# THE PUBLISHER'S PAGE

Our research team continues to grow in strength – see details on pages 5 – 10. This, combined with the increasing number of client interviews and factual submissions from law-firms, has led – I'm proud to say – to ever-improving research.

One sign of this improvement has been the introduction of many new ranking tables devoted to individual lawyers (as contrasted with law-firm tables) – new tables which focus on narrower niche specialisms. These new individuals' tables will be found across the board, in the Nationwide tables as well as in the large and small state tables. They give the reader a nuanced picture of each practice area. There may be only one law-firm table, for instance, but the various specialisms will be picked out in these niche individual tables.

*Michael Chambers*

Published by **Chambers & Partners Publishing**
(a division of Orbach & Chambers Ltd)
39 Parker Street, London WC2B 5PQ
**Tel** +44 207 606 8844
**Fax** +44 207 606 0906

**ISBN** 978 0 85514 443 2

Orders to: Chambers & Partners Publishing

Copyright © 2013 Michael Chambers and Orbach and Chambers Ltd

**Publisher** Michael Chambers
**Editor-in-Chief** Rieta Ghosh
**Executive Publisher** David Lamb

**Editor** Laura Mills
**Deputy Editors** Johanna Hansson, Seth Singh Jennings, Jane Pasquali, Michael Perkin, Christopher Teevan, Peter Whitfield, Richard Winter
**Editorial Assistant** Mario Serna Salazar, Mehri Hudayguliyeva
**Research Coordinators** Jessie Berman, Pippa Summers
**Profiles Manager** Saffeya Shebli
**Production Manager** Jasper John
**Business Development Director** Brad Sirott

**Researchers/writers:**

Matthew Adams
Mersa Auda
Emma Beatty
James Booth
Ed Bradley
Wendy Bremang
Hannah Campaigne
Harriet Carter
Thomas Carter
Angela Castillo-Diaz
Stefan Corre
James Course-Choi
Charles Davies
Andrew Dyer

Sara Fantoni
Mary Gallagher
Francois Gill
Stella Heng
Bryony Hirsch
Ryan Hocking
Calvin Humby
Ara Iskanderian
Clare Joseph
Megan Langham
Fran Latham
Deborah Lewis
Robert Li
Sue Li-Ciraki
Cillian Logue

Loretta Lok
Keziah Mastin
Ben McCarthy
Annie McDermott
Alice McDonald
Becky Millar
Jacob Moffatt
Claire Oxborrow
Ria Pal
Daniel Pang
Steven Preston
Danielle Rabin
Timothy Shaw
Gregory S
Geor

Mandeep Sran
Kimberley Staines
Robyn Stewart
Isabel Story
Kristina Thompson
Christopher Took
Jack Torbet
Indy Tss
Beth

# Contents

## NATIONWIDE RANKINGS

## STATE RANKINGS

# Contents

# Contents

Here you can see our editors, deputy editors and researchers. They are all currently (March 2013) working full-time on our range of guides at our head office in central London. More biographical information can be found on the 'About Us' page of our website.

## The Editors

The Editors are responsible for the overall content of their guides and for managing the research team.

**Rieta Ghosh**
Editor-in-Chief

**Laura Mills**
USA Editor

**David Lamb**
Executive Publisher

**Jonathan Rubin**
UK Editor

**James Cowdell**
Bar Editor

**Andrés Jaramillo Mejía**
Latin America Editor

**Edward Shum**
Global Editor

**Georgia Brooks**
Europe Editor

**Shi-Ning Koay**
Asia-Pacific Editor

**Rieta Ghosh**
Graduated in Ancient History at Durham University. Former Client Information Manager with a European market research agency. Previously worked at a leading business advisory company.

**Laura Mills**
USA Editor. Graduated with a BA in History and Middle Eastern Studies from the University of Pittsburgh and an MA in Middle Eastern Studies from the School of Oriental and African Studies, University of London. Has studied French, Arabic, Spanish and Turkish.

**David Lamb**
Read English and Philosophy at the University of Leeds before converting to law. Has spent a year teaching English in Japan.

**Jonathan Rubin**
UK Editor. Graduated with Honours in Law from the University of Kent in 2006. Completed the LPC at BPP College in London. Qualified as a solicitor in 2009, training with a top American firm in London and Dubai. Studying for an LLM in Law and Political Justice at Birkbeck College, University of London.

**James Cowdell**
UK Bar Editor. Barrister. Read Modern History at The Queen's College, Oxford. Practised at the Criminal Bar for five years and was a fee earner in the family department of a leading London law firm.

**Andrés Jaramillo Mejía**
Latin America Editor. Graduated in Law from the Pontificia Universidad Javeriana in Bogotá, Colombia, and holds a Masters (LLM) Cum Laude in European Intellectual Property Law from Stockholm University. He is a qualified lawyer in Colombia, with significant experience in media, entertainment and intellectual property law.

**Edward Shum**
Editor for Africa, Canada, the Middle East, Caribbean and Global-wide sections. Studied Law at Magdalene College, Cambridge. Previously worked at a South London law firm.

**Georgia Brooks**
Europe Editor. Graduated with an MA in Ancient History from UCL and a BA Hons in Classics from the University of Warwick. Previously worked in marketing and as a freelance translator and travel writer. Speaks Arabic, French and Italian.

**Shi-Ning Koay**
Asia-Pacific Editor. Graduated in Law from the University of Manchester. Completed the Bar Vocational Course and was subsequently called to the Bar in 2005. Trained with a leading Malaysian law firm and was called to the Malaysian Bar in 2006.

## The Deputy Editors

The Deputy Editors work with the Researchers and The Editor to ensure the rankings and commentary are a true reflection of the market.

**Bryony Hirsch**
UK

**Christopher Teevan**
USA

**Crystal Lo**
Asia-Pacific

**Elitsa Yurukova**
Europe

**Emma Dougan**
Global

**Giles Thomas**
UK

**Jamie Horne**
UK

**Jane Pasquali**
USA

**Joanna Haber**
Global

**Jon Comlay**
UK

**Leila Afshar**
Latin America

**Liam Whitton**
UK

**Lidija Liegis**
Europe

**Luke Kenison**
Europe

**Michael Perkin**
USA

**Milena Bellow**
Europe

**Nicolás Obregón Fox**
Latin America

**Peter Whitfield**
USA

**Richard Winter**
USA

**Sarah Kogan**
Asia-Pacific

**Timothy Shaw**
Asia-Pacific

**Ursula Ben-Hammou**
Latin America

**Yvonne Berman**
Asia-Pacific

**Bryony Hirsch**
UK Deputy Editor. Graduated with an honours degree in History from the University of York, did a GDL at the College of Law in York and is currently completing an LPC at the College of Law in Bloomsbury.

**Christopher Teevan**
USA Deputy Editor. Graduated from the University of Warwick in 2006 with Honours in English Literature. Also holds an MA in Creative Writing from Royal Holloway, University of London.

**Crystal Lo**
Asia-Pacific Deputy Editor (based in Hong Kong). Graduated with an MA in Translation and Media from the University of Warwick and a BA in English and Translation Studies from the University of Hong Kong. Worked as a freelance translator/interpreter for the NHS, Thames Valley Police and UBS (Hong Kong), and as a research assistant at CUHK. Speaks Cantonese and Mandarin.

**Elitsa Yurukova**
Europe Deputy Editor. Graduated in Law from the University of Sofia, holds a Master's degree (LL.M.) in Corporate and Commercial Law from the London School of Economics and a Diploma in English and EU Law from the University of Cambridge. Previously worked at the Legal Service of the European Commission in Brussels as well as the Bulgarian Ministry of Justice. Fluent in English and Bulgarian. Oversees research in Russia, Ukraine and throughout Central Eastern Europe.

**Emma Dougan**
Global Deputy Editor. Graduated from Worcester College, Oxford in 2009 with a First in English.

**Giles Thomas**
UK Deputy Editor. Graduated in International Relations from the University of Sussex in 2005.

**Jamie Horne**
UK Deputy Editor. Graduated in 2008 from Emmanuel College, Cambridge, with an honours degree in History.

**Jane Pasquali**
USA Deputy Editor. Graduated with a First in Spanish and Italian from Exeter University in 2007. Has lived and taught in Madrid and Barcelona, and worked for three years in a financial spreadbetting company in London. Awarded a PGCE with Distinction in Primary Education and Spanish in 2011.

**Joanna Haber**
Global Deputy Editor. Graduated in Public Affairs and Management and International Development from Carleton University in Canada and holds a Postgraduate Diploma in Journalism from the London School of Journalism. Speaks French.

**Jon Comlay**
Graduated in History from the University of York in 2005.

**Leila Afshar**
Latin America Deputy Editor. Graduated in Law from King's College London; holds an MSc in Development and Anthropology from the London School of Economics.

**Liam Whitton**
UK Deputy Editor. Graduated in English Literature from Balliol College, Oxford. Worked as a freelance writer and policy researcher for several UK national charities.

**Lidija Liegis**
Europe Deputy Editor. Graduated in Philosophy and Psychology from the University of Edinburgh (MA hons) and also holds a Master's degree in Investigative Journalism from City University. Previously worked in journalism, on a project in collaboration with the Financial Times. Speaks French, Latvian and Spanish. Oversees research in France, Italy, Finland and the Baltics.

**Luke Kenison**
Europe Deputy Editor. Graduated from the University of Warwick in 2010 with a First in English and Comparative Literary Studies.

Oversees research in Belgium, Iceland, Luxembourg and Malta.

**Michael Perkin**

USA Deputy Editor. Graduated in English Language and Linguistics from the University of Sheffield. Worked as a journalist for Hayters Press Agency and has had copy printed in a number of national newspapers, including the Daily Telegraph and the Mail on Sunday.

**Milena Bellow**

Europe Deputy Editor. Graduated in English Literature from the University of Glasgow in 2009. Has previously worked in probate and genealogy research. Oversees research in Austria, Cyprus, Greece, Switzerland and Turkey.

**Nicolás Obregón Fox**

Latin America Deputy Editor. Studied literature in Madrid before gaining substantial journalistic experience with a market-leading consumer magazine. Worked for three years as a researcher/writer for a travel magazine. Speaks fluent Spanish and intermediate French.

**Peter Whitfield**

USA Deputy Editor. Graduated from the University of Newcastle-upon-Tyne with a BA (Hons) in English Literature, and is currently studying towards a Master's degree in Philosophy at Birkbeck, University of London.

**Richard Winter**

USA Deputy Editor. Graduated in English Literature from Loughborough University in 2007. Previously worked for a media intelligence company.

**Sarah Kogan**

Asia-Pacific Deputy Editor. Graduated from Oxford University in 2004 with a degree in English Language & Literature. Worked in the television industry for several years as a Researcher and Associate Producer. Subsequently completed the GDL (Graduate Diploma in Law) in 2011 at the College of Law.

**Timothy Shaw**

Asia-Pacific Deputy Editor. Graduated with a BA (Hons) in French and Spanish from University College London in 2010 and spent a year abroad as an ERASMUS scholar in Paris and Valencia. Subsequently completed the GDL and the LPC. Fluent in Mandarin and a native Cantonese speaker.

**Ursula Ben-Hammou**

Latin America Deputy Editor. Graduated in Law from the Pontificia Universidad Católica del Perú and holds a Master in Laws (LLM) with specialisation in International Business Transactions from the London School of Economics and Political Science. She is a qualified lawyer in Peru, with significant experience in corporate and finance law. Fluent in English and Spanish and also speaks French.

**Yvonne Berman**

Asia-Pacific Deputy Editor. Having completed a law degree (at the University of North London) became a member of the Bar of England and Wales (non-practising) and spent several years in industry and private practice in IP, specialising in trade marks and copyright.

## The Assistant Editors and Senior Researchers

The Assistant Editors and Senior Researchers are responsible for interviewing clients and lawyers and for assisting with the rankings and commentary.

**Angela Castillo-Díaz**
Latin America

**Calvin Humby**
USA

**Charles Procter**
Latin America

**Francesca Lean**
Europe

**Francois Gill**
USA

**Fran Latham**
UK

**Gareth Hewer**
Europe

**Harriet Carter**
Global

**Indy Tsang**
UK/USA

**Isabel Story**
Latin America

**Jurgita Meskauskaite**
Europe

**Kimberley Staines**
USA

**Lucy Craig**
Europe

**Madalena Andrade**
Head of Brazil Research

**Mandeep Sran**
USA

**Mayeni Jones**
Europe

**Miriam Urgelles-Coll**
Europe

**Natalia Tejedor Sanz**
Europe

**Oliver Dimsdale**
Asia-Pacific

**Richard Metcalf**
Europe

**Shuma Hoque**
Europe

**Stefan Corre**
UK

**Talia Addleman**
Europe

**Angela Castillo-Diaz**
Latin America Senior Researcher. Graduated in Journalism from Universidad Central de Venezuela (with a special award, "Magna Cum Laude"), holds a Master's Degree from Universidad Antonio de Nebrija (Madrid, Spain) in Audiovisual Techniques applied to Journalism and an MBA degree in Marketing from University of Wales, Cardiff Institute. Previously worked as Editor for an important London-based Latin American newspaper and as Collaborator for Intereconomía Grupo de Comunicaciones (Spain). Fluent in English and a native Spanish speaker.

**Calvin Humby**
USA Senior Researcher. Graduated with Honours in Law from Canterbury University in New Zealand. He is a qualified lawyer in New Zealand and Australia and practised for three years in commercial dispute resolution.

**Charles Procter**
Graduated from King's College, London in 2011 with a First in Spanish and Portuguese.

**Francesca Lean**
Europe Senior Researcher. Graduated from Newcastle University in 2008 with a BA in French and German, with Spanish. Has previously worked in multilingual financial recruitment. Speaks French and German.

**Fran Latham**
Graduated with a BA in English and Music from the University of Southampton. Holds a Graduate Diploma in Law and Postgraduate Diploma in Legal Practice from The College of Law. Considerable previous experience in corporate communications and PR working for organisations in the media and entertainment sector.

**Francois Gill**
UK Assistant Editor. Graduated with a First in History from University College London in 2006. Went on to complete a Master's in the subject at UCL. Speaks French.

**Harriet Carter**
Global Assistant Editor. Graduated with a First in English from the University of York. Completed an MA in Aberystwyth and a PhD in Creative and Critical Writing at the University of East Anglia. She has taught English literature and creative writing at both school and undergraduate level, and written two novels.

**Gareth Hewer**
Europe Senior Researcher. Graduated in History from Queen Mary, University of London, in 2008, and holds an MA in the History of Political Thought and Intellectual History from University College London. Previously worked as a freelance writer and researcher.

**Jurgita Meskauskaite**
Europe Assistant Editor. Graduated with an MA in Development Management from the University of Westminster in 2007. Previously worked as a business journalist in Lithuania and freelanced in London. Fluent in Russian and Lithuanian.

**Kimberley Staines**
Graduated with a BA in English Literature, Film & Theatre from the University of Reading, before completing the Graduate Diploma in Law and Legal Practice Course at BPP Law School. Previously worked as a fee earner in the Dispute Resolution department of a commercial law firm in Hong Kong and as a fee earner in the Property and Employment departments of a leading London law firm. Has also worked as a freelance writer and is studying for a Diploma in Journalism.

**Lucy Craig**
Europe Assistant Editor for Germany. Graduated from the University of Oxford in 2011 with a BA in French and German. Previously taught English as a foreign language in Germany. Speaks French and German, and is currently learning Russian. Oversees research in Germany.

**Madalena Andrade**
Latin America Head of Brazil Research. Graduated in English Literature with Publishing from Loughborough University. Previous experience includes teaching English as a foreign language and translating. Madalena is a Portuguese national.

**Mandeep Sran**
Graduated in Law from the School of Oriental and African Studies (SOAS) at the University of London, and completed the Legal Practice Course at the Nottingham Law School. Qualified as a solicitor in 2009 specialising in Litigation.

**Mayeni Jones**
Europe Senior Researcher. Graduated from the School of Oriental and African Studies (SOAS) in International Studies and Diplomacy. Also has an BA in Modern Languages from the University of Oxford. Has worked for humanitarian organisations in Brazil and Sierra Leone. Fluent in French, Portuguese and Spanish.

**Miriam Urgelles-Coll**
Europe Senior Researcher. Graduated with an MA in Computational Linguistics before completing a PhD in Theoretical Linguistics, both from Essex University.

**Natalia Tejedor Sanz**
Europe Assistant Editor. Graduated in English Studies from the University of Valladolid (Spain), and holds Postgraduate Certificates in Research Training and Education from the University of Hull. She also obtained a Diploma in Practical Icelandic from the University of Iceland, and attended the University of Salamanca (Spain) and University College Dublin. Speaks Spanish and French. Oversees research in Spain and Portugal.

**Oliver Dimsdale**
Asia-Pacific Senior Researcher. Graduated with an MLitt in Creative Writing from the University of St Andrews in November 2010. Also holds an MA in English Literature from the University of Warwick. Has previously worked as a writing tutor, in Scotland, and as a journalist in Tegucigalpa, Honduras. Speaks Spanish and German. Learning Italian.

**Richard Metcalf**
Europe Assistant Editor. Graduated with a First in German and Italian from the University of Bath in 2008 and holds an MA in Translation Studies from the University of Warwick. Speaks French, German and Italian.

**Shuma Hoque**
Europe Senior Researcher. Holds a law degree and most recently worked in Spain where she completed her legal studies at Universidad Complutense de Madrid.

**Stefan Corre**
Graduated from Leeds University with a degree in Philosophy. Subsequently attended the College of Law in London and qualified and worked as a solicitor in the West End of London.

**Talia Addleman**
Europe Assistant Editor. Graduated from the University of Birmingham in 2008 with a BA in Ancient and Medieval History. Has completed the GDL and LPC at the College of Law. Oversees research in Ireland and Scandinavia.

## The Researchers

The Researchers are responsible for interviewing clients and lawyers and for assembling the data needed for the rankings and commentary.

 Alessandra Sulzer
 Andrew Dyer
 Becky Millar
 Bevil Luck
 Ben McCarthy
 Beth Warin
 Charles Davies
 Christopher Tooke

 Cillian Logue
 Cristina Gonzalez
 David Watson
 Deborah Lewis
 Emma Beatty
 Emma Roche
 Fawkia Hammouda
 Felipe Goralski

 Fredrik Kruse
 Georgina Simmonds
 Georgina Watts
 Graham Gilbert
 Gregory Simkins
 Hannah Campaign
 Jack Torbet
 Jacob Moffatt

 James Booth
 James Course-Choi
 Jamie Yule
 Jenifer Yuen
 Joaquin Sarroca
 Joe Twomey
 Katherine Hughes
 Katherine Yu

 Keziah Mastin
 Kimberley Addison
 Maria Harwood
 Marta Krzeminska
 Matthew Adams
 Matthew James
 Megan Langham
 Mersa Auda

 Raquel Holzmann
 Ria Pal
 Robert Li
 Rupert Wilson
 Sara Fantoni
 Sofia Abasolo
 Stella Heng
 Steven Preston

The Researchers contunued

**Sue Li-Ciraki**  **Tobias Waters**  **William Robertson**  **Wendy Bremang**

# The Rankings

No lawyers are ranked in the *Chambers* tables unless they have strong recommendations from the market. In other words, no one can 'buy their way in'. In addition to the six tier rankings there are six further categories in which attorneys can be ranked. They are as follows:

## Senior statesmen

A senior statesman is a distinguished older partner – often a name partner – who in their senior years remains a principal point of contact for major clients with major matters. They are deeply admired throughout the profession, although they may be seen less frequently on everyday transactions. Sages of their particular legal markets, their contribution is as valuable as ever.

## Star individuals

These players are the first names that roll off everyone's lips, the standard by which others are judged. Beyond that, these attorneys operate in a 'right here, right now' mode, immersing themselves in the most significant work around. At the top of their game, they also bring to the negotiating table a certain degree of gravitas – the kind of influence that sends shivers down the spine of the opposing side. The star category is reserved for those individuals whose profile is far ahead of the pack.

This marketplace authority is cultivated through a long history of excellence, and it usually manifests in the research process through the sheer weight of recommendations compared with their peers. Additionally, they've also managed to change the legal landscape in dramatic ways. For example, rainmaker Larry Sonsini of Wilson Sonsini Goodrich & Rosati is not only a catalyst in the success of his own firm, but also consistently sets industry records for the number of IPOs to his name.

## Up-and-coming individuals

If the senior statesmen are the brains of a firm, then this 'bubbling-under' set is its added brawn. While these individuals do not make or break a firm, they do fuel the firm's growth. This next generation of talent does not necessarily have the industry reputation to warrant a numeric ranking, which is reserved for those with an already established profile. But what they lack in experience, they make up for in energy.

They are the young dynamos that give an operation extra edge. More impor-
tantly, they bridge the practice's present and its future. These operators range in age, but are generally in their 30s and early 40s, partly depending on their areas of specialty; certain fields require more 'seasoning' than others.

## Associates to watch

These lawyers, often the unsung heroes of the most complex cases and biggest deals, are the future of the law firms recommended in *Chambers USA* and so worthy of recognition. While our up-and-coming partners can often be found as headliners on matters, these senior associates have been spotted by clients as they beaver away in the background.

## Specialist table

In certain sections of the guide we spotlight those firms and attorneys who have achieved a ranking for the breadth of their expertise, but also receive praise from commentators for having a particular practice (or industry) specialty as part of their wider skill set.

## Other Notable Practitioners

Other Notable Practitioners are lawyers we have identified as leading individuals, but whose firms are not listed in the Leading Firms tables. Commentary for these individuals can be found under the Other Notable Practitioners heading.

**ADVERTISING:** Covers transactional, regulatory and litigation work. This includes Lanham Act claims, IP suits, consumer class actions, self-regulatory disputes heard before the National Advertising Division of the Better Business Bureau and the representation of clients before federal agencies in relation to print and online media. *See also:* Food & Beverages; IP; Media & Entertainment

**ANTITRUST:** Covers the body of laws that prohibits anti competitive behavior (monopoly) and unfair business practices. This includes practices that hurt business, consumers or both, or that generally violate standards of ethical behavior. Antitrust litigation and M&A-related competition work (such as merger clearance advice) are both covered in *Chambers USA*.

**APPELLATE LAW:** Covers the preparation, drafting and delivery of briefs before the appellate courts (state supreme courts, circuit courts and the US Supreme Court). It also includes interlocutory appeals and writs.

**BANKING & FINANCE:** Covers the representation of both borrowers and lenders in relation to banking transactions. This section takes into account general bank lending, structured finance, leveraged finance and refinancing. Certain banking & finance sections (including New York) also encompass the following: • Acquisition finance covers transactions involving arranging finance for acquisitions. We cover firms and lawyers who act for either the lender or the borrower. • Equipment finance & leasing covers the financing of vehicles, equipment and related assets through leasing, loans and securitization. • Islamic finance covers Shari'a-compliant work such as acquisitions, forming funds to invest in real estate and commercial properties and the issuing of sukuks. • Public finance covers advice on raising money for public bodies such as local, state and federal governments. The section takes into account advice on the allocation of resources and the activity of central banks. *See also:* Bankruptcy/Restructuring; Transportation

**BANKRUPTCY/RESTRUCTURING:** Covers corporate bankruptcy and restructuring and the legal processes related to distressed businesses. Lawyers in this chapter assist clients such as corporate debtors and directors of distressed companies; investors and asset purchasers; secured and unsecured creditors and creditors' committees, bondholders and insurers; and any other interested parties in corporate restructurings and bankruptcy proceedings. *Chambers USA* also takes into account firms and lawyers who advise on acquisition opportunities relating to distressed businesses. We also cover bankruptcy-related litigation, including disputes between parties in connection with distressed companies and with proceedings under multiple Chapters of the Bankruptcy Code.

**CAPITAL MARKETS:** Covers key areas of capital markets. *See also:* Debt & Equity; Derivatives; REITs; Securitization; Structured Finance

**CLIMATE CHANGE:** Focuses on law firms handling projects, regulation and legislation dedicated to preventing or reducing climate change. The types of matters covered include emissions trading, state and regional initiatives, climate change legislation, regulation and policy, corporate risk and the emerging field of climate change litigation outlined above. Clean Development Mechanism (CDM) and joint implementation (JI) projects and other matters related to the Kyoto Protocol are also covered. *See also:* Energy & Natural Resources; Environment

**CONSTRUCTION:** Covers contractual adviser work within the construction industry for both suppliers (such as developers, contractors, engineers and architects), and those clients employing these types of companies (such as corporations or state authorities) on their building plans. *Chambers USA* takes into account both contentious and noncontentious construction work.

**CORPORATE/M&A:** This broad category covers both public company and private equity (including venture capital) matters. It includes company acquisitions, dispositions and related financing arrangements, capitalizations, entity selection, operating and partnership agreements, securities and governance matters. It also covers transactions designed to facilitate restructuring within companies and their subsidiaries. *Chambers USA* places priority on primary representatives (those acting for buyers and sellers) but also considers those acting for financial advisers including underwriters and banks. *See also:* Bankruptcy/Restructuring; Financial Services Regulation; Private Equity: Buyouts

**DEBT & EQUITY:** Equity covers advice on offering transactions such as: initial public offerings (IPOs); follow-on offerings, right offerings, capital increases; ADR/GDR offerings; accelerated bookbuilds and block trades. Debt covers advice on the following transactions: investment grade debt offerings (stand-alone bond issues; MTN programs; Commercial Paper programs), equity-linked offerings (regulatory capital, convertibles and exchangeable offerings) and high-yield debt offerings. *See also:* Capital Markets

**DERIVATIVES:** Covers regulatory and transactional legal advice regarding derivatives products. These include: exchange-traded derivatives; OTC derivatives; securitized derivatives; interest rate, currency, equity, credit and commodity-linked products. The firms and laws featured in *Chambers USA* advise on product development and regulation, market regulation, the structuring and documentation of transactions, related tax issues and litigation. *See also:* Capital Markets

**E-DISCOVERY:** Covers the process through which electronic data is sought, located and secured with the intent of using it as evidence in civil and criminal litigation. *See also:* Litigation; Privacy & Data Security

**EMPLOYEE BENEFITS & EXECUTIVE COMPENSATION:** Covers the full range of benefits and compensation work, from transactional matters to plan design, drafting, implementation and administration. This section also includes health and welfare plans and fringe benefits. On the compensation side, it covers both lawyers who specialize in advising companies and executive compensation committees and those who concentrate on advising senior executives on employment and severance agreements. *See also:* Corporate/M&A; ERISA Litigation

**ENERGY & NATURAL RESOURCES:** Covers both transactional and regulatory work. Key industry sectors include electricity, oil & gas, mining & minerals and nuclear matters. Renewable & alternative energy is considered alongside electricity work because the regulatory framework does not distinguish between forms of electricity besides nuclear. On the transactional side, *Chambers USA* focuses on corporate M&A, commodities trading, private equity investment, structured finance and capital markets issues. Oil & gas work encompasses exploration & production, upstream M&A and reserve-based lending and

MLP matters. The section does not include project development and finance, investment into project-financed assets, or project acquisition & divestiture. On the regulatory side, *Chambers USA* takes into account both state and federal regulation of energy in all its forms. Typically, this means work undertaken before or in accordance with state Public Utility or Public Service Commissions, the Federal Energy Regulatory Commission (FERC), the Commodity Futures Trading Commission (CFTC) and the Nuclear Regulatory Commission (NRC). It does not include environmental permitting. *See also:* Projects

**ENVIRONMENT:** Covers both litigation and advisory/transactional support to clients. Traditional environment work includes regulatory compliance, litigation and enforcement actions related to air, water, wetlands, waste and endangered species. *Chambers USA* also takes into account advice to corporate and financial clients on the environmental aspects of M&A, financings, securities offerings and other transactions (such as merger due diligence and brownfield site development). *See also:* Climate Change; Real Estate

**ERISA LITIGATION:** The Employee Retirement Income Security Act of 1974 (ERISA) is the federal statutory framework that governs the administration of employee benefit plans and the rights of the beneficiaries under the plan. This chapter recognizes firms with expertise in ERISA-related disputes. *See also:* Employee Benefits & Executive Compensation

**FINANCIAL SERVICES REGULATION:** This chapter covers both noncontentious and contentious matters arising out of the financial services industry (including the broker-dealer arena) and advice on all aspects of internal organization and governance, transactions and operations. Noncontentious matters include assistance to banks/financial institution clients on complying with the full range of financial services laws and regulations in their daily operations. This section also encompasses financial institutions business transactions, especially advice on regulatory issues relating to M&A, joint ventures of financial services companies and the implementation of holdings in foreign countries. This section also covers lobbying work done by firms relating to the development of new laws and regulations before Congress or other regulatory agencies. In contentious matters, we include advice related to the defense of financial institutions in criminal and civil examinations,

inspections, investigations, and formal proceedings by federal and state financial regulators and self-regulatory organizations. *See also:* Insurance; Litigation; Securities Regulation

**FOOD & BEVERAGES:** Covers legal advice on FDA regulatory matters, encompassing dietary supplements as well as meat and poultry. *Chambers USA* also takes into account Federal Trade Commission (FTC) issues, such as consumer protection, advertising and point-of-sale. The chapter also covers legislation and litigation in the beverage alcohol sector, relating to the ability of wineries and other vendors to make interstate sales of wine to both consumers and retail customers. *See also:* Advertising; Life Sciences; Product Liability & Mass Torts

**FRANCHISING:** Covers those acting for franchisees and franchisors and takes into account both transactional and contentious work. On the noncontentious side, this includes setting up a franchise arrangement, expanding a system and closing down arrangements.

**GAMING & LICENSING:** Covers the transactional, financing, regulatory and IP issues involved in the formation of entities such as casinos.

**GOVERNMENT:** Covers the full range of government-related issues. *See also:* Government Contracts; Government Relations; Political Law

**GOVERNMENT CONTRACTS:** Refers to supply contract arrangements (with, for example, army, navy, air force and Department of Homeland Security) and bid protests before the agency forum, General Accountability Office (GAO) or Court of Federal Claims (CFC). Litigation arising from the sector includes costs disputes, matters relating to the False Claims Act, and other contractual disputes (such as late completion and overrun costs). Other noncontentious issues include services contracting, scheduling issues and organizational conflicts of interest.

**GOVERNMENT RELATIONS:** Covers legislative lobbying conducted by qualified lawyers for a range of corporate and some nonprofit clients, such as hospitals and universities. This is usually either regarding a specific proposal for legislation (eg asbestos reform) or ongoing appropriations work. This work crosses industries from defense to education.

**HEALTHCARE:** Covers transactional, advisory and contentious matters. Transactional work is primarily

the sale and purchase of some or all of a health system or health insurance company. The section encompasses advice on antitrust issues and assorted regulatory matters for clients such as hospitals, health systems and insurance companies. Litigation includes matters like qui tam (whistle-blower) suits and the defense of parties involved in federal investigations. Advisory and regulatory compliance work includes Medicare Part D, the subsidizing of drugs through the federally run Medicare program. The section also covers Stark Law, which governs referrals of physicians accepting Medicare and Medicaid funds, and the False Claims Act (FCA). It also features advice on pharmaceutical and medical products regulatory issues covering drugs and devices approved by the FDA. *See also:* Life Sciences; Product Liability & Mass Torts

**HEDGE FUNDS:** Covers hedge fund formation and launches, spinouts, strategic acquisitions, distressed debt investments and restructurings. *See also:* Investment Funds

**IMMIGRATION:** Covers all aspects of inbound and outbound immigration, such as work permits and visas, workforce mobility, HSMP and other legislative and regulatory changes. *See also:* Employee Benefit, and Executive Compensation.

**INFORMATION TECHNOLOGY:** Focuses on the startup, development and finance of technology-based businesses, advising startup or later-stage enterprises, venture capital investors, and other financial investors. Issues include private and public capital raisings, joint venture agreements, share listings, corporate governance and M&A.

**INSURANCE:** Includes both contentious and noncontentious insurance and reinsurance matters. On the contentious side, we feature coverage claims litigation, broker's negligence and both 'facultative' and 'treaty' reinsurance disputes for insurers and policyholders. There is also an element of professional negligence issues arising from insurance disputes. On the noncontentious side, we cover all forms of M&A, capital raisings, demutualizations and other regulatory issues.

**INTELLECTUAL PROPERTY:** Covers disputes related to patent, copyright and trademark infringement. Litigation concerning trade secrets also features. Also includes licensing and patent prosecution. *See also:* International Trade; Life Sciences

**INTERNATIONAL ARBITRATION:** Covers advice on the resolution of disputes by one or more neutral parties, either an arbitrator or an arbitration panel. Many contracts – including those imposed on customers by many financial and healthcare organizations – require mandatory arbitration in the event of a dispute. Arbitration institutions include AAA (American Arbitration Association), ICC (International Chamber of Commerce) and ICSID (International Centre for the Settlement of Investment Disputes). *Chambers USA* ranks both arbitration counsel and arbitrators.

**INTERNATIONAL TRADE:** Covers 'classic' trade matters such as antidumping, countervailing duties, export control and other customs/tariff classifications and regulatory work. Also includes matters relating to NAFTA, WTO and GATT trade provisions and the US Foreign Corrupt Practices Act (FCPA), and areas that overlap to some extent with the white-collar crime field. Filings before the Committee on Foreign Investments into the USA (CFIUS) is also taken into account, as is expertise in Section 337 investigations before the ITC. *See also:* Intellectual Property; Litigation

**INVESTMENT FUNDS:** A broad category that covers all aspects of fund work, except private equity buyouts. *See also:* Hedge Funds; Private Equity: Fund Formation; Registered Funds; Venture Capital

**LABOR & EMPLOYMENT:** Covers the full range of labor and employment law. On the labor side, *Chambers USA* takes into account the representation of corporations in connection with union issues, collective bargaining agreements and strike avoidance. Also includes Occupational Safety & Health Act (OSHA) and proceedings before the National Labor Relations Board (NLRB). On the employment side, the guide covers both contentious and noncontentious employment matters relating to day-to-day business issues as well as mergers and takeovers. Includes employment litigation related to sex, race, or age discrimination. Also encompasses class action suits, the avoidance of class action certification and advice on workforce redundancies. *See also:* Employee Benefits & Executive Compensation; ERISA Litigation; Immigration

**LEISURE & HOSPITALITY:** An industry section covering all legal services carried out for clients involved in the leisure industry, ranging from hotels and amusement parks to casinos. Key areas of focus include real estate, employment and Occupational Safety & Health Act (OSHA), corporate/commercial and financing-related matters. *See also:* Corporate/M&A; Labor & Employment; Real Estate

**LIFE SCIENCES:** Focuses on the commercialization of life sciences products (including pharmaceuticals, medical devices and biotech programs). IP issues dominate as large pharmaceuticals seek to obtain innovative, impending blockbuster drugs from biotechs and other pharmaceutical companies. Also includes the licensing and acquisition of new products from other sources (often smaller biotechs to larger suppliers). This section also includes advice on FDA issues and the increased focus on drug and device safety. *See also:* Healthcare; Intellectual Property; Product Liability & Mass Torts

**LITIGATION:** Focuses on commercial proceedings before state and federal court, circuit courts and the US Supreme Court. The section covers pretrial negotiations, documentation and preparation for trial, summary judgment motions, trial, appeals and enforcement proceedings. Alternative dispute resolution, involving non-court mediation, is also featured. *Chambers USA* focuses on two main types of litigation: commercial disputes before civil courts and white-collar crime, including government investigations. In certain key states (such as New York), Chambers also recognizes expertise in securities litigation. Firms and lawyers ranked for general commercial litigation have expertise in business disputes across a variety of industries; for firms and attorneys with a sector-specific focus, please see the relevant practice area (such as insurance, IP, construction or environment). *See also:* Appellate Law; E-Discovery; International Arbitration; Securities Litigation

**MEDIA & ENTERTAINMENT:** Encompasses transactional and contentious work undertaken on behalf of both talent and companies. On the litigation side we identify attorneys who handle significant IP, First Amendment and contract disputes. On the transactional side, the section includes production, financing and distribution, contract, IP and a broad range of corporate matters.

**NATIVE AMERICAN LAW:** Covers the representation of tribes or private companies or state governments in their dealings with tribes. Gaming law and regulatory work and casino development have traditionally been key areas of this market. There is also a growing emphasis on land, energy, water rights and environmental matters. *See also:* Gaming & Licensing

**OUTSOURCING:** Covers major outsourcing agreements relating to IT systems and data storage. *See also:* Information Technology; Privacy & Data Security

**POLITICAL LAW:** Advice on the organization and financing of election campaigns (McCain-Feingold Act) as well as advice to corporations and independent advocacy groups on election activities. Contentious matters include challenging decisions by election authorities (such as the Federal Election Commission).

**PRIVACY & DATA SECURITY:** Covers compliance with US federal and state privacy and information management laws. At the federal level, such laws are predominantly sector-specific and include the Gramm-Leach-Bliley Financial Services Modernization Act, the Health Insurance Portability and Accountability Act (HIPAA), the Controlling the Assault of Non-Solicited Pornography and Marketing (CAN-SPAM) Act and the Children's Online Privacy Protection Act (COPPA). This section also covers advice on data security breaches and related Attorney General and FTC investigation, enforcement or litigation. International work includes advising clients with multinational operations on data security issues relating to cross-border transfers of data. *See also:* E-Discovery; Information Technology; Outsourcing

**PRIVATE EQUITY: BUYOUTS:** Focuses on the transactional aspect of private equity funds work. It takes into account LBO, M&A, recapitalization and restructuring-related matters at both the high-end and mid-market level. *See also:* Corporate/M&A; Private Equity: Fund Formation

**PRIVATE EQUITY: FUND FORMATION:** Covers the formation of private equity funds, ranging from LBOs, secondaries and infrastructure funds to hybrid funds, mezzanine and distressed debt. Particular attention is paid to the sponsor side, because this incorporates the actual structuring of the fund.

**PRODUCT LIABILITY & MASS TORTS:** Covers advice to manufacturers, distributors, suppliers, retailers and others in connection with claims for financial compensation. Such claims encompass allegations of faulty design, food contamination and incorrect product labeling. This section also covers toxic tort, relating to the exposure to chemicals, pharmaceutical drugs or occupational hazards. The majority of pharmaceutical claims are mass tort cases. Occupational toxic tort cases occur where industrial and other workers have been exposed to toxic chemicals. Traditionally, much of the law in this area has focused on asbestos exposure. *See also:* Healthcare; Life Sciences; Litigation

**PROJECTS:** Covers the development, financing (limited and nonrecourse), refinancing and acquisition/divestitures of large projects that arise from the capital-intensive energy and infrastructure markets. Clients in this sector include sponsors, commercial lenders, multilateral agencies, development banks, tax equity investors, private equity investors, bidding consortia for PPP concessions, and local government agencies as sellers on PPP projects. This section encompasses mining & metals, oil & gas (upstream, midstream, downstream and LNG), power (fossil-fuel and nuclear generation), PPP (transportation and social infrastructure) and renewable & alternative energy (all forms of nonconventional fuel sources). *See also:* Energy & Natural Resources

**REAL ESTATE:** Covers corporate, zoning and land use, and real estate finance. Corporate matters related to real estate include M&A of large real estate holding companies, complex fund and real estate investment trusts (REIT) transactions, private equity and public securities. These real estate lawyers are distinct from pure corporate lawyers in that they typically come from a real estate background, have an understanding of the underlying asset and do aspects of 'dirt law' real estate for their clients. The zoning and land use category covers advice on major developments, including zoning regulations and municipal restrictions. This section also includes easement and eminent domain (or condemnation) work. The real estate finance section has an emphasis on lender-side work. *Chambers USA* includes some attorneys with experience of complex debt capital markets – such as securitization – but this is dependent on their understanding of the underlying asset. The real estate table also takes into account a limited amount of structuring and transactional advice provided to REITs. However, it does not include attorneys who focus exclusively on REIT work. *See also:* Bankruptcy/Restructuring: Environment; REITs

**REGISTERED FUNDS:** Covers a broad range of registered funds, including mutual funds. It encompasses fund formation and transactional work, as well as regulatory compliance issues under the 1940 Act. Work for open and closed-ended and exchange traded funds (ETFs) is also covered.

**REITS:** Covers structuring and transactional advice related to specialist real estate investment trusts. Includes IPOs, going private transactions, joint ventures, M&A, REIT formation and investment work, restructurings, REIT tax issues, litigation, 144As that involve REITs, financings, Special Committee representations and UPREIT and downREIT structure implementation. *See also:* Capital Markets; Real Estate

**RETAIL:** An industry table that covers the representation of national retailers. Real estate, planning and land use matters feature prominently, but the section also takes into account expertise in franchise, IP, trademark and e-commerce-related issues. The firms ranked in this section also have experience of employment matters, in addition to tax, advertising, regulatory and consumer protection issues.

**SECURITIES LITIGATION:** Includes insider trading; shareholder disputes; contested merger and acquisition bids; reorganizations and restructurings; corporate governance disputes; director, officer, issuer and investment dealer disclosure and liability matters; and other noncompliance matters. Corporate governance disputes arise where it is alleged that management has breached the rights and responsibilities agreed with shareholders. *See also:* Litigation; Securities Regulation

**SECURITIES REGULATION:** Covers advisory and enforcement matters, internal audits and investigations before the SEC. This includes investigations into accounting irregularities, mortgage and credit market matters, short selling, auction rate securities and matters related to financial fraud. Clients include accounting firms, corporations, investment funds and broker-dealers. *See also:* Financial Services Regulation; Securities Litigation

**SECURITIZATION:** Covers the entire range of asset classes, including: commercial loans; derivatives exposure; bonds and corporate debt; project cash flows; trade receivables; credit card and trade receivables; commercial and residential mortgages; life insurance and annuities; and auto loans. *See also:* Capital Markets

**STRUCTURED FINANCE:** Covers CDOs (both cash and synthetic), repackagings and hybrid synthetic and structured note products. *See also:* Capital Markets

**TAX:** Covers transactional and controversy-related work (the latter area is reviewed at a national level). Tax on the transactional side covers corporate partnership structures, tax planning, spin-offs and negotiating tax-free acquisitions. Tax controversy encompasses any contentious tax issue, predominantly at the federal court stage. This includes tax-based litigation, IRS examinations (usually concerning federal income tax issues) and tax shelter investigations. This section also takes into account transfer pricing, state and local tax and estate planning. *See also:* Employee Benefits & Executive Compensation; Wealth Management

**TECHNOLOGY & OUTSOURCING:** Focuses on contractual agreements in the technology field, often outsourcing contracts between large corporations and suppliers of IT services. This section also includes transactional work such as M&A and financing. The firms covered often work with investors or startup enterprises on a range of business issues including employment law, strategic alliances and joint ventures, stock exchange listings, M&A and corporate governance issues. *See also:* Information Technology; Outsourcing

**TELECOM, BROADCAST & SATELLITE:** Covers a range of issues in the heavily regulated areas of telecom and broadcasting. Work includes transactional, financial and litigation advice to telecom companies, wireless operators, TV and/or radio broadcasters and related regulatory matters. This covers government sponsored-inquiries, investigations or compliance proceedings. Other areas of focus include interconnection and resale laws, multimedia agreements and licensing activity. *See also:* Outsourcing; Technology & Outsourcing

**TRANSPORTATION:** A broad industry category, which covers a number of discrete specialties. Aviation includes finance, regulatory and litigation matters. The finance table concentrates on advice to manufacturers, purchasers and investors (such as hedge and private equity funds) on the sale, leasing and acquisition of portfolios of aircraft. On the litigation side, this section covers traditional accident defense litigation, including advising aviation insurers on coverage and other issues, as well as product liability claims and general commercial disputes affecting the aviation industry. The aviation regulatory table spans representation before the Department of Transportation (DOT), the Federal Aviation Administration (FAA), the Surface Transportation Board (STB) and other federal administrative agencies. The rail section encompasses advice to both railroads and shippers. Key issues include rail rates litigation, fuel supply/surcharges and proceedings before the STB. Road carriage/commercial covers issues of carriage of goods/cargo losses, personal injury matters, bills of lading disputes and cargo security compliance. For firms and attorneys with road infrastructure expertise, please see the Projects chapter, which includes the financing and development of toll roads, rail projects seaports and airports, which can utilize the public-private partnership (PPP) model. Shipping finance, litigation (such as cargo claims and contractual disputes) and regulatory matters are also covered in the transportation section. Shipping finance includes advice to the traditional bank market as well as hedge and private equity funds looking for new investment opportunities. Shipping & maritime litigation involves breach of charterparty disputes, cargo and bills of lading claims, the arrest of vessels and cargoes, marine insurance claims, collision, salvage and environmental liabilities. **See also:** Banking & Finance; Projects

**VENTURE CAPITAL:** Covers work on behalf of emerging growth companies, startups and venture fund managers. It encompasses initial fund formation, early and late-stage venture financings, venture capital partnerships, regulatory compliance issues and IPOs. Emerging markets of focus include technology, life sciences and clean-tech. **See also:** Investment Funds

**WEALTH MANAGEMENT:** Focuses primarily on structuring wealth so as to minimize tax. Often handled by the trusts and estates department (though wealth management or wealth preservation departments exist at some law firms), work in this area includes but is not limited to: charitable planning; wealth transfer; business succession planning; estate, gift and generation-skipping transfer tax planning; life and health insurance planning; the creation and administration of trusts and estates; asset transfer; the taking-public of closely held businesses; and structuring outward and inward investment (for instance, if non-US citizens wish to create trusts for relatives resident in the USA). Contentious matters are also included, such as IRS audits, probate contests and contested wills. Clients are usually high net worth individuals and families, but can include entities such as charities, universities and banks. **See also:** Tax

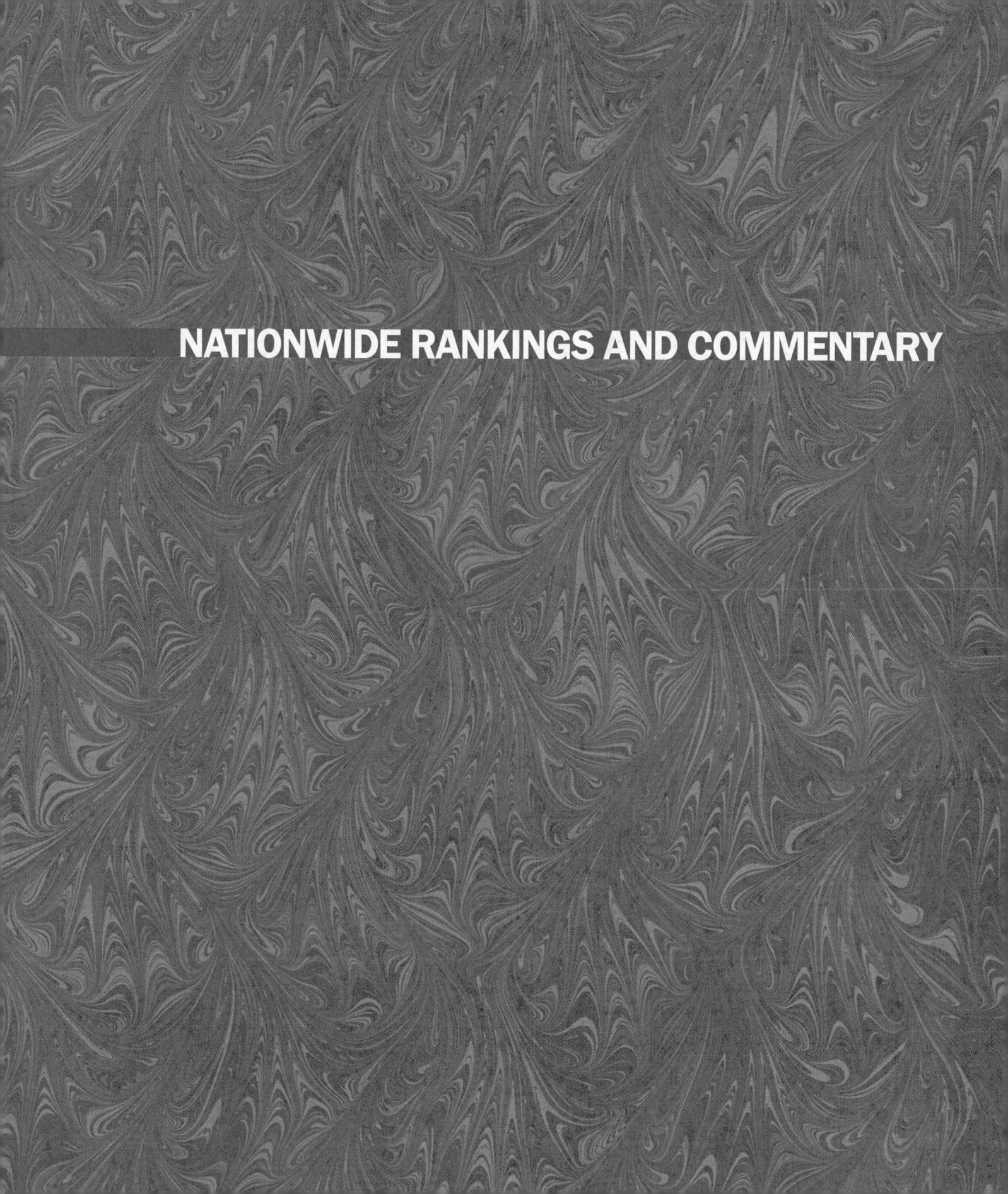

# NATIONWIDE RANKINGS AND COMMENTARY

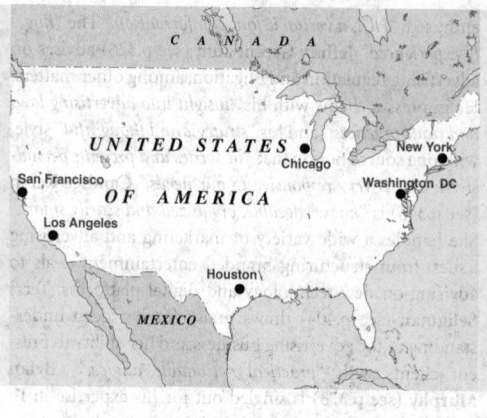

## Contents:

# ADVERTISING

Litigation p.19;  Transactional & Regulatory p.20

Commentary about individuals can be found under their firm's paragraph. If the firm has no paragraph (is not ranked) look at Other Notable Practitioners.

| Advertising: Litigation |
| --- |
| **Leading Firms** |
| **Band 1** |
| Kramer Levin Naftalis & Frankel LLP * |
| Patterson Belknap Webb & Tyler LLP * |
| Proskauer Rose LLP * |
| **Band 2** |
| Debevoise & Plimpton LLP * |
| Kelley Drye & Warren LLP * |
| Manatt Phelps & Phillips LLP * |
| Venable LLP * |
| **Band 3** |
| Kirkland & Ellis LLP * |
| Winston & Strawn LLP * |

*The editorial is in alphabetical order by firm name.*

## Davis & Gilbert LLP

**THE FIRM** This firm is esteemed for its full-service advertising practice, and has a strong reputation for its focus on transactional and regulatory matters. It is renowned for its deep and talented bench, and its significant industry-specific expertise. The team advises a number of global and regional advertising agencies and major brand names, including Apple, Sony, Gap and American Express, on the full spectrum of advertising law issues, including data utilization and security, sponsorship agreements and talent union claims, and online advertising.

**Client Service** *"Excellent. When I call them and need an answer immediately, they do that – sometimes above and beyond normal realms of reason."*

**Commercial Awareness** *"I find D&G to be very practical in their advice based not only on extensive industry knowledge but also general business judgment. We rely on them heavily to make complex risk assessments and to navigate often difficult situations."*

**KEY INDIVIDUALS** Practice group cochair **Ronald Urbach** (see p.419) is *"probably the best attorney in the field today. His advice and counsel is invaluable and he has a very practical business approach to solving problems."* His broad practice covers marketing, promotions, media, IP and technology. *"Ron is a legal expert in the field of advertising and is knowledgeable about the National Advertising Division and its processes,"* said one interviewee, adding: *"He has solid business judgment and is a pleasure to work with."* **Richard Eisert** (see p.309) is praised for his impressive breadth of knowledge. He advises advertising agencies, media and technology companies and traditional publishing organizations on transactional, litigation and regulatory matters. **Joseph Lewczak** (see p.356) *"has a broad knowledge base and is very practical in his approach to dealing with advertising law issues."* **Howard Weingrad** (see p.424) advises a broad array of advertising and media companies on issues ranging from IP, licensing and priva-

*The editorial is in alphabetical order by firm name.*

## Senior Statesmen

**Senior Statesmen:** distinguished older practitioners

| | |
|---|---|
| Morrison Thomas C | *Manatt Phelps & Phillips LLP* |

## Leading Individuals

**Band 1**

| | |
|---|---|
| Weinberger Harold P | *Kramer Levin Naftalis & Frankel LLP* * |
| Weinstein Lawrence I | *Proskauer Rose LLP* |
| Zalesin Steven A | *Patterson Belknap Webb & Tyler LLP* * |

**Band 2**

| | |
|---|---|
| Bernstein David | *Debevoise & Plimpton LLP* |
| Colaizzi Roger | *Venable LLP* * |
| Cole Christopher | *Crowell & Moring LLP (ONP)* † * |
| O'Rourke Brendan | *Proskauer Rose LLP* |
| Villafranco John E | *Kelley Drye & Warren LLP* |

**Band 3**

| | |
|---|---|
| Rose Lewis | *Kelley Drye & Warren LLP* |
| Rosenthal Edward H | *Frankfurt Kurnit Klein & Selz* * |

**Up-and-coming individuals**

| | |
|---|---|
| Simon Norman | *Kramer Levin Naftalis & Frankel LLP* * |

† ONP = Other Notable Practitioner.

### Recommended for Client Service
**Nationwide**

| | |
|---|---|
| Davis & Gilbert LLP | Loeb & Loeb LLP |
| Kelley Drye & Warren LLP | Patterson Belknap Webb & Tyler LLP |

### Recommended for Commercial Awareness
**Nationwide**

| | |
|---|---|
| Davis & Gilbert LLP | Loeb & Loeb LLP |
| Frankfurt Kurnit Klein & Selz | Venable LLP |

## Advertising: Transactional & Regulatory
### Leading Firms

**Band 1**

Davis & Gilbert LLP

Frankfurt Kurnit Klein & Selz

Loeb & Loeb LLP *

**Band 2**

Manatt Phelps & Phillips LLP *

Venable LLP *

**Band 3**

Kelley Drye & Warren LLP *

Sheppard, Mullin, Richter & Hampton LLP *

### Leading Individuals

**Star individuals**

| | |
|---|---|
| Goldstein Linda A | *Manatt Phelps & Phillips LLP* |
| Kurnit Rick | *Frankfurt Kurnit Klein & Selz* * |
| Urbach Ronald R | *Davis & Gilbert LLP* * |

**Band 1**

| | |
|---|---|
| Florin Kenneth R | *Loeb & Loeb LLP* * |
| Greenbaum Jeffrey A | *Frankfurt Kurnit Klein & Selz* * |
| Taylor James D | *Loeb & Loeb LLP* * |
| Wood Douglas J | *Reed Smith LLP (ONP)* † |

**Band 2**

| | |
|---|---|
| Edelstein Jeffrey S | *Manatt Phelps & Phillips LLP* |
| Eisert Richard | *Davis & Gilbert LLP* * |
| Felsten Nancy J | *Davis Wright Tremaine LLP (ONP)* † |
| Kersh Candice | *Frankfurt Kurnit Klein & Selz* * |
| Knowles Jeffrey | *Venable LLP* * |
| Lewczak Joseph J | *Davis & Gilbert LLP* * |
| Lustigman Andrew B | *Olshan Frome Wolosky LLP (ONP)* † * |

**Band 3**

| | |
|---|---|
| Grymes Thompson Christie | *Kelley Drye & Warren LLP* |
| Harrison Todd | *Venable LLP* * |
| Heidelberger Brian L | *Winston & Strawn LLP* * |
| Mulcahy Benjamin R | *Sheppard, Mullin, Richter & Hampton LLP* |
| Murphy Brian | *Frankfurt Kurnit Klein & Selz* * |
| Seligman Terri | *Frankfurt Kurnit Klein & Selz* * |
| Solomon Adam | *Olshan Frome Wolosky LLP (ONP)* † * |
| Weingrad Howard | *Davis & Gilbert LLP* * |

\* Indicates firm / individual with profile.
Alphabetical order within each band. Band 1 is the highest.

cy to the creation, production and promotion of advertising campaigns. *"He is very astute and extremely well liked, and has a strong business approach,"* said one interviewee.

### Debevoise & Plimpton LLP
**See profile on p.1968**

**THE FIRM** The advertising department at this international firm continues to be a major player in litigation, assisting an array of prominent clients in this field. The team is involved in all forms of advertising litigation, representing clients before federal and state courts, the FTC, NAD and NARB. Top clients include Nestlé, Prada and L'Oréal USA. Recent highlights include acting for Bayer HealthCare in front of the NAD, NARB and FTC in a case concerning Merial's advertising campaign for Frontline Plus.

**Sources say:** *"The quality of the lawyers is first-rate."*

**KEY INDIVIDUALS** David Bernstein is a *"rising star"* in advertising litigation. He recently acted for Velcera Pharmaceuticals on a challenge brought before the NAD relating to false comparative claims made by a competitor, and on the preliminary injunction phase of a dispute between competing manufacturers of flea and tick control products.

### Frankfurt Kurnit Klein & Selz

**THE FIRM** This New York-based team is best known for its strength in transactional matters, representing top brand marketers and advertising agencies, including PepsiCo and Staples. It also advises on advertising regulatory law and litigation, and continues to expand its practice into the growing sweepstake, promotions, social media and video game markets.

**Commercial Awareness** *"They have broad industry knowledge and expertise, and give action-oriented advice. They don't just know the field academically, they live it every day, and that means they are in a good position to give you practical solutions."*

**KEY INDIVIDUALS** Star individual **Rick Kurnit** (see p.351) is a well-known name and a *"valuable adviser"* in the advertising arena. *"He is a brilliant attorney and easy to work with, and he deeply understands and empathizes with his clients' needs. He has an intuitive instinct about the best practices with regards to contract negotiations."* One source

enthused: *"He is a veritable font of information."* The *"hugely experienced"* **Jeffrey Greenbaum** (see p.326) advises on advertising regulation and litigation, among other matters. He impresses clients with his *"insight into advertising laws and trade practices,"* and his *"strategic and thoughtful"* style, with one source noting that *"he writes and presents persuasively, and is very responsive to our needs."* **Candice Kersh** (see p.345) is *"knowledgeable, organized and scarily smart."* She handles a wide variety of marketing and advertising issues, from structuring branded entertainment deals to advising on new technology and digital platforms. **Terri Seligman** (see p.404) draws praise for her deep understanding of the advertising business and her ability to present clients with *"practical actionable advice."* **Brian Murphy** (see p.373) is singled out for his expertise in IP matters. He assists an array of advertising and entertainment organizations with the creation and production of traditional and new media campaigns. **Edward Rosenthal's** (see p.395) practice focuses on IP litigation, right of publicity, privacy and advertising disputes. He chairs the firm's IP and litigation groups.

### Kelley Drye & Warren LLP
**See profile on p.1985**

**THE FIRM** This full-service advertising practice is well recognized for its expertise in advertising regulation and consumer protection law, and for its extensive FTC experience. It continues to strengthen its nationwide coverage as well as its advertising litigation practice, which encompasses both Lanham Act litigation and consumer class action cases. The firm recently advised Nestlé Healthcare Nutrition on three class actions related to the advertising for a probiotic product, and acted for Walgreens on negotiations with the FTC to end a potential enforcement action. Other top clients include Ocean Spray, Disney and LG Electronics.

**Client Service** *"Outstanding in all areas: efficient, practical and highly responsive."* *"They are really at the top of their game individually and as a department."*

**KEY INDIVIDUALS** John Villafranco is an *"advertising law and consumer protection dynamo"* who impresses clients with his energy and assertiveness. He has vast experience in state and federal court class action defense, Lanham Act litigation and proceedings before the FTC. Department head **Lewis Rose** is well versed in a broad range of advertising issues. He is commended for his industry expertise, *"common sense and level-headedness."* He focuses on regulation, representing a whole host of clients before various regulatory boards such as the FTC and NAD. **Christie Grymes Thompson** has a strong regulatory-focused advertising practice. Recent work includes a number of FTC investigations and sponsorship agreements for major clients.

### Kirkland & Ellis LLP
**See profile on p.1254**

**THE FIRM** The advertising team at this international firm is part of its large national IP department. The team's skilled and experienced litigators handle a variety of advertising matters, representing clients before the FTC and in

# Advertising **Nationwide**

state and federal courts. It also has extensive experience both defending and challenging NAD claims. Key clients include DIRECTV, Abbott Laboratories and American Standard Brands.

**Sources say:** *"An amazing team."*

**KEY INDIVIDUALS** The team is led by Chicago-based Ross Weisman.

## Kramer Levin Naftalis & Frankel LLP
See profile on p.1987

**THE FIRM** This litigation heavyweight leads the field in advertising. The team regularly advises some of the nation's biggest advertisers on high-profile Lanham Act false advertising cases and class actions. It has also built a particularly strong reputation for its work before the National Advertising Division (NAD) and the National Advertising Review Board (NARB). Recent successes include securing victories for clients such as Procter & Gamble and Neutrogena. Other key clients include AstraZeneca, Johnson & Johnson and Dannon.

**Sources say:** *"They have a great relationship with the NAD, a great understanding of the process and deep knowledge of marketing law."*

**KEY INDIVIDUALS Harold Weinberger** (see p.424) is a *"respected and prominent"* litigator who specializes in marketing law. He advises on a number of high-profile false advertising claims under the Lanham Act, and recently represented Neutrogena in a long-running dispute relating to its sunscreen products. **Norman Simon** (see p.407) is an up-and-coming partner who impresses sources with his boundless energy, and is tipped to take an *"increasingly prominent role"* in the group.

## Loeb & Loeb LLP
See profile on p.689

**THE FIRM** This high-quality practice group has established an excellent reputation in the market for its advertising transactional and regulatory expertise, and is regularly involved in a wide range of high-end matters in this area. It is noted by sources for its work straddling both advertising and entertainment law, and continues to be seen as the go-to firm for advertising work in the technology and social media space. The firm also saw significant growth in NAD work throughout 2012. Its enviable client roster includes Comcast, T-Mobile, Amazon and Facebook.

**Commercial Awareness** *"I think they are the best in the field, in terms of both subject matter expertise and their practical work. They really know the business."*

**Client Service** *"They are extremely responsive."*

**KEY INDIVIDUALS Kenneth Florin** (see p.314) co-heads the firm's advanced media and technology department. He has a broad practice covering regulatory, transactional and litigation matters, and regularly takes a leading role in a range of top cases for major clients. Recent highlights include advising T-Mobile and L'Oréal on various sponsorship agreements, co-venture and social media endorsement deals. **James Taylor** (see p.416) earns praise for his deep understanding of the industry and remains *"the go-to*

lawyer for agency negotiations."* He continues to advise Citibank on a number of regulatory issues.

## Manatt Phelps & Phillips LLP
See profile on p.690

**THE FIRM** Market sources praise this advertising team for its multidisciplinary expertise. It represents some of the biggest names in the field, including Pizza Hut, Ticketmaster, Kimberly-Clark and Disney. It continues to expand into the social media arena, advising on cutting-edge digital campaigns and compliance, and remains strong in its work on more traditional advertising platforms. Recent highlights include assisting General Mills with a review and update of all its promotional campaigns.

**Sources say:** *"We feel very confident with Manatt. They give good business-oriented advice which is useful and practical considering the changing landscape of advertising law."*

**KEY INDIVIDUALS Thomas Morrison** is a highly respected and seasoned litigator with over 30 years of trial experience. He specializes in trademark and Lanham Act cases, representing various major consumer organizations and pharmaceutical companies. **Linda Goldstein** is a *"leading expert in commercial and advertising law,"* handling litigation as well as transactional and regulatory matters. One client enthused: *"I trust her implicitly. She has good gut instincts, and I like the way she treats her clients. She is adaptable, a good leader and extremely savvy."* The *"extremely reliable and available"* **Jeffrey Edelstein** is praised by clients for his deep knowledge of advertising law, supportive nature and ability to *"provide answers in a quick and thorough manner."* He regularly appears before regulatory boards such as the NAD, FTC and NARB.

## Patterson Belknap Webb & Tyler LLP
See profile on p.1995

**THE FIRM** This firm's advertising group handles noteworthy cases on behalf of some of the most prominent names in this space. It has built a strong reputation for its expertise in Lanham Act false advertising litigation, and is acknowledged as a seasoned regular before the NAD. The firm has acted on an increasing number of lawsuits regarding the labeling of products over the past year. In highlights, it successfully represented Coca-Cola in a label claim brought by POM Wonderful concerning the name and labeling of one of its juice products.

**Client Service** *"They can quickly analyze advertising issues and give practical advice. Excellent responsiveness – they make a point of becoming familiar with our business, which I find very impressive."*

**KEY INDIVIDUALS** Department head **Steven Zalesin** (see p.430) is a *"terrific litigator"* with significant trial experience. He focuses on false advertising litigation, and acted for Coca-Cola on the abovementioned labeling dispute.

## Proskauer Rose LLP
See profile on p.2001

**THE FIRM** This group is lauded for its broad-based advertising practice. False advertising litigation remains an irrefutable area of strength, and the firm has also seen a notable increase in class action lawsuits and work before

the NAD. Significant highlights include defending Church & Wright against a consumer class action false advertising case involving its Arm & Hammer deodorant product label statements. The team is also acting for Dyson on a Lanham Act false advertising case brought by competitor Bissell. Other major clients include Colgate-Palmolive, T-Mobile USA and Diageo.

**Sources say:** *"Excellent! Fabulous work – they will do everything they need to bring a case or matter to a successful conclusion. They are energetic and able to handle issues well and with broad experience."*

**KEY INDIVIDUALS Lawrence Weinstein** is a *"superb advertising lawyer with a broad range of experience and many years of handling claims."* He is widely praised by peers and clients alike, who note: *"His strengths include his depth of knowledge and the high respect given to him by peers and members of various self-regulating boards. He is very measured and articulate, and a careful reviewer of the potential impact of actions."* **Brendan O'Rourke** works with a number of high-profile clients on Lanham Act false advertising claims and challenges brought before the NAD and NARB. He recently defended Colgate-Palmolive in two NAD advertising challenges.

## Sheppard, Mullin, Richter & Hampton LLP

**THE FIRM** The advertising, marketing and promotions team at Sheppard Mullin specializes in sports, entertainment and digital marketing. It acts for major brands and studios on cutting-edge campaigns. Recent highlights include advising Chrysler on its Super Bowl halftime spot and its innovative promotional campaign in connection with 'The Dark Knight Rises'.

**Sources say:** *"All of the attorneys have outstanding knowledge and customer service. They are highly expert in their fields."*

**KEY INDIVIDUALS Benjamin Mulcahy** cochairs the advertising and sports industry teams, and represents a broad array of top clients, ranging from major brands and advertising agencies to film studios and television networks. Recent highlights include advising Lionsgate on its highly successful marketing campaign for 'The Hunger Games'.

## Venable LLP
See profile on p.927

**THE FIRM** This firm has built an excellent reputation for its work on the full spectrum of litigation, transactional and regulatory advertising matters. It has a strong national presence, and is highly recommended for its specialization in issues involving the FTC, FDA and NAD. Notably, the team provides ongoing counsel to Kellogg regarding compliance with advertising laws and regulations, including advertising to children, packaging, sweepstakes and data security matters.

**Commercial Awareness** *"I have yet to find an area of advertising law, whether dealing with regulators like the FDA and FTC or issues such as international trade, where Venable does not have a top-tier attorney who understands the law and the realities of my business, and can create a solution that meets the requirements of both."*

**KEY INDIVIDUALS Roger Colaizzi** (see p.297) is a *"smart, tough litigator"* with substantial expertise in FTC matters. *"Roger understands our industry and is a guy you want in your corner,"* said one interviewee. **Jeffrey Knowles** (see p.348) heads the firm's advertising, marketing and new media practice group. He advises on a wide array of advertising matters with a focus on the television industry. *"He is a superb lawyer – everyone in the industry thinks of Jeff as the guy you call when you have a problem and need it fixed."* **Todd Harrison** (see p.331) is rated for his experience before regulatory bodies such as the FTC and FAD, advising clients on guidelines and compliance in relation to the marketing of food products.

### Winston & Strawn LLP
See profile on p.1267
**THE FIRM** This team combines expertise in advertising litigation and transactional matters, and is widely recognized for its work on IP disputes and false advertising claims under the Lanham Act. The team is currently defending the Corn Refiners Association against a high-profile false advertising claim involving high-fructose corn syrup.
**Sources say:** *"They are smart, practical, fearsome competitors, while respectful of clients."*
**KEY INDIVIDUALS** Head of department **Brian Heidelberger** (see p.1211) draws widespread praise from market sources for his deep knowledge of the advertising sector. He has advised the Chicago Sun Times, American Honda and Guggenheim Partners on various promotions, marketing issues and social media campaigns. Sources say: *"He always keeps ahead of the trends."*

## Other Notable Practitioners

**Nancy Felsten** is head of the advertising, marketing and promotions department at Davis Wright Tremaine LLP. She acts for a range of clients from various industries, including media, retail and pharmaceuticals, and regularly appears before the NAD and FTC. **Andrew Lustigman** (see p.359) of Olshan Frome Wolosky LLP has a broad practice covering both regulatory and litigation matters. He impresses sources with his deep knowledge, responsiveness and commercial awareness. Also at Olshan Frome Wolosky, **Adam Solomon** (see p.410) is a *"terrific young lawyer"* who advises on all areas of advertising, marketing, promotions and compliance law. **Christopher Cole** (see p.297) joined Crowell & Moring LLP in January 2013 from Manatt, Phelps & Phillips, and is widely regarded as a *"significant authority"* in advertising litigation. *"He is a good strategist, a strong writer and a practical thinker, who has grown to understand the unique challenges of the advertising business."* **Douglas Wood** cochairs the advertising, technology and media department at Reed Smith LLP. He has over 30 years' experience working with some of media and advertising's biggest clients on a range of issues, from class actions and contract negotiations to celebrity endorsement deals and FTC negotiations.

## ANTITRUST

| Antitrust Leading Firms | Antitrust: Cartel Leading Firms | Recommended for Client Service Nationwide | |
|---|---|---|---|
| **Band 1** | Cleary Gottlieb Steen & Hamilton LLP * | Arnold & Porter LLP * | Gibson, Dunn & Crutcher LLP * |
| Arnold & Porter LLP * | Gibson, Dunn & Crutcher LLP * | Cleary Gottlieb Steen & Hamilton LLP | Jones Day |
| Cleary Gottlieb Steen & Hamilton LLP * | Jones Day * | Covington & Burling LLP | McDermott Will & Emery LLP |
| Gibson, Dunn & Crutcher LLP * | Mayer Brown LLP * | Dechert LLP | WilmerHale |
| Jones Day * | O'Melveny & Myers LLP * | | |
| Skadden, Arps, Slate, Meagher & Flom LLP & Affiliates * | Paul, Weiss, Rifkind, Wharton & Garrison LLP * | **Recommended for Commercial Awareness Nationwide** | |
| **Band 2** | WilmerHale * | Bingham McCutchen LLP | Gibson, Dunn & Crutcher LLP |
| Cravath, Swaine & Moore LLP * | *Indicates firm with profile.* | Cleary Gottlieb Steen & Hamilton LLP | Jones Day |
| Davis Polk & Wardwell LLP * | *Alphabetical order within each band.* | Cravath, Swaine & Moore LLP | Morrison & Foerster LLP |
| Latham & Watkins LLP * | | Davis Polk & Wardwell LLP | WilmerHale |
| Simpson Thacher & Bartlett LLP * | **Band 1** | | |
| Sullivan & Cromwell LLP * | | | |
| Wachtell, Lipton, Rosen & Katz * | ### Arnold & Porter LLP | | |
| **Band 3** | See profile on p.906 | | |
| Covington & Burling LLP * | **THE FIRM** This group remains a potent force in the US antitrust space, despite the departure in January 2013 of global practice co-head Bill Baer to become assistant attorney general of the DOJ's antitrust division. It has strong nationwide scope, and offers particular strength in Washington, DC and California. It is able to cover all aspects of antitrust, with leading practitioners in transactional work as well as litigation. It represented VISA in the payment card interchange fee litigation, and also acted for Sony Corporation of America and Sony/ATV on its $2.2 billion acquisition of EMI's music publishing business. | | |
| Dechert LLP * | | | |
| Hogan Lovells US LLP * | | | |
| Kirkland & Ellis LLP * | | | |
| Mayer Brown LLP * | | | |
| McDermott Will & Emery LLP * | | | |
| O'Melveny & Myers LLP * | | | |
| Weil, Gotshal & Manges LLP * | | | |
| WilmerHale * | | | |
| Wilson Sonsini Goodrich & Rosati * | | | |
| **Band 4** | | | |
| Bingham McCutchen LLP * | | | |
| Boies, Schiller & Flexner LLP * | **Client Service** *"The quality of the different lawyers we work with there is just outstanding, as is their knowledge of our business, cost management and teamwork. It's a model relationship actually."* | | |
| Morrison & Foerster LLP * | | | |
| Paul, Weiss, Rifkind, Wharton & Garrison LLP * | | | |
| Sidley Austin LLP * | **KEY INDIVIDUALS** Following Baer's departure, Deborah Feinstein is now sole head of the firm's practice group and is a highly respected deal lawyer working out of | | |
| Winston & Strawn LLP * | | | |

Washington, DC. She is ably assisted there by Jonathan Gleklen.

### Cleary Gottlieb Steen & Hamilton LLP
See profile on p.1963
**THE FIRM** Cleary Gottlieb has one of the leading antitrust practice groups in the country, and is predominantly based out of Washington, DC. Its capabilities are manifold, with exceptional strength and coverage in civil litigation, cartel investigations and mergers and acquisitions. Among its blue-chip clients is Western Digital, which it represented in its $4.8 billion acquisition of Hitachi's hard disk drive arm. It also gained dismissal in the New York Supreme Court for a number of major financial institutions, including Citi, JPMorgan Chase and Goldman Sachs, in a case of alleged monopolization concerning the financing of airline terminals. The team has also acted for a number of organizations on responding to automotive parts cartel investigations undertaken by authorities on a global scale, demon-

strating its ability to coordinate its impressive worldwide resources.

**Client Service** *"They are so easy to work with – they fit right in, are highly intelligent and I trust them implicitly."*

**Commercial Awareness** *"They bring a unique combination of agency experience, talent and advocacy skills – they are experts in the variety of antitrust issues that arise out of a company's day-to-day operations."*

**KEY INDIVIDUALS** The practice continues to be spearheaded by formidable practitioners George Cary and Mark Leddy.

### Gibson, Dunn & Crutcher LLP
See profile on p.682

**THE FIRM** Few firms can claim to have such strength across such geographical breadth as Gibson, Dunn & Crutcher. Its influence extends well beyond its Californian roots, with high-quality practitioners in New York, Washington, DC and Texas. It is particularly lauded for its cartel-related work, led by legendary cartel figure Gary Spratling, although it offers impressive full-service capability. Its recent work includes acting as lead counsel for Apple on the high-profile eBooks antitrust litigation. It also represented Cox Communications in defense of a putative class action case concerning cable television bundling. The firm's impressive client base also includes Sony, Facebook and Microsoft.

**Client Service** *"They do excellent work, and are responsive and thorough. They can handle any issue that comes up. They are people you can uniformly work with and who are on your side."*

**Commercial Awareness** *"They are very good at analyzing the situation and developing plans to address the issues."*

**KEY INDIVIDUALS** The firm has four lawyers heading up their practice. They are Peter Sullivan in New York, Daniel Swanson in Los Angeles, Sean Royall in Dallas and Gary Spratling in San Francisco.

### Jones Day
See profile on p.919

**THE FIRM** Another giant in the antitrust world, Jones Day has an outstanding national and international legal network. Within the US, its exceptional coast-to-coast coverage sets it apart from many of its competitors. It has a plethora of high-level, high-quality lawyers who cover the gamut of antitrust work from criminal investigations to merger reviews. It represented Goodrich Corporation in one of the largest recent deals in the country, its $18.4 billion acquisition by United Technologies. It also acted for Union Pacific Railway on the defense of antitrust litigation stemming from claims of an alleged conspiracy to fix fuel surcharges.

**Client Service** *"We use them because they know our business – they are pragmatic and efficient and give us concrete advice."*

**Commercial Awareness** *"The firm excels at explaining the rules in a way that is understandable, despite the fact that there are often lots of nuances and tangents."*

**KEY INDIVIDUALS** Highly rated David Wales is the firm's new antitrust practice group leader, based out of the Washington, DC office.

### Skadden, Arps, Slate, Meagher & Flom LLP & Affiliates
See profile on p.2008

**THE FIRM** With leading practices in both New York and Washington, DC, Skadden's sphere of influence for antitrust is based on the East Coast. It is a particularly dominant force in transactional antitrust, and is regularly involved in many of the biggest deals in this space. It also offers strong litigation and criminal cartel aspects to its practice. Its recent representations reflect the team's leading expertise in the arena, and include acting for Express Scripts on its titanic $29.1 billion acquisition of Medco Health Solutions. It is also acting for Anheuser-Busch on its proposed $20.1 billion acquisition of the 50% of Grupo Modelo it does not already own.

**Sources say:** *"They are a good team – detail-oriented, very available and responsive. They were very deep in all of the areas we've needed them for."*

**KEY INDIVIDUALS** New York antitrust litigator Shepard Goldfein heads the global practice group while his colleague Steven Sunshine in Washington, DC is head of the North American antitrust and competition practice.

### Band 2

### Cravath, Swaine & Moore LLP
See profile on p.1966

**THE FIRM** New York-based firm Cravath, Swaine & Moore is known principally for its litigation strength, although it has been boosted on the transactional front by the addition of high-profile former head of the antitrust division at the DOJ, Christine Varney. Despite only having one US office, it is able to stand alongside many of the larger firms in the country, demonstrating the ability to handle a wide range of antitrust matters on a nationwide scale. It has recently acted for American Express on four civil lawsuits concerning alleged breaches of antitrust laws. Other highlights include representing AmerisourceBergen in its $250 acquisition of TheraCom, and providing advice on a range of antitrust matters to Warner Music Group.

**Commercial Awareness** *"They are very practical, they understand our business and I was very pleased with the consistency in quality of their work product."*

**KEY INDIVIDUALS** Christine Varney chairs the firm's antitrust practice group. Fellow antitrust expert Evan Chesler is the firm's presiding partner.

### Davis Polk & Wardwell LLP
See profile on p.442

**THE FIRM** Davis Polk maintains a preeminent antitrust practice in New York, and also offers a strong presence in California. Its leading position in New York is largely predicated on its impressive transactional practice, although it also houses notable litigation capabilities. Partner Arthur Burke continues to have a strong relationship with

Comcast, and the firm has represented it in a number of matters in recent times. This includes its significant victory for Comcast in the cable television bundling class action case. On the transactional side, it recently acted for CNOOC in its $15.1 billion acquisition of Nexen.

**Commercial Awareness** *"They exhibited superb knowledge of the field, had impressive connections with the regulators, formulated a very effective strategy and executed it flawlessly."*

**KEY INDIVIDUALS** Christopher Hockett heads the antitrust practice group out of its Menlo Park, California office. In New York, Ronan Harty is the most prominent antitrust practitioner.

### Latham & Watkins LLP
See profile on p.446

**THE FIRM** Latham is another big name in the antitrust arena, with sources particularly pointing to its strength on the litigation side in addition to undoubted ability in transactional work. Prominent offices in California and Washington, DC confirm its nationwide scope, and it houses a significant bench of high-level, experienced attorneys. It has continued to represent Apple in class action cases relating to the tying of iPhones to the AT&T network, as well as acting for Apple on government investigations into Google and Motorola, and, separately, Samsung Electronics. The team's recent work also includes acting as antitrust counsel to The Carlyle Group on a global scale, work which involved advising on several multibillion-dollar transactions.

**Sources say:** *"They were strong across the board."*

**KEY INDIVIDUALS** The antitrust practice group's three global co-chairs are Michael Egge, who works out of the firm's Washington, DC and Brussels offices, and San Francisco-based Al Pfeiffer and Christopher Yates.

### Simpson Thacher & Bartlett LLP
See profile on p.2006

**THE FIRM** The center of gravity for this firm's antitrust practice is in New York, although it also operates out of other key locations in the country, including Washington, DC. It maintains a strong reputation across both litigation and transactional work, led by the exceptional Kevin Arquit, and works with clients from a wide range of industries. It continues to defend JPMorgan Chase in several civil actions related to the investigation into the alleged fixing of LIBOR rates. It also represented CoStar Group in its $860 million acquisition of LoopNet.

**Sources say:** *"They gave wise and balanced advice and there is no way they could have been any more responsive."*

**KEY INDIVIDUALS** Kevin Arquit remains the lead lawyer in the practice as well as one of the most well-regarded attorneys at the New York antitrust Bar.

### Sullivan & Cromwell LLP
See profile on p.2011

**THE FIRM** Sullivan & Cromwell's antitrust group is predominantly based around its New York office, although it also has some presence in Washington, D.C, Los Angeles and Palo Alto. It is highly skilled at undertaking antitrust litigation, government investigations and merger clearances. It is particularly lauded for its financial services work, and recently acted for Barclays in the LIBOR rate-fixing investigation. It also advised HSBC on the sale of a number of US branches to First Niagara Bank and on the sale of its US card business to Capital One Financial Corporation.

**Sources say:** *"I've yet to run across a partner there that I'm disappointed with and there's very little in this area that they can't deal with."*

**KEY INDIVIDUALS** Yvonne Quinn in New York and Daryl Libow in Washington, DC are the co-heads of the antitrust practice group.

## Wachtell, Lipton, Rosen & Katz
See profile on p.2012

**THE FIRM** Wachtell is highly regarded for its antitrust expertise in mergers and acquisitions, and is considered a leading transactional firm in this area. Based entirely in New York, the firm houses a compact but highly skilled antitrust group whose members are also experienced in handling complex investigations. It has represented clients in some of the biggest recent deals, for instance acting for United Technologies in its $18.4 billion acquisition of Goodrich, and for Motorola Mobility in its $12.5 billion acquisition by Google.

**Sources say:** *"They are the premier transactional firm. Their bench strength is fantastic."*

**KEY INDIVIDUALS** Ilene Knable Gotts continues to be one of the finest transactional lawyers in New York, while Michael Byowitz is also extremely highly regarded.

## Band 3

## Covington & Burling LLP
See profile on p.441

**THE FIRM** This group has an increasing recognized antitrust practice, and houses highly respected practitioners whose experience spans a wide range of litigation and transactional matters in the field. The firm's strength in this area lies predominantly in Washington, DC, although it has a broader geographical presence allowing it to handle matters on a nationwide basis. Its expertise in matters involving agencies is enhanced by the presence of two former assistant attorney generals of the antitrust division of the DOJ. Its recent work includes acting for Expedia in defending several antitrust class actions filed in relation to hotel bookings. It also advised Facebook on its $747 million acquisition of Instagram.

**Client Service** *"They are some of the best lawyers we work with – savvy, pragmatic and usually two steps ahead. They understand our business and understand our goals – everything you'd want in lawyers doing work for you."*

**KEY INDIVIDUALS** The practice is fronted by Thomas Barnett and Deborah Garza, both former heads of the DOJ antitrust division. Both gain praise from peers for their experience and skill in this area.

## Dechert LLP
See profile on p.1969

**THE FIRM** Dechert's US antitrust practice is largely focused around its Washington, DC, New York and Philadelphia offices. It remains the dominant force for antitrust in Pennsylvania, housing an impressive number of skilled practitioners there. It is highly experienced in antitrust litigation and has also had several notable recent representations in the transactional front, including advising Medco Health Solutions on its significant $29.1 billion merger with Express Scripts. Its recent litigation highlights include defending Whole Foods in a class action concerning the acquisition of Wild Oats Market. Class certification was successfully denied.

**Client Service** *"They are cost-effective, cost-conscious and very creative about alternative fee arrangements. They're very relationship-oriented people."*

**KEY INDIVIDUALS** The practice is cochaired by partners George Gordon in Philadelphia and Michael Weiner in New York. Paul Denis also remains a key member of the group.

## Hogan Lovells US LLP

**THE FIRM** This team's power base for antitrust is in its Washington, DC office, although it has notable practitioners in its New York and California offices as well. It has expertise in all areas of antitrust, including cartel work, civil class action litigation and mergers and acquisitions. Among its recent work is acting for IBM in the high-tech antitrust employees investigation and civil litigation. It also acted for Ariba on its acquisition by SAP, a $4.3 billion deal. Another recent highlight is the advice provided to Verizon Communications on the DOJ investigation conducted into the company's agreement to buy wireless spectrum from four cable companies.

**Sources say:** *"They were responsive and communicative, and gave good counsel, while helping us find the right avenues and listening to our concerns."*

**KEY INDIVIDUALS** The antitrust, competition and economic regulation practice group at the firm is headed by two practitioners, Janet McDavid in Washington, DC and Susan Bright in London.

## Kirkland & Ellis LLP
See profile on p.1254

**THE FIRM** Kirkland & Ellis maintains an impressive presence in nationwide antitrust, with strong offices in both Chicago and Washington, DC. The Washington, DC branch is particularly respected for its expertise in transactional matters and has been involved in such major recent matters as acting for Constellation Energy Group on its $7.9 billion merger with Exelon. The firm is also lauded for its litigation expertise, having recently represented, for example, Bain Capital Partners in a putative class action alleging fixing of stock prices.

**Sources say:** *"They were outstanding, not only at addressing the issues of the day, but also planning carefully and anticipating problems down the line."*

**KEY INDIVIDUALS** The leading lawyers in this practice group include Timothy Muris and Mark Kovner in Washington, DC, and James Mutchnik and Daniel Laytin in Illinois.

## Mayer Brown LLP
See profile on p.1257

**THE FIRM** This group is a dominant force in Illinois, hosting an impressive group of top practitioners. It also maintains a strong foothold in the Washington, DC market, and has additional presence in New York. It is particularly noted for its cartel-related work, and acts as co-counsel to ArcelorMittal in allegations of an antitrust conspiracy undertaken by steel producers. It has also been involved in several large transactions, including acting for Nestle in its $11.9 billion acquisition of the infant nutrition arm of Pfizer.

**Sources say:** *"They are very prompt and knowledgeable advisers, giving practical, efficient and actionable advice."*

**KEY INDIVIDUALS** Robert Bloch remains Mayer Brown's global antitrust head.

## McDermott Will & Emery LLP
See profile on p.1258

**THE FIRM** This group has a good breadth of nationwide presence with its well-established offices in Washington, DC and Chicago being joined by an increasingly recognized group in Texas, following the addition there of Allan van Fleet. It covers the gamut of antitrust work, handling both litigation and transactional work with aplomb. Its recent representations include acting for Mars in a case concerning the alleged price fixing of chocolate, and for the Dairy Farmers of America in defense of a putative class action alleging monopolization in the dairy market.

**Client Service** *"They are very responsive and, more importantly, the guidance they give is very clear – they are able to synthesize issues in a coherent way so that I can explain it to my clients. They're an excellent resource for me."*

**KEY INDIVIDUALS** Joseph Winterscheid is head of the practice group. Other notable practitioners at the firm include Joel Chefitz and David Marx in Illinois, and Allan van Fleet in Texas.

## O'Melveny & Myers LLP
See profile on p.693

**THE FIRM** O'Melveny's reputation is largely founded on its strength in antitrust litigation, where it remains a nationally strong practitioner. The firm has a substantial presence in California, and maintains a strong foothold in Washington, DC. Its representations include acting for Apple on both the eBooks investigation and the high-tech employees litigation. The group has also recently represented Samsung Electronics in the cathode ray tube antitrust class action. Its client base is representative of its broad-based capabilities, and also includes Capital One, Honeywell International and SK Hynix.

**Sources say:** *"They are a significant player on a national level."*

**KEY INDIVIDUALS** Richard Parker continues to be head of the antitrust practice group as well as its leading light.

## Weil, Gotshal & Manges LLP
See profile on p.2015

**THE FIRM** The bulk of Weil Gotshal's antitrust strength resides in its Washington, DC office, although it also retains a significant presence in New York. Although practicing across the full breadth of the antitrust spectrum, the group has recently been involved in several high-profile matters on the transactional side. This includes representing Johnson & Johnson in the multibillion-dollar acquisition of Synthes, the largest transaction ever undertaken by the company. It also represented Walgreen in its recent $6.7 billion acquisition of a 45% interest in Alliance Boots.

**Sources say:** *"They have all the know-how and horsepower, but also have a pragmatic and reasoned approach. They understand our goal and are helpful in getting us there."*

**KEY INDIVIDUALS** The head of practice and leading antitrust partner is Steven Newborn, based out of the firm's Washington, DC office.

## WilmerHale
See profile on p.930

**THE FIRM** WilmerHale's sphere of influence is on the East Coast, with particularly strong offices in Boston and Washington, DC. It has an active cartel practice involved in many of the most important ongoing criminal investigations, including the autoparts and freight forwarding investigations, in which it represented DENSO Corporation and Nissin Corporation respectively. In addition, it has been busy in mergers and acquisitions and civil litigation, including acting for the Walt Disney Company in the cable bundling class action case.

**Client Service** *"They support us extremely well – they always give us detailed answers in a timely manner, no matter how urgent. They always try to give us something more than we expect and they always have good suggestions – sometimes things we didn't think of."*

**Commercial Awareness** *"These folks are really, really good lawyers. They're efficient and really customer-focused. They have street savvy and a very good understanding of the formal and informal processes of the DOJ."*

**KEY INDIVIDUALS** The antitrust practice group is cochaired by Michelle Miller in Boston and Thomas Mueller in Washington, DC.

## Wilson Sonsini Goodrich & Rosati
See profile on p.700

**THE FIRM** This team is increasingly establishing itself as a well-regarded firm for antitrust litigation, and has particular expertise in the technology arena. With two strong offices in New York and Washington, DC as well as maintaining a presence in California, it can certainly boast nationwide scope. Its biggest client is Google, which it has acted for on a number of matters, including the government investigation into its search behavior and advertising. Other clients include T-Mobile, which it represented in several acquisitions.

**Sources say:** *"I really love their work – they are fantastic, responsive and easy to work with."*

**KEY INDIVIDUALS** The practice group is co-chaired by two of Wilson Sonsini's most prominent antitrust lawyers,

Susan Creighton in Washington, DC and Jonathan Jacobson in New York.

## Band 4

## Bingham McCutchen LLP
See profile on p.1515

**THE FIRM** Bingham McCutchen enters the rankings on the back of its strong nationwide presence, which comprises substantial antitrust presences in Massachusetts and California, in addition to practitioners in New York and Washington, DC. It focuses primarily on antitrust litigation, and recently represented Intel in the high-tech employees litigation as well as acting for Sharp in opt-out cases related to TFT-LCD televisions.

**Commercial Awareness** *"We've required them to think very creatively and do something they've never done before and they've been amazingly good at it."*

**KEY INDIVIDUALS** Leiv Blad and Frank Hinman head the firm's antitrust and competition practice group.

## Boies, Schiller & Flexner LLP
See profile on p.1958

**THE FIRM** This group continues to have an outstanding reputation for its litigation work and many of its litigators are also skilled in the antitrust space. It has an active presence in both Florida and New York. It undertakes a significant amount of plaintiff-side work and has been involved in cases such as the LCD class action suit on behalf of opt-out plaintiffs.

**Sources say:** *"For pure antitrust litigation, they are excellent."*

**KEY INDIVIDUALS** Two of the named partners at the firm, David Boies and Donald Flexner, remain the firm's antitrust lead lawyers. In Florida, Stuart Singer is the key partner.

## Morrison & Foerster LLP
See profile on p.1990

**THE FIRM** This firm has recently strengthened its presence in Washington, DC, giving it a recognized antitrust practice on the East Coast to go with its established presence in California. Sources praise the group's depth of expertise in the antitrust arena, and highlight its aptitude in technology and IP-related matters. It is also experienced in handling work with cross-border elements, and tackles complex litigation and transactions for a wide range of clients. It recently acted for JPMorgan Chase in the ATM fees antitrust litigation.

**Commercial Awareness** *"What differentiates their partners is that they are not only substantively strong, but also very practical and business-oriented problem solvers. You don't just get the black letter law but also a very practical solution that allows you to apply it to the real world situation."*

**KEY INDIVIDUALS** The practice group heads are Stephen Smith and David Meyer, both based out of the Washington, DC office.

## Paul, Weiss, Rifkind, Wharton & Garrison LLP
See profile on p.1997

**THE FIRM** Litigation specialist Paul Weiss, a new addition to the table, has a growing antitrust presence in Washington, DC and New York. It has an excellent reputation for work within the cartel space in addition to proven success in civil litigation matters. Recently it defended Pfizer in a case concerning alleged anticompetitive conduct related to the drug Neurotonin.

**Sources say:** *"They are a go-to firm for really serious, bet-the-company, high exposure litigation."*

**KEY INDIVIDUALS** The practice group is cochaired by Aidan Synott in the firm's New York office and Joseph Simons in Washington, DC.

## Sidley Austin LLP
See profile on p.1264

**THE FIRM** This group is predominantly active in antitrust litigation, although it is also able to undertake sizeable transactional work for clients. It has a solid presence in both Illinois and California, and covers all aspects of antitrust work for clients based across the country. The US-based practitioners can also draw on the global strength of the firm's antitrust team when handling transactional, regulatory and litigation work. It continues to represent Macmillan in the ongoing eBooks litigation as well as acting for Citi in the payment card interchange fee suit.

**Sources say:** *"They're thorough, fast, efficient professionals who go above and beyond."*

**KEY INDIVIDUALS** The Sidley antitrust practice group is run by the triumvirate of Marie Fiala in San Francisco, Joel Mitnick in New York and John Treece in Chicago.

## Winston & Strawn LLP
See profile on p.1267

**THE FIRM** This team has grown greatly in size of late following the arrival of a large group of antitrust lawyers from Dewey & LeBoeuf, including heavyweight litigators such as Jeffrey Kessler. Its antitrust capabilities are largely on the litigation side, and it features a solid criminal cartel practice. It recently represented Uralkali in the potash civil antitrust litigation, as well as acting for Panasonic on a number of litigation matters.

**Sources say:** *"Excellent in all respects – we have been very pleased with the talent we've been exposed to."*

**KEY INDIVIDUALS** Four partners run the practice group at Winston & Strawn. They are Paul Griffin in San Francisco, Jeffrey Kessler in New York, Mark McCareins in Chicago and Robert Ruyak in Washington, DC.

# APPELLATE LAW

Commentary about individuals can be found under their firm's paragraph. If the firm has no paragraph (is not ranked) look at Other Notable Practitioners.

## Appellate Law
### Leading Firms

**Band 1**
Gibson, Dunn & Crutcher LLP *
Latham & Watkins LLP *
Mayer Brown LLP *
Sidley Austin LLP *
WilmerHale *

**Band 2**
Jones Day *
Kellogg, Huber, Hansen, Todd, Evans & Figel, PLLC

**Band 3**
Akin Gump Strauss Hauer & Feld LLP *
Covington & Burling LLP *
Farr & Taranto
Hogan Lovells US LLP
Jenner & Block LLP *
King & Spalding LLP *
Kirkland & Ellis LLP *
O'Melveny & Myers LLP *
Robbins, Russell, Englert, Orseck, Untereiner & Sauber LLP

**Band 4**
Arnold & Porter LLP *
Bancroft PLLC
Morgan, Lewis & Bockius LLP *
Morrison & Foerster LLP *
Quinn Emanuel Urquhart & Sullivan, LLP
Vinson & Elkins LLP *
Williams & Connolly LLP

### Recommended for Client Service
**Nationwide**

| | |
|---|---|
| Hogan Lovells US LLP | Kirkland & Ellis LLP |
| King & Spalding LLP | Mayer Brown LLP |

### Recommended for Commercial Awareness
**Nationwide**

| | |
|---|---|
| Kirkland & Ellis LLP | WilmerHale |
| Mayer Brown LLP | |

## Appellate Law
### Senior Statesmen

**Senior Statesmen: distinguished older practitioners**

| | |
|---|---|
| Dellinger Walter | O'Melveny & Myers LLP |
| Mahoney Maureen | Latham & Watkins LLP * |

### Leading Individuals

**Star individuals**

| | |
|---|---|
| Clement Paul | Bancroft PLLC |
| Englert Jr Roy | Robbins, Russell, Englert, Orseck, |
| Olson Theodore B | Gibson, Dunn & Crutcher LLP * |
| Phillips Carter G | Sidley Austin LLP (ONP)[†] * |
| Waxman Seth | WilmerHale * |

**Band 1**

| | |
|---|---|
| Blatt Lisa | Arnold & Porter LLP * |
| Estrada Miguel A | Gibson, Dunn & Crutcher LLP * |
| Frederick David C | Kellogg, Huber, Hansen, Todd, Evans |
| Frey Andrew L | Mayer Brown LLP |
| Garre Gregory | Latham & Watkins LLP * |
| Lamken Jeffrey A | MoloLamken LLP (ONP)[†] * |
| Sullivan Kathleen M | Quinn Emanuel Urquhart & Sullivan, LLP |
| Taranto Richard | Farr & Taranto |

**Band 2**

| | |
|---|---|
| Boutrous Jr Theodore J | Gibson, Dunn & Crutcher LLP * |
| Carvin Michael A | Jones Day * |
| Goldstein Thomas C | Goldstein & Russell, P.C. (ONP)[†] |
| Keisler Peter | Sidley Austin LLP * |
| Landau Christopher | Kirkland & Ellis LLP * |
| Long Jr Robert A | Covington & Burling LLP * |
| Millett Patricia A | Akin Gump Strauss Hauer & Feld LLP * |
| Nager Glen | Jones Day * |
| Pincus Andrew J | Mayer Brown LLP |
| Robbins Lawrence | Robbins, Russell, Englert, Orseck |
| Rosenkranz Joshua | Orrick, Herrington & Sutcliffe LLP (ONP)[†] |
| Shanmugam Kannon | Williams & Connolly LLP |
| Shapiro Stephen M | Mayer Brown LLP |
| Smith Paul M | Jenner & Block LLP * |
| Tager Evan M | Mayer Brown LLP |

**Band 3**

| | |
|---|---|
| Axelrad David M | Horvitz & Levy LLP (ONP)[†] * |
| Ayer Donald | Jones Day * |

| | |
|---|---|
| Collins Daniel | Munger, Tolles & Olson LLP (ONP)[†] * |
| DuMont Edward C | WilmerHale * |
| Elwood John | Vinson & Elkins LLP * |
| Farr Bartow | Farr & Taranto |
| Geller Kenneth S | Mayer Brown LLP |
| Hatchell Mike A | Locke Lord LLP (ONP)[†] * |
| Hungar Thomas | Gibson, Dunn & Crutcher LLP * |
| Joseffer Daryl | King & Spalding LLP * |
| Katyal Neal | Hogan Lovells |
| Kellogg Michael | Kellogg, Huber, Hansen, Todd, Evans |
| Maynard Deanne | Morrison & Foerster LLP * |
| Perry Mark A | Gibson, Dunn & Crutcher LLP * |
| Phillips Thomas R | Baker Botts LLP (ONP)[†] * |
| Rogow Bruce S | Alters Law Firm (ONP)[†] |

**Band 4**

| | |
|---|---|
| Baker Miller | McDermott Will & Emery LLP * |
| Cantero Raoul | White & Case LLP (ONP)[†] * |
| Coberly Linda T | Winston & Strawn LLP (ONP)[†] * |
| Dunner Donald R | Finnegan, Henderson, Farabow (ONP)[†] * |
| Franklin Jonathan S | Fulbright & Jaworski LLP (ONP)[†] * |
| Hacker Jonathan | O'Melveny & Myers LLP |
| Hallward-Driemeier Douglas | Ropes & Gray LLP (ONP)[†] |
| Ho Allyson N | Morgan, Lewis & Bockius LLP * |
| Kinnaird Stephen B. | Paul Hastings LLP (ONP)[†] |
| Kolkey Daniel M | Gibson, Dunn & Crutcher LLP * |
| Rothfeld Charles | Mayer Brown LLP |
| Stetson Catherine E | Hogan Lovells US LLP |
| Walker Helgi C | Wiley Rein LLP (ONP)[†] * |
| Wolfson Paul RQ | WilmerHale * |
| Yeates Marie | Vinson & Elkins LLP * |

**Up-and-coming individuals**

| | |
|---|---|
| Ballenger J Scott | Latham & Watkins LLP * |
| Dupree Jr Thomas | Gibson, Dunn & Crutcher LLP * |

* Indicates firm / individual with profile.
[†] ONP = Other Notable Practitioner.

## Band 1

### Gibson, Dunn & Crutcher LLP
See profile on p.682

**THE FIRM** This firm is an obvious leader in the appellate space, featuring an endless supply of top-quality practitioners spread across multiple offices nationwide. The group offers extensive experience in handling complex appellate litigation for a range of clients including Comcast, The Travelers Companies and Walmart. Ongoing cases include the representation of John Wiley & Sons in a dispute concerning the specifics of copyright infringement.
**Sources say:** "*The firm has a variety of advocates who perform appellate work at the highest level.*"

**KEY INDIVIDUALS Theodore Olson** (see p.380) remains a preeminent choice of appellate lawyer, hailed as "*one of the leading Supreme Court advocates in the country*" and "*a wise legal strategist.*" He continues to be involved in some of the country's leading cases in recent times, including acting as co-counsel for the American Foundation for Equal Rights in the historic Proposition 8 litigation. The US Court of Appeals for the Ninth Circuit recently upheld the Perry v Brown district court ruling that confirmed the unconstitutionality of the proposition. The case will be heard by the Supreme Court. The "*tremendously effective advocate*" **Miguel Estrada** (see p.310) cochairs the firm's appellate and constitutional law practice and has displayed superb courtroom abilities in numerous Supreme Court appearances. He is currently working on behalf of Comcast in a dispute regarding the role of district courts in the certification of class actions. He is "*one smart son of a gun,*" according to sources. Fellow practice cochair **Theodore Boutrous** (see p.624) is held in high regard by market commentators for his work as a "*great advocate.*" Following on from his success in the Wal-Mart v Dukes case, Theodore has played a key role in several other significant matters, including the Proposition 8 case referred to above. Other highlights include his representation of Standard Fire before the Supreme Court in what will be the first case at this level to interpret the 2005 Class Action Fairness Act (CAFA). **Thomas Hungar** (see p.338) is an acclaimed appellate lawyer based in Washington, DC and has argued multiple cases at Supreme Court level, as well as numerous arguments before federal and state appellate courts. He recently achieved a substantial victory for Facebook in a patent infringement case brought by Leader Technologies. **Mark Perry** (see p.384) is a seasoned litigator who specializes in complex commercial litigation. After years of extensive litigation on behalf of Janus Capital Management, he led the team that successfully defeated the final case in this matter. This was brought by First Derivative Traders, and was taken to the Supreme Court. **Daniel Kolkey** (see p.647) is a distinguished member of the appellate team, and is based in San Francisco. He currently represents Apple in a California Supreme Court case regarding the recording of a customer's address in an online transaction. **Thomas Dupree** (see p.307) is a new addition to the rankings, backed by a rapidly growing reputation for presenting excellent arguments at appellate level. Peers characterize him as *"a very fine lawyer who is certainly well regarded."*

### Latham & Watkins LLP
See profile on p.446

**THE FIRM** This preeminent appellate group continues to win victory after victory in the federal and supreme courts. It is particularly noted for its ability to handle a diverse caseload, representing a wide range of clients in their most significant cases. It achieved a landmark decision on behalf of a death row inmate Cory Maples in the Supreme Court in the Maples v Thomas case. The team also enjoyed an important win in United States v Home Concrete, a case which significantly impacts the ability of the government to collect tax.

**Sources say:** *"From top to bottom the team is five-star quality."*

**KEY INDIVIDUALS Maureen Mahoney** (see p.360) continues to *"add an enormous amount of value"* to the appellate team. She is described as *"unbelievably good in every respect."* **Gregory Garre** (see p.319) is a force to be reckoned with and is hailed as *"one of the top Supreme Court advocates of his generation."* He is making a huge impact in the appellate community, and his recent high-profile representations include acting for University of Texas at Austin. This Supreme Court case will determine whether the University has the right to use an applicant's race as one of the numerous factors that inform admission choices. **Scott Ballenger** (see p.277) is rapidly gaining praise for his impressive appellate work. His recent work includes representing Union Pacific Railroad Company in its Eighth Circuit case against the US Department of Homeland Security.

### Mayer Brown LLP
See profile on p.1257

**THE FIRM** Mayer Brown remains at the forefront of the appellate field, engaging in many high-stakes appeals at the Supreme Court level. Its impressive client roster spans a diverse range of industries, demonstrating the team's breadth of knowledge. The team is currently working on behalf of Siemens, American Honda Motor, Medtronic and many more. Its recent highlights include acting for Georgia Pacific in a case concerning the Clean Water Act that will be heard before the Supreme Court.

**Client Service** *"They respond immediately to any questions I have; they're always willing to pitch in and do anything, even at the last minute – they have an amazing can-do attitude."*

**Commercial Awareness** *"This is a team of superstars who consistently deliver insightful counsel and, when it's go time, superior advocacy and results."*

**KEY INDIVIDUALS Andrew Frey** is a *"highly regarded and well-known appellate lawyer"* who has amassed an incredible amount of experience at all the varying court levels. *"He is incredibly intelligent and knows the law very, very well – I always feel very confident in his answers to legal questions,"* states one source. **Andrew Pincus** is singled out for being particularly active in the Supreme Court, engaging in several high-profile appeals. Commentators praise the breadth of his practice, and state that he *"gets tapped for the really important matters."* He recently obtained a unanimous summary reversal of a decision made by the West Virginia Supreme Court of Appeals against Clarksburg Nursing Home & Rehabilitation Center. **Stephen Shapiro** maintains an impressive presence in the appellate arena, offering extensive experience in arguing noteworthy cases in the Supreme Court. He handles matters on behalf of clients from a wide range of industries, demonstrating his impressive advocacy skills in multiple high-profile cases. **Evan Tager** is lauded as a *"go-to appellate lawyer"* who is able to *"deliver truly superior advocacy and actionable solutions for complex and high-stakes problems."* He recently succeeded in appealing the decision that CSX Transportation should pay $3.9 million in damages to plaintiff Dominic Choate, who argued that Illinois Harbor Belt Railroad Company should have prevented him from trespassing on its tracks. Managing partner **Kenneth Geller** is a significant member of the appellate team, praised for his *"exquisite understanding of legal issues from both an analytical and practical viewpoint."* Sources also commend his ability to *"devise excellent strategies to promote novel theories."* Special counsel **Charles Rothfeld** is a highly respected appellate advocate who is regarded as *"incredibly successful"* by market sources. He has been involved in a number of matters on behalf of Siemens, Mayo Medical Labs and The Bank of New York Mellon in recent times. Peers also highlight him as being a *"very fine oral advocate."*

### Sidley Austin LLP
See profile on p.1264

**THE FIRM** This highly regarded group of experienced practitioners is capable of handling a broad spread of cases, and has deep-rooted expertise in appearing before all levels of state and federal appellate court. The group recently achieved a victory for Fox Television Stations after a ruling by the Supreme Court determined that certain indecency standards applied by the FCC were unconstitutionally vague.

**KEY INDIVIDUALS Carter Phillips** (see p.384) is one of the leading lights of the appellate Bar, described as *"a truly unique talent"* whose incredible expertise sees him appear frequently before the Supreme Court. He recently obtained the reversal of a ruling made by the federal appeals court against Southern Union Company, which had found his client guilty of storing mercury without a permit. Carter argued that it is the jury, rather than the judge, who has the power to increase the fine set in a criminal case. **Peter Keisler** (see p.344) is singled out as *"one of the most extraordinary advocates"* for his outstanding work on behalf of clients from a wide range of industries. His recent work includes successfully representing transportation company CSX in a case concerning the top level of compensation for disabled workers.

### WilmerHale
See profile on p.930

**THE FIRM** WilmerHale is renowned for its considerable experience within the Supreme Court, and also appears before the federal courts of appeals on a regular basis. The team is adroit at tackling a huge range of appellate cases for clients including American Express, Apple, The Walt Disney Company and Citigroup.

**Commercial Awareness** *"They really delve into issues and understand the most important, fundamental points. They are also really good writers, they produce wonderful briefs which makes them stand out for me."*

**KEY INDIVIDUALS Seth Waxman** (see p.423) is held in the highest esteem by peers and clients for his incredible breadth of experience in appellate litigation. *"When he walks into a courtroom, everybody stops and listens – he just has that command, and he exudes an air of confidence that means he doesn't have to shout or scream,"* comments one impressed source. Having argued 61 cases before the Supreme Court, Waxman maintains a very full caseload and is a popular choice with high-profile clients such as Amgen. **Edward DuMont** (see p.306) has an impressively diverse appellate practice, having amassed experience across a broad array of cases and industries. His recent work includes forming part of the team representing Phoebe Putney Health System in its Supreme Court case against the FTC. **Paul Wolfson** (see p.428) is a highly respected appellate lawyer who is commended for *"his breadth of knowledge and precision."* His recent highlights include being involved in the successful representation of Joel Judulang before the Supreme Court in a case concerning the relief obtainable under Section 212(c) of the Immigration and Nationality Act.

## Band 2

### Jones Day
See profile on p.919

THE FIRM Jones Day houses a highly talented pool of appellate lawyers, many of whom possess extensive government experience. The team's recent work includes representing Kouichi Taniguchi in a Supreme Court case concerning how litigation costs are allocated in civil disputes. The Supreme Court ruled in favor of Jones Day, overturning a ruling previously made by the Ninth Circuit.

Sources say: *"They are efficient and coordinated and do a very good job. They can field large groups when necessary from different offices."*

KEY INDIVIDUALS Practice chair **Glen Nager** (see p.374) is praised for his expertise in appellate law, having argued a significant number of matters before the Supreme Court. He recently achieved a successful result on behalf of Innovation Ventures in a Sixth Circuit appeal looking to reverse a decision made regarding trademark infringements. **Michael Carvin** (see p.292) is renowned for his ability to take on high-profile cases such as the recent healthcare appeal on behalf of the National Federation of Independent Business concerning the Patient Protection and Affordable Care Act. He has a broad practice, handling civil rights, constitutional and civil litigation work alongside his strong appellate caseload. **Donald Ayer** (see p.276) offers extensive experience in the field, and is held in high regard by market commentators. He played a key role in the Taniguchi matter described above. *"He gave one of the most outstanding appellate arguments I've ever seen – he's excellent,"* states one client.

### Kellogg, Huber, Hansen, Todd, Evans & Figel, PLLC

THE FIRM This flourishing Washington, DC-based boutique focuses entirely on trial and appellate litigation. It hosts an excellent team of experienced lawyers who have presented arguments before an impressive range of courts, including the US Supreme Court.

Sources say: *"They have several individuals there who are very smart and talented with long careers of great success."*

KEY INDIVIDUALS **David Frederick** receives praise from market commentators for his experience in appellate work. He offers notable expertise in handling pharmaceutical disputes. **Michael Kellogg** is similarly regarded as *"an exceptional advocate"* who draws on significant experience in arguing cases at the appellate level. His practice includes a particular focus on matters involving the telecommunications industry.

## Band 3

### Akin Gump Strauss Hauer & Feld LLP
See profile on p.904

THE FIRM This respected team can draw upon the notable governmental expertise of its members, two of whom have previously served as appellate court judges. It has the experience and advocacy capabilities to handle a raft of high-profile cases, including the recently concluded Filarsky v Delia appeal in the Supreme Court. The team succeeded in its attempt to reverse a decision previously made in the Ninth Circuit.

Sources say: *"They go out of their way to help us – they provide excellent client service and their work is always of the highest quality."*

KEY INDIVIDUALS Practice head **Patricia Millett** (see p.369) is highly respected for her extensive appellate experience, spanning a myriad of industries including retail, healthcare, insurance and construction. *"She has the ability to distill a case into what she believes the appellate court will be looking for; she knows what judges are thinking and then delivers the case to them couched in exactly their own thought processes – she's been very successful,"* confirms one impressed source.

### Covington & Burling LLP
See profile on p.441

THE FIRM This broad-based appellate team is equipped with substantial government experience and an accomplished track record of success. Clients span a range of industries and include CBS Television Network, Hoffmann-La Roche and Bank of America.

Sources say: *"Covington & Burling is strong across the board of appellate law."*

KEY INDIVIDUALS **Robert Long** (see p.358) chairs the firm's appellate and Supreme Court litigation group. Sources enthuse: *"He gets tremendous respect from the court, and is a brilliant lawyer with the right tenor to be in front of appellate judges."* He has recently acted as amicus curiae in the high-profile Health Care Case, becoming the first attorney to argue before the Supreme Court in this landmark matter.

### Farr & Taranto

THE FIRM This impressive boutique is well versed in appellate law, regularly appearing in key Supreme Court cases. Based in Washington, DC, its highly regarded founding partners handle a range of matters involving constitutional law, antitrust, telecommunications and antitrust.

KEY INDIVIDUALS **Richard Taranto** continues to impress commentators with his preeminent experience in appellate litigation, and maintains a leading position in the market. **Bartow Farr** is also a highly regarded individual in the appellate space. He was recently appointed by the Supreme Court to argue a significant point in the Health Care Case.

### Hogan Lovells US LLP

THE FIRM This flourishing appellate practice is rapidly gaining momentum in the appellate litigation arena. It continues to handle a number of high-profile matters, representing the likes of Google, American Hospital Association and US Airways. It is experienced in appearing before a range of courts, including those at state and federal appellate level, and the Supreme Court.

Client Service *"I was very impressed with them; they did everything we asked of them, and were outstanding. It was, all in all, a great experience."*

KEY INDIVIDUALS Former acting US Solicitor General **Neal Katyal** is swiftly establishing himself as *"a fantastic advocate,"* who offers *"deep experience in appellate issues,"* according to sources. He recently obtained a Supreme Court victory in the recent Knox v SEIU First Amendment case. **Catherine Stetson** cochairs the firm's appellate practice and garners much admiration from the market, with one source praising her as being *"very client conscious and very good at seeing the big picture."* Current clients include US Airways, Yankee Atomic and the University of Virginia.

### Jenner & Block LLP
See profile on p.1252

THE FIRM Jenner & Block continues to act as appellate counsel for a significant range of clients, and houses an experienced group of attorneys dedicated to this field. Its recent work includes obtaining a significant win on behalf of Viacom in a copyright infringement dispute against YouTube. The team is based across the country, allowing it to handle matters with a nationwide scope.

KEY INDIVIDUALS Practice head **Paul Smith** (see p.409) is renowned for dealing with some of the most cutting-edge issues in the area of appellate law: *"He handles big commercial cases but is also the leading gay rights lawyer, which is a very prominent issue in the US right now,"* states one commentator. Smith's recent highlights include leading the Viacom work referred to above.

### King & Spalding LLP
See profile on p.445

THE FIRM King & Spalding maintains a strong presence in the appellate litigation space, impressing clients with its expertise in the field and dedicated approach to client service. Its team features experienced individuals who are experts across a number of areas, including intellectual property, life sciences and energy. It is presently working on behalf of clients such as McKesson Technologies, Google and Allergan.

Client Service *"Their turnaround time is as good as it gets, and they are very thoughtful and proactive – I'm thrilled to be working with them."*

KEY INDIVIDUALS **Daryl Joseffer** (see p.341) heads the firm's appellate practice and is lauded as a *"fantastic oral advocate.* "Sources appreciate that his advice is *"insightful, powerful and pragmatic,"* and highlight his understanding of *"practical effects of broad appellate rules, and how they affect the business."* He recently achieved a substantial victory for McKesson Technologies against Epic Systems.

### Kirkland & Ellis LLP
See profile on p.1254

THE FIRM This large group is adept at handling appellate cases in every possible setting, including the Supreme Court, and state and federal appellate courts. The team purposefully maintains a broad-based approach to litigation, and so can offer an impressive set of skills across a wide range of cases and industries. Current clients range from Barr Pharmaceuticals to Morgan Stanley.

Client Service *"One of the great things about this firm is that if you're hiring them in a new area they catch up very* quickly. They are very adaptable and flexible, and are very open to dialogue."

**Commercial Awareness** *"They are very practical lawyers who know the law extremely well, write brilliant appellate briefs and motions, and try to tie in advice to what the client wants to do from a business perspective."*

**KEY INDIVIDUALS Christopher Landau** (see p.352) is singled out as a *"superb appellate attorney"* who is *"a very effective advocate, both orally and in written briefs."* His recent work includes achieving a significant result for client Morgan Stanley in the Supreme Court in a long-running case concerning Section 16(b) of the Securities Exchange Act of 1934.

## O'Melveny & Myers LLP
See profile on p.693

**THE FIRM** The team is formed of 32 dedicated appellate lawyers who can handle appeals across a wide range of matters. The team recently won a notable landmark victory for Antoine Jones in US v Jones. The Supreme Court ruled unanimously that GPS devices could not be used to survey suspects without a valid warrant.

**Sources say:** *"One of our go-to firms for major appellate matters."*

**KEY INDIVIDUALS** The *"prominent and experienced"* **Walter Dellinger** led the team to victory in the hugely significant US v Jones appeal. Sources praise his *"strong intellectual capabilities, and exceptional trial and appellate skills"* and add that he is *"very client oriented."* **Jonathan Hacker** is increasingly gaining recognition for his appellate practice. He is regarded by the market for his advocacy skills, and currently represents Viad, CompuCredit and Ford Motor Company in ongoing appeals.

## Robbins, Russell, Englert, Orseck, Untereiner & Sauber LLP

**THE FIRM** This litigation boutique is firmly established as a go-to firm for high-quality appellate work. It offers impressive experience in dealing with a range of cases presented before the varying court levels.

**Sources say:** *"The team have been extremely responsive, I couldn't ask for a better service, they are always coming up with new ways to serve client interests really well."*

**KEY INDIVIDUALS** The highly respected **Roy Englert** is hailed as a *"brilliant specialist and Supreme Court advocate"* who maintains a broad appellate practice covering bankruptcy, tax, transportation and more areas. He displays particular expertise in antitrust matters. **Lawrence Robbins** is highly praised by market commentators for his extensive appellate litigation capabilities, and spans both criminal and civil litigation in his practice. He has been involved in several high-profile cases in recent times, and has argued a significant number of them in the Supreme Court.

## Band 4

## Arnold & Porter LLP
See profile on p.906

**THE FIRM** Headed by the revered Lisa Blatt, this flourishing group of 15 appellate lawyers enters the rankings backed by praise for its experience in the field. It currently works with an impressive range of clients, including the Federal Housing Finance Agency, Philip Morris USA and Bank of America. The group has been very active in the last year, appearing in numerous cases before the Supreme Court and the federal and state courts of appeals.

**Sources say:** *"As strategists they developed the themes of our case and the arguments we wanted to make, as well as the preparation for potential responses from the opposition. As technicians they drafted briefing papers that were exquisite in their clarity and force. As advocates they were precise and persuasive. The result was a very significant victory for our company."*

**KEY INDIVIDUALS** Heading the practice is **Lisa Blatt** (see p.284) who holds a superb track record of 30 cases argued before the Supreme Court, 29 of which she has won. Sources are quick to praise her, highlighting her impressive advocacy skills and stating that *"she is client-centric even when she doesn't have to be."* Her recent work includes successfully representing SLM Corporation (Sallie Mae) in an appeal concerning the first-to-file rule in regards to the False Claims Act.

## Bancroft PLLC

**THE FIRM** This highly regarded appellate boutique is a new entry to the rankings, and offers clients extensive experience in arguing cases at the Supreme Court level. Former US Solicitor General Paul Clement is a key name at the firm, but it does also house additional appellate expertise. One example of its recent work is its notable victory representing GlaxoSmithKline in the Supreme Court case Christopher v Smithkline Beecham Corp.

**KEY INDIVIDUALS Paul Clement** has argued a staggering 65 cases before the Supreme Court, earning himself a reputation as a *"spectacular"* appellate attorney. Commentators note that he has *"a very high profile and consistently conducts interesting work,"* as reflected in his impressive caseload.

## Morgan, Lewis & Bockius LLP
See profile on p.2246

**THE FIRM** The Supreme Court and appellate litigation practice at this respected firm maintains a strong presence in the market, and has notable experience across a range of cases. The team recently won a substantial victory for ActiveVideo Networks before the Court of Appeals for the Federal Circuit. The court affirmed the prior decision that Verizon Communications should pay damages of over $260 million to ActiveVideo for patent infringement.

**Sources say:** *"The team were focused, creative, relentless, and effective. They were unfailingly professional, good humored, and responsive."*

**KEY INDIVIDUALS Allyson Ho** (see p.2396) is rapidly becoming a force to be reckoned with in the appellate

community, and is praised by commentators for her ability to *"work very hard and produce high-quality content."* Her recent work includes handling various federal court appeals on behalf of Bayer, Wyeth, and Johnson & Johnson.

## Morrison & Foerster LLP
See profile on p.1990

**THE FIRM** This active firm remains a popular choice for appellate matters, and is particularly experienced in handling complex Supreme Court arguments. The team's impressive work includes achieving an 8-0 win before the Supreme Court in the closely watched RadLAX Gateway Hotel v Amalgamated Bank case, representing the latter party.

**Sources say:** *"I really think their performance is excellent, and they have consistently been very adept as attorneys."*

**KEY INDIVIDUALS Deanne Maynard** (see p.363) chairs the firm's appellate practice, arguing an impressive number of cases before the Supreme Court and is deemed *"very skilled"* by market commentators. She has recently worked on behalf of Synovus Bank, Bank of America and NuVasive.

## Quinn Emanuel Urquhart & Sullivan, LLP

**THE FIRM** This firm enters the rankings after appearing regularly in the Supreme Court and the federal appellate courts. The team is highly regarded for its expertise in handling high-profile disputes for clients such as Shell, Entergy and Google. Its skilled practitioners are able to litigate a broad range of cases, but offer particular expertise in patent appeals.

**Sources say:** *"They're among the best attorneys I've ever worked with; very smart, very diligent – they have an aggressive, creative approach to litigation."*

**KEY INDIVIDUALS** Heading the firm's appellate group is the revered **Kathleen Sullivan**, whose *"absolutely first-rate"* and *"incredibly talented"* practice sees her retained in the most complex of appeals. Her recent work includes representing Shell in the landmark Kiobel v Royal Dutch Petroleum Supreme Court case, which features novel issues under the Alien Tort Statute.

## Vinson & Elkins LLP
See profile on p.2459

**THE FIRM** This experienced appellate group handles an array of cases involving securities, energy, oil & gas, and IP claims, among many more. The team recently won two appeals on behalf of the local officials of The Episcopal Diocese of Fort Worth against breakaway factions of the church claiming a right to still control local church names and property. Its client base also includes The Port of Houston Authority and Shell.

**Sources say:** *"Each member of the team has been very responsive to our needs, and have also been very helpful in negotiating what we think are reasonable rates."*

**KEY INDIVIDUALS** The much-admired **John Elwood** (see p.309) is praised for his advocacy skills before the federal courts of appeals and the Supreme Court. He deals with a broad cross-section of areas, including criminal, employment, and environmental disputes. **Marie Yeates** (see p.2423) cochairs the appellate practice and is singled out as being *"very bright and hard-working."* She currently represents Midstates Petroleum Company before the Louisiana Supreme Court in a $70 million oil and gas dispute against Clovelly Oil Company. Sources add that *"no one is more thorough than Marie when it comes to preparation."*

### Williams & Connolly LLP

**THE FIRM** Williams & Connolly is highly regarded for its general litigation practice, and in recent years its appellate practice has been sharing more and more of the spotlight. The team has extensive experience in appearing before a wide range of appellate courts, and houses an impressive group of Supreme Court advocates.

**Sources say:** *"A prominent litigation shop and now really making an entry in the appellate space."*

**KEY INDIVIDUALS** Department head **Kannon Shanmugam** is hailed as an *"extraordinary advocate"* who possesses *"excellent oral skills and also writes beautifully."* Although Kannon takes on a varied caseload, he has particular expertise in tackling criminal defense matters and also has notable experience in disputes involving pharmaceutical patents.

### Other Notable Practitioners

The *"spectacular"* **Jeffrey Lamken** (see p.351) is credited for *"creating a great appellate practice"* at MoloLamken LLP. He has amassed a tremendous amount of experience arguing cases before the Supreme Court. **Thomas Goldstein** of Goldstein & Russell, P.C. has argued a substantial number of appeals before the Supreme Court

regarding federal patent law, disability law and labor and employment. He maintains his reputation as a *"very good advocate."* **Joshua Rosenkranz** heads the appellate practice at Orrick, Herrington & Sutcliffe LLP and is highlighted as a *"popular choice among clients."* Sources characterize him as *"a superb lawyer who is smart, thinks outside the box and obviously terrific at what he does."* **Daniel Collins** (see p.298) of Munger, Tolles & Olson LLP divides his practice between litigation and appellate work. He is lauded by clients for his impressive levels of *"writing analysis and oral advocacy."* **Mike Hatchell** (see p.2394) heads the appellate department at Locke Lord LLP and has recently achieved a string of victories, including the representation of Ashford Partners against ECO Resources in the Supreme Court of Texas. **Thomas Phillips** (see p.2410) of Baker Botts LLP draws upon his prior experience as Chief Justice of the Texas Supreme Court in his impressive work as an appellate lawyer. Notable highlights include his recent work representing Riley-Huff Energy Group in its appeal of a $95.5 million judgment brought against them at the trial level. **Bruce Rogow** is a prominent Florida-based appellate lawyer at Alters Law Firm. He draws from extensive and wide-ranging experience in this space, and has argued numerous cases before the Supreme Court. **Miller Baker** (see p.277) cochairs McDermott Will & Emery LLP's appellate practice. He recently won a victory at the Sixth Circuit level for Static Control in a case against Lexmark. Former Florida Supreme Court Justice **Raoul Cantero** (see p.987) heads the appellate practice at White & Case LLP. He is respected for his notable experience at the appellate level, and has particular expertise in handling matters before the Florida District Courts of Appeal. **Donald Dunner** (see p.860) of Finnegan, Henderson, Farabow, Garrett & Dunner LLP is praised for his expertise in arguing appeals concerning intellectual property and patents. His *"stature in the Federal Circuit"* sees him held in high esteem by commentators. **Jonathan Franklin** (see p.316) heads the appellate department of Fulbright & Jaworski LLP and is particularly praised for his brief-writing abilities. His recent work includes representing DNA Saves in appellate cases brought before several different courts, including the Supreme Court. **Stephen Kinnaird** of Paul Hastings LLP maintains his impressive reputation in this field, and is experienced in handling cases before a range of appellate courts. His expertise spans a broad array of matters, including those involving energy, criminal and IP law. **Helgi Walker** (see p.898) cochairs the appellate practice of Wiley Rein LLP and is highly regarded as a *"brilliant appellate advocate"* who demonstrates admirable commercial awareness when handling complex matters. She is currently representing Verizon in its challenge to the FCC in relation to its net neutrality rules. **Linda Coberly** (see p.296) is vice chair of the appellate department at Winston & Strawn LLP. She recently acted as part of the team that won a significant victory on behalf of Grant Thornton LLP after Refco admitted having committed criminal fraud. **Douglas Hallward-Driemeier** heads the appellate group at Ropes & Gray LLP and is renowned for being *"extremely thoughtful and strategic about the positioning of his cases."* Notable highlights include the filing of an amicus brief on behalf of a number of HIV-rights groups in the landmark Supreme Court case concerning the validity of the Affordable Care Act. **David Axelrad** (see p.621) of Horvitz & Levy LLP is experienced in handling a wide range of appeals at all levels. His recent work includes successfully handling an appeal on behalf of client Crane in the California Supreme Court in a case concerning the boundaries of product liability.

# BANKING & FINANCE

Commentary about individuals can be found under their firm's paragraph.  If the firm has no paragraph (is not ranked) look at Other Notable Practitioners.

*The editorial is in alphabetical order by firm name.*

### Bingham McCutchen LLP
See profile on p.1515

**THE FIRM** This practice has made a name for itself representing a variety of lenders in the leveraged finance market. Key clients include, on the bank side, HSBC and Bank of America and non-bank lenders such as GE Capital and Ares Capital. It recently represented the latter as the agent, arranger and lender in $385 million of senior secured unitranche credit facilities.

**Sources say:** *"They are my go-to when I need responsive, solid advice. I really trust them on the deals we do."*

**KEY INDIVIDUALS** Senior figure at the firm, **Edwin Smith** (see p.1510) is respected by peers who note *"if you have a Uniform Commercial Code (UCC) question there is nobody better."* He is particularly recognized for his experience in distressed investment work and also demonstrates

strength in leveraged loans and bankruptcy work. Banking and leveraged finance group cochair **Frederick Eisenbiegler** (see p.309) enjoys a fine reputation in the market. He has played a prominent role in many of the firm's highlight matters of late, including acting as the lead attorney on the aforementioned Ares Capital transaction.

### Cahill Gordon & Reindel LLP
See profile on p.1960

**THE FIRM** Cahill is well known for its strong affiliation with financial institutions at the forefront of the lending market. The team possesses a deep bench and stellar expertise across the leveraged finance arena and is recognized as a strong player in transactional deals. It is particularly accomplished at representing institutions in their roles as lead arranger and its impressive highlight list this year includes a $7.2 billion debt financing with JPMorgan

and Bank of America Merrill Lynch and a $1.2 billion term loan facility with UBS.

**Sources say:** *"They have a very deep leveraged finance bench and consistently perform to a high quality."*

**KEY INDIVIDUALS James Clark** (see p.295) continues to garner significant respect from market observers. He is actively involved in representing lenders in capital market

| Recommended for Client Service Nationwide | |
|---|---|
| Cleary Gottlieb Steen & Hamilton LLP | Debevoise & Plimpton LLP |
| Davis Polk & Wardwell LLP | Linklaters |
| | White & Case LLP |

| Recommended for Commercial Awareness Nationwide | |
|---|---|
| Davis Polk & Wardwell LLP | Kirkland & Ellis LLP |
| Fried, Frank, Harris, Shriver & Jacobson LLP | Paul Hastings LLP |

*The editorial is in alphabetical order by firm name.*

## Banking & Finance
### Leading Firms

**Band 1**
Cravath, Swaine & Moore LLP *
Davis Polk & Wardwell LLP *
Simpson Thacher & Bartlett LLP *

**Band 2**
Cahill Gordon & Reindel LLP *
Latham & Watkins LLP *

**Band 3**
Cleary Gottlieb Steen & Hamilton LLP *
Debevoise & Plimpton LLP *
Kirkland & Ellis LLP *
Milbank, Tweed, Hadley & McCloy LLP *
Ropes & Gray LLP *
Shearman & Sterling LLP *
Skadden, Arps, Slate, Meagher & Flom LLP & Affiliates *
Weil, Gotshal & Manges LLP *
White & Case LLP *

**Band 4**
Fried, Frank, Harris, Shriver & Jacobson LLP *
Paul Hastings LLP *
Paul, Weiss, Rifkind, Wharton & Garrison LLP *
Sidley Austin LLP *
Sullivan & Cromwell LLP *

**Band 5**
Bingham McCutchen LLP *
Gibson, Dunn & Crutcher LLP *
Linklaters *

## Banking & Finance
### Senior Statesmen

Senior Statesmen: distinguished older practitioners
Parker C Allen — *Cravath, Swaine & Moore LLP *

### Leading Individuals

**Band 1**

| | |
|---|---|
| Berg Eric L | *White & Case LLP *
| Clark James | *Cahill Gordon & Reindel LLP *
| Cooper James D | *Cravath, Swaine & Moore LLP *
| Cross James | *Simpson Thacher & Bartlett LLP *
| Florack James A | *Davis Polk & Wardwell LLP *
| Goldman Michael S | *Cravath, Swaine & Moore LLP *
| Hanrahan Marc P | *Milbank, Tweed, Hadley & McCloy LLP *
| Hartnett William M | *Cahill Gordon & Reindel LLP *
| Kiessling B Robbins | *Cravath, Swaine & Moore LLP *
| Smith Bradley Y | *Davis Polk & Wardwell LLP *
| Vardell III James C | *Cravath, Swaine & Moore LLP *

**Band 2**

| | |
|---|---|
| Alpert Laurent | *Cleary Gottlieb Steen & Hamilton LLP *
| Brittenham David | *Debevoise & Plimpton LLP*
| Crumbaugh David G | *Latham & Watkins LLP*
| Dokos Daniel S | *Weil, Gotshal & Manges LLP *
| Ezring Gregory | *Paul, Weiss, Rifkind, Wharton LLP *
| Fontana Angela L | *Weil, Gotshal & Manges LLP *
| Guerrera Sal | *Skadden, Arps, Slate, Meagher & Flom *
| Kim Jay | *Ropes & Gray LLP*
| Knight James T | *Simpson Thacher & Bartlett LLP *
| Lindauer Erik D | *Sullivan & Cromwell LLP *
| Mendez John E | *Latham & Watkins LLP*
| Michetti Michael E | *Paul Hastings LLP*
| O'Sullivan Maura | *Shearman & Sterling LLP*
| Penzer Michèle | *Latham & Watkins LLP *
| Peponis Margaret S | *Cleary Gottlieb Steen & Hamilton LLP *
| Plaut Christopher R | *Latham & Watkins LLP *
| Ptashek Jay M | *Kirkland & Ellis LLP *
| Reindel F William | *Fried, Frank, Harris, Shriver LLP *
| Schaffzin Jonathan A | *Cahill Gordon & Reindel LLP *
| Smith Edwin E | *Bingham McCutchen LLP *
| Wesely Marissa C | *Simpson Thacher & Bartlett LLP *
| Zubkoff Daniel J | *Cahill Gordon & Reindel LLP *

**Band 3**

| | |
|---|---|
| Barragate Brett | *Jones Day (ONP)[†] *
| Beekman William | *Debevoise & Plimpton LLP*
| Bilkis David | *White & Case LLP *
| Buchman Emil | *Fried, Frank, Harris, Shriver & Jacobson *
| Clark James | *Sidley Austin LLP *
| Gill Sartaj | *Davis Polk & Wardwell LLP *
| Hilson John F | *Paul Hastings LLP*

| | |
|---|---|
| Koschik David N | *White & Case LLP *
| Kyrwood Jason | *Davis Polk & Wardwell LLP *
| Norton Jeff | *Linklaters*
| Ryan Patrick J | *Simpson Thacher & Bartlett LLP *
| Seale Daniel | *Latham & Watkins LLP *
| Sherman Steven E | *Shearman & Sterling LLP*
| Urquhart Douglas | *Weil, Gotshal & Manges LLP *
| Vance Janet | *Gibson, Dunn & Crutcher LLP *
| Ward Sarah M | *Skadden, Arps, Slate, Meagher & Flom *
| Wieman Lawrence E | *Davis Polk & Wardwell LLP *
| Zobitz George (Jed) E | *Cravath, Swaine & Moore LLP *

**Band 4**

| | |
|---|---|
| Baker Michael | *Paul Hastings LLP*
| Bale Morgan | *Weil, Gotshal & Manges LLP *
| Baptista Robert C | *Mayer Brown LLP (ONP)[†]*
| Bassett Michael | *Linklaters*
| Brusiloff Paul D | *Debevoise & Plimpton LLP*
| Buerstetta Grant E | *Blank Rome LLP (ONP)[†] *
| Cohen Steven N | *Cadwalader, Wickersham & Taft (ONP)[†] *
| Copen Robert A | *Skadden, Arps, Slate, Meagher & Flom *
| Draper Thomas B | *Ropes & Gray LLP*
| Dworkin Adam | *Cahill Gordon & Reindel LLP *
| Eisenbiegler Frederick F | *Bingham McCutchen LLP *
| Esdorn Joerg | *Gibson, Dunn & Crutcher LLP *
| Goodison Eric | *Paul, Weiss, Rifkind, Wharton & Garrison *
| Green Jonathan | *Milbank, Tweed, Hadley & McCloy LLP *
| Joyce David E | *White & Case LLP *
| Leicht Eric F | *White & Case LLP *
| Makich Ann | *Cahill Gordon & Reindel LLP *
| Millard Alden | *Simpson Thacher & Bartlett LLP *
| Miller William | *Cahill Gordon & Reindel LLP *
| Myers Linda K | *Kirkland & Ellis LLP *
| Niebruegge Michael E | *Cadwalader, Wickersham & Taft (ONP)[†] *
| Reamer David C | *Skadden, Arps, Slate, Meagher & Flom *
| Stoddard Marshall C | *Morgan, Lewis & Bockius LLP (ONP)[†] *

**Up-and-coming individuals**

| | |
|---|---|
| Lapushchik Tatiana | *Cravath, Swaine & Moore LLP *
| Le Cren Danelle | *Linklaters*
| Rockwell Alan | *White & Case LLP *
| Ross Jeffrey E. | *Debevoise & Plimpton LLP*
| Steinhardt Brian | *Simpson Thacher & Bartlett LLP *
| Wright Corey | *Cahill Gordon & Reindel LLP *
| Yoon Andrew J | *Weil, Gotshal & Manges LLP *

* *Indicates firm / individual with profile.*
[†]*ONP = Other Notable Practitioner.*

transactions and maintains a significant relationship with regular client Bank of America, which he advised on several significant transactions this year. Firm chairman **William Hartnett** (see p.331) plays a vital role at the firm managing key relationships with institutions such as Deutsche Bank. Alongside this he maintains an active practice providing exceptional representation in a range of lending transactions. This year he has advised a range of top-tier clients including Morgan Stanley, Citigroup, Deutsche Bank and Credit Suisse. **Jonathan Schaffzin** (see p.400) has an extremely broad transactional practice, with skills applicable to a range of transactions including private equity work, M&A and out-of-court debt restructurings. **Daniel Zubkoff** (see p.431) is held in high regard by interviewees. He enjoys a particularly strong relationship with JP Morgan who seek his skills in a significant number of lending transactions. Highlight work for the institution this year includes advising it, along with other lead arrangers, on a $2.5 billion credit facility for Telesat. **Adam Dworkin** (see p.307) offers experience in acquisitions, recapitalizations, restructurings and refinancings. This year he was part of the lead team who represented Bank of America Merrill Lynch and other institutions in a $3 billion debt financing. Away from the traditional bank loan work, **William Miller**'s (see p.369) practice focuses primarily on high yield debt and equity securities. He is regularly involved in acquisition financings and has the abilities and experience to represent either side of the transaction. **Corey Wright** (see p.428) is acknowledged as a growing presence in the market and is regarded by one highly impressed source as *"one of the hardest working people there is, really smart and great to work with. Does it all on every deal – the full package."* **Ann Makich** (see p.361) has experience in a range of leveraged finance transactions. She has been part of the lead team in numerous significant transactions for the firm including advising JPMorgan, Citigroup and Credit Suisse, amongst others, as joint bookrunning managers and co-managers in an acquisition financing by Everest.

*The editorial is in alphabetical order by firm name.*

## Cleary Gottlieb Steen & Hamilton LLP
See profile on p.1963
**THE FIRM** This firm is a popular choice with private equity clients and corporate borrowers. Acquisition financings continue to be a major focus of the practice. Highlights in this area include advising Bausch & Lomb in a refinancing and up-sizing of its credit facilities, the proceeds of which were earmarked for several key acquisitions, and representing the National Copper Corporation of Chile in connection with a $1.867 billion financing for the acquisition of equity shares in Anglo American Sur. It has also been busy lately dealing with several complex restructuring matters.
**Client Service** *"They are dedicated to us: they offer consistency and have a great work ethic. They are always available." "Their turnaround time is so rapid, it is amazing. They have a great bedside manner."*
**KEY INDIVIDUALS Laurent Alpert** (see p.273) is singled out by sources as *"patient and methodical"* and for *"knowing all the provisions that are industry-relevant."* His wealth of experience in loan transactions is particularly valued by clients. **Margaret Peponis** (see p.383) is described as a *"very talented individual who always impresses with her creativity and her intelligence."* She recently advised Biomet in connection with the amendment and restatement of its existing credit facility.

## Clifford Chance US LLP
See profile on p.439
**THE FIRM** This practice is recommended for its strong abilities in equipment finance and leasing. It is particularly adept at handling complex matters in the aviation finance space on behalf of a wide variety of clients including lenders, airlines and lessors. It continues to be recognized for its presence in some of the most sophisticated deals in the market. Highlights over the past year include advising Credit Agricole Securities in connection with an asset backed security (ABS) transaction, involving a $390 million issuance of senior notes secured by 79 aircraft engines.
**Sources say:** *"I get real and immediate answers that provide me with the information to understand the risk and enable me to make an informed decision."*
**KEY INDIVIDUALS John Howitt** (see p.337) is *"an expert: he is always extremely good and has the ability to boil things down to bite sized pieces,"* report sources. His wealth of experience in the aircraft finance space ensures that he is highly sought out as counsel in market leading deals. This year he represented The Milestone Aviation Group in a number of transactions including a financing for 32 helicopters. Commentators describe **Zarrar Sehgal** (see p.403) is *"an excellent lawyer who is dedicated, very knowledgeable and has a great legal mind."* Sehgal focuses on asset finance transactions and, in the past year, he has handled a substantial number of deals for lenders active in the aviation space, including BNP Paribas, Credit Agricole and HSBC. The *"tireless and remarkable"* **Geoffrey White** (see p.425) continues to enjoy a fine reputation in the market. Over the past year he advised LATAM Airlines Group in several issues of bonds totaling $1 billion to finance and refinance a number of aircrafts.

## Cravath, Swaine & Moore LLP
See profile on p.1966
**THE FIRM** Cravath's banking and finance group is affiliated with several of the strongest global financial services firms including JPMorgan, Credit Suisse and Goldman Sachs. As such, the firm is predominantly known for its outstanding lender side representation, offering clients much-lauded expertise across the gamut of lending transactions. The firm also has capabilities on the borrower side, servicing private equity firms and corporate clients in a multitude of financings. In a recent highlight, it acted for Credit Suisse and Citigroup in a $14 billion bridge credit facility related to the merger of Express Scripts and Medco Health Solutions.
**Sources say:** *"Their work stands out on every deal. They always excel – it is truly remarkable that they have the capability to perform to that standard. They offer sound business advice and excellent work quality."*
**KEY INDIVIDUALS Michael Goldman** (see p.322) earns much praise from sources, with one commenting: *"Not only does he offer sound legal advice, but he has a great ability to frame business questions as well."* Of late he has done considerable work with Credit Suisse on several highlight deals including the aforementioned bridge credit facility. **James Cooper** (see p.298) is well respected by market observers. He often works with JPMorgan and recently advised the firm in connection with two credit facilities totaling $8 billion provided to social networking company Facebook. Financial institution practice chair **Robbins Kiessling** (see p.346) remains a prominent figure within the firm. His wealth of experience in lending transactions ensures continued work with clients such as JPMorgan, Citigroup and Bank of America. **James Vardell** (see p.420) has a strong reputation with interviewees. His practice focuses on syndicated bank financings and he regularly represents both corporate borrowers and traditional lenders. He is also well versed in project finance, restructurings and equipment finance. Presiding partner at the firm, **Allen Parker** (see p.382) has a wealth of experience in the field, specifically in syndicated loan transactions, acquisition finance and leveraged recapitalizations. Recent highlights include the representation of Rock Tenn Company and Rock Tenn Company of Canada as borrowers in connection with $3.7 billion of credit facilities. Described as *"a great adviser,"* **Jed Zobitz** (see p.431) is adept at handling syndicated loan transactions, and has particular strengths in acquisition financings, leveraged recapitalizations and M&A. **Tatiana Lapushchik** (see p.352) is a popular choice with several high-profile financial institutions. She recently advised JPMorgan in connection with $7 billion of credit facilities provided to Pfizer.

## Davis Polk & Wardwell LLP
See profile on p.442
**THE FIRM** Davis Polk is renowned as a leading, high-quality banking and finance group. This practice is equally accomplished at representing corporate borrowers and institutional lenders and shows impressive breadth, offering expertise across an extensive catalogue of financial transactions. Alongside this it is proficient in handling workouts and a range of bankruptcy services highlighting strong experience in all the relevant stages of a financial transaction. Unsurprisingly the firm's client roster boasts a succession of high-profile names including Morgan Stanley, Goldman Sachs, Ford and PepsiCo. Highlight

*The editorial is in alphabetical order by firm name.*

work includes representing Facebook in a $5 billion revolving credit facility and $3 billion bridge term loan to fund certain obligations relating to the company's IPO.

**Commercial Awareness** *"They are my first pick for a challenging situation. They have a wealth of experience to draw on and they balance thoroughness and carefulness with commercial creativity." "They are very commercial and understand the market with depth that others do not."*

**Client Service** *"They really stand out in complex, time-consuming work – they are phenomenal on those really complex deals that involve a lot of hand holding." "They work with us to do the best they can for us and our client. They are very responsive and we get great service from them."*

**KEY INDIVIDUALS Bradley Smith** (see p.408) is a well-respected authority in the banking world. His wealth of experience in this sector is highly valued by interviewees who say: *"He has seen it all – if you have a unique challenge and need someone who has been there and done that he is the guy."* His work of late has focused on acquisition finance and a range of secured credit transactions. The *"very experienced and creative"* **James Florack** (see p.314) earns praise from clients who say: *"I appreciate the value that he adds not just with legal advice but from a business standpoint as well."* He has been particularly active in recent times working on a number of highlight transactions including advising Bank of America, Deutsche Bank and Morgan Stanley as joint lead arrangers in a $1.23 billion financing to Providence Equity Partners for its acquisition of Blackboard. **Jason Kyrwood**'s (see p.351) reputation as a significant player in the market continues to grow. He is applauded by interviewees who say: *"He puts so much work into having a comprehensive understanding of the wider market – it is the overall perspective that is so valuable."* His key clients include Citibank and Bank of America. **Lawrence Wieman** (see p.426) is acknowledged for his work as borrowers counsel and recently advised Ford on its $9 billion revolving credit facility. He is also well versed in workouts and debt restructurings. **Sartaj Gill** (see p.320) is described as an *"extremely calm and very smart attorney – he is never fazed and always makes his point calmly and effectively."* He is experienced in acquisition finance and other leveraged finance transactions as well as having strong abilities in restructuring work. He regularly works with clients such as Credit Suisse and Bank of America, as well as a number of corporate borrowers.

## Debevoise & Plimpton LLP
See profile on p.1968

**THE FIRM** This firm is highly regarded for its proficient representation of private equity clients in the leveraged finance market. It has a healthy following, regularly attracting work from some of the most active financial sponsors in the market, including The Carlyle Group, Clayton Dubilier & Rice and Providence Equity Partners. This year the firm also represented regular client Reynolds Group Holdings in its $3.25 billion notes offering, which was one of the largest single-tranche issues in the high-yield market in recent years. The firm is also active in the aviation finance space where it is recognized for its enduring rela-

tionships with multiple airlines, whom it represents across a full range of transactions.

**Client Service** *"They are responsive, very user-friendly and customer-focused." "Their work standard is exceptionally high – they have a great deal of resources and are very client sensitive. We need good legal advice but also have to focus on how clients interact with us and they are top notch at that – they are very sensitive and cognizant of what our clients think."*

**KEY INDIVIDUALS** Seasoned practitioner **William Beekman** is noted for being *"detail-oriented, creative and well versed in market transactions."* **Paul Brusiloff** *"has excellent client focus and is great at bringing a process together,"* report impressed interviewees. He focuses on complex debt and equity financings, as well as refinancings, recapitalizations and restructurings. **David Brittenham** garners significant praise from interviewees: *"He is extremely knowledgeable and brings practical experience – it's very valuable to have such a strong advocate."* He recently represented The Carlyle Group in the financings aspects of the $3.3 billion acquisition of Getty Images. **John Curry** is an admirable presence in aviation finance. Sources say: *"He is a high-quality, intelligent and analytical lawyer."* He continues to work with American Airlines, and is advising it on the financing aspects of an aviation order where committed finance amounted to $13 billion. New addition to the rankings **Jeffrey Ross** is highly valued by clients in the private equity sphere and is described as *"commercial, practical, extraordinarily responsive, smart and creative."*

## Fried, Frank, Harris, Shriver & Jacobson LLP
See profile on p.1975

**THE FIRM** This practice demonstrates abilities across the full spectrum of financial transactions. It is proficient at handling matters for a wide range of clients, providing the practice with a well-rounded view of the overall market. Recent highlights include advising Permira in relation to a $625 million senior secured credit facility related to its $1.5 billion acquisition of Genesys. The firm is also active in fund financings, bankruptcy and restructuring transactions, and real estate development work.

**Commercial Awareness** *"They do a great job to get the best terms the market will stand. They have worked on comparable transactions and help us to understand where we can push. They know what is out there and what we can get."*

**KEY INDIVIDUALS** Sources are quick to single out **William Reindel**'s (see p.391) *"encyclopedic knowledge of deal documentation,"* and also praise his great judgment and calm and thorough approach to matters. He has stellar expertise in the leverage finance space and is particularly noted for his strength in representing borrowers and sponsors in their financial activities. Clients are quick to describe **Emil Buchman**'s (see p.289) knowledge as *"second to none,"* while peers single him out as a *"pleasure to work with."* He recently advised Bank of America Merrill Lynch in a $550 million credit facility matter, and has done several deals on behalf of AEA Investors and its portfolio companies.

## Fulbright & Jaworski LLP
See profile on p.2435

**THE FIRM** Fulbright's equipment finance group is globally active in an array of transactions on behalf of lessors, lenders, manufacturers and airlines. The team maintains a fine reputation in the aviation space and has recently worked on a complex financing funded by a commercial paper facility on behalf of Jackson Square Aviation. Other highlight deals this year include the representation of Apollo Aviation in multiple transactions related to the purchase, lease and disassembly of aircraft and the subsequent sale of parts.

**KEY INDIVIDUALS** Equipment finance practice head **James Tussing** (see p.419) is noted as having *"a tremendous depth of experience."* His expertise in equipment finance, particularly his wealth of knowledge in the aviation space, has been busy in the USA, Europe, Asia and Latin America. Tussing was ably assisted on the aforementioned Jackson Square Aviation and Apollo Aviation matters by associate **Kelli Sallemi** (see p.398), who is regarded as a rising star in equipment finance field.

## Gibson, Dunn & Crutcher LLP
See profile on p.682

**THE FIRM** Traditionally known for its strength on the borrower side, Gibson Dunn continues to attract work from private equity firms, financial sponsors and corporate borrowers. Of late the firm has been involved in a number of acquisition financings, on both sides of the transaction, including advising Del Monte Foods in its $3.45 billion acquisition by an investor group.

**Sources say:** *"They are creative and thoughtful on approaching problems."*

**KEY INDIVIDUALS** Sources are quick to praise **Janet Vance** (see p.420), saying: *"She has that rare component where she cares about our company and wants us to do well."* Recently she has worked on a number of financial transactions including advising Williams Partners in a $2.8 billion revolving bank facility. The *"hard-working and very creative"* **Joerg Esdorn** (see p.310) is focused on leveraged finance transactions where he repents both borrowers and lenders. Lately he has advised UBS Bank on several secured credit facility increase matters.

## Holland & Knight LLP
See profile on p.1028

**THE FIRM** Holland & Knight is a highly esteemed practice in the equipment finance and leasing market. The group is a leading authority in the aviation finance space, where it is particularly experienced in representing airlines and lessors in complex transactions. Among its recent highlights is its counsel to GE Capital Aviation Services in connection with the public issuance of $1.7 billion bonds secured by 137 aircraft on lease to US airlines. The practice also has stellar expertise in the shipping finance arena, drawing on strong capabilities across the field of maritime law. Other strengths include railcar and equipment leasing and finance work.

**Sources say:** *"They offer industry knowledge, attention to detail and close communication with their clients."*

*The editorial is in alphabetical order by firm name.*

KEY INDIVIDUALS Nancy Hengen (see p.333) is a notable figure in the shipping finance space. She recently advised Nordea Bank Finland, as agent and lender, on modification to a $1.4 billion credit facility made to shipping company, Excel Maritime Carriers. San Francisco-based **William Piels** (see p.384) is described as *"very collaborative, thoughtful, thorough and responsive."* He is widely respected as one of the best aviation finance lawyers in the market and is regularly seen representing airlines, lender and lessors in complex transactions. **John Pritchard** (see p.387) is viewed as someone who *"knows the industry and deal matter so well."* Sources say *"he is great at negotiating deals, very reasonable and highly knowledgeable."* *"Smart, analytical lawyer"* **Fred Bass** (see p.279) recently advised GE Capital Rail Services on the acquisition of railcars and the sale of several portfolios of leased locomotives and railcars. He is also experienced in aviation finance transactions.

## Kirkland & Ellis LLP
See profile on p.1254

THE FIRM Kirkland's banking and finance group is an acknowledged presence in the market as counsel to an array of private equity firms, with whom the practice enjoys strong standing. The group's standout deals this year display an array of strengths in areas such as acquisition finance, complex restructuring and refinancing matters. Key work includes its representation of Kerzner International Holdings in a $4 billion out-of-court restructuring.

Commercial Awareness *"They are bright guys who know the market well. They represent a lot of sponsors, from big to small, so they know this work inside and out. The breadth of deals they do is incredible – they have seen it all."*

KEY INDIVIDUALS Jay Ptashek (see p.388) has a strong presence in the market and elicits particular praise for his *"very commercial"* approach to matters. He is noted for his strength in sponsor side representation and also has significant expertise in the leverage finance space. Chicago-based **Linda Myers** (see p.1223) is singled out as possessing *"the relevant experience and a great demeanor in negotiations."* She recently completed a $1.135 billion refinancing for theme park company Six Flags Entertainment.

## Latham & Watkins LLP
See profile on p.446

THE FIRM This distinguished practice is a solid presence in the leveraged and acquisition finance space. It handles transactions for both lenders and sponsors, showing impressive depth and breadth across the market. Within the swath of transactional capabilities the firm offers, it possesses particular expertise in cross-border transactions and large scale acquisition deals, both of which contribute significantly to recent highlights. This year the firm represented Barclays in a bridge, term loan and revolving credit facility matter connected to the $38 billion acquisition of El Paso Corporation by Kinder Morgan.

Sources say: *"In leveraged finance work, across the spectrum, they offer a very broad international coverage. They are strong in the US and are on the ground everywhere here.*

*Offering every product and covering all areas from the one firm."*

KEY INDIVIDUALS Sources say **John Mendez** is *"always available, very focused and involved in the process, with a great knowledge of precedent."* He has wide-ranging experience in representing financial institutions in all manner of lending transactions. Seasoned practitioner **David Crumbaugh**'s Chicago-based practice focuses on secured finance. He specializes in representing financial institutions and commercial lenders in a range of transactions including leveraged buyouts, refinancings and cross-border deals. **Michèle Penzer** (see p.383) is appreciated for being *"responsible and commercial in decisions."* She was the lead attorney on the aforementioned Barclays transaction and has also worked with the institution in a complex financing throughout various stages of an acquisition transaction. *"Deservedly recognized"* **Daniel Seale** (see p.403) is adept at handling transactions in the leveraged finance space. He recently represented Watson Pharmaceuticals in a $1.8 billion financing related to the acquisition of The Actavis Group. **Christopher Plaut** (see p.385) is valued in his role as lender's counsel. He is experienced in acquisition financings, asset-based deals and exit financings. This year he worked with Barclays on a $1.1 billion financing in the telecommunications industry.

## Linklaters
See profile on p.447

THE FIRM Linklaters's New York-based team continues to provide representation across the spectrum of leveraged transactions. With the ability to draw on a comprehensive international network, it is particularly strong at representing clients in transactions that involve a cross-border element. This is evinced by the recent representation of Siam Commercial Bank in its role as agent for a syndicate in connection with a $450 million term loan facility. Other international clients include Australia and New Zealand Banking Group Limited and Banco Bilbao Vizcaya Argentaria (BBVA).

Client Service *"When we seek their counsel we know it will be responsive and timely." "We have demanding clients and deadlines and they are just so responsive no matter what."*

KEY INDIVIDUALS Co-head of the banking practice **Jeff Norton** has a wealth of experience in financial transactions. Recent highlights include representing health insurance company WellPoint in a $3 billion unsecured 364-day bridge term loan credit facility transaction. **Michael Bassett** is a *"very knowledgeable guy – he always responds, never panics or misses a beat,"* reports one impressed source. Basset is adept at handling cross-border transactions – particularly those with a Latin American element. **Danelle Le Cren** draws much praise from the market with sources saying: *"Very impressive – her skill set is excellent, as is her attention to detail. She gets it right the first time and is extremely practical in her advice."*

## Milbank, Tweed, Hadley & McCloy LLP
See profile on p.448

THE FIRM This firm is a heavy hitter in the equipment finance space and is regularly seen on some of the market's most prominent and sophisticated deals. The firm has commendable skills in both aviation and railcar finance – specifically in acquisition, leveraged and asset-based finance. It is regularly seen representing large investment banks that are active in this field. A major highlight of late was the representation of Sumitomo Mitsui Banking in its acquisition of RBS Aviation, which created the world's fourth-largest commercial jet aircraft leasing and finance company. Alongside this the firm's leveraged finance group continues to provide solid representation across the spectrum of financial transactions to a handful of leading financial institutions including Goldman Sachs, Credit Suisse and Barclays. In addition, the practice is an increasing presence as borrowers' counsel, and recently represented MGM Resorts International in a major $5.25 billion refinancing for MGM Grand.

Sources say: *"It has extensive knowledge of all aspects of the aviation finance practice area, from complex securitizations to individual asset tradings. It has a deep bench of partners and associates and provides round the clock service."*

KEY INDIVIDUALS Marc Hanrahan (see p.330) exhibits first-class knowledge in senior lending transactions and is particularly adept when acting as lenders counsel. Unsurprisingly he continues to work with some of the industry's leading global financial service firms. He has recently represented Credit Suisse in connection with several recapitalization matters. **Drew Fine** (see p.312) earns high praise from interviewees: *"He is a dean of the industry – he has extensive knowledge of all aspects of the practice area, from complex securitizations to individual asset trading."* Recent highlights include representing International Lease Finance Corporation in connection with its $1.5 billion term loan. **Helfried Schwarz** (see p.403) is seen as an asset to clients who say: *"He is really valuable to us. He is knowledgeable, easy to work with and business-minded."* He focuses on aircraft and other structured equipment financings. Head of the transportation and space group **Elihu Robertson** (see p.393) is adept at handling all aspects of aviation finance for clients from all areas including lessors, underwriters and airlines. This year he was one of the lead attorneys in the aforementioned Sumitomo Mitsui Banking Corporation matter. Other clients this year have included Citi and Continental Airlines. **Jonathan Green** (see p.325) is a leading figure in the firm's project finance group and is well respected by practitioners active in this field. He is also experienced at handling acquisition and leveraged finance transactions.

## Paul Hastings LLP
See profile on p.1996

THE FIRM Paul Hastings's banking and finance team focuses on the representation of major banks that are active in the leveraged finance market. Recently the firm has handled a number of cash-flow and asset-based loans on behalf of clients including JPMorgan Chase, UBS and Wells Fargo. It also demonstrates notable skills in high-yield bond work such as the representation of RBC Capital Markets, amongst others, as initial purchasers on the high-yield bond offering made in connection with the financing

*The editorial is in alphabetical order by firm name.*

for a $1.6 billion acquisition of 99 Cents Only Stores, by Ares Management.

**Commercial Awareness** *"They are really involved in the market and have good intelligence on what is market standard and what is not." "They have a broad reach and their market experience is amazing."*

**KEY INDIVIDUALS Michael Michetti** earns praise for his *"creative and commercial acumen."* He is highly valued by leading financial institutions and continues to represent them in a broad range of leveraged finance transactions. LA-based **John Hilson** is noted as being a *"very knowledgeable guy."* He is a highly respected presence on the West Coast, where his wealth of experience, particularly in asset-based finance work, continues to attract a significant amount of work. **Michael Baker** is an increasing presence in the leverage finance market. Lately he has played a key role in a number of the firm's highlight deals, including the aforementioned RBC Capital transaction.

## Paul, Weiss, Rifkind, Wharton & Garrison LLP
### See profile on p.1997

**THE FIRM** Paul Weiss dedicates a significant part of its practice to representing private equity firms and corporate clients in all manner of leverage finance transactions. The firm is particularly recognized for its close links with private equity firm Apollo Global Management and its portfolio companies. This year it has represented the group as part of a consortium in the financing related to the $7 billion acquisition of El Paso Corporation. With close links to the firm's impressive bankruptcy team, the practice is also adroit at handling exit finance and refinance matters.

**Sources say:** *"They have great depth and very talented lawyers. They are creative, have strong attention to detail, are good problem solvers, and are able to look at things from a wide angle and fill in the gaps."*

**KEY INDIVIDUALS** Sources say **Eric Goodison** (see p.324) *"has a deep and broad understanding of the current financial market and deal terms."* He recently advised Oak Hill Capital Partners III in a $575 million financing related to a $1 billion acquisition. **Gregory Ezring** (see p.311) is particularly noted for his representation of private equity firms. *"He really truly understands financings – not just the law but the financial implications. The nuance in high-yield deals is that each company has unique peculiarities and he can take them and make a bespoke agreement,"* asserts one satisfied client.

## Pillsbury Winthrop Shaw Pittman LLP
### See profile on p.2000

**THE FIRM** This accomplished team offers services across the spectrum of aviation finance. It maintains a strong reputation for its strength in Ex-Im Bank and other forms of export credit agency (ECA) financing and regularly works on such transactions in the aviation space. The team is well-equipped in handling complex leasing transactions and bankruptcy matters. This year the firm worked with several airlines in their Ex-Im Bank transactions, including a $1.5 billion financing for Ethiopian Airlines and a $1.21 billion financing for Atlas Air.

**KEY INDIVIDUALS William Bowers** is recognized for his knowledge in the structured finance space. This year he represented Willis Lease Finance Corporation in an ABS transaction, involving a $390 million issuance of senior notes. The seasoned **Michael Schumaecker** has worked extensively with airlines in the full range of financial transactions and is a well-known presence in the lending space, representing institutions who are active in aircraft financings. **Payson Coleman** is an experienced figure in the aviation finance arena, where he represents clients from all areas of the market across a broad swath of transactions.

## Ropes & Gray LLP
### See profile on p.1528

**THE FIRM** This banking and finance practice is sought out by some of the leading private equity firms for its substantial talent in leveraged buyouts. Key clients include TPG Capital, which it represented in a $1.695 billion financing to acquire Par Pharmaceuticals Companies, and Bain Capital, which it advised as part of a consortium in the $1.3 billion financing to acquire SkillSoft.

**Sources say:** *"They keep us updated on necessary issues and always translate legal language into business terms, which is useful. They are a very proactive firm."*

**KEY INDIVIDUALS Jay Kim** is *"efficient, direct and always thinks five steps ahead of the deal,"* sources note. He excels at handling leveraged transactions for private equity firms and counts TPG Capital and The Blackstone Group among his regular clients. **Thomas Draper** *"understands business issues, how to document them and how to get a deal done. He has great insight and that is incredibly valuable,"* a satisfied client reports.

## Shearman & Sterling LLP
### See profile on p.2005

**THE FIRM** This broad practice offers capabilities in both lender and borrower side representation in all manner of leveraged finance transactions. The firm's comprehensive international platform allows it to bring a strong network of resources to the table in order to efficiently handle global matters and cross-border deals. The team has been busy on a number of key matters including the representation of Morgan Stanley Senior Funding and other lenders as joint lead arrangers in a $14.5 billion aggregate financing for a prominent pharmaceutical research business.

**Sources say:** *"We are always pleased with their work. They have good market knowledge and are always available to assist with questions or a tough deadline."*

**KEY INDIVIDUALS Maura O'Sullivan** receives much praise from clients, who say: *"She knows her markets and documents cold. She is commercial and flexible, when appropriate."* She recently represented Morgan Stanley in a number of high-value matters including the $14.5 billion financing referenced above. **Steven Sherman** is skilled in handling acquisition and project finance as well as bankruptcy work. He handles work for both corporate clients and major money lenders such as Citigroup Global Markets. **Ji Hoon Hong** is recognized for his presence in the aviation finance sphere. He has experience in structured finance and capital market transactions. In the last

year he has represented several financial institutions in their lending activities to a number of international airlines.

## Sidley Austin LLP
### See profile on p.1264

**THE FIRM** With a stellar presence in Illinois and strong banking and finance teams in New York, California and Texas, Sidley Austin has an impressive nationwide footprint. This practice is well equipped to advise clients from all areas of the market in the full gamut of financial transactions. Recently the group has been particularly busy assisting financial institutions, such as JPMorgan, Wells Fargo, US Bank, Bank of America and Barclays, in a multitude of transactions.

**Sources say:** *"They offer consistent quality. They do not let a deal become adversarial and take a cooperative and consultative approach to prevent issues."*

**KEY INDIVIDUALS** Chicago-based **James Clark** (see p.1202) *"is integral to us in managing our relationship and brings valuable skills to the table,"* asserts one impressed client. He recently advised US Bank as administrative agent in a $450 million acquisition loan finance. Senior counsel **Rory Kelleher** (see p.344) remains an experienced authority for the firm in the equipment finance and leasing space, specifically within the field of aviation finance.

## Simpson Thacher & Bartlett LLP
### See profile on p.2006

**THE FIRM** This practice maintains its reputation as a pre-eminent force in the market, and is much in demand for its strengths in syndicated and leverage finance. It has a particularly strong reputation as borrowers' counsel and counts many of private equity's vanguard among its loyal client base. Highlights this year include the representation of Eaton Corporation in a $6.8 billion financing related to the acquisition of Cooper Industries, and the representation of KKR in financing for the $7.2 billion purchase of Samson Investment Company. The practice is also well-equipped in lender-side representation and recently advised a consortium of top-tier lenders, including JPMorgan, Credit Suisse, Goldman Sachs and UBS, in connection with a $2.2 billion financing related to the acquisition of Pharmaceutical Product Development.

**Sources say:** *"Simpson Thacher are a leader for level of service, quality, depth and knowledge – they are absolutely exceptional."*

**KEY INDIVIDUALS** The very well-regarded **James Cross** (see p.300) is experienced in working with financial institutions, as well as representing corporate borrowers in their finance activities. Recent work includes advising First Data Corporation on a refinancing of outstanding debt. **James Knight** (see p.348) is described as *"a great lawyer who really makes deals run smoothly."* He continues to work with regular client JPMorgan, having this year advised it on a healthcare acquisition finance and a $6.25 billion revolving credit facility for Comcast. Banking and credit practice head **Patrick Ryan** (see p.397) is praised by clients, who emphasize that *"in high-grade acquisition finance his knowledge of precedent in the legal market is unbelievable."*

*The editorial is in alphabetical order by firm name.*

He is particularly valued by financial institutions and acted for JPMorgan, Credit Suisse, Goldman Sachs and UBS on the $2.2 billion financing mentioned above. **Marissa Wesely** (see p.425) has a wealth of experience in leveraged finance and recapitalizations, and frequently represents private equity companies and corporate borrowers. A highlight this year was the representation of Peabody Energy in a financing related to the acquisition of Macarthur Coal. **Alden Millard**'s (see p.369) reputation with his peers continues to grow: *"He is outstanding – excellent for high-yield work,"* sources say. He is accomplished at handling a wide range of financings, with the ability to offer strong representation on either side of a deal. Peers acknowledge **Brian Steinhardt** (see p.412) for his transactional skills. This year he has been particularly active with private equity and corporate clients, acting as the lead attorney in several noteworthy deals, including those for KKR and Eaton Corporation detailed above.

## Skadden, Arps, Slate, Meagher & Flom LLP & Affiliates
### See profile on p.2008

**THE FIRM** With the ability to draw on the firm's impressive M&A platform, this banking and finance team consistently attracts work from corporate clients, representing them in all types of financial transactions. Highlights include advising Coty in its $10.7 billion bid for Avon Products and the associated underwritten bank and bridge loans. While the practice is accustomed to working with borrowers, it also continues to develop significant links on the lender side. Key work this year in this area has included representing Barclays in a highly complex $1.45 billion debtor-in-possessor (DIP) financing.

**Sources say:** *"They are a go-to for corporate finance work. They are very knowledgeable."*

**KEY INDIVIDUALS Sal Guerrera** (see p.327) has a strong presence in the market and is described by interviewees as *"one of the most detail-oriented guys around – a fine lawyer."* He specializes in representing financial institutions in both US and international financings. This year he has handled a number of complex transactions on behalf of regular client Credit Suisse. The *"very practical"* **Sarah Ward** (see p.423) is singled out by sources for her expertise in leverage finance work. In a recent highlight, she was the lead attorney on the Barclays DIP financing noted as being an extremely intricate transaction. The *"very knowledgeable"* **Robert Copen** (see p.298) has worked on a substantial number of acquisition financings for Valeant Pharmaceuticals, and advised on a $7 billion revolving credit facility for Pfizer. The *"terrific"* **David Reamer** (see p.661) is based in Los Angeles and elicits particular praise for his commercial approach and reliability as an advocate.

## Sullivan & Cromwell LLP
### See profile on p.2011

**THE FIRM** With leading talent in the firm's M&A practice and strong expertise in its bankruptcy and capital markets groups, Sullivan's banking and finance practice has the ability to provide clients with experienced, full-service representation in a vast range of transactions. The practice's

expertise is demonstrated in its recent work, which includes advising United Rentals in its merger agreement to acquire RSC Holdings valued at $4.2 billion, and the continued representation of TCW/Crescent Mezzanine as lender in a number of transactions.

**Sources say:** *"They are straightforward and do not miss a thing."*

**KEY INDIVIDUALS Erik Lindauer** (see p.357) is viewed as a valuable asset to the firm for his experience in bank finance work. He is well versed in a broad range of transactions and is noted for his experience in corporate restructurings and bankruptcy matters. Recent work includes advising Eastman Kodak Company in its $650 million debtor-in-possession facility as part of the company's global restructuring.

## Vedder Price PC
### See profile on p.1266

**THE FIRM** Vedder Price retains its admirable reputation in the global aviation finance space, where the firm skillfully handles the full gamut of services including leasings, financings, securitizations, workouts and restructurings. The firm is experienced at representing clients from all sides including lessors, lenders, investors, airlines and manufacturers. It is also highly adept at handling matters in a range of other areas including railcar, maritime and equipment finance. Key deals this year have included acting as bankruptcy counsel to a significant number of creditors in connection with the American Airlines bankruptcy proceedings.

**Sources say:** *"They are proactive, reactive, available and have a very commercial view, which is highly useful for negotiations."*

**KEY INDIVIDUALS** Global transportation finance team chair **Dean Gerber** (see p.319) is in high demand for his top-drawer abilities, particularly in commercial aviation matters. *"His knowledge is incredible and he is easy to work with,"* asserts one impressed client. **Ronald Scheinberg** (see p.400) has an array of experience in aviation, railcar and equipment financing. Clients enthuse: *"He is very helpful to us – his greatest value is his ability to highlight weaknesses that we could strengthen. He really sees it all."* **Edward Gross** (see p.326) is highly valued for his skills in the equipment finance space. Sources say: *"He is just outstanding, he is very knowledgeable and he has great interpersonal skills."* **Joshua Gentner** (see p.319) is a well-known name in the market and specializes in aviation and railcar finance. This year he has represented Amtrak in a Railroad Rehabilitation & Improvement Financing (RRIF) loan from the US government used to finance improvement on the northeast corridor of the US.

## Weil, Gotshal & Manges LLP
### See profile on p.2015

**THE FIRM** This practice demonstrates impressive breadth and depth in both lender and borrower side representation across the gamut of financial transactions. Key strengths include advising private equity clients in acquisition finance as well as representing financial institutions in their lending activities in the leveraged finance space. This

practice is also boosted by the firm's impressive international footprint which attracts highly coveted, cross-border deals. An example of this included acting for a client as part of the consortium which purchased EMI Group's music publishing operations, for $2.2 billion.

**Sources say:** *"They are very hard working, technically strong, detail-oriented and thorough."*

**KEY INDIVIDUALS** Dallas-based **Angela Fontana** (see p.2389) is hailed as *"a very dynamic sponsor lawyer and a real force to be reckoned with."* She recently represented General Growth Properties in a $1 billion revolving credit facility for GGP Limited Partnership and related entities. Global practice head **Daniel Dokos** (see p.305) elicits praise for his ability to *"get things done: he cuts through the case with very practical advice."* He is well versed in financial transactions and has notable expertise in cross-border deals. He acted as the lead attorney in New York in the aforementioned EMI deal. **Douglas Urquhart** (see p.420) is *"responsive, co-operative and helpful in achieving our objectives,"* a satisfied client reports. Recent highlights include the representation of TE Connectivity in a 364-day bridge take-out facility for $700 million concerning the acquisition of The Deutsch Group. The *"excellent"* and *"very detail-oriented"* **Morgan Bale** (see p.277) is a new addition to the rankings following a raft of market praise and impressive work highlights. Standout moments of late include advising Goldman Sachs as lead arranger in a $3.5 billion senior unsecured bridge facility to Walgreens, in connection with the company's investment in Swiss-based group Alliance Boots. Peers are quick to praise **Andrew Yoon** (see p.430): *"He's a very thorough lawyer – he always gets it right."* The representation of private equity firms, particularly in acquisition finance matters, is a key strength.

## White & Case LLP
### See profile on p.451

**THE FIRM** This banking and finance team boasts considerable breadth and depth, offering substantial expertise in a wide range of financial transactions. Predominantly known as a lender side firm, this practice continues to attract work from leading financial institutions including Deutsche Bank, BNP Paribas and Credit Suisse. The group is also recognized for its global strength, and regularly draws on the resources and expertise of the firm's worldwide network, to assist clients in sophisticated cross-border deals. A recent example of such work is the representation of Deutsche Bank in its role as administrative agent and joint lead arranger in a $2.1 billion senior secured credit facility to Colfax Corporation. The firm's breadth is also reflected by its expertise in the equipment finance arena where it is frequently seen representing clients, such as lenders, lessors and airlines, active in the aviation and shipping market.

**Client Service** *"Their senior partners are available throughout the life of the deal. They have a very deep bench and the ability to call on non-US offices, so are very efficient in cross-border deals." "They know how we operate and have a great relationship with us."*

**KEY INDIVIDUALS** Speaking of **Michael Smith**'s (see p.409) experience in the aviation finance space, sources say: "*He is extremely intelligent and meets important criteria for us by being very commercial. We want someone who helps get the deal done and he is excellent at that.*" Global practice head **Eric Berg** (see p.282) continues to do a significant amount of work with regular client Deutsche Bank and was the lead attorney on the aforementioned credit facility deal. Other highlights include advising Morgan Stanley Senior Funding in connection with a $425 million senior secured term loan. **Richard Smith** (see p.409) is recognized for his work in equipment finance and leasing. He earns praise for his ability to "*manage large multibillion-dollar projects involving a huge team. He can bring the work in on time and with the highest quality.*" **David Bilkis**'s (see p.283) expertise in leveraged and acquisition finance continues to attract work from leading financial institutions. Of late he has advised clients such as Deutsche Bank, Citibank and Jefferies Finance in a range of transactions. **David Koschik** (see p.349) is adept at handling leverage finance matters and routinely represents a number of high-profile lenders. Highlights include representing Merrill Lynch as joint lead arranger and joint bookrunner in an amendment and extension of a $3.5 billion senior secured term loan and credit facility. **Eric Leicht** (see

p.354) is noted as being "*unflappable, steady and determined.*" His recent highlights include an array of deals with Deutsche Bank, including a $1.4 billion senior secured term loan facility and revolving credit facility, and a $970 million term loan tranche under an existing credit facility. **Alan Rockwell** (see p.394) is qualified in both the USA and UK and proves to be a valuable resource in deals with an international element. **David Joyce** (see p.341)

### Other Notable Practitioners

The "*calm and unflappable*" **Brett Barragate** (see p.2090) heads Jones Day's banking and finance practice and divides his time between New York and Ohio. He recently acted for PolyOne on its $486 million acquisition of ColorMatrix Group. Of late **Steven Cohen** (see p.297) of Cadwalader, Wickersham & Taft LLP has been active in representing prominent market lenders in a number of financings, including advising BNP Paribas in a sophisticated $1 billion credit facility to a global commodities trading company. At the same firm, Houston-based **Michael Niebruegge** (see p.2407) handles all manner of financial matters. He is a leading figure in the energy industry and is highly experienced at representing clients who are active in that space. **Grant Buerstetta** (see p.289)

of Blank Rome LLP demonstrates expertise in structured asset-backed securities work. A key strength is his experience of collateralized debt obligations. "*Very, very experienced practitioner*" **John Hoyns** (see p.337) of Hughes Hubbard & Reed LLP is well respected in the aviation finance arena. He is particularly commended for his expertise in Enhanced Equipment Trust Certificate (EETC) matters and for his stellar work with Continental Airlines. **Timothy Lynes** (see p.359) of Katten Muchin Rosenman LLP is an experienced practitioner in aviation finance and is particularly knowledgeable in dealings with manufacturers and new aircraft orders. He is also singled out for his expertise in the restructuring of complex agreements in and out of bankruptcy. Morgan, Lewis & Bockius LLP's **Marshall Stoddard** (see p.667) elicits particular praise for his negotiation skills and is also praised for his "*great balance and eloquent, even demeanor.*" His practice is divided between Los Angeles and New York. Key clients include Bank of America and Wells Fargo. Chicago-based **Robert Baptista** of Mayer Brown LLP represents both borrowers and lenders in a range of transactions. He is particularly adept at handling syndicated financings and recently represented Bank of America in a $1.45 billion syndicated credit facility matter.

---

# BANKRUPTCY/RESTRUCTURING

Bankruptcy/Restructuring p.38

Commentary about individuals can be found under their firm's paragraph. If the firm has no paragraph (is not ranked) look at Other Notable Practitioners.

## Band 1

### Akin Gump Strauss Hauer & Feld LLP
See profile on p.904

**THE FIRM** Akin Gump's bankruptcy and restructuring group is considered one of the country's premier creditors' committee practices. With teams spanning New York, Los Angeles, Washington, DC, and Texas, the practice is well-placed to conduct any large-scale, complex committee proceedings. In what has been another successful year, highlights include its appointment as counsel to the unsecured creditors' committee in the Chapter 11 bankruptcy of global oil tanker business Overseas Shipholding. The New York team also represented the unsecured creditors' committee in the bankruptcy of well-known aircraft manufacturer Hawker Beechcraft. Akin's Texas offering provides particular expertise within the oil and gas industry.
**Sources say:** "*The team has a lot of experience; they have a deep bench, are pragmatic and easy to work with.*" "*They are good at client service and very responsive. They understand how I do business and can see issues that might come up.*"
**KEY INDIVIDUALS Daniel Golden** (see p.322) has been instrumental to the firm's prominence this year, with market sources describing him as a "*top-tier, go-to person in the creditors' committee world today.*" His recent highlights

include his role as lead counsel to the unsecured creditors' committee in the Overseas Shipholding bankruptcy. **Fred Hodara** (see p.335) is head of Akin Gump's financial restructuring practice. He is currently playing a leading role alongside Golden in advising the unsecured creditors' committee in the Overseas Shipholding matter. Hodara is described by interviewees as "*a tough and aggressive deal maker.*" **Ira Dizengoff** (see p.305) brings a practical, commercially-focused approach to his cases and is described as "*extremely good at finding ways to navigate through the legal complexities to structure negotiated solutions,*" and for being "*very effective with big picture strategy.*" His recent work includes representing the unsecured creditors' committee in Dynegy Holdings' $4 billion Chapter 11 bankruptcy. **Michael Stamer** (see p.1944) is recognized for his strategic expertise. His foresight and business-oriented approach have garnered recommendations from clients: "*He is calm but sharp-elbowed when necessary.*" **Charles Gibbs** is based in Akin's Dallas, Texas office. He is highly regarded for his expertise in representing both debtors and creditors in oil and gas-related bankruptcies. Interviewees describe him as "*a master of his craft,*" and "*a great strategist who can provide a good road map for how the case will progress.*"

### Davis Polk & Wardwell LLP
See profile on p.442

**THE FIRM** Davis Polk's New York-based insolvency and restructuring team has developed a top-tier reputation in the field. Traditionally considered a preeminent creditor and lender practice, the firm has continued to operate at the highest level, with highlights from the past year including its continued representation of Citibank in relation to $950 million worth of DIP financing for Eastman Kodak.

On the company-side, the firm advised Patriot Coal and Pinnacle Airlines during their respective bankruptcies. The firm also represented the joint administrators of Lehman Brothers International (Europe) in relation to the litigation and settlement of $38 billion in claims between it and Lehman Brothers Inc.

**Commercial Awareness** *"Excellent lawyers, negotiators and businesspeople. They have a firm grasp of the specific nuances of Chapter 11, but can also act as good counselors on making informed business decisions."*

**KEY INDIVIDUALS** Davis Polk's insolvency and restructuring practice is headed by **Donald Bernstein** (see p.282) and **Marshall Huebner** (see p.337), two of the most expe-

rienced and highly regarded practitioners in the industry. The two joined forces recently in advising Citibank on the Eastman Kodak DIP financing. Bernstein is regularly praised for his leadership and sense of strategy, while commentators describe Huebner as *"an excellent negotiator with a strong reputation in court; he has the ability and reputation for being effective in getting to a solution."* Bernstein has played an integral role in the firm's advice to various major finance houses regarding the implementation of the Dodd-Frank Act. Meanwhile, Huebner undertook the debtor-side representations of Patriot Coal and Pinnacle Airlines.

## Jones Day
### See profile on p.919

**THE FIRM** Jones Day's business restructuring and reorganization practice spans offices in New York, Chicago, San Francisco, Los Angeles, Dallas, Cleveland and Columbus. The group has risen to prominence with roles in some of the largest restructurings in history, and its bench strength keeps it well-placed to tackle any debtor or creditor-side engagement. The group continued to represent Hostess Brands in its highly publicized $800 million Chapter 11 bankruptcy. The practice also received a considerable boost following the arrival of LA-based Bruce Bennett from defunct law firm Dewey & LeBoeuf. The firm also recently took the spotlight with the appointment of DC based Kevyn Orr to emergency Financial manager of Detroit.

**Client Service** *"I've been impressed with the quality of their work and their ability to keep fees down. They really try to work to establish long-term relationships."*

**Commercial Awareness** *"They not only have an excellent knowledge of bankruptcy law but a good understanding of the business. Adding to that an ability to be practical and incisive on key and difficult legal points enabled the client to get to a good result."*

**KEY INDIVIDUALS Corinne Ball** (see p.277) is cochair of the firm's business restructuring and reorganization group. She is one of the most well-known practitioners in the industry, with market sources noting that *"she is all business and extremely intelligent; she can see things faster than most,"* and is *"very confident, responsive, bright and very effective."* The *"brilliant and very effective"* **Bruce Bennett** (see p.282) is a new addition to the firm's Los Angeles office. He advises clients across the spectrum of bankruptcy-related situations. His recent highlights have included acting as lead counsel to an ad hoc group of lenders on the MF Global Chapter 11 bankruptcy. Practice group cochair **Paul Leake** (see p.353) is *"practical and a pleasure to deal with,"* according to interviewees, who have been particularly impressed with his leadership qualities, as well as his impact in the court room. The *"smart, savvy and practical"* **Heather Lennox** (see p.2104) is described by commentators as *"very articulate and good at dealing with multiple group entities."* She has quickly developed into one of the more important members in the practice, with one impressed source pointing out that they have *"never seen anyone so well prepared for court with such a grasp of the minute details; her ability to size up a situation quickly and*

*figure out what's going to be a problem is really impressive."* **David Heiman** (see p.2100) operates out of the firm's Cleveland office. He is one of the founding members of Jones Day's practice and is held in high esteem by the wider bankruptcy and restructuring industry. Los Angeles-based **Richard Wynne** (see p.672) is a senior partner in the group. He advises clients on complex distressed situations across the country. His recent highlights include advising FGIC on $1 billion of debt claimed in the ResCap Chapter 11 bankruptcy, on which FGIC is a cochair of the official creditors' committee.

## Kirkland & Ellis LLP
### See profile on p.1254

**THE FIRM** This powerhouse financial restructuring practice has preeminent teams operating out of Chicago and New York. The depth and experience in this group is renowned throughout the US and globally, with the group primed to undertake large-scale, complex debtor-side representations in particular. It also stables increasingly recognized creditor-side expertise. The group's notable highlights include representing well-known aviation businesses Hawker Beechcraft and Global Aviation Holdings in their respective Chapter 11 bankruptcies. It has also successfully completed a number of high-value out-of-court restructurings, including engagements for Barneys New York and luxury resort developer Kerzner International.

**Client Service** *"They worked around our time and our hours but at the same time they were always available to us. They were very good at understanding our business and the sensitivity of the industry – that got us through the bankruptcy a lot quicker."*

**Commercial Awareness** *"There is a depth of experience; the team provides a wide range of expertise and has seen and done just about everything. A strength of theirs is making win-win deals; understanding the desires and needs of all parties but particularly their client."*

**KEY INDIVIDUALS Richard Cieri** (see p.295) is one of the more senior partners in the group, with sources noting that *"he has been around a long time and has great market recognition."* He is described by interviewees as *"outstanding, creative and effective."* He is currently advising Hawker Beechcraft on its Chapter 11 bankruptcy. **James Sprayregen** (see p.411) is one of the leading practitioners in the industry. He divides his time between Kirkland's Chicago and New York offices. Clients look to him as someone who is *"providing leadership and strategic guidance on the big issues."* *"Tireless and very creative,"* Sprayregen is described as *"very good in complicated and difficult situations."* **Paul Basta** (see p.280) recently represented Barneys New York and Kerzner International during their respective out-of-court restructurings. He is praised as a *"very effective lawyer who is practical in his approach."* As part of *"the next generation of leaders,"* **Jonathan Henes** (see p.1902) has built his name on the back of exemplary successes for his clients. He has been *"very active with a strong presence"* during the past year, with highlights including his representation of Global Aviation Holdings in its $495 million bankruptcy proceedings. **Marc Kieselstein** (see p.1909) recently represented

## Bankruptcy/Restructuring

### Senior Statesmen

**Senior Statesmen: distinguished older practitioners**

| | |
|---|---|
| Milmoe J Gregory | *Skadden, Arps, Slate, Meagher & Flom* * |

### Leading Individuals

**Star individuals**

| | |
|---|---|
| Miller Harvey R | *Weil, Gotshal & Manges LLP* * |

**Band 1**

| | |
|---|---|
| Baker D J (Jan) | *Latham & Watkins LLP* * |
| Ball Corinne | *Jones Day* * |
| Bennett Bruce S | *Jones Day* * |
| Bernstein Donald S | *Davis Polk & Wardwell LLP* * |
| Bienenstock Martin J | *Proskauer Rose LLP* |
| Butler Jr John Wm | *Skadden, Arps, Slate, Meagher & Flom* * |
| Cieri Richard M | *Kirkland & Ellis LLP* * |
| Dunne Dennis | *Milbank, Tweed, Hadley & McCloy LLP* * |
| Goffman Jay M | *Skadden, Arps, Slate, Meagher & Flom* * |
| Golden Daniel H | *Akin Gump Strauss Hauer & Feld LLP* * |
| Goldstein Marcia | *Weil, Gotshal & Manges LLP* * |
| Huebner Marshall S | *Davis Polk & Wardwell LLP* * |
| Karotkin Stephen | *Weil, Gotshal & Manges LLP* * |
| Kirpalani Susheel | *Quinn Emanuel Urquhart & Sullivan, LLP* |
| Klee Kenneth N | *Klee, Tuchin, Bogdanoff & Stern LLP* |
| Kornberg Alan W | *Paul, Weiss, Rifkind, Wharton & Garrison* * |
| Mayer Thomas Moers | *Kramer Levin Naftalis & Frankel LLP* * |
| Novikoff Harold S | *Wachtell, Lipton, Rosen & Katz* * |
| Nyhan Lawrence | *Sidley Austin LLP* * |
| Sprayregen James HM | *Kirkland & Ellis LLP* * |

**Band 2**

| | |
|---|---|
| Abrams Marc | *Willkie Farr & Gallagher LLP* * |
| Albergotti Robert | *Haynes and Boone, LLP* |
| Aronzon Paul S | *Milbank, Tweed, Hadley & McCloy LLP* * |
| Basta Paul M | *Kirkland & Ellis LLP* * |
| Bromley James L | *Cleary Gottlieb Steen & Hamilton LLP* * |
| Charles Scott K | *Wachtell, Lipton, Rosen & Katz* * |
| Conlan James F | *Sidley Austin LLP* * |
| Dizengoff Ira S | *Akin Gump Strauss Hauer & Feld LLP* * |
| Eckstein Kenneth H | *Kramer Levin Naftalis & Frankel LLP* * |
| Fife Lori R | *Weil, Gotshal & Manges LLP* * |
| Friedman David M | *Kasowitz, Benson, Torres & Friedman LLP* * |

| | |
|---|---|
| Heller David S | *Latham & Watkins LLP* |
| Hodara Fred S | *Akin Gump Strauss Hauer & Feld LLP* * |
| Lauria Thomas E | *White & Case LLP* * |
| Leake Paul | *Jones Day* * |
| Levin Richard | *Cravath, Swaine & Moore LLP (ONP)* † * |
| Pachulski Richard M | *Pachulski Stang Ziehl & Jones LLP* |
| Pantaleo Peter V | *Simpson Thacher & Bartlett LLP* * |
| Rosenberg Andrew N | *Paul, Weiss, Rifkind, Wharton & Garrison* |
| Sosland Martin | *Weil, Gotshal & Manges LLP* * |
| Ziman Kenneth S | *Skadden, Arps, Slate, Meagher & Flom* * |

**Band 3**

| | |
|---|---|
| Bogdanoff Lee R | *Klee, Tuchin, Bogdanoff & Stern LLP* |
| Davis George A | *Cadwalader, Wickersham & Taft LLP* * |
| Dietderich Andrew G | *Sullivan & Cromwell LLP* * |
| Ellenberg Mark C | *Cadwalader, Wickersham & Taft LLP* * |
| Feldman Matthew A | *Willkie Farr & Gallagher LLP* * |
| Frankel Roger | *Orrick, Herrington & Sutcliffe LLP* * |
| Galardi Gregg M | *DLA Piper LLP (US) (ONP)* † * |
| Gilhuly Peter | *Latham & Watkins LLP* |
| Hansen Kristopher M | *Stroock & Stroock & Lavan LLP (ONP)* † |
| Harris Adam C | *Schulte Roth & Zabel LLP (ONP)* † * |
| Heiman David G | *Jones Day* * |
| Henes Jonathan S | *Kirkland & Ellis LLP* * |
| Holtzer Gary T | *Weil, Gotshal & Manges LLP* * |
| Lennox Heather | *Jones Day* * |
| Levinson Marc A | *Orrick, Herrington & Sutcliffe LLP* * |
| Mason Richard G | *Wachtell, Lipton, Rosen & Katz* * |
| Miller Brett | *Morrison & Foerster LLP* * |
| Palmer Deryck A | *Pillsbury Winthrop Shaw Pittman (ONP)* † |
| Phelan Robin | *Haynes and Boone, LLP* |
| Rapisardi John J | *Cadwalader, Wickersham & Taft LLP* * |
| Reilly Michael J | *Bingham McCutchen LLP* * |
| Sabin Jeffrey S | *Bingham McCutchen LLP* * |
| Schonholtz Margot | *Willkie Farr & Gallagher LLP* * |
| Stamer Michael S | *Akin Gump Strauss Hauer & Feld LLP* * |

| | |
|---|---|
| Stark Robert | *Brown Rudnick LLP* |
| Strubeck Lou | *Fulbright & Jaworski LLP* * |
| Tuchin Michael L | *Klee, Tuchin, Bogdanoff & Stern LLP* |
| Uzzi Gerard | *Milbank, Tweed, Hadley & McCloy LLP* * |
| Weisfelner Edward | *Brown Rudnick LLP* |
| Wynne Richard | *Jones Day* * |
| Zirinsky Bruce R | *Greenberg Traurig, LLP* * |

**Band 4**

| | |
|---|---|
| Bane Mark | *Ropes & Gray LLP* |
| Barr Matthew S | *Milbank, Tweed, Hadley & McCloy LLP* * |
| Beckham, Jr Charles A | *Haynes and Boone, LLP* |
| Bloom Mark D | *Greenberg Traurig, LLP* * |
| Carr James | *Kelley Drye & Warren LLP (ONP)* † |
| Despins Luc A | *Paul Hastings LLP (ONP)* † |
| Dobbs C Edward | *Parker, Hudson, Rainer & Dobbs (ONP)* † |
| Flaschen Evan D | *Bracewell & Giuliani LLP (ONP)* † * |
| Gerber Toby L | *Fulbright & Jaworski LLP* * |
| Gibbs Charles R | *Akin Gump Strauss Hauer & Feld LLP* |
| Giddens James W | *Hughes Hubbard & Reed LLP (ONP)* † * |
| Hahn Richard | *Debevoise & Plimpton LLP* |
| Kieselstein Marc | *Kirkland & Ellis LLP* * |
| Logan III Ben H | *O'Melveny & Myers LLP (ONP)* † |
| Panagakis George N | *Skadden, Arps, Slate, Meagher & Flom* * |
| Perez Alfredo R | *Weil, Gotshal & Manges LLP* * |
| Rosner David S | *Kasowitz, Benson, Torres & Friedman LLP* * |
| Sassower Edward O | *Kirkland & Ellis LLP* * |
| Sathy Anup | *Kirkland & Ellis LLP* * |
| Scheler Brad Eric | *Fried, Frank, Harris, Shriver & Jacobson* * |
| Schweitzer Lisa M | *Cleary Gottlieb Steen & Hamilton LLP* * |
| Seider Mitchell A | *Latham & Watkins LLP* * |
| Seife Howard | *Chadbourne & Parke LLP* * |
| Singerman Paul Steven | *Berger Singerman (ONP)* † * |
| Stewart Dan | *Vinson & Elkins LLP* * |
| Trust Brian | *Mayer Brown LLP* |

\* *Indicates individual with profile.*
† *ONP = Other Notable Practitioner.*

women's fashion retailer United Retail Group in its Chapter 11 bankruptcy proceedings. He is given *"the highest marks"* by interviewees who praise him for *"adding clarity and humor to what can be a dreadful experience."* The *"very smart and practical"* **Anup Sathy** (see p.1229) continues to develop a reputation as a prominent player in the market. He garners respect as *"a great negotiator – he is personable and knows how to talk to a business guy and structure things."* **Edward Sassower** (see p.400) is a *"professional, business-savvy deal-maker."* He is an accomplished practitioner with broad-ranging expertise.

### Milbank, Tweed, Hadley & McCloy LLP
See profile on p.448

THE FIRM Milbank Tweed's nationwide financial restructuring practice advises across the entire bankruptcy spectrum and encompasses leading teams in New York, Los Angeles and DC. The group has experienced a successful year in a strained market, with a slew of high stakes engagements, particularly in advising creditors' committees and bondholder groups. Such highlights include acting for the Official Committee of Unsecured Creditors in the $6.7 billion Chapter 11 bankruptcy of Eastman Kodak. It is also representing the Official Committee of Unsecured Creditors of Arcapita, as well as an ad hoc creditor group of secured noteholders in Residential Capital's (ResCap) $15 billion bankruptcy proceedings.

**Client Service** *"We continue to love working with them every chance we get. They are very responsive to questions."*
**Commercial Awareness** *"Very balanced guys; not chest-thumpers or grenade-throwers – they are problem solvers. They understand issues very quickly and give you the fire power to go back as a business person and make a decision. Very commercially articulate and capable strategists."*
**KEY INDIVIDUALS** *"Fearless leader"* **Dennis Dunne** (see p.307) is based in New York and is cochair of the firm's global financial restructuring practice. Sources describe him as *"very knowledgeable and insightful and, because his demeanor is balanced, it allows him to control the table."* He is equally adept in debtor or creditor-side engagements and is currently leading the Official Committee of Unsecured Creditors in the Eastman Kodak bankruptcy.

Los Angeles-based **Paul Aronzon** (see p.620) cochairs the practice alongside Dunne. *"He has a deep knowledge of the law and process,"* say commentators, who add: *"He has a great ability to evaluate cases and figure out the issue; a very fine strategic-thinker."* **Gerard Uzzi** (see p.1948) has been making a name for himself since his recent move to Milbank from White & Case. He is broadly experienced and works predominantly with creditor-side clients. *"He is able to bring together various parties and reach consensus in highly contentious situations,"* report sources. His recent highlights include advising major ad hoc creditor groups in the bankruptcies of ResCap and American Airlines. **Matthew Barr** (see p.1876) has a diverse practice in which he advises various clients, from debtors to investors in distressed assets. He is currently advising telecom business LightSquared in its Chapter 11 proceedings. *"He is among the most practical lawyers I've dealt with,"* according to an interviewee, who adds: *"He has a good idea of what our end goals are and doesn't get hung up in the weeds."*

## Skadden, Arps, Slate, Meagher & Flom LLP & Affiliates
See profile on p.2008

**THE FIRM** The corporate restructuring practice at Skadden continues to operate at the forefront of the bankruptcy industry. With superb teams in New York, Chicago, Wilmington and Los Angeles, the practice is well-placed to advise on cutting edge national and international bankruptcy issues. Traditionally renowned for large debtor representations, Skadden also undertakes major creditor and investor-side cases, including its ongoing high-profile engagement as counsel to the unsecured creditors' committee in the American Airlines bankruptcy. On the company side, the group demonstrates its far-reaching capabilities in its recent advice to Danish shipping company TORM in its out-of-court restructuring.

**Sources say:** *"Skadden has been very smart and helpful in getting the right result in an extremely complex multijurisdictional case." "It's a combination of knowing the subject matter and being able to help a company make strategic business decisions. They work tirelessly and are available 24/7."*

**KEY INDIVIDUALS** Global head of corporate restructuring **Jay Goffman** (see p.322) is at the forefront of the bankruptcy sector. He has experienced a busy year in which he advised TORM on its restructuring. He is praised by clients as *"exceptionally creative and innovative; he really thinks outside the box and can tackle interesting new problems unconstrained."* *"Industry icon"* **Jack Butler** (see p.290) is based in Chicago. He stands out for *"going beyond a traditional lawyer and thinking about client needs; he is a broad legal business strategist."* One of Skadden's most senior lawyers, clients continue to value his immense experience. New York-based **Kenneth Ziman** (see p.431) is deputy head of the corporate restructuring practice. *"He is very insightful and an excellent technician,"* according to satisfied clients. He recently represented Barclays Bank in a $1.45 billion DIP credit facility for ResCap during its high-profile Chapter 11 case. Fellow practice deputy leader **George Panagakis** (see p.1224) is based in Chicago. He is broadly experienced and acts for a range of creditor and debtor-

side clients. He has played a key role on behalf of TORM. *"One of the fathers in the modern industry of restructuring,"* **Gregory Milmoe** (see p.369) is eminently experienced and renowned throughout the industry. *"His depth of knowledge is fantastic and unusual,"* report sources, who add: *"He has a great, calming demeanor in pressured situations."*

## Weil, Gotshal & Manges LLP
See profile on p.2015

**THE FIRM** Weil Gotshal's business finance and restructuring group is universally considered one of the top practices in the world. The group is headquartered in New York, with strong teams also housed in Dallas and Houston. With near-unrivaled resources and bench strength, Weil is famous for representing companies in many of the biggest bankruptcies in history. Highlights in the past year have included continued advice to the debtors in several large-scale bankruptcies, including AMR, AES Eastern Energy and MF Global UK. The group is not limited to debtor engagements, however, with its Texas offering in particular advising on a full range of bankruptcy issues.

**Client Service** *"The Weil team offers a great breadth of experience. It is very responsive, commercial, hard-working, and they have a very strong bench."*

**KEY INDIVIDUALS** **Harvey Miller** (see p.369) is the founder of Weil's business finance and restructuring practice. He is considered an industry icon, with sources describing him as *"the dean of bankruptcy lawyers; he is a big-picture guy with extensive experience."* He remains active in his practice and interviewees note that he *"is very client-conscious, unbelievably knowledgeable, and has the respect of everyone at the Bar."* Practice group leader **Marcia Goldstein** (see p.323) is admired by commentators as *"insightful, with a strong knowledge base, and gives very practical advice."* Principal among Goldstein's recent highlights is her representation of MF Global UK in the MF Global Chapter 11 bankruptcy. She also acted as lead counsel to Citibank and Barclays in connection with a $500 million DIP credit facility in the Chapter 11 bankruptcy of Patriot Coal. **Stephen Karotkin** (see p.343) is a creative practitioner, lauded by one particular client as: *"A very quick study who gets up to speed on our business and helps us to understand complex bankruptcy issues."* A prominent, nationally respected name, Karotkin has continued to advise is AMR, the parent company of American Airlines, in its high-profile bankruptcy proceedings. **Lori Fife** (see p.312) is a highly experienced practitioner who regularly advises clients on issues across the bankruptcy spectrum. Sources are quick to highlight her as *"very hard-working, thoughtful and helpful in working through difficult problems. She is responsive and has a broad remit of expertise; she's involved in everything."* **Martin Sosland** (see p.2417) is head of Weil's Dallas-based bankruptcy and restructuring team. He is often singled out for his debtor-side expertise, but is adept in all manner of representations, as evidenced by his recent engagement for Macquarie Capital in the implementation of a credit facility and equity investments for Reddy Ice during its bankruptcy proceedings. **Gary Holtzer** (see p.1904) receives a tremendous amount of recognition for his work ethic and technical know-how. He

has broad-ranging bankruptcy expertise, and regularly represents debtors, creditors and lenders. The *"outstanding"* **Alfredo Perez** (see p.2409) heads the restructuring team in Weil's Houston office. He has been praised by interviewees for his business-oriented approach to matters. He plays an integral part in the practice, with leading roles in many of the firm's marquee cases, including advising AMR as a debtor on the American Airlines bankruptcy.

## Band 2

## Cleary Gottlieb Steen & Hamilton LLP
See profile on p.1963

**THE FIRM** Cleary Gottlieb's restructuring and insolvency practice is headquartered in New York. The firm's wider global footprint enables it to conduct engagements in any top-level bankruptcy matter, particularly those involving international and cross-border restructuring elements. The practice has experienced a successful year, and recently filed one of the largest Chapter 11 cases of the past year on behalf of oil tanker business Overseas Shipholding Group.

**Client Service** *"A solid practice with outstanding professional skills and great client focus."*

**KEY INDIVIDUALS** Global practice head **James Bromley** (see p.288) is renowned for his expertise in advising debtor and creditor clients on international restructuring matters. His recent highlights include acting as lead counsel for Overseas Shipholding on its high-value Chapter 11 bankruptcy. He is praised by interviewees as a *"very good, practical lawyer with a calm demeanor."* The *"hard-working and extremely bright"* **Lisa Schweitzer** (see p.1939) enters the nationwide rankings thanks to an excellent year. Sources are quick to identify her prowess in working towards a pragmatic business solution for her clients. Her recent work has included her continued lead for Nortel Networks.

## Kramer Levin Naftalis & Frankel LLP
See profile on p.1987

**THE FIRM** This New York-based corporate restructuring and bankruptcy practice has experienced a stellar year. Kramer Levin's team is able to provide advice to clients working across the bankruptcy spectrum, but is especially renowned for its creditor-side engagements. In this vein, the group has undertaken several high-profile representations including advising the unsecured creditors' committee on ResCap's $15 billion Chapter 11 bankruptcy proceedings. It also acted for unsecured creditors' committees on several other high-value bankruptcies, including the Chapter 11 cases of Hostess Brands, AES Eastern Energy and Patriot Coal.

**Sources say:** *"They have lawyers who are exceptional and top in their fields; highly experienced and very intelligent. They are outstanding at thinking of creative solutions when you are in a particularly difficult situation."*

**KEY INDIVIDUALS** **Thomas Mayer** (see p.363) is cochair of the corporate restructuring and bankruptcy practice. He is *"among the most intellectual of all bankruptcy lawyers,"* say sources, and provides *"thorough, detailed and excellent analysis."* His current highlights include advising the Official Unsecured Creditors' Committees on the Chapter 11 bankruptcies of Hostess Brands and Patriot Coal. Fellow practice group cochair **Kenneth Eckstein** (see p.308) is an expert in a wide range of bankruptcy representations. In recent highlights, he represented the unsecured creditors' committee in the ResCap bankruptcy. *"He has an outstanding reputation and an excellent presence in court,"* according to interviewees, who add: *"He can establish an excellent rapport with the judges."*

### Latham & Watkins LLP
See profile on p.446

**THE FIRM** Latham's restructuring, insolvency and workouts practice is nationally recognized, with a footprint spanning New York, Chicago and Los Angeles. The group is traditionally acclaimed for its expertise in representing creditors, lenders and distressed investors, with recent highlights including acting for US Airways on the Chapter 11 bankruptcy of American Airlines' parent company AMR. The team also boasts debtor-side capabilities, with a notable recent example being its representation of shipping and container business Eagle Bulk Shipping in its $1.2 billion out-of-court restructuring.

**Sources say:** *"They are very strong and particularly excel in marrying bankruptcy strategy with business strategy."*

**KEY INDIVIDUALS Jan Baker** (see p.277) is Latham's global restructuring group cochair. He is described by market sources as *"one of the most senior attorneys in the industry."* Baker has played an integral part in developing the practice's debtor-side capabilities. He recently advised Eagle Bulk Shipping on its $1.2 billion out-of-court restructuring. **David Heller** is chair of the firm's finance group and shares his time between the Chicago and New York offices. He is praised for his extensive experience, with interviewees noting that *"he's got very good judgment, there are not a whole lot of situations out there that he hasn't been through."* Others describe him as *"extremely creative and he always gets results."* **Peter Gilhuly** heads Latham's restructuring and insolvency presence in California. He is a broadly experienced practitioner who is equally adept with creditor or debtor-side engagements. Sources are quick to remark that Gilhuly is a *"fantastic lawyer and in terms of who I'd be looking to hire it'd be Peter."* He recently advised New United Motors Manufacturing, inc (NUMMI) on its high-value out-of-court wind-down, as well as on other insolvency-related issues. **Mitchell Seider** (see p.1939) cochairs the restructuring and workouts group alongside Jan Baker. He is an expert in all types of bankruptcy matter, with interviewees praising him as *"really good at negotiating and guiding towards solutions."* Seider is an expert in Latin American bankruptcy issues, and his recent highlights include acting for Jefferies & Co on its funding of Satelites Mexicanos's exit from its Mexican prepackaged bankruptcy.

### Paul, Weiss, Rifkind, Wharton & Garrison LLP
See profile on p.1997

**THE FIRM** This high-quality bankruptcy and corporate reorganization practice is head-quartered in New York. The team offers a deep bench of experts who are experienced across the spectrum of bankruptcy matters and who are regularly praised for outstanding client service. The group has taken on a number of high-profile engagements, including acting as lead counsel to Houghton Mifflin Harcourt Publishing on a $3.1 billion prepackaged Chapter 11 bankruptcy plan. The group has also continued to advise Silver Point Capital as pre- and post-petition lending agent to Hostess Brands.

**Client Service** *"They have a very talented bench as well as talent the next level down. Creative and great to work with; they are smart, responsive and not afraid to give you a tough answer."*

**Commercial Awareness** *"Their guys are not only intelligent and give concise advice; they get to the bottom line, understand dynamics and are very commercially-oriented."*

**KEY INDIVIDUALS** Practice chair **Alan Kornberg** (see p.349) is considered one of the *"top creditor-side lawyers in country."* *"He is immensely practical, commercial, intelligent and hard-working,"* sources remark. Kornberg recently led the firm's representation of Houghton Mifflin Harcourt Publishing. **Andrew Rosenberg** (see p.394) is similarly well regarded, with one interviewee claiming: *"He is one of the finest bondholder/creditor attorneys I've ever worked with."* Indicative of this are his recent highlights which include acting for the ad hoc committee of bondholders on the Chapter 11 bankruptcy of Dynegy Holdings. He is described as *"somebody who is always a pleasure to work with or opposite."*

### Wachtell, Lipton, Rosen & Katz
See profile on p.2012

**THE FIRM** Wachtell boasts an eminently respected restructuring and finance practice. The team is famed for representing major financial institutions, and private equity and hedge fund clients, in high-profile bankruptcies and distressed M&A situations. It is also increasingly involved in pre- and post-petition litigation. Recent highlights for Wachtell include advising the likes of JPMorgan Chase and Bank of America in the large-scale, complex bankruptcies of MF Global, Hawker Beechcraft and Arcapita Bank.

**Sources say:** *"A really excellent quality firm."*

**KEY INDIVIDUALS Harold Novikoff** (see p.378), who chairs the practice group, is widely regarded as *"a great bankruptcy mind."* He has over 30 years' experience in the industry and has led for Wachtell in many of its flagship cases. One commentator enthused: *"If Congress needed an opinion, he's the guy you'd get to do it."* **Scott Charles** (see p.293) often garners praise for his intellectual prowess and strategic vision. He is tremendously experienced in a full range of bankruptcy matters, and has been particularly active advising investors on distressed acquisitions. **Richard Mason** (see p.362) conducts in- and out-of-court restructurings for creditors and institutional lenders. He

boasts particular expertise within the retail, hotel and resort sectors.

### Willkie Farr & Gallagher LLP
See profile on p.2016

**THE FIRM** Willkie Farr's business reorganization and restructuring group is highly respected by peers, with a broad focus encompassing large debtor engagements as well as creditor and lender-side representations. Highlights from the past year include acting as lead counsel to RG Steel on its $1 billion Chapter 11 bankruptcy. Other notable matters include the team's continued representation of Broadview Networks and K-V Pharmaceutical in their respective bankruptcy proceedings.

**Commercial Awareness** *"Willkie's partners and associates are very business savvy and focus on getting the best business result for their client. They also have the ability to quickly marshal the expertise of others in the firm and tackle any of the complexities that arise in a bankruptcy."*

**KEY INDIVIDUALS Marc Abrams** (see p.271) is the business reorganization and restructuring practice cochair. *"He really knows how to get things done,"* say impressed interviewees, and is *"one of the premier bankruptcy lawyers out there."* He is regularly recommended for his expertise in navigating large companies through bankruptcy and is equally adept at advising creditors. Fellow practice group cochair **Matthew Feldman** (see p.1891) has decades of experience across the spectrum of bankruptcy-related situations. His recent highlights include representing RG Steel and K-V Pharmaceutical in their respective Chapter 11 bankruptcies. The *"practical and assertive"* **Margot Schonholtz** (see p.1938) is an expert in advising institutional creditor and lender clients. She recently acted for Bank of America on the well-publicized bankruptcies of MF Global and Patriot Coal.

### Band 3

### Bingham McCutchen LLP
See profile on p.1515

**THE FIRM** This financial restructuring practice comprises highly regarded teams in New York and Boston. The group is focused on representing creditor and bondholder clients, with a number of leading finance houses among its institutional client-base. The practice is also renowned for its expertise in international and cross-border bankruptcy issues and is able to draw upon Bingham's global network of resources.

**Sources say:** *"They look for a business outcome that works for their clients, sometimes at the expense of their bills. These guys were all about the client, which is rare. The focus is on getting a great result time and time again."*

**KEY INDIVIDUALS** The *"calm and steady-handed"* **Michael Reilly** (see p.391) cochairs Bingham's financial restructuring group alongside **Jeffrey Sabin** (see p.398). Reilly is described as *"a pillar of the bankruptcy Bar; internationally known and respected,"* by impressed commentators; *"he puts people at ease and doesn't inflame a heated situation."* Sabin, meanwhile, is praised by clients as *"very* *deal savvy; and knows the outermost money that his client can get and goes after it.*" Both are highly experienced across the bankruptcy spectrum, with Reilly in particular boasting strong expertise in cross-border matters.

## Brown Rudnick LLP

See profile on p.437

THE FIRM Brown Rudnick's highly respected bankruptcy and restructuring practice spans offices in Boston and New York. It has built a strong reputation for representing creditor and lender clients in contentious situations, where it is particularly well known for its vigorous pursuit of client interests. Recent highlights for the practice include advising an ad hoc consortium of senior unsecured noteholders on the $3 billion Patriot Coal bankruptcy. It is also acting as lead counsel to the Official Committee of Unsecured Creditors of Dewey & LeBoeuf.

Sources say: "*Hard-hitting equity committee guys.*" "*They like to look at situations where you need creative solutions to get where you want be.*"

KEY INDIVIDUALS **Edward Weisfelner** is head of Brown Rudnick's bankruptcy and corporate restructuring practice. He is best known for his strength in creditor and lender-side representations, with sources noting that he "*writes brilliantly and is excellent if you're in a difficult position.*" He is currently lead counsel for the Official Committee of Unsecured Creditors in the $450 million bankruptcy of Dewey & LeBoeuf. **Robert Stark** "*spends a lot of time understanding the client's company itself,*" say sources, and "*is really good at finding creative solutions.*" He recently represented an ad hoc consortium of senior unsecured noteholders in Patriot Coal's $3 billion Chapter 11 bankruptcy.

## Cadwalader, Wickersham & Taft LLP

See profile on p.438

THE FIRM Teams in New York and Washington, DC make up this high-quality financial restructuring department. The practice advises on all types of bankruptcy matter, for both debtor and creditor-side clients. It also harbors expertise in several niche sectors, including the automotive, energy, insurance and real estate industries. The group has been especially active in the energy sector of late, having undertaken notable creditor group representations in the Dynegy, AES Eastern and EME Homer City Generation bankruptcies. The team also represented MBIA Insurance in relation to approximately $2 billion in claims in the ResCap bankruptcy.

Sources say: "*They are a detail-oriented practice which maintains legal and business perspectives; they focus on practical solutions.*"

KEY INDIVIDUALS **George Davis** (see p.1887) cochairs Cadwalader's financial restructuring practice. He is an expert in bankruptcy issues involving the energy sector, and has recently acted for creditor groups in the prominent bankruptcies of Dynegy, AES Eastern and EME Homer City Generation. He is described as "*a real leader in the bankruptcy space.*" Fellow practice group cochair **John Rapisardi** (see p.1929) garners respect among interviewees for his creative, business-oriented approach to matters. He

boasts a tremendous amount of experience, especially in the automotive and healthcare sectors, as well as having expertise in the Chinese Bankruptcy Code. **Mark Ellenberg** (see p.860) "*has seen it all,*" say interviewees, who add: "*He takes a wise approach and a steady hand to make the best of difficult situations.*" Ellenberg works from the firm's Washington, DC office and comes highly recommended for his bankruptcy litigation expertise. He recently advised MBIA Insurance on the ResCap bankruptcy.

## Morrison & Foerster LLP

See profile on p.1990

THE FIRM Morrison & Foerster has experienced another successful year, with its bankruptcy and restructuring team now a fixture among the major players in the industry. The group undertakes the gamut of bankruptcy-related representations, with high-profile recent engagements for both debtor and creditor-side clients. Its recent highlights include advising ResCap on what has been one of the biggest bankruptcy filings of the past year. It also continues to advise the Chapter 11 trustee of MF Global on its highly public bankruptcy case. On the creditor-side, the team is representing the unsecured creditors' committees in both the PMI and Pinnacle Airlines Chapter 11 proceedings.

Commercial Awareness "*They're very commercial and aggressive, with a very good understanding of the market around them. They take into account all aspects of the situation.*"

KEY INDIVIDUALS **Brett Miller** (see p.369) is managing partner of Morrison & Foerster's New York office. He is a "*professional, smart, deal-oriented lawyer,*" according to interviewees, who add: "*He is very bright and gets the whole process – he is great at moving people into positions to get deals done.*" He is currently lead counsel to Louis Freeh, the Chapter 11 trustee in the MF Global bankruptcy, and is also advising the unsecured creditors' committee in the bankruptcy of Pinnacle Airlines.

## Quinn Emanuel Urquhart & Sullivan, LLP

THE FIRM Quinn Emanuel's renowned litigation expertise translates exceptionally well to its bankruptcy and restructuring practice. The group is considered one of the leading bankruptcy litigation shops in the country, and represents a full range of creditors, lenders and committee groups. Its recent work has included the group's involvement in the litigious aspects of the Lehman Brothers, Jefferson County and NewPage bankruptcies. Another prominent recent highlight is the team's representation of practice group chair Susheel Kirpalani in his role as court-appointed examiner in the Dynegy Holdings Chapter 11 bankruptcy.

Commercial Awareness "*Hands-down one of the best firms I've dealt with in terms of understanding all the pieces of the puzzle fitting together. Excellent at identifying points of leverage in a practical way.*"

KEY INDIVIDUALS The "*very creative, aggressive and hard-working*" **Susheel Kirpalani** is head of the firm's bankruptcy department. He has garnered acclaim for his role as court-appointed examiner in the Dynegy Holdings bankruptcy. Interviewees praise his "*incredible skill at*

*piercing through legal issues quickly and coming up with perspective; he is a tremendous courtroom advocate.*"

## Sidley Austin LLP

See profile on p.1264

THE FIRM Sidley Austin's corporate reorganization and bankruptcy practice provides high-level representations in complex issues across a national network of teams spanning Chicago, Los Angeles, New York and Washington, DC. Each branch works collaboratively with the others, increasing the expertise and resources available to tackle any issue, whether it be for debtors or creditors. In recent highlights, the group represented Dynegy Holdings in its high-profile Chapter 11 bankruptcy.

Sources say: "*They are extremely responsive; we feel like we are a priority for them and it makes a difference. What we like is they are not just technical, they have that rare business judgment as well; they come up with business solutions.*"

KEY INDIVIDUALS The "*very smart and practical*" **Lawrence Nyhan** (see p.378) is based in Chicago and cochairs the firm's corporate reorganization and bankruptcy practice. He is described by sources as "*a great bankruptcy strategist with immense experience and terrific judgment,*" with others noting that he is "*very responsive and service-oriented; one of the very best in the business.*" **James Conlan** (see p.1202) cochairs the group alongside Nyhan and is also based in Chicago. Interviewees recommend him as a "*smart, aggressive and creative*" lawyer. He is a specialist in advising distressed companies looking to restructure and masterminded Sidley's representation of Dynegy Holdings.

## Simpson Thacher & Bartlett LLP

See profile on p.2006

THE FIRM Simpson Thacher's bankruptcy and restructuring practice is renowned as a formidable player in the industry, particularly in representing senior lender clients in complex bankruptcies. Leveraging upon the firm's prominent capital markets and M&A practices, the bankruptcy team advises a stable of institutional clients, such as JPMorgan, Deutsche Bank, Blackstone Group, Barclays Capital and Centerbridge Partners. Recent highlights include representing JPMorgan on the MF Global bankruptcy and also on the Chapter 9 bankruptcy of Jefferson County, Alabama.

KEY INDIVIDUALS Practice head **Peter Pantaleo** (see p.381) is a highly respected name in the bankruptcy industry. According to sources, he "*does a fantastic job*" in securing solutions for his senior lender clients. He recently advised JPMorgan on $1.4 billion of claims in the MF Global bankruptcy.

## Band 4

## Greenberg Traurig, LLP

See profile on p.1024

THE FIRM Greenberg Traurig's excellent national business reorganization and financial restructuring practice consists of solid teams in New York, Miami, Atlanta,

Chicago, Dallas, Houston and Wilmington. The group advises clients across the bankruptcy spectrum, with particular expertise in representing debtors, while also being skilled in conducting bankruptcy litigation. With such a strong national and international footprint, the group is also adept at undertaking cross-border representations.

**Sources say:** *"They have very smart lawyers who understand that service and responsiveness are critical."*

**KEY INDIVIDUALS** Practice cochair **Bruce Zirinsky** (see p.431) is based in the firm's New York office. He gains respect from many in the industry for his creditor-side expertise in particular. He is described by impressed interviewees as a *"very talented and tenacious advocate for his clients."* **Mark Bloom** (see p.986) has the *"ability to take complicated issues and translate them clearly, along with providing practical advice which allows us to progress quickly,"* according to commentators. He is a cochair of the practice and is based in Miami. Clients go on to describe Bloom as *"extremely intelligent, capable, articulate, knowledgeable, cordial and professional."*

### Kasowitz, Benson, Torres & Friedman LLP
See profile on p.1983

**THE FIRM** This firm's creditors' rights and bankruptcy practice operates out of the firm's head office in New York. The group is renowned for its expertise in advising creditors, lenders and investors, particularly in complex litigation issues. The group recently represented the Federal Housing Finance Agency in connection with the ResCap Chapter 11 bankruptcy. It is also currently advising the Official Committee of Former Partners of Dewey & LeBoeuf during its bankruptcy proceedings.

**Sources say:** *"They are a strong advocate and great at what they do." "They are diligent, creative, and I think they represent good value."*

**KEY INDIVIDUALS David Friedman** (see p.317) is a cochair of the practice. He is regularly recognized for his pragmatic yet vigorous representations of his clients. Highlights from the past year for Friedman include his role as lead counsel to the Official Committee of Former Partners of Dewey & LeBoeuf, the former powerhouse law firm undergoing bankruptcy proceedings. **David Rosner** (see p.1933) is regularly involved in the practice's flagship engagements. He mirrors the group's profile in that he is considered an expert creditors' rights and bankruptcy litigation lawyer.

### Klee, Tuchin, Bogdanoff & Stern LLP
See profile on p.687

**THE FIRM** Klee Tuchin boasts one of the most prominent boutique bankruptcy practices in the country. The practice is headquartered in Los Angeles and is regularly seen alongside large full-service firms in some of industry's largest bankruptcy cases. It is also considered one of the foremost authorities in the country on Chapter 9 municipal bankruptcy matters. Recent highlights include its continued advice to Jefferson County, Alabama, on its $4 billion Chapter 9 case, as well as more recently advising the town of Mammoth Lakes, California, on its bankruptcy.

**Sources say:** *"Incredibly knowledgeable on the bankruptcy statutes and they are very strategic thinkers." "They are always able to come up with unique approaches and multiple alternatives."*

**KEY INDIVIDUALS** Founding partner and joint managing partner **Kenneth Klee** is described as *"one of the smartest guys around."* He is considered an expert in Chapter 9 municipal bankruptcy situations and is lead counsel to Jefferson County and Mammoth Lakes in their bankruptcies. He is *"incredibly resourceful and creative,"* according to interviewees, who add: *"He gets his hands dirty and is very effective."* Fellow founding partner **Michael Tuchin** *"gets the respect of everybody"* in the market. He is tremendously experienced across a broad range of bankruptcy issues, and is particularly highlighted by sources for being *"exceptional in the courtroom."* He recently represented national sports retailer Pacific Sunwear of California in a successful out-of-court restructuring. **Lee Bogdanoff** is another founding partner who comes highly recommended for his *"excellent strategizing in negotiations and counterarguments."* He recently took center stage with his role acting on behalf of a large group of former Dewey & LeBoeuf partners.

### Pachulski Stang Ziehl & Jones LLP
See profile on p.694

**THE FIRM** Pachulski Stang is a highly regarded bankruptcy boutique based out of Los Angeles, with further offices in San Francisco, Wilmington and New York. Few specialist bankruptcy firms in the country can lay claim to the presence that Pachulski has in this industry. The firm advises clients across the bankruptcy spectrum, with particular expertise in advising large debtor companies. The group's recent highlights include its representation of air carrier business Mesa Air in its Chapter 11 proceedings.

**Sources say:** *"A fantastic firm." "They know everyone and are the ultimate in professionalism."*

**KEY INDIVIDUALS Richard Pachulski** is a favorite among clients. He *"brings instant credibility to any situation,"* remarked one particularly impressed source. He is further described as an *"effective negotiator and lawyer"* and *"by far one of the most prolific attorneys"* on the West Coast. He advises a full range of clients, from prominent debtors to major creditors' committees.

### Proskauer Rose LLP
See profile on p.2001

**THE FIRM** This firm's business solutions, governance, restructuring and bankruptcy practice was bolstered greatly in 2012 following the arrival of a prominent team from Dewey & LeBoeuf. The newly combined team is now primed to challenge some of the bigger names in the industry, with the new complement of experts bringing with it a string of large-scale, high-value engagements that will add to an already strong workload.

**Sources say:** *"A full-service shop with a deep knowledge base and a breadth of partners and senior associates available to provide excellent advice."*

**KEY INDIVIDUALS Martin Bienenstock** was appointed practice chair upon his arrival from Dewey & LeBoeuf. He is a prominent name in the national bankruptcy industry, with interviewees describing him as *"top drawer; a wonderful person, deep strategist – his work is thorough, detailed and clever."* Recent highlights for Bienenstock include continued high-profile representations in the NewPage, MF Global and Capmark Financial bankruptcies.

### White & Case LLP
See profile on p.451

**THE FIRM** White & Case has well-regarded financial restructuring and insolvency teams in New York, Miami and Los Angeles. The firm is recognized for advising a strong client base of major bondholders, lenders and investors. The firm also maintains a worldwide footprint which allows its bankruptcy practice a significant advantage in cross-border and international restructurings. In recent highlights, the group represented a committee of secured lenders in $1.8 billion of claims in the out-of-court restructuring of Danish shipping company TORM.

**Sources say:** *"They have managed to have a thorough understanding of the law, our restrictions and position better than other firms. Their negotiation skills are exemplary."*

**KEY INDIVIDUALS Thomas Lauria** (see p.352) leads the firm's global financial restructuring and insolvency practice. He is immensely experienced across the bankruptcy spectrum, regularly representing a variety of business interests on both debtor and creditor-sides. He plays leading roles in most of the firm's major bankruptcy engagements.

## Band 5

### Chadbourne & Parke LLP
See profile on p.1962

**THE FIRM** Chadbourne & Parke's New York-based bankruptcy and restructuring group is recognized for its full-service offering to its primarily creditor and lender client base. The practice is also well regarded for its cross-border bankruptcy expertise. It is currently advising the court-appointed examiner in the high-profile ResCap Chapter 11 case, the biggest bankruptcy filing of 2012. Additional highlights include advising the overseas liquidators in the high-value Chapter 15 bankruptcies of both Hellas Telecommunications of Greece and ABC Learning Centres of Australia.

**Sources say:** *"Highly competent, very responsive and user-friendly." "A good complement of different types of lawyers who work together well."*

**KEY INDIVIDUALS** Practice chair **Howard Seife** (see p.1939) is particularly experienced in creditor representations and cross-border restructurings. Interviewees praise him as *"an excellent strategist and relationship manager with an established presence; he is calm and deliberate and doesn't come to snap judgments."* Other sources note that Seife is *"good at articulating issues to clients and drawing out the key legal questions in a way that the client can understand."*

### Debevoise & Plimpton LLP
See profile on p.1968

THE FIRM This business restructuring and workout practice represents a full range of debtor and creditor clients. The group is based in New York and is particularly renowned for its expertise in the airline and insurance sectors. The team took the spotlight with its recent representation of institutional client American Airlines, as special aircraft financing counsel, in the bankruptcy proceedings of AMR.

Sources say: "The Debevoise team is always extremely well-prepared and they think about every detail. They are very responsive, creative and give well thought-out responses to difficult questions."

KEY INDIVIDUALS Richard Hahn is cochair of Debevoise's business restructuring and workouts practice. He recently led as special aircraft financing counsel to American Airlines in to the bankruptcy of parent company AMR. "He is a very measured and objective lawyer," report sources.

### Fried, Frank, Harris, Shriver & Jacobson LLP
See profile on p.1975

THE FIRM Fried Frank is a well-known and respected name in the US bankruptcy space. The firm's bankruptcy and restructuring practice offers a full service to a wide range of clients, from distressed companies to creditors and distressed asset investors. It also boasts considerable cross-border restructuring expertise. Recent highlights include representing GS Capital Partners in connection with $2 billion in claimed debts arising out of the high-profile Hawker Beechcraft Chapter 11 proceedings.

Sources say: "We hire them because they are a full-service firm with a deep bench and can give a full range of advice."

KEY INDIVIDUALS Practice chair Brad Eric Scheler (see p.1937) is an ever-present name on a large proportion of the group's most significant engagements. He receives praise for being "really good at bringing about consensus. He's a very smooth guy who knows how to calm a room down; very effective in breaking through conflict and getting people to the table."

### Fulbright & Jaworski LLP
See profile on p.2435

THE FIRM This Texas-based restructuring, bankruptcy and insolvency group is highly regarded for representing a range of clients, including creditors, committees and senior lenders. The practice operates from offices in Dallas and Houston and has recently garnered praise for its expertise in bankruptcy litigation. Prominent institutional clients include JPMorgan Chase, AT&T and Vitro American.

Sources say: "Broad experience, depth of knowledge and responsiveness. Their advice on legal strategy has been excellent."

KEY INDIVIDUALS Dallas-based Lou Strubeck (see p.2418) leads the practice group. He is frequently engaged in work taking place across the country. Interviewees note that "he is very accessible and gives good solid advice; he understands business issues without overwhelming clients

and uses the legal information to inform business decisions." Also based in Dallas, Toby Gerber (see p.2390) has a tremendous amount of experience in the bankruptcy industry, advising creditor and lender clients across a full range of bankruptcy situations. He has particular expertise in the transport and airline sectors. Clients are impressed with his "decades of experience and excellent strategic thinking."

### Haynes and Boone, LLP
See profile on p.444

THE FIRM Haynes and Boone is headquartered in Texas, with bankruptcy and business restructuring teams throughout the state, as well as a strong offering in New York. The practice operates on a national basis, undertaking the gamut of bankruptcy-related cases. The practice offers expertise in a number of industries, with particular recognition paid to its work in the aviation sector. The team's recent highlights include its appointment as conflicts counsel to American Airlines's parent company AMR during its prominent Chapter 11 bankruptcy.

Sources say: "The team is very proactive in looking forward and anticipating developments. When we go to them, the backup and associates are very good and we are pleased with the service – timeliness and availability are strengths."

KEY INDIVIDUALS "Great strategist" Robert Albergotti is one of the most senior partners in the practice. He has many years of bankruptcy experience, and led in the group's representation of AMR. "He is very practical and knows what can and can't be said," say happy clients, who add: "He knows what the best use of time is and what is worth a client's time." The "always impressive" Robin Phelan is described by sources as "one of the deans of the Texas Bar." He is a revered expert in all facets of bankruptcy law, with commentators noting that "he is a recognized genius in the legal field – the guy you go to if you have a question you can't answer." Charles Beckham is lauded as "good in terms of analyzing a situation and communicating what is important." He is based in Dallas and boasts over 25 years of bankruptcy experience.

### Mayer Brown LLP
See profile on p.1257

THE FIRM Mayer Brown's restructuring, bankruptcy and insolvency group has made a name for itself in representing creditors and lenders in complex bankruptcy situations. The practice boasts strong teams in New York and Chicago, and a full complement of large institutional clients including Bank of America, Deutsche Bank, Barclays Bank and BNY Mellon. The practice is not limited to creditor advice, however, and is increasingly recognized for strong debtor-side work. Indicative highlights include its role on behalf of ATP Oil & Gas in its large Chapter 11 bankruptcy.

Sources say: "At all levels of the firm, the depth of knowledge is superior and the service unfailingly professional and efficient. The firm has experience across a multitude of industries and diverse legal disciplines for comprehensive advice."

KEY INDIVIDUALS Global practice co-head Brian Trust is a creditors' rights expert. Impressed sources note that

"his ability to communicate enables him to gain respect and confidence, allowing counterparties to be receptive to and execute on recommended strategies."

### Orrick, Herrington & Sutcliffe LLP
See profile on p.1994

THE FIRM Orrick has a strong bankruptcy and restructuring presence spanning California, New York and Washington, DC. The practice as a whole advises across the spectrum of bankruptcy cases. It is particularly renowned for advising on mass tort and Chapter 9 municipal bankruptcies, in addition to distressed solar energy-related matters. Recent highlights include representing the City of Stockton, California, in its Chapter 9 bankruptcy proceedings.

Sources say: "The firm is staffed by veteran attorneys who are forthright and imaginative in their assessment of our options." "They are good at understanding the big picture and identifying important points, as well as communicating my position to the court."

KEY INDIVIDUALS Marc Levinson (see p.650) is based in Orrick's Sacramento office. He is "emerging as a national expert in Chapter 9 cases" and "has really cornered that market," report many observers. He recently played key roles in the Chapter 9 filings for both the City of Vallejo and the City of Stockton. The vastly experienced Roger Frankel (see p.863) is based in Washington, DC and is cochair of the firm's restructuring group. He leads in a large proportion of the group's most significant matters, and recently acted for Buffalo Thunder Development Authority in its Chapter 11 proceedings. Commentators note that he is "very levelheaded in volatile situations: he is not about ego; it is the way he delivers that garners respect."

### Ropes & Gray LLP
See profile on p.1528

THE FIRM The Ropes & Gray bankruptcy and business restructuring teams in New York and Boston work in tandem to tackle difficult bankruptcy cases, predominantly on behalf of bondholders and lenders. The practice has experienced a busy year, with a number of engagements relating to the energy sector, an area where it boasts particular expertise. Other highlights have included representing an ad hoc group of security holders in ResCap's large-scale Chapter 11 case.

KEY INDIVIDUALS Mark Bane is the head of Ropes & Gray's business restructuring group and is based in the firm's New York office. Distressed debt and equity investors, hedge funds and bondholder group representations make up the majority of his engagements.

### Sullivan & Cromwell LLP
See profile on p.2011

THE FIRM This restructuring and bankruptcy practice group is increasing its standing in the sector, thanks to a strong line of recent successes, including its ground-breaking appointment as lead debtor's counsel to Eastman Kodak. The practice boasts a large presence in New York, where an enviable corporate platform has allowed the group to advise both debtor and lender clients at an early stage and develop strategies.

**Sources say:** *"They have good depth of knowledge and experience. They tend to adopt a team approach to staffing which gives you the benefit of a group of excellent lawyers focusing on your issues."*

**KEY INDIVIDUALS** Sullivan & Cromwell's practice founder and head of restructuring is **Andrew Dietderich** (see p.305). He is equally comfortable in conducting contentious or transactional engagements, and is lead counsel to Eastman Kodak during its Chapter 11 bankruptcy.

### Vinson & Elkins LLP
See profile on p.2459

**THE FIRM** This restructuring and reorganization practice stables superb teams in Dallas, Houston and New York. The group represents both creditor and debtor-side clients, with particular expertise in the real estate, energy and retail industries. In recent years, the team has gained prominence for its work on behalf of private equity funds during distressed asset acquisitions. Its recent highlights include acting for DE Shaw Direct Capital as DIP lender to Seahawk Drilling.

**KEY INDIVIDUALS** Practice founder **Dan Stewart** (see p.2417) is tremendously experienced across all manner of bankruptcy-related situations. Interviewees are quick to praise the gravitas that he brings to their cases, noting his *"long-lasting, outstanding reputation."*

### Winston & Strawn LLP
See profile on p.1267

**THE FIRM** Winston & Strawn has far-reaching national restructuring and insolvency expertise, with the practice boasting strong presence in California, Illinois and New York. The group offers wide-ranging bankruptcy expertise, and is highly commended for its work representing creditors, lenders and investors.

**Sources say:** *"The combined team was incredible."* *"Sophisticated and talented."*

**KEY INDIVIDUALS** Eric Sagerman is chair of Winston & Strawn's restructuring and insolvency practice and is managing partner of the firm's Los Angeles office.

### Other Notable Practitioners

The *"very creative"* **Evan Flaschen** (see p.1893) of Bracewell & Giuliani LLP is praised by commentators for his ability to *"pull deals together when you really feel like all hope is lost."* He is head of the firm's financial restructuring group based in New York and predominantly advises creditors, lenders and investors. *"Consummate professional"* **Paul Steven Singerman** (see p.1007) is cofounder of Miami-based Berger Singerman. He is considered an eminent bankruptcy expert in the region and his practice takes him across the US. Clients note that *"the man is a great negotiator and very well versed in the law. He is amazingly good on his feet in presenting a matter to the court."* Other commentators have admired in Singerman a *"technical expertise I've never seen in anyone before."* **Richard Levin** (see p.355) of Cravath, Swaine & Moore LLP in New York is head of the firm's restructuring practice. He garners tremendous respect from interviewees for an eminent career that encompasses authoring the Bankruptcy Code and chairing the National Bankruptcy Conference. *"Having someone with his gravitas helps during discussions and negotiations,"* note commentators. **Gregg Galardi** (see p.770) of DLA Piper LLP (US) is the firm's national bankruptcy practice head. He divides his time between Delaware, New York and London. He is described by sources as a *"very creative, aggressive and smart bankruptcy person,"* with *"a very strong track record in large debtor cases."* The *"unflappable"* **James Giddens** (see p.1896) of Hughes Hubbard & Reed LLP continues to act as trustee in the Lehman Brothers and MF Global bankruptcies, two of the biggest filings in recent history. He is described as *"tremendously insightful,"* with one particularly impressed source noting: *"In a huge case with lots of adversaries and politics, he puts one foot in front of the other and unwinds these complex negotiations."* **James Carr** is chair of Kelley Drye & Warren LLP's bankruptcy and restructuring practice. He is renowned as a creditors' rights specialist, regularly advising creditors' committees on large scale Chapter 11 cases. He is *"very impressive both in knowledge and results,"* according to clients, who add: *"His strengths are superior intelligence and negotiating win-win resolutions."* His recent highlights include acting for the indenture trustee on the ResCap bankruptcy. **Edward Dobbs** of Parker, Hudson, Rainer & Dobbs LLP is described by interviewees as *"unparalleled"* for bankruptcy work in Georgia, adding that *"it's like watching an artist"* when in court. He has received praise as a *"brilliant negotiator and crafter of creative solutions,"* with other interviewees pointing to his *"good business acumen."* **Ben Logan** of O'Melveny & Myers LLP in Los Angeles is immensely experienced and *"extremely talented."* His practice encompasses a variety of representations spanning the country. He has been involved in many of the firm's most prominent matters, including his recent advice to an ad hoc committee of second lien holders on the AMF Bowling Chapter 11 bankruptcy. **Deryck Palmer** of Pillsbury Winthrop Shaw Pittman LLP is a well-regarded attorney with tremendous experience. He advises debtor and creditor-side clients in all manner of bankruptcy-related issues. He also garners praise for his excellent litigation expertise. Creditors' rights specialist **Luc Despins** is chair of the global restructuring practice at Paul Hastings LLP. He is an expert in acting for creditors' committees. Clients laud his excellent litigation skills and ability to manage parties in complex proceedings. The *"extremely respected"* **Adam Harris** (see p.1901) is head of the bankruptcy department at Schulte Roth & Zabel LLP in New York. Commentators praise his *"superb attention to detail"* and *"innovative structuring of deals and acquisitions."* **Kristopher Hansen** is financial restructuring practice group chair at New York-based Stroock & Stroock & Lavan LLP. He is referred to as a *"practical deal-maker"* who *"is able to bring to bear his business acumen and thought process; he looks at the big picture and is a visionary."*

## CAPITAL MARKETS DEBT & EQUITY

Commentary about individuals can be found under their firm's paragraph.  If the firm has no paragraph (is not ranked) look at Other Notable Practitioners.

*The editorial is in alphabetical order by firm name.*

### Cahill Gordon & Reindel LLP
See profile on p.1960

**THE FIRM** This team attracts the particular respect of the business community for its representation of investment banks in high-yield debt transactions. It also has an impressive track record across the spectrum of debt and equity work. Recent highlights include advising Bank of America Merrill Lynch as sole dealer manager and solicitation agent on a $15.7 billion bond exchange offer by CIT Group.

| Recommended for Commercial Awareness Nationwide | |
| --- | --- |
| Cahill Gordon & Reindel LLP | Simpson Thacher & Bartlett LLP |
| Fried, Frank, Harris, Shriver & Jacobson LLP | Skadden, Arps, Slate, Meagher & Flom LLP & Affiliates |
| Paul, Weiss, Rifkind, Wharton & Garrison LLP | Vinson & Elkins LLP |

| Recommended for Client Service Nationwide | |
| --- | --- |
| Cravath, Swaine & Moore LLP | Proskauer Rose LLP |
| Davis Polk & Wardwell LLP | Simpson Thacher & Bartlett LLP |
| Kirkland & Ellis LLP | Skadden, Arps, Slate, Meagher & Flom LLP & Affiliates |
| Latham & Watkins LLP | |

**Commercial Awareness** *"They take the approach of not just identifying issues, but proactively coming up with solutions."* **KEY INDIVIDUALS William Hartnett** (see p.331) is a favored choice of investment banks and public and private companies to represent them in debt and equity transactions. His recent highlights include advising Morgan Stanley as sole book-running manager on Aircastle's $64.5 million secondary public offering of common stock. **Jonathan Schaffzin** (see p.400) *"knows the issues and makes good judgment calls,"* impressed sources report. He represented Morgan Stanley and others as joint book-running managers, and UBS Investment Bank as co-manager,

*The editorial is in alphabetical order by firm name.*

## Capital Markets: Debt & Equity
### Leading Firms

**Band 1**
Cleary Gottlieb Steen & Hamilton LLP *
Cravath, Swaine & Moore LLP *
Davis Polk & Wardwell LLP *
Simpson Thacher & Bartlett LLP *
Sullivan & Cromwell LLP *

**Band 2**
Latham & Watkins LLP *
Skadden, Arps, Slate, Meagher & Flom LLP & Affiliates *

**Band 3**
Cahill Gordon & Reindel LLP *
Debevoise & Plimpton LLP *
Kirkland & Ellis LLP *
Paul, Weiss, Rifkind, Wharton & Garrison LLP *
Shearman & Sterling LLP *
Sidley Austin LLP *

**Band 4**
Fried, Frank, Harris, Shriver & Jacobson LLP *
Gibson, Dunn & Crutcher LLP *
Morrison & Foerster LLP *
Proskauer Rose LLP *
Ropes & Gray LLP *
Vinson & Elkins LLP *
Weil, Gotshal & Manges LLP *
Wilson Sonsini Goodrich & Rosati *

## Capital Markets: High-Yield Products
### Leading Firms

**Band 1**
Cahill Gordon & Reindel LLP *

**Band 2**
Latham & Watkins LLP *

**Band 3**
Cravath, Swaine & Moore LLP *
Davis Polk & Wardwell LLP *
Kirkland & Ellis LLP *
Simpson Thacher & Bartlett LLP *

in two Rule 144A/Regulation S offerings by Kinetic Concepts of $1.75 billion and $750 million. **James Clark** (see p.295) recently represented JP Morgan Securities and other initial purchasers on a $3.25 billion placement by CIT Group. He is a highly respected capital markets lawyer who is particularly recognized for his expertise in high-yield debt transactions. **John Tripodoro** (see p.419) maintains a formidable reputation for his representation of banks on debt and equity offerings. He recently represented Credit Suisse Securities as lead underwriter in the $97 million offering of common stock by Hercules Offshore. **Douglas Horowitz** (see p.336) is commended by market sources for his highly practical approach. He recently advised Barclays Capital as initial purchaser on a Rule 144A/Regulation S offering by CDW LLC and CDW Finance of $130 million of 8.5% senior notes due 2019.

## Capital Markets: Debt & Equity
### Senior Statesmen

**Senior Statesmen: distinguished older practitioners**

| | |
|---|---|
| Slonaker Norman | Sidley Austin LLP * |
| Tanenbaum James | Morrison & Foerster LLP * |
| Williams Jr William J | Sullivan & Cromwell LLP * |

### Leading Individuals

**Star individuals**

| | |
|---|---|
| Beller Alan | Cleary Gottlieb Steen & Hamilton LLP * |
| Truesdell Richard D | Davis Polk & Wardwell LLP * |

**Band 1**

| | |
|---|---|
| Buckholz Jr Robert E | Sullivan & Cromwell LLP * |
| Clark James | Cahill Gordon & Reindel LLP * |
| Davenport Kirk A | Latham & Watkins LLP * |
| Harms David B | Sullivan & Cromwell LLP * |
| Hartnett William M | Cahill Gordon & Reindel LLP * |
| Heinzelman Kris F | Cravath, Swaine & Moore LLP * |
| Jacob Valerie Ford | Fried, Frank, Harris, Shriver & Jacobson * |
| Jaffe Marc D | Latham & Watkins LLP * |
| Kaplan Michael | Davis Polk & Wardwell LLP * |
| Korff Phyllis G | Skadden, Arps, Slate, Meagher & Flom * |
| Sandler Richard J | Davis Polk & Wardwell LLP * |
| Silverman Leslie N | Cleary Gottlieb Steen & Hamilton LLP * |
| White John W | Cravath, Swaine & Moore LLP * |

**Band 2**

| | |
|---|---|
| Burns Stephen L | Cravath, Swaine & Moore LLP * |
| Denenberg Alan | Davis Polk & Wardwell LLP * |
| Evans III Robert | Shearman & Sterling LLP |
| Goldschmidt David J | Skadden, Arps, Slate, Meagher & Flom * |
| Hinman Jr William H | Simpson Thacher & Bartlett LLP * |
| Kanter Stacy J | Skadden, Arps, Slate, Meagher & Flom * |
| Kennedy John C | Paul, Weiss, Rifkind, Wharton & Garrison * |
| Korff Joshua N | Kirkland & Ellis LLP * |
| Lopez Frank | Proskauer Rose LLP |
| Loughran Peter J | Debevoise & Plimpton LLP |
| Miller Rod | Milbank, Tweed, Hadley & McCloy (ONP)[†] * |
| Petrosky Edward F | Sidley Austin LLP * |
| Pitts Andrew J | Cravath, Swaine & Moore LLP * |
| Reiter Glenn M | Simpson Thacher & Bartlett LLP * |
| Robinson Arthur D | Simpson Thacher & Bartlett LLP * |
| Rogers Jr William P | Cravath, Swaine & Moore LLP * |
| Schaffzin Jonathan A | Cahill Gordon & Reindel LLP * |
| Schiavone Michael J | O'Melveny & Myers LLP (ONP)[†] * |
| Tripodoro John A | Cahill Gordon & Reindel LLP * |
| Whelan III William J | Cravath, Swaine & Moore LLP * |

**Band 3**

| | |
|---|---|
| Beshar Sarah | Davis Polk & Wardwell LLP * |
| Best Edward S | Mayer Brown LLP (ONP)[†] |
| Beveridge David | Shearman & Sterling LLP |
| Bressman Stuart | Proskauer Rose LLP |
| Brod Craig B | Cleary Gottlieb Steen & Hamilton LLP * |
| Clayton Jay | Sullivan & Cromwell LLP * |
| Dallas Bruce | Davis Polk & Wardwell LLP * |
| Ezring Gregory | Paul, Weiss, Rifkind, Wharton & Garrison * |

| | |
|---|---|
| Fogg William V | Cravath, Swaine & Moore LLP * |
| Gandhi Samir A | Sidley Austin LLP * |
| Gelfond Stuart H | Fried, Frank, Harris, Shriver & Jacobson * |
| Grabar Nicolas | Cleary Gottlieb Steen & Hamilton LLP * |
| Healy Peter | O'Melveny & Myers LLP (ONP)[†] * |
| Karpf Jeffrey D | Cleary Gottlieb Steen & Hamilton LLP * |
| Kelly T Mark | Vinson & Elkins LLP * |
| Lebovitz James A | Dechert LLP (ONP)[†] * |
| Lefkowitz David S | Weil, Gotshal & Manges LLP * |
| Lobrano John D | Simpson Thacher & Bartlett LLP * |
| Lopez David | Cleary Gottlieb Steen & Hamilton LLP * |
| Noel Gregg A | Skadden, Arps, Slate, Meagher & Flom [†] |
| Saper Jeff | Wilson Sonsini Goodrich & Rosati |
| Tolley III Edward P | Simpson Thacher & Bartlett LLP * |

**Band 4**

| | |
|---|---|
| Allen Julie M | Proskauer Rose LLP |
| Arcella Craig F | Cravath, Swaine & Moore LLP * |
| Bloch Matthew | Weil, Gotshal & Manges LLP * |
| Bonnie Joshua Ford | Simpson Thacher & Bartlett LLP * |
| Brittenham David | Debevoise & Plimpton LLP |
| Brody Ronald S | White & Case LLP (ONP)[†] * |
| Bursky Daniel J | Fried, Frank, Harris, Shriver & Jacobson * |
| Chambers J Michael | Latham & Watkins LLP |
| Downes Robert W | Sullivan & Cromwell LLP * |
| Fabens Andrew | Gibson, Dunn & Crutcher LLP * |
| Fernicola Gregory | Skadden, Arps, Slate, Meagher & Flom * |
| Giove Stephen | Shearman & Sterling LLP |
| Hall Joseph A | Davis Polk & Wardwell LLP * |
| Haueter Eric S | Sidley Austin LLP * |
| Horowitz Douglas S. | Cahill Gordon & Reindel LLP * |
| Kirkpatrick Deanna | Davis Polk & Wardwell LLP * |
| Levitt Michael | Fried, Frank, Harris, Shriver & Jacobson * |
| Niehoff Philip J | Mayer Brown LLP (ONP)[†] |
| O'Connor James | Sidley Austin LLP * |
| Oelman David | Vinson & Elkins LLP * |
| Rodgers Greg | Latham & Watkins LLP * |
| Slutzky Steven J | Debevoise & Plimpton LLP |
| Soussloff Andrew D | Sullivan & Cromwell LLP * |
| Stolper Antonia E | Shearman & Sterling LLP |
| Tavzel Erik R | Cravath, Swaine & Moore LLP * |
| Tropp Paul D | Fried, Frank, Harris, Shriver & Jacobson * |
| Wallach Kenneth | Simpson Thacher & Bartlett LLP * |
| Woronoff Michael A | Proskauer Rose LLP |

**Up-and-coming individuals**

| | |
|---|---|
| Aftanas Richard | Skadden, Arps, Slate, Meagher & Flom * |
| Breen Justin | Proskauer Rose LLP |
| Schuman Ian | Latham & Watkins LLP * |

\* *Indicates individual with profile.*
[†] *ONP = Other Notable Practitioner.*

*The editorial is in alphabetical order by firm name.*

## Cleary Gottlieb Steen & Hamilton LLP
See profile on p.1963

**THE FIRM** This team maintains its outstanding reputation for advising both issuers and underwriters on key transactions including IPOs, equity offerings, and convertible and secured debt offerings. Highlights include representing Nationstar Mortgage Holdings in its $250 million IPO and Credit Suisse Group as issuer in a $2 billion offering of tier 2 buffer capital notes.

**Sources say:** *"The sheer brain power of their practice is impressive."* *"They are consistently good no matter who the partner is and their associates are also very good."*

**KEY INDIVIDUALS Alan Beller** (see p.281) is *"practical"* and *"in tune with the SEC,"* sources say. Clients recommend his advice on corporate governance matters. **Leslie Silverman** (see p.406) is a lawyer whose advice on complex legal issues related to underwriting is frequently sought by clients. He was counsel to Barclays Capital and Credit Suisse as underwriters on Transocean's public offering of $1.2 billion of shares and a registered public offering of $2.5 billion of senior notes. **Craig Brod** (see p.287) recently advised The Hartford Financial Services Group on a $2.15 billion capital raising which included an offering of 7.875% fixed-to-floating rate junior subordinated debentures due 2042 and a $1.55 billion offering of senior debt in three tranches. **Nicolas Grabar** (see p.1898) is *"smart, calm, thoughtful and quick,"* admiring sources report. He continues to have a particularly impressive reputation for his representation of Mexican and Brazilian companies. **Jeffrey Karpf** (see p.343) has *"great judgment,"* is *"highly thorough"* and *"always calm and collected,"* clients say. He recently represented the underwriters in the sale by the US Department of Treasury of approximately $5.75 billion of American International Group (AIG) common stock. **David Lopez** (see p.358) is praised by sources for his *"highly thoughtful"* and *"collaborative"* approach. His recent highlights include representing LyondellBasell Industries on a $2 billion offering of 5% senior notes due 2019, and a $1 billion offering of 5.75% senior notes due 2024.

## Cravath, Swaine & Moore LLP
See profile on p.1966

**THE FIRM** The strong team at this firm receives plaudits from interviewees for the high quality of its representation of issuers and underwriters on transactions such as IPOs, equity offerings, and high-yield and investment grade debt. Recent highlights include advising Time Warner on its $1 billion registered debt offering and the underwriters, led by Credit Suisse, on Community Health Systems's $1.2 billion registered high-yield senior debt offering.

**Client Service** *"They collaborate seamlessly to ensure they deliver their firm's absolute best on every client matter."*

**KEY INDIVIDUALS Kris Heinzelman** (see p.332) is *"highly thoughtful"* and a *"terrific lawyer,"* sources say. He recently represented the underwriters led by Bank of America Merrill Lynch and others in a $2 billion registered debt offering by Hewlett-Packard. **Stephen Burns** (see p.290) *"gets to the point very quickly,"* *"has a fabulous knowledge of what is going on in the market"* and is *"highly user-friendly,"* sources say. His highlights include advising the

initial purchasers on a $230 million Rule 144A/Regulation S senior convertible debt offering by DFC Global. **Andrew Pitts** (see p.385) *"does his job highly rigorously, but with an attitude and bedside manner that are enviable,"* market sources say. He represented Citigroup as underwriter in FleetCor Technologies' $249 million secondary offering of common stock. **William Fogg** (see p.314) advised the underwriters, led by Bank of America Merrill Lynch and JPMorgan, on Freeport-McMoRan Cooper & Gold's $3 billion registered senior debt offering. Clients highly acclaim his practical judgment on complex issues. **Craig Arcella** (see p.274) frequently represents both corporate clients and financial institutions in a range of capital markets transactions. He recently advised the underwriters led by Barclays Capital, Goldman Sachs and UBS Investment Bank on a $1.5 billion registered debt offering by the State of Israel. **John White** (see p.425) is a *"great thinker"* who sources report *"has a command of the intersection of accounting and disclosure that is really superb."* He represented Rock-Tenn in its $750 million Rule 144A/Regulation S debt offering. **William Rogers** (see p.394) is acclaimed by sources for his commercial understanding and hands-on approach to transactions. His highlights include representing Gaslog in its $329 million IPO. **William Whelan** (see p.425) has *"a complete grasp of all the legal issues, but can give practical advice, too"* and he *"can advise on risk but also on the practicalities of those risks coming to fruition and on ways to minimize risks,"* clients say. He advises investment banks and issuers on IPOs, high-yield and investment grade debt, and equity offerings. **Erik Tavzel** (see p.416) represented DHT in its $80 million offering of common stock and series A participating preferred stock. He counts a number of Canadian public companies among his clients.

## Davis Polk & Wardwell LLP
See profile on p.442

**THE FIRM** This outstanding team is roundly commended by sources for its strength in advising financial institutions and corporates on a range of sophisticated capital markets transactions. Banking clients also highly rate its representation in high-yield product offerings; it recently represented Goldman Sachs as lead underwriter in Hologic's $1 billion high-yield notes offering. Other highlights include advising Cobalt International Energy on its $1.7 billion SEC-registered primary and secondary offering of common stock.

**Client Service** *"The culture of the firm is excellent, they believe in team work and we know we'll always get the best from them."*

**KEY INDIVIDUALS** The *"creative"* **Alan Denenberg** (see p.631) is *"thoughtful, smart and reasonable,"* impressed sources say. His recent highlights include advising Goldman Sachs as lead book-running manager, and the joint book-running managers and co-managers on the $123 million IPO of Yelp. **Sarah Beshar** (see p.283) is *"cool under fire"* and has a *"demeanor and disposition which projects calm and confidence,"* clients say. She advised the joint book-running managers, including Credit Suisse Securities, on the $600 million registered notes offering by

Praxair. **Bruce Dallas** (see p.630) *"knows the markets well"* and *"has a sophisticated understanding of his audience and the ability to communicate at different levels,"* clients say. He advised Comcast on its SEC-registered debt offering of $2.25 billion of notes. **Joseph Hall** (see p.329) advised Citigroup Global Markets and others as representatives of the initial purchasers on ING US's Rule 144A/Regulation S offering of senior notes. Sources say he is a *"highly thoughtful and well respected lawyer."* The *"fantastic"* and *"highly practical"* **Richard Truesdell** (see p.419) is roundly acclaimed by interviewees for his legal knowledge, his extensive experience and his market insight. His recent work highlights include advising Morgan Stanley, JP Morgan Securities and Goldman Sachs as joint book-running managers on the $1.1 billion IPO of Michael Kors. **Michael Kaplan** (see p.343) is *"extremely bright and extremely knowledgeable,"* *"really user friendly"* and *"has precedents at his fingertips and a good understanding of the documents and what works and what does not work and why,"* sources say. He recently advised Merrill Lynch and others as representatives of the underwriters on the $490 million IPO of Rexnord. **Richard Sandler** (see p.399) provides clients with *"business sense and practical advice on a real time basis,"* market sources say. He represented JP Morgan Securities and others as representatives of the underwriters in Vantiv's $575 million IPO. **Deanna Kirkpatrick** (see p.347) is commended by sources for her highly practical approach to advising clients. She advised Cigna on an SEC-registered debt shelf takedown of up to $2.1 billion, and on an SEC-registered equity shelf takedown of up to $650 million.

## Debevoise & Plimpton LLP
See profile on p.1968

**THE FIRM** This team maintains a strong and growing profile for its representation of corporations and financial institutions in the full spectrum of debt and equity transactions. It recently represented The Carlyle Group in the $274.5 million secondary offering of common stock in Triumph Group. Other key clients at this firm include Access Industries, Booz Allen Hamilton and Morgan Stanley.

**Sources say:** *"They are deeply expert, get the job done and are user-friendly."*

**KEY INDIVIDUALS Peter Loughran** is *"smart and knowledgeable"* and a *"hard worker"* with *"good judgment,"* sources say. He is held in high esteem by both issuers and underwriters. Recent highlights include representing The ServiceMaster Company in its $600 million offering of 8% senior notes due 2020. **David Brittenham** is a *"proactive thinker who is able to offer solutions"* and is *"helpful in bringing practical knowledge"* to transactions. He represented HD Supply in its notes offerings totaling $2.382 billion. **Steven Slutzky** recently advised Reynolds Group on its $1.25 billion offering of 9.875% senior notes due 2019. He frequently represents issuers and underwriters in transactions such as IPOs, secondary offerings, private placements and debt offerings.

*The editorial is in alphabetical order by firm name.*

## Fried, Frank, Harris, Shriver & Jacobson LLP
See profile on p.1975

THE FIRM This busy team is highly respected for its balanced practice advising underwriters and corporates on the full spectrum of debt and equity transactions. Recent highlights include representing Humana in its $1 billion senior notes offering.

Commercial Awareness "*They really know market conditions, so get you good terms.*"

KEY INDIVIDUALS Valerie Jacob (see p.339) "*has had decades of experience and access to the investment banking community at the highest levels*" and as a result she "*tells us what is achievable in transactions,*" clients say. She is chairperson of the firm and head of the firm's global capital markets group. Stuart Gelfond (see p.319) is commended by sources for his rigorous and methodical approach to problem-solving. He recently represented the underwriters in Medley Capital's $68.75 million offering of common stock. Daniel Bursky (see p.290) is "*extremely commercial*" and is praised by interviewees for his ability to identify and focus on what is important to clients. He recently represented Bank of America Merrill Lynch as representatives of the underwriters in Armstrong World Industries' public offering of $265.2 million of common stock. Michael Levitt (see p.355) has a "*vast and excellent knowledge of the capital markets,*" clients say. He represented the underwriters in Ares Capital's $428.2 million offering of common stock. Paul Tropp (see p.419) is "*highly thoughtful and willing to be helpful*" and "*always available and always has the team on task in completing things,*" satisfied clients report. He represented the underwriters in Ellington Financial's $87.9 million offering of common stock.

## Gibson, Dunn & Crutcher LLP
See profile on p.682

THE FIRM This team continues to receive strong plaudits from interviewees for the impressive quality of its securities regulation practice and for its transactional work. It recently advised Kraft Foods on a notes offering. Other notable clients include Intel, Williams Partners and Wells Fargo.

Sources say: "*They are all highly bright and knowledgeable and handle things with a great deal of confidence but are also very good to work with.*"

KEY INDIVIDUALS Andrew Fabens (see p.311) is a "*strong and knowledgeable lawyer*" who is highly regarded for his representation of companies on a range of debt and equity transactions. His clients include Heineken, Moody's and Ancestry.com.

## Kirkland & Ellis LLP
See profile on p.1254

THE FIRM The team at this firm is particularly praised by sources for its representation of private equity funds and their affiliate companies on debt and equity transactions including high-yield debt matters. Recent highlights include advising Clear Channel Outdoor on its issue of $2.2 billion senior subordinated notes due 2020 by its subsidiary, Clear Channel Worldwide. Other key clients include Apax, Avis Budget and Kellogg.

Client Service "*They are very prompt and accommodate us no matter how unfair our timetable is.*"

KEY INDIVIDUALS Joshua Korff (see p.349) is "*highly smart,*" "*highly practical*" and is commended by sources for his business-minded approach to issues. He has notable expertise in public and private financings.

## Latham & Watkins LLP
See profile on p.446

THE FIRM The highly sought-after team at this firm is praised by market sources for the high quality of its advice to clients on a range of debt and equity transactions including IPOs, secondary offerings, high-yield and investment grade bonds. Recent highlights include representing Intermolecular in its $96.5 million IPO. It also advised Hyatt Hotels on senior notes offerings totaling $500 million.

Client Service "*Latham & Watkins provides superior service and exceptional legal and business advice.*"

KEY INDIVIDUALS Marc Jaffe (see p.340) has "*deep legal knowledge, but applies it in a user-friendly and commercial way*" and has "*great judgment and is a problem solver,*" impressed clients say. He recently represented soccer club Manchester United in its IPO. Kirk Davenport (see p.301) is "*highly keen on making sure his clients are happy and he'll do anything for his clients.*" He advises a wide array of clients on the full range of capital markets transactions. Ian Schuman (see p.402) is a "*very good adviser*" who "*you want in the trenches with you,*" clients report. His areas of expertise include IPOs, high-yield offerings and public and private equity offerings. Michael Chambers is a Houston, Texas-based lawyer with a good reputation for advising clients on transactions in the oil and gas industry. Clients praise his legal and market knowledge. Greg Rodgers (see p.394) "*really knows the technicalities of what he does*" and is "*always available and has great judgment as well.*" He focuses on high-yield and convertible securities.

## Morrison & Foerster LLP
See profile on p.1990

THE FIRM This team is held in high esteem for its diverse array of transactions including IPOs, preferred stock offerings and investment grade offerings. It represented National Bank of Canada in the establishment of a $5 billion medium-term bank note program. Other clients include Bank of America Merrill Lynch, the Resolution Committee of Landsbanki and RBC Capital Markets.

Sources say: "*They are responsive and highly knowledgeable about the financial markets and financial institutions.*"

KEY INDIVIDUALS James Tanenbaum (see p.415) is praised by sources as a "*highly effective and tough negotiator.*" He represented the underwriters in Capital One Financial's $1.25 billion issue of common stock.

## Paul, Weiss, Rifkind, Wharton & Garrison LLP
See profile on p.1997

THE FIRM This team frequently handles a range of transactions for issuer clients operating in industries which include telecoms, fashion and energy. Recent highlights include representing Michael Kors in its $1.1 billion IPO and its $1.35 billion secondary offering. Other clients of this team include Apollo Global Management, Time Warner and Morgan Stanley.

Commercial Awareness "*We get a business-like service in the sense these are lawyers who come to us with solutions rather than problems.*"

KEY INDIVIDUALS John Kennedy (see p.345) is "*highly knowledgeable and efficient,*" market sources say. He advised the US Department of the Treasury as selling shareholder on several transactions including four private and public auctions of preferred stocks and warrants in 37 different banks and holding companies. Gregory Ezring (see p.311) is praised by market sources for the creativity and elegance of his solutions. He represented EP Energy on a Rule 144A/Regulation S offering of $2 billion of 9.375% senior notes due 2020, and $750 million of 6.875% of senior secured notes due 2019.

## Proskauer Rose LLP
See profile on p.2001

THE FIRM The team at this firm has a balanced and growing practice representing sponsors, corporates and investment banks on high-yield and investment grade bond transactions, IPOs, Rule 144A/Regulation S and private placements. Recent highlights include representing Solera Capital as sponsor and selling stockholder in the $109 million IPO by Annie's. Other clients include Lazard Capital, Piper Jaffray and the National Basketball Association.

Client Service "*They pride themselves on creative solutions and total client service.*" "*It is a very responsive service with advice and counsel that makes sense in the real world in which we operate.*"

KEY INDIVIDUALS Frank Lopez co-heads the global capital markets practice with Julie Allen, and "*combines exceptional technical expertise with a focus on business solutions,*" satisfied clients report. He recently represented Celgene in a $1.5 billion offering of senior unsecured notes. Julie Allen recently represented Grifols in a $1.3 billion offering of ADRs. She is "*absolutely fearless,*" "*bright and driven*" and "*good for when you need a tough lawyer,*" impressed clients say. "*Problem solver*" Stuart Bressman is "*good at taking highly complex issues and being creative about solutions,*" clients state. His highlights include representing Credit Agricole (USA) Securities in an ATM offering by Chicago Bridge & Iron with an approximate value of $300 million. Michael Woronoff represented 99 Cents Only in a $250 million high-yield bond offering. He heads the firm's LA office and its West Coast corporate and securities practice. Justin Breen is "*incredibly hardworking, tireless and also highly smart and creative,*" sources say. He has recently advised Jefferies and Company on several transactions including Acadia Healthcare's $150 million offering of 12.875% senior notes due 2018.

## Ropes & Gray LLP
See profile on p.1528

THE FIRM The team at Ropes & Gray enters the rankings this year due to the plaudits it has received for its work representing corporates, underwriters and other market par-

*The editorial is in alphabetical order by firm name.*

ticipants in a range of transactions. It represented the lead underwriters in Zynga's $1 billion IPO. Other clients include Bain Capital, GoldenTree Asset Management and Ironwood Pharmaceuticals.

**Sources say:** *"They are excellent lawyers and have a very deep bench."*

**KEY INDIVIDUALS** A key contact at the firm is Patrick O'Brien.

## Shearman & Sterling LLP
See profile on p.2005
**THE FIRM** This group is highly regarded for its representation of corporates and financial institutions on a diverse array of securities transactions. It has a significant footprint in Latin America and in Canada. Recent work includes advising B/E Aerospace on its $800 million registered public offering of reopened high-yield senior notes.

**Sources say:** *"They are very user-friendly and adept at understanding the needs and sensitivities of the various stakeholders."*

**KEY INDIVIDUALS David Beveridge** is a *"market leader"* and *"someone who can cut through all of it and get a deal done,"* sources say. He represented Bank of America Merrill Lynch and Goldman Sachs in Steel Dynamics' Rule 144A/Regulation S registered rights offering of $750 million of high-yield senior notes. **Robert Evans** is commended by sources as *"highly even tempered"* and for adopting an approach on transactions which is *"a good mix of academic and practical."* He represented Morgan Stanley and others as joint bookrunners in American Airlines' registered offering of investment grade Class A pass-through certificates. **Stephen Giove** recently represented Viacom in registered offerings of senior notes and debentures totaling $1.6 billion. His areas of expertise include offerings of common stock, preferred stock and high-yield and investment grade debt. **Antonia Stolper** heads the firm's Capital Markets – Americas and Latin America sections. She recently represented Inversiones La Construccion in its global offering of common stock with a value of $468 million.

## Sidley Austin LLP
See profile on p.1264
**THE FIRM** The group at Sidley Austin is a favored choice of issuers, underwriters and other market participants on a range of transactions including IPOs, ATM offerings and investment grade senior and subordinated debt matters. It has recently represented the underwriters in resales by the US Treasury of TARP preferred stock in more than 30 financial institutions. Other key clients include Aon, Caterpillar Financial Services and eBay.

**Sources say:** *"They have much experience in the markets and are a proactive and practical team."*

**KEY INDIVIDUALS** *"Highly practical lawyer"* **Edward Petrosky** (see p.384) is well thought of by interviewees for his focus on finding solutions for his clients. He was recently designated underwriter counsel on two notes offerings by Simon Property Group totaling $3 billion. **Samir Gandhi** (see p.318) recently represented the underwriters in ABB's $2.5 billion notes offering. He frequently

advises clients in the financial services, industrials and clean energy sectors. **Eric Haueter** (see p.640) is commended by sources for his accurate business-oriented advice on a range of capital markets transactions. His highlights include representing the underwriters in Occidental Petroleum's $2.15 billion offering of senior notes. **James O'Connor** (see p.379) recently represented Deutsche Bank as underwriter in Flower Foods' $400 million notes offering. One client said: *"His counsel is not only practical, but highly detailed, understandable and presented in a way that makes it easier for an in-house counsel to do his or her job."* *"Fantastic lawyer"* **Norman Slonaker** (see p.408) is a *"highly smart man and a gentleman, to boot,"* sources say. He was underwriters' counsel on an offering by 3M of $650 million of 1.0% notes due 2017, and $600 million of 2.0% notes due 2022.

## Simpson Thacher & Bartlett LLP
See profile on p.2006
**THE FIRM** This team attracts the respect of the business community for its balanced representation of issuers and underwriters on the full spectrum of debt, equity and equity-linked transactions. It has recently advised Oaktree Capital Group on its IPO and the initial purchasers led by Barclays and others on Kraft Foods' Rule 144A/Regulation S $6 billion offering of notes. Other key clients include L-3 Communications, Peabody Energy and Citigroup Global Markets.

**Client Service** *"They give us top-notch advice." "They are creative, flexible, smart and goal oriented."*

**Commercial Awareness** *"They are very down-to-earth lawyers and give us good, practical advice."*

**KEY INDIVIDUALS Arthur Robinson** (see p.393) is *"highly methodical," "commercial and collaborative"* and he *"understands our business well,"* impressed sources say. He is head of the firm's capital markets group. Palo Alto-based **William Hinman** (see p.642) is *"excellent"* and *"really well connected,"* clients report. He represented the underwriters in Facebook's $16 billion IPO. **Glenn Reiter** (see p.391) has impressed interviewees with his practical know-how. His recent work includes representing BRF-Brasil Foods in a $250 million offering of additional 5.875% senior notes due 2022. **John Lobrano** (see p.357) frequently advises clients on securities offerings including convertible notes and high-yield debt financings. He has advised a range of clients on international securities offerings. **Edward Tolley** (see p.418) is *"commercial, talented and effective in representing his clients,"* sources say. He has recently represented the underwriters notes Philip Morris International's offerings of $2.9 billion of notes. **Joshua Ford Bonnie** (see p.285) is commended by clients for his *"highly practical approach"* and for *"analyzing the risks well."* He recently represented The Carlyle Group in its $671 million IPO. **Kenneth Wallach** (see p.422) is *"highly commercial"* and is *"good at explaining pros and cons,"* clients say. His areas of expertise include representing issuers and underwriters on high-yield bond offerings, IPOs and investment-grade debt offerings.

## Skadden, Arps, Slate, Meagher & Flom LLP & Affiliates
See profile on p.2008
**THE FIRM** This group continues to receive plaudits from impressed market sources for its representation of underwriters and issuers in a range of complex and sophisticated transactions. Its areas of expertise include the biotechnology, e-commerce and consumer products industries. Highlights include representing Pfizer in the 2013 IPO of some 17% of Zoetis.

**Client Service** *"Whenever we needed them they were there and everything was done on time." "They are there 24 hours a day."*

**Commercial Awareness** *"They are extremely knowledgeable on debt instruments and the debt market; they live and breathe it every day."*

**KEY INDIVIDUALS David Goldschmidt** (see p.323) is *"incredibly thoughtful"* and *"really took the time to understand the issues,"* satisfied clients say. He represented Tumi Holdings in its $389 million IPO. **Phyllis Korff** (see p.349) is *"responsive," "quick"* and *"everybody respects her,"* clients report. She represented the bookrunners and the co-managers in The Carlyle Group's $671 million IPO. **Gregg Noel** (see p.657) is a well-respected attorney who has an excellent reputation for his legal expertise and practical approach. He represented Westfield Group (Australia) in its finance subsidiary's $1 billion Rule 144A/Regulation S offering of 4.625% senior guaranteed notes due 2021. **Stacy Kanter** (see p.342) is roundly praised by interviewees, with one client saying: *"She is very good at explaining difficult concepts to management and the board."* **Gregory Fernicola** (see p.312) has advised CEMEX on five exchange offers for approximately $2 billion of outstanding securities which included the issue of high-yield secured notes. He is a respected choice for clients conducting innovative transactions. **Richard Aftanas** (see p.272) is commended by clients for *"connecting a lot of the dots between disciplines."* His highlights include representing Coca-Cola on a series of transactions including a $2.75 billion notes offering in three tranches.

## Sullivan & Cromwell LLP
See profile on p.2011
**THE FIRM** This team has a strong reputation for its representation of issuers and underwriters in complex debt and equity transactions. Recent highlights include representing the underwriters led by Goldman Sachs and others in ADT's $2.5 billion Rule 144A/Regulation S guaranteed bonds offering. It has also represented Barclays Bank as selling stockbroker in BlackRock's $4.61 billion SEC-registered follow-on equity offering of common stock. Other key clients at this firm include CIT Group, Fortescue Metals and Cablevision.

**Sources say:** *"They do first-class work; I think they're one of the best."*

**KEY INDIVIDUALS Robert Buckholz** (see p.289) is *"really knowledgeable, really smart, highly experienced"* and *"has great judgment,"* sources say. He recently represented AIG in its $2 billion registered public notes offering. **David Harms** (see p.330) is described by sources as *"excellent"*

*The editorial is in alphabetical order by firm name.*

and *"terrific."* His highlights include representing a consortium of underwriters in several AT&T notes offerings, including a $3 billion global notes offering. **Robert Downes** (see p.306) recently advised the dealer managers, led by BNP Paribas Securities and others, on Coca-Cola's $2 billion unregistered notes offering and its offer to exchange $2 billion of Coca-Cola Refreshments USA's outstanding debt securities. He is a highly respected choice for public and private equity and debt securities offerings. **Jay Clayton** (see p.296) is praised for his excellent client service skills. He advises a range of clients on the full spectrum of debt and equity offerings. **Andrew Soussloff** (see p.410) recently advised United Rentals, through its unrestricted subsidiary UR Financing Escrow, on offerings of a total $2.825 billion of high-yield debt securities. He regularly represents both domestic and foreign clients in a range of capital markets transactions. **William Williams** (see p.426) is well known for his expertise in international securities offerings. He has considerable experience in advising clients on the regulation of securities offerings.

## Vinson & Elkins LLP
See profile on p.2459

**THE FIRM** This team continues to excel at representing clients on transactions in the energy sector and has notable expertise in master limited partnerships (MLP). It recently represented Plains All American Pipeline in a $455 million common units offering and a $1.25 billion senior notes offering. Other notable clients include Anadarko Petroleum, Southwest Airlines and Barclays Capital.
**Commercial Awareness** *"They are a real powerhouse in the energy world."*
**KEY INDIVIDUALS Mark Kelly** (see p.2399) earns the respect of market participants for his expertise in representing clients in MLP-related transactions. He recently advised Western Gas partners on a $520 million senior

notes offering, and offerings of common units for $219 million and $206 million. **David Oelman** (see p.2407) remains a popular choice for MLPs, exploration and production companies and royalty trusts. He represented Energy Transfer Partners in a $2 billion senior notes offering.

## Weil, Gotshal & Manges LLP
See profile on p.2015

**THE FIRM** This team is highly regarded for its representation of issuers, sponsors and underwriters on all types of debt and equity transactions. It recently represented Vantiv in its $575 million IPO. The client base at this firm includes Barclays, Estée Lauder and Genworth Financial.
**KEY INDIVIDUALS** The *"wonderful"* **David Lefkowitz** (see p.354) recently advised GE Capital on its $2.25 billion issue of fixed-to-floating rate non-cumulative perpetual preferred stock. **Matthew Bloch** (see p.285) *"tells it how it is"* and *"cuts right to the chase,"* impressed clients say. He represented DIRECTV in an issue of $4 billion of investment grade bonds.

## Wilson Sonsini Goodrich & Rosati
See profile on p.700

**THE FIRM** This team maintains its strong profile for representing corporates and investment banks on the full range of transactions, with a notable presence in the technology sector. Highlights include advising Palo Alto Networks, WageWorks and Splunk on IPOs. Other clients include Fusion-io, LinkedIn and Micron Technology.
**Sources say:** *"They have a good market presence and are fine lawyers."*
**KEY INDIVIDUALS Jeff Saper** *"commands the respect of boards of directors and provides sensible, practical advice,"* enthusiastic clients say. He recently represented Guideware Software in its $260 million follow-on offering.

## Other Notable Practitioners

**James Lebovitz** (see p.2222) of Dechert LLP is *"exceptionally responsive,"* *"business-minded"* and gives clients *"sound counsel,"* sources say. He represented Leerink Swann and Cowen and Company as underwriters in the $65.55 million common stock offering by Amicus Therapeutics. **Rod Miller** (see p.369) of Milbank, Tweed, Hadley & McCloy LLP is highly respected in the market for his work on IPOs, follow-on offerings and for issues of securities connected with restructurings. **Edward Best** of Mayer Brown LLP is *"highly user-friendly, dedicated and flexible,"* clients say. His recent highlights include representing Caisse central Desjardins in the establishment of its EUR7 billion global MTN program. **Philip Niehoff** of Mayer Brown LLP is *"meticulous, knowledgeable and forthright"* and *"gives answers which are clear, concise and correct,"* impressed clients report. He advised Home Loan Servicing Solutions on its $196.67 million IPO. **Michael Schiavone** (see p.401) of O'Melveny & Myers LLP joins the team from Shearman & Sterling. *"He understands market standards and where deviations from market standards lie,"* and has *"great presence for difficult conversations,"* sources say. He recently represented the underwriters in the $350 million offering of Markel 4.90% notes due 2022. **Peter Healy** (see p.332) of O'Melveny & Myers LLP is *"highly seasoned"* and is commended for his *"steady hand,"* market sources say. His highlights include representing the underwriters in AvalonBay Communities's $725.4 million common stock offering. **Ronald Brody** (see p.288) of White & Case LLP is commended by sources for his skillful handling of high-yield securities transactions. He continues to be a respected choice of investment banks.

# CAPITAL MARKETS DERIVATIVES & STRUCTURED PRODUCTS

Derivatives p.51; Structured Products p.52

Commentary about individuals can be found under their firm's paragraph. If the firm has no paragraph (is not ranked) look at Other Notable Practitioners.

*The editorial is in alphabetical order by firm name.*

## Allen & Overy LLP
See profile on p.433

**THE FIRM** This team is recognized for the excellence of its advice to clients on cross-border regulatory matters, including OTC clearing. Sources praise the team's detailed knowledge of regulatory regimes in different countries.
**Sources say:** *"They are very bright and strong people there."*
**KEY INDIVIDUALS John Williams** is a *"highly thoughtful"* and *"powerful player,"* who is praised for his *"moderate, no-nonsense approach."* He is a credit derivatives expert. **David Lucking** is much appreciated by sources for his practicality, and has advised clients on the transition from an OTC derivatives market to regulated trading platforms and central clearing houses. He is a frequent choice of

financial institutions to represent them on a range of derivatives and structured finance transactions. The *"very talented and active"* **Deborah North** is well known for her work on OTC derivatives and structured synthetic products. She is a respected option to advise clients on the regulatory reforms affecting derivatives.

## Ashurst
See profile on p.434

**THE FIRM** This team maintains its respected profile for representing clients on CLO transactional work. Its areas of expertise include synthetic CLOs and hybrid transactions.
**KEY INDIVIDUALS** DC-based **Scott Faga** (see p.311) advises issuers and underwriters on a range of transactions, including CLOs and hybrid and synthetic CDOs. He

also has expertise on credit derivatives and other swaps. **William Gray** (see p.325) frequently represents clients on municipal derivative product transactions. He has experience in structured finance transactions.

*The editorial is in alphabetical order by firm name.*

| Capital Markets: Derivatives | |
|---|---|
| **Leading Firms** | |
| **Band 1** | |
| Cleary Gottlieb Steen & Hamilton LLP * | |
| Davis Polk & Wardwell LLP * | |
| **Band 2** | |
| Cadwalader, Wickersham & Taft LLP * | |
| Skadden, Arps, Slate, Meagher & Flom LLP & Affiliates * | |
| Sullivan & Cromwell LLP * | |
| **Band 3** | |
| Allen & Overy LLP * | |
| Mayer Brown LLP * | |
| Shearman & Sterling LLP * | |
| Sidley Austin LLP * | |
| Stroock & Stroock & Lavan LLP * | |
| **Band 4** | |
| Clifford Chance US LLP * | |
| Morrison & Foerster LLP * | |
| Simpson Thacher & Bartlett LLP * | |
| Sutherland Asbill & Brennan LLP | |

## Cadwalader, Wickersham & Taft LLP
### See profile on p.438

**THE FIRM** The derivatives and structured products lawyers at this firm excel at both transactional and regulatory advice to a range of buy and sell-side clients. Sources praise the depth, diversity and technical excellence of Cadwalader's derivatives practice, and it receives plaudits for its expertise on structured products, including liquidating defaulted CDOs, CLO issuances and credit-linked notes. Recent highlights include advising ISDA on an industry-wide effort to amend master agreements governing swaps in light of the Dodd-Frank Act.

**Sources say:** *"They are incredibly innovative, and help us not just with legal documents but with economic strategy, too."*

**KEY INDIVIDUALS Steven Lofchie** (see p.358) is *"insightful and able to get to the issue quickly,"* and *"his broad experience in broker-dealer regulation has been invaluable"* in advising clients on the regulation of derivatives. He cochairs the firm's financial services department. **Richard Schetman** (see p.401) is *"knowledgeable and good humored,"* as well as a *"first-class transactional lawyer,"* sources agree. He recently represented Barclays on a joint venture to acquire Maiden Lane III holdings of Max CDO bonds in NY Fed, with a face value of $7 billion. **Ray Shirazi** (see p.405) is *"super smart"* as well as *"thoughtful about the technical issues, intelligent, and at the same time understands the need to figure out a way to get deals done,"* impressed sources say. His recent highlights include advising UBS on the launch and operation of an automated structured note system. **Lary Stromfeld** (see p.413) is *"one of the best from a strategy perspective,"* and is *"extremely logical and very good at cutting through the surface material to get to the heart of any matter,"* market sources report. He is recommended for his advice on the full range of structured products and derivatives matters, including bankruptcies, close-outs and disputes. **Paul Pantano** (see p.381) is held in high esteem by clients for his advice on Commodities

Futures Trading Commission (CFTC) regulation. The *"tremendous"* **Ivan Loncar** (see p.358) is highly rated by sources for his knowledge of fixed income and credit derivatives. His recent highlights include advising multiple financial institutions and end users on internal policies and documentation on cleared derivatives. **Douglas Donahue** (see p.305) represents a range of market participants on derivatives and structured products regulation and transactions. Impressed clients describe him as *"incredibly fast and really thorough,"* as well as *"extremely smart but practical, too."*

## Cleary Gottlieb Steen & Hamilton LLP
### See profile on p.1963

**THE FIRM** Market sources report that this team is frequently called upon to advise financial institutions on transactions and regulatory matters of the utmost complexity. It has been at the vanguard of shaping and analyzing the Dodd-Frank Act, in addition to advising market-leading clients on the consequences of these reforms. Recent highlights include advising ISDA on implementing an auction settlement mechanism for loan credit derivatives and on documents governing bullet loan credit default swaps.

**Sources say:** *"The service is excellent and their expertise is great."*

**KEY INDIVIDUALS Michael Dayan** (see p.302) is *"detailed, focused and extremely knowledgeable,"* impressed clients say. He has recently advised a credit default swap dealer consortium on the establishment of a credit default swap clearing initiative by the Chicago Mercantile Exchange. **Seth Grosshandler** (see p.327) is exceptionally highly regarded by market participants for his *"great authority and knowledge"* in the field of derivatives and insolvency. He has advised Goldman Sachs, Barclays and Wachovia on derivatives and other exposure to Lehman Brothers. The *"excellent"* **Edward Rosen** (see p.394) has a tremendous reputation for his expertise and experience in advising clients on derivatives and securities transactions and regulation. His recent highlights include advising a clearing joint venture between NYSE and DTCC called New York Portfolio Clearing on commodities and securities law related to the structuring of portfolio margining arrangements. **Michael Mazzuchi** (see p.364) advised BNP Paribas on the disposition of $1.7 billion of structured notes held by Fortis Bank before its acquisition by BNP Paribas. Clients praise his *"breadth of expertise"* as *"highly useful in analyzing new products."*

## Clifford Chance US LLP
### See profile on p.439

**THE FIRM** The team at this firm earns strong market endorsement for the breadth of its derivatives regulatory advice, including matters with an international dimension. It also receives praise for its expertise on CLO and CDO transactions. Recent highlights include advising ISDA on responding to calls for margin requirements for uncleared swaps regulatory proposals.

**Client Service** *"The firm is responsive as the deal progresses."*

| Capital Markets: Derivatives | |
|---|---|
| **Senior Statesmen** | |
| **Senior Statesmen:** distinguished older practitioners | |
| Salzman Jerrold E | Skadden, Arps, Slate, Meagher & Flom * |
| **Leading Individuals** | |
| **Star individuals** | |
| Dayan Michael D | Cleary Gottlieb Steen & Hamilton LLP * |
| Grosshandler Seth | Cleary Gottlieb Steen & Hamilton LLP * |
| Raisler Kenneth M | Sullivan & Cromwell LLP * |
| Rosen Edward J | Cleary Gottlieb Steen & Hamilton LLP * |
| Rothwell James T | Davis Polk & Wardwell LLP * |
| **Band 1** | |
| Brandow John M | Davis Polk & Wardwell LLP * |
| Budofsky Daniel | Davis Polk & Wardwell LLP * |
| Cohn Joshua | Mayer Brown LLP |
| Lofchie Steven | Cadwalader, Wickersham & Taft LLP * |
| Mendez Mark | Davis Polk & Wardwell LLP * |
| Osborn John W | Skadden, Arps, Slate, Meagher & Flom * |
| Shirazi Ray | Cadwalader, Wickersham & Taft LLP * |
| Stromfeld Lary | Cadwalader, Wickersham & Taft LLP * |
| **Band 2** | |
| Bahlke Conrad G | Stroock & Stroock & Lavan LLP |
| Balaban Witold | Latham & Watkins LLP (ONP)† * |
| Felsenthal David | Clifford Chance US LLP * |
| Gilberg David J | Sullivan & Cromwell LLP * |
| Goldman Geoffrey B | Shearman & Sterling LLP * |
| Ibrahim Ray | Davis Polk & Wardwell LLP * |
| Mitchell David S | Fried, Frank, Harris, Shriver (ONP)† * |
| Rance Brian | Freshfields Bruckhaus Deringer US LLP * |
| Sackheim Michael | Sidley Austin LLP * |
| Simmons Rebecca J | Sullivan & Cromwell LLP * |
| Stein Craig | Schulte Roth & Zabel LLP * |
| Williams John | Allen & Overy LLP |
| **Band 3** | |
| Aziz Azam | Shearman & Sterling LLP * |
| Goldstein Marvin | Stroock & Stroock & Lavan LLP |
| Gray William | Ashurst * |
| Kaufman David | Morrison & Foerster LLP * |
| Malyshev Peter | Latham & Watkins LLP (ONP)† * |
| Pantano Paul | Cadwalader, Wickersham & Taft LLP * |
| Parisi Donna | Shearman & Sterling LLP * |
| Rae Mark N | Stroock & Stroock & Lavan LLP |
| Reeder III Robert W | Sullivan & Cromwell LLP * |
| Vebman Yossi | Skadden, Arps, Slate, Meagher & Flom * |
| Xu Joyce Y. | Simpson Thacher & Bartlett LLP * |
| Yeres David | Clifford Chance US LLP * |
| **Up-and-coming individuals** | |
| Donahue Douglas | Cadwalader, Wickersham & Taft LLP * |
| Frey Manuel | Paul, Weiss, Rifkind, Wharton (ONP)† * |
| Loncar Ivan | Cadwalader, Wickersham & Taft LLP * |
| Lucking David | Allen & Overy LLP |
| North Deborah | Allen & Overy LLP |
| Old Gareth | Clifford Chance US LLP * |
| **Associates to watch** | |
| Carruzzo Fabien | Kramer Levin Naftalis & Frankel (ONP)† * |

*Indicates firm / individual with profile.*
†*ONP = Other Notable Practitioner.*

*The editorial is in alphabetical order by firm name.*

**KEY INDIVIDUALS David Felsenthal** (see p.312) is *"extremely smart"* and *"very strong,"* market sources say. He has recently advised several financial institutions, including Morgan Stanley Investment Management, Standard Life Investments and Wells Fargo, on the impact of the Dodd-Frank reforms. **David Yeres** (see p.429) *"gives us precise answers to the questions we pose"* in *"highly accurate, compressed, concentrated advice,"* clients enthuse. He advised the Committee on Investment of Employee Benefit Assets on its response to requirements for clearing swaps. *"Smart lawyer"* **Gareth Old** (see p.379) has expertise in swaps, repos, derivative-related insolvency matters and covered bonds. One client reports: *"You go to him with complicated things and you get a well thought-out response."* **Steven Kolyer** (see p.348) has notable expertise in credit-linked notes, fund derivatives and synthetics, and in commercial lending. He continues to be a respected option for advising clients on CLO and CDO transactions. **Frederick Utley** (see p.420) has *"huge experience"* and *"a perspective that makes him useful for his business as well as his legal opinions,"* interviewees say. He advises clients on a range of matters, including CDOs, CLOs and ABS and CMBS workouts.

## Davis Polk & Wardwell LLP
See profile on p.442

**THE FIRM** This group maintains its exceptional reputation for advising clients on equity derivative transactions, and it also has a strong and growing practice advising clients on the Dodd-Frank regulatory reforms. The team advises a stellar cast of international institutional clients, including Barclays, Citigroup and JPMorgan, on the full array of structured products, including offerings of sophisticated and novel products. Recent highlights include advising Morgan Stanley on an agreement with Mitsubishi UFJ Financial Group to convert preferred stock in Morgan Stanley worth $7.8 billion to common stock.

**Client Service** *"Relying on DPW's expert guidance, best-in-practice advice and excellent work product is, quite frankly, one of the reasons I am able to sleep well at night."* *"DPW delivers the highest quality of service and advice for capital markets products. I have only had good experiences with them."*

**Commercial Awareness** *"They know the market because they almost are the market."*

**KEY INDIVIDUALS John Brandow** (see p.286) recently advised KKR on the repurchase by Legg Mason of $1.25 billion of its senior convertible notes, as well as Legg Mason's issuance of warrants to KKR to purchase Legg Mason's common stock. He heads the firm's derivatives and structured products group and advises an array of clients on equity-related transactions. Sources speak highly of **James Rothwell**'s (see p.396) skills in executing equity derivatives transactions. Recent highlights include advising Goldman Sachs and JPMorgan on a $15 billion accelerated share repurchase for an Irish subsidiary of Johnson & Johnson. **Daniel Budofsky** (see p.289) is *"smart, really cares and has a real depth of knowledge in Dodd-Frank,"* reports one impressed client. He chairs the Exchanges Subcommittee of the New York City Bar Futures and Derivatives Regulation Committee. **Mark Mendez** (see p.367) is a *"great deal lawyer"* who has the *"ability to find solutions,"* and is *"incredibly responsive,"* enthusiastic clients say. His recent highlights include advising Merill Lynch, Fenner & Smith and Goldman Sachs as book-running managers on a $403 million offering of convertible senior notes by NuVasive. **Linda Simpson** (see p.407) is commended by clients for her *"excellent judgment"* and ability to *"to come up with off-the-cuff practical solutions."* Her highlights include advising Credit Suisse on almost 200 structured product offerings, which totaled $10.74 billion. **Ray Ibrahim** (see p.338) is a *"creative and innovative thinker"* who is commended by clients for his excellent legal knowledge and communication skills. His focus is on over-the-counter derivatives, including finance and repurchase transactions, hedging strategies and equity, credit and commodity-linked products. **Warren Motley** (see p.372) remains a popular choice for both domestic and international offerings of structured products. He has recently advised Morgan Stanley on approximately $2.85 billion worth of structured products issuances.

## Freshfields Bruckhaus Deringer US LLP
See profile on p.443

**THE FIRM** This team remains a key choice of financial institutions and hedge funds to represent them on complex structured finance transactions. Highlights include advising JPMorgan Chase on the forward purchase of paper pulp from a major Brazilian paper producer. Other notable clients include Barclays, UBS and The Man Group. **KEY INDIVIDUALS** The *"terrific"* **Brian Rance** (see p.389) is *"thorough and detail oriented,"* as well as an *"effective draftsman,"* sources say. He advised Citi Global Markets as initial purchaser and placement agent on a cash-flow CLO transaction managed by Guggenheim Investment Management, under which $1.013 billion of securities were issued. **Jerome Ranawake** (see p.389) is *"really good at CDOs, CLOs and related derivatives,"* clients say. He recently advised State Street Bank and Trust Company on implementing the Dodd-Frank business conduct rules.

## Mayer Brown LLP
See profile on p.1257

**THE FIRM** This team attracts the respect of the business community for its advice to ISDA on the development of new regulations under the Dodd-Frank Act. Sell-side and buy-side clients continue to hold it in high esteem for its advice on Dodd-Frank matters. It also advises banks on recovering value from transactions damaged in the financial crisis. **KEY INDIVIDUALS** *"Luminary"* **Joshua Cohn** has *"a good handle on why things are the way they are and what they mean,"* and is commended for his technical excellence. He is a primary adviser to ISDA on the development of new regulations under Title VII of the Dodd-Frank Act.

## Milbank, Tweed, Hadley & McCloy LLP
See profile on p.448

**THE FIRM** This team is recommended by clients for the quality of its representation on CLO and specialty finance transactions. It recently advised KKR Asset Management on structuring, issuing and upsizing a $600 million cash flow CLO transaction. Key clients include BNY Mellon, PineBridge Investments and BTMU.

**Sources say:** *"They are all very good, terrific lawyers."*

*The editorial is in alphabetical order by firm name.*

**KEY INDIVIDUALS Eric Moser** (see p.372) advised CIFC Asset Management on the issuance of $464 million of CLOs. He counts a number of banks and hedge funds among his clients.

## Morrison & Foerster LLP
See profile on p.1990

**THE FIRM** This team is active in advising clients on regulatory, transactional and restructuring matters across a range of derivatives asset classes. It is also recognized for its expertise in structuring novel products. Highlights include advising Residential Capital on its insolvency proceedings and derivatives claims. Other clients include the Royal Bank of Canada, UBS and HSBC.
**Commercial Awareness** *"I really get the sense that they have their finger on the pulse."*
**KEY INDIVIDUALS** The *"extremely responsive"* **Anna Pinedo** (see p.385) is *"knowledgeable and diligent," "identifies issues"* and *"gets the deals done,"* impressed clients say. She advised Incapital on the establishment of a $500 million SEC-registered repackaging program. **David Kaufman** (see p.343) *"knows his stuff"* and is *"responsive at communicating market developments and managing overall investment bank relationships,"* clients say. He represented Merrill Lynch on establishing its first Rule 144A structured note program.

## Orrick, Herrington & Sutcliffe LLP
See profile on p.1994

**THE FIRM** The team at this firm is recognized for its expertise on structured products transactions, including mortgage-backed securities, principal financings and restructurings. Interviewees note its particular expertise in representing sponsors of repackagings of municipal bonds.
**KEY INDIVIDUALS** The *"client-friendly"* **Al Sawyers** (see p.400) has *"strong product knowledge,"* and is *"the can-do person who is always trying to find a way to get a deal done,"* impressed sources say. He focuses on structured finance products, derivate and repackaged asset-backed securities.

## Schulte Roth & Zabel LLP
See profile on p.2003

**THE FIRM** This team is a particularly highly regarded option for CLO transactions. It also remains a favored choice of hedge funds, private equity funds and hybrid funds on asset-backed securities and various structured credit products. It recently represented collateral manager Marathon Asset Management on a $356 million CLO issuance.
**Sources say:** *"I am very happy with the firm."*
**KEY INDIVIDUALS Craig Stein** (see p.412) is *"proactive and quick in responding,"* satisfied clients say. His areas of expertise include swaps, credit and fund-linked derivatives. The *"highly responsive"* **Paul Watterson** (see p.423) is praised by one client as *"an old hand at structured products who understands the players and policies, not just the provisions."* He is frequently involved in structured finance transactions involving credit derivatives. **Phillip Azzollini** (see p.276) is commended by clients for his keen attention

to detail and understanding of accounting in addition to the law. He focuses on asset-backed securities offerings.

## Shearman & Sterling LLP
See profile on p.2005

**THE FIRM** The team at this firm is recognized for its regulatory expertise. Recent highlights include advising Merrill Lynch on a variety of matters arising from the implementation of the Dodd-Frank Act. Clients include Citigroup, Intercontinental Exchange and Och-Ziff Capital Management.
**KEY INDIVIDUALS Geoffrey Goldman** (see p.322) has expertise in handling credit and equity derivatives matters. He is advising Merrill Lynch on developing and negotiating client documentation for cleared OTC derivatives. The *"highly commercial"* **Donna Parisi** (see p.382) is applauded by market commentators for her transactional and regulatory expertise on a range of derivatives, including credit, equity, commodity and fixed income. She heads the firm's structured products and derivatives team. **Azam Aziz** (see p.276) *"finds practical solutions and is client service oriented,"* market sources say. He is advising IKB Deutsche Industriebank on enforceability issues related to several synthetic CDO transactions sponsored by Lehman Brothers.

## Sidley Austin LLP
See profile on p.1264

**THE FIRM** This firm is respected by interviewees for its knowledgeable and multidisciplinary representation of buy-side clients on derivatives matters, including the negotiation and modification of platform trading agreements. It is also a frequent choice of market participants on structured product matters. Clients include III Offshore Advisors, BlackRock and Wells Fargo.
**Commercial Awareness** *"They have a strong awareness of our business needs – their advice is reliable, reasoned and solid, and they exercise good judgment."*
**KEY INDIVIDUALS Michael Sackheim** (see p.398) represents the Managed Funds Association on OTC derivatives issues. Market commentators praise his knowledgeable and experienced approach. **Robert Robinson** (see p.393) is a member of the team advising investors and counterparties on issues arising from the Lehman Brothers bankruptcy. He also has an extensive cross-border transactional practice. **Ellen Pesch** (see p.384) co-heads the firm's OTC derivatives cross-practice area team. She frequently handles derivatives, structured finance and securitization transactions for both domestic and international banks.

## Simpson Thacher & Bartlett LLP
See profile on p.2006

**THE FIRM** This compact team represents a growing roster of investment banks and corporations on an array of OTC derivatives matters, as well as on equity-linked transactions. Recent highlights include representing Morgan Stanley and JPMorgan on Micron Technology's $1 billion convertible senior notes issuance. Other key clients include KKR, Credit Suisse and Blackstone.

**KEY INDIVIDUALS Joyce Xu** (see p.429) is praised by market commentators for her strength in representing clients on all areas of derivatives matters, with notable strength in equity derivatives. She heads the firm's derivatives practice.

## Skadden, Arps, Slate, Meagher & Flom LLP & Affiliates
See profile on p.2008

**THE FIRM** This heavy-hitting team maintains its profile as a highly respected option for commodities derivatives transactions. It is also highly regarded for its expertise on CLOs and structured notes. Recent highlights include advising Amerigroup on equity derivatives related to its approximately $4.9 billion purchase by Wellpoint.
**Client Service** *"It's been a long, good relationship of excellent service and expertise, in addition to quality and prompt responses."*
**KEY INDIVIDUALS** *"Terrific lawyer"* **John Osborn** (see p.380) is praised by sources as *"highly competent, direct and technically solid."* He represented BNP Paribas on the sale of its oil and gas reserve-based lending business in the USA and Canada. *"Big name"* **Jerrold Salzman** (see p.399) is an *"impressive force"* in futures regulation and litigation. He is well known for his work representing the Chicago Mercantile Exchange. **Yossi Vebman** (see p.421) receives praise for his knowledgeable approach to transactions. He represented PHH on its $250 million offering of 6.00% convertible senior notes due 2017. **Susan Curtis** (see p.300) ensures her *"advice is tailored to our unique requirements,"* clients say. She represented Apollo Investment as equity investor in Kirkwood Funding. **James Stringfellow** (see p.413) is highly thought of by market sources for his representation of issuers, underwriters, placement agents and other market participants on structured finance transactions. He recently represented Barclays Bank on a $1.45 billion debtor-in-possession credit facility for Residential Capital.

## Stroock & Stroock & Lavan LLP
See profile on p.2010

**THE FIRM** This team is heavily engaged in the commodities and related securities and derivatives markets. Satisfied clients appreciate the high-quality and commercially minded advice received on a range of energy-related transactions. The client roster at this firm includes Constellation Energy Commodities Group, Goldman Sachs and the United Nations Food Programme.
**Commercial Awareness** *"Stroock has a depth of understanding and appreciation for what it is that we do commercially that is unparalleled."*
**KEY INDIVIDUALS Conrad Bahlke** is well respected by market sources for his derivatives and commodities advice. He is increasingly called upon to advise clients on the Dodd-Frank Act. **Marvin Goldstein** is *"extremely responsive to clients' needs,"* and is commended by sources for the breadth and depth of his knowledge. He focuses on derivatives and commodities law, particularly energy and metals transactions. **Mark Rae** is praised by clients for his *"tremendous dedication, thoroughness and preparation."* He

frequently represents energy dealers, producers, users and financial institutions.

## Sullivan & Cromwell LLP
See profile on p.2011

THE FIRM This firm has strong relationships with leading investment banks, and is held in particularly high esteem for its regulatory and transactional expertise in the commodities, futures and derivatives arenas. Interviewees speak with admiration of the team's prowess in advising clients on the implications of the Dodd-Frank Act.
KEY INDIVIDUALS *"Dean of the commodities Bar in the USA"* Kenneth Raisler (see p.389) is a *"tremendous adviser"* with *"an exceptional mind,"* market sources say. He heads the firm's commodities, futures and derivatives group. David Gilberg (see p.320) has an excellent reputation for his advice to clients on a range of securities and derivatives-related transactions and regulatory matters. His clients include broker-dealers, commercial banks, investment banks and corporations. Rebecca Simmons (see p.406) frequently advises clients on a variety of matters, including on the development of financial products and structured transactions. She regularly represents clients in restructuring transactions. Robert Reeder (see p.391) is considered a *"tremendous resource"* by clients for his advice on complex securities law issues. He co-heads the firm's corporate group. Mark Welshimer (see p.424) is recognized for his insightful derivatives law advice to

clients. He focuses on new products and bank regulatory matters.

## Sutherland Asbill & Brennan LLP

THE FIRM This team is held in particularly high esteem for its expertise on energy and commodity derivatives transactions. It is also active in advising clients on equity derivatives, currency hedging, and weather and freight derivatives. Clients include Coca-Cola, CoBank and Oglethorpe Power.
KEY INDIVIDUALS James Cain heads the firm's derivatives and structured products team.

## Weil, Gotshal & Manges LLP
See profile on p.2015

THE FIRM The team at this firm receives recognition for its CLO and CDO experience. It has continued to analyze Lehman Brothers' exposure to structured products and derivatives, and to assist its client to monetize its portfolio.
Sources say: *"They are strong on intra and inter-departmental relationships, and take a highly collaborative approach."*
KEY INDIVIDUALS Robert Chiperfield (see p.294) has impressed sources with his expertise on CDOs, CLOs and credit-linked notes. He counts a number of banks, insurers, investors and asset managers among his clients.

## Other Notable Practitioners

Manuel Frey (see p.316) of Paul, Weiss, Rifkind, Wharton & Garrison LLP is *"extremely analytical and client friendly,"* and is further praised for his *"ability to explain concepts concisely and help you understand highly nuanced rules quickly."* He has notable expertise in OTC derivative products. Witold Balaban (see p.277) of Latham & Watkins LLP is *"extremely experienced"* and *"highly knowledgeable"* on equity derivative and equity-linked product transactions. His highlights include representing Citi and Nomura on a $670 million margin loan transaction secured by Charter Communications' Class A common shares. Peter Malyshev (see p.361), also of Latham, is a *"tireless worker"* who is *"very personable, knowledgeable and energetic,"* market sources say. He has notable expertise on regulatory, compliance and transactional matters related to commodities, securities and derivatives products. Fabien Carruzzo (see p.292) of Kramer Levin Naftalis & Frankel LLP is *"extremely smart and responsive,"* and has *"very good judgment and client skills,"* impressed sources say. He advises clients on the full range of derivatives and structured products transactions. *"Terrific lawyer"* David Mitchell (see p.370) of Fried, Frank, Harris, Shriver & Jacobson LLP is *"very responsive and really knows his stuff,"* impressed clients say. He advises clients on all aspects of commodities, futures and derivatives.

# CAPITAL MARKETS REITS

Commentary about individuals can be found under their firm's paragraph. If the firm has no paragraph (is not ranked) look at Other Notable Practitioners.

## Band 1
## Capital Markets: REITs

### Clifford Chance US LLP
See profile on p.439

THE FIRM This team continues to earn strong market endorsement for its talent in advising clients on the full array of capital market transactions. The team is praised for its cohesive approach to advising clients and its impressive international footprint.
Sources say: *"Their expertise and resources were well suited to our difficult deal."*
KEY INDIVIDUALS The *"delightful"* Jay Bernstein (see p.283) has *"great experience"* and is *"highly knowledgeable,"* sources say. He is roundly recommended by interviewees for his client service skills. Richard Catalano (see p.292) is a tax expert whom sources acclaim for his prowess in advising clients on complex transactions. He advises REITs on the full range of tax demands. The *"seasoned and rea-

sonable"* Larry Medvinsky (see p.366) is commended for his *"bottom line-oriented"* approach. His work on IPOs has won the particular admiration of market sources. Kathleen Werner (see p.424) is an *"extremely hard-working, client-focused and creative lawyer,"* impressed sources report. She has a strong following among REITs.

### Goodwin Procter LLP
See profile on p.1522

THE FIRM This team maintains its outstanding reputation for advising substantial public and private REITs and underwriters on the full range of debt and equity transactions. Recent highlights include advising Boston Properties on the public offering of $1 billion of 3.85% senior unsecured notes due 2023. Other key clients include Archstone, AvalonBay Communities and Barclays Capital. Satisfied clients particularly highlight the consistent partner involvement in transactions.

Client Service *"The turnaround time is amazing and the work is well thought through."*
KEY INDIVIDUALS Gilbert Menna (see p.367) is *"practical and well versed,"* *"highly responsive"* and *"gets the whole picture,"* impressed sources say. He recently represented Retail Properties of America on its initial listing on the NYSE and its IPO as a listed company. Edward Glazer (see

### Capital Markets: REITs
#### Leading Firms

**Band 1**
Clifford Chance US LLP *
Goodwin Procter LLP *
Hogan Lovells US LLP *
Latham & Watkins LLP *
Skadden, Arps, Slate, Meagher & Flom LLP & Affiliates *

**Band 2**
Hunton & Williams LLP *
Sidley Austin LLP *

**Band 3**
Greenberg Traurig, LLP *
Proskauer Rose LLP *
Wachtell, Lipton, Rosen & Katz *

**Band 4**
Alston & Bird LLP *
DLA Piper LLP (US) *
King & Spalding LLP *
Locke Lord LLP *
Morris, Manning & Martin, LLP
Sullivan & Cromwell LLP *

### Capital Markets: REITs: Maryland Counsel
#### Leading Firms

**Band 1**
Venable LLP *

**Band 2**
Ballard Spahr LLP *

### Capital Markets: REITs
#### Senior Statesmen

**Senior Statesmen: distinguished older practitioners**

| | |
|---|---|
| Fass Peter M | Proskauer Rose LLP |

#### Leading Individuals

**Star individuals**

| | |
|---|---|
| Menna Gilbert G | Goodwin Procter LLP * |

**Band 1**

| | |
|---|---|
| Bernstein Jay L | Clifford Chance US LLP * |
| Bonser David W | Hogan Lovells US LLP |
| Brody Michael J | Latham & Watkins LLP |
| Catalano Richard | Clifford Chance US LLP * |
| Feagles Prentiss | Hogan Lovells US LLP |
| Gorrell Jr J Warren | Hogan Lovells US LLP |
| Hanks, Jr James J | Venable LLP * |
| Howell III George C | Hunton & Williams LLP * |
| Rayis John D | Skadden, Arps, Slate, Meagher & Flom * |
| Wright David C | Hunton & Williams LLP * |

**Band 2**

| | |
|---|---|
| Arumi Cristina | Hogan Lovells US LLP |
| Cummins J Gerard | Sidley Austin LLP * |
| Emmerich Adam O | Wachtell, Lipton, Rosen & Katz * |
| Fryer Judith D | Greenberg Traurig, LLP * |
| Genz Peter | King & Spalding LLP * |
| Glazer Edward | Goodwin Procter LLP * |
| Goldschmidt David J | Skadden, Arps, Slate, Meagher & Flom * |
| Kleindorfer Julian T H | Latham & Watkins LLP |
| Kroupa Sharon A | Venable LLP * |
| LeBey Daniel M | Hunton & Williams LLP * |
| Medvinsky Larry | Clifford Chance US LLP * |
| Panovka Robin | Wachtell, Lipton, Rosen & Katz * |
| Petrosky Edward F | Sidley Austin LLP * |
| Santucci Ettore A | Goodwin Procter LLP * |

**Band 3**

| | |
|---|---|
| Colletta Anthony J | Sullivan & Cromwell LLP * |
| Good John A | Bass, Berry & Sims PLC (ONP)† * |
| Goolsby Bryan L | Locke Lord LLP * |

| | |
|---|---|
| Herlihy Scott C | Latham & Watkins LLP * |
| Howe Joseph | Arnold & Porter LLP (ONP)† * |
| Moran Charles R | Ballard Spahr LLP * |
| Schonberger Mark | Goodwin Procter LLP * |
| Sheehan Bartholomew | Sidley Austin LLP * |
| Shenker Joseph C | Sullivan & Cromwell LLP * |
| Slotkin David P | Morrison & Foerster LLP (ONP)† * |
| Thurston Rosemarie A | Alston & Bird LLP * |
| Werner Kathleen L | Clifford Chance US LLP * |

**Band 4**

| | |
|---|---|
| Adler Arthur S | Sullivan & Cromwell LLP (ONP)† * |
| Adler Howard B | Gibson, Dunn & Crutcher LLP * |
| Barr Stuart A. | Hogan Lovells US LLP |
| Bergdolt Robert H | DLA Piper LLP (US) * |
| Burton Richard A | Greenberg Traurig, LLP * |
| Cosby Cameron | Hunton & Williams LLP * |
| Gelfond Stuart H | Fried, Frank, Harris, Shriver (ONP)† * |
| Gelman Bruce L | Kirkland & Ellis LLP (ONP)† * |
| Gilchrist Bruce | Hogan Lovells US LLP |
| McGowan Patricia | Venable LLP * |
| Ponda Ameek Ashok | Sullivan & Worcester LLP (ONP)† * |
| Prevost Lauren | Morris, Manning & Martin, LLP |
| Rock Neil L | Skadden, Arps, Slate, Meagher & Flom * |
| Sandford H Neal | Goodwin Procter LLP * |
| Scheinfeld Steven G | Fried, Frank, Harris, Shriver (ONP)† * |
| Sullivan Jeffrey | Hunton & Williams LLP * |
| Zuppone Michael L | Paul Hastings LLP (ONP)† |

**Up-and-coming individuals**

| | |
|---|---|
| Goode Jason | Alston & Bird LLP * |
| Linsky Heath | Morris, Manning & Martin, LLP |
| Shapiro David | Wachtell, Lipton, Rosen & Katz * |

\* Indicates firm / individual with profile.
†ONP = Other Notable Practitioner.

p.321) is a highly regarded tax specialist who regularly advises clients on structuring collective investment vehicles, real estate securitizations, and forming and operating public and private REITs. One client said: *"Don't leave home without him if you're in the REIT world."* **Ettore Santucci** (see p.399) recently represented Cole Real Estate on the IPO of Cole Real Estate Income Strategy. Sources say he is a *"very thoughtful lawyer"* who is *"easy to work with and practical"* and *"well versed in international legal issues."* **Mark Schonberger** (see p.402) is a *"creative and responsive"* lawyer, market sources say. He regularly advises public and private real estate companies on corporate and securities matters. **Neal Sandford** (see p.1508) advises clients on the tax aspects of the formation, M&A and ongoing compliance matters of REITs. He also represents REITs seeking private letter rulings and closing agreements from the IRS.

## Hogan Lovells US LLP

**THE FIRM** This team is marked out by the high quality of its expertise in representing REITs and underwriters on IPOs and M&A. Both the breadth and depth of this REIT team are much commended by sources. It recently advised Goldman Sachs and Merrill Lynch on the proposed IPO of Empire State Realty Trust. The client base of this firm includes RLJ Lodging Trust, Wells Fargo Securities and Colonial Properties Trust.
**Commercial Awareness** *"They do not just tell you what the problem is – they tell you how to fix it too."*

**KEY INDIVIDUALS Prentiss Feagles** is a tax lawyer who *"explains things in a way which is understandable and he gets to the answer right away,"* impressed clients say. His recent highlights include advising JPMorgan and other underwriters on the $292.56 million IPO of Retail Properties of America. **Warren Gorrell** provides clients with a *"great combination of legal and business advice,"* is *"well rounded"* and is *"very client-focused,"* sources say. He recently advised Morgan Stanley and others as joint bookrunning managers and the co-managers on the $1 billion offering of 4.625% notes due 2021 by ERP Operating, a subsidiary of Equity Residential. *"Talented lawyer"* **David Bonser** is *"very knowledgeable, responsive and well respected within the industry"* and provides clients with a *"high-quality service,"* interviewees report. He recently advised Colony Financial on $248 million in offerings of 8.5% Series A cumulative redeemable perpetual preferred stock. **Cristina Arumi** is *"responsive, smart and thoughtful"* and

sources further praise her abilities to communicate effectively with senior management. Her recent highlights include advising the underwriters on a $198.38 million common stock offering by Hudson Pacific Properties. **Bruce Gilchrist** is a well-respected and experienced REITs lawyer. He advises clients on the full spectrum of capital markets transactions. He is based in Washington, DC. **Stuart Barr** recently advised on a $65 million offering of preferred stock by Dupont Fabros Technologies. Sources acclaim his quick comprehension and solution of key transactional issues.

## Latham & Watkins LLP
### See profile on p.446

**THE FIRM** This superb team attracts the respect of the business community for the strength of its REIT capital market work across the USA, but particular praise is forthcoming for its West Coast presence. Its areas of expertise include IPOs, stock, senior notes and high-yield offerings. It recently represented Spirit Realty Capital on its IPO. Other clients include American Assets Trust, Hudson Pacific Properties and Sunstone Hotel Investors.

**Sources say:** *"They get the whole picture and are the consummate REIT firm."*

**KEY INDIVIDUALS Michael Brody** is a *"phenomenal"* tax REIT expert. His recent highlights include advising Digital Realty Trust on its common stock offering, which raised in excess of $800 million. **Julian Kleindorfer** is *"highly knowledgeable," "well respected"* and *"excellent on IPOs,"* impressed sources say. He frequently advises clients on a range of corporate finance transactions and on the formation of REITs. The *"terrific"* **Scott Herlihy** (see p.334) is highly rated by sources for his advice to clients on a range of corporate and securities matters. He recently advised Host Hotels & Resorts on the issuance of 5.25% Series A senior notes due 2022 with a value of $350 million.

## Skadden, Arps, Slate, Meagher & Flom LLP & Affiliates
### See profile on p.2008

**THE FIRM** This team is praised by interviewees for its technical expertise and the practical focus of its advice to private and public, mortgage, equity, hybrid and special-purpose REITs. It represented Westfield America on its $4.8 billion formation of a joint venture with Canada Pension Plan Investment Board for 12 shopping centers in the USA. Other clients include Apartment Investment & Management, JC Penney and Sonesta Acquisition.

**Client Service** *"Their hallmark is to provide the best possible advice and to bring to bear all necessary resources to facilitate the successful completion of our transactions." "They were creative and they were solution-oriented."*

**Commercial Awareness** *"Skadden moves quickly to handle the matters that we engage them for, many of which are time-sensitive and require around-the-clock guidance and support."*

**KEY INDIVIDUALS John Rayis** (see p.389) is *"absolutely superb," "the gold standard for what a tax partner should be,"* and is able to *"communicate intricate tax issues in a way that someone who isn't a tax lawyer can understand,"* impressed clients say. He is advising Cincinnati Bell as special REIT tax counsel on the proposed IPO of its data center subsidiary, CyrusOne. **David Goldschmidt** (see p.323) is *"a problem solver"* who *"combines good legal knowledge and expertise with good practical application,"* market sources report. His recent highlights include advising American Capital Agency on seven transactions with a total value of over $4.7 billion. **Neil Rock** (see p.393) is an *"extremely user-friendly"* lawyer. He heads the firm's real estate group.

## Band 2
## Capital Markets: REITs

### Hunton & Williams LLP
### See profile on p.2517

**THE FIRM** This team has a balanced practice representing issuers and underwriters on a range of transactions. It has a particular focus in advising on transactions relating to mortgage and hotel REITs. Recent highlights include representing CYS Investments on more than $1.5 billion in aggregate of public offerings of equity securities. Other key clients include New York Mortgage Trust, AG Mortgage Investment Trust and Summit Hotel Properties.

**KEY INDIVIDUALS George Howell** (see p.337) is a *"creative," "practical"* and *"highly commercial"* tax lawyer. He recently advised Citigroup Global Markets, Deutsche Bank Securities and other underwriters on $323.5 million in aggregate of equity and debt securities offerings for NorthStar Realty Finance. **David Wright** (see p.428) is commended by sources as a lawyer who *"gets the deal done"* and is *"a joy to work with."* His recent highlights include representing Pebblebrook Hotel Trust on its $560 million public offerings of common and preferred stock. **Daniel LeBey** (see p.353) receives commendations from sources for his *"good demeanor"* and his *"ability to manage many moving pieces"* of a deal. He recently advised Apartment Trust of America on a $536.5 million recapitalization transaction. **Cameron Cosby** (see p.299) is a tax lawyer with an excellent track record in advising clients on REIT transactions. He recently advised Wells Fargo Securities and other underwriters on $609 million of equity and debt follow-on offerings by CubeSmart. **Jeffrey Sullivan** (see p.414) is a *"really strong securities lawyer"* who *"delivers good results,"* impressed sources say. His work highlights include advising Hatteras Financial on its $539.5 million common stock public offering.

### Sidley Austin LLP
### See profile on p.1264

**THE FIRM** This popular and highly acclaimed firm earns the respect of the business community for its representation of underwriters and issuers on IPOs and debt and equity offerings including at-the-market offerings. It is representing the underwriters on Spirit Realty Capital's potential IPO and PennyMac Investment Trust on its $222.5 million offering of common shares. Other key clients of this team include Banc of America Securities-Merrill Lynch and Aviv Healthcare Properties.

**Client Service** *"They are highly knowledgeable within securities law and within REITs and have been highly responsive to us in all the transactions."*

**Commercial Awareness** *"They provide candid advice with a lot of context."*

**KEY INDIVIDUALS Gerard Cummins** (see p.300) *"understands all aspects of the REITs space,"* market sources report approvingly. He recently advised Starwood Property Trust on its $471.5 million offering of common stock. **Edward Petrosky** (see p.384) recently advised the underwriters on a $351 million common stock offering by Home Properties. He co-heads the firm's capital markets group. **Bartholomew Sheehan** (see p.405) is *"highly practical"* and *"quickly grasps the central issues and highlights them on our behalf,"* appreciative sources report. He recently advised the underwriters on an $85 million offering of preferred shares and a $114.4 million offering of common stock by Pebblebrook Hotel Trust.

## Band 3
## Capital Markets: REITs

### Greenberg Traurig, LLP
### See profile on p.1024

**THE FIRM** This team has a particularly strong reputation for its representation of nontraded REITs. Recent highlights include advising Hines Global REIT on its $1.1 billion IPO and $3.5 billion follow-on offering. Other key clients at this firm include SL Green Realty, Kimco Realty and UDR.

**Client Service** *"The firm has responded to every need we have had with absolute professionalism and expertise."*

**KEY INDIVIDUALS Judith Fryer** (see p.317) recently represented Industrial Income Trust on its $1 billion IPO and its $2.4 billion follow-on offering. Sources say she has *"seen everything,"* is *"highly knowledgeable"* and can *"cut through the underbrush to get transactions completed."* **Richard Burton** (see p.290) is a tax specialist with an excellent reputation for representing clients on REITs capital markets transactions. He also advises REITs on ongoing operational issues.

### Proskauer Rose LLP
### See profile on p.2001

**THE FIRM** This team receives strong market endorsement for its advice on a broad array of REIT-related transactions. It recently advised Ares Commercial Real Estate on its $142.5 million IPO. The client roster at this firm includes AIG Global Investment, The Lightstone Group and Preferred Apartment Communities.

**Sources say:** *"They are doing some of the most creative things in the nontraded REITs space."*

**KEY INDIVIDUALS Peter Fass** represented American Realty Capital Trust on its $2.7 billion IPO. His expertise in advising nontraded REITs is highly acclaimed by sources.

### Wachtell, Lipton, Rosen & Katz
### See profile on p.2012

**THE FIRM** This team maintains a formidable reputation for its work on M&A transactions in the REIT sector. It has a focus on large public company M&A.

**Sources say:** *"They are incredibly hard-working and knowledgeable people and the quality is uniformly high."*

**KEY INDIVIDUALS Adam Emmerich** (see p.1890) is spoken of in admiring terms by sources for his expertise in complex M&A transactions. **Robin Panovka** (see p.1925) is *"highly measured and highly knowledgeable,"* market sources say. He is co-head of real estate and REIT M&A at the firm. **David Shapiro** (see p.1940) is held in high esteem for his expertise in M&A and securities transactions.

## Band 4
## Capital Markets: REITs

### Alston & Bird LLP
### See profile on p.1102

**THE FIRM** This Atlanta-based team has an impressive reputation for its representation of substantial nonlisted

REITs nationwide. Its recent highlights include representing Cogdell Spencer on its $780 million merger with Ventas. Other key clients include Duke Realty, RREEF America Property Income Trust and NorthStar Healthcare Income Trust.

**Commercial Awareness** *"They have been extremely professional and highly execution-oriented."*

**KEY INDIVIDUALS Rosemarie Thurston** (see p.417) is *"highly organized and efficient"* and is commended by clients for her *"in-depth knowledge of REITs."* Her clients include Clarion Partners Property Trust and Jones Lang LaSalle Income Property Trust. **Jason Goode** (see p.323) is a *"highly creative thinker"* who is further praised by clients for his impressive industry knowledge. He is a corporate lawyer with a focus on REIT-related transactions.

### DLA Piper LLP (US)
See profile on p.1971

**THE FIRM** This team maintains an excellent profile for its representation of publicly offered nontraded REITs. It has recently advised W.P. Carey on its conversion to a public REIT. Other key clients include Phillips Edison-ARC Shopping Center REIT, KBS Real Estate Investment Trust II and Behringer Harvard Multifamily REIT I.

**KEY INDIVIDUALS Robert Bergdolt** (see p.282) is a *"highly capable, hard-working and practical guy,"* impressed clients say. His recent highlights include representing Dividend Capital Diversified Property Fund on the registration of a $3 billion public offering.

### King & Spalding LLP
See profile on p.445

**THE FIRM** The integrated REIT team at this firm remains a highly respected option for advising public and private REITs on a range of capital markets transactions. It recently represented Jamestown Premier Property Fund on the formation of a real estate fund, including the acquisition of assets valued at $1.4 billion. Other key clients include GE Capital Real Estate, Prologis and Post Properties.

**KEY INDIVIDUALS Peter Genz** (see p.1082) is commended by sources for his tax expertise. One client said approvingly: *"He is able to provide us with options and with the risks associated with taking those options."*

### Locke Lord LLP
See profile on p.2443

**THE FIRM** This team continues to win the praise of market sources for its committed approach to servicing the needs of its public and private REIT clients. It has recently represented American Campus Communities on several public offerings and acquisitions. The client roster at this firm also includes Hines Global REIT, Plymouth Opportunity REIT and National Health Investors.

**Client Service** *"They are highly responsive, timely and accurate."*

**Commercial Awareness** *"They are available, thorough and they understand the business objectives."*

**KEY INDIVIDUALS** Dallas-based **Bryan Goolsby** (see p.324) has represented Weingarten Realty Investors in multiple public offerings and joint venture deals. He is

praised by sources for his excellent *"attention to detail,"* his *"effectiveness"* and his *"timeliness."*

### Morris, Manning & Martin, LLP
**THE FIRM** This firm enters the rankings this year after earning strong market endorsement for its representation of nonlisted REITs on a range of transactions. Notable recent highlights include advising Cole Credit Property Trust IV on its $4 billion IPO. Other key clients include Griffin-American Healthcare REIT II, United Development Funding and O'Donnell Strategic Industrial REIT.

**Sources say:** *"They are smart, they care and they do a good job of making you feel as if you are their only client."*

**KEY INDIVIDUALS Lauren Prevost** has *"broad and deep technical knowledge along with a keen business sense,"* impressed clients say. She recently represented the underwriters to the fund on a $1.5 billion public offering of common stock by Sierra Income. **Heath Linsky** is recommended by clients, who appreciate his sound judgment. His recent highlights include representing SC Distributors, underwriters to the fund, in RREEF America Property Income Trust's $1.1 billion public offering of stock.

### Sullivan & Cromwell LLP
See profile on p.2011

**THE FIRM** This team has been active on behalf of an impressive roster of clients on multiple offerings and it frequently represents underwriters and issuers. Recent highlights include advising Goldman Sachs, Wells Fargo, Merrill Lynch and KeyBlanc Capital Markets as underwriters on several Glimcher Realty Trust follow-on offerings.

**KEY INDIVIDUALS Arthur Adler** (see p.271) is highly respected for his work on a range of capital markets transactions on behalf of REITs. He frequently advises clients on all areas of commercial real estate and real estate finance. **Anthony Colletta** (see p.298) is commended by market sources for his astute representation of issuers and underwriters on real estate-related transactions. **Joseph Shenker** (see p.1941) recently represented Vornado Realty Trust on a $400 million notes issuance and a $300 million preferred stock issuance. He is chairman of the firm.

## Band 1
## Capital Markets: REITs: Maryland Counsel

### Venable LLP
See profile on p.927

**THE FIRM** This team is a favored choice among many leading REIT lawyers for advice on Maryland law. Its commitment to client service is frequently remarked upon by interviewees, as is its ability to advise clients on complex and novel transactions including IPOs, follow-on offerings and at-the-market offerings. The firm recently acted as Maryland counsel to Healthcare Trust of America on its $150 million offering of Class A common stock.

**Sources say:** *"They are all highly responsive and practical and have a good understanding of the applicable Maryland law."*

**KEY INDIVIDUALS James Hanks** (see p.329) is *"the guru of Maryland law,"* *"has an encyclopedic comprehension of case law,"* and is *"very good in the boardroom,"* enthusiastic interviewees say. He is frequently local counsel on some of the most high-profile and substantial REIT-related transactions in the nation. **Sharon Kroupa** (see p.350) is *"extremely practical, understands the issues and is highly creative,"* impressed sources say. She is praised for her ability to communicate clearly and effectively at all levels and for her high level of responsiveness. **Patricia McGowan** (see p.365) is *"highly accessible and client service-oriented"* and *"highly practical in the way she applies her legal analysis to a transactional setting,"* market sources report. One lawyer said: *"It is always good to get her in on a transaction early."*

## Band 2
## Capital Markets: REITs: Maryland Counsel

### Ballard Spahr LLP
See profile on p.2234

**THE FIRM** Market sources report that they return to this firm again and again for advice on Maryland law, citing the responsiveness of the service and the accuracy of the advice as particular strengths. The multidisciplinary REIT team advises clients on the full array of transactions.

**Sources say:** *"They are terrific on matters of Maryland law and highly practical in their judgments."*

**KEY INDIVIDUALS Charles Moran** (see p.1430) is a *"highly perceptive, bright and helpful"* Maryland lawyer. Sources particularly praise his responsiveness in producing work quickly.

## Other Notable Practitioners

**John Good** (see p.323) of Bass, Berry & Sims PLC is a *"highly practical lawyer"* with *"good business sense,"* impressed sources say. He frequently represents both issuers and underwriters on a range of transactions and his recent highlights include representing AmREIT on its $58.65 million IPO. **Howard Adler** (see p.849) of Gibson, Dunn & Crutcher LLP is commended by sources as a *"highly skillful"* lawyer who is *"easy to work with."* He represents corporations, investment banks and financial institutions on a range of transactions. **David Slotkin** (see p.408) of Morrison & Foerster LLP is highly regarded by sources for his expertise in REIT transactions. He is designated underwriters' counsel on Equity Residential capital markets transactions. **Steven Scheinfeld** (see p.401) of Fried, Frank, Harris, Shriver & Jacobson LLP is recommended by sources for his accurate and highly knowledgeable advice. He represents REITs and financial institutions on a range of matters including public and private offerings. **Stuart Gelfond** (see p.319) of Fried, Frank, Harris, Shriver & Jacobson LLP is *"technically incredibly sound,"* *"understands the issues"* and *"gives very strong advice,"* impressed clients say. Sources further commend the confidence he inspires. **Ameek Ashok Ponda** (see p.1505) of Sullivan & Worcester LLP is a tax specialist who is *"outstanding in his craft"* and has an *"absolutely phenomenal* *command of the REIT rules,"* sources say. Key clients include American Tower, Hospitality Property Trust and CommonWealth REIT. **Joseph Howe** (see p.337) of Arnold & Porter LLP is *"highly committed to providing outstanding client and technical service,"* clients say. He is a highly regarded tax lawyer whose clients include Health Care

REIT and CNL Financial Group. **Bruce Gelman** (see p.319) of Kirkland & Ellis LLP receives positive market feedback for his incisive tax advice. He has represented Charter Hall Group on its $1.71 billion sale of its US assets in Charter Hall Office REIT to Beacon Capital Partners. **Michael Zuppone** of Paul Hastings LLP is admired by

sources for his robust approach to representing substantial clients. His recent highlights include advising Strategic Hotels & Resorts on its $119.6 million common stock offering.

# CAPITAL MARKETS SECURITIZATION

Commentary about individuals can be found under their firm's paragraph. If the firm has no paragraph (is not ranked) look at Other Notable Practitioners.

| Capital Markets: Securitization |
| --- |
| **Leading Firms** |
| **Band 1** |
| Bingham McCutchen LLP * |
| Mayer Brown LLP * |
| Sidley Austin LLP * |
| **Band 2** |
| Cadwalader, Wickersham & Taft LLP * |
| Dentons * |
| Hunton & Williams LLP * |
| Skadden, Arps, Slate, Meagher & Flom LLP & Affiliates * |
| **Band 3** |
| Chapman and Cutler LLP * |
| Dechert LLP * |
| Kaye Scholer LLP * |
| Latham & Watkins LLP * |
| Orrick, Herrington & Sutcliffe LLP * |
| Weil, Gotshal & Manges LLP * |
| **Band 4** |
| Cleary Gottlieb Steen & Hamilton LLP * |
| Clifford Chance US LLP * |
| Katten Muchin Rosenman LLP * |
| Kirkland & Ellis LLP * |
| Milbank, Tweed, Hadley & McCloy LLP * |
| Paul, Weiss, Rifkind, Wharton & Garrison LLP * |
| Simpson Thacher & Bartlett LLP * |
| White & Case LLP * |

*\* Indicates firm with profile.*
*Alphabetical order within each band. Band 1 is the highest.*

| Recommended for Client Service | |
| --- | --- |
| **Nationwide** | |
| Bingham McCutchen LLP | Sidley Austin LLP |
| Katten Muchin Rosenman LLP | Skadden, Arps, Slate, Meagher |
| Kaye Scholer LLP | & Flom LLP & Affiliates |

| Recommended for Commercial Awareness | |
| --- | --- |
| **Nationwide** | |
| Bingham McCutchen LLP | Mayer Brown LLP |
| Dechert LLP | Sidley Austin LLP |
| Hunton & Williams LLP | |

## Band 1

### Bingham McCutchen LLP
See profile on p.1515

**THE FIRM** Market sources speak with particular admiration of this team's prowess in auto loans and leases, RMBS and government agency program-related transactions. It advises big names like Barclays Bank, Credit Suisse and Sallie Mae. The team also has an excellent reputation for representing clients in transactions related to esoterics, and for its regulatory expertise.
**Client Service** *"They are willing to do whatever it takes to get the deal done."*

**Commercial Awareness** *"They are solutions-oriented; identify problems and risks but also work to find solutions." "They are very good at helping us to manage our risk with appropriate solutions."*
**KEY INDIVIDUALS John Arnholz** (see p.274) is well known for his expertise in domestic and international securitization transactions. He was underwriters' counsel on the $1 billion sale of Ford Upgrade Exchange Linked Notes via the FUEL Trust 2011-2. **Matthew Joseph** (see p.341) is a *"practical, hard-working deal-maker,"* clients say. His areas of expertise include the securitization of auto loans and leases, church loans and bonds, and equipment loans. **Steve Levitan** (see p.355) is *"always proactive and has an uncanny ability to foresee potential issues,"* impressed sources say. He has expertise in a wide array of complex securitizations including student loans, credit card receivables and financed insurance premiums. DC-based **Jeffrey Johnson** (see p.340) *"gets to the point very quickly and efficiently"* and *"helps you think through solutions,"* satisfied clients report. His clients include numerous financial institutions, finance companies and government agencies. **Reed Auerbach** (see p.275) is *"extraordinarily knowledgeable and well connected"* and is *"constantly striving to understand his clients and find value for us."* He is viewed by sources as a lawyer at the vanguard of developments in this field.

### Mayer Brown LLP
See profile on p.1257

**THE FIRM** This outstanding team is highly respected for its balanced and comprehensive advice on transactions incorporating a range of asset types and structures. Areas of expertise include MBS, credit cards, and auto and equipment loans and leases. It recently advised Barclays and JPMorgan as lenders on an $850 million fleet lease-backed securitization facility to finance Hertz's acquisition of Donlen.
**Commercial Awareness** *"They know the business extremely well, are commercial and understand that we need to get a deal done." "They understand how US companies are financed and also the ins and outs of the offerings process."*
**KEY INDIVIDUALS** The *"highly professional"* **Carol Hitselberger** *"talks in a language business people can understand,"* impressed clients say. Sources speak particularly

enthusiastically of her domestic and cross-border commercial paper funded securitization work. **Keith Oberkfell** is praised as being incredibly *"smart and practical"* and a *"very strong lawyer with a sense of how to get a deal done,"* sources enthuse. His recent highlights include representing Barclays Bank as sponsor in a $538 million 144A issue of FFELP student loan asset-backed notes by Academic Loan Funding Trust series 2012-1. **Jon Van Gorp** recently advised Carrington Capital Management on the creation of a tax-efficient structure for nonperforming mortgage loans. One client said approvingly: *"We consider him a business partner and not just an outside counsel."* **Paul Jorissen** has impressed clients with both his technical expertise and his *"ability to explain complex issues in plain terms that made sense."* His areas of expertise include residential and commercial mortgage loans, home equity loans and equipment loans and leases. **Stuart Litwin** advised JP Morgan Securities on the $1.4 billion offering of asset-backed notes secured by auto leases issued by Mercedes-Benz Auto Lease Trust 2012-A. Sources say he is *"smart and knows his stuff,"* and he is widely recognized as a leader in areas such as auto loans and leases, FFELP and private student loans, and dealer floorplan receivables. **Mary Fontaine** is highly regarded by sources for her expertise across an array of securitization transactions. She is senior counsel in the firm's Chicago office. **Jason Kravitt** is *"knowledgeable, well known and thoughtful."* He is widely considered to be a leading industry expert. **Angela Ulum** is an *"up-and-coming presence in the auto loan space,"* sources say. She also has expertise on transactions related to equipment leases, home equity loans and trade receivables.

## Capital Markets: Securitisation
### Senior Statesmen

**Senior Statesmen:** distinguished older practitioners

| | |
|---|---|
| Cowan Cameron | *King & Spalding LLP (ONP)[†] \** |
| Kravitt Jason H P | *Mayer Brown LLP* |

### Leading Individuals

**Band 1**

| | |
|---|---|
| Arnholz John | *Bingham McCutchen LLP \** |
| Auerbach Reed D | *Bingham McCutchen LLP \** |
| Gambro Michael S | *Cadwalader, Wickersham & Taft LLP \** |
| Glick Anna H. | *Cadwalader, Wickersham & Taft LLP \** |
| Kudenholdt Stephen S | *Dentons \** |
| Martin Renwick | *Sidley Austin LLP \** |
| Palma Laura | *Simpson Thacher & Bartlett LLP \** |
| Schwartz Jordan M | *Cadwalader, Wickersham & Taft LLP \** |

**Band 2**

| | |
|---|---|
| Blauch Kevin C | *Sidley Austin LLP \** |
| Buckley Kevin J | *Hunton & Williams LLP \** |
| Croke James | *Chapman and Cutler LLP* |
| Cullen William J | *Kaye Scholer LLP \** |
| DiAngelo Christopher | *Katten Muchin Rosenman LLP* |
| Dorris Malcolm S | *Dechert LLP \** |
| Faulkner Andrew M | *Skadden, Arps, Slate, Meagher & Flom \** |
| Hitselberger Carol A | *Mayer Brown LLP* |
| Jorissen Paul A | *Mayer Brown LLP* |
| Klingenberg Erik D | *Dentons \** |
| Litwin Stuart M | *Mayer Brown LLP* |
| Mitchell Michael H | *Chapman and Cutler LLP \** |
| Morriello Henry G | *Kaye Scholer LLP \** |
| Morrison Kenneth P | *Kirkland & Ellis LLP \** |
| Nocco Frank | *Weil, Gotshal & Manges LLP \** |
| Oberkfell Keith F | *Mayer Brown LLP* |
| Quinn Patrick T | *Cadwalader, Wickersham & Taft LLP \** |
| Raff Joshua E | *Orrick, Herrington & Sutcliffe LLP \** |
| Rodriguez Carlos A | *Sidley Austin LLP \** |
| Smith Jason | *Weil, Gotshal & Manges LLP \** |
| Stern Gary | *Sidley Austin LLP \** |
| Van Gorp Jon D | *Mayer Brown LLP* |
| Yarett Jordan | *Paul, Weiss, Rifkind, Wharton & Garrison \** |

**Band 3**

| | |
|---|---|
| Buck Willis | *Sidley Austin LLP \** |
| Cohen Lewis | *Clifford Chance US LLP \** |
| Crost Katharine I | *Orrick, Herrington & Sutcliffe LLP \** |
| Davis Trayton M | *Milbank, Tweed, Hadley & McCloy LLP \** |
| Dedyo John | *Weil, Gotshal & Manges LLP \** |
| Dupler Mitchell S | *Cleary Gottlieb Steen & Hamilton LLP \** |
| Fingeret Kevin | *Latham & Watkins LLP \** |
| Fontaine Mary C | *Mayer Brown LLP* |
| Hartnett Daniel J | *Kaye Scholer LLP \** |
| Hiner Thomas Y | *Hunton & Williams LLP \** |
| Hochberg Kevin J | *Sidley Austin LLP \** |
| Joseph Matthew P | *Bingham McCutchen LLP \** |
| Kadlick Richard F | *Skadden, Arps, Slate, Meagher & Flom \** |
| Levitan Steve | *Bingham McCutchen LLP \** |
| Marks Ellen | *Latham & Watkins LLP* |
| Marlatt Jerry | *Morrison & Foerster LLP (ONP)[†] \** |
| Nedzbala Michael | *Hunton & Williams LLP \** |
| Rudder Richard D | *Kramer Levin Naftalis & Frankel (ONP)[†] \** |
| Schacter Ira J | *Cadwalader, Wickersham & Taft LLP \** |
| Thatch David | *White & Case LLP \** |
| Timperio John M | *Dechert LLP \** |

**Band 4**

| | |
|---|---|
| Barbiere Janet A | *Kaye Scholer LLP \** |
| Camp Lawton | *Allen & Overy LLP (ONP)[†]* |
| Carlson R J | *Sidley Austin LLP \** |
| Donovan John M | *White & Case LLP \** |
| Goldstein Stuart N | *Cadwalader, Wickersham & Taft LLP \** |
| Hardin Elizabeth | *Milbank, Tweed, Hadley & McCloy LLP \** |
| Johnson Jeffrey R | *Bingham McCutchen LLP (ONP)[†] \** |
| Liu Gilbert | *Kramer Levin Naftalis & Frankel LLP \** |
| Lum Dale | *Sidley Austin LLP \** |
| McCarty Joyce | *Cleary Gottlieb Steen & Hamilton LLP \** |
| Midvidy David H | *Skadden, Arps, Slate, Meagher & Flom \** |
| Novetsky Terry D | *Kaye Scholer LLP \** |
| Pisa Albert | *Milbank, Tweed, Hadley & McCloy LLP \** |
| Topolski Joseph P | *Katten Muchin Rosenman LLP* |
| Utley Frederick | *Clifford Chance US LLP \** |
| Zochowski T Robert | *Paul, Weiss, Rifkind, Wharton & Garrison \** |

**Up-and-coming individuals**

| | |
|---|---|
| Barth Giselle | *Sidley Austin LLP \** |
| Cox Brian | *Alston & Bird LLP (ONP)[†] \** |
| Ulum Angela M | *Mayer Brown LLP* |
| Wishnia Jonathan C | *Lowenstein Sandler LLP (ONP)[†] \** |

\* Indicates individual with profile.
[†] ONP = Other Notable Practitioner.

### Sidley Austin LLP
See profile on p.1264

**THE FIRM** This team earns strong market endorsement for the high quality of its technical abilities and commitment to client service. Recent highlights include representing JP Morgan Securities and other financial institutions in the issue by Santander Drive Auto Receivables Trusts of multiple tranches of fixed-rate notes secured by over $4 billion of auto loans. The team also counts Deutsche Bank, Citi and GE Capital among its clients.

**Client Service** *"From senior partners to junior associates, Sidley's attorneys are exceptionally responsive and resourceful." "Everyone at the firm is client service-oriented and is focused on moving to solutions, not simply identifying issues."*
**Commercial Awareness** *"They come at things from an understanding of what our business is and from a highly commercial perspective, but they are not a firm who gloss over real issues – they are real lawyers."*
**KEY INDIVIDUALS** *"Pioneer of securitization"* **Renwick Martin** (see p.362) is a *"legend"* in the industry, sources

say. He has recently represented JPMorgan Securities in four tranches of fixed-rate notes totaling $998.9 million issued by John Deere Owner Trust 2012 backed by sale and loan contracts for construction and agricultural equipment. **Kevin Blauch** (see p.284) is *"highly effective"* in representing clients on all CMBS transactions. Recent highlights include advising Morgan Stanley on two issues of CMBS by MSBAM series 2012-C5 totalling $1.353 billion, and MSC series 2012-C4 totaling $1.098 billion. **Carlos Rodriguez** (see p.394) is widely respected by market sources for the high quality of his advice on a range of securitization and structured finance matters. He has notable expertise in RMBS and CMBS transactions. **Gary Stern** (see p.412) is rated by market sources for the strength of his representation of lenders in transactions related to a variety of asset classes including auto loans, equipment leases and timeshares. He is based in the firm's Chicago office. **Willis Buck** (see p.289) *"comes at everything from a practical perspective,"* impressed market sources report. Sources speak with particular admiration of his expertise in auto leases and loans, commercial paper and credit card receivables. **Kevin Hochberg** (see p.335) is praised by sources for his technical expertise. He represented American Electric Power in an issue of senior secured transition bonds backed by payments from retail electric customers. *"Star in the auto world"* **RJ Carlson** (see p.292) recently represented JPMorgan on three ABS issues of fixed rate notes totaling $3.5 billion by Volkswagen Auto Lease Trust and Volkswagen Auto Loan Enhanced Trust. **Dale Lum** (see p.359) represented Mercedes-Benz Financial Services USA on the offering in four tranches of fixed-rate notes backed by auto leases totaling $1.4 billion. He is based at the firm's San Francisco office. The *"smart and practical"* **Giselle Barth** (see p.279) has advised JP Morgan Securities on the issue of $1 billion of fixed-rate notes backed by interests in automobile leases issued by BMW Vehicle Lease Trust series 2012-1. Clients say: *"Her knowledge of the markets and the law is a tremendous asset."*

### Band 2

### Cadwalader, Wickersham & Taft LLP
See profile on p.438

**THE FIRM** This team is an exceptional player in the securitization market. It has a particularly strong reputation for CMBS work including pooled loan and stand-alone securitizations. Cadwalader continues to win plaudits for its work on ABS transactions.

**KEY INDIVIDUALS** The *"excellent"* **Michael Gambro** (see p.318) is recommended by clients for his *"hardcore understanding of securities law and regulation."* He is well known for his representation of investment banks on residential and CMBS transactions. **Anna Glick** (see p.321) is lauded by sources for her deal structuring, drafting and negotiating abilities. She is particularly highly respected by market participants for her expertise in CMBS. The *"fantastic"* **Jordan Schwartz** (see p.402) is widely considered by sources to be a leading expert in RMBS-related matters. His clients include institutional investors, investment banks, commercial banks and insurance companies. **Patrick Quinn** (see p.388) has notable expertise in public and private CMBS and RMBS. He also advises clients on ABS, including student loans. **Stuart Goldstein** (see p.323) represents issuers, underwriters and institutional investors in products including MBS and CDOs. He is based at the firm's New York and Charlotte, North Carolina offices. **Ira Schacter** (see p.400) is *"bright"* and *"extremely creative,"* sources say. He advises clients on a broad array of securitizations including CDOs, insurance risks and whole company.

## Dentons
See profile on p.449

**THE FIRM** This team is widely acknowledged as a formidable force across the full range of MBS and ABS transactions. It is frequently a favored choice for market participants on RMBS matters. Notable clients include Citi, Wells Fargo and Guggenheim Securities.

**Sources say:** *"They have a good set of expertise across the board."*

**KEY INDIVIDUALS Stephen Kudenholdt** (see p.351) represented Barclays Capital on the issue of $30 billion of government guaranteed asset-backed securities under the National Credit Union Administration guaranteed notes program. He is *"really smart"* and an *"excellent lawyer with a lot of presence,"* sources say. **Erik Klingenberg** (see p.348) is *"concise and understandable,"* *"has a good bedside manner"* and is *"good at keeping his cool and making the argument that is appropriate,"* satisfied clients say. His areas of expertise include CMBS and RMBS, ABS and commercial paper.

## Hunton & Williams LLP
See profile on p.2517

**THE FIRM** The team at this firm has impressed sources with its expertise on RMBS securitizations and resecuritizations, government guaranteed mortgage-backed securities and auto securitizations. It recently represented Bank of America Merrill Lynch as underwriter and placement agent/initial purchaser in a $2.3 billion auto securitization. Other key clients include Government National Mortgage Association (Ginnie May), Wells Fargo and RBS Securities.

**Commercial Awareness** *"They understand our business very well and are a good partner."*

**KEY INDIVIDUALS Kevin Buckley** (see p.289) is *"a firm and fair negotiator"* with *"excellent communication skills,"* clients say. He recently represented RB Commercial Mortgage as issuer's counsel in a $70 million Rule 144A offering of resecuritizations of commercial mortgage-backed certificates. **Thomas Hiner** (see p.334) has *"impressive business acumen"* and is praised for his in-depth understanding of the economics at play in the transactions on which he advises clients. He co-heads the firm's structured finance and securitization practice. **Michael Nedzbala** (see p.375) is highly regarded by sources for his expertise on transactions involving residential and commercial mortgage loans. His clients include issuers, sellers and purchasers.

## Skadden, Arps, Slate, Meagher & Flom LLP & Affiliates
See profile on p.2008

**THE FIRM** This dynamic team is a frequent choice of issuers, underwriters and credit enhancers on transactions related to the securitization of financial assets, and whole company and credit card securitizations for clients like Apollo Investment, Macquarie Leasing and Mitsubishi Motors Credit of America. Notable highlights include advising Domino's Pizza on the issue of $1.575 billion of fixed-rate senior secured term notes, and on establishing a $100 million floating rate, revolving, variable funding note facility.

**Client Service** *"The advice is well thought through, they are experts in the field and the service is excellent."*

**KEY INDIVIDUALS Andrew Faulkner** (see p.311) is a *"strong," "excellent lawyer"* who is *"highly responsive,"* clients say. He has recently represented Chase Bank USA, National Association in several transactions including its sponsorship of Chase Issuance Trusts' issue of $1.5 billion of credit card asset-backed notes. **Richard Kadlick** (see p.341) represented The Blackstone Group on its $277 million acquisition of a controlling stake in Exeter Finance, and on a $600 million structured credit facility. His areas of particular expertise include structured securities backed by mortgage loans, credit card receivables and nonperforming assets. **David Midvidy** (see p.368) is recommended by sources for his intelligent, diligent and efficient transactional work. He is a respected option for securitizations of nonfinancial and consumer finance assets, and whole company securitizations.

# Band 3

## Chapman and Cutler LLP
See profile on p.1244

**THE FIRM** This growing team has an increasingly strong reputation among market participants for its credit card and commercial paper underwriters' and conduits counsel work. It also has a good reputation for its regulatory expertise. Recent highlights include advising Royal Bank of Canada on a $1.2 billion trade receivables securitization for Philips 66. Other notable clients include Bank of America and Citi.

**KEY INDIVIDUALS James Croke** is described by impressed sources as *"knowledgeable and commercial"* and a *"confident and highly competent lawyer."* He advised Cantor Fitzgerald on a new global asset-backed commercial paper conduit. The *"really strong"* **Michael Mitchell** (see p.370) is a *"foremost expert on SEC regulations"* and *"has exceptional securities law expertise,"* enthusiastic commentators say. He is a popular choice of both issuers and underwriters to advise on asset-backed securities issue platforms.

## Dechert LLP
See profile on p.1969

**THE FIRM** The team at this firm continues to win plaudits from sources for its representation of clients in ABS, CLOs

and CMBS transactions. It recently advised Deutsche Bank Securities and others as underwriters on the $1.25 billion Santander Drive Auto Receivables Trust series 2012-3 subprime auto loan securitization.

**Commercial Awareness** *"They are involved in a lot of complex transactions for a lot of lenders so they have a lot of market knowledge."*

**KEY INDIVIDUALS Malcolm Dorris** (see p.306) advised Credit Suisse Securities and others as underwriters on the $1.1 billion AMCAR series 2012-2 public auto loan securitization. He is widely respected for his work on transactions related to a variety of asset types including auto loans and leases, credit cards and trade receivables. **John Timperio** (see p.417) focuses on ABS, structured lending and CLOs. He recently advised Crescent Capital as manager on the $308 million Atlas Senior Loan Fund transaction.

## Kaye Scholer LLP
See profile on p.1984

**THE FIRM** This team attracts the respect of the business community for its advice to investment banks on a range of transactions including public and private ABS, and CMBS and RMBS. It represented Citigroup Commercial Mortgage Securities as issuer in the $674 million issue of UBS-Citigroup Commercial Mortgage Trust series 2011-C1 commercial mortgage pass-through certificates.

**Client Service** *"They will drop everything and get it done by the time we tell them." "They really wrap their arms around all aspects of a transaction."*

**KEY INDIVIDUALS William Cullen** (see p.300) is highly regarded by sources for his expertise on CMBS transactions. He also advises clients on the restructuring of defaulted real estate loans and securities. **Henry Morriello** (see p.371) *"really learns how the institutional client operates"* and *"has a holistic knowledge of the client,"* sources say. He chairs the structured finance and derivatives group. **Daniel Hartnett** (see p.331) is recommended by sources for his multifaceted skill set and practical market knowledge. His areas of expertise include transactions related to RMBS and CMBS, farm credit loans and CLOs. **Janet Barbiere** (see p.278) advises an array of clients on the purchase, sale and acquisition of mortgage securities. She also has expertise in the restructuring and workout of distressed financial assets. **Terry Novetsky** (see p.377) has a *"solution-driven approach to our projects," "can get you out of a tough situation"* and *"relates to the business background,"* impressed clients say. He is a favored choice for financial institutions on complex structured finance transactions.

## Latham & Watkins LLP
See profile on p.446

**THE FIRM** This group maintains a formidable reputation for its advice to clients on transactions related to aircraft leases, cell tower assets, rental car fleets and credit card receivables, and has notable CLO expertise. It represented Deutsche Bank Securities on an acquisition financing for Global Tower Partners' purchase from Goldman Sachs of a portfolio of wireless cell tower easements and ground leases. Key clients include Bank of America Merrill Lynch, Credit Suisse and Zipcar.

**KEY INDIVIDUALS Kevin Fingeret** (see p.312) is widely recommended by sources for his expertise on aircraft and rental car fleet securitizations. He represented US Airways as issuer in a public offering of its series 2012-1 enhanced equipment trust certificates. **Ellen Marks** is *"highly knowledgeable"* and *"has a strong ability to explain things clearly,"* sources say. She represented Discover Bank and Discover Card Master Trust 1 on a $1.65 billion credit card receivables securitization.

## Orrick, Herrington & Sutcliffe LLP
See profile on p.1994

**THE FIRM** This team stands out for its highly adept representation of clients on an array of securitization assets including credit cards, auto loans and tax liens. Notable recent transactions include advising Barclays Bank Delaware as issuer on the creation of its Dryrock credit card securitization program.

**Sources say:** *"They are really good on the skills I need."*

**KEY INDIVIDUALS Joshua Raff** (see p.388) is highly thought of by market sources for his expertise on an array of capital markets transactions. His clients include issuers, underwriters, fund sponsors and other financial institutions. **Katharine Crost** (see p.300) represented Redwood Trust in four securitization transactions totaling $1.4 billion. Her securitization expertise extends across a variety of assets including mortgages, tax liens and tobacco litigation settlements.

## Weil, Gotshal & Manges LLP
See profile on p.2015

**THE FIRM** This team maintains its excellent reputation for advising clients on sophisticated transactions including those relating to auto loan, credit card and trade receivables. It also has expertise in advising clients on restructuring and remediation relating to CMBS exposure. Recent highlights include advising GE Capital on the securitization aspects of the sale of its real estate lending unit, Business Property Lending.

**Sources say:** *"They have a deep substantive knowledge plus a healthy dose of practical business judgment and risk assessment."*

**KEY INDIVIDUALS Jason Smith** (see p.408) is renowned as an *"expert in the rental car securitization space,"* is *"focused on finding solutions"* and *"can get a big deal done."* He represented Hertz in the securitization aspects of its acquisition of Donlen. **Frank Nocco** (see p.376) is *"solutions-oriented, creative and excellent at doing first-time transactions,"* clients say. He heads the firm's structured finance and derivatives practice. **John Dedyo** (see p.303) is praised by sources for his *"calm demeanor"* and *"diligent"* approach. He advised Security National Automotive Acceptance Company on the issue of $350 million of revolving notes backed by auto loans.

## Band 4

## Cleary Gottlieb Steen & Hamilton LLP
See profile on p.1963

**THE FIRM** This team frequently advises underwriters on MBS work and its reputation for CLO work remains strong. Recent highlights include advising Credit Suisse Securities (USA) on two CLO transactions totaling $770 million.

**Sources say:** *"Their strengths are depth of knowledge, the broad resources readily available, the attention to detail, the personal interaction and the ability to share your sense of urgency."*

**KEY INDIVIDUALS** DC-based **Mitchell Dupler** (see p.307) is highly regarded by sources for his transactional and regulatory expertise. He continues to be a frequent choice for underwriters on MBS transactions. **Joyce McCarty** (see p.364) is respected by interviewees for her CLO experience. Her clients include Goldman Sachs, GSO Capital Partners and Merrill Lynch, Pierce, Fenner & Smith.

## Clifford Chance US LLP
See profile on p.439

**THE FIRM** This firm stands out for its high level of expertise on cross-border securitization transactions. Sources speak with particular admiration of the team's capabilities on regulatory issues.

**Sources say:** *"The firm is very professional and knowledgeable about different topics."*

**KEY INDIVIDUALS Frederick Utley** (see p.420) is well regarded for his expertise on the full range of securitized assets. He focuses on advising clients on CLOs and ABS workouts. **Lewis Cohen** (see p.297) is *"smart and reasonable"* and a *"go-to guy for cross-border securitization issues,"* sources say. He represents issuers, credit enhancers and underwriters in the securitization of assets such as credit card and trade receivables, and equipment leases.

## Katten Muchin Rosenman LLP
See profile on p.1253

**THE FIRM** This team is held in high esteem for its expertise on auto, equipment and mortgage finance transactions. Notable highlights include advising PKM Energy on the monetization of coal sale agreements. Other key clients include GM Financial, Fannie Mae and Fortress Investment Group.

**Client Service** *"Their turnaround times are amazing and they are always available."*

**KEY INDIVIDUALS Christopher DiAngelo** gives clients *"strong advice on auto and mortgage-backed securitizations."* He co-heads the structured finance and securitization team at the firm and is highly recommended by clients for his advice on complex transactions. **Joseph Topolski** is much sought after for his advice on auto finance including auto loans, leases and dealer floorplan finance securitizations. His recent highlights include advising Ford Motor Credit and Ford Automotive Credit (China) on establishing a committed purchase facility for dealer floorplan finance receivables in the People's Republic of China.

## Kirkland & Ellis LLP
See profile on p.1254

**THE FIRM** This firm is recognized for its representation of issuers of ABS, particularly those backed by vehicle assets. It is also held in high regard for its underwriter-side practice. Recent highlights include representing Barclays Capital in two offerings and Citigroup Global Markets in one offering of term securities backed by dealer floorplan receivables originated by Ford Motor Credit.

**Sources say:** *"I am impressed with the depth of their knowledge, their response speed and the fact that they give very good advice."*

**KEY INDIVIDUALS** *"Fantastic attorney"* **Kenneth Morrison** (see p.372) is *"extremely intellectual"* but is also praised for speaking in a language businesspeople understand. His highlights include advising Ally Bank and Ally Financial on the $1.2 billion Ally Auto Receivables Trust series 2012-3.

## Milbank, Tweed, Hadley & McCloy LLP
See profile on p.448

**THE FIRM** The team at this firm is recognized for its strength in esoteric securitization matters including transport, alternative energy and infrastructure-related transactions. It recently represented Connecticut Small Business Finance Fund in an offering of notes purchased by private investors for the purpose of making investments in Connecticut companies.

**KEY INDIVIDUALS Trayton Davis** (see p.302) advises a range of clients on the securitization of financial and other assets. He is also sought by clients for advice on RMBS and CMBS workouts. **Elizabeth Hardin** (see p.330) is recommended by sources for her work on auto loan and lease, and aircraft ticket securitization. Her other areas of notable expertise include ABS, CLOs and CDOs. **Albert Pisa** (see p.385) is well regarded for his expertise on esoteric securitization transactions. His clients include corporations, investment banks and private investment funds.

## Paul, Weiss, Rifkind, Wharton & Garrison LLP
See profile on p.1997

**THE FIRM** This team continues to receive plaudits from clients for its expert advice on the securitization of a range of assets including whole businesses, operating assets and media and entertainment industry-related assets. It recently advised Barclays Bank and JPMorgan on an offering of $1.6 billion of senior secured term and variable funding notes backed by a whole business securitization of Domino's Pizza.

**Sources say:** *"The connectivity with other areas of their capital markets practice is the best I have seen."*

**KEY INDIVIDUALS Jordan Yarett** (see p.429) has *"an encyclopedic knowledge of securitization"* and *"an outstanding ability to understand the business motivations behind things and to find solutions,"* satisfied clients say. He represented Amherst Securities as underwriter in the $165 million vacation timeshare securitization issue by Westgate Resorts series 2012-1. **Robert Zochowski** (see p.431) comes recommended for his expertise on film securitization. He recently represented Barclays Bank in the $500 million securitization of the Miramax film library.

## Simpson Thacher & Bartlett LLP
See profile on p.2006

**THE FIRM** This compact but high quality team advises a range of clients on auto loans and leases, timeshare loans, and truck and equipment loan and lease securitizations.
**Sources say:** *"They are doing difficult, interesting work."*
**KEY INDIVIDUALS** *"Big player in auto finance space"* **Laura Palma** (see p.381) is a *"fierce client advocate"* and *"top-notch drafter,"* sources say. Her areas of expertise also include franchise royalty, cell tower and aircraft securitizations.

## White & Case LLP
See profile on p.451

**THE FIRM** This team is recommended by market sources for its expertise on rental car fleet and esoteric products securitizations, and on CLO transactions. Key clients include Anchorage Capital, Commerzbank and Kelson Energy.

**Sources say:** *"I have been impressed with the knowledge base, the quality of the work and the availability of the lawyers."*
**KEY INDIVIDUALS** *"Rising star partner in the securitization world"* **David Thatch** (see p.416) is praised by clients for his *"practical and creative solutions."* He is recommended for his work on esoteric securitizations. The *"always fantastic"* **John Donovan** (see p.305) is *"a good problem solver and gets deals done."* He recently represented Avis Budget Rental Car Funding (AESOP) in its issue of $689.7 million of rental car asset-backed notes.

## Other Notable Practitioners

**Brian Cox** (see p.299) of Alston & Bird LLP is *"highly responsive and competent"* and is further praised for his in-depth understanding of the issues faced by trustee clients on transactions. He is a respected choice for CMBS, RMBS and ABS transactions. **Jerry Marlatt** (see p.361) of Morrison & Foerster LLP advised Royal Bank of Canada Capital Markets on its filing of a registration statement with the US Securities and Exchange Commission, the first ever for covered bonds in the US. Sources speak with con-

siderable admiration of his expertise in the covered bonds area. **Richard Rudder** (see p.397) of Kramer Levin Naftalis & Frankel LLP is recognized by market sources for his expertise on asset-backed transactions including intellectual property, structured settlements and timeshare loan-backed transactions. **Gilbert Liu** (see p.357) also of Kramer Levin Naftalis & Frankel LLP focuses on commercial mortgage, timeshare and student loan-backed securitization transactions. His clients include investment banks, private equity funds and a growing number of issuers. *"All-around exceptional attorney"* **Cameron Cowan** (see p.299) of King & Spalding LLP has a notable focus on China-related transactions. One source said: *"His knowledge is fantastic and his judgment is exceptional."* **Jonathan Wishnia** (see p.427) of Lowenstein Sandler PC specializes in mortgage finance and receivables securitization. He is widely respected for his regulatory and transactional expertise. **Lawton Camp** of Allen & Overy LLP is *"well-rounded in his approach,"* *"highly capable"* and *"very knowledgeable and enjoyable to work with,"* impressed sources say. He advised RBC Capital Markets as dealer, on the first ever registration of a covered bond program with the US Securities and Exchange Commission.

# CLIMATE CHANGE

Commentary about individuals can be found under their firm's paragraph. If the firm has no paragraph (is not ranked) look at Other Notable Practitioners.

| Climate Change |
| --- |
| **Leading Firms** |
| **Band 1** |
| Baker & McKenzie * |
| Hunton & Williams LLP * |
| Latham & Watkins LLP * |
| Sidley Austin LLP * |
| Van Ness Feldman LLP * |
| **Band 2** |
| Baker Botts LLP * |
| Bracewell & Giuliani LLP * |
| Katten Muchin Rosenman LLP * |
| Kirkland & Ellis LLP * |
| **Band 3** |
| Covington & Burling LLP * |
| Crowell & Moring LLP * |
| Hogan Lovells US LLP |
| Morrison & Foerster LLP * |
| Troutman Sanders LLP |
| Vinson & Elkins LLP * |

*Indicates firm with profile.*
*Alphabetical order within each band. Band 1 is the highest.*

## Band 1

### Baker & McKenzie
See profile on p.435

**THE FIRM** This prominent climate change practice is able to harness the firm's global platform in order to successfully serve major clients on an international level, and frequently advises on projects in places as diverse as Malaysia, China and Peru. The group offers in-depth expertise across a broad array of climate change matters, including legislation and regulation, and comes especially recommended for its experience in carbon trading, for which it utilizes the firm's broader capabilities in tax, securities and M&A. Key clients include leading multinational corporations and financial institutions.
**Sources say:** *"They're a powerhouse on carbon credit worldwide."*
**KEY INDIVIDUALS** Head of the North America climate change group **Richard Saines** has significant experience in carbon capture and storage, and is an expert in international carbon trading transactions. Recently, he advised a global food processing company with regards to analysis of EPA's Renewable Fuel Standard. Sources highlight that he *"knows the issues and knows the players."*

| Recommended for Client Service |  |
| --- | --- |
| **Nationwide** | |
| Kirkland & Ellis LLP | Sidley Austin LLP |
| Latham & Watkins LLP | |

| Recommended for Commercial Awareness |  |
| --- | --- |
| **Nationwide** | |
| Bracewell & Giuliani LLP | Sidley Austin LLP |
| Hunton & Williams LLP | Van Ness Feldman LLP |
| Katten Muchin Rosenman LLP | |

### Hunton & Williams LLP
See profile on p.2517

**THE FIRM** The climate change group at this leading firm is highly regarded in the industry, particularly for its well-established expertise in all matters relating to the CAA. It takes a multidisciplinary approach to issues in order to effectively assist clients in the key areas of litigation, regulatory compliance, policy advocacy and carbon-related projects, finance and trading. In a recent work highlight, the team advised on the merger of two carbon asset management companies.
**Commercial Awareness** *"They show a depth of understanding of the CAA and specific industry issues that is difficult to beat."*
**KEY INDIVIDUALS** The *"amazingly intelligent"* **William Brownell** (see p.288) is hailed by interviewees as *"one of the deans of environmental law."* He represents clients in

Europe, as well as the USA, and his broad expertise includes advising on environmental licensing, clean air regulation, and litigation and regulation involving climate change matters.

## Latham & Watkins LLP
See profile on p.446

**THE FIRM** This firm's climate change group offers expertise across the full range of issues, including litigation, project finance, regulation and project development. It acts for clients in a broad range of industries, such as aerospace, power, and oil and gas. In recent highlights, the group advised SCS Energy in connection with the Hydrogen Energy California Project, one of the first large power plants with commercial-scale carbon capture and sequestration. Key clients also include Australia Pacific LNG, Goldman Sachs and California Climate Coalition.
**Client Service** *"Excellent service." "They have given us the attention we desired in a timely manner."*
**KEY INDIVIDUALS** The *"phenomenal"* **Robert Wyman** is widely regarded as *"a real leader in terms of air work."* He is acting on behalf of the California Climate Change Coalition in connection with the development of the state's AB32 carbon cap and trade program. Former Linklaters partner **Jean-Philippe Brisson** joined Latham's New York office in November 2012 as vice chair of the

firm's air quality and climate change practice. He offers significant experience advising financial services firms and oil and gas companies on issues related to climate change.

## Sidley Austin LLP
See profile on p.1264

**THE FIRM** The climate change team at Sidley offers experience across a broad array of issues, including regulatory counseling, permitting and transactional matters. It has also significantly expanded its renewable energy practice recently. The group is frequently involved in major litigation taking place in this area, and recently defended key EPA CAA decisions relating to the regulation of renewable biofuels and biomass on behalf of the National Alliance of Forest Owners. Other notable clients include Chevron, American Chemistry Council and PPG Industries.
**Client Service** *"The service is excellent; they've got a really deep breadth of resources."*
**Commercial Awareness** *"A very solid practice. They have a lot of really great lawyers who handle things well – excellent client service and commercial awareness."*
**KEY INDIVIDUALS** The *"wonderful"* **Roger Martella** (see p.362) is described as *"a really top-notch lawyer,"* who is *"always trying to think of creative solutions."* He provides regular counsel to companies on ways to address issues posed by climate change.

## Van Ness Feldman LLP
See profile on p.926

**THE FIRM** This pioneering practice is frequently involved in working with clients in policy advocacy, influencing the direction of greenhouse gas regulations at both state and federal levels. It also offers significant expertise handling emissions trading transactions and issues relating to automotives. Its recent highlights include advising Toyota in connection with matters stemming from the Obama administration's ongoing action to establish greenhouse gas emission standards under the CAA. The firm also acts for Edison Electric Institute, EKO Asset Management and the Coalition for Emission Reduction Policy.
**Commercial Awareness** *"The group has a high level of experience on federal regulatory matters."*
**KEY INDIVIDUALS** Sources recognize **Kyle Danish** (see p.301) as *"one of the leading lawyers in the world"* on climate change matters. His practice encompasses permitting, regulation and legislation under the CAA. **Stephen Fotis** (see p.315) is an expert in matters relating to the CAA. He regularly acts on behalf of petroleum refineries, electric utilities, governmental entities and power producers.

## Band 2

## Baker Botts LLP
See profile on p.2427

**THE FIRM** This climate change group provides the full range of climate change-related services, on both a domestic and international level. Particular areas of expertise include advising finance and energy clients on project

development, carbon markets and the use of carbon dioxide for enhanced oil recovery. The team recently represented a major clean energy generator in connection with the permitting of a carbon capture facility located next to a coal-fired power plant. Key clients also include Occidental Petroleum, Entergy and Xcel Energy.
**Sources say:** *"A great firm." "They're doing a lot on implementing change."*
**KEY INDIVIDUALS** The *"highly regarded"* **William Bumpers** is hailed by sources as *"a key player"* in the market. He recently represented the Class of '85 Regulatory Response Group, providing an analysis of the EPA's proposed performance standards for existing fossil fuel-fired electric generating units.

## Bracewell & Giuliani LLP
See profile on p.2429

**THE FIRM** A significant number of Bracewell's climate change group have previously held positions at the EPA, and the team wins plaudits for its excellent contacts with the agency. The group's services include regulatory counseling, advocacy, corporate governance and litigation, and it regularly works with key policymakers to help shape the climate change legal landscape. It offers significant expertise in permitting matters, and recently advised Texas-based midstream energy firm Energy Transfer Company in securing greenhouse gas emission permits from the EPA for four proposed gas processing plants at a south Texas site.
**Commercial Awareness** *"They're very current with their knowledge, and they have extremely good contacts."*
**KEY INDIVIDUALS** Head of department **Jeffrey Holmstead** (see p.335) *"knows everything there is to know about the CAA,"* according to interviewees, many of whom appreciate him as *"very thoughtful, intelligent, strategic, and he also has great connections."* He has a wealth of experience guiding clients from various industries through the complicated network of climate change regulations.

## Katten Muchin Rosenman LLP
See profile on p.1253

**THE FIRM** This team offers in-depth assistance with compliance, advocacy and litigation relating to climate change. It is also active advising companies on the potential implications of pending state and federal legislation. The group recently acted on behalf of the Renewable Fuels Association in litigation involving a challenge to the Low Carbon Fuel Standard set by the California Air Resources Board. Other notable clients include GE, the National Association of Manufacturers and the Air Permitting Forum.
**Commercial Awareness** *"They're extremely strategic; they understand the big picture and know how an individual piece of litigation or regulation fits into a broader whole, and they're extremely good at moving from strategy to tactics."*
**KEY INDIVIDUALS** The *"fabulous"* **Chuck Knauss** is described as *"phenomenally good"* when it comes to issues relating to the CAA. Recently, he has been involved in representing SIP/FIP Advocacy Group in litigation questioning EPA rulemaking relating to the implementation of the

federal greenhouse gas permitting program in Texas. **Matthew Paulson** recently joined the team from Baker Botts, and is contributing to its expansion by establishing an Austin office. His expertise includes acting for clients in litigation, regulation and greenhouse gas emissions.

## Kirkland & Ellis LLP
See profile on p.1254

**THE FIRM** Kirkland's climate change group is renowned for its expertise in complex litigation, and regularly acts on behalf of clients in criminal, administrative and civil matters, including toxic tort, Superfund and environmental class actions. The team successfully defended ConocoPhillips in a high-profile case in which the plaintiffs were seeking damages for the alleged effects of global warming on the Alaskan coast. The firm also acts for GM, Suzuki and the US Chamber of Commerce.

**Client Service** "*We could not have asked for better client service.*"

**KEY INDIVIDUALS** The "*really smart*" **Stuart Drake** (see p.306) is highly thought of in the industry. He is a skilled litigator, and has substantial experience advising companies whose products are affected by EPA air pollution control regulations.

## Band 3

### Covington & Burling LLP
See profile on p.441

**THE FIRM** This firm's energy-focused climate change practice advises private equity groups, investors and clean energy clients on issues and opportunities arising out of the gradual shift to a low-carbon energy base. The team recently represented First Wind in connection with the completion of a Hawaii wind farm, and the related implementation of an endangered shorebirds Habitat Conservation Plan. Other key clients include BrightSource Energy, Amazon Forest Carbon Partnership and the Coalition for Green Capital.

**KEY INDIVIDUALS** Practice cochair **Rubén Kraiem** (see p.349) is described as "*extremely intelligent, extremely precise, extremely knowledgeable, extremely careful – all-around exceptional.*" He is an expert in matters involving Latin America, and is particularly focused on integration of US and Mexican renewable energy markets.

### Crowell & Moring LLP
See profile on p.910

**THE FIRM** This robust practice is actively involved in policy-shaping advocacy on behalf of a large client base, which features a substantial amount of trade associations. The group regularly defends or challenges agency decisions in high-profile litigation It recently represented six leading trade associations in a case which involved defending an Endangered Species Act ruling accompanying the designated status of polar bears as a threatened species. Key

clients include the Alliance of Automobile Manufacturers, National Mining Association and Western States Petroleum Association.

**KEY INDIVIDUALS Jeffrey Smith** (see p.1942) is an expert in handling environmental transactional matters. His experience includes underwritings, financings and M&A, as well as corporate governance counseling. **Chet Thompson** (see p.417) is a former deputy general counsel of the EPA. His broad practice encompasses the representation of clients in litigation, advocacy, counseling and enforcement defense under the CAA.

### Hogan Lovells US LLP

**THE FIRM** The group at Hogan Lovells provides a full-service approach to climate change issues on behalf of clients from a wide variety of industry sectors, including aviation, chemical, construction, oil and gas, and energy. In a significant recent matter, the team represented GE Oil & Gas, advising on a legislative strategy to make sure that oil and natural gas technology research and development programs are kept in place. The firm also acts for Black Hills Energy, Denbury Resources and SABIC Innovative Plastics.

**KEY INDIVIDUALS Mary Anne Sullivan** is head of the firm's climate change group. She is an expert in clean energy, and advises clients on both regulatory and transactional climate change matters.

### Morrison & Foerster LLP
See profile on p.1990

**THE FIRM** Morrison & Foerster's climate change group is pivotal to its broader cleantech group, which offers clients significant expertise in matters including corporate, litigation and environment issues. It regularly acts for a broad client base, such as insurers, alternative energy providers and technology platform companies. The group was recently involved in eight lawsuits on behalf of Sierra Pacific Industries, each of which centers around a challenge to the impact analysis of greenhouse gas emissions for almost all of the California timber operations. Key clients also include Ceres, Nature Conservancy and EDF Renewable Energy.

**Sources say:** "*They have been fundamental in guiding our people.*"

**KEY INDIVIDUALS** San Francisco-based William Sloan leads the environmental practice group's carbon team.

### Troutman Sanders LLP

**THE FIRM** This international firm's climate change practice has been actively involved in the sector for nearly 20 years. Sources particularly commend the group's strength in representing clients in the coal and power industries. It offers clients expertise across a broad spectrum of issues, including renewable and alternative energy, carbon trading, litigation, and carbon-related legislation, regulation and policy.

**KEY INDIVIDUALS** Interviewees regard **Peter Glaser** as a leading litigator in this area. He is chair of the firm's climate change group, and regularly acts on behalf of clients in the mining and electric utilities sectors.

### Vinson & Elkins LLP
See profile on p.2459

**THE FIRM** The climate change group at this leading energy firm is at the forefront of advising clients when it comes to energy-related M&A transactions involving climate change matters. The team recently acted on behalf of Duke Energy, in relation to a joint venture with Sumitomo Corporation of America for the development of Duke's Kansas-based 168 MW Ironwood and 131 MW Cimarron II wind energy projects. Other notable clients include Cross Texas Transmission, Sunflower Electric Power and the Coalition for Responsible Regulation.

**KEY INDIVIDUALS** Houston-based Larry Nettles leads the firm's energy practice group, and is a key contact for its climate change activities.

## Other Notable Practitioners

**Kipp Coddington** of Mowrey Meezan Coddington Cloud LLP regularly acts on behalf of investors and developers, advising on issues relating to domestic and international energy projects. He also offers significant experience in carbon capture and storage. **Jonathan Martel** (see p.362) of Arnold & Porter LLP is well regarded in the field. He recently advised PPL Corporation in connection with the implications of new greenhouse gas emission regulations and permitting requirements. Interviewees describe **William Thomas** (see p.417) of Willkie Farr & Gallagher LLP as "*a terrific lawyer and a really wonderful person.*" He offers experience in climate law and policy, as well as carbon finance, and regularly counsels clients on greenhouse gas initiatives at the state, federal and international levels. **Jeffrey Fort** (see p.1207) is co-head of Dentons's climate change group. He assists clients in complicated air permitting and regulation issues, and in matters relating to emission credits trading. **Matthew Adams** (see p.271), also of Denton, has experience across the full spectrum of climate change matters, particularly those arising out of energy and infrastructure projects. Sources highlight that he is "*always responsive and always helpful.*" **Robert McKinstry** (see p.2224) leads the climate change practice at Ballard Spahr LLP. He recently advised the City of Philadelphia Water Department in connection with the implementation and financing of a CWA-required green infrastructure program, which is part of a larger sustainability initiative. The tremendously experienced **Raymond Ludwiszewski** (see p.878) of Gibson, Dunn & Crutcher LLP recently acted for the Association of Global Automakers in litigation, regulatory and rulemaking issues relating to the mandatory use of alternative fuels in motor vehicles.

# CONSTRUCTION

| Construction Leading Firms |
| --- |
| **Band 1** |
| Kilpatrick Townsend & Stockton LLP * |
| Peckar & Abramson, P.C. * |
| Watt, Tieder, Hoffar & Fitzgerald, LLP * |
| **Band 2** |
| Duane Morris LLP * |
| Farella Braun + Martel LLP |
| Holland & Knight LLP * |
| Seyfarth Shaw LLP * |
| **Band 3** |
| Jones Day * |
| Smith, Currie & Hancock LLP * |
| Sutherland Asbill & Brennan LLP |
| **Band 4** |
| Akerman Senterfitt |
| DLA Piper LLP (US) * |
| Moye, O'Brien, O'Rourke, Pickert & Dillon, LLP * |
| Patton Boggs LLP |
| Pepper Hamilton LLP * |
| Pillsbury Winthrop Shaw Pittman LLP * |
| Thompson Hine LLP * |
| *Indicates firm with profile.* |
| *Alphabetical order within each band. Band 1 is the highest.* |

## Band 1

### Kilpatrick Townsend & Stockton LLP
See profile on p.1109

**THE FIRM** This international firm's preeminent construction group comes highly recommended for its expertise in complex projects both in the USA and throughout Europe, Asia, the Middle East and Africa. It offers clients a broad range of expertise in all areas of construction law, including in airport, hospital, power plant and sports arena projects. The team recently represented Archstone in a dispute stemming from property damage in multiple buildings. The firm also acts for the City of Atlanta, American University in Cairo and InterGen.

**Sources say:** *"We have been impressed by the strong litigation skills, the detail in the preparations, the management of the expert witnesses and the efficiency in case management."*

**KEY INDIVIDUALS** Brian Corgan is leader of the firm's construction group. His practice focuses on litigation, alternative dispute resolution and construction contracts.

### Peckar & Abramson, P.C.
See profile on p.1998

**THE FIRM** The team at this impressive construction-focused firm operates across nine offices in the USA, giving it excellent geographic coverage. It is regularly involved in cutting-edge issues, and represents key players, such as major trade associations. The group excels in handling high-profile projects for prominent construction managers and general contractors, with key expertise in risk

management, insurance, litigation and alternative dispute resolution.

**Client Service** *"Very professional, very knowledgeable and very responsive."*

**Commercial Awareness** *"They are well-seasoned veterans in the construction industry and litigation field, and understand how to minimize the risk."*

**KEY INDIVIDUALS** Founding partner Robert Peckar divides his time between the firm's New York and New Jersey offices. He has substantial experience representing leading contractors in construction disputes.

### Watt, Tieder, Hoffar & Fitzgerald, LLP
See profile on p.2522

**THE FIRM** This leading construction boutique is renowned for its ability to effectively handle large, complex disputes, and receives praise from sources for its strength and depth. The team offers experience across the full spectrum of construction law matters, and regularly acts on behalf of major developers, corporations and contractors in national and international matters. In recent highlights, the group represented the largest landowner in Tysons Corner in connection with a breach of contract dispute with Capital One. Its enviable client list also includes Balfour Beatty, URS, Fluor and AECOM.

**Client Service** *"Watt Tieder consistently performs at a level of excellence."*

**KEY INDIVIDUALS** Lewis Baker is the firm's managing partner. His areas of expertise include major construction, engineer and surety claims.

## Band 2

### Duane Morris LLP
See profile on p.2239

**THE FIRM** The experienced construction practice at Duane Morris represents a varied client base, including subcontractors, owners, architects and developers, and others. It provides in-depth knowledge in both litigation and transactional matters, relating to the financing, design and development of projects. The team recently acted for the National September 11 Memorial & Museum in a dispute with the Port Authority of New York & New Jersey in relation to $300 million of construction costs. Other key clients include Zeckendorf Development, Airis Holdings and Columbia University.

**Client Service** *"They're very practical and they've dealt with every situation before, so they always know how to deal with everything that comes up."*

**Commercial Awareness** *"They have a real depth of experience and a very deep understanding of the construction business."*

**KEY INDIVIDUALS** Albert Bates and Robert Prentice, both based in Pennsylvania, are cochairs of the construction practice. Bates concentrates his practice on arbitration, on a domestic and international level, as well as con-

| Recommended for Client Service Nationwide | |
| --- | --- |
| Duane Morris LLP | Sutherland Asbill & Brennan LLP |
| Peckar & Abramson, P.C. | |
| Seyfarth Shaw LLP | Watt, Tieder, Hoffar & Fitzgerald, LLP |

| Recommended for Commercial Awareness Nationwide | |
| --- | --- |
| Duane Morris LLP | Peckar & Abramson, P.C. |

struction litigation. Prentice has extensive experience representing owners, contractors, architects and subcontractors.

### Farella Braun + Martel LLP

**THE FIRM** This firm climbs the rankings after a successful year which saw it earn widespread praise from sources, particularly for the strength of its national practice. It regularly acts on behalf of contractors, subcontractors, owners and design professionals in projects both in the USA and abroad. The group has substantial experience in all elements of the construction process, and its recent matters have included assignments involving hospitals, airports, multifamily developments and power plants.

**Sources say:** *"They're really an outstanding organization. Really top-notch people."*

**KEY INDIVIDUALS** Richard Van Duzer is head of the firm's construction group. His has significant expertise in complex civil trial matters.

### Holland & Knight LLP
See profile on p.1028

**THE FIRM** Holland & Knight's full-service construction group is truly international in scope, handling significant projects in the Middle East and South America, as well as across the USA. The group serves clients in all corners of the industry, with a particular concentration on major contractor and owner representations. The team recently advised the Massachusetts Technology Collaborative in connection with a $70 million fiber-optic cable deployment project. Other notable clients include BCI Construction, Embassy of Sweden and New York Transportation Authority.

**Sources say:** *"Excellent lawyers."*

**KEY INDIVIDUALS** The DC-based Stephen Shapiro is the firm's construction practice group leader. He has broad expertise, including litigation, dispute resolution and procurement, and represents a varied client base.

### Seyfarth Shaw LLP
See profile on p.1262

**THE FIRM** This high-quality construction team has strength in both litigation and transactional matters, and is involved in some of the largest infrastructure projects taking place domestically and overseas. It also offers expertise in construction-related bankruptcy matters, and recently represented Bank of America in connection with its role as lead lender in a high-profile $200 million foreclosure lawsuit on a Chicago mixed-use project. Its impressive client list also includes Ventura Foods, Bigelow Development and CORE Construction.

**Client Service** "*Very hands-on and very responsive.*" "*An exceptional firm and great people to work with.*"

**KEY INDIVIDUALS** Practice group cochair Bennett Greenberg works out of the firm's Washington, DC office. His practice encompasses all aspects of design and construction law, and sources appreciate his pragmatic approach to commercial issues.

## Band 3

### Jones Day
See profile on p.919

**THE FIRM** This firm's construction practice offers clients a soup-to-nuts service, with expertise across the range of issues, from contract preparation and negotiation, to litigation and alternative dispute resolution. The group recently acted on behalf of both San Diego Gas & Electric and Southern California Gas with regards to a pipeline safety enhancement program. Key clients also include El Paso Electric, Chevron, Capital Cement and MGM Resorts International.

**Sources say:** "*Outstanding.*"

**KEY INDIVIDUALS** Key contact Daniel McMillan works out of the firm's Los Angeles office. His expertise includes complex business, commercial and construction litigation.

### Smith, Currie & Hancock LLP
See profile on p.1112

**THE FIRM** This experienced construction team advises clients, including a substantial number of general contractors, in a wide variety of industries, including healthcare, aviation, transportation and infrastructure. In recent highlights the group represented Flatiron West in various issues, including the permitting, drafting, risk management, environmental reviews and litigation relating to the $1.2 billion Presidio Parkway project in San Francisco. Other notable clients include Flatiron Construction, Caddell Construction and Molson Coors.

**Sources say:** "*They are very capable, technology-based and have the ability to react quickly to our needs.*" "*I would highly recommend their services to anyone in the construction market.*"

**KEY INDIVIDUALS** Robert Chambers is the firm's managing partner. His experience includes advising on many types of public and private construction projects, such as power facilities, tunnels, highways and dams.

### Sutherland Asbill & Brennan LLP

**THE FIRM** The well-regarded construction group offers clients a wealth of experience in all construction related issues, and is recognized for its expertise in dispute resolution. Its recent highlights include representing Lend Lease Construction in a $200 million lawsuit concerning the deconstruction of the former Deutsche Bank Building, the final building to be removed from Manhattan's Ground

Zero. The firm also acts for Dragados USA, Lennar and Black & Veatch, among others.

**KEY INDIVIDUALS** Lee Davis is head of the firm's construction practice group. He regularly acts for general contractors, engineers, municipal districts and major engineering, procurement and construction (EPC) contractors.

## Band 4

### Akerman Senterfitt
See profile on p.1014

**THE FIRM** Anchored in Florida, this firm's construction team is involved in major infrastructure projects on both a national and international level, and serves a variety of industries, from government facilities to housing and healthcare entities. The group recently acted on behalf of Resorts World Miami in connection with the development of its new $3 billion resort project on the former Miami Herald site. Key clients also include Dacra Development, The Faena Group and Architect of the Capitol.

**Sources say:** "*A terrific firm.*"

**KEY INDIVIDUALS** Virginia-based Jeffrey Gilmore is head of the construction department. He has expertise across a broad range of construction law matters, including healthcare, power generation and EPC/design-build projects.

### DLA Piper LLP (US)
See profile on p.1971

**THE FIRM** DLA Piper's construction group utilizes the firm's strong international platform, and has developed a strong practice advising major clients in international arbitrations, as well as in high profile domestic matters. The firm recently represented Archstone, both in connection with a $700 million development project, and in a $70 million construction defect case in New York. Other notable clients include Chick-Fil-A and SunEdison.

**Sources say:** "*They have really been able to know and understand us as a client and help us achieve out goals.*"

**KEY INDIVIDUALS** Robert Crewdson and Anthony Meagher act as cochairs of the practice. Georgia-based Crewdson represents developers, owners and contractors in transactions and litigation. Meagher is an expert in construction-related litigation and arbitration, as well as in contract negotiation.

### Moye, O'Brien, O'Rourke, Pickert & Dillon, LLP
See profile on p.1032

**THE FIRM** This Florida-based firm operates out of just one office but is active in some of the largest matters taking place all over the world, including high-profile construction litigation, an area in which the group comes highly regarded. It has also recently been representing a joint venture in connection with its role in the $450 million construction and finance of Florida's new I-4/Lee Roy Selmon Expressway Connector Interchange. The firm also acts for Peter Kiewit & Sons, Odebrecht Construction and PCL Civil Constructors.

**Sources say:** "*Most of their attorneys have some sort of technical background in addition to being lawyers: they understand the detail and understand construction.*"

**KEY INDIVIDUALS** James Moye is managing partner of the firm. Clients appreciate the high level of experience and organization that he brings to projects.

### Patton Boggs LLP

**THE FIRM** The construction group at Patton Boggs represents several major developers, owners, architects and contractors, often in high-value disputes arising from large infrastructure and development projects worldwide. Of recent note, the team acted on behalf of New Jersey Transit Corporation in a dispute with the Department of Transportation stemming from the canceled New Jersey Access to the Region project. Key clients also include the State of Qatar and AECOM.

**Sources say:** "*They are top-notch professionals.*" "*I can think of no other firm that I would want in my corner when it comes to navigating federal government and politics.*"

**KEY INDIVIDUALS** DC-based Robert Brams is chair of the firm's construction department. His practice includes a focus on the matters involving large infrastructure projects, hotels, corporate headquarters and hospitals.

### Pepper Hamilton LLP
See profile on p.2248

**THE FIRM** Pepper Hamilton's construction practice offers commendable trial expertise, and is frequently involved in some of the most high-profile and complex litigation taking place in the USA and overseas, often arising out of major infrastructure projects. It recently acted as counsel for Pepper Construction in substantial arbitration proceedings against a luxury condominium developer relating to the conversion of Chicago's Palmolive Building. Other notable clients include Silverstein Properties, Bechtel Power and The Trump Organization.

**Sources say:** "*They're very valued counsel. I feel very comfortable calling them.*"

**KEY INDIVIDUALS** Practice group head Bruce Ficken is based in Philadelphia. He is a distinguished trial attorney, with almost 40 years of experience in the field.

### Pillsbury Winthrop Shaw Pittman LLP
See profile on p.2000

**THE FIRM** This team is recognized for its skill in construction disputes, and has also experienced a boost to its transactional practice, particularly with regards to infrastructure projects involving foreign investors. The group recently acted on behalf of Lend Lease in litigation concerning $20 million of alleged construction defects at a new San Diego law school building. The firm also represents Brookfield Renewable Power, Chevron and Hunt Construction, among other clients.

**Sources say:** "*They are extremely astute in construction law issues; they have great insight, great energy, and really good ideas when it comes to litigation and disputes.*"

**KEY INDIVIDUALS** John Heisse works out of the San Francisco office. He offers experience in all aspects of the construction industry, and represents developers, builders, designers and owners.

## Thompson Hine LLP
See profile on p.2131
**THE FIRM** Based out of Ohio, this firm's construction group offers clients a balanced practice that includes substantial expertise in transactions, advocacy and consulting. The team recently represented the 49ers Stadium Authority in connection with the $1.2 billion design and construction of the new stadium for the San Francisco 49ers. Other key clients include Kokosing Construction, URS Corporation and Whiting-Turner Contracting.
**Sources say:** *"A market leader in providing risk management counsel for large civil works projects nationwide."*
**KEY INDIVIDUALS** Ohio-based Jeffrey Appelbaum is head of the construction group. He is an experienced trial and transactional attorney, and represents construction managers, design professionals and owners.

# CORPORATE/M&A

| Corporate/M&A: The Elite Leading Firms |
| --- |
| **Band 1** |
| Cravath, Swaine & Moore LLP * |
| Latham & Watkins LLP * |
| Simpson Thacher & Bartlett LLP * |
| Skadden, Arps, Slate, Meagher & Flom LLP & Affiliates * |
| Sullivan & Cromwell LLP * |
| Wachtell, Lipton, Rosen & Katz * |
| **Band 2** |
| Cleary Gottlieb Steen & Hamilton LLP * |
| Davis Polk & Wardwell LLP * |
| Debevoise & Plimpton LLP * |
| Gibson, Dunn & Crutcher LLP * |
| Kirkland & Ellis LLP * |
| Weil, Gotshal & Manges LLP * |
| **Band 3** |
| Fried, Frank, Harris, Shriver & Jacobson LLP * |
| Jones Day * |
| Paul, Weiss, Rifkind, Wharton & Garrison LLP * |
| Ropes & Gray LLP * |
| Shearman & Sterling LLP * |
| Sidley Austin LLP * |
| **Band 4** |
| Baker Botts LLP * |
| Hogan Lovells US LLP |
| Morrison & Foerster LLP * |
| Vinson & Elkins LLP * |
| Willkie Farr & Gallagher LLP * |
| *Indicates firm with profile.* |
| *Alphabetical order within each band. Band 1 is the highest.* |

| Corporate/M&A: Highly Regarded Leading Firms |
| --- |
| **Band 1** |
| Dechert LLP * |
| Goodwin Procter LLP * |
| Morgan, Lewis & Bockius LLP * |
| White & Case LLP * |
| Wilson Sonsini Goodrich & Rosati * |
| **Band 2** |
| Bingham McCutchen LLP * |
| Cadwalader, Wickersham & Taft LLP * |
| DLA Piper LLP (US) * |
| Greenberg Traurig, LLP * |
| McDermott Will & Emery LLP * |
| Proskauer Rose LLP * |
| **Band 3** |
| Bracewell & Giuliani LLP * |
| Covington & Burling LLP * |
| Jenner & Block LLP * |
| K&L Gates * |
| King & Spalding LLP * |
| Paul Hastings LLP * |
| Pillsbury Winthrop Shaw Pittman LLP * |

| Recommended for Client Service Nationwide | |
| --- | --- |
| Baker Botts LLP | Paul Hastings LLP |
| Davis Polk & Wardwell LLP | Pillsbury Winthrop Shaw Pittman LLP |
| Debevoise & Plimpton LLP | |
| Gibson, Dunn & Crutcher LLP | Skadden, Arps, Slate, Meagher & Flom LLP & Affiliates |
| Greenberg Traurig, LLP | |
| Kirkland & Ellis LLP | Wachtell, Lipton, Rosen & Katz |
| Latham & Watkins LLP | Weil, Gotshal & Manges LLP |
| | Willkie Farr & Gallagher LLP |

| Recommended for Commercial Awareness Nationwide | |
| --- | --- |
| Covington & Burling LLP | Latham & Watkins LLP |
| Davis Polk & Wardwell LLP | Morrison & Foerster LLP |
| Fried, Frank, Harris, Shriver & Jacobson LLP | Paul, Weiss, Rifkind, Wharton & Garrison LLP |
| Gibson, Dunn & Crutcher LLP | Simpson Thacher & Bartlett LLP |
| Jones Day | |
| Kirkland & Ellis LLP | Wachtell, Lipton, Rosen & Katz |

## Band 1
## Corporate/M&A: The Elite

### Cravath, Swaine & Moore LLP
See profile on p.1966
**THE FIRM** Famed as a powerhouse in the representation of sophisticated clients such as BAE Systems, Johnson & Johnson and Unilever, this firm continues to garner respect from market observers. Its New York office houses a deep bench of talented attorneys who have honed their skills over countless mergers, acquisitions, joint ventures and divestitures. By virtue of this towering reputation, the team is the regular recipient of some of the most demanding and complex mandates around, including the $4.6 billion acquisition of Lincare Holdings by The Linde Group.
**Sources say:** *"Their knowledge of substance and procedure is complete, they are extremely responsive, and frankly, very nice people to work with."*
**KEY INDIVIDUALS** Chair of the M&A department Philip Gelston and his colleague Mark Greene are prominent members of this practice.

### Latham & Watkins LLP
See profile on p.446
**THE FIRM** Although it has deep roots on the West Coast, this hugely successful firm has more than made its presence felt among its East Coast competitors. The talented corporate team attracts a steady flow of high-profile mandates from its diverse stable of clients and frequently handles deals in the energy, pharmaceuticals and technology sectors. Its lawyers acted on Watson Pharmaceuticals' acquisition of Actavis Group for some EUR4.25 billion, leading the deal from Orange County and coordinating seamlessly with personnel in London.

**Client Service** *"Extremely responsive on a short timeline, and they do whatever it takes to get the work done. They are the best."*
**Commercial Awareness** *"Tremendous knowledge of the M&A market and tremendous strategic knowledge."*
**KEY INDIVIDUALS** New-York based Adel Aslani-Far and Mark Gerstein, who splits his time between the New York and Chicago offices, act as global cochairs of Latham's M&A practice.

### Simpson Thacher & Bartlett LLP
See profile on p.2006
**THE FIRM** Private equity titan Simpson Thacher retains its fantastic reputation for handling some of the most lucrative and complex deals in the market. The firm prides itself on its one-stop shop offering, incorporating leading finance and capital markets expertise into its M&A practice. Ingersoll Rand, Microsoft and Petrohawk Energy are all notable clients, serviced by a deep bench of lawyers spanning the firm's New York, Houston, Palo Alto, Los Angeles and Washington, DC offices. McKesson's $2.1 billion acquisition of PSS World Medical was one of a number of multibillion-dollar highlights for the team this past year.
**Commercial Awareness** *"They are excellent, probably some of the most knowledgeable people in the M&A world."*

**KEY INDIVIDUALS** Respected practitioner Lee Meyerson heads the M&A group from New York, while Richard Capelouto and Dan Clivner lead in Palo Alto and Los Angeles.

## Skadden, Arps, Slate, Meagher & Flom LLP & Affiliates
See profile on p.2008

**THE FIRM** As one of the foremost corporate shops in the nation, Skadden consistently invites a raft of headline-grabbing mandates. Lawyers provide exceptional all-around service to mammoth clients such as Disney and GenOn Energy, and recently assisted Sprint Nextel with the $20.1 billion sale of a 70% stake to Softbank. The deal is the largest ever overseas acquisition by a Japanese company, emphasizing the team's unarguable preeminence in cross-border transactions.
**Client Service** *"Unbelievably professional in the way they do things. They make themselves available and are high-quality people."*
**KEY INDIVIDUALS** Peter Krupp in Chicago and New York-based Howard Ellin serve as global co-heads of the firm's corporate transactions and M&A practices.

## Sullivan & Cromwell LLP
See profile on p.2011

**THE FIRM** At the heart of Sullivan & Cromwell's corporate offering is its commitment to seamless multidisciplinary coordination across its New York, Palo Alto, Los Angeles and Washington, DC offices. Major clients such as Goldman Sachs, Amgen and AT&T reward this dedication with mandates to act on some of the largest deals in the market, such as the $4.1 billion acquisition of Amil by UnitedHealth. The group's expertise extends far beyond national borders, garnering a reputation as one of the most active groups in the market on international transactions.
**Sources say:** *"Sullivan has a broad geographic presence and that hasn't diluted its quality, high-end, broad presence."*
**KEY INDIVIDUALS** New York-based Joseph Frumkin is managing partner of the M&A group and Alison Ressler oversees the firm's California practice.

## Wachtell, Lipton, Rosen & Katz
See profile on p.2012

**THE FIRM** Wachtell's dynamic corporate team has once again been active across a staggering array of high-profile transactions. Housed exclusively in New York, this talented bench represents energy, financial services and technology companies among others, in multibillion-dollar M&A transactions, utilizing resources and talent from across the firm to best serve the needs of corporate giants. Noteworthy transactions of late include the representation of Deutsche Telekom in its proposed merger of T-Mobile with MetroPCS.
**Client Service** *"Exceptional service. You call on a Sunday night and they find you the person you need and you speak to them. The advice and the understanding were exceptional – I have never seen anything like it."*
**Commercial Awareness** *"They have really good people and a lot of experience. They can walk into any M&A deal at any*

point and have a good sense of what to do and how to do it. They can negotiate and execute without wasted time learning the deal or the area, and have really good judgment."*
**KEY INDIVIDUALS** Founding partner Martin Lipton and cochair of the corporate practice Andrew Brownstein are key contacts.

## Band 2
## Corporate/M&A: The Elite

## Cleary Gottlieb Steen & Hamilton LLP
See profile on p.1963

**THE FIRM** The dexterity and experience of this firm's New York and Washington, DC teams allow it to remain at the vanguard of corporate activity, especially in the technology, IP and pharmaceutical industries. Lawyers have been prominent on some of the largest deals of the year, such as the $3.6 billion acquisition of Human Genome Sciences by long-standing client GlaxoSmithKline. Its reputation as a go-to firm for high-value transactions has attracted many other industry behemoths including Google, Coca-Cola and Sony.
**Sources say:** *"I think the Cleary team was very professional, knew what it was doing, and all the legal processes were done very slickly."*
**KEY INDIVIDUALS** New York partners Victor Lewkow, Paul Shim and Michael Ryan are all key contacts for the corporate practice.

## Davis Polk & Wardwell LLP
See profile on p.442

**THE FIRM** Davis Polk has a well-earned reputation for its prowess in running the gamut of corporate transactions and for promoting an innovative approach to solving complex M&A problems. Spanning the firm's California, New York and Washington, DC offices, this creative bench represents a string of international household names such as AstraZeneca, Comcast and Oracle. Notable transactions of the year include acting for Citi on the sale of a 14% stake in Morgan Stanley Smith Barney for $4.725 billion.
**Client Service** *"They are highly responsive, proactive in their engagement, they proactively raise issues and concerns that we should be following, and they are sensitive to and understand our business issues as we go through."*
**Commercial Awareness** *"They have subject matter expertise, offer practical legal/business advice, have exposure to a great deal of deal flow and, consequently, have a sense of what is 'market'."*
**KEY INDIVIDUALS** Distinguished partners David Caplan and George Bason serve as global co-heads of the M&A practice from New York.

## Debevoise & Plimpton LLP
See profile on p.1968

**THE FIRM** Debevoise excels in high-end transactional activity, with an impressive client roster composed largely of private equity firms, corporations and financial institutions. Its international profile augments its standing in the US market, attracting distinguished global players such as

Amazon.com and Verizon. Private equity powerhouse The Carlyle Group recently engaged the group as counsel on its $3.3 billion acquisition of Getty Images.
**Client Service** *"They really are a true partnership; they really believe that a client of the firm is a client of the whole firm, so other partners are able to step in and handle the matter in a seamless way."*
**KEY INDIVIDUALS** Experienced New York partner Jeffrey Rosen heads the corporate group here.

## Gibson, Dunn & Crutcher LLP
See profile on p.682

**THE FIRM** The influence of this firm extends far beyond its California origins, ensuring that it is frequently enlisted on some of the most significant transactions in the market. This year saw lawyers engaged by Lazard Freres as financial adviser to Walgreens in its $6.7 billion acquisition of a 45% equity stake in Boots. Williams Partners also gave the team an opportunity to demonstrate its prowess in the energy and natural resources sector in its mandate to act on the $2.5 billion acquisition of Caiman Eastern Midstream.
**Client Service** *"They are first-rate, the advice is very sound, and customer service is unparalleled."*
**Commercial Awareness** *"Knowledgeable, commercially unbelievable – you don't generally find lawyers that can blend law and commerciality to give balanced advice. They are very knowledgeable on overall markets."*
**KEY INDIVIDUALS** Washington, DC-based Stephen Glover, Jeffrey Chapman in Dallas and Barbara Becker in New York are the global cochairs of the corporate practice.

## Kirkland & Ellis LLP
See profile on p.1254

**THE FIRM** Having firmly established itself as a driving force on the national M&A scene, Kirkland continues to assert its strength across its New York, California, Washington, DC and Illinois bases. It invites mandates from some of the most active and distinguished players in the market, including Bristol-Myers Squibb, Teva and Burger King Worldwide. Marquee private equity clients also flock to this firm for guidance on major transactions; Kirkland recently acted for Bain Capital on its $1.6 billion purchase of Apex Tool Group, and for Oaktree Capital Management and JSA International Holdings on the $1.4 billion disposal of Jackson Square to Mitsubishi.
**Client Service** *"Client service is also great as the team is always available regardless of hour. We get high-level partner attention when needed, but less vital work is appropriately shared with junior resources to help defray costs."*
**Commercial Awareness** *"They are most commercially minded, and are able to think like me better than any other group I work with."*
**KEY INDIVIDUALS** New York partners David Fox and Daniel Wolf are key members of the corporate team.

## Weil, Gotshal & Manges LLP
See profile on p.2015

**THE FIRM** Lawyers in this group have cultivated a reputation as prolific deal-makers, acting on a glut of blockbuster deals in the past year. The firms caters to an enviable selec-

tion of clients, drawn from a diverse range of industries, with key names including Kinder Morgan, eBay and Symantec. A recent mandate by Medicis Pharmaceutical to act on its $2.6 billion sale to Valeant Pharmaceuticals International is a firm indication of the team's strong standing in the market. As well as its key New York component, the corporate team acts out of nine other national bases and coordinates with a global network of 11 offices.
**Client Service** *"The firm has done an excellent job from the top down to make sure we get the service that we need and are introduced to people that could be helpful to us. They are very focused on building their client relationships."*
**KEY INDIVIDUALS** Michael Aiello in New York is chair of Weil's private equity and M&A department.

## Band 3
## Corporate/M&A: The Elite

### Fried, Frank, Harris, Shriver & Jacobson LLP
See profile on p.1975
**THE FIRM** Offices in New York and Washington, DC are at the heart of Fried Frank's corporate offering, placing it in prime position to receive sophisticated engagements from some of the country's most active clients. Public companies, private equity firms and financial institutions alike regard this firm as a leading choice for the entire life cycle of a deal, due to its well-established expertise in the tax, regulatory and capital markets arenas. A recent highlight saw lawyers advising long-standing client Goldman Sachs as financial adviser to Catalyst Healthcare Solutions on its $4.4 billion merger agreement with SXC Health Solutions.
**Commercial Awareness** *"We are consistently impressed with how standout FF are: they have experience throughout the firm and what they believe to be market standard is always accurate and on trend. They have a lot of credibility and are great for negotiating when they have that kind of knowledge."*
**KEY INDIVIDUALS** Brian Mangino is a Washington, DC partner with valuable experience in the corporate arena.

### Jones Day
See profile on p.919
**THE FIRM** Enjoying an extensive national and global network, this firm is able to marshal considerable resources to take on high-profile mandates from clients such as Procter & Gamble, Eastman Chemical and SAP. Hubs of practice expertise can be found across the country, with its Ohio and Georgia teams particularly impressing market commentators of late. Cumulus Media engaged the Georgia team as counsel on its $610 million senior notes exchange offer and subsequent acquisition of Citadel Broadcasting for $2.4 billion.
**Commercial Awareness** *"They all think very commercially. They understand that winning every single legal point, but not getting the deal done, is not in anyone's best interests. They have the experience and the wisdom to know what's important to us and what is not."*

**KEY INDIVIDUALS** New York partner Robert Profusek chairs the firm's global M&A practice.

### Paul, Weiss, Rifkind, Wharton & Garrison LLP
See profile on p.1997
**THE FIRM** Situating itself firmly at the forefront of the M&A action flowing out of the New York and Washington, DC markets, this firm has built a sophisticated practice capable of addressing the needs of high-level clients such as Citi and Time Warner Cable. Recent highlights include the representation of Apollo Global Management in its $7.15 billion acquisition of El Paso's energy business.
**Commercial Awareness** *"They're incredibly commercially oriented. It's that extra little bit that makes a huge difference in a negotiation."*
**KEY INDIVIDUALS** Robert Schumer heads the corporate department and cochairs the M&A group from the firm's New York office.

### Ropes & Gray LLP
See profile on p.1528
**THE FIRM** This Boston institution also has solid bases in New York, Chicago and Washington, DC, as well as a growing West Coast presence. The team exhibits strength in representations of private equity firms, pharmaceutical and healthcare companies and financial institutions, such as acting for Alexion Pharmaceuticals on its $1.08 billion acquisition of Enobia Pharma. The team's experience is well balanced between buy and sell work, making it a strong choice for companies considering transactions of any nature.
**Sources say:** *"It's a big firm with a lot of firepower on the big deals and public company mergers. They can do really sophisticated, high-end, resource-intensive work."*
**KEY INDIVIDUALS** Paul Kinsella and Patrick O'Brien, both Boston partners, co-head the securities and public companies group at Ropes.

### Shearman & Sterling LLP
See profile on p.2005
**THE FIRM** The New York office of this well-established firm contains its largest concentration of corporate expertise, with substantial additional teams located in DC and California. This outfit excels at handling transactions with a global flavor, recently serving as counsel to Sony Corporation of America as part of a consortium purchasing patents from Nortel Networks for $4.5 billion, a deal which saw the US lawyers liaising with their counterparts in the Brussels office.
**Sources say:** *"They are a substantial firm and their strength in depth is a very valuable asset in M&A transactions as it enables them to meet the tight turnaround times that we require."*
**KEY INDIVIDUALS** Global co-head of the M&A group George Casey is based in New York.

### Sidley Austin LLP
See profile on p.1264
**THE FIRM** This firm's representation of prominent players across a diverse range of industries has earned it considerable market recognition. It maintains a dominant position in its native Illinois and has robust practices in Texas, California, New York and Washington, DC. New York and Chicago lawyers recently pulled together on a mandate by Athene Annuity & Life Assurance to represent it in its $415 million acquisition of Presidential Life.
**Sources say:** *"We are happy with them, they are very smart, experienced and client-focused and we have gotten very good results."*
**KEY INDIVIDUALS** Co-heads of the M&A and private equity group Scott Freeman and Frederick Lowinger are based out of the firm's New York and Chicago offices respectively.

## Band 4
## Corporate/M&A: The Elite

### Baker Botts LLP
See profile on p.2427
**THE FIRM** Baker Botts consistently impresses observers with its significant market share in the energy sector and its technical abilities across a range of other industries. Its corporate offering spans the country, with key practice hubs situated in Texas, New York, DC and California. Some notable clients include LINN Energy, Halliburton and Marathon Oil. In a recent practice highlight, lawyers were engaged by El Paso Energy to act on its $7.15 billion acquisition by Apollo Global Management.
**Client Service** *"The strongest points are client service levels and attention to detail. Baker Botts's lawyers are extremely thorough and top-notch in terms of client service."*
**KEY INDIVIDUALS** Houston-based David Kirkland heads the firm's corporate practice group.

### Hogan Lovells US LLP
**THE FIRM** National and multinational corporations alike regularly draw upon the corporate expertise of this substantial global player. With 12 offices across the country and a further 31 around its global network, the firm is able to provide advice on large and midcap M&A deals in the aerospace, life sciences and telecom industries, among others. In a recent highlight, the transactions committee of the board of Knology engaged the team to act on its $1.5 billion sale to WOW. Washington, DC and Northern Virginia-based partners collaborated effectively on this complex transaction.
**Sources say:** *"Fantastic advisers, fantastic lawyers, fantastic people. I felt like they always gave us great advice, which was very direct."*
**KEY INDIVIDUALS** Washington, DC-based Stuart Stein is the global co-head of the corporate practice group.

## Morrison & Foerster LLP
See profile on p.1990

**THE FIRM** This robust firm has a corporate presence across the country, notably featuring highly rated practices on both coasts. Its recent engagement by Softbank to act on its acquisition of a 70% stake in Sprint Nextel for $20.1 billion propelled this ambitious global firm into the limelight. Its technology, life sciences and healthcare sector expertise makes it an attractive prospect for a wide range of corporate clients, including the likes of DaVita, Intel and Hitachi.

**Commercial Awareness** *"I would say that they are pragmatic lawyers, they understand the big picture and the business objectives, and are not overly legalistic in their analysis."*

**KEY INDIVIDUALS** Scott Stanton chairs the firm's global corporate group from its San Diego office.

## Vinson & Elkins LLP
See profile on p.2459

**THE FIRM** Unquestionably a leader in the oil and gas field, Vinson & Elkins also houses an energetic and talented bench of corporate attorneys in its Texas, New York, California and DC offices. Recent high-level mandates have included acting for The Shaw Group on its $3 billion merger with Chicago Bridge & Iron as well as the sale of its chemicals division to Paris-based Technip. It also represented Dart Container in the $1 billion purchase of Solo Cup, coordinating with the firm's solid antitrust, tax, employee benefits and executive compensation teams on both transactions.

**Sources say:** *"Excellent. They've been very strong as a firm and provide very high-quality service; they're responsive, thoughtful and they know the market very well."*

**KEY INDIVIDUALS** Head of the M&A and private equity group Keith Fullenweider is based in the Houston office.

## Willkie Farr & Gallagher LLP
See profile on p.2016

**THE FIRM** This highly rated practice operates out of New York and Washington, DC strongholds, servicing an enviable list of corporate clients such as Ventas, Insight Venture Partners and Allied World Assurance. It is equally comfortable acting for buyers, sellers, investors and financial advisers, and covers the full range of transactions. Its industry specializations include insurance, REITs and communications; it recently demonstrated its abilities in the latter through its representation of Telcordia Technologies, Warburg Pincus and Providence Equity Partners in the $1.15 billion sale of Telcordia to Ericsson.

**Client Service** *"The team gives us a level of responsiveness and professionalism with a focus on being trusted advisers to us that I think is unmatched. What differentiates Willkie for me is really the personalization and the feeling that we're one of their premier clients – we may not be but they sure make us feel like we are."*

**KEY INDIVIDUALS** Steven Seidman and David Boston cochair the M&A group from the New York office.

## Band 1
## Corporate/M&A: Highly Regarded

## Dechert LLP
See profile on p.1969

**THE FIRM** Successful international expansion bolsters Dechert's standing in the US corporate market this year, increasing its appeal to a global client base. The practice concentrates its efforts on the financial services, life sciences and healthcare sectors, as demonstrated by its impressively full deal list, which features mandates from the likes of Dow Chemical, Celgene and Monster Worldwide. A notable highlight was acting on behalf of Siemens in its acquisition of eMeter, showcasing the team's technical and cross-border abilities.

**Sources say:** *"They have worked very hard. They are smart and consistent, and most importantly, down-to-earth."*

**KEY INDIVIDUALS** Mark Thierfelder spearheads the New York practice, while Henry Nassau in the firm's Philadelphia base is a key contact.

## Goodwin Procter LLP
See profile on p.1522

**THE FIRM** Working out of seven nationwide offices, this native Boston firm has significant coverage of the prime commercial centers. It represents clients drawn from the private equity, life sciences and technology sectors, as well as financial institutions such as Boston Private Financial Holdings. Zoll Medical, a client of the firm from its inception, engaged the team to act on its $2.2 billion sale to Japanese manufacturer Asahi Kasei.

**Sources say:** *"I found the firm to be exceptional at all levels."*

**KEY INDIVIDUALS** Chair of the M&A and corporate governance practice at Goodwin Procter, Joseph Johnson is a key contact.

## Morgan, Lewis & Bockius LLP
See profile on p.2246

**THE FIRM** The majority of corporate work handled by this firm passes through its Philadelphia and New York offices, although clients benefit from the resources of the 22 other offices of its impressive global network. The practice represents a wide variety of market participants, counting Apollo, Ares Capital and Pearson among its enviable client roster. Of the transactions completed this year, the representation of ConocoPhillips in the $1.15 billion sale of its interest in Seaway Crude Pipeline Company has been a highlight for these attorneys and reflects their capabilities in the energy sector.

**Sources say:** *"They are knowledgeable people who are in touch with the sector and show good subject matter expertise. Very professional."*

**KEY INDIVIDUALS** Richard Aldridge in Philadelphia and Steven Navarro in New York are cochairs of the practice and key contacts.

## White & Case LLP
See profile on p.451

**THE FIRM** This firm fields a highly integrated corporate group out of its New York stronghold, acting on behalf of major players such as ICBC, Disney and Calpine in complex M&A and restructuring transactions. In a highly publicized transaction, the team recently represented Sony in its $2.2 billion acquisition of EMI Music Publishing from Citi, evincing its undeniable talent in market-leading transactional activity.

**Sources say:** *"They deliver, they're trustworthy, and they provide a seamless process and end-to-end service that is well coordinated with great communication."*

**KEY INDIVIDUALS** Global heads of the M&A practice John Reiss and Oliver Brahmst are key contacts based in New York.

## Wilson Sonsini Goodrich & Rosati
See profile on p.700

**THE FIRM** Originating in Palo Alto, this West Coast stalwart has successfully gained recognition as a driving force in nationwide M&A, ably competing against some of the most established East Coast firms in the market. The technology industry continues to be a key area of concentration for this vibrant practice, with names such as Electronic Arts, LinkedIn and Zipmark appearing on its illustrious client roster. Its lawyers represented Bank of America as financial adviser on several transactions recently, including the $1.3 billion merger of Ardea Biosciences with AstraZeneca.

**Sources say:** *"They're very oriented to practicality; they don't really get hung up on a lot of arcane lawyer points and can see the bigger picture." "Strengths are their knowledge of the subject matter; they're experts."*

**KEY INDIVIDUALS** Co-managing partner of the firm Jack Sheridan is based out of the firm's Palo Alto office.

## Band 2
## Corporate/M&A: Highly Regarded

## Bingham McCutchen LLP
See profile on p.1515

**THE FIRM** Six offices across the country comprise Bingham's acclaimed corporate group, with expertise located on both the East and West Coasts. By virtue of its leading technology practice, lawyers have been involved in numerous lucrative deals in the industry of late, for example representing NetLogic Microsystems in its sale to Broadcom for $3.7 billion. Other A-list clients include Oracle and Honeywell. Financial services M&A and Asia-based deals are also key strengths of this group.

**Sources say:** *"Excellent. They're extremely efficient, analytical and strategic. Very good at distilling the legal matters and separating the business matters. They don't create barriers to getting deals done."*

**KEY INDIVIDUALS** Boston-based Steven Browne and David Robbins in Los Angeles are cochairs of the corporate practice.

## Cadwalader, Wickersham & Taft LLP
See profile on p.438

**THE FIRM** The selling point of this practice is the impressive breadth of experience accumulated by its talented practitioners across the full spectrum of M&A matters. Lawyers are able to offer tailored guidance to a sophisticated client base which includes Elan Corporation, Barclays and JPMorgan. The team recently presided over the $372 million acquisition of Navilyst Medical by medical manufacturer client AngioDynamics, supplementing its advice with guidance from core related areas such as tax and antitrust.

**Sources say:** *"They have great substantive expertise and tend to keep the people working on your matters relatively streamlined. The team really immerses itself in our transactions."*

**KEY INDIVIDUALS** New York-based Louis Bevilacqua heads the corporate practice here.

### DLA Piper LLP (US)
See profile on p.1971

**THE FIRM** DLA Piper remains a popular choice for major corporations throughout the country, offering expertise on the ground in the nation's principal corporate centers and integrating effectively across its global platform. Lawyers have demonstrated their acumen in the pharmaceutical space through their representation of Human Genome Sciences throughout its sale to GlaxoSmithKline for $3.6 billion. Key clients also include Pfizer and W.P. Carey.

**Sources say:** *"They're able to coordinate knowledge across their firm very efficiently and seamlessly. They are able to marshal their resources very quickly."*

**KEY INDIVIDUALS** Chair of the M&A practice Jonathan Klein operates from the New York office, while Jay Rains in San Diego and Jay Smith in Baltimore are key contacts.

### Greenberg Traurig, LLP
See profile on p.1024

**THE FIRM** Miami and New York are this firm's corporate strongholds, ably supported by a broad geographic spread of teams throughout the country. Well respected in the market, this group consistently draws in large mandates from clients such as Deutsche Bank Securities, Berggruen Holdings and Bank of America Merrill Lynch. The team is noted for its representation of investment banks as financial adviser on high-value deals. It also holds its own on complex company-side mandates, such as the purchase of over 2,000 tower sites in the USA and Central America by client SBA Communications for some $1.093 billion.

**Client Service** *"They are a large firm, but some of their partners operate like small firms and provide a very personalized approach."*

**KEY INDIVIDUALS** Global M&A cochair David Schwartzbaum is a key contact for the practice.

### McDermott Will & Emery LLP
See profile on p.1258

**THE FIRM** Thriving in the face of challenging market conditions, this Chicago-headquartered firm is an attractive choice for players in the middle and upper-middle market. Its strong healthcare focus provides it with healthy deal flow from names like Merck and Siegfried, and it is also gaining substantial traction representing private equity firms such as The ComVest Group and H.I.G. Capital.

Lawyers have additionally found themselves occupied on deals originating from the life sciences, metals and mining and sports law sectors of late.

**Sources say:** *"There are many talented law firms in our space, but relationships and responsiveness are very important and, in this regard, McDermott is excellent." "They're team players. Very knowledgeable and they don't hoard work, they spread it among their team."*

**KEY INDIVIDUALS** David Goldman, head of the global corporate practice, is a valuable contact.

### Proskauer Rose LLP
See profile on p.2001

**THE FIRM** Proskauer's robust M&A team operates out of its New York, Los Angeles and Washington, DC offices. The group has carved out an excellent position in the national landscape, attracting a number of multibillion-dollar mandates from notable names such as Ares Management, Neuberger Berman and Arkema. This past year has seen lawyers engaged on the $2.95 billion merger of two major REITs, representing American Realty Capital Trust across the table from Realty Income Trust.

**Sources say:** *"Excellent interface, superb mastery of the other party's requirements and excellent integration of the many skills that are required in an M&A deal."*

**KEY INDIVIDUALS** Michael Woronoff heads the firm's Los Angeles office and co-heads the global M&A group with New York-based Ron Papa.

## Band 3
## Corporate/M&A: Highly Regarded

### Bracewell & Giuliani LLP
See profile on p.2429

**THE FIRM** This Texas energy stalwart has a shining track record representing energy industry clients such as Apache, Chesapeake Energy and Kinder Morgan. Its New York team handles a healthy volume of distressed transaction work, integrating smoothly with the firm's restructuring team to best serve clients. Besides its highly publicized role as counsel to Kinder Morgan in its $38 billion acquisition – including debt – of El Paso, the team has also acted for Apache throughout its purchase of Cordillera Energy Partners for $2.85 billion.

**Sources say:** *"They are highly competent attorneys who understand how to contextualize the legal needs within the overall transaction, including the complexity and value of the transaction."*

**KEY INDIVIDUALS** Greg Bopp heads the firm's business and regulatory department from Houston, and Rob Tretter is a key contact in the firm's New York office.

### Covington & Burling LLP
See profile on p.441

**THE FIRM** Fielding strong teams out of its New York and Washington, DC offices, Covington & Burling is well placed to act on a range of transactions that are notable for their complexity as well as their dollar value. The group has a strong foothold in the life sciences, technology, media

and energy sectors, and clients benefit from high levels of integration with the firm's stellar regulatory practice. SandRidge Energy recently sought the advice of this team on its $1.275 billion acquisition of Dynamic Offshore Resources and related financing arrangements of $725 million.

**Commercial Awareness** *"Experts in this field. Very willing to listen to a company's business needs and strategies, also taking into account different companies' risk profiles and tailoring their advice."*

**KEY INDIVIDUALS** New York-based Scott Smith and Catherine Dargan in Washington, DC are the cochairs of the M&A practice here.

### Jenner & Block LLP
See profile on p.1252

**THE FIRM** Recent engagements by household names General Dynamics, News Corporation and Hertz exemplify Jenner & Block's strong standing in the national corporate arena. Based out of the firm's Chicago, Los Angeles, Washington, DC and New York offices, the group ably handles the full range of transactional activity. Of the deals completed this past year, the representation of GM in a $5.5 billion share repurchase transaction stands out as among the most significant. During the transaction, the team demonstrated its ability to act effectively on a cross-disciplinary basis.

**KEY INDIVIDUALS** Chicago-based Joseph Gromacki is chair of the firm's corporate practice and Wesley Fredericks leads the New York corporate practice.

### K&L Gates
See profile on p.2245

**THE FIRM** K&L Gates runs a highly integrated corporate practice out of its 21 nationwide offices, calling upon the resources of its tremendous international network as required. Its broad geographic spread lends itself to the representation of numerous foreign-based companies such as Renren, the Chinese social networking company. The group's most recent highlights include acting on behalf of State Street Bank & Trust on the $26 billion pension plan offered by GM to certain salaried retirees.

**Sources say:** *"I think the firm is extremely professional in its approach and the quality of its work is top-notch. They make you feel as though they are working with you and not for you, a subtle but important difference."*

**KEY INDIVIDUALS** Robert Zinn is the corporate practice area leader, based out of the firm's New York and Pittsburgh offices.

### King & Spalding LLP
See profile on p.445

**THE FIRM** Originating in Georgia, this midmarket-focused firm has recently experienced buoyant levels of transactional activity across its Atlanta base and in its New York, Washington, DC, California and Texas offices. Significant representations of late have included acting for Winn-Dixie on its merger with Bi-Lo, a $560 million deal. The Texas practice is focused on the vibrant energy industry in the state and counts Endicott Biofuels and Haddington Energy Partners among its client roster.

**Sources say:** *"They do a very good job of keeping the core team on the transaction very tight, making sure the client doesn't feel like they're getting lost among thousands of lawyers. You feel like you're getting personal attention."*

**KEY INDIVIDUALS** Atlanta-based Ray Baltz heads the firm's corporate department.

## Paul Hastings LLP
See profile on p.1996

**THE FIRM** A favorite with clients in the real estate, technology and healthcare industries, Paul Hastings is committed to the consummate provision of cross-border services, regularly utilizing the talents of its corporate attorneys

housed across 18 global offices. It was recently engaged to act as counsel to DDi Corp on its $268 million sale to Viasystems Group. Noteworthy clients include Ardea Biosciences, Madison Capital and The Home Depot.

**Client Service** *"They are available 24/7 and simply do not miss deadlines. They remain a go-to firm for us based on the combination of skill, speed, practicality and cost."*

**KEY INDIVIDUALS** Based in the firm's San Diego office, Carl Sanchez serves as the firm's global M&A chair.

## Pillsbury Winthrop Shaw Pittman LLP
See profile on p.2000

**THE FIRM** Pillsbury's corporate lawyers have lately enjoyed an abundance of impressive deals across their New York, North Virginia, California and Washington, DC

offices. One such transaction saw the Silicon Valley team representing Nicira in its sale to VMware for $1.26 billion. The firm's strong technology, life sciences and communications focus provides it with an excellent platform to attract the numerous cutting-edge and innovative clients on its books.

**Client Service** *"Pillsbury was extremely good and focused on achieving results that protected the client. They continually went above the standard that the client expected."*

**KEY INDIVIDUALS** Robert Robbins is a key practice contact based in the Washington, DC office.

# EMPLOYEE BENEFITS & EXECUTIVE COMPENSATION

Commentary about individuals can be found under their firm's paragraph. If the firm has no paragraph (is not ranked) look at Other Notable Practitioners.

| Employee Benefits & Executive Compensation Leading Firms |
| --- |
| **Band 1** |
| Cleary Gottlieb Steen & Hamilton LLP * |
| Groom Law Group * |
| Morgan, Lewis & Bockius LLP * |
| **Band 2** |
| Davis Polk & Wardwell LLP * |
| McDermott Will & Emery LLP * |
| Simpson Thacher & Bartlett LLP * |
| Skadden, Arps, Slate, Meagher & Flom LLP & Affiliates * |
| Steptoe & Johnson LLP |
| Sullivan & Cromwell LLP * |
| **Band 3** |
| Covington & Burling LLP * |
| Latham & Watkins LLP * |
| Proskauer Rose LLP * |
| **Band 4** |
| Mayer Brown LLP * |
| Ropes & Gray LLP * |
| Sidley Austin LLP * |

*The editorial is in alphabetical order by firm name.*

## Band 1

### Cleary Gottlieb Steen & Hamilton LLP
See profile on p.1963

**THE FIRM** Cleary Gottlieb stands out for its prominence in four main areas: executive compensation, private equity, ERISA fiduciary matters and M&A. The team boasts an impressive client list which features the likes of banking powerhouses Barclays, BNP Paribas and Deutsche Bank, as well as global corporations such as McDonald's. In recent highlights the New York-based firm advised Google on its acquisition of Motorola Mobility, and represented

Mexican food giant Grupo Bimbo in its deal to buy the bakery assets of Sara Lee.

**Sources say:** *"A very high-quality firm and practice."*

**KEY INDIVIDUALS** The eminent **Brick Susko** (see p.415) has a broad skill set, with work including the tax and fiduciary aspects of executive compensation as they relate to incentives such as stock options and golden parachutes. Of late, he has advised a number of large financial groups on ERISA fiduciary matters. **Arthur Kohn** (see p.348) advises on pension compliance and executive compensation, acting for clients such as McDonald's and American Express. *"He is absolutely first-rate,"* say sources.

### Groom Law Group
See profile on p.915

**THE FIRM** Groom Law Group remains at the forefront of the employee benefits field in the USA. Operating out of DC, the firm has a great platform from which to influence policy and legislation, and is widely acknowledged as a go-to group for advice on fiduciary responsibility, plan design, funding and restructuring, as well as multiemployer and government plans. It represents clients including Pfizer, Toshiba and the American Benefits Council in a wide array of benefits issues.

**Sources say:** *"They provide excellent service. They are extremely knowledgeable, quick to respond, focused on our long-term goals and careful about spending our money."*

**KEY INDIVIDUALS Gary Ford** (see p.315) has *"unmatched experience"* in the employee benefits field, according to interviewees. He specializes in plan funding and restructuring and is noted for his Pension Benefits Guaranty Corporation (PBGC) work. He regularly advises on the consequences and implications of bankruptcies for benefit plans. **Louis Mazawey** (see p.363) is described as *"a careful and thoughtful lawyer"* by his peers. He heads the group's plan design and taxation practice, and advises a range of clients, including Fortune 100 companies, on the inception and upkeep of their plans. He has a wide range

of experience in this area, which includes advising on employee stock ownership and qualified plans.

### Morgan, Lewis & Bockius LLP
See profile on p.2246

**THE FIRM** This highly regarded practice group is acclaimed for its national footprint and manpower, and has a growing reputation for its representation of senior management in the context of large transactions. Notably, the firm advised the management of the Kenexa Group on the executive compensation and employee benefits aspects of its acquisition by IBM. It is also singled out for its strength in ERISA fiduciary matters. Other key clients include Aramark, Google and Goldman Sachs.

**Sources say:** *"They coordinate well between offices – they bring in the best of the best. They are down to earth and fun to work with, and treat our employees well."*

**KEY INDIVIDUALS** Working out of the firm's Palo Alto office, **James DiBernardo** (see p.632) is praised for his responsiveness and subject matter expertise. He focuses on deferred and equity compensation, and related tax and securities issues. Recent highlights include advising Gilead Sciences in relation to various acquisitions of both private and public entities.

## Band 2

### Davis Polk & Wardwell LLP
See profile on p.442

**THE FIRM** This New York-based group is best known for its focus on transactional work, and stands out for its knowledge and experience across a broad range of deal types. Recent work of note includes representing Japan's Daikin Industries in the compensation and benefits issues surrounding its $3.7 billion acquisition of Goodman Global, and advising Santander México on its $4.1 billion global IPO. Other clients include oil and gas giant ExxonMobil and PepsiCo.

*The editorial is in alphabetical order by firm name.*

**Sources say:** *"Their performance is top-notch. They are leaders in the field, stay on top of changes and give very smart and practical advice."*
**KEY INDIVIDUALS Edmond FitzGerald** (see p.313) is *"an outstanding lawyer, who is very smart and has real talent."* He has significant experience acting for companies, boards and compensation committees on the creation of employment agreements, equity, and deferred compensation and incentive plans. He recently represented Campbell's in its $1.55 billion acquisition of Bolthouse Farms.

## McDermott Will & Emery LLP
See profile on p.1258

**THE FIRM** This firm has a huge amount of experience and expertise within its employee benefits practice. It is recognized for its focus on plan design and administration, including both 401(k) and defined benefit plans. The group also advises on all manner of ERISA litigation. Highlights include representing Fortune Brands in the separation of its spirits and home and security businesses, including the division of retirement assets of more than $3 billion.
**Sources say:** *"They're always ahead of the curve."*
**KEY INDIVIDUALS Andrew Liazos** (see p.1500) advises on the securities and tax issues surrounding executive compensation. Notable work includes acting for Demoulas Supermarkets in connection with the dismissal of a lawsuit concerning an alleged breach of fiduciary duty. Sources say: *"Andrew is very bright and passionate about his area of expertise."*

## Simpson Thacher & Bartlett LLP
See profile on p.2006

**THE FIRM** The group is renowned for its transactions-based benefits and compensation work for private equity groups. The team advises on the issues arising from the public offerings of portfolio companies, as well as on the creation and implementation of equity compensation schemes for senior executives. Recent highlights include representing The Blackstone Group in a deal worth approximately $2 billion to acquire Vivint. The group also acts for public companies such as Sealy and Del Monte.
**KEY INDIVIDUALS Brian Robbins** (see p.1931) heads the firm's employee benefits and executive compensation practice, and is considered an *"excellent lawyer"* by peers. He advises both public and private entities on benefits, compensation and ERISA matters and recently acted for the Eaton Corporation on its $11.8 billion cross-border acquisition of Cooper Industries.

## Skadden, Arps, Slate, Meagher & Flom LLP & Affiliates
See profile on p.2008

**THE FIRM** This firm is highly rated for its representation of private equity groups and public companies in a wide range of M&A-related executive compensation and employee benefits matters. Highlights include advising Sprint Nextel on the benefits and compensation issues arising from its sale of a 70% stake to Japan's Softbank. The firm also acted for RailAmerica on its $2.8 billion merger with Genesee & Wyoming.
**Sources say:** *"They are exceptionally creative, very client-focused and able to deliver very complicated projects on very tight deadlines."*
**KEY INDIVIDUALS Regina Olshan** (see p.1925) is the head of the firm's global employee benefits and executive compensation practice. Noted for her *"unquestionable expertise," "good judgment, sound legal advice and great commercial awareness,"* she focuses on the regulatory aspects of benefits and compensation. **Joseph Yaffe** (see p.673) heads the firm's West Coast practice from Palo Alto,

and regularly advises high-profile new media and technology executives. Sources laud him as a *"patient yet effective negotiator."*

## Steptoe & Johnson LLP

**THE FIRM** This prominent DC-based firm is well known for its expertise in employee benefits and ERISA law, advising on Title I, Title II, Title IV and public plans. The team has substantial experience advising on IRS and DOL reviews and government investigations, as well as providing counsel to a range of interests, including plan sponsors, fiduciaries, banks and others. Key clients include the National Electrical Benefit Fund, Deutsche Bank and Morgan Stanley. The firm also represents the pension plans of several states.
**KEY INDIVIDUALS Melanie Nussdorf** is described as a *"magnificent lawyer,"* and a *"star in terms of breadth of practice and high-profile projects."* She focuses on ERISA fiduciary matters, and has recently worked with the DOL on exemptions relating to Dodd-Frank.

## Sullivan & Cromwell LLP
See profile on p.2011

**THE FIRM** This New York-based firm has built a highly successful practice focusing on transactional benefits and compensation work. The team has a great deal of M&A experience and regularly advises on related issues such as pension liabilities and the compensation of senior executives. In recent highlights, it advised Ally Financial on the divestiture of its international operations. Other clients include ING and Goldman Sachs.
**Sources say:** *"The level of expertise and responsiveness is incredible."*
**KEY INDIVIDUALS** Of counsel **Max Schwartz** (see p.402) handles corporate governance and tax matters relating to executive compensation, and wins praise for both his *"business-oriented focus"* and *"great intellect."* He continues to advise the compensation committee of Activision Blizzard on a wide range of executive compensation matters. **Marc Trevino** (see p.1947) is the managing partner of the firm's employee benefits and executive compensation practice. Clients appreciate his creative approach, while peers laud him as a *"leader of the next generation."* He has an extensive practice which covers governance and regulatory issues, and recently acted for AIG on a number of matters, including the appointment of its executive chairman.

### Band 3

## Covington & Burling LLP
See profile on p.441

**THE FIRM** This group is well regarded for its expertise across the full range of employee benefits matters. The group covers areas such as taxation, fiduciary responsibility and healthcare plans, and is noted for its involvement in regulatory matters and legislative development. The firm recently acted as ERISA counsel to Verizon on the transfer of $7.5 billion in pension liabilities to Prudential Financial.

*The editorial is in alphabetical order by firm name.*

**Sources say:** *"They provide a good service. They're responsive, smart, and think outside the box."*
**KEY INDIVIDUALS** Amy Moore is the head of the department. She is based in DC.

## Latham & Watkins LLP
See profile on p.446

**THE FIRM** This global law firm has a flourishing compensation and benefits practice in the USA. It has a strong deal-based practice, with a focus on executive incentive plans and a great deal of experience working with both public companies and private equity groups. Recent highlights saw the team advise Manchester United on disclosure and complex compensation issues relating to the English soccer team's IPO on the NYSE.
**Sources say:** *"The group is excellent – knowledgeable and responsive."*
**KEY INDIVIDUALS Jim Barrall** is described as *"one of the best executive compensation lawyers in the entire country."* He is the department's global chair, and offers extensive expertise in executive compensation, with a noted specialty in regulatory and disclosure issues. He recently advised Medicis Pharmaceutical on its $2.6 billion acquisition by Valeant Pharmaceuticals.

## Proskauer Rose LLP
See profile on p.2001

**THE FIRM** This highly regarded New York group focuses on representing Fortune 500 companies in significant M&A deals, while also offering nontransactional advice to boards, compensation committees and individual executives. In recent highlights, the group advised the compensation committee of Yahoo! on the high-profile hiring of Marissa Mayer from Google.
**Sources say:** *"A very deep firm."*
**KEY INDIVIDUALS Michael Sirkin** is *"a true benefits man,"* who focuses on nonqualified arrangements relating to executive compensation as well as stock option plan design. He recently advised the management of Neuberger Berman as it sought to spin the group off from Lehman Brothers. One peer commented: *"If I were a CEO, I'd want him on my side."* Based in DC, **Paul Hamburger** co-heads the firm's employee benefits, executive compensation and ERISA practice. Described as *"very skilled"* by peers for his expertise in ERISA law, he advises clients on a range of benefits issues, with a focus on tax-qualified retirement plans.

## Band 4

## Mayer Brown LLP
See profile on p.1257

**THE FIRM** This firm focuses on the representation of tax-exempt employers and Fortune 500 companies. The team specializes in ERISA fiduciary matters as well as transactional benefits and compensation work. Recent highlights include advising Caterpillar on its acquisition of Bucyrus International. Other clients include Prologis, Northern Trust and American Realty Advisors.

**Sources say:** *"Top-notch on service, awareness and operations."*
**KEY INDIVIDUALS** Maureen Gorman is a key contact.

## Ropes & Gray LLP
See profile on p.1528

**THE FIRM** This well-established team is recognized for its all-encompassing benefits practice, with broad expertise covering ESOP and 401(k) plans as well as executive compensation. The firm regularly advises tax-exempt employers such as Harvard University and Children's Hospital Boston, as well as private equity firms including Bain Capital and Thomas H Lee Partners. It recently represented TPG Capital in relation to the executive compensation and employee benefits aspects of its $1.9 billion acquisition of Par Pharmaceuticals.
**Sources say:** *"They are wonderful partners. Very qualified, and capable of providing support."*
**KEY INDIVIDUALS Jonathan Zorn** heads the firm's ERISA practice, and is praised by peers for his work in this area. He continues to advise the employee benefits committee and master trust of the Tribune Company relating to ongoing ERISA concerns arising from its 2007 bankruptcy filing. **Peter Rosenberg** handles the full spectrum of ERISA work, including compliance and prohibited transactions. He has significant expertise counseling private equity groups on fund structure relating to ERISA compliance, and recently advised Bain Capital on the formation of a seed investment fund.

## Sidley Austin LLP
See profile on p.1264

**THE FIRM** This well-known firm has a wide range of executive compensation and employee benefits expertise, which covers qualified retirement plans, welfare plans, ERISA litigation and executive compensation. The team acts as primary outside counsel for eBay, and recently advised the company on the reorganization of its equity compensation plans. Other notable clients include Aon and AT&T.
**KEY INDIVIDUALS Priscilla Ryan** (see p.1229) is a *"very good and careful lawyer,"* who is singled out for her client relationship skills. Working out of Chicago, she focuses on employee benefits matters, including plan design and implementation. She recently advised RR Donnelly & Sons in connection with the new requirements imposed on group health plans by the Patient Protection and Affordable Care Act.

## Other Notable Practitioners

**Lawrence Cagney** is the chair of the employee benefits and executive compensation practice at Debevoise & Plimpton LLP. Considered an *"outstanding attorney"* by other practitioners, his practice focuses on structuring compensation plans for public and private entities. **Broni Grala** (see p.325) of Cadwalader, Wickersham & Taft LLP is nationally recognized for his eminence in the ERISA arena. Sources say: *"He is at the top level of the profession – we all value him tremendously."* He recently advised BlackRock on the

ERISA implications of its acquisition of Barclays Global Investors. **Susan Serota** of Pillsbury Winthrop Shaw Pittman LLP is acclaimed for the depth and breadth of her ERISA experience. *"She is extraordinary,"* sources agree. She also advises on cross-border M&A and equity compensation plans. **John Cleary** (see p.1488) of Goodwin Procter LLP *"has a very good understanding of the law, and can give you insight that very few people can in terms of novel and new issues."* He is experienced in matters relating to Title I of ERISA, as well as transactional corporate and real estate work. He recently advised The Bank of New York Mellon on ERISA issues relating to new DOL regulations. **Andrew Oringer** (see p.380) is the leader of the national fiduciary practice group at Dechert LLP. Based in New York, he regularly advises clients on benefits issues relating to 401(k), health and welfare plans, and ERISA. **Robert Fleder** (see p.1893) of Paul, Weiss, Rifkind, Wharton & Garrison LLP is noted for his work advising private equity groups on ERISA fiduciary matters. He also advises on transactions, and recently acted for RSC Holdings on its merger with United Rentals. *"He is an excellent lawyer,"* say sources. Vice chair of the firm's employee benefits and executive compensation practice, **Pamela Baker** (see p.1197) of Dentons is highly regarded by peers. *"She is an awfully good lawyer,"* said one source, while another added: *"She is the most prolific writer in the EBEC area."* **Ethan Lipsig** of Paul Hastings LLP is *"one of the best ERISA lawyers in the USA,"* sources say. Clients appreciate his *"personal touch"* and ability to clearly explain difficult issues. A recent highlight saw him advise a group of US pension funds in relation to European tax rebates. **Edward Burmeister** (see p.626) of Baker & McKenzie specializes in executive and equity compensation. His practice has an international component, and he regularly advises multinational companies on global equity compensation. **Gregory Brown** of Katten Muchin Rosenman LLP is *"one of the leading ESOP lawyers in Illinois,"* according to interviewees. His expertise extends across the entire ERISA arena, and he is often sought out for his advice on ERISA fiduciary matters. **Marian Tse** (see p.1512) of Goodwin Procter LLP is highlighted for her experience in the drafting and implementation of compensation plans, as well as related tax and securities issues. Work of note includes representing Brookline Bancorp in its acquisition of Bancorp Rhode Island. **Michael Segal** (see p.1939) of Wachtell, Lipton, Rosen & Katz counsels clients on the benefits and compensation implications of M&A and joint ventures. He is widely praised by peers, who describe him as a *"terrific lawyer."* **Alden Bianchi** (see p.1485) of Mintz Levin Cohn Ferris Glovsky and Popeo PC specializes in healthcare benefits, and also advises on standard benefits issues, retirement plans and stock options. Client praise his level of service, saying he is *"a pleasure to deal with – thoughtful, and a good listener."* **Robert Stucker** (see p.1234) of Vedder Price PC acts for individuals, boards and compensation committees on executive compensation matters in both a transactional and nontransactional context. Peers note that he is *"very effective for his clients."* He recently advised Hillshire Brands on the employment agreement for its new CEO.

# ENERGY & NATURAL RESOURCES

Electricity (Finance) p.75; Electricity (Regulatory & Litigation) p.75; Electricity (Transactional) p.77; Mining & Metals (Transactional) p.77; Nuclear (Regulatory & Litigation) p.77; Oil & Gas (Regulatory & Litigation) p.78; Oil & Gas (Transactional) p.79

Commentary about individuals can be found under their firm's paragraph. If the firm has no paragraph (is not ranked) look at Other Notable Practitioners.

## Energy: Electricity (Regulatory & Litigation)
### Leading Firms

**Band 1**
Skadden, Arps, Slate, Meagher & Flom LLP & Affiliates *
Steptoe & Johnson LLP

**Band 2**
King & Spalding LLP *
Van Ness Feldman LLP *

**Band 3**
Alston & Bird LLP *
Dickstein Shapiro LLP *
Latham & Watkins LLP *
Troutman Sanders LLP
White & Case LLP *
Wright & Talisman PC

**Band 4**
Bracewell & Giuliani LLP *
Covington & Burling LLP *
Hunton & Williams LLP *
Morgan, Lewis & Bockius LLP *
Sutherland Asbill & Brennan LLP
Vinson & Elkins LLP *
Winston & Strawn LLP *

**Band 5**
Akin Gump Strauss Hauer & Feld LLP *
Andrews Kurth LLP *
Cadwalader, Wickersham & Taft LLP *
Chadbourne & Parke LLP *
Dentons *
Hogan Lovells US LLP
Jones Day *
K&L Gates *
Miller, Balis & O'Neil, PC
Stinson Morrison Hecker LLP
Thompson Coburn LLP

*Indicates firm / individual with profile.*
*Alphabetical order within each band. Band 1 is the highest.*

*The editorial is in alphabetical order by firm name.*

## Akin Gump Strauss Hauer & Feld LLP
See profile on p.904

**THE FIRM** This firm wins acclaim from clients for its timely completion of transactions and dedication to their business needs. It has a particularly prominent oil and gas practice, members of which act on a range of big-ticket transactions for an enviable roster of clients including Baker Hughes, El Paso Pipeline Partners and Genesis Energy. Its recent representation of Memorial Production Partners drew on its securities expertise, and the group also

## Energy: Electricity (Finance)
### Leading Individuals

| **Band 1** | |
|---|---|
| Baxter David | *Pillsbury Winthrop Shaw Pittman LLP* |
| Delaney Jeffrey J | *Pillsbury Winthrop Shaw Pittman LLP* |
| Ellis Emmett N | *Hunton & Williams LLP* * |
| Fitzpatrick Jr Michael F | *Hunton & Williams LLP* * |
| Giblin Jr Thomas P | *Morgan, Lewis & Bockius LLP* * |
| O'Brien Peter | *Hunton & Williams LLP* * |
| Reger Jr Robert J | *Morgan, Lewis & Bockius LLP* * |
| Rod Jonathan | *Latham & Watkins LLP* |
| Terrell J Anthony | *Pillsbury Winthrop Shaw Pittman LLP* |

advised Laredo Petroleum on its $1 billion acquisition of an oil and gas exploration company. On the electricity side, the energy team is highly praised for its strong FERC capabilities, which have been bolstered by the recent hire of several attorneys with previous experience of working for the regulatory body.

**Client Service** *"Their client service is exceptional – we can just pick up the phone and speak to a partner right away."*
**KEY INDIVIDUALS** Christine LaFollette (see p.2400) is hailed as *"a consummate professional in all respects: she consistently assembles a working team of Akin Gump professionals necessary to fulfill any needs of the client in an efficient and timely manner."* LaFollette and her team recently represented Laredo Petroleum in the aforementioned matter, and also advised the Conflicts Committee of Exterran Partners on its acquisition of assets worth some $184 million. **Suedeen Kelly** (see p.344) is one of three prominent attorneys who have recently moved to the firm from Patton Boggs. The former FERC commissioner receives glowing feedback from sources who praise her *"substantial energy policy experience,"* *"great litigation skills"* and responsiveness. In the words of a client, *"she is terrific – she is very bright, articulate and very well informed about industry issues, and has excellent judgment."* **George Cannon** (see p.291) has also recently joined the firm from Patton Boggs, bringing with him a broad array of expertise, and is well versed in the gamut of regulatory issues arising out of acquisitions, divestitures and financings. As one client notes, *"he has impressed our team with his determination and ability to master information and to translate his understanding and the issues into language that can be understood in a legal context."* The *"very accomplished"* **Cynthia Marlette** (see p.361) debuts in the rankings this year after receiving universal praise from peers and clients alike. She is another lawyer who was formerly part of the Patton Boggs team, and her previous substantial experience as general counsel at FERC has left her in good stead to advise

| **Recommended for Client Service** | |
|---|---|
| **Nationwide** | |
| Akin Gump Strauss Hauer & Feld LLP | King & Spalding LLP |
| Baker Botts LLP | Morgan, Lewis & Bockius LLP |
| Bracewell & Giuliani LLP | Steptoe & Johnson LLP |
| Gardere Wynne Sewell LLP | Vinson & Elkins LLP |
| Hogan Lovells US LLP | Wright & Talisman PC |

| **Recommended for Commercial Awareness** | |
|---|---|
| **Nationwide** | |
| Bracewell & Giuliani LLP | Morgan, Lewis & Bockius LLP |
| Chadbourne & Parke LLP | Simpson Thacher & Bartlett LLP |
| Dentons | |
| K&L Gates | Sutherland Asbill & Brennan LLP |

electricity clients on the full range of regulatory and policy concerns.

## Alston & Bird LLP
See profile on p.1102

**THE FIRM** Alston & Bird earns unanimous client and peer praise for its comprehensive regulatory practice, specifically its ability to handle transmission-related matters. The team regularly acts for some of the largest industry participants, including FirstEnergy, California ISO and enXco. Notably, it recently assisted National Grid with making FERC applications in order to obtain permissions concerning a $2 billion transmission line project.
**Sources say:** *"The attorneys are great to work with, smart, and possess a very strong understanding of the industry."*
**KEY INDIVIDUALS** Peers have a *"very high opinion"* of *"excellent lawyer"* **Kenneth Jaffe** (see p.340), while clients applaud him for his *"broad knowledge of FERC rules and precedent and his ability to offer creative solutions to problems."* Recent examples of his work include leading the team on the National Grid matter, and he is also representing FirstEnergy in a number of FERC and appellate matters. *"Great lawyer and great gentleman"* **Sean Atkins** (see p.275) continues to represent a range of electric utilities in complex matters and is currently helping California ISO with regulatory compliance and litigation arising out of a transmission planning matter.

## Andrews Kurth LLP
See profile on p.2426

**THE FIRM** This longstanding firm is widely recognized for its leading energy practice. The team receives consistently positive feedback for its expertise in the oil and gas space, with clients particularly quick to commend its advice on FERC regulatory concerns as well as its ability to handle large-scale and complex transactions including

## Energy: Electricity (Regulatory & Litigation)
### Leading Individuals

**Star individuals**

| | |
|---|---|
| Naeve Clifford M | Skadden, Arps, Slate, Meagher & Flom * |

**Band 1**

| | |
|---|---|
| Eisenstat Larry | Dickstein Shapiro LLP * |
| Estes III John N | Skadden, Arps, Slate, Meagher & Flom * |
| Green Douglas G | Steptoe & Johnson LLP |
| Jaffe Kenneth G | Alston & Bird LLP * |
| Levy Neil L | King & Spalding LLP * |
| Moot John S | Skadden, Arps, Slate, Meagher & Flom * |
| O'Donnell Earle | White & Case LLP * |
| Pantano Paul | Cadwalader, Wickersham & Taft LLP * |
| Raskin David | Steptoe & Johnson LLP |
| Roberts Richard | Steptoe & Johnson LLP |
| Spector Barry S | Wright & Talisman PC |

**Band 2**

| | |
|---|---|
| Acker Lawrence G | Van Ness Feldman LLP * |
| Attanasio Donna | White & Case LLP * |
| Blackburn Thomas | Schiff Hardin LLP (ONP)† |
| Caplan Stuart A | Dentons * |
| Gergen Michael | Latham & Watkins LLP * |
| McGrane John D | Morgan, Lewis & Bockius LLP * |
| Moore Margaret | Van Ness Feldman LLP * |
| Scherman William S | Gibson, Dunn & Crutcher LLP (ONP)† * |
| Schwartz David L | Latham & Watkins LLP * |
| Smith Douglas | Van Ness Feldman LLP * |
| Tewksbury David | King & Spalding LLP * |

**Band 3**

| | |
|---|---|
| Angle Stephen | Vinson & Elkins LLP * |
| Bachman Gary | Van Ness Feldman LLP * |
| Conway Jr William B | Skadden, Arps, Slate, Meagher & Flom * |
| Decker John S | Vinson & Elkins LLP * |
| Doot David T | Day Pitney LLP (ONP)† * |
| Larcamp Daniel | Troutman Sanders LLP |
| Massey William L | Covington & Burling LLP * |
| McCarthy Catherine | Bracewell & Giuliani LLP * |
| McCrea Keith R | Sutherland Asbill & Brennan LLP |
| Norton IV Floyd L | Morgan, Lewis & Bockius LLP * |
| Perlis Mark | Dickstein Shapiro LLP * |
| Podgorsky Arnold | Wright & Talisman PC |
| Reed Wendy N | Wright & Talisman PC |
| Ross Steven | Steptoe & Johnson LLP |
| Shapiro Howard | Van Ness Feldman LLP * |
| Walsh Linda | Hunton & Williams LLP * |
| Wenner Adam | Orrick, Herrington & Sutcliffe LLP |
| Williams Mark C | Bingham McCutchen LLP (ONP)† * |
| Wiseman Kenneth L | Andrews Kurth LLP * |

**Band 4**

| | |
|---|---|
| Barancik Tia S | Sullivan & Cromwell LLP * |

| | |
|---|---|
| Barrowes Brooksany | Baker Botts LLP * |
| Berman Stan | Sidley Austin LLP * |
| Bloom David I | Mayer Brown LLP (ONP)† |
| Bruner Becky M | Davis Wright Tremaine LLP (ONP)† |
| Clair Adrienne E | Stinson Morrison Hecker LLP |
| Fagan Joseph H | Day Pitney LLP (ONP)† * |
| Kaplan Donald | K&L Gates * |
| Kelly Suedeen G. | Akin Gump Strauss Hauer & Feld LLP * |
| King Deanna E | Bracewell & Giuliani LLP * |
| Krupka Catherine M | Sutherland Asbill & Brennan LLP |
| Lehfeldt Richard | Dickstein Shapiro LLP * |
| Lilyestrom John | Hogan Lovells US LLP * |
| Mullins Todd | McGuireWoods LLP (ONP)† |
| Nordhaus Robert | Van Ness Feldman LLP * |
| Reiter Harvey L | Stinson Morrison Hecker LLP |
| Richardson Bruce L | King & Spalding LLP * |
| Rizzo Sandra E | Bracewell & Giuliani LLP * |
| Shapiro Robert | Chadbourne & Parke LLP * |
| Sikora Clifford S | Troutman Sanders LLP |
| Vasile James | Davis Wright Tremaine LLP (ONP)† |
| Walsh Elaine | Baker Botts LLP |
| Watkiss Jeffrey D | McDermott Will & Emery LLP (ONP)† * |
| Wuslich Raymond | Winston & Strawn LLP * |
| Yuffee Michael | Fried, Frank, Harris, Shriver (ONP)† * |

**Band 5**

| | |
|---|---|
| Atkins Sean | Alston & Bird LLP * |
| Bernstein Glen S | Morgan, Lewis & Bockius LLP * |
| Blair Bonnie S | Thompson Coburn LLP |
| Bogorad Cynthia | Spiegel & McDiarmid (ONP)† |
| Cannon Jr George D | Akin Gump Strauss Hauer & Feld LLP * |
| DeGrandis William D | Paul Hastings LLP (ONP)† |
| Fox Paul W | Bracewell & Giuliani LLP * |
| Frank Daniel | Sutherland Asbill & Brennan LLP |
| Gianvecchio Natasha | Latham & Watkins LLP * |
| Hillard Hugh | O'Melveny & Myers LLP (ONP)† |
| Hollis Sheila Slocum | Duane Morris LLP (ONP)† |
| Lawrence Gregory | Cadwalader, Wickersham & Taft LLP * |
| Marlette Cynthia A | Akin Gump Strauss Hauer & Feld LLP * |
| Shafferman Howard H | Ballard Spahr LLP (ONP)† * |
| Statman Alan | Wright & Talisman PC |
| Stough John | Hogan Lovells US LLP * |
| Symons Noel | McGuireWoods LLP (ONP)† |
| Vince Clinton A | Dentons * |
| Warren Wendy | Wright & Talisman PC |

**Up-and-coming individuals**

| | |
|---|---|
| Lim Stephanie | King & Spalding LLP * |
| McNaul Margaret E | Thompson Coburn LLP |

\* Indicates individual with profile.

†ONP = Other Notable Practitioner.

acquisitions, sales and joint ventures. The team recently assisted Hilcorp Resources with the $3.5 billion sale of its shale oil and gas assets to Marathon Oil, and also acted for Bison Pipeline on the regulatory aspects of the development of a $610 million oil and gas pipeline. It also advises high-profile clients such as TransCanada, Kansas Corporation Commission and Midwest ISO on a range of electric power matters.

**Sources say:** "*We have received very good service and high-quality advice and counsel from Andrews Kurth. This is due to having direct access to senior partners who can quickly answer questions and help resolve issues.*"

**KEY INDIVIDUALS** The "*excellent and vastly experienced*" **Michael O'Leary** (see p.2407) regularly handles a range of transactional matters for major energy companies including First Reserve, Cordillera Energy Partners and GSO Capital Partners. **Mark Sundback** (see p.414) is a "*very hard-working, thorough attorney with a deep understanding of FERC regulation, policy and precedent,*" an impressed client notes. He is best known for his work in the interstate pipeline arena, where he continues to advise the likes of Bison Pipeline before FERC. **Kenneth Wiseman** (see p.427) climbs the electricity rankings this year after receiving strong market recognition for his "*in-depth knowledge of FERC procedures.*" He recently teamed up with Sundback to defend TransCanada in FERC proceedings brought against it by numerous parties. A very positive result was achieved for the client, a claim for $50 million in refunds being rejected. Over the past year, **Shemin Proctor** (see p.387) has acted on behalf of Enterprise Products Partners on a $3.3 billion merger with Duncan Energy Partners, and has also represented DCP Midstream Partners in the development of a natural gas processing plant and the acquisition of shale assets. **Thomas Bateman** (see p.280) continues to impress sources with his very active oil and gas transactional practice. He was recently part of the team representing Maritech Resources in the disposal of several offshore assets located in the Gulf of Mexico valued at several million dollars.

## Baker Botts LLP
### See profile on p.2427

**THE FIRM** This group wins accolades for its broad oil and gas capabilities, with strong depth and breadth in both regulatory and transactional matters. Its loyal clients are drawn from all corners of the industry and include high-profile organizations such as ExxonMobil, Shell and Marathon Oil. It specializes in handling complex and high-value disputes and recently represented Murphy Oil Exploration & Production in several claims and disputes relating to the Eagle Ford shale play in south Texas. It also successfully acted for ExxonMobil and BP West Coast Products, among others, on a pipeline rates case valued at $350 million.

**Client Service** "*All the attorneys were outstandingly efficient and very responsive.*"

**KEY INDIVIDUALS** The highly regarded **Brooksany Barrowes** (see p.279) continues to impress market sources with her expert handling of electricity regulatory and litigation matters. She recently defended Ameren in a dispute over an interconnection agreement and is currently assisting Shell with the configuration of a range of complicated transactions in the Community Choice Aggregation program, which are to take place between Shell and various parties including the City of San Francisco. "*First-rate lawyer*" **Thomas Eastment** (see p.308) leads the firm's energy regulatory practice. He continues to impress clients with his "*profound understanding*" of oil and gas regulatory and litigation matters. He has enjoyed an active year representing a number of major oil and gas companies including Repsol, ExxonMobil, BP West Coast Products and HollyFrontier before the appeal courts in pipeline rate

## Energy: Electricity (Transactional)
### Leading Firms

**Band 1**
Latham & Watkins LLP *
Skadden, Arps, Slate, Meagher & Flom LLP & Affiliates *

**Band 2**
Kirkland & Ellis LLP *
Milbank, Tweed, Hadley & McCloy LLP *
Simpson Thacher & Bartlett LLP *
Vinson & Elkins LLP *

**Band 3**
Chadbourne & Parke LLP *
Morgan, Lewis & Bockius LLP *
Sullivan & Cromwell LLP *
White & Case LLP *

**Band 4**
Debevoise & Plimpton LLP *
Jones Day *
Orrick, Herrington & Sutcliffe LLP *
Pillsbury Winthrop Shaw Pittman LLP *

## Energy: Electricity (Transactional)
### Senior Statesmen

**Senior Statesmen: distinguished older practitioners**
Baker Jr William T — *Day Pitney LLP (ONP)†*

### Leading Individuals

**Band 1**

| | |
|---|---|
| Adler Sheldon S | Skadden, Arps, Slate, Meagher & Flom * |
| Frumkin Joseph B | Sullivan & Cromwell LLP * |
| Hertz Mitchell F | Kirkland & Ellis LLP |
| Klauberg John G | Bracewell & Giuliani LLP * |
| Lamb William S | Baker Botts LLP * |
| Rod Jonathan | Latham & Watkins LLP |

**Band 2**

| | |
|---|---|
| Barancik Tia S | Sullivan & Cromwell LLP * |
| Shenberg Michael | White & Case LLP * |
| Sinha Pankaj K | Skadden, Arps, Slate, Meagher & Flom * |
| Sonnenschein Edward | Latham & Watkins LLP |
| Walsh Elaine | Baker Botts LLP |

**Band 3**

| | |
|---|---|
| Backus Marcia E | Vinson & Elkins LLP * |
| Bell Crayton L | King & Spalding LLP * |
| Cohen David | Vinson & Elkins LLP * |
| Cusick Michael F | Sole Practitioner (ONP)† |
| Davidson Douglas E | Morgan, Lewis & Bockius LLP * |
| Fitts Sarah | Debevoise & Plimpton LLP |
| Henze II William F | Jones Day * |
| Hood John T | Morgan, Lewis & Bockius LLP * |
| Hord Charles | Chadbourne & Parke LLP * |
| Lieberman David M | Simpson Thacher & Bartlett LLP * |

**Band 4**

| | |
|---|---|
| Belval Paul | Day Pitney LLP (ONP)† |
| Danti Anthony M | Fulbright & Jaworski LLP * |
| Hawkins Ann A | Skadden, Arps, Slate, Meagher & Flom * |

## Energy: Mining & Metals (Transactional)
### Leading Firms

**Band 1**
Cleary Gottlieb Steen & Hamilton LLP *
Debevoise & Plimpton LLP *
Sullivan & Cromwell LLP *

disputes. **Joshua Davidson** (see p.2386) continues to drive the group's work in MLPs, representing the likes of Pacific Coast Oil Trust, Plains All American Pipeline and TC Pipelines in oil and gas public offerings valued in excess of $350 million each. *"Terrific, talented lawyer"* **Elaine Walsh** is fluent in both regulation and litigation as well as transactional issues. In a recent highlight, she acted for NRG Energy on its $200 million purchase of Energy Plus Holdings. *"Phenomenal lawyer"* **William Lamb** (see p.351) is lauded for his *"market knowledge and sound judgment,"* and for being *"incredibly insightful and savvy."* Enthusiastic clients report that he can *"always quickly devise a clever solution to the multitude of challenges that arise in any complicated transaction."* Oil and gas department head **Hugh Tucker** (see p.419) is described as a *"very good listener and project driver."* Over the past year, he has been active on a wide range of transactional work including joint ventures, divestitures, acquisitions and disposals. Highlights include acting for Hess Corporation on its $594 million purchase of half of CNX Gas's interest in the Utica Shale in eastern Ohio. **Thomas Moore** (see p.371) has recently moved to the firm from Dewey & LeBoeuf, bringing with him vast experience of the domestic and international oil and gas transactional markets. He is well versed in a variety of matters ranging from LNG and gas trading projects to divestitures and acquisitions. **Hillary Holmes** (see p.335) is *"absolutely excellent,"* say clients. She recently played an instrumental part in the representation of the John Wood Group in the disposal of its Well Support Division to GE Energy Manufacturing, a $2.8 billion transaction. The *"outstandingly efficient and very responsive"* **Anthony Speier** (see p.411) makes his debut in the oil and gas transactional table this year following market acclaim. *"He is a great up-and-coming lawyer who has the ability to influence and negotiate in a way that's very appealing,"* reports one client. He specializes in executing M&A and joint venture transactions on behalf of a wide spectrum of clients including Rosneft and Marathon Oil.

### Balch & Bingham LLP
See profile on p.475

**THE FIRM** This firm offers an impressive depth of expertise in nuclear matters ranging from licensing requiring representation before the Nuclear Regulatory Commission (NRC), to helping providers of nuclear-related products achieve compliance with regulatory provisions. Impressively, the group recently helped a consortium of licensees apply for a combined license in connection with the first two new nuclear units to be developed in conjunction with the NRC's Part 52 licensing system. Other notable clients include Southern Nuclear Operating and Exelon.

## Energy: Nuclear (Regulatory & Litigation)
### Leading Firms

**Band 1**
Morgan, Lewis & Bockius LLP *

**Band 2**
Pillsbury Winthrop Shaw Pittman LLP *

**Band 3**
Balch & Bingham LLP *
Hogan Lovells US LLP
Winston & Strawn LLP *

### Senior Statesmen

**Senior Statesmen: distinguished older practitioners**
Edgar George L — *Morgan, Lewis & Bockius LLP *

### Leading Individuals

**Band 1**

| | |
|---|---|
| Gutierrez Jay M | Morgan, Lewis & Bockius LLP * |
| Repka David A | Winston & Strawn LLP * |
| Silberg Jay | Pillsbury Winthrop Shaw Pittman LLP * |
| Sutton Kathryn M | Morgan, Lewis & Bockius LLP * |

**Band 2**

| | |
|---|---|
| Blanton M Stanford | Balch & Bingham LLP |
| Frantz Steven P | Morgan, Lewis & Bockius LLP * |
| Lewis David | Pillsbury Winthrop Shaw Pittman LLP * |
| Stenger Daniel | Hogan Lovells US LLP |

**Band 3**

| | |
|---|---|
| Garfield Gerald | Day Pitney LLP (ONP)† * |
| Irwin Donald P | Hunton & Williams LLP * |
| Matthews John E | Morgan, Lewis & Bockius LLP * |
| O'Neill Jr John H | Pillsbury Winthrop Shaw Pittman LLP |
| Peterson Charles | Pillsbury Winthrop Shaw Pittman LLP |

**Band 4**

| | |
|---|---|
| Domby Arthur H | Troutman Sanders LLP |
| Meserve Richard | Covington & Burling LLP * |
| Polonsky Alex | Morgan, Lewis & Bockius LLP * |
| Silverman Donald J | Morgan, Lewis & Bockius LLP * |
| Sullivan Mary Anne | Hogan Lovells US LLP |

**Up-and-coming individuals**

| | |
|---|---|
| Kuntamukkala Ajay | Hogan Lovells US LLP |
| Smith Tyson | Winston & Strawn LLP * |

**Associates to watch**

| | |
|---|---|
| Roma Amy C | Hogan Lovells US LLP |

* Indicates firm / individual with profile.
†ONP = Other Notable Practitioner.

**Sources say:** *"A group of stellar individuals who provide excellent counsel."*

**KEY INDIVIDUALS** The *"fantastic"* **Stanford Blanton** attracts widespread praise from the market, with one client saying they *"work almost exclusively with Balch & Bingham because of people like Stan Blanton."* Another source was quick to celebrate his *"ability to summarize an issue and explain all aspects in a concise fashion as well as provide excellent counsel."*

## Energy: Oil & Gas (Regulatory & Litigation)
### Leading Firms

**Band 1**
Steptoe & Johnson LLP
Vinson & Elkins LLP *

**Band 2**
Baker Botts LLP *
Bracewell & Giuliani LLP *
Sidley Austin LLP *
Skadden, Arps, Slate, Meagher & Flom LLP & Affiliates *

**Band 3**
Andrews Kurth LLP *
Fulbright & Jaworski LLP *
Greenberg Traurig, LLP *
Hogan Lovells US LLP *
Van Ness Feldman LLP *

**Band 4**
Cadwalader, Wickersham & Taft LLP *
Covington & Burling LLP *
King & Spalding LLP *
Morgan, Lewis & Bockius LLP *
Venable LLP *
Wright & Talisman PC

## Energy: Oil & Gas (Regulatory & Litigation)
### Senior Statesmen

**Senior Statesmen: distinguished older practitioners**

| | | | | |
|---|---|---|---|---|
| Loeffler Robert H | Morrison & Foerster LLP (ONP)† | | O'Neill Brian D | Van Ness Feldman LLP * |
| May Jr Henry S | Vinson & Elkins LLP * | | Tabor Bert | Vinson & Elkins LLP * |

### Leading Individuals

**Band 1**

| | |
|---|---|
| Andril David T | Vinson & Elkins LLP * |
| Brose Steven | Steptoe & Johnson LLP |
| Caldwell Charles | Vinson & Elkins LLP * |
| Eastment Thomas | Baker Botts LLP * |
| Elrod Eugene R | Sidley Austin LLP * |
| Haskell Mark R | Morgan, Lewis & Bockius LLP * |
| Moore Charles A | Morgan, Lewis & Bockius LLP * |
| Naeve Clifford M | Skadden, Arps, Slate, Meagher & Flom * |
| Reed Steven | Steptoe & Johnson LLP |
| Shoneman Charles H | Bracewell & Giuliani LLP * |

**Band 2**

| | |
|---|---|
| Acker Lawrence G | Van Ness Feldman LLP * |
| Bowe Jr James F | King & Spalding LLP * |
| Heeg Peggy A | Fulbright & Jaworski LLP * |
| Kennedy John | Vinson & Elkins LLP * |
| Leggette Poe | Fulbright & Jaworski LLP * |
| Lewis Mark K | Bracewell & Giuliani LLP * |
| Lipson Kevin J | Hogan Lovells US LLP * |
| Minesinger Kenneth M | Greenberg Traurig, LLP * |
| Moffatt J Curtis | Van Ness Feldman LLP * |
| Nevins Patrick | Hogan Lovells US LLP * |
| Scherman William S | Gibson, Dunn & Crutcher LLP * |
| Sundback Mark | Andrews Kurth LLP * |
| Tonery Lisa | Fulbright & Jaworski LLP * |
| Wilson Anita | Vinson & Elkins LLP * |

**Band 3**

| | |
|---|---|
| Alexander Lee | DLA Piper LLP (US) * |
| Crowley Lisanne | Troutman Sanders LLP |
| Koury Joseph S | Wright & Talisman PC |
| Poynor Daniel | Steptoe & Johnson LLP |
| Williams William A | Sidley Austin LLP * |

**Band 4**

| | |
|---|---|
| Avil Richard | Jones Day * |
| Barr Christopher J. | Post & Schell, P.C. (ONP)† |
| Edwards Katherine | Edwards & Associates (ONP)† |
| Fleishman Robert S | Covington & Burling LLP * |
| Gibbs Kirstin E | Bracewell & Giuliani LLP * |
| Irvin Kenneth W | Cadwalader, Wickersham & Taft LLP * |
| Korman Paul | Van Ness Feldman LLP * |
| Krantz Stefan | Hogan Lovells US LLP * |
| Levy Neil L | King & Spalding LLP * |
| Lowther Frederick M | Dickstein Shapiro LLP * |
| Massey William L | Covington & Burling LLP * |
| Nelson Howard L | Greenberg Traurig, LLP * |
| Powers Richard | Venable LLP * |
| Rich Randall S | Pierce Atwood LLP (ONP)† * |
| Wiggins Dena E | Ballard Spahr LLP (ONP)† * |
| Wiseman Kenneth L | Andrews Kurth LLP * |

**Band 5**

| | |
|---|---|
| Adducci Steven | Venable LLP * |
| Decker John S | Vinson & Elkins LLP * |
| Lyons Christopher | Sidley Austin LLP * |
| McClure Daniel M | Fulbright & Jaworski LLP * |
| Morgan II Kirk D | Bracewell & Giuliani LLP * |
| Newman Karol Lyn | McDermott Will & Emery LLP (ONP)† * |
| Proctor Shemin | Andrews Kurth LLP * |
| Seegers James D | Vinson & Elkins LLP * |
| Sweeney Kevin | John & Hengerer (ONP)† |
| Thompson Michael | Wright & Talisman PC |
| Waters Jennifer N | Crowell & Moring LLP (ONP)† * |

**Up-and-coming individuals**

| | |
|---|---|
| Perez Tania | Fulbright & Jaworski LLP * |

\* Indicates firm / individual with profile.
†ONP = Other Notable Practitioner.

## Bracewell & Giuliani LLP
See profile on p.2429

**THE FIRM** This established group has a standout reputation for energy work, and in this space the team has both the bench strength and expertise to handle the most complex issues. On the oil and gas front, the team is particularly noted for its adept handling of regulatory matters for a variety of clients including Kinder Morgan, PetroLogistics Natural Gas Storage and Shell. On the electric side, the group is especially lauded for its litigation strengths, of which a current example is its representation of Powerex before FERC in a litigation matter involving the interpretation of a range of complicated issues arising under various legislation including the Federal Power Act and the Foreign Sovereign Immunities Act.

**Client Service** *"An excellent firm. It has a good cross-section of experienced energy regulatory attorneys who are easy to work with and extremely responsive to the client's needs."*

**Commercial Awareness** *"Their particular strengths are strategy and door opening."*

**KEY INDIVIDUALS** New addition to the firm **Catherine McCarthy**'s (see p.364) *"advice and advocacy protect the company and advances our business interests,"* one client enthuses. Peers are quick to acknowledge her very active electric transmissions practice, which involves advising on compliance matters and transmission formula rate work, as well as representing clients including transmission owners before FERC. *"Terrific litigator"* **Deanna King** (see p.347) is mostly active on the electric side and is singled out as *"extremely knowledgeable, responsive and well connected."* Energy regulatory practice head **Sandra Rizzo** (see p.393) is lauded for her *"excellent knowledge on FERC electric regulatory matters."* She is also singled out for being *"extremely bright, knowledgeable and thorough"* and a *"great pleasure to deal with."* Of late, she has been active on

behalf of a range of electricity companies including Rockland Capital Partners, ConocoPhillips and Kinder Morgan. *"Seasoned lawyer"* **Paul Fox** (see p.315) is praised by clients for his *"very client-oriented"* approach. He is acting on behalf of Powerex in the contentious FERC-related matters mentioned above. Clients are appreciative of **John Klauberg**'s (see p.347) *"very valuable advice."* He recently joined the firm from Dewey & LeBoeuf and comes recommended for his strengths in the arrangement and implementation of transactions on behalf of unregulated companies and regulated utilities. Sources commend **Mark Lewis**'s (see p.356) *"tremendous amount of experience in dealing with energy regulatory and midstream energy issues."* He is also highlighted for his excellent client service. He recently acted for Caisse de dépôt et placement du Québec in connection with its $850 million acquisition of 16.55%

of Colonial Pipeline. The *"impressive"* **Charles Shoneman** (see p.406) is a well-known figure in the world of energy regulatory matters. He has an enviable client list which includes the likes of Shell LNG and ConocoPhillips, and is currently acting for the latter in a FERC Office of Enforcement investigation. **Kirstin Gibbs** (see p.320) is particularly focused on oil and gas matters, acting for a broad range of clients including traders, natural gas pipelines and local distribution companies. Recent examples of her work include representing Statoil in cutting-edge FERC litigation concerning rate and tariff issues. **Kirk Morgan** (see p.371) is a rising name in the oil and gas space and is lauded for his *"strong negotiation talent."* He is also recognized as a *"very talented regulatory lawyer, particularly with regard to matters before FERC."* *"Very capable transactional lawyer"* **Alan Rafte** (see p.389) remains a big

## Energy: Oil & Gas (Transactional)
### Leading Firms

**Band 1**
Baker Botts LLP *
Vinson & Elkins LLP *

**Band 2**
Andrews Kurth LLP *

**Band 3**
Akin Gump Strauss Hauer & Feld LLP *
Bracewell & Giuliani LLP *
Fulbright & Jaworski LLP *
Latham & Watkins LLP *
Morgan, Lewis & Bockius LLP *

**Band 4**
DLA Piper LLP (US) *
Gardere Wynne Sewell LLP *
Locke Lord LLP *
Porter Hedges LLP *
Skadden, Arps, Slate, Meagher & Flom LLP & Affiliates *
Thompson & Knight LLP *

attraction to clients for his *"deep experience in the energy business."* He recently led the team advising Chesapeake Energy on two separate joint ventures, with EIG Global Energy Partners and GSO Capital Partners. The aggregate value of both transactions was $2.5 billion. **James McAnelly** (see p.364) advises on a wide range of transactions, ranging from the financing, acquisition and disposal of exploration and production assets to providing assistance with the creation of joint ventures. He successfully represented Kinder Morgan in its $38 billion purchase of El Paso and its subsequent disposal of El Paso's exploration and production assets.

### Cadwalader, Wickersham & Taft LLP
See profile on p.438
**THE FIRM** This firm's energy and natural resources group possesses indisputable strength in regulatory and litigation concerns affecting both the oil and gas and electricity sectors. The group comes highly recommended in the energy trading arena, where the firm's acknowledged primacy in the commodities industry has seen it represent a number of leading financial institutions including international banks, hedge funds and commercial companies before the Commodity Futures Trading Commission (CFTC). The team has also been particularly active in matters pertaining to the Dodd-Frank Act, the Federal Power Act and FERC investigations. A recent highlight saw it represent Morgan Stanley, South Carolina Electric & Gas and others in natural gas pipeline rate proceedings before FERC.
**KEY INDIVIDUALS Paul Pantano** (see p.381) remains a strong choice for clients seeking advice on complex enforcement matters. In the words of one client, *"he is super plugged-in when it comes to CFTC matters. He is very good at predicting outcomes and at explaining the bigger picture in a way that clients can understand."* **Gregory Lawrence** (see p.352) concentrates on representing clients ranging from financial institutions and funds to project developers and major energy consumers in a broad array

## Energy: Oil & Gas (Transactional)
### Senior Statesmen

**Senior Statesmen: distinguished older practitioners**
Kutzschbach George   *Fulbright & Jaworski LLP* *

### Leading Individuals

**Star individuals**
Asmus David   *Morgan, Lewis & Bockius LLP* *
Cogan Jr John P   *Cogan & Partners LLP (ONP)* [†]

**Band 1**
Backus Marcia E   *Vinson & Elkins LLP* *
Bland Douglas S   *Vinson & Elkins LLP* *
Irvin Michael P   *Fulbright & Jaworski LLP* *
Rafte G Alan   *Bracewell & Giuliani LLP* *

**Band 2**
Darden Michael P   *Latham & Watkins LLP*
Langlois Jack J   *DLA Piper LLP (US)* *
Moore Thomas J   *Baker Botts LLP* *
O'Leary Michael   *Andrews Kurth LLP* *
Rosenwasser Michael   *Vinson & Elkins LLP* *

**Band 3**
Atnipp Douglas C   *Greenberg Traurig, LLP* *
Fredrickson Robin S   *Latham & Watkins LLP*
Gitomer Deborah   *Fulbright & Jaworski LLP* *
King Michael   *Latham & Watkins LLP*
LaFollette Christine B   *Akin Gump Strauss Hauer & Feld LLP* *
McAnelly III W James   *Bracewell & Giuliani LLP* *
Rice James   *Sidley Austin LLP* *
Stephens Robert   *Cadwalader, Wickersham & Taft LLP* *
Tucker Hugh   *Baker Botts LLP* *

**Band 4**
Bateman Thomas   *Andrews Kurth LLP* *
Byrd Michael   *Baker & McKenzie (ONP)* [†] *
Cohen David   *Vinson & Elkins LLP* *
Connally IV John B   *Vinson & Elkins LLP* *
Davidson Joshua   *Baker Botts LLP* *
Derman Andrew B   *Thompson & Knight LLP* *
Eyberg Doug   *Gardere Wynne Sewell LLP* *
Fullenweider Keith   *Vinson & Elkins LLP* *
King C Randall   *Porter Hedges LLP* *
Moore Rodney L   *Weil, Gotshal & Manges LLP (ONP)* [†] *
Munoz Jeff   *Latham & Watkins LLP*
Patton David   *Locke Lord LLP* *
Rain John W   *Thompson & Knight LLP* *
Stevens III N L (Larry)   *Gardere Wynne Sewell LLP* *
Thomas Robert   *Porter Hedges LLP* *

**Up-and-coming individuals**
Holmes Hillary H.   *Baker Botts LLP* *

**Associates to watch**
Speier Anthony   *Baker Botts LLP* *

\* *Indicates firm / individual with profile.*
[†] *ONP = Other Notable Practitioner.*

of power matters, including FERC regulatory and enforcement proceedings, and transactions. He recently represented Dayton Power & Light before FERC in connection with various regulatory matters relating to its $4.7 billion merger with AES. **Kenneth Irvin** (see p.339) is heavily involved in the energy trading space and was recently part of the

team acting on the natural gas pipeline rate proceedings. **Robert Stephens** (see p.412) plays a central role in much of the group's oil and gas transactional and financing work, acting on behalf of a broad spectrum of clients including energy companies, private investors and financial institutions. He recently took the lead on a $500 million project financing on behalf of Gainesville Renewable Energy Center.

### Chadbourne & Parke LLP
See profile on p.1962
**THE FIRM** The market sees this firm as a go-to outfit for transactional matters in the electricity space, particularly in M&A and securities-related issues. The group recently represented Credit Suisse in the $935 million financing for a solar thermal project and also recently acted for TPF Holdings on the disposal of an 800 MW gas-fired power plant. The team is also active on regulatory and litigation matters, regularly acting for some of the largest financial institutions in the world, including GE Capital, Union Bank and Siemens Financial Services, as well as sponsors and developers such as First Wind.
**Commercial Awareness** *"The key is that they are able to balance the legal issues with the business issues, which is a delicate balance."*
**KEY INDIVIDUALS Robert Shapiro** (see p.404) is a project finance lawyer with a real strength in electricity matters. He has enjoyed an active year, representing the likes of Bloom Energy, which he is currently acting for in all the financing and regulatory aspects of its solid waste project. **Charles Hord** (see p.336) is *"extremely knowledgeable, and a good negotiator who always remains cool under pressure,"* according to one impressed client. Sources also appreciate his ability to *"promptly react to a situation as soon as it arises."* He applies his corporate and finance expertise to a wide range of matters, including joint ventures and restructurings for the benefit of various energy companies and financial institutions.

### Cleary Gottlieb Steen & Hamilton LLP
See profile on p.1963
**THE FIRM** This firm is best known for its expertise in mining and metals transactions. The group handles sales, securities offerings and purchases for a range of top-drawer clients including Vale, Codelco and Citi. The team has been active over the past year advising on a number of the leading deals in this space, including representing Alpha Natural Resources in its $8.5 billion purchase of Massey Energy, a groundbreaking transaction that has led to the formation of one of the largest coal groups in the USA. In similar fashion, the group also recently acted for Citi, which was leading the biggest rights offering made by a Canadian issuer to date. The firm is also known for its ongoing representation of the likes of Petrobras and Petróleos Mexicanos in a range of oil and gas matters.
**Sources say:** *"The attorneys are all exceptional: they are assertive and able to manage difficult situations very well, and always look for solutions."*
**KEY INDIVIDUALS** Richard Cooper and Jeffrey Lewis are key contacts in New York.

## Covington & Burling LLP
See profile on p.441

THE FIRM This group has acted as counsel to some of the biggest names within the electricity arena including utilities such as Public Service Enterprise Group and the COMPETE Coalition. On the oil and gas side, the group is well equipped to handle a wealth of litigation and regulatory issues, and is currently representing ExxonMobil in two cross-border arbitration matters.

Sources say: "A group of brilliant lawyers who are courteous, extremely efficient and work very hard to understand the needs of the client."

KEY INDIVIDUALS Sources particularly appreciate the experience William Massey (see p.363) gained as a former FERC commissioner, which they say has left him "very well connected" and possessing a "very broad understanding of public policy." Peers concede that he has "had a great deal of success" in the past year, such as in his work on behalf of the COMPETE Coalition. Clients flock to the firm due to Richard Meserve's (see p.367) strong reputation, especially when it comes to regulatory and litigation work within the nuclear arena. "He has excellent judgment," reports one impressed source. Robert Fleishman (see p.314) is another highly experienced regulatory and litigation attorney, serving a range of oil and gas clients including the American Gas Association and Clean Energy Fuels. His practice maintains a particular focus on Dodd-Frank and FERC enforcement matters.

## Debevoise & Plimpton LLP
See profile on p.1968

THE FIRM This team includes attorneys who are skilled in the full range of corporate metals and mining work, advising domestic and international clients on a range of transactional matters including M&A, securities offerings, project financings and joint ventures. In one standout matter, the team represented Mitsui in the granting of a $5.8 billion short-term loan to leading copper manufacturer CODELCO. The group also has a heavyweight power practice which attracts a highly prestigious client base, including names such as Tenaska and the US Department of Energy (DOE). The team is currently assisting the latter with $1.6 billion in loan guarantees on three solar power plants. Its workload also includes oil and gas advice to industry giants including ExxonMobil and Mobil Oil.

KEY INDIVIDUALS Peers "think very highly" of Sarah Fitts, who has a sterling reputation for her extensive experience in M&A transactional, restructuring and projects work. She was part of the team dealing with the big-ticket Mitsui matter above.

## Dentons
See profile on p.449

THE FIRM This global firm attracts tremendous praise from clients for its exceptional industry knowledge and responsiveness. Over the past year, the electricity group has been particularly active on representing clients such as Otter Tail Power and New York Regional Interconnect in transmission issues. Notably, the team has been appointed as regulatory counsel for the City of New Orleans in multiple cases that are to be heard before FERC and at all levels of the court system.

Commercial Awareness "In addition to significant expertise at FERC, the lawyers understand how the markets function." "I value their strategic advice in resolving complex political issues."

KEY INDIVIDUALS "Excellent regulatory lawyer" Stuart Caplan (see p.291) continues to impress clients, who report: "He is incredibly thoughtful, bright, diligent and a real pleasure to work with." Recent high-profile highlights include serving as FERC counsel on behalf of Bayonne Energy Center in various issues arising out of a major gas-fired power plant project. Clinton Vince (see p.421) is another accomplished attorney at the firm and is lauded by market sources for his "excellent advice and counsel" and "broad industry experience," which clients say is "invaluable in dealing with our challenges."

## Dickstein Shapiro LLP
See profile on p.911

THE FIRM The primary focus of this firm's electricity and regulatory practice is transmission power supply and interconnection issues, in which it has one of the strongest reputations in the country. The team is very well versed in the representation of clients before various federal and state bodies including FERC and the DOE, as well as the public service commissions of numerous states. It has notably been representing Invenergy and the American Wind Energy Association (AWEA) before FERC in their challenge to various fees, including transmission rates, intended to be charged by Puget Sound Energy. The team also continues to carve out a reputation for itself in the transactional sphere, and has recently won instructions from clients such as Competitive Power Ventures, Poseidon Water and Constellation Energy.

Sources say: "We have been clients of the firm for many years. This long tenure is indicative of our confidence in the firm's attorneys, their expertise, professionalism and can-do attitudes."

KEY INDIVIDUALS Larry Eisenstat (see p.309) continues to serve as practice group head at the firm and is described by one impressed peer as "very aggressive and very effective in representing his clients." He led on the Invenergy and AWEA matter, and is currently assisting Competitive Power Ventures with administrative litigation relating to the development of the Maryland Power plant, alongside Richard Lehfeldt (see p.354). Lehfeldt is another highly experienced electricity attorney, who is frequently called upon to handle a wide range of issues including complicated acquisitions and matters requiring expertise in federal and state legislation. Mark Perlis (see p.383) is renowned for his wide-ranging regulatory and litigation expertise, helping electric utilities with industry restructuring matters as well as FERC-related concerns. The "highly experienced" and "deeply knowledgeable" Frederick Lowther (see p.359) is lauded for his broad-based electricity practice. "Whether the issues are regulatory, transactional or litigation-based, his support and advice are high-quality, insightful and extremely timely," clients enthuse.

## DLA Piper LLP (US)
See profile on p.1971

THE FIRM This team is a strong choice for oil and gas transactional matters and is currently assisting BP with a broad array of concerns including M&A, joint ventures and alternative energy projects. The group comes highly recommended by clients, who extend praise to the responsiveness and broad expertise of its attorneys.

Sources say: "Both experienced and professional – they have exceeded all expectations." "The group has demonstrated a flexibility and willingness to do what it takes to get the job done."

KEY INDIVIDUALS Lee Alexander (see p.272) concentrates on transactional energy and federal regulatory concerns. He and other members of the team are currently assisting NiSource with Dodd-Frank and CFTC regulatory compliance issues in a pipeline modification matter. Jack Langlois (see p.352) is a well-respected transactional lawyer who has recently been involved in several big-ticket matters on behalf of Kayne Anderson Capital Advisors, HighMount Exploration & Production, MatlinPatterson Global Advisors and others.

## Fulbright & Jaworski LLP
See profile on p.2435

THE FIRM This oil and gas team counsels a wide range of clients on the financing and development of energy projects, together with advising on acquisitions and sales. It has recently been acting for Total on its $2.3 billion purchase of oil and gas assets. Additionally, it also possesses considerable strength in litigation matters, and the past year has seen it act for many leading clients from the upstream, midstream and downstream areas including Shell, ConocoPhillips and BP. Notably, the firm is defending BP in a high-profile False Claims Act case estimated at £25 billion.

Sources say: "It is an excellent firm. The quality of work is high and it is done right."

KEY INDIVIDUALS Anthony Danti (see p.301) continues to focus on electric power generation concerns and recently represented Brookfield Renewable in its purchase of wind facilities. Peggy Heeg (see p.332) has particular expertise in a variety of concerns including the development of regulatory compliance programs, corporate malfeasance and market manipulation. Her clients typically include leading energy companies and special committees as well as individuals. The "highly regarded" Poe Leggette (see p.354) is hailed as a "very impressive lawyer." A renowned expert in both administrative and judicial litigation, he is currently leading the firm's work on behalf of Rockies Express Pipeline, which is seeking up to $176 million in damages in a breach of contract matter. This case will be heard before the Civilian Board of Contract Appeals. The "terrific" Lisa Tonery (see p.418) is highly experienced in appearing before FERC and the DOE, and has been busy in the past year advising parties on the big-ticket Sabine Pass LNG liquefaction project, which has included obtaining the required authorizations from both FERC and the DOE, as well as advising on the financing aspects. The "truly outstanding" Daniel McClure (see p.2404) is a talented litigator who regularly appears before state and federal courts on behalf of oil and gas clients. Notably, he recently successfully defended Anadarko against a $330 million damages claim relating to an alleged breach of the terms of a joint exploration agreement. **Michael Irvin** (see p.339) is *"very practical, pragmatic, and highly knowledgeable in different international arenas and business structures."* He is currently the lead counsel acting for EOG Resources on its intended $4 billion natural gas liquefaction plant and export terminal project. The highly experienced **Deborah Gitomer** (see p.321) continues to provide clients with comprehensive advice on the purchase and sale of various energy assets including oil and gas exploration and producing properties and gas processing plants. Her recent workload has included acting for Sinopec on its $2.5 billion acquisition of multiple shale plays. Of counsel **George Kutzschbach** (see p.351) recently acted for Diamond Offshore Drilling on the amendment of various agreements and contracts. He has a substantial amount of experience acting on a broad array of transactions on both a domestic and international level. **Tania Perez** (see p.383) has a wealth of experience in oil and gas transactions, particularly those concerning the establishment of energy infrastructure, such as pipelines, natural gas storage and LNG terminals. She is frequently required to appear before FERC and other regulatory bodies on behalf of clients, and is currently working alongside Tonery on the Sabine Pass LNG liquefaction project.

### Gardere Wynne Sewell LLP
See profile on p.2436

**THE FIRM** This team is recognized for its strength in transactional matters, with particular expertise in handling cross-border transactions on behalf of domestic clients in Latin America. The team has been engaged by BP in a range of matters including the disposal of oil and gas assets valued at more than $1.2 billion, and the sale of a midstream gas plant to Anadarko for $575 million.
**Client Service:** *"It is an excellent firm: very responsive to our needs and it offers a wide range of legal services and products to our company."* *"Completely client-focused – almost like part of my internal legal team."*
**KEY INDIVIDUALS** Energy practice leader **Doug Eyberg** (see p.311) debuts in the rankings this year following glowing praise from market sources. Clients say: *"He has a deep knowledge of the client's business and the wider industry"* and is *"exceptionally good at negotiations."* Peers attest to his very active practice over the past year, which has involved work on behalf of the firm's most significant clients including BP and Boardwalk Pipeline Partners. **Larry Stevens** (see p.412) is another strong transactional attorney at the firm and is best known for his M&A and debt and equity financing work. Recent highlights include representing Sidewinder Drilling in a $150 million capital financing matter, which will enable it to purchase state-of-the-art drilling rigs.

### Greenberg Traurig, LLP
See profile on p.1024

**THE FIRM** Greenberg Traurig is most noted for its work in the oil and gas regulatory and litigation arenas, particularly for its ability to represent clients in major FERC matters. Clients include a variety of big names from the oil and gas industry including major pipelines such as ANR Pipeline and Mojave Pipeline as well as regulators and governments including the State of Alaska. The firm also has the capacity to handle a range of transactional matters, including the financing and refinancing of projects for the likes of JPMorgan Chase and Schlumberger.
**Sources say:** *"I can scarcely begin to describe to you the excellence of FERC practice at Greenberg Traurig. All in all, this team gets the highest marks."*
**KEY INDIVIDUALS Kenneth Minesinger** (see p.369) is celebrated for *"performing exquisitely"* when arguing cases. In addition to his litigation expertise, he is also lauded for his excellent written work, *"strategic thinking"* and ability to *"deftly problem-solve."* The *"impressive"* **Howard Nelson** (see p.375) also comes recommended for his skills in the courtroom and consistently provides *"tireless legal advice and work product."* **Douglas Atnipp** (see p.275) serves as cochair of the national energy and natural resources team and offers clients over two decades of experience in transactions ranging from the purchase and sale of energy-related property to energy finance.

### Hogan Lovells US LLP

**THE FIRM** Market sources praise this firm's brilliant nuclear practice and also highlight its impressive national and worldwide profile. Clients are particularly quick to commend the group's excellent client service and its ability to handle complex matters. Notably, the group recently represented Constellation Energy before the NRC in licensing matters relating to its $7.9 billion merger with Exelon. It also continues to represent Toshiba in several nuclear-related concerns. The team also comes much recommended for its expertise on regulatory matters and litigation in the oil and gas and electricity space.
**Client Service** *"The client service is first-rate."* *"I would single out their capacity for understanding our company's needs and providing the most appropriate service."*
**KEY INDIVIDUALS** The esteemed **John Stough** has much experience in advising lenders and electric utilities on rate approval and transmission-related matters, among others. He is also recognized for his abilities acting before FERC and various other public utility commissions in asset transaction permissions and mergers, such as the ongoing matter he is currently handling for Cleco. *"Excellent nuclear lawyer"* **Daniel Stenger** is currently acting as nuclear counsel for Constellation Energy Nuclear Group on several matters and is also leading the team's efforts on behalf of Louisiana Energy Services in various regulatory and legislative concerns. The *"very talented"* **Mary Anne Sullivan** is also well known for her strength in nuclear matters, and has had an active year providing stellar advice to a broad range of clients. The *"extremely knowledgeable and well-connected"* **Ajay Kuntamukkala** stands out for his expertise in nuclear export and nonpro-

liferation concerns, and has been involved in many of the firm's significant mandates including the Louisiana Energy Services, Constellation Energy and Toshiba matters. **Amy Roma** has particular expertise in assisting clients with regulatory matters entailing the approval of the NRC and the DOE, and is currently working with Daniel Stenger for the Central Vermont Public Service Corporation, helping it to obtain permissions from the NRC relating to its intended $472 million merger with Gaz Metro of Canada. The *"highly regarded"* **Patrick Nevins** is the first port of call for several of his peers when it comes to referrals in the oil and gas space. He continues to focus on the regulatory concerns of various prominent clients including Dominion Cove Point LNG, Chevron Pipeline and Dominion Resources. He has recently been representing Southern California Edison in several FERC litigation matters, including a complaint initiated by Texas Gas Services. The *"very strong"* **John Lilyestrom** (see p.357) continues to advise his electricity clients on transmission and reliability concerns as well as power generation issues. Alongside **Kevin Lipson** (see p.357), he is currently representing a leading public power authority, in FERC enforcement proceedings. Lipson is described as an *"accomplished and effective"* attorney and enjoys a fine reputation for being an *"excellent oil and gas litigator."* **Stefan Krantz** (see p.350) recently joined the firm from Hogan Lovells and is particularly well known for his wealth of experience in handling matters for a variety of oil and gas industry clients.

### Hunton & Williams LLP
See profile on p.2517

**THE FIRM** Hunton & Williams remains a leading choice for electricity clients requiring representation in international and domestic complex financing matters, including capital markets and securities transactions. Its impressive lawyers also undertake traditional electricity regulatory and litigation work for a whole host of clients including investor-owned utilities and transmission entities before various bodies including FERC and the CFTC. The firm also has a significant presence in the nuclear arena, and is well versed in the gamut of regulatory work including licensing and relicensing applications, as well as representing clients before the NRC in rulemaking and enforcement proceedings.
**Sources say:** *"Excellent firm."* *"The entire team is client-oriented."*
**KEY INDIVIDUALS** According to clients, **Emmett Ellis** (see p.309) *"is an icon in the industry"* whose *"knowledge and ever-calm demeanor are impressive."* Peers are also quick to highlight his outstanding reputation and strength in providing energy companies advice on capital markets transactions. *"Top-notch"* attorney **Michael Fitzpatrick** (see p.314) continues to represent various utilities in securities transactions and other financing concerns. He recently acted on behalf of a number of banks including Goldman Sachs and Citi on CenterPoint Energy Transition Bond's sale of almost $1.7 billion in secured transition bonds. The *"exceptional"* **Peter O'Brien** (see p.379) also receives strong praise from his peers, with one source commenting: *"He is very aware of what is happening in the*

*industry and would be first choice for referral in a conflict situation.*" He is another member of the team who is highly experienced in energy financing matters. The *"excellent"* **Linda Walsh** (see p.422) plays a central role in much of the group's electricity regulatory work for its utility clients. She is also adept at handling North American Electric Reliability Corporation (NERC) reliability issues, as well as contentious work relating to rates and administrative concerns. **Donald Irwin** (see p.339) handles nuclear regulatory concerns on behalf of utilities, regularly appearing before the NRC in licensing matters. He is lauded by clients, one of whom says: "*The advice and counsel of Mr Irwin is exemplary. His particular knowledge of the nuclear industry here in the USA is without peer.*"

## Jones Day
### See profile on p.919

**THE FIRM** This multidisciplinary team guides electricity businesses through a wide variety of energy regulatory proceedings and transactions on both a domestic and international level. Clients such as EON, NRG Energy and El Paso Electric take advantage of the firm's expertise in M&A, and FERC-related regulatory work. The team also helps companies achieve compliance with the Dodd-Frank Act. In addition, the team is noted for its proficiency on the oil and gas side, advising on matters such as oil and gas shale plays and regulatory concerns relating to the Natural Gas Act and the Natural Gas Policy Act.
**Sources say:** "*An efficient team that is very thorough and always does its very best to help us get the deal done.*"
**KEY INDIVIDUALS William Henze** (see p.333) is a go-to figure for clients requiring guidance on energy transactions. He regularly advises high-profile clients including the likes of El Paso Electric, which he recently represented in negotiations with an affiliate of NRG Energy regarding the amendment of a power purchase agreement. "*Very skilled lawyer*" **Richard Avil** (see p.275) commands high levels of respect from the field. He is heavily involved in regulatory and litigation matters on behalf of oil and gas clients, including natural gas pipelines and local distribution businesses.

## K&L Gates
### See profile on p.2245

**THE FIRM** This group offers broad-based advice on all aspects of regulatory compliance, and has recently been highly active on behalf of major clients such as Duquesne Light and CP Energy Marketing in Dodd-Frank matters. The firm also maintains a highly successful litigation practice, and is currently acting for the Northwest & Intermountain Power Producers Coalition on a cutting-edge matter concerning the jurisdictional power of regulatory bodies including FERC.
**Commercial Awareness** "*We continue to use them on issues that are complex and need tough strategic thinking – that's where they really excel.*"
**KEY INDIVIDUALS** The *"fantastic"* **Donald Kaplan** (see p.342) "*is very skilled and has a loyal client following,*" notes one contemporary. He acts as counsel to the firm's long-standing client PPL Corporation, and is currently repre-

senting it before FERC in the issue of rate incentives applicable in a transmission project.

## King & Spalding LLP
### See profile on p.445

**THE FIRM** This established practice is famed for its very strong regulatory capabilities, particularly on behalf of IPPs in the electricity arena. The group is currently acting for Electric Power Supply Association (EPSA) on several challenges before FERC, including a significant rulemaking, the decision on which will heavily impact upon energy prices for EPSA members and other providers. This solid practice also continues to build on its reputation within the oil and gas sector. In recent highlights, the group represented Chevron in both the regulatory and litigation matters arising out of the Deepwater Horizon oil spill.
**Client Service** "*They are very responsive.*" "*They have high-quality people and are easy to work with.*"
**KEY INDIVIDUALS** The *"extraordinarily talented"* **Neil Levy** (see p.356) is applauded for its strong commercial awareness and "*sharp legal mind.*" Together with **David Tewksbury** (see p.416), he successfully acted for Calpine and several of the subsidiaries of Dynergy, GenOn Energy, NRG Energy and Tenaska on a judicial review case before FERC, overturning longstanding rules for generators which self-supply station power. Tewksbury receives significant praise from clients, who say he has a "*very strong understanding of the legal market, and the rules and regulations of regulatory commissions, and has a good sense for how the legal environment operates and how it impacts business-es.*" **Bruce Richardson** (see p.392) is known for his activity in the electricity regulatory arena, acting for a broad spectrum of clients including independent power producers, electric power marketers, energy asset managers and generation-owning industrial businesses. He is notably advising several of the firm's key clients, including EPSA, AES and Tenaska, on NERC-related compliance issues. **Crayton Bell** (see p.281) continues to build an impressive electricity transactional practice and recently advised Gateway Energy Services on its sale to Direct Energy, a transaction valued at $90 million. **James Bowe** (see p.286) recently joined the firm from Dewey & LeBoeuf. He stands out for his advice to owners and developers on natural gas pipeline storage projects and recently assisted Atlas Pipeline Mid-Continent WestTex with the development of a pipeline project, obtaining all necessary approvals from FERC. The "*smart and hard-working*" **Stephanie Lim** (see p.357) debuts in the table this year amid significant market acclaim. She has been present on a number of the firm's major electricity regulatory highlights over the past year, including the EPSA matters, and also assisted Levy with the representation of LS Power in a contentious FERC matter.

## Kirkland & Ellis LLP
### See profile on p.1254

**THE FIRM** This firm draws plaudits for its transactional expertise in the electricity space, and has been involved in some truly significant work over the past year. It has handled a number of matters for NRG Energy, including

advising it on a $3 billion refinancing matter, as well as assisting with its purchase of Energy Plus Holdings, a large, independent energy company. Other clients include National Grid, BP Pipelines and Constellation Energy.
**Sources say:** "*They are as always doing a fantastic job for us. They have very talented, efficient lawyers.*"
**KEY INDIVIDUALS** Clients are full of praise for the "*fantastic*" **Mitchell Hertz**, who serves as chair of the firm's energy practice. Sources highlight him for his "*superior negotiating abilities*" and excellent client management skills. In addition to advising NRG on various matters, he is assisting Sumitomo Corporation of America with completing its $353 million joint venture with Duke Energy Renewables.

## Latham & Watkins LLP
### See profile on p.446

**THE FIRM** The broad and deep energy group at this well-regarded firm is without doubt among the very best across the USA. It offers the full spectrum of energy-related services, ranging from M&A and corporate finance to renewable energy projects, and features a particularly strong power subgroup. Typical highlights from the past year include advising Barclays Capital on Duke Energy's $25.9 billion purchase of Progress Energy, and assisting JPMorgan Securities with its provision of $7.9 billion for the financing of the merger between Exelon and Constellation Energy. Observers also note its increasing strength in the oil and gas space, where it acts for clients including The Blackstone Group, Energy Transfer Partners and Continental Resources.
**Sources say:** "*This is a super firm.*"
**KEY INDIVIDUALS** The "*absolutely terrific*" **Jonathan Rod** serves as chair of the energy power industry group, and is noted for his strengths in the oil and gas and power financing space. He recently led on a high-value debt refinancing matter on behalf of Goldman Sachs and Credit Suisse. **Michael Gergen** (see p.320) is an "*excellent attorney*" who sources say they would "*trust to handle the most complicated of work.*" He enjoys a fine track record in regulatory matters, representing a range of clients including Duquesne Light and LS Power Equity Advisors. The "*very smart*" and "*pragmatic*" **David Schwartz** (see p.402) is a "*great energy attorney with a clear sense of what drives the industry.*" His areas of expertise include representing clients before various bodies including FERC, the DOJ and the DOE. He recently secured an advantageous settlement on behalf of Duquesne Light in its conflict with Midwest Independent Transmission System Operator. The "*fantastic*" **Natasha Gianvecchio** (see p.320) continues to act for a wide range of electric and oil and gas clients, including natural gas companies, electric utilities and financial institutions, on a variety of regulatory matters. In a recent highlight, she advised FirstEnergy on market concerns relating to the PJM organization arising out of the closure of numerous coal-fired plants. **Edward Sonnenschein** continues to apply his corporate expertise for the benefit of energy clients, and recently acted for Brookfield Asset Management on its $13 billion purchase of a renewable fund. **Michael Darden** has an established practice repre-

senting clients such as Plains Exploration and Continental Resources in a number of high-value acquisitions, joint ventures, disposals and divestitures. He recently assisted Red Leaf Exploration with its high-profile joint venture with Total. **Robin Fredrickson** joined the group from Vinson & Elkins in 2012 and is a favorite among clients for transactional work. Clients say she is *"a joy to work with"* and enthuse about her *"incredible knowledge."* Houston-based **Michael King** has an accomplished transactional practice covering oil and gas upstream and midstream work. On the upstream side, he has a special concentration on divestitures, acquisitions and, on midstream, joint ventures. He is currently acting on behalf of Energy Transfer on its purchase of Southern Union, a transaction which represented the biggest acquisition of a pipeline company within the past year. New entrant to the oil and gas transactional rankings **Jeff Munoz** is noted for his ability to handle major transactions: *"He helped us with several very complex multibillion-dollar transactions. He is a very good lawyer who is very knowledgeable about the industry and is also a very good negotiator,"* enthuses one very impressed client.

### Locke Lord LLP
See profile on p.2443

**THE FIRM** This talented oil and gas group advises energy companies including new business ventures and large multinationals on a broad array of concerns including M&A work, finance, litigation and regulatory concerns requiring representation before FERC. Recent highlights include assisting Southern Union with its $9.7 billion merger with Sigma Acquisition, as well as acting for El Paso Corporation on the disposal of its exploration and production business valued at over $7 billion.

**KEY INDIVIDUALS David Patton** (see p.382) serves as cochair of the firm's energy practice, and has over three decades' experience in oil and gas matters. Of late, he has been involved in some of the firm's big-ticket transactions, including acquisitions and restructurings.

### Milbank, Tweed, Hadley & McCloy LLP
See profile on p.448

**THE FIRM** This excellent firm is noted for its solid state-to-state offering. It has a strong transactional practice and focuses primarily on the representation of major financial organizations as well as prominent power companies, on a range of concerns including transmission matters, and the development, financing, acquisition and sale of projects in the renewable and alternative energy space.

**Sources say:** *"An excellent firm: it has enormous coverage and its work is always of a very high quality."*

**KEY INDIVIDUALS** Eric Silverman and Jonathan Green cochair the New York project finance group.

### Miller, Balis & O'Neil, PC

**THE FIRM** This compact but highly respected firm has been a presence in Washington, DC for over 30 years and is relied upon for advice on a broad spectrum of electric power issues, ranging from providing representation in FERC proceedings, including licensing and permitting

matters relating to hydroelectric facilities, to facilitating the formation of power purchase and interconnection agreements. The experienced group also represents clients in electricity transactions.

**Sources say:** *"A very good boutique firm."*

**KEY INDIVIDUALS** James Choukas-Bradley is a key practice contact.

### Morgan, Lewis & Bockius LLP
See profile on p.2246

**THE FIRM** Morgan Lewis's nuclear practice continues to be one of the most formidable and successful in the country, with market competitors conceding it is wholly deserving of its exclusive position at the top of the table. Clients are universal in their praise for the team, highlighting its deep-rooted understanding of the nuclear industry as well as its clear ability to appreciate clients' needs. It is regularly employed on some of the most high-value and high-profile matters both nationally and globally. Of late it has been very active advising the likes of South Carolina Electric & Gas and Nuclear Innovation North America on obtaining various approvals and operating licenses from the NRC. The team also enjoys a fine reputation for its work in the electricity and oil and gas arenas. On the electricity side, it regularly acts for clients such as Exelon, National Grid and Entergy Services. The oil and gas team has been busy representing the likes of BP and Mitsui in a variety of matters such as domestic and international upstream M&A, including the acquisition and development of shale gas properties. One major highlight for the team was acting for ConocoPhillips on the highly publicized $1.15 billion disposal of its interest in Seaway Crude Pipeline Company to a Canadian company.

**Client Service** *"One thing that sets them is apart is that they work very well as a team and are particularly good at getting individuals with particular expertise to help out and work on different types of matters and issues – that's very beneficial from a client's perspective."*

**Commercial Awareness** *"Great commercial judgment – we value attorneys who do their best for clients by understanding their broader objectives, and all the people here at this firm demonstrate that."*

**KEY INDIVIDUALS Thomas Giblin** (see p.320) is known among peers for his ability to *"get deals done"* and is top of the list for referrals from peers in conflict situations. Giblin is particularly noted for his knowledge of capital markets, especially within the utilities and energy space. Market sources are keen to point out **Robert Reger's** (see p.391) experience in the energy finance arena, with one saying: *"He is one of the deans of the profession – there is nothing he has not done or seen."* Both Reger and Giblin recently acted for Florida Power & Light on several issues, and their sale, of bonds valued at $1.45 billion. **John McGrane** (see p.365) moves up the rankings this year having attracted widespread praise from market sources, drawing particular praise for the quality of his work product and his management of client relations. He concentrates on advising electric utilities such as PacifiCorp, National Grid and TECO Energy on the full range of electricity regulation and structure concerns. **Floyd Norton** (see p.377) specializes in elec-

tric utility concerns, with a particular focus on utility responses to competition and utility regulation. He is well known for acting on behalf of various clients who are under scrutiny for transmission access and electric trading practices. **Glen Bernstein** (see p.283) is a seasoned attorney in matters involving electric utility regulation and deregulation. He has recently taken the lead on a series of major matters, including helping Entergy Services in a civil investigation initiated by the DOJ, as well as representing the company before FERC in its application to become a part of the regional transmission organization.

**John Hood** (see p.336) has enjoyed another active year advising clients on a wide range of finance transactions including public offerings, debt and equity offerings, public offerings, structured finance and bank lending matters. Recent highlights include representing Entergy in two separate public offerings totaling $750 million, as well as acting for it and several of its subsidiaries on the division and rearrangement of its transmission businesses. According to market sources **Jay Gutierrez** (see p.328) does a *"wonderful job on everything."* During the past year he has continued to focus on the development of the international side of the group's nuclear practice, which has seen him head a variety of newbuild ventures in countries ranging from Europe to the Middle East, representing clients such as the King Abdullah City for Atomic & Renewable Energy and Polska Grupa Energetyczna. Peers and clients alike are full of praise for the energy group leader, **Kathryn Sutton** (see p.415). She is *"extremely client-focused,"* say impressed sources, with one client reporting that she *"understands our business and is very good at leading the team that services us."* A large part of her workload consists of advice on commercial nuclear reactors and the latest stage of nuclear power plants in the USA, in which she has helped several clients including Entergy, Tennessee Valley Authority and South Carolina Electric & Gas to obtain the required licenses and permits. **Steven Frantz** (see p.316) has recently been helping Nuclear Innovation North America with obtaining a combined construction and operating license for a newly developed power plant, the first ever application of its kind. His typical clients include electric utilities, materials licensees and reactor producers. The highly regarded **John Matthews** (see p.363) is also very experienced in acquiring NRC permissions, specifically for cutting-edge commercial projects relating to nuclear power plants. He is also very well versed in handling complicated commercial litigation associated with nuclear assets and representing clients before the NRC in cases where there is a license dispute. The *"very smart"* **Alex Polonsky** (see p.386) focuses on NRC litigation and licensing, with particular expertise in matters requiring representation before the NRC's Atomic Safety and Licensing Boards. He recently helped Exelon obtain a power uprate from the NRC within a very impressive timeframe. **Donald Silverman** (see p.406) is another highly respected nuclear attorney, with particular experience in acting for DOE contractors before the NRC. He is an *"extraordinarily good attorney,"* enthuse clients, who also appreciate his excellent management of transactions. Senior statesman **George Edgar** (see p.308) continues to assist clients with an array of nuclear matters. Respect for his extensive capabilities is apparent among sources, who do not hesitate in singling him out as an *"outstanding nuclear lawyer"* who provides *"invaluable advice."*

As far as market sources are concerned, there is *"nothing"* **Mark Haskell** (see p.331) *"can't do."* One client goes so far as to say: *"If I asked him to build a replica of the Vatican, he would find an easy way to do it because he is just amazing."* He is best known for his expertise in FERC matters for producers, and over the past year has worked closely with BP and several other confidential clients on CFTC investigations. **Charles Moore** (see p.370) is a very well-respected individual in the oil and gas regulatory space who offers clients the advantage of many years of experience in energy-related roles within government, including as general counsel at FERC. **David Asmus** (see p.274) chairs the energy transactional practice and offers significant expertise in divestitures and acquisitions, oil and gas development projects, and energy-related financings. He recently acted for Mitsui on its big-ticket purchase of 12.5% of SM Energy's position in the Eagle Ford Shale. Clients and peers alike are full of praise for this *"supersmart, fantastic, hard-working lawyer,"* with universal agreement that he *"is a definite star in this area."* *"The attentive and commercial"* **Douglas Davidson** (see p.301) is highly recommended for his expertise in capital markets. One client reports: *"He understands our objectives and works in a fast, efficient manner."* He undertakes work ranging from electricity finance and regulation to purchases and divestitures, for a diverse range of clients including investor-owned utilities and private equity firms.

## Orrick, Herrington & Sutcliffe LLP
See profile on p.1994

**THE FIRM** This robust practice has been busy advising on the financing aspects of energy transactions of late, for clients including Rim Rock Financing, NextEra Energy and Wellhead Electric. Its attorneys are also skilled in acting on the various other aspects of electricity transactions, ranging from advising on power purchase and asset purchase agreements to acquisitions and disposals.

**KEY INDIVIDUALS** The highly regarded **Adam Wenner** recently advised NextEra Energy on the $225 million financing of its Capricorn Wind Farm.

## Pillsbury Winthrop Shaw Pittman LLP
See profile on p.2000

**THE FIRM** This talented group attracts particular praise from clients and peers alike for its strength in nuclear issues, both domestic and international. Of late, the group has appeared before the NRC in licensing proceedings on behalf of clients. The team also offers counsel on the full range of electricity transactional matters, including energy company financings, as well as power generation and transmission projects ranging from hydro and coal to renewable energy. Clients applaud its vast knowledge of the US electric utility industry and the respect it garners among the underwriter community. Notably, the team is currently representing Barclays Capital, JPMorgan Securities and other underwriters in a $300 million refi-

nancing offering for Northeast Utilities. The group continues to represent a variety of other high-profile clients, including Merrill Lynch, Deutsche Bank Securities and Goldman Sachs.

**Sources say:** *"The attorneys are excellent – knowledgeable in their field, hard-working and responsive."*

**KEY INDIVIDUALS** Leading practitioner **David Baxter** assists energy clients with M&A transactions and securities matters and *"works efficiently to complete transactions on time and with a minimum of fuss,"* reports one enthusiastic source. Recent highlights include helping Merrill Lynch, Citigroup Global Markets and others in numerous capital markets issues by CMS Energy. **Jeffrey Delaney** serves as cochair of the firm's global energy industry group. He maintains an excellent reputation among his numerous energy and utility clients for his work as underwriters' and issuers' counsel. *"He is an extremely skilled lawyer; very knowledgeable and practical and is able to break down tough issues into more easily understandable terms,"* notes one impressed commentator. **Anthony Terrell** is a talented attorney who specializes in public and private offerings of a broad array of securities for a variety of issuers and underwriters, including Avista and PPL Electric Utilities. Interviewees say of **Jay Silberg** (see p.406): *"He is extremely dedicated and competent,"* and is praised for his *"vast knowledge"* in all matters nuclear. He regularly appears before the NRC, DOE and courts in licensing matters as well as nuclear waste concerns. Peers and clients highlight **David Lewis** (see p.356) for his license renewal work, hailing him as *"a very strong expert on the subject matter."* Additionally, he is commended for his extensive industry knowledge and excellent writing skills. **John O'Neill** has advised a large number of nuclear companies and electric utilities on their nuclear transactions and a broad spectrum of issues including the purchase and disposal of power plants and nuclear fuels and services. He is also well versed in helping clients achieve compliance with US nuclear regulatory provisions. **Charles Peterson** has an internationally focused practice and regularly represents utilities in relation to the licensing concerns arising out of the development of nuclear reactors, as well as nuclear fuel procurement.

## Porter Hedges LLP
See profile on p.2450

**THE FIRM** This team is commended by clients for its high-quality practice, and counsels a wide range of clients including oilfield service entities, natural gas pipelines and exploration and production companies on transactional matters. Its diverse workload includes M&A, sales, divestitures and the financing of energy companies. In a recent high-value matter, the team successfully represented Noble Energy in a joint venture with CONSOL Energy. Other major names on its client roster include Kinder Morgan, Petrohawk Energy and Talisman Energy.

**Sources say:** *"It is a good law firm that has provided us with a very reliable and dependable service. Everyone at the firm has impressed us."* *"They have great experience in oil and gas transactions."*

**KEY INDIVIDUALS Randall King** (see p.347) led the team on the high-profile Noble Energy matter and is described by loyal clients as a *"very practical and knowledgeable attorney who is very solutions-focused in his practice."* Clients also compliment the way in which he and colleague **Robert Thomas** (see p.417) *"have really taken the time to get to know our business and company."* Clients also laud Thomas for his *"knowledge and experience of the oil and gas industry, which makes him excellent from a commercial point of view."*

## Sidley Austin LLP
See profile on p.1264

**THE FIRM** This strong group is principally known for its expertise in the realm of oil and gas regulatory and litigation matters, focusing largely on the representation of major oil pipelines. The team continues to represent ExxonMobil Pipeline in various FERC proceedings including a challenge to the rates for transportation services over the Trans-Alaska Pipeline System. Other work has involved helping the likes of Explorer Pipeline, Mobil Pipe Line and Magellan Pipeline file petitions for declaratory orders at FERC.

**Sources say:** *"Very high-quality, professional and knowledgeable about energy issues."*

**KEY INDIVIDUALS** *"Very good lawyer"* **Stan Berman** (see p.282) is highlighted by observers for his strong litigation and regulatory capabilities in the power arena. He is currently acting for Pacific Gas on high-profile litigation relating to the California electric crisis FERC litigation. Market sources single out **Eugene Elrod** (see p.309) as a leading figure in this field. He is very well respected among peers, with one saying that in a conflict situation, *"I would always ask Gene Elrod first."* Another key member of the oil and gas team is the *"terrific"* **William Williams** (see p.426). He specializes in representing interstate oil and gas pipelines in FERC-related matters, including enforcement proceedings. He is currently helping Explorer Pipeline with its efforts to obtain a declaratory order from FERC. *"Exceptionally able lawyer"* **Christopher Lyons** (see p.359) offers clients considerable expertise in a variety of oil and gas regulatory and litigation matters. Over the past year he has been involved in several of the firm's most significant mandates for an enviable roster of clients including ExxonMobil, Enterprise Products Pipeline and Mobil Pipe Line. As one loyal client puts it, **James Rice** (see p.392) is *"a very thoughtful negotiator"* who *"helped us understand the ins and outs of the oil and gas industry."* His practice involves representing energy companies such as Grupo Transmerquim in a broad array of transactions ranging from joint ventures to bank financings and debt restructurings.

## Simpson Thacher & Bartlett LLP
See profile on p.2006

**THE FIRM** This firm enjoys a sound reputation for its skilled handling of issues in the electricity financing, acquisitions and divestiture arenas. It acts for substantial, well-known clients such as Barclays Capital, RBS and First Reserve. Notably, the firm recently represented Eaton

Corporation in its $11.8 billion acquisition of Cooper Industries.

**Commercial Awareness** "*The team is made up of very practical, business-minded lawyers who always try to find solutions to problems.*"

**KEY INDIVIDUALS** The "*very talented*" **David Lieberman** (see p.356) is applauded for the "*knowledge that he brings to the table*" and his ability to "*get everybody focused on business.*" Recent examples of his work include acting on behalf of the lenders in a $460 million financing to Blythe Energy.

## Skadden, Arps, Slate, Meagher & Flom LLP & Affiliates
### See profile on p.2008

**THE FIRM** The Skadden energy and natural resources practice remains very strong on a variety of fronts. The electricity regulatory and litigation group continues to be seen as one of the leading teams in the country, representing a desirable list of industry names including Duke Energy, GenOn Energy and FirstEnergy. Just one example of its many recent highlights is the representation of Exelon in settlement negotiations relating to a FERC investigation. The team is renowned for its involvement in notable M&A matters, such as the $9.5 billion merger between Northeast Utilities and NSTAR, which has led to the formation of one of the biggest energy utility companies worldwide. It also offers superior advice on natural gas and LNG issues to the likes of Exelon and JPMorgan Chase.

**Sources say:** "*It is the gold standard in the industry – it has many, many strong lawyers.*" "*For anything of significance, it is our law firm of choice.*"

**KEY INDIVIDUALS** "*The king of energy regulation,*" **Clifford Naeve** (see p.374) is "*head and shoulders above the rest,*" market sources report. This "*brilliant lawyer*" has enjoyed an active year acting on some of the most cutting-edge deals in industry. By way of example, he acted on Duke Energy's $13.7 billion merger with Progress Energy, a deal which resulted in the creation of the biggest utility in the USA. He also led on the Exelon matter above. "*Excellent attorney*" **John Estes** (see p.310) has "*great command of the industry*" and is "*always very effective.*" He specializes in judicial review and FERC enforcement and litigation cases, and is currently active in the defense of several market manipulation cases including on behalf of Kansas City Power & Light and Dynegy. "*The very bright and very capable*" **John Moot** (see p.371) has wide-ranging electricity regulation and litigation experience that includes M&A, enforcement matters, rates and transmission access issues. One very satisfied client reports: "*In addition to his sheer legal capabilities and brilliance, he is able to understand the bigger picture and can therefore counsel the client in a balanced manner about their various options.*" The highly regarded **William Conway** (see p.298) has advised a number of major names including AES and Citizens Sunrise Transmission on a broad range of regulatory matters. **Sheldon Adler** (see p.271) is particularly renowned for his public utility merger work, recently acting for National Grid on its $285 million disposal of two

companies to a subsidiary of a Canadian utility. M&A guru **Pankaj Sinha** (see p.407) recently acted for AES on its $4.7 billion purchase of an electric utility business. The "*excellent*" **Ann Hawkins** (see p.332) has been heavily involved in a series of transactional matters, including acting for renewable energy power company GreenTech Global Energy on its purchase of a solar power property.

## Steptoe & Johnson LLP

**THE FIRM** Steptoe & Johnson is a powerhouse in the world of energy regulatory matters, with sources particularly quick to commend its strength in oil pipeline matters, especially when it comes to representation before FERC. The team is currently acting for ConocoPhillips on numerous Trans-Alaska Pipeline System-linked concerns. Market commentators are impressed by the attorneys' unrivaled experience and the high-quality advice that they provide, and do not hesitate to say that it is the preeminent firm when it comes to rates cases. The group has also seen considerable success in the electricity arena over the past year, particularly in its continued efforts in the electric transmissions legal market, in which it regularly acts for major clients such as Duke Energy, Enbridge and AEP.

**Client Service** "*The attorneys are great. They are consistently very responsive. We always feel we have the best in the whole industry.*"

**KEY INDIVIDUALS** **Douglas Green** "*is a standout in the area of regulatory law and representation,*" say market sources. According to them, "*this is an area where in-depth knowledge of the regulator, as well as the law, is required for valuable counseling and representation, and he possesses this special skill.*" He is also praised for his excellent litigation skills and his involvement in some of the largest cases in this space. His colleague **David Raskin** is also singled out for being a "*great regulatory lawyer and very able litigator*" and is lauded by clients for his breadth of experience. He continues to lead the firm's transmissions work and is notably representing Northeast Utilities in a return on equity complaint that is imminently due to be heard before FERC. The result of this case will be very significant, not only for the client, but also for the wider community of developers alike in terms of their return on equity. Clients and peers alike have high regard for **Richard Roberts**, who is "*very smart, creative and thoughtful, and handles relationships with co-counsel and opposing counsel and regulators very well.*" This "*superb trial lawyer*" has been involved in many high-profile matters such as the ongoing Southern California Edison refund matter, in which he recently managed to secure the highest-value refund claim to have been granted in the USA to date. **Steven Brose** has an excellent reputation among peers, who describe him as "*top of the heap in pipeline work.*" Clients laud his experience and knowledge of FERC matters and the respect that he is awarded by the regulators, judges and opposing counsel. "*The very highly regarded*" **Steven Reed** enjoys a significant practice in the oil pipelines area and is singled out for his "*absolute wealth of knowledge in relation to the industry,*" "*excellent judgment*" and "*very good negotiation skills.*" He has recently been acting for Enbridge on a variety of matters including the defense of the spot tariff rates imposed

for US shippers. The "*outstanding*" **Daniel Poynor** is another well-respected oil pipeline lawyer at the firm and is lauded for his "*great depth of knowledge*" and excellent writing skills. He is adept in the gamut of pipeline rates and regulatory matters and is currently representing TEP-PCO in a cost of service matter valued at $350 million. "*Very strong performer*" **Steven Ross** has been involved in work on behalf of a number of key clients including American Electric Power, Enbridge, Duke Energy and Westar Energy.

## Stinson Morrison Hecker LLP

**THE FIRM** This solid team continues to build on its healthy reputation in regulatory and transactional concerns on behalf of public sector electricity clients. It is particularly known for its representation of municipally owned utilities and state regulatory commissions, having represented clients such as Sacramento Municipal Utility District and Arkansas Public Service Commission.

**Sources say:** "*Very satisfied: they have pulled our cookies out of the oven when they were close to burning.*"

**KEY INDIVIDUALS** The "*very knowledgeable and very attentive*" **Harvey Reiter** is "*an excellent regulatory lawyer,*" sources report. He is currently working alongside the "*fantastic*" **Adrienne Clair** on behalf of a number of key clients in FERC proceedings relating to transmission issues.

## Sullivan & Cromwell LLP
### See profile on p.2011

**THE FIRM** This team houses one of the premier mining and metals practice in the country. The firm's ability reflects its instructions on big-ticket matters for a strong client base that includes Nippon Steel, Sumitomo Metal Mining and Cameco. A significant example of the group's work includes its recent representation of CST Mining in the $505 million sale of its 70% stake in a copper project in Peru. The firm also maintains a strong focus on helping utilities with their M&A work and recently advised BHP Billiton on its $15.1 billion purchase of Petrohawk Energy. **KEY INDIVIDUALS** **Joseph Frumkin** (see p.317) specializes in M&A, frequently acting as lead attorney on cross-border matters. Recent examples of his work include the representation of Southern Union in its $9.4 billion merger with Energy Transfer Equity. The highly regarded **Tia Barancik** (see p.277) played an integral part in the Southern Union transaction and is also very active on the regulatory side, recently assisting Mitsubishi UFJ Financial Group with FERC issues arising out of its proposed investment in Morgan Stanley.

## Sutherland Asbill & Brennan LLP

**THE FIRM** This expanding energy practice is regularly engaged in a variety of regulatory matters. It has recently been very active in advising on compliance issues concerning the Dodd-Frank Act, and is well versed in handling matters before FERC, CFTC, NERC and EPA. Key clients include Calpine, Oglethorpe Power and Vitol.
**KEY INDIVIDUALS** **Keith McCrea** continues to be highly thought of by peers. He is adept at representing clients in investigations and contentious matters before FERC, and

has recently been helping clients with CFTC regulatory compliance issues. **Catherine Krupka** heads the power and natural gas regulatory group and of late has been particularly active in representing several of the firm's commodity-trading clients in their regulatory and transactional concerns. **Daniel Frank** has a broad electricity practice and is regularly sought by transmission clients on regulatory compliance issues. He is praised by clients for his thoughtful approach.

## Thompson Coburn LLP

**THE FIRM** This compact team packs a considerable punch in energy electricity matters. The group handles a range of regulatory and litigation matters. Notable clients include American Municipal Power, Lafayette Utilities System and Louisiana Energy & Power Authority.

**Sources say:** *"They are very responsive. We are deadline-driven and often have last-minute issues but they always meet our needs."*

**KEY INDIVIDUALS Bonnie Blair** is highly acclaimed for her extensive knowledge and technical expertise, with clients enthusing: *"She's so well respected that we are always very proud to throw her name out and say Bonnie Blair did this for us. That always gets people's attention – judges and attorneys alike."* **Margaret McNaul** is a new addition to the electricity regulatory and litigation table, following excellent client appraisals. She is highlighted as an emerging name in this sector, with sources hailing her as *"fantastic"* and *"very collaborative,"* especially when it comes to the settlement of cases.

## Thompson & Knight LLP
See profile on p.2458

**THE FIRM** This team provides its clients with a broad range of transactional services, and its members are especially recommended by commentators for their ability to handle complex matters. Of late, the firm has been instructed in several cross-border highlights and recently acted for Brigham Exploration on its sale to Norway-based oil and gas production company Statoil. The group was also called upon by Samsung C&T to assist with its acquisition of Parallel Petroleum, a transaction valued at some $800 million.

**Sources say:** *"An excellent law firm with a number of very, very talented attorneys."*

**KEY INDIVIDUALS Andrew Derman** (see p.304) is *"very client-focused and proactive at fulfilling our needs,"* a satisfied client asserts. He is specifically highlighted for his international expertise, and recently led the team on the Samsung C&T matter. **John Rain** (see p.2411) has renowned expertise in representing capital consumers and suppliers in transactions involving volumetric production payments. He was recently part of the team acting for Cinco Resources on a securities matter.

## Troutman Sanders LLP

**THE FIRM** This energy group specializes in electricity regulatory concerns on behalf of a variety of investor-owned utilities. A significant proportion of the team's work over the past year has involved assisting such clients with

obtaining FERC permissions under Section 203 of the Federal Power Act for acquisitions and disposals. Other recent highlights have included the ongoing representation of Indiana Public Service Company in its dispute with a transmission developer concerning a proposed regional transmission project. The firm also maintains an active oil and gas practice, helping clients such as Atlanta Gas Light and Pivotal LNG.

**KEY INDIVIDUALS Daniel Larcamp** heads the federal regulation of electricity and gas practice group at the firm. Armed with over two decades' experience of working at FERC, he is adept at handling a broad spectrum of issues ranging from Federal Power Act concerns such as rate proceedings and mergers, to FERC enforcement matters. He has recently been leading the firm's work, alongside **Clifford Sikora**, for its investor-owned utility clients. Sikora is also held in high regard for his FERC-related work, acting for a variety of clients, including transmission entities, conventional utilities and banks. **Arthur Domby** is particularly focused on providing advice on the regulatory concerns affecting the firm's nuclear clients, specifically on power plant and material licensing matters. **Lisanne Crowley** is an experienced litigator, frequently acting for natural gas pipeline and storage entities and natural gas distribution businesses on a range of administrative proceedings including ratemaking, rulemaking and enforcement issues. She is currently leading the firm's work on behalf of Atlanta Gas Light, with the aim of securing a settlement in a contentious FERC rates case.

## Van Ness Feldman LLP
See profile on p.926

**THE FIRM** Van Ness retains its reputation for excellence in regulatory and litigation work, both on the electricity and oil and gas sides. The attorneys' previous experience working for the regulators has left them well equipped to represent clients in all manner of FERC issues. The electricity group has particular expertise in hydropower concerns, specifically licensing and relicensing of such projects, and has recently acted on some of the largest matters in this arena. The group recently achieved victory for a number of licensees including Idaho Power and PacifiCorp before FERC and the US Court of Appeals, securing refunds of over $20 million. The oil and gas team continues to represent major oil pipelines in FERC proceedings as well as providing advice on compliance with changing regulatory policies. In a recent highlight the team successfully represented the Texas Pipeline Association before FERC.

**Sources say:** *"There is just so much depth at this firm. It is a great group of very qualified attorneys who are very well regarded and highly competent."*

**KEY INDIVIDUALS** The *"terrific"* **Lawrence Acker** (see p.271) has recently joined the firm from Dewey & LeBoeuf. He is a popular choice for natural gas and electric power issues and is praised for his expertise in such matters. He was recently part of the team which helped Idaho Power obtain a declaratory order for the extinguishment of a settlement. Peers applaud **Margaret Moore's** (see p.371) *"vast knowledge"* of the regulatory space, where she frequently advises a range of clients including electric utilities, inde-

pendent power companies and financial institutions. Recent mandates include advising Blackstone Energy Partners on federal regulatory concerns relating to its $1.5 billion investment in Cheniere Energy Partners. *"Very smart lawyer"* **Douglas Smith** (see p.408) is a former general counsel at FERC and deputy general counsel for energy policy at the DOE, and is much sought for his expertise in areas including rulemaking, rates issues and energy efficiency regulation. Clients appreciate his *"very strong understanding of both business and legal issues."* The *"very thoughtful"* **Gary Bachman** (see p.276) is well versed in defending clients in FERC investigations and disputes. He is also routinely called upon to advise on NERC and FERC regulatory compliance issues. **Howard Shapiro** (see p.404) was recently part of the team assisting the various hydroelectric licensees with FERC litigation, and continues to help Resale Power Group of Iowa with a complaint filed with FERC in relation to transmission service charges. **Robert Nordhaus** (see p.377) is particularly focused on FERC matters as they relate to the electric power industry, counting organizations such as the Large Public Power Council and Carnegie Mellon's Department of Engineering & Public Policy among his clients. **Curtis Moffatt** (see p.370) maintains a strong presence in the market, with over 30 years' experience in the oil and gas space. Recent work highlights include acting as lead lawyer for Kinder Morgan on its purchase of El Paso Corporation. According to clients, **Paul Korman** (see p.349) *"has a deep base of knowledge and experience and stays in tune with industry. He does a good job of staffing cases efficiently and excels at picking the battles that matter in litigation."* Peers have the *"highest respect and regard"* for **Brian O'Neill** (see p.380). He recently moved to the firm from Dewey & LeBoeuf, and specializes in regulatory matters on behalf of major participants in the energy industry such as pipelines, oil and gas businesses, and LNG companies.

## Venable LLP
See profile on p.927

**THE FIRM** This firm has a highly respected oil and gas practice and a particularly strong reputation for undertaking pipeline-related concerns. Over the past year, the group has been appointed to act as counsel for a range of leading clients including ConocoPhillips. The team is also famed for its work on behalf of airlines, including Continental, Delta and United, and also has a fine track record handling rates cases before FERC.

**Sources say:** *"Venable is extremely knowledgeable about the pipeline industry and has great relationships."*

**KEY INDIVIDUALS Richard Powers** (see p.387) garners much praise from the market: *"He skillfully navigates complex regulatory issues and develops viable, and ultimately successful, strategies,"* according to one well-placed commentator. Another source was quick to praise his *"depth, experience and institutional knowledge in understanding various pipeline issues."* **Steven Adducci** (see p.271) rises up the rankings this year after strong recommendations from market sources and an impressive list of highlight matters. Peers attest to his very active practice and say that they have *"referred many matters to him and he has done very well."*

## Vinson & Elkins LLP
See profile on p.2459

THE FIRM Vinson & Elkins's energy group maintains its stellar reputation as one of the nation's best. Sources hold it in high regard for its attorneys' vast expertise and ability to handle the largest and most complex matters. With one of the largest teams in the area, the group is well equipped to advise on leading oil and gas mandates, and is ever-present before FERC and other bodies on various regulatory and litigation matters. It has developed strong, longstanding relationships with many large clients, including BG Group, Kinder Morgan and Apollo Global Management. On the transaction side, the group's vast experience in gas value stream cross-border work saw it instructed in the high-profile Statoil $4.7 billion acquisition of Brigham Exploration. The team also receives acclaim for its capabilities in the electricity space. It works with clients on a variety of issues including transmission matters and is highly experienced in appearing before FERC and the DOE. A recent highlight saw the practice represent LS Power Transmission in the $600 million financing of a transmission project.

Client Service *"They will do whatever is necessary to keep clients very happy."*

KEY INDIVIDUALS **Stephen Angle** (see p.273) was formerly the assistant general counsel for electricity litigation at FERC, and sources say that he *"really knows his stuff."* His practice includes representing the likes of TransAlta Energy Marketing and Clean Line Energy Partners in NERC compliance matters and FERC enforcement inquiries. **John Decker** (see p.303) is lauded for his ability to *"provide advice on tricky, less obvious questions."* He has been very active over the past year, providing regulatory and transactional advice to both electric and oil and gas entities. **Marcia Backus** (see p.276) heads the transactional team, and continues to assist prominent energy companies, at home and abroad, with a wide spectrum of matters ranging from joint ventures and M&A for power generation facilities to natural gas pipeline concerns and shale mergers. She was recently entrusted by SandRidge Energy to handle a large-scale shale transaction worth $1.5 billion. Corporate lawyer **David Cohen** (see p.297) regularly turns his hand to energy concerns, and over the past year has acted on behalf of clients such as the BG Group and GasAtacama, assisting them with major LNG projects. Clients turn to **David Andril** (see p.273) because *"the level of his knowledge and the number of projects he has worked on is great."* He is also praised for his ability to handle LNG concerns, with one client commenting that *"his management of these transactions is extraordinary."* **Charles Caldwell** (see p.291) is highlighted this year for his excellent advocacy skills. In the words of one peer, *"I have seen him argue in court and can say that he is top-notch."* He is an expert in oil and gas pipeline work, and has recently led on a number of public utilities commission and FERC-related matters for Kinder Morgan. **Anita Wilson** (see p.427) stands out for her solid advice on FERC-related

issues. She teamed up with colleague Decker to advise the BG Group on FERC proceedings concerning an LNG export matter. **John Kennedy** (see p.345) has extensive experience and continues to represent leading names within the oil and gas pipelines arena. He is adept at representing clients before a range of bodies including FERC, the US Supreme Court and state public utilities commissions. **Bert Tabor** (see p.415) is another experienced FERC lawyer, and is regularly called upon by clients from the energy industry to handle matters such as the purchase, sale, financing, regulation and operation of oil and gas pipelines. He was recently part of the team that successfully appeared before FERC on behalf of Kinder Morgan's subsidiary SFPP in a significant rates case. **Henry May** (see p.363) enjoys an excellent reputation, representing high-profile clients nationwide in a variety of matters including transactions, regulatory concerns and policy issues. He is particularly well known for his regulatory representations before FERC and the courts. **Douglas Bland** (see p.284) is well versed in a broad array of upstream, midstream and downstream transactional work, and is also frequently sought to advise on clean energy concerns. He is assisting Backus with the shale transaction for SandRidge Energy. **Michael Rosenwasser** (see p.395) comes recommended for his wealth of experience in M&A, particularly in oil and gas pipeline projects. **Keith Fullenweider** (see p.2390) continues to be recognized for his adroit handling of transactions in the oil and gas arena. **John Connally** (see p.298) has a large practice and significant cross-border capabilities, regularly working with companies across all continents. He recently assisted Devon Energy with a $2.2 billion joint venture sale to Sinopec. **James Seegers** (see p.403) enters the rankings after having earned widespread praise for his regulatory practice. In the words of one peer, he is a *"great general oil and gas attorney."* He counts Spectra Energy as a key client.

## White & Case LLP
See profile on p.451

THE FIRM This firm continues to excel in the gamut of regulatory, litigation and transactional concerns affecting the electricity industry. On the regulatory and litigation front, the group continues to be involved in major transmission and power generation projects, both within the USA and internationally, acting for clients including DTE Energy, PG&E and Hess Corporation. On the transactional side, the team has had its fair share of big-ticket work including acting on the $1.5 billion purchase of American-owned CH Energy by Canadian utility Fortis, as well as representing Morgan Stanley in connection with the $1 billion financing of a natural gas-fired plant project.

Sources say: *"They do a really good job and are committed to helping clients achieve their objectives."*

KEY INDIVIDUALS Leading regulatory lawyer **Earle O'Donnell** (see p.379) has had another active year acting on significant matters including the $230 million Gratiot County Wind Project, where he represented Detroit Edison. Clients afford him particular praise for his *"excellent industry connections"* and the way in which he can aptly *"find out what the real issue is and work with regulators to get

things done."* **Donna Attanasio** (see p.275) is another highly experienced regulatory lawyer, who recently collaborated with O'Donnell on the Fortis and CH Energy matter. She also served as lead lawyer to PG&E in relation to various matters involving renewable power transactions and regulatory compliance. The *"talented"* **Michael Shenberg** (see p.405) is *"a pleasure to work with,"* sources say. He is the lead lawyer on a number of the firm's transactional matters, acting for a range of prominent clients including Russell City Energy and Kelson Energy.

## Winston & Strawn LLP
See profile on p.1267

THE FIRM Winston & Strawn is a longstanding and highly respected name in the nuclear power arena. The firm also boasts a strong electric power practice undertaking the gamut of regulatory issues and litigation concerns. The group is particularly well versed in acting on behalf of clients requiring representation in California state administrative agencies, and recently helped California Cogeneration Council reach a settlement with the State of California on the development of a combined heat and power project. On the nuclear side, the team has been actively engaged in helping various clients such as Unistar Nuclear Energy and DTE Energy make license applications to the NRC for the development and use of new nuclear power plants, as well as handling renewal applications on existing plants.

Sources say: *"They have several outstanding people."*

KEY INDIVIDUALS The *"very effective"* **Raymond Wuslich** (see p.429) is experienced in handling federal regulatory concerns, and is currently acting for Terra-Gen Power in FERC proceedings relating to a transmission matter. The *"very talented"* and *"outstanding nuclear lawyer"* **David Repka** (see p.391) is highlighted in particular for his excellent licensing work. He recently acted for Entergy in respect of alleged NRC breaches. **Tyson Smith** (see p.409) has been heavily involved in helping clients with licensing matters relating to both new and existing plants, and recently acted on behalf of PG&E Co on a license renewal matter.

## Wright & Talisman PC

THE FIRM Wright & Talisman earns unanimous client praise for its comprehensive regulatory and litigation offering, particularly for its ability to handle the full array of FERC-related matters. Peers also attest to its active presence on both the electric and oil and gas sides, and deep bench of strong attorneys. The electric power team typically works for sizable companies including various transmission groups such as PJM Interconnection and Southwest Power Pool, while the robust oil and gas group is highlighted for its representation of interstate pipelines such as the Transcontinental Gas Pipe Line and the Millennium Pipeline. Recent standout work includes successfully representing the MISO Transmission Owners, a group made up of over 27 utilities, in regional transmission organization withdrawal charges of over $700 million. It also represented Anadarko before FERC in a contentious rates matter valued at over $350 million.

**Client Service** "*Wright & Talisman has mastered the art of providing exceptional and quality service and expertise to its clients.*" **KEY INDIVIDUALS** The very well-respected **Barry Spector** is responsive and "*provides great legal and practical advice,*" commentators note. He has been at the forefront of the firm's most significant work, including both prosecuting and defending FERC litigation on behalf of PJM Interconnection. **Arnold Podgorsky** is also very well versed in handling regulatory and litigation-related matters before FERC and various other agencies, and was recently called upon by WSPP to advise it on regulations applicable to a contemplated Energy Imbalance Market. **Wendy Reed** is another of the team's standout performers, with one client asserting: "*Wendy is a super attorney with remarkable FERC regulatory knowledge.*" She is also lauded for her "*exceptional skill, finesse, determination and dedication.*" She is currently leading the team on the MISO Transmission Owners matter. **Alan Statman** and **Wendy Warren** win praise for maintaining "*terrific relationships within the FERC regulatory arena*" and for being "*very good strategic thinkers.*" Both are highly experienced in transmission matters. **Joseph Koury** recently represented Anadarko before FERC in a contentious rates matter valued at over $350 million. **Michael Thompson** stands out for his "*vast knowledge.*" He also earns credit for his responsiveness and efficient approach. In the past year he has worked for the likes of Guardian Pipeline and Kern River Gas Transmission.

## Other Notable Practitioners

Senior statesman **William Baker** (see p.277) of Day Pitney LLP receives much praise for his "*wealth of knowledge and experience in utility industry matters.*" Post & Schell, P.C.'s **Christopher Barr** is highlighted for his strong capabilities within the oil and gas sphere and is regarded as "*a walking encyclopedia on FERC issues.*" The "*fantastic*" **Paul Belval** at Day Pitney LLP, is noted for his transactional strengths on behalf of energy companies and is described by clients as an "*invaluable resource.*" Schiff Hardin LLP's **Thomas Blackburn** is a well-known player in the electric power space, particularly in connection with FERC regulation matters. "*Great regulatory and FERC counsel*" **David Bloom** of Mayer Brown LLP continues to advise a range of leading clients including energy producers, financial institutions and major energy consumers. **Cynthia Bogorad** of Spiegel & McDiarmid receives rave reviews from clients: "*She is an amazing resource for developing strategy and overall goals,*" reports one source, while another interviewee describes her a "*tireless worker*" who provides "*great customer service.*" She receives particular recognition for her work on behalf of the Transmission Access Policy Study Group, and for her expertise in matters concerning the Federal Power Act. **Becky Bruner** of Davis Wright Tremaine LLP is a strong choice for clients seeking advice on state and federal energy regulation issues. A former FERC legal adviser, she recently represented American Electric Power Service before both FERC and the Washington, DC Circuit Court of Appeals in a complicated litigation matter. "*She is very good, especially when it comes to matters concerning cutting-edge policy issues,*" notes one impressed peer. **Michael Byrd** (see p.291) at Baker & McKenzie receives plaudits for his high-quality work and excellent negotiation skills. In the words of one client, "*we rely upon him for major acquisitions because he has a lifetime's experience in the oil industry,*" while peers say that they "*would definitely refer to him in a conflict situation.*" The "*very fine*" **John Cogan** of Cogan & Partners LLP has built a reputation as a go-to attorney for both domestic and international oil and gas transactional matters, particularly in relation to LNG projects. Sole practitioner **Michael Cusick** is particularly well known for his advice to public utilities on a range of transactional matters including acquisitions, restructurings and dispositions. Corporate attorney **William DeGrandis** of Paul Hastings LLP continues to impress clients with his high level of knowledge and experience in the energy field, as well as for his "*hard-working and helpful*" manner. He recently acted for Korea East-West Power in connection with several regulatory matters including the negotiation of various agreements arising out of its purchase of an interest in a subsidiary of Marubeni. The "*excellent*" **David Doot** (see p.305) is head of the energy and utility law team at Day Pitney LLP and has had a very busy year acting on behalf of several of the firm's utility clients including New England Power Pool. He is described as "*extremely knowledgeable about industry and regulatory issues,*" and is also commended for his active involvement in the "*bulk of very significant and high-dollar, intricate disputes involving rights to transmission and power pricing.*" **Katherine Edwards** of Edwards & Associates is very well respected for her FERC work, acting on behalf of her substantial oil and gas client base. She elicits particular praise for her client skills. Also at Day Pitney LLP, **Joseph Fagan** (see p.311) is noted for his ability to handle a variety of FERC matters. He acts for a wide spectrum of electricity clients including utilities and renewable power developers. Day Pitney is home to **Gerald Garfield** (see p.318) as well, who is described as "*very knowledgeable on anything related to nuclear*" and is also lauded for "*his ability to take on projects that have very little precedent and figure out how to get them done successfully.*" **Hugh Hilliard** recently joined O'Melveny & Myers LLP from Dewey & LeBoeuf, and is experienced in advising clients on the regulatory aspects of alternative energy projects and FERC compliance issues. **Robert Loeffler** of Morrison & Foerster LLP offers clients over three decades' experience in handling regulatory matters on behalf of various oil and gas industry participants. He is noted for his work with the State of Alaska, and is currently representing it before both FERC and the Regulatory Commission of Alaska in a rates case. At McDermott Will & Emery LLP is **Karol Lyn Newman** (see p.376), who is recognized for her work with natural gas entities, handling a range of FERC-related regulatory matters. **Rodney Moore** (see p.371) of Weil, Gotshal & Manges LLP is lauded for his "*excellent demeanor when dealing with difficult members of counterparty teams,*" and is also singled out for his excellent drafting abilities. **Todd Mullins** of McGuireWoods LLP is recommended for his strengths in enforcement and compliance matters. He regularly represents clients before various regulatory bodies including FERC, the CFTC and NERC. Pierce Atwood LLP's **Randall Rich** (see p.392) has had an active year advising an impressive roster of clients on pipeline rate proceedings before FERC. He is also well versed in handling a range of other compliance and enforcement concerns. The "*very effective*" **William Scherman** (see p.401) of Gibson, Dunn & Crutcher LLP is known for his abilities on complex matters on the electricity regulatory side, both in the USA and internationally. He recently arrived from Skadden. **Howard Shafferman** (see p.404) of Ballard Spahr LLP handles a range of regulatory matters for his electric power client base, which includes the likes of New York Independent System Operator and NV Energy. "*The extremely well-respected*" **Sheila Slocum Hollis** of Duane Morris LLP "*has done an excellent job representing our interests,*" a satisfied client asserts. She has a wealth of experience in the gamut of regulatory issues including compliance concerns and in investigations, and was recently called upon by Trinity River Authority to represent it before FERC in a hydroelectric licensing issue. "*Very fine lawyer*" **Kevin Sweeney** of John & Hengerer maintains a strong reputation for his work assisting gas producers with their regulatory concerns. **Noel Symons** at Davis Wright Tremaine LLP acts for a strong electric power client base includes various utilities, financial institutions and merchant transmission developers. He impresses sources with his "*knowledge of FERC law and precedent, wealth of experience practicing before FERC, extreme attentiveness to detail and responsiveness to a client's legal needs.*" **James Vasile** at the same firm offers counsel on FERC-related issues to his electric power client base. Of late, a large proportion of his workload has involved acting for clients such as Public Utility District No. 1 of Douglas County and Idaho Power on relicensing matters before FERC. **Jennifer Waters** (see p.423) of Crowell & Moring LLP continues to be active on pipeline matters, and recently successfully defended Enterprise Products Partners and Enbridge in litigation concerning transportation rates. **Jeffrey Watkiss** (see p.423) of McDermott Will & Emery LLP assists a range of companies, including electric utilities, with a broad array of transactions as well as complicated lawsuits and investigations. Ballard Spahr's **Dena Wiggins** (see p.426) is heavily praised by clients for her ability to "*explain complicated issues in terms that are easily understood,*" as well as for being "*well connected with key people in FERC and in the broader natural gas community.*" She is specifically highlighted for her excellent understanding of US natural gas pipeline and utility distribution tariffs. Bingham McCutchen LLP's **Mark Williams** (see p.426) continues to receive praise for his "*thorough knowledge of FERC rules, regulations and precedent*" as well as his "*extremely responsive and excellent customer service.*" He recently advised Kleen Energy Systems on the various regulatory matters arising for its new project after a fatal explosion. The "*very impressive*" **Michael Yuffee** (see p.430) recently joined Fried, Frank, Harris, Shriver & Jacobson LLP from Hogan Lovells. He represents a fine choice of counsel for clients on FERC regulatory matters.

# ENVIRONMENT

## Band 1

### Hunton & Williams LLP
See profile on p.2517

**THE FIRM** The environmental group at this preeminent firm comes highly recommended for its expertise in the CAA, and remains at the forefront of litigation, regulatory proceedings and policymaking. It is often successful in leading precedent-setting challenges, and also offers significant experience in the Endangered Species Act and CWA. Recent highlights include representing the Electric Power Research Institute in the introduction of its water quality trading project in Ohio. Other key clients include Arch Coal, Utility Air Regulatory Group and Southern Company.
**Client Service** *"Hunton & Williams is one of the top firms for environmental law. They are knowledgeable, incredibly client-focused and technically sound."*
**KEY INDIVIDUALS** The department is cochaired by Virginia-based Brooks Smith and Washington, DC-based Bill Wehrum. Smith is particularly involved in all matters relating to the CWA, while Wehrum offers expertise on a wide range of air quality issues.

### Latham & Watkins LLP
See profile on p.446

**THE FIRM** This leading firm is commended by peers for its skill in transactional matters, and is regularly involved in some of the most high-profile environmental projects taking place across the country. The diverse practice also offers clients expertise in contentious matters, with recent highlights including its representation of Oakley Generating Station in connection with threatened litigation relating to the Endangered Species Act and CAA. Key clients also include Edison Mission Energy, San Diego Gas & Electric Company and Georgia-Pacific.
**Sources say:** *"Top-notch lawyers, well versed in the field and worthy adversaries."*
**KEY INDIVIDUALS** Los Angeles-based Robert Wyman is the global chair of the firm's environment, land and resources department. He is lauded as one of the most influential environmental attorneys in the country.

### Sidley Austin LLP
See profile on p.1264

**THE FIRM** Sidley Austin's impressive environmental group is one of the largest in the country, and it saw further expansion in the past year, with the opening of a new, strategically located Houston office. Sources hold the team in high regard and particularly praise its deep bench's ability to handle any type of environmental matter effectively. The team has been highly active on significant litigious issues, including successfully representing a number of utility companies in the high-profile Comer v Murphy Oil case involving claims relating to greenhouse gas emissions. Its enviable client list also includes BP, Chevron, Morgan Stanley and ExxonMobil.
**Commercial Awareness** *"They prepare excellent and timely work that really adds value to our business."*
**Client Service** *"Excellent lawyers focused on providing excellent client service across a wide spectrum of areas and issues."*
**KEY INDIVIDUALS** The environmental group is jointly led by Robert Olian from the Chicago office, Judith Praitis from the California office and David Buente in Washington, DC. Olian primarily focuses his practice on contentious matters relating to enforcement. Praitis advises clients on the permitting and compliance of water, air and waste management. Buente offers a broad base of experience in Superfund, CAA and toxic tort issues.

## Band 2

### Beveridge & Diamond PC
See profile on p.907

**THE FIRM** The attorneys at this leading boutique firm provide superb services across all areas of environmental law, with many having previously held high-level positions at the EPA. It has in-depth knowledge of product-related requirements, and advises many large international clients

on such issues. The team recently represented leading trade association the Information Technology Industry Council in Basel Convention negotiations regarding the requirements for the process of managing, and disposing of, end-of-life and used electronic equipment around the world. The firm also acts for Dow Chemical, Sunoco and Syngenta Crop Protection.
**Client Service** *"They've been top-notch. They're effective, they communicate well and develop a good plan."*
**KEY INDIVIDUALS** The firm's chairman, Washington, DC-based Benjamin Wilson, offers a wealth of expertise in environmental matters, and has represented many leading corporations and developers in complex environmental litigation.

## Band 3

### Arnold & Porter LLP
See profile on p.906

**THE FIRM** This high-quality team offers expertise across the full spectrum of environmental matters, from enforcement and toxic torts to hazardous waste and contaminated property cleanups. The practice has particular skill in the area of environmental litigation, and continues to act as primary counsel to BP on ongoing issues relating to the Deepwater Horizon oil spill. Another recent highlight saw the group successfully challenge new water regulations in Florida on behalf of The Mosaic Company.
**Sources say:** *"The lawyers we work with at Arnold & Porter are completely invested in our success. The time, effort and commitment they display has impressed us all."*
**KEY INDIVIDUALS** Lester Sotsky is the firm's environment practice head. He works out of the Washington, DC office, and is commended for his expertise in major enforcement litigation.

### Baker Botts LLP
See profile on p.2427

**THE FIRM** The environmental team at Baker Botts works out of offices in Washington, DC and Texas, and is celebrated for its expertise in the energy sector, which includes involvement in upstream oil and gas, petrochemicals, refining and renewable energy matters, among other issues. The group recently defended an agricultural com-

pany in an ongoing toxic tort class action suit in Iowa. Key clients include Marathon Petroleum, BP and NRG Energy.
**Sources say:** *"The service we receive is outstanding."* *"They have just been terrific, and one of the best firms I've had the pleasure of working with."*
**KEY INDIVIDUALS** Steven Leifer chairs the environmental department from Washington, DC. He specializes in environmental litigation, including product liability, toxic tort and bankruptcy cases.

## Bracewell & Giuliani LLP
See profile on p.2429

**THE FIRM** This diverse group is frequently involved in high-profile matters for leading clients, and offers enforcement and litigation defense, as well as counseling, relating to all key environmental issues and statutes. The group has continued its representation of Halliburton, defending the company against civil and criminal investigations stemming from the Deepwater Horizon oil spill. Other key clients include Cabot Oil & Gas, Apache and Kinder Morgan.
**Sources say:** *"It is all seamless; they work together really well and I think they do a very good job on client service as a firm."*
**KEY INDIVIDUALS** Tim Wilkins is head of the firm's environment and natural resources practice group, and is also managing partner of its Austin office. His practice encompasses environmental counseling, enforcement actions and remediation.

## Crowell & Moring LLP
See profile on p.910

**THE FIRM** This team climbs the rankings after a successful year, which included victories in a number of high-profile litigation matters, as well as the lateral hires of two highly regarded attorneys. Former Cravath partner Jeff Smith and former Wyoming governor David Freudenthal joined the firm, significantly bolstering its strength in this area. The group is at the forefront of national rulemakings, frequently engaging in advocacy on behalf of a number of trade association clients, helping to shape future developments in this field.
**Commercial Awareness** *"They provide good practical advice that takes into account the total business environment, not just technical legal considerations."*
**KEY INDIVIDUALS** The firm's environment and natural resources group is led by former EPA deputy general counsel Chet Thompson, who works out of the firm's Washington, DC office.

## Hogan Lovells US LLP

**THE FIRM** This team offers experience across the whole spectrum of environmental law issues, from litigation to permitting, and is increasingly active on work in the mining and energy development sectors. In recent highlights, the group achieved a significant legal victory for Daimler Trucks North America/Detroit Diesel in a challenge against the EPA. Key clients also include Lockheed Martin, 3M, Duke Energy and Bridgelux.

**Sources say:** *"Excellent service, everything is on time, and everything is extremely accurate."*
**KEY INDIVIDUALS** The Denver-based Scott Reisch leads the firm's environment practice group. He has a broad-ranging practice encompassing contentious and transactional work, and is best known for his work in contamination, Superfund and compliance work.

## Jones Day
See profile on p.919

**THE FIRM** Jones Day's excellent environment practice group is recognized for its ability to handle substantial transactions, litigation and regulatory issues, including hydraulic fracturing and climate change matters, for a diverse client base. The team recently advised Eastman Chemical on all environmental aspects related to its $4.8 billion acquisition of material and chemical manufacturer Solutia. Other notable clients include Oglethorpe Power, Bridgestone and Georgia Gulf.
**Sources say:** *"Good expertise and experience in the environmental area."*
**KEY INDIVIDUALS** Kevin Holewinski is head of the firm's global environmental practice. He is an experienced trial lawyer who handles toxic tort, climate change, cost recovery and OSHA regulation matters.

## King & Spalding LLP
See profile on p.445

**THE FIRM** King & Spalding's environmental practice comes especially recommended for its expertise in Superfund matters, where it offers clients expertise in both litigation and counseling. The group has been representing core client Chevron in the high-profile Comer litigation. Key clients also include Shell, ConocoPhillips and Power4Georgians.
**Sources say:** *"An excellent firm for the Superfund space."*
**KEY INDIVIDUALS** Atlanta-based Patricia Barmeyer is head of the firm's environmental group. She focuses her practice on air, water and waste litigation.

## Kirkland & Ellis LLP
See profile on p.1254

**THE FIRM** The environmental group at this firm excels in major litigation, offering clients a wealth of trial experience at the local, state and federal levels. The team also comes highly recommended for its skill in transactional matters. Recent highlights include its representation of Berry Plastics in its acquisition of LINPAC Packaging Filmco. The team's impressive client list also includes Dow Chemical, GM and BP.
**Sources say:** *"They're a good team; it's always a pleasure to work with them."*
**KEY INDIVIDUALS** Granta Nakayama works out of the firm's Washington, DC office. His expertise includes representing clients in Congressional matters and agency rulemakings, as well as regulatory litigation and enforcement defense.

## Morgan, Lewis & Bockius LLP
See profile on p.2246

**THE FIRM** This firm's environmental group operates out of the Washington, DC office, and has experience acting for clients from a broad array of industries, including chemicals, transportation, manufacturing and energy. The group is often involved in significant rulemakings, due in part to its strong trade association client base. Recent highlights include its representation of the Campbell Group in connection with opposition to designating some of its land as 'critical habitat' for an endangered species. The firm also acts for Mellon Foundation, Vertellus Specialties and Minnesota Power.
**Sources say:** *"The resources they were able to bring to accomplish the project quickly were really pretty tremendous – very well organized and the quality of the legal work was very good."*
**KEY INDIVIDUALS** John McAleese from the Philadelphia office, and Ronald Tenpas who is based in the Washington, DC office, cochair the firm's environmental practice. McAleese offers experience in compliance counseling, Superfund cost recovery and regulatory negotiations. Tenpas's practice includes advising clients under environment-related criminal investigations.

## Pillsbury Winthrop Shaw Pittman LLP
See profile on p.2000

**THE FIRM** This firm's environmental group has deep knowledge of developing policy and regulation, on both the national and international level. It has particular expertise in the area of catastrophic events, and in 2012 launched its Crisis Management Resource Center. A recent highlight saw the group advise Gibson Guitar on the company's importation of exotic hardwood, and the environmental white-collar issues arising from that. Other significant clients are Mitsui Oil Exploration, Chevron and Association of American Railroads.
**Sources say:** *"A superstrong environmental firm."*
**KEY INDIVIDUALS** Mark Farley heads up the firm's environmental, health and safety practice. A core focus of his practice is advising companies on how to prevent and prepare for catastrophic events.

## Vinson & Elkins LLP
See profile on p.2459

**THE FIRM** The team at Vinson & Elkins is widely celebrated for its expertise in energy-related environmental matters, particularly in the oil and gas industries. The group recently represented Caiman Energy in the $2.5 billion sale of its shale gas processing subsidiary Caiman Eastern Midstream to Williams Partners. The firm also acts for El Paso Electric, Sandy Creek Energy and White Stallion Energy Center.
**Sources say:** *"They have a high profile and good lawyers."*
**KEY INDIVIDUALS** Carol Dinkins is chair of the firm's environmental group, and works out of both Houston and Washington, DC. Her practice includes business transaction counseling, civil litigation, criminal defense and mediation.

## Band 4

### Bingham McCutchen LLP
See profile on p.1515

THE FIRM This practice offers expertise in a broad array of environmental issues, including emerging sectors such as hydraulic fracturing, greenhouse gas regulation and environmental bankruptcies. The group is commended for its skill in litigation, and recently represented Anadarko in a significant legacy liability-related dispute with Tronox. Key clients also include Cogentrix, SunCoke Energy and Schnitzer Steel Industries.

Client Service *"The attorneys are very receptive to our emergency calls and will look at something for us immediately."*

KEY INDIVIDUALS Rick Rothman, Ella Foley Gannon and Michael Wigmore cochair the group. Rothman concentrates on litigation and counseling related to energy and environment. Foley Gannon offers expertise in the areas of land use entitlement, natural resources permitting and environmental law at the state and federal level. Wigmore is best known for his roles on behalf of investors, energy companies, trade associations, and oil and gas companies in natural resource and public land matters.

### Greenberg Traurig, LLP
See profile on p.1024

THE FIRM Greenberg Traurig's environmental group comes highly recommended by clients for its ability to effectively handle complex legal situations. The team offers experience in several key sectors, including mining, natural gas, pharmaceuticals and renewable energy. In one standout project, it represented wind farm developer Wind Capital Group in the permitting for a proposed new development in Florida. The group also represents Exelon, Kinder Morgan and CEMEX.

Commercial Awareness *"Excellent. They completely understand environmental law, but are good businesspeople."*

KEY INDIVIDUALS Kerri Barsh and David Mandelbaum cochair the environmental group. Barsh has a broad practice encompassing litigation, compliance, permitting, land use and brownfield counseling. Mandelbaum's practice includes complex litigation and permit appeals under the laws governing solid waste, air pollution and water pollution.

### Holland & Hart LLP
See profile on p.727

THE FIRM This top-notch firm has adapted successfully to evolving environmental trends, and regularly represents clients in the oil and gas, mining and coal sectors. It also has a large dedicated water team. The group acts as US counsel to Principal Power, a developer of floating platforms for wind turbines, which is in the process of bringing an advanced prototype project to the USA. Other key clients are Sapphire Energy and Syngenta Seeds.

Sources say: *"Responsive, insightful and bring a good mix of political and legal expertise." "The firm has experts in every area of our business."*

KEY INDIVIDUALS Kelly Johnson heads the firm's environment, energy and natural resources group. She provides strategic and legal advice on regulatory and legislative matters.

### Holland & Knight LLP
See profile on p.1028

THE FIRM This firm's environmental practice offers clients a holistic service in matters related to wetlands, hazardous waste, endangered species and brownfield redevelopment by working seamlessly with the firm's land use and zoning practice. The team recently represented the National Association of Clean Water Agencies in CWA amendments relating to federal government stormwater pollution cleanup payments. The firm also acts for Invesco Advisers, CEMEX and American Road & Transportation Builders Association.

Sources say: *"Very good in legal and personal skills and in the ability to manage and work with us on cases."*

KEY INDIVIDUALS Amy Edwards is cochair of the firm's nationwide environmental team. She is an expert in brownfield development, and routinely counsels corporations, developers and financial institutions on environmental issues.

### K&L Gates
See profile on p.2245

THE FIRM The environmental group at this international firm operates out of offices spread across the country, and offers clients in-depth expertise in a diverse range of issues, with particular experience in contaminated sites. The team recently represented a major client in relation to the exploration for, and production of, shale gas, advising on cutting-edge regulatory developments as well as handling litigation and policy matters arising from the process. Notable clients also include Hess Corporation, United Technologies and Chesapeake Energy.

Commercial Awareness *"Superb advocates who are very knowledgeable about government restrictions and government rules."*

Client Service *"Sophisticated and sensitive to client needs."*

KEY INDIVIDUALS Craig Wilson from the Harrisburg office and David Franchina from the Charlotte office are cochairs of the environmental, land and natural resources group. Wilson's experience includes advising clients in the natural gas exploration, production and transport sectors. Franchina has a broad practice which includes counseling on the regulation of air pollution, wetlands, chemicals and hazardous waste.

### Perkins Coie LLP
See profile on p.2548

THE FIRM This group has great expertise in handling the permitting and strategies for major development projects, including airports, water supplies, clean energy and substantial infrastructure projects. In a significant recent matter, the group represented Stanford University in the regulatory and compliance issues affecting the $5 billion construction of a new hospital, medical office, clinic and academic facilities. Key clients also include Donlin Gold, BP Alaska and Teck Resources.

KEY INDIVIDUALS Chicago-based Tom Lindley is chair of the firm's environment, energy and resources group. He has more than 25 years' experience advising clients on cutting-edge environmental issues.

### Van Ness Feldman LLP
See profile on p.926

THE FIRM Anchored in the Pacific Northwest, this firm's environmental team is best known for its expertise in transportation matters, as well as in CAA issues. The group recently acted as lead counsel to Alaska Energy Authority on the environmental, energy and resource matters related to the development of the proposed Susitna-Watana Hydroelectric project. Other notable clients include American Electric Power, Cascade Water Alliance and Bipartisan Policy Center.

Commercial Awareness *"Very responsive and they're also knowledgeable about the key players affecting regulations."*

Client Service *"Outstanding – they've very responsive, very insightful and very practical."*

KEY INDIVIDUALS Stephen Fotis is head of the firm's environment, natural resources and public lands group. He is an expert in CAA regulations for stationary source emissions.

# ERISA LITIGATION

Commentary about individuals can be found under their firm's paragraph. If the firm has no paragraph (is not ranked) look at Other Notable Practitioners.

## ERISA Litigation
### Leading Firms

**Band 1**
Morgan, Lewis & Bockius LLP *
O'Melveny & Myers LLP *
Proskauer Rose LLP *
Steptoe & Johnson LLP

**Band 2**
Alston & Bird LLP *
Covington & Burling LLP *
Gibson, Dunn & Crutcher LLP *
Groom Law Group *
McDermott Will & Emery LLP *
Sidley Austin LLP *

**Band 3**
Jones Day *
Paul Hastings LLP *
Paul, Weiss, Rifkind, Wharton & Garrison LLP *
Seyfarth Shaw LLP *

## ERISA Litigation
### Senior Statesmen

**Senior Statesmen: distinguished older practitioners**

| | |
|---|---|
| Eccles Bob | O'Melveny & Myers LLP * |

### Leading Individuals

**Band 1**

| | |
|---|---|
| Jackson Charles C | Morgan, Lewis & Bockius LLP * |
| Ondrasik Paul | Steptoe & Johnson LLP |
| Shapiro Howard | Proskauer Rose LLP |

**Band 2**

| | |
|---|---|
| Braden Gregory C | Morgan, Lewis & Bockius LLP * |
| Cohen (formerly Flowe) Carol Connor | (ONP)† * |
| Hinson H Douglas | Alston & Bird LLP * |
| Huvelle Jeffrey | Covington & Burling LLP * |
| Kilberg William J | Gibson, Dunn & Crutcher LLP * |
| Miller Evan | Jones Day * |
| Ortelere Brian T | Morgan, Lewis & Bockius LLP * |
| Prame Michael | Groom Law Group * |
| Ross Nancy | McDermott Will & Emery LLP |
| Rumeld Myron D | Proskauer Rose LLP |
| Shelley Anthony | Miller & Chevalier Chartered (ONP)† * |

**Band 3**

| | |
|---|---|
| Blankenstein Paul | Gibson, Dunn & Crutcher LLP * |
| Blocker Mark B | Sidley Austin LLP * |
| Boies Bill | McDermott Will & Emery LLP * |
| Boyle Brian | O'Melveny & Myers LLP * |
| Casciari Mark | Seyfarth Shaw LLP * |
| Clayton Lewis R | Paul, Weiss, Rifkind, Wharton & Garrison * |
| DiCarlo Patrick | Alston & Bird LLP * |
| Golumbic Lars | Groom Law Group * |
| Kallstrom D Ward | Seyfarth Shaw LLP * |
| Rea Anne E | Sidley Austin LLP * |
| Scallet Edward | Groom Law Group * |

\* Indicates firm / individual with profile.
Alphabetical order within each band. Band 1 is the highest.

## Recommended for Client Service
### Nationwide

| | |
|---|---|
| Groom Law Group | Proskauer Rose LLP |

## Recommended for Commercial Awareness
### Nationwide

| | |
|---|---|
| Groom Law Group | Sidley Austin LLP |
| Morgan, Lewis & Bockius LLP | |

## Band 1

### Morgan, Lewis & Bockius LLP

See profile on p.2246

**THE FIRM** Widely recognized for its broad practice and solid presence within the ERISA litigation market, this firm continues to be one of the leading names in the field. It deals with a variety of sophisticated ERISA class action suits and cases, involving matters such as life insurance benefits and 401(k) stock drops. A large team dedicated to ERISA litigation operates across the nation, and combines vast experience with the energetic approach that characterizes the firm. Its recent work includes defending CIGNA in a class action concerning allegations of breach of fiduciary duty. The group's client base also includes GlaxoSmithKline, Towers Watson and DHL Express.

**Commercial Awareness** *"They are not only technically competent and professional, but wonderful communicators too. Our matters were complex and they have been able to explain and teach with a wonderful balance. They have empowered us through knowledge so that we can make wise business decisions."* *"Their ERISA expertise is second to none."*

**KEY INDIVIDUALS Charles Jackson** (see p.339) has been described by his clients as *"the epitome of a trial attorney, very good at cutting through legalities and getting to the essence of the case."* He has recently worked on a number of complex cases for clients including CIGNA. **Gregory Braden** (see p.286) is co-leader of the firm, and is praised for his expertise in the field. His recent work includes leading the team defending Principal Financial Group in an investigation conducted by the DOL. **Brian Ortelere** (see p.380) is praised by his clients for his *"encyclopedic knowledge of litigation,"* and is *"a pleasure to work with."* His

recent highlights include acting as lead partner on one of the largest ERISA class action suits in the nation.

### O'Melveny & Myers LLP

See profile on p.693

**THE FIRM** Combining ERISA expertise with a broad knowledge of labor law, this leading firm has been active on a large number of investment, retirement and healthcare-related matters. It continues to attract high-profile work, and maintains an impressive client base. The team's recent highlights include successfully representing UnitedHealth Group in the Third Circuit, achieving the dismissal of a nationwide class action. Commentators are quick to highlight the group's impressive ability to provide versatile interdisciplinary support to clients.

**KEY INDIVIDUALS Bob Eccles**'s (see p.308) undisputed reputation makes him a pillar of the firm. He continues to play a key role in the firm's ERISA matters, and is lauded

for his extensive experience and expertise in the field. **Brian Boyle** (see p.286) chairs the firm's financial services practice. His focus also extends to representing healthcare companies, and he has recently obtained victories for Fidelity Investments and UnitedHealth.

### Proskauer Rose LLP

See profile on p.2001

**THE FIRM** Proskauer has handled a great variety of ERISA matters over the past year, and ably tackles issues of any size or import. Highlights include working with clients such as Honeywell International and Bausch & Lomb on a range of matters. The team has also handled a number of significant and successfully resolved stock drop cases. By applying a creative approach to the work at hand, the firm has maintained a good record of finding innovative solutions before and during trials.

**Client Service** *"There is not much Proskauer could do to improve its services – I consider it the gold standard."*

**KEY INDIVIDUALS Howard Shapiro** is held in high regard by market commentators for his excellent work in the space. He has been very active in several high-profile cases of late, including leading the representation of Honeywell International in all of its ERISA litigation matters. **Myron Rumeld** is lauded as *"a brilliant ERISA litigator, who is also a pragmatic problem solver and very easy to work with."* His recent work includes representing Phibro Animal Health in defending a putative class action relating to its benefit retirement plan.

### Steptoe & Johnson LLP

**THE FIRM** Steptoe & Johnson regularly represents clients from a broad range of industries, and continues to successfully handle cases involving employer stock drops and excessive fees in 401(k) plans. The team has recently represented prestigious clients such as American Express and Bear Stearns Companies in complex disputes on a nationwide scale. A key highlight from the past year is acting as co-lead defense counsel for BP on obtaining the dismissal of a putative class action concerning breach of ERISA fiduciary duties.

**Sources say:** *"I would recommend them to anyone who needed help with ERISA litigation."*

**KEY INDIVIDUALS Paul Ondrasik** is widely recognized as one of the leading lawyers within the field. His peers agree that he is *"very talented and very knowledgeable,"* and characterize him as *"a key player, with a good way of approaching cases."*

## Band 2

### Alston & Bird LLP
See profile on p.1102

**THE FIRM** Alston & Bird has an impressive track record of employer stock cases, and maintains a strong appellate practice. It continues to represent a range of high-profile clients including Delta Air Lines, Nokia and AIG/FSC Securities. The team's recent work includes representing Prudential Financial in the defense of a large number of ERISA claims on a nationwide basis.

**KEY INDIVIDUALS Douglas Hinson** (see p.334) handles all aspects of ERISA litigation for clients from a wide range of industries. He is lauded by market commentators as *"a great lawyer – his resume speaks for itself."* **Patrick DiCarlo** (see p.304) has represented some of the nation's largest employers, and has notable experience in ERISA litigation. His recent work includes representing Delta Air Lines in a class action concerning amendments made to the company retirement plan.

### Covington & Burling LLP
See profile on p.441

**THE FIRM** Covington's highly experienced ERISA team draws on impressive capabilities across a number of relevant departments when working with its broad client base. It has played a key role in several industry-changing cases, demonstrating its depth of expertise in the field, and recently obtained the dismissal of a case brought against IBM by former employees who had been transferred from AT&T. Key highlights also include a Supreme Court amicus curiae appointment in the benchmark Health Care Case.

**Sources say:** *"They are very creative and we rate them very highly."*

**KEY INDIVIDUALS Jeffrey Huvelle** (see p.338) maintains his reputation as an impressively experienced litigator in this arena, and has recently been active on a number of landmark cases involving pension plans. This includes work with clients such as Verizon, IBM and PhRMA.

### Gibson, Dunn & Crutcher LLP
See profile on p.682

**THE FIRM** Gibson Dunn continues to represent an array of high-profile clients, including Boeing and Textron. The experienced ERISA team's recent work has included a number of stock drop cases and pension plan matters, and it is adept at handling matters on a nationwide scale. This is exemplified by its representation of Aetna in multidistrict litigation concerning a number of claims linked to alleged breaches of fiduciary duty and reimbursement policies. An additional strength of the practice is the notable government experience of several of its attorneys.

**Sources say:** *"Their reputation is strong and their practice is well balanced."*

**KEY INDIVIDUALS William Kilberg** (see p.874) is highly regarded for his longstanding expertise in ERISA law. He continues to work with Boeing on a number of matters in this space, and is described by sources as a *"wonderful guy with a great reputation."* **Paul Blankenstein** (see p.284) specializes in complex commercial litigation, and has a notable focus on ERISA-related cases. He has recently been active on a number of stock drop cases, representing clients such as Textron, KV Pharmaceutical and Eastman Kodak, among others.

### Groom Law Group
See profile on p.915

**THE FIRM** This firm is held in high esteem for its deep expertise in ERISA matters, and houses an impressive bench of experienced attorneys. It recently acted as lead counsel for American Airlines on pension matters following on from the company's bankruptcy proceedings, and continues to advise Eastman Kodak on similar matters. The group has also handled a number of ESOP transactions of late.

**Commercial Awareness** *"They are experts in their field and tremendous to work with. They make sure they respond to our questions quickly, efficiently and accurately, and provide advice which will assist us with providing services rather than just telling us what the law says."*

**Client Service** *"They are extremely cost-efficient, and provide excellent results and creative solutions – I always look forward to working with them."*

**KEY INDIVIDUALS Michael Prame** (see p.387) has been praised for always *"ensuring that issues are addressed in a timely and efficient manner."* Clients go on to comment: *"Michael can anticipate issues, which allows us to be proactive rather than just reactive because he understands our business. He is an outstanding attorney."* Among other cases, he has continued to defend Regions Bank and Wilmington Trust in putative class action lawsuits. **Edward Scallet** (see p.400) offers extensive experience in ERISA matters, and has a particular focus on preemption issues. His recent work includes representing Conrad Siegel Actuaries in a case concerning allegations of malpractice. He has also defended a number of clients involved in DOL investigations. **Lars Golumbic** (see p.323) specializes in ERISA litigation, and is highly regarded by clients for his strategic approach to complex matters. His recent highlights include acting for a national pension fund during a DOL investigation.

### McDermott Will & Emery LLP
See profile on p.1258

**THE FIRM** This group offers a focused ERISA litigation practice, and draws on vast experience in the courtroom. It represents clients across a number of industries, and works closely with its employee benefits and executive compensation practice. Prominent work from the past year includes working on 401(k) plan matters for Bank of America, and handling an ERISA class action for Northrop Grumman which resulted in a significant $1 billion victory for the client.

**KEY INDIVIDUALS Nancy Ross** heads the team, and offers impressive expertise in ERISA litigation. She is active in several areas of the field, and led on the Northrop Grumman matter. She is also acting for Liberty Mutual Insurance Company on a significant ERISA-related challenge to the State of Vermont. **Bill Boies** (see p.285) focuses mainly on acting for benefit plan sponsors and fiduciaries. A recent important achievement was the successful representation of State Street Bank in a putative class action brought by former Chrysler executives. He also maintains a significant portfolio of work in the healthcare space.

### Sidley Austin LLP
See profile on p.1264

**THE FIRM** Sidley Austin has a well-established ERISA litigation practice, with a notable presence in Chicago, Los Angeles, New York and Washington, DC. Its expertise spans a wide range of matters in the field, and the experienced practitioners have significant litigation capabilities. The team's recent work includes successfully representing American United Life Insurance in an ERISA class action. It also successfully defended a class action on behalf of Exelon.

**Commercial Awareness** *"I have not found a topic they did not have complete expertise in, or at least burgeoning expertise. They're involved in cutting-edge matters which they are able to address in a very constructive way. Their knowledge of the industry is extraordinary."*

**KEY INDIVIDUALS Mark Blocker** (see p.285) has extensive experience in representing trustees in breach of fiduciary duty claims, and handles a wide range of ERISA class actions. Clients state: *"He is incredibly prepared and has very strong analytical powers and an understanding of complex matters. He is also very personable, and able to relate complex information by distilling it into something simple."* **Anne Rea** (see p.390) has acted as counsel for a number of defendants at trial and appellate level. She is the global coordinator of the firm's ERISA litigation group.

## Band 3

### Jones Day
See profile on p.919

**THE FIRM** Jones Day's dedicated ERISA team has been particularly active of late in retirement plan cases. It recently represented Xerox in a retiree healthcare plan case; its client base also includes The Washington Post Company and GM.

**KEY INDIVIDUALS** Highly regarded by peers, **Evan Miller** (see p.369) works across a range of ERISA matters, and is familiar with the field's most intricate aspects. His most salient recent cases includes advising GM on a $29 billion pension plan transfer. He cochairs the firm's employee benefits and executive compensation practice.

## Paul Hastings LLP
See profile on p.1996
THE FIRM This team is highly experienced in handling varied cases for Fortune 500 companies, and is known for providing practical, insightful advice to clients. It draws on a wide range of expertise within the firm to provide a comprehensive approach to ERISA matters. It represents prestigious companies such as Credit Suisse, American Airlines and the Economist Newspaper Group.
Sources say: *"They always give us analytical, commercial and legally sound advice. I like them for the broad perspective they bring."*
KEY INDIVIDUALS Lawrence Hass and Mark Poerio are key contacts at the firm, and are the cochairs of the ERISA and global benefits practice.

## Paul, Weiss, Rifkind, Wharton & Garrison LLP
See profile on p.1997
THE FIRM This team has recently been involved in a number of significant pension and benefits litigation cases. It hosts an impressive bench of experienced litigators, and can also offer clients the expertise of a number of complementary practice groups. Its recent work includes representing Time Warner in a number of ERISA litigation mat-

ters, and successfully representing Bear Stearns in an ERISA stock drop class action. Other high-profile clients include AIG and JPMorgan Chase.
KEY INDIVIDUALS Lewis Clayton (see p.296) cochairs the firm's ERISA, pensions and benefits litigation group. He has an impressive depth of knowledge in ERISA litigation, and has been involved in some of the leading cases in that arena in the past year. His recent caseload includes acting for JPMorgan Chase on a number of class actions concerning allegations of breach of fiduciary duty.

## Seyfarth Shaw LLP
See profile on p.1262
THE FIRM Seyfarth Shaw has an impressive footprint across the nation, and can draw on the additional expertise of its employee benefits group when handling ERISA matters for clients. It maintains up-to-date knowledge of ERISA regulations, and works with an impressive list of employers from across the country. Its most recent prominent cases include an ERISA class action for Kraft Foods Global on class certification, which was once again successfully denied.
Sources say: *"They're excellent – very responsive and they provide us with practical advice."* KEY INDIVIDUALS Mark Casciari (see p.292) has considerable experience in

representing employers, plan sponsors and fiduciaries, and offers great expertise as a litigator in a variety of settings. His recent work includes obtaining the dismissal of an ERISA class action filed against client Accenture. Ward Kallstrom's (see p.645) litigation practice is mainly focused on federal court class actions, but he has worked on virtually every type of ERISA case. Among recent work is a significant victory for Pacific Maritime Association.

## Other Notable Practitioners
Anthony Shelley (see p.405) of Miller & Chevalier Chartered is regarded by clients as *"excellent in all respects, with vast expertise in ERISA litigation and federal procedure."* His recent work includes representing Blue Cross and Blue Shield of Montana in a putative class action. He also represented CareFirst in federal litigation related to the payment of medical providers for services given to participants in ERISA plans. Carol Cohen (see p.297)(formerly Flowe) heads the ERISA litigation practice at Arent Fox LLP, and is held in high regard by commentators for her expertise in the area. She is praised for her ability to *"communicate expertise with practical strategic advice,"* and offers *"nuanced understanding of the law."*

# FINANCIAL SERVICES REGULATION

Commentary about individuals can be found under their firm's paragraph. If the firm has no paragraph (is not ranked) look at Other Notable Practitioners.

*The editorial is in alphabetical order by firm name.*

## Allen & Overy LLP
See profile on p.433
THE FIRM Allen & Overy is recognized for the continued development of its regulatory practice in the USA, and is particularly noted for its respected broker-dealer team. The firm provides regulatory advice across a wide range of issues including representation before federal agencies and Dodd-Frank Act compliance to the trading arms of major global financial institutions. Key clients include HSBC, ING, Bank of America and UBS.
Client Service *"I have been delighted with their work product, timeliness of responses and high-caliber work. They are willing to go the extra mile."*
KEY INDIVIDUALS Broker-dealer regulatory expert Barbara Stettner *"has a great depth of knowledge about that part of the industry and is concise and to the point in her advice."* Sources praise her *"masterful ability to really focus the questions."* Christopher Salter is *"remarkably dedicated to clients"* and *"is a strong advocate,"* say sources. He advis-

es broker-dealer and investment clients on regulatory and enforcement issues.

## Arnold & Porter LLP
See profile on p.906
THE FIRM Arnold & Porter remains prominent in the bank regulatory arena and is considered to have a deep understanding of the technical complexities of both current and historical regulatory regimes. It is noted for its strong connections to the governmental and regulatory heartland, and for its knowledge of the political context of legislative change. An area of particular strength is the firm's investigations and enforcement practice. The team continues to advise significant financial institutions embroiled in the fallout from the financial crisis, including Lehman Brothers subsidiaries Woodlands Commercial Bank and Aurora Bank. On the compliance side, the team has assisted Banco do Brasil in achieving US holding company status as part of its expansion plans, and counsels clients such as State Farm and Toyota Financial Services on regulatory strategy relating to ongoing banking reform.

### Recommended for Client Service
#### Nationwide
| | |
|---|---|
| Allen & Overy LLP | Debevoise & Plimpton LLP |
| Arnold & Porter LLP | Morrison & Foerster LLP |
| Ballard Spahr LLP | Paul Hastings LLP |
| Bingham McCutchen LLP | Sullivan & Cromwell LLP |
| Davis Polk & Wardwell LLP | WilmerHale |

### Recommended for Commercial Awareness
#### Nationwide
| | |
|---|---|
| Arnold & Porter LLP | Debevoise & Plimpton LLP |
| Bracewell & Giuliani LLP | K&L Gates |
| BuckleySandler LLP | Morrison & Foerster LLP |
| Cleary Gottlieb Steen & Hamilton LLP | Paul Hastings LLP |
| | Sullivan & Cromwell LLP |

Client Service *"Arnold & Porter is one of the key firms in the federal preemption space. They have good government contacts, and they are pragmatic and are great at client service."*
Commercial Awareness *"I look to them for very specific questions that are highly technical relating to corporate structure: things a financial regulator can oversee but that are not

## Financial Services Regulation: Banking (Compliance)
### Leading Firms

**Band 1**
Cleary Gottlieb Steen & Hamilton LLP *
Davis Polk & Wardwell LLP *
Sullivan & Cromwell LLP *

**Band 2**
Arnold & Porter LLP *
Covington & Burling LLP *
Debevoise & Plimpton LLP *
Skadden, Arps, Slate, Meagher & Flom LLP & Affiliates *

**Band 3**
Dechert LLP *
Morrison & Foerster LLP *
Sidley Austin LLP *
Simpson Thacher & Bartlett LLP *

**Band 4**
Goodwin Procter LLP *
Hogan Lovells US LLP *
Mayer Brown LLP *
Shearman & Sterling LLP *
Venable LLP *
WilmerHale *

**Band 5**
Bingham McCutchen LLP *
Bracewell & Giuliani LLP *
Paul Hastings LLP *
White & Case LLP *
Winston & Strawn LLP *

## Financial Services Regulation: Banking (Compliance)
### Leading Individuals

**Star individuals**

| | |
|---|---|
| Cohen H Rodgin | Sullivan & Cromwell LLP * |
| Sweet Jr William J | Skadden, Arps, Slate, Meagher & Flom * |
| Tortoriello Robert L | Cleary Gottlieb Steen & Hamilton LLP * |

**Band 1**

| | |
|---|---|
| Bush Derek M | Cleary Gottlieb Steen & Hamilton LLP * |
| Dugan John C | Covington & Burling LLP * |
| Guynn Randall | Davis Polk & Wardwell LLP * |
| Lee Paul L | Debevoise & Plimpton LLP |
| Lyons Gregory J | Debevoise & Plimpton LLP |
| Stock Stuart C | Covington & Burling LLP * |
| Vartanian Thomas | Dechert LLP * |
| Wiseman Michael M | Sullivan & Cromwell LLP * |

**Band 2**

| | |
|---|---|
| Anenberg Scott | Mayer Brown LLP |
| Barnard Kevin | Arnold & Porter LLP * |
| Bruemmer Russell | WilmerHale * |
| Doyle Patrick | Arnold & Porter LLP * |
| Eitel Mitchell S | Sullivan & Cromwell LLP * |
| Escue Michael T | Sullivan & Cromwell LLP * |
| Glancz Ronald R | Venable LLP * |
| Horn Charles M | Morrison & Foerster LLP * |
| Kim Richard K | Wachtell, Lipton, Rosen & Katz * |
| Kini Satish M. | Debevoise & Plimpton LLP |
| Meyerson Lee | Simpson Thacher & Bartlett LLP * |
| Sabel Bradley K | Shearman & Sterling LLP * |
| Sahr David | Mayer Brown LLP |
| Stein Stuart | Hogan Lovells US LLP |
| Tahyar Margaret | Davis Polk & Wardwell LLP * |
| Toumey Donald J | Sullivan & Cromwell LLP * |

**Band 3**

| | |
|---|---|
| Barr Lynne B | Goodwin Procter LLP * |
| De Ghenghi Luigi L | Davis Polk & Wardwell LLP * |
| Eckland William S | Sidley Austin LLP * |
| Fields Henry M | Morrison & Foerster LLP * |

| | |
|---|---|
| Freeman Jr David F | Arnold & Porter LLP * |
| Ireland Oliver I | Morrison & Foerster LLP * |
| Krimminger Michael | Cleary Gottlieb Steen & Hamilton LLP * |
| Kroener William F | Sullivan & Cromwell LLP * |
| Landy Douglas J | Milbank, Tweed, Hadley & McCloy LLP * |
| Loeser Julius | Winston & Strawn LLP * |
| Maxwell Robin JH | Linklaters (ONP) † |
| Mendelson Barbara R | Morrison & Foerster LLP * |
| Menting Mark J | Sullivan & Cromwell LLP * |
| Patrikis Ernest T | White & Case LLP * |
| Plotkin Mark E | Covington & Burling LLP * |
| Rockett James M | Bingham McCutchen LLP * |
| Rubenstein William S | Skadden, Arps, Slate, Meagher & Flom * |
| Smith Dwight C | Nelson Mullins Riley & Scarborough LLP |
| Vitale Joseph P | Schulte Roth & Zabel LLP (ONP) † * |
| Yingling Ed | Covington & Burling LLP * |

**Band 4**

| | |
|---|---|
| Avery Alan | Latham & Watkins LLP * |
| Beaty John B | Venable LLP * |
| Brown Sanford M | Bracewell & Giuliani LLP * |
| Comizio V. Gerard | Paul Hastings LLP |
| Edwards Christine A | Winston & Strawn LLP * |
| Friesen Connie M | Sidley Austin LLP * |
| Ledig Robert H | Dechert LLP * |
| McGinn Stacie E. | Simpson Thacher & Bartlett LLP * |
| Robinson Patricia | Wachtell, Lipton, Rosen & Katz * |
| Sandler Andrew L | BuckleySandler LLP * |
| Schaberg Richard A | Hogan Lovells US LLP |
| Sharpe Ralph E | Venable LLP * |

**Up-and-coming individuals**

| | |
|---|---|
| Chatterjee Whitney | Sullivan & Cromwell LLP * |
| Harris Gutierrez Franca | WilmerHale * |
| Mooney Carroll Katherine | Cleary Gottlieb Steen & Hamilton * |
| Stengel Scott | King & Spalding LLP (ONP) † * |

\* Indicates firm / individual with profile.
†ONP = Other Notable Practitioner.

straightforward. They understand our statute well and give appropriate advice."

**KEY INDIVIDUALS** Practice co-head **Patrick Doyle** (see p.306) "is experienced in the US banking world and his connections in Washington, DC are invaluable; there isn't much he hasn't seen or heard," explains one client. Doyle advises financial institutions including large insurers and Fortune 100 and investment companies on the impact and implications of the Dodd-Frank Act. **Kevin Barnard** (see p.278) is a "good and strong lawyer" with a "good background in state and federal regulation," comment sources. He co-heads the firm's financial service team alongside Doyle and has been advising a number of foreign banks including Banco do Brasil in relation to the ongoing development of the US banking regulations. **David Freeman** (see p.316) advises a range of financial institutions and broker-dealers on regulatory matters. He has been advising Toyota Financial Services on its regulatory strategy and response to the ongoing Dodd-Frank rulemaking. "Superb lawyer" **Richard Alexander** (see p.272) excels in the area of banking enforcement and investigations. He serves as the firm's managing partner and has represented clients in matters brought by the Federal Reserve, the Office of the Comptroller of the Currency (OCC) and the Office of Thrift Supervision, among others. **Brian McCormally's** (see p.364) knowledge of federal enforcement action pro-

cedures is appreciated by respondents. He has "developed a solid practice" following his move to private practice after careers at both the OCC and the Office of Thrift Supervision. Sources note that he "performs at the highest level." Washington, DC-based litigator **Howard Cayne** (see p.293) has been active in some of the financial services industry's landmark litigations. He has cemented a reputation in high-stakes preemption litigation and is valued by clients for his "very vigorous and very careful" approach. **Michael Mierzewski** (see p.368) counsels clients on both regulatory compliance and enforcement actions in the banking and consumer finance areas. He is adept at counseling clients on fair lending issues and continues to advise Visa on a range of litigious and antitrust issues. **John Hawke** (see p.332) is considered to be a legend in US banking regulation. He continues to employ his considerable experience to advise clients on enforcement and compliance matters. Financial services company Federated Investors has recently sought his expertise in response to a

federal regulators review of money funds prompted by the implementation of the Dodd-Frank Act.

### Ballard Spahr LLP
See profile on p.2234
**THE FIRM** Ballard Spahr houses a premium consumer finance team with significant expertise in handling complex class action and litigation defense and impressive regulatory compliance capabilities. The 37-partner team has considerable experience in advising mortgage finance sector clients on federal investigations and civil litigation. In other areas it has been counseling First Niagara Financial Group in connection with its purchase of a number of retail branches from HSBC and their associated credit card lending portfolios. Multiple clients have turned to the firm for guidance on the remit and proposed rulemaking of the Consumer Finance Protection Bureau (CFPB) including advice on meeting investigative requirements. Additionally, it has been active in helping non-bank organ-

*The editorial is in alphabetical order by firm name.*

## Financial Services Regulation: Banking (Enforcement & Investigations)
### Leading Firms

**Band 1**
Arnold & Porter LLP *
Cleary Gottlieb Steen & Hamilton LLP *
Sullivan & Cromwell LLP *

**Band 2**
BuckleySandler LLP *
Covington & Burling LLP *
Skadden, Arps, Slate, Meagher & Flom LLP & Affiliates *
Venable LLP *

**Band 3**
Davis Polk & Wardwell LLP *
Dechert LLP *
Hogan Lovells US LLP
Paul, Weiss, Rifkind, Wharton & Garrison LLP *

**Band 4**
Mayer Brown LLP *

## Financial Services Regulation: Banking (Enforcement & Investigations)
### Senior Statesmen

**Senior Statesmen: distinguished older practitioners**

| | |
|---|---|
| Hawke Jr John D | Arnold & Porter LLP * |

### Leading Individuals

**Band 1**

| | |
|---|---|
| Alexander Richard M | Arnold & Porter LLP * |
| Cohen H Rodgin | Sullivan & Cromwell LLP * |
| Glancz Ronald R | Venable LLP * |
| Sandler Andrew L | BuckleySandler LLP * |
| Tortoriello Robert L | Cleary Gottlieb Steen & Hamilton LLP * |
| Vartanian Thomas | Dechert LLP * |
| Veta D Jean | Covington & Burling LLP * |
| Villa John K | Williams & Connolly LLP (ONP) † |
| Wiseman Michael M | Sullivan & Cromwell LLP * |

**Band 2**

| | |
|---|---|
| Boucher Jamie L | Skadden, Arps, Slate, Meagher & Flom * |
| Ledig Robert H | Dechert LLP * |
| McCormally Brian C | Arnold & Porter LLP * |
| Rudnick Amy G | Gibson, Dunn & Crutcher LLP (ONP) † * |
| Stock Stuart C | Covington & Burling LLP * |

**Band 3**

| | |
|---|---|
| Cayne Howard N | Arnold & Porter LLP * |
| Delaney Thomas J | Mayer Brown LLP |
| Karp Brad S | Paul, Weiss, Rifkind, Wharton & Garrison * |
| Klubes Benjamin B | BuckleySandler LLP * |
| Mierzewski Michael B | Arnold & Porter LLP * |
| Seymour Karen Patton | Sullivan & Cromwell LLP * |
| Seymour Samuel W | Sullivan & Cromwell LLP * |
| Sharpe Ralph E | Venable LLP * |
| Soldo Linda J | Cleary Gottlieb Steen & Hamilton LLP * |
| Stein Stuart | Hogan Lovells US LLP |

**Up-and-coming Individuals**

| | |
|---|---|
| Mancusi Michael A. | Kilpatrick Townsend & Stockton (ONP) † |

izations comply with anti-money laundering regulations which came into force in August 2012. Notable clients of the team include Discover Financial Services, JPMorgan Chase and Sallie Mae.

**Client Service** *"They have been fantastic and by far the best firm in putting out 'webinars' – updates to the field. They're on top of any big issue that arises and they're extremely helpful."*

**KEY INDIVIDUALS** *"First-class"* consumer finance attorney **Alan Kaplinsky** (see p.343) is described as an *"outstanding lawyer"* who is *"extremely knowledgeable, detailed and articulate."* Kaplinsky has been fundamental to the firm's response and guidance in relation to CFPB compliance and enforcement matters. **Jeremy Rosenblum** (see p.395) is an accomplished litigator with a solid consumer finance practice. One source states: *"He's terrific and I've worked with him on many briefs. He is very bright and talented."* **Stanley Mabbitt** (see p.360) is a *"knowledgeable and well-known consumer attorney"* who has a *"good background in consumer finance laws"* and is a *"fabulous mortgage lawyer,"* comment sources. The *"bright"* **Mark Furletti** (see p.318) is praised by sources as a *"terrific young man and lawyer."* He continues to win plaudits as a future leader in the consumer finance arena.

## Bingham McCutchen LLP
**See profile on p.1515**

**THE FIRM** Bingham McCutchen is highly rated in the financial services sector and is noted for its presence in the banker compliance and broker-dealer spaces. Recent matters include advising Altrinsic Global advisors on regulatory matters concerning its conversion to a bank holding company affiliate. An impressive client roster also includes Bank of America, Barclays and Stade street Bank..

**Client Service** *"The firm has knowledge on the breadth of the financial services world. I can go to them with any question in this area and get prompt, well-informed answers and judgment. They give clear information that is reliable and quick."*

**KEY INDIVIDUALS David Boch** (see p.285) is a well-known and skilled broker-dealer attorney. He counsels multinational financial institutions on a broad array of regulatory requirements at both a state and federal level. **James Rockett** (see p.393) cochairs the firm's financial institutions corporate and regulatory group. He is active in advising clients on banking compliance, corporate governance and regulatory issues. Sources praise him as a *"terrific lawyer"* who is *"responsive, knowledgeable, experienced and practical."*

## Bracewell & Giuliani LLP
**See profile on p.2429**

**THE FIRM** This Texas-headquartered firm has carved out a solid reputation in the financial services arena with a broad practice that encompasses regulatory advice, investigations and transactional support for financial institutions. It has represented Main Street Bank, Texas Capital Bank and United Central Bank in varied compliance matters. The team has also advised MetroCorp subsidiaries Metro Bank and Metro United Bank on the lifting of control orders imposed by the OCC, FDIC and California

Department of Financial Institutions. Notable M&A clients include Prosperity Bancshares and WashingtonFirst Bankshares.

**Commercial Awareness** *"We appreciate their broad and deep knowledge of the industry and space in which we operate. We have found them to be accessible, on-target and consistently solid advisers."*

**KEY INDIVIDUALS Sanford Brown** (see p.288) is a respected bank regulatory attorney. He has a strong financial institutions M&A practice and has recently been advising DFW Capital Holdings on its acquisition of Texas-based Schwertner State Bank. One commentator remarks: *"I am a huge fan of Sandy. I have had great dealings with him and he is a successful lawyer."* **Julian Rainero** (see p.389) is a respected broker-dealer regulatory compliance attorney. Respondents agree that he *"is knowledgeable, provides good practical advice and is soundly grounded in securities law and regulation."* Head of department and M&A regulatory lawyer **William Luedke** (see p.359) *"knows all the players and agencies, which makes it easier to negotiate and get a deal done,"* say sources. He advised Texas-based holding company Prosperity Bancshares on its merger with American State Financial including gaining regulatory approval.

## BuckleySandler LLP
**See profile on p.908**

**THE FIRM** BuckleySandler is acclaimed as one of the most enterprising firms in the financial services sector. The firm's significant reputation in the consumer finance space is illustrated by its provision of a broad range of consumer regulatory advice to some of the country's biggest banking brands including ISIS, Citibank, Bank of America and Morgan Stanley. It has been retained by a leading national bank to provide it with an outline of the scope and application of rulemaking post-Dodd-Frank in relation to its student and residential mortgage lending operations. The team also maintains a stellar profile in consumer finance litigation and represented Wells Fargo in relation to alleged unfair lending practices.

**Commercial Awareness** *"Any mortgage lender, servicer or real estate specialty firm would be myopic to overlook BuckleySandler for legal representation and counsel. They stay informed and do an impeccable job of keeping their clients informed of current developments."*

**KEY INDIVIDUALS Andrew Sandler** (see p.399) continues to win unanimous praise from the market. Sandler's *"exemplary professionalism and problem-solving approach, coupled with his well-developed relationships and credibility with regulators, make him one of the premier enforcement and litigation attorneys for consumer-facing financial institutions."* He has a broad regulatory skill set and is particularly noted for his excellence in consumer enforcement and litigation matters, while he is often considered one of the nation's preeminent attorneys in the fair lending space. The *"top-notch"* **Benjamin Klubes** (see p.348) is highly rated by respondents as an *"extremely able"* financial services regulation attorney. He has particular strength in enforcement and consumer litigation matters. **Joseph Kolar** (see p.348) is seen as a *"talented lawyer"* and one of

*The editorial is in alphabetical order by firm name.*

### Financial Services Regulation: Broker Dealer (Compliance & Enforcement)
#### Leading Firms

**Band 1**
Davis Polk & Wardwell LLP *
WilmerHale *

**Band 2**
Bingham McCutchen LLP *
Cadwalader, Wickersham & Taft LLP *
Cleary Gottlieb Steen & Hamilton LLP *
Morgan, Lewis & Bockius LLP *
Sidley Austin LLP *

**Band 3**
Allen & Overy LLP *
Latham & Watkins LLP *

**Band 4**
Bracewell & Giuliani LLP *
Milbank, Tweed, Hadley & McCloy LLP *

### Financial Services Regulation: Broker Dealer (Compliance)
#### Leading Individuals

| Star Individuals | |
| --- | --- |
| Nazareth Annette | Davis Polk & Wardwell LLP * |
| **Band 1** | |
| Callcott W Hardy | Bingham McCutchen LLP * |
| Fleischman Dana G | Latham & Watkins LLP * |
| Lee Yoon-Young | WilmerHale * |
| Lofchie Steven | Cadwalader, Wickersham & Taft LLP * |
| Schwartz Lanny | Davis Polk & Wardwell LLP * |
| Stone Steven W | Morgan, Lewis & Bockius LLP * |
| **Band 2** | |
| Kramer Howard L | Willkie Farr & Gallagher LLP (ONP)† * |
| Mendelson Robert C | Morgan, Lewis & Bockius LLP * |
| Newman Bruce H | WilmerHale * |
| Owens Andre | WilmerHale * |
| Prezioso Giovanni | Cleary Gottlieb Steen & Hamilton LLP * |
| Wink Stephen | Latham & Watkins LLP * |
| **Band 3** | |
| Aman David | Cleary Gottlieb Steen & Hamilton LLP * |
| Ayanian John V | Morgan, Lewis & Bockius LLP * |
| Bartlett Maurine R | Cadwalader, Wickersham & Taft LLP * |
| Boch David C | Bingham McCutchen LLP * |
| Brigagliano James | Sidley Austin LLP * |
| Campion Kevin | Sidley Austin LLP * |
| Grafton Susan | K&L Gates * |
| Hensley Dennis C | Sidley Austin LLP * |
| Pruitt Laura | Alston & Bird LLP (ONP)† * |
| Rainero Julian | Bracewell & Giuliani LLP * |
| Roche Jerome J | Mayer Brown LLP * |
| Sacks Russell | Shearman & Sterling LLP * |
| Salter Christopher | Allen & Overy LLP |
| Sharp Richard T | Milbank, Tweed, Hadley & McCloy LLP * |
| Smith Holly | Sutherland Asbill & Brennan LLP (ONP)† |
| Stettner Barbara | Allen & Overy LLP |

| Up-and-coming individuals | |
| --- | --- |
| Nicolas Stephanie | WilmerHale * |

\* Indicates individual with profile.
†ONP = Other Notable Practitioner.

### Financial Services Regulation: Broker Dealer (Enforcement)
#### Leading Individuals

| **Band 1** | |
| --- | --- |
| Merrill Susan | Bingham McCutchen LLP * |
| Nazareth Annette | Davis Polk & Wardwell LLP * |
| Sullivan Neal E | Bingham McCutchen LLP * |
| **Band 2** | |
| Boch David C | Bingham McCutchen LLP * |
| Callcott W Hardy | Bingham McCutchen LLP * |
| Sharp Richard T | Milbank, Tweed, Hadley & McCloy LLP * |
| **Band 3** | |
| Aaron Wayne M | Milbank, Tweed, Hadley & McCloy LLP * |
| Gatti Steven | Clifford Chance US LLP (ONP)† * |
| Grafton Susan | K&L Gates * |
| Prezioso Giovanni | Cleary Gottlieb Steen & Hamilton LLP * |

the country's leading experts in the mortgage arena. Co-managing partner **John Kromer** (see p.350) advises clients on consumer finance compliance matters at both state and federal level. He headed up a team that has conducted an expansive review of state consumer laws for six leading national banks in relation to compliance and federal pre-emption law changes. **Jeffrey Naimon** (see p.374) *"really stands out"* for advice on mortgage lending and servicing issues, according to respondents. One interviewee reports: *"I have worked with him regarding regulatory questions on transactions and he is one of the smartest people I know."* One of the elder statesmen of the industry, founding partner **Jeremiah Buckley** (see p.289) is a highly respected consumer finance practitioner and has incredible depth of expertise in the mortgage sector. Rising star **Clinton Rockwell** (see p.394) is *"unquestionably one of the most practical and user-friendly lawyers in the regulatory compliance and licensing space for consumer-facing financial institutions,"* relates one highly impressed source. Rockwell advises banks, mortgage companies and auto lenders on a range of regulatory matters.

### Cadwalader, Wickersham & Taft LLP
See profile on p.438

**THE FIRM** This firm's 17-partner financial services team excels in the provision of regulatory compliance and enforcement counsel in the broker-dealer space. Notable matters include advising a host of systemically important financial institutions such as JPMorgan Chase in connection with the establishment of swap dealer compliance procedures. In addition, the firm has been advocating on behalf of numerous foreign banks in relation to the Volcker Rule and its global impact. Clients include Wells Fargo, Standard Chartered and Morgan Stanley.
**Sources say:** *"They respond quickly and they are knowledgeable and approachable."*
**KEY INDIVIDUALS Steven Lofchie** (see p.358) heads the firm's financial services team and has a *"superb reputation"* for providing high-level broker-dealer regulatory advice. Sources describe him as *"a smart guy who thinks outside the*

box and can solve problems." The *"knowledgeable"* Maurine Bartlett (see p.279) is considered to be *"good at explaining and translating things from legalese."* She counsels broker-dealers and large financial institutions on compliance and enforcement issues including proceedings brought by the SEC and FINRA.

### Cleary Gottlieb Steen & Hamilton LLP
See profile on p.1963

**THE FIRM** Cleary Gottlieb maintains its position at the cutting edge of financial services regulation and reform. The firm has cultivated an experienced team of specialist practitioners and continues to attract new talent from the regulatory community. The team's broad spectrum of capabilities across compliance, enforcement and transactional matters is highly valued by clients, which include some of the county's leading financial institutions. It has been advising Bank of America on a broad array of trans-

actional, compliance and enforcement matters regarding its merger with Merrill Lynch. Other notable clients include Credit Suisse, HSBC, BNP Paribas and Citibank.
**Commercial Awareness** *"They have an extremely good understanding of the business and market risks. They give pragmatic solutions and advice that you can 'operationalize' and work well with the regulators on."*
**KEY INDIVIDUALS Robert Tortoriello** (see p.418) operates in the highest levels of the bank regulatory sphere. One interviewee reports: *"He is brilliant! A legend who has impeccable client service despite what must be enormous demands."* Tortoriello is considered by peers to be *"a world leader and recognized authority on international banking law in the USA."* He is particularly noted for his strength in compliance and enforcement matters, and is increasingly recognized for his handling of financial institution transactions. **Derek Bush** (see p.290) is *"superstrong on institutional knowledge,"* relate sources, who also comment that *"he is very invested in his clients, is smart and practical, and definitely thinks about things from a business perspective."* Bush enjoys a reputation as a *"top-flight adviser"* in both domestic and international bank regulation and legislation. **Michael Krimminger** (see p.350) joins the firm this year from the Federal Deposit Insurance Corporation (FDIC), where he served as general counsel. His recent regulatory experience and insight are considered to be of great strength to the firm. One source comments: *"I think the world of him; he is the next generation."* **Katherine Mooney Carroll** (see p.370) continues to impress sources with her commitment to client service and maturity in relation to regulatory matters. *"She is pleasant to work with, smart and practical,"* comments one source. *"First-rate"* partner **Giovanni Prezioso's** (see p.387) expertise spans broker-dealer regulatory advice and securities law. He *"brings a lot of value through his SEC tenure and has a real presence in the industry."* Recent highlights have included the representation of the Securities Industry & Financial Markets Association (SIFMA) in a number of SEC enforcement action appeals. **David Aman's** (see p.273) strength, according to one source, is his *"historical knowledge: he is very good at the nitty-gritty detail of the rules as well as understanding the politics, interpretations and background to the*

*The editorial is in alphabetical order by firm name.*

| Financial Services Regulation: Consumer Finance (Compliance & Litigation) Leading Firms | |
| --- | --- |
| **Band 1** | |
| Ballard Spahr LLP * | |
| BuckleySandler LLP * | |
| K&L Gates * | |
| Morrison & Foerster LLP * | |
| **Band 2** | |
| Goodwin Procter LLP * | |
| Hudson Cook LLP | |
| **Band 3** | |
| McGlinchey Stafford PLLC * | |
| Sidley Austin LLP * | |
| Skadden, Arps, Slate, Meagher & Flom LLP & Affiliates * | |

| Financial Services Regulation: Consumer Finance (Compliance) Senior Statesmen | |
| --- | --- |
| **Senior Statesmen: distinguished older practitioners** | |
| Buckley Jeremiah S | *BuckleySandler LLP* * |

| Leading Individuals | |
| --- | --- |
| **Star individuals** | |
| Fischer L Richard | *Morrison & Foerster LLP* * |
| Platt Laurence E | *K&L Gates* * |
| **Band 1** | |
| Barr Lynne B | *Goodwin Procter LLP* * |
| Cook Robert A | *Hudson Cook LLP* |
| Ireland Oliver I | *Morrison & Foerster LLP* * |
| Kaplinsky Alan S | *Ballard Spahr LLP* * |
| Kolar Joseph M | *BuckleySandler LLP* * |
| Koren Bennet S | *McGlinchey Stafford PLLC* * |
| Sandler Andrew L | *BuckleySandler LLP* * |
| Zalenski Walter E | *Weil, Gotshal & Manges LLP (ONP)* † * |
| **Band 2** | |
| Brody Melanie | *K&L Gates* * |
| Dreher Darrell L | *Dreher Tomkies Scheiderer LLP (ONP)* † |
| Hudson Thomas | *Hudson Cook LLP* |
| Kaplan Steven M | *K&L Gates* * |
| Lampe Donald C | *Dykema Gossett PLLC (ONP)* † |
| Mierzewski Michael B | *Arnold & Porter LLP* * |
| Schulman Phillip | *K&L Gates* * |
| Teitelbaum David E | *Sidley Austin LLP* * |
| **Band 3** | |
| Chanin Leonard | *Morrison & Foerster LLP* * |
| Huizinga James A | *Sidley Austin LLP* * |
| Kromer John | *BuckleySandler LLP* * |
| Lifset Marc | *McGlinchey Stafford PLLC* * |
| Mabbitt Stanley | *Ballard Spahr LLP* * |
| Naimon Jeffrey | *BuckleySandler LLP* * |
| Rockwell Clinton | *Buckleysandler LLP* * |
| **Up-and-coming individuals** | |
| Douglass Duncan B | *Alston & Bird LLP (ONP)* † * |
| Garwood Suzanne | *Venable LLP* * |
| Harris Gutierrez Franca | *WilmerHale* * |
| **Associates to watch** | |
| Furletti Mark J. | *Ballard Spahr LLP* * |

\* *Indicates individual with profile.*
† *ONP = Other Notable Practitioner.*

| Financial Services Regulation: Consumer Finance (Litigation) Leading Individuals | |
| --- | --- |
| **Star individuals** | |
| Sandler Andrew L | *BuckleySandler LLP.* * |
| **Band 1** | |
| Hefferon Thomas M | *Goodwin Procter LLP* * |
| Platt Laurence E | *K&L Gates* * |
| Rosenblum Jeremy T | *Ballard Spahr LLP* * |
| **Band 2** | |
| Agoglia Michael J | *Morrison & Foerster LLP* * |
| Barloon Joseph L | *Skadden, Arps, Slate, Meagher & Flom* * |
| Gottlieb Richard E | *Dykema Gossett PLLC (ONP)* † |
| Huizinga James A | *Sidley Austin LLP* * |
| Ladner Mark P | *Morrison & Foerster LLP* * |
| Mierzewski Michael B | *Arnold & Porter LLP* * |
| Raman Anand S | *Skadden, Arps, Slate, Meagher & Flom* * |
| **Band 3** | |
| Klubes Benjamin B | *BuckleySandler LLP* * |

regulations." He has been particularly active in the representation of trade organizations such as SIFMA as well as financial institutions participating in the ongoing dialog with the regulators. The *"highly regarded"* **Linda Soldo** (see p.410) is considered to be *"a great practitioner"* in regulatory enforcement and investigations.

## Covington & Burling LLP
See profile on p.441

**THE FIRM** Covington & Burling is recognized for its fine bank regulatory and enforcement practices. The firm's financial institutions advisory practice continues to go from strength to strength. The firm has developed a team which combines broad regulatory expertise in the financial services sector with high-level federal agency experience. It provides guidance on implications of the Dodd-Frank Act to industry associations such as SIFMA and the American Banking Association and both domestic and foreign banking entities. In the enforcement arena, the team has had a busy year representing Wells Fargo and Citi in Federal Reserve Board actions, as well as a range of clients involved in OCC and FDIC matters.

**Sources say:** *"What impresses me the most is the high degree of professionalism and the fact that they are smart and they give us good opinion and advice. They are humble, straight shooters and incredibly talented people."*

**KEY INDIVIDUALS** Former Comptroller of the Currency **John Dugan** (see p.306) has an international banking law practice and the *"political acumen, substantive knowledge and ability to give great advice"* to help clients navigate the regulatory arena. He heads the team and is noted for his ability to *"put into context what's coming out in the new regulations and the expectations of the examiners."* **Stuart Stock** (see p.413) is described as *"smart and well informed,"* while sources point to the *"scope and depth of the legal knowledge he always brings to the table."* He advised Wells Fargo in relation to an investigation and financial consent order brought by the Federal Reserve Board. **Mark Plotkin** (see p.385) has a wealth of experience in banking compliance matters and is considered to be a strong regulatory lawyer. He also has knowledge of financial technology and data privacy issues and advises both banks and non-banks on wide-ranging financial services compliance and investi-

gatory concerns. *"Sophisticated"* former president and CEO of the American Bankers Association **Ed Yingling** (see p.429) has *"superb intellect, great breadth of knowledge and political acumen,"* say sources. He provides thought leadership on regulatory, legislative and policy matters to financial institutions and industry associations. Prominent regulatory attorney **Jean Veta** (see p.421) is acknowledged for her advice and representation in regulatory investigations. She *"comes up with questions about corporate governance and is valuable for her links in Washington and to the regulators,"* explains one source.

## Davis Polk & Wardwell LLP
See profile on p.442

**THE FIRM** The premier financial regulation group at Davis Polk has an outstanding reputation as industry thought leaders on the implementation of the Dodd-Frank Act. The team provides elite counseling and regulatory advice to US banking giants The Bank of New York Mellon, Bank of America and Goldman Sachs as well as global entities Santander and RBS. Its market-dominant, web-based Dodd-Frank tracking service has been heralded by clients as a vital resource on the changing regulatory regime. The team has been advising industry trade organizations including SIFMA on compliance issues and has also been engaged by two financial institutions to advise in relation to Libor agency investigations.

**Client Service** *"They have great depth at multiple levels, which means you can mine the team at various cost bases. They also have outstanding historical experience in various in-house roles and you get that wealth of experience brought to bear. I give them the highest marks as a group."*

**KEY INDIVIDUALS** Practice head **Randall Guynn** (see p.328) is a standout financial services lawyer with strength in banking compliance and financial institution transactions. He is considered by sources to have *"a deeper understanding than probably anyone on the likely evolution of the regulatory environment. He is a thought leader in the area."* He has been advising a number of domestic and foreign banks, including Deutsche Bank and Barclays, on compliance matters in relation to the Swaps Pushout Rule of the Dodd-Frank Act. **Margaret Tahyar** (see p.415) has an *"impressive"* reputation in bank regulatory matters. She *"is widely recognized as the authority on Dodd-Frank and her advice is widely sought after,"* according to one source. Tahyar is considered to be an *"expert on the Volcker Rule"* and has been active in authoring responses to regulators on behalf of SIFMA and other stakeholders in relation to rulemaking proposal. *"Savvy lawyer"* **Luigi De Ghenghi** (see p.302) is *"front and center of the regulatory space. He is in constant dialog with the regulators, which gives us confi-*

*The editorial is in alphabetical order by firm name.*

dence in his interpretation of existing and proposed rules," one source comments. De Ghenghi advised prepaid card company Green Dot on its unique multimillion-dollar purchase of Bonneville Bancorp and its successful application to the Federal Reserve Board. **Annette Nazareth** (see p.374) is widely regarded as an outstanding broker-dealer adviser who has strong connections within the regulatory community at all levels. Sources have the utmost "*respect for her view and judgment,*" and her wealth of in-house experience at the SEC is reflected in her understanding of the rulemaking proposals and implementation. She "*has a unique skill set and great credibility, and is highly technical and strategic,*" sources say. Another valued member of the firm's broker-dealer advisory practice is partner **Lanny Schwartz** (see p.402). His experience and expertise span the regulation of trading and markets, broker-dealers, banks and related transactions. He advises a range of clients including exchanges, financial institutions and trade associations. **George Bason** (see p.279) co-heads the firm's global M&A practice and has a respected financial institutions transactional practice. He advises investors and boards of directors on a range of matters including restructures, joint ventures and corporate governance issues.

## Debevoise & Plimpton LLP
### See profile on p.1968
**THE FIRM** Debevoise & Plimpton's thriving financial services practice is underpinned by its status as go-to regulatory counsel for organizations in the insurance industry. The team, which includes a large contingent of regulatory alumni, is noted for its business-focused and strategic compliance advice on both a domestic and international level. The team advises a wide array of industry associations and their members in relation to regulatory changes in the USA and abroad including the Financial Services Roundtable and Risk Management Association. Additionally, the team maintains an active practice in the financial institutions M&A arena and has represented Goldman Sachs and AIG in recent high-level transactions.
**Client Service** "*They are knowledgeable, thoughtful, flexible and solution-oriented. They have been willing to help in a variety of ways, based on our needs. I appreciate the insights they provide, whether we're working on a major matter or seeking a discrete piece of advice.*"
**Commercial Awareness** "*Debevoise is a leading firm in financial services regulation. The firm includes many former regulators and is adept at understanding the nuances of federal and state regulatory agencies. They are on the cutting edge of regulatory advisory and transactional work.*"
**KEY INDIVIDUALS** "*I appreciate that* **Paul Lee** *is intelligent and very detailed, really understands the issues and has historical perspective. He also has credibility with the regulators, Capitol Hill and other people in the industry,*" explains one source. Lee has been involved in advising a number of leading international financial institutions including American Express, Credit Suisse and Prudential Financial on compliance issues and the impact of ongoing regulatory reforms. **Gregory Lyons** has a broad financial services practice and "*deep regulatory and transactional knowledge,*"

according to sources. He recently represented Admirals Bank in a joint venture agreement regarding the $1 billion purchase of distressed loans. **Satish Kini** is "*a trusted adviser who is thoughtful, strategic, responsive and extremely knowledgeable,*" and whose expertise is relied upon for "*many sensitive and significant matters.*" He advises a wide range of financial institutions on strategic regulatory matters including guidance on the ongoing Dodd-Frank reforms. **Nicholas Potter** has a strong transactional practice. He has advised a number of significant corporations on regulatory and transactional matters, including CIGNA and Goldman Sachs. **John Vasily** is considered to be an "*exceptional*" transactional and M&A lawyer. He has a strong international practice and advised AIG on its sale of Nan Shan Life Insurance to Ruen Chen Investment for $2.16 billion.

## Dechert LLP
### See profile on p.1969
**THE FIRM** Dechert has continued to cement its position in the financial regulation space following the arrival of its specialist regulatory team in 2010. The banking and financial institutions team has gone from strength to strength in the enforcement arena, where it has advised the Federal Home Loan Bank of Chicago in relation to a cease and desist order imposed by the Federal Housing Finance Agency. Transactional work has included the representation of Citadel LLC in the $100 million sale of hedge fund Omnium to Northern Trust.
**Sources say:** "*Dechert is outstanding for thinking outside the box and it is number one at keeping us abreast of regulatory changes.*"
**KEY INDIVIDUALS** Head of department **Thomas Vartanian** (see p.420) "*brings unparalleled experience and judgment to difficult decision-making both as a deal-maker and regulatory guru,*" comments one source. Vartanian advised the US directors of ING Direct on its sale to Capital One Financial for $9 billion. **Robert Ledig** (see p.353) plays a key role in some of the firm's largest bank regulatory compliance and enforcement matters. He has a "*great analytical mind*" and "*the key ability to make sure every stone is turned and the issues addressed,*" sources comment. The "*responsive and pragmatic*" **David Ansell** (see p.274) "*regularly demonstrates a very high level of proficiency in the bank regulatory area,*" comment sources. He has a strong transactional practice and recently represented an investment management firm in connection with a fund formation.

## Goodwin Procter LLP
### See profile on p.1522
**THE FIRM** Goodwin Procter's national practice combines broad geographical scope with deep expertise in bank regulatory, consumer finance and M&A transactions. Its consumer finance team is noted for its ability to defend complex class actions as well as provide strategic compliance and regulatory enforcement advice in areas such as mortgage and credit card lending, electronic payment services and insurance products. A highlight was the team's US Supreme Court victory for client Quicken Loans in a case

*The editorial is in alphabetical order by firm name.*

concerning the Real Estate Settlement Procedures Act. The team also provides regulatory counseling to an array of financial institutions including advice on compliance, legislative reform and transactions. On the M&A side, the firm represented Brookline Bancorp in its purchase of Bancorp Rhode Island.

**Sources say:** *"An outstanding firm. I've been very happy with their response time."*

**KEY INDIVIDUALS** *"First-class"* banking and consumer finance attorney **Lynne Barr** (see p.278) leads the firm's consumer financial services team. She advises leading financial institutions including American Express and US Bank on a broad spectrum of regulatory compliance matters. Sources describe her as an *"exceptional lawyer"* who has *"put together a good and effective group."* **Thomas Hefferon** (see p.332) is an *"experienced, reliable and strong"* consumer finance attorney. He handled the aforementioned matter for Quicken Loans. Chair of the firm's banking practice **William Mayer** (see p.1501) is a *"superb lawyer"* who has a reputable practice at both a state and national level. He has an active M&A regulatory practice and has represented clients such as Brookline Bancorp and Camden National Bank in connection with transactional matters. **Regina Pisa** (see p.385) is considered to be an important player in the financial services M&A market. She continues to participate in counseling the firm's banking clients on regulatory and transactional matters.

## Hogan Lovells US LLP

**THE FIRM** The Hogan Lovells financial institutions group maintains its respected showing in the regulatory space. The team is skilled at helping international banks to navigate the US regulatory system. It is also well versed in the community bank space and advises Bangor Bancorp, Eagle Bank and Watertown Savings Bank on a range of regulatory matters. On the M&A side, the team recently represented BankAtlantic Bancorp in the holding company's intended sale of Florida-based subsidiary BankAtlantic.

**KEY INDIVIDUALS Stuart Stein** has a broad compliance, enforcement and transactional practice and is co-head of the firm's global corporate practice group. He recently advised Banco Industrial de Venezuela on a range of US regulatory compliance matters. **Richard Schaberg** is co-head of the firm's financial institutions practice. *"He has a good legal knowledge base and brings a good business perspective to his legal work,"* comments one source.

## Hudson Cook LLP

**THE FIRM** This specialist consumer finance and privacy firm is noted for its expertise in the full array of financial products and services including mortgage lending, payment cards and auto finance. The team advises clients on regulatory compliance at both a state and federal level. Representative clients include auto financiers BMW Financial Services and Capital One Auto Finance, banking organizations Citibank and OneWest Bank, and numerous trade associations.

**KEY INDIVIDUALS** The *"outstanding"* **Robert Cook** is an experienced consumer finance attorney who counsels a diverse range of financial institutions including banks,

lenders and credit unions on regulatory compliance. **Thomas Hudson** also handles consumer finance matters. Sources name him *"a very fine lawyer."*

## K&L Gates
### See profile on p.2245

**THE FIRM** K&L Gates has a standout financial services team with impressive strength in the consumer finance area. The team has been engaged in a multitude of complex enforcement and litigation matters on behalf of three of the country's largest banking institutions. Recent matters include representing Bank of America in securing a significant $1 billion settlement relating to a Federal Housing Administration mortgage insurance False Claims Act case. It also counsels clients on consumer lending and payment system regulations. Other clients include American Express and HSBC.

**Commercial Awareness** *"They are the go-to team when discussing state and federal regulation in the mortgage arena – it's their breadth of experience and relationships with federal and state regulators. They also provide an ongoing webinar and a very extensive newsletter – invaluable resources for the industry in what's going on."*

**KEY INDIVIDUALS Laurence Platt** (see p.385) is a stalwart of the consumer finance regulation sector and receives high praise for his sheer breadth of knowledge. His expertise is particularly respected and valued in the mortgage arena, where he is seen by peers and clients alike as a leading attorney. One source comments: *"In anything dealing with government-related loans, loan origination or loan underwriting, he is the man."* **Steven Kaplan's** (see p.343) reputation continues to grow in the consumer finance compliance space. Respondents appreciate his *"knowledge of consumer products and federal and state laws"* and provision of *"good practical advice."* The *"talented"* **Melanie Brody** (see p.288) advises clients on regulatory enforcement and compliance relating to consumer finance products and services. She has been involved in counseling Goldman Sachs prior to an examination by the CFPB. **Phillip Schulman** (see p.402) is considered to be a *"fantastic lawyer who develops good working relationships with counterparties."* He has expertise in Federal Housing Administration insured loans and was instrumental in advising Bank of America in relation to its aforementioned False Claims Act settlement. He is particularly recommended for his expertise in HUD matters. **Susan Grafton** (see p.325) joined the firm's investment management and broker-dealer practice groups in June 2012 from Gibson Dunn. She has a strong reputation in the industry and advises the securities working group of the Financial Services Roundtable on regulatory reform issues relating to the Dodd-Frank Act.

## Latham & Watkins LLP
### See profile on p.446

**THE FIRM** Latham & Watkins has a respected financial services practice in the broker-dealer space. The respected team recently advised Credit Suisse on regulatory and structural matters regarding the merger of its Switzerland-based brokerage CSPA and its US equivalent Credit Suisse

Securities. Other clients include Morgan Stanley and Barclays.

**Sources say:** *"They are very client-centric and extremely responsive."*

**KEY INDIVIDUALS Dana Fleischman** (see p.314) is applauded as *"one of the top lawyers"* in the broker-dealer space. Sources note that a key strength of her practice is her expertise at the intersection between broker-dealer regulation, research and capital markets. The *"talented and skilled"* **Stephen Wink** (see p.427) *"is a trusted adviser: he's patient, calm and always available, and his advice is well received,"* report interviewees. He provides advice to broker-dealers and industry organizations on regulatory compliance and rule changes. **Alan Avery** (see p.275) is a respected financial services advisory lawyer who is considered to have *"extremely high credibility and knowledge of the latest regulations."*

## Mayer Brown LLP
### See profile on p.1257

**THE FIRM** Mayer Brown is commended by respondents for its expertise in financial services regulation. It has been advising the Royal Bank of Canada on challenges posed by the ongoing regulatory changes including the proprietary trading restrictions under the Volcker Rule. On the enforcement side, the group represented Ally Bank and HSBC in investigations brought by multiple government agencies relating to MBS issues. Other significant clients include Capital One and Wells Fargo.

**Sources say:** *"The firm has prepared and updated an analysis of how the Dodd-Frank Act will affect the operations of my organization. That analysis, with the teleconferences and tailored advice specific to my situation, has materially assisted in focusing our attention on high-priority, high-impact aspects of its implementation."*

**KEY INDIVIDUALS Scott Anenberg** cochairs the firm's financial services regulatory and enforcement group. He is a respected regulatory attorney and provides advice to financial institutions in relation to expansion considerations and transactional requirements. Sources comment that the knowledgeable and approachable **David Sahr** is a *"prominent expert in banking and securities law."* He advises financial institutions on the domestic and global impact of US regulations and Dodd-Frank implementation considerations. **Jerome Roche** maintains a strong profile counseling broker-dealers on regulatory compliance matters particularly in connection to Dodd-Frank implementation. He is a *"dynamic lawyer"* who has *"good substantive knowledge,"* say sources. **Thomas Delaney** has been active advising clients on the implications and requirements of the Dodd-Frank Act. Respondents consider him to be *"knowledgeable about banking laws in general, and enforcement actions in particular."*

## McGlinchey Stafford PLLC
### See profile on p.1382

**THE FIRM** This firm is particularly noted for its presence in the mortgage and lending space. The team is highly rated for its ability to advise clients on statewide licensing and regulation requirements and how they interact with federal consumer finance regulation. It has been actively involved in counseling mortgage industry clients through the fall-out from the foreclosure crisis and increased regulatory scrutiny. Clients include Capital One, Clayton Homes and Regions Bank.

**Sources say:** *"McGlinchey Stafford is absolutely top-notch and puts together the best two-day seminar. The topics are fantastically relevant to what we do day in, day out."*

**KEY INDIVIDUALS** Consumer finance regulation expert **Bennet Koren** (see p.349) receives praise for his *"understanding of the regulatory schemes and practical application of the rules."* He heads the firm's financial services practice and provides ongoing counsel to national organizations such as Consumer Portfolio Services. **Marc Lifset** (see p.356) is widely considered to be a *"national expert in the mortgage and manufactured housing lending area."* He is *"one of the most knowledgeable people I know to do deep dive on highly technical legal issues for the mortgage industry,"* attests one market observer.

## Milbank, Tweed, Hadley & McCloy LLP
See profile on p.448

**THE FIRM** This firm has a team of respected broker-dealer regulatory advisers. Increasingly they have been advising clients on compliance and investigatory issues at the intersection between technology and the securities industry. The firm is particularly known for its work in enforcement matters pertaining to the broker-dealer space and the assistance it provides with respect to internal regulatory compliance procedures.

**KEY INDIVIDUALS** Broker-dealer enforcement and advisory expert **Richard Sharp** (see p.405) is a partner in the firm's litigation and arbitration group. According to sources he *"understands litigation risks, helps guide you through difficult pre-litigation scenarios and is a good adviser in structured products and broker-dealer issues."* **Wayne Aaron** (see p.271) advises clients in the securities arena including broker-dealers that are involved in enforcement and investigation proceedings brought by the SEC and other regulatory organizations. The *"knowledgeable"* **Douglas Landy** (see p.352) recently joined the team from Allen & Overy. He advises domestic and international banking clients on compliance matters.

## Morgan, Lewis & Bockius LLP
See profile on p.2246

**THE FIRM** This respected firm handles a wide variety of broker-dealer regulatory matters for its portfolio of leading banking and brokerage clients. One of the team's recent highlights was its representation of Penson Worldwide with regard to its exit from the clearing business. The group is also adept at handling regulatory enforcement actions in the broker-dealer space, and has experience representing clients in investigations by federal agencies, including the OCC, SEC, FINRA and Commodity Futures Trading Commission. An enviable client roster also includes Barclays Capital and Goldman Sachs.

**Sources say:** *"We use Morgan Lewis for general broker-dealer regulatory advice. They are experts in the field. They are responsive and their billing practices are reasonable."*

**KEY INDIVIDUALS** The respected **Steven Stone** (see p.413) heads the firm's investment management group and handled the matter for Penson Worldwide described above. Sources name him *"a great broker-dealer lawyer."* **Robert Mendelson** (see p.367) is particularly noted for his broker-dealer compliance and enforcement practice. He impresses sources with his practical approach to issues and solid judgment. Mendelson recently acted for Lehman Brothers International Europe in a range of claims before the Securities Investor Protection Corporation. **John Ayanian** (see p.275) is also a respected member of the firm's broker-dealer advisory practice. He advises clients on both compliance and transactional matters. Recently he assisted Wells Fargo Securities with regulatory considerations in relation to its purchase of brokerage technology and services business Merlin Securities.

## Morrison & Foerster LLP
See profile on p.1990

**THE FIRM** Sources note that the strength of the Morrison & Foerster regulatory practice is its depth of knowledge and expertise in the consumer finance space. The team has been advising financial services giants including JPMorgan Chase, Capital One Financial and ING on the regulatory compliance considerations surrounding consumer product portfolios and transactional matters. It has been active in helping clients to comply with credit card regulatory requirements imposed by the Credit Card Accountability, Responsibility and Disclosure (CARD) Act. It also draws upon the firm's broad international platform to advise non-US banking entities on US regulatory matters, notably gaining regulatory approvals on behalf of Bank of Communications, a Chinese financial institution, for a new West Coast branch.

**Client Service** *"They are easy to work with and they give great advice. They are always available and accessible when we need them."*

**Commercial Awareness** *"They have the expertise and depth to provide quick concise legal analysis for us to understand not only the legal aspects but also the political context."*

**KEY INDIVIDUALS Richard Fischer** (see p.313) is described by sources as the *"dean of consumer lawyers."* He is *"knowledgeable on both historical and current regulatory trends"* and is *"creative in his ability to ensure that you can get to the right answer."* Fischer's particular forte is in the credit card arena and he has been advising Capital One on the new compliance requirements imposed by the CARD Act. **Oliver Ireland** (see p.339) advises the firm's banking clients on regulatory compliance issues. He is considered to be a preeminent expert on consumer finance payment system issues, with sources noting that he has *"superb insights"* and moreover *"helps us navigate a very complex regulatory environment and is an incredibly valuable resource."* San Francisco-based **Michael Agoglia** (see p.272) is an active and well-respected litigator practicing in the consumer finance arena. He is cochair of the firm's financial services litigation group and is noted for his handling of consumer class actions. **Charles Horn** (see p.336) advises clients on banking regulations including the Dodd-Frank Act and the Volcker Rule. Sources admire his ability

to *"decipher and understand what the implications of the rules are for banks of all sizes."* Respondents consider Los Angeles-based **Henry Fields** (see p.312) to be *"experienced, knowledgeable and creative when it comes to regulation and M&A."* Fields has particular strength in the West Coast market and is valued for his knowledge of *"all the pitfalls and regulatory options and his ability to explain them."* Respected banking lawyer **Barbara Mendelson** (see p.367) provides regulatory counseling to domestic and international banks and assists clients to obtain necessary regulatory approvals in relation to transactions. She handled the aforementioned matters for the Bank of Communications. New York-based consumer finance litigator **Mark Ladner** (see p.351) gains recognition for his expertise in the payment card and systems arena and is an accomplished consumer class action attorney. Highly respected consumer regulatory specialist **Leonard Chanin** (see p.293) joins the firm from the CFPB, where he served as assistant director. He is tipped to be an important player and a future leader in regulatory compliance matters at a federal level.

## Paul Hastings LLP
See profile on p.1996

**THE FIRM** This firm is committed to helping its clients to review regulatory compliance programs and policies in light of changes wrought by the Dodd-Frank Act. The four-partner regulatory team is praised for the strength of its advice across both banking and consumer compliance issues. Key highlights include providing social commerce regulatory advice to Facebook and counsel to Scottrade Financial Services on compliance requirements and FDIC issues.

**Client Service** *"They're very business-focused, and willing to provide business advice in addition to stellar legal advice."*

**Commercial Awareness** *"They are gifted at being able to cull down complex information into understandable terms and are proactive in terms of keeping us updated about anything on the horizon."*

**KEY INDIVIDUALS Gerard Comizio** is *"a knowledgeable and proactive attorney who works as a solid team leader, a quality second to none,"* relates one interviewee. Practice head Comizio has been assisting Brooklyn Federal Bancorp on its agreed merger with Investors Bancorp.

## Paul, Weiss, Rifkind, Wharton & Garrison LLP
See profile on p.1997

**THE FIRM** This firm has a reputable portfolio of financial institution clients including UBS, JPMorgan Chase and Deutsche Bank. The team includes a number of former prosecutors and has significant expertise in defending clients involved in complex litigious matters. It provides a broad range of advice to organizations involved in investigations brought by US agencies such as the DOJ and the SEC.

**Sources say:** *"Paul Weiss has world-class expertise for any area of litigation or regulatory exposure I have encountered."*

**KEY INDIVIDUALS** The *"smart and savvy"* **Brad Karp** (see p.343) impresses respondents with the depth and breadth of his practice. He is a highly respected litigator

*The editorial is in alphabetical order by firm name.*

who is well known in the New York Bar and is active in regulatory investigations. Recently he represented MasterCard in a DOJ investigation and antitrust litigation relating to merchant fees.

## Shearman & Sterling LLP
See profile on p.2005

THE FIRM This firm is recommended for its knowledge and expertise in banking and broker-dealer compliance matters. The team has represented a number of financial institutions and broker-dealer clients requiring regulatory advice ranging from transactional matters to Dodd-Frank implementation requirements. Notable highlights include advising Natixis on the creation of Natixis Securities North America, involving the consolidation of two broker-dealers linked to different exchanges.

KEY INDIVIDUALS **Bradley Sabel** (see p.398) is a *"well-known and excellent lawyer,"* comment respondents. He is active in transactional and compliance matters and continues to advise ICE Clear Credit in relation to Commodity Futures Trading Commission, SEC and Dodd-Frank requirements and clearing system development. **Russell Sacks** (see p.398) is a respected attorney who gains recognition for his expertise in broker-dealer compliance. One source comments that his *"legal analysis is rigorous and I trust his due diligence and analysis."*

## Sidley Austin LLP
See profile on p.1264

THE FIRM Sidley Austin's national financial services practice advises both US and foreign financial institutions on a range of issues, from discrete projects to ongoing compliance matters. The team has been acting for UBS and Morgan Stanley in relation to the impact of the Truth in Lending Act exemption changes brought about by the Dodd-Frank Act. On the consumer side, the firm enjoys a strong reputation in the credit card space with recent clients including MasterCard and Green Dot. The firm's greatest strength is arguably in the broker-dealer arena, where its dedicated team represents some of the leading brokerage firms before securities regulators and advises them on the full spectrum of compliance considerations. Notable clients in this area include BNP Paribas Securities Services and Goldman Sachs. Shortly before going to press, Sidley welcomed a sizeable bbroker-dealer team from Bingham McCutchen.

Sources say: *"Sidley has a deep bench in broker-dealer regulatory advice and a top-notch transactional practice."*

KEY INDIVIDUALS **William Eckland** (see p.308) has vast bank regulatory expertise and provides a range of advice to domestic and international clients on compliance matters. He provides *"sophisticated analysis and is excellent at understanding how the banking regulators view the market,"* say sources. **James Brigagliano** (see p.287) is considered to be a *"real asset"* to the firm's broker-dealer regulatory practice and brings with him a considerable amount of technical experience in securities and market trading. *"In addition to his extensive and invaluable contacts in the regulatory world, he has unique insights into recent regulatory initiatives,"* say sources. **Kevin Campion** (see p.291) is a respect-

ed broker-dealer regulatory attorney. He provides broad advice including SEC and FINRA research rules, record keeping and registration matters, and is considered to have extensive knowledge of short sale regulatory requirements. **Dennis Hensley** (see p.333) has significant experience in advising clients on compliance and enforcement matters in the broker-dealer space. Recently he acted for a sovereign wealth fund on its purchase of a broker-dealer business. Consumer finance compliance and litigation expert **James Huizinga** (see p.337) provides *"an extraordinary synthesis of the law and the facts,"* note interviewees. He recently represented the Consumer Bankers Association in its response to proposed CFPB rules affecting prepaid credit cards. **David Teitelbaum**'s (see p.416) experience and expertise cover a wide range of regulatory matters, notably with respect to the consumer finance arena. He has particular knowledge of electronic payment systems and is considered to be an *"extremely smart and capable lawyer"* who is *"technically excellent, practical, responsive and efficient."* **Connie Friesen** (see p.317) advises clients on bank regulatory compliance matters. She has an active practice advising foreign-based financial institutions particularly from Europe, China, Singapore and Australia on their US expansion plans and regulatory compliance. **Hardy Callcott** (see p.291) had a strong reputation in broker-dealer advisory and compliance matters. He is recognized for his work on transactional matters and his solid regulatory practice. At his previous firm he represented Citigroup Global Markets in the settlement of a number of FINRA inquiries. **Neal Sullivan** (see p.414) maintains a strong reputation in the broker-dealer compliance and enforcement arena. Sources attest that he *"communicates our message and helps us to understand what the regulatory concerns are."* Former FINRA head of enforcement **Susan Merrill** (see p.367) heads up the firm's securities enforcement department. *"Her ability to communicate with the regulators and know who to reach out to is a real strength,"* says one respondent. Merrill is described as a *"fantastic"* attorney who is thought of highly for her knowledge and understanding of the regulatory enforcement process.

## Simpson Thacher & Bartlett LLP
See profile on p.2006

THE FIRM Simpson Thacher & Bartlett has an outstanding corporate and transactional practice which is reflected by its robust showing in the financial institutions M&A space. Recent work includes the representation of The Carlyle Group during its $671 million IPO. The team also provides clients with cutting-edge advice in relation to Dodd-Frank and Basel III and continues to guide the US Treasury in relation to its Troubled Asset Relief Program implementation.

Sources say: *"They are sharp and professional, and have been very generous with their time."*

KEY INDIVIDUALS According to sources **Lee Meyerson** (see p.368) has *"terrific judgment about regulatory questions"* and is a *"very commercial thinker."* He heads the firm's financial services and M&A groups and is highly regarded for his banking compliance acumen and transactional advice. **Stacie McGinn** (see p.365) has provided

bank regulatory advice on a number of the firm's key financial institution transactions including the aforementioned matter for The Carlyle Group. She is considered to be a *"strong technical lawyer"* with *"broad expertise across banking and consumer regulation."* The well-regarded **Maripat Alpuche** (see p.273) advises clients on financial institution M&A transactions. Interviewees value her *"detail-oriented and helpful"* approach. **Elizabeth Cooper** (see p.298) is described as *"an absolute star"* and is acknowledged by sources as a rising star of the financial services regulatory sphere.

## Skadden, Arps, Slate, Meagher & Flom LLP & Affiliates
See profile on p.2008

THE FIRM This firm draws on its global expertise to provide both US and foreign financial institutions and non-banking clients with a full spectrum of regulatory advice, particularly in relation to the impact of the Dodd-Frank Act and subsequent rulemaking. The regulatory team is widely acknowledged for its ability to handle considerable cross-border M&A transactions. Its work in this area includes advising BNP Paribas in relation to the sale of the bank's North American lending business to Wells Fargo. In addition, the firm has considerable expertise in representing clients involved in litigious and investigative matters involving the FDIC, DOJ, CFPB and Office of Foreign Assets Control. It has an active consumer finance practice in this area and recently represented online poker giant PokerStars in a DOJ action.

Sources say: *"The team is instrumental in moving applications along and getting quick responses to things."*

KEY INDIVIDUALS The *"talented"* **William Sweet** (see p.415) has *"extremely good knowledge of the regulatory players"* and is a *"technical lawyer with a great academic mind,"* say sources. He is considered to be one of the world's leading banking lawyers and has been instrumental in advising a number of the firm's leading financial services clients in relation to Dodd-Frank, regulatory compliance and transactions. **William Rubenstein** (see p.396) has been active in advising US investment bank Keefe Bruyette & Woods in its role as financial adviser to a number of transactions in the financial services industry. Respondents describe him as a *"practical lawyer"* who is valued for his efficient and concise approach. The *"highly skilled"* **Jamie Boucher** (see p.285) has a solid reputation in the bank regulatory sector, particularly in relation to enforcement actions, investigations and financial sanctions compliance. Well-respected consumer finance litigator **Joseph Barloon** (see p.278) is *"analytical, detail-oriented, and good at asking the right questions and getting deep into issues."* **Anand Raman** (see p.389) advises clients on investigatory and enforcement matters in the consumer finance space. He recently represented PokerStars in the DOJ matter alluded to above. **Brian Christiansen** (see p.294) takes a *"pragmatic approach to things and is quick to offer constructive opinions,"* comment interviewees. He advises financial institutions including BankUnited on regulatory compliance matters and Dodd-Frank considerations.

*The editorial is in alphabetical order by firm name.*

## Sullivan & Cromwell LLP
See profile on p.2011

**THE FIRM** Sullivan & Cromwell houses one of the country's most respected bank regulatory teams. It has formidable expertise in banking compliance matters and provides big-picture strategic regulatory advice in relation to the Dodd-Frank Act. It maintains an active practice in the M&A space, advising leading global financial institutions on complex domestic and cross-border transactions. It represented HSBC in the $2.6 billion disposal of its US credit card business to Capital One and its sale of 195 US branches to the First Niagara Bank for $1 billion. On the enforcement side, the team has counseled Goldman Sachs and Moody's in high-profile government investigations relating to the fallout from the MBS crisis. Its enviable client base includes the nation's top five banks plus leading non-US financial institutions such as BNP Paribas, Deutsche Bank, ING, Barclays Bank and RBS.

**Client Service** *"They're there to help us. They're knowledgeable about the industry but they're not a firm wanting to clock up the hours. They make it easy because they're responsive to our needs."*

**Commercial Awareness** *"They are very well versed in the intricacies of financial regulation and the dos and don'ts of executing in such a regulated environment."*

**KEY INDIVIDUALS Rodgin Cohen** (see p.297) retains his legendary status as trusted counsel and industry *"standard-bearer,"* and *"continues to be spectacular"* at the forefront of the ongoing reform of banking industry regulations. His ability to *"cut through issues that may hang up others"* and find creative solutions cements his position as arguably the preeminent attorney in the field. Cohen is considered to have particular strength in facilitating complex M&A deals, advising clients on overarching regulatory challenges and understanding regulatory dynamics. One source captures market feeling by commenting that he is *"a role model of impeccable conduct, extreme professionalism and judgment,"* and attests that *"he is simply one of the most amazing people I have ever worked with."* **Michael Wiseman** (see p.427) is considered to be a *"forward thinker"* who *"provides strategic advice"* and *"comes to the fore to provide a position on the form of new banking legislation and how it is likely to be resolved."* He advises a broad portfolio of some of the world's leading financial institutions on compliance, enforcement and transactional matters. **Michael Escue** (see p.310) has a *"comprehensive knowledge of banking laws, regulation and regulatory supervision,"* say sources. He advises on a range of regulatory issues including Dodd-Frank, and provides ongoing counsel to clients such as American Express and CIT. **Donald Toumey** (see p.418) is described as a *"guru in New York"* for his *"substantive knowledge of banking regulations."* He has both a national and global reputation in compliance matters. While he advises a range of major financial institutions, he is considered to have particular strength in counseling international banks on the impact of US banking regulations on their operations in the USA and abroad. Former FDIC general counsel **William Kroener** (see p.350) is valued for his advice in relation to banking matters, and particularly FDIC regulations. **Mitchell Eitel** (see p.309) has a signifi-

cant reputation in financial institutions M&A and related regulatory issues. Sources report: *"He's extremely smart, dedicated and commercial, and will deliver a point of view even if it's not what you want to hear. He's seen it all with regards to execution so one is well advised to go with his advice."* **Mark Menting** (see p.367) is a respected banking compliance and transactional lawyer who is *"impressive on complex matters,"* according to sources. He is strongly recommended for his *"careful, thoughtful"* approach and consideration of clients. He advised EverBank Financial on its multibillion-dollar purchase of Business Property Lending. **Karen Patton Seymour** (see p.1940) has a fine reputation in regulatory investigation matters. She represents Goldman Sachs in a range of enforcements and investigations brought by a number of regulatory and governmental agencies. *"Her major strength is in relation to her management skills and ability to bring issues to resolution in a calm and rational way,"* note sources. **Samuel Seymour** (see p.1940) has been advising HSBC in relation to an ongoing governmental investigation relating to Office of Foreign Assets Control sanctions and anti-money laundering issues. The *"talented"* **Andrew Gerlach** (see p.320) is described by sources as a *"smart and accomplished lawyer"* who is *"diligent, good at seeing the issues and a good communicator."* He worked with Cohen to advise The Bank of East Asia on the sale of an 80% stake in its US subsidiary to Industrial & Commercial Bank of China, and to gain Federal Reserve board approval for the deal. Tipped as a rising star in the financial services arena, **Whitney Chatterjee** (see p.293) is praised as a *"thoughtful, constructive, and commercial"* attorney who is *"not afraid to take a view and make a decision."*

## Venable LLP
See profile on p.927

**THE FIRM** This firm enjoys an excellent national reputation in the financial services sector. The banking and finance group represents senior executives, shareholders and financial institutions in regulatory compliance, enforcement matters and investigative actions brought by federal agencies such as the OCC and FDIC. The team recently advised directors and officers of Cooperative Bank in an action brought by the FDIC. Other notable clients include Auto Club Trust, USAA Federal Savings Bank and ING Direct.

**Sources say:** *"On bank operational issues the team has outstanding technical and analytical expertise."*

**KEY INDIVIDUALS** Department chair **Ronald Glancz** (see p.321) is *"very client-oriented"* and *"easy to work with,"* comment respondents. His command and understanding of Dodd-Frank and what it means for clients is highlighted as a key strength of his practice. Respondents appreciate **John Beaty's** (see p.280) *"knowledge base, work product and style."* He is considered to have *"outstanding technical and analytical expertise"* in relation to bank operational issues. **Ralph Sharpe** (see p.405) is considered to be a *"fabulous lawyer who knows enforcement and compliance incredibly well."* His advice is of great value to clients as it *"always incorporates a unique perspective and a variety of alternatives on how best to resolve a particular issue."* New partner

**Suzanne Garwood** (see p.319) stands out in the consumer space according to sources. One client reports: *"We have drawn on her expertise in the subprime consumer space and her knowledge of how to navigate Washington, and I have been thoroughly impressed."*

## Wachtell, Lipton, Rosen & Katz
See profile on p.2012

**THE FIRM** Wachtell is considered to be a major player in the bank M&A space. Its superior corporate practice includes regulatory specialists with a wealth of experience and expertise in sophisticated US and cross-border transactions. The team advised Capital One Financial in connection with numerous acquisitions including that of ING Direct USA. Other notable clients include PNC, Morgan Stanley and JPMorgan Chase.

**Sources say:** *"On the M&A side, they are as prominent as they come and their regulatory work is of a high level as it relates to M&A transactions." "They're extraordinary – those guys are unbelievable in the corporate M&A and corporate governance arenas."*

**KEY INDIVIDUALS** The *"talented"* **Edward Herlihy** (see p.334) earns *"enormous respect"* from sources in relation to the scale and complexity of deals he has worked on. He ascends to the star ranking for M&A lawyers in the financial services space after receiving outstanding feedback from market observers. **Richard Kim** (see p.346) maintains a prominent reputation in the industry. He is noted for his ability to advise clients on both regulatory and transactional matters. Respondents have a *"world of confidence in him"* and peers hold him in high regard as someone who is *"easy to work with"* on M&A deals. Corporate partner **Nicholas Demmo** (see p.303) is an accomplished deal lawyer with a practice centered on advising banks and other financial institutions involved in complex M&A transactions. **Patricia Robinson** (see p.393) enters the rankings this year following strong praise and recognition from sources. Interviewees highlight her *"wealth of knowledge in banking law compliance."*

## White & Case LLP
See profile on p.451

**THE FIRM** This firm's financial institutions advisory practice provides regulatory advice to bank and non-bank clients. It has strong transactional expertise and can also draw on the firm's global platform to counsel clients on cross-border regulatory considerations. The team represents a number of highly respected international organizations including Credit Suisse, Deutsche Bank and BNP Paribas. It is also playing an active role in the investigation by US regulators into the Libor scandal and represents two non-US financial institutions.

**KEY INDIVIDUALS** Co-head of the firm's global financial institutions advisory group **Ernest Patrikis** (see p.382) is a *"font of knowledge in the bank regulatory area,"* according to respondents. He advises a number of non-US banks including ICBC and Bank of China in relation to Federal Reserve applications and regulatory compliance requirements.

*The editorial is in alphabetical order by firm name.*

## WilmerHale
See profile on p.930

**THE FIRM** WilmerHale's financial institutions regulatory team provides a unified regulatory offering spanning compliance, enforcement and transactional advice. It has recently advised HSBC and Nationwide on a range of investigative and regulatory matters, in addition to providing ongoing guidance in relation to the Dodd-Frank Act. The firm also has a preeminent broker-dealer practice that provides a full range of regulatory advice in this area. Significant clients include Credit Suisse, Goldman Sachs and SIFMA.

**Client Service** *"They do a great job for us. They are very responsive and timely, and they have learned a great deal about our business, so we have developed some synergies based on their knowledge of what we do."*

**KEY INDIVIDUALS** The highly respected **Yoon-Young Lee** (see p.353) receives praise as a *"solid and experienced compliance lawyer."* She has a strong broker-dealer regulatory compliance and enforcement practice, and particular strength in research issues. She works closely with industry associations including SIFMA and the Loan Syndications & Trading Association on regulatory reform issues. Respondents praise **Russell Bruemmer**'s (see p.288) considerable knowledge and experience in bank regulatory compliance matters. His ability to provide clients with strategic advice and assist them in managing issues is noted as a key strength. One interviewee reports that *"from a big-picture standpoint he was very good."* **Franca Harris Gutierrez** (see p.331) continues to be noted by interviewees as a talented regulatory compliance lawyer. Sources attest to her *"deep subject matter expertise"* and note that *"she is good at partnering with clients and understanding large organizations."* **Bruce Newman** (see p.376) *"knows how the regulators think, has incredibly good insights and judgment and you trust what he says,"* explains one client. Newman has a strong reputation advising broker-dealer clients on compliance and enforcement matters. **Andre Owens** (see p.381) is considered by sources to be *"one of the best broker-dealer compliance lawyers."* He advises clients on regulatory and compliance matters and is described as *"smart"* with *"really good client skills."* **Stephanie Nicolas** (see p.376) joins the rankings and is highlighted as a *"smart, super-responsive, practical and forward-thinking"* attorney who has strength in the broker-dealer space.

## Winston & Strawn LLP
See profile on p.1267

**THE FIRM** This firm represents both domestic and foreign financial institutions and provides advice on a broad range of transactional and regulatory matters. The financial services team has been involved in providing industry association the Financial Services Roundtable with advice and guidance on the impact of the Dodd-Frank Act and its implementation. Other notable clients include Bank of Hawaii and Continental Investors.

**Sources say:** *"The firm has knowledge across the breadth of the financial services world. I can go to them with any question and get a prompt, well-informed answer and judgment."*

**KEY INDIVIDUALS Julius Loeser** (see p.358) is described by sources as a *"great financial institution attorney"* who is *"skilled and responsive."* He provides bank regulatory advice on matters such as Dodd-Frank implementation to a range of financial organizations. **Christine Edwards** (see p.308) heads the firm's financial services regulation department. She advises financial institutions and boards of directors in the banking and securities sectors on regulatory compliance and corporate governance matters.

## Other Notable Practitioners

The *"talented"* **Robin Maxwell** of Linklaters is *"knowledgeable in banking matters"* and described as a *"thoughtful and energetic counselor."* She provides a broad range of financial regulatory advice and is seen as *"an important bridge for the firm's international client base seeking to understand US markets."* Bank regulatory attorney **Scott Stengel** (see p.412) of King & Spalding LLP secures a place in this year's rankings following a raft of praise from sources. He is considered to have a *"tangible and deep knowledge of a broad range of issues,"* and *"his advice is always well thought out and pragmatic."* Leading attorney **John Villa** of Williams & Connolly LLP has a stellar reputation in the bank regulatory enforcement and investigations area. He is considered to be an experienced and versatile financial services litigator who is also active in the representation of individuals in malpractice defense cases. Practicing from Gibson, Dunn & Crutcher LLP's Washington, DC office, **Amy Rudnick** (see p.397) *"has a great reputation"* for her banking enforcement and investigations expertise. She cochairs the firm's financial institutions group and has particular expertise in anti-money laundering compliance. **Laura Pruitt** (see p.387) recently joined Alston & Bird LLP and is praised for her *"depth of expertise"* in broker-dealer compliance and knowledge of alternative trading systems. SEC alumna **Holly Smith** of Sutherland Asbill & Brennan LLP is highly regarded by commentators for her ability to

understanding the cutting-edge issues in the market, and for her deep industry expertise. Ohio-based **Darrell Dreher** is a respected consumer finance attorney and heads the practice at Dreher Tomkies Scheiderer LLP. He is active advising clients in the credit card and consumer lending space on regulatory compliance. **Joseph Vitale**'s (see p.421) *"counsel runs the gamut from transactions to regulatory issues and his advice stands the test of time,"* explains one source. Vitale is at Schulte Roth & Zabel LLP, and wins praise from a number of sources for his knowledge of the regulatory environment. Consumer finance expert **Duncan Douglass** (see p.306) of Alston & Bird LLP is *"an experienced and knowledgeable payments attorney with a clear understanding of all aspects of the various card products and the legal relationships among issuers, processors and payment networks,"* explains one source. Banking regulatory attorney **Michael Mancusi** of Kilpatrick Townsend & Stockton LLP makes his debut in the rankings and is flagged by sources as a key player in the enforcement arena. He has recently been involved in representing clients involved in FDIC investigations and enforcement matters. **Howard Kramer** (see p.350) is a securities regulation expert at Willkie Farr & Gallagher LLP who focuses on broker-dealer compliance matters and is also highlighted for his market structure knowledge. Kramer is described by respondents as *"incredibly knowledgeable"* and *"tenacious and a strong advocate."* **Steven Gatti** (see p.319) of Clifford Chance US LLP joins the rankings this year as a respected attorney with noted expertise in broker-dealer enforcement matters. Clients describe him as a *"solid performer"* who provides *"good commercial advice."* Respondents consider Weil, Gotshal & Manges LLP's **Walter Zalenski** (see p.430) to have a fine reputation in the consumer finance regulatory space. He has provided advice on a number of transactional matters, recently representing Advent International in its purchase, with Goldman Sachs, of consumer credit reporting company TransUnion. Dykema Gossett PLLC's head of financial services regulatory and compliance **Donald Lampe** is considered to be a talented attorney who *"really gets into the fight on issues."* He represents a range of financial service providers on consumer regulatory matters, with a focus on mortgage-related compliance issues. At the same firm, Chicago-based **Richard Gottlieb** is applauded for his knowledge and problem-solving abilities. Gottlieb has particular expertise in consumer finance matters and is described as *"incredibly client-focused."* *"The outstanding"* Dwight Smith of Nelson Mullins Riley & Scarborough LLP provides clients with guidance on Dodd-Frank implementation and represents financial institutions before Federal agencies including the Federal Reserve Board.

# FIRST AMENDMENT LITIGATION

| First Amendment Litigation Leading Individuals | |
| --- | --- |
| **Star individuals** | |
| Abrams Floyd | Cahill Gordon & Reindel LLP * |
| Levine Lee | Levine Sullivan Koch & Schulz LLP * |
| Sager Kelli L | Davis Wright Tremaine LLP |
| **Band 1** | |
| Babcock Charles | Jackson Walker LLP * |
| Baine Kevin T | Williams & Connolly LLP |
| Handman Laura R | Davis Wright Tremaine LLP |
| Kelley Thomas | Levine Sullivan Koch & Schulz LLP * |
| Schulz David A | Levine Sullivan Koch & Schulz LLP * |
| Smith Paul M | Jenner & Block LLP * |
| Tobin Charles D | Holland & Knight LLP * |
| **Band 2** | |
| Boutrous Jr Theodore J | Gibson, Dunn & Crutcher LLP * |
| Canfield Peter C | Dow Lohnes PLLC * |
| Johnson Bruce | Davis Wright Tremaine LLP |
| Julin Thomas R | Hunton & Williams LLP * |
| Kovner Victor A | Davis Wright Tremaine LLP |
| McNamara Elizabeth A | Davis Wright Tremaine LLP |
| Sanford Bruce W | Baker & Hostetler LLP * |
| Sullivan Michael D | Levine Sullivan Koch & Schulz LLP * |
| Wimmer Kurt A | Covington & Burling LLP * |
| **Band 3** | |
| Albano Jonathan M | Bingham McCutchen LLP * |
| Balin Robert | Davis Wright Tremaine LLP |
| Bodney David J | Steptoe & Johnson LLP |
| Corn-Revere Robert | Davis Wright Tremaine LLP |
| Leatherbury Thomas S | Vinson & Elkins LLP * |
| Steinfeld Joseph D | Prince Lobel Tye LLP |
| Yannucci Thomas D | Kirkland & Ellis LLP * |

* Indicates individual with profile.
Alphabetical order within each band. Band 1 is the highest.

## Star individuals

### Floyd Abrams
**Cahill Gordon & Reindel LLP**

Floyd Abrams is revered by his peers and considered by many as *"the godfather of the media Bar."* He is unquestionably regarded as a *"star"* in this space and described as *"the best First Amendment lawyer in the USA."* He has been busy with a variety of cases, including numerous lawsuits brought by Lorillard Tobacco Company challenging FDA restrictions on cigarette advertising and marketing as unconstitutional under the First and Fifth Amendments.

### Lee Levine
**Levine Sullivan Koch & Schulz LLP**

Superlatives abound in the commentary for Lee Levine, who is lauded by peers and clients alike as *"a recognized expert with unparalleled knowledge"* in First Amendment litigation. One source enthused: *"He is one of the smartest lawyers I know – he is incredibly knowledgeable and a brilliant strategist, with great common sense and great judg-*

*ment. He knows this area better than anyone else."* Levine's practice includes libel, copyright, invasion of privacy and First Amendment cases. Recent successes include defending CBS Interactive in a defamation lawsuit brought by a Hall of Fame basketball star.

### Kelli L Sager
**Davis Wright Tremaine LLP**

Kelli Sager receives exceptional feedback for her expertise in this area, and is praised by sources as *"a real star,"* who is *"a leader in this field."* 2012 highlights saw her defend a number of prominent media companies, including Electronic Arts, Microsoft and Lions Gate Entertainment, against right of publicity claims. She also successfully defended the Los Angeles Times in a series of related defamation cases arising out of the newspaper's reporting on the 1-800-GET-THIN ad campaign and the surgery centers associated with that company.

## Band 1

### Charles Babcock
**Jackson Walker LLP**

Charles Babcock continues to expand and strengthen his presence on the First Amendment stage across the USA. The *"extraordinary"* Texan litigator is particularly well known for his considerable jury trial experience. He is currently representing Dr Phil McGraw in a long-running defamation case related to the disappearance of Natalee Holloway. *"He is a nationally renowned First Amendment lawyer,"* sources agree.

### Kevin T Baine
**Williams & Connolly LLP**

Kevin Baine is renowned for his long-standing presence in the First Amendment field. He is regarded as the *"gold standard"* of attorneys in libel law cases, and noted by sources for his considerable jury trial experience. As well as First Amendment matters, his practice also covers copyright, trademark, contract and other commercial disputes.

### Laura R Handman
**Davis Wright Tremaine LLP**

Laura Handman is described by peers as *"a terrific public appellate lawyer – she is a great writer, a great speaker and terrific with clients."* She operates a broad media practice, with a strong focus on First Amendment litigation. 2012 highlights saw her act on a number of anti-SLAPP (Strategic Lawsuits Against Public Participation) cases in Washington, DC. She also represented a coalition of media organizations in a $20 million defamation lawsuit concerning the reporting of a story involving an arrest and alleged threats to shoot the president. Sources say: *"She is a zealous advocate for the First Amendment – truly dedicated to this area of practice."*

### Thomas Kelley
**Levine Sullivan Koch & Schulz LLP**

The impressive Thomas Kelley is a seasoned litigator with a national practice, representing top media clients in privacy, libel, copyright and other First Amendment disputes. In highlights, he recently successfully obtained a court order recognizing a First Amendment right of access to judicial records in the prosecution of the individual accused of the movie theater shootings in Aurora, Colorado. *"He is very strong and a smart guy. On a national level he is a terrific lawyer."*

### David A Schulz
**Levine Sullivan Koch & Schulz LLP**

David Schulz is an *"outstanding"* litigator who is well known for his work in this field. He stands out for his expertise in access cases, and regularly represents both the public and the press in matters concerning the First Amendment right to access court proceedings. Notably, he continues to be involved in litigation in connection with the efforts of media organizations to access information about detainees in Guantanamo Bay.

### Paul M Smith
**Jenner & Block LLP**

Paul Smith is a US Supreme Court specialist with an extensive history in First Amendment and copyright dispute resolution. He is seen as a go-to litigator in cases regarding new technology, and is lauded by peers as an *"extraordinary bright light of the Bar."* Smith leads the firm's appellate and Supreme Court practice, and cochairs its media and First Amendment, election law and redistricting groups.

### Charles D Tobin
**Holland & Knight LLP**

Charles Tobin rises through the ranks due to exceptional client feedback and high-profile work. His national practice focuses on First Amendment litigation for news media, with an emphasis on libel, privacy and access to information matters. Recent highlights include representing 17 major media organizations in an intervention seeking to obtain access to court records in the widely publicized Trayvon Martin shooting prosecution. Of note, he was also involved in a precedent-setting case involving the release of FBI documents under the Freedom of Information Act in relation to civil rights photographer Ernest Withers.

## Band 2

### Theodore J Boutrous Jr
**Gibson, Dunn & Crutcher LLP**

Theodore Boutrous divides his time between Los Angeles and Washington, DC, from where he operates a broad practice covering media, entertainment and technology. He represents clients in defamation, news gathering, freedom of information and access cases, and has substantial experience in both federal and state appellate courts nationwide.

### Peter C Canfield
**Dow Lohnes PLLC**

Atlanta-based Peter Canfield is well known for his First Amendment litigation practice and earns widespread acclaim from his peers in the field nationwide. He is *"an excellent lawyer"* with more than 20 years of experience in courtrooms across the country, and maintains a broad practice covering IP, entertainment, sports, libel, First Amendment and commercial cases.

### Bruce Johnson
**Davis Wright Tremaine LLP**

Bruce Johnson chairs the firm's privacy and security practice, and is regarded as one of the strongest First Amendment litigators on the West Coast. He operates a national practice, regularly defending reporters and editors in journalist privilege matters, as well as other national media clients in privacy, defamation and internet liability cases. *"He is an excellent lawyer,"* say interviewees.

### Thomas R Julin
**Hunton & Williams LLP**

Miami litigator Thomas Julin is highly regarded for expertise in First Amendment litigation and media law, advising clients on cases nationwide. One source said: *"I think he is one of the most impressive people I have had the pleasure of knowing. His desire to take a stand for what he believes in means he will go the distance for his clients."* Julin recently assisted a group of healthcare organizations in securing an injunction to enjoin the enforcement of a law which would prohibit doctors from discussing firearm safety with their patients.

### Victor A Kovner
**Davis Wright Tremaine LLP**

Victor Kovner is a long-standing authority in First Amendment litigation and considered *"a world expert on invasion of privacy cases."* He continues to offer pre-publication and pre-broadcast counsel to an assortment of media organizations.

### Elizabeth A McNamara
**Davis Wright Tremaine LLP**

New York-based Elizabeth McNamara is admired by peers and clients as an *"extremely dependable"* litigator, whose work is always of the highest standard. She continues to focus on significant nationwide IP and First Amendment matters for clients from the film, newspaper, television and book-publishing industries. Recent work highlights include defending the distributors of the film 'Savage Grace' against a libel lawsuit brought by an art dealer who claimed to have been falsely portrayed in the movie.

### Bruce W Sanford
**Baker & Hostetler LLP**

Bruce Sanford heads the firm's IP, technology and media department and is considered a *"top-of-the-line"* First Amendment litigator. He is esteemed by peers for his expertise in libel and privacy law, and described by clients as *"proactive, experienced and commercially aware."* Recent highlights include representing blogger Larry O'Connor in respect of an anti-SLAPP motion to dismiss a libel lawsuit brought by former USDA official Shirley Sherrod.

### Michael D Sullivan
**Levine Sullivan Koch & Schulz LLP**

Michael Sullivan is a highly respected trial lawyer with decades of experience defending important media entities in libel, copyright and First Amendment disputes. He continues to act for The Virgin Island Daily News on an appeal of a defense judgment secured in a 2010 defamation case. He impresses sources with his courtroom skills: *"He is unflappable – capable of rolling with the punches. He is a force to be reckoned with."*

### Kurt A Wimmer
**Covington & Burling LLP**

Kurt Wimmer is an *"outstanding"* attorney with a diverse practice including privacy and copyright, as well as First Amendment litigation. He continues to work with various trade associations, new media content providers and newspapers, and regularly handles amicus curiae work and briefs. Notable clients include Facebook, National Geographic and the Washington Post.

## Band 3

### Jonathan M Albano
**Bingham McCutchen LLP**

Jonathan Albano is the head of the litigation department at Bingham McCutchen. He is a seasoned trial lawyer, with extensive experience representing traditional news organizations in First Amendment matters. Recent highlights include defending new client HarperCollins in an invasion of privacy lawsuit. He also continues to assist long-standing client The Boston Globe with a variety of matters, and is praised for his *"speedy legal and tactical advice, which is always expressed in concise and clear language."*

### Robert Balin
**Davis Wright Tremaine LLP**

Robert Balin cochairs the firm's media and First Amendment department. He advises on a broad spectrum of media matters including IP, privacy, libel and other First Amendment issues. He advises a variety of international as well as domestic clients including publishers, broadcasters and new media organizations.

### David J. Bodney
**Steptoe & Johnson LLP**

Phoenix-based David Bodney receives a wealth of praise for his litigation practice. He handles a wide array of matters, and is singled out for his specialization in First Amendment cases, where he represents both newspapers and television broadcasters. One source enthused: *"I think he is the top First Amendment litigator bar none in Arizona. He takes very reasonable but aggressive positions, and is a very effective advocate for First Amendment rights."*

### Robert Corn-Revere
**Davis Wright Tremaine LLP**

New to the nationwide rankings, Robert Corn-Revere is greatly admired for his focus on the First Amendment aspects of media law. According to interviewees, he is *"ubiquitous"* in this area, and is praised for his *"superb legal work"* and *"top of the line"* briefs. He is singled out for his experience in relation to indecency cases, and also handles matters involving regulatory and telecommunications law. He successfully represented CBS before the US Supreme Court in a widely publicized battle challenging FCC indecency fines imposed following the 2004 Super Bowl halftime show.

### Thomas S Leatherbury
**Vinson & Elkins LLP**

The *"tremendous"* Thomas Leatherbury receives widespread recognition for his First Amendment practice in Texas and his increasing presence on the national stage. He impresses sources with his *"intellectual firepower"* and jury trial experience, and is acknowledged as an *"extraordinarily good lawyer in this area."* One client enthused: *"Tom is an extremely responsive, creative and hard-working lawyer."*

### Joseph D Steinfield
**Prince Lobel Tye LLP**

With over 35 years of experience in the field, Joseph Steinfield is well known and respected for his long-standing dedication to First Amendment litigation. He has both a strong trial and arbitration background, advising clients from all corners of the media space, including newspapers, broadcasters and internet and new media content providers. Recent experience includes access cases and defamation disputes.

### Thomas D Yannucci
**Kirkland & Ellis LLP**

Thomas Yannucci stands out for his focus on plaintiff-side representation in First Amendment litigation. He advises on both individual and class action cases involving defamation, IP, antitrust and regulatory matters. *"He is a fabulous lawyer,"* sources say.

# FOOD & BEVERAGES

Commentary about individuals can be found under their firm's paragraph. If the firm has no paragraph (is not ranked) look at Other Notable Practitioners.

## Food & Beverages: Regulatory & Litigation

### Leading Firms

**Band 1**
Covington & Burling LLP *
Hogan Lovells US LLP

**Band 2**
Hyman Phelps & McNamara
Keller and Heckman LLP *
Olsson Frank Weeda Terman Matz PC *

**Band 3**
Faegre Baker Daniels
King & Spalding LLP *
Patton Boggs LLP

### Senior Statesmen

| Senior Statesmen: distinguished older practitioners | |
| --- | --- |
| Ely Jr Clausen | Covington & Burling LLP * |

### Leading Individuals

**Band 1**

| | | |
| --- | --- | --- |
| Degnan Frederick H | King & Spalding LLP * | |
| Hutt Peter Barton | Covington & Burling LLP * | |
| Levitt Joseph A | Hogan Lovells US LLP | |
| Pape Stuart M | Patton Boggs LLP | |

**Band 2**

| | | |
| --- | --- | --- |
| Frank Richard L | Olsson Frank Weeda Terman Matz PC * | |
| Hahn Martin J | Hogan Lovells US LLP | |
| Kushner Gary Jay | Hogan Lovells US LLP | |
| Roller Sarah E (Taylor) | Kelley Drye & Warren LLP (ONP)[†] | |
| Silverman Richard S | Hogan Lovells US LLP | |
| Steinborn Steven B | Hogan Lovells US LLP | |

**Band 3**

| | | |
| --- | --- | --- |
| Beckwith Van | Baker Botts LLP (ONP)[†] * | |
| Brew Sarah L. | Faegre Baker Daniels | |
| Guggenheim Miriam J | Covington & Burling LLP * | |
| Krasny Leslie T | Keller and Heckman LLP | |
| McColl Diane B | Hyman Phelps & McNamara | |
| Norris Trenton H | Arnold & Porter LLP (ONP)[†] * | |
| Thorpe Jane F | Alston & Bird LLP (ONP)[†] * | |

* Indicates firm / individual with profile.
[†] ONP = Other Notable Practitioner.

## Band 1

### Covington & Burling LLP
**See profile on p.441**

**THE FIRM** This renowned Washington, DC regulatory firm advises its clients on a wide range of food regulatory and litigation issues. It is home to a number of former FDA and FTC lawyers, which gives it an advantage when advising on government and regulatory matters. Its broad client list includes a number of trade associations, large food companies, dietary supplement suppliers and emerging food companies, particularly from the biotechnology sector. Covington advises the American Bakers Association on regulatory and legislative issues, including providing analysis on the Food Safety Modernization Act (FSMA) of 2011. Other clients of the firm include Archer Daniels Midland, Mars, Campbell's, Council for Responsible Nutrition and Roll Global.

**Commercial Awareness** *"We have been thoroughly impressed with these individuals, mainly as a result of their deep knowledge of regulatory matters related to our industry, their detail-oriented nature, and their very practical, efficient-to-apply legal counsel."*

**KEY INDIVIDUALS Clausen Ely** (see p.310) focuses on representing clients with regard to FDA and FTC regulations pertaining to areas such as biotechnology, antimicrobial food products, food additives, food contact material, and advertising and labeling issues. Sources describe him as an *"excellent lawyer and a real gent,"* and add: *"He is strong and good on pure regulatory issues."* **Miriam Guggenheim** (see p.327) advises food and dietary supplement companies on regulatory and legal compliance in areas such as product development, food labeling and food marketing. She has worked extensively with Mars, providing the company with guidance relating to its various food, pet food and dietary supplement products. Sources say: *"She is good at giving really thoughtful and practical advice to her clients and she is a person who stays calm in a crisis."* **Peter Barton Hutt** (see p.870) is viewed by market sources as *"one of the deans of the US food and drug law Bar."* His extensive practice in the field encompasses advising trade associations, food companies, biotechnology companies and dietary supplement companies on the legislative and regulatory issues they may face. He is a former FDA general counsel and is therefore seen as a good choice for companies with FDA-related problems. His clients include the Council for Responsible Nutrition, a leading dietary supplement trade association, which he represents in its relationship with the FDA.

### Hogan Lovells US LLP

**THE FIRM** This leading firm offers its clients an extremely broad offering in the food sphere and is one of the few firms that is seen as equally adept at dealing with the FDA and the USDA. The firm advises leading food producers, food retailers and trade associations, among others. It advises on new legislative and regulatory programs and is able to provide litigation support to food companies, particularly in food consumer class actions.

**Sources say:** *"The food law practice at Hogan Lovells is first-rate. It is a leader in the field and offers bench depth that few, if any, firms can match."*

**KEY INDIVIDUALS Joseph Levitt** is *"very much an FDA expert,"* due to his past as director of the FDA's Center for Food Safety & Applied Nutrition. He focuses on advising clients on regulatory and legislative issues, and according to one source *"he is the leading expert on the recent FSMA legislation."* Sources say: *"He is extremely good at predicting where the FDA is headed and what its thinking is, and advising companies how to maneuver in light of that."* **Martin Hahn** is a well-regarded attorney who advises his clients on regulatory compliance and enforcement actions relating to the FDA, USDA and FTC. Sources appreciate his creative style and one praised his *"think-outside-the-box original approach to problem solving."* Sources say: *"A particular skill set he brings to the table is an aptitude for dealing with technical and scientific folks and speaking their language."* **Gary Jay Kushner** is recognized by market sources for his strong USDA regulatory practice. He advises his clients, including trade organizations and food companies, on a wide variety of regulatory compliance and enforcement issues. Sources say: *"Gary brings an extraordinary institutional knowledge to the table."* **Richard Silverman** is a well-regarded regulatory attorney who has worked for the FDA and as in-house counsel for a major food company. This varied background is appreciated by his clients, one of whom said: *"He probably has more experience than any other US lawyer dealing with product recall-type matters."* Sources praise his client-centric approach, with one saying: *"He is very responsive and always seeking feedback on the firm and what they can do to improve the relationship."* **Steven Steinborn** advises his clients on a wide variety of regulatory compliance issues and regularly represents clients facing enforcement actions by the USDA and FDA. Sources say: *"He is very thorough, he is available in a crisis and he offers very practical, good advice."*

## Band 2

### Hyman Phelps & McNamara

**THE FIRM** This DC boutique has a broad food law practice which covers both regulatory and litigation work. The firm advises food and dietary supplement companies on a wide range of issues including food labeling, food ingredients, advertising and marketing. The firm advises its clients on both litigation and regulatory enforcement actions by the FDA and FTC.

**KEY INDIVIDUALS Diane McColl** is a well-regarded DC food lawyer. One client said: *"I have been very impressed with her work."*

### Keller and Heckman LLP
**See profile on p.920**

**THE FIRM** This DC firm has a great depth of expertise in the area of food packaging. The firm has a strong bench of experienced attorneys who work closely with its in-house scientists to advise clients on packaging compliance issues. The firm regularly submits Food Container Notifications (FCN) to the FDA in order to get regulatory approval for new food packaging substances. In one recent example, the firm acted for Cytec Industries on preparing and submitting an FCN for a component of adhesive formulations; the firm successfully guided its client through the process and received pre-market clearance for the product. Additionally, the firm advises on product recalls and litigation, including the defense of consumer class actions.

**Client Service** *"The breadth and depth of their knowledge of food packaging requirements is excellent. They are easy to work with. They responded quickly and appropriately to requests and they made the effort to understand our business needs."*

**KEY INDIVIDUALS Leslie Krasny** is a regulatory lawyer who practices from the firm's San Francisco office. She focuses on issues such as regulatory compliance, product recalls, food labeling, health claims and California's Proposition 65. Sources say: *"She has a deep understanding of the regulations, and more significantly, a deep understanding of both the related science and the business implications."*

## Olsson Frank Weeda Terman Matz PC
See profile on p.924

**THE FIRM** This regulatory boutique focuses on serving its clients in the spheres of FDA and USDA law. The firm lobbies lawmakers on its clients' behalf, as well as assisting them in interpreting new legislation and regulations, providing compliance advice and representing clients in enforcement matters. Additionally, lawyers from the firm's strong USDA practice advise clients on the full food-to-table spectrum of food safety issues.

**Sources say:** *"It is the firm to go to on USDA matters."*

**KEY INDIVIDUALS Richard Frank** (see p.315) is recognized by sources for his strong USDA practice and also advises clients on a wide variety of FDA and FTC-related issues. Sources say: *"Rick Frank is a superb USDA food lawyer."*

## Band 3

## Faegre Baker Daniels
**THE FIRM** This firm provides its clients with full litigation and regulatory support service in the food arena. The firm acts for food companies, animal feed companies and dietary supplements companies on matters such as food safety advice, product recalls, food labeling advice and defense of litigation. The firm represented Cargill in the litigation and regulatory issues surrounding the company's 2011 withdrawal of 36 million pounds of ground turkey products due to alleged Salmonella Heidelberg links. Other clients of the firm include MOM Brands, Dole Food, Pharmavite, Muller Quaker Dairy, Reckitt Benckiser and Flint Hills Resources.

**KEY INDIVIDUALS Sarah Brew** is the head of the firm's food litigation and regulatory group. She represents her clients in a wide variety of matters including consumer class actions and food-borne illness and contamination cases.

## King & Spalding LLP
See profile on p.445

**THE FIRM** This well-respected firm represents its food clients in the full range of regulatory matters. It acts for major food manufacturers and producers with regard to labeling issues, food safety issues and advice on biotechnology matters. The firm is particularly strong on FDA regulations, as it is home to a number of ex-FDA lawyers.

**KEY INDIVIDUALS Frederick Degnan** (see p.303) is a well-known figure in the food law world. He is a former FDA counsel and has a practice that focuses on advising food companies on issues such as biotechnology, labeling and food safety. Sources say: *"Fred's combination of experience, knowledge, connections with the regulators and his ability to bridge between the science and the law involved in the regulation of food makes him extraordinarily good at what he does."*

## Patton Boggs LLP
**THE FIRM** This firm's food group is based in DC and focuses on representing its clients with regard to legislative and regulatory matters. The firm's lawyers regularly counsel their clients on issues relating to the FDA, the FTC and the USDA. Additionally, the group advises its clients on

legislative issues and defends clients facing Congressional investigations.

**Sources say:** *"They are highly regarded for their lobbying and public policy work."*

**KEY INDIVIDUALS Stuart Pape** is an experienced and well-respected food lawyer whose practice focuses on FDA and Congressional representation. He is particularly noted for his work representing the soft drinks industry and his work for dietary supplement companies.

## Other Notable Practitioners

**Jane Thorpe** (see p.417) of Alston & Bird LLP is a mass tort litigator who is *"very smart, appropriately aggressive and trusted by colleagues and clients."* She handles food and beverage cases with respect to consumer class actions and investigations by the FTC or state attorney generals. Sources say: *"She comes at cases from a science angle and she is every bit a trial lawyer."* **Sarah Roller** of Kelley Drye & Warren LLP chairs the firm's DC food group. She has a strong food and government background, having worked as a nutritionist and a Congressional researcher. This helps inform her practice, and according to one source, *"she is well wired in with the folks at the FDA."* Sources say: *"She has a deep historical understanding of the evolution of the regulatory framework that allows her to spot trends and provide solid, timely counsel."* **Van Beckwith** (see p.281) of Baker Botts LLP is a litigator who handles cases in the food and beverage space. His experience in the sector includes successfully defending the Dr Pepper Snapple Group in putative class actions in New York, New Jersey and California. The District Court in New York denied class certification, and then granted summary judgment for Beckwith's client, which led to the plaintiffs dropping their suits in California and New Jersey. **Trenton Norris** (see p.657) of Arnold & Porter LLP is a California-based attorney who defends food and beverage clients in litigation, particularly related to consumer class actions. In one case, he represented seven national restaurant chains in a case brought by an animal rights group claiming that his clients failed to provide customers with a Proposition 65 warning for the chemical PhIP in grilled chicken products. Sources say: *"He is creative in coming up with alternative approaches and strategies. He seeks to understand the whole scope of the situation and tries to understand what is motivating the other party."*

# FOOD & BEVERAGES ALCOHOL

Commentary about individuals can be found under their firm's paragraph. If the firm has no paragraph (is not ranked) look at Other Notable Practitioners.

## Food & Beverages: Alcohol
### Leading Firms

**Band 1**
GrayRobinson, PA
McDermott Will & Emery LLP *

**Band 2**
Buchman Law Firm, LLP
Hinman & Carmichael LLP
Holland & Knight LLP *
Pillsbury Winthrop Shaw Pittman LLP *

**Band 3**
Davis Wright Tremaine LLP *
Dickenson, Peatman & Fogarty *
Stoel Rives LLP

## Food & Beverages: Alcohol
### Senior Statesmen

| Senior Statesmen: distinguished older practitioners | |
| --- | --- |
| Mendelson Richard P | Dickenson, Peatman & Fogarty |
| O'Brien Vincent | Nixon Peabody LLP (ONP) † |
| Schreiber William B | Wormser, Kiely, Galef & Jacobs LLP (ONP) † |
| Siegel Mort | Siegel Moses & Schoenstadt PC (ONP) † |

### Leading Individuals

| Star individuals | |
| --- | --- |
| Sorini Marc | McDermott Will & Emery LLP * |

| Band 1 | |
| --- | --- |
| Blau Richard M | GrayRobinson, PA * |
| Hinman John A | Hinman & Carmichael LLP |
| Newman Michael B | Holland & Knight LLP * |
| Seff James M | Pillsbury Winthrop Shaw Pittman LLP * |

| Band 2 | |
| --- | --- |
| Bergman Nicholas J | Buchman Law Firm, LLP |
| Carmichael Lynne A | Hinman & Carmichael LLP |
| Davis J Daniel | Sole Practitioner (ONP) † |
| Hermann Christopher R | Stoel Rives LLP |
| Webster James | Webster Powell (ONP) † |

| Band 3 | |
| --- | --- |
| Behmke Jay M. | Carle, Mackie, Power & Ross LLP (ONP) † |
| DeCelle Arthur J | McDermott Will & Emery LLP * |
| DeConti Elizabeth A | GrayRobinson, PA * |
| Lyon Jesse D | Davis Wright Tremaine LLP |
| Terry James W | Dickenson, Peatman & Fogarty |

| Up-and-coming individuals | |
| --- | --- |
| Yang Grace | GrayRobinson, PA * |

\* Indicates individual with profile.

† ONP = Other Notable Practitioner.

## Band 1

### GrayRobinson, PA

**THE FIRM** This Florida-based firm represents clients in a wide variety of alcohol regulatory matters. The firm acts for all segments and tiers of the market and is home to a strong team of lawyers and other licensing professionals. In one recent matter, the firm acted for private equity group Olympus Partners and dealt with the alcohol regulatory aspects of its acquisition of Centerplate, a nationwide event hospitality company. Other clients include Bacardi, Walgreen and 7-Eleven.

**Sources say:** "The team's work is excellent time after time."

**KEY INDIVIDUALS Richard Blau** (see p.284) chairs the firm's alcohol group and focuses on providing regulatory guidance to clients. In one recent example, he advised Southwest Airlines on the alcohol regulatory components of its acquisition of AirTran Airways. According to commentators, "he is really a very bright, sharp guy and he definitely knows his stuff." **Elizabeth DeConti** (see p.303) advises alcohol companies, retailers and marketing companies on regulatory issues. She has recently advised Catalina Marketing on ensuring its marketing and brand promotion campaigns comply with state and federal alcohol law. **Grace Yang** (see p.429) is praised by clients for her "effective and diligent" approach. Her practice focuses on regulatory compliance and alcohol licensing issues.

### McDermott Will & Emery LLP
See profile on p.1258

**THE FIRM** This highly regarded group is based in Washington, DC, and is primarily recognized for its practice representing alcohol suppliers. The firm has a strong federal practice, which encompasses the representation of clients in investigations by the Alcohol and Tobacco Tax and Trade Bureau (TTB) and FTC, and lobbying and other legislative work on Capitol Hill. In addition to its strong supplier practice, the firm represents trade associations and a number of specialist alcohol retailers.

**Commercial Awareness** "Their breadth of knowledge never ceases to amaze. We've yet to have an issue they couldn't help us navigate."

**KEY INDIVIDUALS Marc Sorini** (see p.410) earns extensive praise from across the market. He services an impressive client list of major alcohol suppliers and producers in matters such as investigations by the FTC and TTB, and distribution and regulatory advice. One client says: "I feel like I am his only client even though I know he represents many others. He is an excellent communicator and always accessible." **Arthur DeCelle** (see p.303) brings "a vast wealth of industry background" to his work for clients. His practice focuses on public policy issues and lobbying. "He has a very sophisticated, subtle understanding of the legal principles and a great degree of care and consideration for the client's interests," say sources.

## Recommended for Client Service
### Nationwide

| | |
| --- | --- |
| Holland & Knight LLP | Pillsbury Winthrop Shaw Pittman LLP |

## Recommended for Commercial Awareness
### Nationwide

| | |
| --- | --- |
| Buchman Law Firm, LLP | Stoel Rives LLP |
| McDermott Will & Emery LLP | |

## Band 2

### Buchman Law Firm, LLP

**THE FIRM** This alcohol regulatory boutique operates across the country from offices in New York, San Francisco, New Jersey and Washington, DC. The firm provides licensing services to every tier of the industry, advising companies on the import and distribution of alcohol, and on trademark and label approvals and trade practices.

**Commercial Awareness** "They are very capable and very knowledgeable, and have a lot of institutional knowledge."

**KEY INDIVIDUALS** New York partner **Nicholas Bergman** has a varied practice which encompasses licensing, import and distribution, franchise protection and trade practices. Sources describe him as a "bright, personable and capable" attorney.

### Hinman & Carmichael LLP

**THE FIRM** This well-respected alcohol boutique based in San Francisco advises clients on a wide variety of regulatory matters, including TTB and California Department of Alcoholic Beverage Control (ABC) enforcement actions and stings. Additionally, the firm has a strong reputation when it comes to handling complex licensing matters.

**Sources say:** "They give quick and easy answers."

**KEY INDIVIDUALS John Hinman** has a national reputation in the industry, but is particularly associated with the California wine trade, with one source calling him "the wine shipping guru." Additionally, he is noted for his representation of clients in enforcement actions and investigations by the ABC and TTB. "He is smart, feisty and a bit of a bulldog in a good way," say sources. **Lynne Carmichael** focuses on licensing and transactions involving licensed premises. According to commentators, "she is really skilled and well respected in licensing."

### Holland & Knight LLP
See profile on p.1028

**THE FIRM** This San Francisco-based group focuses on alcohol regulatory issues. While the firm is known for its work in the California wine industry, it also provides advice to clients all over the country. A flourishing area of activity for the firm is advising on issues surrounding online alcohol distribution and marketing. Its clients include 5th Rock, Francis Coppola Winery, MGM Resorts International and Pernod Ricard.

**Client Service** *"They are really responsive and don't waste time. They work with a sense of urgency that nobody else does."*
**KEY INDIVIDUALS Michael Newman** (see p.376) recently advised Fidelity National Financial on the alcohol regulatory components of its purchase of O'Charley's Restaurant Chain. *"He understands where regulators are coming from and understands what his clients want and does a very good job of balancing those interests,"* say interviewees.

## Pillsbury Winthrop Shaw Pittman LLP
See profile on p.2000
**THE FIRM** This San Francisco-centered practice represents its clients in a wide range of regulatory issues. Its lawyers regularly interact with the TTB and other state regulators, as well as handling licensing, trademark, transactional and litigation matters. In one recent case, the firm acted for the California Grocers Association in a legal challenge against a decision by the ABC to restrict sales of alcohol through self-service grocery lanes. Other clients of the firm include Anheuser-Busch, Silverado Vineyards and Moët Hennessy.
**Client Service** *"They are intelligent and competent, and respond quickly and thoroughly to all of our questions. Particularly when we have a pressing matter, they make themselves available on short notice."*
**KEY INDIVIDUALS James Seff** (see p.403) has a broad-based alcohol regulatory practice and is well known among peers in the sector who note his deep industry knowledge. According to sources, *"he knows the regulators well and knows what will and won't fly. He has the ability to fix problems for clients that other people may not be able to fix."*

## Band 3

### Davis Wright Tremaine LLP
See profile on p.2544
**THE FIRM** This firm's alcohol group is increasingly building a national reputation in the sector and expanding beyond its traditional power base in the Pacific Northwest. The firm advises clients on a range of matters including regulatory compliance, marketing, licensing and distribution. Key clients include Matador Restaurants and Sundance Cinemas.
**KEY INDIVIDUALS Jesse Lyon** has a varied practice that includes handling regulatory and transactional matters for clients in the alcohol industry. He recently oversaw a multistate review of Alaska Airlines' alcohol service, liquor licensing and alcohol-related operations.

### Dickenson, Peatman & Fogarty
See profile on p.678
**THE FIRM** This California firm draws much of its clientele from the state's many winemakers, but additionally acts for restaurants, hotels, and wine importers and distributors. Much of the firm's practice is devoted to regulatory issues and its lawyers often deal with the ABC and TTB on behalf of clients.
**KEY INDIVIDUALS James Terry** is an experienced alcohol attorney with a practice that focuses heavily on winemaking. *"I like working with him on the other side of the table,"* says one source. **Richard Mendelson** remains an esteemed player in the field. According to commentators, *"clients that have the luxury of him representing them have a very good lawyer."*

### Stoel Rives LLP
**THE FIRM** This firm has a strong base in the Pacific Northwest and additionally handles regulatory and acquisition work for its clients on a nationwide basis. The firm is particularly renowned in the winemaking sector, but also has strong brewery, restaurant and retail expertise. Recent highlights include acting for Anheuser-Busch on its purchase of a Washington State Budweiser distributor, with the firm's attorneys handling the licensing and regulatory compliance aspects of the transaction.
**KEY INDIVIDUALS Christopher Hermann** is noted for his knowledge of the wine trade, and his ability in handling winery transactions.

## Other Notable Practitioners

**Jay Behmke** of Carle, Mackie, Power & Ross LLP in California focuses on assisting wineries, distributors, importers and restaurants with transactional, trademark and licensing matters. Sole practitioner **Daniel Davis** is widely respected by his peers, and is noted for his deep industry knowledge. Sources praise his practical and analytical approach. **James Webster** of Webster Powell is based in Chicago and is particularly noted for his work in the trade practice area and in TTB-related matters. Clients particularly praise his dedication to and understanding of their needs. **Vincent O'Brien** (see p.379) of Nixon Peabody LLP is a New York-based attorney who has a distinguished track record in the field. He is noted for his strong wine-based practice and close relationships with regulators, with clients saying: *"His network of contacts and long-term understanding of the law and its evolution have been instrumental to us."* New York practitioner **William Schreiber** of Wormser, Kiely, Galef & Jacobs LLP represents clients from across the industry including distributors, importers, producers and hotel and restaurant companies. *"It might be a stretch to call him Gandalf but he is pretty close to it. Clients love him because he is so bright and he has a deep understanding of the law,"* say sources. **Mort Siegel** of Siegel Moses & Schoenstadt PC is highly respected in the industry for his depth of institutional knowledge. *"If you are in a tough situation and need something creative you would go with Mort,"* say commentators.

# FRANCHISING

Commentary about individuals can be found under their firm's paragraph. If the firm has no paragraph (is not ranked) look at Other Notable Practitioners.

## Band 1

### DLA Piper LLP (US)
See profile on p.1971
**THE FIRM** This firm's franchising and distribution practice continues to stand head and shoulders above its competitors. Sources speak of its enduring high profile in franchisor representation and note that the firm's impressive global footprint allows it to assist with international matters. Highlights for the practice include advising on franchising issues surrounding the sale of BP's Southwest Fuels Value Chain. An impressive client roster includes Hilton, Ace Hardware and Procter & Gamble.

**Commercial Awareness** *"DLA Piper is certainly a leader in this area. The lawyers are all very knowledgeable and their extensive network around the world fits well with our global needs."*
**KEY INDIVIDUALS Dennis Wieczorek** (see p.426) chairs the firm's franchise and distribution practice group. He had a lead role for BP on the Southwest Fuels Value Chain matter. Clients describe his service as *"complete, thorough and professional."* The highly experienced **Michael Brennan** (see p.287) is recognized by market observers for his strength in international franchising matters, routinely advising on transactional matters and franchise launches and operations. His client base includes major retail chains, restaurant franchisors and Fortune 500 companies.

**Bret Lowell** (see p.358) acts for clients from a range of sectors including hospitality, car hire and financial services. Areas of excellence include the drafting of franchise license agreements and the termination and renewal of obligations. Sources report: *"He is extremely knowledgeable with a lot of experience and always provides helpful, practical*

| Franchising | |
|---|---|
| **Leading Firms** | |
| **Band 1** | |
| DLA Piper LLP (US) * | |
| **Band 2** | |
| Faegre Baker Daniels | |
| Gray Plant Mooty * | |
| Haynes and Boone, LLP * | |
| Nixon Peabody LLP * | |
| Wiggin and Dana LLP * | |
| **Band 3** | |
| Bryan Cave LLP | |
| Foley & Lardner LLP * | |
| Greensfelder, Hemker & Gale, P.C. | |
| Larkin Hoffman Daly & Lindgren, Ltd. * | |
| Plave Koch PLC | |
| **Band 4** | |
| Baker Botts LLP * | |
| Ballard Spahr LLP * | |
| Cheng Cohen LLC | |
| Day Pitney LLP * | |
| Fisher Zucker, LLC | |
| Kaufmann Gildin Robbins & Oppenheim LLP | |
| Kilpatrick Townsend & Stockton LLP * | |
| Snell & Wilmer LLP * | |
| Wiley Rein LLP * | |

*advice."* **Erik Wulff** (see p.428) recently represented Loblaw's in a license and distribution agreement relating to the opening of 700 Joe Fresh boutiques in JC Penney stores across the US. He has also acted on international franchise and product distribution work. The *"well-respected"* **Stuart Hershman** (see p.334) advises on the structuring, documentation and implementation of franchising programs. The *"very knowledgeable"* **Joseph Sheyka** (see p.405) is praised by sources for a *"great skill set"* that encompasses the negotiation of distribution agreements and franchising issues surrounding transactions. **Norman Leon** (see p.354) is a talented trial lawyer with a focus on disputes in the franchising arena. Areas of expertise include disputes stemming from breach of contract, encroachment or fraud. The widely admired **Philip Zeidman** (see p.430) is a senior partner in the franchise group and garners considerable respect as *"one of the prime attorneys in the franchising world."* He is noted for his knowledge of domestic and international franchising law. **Tao Xu** (see p.429) is recognized for his handling of international franchising and distribution matters. He has been closely involved in lobbying the Chinese government to adopt a new franchising regulatory system. **Richard Morey** (see p.371) is a younger partner in the franchising and corporate groups. His experience includes advising on the structuring and compliance aspects of franchising. He attracts market praise as *"a sharp up-and-comer."*

| Franchising | |
|---|---|
| **Senior Statesmen** | |
| **Senior Statesmen: distinguished older practitioners** | |
| Silberman Alan H | *Dentons (ONP)*[†] * |
| Zeidman Philip F | *DLA Piper LLP (US)* * |

**Leading Individuals**

| **Band 1** | | | | |
|---|---|---|---|---|
| Baer John RF | *Greensfelder, Hemker & Gale, P.C.* | | Sheyka Joseph W | *DLA Piper LLP (US)* * |
| Barkoff Rupert M | *Kilpatrick Townsend & Stockton LLP* | | Vines Leonard D. | *Greensfelder, Hemker & Gale, P.C.* |
| Dienelt John F | *Quarles & Brady LLP (ONP)*[†] * | | **Band 4** | |
| Dunham Edward Wood | *Wiggin and Dana LLP* * | | Appleby Bethany L | *Wiggin and Dana LLP* * |
| Mazero Joyce G | *Haynes and Boone, LLP* | | Beyer David | *Quarles & Brady LLP (ONP)*[†] * |
| Plave Lee J | *Plave Koch PLC* | | Brimer Jeffrey A | *Faegre Baker Daniels* |
| Pressman Arthur L | *Nixon Peabody LLP* * | | Cheng Amy | *Cheng Cohen LLC* |
| Solish Jonathan C | *Bryan Cave LLP* | | Collin Thomas J | *Thompson Hine LLP (ONP)*[†] * |
| Wieczorek Dennis E | *DLA Piper LLP (US)* * | | Curran Leslie D. | *Plave Koch PLC* |
| **Band 2** | | | Feirman Steven | *Nixon Peabody LLP* * |
| Brennan Michael G | *DLA Piper LLP (US)* * | | Fisher Lane | *Fisher Zucker, LLC* * |
| Cohen Fredric A | *Cheng Cohen LLC* | | Gilbert Jan S. | *Gray Plant Mooty* |
| Coldwell Deborah S | *Haynes and Boone, LLP* | | Hein Kevin | *Faegre Baker Daniels* |
| Costello Kenneth R | *Bryan Cave LLP* | | LaFiura Dennis R | *Day Pitney LLP* * |
| Fittante Joseph J | *Larkin Hoffman Daly & Lindgren, Ltd.* | | Leon Norman | *DLA Piper LLP (US)* * |
| Grueneberg Susan A | *Snell & Wilmer LLP* | | MacPhee Leonard | *Perkins Coie LLP (ONP)*[†] |
| Hurwitz Ann | *Baker Botts LLP* * | | McCullough Kim | *Ballard Spahr LLP* * |
| Joblove Michael D | *Genovese Joblove & Battista, PA (ONP)*[†] | | Miller Charles G | *Bartko, Zankel, Tarrant & Miller (ONP)*[†] * |
| Killion William L | *Faegre Baker Daniels* | | Oppenheim David | *Kaufmann Gildin Robbins & Oppenheim* |
| Klarfeld Peter J | *Gray Plant Mooty* | | Sager David S | *Lowenstein Sandler LLP (ONP)*[†] * |
| Lindsey Michael K | *Paul Hastings LLP (ONP)*[†] | | Santa Maria Michael E | *Baker & McKenzie (ONP)*[†] * |
| Lockerby Michael J | *Foley & Lardner LLP* | | Schott Max | *Gray Plant Mooty* |
| Loewinger Andrew P | *Nixon Peabody LLP* * | | Smith Mary Leslie | *Foley & Lardner LLP* |
| Lowell Bret | *DLA Piper LLP (US)* * | | Smith Robert A | *Wiley Rein LLP* * |
| Modell Charles S | *Larkin Hoffman Daly & Lindgren, Ltd.* | | Tractenberg Craig R | *Nixon Peabody LLP* * |
| Morency Paula J | *Schiff Hardin LLP (ONP)*[†] | | Woods Will K | *Baker Botts LLP* * |
| Spandorf Rochelle Buchsbaum | *Davis Wright Tremaine (ONP)*[†] | | Wulff Erik B | *DLA Piper LLP (US)* * |
| **Band 3** | | | Yaffe Eric | *Gray Plant Mooty* |
| Bundy Kerry | *Faegre Baker Daniels* | | Zwisler Carl | *Gray Plant Mooty* |
| Fournaris Dean | *Wiggin and Dana LLP* * | | **Up-and-coming individuals** | |
| Hershman Stuart | *DLA Piper LLP (US)* * | | Dillon Liz | *Gray Plant Mooty* |
| Joseph Robert T | *Dentons (ONP)*[†] * | | Krakus Beata | *Greensfelder, Hemker & Gale, P.C.* |
| Kaufmann David J | *Kaufmann Gildin Robbins & Oppenheim* | | Lauer Robert A. | *Haynes and Boone, LLP* |
| Knack Gaylen L | *Gray Plant Mooty* | | Morey Richard J. | *DLA Piper LLP (US)* * |
| Koch David W | *Plave Koch PLC* | | Prince Rebekah | *Eisner, Kahan & Gorry (ONP)*[†] |
| | | | Xu Tao | *DLA Piper LLP (US)* * |

\* *Indicates firm / individual with profile.*
[†] *ONP = Other Notable Practitioner.*

## Band 2

### Faegre Baker Daniels

**THE FIRM** This firm is well respected for the quality of its work in the franchising and distribution space. The team is noted for its handling of the full spectrum of contentious franchising matters, while it continues to advise franchisor clients on transactional matters and the structuring, negotiation and implementation of distribution agreements. Recent highlights include acting for Jani-King International on a number of federal court cases alleging consumer fraud. Other clients include International Dairy Queen and Johnny Rockets.

**KEY INDIVIDUALS Bill Killion** provided input on the Jani-King International cases and is a highly respected litigator in the franchising sphere. **Kerry Bundy** was lead trial counsel on the Jani-King International matters. She has also acted for Buffalo Wild Wings and International Dairy Queen. **Jeffrey Brimer** recently advised Johnny Rockets on intellectual property issues arising from the company's expansion plans. He advises clients on all aspects of domestic and international franchising and distribution law. **Kevin Hein** heads the team and is noted by interviewees for his handling of international transactional, structuring and implementation matters in the franchising space.

## Gray Plant Mooty
See profile on p.1585

**THE FIRM** This firm's franchising and distribution group handles the full range of advisory matters and is particularly recognized by interviewees for its strengths in the contentious aspects of franchising law, including trial and appellate work. Recent highlights include the team's representation of Outdoor Lighting Perspectives Franchising in two cases against former franchisees who had violated post-expiration noncompete provisions. Other clients include Dunkin' Brands and Domino's Pizza Franchising.
**KEY INDIVIDUALS Peter Klarfeld** is renowned in franchising circles as *"a strong and smart litigator,"* and is also experienced in competition matters. He recently acted for H&R Block Tax Services on litigation surrounding the renewal rights of 300 franchisees. **Gaylen Knack** recently advised Smoothie King Systems on its sale by merger to the franchisor's largest franchisee. Sources name him *"a solid transactional disclosure lawyer."* **Max Schott** advises franchisor clients on the negotiation of agreements and the drafting of documentation. **Eric Yaffe** recently acted for Dunkin' Brands in a high-value dispute with franchisee Progressive Foods concerning the termination of development rights. Sources praise him as *"a very good litigator."* **Carl Zwisler** is *"a good transactional and international lawyer,"* say sources. He recently helped negotiate the resolution of a number of franchising disputes in the healthcare arena. **Liz Dillon** handles the negotiation and preparation of agreements on behalf of franchisors. She was recently involved in the Smoothie King Systems matter. **Jan Gilbert** has advised on M&A, compliance and the drafting of agreements in the franchising arena. Sources describe him as *"a strong negotiator."*

## Haynes and Boone, LLP
See profile on p.444

**THE FIRM** This firm's franchising and distribution group has built an impressive reputation in domestic and international contentious and transactional matters. A raft of household names seek its services in this area, including Shell Oil, Hilton Worldwide and Krispy Kreme. Recent matters include the representation of RadioShack in a franchise transaction for the development of 1,000 stores in 11 countries.
**KEY INDIVIDUALS Joyce Mazero** heads the team and focuses her practice on domestic and international franchising matters. Sources say: *"She has a robust transactional practice,"* and is *"an expert in her field."* **Deborah Coldwell** is a high-profile contentious lawyer and *"a wonderful litigator,"* according to sources. She recently defended Party City in a trial concerning allegations of breach of contract brought by a former franchisee. **Robert Lauer** played a key role in the RadioShack matter. He concentrates his practice on domestic and international franchising transactions.

## Nixon Peabody LLP
See profile on p.1526

**THE FIRM** Market observers speak highly of the talent and scope of this firm's franchising practice. The group routinely handles the structuring, negotiation and licensing of franchise agreements, advises on franchising issues emerging from mergers and acquisitions and represents clients in franchise disputes. The team advises a number of high-profile franchisors including Dunkin' Brands, Burger King and Hard Rock Cafe.
**Sources say:** *"They have some excellent lawyers and are a good, balanced group."*
**KEY INDIVIDUALS Arthur Pressman** (see p.387) has a national franchise disputes practice and is described by sources as *"a very good litigator."* His clients include Fantastic Sams Franchise Corporation. **Andrew Loewinger** (see p.358) handles domestic and international franchising matters. He has recently advised franchisor clients on a number of franchisee bankruptcies and workouts. **Steven Feirman** (see p.312) is highly rated by market observers. He handles contentious and noncontentious work for domestic and international franchisors in addition to offering a strong knowledge of antitrust issues. **Craig Tractenberg** (see p.418) chairs the franchise and distribution practice group. He is recognized for his handling of contentious franchising matters, including disputes stemming from franchisee bankruptcies.

## Wiggin and Dana LLP
See profile on p.752

**THE FIRM** This firm is well regarded for its representation of franchisors from a wide range of industry sectors including hospitality, retail, food and automotive. The franchise and distribution practice group is particularly noted by market observers for its expertise in contentious matters, recently representing Doctor's Associates in a dispute concerning the exclusivity of development rights. Other marquee clients include Direct Buy.
**KEY INDIVIDUALS Jack Dunham** (see p.307) receives warm praise from commentators for his contentious franchising practice. He recently provided strategic advice on the Doctor's Associates matter. The *"very smart"* **Dean Fournaris** (see p.315) cochairs the franchise and distribution practice. He continues to provide strategic advice to childcare franchising company Goddard Systems. Sources describe him as *"knowledgeable, assertive and responsive."* *"Outstanding"* practitioner **Bethany Appleby** (see p.274) cochairs the group alongside Fournaris. She is praised for her handling of contentious franchising matters, and led in the Doctor's Associates dispute.

### Band 3

## Bryan Cave LLP

**THE FIRM** This firm is well regarded for its representation of franchisors from a range of industries including the restaurant, hotel and automotive sectors. The group is experienced in domestic and international transactional advisory work, including the structuring, drafting and negotiation of franchise agreements. In addition, it handles a broad range of contentious franchising matters including termination and encroachment disputes.
**KEY INDIVIDUALS Jonathan Solish** is a litigator with an excellent reputation as a franchise attorney. Sources praise his analytical skills and preparedness. **Kenneth Costello** is acclaimed as a strong private equity transactional and disclosure lawyer in particular. He is noted for his negotiation skills and structuring of agreements in the franchising and distributorship arena.

## Foley & Lardner LLP
See profile on p.2588

**THE FIRM** This firm's distribution and franchise practice represents clients in the establishment of franchise networks, the negotiation and drafting of agreements and the merging of distribution channels. It is also noted for its handling of contentious matters. Key clients of the practice include Harley-Davidson and Carlson Restaurants. The team recently acted for MillerCoors on the defense of allegations of price discrimination.
**KEY INDIVIDUALS Michael Lockerby** cochairs the practice. *"He is very effective, and has acted on some very important litigation,"* according to sources, who also note his *"great courtroom presence."* He was lead attorney on the MillerCoors price discrimination matter. Miami-based **Mary Leslie Smith** is a talented litigator with a focus on franchising and distribution disputes. Her franchisor clients include entities from the automotive and hospitality sectors.

## Greensfelder, Hemker & Gale, P.C.

**THE FIRM** This firm is noted for its handling of litigation and transactional franchising matters. The team was recently successful in its defense of BP in litigation stemming from a dispute over a gasoline station franchise offering. The group also acted for Shell Oil on a high-value price discrimination case. Other clients include Culligan International and Teixeira Development Group.
**Client Service** *"They were extremely thorough, prompt on responses and deadlines, very knowledgeable, and gave us the tools and information needed for our endeavor."*
**KEY INDIVIDUALS John Baer** handles domestic and international franchising work, including assisting clients with expansion overseas. Sources agree he is deserving of the highest recognition since *"he understands commercial law fundamentally."* Clients praise the *"top-level quality of work and input"* from **Leonard Vines**, with one interviewee noting that *"he worked within tight timeframes and provided us with the needed information and feedback."* Recent matters include advising the lender on the financing of a multistate food franchise chain. **Beata Krakus** advises on the negotiation and drafting of agreements, as well as franchising-related compliance and registration work. She is noted for her international franchising transaction activity.

## Larkin Hoffman Daly & Lindgren, Ltd.
See profile on p.1586

**THE FIRM** This Minneapolis firm is well respected for its work in the franchise and distribution arena. Its comprehensive practice includes the negotiation, drafting and registering of agreements, while it continues to assist clients with contentious matters. Clients include startups and Fortune 500 companies from a range of industries, including hospitality, retail and fitness.

**KEY INDIVIDUALS Joseph Fittante** is praised for his *"good experience and outstanding judgment."* His practice includes advising on all aspects of the franchising relationship, including distribution agreements and the registration of documentation. **Charles Modell** chairs the franchise and distribution group. He has considerable experience of advisory and transactional work, while he is also recognized for his comprehensive experience of contentious franchising matters.

## Plave Koch PLC
**THE FIRM** This compact franchising boutique represents franchisor clients in a broad range of domestic and international matters. The firm's wide expertise includes brand acquisitions, franchisee-relationship management and program launches. It also has a recognized track record in franchise litigation, representing clients in disputes such as noncompete violations, encroachment and lack of support.

**KEY INDIVIDUALS** Cofounder **Lee Plave** advises franchisors on system formation and international agreements, as well as IP matters including domain name disputes. **David Koch** cofounded the firm alongside Plave. He handles franchising, licensing and supply chain issues for entities from a broad range of industry sectors. **Leslie Curran** has advised franchisors and manufacturers on the negotiation, renegotiation and expansion of domestic and international franchising systems.

### Band 4

## Baker Botts LLP
See profile on p.2427

**THE FIRM** The Baker Botts franchising and distribution practice continues to handle a broad range of domestic and international distribution matters. Recent highlights include advising Marriott International on the spin-off of its timeshare and residential businesses into a new company, Marriott Vacations Worldwide Corporation. Marquee clients also include notable retail and hospitality entities such as 7-Eleven and La Quinta Inns.

**KEY INDIVIDUALS Ann Hurwitz** (see p.338) chairs the franchise and distribution law practice and is closely involved in much of the team's work for Marriott International. In addition, she serves as franchise counsel to Jamba Juice on program development and international tax issues. **Will Woods** (see p.428) took the lead role in the Marriott International matter. Areas of expertise include the structuring and registration of domestic and international franchise agreements.

## Ballard Spahr LLP
See profile on p.2234

**THE FIRM** This firm is noted for its handling of transactional, regulatory and litigious matters for franchisors at every stage of their development. Recent matters include the defense of Choice Hotels International with respect to an improper termination claim made by a multiunit franchisee. Other clients include Multivista Systems and Precision Franchising.

**KEY INDIVIDUALS Kim McCullough** (see p.365) heads the firm's franchise and distribution practice group. She represents franchisors in registration and disclosure, international expansion and M&A.

## Cheng Cohen LLC
**THE FIRM** This compact boutique firm represents clients in the full range of domestic and international matters. The group routinely advises on the structuring of franchise programs, the management of franchisee relationships, international expansion and litigation. In addition, the firm has experience in advising private equity clients on the acquisition of franchise companies.

**KEY INDIVIDUALS Fredric Cohen** is recognized for his astute handling of contentious work on behalf of franchisor clients. Sources agree he is *"a very good litigator."* He can call on broad experience as a seasoned trial and appellate lawyer. **Amy Cheng** wins plaudits as a *"really good transactional lawyer."* Her broad transactional franchising practice includes advising on M&A and joint ventures for clients from the restaurant and retail sectors.

## Day Pitney LLP
See profile on p.1753

**THE FIRM** This firm has a solid reputation for contentious and noncontentious franchisor representation and is noted for its close ties to the automotive and hospitality sectors. The team recently represented Ford in a class action brought by its former heavy truck dealer franchisees. Other clients include Avis, Hyundai and Wyndham Worldwide.

**Sources say:** *"These are the attorneys that I would turn to in the event that my company's life was at stake. Their intellect and dedication are unmatched."*

**KEY INDIVIDUALS Dennis LaFiura** (see p.1740) has a strong reputation in franchise litigation and led the team in the Ford matter. One source praises his *"unmatched legal analysis of any franchise legal issue."*

## Fisher Zucker, LLC
**THE FIRM** This boutique firm has built a loyal following for its astute command of franchise law. The group recently acted for a number of franchisors on negotiating the terms of their appearance on the reality television show Undercover Boss. The firm also advises franchisors such as Mister Softee, Pet Supplies Plus and California Closets.

**Client Service** *"They are unique in that they approach problems in a collaborative way. You have access to all of the principal partners of the firm with respect to all matters you send them. That personal attention by multiple partners sets them apart from other similarly sized firms."*

**KEY INDIVIDUALS Lane Fisher** (see p.313) took the lead in the negotiations for the Undercover Boss matter. Sources say: *"He does not rest on his laurels. He is persistent and inquisitive, and he uses both of these qualities to ensure that if we have a position, it is defensible."*

## Kaufmann Gildin Robbins & Oppenheim LLP
**THE FIRM** New York-based Kaufmann Gildin is a boutique firm with a healthy reputation in the franchising and distribution space. The group offers a broad service to franchisor clients including startup counseling, dispute resolution, program drafting and the negotiation of agreements.

**KEY INDIVIDUALS David Kaufmann** is a respected figure in the New York franchising Bar. He is an experienced counselor and litigator whose clients include Yum! Brands and Hilton Hotels. **David Oppenheim** handles a range of matters including the structuring and registration of franchising programs. He is also experienced in representing clients in complex franchise disputes.

## Kilpatrick Townsend & Stockton LLP
See profile on p.1109

**THE FIRM** The firm is recognized for its handling of the full range of contentious and noncontentious franchising matters. The team has been particularly active on franchise-related litigation, representing franchisor clients in disputes concerning trademark violations, breach of contract and franchisee bankruptcy matters.

**KEY INDIVIDUALS** Atlanta partner **Rupert Barkoff** chairs the franchising group. Market observers consider him to be *"extremely well regarded"* in the franchise Bar. He advises startup and mature franchisors on contentious and noncontentious matters.

## Snell & Wilmer LLP
See profile on p.517

**THE FIRM** This dedicated franchise practice remains busy advising on transactional and compliance matters as well as associated litigation. A number of impressive brands rely on its counsel, including Quiznos, Starbucks and Great Steak & Potato. The team recently represented Domino's Pizza in a California Supreme Court matter concerning vicarious liability.

**Sources say:** *"Excellent franchise counsel."*

**KEY INDIVIDUALS Susan Grueneberg** is commended for her *"firm grasp of the statutory requirements"* and *"good understanding of the regulatory environment."* She continues to provide strategic brand and restructuring consultancy to a number of national franchisors.

## Wiley Rein LLP
See profile on p.928

**THE FIRM** This nine-lawyer franchise group acts for clients including Pizza Inn and Noodles & Company. The team has recently advised Carl Karcher Enterprises and Hardee's Food Systems on a number of franchise transactions in Asia, South America and Europe. Other highlights include acting for Yoforia on a franchisee dispute concerning system changes and termination.

**KEY INDIVIDUALS Robert Smith** (see p.409) chairs the franchising practice. He advises clients on a range of franchising matters such as drafting contracts, disclosure documents and facilitating the purchase or sale of systems. He anchors the firm's work for Carl Karcher Enterprises and Hardee's Food Systems.

## Other Notable Practitioners

**John Dienelt** (see p.304) of Quarles & Brady LLP is a highly commended trial and appellate counsel. Sources praise his handling of contentious franchising matters, describing him as *"a real thinker, very strategic and very bright."* At the same firm, **David Beyer**'s (see p.283) franchise practice includes program formation, distribution agreements and disclosure matters. His clients include franchisors and dealers, and he has advised entities from the healthcare, automotive and real estate sectors. **Michael Joblove** heads the commercial litigation group at the Miami office of Genovese Joblove & Battista, PA. He is noted for his expertise in franchising disputes. His impressive client list includes Burger King, Denny's and Jamba Juice. **Michael**

**Lindsey** of Paul Hastings LLP advises clients on a range of matters including franchise structure, disclosure and compliance. He wins plaudits as an *"extremely knowledgeable and effective"* lawyer who is *"detail-oriented"* and *"terrific to work with."* *"Excellent litigator"* **Paula Morency** practices at Schiff Hardin LLP's Chicago office. Sources describe her as a *"good, solid counselor"* in the franchising space. **Shelley Spandorf** of Davis Wright Tremaine LLP garners notable market support for her practice. Sources report: *"She is extremely knowledgeable and efficient, and has an incredible background in franchise law."* **Robert Joseph** (see p.341) of Dentons is a widely respected lawyer who has represented clients including McDonald's and Sun Microsystems. He is noted for his handling of disputes at the intersection of franchising and antitrust law. **Thomas Collin** (see p.2093) heads Thompson Hine LLP's competition, antitrust and white-collar criminal section. Highlights include acting for Husqvarna Group on state franchise and dealer compliance regulatory issues. **Leonard MacPhee** of Perkins Coie LLP handles disputes involving IP and noncompete issues. He advised Quiznos on an action brought by a franchisee alleging fraud, breach of contract and RICO Act violations.

The *"terrific"* **Charles Miller** (see p.369) of Bartko, Zankel, Tarrant & Miller, PLC is *"a big-picture thinker and a great strategist,"* according to sources. He has acted for franchisors on class action litigation brought by both franchisees and consumers. **David Sager** (see p.398) heads the franchise and distribution group at Lowenstein Sandler PC. Sources describe him as a *"meticulous attorney"* who is *"very detail-oriented and takes client work very seriously."* **Michael Santa Maria** (see p.399) of Baker & McKenzie is recognized for his handling of international franchisor matters, and is noted for his knowledge of Latin American markets. **Alan Silberman** (see p.406) of Dentons handles antitrust disputes in the franchise space. *"He has a long and significant reputation as an antitrust litigator and is well respected,"* say sources. **Rebekah Prince** is of counsel in the corporate department at Eisner, Kahan & Gorry. Her broad corporate law experience extends to counseling and negotiating franchising agreements, as well as the purchase and sale of existing systems.

# FRANCHISING MAINLY FRANCHISEE

Commentary about individuals can be found under their firm's paragraph. If the firm has no paragraph (is not ranked) look at Other Notable Practitioners.

### Franchising: Mainly Franchisee

**Leading Firms**

**Band 1**
Dady & Gardner, PA *

**Band 2**
Einbinder & Dunn LLP
Marks & Klein, LLP
Zarco Einhorn Salkowski & Brito, PA

**Leading Individuals**

**Band 1**

| | | |
|---|---|---|
| Abrams Lee N | Mayer Brown LLP | |
| Dady J Michael | Dady & Gardner, PA * | |
| Gardner Ronald K | Dady & Gardner, PA * | |

**Band 2**

| | | |
|---|---|---|
| Garner W. Michael | W. Michael Garner, P.A. | |
| Green-Kelly Diane | Reed Smith LLP | |
| Karp Eric H | Witmer, Karp, Warner & Ryan | |
| Korzenowski Scott E | Dady & Gardner, PA * | |
| Selden Andrew | Briggs and Morgan * | |

**Band 3**

| | | |
|---|---|---|
| Chernow Harris J | Chernow Katz, LLC | |
| Einbinder Michael | Einbinder & Dunn LLP | |
| Einhorn Robert M | Zarco Einhorn Salkowski & Brito, PA | |
| Haff Jeffery S | Dady & Gardner, PA * | |
| Klein Justin | Marks & Klein, LLP | |
| Zarco Robert | Zarco Einhorn Salkowski & Brito, PA | |

*\* Indicates firm / individual with profile.*
*Alphabetical order within each band. Band 1 is the highest.*

## Band 1

### Dady & Gardner, PA
See profile on p.1582

**THE FIRM** This Minneapolis firm has an outstanding reputation for its representation of franchisees and distributors in the full range of matters including contentious and transactional work. It has previously acted for individual franchisees and franchisee groups of a host of famous restaurant names, such as McDonald's and Domino's Pizza.
**Sources say:** *"It is excellent, and does a good job."*
**KEY INDIVIDUALS** The *"excellent"* **Michael Dady** (see p.301) is widely recognized for his effective work for franchisees and dealers. Sources describe him as *"probably the best plaintiff lawyer in the country in this area of law. He is extremely knowledgeable and tenacious, but also fair."* **Ronald Gardner** (see p.318) is *"a good lawyer and litigator,"* according to sources. He regularly advises on franchisee terminations, breach of agreements and unreasonable conduct matters. **Scott Korzenowski** (see p.349) is a respected litigator in franchisor-franchisee disputes. He has a *"very good reputation,"* say sources. **Jeffery Haff** (see p.328) is recognized for his handling of contentious matters, including arbitrations and appellate proceedings. Clients he has advised include franchisees of Deere & Company.

## Band 2

### Einbinder & Dunn LLP
**THE FIRM** This New York franchise law boutique represents both franchisors and franchisees, and is particularly noted for its handling of franchisee matters. The team counsels clients on the full range of transactional and contentious matters, including breach of contract, fraud and unfair competition.
**KEY INDIVIDUALS Michael Einbinder** wins plaudits as a tenacious litigator with a focus on franchisee matters. His broad contentious capabilities include litigation, appellate, and alternative dispute resolution.

### Marks & Klein, LLP
**THE FIRM** This firm continues to advise franchisee clients on matters such as disclosure, contract review and leasing. It is also experienced in contentious work in the franchise space, and is noted for its handling of class and collective actions for franchisees.
**KEY INDIVIDUALS Justin Klein** is a litigator who is well regarded for his handling of high-value class and collective actions for franchisees. He has previously advised a group of Quiznos franchisees.

### Zarco Einhorn Salkowski & Brito, PA
**THE FIRM** This boutique firm advises on transactions and disputes in the franchising and licensing areas. It has previously acted for a number of hospitality and leisure clients, including franchisees of Holiday Inn, KFC and Domino's Pizza. It also advises on regulatory, noncompete and labor and employment matters.

**Sources say:** *"It is certainly well known for the diligent representation of franchisees."*
**KEY INDIVIDUALS Robert Einhorn** is the firm's managing partner. He is a highly regarded attorney in the franchising space and routinely represents clients in contentious matters at state, federal and appellate levels. **Robert Zarco** has advised franchisees of a number of high-profile brands including McDonald's, 7-Eleven and Johnny Rockets. He handles matters that are both domestic and international in scope, having represented clients throughout Europe and the Americas.

## GAMING & LICENSING

| Gaming & Licensing Leading Individuals | |
|---|---|
| **Star individuals** | |
| Cabot Anthony N | Lewis and Roca LLP |
| Faiss Robert D | Lionel Sawyer & Collins |
| Schreck Frank A | Brownstein Hyatt Farber Schreck, LLP |
| **Band 1** | |
| Casiello Jr Nicholas | Fox Rothschild LLP * |
| Stocker II Robert W | Dickinson Wright PLLC * |
| **Band 2** | |
| Clayton Mark | Lionel Sawyer & Collins |
| Duncan J Kelly | Jones Walker LLP * |
| Staudenmaier Heidi M | Snell & Wilmer LLP |
| West Paul | Baker, Donelson, Bearman, Caldwell * |
| **Band 3** | |
| Arrajj David R | Brownstein Hyatt Farber Schreck, LLP |
| Dayanim Behnam | Paul Hastings LLP |
| O'Gara Paul | Brownstein Hyatt Farber Schreck, LLP |
| Richey Kent E | Faegre Baker Daniels |
| Silver Jeffrey | Gordon Silver * |
| Waddell David | Regulatory Management Counselors, PC |

*\* Indicates individual with profile.*
*Alphabetical order within each band. Band 1 is the highest.*

## Star individuals

### Anthony N Cabot
**Lewis and Roca LLP**

Anthony Cabot of Lewis and Roca LLP is a *"Mensa-league genius"* who is at the forefront of internet gaming law and writes and speaks prolifically on the subject; one source said: *"With iGaming he doesn't have any peers."* Cabot's recent mandates include advising Entertainment Properties and American Casino on interactive gaming regulations in Nevada.

### Robert D Faiss
**Lionel Sawyer & Collins**

Robert Faiss of Lionel Sawyer & Collins is a Las Vegas-based regulatory attorney who is considered a *"legend among gaming lawyers."* He is widely respected and his

## Other Notable Practitioners

**Lee Abrams** of Mayer Brown LLP is *"very knowledgeable and extremely well regarded,"* according to sources. He is a commercial litigator with a focus on antitrust and franchising matters. **Diane Green-Kelly** of Reed Smith LLP advises franchisee clients on commercial and regulatory disputes including antitrust matters. Sources attest that she is *"well regarded"* in the franchising space. **Michael Garner** of W. Michael Garner, P.A. is a respected attorney in the franchisee and dealer representation arena. He has advised the franchisees of a number of prominent brands includ-

experience includes testifying before the Nevada legislature on gaming matters and advising countries such as Taiwan and Singapore on the creation of gaming control regimes. One enthusiastic commentator states: *"If you have seen anyone appear before a gaming board you ain't seen nothing until you have seen Bob Faiss."*

### Frank A Schreck
**Brownstein Hyatt Farber Schreck, LLP**

Frank Schreck of Brownstein Hyatt Farber Schreck, LLP is a Las Vegas-based attorney whom numerous sources describe as *"an icon in the industry."* His practice focuses on the regulatory aspects of land-based gaming; however, he is increasingly sought after for advice on internet gaming issues. Sources say that *"when it comes to difficult regulatory issues, in Nevada and on a national scale, he is very experienced, very sage and very practical."*

## Band 1

### Nicholas Casiello Jr
**Fox Rothschild LLP**

Nicholas Casiello of Fox Rothschild LLP *"has been involved in so many types of transactions that he is a quick study on whether or not something is able to be done or whether it would cause a problem."* He is a New Jersey-based attorney with a gaming practice that spans licensing, joint ventures, and land-based and internet regulatory work. In one recent matter, he advised Irish gaming group Paddy Power on US internet gaming laws and assisted with its application for a license in New Jersey.

### Robert W Stocker II
**Dickinson Wright PLLC**

Robert Stocker of Dickinson Wright PLLC, who advises clients from Lansing, Michigan, has a significant practice that focuses on land-based gaming and regulatory work. He advises gaming companies, state governments, investors and Indian tribes on a wide variety of matters including the refinancing, expansion and licensing of casinos. Impressed sources describe him as *"omnipresent"* and speak admiringly of his knowledge of the key players in the

ing Supercuts, Holiday Inn and Deere & Company. **Eric Karp** of Witmer, Karp, Warner & Ryan advises franchisees on the negotiation of agreements, disclosure and transfers. His key clients include franchisees of Dunkin' Donuts, McDonald's and Choice Hotels. **Andrew Selden** (see p.404) chairs the franchise group at Briggs and Morgan. He advises franchisee clients on the full range of contentious franchising matters. **Harris Chernow** of Chernow Katz, LLC is regarded by sources as an *"expert in franchise law."* His client list includes franchisee groups and individuals.

industry: *"If you call Bob, he can always introduce you to someone."*

## Band 2

### Mark Clayton
**Lionel Sawyer & Collins**

Mark Clayton of Lionel Sawyer & Collins is a well-respected Nevada attorney with a great deal of experience, both in private practice and as a gaming regulator. In one recent matter, he advised Caesars Interactive Entertainment on its application for a license to operate an in-state internet poker system in Nevada. One impressed client lists several of Clayton's finest traits: *"He is a former regulator with a very deep knowledge base, particularly on the complex minutiae of casino regulations. He is really in the know on aspects of slots technology and casino internal controls, and he brings that knowledge from regulation out to his private-sector clients."*

### J Kelly Duncan
**Jones Walker LLP**

Kelly Duncan of Jones Walker LLP is *"just great; a wonderful person, he knows the laws, he has great relationships with the regulators and is very well respected, which is important in this area."* He is based in New Orleans and has a broad gaming practice. He represents manufacturers, casino companies, casino suppliers and lenders in casino licensing, regulatory compliance, litigation and administrative hearings.

### Heidi M Staudenmaier
**Snell & Wilmer LLP**

Heidi Staudenmaier of Snell & Wilmer LLP is viewed by sources as *"the go-to person for anything to do with Native American gaming."* Her practice includes regulatory and legislative aspects, and she regularly deals with bodies such as the National Indian Gaming Commission, as well as various state and local governmental bodies. Additionally, she handles financing work, and indeed much of her recent work has focused on restructurings in the Indian gaming sector. Sources say: *"She is one of the finest tribal lawyers in the country."*

### Paul West
**Baker, Donelson, Bearman, Caldwell & Berkowitz, PC**

Paul West of Baker, Donelson, Bearman, Caldwell & Berkowitz, PC is a well-regarded New Orleans gaming regulatory attorney. *"He is very fair, methodical and logical; there are no surprises with him, you know what you are going to get,"* according to clients. He is noted for his relationships with regulators and industry figures and sources describe him as *"a good communicator."* He represents a wide array of clients, including gaming equipment manufacturers, developers, operators, investors and lenders.

## Band 3

### David R Arrajj
**Brownstein Hyatt Farber Schreck, LLP**

Commentators say that David Arrajj of Brownstein Hyatt Farber Schreck, LLP is an *"enormously talented and experienced gaming lawyer."* He has a great deal of experience in the sector; prior to establishing himself in Las Vegas he had stints as a gaming regulator in New Jersey and as an in-house counsel to a major gaming company. That experience prompted sources to say that *"he really understands the ramifications of gaming law because he has been a regulator and really studied the gaming law arena for so long."*

### Behnam Dayanim
**Paul Hastings LLP**

Behnam Dayanim of Paul Hastings LLP is a Washington, DC trial lawyer who has developed a specialty in the area of internet and social gaming. He is particularly noted for his work dealing with the DOJ and other law enforcement agencies on behalf of internet gaming clients. Sources say: *"His attention to detail is great and he grasps concepts quickly and also works to find solutions to further his client's goals."*

### Paul O'Gara
**Brownstein Hyatt Farber Schreck, LLP**

Paul O'Gara of Brownstein Hyatt Farber Schreck, LLP is an experienced gaming lawyer who recently joined the firm, along with a small team, to establish its first Atlantic City office. He is described as *"a creative guy who works well with the regulators trying to find solutions."* His practice includes representing gaming investors and handling acquisitions in the sector, in addition to representing casino operating companies and casino holding companies.

### Kent E Richey
**Faegre Baker Daniels**

Kent Richey of Faegre Baker Daniels is a *"talented and experienced lawyer"* who focuses on tribal gaming. His practice includes handling corporate work and financing in gaming projects, as well as interacting with regulators such as the National Indian Gaming Commission (NIGC)

and the Bureau of Indian Affairs. Sources say: *"He understands the regulatory process as well as anyone and will move heaven and earth to get the NIGC to act quickly."*

### Jeffrey Silver
**Gordon Silver**

Jeffrey Silver of Gordon Silver is a well-regarded gaming regulatory lawyer based in Las Vegas. Commentators note that *"he has a way of getting his point across and doing so in a manner that makes him highly respected."* He is praised for his abilities as a business lawyer and noted for his significant gaming industry background, which included a period working as a regulator.

### David Waddell
**Regulatory Management Counselors, PC**

David Waddell of Regulatory Management Counselors, PC is a gaming attorney based in Michigan. He is described by market sources as *"an extremely experienced and well-respected lawyer in the regulatory arena."* His specialist practice focuses exclusively on regulatory issues including licensing, gaming equipment compliance, internet gambling and corporate structuring. Sources say: *"He is the kind of guy who knows the regulators, knows the law and gets the job done without making a big deal about everything."*

# GOVERNMENT GOVERNMENT CONTRACTS

Commentary about individuals can be found under their firm's paragraph. If the firm has no paragraph (is not ranked) look at Other Notable Practitioners.

## Band 1

### Arnold & Porter LLP
See profile on p.906

**THE FIRM** Arnold & Porter remains a sound choice for contractors with a focus on national security matters and classified projects. The team numbers 57 attorneys and is home to former general counsels of the CIA and NSA. The firm continues its representation of leading technology companies such as Raytheon and Computer Sciences Corporation, while also representing a mix of companies from the professional services, communications and pharmaceuticals industries. In the past year, the group also successfully represented the Wisconsin Physicians Services Insurance Corporation in Government Accountability Office (GAO) protests involving two major Medicare administration contracts.
**Client Service** *"A very responsive, customer-centric and knowledgeable firm that appears to pay close attention to the quickly changing environment of government contracting, and ensures its clients are kept similarly knowledgeable."*
**Commercial Awareness** *"Arnold & Porter has lawyers who were formerly officials at government administrations. They*

*have a depth and breadth of skills that we find particularly helpful."*
**KEY INDIVIDUALS** Department head **Mark Colley** (see p.298) *"continues to distinguish himself,"* according to sources, and his practice focuses on False Claims Act and bid protest matters. Colley is chair of the American Bar Association public contract law section, and has assisted a number of organizations performing highly classified contracts supported by the US armed forces and intelligence agencies outside of the USA. **Paul Pompeo**'s (see p.386) reputation for high-quality work in the cost accounting and cost dispute arena continues unabated. The *"absolutely excellent and very knowledgeable"* **Ronald Schechter** (see p.400) is admired for his understanding of how the federal contracting system works. Schechter also represented the Wisconsin Physicians Service Insurance Corporation in the protests outlined above. **Jeffrey Smith** (see p.409) is renowned for his work in the field of national security, and is described by clients as being *"extremely well connected."*

### Crowell & Moring LLP
See profile on p.910

**THE FIRM** The team at Crowell & Moring is comprised of over 50 government contracts specialists, and has growing expertise in bid protests. Notable clients include BAE Systems and the Military & Veterans Services wing of UnitedHealth Group, but the firm also continues to see expansion in its client base of small and mid-sized businesses. The past year saw the team successfully defend an award made to Spectrum Healthcare Resources, and then defeat a subsequent appeal relating to the contract to build and operate two family health clinics for the Department of Defense, which was valued at over $220 million. Crowell

## Government: Government Contracts
### Leading Firms

**Band 1**
Arnold & Porter LLP *
Crowell & Moring LLP *
McKenna Long & Aldridge LLP *
Wiley Rein LLP *

**Band 2**
Gibson, Dunn & Crutcher LLP *
Hogan Lovells US LLP *
Jenner & Block LLP *
Rogers Joseph O'Donnell *
Sheppard, Mullin, Richter & Hampton LLP

**Band 3**
Fried, Frank, Harris, Shriver & Jacobson LLP *
Holland & Knight LLP *
Mayer Brown LLP *
Pillsbury Winthrop Shaw Pittman LLP *
Smith Pachter McWhorter PLC *
Venable LLP *

**Band 4**
Covington & Burling LLP *
Dickstein Shapiro LLP *
DLA Piper LLP (US) *
Foley & Lardner LLP *
Vinson & Elkins LLP *

## Government: Government Contracts
### Senior Statesmen

**Senior Statesmen: distinguished older practitioners**

| | |
|---|---|
| Dees C Stanley | McKenna Long & Aldridge LLP |
| Doke Jr Marshall J | Gardere Wynne Sewell LLP (ONP)[†] * |

### Leading Individuals

**Band 1**

| | |
|---|---|
| Albertson Terry | Crowell & Moring LLP * |
| Allen Rand L | Wiley Rein LLP * |
| Chierichella John W | Sheppard, Mullin, Richter & Hampton LLP |
| Churchill David A | Jenner & Block LLP * |
| Joseph Allan J | Rogers Joseph O'Donnell |
| Khoury Paul F | Wiley Rein LLP * |
| Madsen Marcia G | Mayer Brown LLP |
| Manos Karen L | Gibson, Dunn & Crutcher LLP * |
| McCullough James J | Fried, Frank, Harris, Shriver & Jacobson * |
| O'Donnell Neil | Rogers Joseph O'Donnell |

**Band 2**

| | |
|---|---|
| Charness Michael | Vinson & Elkins LLP * |
| Colley Mark | Arnold & Porter LLP * |
| DeVecchio W Jay | Jenner & Block LLP * |
| Gallagher James J | McKenna Long & Aldridge LLP * |
| Humphrey Thomas P | Crowell & Moring LLP * |
| McCaleb Scott M | Wiley Rein LLP * |
| McGovern III Thomas L | Hogan Lovells US LLP |
| Pachter John | Smith Pachter McWhorter PLC |
| Papson Thomas C | McKenna Long & Aldridge LLP * |
| Rector Richard P | DLA Piper LLP (US) * |
| Smith Gregory A | Smith Pachter McWhorter PLC |
| West Joseph D | Gibson, Dunn & Crutcher LLP * |

**Band 3**

| | |
|---|---|
| Mason Michael F | Hogan Lovells US LLP |
| Nadler David | Dickstein Shapiro LLP * |

| | |
|---|---|
| Johnson W Stanfield | Crowell & Moring LLP * |
| Madden Thomas J | Venable LLP * |
| Vacketta Carl Lee | DLA Piper LLP (US) * |

| | |
|---|---|
| Nibley Stuart B | K&L Gates (ONP)[†] * |
| Pompeo Paul E | Arnold & Porter LLP * |
| Tomaszczuk Alex | Pillsbury Winthrop Shaw Pittman LLP * |
| Vacura Richard J | Morrison & Foerster LLP (ONP)[†] * |

**Band 4**

| | |
|---|---|
| Abbott Thomas M | McKenna Long & Aldridge LLP |
| Belkin Jeffrey A | Alston & Bird LLP (ONP)[†] * |
| Biagini Ray | McKenna Long & Aldridge LLP * |
| Black David | Holland & Knight LLP * |
| Campos Lorraine | Reed Smith LLP (ONP)[†] |
| Debolt Paul A | Venable LLP * |
| Dover Agnes | Hogan Lovells US LLP |
| Dowd David F | Mayer Brown LLP |
| Graham Daniel P | Wiley Rein LLP * |
| Hommer Scott | Venable LLP * |
| Jensen John E | Pillsbury Winthrop Shaw Pittman LLP |
| Johnson David R | Vinson & Elkins LLP * |
| Mullen Kevin | Jenner & Block LLP * |
| Pemberton Alan | Covington & Burling LLP * |
| Ralston David | Foley & Lardner LLP |
| Schechter Ronald A | Arnold & Porter LLP * |
| Smith Jeffrey | Arnold & Porter LLP * |
| Styles Angela B | Crowell & Moring LLP * |

**Up-and-coming individuals**

| | |
|---|---|
| Carey Jason | McKenna Long & Aldridge LLP * |
| Forman Daniel R | Crowell & Moring LLP * |
| Owren-Wiest Nicole J | Wiley Rein LLP * |

\* Indicates firm / individual with profile.
[†]ONP = Other Notable Practitioner.

achieved victory on behalf of its client after multiple rounds of bid protests.

**Client Service** *"They keep us updated on things they do in our area, which allows us to key our strategy in a particular direction. I feel like they're an extension of our company and can't imagine not having the firm at our fingertips. Our company would be less well off if they weren't around."*

**KEY INDIVIDUALS** Chair of the group **Angela Styles** (see p.414) maintains a practice focused primarily on suspension and debarment matters. Clients sing **Terry Albertson**'s (see p.272) praises for his work in the government contracts arena, saying: *"He really is one of the leading lights in that regard."* Albertson represents a number of defense contractors, and has amassed great expertise in counseling on matters relating to contract costs, price, accounting and termination issues. Sources are impressed by **Thomas Humphrey**'s (see p.337) *"extraordinary wisdom in analyzing cases."* In the past year, Humphrey has demonstrated his dynamism in bid protests, successfully defending an award made by the Army to BAE Systems in relation to the development of a 'next-generation common infrared countermeasure system for helicopters'. **Stanfield Johnson** (see p.340) continues to counsel clients in the most complex government contracting issues. **Daniel Forman** (see p.315) is gaining increased recognition for his expertise in technology-related bid protests, and is championed by clients as an *"excellent advocate."*

### McKenna Long & Aldridge LLP
See profile on p.922

**THE FIRM** This formidable group numbers in excess of 80 government contracts professionals, and boasts the expert-

ise to cater to a broad client base which includes Lockheed Martin, UnitedHealth, IBM and BP North America. The firm is currently representing Honeywell International in the face of ongoing potential debarment issues arising out of the 2012 Appropriations Act, and has assisted the client in avoiding any associated loss of federal work or projects in connection with this matter to date. McKenna also has a large number of attorneys in possession of top-level security clearances, enabling it to adeptly handle classified program matters.

Sources say: *"Their advice has been excellent across the board."* *"They have deep government contracts expertise, so if a related question needs to be pursued they have the best people to pursue those matters."*

**KEY INDIVIDUALS** Based in Los Angeles, **James Gallagher** (see p.318) and **Thomas Abbott** spearhead the West Coast limb of McKenna's government contracts team. Clients are hugely impressed by Gallagher, remarking: *"He's a terrific lawyer – very knowledgeable about government contracts-related issues. We have full faith in him."* **Ray Biagini** (see p.283) has developed a niche in obtaining

SAFETY Act coverage for clients so as to minimize tort liability arising out of terrorist attacks for organizations that develop and deploy anti-terror products and services. Biagini assists the Port Authority of New York/New Jersey in obtaining coverage for the numerous high-value terrorist targets situated within the region. He also has a successful track record in tort litigation, and sources praise his persuasive arguments in addition to his *"ability to build a rapport with judges quickly."* **Thomas Papson** (see p.381) worked with **Jason Carey** (see p.292) in a successful protest on behalf of AT&T which challenged the terms of a contract solicitation and excluded AT&T from the competitive range. The duo were successful on both counts, and similar successes have led observers to enthuse about Papson's *"top-drawer"* approach within the world of bid protests. *"It's a bit like a chess match and he's very good – a bright litigator,"* say sources. Similarly, observers admire Carey's *"keen intellect – he's able to see the issues and evidence, and craft an argument in a compelling way which is clearly articulated."* **Stanley Dees**'s practice embraces all elements of government contracts law, and has included false claims and debarment actions in addition to bid protests and costs recovery.

## Wiley Rein LLP
See profile on p.928

**THE FIRM** Wiley Rein's continuing dominance in the world of government contracts can be attributed to its strong relationships with Fortune 500 companies such as Fluor, AECOM and Hewlett-Packard. The firm continues its ongoing representation of long-standing client Boeing, handling bid protests, convenience terminations, claims assessment and litigation, compliance matters, pricing issues, audits before the Defense Contract Audit Agency and internal investigations on its behalf. The sizable group comprises 39 attorneys based predominantly in DC.
**Client Service** "The group works very well – they staff effectively, respond quickly to client desires, and understand how we operate and expect them to operate."
**KEY INDIVIDUALS** "Exceptional" **Rand Allen** (see p.272) secured a victory on behalf of Booz Allen Hamilton, successfully opposing a proposed debarment of its San Antonio location and securing an administrative agreement in the client's favor. **Paul Khoury** (see p.346) is renowned for being "a fantastic bid protest attorney." He was victorious in a bid protest on behalf of Verizon Wireless, which challenged the terms of a General Services Administration (GSA) solicitation estimated at around $1.6 billion. Observers state that **Scott McCaleb** (see p.364) is "going great guns" at Wiley. In the past year, he has counseled CGI Federal on a broad range of matters, including bid protests and general compliance matters. **Daniel Graham** (see p.325) continues to gain ground in this field, with clients affirming that "Dan Graham leads the next generation of Wiley protest lawyers. He does outstanding work and gets good results for us." **Nicole Owren-Wiest** (see p.381) is praised by sources for her "outstanding efforts," and assisted Allen in facing the proposed debarment of Booz Allen Hamilton outlined above.

## Band 2

## Gibson, Dunn & Crutcher LLP
See profile on p.682

**THE FIRM** Gibson Dunn has a particular focus on representing aerospace and defense contractors in high-value government contract litigation. This global firm is revered by sources for its extensive resources and ability to marshal assistance from other practice groups as needed. Notable clients include Northrop Grumman and Raytheon, on whose behalf the group won a significant $59.2 million judgment in a case which arose pursuant to the sale of four Raytheon businesses with underfunded post-retirement benefit plans. The team also defeated government counterclaims totaling over $18 million in the process.
**Sources say:** "The team at Gibson Dunn is highly aware of our commercial operations and need for pragmatic solutions." "They have an expert-level knowledge of suspensions and debarment and government administrative actions."
**KEY INDIVIDUALS Karen Manos** (see p.361) is once again highlighted for her impressive skill in handling cost disputes and cost accounting issues. The aforementioned Raytheon matter is one in which she excelled, and sources report that Manos is "extremely confident and capable. She is very good at making rational arguments and explaining them so that non-accountants can understand." **Joseph West** (see p.899) has great experience in handling suspension and debarment matters. Observers are impressed, attesting that "he is a fierce advocate for the client. He's willing to take a tough position with government representatives." West's recent work includes providing ongoing counseling to a diverse group of clients, including the Bank of New York Mellon and Enterprise Rent-a-Car.

## Hogan Lovells US LLP

**THE FIRM** This firm is well known for its impressive abilities in federal procurement law, regulatory compliance and IT government contracting, and for its adeptness at dealing with a range of government agencies. In the past year, Hogan Lovells has experienced significant growth in its bid protest practice, achieving success in protests on behalf of Lockheed Martin in relation to a contract worth over $4 billion governing the operation and maintenance of information systems managed by the US Defense Information Systems Agency. This global firm caters to government contractors across a broad spectrum of industries, including pharmaceuticals, biotechnology, federal research and energy. Clients include Pfizer, General Dynamics, Accenture and Google.
**Commercial Awareness** "They understand everything immediately. They are thoughtful, prepared and have the trust of the government, which makes things easy. They can distill very complicated things into easy to understand pieces, which is helpful."
**KEY INDIVIDUALS Agnes Dover** is considered by sources to be "a go-to person in respect of regulatory compliance, particularly in the Department of Energy and defense spaces." Dover's practice also focuses on Department of Homeland Security issues and federal contracts matters arising in the education sector. **Thomas McGovern** is a leading figure in the growing bid protest practice at Hogan Lovells, and has special expertise in the fields of aerospace and defense. Clients appreciate the close attention he pays them, with one reporting that "Tom provides an efficient service and keeps us up to date on the latest legal and regulatory developments." **Michael Mason** led on the Lockheed Martin matter outlined above, and has also represented TechAmerica in government procurement matters. Mason impresses sources, who state that "he is a phenomenal lawyer."

## Jenner & Block LLP
See profile on p.1252

**THE FIRM** Jenner & Block handles matters on behalf on major US defense contractors, including L-3 Communications and General Dynamics. The group comprises approximately 20 attorneys based primarily in DC, and has substantial experience handling fast-paced bid protests before the GAO and US Federal Claims Court. The firm deals with both government contracts litigation and transactional work, including handling contractor mergers and acquisitions.
**Sources say:** "The firm does an exceptional job for us on a number of matters."
**KEY INDIVIDUALS David Churchill** (see p.295) and **Jay DeVecchio** (see p.304) are cochairs of the practice and have an impressive number of government dispute victories between them. Churchill is praised by sources for his versatility: "He's a very good government contracts generalist and also an exceptional litigator – those skills have been well honed." Meanwhile, observers are quick to enthuse about DeVecchio's specific areas of focus, stating: "Jay is terrific at government contracts data rights and intellectual property issues." DeVecchio successfully resolved a costs dispute in favor of Lockheed Martin, recovering $107.6 million from the Air Force in relation to the F-22 aircraft program. **Kevin Mullen**'s (see p.372) ongoing work in the bid protest world is highly regarded by sources, who report that "Kevin is a top protest lawyer. He is somebody that I have a lot of respect for in this arena."

## Rogers Joseph O'Donnell
See profile on p.697

**THE FIRM** This well-regarded litigation boutique has offices in San Francisco and DC. The firm is renowned for its bid protest work, and also has a particularly strong presence on the West Coast. In the last year, the group successfully represented Assisted Housing Services and the North Tampa Housing Development Corporation in a GAO bid protest of the Department of Housing and Urban Development's proposed use of cooperative agreements to obtain services. The group's success enabled an entire class of qualified contractors to meaningfully compete for a minimum ten-year contract to the value of around $260 million a year.
**Sources say:** "It is an extremely good value proposition using the firm." "Rogers Joseph O'Donnell has conducted work well, and the attorneys here always make themselves available to me if I need information on federal procurement."

**KEY INDIVIDUALS** The *"terrific"* **Neil O'Donnell** receives praise for his pragmatism and depth of experience: *"I like going to Neil for things that are not so run of the mill and which require more in-depth analysis. He's very good at thinking through how things will work in the long term."* O'Donnell continues to impress in bid protest matters for pubic construction and infrastructure companies. **Allan Joseph** receives plaudits for his dedicated service in the government contracts field. He advises the Electric Power Research Institute on the implementation of a grant from the Department of Energy to the South Coast Air Quality Management District.

### Sheppard, Mullin, Richter & Hampton LLP

**THE FIRM** This team comprises 45 attorneys with broad government contracts expertise, enabling it to guide clients through a wide range of issues, including bid protests, fraud investigations, costs control and costs recovery work, small business subcontracting reviews, country of origin compliance reviews, patent litigation and audits. Clients hail from a varied selection of industries, including hi-tech, aerospace and defense, healthcare, power and utilities.

**KEY INDIVIDUALS** The past year has seen **John Chierichella** assist clients in matters relating to the False Claims Act, as well as with audit responses and claims against various government agencies. Sources admire his ability to get to grips with a matter, stating that *"he's a quick study – he homes in on the issue rapidly and asks relevant questions to get the information he needs. We appreciate that efficiency."*

### Band 3

### Fried, Frank, Harris, Shriver & Jacobson LLP
See profile on p.1975

**THE FIRM** The Fried Frank team has vast experience in representing clients in bid protests before the GAO and US Federal Claims Court. In the past year, one significant victory for the firm was achieved in reinstating Hawker Beechcraft Defense in the competition for a US Air Force award of $355 million for the manufacture of 20 light air support aircraft to be used in Afghanistan. Other key matters include counseling in government investigations, contracts-related litigation, and handling corporate transactions between contractors.

**Sources say:** *"The group offers efficient, effective representation."*

**KEY INDIVIDUALS** James McCullough (see p.365) leads the Fried Frank team in handling post-award disputes and contract formation matters. He has extensive experience in enforcement matters which involve voluntary disclosure and suspension and debarment issues. McCullough has also honed his skills in resolving contract disputes via mediation and arbitration.

### Holland & Knight LLP
See profile on p.1028

**THE FIRM** This group maintains its focus on bid protests, and is defending Raytheon's Missile Systems Division against a protest in relation to a multimillion-dollar weapons contract awarded by the US Marine Corps. The team has also enjoyed success in suspension and debarment proceedings, and is positioning itself well in the growing field of state government contracting. Holland & Knight's additional proficiency in the areas of white-collar crime and compliance further strengthen its ability to counsel contractor clients operating within this sphere.

**Commercial Awareness** *"They helped us position ourselves during a time-consuming, complex renegotiation of a contract. We've relied greatly on these attorneys."*

**KEY INDIVIDUALS** The past year has seen **David Black** (see p.284) represent Blackstone Consulting in protests before the GAO, in addition to providing general counseling services in relation to contract compliance and administration. Black is equally adept at responding to government investigations and audits, as well as assisting clients with issues arising out of terminations. Sources are enthusiastic about his skills: *"David understands business. I'll shoot off a quick query and he doesn't filter the work down or accrue unnecessary hours – he'll give a quick response."*

### Mayer Brown LLP
See profile on p.1257

**THE FIRM** In the past year, Mayer Brown successfully represented Lockheed Martin in a high-profile bid protest relating to a contract valued at approximately $1.8 billion for support of the US Antarctic Program. The group also assists with a high number of FCA recoveries and civil fraud investigations, working with traditional government contractors in addition to companies that do not traditionally work within the procurement industry. Other notable clients include BAE Systems, Bechtel Infrastructure and Siemens.

**Client Service** *"The team at Mayer Brown is cost conscious in the fact that they don't chase down every possible alleyway for no good reason – they know what will lead to success."*

**KEY INDIVIDUALS** Best known for her substantial work in bid protests, **Marcia Madsen** took the lead on the Lockheed Martin matter outlined above. Along with colleague **David Dowd**, Madsen receives impressive feedback from sources, who state: *"She knows when to arc in and when not to. The combination of the two of them is dynamic – you don't need to deal with anyone else. They are value for money."* Alongside Madsen, Dowd also continues to counsel Lockheed Martin in multiple ongoing government contracts and litigation matters.

### Pillsbury Winthrop Shaw Pittman LLP
See profile on p.2000

**THE FIRM** Pillsbury fields 26 lawyers with experience handling government contracts matters from DC to the West Coast. The group has particular expertise in assisting clients with bid protests, conducting internal investigations and defending clients in cases concerning alleged viola-

tions of the False Claims Act, in addition to advising on international government contracting opportunities.

**Sources say:** *"The attorneys with whom I work are excellent – they are knowledgeable in their field, hard-working and responsive."*

**KEY INDIVIDUALS** Clients clearly rely on **Alex Tomaszczuk** (see p.418), stating that *"he is amazingly available when we need him to be."* Tomaszczuk's work predominantly involves high-value government contracts litigation and advising on ethics issues relating to contracts. Similarly, observers admire **John Jensen**'s abilities, stating that *"he is a tenacious advocate for his clients and very diligent in what he does – a worthy adversary."* Jensen leads the group at Pillsbury, and focuses on assisting clients with matters pertaining to federal government contract law.

### Smith Pachter McWhorter PLC
See profile on p.2521

**THE FIRM** This boutique firm specializes in government contracts and construction law. The group's industries of focus include large weapon systems, IT, food services and electronics. The firm is based in Tysons Corner, Virginia, and comprises approximately 19 practicing government contracts professionals.

**Sources say:** *"Smith Pachter McWhorter is a premier boutique in this area – the group is very capable."*

**KEY INDIVIDUALS** Sources tell us that the *"terrific"* **John Pachter** is *"very knowledgeable and well respected – you can rely on him."* Pachter's bid protest experience has seen him litigate before the Boards of Contract Appeals, the US Federal Claims Court and the GAO. Meanwhile, clients are thrilled with **Gregory Smith**'s skill in costs matters: *"I consider him to be the person for cost accounting issues. This can be a minefield for businesses, and our team holds the cost accounting work he does for us in really high regard."*

### Venable LLP
See profile on p.927

**THE FIRM** Venable's growing practice incorporates 15 attorneys, and notable clients include Dell Federal, E-Merging Technologies and Securitas Security Services. The past year has seen the group counseling clients on the potential impact of sequestration, advising on matters arising in relation to the GSA schedule and claims litigation, investigations, and suspension and debarment matters. Additionally, the team is populated by a number of former government officials, boosting the firm's resources.

**Client Service** *"They operate effectively and coordinate very well between practice groups to ensure the client gets the benefit of the advice of various experts. They are aware of the commercial environment and the economic challenges that their clients face, and work well with them. They have always been very responsive to my needs and realistic in their approach to helping me address the issue."*

**KEY INDIVIDUALS** Thomas Madden (see p.360) is praised by observers for his depth of knowledge in this field: *"He is one of the go-to lawyers in the country in this area. He's one of a handful of guys who knows US government contract law like the back of his hand."* Cochairs **Scott Hommer** (see p.335) and **Paul Debolt** (see p.303) also draw positive reviews. Clients are impressed with Hommer's knowledge of the bid protest process as well as his "*ability to ensure fair treatment by the government in contract disputes.*" Similarly, "*Paul pursues cost-effective solutions, always displaying an understanding of the economic pressures that are exerted on companies that deal directly or indirectly with the government.*" Debolt's knowledge extends to the competitive source selection process, and he also has vast experience in the corporate aspects of government contracting, having dealt with contractor mergers and acquisitions.

## Band 4

### Covington & Burling LLP
See profile on p.441

THE FIRM This 23-attorney group carries out ongoing representation of PAE Government Services as protestor of the award of a Navy contract for support services at the Navy support facility in Diego Garcia, as well as as an intervenor in a protest against the award of a contract to PAE from the Department of State for its work providing support services at the US embassy in Baghdad. Other clients include Microsoft, Johnson & Johnson, and Novartis Vaccines & Diagnostics.

Sources say: "*They really know how to deal with people. They are great listeners, and are able to put things in layman's terms.*"

KEY INDIVIDUALS Alan Pemberton (see p.383) is cochair of the practice at Covington & Burling, and impresses sources with his ability to get things done. "*He's never failed to work with us and help us make things happen,*" said one interviewee. Pemberton's areas of expertise include bid protests and procurement litigation, in addition to performance and compliance of contracts and suspension and debarment issues.

### Dickstein Shapiro LLP
See profile on p.911

THE FIRM Dickstein Shapiro has six offices spanning the USA, incorporating 19 practicing government contracts professionals. Clients include leading helicopter services companies such as Caron Helicopters and VIH Cougar Helicopters. The group assists clients in navigating the complex regulations affecting their abilities to succeed in securing government contracts, and provides effective counsel in associated litigation. The team also has experience in False Claims Act investigations and congressional investigations.

Commercial Awareness "*It's a very cohesive group which brings common sense skills and unique capabilities together for collaborative purposes. They also get to issues cleanly and understand the nuances of a matter. We rely on Dickstein and have confidence in their results.*"

KEY INDIVIDUALS Clients of David Nadler (see p.374) are immensely satisfied: "*He pays attention to us as a client, and he'll make sure our matters are appropriately handled. He makes us feel we're his number-one client.*" In addition to

the general matters handled by the practice, Nadler has expertise in bid protests, cost accounting issues and matters arising in relation to the Foreign Corrupt Practices Act.

### DLA Piper LLP (US)
See profile on p.1971

THE FIRM The practice at DLA Piper incorporates 16 dedicated government contracts attorneys, able to draw on the additional strength of an impressive task force of over 50 experienced procurement, defense, and infrastructure lawyers across the globe. Clients include GE and UPS, and in the past year the firm acted as lead negotiator for Accenture on a substantial contract to put in place a statewide health insurance exchange, known as the California Healthcare Enrollment, Eligibility and Retention System.

Sources say: "*They send along other reminders and updates that are useful to our day-to-day business. They look after our best interests, and I can just pick up the phone and ask them anything.*"

KEY INDIVIDUALS Carl Lee Vacketta (see p.420) assists Trade Center Management Associates, advising on administration, compliance and negotiations relating to a multiyear contract with the GSA to operate the Ronald Reagan Building and International Trade Center in DC. Sources tell us: "*Carl brings a lot of weight to our discussions – if he's involved then people know he'll be fair. He understands the outcome and imparts a lot of wisdom to our team.*" Head of department Richard Rector (see p.390) filed a successful state-level bid protest on behalf of UPS challenging an award to a competitor of a contract for statewide delivery of small packages. The contract was ultimately awarded to UPS. Observers state that "*his depth of knowledge and ability to take relatively complex issues and craft them in a manner that works at a business level are really impressive.*"

### Foley & Lardner LLP
See profile on p.2588

THE FIRM The government procurement team at Foley & Lardner caters to a broad spectrum of clients across a range of industries, including healthcare, energy and defense. The firm has 19 offices across the US and a dedicated contracts group comprising 11 attorneys. Clients include Oshkosh, Cisco Systems, BAE Systems and Sony Corporation of America, and the group is adept at counseling contractors through the bid process, including handling contract negotiations, in addition to representing clients before federal and international tribunals in suspension or debarment matters.

Sources say: "*There is excellent communication between the firm's various offices.*" "*These people are wonderfully detail-oriented, which is critically important.*"

KEY INDIVIDUALS In addition to the matters outlined above, department chair David Ralston has great experience in bid protests, defending contractors against fraud and bribery charges and assisting clients in the face of corporate investigations. Clients value his communication

skills, explaining that "*David puts language in a businessperson's framework.*"

### Vinson & Elkins LLP
See profile on p.2459

THE FIRM Vinson & Elkins's client base includes illustrious names like AREVA, BAE, Fluor, GE and Shell. In the past year, the group represented Kuwaiti company KGL Food Services in a successful bid protest at the GAO relating to a multibillion-dollar contract covering the supply of food products to US troops. The team also represented TriWest Healthcare, which provides healthcare to the armed forces, in one of the largest bid protests ever to be filed at the GAO.

KEY INDIVIDUALS Michael Charness (see p.293) led on the KGL bid protest, and handles complex commercial litigation arising out of government contracts. One client enthused: "*Mike is easy to work with and watches my back.*" Similarly, sources affirm that David Johnson (see p.340) "*coordinates all activities well. His counsel is invaluable in identifying practical and pragmatic approaches for resolving issues.*" Johnson played an active role in the TriWest Healthcare bid protest outlined above, and has also litigated before the Federal Aviation Administration and US Federal Claims Court.

## Other Notable Practitioners

In the past year, Alston & Bird LLP practice head Jeffrey Belkin (see p.281) successfully obtained a dismissal in a qui tam suit against his clients Dell, Insight, PC Mall and PC Specialists. Sources admire "*his understanding of the law and his ability to take the facts and figure out a good strategy moving forward. He gets a really sound resolution.*" Marshall Doke (see p.305) of Gardere Wynne Sewell LLP is considered by observers to be "*the preeminent government contracts lawyer in the country. His advice and counsel are exemplary – he's very well respected.*" At K&L Gates, Stuart Nibley (see p.376) has shown great skill in representing civilian and defense contractors in a range of government contracts contexts, including boards of contract appeals, federal and state courts, and international arbitration forums. Commentators affirm that Nibley is "*incredibly knowledgeable.*" Richard Vacura (see p.420) of Morrison & Foerster LLP is representing Global Linguistics Solutions before the Court of Federal Claims in defense of a multiple contract award for foreign language support services made by the US Army to the value of $7.6 billion. Other clients include Honeywell and DynCorp International. Lorraine Campos is new to the rankings, and is thought of by clients as "*very practical in her advice: Lorraine is good at pointing out the strengths and weaknesses of different approaches.*" Campos leads the team at Reed Smith LLP, where she provides ongoing counsel to McKesson in relation to a US Department of Veterans Affairs pharmaceuticals contract valued at approximately $4 billion a year to supply pharmaceuticals to more than 700 locations.

# GOVERNMENT GOVERNMENT RELATIONS

Commentary about individuals can be found under their firm's paragraph. If the firm has no paragraph (is not ranked) look at Other Notable Practitioners.

## Government: Government Relations
### Leading Firms

**Band 1**
Akin Gump Strauss Hauer & Feld LLP *
Hogan Lovells US LLP
Patton Boggs LLP

**Band 2**
Covington & Burling LLP *
DLA Piper LLP (US) *
Holland & Knight LLP *
K&L Gates *

**Band 3**
Alston & Bird LLP *
Arnold & Porter LLP *
Bingham McCutchen LLP *
Dentons *
Dickstein Shapiro LLP *
King & Spalding LLP *
Mayer Brown LLP *
Steptoe & Johnson LLP
Van Ness Feldman LLP *
Williams & Jensen PLLC
WilmerHale *

## Government: Government Relations
### Senior Statesmen

**Senior Statesmen: distinguished older practitioners**

| | |
|---|---|
| Hand Lloyd | King & Spalding LLP * |

### Leading Individuals

**Star individuals**

| | |
|---|---|
| Boggs Jr Thomas Hale | Patton Boggs LLP |

**Band 1**

| | |
|---|---|
| Gorelick Jamie | WilmerHale * |
| House W Michael | Hogan Lovells US LLP |
| Jankowsky Joel | Akin Gump Strauss Hauer & Feld LLP * |

**Band 2**

| | |
|---|---|
| Hart J Steven | Williams & Jensen PLLC |
| Hester Theodore M | King & Spalding LLP * |
| Merrigan John A | DLA Piper LLP (US) * |
| Nash Bernard | Dickstein Shapiro LLP * |
| Rouvelas Emanuel L | K&L Gates * |
| Sinder Scott | Steptoe & Johnson LLP |
| Spulak Thomas | King & Spalding LLP * |

**Band 3**

| | |
|---|---|
| Allard Nicholas W | Patton Boggs LLP |
| Blanchard James J | DLA Piper LLP (US) * |
| Boyd Thomas M | DLA Piper LLP (US) * |
| Cochran Martha L | Arnold & Porter LLP * |
| DeArment Roderick | Covington & Burling LLP * |
| Gold Martin | Covington & Burling LLP * |
| Gold Richard M | Holland & Knight LLP * |
| Jones Robert C | Alston & Bird LLP * |
| Moeller Elizabeth V | Pillsbury Winthrop Shaw Pittman (ONP)[†] * |
| Smith Russell L | Willkie Farr & Gallagher LLP (ONP)[†] * |
| Whitestone David | Holland & Knight LLP * |

**Up-and-coming individuals**

| | |
|---|---|
| Fechner Holly | Covington & Burling LLP * |
| Waltzman Howard | Mayer Brown LLP |

\* Indicates firm / individual with profile.
[†] ONP = Other Notable Practitioner.

## Recommended for Client Service
### Nationwide

| | |
|---|---|
| Covington & Burling LLP | K&L Gates |
| DLA Piper LLP (US) | Patton Boggs LLP |

## Recommended for Commercial Awareness
### Nationwide

| | |
|---|---|
| Covington & Burling LLP | Steptoe & Johnson LLP |
| Dentons | |

## Band 1

### Akin Gump Strauss Hauer & Feld LLP
See profile on p.904

**THE FIRM** Akin Gump's marquee public law and policy practice comprises 55 lawyers and professional advisers. The team is equipped to assist clients with complicated legal reform and policy issues arising across a range of sectors, including healthcare, energy and environment, education, tax and transportation. The subpractice of political law and government ethics operates seamlessly alongside a number of other dedicated groups at the firm, catering to sovereign government policy as well as Congressional investigations, coalitions and organizations, enabling the firm to assist clients with a comprehensive range of matters. The group is also home to a number of former members of Congress, bolstering the firm's strong ties to the government and benefiting clients who seek lobbying assistance.
**Sources say:** *"This is a long-standing, well-established practice."*
**KEY INDIVIDUALS** Renowned government relations expert **Joel Jankowsky** (see p.340) is held in high regard for his expertise in public policy matters. He has particular strength within the fields of telecom, technology and entertainment.

### Hogan Lovells US LLP

**THE FIRM** The legislation and political law compliance group at Hogan Lovells boasts 59 attorneys, with high-pro-

file clients including Nissan, Barclays Capital and Nestlé. In the past year, the practice has maintained its focus on assisting clients with federal funding matters, as well as navigating the federal grants and Congressional appropriations processes. The group's clients include hospital research centers, universities, and for-profit and nonprofit companies, among others. The team also continues to assist the Bowl Championship Series (BCS) with its communications with Congress and the development of an outreach strategy relating to the structure of post-season college football.
**Sources say:** *"A leader here in DC."*
**KEY INDIVIDUALS** Department head **Michael House** is involved in the representation of BCS outlined above. He has assisted with communications with members of Congress relating to specific legislation, as well as in edu-

cating individuals about BCS and its impact on both students and educational institutions.

### Patton Boggs LLP

**THE FIRM** Patton Boggs is recognized for the extensive service it offers clients, which includes monitoring legislation, analyzing public policy, and lobbying on behalf of clients at both state and federal level. The firm's sizable public policy department is made up of over 100 attorneys representing organizations such as SICPA, McLane Company and the National Football League Players Association. A key matter for the team in the past year was advising the University of Minnesota on legislative issues relating to the implementation of a $1 billion light rail line that will run through the university campus between St. Paul and Minneapolis.
**Client Service** *"This is a large firm, so the group is readily able to tap into a number of areas. There are partners to go to quickly for an answer, and with their depth of knowledge you can get answers very quickly."*
**KEY INDIVIDUALS Thomas Hale Boggs** is lauded by peers as *"the best in town."* One particularly impressed client asserts that *"there's no brighter mind or person more experienced in Washington. He is always available with insight and guidance."* **Nicholas Allard** counseled the University of Minnesota in the aforementioned matter, helping it secure the Congress-approved funding which was required to mitigate potential environmental and safety risks posed by the rail line. Clients describe Allard as *"thoughtful and intelligent – he always finds different ways of tackling our problems. He's very effective."*

## Band 2

### Covington & Burling LLP
See profile on p.441

**THE FIRM** The government affairs department at Covington is home to a number of former government officials, and has expanded the group by securing some significant new hires in the past year. Clients of the firm include Wells Fargo, the National Association of Broadcasters and Amazon.com, which the group assists with matters of public policy. Work carried out by the team includes providing strategic advice on legislative matters and helping clients access key individuals within the government who are involved in decision-making processes.

**Client Service** *"Covington has a very professional operation. It responds well to our problems and constantly keeps us updated."*

**Commercial Awareness** *"The firm has a breadth of experience from the top levels of Congress."*

**KEY INDIVIDUALS** Clients are pleased with **Roderick DeArment** (see p.302), who is considered *"resourceful, energetic and collaborative."* DeArment led in assisting Alcatel-Lucent successfully secure an amendment to the Internal Revenue Code, which will allow for continued payment of benefits to approximately 90,000 company retirees. Sources say that **Martin Gold** (see p.322) is *"highly regarded in debarment."* Gold also assisted the 1882 Project successfully seek redress from Congress for a series of Acts discriminating against persons of Chinese origin published between 1879 and 1904. Gold's work resulted in an official expression of regret for this legislation. **Holly Fechner** (see p.311) assisted DeArment in representing Alcatel-Lucent as outlined above, and also assisted the ERISA Industry Council organize a coalition with the purpose of educating members of Congress about proposed regulations governing hybrid pension plans. Fechner continues to receive praise from clients, who affirm that she is *"smart, effective and persistent."*

## DLA Piper LLP (US)
See profile on p.1971

**THE FIRM** The government affairs team at this global giant has had an active year, having represented ZTE, a global supplier of telecom equipment, counseling the company through investigation by the House Intelligence Committee and making presentations to Congress. The firm also assists a US joint venture with Japan Central Railroad for the purpose of developing a maglev high-speed rail system in the Northeast Corridor, which requires the firm to advise on environmental issues, legislative authorization and appropriation issues.

**Client Service** *"They're very good at bringing together a team and working collaboratively. They'll often preempt our needs."*

**KEY INDIVIDUALS** Sources enthuse that **John Merrigan** (see p.367) is an *"eminent name"* in the government relations sphere. Clients are impressed, stating that he is *"resourceful and very well connected."* Merrigan led on both the ZTE and maglev matters outlined above. **James Blanchard** (see p.284) has represented Public Affairs Associates on one of the largest infrastructure projects in North America, working with government officials to authorize a new bridge between Detroit, Michigan and Windsor, Canada. Observers note that Blanchard is *"very execution-oriented – he engages in an action plan and carries out the elements required. James is also very helpful with high-level strategy."* Interviewees affirm that **Thomas Boyd** (see p.286) is *"a very fine lawyer."* Boyd assisted with the ZTE matter, and continues as counsel to the National Business Coalition on E-Commerce & Privacy.

## Holland & Knight LLP
See profile on p.1028

**THE FIRM** The public policy and regulation group at Holland & Knight supports clients including Blue Cross Blue Shield of Tennessee, Alliance for Regenerative Medicine, Dow Chemical, FirstEnergy and Thomson Reuters Legal. The group has grown over the past year, and has a deep bench of lawyers accompanied by a large number of nonlegal professionals able to expertly advise in policy matters. The federal healthcare policy team recently achieved significant success assisting a number of clients across a range of sectors optimize opportunities arising out of the Food and Drug Administration Safety and Innovation Act.

**Sources say:** *"I am pleased with the firm's performance. The team that works with us is professional in every way, and their attention to detail is impressive."*

**KEY INDIVIDUALS Richard Gold**'s (see p.322) impressive practice covers a broad range of fields, including transportation, food safety, energy and environment. **David Whitestone** (see p.426) is chair of the firm's transportation industry practice, which sees him counseling a vast number of rail, aviation and maritime clients in relation to their regulatory and public policy work. Sources admire Whitestone, saying that *"he's extremely well liked, smart and a good strategist."*

## K&L Gates
See profile on p.2245

**THE FIRM** K&L Gates maintains a strong reputation in the government relations field, with a bipartisan team comprising 50 lawyers and nonlawyer public policy professionals. The team is home to a vast number of individuals with experience working on Capitol Hill and in government agencies, including a number of former Congressmen. The firm's global government solutions initiative relies on smart interaction between 40 offices worldwide. This service is ideally suited to support clients whose policy objectives extend beyond the USA. Notable clients include Annaly Capital, BNSF Railway, Boeing Employees' Credit Union and Columbia University.

**Client Service** *"They work as a team and will draw on another partner as needed according to what the issue requires, yet still keep costs level."*

**KEY INDIVIDUALS Emanuel Rouvelas** (see p.396) is founder and leader of the public policy and law group. Rouvelas is well respected for his specialty in maritime law and represents leading companies and trade associations across a broad range of sectors, including telecom, transportation, hospitality and the manufacturing industry.

## Band 3

## Alston & Bird LLP
See profile on p.1102

**THE FIRM** The legislative and public policy group at Alston & Bird has a strong bench that provides strategic counseling to clients including Experian, Navistar and the National Geographic Education Foundation. The firm also

represents Safeway, having provided assistance in tax and pensions issues, as well as advising the company in debates relating to healthcare reform, derivatives reform, climate change and food safety.

**Sources say:** *"They have very good FTC, corporate and lobbying practices in DC."*

**KEY INDIVIDUALS Robert Jones** (see p.341) is leader of the group and has personally counseled Safeway as outlined above, in addition to assisting Autoliv in communications with the Department of Defense, Department of Energy and Nuclear Regulatory Commission. Sources have been impressed: *"He is energetic, willing and happy to help."*

## Arnold & Porter LLP
See profile on p.906

**THE FIRM** Clients of Arnold & Porter's legislative and public policy group include illustrious names such as Lloyd's, which the firm advises in relation to a broad spectrum of legislative and regulatory issues affecting its trading position in the USA. This relationship sees the firm providing guidance on issues potentially arising in connection with natural catastrophe financing, massive pollution, aviation war risk and political risk. The team also represents the Association for Advanced Life Underwriting and the Coalition to Insure Against Terrorism.

**Sources say:** *"They've always been responsive and willing to work with us. They make sure we're satisfied."*

**KEY INDIVIDUALS Martha Cochran** (see p.296) is noted for her work with asset managers and financial institutions, including the Association for Advanced Life Underwriting. Sources affirm that *"Martha knows the ins and outs of securities law and has a significant background in this work, in addition to high-level relationships with commissioners at the SEC and the Financial Industry Regulatory Authority."*

## Bingham McCutchen LLP
See profile on p.1515

**THE FIRM** This small but dynamic government affairs group packs a mighty punch in DC, counseling high-profile companies which include Universal Music Group and GE. The team provides ongoing counseling to New York-based technology company Aereo, which it has advised in relation to possible legislation and Congressional inquiries related to telecom and copyright policy.

**Sources say:** *"They have helped us deepen our relationship with key government offices, and also helped us understand which issues are important to those offices."*

**KEY INDIVIDUALS** Gary Slaiman is the leader of Bingham's government affairs practice group.

## Dentons
See profile on p.449

**THE FIRM** Dentons's clients span the healthcare, finance, manufacturing, transportation and energy sectors, and include companies such as KV Pharmaceutical, Morgan Stanley, NextEra Energy and Allstate. The group has numerous former federal, state and local government employees, in addition to a number of former state attorneys general. The team is presently assisting the California

State Parks Foundation in conducting a study of methods by which parks threatened with closure due to state budget cuts can utilize private funding in order to stay open.

**Commercial Awareness** "*I have been extremely impressed by the Dentons government relations group, in particular their comprehensive problem-solving skills, their knowledge of the inner workings of federal agencies and the media, and their ability to work well on a personal level with diverse groups of people in our organization and in government.*"

**KEY INDIVIDUALS** Mike McNamara is chair of the public policy and regulation practice, and also leads the worldwide government sector team at Dentons.

### Dickstein Shapiro LLP
See profile on p.911

**THE FIRM** The government law and strategy group at Dickstein Shapiro is bolstered by the work carried out by the firm's long-running and highly reputed state attorneys general practice. Clients of the firm include Peabody Energy, the US Chamber of Commerce, MasterCard, Walmart and PepsiCo. In the past year, the group has advised McAfee in relation to educating Congress about federal government cybersecurity programs, in addition to counseling on legislation that could enhance cybersecurity throughout the USA.

**KEY INDIVIDUALS** Bernard Nash (see p.374) continues to represent Pfizer, assisting the company with legal and policy matters, as well as providing advice in the face of a number of investigations and litigations by attorneys general in relation to the marketing and sale of Pfizer products. Observers state that Nash is "*very focused*" and has "*cornered the market among state attorneys general.*"

### King & Spalding LLP
See profile on p.445

**THE FIRM** In the past year, King & Spalding undertook significant effort on behalf of multiple US manufacturing companies to overturn a US Court of Appeals decision prohibiting the use of countervailing duty law to counteract illegal subsidies on goods from non-market economy countries, including China. The team was successful in its substantial three-month lobbying campaign, resulting in a law which overturned the court decision being enacted in less than one month. The law, passed in March 2012, assists US companies facing unfair competition from foreign competitors selling products at artificially low prices. The firm also represents notable clients including Toyota, Embraer, JMC Steel Group and Raytheon.

**Sources say:** "*This is a cohesive group with a lot of good talent on the government affairs side. They understand the environment that we inhabit, and they're happy doing work for us without rocking the boat.*"

**KEY INDIVIDUALS** One client says that Lloyd Hand (see p.329) is "*a Washington institution in and of himself.*" Hand is considered to be particularly well connected with senior members of Congress, and he has great experience in providing counsel to Fortune 500 companies and foreign governments on legislative, administrative, regulatory and international trade issues. Thomas Spulak (see p.411) is

chair of the group and a former general counsel to the House of Representatives. Spulak has developed a niche in understanding the political rules regulating campaign finance and Congressional ethics, and sources are quick to praise him: "*His word is golden. He has incredible contacts, a good grasp of the law and terrific political instincts.*" Theodore Hester (see p.334) has amassed great experience in representing companies in Congressional investigations, and observers enthusiastically note that he is "*terrific.*"

### Mayer Brown LLP
See profile on p.1257

**THE FIRM** The government relations team at Mayer Brown is able to draw on an impressive wealth of state and local government experience amassed throughout its seven US offices, particularly its Los Angeles and Chicago branches. The firm also has significant experience in handling government affairs at both a federal level and on the international stage. The group has been representing Google in its driverless car project, assisting by obtaining permission for the vehicles to be tested within the states of Nevada, Florida and California, as well as in presenting the technology to the US Department of Transportation and the National Highway Traffic Safety Administration.

**Sources say:** "*The firm operates cohesively, and the individuals we work with are responsive and stay on top of our particular area of business. Government relations are a very strong area for the firm, and we are able to draw on their contacts in both parties in Congress.*"

**KEY INDIVIDUALS** The "*very talented*" Howard Waltzman is a former chief counsel for the House Energy & Commerce Committee, focusing on telecom and the internet. Waltzman has a particular specialty in privacy compliance, communications and internet law.

### Steptoe & Johnson LLP

**THE FIRM** The firm represents Kia Motors and CRE Finance Council, among other illustrious names. It also provides ongoing counseling to AOL and Facebook on legislative and regulatory issues relating to internet privacy and telecoms, requiring the team to effectively liaise with the FTC and FCC. The group has also represented the National Association of Convenience Stores and the Society of Independent Gasoline Marketers of America, successfully campaigning for the inclusion of language in the Moving Ahead for Progress in the 21st Century Act to clarify the meaning of tobacco 'manufacturers', which subsequently clarifies the tax position for these manufacturers.

**Commercial Awareness** "*They are a law firm and lobby shop. They serve as regulatory counsel and help draft compliance guidelines for us. They've looked at our needs and are hired to service them, so I'm aware that when we have a need they'll help us.*"

**KEY INDIVIDUALS** The "*talented*" Scott Sinder is praised by clients, who state that "*he is extremely well positioned and he gives us tremendous strategic and legal advice.*" Sinder is head of the department, and continues to represent the Council of Insurance Agents & Brokers following the Dodd-Frank financial services overhaul, liaising with

the National Association of Insurance Commissioners and the new Federal Insurance Office to ensure that state implementation efforts progress.

### Van Ness Feldman LLP
See profile on p.926

**THE FIRM** Van Ness Feldman provides ongoing counsel to BrightSource Energy, which has included advocacy work on Capitol Hill in relation to a number of solar industry tax incentives, as well as representation during a Congressional investigation into a Department of Energy loan guarantee program relating to several Department of Defense energy initiatives. Other clients include the Coal Utilization Research Council, Puget Sound Energy, Kinder Morgan, McKesson and TransCanada.

**KEY INDIVIDUALS** Bob Szabo is a key contact and the practice business development coordinator.

### Williams & Jensen PLLC

**THE FIRM** This specialist government affairs firm based in DC manages dedicated practices in federal appropriations, Congressional oversight and investigations, and international government affairs. The firm has particular specialty in financial services and tax policy, and has great experience in dealing with the Treasury Department and IRS to advance the objectives of its clients.

**Sources say:** "*A leading law firm in tax reform.*"

**KEY INDIVIDUALS** Steven Hart is "*well regarded*" by peers and considered a prominent lobbyist in DC. He is highly renowned for his proficiency in tax matters.

### WilmerHale
See profile on p.930

**THE FIRM** The defense, national security and government contracts practice at WilmerHale comprises 29 attorneys who are highly adept at assisting clients with government affairs matters across a broad range of industries. The firm has seven offices across the USA, and the team is home to a number of attorneys who have formerly held senior positions in various government departments and agencies, including the DOJ.

**KEY INDIVIDUALS** The "*outstanding*" Jamie Gorelick (see p.324) is praised for her strategic advice in addition to her experience as "*a major player in DC.*" Gorelick is chair of the department, and has particular expertise in public policy, regulatory and enforcement matters.

### Other Notable Practitioners

The "*highly regarded*" Russell Smith (see p.409) of Willkie Farr & Gallagher LLP represented Telcordia Technologies during a review by the Committee on Foreign Investment in the United States of the $1.5 billion acquisition of the company by Ericsson. Elizabeth Moeller (see p.370) is head of the practice at Pillsbury Winthrop Shaw Pittman LLP, and is respected by peers for her work representing clients in the water, energy and transportation industries, among others.

# GOVERNMENT POLITICAL LAW

Commentary about individuals can be found under their firm's paragraph. If the firm has no paragraph (is not ranked) look at Other Notable Practitioners.

## Government: Political Law
### Leading Firms

**Band 1**
Perkins Coie LLP
Skadden, Arps, Slate, Meagher & Flom LLP & Affiliates *
Wiley Rein LLP *

**Band 2**
Caplin & Drysdale *
Covington & Burling LLP *
Patton Boggs LLP
Sandler, Reiff, Young & Lamb, P.C

**Band 3**
Arent Fox LLP *
McDermott Will & Emery LLP *
McKenna Long & Aldridge LLP *
Pillsbury Winthrop Shaw Pittman LLP *

## Government: Political Law
### Senior Statesmen

**Senior Statesmen: distinguished older practitioners**
Utrecht Lyn          Utrecht & Phillips, PLLC (ONP)[†]

### Leading Individuals

**Band 1**

| | |
|---|---|
| Baran Jan W | Wiley Rein LLP * |
| Bauer Robert F | Perkins Coie LLP |
| Elias Marc Erik | Perkins Coie LLP |
| Ginsberg Benjamin L | Patton Boggs LLP |
| Gross Kenneth A | Skadden, Arps, Slate, Meagher & Flom * |
| Hong Ki P | Skadden, Arps, Slate, Meagher & Flom * |
| Kelner Robert K | Covington & Burling LLP * |
| Nielsen Chip | Nielsen Merksamer Parrinello Gross (ONP)[†] |
| Sandler Joseph E | Sandler, Reiff, Young & Lamb, P.C |
| Toner Michael E | Wiley Rein LLP * |

**Band 2**

| | |
|---|---|
| Birkenstock Joseph | Caplin & Drysdale |
| Engle Craig | Arent Fox LLP * |
| Lowell Frederick K | Pillsbury Winthrop Shaw Pittman LLP * |
| Minor William | DLA Piper LLP (US) (ONP)[†] * |
| Potter Trevor | Caplin & Drysdale |

**Band 3**

| | |
|---|---|
| Berke Elliot | McGuireWoods LLP (ONP)[†] |
| Burchfield Bobby R | McDermott Will & Emery LLP * |
| Burns Caleb P | Wiley Rein LLP * |
| Jacobs Ronald | Venable LLP (ONP)[†] * |
| Lenhard Robert | Covington & Burling LLP * |
| Mitchell Cleta D | Foley & Lardner LLP (ONP)[†] |
| Norton Lawrence H | Venable LLP (ONP)[†] * |
| Passantino Stefan | McKenna Long & Aldridge LLP |
| Spies Charles | Clark Hill PLC (ONP)[†] * |
| Thomas Scott | Dickstein Shapiro LLP (ONP)[†] * |

### Up-and-coming individuals

| | |
|---|---|
| Bobys Matthew | Skadden, Arps, Slate, Meagher & Flom * |
| Gordon Rebecca | Perkins Coie LLP |
| McGinley William | Patton Boggs LLP |

*  Indicates firm / individual with profile.
[†] ONP = Other Notable Practitioner.

## Recommended for Client Service
### Nationwide

Skadden, Arps, Slate, Meagher     Wiley Rein LLP
& Flom LLP & Affiliates

## Recommended for Commercial Awareness
### Nationwide

Perkins Coie LLP          Skadden, Arps, Slate, Meagher
& Flom LLP & Affiliates

## Band 1

### Perkins Coie LLP
See profile on p.2548

**THE FIRM** This has been a stellar year for political law heavyweight Perkins Coie, with a client base including high-profile names such as Obama for America, Google, the Democratic Senatorial Campaign Committee, Facebook, EMILY's List and TechNet. The team has also represented the Democratic Congressional Campaign Committee, which it advised on matters relating to federal campaign finance law compliance, election administration and recount issues, commercial law issues and ethics compliance.

**KEY INDIVIDUALS Robert Bauer** has had a phenomenal year as general counsel to the successful Obama for America presidential campaign. Bauer also provides strategic advice to the Democratic National Committee as general counsel. Head of department **Marc Elias** receives excellent client feedback as a deeply well-connected and thoroughly knowledgeable government and political practitioner. The past year has seen him working with up-and-comer **Rebecca Gordon** in counseling Facebook on its US-wide state-level lobbying program. Peers remark positively on Gordon's rising profile and note that they have enjoyed working with her.

### Skadden, Arps, Slate, Meagher & Flom LLP & Affiliates
See profile on p.2008

**THE FIRM** Skadden is widely considered to be a front-line firm for corporate political activity. The group's areas of specialty include campaign finance, lobbyist registrations, activity reports, handling political contributions and gifts to public officials and assisting with pay-to-play program consulting matters. Skadden's clients inhabit a broad range of industries, from energy and pharmaceuticals to media and insurance, and include high-profile corporations including ExxonMobil, Prudential, Viacom and Novartis.
**Client Service** "This is a very collaborative and client-focused group. It provides outstanding client alerts and holds an annual client seminar which is useful and informative."
**Commercial Awareness** "These individuals are the best in the industry when it comes to political activity program consulting and legal consulting for procurement lobbying and pay-to-play."
**KEY INDIVIDUALS** One source commends **Ki Hong** (see p.336) for his skill in this field: "Ki is the beginning, middle and end of all things having to do with political lobbying in the United States." Another client affirms both Hong's and

**Kenneth Gross's** (see p.327) expertise: "They are the go-to individuals for all areas of campaign finance, lobbying and pay-to-play." Both Hong and Gross have counseled several companies on political compliance issues relevant to M&A, including Kraft, CIGNA and Goldman Sachs. Interviewees note that **Matthew Bobys** (see p.285) is "extremely responsive, thorough and practical in his application."

### Wiley Rein LLP
See profile on p.928

**THE FIRM** The election law and government ethics practice at this Republican-focused firm numbers 16 attorneys dedicated to counseling clients on all areas of political law, including political action committees, political contributions, federal and state regulation of lobbying and the use of corporate facilities for the purpose of political activities. Clients include the Speaker of the House of Representatives (Congressman John Boehner), the Republican National Committee, the National Association of Business Political Action Committees and Microsoft.
**Client Service** "We have a very high opinion of them. We have a steady diet of questions for them and they give prompt, practical advice on short notice – all are experts in their fields."
**KEY INDIVIDUALS** The "exceptional" **Jan Baran** (see p.277) is a distinguished practitioner of political law described by peers as "both counselor and teacher to his clients." Baran represented the US Chamber of Commerce, on whose behalf he filed an amicus brief with the US Supreme Court contributing to the successful reversal of a Montana Supreme Court ruling which curtailed corporate political speech and First Amendment rights. The "excellent" **Michael Toner** (see p.418) is a former chairman of the Federal Election Commission (FEC) and widely recognized for his work with Republican clients. Sources have been impressed by **Caleb Burns** (see p.290), enthusing that "he's just a real expert in the political law arena, so can give us instantaneous guidance on issues. He's right on top of the latest developments in this very complex area."

## Band 2

### Caplin & Drysdale
See profile on p.909

**THE FIRM** The team at Caplin & Drysdale receives praise for its handling of FEC, state and local pay-to-play and political contribution matters, in addition to its general government affairs work. The firm's client base is broad, incorporating political candidates, for-profit and nonprofit organizations and trade associations, including Visa, Verizon Wireless, Stephen Colbert, Rolls-Royce and NBCUniversal.
**Sources say:** *"They are such an extension of what I do and so ingrained and involved in all the projects I work with them on, they are more of a partner than just our counsel."*
**KEY INDIVIDUALS** Clients speak highly of their positive experiences working with **Joseph Birkenstock**: *"He's very commercially oriented. He gives his legal interpretation and at the same time provides a very common-sense, real-world approach."* Head of department **Trevor Potter** is very involved in campaign finance reform and clients are quick to affirm his skills: *"He's smart as a whip. He's an attorney who works with you to find a good answer."*

### Covington & Burling LLP
See profile on p.441

**THE FIRM** The election and political law group at Covington & Burling assists clients with lobbying compliance work, government ethics law and state campaign finance. The team has great experience in representing clients from both the political and corporate spheres who face FEC and DOJ civil and criminal investigations into campaign finance matters. Covington's client base includes high-profile names such as the Republican National Committee, Bank of America, Procter & Gamble, the NFL and Grocery Manufacturers of America.
**Sources say:** *"They have massive infrastructure in place, are a huge firm with the associated resources and are strong practitioners."*
**KEY INDIVIDUALS Robert Kelner** (see p.345) is head of the department and is considered by peers to be *"a fine attorney who is growing increasingly experienced and has taken the initiative to develop the practice at Covington."* Kelner represents John Lopez, the former chief of staff to former senator John Ensign, in a high-profile Senate Ethics Committee investigation and a DOJ criminal investigation into Ensign's conduct. **Robert Lenhard** (see p.354) *"is bright, attentive and always willing to help you find a way to do something,"* according to clients. Lenhard provides ongoing counsel to Priorities USA Action, the Democratic super PAC.

### Patton Boggs LLP

**THE FIRM** Patton Boggs is a real powerhouse within the Republican establishment, having represented Mitt Romney's 2012 presidential campaign. The firm has particular expertise in counseling clients on state and federal rules governing lobbying compliance, in addition to assisting businesses, trade associations, donors and political candidates and committees with campaign finance matters.
**Sources say:** *"Patton Boggs is a fine practice."*
**KEY INDIVIDUALS** One source admires the *"substantial body of business and leadership excellence"* at Patton Boggs, which they attribute primarily to **Benjamin Ginsberg**, who provided substantial support for the Romney presidential campaign. Up-and-comer **William McGinley** continues to receive praise for his election law practice and is described by peers as *"very knowledgeable."*

### Sandler, Reiff, Young & Lamb, P.C

**THE FIRM** This highly renowned political law boutique situated in Washington, DC is adept at catering to the needs of clients seeking specialist assistance in matters of campaign finance and election law, in addition to government ethics and the applicable federal, state and local laws which govern lobbying. The firm is also greatly experienced in counseling candidates for federal, state and local office, in addition to businesses and unions, nonprofit organizations and PACs and political party committees.
**Sources say:** *"This is a very strong bread-and-butter election law firm – its strength lies in core compliance matters."*
**KEY INDIVIDUALS Joseph Sandler** is admired for his significant experience in representing state political parties, in particular branches of the Democratic Party. Sandler's areas of focus include assisting with campaign finance and providing guidance on the corporate and tax issues affecting activities of a political or advocacy nature.

## Band 3

### Arent Fox LLP
See profile on p.905

**THE FIRM** The Arent Fox political law group utilizes the talents of 15 highly skilled legal professionals supported by a number of policy experts with past experience on Capitol Hill. The team has great collective experience of having made representations before the FEC in enforcement and campaign finance matters, and has also advised clients facing audits and ethics and Congressional investigations.
**KEY INDIVIDUALS** Founder of the group **Craig Engle** (see p.310) is well known in the political law space. Engle played a pivotal role in developing the legal framework for a system which ultimately enabled donors to make political contributions via text message during the presidential election.

### McDermott Will & Emery LLP
See profile on p.1258

**THE FIRM** The areas of focus deftly handled by McDermott's ten political law specialists include representation of high-profile politicians in white-collar investigations, in addition to a broad range of matters spanning election and campaign finance law. The firm's broad client base includes the US Chamber of Commerce, the National Republican Senatorial Committee, Congressman Michael McCaul, the Republican Party of Louisiana and AstraZeneca.

**KEY INDIVIDUALS Bobby Burchfield** (see p.289) receives praise for his diligence in handling client matters: *"Bobby prides himself on being as prepared as possible – there's never a fear that something is slipping through the cracks."* Long-standing clients include the Republican National Committee and the Republican Governors Association.

### McKenna Long & Aldridge LLP
See profile on p.922

**THE FIRM** This political law department's client base is impressively diverse, including Newt Gingrich's presidential campaign 'Newt 2012', Forest Laboratories, Primerica, the National Mining Association, the American Council on Education and Century Strategies. The firm receives praise for its skill in advising clients on lobbying laws and regulations and general political law matters, in addition to monitoring corporate activities on behalf of clients and helping them to deal with political contributions appropriately.
**Sources say:** *"The team has a great reputation."*
**KEY INDIVIDUALS** According to clients, **Stefan Passantino** *"has an ability to summarize very complex legal material for nonlegal professionals."* Sources are pleased with the way in which his assistance helps them achieve their objectives: *"Stefan is an excellent communicator. He makes it easy for us to understand and execute things from our end."*

### Pillsbury Winthrop Shaw Pittman LLP
See profile on p.2000

**THE FIRM** Widely renowned for its strong presence on the West Coast, the Pillsbury team is noted for its skill in handling political matters throughout California, in addition to advising on federal issues relating to national elections. Key recent highlights include advising various Schwarzenegger committees and assisting Chevron with its political law compliance program. Clients include AT&T, Bechtel, Charles Schwab & Co, McKesson and Stanford University.
**Sources say:** *"They have always been responsive and well tuned to our needs."*
**KEY INDIVIDUALS** Peers affirm that **Frederick Lowell** (see p.358) is held in high regard: *"Our experience working with Fred and his team has been wonderful."* Lowell also served on the 2012 Romney campaign's judicial and legislative policy committee.

### Other Notable Practitioners

A former FEC chairman, **Scott Thomas** (see p.417) at Dickstein Shapiro LLP is praised by clients for his *"expert guidance"* and *"ready availability and immediate understanding of an issue."* Thomas's particular specialties include lobbying law and matters relating to campaign finance and ethics. At DLA Piper LLP (US), clients have been particularly impressed by **William Minor** (see p.369), who *"does a terrific job of explaining complex legal concepts and demonstrating clearly how they apply to a given set of facts."* The same source relates: *"We have run a very broad* variety of issues past him and have yet to stump him." **Cleta Mitchell** of Foley & Lardner LLP has experience appearing before the FEC and Congress ethics committees. Mitchell is well known for her corporate work and assists corporations preparing compliance and ethics policies. **Chip Nielsen** of Nielsen Merksamer Parrinello Gross & Leoni LLP is considered to be *"one of the most eminent names"* in this market. Nielsen is the senior political law partner at this boutique government and political law firm, and his areas of focus include pay-to-play and campaign finance law. **Charles Spies** (see p.411) is leader of the political law

practice at Clark Hill PLC and is considered by sources to be *"a very skilled election lawyer."* Spies has had significant involvement in Restore Our Future, a super PAC created to support of Mitt Romney's presidential campaign. Sources affirm **Ronald Jacobs** (see p.339) of Venable LLP is *"technically proficient and committed to the cause."* Jacobs cochairs Venable's political law group alongside **Lawrence Norton** (see p.377), who is described by one client as *"my go-to person for political compliance matters – his availability and wealth of knowledge make him a perfect combination for us."* Venable clients include Time Warner and Marriott

International. The hugely respected **Lyn Utrecht** is a founding partner of Utrecht & Phillips, PLLC, where she has established an extraordinary reputation for representing Democratic candidates in elections past. At McGuireWoods LLP, **Elliot Berke** provides legal guidance to prominent lobbying firm Ogilvy Government Relations, The Blackstone Group and the American Energy Alliance/Institute for Energy Research. Berke is praised by peers for his ability in the political law field.

# HEALTHCARE

Commentary about individuals can be found under their firm's paragraph. If the firm has no paragraph (is not ranked) look at Other Notable Practitioners.

| Healthcare |
| --- |
| **Leading Firms** |

**Band 1**
McDermott Will & Emery LLP *

**Band 2**
Epstein Becker & Green PC *
Hogan Lovells US LLP *
King & Spalding LLP *

**Band 3**
Foley & Lardner LLP *
Ober Kaler Grimes & Shriver *
Reed Smith LLP *
Ropes & Gray LLP *
Sidley Austin LLP *

**Band 4**
Arent Fox LLP *
Baker, Donelson, Bearman, Caldwell & Berkowitz, PC *
Fulbright & Jaworski LLP *
Jones Day *
Latham & Watkins LLP *
Manatt Phelps & Phillips LLP *
Skadden, Arps, Slate, Meagher & Flom LLP & Affiliates *

\* Indicates firm with profile.

## Band 1
## Healthcare

### McDermott Will & Emery LLP
See profile on p.1258
**THE FIRM** McDermott Will & Emery retains its leading position in the healthcare market, and is held in high esteem by commentators for its extensive expertise across the full spectrum of regulatory and transactional matters. Its attorneys are based in key locations across the nation, with a notable presence in New York, California, Illinois, Massachusetts and DC, among other areas. Recent highlights include assisting TeamHealth in its acquisition of The Exigence Group and acting for Ascension Health in connection with its purchase of Daughters of Charity

Health System, the latter being the largest nonprofit acquisition of 2012 in the USA.

**Client Service** *"They are excellent, the go-to firm for virtually all of our legal issues. They have the highest quality of legal talent and extraordinary responsiveness."*

**KEY INDIVIDUALS** The *"very talented"* **Ira Coleman** (see p.297) heads the firm's Miami health industry advisory practice and is an excellent choice of counsel on M&A and private equity healthcare matters. Sources are particularly quick to praise his *"client service-oriented"* approach to matters. **Gary Scott Davis** (see p.301) is particularly noted for his managed care work, in which he advises on M&A, joint ventures, strategic restructurings and reorganizations, and health benefit plans. *"He supports his client's position and is a great adviser,"* reports one impressed source. **Joel Michaels** (see p.368) is based in the firm's DC office and is recognized for his strengths in insurance matters relating to the healthcare sector. **Stephen Bernstein** (see p.1484) is an authority on e-health matters and is also routinely called upon to handle M&A and joint ventures for healthcare institutions. The seasoned **Bernadette Broccolo** (see p.1200) has over the three decades' worth of experience in the sector and maintains a fine track record for healthcare-related IT matters. **Eric Gordon** (see p.638) is adept in healthcare-related transactions, in addition to advising on compliance issues and fraud and abuse matters. **Christopher Jedrey** (see p.1496) is cochair of the firm's academic medical centers practice. He is well versed in M&A and joint ventures, acting for a range of provider and HMO clients. He also advises on issues concerning taxable to tax-exempt status conversions. **Michael Peregrine** (see p.1225) is frequently sought after to assist clients on matters related to corporate structure, governance, fiduciary duties and D&O liability. He is also renowned for his work pertaining to charitable trust law. *"Terrific lawyer"* **Michael Anthony** (see p.274) is senior counsel at the firm and continues to be highly regarded for his wealth of experience in transactional work.

| **Recommended for Client Service** | |
| --- | --- |
| **Nationwide** | |
| Akin Gump Strauss Hauer & Feld LLP | McDermott Will & Emery LLP |
| Foley & Lardner LLP | Proskauer Rose LLP |
| King & Spalding LLP | Skadden, Arps, Slate, Meagher & Flom LLP & Affiliates |
| Manatt Phelps & Phillips LLP | |

| **Recommended for Commercial Awareness** | |
| --- | --- |
| **Nationwide** | |
| Epstein Becker & Green PC | Manatt Phelps & Phillips LLP |
| Foley & Lardner LLP | Reed Smith LLP |
| Hogan Lovells US LLP | Skadden, Arps, Slate, Meagher & Flom LLP & Affiliates |

## Band 2

### Epstein Becker & Green PC
See profile on p.1972
**THE FIRM** This fine practice provides excellent counsel in healthcare-related transactions and disputes, and also maintains a superb reputation for its regulatory and Medicare reimbursement work. In a recent highlight, it acted for American Air Liquide in its bid for home oxygen provider Lincare Holdings. The group also counts The Mount Sinai Medical Center, Gold Health Strategies, Community Health Network and Riverside Health System among its most noteworthy clients.

**Commercial Awareness** *"They are very skilled at understanding the balance, and helping us to identify ways to mitigate risk within our business model."*

**KEY INDIVIDUALS** The *"very creative and ridiculously smart"* **Jeffrey Becker** is a cofounder of the firm and is renowned for his expertise in a broad array of transaction and regulatory work. The highly regarded **Douglas Hastings** (see p.331) also commands much respect in the market for his regulatory and transactional strengths. He elicits particular praise for his ability to keep up to date with the future implications of the healthcare reform.

## Healthcare: Regulatory & Litigation
### Senior Statesmen

**Senior Statesmen: distinguished older practitioners**

| | |
|---|---|
| Nadel Peter F | Katten Muchin Rosenman LLP (ONP)[†] |

### Leading Individuals

**Band 1**

| | |
|---|---|
| Barry Dennis M | King & Spalding LLP * |
| Brennan Jr John T | Crowell & Moring LLP (ONP)[†] * |
| Bulleit Jr Thomas N | Hogan Lovells US LLP |
| Carder-Thompson Elizabeth | Reed Smith LLP |
| Imperato Gabriel L | Broad and Cassel (ONP)[†] |
| Keough Christopher L | Akin Gump Strauss Hauer & Feld LLP * |
| Kornreich Edward S | Proskauer Rose LLP |
| Leibenluft Robert F | Hogan Lovells US LLP |
| Luce Gregory M | Skadden, Arps, Slate, Meagher & Flom * |
| Michaels Joel | McDermott Will & Emery LLP * |
| Miles John J | Ober Kaler Grimes & Shriver |
| Robinson Frederick | Fulbright & Jaworski LLP * |
| Salcido Robert S | Akin Gump Strauss Hauer & Feld LLP * |
| Schneider Jeffrey G | Hogan Lovells US LLP |
| Teplitzky Sanford V | Ober Kaler Grimes & Shriver |
| Warnke Stephen A | Ropes & Gray LLP |

**Band 2**

| | |
|---|---|
| Becker Scott | McGuireWoods LLP (ONP)[†] * |
| Bookman Lloyd A | Hooper Lundy & Bookman PC (ONP)[†] * |
| Gordon Eric B | McDermott Will & Emery LLP * |
| Hooper Patric | Hooper Lundy & Bookman PC (ONP)[†] |
| Lipton M Steven | Hooper Lundy & Bookman PC (ONP)[†] |
| Millock Peter J | Nixon Peabody LLP (ONP)[†] * |
| Robfogel Susan S | Nixon Peabody LLP (ONP)[†] * |
| Singer Toby G | Jones Day * |
| Vickery Ann Morgan | Hogan Lovells US LLP |

**Band 3**

| | |
|---|---|
| Bernstein William S | Manatt Phelps & Phillips LLP |
| Callahan Michael R | Katten Muchin Rosenman LLP (ONP)[†] * |
| Eiland Gary | King & Spalding LLP * |
| Erde Joanne B | Duane Morris LLP (ONP)[†] |
| Foster Hope S | Mintz Levin Cohn Ferris Glovsky and Popeo * |
| Hilgers David W | Brown McCarroll, L.L.P. (ONP)[†] |
| Holden S Craig | Ober Kaler Grimes & Shriver |
| Immelt Stephen | Hogan Lovells US LLP |
| Iselin Harold N | Greenberg Traurig, LLP (ONP)[†] * |
| Kadzielski Mark A | Fulbright & Jaworski LLP * |
| Lerner Arthur N | Crowell & Moring LLP (ONP)[†] * |
| Lopez Jr Jorge | Akin Gump Strauss Hauer & Feld LLP * |
| Reed Glen | King & Spalding LLP * |
| Root Jr George L | Procopio, Cory, Hargreaves (ONP)[†] |
| Sarraille William A | Sidley Austin LLP * |
| Schmidt Donald R | Carlton Fields, P.A. (ONP)[†] * |
| Shackelford Richard L | King & Spalding LLP * |
| Wild Robert Andrew | Garfunkel Wild P.C. (ONP)[†] |

\* Indicates firm / individual with profile.
[†] ONP = Other Notable Practitioner.

### Hogan Lovells US LLP
**THE FIRM** This superb practice is well equipped to handle the entire gamut of healthcare work. It maintains a particularly fine reputation for its regulatory capabilities, and is also renowned for its strengths in the medical device and

## Healthcare: Transactional
### Senior Statesmen

**Senior Statesmen: distinguished older practitioners**

| | |
|---|---|
| Anthony Michael F | McDermott Will & Emery LLP * |

### Leading Individuals

**Band 1**

| | |
|---|---|
| Becker Jeffrey H | Epstein Becker & Green PC |
| Coleman Ira | McDermott Will & Emery LLP * |
| Davis Gary Scott | McDermott Will & Emery LLP * |
| Fitzgerald Mark R | Powers Pyles Sutter & Verville PC (ONP)[†] |
| Hastings Douglas A | Epstein Becker & Green PC * |
| Kornreich Edward S | Proskauer Rose LLP |
| Michaels Joel | McDermott Will & Emery LLP * |
| Sullivan T J | Drinker Biddle & Reath LLP * |

**Band 2**

| | |
|---|---|
| Becker Scott | McGuireWoods LLP |
| Bernstein Stephen W | McDermott Will & Emery LLP * |
| Blau Michael L | Foley & Lardner LLP |
| Broccolo Bernadette | McDermott Will & Emery LLP * |
| Higgins Daniel B | Manatt Phelps & Phillips LLP |
| Jedrey Christopher M | McDermott Will & Emery LLP * |
| Johnstone Debbi M | Fulbright & Jaworski LLP * |
| Mancino Douglas M | Hunton & Williams LLP (ONP)[†] * |
| Peregrine Michael W | McDermott Will & Emery LLP * |
| Segal Mike | Broad and Cassel (ONP)[†] |

**Band 3**

| | |
|---|---|
| Bell Jerry | Fulbright & Jaworski LLP * |
| Currier Maria | Holland & Knight LLP (ONP)[†] * * |
| Dube Monte I | Proskauer Rose LLP |
| Fahey Thomas M | Ungaretti & Harris LLP (ONP)[†] * |
| Garvin Michele M | Ropes & Gray LLP |
| Hinkley Gerry | Pillsbury Winthrop Shaw Pittman (ONP)[†] |
| Schwartz James R | Manatt Phelps & Phillips LLP |
| Zall Richard J | Proskauer Rose LLP |

## Healthcare: East Coast
### Leading Firms

**Band 1**

Mintz Levin Cohn Ferris Glovsky and Popeo PC *
Proskauer Rose LLP *

**Band 2**

Akin Gump Strauss Hauer & Feld LLP *
Alston & Bird LLP *

**Band 3**

Drinker Biddle & Reath LLP *

pharmaceuticals arena. Recent work includes providing regulatory and compliance counsel to LabCorp, and also assisting the company with regard to its $240 million acquisition of Medtox Scientific. Its distinguished roster of clients includes Abbott Laboratories, GE Healthcare and American Hospital Association (AHA).
**Commercial Awareness** *"Practical, sound business advice."*
**KEY INDIVIDUALS Thomas Bulleit** is singled out for his *"deep understanding of regulatory healthcare structure."* He is particularly noted for his work with academic medical centers and medical device and pharmaceutical manufacturers, and counts GE Healthcare as a key client. **Robert**

**Leibenluft** is highly regarded for his expertise in antitrust-related matters affecting the healthcare sector. He wins praise for his communication skills and is also lauded for his strengths in contentious healthcare matters. **Jeffrey Schneider** is *"an absolute pleasure to work with,"* a satisfied client reports. He is well versed in regulatory and transactional matters, and is also sought after for his expertise in disputes. **Ann Vickery** maintains a fine track record in Medicare and Medicaid regulatory issues, acting for healthcare providers, manufacturers and trade associations. **Stephen Immelt** comes recommended for his expertise in litigation and governmental investigations, and counts healthcare providers, academic health centers and medical schools, and medical device and pharmaceutical companies among his client base.

### King & Spalding LLP
See profile on p.445
**THE FIRM** King & Spalding continues to impress with its expertise in regulatory and transactional matters. Medicare and Medicaid concerns represent a particular area of strength, and in a recent highlight, it successfully acted for Oakwood Health System in a Medicare reimbursement review concerning a graduate medical education program. On the transactional side, it represented Piedmont Healthcare as it finalized the $150 million purchase of Henry Medical Center. Other key clients include Medtronic, Allergan and Christus Health System.
**Client Service** *"The practice is terrific. It has first-rate lawyers, who are closely aligned with our company's objectives; they are dedicated, responsive, able to work with a lot of moving pieces, and able to see the big picture. I would recommend them without hesitation."*
**KEY INDIVIDUALS Dennis Barry** (see p.279) comes recommended for his Medicare and Medicaid work and is also singled out for his adept handling of reimbursement and compliance matters. He acted as lead partner in the aforementioned Oakwood Health System matter. **Gary Eiland** (see p.2388) is *"incredibly responsive and really thoughtful in the way he approaches problems,"* an enthusiastic client asserts. He has over three decades' worth of experience in the sector, and is routinely sought after by healthcare providers for counsel on regulatory matters. Healthcare practice chair **Glen Reed** (see p.1094) is well versed in issues concerning compliance, fraud and abuse, managed care and healthcare policy, acting on behalf of a client list that includes healthcare systems and pharmaceutical, medical device and healthcare-related technology companies. **Richard Shackelford** (see p.1096) is *"not afraid to roll up his sleeves and be creative,"* reports one impressed commentator. He is noted for his wealth of litigation experience and, in a recent highlight, he successfully defended Omnicare against allegations of improper submission of prescriptions.

## Band 3
## Healthcare

### Foley & Lardner LLP
See profile on p.2588

THE FIRM Foley & Lardner handles a broad spectrum of healthcare work and is particularly highly regarded for its strengths in strategic planning and compliance matters. It is also recognized for its adroit handling of healthcare transactions, and recently acted for West Clinic in its affiliation with Methodist Health System, in one of the largest conversion transactions in the USA in recent years. Notable clients include Johns Hopkins Health System, Dartmouth Hitchcock and Baptist Health System.
**Client Service** *"Fantastic people – very service-oriented."*
**Commercial Awareness** *"Very creative and pragmatic."*
**KEY INDIVIDUALS** Healthcare venture practice chair **Michael Blau** is regularly sought after by private equity clients to handle healthcare-related transactions. Blau enjoys a fine reputation in the market, with one impressed peer quick to say of him: *"He's so good it's frustrating!"*

### Ober Kaler Grimes & Shriver
See profile on p.1439

THE FIRM Medicare and Medicaid regulatory issues and fraud and abuse matters remain a key area of strength for this practice, which acts for a range of academic and community hospitals, health systems, long-term care facilities, physicians groups and healthcare trade organizations. The group also comes recommended for its work with clinical laboratories, pharmacies and biotechnology clients.
**Sources say:** *"Excellent healthcare firm: they have some really fabulous people there."*
**KEY INDIVIDUALS** *"High-quality attorney"* **Sanford Teplitzky** is frequently called upon to represent large healthcare companies before federal and state investigations, and maintains a fine track record in fraud and abuse matters. He cochairs the firm's health law group. **John Miles** represents a fine choice of counsel for hospitals, health systems and physician practices in governmental investigations and healthcare-related antitrust matters. The *"highly regarded"* **Craig Holden** is the firm's president and CEO. He is noted for his assistance in compliance matters and is also recognized for his adept handling of Medicare and Medicaid matters.

### Reed Smith LLP

THE FIRM Reed Smith remains an established player in regulatory and transactional matters and also enjoys a fine reputation for its disputes work. The group continues to be sought after for its strength in corporate compliance programs and issues concerning privacy laws and HIPAA. In a recent highlight, it achieved a successful settlement for Voyager HospiceCare in connection with a long-running qui tam suit filed by the DOJ. The team also counts Kindred Healthcare, HCR ManorCare and Omnicare among its other key clients.
**Commercial Awareness** *"The firm was able to provide not only legal advice, but also practical advice on how to position*

arguments and communicate them to the FDA in a manner that would be most effective and efficient."
**KEY INDIVIDUALS** Clients single out **Elizabeth Carder-Thompson**'s *"excellent service and quality of work."* She is much in demand for her expertise in regulatory, legislative, and enforcement matters.

### Ropes & Gray LLP
See profile on p.1528

THE FIRM This group is adept in all areas of regulatory, transactional and disputes-related healthcare matters, acting for major healthcare providers, community hospitals and academic medical centers, and managed care organizations. The team is also noted for its work in pharmaceutical, medical device and biotech arenas. In a recent highlight, it assisted Partners Healthcare System in settling an enforcement action brought against Massachusetts General Hospital by the Office of Civil Rights. It is also advising North Shore Long Island Jewish Health System in several matters, including in connection with DOJ investigations and transactional issues.
**Sources say:** *"They master a broad scope of knowledge and are completely accessible."*
**KEY INDIVIDUALS** **Stephen Warnke** is *"terrific, very precise and exact and clear – he leaves no stone unturned."* Regulatory compliance and Medicare and Medicaid reimbursement represent particular areas of strength. *"Very fine lawyer"* **Michele Garvin** is noted for her adroit handling of matters relating to healthcare regulation and compliance. She is also well regarded for her work concerning academic medical center and medical school relationships.

### Sidley Austin LLP
See profile on p.1264

THE FIRM Sidley Austin's broad-ranging practice covers the full spread of healthcare work, from governmental investigations, disputes and transactions to regulatory compliance and enforcement, FDA issues and antitrust matters. Recent work has seen it represent Medtronic in a complicated strategic alliance transaction involving LifeTech Scientific. In a another highlight, it is acting for Celgene in a DOJ investigation concerning the promotion and marketing of products. It also counts SXC Health Solutions, Pfizer, GlaxoSmithKline and Roche Diagnostics as key clients.
**Sources say:** *"Sidley Austin has deep expertise in healthcare matters."*
**KEY INDIVIDUALS** *"Terrific regulatory healthcare lawyer"* **William Sarraille** (see p.889) is widely respected for his expertise in fraud and abuse matters and issues relating to Medicare and Medicaid reimbursement.

## Band 4
## Healthcare

### Arent Fox LLP
See profile on p.905

THE FIRM Regulatory compliance and government enforcement matters represent key areas of strength for

this practice, which is also noted for its accomplished work on the transactional side. Recent highlights have seen it represent public hospital district Broward Health in ongoing compliance and regulatory issues, including False Claims Act investigations. Other clients include Maxim Healthcare Services and Fundamental Long Term Care.
**Sources say:** *"I'm impressed with the team's responsiveness, reliability, accessibility, professionalism and quality of work product."*
**KEY INDIVIDUALS** Lisa Estrada is chair of the healthcare practice and a key contact at the firm.

### Baker, Donelson, Bearman, Caldwell & Berkowitz, PC
See profile on p.2313

THE FIRM This practice undertakes all manner of regulatory and transactional work and comes particularly recommended for its strengths in HIPAA compliance issues. Its clients include major hospitals and health systems, academic medical centers, physician organizations and specialty care providers, and it is additionally routinely sought out to advise pharmaceutical companies and medical device manufacturers. The group also has a fine track record in healthcare-related disputes and antitrust issues.
**KEY INDIVIDUALS** Thomas Baker heads the healthcare department and is a key client.

### Fulbright & Jaworski LLP
See profile on p.2435

THE FIRM Fulbright & Jaworski's health law team continues to impress with its expertise in regulatory and compliance matters and remains a go-to practice for Medicare and Medicaid reimbursement issues. In addition, the group is noted for its assured handling of high-value healthcare-related transactions and is a fine choice of counsel for complex disputes and government investigations. Medical staffing issues are another notable area of strength for the practice. Baylor College of Medicine, BJC Healthcare, Seton Family of Hospitals and Boston Scientific are all key clients.
**Sources say:** *"Fulbright truly is a full-service firm and the people I've engaged with have been exceptional in going the extra mile to make sure our questions are answered."*
**KEY INDIVIDUALS** **Frederick Robinson** (see p.393) maintains a fine track record for his work in government investigations and prosecutions. In a recent highlight, he acted for Universal Health Services, defending the organization against allegations that it had violated the False Claims Act by submitting false claims for payment to the Virginia Medicaid program. **Debbi Johnstone** (see p.2397) continues to win praise for her expertise in regulatory matters and is also highly regarded for her strengths in reimbursement issues. **Jerry Bell** (see p.2380) is recognized for his fine transactional and regulatory capabilities, and acts for a range of hospitals, medical schools and HMOs. He is also frequently called upon to advise on hospital medical staff issues. **Mark Kadzielski** (see p.644) is highly regarded for his work in the regulatory arena, acting for a range of hospitals and managed care entities. He is also regularly sought after to provide counsel on medical staff matters.

## Jones Day
See profile on p.919

**THE FIRM** This group is noted for its wealth of transactional expertise and also comes recommended for compliance, investigation and enforcement work. The team is especially esteemed for its healthcare financing work, particular in the area of tax bond issues. In addition, the practice is also well regarded in healthcare-related antitrust and IP matters. Its key clients include Premier Health Partners, Regional Health and Stanford Hospital and Clinics.
**Sources say:** *"Very fine lawyers."*
**KEY INDIVIDUALS Toby Singer** (see p.892) continues to be in much demand for her strengths in transactions, government investigations and antitrust matters as they relate to the healthcare sector. In a recent highlight, she acted for CIGNA, handling antitrust issues concerning its $3.8 billion purchase of HealthSpring.

## Latham & Watkins LLP
See profile on p.446

**THE FIRM** Latham & Watkins is well versed in the full spectrum of regulatory, transactional and disputes-related healthcare matters. It is particularly recognized for its strengths in the FDA space and also has a good track record for its work in the pharmaceutical and medical device arena. In a recent highlight, it defended HCA alongside other hospitals in a DOJ investigation concerning reimbursement of hospital equipment.
**Sources say:** *"I've been extremely happy with the firm's work. They have deep healthcare expertise, as well as knowledge and experience of working with government programs."*
**KEY INDIVIDUALS** Daniel Meron is global cochair of the healthcare and life sciences practice and a key contact at the firm.

## Manatt Phelps & Phillips LLP
See profile on p.690

**THE FIRM** This group is renowned for its work in the healthcare IT arena and is also recognized for its expertise in reform issues. The group is also a fine choice of counsel for healthcare-related disputes and government investigations, and is also noted for adept handling of Medicaid matters. Among its notable clients are California Hospital Association, Adventist Health, Health Plus and Sun Healthcare Group.
**Client Service** *"They have a collegial, flexible and supportive way of working with me as a client." "The firm knows how to deliver work product that is useful to the client – it provides excellent customer service."*
**Commercial Awareness** *"I appreciate their command of the subject matter, and their ability to clearly explain and summarize complex concepts." "The team's work is detailed, insightful, and offers a clear analysis of evolving legal and policy matters. They are top-rate subject matter experts, many of whom have held leadership positions in government agencies relevant to our business."*
**KEY INDIVIDUALS Daniel Higgins** maintains an excellent reputation for his finance and transactional strengths in the medical space. In a recent highlight, he acted for nonprofit healthcare network Sutter Health in connection

with bond issuances by the California Health Facilities Financing Authority and the California Statewide Communities Development Authority, valued at $465 million. Healthcare department chair **William Bernstein** continues to be sought after for his advice to provider organizations and managed care companies, in addition to financial institutions handling work in the healthcare sector. He is especially well regarded for his strengths in matters pertaining to healthcare reform. **James Schwartz** is well versed in issues relating to corporate governance, fiduciary duties, and alliances and conversions, and is particularly commended for his work with nonprofit organizations. He is also noted for his expertise in D&O liability issues.

## Skadden, Arps, Slate, Meagher & Flom LLP & Affiliates
See profile on p.2008

**THE FIRM** This group acts for health systems, pharmaceutical and medical device manufacturers, and other healthcare providers in high-value transactions and is also known for its sophisticated regulatory and disputes work. The team is especially adept in its representation of clients before false claims and qui tam proceedings, and is also well versed in product liability, securities and IP litigation affecting the healthcare arena.
**Client Service** *"Client service is very good – highly responsive to requests and always available on short notice.*
**Commercial Awareness** *"Extremely knowledgeable and experienced attorneys able to give practical and business-focused legal advice." "The attorneys at Skadden are experts and know the subject matter extremely well. They are also exceptionally creative with solutions to issues. I give them a ten for their creativity."*
**KEY INDIVIDUALS Gregory Luce** (see p.359) is *"one of the preeminent healthcare litigators in the country"* and is particularly sought after for his wealth of expertise in civil and criminal disputes and regulatory issues affecting the sector.

# Band 1
## Healthcare: East Coast

## Mintz Levin Cohn Ferris Glovsky and Popeo PC
See profile on p.1523

**THE FIRM** This tremendous East Coast group maintains a fine reputation for its transactional and regulatory work. It acts for clients throughout the healthcare sector, from providers, pharmacies and manufacturers to payors, distributors, lenders and investors. Healthcare IT issues and physician residency programs are particular areas of strength for the team, as are antitrust and IP matters affecting the industry. In recent work, the practice provided corporate and regulatory counsel to Catalyst Health Solutions in connection with Medicare and fraud and abuse compliance issues.
**Sources say:** *"The firm understands the healthcare business, and has expertise in the associated legal issues and good relationships with regulators."*

**KEY INDIVIDUALS** Healthcare enforcement defense group chair **Hope Foster** (see p.862) is singled out as *"practical, resourceful and very responsive."* She is acclaimed for her regulatory expertise and is particularly noted for her strengths in fraud and abuse and reimbursement issues.

## Proskauer Rose LLP
See profile on p.2001

**THE FIRM** This superb team represents a fine choice of counsel on regulatory and compliance matters, and reimbursement and fraud and abuse work. It also maintains a strong transactional and finance practice, and is additionally recognized for its strengths in labor, tax, real estate and IP issues concerning the healthcare sector. The practice recently acted for Richmond University Medical Center in the development of a clinical affiliation with Mount Sinai Medical Center. Ascension Health Care Network and AthenaHealth also feature among its key clients.
**Client Service** *"Extremely responsive and very timely. They concentrate on getting the deal done and never lose sight of the client's interests."*
**KEY INDIVIDUALS** Seasoned practitioner **Edward Kornreich** is noted for his strengths in healthcare payment issues, in addition to transactions and regulatory compliance, and acts for a range of healthcare providers, HMOs, and medical device and pharmaceutical companies. **Monte Dube** is well known for his work in high-value M&A matters on behalf of hospital clients. Sources are quick to celebrate his excellent communication abilities. Healthcare group chair **Richard Zall** *"is incredibly responsive, knowledgeable, clear and concise,"* a satisfied client reports. Zall continues to impress with his expertise in transactions and regulatory compliance work.

# Band 2
## Healthcare: East Coast

## Akin Gump Strauss Hauer & Feld LLP
See profile on p.904

**THE FIRM** Reimbursement, fraud and abuse, and legislative and regulatory advocacy and compliance continue to be areas of particular strength for this excellent team. In a recent highlight, it successfully acted for LabCorp, obtaining dismissal of a qui tam case concerning the False Claims Act and Anti-Kickback Statute. Pfizer, Golden Living Centers and Barnabas Health are also counted among its roster of clients.
**Client Service** *"I can't think of any areas for improvement. On all points that are important to me – responsiveness, technical expertise and general overall quality – their services are excellent."*
**KEY INDIVIDUALS** Medicare and Medicaid reimbursement and compliance continues to be an area of key strength for **Christopher Keough** (see p.345). In a recent highlight he acted for MD Anderson Cancer Center in a reimbursement appeal to the Department of Health & Human Services. Keough also singled out for his expertise in false claim matters. The *"extremely diligent"* **Robert Salcido** (see p.398) is renowned for his expertise in gov-

ernmental civil and criminal investigations. Sources also reserve praise for his *"tremendous subject matter expertise."* National health industry practice head **Jorge Lopez** (see p.878) is noted for his *"superb knowledge"* and *"ability to get issues resolved regarding legislation."* Medicare appeals and cancer care policy and regulation constitute particular areas of specialty.

## Alston & Bird LLP
See profile on p.1102

**THE FIRM** This fine group continues to be in much demand for its transactional and regulatory prowess. In recent work, it has acted for Getinge in several large-scale acquisitions, including the $680 million purchase of Atrium Medical. Issues relating to antitrust, insurance and FDA are also well-known areas of expertise. The practice also counts Emory Healthcare, Preferred Care Partners and PSS World Medical among its clients.

**Sources say:** *"They have a broad base of healthcare knowledge that makes them an invaluable resource."*

**KEY INDIVIDUALS** Jennifer Butler is a key contact at the firm.

## Band 3
## Healthcare: East Coast

## Drinker Biddle & Reath LLP
See profile on p.2238

**THE FIRM** This practice is notable for its accomplished handling of transactional and finance matters, and also offers considerable expertise in the regulatory and disputes arenas. In addition to this, the group is noted for its abilities in physician and executive compensation, and labor and employment issues concerning the healthcare environment. Atlantic Health System, Geisinger Health System Foundation, Lahey Clinic and Bon Secours Health System are among its key clients.

**Sources say:** *"Experienced, thorough and responsive."*

**KEY INDIVIDUALS** T J Sullivan (see p.414) is a leading light in the tax exemption field and impresses with his abilities in assisting tax-exempt organizations in regulatory and business matters.

## Other Notable Practitioners

**Scott Becker** chairs McGuireWoods LLP's healthcare group and is equally adept on regulatory and transactional matters in the healthcare arena. He is especially noted for his knowledge of surgery center issues. **Lloyd Bookman** of Hooper Lundy & Bookman PC is an authority on Medicare and Medicaid issues and is frequently called upon to assist clients with matters relating to false claims and antikickback. **John Brennan** (see p.287) is cochair of the healthcare team at Crowell & Moring LLP. He enjoys a fine track record for his work concerning fraud and abuse matters and the False Claims Act. **Michael Callahan** of Katten Muchin Rosenman LLP has more than three decades' worth of experience in the healthcare arena, advising on a wide variety of matters, from antitrust issues, HIPAA and regulatory compliance to medical staff credentialing, hospital and medical staff relations, and general corporate matters. The *"very knowledgeable"* **Maria Currier** (see p.989) heads the healthcare and life sciences group at Holland & Knight LLP. She is routinely sought after to advise clients on transactions and regulatory issues, and recently played a leading role in Express Scripts' $29.1 billion acquisition of Medco Health Solutions. Duane Morris LLP's **Joanne Erde** is recognized as a leading light in Medicare and Medicaid arena, and is well versed in handling cases across the country before the Provider Reimbursement Review Board, state administrative agencies and the federal courts. The *"well-respected"* **Thomas Fahey** (see p.1206) is managing partner at Ungaretti & Harris LLP and chairs its healthcare group. He is noted for his wealth of experience in the healthcare arena, where he is routinely sought after to advise on both transactional and regulatory matters. *"Very fine lawyer"* **Mark Fitzgerald** of Powers Pyles Sutter & Verville PC continues to command respect from the market for his Medicare fraud and abuse work. **David Hilgers** of Brown McCarroll, L.L.P. is *"professional, very accessible and customer service-oriented,"* reports one enthusiastic client. He is well known for his expertise in corporate and administrative matters, acting for a client base including healthcare providers, health systems and managed care organizations. **Gerry Hinkley** of Pillsbury Winthrop Shaw Pittman LLP has over three decades of experience in the market and impresses with his expertise in corporate matters facing healthcare organizations. He is also known for his adept handling of board governance issues. At Hooper Lundy & Bookman PC, former Deputy Attorney General **Patric Hooper** is much noted for his expertise in healthcare disputes, particularly with regard to cases against federal and state governments,

and acts for both profit and nonprofit organizations. Broad and Cassel's **Gabriel Imperato** maintains a fine track record acting for individuals and organizations facing fraud and internal investigations, and is also renowned for his corporate governance work. The *"excellent, very intelligent and responsive,"* **Harold Iselin** (see p.1906) of Greenberg Traurig, LLP is much in demand for his knowledge of governmental affairs, healthcare plans and reimbursement, and receives praise for his results-oriented approach to matters. Crowell & Moring LLP's group cochair **Arthur Lerner** (see p.876) is recognized for experience in antitrust and fraud and abuse issues affecting the healthcare sector, and in recent work, assisted Coventry Health Corporation with regard to antitrust matters concerning its $7.2 billion sale to Aetna. Hooper Lundy & Bookman's **Steven Lipton**, who principally acts for hospitals in healthcare transactions, regulatory and compliance issues, and matters concerning physician contracting. Representation in EMTALA investigations and fraud and abuse cases are particularly notable areas of strength. **Douglas Mancino** (see p.651) is co-head of the healthcare team at Hunton & Williams LLP. He is highly regarded for his tax-exempt practice and represents a sound choice for tax-exempt organizations involved in joint ventures. **Peter Millock** (see p.1919) of Nixon Peabody LLP is much in demand for his strengths concerning regulatory and policy matters. At Katten Muchin Rosenman LLP, the seasoned **Peter Nadel** is highly regarded for his regulatory and litigation capabilities, and is also sought after for his expertise in healthcare-related transactions. Nixon Peabody LLP's **Susan Robfogel** (see p.393) continues to command a great deal of respect for her expertise in labor and employment issues affecting the healthcare and life sciences arena. **George Root** heads the practice at Procopio, Cory, Hargreaves & Savitch LLP. The formation of integrated delivery systems and medical staff relations are two areas of particular strength for him. Key clients include OxyHeal Health Group and Alliance Healthcare Foundation. The highly experienced **Donald Schmidt** (see p.1006) of Carlton Fields, P.A. maintains a fine reputation for his expertise concerning healthcare disputes and remains a fine option for both regional and national healthcare clients facing investigations by enforcement agencies. At Broad and Cassel, health law practice chair **Mike Segal** comes recommended for his work representing physician groups in a variety of matters. The *"fantastic"* **Robert Andrew Wild** of Garfunkel Wild P.C. is renowned for his regulatory and compliance strengths. He is also frequently called upon to advise clients on reimbursement and professional conduct issues.

# IMMIGRATION

Commentary about individuals can be found under their firm's paragraph. If the firm has no paragraph (is not ranked) look at Other Notable Practitioners.

## Immigration
## Leading Firms

### Band 1
Fragomen, Del Rey, Bernsen & Loewy, LLP *

### Band 2
Berry Appleman & Leiden LLP
Greenberg Traurig, LLP *
Klasko Rulon Stock & Seltzer
Kramer Levin Naftalis & Frankel LLP *
Seyfarth Shaw LLP *

### Band 3
Baker & McKenzie *
Duane Morris LLP *
FosterQuan, LLP
Mintz Levin Cohn Ferris Glovsky and Popeo PC *
Morgan, Lewis & Bockius LLP *
Pearl Law Group
Proskauer Rose LLP *

## Recommended for Client Service
## Nationwide
| Berry Appleman & Leiden LLP | Seyfarth Shaw LLP |

## Recommended for Commercial Awareness
## Nationwide
| Berry Appleman & Leiden LLP | Pearl Law Group |

## Immigration
## Senior Statesmen

**Senior Statesmen:** distinguished older practitioners
| Virtue Paul | Baker & McKenzie |

## Leading Individuals

### Band 1
| Buffenstein Daryl | Fragomen, Del Rey, Bernsen and Loewy |
| Grunblatt David | Proskauer Rose LLP |
| Klasko H Ronald | Klasko Rulon Stock & Seltzer |
| Kurzban Ira J | Kurzban, Kurzban, Weinger, Tetzeli (ONP) [†] |
| Leiden Warren R | Berry Appleman & Leiden LLP |
| Paparelli Angelo | Seyfarth Shaw LLP * |
| Pelta Eleanor | Morgan, Lewis & Bockius LLP * |
| Sabagh Denyse | Duane Morris LLP |
| Walker Kathleen Campbell | Cox Smith Matthews (ONP) [†] |
| Wolfsdorf Bernard | Wolfsdorf Immigration Law Group (ONP) [†] |
| Yale-Loehr Stephen W | Miller Mayer LLP (ONP) [†] |

### Band 2
| Appleman Jeff T | Berry Appleman & Leiden LLP |
| Berry David P | Berry Appleman & Leiden LLP |
| Cohen Susan | Mintz Levin Cohn Ferris Glovsky and Popeo * |
| Foster Charles C | FosterQuan, LLP |
| Fox-Isicoff Tammy | Rifkin and Fox-Isicoff PA (ONP) [†] |
| Fragomen Jr Austin T | Fragomen, Del Rey, Bernsen & Loewy, LLP |
| Gonzalez Josie | Gonzalez & Harris PC (ONP) [†] |
| Kuck Charles H | Kuck Immigration Partners LLC (ONP) [†] |
| Mehlman Sharon R | Larrabee Mehlman Albi Coker LLP (ONP) [†] |
| Pearl Julie | Pearl Law Group |
| Quan Gordon J | FosterQuan, LLP |
| Ruthizer Theodore | Kramer Levin Naftalis & Frankel LLP * |
| Shusterman Carl | The Law Offices of Carl Shusterman (ONP) [†] |
| Stock William | Klasko Rulon Stock & Seltzer |
| Zulkie Paul L | Zulkie Partners LLC (ONP) [†] |

### Band 3
| Catillaz Margaret A | Harter, Secrest & Emery LLP (ONP) [†] |
| Chiappari Ted | Satterlee Stephens Burke & Burke (ONP) [†] |
| Cooper Bo | Fragomen, Del Rey, Bernsen & Loewy, LLP |
| Ginsburg Jonathan | Fettman Ginsburg (ONP) [†] |
| Hammond Denise | Hammond Immigration Law, P.C. (ONP) [†] * |
| Ivener Mark | Ivener & Fullmer LLP (ONP) [†] * |
| Koestler Mark D | Kramer Levin Naftalis & Frankel LLP * |
| Ladik Steven M | Berry Appleman & Leiden LLP |
| Mehta Cyrus D | Cyrus D Mehta & Associates PLLC (ONP) [†] |
| Morell Avram E | Pryor Cashman LLP (ONP) [†] |
| Moseley Thomas | The Law Offices of Thomas Moseley |
| Newman George | Stinson Morrison Hecker LLP (ONP) [†] |
| Notkin Deborah | Barst Mukamal & Kleiner LLP (ONP) [†] |
| Patrick Michael D | Fragomen, Del Rey, Bernsen & Loewy, LLP |
| Reiff Laura Foote | Greenberg Traurig, LLP * |
| Schoonover Martha J | Greenberg Traurig, LLP * |
| Seltzer Suzanne | Klasko Rulon Stock & Seltzer |
| Stern Elizabeth Espin | Baker & McKenzie |
| Stump T Douglas | Stump & Associates (ONP) [†] |
| Swapp Russell | Seyfarth Shaw LLP * |
| Tobocman Sarah Lea | Gunster (ONP) [†] |
| Vázquez-Azpiri A James | Morgan, Lewis & Bockius LLP * |
| Yanni Palma | Dickstein Shapiro LLP (ONP) [†] * |

### Up-and-coming individuals
| Sauer Ari J | Siskind Susser, PC (ONP) [†] |

\* Indicates firm / individual with profile.
[†] ONP = Other Notable Practitioner.

## Band 1

### Fragomen, Del Rey, Bernsen & Loewy, LLP
See profile on p.1974

THE FIRM Fragomen is well known as the largest immigration boutique in the country, with an impressive number of offices scattered across the USA. The firm has earned its stellar reputation through its ability to service the migration needs of small to large corporations on a local, national and global scale. The group covers the whole spectrum of business immigration matters, including compliance, investment and export control issues, as well as related family petitions and student matters.
Sources say: *"Their network is superior."*
KEY INDIVIDUALS The *"very high-caliber"* **Daryl Buffenstein** is based in the Atlanta office and enjoys a fine reputation as an expert in government policy and legislation. **Bo Cooper** *"has a very strong command of the developments and the players at the USCIS,"* according to commentators. He operates out of Washington, DC and specializes in advising clients on their corporate immigration strategies. **Austin Fragomen**, in New York, is a seasoned authority in the immigration law arena. He has frequently testified before Congress. Also in New York is the *"excellent"* **Michael Patrick**, a longstanding immigration and nationality law specialist. He assists clients with compliance issues, and is also well versed in advising on develop-

ing immigration policies and with immigration due diligence.

## Band 2

### Berry Appleman & Leiden LLP
THE FIRM This growing immigration boutique provides top-quality corporate services to clients from a network of US offices. As one of the largest immigration practices in the country, the team has experts across a comprehensive range of areas including nonimmigrant visas, naturalization and permanent residence, and can also be counted on for its advice regarding compliance, government relations and global migration.
Client Service *"Service to their clients is very thorough." "Very responsive."*

Commercial Awareness *"They understand the company and how we work."*
KEY INDIVIDUALS **Warren Leiden** is very active in the immigration law community and on issues involving government relations, and according to sources is *"responsible for thought-leading discussion."* Leiden currently heads several teams representing large companies in their immigration programs. **David Berry** focuses on managing immigration programs for multinational clients and advising on corporate compliance, and is also sought for assistance with immigration implications for M&A. Dallas-based **Steven Ladik** is *"a big part of supporting our organization,"* according to one satisfied client. He is well known in the field for his expertise in labor certification issues and also advises on other areas where there may be immigration implications, such as due diligence and workforce reductions. The *"extremely knowledgeable"* **Jeff Appleman** is a

seasoned figure in the market and elicits much admiration for his dedication to client service.

## Greenberg Traurig, LLP
See profile on p.1024
**THE FIRM** This expanding immigration team services clients on the full range of immigration matters. Lately the firm has handled a significant amount of work in the area of compliance and has been particularly active in handling EB-5 work with dozens of regional centers. The practice represents high-profile individuals and large organizations from a diverse range of sectors, but is particularly recommended for its immigration work concerning the entertainment industry.
**Sources say:** *"A very solid practice."*
**KEY INDIVIDUALS** *"Excellent attorney"* **Laura Foote Reiff** (see p.887) is a client favorite and has recently been active in dealing with EB-5 investor category matters, assisting companies to plan for proposed legislation and helping them to ensure compliance with regulations. Business immigration specialist **Martha Schoonover** (see p.890) *"knows her stuff"* according to impressed commentators, and is particularly appreciated by clients for the very personalized attention she affords.

## Klasko Rulon Stock & Seltzer
**THE FIRM** Klasko Rulon Stock & Seltzer is a nationally recognized immigration boutique, operating out of offices in New York and Philadelphia. The team handles all aspects of employment-based immigration matters, assisting everyone from individuals to large corporations, and has a strong track record for its work on behalf of public institutions such as universities and hospitals.
**Sources say:** *"They have a reputation for being involved in some of the most complex and difficult areas."*
**KEY INDIVIDUALS** Managing partner **Ronald Klasko** is *"a fixture in the immigration Bar"* and represents clients from a diverse range of industries and sectors, including biotech, manufacturing and healthcare. **William Stock** elicits praise for his creativity in litigation and is also described as an *"impressive strategist around immigration issues."* Stock concentrates on assisting individuals and domestic and international companies with their immigration needs and related litigation. **Suzanne Seltzer** is a well-known figure in the immigration law community and advises many universities, hospitals and research institutions on J-1, national interest waiver and extraordinary ability visas.

## Kramer Levin Naftalis & Frankel LLP
See profile on p.1987
**THE FIRM** This fine business immigration group is based in New York and comes particularly recommended for its work in investment and employer sanctions. It also maintains a fine track record handling the immigration consequences of corporate transactions.
**Sources say:** *"They are very timely and their advice has been consistently accurate – I trust their judgment."*
**KEY INDIVIDUALS** The *"very well-regarded"* **Theodore Ruthizer** (see p.1934) cochairs the firm's business immi-

gration practice and has over three decades' experience in the space. **Mark Koestler** (see p.1910) is well known in the field, particularly for his representation of clients in the entertainment industry, but also represents a fine choice of counsel for individuals and organizations in other sectors including financial services and insurance.

## Seyfarth Shaw LLP
See profile on p.1262
**THE FIRM** Seyfarth Shaw's integrated immigration group manages the immigration needs of local, national and international clients. The firm's new client service model, Seyfarth*Lean*, attests to the group's commitment to the field. The team handles the gamut of immigration matters from visa petitions to corporate strategy, and the training of human resources staff.
**Client Service** *"Responsive and customer-oriented." "Very flexible and willing to work with us to accelerate matters."*
**KEY INDIVIDUALS** **Angelo Paparelli** (see p.658) is regarded as *"a real powerhouse and a thought leader."* Paparelli is renowned for his problem-solving and adept command of the most complex immigration matters. Boston-based **Russell Swapp** (see p.415) is praised by sources for his trustworthiness and ability to communicate complicated concepts. Swapp represents various individuals, institutions and corporations in their immigration needs.

## Band 3

## Baker & McKenzie
See profile on p.435
**THE FIRM** The global immigration and mobility practice group at Baker & McKenzie focuses on all areas of business immigration, policy and enforcement. The firm takes a holistic approach to compliance issues and also comes recommended for its advice concerning other potentially related issues that can arise in the movement of personnel, including corruption and bribery, cyber security and data privacy. In addition, the group enjoys a fine reputation for its work concerning employee benefits and tax issues.
**KEY INDIVIDUALS** **Paul Virtue** is *"one of the best-known immigration attorneys in the USA and a thought leader."* He is a former general immigration counsel of the Immigration and Naturalization Service and has extensive experience representing individuals, businesses and institutions in immigration matters. According to sources, **Elizabeth Espin Stern** *"makes sure that things get done"* and is *"very experienced, and able to identify the key points in cases that really influence what the direction should be."* She manages global migration programs for major companies.

## Duane Morris LLP
See profile on p.2239
**THE FIRM** This fine immigration practice focuses on corporate immigration and related litigation. The team has substantial experience in a full set of immigration matters including immigrant and nonimmigrant visas, and com-

pliance and training, and is also noted for its adroit handling of removals issues and corporate transactions.
**Sources say:** *"Responsive and extremely knowledgeable."*
**KEY INDIVIDUALS** The *"absolutely stellar"* **Denyse Sabagh** heads the immigration group and is admired for the passion she exudes throughout her work in assisting corporate clients with managing their immigration programs. She also maintains a strong track record in removal litigation.

## FosterQuan, LLP
**THE FIRM** This dedicated immigration law firm has offices in Washington, DC, as well as Houston, Austin, San Antonio, Rio Grande Valley and Mexico City. The group offers a comprehensive immigration service to individuals and corporations for employment-based, family-based and asylum work. Lately, the team has handled a large number of investor category matters and is also noted as a fine choice of counsel for foreign diplomats.
**Sources say:** *"A quality immigration shop – an outstanding practice."*
**KEY INDIVIDUALS** The *"terrific"* chairs **Charles Foster** and **Gordon Quan** both operate out of Houston and are well-known figures in the immigration law field.

## Mintz Levin Cohn Ferris Glovsky and Popeo PC
See profile on p.1523
**THE FIRM** This integrated immigration practice group collaborates with other departments to provide comprehensive services to individuals, businesses and organizations. The group has recently been actively engaged in high-caliber investment work in tandem with the firm's securities department.
**Sources say:** *"They took our concerns, gave us support and made the work we needed to do easy."*
**KEY INDIVIDUALS** Founder and chair of the firm's immigration practice, **Susan Cohen** (see p.297) is appreciated for her *"empathy and compassion."* Cohen is recognized nationally for the breadth and depth of her experience across the spectrum of immigration law.

## Morgan, Lewis & Bockius LLP
See profile on p.2246
**THE FIRM** Through this firm's immigration and nationality practice group, clients are offered a full set of business immigration services. The team works with a diverse clientele, from small companies to major corporations, managing their global migration needs, and assisting with compliance matters and policy development. The group also has experience in a range of family-based matters.
**Sources say:** *"I would highly recommend the firm to any of my corporate peers."*
**KEY INDIVIDUALS** The *"phenomenal"* **Eleanor Pelta** (see p.885) has earned an excellent national reputation in the immigration law community. Based in Washington, DC, she assists clients from a variety of industries with all matters relating to the transfer of personnel. **James Vázquez-Azpiri** (see p.670) impresses sources with his wealth of knowledge and expertise in corporate immigra-

tion law. He is described as *"a scholar par excellence in terms of his knowledge of immigration law,"* and elicits praise for his calm demeanor, accessibility and diligent approach to matters.

## Pearl Law Group

**THE FIRM** This San-Francisco based firm devotes its expertise to all areas of business immigration law and is highly regarded for its widely used immigration management system, ImmigrationTracker. The team is particularly noted for its expertise in trusted traveler programs.

**Commercial Awareness** *"They go above and beyond taking care of their clients and understanding our business."*

**KEY INDIVIDUALS Julie Pearl** is a well-known figure in the immigration law community and is commended for her *"very energetic"* approach to matters. Another source adds: *"She is very good at helping us streamline and make our program more efficient."*

## Proskauer Rose LLP

See profile on p.2001

**THE FIRM** Proskauer Rose's immigration and nationality practice is based in Newark and operates on a national level for clients throughout the country. The team handles work for high net worth individuals, investors, entrepreneurs, businesses and other organizations. It counts HSBC, Coach, Willis and The New York Times among its key clients.

**Sources say:** *"A comprehensive job – no shortcuts."*

**KEY INDIVIDUALS** The *"fabulous"* **David Grunblatt** heads the immigration and nationality practice group and has wide-ranging experience, with particular expertise in I-9 and E-Verify compliance and the immigration consequences of corporate transactions. *"His familiarity with the subject area is unparalleled,"* asserts one impressed commentator.

## Other Notable Practitioners

Rochester-based **Margaret Catillaz** of Harter, Secrest & Emery LLP practices in business immigration matters and often represents clients from the healthcare industry. She has recently been involved in important litigation involving licensing and discrimination against foreign professionals. **Ted Chiappari** of Satterlee Stephens Burke & Burke LLP also operates out of New York. He is routinely sought to advise companies on business immigration matters, including temporary work permits and permanent resident status applications. Rifkin and Fox-Isicoff PA's **Tammy Fox-Isicoff** has a background in enforcement and is singled out as a *"really strong advocate."* She has particular expertise in the EB-5 investor category. **Jonathan**

Ginsburg of Fettmann Ginsburg PC practices in a broad range of immigration matters and has notable experience in the complex areas of national interest waivers and aliens of extraordinary ability. Sources commend him for his creativity and for his representation of clients in the arts space. *"Fine lawyer"* **Josie Gonzalez** of Gonzalez & Harris PC has earned an excellent reputation, particularly in the areas of employer sanctions, labor certification and I-9 compliance. *"Fabulous"* sole practitioner **Denise Hammond** (see p.868) *"has an incredible client service approach – her personal attention to each case is fantastic,"* according to commentators. She is recognized for her work serving the immigration needs of individuals, families and companies that are leaders in their industries. Ivener & Fullmer LLP's **Mark Ivener** (see p.643) is based in Los Angeles and has an excellent reputation particularly in the area of EB-5 investor visas. He also handles nonimmigrant visas and corporate compliance issues. *"Tremendous lawyer"* **Charles Kuck** of Kuck Immigration Partners LLC is recognized nationally as a *"fierce advocate for his clients."* He has extensive experience in a full range of matters relating to immigration, nationality and asylum law. **Ira Kurzban** of Kurzban, Kurzban, Weinger, Tetzeli & Pratt is considered by sources to be among those attorneys who are *"advancing immigration law."* He is the author of the definitive sourcebook in the immigration law field and highly regarded in the industry especially for his federal litigation work.

The *"extremely knowledgeable"* **Sharon Mehlman** of Larrabee Mehlman Albi Coker LLP has broad experience in business immigration matters and is respected by peers for being at the forefront of current developments. **Cyrus Mehta** of Cyrus D Mehta & Associates PLLC is *"very straightforward and obviously knows what he's doing,"* according to sources. He has experience in a vast array of immigration matters, and among recent matters has been assisting clients with navigating issues concerning roaming employees. **George Newman** at Stinson Morrison Hecker LLP enjoys a fine reputation for his work in the healthcare industry, acting for physicians, researchers and scientists, and is also noted for his counsel to medical schools and hospitals. He elicits particular praise from interviewees for his communication skills. The *"wonderful"* **Deborah Notkin** of Barst Mukamal & Kleiner LLP is based in New York and known nationally for her immigration law expertise, particularly in the area of PERM matters. Pryor Cashman LLP's **Avram Morell** is based in New York and is hailed by sources as a very thorough, knowledgeable attorney with an excellent ability to communicate clearly. He has a wide range of experience within immigration, nationality and asylum law and related litigation. **Thomas Moseley** of The Law Offices of Thomas Moseley is a wide-

ly respected advocate based in Newark and is a fine choice of counsel for immigration-related federal court litigation and removal defense. **Ari Sauer** is at the well-established Tennessee firm Siskind Susser, PC. A rising star in the arena, he is developing a fine reputation for acting on behalf of both individuals and businesses, and comes particularly recommended for his work on permanent residency and citizenship. The highly regarded **Carl Shusterman** of The Law Offices of Carl Shusterman is much noted for his work in employment-based matters, especially in the healthcare, IT and entertainment arenas. Additionally, he is also heavily involved in federal court litigation, winning much praise for his advocacy skills, and comes particularly recommended for his expertise in family-based and asylum and deportation cases. President-elect of the American Immigration Lawyers Association (AILA), **Douglas Stump** of Stump & Associates in Oklahoma is recognized as an extremely knowledgeable practitioner. Although his practice is focused on employment-based immigration, he also excels in difficult deportation cases, family-based immigration and federal court litigation.

Gunster's **Sarah Lea Tobocman** draws much praise for her wealth of knowledge in the immigration arena, with one impressed source saying: *"It is not often that she has to look something up."* She is noted for her work in the healthcare industry and in recent matters has been busy engaged in investor category work. **Kathleen Campbell Walker** of Cox Smith Matthews Incorporated is a recognized practitioner of immigration law, especially for *"her expertise in increasingly complex issues of immigration compliance and worksite enforcement."* **Bernard Wolfsdorf** of Wolfsdorf Immigration Law Group in Los Angeles and New York receives continual praise from sources. One commentator appreciated that *"his persistent and strategic approach meant that a complicated application was awarded."* Wolfsdorf's practice is mainly focused on business immigration matters and he has been particularly busy of late with investor category work. Ithaca-based **Stephen Yale-Loehr** of Miller Mayer LLP has over three decades of experience in the immigration arena and is regarded by commentators as *"the premier guy on EB-5 cases."* Clients respect **Palma Yanni** (see p.901) of Dickstein Shapiro LLP for being *"very accessible and personable"* as well as for her ability to *"come up with solutions."* Yanni has a strong reputation for her work representing physicians but also assists other individuals and businesses with their employment-based immigration needs. **Paul Zulkie** of Zulkie Partners LLC in Chicago, is a well-respected business immigration practitioner and, as a former president of AILA, is recognized as a leading figure in the immigration law community.

## INSURANCE DISPUTE RESOLUTION: INSURER

Commentary about individuals can be found under their firm's paragraph. If the firm has no paragraph (is not ranked) look at Other Notable Practitioners.

### Insurance: Dispute Resolution: Insurer
#### Leading Firms

**Band 1**
Simpson Thacher & Bartlett LLP *

**Band 2**
Dentons *
Duane Morris LLP *
Steptoe & Johnson LLP *

**Band 3**
Cahill Gordon & Reindel LLP *
Cozen O'Connor *
Crowell & Moring LLP *
O'Melveny & Myers LLP *
Sidley Austin LLP *
Troutman Sanders LLP

**Band 4**
Hogan Lovells US LLP *
Locke Lord LLP *

### Insurance: Dispute Resolution: Insurer
#### Senior Statesmen

**Senior Statesmen:** distinguished older practitioners
Newman Thomas R    *Duane Morris LLP*

#### Leading Individuals

**Band 1**

| | | |
|---|---|---|
| Dixon Gary | *Troutman Sanders LLP* | |
| Glad Paul E B | *Dentons* * | |
| Matthews Philip R | *Duane Morris LLP* | |
| Nonna John M | *Patton Boggs LLP (ONP)* [†] | |
| Ostrager Barry R | *Simpson Thacher & Bartlett LLP* * | |
| Rocap III James | *Steptoe & Johnson LLP* | |
| Vyskocil Mary Kay | *Simpson Thacher & Bartlett LLP* * | |
| Warin Roger | *Steptoe & Johnson LLP* | |

**Band 2**

| | |
|---|---|
| Ashinoff Reid | *Dentons* * |
| Barr Michael H | *Dentons* * |
| Koepff Paul | *Clyde & Co US LLP (ONP)* [†] |
| Krugman Edward P | *Cahill Gordon & Reindel LLP* * |
| Ruggeri James | *Shipman & Goodwin LLP (ONP)* [†] |

**Band 3**

| | |
|---|---|
| Cozen Stephen A | *Cozen O'Connor* * |
| Goetz Richard | *O'Melveny & Myers LLP* |
| Gordon Andrew K | *Duane Morris LLP* |
| Hendler Clifford B | *Crowell & Moring LLP* * |
| Kalish Paul W | *Crowell & Moring LLP* * |
| Kent Ronald D | *Dentons* * |
| Rosenthal Thorn | *Cahill Gordon & Reindel LLP* * |
| Schiavoni Tancred | *O'Melveny & Myers LLP* |
| Shelley William | *Gordon & Rees, LLP (ONP)* [†] |
| Warner Margaret H | *McDermott Will & Emery LLP (ONP)* [†] * |

### Recommended for Client Service
#### Nationwide

| | |
|---|---|
| Crowell & Moring LLP | Steptoe & Johnson LLP |
| Sidley Austin LLP | Troutman Sanders LLP |

### Recommended for Commercial Awareness
#### Nationwide

| | |
|---|---|
| Cozen O'Connor | Steptoe & Johnson LLP |
| Simpson Thacher & Bartlett | Troutman Sanders LLP |

### Insurance: Dispute Resolution: Reinsurance
#### Leading Individuals

**Band 1**

| | |
|---|---|
| Chaffetz Peter | *Chaffetz Lindsey LLP (ONP)* [†] * |
| Krugman Edward P | *Cahill Gordon & Reindel LLP* * |
| Nonna John M | *Patton Boggs LLP* |
| Ostrager Barry R | *Simpson Thacher & Bartlett LLP* * |
| Raim David | *Chadbourne & Parke LLP (ONP)* [†] * |
| Rubin James I | *Butler Rubin Saltarelli & Boyd LLP (ONP)* [†] * |
| Schwartz Steven | *Locke Lord LLP* * |
| Stone Susan | *Sidley Austin LLP* * |
| Vyskocil Mary Kay | *Simpson Thacher & Bartlett LLP* * |

\* *Indicates firm / individual with profile.*
[†] *ONP = Other Notable Practitioner.*

## Band 1

### Simpson Thacher & Bartlett LLP
**See profile on p.2006**

**THE FIRM** Simpson Thacher & Bartlett continues to be the star firm in the nationwide insurance market. Clients do not hesitate in referring big-ticket insurance and reinsurance matters to the capable hands of the firm's attorneys. The group has a reputation in the market for a track record of very good results. The team furnishes advice to some of the world's most significant insurance groups including The Travelers Companies, Berkshire Hathaway, Equitas and American Nuclear Insurers. Acting for Travelers affiliates USF&G, the team recently secured a high-profile summary judgment before the New York Appellate Division in a historic asbestos case.
**Commercial Awareness** *"They understand our business very well and send updates on the law when it changes."*
**KEY INDIVIDUALS** *"Excellent"* **Barry Ostrager** (see p.381) is nationally recognized as *"a big name"* both in the insurance and the reinsurance fields. Clients recommend him for asbestos bankruptcy cases and praise him for his impressive leadership and willingness to be in the front line in facing difficult points. *"Sophisticated"* attorney **Mary Kay Vyskocil** (see p.422) *"stands out"* in the nationwide insurance as well as the reinsurance rankings. The scope of her expertise encompasses securities, financial services industry and general coverage disputes. Commentators emphasized that she has *"had another really great year, a spectacular year."*

### Dentons
**See profile on p.449**

**THE FIRM** This widely acclaimed firm houses a formidable insurance practice, with 15 US-based offices and over 60 worldwide. Dentons has experience in dealing with a diverse range of financial, property and casualty, class action and bad faith coverage cases. Clients praise it for taking a result-oriented approach which they find to be ideal for high-exposure cases.
**Sources say:** *"Top-notch firm, very good results with them. They are good litigators, good strategists, and they understand the insurance industry."*
**KEY INDIVIDUALS** *"Extremely well-respected"* California-based **Paul Glad** (see p.321) is *"a legend"* and *"definitely a top practitioner."* Cochair of the firm's appellate litigation practice, he appears in cases relating to general liability, bad faith and class actions. Highly recommended **Reid Ashinoff** (see p.274) is *"a good strategic thinker on a pragmatic level"* according to sources. He has been busy acting for Genworth Financial Wealth Management in several class actions involving federal securities and mortgage-related consumer protection lawsuits. Cochair of Dentons's global insurance sector, **Michael Barr** (see p.278) is *"strong on strategy, argument, case management and very good in resolution settings as*

well." He has been heavily involved in cases relating to the financial industry crisis, for example representing Royal Indemnity in a surety-related fraud trial. Litigator **Ronald Kent** (see p.646) is a favorite among clients, who comment that *"his calm demeanor and good sense of humor only add to the effectiveness of his thoughtful but aggressive approach to litigation."* His practice focuses on natural and man-made catastrophic losses, but he has wide experience also in general insurance matters.

## Band 2

### Duane Morris LLP
**See profile on p.2239**

**THE FIRM** Duane Morris is known as a leader in the California insurance Bar. With 20 offices across the USA and international branches in Vietnam, Singapore and the UK, Duane Morris has expanded to affirm its presence globally. The team is prominent in insurance coverage disputes, with core expertise in environmental and professional liability matters.
**Sources say:** *"We found them to be very proficient in arbitration but also in general matters – very bright lawyers and their work is of very high quality."*
**KEY INDIVIDUALS Philip Matthews** is a highly esteemed insurance litigator. He is known as *"somebody who pursues a client's case thoroughly and is incredibly professional in doing it."* He has recently dealt with the Thorpe Insulation bankruptcy arising out of asbestos cases. Senior

statesman **Thomas Newman** *"knows the business inside and out."* He has wide experience in appellate courts, where he argues reinsurance and insurance coverage disputes. **Andrew Gordon** enjoys a *"good reputation for London market issues."* He recently acted for CNA in settling a London market coverage case just before jury selection.

### Steptoe & Johnson LLP

THE FIRM This highly respected practice group advises insurers in big-ticket coverage matters from D&O to environmental. With an extensive domestic coverage, the firm boasts offices in Century City, Chicago, Los Angeles, New York, Phoenix and Washington, DC. Clients speak at length about the team's bench strength that enables it to seamlessly try large and complex cases. Steptoe & Johnson is playing an instrumental role acting for The Hartford in the high-profile NFL concussions case.

**Client Service** *"The firm is highly responsive, outcome-focused and willing to partner with us in finding solutions."*
**Commercial Awareness** *"They have great knowledge across the board, and they are very sensitive to the company's particular outlook on cases. There is no need to reinvent the wheel with them."*
**KEY INDIVIDUALS** *"Very fine lawyer"* **James Rocap** is an undisputed *"leader in his field."* He focuses on environmental matters and is frequently chosen to counsel The Hartford in complex insurance cases. *"Very effective lawyer"* **Roger Warin** has a reputation in the market for his insurance work in connection to professional liability matters. Peers describe him as a *"formidable"* and *"tough but fair adversary."*

### Band 3

### Cahill Gordon & Reindel LLP
See profile on p.1960

THE FIRM This firm is one of the best in New York and has also carved out a strong presence for itself in the nationwide market. The team is well known for its prominent role in representing prominent insurance clients, such as AIG, Chartis and National Union Fire Insurance. Acting on behalf of the latter, the group secured a victory against Everest Re in connection to a historical environmental cleanup case.

**Sources say:** *"They are really good at what they do. They are good because they are very smart, they have lots of experience and their approach to litigation or arbitration is really very sound."*
**KEY INDIVIDUALS Edward Krugman** (see p.350) combines sound legal knowledge with a sharp analytical mind. Peers would be happy to refer work to him, finding him an *"extremely intelligent guy, creative and effective."* He has long-standing insurance and reinsurance expertise, having recently represented Chartis International in a political risk insurance dispute. *"Fantastic"* **Thorn Rosenthal** (see p.1933) is recognized as *"one of the new leaders in the market."* He is involved in insurance and reinsurance disputes

### Cozen O'Connor
See profile on p.2237

THE FIRM Cozen O'Connor has a nationally known insurance practice, with a particular stronghold in Pennsylvania. The group's impressive client portfolio features giant property and casualty insurer Chubb Group and reinsurance companies such as Munich Re and Everest Re. The firm acted for ACE American Insurance against American Medical Response Northwest, seeking coverage for lawsuits relating to sexual abuse allegations.
**Commercial Awareness** *"They are smart, strategic and practical. They are experienced coverage attorneys that listen to the client, have innovative ideas and are results-oriented. They also work well with other insurer counsel."*
**KEY INDIVIDUALS Stephen Cozen** (see p.299), founder and chairman of the firm, is based in the Philadelphia office. He is highly praised by sources, who describe him as a *"very fine lawyer and very fine person."* He is experienced in litigating insurance coverage issues on behalf of insurers.

### Crowell & Moring LLP
See profile on p.910

THE FIRM Peers recognize this firm as a key player in the US insurance space, with offices in Washington, DC, San Francisco, Los Angeles, Irvine and New York. The team is recognized as a leader in reinsurance and complex insurance coverage in mass torts from asbestos to medical devices-related lawsuits. The firm has been busy representing ACE in several high-stakes coverage disputes.
**Client Service** *"We have found that C&M lawyers are all experts in their areas and have very good client service ethos."*
**KEY INDIVIDUALS** *"Experienced"* **Clifford Hendler** (see p.868) is recognized in the market for playing a front-line role in asbestos disputes. Clients single him out for his *"superb"* ability to understand their needs and develop productive relationships with adversaries. Cochair of Crowell's insurance and reinsurance group, **Paul Kalish** (see p.873) has a national reputation in connection to reinsurance and insurance coverage asbestos and D&O issues. Clients say: *"He is extremely responsive and is prepared for emergencies."*

### O'Melveny & Myers LLP
See profile on p.693

THE FIRM This team is active in insurance coverage matters and reinsurance cases. The group acts for a wide range of market players, including major insurance companies such as ACE and CIGNA. One recent highlight is the representation of Century Indemnity in the ongoing insurance litigation against Montrose Chemical Corporation of California relating to the manufacturing and distribution of insecticide DDT.
**Sources say:** *"They are easy to deal with, strategic and good partners."*
**KEY INDIVIDUALS** Head of the firm's insurance practice **Richard Goetz** is *"one of the best oral advocates"* and is

*"very strategic, thoughtful and very bright,"* according to sources. Recent clients include Century Indemnity and Resolute Management. Commentators endorse **Tancred Schiavoni** as a *"bulldog of a litigator."* An experienced insurance practitioner, he recently secured a victory on behalf of Resolute Management before the Ninth Circuit allowing insurers to challenge certain bankruptcy reorganization plans in the context of the Thorpe Insulation litigation.

### Sidley Austin LLP
See profile on p.1264

THE FIRM With eight offices nationwide, this insurance outfit is seen to be expanding on a global scale. Market commentators praise the firm for its high standing in reinsurance and insurance bankruptcy-related matters. The group recently secured a win for TIG Insurance in the California Court of Appeal in a reinsurance dispute with Transport Insurance Company.
**Client Service** *"They are willing at any time to make accommodation to provide us with the advice we are seeking." "We have significant contact with them and are able to obtain advice we need on a very quick basis."*
**KEY INDIVIDUALS** Chicago-based attorney **Susan Stone** (see p.413) is considered *"very prominent"* in the reinsurance arena. She recently acted for Chartis/AIG in an appellate case involving workers' compensation insurance premiums.

### Troutman Sanders LLP

THE FIRM This well-regarded team is spread across the USA with 12 offices from San Diego to New York. The firm handles the full range of insurance coverage matters including D&O, E&O, medical malpractice and toxic tort. Clients heap praise on the attorneys' practical style as well as on their consistent approach across the board. Troutman Sanders recently represented HCC Insurance Holdings and XL Insurance in multiple coverage actions arising out of MF Global Holdings' 2011 bankruptcy.
**KEY INDIVIDUALS Gary Dixon** is a nationally established insurance practitioner, whose practice focuses on D&O, property and casualty, and financial issues. Clients praise his sensitivity to their needs and his strategic thinking skills.

### Band 4

### Hogan Lovells US LLP

THE FIRM Hogan Lovells remains a stronghold in the insurance field, with over 40 offices around the world and ten in the USA. Clients speak at length about the group's commitment to their needs and its ability to build solid business relationships. The team represents insurers in coverage matters mainly in the financial and healthcare industries.
**Sources say:** *"Hogan Lovells does an excellent job of being a diligent advocate on behalf of its client."*
**KEY INDIVIDUALS** Litigator David Hensler, based in Washington, DC, is a point person for the firm.

## Locke Lord LLP

**See profile on p.2443**

**THE FIRM** This litigation boutique is known for the deep expertise of its attorneys when it comes to insurance and reinsurance disputes. The team boasts a long-standing relationship with the London market and experience in dealing with life insurance matters. The top-drawer client roster includes Hannover Re, Berkshire Hathaway and Catlin Group.

**Sources say:** *"They are very confident and timely; they are creative and very knowledgeable."*

**KEY INDIVIDUALS** Sources emphasize that **Steven Schwartz** (see p.403) has a sound knowledge of how the industry works and is *"very competent."* His practice focuses on reinsurance arbitrations.

## Other Notable Practitioners

Considered *"one of the best,"* **James Rubin** (see p.1228) of Butler Rubin Saltarelli & Boyd LLP has a significant presence in the reinsurance space. Peers observe that he is *"effective in arbitrations."* He is busy representing Liberty Mutual Insurance in a workers' compensation matter against AIG. According to sources, **James Ruggeri** of Shipman & Goodwin LLP is *"really extremely well versed in coverage issues and in big, complex cases."* His areas of expertise includes environmental and D&O liability issues, with particular knowledge of asbestos cases. DC-based **David Raim** (see p.389) of Chadbourne & Parke LLP is a well-established reinsurance practitioner. He recently acted for St. Paul Reinsurance, a subsidiary of The Travelers Companies, in a retrocessional losses coverage arbitration against Scandinavian Reinsurance. Popular with clients, he has the *"ability to manage complex, unusual issues arising in reinsurance."* Sources enthuse about **Peter Chaffetz** (see p.293) of Chaffetz Lindsey LLP, a *"very bright and experienced"* attorney, who *"provides very sound practical advice."* He divides his time between complex reinsurance arbitrations and insurance commercial dis-

putes. Much admired in the insurance arena, **Paul Koepff** of Clyde & Co US LLP is considered *"a true leader"* and peers admire him for his amazing track record of arbitration victories. He was engaged in IMG v Westchester Fire, a jury trial in Ohio relating to a coverage suit in an underlying fraud claim alleging loss of property use by a group of investors. **Margaret Warner** (see p.898) of McDermott Will & Emery LLP is a leading name in the world of insurance representation. Clients highly value that *"she is deeply aware of insurance company rights and obligations and is a common-sense businessperson."* Former Dewey & LeBoeuf partner **John Nonna** of Patton Boggs LLP retains a superb reputation in both the insurance and reinsurance arenas. Sources invariably identify him as a *"very good litigator operating at a very high level"* who is *"preeminent in the field."* He recently acted for Tower Insurance Company of New York against Munich Re in a complex reinsurance dispute. **William Shelley** recently joined Gordon & Rees, LLP from Cozen O'Connor. He is identified as *"terrific, top-flight and very smart"* by commentators. He is heavily involved in insurance commercial disputes acting on behalf of major carriers.

# INSURANCE DISPUTE RESOLUTION: POLICYHOLDER

| Insurance: Dispute Resolution: Policyholder Leading Firms |
| --- |
| **Band 1** |
| Covington & Burling LLP * |
| **Band 2** |
| Anderson Kill & Olick, P.C. * |
| Jenner & Block LLP * |
| Kasowitz, Benson, Torres & Friedman LLP * |
| Reed Smith LLP |
| **Band 3** |
| Dickstein Shapiro LLP * |
| K&L Gates * |
| Latham & Watkins LLP * |
| Morgan, Lewis & Bockius LLP * |
| Proskauer Rose LLP * |

*Indicates firm with profile.*
*Alphabetical order within each band. Band 1 is the highest.*

**Client Service** *"They are aware of our budget concerns and attempt to address them. They are nice people, not arrogant. This makes it more fun to work with them, and it goes down well with opponents."*

**Commercial Awareness** *"They are the best law firm in the country on the policyholder side. They know the subject matter, they have a deep bench, and their associates are very good."*

**KEY INDIVIDUALS** *"Excellent"* California partner **Donald Brown** (see p.625) earns unanimous acclaim for his work in coverage matters, in particular relating to environmental issues. Peers say that he *"fights over what matters, and is very sharp and to the point."* His key clients include ExxonMobil and the NFL. **Mitchell Dolin** (see p.305) chairs the practice from DC and is a favorite among clients, who describe him as *"great"* and *"terrific."* He is involved in disputes both nationally and worldwide, and has recently appeared in a loss of goods matter for a large pharmaceutical company. On the West Coast, **David Goodwin** (see p.324) is highly respected for his admirable knowledge of insurance coverage law. He is considered *"technically great"* and able to offer a *"well-rounded"* set of skills and knowledge. He has been playing a key role in the Deepwater Horizon oil spill coverage matter, acting on behalf of BP America and related entities. Highly regarded DC player **William Greaney** (see p.325) frequently appears in the front line in prominent arbitration proceedings and mediations. Sources describe him as *"very incisive but agreeable, and extremely clear in the way in which he covers matters."* He recently handled a dispute for National Grid involving a number of environmental coverage lawsuits. **William Skinner** (see p.407) comes highly recommended by peers and clients. He has recently acted on behalf of

| Recommended for Client Service Nationwide | |
| --- | --- |
| Anderson Kill & Olick, P.C. | K&L Gates |
| Covington & Burling LLP | |

| Recommended for Commercial Awareness Nationwide | |
| --- | --- |
| Anderson Kill & Olick, P.C. | Jenner & Block LLP |
| Covington & Burling LLP | Kasowitz, Benson, Torres & Friedman LLP |
| Dickstein Shapiro LLP | |

Chiquita Brands International in a complex coverage case relating to alleged money extortion. **John Buchanan** (see p.855) is a highly thought-of attorney with a solid reputation in the insurance arena. His practice focuses on environmental, pharmaceutical and financial matters on behalf of policyholders. Well-respected San Francisco partner **Lawrence Hobel** (see p.335) practices as a litigator and settlement lawyer on a nationwide scale. He has long-standing experience in representing insureds in environmental and business interruption coverage.

## Band 2

### Anderson Kill & Olick, P.C.
**See profile on p.1954**

**THE FIRM** The firm continues to rank among those leading the pack in the representation of policyholders in insurance cases. While well known in New York, the group also has a presence in DC and California. The team is very active in the areas of environmental, asbestos, business interruption and data breach coverage. It recently secured

## Band 1

### Covington & Burling LLP
**See profile on p.441**

**THE FIRM** This team is firmly settled at the pinnacle of the nationwide insurance policyholder Bar. It enjoys a standout reputation from coast to coast for its leadership in a wide range of coverage matters. In particular, the group regularly plays a central role in asbestos and environmental disputes. The firm is on the front line in the nationwide representation of the NFL in the headline concussions-related lawsuits filed by former players and their relatives.

## Insurance: Dispute Resolution: Policyholder
### Leading Individuals

**Star individuals**

| | |
|---|---|
| Oshinsky Jerold | Jenner & Block LLP * |

**Band 1**

| | |
|---|---|
| Brown Donald W | Covington & Burling LLP * |
| Cohen Robin L | Kasowitz, Benson, Torres & Friedman LLP * |
| Dolin Mitchell F | Covington & Burling LLP * |
| Goodwin David B | Covington & Burling LLP * |
| Greaney William | Covington & Burling LLP * |
| Heintz John | Dickstein Shapiro LLP * |
| Horkovich Robert M | Anderson Kill & Olick, P.C. * |
| Lundberg G Andrew | Latham & Watkins LLP |
| Pasich Kirk A | Dickstein Shapiro LLP * |
| Skinner William P | Covington & Burling LLP * |
| Steuber David W | Jones Day (ONP) † * |
| Vishneski John S | Reed Smith LLP |

**Band 2**

| | |
|---|---|
| Buchanan John | Covington & Burling LLP * |
| Burns Timothy W | Perkins Coie LLP (ONP) † |
| Childress Tyrone R | Jones Day (ONP) † * |
| Cohen Nancy S | Proskauer Rose LLP |
| Halbreich David M | Reed Smith LLP |
| Hobel Lawrence | Covington & Burling LLP * |
| Horton Michel Yves | Morgan, Lewis & Bockius LLP * |
| Masters Lorelie S | Jenner & Block LLP * |
| Passannante William G | Anderson Kill & Olick, P.C. * |
| Plumer Mark J | Orrick, Herrington & Sutcliffe LLP (ONP) † |
| Shugrue John | Reed Smith LLP |
| Zevnik Paul A | Morgan, Lewis & Bockius LLP * |

**Band 3**

| | |
|---|---|
| Berkeley Jill B | Neal, Gerber & Eisenberg LLP (ONP) † * |
| Goldberg Stephen | Dickstein Shapiro LLP * |
| Kellner Leon B | Perkins Coie LLP (ONP) † |
| Reidy Andrew | Dickstein Shapiro LLP * |
| Schafler Seth B | Proskauer Rose LLP |

† *Indicates individual with profile.*
† ONP = Other Notable Practitioner.

a jury victory on behalf of the State of California in a hazardous waste disposal coverage claim.

**Client Service** *"Billing practices are flexible to accommodate client needs."*

**Commercial Awareness** *"That is what they do and what they have done for decades. They really know their stuff. Insureds' matters are in their DNA."*

**KEY INDIVIDUALS** *"Very strong lawyer"* **Robert Horkovich** (see p.336) is recognized in the market for his leading trial and negotiation skills. With an undisputed national presence, he covers asbestos and bankruptcy claims. **William Passannante** (see p.382) remains a *"go-to figure for high-dollar insurance coverage litigation,"* according to clients. His practice focuses on D&O and asbestos-related insurance matters.

### Jenner & Block LLP
See profile on p.1252

**THE FIRM** Clients are extremely pleased with the practical legal advice offered by this firm. With a strong presence in California, DC and Illinois, Jenner & Block takes a lead role in insurance disputes all over the country. A recent highlight is their involvement in the Gerald Sandusky scandal. The group is acting on behalf of Penn State University in insurance coverage issues related to the $2 billion multiple claims and investigations arising out of the sexual misconduct allegations made against Gerald Sandusky.

**Commercial Awareness** *"They delve into issues well and have depth of understanding. That is the most helpful skill, giving me the perspective I need."*

**KEY INDIVIDUALS** Star performer **Jerold Oshinsky** (see p.380) is a *"passionate advocate"* with a wealth of experience in representing insurance policyholders in long exposure matters. He was recently involved in the Tyson Foods environmental coverage litigation involving chicken waste contamination. *"Very strong lawyer."* **Lorelie Masters** (see p.880) is a much-admired practitioner, with impressive expertise in the London market and Bermuda Form arbitrations.

### Kasowitz, Benson, Torres & Friedman LLP
See profile on p.1983

**THE FIRM** This New York-headquartered firm has quickly established itself at the heart of the insurance marketplace. The team is lauded for its work on behalf of insureds in connection to mass torts, environment, asbestos, product liability and professional liability matters. The firm's client list includes Syracuse University, Visa and Philips.

**Commercial Awareness** *"They are clearly experts in their field – they know the players and the law." "They are exceptionally well prepared, they are bright and knowledgeable, and they are willing to consider all suggestions to produce an excellent result."*

**KEY INDIVIDUALS** Highly regarded litigator **Robin Cohen** (see p.297) rises to the top band following an impressive year representing policyholders in insurance coverage disputes. Sources state that *"she is outstanding in all aspects, whether it is communicating with the client, with opposing counsel or with the court."* She is also described as *"exceptionally well prepared, dedicated, thorough, smart, knowledgeable and persuasive."*

### Reed Smith LLP

**THE FIRM** This outstanding international powerhouse is a widely recognized player on the policyholder side of insurance coverage disputes. Clients appreciate the small-firm feel they get while having access to all the resources they need. Historically strong in the toxic tort arena, Reed Smith also has a key focus in the financial, life sciences and energy and natural resources sectors. The firm was recently retained by Anadarko in connection with the explosion of the Deepwater Horizon drilling rig in the Gulf of Mexico.

**Sources say:** *"They are one of the firms that have the depth and breadth of experience that most other firms do not have. I have been impressed by way they approach a case, and by their knowledge."*

**KEY INDIVIDUALS** Chicago leader **John Vishneski** enjoys *"a very good reputation"* in the insurance arena. He is known for his expertise in mortgage insurance matters and first-party property. He recently acted for Bank of America in a matter relating to the resort and casino complex Fontainebleau, a failed construction project in Las Vegas. Also in Chicago, the highly regarded **John Shugrue's** expertise ranges from fiduciary liability to product recall issues, with particular knowledge of the energy and natural resources industry. Recent clients include the Tribune Company and Anadarko. Los Angeles-based **David Halbreich** recently acted for Bank of America/Countrywide in a complex mortgage-related insurance dispute. According to clients, he is *"a very smart guy, very personable, and somebody who puts a great effort into client service."*

**Band 3**

### Dickstein Shapiro LLP
See profile on p.911

**THE FIRM** This long-standing insurance group remains an active player representing policyholders on both coasts. The firm is engaged in insurance coverage matters relating to business interruption, political risk, environmental disasters and professional liability claims. Dickstein Shapiro is often involved in headline cases such as the Beebe Medical Center matter, in which it represented the hospital that had employed pediatrician Dr Earl Bradley, convicted of sexual abuse of over 100 minors, dealing with the insurance aspects concerning the victims.

**Commercial Awareness** *"They are second to none in terms of knowledge and skill on coverage issues. They are aggressive and creative, and the carriers know that they are willing to fight to get the coverage for which their insureds bargained."*

**KEY INDIVIDUALS** Widely respected DC partner **John Heintz** (see p.332) is applauded for his *"enormous amount of common sense and credibility."* Clients appreciate how he is *"always candid with his assessment of the situation without overstating strengths, and clearly outlines options."* **Kirk Pasich** (see p.382) is *"the anchor of the practice in California,"* and appears *"on anyone's list of top policyholder lawyers."* He has deep experience in dealing with insurance coverage matters, and is especially known in the entertainment industry. Also on the West Coast, **Stephen Goldberg** (see p.322) is a *"strong lawyer"* who comes highly recommended by commentators. His practice focuses on the representation of policyholders in D&O, E&O and business interruption liability disputes. DC-based **Andrew Reidy** (see p.887) is praised by market sources, who describe him as *"very levelheaded and very helpful in laying out the pros and cons and various courses of action."*

### K&L Gates
See profile on p.2245

**THE FIRM** This client favorite continues to flourish on a nationwide scale from its headquarters in Pennsylvania. The firm is active in the representation of policyholders in a range of disputes, including D&O, product liability, environmental and employment coverage matters. K&L Gates has recently counseled significant clients including Guess, Universal Music Group, Alcoa and Babcock & Wilcox.

**Client Service** *"They are very client-oriented. They have listened to what the company needs, they are very concerned with costs, and they have kept us very well informed. They are responsive and available."*

**KEY INDIVIDUALS** Pittsburgh-based litigator Thomas Birsic is the practice contact.

## Latham & Watkins LLP

See profile on p.446

**THE FIRM** An 11-office nationwide insurance network possessing international offices across Asia, Europe and the Middle East allows this firm to maintain a robust presence in the market. Latham & Watkins advises policyholders on insurance coverage issues, from environmental coverage to professional liability matters. The team has recently handled complex asbestos claims on behalf of Fluor related to bodily injuries caused by exposure on construction sites. Other notable clients include Westfield, Los Angeles Dodgers and Montrose Chemical.

**Sources say:** *"They have a large resource base, which enables them to respond promptly."*

**KEY INDIVIDUALS** Global practice cochair **Andrew Lundberg** receives much praise from peers and clients, who describe him as *"outstanding," "very savvy"* and *"very inventive."* He has served as lead counsel for Rockwell Automation, Meritor and Invensys in asbestos coverage litigation with over 25,000 underlying lawsuits.

## Morgan, Lewis & Bockius LLP

See profile on p.2246

**THE FIRM** This team is well known for its extensive expertise in the insurance arena, with 16 offices across the USA. Attorneys are able to advise on coverage matters including property and casualty, D&O and toxic tort matters. The team recently led a high-stakes asbestos and environmental coverage litigation representing PepsiCo relating to discontinued operations. Other key clients include Sunoco, Kimberly-Clark and Kraft.

**Sources say:** *"High marks for creativity and strategic thought."*

**KEY INDIVIDUALS** *"Outstanding attorney"* **Michel Yves Horton** (see p.337) comes highly recommended by market sources. He played an instrumental role in a number of big-ticket asbestos coverage matters, including acting on behalf of PepsiCo and Goulds Pumps. **Paul Zevnik** (see p.431) impresses clients, who describe him as *"very energetic, very articulate, proactive"* and with *"good common sense."* He recently secured a settlement for United Technologies in two coverage disputes involving complex corporate transactions, retrospective premium obligations and asbestos liabilities.

## Proskauer Rose LLP

See profile on p.2001

**THE FIRM** With eight offices nationwide, Proskauer Rose has a robust presence across the country. Particularly prominent in New York, the team is at the forefront of cases relating to financial issues. A top-drawer client list includes JPMorgan Chase, Credit Suisse Securities, Foot Locker and Alpha Therapeutic.

**Sources say:** *"Very good, experienced lawyers."*

**KEY INDIVIDUALS** Highly sought-after **Nancy Cohen** is a reputable litigator with extensive experience in trying cases before juries. Sources applaud her courtroom style, saying she is a *"real tough, hard-nosed litigator, who by sheer force of her determination gets very good outcomes."* *"Fine*

*lawyer"* **Seth Schafler** is active in the insurance coverage space. Sources emphasize his commercial approach with clients. His policyholder practice ranges from mutual funds to life insurance matters.

## Other Notable Practitioners

Wisconsin-based **Timothy Burns** of Perkins Coie LLP is lauded as a good strategist by his clients. His practice focuses on D&O liability coverage matters, class actions and business interruption losses. Also at Perkins Coie, **Leon Kellner** works from the firm's DC office. He has been busy representing the Tennessee Valley Authority in a dispute against its property and liability insurers concerning a $1 billion loss. Los Angeles-based **David Steuber** (see p.412) of Jones Day stands out as *"one of best lawyers in the USA,"* according to market commentators. He often assists policyholder clients with toxic tort, environmental, fidelity bond and construction defect insurance coverage claims as part of a broad practice. Client favorite **Tyrone Childress** (see p.294) of Jones Day's Los Angeles office is *"expert with his knowledge of the intricacies of insurance recovery."* He has recently acted as lead counsel for Dell in a copyright infringement insurance coverage action against Lloyd's. Highly recommended DC partner **Mark Plumer** of Orrick, Herrington & Sutcliffe LLP is experienced in representing policyholders in insurance coverage matters, particularly in environmental disputes. Sources highlight that *"he is very knowledgeable, experienced and effective."* Chair of the firm's insurance policyholder practice group, **Jill Berkeley** (see p.1198) of Neal, Gerber & Eisenberg LLP in Chicago is recognized by peers as having a *"great stature nationally"* and being *"a pillar of the policyholder community."* Her recent clients include Ameren and ExxonMobil.

---

# INSURANCE TRANSACTIONAL & REGULATORY

Commentary about individuals can be found under their firm's paragraph. If the firm has no paragraph (is not ranked) look at Other Notable Practitioners.

| Insurance: Transactional & Regulatory |
| --- |
| **Leading Firms** |
| **Band 1** |
| Debevoise & Plimpton LLP * |
| Sidley Austin LLP * |
| Willkie Farr & Gallagher LLP * |
| **Band 2** |
| Skadden, Arps, Slate, Meagher & Flom LLP & Affiliates * |
| Sullivan & Cromwell LLP * |
| **Band 3** |
| Dentons * |
| Sutherland Asbill & Brennan LLP |

*Indicates firm with profile.*
*Alphabetical order within each band. Band 1 is the highest.*

## Band 1

### Debevoise & Plimpton LLP

See profile on p.1968

**THE FIRM** This established New York M&A firm is one of the nationwide leaders in transactional and regulatory insurance matters. Sources particularly highlight its commanding position in the life insurance sector, illustrated by its work for Prudential Financial in the acquisition of The Hartford's individual life insurance business. In another significant deal, the team advised on Goldman Sachs Reinsurance Group's acquisition of Ariel Holdings' Bermuda-based reinsurance operations.

**Commercial Awareness** *"They are strong in industry knowledge, and in transactional skills and experience."*

**KEY INDIVIDUALS** Peers strongly praise **Nicholas Potter**, who *"thinks in the right way about the transaction and the clients."* His work is highly respected in the life

| Recommended for Client Service | |
| --- | --- |
| **Nationwide** | |
| Sidley Austin LLP | Skadden, Arps, Slate, Meagher & Flom LLP & Affiliates |

| Recommended for Commercial Awareness | |
| --- | --- |
| **Nationwide** | |
| Debevoise & Plimpton LLP | Willkie Farr & Gallagher LLP |
| Sidley Austin LLP | |

insurance and fund areas. His clients include Prudential Financial and Pan-American Life Insurance. **Thomas Kelly** is described by one source as a *"strong, thoughtful and well-rounded insurance-focused transactional lawyer."* He has assisted the Principal Financial Group in its $1.5 billion acquisition of Chilean pension manager Cuprum. Of counsel **Wolcott Dunham** is considered by many to be *"the dean of transactional work"* in New York, and a lawyer who has *"heavily influenced and shaped law in demutualization."*

## Sidley Austin LLP

See profile on p.1264

**THE FIRM** This firm has moved to expand its team and maintain an imposing presence in both the Midwest and in New York. Sidley Austin has particular strength in M&A, life settlement insurance, insurance securitisation and private equity funds. One recent highlight is the firm's representation of Transatlantic Reinsurance in a $3.4 billion merger deal with Alleghany Corporation. The team regularly represents a series of major industry clients and financial institutions, including Aegon, UBS and Morgan Stanley.

**Client Service** *"They provide strong legal advice tailored to the goals of our firm, and they provide excellent responsive service."*

**Commercial Awareness** *"The key factors that we enjoy in dealing with them are their authority and their judgment. Their depth of understanding of issues and judgment is excellent, and comes from deep, deep experience."*

**KEY INDIVIDUALS** New York insurance practice head **Jeff Liebmann** (see p.356) is particularly experienced in life insurance and insolvency matters. Clients are impressed by his knowledge base and remark how *"he has it at his fingertips, and is very on top of things."* **Jonathan Freedman** (see p.316) is active in the insurance insolvency, regulatory and life fields, and sources have *"tremendous respect for him."* He has recently assisted Credit Suisse Securities in a $300 million senior notes issuance by Montpelier Re. He is also based in New York. Co-head of the firm's global insurance and financial services group **Michael Goldman** (see p.1209) is a known and respected player in the market, particularly in his Chicago base. He

recently acted as lead counsel in Transatlantic Reinsurance's merger transaction with Alleghany. Chicago partner **Perry Shwachman** debuts in the nationwide rankings following strong market feedback. He is a renowned practitioner in the insurance and reinsurance finance space.

## Willkie Farr & Gallagher LLP

See profile on p.2016

**THE FIRM** This New York firm rises to the top of the rankings following a year of consistently impressive performances. The team has gone from strength to strength following an influx of major lateral hires from the now-defunct Dewey & LeBoeuf. The expanded practice group's expertise spans now from M&A, capital markets, structured finance and reinsurance to regulatory and tax matters. Its impressive client portfolio includes Zurich Financial, MetLife, Aviva, Aegon and Aspen.

**Commercial Awareness** *"We have used them as counsel on numerous debt and equity underwritings, as well as M&A counsel. They are all excellent lawyers – knowledgeable, transaction-oriented and responsive. True problem solvers."*

**KEY INDIVIDUALS Alexander Dye** (see p.307) comes wholeheartedly recommended by peers and clients alike, who describe him as a *"very bright, down-to-business"* attorney. He is very active in the New York transactional space. **Michael Groll** (see p.326) is highly trusted by clients, who describe him as *"probably the best for client service in the industry."* He also earns great respect among his peers, who laud his *"stellar reputation in the industry."* **Donald Henderson** (see p.333) is *"one of the best technicians out there,"* according to sources. His field of expertise covers a series of major financial transactions. He acts for clients including The Prudential, Assurant and Ariel Reinsurance. The *"very talented"* **John Schwolsky** (see p.1939) has recently represented MetLife in the big-ticket sale of Caribbean and Central American-based Alico Operations to Pan-American Life Insurance. His practice focuses on corporate matters on a national and international scale.

## Band 2

## Skadden, Arps, Slate, Meagher & Flom LLP & Affiliates

See profile on p.2008

**THE FIRM** This corporate powerhouse has a healthy reputation in related insurance deals. With eight offices nationwide, the firm has a strong presence across the country, and is identified by commentators for its involvement in sophisticated securitization and M&A work. The group has been active in securing high-stakes deals for the likes of Merrill Lynch, Jackson National Life Insurance and Barclays Bank.

**Client Service** *"Their client communication was exemplary, and their preparedness and counsel clearly made a difference in the transaction outcome."*

**KEY INDIVIDUALS** New York partner **Robert Sullivan** (see p.414) is considered to be one of the top insurance

M&A practitioners in the country. Sources comment that *"he never loses focus of the business objective, and works creatively to get both sides where they want to go."* They add that *"he has great knowledge of the regulatory environment and how to avoid regulatory pitfalls."*

## Sullivan & Cromwell LLP

See profile on p.2011

**THE FIRM** This New York firm remains one of the US insurance industry's go-to providers for transactional services, with expertise spanning from M&A to capital markets. Sources highlight Sullivan & Cromwell's influential presence in major deals across the insurance market. The team has recently been involved in the sale of a portion of Swiss Re's Admin Re division, and is involved in a number of big-ticket deals on behalf of ING and AIG.

**Sources say:** *"We are very satisfied. They are very knowledgeable about insurance coverage issues, very smart, very responsive and very good at what they do."*

**KEY INDIVIDUALS** *"Outstanding"* regulatory and securities lawyer **Andrew Rowen** (see p.1933) is considered among commentators to be *"very influential on insurance transactions."* He has recently played an instrumental role in Swiss Re's $900 million sale of one of its divisions.

## Band 3

## Dentons

See profile on p.449

**THE FIRM** With impressive resources across the nation and worldwide, this firm offers the full range of insurance regulatory services to clients. Alongside a strong California presence, Dentons has 15 offices across the USA. The group remains strong in the reinsurance space, where it advises clients, including Fortune 500 companies, on regulatory matters.

**Sources say:** *"Lawyers are top notch in their field and are recognized as such in the industry. They have the right relationship and expertise."*

**KEY INDIVIDUALS** Head of the firm's insurance regulation practice, San Francisco partner Kara Baysinger works on regulatory and transactional matters on behalf of clients in the insurance and reinsurance space.

## Sutherland Asbill & Brennan LLP

**THE FIRM** This group has a significant presence on the East Coast as well as being prominent in the Texas and Georgia markets. The firm's core expertise focuses on the insurance aspects of property and casualty, captive insurance and financial services. Well-known clients include The Hartford, Swiss Re and Lloyd's. Sources particularly praise the team's expertise in the captive insurance and taxation space.

**KEY INDIVIDUALS David Massey** is based in DC and has a well-recognized position in the insurance transactional space. His client portfolio includes The Hartford, Cetera Financial and Wilton Re. He has recently co-advised The Hartford in the $615 million sale of its individual life business to Prudential Financial. Co-head of the firm's insurance transactions and products practice and leader of the financial services practice, DC partner **Stephen Roth** focuses his work on life insurance matters. He has served as lead counsel advising the Committee of Annuity Insurers in connection to rule proposals and initiatives, including the Dodd-Frank Act and FINRA.

## Other Notable Practitioners

**Paul Meyer** (see p.1919) of Clifford Chance US LLP's New York office is held in high regard by his clients for being *"very well informed"* on complex industry issues affecting insurance transactions. His niche is in life insurance, where he has recently been advising General Motors Asset Management on the restructuring of its pension plan's group annuity contracts. **Thomas Jones** (see p.1213) of McDermott Will & Emery LLP in Chicago is a recognized captive insurance expert, with experience in dealing with related tax and insurance regulatory aspects. His clients are mainly within the healthcare, construction and insurance industries.

# INTELLECTUAL PROPERTY

Commentary about individuals can be found under their firm's paragraph. If the firm has no paragraph (is not ranked) look at Other Notable Practitioners.

## Intellectual Property
### Leading Firms

**Band 1**
Finnegan, Henderson, Farabow, Garrett & Dunner LLP *
Fish & Richardson PC
Kirkland & Ellis LLP *
WilmerHale *

**Band 2**
Covington & Burling LLP *
Fitzpatrick, Cella, Harper & Scinto *
Irell & Manella *
Jones Day *
Morrison & Foerster LLP *
Quinn Emanuel Urquhart & Sullivan, LLP
Ropes & Gray LLP *
Sidley Austin LLP *
Weil, Gotshal & Manges LLP *

**Band 3**
Baker Botts LLP *
Cooley LLP
DLA Piper LLP (US) *
Keker & Van Nest LLP
Latham & Watkins LLP *
McDermott Will & Emery LLP *
McKool Smith *
Orrick, Herrington & Sutcliffe LLP *

**Band 4**
Cravath, Swaine & Moore LLP *
Fulbright & Jaworski LLP *
Goodwin Procter LLP *
Haynes and Boone, LLP *
Kaye Scholer LLP *
Kenyon & Kenyon LLP
Knobbe Martens Olson & Bear
Perkins Coie LLP
Skadden, Arps, Slate, Meagher & Flom LLP & Affiliates *
Vinson & Elkins LLP *

* *Indicates firm with profile.*
*Alphabetical order within each band. Band 1 is the highest.*

## Intellectual Property:
### Trademark, Copyright & Trade Secrets
### Leading Firms

**Band 1**
Arnold & Porter LLP *
Debevoise & Plimpton LLP *
Fross Zelnick Lehrman & Zissu PC *

**Band 2**
Arent Fox LLP *
Kilpatrick Townsend & Stockton LLP *

**Band 3**
Foley & Lardner LLP *

## Recommended for Client Service
### Nationwide

| | |
|---|---|
| Arent Fox LLP | Jones Day |
| Arnold & Porter LLP | Kenyon & Kenyon LLP |
| Covington & Burling LLP | Kilpatrick Townsend & Stockton LLP |
| Debevoise & Plimpton LLP | Sidley Austin LLP |
| Fish & Richardson PC | Skadden, Arps, Slate, Meagher & Flom LLP & Affiliates |
| Irell & Manella | |

## Recommended for Commercial Awareness
### Nationwide

| | |
|---|---|
| Covington & Burling LLP | Quinn Emanuel Urquhart & Sullivan, LLP |
| Fish & Richardson PC | Ropes & Gray LLP |
| Fross Zelnick Lehrman & Zissu | Vinson & Elkins LLP |
| Kirkland & Ellis LLP | WilmerHale |
| Latham & Watkins LLP | |

## Band 1
### Intellectual Property

### Finnegan, Henderson, Farabow, Garrett & Dunner LLP
See profile on p.912
**THE FIRM** This firm has a truly comprehensive, first-class IP practice which receives plaudits for both its geographical reach as well as the range of its skills. It is one of the largest firms devoted to IP in the USA, and is staffed by a veritable army of experts in all manner of scientific disciplines and industry sectors. In addition to its noncontentious work and formidable prowess in state and federal courts, the firm is also noted as a leader in Section 337 actions before the ITC. It has clients such as Philips, Caterpillar, Yahoo! and Starbucks.
**Sources say:** *"A high standard of quality of service across the firm." "A fantastic firm."*
**KEY INDIVIDUALS** Donald Dunner, well known for his skills as a litigator and an adviser to technology-reliant companies, is based in the firm's DC office.

### Fish & Richardson PC
**THE FIRM** Fish & Richardson is one of the world's largest IP and technology-focused law firms, so no case or matter, however legally or technically complex, is beyond the ken of the attorneys based in offices throughout the country. Its lawyers have argued cases at all levels of the US court system, and are regularly before the courts on some of the most competitive IP hotspots. Clients include Allergan, Honda, Microsoft and Samsung Electronics.
**Commercial Awareness** *"Each attorney has deep knowledge and an excellent strategic view."*
**Client Service** *"They're just so reliable in terms of meeting targets, budgets and deadlines – there are never any surprises."*
**KEY INDIVIDUALS** Ruffin Cordell, based in the DC office, is one of the firm's most celebrated IP litigators.

### Kirkland & Ellis LLP
See profile on p.1254
**THE FIRM** One of the top IP practices in the country, this group is known in particular for taking on heavyweight, precedent-setting cases. It has a nationwide structure and so staffs matters from the pick of its offices across the country. The firm's already muscular patent litigation practice, traditionally weighted toward high-technology electronics, has in recent years been boosted by the recruitment of top partners specializing in life sciences. Its clients range from the Associated Press, Colgate-Palmolive and Fox Entertainment to IBM and the Tetris Company.
**Commercial Awareness** *"Everyone there knows what's going on, and we get answers really quickly. From a strategy perspective they are one of the most creative firms."*

**KEY INDIVIDUALS** William Streff, one of the cochairs of the IP practice, is based in Chicago, while Robert Krupka in Los Angeles is one of the firm's premier IP litigators.

## WilmerHale
See profile on p.930

**THE FIRM** Clients and peers consistently acclaim WilmerHale as one of the highest quality and most comprehensive nationwide IP practices. Its offices all over the country brim with talent and resources and it is particularly well known for the caliber of its litigators, although this does not overshadow the quality of its work regarding the registration, exploitation and transfer of IP assets. Clients include Abbott Laboratories, Cisco Systems, Intel and Procter & Gamble.

**Commercial Awareness** *"They bring especially strong trial skills and couple that with some very well-reasoned and shrewd strategic counseling skills as well."*

**KEY INDIVIDUALS** Boston-based William Lee has a national reputation as a patent litigator and trial lawyer.

## Band 2
## Intellectual Property

## Covington & Burling LLP
See profile on p.441

**THE FIRM** Covington & Burling has offices in New York and DC on the East Coast, and San Diego, San Francisco and Silicon Valley on the West, and so offers excellent local and national coverage. The group has an established reputation for high-stakes patent litigation and actions before the ITC on behalf of clients such as AstraZeneca, Hewlett-Packard and SAMSUNG.

**Client Service** *"They were very responsive to our direction and flexible in approach."*

**Commercial Awareness** *"We rate the depth of the local legal team to handle multiple time-critical issues in multiple venues, and the depth of the overall firm's resources and the technical knowledge of the attorneys relevant to our business."*

**KEY INDIVIDUALS** Christopher Sipes in DC and Robert Fram in San Francisco cochair the IP department.

## Fitzpatrick, Cella, Harper & Scinto
See profile on p.1973

**THE FIRM** This firm is dedicated solely to IP and technology law from offices in New York, DC and Orange County. It offers a full and highly polished IP service, from registration, enforcement and transactional matters through to litigation. The firm is particularly well known for its excellent patent litigation skills, not least with regard to pharmaceutical and life sciences cases. Clients include AstraZeneca, IBM, Merck and Sanofi.

**Sources say:** *"The firm really stands out."*

**KEY INDIVIDUALS** Robert Baechtold, in New York, is a leading life sciences litigation expert.

## Irell & Manella
See profile on p.686

**THE FIRM** From its base in California, Irell & Manella has built a renowned practice which attracts both national and international clients. The firm handles litigation on the full spectrum of IP rights for clients in high-technology electronics, life sciences and pharmaceuticals and also maintains a busy prosecution practice. Clients include Ariosa Diagnostics, Research In Motion and TiVo.

**Client Service** *"They deliver what they promise and often exceed my expectations."*

**KEY INDIVIDUALS** Morgan Chu, based in Los Angeles, is a much-admired IP litigator and key partner at the firm.

## Jones Day
See profile on p.919

**THE FIRM** Jones Day's IP practice group offers a comprehensive, high-quality service to leading technology and brand-reliant companies from offices throughout the country. As well as high-stakes patent litigation, the group is well respected for its work in non-patent disputes, and its noncontentious transactional and prosecution services are noted for their sophistication and accomplishment. Life sciences and high-technology companies of multinational reach are key clients, such as Apple, BMW, Celgene, IBM and Johnson & Johnson.

**Client Service** *"They are very responsive and have delivered great work product under intense time pressure."*

**KEY INDIVIDUALS** Brian Poissant in Washington, DC and Anthony Insogna in San Diego chair the global practice group.

## Morrison & Foerster LLP
See profile on p.1990

**THE FIRM** This large and distinguished practice group has a very strong market presence, above all in California and Washington, DC. The formidable IP litigation practice has been at the forefront of some of the most significant high-technology and life sciences cases: notably, it acted for Bayer HealthCare where a federal court found that certain patents were not enforceable against Bayer due to the principle of inequitable conduct. The case has attracted considerable attention. The group's accomplished copyright, patent and trademark prosecution and transactional resources are also well regarded.

**KEY INDIVIDUALS** Rachel Krevans and Michael Ward, both based in San Francisco, are the group practice heads.

## Quinn Emanuel Urquhart & Sullivan, LLP

**THE FIRM** Quinn Emanuel's IP litigation group is widely considered in the market to be one of the best in the country. Its expanding DC office is a reflection of the group's increased presence in the ITC, adding further luster to its reputation. It has handled a number of high-profile cases in the past year and includes Genentech, Google, IBM and Sony Corporation of America among its clients.

**Commercial Awareness** *"We work with them regularly because they all have similarly deep knowledge of the patent system and our business and know how to get the job done."*

**KEY INDIVIDUALS** Ed DeFranco in New York and David Nelson in Chicago cochair the national IP litigation practice.

## Ropes & Gray LLP
See profile on p.1528

**THE FIRM** Ropes & Gray's IP group covers the spectrum of litigation, prosecution, and technology and IP-related transactional work. Some of the biggest technology-driven and brand-reliant names in the world rely on the firm for work in all these areas, and the group's trial lawyers are seasoned veterans of major litigations in the nation's most competitive jurisdictions. The group's prestigious client roster includes Bayer HealthCare, Hyundai Motor America, Pfizer and Ricoh Americas.

**Commercial Awareness** *"The firm is particularly well situated to add value to complex, high-value matters."*

**KEY INDIVIDUALS** Gene Lee is an IP litigation practice leader based in New York.

## Sidley Austin LLP
See profile on p.1264

**THE FIRM** This global firm has talented IP lawyers based all over the country, and its litigators fight some of the toughest actions. The IP group is particularly well known for its depth and breadth of expertise and trial experience in cases involving life sciences and consumer electronics. One highlight saw the team win a Bench trial on behalf of Merck, upholding the validity of a patent covering the client's blockbuster drugs Zetia and Vytorin.

**Client Service** *"I have used patent prosecution firms and several litigation firms and the level of service and expertise at Sidley is unsurpassed."*

**KEY INDIVIDUALS** David Pritikin in Chicago chairs the firm's national practice.

## Weil, Gotshal & Manges LLP
See profile on p.2015

**THE FIRM** Weil Gotshal's national IP group is located in key areas of the country such as Silicon Valley, Texas, New York and DC. The group is noted for its command of high-technology electronics matters, and continues to grow its life sciences practice. It also has a very active copyright, trademarks and music licensing practice led from the New York office. Clients include Apple, eBay, Merck and HarperCollins Publishers.

**Sources say:** *"Weil Gotshal has some of the best and most talented lawyers."*

**KEY INDIVIDUALS** Jared Bobrow chairs the firm's patent litigation practice from the Silicon Valley office.

## Band 3
## Intellectual Property

## Baker Botts LLP
See profile on p.2427

**THE FIRM** This practice is well known for its patent litigation skills, although this view overlooks the sterling work done by its attorneys in patent prosecution, licensing and the handling of IP assets in M&A. The group also offers a real depth of technical expertise serving clients in industries such as energy, life sciences, and consumer and high-technology electronics. Clients include AT&T, Cisco Systems, Facebook and Brother Industries.

**Sources say:** *"A very formidable force to have on your side."*
**KEY INDIVIDUALS** Bart Showalter, in Dallas, leads the firm's IP practice.

## Cooley LLP

**THE FIRM** Headquartered in Palo Alto, Cooley maintains its reputation for taking on some big-ticket patent litigation for clients in the high-technology, software and life sciences fields. The firm assists tech startups as well as established businesses, giving them the added benefit of its considerable resources in prosecution, portfolio and brand management. In recent work, the group has handled a number of patent infringement matters for Facebook and also counts LinkedIn, Lonely Planet, Onyx Pharmaceuticals and HTC among its clients.
**KEY INDIVIDUALS** Based in Broomfield, Colorado, Jim Brogan chairs Cooley's IP practice.

## DLA Piper LLP (US)
See profile on p.1971

**THE FIRM** This international firm continues to consolidate its position among the best IP firms in the USA, and its cohort of talented attorneys is growing apace. The group's patent litigation bench is impressive and is engaged in challenging cases for leaders in technology and life sciences, while its copyright and trademarks practice is spearheaded by acknowledged leaders in brand management and protection. In recent work, it acted for CSR subsidiary Zoran in an ITC matter and for Motorola Mobility and Time Warner Cable in a patent enforcement case.
**Sources say:** *"They are real experts at IP. Their engagement is very proactive; they have caught things that other providers haven't picked up on."*
**KEY INDIVIDUALS** John Allcock, who divides his time between San Diego and Palo Alto, chairs the IP and technology group; Ann Ford, who is based in DC and New York, leads the firm's trademarks, copyright and media practice.

## Keker & Van Nest LLP

**THE FIRM** Although based in San Francisco, Keker & Van Nest's reputation extends well beyond the Bay Area. This bespoke litigation group has a loyal client following including market leaders in the life sciences, high-technology electronics and software fields who rely on its attorneys to win business-critical trials in the various 'rocket dockets' for IP disputes nationwide. Clients include Electronic Arts, Facebook, HTC and Medtronic.
**Sources say:** *"Very good trial attorneys."*
**KEY INDIVIDUALS** Robert Van Nest is a highly respected IP litigator.

## Latham & Watkins LLP
See profile on p.446

**THE FIRM** This international firm has a network of offices throughout the USA and its IP group undertakes the full range of IP work involving utility and design patents, from prosecution and portfolio management to litigation and trials at the highest level. The firm as a whole has a strong appellate practice, and its IP litigators are augmenting its presence and reputation with regard to ITC Section 337 hearings.
**Commercial Awareness** *"Latham made it a point to understand our business objectives and pursued the litigation with those objectives as paramount."*
**KEY INDIVIDUALS** Maximilian Grant and Perry Viscounty are cochairs of the IP litigation practice group based in DC and Los Angeles respectively.

## McDermott Will & Emery LLP
See profile on p.1258

**THE FIRM** This firm's IP offering is highly polished and comprehensive, with deep resources devoted to specialist representation in matters litigious and noncontentious regarding copyright, trademarks and patents. The group acts for companies operating in all sectors of the industrial landscape and has long-standing engagements from high-technology clients from Asia and the Pacific Rim as well as US corporates. Of late, the team is handling a number of cases for Siemens, including defending the Germany-based engineering conglomerate in a patent infringement case.
**Sources say:** *"They are very responsive to our needs and are aware of and sensitive to the internal workings of our company."*
**KEY INDIVIDUALS** Sarah Columbia in Boston chairs the firm's global IP litigation practice group.

## McKool Smith
See profile on p.2446

**THE FIRM** McKool Smith is gaining increasing national prominence beyond the firm's Texas heartland. Already a go-to practice for clients dealing with the 'rocket docket' Eastern District of Texas, McKool Smith and its trial team is much sought after for its patents skills in state and federal courts nationwide, and for representations before the ITC. The team is sought out by clients such as American Airlines, Ericsson, Massachusetts Institute of Technology and WiLAN.
**KEY INDIVIDUALS** Mike McKool in Dallas is a principal and founding partner.

## Orrick, Herrington & Sutcliffe LLP
See profile on p.1994

**THE FIRM** This comprehensive practice has an excellent pool of talented and seasoned lawyers based across the country. While its noncontentious offering is highly accomplished, it is perhaps best known for its litigation prowess, having represented clients at all levels of US courts and the ITC. Notable work from the past year includes handling a number of matters for Microsoft including a patent infringement case.

**Sources say:** *"A very professional, accurate, caring and sincere high-class service."*
**KEY INDIVIDUALS** Neel Chatterjee in San Francisco and Steven Routh in Washington, DC together head the IP department.

## Band 4

## Cravath, Swaine & Moore LLP
See profile on p.1966

**THE FIRM** Based in New York, this firm is small relative to some of the international giants; however, it is roundly recognized as a litigation practice of the highest quality. Although patent litigation for life sciences and high-technology electronics companies is the IP group's mainstay, the firm undertakes copyright and trademarks cases and often bests firms many times its size.
**Sources say:** *"I was very impressed with the level of focus that they can maintain."*
**KEY INDIVIDUALS** Evan Chesler is the firm's presiding partner.

## Fulbright & Jaworski LLP
See profile on p.2435

**THE FIRM** This Texas-based firm has tremendous resources across the USA and internationally from which the IP group benefits while still being attuned to the realities of the local jurisdictions. This full-service group handles a range of patent, trademark, domain name and anti-counterfeiting matters, including prosecution matters and portfolio management. Its clientele includes General Mills, Louis Vuitton, Mars and The Capital Group Companies.
**KEY INDIVIDUALS** James Repass heads the department from the Houston office.

## Goodwin Procter LLP
See profile on p.1522

**THE FIRM** This full-service practice takes on disputes and noncontentious work across the range of IP rights. It is widely recognized as being one of the leading firms in the country for Hatch-Waxman Act litigation on behalf of generic pharmaceuticals companies. The group has strong client followings in the high-technology electronics and software arenas as well as in financial services. Key clients include Hewlett-Packard, JPMorgan Chase and Teva.
**Sources say:** *"They just have a very deep bench and they leave no stone unturned."*
**KEY INDIVIDUALS** Boston-based Anthony Downs chairs the IP litigation group.

## Haynes and Boone, LLP
See profile on p.444

**THE FIRM** This Texas firm continues to cut a dash in the national IP landscape, ever growing and developing its capability in offices throughout the country. The group is noted for its achievements in major patent disputes, but also places a strong emphasis on patent prosecution and reexaminations. The group's copyright and trademark expertise is also an area of growth, particularly at the firm's recently opened New York office.

**KEY INDIVIDUALS** The firmwide head of IP is Dallas-based Randall Brown.

## Kaye Scholer LLP
See profile on p.1984

**THE FIRM** With offices in New York, Palo Alto, Los Angeles, DC and Chicago, Kaye Scholer is ideally placed to advise national and international IP-reliant businesses. The group is best known for its high-stakes patent litigation work, as well as for IP-based transactions and agreements, and the treatment of IP rights in the context of M&A. Clients include Amazon.com, GlaxoSmithKline, Time Warner Cable and Pfizer.

**Sources say:** *"They are exceptional attorneys, specialists in their field."*

**KEY INDIVIDUALS** Aaron Stiefel, based in Washington, DC, is cochair of the IP practice group.

## Kenyon & Kenyon LLP

**THE FIRM** Kenyon & Kenyon has offices in New York, Washington, DC and Palo Alto, an excellent geographic spread for a firm devoted to the practice of IP law. The firm is celebrated for its patent litigation work, in particular Hatch-Waxman Act generic pharmaceuticals-related disputes. However, the firm serves leading players in most industries, and has thriving copyright, trademark and patent prosecution practices.

**Client Service** *"They really do put client service first."*

**KEY INDIVIDUALS** Michael Loughnane is the managing partner based in New York.

## Knobbe Martens Olson & Bear

**THE FIRM** This IP and technology specialist firm has several offices in its California heartland as well as Seattle and Washington, DC. The firm has an exhaustive practice, which includes prosecution, transactional, portfolio management and litigation work in all IP rights across a range of industries, with life sciences, electronics and IT being particularly well represented.

**KEY INDIVIDUALS** Joseph Re is a nationally recognized IP litigator based in the firm's Orange County office. Based in Irvine, California, Don Martens is an arbitrator and special master in IP disputes.

## Perkins Coie LLP
See profile on p.2548

**THE FIRM** Perkins Coie has an established reputation on the national IP stage as well as in its Pacific Northwest origins. This is a comprehensive IP service delivered from a host of offices throughout the country, a service which takes in prosecution, technology transfers, and litigation before state and federal courts and the ITC. Clients include Amazon.com, Goldman Sachs and Nintendo.

**KEY INDIVIDUALS** Jonathan James, based in Phoenix, and Michael Wamecke in Chicago cochair the patent litigation practice group.

## Skadden, Arps, Slate, Meagher & Flom LLP & Affiliates
See profile on p.2008

**THE FIRM** This IP group has a reputation for attracting high-stakes, high-value litigation. The group concentrates on major patent disputes in the technology and life sciences spheres, as well as copyright, trademark and related antitrust actions before federal and state courts, as well as the ITC. In one recent highlight, it was successful in defending its client Medtronic in a Bench trial regarding patent infringement accusations.

**Client Service** *"They truly take the client's interests to heart."*

**KEY INDIVIDUALS** Edward Filardi in New York heads the patent litigation practice.

## Vinson & Elkins LLP
See profile on p.2459

**THE FIRM** Vinson & Elkins has a full-service IP practice, with a strong emphasis on patent litigation. Life sciences and pharmaceuticals, hi-tech electronics, semiconductors, internet and digital media are industry sectors within which the firm has a particularly strong reputation. The firm also has a sophisticated IP prosecution, technology transfer and transactions practice.

**Commercial Awareness** *"They are attuned to our commercial interests and understand the need for balance between legal and commercial issues."*

**KEY INDIVIDUALS** David Weaver in Austin and Peter Mims in Houston head the department.

## Band 1

## Arnold & Porter LLP
See profile on p.906

**THE FIRM** Arnold & Porter continues to house leading practices in many of the most important US jurisdictions for IP transactions and litigation. The firm's work with regard to copyright, trademarks and related advertising and branding work is particularly well thought of, and the firm represents leading media, entertainment and fashion clients such as Fox, Google, Gucci America and Disney.

**Client Service** *"They bend over backwards to meet you."*

**KEY INDIVIDUALS** Renowned trademark law specialist Louis Ederer is based in the firm's New York office.

## Debevoise & Plimpton LLP
See profile on p.1968

**THE FIRM** Based primarily in the firm's New York offices, Debevoise & Plimpton has a celebrated practice in anti-counterfeiting, copyright, trade dress and trademark law, attracting high-value and innovative work. Its impressive client roster includes Yves Saint Laurent, Disney and Sony Pictures Entertainment. The team recently advised Prada regarding the luxury brand's campaign to block sales of counterfeit and gray market goods via discount stores and websites.

**Client Service** *"They are pleasant and responsive and they really value service to the client."*

**KEY INDIVIDUALS** Bruce Keller and David Bernstein lead the IP litigation group.

## Fross Zelnick Lehrman & Zissu PC
See profile on p.1976

**THE FIRM** Fross Zelnick is undoubtedly one of the largest and most accomplished firms handling non-patent IP law in the USA and globally. Operating from offices in New York and Washington, DC, the firm's attorneys advise household-name brands on the registration, exploitation and protection of their portfolios at home and in overseas jurisdictions. The firm's litigation capability is well noted, taking on cutting-edge cases which go to the heart of how the internet is changing the landscape affecting copyright, trademarks and other rights. Notable work included successfully defending The Gap in connection with trademark infringement and unfair competition actions.

**Commercial Awareness** *"Their prices are reasonable and the quality we get for it is unmatched." "They work hard to give practical and efficient advice."*

**KEY INDIVIDUALS** Roger Zissu, based in New York, is a founding partner of the firm and one of the most distinguished copyright, trademark and unfair competition experts in the country.

## Band 2
## Intellectual Property: Trademark, Copyright & Trade Secrets

## Arent Fox LLP
See profile on p.905

**THE FIRM** With offices in Washington, DC, New York and Los Angeles, this practice has a full-service offering but is particularly well known for its copyright, trade secrets and trademark practice. The team's stellar client roster includes the likes of Benetton, Mars, NYSE Euronext, Pixar and Warner Bros. Its experience encompasses virtually all industries, from all manner of consumer goods to internet services and life sciences and it is especially active in the media and entertainment fields.

**Client Service** *"They have handled all matters in a measured, informed and responsible fashion, finding creative solutions and expeditious resolutions."*

**KEY INDIVIDUALS** Anthony Lupo, based in the DC office, cochairs the IP practice group.

## Kilpatrick Townsend & Stockton LLP
See profile on p.1109

**THE FIRM** This firm offers a balanced and comprehensive IP service from an extensive yet integrated network of offices from coast to coast. Domestic and international copyright and trademark registration, exploitation and enforcement are notable areas of strength, as are noncontentious and litigious patent work across a range of high-technology industries. Adidas, AT&T, Intercontinental Hotels Group and Logitech are among the group's key clients.

**Client Service** *"The high work ethic, and very present communication skills, make my in-house job possible."*

**KEY INDIVIDUALS** Atlanta-based John Pratt heads up the IP practice.

## Band 3

### Foley & Lardner LLP
See profile on p.2588

**THE FIRM** Foley & Lardner enters the rankings this year on the strength and consistency of the full IP service on offer across its US offices. It handles copyright, trademark and patent matters, both contentious and noncontentious, such as patent prosecution and licensing, and has a particularly polished post-grant and reexamination offering. It attracts clients of the order of Kraft, Toshiba, Google and Unilever.

**Sources say:** *"Foley has excellent lawyers who are well versed in their specialties and take a business approach to IP."*

**KEY INDIVIDUALS** Pavan Agarwal in Washington DC is the head of department.

# INTERNATIONAL ARBITRATION

International Arbitrators p.146
Commentary about individuals can be found under their firm's paragraph. If the firm has no paragraph (is not ranked) look at Other Notable Practitioners.

| International Arbitration |
| --- |
| **Leading Firms** |
| **Band 1** |
| Debevoise & Plimpton LLP * |
| Freshfields Bruckhaus Deringer US LLP * |
| White & Case LLP * |
| **Band 2** |
| Arnold & Porter LLP * |
| Covington & Burling LLP * |
| Hughes Hubbard & Reed LLP * |
| King & Spalding LLP * |
| Skadden, Arps, Slate, Meagher & Flom LLP & Affiliates * |
| WilmerHale * |
| **Band 3** |
| Allen & Overy LLP * |
| Baker Botts LLP * |
| Cleary Gottlieb Steen & Hamilton LLP * |
| Fulbright & Jaworski LLP * |
| Sidley Austin LLP * |
| Simpson Thacher & Bartlett LLP * |
| **Band 4** |
| Astigarraga Davis * |
| Baker & McKenzie * |
| Chadbourne & Parke LLP * |
| Chaffetz Lindsey LLP |
| Shearman & Sterling LLP * |
| Sullivan & Cromwell LLP * |
| Weil, Gotshal & Manges LLP * |
| **Band 5** |
| Crowell & Moring LLP * |
| Curtis, Mallet-Prevost, Colt & Mosle LLP * |
| DLA Piper LLP (US) * |
| Fried, Frank, Harris, Shriver & Jacobson LLP * |
| Hogan Lovells US LLP |
| Jenner & Block LLP * |
| Mayer Brown LLP * |
| Milbank, Tweed, Hadley & McCloy LLP * |
| Morrison & Foerster LLP * |
| Paul Hastings LLP * |
| Quinn Emanuel Urquhart & Sullivan, LLP |

*Indicates firm with profile.*
*Alphabetical order within each band. Band 1 is the highest.*

## Band 1

### Debevoise & Plimpton LLP
See profile on p.1968

**THE FIRM** The international arbitration group at Debevoise enjoys impressive levels of success in its commercial and investment treaty arbitration practice. The practice is held in the highest regard by clients and peers alike for its depth of knowledge and strong global reach. The talented team obtained a $1.77 billion award plus interest on behalf of Occidental, which was seeking damages against the Republic of Ecuador, in one of the most high-profile ICSID arbitrations of recent times. It also counts Tethyan Copper, Perenco and ExxonMobil among its distinguished client base.

**Client Service** *"The work product is stellar: the team is incredibly attentive, works with a common-sense approach and is extremely helpful in dealing with legal and political strategies. Top of the heap – first-class."*

**KEY INDIVIDUALS Donald Francis Donovan** maintains a preeminent reputation as an arbitrator and advocate, and is described by market sources as *"extremely knowledgeable"* and *"hands-on, accessible, client-friendly and extremely hard-working."* His recent work includes representing Detroit International Bridge Company in a $1 billion NAFTA arbitration brought against Canada. **Dietmar Prager** enters the rankings backed by significant praise for his expertise in Latin America-based work, with sources claiming: *"In the near future he will be one of the best lawyers working with matters involving Brazil."* Clients speak highly of his qualities, saying: *"He's dynamic, intelligent, accessible and knowledgeable."* **David Rivkin** has extensive experience in serving as counsel and arbitrator, and demonstrates a particular aptitude for complex, high-stakes disputes. Sources report: *"He has a huge presence in the courtroom and his advocacy skills are without parallel."* He was lead partner on the aforementioned matter for Occidental. **Mark Friedman** has an impressive track record of success as an advocate, with his representation of Perenco Ecuador in a $3.5 billion ICSID arbitration against Ecuador being among his recent highlights. He elicits praise for his *"in-depth knowledge of disputes and corporate and commercial issues,"* and is also commended for *"implementing strategies in the most efficient, top-quality way."* **Catherine Amirfar** particularly impresses clients with her cross-examination skills. She recently began representing Grupo Diniz in an ICC arbitration. She is praised for her *"very proactive and experienced"* approach to matters.

### Freshfields Bruckhaus Deringer US LLP
See profile on p.443

**THE FIRM** With established US bases in New York and DC, this excellent practice is regarded by clients as a first choice for both commercial and investor-state disputes. Equipped with great strength in numbers and plentiful global resources, the group has the breadth and depth required of a market leader. It recently secured a major victory for the Republic of Guatemala in an ICSID arbitration brought by Iberdrola Energía, in which the tribunal rejected the Spanish company's claim and ordered it to reimburse the $5.3 million cost of the proceedings to the Republic. The team also works for investors, and notably represented Crystallex International in $3.2 billion arbitration against Venezuela concerning one of the world's largest untapped gold mines.

**Sources say:** *"The team is well organized and offers very good advice and recommendations."*

**KEY INDIVIDUALS Nigel Blackaby** (see p.284) is widely renowned for his extensive work in the energy sector and in disputes involving Latin America. Sources single out his imaginative ability when it comes to preparing strategy and arguments. Blackaby is currently representing Burlington Resources in an ICSID arbitration against Ecuador. **Brian King** (see p.346) elicits much praise for his work as an advocate and arbitrator. *"He possesses a great understanding of how to prepare for an arbitration,"* report commentators. He is currently representing

| **Recommended for Client Service** | |
| --- | --- |
| **Nationwide** | |
| Chadbourne & Parke LLP | Debevoise & Plimpton LLP |
| Chaffetz Lindsey LLP | |

| **Recommended for Commercial Awareness** | |
| --- | --- |
| **Nationwide** | |
| Chaffetz Lindsey LLP | Covington & Burling LLP |
| Cleary Gottlieb Steen & Hamilton LLP | Milbank, Tweed, Hadley & McCloy LLP |

## International Arbitration
### Senior Statesmen

**Senior Statesmen: distinguished older practitioners**

| | | |
|---|---|---|
| Carter James H | WilmerHale * | |

### Leading Individuals

**Band 1**

| | |
|---|---|
| Astigarraga José I | Astigarraga Davis * |
| Bishop Doak | King & Spalding LLP * |
| Blackaby Nigel | Freshfields Bruckhaus Deringer LLP * |
| Donovan Donald Francis | Debevoise & Plimpton LLP |
| Friedland Paul | White & Case LLP * |
| Lamm Carolyn B | White & Case LLP * |
| Rivkin David W | Debevoise & Plimpton LLP |
| Townsend John M | Hughes Hubbard & Reed LLP * |

**Band 2**

| | |
|---|---|
| Alexandrov Stanimir A | Sidley Austin LLP * |
| Ali Arif H | Weil, Gotshal & Manges LLP * |
| Baker Mark | Fulbright & Jaworski LLP * |
| Bowman John | King & Spalding LLP * |
| Di Rosa Paolo | Arnold & Porter LLP * |
| Fellas John | Hughes Hubbard & Reed LLP * |
| Gardiner John L | Skadden, Arps, Slate, Meagher & Flom * |
| Garibaldi Oscar M | Covington & Burling LLP * |
| Kalicki Jean E | Arnold & Porter LLP * |
| Kehoe Edward | King & Spalding LLP * |
| Lindsey David | Chaffetz Lindsey LLP * |
| Neuhaus Joseph E | Sullivan & Cromwell LLP * |
| Nolan Michael D | Milbank, Tweed, Hadley & McCloy LLP * |
| Shore Laurence | Herbert Smith Freehills (ONP) † |
| Smit Robert H | Simpson Thacher & Bartlett LLP * |
| Smutny Abby Cohen | White & Case LLP * |

**Band 3**

| | |
|---|---|
| Aguilar-Alvarez Guillermo | King & Spalding LLP * |
| Armas Oliver J | Chadbourne & Parke LLP * |
| Beckett Mark | Chadbourne & Parke LLP * |
| Friedman Mark W | Debevoise & Plimpton LLP |
| Goldberg Michael S | Baker Botts LLP * |
| Hammond Steven A | Hughes Hubbard & Reed LLP * |
| Hanessian Grant | Baker & McKenzie * |
| Kimmelman Louis B | Allen & Overy LLP |
| Pierce John V H | WilmerHale * |
| Polebaum Elliot E | Fried, Frank, Harris, Shriver & Jacobson * |
| Schaner Lawrence | Jenner & Block LLP * |
| Schiller Jonathan D | Boies, Schiller & Flexner LLP (ONP) † |
| Sherwin Peter J W | Proskauer Rose LLP (ONP) † |
| Weisburg Henry | Shearman & Sterling LLP |
| Ziegler Richard F | Jenner & Block LLP * |

**Band 4**

| | |
|---|---|
| Amirfar Catherine | Debevoise & Plimpton LLP |
| Bédard Julie | Skadden, Arps, Slate, Meagher & Flom * |
| Bravin Mark N | Winston & Strawn LLP (ONP) † * |
| Chao Cedric | DLA Piper LLP (US) * |

| | |
|---|---|
| González Daniel E | Hogan Lovells US LLP |
| Goodman Ronald | Foley Hoag LLP (ONP) † * |
| Gulland Eugene D | Covington & Burling LLP * |
| Hosking James | Chaffetz Lindsey LLP * |
| King Brian | Freshfields Bruckhaus Deringer US LLP * |
| Knull William H | Mayer Brown LLP |
| Nelson Timothy G | Skadden, Arps, Slate, Meagher & Flom * |
| O'Gorman Kevin | Fulbright & Jaworski LLP * |
| Ordway Eric | Weil, Gotshal & Manges LLP * |
| Profaizer Joseph R | Paul Hastings LLP |
| Rosenthal Jeffrey | Cleary Gottlieb Steen & Hamilton LLP * |
| Sabater Aníbal Martin | Fulbright & Jaworski LLP * |
| Salomon Claudia T | Latham & Watkins LLP (ONP) † * |
| Sarles Jeffrey | Mayer Brown LLP |
| Smith Jennifer M | Baker Botts LLP * |
| Smith Steven | Jones Day (ONP) † |
| Yanos Alexander | Freshfields Bruckhaus Deringer US LLP * |
| Zaslowsky David | Baker & McKenzie * |

**Band 5**

| | |
|---|---|
| Burnett Henry Guy | King & Spalding LLP * |
| Cymrot Mark A | Baker & Hostetler LLP (ONP) † * |
| de Gramont Alexandre | Weil, Gotshal & Manges LLP * |
| Green Allen B. | McKenna Long & Aldridge LLP (ONP) † * |
| Haridi Samaa | Weil, Gotshal & Manges LLP * |
| Kahale III George | Curtis, Mallet-Prevost, Colt & Mosle LLP * |
| Kent Rachael D | WilmerHale * |
| Lennon Jr Michael P | Baker Botts LLP * |
| Lew Darryl | White & Case LLP * |
| Loftis James | Vinson & Elkins RLLP (ONP) † * |
| Miles Craig | King & Spalding LLP * |
| O'Brien William | McKenna Long & Aldridge LLP (ONP) † * |
| Paparella Christopher | Hughes Hubbard & Reed LLP * |
| Reisenfeld Kenneth B | Patton Boggs LLP (ONP) † |
| Santens Ank A | White & Case LLP * |
| Suarez Anzorena Ignacio | Clifford Chance US LLP (ONP) † * |
| Whitesell Anne Marie | Dechert LLP (ONP) † * |
| Zelbo Howard | Cleary Gottlieb Steen & Hamilton LLP * |

**Up-and-coming individuals**

| | |
|---|---|
| Boehning H Christopher | Paul, Weiss, Rifkind, Wharton (ONP) † * |
| Cárdenas M Cristina | Astigarraga Davis * |
| Cheek Marney | Covington & Burling LLP * |
| Lahlou Yasmine | Chaffetz Lindsey LLP * |
| Marigo Noiana Paula | Freshfields Bruckhaus Deringer US LLP * |
| Prager Dietmar | Debevoise & Plimpton LLP |
| Ryan Chris | Shearman & Sterling LLP |
| Tan Daniel | Dan Tan Law (ONP) † |

\* Indicates individual with profile.

† ONP = Other Notable Practitioner.

ConocoPhillips in a number of significant arbitrations. **Alexander Yanos** (see p.429) is particularly recognized for his impressive investment treaty practice, while still offering expertise across a broad spread of arbitration disputes.

He played a leading role in the aforementioned matter for Burlington Resources, alongside Nigel Blackaby. Yanos also counts National Grid and BG Group among his key clients. Rising star **Noiana Paula Marigo** (see p.361) is a new entry

to the table, and centers her practice on arbitrations involving Latin America. She formed part of the team that acted for the Republic of Guatemala in the aforementioned ICSID arbitration.

### White & Case LLP
**See profile on p.451**

**THE FIRM** This leading international arbitration practice has a strong track record of success in investor-state arbitrations, representing both investors and states. The highly esteemed practitioners have a breadth and depth of knowledge across a range of industry sectors, including energy, transportation and financial services, and they have particular expertise in complex international arbitration relating to the construction arena. Recent highlights include achieving a landmark $58 million award for Société Générale de Surveillance (SGS) against the Republic of Paraguay. The team also acted for Gold Reserve in a $2 billion ICSID arbitration against Venezuela.

**Sources say:** *"A good, strong firm."*

**KEY INDIVIDUALS** The *"terrific"* **Carolyn Lamm** (see p.351) is recognized by clients and peers alike as *"one of the best international arbitrators in the world."* She acts as both advocate and arbitrator. Recent highlights include representing thousands of Italian claimants in a $1.3 billion ICSID arbitration against the Argentine Republic. She is also representing the Republic of the Philippines in three separate arbitrations. The *"very smart, knowledgeable, calm and detail-oriented"* **Paul Friedland** (see p.316) is similarly highly regarded for his abilities as both an arbitrator and an advocate. He led on the aforementioned matter for SGS, and handles both investment treaty and commercial disputes. **Abby Cohen Smutny** (see p.409) is well versed in both commercial and investment treaty arbitrations. She is currently handling a number of arbitrations for the Republic of Bulgaria and, alongside **Darryl Lew** (see p.356), handled the $2 billion ICSID arbitration for Gold Reserve mentioned above. Lew remains an integral and much-respected member of the international arbitration team. *"Great lawyer"* **Ank Santens** (see p.399) is tipped by market sources as a *"future leader of the profession,"* and is currently involved in a number of matters for key clients of the firm. She handles investment treaty and commercial arbitrations with equal aplomb.

### Band 2

### Arnold & Porter LLP
**See profile on p.906**

**THE FIRM** This hugely experienced group is held in high regard for its expertise in both investment treaty arbitrations and commercial arbitrations. The talented practitioners handle disputes across a wide range of areas, demonstrating a notable breadth of arbitration capabilities. The team offers particular expertise in representing sovereign states, with recent clients on this side including the Dominican Republic, Costa Rica and Hungary. The group has also earned notable respect for its strength in Latin America-related matters.

Sources say: *"The team was extremely professional, fast and accurate. It was able to dive in to the details of very complex cases."*

KEY INDIVIDUALS **Paolo Di Rosa** (see p.304) heads the firm's international arbitration group, and is highly regarded for his extensive experience in dealing with disputes relating to Latin America. Clients state that *"he is well prepared and articulate,"* and praise his cross-examination capabilities. His recent work includes obtaining a $202 billion award for EDF International, SAUR International and León Participaciones in an ICSID arbitration brought against Argentina. **Jean Kalicki** (see p.342) is a celebrated presence in the market who is *"creative and business-minded,"* and has *"great presence before a tribunal,"* according to sources. She continues to represent the Republic of Hungary in a number of arbitrations, including an Energy Charter Treaty case involving a $700 million claim.

## Covington & Burling LLP
### See profile on p.441

THE FIRM This diverse practice maintains a balanced docket of commercial and investor-state cases spanning a range of industries. The truly integrated practice has dealt with disputes involving parties from a broad spread of jurisdictions, including Latin America, Europe and the Middle East. Its impressive client roster includes

ExxonMobil and former Asian Football Confederation president Mohamed Bin Hammam. The team recently achieved a significant victory in its representation of the Spanish investors in YUKOS in an arbitration brought against Russia.

**Commercial Awareness** *"The group operates well as an integrated team, and provides responsive and fulsome advice. They have a deep understanding of the international law principles that apply to cases and a more general awareness of the issues that tend to drive such disputes and their resolution."*

KEY INDIVIDUALS **Oscar Garibaldi** (see p.319) is renowned for his impressive investment treaty practice, with sources stating that *"his education in both civil and common law and his complete fluency in Spanish and English make him an ideal choice to present cases before international panels."* Clients also report that *"his oral and written advocacy is thorough, convincing, sophisticated and eloquent."* **Eugene Gulland** (see p.327) draws upon his extensive litigation experience when conducting commercial and investment treaty arbitrations. He is described as *"an outstanding strategist who sees angles and arguments others miss."* Recent highlights include reversing the lifetime soccer ban given by FIFA to former Asian Football Confederation president Mohamed Bin Hammam. **Marney Cheek** (see p.294) is rapidly gaining an impressive track record in the market after forming part of the team that acted on behalf of Spanish investors in YUKOS, as described above. She also represented Metal-Tech in a bilateral investment treaty (BIT) claim against Uzbekistan.

## Hughes Hubbard & Reed LLP
### See profile on p.1981

THE FIRM Hughes Hubbard & Reed works across a diverse range of industries, representing clients in both commercial and investment treaty arbitrations. The firm acts for an impressive and varied client roster, including Forest Laboratories, Suzlon Energy and RosInvestCo UK. The team successfully defended the government of Canada in an LCIA arbitration brought by the USA. The tribunal ruled in the client's favor on every point and rejected the claimant's demand of $500 million in its entirety.

Sources say: *"Every aspect of their case strategy was reflected in the tribunal's award – their advocacy was faultless."*

KEY INDIVIDUALS **John Fellas's** (see p.312) extensive experience enables him to be *"involved in every role imaginable,"* and he handles cases as both arbitrator and advocate. His recent highlights include appearing in federal court to successfully defend an International Centre for Dispute Resolution (ICDR) award issued in favor of firm client Tele2 Sverige. Well established as both an arbitrator and an advocate, **Steven Hammond** (see p.329) is praised for *"providing very good insight into the positioning of arguments – he understands what will work and what won't."* He is currently representing Türkiye Petrolleri Anonim Ortakligi in an ICSID arbitration against the Republic of Kazakhstan. **John Townsend** (see p.418) is acclaimed for his prominence as an arbitrator and advocate. Sources agree that *"his depth of understanding and ability to take a complex case and present a clear, compelling argument are*

*second to none."* He recently defended Canada in the LCIA arbitration referred to above. **Christopher Paparella** (see p.381) is praised for his *"very intelligent and responsive"* approach to international arbitration. He chairs the firm's construction law group, and has particular experience in matters related to the energy sector.

## King & Spalding LLP
### See profile on p.445

THE FIRM This well-known firm is held in high regard by market commentators, and maintains a strong bench of practitioners based in key locations across the country. The team remains particularly focused on the energy sector, with a specific emphasis on oil and gas, and handles a mixture of commercial arbitration and investment treaty arbitration. The firm continues to bolster its global presence, offering clients access to an impressive network of attorneys. It continues to represent Chevron in litigation related to its high-profile UNCITRAL arbitration against Ecuador.

Sources say: *"They do fabulous work for us in international arbitration, and have really batted a thousand – I can't think of anything where they haven't gotten us success."*

KEY INDIVIDUALS **Doak Bishop** (see p.283) is the respected co-head of the firm's international arbitration practice and is renowned for his experience as arbitrator and advocate. Clients report that *"he has a tremendous instinct for how things work in the arbitration realm – his insight is invaluable."* Fellow practice co-head **Edward Kehoe** (see p.344) has a diverse practice and handles both commercial and investment treaty arbitrations covering a range of industries. He continues to represent The Renco Group in its $800 million arbitration against Peru held under the UNCITRAL rules. **Guillermo Aguilar-Alvarez** (see p.272) earns praise for his experience in acting as both arbitrator and counsel. Sources describe him as *"very well prepared and completely fluent in civil and common law culture."* His practice includes advocating under a wide range of arbitral rules in both commercial and investment treaty disputes. **Craig Miles** (see p.368) is experienced across the board in the international arbitration arena, and has particular expertise in energy disputes. Recent highlights include successfully representing Exterran in an ICSID arbitration brought against Venezuela. Another prominent team member, **John Bowman** (see p.286) provides expert knowledge on the energy sector, with a specific focus on oil and gas arbitration. **Harry Burnett** (see p.290) is a new addition to the group from Crowell & Moring, and is highly praised for his advocacy skills as an *"outstanding litigator."* He is experienced in acting as counsel and sitting as arbitrator in a wide range of disputes.

## Skadden, Arps, Slate, Meagher & Flom LLP & Affiliates
### See profile on p.2008

THE FIRM This reputable firm attracts great praise for the breadth and depth of its international arbitration group, and handles investor-state and commercial disputes with equal aplomb. The group is currently representing Devas Multimedia in two arbitrations against a company completely owned by the government of India. These disputes concern the alleged wrongful cancellation of a highly valuable satellite contract, and total over $2.6 billion in claims. It is also acting for private equity company Castle Harlan in a dispute involving a $225 million fraud claim by a Luxembourg company.

**Sources say:** "*It's a great firm, and gets superior results.*"

**KEY INDIVIDUALS** As co-head of the firm's international litigation and arbitration group, **John Gardiner** (see p.318) has extensive experience in appearing before a wide range of arbitral institutions. Clients report that "*he is very analytical and as a result can merge complicated concepts and legal facts into something that makes pragmatic sense.*" **Julie Bédard** (see p.281) has a distinguished reputation within the international arbitration community, and offers particular experience in investor-state arbitrations. She is currently representing Gambrinus in a $150 million ICSID arbitration against Venezuela. **Timothy Nelson** (see p.375) has significant experience in handling international arbitration and litigation on behalf of a wide range of clients. "*He is always very well prepared and demonstrates great pragmatism and experience,*" according to impressed clients. His current clients include Devas Multimedia and Gambrinus. **Barry Garfinkel** (see p.318) is held in extremely high regard for his extensive experience serving both as a party-nominated arbitrator and as chairman in arbitrations held under the auspices of a wide range of institutions.

## WilmerHale
See profile on p.930

**THE FIRM** This group is staffed with the highest caliber of advocates, including an impressive team entirely dedicated to international arbitration matters. The US-based practice is closely integrated with international offices in London and other key locations across the globe, giving clients access to a rich pool of lawyers with a range of expertise. The group is experienced in handling both commercial and investment treaty arbitrations, and is making efforts to grow the latter practice.

**Sources say:** "*They are very smart people who are very knowledgeable about the rules and procedures of international arbitration.*"

**KEY INDIVIDUALS** A new addition to the New York office, **James Carter** (see p.292) brings extensive experience serving as counsel and has an internationally recognized reputation as a leading arbitrator. "*He is one of the leading international arbitrators and would always be at the top of my list,*" states one impressed commentator. **John Pierce** (see p.384) is celebrated by sources for his commercial awareness: "*He's very practical in terms of advice – it's not just legal advice. He takes into consideration a wider set of risks that may be applicable, such as long-term costs.*" He splits his time between the firm's London and New York offices. **Rachael Kent** (see p.345) is vice chair of the firm's international arbitration practice. She focuses on both investment treaty and commercial disputes, and impresses sources with the "*great judgment*" and dedication she shows when handling a wide range of matters.

Band 3

## Allen & Overy LLP
See profile on p.433

**THE FIRM** This firm has a truly integrated global network, offering clients a seamless approach to investor-state and commercial international arbitrations. It houses a highly experienced team of attorneys whose broad-based expertise and multilingual capabilities enable it to tailor its approach to the exact needs of each client. Its recent work includes acting for a number of lenders involved in a $500 million ICSID arbitration brought against the Republic of Ecuador. Additional clients include the Republic of Peru and Petrotrin.

**Sources say:** "*The matter the team dealt with was highly complex and required a huge amount of willpower and endurance.*"

**KEY INDIVIDUALS** "*Outstanding advocate*" **Louis Kimmelman** is respected by market sources for his extensive experience across the board in international arbitration. He is described as a "*really practical attorney*" whose strategic approach is particularly appreciated by clients. His recent work includes representing Petrotrin in separate ICC and LCIA arbitrations against World GTL.

## Baker Botts LLP
See profile on p.2427

**THE FIRM** This leading firm continues to conduct challenging, high-value commercial and investment treaty arbitrations. The scope of the practice is impressive, with practitioners acting for respondents and claimants across a wide range of industries. The US-based team is split between offices in Washington, DC and Houston, and coordinates closely with the firm's foreign offices. Its client base reflects the breadth of the team's expertise, and includes Sangatta Holdings, Kia Motors and the Russian Federation.

**Sources say:** "*It is a strong and disciplined team of professional lawyers with branch offices all over the world, giving it a wide scope and a strong network of local professionals.*"

**KEY INDIVIDUALS Michael Goldberg** (see p.322) cochairs the international arbitration and dispute resolution practice, and has long-standing experience in the field. Sources praise "*his ability to analyze issues in multiple jurisdictions.*" He offers expertise in acting as counsel and arbitrator in a wide range of disputes. **Jennifer Smith** (see p.409) focuses on commercial arbitration and is praised as being "*very bright, hard-working and well organized.*" She is currently involved in a number of arbitrations relating to the energy and technology industries. **Michael Lennon** (see p.354) is highly respected as "*the consummate professional – he's always reachable, very patient and understanding, full of good ideas and knows exactly how to handle all the parties on a case.*" He offers particular expertise in disputes involving the energy sector.

## Cleary Gottlieb Steen & Hamilton LLP
See profile on p.1963

**THE FIRM** This flourishing firm continues to bolster its global strength by recently opening additional offices in South Korea, Abu Dhabi and Brazil. The prominent group is held in high esteem for its strong investment treaty and commercial arbitration practices, and clients especially appreciate its commercial awareness. The group's significant client roster includes several sovereign states and companies across the globe. Notable highlights include representing the Russian Federation in three parallel UNCITRAL arbitrations brought by former shareholders of YUKOS, with damages claims surpassing $100 billion.

**Commercial Awareness** "*All the lawyers possess great knowledge of international arbitration and the law in many different countries. They focus not only on the legal aspects of the arbitration but also on the business aspects, providing a valuable business-oriented solution.*"

**KEY INDIVIDUALS Jeffrey Rosenthal** (see p.395) offers extensive experience in handling a range of complex arbitrations, and recently represented Citigroup Financial Products in an ICC arbitration regarding its purchase of a EUR2 billion portfolio of German loans from Eurohypo. Commentators acknowledge that "*he is very diligent and a pleasure to work with.*" **Howard Zelbo** (see p.430) has a varied portfolio of investor-state and commercial arbitrations, and also handles commercial litigation. He is part of the team serving as counsel to the Argentine Republic in a multibillion-dollar ICSID arbitration brought by bondholders under the Argentina-Italy BIT.

## Fulbright & Jaworski LLP
See profile on p.2435

**THE FIRM** This international arbitration powerhouse has built a renowned practice on a solid foundation of experience within the energy industry. The dynamic group is held in high regard for its creative and flexible approach to disputes, and specializes in both investment treaty and commercial arbitration. The firm acts for a diverse cross-section of clients, including Baker Hughes, Conoco Phillips, YUKOS and Noble Energy.

**Sources say:** "*The group has a deep bench full of world-class advocates.*"

**KEY INDIVIDUALS Mark Baker** (see p.277) is an undeniable force in the international arbitration arena, bringing a great depth of knowledge and expertise to his work as advocate and arbitrator. Sources single him out as "*a very thoughtful, talented attorney who knows his business and provides precise legal and strategic advice.*" **Aníbal Sabater** (see p.398) handles a wide range of investor-state and commercial arbitrations in his respected practice, and is equally adept at advocating in Spanish and English. "*He really takes an interest in matters which affect our company,*" say appreciative clients. **Kevin O'Gorman** (see p.379) is praised as "*one of the most client-focused lawyers out there,*" and "*does a good job anticipating things that might arise in the future.*" His arbitration practice is enhanced by his expertise in the energy arena.

## Sidley Austin LLP
See profile on p.1264

**THE FIRM** The heart of Sidley Austin's US-based international arbitration practice rests in Washington, DC, but it draws strength from an impressive network of offices across the globe. The celebrated group has a successful investment treaty practice, evidenced by its continued representation of the Republic of Peru in two ICSID arbitrations, one of which involves defending against a $2.5 billion claim regarding coastal properties. The team also conducts commercial arbitrations, most recently involving Korean, Russian and Latin American companies.

**Sources say:** *"They are experts in the field. They understand the process, the issues, the players and how to win."*

**KEY INDIVIDUALS Stanimir Alexandrov** (see p.272) has an excellent reputation for his impressive investment treaty expertise. He represents both investors and states, and also handles complex commercial arbitrations. He is recognized as having *"tremendous experience and unique insights specific to international arbitration that have proven invaluable."*

## Simpson Thacher & Bartlett LLP
### See profile on p.2006

**THE FIRM** Simpson Thacher has an impressive bench of distinguished litigators with extensive arbitration experience in both investor-state and commercial disputes. It also attracts clients through its strong insurance and reinsurance arbitration practice, and its notable presence in several key jurisdictions across the globe. Recent highlights include successfully opposing the enforcement of a $55 million ICC arbitration award levied against its client MatlinPatterson.

**Sources say:** *"They have won every case that they have handled for us, even cases that others had deemed unwinnable."*

**KEY INDIVIDUALS Robert Smit** (see p.408) maintains his position as a key player in the arbitration world. He is recognized as a *"master strategist"* who regularly takes on disputes both as advocate and arbitrator. According to interviewees, *"he is absolutely brilliant as an advocate as he understands his clients' needs and sensitivities."*

## Band 4

### Astigarraga Davis
#### See profile on p.1015

**THE FIRM** This boutique firm is well respected within the international arbitration market for its specialized litigation and arbitration practice. It acts for an impressive range of clients attracted by the team's extensive experience and adaptability. Having traditionally focused solely on commercial arbitration, in recent years the firm's investor-state practice has been growing rapidly. The group also has a stellar reputation for its work involving Latin America-related disputes.

**Sources say:** *"Their work quality and expertise are second to none. Plus their rates are very competitive." "They are highly customer-oriented."*

**KEY INDIVIDUALS José Astigarraga** (see p.275) has a wealth of experience within the international arbitration domain and receives abundant praise for his consistent level of excellence. Sources describe him as *"a highly recognized and respected professional who is respectful of his clients, and sharp when it comes to strategy."* **Cristina**

Cárdenas (see p.292) is increasingly recognized for her dedication to international arbitration and litigation, and is praised by clients for her ability to *"know every single piece of detailed information on the dispute."*

## Baker & McKenzie
### See profile on p.435

**THE FIRM** This large, well-connected group has traditionally focused on commercial arbitrations but has been strengthening its investment treaty practice in recent years. With nationwide resources across multiple US offices and a highly reputed global reach, Baker & McKenzie is well equipped to resolve international disputes. For example, lawyers from offices in New York, Chicago and Brazil worked seamlessly together to successfully represent Petrobras in an ad hoc arbitration against Kellogg Brown & Root LLC. The team is active in a range of sectors, including energy, engineering and construction, and other commercial areas.

**Sources say:** *"They have lots of international offices and good resources, so they can provide advice in countries we start working in. Their network is very wide."*

**KEY INDIVIDUALS Grant Hanessian** (see p.329) is *"well respected and focused in this field,"* and is *"very experienced, hugely knowledgeable and effective,"* according to interviewees. He is applauded for his expertise in both sitting as an arbitrator and serving as counsel in a wide range of disputes. Recent highlights include the victory for Petrobras referred to above. **David Zaslowsky** (see p.430) is praised for his experience in acting in both arbitration and litigation. He has a particular focus on commercial arbitration, and sources note that *"he is excellent on his feet."*

## Chadbourne & Parke LLP
### See profile on p.1962

**THE FIRM** This group houses an impressive group of experienced practitioners. The team deals with both commercial and investment treaty arbitrations, and is held in particularly high regard for its adaptability and strategic approach. The group's growing global footprint enables it to handle matters involving parties from areas such as Asia and Latin America. It recently represented St. Paul Reinsurance in its attempts to recover unpaid losses of $275 million in a dispute with Scandinavian Reinsurance. Other clients include AES, Enel and Bechtel.

**Client Service** *"They are always well prepared and provided us with real and specific answers to our numerous questions. They also kept us informed all the time and were responsive to our inquiries."*

**KEY INDIVIDUALS** Department head **Oliver Armas** (see p.274) is considered to be *"very thoughtful and inventive; he created arguments others wouldn't have thought of."* Commentators also commend him for *"providing key strategic advice – he always thinks a few steps ahead."* **Mark Beckett** (see p.281) is a recent addition to the practice, arriving from Latham & Watkins in late 2012. He is experienced in handling both investment treaty and commercial disputes. He is *"extremely bright and hard-working,"* with *"excellent rhetorical skills and a thorough approach to research."*

## Chaffetz Lindsey LLP

**THE FIRM** This New York-based boutique focuses on international arbitration, and has a well-regarded practice spanning a wide range of industries. Practitioners are commended for their depth and breadth of knowledge, especially in complex arbitrations, which stems partially from their experience of sitting as arbitrators. The impressive client base reflects the team's ability to handle a wide range of investment treaty and commercial disputes, including AEI, the Islamic Republic of Iran and AES. Recent work includes acting for a Turkish company in a large dispute involving three different arbitration proceedings in Europe. This matter demonstrates the group's ability to work seamlessly alongside foreign co-counsel, and to handle complex enforcement matters.

**Client Service** *"They are as responsive, flexible and adaptable as possible. They are able to adapt to clients' needs."*

**Commercial Awareness** *"They are highly specialized in international arbitration, and have a deep knowledge of the relevant law. They are also experienced litigators, and are used to handling complex disputes. They render tailormade services that are specifically designed for the client and case."*

**KEY INDIVIDUALS David Lindsey** (see p.357) is a rising force in the market and is described as *"a well-known expert in international arbitration circles"* by commentators. He attracts enthusiastic recommendations from clients and peers alike, with one interviewee saying: *"His experience allows him to anticipate movements the other party might make, which is very good for strategy planning."* **James Hosking** (see p.337) is highly recommended by sources, who say: *"He has an amazing amount of energy and dives right in to matters – the level of his commitment is quite remarkable."* He has impressive expertise in disputes relating to Latin America, and draws on experience in handling arbitrations held under the auspices of all major institutions. Clients are hugely impressed by **Yasmine Lahlou** (see p.351) and her thorough approach, stating: *"She has such knowledge of even the most minor aspects of the case."* She is fluent in Italian, English and French, and has particular expertise in Middle Eastern and European disputes.

## Shearman & Sterling LLP
### See profile on p.2005

**THE FIRM** This group's impressive caseload continues to grow by the year and covers a diverse cross-section of industries, including energy, natural resources and financial disputes. The group's broad expertise within the arbitration sphere includes investment treaty and commercial arbitration experience. Major highlights include successfully representing a key client in an ICC arbitration against Petrochemicals Industries Company, in which the tribunal issued one of the largest commercial arbitration awards ever, at more than $2 billion.

**Sources say:** *"Strong, very experienced players. They are very good on strategy, and excellent in hearings."*

**KEY INDIVIDUALS Henry Weisburg** has long-standing experience in the international arbitration arena, and is hailed as being *"excellent at preparing a case."* As well as regularly representing parties in commercial and investment treaty arbitrations, he also conducts high-stakes enforcement proceedings. **Chris Ryan** has a versatile practice, handling both commercial and investment treaty arbitrations. He is currently representing a sovereign state in three ICSID arbitrations.

### Sullivan & Cromwell LLP
See profile on p.2011

**THE FIRM** Sullivan & Cromwell has extensive experience in the international arbitration arena. It concentrates on both commercial and investor-state arbitrations, and also offers notable litigation capabilities. Recent highlights include achieving a victory for TeliaSonera in an ICC arbitration against Turkish companies related to a joint venture; TeliaSonera was awarded $932 million, which is believed to be the largest commercial arbitration award ever given.
**KEY INDIVIDUALS Joseph Neuhaus** (see p.375) coordinates the arbitration practice and is widely respected within the international arbitration community. He is noted for his experience as arbitrator and counsel. He is currently representing a European bank in three ICDR arbitrations brought by Latin American investors regarding the Madoff Ponzi scheme.

### Weil, Gotshal & Manges LLP
See profile on p.2015

**THE FIRM** This thriving nationwide group continues to flourish in the international arbitration space. The firm is able to draw on its multijurisdictional and multilingual capabilities to tailor its service to each client and specific dispute. It is held in particularly high esteem for its investment treaty practice, and also has a successful commercial practice, representing companies such as Employ Media LLC in ongoing disputes. Recent highlights include securing a victory for The Williams Companies in a $400 million ICSID arbitration against Venezuela.
**Sources say:** "*The team has been straightforward, hardworking and diligent. It is as dedicated to the business as I am.*"
**KEY INDIVIDUALS Arif Ali** (see p.272) cochairs the firm's international arbitration practice and is extremely well regarded by interviewees, who say: "*He is absolutely marvelous – very cooperative and always available day or night.*" He is adept in both investor-state and commercial arbitration. "*He is an excellent oral advocate and he really strives to understand the business,*" add sources. **Eric Ordway** (see p.380) is highly respected in the international arbitration field and has extensive experience in handling disputes involving a wide range of jurisdictions. He led the representation of The Williams Companies in the ICSID arbitration described above. **Samaa Haridi** (see p.330) is singled out by clients for her "*very supportive and intelligent*" approach, and regularly handles commercial and investor-state arbitrations involving the Middle East. Sources also acknowledge her as being "*hard-working and very entrepreneurial.*" **Alexandre de Gramont** (see p.302) maintains a strong investor-state practice and also conducts commercial arbitrations. He handles disputes arising from a wide range of sectors and jurisdictions. Sources

particularly praise his dedication to matters, stating that "*his attention to detail is excellent.*"

### Band 5

### Crowell & Moring LLP
See profile on p.910

**THE FIRM** This respected firm is experienced in dealing with investment treaties and commercial arbitrations. It regularly represents clients in high-value cases and displays a particular aptitude in investor-state cases. The firm is committed to supporting clients' best interests by providing alternative fee arrangements. Current clients include Khan Resources, H&H Enterprises and Marriott International.
**Sources say:** "*The group is very client-oriented.*"
**KEY INDIVIDUALS Ian Laird** is a key contact at the firm.

### Curtis, Mallet-Prevost, Colt & Mosle LLP
See profile on p.1967

**THE FIRM** This firm enters the rankings thanks to its rapidly rising reputation in the commercial and investment treaty arbitration arena. The group exclusively represents states and state-owned entities when tackling investor-state disputes, and has built up considerable expertise in this space. The team is split between offices in Washington, DC and New York, and maintains solid connections to Latin America.
**Sources say:** "*The team was able to establish a good and respectful relationship with our local team of lawyers and other professionals. That was actually the key to our success.*"
**KEY INDIVIDUALS George Kahale** (see p.342) cochairs the group and is characterized as being "*very smart, with excellent presentation skills, superb at team-building, and able to see situations from all points of view.*" He has recently represented several sovereign states in significant disputes.

### DLA Piper LLP (US)
See profile on p.1971

**THE FIRM** This international powerhouse continues to expand its international arbitration practice with internal promotions and hires from Dewey & LeBoeuf and Grant Thornton. The group handles arbitration across a broad range of sectors, including aviation, energy and media. The team currently represents the Ministry of Transportation of the Republic of Turkey in an EUR800 million ICC arbitration brought by Alstom Transport regarding a railroad line. Other notable clients include Ghana and Blue Bank International & Trust.
**KEY INDIVIDUALS** According to market commentators, **Cedric Chao** (see p.293) is "*outstandingly able, conscientious, hard-working and astute,*" as well as "*very detail-oriented and a good negotiator.*" He cochairs the practice, and also acts as an arbitrator alongside serving as counsel.

### Fried, Frank, Harris, Shriver & Jacobson LLP
See profile on p.1975

**THE FIRM** This talented group is commended for the strength of its commercial arbitration practice. Its practitioners have a wide range of industry expertise, and are also experienced in acting as both counsel and arbitrator. Recent highlights include acting for Thales Alenia Space France in an ICDR arbitration against Globalstar, in which Globalstar's EUR350 million claim was dismissed. Globalstar was then ordered to pay the respondent's counterclaim of EUR53 million.
**KEY INDIVIDUALS** Group head **Elliot Polebaum** (see p.386) has a versatile practice serving as counsel and arbitrator. Market sources praise him as "*a very able litigator who picks up the rhythm and tone of arbitration very well and does an excellent job for clients.*"

### Hogan Lovells US LLP

**THE FIRM** This well-known group has experience representing clients in both commercial disputes and bilateral and multilateral investment treaty arbitrations. Its portfolio demonstrates a specific aptitude for complex commercial matters, and particular expertise in disputes related to Latin America.
**KEY INDIVIDUALS Daniel González** is highly experienced in sitting as an arbitrator and serving as counsel in a wide range of disputes. He offers notable strength in arbitrations involving Latin America, aided by his fluency in Spanish.

### Jenner & Block LLP
See profile on p.1252

**THE FIRM** Jenner & Block maintains a significant presence within the international arbitration domain, and is praised and respected for its commercial practice. The firm has a broad scope of industry experience, and handles disputes for a wide range of clients. Notable highlights include defending Ritz-Carlton against $140 million claims in an ICDR arbitration brought by resort owners in Jamaica.
**Sources say:** "*The team is exceptionally professional and very responsive.*"
**KEY INDIVIDUALS Richard Ziegler** (see p.431) cochairs the practice and is also the managing partner of the firm's New York office. Market sources praise his abilities as "*an excellent cross-examiner.*" Fellow cochair **Lawrence Schaner** (see p.400) specializes in commercial arbitration and litigation. Sources note that he is "*very familiar with the international arbitration community, as well as the Bar.*"

### Mayer Brown LLP
See profile on p.1257

**THE FIRM** This impressive group is singled out for its fully integrated approach, and can draw on the strength of numerous key offices around the globe to create teams tailored to each case and client. It recently represented Lufthansa in a EUR70 million ICC arbitration regarding the performance of an outsourced IT contract to handle the airline's flight features.

**KEY INDIVIDUALS Philip Lacovara** is highlighted as a "*first-rate lawyer*" and is held in high esteem for his extensive experience of serving as arbitrator. Market sources praise his "*creative writings.*" **William Knull** has a great depth of knowledge across a wide array of industries, including particular expertise in the oil and gas sector. Commentators characterize him as "*a very smart fellow who has a good courtroom demeanor which translates very well in international arbitration.*" **Jeffrey Sarles** is the highly respected co-head of the firm's Supreme Court and appellate group, and divides his practice between appellate, international arbitration and litigation work.

## Milbank, Tweed, Hadley & McCloy LLP
See profile on p.448

**THE FIRM** This firm is a new addition to the rankings and has built a solid reputation for its handling of investor-state disputes. The US team is spread across offices in New York, Washington, DC and Los Angeles, and also draws on Milbank's impressive global presence. It is renowned for establishing long-term client relationships through its efficiency and commitment to client service. The team recently defended Mongolia against a $1 billion claim brought by Russian claimants relating to gold mining.
**Commercial Awareness** "*Milbank is very good at working with us to understand our strategic objectives and combines skills to function effectively as a team, which leads to the best results. We are impressed by Milbank's ethic of hard work and energy. The quality of the technical lawyering is very high.*"
**KEY INDIVIDUALS** Sources praise **Michael Nolan's** (see p.377) experience serving as both counsel and arbitrator. Sources say he "*is equipped with plenty of experience to handle diverse cultures and situations. His tactical and thoughtful decision-making is critical for case management and outcome.*"

## Morrison & Foerster LLP
See profile on p.1990

**THE FIRM** Morrison & Foerster maintains a notable presence in the international arbitration arena, and has core strength in trial advocacy skills. It has particular expertise in IP-related matters and disputes arising from the technology industry. It also has a particular focus on arbitrations involving Asia. The group recently represented SUSE Linux in an ICC arbitration against The SCO Group that involved claims of copyright infringement.
**KEY INDIVIDUALS** San Francisco-based James Schurz is a key contact.

## Paul Hastings LLP
See profile on p.1996

**THE FIRM** This firm's strong US group is split between New York and Washington, DC offices and coordinates with offices in Asia and Europe to offer clients a truly integrated service. The international arbitration group specializes in political risk insurance arbitration as well as commercial and investment treaties. It also offers impressive expertise in handling complex enforcement proceedings. The firm continues to represent the Republic of the Philippines in a $2.4 billion UNCITRAL arbitration relating to a build-lease-transfer agreement with Metro Rail Transit Corporation.
**Sources say:** "*They dedicate the resources and the competency levels necessary to root out the real issues and then implement a detailed strategy to defend their clients. Then they present well and understand what the arbitrators are looking for. And they do it all with a great sense of humor and passion.*"
**KEY INDIVIDUALS Joseph Profaizer** divides his practice between commercial arbitration and investment treaties. Sources praise his "*great presentation style and inquisitive nature,*" and one client enthuses that "*it's comforting to have him on our side – he not only sees his role as 'fighting the battle' but more importantly, 'how can we avoid the battle', while not sacrificing our overall position materially.*"

## Quinn Emanuel Urquhart & Sullivan, LLP

**THE FIRM** Quinn Emanuel has significantly expanded its international arbitration practice in recent years. The firm has traditionally focused on commercial arbitrations, but has lately shifted its focus to investment treaties, representing both investors and states. With highly qualified lawyers, the team has a great depth of technical knowledge covering a wide range of areas, including financial, patent, aerospace and financial disputes.
**Sources say:** "*The team is very thorough, provides good briefs, and really thinks about all the possible outcomes, ensuring we get the best result.*"
**KEY INDIVIDUALS Fred Bennett** is a key contact at the firm.

## Other Notable Practitioners

Market sources highlight **Gerald Aksen** as an outstanding sole practitioner, with one saying: "*He's the god of arbitration.*" Based in New York, Aksen has sat as arbitrator in more than 200 cases, illustrating his impressive popularity. The "*outstanding*" **George Bermann** of Columbia Law School is held in high regard for his long-standing experience and expertise in international arbitration. He regularly sits as arbitrator in a wide range of institutional and ad hoc arbitrations. **Christopher Boehning** (see p.285) is a highly regarded arbitration practitioner at Paul, Weiss, Rifkind, Wharton & Garrison LLP. Clients appreciate the broad scope of his experience, which ranges from complex litigation to insurance matters. He is characterized as "extremely bright, calm and very articulate – he always plans his strategies four moves in advance." **Mark Bravin** (see p.286) is the cochair of Winston & Strawn LLP's global international arbitration practice, based in the Washington, DC office. He is respected for his expertise in both commercial and investor-state arbitrations, and is currently representing McKesson in a complex arbitration against the Islamic Republic of Iran. **Charles Brower** of 20 Essex Street draws on an incredible depth of expertise in international disputes in his role as a leading arbitrator. He maintains his role serving as a judge of the Iran-United States Claims Tribunal. As president of the American Society of International Law, **David Caron** of 20 Essex Street has a diverse practice, serving as arbitrator and counsel in both investor-state and commercial arbitration proceedings. He is highly respected for his long-standing experience in the field. **Louis Craco** of Craco & Ellsworth, LLP is a highly regarded international arbitrator, and offers particular expertise in arbitrating commercial proceedings. **Mark Cymrot** (see p.300) is head of Baker Hostetler's international arbitration practice and enters the rankings having earned significant praise from market sources. Described as "*very experienced and intelligent,*" he is considered an expert in commercial disputes. One client enthuses: "*I was absolutely flabbergasted by his way of combining strategic insight and an immediate and profound understanding of the client's needs.*" Commentators single out **Robert Davidson** of JAMS as a "*fountain of knowledge*" who is "*always at the forefront of cutting-edge arbitration issues.*" He dedicates his practice to mediation and arbitrating complex international and domestic disputes. **Ronald Goodman** (see p.324) attracts extensive praise for his experience as counsel in commercial and investor-state arbitrations. He cochairs Foley Hoag LLP's international litigation and arbitration practice, and also teaches at the American University School of Law. **Allen Green** (see p.325) of McKenna Long & Aldridge LLP specializes in investor-state disputes. He is praised for his extensive expertise in the arena and his notable advocacy skills. Commentators particularly emphasize his international experience: "*He's come across every situation seven times in four different countries!*"

**Horacio Grigera Naón** of the Washington College of Law, American University is classified as "*a helpful and supportive co-arbitrator*" as well as an outstanding sole arbitrator for both commercial and investor-state arbitrations. Market sources also hail him as "*the leading arbitrator in Latin American-related matters.*" Sole practitioner **Mark Kantor** is identified as an influential force in the international arbitration community. He has sat as an arbitrator in a wide range of disputes, and offers particular expertise in the M&A space. He teaches at the Georgetown University Law Center. **Judd Kessler** (see p.346) of Porter Wright Morris & Arthur LLP is considered a "*first-rate lawyer*" and excellent arbitrator, with a particular specialty in investment treaty arbitrations. **James Loftis** (see p.358) is the head of Vinson & Elkins RLLP's international arbitration practice and handles both investment treaty and commercial arbitrations, with particular expertise in Latin American disputes. Clients highlight him as "*a highly experienced lawyer who must be considered among the elite few who are 'go-to' lawyers in large international arbitration matters.*" **William O'Brien** (see p.379) of McKenna Long & Aldridge LLP is a new entry to the rankings, highlighted for his extensive experience in handling commercial arbitrations. Sources regard him as "*highly qualified and very personable,*" with one client noting: "*He's also an excellent leader with perfect oratory skills.*" Market sources enthuse that **William Park** (see p.382) is "*legendary*" due to his accomplishments within the international arbitration arena. Alongside teaching law at Boston University, he arbitrates numerous disputes and has been appointed to the ICSID Panel of Arbitrators, as well as holding the title of president of the LCIA. **Kenneth Reisenfeld** is the highly recommended chair of Patton Boggs LLP's international arbitration practice. *"He is extremely thorough, thoughtful and diligent – he leaves no stone unturned,"* say interviewees. He is currently representing DRC in its attempt to enforce an $80 million award issued by an UNCITRAL panel against the Republic of Honduras. **Michael Reisman** is distinguished as a celebrated author, experienced arbitrator and advocate. He also acts as professor of international law at Yale Law School. One source enthused: *"He is one of the smartest and best writers in this field."* Commentators highlight **Charles Renfrew** as an illustrious leading arbitrator who can draw upon his prior experience as a District Judge and US Deputy Attorney General. **Claudia Salomon** (see p.399) recently joined Latham & Watkins LLP from DLA Piper. She is highly commended for her expert knowledge of investment treaty arbitrations. She is regarded as *"very responsible, capable and hard-working"* by market sources. As cofounder and managing partner of Boies, Schiller & Flexner LLP, **Jonathan Schiller** focuses his practice on litigation and international arbitration. Observers praise his depth of expertise in handling complex disputes. **Peter Sherwin** is a *"very well-rounded lawyer"* who is experienced in handling a wide range of disputes. Sources are quick to praise the breadth of his practice, noting that he is *"really good counsel and a very good arbitrator."* He is head of the international arbitration practice at Proskauer Rose and is currently representing a European biotech company in a $350 million ICDR arbitration against Bayer. **Laurence Shore** recently joined Herbert Smith Freehills from Gibson, Dunn & Crutcher. He is held in high regard for his extensive knowledge and insight into international arbitration disputes. Sources describe him as a *"prodigious worker and outstanding analyst of case issues,"* as well as a *"world-class expert on ICC arbitration policies and practices."* **Steven Smith** recently moved from O'Melveny & Myers to Jones Day. He is highly regarded by peers and clients for his experience in a wide range of commercial arbitrations. He has also acted in disputes involving sovereign states, and sits as an arbitrator as well as serving as counsel. **Abraham Sofaer** has amassed a significant amount of experience in his roles as former District Judge for the Southern District of New York and legal adviser to the US Department of State. Market sources regard him as *"incredibly dynamic."* **Ignacio Suarez Anzorena** (see p.414) has returned to Clifford Chance US LLP after spending several years in Chadbourne & Parke's international dispute resolution team. Market sources highlight his *"proactive capacity to understand complex issues in a very short amount of time."* He continues to focus much attention on disputes relating to Latin America. Rising star **Daniel Tan** is the principal of Dan Tan Law, an international arbitration and litigation boutique based in New York and San Francisco. Sources agree that he is *"a very entrepreneurial lawyer"* whose *"practice is very impressive."* He is currently defending US and Canadian companies against a claim of at least $25 million in an ICDR arbitration concerning distribution agreements. **Robert von Mehren** receives international respect as a senior arbitrator. Market sources describe him as *"the dean of international arbitration and a wonderful person."* **Anne Marie Whitesell** (see p.425) is based in the Washington, DC office of Dechert LLP, and also spends time in the firm's Paris office. She has extensive expertise in matters related to the ICC, and acts as counsel and arbitrator in a wide range of disputes.

# INTERNATIONAL TRADE

Commentary about individuals can be found under their firm's paragraph.  If the firm has no paragraph (is not ranked) look at Other Notable Practitioners.

## Band 1

### Covington & Burling LLP
See profile on p.441

**THE FIRM** This firm has an enduring reputation as a leading international trade practice. The team receives praise for its expertise across a range of areas and has a deep bench of practitioners dedicated to these fields. In the trade policy arena, clients include Microsoft and the Economic Cities Authority of Saudi Arabia, the latter of which engaged the group's services in developing new regulatory infrastructure. A busy export controls and sanctions practice includes representing major US companies in matters such as potential International Traffic in Arms Regulations (ITAR) violations and issues relating to Iran and Syria. The Foreign Corrupt Practices Act (FCPA) team also advises on investigations, risk assessments and compliance for clients in a wide range of industries.

**Client Service** *"They give us great advice and are very responsive to our requirements and concerns."* *"They're personable, they provide common-sense legal advice and they understand the nuances of the subject matter."*

**KEY INDIVIDUALS** Peter Trooboff (see p.419) is a well-respected senior counsel in the area of export controls and sanctions. The head of the firm's international practice, **Stuart Eizenstat** (see p.309) is a leading figure for trade policy work. His experience from his time in several government positions informs his advice on international business regulations. Sources regard **David Fagan** (see p.311) as one of the top practitioners in the country for Committee on Foreign Investment in the United States (CFIUS) matters, commenting that *"he has been doing topflight work for decades and is very well regarded."* Peers are happy to refer clients seeking export control expertise to **Peter Flanagan** (see p.314), and clients report that he is *"knowledgeable, accurate and timely with his advice."* **Peter Lichtenbaum** (see p.356) is admired by peers and clients alike for his *"devoted expertise"* in export control enforcement, and his sharp judgment when advising clients. According to one source, he is *"terrific and gives very practical advice – very down to earth."* In the CFIUS arena, **Mark Plotkin** (see p.385) is highly regarded for his transactional advice, and assisted Northrop Grumman with the sale of its Viper Strike business. Clients particularly appreciate his depth of experience in this area: *"The insight is really spot-on."* Clients are happy to recommend **Donald Ridings** (see p.392) for FCPA work, saying that *"he really knows his stuff"* and *"manages his team very well."* **John Veroneau** (see p.421) receives high praise for his comprehensive handling of trade matters: *"He is able to go from the highest levels of business strategy to the most precise details of execution."*

| Recommended for Client Service Nationwide | |
|---|---|
| Akin Gump Strauss Hauer & Feld LLP | Davis Polk & Wardwell LLP |
| Arent Fox LLP | Miller & Chevalier Chartered |
| Arnold & Porter LLP | Sheppard, Mullin, Richter & Hampton LLP |
| Baker & McKenzie | Steptoe & Johnson LLP |
| Covington & Burling LLP | WilmerHale |

| Recommended for Commercial Awareness Nationwide | |
|---|---|
| Arnold & Porter LLP | Kelley Drye & Warren LLP |
| Baker & McKenzie | Miller & Chevalier Chartered |
| Davis Polk & Wardwell LLP | Sidley Austin LLP |
| Hughes Hubbard & Reed LLP | WilmerHale |

### Hogan Lovells US LLP

**THE FIRM** This firm's array of international trade work includes numerous mandates relating to international sanctions, which has been an especially active arena for firms across the board. The team also provides expert guidance in various trade remedies and export controls investigations. Hogan Lovells's trade remedies and trade policy practice is extremely well regarded among commentators, and ongoing matters include advising the government of China on antidumping and countervailing duty investigations in the solar panel manufacturing industry.

The team also offers expertise in CFIUS, import strategy and anticorruption compliance.

**Sources say:** "*Hogan has so many terrific practice areas that it always has an expert even in a niche area.*"

**KEY INDIVIDUALS Jeanne Archibald** is active in sanctions advisory work and assisting clients achieve CFIUS clearance. She leads the firm's government regulatory practice group. Peers comment that they wouldn't hesitate to recommend **Mark McConnell** for a referral, and clients are equally impressed with his services: "*There's no one else we would call – he is truly an asset to us.*" **Beth Peters** garners high praise from commentators for her level of knowledge,

and is regarded as "*a fantastic attorney*" in the field of export controls and sanctions. Commentators admire the quality of **Deen Kaplan**'s work and clients appreciate his "*really useful perspective – the ability to step outside of it all and see trade in its political context.*" **Lewis Leibowitz** handles matters including trade remedies, negotiations and free trade agreements.

## Sidley Austin LLP
### See profile on p.1264

**THE FIRM** WTO work is a particular forte of this practice, which also handles a high volume of trade remedies, policy and sanctions work. The team continues to advise Airbus on an ongoing WTO dispute, and represents LG Electronics in antidumping and countervailing investigations into refrigerators imported from South Korea and Mexico. The firm's customs practice is also well regarded for its work on issues such as duty drawback and Trans-Pacific Partnership negotiations. Recent mandates include litigation regarding tariff classification for GE.

**Commercial Awareness** "*First-rate commercial awareness.*" "*This work requires good insights and knowledge, and we use Sidley for that.*"

**KEY INDIVIDUALS** "*An outstanding customs and trade attorney,*" **Richard Belanger** (see p.281) receives praise for both his detailed understanding of complex customs issues and his strategic thinking when navigating matters more widely. **Andrew Shoyer** (see p.406) is regarded as a standout practitioner, especially in the field of WTO litigation. One source comments: "*You can't touch him for WTO matters.*" Clients appreciate **Lisa Crosby**'s (see p.299) commitment to their export controls and sanctions mandates. She receives excellent feedback for "*her reliable, practical legal advice,*" and is described as "*very responsive and diligent.*"

## Steptoe & Johnson LLP

**THE FIRM** Steptoe & Johnson is a well-known name in international trade across the globe, and the firm is often called on for its expertise in Asia-Pacific work. The group's considerable activity in WTO litigation has grown of late to include significant new mandates. The team represents respondents in numerous proceedings, and advised SKF on antidumping administrative reviews of imports of bearings. FCPA is another area of strength, and highlights include a multijurisdictional investigation for Hercules Offshore. The firm's skill set is rounded out by in-demand expertise in export controls and sanctions.

**Client Service** "*I appreciate the quality of their service and enjoy our interaction. They are quite responsive and prompt.*"

**KEY INDIVIDUALS** "*The patriarch of the practice,*" **Richard Cunningham** played a lead role in the firm's defense of LG Electronics in connection with its imports of bottom-mount refrigerator-freezers from South Korea and Mexico, as well as wider work relating to South Korea. **Edward Krauland** is a popular choice for referrals among peers in the export controls arena. Clients value the fact that he is "*really a specialist, and obviously did the right thing in both solving our problems and advising us at earlier stages.*" **Lucinda Low** impresses commentators with her level of expertise – clients report that "*she gave good advice and was practical and friendly.*" Another source enthused that she is "*one of the best in the world at what she does.*" **Mark Moran** is a lead partner in the firm's WTO work and is described as "*a spectacular lawyer.*" He receives excellent feedback for his calm strategic reasoning as well as the strength of his technical legal advice. **Stewart Baker** is frequently sought out for his CFIUS expertise, and sources are confident in relying on his abilities: "*He was great, he was in the trenches with us and he was very attentive to our client.*" Chair of the firm's international department, **Susan Esserman** is particularly active on trade policy matters and Chinese antidumping investigations. Her clients include global packaging company MeadWestvaco. Partner **Stephen Heifetz** maintains a substantial CFIUS practice and is highly regarded for his knowledge of the field.

## WilmerHale
### See profile on p.930

**THE FIRM** This team's wide range of work includes CFIUS, export controls and sanctions advice as well as trade remedies mandates. Ongoing matters for Boeing and the Alliance for Clean Technology Innovation demonstrate the team's WTO abilities, and the team also advises a number of clients on Trans-Pacific Partnership negotiations. High-level clients seek out the firm's anticorruption practice for its advice on FCPA compliance and investigations.

**Client Service** "*WilmerHale has been extremely helpful and value-adding – they have such a broad reach that they're able to identify other issues as well.*"

**Commercial Awareness** "*One of the things they do especially well is that they clarify the business implications of the legal work.*" "*Very commercial and practical.*"

**KEY INDIVIDUALS Charlene Barshefsky** (see p.279) brings "*very important overall strategic guidance and insights*" to the firm's high-level trade remedies mandates.

Market commentators are unanimous in their respect for **Roger Witten** (see p.427). He leads the firm's renowned FCPA practice, assisting clients from a wide variety of industries with FCPA investigations, risk assessments, transactions and compliance training. **Ronald Meltzer** (see p.366) provides export and sanctions compliance advice in high-stakes situations for clients across a range of sectors. Co-managing partner of the firm, **Robert Novick** (see p.378) is valued for his attentive representation in major cases, such as the firm's work for Boeing. **Kimberly Parker** (see p.382) moves up in the rankings this year following outstanding feedback from clients, who rate her as "*phenomenal for FCPA work.*" **Benjamin Powell** (see p.387) is respected as a go-to adviser for CFIUS advice. According to one commentator, "*he is extremely strong, and I think very highly of him.*" Sources admire **David Weller**'s (see p.424) knowledge of trade policy issues and he frequently takes a lead role representing clients in negotiations.

## Band 2

### Akin Gump Strauss Hauer & Feld LLP
See profile on p.904

THE FIRM This firm's recent major mandates include advising on high-level trade policy negotiations, antidumping defense, ITAR compliance and antibribery issues. In one highlight, the firm represented the government of British Columbia in the longstanding lumber dispute between the USA and Canada. On the sanctions side, the team assists clients with regulatory compliance and voluntary disclosures. The customs team receives excellent feedback, and advises on the full spectrum of issues facing importers.
Client Service "*Awesome customer service – I couldn't recommend them enough.*"
KEY INDIVIDUALS **Edward Rubinoff** (see p.396) is head of the firm's export controls and economic sanctions prac-

tice, and is held in high regard for his work in both areas. The key contact for customs matters is the versatile **Lars-Erik Hjelm** (see p.334). Sources praise his breadth of experience, and one impressed client comments: "*He has a good working knowledge of the business, I like his pragmatic approach, and his responsiveness is off-the-charts good.*" **Warren Connelly** (see p.298) led the firm's representation of Samsung Electronics in its response to Whirlpool's allegations of refrigerator dumping in the US market. Department head **Valerie Slater** (see p.408) leads antidumping and countervailing mandates, and clients appreciate the experience she brings to bear on their cases. **Hal Shapiro** (see p.404) advises on international business and trade policy issues, including extensive high-level discussions between the USA and its trading partners.

### Arent Fox LLP
See profile on p.905

THE FIRM The trade team at Arent Fox comprises experts in numerous areas of regulation that affect international businesses. Perceived by the market as an extremely strong contender for compliance work, the group counsels clients on economic sanctions, import-export matters, and wider antiboycott and FCPA concerns. The trade remedies team handles sunset reviews for household-name clients, as well as advising on longstanding disputes such as cases ongoing in the steel and lumber industries.
Client Service "*Very high level of client service – I always get a very timely response. They are also very up to date with current legislative and regulatory activity, and I have nothing but praise for the firm.*"
KEY INDIVIDUALS The "*very responsive and very helpful*" **Kay Georgi** is particularly highly regarded for her work in export controls. She represents clients including 3M and G4S International. One interviewee describes **Matthew Clark** (see p.295) as "*a spectacular lawyer and a supreme advocate.*" He represented the government of Québec before the Court of International Arbitration in the softwood lumber case. **Matthew Nolan** (see p.376) heads the firm's international trade practice. His recent work includes advising leading Mexican tomato producer NatureSweet on a trade dispute regarding the alleged dumping of tomatoes in the US market. **John Gurley** is active in both customs and trade relief proceedings. He represented Trina Solar, a Chinese manufacturer of solar panel components, in the headline-grabbing US investigation into the Chinese solar panel industry.

### Arnold & Porter LLP
See profile on p.906

THE FIRM This firm's workload encompasses a broad range of international issues, including trade remedies, export controls, CFIUS, customs and FCPA advice. The team successfully represented BAE Systems in its consent agreement negotiations with the US State Department, resolving a civil claim brought under ITAR. The sanctions practice is increasingly sought out for advice on the changes in US restrictions to trade with Iran, Syria and Myanmar. In one trade remedies highlight, the firm repre-

sented Tjiwi Kimia in the successful revocation of antidumping and countervailing duty orders following a sunset review.
**Client Service** *"Very responsive, and this area of law is fairly urgent and immediate."*
**Commercial Awareness** *"They have real experience and give good advice – their legal advice takes the business challenges properly into perspective."*
**KEY INDIVIDUALS John Barker** (see p.278) is appreciated for his knowledge of export controls and wide experience dealing with the State, Commerce and Treasury departments. He is known as a go-to specialist in the arena, and *"people trust his judgment and leadership."* According to clients, **Lawrence Schneider** (see p.401) *"understands our concerns very well and can share his valuable experience with us."* He is head of the firm's international trade practice, and highlights include ongoing representation of the government of Israel and the Canadian province of Alberta. **Michael Shor** (see p.406) takes a lead role in

antidumping and countervailing duty investigations work, and represented Tjiwi Kimia in the abovementioned sunset review.

## Gibson, Dunn & Crutcher LLP
### See profile on p.682
**THE FIRM** This firm receives excellent feedback for all aspects of its international trade work. Recent highlights include representing the National Bank of Abu Dhabi in Office of Foreign Assets Control (OFAC) compliance issues, while other sanctions clients include household names such as Facebook and McDonald's. The firm's white-collar defense and investigations group has a well-respected FCPA practice that handles major internal investigations and routinely advises on compliance programs. Customs and trade remedies mandates further round out the firm's workload.
**Sources say:** *"We are very impressed with the firm and very happy with its work."*

**KEY INDIVIDUALS Joseph Warin** (see p.423) enjoys a top-tier reputation for his *"real breadth of experience"* in FCPA enforcement and compliance. He serves as compliance monitor to several industry-leading companies. Customs expert **Donald Harrison** (see p.331) advises on valuation, classification and country of origin issues, among other specialized areas. His clients include Honda and the Alliance of Automobile Manufacturers. **Judith Lee** (see p.353) is a popular choice for export controls, economic sanctions and CFIUS advice: *"She's very sure-footed on the law, and has an excellent manner."*

## Band 3

## Curtis, Mallet-Prevost, Colt & Mosle LLP
### See profile on p.1967
**THE FIRM** The international trade team at Curtis Mallet-Prevost can draw on decades of experience in representing clients from across the world. Import and export issues both contribute to its workload, and the firm has a sterling reputation for its expertise in WTO and trade remedy litigation. Recent work highlights include advising Deosen USA and Shelter Forest International on antidumping investigations, and acting for Vietnamese shrimp importers on sunset reviews.
**Sources say:** *"An exceptionally talented group of lawyers."*
**KEY INDIVIDUALS William Barringer** (see p.279) is described as *"one of the best trade lawyers in town."* He has particular experience in the Chinese market, and has defended the Ministry of Commerce of the People's Republic of China (MOFCOM) in several WTO and subsidy cases. **Christopher Dunn's** (see p.307) client roster includes key clients in Asia and Latin America, and he advised the Embassy of Colombia on the implementation of the Colombia Free Trade Agreement. **James Durling** (see p.307) is a *"very high-quality lawyer,"* and a key member of the trade remedies team. **Daniel Porter** (see p.386) rises in the rankings following particularly good feedback from market sources. He has an excellent reputation for handling high-profile matters such as his continued trade remedies work for GPX International Tire.

## Hughes Hubbard & Reed LLP
### See profile on p.1981
**THE FIRM** This firm enjoyed particular success in 2012 with the dismissal of all US claims in the widely publicized US-Canada lumber arbitration, in which it represented the Canadian government. The diversity of the firm's trade practice wins praise from commentators, with export compliance and import counseling numbering among the firm's strengths. Major international clients such as ThyssenKrupp Steel Europe use the partners' expertise across several areas.
**Commercial Awareness** *"They made a massive effort to understand the market and they couldn't have done better – their advocacy was faultless."*
**KEY INDIVIDUALS** Clients including Eaton and the LED innovator Cree engage **Amanda DeBusk's** (see p.303) talents in many aspects of export compliance. **Joanne**

**Osendarp** (see p.380) was a key figure in the firm's above-mentioned representation of the government of Canada, and is lauded for her strategic skills. Peers and clients alike recommend **Kenneth Pierce** (see p.384). According to one interviewee, he is *"knowledgeable, very practical, and his client service is phenomenal."* He heads the international trade remedies and customs group. The *"very thorough and focused"* **Matthew Nicely** (see p.376) moved to Hughes Hubbard & Reed from Thompson Hine in January 2013, further boosting the firm's bench strength in international trade matters. His experience includes representing a consortium of clients in the Vietnamese shrimp industry.

## King & Spalding LLP
### See profile on p.445
**THE FIRM** The quality of this firm's trade remedies practice is universally applauded by market commentators. The team is very well known for its work on the petitioners' side, and the firm's recent highlights in this area include representing US Magnesium in antidumping proceedings regarding imports from China and Russia. The team's wider capacities include FCPA investigations and CFIUS transactional advice.

Sources say: *"A very complete team of experts in trade issues with very high professional standards and easy communication."*
**KEY INDIVIDUALS** The founding partner of the firm's international trade practice group, **Joseph Dorn** (see p.306) is described as *"one of best trade lawyers in the USA – extremely well respected and knowledgeable."* Peers are impressed by **Gilbert Kaplan's** (see p.343) experience in representing petitioners. He takes a lead role in antidumping and countervailing duty filings on behalf of key clients. **Stephen Orava** (see p.380) has particular expertise in WTO agreements and dispute settlements, and has practiced across a range of global jurisdictions.

## Skadden, Arps, Slate, Meagher & Flom LLP & Affiliates
### See profile on p.2008
**THE FIRM** The steel industry remains a significant source of work for this firm, and US Steel is a prominent client which has contributed substantially to its workload. A renowned CFIUS practice benefits from the firm's healthy deal flow, and advises clients on an array of high-level transactions. Highlights include representing Sprint Nextel in its sale of a 70% stake worth $20.1 billion to the Japanese telecoms and internet company SOFTBANK.
Sources say: *"Extremely helpful in giving us the information and very timely responses to the issues as they come up. They take us through the whole criteria to help us figure out what we should do."*
**KEY INDIVIDUALS Ivan Schlager** (see p.401) is regarded as a top-notch lawyer with *"an enormous amount of experience"* in structuring transactions for CFIUS approval. As one source puts it, *"he's top of his game – incredibly good."* Commentators on the firm's trade remedies practice are complimentary about **James Hecht's** (see p.332) pragmatic approach: *"I find him very thoughtful, and he's got a good sense of the practical way to accomplish things."* Head of the international trade department, **Robert Lighthizer** (see p.357) *"combines astute legal analysis and advocacy with insightful political skills."*

## White & Case LLP
### See profile on p.451
**THE FIRM** The well-established team at White & Case has wide-ranging experience that covers a variety of trade matters. The group's client roster includes names from across the world, as illustrated by recent antidumping work for Saudi Aramco, Hyundai Heavy Industries and a Mexican galvanized steel wire manufacturer. WTO work is also a busy area, in which the firm can draw on its global capacity and Geneva-based experts.
Sources say: *"We know that we'll get detailed responses and they tend to present us with several different options depending on commercial considerations."*
**KEY INDIVIDUALS** Feedback for **Gregory Spak** (see p.411) details that he *"provides on-time, accurate analysis based on a thorough knowledge of the regulations."* **Walter Spak** (see p.411) heads the group, and clients appreciate the tenor of his input: *"Walter is 100% familiar with the underlying factual issues, and can handle things very aptly*

*from a high level."* **William Clinton** (see p.296) is an experienced trade lawyer whose expertise is called on by clients including Fujifilm and Saudi Aramco.

## Wiley Rein LLP
### See profile on p.928
**THE FIRM** This firm has advised a number of US manufacturers on defending their commercial interests against increasing imports of low-cost products from abroad. In one high-profile example, the team represented SolarWorld Industries America in filing petitions against the imports of Chinese solar cells and modules. More broadly, the team includes experts in export controls, economic sanctions and CFIUS compliance.
Sources say: *"We found Wiley Rein to be assertive and very responsive, and they came in with good documentation."*
**KEY INDIVIDUALS** Senior figure **Charles Verrill** (see p.421) has long experience across a broad range of trade dispute and policy matters. **Alan Price** (see p.387) is a highly active adviser, who spearheads the firm's representation of clients such as Nucor and the Wind Tower Trade Coalition. Sources are glowing in their praise of **Timothy Brightbill** (see p.287), and full of confidence in his handling of high-stakes matters: *"He was masterful in orchestrating the effort – he gave good counsel, and was extremely responsive and precise."*

### Band 4

## Baker & McKenzie
### See profile on p.435
**THE FIRM** Baker & McKenzie rises up the rankings this year following excellent feedback for the broad spectrum of services on offer. These include advice on customs and export matters, as well as trade remedies cases. The group represented NTN Corporation in all aspects of its trade concerns, including NAFTA audits, classification issues and antidumping proceedings. A burgeoning FCPA practice handles global investigations and acts as anticorruption counsel to numerous multinationals.
**Client Service** *"They've been incredibly customer-oriented, and they bring teams of lawyers to our office and go through recent developments. The huge global footprint of Baker is also particularly helpful in this area."*
**Commercial Awareness** *"They have exceeded our expectations – the firm strives to see issues from the business perspective."*
**KEY INDIVIDUALS Stuart Seidel** (see p.403) has long been regarded as a leading authority on customs matters such as classification, valuation and country of origin. He is a popular choice for peer referral and receives a range of positive reports from clients. **Richard Dean** (see p.302) is *"extremely experienced and savvy"* in anticorruption issues, and receives recommendation for his expertise in Russian matters. **Robert Tarun** (see p.416) is well known as the author of a leading guide to the FCPA, and is also praised for his commitment to client service. **Michael Murphy** (see p.373) is frequently picked out by commentators as an up-and-comer in the customs arena. He is valued for his

"*particularly commercial and practical*" advice, and for being "*really willing to do what it takes.*"

## Cassidy Levy Kent LLP

THE FIRM This specialist firm has boosted its bench strength, and can now offer the expertise of nine partners. The team receives excellent feedback for its cumulative experience and talent in the trade remedies arena. The group represents both US and foreign clients in antidumping and antisubsidy cases, acting for major names in steel, lumber and consumer goods.

KEY INDIVIDUALS John Greenwald (see p.326) focuses on antidumping and countervailing duty investigations, and is regarded as an excellent attorney in the field. Jack Levy (see p.356) is called on for a range of trade remedies advice, and has represented numerous US companies in their concerns over foreign imports.

## Crowell & Moring LLP
See profile on p.910

THE FIRM Export and import issues are the mainstays of this firm's practice, and the group handles a variety of work on each side. The team provides customs advice to a wide array of clients, including the Toyota affiliate Aisin and golfing equipment manufacturer Acushnet. Trade remedies work is an active area, and the firm represented GM in an antidumping and countervailing duty investigation.

Sources say: "*They provide a very good standard of service – very knowledgeable in the area from both a legal and a business perspective.*"

KEY INDIVIDUALS Practice head Jeffrey Snyder (see p.410) has wide-ranging experience: "*He's quite terrific – he's not only got a good sense of US law but also has good oversight.*" He is particularly well regarded for his advice on export control regulations such as ITAR and Export Administration Regulations (EAR). Clients describe John Brew (see p.287) as "*extremely good, and very responsive.*" His workload includes classification disputes, audits, prior disclosures and duty drawback.

## Davis Polk & Wardwell LLP
See profile on p.442

THE FIRM The sanctions arena has been a busy area for this firm of late, and Davis Polk's diverse client base in the field includes several high-profile financial institutions. In one highlight, the team achieved the termination of investigations into the Italian bank Intesa Sanpaolo. The group is also active in export controls work, as well as representing acquirers and targets before CFIUS. In FCPA matters, the firm has advised giants in the financial, mining and pharmaceutical sectors, and acted for BHP Billiton on a multijurisdictional investigation.

Client Service "*They not only kept me totally informed on a real-time basis, but were available to speak with me at any time, day or night, weekday or weekend.*"

Commercial Awareness "*Extremely knowledgeable and very commercial in understanding what we do.*" "*They are often the go-to firm for analysis when there's a change in leg-*

islation or regulation – they do the most thoughtful and complete analyses of issue-spotting.*"

KEY INDIVIDUALS John Reynolds (see p.392) "*has a reputation as a straight shooter,*" and is also "*respected for his knowledge and sensitivity.*" Sources comment on his particular excellence in handling sanctions issues for financial institutions. New York-based Scott Muller (see p.372) is a noted litigator who handles high-level international corruption mandates. Clients are pleased with his "*experienced, pragmatic and responsive*" representation.

## Kaye Scholer LLP
See profile on p.1984

THE FIRM This firm is best known for its market-leading CFIUS practice. The team receives praise for its in-depth knowledge of the relevant industries as well as the technical side of the process. It advised EADS on the ultimately terminated merger negotiations with BAE Systems, and represented Hawker Beechcraft Acquisition Company in the $1.39 billion sale of its commercial business to Superior Aviation Beijing.

Sources say: "*A preeminent firm for the defense industry in the USA.*"

KEY INDIVIDUALS Christopher Griner (see p.326) is chair of the national security/CFIUS practice group, and is unanimously acknowledged as a leader in the field of defense and security. Clients describe Farhad Jalinous (see p.340) as "*incredibly knowledgeable,*" and commend his ability to apply this knowledge to individual business circumstances. One source commented: "*He's my go-to person, he's brilliant.*"

## Kelley Drye & Warren LLP
See profile on p.1985

THE FIRM This team is well known for its skilled handling of trade remedies cases on behalf of petitioners, and its workload includes proceedings in the steel, agriculture and food industries. In standout matters, the firm represented several US producers of brass sheeting in connection with the potential revocation of an antidumping duty order on imports from Europe and Japan. The export control and sanctions team also receives strong feedback, and is active on a range of work including counseling clients on compliance with export controls.

Commercial Awareness "*They do a good job researching their clients both individually and as an industry. They want to determine the best strategy to ensure success.*"

KEY INDIVIDUALS David Hartquist is held in high respect, and clients note that he "*doesn't waste words, and when he speaks people listen.*" Interviewees "*would not hesitate to recommend*" Paul Rosenthal, particularly on the petitioner side of trade remedies cases. Among many other mandates, he defended US pasta producers against an Italian plaintiff's challenge to antidumping duty rates. Export controls specialist Eric McClafferty is commended for the practical perspective afforded by his thorough regulatory understanding: "*He is good at coming up with systemic broad approaches rather than just covering individual cases on a one-off basis.*" Chair of the international trade and customs group Kathleen Cannon has long experience

handling trade disputes. Described as "*outgoing and engaging*" by one source, "*she has the ability to draw out pertinent information.*"

## Mayer Brown LLP
See profile on p.1257

THE FIRM Trade remedies work and export controls and sanctions issues form the key strengths of this team, which also offers expertise in FCPA, CFIUS and customs work. The group has been called on by a number of major clients seeking advice on changing US trade sanctions. Kodak and its affiliates have engaged the firm's services in antidumping proceedings in China and India, and the firm has also been busy handling matters for the Renewable Fuels Association, Visa and Ralph Lauren.

KEY INDIVIDUALS The multitalented Simeon Kriesberg advises on a range of trade matters, and counsels global clients on export controls and economic sanctions compliance. Michael Kantor can draw on his experience in a number of governmental roles to advise on the firm's top trade instructions.

## McDermott Will & Emery LLP
See profile on p.1258

THE FIRM The trade team at this firm is highly active in the WTO area, and also represents clients' interests in the negotiation of free trade agreements including the Trans-Pacific Partnership. The group acts for a variety of clients from the agribusiness industry, and represents a coalition of US producers in defending domestic interests. Import-export work is also a core element of the practice, and the anticorruption team assists clients with FCPA issues.

Sources say: "*They were all very easy to work with, easy to communicate with, and their work was good quality – very thorough and detailed.*"

KEY INDIVIDUALS "*Practical, knowledgeable and thoughtful,*" David Levine (see p.355) impresses with both his area expertise and communication skills. One source also values the fact he is "*deeply committed to understanding our business and partnering with my team.*"

## Miller & Chevalier Chartered
See profile on p.923

THE FIRM Miller & Chevalier fields a stellar FCPA team as well as a strong practice in export compliance. The group assists clients with ongoing strategies and classification issues, as well as handling investigations and voluntary disclosures. The anticorruption group provides compliance counseling and due diligence services to an array of clients, and conducts a variety of cross-border internal investigations.

Client Service "*Very good client relationship skills.*" "*They're great partners – they are flexible when they can be and support us when we can't be flexible.*"

Commercial Awareness "*They really understand our business and are able to see the business context of the legal advice they're delivering.*"

KEY INDIVIDUALS The "*exceptionally well-respected*" Homer Moyer (see p.372) "*has superb client relation skills and judgment.*" He is regarded as a top authority for FCPA work. **Larry Christensen** (see p.294) counsels clients from a variety of sectors on trade compliance under OFAC, ITAR and EAR. He is well known for his expertise in issues involving the US Department of Commerce. **Kathryn Atkinson** (see p.275) earns high praise for her knowledge and practical approach: *"She's a delight to work with – responsive and pragmatic. I can't recommend her highly enough."* **William Clements** (see p.296) is of counsel to the firm, and is commended for his capabilities in compliance issues.

## Morris, Manning & Martin, LLP

**THE FIRM** This team of international trade experts is regarded as a strong choice for trade remedies work, and its practitioners have extensive experience in the field. In one highlight, the group assisted the UAE company Universal Tube & Plastic Industries with an antidumping and countervailing duty investigation. Other significant clients in the area include Electrolux and Hyundai HYSCO.

**KEY INDIVIDUALS Donald Cameron** is described as *"somewhat of an institution"* and an excellent advocate: *"Very impressive, does a great job for his clients – fights for them and won't leave any stone unturned."* **Julie Mendoza** also receives excellent feedback and is particularly noted for her work in Latin America. The partners' teamwork is afforded considerable respect: *"They are both passionate about zealously representing clients and are respected by judges, government officials and other members of the Bar."*

## O'Melveny & Myers LLP
See profile on p.693

**THE FIRM** O'Melveny & Myers handles an impressive range of international trade work. It has handled policy issues for the likes of Rio Tinto and Goldman Sachs, and is also involved in trade remedy proceedings in the solar industry. The team includes several individuals with notable expertise in export controls, and represents a wide range of companies in this area. The firm's services also include expert anticorruption advice, and it has assisted clients with FCPA risk assessment, due diligence and training.

**Sources say:** *"I think the practice is extremely good, and the customer service is excellent."*

**KEY INDIVIDUALS** Peers will happily refer CFIUS matters to **Theodore Kassinger**: *"He's very good and would take good care of clients."* He has decades of experience from his time in both government roles and private practice. **Greta Lichtenbaum** is a *"fantastic lawyer,"* whose experience inspires trust and respect when representing clients before OFAC. Sources report that **Richard Grime**'s background at the SEC *"has been extremely helpful, along with his international experience."* He is also described as *"insightful, knowledgeable and practical."*

## Pillsbury Winthrop Shaw Pittman LLP
See profile on p.2000

**THE FIRM** This firm is well regarded for its work on international trade disputes, as well as for its broad range of compliance and enforcement expertise. The team is highly active in WTO matters, and also advises on trade agreements such as NAFTA. Numerous compliance highlights include advising the Electric Power Research Institute on ongoing export controls matters. Other corporations in the financial services, energy and defense sectors round out the impressive client roster of this busy practice.

**Sources say:** *"Very experienced in these highly technical and specialized areas of law."*

**KEY INDIVIDUALS Christopher Wall** (see p.422) leads the firm's work in the export controls and sanctions area, and is also recognized for his CFIUS expertise. His clients include major names such as Rolls-Royce, American Express and Saab. **Stephan Becker** (see p.281) heads the international trade practice, and sources are impressed by his *"multi-industry, multi-issue knowledge of all that's going on."* **Nancy Fischer** (see p.313) advises on a variety of trade controls matters, including OFAC and ITAR enforcement, and has also been engaged on antiboycott and FCPA mandates.

## Stewart & Stewart

**THE FIRM** This boutique firm receives outstanding feedback from its loyal clients. The team has extensive experience in antidumping and countervailing duty disputes, which include significant cases in the steel, agriculture and automotive sectors. Its workload also includes a number of sanctions and export controls mandates.

**Sources say:** *"It's phenomenal – they're absolutely focused on every tiny nuanced aspect of the case, which gives me confidence that they'll handle things perfectly every time."*

**KEY INDIVIDUALS Terence Stewart** leads the practice and receives high praise for his skills and *"unwavering commitment to the best goals of the client."*

## Band 5

## Alston & Bird LLP
See profile on p.1102

**THE FIRM** Customs and export matters form the dual mainstays of this group's practice, and the firm's experience covers a broad swath of trade areas. Highlights include representing PPG Industries in connection with the obligations of its nonprosecution agreement with the DOJ. Customs mandates include the submission of prior disclosures, enforcement defense and ongoing strategy development. The group's varied client roster includes names such as Bayer, UPS and the government of the Russian Federation.

**Sources say:** *"The customer service is good and they work well together."*

**KEY INDIVIDUALS Kenneth Weigel**'s (see p.424) *"well-rounded"* practice includes both export compliance advice and high-stakes customs matters. **Thomas Crocker** (see p.299) has decades of experience in export regulations and enforcement, and, according to sources, is a renowned adviser on sanctions. On the customs side, **Jon Fee**'s (see p.311) practice includes criminal investigations and Trans-Pacific Partnership strategy as well as general compliance advice.

## DLA Piper LLP (US)
See profile on p.1971

**THE FIRM** This group has had a particularly active year in the export controls and sanctions arena. Clients such as Renault, General Reinsurance and Saudi Aramco sought the firm's advice on compliance with several sets of federal regulations. The team also handles trade remedies work and has represented several US producers in connection with sunset reviews of antidumping orders.

**KEY INDIVIDUALS Richard Newcomb**'s (see p.375) long experience as the director of OFAC lends extra insight to his advice on sanctions issues.

## Greenberg Traurig, LLP
See profile on p.1024

**THE FIRM** This firm continues to represent clients in WTO issues, including state-level entities in Brazil and Mexico. Trade policy has been a busy area overall, and the group has been engaged in matters pertaining to the Central American Free Trade Agreement (CAFTA). More widely, clients such as Volvo have consulted the firm regarding export controls and CFIUS clearance.

**KEY INDIVIDUALS James Bacchus** (see p.276) chairs the firm's global practice group, and can call on his background as a member of the WTO's appellate body and a member of Congress. His highlights include representing the National Fisheries Institute regarding the regulation of catfish in the US market. **Philippe Bruno** (see p.289) takes a lead role in many of the firm's antidumping and countervailing duty instructions, and he is valued for the quality of his representation.

## Latham & Watkins LLP
See profile on p.446

**THE FIRM** Market commentators highlight this firm's impressive strength in export controls and economic sanctions. Recent mandates include issues involving Iran, Syria, Cuba, Sudan and Somalia, and the firm represents several nonprofit humanitarian organizations as well as multinational corporations. Other areas of expertise include customs and CFIUS compliance.

**KEY INDIVIDUALS** Peers consider **William McGlone** (see p.365) a leading figure in the export controls field, and have a high regard for his expertise in ITAR, EAR and OFAC matters.

## McKenna Long & Aldridge LLP
See profile on p.922

**THE FIRM** This team has been bolstered by the addition of four lateral hires, including ex-Dewey & LeBoeuf specialist Alan Wolff. The group represents clients in a variety of areas, from WTO litigation to export compliance and customs issues. In one highlight, the team acted for the Semiconductor Industry Association in connection with the elimination of tariffs on semiconductor products. Clients in multiple sectors have also sought the firm's advice on voluntary disclosures to OFAC.

**KEY INDIVIDUALS** Senior counsel **Alan Wolff** (see p.428) has long experience in litigation and regulatory counseling, and sources admire his expertise in trade policy matters.

## Sheppard, Mullin, Richter & Hampton LLP

**THE FIRM** Sheppard Mullin represents both US and global clients in a range of international trade concerns including export controls, economic sanctions, customs and FCPA. Its client base spans sectors such as defense, manufacturing and telecoms. The team receives high praise for its responsiveness and smooth management of client relations.

**Client Service** *"Wonderfully responsive to the questions we've had; they provided timely advice to help us navigate things and very much took our needs into account."*

**KEY INDIVIDUALS** Interviewees value the experience and expertise offered by **Scott Maberry** when dealing with federal agencies. One source also comments: *"I can pick up the phone and reach him wherever he is working."* **Thaddeus McBride** joins the export controls and economic sanctions rankings this year following excellent client feedback. He is described as *"very focused and sincere in his desire to help the business."*

## Sullivan & Cromwell LLP
See profile on p.2011

**THE FIRM** This firm receives strong feedback across several areas of international trade practice. Sanctions matters have been a highly active area of late, and the team has advised a number of top international financial institutions on related issues. The white-collar group is active in FCPA investigations for clients such as Tenaris and Diageo.

**KEY INDIVIDUALS** Eric Kadel and Elizabeth Davy are key contacts for export compliance, as is Karen Seymour for FCPA matters.

## Vinson & Elkins LLP
See profile on p.2459

**THE FIRM** This firm has considerable expertise in handling compliance and investigations into potential violations of export controls and sanctions. Several multinational companies have sought its counsel regarding amendments to the Iran Sanctions Act, and Syria, Libya and Sudan have also been areas of concern. Other work includes conducting export audits and assisting with voluntary disclosures.

**Sources say:** *"Good practical advice: they always give you quick guidance and are also able to give you the in-depth coverage when you need that as well."*

**KEY INDIVIDUALS Kathleen Little** (see p.357) is popular with clients, who appreciate her *"methodical and process-oriented"* approach, and peers are also complimentary: *"She does a very good job and I hold her in very high regard."* Practice head **David Johnson** (see p.340) regularly counsels clients on export regulations. According to one interviewee, *"what stands out about David is his practical approach and strategic thinking."*

## Weil, Gotshal & Manges LLP
See profile on p.2015

**THE FIRM** This firm continues to advise on trade remedies and policy matters for a roster of clients that includes Philip Morris, which sought the group's advice on the negotiation of the Trans-Pacific Partnership. In other standout matters, the team acted for Banc of America Securities and its subsidiary Blue Ridge Investments on the enforcement of an arbitral award in a trade dispute with the Argentine Republic. FCPA work is also handled for significant clients across various sectors.

**KEY INDIVIDUALS Charles Roh** (see p.394) is highlighted as a *"good strategic thinker."* His experience in the office of the United States Trade Representative lends insight to some of the firm's top-level mandates.

## Other Notable Practitioners

**Josephine Aiello LeBeau** of Wilson Sonsini Goodrich & Rosati counsels clients on a range of export controls and sanctions matters, and is considered a particular specialist in the technology industry. **Michael Burton** recently left Arent Fox to become a founding partner of Joiner Burton. He is commended for his knowledge of ITAR and excellent level of responsiveness. He also advises on antiboycott and anticorruption issues. **David Christy** (see p.294) of Thompson Hine LLP is noted particularly for his expertise in WTO matters and has recently acted for clients including Diageo. **Harry Clark** leads the international trade and compliance group at Orrick, Herrington & Sutcliffe LLP. He has experience in many areas affecting clients' international business and receives especially good feedback for his advice on export compliance. The highly respected **Peter Clark** (see p.295) of Cadwalader, Wickersham & Taft LLP is known for his extensive background as a thought leader in the FCPA Bar. **Gail Cumins** of the specialist firm Sharretts, Paley, Carter & Blauvelt, P.C. is regarded as a knowledgeable resource on customs issues. **Timothy Dickinson** of Paul Hastings LLP is *"one of the premier attorneys in the area of anticorruption,"* and is complimented for the sensitivity of his compliance advice: *"I find his judgment excellent, and I have a high level of comfort that he gives superb advice."* **Elliot Feldman** (see p.312) of Baker Hostetler LLP is a trade remedies lawyer who *"brings very interesting issues and perspectives to the table."* His clients have included foreign governments, domestic and international organizations and individuals. At Berliner, Corcoran & Rowe, LLP, **Benjamin Flowe** receives high praise as *"a really good nitty-gritty guy when it comes to encryption and export controls."* He regularly assists clients with voluntary disclosures and in-house compliance, as well as guiding them through enforcement proceedings. **Lawrence Friedman** (see p.317) of Barnes, Richardson & Colburn joins the rankings this year following recognition for his prominence in the field and his impressive skill set: *"He is knowledgeable on the subject and gives practical advice."* **Gary Horlick** of Law Offices of Gary N. Horlick is seen by peers as a good pair of hands in the trade remedies and trade policy area. He advised internet industry clients on the Trans-Pacific Partnership as well as handling trade remedy cases across several continents. **Doug Jacobson** practices at the Law Offices of Douglas N. Jacobson, PLLC, and receives glowing feedback from peers for his experience and the quality of his work. At Clifford Chance US LLP, **George Kleinfeld** (see p.348) is active in trade matters extending through the full range of export control matters, and can offer expert guidance to clients seeking CFIUS clearance for their transactions. With over 25 years of experience in the customs arena, **Peter Klestadt** of Grunfeld, Desiderio, Lebowitz, Silverman & Klestadt LLP is a highly regarded figure in the field. Clients are highly impressed, and one reported: *"He is amazing and did a wonderful job."* **Susan Kohn Ross** in the Los Angeles office of Mitchell Silberberg & Knupp LLP regularly advises clients on their interaction with US Customs & Border Protection.

**Trip Mackintosh** (see p.360) of Holland & Hart LLP receives resounding praise from clients: *"There don't seem to be any holes in his expertise – he has vast experience with all the regulators in this area, his advice always seems spot-on and he's easy to work with."* **John Magnus** of Tradewins LLC is engaged in various trade policy matters, and is also active on antidumping and countervailing duty mandates. Market sources identify **Paul Marquardt** (see p.362) of Cleary Gottlieb Steen & Hamilton LLP as an expert in managing CFIUS filings, and they also praise his client service: *"He's been there for me, helping me understand everything – he's practical, easygoing and pleasant to deal with."* In the export controls and sanctions arena, **Richard Matheny** (see p.363) of Goodwin Procter LLP is lauded by clients, who appreciate his guidance in potentially difficult situations. One source comments that *"his diligence and depth of knowledge were very impressive,"* and another adds: *"He was just outstanding, and you got the feeling that we were his only client."*

With *"seasoned experience"* in customs law, **Matthew McGrath** of Barnes, Richardson & Colburn advises on the full spectrum of issues affecting importers. He continues to represent the Pharmaceutical Research & Manufacturers of America regarding tariff elimination for drugs among member countries of the WTO. **Mark Mendelsohn** (see p.367) of Paul, Weiss, Rifkind, Wharton & Garrison LLP is *"a big name and has a lot of experience from the enforcement side."* He is frequently identified as a leading expert in FCPA counseling work and represents a number of sector-significant clients. **Lindsay Meyer** (see p.368) is co-managing partner of Venable LLP and head of the firm's international trade practice. Her considerable experience in customs matters leads clients to take important issues straight to her: *"She has a really good ability to explain these difficult questions and concepts to a range of businesspeople."* Also well recognized in the customs area, **Kathleen Murphy** (see p.373) of Drinker Biddle & Reath LLP assists clients in negotiating audits, investigations and self-assessment. In the FCPA field, **Danforth Newcomb** (see p.375) is a founding member of Shearman & Sterling LLP's anticorruption practice. He is held in universal esteem, and his long experience includes numerous SEC and DOJ proceedings. **John Peterson** of Neville Peterson LLP is described as *"a big-time customs litigator,"* and is recommended for the level of dedication he shows to clients' cases. Clients are unreserved in their recommendation of **Robert Pisani** of Pisani & Roll LLP and regularly consult his expertise on customs matters: *"He is exceptionally good at what he does, and is very pragmatic – he has good business sense and knows what is important and what is not."* **Michael Roll** is another valued partner at the customs specialist firm Pisani & Roll LLP. He is described as *"extremely knowledgeable,"* and according to one client *"his pragmatism and incisiveness help us to resolve problems in a very efficient manner."* Miami-based **Peter Quinter** (see p.388) of GrayRobinson, PA has notable customs expertise and is a vice chair of the ABA Customs Law Committee. Clients elucidate the qualities he brings to their cases: *"His strengths include his ability to clearly explain complicated matters and effectively resolve them."* **Lee Sandler** is a founding member of bou-

tique customs practice Sandler, Travis & Rosenberg. He has decades of experience across the board and is well respected by commentators. **Roger Schagrin** of Schagrin Associates is *"a very prominent trade lawyer"* who is active on trade remedies cases, especially in the steel industry. **Melvin Schwechter** (see p.403) of Baker Hostetler LLP is ranked for his work in both export controls and customs, and sources appreciate the breadth of his expertise. One source likened him to *"a walking encyclopedia – he can recite different cases and has a wealth of knowledge."* He is also valued for his *"sincere desire to help his clients to achieve what they need to achieve."* **Laurence Urgenson** (see p.420) specializes in FCPA work at Kirkland & Ellis LLP, and is known for his experience in high-stakes investigations. According to interviewees, **Philip Urofsky** of Shearman & Sterling LLP *"works hard and is really thoughtful."* He takes

a lead role in the firm's FCPA mandates, and has considerable experience from his time as a federal prosecutor as well as in private practice. **Martin Weinstein** (see p.424) of Willkie Farr & Gallagher LLP is active on FCPA matters for clients such as Tyco International. Interviewees report that they are impressed by the level of service received: *"He always gets back to us promptly and follows up to make sure we're satisfied."* Respected white-collar defense lawyer **Bruce Yannett** of Debevoise & Plimpton LLP regularly acts on prominent DOJ and SEC investigations for heavyweight clients. He is highly regarded by peers, who consider him a *"very talented lawyer."* Chicago-based **Mark Zolno** of Katten Muchin Rosenman LLP has years of experience in customs law, including tariff classifications, country of origin determinations and valuation.

# INTERNATIONAL TRADE INTELLECTUAL PROPERTY (SECTION 337)

Commentary about individuals can be found under their firm's paragraph. If the firm has no paragraph (is not ranked) look at Other Notable Practitioners.

| International Trade: Intellectual Property (Section 337) Leading Firms |
| --- |
| **Band 1** |
| Adduci, Mastriani & Schaumberg LLP * |
| Finnegan, Henderson, Farabow, Garrett & Dunner LLP * |
| Fish & Richardson PC |
| **Band 2** |
| Covington & Burling LLP * |
| Foster, Murphy, Altman & Nickel, PC * |
| **Band 3** |
| Kirkland & Ellis LLP * |
| Morrison & Foerster LLP * |
| Sidley Austin LLP * |
| Steptoe & Johnson LLP |
| Weil, Gotshal & Manges LLP * |
| WilmerHale * |
| **Band 4** |
| DLA Piper LLP (US) * |
| Kenyon & Kenyon LLP |
| Quinn Emanuel Urquhart & Sullivan, LLP |

\* *Indicates firm with profile.*
*Alphabetical order within each band. Band 1 is the highest.*

## Band 1

### Adduci, Mastriani & Schaumberg LLP
See profile on p.903

**THE FIRM** This firm has long been regarded as a top choice for counsel in the Section 337 arena, and is regularly called on by other legal practices for its specialist expertise. The firm advises a range of prestigious clients on high-stakes ITC cases, including Apple, Tessera and Seiko Epson. In standout matters, it advised silicone smartphone case manufacturer Otter Products on the unfair acts aspects of an ITC case against multiple respondents. Further highlights include acting for Honeywell on a case regarding the importation of GPS devices.

**Sources say:** *"The experience lives up to the reputation – they're very good at providing support and advice." "They're very good at what they do and the sheer volume of the cases they handle is top-notch."*

**KEY INDIVIDUALS** Sources are highly impressed by managing partner **James Adduci**, who is regarded as one of the preeminent practitioners in the field. Interviewees are just as complimentary about **Louis Mastriani**, who is *"widely respected – no doubt about that."* He led the firm's representation of Garmin in its successful defense against a claim by Rambus. **Tom Schaumberg** takes a lead role in acting for respondents and petitioners, including Intellectual Ventures and 3M. He is well respected for his long experience in the field.

### Finnegan, Henderson, Farabow, Garrett & Dunner LLP
See profile on p.912

**THE FIRM** This highly regarded IP firm is a dominant participant in ITC work. In one highlight, the team repre-

sented LG Electronics in multiple patent infringement cases against several different complainants. It also continued to represent HTC and its subsidiary S3 Graphics in a series of cases against Apple that formed one of the principal battles of the 'smartphone wars'. The firm's impressive client list also includes Research In Motion and Mitsubishi Heavy Industries.

**Sources say:** *"One of the firms which substantively stand out for big matters."*

**KEY INDIVIDUALS** **Thomas Jarvis** (see p.340) has decades of experience litigating IP cases in the ITC, and has acted as lead trial counsel for an array of technology sector clients. The *"very strong"* **Smith Brittingham** (see p.287) is praised for his assertiveness and clear thinking. He represented Korean company SKC Kolon in a polyimide film patent infringement case.

### Fish & Richardson PC

**THE FIRM** This firm receives high praise for both its dedicated ITC expertise and its superb litigation ability. These combined strengths attract a range of high-stakes cases, including mandates for several manufacturers of wireless devices. Its sector-spanning client base includes LG Electronics and SAMSUNG, as well as Honda.

**Sources say:** *"Known as a preeminent firm in the area." "A top-tier ITC practice."*

**KEY INDIVIDUALS** Esteemed patent litigator **Ruffin Cordell** is held in high regard for his ITC work. He is known for his prolific practice, and one source commented that he appeared to be *"active in everything everywhere."* **Michael McKeon** rises in the rankings this year after receiving consistently impressive feedback. Peers respect his knowledge of the Section 337 arena, and assert that clients *"certainly can't go wrong"* by engaging his services.

## Band 2

### Covington & Burling LLP
See profile on p.441

THE FIRM This firm's renowned international trade capabilities include impressive expertise in high-level Section 337 work. Key clients in the pharmaceutical, electronics and wireless technology industries seek the team's expert advice on prominent cases. One highlight saw the firm representing Samsung Electronics and Samsung LED in parallel litigations against OSRAM regarding LED patent infringement.
Sources say: *"A very good ITC team."*
KEY INDIVIDUALS Sturgis Sobin (see p.410) is a notable Section 337 lawyer, with experience across a broad swath of technological issues. His clients include heavyweights such as Merck and Huawei. **Maureen Browne** (see p.288) is lauded for both her technical knowledge and litigation skills. One peer comments: *"She's a fantastic ITC litigator and I think she does a great job."*

### Foster, Murphy, Altman & Nickel, PC
See profile on p.913

THE FIRM This boutique firm is dedicated to counseling clients and third parties on ITC proceedings. Collectively, the team offers an impressive range and depth of experience, and receives standout feedback for its stellar knowledge and ease of interaction. Recent work highlights include cases on behalf of HTC and several respondents in the semiconductor industry.
Sources say: *"Outstanding lawyers – they're always thinking about how to do better for the client and do things strategically."*
KEY INDIVIDUALS *"A fixture at the ITC,"* David Foster (see p.315) is a respected figure with enormous Section 337 experience. He takes a lead in many of the firm's highest-profile mandates, including cases for HTC against Apple and Kodak. Sources are glowing in their praise of **Barbara Murphy** (see p.373), commending both her depth of knowledge and communication skills. **James Altman's** (see p.273) diverse client base includes uPI Semiconductor, which sought his advice as a respondent in a dispute over DC-DC controllers. He is a former president of the ITC Trial Lawyers Association. **David Nickel** (see p.376) is described as an *"extraordinarily good technical guy,"* and represents major industry names such as LSI and Alcatel-Lucent.

## Band 3

### Kirkland & Ellis LLP
See profile on p.1254

THE FIRM Kirkland & Ellis represents an impressive array of technology industry clients as both complainants and respondents. The team advised Cisco Systems on several cases, including one claim brought by a patent licensing firm and another brought by ChriMar Systems. In other highlights, the firm achieved a successful result for IBM in a dispute over the alleged infringement of two patents.
Sources say: *"An excellent firm which I'd happily refer others to."*
KEY INDIVIDUALS Gregory Arovas (see p.1874) joins the rankings this year following strong feedback from interviewees, who describe him as *"really a superb lawyer."*

### Morrison & Foerster LLP
See profile on p.1990

THE FIRM This firm maintains a very active ITC practice, and attracts plaudits for both the strength of its team and the caliber of its clients. The team has been heavily involved in the 'smartphone wars', and is also handling cases involving numerous other technologies. Highlights include representing Hitachi Metals in a case regarding patents for rare earth magnets used in household, automobile and military products. The group also defended Fujitsu against claims that two flash memory reader patents had been infringed.
Sources say: *"They kept us fully informed through every phase, and were very responsive and available."*
KEY INDIVIDUALS Brian Busey (see p.290) is a respected ITC trial lawyer who is a real hit with clients: *"He has good insight and can give us strategic advice regarding the whole direction of a case."* According to one impressed source, **Alexander Hadjis** (see p.328) *"has intensive experience of ITC litigation and can communicate with the client very well on either team management, strategy or detailed technology issues."*

### Sidley Austin LLP
See profile on p.1264

THE FIRM This firm continues to represent top-level manufacturers of portable devices and associated software in multiple patent litigation cases. Clients in the smartphone arena include Microsoft and Research In Motion. In other areas, the team represented LG Electronics in defense of a claim brought by Walker Digital over Blu-ray disc players.
KEY INDIVIDUALS Brian Nester (see p.375) is held in high regard by peers, who commend his active practice and specialized skills: *"He's an excellent lawyer and has a tremendous amount of ITC experience."*

### Steptoe & Johnson LLP

THE FIRM Steptoe & Johnson has handled many major smartphone cases as part of its ITC practice. Motorola and SAMSUNG are both highly active participants which call on the firm for assistance. The firm's wider practice includes cases involving television and video technology, GPS equipment and luxury goods. The team also represented Louis Vuitton Malletier in an investigation against US and Chinese respondents accused of importing and selling counterfeit products.
KEY INDIVIDUALS According to interviewees, **Charles Schill** is *"a wonderful guy"* who is *"widely respected."* He leads the team at Steptoe that handles ITC work and he has extensive experience in this area. **Alice Kipel's** practice includes a variety of international trade areas and considerable involvement in Section 337 investigations. She advised Dura Magnetics as respondent on a claim filed by Hitachi Metals.

### Weil, Gotshal & Manges LLP
See profile on p.2015

THE FIRM This firm's workload includes cases involving cell phone, television and semiconductor technologies. Apple is a prominent client on the firm's roster, and has called on the team for advice on disputes with Kodak and Motorola. The group also represented the California Institute of Technology in an investigation into the alleged violation of its patents by chips in imported Research In Motion and Nokia smartphones.
KEY INDIVIDUALS Mark Davis (see p.301) is commended for his *"experienced, talented and well-balanced"* practice. He leads the group's representation of clients including Microsoft and Apple.

## WilmerHale
See profile on p.930

THE FIRM WilmerHale's renowned IP department is regularly called on to lead high-stakes cases for industry-leading clients. The firm's workload has been dominated by cases in the smartphone arena of late, and the team also represents technology producers and retailers of a range of imported products.

KEY INDIVIDUALS William Lee's (see p.353) sterling reputation in the IP arena means that he is often called on for representation in big-ticket ITC cases. *"He's as good as they come in terms of handling the trial work,"* says one source.

### Band 4

## DLA Piper LLP (US)
See profile on p.1971

THE FIRM This firm offers expert guidance throughout all stages of ITC proceedings, advising a range of respondents and complainants. In one highlight, DLA Piper lawyers represented Apple in a major case brought by HTC alleging infringement of five patents, which resulted in the ITC finding no violation. The team also successfully

defended GSI Technology in an investigation into its SRAM chips.

KEY INDIVIDUALS Mark Fowler (see p.315) *"is a superb attorney"* who leads much of the firm's top-level Section 337 work. He cochairs the firm's patent litigation practice, and is well known for his technological expertise and oral advocacy skills.

## Kenyon & Kenyon LLP
THE FIRM Household name clients from a variety of sectors seek out this firm's specialist advice on ITC disputes. These include Apple and Sony, which engaged the firm's services in cases regarding imports of portable communication devices. The team also represented Audi and Volkswagen in a complaint issued by Beacon Navigation, and acted for Bosch as a complainant against several wiper blade manufacturers.

KEY INDIVIDUALS Practice chair Marcia Sundeen receives high praise, and interviewees describe her as a *"terrific lawyer"* who *"does great work."*

## Quinn Emanuel Urquhart & Sullivan, LLP
THE FIRM This firm is a frequent participant in disputes between multinational technology companies. It has risen in prominence due to its expanding team and involvement

in notable cases. In the smartphone arena, the group represented Motorola in a case brought by Microsoft claiming violation of multiple patents. The team also advised a group of chip suppliers including Broadcom on a case brought by Rambus.

KEY INDIVIDUALS Paul Brinkman is an ITC specialist who brings dedicated knowledge and experience to the firm's patent litigation team. He leads the firm's Section 337 practice and sources describe his move to Quinn as *"a big deal – he's very good."*

### Other Notable Practitioners

At Latham & Watkins LLP, Bert Reiser (see p.391) is considered a go-to lawyer for advice on Section 337 proceedings. He leads the firm's representation of clients including the LCD display manufacturer AU Optronics and General Imaging. Gary Hnath of Mayer Brown LLP is well known as an experienced ITC specialist. Clients value his practicality and responsiveness, and report that *"he's extremely smart in understanding technical issues very quickly."*

# INVESTMENT FUNDS HEDGE FUNDS

Investment Funds: Hedge Funds p.162

Commentary about individuals can be found under their firm's paragraph. If the firm has no paragraph (is not ranked) look at Other Notable Practitioners.

### Band 1

## Schulte Roth & Zabel LLP
See profile on p.2003

THE FIRM Universally recognized as a top performer in the hedge funds space, this team is frequently engaged by industry behemoths such as The Blackstone Group and Centerbridge Partners. The group's strength is derived from a deep bench of top practitioners whose experience spans a multitude of fund formations, structurings and M&A transactions. Support from the firm's stellar regulatory and compliance teams is also a valuable resource for the hedge funds team. The team recently presided over new fund launches for a number of notable investment advisers, including Perella Weinberg Partners.

Sources say: *"I have a very high regard for their legal skills, responsiveness and common-sense approach to disputes."*

KEY INDIVIDUALS Cochair of the group Stephanie Breslow (see p.287) is considered a leading figure in the field. She is highly experienced in a range of hedge fund matters, and recently assisted Centerbridge Partners in the $1.95 billion formation of a new credit fund. Steven Fredman (see p.316) also cochairs the practice. He is iden-

tified by sources as *"one of the best in the business,"* winning the respect of the market for his illustrious client roster. His clients appreciate his commitment to *"making sure we are properly protected wherever we go."* David Nissenbaum (see p.376) has recently been engaged by Perella Weinberg Partners Capital Management on the complex acquisition from Deutsche Bank of a proprietary trading team. Clients are quick to praise his *"intelligent and personable"* approach. Paul Roth (see p.396) maintains a towering reputation in the hedge funds sphere, and is recognized as a *"great figure in the industry."* He chairs the investment management practice.

## Sidley Austin LLP
See profile on p.1264

THE FIRM Sidley Austin receives outstanding endorsements from the market for its leading hedge funds practice. The team's longstanding representation of a diverse and sophisticated client base, which includes the likes of The BlackRock Funds and Marathon Asset Management, has earned it the respect of key industry players. Lawyers have recently been busy with several ongoing projects, including the expansion of Credit Suisse's HedgeFocus

| Recommended for Client Service Nationwide | |
|---|---|
| Fried, Frank, Harris, Shriver & Jacobson LLP | Paul, Weiss, Rifkind, Wharton & Garrison LLP |
| | Willkie Farr & Gallagher LLP |

| Recommended for Commercial Awareness Nationwide | |
|---|---|
| Akin Gump Strauss Hauer & Feld LLP | Davis Polk & Wardwell LLP |
| | Sidley Austin LLP |

feeder platform. The team remains impressively well informed on the impact of regulatory changes across the investment management industry.

Commercial Awareness *"I think they have a better handle on the market than almost anyone out there, and they are very deep on the regulatory and compliance side."*

KEY INDIVIDUALS William Kerr (see p.345) *"makes everything very seamless and easy,"* according to happy clients. His recent work includes acting for Deutsche Bank London on the formation of a capital fund aimed at seed managers of hedge funds. David Sawyier (see p.400) receives glowing endorsements from market sources for the "*incredibly high quality*" of his practice. "*It is like working with someone who has 100 years of experience,*" said one client. Talented attorney **Michael Schmidtberger** (see p.401) is held in high esteem for his "*fabulous judgment,*" and regularly represents major names in the hedge funds world such as Credit Suisse and Morgan Stanley. Clients are quick to praise his "*very broad view of the market and regulatory landscape.*"

## Band 2

### Akin Gump Strauss Hauer & Feld LLP
See profile on p.904

**THE FIRM** This firm houses a highly successful hedge funds group that is comprehensive in the scope and variety of its representations. The team acts for high-end sponsors and investors such as Angelo, Gordon & Co and Caspian Capital. It devotes considerable time to developing funds in vibrant emerging markets, such as India. The hedge funds lawyers have cultivated an excellent reputation for offering clients a full-service approach across asset classes and complementary departments such as tax, regulatory and litigation.

**Commercial Awareness** "*They have an extraordinarily deep bench of lawyers who work in the space. They are extremely knowledgeable about best practices and what other funds are doing.*"

**KEY INDIVIDUALS** Standout name **Stephen Vine** (see p.421) has an exceptional reputation in this field. He is renowned as an authority on private investment funds, covering matters such as formation, regulatory compliance and transactional activity. He is acclaimed as a "*leading hedge funds lawyer*" on a global scale, and is praised for his creativity and ability to see the big picture. The "*extremely experienced*" **Eliot Raffkind** focuses on guiding domestic and offshore hedge funds through the full range of formation and investing activity. He has a solid reputation for his representation of investment managers.

### Dechert LLP
See profile on p.1969

**THE FIRM** Dechert's talented hedge funds attorneys maintain an impressive global outlook, and have been involved in numerous cross-border matters of late. A sig-

nificant fund of funds client recently called upon the team to assist it in expanding into several new geographic areas, including Singapore, Russia and China. The firm's extensive global network of offices and its wealth of experience in the international funds industry are consistently cited as valuable assets for its diverse client base.

**Sources say:** "*A very strong team that comes from different areas and is able to marry together practical business knowledge with precision and depth in regulatory understanding.*"

**KEY INDIVIDUALS** **George Mazin** (see p.364) is popular with clients, who praise his "*tremendous breadth of experience across all different types of matters.*" He recently represented a Danish fund manager looking to invest in Scandinavian equities and targeting US investors.

### Fried, Frank, Harris, Shriver & Jacobson LLP
See profile on p.1975

**THE FIRM** This nationally acclaimed group operates across the full spectrum of hedge fund activity, providing comprehensive guidance to its roster of market-leading institutional clients. Clients remain notably impressed with the high levels of client service demonstrated across the board. The team possesses deep expertise covering a wide variety of asset classes, allowing it to handle the development of cutting-edge hybrid funds, integrating private equity, real estate and hedge fund knowledge and structures.

**Client Service** "*Incredible client service and thoughtful problem solvers.*" "*Their strongest point is their commitment to working with us as a partner.*"

**KEY INDIVIDUALS** Peers and clients sing the praises of asset management group head **Lawrence Barshay** (see p.279). He is described as "*one of the sharpest minds in the industry,*" and is lauded for his "*commitment to working with clients at the highest level possible.*" He acts on behalf of some of the largest and most active names in the market. Operating out of the firm's Washington, DC office, **Walid Khuri** (see p.346) has a strong handle on the alternative investment area, concentrating particularly on the structuring and offering of hedge funds and funds of funds. **David Selden** (see p.404) is "*extremely hard-working,*" according to sources, and is "*able to keep the big picture in focus when providing advice.*" As well as ably advising traditional hedge funds on the full spectrum of matters, he also offers guidance to hybrid funds and funds of funds. **Lisa Schneider** (see p.401) enters the rankings with substantial feedback from sources. She is identified as "*very responsive,*" and is also respected for her work across a host of alternative investment products.

### Ropes & Gray LLP
See profile on p.1528

**THE FIRM** The full-service approach offered by the hedge funds team at Ropes & Gray has cemented its position as a favored destination for clients seeking advice on everything from new product launches to spinouts and compliance questions. Major client PIMCO regularly calls upon this team for ongoing operational advice as well as guidance on the formation of new hedge fund products. The firm also houses a specialist team handling hedge fund transactional matters.

**Sources say:** *"They think outside of the box. They never grasp for the obvious without clear and patient consideration of all variables."*

**KEY INDIVIDUALS Sarah Davidoff** focuses on the representation of institutional and independent sponsors of private funds. She has recently acted for a key client on designing and launching aggregation vehicles to target high net worth US clients. She and her colleague **Laurel FitzPatrick** are highlighted by one satisfied client as *"two of the best hedge fund lawyers I have had the chance to work with."* FitzPatrick has had a busy year working on matters for Commonfund Asset Management, PIMCO and The Blackstone Group.

### Seward & Kissel LLP
See profile on p.2004

**THE FIRM** Seward & Kissel fields a highly rated bench of hedge funds practitioners and is well placed to advise notable funds clients such as Tiger Global Management and Marathon Asset Management on high-profile and complex matters. It has deep roots in the industry and a wealth of experience in handling every stage of the hedge fund life cycle, encompassing formation, investment and transactional activity. In a recent highlight, lawyers from the group helped engineer the acquisition by Arden Asset Management of Robeco Sage.

**Sources say:** *"They are quick and reactive to issues, and the fact that they are proactive is of huge benefit to us."*

**KEY INDIVIDUALS John Cleary** (see p.296) is highly popular with clients, who appreciate his straightforward approach: *"He is the best person I have ever encountered at not only giving the legal answer but giving me the commercial answer too."* A recent highlight saw him representing Emerging Sovereign Group throughout The Carlyle Group's acquisition of a 55% ownership stake in the business. Head of department **John Tavss** (see p.416) maintains an excellent reputation for hedge funds work and his wide knowledge of the industry as a whole. His experience in the investment management space sees him handle a range of tax, commercial and securities matters. **Steven Nadel** (see p.373) impresses with his deep expertise in this space, and *"stays very close to the actual practice of everyday law for hedge funds, so he has a very good perspective."* Of late, he has been engaged by a US investment manager to assist with all aspects of a merger with a UK-based manager.

### Willkie Farr & Gallagher LLP
See profile on p.2016

**THE FIRM** Commentators are quick to note the standout client service experienced by clients of this practice group, a significant factor in the successful maintenance of relationships with some of the highest-caliber fund managers in the market. Willkie's hedge funds attorneys are highly conversant across the full range of matters facing their clients, and are particularly admired for their in-depth knowledge of the rules and regulations affecting the private funds industry. Of late, Commodity Futures Trading

Commission and SEC registration issues and the provisions of the Dodd-Frank Act have been occupying much of the team's time.

**Client Service** *"They continue to be incredibly responsive. I feel like I'm treated as a valued member of the entire firm."*

**KEY INDIVIDUALS Barry Barbash** (see p.278) is recognized as a gifted adviser who is *"incredibly knowledgeable about every aspect of the industry."* His assessment management experience is extremely broad, and he is regularly called upon to offer regulatory and compliance advice to hedge fund clients. **Daniel Schloendorn** (see p.401) draws admiration for his wide-ranging practice and broad-based experience. He acts on matters ranging from M&A activity in the financial services sector to the formation of US and offshore hedge funds.

## Band 3

### Bingham McCutchen LLP
See profile on p.1515

**THE FIRM** By virtue of its cohesive integration with the firm's wider investment management practice, Bingham's hedge funds group is well equipped to shepherd clients through a wide array of formation, regulatory and transactional matters. Its recent work includes working with SeaStone Capital to oversee the launch of its new hedge fund. The team has also been busy assisting various fund managers with SEC and Commodity Futures Trading Commission registration issues.

**Sources say:** *"Their main strengths are their subject area knowledge, decisiveness and communication."*

**KEY INDIVIDUALS** Boston-based **Richard Goldman**'s (see p.1493) *"practical advice"* and *"substantive knowledge"* of his subject are prized by clients. He has recently advised a major client on pending securities law changes.

### Davis Polk & Wardwell LLP
See profile on p.442

**THE FIRM** The quality of Davis Polk's hedge funds practice is demonstrated by the extensive list of clients frequently calling upon the services of the team, including Avenue Capital, Perella Weinberg and Citadel Investment Group. Highly prized for their Dodd-Frank expertise, attorneys in this group are also commended for their insight into industry developments. A recent mandate by Ramius Trading Strategies saw attorneys handling the launch of the investment adviser's new managed futures fund.

**Commercial Awareness** *"Their strength is their insight not only into the law surrounding hedge funds but also into how other hedge funds, businesses and peers are functioning."*

**KEY INDIVIDUALS Nora Jordan** (see p.341) attracts excellent reviews for her *"smart and practical"* approach to the evolving rules and regulation affecting the hedge funds world. *"Her advice is very crisp and to the point,"* enthuses one interviewee. The *"wise and experienced"* **Leor Landa** (see p.351) possesses *"incredibly sound judgment,"* and gives his clients *"ways of accomplishing goals so as to reduce

risk."* He is experienced in all aspects of private investment fund formation and operation.

### Goodwin Procter LLP
See profile on p.1522

**THE FIRM** A long-established presence in the hedge funds world, Goodwin Procter continues to attract the business of highly regarded industry names such as Sequoia Capital and Arrowstreet Capital Management. The group draws on the firm's strong transactional and regulatory practices to provide an excellent platform for hedge fund clients seeking advice on strategic transactions. The team is also skilled in accommodating its clients' wider business needs, drawing upon tax and ERISA expertise as required.

**KEY INDIVIDUALS Elizabeth Shea Fries** (see p.1492) has experience across the spectrum of hedge funds matters, and is particularly highlighted for her compliance and fund formation knowledge. She regularly acts for clients such as HighVista Strategies and Regiment Capital Management.

### Katten Muchin Rosenman LLP
See profile on p.1253

**THE FIRM** The lawyers comprising Katten's hedge funds group possess deep expertise in this space, accumulated through years of working on behalf of clients such as Renaissance Technologies and AIG Asset Management. The team has recently been providing tailored compliance and tax guidance to Man Investments, ensuring it meets the requirements of both UK and USA regulatory bodies. It represents funds, brokers, investors and financial institutions in hedge funds matters, providing it with a broad and varied insight into industry trends and the impact of regulatory changes.

**KEY INDIVIDUALS Henry Bregstein** is *"well respected and trusted by clients,"* who appreciate his considerable market experience. Among other high-profile representations, he provides ongoing advice to PineBridge Investments on its existing funds, and assists in the structuring of new products.

### Morgan, Lewis & Bockius LLP
See profile on p.2246

**THE FIRM** The hedge funds team at this firm enjoys a robust reputation for its representation of leading fund managers and investors such as Och-Ziff Capital Management, CalPERS and Fortress Investment Group. Its lawyers expertly handle fund formation, investment management, regulation and enforcement issues. Its clients can also benefit from a considerable European network through which international investments and transactions can be seamlessly facilitated.

**Sources say:** *"The team has knowledge and understanding of complex structures and of current developments in the market. They work diligently to achieve their clients' objectives."*

**KEY INDIVIDUALS Jedd Wider** (see p.426) continues to work closely with a range of clients in this area, and also encounters a great deal of activity relating to offshore hedge funds matters in the British Virgin Islands and the Cayman Islands.

## Paul, Weiss, Rifkind, Wharton & Garrison LLP
See profile on p.1997

**THE FIRM** This firm's representation of major industry players such as Apollo, Blackstone and KKR Asset Management in hedge funds matters has earned it market recognition. It is frequently the recipient of high-quality mandates such as the $2.8 billion final closing of Avenue Capital's Europe Special Situations Fund II. The wide-ranging experience of the team attracts clients seeking advice on a diverse range of structures, covering different types of hedge and hybrid funds. The team's proactive approach to client service is further highlighted as a key draw.

**Client Service** *"They think outside the box, and they really do get back to their clients; they are good at client service."*

**KEY INDIVIDUALS** Udi Grofman (see p.326) invites glowing reviews for his experience in this area. He is praised as being *"very pragmatic and responsive, with a good understanding of the business."* Hutchin Hill Capital recently selected him to guide it through the launch of its liquid credit fund, with a target size of $600 million. Chair of the corporate department **Marco Masotti** (see p.363) demonstrates notable expertise across the alternative asset management sphere. According to admiring observers, he *"exudes knowledge, confidence and gravitas."* He has recently overseen multibillion-dollar matters for Avenue Capital and Reservoir Capital.

## Proskauer Rose LLP
See profile on p.2001

**THE FIRM** This team has recently acted on behalf of new client Altana Funds during the launch of three offshore hedge funds. The representation of this London-based manager emphasizes Proskauer's ability to act on hedge funds matters on a global basis, coordinating US and UK expertise to best serve its clients' needs. Attorneys are highly regarded for their comprehensive coverage of regulatory, M&A and fund formation matters.

**KEY INDIVIDUALS** Christopher Wells spearheaded the team leading Neuberger Berman through the $2 billion sale of its commodities asset management business. He is described by one commentator as *"outstanding in all respects."*

## Shartsis Friese LLP

**THE FIRM** A new entrant to the rankings, Shartsis Friese's hedge funds practice is firmly established as an active and vibrant industry presence on a national basis. Attorneys focus on the representation of investment advisers in a wide range of matters, drawing especially on the wider practice group's regulatory knowledge to guide clients through registration and compliance matters.

**Sources say:** *"They have a very good client base and devote a lot of attention to the business and the industry."*

**KEY INDIVIDUALS** San Francisco-based **John Broadhurst** is a respected figure in the hedge funds industry. He advises on a host of investment managements issues, including the formation and operation of investment advisory firms, and regulatory and compliance issues.

## Shearman & Sterling LLP
See profile on p.2005

**THE FIRM** With expertise on both the sponsor and the investor side, this group has good depth of experience across a range of industries and fund types. The team provides ongoing representation to notable clients such as Och-Ziff Capital Management Group on matters relating to derivatives, compliance, tax and fund formations.

**Sources say:** *"This practice has spectacular lawyers of all types."*

**KEY INDIVIDUALS** Azam Aziz is a key partner in the investment funds group.

## Skadden, Arps, Slate, Meagher & Flom LLP & Affiliates
See profile on p.2008

**THE FIRM** Skadden's hedge funds team is able to undertake a variety of sponsor and investor-side mandates on both a domestic and international basis, drawing on the resources of highly skilled global specialists. Major names

such as BlackRock, Banco BTG Pactual and JPMorgan regularly seek the expertise of the experienced practitioners within the team.

**Sources say:** *"They are very good from top to bottom – they have extremely capable lawyers in every field you would go to. For any kind of novel issue that comes up, they are one of the firms you think of that has done it before or will be best at that type of transaction; very strong across the board."*

**KEY INDIVIDUALS** The *"very talented"* **Philip Harris** (see p.331) is widely acclaimed as a leader in this field. He has recently been active on matters for major clients Advent Capital, Fortress Investment Group and Optima Fund Management. Commentators are also quick to highlight his strong technical skills.

## Other Notable Practitioners

**Timothy Selby** (see p.404) of Alston & Bird LLP attracts positive commentary on his technical prowess, with one source noting his strength in *"coming up with creative solutions to complex issues related to strategic partnerships."* **Drew Chapman** (see p.293) operates out of WilmerHale's New York office and heads the firm's alternative investment practice. His work covers the representation of sponsors in hedge funds matters, and his client base also includes a range of other funds. **Scott MacLeod** (see p.360) of Holland & Knight LLP comes highly recommended for his strong commitment to client service: *"We find that he consistently goes above and beyond the call of duty for us,"* says one source. MacLeod offers experience across a range of investment management matters. **Gregory Nowak** (see p.378) of Pepper Hamilton LLP has a robust practice encompassing the full range of hedge funds activity. He also has a wider focus on securities law, M&A and tax matters relating to the investment industry. The *"very patient and responsive"* **William Thomas** (see p.416) of Gibson, Dunn & Crutcher LLP has recently guided clients Arcapita and TRB Advisors through various investment management matters. **Olga Gutman** (see p.328) of Simpson Thacher & Bartlett LLP acts on behalf of hedge and private equity fund sponsors. She is highly regarded by market commentators for her experience in this arena.

# INVESTMENT FUNDS PRIVATE EQUITY: FUND FORMATION

Commentary about individuals can be found under their firm's paragraph. If the firm has no paragraph (is not ranked) look at Other Notable Practitioners.

## Investment Funds: Private Equity: Fund Formation
### Leading Firms

**Band 1**

Debevoise & Plimpton LLP *

Kirkland & Ellis LLP *

Simpson Thacher & Bartlett LLP *

**Band 2**

Cleary Gottlieb Steen & Hamilton LLP *

Davis Polk & Wardwell LLP *

Paul, Weiss, Rifkind, Wharton & Garrison LLP *

Ropes & Gray LLP *

Weil, Gotshal & Manges LLP *

**Band 3**

Akin Gump Strauss Hauer & Feld LLP *

Fried, Frank, Harris, Shriver & Jacobson LLP *

Gibson, Dunn & Crutcher LLP *

Latham & Watkins LLP *

Linklaters *

Morgan, Lewis & Bockius LLP *

Proskauer Rose LLP *

Skadden, Arps, Slate, Meagher & Flom LLP & Affiliates *

**Band 4**

Clifford Chance US LLP *

Covington & Burling LLP *

DLA Piper LLP (US) *

Goodwin Procter LLP *

Mayer Brown LLP *

Nixon Peabody LLP *

Paul Hastings LLP *

### Recommended for Client Service
**Nationwide**

| | |
|---|---|
| Debevoise & Plimpton LLP | Kirkland & Ellis LLP |
| Fried, Frank, Harris, Shriver & Jacobson LLP | |

### Recommended for Commercial Awareness
**Nationwide**

| | |
|---|---|
| Debevoise & Plimpton LLP | Nixon Peabody LLP |
| Latham & Watkins LLP | Simpson Thacher & Bartlett LLP |

## Investment Funds: Private Equity: Fund Formation
### Leading Individuals

**Band 1**

| | |
|---|---|
| Bell Thomas | Simpson Thacher & Bartlett LLP * |
| Ettelson Bruce I | Kirkland & Ellis LLP * |
| Gerstenzang Michael A | Cleary Gottlieb Steen & Hamilton LLP * |
| Harrell Michael P | Debevoise & Plimpton LLP |
| Kawata Yukako | Davis Polk & Wardwell LLP * |
| Wolf Barry M | Weil, Gotshal & Manges LLP * |
| Wolitzer Michael | Simpson Thacher & Bartlett LLP * |

**Band 2**

| | |
|---|---|
| Barshay Lawrence N | Fried, Frank, Harris, Shriver & Jacobson * |
| Bowie Scott O | Linklaters |
| Burleigh Jennifer J | Debevoise & Plimpton LLP |
| Covit Barrie B | Simpson Thacher & Bartlett LLP * |
| Jacobs Charles P | Nixon Peabody LLP * |
| Landa Leor | Davis Polk & Wardwell LLP * |
| Masotti Marco | Paul, Weiss, Rifkind, Wharton & Garrison * |
| Painter Robin A | Proskauer Rose LLP |
| Rosh Kenneth I | Fried, Frank, Harris, Shriver & Jacobson * |
| Sarno Glenn R | Simpson Thacher & Bartlett LLP * |
| Schwartz David J | Debevoise & Plimpton LLP |
| Silberstein Rebecca F | Debevoise & Plimpton LLP |
| Singer Louis H | Morgan, Lewis & Bockius LLP * |
| Sopher Edward D | Gibson, Dunn & Crutcher LLP * |
| Tabak Jeffrey E | Weil, Gotshal & Manges LLP * |

**Band 3**

| | |
|---|---|
| Ansbacher Richard I | Fried, Frank, Harris, Shriver & Jacobson * |
| Berthou Erica | Debevoise & Plimpton LLP |
| Clark Barton B | Latham & Watkins LLP * |
| Culhane Stephen | Kaye Scholer LLP (ONP)† * |
| Hirsh Robert M | Paul, Weiss, Rifkind, Wharton & Garrison * |
| Klein Scott P | Latham & Watkins LLP |
| Mehta Prakash | Akin Gump Strauss Hauer & Feld LLP * |
| Milner Ann L | Ropes & Gray LLP |

| | |
|---|---|
| O'Neil John R | Kirkland & Ellis LLP * |
| Rowe Larry Jordan | Ropes & Gray LLP |
| Schaefer Georgette A | Morgan, Lewis & Bockius LLP * |
| Singer Roger | Clifford Chance US LLP * |
| Smith Joseph A | Schulte Roth & Zabel LLP (ONP)† * |
| Soler Jonathon G | Weil, Gotshal & Manges LLP * |
| Winter David A | Hogan Lovells US LLP (ONP)† |

**Band 4**

| | |
|---|---|
| Caccia John | Skadden, Arps, Slate, Meagher & Flom * |
| Clark Timothy | Sidley Austin LLP (ONP)† * |
| de Brito Carl A | Dechert LLP (ONP)† * |
| Friedrich Laura S | Shearman & Sterling LLP (ONP)† * |
| Goldstein David A | DLA Piper LLP (US) * |
| Grossman Shukie | Weil, Gotshal & Manges LLP * |
| Kallos Chris P | Kirkland & Ellis LLP * |
| Kirson Sarah E | Kirkland & Ellis LLP * |
| Koeppel John | Nixon Peabody LLP * |
| Lenas Elizabeth | Cleary Gottlieb Steen & Hamilton LLP * |
| Marphatia Raj | Ropes & Gray LLP |
| McCormack William F | Ropes & Gray LLP |
| Murray Jordan C | Debevoise & Plimpton LLP |
| Nelson Edward D | Gibson, Dunn & Crutcher LLP * |
| Phleger Peter M | Morgan, Lewis & Bockius LLP * |
| Rothermel Sarah | WilmerHale (ONP)† * |
| Shapiro David I | Fried, Frank, Harris, Shriver & Jacobson * |
| Shaw-Lorello Loretta | Covington & Burling LLP * |
| Sternoff Joshua H | Paul Hastings LLP |
| Wright Andrew | Kirkland & Ellis LLP * |

**Up-and-coming individuals**

| | |
|---|---|
| Herman Jason | Simpson Thacher & Bartlett LLP * |

**Associates to watch**

| | |
|---|---|
| Storms Justin | Linklaters |

\* Indicates firm / individual with profile.

† ONP = Other Notable Practitioner.

## Band 1

### Debevoise & Plimpton LLP
**See profile on p.1968**

**THE FIRM** Market observers are unequivocal in their support for this firm's rating as a top fund formation shop. Having attracted some of the brightest talents in the industry, Debevoise houses a deep and experienced bench that is equipped to handle the most sophisticated of mandates. Lawyers work across an impressive range of industries and asset classes, from mega buyout funds to sector-focused funds in energy, healthcare and telecommunications. As well as providing stellar formation and structuring guidance, the team also ensures its clients are kept abreast of current regulatory conditions. Oaktree Capital Management, HarbourVest Partners and Stone Point Capital are a selection of the private equity giants that make up this team's impressive client roster.

**Client Service** *"They all have a delightful personal touch, very user friendly – it is part of their culture. They do place client service at a premium – responsiveness has been ingrained into their psyche."*

**Commercial Awareness** *"They are knowledgeable on a global basis; they understand the implications and laws in the various locales throughout the world, so we consider them one of the best in the business."*

**KEY INDIVIDUALS** Distinguished partner **Michael Harrell** continues to work closely with key client Oaktree Capital Management and is described by market sources as one of the *"deans of the industry."* He has recently been occupied with the impact of regulatory changes wrought by the Dodd-Frank reforms on the private equity industry. **Jennifer Burleigh** is lauded for her *"outstanding technical knowledge of market and legal private equity fundraising issues."* She spearheaded the team representing Tenex Capital on its $450 million fund focusing on investments in distressed companies. Cochair of the private equity funds group **David Schwartz** has lately been active on a significant emerging markets fund formed by Capital International which, at $3 billion, is one of the largest of its kind in recent years. **Rebecca Silberstein** attracts glowing endorsements for her *"incredibly thoughtful and business-minded approach,"* with one source adding: *"She is very, very meticulous in the work that she does."* She continues to work with clients such as Stone Point Capital in significant matters. *"Fantastic lawyer"* **Erica Berthou** is also highly appreciated by her clients, who describe her as *"very hard-working and dynamic."* She has overseen some of the team's largest mandates of late, including an $8.25 billion fund for Global Infrastructure Partners, the largest fund of its kind ever to be raised. **Jordan Murray** is increasingly gaining recognition through his involvement with major clients such as Providence Equity Partners, for whom he recently closed a media-focused fund. One enthusiastic source comments: *"I think the world of his work."*

## Kirkland & Ellis LLP
See profile on p.1254

**THE FIRM** Kirkland's fund formation team stands out for its stellar relationships with numerous private equity luminaries such as Golden Gate Capital, CVC and Starwood Capital Group. It is frequently the recipient of complex and cutting-edge mandates, and is particularly noted for its ability to handle global work due to its seamless integration across all offices in its network. Capitalizing on its impressive capabilities in fund formation, Kirkland has developed leading emerging markets and secondaries practices in order to best serve clients in the constantly evolving private equity landscape. The team's work is supported by sophisticated tax, ERISA and regulatory lawyers throughout the firm.

**Client Service** *"They are extremely smart and thoughtful. I'm constantly amazed at the response time, the thoughtfulness and how quickly they provide really good advice on anything I ask them."*

**KEY INDIVIDUALS Bruce Ettelson's** (see p.310) clients are consistently impressed with his thorough and dedicated approach, praising him as an *"authority on private equity fund work and structuring."* He recently acted on the Golden Gate Capital Opportunity Fund's final closing, which raised approximately $3.7 billion in commitments. *"Phenomenal lawyer"* **John O'Neil** (see p.380) is acknowledged for his strong track record representing large sponsors. Water Street Healthcare Partners selected him to guide its buyout fund to a $750 million final closing. **Chris Kallos** (see p.342) offers experience in representing clients on both the sponsor and investor side. He acts for some of the firm's largest clients in a wide range of private equity fund activity, including formation, spin-outs and investments. **Sarah Kirson** (see p.347) is praised for her leadership abilities, with one source describing her as *"extraordinarily effective."* A recent highlight saw her acting on behalf of Symphony Technology Group on its $871 million buyout fund. New York-based **Andrew Wright** (see p.428) is praised by one client as being *"a genuine partner in our business."* He is highlighted as an *"extraordinarily knowledgeable and responsive"* attorney, who *"stands out for his breadth of expertise."*

## Simpson Thacher & Bartlett LLP
See profile on p.2006

**THE FIRM** This firm has a deep reservoir of fund formation talent spanning its New York, Los Angeles and Palo Alto offices. The firm continues to defy market conditions

and grow its formidable private funds practice, and invites a remarkable volume of work from private equity giants such as Apax, Blackstone and The Carlyle Group. The team specializes in raising large buyout funds for such clients, but has also experienced an uptick in work flowing from other asset classes such as energy, infrastructure and emerging markets.

**Commercial Awareness** *"They are very current on market innovations, structures and what the latest thinking is. They are very commercial and focused on trying to get the deal done."*

**KEY INDIVIDUALS Thomas Bell** (see p.281) is universally recognized as a leader in the private funds field. He is credited with possessing an *"outstanding command of the market"* and *"a super knowledge of the industry overall."* His practice covers the full range of fund types, and his deep experience attracts some of the most sophisticated clients in the business. Esteemed partner **Michael Wolitzer** (see p.428) consistently delivers high-quality work to his roster of clients, who commend his *"incredibly patient"* approach and his availability. He is *"very good at synthesizing information,"* according to one impressed observer. **Barrie Covit** (see p.299) is highly respected in the market for his broad-ranging funds practice. He frequently acts on behalf of marquee clients such as KKR, The Carlyle Group and Lexington Partners. *"He is an excellent fund lawyer, extremely responsive and very well versed in the agreements and practices in the marketplace,"* states one source. **Glenn Sarno** (see p.400) covers the full spectrum of asset classes in his well-established practice. He has developed an excellent reputation for his work on behalf of sponsors of fund of funds products. **Jason Herman** (see p.334) enters the rankings backed by exceptional client feedback on his thriving practice. He works across a variety of asset categories, and is lauded as *"an incredibly strong service provider."* He is also noted for his ability to *"approach issues with a great sense of practicality."*

## Band 2

## Cleary Gottlieb Steen & Hamilton LLP
See profile on p.1963

**THE FIRM** Cleary Gottlieb's private funds team has racked up an impressive deal list forming funds for a number of prominent industry players such as TPG, KKR and JPMorgan. Its lawyers have made an impressive mark on the international stage, and demonstrate notable skill in forming private equity funds with global elements. The team's recent work includes advising Victoria Capital Partners on its Latin American-based second fund. It offers clients the benefit of its extensive market perspective, gained through years of working with major industry players.

**KEY INDIVIDUALS Michael Gerstenzang** (see p.320) enjoys a sterling reputation in the private funds space, and is hailed by one commentator as *"a thought leader"* in the space. He recently formed two Asia-focused funds for private equity giant KKR. **Elizabeth Lenas** (see p.354) has cultivated a strong reputation in the field, acting on behalf

of major industry names such as TPG, KKR and Blackstone Alternative Asset Management.

## Davis Polk & Wardwell LLP
See profile on p.442

**THE FIRM** This firm has cemented its position as a go-to adviser for private equity firms and institutional groups seeking a holistic approach to fund formation matters. It is credited with housing considerable expertise on the regulatory and compliance implications of formations and structurings. Credit Suisse, Morgan Stanley Infrastructure and Tailwind Capital partners have all recently called upon the guidance of Davis Polk practitioners in matters related to Dodd-Frank and the Consumer Protection Act. The team has also recently advised a key client on the formation of a series of feeder funds.

**Sources say:** *"As a team they work very closely together and with the various departments of the firm."* *"They are very practical, and have hands-on knowledge of issues."*

**KEY INDIVIDUALS** The *"thoughtful and decisive"* **Yukako Kawata** (see p.344) remains a top choice for private equity funds clients. She is particularly highlighted for the huge breadth of her experience, and her deep industry ties: *"She has a lot of connectivity to other experts in the industry and a pulse on the finger of the regulators."* **Leor Landa** (see p.351) is identified as an *"outstanding private funds lawyer,"* and a *"strategic player in terms of new structures and solutions."* His recent work includes providing ongoing advice to Credit Suisse Partners on secondary transactions.

## Paul, Weiss, Rifkind, Wharton & Garrison LLP
See profile on p.1997

**THE FIRM** This vibrant team has been highly visible in the market of late. It demonstrates particular skill in high-value and innovative mandates, such as the launch of a fund for BlackRock which will target investors in the renewable energy industry. Its illustrious client roster includes some of the most notable names in the industry, including Oaktree Capital Management, Blackstone and Apollo. The team maintains a strong market profile due in large part to its talented and prominent bench of practitioners. It is highly adept across the full range of fund types, including buyout, mezzanine, infrastructure and hybrid funds.

**KEY INDIVIDUALS Marco Masotti** (see p.363) has presided over some of the firm's most important private funds mandates of late. These include Apollo Global Management's strategic partnership with the Teacher Retirement System of Texas, worth $3 billion in commitments. **Robert Hirsh** (see p.334) *"has seen it all, and his experience is invaluable,"* according to market commentary. Roark Capital Management has recently engaged him to act on its third fund, which has so far raised over $1.2 billion.

## Ropes & Gray LLP
See profile on p.1528

**THE FIRM** This agile team located across several of Ropes & Gray's national offices advises virtually every type of stakeholder in the market on fund formation, investments, secondary transactions and regulatory issues. The group regularly advises PIMCO on the operation of its funds, and recently assisted it with the launch of a series of funds across various credit sectors. Boston Ventures, Landmark Capital and Brown University are also established clients of the team. Sources highlight the firm's excellent market understanding as a key attraction.

**Sources say:** "*Depth and breadth of experience, in particular the fact that they can really bring inter-disciplinary teams to the table when we need them to. They are very accessible, responsive, everything you would want.*"

**KEY INDIVIDUALS Ann Milner** is highly praised for her expertise in handling fund formation issues. She recently formed part of the team acting for Thomas H Lee Partners on the fundraising for its seventh fund. **Larry Jordan Rowe** is known for his strength on both the investor and sponsor sides, regularly taking on work from large institutions such as Goldman Sachs and Harvard University. Clients appreciate that he is "*very accessible and responsive.*" **Raj Marphatia** recently relocated to the firm's Silicon Valley office, boosting its West Coast presence. His broad-based experience sees him cover a wide range of matters for clients, including advising sponsors on formation, operation and investment matters. He also advises institutional investors on a range of investment activity. **William McCormack**'s private funds experience covers the gamut of sponsor representations on both a domestic and an international basis, and is experienced across a variety of asset classes.

### Weil, Gotshal & Manges LLP
See profile on p.2015

**THE FIRM** The strength of this practice is enhanced by the highly effective coordination of Weil's private funds expertise across the globe. The US-based team is able to offer clients comprehensive coverage of a huge range of fund types and industry participants, supplemented by extensive firmwide capabilities in tax, regulation and transactional activity. Key clients who have been attracted by this diverse offering include The Gores Group, Brookfield Asset Management and Berkshire Partners. The team's recent work includes assisting Berkshire Partners with the formation of a $4.5 billion buyout fund.

**Sources say:** "*They are a very good firm, and you can see that they are right up there.*"

**KEY INDIVIDUALS Barry Wolf** (see p.427) impresses clients with his creative approach: "*He looks for solutions as opposed to problems,*" noted one client. The Gores Group recently engaged him to work on its $300 million buyout fund focusing on lower middle market companies across a range of industries. Founding member of the private funds team at Weil, **Jeffrey Tabak** (see p.415) is highly valued by clients. He is well versed in sponsor and investor-side representation, as well as corporate and securities matters. **Jonathon Soler** (see p.410) is widely admired for the breadth of his practice. He handles high-value matters for private equity funds, investment firms and institutional investors. He is co-head of the private funds group. Talented partner **Shukie Grossman** (see p.327) has lately

represented key client Credit Suisse Group throughout the acquisition of an ownership interest in South American private equity firm Victoria Capital Partners.

## Band 3

### Akin Gump Strauss Hauer & Feld LLP
See profile on p.904

**THE FIRM** Akin Gump is a well-recognized name among market sources, particularly in the emerging markets space. It has cultivated a leading practice focusing on the formation of and investment into Asia-based funds. The team is acclaimed for its work on the investor side, where notable names such as Oak Hill frequently seek out its advice. It is also growing in stature on the sponsor side, and was recently the recipient of a number of fund formation mandates from key industry players.

**KEY INDIVIDUALS Prakash Mehta** (see p.366) has been instrumental in the expansion of this group's investor-side practice of late, representing names such as Oak Hill Investment Management and Texas Teacher's Retirement System in high-value investment activity on a global basis.

### Fried, Frank, Harris, Shriver & Jacobson LLP
See profile on p.1975

**THE FIRM** The strategic expertise of this team continues to see it retained by sophisticated financial institution and fund sponsor clients. New domestic and international mandates on both the formation and investment side have kept this highly experienced bench busy of late, with noteworthy matters flowing from relationships with clients such as Fortress Investment Group, Goldman Sachs and Neuberger Berman. The team's dedicated approach to client service is particularly highlighted by sources.

**Client Service** "*They are outstanding and responsive; they own the work that we give them. and I really feel like when you give them an assignment they treat it as if it were their own.*"

**KEY INDIVIDUALS Lawrence Barshay** (see p.279) is popular among industry peers, who acknowledge his strength in private equity funds matters as well as on the alternative asset management side. He is consistently engaged as counsel to some of the firm's most notable clients. **Kenneth Rosh** (see p.395) "*understands both sides of the market so he can advocate with a very calm, measured demeanor,*" according to one satisfied client. He heads the private equity fund formation group. **Richard Ansbacher** (see p.274) operates out of the firm's DC office and spends much of his time advising domestic and international clients on formation and structuring issues. He demonstrates notable skill when handling matters with a global flavor. The "*excellent*" **David Shapiro** (see p.1940) adeptly handles a wide variety of asset management issues, and has particular experience in merger and acquisition transactions by private equity entities. "*He knows our space very well,*" one interviewee enthuses.

### Gibson, Dunn & Crutcher LLP
See profile on p.682

**THE FIRM** This firm houses a skilled team that is capable of handling work across the full spectrum of private investment funds matters. Of late, lawyers have been involved in significant fundraising for buyout, distressed real estate, secondary and environmental infrastructure funds. Leonard Green & Partners, Investcorp and JPMorgan are all distinguished clients of the team, and lawyers are frequently enlisted by such names to assist on the full scope of regulatory, transactional and investment activity.

**Sources say:** "*Their main strengths are their market knowledge and experience.*"

**KEY INDIVIDUALS** Cochair of the group **Edward Sopher** (see p.410) is a go-to attorney for "*judgments on tricky questions,*" providing "*pragmatism as well as protection, and business savvy responses.*" He works skillfully across a wide range of asset classes, and has a wealth of experience representing fund managers, sponsors and institutional investors. **Edward Nelson** (see p.375) receives enthusiastic recommendations from sources, one of whom comments: "*I would recommend him to absolutely any firm, large or small.*" His "*fair-minded approach*" draws particular praise.

### Latham & Watkins LLP
See profile on p.446

**THE FIRM** Benefiting from a renowned international presence, this firm is engaged by many global players in the private equity sphere to advise upon fund formation as well as complex investment, structuring or transactional arrangements. The team has been highly active in the market this year, as is evidenced by its extensive deal list. Formations on behalf of Milestone Capital, Panda Power and Denham Capital Management, among others, have kept lawyers occupied of late.

**Commercial Awareness** "*They really understand where the market is and provide good context.*" "*The caliber of their attorneys was phenomenal.*"

**KEY INDIVIDUALS Barton Clark** (see p.295) is highly prized by his clients, one of whom describes him as "*one of the most important individuals*" to his company. A recent highlight saw him acting on behalf of Denham Capital Management on the formation of a $3 billion global energy fund. Global practice cochair **Scott Klein** has lately been occupied on the formation of a $1 billion private equity fund for BDT Capital and is highly praised by sources for his expertise in funds creation.

### Linklaters
See profile on p.447

**THE FIRM** This firm earns plaudits for its strong international capacity and its collaborative approach to working with counterparties. The team works effectively across the full range of private equity fund issues, including formation, structuring and regulation. It acts on behalf of prominent institutional investors as well as fund sponsors, and works closely with its accomplished tax, compliance and securities lawyers to provide a fully rounded service to its clients.

**Sources say:** *"They are technically capable, great to deal with and very pleasant – they tick all of the boxes that we would want to see."*

**KEY INDIVIDUALS Scott Bowie** is highly respected for his well-established private equity funds practice. He is able to advise across the board on investment management issues, and his reputation attracts some of the largest names in the industry onto his client roster. **Justin Storms** continues to be a valuable member of the investment management group, gaining praise from market commentators for his expertise and skill in handling cross-border fund matters.

## Morgan, Lewis & Bockius LLP
See profile on p.2246

**THE FIRM** Morgan Lewis is praised by market sources as being a vibrant presence in the market, and has a significant institutional investor practice as well as considerable talent on the fund sponsor side. The team is highly appreciated by clients for its ability to tap into the wider resources of the firm and transform it into a one-stop shop for all their needs. Major clients such as Credit Suisse, CalPERS and Pantheon Ventures have all been attracted to the diversity and efficiency of this practice. The formation of secondary funds and fund of funds is a further key strength of the team here.

**Sources say:** *"Their strengths include their knowledge and understanding of complex deal structures, and how best to achieve our objectives within these structures."*

**KEY INDIVIDUALS** Sources particularly appreciate **Louis Singer**'s (see p.407) dedication to client service and technical prowess in the private funds arena. He has overseen the formation of numerous funds and fund of funds as well as being heavily involved in the firm's strong investor-side practice. **Georgette Schaefer** (see p.400) is relied upon by her clients to deal with highly complex matters, and is experienced across a range of transactional and regulatory matters impacting funds. **Peter Phleger** (see p.384) stays abreast of current market trends through his extensive representations of sponsors and institutional investors. He also possesses particular expertise in secondary transactions.

## Proskauer Rose LLP
See profile on p.2001

**THE FIRM** The representation of highly active market players such as Ares Management, Adams Street Partners and Lexington Partners marks Proskauer Rose out as a solid contender in the fund formation space. Lawyers possess a strong grasp of the needs of their sponsor and institutional investor clients, garnered through a consistently healthy volume of mandates from both types of stakeholder. The breadth of this practice is held in high regard by clients, who know that they can rely on the team across the full spectrum of asset classes.

**Sources say:** *"Due to their longstanding tenure in the space they have critical mass and a huge perspective of the market."*

*The team I worked with was just so technically strong; brilliant lawyers."*

**KEY INDIVIDUALS Robin Painter**'s client roster includes many significant industry players who frequently seek her perspective on a variety of private equity matters. She co-heads the firm's global private investment funds group.

## Skadden, Arps, Slate, Meagher & Flom LLP & Affiliates
See profile on p.2008

**THE FIRM** Skadden's fund formation team continues to impress market observers, who praise the team's excellent coordination on both a cross-departmental and multi-jurisdictional basis. As part of the firm's wider investment management practice, its client roster features many notable industry names, including Deutsche Bank and AXA Private Equity. Its recent highlights include acting on the formation of a $200 million Brazilian private equity fund for Graycliff Partners. Clients further appreciate the heavyweight tax and ERISA support available to them.

**Sources say:** *"The team at Skadden is incredibly well integrated with other specialties and can anticipate issues that may arise."*

**KEY INDIVIDUALS John Caccia** (see p.291) is held in high regard for his expertise in fund formation and transactional matters for investors and sponsors. He is lauded for his *"good strategic advice"* and keen understanding of the space.

## Band 4

## Clifford Chance US LLP
See profile on p.439

**THE FIRM** This international firm offers strength in handling regulatory developments in the private funds industry both in the USA and in Europe. As well as forming funds and advising on structures and operations for key clients, the team offers a comprehensive overview of compliance with new regulations. Its lawyers are recognized for their strength in the niche of private equity real estate and for their proactivity in keeping ahead of the curve in terms of market knowledge.

**Sources say:** *"They have excellent market knowledge and are able to provide up-to-date and relevant advice on the latest developments and key issues."*

**KEY INDIVIDUALS** Described by one source as a *"walking encyclopedia of knowledge,"* **Roger Singer** (see p.407) attracts positive commentary on his legal and commercial acumen. He is a *"great businessperson's attorney"* whose receptive and forward-thinking approach is highly valued by clients.

## Covington & Burling LLP
See profile on p.441

**THE FIRM** This group continues to work with an impressive proportion of highly active funds clients, including the likes of Neuberger Berman, Pantheon Ventures and The Hampshire Companies. It has also attracted several new clients of late, with sources citing the breadth of practice

and the firm's international capacity as strong factors in its favor. The firm's vibrant secondaries practice adds to its solid reputation among industry players.

**Sources say:** *"Across a wide variety of issues, they have a very good understanding of the law and business. They provide very good business-oriented advice and are keenly attuned to the business needs of a transaction or structure."*

**KEY INDIVIDUALS** Accomplished attorney **Loretta Shaw-Lorello** (see p.405) is commended for her *"client-focused"* approach as well as her excellent knowledge of fund practices and terms. She is picked out as an effective negotiator who regularly handles sophisticated work on behalf of her clients.

## DLA Piper LLP (US)
See profile on p.1971

**THE FIRM** DLA Piper's private funds group is admired for its wide-ranging and practical approach to the gamut of issues faced by its clients. Of late, the team has experienced an uptick in the volume of work received from institutional investors such as Gávea Investimentos, Korea Investment Corporation and Arbor Investments. Lawyers were recently engaged by the latter to act on a lower middle market buyout fund, which closed at $400 million. The firm's extensive global network allows the team to call upon the support of transactional, tax and regulatory experts around the world in order to best assist its clients.

**KEY INDIVIDUALS** The *"extremely knowledgeable"* **David Goldstein** (see p.323) spearheads the department, and is responsible for some of the team's largest matters. His recent work includes acting for Gávea Investimentos in the $2 billion final closing of its fourth fund.

## Goodwin Procter LLP
See profile on p.1522

**THE FIRM** This firm remains a solid choice for both fund sponsor and investor clients, and offers an impressive breadth of practice. Attorneys have gained experience across the whole range of private investment vehicles, and are noted for the excellent value proposition they provide. Real estate funds remain a key specialty of this Boston-headquartered practice.

**KEY INDIVIDUALS** David Watson chairs the firm's private investment funds practice, and is a key contact for the group.

## Mayer Brown LLP
See profile on p.1257

**THE FIRM** Mayer Brown maintains a solid reputation in the market. It is experienced in forming funds for a diverse range of clients, from major fund managers to banks and insurance companies. Cohesive integration between practices is a strong component of its fund formation offering, with support drawn from solid corporate and securities, tax and ERISA departments across multiple jurisdictions. The team's experience extends across the full spectrum of fund types, including infrastructure and agriculture funds alongside more traditional private equity offerings.

**Sources say:** *"A good firm with a broad team of accomplished lawyers."*

**KEY INDIVIDUALS** John Noell is a key contact at the firm.

## Nixon Peabody LLP
See profile on p.1526

**THE FIRM** This team is credited for its high levels of activity representing institutional investors in many of the world's most important financial centers. Its sponsor-side practice is also gaining traction in the market, supported by considerable talent on ERISA issues facing public and private pension funds. The team is popular with clients, who highlight the experience and in-depth market knowledge of its accomplished bench.

**Commercial Awareness** *"They've been very helpful; they have a broad range of clients both on the investor side, and on the fund formation side and that helped to bring a sense of what the market really is."*

**KEY INDIVIDUALS Charles Jacobs** (see p.339) offers tailored advice to his clients and *"really takes the time to understand the whole business."* He is further praised for his responsive and extensive market experience. **John Koeppel** (see p.348) *"really has a sense of how to advise us from a business perspective,"* according to one impressed interviewee. He chairs the firm's private equity and investment funds group.

## Paul Hastings LLP
See profile on p.1996

**THE FIRM** This team is highly experienced in forming innovative and high-value real estate funds for sponsors such as Perella Weinberg, Prudential Real Estate Investors and Apollo Global Real Estate. Lawyers have substantial expertise in this niche, and also demonstrate strong technical ability when acting on funds with other investment strategies, including buyout and infrastructure funds. The team is also frequently enlisted to advise upon regulatory changes impacting the private funds industry.

**Sources say:** *"The team is highly motivated to do whatever it takes to get your matter handled in a satisfactory manner and has good bench strength."*

**KEY INDIVIDUALS** Identified by one client as *"outstanding in all respects,"* **Joshua Sternoff**'s *"main strength is the ability to navigate through complex situations."* He has lately been active on a number of private equity real estate matters for clients such as Artemis Real Estate Partners and Prudential Real Estate Investors.

## Other Notable Practitioners

**Stephen Culhane** (see p.300) has continued to impress sources since his move to Kaye Scholer LLP. One commentator describes him as *"a good quality fund formation lawyer,"* whose thoughtfulness and skill has attracted the business of clients such as MSouth Equity Partners and AXA Real Estate Investment Management. The *"exceptional"* **Joseph Smith** (see p.409) of Schulte Roth & Zabel LLP is well liked by both peers and clients, and is described as a *"pleasure to work with."* His recent work has included acting for DRA Advisors in the formation of a $1 billion private equity fund and other related matters. **Timothy Clark** (see p.295) of Sidley Austin LLP is praised for his *"experience, credibility and track record,"* impressing market sources with his expertise. **Carl de Brito** (see p.302) cochairs Dechert LLP's private equity fund formation group and maintains an impressively varied practice. He has a good reputation for his work counseling public and private companies. **Laura Friedrich** (see p.317) of Shearman & Sterling LLP has this year been involved in fund formations for high-profile clients such as Citi Private Bank, GTIS Partners and NGP Energy Capital Management. **Sarah Rothermel** (see p.1507) of WilmerHale is lauded for her *"very customer and business-oriented"* approach. She is a talented fund formation lawyer with a particular focus on the representation of venture capitalists. Co-head of the group at Hogan Lovells US LLP, **David Winter** is a *"really good asset"* to his clients, according to market feedback. He recently acted for Bluestone Capital Partners on the formation of a government services-focused fund.

# INVESTMENT FUNDS REGISTERED FUNDS

Commentary about individuals can be found under their firm's paragraph. If the firm has no paragraph (is not ranked) look at Other Notable Practitioners.

| Investment Funds: Registered Funds Leading Firms |
|---|
| **Band 1** |
| Dechert LLP * |
| Ropes & Gray LLP * |
| **Band 2** |
| Bingham McCutchen LLP * |
| Goodwin Procter LLP * |
| K&L Gates * |
| Paul Hastings LLP * |
| Sidley Austin LLP * |
| Stradley Ronon Stevens & Young LLP * |
| Stroock & Stroock & Lavan LLP * |
| Willkie Farr & Gallagher LLP * |
| **Band 3** |
| Debevoise & Plimpton LLP * |
| Drinker Biddle & Reath LLP * |
| Kramer Levin Naftalis & Frankel LLP * |
| Morgan, Lewis & Bockius LLP * |
| Simpson Thacher & Bartlett LLP * |
| Skadden, Arps, Slate, Meagher & Flom LLP & Affiliates * |
| Sullivan & Cromwell LLP * |
| Sutherland Asbill & Brennan LLP |

*Indicates firm with profile.*
Alphabetical order within each band. Band 1 is the highest.

## Band 1

### Dechert LLP
See profile on p.1969

**THE FIRM** Dechert has attracted the business of many of the most significant fund complexes in the industry by virtue of its far-reaching international presence, and has carved out a dominant position in the US market. The depth of the team attracts consistently favorable reviews from clients, many noting the valuable experience of numerous lawyers as in-house counsel or as members of key regulatory bodies. The team has recently been working on a range of issues, including open and closed-end fund formation and regulatory advice in M&A transactions. It also provides ongoing counsel to numerous financial institutions, fund boards and broker-dealers.

**Commercial Awareness** *"They have very talented partners who have a broad depth of understanding of the industry, and that depth of understanding allows them to weigh in and be very helpful on a wide variety of issues."*

**KEY INDIVIDUALS Robert Helm** (see p.333) *"has an exceptionally deep background in the industry, and is very creative and engaging."* He is co-head of the department, and is regularly engaged as fund counsel to some of the biggest players in the market. He is identified as *"a very good lawyer in every sense of the word."* Co-head of the registered funds practice **Jack Murphy** (see p.373) demonstrates *"exceptional skill and knowledge"* in the course of his

| Recommended for Client Service Nationwide | |
|---|---|
| Bingham McCutchen LLP | Willkie Farr & Gallagher LLP |
| Stradley Ronon Stevens & Young LLP | |

| Recommended for Commercial Awareness Nationwide | |
|---|---|
| Dechert LLP | Sidley Austin LLP |
| Drinker Biddle & Reath LLP | Skadden, Arps, Slate, Meagher & Flom LLP & Affiliates |

dealings with clients. His practice covers the spectrum of mutual funds matters, including organizing new funds, structuring derivatives transactions and management representation. Experienced practitioner **Geoffrey Kenyon** (see p.1498) has garnered wide respect in the industry for his representation of domestic and international participants in the US mutual funds market. He is described by one commentator as *"knowledgeable and effective,"* and has a *"good understanding of the industry in general."* **John O'Hanlon** (see p.379) is held in high regard by market commentators for his expertise in the field. He has a wealth of experience handling securities law, corporate and regulatory matters for a range of financial institution clients. **Jeffrey Puretz** (see p.388) is highly praised for his *"great depth of technical knowledge"* within this space. His practice particularly focuses on registered funds matters within the insurance sector. Clients highly appreciate his strong interpersonal skills. **Joseph Fleming** (see p.314) maintains an excellent reputation in the mutual funds market, and his advice is frequently sought by insurance companies, banks, investment funds and managers. **Christopher Harvey** (see p.1495) receives enthusiastic recommendations from peers and clients, who describe him as *"extremely knowledgeable, always well prepared, readily accessible and very thoughtful in his approach."* **Jane Kanter** (see p.342) is highly regarded for her work as counsel to numerous investment advisory firms, as well as her knowledge of the exchange-traded fund (ETF) space. She is known as a *"very strong advocate for her clients."* **Stuart Strauss** (see p.413) is held in high esteem by clients and continues to be a prominent figure in the world of ETFs.

## Ropes & Gray LLP
See profile on p.1528

**THE FIRM** Ropes & Gray's registered funds team maintains its stellar reputation as one of the best in the country. As well as serving the broad-ranging requirements of its sophisticated client base, the team has a deep understanding of the overarching trends and developments affecting the wider market. Derivatives and commodities reform and the increasing prominence of ETFs have been two such issues occupying the registered funds team of late. Its lawyers provide advice to some of the most prominent names in the industry, including Stone Harbor, the DoubleLine Funds and Schroders. The team has recently overseen closed-end fund launches for Cohen & Steers Capital Management and the DoubleLine Funds, raising approximately $690 million and $326 million respectively. **Sources say:** *"One of the ways they deliver value is being very to the point and focused."* *"I really like their approach to issues, as well as their professional and calm attitude."*

**KEY INDIVIDUALS John Loder** continues in his role as head of the firm's extensive investment management group, and is highly thought of in the market. His recent work has seen him advise key clients such as Artisan Funds, Natixis Global Asset Management and ProFund Advisors. He is identified by market observers as *"a leader of the pack."* **Gregory Sheehan** also maintains a strong reputation in the registered funds area. He continues to play a key role in working with clients such as Pyxis Capital on a broad spread of regulatory and operational matters. Experienced practitioner **John Gerstmayr** has a strong track record in representing investment companies and

advisers. He is also highly skilled in trustee representation, as demonstrated by his recent and ongoing guidance to the independent trustees of the DWS Funds. **Bryan Chegwidden** continues to make a positive impression on the market, with one interviewee declaring him to be *"deeply knowledgeable, practically minded and easy to work with."* Talented partner **Thomas Hiller** is a valuable member of the team representing the independent trustees of the DWS Funds, and is recognized by interviewees as *"a very strong lawyer."* **David Sullivan** was engaged by major client Allianz Global Investors to act as fund counsel to a series of open-ended funds. He also advised on more than 20 closed-ended funds managed by Allianz and sub-advised by PIMCO.

## Band 2

### Bingham McCutchen LLP
See profile on p.1515

**THE FIRM** The registered funds team at Bingham McCutchen continues to go from strength to strength, and has recently taken on several lateral hires from Morgan, Lewis & Bockius, significantly increasing the depth of its bench. Lawyers have recently gained several significant new client wins, including State Street Global Advisers, Nuveen Funds and Western Asset Management. The team also draws on strong support from its deep pool of regulatory enforcement and compliance lawyers, allowing it to take on complex mandates which incorporate innovative structures.

**Client Service** *"The attorneys are highly responsive, and provide valuable real-world advice and solutions to help address matters referred to them."*

**KEY INDIVIDUALS Lea Anne Copenhefer**'s (see p.299) focused guidance has proven extremely valuable to her clients, allowing them to make informed choices on a range of registered funds issues. She is a valuable member of the team acting as fund counsel to Capital Research and Management. **Thomas Harman** (see p.330) offers registered funds and their boards the benefit of his years of industry experience, including a considerable stint at the SEC. He provides clients with *"a high level of support,"* and is praised for the practicality of his advice. Head of the investment management practice **Roger Joseph** (see p.1496) is held in high regard in the registered funds space, and has recently been involved in complex and innovative projects for several high-profile clients. **John McGuire** (see p.365) is lauded for his collaborative approach, and is described as *"very approachable, responsive and easy to work with"* by interviewees. He enjoys a robust reputation for his work with ETFs, and has lately been working on behalf of major client State Street Global Advisors. **Michael Glazer** (see p.321) wins significant approval from market commentators, with one interviewee enthusing: *"He has unparalleled experience and a practical approach to solving problems."* Glazer acts as counsel to names such as Capital Research and Management, and also works with the independent directors of several other mutual funds.

## Goodwin Procter LLP
See profile on p.1522

**THE FIRM** The registered funds team at Goodwin Procter has a loyal stable of high-profile mutual fund clients such as Wells Fargo, Van Eck Funds and Prudential Insurance Funds. Its lawyers are highly regarded for their representation of the independent directors and independent trustees of numerous other fund complexes, and observers are quick to note the team's ability to operate on an international basis advising offshore and non-US funds. Recent highlights include advising the independent trustees of Invesco Funds on several fund mergers and formations. **Sources say:** *"I would point to their vast experience, depth of knowledge and very good judgment as being their main strengths."*

**KEY INDIVIDUALS** Talented partner **Robert Kurucza** (see p.351) is well known in the space, and is particularly highlighted for his work on bank-related mutual funds. He continues to advise the Columbia Funds on various regulatory matters. **Philip Newman** (see p.1504) garners praise for his *"good bedside manner and diplomatic way of dealing with the fine lines,"* and provides an impressive understanding of his clients' business needs. The independent trustees of the Eaton Vance Funds rely on his expertise in the registered funds area, particularly with regards to shareholder demand letters. Recognized by interviewees as a *"problem solver, not a problem creator,"* **Christopher Palmer** (see p.381) *"deals with issues almost before they arise."* He provides ongoing representation to Prudential Insurance Funds, as well as to the independent directors of several large mutual funds groups. **Marco Adelfio** (see p.271) is held in high esteem by commentators for his expertise in this area. He represents Wells Fargo Advantage Funds, and has also worked with the independent trustees of Invesco Funds.

## K&L Gates
See profile on p.2245

**THE FIRM** This firm's strength in the registered funds space is illustrated by the impressive volume of work handled by the team of late. It counts the likes of Neuberger Berman, John Hancock Financial Services and AXA Equitable Life among its extensive client roster. Exchange-traded fund complex Invesco Powershares recently mandated the team to act as its fund and adviser counsel. Other highlights include acting for Salient Absolute Return Funds on the formation and launch of a complex of alternative strategy mutual funds. **Sources say:** *"The strongest points are the team's reliability, expertise and competence."*

**KEY INDIVIDUALS** **Robert Zutz** (see p.431) is consistently recognized as a distinguished figure in the market, and is able to call upon over 30 years of experience when representing a wide variety of mutual funds clients. Interviewees highlight **Paul Dykstra** (see p.308) as a *"very knowledgeable and effective attorney"* within the industry. His recent work includes acting on behalf of the independent trustees on the creation of a new family of exchange-traded funds.

## Paul Hastings LLP
See profile on p.1996

**THE FIRM** This high-quality team continues to offer significant depth of experience and expertise when handling all types of matters for its distinguished client base. It remains a strong choice for clients seeking assured regulatory support, such as guidance on exemptions from the Investment Company Act, SEC enforcement issues and M&A activity. The team represents Tocqueville Trust as fund counsel, and has also acted for TCW Group and Metropolitan West Funds of late. Another attractive feature of the practice is the high level of communication between related departments such as ERISA and securities law. **Sources say:** *"An excellent approach to the legal requirements and really practical business guidance."*

**KEY INDIVIDUALS** **Domenick Pugliese** is highly praised for his *"ability to explain the intricacies of 40 Act regulations in layman's language."* He is renowned for his comprehensive understanding of the Investment Company Act and Investment Advisers Act. **David Hearth** has lately been working on behalf of a significant funds complex with regards to the regulatory implications of a proposed transaction. He is praised for his excellent understanding of the field. **Michael Rosella** advises Tocqueville Trust as fund counsel, and is appreciated by sources for his *"ability to give practical advice in real time. He is a strong leader, and a smart and thoughtful advocate for his clients."*

## Sidley Austin LLP
See profile on p.1264

**THE FIRM** The impressive registered funds group at Sidley Austin is consistently at the forefront of industry developments, regularly handling matters connected to alternative investment vehicles, business development companies (BDCs) and money market funds. Clients benefit from the vast knowledge base of Sidley's global registered funds team, which is well equipped to work alongside the US team on cross-border issues. The group provides ongoing counsel to a range of mutual funds players such as BlackRock, Ironwood Capital Management and new client Prudential Investments.

**Commercial Awareness** *"The benefits are their expertise in the field and ability to apply that knowledge. The combination of technical expertise and practical application adds true value to the client."*

**KEY INDIVIDUALS** **Frank Bruno** (see p.289) *"is one of the best technical resources in the industry,"* and *"instills high levels of confidence"* in his clients. Major names such as BlackRock regularly call upon his expertise in the mutual funds area. Co-head of the practice group **John MacKinnon** (see p.360) possesses *"gravitas based on years of experience."* He represents the likes of Mirae Funds in its investment management matters.

## Stradley Ronon Stevens & Young LLP

**THE FIRM** For decades this firm has been one of the top choices for registered funds work, and it continues to attract high-quality mandates from mutual funds giants such as Franklin Templeton Investments, UBS Funds and Delaware Investments. Attorneys support such clients on the full range of issues facing them and the industry at large, and are especially trusted advisers on issues emerging from the Investment Company Act. The team recently assisted Old Mutual Funds in the disposition of its $2 billion retail mutual funds business to three buyers. **Client Service** *"One of the things that I most appreciate about working with Stradley is the high degree of accessibility and responsiveness."*

**KEY INDIVIDUALS** **Bruce Leto** is a renowned practitioner in this space, frequently representing investment advisers and companies as well as independent trustees in a range of funds matters. Franklin Advisers recently mandated him to advise on an exemptive application to the SEC. He is lauded as *"responsive, practical and very effective,"* alongside his colleague **Ruth Epstein**. Epstein offers notable experience in a wide range of investment funds matters. **Michael O'Hare** ably assists his clients with the registration, regulation and operation of registered funds, as well as the formation and launch of new fund products. He is held in high regard by market commentators for his expertise in the space.

## Stroock & Stroock & Lavan LLP
See profile on p.2010

**THE FIRM** Stroock's deep bench in the registered funds area comprises a strong group of professionals whose industry and academic experience inspire confidence in the most sophisticated of clients. Its attorneys receive particular recognition for their assured representation of independent board members. They also possess an excellent track record working on behalf of mutual funds and advisers such as Lazard Funds and the Dreyfus Family of Funds. The team coordinates smoothly with the firm's tax, litigation and ERISA departments in order to provide clients with the most comprehensive support. **Sources say:** *"A really superb mutual funds practice."* *"They are extremely responsive and very knowledgeable, and really get to the heart of the matter."*

**KEY INDIVIDUALS** Chair of the practice group **Stuart Coleman** continues to garner significant praise from commentators, who describe him as *"deeply knowledgeable,"* *"extraordinarily effective"* and simply *"first class."* **Joel Goldberg** is a hugely experienced practitioner with many years of experience at the SEC under his belt. According to one source, *"there are very few lawyers who have the judgment and ability to strategize on the same level as Joel"* when it comes to 40 Act matters. **Gary Granik** has a strong track record in handling registered funds matters on a domestic and international basis. He *"works tirelessly, and has a comprehensive knowledge of securities law."* **Burton Leibert's** *"knowledge base is deep and wide,"* and he is recognized for his proactive approach to client service. *"He is always fully prepared and thoughtful in the dispensing of his advice,"* one interviewee notes appreciatively. The *"bright, knowledgeable and pleasant"* **David Stephens** is praised for his ability to act as a *"key resource, guide and mentor"* in mutual funds matters, particularly those pertaining to the Investment Company Act.

## Willkie Farr & Gallagher LLP
See profile on p.2016

**THE FIRM** Willkie Farr & Gallagher has long held a strong reputation in the registered funds sphere, housing a highly experienced team of practitioners across several offices. Its dedicated commitment to client service impresses market commentators, as does the team's ability to accept mandates across the full spectrum of registered funds matters. It expertly guides exchange-traded funds, business development companies, and open and closed-end funds clients through operations, regulation and M&A activity.

**Client Service** *"We get great service, and the team is extremely responsive and flexible in meeting our needs and timeframes. They are always available to discuss any new or emerging issues."*

**KEY INDIVIDUALS** The excellent **Barry Barbash** (see p.278) attracts compliments from numerous sources, who note his *"strong knowledge, judgment and political savvy"* in the registered funds area. He is universally recognized as a highly prominent figure, and highlighted for his longstanding experience in all aspects of mutual funds matters. **Margery Neale** (see p.374) has cultivated a reputation as *"one of the best, most well-respected 40 Act lawyers in the industry."* She is able to act on registered funds issues on both a domestic and cross-border basis. **Rose Di Martino** (see p.304) is highly regarded by her registered funds clients for providing *"exceptional, timely and practical advice."* She is further commended for her responsiveness and client-oriented approach.

## Band 3

## Debevoise & Plimpton LLP
See profile on p.1968

**THE FIRM** This firm houses a robust registered funds practice that consistently garners wide acclaim from industry insiders. By virtue of its extensive connections within the funds industry, the team maintains an enviable client base, including BlackRock, HarbourVest Partners and Clayton, Dubilier & Rice. Attorneys at Debevoise are highlighted for their experience in representing independent directors, as well as their ability to efficiently pool expertise with other practices within the firm.

**KEY INDIVIDUALS Kenneth Berman** maintains a *"tremendous reputation"* within the registered funds sphere. His practice focuses on the representation of financial services clients, to which he offers regulatory and compliance guidance.

## Drinker Biddle & Reath LLP
See profile on p.2238

**THE FIRM** Drinker Biddle's registered funds team is well established as a vibrant presence in the market, attracting high-caliber clients such as Northern Funds, the RBB Fund and Hatteras Funds. The registered funds practitioners are able to marshal the resources of the full-service investment management practice housed within the firm in order to best serve their clients. A recent highlight saw the team acting on behalf of FlexShares Trust throughout the structuring and launch of a series of cutting-edge ETF products.

**Commercial Awareness** *"They understand the landscape of the industry and the rules very well, and their advice is always very practical." "Their strategic advice has been extremely timely and helpful."*

**KEY INDIVIDUALS Joshua Deringer** (see p.303) is the recipient of enthusiastic praise from sources, who emphasize his *"hands-on and responsive"* style. Hatteras Funds recently engaged him to advise on the formation of a strategic variable mutual insurance fund. Head of the group **Michael Malloy** (see p.361) *"understands the boardroom and the industry very well,"* and is highly regarded by market observers. He has recently acted for key clients such as the independent trustees of Credit Suisse Funds and the RBB Fund on new fund offerings.

## Kramer Levin Naftalis & Frankel LLP
See profile on p.1987

**THE FIRM** The registered funds team at Kramer Levin offers significant experience in representing independent directors of mutual funds. The firm fields a solid bench of accomplished attorneys whose representation of numerous high-quality clients attracts admiration from market sources. The independent directors of Oppenheimer Funds, Morgan Stanley and First Eagle regularly call upon the guidance of this team on the full spectrum of matters affecting their businesses, including risk management, compliance, litigation and strategic matters.

**Sources say:** *"They have a deep bench and a team that is deeply admired. They have real expertise and a lot of experience."*

**KEY INDIVIDUALS Carl Frischling** (see p.317) garners significant praise for the depth of his expertise in this arena, and is *"extraordinarily well connected,"* according to sources. He is highly respected for his representation of the independent directors and independent trustees of major investment funds complexes. **Ronald Feiman** (see p.312) enters the rankings on the back of significant positive commentary on his abilities in the registered funds area. He is praised for his significant expertise in the industry, as well as the strategic approach he brings to complex matters.

## Morgan, Lewis & Bockius LLP
See profile on p.2246

**THE FIRM** This firm maintains a solid presence in the registered funds space, and its key client relationships with Manning and Napier Funds, Goldman Sachs and ING Investment Management continue to thrive. Attorneys cover the gamut of mutual funds matters, including product development, compliance issues and commodities regulation, and are praised for their excellent value proposition.

**Sources say:** *"The team has strong experience and a broad client base that allows for a valuable perspective on industry matters. The attorneys are highly responsive, and provide valuable real-world advice and solutions to help address matters referred to them."*

**KEY INDIVIDUALS** The *"business-savvy"* **Timothy Levin** (see p.355) impresses with his *"great ability to think outside the box."* Operating out of the firm's Philadelphia office, his practice covers the full spectrum of registered funds work.

## Simpson Thacher & Bartlett LLP
See profile on p.2006

**THE FIRM** This firm's expertise in the registered funds area is held in high esteem by peers and clients alike. It offers comprehensive 40 Act guidance to clients such as Legg Mason Closed-End Funds, Morgan Stanley and UBS Securities. The firm's strong foundation in transactional work lends itself to the assistance of registered funds clients in a variety of capital markets transactions. Of late, the team has been working on numerous closed-end public fund offerings.

**Sources say:** *"The team is extremely knowledgeable, pragmatic and technically sound. They hit the nail on the head."*

**KEY INDIVIDUALS** Head of the investment management practice **Sarah Cogan** (see p.296) is picked out by one commentator as being *"among the best of the lawyers I work with."* She has a broad practice representing investment companies, funds and independent directors.

## Skadden, Arps, Slate, Meagher & Flom LLP & Affiliates
See profile on p.2008

**THE FIRM** This firm's registered funds practice continues to rise in the estimation of market observers. Drawing on its impressive portfolio of firmwide relationships, the practice represents the likes of TCP Capital, BlackRock and Guggenheim Funds Distributors across the board on mutual funds matters. The practice is known as a hub for innovation in relation to investment company work, and has recently been involved in developing registered private equity funds and new offering structures for closed-end funds.

**Commercial Awareness** *"Skadden's strength as a law firm is in dealing with complicated, sensitive and/or high-profile projects." "Their expertise is helpful and their background is helpful to us – they know what else is being done in the market."*

**KEY INDIVIDUALS Richard Prins** (see p.387) is *"very knowledgeable"* across a range of registered funds matters. Prospect Capital engaged him to guide it through a series of offerings of stock and senior notes, as well as an acquisition and debt financing worth $266 million. **Michael Hoffman** (see p.335) is highly esteemed for his strong negotiation skills. Sources say: *"He stays firm in negotiations, and sticks to the facts."* He recently assisted TCP Capital in its $285 million conversion from a closed-end fund to a BDC.

## Sullivan & Cromwell LLP
See profile on p.2011

**THE FIRM** Sullivan & Cromwell's registered funds team commands respect for its strong grasp of the regulatory, transactional and advisory issues facing its clients in the registered funds arena. Focused collaboration with other departments such as tax, ERISA and M&A forms a key attractive factor for clients. Bank of America, Centaurus

Advisors and Skylar Capital have all called upon the expertise of this team of late.

**Sources say:** *"It is a terrific firm and it has notable people in this space." "They are very good on quality."*

**KEY INDIVIDUALS** *"High-quality lawyer"* **John Baumgardner** (see p.280) maintains an outstanding reputation among peers and clients, and is described as an *"absolute industry-leading individual."* He is known for his representation of some of the most important investment companies in the US.

### Sutherland Asbill & Brennan LLP

**THE FIRM** Sutherland's registered funds lawyers are routinely described by market commentators as the leading experts in BDC matters. The team is also highly rated for its work with ETFs and unit investment trusts, and for its regulatory prowess. A recent engagement by CION Investment saw attorneys acting on the registration of common equity worth $1 billion in a non-traded BDC. Other notable names on the client roster include Ares Capital and Metropolitan Life Insurance Company.

**KEY INDIVIDUALS Steven Boehm** is commended by interviewees for his deep industry experience and market understanding. Highlights of the past year include representing key clients Main Street Capital and GSV Capital in follow-on private equity offerings of $97 million and $112 million, respectively. **Stephen Roth** has recently undertaken work on behalf of the Committee of Annuity Insurers, working with insurance companies and broker-dealers to deal with the implications of SEC and CFTC rules and proposals. His extensive understanding of the field is particularly singled out by commentators.

### Other Notable Practitioners

Chair of WilmerHale's investment management group **James Anderson** (see p.273) is highly regarded within the registered funds community, and is noted by clients for his *"depth of knowledge and ability to add value"* when handling their matters. According to interviewees, he *"offers tremendous judgment and reliable advice."* **Jay Baris** (see p.278) heads up Morrison & Foerster LLP's investment management practice, and is regarded as an *"incredibly knowledgeable"* attorney who *"works tirelessly for his clients."* He is further praised for his *"creative and flexible approach to solutions."* He acts as fund counsel to The Victory Funds. **Nathan Greene** (see p.326) of Shearman & Sterling LLP has had a busy year advising a range of financial institutions and funds on their registered funds activities. Notable clients include SkyBridge Capital, Cantor Fitzgerald and First Eagle Funds. **Stephanie Monaco** of Mayer Brown LLP is respected by market sources for her funds practice, and calls upon her experience of working at the SEC to offer investment management clients sound regulatory counsel. **Cathy Gonzales O'Kelly** (see p.323) of Vedder Price PC is a new entrant to the rankings, receiving enthusiastic recommendations from a variety of sources. She is highlighted as being *"detail-oriented and fully knowledgeable about the industry,"* and is adept at maintaining *"the best possible collegiality"* with her clients.

# INVESTMENT FUNDS VENTURE CAPITAL

Commentary about individuals can be found under their firm's paragraph. If the firm has no paragraph (is not ranked) look at Other Notable Practitioners.

| Investment Funds: Venture Capital |
| --- |
| **Leading Firms** |
| **Band 1** |
| Cooley LLP |
| Fenwick & West LLP * |
| Gunderson Dettmer Stough Villeneuve Franklin & Hachigian |
| Wilson Sonsini Goodrich & Rosati * |
| **Band 2** |
| DLA Piper LLP (US) * |
| Goodwin Procter LLP * |
| Latham & Watkins LLP * |
| **Band 3** |
| Hogan Lovells US LLP |
| Morgan, Lewis & Bockius LLP * |
| Orrick, Herrington & Sutcliffe LLP * |
| Perkins Coie LLP |
| Pillsbury Winthrop Shaw Pittman LLP * |
| WilmerHale * |
| **Band 4** |
| Blank Rome LLP * |
| Dentons * |
| Gibson, Dunn & Crutcher LLP * |

\* Indicates firm with profile.
Alphabetical order within each band. Band 1 is the highest.

## Band 1

### Cooley LLP

**THE FIRM** A favorite with technology clients and their institutional investors, Cooley remains a dominant presence in the venture capital world. Clients appreciate the high levels of support provided by the highly skilled securities, tax and ERISA lawyers who work seamlessly alongside the team. Matters range from early-stage fund-raising all the way through to multimillion-dollar closings, with a prime example of its abilities being the team's recent advice on a $1 billion fund for Institutional Venture Partners. This fund's focus on the internet, digital media and mobile technology spaces played to the key strengths of Cooley's talented bench.

**KEY INDIVIDUALS** The highly regarded **Craig Dauchy** heads up the practice at Cooley, and recently represented Foundation Capital in the formation of its $400 million seventh fund. He is particularly praised for his ability to draw on industry connections when working in this space. **Mark Tanoury** is based in the firm's Palo Alto office, and maintains a strong presence in the field. Drawing upon his considerable experience in venture fund formations, he recently assisted JAFCO Technology Partners through the formation of its fifth fund. **Eric Jensen** has a broad corporate and securities practice with particular experience in the representation of emerging and public technology clients. He is highly regarded for his practical approach to matters. **Barbara Kosacz** continues in her role as head of the life sciences practice, and is respected for her strategic investment, financing and M&A knowledge. Esteemed partner **Fred Muto** has developed an excellent reputation for his guidance of investment banks and venture capital investors. He also acts on behalf of startups, emerging growth companies and public companies in the technology sector.

| Recommended for Client Service Nationwide | |
| --- | --- |
| Gunderson Dettmer Stough Villeneuve Franklin & Hachigian | Latham & Watkins LLP |
| | WilmerHale |

| Recommended for Commercial Awareness Nationwide | |
| --- | --- |
| Blank Rome LLP | Wilson Sonsini Goodrich & Rosati |
| Perkins Coie LLP | |

### Fenwick & West LLP
See profile on p.680

**THE FIRM** Fenwick & West has a strong presence in Silicon Valley, consistently attracting a wealth of highly active technology clients to its practice. Lawyers are equipped to shepherd clients through every stage of the venture capital life cycle, from seed funding through to a variety of liquidity events. The group's long history in this field means it has strong ties with local industry players, benefiting both emerging companies and investors through its knowledge of their business models.

**Sources say:** *"They are all good attorneys who individually have long histories in the space."*

**KEY INDIVIDUALS Gordon Davidson** (see p.631) is a well-known figure in Silicon Valley, and is highly regarded for his expertise in venture capital. His clients are largely drawn from the technology, life sciences and clean technology sectors. Identified by interviewees as *"very smart and focused,"* **Mark Stevens** (see p.412) has a broad client roster of IT and media clients, which he represents in M&A transactions, IPOs and complex strategic alliances. Accomplished attorney **Barry Kramer** (see p.350) operates out of the firm's Mountain View office, counseling technology and life sciences companies on a broad range of venture capital issues.

## Gunderson Dettmer Stough Villeneuve Franklin & Hachigian

**THE FIRM** This firm's strong venture capital tradition and proven capabilities in the sphere are key selling points. Startup companies and venture capital funds regularly turn to the guidance of the experienced team at Gunderson, which is notably busy on the fund formation side. The team has recently formed funds for noteworthy client Andreessen Horowitz, among others. Its dedication to excellent client service is a further key draw of this practice.

**Client Service** *"They provide top-tier service. They are experts in their field and are very thoughtful in their advice."*

**KEY INDIVIDUALS Scott Dettmer** is praised as being a *"terrific guy to work with."* His reputation has attracted the business of numerous life sciences and technology companies. **Steven Franklin** has recently advised on a raft of mat-

ters for clients such as Altira, Corsa Ventures and First Round Capital. He spearheads the firm's venture fund practice. **Bob Gunderson** is respected as a leading figure in the market. By virtue of his long tenure in the space, he has a wealth of experience in M&A, financing and IPO activity for Silicon Valley's most significant players.

## Wilson Sonsini Goodrich & Rosati
### See profile on p.700

**THE FIRM** This practice continues to go from strength to strength, spanning an impressive range of industry sectors in its work, including energy, media and entertainment and information services. It has attracted the business of some of the most active and innovative players in the venture capital market, including Accel Partners, Apptio and GreenVolts. Numerous venture financings have kept the team occupied of late, and it has also provided nuanced investment advice to venture capital and private equity firms.

**Commercial Awareness** *"They have an exceptional network and grasp of what is happening in the market."*

**KEY INDIVIDUALS Jeff Saper** is lauded for his strong expertise and experience in the space. His practice spans the representation of emerging growth companies, investment banks and corporate issuers in domestic and cross-border matters. **Steven Bochner** offers huge depth of experience in the venture capital world, and has acted as counsel on a multitude of IPOs, merger transactions and financings for virtually every type of stakeholder in the market. **Larry Sonsini** is a well-recognized figure in the industry. He is the chairman of the firm, and has a global reputation for his work on significant M&A and IPO transactions. **Michael Danaher** is praised for the level of service he has provided to his technology client base. He recently assisted Shocking Technologies on its $10.5 million Series C financing. **Robert O'Connor** *"is willing to be helpful and provide active introductions for companies,"* comment clients. He is particularly praised for his experience in the cleantech arena.

### Band 2

## DLA Piper LLP (US)
### See profile on p.1971

**THE FIRM** Capitalizing on its globally renowned corporate practice, DLA Piper represents a raft of technology companies and venture funds in financing and M&A transactions. New Enterprise Associates, Steamboat Ventures and Groupon are among the high-profile names that regularly call upon the services of this team. Its recent work includes handling a $25 million Series D financing for Global Analytics. Clients appreciate the firm's tremendous international presence and high levels of coordination across relevant jurisdictions.

**Sources say:** *"They have a very broad practice and very broad geographic footprint. These folks really understand our business better than most."*

**KEY INDIVIDUALS Jeffrey Leavitt** (see p.353) possesses a *"unique set of contacts in this industry."* He is respected for

his skilled representation of entrepreneurs, and *"understands the dynamics"* of the venture capital space. **Jeffrey Lehrer** (see p.2511) is a *"go-to attorney"* for his clients, who rely on his *"service-oriented and good business sense"* to guide them through a wide range of financing and transactional activity.

## Goodwin Procter LLP
### See profile on p.1522

**THE FIRM** Goodwin Procter's hubs of venture capital expertise can be found in Boston, New York, California and DC, offering clients comprehensive coverage on a nationwide basis. The practice represents emerging technology companies, investment banks and private equity firms, and translates its experience acting for a diverse range of market participants into creative solutions for its clients. The team was recently engaged by Sequoia Capital to restructure its $2 billion India funds family.

**Sources say:** *"They are real specialists in this area."*

**KEY INDIVIDUALS Jonathan Axelrad** (see p.275) is praised for his excellent practice on the fund formation side. He recently handled the formation of a third fund for Axiom Asia Private Capital. **John Egan** (see p.1490) has been highly occupied in assisting clients with exits in recent times, representing Admeld in its sale to Google, and Q1 Labs in its sale to IBM.

## Latham & Watkins LLP
### See profile on p.446

**THE FIRM** With high visibility across some of the most important venture capital industries, Latham & Watkins is well placed to advise its broad clientele on all aspects of the venture capital life cycle. Its geographic spread also lends itself to a vibrant presence in the market, with lawyers operating out of nine offices across the country. ActiFio, BIND Biosciences and Data Gravity have all recently called upon the team to assist on multimillion-dollar venture financings.

**Client Service** *"They have a high level of professionalism, promptness and a real sense of customer advocacy."*

**KEY INDIVIDUALS** Silicon Valley-based **Christopher Kaufman** (see p.343) is lauded as *"a fantastic lawyer"* who has a leading venture capital practice. His expertise in M&A and corporate finance matters is greatly appreciated by his high-technology client base. The *"professional and personable"* **John Chory** is *"very knowledgeable about all areas of corporate law."* He is a new entry to the nationwide rankings, and is based in Massachusetts. **Patrick Pohlen** (see p.659) continues to be very active in the emerging companies space, recently acting on a $30 million Series C financing for Siluria Technologies.

### Band 3

## Hogan Lovells US LLP

**THE FIRM** Hogan Lovells has cemented its position as a strong choice for virtually every type of stakeholder in the venture capital market. Its expertise and experience on cross-border matters make it a favored destination for clients such as ABS Capital Partners and Supponor. The team has also been active on several significant IPOs of late, demonstrating its ability to represent clients from startup throughout their expansion.

**Sources say:** *"Their strongest points are legal thoroughness and a focus on the client."*

**KEY INDIVIDUALS** Jeffrey Hurlburt and Michael Williams are the key contacts for this practice.

### Morgan, Lewis & Bockius LLP
See profile on p.2246

**THE FIRM** This team has had a busy year, acting on numerous financing rounds for key clients such as Better Place, Valeritas and Flowonix Medical. Lawyers develop and cultivate close relationships with key financial institutions across the country, and work effectively across many sectors, including digital media, cleantech and IT.

**KEY INDIVIDUALS** Cochairs of the emerging business and technology group Steve Cohen and Tom Kellerman are the key contacts for this practice.

### Orrick, Herrington & Sutcliffe LLP
See profile on p.1994

**THE FIRM** Orrick houses a well-regarded venture capital team based out of Silicon Valley. Its clientele is mostly composed of technology industry participants drawn from the worlds of social media, cloud computing and education technology, among other sectors. Generation Investment Management recently mandated the team to act on its $110 million Series C investment into a renewable energy company.

**KEY INDIVIDUALS** John Bautista heads the firm's emerging companies group, and is a key contact.

### Perkins Coie LLP
See profile on p.2548

**THE FIRM** This team has a notable presence across the full spectrum of venture capital matters, and is especially highlighted for its expertise representing digital media, social media and music companies seeking funding. Venture capital firms looking to invest are able to turn to the firm's considerable network, and can rely upon the team's noted efficiency in negotiations. The team also skillfully handles exit transactions such as the recent $168 million sale of PowerReviews to Bazaarvoice.

**KEY INDIVIDUALS** Michael Glaser continues to attract significant praise from commentators. Clients praise his high standards of service and pragmatic approach to complicated matters.

### Pillsbury Winthrop Shaw Pittman LLP
See profile on p.2000

**THE FIRM** This firm has a strong track record of guiding companies from startup to IPO and beyond, presiding over financing rounds for key clients Apigee, Tilera and Svaya Nanotechnologies in the past year. Technology and life sciences are key areas of focus for this agile team.

**Sources say:** *"Smart, hard-working, experienced partners and comprehensive capabilities as a firm."*

**KEY INDIVIDUALS** Jorge del Calvo maintains a stellar reputation among peers and clients. He offers an impressive depth of experience in the technology sector.

### WilmerHale
See profile on p.930

**THE FIRM** WilmerHale is an attractive one-stop shop for startups and emerging companies, and offers clients an assured multidisciplinary approach that includes antitrust, IP and regulatory advice. The sale of Rhythmia Medical to Boston Scientific for $265 million is a prime example of the success of lawyers in representing a company throughout its life cycle from startup to exit.

**Client Service** *"They are agile and supportive, and I feel that they are an extended part of our team. I have a feeling that we are going to be doing business again and again."*

**KEY INDIVIDUALS** Sarah Rothermel (see p.1507) is a highly active presence in the industry. A fund formation specialist, she frequently represents venture capital funds and other private investment vehicles.

## Band 4

### Blank Rome LLP
See profile on p.2235

**THE FIRM** This firm has cultivated a solid presence in the emerging growth sector, working closely with IT, life sciences and clean technology companies through every stage of their growth. The team has been involved in numerous venture financing transactions of late, and counts Edison Ventures, Greenphire and Halfpenny Technologies among its vibrant clientele.

**Commercial Awareness** *"Great technical lawyers."* *"They are extremely thorough yet also very business-minded. They really understand the space and are very efficient; a hidden gem in venture capital work."*

**KEY INDIVIDUALS** Louis Rappaport (see p.389) *"simplifies rather than complicates,"* making him a popular choice for venture capital clients. *"We know that we can*

depend on him, and at the end of the day that is what matters most,"* explains one client.

### Dentons
See profile on p.449

**THE FIRM** The dynamic team at Dentons operates across the full spectrum of venture capital activity, representing emerging growth companies as well as investment banks and notable venture capital firms, including Canaan Partners. Leveraging a global network of expertise in the space, the team is able to support its clients in all nature of transactions, from financings and investments to exit strategies.

**KEY INDIVIDUALS** Chicago-based **Michael Rosenthal** has extensive experience assisting investors of all types as well as forming funds for private equity and venture capital sponsors. **Paul Gajer** (see p.318) was lately called upon by MCMC to guide it through a $15 million Series C offering and related acquisitions.

### Gibson, Dunn & Crutcher LLP
See profile on p.682

**THE FIRM** Housing considerable expertise in the mid and late stages of emerging growth companies as well as a wealth of experience with corporate investors, Gibson Dunn has proved an attractive prospect to clients such as Intel Capital, Shazam Entertainment and Adknowledge. Attorneys are identified as being adept in complex transactional activity, including cross-border and offshore work.

**Sources say:** *"I believe that money spent on attorneys can deliver incredibly good value when you get the right team – with Gibson, we got the right team."*

**KEY INDIVIDUALS** Experienced practitioner **Gregory Davidson** (see p.301) was recently engaged by Accuray to act on a $15.35 million investment in Compact Particle Acceleration and to coordinate relevant licensing arrangements.

## Other Notable Practitioners

**David Gitlin** (see p.321) of Greenberg Traurig, LLP is a talented corporate and securities attorney, with substantial experience conducting cross-border transactions and representing foreign venture capital funds.

# LABOR & EMPLOYMENT

| Labor & Employment Leading Firms |
| --- |
| **Band 1** |
| Jones Day * |
| Morgan, Lewis & Bockius LLP * |
| Paul Hastings LLP * |
| Proskauer Rose LLP * |
| **Band 2** |
| Seyfarth Shaw LLP * |
| **Band 3** |
| Gibson, Dunn & Crutcher LLP * |
| Jackson Lewis LLP * |
| Littler Mendelson, PC * |
| Ogletree, Deakins, Nash, Smoak & Stewart, PC * |
| **Band 4** |
| Akin Gump Strauss Hauer & Feld LLP * |
| Fisher & Phillips LLP * |
| Orrick, Herrington & Sutcliffe LLP * |

*Indicates firm with profile.*
*Alphabetical order within each band. Band 1 is the highest.*

## Band 1

### Jones Day
See profile on p.919

**THE FIRM** This global law firm is renowned for its outstanding labor and employment practice. The depth and breadth of its expertise in this area attracts huge corporate clients such as McDonald's, Verizon, and Continental Airlines. The firm is highly skilled at collective bargaining, and has particular expertise regarding the Railway Labor Act. The National Railway Labor Conference recently sought help from the team when conducting complex multiemployer collective bargaining. It is also adept at defending collective and class actions, and was recently employed by Abbott Laboratories to advise on a collective action brought by current and former sales representatives. The team convinced the Seventh Circuit Court to reverse a previous judgment, saving Abbott $3.5 million in the process.
**Sources say:** *"The group provides consistent advice and excellent representation." "Very responsive and thorough."*
**KEY INDIVIDUALS** Lawrence DiNardo is the global head of the firm's labor and employment practice.

### Morgan, Lewis & Bockius LLP
See profile on p.2246

**THE FIRM** This firm has an impressive nationwide footprint, housing a large number of labor and employment specialists based in key locations across the country. The team has a great deal of experience in handling complex labor and employment issues including single plaintiff discrimination claims. Of late, it successfully defended Dell against claims of gender discrimination brought by a former executive. Further areas of expertise include class and collective actions, with a recent example being its representation of Lockheed Martin in successfully arguing against class certification in a gender discrimination suit. The firm's excellence in this area attracts many other notable clients, including American Airlines, Citi and Rolls-Royce.
**KEY INDIVIDUALS** Joseph Costello heads the firm's labor and employment department, and is based in the Philadelphia office.

### Paul Hastings LLP
See profile on p.1996

**THE FIRM** This highly regarded firm is widely recognized as having one of the leading labor and employment practices in the USA. Its expertise in the area draws prominent clients such as Goldman Sachs, IBM and Microsoft. Known for its particular focus on class actions, the team recently represented GlaxoSmithKline before the Supreme Court and achieved an important victory for the company. The group is also renowned for its ability in labor negotiations, representing groups such as the Long Beach/Los Angeles Harbor Employers Association and American Airlines. The team advised the latter on negotiations with three separate unions following its Chapter 11 bankruptcy filing.
**Commercial Awareness** *"They are incredibly strategic and practical in terms of the advice they give us."*
**KEY INDIVIDUALS** Nancy Abell chairs the firm's global employment law department, and is based in the Los Angeles office.

### Proskauer Rose LLP
See profile on p.2001

**THE FIRM** Proskauer has an eminent labor and employment practice with a national reach. It regularly counsels clients in the financial services industry, the entertainment business and the sports world. Renowned for its work in this last area, the team is retained by the NBA, NFL, NHL and MLB to handle collective bargaining as well as wider employment issues. It also has a great deal of experience advising on class actions and recently achieved a positive settlement for the Creative Artists Agency relating to age discrimination claims. The group also focuses on noncompete litigation, and recently advised Sientra on 13 different noncompete issues relating to a number of their employees.
**Client Service** *"I like their responsiveness – you reach out to them, and they get back to you day and night, and in between."*
**Commercial Awareness** *"They pull together the right people – they know our company and put the right lawyer in." "You call them, and you get practical expertise which adds value."*
**KEY INDIVIDUALS** The department is cochaired by Paul Salvatore and Elise Bloom, both of whom are based in New York.

| Recommended for Client Service Nationwide | |
| --- | --- |
| Akin Gump Strauss Hauer & Feld LLP | Proskauer Rose LLP |
| Ogletree, Deakins, Nash, Smoak & Stewart, PC | Seyfarth Shaw LLP |

| Recommended for Commercial Awareness Nationwide | |
| --- | --- |
| Jackson Lewis LLP | Proskauer Rose LLP |
| Paul Hastings LLP | |

## Band 2

### Seyfarth Shaw LLP
See profile on p.1262

**THE FIRM** This multiservice firm continues to stand out because of its extensive and broad-reaching labor and employment expertise. It covers the full gamut of work in this area, and is particularly well known for its experience in labor relations. An example of this is its recent representation of Hotel Association of Washington, DC in collective bargaining negotiations affecting 6,000 staff. Seyfarth also excels at defending EEOC investigations and is currently representing Kaplan against claims of racial discrimination. Other clients of note include Family Dollar, Aaron's and BP America.
**Client Service** *"What stands out for me is their customer service – they treat each thing as very important and turn things around very quickly for me. I feel like I'm their largest customer although I know I'm not!"*
**KEY INDIVIDUALS** Lisa Damon chairs the firm's labor and employment department, and is based in the Boston office.

## Band 3

### Gibson, Dunn & Crutcher LLP
See profile on p.682

**THE FIRM** This firm is noted for its high-end labor and employment practice, and regularly advises on big-ticket cases for corporate giants such as Walmart and Starbucks. It is hugely experienced in representing clients in class and collective actions, and recently advised Northrop Grumman in a wage and hour class action. The team succeeded in having the class action dismissed in favor of individual non-class arbitration proceedings. It is also skilled at handling single plaintiff defense and recently advised the Ports America Management Corporation in a complex wrongful termination case.
**Sources say:** *"Customer service is beyond any other firm I have experienced. The lawyers are quick to respond and are very aware of current trends." "They are exceptional lawyers; they have the ability to gain insight into our business to allow them to attain exceptional results."*

**KEY INDIVIDUALS** The firm's labor and employment department is headed by DC-based Eugene Scalia and Los Angeles-based Catherine Conway.

## Jackson Lewis LLP
See profile on p.1982

**THE FIRM** This much-admired labor and employment specialist is highly regarded for its representation of employers in a wide range of matters. The group regularly counsels on discrimination cases and recently represented the Cincinnatian Hotel in a federal jury trial. The firm successfully defended the company against a claim of alleged age discrimination filed by a job applicant. The group is also adept at defending both single plaintiff cases and class actions. Recently, it acted on behalf of the Benefits Administration Council and succeeded in getting a number of claims made under ERISA and the ADEA dismissed.

**Commercial Awareness** *"They are exceptional attorneys who do work in multiple states. They only do labor and employment work, which gives them an extremely strong base for this sphere. What they do, they do exceptionally well with laser precision."*

**KEY INDIVIDUALS** Vincent Cino chairs the firm, and is based in the Morristown office.

## Littler Mendelson, PC
See profile on p.688

**THE FIRM** This vibrant group focuses exclusively on labor and employment work and is renowned for its deep, high-quality bench. It offers clients an impressive geographical footprint across the country. The group covers the full spectrum of law affecting the workplace, and counsels clients such as Coca-Cola, Safeway, Securitas and Tenet Healthcare. Recently, it advised Tenet during its positive renegotiation of national labor accords. Further noteworthy work includes representation of Securitas in a class action where the class consists of 60,000 people.

**Sources say:** *"They are extremely organized, knowledgeable and experienced. They are able to communicate complicated legal scenarios and possible outcomes in lay terms."*

**KEY INDIVIDUALS** Thomas Bender and Jeremy Roth are the co-presidents and co-managing directors of the firm. Bender is based in Philadelphia, and Roth in San Diego.

## Ogletree, Deakins, Nash, Smoak & Stewart, PC
See profile on p.1110

**THE FIRM** This labor and employment firm works with such high-profile clients as Dell, Target, Honeywell and Boeing. The team handles the full spectrum of labor and employment work with supplementary practices focusing on employee benefits, immigration and affirmative action. It recently successfully defended the Boston Police Department against claims made under Title VII of the Civil Rights Act. The win saved the city of Boston between $15 million and $20 million in possible damages.

**Client Service** *"They're very effective and efficient. Of all the law firms I employ they are the top in terms of customer satisfaction."*

**KEY INDIVIDUALS** Kim Ebert is the managing partner of the firm, and is based in Indianapolis.

## Band 4

### Akin Gump Strauss Hauer & Feld LLP
See profile on p.904

**THE FIRM** This robust firm maintains an impressive labor and employment practice. Its offices across the country advise on a wide range of matters including EEOC advocacy, FLSA counseling and litigation, as well as general defense of class actions. The group is retained by Home Depot and has recently defended the retail giant in a number of matters including class actions and wage and hour suits. Other clients of note include the NFL, Starbucks, and Ernst & Young.

**Client Service** *"The teamwork and interaction between offices is excellent – they are very well prepared, and they spend the appropriate amount of time ensuring that their clients are prepared for all eventualities."*

**KEY INDIVIDUALS** Robert Lian heads the firm's labor and employment practice, and is based in the Washington, DC office.

## Fisher & Phillips LLP
See profile on p.1107

**THE FIRM** This dedicated labor and employment firm has over 250 attorneys working from multiple offices across the country. Its national profile is boosted by its recognition as a leading firm in this area across several different states, including its home state of Georgia. The group works across a large number of practice areas including litigation and employment disputes, wage and hour law and workers' compensation. The firm also operates specialist practice groups focusing on areas such as the retail industry and automotive manufacturing.

**Sources say:** *"It has devotion to excellence, attention to detail, extraordinary preparation, the desire to achieve the best results for the company, but most importantly, the ability to understand the company's short and long-term goals and align its services and advice accordingly."*

**KEY INDIVIDUALS** Roger Quillen is the chairman and managing partner of the firm, and works out of the Atlanta office.

## Orrick, Herrington & Sutcliffe LLP
See profile on p.1994

**THE FIRM** With a significant bench of labor and employment lawyers working across the USA, this firm represents a broad range of clients including Credit Suisse, Facebook and Microsoft. The group offers extensive expertise in advising financial service providers and technology and retail clients, and recently acted on behalf of Morgan Stanley in obtaining the dismissal of a wage and hour class action suit. The team also counsels clients on Dodd-Frank whistle-blower defense and employment issues relating to trade secrets.

**Sources say:** *"They have been just exactly what we wanted and needed... what every attorney-client relationship should be and what clients hope it will be."*

**KEY INDIVIDUALS** Mike Delikat chairs the firm's global employment group, and is located in the New York office.

# LEISURE & HOSPITALITY

Commentary about individuals can be found under their firm's paragraph. If the firm has no paragraph (is not ranked) look at Other Notable Practitioners.

## Leisure & Hospitality
### Leading Firms

**Band 1**
Paul Hastings LLP *
Dentons *

**Band 2**
DLA Piper LLP (US) *
Greenberg Traurig, LLP *
Perkins Coie LLP

**Band 3**
Baker & Hostetler LLP *
Gardere Wynne Sewell LLP *
Goodwin Procter LLP *
Hogan Lovells US LLP
Holland & Knight LLP *
Latham & Watkins LLP *
Milbank, Tweed, Hadley & McCloy LLP *
Proskauer Rose LLP *
Sidley Austin LLP *

**Band 4**
Arent Fox LLP *
Bickel & Brewer
Goulston & Storrs
Hunton & Williams LLP *
Jeffer, Mangels, Butler & Mitchell LLP
Seyfarth Shaw LLP *
Steptoe & Johnson LLP
Venable LLP *

*\* Indicates firm with profile.*
*Alphabetical order within each band. Band 1 is the highest.*

## Band 1

### Dentons
See profile on p.449

**THE FIRM** The lawyers at this firm are recognized for their deep understanding of the leisure industry and ability to apply this knowledge in a wide variety of matters. The firm focuses on advising its clients on hotel acquisitions, developments and operations, in addition to being particularly respected in negotiating hotel management agreements. Recent highlights include representing KSL Capital in its joint venture partnership for the purchase of the Essex Hotel in New York.
**Commercial Awareness** *"They understand how the lodging industry works. This experience alone sets them apart from most other firms who treat hotels simply as an extension of their real estate practice."*
**KEY INDIVIDUALS Richard Ross** (see p.396) is praised by market sources for his knowledge of the sector and outstanding technical skills. He advises owners, operators, developers and lenders on a wide variety of operational and transactional matters. Sources respect him for being *"perfectly realistic about where the deal is going."* **Meghan**

Cocci (see p.296) represents hotel operators, investors and owners in a wide variety of negotiations and transactions. Sources say: *"She is wonderful – she is approachable, knowledgeable and responsive."* **Mark Daliere** (see p.301) has a practice that focuses on representing hotel developers, owners, operators and investors in a wide variety of matters. He is particularly noted for his ability in the negotiation of hotel management agreements.

### Paul Hastings LLP
See profile on p.1996

**THE FIRM** This standout firm has a fine reputation in the hospitality industry and is particularly noted for its work representing hotel owners, lenders and developers. The firm represented Baha Mar in the negotiation of management agreements with three hotel operating companies, relating to a $3.5 billion resort under development in the Bahamas. Other clients of the firm include Oaktree Capital, Starwood Capital and Hersha Hospitality Trust.
**Client Service** *"We get value for the dollars we spend and even when projects become much more complicated than originally expected, they ensure that the billing works for us and our budget. They are very much about the long-term relationship and health of their client."*
**KEY INDIVIDUALS Rick Kirkbride** is acknowledged by peers and industry insiders as one of the leaders of the leisure and hospitality field. His practice focuses on representing hotel owners, developers and investors, in the financing, development and acquisition of hotels and resorts. *"He truly cares about his clients and ensures that their needs are met and that their business goals are achieved,"* say sources. Associate **Lauren Giovannone** represents owners, developers and lenders in the development and acquisition of hotels and resorts. In addition, she regularly negotiates management and licensing agreements on behalf of her clients.

## Band 2

### DLA Piper LLP (US)
See profile on p.1971

**THE FIRM** This firm handles a variety of high-level work within the leisure and hospitality sector. The team represents hotel operators, developers, investors, lenders and franchisors in a range of transactional and financing matters. In a recent highlight, the group acted for Shell Vacations on its acquisition by Wyndham Worldwide. Key clients include a series of major resort industry players, such as Marriott International and Hilton Worldwide.
**Commercial Awareness** *"They knew a lot of the nuances and we wouldn't have been able to close the sale without them. Their skills and knowledge were unparalleled."*

### Recommended for Client Service
**Nationwide**

| | |
|---|---|
| Baker & Hostetler LLP | Proskauer Rose LLP |
| Goulston & Storrs | Seyfarth Shaw LLP |
| Paul Hastings LLP | Venable LLP |

### Recommended for Commercial Awareness
**Nationwide**

| | |
|---|---|
| DLA Piper LLP (US) | Hogan Lovells US LLP |
| Dentons | Perkins Coie LLP |
| Goodwin Procter LLP | |

**KEY INDIVIDUALS Sandra Kellman** (see p.344) is noted as a lawyer who is able to handle work for hotel operators and owners at the highest level. *"Sandy is extraordinarily experienced and she will get the deal done. If I need someone with creative solutions on complex matters she is terrific,"* said one commentator.

### Greenberg Traurig, LLP
See profile on p.1024

**THE FIRM** This large firm has extensive capability within the hospitality sector and handles work across the USA and the Caribbean. Its experienced lawyers have the ability to handle diverse issues including fractional ownership structures, brand management agreements and condominium development agreements. Clients of the firm include Starwood Capital, Seminole Hard Rock International, Affinia Hospitality, Intrawest and Starwood Hotels & Resorts.
**Sources say:** *"I like the fact they work quickly and efficiently, that they are always available to us and that they are exceedingly knowledgeable."*
**KEY INDIVIDUALS Nelson Migdal** (see p.368) is noted for his knowledge of the leisure industry and expertise when it comes to hotel management and franchise agreements. *"He is a very prominent guy and he always has the big-picture view so he is good for strategy,"* say sources. **Michael Sullivan** (see p.1010) is based in Orlando and handles a wide variety of leisure and hospitality matters. According to interviewees, *"he is one of a few guys who have done a lot on the developer and the brand side. That gives him some good insights into both sides of transactions."* **Richard Davis** (see p.302) is noted by interviewees for his experience in the timeshare and fractional use sector. *"His goal is to get to the right compromise and not just show how smart he is, and as a result, you get real critical thinking through issues to get the right answer,"* say sources.

### Perkins Coie LLP
See profile on p.2548

**THE FIRM** This well-regarded firm focuses on representing hotel owners in a wide variety of matters. The team is also notable for its strong hotel bankruptcy practice. In one recent matter, lawyers from the firm represented Strategic Hotels in its joint venture acquisition of the Essex Hotel in

## Leisure & Hospitality
### Senior Statesmen

Senior Statesmen: distinguished older practitioners

| | | |
|---|---|---|
| Norman James M | Holland & Knight LLP * | |

### Leading Individuals

**Band 1**

| | |
|---|---|
| Benudiz P Peter | Milbank, Tweed, Hadley & McCloy LLP * |
| Kirkbride Rick S | Paul Hastings LLP |
| Ross Richard F | Dentons * |

**Band 2**

| | |
|---|---|
| Axelrod Gary | Latham & Watkins LLP |
| Cocci Meghan | Dentons * |
| Fanelli Cecelia L | Steptoe & Johnson LLP |
| Horwitz Jeffrey A | Proskauer Rose LLP |
| Hudak Timothy Q | Eckert Seamans Cherin & Mellott (ONP)† |
| Kellman Sandra Y | DLA Piper LLP (US) * |
| Melicharek Jr John | Baker & Hostetler LLP * |
| Migdal Nelson F | Greenberg Traurig, LLP * |
| Neff David M | Perkins Coie LLP |
| Parmley Bruce E | Hogan Lovells US LLP |
| Risman Clifford J | Gardere Wynne Sewell LLP * |
| Robins Andrew S | Akerman Senterfitt (ONP)† |
| Sullivan Michael J | Greenberg Traurig, LLP * |
| Weld King Carol | Hogan Lovells US LLP |

**Band 3**

| | |
|---|---|
| Barker Christopher B | Goodwin Procter LLP * |
| Butler Jr James R | Jeffer, Mangels, Butler & Mitchell LLP |
| Cadwalader Lynn K | Holland & Knight LLP * |
| Davis Richard F | Greenberg Traurig, LLP * |
| Goebel Teresa | Goodwin Procter LLP * |
| Gordon Phillip | Perkins Coie LLP |
| Marre Daniel GM | Perkins Coie LLP |
| Nelson Cynthia | Gardere Wynne Sewell LLP * |
| Salaman Christian A | Pillsbury Winthrop Shaw Pittman (ONP)† * |
| Stahler Harold | Goulston & Storrs |
| Weil Alan S | Sidley Austin LLP * |

**Band 4**

| | |
|---|---|
| Bickel John | Bickel & Brewer |
| Bosch William M. | Steptoe & Johnson LLP |
| Brewer Bill | Bickel & Brewer |
| Brown Banks | McDermott Will & Emery LLP (ONP)† * |
| Capute Courtney G | Venable LLP * |
| Cole Alexandra | Perkins Coie LLP |
| Daliere Mark | Dentons * |
| Goodwin Michael | Arnold & Porter LLP (ONP)† * |
| Guay Joseph | Holland & Knight LLP * |
| Maganuco Robert J | Sidley Austin LLP * |
| Margalit Nir | Foley & Lardner LLP (ONP)† |
| Ressa Gregory J | Simpson Thacher & Bartlett LLP (ONP)† * |
| Rosenblatt Brett P | Latham & Watkins LLP * |
| Wachen Kimberly | Arent Fox LLP * * |
| Webb Robert J | Baker & Hostetler LLP * |

**Up-and-coming individuals**

| | |
|---|---|
| Docks Adam | Perkins Coie LLP |

**Associates to watch**

| | |
|---|---|
| Giovannone Lauren | Paul Hastings LLP |
| Wilk Corey | Goulston & Storrs |

*\* Indicates individual with profile.*

*†ONP = Other Notable Practitioner.*

New York. Other clients include Rosewood Hotels & Resorts, Shamrock-Hostmark, Maritz, Wolff & Co and Sun Development & Management.

KEY INDIVIDUALS **David Neff** has a niche practice that focuses on dealing with bankruptcies in the hotel sector. He represented the owners of the Radisson Hotel at Los Angeles International Airport in a Chapter 11 reorganization. **Daniel Marre** focuses on handling the development, acquisition and financing of hotel projects, and the negotiation of hotel management agreements. Sources describe him as a pleasure to work with. **Alexandra Cole** is well regarded for her abilities in transactional matters. She recently represented Maritz, Wolff & Co in its $192 million refinancing and sale of a hotel property. **Phillip Gordon** is the chair of the firm's hospitality group and has a practice that focuses on hotel financing, hotel acquisitions, and the negotiation of management agreements. He represented a hotel management company when it was sold, along with five hotel properties, to a Chinese company. **Adam Docks** has experience in areas such as hotel acquisitions, franchise agreements and operational matters among others. Sources praise his conscientious and practical approach.

### Band 3

#### Baker & Hostetler LLP
See profile on p.2119

THE FIRM This firm's Florida-based practice handles hotel and leisure matters across the USA and Caribbean, and is particularly noted for its timeshare and mixed-use work. The team represented Fortune Hotels in its redevelopment of an 800-room resort, which included the restructuring of a $60 million financing facility and the conversion of part of the resort into timeshares. Other clients of the firm include Hard Rock Hotels, Marriott Vacations Worldwide and Spottswood Companies.

Client Service *"I am very pleased with their responsiveness. Sometimes I have to tell them they don't have to work over the weekend and that next week is fine – they are willing to drop everything for me."*

KEY INDIVIDUALS **John Melicharek** (see p.366) is chair of the firm's leisure and hospitality group. He recently represented Melia Hotels in its acquisition of an Orlando hotel out of bankruptcy. *"I would say he is a good listener, he is down to earth, understands the problems and has a cool head,"* said one interviewee. **Robert Webb** (see p.423) enjoys a fine reputation in the timeshare and mixed-use industry. He practices across the USA and throughout the Caribbean and is held in high regard by market commentators.

#### Gardere Wynne Sewell LLP
See profile on p.2436

THE FIRM This firm represents its clients throughout the USA and Latin America in a wide variety of hotel, luxury resorts and mixed-use projects. The firm has acted for REIT Ashford Hospitality on its hotel acquisitions, dispositions and financings in a number of different states.

Other clients of the firm include Aimbridge Hospitality, KSL Capital Partners and LQ International.

Sources say: *"They were result-oriented and easy to deal with."*

KEY INDIVIDUALS **Clifford Risman** (see p.392) has a varied hospitality practice which encompasses the acquisition, development, operation and financing of hotels and resorts, for a wide variety of investors, developers and hotel owners. He recently represented Aimbridge Hospitality in its formation of an equity venture with a private equity firm to buy a portfolio of over 100 hotels out of bankruptcy. **Cynthia Nelson** (see p.375) is a real estate attorney with significant experience handling acquisitions, financing and leasing in the hospitality sector. According to one impressed client, *"she is very fast, very efficient and understands what I want."*

### Goodwin Procter LLP
See profile on p.1522

THE FIRM This firm's leisure and hospitality team is home to lawyers with experience in many facets of the sector, including financing, M&A, operational matters and litigation. The firm represents hotel operators and brands, in addition to acting for REITs and other investors. It has recently assisted Rockwood Capital Partners in a number of deals, including its purchase of San Juan Marriott Resort and Stellaris Casino in a joint venture with a Puerto Rico-based investment group.

Commercial Awareness *"They are obviously very experienced in hospitality transactions. They knew what was coming and what was expected. They were always one step ahead of the game."*

KEY INDIVIDUALS **Christopher Barker** (see p.278) is well known in the hospitality world and is recognized as a lawyer with significant experience in the transactional side of the business. He is particularly noted for his work representing REITs such as HEI Hotels in matters including hotel acquisitions and franchise agreements with hotel operators. **Teresa Goebel** (see p.321) is a *"smart, detail-oriented"* lawyer whose practice focuses on representing hotel operators and investors in a wide variety of matters. She regularly advises Four Season Hotels on hotel agreements and recently negotiated a series of agreements relating to the rebranding and management of the Four Seasons Rancho Encantado, Santa Fe.

### Hogan Lovells US LLP

THE FIRM This firm focuses on representing investors and hotel owners in the full spectrum of leisure acquisitions, financing and negotiations. It recently represented Gaylord Entertainment in the $210 million sale of its hotel management business to Marriot International. Other significant clients include the Abu Dhabi Investment Authority, Morgans Hotel Group and Bayshore Capital.

Commercial Awareness *"The hotel companies couldn't get anything past them – they knew the business better than anyone."*

KEY INDIVIDUALS **Bruce Parmley** has a wealth of transactional experience in the leisure and hospitality sector. He advised a UAE-based investment group on the development of the new Four Seasons Resort Dubai at Jumeirah Beach. Sources say: *"He is full of personality, very intellectual, clear-minded and a good negotiator."* **Carol Weld King** represents hotel and equity groups in transactions and developments throughout the USA. In one recent deal, she advised LoF Bethesda L.P. on the sale of a Residence Inn for $64.5 million to RLJ Lodging Trust. *"If it takes working round the clock to get the deal done she will do it – she would walk through fire for her clients,"* according to impressed commentators.

## Holland & Knight LLP
See profile on p.1028
**THE FIRM** This firm has a broad-based hospitality practice which encompasses the hotel and timeshare sector and includes work such as management agreements, financing, acquisitions and related litigation. The team focuses on representing hotel brands, exemplified by its work for Intercontinental Hotel Group on two franchise agreements with the developers of two new Holiday Inn hotels in Colombia.
**Sources say:** *"They have very strong experience in the hospitality arena and they understand and know our company and its objectives."*
**KEY INDIVIDUALS Lynn Cadwalader** (see p.291) is an experienced leisure and hospitality lawyer who regularly handles both hotel and mixed-use work. She recently represented the Ritz-Carlton Hotel company in connection with the management and licensing of a branded condominium project under development in Hawaii. **Joseph Guay** (see p.327) is a real estate and finance lawyer with a proven track record in the hospitality sector. Sources say: *"He is extremely responsive and technically proficient, and has a terrific bedside manner. He is always positive and upbeat."* **James Norman** (see p.377) is respected by his peers and clients, and praised for his *"levelheaded, business-sense approach to the legal aspects of any deal."* He continues to carry out a consultancy role and is active in arbitration and mediation work.

## Latham & Watkins LLP
See profile on p.446
**THE FIRM** This firm's leisure and hospitality practice is largely recognized in the market for its role in the financing of developments and acquisitions. The firm represented Loews Hotels in such work relating to the Renaissance Hollywood Hotel & Spa. Key clients include Caesars Entertainment, Pinnacle Entertainment and Host Hotels & Resorts.
**Sources say:** *"It is a fine law firm that produces a quality product."*
**KEY INDIVIDUALS Gary Axelrod** focuses on representing hotel owners in transactions, development projects and the negotiation of management agreements. He recently acted for Starwood Capital Group on the $81.8 million acquisition of a portfolio of nine hotels. *"He is good to negotiate with, smart and principled, and not a table pounder,"* say sources. **Brett Rosenblatt** (see p.395) focuses on financing gaming and hospitality projects, and acquisi-

tions. He is described by sources as *"very effective"* and a *"good resource."*

## Milbank, Tweed, Hadley & McCloy LLP
See profile on p.448
**THE FIRM** This firm represents owners, investors and operators in a wide variety of leisure and hospitality transactions. The firm has the capacity to handle complex cross-border deals involving both hotels and mixed-use resorts. Its clients include Plaza Hotel and Beverly Hilton.
**KEY INDIVIDUALS Peter Benudiz** (see p.282) is recognized for his involvement in financing as well as his technical expertise when it comes to management agreements. *"He is willing to listen – he is not abrasive and gives everyone a chance to make their point,"* according to interviewees.

## Proskauer Rose LLP
See profile on p.2001
**THE FIRM** This firm represents investors and owners, as well as hotel brands and developers, in a variety of leisure and hospitality matters. The firm regularly represents REITs, private equity groups, sovereign wealth funds and high net worth individuals, in investments and acquisitions within the sector. Additionally, it represents a number of boutique developers and non-US-based hotel brands in developments, acquisitions and management agreement work.
**Client Service** *"They take the time to understand the objective of what we want to accomplish, and they try to understand the business objectives of what we need."*
**KEY INDIVIDUALS Jeffrey Horwitz** is a corporate and securities lawyer with extensive expertise in the leisure and hospitality sector. *"He is very practical. He is not only a very talented lawyer: he has got great experience which comes to bear in different situations,"* say sources.

## Sidley Austin LLP
See profile on p.1264
**THE FIRM** This experienced hotel group represents owners, operators and financial institutions in a wide variety of acquisitions, transactions and restructurings, in addition to handling licensing and management agreements. The firm recently represented GE Asset Management in the modification and sale of an $80 million mezzanine loan related to three hotels.
**KEY INDIVIDUALS Alan Weil** (see p.424) is a real estate lawyer with a great deal of experience in hospitality financings and acquisitions. He recently represented Starwood Property Trust in the purchase of a $35 million participation interest in a subordinate loan secured by a ski resort complex. **Robert Maganuco** (see p.360) handles hotel financing and restructuring deals. Sources say: *"He is the kind of guy that focuses on getting a deal done; he knows his stuff and doesn't have to hesitate."*

## Band 4

## Arent Fox LLP
See profile on p.905
**THE FIRM** This firm's leisure and hospitality group is based on its strong real estate practice and clients include developers, owners, operators and franchisors. The firm has a close relationship with Marriott International, and recently assisted in the development of hotels in Manhattan and Miami Beach on its behalf.
**Sources say:** *"They are thorough and practical." "They are good on the franchise side."*
**KEY INDIVIDUALS Kimberly Wachen** (see p.897) is visible in the market due to the work she carries out with Marriott International. Matters she has handled include the acquisition of the Grand Cayman Beach Resort hotel, which included equity, development and contractual issues.

## Bickel & Brewer
**THE FIRM** This Texas litigation boutique has established a strong reputation in the hospitality industry for its representation of hotel owners in disputes with operators. The firm has been involved at the cutting edge of litigation in the sector and has a proven track record in big hospitality cases.
**Sources say:** *"I would rate them as an A-team of litigators."*
**KEY INDIVIDUALS John Bickel** is a well-known litigator in the leisure and hospitality field. Sources say: *"He makes a good impression in the courtroom."* Litigator **Bill Brewer** is *"certainly very knowledgeable about the industry,"* according to commentators.

## Goulston & Storrs
**THE FIRM** This Boston-centered firm has a US-wide practice which represents REITs, owners, developers, operators and financial institutions, in acquisitions, financing and the negotiation of management agreements. The firm recently represented Pebblebrook Hotel Trust in the acquisition of a hotel in California, and additionally negotiated the hotel management agreements with the operator.
**Client Service** *"They really understand us as a firm which enables us to move expeditiously and not to have to bring them up to speed on deals."*
**KEY INDIVIDUALS Harold Stahler** has a practice focused on acquisitions, financing, joint venture transactions and management issues. He has acted for Pyramid Hotel Group on a variety of matters, including negotiating hotel management and equity investment agreements and acting as a court-appointed receiver. **Corey Wilk** is a well-regarded associate who regularly practices in the leisure and hospitality sector. *"He is very articulate, very quick in his work but very accurate and has great expertise in the hotel space and dealing with brands,"* say impressed sources.

### Hunton & Williams LLP
See profile on p.2517

**THE FIRM** This firm's hospitality group is particularly noted for its REIT practice, and is regularly involved in REIT IPOs and restructurings, CMBS loans, secured and unsecured credit lines, management agreements and franchise agreements. Clients include Pebblebrook Hotel Trust, Hersha Hospitality Trust and Chatham Lodging Trust.

**KEY INDIVIDUALS** Daryl Robertson is a key contact at the practice.

### Jeffer, Mangels, Butler & Mitchell LLP

**THE FIRM** This West Coast firm has a hospitality practice that is well known in the industry and handles a significant volume of work. The firm's lawyers have experience negotiating hotel management agreements, assisting with hotel finance, structuring joint ventures, and advising hotels on labor and employment issues. The firm has handled a wide variety of matters related to hotels, resorts, mixed-use projects and timeshares.

**KEY INDIVIDUALS** James Butler is a transactional lawyer and litigator with a high profile in the hospitality space. Sources say: *"He has established a reputation in the industry for being on the cutting edge of new litigation."*

### Seyfarth Shaw LLP
See profile on p.1262

**THE FIRM** This firm's reputation in the industry is built on its strong labor and employment practice. The team is particularly respected for its expertise in union relations. In one example, the firm represented Washington, DC's leading unionized hotels in collective negotiations covering over 6,000 employees. Additionally, the group represents clients in the hospitality industry in wage and hour class actions, employment issues and employee benefit work.

**Client Service** *"One thing I like about all the people at the firm is that they are readily available and you always get a call back – they are very responsive."*

**KEY INDIVIDUALS** Ronald Kramer heads the hospitality practice.

### Steptoe & Johnson LLP

**THE FIRM** This firm is recognized for its participation in sector-leading litigation on behalf of its clients, and is also known for its work in transactions and negotiating hotel management agreements. The firm draws clients from all sectors of the industry including hotel owners, operators and developers, investors, franchisors and franchisees.

**Sources say:** *"They are very good litigators – smart and thoughtful."*

**KEY INDIVIDUALS** Cecelia Fanelli is well respected in the hotel industry for her extensive litigation experience. Additionally, she has handled arbitrations, mediations and transactional matters for her clients. *"When she speaks she knows what she is talking about, and it tends to be very persuasive, not just to the court but to her opposition,"* say sources. **William Bosch** is a trial lawyer with a great deal of experience representing clients in the hospitality industry. According to commentators, *"he is creative and thorough, and takes advantage of all the avenues that are open."*

### Venable LLP
See profile on p.927

**THE FIRM** This firm represents hotel developers, owners and operators in a wide variety of hospitality matters. The firm's work includes negotiating hospitality agreements, licensing agreements and franchise agreements. Clients include Authentic Entertainment, Marriott International and White Lodging Services Corporation.

**Client Service** *"I think they are excellent in terms of responsiveness. They are very quick to respond and if they can't get an answer quickly they are very quick to give their analysis timeframes. They do a very good job of managing expectations, and they are pleasant to work with and very knowledgeable – everything you would like in a law firm."*

**KEY INDIVIDUALS** Courtney Capute (see p.292) is a transactional and real estate lawyer who is regularly involved in hospitality work. She assists her clients in acquisitions, dispositions and financing, as well as negotiating management and franchising agreements on her clients' behalf.

### Other Notable Practitioners

**Andrew Robins** of Akerman Senterfitt is a *"very creative thinker,"* who represents hotel operators, owners, developers and investors in a wide variety of matters. He has a particular strong suit in structuring mixed-use developments, but his wide experience also includes the negotiation of hotel management and licensing agreements, and involvement in acquisitions and financing. **Michael Goodwin** (see p.866) of Arnold & Porter LLP is a real estate lawyer whose hospitality practice focuses on representing owners and developers. Sources describe him as *"a terrific development lawyer,"* and he is also active in acquisitions. He recently represented Host Hotels in its acquisition of the 888-key Grand Hyatt Washington Center. **Nir Margalit** of Foley & Lardner LLP is a well-regarded hospitality lawyer whose experience includes handling issues such as management agreements, transactions, branding, financing, structuring and intellectual property. **Christian Salaman** (see p.398) of Pillsbury Winthrop Shaw Pittman LLP is a corporate lawyer who advises owners, operators and lenders in the hospitality space. Sources say: *"He does lots of management contracts so he knows the ins and outs very well and is a very practical guy."* **Gregory Ressa** (see p.392) of Simpson Thacher & Bartlett LLP is a real estate lawyer whose practice in the sector is focused on representing private equity groups, banks and other investors. Sources say: *"He is very smart and very fast."* **Timothy Hudak** of Eckert Seamans Cherin & Mellott, LLC handles hotel management agreements, structuring joint ventures and working on hotel acquisitions for clients such as Interstate Hotels and FFC Capital. *"He is just completely unflappable – I have never encountered a situation where Tim is anything but completely calm,"* said one interviewee. **Banks Brown** (see p.288) of McDermott Will & Emery LLP is a litigator who focuses on the operational side of the hospitality sector. He has acted as general counsel to leading trade group the American Hotel & Lodging Association. *"He has a very good perspective on the compliance and regulatory issues facing the industry,"* say commentators.

# LIFE SCIENCES

Patent Litigation p.183    Regulatory/Compliance p.183

Commentary about individuals can be found under their firm's paragraph. If the firm has no paragraph (is not ranked) look at Other Notable Practitioners.

## Life Sciences
### Leading Firms

**Band 1**
Cooley LLP
Covington & Burling LLP *
Latham & Watkins LLP *
Ropes & Gray LLP *
WilmerHale *

**Band 2**
Arnold & Porter LLP *
Dechert LLP *
Finnegan, Henderson, Farabow, Garrett & Dunner LLP *
Goodwin Procter LLP *
Hogan Lovells US LLP *
Kaye Scholer LLP *
Sidley Austin LLP *
Wilson Sonsini Goodrich & Rosati *

**Band 3**
McDermott Will & Emery LLP *
Morgan, Lewis & Bockius LLP *
Morrison & Foerster LLP *
Pillsbury Winthrop Shaw Pittman LLP *
Reed Smith LLP

**Band 4**
Baker Botts LLP *
DLA Piper LLP (US) *
Kirkland & Ellis LLP *
Mintz Levin Cohn Ferris Glovsky and Popeo PC *
O'Melveny & Myers LLP *

*Indicates firm with profile.*
†*ONP = Other Notable Practitioner.*

## Life Sciences: Corporate/Commercial
### Leading Individuals

**Star individuals**

| | |
|---|---|
| Mendelson Alan C | Latham & Watkins LLP * |
| Singer Steven D | WilmerHale * |

**Band 1**

| | |
|---|---|
| Hurvitz John A | Covington & Burling LLP * |
| Jones Robert | Cooley LLP |
| Kosacz Barbara | Cooley LLP |
| Redlick David E | WilmerHale * |
| Rubenstein Marc A | Ropes & Gray LLP |
| Wiesen Jeffrey M | Mintz Levin Cohn Ferris Glovsky and Popeo * |

**Band 2**

| | |
|---|---|
| Clark Kenneth A | Wilson Sonsini Goodrich & Rosati |
| Davis Geoffrey B | Ropes & Gray LLP |
| Golden Adam | Kaye Scholer LLP * |
| Hasko Judith A | Latham & Watkins LLP * |
| Kravetz Jonathan | Mintz Levin Cohn Ferris Glovsky and Popeo * |
| Leonard Emily I | Covington & Burling LLP * |
| McGlynn Casey | Wilson Sonsini Goodrich & Rosati |
| Muto Fred | Cooley LLP |
| Taft Kingsley L | Goodwin Procter LLP * |
| Wilcox Steven A | Ropes & Gray LLP |

**Band 3**

| | |
|---|---|
| Frenier Diane M | Reed Smith LLP |
| Grossman Daryn A | Proskauer Rose LLP (ONP)† |
| Parker Steve | Arnold & Porter LLP * |
| Snipes James C | Covington & Burling LLP * |
| Zucker Sam | O'Melveny & Myers LLP |

### Recommended for Client Service
### Nationwide

| | |
|---|---|
| Arnold & Porter LLP | Goodwin Procter LLP |
| Covington & Burling LLP | Kaye Scholer LLP |
| Dechert LLP | WilmerHale |

### Recommended for Commercial Awareness
### Nationwide

| | |
|---|---|
| Kaye Scholer LLP | Sidley Austin LLP |
| Ropes & Gray LLP | |

## Band 1

### Cooley LLP

**THE FIRM** Cooley's highly regarded life sciences practice operates out of five locations across California as well as offices in Seattle and along the East Coast. With corporate, partnering, IP, licensing, financing and transactional abilities, the firm is well placed to assist life sciences companies and industry-focused investors. In particular, Cooley has a strong reputation in the representation of startups and early-stage businesses. Biotechnology and pharmaceuticals are key areas of expertise.

**KEY INDIVIDUALS Robert Jones** in the Palo Alto office has a practice focus on transactional and corporate matters, including securities, financing, licensing, partnering and fiduciary duties. He specializes in biotechnology. **Barbara Kosacz** is a highly regarded corporate attorney based in the firm's Palo Alto office. Sources highlight venture capital work as a strength of her practice, which also covers M&A, strategic partnerships, strategic investment and public offerings. **Fred Muto** is acknowledged as having a significant market presence in the venture capital arena, with experience representing investors as well as biotechnology and medical device companies. His practice also covers corporate and commercial transactions, including M&A, collaboration agreements and public offerings.

### Covington & Burling LLP
See profile on p.441

**THE FIRM** Covington's nationwide life sciences practice comprises over 200 attorneys, including the recent addition of seven corporate and transactional partners formerly at Dewey & LeBoeuf and Wilson Sonsini. The firm is synonymous with excellence in the FDA regulatory space and has capabilities in corporate, transactional and collaboration matters. The firm works with clients like Abbott Laboratories, AstraZeneca and GlaxoSmithKline through its offices in DC, San Francisco, Silicon Valley, San Diego and New York.

**Client Service** *"They have a lot of depth, so if a peculiar issue arises they have always had someone on staff who not only* has experience, but is probably an expert in the field. That's terrific, to be able to keep that in one firm."

**Commercial Awareness** *"They have a wonderful approach: brilliant strategies and great technical skill."*

**KEY INDIVIDUALS John Hurvitz** (see p.338) is cochair of the firm's life sciences practice as well as an *"excellent"* corporate and transactional attorney. He recently acted for AstraZeneca on the $1.26 billion acquisition of biotechnology company Ardea Biosciences. He is based in the DC office. DC-based **Richard Kingham** (see p.347) is a well-known figure in the FDA space and one whom peers describe as *"outstanding."* His practice covers advising biotechnology companies as well as representing pharmaceutical clients in administrative investigations, Congressional hearings and criminal prosecutions. One client praised him as *"the go-to guy for us when we want to get very good, solid guidance and counseling. He is very pragmatic and is a great guide through the gray areas."* **Emily Leonard's** (see p.354) practice covers both IP and corporate matters, including partnership agreements, licensing and technology transfer. She advises clients of all sizes on the life cycle of drugs and devices, from technology evaluation to co-promotion agreements. Leonard is based in the Silicon Valley office. **Peter Safir** (see p.889) is *"very well regarded"* in the FDA field, and heads the food and drug practice at Covington. He advises pharmaceutical companies on marketing, life cycle management, manufacturing and drug quality issues, as well as defending companies subject to enforcement action by the FDA. He is based in DC. **James Snipes** (see p.666) in the San Francisco office is *"a very substantial figure in the life sciences space,"* according to market commentators. He focuses on corporate and transactional matters in the biopharmaceutical field, including M&A, licensing, venture investment, collaborations and spinouts.

### Latham & Watkins LLP
See profile on p.446

**THE FIRM** Latham & Watkins is a national, multiservice firm with an international footprint. It has a reputation in the life sciences market for its high-quality corporate and transactional practice, which comprises M&A and capital

## Life Sciences: IP/Patent Litigation

### Senior Statesmen

| Senior Statesmen: distinguished older practitioners | |
|---|---|
| Baechtold Robert L | Fitzpatrick, Cella, Harper & Scinto (ONP)† |
| Murashige Kate H | Morrison & Foerster LLP * |
| Sobel Gerald | Kaye Scholer LLP * |

### Leading Individuals

| Star individuals | |
|---|---|
| Lee William F | WilmerHale * |
| **Band 1** | |
| Ben-Ami Leora | Kirkland & Ellis LLP * |
| Goldstein Jorge A | Sterne, Kessler, Goldstein & Fox (ONP)† |
| Lipsey Charles E | Finnegan, Henderson, Farabow, Garrett * |
| **Band 2** | |
| Becker Daniel | Dechert LLP * |
| Chesler Evan R | Cravath, Swaine & Moore LLP (ONP)† * |
| Marsh David | Arnold & Porter LLP * |
| **Band 3** | |
| Caviani Pease Ann M | Dechert LLP * |
| de Bodo Richard | DLA Piper LLP (US) * |
| Elrifi Ivor R | Mintz Levin Cohn Ferris Glovsky and Popeo * |
| Flattmann Gerald J | Paul Hastings LLP (ONP)† |
| Hoyng Charles F | Latham & Watkins LLP * |
| Rakoczy William A | Rakoczy Molino Mazzochi Siwik (ONP)† |
| Sandercock Colin G | Perkins Coie LLP (ONP)† |
| Wise Michael | Perkins Coie LLP (ONP)† |

## Life Sciences: Regulatory/Compliance

### Senior Statesmen

| Senior Statesmen: distinguished older practitioners | |
|---|---|
| Brady Robert P | Hogan Lovells US LLP |

### Leading Individuals

| **Band 1** | |
|---|---|
| Beardsley Kate C | Zuckerman Spaeder LLP (ONP)† |
| Kingham Richard F | Covington & Burling LLP * |
| **Band 2** | |
| Bass Scott | Sidley Austin LLP * |
| Fox David | Hogan Lovells US LLP |
| Klasmeier Coleen | Sidley Austin LLP * |
| Safir Peter O | Covington & Burling LLP * |
| Sanzo Kathleen M | Morgan, Lewis & Bockius LLP * |
| **Band 3** | |
| Basile Edward | King & Spalding LLP (ONP)† * |
| Minsk Alan | Arnall Golden Gregory LLP (ONP)† * |
| Shapiro Robyn | Drinker Biddle & Reath LLP (ONP)† * |
| Torrente Josephine | Hyman Phelps & McNamara (ONP)† |

*Indicates firm / individual with profile.*
†ONP = Other Notable Practitioner.

### Ropes & Gray LLP
See profile on p.1528

**THE FIRM** This multiservice firm has a strong reputation and a broad practice in life sciences, with sources particularly noting its government investigations, IP and transactional work. The firm also has regulatory and litigation expertise. Recent work includes acting as governance and disclosure counsel for Pfizer, as well as assisting the company in relation to its collaborative Centers for Therapeutic Innovation program. Other key clients include Johnson & Johnson, Genzyme and Biogen Idec. The life sciences team operates out of Boston, Chicago, New York, San Francisco, Silicon Valley and DC.

**Commercial Awareness** "When it comes to a unique life sciences issue, they are as good as it gets." "They can answer any question on any subject around the periphery of the deal."

**KEY INDIVIDUALS** Clients are full of praise for **Marc Rubenstein**, whom they commend as "a true expert in this area," "very bright, hard-working and responsive" and "one of the best lawyers I've ever dealt with." His focus is on licensing, collaboration agreements, M&A and securities offerings, as well as a variety of other commercial agreements. He recently acted for Biogen Idec on two collaboration agreements with Isis Pharmaceuticals. **Geoffrey Davis** focuses on corporate partnership, licensing and financing for pharmaceutical, biotechnology, biomedical and medical device companies. Recent work includes handling licensing and collaboration matters for Pfizer in relation to its Centers for Therapeutic Innovation program. Clients are "enormously pleased with his team and his work." **Steven Wilcox**'s practice covers licensing, collaborations, M&A and financing, including public offerings and venture capital investments. He recently acted for Salient Surgical Technologies on its $525 million acquisition by Medtronic. He is based in the Boston office.

### WilmerHale
See profile on p.930

**THE FIRM** WilmerHale has a broad life sciences practice, handling IP, transactional, corporate, finance and antitrust matters. The firm is particularly known for its litigation and transactional capabilities. Recent work includes acting for Thermo Fisher Scientific on its public offering of $1.3 billion of senior notes. Key clients include Novartis, Bristol-Myers Squibb and Abbott Laboratories.

**Client Service** "Consistently excellent people. Very responsive."

**KEY INDIVIDUALS William Lee** (see p.353) is a renowned trial attorney focusing on commercial and patent litigation. Recent work in the life sciences field includes acting for Wyeth (now Pfizer) and Altana Pharma (now Nycomed) in a patent infringement action against Teva, Sun Pharmaceutical Industries and KUDCo in relation to the patented active ingredient Protonix. Sources describe him as "just excellent" and name him as "a leader in the legal space." **Steven Singer** (see p.407) is chair of the transactional department and cochair of the life sciences group at WilmerHale, with a practice focus on venture capital, public offerings, strategic alliances, joint ventures and other corporate matters. He recently acted for Constellation Pharmaceuticals on a collaboration agreement with Genentech. **David Redlick** (see p.390) is an "exceptional" attorney considered by many people to be "one of the best pharmaceutical transactional attorneys in the country." His practice focus is on public offerings, collaborations, M&A and venture capital transactions. He acted for Merrimack Pharmaceuticals on its IPO.

### Band 2

### Arnold & Porter LLP
See profile on p.906

**THE FIRM** This firm has breadth across a number of practice areas in the life sciences sector, with IP, litigation, regulatory and antitrust capabilities. Particularly active areas of practice are the pharmaceutical and biotechnology spaces. Life sciences-focused attorneys work out of offices in San Francisco, Silicon Valley, Los Angeles, DC and New York.

**Client Service** "I love them! They're always available: if I have a question and send an e-mail, they schedule a call or send an e-mail within the day."

**KEY INDIVIDUALS** Cochair of the firm's IP practice **David Marsh** (see p.362) is focused on counseling, reexaminations, interferences and Hatch-Waxman matters. He also assists clients in patent procurement relating to chemical, pharmaceutical, biotechnology and medical device subjects. **Steve Parker** (see p.2513) focuses on technology transactions and licensing, as well as M&A, collaborations and other partnership agreements. Clients describe him as "really knowledgeable."

---

markets work, financing and corporate partnership. The firm also offers regulatory services and has growing IP capabilities. Recent work includes Watson Pharmaceuticals' acquisition of Actavis Group, a Swiss pharmaceutical company. The life sciences practice primarily operates out of the San Diego and Silicon Valley offices, as well as the more recently opened Boston office.

**Sources say:** "They are high-quality lawyers with terrific experience; they are extremely responsive on a short timeline and they do whatever it takes to get the work done."

**KEY INDIVIDUALS Alan Mendelson** (see p.367) is an experienced and highly regarded corporate attorney focused on strategic alliances, M&A, venture capital financings and public offerings. He recently acted for Kythera Biopharmaceuticals on its IPO, which raised upwards of $80 million. **Judith Hasko** (see p.331) in the Silicon Valley office is a corporate and transactional attorney. She advises and acts for clients on corporate partnership arrangements, including joint ventures, co-promotion, co-development and profit-sharing agreements. She recently represented KAI Pharmaceuticals in its $315 million acquisition by Amgen. **Charles Hoyng** (see p.643) counsels clients on technology transactions, licensing and commercial agreements. He recently assisted BIND Biosciences and Selecta Biosciences on their financing by RUSNANO and the related technology licensing. He works from both the Boston and Silicon Valley offices.

## Dechert LLP

See profile on p.1969

**THE FIRM** This firm has a good national and international footprint, with life sciences-focused attorneys based in the Austin, Philadelphia, New York, Princeton, DC and Silicon Valley offices. The broad practice covers corporate, transactional, IP, antitrust, product liability and dispute resolution matters. Key clients include Pfizer, Endo Pharmaceuticals, Celgene and GlaxoSmithKline.

**Client Service** *"They have distinguished themselves from any other firm I have worked with in that they have just taken the initiative. Bills are reasonable and have tended to come in lower than other firms we have worked with."*

**KEY INDIVIDUALS Daniel Becker** (see p.280) is a registered patent attorney, a qualified medical doctor and, according to clients, *"an IP guru."* His practice focus is primarily on patent counseling, both domestically and in Europe. Clients say: *"His knowledge and his ability to come to a solution are pretty spectacular."* **Ann Caviani Pease** (see p.293) is cochair of the IP group at Dechert and focuses on patent portfolio development, due diligence analyses and opinion work, including noninfringement and invalidity opinions. Sources say she provides *"the highest quality of advice."*

## Finnegan, Henderson, Farabow, Garrett & Dunner LLP

See profile on p.912

**THE FIRM** This highly regarded national IP boutique has offices in DC, Boston, Palo Alto, Atlanta and Reston. The team focuses on counseling, prosecution, portfolio management, licensing and litigation. Brand-side Abbreviated New Drug Application litigation is a particular area of strength. Recent work includes successfully representing Galderma Laboratories in a patent infringement claim against Tolmar relating to Differin Gel 0.3% acne medicine.

**Sources say:** *"Finnegan has a very strong life sciences IP capability." "Top IP patent litigation."*

**KEY INDIVIDUALS Charles Lipsey** (see p.357) has a diverse practice with a particular focus on biotechnology and pharmaceutical chemistry. Sources describe him as *"a fabulous lawyer in patent litigation."* In addition to the Galderma Laboratories matter listed above, Lipsey recently represented Eli Lilly and Avid Radiopharmaceuticals in a patent infringement case brought by Alzheimer's Institute of America.

## Goodwin Procter LLP

See profile on p.1522

**THE FIRM** This multiservice, national firm services life sciences clients from its Boston, San Diego and DC offices. Along with IP and regulatory work, the team is active in corporate and financing matters. The firm recently acted for Avila Therapeutics on its $350 million acquisition by Celgene, and for Foundation Medicine on its $42.5 million Series B financing.

**Client Service** *"Very effective. We're not paying hourly rates for a partner when someone more junior and less expensive can resolve it. They're really smart, they work all night and*

day to get things done, and they focus on doing things well and efficiently."

**KEY INDIVIDUALS** Cochair of the firm's life sciences practice **Kingsley Taft** (see p.415) is a corporate attorney focusing on financings, M&A and partnering. Clients praise him as *"highly knowledgeable"* and *"an excellent adviser who is thoughtful with his billing approach."*

## Hogan Lovells US LLP

**THE FIRM** This international firm is recognized by market commentators for its broad practice and, in particular, its strong regulatory capabilities. Litigation and transactional matters are also key areas of activity. The team recently worked with TESARO on its $81 million IPO, follow-on issuance of $58.5 million Series B preferred stock and Series B preferred stock financing. The life sciences group practices out of offices in DC, Pennsylvania, California, Florida, Maryland and New York.

**Sources say:** *"An excellent all-around firm." "Tremendous firm. They are smart, pragmatic and always impressive."*

**KEY INDIVIDUALS David Fox** in the DC office focuses on FDA regulation relating to generic and follow-on products, as well as new drugs and biologics. He advises clients on compliance and approval. Sources highlight his *"tremendous expertise"* in product development. **Robert Brady** is based in the DC office. His practice focuses on advising clients on FDA regulatory matters, with particular expertise in Hatch-Waxman matters and product approval.

## Kaye Scholer LLP

See profile on p.1984

**THE FIRM** Kaye Scholer is renowned for its litigation capabilities, particularly in the product liability and patent litigation spaces. In addition, the life sciences practice assists clients in regulatory and corporate matters across its offices in Los Angeles, New York, DC and Palo Alto. Key clients include Affymetrix, Pfizer, Purdue Pharma and Genentech.

**Client Service** *"Not until I dealt with Kaye Scholer did I come to recognize a new level of client service existed and was willingly provided."*

**Commercial Awareness** *"They see the bigger picture of what the case means and how to get it done. From A to Z, they have a plan in place."*

**KEY INDIVIDUALS** Sources praise **Adam Golden** (see p.322) in the New York office as being *"smart, levelheaded and easy to work with."* His practice focuses on IP licensing, M&A, securities, joint ventures and corporate partnership. He recently represented Sandoz/Novartis in the $1.525 billion purchase of Fougera Pharmaceuticals. **Gerald Sobel** (see p.410) is an experienced litigator with a practice focused on antitrust, IP and patent litigation. He is special counsel in the New York office.

## Sidley Austin LLP

See profile on p.1264

**THE FIRM** This firm has a broad practice in life sciences and has offices in DC, New York, Los Angeles, San Francisco, Palo Alto, Chicago and Dallas. It is particularly

known for its strong regulatory and IP work, while corporate, transactional, litigation and investigations are also key areas of activity. Notable clients include Bayer HealthCare, Genentech, GlaxoSmithKline and Pfizer.

**Commercial Awareness** *"Creative in finding solutions." "Their knowledge of this industry is high."*

**KEY INDIVIDUALS Scott Bass** (see p.280) is head of the life sciences team at Sidley Austin and specializes in FDA regulatory and enforcement matters. His practice covers audits and investigations into such areas as off-label promotion, pharmacovigilance, and fraud and abuse. Clients say he *"offers valuable perspectives on FDA law."* **Coleen Klasmeier** (see p.347) is head of the food, drug and medical device regulatory practice at the firm, and *"a walking dictionary of FDA case law,"* according to one happy client. Klasmeier's practice is focused on advising manufacturers on FDA issues and also includes compliance, enforcement, transactional and litigation work.

## Wilson Sonsini Goodrich & Rosati

See profile on p.700

**THE FIRM** Wilson Sonsini has a particularly strong presence in the California market and the team is known for corporate and transactional work, and particularly for its experience in venture capital investments and in representing early-stage biotechnology clients. Recent highlights include advising Fluidigm on its $60 million underwritten offering, and acting for KAI Pharmaceuticals on its licensing agreement and collaboration with Ono Pharmaceuticals.

**KEY INDIVIDUALS Kenneth Clark** is a highly regarded corporate attorney focused on strategic alliances, financing and technology transactions. Sources commend him as being *"practical and in tune with his clients' interests."* He also acts as general counsel to biotechnology companies and their boards of directors. **Casey McGlynn** is known for his representation of startup and emerging growth life sciences companies. He assists clients with finding investors and corporate partners, as well as representing companies in IPOs and secondary offerings.

## Band 3

## McDermott Will & Emery LLP

See profile on p.1258

**THE FIRM** The team at McDermott Will & Emery advises life sciences clients on corporate, transactional, regulatory, antitrust and IP matters. Clients include medical device, pharmaceutical and biotechnology companies, from startups to multinationals. Recent work includes acting for Novartis in interference proceedings against Sanofi.

**KEY INDIVIDUALS Byron Kalogerou** is chair of the life sciences group and a key contact.

## Morgan, Lewis & Bockius LLP

See profile on p.2246

**THE FIRM** Morgan, Lewis & Bockius is noted for the breadth of its life sciences team, which assists clients from early stage financing through IP strategy and regulatory issues to corporate partnership and M&A. The firm represents the full range of life sciences companies, with the pharmaceuticals space a particular area of activity. Clients include AstraZeneca, Pfizer, Merck and Teva. The firm recently advised Lundbeck, a Danish pharmaceutical company, on its commercialization agreements with Japanese counterpart Otsuka Pharmaceutical.

**Sources say:** *"Very responsive, well connected and highly intelligent. They give practical advice."*

**KEY INDIVIDUALS Kathleen Sanzo** (see p.399) focuses her practice on a range of FDA compliance and regulatory matters, including advising on testing, approval, marketing and labeling. Sources say she is *"prompt, skilled, experienced and client-focused."*

## Morrison & Foerster LLP
See profile on p.1990

**THE FIRM** This multiservice firm has a strong West Coast practice in addition to offices in New York, DC, Denver and Northern Virginia. The team is particularly known for its work with Asian companies and US companies in the Asian market. In addition to IP and corporate capabilities, the firm also assists clients in product liability cases. Recent work includes representing Japanese company Terumo in the $2.6 billion purchase of CaridianBCT, the US medical device company.

**Sources say:** *"They have made huge inroads into the Japanese market and are really considered leaders."*

**KEY INDIVIDUALS** Sources describe **Kate Murashige** (see p.372) as *"the mother of biotechnology litigation"* in California. An experienced life sciences attorney, she advises clients on patent prosecution, due diligence, opinion work and reexaminations.

## Pillsbury Winthrop Shaw Pittman LLP
See profile on p.2000

**THE FIRM** This firm's life sciences practice works from offices across the USA and has a good presence in California, with offices in San Diego, Silicon Valley, Los Angeles and Sacramento. The team focuses on IP, litigation, financing and corporate transactions, including collaboration agreements. Notable clients include AstraZeneca, Research Laboratories USA and Merck.

**Sources say:** *"Pillsbury has impressed us because it is prepared to throw its weight behind a small startup. We have never been made to feel we are low on its list of priorities."*

**KEY INDIVIDUALS** John Wetherell and Steven Meltzer are co-heads of the life sciences practice.

## Reed Smith LLP

**KEY INDIVIDUALS** This national firm has a broad reach, working with life sciences clients through numerous offices on the East and West Coasts. The team is particularly known for transactional, licensing and corporate work. Recent work includes representing US venture capital firm Domain Associates in a partnership agreement with RUSNANO involving co-investment in around 20 US-based life sciences companies.

**KEY INDIVIDUALS Diane Frenier** focuses on life sciences transactions, including strategic alliances, collabora-

tions, licensing, M&A and other commercial agreements. Her practice covers biotechnology, pharmaceuticals, biopharmaceuticals and medical devices. She recently represented Dr. Reddy's Laboratories in a partnership with Merck Serono aimed at developing biosimilar compounds with oncological applications.

## Band 4

## Baker Botts LLP
See profile on p.2427

**THE FIRM** Baker Botts's life sciences team works out of offices in Texas, New York, Palo Alto and DC. The practice covers products-related litigation, corporate transactions and IP. Abbreviated New Drug Application and other patent litigation is an area of particular activity. Clients include Merck, AstraZeneca, Novartis and three Novartis subsidiaries. The team continues its ongoing representation of AstraZeneca in the high-profile Seroquel personal injury litigation.

**KEY INDIVIDUALS Earl Austin** heads the life sciences practice.

## DLA Piper LLP (US)
See profile on p.1971

**THE FIRM** This international multiservice firm advises life sciences companies on corporate, financing, consumer class action and product liability litigation, and has a strong reputation for its IP work. The team recently represented Human Genome Science in its forthcoming $3.6 billion purchase by GlaxoSmithKline. Other high-profile clients include Abbott Laboratories, Amgen, Novartis and Baxter.

**Sources say:** *"They do excellent deal work."*

**KEY INDIVIDUALS Richard de Bodo** (see p.631) is cochair of the patent litigation practice and focuses on IP issues within the life sciences sector. Recent work includes acting for Pfizer in a patent infringement case brought by AntiCancer, relating to gene expression tracking methods and mouse models used to determine optimal dosing.

## Kirkland & Ellis LLP
See profile on p.1254

**THE FIRM** Kirkland & Ellis works with life sciences clients on M&A, antitrust litigation, product liability litigation, licensing and regulatory matters. The firm has a well-regarded IP litigation practice, bolstered by the recent addition of six former Kaye Scholer lawyers, including patent and appellate litigator Leora Ben-Ami. Key clients include Pfizer, Teva, Bristol-Myers Squibb and GlaxoSmithKline.

**KEY INDIVIDUALS Leora Ben-Ami** (see p.282) is an IP specialist and *"fantastic trial lawyer,"* whose practice covers pharmaceuticals, biotechnology, chemistry and medical devices. One client comments: *"I have immense confidence in her presenting cases, taking very complex concepts and making them understandable for judge and jury."*

## Mintz Levin Cohn Ferris Glovsky and Popeo PC
See profile on p.1523

**THE FIRM** The life sciences practice at Mintz Levin covers corporate, regulatory and IP matters. The team is particularly noted for its transactional work, which includes angel and venture capital investment, M&A, securities offerings and strategic alliances. The team operates out of offices in New York, Boston, DC and Stamford as well as three California offices.

**KEY INDIVIDUALS** Chair of the life sciences practice **Jeffrey Wiesen** (see p.426) is based in the Boston office. He focuses on M&A, financing, technology transfer, strategic alliances and joint ventures. Clients range from startups to public companies in biotechnology, pharmaceuticals and chemicals. Sources describe **Jonathan Kravetz** (see p.350) as *"a wonderful lawyer and a wonderful guy."* A corporate attorney, Kravetz handles equity and debt financings, advises on securities compliance issues and counsels on M&A transactions. He is based in the Boston office. **Ivor Elrifi** (see p.309) is cochair of the IP practice and focuses on patent prosecution, licensing, transactions, litigation and arbitration. His clients hail from the biotechnology, genetics, diagnostics, medical devices and drug formulation fields. Sources say he *"is experienced and does a good job."*

## O'Melveny & Myers LLP
See profile on p.693

**THE FIRM** The life sciences team at O'Melveny & Myers works with startups, publicly traded companies, research institutions, investors and universities. The practice covers financings, corporate transactions, securities work and IP, as well as pharmaceuticals litigation, including product liability and class actions. Recent work includes representing medical device company LifeTech Scientific in its $32 million IPO on the Hong Kong stock exchange.

**KEY INDIVIDUALS** Based in Silicon Valley and New York, **Sam Zucker** is a corporate attorney with a focus on M&A, joint ventures and strategic alliances, financing and securities offers. His practice covers both domestic and overseas transactions.

## Other Notable Practitioners

**Kate Beardsley** of Zuckerman Spaeder LLP is an experienced FDA regulatory counselor to biologics, pharmaceutical and medical device companies. Her expertise covers approval, clinical studies, manufacturing practice obligations and other compliance issues. Sources say she *"has superb judgment and a pleasant manner"* and is *"very responsive."* **Evan Chesler** (see p.294) of Cravath, Swaine & Moore LLP is chairman of the firm and has a broad trial and appellate practice, which includes securities and patent litigation in the pharmaceutical industry. He is *"an extremely persuasive advocate, who is personable and responsive,"* according to clients. **Gerald Flattmann** of Paul Hastings LLP focuses on IP matters in the biotechnology and pharmaceutical fields, including licensing, counseling and litigation. He recently acted for Galderma

Laboratories, Research Foundation of State University of New York and New York University in a patent infringement action against Mylan relating to the Oracea drug. **Robert Baechtold** (see p.276) of Fitzpatrick, Cella, Harper & Scinto focuses on IP litigation in the pharmaceutical, chemical, biotechnology and polymeric fields. Peers describe him as "*the dean of pharmaceutical patent litigation.*" **Colin Sandercock** of Perkins Coie LLP is an IP attorney who handles patent portfolio management and enforcement, patent litigation, licensing and opinion work. He is sought after for his expertise in matters concerning diagnostics, pharmaceuticals, biotechnology, organic chemistry, medical devices and biochemical engineering technologies. **Jorge Goldstein** of Sterne, Kessler, Goldstein & Fox P.L.L.C. is head of the biotechnology group at the firm and "*a great name in the industry.*" He focuses on patents relating to such fields as pharmaceutical products, recombinant DNA, transgenics, molecular and cell biology, and stem cells. He has a strong academic pedigree in chemistry and biochemistry, and speaks Spanish and German. Sources are full of praise for **Alan Minsk** (see p.370), head of the food and drug practice at Arnall

Golden Gregory LLP, who they say is "*thoughtful, creative, hard-working, available and a problem solver.*" One happy client named him as "*possibly the most knowledgeable person I know in relation to orphaned drugs, product labeling and exclusivity.*" **Daryn Grossman** of Proskauer Rose LLP is head of the life sciences practice at the firm and is based in the New York office. Her focus is on transactional work, including development, licensing and distribution agreements, corporate partnering, equity investments and evaluating IP portfolios. She recently represented Celgene in a worldwide and exclusive co-development agreement with VentiRx Pharmaceuticals. **Michael Wise** is cochair of the life sciences practice at Perkins Coie LLP and is praised by sources for his thorough approach. His practice covers IP matters including litigation and patent portfolio work, due diligence and interferences. He is also noted for his China practice. **Robyn Shapiro** (see p.404) of Drinker Biddle & Reath LLP is experienced in regulatory and licensing issues in the life sciences space, representing pharmaceutical and medical device companies as well as research centers. She has particular expertise in the area of bioethics. Clients say: "*She combines the highest level of subject matter expertise

with a continual willingness to creatively solve problems.*" **Josephine Torrente** of Hyman Phelps & McNamara focuses on new drug and biologics approval, as well as Investigational New Drug and New Drug Application matters such as orphan drugs, special protocol assessments, and risk evaluation and mitigation strategies. Sources say she is "*very responsive and very knowledgeable.*" **William Rakoczy** of Rakoczy Molino Mazzochi Siwik LLP handles litigation and regulatory matters in the pharmaceutical, chemical and biotechnology fields. He has both trial and appellate experience in Hatch-Waxman cases, as well as expertise in Abbreviated New Drug Applications, Section 505(b)(2) applications and new drug applications before the FDA. He is based in Chicago. **Edward Basile** (see p.851) of King & Spalding LLP is chair of the FDA and life sciences practice, and is based in the DC office. He advises pharmaceutical, biotechnology and medical device clients of all sizes in relation to FDA approval and compliance. He also represents companies in criminal investigations, labeling matters, inspections and litigation with the FDA.

# LITIGATION TRIAL LAWYERS

| Litigation: Trial Lawyers | |
| --- | --- |
| **Senior Statesmen and Eminent Partners** | |
| **Senior Statesmen:** distinguished older practitioners | |
| Bartlit Jr Fred | Bartlit Beck Herman Palenchar & Scott LLP |
| Bird Terry W | Bird, Marella, Boxer, Wolpert, Nessim * |
| Blecher Maxwell M | Blecher & Collins |
| Brosnahan James | Morrison & Foerster LLP * |
| Cooper Robert E | Gibson, Dunn & Crutcher LLP * |
| Nussbaum Bernard W | Wachtell, Lipton, Rosen & Katz * |
| Reasoner Harry M | Vinson & Elkins LLP * |
| Terrell Irv | Baker Botts LLP * |
| Wachtell Herbert M | Wachtell, Lipton, Rosen & Katz * |

*Indicates individual with profile.*
*Alphabetical order within each band.*

## Senior statesmen
## Litigation: Trial Lawyers

### Fred Bartlit Jr
**Bartlit Beck Herman Palenchar & Scott LLP**

Bartlit Beck Herman Palenchar & Scott LLP houses the highly regarded trial lawyer Fred Bartlit, who continues to garner praise for his levels of energy and expertise. His broad-based practice has seen him try multiple cases across the country.

### Terry W Bird
**Bird, Marella, Boxer, Wolpert, Nessim, Drooks & Lincenberg PC**

Bird, Marella, Boxer, Wolpert, Nessim, Drooks & Lincenberg PC's Terry Bird is considered a leading trial lawyer, and is esteemed for his longstanding experience in handling both criminal and civil disputes.

### Maxwell M Blecher
**Blecher & Collins**

The founding partner of Blecher & Collins, Maxwell Blecher has long held sway as a highly respected litigator whose practice focuses mainly on plaintiff-side antitrust matters. He is applauded for his impressive experience in litigating cases at trial and appellate level.

### James Brosnahan
**Morrison & Foerster LLP**

Morrison & Foerster LLP's James Brosnahan is described as "*one of the greatest trial lawyers in the country.*" His command of criminal and civil litigation is consistently applauded by commentators, and his practice draws on extensive experience of having tried manifold cases to verdict.

### Robert E Cooper
**Gibson, Dunn & Crutcher LLP**

The "*really talented*" Robert Cooper is "*a leading antitrust lawyer*" based at Gibson, Dunn & Crutcher LLP. He maintains his position as a highly respected trial lawyer, who has

amassed extensive experience in antitrust-related litigation.

### Bernard W Nussbaum
**Wachtell, Lipton, Rosen & Katz**

Bernard Nussbaum is renowned as an impressive commercial litigator at Wachtell, Lipton, Rosen & Katz. He draws on longstanding experience as a trial lawyer, and is considered a true veteran of the Bar.

### Harry M Reasoner
**Vinson & Elkins LLP**

Vinson & Elkins LLP's Harry Reasoner is applauded as a "*very seasoned litigator.*" He focuses on civil litigation, and is praised as a "*very strategic thinker who is deeply knowledgeable about the federal courts.*"

### Irv Terrell
**Baker Botts LLP**

Irv Terrell is based in the Houston office of Baker Botts LLP, and is highly regarded for his nationwide trial expertise. He offers a notable breadth of experience in commercial litigation, and acts for clients in a wide range of complex disputes.

### Herbert M Wachtell
**Wachtell, Lipton, Rosen & Katz**

Sources confirm Herbert Wachtell's extensive expertise in trial work, and venerate him as a leading authority on

## Litigation: Trial Lawyers
### Leading Individuals

**Star individuals**

| | | |
|---|---|---|
| Boies David | Boies, Schiller & Flexner LLP | |
| Sullivan Jr Brendan V | Williams & Connolly LLP | |
| Weingarten Reid | Steptoe & Johnson LLP | |
| Wells Jr Theodore V | Paul, Weiss, Rifkind, Wharton & Garrison * | |

**Band 1**

| | |
|---|---|
| Arguedas Cristina C | Arguedas, Cassman & Headley, LLP |
| Beck David J | Beck Redden LLP |
| Beck Philip | Bartlit Beck Herman Palenchar & Scott LLP |
| Berke Barry H | Kramer Levin Naftalis & Frankel LLP * |
| Brian Brad D | Munger, Tolles & Olson LLP * |
| Chesler Evan R | Cravath, Swaine & Moore LLP * |
| Chu Morgan | Irell & Manella * |
| Green Thomas C | Sidley Austin LLP * |
| Hennigan J Michael | McKool Smith * |
| Jeffress Jr William H | Baker Botts LLP * |
| Keker John | Keker & Van Nest LLP |
| Marmaro Richard | Skadden, Arps, Slate, Meagher & Flom * |
| Naftalis Gary P | Kramer Levin Naftalis & Frankel LLP * |
| Neal Stephen C | Cooley LLP |
| Nolan Thomas J | Skadden, Arps, Slate, Meagher & Flom * |
| Quinn James W | Weil, Gotshal & Manges LLP * |
| Quinn John B | Quinn Emanuel Urquhart & Sullivan, LLP |
| Roberts Michele A | Skadden, Arps, Slate, Meagher & Flom * |
| Ruby Allen J | Skadden, Arps, Slate, Meagher & Flom * |

| | |
|---|---|
| Webb Dan K | Winston & Strawn LLP * |

**Band 2**

| | |
|---|---|
| Babcock Charles | Jackson Walker LLP * |
| Clary Richard W | Cravath, Swaine & Moore LLP * |
| Cotchett Joseph | Cotchett, Pitre & McCarthy |
| Davis Varner Chilton | King & Spalding LLP * |
| Gibbs Robin C | Gibbs & Bruns LLP * |
| Godfrey H Lee | Susman Godfrey LLP |
| Greenberg Gordon A | McDermott Will & Emery LLP * |
| Grossman Marshall B | Bingham McCutchen LLP * |
| Jones Christy D | Butler, Snow, O'Mara, Stevens & Cannada * |
| Lee William F | WilmerHale * |
| Levander Andrew J | Dechert LLP * |
| Lukey Joan | Ropes & Gray LLP |
| Maledon William J | Osborn Maledon PA * |
| McKool Mike | McKool Smith * |
| Ostrager Barry R | Simpson Thacher & Bartlett LLP * |
| Phelan Rod | Baker Botts LLP * |
| Pomerantz Mark F | Paul, Weiss, Rifkind, Wharton & Garrison * |
| Reidy Daniel E | Jones Day * |
| Susman Stephen D | Susman Godfrey LLP |
| Valukas Anton R | Jenner & Block LLP * |
| Ware Jr Paul F | Goodwin Procter LLP * |
| Wheeler Malcolm | Wheeler Trigg O'Donnell LLP * |

## Litigation: E-Discovery
### Leading Individuals

**Band 1**

| | |
|---|---|
| Esteban Amor A. | Shook, Hardy & Bacon LLP |
| Kessler David | Fulbright & Jaworski LLP * |
| Owen Robert D | Sutherland Asbill & Brennan LLP |
| Redgrave Jonathan | Redgrave LLP * |
| Rosenthal John J | Winston & Strawn LLP * |

**Band 2**

| | |
|---|---|
| Brady Kevin F | Eckert Seamans Cherin & Mellott, LLC |
| Lackey Michael | Mayer Brown LLP |
| Stanton David | Pillsbury Winthrop Shaw Pittman LLP |
| Thomas Jeane | Crowell & Moring LLP * |
| Weiner Paul | Littler Mendelson, PC |
| Woods John W | Baker & McKenzie |

**Band 3**

| | |
|---|---|
| Barnett Benjamin R | Dechert LLP * |
| Blair Stephanie | Morgan, Lewis & Bockius LLP * |
| Capone Kirk Shannon | Ropes & Gray LLP |
| Carlson Scott A | Seyfarth Shaw LLP * |
| Fowler Jeffrey | O'Melveny & Myers LLP * |
| Grossman Maura | Wachtell, Lipton, Rosen & Katz * |
| King Christopher Q | Dentons * |
| Rippey Edward | Covington & Burling LLP * |
| Solomon Ronni | King & Spalding LLP * |

*\* Indicates individual with profile.*
*Alphabetical order within each band. Band 1 is the highest.*

---

commercial litigation. He is a founding member of Wachtell, Lipton, Rosen & Katz.

## Star individuals
## Litigation: Trial Lawyers

### David Boies
**Boies, Schiller & Flexner LLP**

David Boies is the chair of Boies, Schiller & Flexner LLP, and is endorsed by commentators as being *"at the top of the list of trial lawyers in national practice."* He remains at the forefront of complex and highly significant commercial litigation, and also offers significant expertise in antitrust.

### Brendan V Sullivan Jr
**Williams & Connolly LLP**

Brendan Sullivan is recognized as an outstanding trial lawyer, and is an experienced member of the litigation team at Williams & Connolly LLP. His expertise encompasses civil and white-collar criminal disputes, and he is acclaimed as being *"on the list of people you would call when you have a big problem."*

### Reid Weingarten
**Steptoe & Johnson LLP**

Reid Weingarten is *"an outstanding trial lawyer,"* who is considered *"one of the best white-collar criminal defense practitioners in the field."* He works out of the New York and Washington, DC offices of Steptoe & Johnson LLP, and has a nationwide trial practice. He is *"incredibly effective in*

*front of juries,"* and is applauded for his extensive experience in litigating cases.

### Theodore V Wells Jr
**Paul, Weiss, Rifkind, Wharton & Garrison LLP**

Theodore Wells upholds his position as a *"great trial lawyer and strategist,"* and is highly respected for his expertise in commercial and white-collar criminal defense litigation. Sources commend his notable trial experience, and confirm his preeminent position as a *"complete star"* on a nationwide scale. He is based in the New York office of Paul, Weiss, Rifkind, Wharton & Garrison LLP.

## Band 1
## Litigation: Trial Lawyers

### Cristina C Arguedas
**Arguedas, Cassman & Headley, LLP**

Cristina Arguedas has long held sway as a *"superb trial lawyer,"* and focuses her leading litigation practice on white-collar criminal defense matters. Her trial skills are highlighted repeatedly by impressed commentators, and she upholds her nationwide reputation for excellence. She is based at Arguedas, Cassman & Headley, LLP.

### David J Beck
**Beck Redden LLP**

David Beck is highly recommended for his experience in commercial litigation, and consistently earns the respect of commentators for his excellent trial skills. His expertise

spans a wide range of disputes, including insurance coverage and energy-related matters. He is a founding member of Beck Redden LLP.

### Philip Beck
**Bartlit Beck Herman Palenchar & Scott LLP**

Bartlit Beck Herman Palenchar & Scott LLP's Philip Beck is highly respected as a trial lawyer, and is seen as a leading litigator capable of representing clients involved in commercial, product liability and IP-related disputes, among other areas. Impressed commentators are quick to praise his expert oral advocacy skills.

### Barry H Berke
**Kramer Levin Naftalis & Frankel LLP**

Kramer Levin Naftalis & Frankel LLP houses *"accomplished trial lawyer"* Barry Berke, whose litigation expertise extends to commercial disputes, and white-collar criminal defense matters. Sources underline the extensive trial experience he offers as a former member of the Federal Defender's Office for the Southern District of New York. His *"strategic advice and deep, analytical thinking"* garner particular praise, as does his *"very creative and engaging approach."*

### Brad D Brian
**Munger, Tolles & Olson LLP**

Brad Brian works from the Los Angeles office of Munger, Tolles & Olson LLP, and continues to garner significant praise for his expertise in white-collar criminal and civil litigation. He is praised as an *"outstanding trial advocate,"* with one source confirming that *"he is the go-to guy for a bet-the-company case."* He plays a key role in representing Transocean in all litigation related to the Deepwater Horizon oil spill.

## Evan R Chesler
### Cravath, Swaine & Moore LLP
Cravath, Swaine & Moore LLP's presiding partner Evan Chesler is hailed as a *"preeminent litigator in the United States,"* and has an impressively extensive trial practice. His *"effective and efficient"* way of handling cases sees him represent clients in disputes across a range of areas, including patent-related matters, antitrust and general commercial litigation.

## Morgan Chu
### Irell & Manella
The *"phenomenal"* Morgan Chu is a highly regarded trial lawyer based at Irell & Manella. He is recognized as a *"premier patent litigator in the country,"* and chairs the firm's litigation group. His practice encompasses a wide range of disputes, including antitrust, appellate and commercial litigation.

## Thomas C Green
### Sidley Austin LLP
Described as *"a trial lawyer's trial lawyer,"* Thomas Green is a preeminent white-collar and civil litigation expert. He is based in the Washington, DC office of Sidley Austin LLP, and is highly experienced in representing clients in the most high-profile of cases. One source noted: *"If I was in trouble and going to trial, I would want to be sitting next to him. As far as trial lawyers go, and in terms of knowing how to deal with people, he is the person I would want at the table representing me."*

## J Michael Hennigan
### McKool Smith
Founding principal of McKool Smith, Michael Hennigan offers an *"unmatched history of trial experience,"* according to one source. He is a highly experienced commercial litigator, and has a particular focus on plaintiff-side representation. His extensive expertise sees him represent clients at both trial and appellate level.

## William H Jeffress Jr
### Baker Botts LLP
Baker Botts LLP's William Jeffress is a *"litigation star"* who is held in high regard for his expertise in white-collar criminal and commercial litigation. He is *"very well respected as an outstanding lawyer."* His recent work includes representing the Drummond Company, and others, in defending a case involving claims of payments made to Colombian paramilitaries.

## John Keker
### Keker & Van Nest LLP
John Keker of Keker & Van Nest LLP is renowned as a leading trial lawyer nationally, and handles both criminal and civil disputes with equal aplomb. Sources highlight his extensive oral advocacy skills, praising him as being *"really good in court."* His experience sees him represent clients in cases across a range of IP, commercial and white-collar defense matters.

## Richard Marmaro
### Skadden, Arps, Slate, Meagher & Flom LLP & Affiliates
Skadden, Arps, Slate, Meagher & Flom LLP & Affiliates houses *"real superstar"* Richard Marmaro, whose expertise in the white-collar criminal defense and securities enforcement space garners him significant praise from peers and clients. He is *"all around one of the top people, and is good on his feet in court."* He offers substantial expertise in trying cases on behalf of individuals and entities, and has represented clients in multiple headline disputes in recent times.

## Gary P Naftalis
### Kramer Levin Naftalis & Frankel LLP
Gary Naftalis is applauded as a *"tremendous asset"* at Kramer Levin Naftalis & Frankel LLP whose *"high-profile"* trial practice covers both civil and white-collar criminal defense litigation. He is widely confirmed as a leading trial lawyer both in the New York market and on a nationwide scale.

## Stephen C Neal
### Cooley LLP
Cooley LLP's chairman Stephen Neal is highly commended for his broad-based litigation practice. He is applauded for his superb courtroom skills, and has tried a significant number of cases across a wide range of areas. He is highly praised for his ability to handle commercial, patent and securities litigation, among other types of dispute.

## Thomas J Nolan
### Skadden, Arps, Slate, Meagher & Flom LLP & Affiliates
Thomas Nolan works from the Los Angeles office of Skadden, Arps, Slate, Meagher & Flom LLP & Affiliates, and is a leading expert in litigating both civil and criminal trials. He is recognized for his *"very good courtroom demeanor,"* and is highlighted as being *"fantastic – just so smart, strategic and practical."* He recently represented Toyota in the highly significant litigation arising from claims of a flaw in its vehicle throttle systems.

## James W Quinn
### Weil, Gotshal & Manges LLP
James Quinn is highly praised as a *"leading litigator in the United States,"* who is noted as a *"great strategic mind"* and a *"real trial lawyer."* He cochairs Weil, Gotshal & Manges LLP's global litigation practice, and focuses on a broad array of disputes as a trial attorney. His practice includes a strong focus on matters involving sports law, as well as an impressive number of other areas.

## John B Quinn
### Quinn Emanuel Urquhart & Sullivan, LLP
John Quinn is described as a *"leading icon of the trial Bar,"* and is based in the Los Angeles office of Quinn Emanuel Urquhart & Sullivan, LLP. He draws on extensive litigation experience in his practice, and covers a wide range of disputes for a high-profile client base. Commentators observe that he is *"exceptional"* in his trial skills, and clients are quick to highlight his dedicated approach, stating that *"you know he will fight for you, and is always there and involved."*

## Michele A Roberts
### Skadden, Arps, Slate, Meagher & Flom LLP & Affiliates
Michele Roberts is a *"truly gifted trial lawyer"* who is based in the Washington, DC office of Skadden, Arps, Slate, Meagher & Flom LLP & Affiliates. She has impressive experience in trying a significant number of cases to verdict, and her practice spans white-collar criminal defense matters and commercial litigation.

## Allen J Ruby
### Skadden, Arps, Slate, Meagher & Flom LLP & Affiliates
Allen Ruby is based in the Palo Alto office of Skadden, Arps, Slate, Meagher & Flom LLP & Affiliates. He is acclaimed as an *"extraordinary lawyer"* whose highly respected trial practice sees him handle a wide array of civil and criminal litigation. This broad-based experience is highlighted by commentators, with one source stating that he is *"very versatile and can try any kind of case."*

## Dan K Webb
### Winston & Strawn LLP
Dan Webb is commended as an *"outstanding, extremely insightful and unbelievably experienced"* trial attorney, whose reputation as a *"truly top-flight courtroom lawyer"* sees him retained by clients in their most complex of cases. He works out of the Chicago office of Winston & Strawn LLP, and covers a highly impressive range of product liability, commercial, IP and white-collar criminal matters in his litigation practice.

## Band 2
## Litigation: Trial Lawyers

## Charles Babcock
### Jackson Walker LLP
Charles Babcock of Jackson Walker LLP is highly regarded as a nationwide First Amendment litigator. He also maintains a strong commercial litigation practice. He successfully represented Celanese in a case brought by Southern Chemical, obtaining a significant verdict following on from a trial lasting four weeks. He is described as *"thorough, dedicated, hard-working, and great at both trial preparation and trial itself."*

## Richard W Clary
### Cravath, Swaine & Moore LLP
Richard Clary is a highly regarded securities litigator, operating out of the Cravath, Swaine & Moore LLP New York office. His strategic approach and strong trial skills are highlighted by sources, and his significant experience in litigating heavyweight cases sees him lead work for high-profile clients such as Credit Suisse.

### Joseph Cotchett
**Cotchett, Pitre & McCarthy**

Joseph Cotchett is a *"force to be reckoned with"* in the litigation arena, and is well versed in handling securities and commercial matters for clients. He offers impressive experience at trial level across the country, and is at Cotchett, Pitre & McCarthy.

### Chilton Davis Varner
**King & Spalding LLP**

Chilton Davis Varner is highly praised as a *"fantastic lawyer who can practice in lots of different areas,"* and is *"incredibly effective in the courtroom."* She works from King & Spalding LLP's Atlanta office, and is impressively experienced in handling disputes in the general commercial and product liability arenas.

### Robin C Gibbs
**Gibbs & Bruns LLP**

Robin Gibbs maintains an impressive broad-based litigation practice, and is acclaimed as being *"great in any forum."* His trial skills see him retained by clients in the most challenging of disputes, and he is described as *"extremely well prepared and able to digest a lot of complex issues, simplify them and communicate them efficiently in front of the judge and jury."* He founded Houston-based firm Gibbs & Bruns LLP.

### H Lee Godfrey
**Susman Godfrey LLP**

Lee Godfrey is *"wonderful trial lawyer"* who represents clients in a diverse range of cases. He focuses on general commercial litigation, and is also noted for his expertise in antitrust-related disputes. He is a founder of Susman Godfrey LLP.

### Gordon A Greenberg
**McDermott Will & Emery LLP**

Gordon Greenberg is a highly regarded litigator based in the Los Angeles office of McDermott Will & Emery LLP. He centers his trial practice on white-collar criminal defense disputes, and is characterized as *"a tough advocate who is a very strong warrior for his clients."*

### Marshall B Grossman
**Bingham McCutchen LLP**

Marshall Grossman splits his time between the Los Angeles and Santa Monica offices of Bingham McCutchen LLP. He is commended as *"a great orator"* and a *"very well-known trial lawyer."* His practice encompasses a wide range of civil disputes, with recent work including his successful representation of Leonard Tweten in a trial setting a precedent in the estate tax space.

### Christy D Jones
**Butler, Snow, O'Mara, Stevens & Cannada, PLLC**

Christy Jones of Butler, Snow, O'Mara, Stevens & Cannada, PLLC is recognized as a star in product liability disputes on a nationwide scale, and is praised as a *"terrific advocate for clients."* She is also considered a leader in her general commercial litigation practice, and is commended for her superb trial skills.

### William F Lee
**WilmerHale**

WilmerHale's William Lee is a highly regarded litigator with tremendous expertise in IP and life science disputes. He is praised as being *"the real deal – a true trial lawyer,"* and is acclaimed by one source for his extensive experience in this area: *"He is as good as they come in terms of handling the trial work."*

### Andrew J Levander
**Dechert LLP**

*"Superstar"* Andrew Levander is based in Dechert LLP's New York office, and is a preeminent litigator who focuses his practice on securities and white-collar crime-related disputes. He is praised as *"a terrific oral advocate,"* and continues to try a wide range of cases. His recent work includes representing Rubin Schron in multiple commercial cases brought before numerous courts.

### Joan Lukey
**Ropes & Gray LLP**

Ropes & Gray LLP's Joan Lukey is commended for her *"stellar reputation in Boston, and throughout the USA."* Her highly impressive trial experience sees her handle a broad range of high-profile cases for clients across multiple practice areas. She is praised for her *"directed and extremely focused"* approach, and is highlighted for her impressive oral advocacy skills.

### William J Maledon
**Osborn Maledon PA**

William Maledon is lauded as *"one of the best litigators"* in Arizona, where he is based at Osborn Maledon PA. His *"phenomenal"* commercial practice sees him try an impressive range of cases, handling the most complex of disputes for clients.

### Mike McKool
**McKool Smith**

Mike McKool is a founding member of McKool Smith, and is commended as *"an excellent trial lawyer, who is well known nationally."* He is highly experienced in handling commercial litigation and IP-related disputes, with recent highlights including his representation of Unwired Planet in patent cases brought against Apple and Google.

### Barry R Ostrager
**Simpson Thacher & Bartlett LLP**

Barry Ostrager is a senior partner in the New York office of Simpson Thacher & Bartlett LLP. He is recognized as a *"well-known and prominent litigator."* He offers widespread experience in cases involving insurance disputes, and is also acclaimed as a *"top-drawer commercial litigator."* He recently acted for Ingersoll Rand in defending a class action related to bonus claims made by numerous employees.

### Rod Phelan
**Baker Botts LLP**

Rod Phelan is a highly regarded commercial litigator based in the Dallas office of Baker Botts LLP. His extensive trial experience sees him represent clients in a broad spread of cases, including professional liability and IP-related disputes.

### Mark F Pomerantz
**Paul, Weiss, Rifkind, Wharton & Garrison LLP**

Mark Pomerantz is a preeminent white-collar criminal defense practitioner operating out of Paul, Weiss, Rifkind, Wharton & Garrison LLP's New York office. He is *"incredibly well regarded"* within the litigation arena, and receives acclaim for his superb trial skills.

### Daniel E Reidy
**Jones Day**

Chicago-based Daniel Reidy of Jones Day has impressive trial practice encompassing both white-collar criminal disputes and civil litigation. He is highly praised for his experience in the field, and *"does a phenomenal job"* for the individuals and companies that he represents.

### Stephen D Susman
**Susman Godfrey LLP**

Stephen Susman comes highly recommended as a seasoned commercial litigator, and is a founding member of Susman Godfrey LLP. Sources praise his ability to handle the *"big-ticket commercial cases"* with aplomb, and highlight his expertise in trying cases on behalf of plaintiffs. His expertise also encompasses antitrust and IP-related cases.

### Anton R Valukas
**Jenner & Block LLP**

Anton Valukas is a highly regarded litigator at Jenner & Block LLP, and is praised for his strength in handling a wide range of disputes. He tries cases involving both white-collar criminal defense and complex commercial issues, and offers impressive experience in representing entities and individuals.

### Paul F Ware Jr
**Goodwin Procter LLP**

Boston-based Paul Ware of Goodwin Procter LLP is described as an *"excellent trial lawyer"* by market commentators. His *"A-plus quality"* as a litigator applies to the wide range of disputes he handles for clients, including general commercial and IP matters. He recently defended Philip Morris against a case brought to federal court by family members of a smoker. He also remains lead trial lawyer in defending a number of civil disputes brought against Countrywide and Bank of America regarding allegations of fraud.

### Malcolm Wheeler
**Wheeler Trigg O'Donnell LLP**

Malcolm Wheeler is a highly regarded litigator whose trial expertise extends across a wide range of product liability and general commercial disputes. He is based at Wheeler

Trigg O'Donnell LLP, and garners praise for the nationwide scope of his practice.

## Band 1
### Litigation: Trial Lawyers

### Amor A. Esteban
**Shook, Hardy & Bacon LLP**

Amor Esteban is widely regarded as a leading practitioner in the e-discovery arena, and is an attorney at Shook, Hardy & Bacon LLP. He is extensively experienced in representing organizations in all matters related to electronically stored data in the context of litigation and investigations. He is increasingly noted as *"the go-to guy on cross-border issues."*

### David Kessler
**Fulbright & Jaworski LLP**

David Kessler is the New York-based cochair of Fulbright & Jaworski LLP's e-discovery and information governance practice. His respected practice sees him counsel clients across all advisory and litigation matters related to electronic discovery. He is praised for his ability to *"describe complex technical matters in an understandable way."*

### Robert D Owen
**Sutherland Asbill & Brennan LLP**

Robert Owen co-heads the e-discovery and information management team at Sutherland Asbill & Brennan LLP. He is highly regarded for the depth of his expertise in this field, and his respected practice is enhanced by his experience in working with complex technology.

### Jonathan Redgrave
**Redgrave LLP**

Jonathan Redgrave established Redgrave LLP in 2010 as a dedicated e-discovery and information law practice. He is held in high regard as a *"true expert in his field"* and *"a leading electronic discovery lawyer in the country."* He is highly experienced in acting as national counsel in this arena for large companies, and is also an expert in handling e-discovery matters for clients involved in complex litigation.

### John J Rosenthal
**Winston & Strawn LLP**

Experienced litigator John Rosenthal is a partner in the Washington, DC office of Winston & Strawn LLP. He chairs the firm's e-discovery group, and is highly praised for his expertise in the arena and commitment to developing the practice. One source commented: *"He has always impressed me with his analytical approach to issues."* Rosenthal's experience in the field sees him retained by key clients such as Union Pacific to act as national e-discovery counsel.

## Band 2
### Litigation: Trial Lawyers

### Kevin F Brady
**Eckert Seamans Cherin & Mellott, LLC**

Kevin Brady is an experienced e-discovery practitioner based at Eckert Seamans Cherin & Mellott, LLC. He is an experienced commercial litigator whose practice sees him cover a wide range of disputes for clients, as well as related e-discovery matters.

### Michael Lackey
**Mayer Brown LLP**

Michael Lackey is the lead partner in Mayer Brown LLP's Washington, DC office and is the chair of the firm's electronic discovery services group. He can draw on extensive experience as a litigator in a wide range of disputes when advising clients on all matters related to e-discovery, and has played a lead role in several key cases in the field.

### David Stanton
**Pillsbury Winthrop Shaw Pittman LLP**

Pillsbury Winthrop Shaw Pittman LLP's David Stanton is credited as being *"exceptionally knowledgeable, with respect to both e-discovery and information governance."* Backed by extensive experience, he represents an impressive roster of clients in these matters, and is praised for his *"clear understanding of the strategic value of e-discovery."*

### Jeane Thomas
**Crowell & Moring LLP**

Crowell & Moring LLP's Jeane Thomas is praised for her extensive experience in the e-discovery arena. Commentators point to the depth of her subject matter expertise, stating that she *"is always at the highest level of being articulate and up to speed on hot issues."* Her recent work advising UTC on the e-discovery aspects of its proposed acquisition of Goodrich demonstrates her ability to operate at the intersection of antitrust and information management.

### Paul Weiner
**Littler Mendelson, PC**

Paul Weiner heads the e-discovery practice at Littler Mendelson, PC, and is considered a *"talented lawyer"* in the space. Clients seek out his dedicated and extensive expertise in all matters related to this field, as well as his prior experience as a commercial litigator.

### John W Woods
**Baker & McKenzie**

Baker & McKenzie's John Woods is noted as a *"great strategist"* when advising clients on matters relating to e-discovery. He has a prominent practice focusing on representing clients with respect to investigations and litigation involving data privacy and e-discovery issues. He is based in the firm's Washington, DC office.

## Band 3
### Litigation: Trial Lawyers

### Benjamin R Barnett
**Dechert LLP**

Benjamin Barnett is an experienced commercial litigator at Dechert LLP who works with clients on a range of e-discovery matters. He offers extensive expertise in advising clients on the discovery process during the course of litigation, and also works with companies to improve e-discovery processes.

### Stephanie Blair
**Morgan, Lewis & Bockius LLP**

Tess Blair is based in the Philadelphia office of Morgan, Lewis & Bockius LLP, and heads its eData practice. She is highlighted as being a *"very experienced lawyer who has a wealth of knowledge, not only in her area of expertise but through interrelated subject matters."*

### Shannon Capone Kirk
**Ropes & Gray LLP**

Shannon Capone Kirk is a highly regarded entry to the e-discovery rankings, and is based in the Boston office of Ropes & Gray LLP. There is no shortage of praise for her expertise in this field, and sources note that *"she is very knowledgeable about the subject area, has thought through trends and has dug into the dynamics of a case."* She is also considered *"responsive, smart and organized – a real pleasure to work with, as well as an expert."*

### Scott A Carlson
**Seyfarth Shaw LLP**

Scott Carlson is recognized for his sterling e-discovery practice, and is commended by clients for his ability to draw on extensive experience as a litigator. He is also equally praised for his skills in technology-related issues. He heads the practice group at Seyfarth Shaw LLP, and is characterized as *"very easy to deal with and always accessible."*

### Jeffrey Fowler
**O'Melveny & Myers LLP**

Jeffrey Fowler of O'Melveny & Myers LLP is a new entry to the rankings, and is strongly supported by feedback praising his expertise in the e-discovery field. He is *"very experienced and practical,"* say sources, *"and someone who really understands e-discovery."* His recent work includes acting as national e-discovery counsel for General Mills.

### Maura Grossman
**Wachtell, Lipton, Rosen & Katz**

Market commentators are quick to praise Maura Grossman for her impressive breadth of experience in handling all aspects of e-discovery for clients. She offers particular expertise in matters related o technology-assisted review, and is also experienced as a litigator. She is counsel at Wachtell, Lipton, Rosen & Katz.

## Christopher Q King
**Dentons**

Christopher King is based in the Chicago office of Dentons, and is an experienced litigator with a particular focus on e-discovery. Sources praise the seamless way in which he partners with other attorneys involved in a case, stating that he *"gets involved in every aspect"* of the process, and is *"very detail-oriented, and great on follow-ups and client service."*

## Edward Rippey
**Covington & Burling LLP**

The *"very technologically savvy and forward-thinking"* Edward Rippey chairs the e-discovery practice at Covington & Burling LLP, and enters the rankings on the back of strong praise from sources. He is highlighted for both his litigation expertise and significant experience in handling e-discovery matters for clients. *"He is a litigator by training,"* notes an interviewee, *"so he understands not just the technical e-discovery pieces but also the implications for active litigation."*

## Ronni Solomon
**King & Spalding LLP**

Ronni Solomon heads the e-discovery practice at King & Spalding LLP, and joins the rankings having received extensive praise for her *"superior expertise in e-discovery issues."* Her recent work includes acting as national e-discovery counsel to UPS.

---

# NATIVE AMERICAN LAW

Commentary about individuals can be found under their firm's paragraph. If the firm has no paragraph (is not ranked) look at Other Notable Practitioners.

| Native American Law |
|---|
| **Leading Firms** |
| **Band 1** |
| Akin Gump Strauss Hauer & Feld LLP * |
| Drinker Biddle & Reath LLP * |
| Faegre Baker Daniels |
| Sonosky, Chambers, Sachse, Miller & Munson LLP |
| **Band 2** |
| Dentons * |
| Hobbs Straus Dean & Walker LLP |
| Holland & Knight LLP * |
| Modrall, Sperling, Roehl, Harris & Sisk, PA |
| Orrick, Herrington & Sutcliffe LLP * |
| **Band 3** |
| Dorsey & Whitney LLP * |
| Greenberg Traurig, LLP * |
| Hogan Lovells US LLP |
| Holland & Hart LLP * |
| Jacobson, Buffalo, Magnuson, Anderson & Hogen |
| Kanji & Katzen PLLC |
| Kilpatrick Townsend & Stockton LLP * |
| Nixon Peabody LLP * |
| Nordhaus Law Firm LLP |
| Patton Boggs LLP |
| Pillsbury Winthrop Shaw Pittman LLP * |
| Sheppard, Mullin, Richter & Hampton LLP |
| Tilden McCoy + Dilweg LLP |
| Van Ness Feldman LLP * |
| WilmerHale * |
| * Indicates firm with profile. |
| Alphabetical order within each band. Band 1 is the highest. |

## Band 1

### Akin Gump Strauss Hauer & Feld LLP
See profile on p.904
**THE FIRM** This large DC practice is well placed to advise on all Native American law matters at a federal level. It is known for its particular strength in matters concerning financing, gaming, and energy and natural resources. Recent work highlights include the firm's representation of the Gila River Indian Community in its opposition to EPA measures concerning an electric power plant in Arizona.
**Sources say:** *"An exceptionally good practice."*
**KEY INDIVIDUALS** Department head **Donald Pongrace** (see p.386) led the team advising the Gila River Indian Community on the aforementioned environmental matter, and has represented the same client in the protection of its Arizona tribal gaming compact. **Michael Rossetti** (see p.396) specializes in matters of tribal governance, economic development and gaming. He recently acted for the Gila River Indian Community in connection with the Homeless Emergency Assistance and Rapid Transition to Housing (HEARTH) Act's passage through Congress.

### Drinker Biddle & Reath LLP
See profile on p.2238
**THE FIRM** This DC-based practice acts chiefly for tribal governments and related businesses across a broad range of transactional and government relations work. It recently secured a $193 million settlement for the Confederated Tribes of the Colville Reservation in one of the largest ever Indian trust mismanagement cases. The same client has also sought the firm's advice on persuading Congress and Federal agencies to favor the development of biomass and biofuel energy projects on Indian land.
**Sources say:** *"Highly competent, motivated and respected."* *"Exceptional in Congressional issues."*
**KEY INDIVIDUALS Paul Moorehead** (see p.371) concentrates exclusively on matters of Federal Indian law and pol-

icy. He is described as *"a very good legislative lobbyist"* who is *"very strategic in his approach and has a valuable ability to work well with both Democrats and Republicans."* He lately represented the Enterprise Rancheria of Maidu Indians of California with regard to the taking into trust of land for gaming purposes. **Kevin Wadzinski** (see p.422) is widely respected by both clients and peers in this practice area. He specializes in matters of gaming, economic development, and labor and employment law. *"Smart and diligent"* practice head **Brian Gunn** (see p.328) was lead partner in the aforementioned matters for the Confederated Tribes of the Colville Reservation.

### Faegre Baker Daniels

**THE FIRM** Faegre Baker Daniels fields one of the largest teams in this practice area, and is noted for its strong expertise in tribal financing and gaming matters. It recently acted as federal Indian law counsel to the Mohegan Tribal Gaming Authority with regard to the refinancing of $1.6 billion in debt which financed its Mohegan Sun casino and other enterprises.
**KEY INDIVIDUALS** Group head **Kent Richey** commands widespread respect for his Native American law practice. He led the team advising the Mohegan Tribal Gaming Authority on its debt refinancing. **Aaron Harkins** is widely recognized as an up-and-coming lawyer for both finance and gaming law matters.

### Sonosky, Chambers, Sachse, Miller & Munson LLP

**THE FIRM** This universally respected practice covers the nation from offices in DC, Alaska, California and New Mexico. It is exclusively dedicated to the representation of tribal interests, and acts for Native American governments, regional confederations and tribal service providers at every level, from local tribunals to the Supreme Court, Congress, and federal agencies and authorities.

**KEY INDIVIDUALS Reid Chambers** possesses some 40 years of Indian law experience, and is widely acknowledged to be at the top of his profession. He acts frequently for Native Alaskan interests across a broad range of gaming, natural resources and tribal rights matters. **Harry Sachse** is *"a senior and experienced lawyer with a stellar reputation,"* say sources. He is especially adept in matters concerning land claims, gaming rights and natural resources issues. **Lloyd Miller** is attracting increasing attention for his handling of tribal jurisdiction litigation, as well as Indian gaming, health and employment law issues.

## Band 2

### Dentons
See profile on p.449

**THE FIRM** Dentons offers a comprehensive Indian law service, covering both regional and federal issues, and acting primarily for tribal governments. The team is highly regarded for its expertise in Congressional and government agency lobbying, and also covers finance and development matters. Recent work highlights have included representing the Tohono O'odham Nation in a complex series of legal processes related to the nation's land claim settlement.
**Sources say:** *"They have vast resources in legal and government relations services, deployed expertly in the service of clients."*
**KEY INDIVIDUALS** Practice head **Heather Sibbison** (see p.406) draws praise for her handling of especially complex issues, particularly those with a government relations aspect. She is characterized as *"a very talented and creative strategic thinker"* who puts clients' interests first. **Steven McSloy** (see p.366) is *"a tremendous practitioner,"* whose arrival at Dentons has been described as *"a big coup"* for the firm. He represents both Indian tribes and financial institutions in the negotiation of major financing agreements. **Nicholas Yost** (see p.430) is particularly well known for his expertise in regulatory and environmental law, and he has recently acted on behalf of several tribal governments with regard to the opening of casinos on their lands.

### Hobbs Straus Dean & Walker LLP

**THE FIRM** This firm has represented the interests of Native American and Alaskan peoples for nearly 30 years, operating from offices in DC, Alaska, California, Oklahoma and Oregon. Sources draw particular attention to its strong performance in matters involving environmental issues, multiparty negotiations, and the protection of its clients' natural and cultural resources. In addition to its representation of individual tribal governments and corporations, it handles a significant volume of work for such bodies as the National Congress of American Indians (NCAI) and Americans for Indian Opportunity.
**Sources say:** *"A very good firm with a large geographical footprint."*
**KEY INDIVIDUALS** Founding partner **Jerry Straus** is renowned for his land and water rights expertise, while

sources especially highlight his capabilities in the Indian gaming sphere.

### Holland & Knight LLP
See profile on p.1028

**THE FIRM** This large national practice maintains offices in DC, New York and California, and acts for tribal governments, as well as companies seeking to do business with Indian nations. The firm's key strengths include expertise in federal, state and tribal tax issues, as well as government relations matters. Recent work highlights have included a notable victory for the Blue Lake Rancheria tribe in a significant tax refund case.
**KEY INDIVIDUALS Jerome Levine** (see p.355) heads the practice from the firm's Los Angeles office. He is described by one commentator as *"the dean of Native American gaming counsel."* **Philip Baker-Shenk** (see p.277) is renowned for his federal relations advocacy skills on behalf of tribal governments and organizations, as well as companies conducting business with Indian tribal entities.

### Modrall, Sperling, Roehl, Harris & Sisk, PA

**THE FIRM** This New Mexico firm's Native American Law practice is active in over 20 states, while its lawyers' expertise spans energy, environment and taxation matters. The team is noted especially for its representation of non-tribal companies and other entities seeking to do business in Indian country. The group recently acted successfully for K Road Solar Energy on securing the necessary agreements and approvals for the development of a large-scale solar power facility in Nevada.
**Sources say:** *"A very sound, skilled and professional firm, well versed and superior in its areas of expertise."*
**KEY INDIVIDUALS** Practice head **Lynn Slade** is known for his breadth of practice area knowledge, but also for his *"extremely good client service"* and *"superior command of an extensive documentation."* Sources note his renewable energy expertise, which he applied as lead partner in the aforementioned K Road matter. **Walter Stern** is highlighted for his *"keen knowledge of day-to-day dealings with tribes and good perspective on previous deals."* He recently acted on behalf of the BHP Navajo Coal Company with regard to environmental issues concerning the renewal of the company's permit to operate in Colorado.

### Orrick, Herrington & Sutcliffe LLP
See profile on p.1994

**THE FIRM** This firm houses a specialized Indian tribal finance group with particular expertise in tribal bond and gaming finance issues. The group acts for Indian governing bodies, major financial institutions and other organizations doing business in Indian country. Recent work highlights include assisting with the financing of land acquisitions, governmental and social infrastructure, and leisure facilities for a range of clients.
**KEY INDIVIDUALS Townsend Hyatt** leads the practice from the firm's Portland, Oregon office, and is widely cited as one of the country's leading tribal finance specialists. His skill as a bond counsel and in taxation issues attracts particular praise from sources. Los Angeles-based **Ramon**

Galvan (see p.318) is particularly well known for his experience in handling financing matters for Indian tribal entities, and he has acted as lead counsel in some of the largest transactions on the West Coast. He is especially well versed in the financial aspects of casino construction and expansion.

## Band 3

### Dorsey & Whitney LLP
See profile on p.1583
**THE FIRM** This practice is notable for offering a full Native American law service to both tribal and non-tribal clients nationwide. Key areas of specialization include taxation, financing transactions, employment law and tribal sovereignty issues. Recent work highlights include a notable success on behalf of the Mashantucket Pequot Tribe with regard to the taxation of its Foxwoods Casino. In another case, the firm represented Crescent Point Energy in its $800 million acquisition of a largely Indian-owned petroleum and natural gas exploration and production company.
**KEY INDIVIDUALS** Practice co-head **Skip Durocher** is described as *"an exceptional lawyer"* and *"excellent litigator"* whose combination of federal litigation and Indian law experience constitutes *"a consistent and reliable resource."* He acted as lead partner in the firm's work for the Mashantucket Pequot Tribe. Fellow co-head **Mary Streitz** is strongly praised by both peers and clients for her *"extensive knowledge of tax matters"* and their interaction with Native American law. She specializes in the handling of sensitive tax audits and controversies with the IRS.

### Greenberg Traurig, LLP
See profile on p.1024
**THE FIRM** This large practice offers excellent national coverage, with over 24 lawyers offering a full service to Native American clients in addition to companies and other organizations which interact with them. Recent significant mandates include representing the Ute Mountain Ute Tribe in a complex dispute over its responsibility to pay New Mexico oil and gas production taxes, and acting for Uranium Resources with regard to environmental and Indian law aspects of its proposed uranium in situ recovery project on the Navajo Nation reservation.
**KEY INDIVIDUALS** **Troy Eid** (see p.309) cochairs the practice, and is identified as a *"very strong team leader"* with key expertise in Indian law issues involving energy and natural resources, environmental and other regulatory aspects. He served as lead partner advising Uranium Resources in the aforementioned matter. Fellow cochair **Jennifer Weddle** (see p.424) is lauded by one client as *"a top-notch attorney"* who has *"provided consistently excellent assistance."* She specializes in energy-related matters, and acted as lead partner in the aforementioned Ute Mountain Ute Tribe matter.

### Hogan Lovells US LLP
**THE FIRM** This team has a strong commitment to assisting Native American peoples on cultural and environmental matters, representing them before courts, Congress and federal agencies, as well as advising on business and tax affairs, and natural resources issues. It recently acted for BHP Billiton on its collaborative effort with the Navajo Nation to redevelop the Four Corners Power Plant on the Navajo reservation in New Mexico.
**KEY INDIVIDUALS** Raymond Calamaro heads Hogan Lovells's Native American law practice, now part of the firm's global native peoples practice.

### Holland & Hart LLP
See profile on p.727
**THE FIRM** This practice acts for both tribal and non-tribal clients from 14 offices across the Mountain West and another in DC. Key areas of expertise include government relations, energy and natural resources, tribal governance and a range of taxation matters. Key clients include the Blue Lake Rancheria Tribe of California, Cherokee Nation Entertainment and the Choctaw Nation of Oklahoma.
**KEY INDIVIDUALS Thomas Sansonetti** (see p.399) is an environmental and natural resources specialist with extensive government service, litigation and Indian law experience. He is particularly familiar with the workings of the Bureau of Indian Affairs and the provisions of the Indian Regulatory Gaming Act. **Mark Sheridan** (see p.1774) is a widely respected litigator whose Native American law expertise is especially notable in matters concerning natural resources and water rights.

### Jacobson, Buffalo, Magnuson, Anderson & Hogen
**THE FIRM** This Minnesota boutique represents both Native American clients and non-tribal entities doing business with them. Its 17 lawyers handle a comprehensive range of Indian law matters, including tribal governance, gaming, natural resources and intergovernmental relations. One notable specialty is the provision of intellectual property services, and the firm has lately extended its capacity to advise clients on the negotiation of construction contracts for tribal development projects.
**KEY INDIVIDUALS Vanya Hogen** commands the respect of her peers as a skilled litigator at tribal, state and federal level, where she has scored notable successes in cases concerning taxation and Indian Gaming Regulatory Act issues.

### Kanji & Katzen PLLC
**THE FIRM** This boutique practice, operating from offices in Ann Arbor, Seattle and DC, is acquiring increased recognition in the market. It acts exclusively for Indian nations, their governments and individual members nationwide, advising on all issues affecting their sovereignty or economic development, with a particular focus upon litigation. It also specializes in advising tribes on the development of their own legislative and judicial systems, and acts in close conjunction with such bodies as the NCAI and the Native American Rights Fund.

**Sources say:** *"A small firm, but very highly regarded throughout the country."*
**KEY INDIVIDUALS** Founding partner **Riyaz Kanji** is described as *"an extraordinary lawyer at the top of his game"* and *"one of the stars of the practice area."* He is widely regarded as a leading lawyer for trials and appellate hearings concerning Indian tribes and nations.

### Kilpatrick Townsend & Stockton LLP
See profile on p.1109
**THE FIRM** With 12 offices, this firm is well placed to provide nationwide Native American law and public policy advice to its predominantly tribal entity client base. Key areas of expertise include government relations, energy and litigation matters. The group recently negotiated multimillion-dollar settlements for three tribes whose trust account funds had been mismanaged by the federal government.
**Sources say:** *"They are known as strong advocates for tribes in class actions."*
**KEY INDIVIDUALS Keith Harper** is cochair of the Native American Affairs team, and is lauded for his *"very good sense of the Native American scene and the issues confronting Native Americans nationally."* He played a key role in the trust mismanagement suits, coordinating the approaches of 75 tribes.

### Nixon Peabody LLP
See profile on p.1526
**THE FIRM** This firm's Indian law and gaming team acts predominantly for non-tribal clients negotiating municipal service agreements with tribal entities, and is particularly well known for its handling of matters concerning Native American land claims and high-stakes gaming enterprises. Recent noteworthy mandates include acting successfully for New York's Madison and Oneida counties in litigation concerning a land claim by the Oneida Indian Nation.
**KEY INDIVIDUALS** Practice cochair Michael Cohen, based in the Long Island office, is a key contact.

### Nordhaus Law Firm LLP
**THE FIRM** This boutique acts solely for Native American nations and their organizations, and represents over 30 such entities from offices in New Mexico and DC. It advises clients on external matters such as traditional land reclamation, government relations and the creation of leisure industries, but also internal issues of legislative and infrastructural development.
**KEY INDIVIDUALS** DC-based **Jill Grant** specializes in handling administrative, environmental and natural resources matters for her tribal clients, and is respected as an effective litigator and negotiator. **Dan Rey-Bear** is described as *"a good, smart appellate lawyer."* Based in Albuquerque, he is best known as a litigator in tribal jurisdiction and federal trust duty cases, as well as for his expertise in handling fee land and trust land acquisitions.

## Patton Boggs LLP

**THE FIRM** Patton Boggs's Native American Affairs practice represents American Indians, Native Alaskans, Native Hawaiians, and non-tribal entities seeking to conduct responsible and economically beneficial business with them. Key areas of expertise include business development and the expanding field of tribal online lending and internet commerce.

**Sources say:** *"An outstanding firm to work with."*

**KEY INDIVIDUALS** **Walter Featherly** heads the Anchorage practice, and specializes in assisting Native American, and especially Alaskan, peoples in the development of their economies. Clients enthusiastically praise his *"great knowledge of all business dealings,"* characterizing him as *"a rainmaker, and one of the best resources for federal preference contracting."*

## Pillsbury Winthrop Shaw Pittman LLP

See profile on p.2000

**THE FIRM** This firm's Indian law practice operates from five offices in California and five more in New York, Texas, Virginia and DC. It acts both for tribes and for companies doing business with them, and is closely integrated with Pillsbury's regulatory and public policy teams. Key specialisms include tribal governance and gaming matters, and the firm also offers advice on the provision of internet and other communications facilities to native communities.

**Sources say:** *"We are very impressed by their depth of engagement."*

**KEY INDIVIDUALS** San Francisco-based partner Blaine Green leads the practice.

## Sheppard, Mullin, Richter & Hampton LLP

**THE FIRM** This practice operates from offices in California, New York and DC, servicing both tribal and non-tribal clients in major financing transactions, particularly those funding high-profile gaming or resort projects. Other key strengths include land use litigation and water rights settlement. The team recently acted for Wells Fargo and Merrill Lynch on their $850 million financing of a casino development for the Federated Indians of the Graton Rancheria.

**Sources say:** *"Strong on the banking side, and provides good advice on lending in the gaming space."*

**KEY INDIVIDUALS** **Christine Swanick** is based in New York and attracts extensive client praise as a lawyer who *"understands Indian law issues very well"* and is *"especially strong in banking matters and on the documentation of tribal lending."* **Charbel Lahoud** is a Los Angeles-based

financing specialist who is also *"extremely well versed in Native American law"* and *"always takes time, when reviewing loan documentation, to make sure you understand the implications of the decisions made."*

## Tilden McCoy + Dilweg LLP

**THE FIRM** This respected boutique, operating from Colorado and Los Angeles, acts for tribal governments and their business partners. It concentrates most notably on matters of tribal governance and federal acknowledgement, land issues, gaming and other economic enterprises, as well as litigation at both state and federal level. The team has particular expertise in advising tribal businesses, developers and investors on the financing of casino, hotel and infrastructural developments.

**KEY INDIVIDUALS** Denver-based **Padraic McCoy** is widely respected for his mastery of a wide range of Indian law issues, including particular strengths in land rights and tribal financing transactions. **Mark Tilden** enjoys an excellent reputation in the practice area, with a notable proficiency in federal acknowledgement, gaming and environmental issues.

## Van Ness Feldman LLP

See profile on p.926

**THE FIRM** This team focuses on the business needs of Indian tribes, Native Alaskan corporations and the companies which partner with them. It is particularly noted for its expertise in renewable energy projects on tribal lands, and recently acted for the Confederated Salish and Kootenai Tribes with regard to their acquisition of the federally licensed Kerr Hydroelectric Project in Montana. The firm's prominence in the Alaskan sphere is illustrated by its selection to act as outside federal legal counsel to the Alaska Federation of Natives, advising it on government relations, land and natural resources issues.

**KEY INDIVIDUALS** **Dan Press** leads the team from the DC office.

## WilmerHale

See profile on p.930

**THE FIRM** This DC-based practice specializes in the representation of tribal governments in complex or high-stakes matters of federal law and government policy, including land claims, gaming issues and breach of trust actions. The team has lately acted for the Tohono O'odham Nation in three distinct lawsuits concerning the nation's acquisition of a parcel of land in Arizona for gaming purposes.

**Sources say:** *"While newer to Native American law practice, WilmerHale has provided first-rate service in this area."*

**KEY INDIVIDUALS** **Seth Waxman** chairs the firm's Appellate and Supreme Court Litigation practice and is a key contact for matters of Native American law.

## Other Notable Practitioners

**Robert Gips** (see p.320) of Drummond Woodsum & MacMahon in Portland, Maine has 30 years of experience in advising Indian tribal governments on their business and financial transactions, and has particular expertise on gaming matters. **Nancy Appleby** heads Appleby Law PLLC, and is *"recognized at the national level as a real expert in this area."* She specializes in advising companies seeking to do business in Indian country, and is noted for her expertise in real estate, energy development and credit arrangements. She recently acted for Wells Fargo on a debt restructuring matter concerning Indian-owned business. **George Forman** of Forman & Associates in San Rafael is *"an excellent practitioner"* who acts exclusively for tribal entities and their communities. He is best known for his work in the gaming sector and his acumen as a litigator. **Charles Curtis** (see p.2582) of Arnold & Porter LLP is a *"first-rate litigator,"* best known for his representation of individual, corporate and government clients in their dealings with tribal entities. He lately acted for Philip Morris USA with regard to a number of tobacco taxation and brand protection issues. **Howard Dickstein** of Dickstein Law Offices in Sacramento is *"a force of nature for his clients"* and *"very well recognized in California,"* where he is particularly skilled at *"navigating the political waters."* He is especially well known for advising tribal clients on their gaming enterprises. **Glenn Feldman** (see p.312) of Dickinson Wright Mariscal Weeks in Phoenix acts exclusively in matters of federal Indian law. He is widely admired for his ability to advise clients on gaming matters. **Arlinda Locklear** of the Law Office of Arlinda Locklear attracts enthusiastic praise from sources, who describe her as a *"terrific and very knowledgeable practitioner"* as well as an *"outstanding land rights lawyer."* She represents tribal clients on such federal issues as treaty and water rights, boundary disputes and taxation. **Heidi Staudenmaier** of Snell & Wilmer LLP's Phoenix office has been called *"the go-to person for anything to do with Native American gaming."* She acts for both tribal and non-tribal clients.

# OUTSOURCING

Commentary about individuals can be found under their firm's paragraph. If the firm has no paragraph (is not ranked) look at Other Notable Practitioners.

## Outsourcing
### Leading Firms

**Band 1**
Gibson, Dunn & Crutcher LLP *
K&L Gates *
Mayer Brown LLP *
Pillsbury Winthrop Shaw Pittman LLP *

**Band 2**
Baker & McKenzie *
Dentons *
Latham & Watkins LLP *
Morgan, Lewis & Bockius LLP *
Morrison & Foerster LLP *

**Band 3**
Baker Botts LLP *
DLA Piper LLP (US) *
Hunton & Williams LLP *
Kirkland & Ellis LLP *
Loeb & Loeb LLP *
Skadden, Arps, Slate, Meagher & Flom LLP & Affiliates *
White & Case LLP *

**Band 4**
Alston & Bird LLP *
Kilpatrick Townsend & Stockton LLP *
Sutherland Asbill & Brennan LLP *
Weil, Gotshal & Manges LLP *
WilmerHale *

### Recommended for Client Service
**Nationwide**

| | |
|---|---|
| Gibson, Dunn & Crutcher LLP | Kirkland & Ellis LLP |
| Kilpatrick Townsend & Stockton LLP | Loeb & Loeb LLP |
| | Mayer Brown LLP |

### Recommended for Commercial Awareness
**Nationwide**

| | |
|---|---|
| Baker & McKenzie | Pillsbury Winthrop Shaw Pittman LLP |
| Gibson, Dunn & Crutcher LLP | |
| Morrison & Foerster LLP | Sutherland Asbill & Brennan LLP |

## Outsourcing
### Senior Statesmen

**Senior Statesmen: distinguished older practitioners**

| | |
|---|---|
| Millstein Julian S | Moses & Singer LLP (ONP)[†] |

### Leading Individuals

**Star individuals**

| | |
|---|---|
| Howell John E | K&L Gates * |
| Zahler Robert | Pillsbury Winthrop Shaw Pittman LLP |

**Band 1**

| | |
|---|---|
| Alberg James L | Pillsbury Winthrop Shaw Pittman LLP * |
| Eisner Rebecca S | Mayer Brown LLP |
| Finkel Robert | WilmerHale * |
| Guedry David N | K&L Gates * |
| Howard Nigel L | Covington & Burling LLP (ONP)[†] * |
| Masur Daniel A | Mayer Brown LLP |
| Melby Barbara Murphy | Morgan, Lewis & Bockius LLP * |
| Mensik Michael S | Baker & McKenzie * |
| Mummery Daniel | Gibson, Dunn & Crutcher LLP * |
| Nagel Trevor | White & Case LLP * |
| Peters William J | Gibson, Dunn & Crutcher LLP * |
| Peterson Brad L | Mayer Brown LLP |
| Roy Paul J N | Mayer Brown LLP |

**Band 2**

| | |
|---|---|
| Brito Michael James | Akin Gump Strauss Hauer & Feld (ONP)[†] |
| Delaney John | Morrison & Foerster LLP * |
| Docksey Ross | Dentons * |
| Ford Christopher D | Morrison & Foerster LLP * |
| Hansen Edward J | Baker & McKenzie * |
| Hanson Vivian L | Morrison & Foerster LLP * |
| Hirshman Neil S | Kirkland & Ellis LLP * |
| Hobby Scott M | Sutherland Asbill & Brennan LLP |
| Kirchhoefer Gregg | Kirkland & Ellis LLP * |
| Klein Allen | Latham & Watkins LLP * |
| Krieser Jason D | K&L Gates * |
| Levi Stuart D | Skadden, Arps, Slate, Meagher & Flom * |
| Murphy Michael | Pillsbury Winthrop Shaw Pittman LLP * |
| Nash Glenn | Sidley Austin LLP (ONP)[†] * |
| Nordahl Stephen D | Gibson, Dunn & Crutcher LLP * |

| | |
|---|---|
| Oser Aaron M | Pillsbury Winthrop Shaw Pittman LLP |
| Parks Randall S | Hunton & Williams LLP * |
| Sanchez Vincent | DLA Piper LLP (US) * |
| Stern Akiba | Loeb & Loeb LLP * |
| Tanenbaum William A | Kaye Scholer LLP (ONP)[†] * |

**Band 3**

| | |
|---|---|
| Adler Kenneth A | Loeb & Loeb LLP * |
| Andrews Jeffrey B | Bracewell & Giuliani LLP (ONP)[†] * |
| Fisher Todd A | K&L Gates * |
| George Peter R | Baker & McKenzie * |
| Gullikson Rosemary L | Dentons * |
| Harvey James A | Alston & Bird LLP * |
| Kennedy John B | Wiggin and Dana LLP (ONP)[†] * |
| Marple J D | Latham & Watkins LLP * |
| Martin John | Baker Botts LLP * |
| Pillion Michael L | Morgan, Lewis & Bockius LLP * |
| Porter Philip | Hogan Lovells US LLP (ONP)[†] |
| Radcliffe Mark F | DLA Piper LLP (US) * |
| Raysman Richard | Holland & Knight LLP (ONP)[†] * |

**Band 4**

| | |
|---|---|
| Brockland John P | Weil, Gotshal & Manges LLP * |
| Harvey Jeffrey L | Hunton & Williams LLP * |
| Konvisser Joshua B | Pillsbury Winthrop Shaw Pittman LLP * |
| Kramer Samuel | Baker & McKenzie * |
| Maccoby Matthew F | Arnold & Porter LLP (ONP)[†] * |
| Meadows James E | FSB FisherBroyles (ONP)[†] |
| Nishawala Vipul N | Pillsbury Winthrop Shaw Pittman LLP * |
| Osterman Jeffrey D | Weil, Gotshal & Manges LLP * |
| Paine James | Kilpatrick Townsend & Stockton LLP |
| Steinberg James | Kilpatrick Townsend & Stockton LLP |

**Up-and-coming individuals**

| | |
|---|---|
| Helms Shawn C | K&L Gates * |

* Indicates individual with profile.
[†]ONP = Other Notable Practitioner.

## Band 1

### Gibson, Dunn & Crutcher LLP
See profile on p.682

**THE FIRM** Gibson Dunn's strategic sourcing and technology transactions practice continues to go from strength to strength. The team regularly advises market leaders on the most complex and high-value domestic and international outsourcing transactions. Leading lawyers on both the East and West Coasts offer a wide range of experience that includes structuring and negotiating agreements such as shared services, restructuring and offshore arrangements. The team advises Symantec on its outsourcing matters, and recently acted on the renegotiation of a business process outsourcing (BPO) transaction with Infosys.

**Commercial Awareness** *"Gibson Dunn knows my business, fiercely protects my interests and provides high-value, strategic business and legal advice."*
**Client Service** *"They have provided superior client service. They take the time to understand our business."*
**KEY INDIVIDUALS** The highly regarded **Daniel Mummery** (see p.656) has a sterling reputation in the outsourcing community. His practice is focused on onshore and offshore BPO and information technology outsourcing (ITO) transactions. He recently represented Con-way on a range of outsourcing agreements. Sources say he is *"a leading authority in his field."* **William Peters** (see p.384)

wins plaudits for his *"deep understanding of the business landscape in the outsourcing arena."* Recent work highlights include advising Battelle Memorial Institute on the migration of its enterprise resource planning system to AT&T's platform. Interviewees commend **Stephen Nordahl** (see p.377) as an excellent lawyer, noting the *"active leadership"* he demonstrates when handling business critical matters. As leader of the New York practice he guides clients through the structuring and negotiation of ITO and BPO transactions and strategic alliances.

## K&L Gates
See profile on p.2245

THE FIRM This leading outsourcing practice provides an expert understanding of both the customer and vendor side of transactions. A large team of high-caliber lawyers offers a vast range of experience across the ITO and BPO spectrum. Recent work highlights include advising a leading global telecommunications company on the outsourcing of its customer-facing wireline network to a Tier 1 provider. High-profile clients include American Express, Fujitsu America and Sprint Nextel.

Sources say: *"Very strong in the business process outsourcing arena."*

KEY INDIVIDUALS Established practitioner **John Howell** (see p.337) is revered for his *"incredible depth of knowledge and experience in outsourcing"* across a range of industries. Recently, he advised Travelport on a long-term agreement that saw Axess International Network outsourcing its global distribution system to Travelport. **David Guedry** (see p.327) *"stays current on trends in the industry so as to provide excellent practical advice,"* say sources. He represented Fujitsu America in a complex transaction involving its acquisition of the data center of Blue Cross Blue Shield, and the outsourcing to Fujitsu of a range of related services. **Jason Krieser** (see p.2400) recently advised Clean Harbors on a five year outsourcing of application development services to Accenture. Sources say he is *"an excellent technology lawyer."* Prominent attorney **Todd Fisher** (see p.2389) is recognized for the international scope of his work. Fisher advises Deere & Company on its global outsourcing initiatives. **Shawn Helms** (see p.2395) continues to go from strength to strength in the outsourcing arena. Interviewees remark upon his *"tremendous subject matter expertise, judgment and client focus,"* and his keen understanding of industry trends and developments.

## Mayer Brown LLP
See profile on p.1257

THE FIRM Mayer Brown maintains its enviable national standing in the outsourcing arena. Commentators value the firm's attention to efficient staffing, and applaud its dedication to ensuring that junior attorneys are of the highest standard. The business and technology sourcing practice offers an array of expertise in the fields of ITO and BPO that includes guiding clients through the development, renegotiation and termination of strategic sourcing transactions. Clients include AT&T, Motorola and United Airlines.

Client Service *"Very efficient, capable and knowledgeable with an excellent customer approach."*

KEY INDIVIDUALS Market commentators attest to **Rebecca Eisner**'s extensive industry knowledge and commend her *"excellent"* negotiating skills. Recent highlights include the negotiating of an outsourcing service agreement for CoreLogic. **Daniel Masur** retains his reputation as *"a phenomenal lawyer."* He guides both emerging and established entities through business critical outsourcing transactions, and is recognized for his understanding of a range of industries including banking, telecommunications, pharmaceuticals and insurance. Sources respect

**Brad Peterson** as a *"brilliant, strategic deal guy."* He is a vastly experienced practitioner with a keen awareness of the commercial realities that clients face. **Paul Roy** is held in high esteem by sources, with one interviewee describing him as *"among the best negotiators that I have had the pleasure to work with."* Roy represents clients with respect to a range of offshore, onshore and nearshore BPOs and ITOs.

## Pillsbury Winthrop Shaw Pittman LLP
See profile on p.2000

THE FIRM Pillsbury's global sourcing practice continues to be recognized for the business acumen that informs the team's approach. A commanding team of attorneys offers expertise in the full spectrum of outsourcing transactions, impressing interviewees with work of the highest quality. Clients include financial institutions, healthcare systems and other multinational companies.

Commercial Awareness *"We rely on their legal counsel, but more importantly, they are a key business resource for business decisions."* *"They have an advanced, sophisticated and commercially informed practice with a deep bench and outstanding forms, precedents and protocols."*

KEY INDIVIDUALS **Robert Zahler** impresses interviewees with his *"pragmatic and knowledgeable approach to technology contract issues."* Clients regularly look to him to guide them through business critical outsourcing agreements. **James Alberg** (see p.272) *"brings a high level of customer service and an understanding of how large organizations operate,"* say sources. He advises prominent clients on high-value deals, including a recent transformational transaction involving global IT infrastructure and application software maintenance. Commentators highlight **Michael Murphy**'s (see p.373) attention to detail and client-focused approach. One source notes: *"Michael's main strength is his ability to put the legal issues in context for our business folks."* Murphy's practice covers the full range of outsourcing transactions. Sources speak warmly of **Aaron Oser**, remarking that they *"cannot recommend him highly enough."* His clients have included American Express, Goodyear and Starwood. The highly experienced **Vipul Nishawala** (see p.1923) is well known for the strength of his capabilities, regularly representing market leaders on substantial deals. **Joshua Konvisser** (see p.1910) wins praise for his awareness of market developments, with one interviewee reporting that *"he understands our business and is fully integrated in our business operations."* He represents buyers and sellers in a wide range of outsourcing transactions.

## Band 2

## Baker & McKenzie
See profile on p.435

THE FIRM Baker & McKenzie's global presence attracts clients to its high-caliber outsourcing practice. The practice is at its strongest in the New York, Illinois and California offices, while the team is widely recognized for its industry knowledge. A diverse range of clients includes

Bausch & Lomb, Universal Music Group and Hewlett-Packard.

Commercial Awareness *"I find them to be very smart and knowledgeable about the entire IT and outsourcing space."*

KEY INDIVIDUALS The respected **Michael Mensik** (see p.367) remains an active and important presence in the field. He is the cochair of the firm's North American sourcing practice and is regarded as an expert in domestic and international outsourcing transactions. He has advised Cardinal Health on a number of matters. **Edward Hansen** (see p.1900) is widely considered to be *"a recognized industry authority with extensive experience in major sourcing initiatives."* He has amassed a wealth of expertise in complex BPO and ITO transactions for clients of the caliber of Estée Lauder and Universal Music Group. **Peter George** (see p.1208) receives warm praise from sources, with one interviewee commenting: *"I am fully confident that he will handle every aspect of the matter extremely well."* Recent clients include Wells Fargo Bank. **Samuel Kramer** (see p.1216) acts for industry leaders such as Boston Scientific. Sources report: *"Sam has a deep knowledge of international outsourcing contracts and is able to recommend positions and predict outcomes during negotiations, allowing discussions to come to an agreeable position quickly."*

## Dentons
See profile on p.449

THE FIRM Dentons maintains a strong strategic sourcing practice, most notably from its Texas and Illinois offices. Members of the team regularly handle a range of international transactions for market leaders from a variety of industries including healthcare, finance, insurance and energy.

KEY INDIVIDUALS Peers hold established practitioner **Ross Docksey** (see p.1204) in the *"highest regard."* He represents buyers and vendors in BPO and ITO transactions. **Rosemary Gullikson** (see p.1210) wins praise for her business acumen, with one interviewee noting that she has *"a very strong understanding of the marketplace – she has an understanding of what is doable."* Gullikson chairs the firm's US outsourcing practice.

## Latham & Watkins LLP
See profile on p.446

THE FIRM Latham & Watkins's outsourcing team is well known for its expertise in customer-side transactions. The group has represented clients in countless ITO and BPO transactions such as asset and fund management and human resources. The practice attracts blue-chip clients such as Avery Dennison, Sony Online Entertainment and BASF.

Sources say: *"Latham is extraordinarily capable in a wide variety of subject matters."*

KEY INDIVIDUALS The *"excellent"* **Allen Klein** (see p.874) is recognized for his expert handling of complex outsourcing transactions. Recent highlights include advising Old Mutual Life Assurance in a multi-year, multiparty managed network services transaction. Clients applaud **J D Marple**'s (see p.652) ability to maintain *"the highest levels of professionalism and ability in terms of knowledge, respon-*

*siveness and service."* Recent highlights include representing Avery Dennison in a deal involving the outsourcing of the design and building of a worldwide financial management system.

## Morgan, Lewis & Bockius LLP
See profile on p.2246

THE FIRM This established outsourcing and technology transactions group is well known for its outsourcing expertise in key areas such as cloud computing and data analytics. The team works with leaders from a number of industries including life sciences, energy and financial services. Key clients include AllianceBernstein and Colgate-Palmolive.

Sources say: *"They have a great depth of expertise in a number of areas that impact technology companies."*

KEY INDIVIDUALS **Barbara Melby** (see p.366) is described by sources as a *"truly exceptional attorney, negotiator and adviser."* She handles the full range of information technology and business process outsourcing. **Michael Pillion** (see p.384) handles outsourcing matters for high-profile clients such as Independence Blue Cross. He receives strong endorsements from the market, with commentators noting that *"he has been a strong advocate for us and has provided key industry insight, which has allowed us to make informed judgment calls which directly impact our business."*

## Morrison & Foerster LLP
See profile on p.1990

THE FIRM Morrison & Foerster's global sourcing group attracts a stellar lineup of clients from a range of industries such as pharmaceuticals, financial services and cleantech. The team assisted Bank of America in a transaction to outsource processing services for its credit card portfolio. Clients also include Ingersoll Rand and Residential Capital.

Commercial Awareness *"All aspects of their work are excellent – particularly their commercial acumen, understanding of our business priorities and negotiating skills."*

KEY INDIVIDUALS **John Delaney** (see p.1888) is noted for the hi-tech expertise that complements his outsourcing capabilities. Clients range from emerging companies to established entities, while sources comment that *"he is very focused on adding value, has a tremendous level of experience and is very practical."* Market leaders recommend **Christopher Ford** (see p.314) for his *"expertise, diligence and sound guidance."* The global sourcing group chair centers his practice around high-value ITO and BPO transactions for clients such as Ingersoll Rand. **Vivian Hanson**'s (see p.330) knowledge and experience are held in high regard by both peers and clients, with one interviewee remarking that *"I'm always glad she's on my side of the table."* Hanson is notable for her expert handling of large-scale transactions involving a diverse range of industries, and for her specialist knowledge of the Japanese market.

## Band 3

### Baker Botts LLP
See profile on p.2427

THE FIRM Baker Botts's Texas-based practice has a long-standing presence in the outsourcing sector. The team is notable for its skill in representing service providers in numerous ITO and BPO transactions. Expertise includes electronic security, private cloud and procurement and supply chain management. Clients include Accenture and Dell.

KEY INDIVIDUALS Technology group head **John Martin** (see p.2403) retains a significant outsourcing practice. Sources hold him in high regard as an established practitioner with a commendable understanding of the key issues facing clients.

### DLA Piper LLP (US)
See profile on p.1971

THE FIRM This firm's technology, sourcing and commercial team acts for both customers and vendors, and offers clients the benefit of an impressive global platform. The team recently acted for the OpenStack Foundation on developing a framework to govern a group providing cloud services. Other clients include eBay, Sony and Hyatt.

KEY INDIVIDUALS Department head **Vincent Sanchez** (see p.1229) remains an energetic player in the market, impressing commentators with his *"ability to absorb and retain large amounts of information."* Interviewees regard him as a *"go-to"* counsel for large and complex deals. He acts on behalf of high-profile clients such as RBS Citizens and Groupon. The *"excellent"* **Mark Radcliffe** (see p.660) is singled out for his prowess in the open source space. He has built up an impressive practice during the course of his long career and led the team in the aforementioned matter for the OpenStack Foundation.

### Hunton & Williams LLP
See profile on p.2517

THE FIRM Hunton & Williams continues its solid showing in the outsourcing space. The team is experienced in a range of outsourcing matters including IT, procurement, software as a service (SaaS) and cloud-related transactions. The group recently represented Baylor Health Care System in the cloud-based outsourcing of a health information exchange. Other clients include Blockbuster and WNS Global Services.

KEY INDIVIDUALS Practice head **Randall Parks** (see p.382) is held in high regard by fellow practitioners for his *"in-depth knowledge of the important factors in transactions."* He handles the full range of business process and information technology transactions. **Jeffrey Harvey** (see p.331) is noted for his active outsourcing practice. He has worked with Dana Holding on a number of transactions including data center service agreements and engineering systems outsourcing transactions.

### Kirkland & Ellis LLP
See profile on p.1254

THE FIRM Kirkland & Ellis continues to be respected as a strong presence in the outsourcing field. The team recently represented National Grid in the completion of a series ITO transactions dating back to 2009, and also represented Xchanging as the vendor in a high-value outsourcing agreement with BAE Systems. Other key clients include Goldman Sachs and Cigna.

Client Service *"From a client perspective they just do a fantastic job of training lawyers to be business-minded and responsive. This is important and rare."*

KEY INDIVIDUALS **Neil Hirshman**'s (see p.334) *"excellent business judgment"* and *"realistic advice"* show an understanding of the market that is valued by those who work with him. His practice is focused on IP and technology-related transactions such as the ITO matters for National Grid. Group leader **Gregg Kirchhoefer** (see p.1214) stands out as *"a real go-to guy for the tough issues."* Interviewees think very highly of him, noting that *"he commands the room and the respect of everyone."* He advises on technology, IP and communications-focused matters.

### Loeb & Loeb LLP
See profile on p.689

THE FIRM Loeb & Loeb wins plaudits for the strength of its outsourcing practice. Interviewees are quick to praise the breadth of knowledge and experience shown by members of the team. Lawyers are experienced in the handling of a range of transactions such as those that involve HR, facilities management and procurement. The team also offers significant expertise in the field of cloud computing. Clients include Comcast and Harvard Pilgrim HealthCare.

Client Service *"The firm is excellent in terms of client service as it is highly responsive and easily accessible."*

KEY INDIVIDUALS **Akiba Stern** (see p.412) *"is a business lawyer who understands the business as well as legal issues"* and is widely regarded as a *"top-notch lawyer."* Sources also commend his effective negotiating style. He has recently completed major outsourcing transactions for Citi and IMG Worldwide. Interviewees praise **Kenneth Adler**'s (see p.1872) *"encyclopedic knowledge of the industry"* and value his lengthy experience in the outsourcing sector: *"If you're doing something, he has seen it."* His clients include Comcast and Harvard Pilgrim HealthCare.

### Skadden, Arps, Slate, Meagher & Flom LLP & Affiliates
See profile on p.2008

THE FIRM Skadden's New York-based team expertly guides clients throughout the outsourcing process. The team offers a breadth of experience that attracts a number of industry-leading companies to the practice. The group is particularly adept at handling transactions that involve IT services, procurement, HR and call centers. Clients include Citi and American Express.

KEY INDIVIDUALS The *"indefatigable"* **Stuart Levi** (see p.1913) maintains a broad practice as both outsourcing practice head and IP and technology group co-head. Sources appreciate his hands-on approach and the ease with which he guides clients through complex legal concepts. Recent work highlights include representing the McGraw-Hill Companies in several large outsourcing transactions.

## White & Case LLP
### See profile on p.451
THE FIRM White & Case continues to impress in the field of strategic sourcing, with clients benefiting from the firm's global reach. Recent work highlights include representing Coca-Cola in connection with a large-scale pan-Atlantic BPO transaction. Other clients include Best Buy and Royal Bank of Canada.
KEY INDIVIDUALS Trevor Nagel (see p.374) is held in high regard as an "extraordinarily good lawyer." He has recently handled a long-term sourcing project on behalf of The Commonwealth Bank of Australia.

## Band 4

### Alston & Bird LLP
#### See profile on p.1102
THE FIRM Alston & Bird offers a full spectrum outsourcing practice, and is notable for its international capabilities. The team is predominantly focused on customer-side representation, but has significant supplier-side capability. Clients are drawn from the insurance, supply, logistics and financial services space. The group recently advised Sabre Holdings in connection with an $800 million IT infrastructure transaction with HP.
KEY INDIVIDUALS James Harvey (see p.331) was recently part of a team advising the State of Georgia in connection with the outsourcing of its electricity grid to GE's cloud-based smart grid system. Market observers attest to his continuing prominence in the outsourcing community.

### Kilpatrick Townsend & Stockton LLP
#### See profile on p.1109
THE FIRM Kilpatrick Townsend & Stockton's global sourcing and technology team is noted for its experience with overseas transactions. The Atlanta-based lawyers offer highly respected expertise across the transactional spectrum, representing leading clients throughout complex BPO, ITO, ERP matters and strategic alliances. The team is regularly engaged by international entities that value the firm's overseas reach.
Client Service "The quality of their work is outstanding."
KEY INDIVIDUALS James Paine is a highly regarded strategic outsourcing expert. He regularly advises on matters that involve HR services, IT infrastructure support and application development and maintenance services. James

Steinberg is singled out for the quality of his work, with customer service and timeliness recognized as particular attributes. His outsourcing practice is notable for its cross-border capabilities, and is given added depth by his wider corporate and commercial experience.

## Sutherland Asbill & Brennan LLP
THE FIRM This firm's outsourcing practice is focused on customer-side representation, advising clients on a variety of business critical transactions. Areas of expertise include data center arrangements, SaaS arrangements and BPO. The team assists clients on a global scale, with sources praising the group's understanding of the commercial realities that inform clients' business needs. Clients include Hilton Worldwide, ScanSource and Hershey.
KEY INDIVIDUALS Market commentators are full of praise for Scott Hobby, highlighting his ability to bring a business-focused approach to handling diverse matters.

## Weil, Gotshal & Manges LLP
### See profile on p.2015
THE FIRM This firm's technology and IP transactions team focuses its outsourcing capabilities on ITO and BPO transactions. The team employs a collaborative approach, and clients benefit from the firm's corporate and litigation strengths. Clients represent a broad range of industries such as banking, telecommunications and life sciences, and include GE and Thomson Reuters.
Sources say: "The quality of work is very high and they are very responsive."
KEY INDIVIDUALS John Brockland (see p.625) "is a true professional who understands the needs of clients," report admiring sources. He offers extensive outsourcing experience from his Silicon Valley base. Jeffrey Osterman (see p.1925) is commended for his expert handling of highly complex matters. He recently represented Summit Partners in the acquisition of data center automation, security and business intelligence solutions provider Help/Systems.

## WilmerHale
### See profile on p.930
THE FIRM WilmerHale's technology transactions and licensing department has bolstered its outsourcing capabilities with the arrival of Robert Finkel from Dewey & LeBoeuf. The practice attracts high-caliber clients, offering specialist knowledge of regulated industries such as pharmaceuticals and financial services. Clients include State Street and Boehringer Ingelheim.
KEY INDIVIDUALS The enormously respected Robert Finkel (see p.313) is "clearly a thought leader in the sourcing industry and has been recognized as such for many years." His "unparalleled" industry knowledge ensures that "his

personal brand is well known and highly respected in the sourcing marketplace by both buyers and suppliers of outsourced services."

## Other Notable Practitioners

"Tremendous attorney" Nigel Howard (see p.337) of Covington & Burling LLP is commended by interviewees who value his depth of knowledge, and his ability to understand the business needs of clients. He recently advised Etihad Airways on a Request for Bid (RFB) process with Amadeus and Sabre. Texas-based Michael Brito of Akin Gump Strauss Hauer & Feld LLP is well regarded in the outsourcing community, and recognized for the breadth and depth of his expertise. His practice attracts a wide range of clientele on both the customer and vendor side. Market leaders single out Philip Porter of Hogan Lovells US LLP as a trusted adviser. He is valued for his ability to translate complex legal concepts into client-focused guidance, with sources noting that "he helps us come to an agreement on contract issues without compromising our business objectives or assuming unnecessary business risk." Richard Raysman (see p.1930) of Holland & Knight LLP has extensive experience in the outsourcing sector. Sources recognize him as an expert in technology-focused transactions. Matthew Maccoby (see p.651) of Arnold & Porter LLP is described as "extremely bright, responsive, concerned and results-driven." He is well known for his ability to handle complex matters with ease. The "unflappable" James Meadows of FSB FisherBroyles is praised for his perseverance in moving deals forward and his "wonderful understanding" of how to get the results a client needs. Glenn Nash (see p.656) of Sidley Austin LLP retains an excellent reputation in the outsourcing community and is a recognized specialist in the area. Sources report: "Glenn understands the delicate balance between getting a deal done and minimizing the client's legal risks." Thought leader William Tanenbaum (see p.1946) of Kaye Scholer LLP takes a "smart, practical, tactical and highly strategic" approach. His clients include Novartis and CLS Bank. Jeffrey Andrews (see p.2378) of Bracewell & Giuliani LLP is valued for his "exemplary" client-focused approach. One interviewee comments: "Jeff is a tough negotiator and knows his subject matter extremely well." John Kennedy (see p.345) of Wiggin and Dana LLP is noted for his work in ITO transactions and cloud-based outsourcing solutions. Sources note his "keen understanding of the issues that are current for the day." Senior statesman Julian Millstein of Moses & Singer LLP is a venerated figure in the outsourcing field. His knowledge and experience continue to inspire peers who hold him in high esteem.

# PRIVACY & DATA SECURITY

Commentary about individuals can be found under their firm's paragraph. If the firm has no paragraph (is not ranked) look at Other Notable Practitioners.

## Privacy & Data Security
### Leading Firms

**Band 1**
Hogan Lovells US LLP
Hunton & Williams LLP *
Morrison & Foerster LLP *

**Band 2**
Baker & McKenzie *
Covington & Burling LLP *
DLA Piper LLP (US) *
Kelley Drye & Warren LLP *
Perkins Coie LLP
Sidley Austin LLP *
Venable LLP *
Wiley Rein LLP *

**Band 3**
Alston & Bird LLP *
Arnold & Porter LLP *
Baker & Hostetler LLP *
Edwards Wildman Palmer *
Foley & Lardner LLP *
Gibson, Dunn & Crutcher LLP *
InfoLawGroup
McDermott Will & Emery LLP *
Patton Boggs LLP
Pillsbury Winthrop Shaw Pittman LLP *
Proskauer Rose LLP *
Ropes & Gray LLP *
WilmerHale *
ZwillGen PLLC *

### Recommended for Client Service
**Nationwide**

| | |
|---|---|
| Baker & Hostetler LLP | Hunton & Williams LLP |
| Edwards Wildman Palmer LLP | Proskauer Rose LLP |
| Hogan Lovells US LLP | Sidley Austin LLP |

### Recommended for Commercial Awareness
**Nationwide**

| | |
|---|---|
| Baker & Hostetler LLP | Kelley Drye & Warren LLP |
| Baker & McKenzie | Patton Boggs LLP |
| Hunton & Williams LLP | Proskauer Rose LLP |

## Privacy & Data Security
### Leading Individuals

**Star individuals**
| | |
|---|---|
| Sotto Lisa J | Hunton & Williams LLP * |

**Band 1**
| | |
|---|---|
| Fischer L Richard | Morrison & Foerster LLP * |
| Freeman D Reed | Morrison & Foerster LLP * |
| Gidari Albert | Perkins Coie LLP |
| Ingis Stuart P | Venable LLP * |
| Nahra Kirk J | Wiley Rein LLP * |
| Raul Alan Charles | Sidley Austin LLP * |
| Wolf Christopher | Hogan Lovells US LLP |
| Wugmeister Miriam | Morrison & Foerster LLP * |

**Band 2**
| | |
|---|---|
| Cividanes Emilio W | Venable LLP * |
| DeMarco Joseph V | DeVore & DeMarco LLP (ONP)† * |
| Gilbert Françoise | IT Law Group (ONP)† |
| Halpert James J | DLA Piper LLP (US) * |
| Lee Ronald D | Arnold & Porter LLP * |
| Mathews Kristen | Proskauer Rose LLP |
| McNicholas Edward R | Sidley Austin LLP * |
| Perkins Nancy L | Arnold & Porter LLP * |
| Rosenfeld Dana | Kelley Drye & Warren LLP |
| Serwin Andrew B | Foley & Lardner LLP |
| Smedinghoff Thomas J | Edwards Wildman Palmer * |
| Wilder Marcy | Hogan Lovells US LLP |
| Zwillinger Marc J | ZwillGen PLLC |

**Band 3**
| | |
|---|---|
| Ballon Ian C | Greenberg Traurig, LLP (ONP)† * |
| Boyd Thomas M | DLA Piper LLP (US) * |

## Privacy & Data Security: Healthcare
### Leading Firms

Arnold & Porter LLP *
Baker & McKenzie *
Hogan Lovells US LLP
McDermott Will & Emery LLP *
Ropes & Gray LLP *
Sidley Austin LLP *
Wiley Rein LLP *

* Indicates firm / individual with profile.
† ONP = Other Notable Practitioner.

| | |
|---|---|
| Determann Lothar | Baker & McKenzie * |
| Eisenhauer Margaret P | Privacy & Information Management (ONP)† |
| Fagan David N | Covington & Burling LLP * |
| Freedman Linn F | Nixon Peabody LLP (ONP)† * |
| Heitmann John | Kelley Drye & Warren LLP |
| Hengesbaugh Brian | Baker & McKenzie * |
| Hutnik Alysa Zeltzer | Kelley Drye & Warren LLP |
| Jolly Ieuan | Loeb & Loeb LLP (ONP)† * |
| Kahn Benita A | Vorys, Sater, Seymour and Pease (ONP)† * |
| Kashatus Jennifer | DLA Piper LLP (US) * |
| Keating David C | Alston & Bird LLP * |
| Kobus III Theodore J | Baker & Hostetler LLP * |
| Larose Cynthia | Mintz Levin Cohn Ferris Glovsky (ONP)† * |
| Martino Paul G | Alston & Bird LLP * |
| Meal Douglas H | Ropes & Gray LLP |
| Melodia Mark S | Reed Smith LLP (ONP)† |
| Parnes Lydia B | Wilson Sonsini Goodrich & Rosati (ONP)† |
| Plotkin Mark E | Covington & Burling LLP * |
| Sabett Randy V | ZwillGen PLLC |
| Smith Andrew M | Morrison & Foerster LLP * |
| Sussmann Michael | Perkins Coie LLP |
| Thoren-Peden Deborah S | Pillsbury Winthrop Shaw Pittman LLP * |
| Vatis Michael A | Steptoe & Johnson LLP (ONP)† |

**Up-and-coming individuals**
| | |
|---|---|
| Beringer Ashlie | Gibson, Dunn & Crutcher LLP * |
| Simpson Aaron P | Hunton & Williams LLP * |

**Associates to watch**
| | |
|---|---|
| Gates Melodi | Patton Boggs LLP |

## Band 1

### Hogan Lovells US LLP

**THE FIRM** This established firm's privacy and information management team is well known for its skillful handling of policy and regulatory matters. Lawyers represent clients from a wide range of industries, and have significant expertise in the healthcare field. The team's expertise is illustrated by its recent work for the Utah Department of Health following a high-profile data breach. Other clients include WebMD and Lexis Nexis.

**Client Service** "Outstanding client service and scope of knowledge."

**KEY INDIVIDUALS Christopher Wolf** impresses market commentators, who note that he is "truly an international expert in privacy law." Sources appreciate that he "combines deep legal insight with great communication skills and a fine sense for commercial and political realities." He offers expertise in breach notification, compliance and FTC-related matters. Established practitioner **Marcy Wilder** is highly regarded by peers. Her practice is focused on the healthcare space, and she took the lead in the aforementioned work for the Utah Department of Health.

### Hunton & Williams LLP
See profile on p.2517

**THE FIRM** Hunton & Williams maintains a stellar privacy and data security practice, representing a host of industry leaders. The team is notable for its expertise in the international sphere and has advised on numerous cross-border data breaches, while lawyers are also highly experienced in the handling of compliance issues. Recent highlights include acting for GE on a range of global privacy and information security issues.

**Client Service** "Their client service has been excellent. They are responsive almost 24 hours a day, seven days a week."

**Commercial Awareness** "Hunton & Williams is very strong in all major aspects you look to in counselors: subject matter expertise and experience, ability to give practical advice informed by real-world cases, and an understanding of our particular business and culture."

**KEY INDIVIDUALS** Peers attest to **Lisa Sotto** (see p.410) outstanding reputation in the legal community, noting that she "provides unsurpassed industry and regulatory expertise." She led an international team of lawyers in the aforementioned work for GE. **Aaron Simpson** (see p.407) wins plaudits for his practical, business-friendly approach. Those who work with him consider him to be "absolutely *outstanding in terms of his knowledge, his accessibility and his willingness to get to know our business."* His clients include Estée Lauder, which he advises on global data protection and privacy matters.

## Morrison & Foerster LLP
See profile on p.1990

**THE FIRM** This continues to be considered one of the nation's premier firms for privacy and data security issues. The team's expertise includes data security breaches, regulatory investigations, and data protection and privacy policy implementation. The team has particularly close ties with the financial services sector, and recently represented Citibank in two consumer class actions stemming from allegations of data security breach. Other clients include Capital One Financial, Visa and Bed Bath & Beyond.
**Sources say:** *"With regard to international data privacy and security issues, they have more lawyers who are knowledgeable in this area, more collective experience and better worldwide resources."*
**KEY INDIVIDUALS Richard Fischer** (see p.313) remains a leading figure who peers regard as *"brilliant."* He is notable for his expert handling of matters involving clients from the financial industry, but offers experience of a wide range of industries. **Reed Freeman** (see p.316) has a commendable breadth of industry knowledge, and is notable for his capable handling of FTC matters. Global privacy and data security chair **Miriam Wugmeister** (see p.428) advises high-profile clients on the collection, use, disclosure and transfer of information. Sources attest that she is a *"great"* attorney and *"a real force"* in the privacy and data security Bar. Privacy expert **Andrew Smith** (see p.408) routinely advises clients from the financial sector. He is well known for his regulatory expertise, and sources describe him as *"a thoughtful, sensible legal thinker."*

## Band 2

### Baker & McKenzie
See profile on p.435

**THE FIRM** This firm is recognized for the global reach of its privacy and data protection practice. The team provides a broad service that covers the full spectrum of clients' regulatory compliance and breach management needs. Lawyers are equipped to advise a range of industries including healthcare, financial services and social media. Recent clients include NetSuite and Trend Micro.
**Commercial Awareness** *"The lawyers are commercial, easy to deal with and provide sound legal advice."*
**KEY INDIVIDUALS** California-based **Lothar Determann** (see p.631) is recognized for the international scope of his privacy practice. He represents international technology companies in global compliance issues. Clients include Yelp and AIRBNB. Peers attest to the caliber of **Brian Hengesbaugh**'s (see p.333) work in the privacy field. Working from the Chicago office, he specializes in breach notification and policy implementation. He has recently represented Priceline.

### Covington & Burling LLP
See profile on p.441

**THE FIRM** Covington & Burling's global privacy and data security practice is recognized for its experience in a range of sectors, including healthcare, financial, technology and communications. Over the last twelve months the practice has been retained by market leaders such as Facebook, advising on privacy and data security matters and on compliance with the Children's Online Privacy Protection Act. An impressive client roster also includes Microsoft and SAMSUNG.
**Sources say:** *"They are experienced, trusted advisers. I would recommend the firm wholeheartedly."*
**KEY INDIVIDUALS Mark Plotkin**'s (see p.385) practice is focused on compliance and breach handling. He has recently advised a number of financial institutions on regulatory compliance matters, and is noted for his expertise in this area. The *"quite knowledgeable"* **David Fagan** (see p.311) wins plaudits for the strength of his practice. He offers expert advice in the field of breach handling. Recent work highlights include acting for Microsoft on a wide range of issues.

### DLA Piper LLP (US)
See profile on p.1971

**THE FIRM** DLA Piper's IP and technology practice houses a team of expert privacy and data security lawyers. The team is best known for its knowledge of new regulatory requirements and its strength in class action defense, with clients benefiting from the firm's international reach. The team has been retained by clients of the caliber of Accenture, Hilton Worldwide and Pfizer, and offers noted strength in the communications, cloud computing and financial services sectors.
**Sources say:** *"They were able to assist on a global basis using a single contact point, and provided clear strategies to assist us in developing a comprehensive and effective global data privacy policy that was neither burdensome nor overly complicated."*
**KEY INDIVIDUALS James Halpert**'s (see p.329) *"robust, international practice"* attracts strong praise from the market, with sources also noting that he is *"very well connected in this field, with a lot of information about what's going on."* Recent work highlights include acting as general counsel to the State Privacy & Security Coalition. Peers attest to the deep knowledge that informs **Thomas Boyd**'s (see p.286) advice. He is recognized for his skill in handling privacy-related regulatory issues. **Jennifer Kashatus** (see p.343) is highly recommended by market commentators, who value her *"encyclopedic knowledge of industry and data protection."* She is an experienced adviser on global issues, with one interviewee commenting on her ability to provide *"clear and concise strategies, templates and advice to develop and implement a global data privacy program."*

### Kelley Drye & Warren LLP
See profile on p.1985

**THE FIRM** The Kelley Drye & Warren privacy and information security team is best known for its strength in the advertising and marketing sphere. The team is also recog-

nized for its expert handling of FTC investigations and privacy and data protection litigation. Clients include Toshiba and DISH Network, with the former retaining the firm to give privacy policy and training development for a VoIP product launch.
**Commercial Awareness** *"They truly appreciate the delicate balance between having a high degree of legal acumen, understanding and preparedness and the need to make smart, efficient and often quick decisions in a real-time business situation."*
**KEY INDIVIDUALS** Practice leader **Dana Rosenfeld** is singled out as a highly visible force in the market with a practice that encompasses all aspects of privacy and data security. She recently represented Disney in its response to proposed revisions to the Children's Online Privacy Protection Act. The *"outstanding"* **Alysa Zeltzer Hutnik** worked closely with Rosenfeld on the Disney matter. She handles domestic and global privacy, data security and consumer protection issues. **John Heitmann** is well known as a privacy and data security expert. Interviewees strongly recommend him, noting that *"his knowledge in this field, his responsiveness and his attention to client needs are exemplary."* Sources also describe him as *"a strong practitioner in providing cutting-edge advice on social media and mobile privacy issues."*

### Perkins Coie LLP
See profile on p.2548

**THE FIRM** Perkins Coie is highly regarded for its work in the retail and e-commerce sectors. The firm's Electronic Communications Privacy Act practice attracts industry leaders that value the team's cross-border expertise. Lawyers recently represented Twitter in privacy-related litigation, and also represented Google in litigation and regulatory matters stemming from the company's Street View service.
**KEY INDIVIDUALS Albert Gidari** is highly rated in the market for his ability to navigate through complex issues. The last year saw take the lead in the Google matter described above. **Michael Sussmann** offers a breadth of privacy-related expertise, specializing in regulatory issues, compliance, internet security and electronic surveillance. He has advised a range of industry leaders on compliance with the Electronic Communications Privacy Act.

### Sidley Austin LLP
See profile on p.1264

**THE FIRM** Sidley Austin's privacy, data security and information law practice is shaped by a team of interdisciplinary lawyers who have wide-ranging expertise on a global scale. The breadth of knowledge on offer includes cybersecurity, data protection and health-related privacy matters. Clients are drawn predominantly from the healthcare, financial, telecommunications and media sectors.
**Client Service** *"Sidley is highly capable, and very responsive and client-friendly. They combine deep and technical knowledge of the law with a sense of the need for its practical application."*
**KEY INDIVIDUALS** Peers applaud the highly respected **Alan Raul** (see p.389), describing him as a true *"ambassa-*

_dor"_ for the privacy sector. He is particularly active in data breach and cyber-security matters and related litigation. **Edward McNicholas** (see p.366) wins praise for his _"depth of experience and ability to bring technology issues together to provide information we can act on."_ The FTC specialist continues to be involved in a wide range of privacy matters.

## Venable LLP
See profile on p.927

**THE FIRM** Venable remains a firm of choice for regulatory matters in the privacy and data security arena. The team is highly experienced in the defense of enforcement actions and the formation of privacy policies, while market commentators attest to the caliber of its bench and the quality work handled by the practice. Key clients include Experian and Reed Elsevier.
**Sources say:** _"They are really good when it comes to this space."_
**KEY INDIVIDUALS Stuart Ingis** (see p.338) has _"unparalleled domain knowledge, great business judgment and an extensive network of contacts in the public and private sectors,"_ according to impressed sources. He recently advised the Association of National Advertisers on the implementation of privacy principles for online behavioral advertising. **Emilio Cividanes** (see p.295) receives warm praise from the market, with clients remarking that he is _"passionate about supporting us and what we do, proficient in making cases and knowledgeable about how the process works."_

## Wiley Rein LLP
See profile on p.928

**THE FIRM** Wiley Rein is best known its specialist knowledge of healthcare privacy and data security issues. The team offers expert advice in a range of areas including the formation of security policies and the handling of data breach events. Industry leaders such as PwC, Dell and the Blue Cross Blue Shield Association look to the group to guide them through business-critical issues.
**Sources say:** _"I would give them extremely high marks in all categories, including prompt response time."_
**KEY INDIVIDUALS** Privacy chair **Kirk Nahra** (see p.374) is recognized for his focus on healthcare-related matters. Sources consider him to be _"highly knowledgeable and sensitive to both costs and delivering results on time,"_ and remark that he is in _"the top echelon"_ of data privacy lawyers.

## Band 3

## Alston & Bird LLP
See profile on p.1102

**THE FIRM** This firm's privacy and security practice is characterized by its international expertise, with lawyers regularly handling data protection matters in Asia, Latin America and the EU. The team also provides experienced counsel on cyber-risk, breach management, regulatory compliance and privacy litigation. Members of the practice

are regularly retained by blue-chip clients such as UPS and Experian.
**KEY INDIVIDUALS David Keating** (see p.344) concentrates his practice on guiding clients through the impact of pending and enacted legislation at national and EU level. His clients include UPS, for which he acts as global privacy counsel. **Paul Martino** (see p.362) handles complex data protection compliance initiatives on a global scale. Recent work highlights include advising the National Retail Federation on a variety of public policy and federal legislative issues.

## Arnold & Porter LLP
See profile on p.906

**THE FIRM** Arnold & Porter has a solid reputation in the privacy and data security sphere. Lawyers offer a range of experience that includes healthcare-related matters, EU Directive compliance, breach management and national security issues. Clients include market leaders from the financial sector, communications and pharmaceutical industries.
**KEY INDIVIDUALS** Established practitioner **Ronald Lee** (see p.353) remains a respected member of the legal community. He has recently represented a number of clients in connection with national security and electronic surveillance restrictions. **Nancy Perkins** (see p.383) is highly regarded for her specialist regulatory knowledge in the privacy space. She has recently advised several substantial pharmaceutical and biotech companies on EU data protection laws.

## Baker & Hostetler LLP
See profile on p.2119

**THE FIRM** BakerHostetler's privacy and data security team has won considerable praise for its handling of security breaches and privacy-related risks. Recent matters include defending Eisenhower Medical Center with respect to a putative class action stemming from a data breach complaint. Other clients include QVC and Farm Credit Council Services.
**Client Service** _"The team looks to get the job done in a manner that is in the best interests of the client, in a professional and cost-effective manner, which is exactly what we look for in counsel."_
**Commercial Awareness** _"It has a very strong team and we look for it to be our go-to firm on these issues given its deep capability, its dedicated service to clients and its commercial awareness."_
**KEY INDIVIDUALS** The _"excellent"_ **Theodore Kobus** (see p.348) is widely regarded as _"an expert and a leader in the field."_ He has taken the lead role in the aforementioned matter for the Eisenhower Medical Center.

## Edwards Wildman Palmer
See profile on p.1520

**THE FIRM** Edwards Wildman Palmer's privacy and data protection practice is shaped by a multidisciplinary approach incorporating litigation, IP, insurance and compliance expertise. The firm recently assisted Kia Motors with privacy and security issues relating to the launch of its

UVO2 vehicle navigation system. Other clients include Thomson Reuters and Myspace.
**Client Service** _"Client service has always been excellent."_
**KEY INDIVIDUALS Thomas Smedinghoff** (see p.1232) is an authority on information law and electronic business. Over the last twelve months he has counseled a number of clients, including Thomson Reuters and Lexis Nexis, in connection with online identity management.

## Foley & Lardner LLP
See profile on p.2588

**THE FIRM** Foley & Lardner is considered a firm of choice for privacy and data security issues. The team structures international privacy programs and gives regulatory compliance advice to industry leaders such as eBay, Qualcomm and Playdom. Recent matters include representing Wyndham Worldwide in a class action alleging the improper recording of telephone calls.
**KEY INDIVIDUALS** Privacy, security and information management chair **Andrew Serwin** is commended for the strength of his practice. Recent work highlights include acting on behalf of Spokeo in an FTC matter alleging improprieties following the sale of internet information, and leading in the aforementioned matter for Wyndham Worldwide.

## Gibson, Dunn & Crutcher LLP
See profile on p.682

**THE FIRM** Gibson, Dunn & Crutcher enjoys a solid reputation in the privacy space. The IT and data privacy practice handles a variety of complex class action litigation, and advises on compliance programs and investigations. Key work highlights include representing Facebook in a significant FTC investigation.
**KEY INDIVIDUALS** Peers hold **Ashlie Beringer** (see p.282) in high regard, describing her work as _"groundbreaking."_ Clients value her impressive industry knowledge and understanding of their business needs. She has recently successfully defended Flurry, Inc and Pinch Media in class action litigation alleging that the defendants had illegally collected and distributed the personal data of iPhone app users.

## InfoLawGroup

**THE FIRM** Highly regarded boutique InfoLawGroup is noted for its strength in the privacy and data security space. Lawyers regularly guide clients through privacy and data security concerns relating to corporate and outsourcing transactions, assist with respect to data breach management and advise on the development of compliance programs. The firm is retained by BrightTag to act as outside privacy counsel.
**Commercial Awareness** _"The firm is able to strike a balance between legal responsibility and practical business advice."_
**KEY INDIVIDUALS** Justine Gottshall is a key contact.

## McDermott Will & Emery LLP
See profile on p.1258

**THE FIRM** McDermott Will & Emery maintains an impressive global privacy and data security practice from its Los Angeles, Boston and Chicago offices. Lawyers regularly advise on privacy policies and the data security aspects of transactions that include M&A, data purchase and data licensing. The team has recently advised a number of industry leaders on electronic data strategic partnerships and the development of privacy and security infrastructures.

**KEY INDIVIDUALS** Daniel Gottlieb is a key contact.

## Patton Boggs LLP

**THE FIRM** The Patton Boggs privacy and data security practice is praised for its deep industry knowledge and attendant commercial acumen. The group handles compliance issues, privacy policy implementation and breach management matters. Recent work highlights include advising the Colorado Regional Health Organization on privacy and data security policies.

**Commercial Awareness** *"They have subject matter expertise, understand the commercial aspects of the business and follow through consistently."*

**KEY INDIVIDUALS Melodi Gates** comes highly recommended by interviewees, who note her outstanding responsiveness. She *"is highly capable, service-minded and prompt, and understands all commercial issues in this area."*

## Pillsbury Winthrop Shaw Pittman LLP
### See profile on p.2000

**THE FIRM** Pillsbury provides clients with the full spectrum of privacy and data security advice. The team advises clients from a range of sectors including healthcare, finance and hospitality. Members of the team continue to represent Blackhawk Network and Dun & Bradstreet.

**KEY INDIVIDUALS** Practice head **Deborah Thoren-Peden** (see p.417) maintains an active practice and is recognized for her representation of financial services clients. She continues to advise Netspend on privacy, regulatory and compliance matters.

## Proskauer Rose LLP
### See profile on p.2001

**THE FIRM** Proskauer's respected privacy and data security practice is supported by the firm's wider corporate and litigation expertise. Clients are drawn from a wide range of sectors including telecommunications, financial services and media, while the firm's global footprint enables it to operate seamlessly with offices overseas.

**Commercial Awareness** *"They are very knowledgeable about the substantive law but also very aware of the commercial settings and the need to serve the specific client."*

**Client Service** *"I would rate Proskauer extremely highly in terms of client service."*

**KEY INDIVIDUALS** Highly specialized practitioner **Kristen Mathews** is widely praised by market observers. Interviewees value her ability to *"take the specific circumstances of an individual client and formulate a policy and statement that work both from the legal perspective and for the particular commercial situation."*

## Ropes & Gray LLP
### See profile on p.1528

**THE FIRM** This firm is best known for its handling of large-scale data security breaches, advising clients across a wide range of industries. The team also guides clients through regulatory compliance issues, offering both transactional and litigation expertise. Clients include Sony Computer Entertainment America and The Blackstone Group.

**KEY INDIVIDUALS Douglas Meal** is *"not only an excellent lawyer, he is also a very smart businessperson,"* say sources, while he is also noted for his *"reputation for getting results."* He specializes in payment card breaches.

## WilmerHale
### See profile on p.930

**THE FIRM** WilmerHale's communications, privacy and internet law group advises clients on regulatory compliance, security breach management and investigations. The team has specialist knowledge on the application of the Electronic Communications Privacy Act. The group has recently represented Verizon and the International Franchise Association.

**KEY INDIVIDUALS** Jonathan Nuechterlein is a key contact.

## ZwillGen PLLC
### See profile on p.932

**THE FIRM** ZwillGen is a highly respected boutique commended for its technical expertise and prowess in litigation matters surrounding data security and privacy issues. Clients are drawn from a range of industries including the technology and media sectors.

**KEY INDIVIDUALS Marc Zwillinger** is respected for his knowledgeable, practical approach. He offers a wealth of expertise in regulatory compliance, with clients benefiting from his breadth of industry experience. **Randy Sabett**'s practice is centered on data breach policy and management and privacy-related legislation.

## Other Notable Practitioners

**Ian Ballon** (see p.621) of Greenberg Traurig, LLP maintains his active practice. He is a well-known litigator with a strong reputation in the privacy and data security field. Clients include leading technology and social media companies. **Ieuan Jolly** (see p.340) of Loeb & Loeb LLP is noteworthy for the international scope of his experience. Recent work highlights include advising SC Johnson on global privacy strategy. **Margaret Eisenhauer** of Privacy & Information Management Services—Margaret P. Eisenhauer, P.C. is recognized for her established presence in the legal community. Clients benefit from her commendable knowledge of data management and compliance-related issues. **Benita Kahn** (see p.342) of Vorys, Sater, Seymour and Pease LLP is *"very knowledgeable in the area and also takes the time to understand the business concerns or aspects behind the issue,"* say sources. Practice leader **Mark Melodia** of Reed Smith LLP is widely regarded as a *"very skilled lawyer."* He is known for his expertise in the field of litigation, most notably putative class actions. He has recently represented Macy's and JC Penney in a number of flash cookie class action litigations. **Lydia Parnes** of Wilson Sonsini Goodrich & Rosati offers a wealth of data security enforcement and data breach expertise. She recently advised Evidon on compliance issues. **Michael Vatis** of Steptoe & Johnson LLP is a respected member of the legal community. Areas of expertise include international breach management and compliance issues. Peers consider **Joseph DeMarco** (see p.303) of DeVore & DeMarco LLP to be *"the real deal."* Interviewees value his ability to condense complex legal terminology into business-focused advice. He recently advised Sotheby's on a range of privacy and security-related issues. **Linn Freedman** (see p.316) of Nixon Peabody LLP specializes in healthcare-related matters, with particular expertise in compliance and data breaches. Commentators describe her as *"prompt, effective, personable and very much on top of the substantive area of law."* **Françoise Gilbert** of IT Law Group has an excellent reputation among peers as a pioneer in the field. She is notable for her European expertise and as a result attracts an impressive international clientele. Peers attest to the strength of her practice. **Cynthia Larose** (see p.352) of Mintz Levin Cohn Ferris Glovsky and Popeo PC impresses sources with her *"comprehensive knowledge of this complex and evolving area, as well as her ability to apply that knowledge in a meaningful way for our lines of business."* She provides privacy and information management services to clients from a range of sectors, including energy and media

# PRIVATE EQUITY BUYOUTS

Commentary about individuals can be found under their firm's paragraph. If the firm has no paragraph (is not ranked) look at Other Notable Practitioners.

## Private Equity: Buyouts
### Leading Firms

**Band 1**
Kirkland & Ellis LLP *
Simpson Thacher & Bartlett LLP *

**Band 2**
Cleary Gottlieb Steen & Hamilton LLP *
Debevoise & Plimpton LLP *
Latham & Watkins LLP *
Ropes & Gray LLP *
Weil, Gotshal & Manges LLP *

**Band 3**
Davis Polk & Wardwell LLP *
Fried, Frank, Harris, Shriver & Jacobson LLP *
Gibson, Dunn & Crutcher LLP *
Goodwin Procter LLP *
Paul, Weiss, Rifkind, Wharton & Garrison LLP *
Proskauer Rose LLP *
Skadden, Arps, Slate, Meagher & Flom LLP & Affiliates *
Willkie Farr & Gallagher LLP *

**Band 4**
Dechert LLP *
White & Case LLP *

### Recommended for Client Service
#### Nationwide

| | |
|---|---|
| Debevoise & Plimpton LLP | Ropes & Gray LLP |
| Gibson, Dunn & Crutcher LLP | Simpson Thacher & Bartlett LLP |
| Proskauer Rose LLP | |

### Recommended for Commercial Awareness
#### Nationwide

| | |
|---|---|
| Davis Polk & Wardwell LLP | Paul, Weiss, Rifkind, Wharton & Garrison LLP |
| Debevoise & Plimpton LLP | |
| Dechert LLP | Proskauer Rose LLP |
| | Simpson Thacher & Bartlett LLP |

## Band 1

### Kirkland & Ellis LLP
See profile on p.1254

**THE FIRM** This market-leading private equity team continues to enjoy a fine reputation in the field, and represents a significant volume of high-end and midmarket funds. Notable recent highlights for the group include representing Bain Capital in its acquisition of Apex Tool Group, valued at $1.6 billion. The team also acted on behalf of Spectrum Equity Fund as part of a buyout group led by Permira in connection with the $1.6 billion acquisition of Ancestry.com.

**Sources say:** *"Very responsive and commercial, and very thorough in their work."*

**KEY INDIVIDUALS** The *"excellent"* **Kirk Radke** (see p.388) has a wealth of experience handling all aspects of

## Private Equity: Buyouts
### Senior Statesmen

**Senior Statesmen:** distinguished older practitioners

| | |
|---|---|
| Beattie Richard I | Simpson Thacher & Bartlett LLP * |
| Cogut Charles 'Casey' | Simpson Thacher & Bartlett LLP * |
| Hammes Jeffrey C | Kirkland & Ellis LLP * |
| Malt R Bradford | Ropes & Gray LLP |

### Leading Individuals

**Band 1**

| | |
|---|---|
| Blassberg Franci J | Debevoise & Plimpton LLP |
| Chapin David C | Ropes & Gray LLP |
| Davenport Margaret Andrews | Debevoise & Plimpton LLP |
| Horowitz Gary I | Simpson Thacher & Bartlett LLP * |
| Neely Wilson S | Simpson Thacher & Bartlett LLP * |
| Radke Kirk A | Kirkland & Ellis LLP * |
| Rose Alfred O | Ropes & Gray LLP |
| Ryan Michael L | Cleary Gottlieb Steen & Hamilton LLP * |

**Band 2**

| | |
|---|---|
| Bird Paul S | Debevoise & Plimpton LLP |
| Capelouto Richard | Simpson Thacher & Bartlett LLP * |
| Gartner Steven J | Willkie Farr & Gallagher LLP * |
| Lennon Daniel | Latham & Watkins LLP * |
| Nugent Eileen T | Skadden, Arps, Slate, Meagher & Flom * |
| Schwenkel Robert C | Fried, Frank, Harris, Shriver & Jacobson * |
| Shim Paul J | Cleary Gottlieb Steen & Hamilton LLP * |
| Stadler Brian M | Simpson Thacher & Bartlett LLP * |
| Stillwell R Newcomb | Ropes & Gray LLP |
| Warner Douglas | Weil, Gotshal & Manges LLP * |

**Band 3**

| | |
|---|---|
| Bason Jr George R | Davis Polk & Wardwell LLP * |
| Coco Joseph A | Skadden, Arps, Slate, Meagher & Flom * |
| Cross James | Simpson Thacher & Bartlett LLP * |
| Duffell David K | Weil, Gotshal & Manges LLP * |
| Ewan Christopher | Fried, Frank, Harris, Shriver & Jacobson * |
| Gessner Douglas C | Kirkland & Ellis LLP * |
| Jones Julie H | Ropes & Gray LLP |
| Prounis Othon A | Ropes & Gray LLP |
| Reiss John | White & Case LLP * |
| Schneirov Allison R | Skadden, Arps, Slate, Meagher & Flom * |

| | |
|---|---|
| West Glenn D | Weil, Gotshal & Manges LLP * |
| Woronoff Michael A | Proskauer Rose LLP |

**Band 4**

| | |
|---|---|
| Bellah Maguire Jennifer | Gibson, Dunn & Crutcher LLP * |
| Caplan Gordon | Willkie Farr & Gallagher LLP * |
| Kennedy Robert | Jones Day (ONP)[†] |
| LeClaire John R | Goodwin Procter LLP * |
| Lin Raymond Y | Latham & Watkins LLP * |
| O'Donnell G Daniel | Dechert LLP * |
| Reisner Carl L | Paul, Weiss, Rifkind, Wharton & Garrison * |
| Schmidt Kevin M | Debevoise & Plimpton LLP |
| Schwed Robert | WilmerHale (ONP)[†] * |
| Weisser Michael E | Weil, Gotshal & Manges LLP * |

**Band 5**

| | |
|---|---|
| Austin Christopher E | Cleary Gottlieb Steen & Hamilton LLP * |
| Blittner David | Weil, Gotshal & Manges LLP * |
| Brahmst Oliver | White & Case LLP * |
| Burnett Mark | Goodwin Procter LLP * |
| Dawson R Alec | Morgan, Lewis & Bockius LLP (ONP)[†] * |
| Griffiths Sean P. | Gibson, Dunn & Crutcher LLP * |
| Hopkinson R Ronald | Cadwalader, Wickersham & Taft (ONP)[†] * |
| Kagan Stewart | Cadwalader, Wickersham & Taft (ONP)[†] * |
| Mangino Brian | Fried, Frank, Harris, Shriver & Jacobson * |
| Marcus Craig | Ropes & Gray LLP |
| Nassau Henry N | Dechert LLP * |
| Pollack Richard A | Sullivan & Cromwell LLP (ONP)[†] * |
| Rosen Jeffrey J | Debevoise & Plimpton LLP |
| Rubin Stephen W | Proskauer Rose LLP |
| Shoemate Steven R | Gibson, Dunn & Crutcher LLP * |
| Welch Richard J | Bingham McCutchen LLP (ONP)[†] * |

\* Indicates firm / individual with profile.
[†] ONP = Other Notable Practitioner.

private equity transactions, representing sponsors and public entities across a broad range of industries. Sources say: *"He's a smart and capable lawyer."* **Jeffrey Hammes** (see p.1211) enjoys a strong reputation among peers, and concentrates his practice on complex business transactions, including leveraged buyouts and private equity compensation matters. **Douglas Gessner** (see p.320) represents private equity and venture capital sponsors in a wide range of matters, including leveraged buyouts, growth equity investments and recapitalizations.

### Simpson Thacher & Bartlett LLP
See profile on p.2006

**THE FIRM** This preeminent firm has a global private equity practice, and is widely recognized as a leader in the field. Simpson Thacher has longstanding relationships with numerous top-tier private equity firms, and regularly handles complex and sophisticated deals on behalf of its clients. Illustrative of this is its recent representation of KKR and a consortium of others in the $7.2 billion acquisition of Samson Investment Company. Attorneys are particularly skilled at managing leveraged buyout transactions, and have significant experience handling energy-related investments for prestigious clients, including Blackstone and First Reserve Corporation.

**Client Service** *"They know the business and offer very good client service. I hold them in the top handful of firms in the USA, as they're very good at being practical."*

**Commercial Awareness** *"They're very good at understanding what we do and what we are trying to do, and they are able to juxtapose that against the legal realities within the marketplace."*

**KEY INDIVIDUALS Gary Horowitz** (see p.336) recently represented KKR and Alliance Boots in connection to the $6.7 billion acquisition of a 45% equity stake in Alliance Boots by Walgreens. Sources say: *"He's a star at the top of the industry."* Sources recognize that **Wilson Neely** (see p.375) *"knows his way around the private equity marketplace"* and has a *"vibrant practice."* Recent highlights include representing Centerbridge Partners in connection with the acquisition of a stake in Santander Consumer USA. **Richard Capelouto** (see p.627) is highly regarded in the private equity arena, and is described by sources as a *"phenomenal lawyer"* with a well-respected practice. Notable transactions include the representation of Hellman and Friedman in relation to Blackstone's acquisition of a controlling interest in Emdeon. **Brian Stadler** (see p.411) regularly advises large private equity firms on a wide range of matters, including acquisitions, dispositions and leveraged buyouts. Notable clients include Blackstone. **James Cross** (see p.300) enjoys an excellent reputation for his debt work and financing transactions. He has represented large private equity firms, including KKR, General Atlantic and Silver Lake. Esteemed practitioner **Richard Beattie** (see p.280) is described by interviewees as an *"impressive lawyer"* and a *"legend in the field."* He specializes in M&A and leveraged buyouts. **Casey Cogut** (see p.296) is an experienced practitioner with a diverse and respected private equity practice. He has particular expertise in handling complex multijurisdictional matters.

## Band 2

### Cleary Gottlieb Steen & Hamilton LLP
See profile on p.1963

**THE FIRM** This solid firm has a well-established international private equity practice with cross-border capabilities across Europe and Asia. The team has impressive expertise across the full gamut of matters, ranging from M&A and leveraged buyouts to portfolio company transactions and fund formation. Notable cases of late include handling multiple matters for long-standing client TPG. The team also managed numerous transactions for Warburg Pincus, including its acquisition of Endurance International from Accel-KKR.

**Sources say:** *"A great firm that is well established in the area."*

**KEY INDIVIDUALS** *"Terrific lawyer"* **Michael Ryan** (see p.397) has broad experience across a range of corporate and financial matters, and serves as principal outside counsel to TPG. **Paul Shim** (see p.405) recently provided

counsel to TPG in a number of matters, including a $1.7 billion recapitalization of Savers together with Leonard Green & Partners. The *"very experienced, very responsive and very thoughtful"* **Christopher Austin** (see p.1875) receives extensive praise, with one client describing him as *"very good in a contentious negotiation"* and *"the best I deal with in terms of his ability to get a deal done."*

### Debevoise & Plimpton LLP
See profile on p.1968

**THE FIRM** This prominent private equity practice is highly regarded in the marketplace, and has enjoyed a busy year handling a large volume of significant transactions for high-profile clients. With a deep bench of attorneys, the group is well equipped to tackle complex and sophisticated private equity matters. This is exemplified by its recent representation of Access Industries and a consortium of firms in its $7.15 billion acquisition of energy producer El Paso.

**Client Service** *"The quality and consistency of their lawyers and their service is distinguished. They do a good job of integrating their practices and making themselves easy to work with. They present a very efficient legal solution for a PE firm."*

**Commercial Awareness** *"Debevoise has a broad and deep understanding of our business. They help us manage risk, and they help us capitalize on the opportunities we develop. We view our relationship with Debevoise as a true partnership between client and counsel."*

**KEY INDIVIDUALS Franci Blassberg** is recognized as *"one of the deans of the private equity legal community."* She receives high praise from sources, with one client commenting: *"Her good judgment and creativity have helped us navigate many novel and interesting transactions over the years."* Blassberg recently counseled Clayton, Dubilier & Rice in its sale of Diversey Holdings to Sealed Air, valued at $4.3 billion. **Peggy Davenport** has *"very good business sense,"* and recently led the team advising Kelso & Company on numerous investments. One client notes: *"She knows what's important to us, and is an effective lawyer and negotiator for us."* Recent highlights for **Paul Bird** include handling the $3.3 billion acquisition of Getty Images for prestigious private equity firm The Carlyle Group. Interviewees praise his abilities, commenting: *"He had great judgment as well as an even-handed approach and demeanor, which serve him – and his clients – very well."* The *"smart, efficient and thoughtful"* **Kevin Schmidt** recently led the team advising healthcare organization Oceana Therapeutics on its sale to Salix Pharmaceuticals. Clients appreciate that he *"works hard and gets it all done, knows what's important to us, and has good business sense."* **Jeffrey Rosen** is hailed by one commentator as *"one of the best lawyers I've ever known. He is phenomenally intelligent."* He recently represented The TCW Group in connection with its sale to The Carlyle Group.

### Latham & Watkins LLP
See profile on p.446

**THE FIRM** This globally renowned firm has a robust private equity practice with a deep bench of attorneys. The

group has strong industry expertise across a range of sectors, including life sciences and technology. Latham also has particular strength in the energy space, as illustrated by its recent representation of Blackstone Energy Partners in connection with its $1.5 billion investment in Cheniere Energy. Other recent highlights include advising The Carlyle Group on its $4.9 billion acquisition of DuPont.

**Sources say:** *"Really terrific – very, very strong across the board. We are very pleased with their work."*

**KEY INDIVIDUALS Daniel Lennon** (see p.876) recently advised BC Partners and The Carlyle Group on the $3.5 billion acquisition of Hamilton Sundstrand Industrial from United Technologies. Sources note that he *"knows what he's doing and things get done properly."* **Raymond Lin** (see p.357) is particularly adept at handling initial public offerings, as well as debt financing and restructurings. Recent transactions include the representation of BC Partners and other investors in its acquisition of Suddenlink Communications.

### Ropes & Gray LLP
See profile on p.1528

**THE FIRM** This firm has expanded its private equity practice with added international capabilities in London and Hong Kong. The group represents a large number of megafunds such as Silver Lake Partners, and also has a substantial midmarket presence. Recent highlights include advising Bain Capital on its $1 billion acquisition of Genpact, as well as numerous transactions for TPG.

**Client Service** *"They are extremely responsive. They work tirelessly. They will do whatever it takes to get the job done. They have excellent business judgment."*

**KEY INDIVIDUALS Alfred Rose** is widely respected by peers and clients alike. He regularly represents major private equity sponsors, and recently handled a variety of matters for TPG, including a $200 million PIPE investment in REIT Parkway Properties. Recognized for his strong and diverse private equity practice, **David Chapin** recently represented Skillsoft, a portfolio company of Berkshire Partners, in connection with its acquisition of Element K. Recent highlights for **Newcomb Stillwell** include representing Blackstone in its high-profile $3 billion acquisition of Emdeon. The *"pragmatic, dynamic and focused"* **Julie Jones** is well respected in the private equity space. She recently represented Bain Capital in relation to its $3.3 billion sale of Warner Music Group. One client notes: *"She brings a unique perspective to transactions. Because she's so hands-on we feel like we get top-level advice."* **Othon Prounis** is favorably described as *"smart, with a good demeanor."* He represents Welsh, Carson, Anderson & Stowe in a wide range of matters, including a number of high-value acquisitions and dispositions. **Craig Marcus** heads the firm's executive compensation practice, and has significant experience representing private equity sponsors and portfolio companies. He recently assisted Thomas H Lee Partners with the sale of its interest in a quick-service food chain. **Bradford Malt** founded the firm's private equity practice group, and has a strong reputation in the marketplace. His broad experience ranges from financings and portfolio company matters to fundraising issues and strategic initiatives.

## Weil, Gotshal & Manges LLP
See profile on p.2015

**THE FIRM** This leading firm has a diverse private equity practice representing a large number of clients in significant transactions, as illustrated by its recent representation of Advent International in multiple matters, including its acquisition of AOT Bedding Super Holdings. The team handles a large volume of multifaceted transactions, and is able to seamlessly integrate its knowledge and experience in other practice areas, ranging from M&A and tax to litigation and real estate, in order to provide well-coordinated and high-quality counsel.
**Sources say:** *"All-around excellent – timely, efficient and good value."*
**KEY INDIVIDUALS Douglas Warner** (see p.423) represents prestigious clients such as CVC and Oak Hill, and recently advised Centerbridge Partners on its acquisition of an international restaurant chain. **David Duffell** (see p.2257) has notably advised Providence Equity Partners on numerous matters, including its $1.1 billion acquisition of Q9 Networks. Sources say he has *"everything you want in an attorney."* *"Technically very strong"* **Glenn West** (see p.2421) recently acted on behalf of PL Logistics, a portfolio company of Lindsay Goldberg, on the sale of oil and gas supplier PL Midstream. **Michael Weisser's** (see p.424) recent highlights include advising American Securities on its $750 million leveraged buyout of auto components supplier HHI Intermediate Group. **David Blittner** (see p.285) has extensive experience handling leveraged buyouts and dispositions, and recently represented Avista in connection with the sale of portfolio company BioReliance.

## Band 3

### Davis Polk & Wardwell LLP
See profile on p.442

**THE FIRM** This growing private equity practice has an international scope, and is routinely called upon to handle complex and sophisticated transactions, ranging from debt financing for portfolio companies to fund formation and recapitalization transactions. Recent highlights for the group include the representation of Getty Investments with regards to the acquisition of Getty Images by The Carlyle Group, a transaction valued at $3.3 billion. Other notable clients include General Atlantic and GS Capital Partners.
**Commercial Awareness** *"They help to bring a commercial element to the deal."*
**KEY INDIVIDUALS George Bason** (see p.279) is *"very well regarded in the community."* He recently played a key role in advising Japanese manufacturing company Daikin Industries on its acquisition of Texas-based Goodman Global.

## Fried, Frank, Harris, Shriver & Jacobson LLP
See profile on p.1975

**THE FIRM** This firm has a long-established presence in the private equity space, and continues to represent major names in the industry. Not only does the team represent megafunds such as Permira and Goldman Sachs, but it also acts for important clients in the midmarket, including New Mountain and Onex. The group handles all aspects of private equity matters, including fund formation and portfolio company transactions. Highlights of late include representing Permira in its $1.6 billion acquisition of Ancestry.com, as well as a number of other deals.
**KEY INDIVIDUALS Robert Schwenkel** (see p.403) heads the firm's private equity team, and handles major deals including the recent $6.6 billion sale of Suddenlink. **Christopher Ewan** (see p.310) is described as an *"extremely good negotiator,"* and clients appreciate his responsiveness. He recently advised Onex on its agreement to acquire SGS International. Notable transactions for **Brian Mangino** (see p.879) include the aforementioned acquisition of Ancestry.com by client Permira.

## Gibson, Dunn & Crutcher LLP
See profile on p.682

**THE FIRM** Attorneys at this private equity practice coordinate efforts with lawyers in other practice areas, including tax and M&A, in order to provide comprehensive advice and excellent service to clients. The group has an extensive list of major clients, and recently handled multiple transactions for Centerview Partners and Aurora Capital Group. The practice also benefits from the firm's international reach, enabling attorneys to effectively manage transactions involving cross-border elements.
**Client Service** *"They dedicate their most sophisticated resources to us."*
**KEY INDIVIDUALS** Based in Los Angeles, **Jennifer Bellah Maguire** (see p.623) concentrates her practice on private equity fund formation and M&A. **Sean Griffiths** (see p.326) recently represented CVC Capital Partners in its acquisition of a majority interest in AlixPartners. One client notes: *"He is a pragmatic and effective problem solver in complex and tense transaction negotiations."* **Steven Shoemate** (see p.406) has strong expertise in the private equity arena, and has recently handled numerous transactions for Catterton Partners, including multiple investments.

## Goodwin Procter LLP
See profile on p.1522

**THE FIRM** This well-regarded private equity practice continues to strengthen its team, and recently added a number of attorneys from Dewey & LeBoeuf. The team has deep industry expertise across a wide range of sectors, including financial services, life sciences, healthcare and technology. Attorneys handle a large volume of deals, ranging from leveraged buyouts to portfolio company transactions and recapitalizations, primarily on behalf of midmarket clients. Recent highlights include representing The Halifax Group in its leveraged buyout of XL Associates.

**Sources say:** *"They seem to be able to get the transaction done efficiently, professionally and smoothly, with our interests in mind."*
**KEY INDIVIDUALS John LeClaire** (see p.1499) heads the firm's private equity group, and has an impressive client roster. He has handled numerous private equity transactions on behalf of Leeds Equity Partners of late, including the leveraged buyout of Evanta Ventures. **Mark Burnett** (see p.1487) is lead partner for JMI Equity on multiple transactions, including the $1 billion acquisition of Paradigm and a number of large buyouts.

## Paul, Weiss, Rifkind, Wharton & Garrison LLP
See profile on p.1997

**THE FIRM** This solid firm has a broad base of clients, including long-standing relationships with major firms such as Oak Hill Capital and General Atlantic. In addition to the representation of megafunds, the group also has a strong midmarket practice which regularly handles transactions for the likes of CI Capital, KPS and TowerBrook Capital Partners, among others. Recent highlights include one of the largest private equity transactions of the year, involving the representation of Apollo Global Management and other investors in a $7.15 billion acquisition of El Paso's energy and power business.
**Commercial Awareness** *"Fantastic. Very creative and very commercial. Fair billing, good value for money, efficient and timely. They are very, very strong across major dimensions."*
**KEY INDIVIDUALS Carl Reisner** (see p.391) recently advised KPS Capital Partners in connection with the disposition of portfolio company HHI Group to American Securities.

## Proskauer Rose LLP
See profile on p.2001

**THE FIRM** This team regularly handles high-value sophisticated transactions for prestigious clients, as illustrated by its recent representation of Ares Management in a number of matters, including the $1.6 billion acquisition of 99 Cents Only Stores. Renowned for excellent client service, the firm represents an impressive roster of private equity firms and manages deals across a broad range of industries.
**Commercial Awareness** *"They were across the board fantastic to work with. They did a great job of understanding the clients' needs and the ultimate business objectives. They put the clients' needs first."*
**Client Service** *"Their quality of advice, responsiveness and legal knowledge are all excellent. They are a really good partner to us. They have been really helpful and we've been really, really impressed."*
**KEY INDIVIDUALS Michael Woronoff** has extensive experience in the private equity field, and continues to provide counsel to Ares Management in a variety of transactions. **Stephen Rubin** routinely handles all types of private equity deals, and has extensive experience in debt offerings and subordinated loan transactions.

## Skadden, Arps, Slate, Meagher & Flom LLP & Affiliates

See profile on p.2008

THE FIRM This highly regarded firm has a robust private equity practice representing a broad client base, including high-profile megafunds as well as midmarket funds. The team has strong industry knowledge across a range of sectors, particularly within healthcare and technology. Recent highlights include representing interactive software developer NDS Group and its owners in its sale to Cisco Systems, valued at approximately $5 billion.
Sources say: *"They provide sophisticated advice for complex transactions."*
KEY INDIVIDUALS **Eileen Nugent** (see p.378) continues to represent Medtronic, and recently acted on behalf of Norwest Equity in connection with its investment in firearms manufacturer Savage Sports. **Joseph Coco** (see p.296) recently represented RailAmerica in its acquisition by Genesee & Wyoming. Clients say: *"He's got deep industry knowledge and awareness. He's a sophisticated adviser, he's practical, he's solution-oriented, and he's very timely with his response."* **Allison Schneirov** (see p.402) is the relationship partner for significant private equity firms, including Permira Funds and Blackstone. Recent work highlights include representing Dell in its $2.4 billion acquisition of Quest Software.

## Willkie Farr & Gallagher LLP

See profile on p.2016

THE FIRM With a deep bench of skilled attorneys, this firm is adept at representing both national and international private equity firms and portfolio companies. The group has an impressive client roster, and handles a large number of high-profile private equity deals across a range of industries. Recent transactions include the representation of Riverstone Holdings in relation to its acquisition of El Paso's oil and gas business.
Sources say: *"They are very strong, good, smart lawyers, and very responsive."*
KEY INDIVIDUALS **Steven Gartner** (see p.319) recently acted on behalf of Warburg Pincus in connection with the sale of MLM Information Services Holdings. Sources say: *"He's a businessman as well as a lawyer,"* and praise his

negotiation skills and ability *"to get to a good outcome and result, and push negotiations forward."* Chair of the firm's private equity group, **Gordon Caplan** (see p.1882) recently advised Insight Venture Management on its $2 billion acquisition of Quest Software.

## Band 4

### Dechert LLP

See profile on p.1969

THE FIRM Attorneys at this national powerhouse are able to draw on their expertise in other practice areas such as tax, M&A and corporate finance to provide clients with comprehensive interdisciplinary advice in a range of private equity deals. The team regularly handles all aspects of private equity, including fund formation and investments and portfolio company transactions. Recent representations include providing counsel to One Equity Partners in relation to its high-value acquisition of MModal.
**Commercial Awareness** *"The worldwide resources of Dechert support our transactions wherever we might go, and their deep bench covers every aspect of our legal work."*
KEY INDIVIDUALS **Daniel O'Donnell** (see p.2226) is praised for his responsiveness and availability. One source notes: *"He is immensely talented because he is able to simplify issues and get to the crux of the matter. His work ethic is unbelievable."* Notable transactions include handling an acquisition for Court Square Capital Partners. Described by clients as *"very strategic and very helpful,"* **Henry Nassau** (see p.2226) recently represented Graham Partners in its acquisition of Henry Company.

### White & Case LLP

See profile on p.451

THE FIRM This full-service firm has a respected private equity group with an international reach. The team assists clients across a wide range of industries, including healthcare, technology, and oil and gas. Recent highlights include representing private equity fund manager Pegasus Capital Advisors in connection with its acquisition of Six Senses Resorts & Spas, as well as the sale of one of its portfolio

companies. The deal involved numerous cross-border elements.
Sources say: *"They are very reliable. A good set of people and a strong bench."*
KEY INDIVIDUALS **John Reiss** (see p.1930) is lauded by one source as *"the best lawyer I've ever worked with. He's commercial, aggressive and smart."* Recent transactions include an acquisition and a number of dispositions for Quad-C Management. **Oliver Brahmst** (see p.286) receives high praise from clients as *"someone who is capable of not only being immersed in the detail, but who can also take a step back and view the bigger picture. He's creative in coming to a resolution that works for everyone, and has a commercial view on things."*

## Other Notable Practitioners

**Stewart Kagan** (see p.342) of Cadwalader, Wickersham & Taft LLP has extensive experience in dealing with financial restructurings and leveraged buyouts. He represents a broad range of clients on debt financings. **Ronald Hopkinson** (see p.336), also of Cadwalader, heads the firm's private equity group, and handles high-profile leveraged buyouts and private equity transactions for major entities. Recent highlights for **Richard Welch** (see p.672) of Bingham McCutchen LLP include advising Levine Leichtman Capital Partners in connection with its acquisition of McKenzie Sports Products. **Robert Kennedy** (see p.345) of Jones Day regularly advises an array of clients, including private equity funds and strategic buyers and sellers, in a wide range of investments and transactions. **Alec Dawson** (see p.1888) of Morgan, Lewis & Bockius LLP is well respected in the private equity field, and recently represented Ares Capital in relation to the sale of its controlling interest in Penn Power Group. **Robert Schwed** (see p.403) of WilmerHale recently represented Cerca Group in connection with the acquisition of Samba Holdings. Sources say: *"He's exceptionally intelligent, innovative and entrepreneurial."* **Richard Pollack** (see p.386) co-heads Sullivan & Cromwell LLP's private equity group, and has significant experience across a wide range of industries. He has recently assisted Rhône Capital with numerous investments.

# PRODUCT LIABILITY & MASS TORTS

Commentary about individuals can be found under their firm's paragraph.  If the firm has no paragraph (is not ranked) look at Other Notable Practitioners.

## Product Liability & Mass Torts
### Leading Firms

**Band 1**
Bartlit Beck Herman Palenchar & Scott LLP
Kaye Scholer LLP *
Shook, Hardy & Bacon LLP *
Sidley Austin LLP *
Skadden, Arps, Slate, Meagher & Flom LLP & Affiliates *
Williams & Connolly LLP

**Band 2**
Bowman and Brooke LLP
Covington & Burling LLP *
Dechert LLP *
Jones Day *
King & Spalding LLP *
Kirkland & Ellis LLP *
Pepper Hamilton LLP *
Wheeler Trigg O'Donnell LLP *

**Band 3**
Arnold & Porter LLP *
Butler, Snow, O'Mara, Stevens & Cannada, PLLC *
Campbell Campbell Edwards & Conroy PC *
DLA Piper LLP (US) *
Fulbright & Jaworski LLP *
Goldman Ismail Tomaselli Brennan & Baum LLP
Hogan Lovells US LLP
Hughes Hubbard & Reed LLP *
Nelson Mullins Riley & Scarborough LLP *
Orrick, Herrington & Sutcliffe LLP *
Reed Smith LLP
Winston & Strawn LLP *

**Band 4**
Baker Botts LLP *
Faegre Baker Daniels
Greenberg Traurig, LLP *
Holland & Knight LLP *
Mayer Brown LLP *
McGuireWoods LLP *
Morgan, Lewis & Bockius LLP *
Morrison & Foerster LLP *
O'Melveny & Myers LLP *
Perkins Coie LLP
Tucker Ellis
Venable LLP *
Watkins & Eager PLLC *

*  Indicates firm with profile.
Alphabetical order within each band. Band 1 is the highest.

## Band 1

### Bartlit Beck Herman Palenchar & Scott LLP

**THE FIRM** Trial work is held to be this firm's forte, and the group also stands out for the consistent strength of its lawyers throughout the team. Pharmaceutical work is a particular focus, and the firm recently handled multidistrict litigation relating to Bayer's oral contraceptive YAZ and to Trasylol, a drug used to prevent excessive bleeding during complex surgery. Another key client is DuPont, which the firm defends in relation to the herbicide Imprelis.

**KEY INDIVIDUALS Philip Beck** is lauded for his extensive trial expertise. Commentators applaud his openness and notable cross-examination capabilities. He serves as lead trial counsel in the YAZ and Trasylol litigation. **Adam Hoeflich** is praised as being an experienced strategist whose scope of work includes pharmaceutical withdrawals, mass torts and class actions. He acts as lead counsel on the YAZ litigation in the Southern District of Illinois and on the Imprelis multidistrict litigation in the Eastern District of Pennsylvania. Trial lawyer **Donald Scott** impresses with his detailed and committed approach to case preparation and execution. He is recognized by peers for his success in major litigation relating to lead pigment and lead paint, including recently on behalf of NL Industries.

### Kaye Scholer LLP
See profile on p.1984

**THE FIRM** Commentators highlight this firm's extensive experience in this field and the range of matters its team is able to handle. It maintains a formidable reputation for pharmaceuticals work, acting as global strategy counsel and national counsel for two Pfizer units on the hormone therapy litigation, in which it coordinates regional and local counsel on over 10,000 claims. It also defended AstraZeneca as national coordinating counsel in relation to the antipsychotic drug Seroquel. Major nonpharmaceutical clients include Knauf Plasterboard Tianjin and ExxonMobil.
**Client Service** "*They really understand the client. I've been very impressed. They're very responsive and tenacious.*"
**Commercial Awareness** "*They are incredibly creative and receptive. The product result is absolutely perfect and they tend to be very strategic.*"
**KEY INDIVIDUALS Steven Glickstein** (see p.321) is singled out in the products and mass torts space as being "*very good at strategic thinking,*" and "*collaborative, informative and responsive.*" **Jay Mayesh** (see p.363) is highly regarded for his experience in this arena, and garners particular praise for his trial expertise. With Glickstein, he led the firm's successful defense of Knauf Plasterboard in liti-

gation relating to drywall products manufactured in China. Newly ranked **Arthur Brown** (see p.288) is "*smart, practical and incredibly strategic.*" He is also noted for his strong organizational capabilities and ability to build an effective team. He led the team's work in the Seroquel litigation for AstraZeneca.

### Shook, Hardy & Bacon LLP
See profile on p.1644

**THE FIRM** This firm is a major player in the tobacco sphere and is widely respected for its track record at trial level. Pharmaceuticals and toxic torts are other areas of note, with recent work including continuing to act as national counsel for Mylan Pharmaceuticals in litigation relating to the heart failure and arrhythmia drug Digitek. Additional highlights include the successful representation of Centocor at the appellate level in a case concerning prescription drugs. This resulted in a previous award of $4.6 million being overturned. The firm's other leading clients include Philip Morris, Ford and Coca-Cola.
**Sources say:** "*They have done a phenomenal job, handling the cases in an efficient and straightforward manner.*"
**KEY INDIVIDUALS Harvey Kaplan** is chair emeritus of the firm's pharmaceutical and medical device practice. He is praised by one source as "*the dean of the pharmaceuticals defense Bar; someone who has a lot of knowledge and information at his fingertips.*" He took the lead in the Digitek litigation for Mylan Pharmaceuticals. **Kenneth Reilly** is lauded as "*one of the most wonderful trial lawyers.*" "*He applies a creative and innovative approach to these cases and is always seeking ways to improve our trial performance and outcomes,*" sources comment. He represents Philip Morris in the Engle Progeny trials. **Sean Wajert** wins praise for his broad-based expertise in litigation. He currently acts as national counsel to Firmenich on nationwide litigation relating to the chemical diacetyl, exposure to which is alleged to have caused plaintiffs lung injuries.

## Recommended for Client Service
### Nationwide

| | |
|---|---|
| Butler, Snow, O'Mara, Stevens & Cannada, PLLC | King & Spalding LLP |
| Holland & Knight LLP | Pepper Hamilton LLP |
| Kaye Scholer LLP | Watkins & Eager PLLC |

## Recommended for Commercial Awareness
### Nationwide

| | |
|---|---|
| Butler, Snow, O'Mara, Stevens & Cannada, PLLC | Mayer Brown LLP |
| Covington & Burling LLP | Pepper Hamilton LLP |
| Kaye Scholer LLP | Williams & Connolly LLP |

## Product Liability & Mass Torts
### Senior Statesmen

**Senior Statesmen:** distinguished older practitioners

| | |
|---|---|
| **Grossi** Peter | Arnold & Porter LLP * |
| **Tottenham** Terry O | Fulbright & Jaworski LLP * |

### Leading Individuals

**Star individuals**

| | |
|---|---|
| **Beck** Philip | Bartlit Beck Herman Palenchar & Scott LLP |
| **Birnbaum** Sheila L | Skadden, Arps, Slate, Meagher & Flom * |
| **Jones** Christy D | Butler, Snow, O'Mara, Stevens & Cannada * |
| **Wheeler** Malcolm | Wheeler Trigg O'Donnell LLP * |

**Band 1**

| | |
|---|---|
| **Beisner** John H | Skadden, Arps, Slate, Meagher & Flom * |
| **Brock** Robert C. | Covington & Burling LLP * |
| **Brown** Michael K | Reed Smith LLP |
| **Davis** Varner Chilton | King & Spalding LLP * |
| **Gussack** Nina M | Pepper Hamilton LLP * |
| **Kaplan** Harvey | Shook, Hardy & Bacon LLP |
| **Marvin** Douglas R | Williams & Connolly LLP |
| **Sullivan** Diane P | Weil, Gotshal & Manges LLP * |
| **Webb** Dan K | Winston & Strawn LLP * |

**Band 2**

| | |
|---|---|
| **Bicks** Peter A | Orrick, Herrington & Sutcliffe LLP * |
| **Boutrous Jr** Theodore J | Gibson, Dunn & Crutcher LLP (ONP) † * |
| **Campbell** James M | Campbell Campbell Edwards & Conroy PC |
| **Cereghini** Paul G | Bowman and Brooke LLP * |
| **Cheffo** Mark S | Skadden, Arps, Slate, Meagher & Flom * |
| **Cohen** Lori G | Greenberg Traurig, LLP * |
| **Davis** Michael W | Sidley Austin LLP * |
| **Dukes** David E | Nelson Mullins Riley & Scarborough LLP * |
| **Gourley** Sara J | Sidley Austin LLP * |
| **Hubbard** Heidi K | Williams & Connolly LLP |
| **Ismail** Tarek | Goldman Ismail Tomaselli Brennan & Baum |
| **Platt** Warren | Snell & Wilmer LLP (ONP) † |
| **Pole** Debra E | Sidley Austin LLP * |
| **Trigg** John | Wheeler Trigg O'Donnell LLP * |
| **Tucker** Robert | Tucker Ellis |

**Band 3**

| | |
|---|---|
| **Denny** Otway | Fulbright & Jaworski LLP * |
| **Glickstein** Steven | Kaye Scholer LLP * |
| **Goodman III** Will | Watkins & Eager PLLC * |
| **Heard III** F Lane | Williams & Connolly LLP |
| **Irwin** James | Irwin Fritchie Urquhart & Moore (ONP) † |
| **Mayer** Theodore VH | Hughes Hubbard & Reed LLP * |
| **Mayesh** Jay | Kaye Scholer LLP * |

| | |
|---|---|
| **Raber** Stephen | Williams & Connolly LLP |
| **Reilly** Kenneth J | Shook, Hardy & Bacon LLP |
| **Rosenberg** Ezra D | Dechert LLP * |
| **Stengel** James L | Orrick, Herrington & Sutcliffe LLP * |

**Band 4**

| | |
|---|---|
| **Bayman** Andrew T | King & Spalding LLP * |
| **Brown** Loren H | DLA Piper LLP (US) * |
| **Conroy** William J | Campbell Campbell Edwards & Conroy PC |
| **Curtis** Philip | Arnold & Porter LLP * |
| **Dwyer** Susan | Herrick, Feinstein LLP |
| **Fitzpatrick** John | Wheeler Trigg O'Donnell LLP * |
| **Frederick** Thomas | Winston & Strawn LLP * |
| **Goodell Jr** Charles P | Goodell, DeVries, Leech & Dann (ONP) † * |
| **Grossman** Theodore | Jones Day * |
| **Heim** Robert C | Dechert LLP * |
| **Hoeflich** Adam | Bartlit Beck Herman Palenchar & Scott LLP |
| **Ichel** David W | Simpson Thacher & Bartlett LLP (ONP) † * |
| **Lavelle Jr** John P | Morgan, Lewis & Bockius LLP * |
| **Lumish** Wendy F | Carlton Fields, P.A. (ONP) † * |
| **Miller** Jessica Davidson | Skadden, Arps, Slate, Meagher & Flom * |
| **Morrison** Stephen G | Nelson Mullins Riley & Scarborough LLP * |
| **Norwood Jr** Colvin G | McGlinchey Stafford PLLC (ONP) † * |
| **Parsigian** Kenneth J | Latham & Watkins (ONP) † |
| **Pohl** Paul M | Jones Day * |
| **Price** Joseph M | Faegre Baker Daniels |
| **Rubel** Eric | Arnold & Porter LLP * |
| **Scheve** Stephen | Baker Botts LLP * |
| **Schmidt** Paul W | Covington & Burling LLP * |
| **Schoon** Eugene A | Sidley Austin LLP * |
| **Scott** Donald E | Bartlit Beck Herman Palenchar & Scott LLP |
| **Scott** Michael T | Reed Smith LLP |
| **Skidmore** Jonathan B | Fulbright & Jaworski LLP * |
| **Smith** Colin P | Holland & Knight LLP * |
| **Smith** Joel H | Bowman and Brooke LLP * |
| **Strain** Paul | Venable LLP * |
| **Tomaselli Jr** Joe W | Goldman Ismail Tomaselli Brennan & Baum |
| **Urquhart, Jr.** Quentin F | Irwin Fritchie Urquhart & Moore (ONP) † |
| **Winter** John D | Patterson Belknap Webb & Tyler (ONP) † * |
| **Zarov** Herbert L | Mayer Brown LLP |

**Band 5**

| | |
|---|---|
| **Agneshwar** Anand | Arnold & Porter LLP * |
| **Anderson** Brian | O'Melveny & Myers LLP * |
| **Bassett** W Randall | King & Spalding LLP * |
| **Brown** Arthur | Kaye Scholer LLP * |
| **Buente** David | Sidley Austin LLP * |
| **Campion** Thomas | Drinker Biddle & Reath LLP (ONP) † * |
| **Cohen** Charles W | Hughes Hubbard & Reed LLP * |
| **Crawford** Vaughn | Snell & Wilmer LLP (ONP) † |
| **Dameris** Thad | Hogan Lovells US LLP |
| **Davies** Colleen T | Reed Smith LLP |
| **Davies** Patrick S | Covington & Burling LLP * |
| **Dillow** John | Perkins Coie LLP |
| **Dodd** Jan E | Fulbright & Jaworski LLP * |
| **Eaton** Maja C | Sidley Austin LLP * |
| **Fahey** Sean P | Pepper Hamilton LLP * |
| **Fitzpatrick** James C | Hughes Hubbard & Reed LLP * |
| **Harburg** Stephen J | Skadden, Arps, Slate, Meagher & Flom * |
| **Hooper** James E | Wheeler Trigg O'Donnell LLP * |
| **Hooper** John | Reed Smith LLP |
| **Kleinberg** Norman | Hughes Hubbard & Reed LLP |
| **Marshall** Steve | Venable LLP * |
| **McGaan** Andrew R. | Kirkland & Ellis LLP * |
| **Newton** Peter B | Neal, Gerber & Eisenberg LLP (ONP) † * |
| **Parker** Bruce | Venable LLP * |
| **Pigott** Ginger | Greenberg Traurig, LLP * |
| **Ring** Daniel | Mayer Brown LLP |
| **Schneider** Richard A | King & Spalding LLP * |
| **Smith** Leslie M | Kirkland & Ellis LLP * |
| **Socha** Charles Q | Tucker Ellis |
| **Thomasch** Daniel J | Gibson, Dunn & Crutcher LLP (ONP) † * |
| **Thorpe** Jane F | Alston & Bird LLP (ONP) † * |
| **Voorhees Jr** Theodore | Covington & Burling LLP * |
| **Wajert** Sean P | Shook, Hardy & Bacon LLP |
| **Walters** Neal | Ballard Spahr LLP (ONP) † * |
| **Wilkinson** Phoebe A | Chadbourne & Parke LLP (ONP) † * |
| **Williams** Steven R | McGuireWoods LLP |
| **Yelenick** Mary T | Chadbourne & Parke LLP (ONP) † * |

\* Indicates individual with profile.

† ONP = Other Notable Practitioner.

---

## Sidley Austin LLP
**See profile on p.1264**

**THE FIRM** This firm offers a high level of expertise in both trial and appellate work, and is particularly experienced in class action and pharmaceutical matters. It acts for Armour Pharmaceutical on allegations that blood derivatives used by hemophilia patients transmitted HIV and hepatitis C. Consumer fraud class action work is a growing area for the firm, which obtained a motion to dismiss for American Honda Motor in a case concerning the paint used on the manufacturer's automobiles. The group also has substantial experience in environmental, aviation and food product litigation.

**Sources say:** *"A terrific products department." "Their legal reasoning and research skills are superior."*

**KEY INDIVIDUALS** *"Marvelous courtroom lawyer"* **Debra Pole** (see p.386) is renowned for her effectiveness in a trial setting and her ability to present facts persuasively. *"She is a consistently good mass tort defense attorney,"* say sources. She is acting on the Fosamax class action litigation on behalf of Merck. Highly regarded **Sara Gourley** (see p.325) is a *"good strategic thinker"* and is particularly lauded for her work in the pharmaceutical sphere. Current highlights include representing Armour Pharmaceutical in blood derivatives litigation. **Eugene Schoon** (see p.402) also receives praise for his strategic skills, and is described as *"one of those guys who can do anything – write, argue a motion or appeal, take a deposition, and try a case."* He is currently handling a number of matters for Bayer, including the Yasmin and YAZ litigation. **Maja Eaton** (see p.308)

## Product Liability: Automobile
### Leading Individuals

| | |
|---|---|
| Campbell James M | Campbell Campbell Edwards & Conroy PC |
| Cereghini Paul G | Bowman and Brooke LLP * |
| Dwyer Susan | Herrick, Feinstein LLP (ONP)[†] |
| Norwood Jr Colvin G | McGlinchey Stafford PLLC * |
| Platt Warren | Snell & Wilmer LLP |
| Smith Colin P | Holland & Knight LLP * |
| Smith Joel H | Bowman and Brooke LLP * |
| Wheeler Malcolm | Wheeler Trigg O'Donnell LLP * |

## Product Liability: Pharmaceutical
### Leading Individuals

| | |
|---|---|
| Beck Philip | Bartlit Beck Herman Palenchar & Scott LLP |
| Cheffo Mark S | Skadden, Arps, Slate, Meagher & Flom * |
| Cohen Lori G | Greenberg Traurig, LLP * |
| Goodell Jr Charles P | Goodell, DeVries, Leech & Dann, LLP * |
| Gussack Nina M | Pepper Hamilton LLP * |
| Jones Christy D | Butler, Snow, O'Mara, Stevens & Cannada * |
| Kaplan Harvey | Shook, Hardy & Bacon LLP |
| Marvin Douglas R | Williams & Connolly LLP |
| Sullivan Diane P | Weil, Gotshal & Manges LLP (ONP)[†] * |

is praised as being *"very good with clients and thinking ahead to the big picture."* Clients appreciate her business acumen and deep understanding of the product liability arena. She currently acts for GE and Schering on a range of complex matters. **David Buente** (see p.855) is acclaimed as an expert on environmental law, earning praise as the *"best in class when it comes to environmental enforcement matters."* He has considerable experience in climate change litigation. **Michael Davis** (see p.302) is highly regarded for his product liability work, which encompasses pharmaceuticals, chemicals, consumer and food products. His recent highlights include representing Beiersdorf in consumer fraud class action litigation.

### Skadden, Arps, Slate, Meagher & Flom LLP & Affiliates
See profile on p.2008

**THE FIRM** This preeminent firm impresses interviewees with its capacity for strategic management, which enables it to handle large, complex matters. It maintains strong relationships with various leading organizations, including pharmaceutical, medical device and consumer goods companies. Major recent work includes acting as lead counsel for Lincoln Electric and other defendants on multiple mass tort proceedings relating to claims of injury caused by the inhalation of manganese while working with welding equipment. Other clients include Electrolux, Johnson & Johnson, Pfizer and Toyota.
**Sources say:** *"They are just remarkably responsive and have a deep bench of people."*
**KEY INDIVIDUALS** The *"outstanding"* **Sheila Birnbaum** (see p.283) co-heads the practice and is *"tremendous to have on any case; her judgment and sense of what is going on are phenomenal."* She continues to defend Pfizer in major litigation and has a distinguished track record for mass torts. Group co-head **John Beisner** (see p.281) is particu-

## Product Liability: Plaintiffs
### Senior Statesmen: distinguished older partners

| | |
|---|---|
| Motley Ronald L | Motley Rice LLC (ONP)[†] |

### Leading Individuals
#### Band 1

| | |
|---|---|
| Cabraser Elizabeth J | Lieff Cabraser Heimann & Bernstein (ONP)[†] |
| Lanier W Mark | The Lanier Law Firm PLLC (ONP)[†] |
| Seeger Christopher A | Seeger Weiss LLP (ONP)[†] |

#### Band 2

| | |
|---|---|
| Blizzard Edward F | Blizzard, McCarthy & Nabers (ONP)[†] |
| Girardi Thomas V | Girardi & Keese (ONP)[†] |
| Gordon Robert J | Weitz & Luxenberg, PC (ONP)[†] |
| Herman Russ M | Herman, Herman & Katz LLC (ONP)[†] |
| Weitz Perry | Weitz & Luxenberg, PC (ONP)[†] |

#### Band 3

| | |
|---|---|
| Birchfield Jr Andy | Beasley, Allen, Crow, Methvin (ONP)[†] |
| Ciresi Michael V | Robins, Kaplan, Miller & Ciresi LLP[†] * |
| Littlepage Zoe | Littlepage Booth (ONP)[†] |
| Robinson Mark | Robinson, Calcagnie & Robinson (ONP)[†] |
| Shkolnik Hunter J | Napoli Bern Ripka Shkolnik LLP (ONP)[†] |

## Product Liability: Tobacco
### Leading Individuals

| | |
|---|---|
| Grossman Theodore | Jones Day S |
| Parsigian Kenneth J | Latham & Watkins |
| Reilly Kenneth J | Shook, Hardy & Bacon LLP |

## Product Liability: Toxic Torts
### Leading Individuals

| | |
|---|---|
| Bicks Peter A | Orrick, Herrington & Sutcliffe LLP * |
| Buente David | Sidley Austin LLP * |
| Curtis Philip | Arnold & Porter LLP * |
| Denny Otway | Fulbright & Jaworski LLP * |

* Indicates firm / individual with profile.
[†] ONP = Other Notable Practitioner.

larly known for his successes on class action and multidistrict litigation, and was one of the lead attorneys on the Lincoln Electric matter. He has also advised Johnson & Johnson and various subsidiaries on a range of cases recently. Commentators agree that he is *"very strategic and always looks for a way to get good results."* The *"extremely talented"* **Mark Cheffo** (see p.294) wins praise for his strategic thinking and his *"deep understanding of the client."* He is representing Pfizer in multidistrict litigation relating to the antidepressant Zoloft. **Jessica Miller** (see p.369) offers extensive expertise in briefing and appellate work, and is particularly singled out for her writing skills. Her broad range of recent work includes acting as part of the team defending Electrolux in class actions regarding allegedly defective washing machines. She is described by one source as *"the master of the argument."* **Stephen Harburg** (see p.330) handles a range of consumer fraud and product liability class actions. He serves as national coordinating counsel for Lincoln Electric in the fumes inhalation matter. Sources reveal:*"This is a man who can manage every little detail across multiple cases with multiple

plaintiff lawyers, regardless of how many cases he has active at one time."*

### Williams & Connolly LLP
**THE FIRM** This firm is recognized for its strength in both settling and trying cases, with commentators particularly noting its strategic capabilities. It is also sought out for its wealth of experience in handling pharmaceutical matters. It acts as co-lead national counsel for Pfizer on the smoking cessation aid Chantix. In a notable development in this litigation, the multidistrict litigation court recently upheld the adequacy of the Chantix label. Other key clients of the firm include Bayer, Genentech and GE.
**Commercial Awareness** *"The breadth and variety of their experience has enabled them to cultivate a very impressive array of substantive expertise."*
**KEY INDIVIDUALS** **Douglas Marvin** is lauded as being *"great strategically, and someone who has the ability to coordinate well during mass litigation."* He leads the firm's defense of Bayer in the YAZ/Yasmin marketing and sales practices and product liability litigation. **Heidi Hubbard** draws praise as a *"terrific trial lawyer."* Particularly experienced in pharmaceuticals work, she is one of the lead lawyers in the firm's representation of Pfizer in the Chantix litigation. **Lane Heard** is a *"great, dynamic strategist who is great at oral argument."* Together with Heidi Hubbard, he led the firm's defense of Wyeth in federal multidistrict and state court litigation regarding the hormone therapy medicines Prempro and Premarin. **Stephen Raber** garners praise for his work as a *"very experienced courtroom trial lawyer."* He has been involved in several high-profile matters of late, including representing clients such as Genentech.

### Band 2

### Bowman and Brooke LLP
**THE FIRM** This team's ability to apply its excellent understanding of vehicle technology to the demands of litigation wins it mandates from various leading automotive companies, including Toyota, Ford and Nissan North America. It represents Toyota as lead product liability defense counsel in the unintended acceleration litigation. The practice spans a range of other sectors, with recent work including defending medical device manufacturer Breg in relation to pain relief pumps alleged to cause deterioration of joint cartilage.
**Sources say:** *"They are very good trial lawyers with lots of experience in individual cases."*
**KEY INDIVIDUALS** **Paul Cereghini** (see p.293) is an *"outstanding lawyer in every regard,"* according to sources. He offers particular expertise in automotive litigation, and is representing Honda in a putative national consumer class action relating to alleged window regulator defects. He also leads the firm's defense of Riddell in litigation concerning allegations of defective helmets. **Joel Smith** (see p.2272) also has notable experience in matters related to automotive litigation. Commentators praise his *"very strong communication skills,"* and have *"a lot of confidence

*in his courtroom abilities."* His recent highlights include representing Toyota in the unintended acceleration litigation.

## Covington & Burling LLP
See profile on p.441

**THE FIRM** This practice is highly regarded for its strengths in handling litigation and regulatory matters within the product liability arena. While the group focuses on pharmaceutical and medical device work, recent work highlights have included acting as lead trial counsel to BP in multidistrict litigation relating to the Deepwater Horizon explosion. The group also has a strong appellate division, recently reversing three jury verdicts against Hoffmann-La Roche in relation to the acne medication Accutane. Interviewees are particularly impressed by both the writing and the trial skills of the firm's lawyers.

**Commercial Awareness** *"They have a top-notch knowledge of my industry and business."*

**KEY INDIVIDUALS Mike Brock** (see p.287) is *"an excellent trial lawyer"* who is *"hugely experienced and knows what matters and what doesn't – he is strategic at a high level."* In addition to taking a lead role on the work for BP, he also handles litigation relating to the cancer medicine Avastin on behalf of Genentech. **Paul Schmidt** (see p.401) represented Hoffmann-La Roche at trial and appellate level in the Accutane disputes. *"He's been extremely helpful and informative. He's kept me in the loop on everything and has been excellent when prepping witnesses for discovery,"* enthuses a client. **Patrick Davies** (see p.301) is *"an excellent strategist"* and is *"as personable a lawyer as you'll ever meet."* He is particularly experienced at handling pharmaceutical product liability and mass tort cases. He is currently defending Chiquita in the USA against thousands of claims made by foreign nationals under the Alien Tort Statute. **Theodore Voorhees** (see p.421) is highly regarded for his product liability practice. He also handles antitrust and consumer protection matters. He has worked with clients across a wide range of industries.

## Dechert LLP
See profile on p.1969

**THE FIRM** Dechert continues to attract an impressive range of work from distinguished clients. It is highly experienced in litigation at trial and appellate level, and handles matters for companies from a broad spread of industries. Recent highlights include representing Union Carbide in various ongoing matters and acting for Pfizer on hormone therapy litigation. Other clients include Philip Morris, Google and Golden Living.

**Sources say:** *"The quality of analysis, creativity of thought, depth of research and quality of briefing are exceptional."*

**KEY INDIVIDUALS Ezra Rosenberg's** (see p.1746) well-respected practice focuses on pharmaceutical and tobacco product liability cases. Recent work includes acting for Pfizer on the hormone therapy litigation. He offers expertise in litigating cases at both trial and appellate level. **Robert Heim** (see p.2219) is *"extraordinarily well thought of"* by market commentators, and is noted for his extensive trial experience. Work highlights include representing

Pfizer in the hormone therapy litigation, and in the multidistrict Zoloft litigation.

## Jones Day
See profile on p.919

**THE FIRM** This firm wins accolades for its dedication, depth of expertise and broad-based approach. Traditionally recognized for its excellent tobacco practice, this group handles a diverse range of products work, including automotive and consumer products matters. Recent highlights include serving as national counsel for The Sherwin-Williams Company on various lawsuits concerning lead paints and pigments, and defending Pilatus Aircraft in four aircraft accident cases. Other clients include Abbott Laboratories, ExxonMobil and Yamaha.

**Sources say:** *"I can't say enough good about them. They are a phenomenal firm."*

**KEY INDIVIDUALS Paul Pohl** (see p.385) heads Jones Day's US business and tort litigation practice. He is praised as being a *"good leader with excellent judgment."* Prominent work includes acting for The Sherwin-Williams Company on the lead paint and pigment lawsuits. **Theodore Grossman** (see p.2098) is singled out as *"one of the principal strategic thinkers in tobacco litigation as it's morphed over the years."* His tobacco work forms a key part of his broad commercial and tort litigation portfolio.

## King & Spalding LLP
See profile on p.445

**THE FIRM** The practice is singled out for its expertise in regulatory and litigation matters, and houses an impressive bench of trial lawyers. It has particular experience in pharmaceutical, tobacco and automotive matters. Recent headline matters include defending GlaxoSmithKline against allegations that its antidepressant Paxil caused birth defects. It also represented Halliburton in toxic tort cases stemming from groundwater contamination.

**Client Service** *"They are terrific – first-rate lawyers closely aligned with my company's objectives who are dedicated, responsive and able to work with a lot of moving pieces and to see the big picture. I would recommend them without hesitation."*

**KEY INDIVIDUALS Chilton Davis Varner** (see p.302) is *"one of the finest trial lawyers in the country,"* and has a *"brilliant court presence."* Her *"smart and practical"* approach sees her held in high regard by peers and clients alike. Her impressive experience includes acting as lead trial and appellate counsel for leading pharmaceutical and medical device companies. Department head **Andrew Bayman** (see p.280) is highly regarded by commentators, and *"moves heaven and earth to accommodate clients' needs and requests."* He took the lead in the Paxil litigation. **Randall Bassett** (see p.280) is praised for his ability to *"understand the law and engage in complex reasoning."* Highlights include taking a lead role on the firm's representation of R.J. Reynolds in multiple Engle Progeny cases. In addition to tobacco companies, he also represents automotive and pharmaceutical manufacturers. **Richard Schneider** (see p.1096) is renowned for his automotive and tobacco work. He was on the team that secured two

victories at appellate level for R.J. Reynolds in the Engle Progeny litigation. He also has substantial experience in trial work.

## Kirkland & Ellis LLP
See profile on p.1254

**THE FIRM** Market commentators applaud this firm's litigation capabilities and deep bench of experienced trial lawyers. Toxic torts, pharmaceutical, tobacco and aviation work are some of the areas in which the group has particular expertise. It serves as nationwide counsel for Abbott in litigation concerning allegations that the company failed to warn about severe side effects from its drug Humira. Other key clients include BP America, Teva Pharmaceuticals and Boeing.

**Sources say:** *"They deliver not only thoughtful but also practical advice. They are at the top of my list in terms of go-to firms."*

**KEY INDIVIDUALS Andrew McGaan** (see p.365) garners praise for his advocacy skills, with one source commenting that he is *"good on his feet and a good person to work with."* He is particularly known for his tobacco work. He acts for R.J. Reynolds on the recovery of contested reductions in its yearly payments under the Tobacco Litigation Master Settlement Agreement. **Leslie Smith** (see p.409) is another talented litigator highly regarded in the pharmaceuticals sector. *"She absolutely spoils me in terms of how accommodating and easy to work with she is. She is very good at understanding our strategic goals and working towards achieving them,"* reports a client.

## Pepper Hamilton LLP
See profile on p.2248

**THE FIRM** This team is primarily sought for its expertise in medical device and pharmaceutical product litigation. It recently represented longstanding client GlaxoSmithKline in litigation concerning claims that its diabetes medication Avandia causes heart attacks and other complications. Demonstrating the practice's capacity to handle highly complex cases, the matter entailed a raft of claims across a wide range of fora and included federal multidistrict litigation and consumer fraud actions. The firm continues to act for other leading clients including Eli Lilly, Merck and Medtronic on major matters.

**Client Service** *"They are quick to put together the right team and right approach. They know my company very well and have been a tremendous partner."*

**Commercial Awareness** *"They really made a Herculean effort to get their arms around the issues and translate them in the best way, managing the work in a manner that reflected the demands of the industry and the client's needs."*

**KEY INDIVIDUALS** *"First-rate"* **Nina Gussack** (see p.328) earns extensive praise as a *"good strategist"* who *"works nonstop"* for her clients. She took the lead on the Avandia matter for GlaxoSmithKline and continues to handle major work for Eli Lilly. **Sean Fahey** (see p.311) is highly commended for his strategic and analytical skills and is described as *"great to work with."* He focuses on pharmaceuticals and medical devices, and recently co-led various matters for Medtronic.

### Wheeler Trigg O'Donnell LLP
See profile on p.730

**THE FIRM** This relatively compact firm punches well above its weight, housing an acclaimed products practice that excels both at the strategic planning stage and in the courtroom. It is hailed as a major player in pharmaceutical and automobile matters. It has recently been engaged on work for Ford, Advanced Bionics and GE. It is also acting as Pfizer's national trial counsel in litigation relating to Zoloft, Neurontin and hormone replacement therapy medication.

**Sources say:** *"They are brilliant strategists and very good at helping me select experts. The work product is also excellent."*

**KEY INDIVIDUALS John Fitzpatrick** (see p.718) is an *"outstanding, charismatic trial lawyer"* whose *"ability to connect with the jury is phenomenal."* He has a reputation for trying complicated cases in challenging jurisdictions. He currently acts for GE on claims that its gadolinium-based contrast agent Omniscan causes a serious disease known as nephrogenic systemic fibrosis. **James Hooper** (see p.336) has a well-regarded practice that focuses on disputes involving pharmaceuticals, medical devices, building materials and a range of other products. He leads Wheeler Trigg O'Donnell's defense of Pfizer in the Zoloft, Neurontin and HRT litigation. **Malcolm Wheeler** (see p.425) has a *"stellar reputation"* as a trial lawyer and is a *"thought leader"* in this space. Clients applaud his *"in-depth knowledge of how the product functions and ability to organize and present a complex technical case so that it can be understood by a lay jury."* He has substantial experience representing automobile companies including Ford and Nissan, and works alongside Hooper on the Pfizer litigation. **John Trigg** (see p.419) is known for his *"excellent trial skills"* and offers extensive expertise in defending major organizations as national trial counsel in product liability and class action litigation.

## Band 3

### Arnold & Porter LLP
See profile on p.906

**THE FIRM** This firm has experience across a broad spectrum of matters, including those related to pharmaceuticals and medical devices, consumer products and tobacco. Recent work includes representing Philip Morris in both the Engle Progeny litigation and the 'light cigarettes' class action litigation alleging breaches of consumer protection law and misleading marketing. Toxic torts is another forte, and the group represents Honeywell in a number of such matters, including a class action litigation in which a community in Florida claims to have been exposed to trichloroethylene.

**Sources say:** *"They've done a terrific job of organizing and strategizing with us to come up with the best possible approach."*

**KEY INDIVIDUALS Philip Curtis** (see p.300) is an experienced and respected figure in the product liability and mass torts field. He plays a central role in the team's work for Philip Morris, and also in defending BP in various tort

and public nuisance cases involving claims of injury caused by the company's emissions. Practice co-head **Anand Agneshwar** (see p.272) not only takes a long-term strategic view for his clients but also *"cares about and thinks about your cases as much as you do,"* according to sources. He currently handles major litigation on behalf of Bristol-Myers Squibb and Sanofi-Aventis. **Eric Rubel** (see p.396) is the fellow cochair of the practice. He has substantial experience in consumer product safety and related litigation, and is currently representing several clients in civil penalty investigations conducted by the US Consumer Product Safety Commission into alleged violations of the Consumer Product Safety Act. **Peter Grossi** (see p.327) is acclaimed as an *"intellectual deep thinker"* and an excellent strategist. Recent highlights include his continuing role in the representation of Philip Morris in the Engle Progeny litigation.

### Butler, Snow, O'Mara, Stevens & Cannada, PLLC
See profile on p.1613

**THE FIRM** This group offers an impressive nationwide products practice, with a particular emphasis on pharmaceuticals and medical devices. The firm serves as national multidistrict litigation counsel for Johnson & Johnson/Ethicon in litigation concerning allegations that the use of pelvic mesh led to severe complications in patients. Animal health products are another burgeoning area for the firm, with Merial among clients recently attracted by this expertise.

**Client Service** *"Their customer relations are very good. They're timely in responding and always on top of things without me having to ask."*

**Commercial Awareness** *"They have a great depth of experience in multiple courts and are very, very good communicators. They know the industry and business very well."*

**KEY INDIVIDUALS Christy Jones** (see p.341) is acclaimed as *"a phenomenon"* who offers extensive nationwide trial experience, and she is able to *"do a great job in a difficult situation."* One interviewee enthuses: *"She has enormous confidence in the courtroom."* Highlights include taking the lead in defending Johnson & Johnson in the pelvic mesh litigation and in trials relating to Children's MOTRIN, and representing Merck in the Fosamax medication litigation.

### Campbell Campbell Edwards & Conroy PC
See profile on p.1516

**THE FIRM** This boutique trial and appellate firm offers clients a broad product liability practice that encompasses automotive, aviation, pharmaceuticals and asbestos matters. Its particularly renowned automotive product liability team recently represented Honda North America in litigation concerning hybrid fuel economy. Other key clients include Caterpillar and GE.

**Sources say:** *"They have done an excellent job."*

**KEY INDIVIDUALS** Department head **James Campbell** stands out for his *"tenacity and extremely strong trial skills."* He has recently dedicated his extensive product liability experience to a number of major automobile cases, includ-

ing the Honda hybrid fuel matter. **William Conroy** is praised as a *"really excellent trial lawyer"* who has handled numerous challenging cases. He offers particular expertise in automobile litigation matters, and recently represented Ford in a significant case.

### DLA Piper LLP (US)
See profile on p.1971

**THE FIRM** This firm is singled out for its strategic approach, and is typically called upon to work on high-stakes cases. It has considerable expertise in pharmaceuticals, food, automotive and consumer product cases. Recent work highlights include representing Pfizer as co-lead national counsel regarding the smoking cessation aid Chantix and in the hormone therapy litigation, in which it drew on its considerable trial and appellate resources. Other leading clients include Harley-Davidson, Bayer and Lorillard Tobacco.

**Sources say:** *"They're always responsive and on top of the work, fighting hard."*

**KEY INDIVIDUALS Loren Brown** (see p.288) cochairs the practice and focuses on the pharmaceutical and mass tort areas. He is particularly lauded for his deep technical expertise in this field. Commentators also describe him as *"an expert trial lawyer and as strong as they get for overall strategy."* He is a central figure in the work for Pfizer.

### Fulbright & Jaworski LLP
See profile on p.2435

**THE FIRM** Fulbright & Jaworski offers a broad product liability practice spanning diverse industries, from pharmaceutical and medical device to automotive and aerospace. It offers notable experience in representing clients in a range of disputes, including multidistrict litigation and class action lawsuits. It also helps clients tackle the risk of litigation by providing preventive advice.

**Sources say:** *"They have the legal knowledge and know how to apply it, and they also have the resources and staff to handle matters when they end up in the courtroom. From a strategy perspective, they are very smart at looking at all the chess pieces and coming up with a masterplan."*

**KEY INDIVIDUALS Otway Denny** (see p.2387) is a *"real trial lawyer"* with an *"excellent reputation."* As chair of the firm's global litigation practice, he has substantial experience defending companies in cases concerning chemicals, automobiles and construction equipment. **Jonathan Skidmore** (see p.407) is reputed to be an impressive trial lawyer. He focuses on pharmaceutical and medical device product liability, and has substantial experience in mass torts. **Jan Dodd** (see p.305) has an acclaimed products practice that focuses on pharmaceutical products and medical devices. She is an experienced trial lawyer with an excellent track record in state and federal courts. **Terry Tottenham** (see p.418) chairs the firm's pharmaceutical and medical device litigation practice and has longstanding experience in the field. He is renowned as an *"excellent strategist,"* and defends major companies in the electronic, pharmaceutical and technology industries.

## Goldman Ismail Tomaselli Brennan & Baum LLP

**THE FIRM** This Chicago-based trial and litigation boutique moves up the rankings following consistent praise from peers and clients alike. Observers highlight the firm's deep bench of outstanding trial lawyers and detailed approach to cases. The attorneys also impress with their thorough knowledge of clients' businesses. Demonstrating its expertise in pharmaceutical and medical device litigation, the firm acts as trial counsel for Merck on the Fosamax litigation. It also recently obtained a settlement on behalf of Pfizer in a consolidated trial in which three plaintiffs alleged that their use of hormone replacement therapy drugs caused them to develop breast cancer.

**Sources say:** "They're exceptionally responsive and very good at putting a case together and arguing it. I'm just a big fan of these people."

**KEY INDIVIDUALS** Department head **Tarek Ismail**'s "talents and trial skills set him apart." Commentators recommend him for his track record in winning highly challenging cases. In addition to his work on the Fosamax litigation and the hormone therapy litigation, he serves as lead trial counsel for Bayer on litigation concerning Magnevist, its MRI contrast agent. **Joe Tomaselli** wins praise for his extensive expertise in pharmaceutical matters and ability to "explain technical issues to clients and juries." Highlights include defending Medtronic in litigation concerning claims that plaintiffs were injured by defective defibrillation leads in implantable cardiac defibrillators.

## Hogan Lovells US LLP

**THE FIRM** This well-reputed group advises clients on claims across industries including pharmaceutical, automobile, aviation and food. As well as maintaining its excellent reputation for aviation work in continuing to represent Airbus in major regional and international litigation matters, it recently defended ConAgra Foods in consumer class actions concerning allegedly misleading food labeling and advertising.

**Sources say:** "We've been very pleased with their services. They are very responsive and proactive and partner closely with us."

**KEY INDIVIDUALS** Aviation expert **Thad Dameris** is praised for his "good substantive knowledge" in this space. He is the lead partner on matters for Airbus, and also acts for Costa Crociere and Carnival Corporation on all US-based litigation relating to the grounding of the 'Costa Concordia' off Giglio Island, Italy.

## Hughes Hubbard & Reed LLP
See profile on p.1981

**THE FIRM** This broad practice has a particular focus on pharmaceuticals and tobacco product liability work, and also has considerable experience in toxic torts. Recent notable developments include being selected by Lorillard for the role of national coordinating counsel in the Engle Progeny and Kent Filter litigation. Other clients include Pfizer and the American Bureau of Shipping.

**Sources say:** "They are excellent across the board. They view our cases in a very strategic way. There are attorneys there with an incredible grasp of scientific issues."

**KEY INDIVIDUALS Theodore Mayer** (see p.363) is renowned for "setting the strategic tone of the firm and taking a broad view of matters." Recent highlights include working on the Engle Progeny litigation for Lorillard, and representing Bureau Veritas Consumer Products Services in a recent lawsuit. **Charles Cohen** (see p.296) attracts praise for his expertise in discovery issues. He has a broad-based product liability practice, and is an experienced litigator. **James Fitzpatrick** (see p.313) is a pharmaceuticals expert who wins accolades for his scientific knowledge and excellent communication skills with clients. He and Cohen both worked alongside Mayer on the Engle Progeny litigation. **Norman Kleinberg** concentrates on product liability, insurance coverage and complex civil litigation in his respected practice.

## Nelson Mullins Riley & Scarborough LLP
See profile on p.2276

**THE FIRM** This practice offers a diverse range of expertise, having worked on cases concerning products ranging from pharmaceuticals and medical devices to automobiles and asbestos. It is particularly well positioned to advise clients based on the East Coast. Clients are pleased that the firm offers not only excellent litigation support but also regulatory advice and business counseling.

**Sources say:** "They are very thorough and efficient, putting the right people in the right places when staffing cases and getting the best results for their clients."

**KEY INDIVIDUALS David Dukes** (see p.2268) is a "very talented trial lawyer who is very skilled in his examinations." His charismatic approach and ability to try cases in challenging jurisdictions also win him praise. He is highly experienced in medical device and pharmaceutical matters. **Stephen Morrison** (see p.2271) also wins accolades for his trial skills: "He's very wise, methodical and thorough – juries love him." His considerable experience includes representing clients in the technology, chemical and automotive industries.

## Orrick, Herrington & Sutcliffe LLP
See profile on p.1994

**THE FIRM** Orrick is singled out as a go-to firm for toxic torts. The group has particular expertise in the chemical, manufacturing, pharmaceutical and medical device industries. It continues to defend longstanding client Dow Chemical in major litigation, including recently in a mass tort case concerning float-sink testing. The firm also has an impressive international dimension and is able to draw on its offices in Asia to serve the clients it has recently attracted from the region.

**Sources say:** "They do phenomenal work. They are very efficient and get the results for their clients."

**KEY INDIVIDUALS Peter Bicks** (see p.283) is a renowned trial lawyer praised for his strategic skills. He is described as "very good at working out how best to communicate technically difficult points to judges and doing it persuasively." He handles various major matters for Dow Chemical, including the float-sink matter. **James Stengel** (see p.412) works alongside Bicks on the float-sink testing matter for Dow Chemical. He also serves as national coordinating counsel for Union Carbide in asbestos personal injury litigation. He is praised as being "great on strategy, and excellent at managing large cases."

## Reed Smith LLP

**THE FIRM** This firm is applauded for its broad product liability practice. It represents clients in a number of sectors, including pharmaceuticals and medical devices, aviation and automotive. Current work includes acting as strategic counsel for C.R. Bard in litigation relating to its Avaulta surgical mesh products. The group also has considerable expertise in toxic torts, recently defending a key client in asbestos and silica litigation.

**Sources say:** "They are really exceptional advocates for the legal theories relevant to product liability."

**KEY INDIVIDUALS Michael Brown** is a "great trial lawyer" who "has great depth of experience in medical device litigation and knows the ins and outs of practicing in tough jurisdictions." He also stands out for his knowledge of federal preemption law and his understanding of clients' products. Current work includes representing C.R. Bard in the Avaulta litigation. **Michael Scott** is praised for his detailed approach and sound judgment. Pharmaceutical products are at the heart of his litigation practice, and he continues to represent GlaxoSmithKline in litigation concerning alleged injuries caused by the drug thalidomide. **Colleen Davies** also wins accolades for her work in pharmaceutical litigation. She currently represents American Medical Systems in litigation concerning surgical mesh products that plaintiffs allege are defectively designed and carry inadequate warnings. **John Hooper** is praised for his "big strategy approach" to cases, and has experience in handling trials, mediations and settlements. Recent highlights from his broad practice include working alongside Brown in the Avaulta litigation.

## Winston & Strawn LLP
See profile on p.1267

**THE FIRM** This practice is sought after for its excellent track record defending leading pharmaceutical, tobacco and automotive companies. The team acts as lead counsel for Philip Morris in the NPM adjustment arbitration, which concerns a reduction in annual payments owed by tobacco companies to 46 states for the recovery of tobacco-related healthcare costs. On the pharmaceutical and medical devices side, the team acts for Abbott Laboratories on a class action alleging illegal marketing of enteral feeding products.

**Sources say:** "They're very responsive. They research everything thoroughly and exercise judgment well so that they know what to hold back on and when to move forward."

**KEY INDIVIDUALS** "First-rate" **Dan Webb** (see p.1236) is a "very talented trial lawyer with decades of experience and a tremendous amount of energy." He is highly renowned for handling difficult, complex cases, and also offers extensive experience in handling commercial and white-collar criminal cases. Department head **Thomas Frederick** (see p.316) is highly recommended for his product liability practice, and has particular expertise in tobacco litigation. He takes the lead in the NPM adjustment arbitration for Philip Morris.

## Band 4

### Baker Botts LLP
See profile on p.2427

**THE FIRM** Baker Botts focuses on product liability cases in the pharmaceutical, chemical and energy sectors. It represents Elan Pharmaceuticals as national counsel in litigation concerning the multiple sclerosis drug Tysabri. Toxic tort work is another staple of the practice, which is currently acting for a major petroleum company on lawsuits alleging property damage and personal injuries from a release of gasoline. Other clients include Merck, BASF and Union Carbide.
**Sources say:** *"They provide an excellent service in all of the work they do for us."*
**KEY INDIVIDUALS Stephen Scheve** (see p.401) is cochair of the firm's pharmaceutical litigation practice, and maintains an impressive reputation in the area. He takes a lead role in the Tysabri litigation for Elan Pharmaceuticals.

### Faegre Baker Daniels

**THE FIRM** Faegre Baker Daniels undertakes product liability work on behalf of clients in a wide range of industries. It has a particularly strong presence in the Midwest, and is singled out for its expertise in the agricultural sector and its efforts to understand the business objectives of clients. Recent work highlights include acting as lead trial counsel to Novartis in litigation concerning the prescription medications Aredia and Zometa, which are alleged to cause osteonecrosis of the jaw. Other clients include Syngenta Crop Protection, Dole Foods and Cargill.
**KEY INDIVIDUALS Joseph Price** is a massively experienced attorney in this space, with a practice that focuses on mass tort and class action products liability defense. He takes a lead role in the Novartis litigation.

### Greenberg Traurig, LLP
See profile on p.1024

**THE FIRM** Clients are impressed by this team's broad expertise and its sector-specific knowledge and experience, particularly in the pharmaceutical field. Recent work includes acting for Medtronic in multiple product liability suits at both federal and state level. Tobacco is another area of expertise; the firm currently represents Lorillard in the NPM adjustment arbitration.
**Sources say:** *"They are a 24/7 operation in terms of responsiveness, and provide excellent results for us."*
**KEY INDIVIDUALS Lori Cohen** (see p.1078) heads the pharmaceutical, medical device and healthcare practice. She is classed as a *"bright, phenomenal trial lawyer who really understands the issues."* She provides national counsel to Medtronic on various key product liability matters. Recent arrival **Ginger Pigott** (see p.384) has a respected

practice focused on pharmaceutical and medical device product liability litigation. She works alongside Cohen on various matters for Medtronic and other key clients.

### Holland & Knight LLP
See profile on p.1028

**THE FIRM** Transport is the key forte of this practice, with key clients from the sector including Bridgestone, Continental Tire and Enterprise Leasing Company of Florida. The practice drew on its considerable toxic tort expertise in litigation on behalf of Chr. Hansen concerning exposure to diacetyl, a constituent of butter flavoring in popcorn, which plaintiffs allege caused them lung injuries.
**Client Service** *"They are very proactive in partnering with the client."*
**KEY INDIVIDUALS Colin Smith** (see p.408) is *"completely dedicated and focused, and knows the product and design better than the engineers. He's the guy I would want to be in the trenches for me."* Recent highlights include his continuing defense of Bridgestone in several significant cases.

### Mayer Brown LLP
See profile on p.1257

**THE FIRM** This firm houses an accomplished product liability practice that covers a broad spread of industries. Further demonstrating the breadth of its expertise, the team is representing NXP Semiconductors and Philips in toxic tort actions concerning claims that semiconductor manufacturing workers were exposed to chemicals and substances that resulted in birth defects. The group receives particular accolades for its strategic approach and appellate work.
**Commercial Awareness** *"They're the kind of firm you can throw into very complicated matters, and they pick up and understand the issues. They quickly understand what needs to be done."*
**KEY INDIVIDUALS Herbert Zarov** is lauded as an *"appellate guru"* who is *"great at brief writing and strategy."* Recent highlights include defending Dow Chemical against allegations that the company's greenhouse gas emissions indirectly increased the damage that Hurricane Katrina caused to the Mississippi-based plaintiffs' property. **Daniel Ring** is described as an *"exceptional strategist who understands the big picture and is able to manage a large team in complex litigation."* He focuses his practice on product liability, mass and toxic tort claims, as well as complex commercial disputes.

### McGuireWoods LLP
See profile on p.2519

**THE FIRM** This group has a wealth of experience in mass torts and in product liability litigation concerning food, asbestos, automobiles and various consumer products. Recent standout matters include defending Invensys against claims that defects in its products contributed to fires and explosions that resulted in death and personal injury. The team also continues to defend Ford in various high-stakes matters.
**Sources say:** *"They are very highly regarded, and had a very business-focused approach to the advice they gave us."*

**KEY INDIVIDUALS Steven Williams** has significant experience in toxic tort and environmental litigation. He acts as national coordinating counsel and trial counsel to a variety of clients. Recent highlights include defending DuPont in lead paint litigation.

### Morgan, Lewis & Bockius LLP
See profile on p.2246

**THE FIRM** This group has substantial experience handling environmental mass torts and asbestos, pharmaceutical and medical device product liability cases on a nationwide level. Its recent work includes defending Medtronic in a variety of product liability and personal injury lawsuits. Other prominent clients include Tyco International, Philips and Zimmer.
**KEY INDIVIDUALS John Lavelle** (see p.2222) is highlighted as a *"very good strategist and brief writer,"* and is known for his medical device work. Recent successes include acting for Medtronic on obtaining the dismissal of a series of lawsuits based on federal preemption.

### Morrison & Foerster LLP
See profile on p.1990

**THE FIRM** This firm maintains a solid presence in the market, offering experience in a range of matters including toxic torts and pharmaceutical product liability. The trial team receives particular praise from market commentators. Recent work highlights include defending APP Pharmaceuticals in multidistrict litigation and in state consolidated cases concerning the generic form of a cancer treatment. Other clients include Bayer, Lucasfilm and MD Helicopters.
**Sources say:** *"I'm always pleased with what they do for us. They work efficiently and have some very good talent and depth."*
**KEY INDIVIDUALS Erin Bosman** leads the practice from the firm's San Diego office.

### O'Melveny & Myers LLP
See profile on p.693

**THE FIRM** This group's broad industry knowledge covers a range of areas, including aviation, medical devices and consumer goods. According to sources, the firm stands out for its consistent quality at all stages of litigation, from initial research to making closing arguments at trial. Recent highlights include acting for Amylin in personal injury cases concerning the diabetes drug Byetta. Other clients include Johnson & Johnson, ExxonMobil and Ford.
**Sources say:** *"They are a very strategic partner and their communication is excellent. I can't say enough positive things about how they've managed the process."*
**KEY INDIVIDUALS Brian Anderson** (see p.273) is an *"extremely talented class action lawyer"* who handles product liability cases at both trial and appellate level. Recent work includes representing Ford in class actions concerning allegations of defective engines. He has also defended leading companies in the food and pharmaceutical sectors.

## Perkins Coie LLP

See profile on p.2548

THE FIRM This firm receives accolades for its highly experienced aviation practice, and defends Boeing in litigation stemming from the fatal crash of a Mandala Airlines 737 aircraft. The team also defends clients from a range of other industries, including automotive and food and beverage companies. It counts Honeywell, Intel and Nintendo among its clients.

KEY INDIVIDUALS John Dillow comes highly recommended for his expertise in the aviation sector and his diligent approach to litigation. Recent work includes taking the lead on the Boeing 737 matter.

## Tucker Ellis

THE FIRM This firm has a distinguished track record in handling pharmaceutical and medical device product liability litigation and mass torts. Notable recent successes include its defense of PharmaJet in litigation concerning the use of a jet injector to administer flu shots. The team also continues to handle a substantial workload of asbestos litigation on behalf of Rockwell Automation, McCord and Carrier Corporation, acting in national coordinating counsel roles for all three.

Sources say: "They have very good depth across the board and are able to get in there and strategize."

KEY INDIVIDUALS Robert Tucker is recognized as "terrific in court" and is credited with playing significant roles in hip implant and drug litigation. Current highlights include serving as national co-lead and liaison counsel for the Johnson & Johnson subsidiary DePuy Orthopaedics in litigation arising from its recall of metal-on-metal hip implants. Charles Socha has extensive experience acting as a litigator in a range of product liability matters, and worked alongside Tucker on the DePuy Orthopaedics matters.

## Venable LLP

See profile on p.927

THE FIRM This practice enjoys an excellent reputation in the product liability sphere, especially for its expertise in pharmaceuticals cases. The team also wins accolades for its responsiveness and fast turnaround. It acts as national counsel for Merck on its Fosamax litigation and as primary counsel for the company in litigation concerning vaccine products. Other major clients include Abbott Laboratories, Boehringer Ingelheim Pharmaceuticals and Johnson & Johnson.

Sources say: "A team of very talented lawyers. I wholeheartedly endorse them."

KEY INDIVIDUALS Bruce Parker (see p.382) has a "great reputation as a trial lawyer in the product liability field." Current work includes representing Boehringer Ingelheim Pharmaceuticals as national counsel in litigation concerning allegations that the Parkinson's disease drug Mirapex causes impulse control disorders. Paul Strain (see p.1433) is an "excellent strategist who tries cases well." He currently brings his substantial experience in pharmaceutical and medical device product litigation to the representation of Takeda Pharmaceuticals in allegations that users of its diabetes medication Actos developed bladder cancer. "Excellent courtroom lawyer" Steve Marshall (see p.362) earns praise for his technical competence on pharmaceutical and medical device cases and his impressive trial experience. He works alongside Strain in the Fosamax and vaccine product cases.

## Watkins & Eager PLLC

See profile on p.1617

THE FIRM Commentators highlight this firm's impressive trial team, communication skills and responsiveness as being particular strengths. Its broad expertise spans pharmaceutical, automotive, tobacco and manufacturing products. Current highlights include representing Bayer CropScience in litigation alleging the presence of genetically engineered rice in the commercial rice supply. It also continues to defend various clients, including Lincoln Electric and Union Carbide, in welding fumes litigation.

Client Service "They are very professional, very accessible and extremely responsive. They are also easy and practical to work with."

KEY INDIVIDUALS Will Goodman (see p.324) is recognized as a "truly excellent trial attorney" who is "very practical and can really connect with jurors." He continues to represent Bayer HealthCare in litigation concerning the drugs Baycol, Trasylol, Levitra and Yasmin/YAZ.

## Other Notable Practitioners

Andy Birchfield of Beasley, Allen, Crow, Methvin, Portis & Miles, PC is praised as someone who "is not only a strategist – he gets in the trenches and will actually try the cases as well," according to sources. He is experienced in acting for plaintiffs on a range of matters. Edward Blizzard of Blizzard, McCarthy & Nabers "has learned more about the business of pharmaceuticals and medical devices than many others; he has great mastery of the facts." He has worked on several major matters in the pharmaceutical and medical device arena in his plaintiff-side practice. Theodore Boutrous (see p.624) of Gibson, Dunn & Crutcher LLP is a "phenomenal lawyer who is outstanding on his feet and in oral arguments." His appellate practice is particularly highly regarded. Within product liability, he has a distinguished reputation for automobile work, recently representing Toyota in the unintended acceleration litigation. His other highlights include defending Chevron in litigation concerning allegations of environmental damage in the Amazon. Plaintiff lawyer Elizabeth Cabraser of Lieff Cabraser Heimann & Bernstein, LLP is widely praised as a "fierce advocate for her clients" and a "true legal mind." She has handled cutting-edge litigation and maintains an active caseload in this area. Thomas Campion (see p.1732) of Drinker Biddle & Reath LLP is renowned for his experience in pharmaceuticals litigation, having defended various major companies as national coordinating counsel. Michael Ciresi (see p.1578) of Robins, Kaplan, Miller & Ciresi LLP has a "well-earned reputation" as a talented plaintiffs' lawyer who is "very good in front of a jury." His product liability work forms part of a broad litigation practice. He has recently undertaken work on a number of pharmaceutical and tobacco claims. Automobile litigation expert Vaughn Crawford is based at Snell & Wilmer LLP. He is praised as a "top-of-the-line defense trial lawyer" and stands out for his strong advocacy skills. He also has substantial experience in pharmaceutical and medical device litigation. Susan Dwyer of Herrick, Feinstein LLP brings to bear extensive experience in automobile product liability issues. "She knows the ins and outs of product liability issues both on the legal side and on the business side," a source comments. Recent highlights include the successful defense of Bridgestone in class actions concerning an innovative tire design. Thomas Girardi of Girardi & Keese is highly recommended as a "high-profile plaintiff lawyer" who offers significant experience in the product liability space. Charles Goodell (see p.323) of Goodell, DeVries, Leech & Dann, LLP counts Bayer and AstraZeneca among his clients, and is highly experienced in the pharmaceutical and medical device space. "He is extremely knowledgeable about his cases and always well prepared – juries and judges trust him," report peers. Robert Gordon of Weitz & Luxenberg, PC is praised as a "good trial counsel" and as being "very good on his feet." He has extensive experience in representing plaintiffs in a wide range of matters. Russ Herman of Herman, Herman & Katz LLC is "an excellent trial lawyer and excellent manager of litigation for the plaintiff Bar." He is renowned for his expertise in pharmaceutical disputes, and matters relating to tobacco and automotive claims.

David Ichel (see p.1905) of Simpson Thacher & Bartlett LLP is "very smart and encyclopedic in his knowledge of the law." He is particularly renowned for his work acting for leading alcoholic beverage companies and organizations. Demonstrating the breadth of his practice, recent work highlights include successfully defending Ducati in a nationwide consumer class action concerning allegedly defective thermoplastic fuel tanks. James Irwin of Irwin Fritchie Urquhart & Moore is a "very good trial lawyer" who offers extensive experience in pharmaceutical litigation. Commentators report that he is "depended on by clients to handle really tough problems." Peers describe Mark Lanier of The Lanier Law Firm PLLC as "very engaging" and a "talented jury trial lawyer" who "makes extraordinarily cogent and clear arguments." He has handled a range of pharmaceutical, asbestos and other toxic product cases. Plaintiff lawyer Zoe Littlepage of Littlepage Booth is "a tenacious trial lawyer" when pursuing clients' cases. Peers highlight her experience in pharmaceutical trials, and single out her skillful handling of hormone therapy litigation as a key example of her expertise. Wendy Lumish (see p.998) of Carlton Fields, P.A. is a "brilliant appellate lawyer" with a broad product liability practice encompassing automobiles, chemicals and pharmaceutical products, among others. Ronald Motley of Motley Rice LLC is a highly respected authority in the plaintiff-side product liability litigation arena. Sources confirm that he remains a notable figure in the field, stating that "there's no denying his talent." Peter Newton (see p.376) of Neal, Gerber & Eisenberg LLP receives accolades for his technical knowledge concerning product liability and tort claims following fires and explosions. He recently defended Engineered

Controls against a claim that a propane explosion in which the plaintiff was severely and permanently injured resulted from a defective propane system. **Colvin Norwood** (see p.377) of McGlinchey Stafford PLLC is sought by major automobile clients because he is *"completely at ease with the technical sides of cases and with concepts that other lawyers take a while to get comfortable with."* He has recently handled work for Bell Helicopter, BMW and Caterpillar, among other big names. **Kenneth Parsigian** of Latham & Watkins is a leading product liability and class action lawyer for tobacco claims. Peers describe him as a *"top trial lawyer"* and have *"a lot of confidence in his judgment."* He currently represents Altria and long-term client Philip Morris in various matters. **Warren Platt** of Snell & Wilmer LLP has earned widespread recognition as a leading figure for automobile product liability litigation and counts major companies such as Ford among his clients. He impresses sources with his *"vast experience as a trial lawyer."* A peer comments: *"He is a very strategic thinker who can take complex problems and think through the best way to resolve them."* Plaintiff lawyer **Mark Robinson** of Robinson, Calcagnie & Robinson PC is a *"skilled trial lawyer who can't be taken lightly in the courtroom."* He is renowned for his work on major automobile and pharmaceutical cases. **Christopher Seeger** of Seeger Weiss LLP is recognized as a *"very savvy, talented plaintiff lawyer who is able to do well both in the courtroom and in the settlement room."* Market commentators also highlight his negotiation skills and knowledge of business matters. He has a renowned mass torts practice and has substantial experi-

ence in handling pharmaceutical claims. **Hunter Shkolnik** of Napoli Bern Ripka Shkolnik LLP is highlighted by peers as being *"talented with a wide range of expertise across industries."* His substantial experience at trial level has seen him handle claims relating to a wide range of products. **Diane Sullivan** (see p.414) of Weil, Gotshal & Manges LLP is applauded as an *"outstanding and tough trial lawyer."* Sources particularly praise her work on large class action cases and her skill in cross-examining expert witnesses. Current matters include acting as lead trial counsel for Johnson & Johnson subsidiary Ortho-McNeil in hormone therapy litigation and defending longstanding client Philip Morris in a class action case concerning medical monitoring. **Daniel Thomasch** (see p.1947) of Gibson, Dunn & Crutcher LLP is a *"strategic thinker"* who is *"very good at distilling complex technical issues and making persuasive presentations to a court."* He cochairs the firm's product liability and mass torts group. **Jane Thorpe** (see p.417) of Alston & Bird LLP is characterized as a *"science guru"* who offers extensive expertise in the products space. She recently obtained a dismissal on behalf of client McDonald's, successfully disputing claims that the company violates consumer protection statutes by marketing Happy Meals that contain toys to children. **Quentin Urquhart** is based at Irwin Fritchie Urquhart & Moore, and has a well-regarded practice that focuses on pharmaceutical and medical device product liability, and environmental and toxic tort litigation. **Neal Walters** (see p.1749) of Ballard Spahr LLP impresses leading clients with his litigation coordination skills and technical expertise in automotive products. *"He*

*is always concerned about knowing our business and that enables him to make broader connections that aid our relationship in the long term,"* a satisfied client explains. Walters represents Kia Motors in an 8,000-member class action concerning allegations of consumer fraud. Based at Weitz & Luxenberg, PC, **Perry Weitz** is recognized as having been *"enormously successful"* in a diverse range of cases. Commentators highlight his impressive experience in acting for plaintiffs, and his notable advocacy skills. **Phoebe Wilkinson** (see p.426) of Chadbourne & Parke LLP has substantial experience in medical device and pharmaceutical matters, and is praised for *"going the extra mile with her clients"* and *"having a sense of what wins and what doesn't."* She represents Purdue Pharma in defending claims of personal injury caused by ingestion of the drug OxyContin. **John Winter** (see p.427) of Patterson Belknap Webb & Tyler LLP focuses his well-regarded practice on pharmaceutical cases. He is praised for his *"very good judgment"* and for being *"always accessible and very responsive"* to his clients. Recent highlights include representing Biomet in multidistrict litigation concerning metal-on-metal hip implants. **Mary Yelenick** (see p.429) is based at Chadbourne & Parke LLP and is described as a *"really smart strategist"* who has great *"analytical power."* Recent highlights include acting as national counsel to Beam Global Spirits & Wine and Jim Beam Brands on defending consumer fraud class actions at both the state and nationwide level.

# PROJECTS

Commentary about individuals can be found under their firm's paragraph. If the firm has no paragraph (is not ranked) look at Other Notable Practitioners.

| Projects: Mining & Metals Leading Firms |
| --- |
| **Band 1** |
| Milbank, Tweed, Hadley & McCloy LLP * |
| Sullivan & Cromwell LLP * |
| **Band 2** |
| Shearman & Sterling LLP * |
| **Band 3** |
| Freshfields Bruckhaus Deringer US LLP * |

*Indicates firm with profile.*
*Alphabetical order within each band. Band 1 is the highest.*

*The editorial is in alphabetical order by firm name.*

## Akin Gump Strauss Hauer & Feld LLP
See profile on p.904

**THE FIRM** Sources consider this firm a strong choice for developers of renewable energy projects. The group represents clients in some of the sector's most significant projects, and was recently instructed by Abu Dhabi-based

Masdar to provide advice in relation to the development of a solar photovoltaic project, as well as in connection with its joint venture with E.ON. The group is also adept at handling the financing aspects of projects.
**Sources say:** *"We have sought to bring them in on all our deals because they are so very good."*
**KEY INDIVIDUALS** According to market commentators, **Adam Umanoff** (see p.419) *"is by far one of the best project finance attorneys out there."* Clients appreciate that *"he is a real partner in the process and understands the business side of issues."* He recently led the team on a financing for EverPower Wind Holdings. **Edward Zaelke** (see p.430) is hailed as *"a very competent transactional lawyer."* His practice runs the gamut of alternative and renewable concerns, and he regularly acts for a range of notable clients including Cielo Wind Energy and Western Wind Energy.

## Allen & Overy LLP
See profile on p.433
**THE FIRM** The recent arrival of preeminent practitioners Kent Rowey and Dolly Mirchandani from Freshfields has

| Recommended for Client Service Nationwide | |
| --- | --- |
| Andrews Kurth LLP | Skadden, Arps, Slate, Meagher & Flom LLP & Affiliates |
| Baker Botts LLP | |
| Chadbourne & Parke LLP | Vinson & Elkins LLP |
| Orrick, Herrington & Sutcliffe LLP | White & Case LLP |

| Recommended for Commercial Awareness Nationwide | |
| --- | --- |
| Allen & Overy LLP | Orrick, Herrington & Sutcliffe LLP |
| Bingham McCutchen LLP | |
| Hunton & Williams LLP | Skadden, Arps, Slate, Meagher & Flom LLP & Affiliates |
| Nossaman LLP | Sullivan & Cromwell LLP |

significantly boosted this firm's already impressive capabilities in PPP work. The team has recently been involved in several cutting-edge projects, including acting for the consortium of lenders financing the first ever major airport privatization project to take place in Puerto Rico. As well as representing financiers in projects, the team is equally

*The editorial is in alphabetical order by firm name.*

## Projects
### Leading Individuals

| Band 1 | | | Band 3 | | Zaelke Edward W | Akin Gump Strauss Hauer & Feld LLP * |
|---|---|---|---|---|---|---|

**Band 1**

| | | |
|---|---|---|
| Alexander Troy | White & Case LLP * | |
| Asmus David | Morgan, Lewis & Bockius LLP * | |
| Cogan Jr John P | Cogan & Partners LLP (ONP)† | |
| DeSantis Victor J | White & Case LLP * | |
| Fitzgerald Peter F | Chadbourne & Parke LLP * | |
| Gordon David A | Latham & Watkins LLP * | |
| Green Jonathan | Milbank, Tweed, Hadley & McCloy LLP * | |
| Greenberg Jeffrey | Latham & Watkins LLP | |
| Klepper Martin | Skadden, Arps, Slate, Meagher & Flom * | |
| Machlin Barry N | Mayer Brown LLP | |
| Martin Keith | Chadbourne & Parke LLP * | |
| McIsaac Christopher | Clifford Chance US LLP * | |
| Moore Harold F | Skadden, Arps, Slate, Meagher & Flom * | |
| Rich Frederic C | Sullivan & Cromwell LLP * | |
| Rod Jonathan | Latham & Watkins LLP | |
| Scavone Arthur A | White & Case LLP * | |
| Shutran Richard | O'Melveny & Myers LLP (ONP)† | |
| Urda Kassis Cynthia | Shearman & Sterling LLP | |
| Wachsberger Chaim | Chadbourne & Parke LLP * | |

**Band 2**

| | |
|---|---|
| Bice William B | Milbank, Tweed, Hadley & McCloy LLP * |
| Chida Junaid H | O'Melveny & Myers LLP (ONP)† |
| Czarniak Julia A | Skadden, Arps, Slate, Meagher & Flom * |
| Freedman Robert | Shearman & Sterling LLP |
| Fried Douglas M | Chadbourne & Parke LLP * |
| Harris Gregg | Fulbright & Jaworski LLP * |
| Irvin Michael P | Fulbright & Jaworski LLP * |
| Lieberman David M | Simpson Thacher & Bartlett LLP * |
| Mann Christopher L | Sullivan & Cromwell LLP * |
| Marks Allan T | Milbank, Tweed, Hadley & McCloy LLP * |
| Mattei Ivan E | Debevoise & Plimpton LLP * |
| Mauel John G | Pillsbury Winthrop Shaw Pittman LLP * |
| Neaher Jr Ned | White & Case LLP * |
| Pinkusiewicz Tomer | Gibson, Dunn & Crutcher LLP (ONP)† * |
| Rafte G Alan | Bracewell & Giuliani LLP * |
| Sachs John | Latham & Watkins LLP * |
| Spradling Mark | Vinson & Elkins LLP * |
| Umanoff Adam S | Akin Gump Strauss Hauer & Feld LLP * |
| Weitzel Mark P | Orrick, Herrington & Sutcliffe LLP |

**Band 3**

| | |
|---|---|
| Alexander Todd E | Chadbourne & Parke LLP * |
| Arrington Scott J | McDermott Will & Emery LLP * |
| Ayali Noam | Chadbourne & Parke LLP * |
| Bartfeld Daniel D | Milbank, Tweed, Hadley & McCloy LLP * |
| Brasher Lance T | Skadden, Arps, Slate, Meagher & Flom * |
| Chaudhry Rohit | Chadbourne & Parke LLP * |
| Chester Jeffrey A | Kaye Scholer LLP (ONP)† * |
| Culotta Kenneth S | King & Spalding LLP * |
| Friedman Ellen S | Nixon Peabody LLP (ONP)† * |
| Gale Kelley | Latham & Watkins LLP * |
| Galvis Sergio J | Sullivan & Cromwell LLP * |
| Gedanken Lynne E | Chadbourne & Parke LLP * |
| Goldstein Maura | Baker Botts LLP * |
| Groobey Christopher | Wilson Sonsini Goodrich & Rosati |
| Hammes Patricia | Shearman & Sterling LLP |
| Hansen Kenneth W | Chadbourne & Parke LLP * |
| Higgins Tara A | Orrick, Herrington & Sutcliffe LLP |
| Hunt Paul J | Latham & Watkins LLP * |
| Kartheiser Robert | Allen & Overy LLP |
| Kayukov Edward V | Milbank, Tweed, Hadley & McCloy LLP * |
| Kenney John H | Latham & Watkins LLP * |
| Maizel Jonathan | Milbank, Tweed, Hadley & McCloy LLP * |
| Mathews Daniel A | Orrick, Herrington & Sutcliffe LLP |
| Miles Steven | Baker Botts LLP * |
| Moore III Thomas O | Bracewell & Giuliani LLP * |
| Pozzerle Sergio A | Sidley Austin LLP * |
| Reardon Marc A | Bingham McCutchen LLP * |
| Rowey Kent | Allen & Overy LLP |
| Schmidt John R | Mayer Brown LLP |
| Schroeder Jeff | Hunton & Williams LLP * |
| Silverman Eric | Milbank, Tweed, Hadley & McCloy LLP * |
| Slade David | Allen & Overy LLP |
| Smith Gregory K | Allen & Overy LLP |
| Spivak Mark | Vinson & Elkins LLP * |
| Tan Gregory | Shearman & Sterling LLP |
| Unger Timothy | Andrews Kurth LLP * |
| Weber Paul L | Chadbourne & Parke LLP * |
| Winburne Blake H | McDermott Will & Emery LLP * |
| Wong Karen | Milbank, Tweed, Hadley & McCloy LLP * |
| Wyman Kenneth | Simpson Thacher & Bartlett LLP * |

**Band 4**

| | |
|---|---|
| Archer Matt | McDermott Will & Emery LLP * |
| Baecher John | Chadbourne & Parke LLP * |
| Bean Lori Ann | Clifford Chance US LLP * |
| Bradshaw Brian A | Morgan, Lewis & Bockius LLP * |
| Callahan Timothy P | Paul Hastings LLP (ONP)† |
| Chung Ernest | Blank Rome LLP (ONP)† * |
| Evans David | Clifford Chance US LLP * |
| Glascock Thomas B | Orrick, Herrington & Sutcliffe LLP |
| Goodman Jeffrey H | Fulbright & Jaworski LLP * |
| Hadley Joseph P | Davis Polk & Wardwell LLP (ONP)† * |
| Henegar Matthew | Latham & Watkins LLP * |
| Holcomb Ryan S | Bracewell & Giuliani LLP * |
| Kelley Jay D | Jay D Kelley (ONP)† |
| Keneally Walter S | Bracewell & Giuliani LLP * |
| Koenigsberg Benjamin Y | Chadbourne & Parke LLP * |
| Kraske Paul S | Skadden, Arps, Slate, Meagher & Flom * |
| Larson Keith D | Hogan Lovells US LLP |
| Lewis Jeffrey S | Cleary Gottlieb Steen & Hamilton LLP * |
| Lilien Warren H | Latham & Watkins LLP * |
| Lincer Richard S | Cleary Gottlieb Steen & Hamilton LLP * |
| McCarthy Catherine | Clifford Chance US LLP * |
| Pinkerton Glenn | Sidley Austin LLP * |
| Raciti-Knapp Melissa | Freshfields Bruckhaus Deringer US LLP * |
| Rotter Irving L | Sidley Austin LLP * |
| Shortz Richard | Morgan, Lewis & Bockius LLP * |
| Song Wayne W | Morgan, Lewis & Bockius LLP * |
| Stein Jane Wallison | Pillsbury Winthrop Shaw Pittman LLP |
| Tato Joseph A | DLA Piper LLP (US) (ONP)† * |
| Thompson Dahl | Andrews Kurth LLP * |
| Thorpe Gregory | O'Melveny & Myers LLP (ONP)† |
| Thurber Mark | Andrews Kurth LLP * |
| Walther-Meade Carolina | Milbank, Tweed, Hadley & McCloy LLP * |
| Warner E Waide | Davis Polk & Wardwell LLP (ONP)† * |

**Up-and-coming individuals**

| | |
|---|---|
| Michalchuk Daniel J | Milbank, Tweed, Hadley & McCloy LLP * |
| Reese Michael T | Pillsbury Winthrop Shaw Pittman LLP * |

**Associates to watch**

| | |
|---|---|
| Hutchings Julie | Pillsbury Winthrop Shaw Pittman LLP * |

\* *Indicates individual with profile.*
†*ONP = Other Notable Practitioner.*

experienced in acting for bidders and leading public authorities including the Port Authority of New York & New Jersey and the Queensland Investment Corporation. This international firm also tackles complex energy projects by drawing on its specialties in the oil and gas and power arenas.
**Commercial Awareness:** *"They are amazing. With them on our side, we are always confident that a transaction will work because they know what they are doing." "They are very knowledgeable about the industry, and work hard to keep track of what is going on in both the domestic and international sphere."*

**KEY INDIVIDUALS** The *"very strong"* and *"pragmatic"* **Kent Rowey** commands high levels of respect from the field. He recently moved to the firm from Freshfields, bringing with him a wealth of experience in PPP matters. He has recently led the firm's work on behalf of KKR and United Water on the $150 million Bayonne Water Concession Project. **David Slade** is a prominent adviser of various lenders and project endorsers in connection with a broad array of projects, including transportation, infrastructure oil and gas field development, and electricity generation. He has represented multiple lenders, including Inter-American Development Bank and Export Development Canada, in connection with a $4.5 billion

cross-border petrochemical project. **Andrew Fraiser** handles the full range of PPP projects. Of late, he has been active in various projects, including leading the team on behalf of the Port Authority of New York and New Jersey in relation to a $1.5 billion bridge replacement venture in New York City. *"Fine attorney"* **Dolly Mirchandani** is another new recruit from Freshfields, who has impressed clients and peers with her *"very strong"* project finance practice. She is particularly adept at handling energy and infrastructure projects, and has recently been active on a number of big-ticket matters for the likes of ACS Infrastructure Development. **Gregory Smith** is recommended as a *"pragmatic, constructive and knowledgeable"*

## Projects: LNG
### Leading Individuals

**Band 1**

| | |
|---|---|
| Cogan Jr John P | *Cogan & Partners LLP* |
| Culotta Kenneth S | *King & Spalding LLP* * |
| Mauel John G | *Pillsbury Winthrop Shaw Pittman LLP* |
| Miles Steven | *Baker Botts LLP* * |

## Projects: Oil & Gas
### Leading Firms

**Band 1**

Baker Botts LLP *
Vinson & Elkins LLP *

**Band 2**

Fulbright & Jaworski LLP *
Latham & Watkins LLP *
Milbank, Tweed, Hadley & McCloy LLP *
Skadden, Arps, Slate, Meagher & Flom LLP & Affiliates *
Sullivan & Cromwell LLP *
White & Case LLP *

**Band 3**

Andrews Kurth LLP *
Bracewell & Giuliani LLP *
King & Spalding LLP *

**Band 4**

Allen & Overy LLP *
Pillsbury Winthrop Shaw Pittman LLP *

* Indicates firm / individual with profile.
† ONP = Other Notable Practitioner.

## Projects: Power
### Leading Firms

**Band 1**

Chadbourne & Parke LLP *
Latham & Watkins LLP *
Milbank, Tweed, Hadley & McCloy LLP *
Skadden, Arps, Slate, Meagher & Flom LLP & Affiliates *

**Band 2**

Shearman & Sterling LLP *
Vinson & Elkins LLP *
White & Case LLP *

**Band 3**

Allen & Overy LLP *
Clifford Chance US LLP *
Hunton & Williams LLP *
Simpson Thacher & Bartlett LLP *

**Band 4**

Bingham McCutchen LLP *
Bracewell & Giuliani LLP *
Fulbright & Jaworski LLP *
McDermott Will & Emery LLP *
Sidley Austin LLP *

## Projects: PPP
### Leading Firms

**Band 1**

Allen & Overy LLP *
Mayer Brown LLP *
Milbank, Tweed, Hadley & McCloy LLP *
Nossaman LLP *

**Band 2**

Orrick, Herrington & Sutcliffe LLP *

**Band 3**

Chadbourne & Parke LLP *
Debevoise & Plimpton LLP *
White & Case LLP *

**Band 4**

Bracewell & Giuliani LLP *
Cleary Gottlieb Steen & Hamilton LLP *
Greenberg Traurig, LLP *
Hunton & Williams LLP *
Shearman & Sterling LLP *

### Leading Individuals

**Band 1**

| | |
|---|---|
| Marks Allan T | *Milbank, Tweed, Hadley & McCloy LLP* * |
| Mathews Daniel A | *Orrick, Herrington & Sutcliffe LLP* |
| Pinkusiewicz Tomer | *Gibson, Dunn & Crutcher LLP* * |
| Rowey Kent | *Allen & Overy LLP* |
| Schmidt John R | *Mayer Brown LLP* |
| Yarema Geoffrey S | *Nossaman LLP* |

**Band 2**

| | |
|---|---|
| Fraiser Andrew | *Allen & Overy LLP* |
| Fried Douglas M | *Chadbourne & Parke LLP* * |
| Harder Patrick D | *Nossaman LLP* |
| Lincer Richard S | *Cleary Gottlieb Steen & Hamilton LLP* * |
| Mattei Ivan E | *Debevoise & Plimpton LLP* |
| Mirchandani Dolly | *Allen & Overy LLP* |
| Richards Eric A S | *O'Melveny & Myers LLP (ONP)* † * |
| Slade David | *Allen & Overy LLP* |

**Band 3**

| | |
|---|---|
| Devlin Roderick N. | *Greenberg Traurig, LLP* * |
| Lee Young J | *Orrick, Herrington & Sutcliffe LLP* |
| Moore III Thomas O | *Bracewell & Giuliani LLP* * |
| Moser Joel H | *Kaye Scholer LLP (ONP)* † * |
| Pulley III J Waverly | *Hunton & Williams LLP* * |

project finance attorney. Of particular note was his recent representation of financial institutions HSBC, IFC and Korea Export-Import Bank as financiers of a $176 billion transport project in Colombia. **Robert Kartheiser** is highly respected and well known in the project finance space. He is recognized as a preeminent expert in matters involving emerging markets, and represents the likes of Deutsche Bank, Calyon and AES.

## Andrews Kurth LLP
### See profile on p.2426

**THE FIRM** This firm is renowned for its ability to handle oil and gas-related projects, and receives particular praise from clients this year for its high level of knowledge in this area. The team handles a wide range of matters, including entity and asset purchases and transactions concerning exploration, production, development and transportation. The group recently advised Sabine Pass Liquefaction in connection with the $3.6 billion financing of an LNG export project. Additionally, Andrews Kurth's renewables team is praised for its expert handling of large and complex financings of wind projects.

**Client Service** *"Extremely timely and responsive to what we have needed. We are very pleased across the board, everything has been great."*

**KEY INDIVIDUALS** *"Excellent lawyer"* **Dahl Thompson** (see p.417) is highlighted as one of the leading members of the projects team. Clients applaud him for his *"outstanding knowledge,"* and are particularly impressed with his expert-

ise in financings and power purchase agreements. **Mark Thurber** (see p.417) continues to garner strong praise from peers for his strong renewables and alternative energy practice. He has recently been highly active advising clients such as Viento Blanco in connection with wind power projects. **Timothy Unger** (see p.419) is known to be a *"very good oil and gas attorney."* He brings deep experience in energy matters, which he recently applied for the benefit of Pattern Energy in relation to its proposed development of a wind farm and transmission system in Hawaii.

## Baker Botts LLP
### See profile on p.2427

**THE FIRM** Baker Botts's oil and gas projects group is one of the most formidable in the country. The practice is valued for its wide-ranging project finance expertise and dedication to its clients, which include leading energy companies such as ExxonMobil and Reliance. The team has vast experience in handling a broad array of projects, ranging from domestic and international midstream and downstream projects, to upstream development in the Gulf of Mexico. It continues to dedicate a large proportion of its time to transactional work relating to shale plays, and recently represented KKR in relation to its participation in the development of the Eagle Ford Shale in Texas.

**Client Service** *"Our experience with Baker Botts has been extraordinary. They are very attentive to the client's needs, are effective negotiators and have a wonderful variety of project finance experience. We would rate them among the highest in this area."*

**KEY INDIVIDUALS** Clients are quick to recommend **Steven Miles** (see p.368) as a *"very service-oriented, highly responsive and very commercially aware"* practitioner. He has recently acted on several of the firm's significant mandates, an example of which is his advice to Cheniere

Energy Partners in connection with the extension of its Sabine Pass LNG terminal. **Maura Goldstein** (see p.323) has had another busy year representing clients in relation to various renewables and alternative energy projects. In a recent highlight, she represented Buchanan Renewables in connection with a cross-border electric power generation project valued at $290 million.

## Bingham McCutchen LLP
### See profile on p.1515

**THE FIRM** This firm is nationally renowned for its strong traditional power capabilities and its renewables and alternative energy expertise. The group is prized for its ability to handle big-ticket renewable energy projects, a recent

*The editorial is in alphabetical order by firm name.*

example of which was its advice to longstanding client GE in connection with a multimillion-dollar tax equity financing of a wind energy project in Michigan. On the power side, the team has had an active year acting for high-profile clients, including the representation of SCS Energy in connection with the Hydrogen Energy California project.

**Commercial Awareness** *"The Bingham relationship is valued for its depth in energy project finance as well as its breadth across regulatory, environmental and restructuring practices."*

**KEY INDIVIDUALS** The highly experienced **Marc Reardon** (see p.390) also draws great praise from market sources, who describe him as an *"excellent lawyer who has very good business judgment, is extremely responsive and provides excellent customer service."* He has played an integral role in some of the firm's most significant matters for major clients.

## Bracewell & Giuliani LLP
See profile on p.2429

**THE FIRM** This firm has a balanced projects practice covering a mix of conventional power, oil and gas, and PPP work, frequently handling high-value instructions. On the oil and gas side, the group has recently seen an uptick in shale-related transactions, and has assisted several high-profile clients such as Chesapeake Energy, Apache and Three Rivers Operating Company in both acquisitions and sales. Power mandates include assisting Entergy in connection with its $409 million purchase of a natural gas-fired plant. On the PPP side, the team's reputation for energy, transportation and social infrastructure advice attracts instructions from national and international clients, including Cintra Infraestructuras and Dallas Police & Fire Pension System.

**Sources say:** *"We just love working with them. Their internal communication is excellent, they understand fully what our risk profile is, and are very good in negotiations with counterparties. Their drafting skills are also excellent."*

**KEY INDIVIDUALS Thomas Moore** (see p.371) is well versed in guiding domestic and international clients through project development and finance matters, and is currently acting for Cintra Infraestructuras and Meridiam Infrastructure in connection with the $1.6 billion North Tarrant Express project. **Alan Rafte** (see p.389) is hailed by market sources as *"excellent; very experienced and highly skilled."* He is known nationwide for his representation of clients including utilities, financial institutions and private equity investors in oil and gas-related projects. **Ryan Holcomb** (see p.335) continues to impress his clients, who say that he *"drafts well, presents ideas in a clear, straightforward manner, has a calm, relaxed temperament, and possesses excellent recall."* He is well versed in both the oil and gas and power sides. **Walter Keneally** (see p.345) *"has a good perspective and is a good advocate for us,"* say clients. Additionally, they report that he is *"thorough and gives a lot of insight for us, and draws on other expertise when he needs to."*

## Chadbourne & Parke LLP
See profile on p.1962

**THE FIRM** This preeminent team is sought out for its sophisticated work on project development and finance matters. Complex power and renewable and alternative energy projects are all handled by this group, and a substantial amount of its work is international in scope. On the power side, the group continues to represent the Department of Energy in connection with the financings of several projects, including a $14 billion nuclear project. The renewables and alternative energy arm of the team has recently been instructed in several high-profile wind and solar projects. The team also handles PPP work and continues to advise on infrastructure development, both at home and abroad.

**Client Service:** *"A top-notch firm with highly regarded professionals who can provide a broad range of services to clients. It delivers value to our company and is a strong advocate of our business interests."*

**KEY INDIVIDUALS** Sources hail the *"phenomenal"* **Keith Martin** (see p.362) as the *"dean of the renewable energy tax Bar."* Clients praise him for his calm demeanor and the fact that he *"knows the industry inside out."* He serves as head of the firm's project finance team, and clients benefit from his deep experience in project finance and tax matters. **Todd Alexander** (see p.272) is applauded as an excellent project finance lawyer, who is *"exceedingly knowledgeable in the renewable field."* He regularly represents large sponsors and lenders in energy projects ranging from wind and solar to clean coal facilities. He recently acted for LS Power, the sponsors of a $550 million solar photovoltaic project. **Douglas Fried** (see p.316) enjoys a solid reputation for providing advice on PPP projects, with sources particularly highlighting his *"very high knowledge of the infrastructure industry."* He is also adept at handling large and complex energy matters. The *"excellent"* **Peter Fitzgerald** (see p.313) is an industry leader in project finance and development, attracting a host of high-profile clients. He is *"extremely experienced, knowledgeable and just great,"* according to sources. Commentators laud **Chaim Wachsberger** (see p.422) as *"very experienced and knowledgeable in the finance area, and he understands well how to deal with difficult situations."* Notable clients in the past year include Duke Energy and several prominent financial institutions funding power-related projects. The *"very good"* and *"highly accomplished"* **Rohit Chaudhry** (see p.294) is noted for his international capabilities, and recently acted for investment fund Macquarie Capital in connection with the largest wind farm project in Latin America to date. **Noam Ayali** (see p.275) serves as chair of the oil and gas project finance group, but is also highly experienced in matters concerning power and renewable energy. He has had a busy year leading the team on some of the largest oil and gas financings of the past year, including in relation to the Sabine Pass LNG liquefaction project, which involved the representation of multiple lenders. **Paul Weber** (see p.423) continues to assist clients with a wide range of energy-related transactions, and has recently acted on behalf of GE Energy Financial Services in connection with the purchase of shares in two big-ticket wind projects. **John Baecher** (see p.276) focuses his project finance practice on the private power sector, and has continued to act for the AES Corporation in a variety of projects. **Kenneth Hansen** (see p.330) has extensive expertise in alternative energy projects, and was recently part of the team representing a subsidiary of Ormat Technologies in connection with the refinancing of a geothermal power complex. The deeply experienced **Lynne Gedanken** (see p.319) is able to offer developer and lender clients a range of services, including advice in relation to both international and domestic transmission and electricity generation projects. She is also involved in advising governmental bodies in connection with utilities-related privatization. New York-based attorney **Benjamin Koenigsberg** (see p.348) moves up in this year's rankings following an impressive year. He has played an integral part in the firm's oil and gas project work, as well as in PPP matters.

### Cleary Gottlieb Steen & Hamilton LLP
See profile on p.1963

**THE FIRM** A big name within the PPP community, Cleary Gottlieb continues to handle domestic and international infrastructure, energy, and various other projects on behalf of several longstanding clients, including Highstar Capital, DP World, Codelco and Alpha Natural Resources. The firm is frequently instructed in relation to innovative projects, as well as those that call for cross-border expertise. The group was retained by the US-located Fintech Energy in connection with its acquisition of shares in an Argentine gas distribution business which is involved in major renewables projects in Argentina.
**KEY INDIVIDUALS** Strong market endorsement has enabled *"very strong lawyer"* **Richard Lincer** (see p.357) to climb the PPP rankings this year. In the past year he has handled a series of big-ticket matters for the likes of DP World, Cascade Investment and Aerostar Airport Holdings. The *"exceptional"* **Jeffrey Lewis** (see p.1914) is commended by clients for his *"tremendous ability to manage difficult situations very well."* He has recently led the team's work on behalf of DB Masdar Clean Tech Fund in connection with its private equity investment in a solar cell manufacturing project.

### Clifford Chance US LLP
See profile on p.439

**THE FIRM** This 22-strong project finance group continues to impress observers with its extensive international reach alongside impressive teams in New York and DC. The group primarily serves clients from the electrical power and renewable and alternative energy sectors, providing a wide range of services, including advice on the financing aspects of wind and solar projects, as well as hydroelectric and geothermal projects. In the last year, it has represented Acconia Energy in connection with the $135 million financing for a wind generation plant.
**KEY INDIVIDUALS** Americas energy and projects practice cochair **Christopher McIsaac** (see p.365) is a well-known figure in the national and international projects space. He has recently acted on a number of the team's major international matters, including several on behalf of

the US Ex-Im Bank, such as in relation to a wind power generation facility in Uruguay. **Lori Ann Bean** (see p.280) wins acclaim from clients for her *"smooth negotiation skills and high degree of pragmatism."* She continues to assist clients including IFC, Technip and Santander with the financing and development of international and domestic energy and infrastructure projects. **David Evans** (see p.310) has made an impression on clients and peers alike. In the words of one client, *"he has really impressed me; based on his experience he did a good job of presenting issues and questions, and he always provides a very rapid response."* Peers describe him as a *"great energy practitioner."* Banking and finance expert **Catherine McCarthy** (see p.364) recently represented a range of financial institutions, including Inter-American Development Bank, HSBC and others in a $693 million financing connected to what will be the largest wind farm in Latin America.

### Cooley LLP

**THE FIRM** The attorneys at Cooley are a prominent force in the nationwide renewables and alternative energy projects market, with substantial capabilities in clean energy and technologies. The experienced group comprises 35 dedicated lawyers spread across the firm's DC, New York and San Francisco offices. The team recently counseled Southeast Renewables in connection with the development and subsequent disposal of multiple biomass projects in South Carolina. Its international capabilities are also demonstrated by its recent representation of KMRI in various utility-scale generation projects in numerous emerging markets.
**KEY INDIVIDUALS** **Thomas Amis** continues to serve as co-head of the firm's clean energy and technologies practice, and possesses considerable experience in the finance and development aspects of renewable energy projects. He has taken a lead role in the firm's work for KMRI. **Nikesh Patel** makes his way up this year's renewables and alternative energy rankings following widespread market endorsement. He is flagged up by market commentators as a future star in this area.

### Debevoise & Plimpton LLP
See profile on p.1968

**THE FIRM** Debevoise is an internationally renowned projects firm that has a strong reputation for PPP work. On the project finance side, the team has recently been representing Mitsui in connection with a joint venture transaction involving a $1.8 billion financing. In the past year, the firm has attracted numerous sophisticated clients, including Footprint Power, Sithe Global and the US Department of Energy. Clients praise the team for its creativity and deep industry knowledge.
**Sources say:** *"They are very good. They have great experience in representing clients in project finance matters."*
**KEY INDIVIDUALS** Clients continue to heap praise on the *"very smart"* **Ivan Mattei**. A recognized expert within the PPP community, he is applauded for being *"very strong technically, with a good analytical and commercial understanding."*

### Freshfields Bruckhaus Deringer US LLP
See profile on p.443

**THE FIRM** Freshfields has a strong track record in advising mining and metals clients on project finance concerns, both nationwide and those with cross-border elements. Recent work has included advice on complex copper mining and iron ore projects. Noted for its worldwide reach, the group advises a wide range of international clients.
**KEY INDIVIDUALS** **Melissa Raciti-Knapp** (see p.388) is best known for her expertise in domestic and Latin American project finance matters. A large part of her practice focuses on mining and metals, but she is also adept at handling matters for clients from the power, oil and gas, wastewater and infrastructure sectors.

### Fulbright & Jaworski LLP
See profile on p.2435

**THE FIRM** Fulbright has a well-regarded oil and gas projects practice with a considerable depth of resources. The team has recently represented a number of oil and gas entities in connection with joint venture transactions in shale plays, including Sinopec and Total. They are also adept at handling LNG-related matters, recently acting for EOG Resources in connection with its purchase of the entire shares in an LNG company, and the subsequent development of a $4 billion LNG plant in Canada. The group also has specialized expertise in counseling a range of renewable energy and power clients.
**Sources say:** *"Very professional and qualified in every area where we have required subject matter expertise."*
**KEY INDIVIDUALS** Peers attest to **Gregg Harris** (see p.331) and **Michael Irvin**'s (see p.339) active practices and note their strong capabilities, particularly in relation to agency work. Harris serves as chair of the global structured and project finance group and cochair of its global infrastructure group, and has a particular focus on the financing of power projects. Irvin is an oil and gas specialist, and has recently led the team's work on behalf of prominent clients, including EOG Resources, Noble Energy and Anadarko. Clients laud **Jeffrey Goodman** (see p.324) as a *"wise business adviser."* He is heavily involved in international work, ranging from real estate and electric projects to water projects.

### Greenberg Traurig, LLP
See profile on p.1024

**THE FIRM** This firm has a multidisciplinary capacity, and comes highly recommended for its PPP projects practice. It is also noted for its recent participation in numerous significant projects in this arena. Highlights include acting for OTOW in connection with a public-private agreement with Bay Laurel Center Community Development for the provision of water and sewer utility facilities. Other notable clients include Citigroup Global Markets, The Atlanta Development Authority and the State of Georgia.
**KEY INDIVIDUALS** The *"very capable"* **Roderick Devlin** (see p.304) is singled out by clients for his responsiveness to their needs. He has recently handled a number of significant PPP mandates.

*The editorial is in alphabetical order by firm name.*

## Hogan Lovells US LLP

THE FIRM Sources are quick to praise the nationally acclaimed renewables and alternative energy project finance practice at this firm, highlighting its high-quality advice and understanding of client needs as particular strengths. It enjoys a diverse client roster consisting of domestic and international financial institutions, private equity funds and project sponsors, among others. Of late, the practitioners have been heavily involved in advising on the development, financing and M&A aspects of solar projects.

Sources say: *"Very capable with a strong work ethic, deep bench, very accessible, and willing to jump in and assist in whatever capacity needed. They can take a whole project and run with it."*

KEY INDIVIDUALS **Brian Chappell** is highly rated for his expert advice on the development and financing aspects of energy projects. He is applauded as *"a very strong lawyer all around,"* and is said to be *"absolutely outstanding on matters that require technical knowledge."* **Keith Larson** was recently part of the team representing NextEra Energy Resources in connection with the $250 million financing of a wind energy project in California.

## Holland & Hart LLP
See profile on p.727

THE FIRM This group enjoys a strong reputation for renewable and alternative energy matters, and is noted for being particularly strong in wind energy projects, in which it has recently acted for Duke Energy Renewables and Cook Inlet Region. It is also adept at handling major solar projects. Sources extend praise for its excellent industry knowledge, responsiveness and deep bench of attorneys.

Sources say: *"They possess a very good understanding of the wind energy space."*

KEY INDIVIDUALS Head of the energy and infrastructure team **Mark Safty** is a key contact at the firm.

## Hunton & Williams LLP
See profile on p.2517

THE FIRM This dedicated projects practice has gained a reputation for its commitment to clients' business needs as well as its consistent high-quality service. The team has extensive experience in handling renewable energy projects on behalf of both investors and developers. The firm's expertise in tax energy concerns such as grants and energy tax credits attracts major tax equity investors to the firm. Recent highlights include the representation of Mitsubishi on all facets of its purchase of shares in a high-value wind power generation project in Mexico. The firm is also active in power matters, and provides clients with a comprehensive PPP service.

Commercial Awareness: *"Knowledgeable, experienced attorneys who know not only their profession but the business side of things, which provides that extra something, differentiating them from other firms."*

KEY INDIVIDUALS **Laura Ellen Jones** (see p.341) continues to amass praise from market commentators for her strength in tax matters, and has recently been involved in much of the firm's work on behalf of tax equity investor

clients. The highly regarded **Waverly Pulley** (see p.388) is based in the Richmond office and serves as chair of the firm's transportation infrastructure team. He centers his practice on infrastructure projects and PPP. **Jeff Schroeder** (see p.402) receives strong praise for his ability to handle complicated transactions, particularly in the power arena. He recently acted for JPMorgan and Morgan Stanley in relation to a tax equity investment in various wind farms across several US states.

## King & Spalding LLP
See profile on p.445

THE FIRM Operating out of several locations across the USA, the team here offers its clients the full range of energy-related project finance services, but is especially strong in advising on oil and gas matters, and has recently seen an increase in instructions relating to cutting-edge LNG projects. Highlights include representing Freeport LNG in connection with the development of a multibillion-dollar LNG export terminal in Texas. Other notable clients include Anadarko, Cheniere Energy and Inergy Midstream.

Sources say: *"A very good group that is extremely adept at working with the client. They also possess a very good understanding of the industry."*

KEY INDIVIDUALS **Kenneth Culotta** (see p.300) secures a place in the LNG rankings this year following strong peer support and an impressive list of work highlights in this area. He is also strongly received by clients, who rave that *"his understanding of project finance and how it applied to actual contracts is phenomenal."* He has been at the forefront of much of the firm's significant oil and gas and LNG work.

## Latham & Watkins LLP
See profile on p.446

THE FIRM This global powerhouse provides top-drawer counsel on the gamut of project finance and development matters to a wide range of clients, including major financial institutions, electric energy, and oil and gas developers. The team is highly recommended for its outstanding power-related project work, with sources citing its deep global bench as a major strength. Recent highlights include the representation of South Jamaica Power in connection with the financing and development of a gas-fired power project, the first of its kind in Jamaica. The group also receives high marks for its work in renewables and alternative energy, and in oil and gas.

Sources say: *"The attorneys are extremely smart, very responsive and a pleasure to work with. They are excellent when it comes to understanding complex transactions and very good at training up their younger members, who are all very good."*

KEY INDIVIDUALS **David Gordon** (see p.324) rises up the rankings this year following glowing reviews from clients and peers alike. Although he has a very broad-based practice, he is particularly experienced in guiding clients through private power projects. The *"excellent and very effective"* **Jeffrey Greenberg** also earns widespread peer endorsement. He is sought out by clients seeking advice in

relation to the development and financing of the full range of energy and natural resource projects, but has been particularly active this year in power projects for the likes of Energy Capital Partners, Codan Trust and LS Power Associates. **Jonathan Rod** is an *"excellent lawyer who is very knowledgeable and very good, especially when it comes to project finance."* He serves as head of the energy power industry team, and is additionally adept at handling the financing of gas, oil and infrastructure projects. He has recently been active on several of the firm's renewables and alternative energy projects. **John Sachs** (see p.398) is lauded by clients for the way in which he *"really understands the deals that we do,"* while peers say that it is *"always good to work with him."* He has been instructed by a diverse range of clients, including Tenaska and South Jamaica Power. **Paul Hunt** (see p.338) continues to impress sources with his successful project finance work in the power and alternative energy sectors. He recently led the firm's representation of Summit Power in connection with the financing and development of a $3 billion Texas Clean Energy Project. The *"very competent"* **John Kenney** (see p.345) is lauded by clients for his *"practical and problem-solving"* approach to matters. He is highlighted for maintaining good relationships with his clients, who include the likes of Wind Capital Group and Union Bank. **Warren Lilien** (see p.357) is another member of the team who is particularly experienced and highly active in energy-related projects. He recently led the team's work in relation to the Panda Temple Power Plant project. Global head of the firm's project finance practice **Kelley Gale** (see p.318) is an *"excellent attorney,"* focusing his practice on renewable and alternative energy projects. He recently collaborated with the highly reputed **Matthew Henegar** (see p.333) on a range of matters, including the Desert Sunlight project and the financing of the Arlington Valley Solar Energy II project.

## Mayer Brown LLP
See profile on p.1257

THE FIRM Mayer Brown is highly respected in the PPP market, and receives particular praise for its expertise in government representations and infrastructure transactions. The team is regularly instructed in first-of-its-kind matters, and has notably acted for Puerto Rico Public-Private Partnerships Authority in connection with a $2,6 billion leasing transaction. It also receives additional recognition for its deep knowledge of the renewables industry. The group is particularly strong in assisting with solar and wind energy projects on behalf of major developers, owners and lenders, including Bank of America and BP Wind. Clients applaud the team for its depth and breadth as well as its responsiveness.

Sources say: *"The group is very professional, responsive and extremely knowledgeable in project finance." "They see a lot of deals and this gives them inherent critical mass. They know how counterparties and the various government agencies will react."*

KEY INDIVIDUALS The *"fabulous"* **John Schmidt** remains at the forefront of the PPP world. Peers attest to his active presence and impressive capabilities on the government side. He was recently appointed as lead lawyer on behalf of the Puerto Rico Public-Private Partnerships Authority matter. **Barry Machlin** continues to serve as cochair of the firm's global practice team, and has an impressive reputation among peers owing to his extensive experience in complex infrastructure and project finance transactions.

## McDermott Will & Emery LLP
See profile on p.1258

THE FIRM The strengths of this team lie in representing lenders, sponsors and developers on electrical power and alternative energy projects. The group is frequently sought out by tax and private equity investors for its project finance expertise, an example of which includes its recent work on behalf of Energy Investors Funds in relation to the financing of a coal-fired power plant in Morgantown. With a global footprint, it is also well equipped to handle cross-border matters. One of its most noteworthy recent matters is the representation of International Power/GDF SUEZ in connection with its bid to develop and operate a natural gas-fired power plant in Mexico.
**Sources say:** *"They really understand what the client's goals are, and understand that speed is important."*
KEY INDIVIDUALS Scott Arrington (see p.274) is based in the Houston office and continues to focus his practice on the power, mining, and oil and gas sectors. He has been particularly busy over the past year negotiating a wide range of agreements, including power purchase and joint venture agreements. **Blake Winburne** (see p.427) is a project finance lawyer with experience in the full range of renewable energy projects. He continues to represent BP Wind Energy in a variety of alternative energy ventures, including its recent project involving the development of a wind farm complex. **Matt Archer** (see p.274) has also been active in the renewable energy space, having represented NRG Solar in relation to the development of a solar project in Arizona. He has also acted for various other notable clients over the past year, including EDP Renewables North America and BP Wind Energy.

## Milbank, Tweed, Hadley & McCloy LLP
See profile on p.448

THE FIRM This team is acknowledged by its competitors as a frontrunner in the projects space. The strong group of over 100 attorneys offers exceptional expertise across the full range of energy and PPP matters, and clients benefit from the firm's strong international network and praise its full-service capabilities. On the PPP side, the team is regularly called upon by clients for their most innovative and complex of infrastructure projects. Its talented group of mining and metals attorneys recently represented a consortium of lenders in relation to the over $1.8 billion financing of Sierra Gorda copper mine. The firm has also had a run of successes in the conventional power and renewables and alternative energy arenas of late, including its representation of the lenders in connection with El Arrayán wind farm, which will be Chile's biggest wind farm to date. The oil and gas team has had an active year advising various international lenders on a number of cross-border projects. Notable clients of the firm for the

past year include Google, Bank of Tokyo-Mitsubishi UFJ, Deutsche Bank and HSBC.
**Sources say:** *"They are the market leader when it comes to representing banks on project financings." "I am a big fan of the team here – they are all great attorneys."*
KEY INDIVIDUALS The well-regarded **Edward Kayukov** (see p.344) *"is a really good project finance lawyer,"* according to sources. He specializes in renewable and alternative energy matters, and has recently represented a number of lenders in relation to the financing of various big-ticket solar matters, including in connection with the Mount Signal Solar project. The *"very talented"* **Allan Marks** (see p.361) maintains a healthy reputation in the PPP field, counseling clients on a variety of transportation and infrastructure concerns. He was recently retained by the lenders financing the development of the Presidio Parkway transmission cable. **Jonathan Green** (see p.325) continues to garner praise from market sources this year. *"He is a very smart attorney with a can-do attitude,"* say clients. He continues to be sought out by organizations seeking both project finance and development advice in relation to various domestic and cross-border energy projects. **William Bice** (see p.283) is a *"very sharp and fine lawyer"* whose recent highlights include acting for JPM Ventures Energy in relation to the $1 billion financing of wind farms in various locations across the USA, as well as assisting MACH Gen in connection with the $160 million financing of gas-fired generation plants. **Daniel Bartfeld** (see p.1876) continues to build a successful projects practice. Of late, he has been representing a number of European and Asian lenders who are providing the financing for various oil and gas ventures, including in relation to the development of a gas transmission pipeline in Mexico. The *"very strong"* **Jonathan Maizel** (see p.360) serves as head of the project finance group in DC. He has a wealth of experience in multisourced finance transactions in the energy sector. Co-head of the firm's overall project finance department **Eric Silverman** (see p.406) specializes in the development and financing of energy and infrastructure assets, both at home and abroad. He is particularly adept at handling power projects. **Karen Wong** (see p.428) has a great deal of experience in the renewables and alternative energy sector, and has been active during the past year on behalf of the likes of Google, SAIC, Union Bank and Investec. **Carolina Walther-Meade** (see p.422) focuses on cross-border finance transactions, especially in mining and energy, and infrastructure projects across Latin America. She recently acted for Brazil-based USJ Açúcar e Alcool in connection with a $275 million export prepayment facility. **Daniel Michalchuk** (see p.368) continues to be recognized as a rising star within the projects community, and has had a busy year advising on the financing of various high-value projects. Highlights include acting for Crédit Agricole and CorpBanca in connection with the $80 million financing of transmission lines in Chile.

## Morgan, Lewis & Bockius LLP
See profile on p.2246

THE FIRM This firm is highly regarded by market sources for its depth of experience in the renewables sector, partic-

ularly in relation to the financing of wind energy projects. Notable highlights include its recent representation of First Wind in relation to a wind energy project in Hawaii valued at $236 million. Its diverse client base ranges from utilities to developers and investors. Clients also utilize the group for advice on oil and gas and power matters.
**Sources say:** *"They get the job done without fielding large teams and never make us feel like they are stretched too thin. Their work is excellent."*
KEY INDIVIDUALS *"Excellent lawyer"* **David Asmus** (see p.274) is well respected for his broad spectrum of expertise, but receives particular acclaim for his *"first-rate oil and gas expertise."* He has recently represented leading industry participants in a variety of oil and gas development projects. **Brian Bradshaw** (see p.286) is another talented projects lawyer with a focus on oil and gas concerns. He recently assisted Contango Oil & Gas with the development of a drilling program valued at $380 million. Clients describe **Richard Shortz** (see p.406) as an *"excellent lawyer and a terrific business partner, who is talented, honest, and practical."* With a background in business finance, he is well versed in handling M&A and financing concerns on behalf of the full range of energy companies. Noted by market sources for his particularly active renewables practice, **Wayne Song** (see p.410) makes his debut in the alternative energy and renewables rankings this year. He attracts praise for his *"superior level of service, attention to detail and work product."*

## Morrison & Foerster LLP
See profile on p.1990

THE FIRM This practice stands out for its strength in renewables and alternative energy projects, representing clients such as First Solar, CleanPath Ventures and Petra Solar. Recent work highlights include representing the Department of Energy in relation to its funding for a $2 billion solar thermal project, and being involved in connection with the big-ticket financing of a hydroelectric power plant in Peru.
KEY INDIVIDUALS Nicholas Spiliotes is a key contact at the firm.

## Nossaman LLP
See profile on p.692

THE FIRM Nossaman is nationally renowned as a leader in PPP matters. The 32-strong infrastructure team represents clients in more than 30 states in major projects. Recent highlights include its representation of Indiana Finance Authority in connection with the development and financing aspects of the East End Crossing project valued at $1.2 billion, as well as advising the California Department of Transportation in relation to the Presidio Parkway project, which is the first transaction of its kind since the implementation of new laws concerning availability payment PPP. Clients enthuse about the group's highly specialized industry knowledge, and its ability to negotiate complex agreements while safeguarding both the clients' and the public interest.
**Commercial Awareness:** *"They work extremely hard to get the job done, even when faced with very challenging sched-*

*The editorial is in alphabetical order by firm name.*

ules." "We chose it because it is certainly one of the preeminent firms in the USA working in PPP. The team brings a deep experience on public-side representation."

**KEY INDIVIDUALS Geoffrey Yarema** is a well-connected and active practitioner who is widely recognized as a leader in projects involving PPP. Sources highlight his deep knowledge of the industry and experience in handling the most complex of matters. **Patrick Harder** was recently appointed as head of the firm's infrastructure team. He is part of the team acting for the New York State Thruway Authority and the New York State Department of Transportation in relation to a design-build contract matter for the development of a new toll bridge which will be the furthest-reaching in the state.

## Orrick, Herrington & Sutcliffe LLP
See profile on p.1994

**THE FIRM** Orrick is best known for representing topdrawer renewables and alternative energy companies in cutting-edge wind and solar projects. Recent examples include advising NextEra on the $225 million financing for a wind farm project in Texas, and acting for SunEdison in connection with the disposal of a solar photovoltaic project. Also prominent is the firm's work in the PPP arena, with the team handling transactions for a variety of leading clients from the transport infrastructure sector, including lenders and private developers.

**Client Service** *"We are very happy with the whole team, from the partners down to the associates. It's a very high-level team which is very client-focused, but also very knowledgeable of both the law and the industry."*

**Commercial Awareness** *"We have placed our trust in Orrick for our largest and most sensitive transactions. We consider our partnership with Orrick to be one of our strategic and competitive advantages."*

**KEY INDIVIDUALS** Sources heap praise on the *"fabulous"* **Mark Weitzel**. He enjoys a strong standing in the renewables and alternative energy space, and is lauded for being *"really fantastic in navigating a path to success in very complicated matters."* He recently represented a polysilicon manufacturer in connection with the $266 million financing of its Alpaugh Solar project. **Leslie Sherman** and **David Spielberg** are singled out for being *"very thorough and responsive, and friendly to work with or against."* Leading clients seek them out for renewables and alternative energy matters, including solar and wind project transactions. They have recently acted on a project for 21 renewable energy development entities in connection with a multibillion-dollar project for the provision of renewable energy to three California utilities. **Daniel Mathews** continues to collect praise from market sources across the board for his active presence in the PPP area. Over the past year, he has represented a strong clientele comprising the likes of Fluor Enterprises, Skanska and Macquarie Capital. **Young Lee** makes her way up the PPP rankings this year following extensive praise from all corners of the market. She is applauded for the way in which she *"really goes the extra mile on transactions,"* and recently represented a consortium of bidders including ACS and Skanska Infrastructure in relation to the development of a crossing

as part of the Ohio River Bridges project. **Thomas Glascock** is highlighted for his ability in project debt financing matters. Although he has a broad-based practice, he is particularly active in the renewables and alternative energy space, where he has successfully acted for the likes of GCL Solar and Recurrent Energy in the financings of utility scale solar projects. **Christopher Moore** has gone from strength to strength in the past year. In the words of one client, *"he has exceeded all expectations: he is a client's dream lead as he is a professional through and through, highly respected by his peers and a true expert in the field."* Recent highlights include acting for Gamesa Energy USA in relation to a major renewables project. Renewable energy project finance expert **Tara Higgins** recently joined the firm from Bingham McCutchen. She is held in high regard by interviewees, who say she is *"very technically able, practical, has an excellent demeanor and is very protective of her clients."*

## Pillsbury Winthrop Shaw Pittman LLP
See profile on p.2000

**THE FIRM** This firm offers a comprehensive oil and gas projects service, and is particularly well known for its LNG prowess, having recently represented high-profile clients in several big-ticket cross-border matters. Recent highlights include representing Tesoro Corporation in connection with its purchase of $2.5 billion worth of BP oil and gas assets in Southern California, as well as assisting Chevron in completing various transactions for the lease of gas and coal facilities.

**KEY INDIVIDUALS John Mauel** is highly respected for his wealth of experience in the LNG sector. Clients praise his deep understanding of their business requirements, while peers describe him as *"simply fantastic."* **Jane Wallison Stein** has led the team's efforts on behalf of Tenaska in relation to the financing of several solar photovoltaic power projects. She was assisted by rising star **Michael Reese** (see p.391), who continues to impress peers with his project finance capabilities. Associate **Julie Hutchings** (see p.338) has developed a strong reputation among sources, who say: *"We think the world of her – she is responsible for getting things done, and does so promptly and thoroughly."* She is also said to be a *"superb lawyer and very commercial-minded."*

## Shearman & Sterling LLP
See profile on p.2005

**THE FIRM** This firm offers expertise across the full range of financial sources and structures employed in the projects arena. The 85-strong project development and finance group has impressive domestic and Latin American capabilities, acting for an enviable list of clients consisting of large financial institutions and major energy companies. The team is particularly well regarded for its strength in the power and mining and metals space, and over the last year has been instructed on various big-ticket matters. The team has also been active in the PPP sector.

**Sources say:** *"A tremendous law firm made up of a terrific team of highly professional lawyers."*

**KEY INDIVIDUALS** The *"phenomenal"* **Cynthia Urda Kassis** has substantial project development and project finance experience. Her practice includes advising a broad array of clients including lenders and sponsors from a diverse range of industries, from energy and infrastructure to mining and metals. **Robert Freedman** is another highly respected member of the project finance community. A wide spectrum of clients including Credit Suisse, ING and Citicorp benefit from his extensive experience in restructurings and workouts of infrastructure property, purchases and sales, and finance and development. **Patricia Hammes** recently acted for the lenders in relation to the $345 million financing of the West Deptford Merchant Power Plant. Her renewables expertise continues to attract high-profile clients such as the Department of Energy, which she and the firm continue to represent on numerous renewables projects. **Gregory Tan** was recently appointed as co-deputy chair of the global developments project finance group. He has extensive experience in a variety of energy and infrastructure projects, and is well reputed for his representation of various leading lenders, including the likes of Morgan Stanley and Credit Suisse.

## Sidley Austin LLP
See profile on p.1264

**THE FIRM** This group is a popular port of call for renewables-related projects. It has recently been busy with solar matters, acting on behalf of an enviable roster of clients including AES Solar Power, KDC Solar and Exeron Generating. The team is also well versed in advising clients on power concerns, and recently assisted a sovereign wealth fund in acquiring a sizable share in two power plants.

**Sources say:** *"The team is very skilled in this field and brilliant at negotiating with counterparties. They are also very responsive."*

**KEY INDIVIDUALS** According to clients, **Sergio Pozzerle** (see p.387) *"is one of the best lawyers in the renewable energy space. If something was very complicated, new or difficult, we would use Sergio because he is the best we know."* **Glenn Pinkerton**'s (see p.385) clients say he is an *"experienced and sharp lawyer."* He is singled out for his expertise in electrical power projects. **Irving Rotter** (see p.396) *"has been an absolutely invaluable, reliable and expert adviser,"* report clients. Over the past year, he has acted for the likes of Alaska Communications Systems Group and Chamisa Energy.

## Simpson Thacher & Bartlett LLP
See profile on p.2006

**THE FIRM** This team's reputation is dominated by its project finance work in the power and renewable and alternative energy sectors, as evidenced by its recent representation of high-profile lenders responsible for financing such projects. For example, the team recently represented Union Bank and RBS in connection with their provision of $650 million for the development of two wind projects as part of the major Terra-Gen Alta Wind Energy Center. On the conventional power side, the firm has recently represented

*The editorial is in alphabetical order by firm name.*

leading clients including Central Térmica Santa Rosa and Kinder Morgan.

**Sources say:** *"An extraordinarily good firm."*

**KEY INDIVIDUALS David Lieberman** (see p.356) rises to the top of the rankings this year on the back of ringing endorsement from clients, who say: *"He has an outstanding work ethic, strong familiarity with market terms, and provides solutions in difficult negotiating situations."* He has a broad projects practice and recently led the team in a financing for Redwood Trails Wind on behalf of Lloyds TSB. **Kenneth Wyman** (see p.429) is also applauded by clients for being *"practical and solution oriented; he approaches transactions on a collaborative rather than confrontation basis."* He has had an active year in the renewables space, and has been heavily involved in both wind and energy projects for the likes of KKR and the First Energy Reserve Infrastructure Fund.

### Skadden, Arps, Slate, Meagher & Flom LLP & Affiliates
See profile on p.2008

**THE FIRM** This team is a major presence in the power project arena, with a deep bench of highly experienced partners. The group attracts important clients such as the US Department of Energy, SolarReserve and Merrill Lynch. The team also has an impressive reputation for renewables project work, and continues to be at the forefront of some of the largest wind and solar financings. The team has represented First Solar in a number of projects over the past year, including in connection with the financing aspects of a $1.93 billion solar farm project. These successes are mirrored in the oil and gas sphere, with the team continuing to represent private equity investors and lenders in a broad range of financings and development projects on every continent. Notably, they recently represented RBS in connection with the financing of a high-profile joint venture between ExxonMobil and Qatar Petroleum.

**Client Service** *"Excellent service and a very high-quality work product."*

**Commercial Awareness** *"Their industry knowledge is extremely good – they regularly provide mailings and hold seminars for clients. They are also very understanding of clients' business needs, and very willing to pull out all the stops and throw the whole team in when needed."*

**KEY INDIVIDUALS Martin Klepper**'s (see p.348) considerable expertise in the project finance realm is praised by market commentators, who say: *"We are very impressed by him – his experience and knowledge rank very high."* He is principally recognized for his work in the renewables and alternative energy space, and has acted for First Solar and SolarReserve. **Harold Moore** (see p.371) commands an outstanding reputation in the field. He recently assisted South Korean fund Troika Resources Investment PEF in connection with the acquisition of an interest in oil and gas assets in Texas. **Julia Czarniak** (see p.300) impresses sources with her industry-savvy advice and *"great ability."* She specializes in the financing side of projects, and is regularly called upon by top-drawer clients such as RBS. She is adept at handling matters of both a national and inter-

national nature, and of late she has been particularly active in the Middle East. **Lance Brasher**'s (see p.286) highlights showcase a very active year in the renewables area. He was part of the various teams acting on multiple matters for First Solar, and recently assisted Solar Reserve with obtaining a loan of $737 million for a solar farm project. **Paul Kraske** (see p.350) handles the developmental, financing and acquisition aspects of a number of energy and infrastructure projects out of DC. He recently represented Citizens Sunrise Transmission in relation to the lease of a California transmission line worth over $98 million.

### Stoel Rives LLP

**THE FIRM** Stoel Rives's renewable and alternative energy projects team continues to garner praise for its representation of developers and investors. Clients from a range of industries retain the group and the past year has seen it handle numerous wind projects, including the financing aspects of the Prairie Rose Wind Farm project. The team has also been highly active on the solar side for clients including Capital Dynamics and Solar Frontier. The firm's international capabilities are a further draw for clients, particularly those from China and Europe seeking to invest in the renewables sector in the USA.

**KEY INDIVIDUALS** Renewables project finance and development expert **Edward Einowski** is based in Portland, and has been at the forefront of much of the firm's high-profile wind work. He recently handled the financing of the $375 million Chisholm View Wind Project, as well as acting on the Prairie Rose project on behalf of Enel Green Power. **Alan Merkle** recently led the team acting on behalf of Ireland's Mainstream Renewable Power in connection with various project agreements, and the financing relating to the development of a wind farm in South Africa. **Howard Susman** is a well-known player in the renewables community. Clients benefit from his deep experience in handling wind and solar projects.

### Sullivan & Cromwell LLP
See profile on p.2011

**THE FIRM** Sullivan & Cromwell enjoys a reputation as a first-class mining and metals projects firm. It is known for representing sponsors and borrowers on various projects at home and abroad, and highlights over the past year include acting for the sponsors in the Constancia project in Peru and the First Bauxite refractory grade bauxite project in Guyana. Peers are quick to highlight its preeminent ability in the project finance arena, particularly in relation to work on some of the highest-value transactions in this space. An example of this is its work for Minera Antucoya in relation to a $1.6 billion copper project in Chile. The group also performs well in oil and gas matters, exemplified by its recent employment by Australia Pacific LNG in connection with a multibillion-dollar LNG project in Australia.

**Commercial Awareness** *"Sullivan is our firm of choice – they are terrific, time after time. The work is of a very high quality, and they understand our commercial intentions as well as the legal issues."*

**KEY INDIVIDUALS** The *"very smart"* **Frederic Rich** (see p.392) is *"first-rate for work with oil and gas projects,"* with several peers singling him out as a top candidate for referrals in this area. He has continued to act for Australia Pacific LNG in relation to its big-ticket LNG project, as well as advising the likes of Sempra Energy and Tengizchevroil LLP. Clients turn to **Christopher Mann** (see p.361) for advice in relation to a wide array of energy and infrastructure projects. He has led on many of the firm's infrastructure projects, including serving as counsel to Chrysler Group in relation to the financing and other aspects of a sizable automobile joint venture project in Russia. Clients report that **Sergio Galvis** (see p.1895) is *"very good at judging what is important and what is not in a transaction, and always finds a solution that is very good for us."* He works on a wide range of project finance transactions, but stands out for his sophisticated mining and metals work.

### Vinson & Elkins LLP
See profile on p.2459

**THE FIRM** Vinson & Elkins possesses one of the finest oil and gas projects practices in the USA, with significant cross-border capabilities. Its prominent reputation in this sector is strongly linked to its preeminence in the energy and natural resources space. The group is heralded for its deep bench and profound project development and finance expertise in all aspects of the oil and gas value stream, as well as LNG matters. The team has had a successful year, winning a range of new clients to add to its already impressive client roster, which includes the likes of Statoil, Apollo Global Management and Spectra Energy. The group also receives glowing praise for its power projects work, which includes its recent representation of American Electric Power in connection to a joint venture with Great Plains Energy for the national development of transmission lines. The firm also enjoys a strong presence in the renewables space.

**Client Service:** *"Very credible, highly specialized service."* *"They are very responsive to our needs, produce excellent quality work, and have been very thoughtful in addressing the business needs of our company."*

**KEY INDIVIDUALS Mark Spradling** (see p.411) has acted on several big-ticket oil and gas projects, including for Peregrine Midstream Partners in connection with the $145 million financing of the Ryckman Creek natural gas storage project, as well as assisting China National Petroleum Corporation International with the legal aspects of the $1.2 billion Costa Rica refinery project. According to clients, **Mark Spivak** (see p.411) is *"a highly experienced and capable project development and project finance lawyer."* He focuses on the financing of renewables and power projects, and recently led the team's representation of Goldman Sachs in relation to the funding of a New Mexico electric transmission line project.

### White & Case LLP
See profile on p.451

**THE FIRM** White & Case is a highly respected option for power and oil and gas projects, particularly those involving

223

*The editorial is in alphabetical order by firm name.*

multidisciplinary and cross-border elements. With 84 lawyers spread across its DC, Miami and New York offices, this diverse practice has the breadth and depth to represent a range of top-drawer clients, including Calpine, ExxonMobil and Santander. On the power side, the group is fully versed in handling both traditional and renewable power generation projects, and recently represented Morgan Stanley in connection with the financing aspects of the Panda Temple Power Project. The highly acclaimed oil and gas team offers a wide range of services to clients, and the firm also upholds significant strength on the PPP side.

**Client Service** *"The service is terrific. They take a seamless approach across the board."*

**KEY INDIVIDUALS** *"Fabulous lawyer"* **Victor DeSantis** (see p.304) focuses on the representation of lenders in international project finance and cross-border matters. He recently represented ING, Citi and BNP Paribas in connection with the $900 million financing of the Amaralina Star and Laguna Star drillships. **Arthur Scavone** (see p.400) is known for his energy-related projects expertise, and recently represented Germany-based BayernLB and others in connection with the big-ticket financing of Post Rock Wind Farm in the USA. Another favorite among sources is the *"fantastic"* **Ned Neaher** (see p.374). He has represented clients ranging from the oil and gas and power arenas to PPP projects concerning airports and toll roads. Recent highlights include acting for a consortium of in connection with the financing of wind farm projects in Mexico. **Troy Alexander** (see p.272) specializes in the financing of energy projects, and was recently part of the team acting for Qatar Petroleum and ExxonMobil in relation to their role as sponsors of the Barzan Gas Project in Qatar. The project financing was valued at $10.3 billion, and represented the largest ever single financing in Qatar.

## Wilson Sonsini Goodrich & Rosati
See profile on p.700

**THE FIRM** This highly regarded projects practice is particularly well known for its strength in renewable energy and clean technology work, handling many of the biggest projects in the sector. The team continues to assist in the development and financing of a variety of projects including wind, solar, biomass and hydropower, on behalf of an enviable roster of clients featuring the likes of Clean Path Ventures, SunRun and Own Energy. Sources are particularly quick to highlight the group's prominence in the solar area, and a recent example of its success was its representation of Agile Solar Holdings in relation to a 150 MW solar project.

**Sources say:** *"A very good firm. The attorneys are very client-focused, highly practical and deal-oriented."*

**KEY INDIVIDUALS** The *"truly exceptional"* **Todd Glass** continues to offer a high level of skill in a range of renewable and alternative energy matters. Commentators attest

to his active practice over the past year, which has included assisting with the development and financing of several solar projects including on behalf of Clean Path Ventures, TUUSSO Energy and North Star Solar. **Peter Mostow**'s expertise covers the full range of energy and cleantech matters, and he has been retained by Foundation WindPower in connection with its efforts to facilitate multiple wind projects. Clients say he is *"outstanding in all regards, knowledgeable, creative, fair-minded and hardworking."* *"Great talent"* **Christopher Groobey** makes his way up the projects table this year after receiving very strong feedback from clients and peers alike. He maintains a national practice advising energy and clean technology clients in project finance and M&A transactions. He recently advised Union Bank in connection with the financing of over 20 landfill gas facilities across the USA.

## Winston & Strawn LLP
See profile on p.1267

**THE FIRM** This firm moves up the rankings this year, backed by strong support from clients and peers alike. The alternative energy and renewables team represents both lenders and sponsors with ease in connection with biomass, hydroelectric, wind, geothermal and solar projects. The group has recently conducted a large amount of work on behalf of Santander, helping with its efforts to make investments in various renewables projects in the USA. Other notable clients of the firm include enXco, Solar Reserve and Atlantic Wind Connection.

**Sources say:** *"We relish the opportunity to work with them – they are extremely knowledgeable and very easy to work with."*

**KEY INDIVIDUALS** Clients marvel that the *"excellent"* **Jerry Bloom** (see p.285) is *"very respectful of the process and knowledgeable on the issues we are faced with."* He has recently acted for Soitec Solar in connection with a wide range of transactional matters.

## Other Notable Practitioners

*"The legendary and very knowledgeable"* **John Cogan** of Cogan & Partners LLP maintains a superb reputation for oil and gas projects work, and continues to be a popular choice for clients seeking representation in LNG-related matters. **Thomas Hoffmann** (see p.335) of Ballard Spahr LLP specializes in advising lenders, sponsors, investors and developers on a variety of renewable energy projects including biomass, wind and solar power. **Jeffrey Chester** (see p.294) of Kaye Scholer LLP is *"very entrepreneurial and commercially oriented, with a firm grasp of both the law and what it takes to actually get a deal done."* He recently represented RPM in connection with the $116 million financing of several wind energy projects. Also at Kaye Scholer LLP, **Joel Moser** (see p.372) maintains a particular emphasis on PPP matters. Clients are thoroughly pleased

with his performance this year, commenting that he displays *"an excellent blend of business insight and legal context."* **Tomer Pinkusiewicz** (see p.385) is a recent addition to the projects team at Gibson, Dunn & Crutcher LLP. Clients say he *"provides sound and trusted professional legal advice, is a creative thinker and is able to navigate through tough negotiations while protecting his client's interest."* **Ernest Chung** (see p.294) of Blank Rome LLP continues to impress clients with his high levels of responsiveness while peers praise his *"strong knowledge of finance"* and *"detail-oriented"* approach. He recently acted for Dutch bank FMO in connection with its $200 million loan to multiple Latin American companies for the financing of various projects. Project finance specialist **Joseph Hadley** (see p.328) of Davis Polk & Wardwell LLP continues to collect praise from clients and peers alike. Peers say that he is *"a very smart and a very polished lawyer,"* while clients describe him as *"one of the best we have ever used."* At the same firm, **Waide Warner** (see p.423) continues to serve as head of the project finance team, and has recently acted for clients including Línea Amarilla, Credit Suisse, Morgan Stanley and Solar Solutions. Solo practitioner **Jay Kelley** is highly recommended for his broad-based projects practice. He regularly handles LNG matters for oil and gas companies. **Joseph Tato** (see p.416) has recently moved to DLA Piper LLP (US) from Dewey & LeBoeuf. He serves energy clients on a wide range of project finance matters. He recently represented Biotherm Energy in connection with several renewable energy projects. **Richard Shutran** of O'Melveny & Myers LLP is described as *"a very creative lawyer who has an enormous amount of knowledge."* He recently joined the firm from Dewey & LeBoeuf, and continues to assist clients ranging from lenders and investments funds to public and private entities. The *"simply outstanding"* **Junaid Chida**, also of O'Melveny & Myers LLP, is another attorney who has recently moved over from Dewey. Clients highlight him for his impressive energy project finance expertise, which covers a wide range of concerns including renewable energy projects, oil and gas projects and nuclear and hydroelectric projects. **Eric Richards** (see p.392) of O'Melveny & Myers LLP has a pre-eminent profile in the PPP field, with a particular focus on infrastructure project finance and development. Fellow O'Melveny & Myers LLP partner **Gregory Thorpe** is described by clients as *"experienced, unflappable, knows our company and works well with our internal teams."* He is best known for his renewables projects expertise. **Ellen Friedman** (see p.317) of Nixon Peabody LLP has had an active year representing various clients in renewable energy projects. She recently acted for US Bancorp, a tax equity investor, in connection with its investment in a big-ticket solar power project. **Timothy Callahan** of Paul Hastings LLP is well respected for his work in relation to power projects, and has recently acted on mandates for KeyBank, REpower USA and EWP Renewable.

# REAL ESTATE

| Real Estate Leading Firms |
|---|
| **Band 1** |
| Greenberg Traurig, LLP * |
| Skadden, Arps, Slate, Meagher & Flom LLP & Affiliates * |
| Sullivan & Cromwell LLP * |
| **Band 2** |
| DLA Piper LLP * |
| Fried, Frank, Harris, Shriver & Jacobson LLP * |
| Paul Hastings LLP * |
| Sidley Austin LLP * |
| Simpson Thacher & Bartlett LLP * |
| **Band 3** |
| Cadwalader, Wickersham & Taft LLP * |
| Cleary Gottlieb Steen & Hamilton LLP * |
| Dechert LLP * |
| Gibson, Dunn & Crutcher LLP * |
| Goodwin Procter LLP * |
| Holland & Knight LLP * |
| Proskauer Rose LLP * |
| **Band 4** |
| Baker Botts LLP * |
| Bingham McCutchen LLP * |
| Debevoise & Plimpton LLP * |
| Hogan Lovells US LLP |
| Jones Day * |
| Katten Muchin Rosenman LLP * |
| Kaye Scholer LLP * |
| Kirkland & Ellis LLP * |
| Latham & Watkins LLP * |
| Mayer Brown LLP * |
| Pillsbury Winthrop Shaw Pittman LLP * |
| Weil, Gotshal & Manges LLP * |
| Willkie Farr & Gallagher LLP * |

* Indicates firm / individual with profile.
Alphabetical order within each band. Band 1 is the highest.

## Band 1

### Greenberg Traurig, LLP
See profile on p.1024

**THE FIRM** This real estate powerhouse operates out of 30 offices across the USA, offering expertise across the full spectrum of real estate matters, including commercial leasing, joint ventures and restructurings. In standout matters, the team acted for Swire Properties on the acquisition, development and retail leasing of the $1 billion Brickell CitiCentre project in Miami. Other key clients include Invesco, Square Mile Capital and Kimco Realty.
**Sources say:** *"A very fine firm, staffed with very savvy real estate attorneys." "A tremendous national practice."*
**KEY INDIVIDUALS** Head of the firm's global real estate group, **Robert Ivanhoe** (see p.339) is *"one of the best*

| Real Estate Leading Individuals | |
|---|---|
| **Band 1** | |
| Altschuler Fredric L | Cadwalader, Wickersham & Taft LLP * |
| Epstien Jay | DLA Piper LLP (US) * |
| Fries Richard S | Bingham McCutchen LLP * |
| Horowitz Steven G | Cleary Gottlieb Steen & Hamilton LLP * |
| Ivanhoe Robert J | Greenberg Traurig, LLP * |
| Klein Frederick L | DLA Piper LLP (US) * |
| Mechanic Jonathan L | Fried, Frank, Harris, Shriver & Jacobson * |
| Mermelstein Joshua | Fried, Frank, Harris, Shriver & Jacobson * |
| Pinover Eugene | Willkie Farr & Gallagher LLP * |
| Ressa Gregory J | Simpson Thacher & Bartlett LLP * |
| Sharf Jesse | Gibson, Dunn & Crutcher LLP * |
| Uris Harvey R | Skadden, Arps, Slate, Meagher & Flom * |
| **Band 2** | |
| Adler Arthur S | Sullivan & Cromwell LLP * |
| Beard James | DLA Piper LLP (US) * |
| Colletta Anthony J | Sullivan & Cromwell LLP * |
| Glazer Michael H | Goodwin Procter LLP * |
| Heil Joseph B | Dechert LLP * |
| McInerney William P | Cadwalader, Wickersham & Taft LLP * |
| Rosenthal Barry P | Bingham McCutchen LLP * |
| Wasserstrom Neil | Mayer Brown LLP |

*lawyers around,"* according to interviewees. His expertise covers complex financings, restructurings and workouts involving real estate.

### Skadden, Arps, Slate, Meagher & Flom LLP & Affiliates
See profile on p.2008

**THE FIRM** The real estate practice group at this preeminent firm represents developers, investors, funds and REITs in both domestic and cross-border transactions. It has significant real estate finance capabilities, and regularly handles high-profile restructurings, workouts and securitized lending transactions. The group advised affiliates of Divco West and TPG Realty on their $798 million acquisition of Mission West Properties' real estate assets. Its enviable client list also includes SL Green Realty, Black Diamond Capital Management and PensionDanmark.
**Sources say:** *"Very high quality and very responsive – these are people who are used to delivering white-glove service."*
**KEY INDIVIDUALS Harvey Uris** (see p.420) heads the firm's global real estate practice and is widely regarded as a leading figure in the industry. He concentrates on public and private REITs, loan originations and securitization, and real estate capital markets transactions.

| Recommended for Client Service Nationwide | |
|---|---|
| Bingham McCutchen LLP | Jones Day |
| Gibson, Dunn & Crutcher LLP | Mayer Brown LLP |
| Holland & Knight LLP | |

| Recommended for Commercial Awareness Nationwide | |
|---|---|
| Bingham McCutchen LLP | Kirkland & Ellis LLP |
| Holland & Knight LLP | Paul Hastings LLP |

### Sullivan & Cromwell LLP
See profile on p.2011

**THE FIRM** This firm's real estate group is esteemed for its multidisciplinary approach, and assists clients with a broad range of real estate transactions, including acquisitions, dispositions, capital markets issuances and joint ventures. It is highly recommended for its representation of private equity clients, and offers substantial experience in the formation and structuring of new funds for real estate investments. The team recently represented Lazard Alternative Investments in a $1.1 billion secondary sale of shares of Ventas. The firm also acts for Vornado Realty, Forest City Enterprises and ING Group.
**Sources say:** *"I think they're the best real estate practitioners in the USA. They have a very good understanding of what we need and what's important to us in each deal. They have a very keen ability to know which points are critical." "They are really on top of every piece of the market – I've never run into an area they can't handle. The consistency is great – everyone we've dealt with has extraordinarily good judgment."*
**KEY INDIVIDUALS Arthur Adler** (see p.271) offers expertise across a broad range of commercial real estate matters, with a focus on real estate finance. He recently advised Vornado Realty on its $2.5 billion revolving credit facility. **Anthony Colletta** (see p.298) is *"good at taking a measured approach to what can be intense situations."* His extensive experience includes loan workouts and restructurings, private equity transactions, joint ventures and other corporate matters.

## Band 2

### DLA Piper LLP
See profile on p.1971

**THE FIRM** This international firm utilizes its broad and diverse skill set to handle complex matters for its investor, developer and lender clients. Regularly involved in high-value, high-profile matters, the team offers expertise in financing, leasing, land use and litigation. Recent highlights include advising Macerich on a swap transaction in which the company purchased a one-third ownership interest in Arrowhead Towne Center and Superstition

Springs Mall from General Growth Properties. Other significant clients include Tishman Speyer Properties, AEW Capital Management and Oxford Properties Group.

**Sources say:** *"DLA has tremendous national real estate capacities."*

**KEY INDIVIDUALS** The *"extremely bright and extremely experienced"* **Jay Epstien** (see p.310) is head of the firm's US real estate group. He is experienced in all types of real estate transactions, and represents developers, users and owners. Interviewees say **Frederick Klein** (see p.347) is *"responsive, hard-working and savvy"* in his approach. He has handled numerous transactions for Tishman Speyer, including the purchase and financing of a 380,000 sq ft office building in Arlington, Virginia. The *"outstanding"* **James Beard** (see p.1198) earns praise from commentators for his *"very practical"* approach. He has substantial expertise in handling workouts and the restructuring of troubled real estate assets for institutional lenders and developers.

## Fried, Frank, Harris, Shriver & Jacobson LLP
See profile on p.1975

**THE FIRM** This team serves clients across the complete spectrum of real estate issues, including leasing, financing, restructuring and litigation. It regularly advises on significant matters across the country, representing a diverse client base that includes REITs, owners, lenders and investors, and working closely with the firm's litigation, tax and bankruptcy departments. Its impressive clientele includes Credit Suisse, Aria Investment Partners, Google and Highgate Hotels.

**Sources say:** *"A terrific, top-quality real estate group."*

**KEY INDIVIDUALS** The *"phenomenal"* **Jonathan Mechanic** (see p.1918) chairs the firm's real estate group. His broad expertise encompasses the acquisition and disposal of hotels, offices and mixed-use properties. **Joshua Mermelstein** (see p.367) regularly represents developers, financial institutions and owners in a wide array of real estate matters, such as fund formation, financing and joint ventures. He also has significant experience in advising clients on complex workouts and loan restructurings.

## Paul Hastings LLP
See profile on p.1996

**THE FIRM** This firm's real estate department is highly regarded for its involvement in complicated and high-profile bankruptcy matters. Its 120-strong team offers considerable expertise across a broad range of issues, including financing, acquisitions and land use. The group has handled a significant number of deals for key client Oaktree Capital Management of late, including its acquisition of more than $1.5 billion nonperforming real estate loans from the Federal Deposit Insurance Corporation (FDIC) and other institutions. The firm also acts for Rockwood Capital, Lennar and Facebook.

**Commercial Awareness** *"They are very practical, business-minded and deal-oriented – they understand the business side."*

**KEY INDIVIDUALS** Los Angeles-based Phil Feder is head of the firm's global real estate practice.

## Sidley Austin LLP
See profile on p.1264

**THE FIRM** The real estate group at Sidley Austin is highlighted for its expertise in capital markets transactions, and across a range of complicated financing structures, including secured and unsecured credit facilities, mezzanine loans and CMBS. It represents developers, owners, lenders and investors in an array of issues throughout the USA and overseas. The team recently assisted Starwood Property Trust with the purchase and financing of 26 performing mortgage loans from Citibank.

**Sources say:** *"They're very good at what they do – it's a very high-quality practice."*

**KEY INDIVIDUALS** Alan Weil in New York, Marc Hayutin in Los Angeles and Charles Schrank in Chicago are the global coordinators of the firm's real estate practice.

## Simpson Thacher & Bartlett LLP
See profile on p.2006

**THE FIRM** This firm's sophisticated real estate group regularly assists prominent funds and private equity houses with major transactions. The team recently acted for key client The Blackstone Group on its $2 billion acquisition of the CalWest Industrial Portfolio, located across six states. In other notable work, it advised the Carlyle Real Estate Fund on a $900 million recapitalization of debt and equity for Class A retail and office building 650 Madison Avenue in New York.

**Sources say:** *"The best private equity real estate firm."*

**KEY INDIVIDUALS** The *"terrific"* **Gregory Ressa** (see p.392) heads the firm's real estate group. His practice encompasses all areas of real estate law, with a particular focus on representing opportunity funds, as well as real estate finance and M&A transactions.

## Band 3

## Cadwalader, Wickersham & Taft LLP
See profile on p.438

**THE FIRM** This prominent real estate finance group is well equipped to assist clients across the full range of transactions, and is particularly adept in mortgage and mezzanine loans. The team frequently represents institutional clients in loan originations, purchases, sales and workouts. In highlights, it acted for HSBC on the $500 million syndicated financing of the Empire State Building. Other key clients include Vornado Realty, Deutsche Bank and Macquarie.

**Sources say:** *"A preeminent real estate finance firm. We're delighted when they're on the other side."*

**KEY INDIVIDUALS** **Fredric Altschuler** (see p.273) is described as *"hard-working, very responsive"* and good at *"balancing legal risk with accomplishing business objectives."* He represents investment banks, public entities, and developers, among other clients, in the financing of their major real estate projects. Practice group chair **William McInerney** (see p.365) is experienced across the full spectrum of real estate-related transactions, and frequently acts on behalf of leading investors and financial institutions.

Notable work includes acting for a group of banks on the financing for The Blackstone Group's $1.9 billion acquisition of the Motel 6 chain.

## Cleary Gottlieb Steen & Hamilton LLP
See profile on p.1963

**THE FIRM** This versatile real estate group handles complex financing, securitization and capital markets transactions, drawing on its deep bench of highly skilled and specialized attorneys. It also offers significant experience in bankruptcy matters, restructurings and workouts, and recently represented affiliates of the Simon Property Group in a $300 million mortgage loan restructuring. Other notable clients include Colony Capital, Goldman Sachs and OneWest Bank.

**Sources say:** *"A very good, diversified practice."*

**KEY INDIVIDUALS** Sources hold **Steven Horowitz** (see p.337) in high esteem, describing him as *"a truly outstanding practitioner."* He is experienced across a broad range of transactions, acting for investors, banks and owners on matters both in the USA and around the world.

## Dechert LLP
See profile on p.1969

**THE FIRM** Dechert is a key player in the area of CMBS, regularly acting for underwriters, loan originators, major issuers and structured investment vehicles, among others. Other areas of expertise include fund formation, mortgage finance and loan origination. Notable highlights saw the team act for Pacific Life Insurance Company on the origination of a $325 million office building-secured leasehold. Other clients include H/2 Capital Partners, Berkadia Commercial Mortgage and Rialto Capital.

**Sources say:** *"Their prominence in the securitization space is important to us. They're really smart people, and they do a good job of leveraging attorneys and other professionals in a way that makes the transaction efficient."*

**KEY INDIVIDUALS** Interviewees describe **Joseph Heil** (see p.332) as *"extremely responsive and extremely sharp."* He is highly respected as an expert in CMBS lending, and also handles workouts, debt funds and equity transactions.

## Gibson, Dunn & Crutcher LLP
See profile on p.682

**THE FIRM** This firm's real estate group has extensive expertise across a broad range of matters, including leasing, development, acquisitions and dispositions. It provides clients with a well-rounded service by drawing on the firm's bankruptcy, litigation and corporate capabilities. The team recently acted for Wells Fargo on the $3.3 billion acquisition of Irish Bank Resolution Corporation's portfolio of 61 US-based commercial real estate loans. Other key clients include Woodridge Capital, Fortress and Deutsche Bank.

**Client Service** *"They have great business acumen, attention to detail and overall client service."*

**KEY INDIVIDUALS** **Jesse Sharf** (see p.404) is *"a relationship source and a deal maker"* who *"drills down to what's meaningful"* in a transaction, according to sources. He specializes in real estate-related high-end equity and debt finance.

## Goodwin Procter LLP
See profile on p.1522

**THE FIRM** This firm's real estate team offers a deep bench of attorneys skilled in a wide range of matters, from public finance and real estate capital markets to large-scale development and permitting. In standout matters, the group acted for Equity One on the sale of its $473 million multistate shopping center portfolio to Blackstone. Notable clients also include AvalonBay Communities and Four Seasons Hotels & Resorts.

**Sources say:** "*They produce very good work and they're very client service-oriented.*"

**KEY INDIVIDUALS** Michael Glazer (see p.1493) has extensive expertise in advising funds, investors and managers on their real estate investments. Sources say he is "*thorough, very good at thinking through all the issues, good at overseeing a team, and conscientious.*"

## Holland & Knight LLP
See profile on p.1028

**THE FIRM** This international firm's real estate group offers broad geographic coverage, with 200 lawyers working out of offices across the country. It has significant experience across the full spectrum of real estate matters, including land use and finance, and stands out for its work in the hospitality sector. The group has been advising Starwood Capital Group and Tribeca Associates on the $500 million development of the Manhattan-based, five star flagship Baccarat Hotel and Residences. Other clients include Extell Development, Stark Properties and New York Life Insurance.

**Client Service** "*They have been absolutely excellent – they're responsive and prompt, and understand what the client needs. They are a pleasure to work with.*"

**Commercial Awareness** "*A professional firm with high standards and high integrity, that understands practical and business concerns.*"

**KEY INDIVIDUALS** Joe Guay is head of the real estate group, and the main contact for the firm.

## Proskauer Rose LLP
See profile on p.2001

**THE FIRM** Proskauer Rose represents some of the most prominent owners, developers, funds and financial institutions, and is regularly involved in some of the most complex, high-profile projects in the real estate market. The team advised Guggenheim Partners on the origination of more than $500 million of US-based mortgage loans, including shopping centers in California and Arkansas, and a Pennsylvania office building portfolio. The firm also represents CBRE, AIG Global Investment and Donna Karan New York.

**Sources say:** "*They are service-oriented and will do what it takes to keep up with the pace of the transaction. I have the utmost confidence in the firm.*"

**KEY INDIVIDUALS** New York-based Ronald Sernau is the group's main contact.

Band 4

## Baker Botts LLP
See profile on p.2427

**THE FIRM** This firm has a wealth of experience across all traditional real estate transactions, including financing, leasing, joint ventures and development. It also has extensive experience advising on the full life cycle of funds, from establishment to portfolio disposition and asset liquidation. The team has handled several important matters for key client Hines in recent months, including the development of a Class A office building overlooking Bryant Park. Other clients include Coventry Development Group, E2M Partners and the Dallas Center for the Performing Arts Foundation.

**Sources say:** "*Tremendous lawyers.*"

**KEY INDIVIDUALS** Dallas-based Patricia Stanton chairs the firmwide real estate group.

## Bingham McCutchen LLP
See profile on p.1515

**THE FIRM** This real estate group excels in all elements of major distressed loan and business workouts, including financings, foreclosures and restructurings. The team has been advising private equity client Silverpeak Real Estate Partners on the restructuring of over $2 billion of distressed development projects, joint venture interests and mezzanine loans. It also represents Citibank, Stanford University, Wells Fargo and M&T Bank.

**Client Service** "*Bingham is a fantastic firm. Our experience with its attorneys has been exceptional.*"

**Commercial Awareness** "*Bingham is a premium service provider that can be expected to quickly understand the nuances of a complex transaction and meet a difficult deadline.*"

**KEY INDIVIDUALS** Richard Fries (see p.317) has "*a depth of knowledge and experience that is invaluable in handling the unexpected and unique challenges of real estate workout transactions.*" He regularly advises on the distressed real estate issues of developers, owners, investment banks and lenders. "*Really smart and very practical,*" **Barry Rosenthal** (see p.888) earns praise from interviewees for his "*very good business sense coupled with common sense.*" He offers expertise in all facets of real estate transactions, including joint ventures, leasing and acquisitions.

## Debevoise & Plimpton LLP
See profile on p.1968

**THE FIRM** This firm's real estate practice group offers expertise across a broad range of matters, including joint venture investments, financings, workouts and restructurings. It has significant experience advising on the sales and acquisitions of major shopping centers, hotels and office buildings. In highlights, the team acted for Rockefeller Group International on its acquisition of San Francisco's 50 Beale Street, in a joint venture with Mitsubishi Estate New York. Other notable clients include the Westfield Group, Clayton, Dubilier & Rice and Beacon Capital Partners.

**Sources say:** "*I've never encountered anyone as responsive as they are.*"

**KEY INDIVIDUALS** The team's main contact is Peter Irwin in New York.

## Hogan Lovells US LLP

**THE FIRM** The real estate department at Hogan Lovells brings together expertise from the firm's hotels, tax, REITs and corporate teams, in order to effectively represent clients in major projects both in the USA and around the world. The group recently advised the Schwan Foundation on the $200 million restructuring of its ownership positions, with Florida Farm and Ice Company, in a major development in Costa Rica. Other key clients include Kingdom Hotel Investments, Quadrangle Development and Gaylord Entertainment.

**Sources say:** "*A great law firm with very good lawyers.*"

**KEY INDIVIDUALS** Bruce Parmley heads the department.

## Jones Day
See profile on p.919

**THE FIRM** This firm's real estate group represents banks, REITs, funds and developers in all types of transactions, and has particular strength in fund formation, substantial M&A deals and private equity investments. Recent highlights saw the group act for DDR Group on a joint venture formation with The Blackstone Group, and on the negotiation for its subsequent purchase of a $1.43 billion, 46 shopping center portfolio. The firm also acts for Trammell Crow Residential, Capital One Bank and Mill Creek Residential Trust.

**Client Service** "*They provide a very high-quality service in terms of professionalism and the advice that they dispense.*"

**KEY INDIVIDUALS** Chicago-based Robert Lee and David Lowery in Dallas cochair the firm's US real estate practice.

## Katten Muchin Rosenman LLP
See profile on p.1253

**THE FIRM** This firm's diverse real estate group is highly recommended for its expertise in handling matters on both the debt and equity sides of real estate capital markets transactions and financings. The team recently acted for Freddie Mac on a series of multifamily transactions financed nationwide with tax-exempt bonds. Other key clients include Macquarie Bank, Resort Gaming Group and Chesapeake Lodging Trust.

**Sources say:** "*The attorneys are very knowledgeable and responsive, and work well together.*"

**KEY INDIVIDUALS** Chicago-based David Bryant heads the firm's real estate department.

## Kaye Scholer LLP
See profile on p.1984

**THE FIRM** This real estate practice group is well known for its representation of lenders, and is particularly experienced in loan originations, including the structuring of large CMBS loans. It recently advised the Canada Pension Plan Investment Board on the origination of $145 million of senior mezzanine debt financing for New York's Carousel and Destiny USA Malls. The firm also represents HSH Nordbank, Bank of America and Crédit Agricole CIB.

**Sources say:** *"They're supersophisticated on the debt side."*

**KEY INDIVIDUALS** Key contacts include Warren Bernstein and Stephen Gliatta in New York.

## Kirkland & Ellis LLP
See profile on p.1254

**THE FIRM** Kirkland & Ellis is rated for its expertise in the real estate funds space. It represents prominent private equity fund sponsors, pension organizations, investors and sovereign wealth funds, among others. The team recently assisted General Growth Properties with the formation of a joint venture with Canada Pension Plan Investment Board for the $500 million acquisition of St. Louis shopping center Plaza Frontenac. Other key clients include Garrison Investment Group, Archstone and Equity Lifestyle Investments.

**Commercial Awareness** *"They are responsive and commercially oriented – they focus on the context of the transaction, and on getting it done."*

**KEY INDIVIDUALS** Key contacts include Daniel Perlman and Andrew Small in Chicago.

## Latham & Watkins LLP
See profile on p.446

**THE FIRM** This team offers deep experience across a broad range of real estate matters, including mezzanine debt, REIT financing, leasing and development. It benefits from the firm's global footprint, and regularly represents clients in cross-border transactions. In a standout matter, the group handled the $2.3 billion restructuring of a mortgage loan for Atlantis Paradise Island Hotel, Resort & Casino. Other significant clients include BlackRock, Colony Capital, Jefferies and TimeWarner.

**Sources say:** *"They have a very deep bench and are very willing to bring the right talent in to help the client be as efficient as possible."*

**KEY INDIVIDUALS** New York-based James Hisiger is global cochair of the firm's real estate practice, and the main contact in the USA.

## Mayer Brown LLP
See profile on p.1257

**THE FIRM** This firm's real estate team regularly acts for leading private equity firms, investors, banks and joint ventures, among others. It is experienced in all types of real estate-related transactions, and recently acted for Australian REIT Charter Hall Office Management on the $1.7 billion sale of its US portfolio, which included interests in 14 office properties. Other key clients include GM, Clarion Partners and Prudential Financial.

**Client Service** *"The lawyers at Mayer Brown have been extremely responsive, professional, fair, and a great bargain for the quality of service provided."*

**KEY INDIVIDUALS** **Neil Wasserstrom** *"is very knowledgeable about real estate law and gives solid, practical counsel."* One client enthused: *"He is one of the most responsive, user-friendly lawyers I've ever worked with."* Wasserstrom is based in Houston, and concentrates on energy-related real estate matters.

## Pillsbury Winthrop Shaw Pittman LLP
See profile on p.2000

**THE FIRM** This real estate group has significant experience across a wide array of real estate projects, including shopping centers, universities, office buildings and sports complexes. In recent highlights, it represented Midway Cos., in partnership with Canyon Partners and basketball legend Magic Johnson, in its $200 million acquisition of the Houston Pavilions. The firm also acts for CommonWealth Partners, Clark Realty Capital and In-N-Out Burger.

**Sources say:** *"They are solution-oriented, and don't lose sight of the business aspects when they are doing a deal."*

**KEY INDIVIDUALS** Robert Herr is the key contact for the real estate department, and leads the group from San Francisco.

## Weil, Gotshal & Manges LLP
See profile on p.2015

**THE FIRM** This sophisticated practice group is frequently involved in cutting-edge matters across the country, including financings, development and leasing matters, and major M&A deals. In a recent highlight, the team advised Brookfield Asset Management on its $400 million joint venture with Texas-based Hillwood Development to acquire and develop industrial properties in the USA. The team is also highlighted for its expertise in insolvency-related real estate work.

**Sources say:** *"Our matters always have successful outcomes, as a result of their sage counsel, expertise and execution."*

**KEY INDIVIDUALS** Philip Rosen and Michael Bond cochair the practice from New York.

## Willkie Farr & Gallagher LLP
See profile on p.2016

**THE FIRM** This highly regarded real estate group represents a broad mix of clients, including hedge funds, developers and institutional investors, in significant matters across the USA. Notably, the team has recently been involved in several complicated and highly visible restructuring matters. It also has substantial experience in the acquisition and financing of commercial properties, including hotel portfolios, shopping centers and casinos. Key clients include Sunrise Senior Living, Brookfield and The Paramount Group.

**Sources say:** *"They're very professional, with very high standards."*

**KEY INDIVIDUALS** Practice group cochair **Eugene Pinover** (see p.385) is widely recognized for his extensive experience handling financings, restructurings, acquisitions and dispositions for a client base of both foreign and domestic real estate companies.

# RETAIL

| Retail |
|---|
| **Leading Firms** |
| **Band 1** |
| DLA Piper LLP (US) * |
| Greenberg Traurig, LLP * |
| Jones Day * |
| Perkins Coie LLP |
| **Band 2** |
| Fulbright & Jaworski LLP * |
| Gibson, Dunn & Crutcher LLP * |
| Goulston & Storrs |
| Holland & Knight LLP * |
| Morgan, Lewis & Bockius LLP * |
| Seyfarth Shaw LLP * |
| **Band 3** |
| Cravath, Swaine & Moore LLP * |
| Davis Polk & Wardwell LLP * |
| Latham & Watkins LLP * |
| Paul, Weiss, Rifkind, Wharton & Garrison LLP * |
| Sills Cummis & Gross P.C. * |

*Indicates firm with profile.*
*Alphabetical order within each band. Band 1 is the highest.*

## Band 1

### DLA Piper LLP (US)
See profile on p.1971

THE FIRM This global heavyweight is widely recognized as a major force in the industry and is particularly noted for its exceptional franchising and brand protection expertise. In recent highlights, the group represented PF Chang's China Bistro in its merger with Centerbridge. The team consists of highly experienced lawyers from various practices working together across its global network. This has attracted a significant portfolio of clients including lululemon athletica, The Home Depot, Harley Davidson and Porsche.
Sources say: *"We work with them across the world. They are responsive – the advice is good and practical."*
KEY INDIVIDUALS Seattle-based corporate partner John Steel heads the firm's retail and consumer product practice and is a main point of contact.

### Greenberg Traurig, LLP
See profile on p.1024

THE FIRM This full-service firm combines a distinguished mix of experienced lawyers across its department to offer one of the strongest retail practices in the country. The group continues to be very busy handling anticounterfeiting cases as high-end retailers turn to the team for its strong track record in this area.
Sources say: *"The service, coordination and communication were very good."*
KEY INDIVIDUALS Chair of the global retail practice Warren Karp is the key contact.

### Jones Day
See profile on p.919

THE FIRM This powerhouse is home to one of the most well-respected retail teams in the country. It represents long-standing client DDR, one of the largest shopping mall developers in the country, in a wide range of matters including its joint venture with The Blackstone Group to acquire EPN Group's portfolio of 46 shopping centers for $1.43 billion. The team is also well versed in litigation, having recently represented Abercrombie & Fitch in various class actions. Other notable highlights include advising Harry Winston on its $300 million senior secured credit facility to finance its domestic and international operations.
KEY INDIVIDUALS Cleveland-based Lyle Ganske heads the retail practice and is the main contact.

### Perkins Coie LLP
See profile on p.2548

THE FIRM This esteemed firm enjoys a prominent position at the top of the table thanks to its preeminent strength in e-commerce and IP issues. Its strong track record in this field has attracted a strong client following, including Microsoft, Google, Starbucks, General Mills and several major e-commerce players. The team represents a whole range of clients ranging from startups and small entrepreneurial businesses to major industry-leading companies. Recent highlights include acting for Costco in its $760 million acquisition of the 50% stake it did not own of Costco de México.
KEY INDIVIDUALS Kevin Hamilton chairs the firm's retail and consumer products practice and is based in Seattle.

## Band 2

### Fulbright & Jaworski LLP
See profile on p.2435

THE FIRM Fulbright & Jaworski is a significant player in the market and maintains a strong foothold in the retail industry. The group has been highly active in significant litigation mandates involving trademark infringement, employment and enforcement issues. Recent highlights include representing EPN in the $1.43 billion sale of its portfolio of 46 shopping malls in 22 states to a joint venture between DDR and The Blackstone Group. In addition, it currently advises Toyota Motor Engineering & Manufacturing North America on the development and construction of Phase II of its vehicle manufacturing plant in Texas.
Commercial Awareness *"We're very pleased with the way they tackle the job – they do a good job of looking not just at the legal aspects but at business ramifications, which is a huge help."*
KEY INDIVIDUALS Austin-based Jane Smith is a key contact in the group.

| Recommended for Client Service Nationwide | |
|---|---|
| Goulston & Storrs | Paul, Weiss, Rifkind, Wharton & Garrison LLP |
| Latham & Watkins LLP | |
| | Sills Cummis & Gross P.C. |

| Recommended for Commercial Awareness Nationwide | |
|---|---|
| Davis Polk & Wardwell LLP | Morgan, Lewis & Bockius LLP |
| Fulbright & Jaworski LLP | Paul, Weiss, Rifkind, Wharton & Garrison LLP |

### Gibson, Dunn & Crutcher LLP
See profile on p.682

THE FIRM Gibson Dunn's acclaimed strength across the board, and its dedication to the industry, ensure its position as a prominent player in retail issues. With offices in strategic locations across the world, it is well positioned to advise all manner of clients, ranging from startups to international corporations. As counterfeiting continues to be of growing concern in the industry, the team is frequently sought after by major clients such as Bottega Veneta, Balenciaga, Chloé, Yves Saint Laurent and Gucci in trademark infringement actions against website operators selling counterfeit products. It also offers strong litigation capabilities, representing Apple in numerous cases, including its much-publicized dispute with SAMSUNG.
Sources say: *"Excellent and they were very easy to work with."*
KEY INDIVIDUALS The New York-based Lois Herzeca and David Wilf cochair the fashion, retail and consumer products practice.

### Goulston & Storrs

THE FIRM This long-standing market player continues to be a force in the retail industry and is best known for its strengths in real estate and leasing. For example, the team represents Tory Burch in retail leasing matters across the country, including in negotiations for the retail roll-out of its flagship store on Rodeo Drive. The group is also very active in airport retail leasing and management, recently advising MarketPlace Development on leasing, marketing and management of retail concessions at the Ronald Reagan Washington National Airport, Philadelphia International Airport and Dulles International Airport.
Client Service *"I've been impressed with them – the number-one thing is their availability and the high level of quality. They are extremely responsive and the work is very good across the board."*
KEY INDIVIDUALS Nancy Davids, Matthew Epstein and David Rabinowitz cochair the practice group.

### Holland & Knight LLP
See profile on p.1028

THE FIRM This renowned firm is a prominent feature in the retail industry. Its core strength in commercial real estate and leasing makes it a significant player in the sector, and its tremendous expertise across various industries and practice areas makes it a go-to firm for major retail clients. It also has a strong restaurant practice within the retail department, with a group of lawyers dedicated to advising key clients such as McDonald's, Nando's Restaurant Group and Wagamama. It also currently represents Pie-Face Holdings, a successful Australian bakery/café chain, in its expansion into the USA.

**Sources say:** *"The team is consistent and no matter who you get, they all do a good job."*

**KEY INDIVIDUALS** Deborah De Luca and Tara Scanlon cochair the retail developments practice.

## Morgan, Lewis & Bockius LLP
See profile on p.2246

**THE FIRM** This firm's labor and employment expertise earns it a great deal of respect from the market and attracts significant class action mandates from the retail industry. Notably, the team successfully obtained a voluntary dismissal by the plaintiff in a wage and hour class action claim against PetSmart. On the transactional side, it recently acted for Claire's Stores in its $625 million sale of 9% senior secured first-lien notes due 2019. Other key clients include ARAMARK, Toys R Us, Office Depot and Best Buy.

**Commercial Awareness** *"We appreciate their knowledge and expertise in the retail industry, responsiveness and ability to provide good practical advice."*

**KEY INDIVIDUALS** Co-heads of the retail group Anne Marie Estevez and Greg Parks are based in Miami and Philadelphia respectively.

## Seyfarth Shaw LLP
See profile on p.1262

**THE FIRM** This market stalwart remains a go-to group for retail clients seeking expertise in labor and employment matters. It has an outstanding track record of representing retailers in class actions across the country. For example, the team recently successfully represented Family Dollar in a significant nationwide sex discrimination class action. It also has a strong real estate offering and represents 7-Eleven in real estate matters across the country. Other notable clients include Hermes of Paris, Ferragamo, Groupon, The Gap and Whole Foods Market.

**KEY INDIVIDUALS** Boston-based Lynn Kappelman leads the firm's retail practice.

## Band 3

## Cravath, Swaine & Moore LLP
See profile on p.1966

**THE FIRM** This firm is highly respected for its corporate transactional capabilities and is frequently instructed on some of the largest mandates in the retail industry. The team currently represents Hertz in its $2.3 billion acquisition of Dollar Thrifty Automotive Group. It has also advised JPMorgan on numerous credit facilities for companies such as JC Penney, Walmart and Best Buy.

**Sources say:** *"Outstanding – they did a terrific job and if we had a similar situation, we would turn to them immediately."*

**KEY INDIVIDUALS** Minh Van Ngo is a key contact at the firm.

## Davis Polk & Wardwell LLP
See profile on p.442

**THE FIRM** This group has a respected profile in the retail industry and is especially noted for its outstanding financing practice. The team has acted as underwriters' counsel in numerous significant transactions, advising the likes of JPMorgan, Bank of America Merrill Lynch and Credit Suisse. It is also well recognized for M&A work, and recently represented Campbell's in its $1.55 billion acquisition of Bolthouse Farms. Other highlights include acting for Limited Brands in its sale of a 51% stake in Mast Global Fashions to Sycamore Partners, as well as in its $1 billion senior notes SEC-registered offering.

**Commercial Awareness** *"They are extremely competent, very talented and give me advice that is very practical and creative, and that I can rely on."*

**KEY INDIVIDUALS** David Caplan and Sarah Beshar are key contacts in the group.

## Latham & Watkins LLP
See profile on p.446

**THE FIRM** This renowned corporate firm makes its debut in the rankings this year following tremendous praise from the market. It is respected for its corporate strength as well as for its experienced team of IP and litigation experts. Highlights include representing Tilly's in its $142.6 million IPO, and Skullcandy in its $188.8 million IPO. The team also handled a significant number of transactions for Leonard Green & Partners, including its $1.7 billion investment in Savers through a recapitalization.

**Client Service** *"The quality of their work is great, and what sets them apart from others is their responsiveness; they seem to be on call 24/7, they reply immediately and it's unbelievable."*

**KEY INDIVIDUALS** New York-based Gregory Rodgers and the Silicon Valley-based Anthony Richmond are key contacts in the global retail practice.

## Paul, Weiss, Rifkind, Wharton & Garrison LLP
See profile on p.1997

**THE FIRM** This corporate heavyweight has a strong reputation in the retail industry for its transactional strength. The nine-partner team undertakes a significant number of high-profile IPOs and financing transactions. Indicative work highlights include the team's recent representation of Michael Kors Holdings in its two secondary offerings, having handled its $1.1 billion IPO in 2011. Fast Retailing USA is one of the firm's long-standing clients, which the team recently advised on licensing matters as well as on internal restructuring to separate its two principal brands, UNIQLO and Theory, in the USA.

**Client Service** *"They are incredibly responsive and comprehensive in their advice."*

**Commercial Awareness** *"They have a very good understanding of our operating business and a decent idea of our business objectives."*

**KEY INDIVIDUALS** New York-based Valerie Radwaner is a key contact.

## Sills Cummis & Gross P.C.
See profile on p.1762

**THE FIRM** This compact but highly effective outfit is a strong contender in the market and is able to provide a dedicated team of experts to advise on all aspects of the retail industry. It has established a strong reputation for its commercial real estate and leasing work, including real estate-related litigation.

**Client Service** *"Their performance for us has been outstanding – they use the right level of lawyers and staffing to minimize the costs, are always accessible, very on top of things and responsive in the turnaround for any aspect of our projects."*

**KEY INDIVIDUALS** Co-managing partner of the New York office, Michael Goldsmith chairs the firm's retail practice.

# SECURITIES

Commentary about individuals can be found under their firm's paragraph.  If the firm has no paragraph (is not ranked) look at Other Notable Practitioners.

## Securities: Litigation
### Leading Firms

**Band 1**
Cravath, Swaine & Moore LLP *
Paul, Weiss, Rifkind, Wharton & Garrison LLP *
Simpson Thacher & Bartlett LLP *
Skadden, Arps, Slate, Meagher & Flom LLP & Affiliates *
Sullivan & Cromwell LLP *

**Band 2**
Cleary Gottlieb Steen & Hamilton LLP *
Davis Polk & Wardwell LLP *
Gibson, Dunn & Crutcher LLP *
Wachtell, Lipton, Rosen & Katz *
Weil, Gotshal & Manges LLP *

**Band 3**
Debevoise & Plimpton LLP *
Goodwin Procter LLP *
Latham & Watkins LLP *
Munger, Tolles & Olson LLP *
O'Melveny & Myers LLP *
WilmerHale *

**Band 4**
Jenner & Block LLP *
Katten Muchin Rosenman LLP *
Kaye Scholer LLP *
Milbank, Tweed, Hadley & McCloy LLP *
Morrison & Foerster LLP *
Orrick, Herrington & Sutcliffe LLP *
Ropes & Gray LLP *
Shearman & Sterling LLP *
Sidley Austin LLP *
Williams & Connolly LLP
Willkie Farr & Gallagher LLP *

*The editorial is in alphabetical order by firm name.*

## Arnold & Porter LLP
See profile on p.906

**THE FIRM** Arnold & Porter's national securities practice is recognized for its ability to guide clients through complex investigations. The team provides representation in enforcement preceedings before securities regulators the Financial Industry Regulatory Authority (FINRA) and the SEC, as well as other federal agencies. Clients include iStar Financial and Ernst & Young.
**Sources say:** *"The team always goes over and above to provide exceptional service. In addition to their level of knowledge, it's what sets them apart."*
**KEY INDIVIDUALS** Michael Trager (see p.418) handles securities enforcement actions for clients and chairs the firm's practice group in this area. He is described as *"exceptionally knowledgeable about the handling of SEC investiga-*

tions" and is commended for his provision of *"outstanding client support."*

## Bernstein Litowitz Berger & Grossmann LLP
See profile on p.1957

**THE FIRM** This firm is highlighted by peers around the country as one of the leading practices focusing on the representation of plaintiffs in complex, high-stakes securities class actions. It pursues claims on behalf of both institutions and individuals in relation to the subprime mortgage crisis, securities fraud and shareholder actions, and acts for whistle-blowers on SEC investigations. The team has been involved in some of the nation's biggest securities fraud cases and was instrumental in achieving a multibillion-dollar settlement for shareholders from Bank of America relating to its Merrill Lynch purchase.
**Sources say:** *"It has a lot of big, high-profile cases and is the leading firm right now in terms of the quality of cases."*
**KEY INDIVIDUALS** Standout attorney **Max Berger** (see p.1878) is a household name in securities litigation circles and is considered across the board to be a dean of the Bar in this area. *"I like* **Salvatore Graziano** (see p.1899)," comments one peer, who adds: *"He is professional, worthy and makes you work hard in a legitimate way."* His client base includes hedge funds and institutional investors. **Steven Singer** (see p.1942) is an influential player in the securities litigation arena according to sources. He was lead lawyer in claims against Bank of America which recovered $2.43 billion on behalf of shareholders and investors.

## Bingham McCutchen LLP
See profile on p.1515

**THE FIRM** Bingham McCutchen is acknowledged for its work in the securities enforcement space and has played a significant role in representing some of the nation's leading financial institutions in high-stakes investigations and enforcement actions, often in the broker-dealer space. The team offers significant experience before securities regulatory bodies and provides ongoing advice to a high profile roster of clients including Bank of America Merrill Lynch.
**KEY INDIVIDUALS** Head of the firm's securities and financial institutions litigation department, **Jeffrey Smith** (see p.409) is considered to be a leading securities litigator. He recently represented Credit Suisse Securities in a multidistrict litigation relating to asset-backed security fraud. **David Boch** (see p.285) is a *"smart guy"* who is well regarded for his broker-dealer regulatory advice and his representation of clients in SEC and FINRA enforcement matters. Financial services cochair **Timothy Burke** (see p.289) handles complex securities enforcement and litigation matters for a range of investment advisers and brokerage firms.

## Recommended for Client Service
### Nationwide

| | |
|---|---|
| Cleary Gottlieb Steen & Hamilton LLP | Morgan, Lewis & Bockius LLP |
| Cravath, Swaine & Moore LLP | Morrison & Foerster LLP |
| Debevoise & Plimpton LLP | Paul, Weiss, Rifkind, Wharton & Garrison LLP |
| Dechert LLP | Richards Kibbe & Orbe LLP |
| Katten Muchin Rosenman LLP | Skadden, Arps, Slate, Meagher & Flom LLP & Affiliates |

## Recommended for Commercial Awareness
### Nationwide

| | |
|---|---|
| Cravath, Swaine & Moore LLP | Paul, Weiss, Rifkind, Wharton & Garrison LLP |
| Dechert LLP | |
| Gibson, Dunn & Crutcher LLP | Skadden, Arps, Slate, Meagher & Flom LLP & Affiliates |
| | WilmerHale |

## Cleary Gottlieb Steen & Hamilton LLP
See profile on p.1963

**THE FIRM** This premier firm stands out for its ability to guide clients through national and international regulatory challenges in the securities arena. From both an advisory and enforcement standpoint, the firm is able to provide its client base with a full response to regulatory and litigious securities matters. An experienced and knowledgeable team of regulatory experts includes a raft of former federal prosecutors and senior SEC executives. The group is engaged on some of the industry's highest-profile investigative proceedings including multiple actions relating to the 2011 collapse of brokerage firm MF Global, the multi-agency LIBOR investigation and the Facebook IPO. On the securities litigation side, the team remains on the front line of a number of significant matters and represents financial groups including BNP Paribas, Citi and HSBC.
**Client Service** *"They have good solid experience and provide good practical advice. Their client service is good. They understand customer service and get the right expert to us."*
**KEY INDIVIDUALS** Mitchell Lowenthal (see p.359) is a *"seasoned litigator"* who gives *"practical advice,"* and *"recognizes the pros and cons of going for settlement or discovery."* He continues to provide counsel to some of the world's leading financial institutions embroiled in securities class actions following the demise of Lehman Brothers. Key clients include HSBC and ING. SEC alumnus **Alan Beller** (see p.281) has a formidable reputation in the securities advisory arena. His firsthand knowledge of the inner workings of the SEC enables him to bring great insight to the table to counsel clients on regulatory and corporate governance. **Giovanni Prezioso** (see p.387) has *"wonderful judgment and is a terrific adviser,"* says one interviewee. The former SEC general counsel provides regulatory advice and representation in securities enforcement and litigation matters. **David Becker** (see p.280) is recommended for his

*The editorial is in alphabetical order by firm name.*

## Securities: Litigation

### Senior Statesmen

**Senior Statesmen:** distinguished older practitioners

| | | |
|---|---|---|
| DiBlasi Gandolfo V | Sullivan & Cromwell LLP * | |
| Lerner Jonathan J | Skadden, Arps, Slate, Meagher & Flom LLP & Affiliates * | |

### Leading Individuals

**Star individuals**

| | |
|---|---|
| Karp Brad S | Paul, Weiss, Rifkind, Wharton & Garrison * |

**Band 1**

| | |
|---|---|
| Angiolillo Bruce | Simpson Thacher & Bartlett LLP * |
| Clary Richard W | Cravath, Swaine & Moore LLP * |
| Giuffra Jr Robert J | Sullivan & Cromwell LLP * |
| Kasner Jay B | Skadden, Arps, Slate, Meagher & Flom * |
| Kramer Daniel J | Paul, Weiss, Rifkind, Wharton & Garrison * |
| Lowenthal Mitchell | Cleary Gottlieb Steen & Hamilton LLP * |
| Mirvis Theodore N | Wachtell, Lipton, Rosen & Katz * |
| Warin Joseph | Gibson, Dunn & Crutcher LLP * |

**Band 2**

| | |
|---|---|
| Allerhand Joseph S | Weil, Gotshal & Manges LLP * |
| Aronson Seth | O'Melveny & Myers LLP |
| Baron Robert | Cravath, Swaine & Moore LLP * |
| Benedict James | Milbank, Tweed, Hadley & McCloy LLP * |
| Bodner Randall W | Ropes & Gray LLP |
| Curnin Paul C | Simpson Thacher & Bartlett LLP * |
| Donovan John D | Ropes & Gray LLP |
| Dougherty Thomas J | Skadden, Arps, Slate, Meagher & Flom * |
| Edelman Scott | Milbank, Tweed, Hadley & McCloy LLP * |
| Eggleston W Neil | Kirkland & Ellis LLP (ONP) † * |
| Eth Jordan | Morrison & Foerster LLP * |
| Feldman Boris | Wilson Sonsini Goodrich & Rosati (ONP) † |
| Holland Mark | Goodwin Procter LLP * |
| Kirsch Mark | Gibson, Dunn & Crutcher LLP * |
| Kitchens Dean | Gibson, Dunn & Crutcher LLP * |
| Maguire William R | Hughes Hubbard & Reed LLP (ONP) † * |
| Markel Gregory A | Cadwalader, Wickersham & Taft (ONP) † * |

| | |
|---|---|
| Musoff Scott | Skadden, Arps, Slate, Meagher & Flom * |
| Pastuszenski Brian E | Goodwin Procter LLP * |
| Patrick Kathy | Gibbs & Bruns LLP (ONP) † * |
| Polkes Jonathan | Weil, Gotshal & Manges LLP * |
| Portnoy Lawrence | Davis Polk & Wardwell LLP * |
| Rosen Richard | Paul, Weiss, Rifkind, Wharton & Garrison * |
| Rudman Jeffrey | WilmerHale * |
| Ruthberg Miles | Latham & Watkins LLP * |
| Sacks Robert A | Sullivan & Cromwell LLP * |
| Siegel David | Irell & Manella (ONP) † * |
| Smith Jeffrey Q | Bingham McCutchen LLP * |
| Spiegel John | Munger, Tolles & Olson LLP * |
| Vizcarrondo Jr Paul | Wachtell, Lipton, Rosen & Katz * |
| Wald Peter A | Latham & Watkins LLP * |
| Young Michael | Willkie Farr & Gallagher LLP * |

**Band 3**

| | |
|---|---|
| Baskin Stuart | Shearman & Sterling LLP * |
| Davison Douglas | WilmerHale * |
| Downey Kevin | Williams & Connolly LLP * |
| Ferrara Ralph C | Proskauer Rose LLP (ONP) † |
| Kilduff Jeffrey | O'Melveny & Myers LLP |
| Levander Andrew J | Dechert LLP * |
| Shea Daniel F | Hogan Lovells US LLP |
| Tuttle Jonathan | Debevoise & Plimpton LLP |
| Villa John K | Williams & Connolly LLP * |
| Youngwood Jonathan K | Simpson Thacher & Bartlett LLP * |

**Up-and-coming individuals**

| | |
|---|---|
| Ryan Antony | Cravath, Swaine & Moore LLP * |

## Securities: Regulation: Advisory

### Leading Individuals

**Band 1**

| | |
|---|---|
| Beller Alan | Cleary Gottlieb Steen & Hamilton LLP * |
| Dunn Martin | O'Melveny & Myers LLP * |
| Dye Alan L | Hogan Lovells US LLP |
| Lane Brian | Gibson, Dunn & Crutcher LLP * |
| Martin David | Covington & Burling LLP * |
| Nazareth Annette | Davis Polk & Wardwell LLP * |
| Olson John | Gibson, Dunn & Crutcher LLP * |
| Prezioso Giovanni | Cleary Gottlieb Steen & Hamilton LLP * |
| Romeo Peter J | Hogan Lovells US LLP |
| Stettner Barbara | Allen & Overy LLP (ONP) † |
| White John W | Cravath, Swaine & Moore LLP * |

**Band 2**

| | |
|---|---|
| Breheny Brian V. | Skadden, Arps, Slate, Meagher & Flom * |
| Goodman Amy | Gibson, Dunn & Crutcher LLP * |
| Griggs Linda L | Morgan, Lewis & Bockius LLP |
| Groskaufmanis Karl A | Fried, Frank, Harris, Shriver & Jacobson * |
| Hensley Dennis C | Sidley Austin LLP * |
| Lynn David | Morrison & Foerster LLP * |
| McLaughlin Joseph | Sidley Austin LLP * |
| Odoner Ellen J | Weil, Gotshal & Manges LLP * |
| Rosenberg Marc S | Cravath, Swaine & Moore LLP * |
| Webster Susan | Cravath, Swaine & Moore LLP * |

**Up-and-coming individuals**

| | |
|---|---|
| Gumbs Keir D | Covington & Burling LLP * |
| Plesnarski Rob | O'Melveny & Myers LLP * |

* Indicates individual with profile.
† ONP = Other Notable Practitioner.

---

deep knowledge of SEC rulemaking and the broader securities regulatory. One source reports: *"He is a sound lawyer with good judgment. If you have a thorny issue you can call him and he's great at giving advice."*

## Covington & Burling LLP
See profile on p.441

**THE FIRM** This firm has a respected regulatory practice in the securities arena and is noted for its expertise in government enforcement actions. It offers clients a combined team with capabilities across securities litigation, enforcement and white-collar crime defense. The team has a large public company client base and advises the likes of Verizon, Microsoft and Procter & Gamble in addition to individual officers and boards of directors. During the high-profile 'flash crash' investigation brought by the SEC the team represented the interests of NYSE Euronext, successfully reaching settlement in 2012.

**Sources say:** *"They are good at corralling and working together, do very well in document management discovery issues, and are client-friendly and smart."*

**KEY INDIVIDUALS** Securities team cochair **David Martin**'s (see p.362) previous regulatory experience and contacts at the SEC are flagged by multiple respondents as a key strength of his advisory practice. He is noted as a *"thought leader in securities regulation."* **Bruce Baird** (see p.276) is a *"tremendous lawyer and does a great job,"* comments one source. He leads the firm's white-collar defense and investigations practice and draws upon a well-established reputation and solid litigation background to advocate on behalf of individuals and companies in high-stake investigations. **David Kornblau** (see p.349) cochairs the securities enforcement practice and one source comments that he is *"knowledgeable about the area of the law and manages it cost-effectively. I trust his judgment."* **Keir Gumbs** (see p.328) demonstrates tremendous potential in securities regulatory matters, with interviewees commenting that *"beyond the technical perspective he has an invaluable amount of experience dealing with the SEC."*

## Cravath, Swaine & Moore LLP
See profile on p.1966

**THE FIRM** Cravath, Swaine & Moore has one of the industry's leading securities litigation practices and handles some of the most significant class action and civil litigation matters. The firm's litigation team remains active in the defense of cases relating to the MBS fallout, notably acting as coordinating counsel to Credit Suisse on all such matters. In addition, the group represents companies, directors and present and former officers in shareholder derivative suits and class actions relating to M&A activity, fraud allegations and subprime asset issues. Notable clients include Barnes & Noble, Deloitte & Touche and JPMorgan Chase.

**Client Service** *"They're incredibly bright, professional and totally focused on the client and what works for the client."*
**Commercial Awareness** *"They are as good a subject matter expert as you would hope to find. They apply a deep analysis and think about things and how they will pan out."*
**KEY INDIVIDUALS** **Richard Clary** (see p.295) has an illustrious reputation as one of the security industry's most prominent and successful litigators. He has represented the outside directors of Citi in shareholder derivative actions filed in Delaware and New York and continues to act as coordinating counsel on the defense of all RMBS claims brought against Credit Suisse. Managing partner **Robert**

*The editorial is in alphabetical order by firm name.*

### Securities: Regulation: Enforcement
### Leading Individuals

**Star individuals**

| | |
|---|---|
| McLucas William | *WilmerHale* * |

**Band 1**

| | |
|---|---|
| Berger Paul | *Debevoise & Plimpton LLP* |
| Goldsmith Barry | *Gibson, Dunn & Crutcher LLP* * |
| Janick III Herbert F | *Sidley Austin LLP* * |
| Levander Andrew J | *Dechert LLP* * |
| Mahoney Colleen P | *Skadden, Arps, Slate, Meagher & Flom* * |
| Warin Joseph | *Gibson, Dunn & Crutcher LLP* * |
| Weiss Harry J | *WilmerHale* |

**Band 2**

| | |
|---|---|
| Baird Bruce | *Covington & Burling LLP* * |
| Baker III William R | *Latham & Watkins LLP* |
| Bruch Gregory S | *Willkie Farr & Gallagher LLP* * |
| Ceresney Andrew J | *Debevoise & Plimpton LLP* |
| Davidow Charles E | *Paul, Weiss, Rifkind, Wharton & Garrison* * |
| Eggleston W Neil | *Kirkland & Ellis LLP* * |
| Ferrara Ralph C | *Proskauer Rose LLP* |
| Johnson Dixie L | *Fried, Frank, Harris, Shriver & Jacobson* * |
| Mann Michael D | *Richards Kibbe & Orbe LLP* |
| Prezioso Giovanni | *Cleary Gottlieb Steen & Hamilton LLP* * |
| Sturc John | *Gibson, Dunn & Crutcher LLP* * |
| Sullivan Neal E | *Sidley Austin LLP* * |
| Trager Michael D | *Arnold & Porter LLP* * |
| Winer Samuel J | *Foley & Lardner LLP (ONP)* † |

**Band 3**

| | |
|---|---|
| Becker David M | *Cleary Gottlieb Steen & Hamilton LLP* * |
| Chatman Thomsen Linda | *Davis Polk & Wardwell LLP* * |

* Indicates firm / individual with profile.
† ONP = Other Notable Practitioner.

| | |
|---|---|
| Crimmins Stephen J | *K&L Gates* * |
| Flannery Anne C | *Morgan, Lewis & Bockius LLP* * |
| Gray Elizabeth P. | *Willkie Farr & Gallagher LLP* * |
| Indek Ben | *Morgan, Lewis & Bockius LLP* * |
| Kornblau David | *Covington & Burling LLP* * |
| Lawrence Carmen J | *Fried, Frank, Harris, Shriver & Jacobson* * |
| Morvillo Richard J | *MORVILLO LLP (ONP)* † |
| Ricciardi Walter G | *Paul, Weiss, Rifkind, Wharton & Garrison* * |
| Richards III Lee S | *Richards Kibbe & Orbe LLP* |
| Romatowski Peter J | *Jones Day (ONP)* † * |
| Schwartz Erich T | *Skadden, Arps, Slate, Meagher & Flom* * |
| West Lawrence | *Latham & Watkins LLP* * |

**Band 4**

| | |
|---|---|
| Boch David C | *Bingham McCutchen LLP* * |
| Burke Timothy P | *Bingham McCutchen LLP* * |
| Firestone Frederic | *McDermott Will & Emery LLP (ONP)* † * |
| Hellerer Mark R | *Pillsbury Winthrop Shaw Pittman (ONP)* † |
| Mixter Christian J | *Morgan, Lewis & Bockius LLP* * |
| Newkirk Thomas | *Jenner & Block LLP* * |
| Rashkover Barry | *Sidley Austin LLP* * |
| Romano Robert M | *Morgan, Lewis & Bockius LLP* * |
| Salehi Nader H | *Sidley Austin LLP* * |
| Shea Daniel F | *Hogan Lovells US LLP* |
| Shepard Michael J | *Hogan Lovells US LLP* |
| Wolk Michael D | *Sidley Austin LLP* * |
| Zornow David M | *Skadden, Arps, Slate, Meagher & Flom* * |
| Zweifach Lawrence J. | *Gibson, Dunn & Crutcher LLP* * |

### Securities: Litigation: Mainly Plaintiff
### Leading Firms

**Band 1**

| |
|---|
| Bernstein Litowitz Berger & Grossmann LLP * |
| Grant & Eisenhofer PA * |
| Labaton Sucharow LLP * |
| Quinn Emanuel Urquhart & Sullivan, LLP |
| Robbins Geller Rudman & Dowd LLP * |

Baron (see p.278) advises global pharmaceutical and healthcare company Merck on numerous federal securities claims arising out of the market withdrawal of its Vioxx product. He continues to be recognized for his broad securities litigation expertise. For "*corporate advice and board procedure,*" **John White** (see p.425) is "*one of the best I've ever met,*" comments one source. The former SEC staffer is a highly respected regulatory adviser and is cochair of the firm's corporate governance and board advisory practice. **Marc Rosenberg** (see p.395) "*has become an invaluable securities law and governance adviser to us on a host of matters. We turn to him for our hardest questions in this area,*" explains one source. He cochairs the firm's corporate governance and board advisory team alongside White and provides ongoing regulatory advice to corporate entities including IBM and the audit committee of GE. **Susan Webster** (see p.423) is valued for her "*depth of knowledge, high level of engagement, problem-solving and strategic advice.*" She advised the Huron Consulting Group nonexecutive directors on an SEC investigation and settlement, and other related litigation matters. **Antony Ryan** (see p.397) receives warm praise from the market as an "*extremely smart and capable*" securities litigator. He is applauded for his recent representation of AIG auditors PwC in a major securities class action, which reached an

agreed settlement in the Southern District of New York affirmed by the Second Circuit Court of Appeals.

### Davis Polk & Wardwell LLP
See profile on p.442

**THE FIRM** Davis Polk's outstanding reputation at the heart of the financial services sector continues to feed its expansive securities practice. The team has a consistency of strength across both regulatory enforcement and advisory matters and securities litigation. On the enforcement side it successfully represented Italian bank Intesa Sanpaolo in a significant multiagency civil and criminal investigation into US sanction violations, which resulted in no actions being brought. Financial institutions including Barclays Capital, Deutsche Bank and RBS are the recipients of ongoing regulatory guidance on reforms and compliance matters. It has also represented some of the financial industry's leading firms in securities class actions including the multiple underwriters involved in securities class actions relating to Facebook's 2012 IPO. Other notable clients include Morgan Stanley and JPMorgan Chase.

**Sources say:** "*For regulatory work and securities they provide excellent service.*"

**KEY INDIVIDUALS** The "*terrific*" **Lawrence Portnoy** (see p.1928) has had a successful year achieving a significant pretrial win for Credit Suisse in its defense of a multibil-

lion-dollar class action brought by Time Warner investors. He is "*easy to work with*" and "*down-to-earth,*" comment sources. **Annette Nazareth** (see p.374) is one of the financial services sector's recognized authorities in securities regulatory matters. She advises many of the firm's leading financial institution clients and is particularly noted for her preeminence in the broker-dealer space. Former SEC head of enforcement **Linda Chatman Thomsen** (see p.293) garners huge praise from peers and clients alike for her deep level of knowledge and expertise coupled with strong diplomacy and advocacy skills. The independent directors of MF Global remain a key client.

### Debevoise & Plimpton LLP
See profile on p.1968

**THE FIRM** Sources emphasize this firm's strength across both securities litigation and regulatory matters. The firm fields a combined securities practice and covers a full spectrum of advice for financial institutions, public companies, individual executives and boards of trustees and directors. It has a robust enforcement practice which has earned the respect of the industry for its handling of a number of key matters. The team defends MetLife and a number of its current and former directors in multiple cases relating to an industrywide investigation into the alleged use of false data. It also acts for the former CEO and chairman of Bank of America on litigation concerning the bank's acquisition of Merrill Lynch.

**Client Service** "*I have never worked with better partners in my life. They are extremely responsive, extremely knowledgeable and able to see the big picture. They make you feel like the number-one client.*"

**KEY INDIVIDUALS** Shortly before going to press **Mary Jo White,** one of the luminaries of the white collar criminal defense and securities enforcement spaces was confirmed by the Senate as the next chair of the SEC. **Jonathan Tuttle** represents clients in regulatory investigations and enforcement actions and is an expert in accounting violations. Sources say he is "*flawless in his execution and attention to detail.*" **Paul Berger** is valued for his insider understanding of the regulatory process. Sources consider him to be "*one of the most experienced securities practitioners, with great attention to detail, encyclopedic knowledge of anticorruption practices and a broad knowledge base.*" Following his tenure at the US Attorney's Office for the Southern District of New York, enforcement specialist **Andrew Ceresney** brings "*an unbelievable expertise*" and the "*ability to marry understanding of the DOJ with how business works.*" He "*has the unique skill to truly understand something very complex and explain it in straightforward terms,*" say sources.

*The editorial is in alphabetical order by firm name.*

## Securities: Regulation
### Leading Firms

**Band 1**
Cleary Gottlieb Steen & Hamilton LLP *
Gibson, Dunn & Crutcher LLP *
WilmerHale *

**Band 2**
Bingham McCutchen LLP *
Davis Polk & Wardwell LLP *
Debevoise & Plimpton LLP *
Sidley Austin LLP *
Skadden, Arps, Slate, Meagher & Flom LLP & Affiliates *

**Band 3**
Covington & Burling LLP *
Cravath, Swaine & Moore LLP *
Dechert LLP *
Fried, Frank, Harris, Shriver & Jacobson LLP *
Hogan Lovells US LLP
Latham & Watkins LLP *
Morgan, Lewis & Bockius LLP *
Paul, Weiss, Rifkind, Wharton & Garrison LLP *
Willkie Farr & Gallagher LLP *

**Band 4**
Arnold & Porter LLP *
K&L Gates *
O'Melveny & Myers LLP *
Richards Kibbe & Orbe LLP *
Shearman & Sterling LLP *
Weil, Gotshal & Manges LLP *

## Securities: Litigation: Mainly Plaintiff
### Senior Statesmen

Senior Statesmen: distinguished older practitioners
Sucharow Lawrence | Labaton Sucharow LLP *

### Leading Individuals

**Star individuals**
Berger Max W | Bernstein Litowitz Berger & Grossmann *

**Band 1**
Dubbs Thomas | Labaton Sucharow LLP *
Eisenhofer Jay W | Grant & Eisenhofer PA *
Grant Stuart M | Grant & Eisenhofer PA *

**Band 2**
Bernstein Stanley | Bernstein Liebhard LLP (ONP)†
Dumain Sanford P | Milberg LLP (ONP)†
Graziano Salvatore J | Bernstein Litowitz Berger & Grossmann *
Rudman Samuel | Robbins Geller Rudman & Dowd LLP *
Selendy Philippe Z. | Quinn Emanuel Urquhart & Sullivan, LLP
Singer Steven | Bernstein Litowitz Berger & Grossmann *

\* Indicates individual with profile.
†ONP = Other Notable Practitioner.

### Dechert LLP
See profile on p.1969

**THE FIRM** Dechert has a team of 32 partners handling the defense of public and private companies and key executives, investment advisers and brokerage firms in regulatory actions and civil litigation proceedings. It has experience advocating on behalf of clients before federal and state regulators in investigations conducted by agencies including FINRA, the SEC, the DOJ and the Commodities & Futures Trading Commission (CFTC). The team has represented former MF Global CEO Jon Corzine in relation to class actions filed following the brokerage firm's bankruptcy.
**Client Service** *"They are outstanding. What impresses me is their grasp of the issues, willingness to put more resources on when necessary and the way they bring expertise in when they need it from within the firm."*
**Commercial Awareness** *"They have deep and broad expertise, an excellent familiarity with the people and personalities at the regulatory agencies and an ability to be creative and apply themselves in different ways."*
**KEY INDIVIDUALS** First-rate attorney **Andrew Levander** (see p.1913) is *"extraordinarily perceptive and experienced,"* say sources. He represented Jon Corzine in the MF Global proceedings and is highly rated for his expertise in matters at the intersection of securities enforcement and white-collar criminal defense.

### Fried, Frank, Harris, Shriver & Jacobson LLP
See profile on p.1975

**THE FIRM** This firm's securities practice centers on the provision of a combined regulatory, criminal and civil litigation defense service. Its team represents a wide range of organizations, including public companies and accounting firms, in addition to individual directors, officers and other professionals. Present in the firm's New York, Washington, DC and London offices, the team is well positioned to provide guidance on the changing domestic and international regulatory landscape.
**KEY INDIVIDUALS** One interviewee comments that corporate partner and regulatory attorney **Karl Groskaufmanis** (see p.326) is *"available all the time, he is thoughtful and keeps a great balance between protection and commerciality."* **Dixie Johnson** (see p.340) co-leads the firm's securities enforcement and regulation group. Sources comment: *"She has excellent judgment and many years of practical securities-related experience. She is particularly adept at advising on sensitive and complex securities law issues and questions relating to the requirements of and interactions with the SEC."* **Carmen Lawrence** (see p.352) is *"outstanding"* and has an active enforcement and investigations practice. She has *"a very fine reputation"* in the industry and has previous senior experience at the SEC.

### Gibson, Dunn & Crutcher LLP
See profile on p.682

**THE FIRM** Gibson, Dunn & Crutcher houses a spectacular securities regulatory group and expanding litigation team. On the advisory side, the team counsels clients on the impact of regulatory change in the wake of the Dodd-Frank Act and is considered an industry thought leader on the impact of the JOBS Act. With an impressive stable of former officers from FINRA, the SEC, CFTC and the DOJ, the team is well equipped to handle complex regulatory enforcement proceedings. It represents a number of industry associations including the Securities Industry & Financial Markets Association (SIFMA) in CFTC rulemaking and rule amendments. Its litigation team continues to play a lead role in complex litigation linked to the fallout from the RMBS crisis, advising the independent board members of JPMorgan Chase on ongoing lawsuits relating to the rogue activities of the so-called 'London Whale' trader.
**Commercial Awareness** *"They are incredibly knowledgeable about securities rules and laws and very able to translate the knowledge into productive action. They provide great counsel on complex and challenging subjects and represent clients very effectively before regulatory agencies."*
**KEY INDIVIDUALS** The venerable **Joseph Warin** (see p.423) is a *"first-rate"* attorney with a broad practice which includes securities litigation, government investigations and white-collar crime. One source notes that he is *"perceived as one of the leading lawyers in the Foreign Corrupt Practices Act space internationally and I think his reputation in the Bar is incredibly high."* Experienced trial attorney and cochair of the firm's litigation practice **Mark Kirsch** (see p.1909) is praised by sources for his *"technical knowledge – he knows what to do and how to do it – and his tactical ability to accomplish things within that realm."* He recently acted for UBS on a class action sparked by losses incurred by rogue London-based trader Kweku Adoboli. Los Angeles-based **Dean Kitchens** (see p.347) has a nationally recognized securities litigation practice. One interviewee names him a *"terrific and savvy"* lawyer who *"gets good results."* **Barry Goldsmith** (see p.323) is *"terrific for regulatory matters,"* with sources reporting that *"he is knowledgeable, approachable, smart, liked by the regulators, thoughtful and has excellent technical knowledge."* He has a leading practice advising clients engaged in regulatory enforcement and investigations before agencies such as the SEC and FINRA. **Brian Lane** (see p.352) advises clients on federal securities law compliance. He impresses sources and according to one respondent is considered to be *"one of the most knowledgeable securities attorneys that I have worked with. He gives practical advice and has superb judgment."* **John Olson** (see p.380) is a *"wonderful adviser; he has that balance and sense that I think is almost unique,"* explains one client. As founding partner of the firm's securities practice and Washington, DC office, Olson is a seasoned and widely respected regulatory practitioner. Securities regulatory adviser **Amy Goodman** (see p.324) cochairs the firm's practice group in this area. She has served at the SEC and has particular expertise on the Dodd-Frank Act provisions relating to securities and governance. Her clients include Hewlett-Packard and Johnson & Johnson. **John Sturc** (see p.413) co-heads the firm's securities enforcement practice and is one of the team representing oil rig operator Noble Corporation's executive Jim Ruehlen in a Foreign Corrupt Practices Act (FCPA) case brought by the SEC, one of few contested cases to be brought to trial. He is described as a *"sound guy with good judgment, and a first-rate enforcement lawyer."* **Lawrence Zweifach** (see p.1953) is involved in advising clients on significant multiagency investigative actions. He is praised for his ability to strategize and steer clients in the right direction.

## Goodwin Procter LLP
See profile on p.1522

**THE FIRM** Goodwin Procter has an esteemed securities litigation and enforcement practice. The team continues to defend Bank of America and its subsidiary Countrywide in a raft of class actions and civil claims that stem from the subprime mortgage crisis. In one example, the team was successful before the Second Circuit Court of Appeals, which affirmed a previous judgment dismissing claims filed by SRM Global relating to the firm's merger with Bank of America. The team names Credit Suisse, Citibank, Goldman Sachs and UBS Securities among an impressive client roster.

**Sources say:** *"They are incredibly talented, responsive and helpful."*

**KEY INDIVIDUALS** Mark Holland (see p.335) is highly recommended by sources as a trusted adviser: *"Mark worked with us beautifully, he made everything very clear to us,"* stated one client. Holland recently represented Bank of America/Countrywide in fraud and breach of contract claims filed by four monoline insurers relating to RMBS. The *"phenomenal"* **Brian Pastuszenski** (see p.1504) cochairs the firm's securities litigation and enforcement practice and rises in the rankings this year due to a stellar performance as lead attorney for Bank of America/Countrywide. He is *"a really intelligent lawyer"* who is *"tireless, responsive and experienced,"* relate sources.

## Grant & Eisenhofer PA
See profile on p.780

**THE FIRM** Grant & Eisenhofer is a boutique litigation practice representing institutional investors in nationally significant securities litigation and class actions. It represents the plaintiff class in an ongoing federal court action against Pfizer concerning its drug Vioxx, which was withdrawn from the market in 2004. The team has recently acted for a number of investors in litigation against Citi alleging that the defendant violated UK financial regulations.

**Sources say:** *"They are a very effective group with very capable lawyers. They've developed a good practice, do good work and achieve good results."*

**KEY INDIVIDUALS** Jay Eisenhofer (see p.770) is a *"smart and formidable"* securities litigator, according to sources. He continues to develop a leading reputation at both a national and international level and is described as a *"great strategist."* **Stuart Grant** (see p.771) is a respected plaintiff attorney who routinely represents major institutional investors in securities litigation claims. He has been closely involved in the Citi litigation.

## Hogan Lovells US LLP

**THE FIRM** Hogan Lovells has an active securities practice with over 60 partners based in the global firm's key offices including Washington, DC, New York, Denver, San Francisco and Silicon Valley. Its advisory team counsels a range of blue-chip public companies on corporate governance and securities regulatory requirements. The firm is also noted for its handling of enforcement matters and investigations before bodies such as the SEC.

**KEY INDIVIDUALS** Denver-based litigator **Daniel Shea** represents individual directors and officers and corporate bodies in civil lawsuits, regulatory investigations and criminal proceedings. *"He is great at spotting issues,"* says one peer. **Alan Dye** has an outstanding reputation in regulatory circles especially in relation to executive trading and SEC filing requirements for officers, directors and other specified persons under the Securities Exchange Act of 1934. **Peter Romeo** also provides regulatory counsel pertaining to SEC filing requirements and Securities Exchange Act of 1934 matters. He is considered to be a subject matter expert on the Section 16 provisions of the 1934 Act. San Francisco-based **Michael Shepard** is a respected advocate and skilled tactician whose practice combines white-collar criminal defense and regulatory enforcement and investigation representation.

## Jenner & Block LLP
See profile on p.1252

**THE FIRM** This premier Chicago-headquartered litigation firm has a strong reputation in the securities arena. The litigation team not only defends class action and lawsuits on behalf of individuals and corporate clients, but also acts on behalf of institutional plaintiffs to bring securities and derivative claims. The team acted on behalf of the Lehman Brothers bankruptcy examiner on an investigation into the culpability and conduct of its directors and officers in relation to the organization's collapse.

**KEY INDIVIDUALS** Thomas Newkirk (see p.375) cochairs the Jenner & Block securities litigation and enforcement group and has a long-standing career in the sector which includes almost two decades at the SEC. He is considered to be a *"smart lawyer"* who *"knows the practice well."*

## K&L Gates
See profile on p.2245

**THE FIRM** This internationally renowned firm offers clients regulatory advice, SEC enforcement representation and guidance on both federal and internal investigations. The team offers broad geographical scope with practitioners located in many of the major US cities as well as global regulatory expertise through its offices in London, Berlin and Hong Kong. It acts for some of the nation's biggest financial institutions on ongoing RMBS investigations relating to the financial crisis and counsels the Securities Working Group of the Financial Services Roundtable on Dodd-Frank and regulatory issues and rulemaking.

**KEY INDIVIDUALS** Stephen Crimmins (see p.299) has a successful practice representing executives and public companies in enforcement proceedings. He is described as a *"master of every detail,"* and is recognized for his insider trading liability expertise, acting for the former general counsel of Heartland Advisors on appeal on one such case.

## Katten Muchin Rosenman LLP
See profile on p.1253

**THE FIRM** This firm has a reputable securities litigation practice. It has been involved in the representation of business executives, financial institutions and public compa-

nies in shareholder class actions and civil lawsuits as well as multiagency investigations. The team, which has a presence in the firm's Chicago, Washington, DC, New York and Los Angeles offices, has recently handled cases on behalf of clients in the financial services, technology and IT sectors, among others.

**Client Service** *"Their handling of complex issues and client service is exceptional. We've raised issues and they have addressed them very quickly."*

**KEY INDIVIDUALS** New York-based Bruce Vanyo is a key contact and co-heads the firm's national securities litigation practice.

## Kaye Scholer LLP
See profile on p.1984

**THE FIRM** Kaye Scholer joins the rankings this year following a wealth of recommendations outlining the firm's strategic prowess and collaborative work ethic. Its securities and derivatives team acts for named individuals on major securities litigation matters as well as public companies. Notable representations include that of Howard Smith, former CFO of AIG, in multiple litigation claims including a substantial securities fraud class action.

**Sources say:** *"Kaye Scholer has shown a great ability to jump into complex cases on a moment's notice and then do a great job of bringing the case to a successful resolution."*

**KEY INDIVIDUALS** Vincent Sama is chair of the securities and derivatives litigation team.

## Labaton Sucharow LLP
See profile on p.1988

**THE FIRM** Leading plaintiff firm Labaton Sucharow has considerable experience in handling litigation on behalf of investors and shareholders. It is active in MBS litigation and other claims kindled by the fallout from the financial crisis. The team has played a fundamental role in achieving settlements on behalf of clients in key actions against the likes of AIG. It also represented the Michigan Retirement Systems in the Bear Stearns securities class action, successfully achieving a settlement of $275 million.

**Sources say:** *"We chose Labaton Sucharow to represent us because of the firm's nationally recognized litigation skills and demonstrated commitment to shareholder advocacy."*

**KEY INDIVIDUALS** Chairman and renowned litigator **Lawrence Sucharow** (see p.1945) *"is a wonderful lawyer, a deeply thoughtful strategist, and a man whose word you can cash at any financial institution,"* say sources. **Thomas Dubbs** (see p.1889) is a respected plaintiff attorney and represents institutional investors in high-profile securities litigation claims. He played a lead role in both the AIG and Bear Stearns class actions.

## Latham & Watkins LLP
See profile on p.446

**THE FIRM** Latham & Watkins is a globally renowned multiservice law firm with an impressive national and international coverage. Sources consider it to have a strong bench of expertise in both securities regulation and litigation. The firm has an excellent reputation on the litigation side as a key representative for the Big Four accountancy

*The editorial is in alphabetical order by firm name.*

firms, illustrated by its successful defense of Ernst & Young in a securities fraud class action relating to the IndyMac bank failure. On the regulatory side it represented soccer club Manchester United in its IPO, while it provides ongoing regulatory advice to Omnicom and Kimco.

**Sources say:** *"They're helpful at getting on top of the regulations and are on the front line of guiding and advising banks. They're also good at approaching things from the underwriter side."*

**KEY INDIVIDUALS** The *"talented"* **Miles Ruthberg** (see p.397) is an exceptionally well-regarded trial attorney who is considered to be a *"national force in securities litigation."* He was a lead partner in the successful defense of Ernst & Young in multiple securities claims relating to the demise of Lehman Brothers. **Peter Wald** (see p.422) is *"brilliant,"* and *"a leading light in the securities litigation Bar,"* comments interviewees. He was a lead attorney representing Deloitte & Touche in claims relating to the Washington Mutual bankruptcy. **William Baker** is acknowledged as an outstanding regulatory specialist with particular strength in securities enforcement matters. He is commended for his *"encyclopedic knowledge of regulatory issues and the subtleties of Washington, DC representation."* Fellow regulatory partner **Lawrence West** (see p.425) is also praised for his command of the intricacies of the securities enforcement process. This *"knowledgeable"* SEC alumnus represents organizations and individuals before the SEC, the Public Company Accounting Oversight Board (PCAOB) and other investigative agencies.

## Milbank, Tweed, Hadley & McCloy LLP
See profile on p.448

**THE FIRM** This reputable Manhattan-headquartered firm has carved out a solid reputation for counseling investment advisers on securities and derivatives litigation. The team successfully defended investment manager Capital Research & Management Company in a $15 billion excessive fee action at trial. It also represents Rabobank in class actions relating to alleged LIBOR manipulation.

**KEY INDIVIDUALS** Litigation expert **James Benedict** (see p.1877) is noted as *"one of the best in the business"* by sources. The litigation and arbitration group chair is *"clearly the dean of the Investment Company Act Bar – he created much of the law that matters in that area and I have a lot of admiration for him,"* relates one source. One interviewee reports that securities litigator **Scott Edelman** (see p.308) is *"superb, smart and if you need a trial lawyer this is your guy!"* Edelman represented the underwriters, which included Citigroup Global Markets and UBS Securities, in a securities fraud claim relating to a preferred securities offering.

## Morgan, Lewis & Bockius LLP
See profile on p.2246

**THE FIRM** The reputation of the Morgan Lewis securities regulatory practice is augmented by the firm's expansive and long-established governmental and public policy department. The team advises financial sector clients and public companies on a host of regulatory and litigation matters. It recently acted for Oracle on the negotiation of a

$2 million settlement with the SEC in an FCPA investigation. Other clients include Penson Worldwide and Barclays Capital.

**Client Service** *"Morgan Lewis is well known for securities enforcement defense work and has good client service."*

**KEY INDIVIDUALS Ben Indek** (see p.338) is praised for his understanding of the securities enforcement arena. He advised UBS Securities on its $12 million settlement with FINRA. Sources consider him to be a *"terrific regulatory lawyer"* who is *"excellent with regulators, provides good client service and is smart and likable."* **Anne Flannery** (see p.314), who also led on the UBS Securities FINRA negotiations, has impressed clients, one of whom notes that she *"deserves the highest praise."* Washington, DC-based **Christian Mixter** (see p.370) represented hedge fund Quantek Asset Management in the settlement of an SEC investigation into the firm's trading practices. He is *"one of the smartest lawyers I've met,"* comments one observer. **Robert Romano** (see p.394) is an *"excellent lawyer"* and plays a lead role in the defense of individuals, companies and financial institutions involved in investigations and actions brought by the SEC, FINRA and other regulators. New entrant **Linda Griggs** previously served as lead counsel to the SEC's chief accountant. *"She's terrific,"* comment sources, who also observe that *"her great strength is that she really knows accounting."*

## Morrison & Foerster LLP
See profile on p.1990

**THE FIRM** Morrison & Foerster provides broad-spectrum securities advice delivered by a geographically dispersed but operationally integrated team. The team is applauded for its thorough and creative litigation defense capabilities and acts for some of the world's biggest household names on securities and derivatives lawsuits. It has represented Yahoo!, Capital One, Zynga and various officers and directors in recent class and shareholder actions.

**Client Service** *"An excellent firm to work with: very capable attorneys, reasonable billed hours and very customer service-oriented."*

**KEY INDIVIDUALS** *"First-rate"* **Jordan Eth** (see p.634) is located in San Francisco and cochairs the litigation, enforcement, and white-collar defense practice group. An accomplished securities litigator, Eth is praised for his passion and efficiency and has played a lead role in noteworthy cases for the key brands mentioned above. **David Lynn** (see p.359) cochairs the firm's 25-partner public companies group. He advises clients on securities regulation compliance and has a special focus on executive compensation disclosure and reporting requirements.

## Munger, Tolles & Olson LLP
See profile on p.691

**THE FIRM** Elite West Coast firm Munger, Tolles & Olson has a talented group of litigators who appear in some of the nation's most significant securities litigation cases. On the public company side, the team has advised Facebook's board of directors on multiple IPO-related class actions, and Google founders Larry Page and Sergey Brin on a shareholder action linked to a proposed offering by the

search engine. The team also advises financial institutions Bank of America, Citigroup Global Markets and Wells Fargo, particularly on ongoing litigation relating to the RMBS crisis.

**Sources say:** *"They are very specialized, smart counselors on the litigation side and are our go-to firm."*

**KEY INDIVIDUALS John Spiegel** (see p.666) has a well-rounded litigation practice incorporating both civil and criminal defense representation. Sources point to his *"good judgment and high energy."* He leads the Facebook and Google representations.

## O'Melveny & Myers LLP
See profile on p.693

**THE FIRM** This firm receives resounding praise for its ongoing accomplishments in the securities space. The team continues to act for prestigious organizations including Bank of America, UBS and Fannie Mae. It has established itself as a go-to firm for China-related securities litigation, representing both US public companies based in China and Chinese firms facing litigious action in the USA. On the regulatory side, the team advises financial institutions, institutional investors and Fortune 500 companies on SEC, FINRA and other regulatory requirements.

**Sources say:** *"They are top-notch. It is a deep group and led by some very good lawyers who are thoughtful and attentive, and we get good results."*

**KEY INDIVIDUALS** Based in the firm's Los Angeles office, the *"absolutely terrific"* **Seth Aronson** is highly regarded and has an active securities litigation practice. He is a driving force behind the team's burgeoning representation of Chinese companies in the USA. **Jeffrey Kilduff** is lead counsel to Fannie Mae and has represented the organization in multiaction cases filed in the US District Court for the District of Columbia as well as pending cases in the Southern District of New York. Sources report: *"He is able to consolidate the intricacies of the case into understandable propositions that a court can understand, and has a phenomenal courtroom demeanor."* **Martin Dunn** (see p.307) is an immensely respected regulatory expert who spent two decades at the SEC prior to joining the firm. He provides high-end securities counseling on regulatory compliance and transactional matters. **Rob Plesnarski** (see p.385) also provides counseling on securities regulatory matters. He continues to carve out a strong reputation in the sector.

## Orrick, Herrington & Sutcliffe LLP
See profile on p.1994

**THE FIRM** The securities litigation and enforcement practice at Orrick, Herrington & Sutcliffe reaches from coast to coast with key members of the team based in New York, Washington, DC, San Francisco and Los Angeles. The firm maintains an active litigation defense practice and the team has a diverse client base that includes financial institutions, accounting firms, public companies and business executives. Key clients include Ernst & Young and Iron Planet.

**KEY INDIVIDUALS** San Francisco-based Michael Torpey leads the firm's practice in this area.

*The editorial is in alphabetical order by firm name.*

## Paul, Weiss, Rifkind, Wharton & Garrison LLP
See profile on p.1997

**THE FIRM** Paul Weiss has a phenomenal litigation and enforcement practice with a stellar cast of trial attorneys and litigators who perform center stage in some of the nation's biggest securities cases. Sources unanimously attest to the firm's excellence and praise the strength and depth of its securities bench. Its enviable client roster lists some of the world's leading financial institutions and corporations including JPMorgan Chase, Morgan Stanley, Bank of America, AIG and Deutsche Bank. The team recently represented Citigroup Global Markets in reaching a $285 million settlement with the SEC including no admission or denial of the regulator's allegations, a decision that was subsequently blocked in a landmark ruling by a federal district judge and is ongoing before the Second Circuit Court of Appeals.

**Client Service** *"Best in the business. We never feel we are competing with other clients for time and attention or the very best resources. Their responsiveness and client service are better than any other law firm with which I have worked."*

**Commercial Awareness** *"I like that they are highly sophisticated: they know the space cold, they are current, they are on it. I can call them and ask their opinion and they are so deeply involved in securities litigation that they will often be representing other people in similar positions."*

**KEY INDIVIDUALS** Chair of the firm **Brad Karp** (see p.343) is a superstar of the litigation Bar and has an impressive reputation among peers and clients for his judgment, experience and leadership in court. One source comments: *"He is someone that every major bank turns to if there is a crisis. He is someone who is recognized as just having excellent skills at providing advice."* Leading litigator and securities litigation practice group cochair **Daniel Kramer** (see p.350) is described as a *"terrifically talented lawyer"* who is *"brilliant, passionate, highly accessible and possesses sound business judgment."* **Richard Rosen** (see p.394) cochairs the firm's securities litigation practice alongside Kramer and is an active trial attorney. He has been involved in multiple class actions and civil lawsuits for Citi and is described by peers as *"smart and detail-oriented."* The third practice cochair **Charles Davidow** (see p.301) is respected for his representation in DOJ and SEC investigations. He has been part of a team acting for The Bank of New York Mellon on ongoing investigations by the New York, Virginia and Massachusetts Attorney Generals. Former SEC deputy director of enforcement **Walter Ricciardi** (see p.392) plays a key role in some of the industry's most significant investigations and is recognized for his deep expertise.

## Quinn Emanuel Urquhart & Sullivan, LLP

**THE FIRM** This firm plays a key role in attempting to remedy the considerable repercussions of the RMBS crisis in 2008. It represents the Federal Housing Finance Agency (FHFA) on behalf of Fannie Mae and Freddie Mac in actions against multiple financial institutions including UBS, Bank of America, JPMorgan Chase and RBS for representations made relating to mortgage loans. It has also acted for AIG on a claim to recover RMBS losses from Bank of America, Countrywide and Merrill Lynch.

**Sources say:** *"They are always trying to anticipate arguments and their diversity of experience in the field brings a lot to bear."*

**KEY INDIVIDUALS Philippe Selendy** cochairs the firm's structured finance litigation group and leads the RMBS team. Sources comment: *"Philippe conveys a great deal of confidence; he is an easygoing person who is interactive with clients in a very positive way."*

## Richards Kibbe & Orbe LLP
See profile on p.2002

**THE FIRM** Richards Kibbe & Orbe's securities practice offers a knowledge and understanding of both regulatory and criminal proceedings. Its compact and nimble team is praised by sources for its creative approach to problem-solving, its consistency of service and its collaborative approach. Notable clients include Citigroup Global Markets, Morgan Stanley and Financial Guaranty Insurance Company (FGIC).

**Client Service** *"They are incredibly thoughtful and really care about their clients, and come up with advice that really takes client interests into account."*

**KEY INDIVIDUALS** Respondents praise **Michael Mann**'s *"global vision,"* which he has continued to develop following his tenure as head of the SEC's Office of International Affairs. Sources comment: *"The international operation of regulatory restraints for companies has become absolutely crucial and Michael is unparalleled. He's in a league of his own."* **Lee Richards** co-heads the firm's securities practice with Mann. His work encompasses criminal and civil litigation defense and the representation of clients in regulatory investigations and enforcement matters. *"He is, in every sense of the term, a real counselor and he knows how to work with clients,"* say sources.

## Robbins Geller Rudman & Dowd LLP
See profile on p.696

**THE FIRM** Robbins Geller is regarded as one of the nation's preeminent plaintiff litigation firms. It has a considerable securities litigation team based in the firm's San Diego office as well as senior-level expertise in New York and San Francisco. The team is active on a considerable number of securities fraud class actions and in 2012 led a claim against Motorola Solutions on behalf of shareholders, securing a $200 million settlement before trial.

**Sources say:** *"They are tenacious, knowledgeable and experienced and also have the resources to stand up against big corporations."*

**KEY INDIVIDUALS** Former SEC attorney **Samuel Rudman** (see p.1934) investigates and pursues securities litigation cases on behalf of shareholders. He is *"incredibly entrepreneurial and a very good lawyer."*

## Ropes & Gray LLP
See profile on p.1528

**THE FIRM** The Boston-headquartered securities practice at this reputable firm maintains a solid profile as a leading national player in mutual funds and public company litigation. It recently represented fund managers Harris Associates and Ameriprise Financial Services in excessive fee litigation, and State Street in multiple class actions relating to the RMBS crisis. On the shareholder litigation side, the team won a dismissal of multiple class actions filed in the US District Court of Massachusetts for biotech client Genzyme. The team has seen an increase in the number of M&A cases and represented TPG Capital in litigation concerning its $3 billion purchase of J.Crew Group.

**Sources say:** *"Very smart and responsive people at all levels. They are excellent in terms of efficiency and service."*

**KEY INDIVIDUALS** *"First-rate"* **Randall Bodner** is a highly respected advocate and cochairs the firm's business and securities litigation team. He is lead counsel to the officers of Freddie Mac in ongoing securities fraud class actions. **John Donovan** is a seasoned securities litigator whose experience, expertise and courtroom acumen are held in high regard. He was lead lawyer in the Genzyme litigation.

## Shearman & Sterling LLP
See profile on p.2005

**THE FIRM** Shearman & Sterling's securities practice incorporates expertise from its litigation and financial institutions regulatory groups. It is well equipped to represent clients in multiagency investigations and enforcement actions as well as complex civil lawsuits. The team has been advising Countrywide Financial on numerous state and federal RMBS claims against it. On the regulatory side, it advises domestic banking organizations including Bank of America Merrill Lynch on SEC investigations and enforcement actions.

**Sources say:** *"They are deep and broad in their expertise, particularly for Wall Street clients."*

**KEY INDIVIDUALS** Litigator **Stuart Baskin** is *"extremely well known and highly regarded,"* comments interviewees. His practice spans securities, transactional and white-collar defense, while his clients include financial institutions and public companies.

## Sidley Austin LLP
See profile on p.1264

**THE FIRM** Sidley Austin has a distinguished national securities regulation practice with a large team housed in its New York, Chicago, Washington, DC and Los Angeles offices. It works with financial institutions, including banks and brokerage firms, to ensure their compliance with SEC and FINRA rules including requirements under the JOBS Act. Its specialist team, peppered with former in-house regulatory counsel, is noted for having strength in guiding clients through enforcement and ongoing representations before agencies including the CFTC, DOJ and SEC. The litigation team acts for major investment banks, public companies and advisory firms on federal class actions, shareholder litigation and excessive fee litigation. Shortly before going to press, Sidley welcomed a sizeable regulatory team from Bingham McCutchen.

**KEY INDIVIDUALS Dennis Hensley** (see p.333) is a seasoned securities professional with a deep knowledge and understanding of the regulatory environment. He advises

*The editorial is in alphabetical order by firm name.*

financial institutions on the full range of enforcement and compliance matters. Senior counsel **Joseph McLaughlin** (see p.366) is *"simply one of the very knowledgeable people who understands the industry, the questions and the issues,"* say sources. He advises clients on regulatory issues and international securities offerings. **Barry Rashkover** (see p.1929) is based in New York and has been active in defending clients against regulatory actions relating to MBS and short selling. *"You'd be in good hands with him,"* comments one peer. Portland-based **Herbert Janick** (see p.340) has a fine reputation as a securities enforcement attorney. One interviewee describes him as *"thorough and detail-oriented,"* while he is commended for his ability to *"interact with regulators and know when it is appropriate to be forceful and when to be accommodating."* **Neal Sullivan** (see p.414) represents clients in federal securities actions, in which he is considered to also play a strong role at a state level. Sources report that he is *"just a great lawyer."* Enforcement attorney **Nader Salehi** (see p.398) *"knows the industry well and is very client-responsive,"* notes one source. Another reports: *"He is a great lawyer for regulated investments, and is easygoing, detail-oriented and has great understanding."* **Michael Wolk** (see p.428) is a regulatory attorney whose practice focuses on guiding clients through securities investigations brought by agencies including the SEC and FINRA.

## Simpson Thacher & Bartlett LLP
See profile on p.2006

**THE FIRM** The litigation practice at Simpson Thatcher remains one of the industry's go-to providers of complex securities class action and multilawsuit defense. It continues to occupy a prominent position in cases flowing from the aftermath of the financial crisis. In the RMBS arena, the team has amassed a raft of achievements, including successes for RBS. It has also been retained to defend JPMorgan Chase in all actions brought against the institution relating to the internationally significant LIBOR manipulation allegations. With heavyweight expertise on the East Coast in New York, and a West Coast presence in Palo Alto and Los Angeles, the team has both the depth and geographical scope to handle a broad range of matters. **Sources say:** *"I have found them to be uniformly talented lawyers who are especially experienced and well versed in securities litigation."*

**KEY INDIVIDUALS** The *"impressive"* **Bruce Angiolillo** (see p.273) is a *"wonderfully gifted and talented litigator"* who is *"good on his feet, great with judges and skilled in legal argument."* As head of department, he is engaged in many of the firm's most prominent cases in this area. **Paul Curnin** (see p.300) practices at the intersection between white-collar criminal defense and complex securities litigation. Interviewees describe him as *"outstanding"* and *"top-notch."* **Jonathan Youngwood** (see p.1952) is a rising star of the securities litigation Bar and a new entrant in the nationwide table. He is noted as a *"strong and effective securities litigator"* with a flair for written work and oral advocacy, according to sources.

## Skadden, Arps, Slate, Meagher & Flom LLP & Affiliates
See profile on p.2008

**THE FIRM** This elite, multiservice global law firm houses a thriving securities litigation practice. The team, which draws upon expertise from the firm's national and international network of litigators and trial attorneys, has played a prominent role in the defense of securities claims for some of the most significant corporations and financial institutions including JPMorgan Chase, Deutsche Bank and GenOn Energy. Recent matters have included the representation of Amerigroup and its board in the defense of an M&A-related shareholder action, and Morgan Stanley Private Equity Asia concerning a proposed MBO of China-based producer FEIHE International. The firm also has a deep regulatory enforcement and investigations practice, advising private and public organizations, management, boards of directors and board committees on the full range of regulatory agency matters.

**Client Service** *"Any communication to the firm receives a response almost instantly – they bend over backward to make sure I get all the support I need as in-house counsel, and it is the only major firm I work with that endeavors to keep me completely informed about important legal developments at all times. No other firm provides the level of service that I get from Skadden, period."*

**Commercial Awareness** *"Skadden has committed serious resources to being up-to-the-minute in this area of law and deserves the stellar reputation the firm has built. My relationship with Skadden keeps me informed – in real time – about all major legal developments (whether related to cases where Skadden is involved or not) and allows me to disseminate this information internally and evaluate it in making important strategic decisions. This is invaluable to me."*

**KEY INDIVIDUALS Jay Kasner** (see p.1907) impresses clients with his strategic acumen and creativity in complex cases. According to one interviewee, *"he tries consistently to think of new and innovative solutions to problems, and no other senior partner or firm is as responsive or as committed to client service. Jay takes this to another level entirely."* According to sources, the *"superb"* **Colleen Mahoney** (see p.360) stands out as one of the leading lights in securities enforcement representation. She is based in the firm's Washington, DC office and is *"one of the first people I would turn to in regulatory matters and civil litigation with regulatory aspects,"* a client explains. **Thomas Dougherty** (see p.1490) leads the Boston litigation team and predominantly acts for companies and officers, including a large number of hi-tech businesses, in civil securities actions and SEC matters. He *"has an absolute mastery of the law, is a great presenter of the facts and has a commanding presence,"* say sources. Commended for his *"outstanding strategic judgment,"* **Scott Musoff** (see p.373) represents financial institutions in complex securities cases and recently advised Deutsche Bank, as agent in a stock offering by DryShips, on a class action which resulted in a voluntary dismissal by the plaintiffs. Musoff *"has a keen understanding of the legal issues and his substantive work is excellent,"* remark interviewees. **Jonathan Lerner** (see p.355) *"comes with a formidable reputation that is brought to bear in practice. He is a per-*

suasive writer, thinker and arguer,"* comments one source. His practice focuses on federal securities cases and commercial arbitration. **Erich Schwartz** (see p.402) concentrates on regulatory enforcement actions and represented Symmetry Medical in an internal investigation and subsequent settlement with the SEC. He is an *"excellent lawyer and great technician; someone I would call in a heartbeat,"* commends one interviewee. Following his move from the SEC to Skadden in 2010, **Brian Breheny** (see p.286) has developed an active practice. He joins the rankings this year on the recommendation of many who value the depth of experience and understanding he brings to the team. **David Zornow** (see p.1953) is *"absolutely outstanding in the courtroom"* and defends individuals and corporations in high-end federal and state civil and criminal proceedings and regulatory securities enforcement actions.

## Sullivan & Cromwell LLP
See profile on p.2011

**THE FIRM** Sullivan & Cromwell is a premier international firm with a sophisticated securities litigation group. The prestigious team handles a range of matters including securities class actions, shareholder derivative suits and M&A litigation. The team recently acted for Barclays on the highly publicized LIBOR rate-fixing allegations. Additionally, it continues to represent JPMorgan Chase as coordinating counsel in the defense of multiple RMBS lawsuits. An enviable client base of leading financial institutions and global corporations includes UBS, Goldman Sachs and BP.

**Sources say:** *"The people are terrific and prominent and great in litigation. They're strong and have a fantastic group."*

**KEY INDIVIDUALS Robert Giuffra** (see p.321) recently represented Porsche in litigation alleging fraud in its 2008 attempt to acquire Volkswagen. Sources attest that he *"has a deep and vast experience, excellent judgment, thinks through all the issues at an early stage and is very focused in his approach."* **Robert Sacks** (see p.663) heads up the firm's Los Angeles office and is *"very strategic in his thinking,"* say sources. He recently achieved a significant victory for JPMorgan Chase in defense of a securities class action relating to its liability to defrauded Millennium Bank Ponzi scheme investors. The much-venerated **Gandolfo DiBlasi** (see p.304) is a stalwart of the securities Bar and is described by sources as *"one of the best securities lawyers in the country."* He has played a key role in counselling the firm's leading banking clients engaged in contentious and investigatory matters.

## Wachtell, Lipton, Rosen & Katz
See profile on p.2012

**THE FIRM** Wachtell has a substantial national profile as a go-to firm for securities litigation. The firm handles a range of complex litigious matters for financial institutions and corporate entities. The group played a key role acting for Bank of America on its $8.5 billion settlement of claims relating to Countrywide-issued MBS following the subprime crisis. It is also handling the defense of a class action launched by shareholders of AOL following the corporation's sale of a patent portfolio to Microsoft in 2012.

**Sources say:** *"A great law firm, with really smart people."*
**KEY INDIVIDUALS Theodore Mirvis** (see p.370) is considered to be a *"leading light in securities litigation"* and headlines some of the firm's most significant representations. He is *"one of the quickest, smartest and most creative around,"* according to one peer. **Paul Vizcarrondo** (see p.421) *"is a top-quality litigator who has great knowledge of the securities laws,"* explains sources. His practice encompasses civil, criminal and regulatory representation and he is routinely called upon to advise in complex securities fraud cases.

### Weil, Gotshal & Manges LLP
See profile on p.2015

**THE FIRM** This firm has a deserved reputation in the securities arena with an enviable proficiency in both the litigation and regulatory spaces. Its public company advisory group provides ongoing counseling on corporate governance and regulatory compliance issues. The team's key clients in this area include the audit committee of Cablevision, and Willis Group Holdings. The firm's 17-partner securities litigation team has noted expertise in transaction-related claims and shareholder actions. It continues to act as nationwide counsel for AIG on the defense of various cases relating to the subprime crisis, and also represents GE in three federal securities class actions and corresponding derivative matters. The team also represents clients in regulatory enforcement proceedings and investigations.
**Sources say:** *"They understand our goals and are helpful in getting us there while ensuring that we are covered from a legal perspective."*
**KEY INDIVIDUALS Joseph Allerhand** (see p.273) is co-head of the firm's securities litigation team and leads AIG's defense. Sources refer to his *"great judgment in terms of strategizing."* **Jonathan Polkes** (see p.386) also co-heads the team and has a practice that spans civil and criminal securities litigation, as well as investigations and regulatory advice. *"He really knows his way around a courtroom,"* note sources. **Ellen Odoner** (see p.379) receives warm praise from market observers. One interviewee reports: *"She is highly intelligent but extremely calm – an important trait when dealing with highly charged issues – and she has done a really good job at marshaling the right talent and resources."*

### Williams & Connolly LLP

**THE FIRM** Williams & Connolly has a reputable securities practice with strength in representing senior executives, directors and officers in civil litigation and SEC regulatory actions. The team also represents accounting firms, legal practices and investment companies. Notable clients in this area include former Fannie Mae CEO Franklin Raines, The Carlyle Group and Greenberg Traurig.
**Sources say:** *"They are very professional. Strategically they know exactly what they are doing and have done it before."*
**KEY INDIVIDUALS John Villa** is a Washington, DC stalwart with considerable experience defending clients in banking, securities and legal malpractice litigation and regulatory proceedings. Sources describe him as *"a leading*

*light"* of the securities Bar. **Kevin Downey** has expertise in both criminal and civil proceedings in the securities arena. He is *"a zealous advocate who is extremely intense in court but his presentation is professorial and incredibly persuasive,"* note sources.

### Willkie Farr & Gallagher LLP
See profile on p.2016

**THE FIRM** The Willkie Farr securities practice is noted for its proficiency across both enforcement and litigation issues. The team has been involved in the defense of securities cases for an illustrious roster of clients including Facebook and AIG. In a notable highlight, the team represented Goldman Sachs and other underwriters in class actions relating to a $12 billion offering by GE in 2008, resulting in the dismissal of all claims and subsequent denial of the plaintiff's request for reconsideration using new assertions.
**KEY INDIVIDUALS** Preeminent New York litigator **Michael Young** (see p.1952) is chair of the securities litigation and enforcement practice group. One client states: *"You couldn't envision a more client-focused lawyer. You feel like you are his only client."* **Gregory Bruch** (see p.854) practices in Washington, DC and is considered to be a *"great guy"* with *"excellent judgment."* He has acted on behalf of IndyMac Bancorp CFO Scott Keys in all investigative and regulatory matters following the bank's failure and FDIC takeover in 2008. **Elizabeth Gray** (see p.325) is valued for her ability to interface with regulators and has *"great communication skills,"* sources say.

### WilmerHale
See profile on p.930

**THE FIRM** WilmerHale is widely considered to be a market leader with outstanding expertise and knowledge of the securities regulatory arena. It has a powerful enforcement and investigations practice, which dovetails effectively with the firm's active civil litigation defense team to provide a uniform approach in contentious matters. On the enforcement side, it has been involved in a number of prominent representations including an SEC investigation into the alleged misconduct of a senior executive of a major retailer. Its client base includes major financial institutions, corporations, global accountancy firms and trade associations. The team advised numerous underwriters including Deutsche Bank Securities, RBS Securities and Wells Fargo Securities on the successful defense of an action relating to Bank of America's Common Equivalent Securities offering.
**Commercial Awareness** *"They provide a quality service which is commercial. They want to understand the business."*
**KEY INDIVIDUALS William McLucas** (see p.366) chairs the securities department. He is one of the country's most celebrated regulatory attorneys and is considered to offer unquestionable strength in representing corporations and individuals in investigations and enforcement proceedings brought by the SEC. Sources say: *"He is the go-to guy when it comes to SEC enforcement matters. He is absolutely phenomenal. He has deep knowledge and his style is very effective – not overbearing or pretentious."* *"I think* **Harry Weiss**

knows the SEC and how that process works probably better than anyone in the country,"* comments one client. The former SEC associate director of enforcement chairs the firm's practice in this area and impresses sources with the quality of his advice. Industry stalwart **Jeffrey Rudman** (see p.1507) is an *"encyclopedia of experience and knowledge"* and is deeply respected by peers. He leads some of the firm's key litigation matters and is skilled at defending shareholder class actions. Vice chair of the securities group **Douglas Davison** (see p.302) makes his debut in the rankings this year. He receives high praise from sources, who comment: *"He is a very smart securities litigator who understands when it is appropriate to be cost-conscious and provides extremely practical and sound advice."*

### Other Notable Practitioners

Irell & Manella's **David Siegel** (see p.665) is a highly rated Californian securities litigator. He has a nationally recognized practice and has been acting on behalf of Angelo Mozilo, Countrywide Financial's former chairman and CEO, in multiple lawsuits and government actions relating to the mortgage lender's collapse in 2008. **Boris Feldman** of Wilson Sonsini Goodrich & Rosati is an accomplished securities litigator and *"standout name"* in the sector. Feldman is considered to be a *"real leader in the area of securities litigation involving technology and startup companies."* **Neil Eggleston** (see p.860) has *"good judgment"* and is the *"person you want to have fighting your corner,"* comment interviewees. From the Washington, DC office of Kirkland & Ellis LLP, he represents companies and individuals in securities litigation, enforcement and white-collar crime actions. **William Maguire** (see p.360) of Hughes Hubbard & Reed LLP is a *"terrific"* attorney who specializes in complex securities litigation. He *"has a good rapport with clients, gives you a sense of confidence that he knows what he is doing and is experienced in the industry,"* comments one respondent. **Gregory Markel** (see p.361) cochairs Cadwalader, Wickersham & Taft LLP's litigation practice and is an experienced securities attorney who has been involved in some of the sector's biggest cases. Sources name him a *"talented"* and *"sincere"* attorney. The *"talented"* **Kathy Patrick** (see p.2409) of Gibbs & Bruns LLP has *"great presence and confidence,"* applaud sources. She represents corporations and institutional investors in sophisticated securities litigation. **Ralph Ferrara** of Proskauer Rose LLP is considered to be *"a brilliant strategist with unlimited energy who is always ten steps ahead of the opposition."* His practice fuses broad experience in civil, criminal, investigative and enforcement defense to provide clients with a unified approach. **Barbara Stettner** of Allen & Overy LLP is recognized as a leading regulatory attorney in the securities arena. One interviewee comments that she has *"great depth of knowledge of that part of the industry and is concise and to the point in her advice."* Key enforcement attorney **Samuel Winer**'s practice is highly regarded in the sector. He is a member of Foley & Lardner LLP's full-service regulatory, litigation and transactional securities practice, and peers regard him as *"smart"* and *"talented."* **Richard Morvillo** practices from the offices of boutique litigation practice MORVILLO LLP. Sources praise him as a "*very good lawyer who is good in the courtroom and good on his feet.*" Jones Day's litigation and SEC enforcement group is headed by reputable Washington, DC-based attorney **Peter Romatowski** (see p.888). Interviewees praise him as a "*terrific lawyer.*" **Frederic Firestone** (see p.313) of McDermott Will & Emery LLP "*understands the nature of client relationships very well,*" say sources. He recently won a key acquittal for State Street's former chief investment officer in the high-profile SEC subprime securities investigation. **Mark Hellerer** of Pillsbury Winthrop Shaw Pittman LLP has a broad litigation practice which includes the representation of defendants involved in securities enforcement actions and criminal proceedings. According to sources he has "*an incredible work ethic and dedication to clients*" and is a "*smart, knowledgeable and careful lawyer.*" Bernstein Liebhard LLP's founding partner **Stanley Bernstein** is a well-respected litigator who represents plaintiffs in some of the nation's largest securities class actions. One source comments: "*He has a nice argument style which is not overbearing, he is very effective and does an excellent job.*" New York-based plaintiff attorney **Sanford Dumain** of Milberg LLP is recognized as a key practitioner acting as lead counsel in complex securities class actions.

# SPORTS LAW

Athletic Disputes p.241

Commentary about individuals can be found under their firm's paragraph. If the firm has no paragraph (is not ranked) look at Other Notable Practitioners.

### Sports Law
### Leading Firms

**Band 1**

Covington & Burling LLP *
Proskauer Rose LLP *
Skadden, Arps, Slate, Meagher & Flom LLP & Affiliates *

**Band 2**

Arent Fox LLP *
Debevoise & Plimpton LLP *
DLA Piper LLP (US) *
Foley & Lardner LLP *
O'Melveny & Myers LLP *
Winston & Strawn LLP *

**Band 3**

Arnold & Porter LLP *
Bryan Cave HRO
Katten Muchin Rosenman LLP *
Weil, Gotshal & Manges LLP *

* Indicates firm with profile.

## Band 1

### Covington & Burling LLP
See profile on p.441

**THE FIRM** This giant in the world of sports law has a raft of high-quality practitioners who dedicate the vast majority of their time to representing several of the biggest sports leagues and teams. In particular, the team is known for its continuing work for the NFL, which regularly uses Covington as its primary counsel, including in major recent matters such as the litigation arising from the 'Bountygate' scandal and issues relating to the salary cap. The firm also increasingly acts for the NBA.
**Client Service** "*They're very thorough. You hear that all the time but I've witnessed it – they don't make mistakes. Their temperament is easy to work with and exactly what you'd want.*"

**Commercial Awareness** "*They've got deep experience in the media space and a real grasp on the rapidly changing technology environment, and are very proficient at understanding the political dynamic.*"
**KEY INDIVIDUALS** Sources variously call **Gregg Levy** (see p.355) an "*A-list guy*" and "*one of the smartest people I've ever met.*" His litigation strategy is particularly well regarded, with one commentator saying: "*There is no way to out-think this guy!*" Levy has long-standing experience as lead outside counsel for the NFL, for which he led the firm's representation in both the bounty litigation and the salary cap dispute. **Douglas Gibson** (see p.320) is described as an "*intelligent, thoughtful, detail-oriented and knowledgeable sports lawyer,*" and "*one of the best corporate sports guys out there.*" He regularly advises the major leagues on corporate and sports media transactions, and recently advised the NFL on its credit facilities available to franchises. **Bruce Wilson** (see p.427) undertakes sports work in addition to other corporate matters. He recently advised the owner of the New Orleans Saints, Tom Benson, on his acquisition of the New Orleans Hornets. **Peter Zern** (see p.431) is known as "*one of the preeminent new media guys*" and a "*great negotiator whose opinion is based on practicality and extreme knowledge.*" He focuses on transactional sports work and media-based deals, although he was also part of the team involved in the recent NFL credit facilities matter. Senior counsel **Paul Tagliabue** (see p.415) is one of the most recognizable names in US sports administration following his nearly 17 years as commissioner of the NFL. He continues to advise clients in relation to sports, and notably recently presided over the appeals of the players suspended in the NFL bounty scandal.

### Proskauer Rose LLP
See profile on p.2001

**THE FIRM** Proskauer continues to be a dominant force in this area, representing every major league in some capacity and playing an integral part in a large proportion of the

major cases in the last year. These include the NHL, NBA and MLB collective bargaining agreements, and the acquisitions of the Jacksonville Jaguars and Cleveland Browns. The team has also been active in the establishment of a series of regional sports networks on behalf of NASCAR, Time Warner and CBS.
**Commercial Awareness** "*They are so aware and tailor their work to fit the league rules and conventions. There is no weakness that I have ever seen in them.*"
**KEY INDIVIDUALS** Peers consider the "*terrific*" **Howard Ganz** to be one of the "*top-flight*" labor litigators working in sports law. His impressive recent activity includes serving as outside counsel to the NBA in the continuing fallout from the 2011 lockout, and performing a similar role in relation to the MLB collective bargaining agreement. Sources describe **Joseph Leccese** as "*the top corporate sports guy,*" and as a "*really talented client-facing person.*" His recent work has included advising on the acquisitions of the Houston Astros and Jacksonville Jaguars, and working on the creation of a number of major regional sports networks. Leading labor lawyer **Robert Batterman**'s stellar year has included key roles in the high-profile and controversial NHL lockout and a similar work stoppage by NFL officials. Clients describe him as "*very practical, very smart and a very good negotiator.*" **Wayne Katz** is admired for his "*coolness under pressure, in addition to being brilliant, which is a given.*" His primary focus is on transactional and

| Recommended for Client Service | |
| Nationwide | |
| --- | --- |
| Arent Fox LLP | Covington & Burling LLP |
| Bryan Cave HRO | Skadden, Arps, Slate, Meagher & Flom LLP & Affiliates |

| Recommended for Commercial Awareness | |
| Nationwide | |
| --- | --- |
| Covington & Burling LLP | Proskauer Rose LLP |
| Katten Muchin Rosenman LLP | Winston & Strawn LLP |

## Sports Law
### Senior Statesmen

**Senior Statesmen: distinguished older practitioners**

| | |
|---|---|
| Tagliabue Paul | Covington & Burling LLP * |

### Leading Individuals

**Band 1**

| | |
|---|---|
| Batterman Robert | Proskauer Rose LLP |
| Ganz Howard | Proskauer Rose LLP |
| Goldfein Shepard | Skadden, Arps, Slate, Meagher & Flom * |
| Kessler Jeffrey L | Winston & Strawn LLP * |
| Leccese Joseph M | Proskauer Rose LLP |
| Levy Gregg | Covington & Burling LLP * |
| Mishkin Jeffrey A | Skadden, Arps, Slate, Meagher & Flom * |

**Band 2**

| | |
|---|---|
| Braza Mary K | Foley & Lardner LLP |
| Calabrese Joseph | O'Melveny & Myers LLP |
| Gibson Douglas G | Covington & Burling LLP * |
| Katz Wayne D | Proskauer Rose LLP |
| Keller Bruce P | Debevoise & Plimpton LLP |
| Klein Adam | Katten Muchin Rosenman LLP |
| Oram Jon | Proskauer Rose LLP |
| Quinn James W | Weil, Gotshal & Manges LLP * |
| Ruskin Bradley I | Proskauer Rose LLP |
| White Peter C | DLA Piper LLP (US) * |
| Wilson Bruce S | Covington & Burling LLP * |
| Zern Peter | Covington & Burling LLP * |

**Band 3**

| | |
|---|---|
| Baker Charles H | DLA Piper LLP (US) * |
| Braham Denis Clive | Winstead PC (ONP)[†] * |
| Brand Richard L | Arent Fox LLP * |
| Curtner Gregory L | Schiff Hardin LLP (ONP)[†] |
| Feher David G | Winston & Strawn LLP * |
| Garrett Robert A | Arnold & Porter LLP * |
| Gowan Thomas W | Skadden, Arps, Slate, Meagher & Flom * |
| Henn Jr R Charles | Kilpatrick Townsend & Stockton (ONP)[†] |
| Levinstein Mark S | Williams & Connolly LLP (ONP)[†] |
| Meyer Bruce S | Weil, Gotshal & Manges LLP * |
| Nash Daniel L | Akin Gump Strauss Hauer & Feld (ONP)[†] * |
| Smith Steven B. | Bryan Cave HRO |
| Whitaker Mark | DLA Piper LLP (US) * |

**Up-and-coming individuals**

| | |
|---|---|
| Jones Alicia Grahn | Kilpatrick Townsend & Stockton (ONP)[†] |
| Young Jason | Clifford Chance US LLP (ONP)[†] * |

## Sports Law: Athletic Disputes
### Leading Individuals

**Band 1**

| | |
|---|---|
| Jacobs Howard L | Law Offices of Howard L Jacobs (ONP)[†] * |
| Suh Maurice | Gibson, Dunn & Crutcher LLP (ONP)[†] * |
| Young Richard R | Bryan Cave HRO |

\* Indicates firm / individual with profile.

[†] ONP = Other Notable Practitioner.

### Skadden, Arps, Slate, Meagher & Flom LLP & Affiliates
See profile on p.2008

**THE FIRM** This prominent sports group includes two of the most notable practitioners in sports litigation work. It represents the major leagues, and has recently been extensively active for the NHL, including on collective bargaining agreements with the NHLPA and the league's $400 million credit facility. The team is also acting for several of the leading leagues in a case brought against the governor of New Jersey concerning sports gambling.

**Client Service** *"They respond quickly to demands, turn around briefs and are responsive to requests for additional information."*

**KEY INDIVIDUALS** Sources are effusive about **Shepard Goldfein** (see p.322), describing him as a *"standout general all-around legal counsel – exceedingly smart, very creative in finding solutions to problems, incredibly responsive and very proactive."* He was among the lead lawyers representing the NHL in its collective bargaining agreement negotiations. Sources describe **Jeffrey Mishkin** (see p.370) as a *"top-notch litigator,"* with one adding: *"I don't know of anybody who's a better advocate in court."* Mishkin continues to be the first person the NBA turn to when they need a litigator. He was recently part of the Skadden team representing the NBA and former ABA teams in an antitrust suit brought by the former Spirits of St. Louis team. Working with **Thomas Gowan** (see p.325) *"is almost like having an in-house lawyer,"* says one source, praising his responsiveness, proactivity and *"in-depth knowledge and feel for our business."* Gowan has recently represented the NHL in several finance transactions relating to NHL teams.

## Band 2

### Arent Fox LLP
See profile on p.905

**THE FIRM** This group is extremely active in various sports law fields, including media rights deals, franchise acquisitions and sponsorship matters. Its recent highlights include handling the purchase of the IP rights of soccer legend Pelé for client Sport 10 IP, and acting for the Brooklyn Events Center on the New York Islanders' move to the Barclays Center.

**Client Service** *"They always bring a friendly approach and their billing was very fair."*

**KEY INDIVIDUALS Richard Brand** (see p.286) is an *"excellent,"* *"all-purpose utility player,"* noted for his familiarity and experience with broadcasting rights matters. He was a key part of the team representing the Brooklyn Events Center.

### Debevoise & Plimpton LLP
See profile on p.1968

**THE FIRM** Led by the excellent Bruce Keller, Debevoise's sports practice is a strong player in IP-related sports law, particularly in matters relating to trademark and copyright infringement. It acts for some of the major sports leagues, including the NFL, which it represents in several litigation matters concerning the use of players' identities by NFL Films after their retirement.

**Sources say:** *"An extremely highly skilled group."*

**KEY INDIVIDUALS Bruce Keller** is at the forefront of IP-related sports law, with sources praising him as a *"widely respected"* lawyer and *"one of the most knowledgeable privacy and IP players."* He advised the Brooklyn Nets on advertising and on updating the team's mascot.

### DLA Piper LLP (US)
See profile on p.1971

**THE FIRM** This group practices across a wide range of sports law, although it is perhaps best regarded for its stadium financing work, which has recently included acting for the San Francisco 49ers on an $850 million loan for a new stadium. The team has also acted as counsel to Pac-12 Enterprises in a variety of areas. Other key clients include the Chicago Cubs and European soccer clubs AS Roma and Manchester City.

**KEY INDIVIDUALS Peter White** (see p.425) *"does a tremendous job on financing,"* according to sources, who praise him for *"always being very good at thinking outside the box"* and creating innovative solutions. He led the representation of the San Francisco 49ers in the matter above, and also acted for several bidders on the Los Angeles Dodgers sale. **Charles Baker** (see p.276) concentrates his sports practice on financing and M&A. His clients include major worldwide soccer teams such as Manchester City, which he represented in a sponsorship deal with Nike. Experienced practitioner **Mark Whitaker** (see p.425) is *"held in high regard"* for his *"tremendously detail-oriented approach."* His practice is largely focused on sports financing.

### Foley & Lardner LLP
See profile on p.2588

**THE FIRM** Undoubtedly the highlight of the Foley sports group's year was the representation of Guggenheim Baseball Management in its $2 billion-plus acquisition of the Los Angeles Dodgers, which cemented the group's reputation as an expert in MLB-related matters. Aside from baseball, the firm also represented the Green Bay Packers in a new $67 million stock offering.

**KEY INDIVIDUALS** Sources call **Mary Braza** *"a great practitioner"* in her field, and she is regularly seen in sports matters across a range of areas. Her clients includes MLB Advanced Media, which she represents in a variety of IP-related matters.

financing work, and he was part of the team that recently advised Jimmy Haslam on his acquisition of the Cleveland Browns. Another corporate and financing partner, **Jon Oram** continues to stand out for his impressive work for major clients, which includes securing credit facilities for the NFL, MLB and MLS. The *"tremendous"* and *"amazing"* **Bradley Ruskin** rounds off Proskauer's offering. An experienced litigator, he has overseen various major disputes of late, including defending the ATP Tour against claims of monopolization.

## O'Melveny & Myers LLP
See profile on p.693

THE FIRM This group's traditional strength is in the entertainment and broadcast rights sector of sports. It has acted for the International Olympic Committee for more than 20 years, recently representing it in negotiations with the USOC. The team also has a niche in boxing representation, and an increasing M&A aspect to its practice.

Sources say: *"They achieve unbelievable results and prepare like no one else I've ever seen."*

KEY INDIVIDUALS **Joseph Calabrese** is predominantly known for his expertise in entertainment law, but also has extensive experience in the sports arena. Sources highlight his knowledge and client-handling skills. He was part of the team involved in representing the IOC.

## Winston & Strawn LLP
See profile on p.1267

THE FIRM Winston & Strawn has shot to prominence on the sports front following the mass arrival of Dewey & LeBoeuf's sports practice in May 2012. Led by Jeffrey Kessler, the Winston group is present in most labor disputes for players' associations, and has recently represented the NFLPA and NBPA in various disputes, such as the NFL 'Bountygate' litigation and an arbitration concerning NBA players.

Commercial Awareness *"They are very experienced in our business, which is so important, not wasting time on theories that don't really work. There's lots of people practicing this type of law, so specific knowledge and history of dealing with us previously on similar matters is invaluable."*

KEY INDIVIDUALS **Jeffrey Kessler** (see p.346) is *"a star,"* according to sources, who highlight his creativity as a litigator. He is arguably the country's leading lawyer representing player unions in sports labor disputes, most recently acting for the NFLPA on the bounty scandal and for the NBPA in arbitration against the NBA. **David Feher** (see p.312) is praised by sources for his *"exemplary"* work and *"very detail-oriented"* approach. He practices across sports law, including representing clients in sponsorship matters and individual athletes' disputes.

## Band 3

## Arnold & Porter LLP
See profile on p.906

THE FIRM Arnold & Porter's sports practitioners focus on aspects of IP and broadcasting, particularly areas such as copyright royalties. The team represents Joint Sports Claimants, which comprises most of the major sports leagues including the MLB, NFL, NHL, NBA and NCAA, before the Copyright Royalty Board.

KEY INDIVIDUALS **Robert Garrett** (see p.864) is recognized by peers for his expertise in the copyright area of

sports law and related IP areas. He represented a coalition of sports leagues in front of the World Intellectual Property Organization concerning the illegal streaming of live internet feeds worldwide.

## Bryan Cave HRO

THE FIRM Following the 2012 merger of Bryan Cave and Holme Roberts & Owen, this group is now active in two significant areas in sports law. As well as undertaking cases involving arena naming rights and sponsorship, it also acts for a large number of US Olympic teams and governing bodies as well as the US Anti-Doping Agency (USADA) and the World Anti-Doping Agency (WADA). It recently advised USADA on various aspects of the case against Lance Armstrong.

KEY INDIVIDUALS **Richard Young** is renowned for his expertise in matters related to doping in sports, where he is described as having global understanding and knowledge. He led the team acting for WADA on potential changes in the World Anti-Doping Code, and has also represented USADA since its creation in 2000. **Steven Smith** is highly commended for his focus and understanding in all facets of sports law. Along with Richard Young, he acts as general counsel for the Mountain West Conference.

## Katten Muchin Rosenman LLP
See profile on p.1253

THE FIRM The Katten team focuses mainly on the corporate side of sports law, in particular representing clients in transactional, financing and sponsorship deals. It represents many major franchises and teams such as the Chicago Bulls, for which it acted on sponsorship and revenue sharing matters. The team has also worked with Time Warner Cable in relation to regional sports networks.

Commercial Awareness *"They understand what it's about because they've been working with us and other sports clients for over 30 years. Adam and his people are very, very expert."*

KEY INDIVIDUALS *"Top negotiator"* **Adam Klein** stands out for his ability to *"reduce complicated matters into simple language."* According to sources, his specialty lies in representing franchises in transactions. He recently represented the Oakland Athletics in the arrangement of a credit facility.

## Weil, Gotshal & Manges LLP
See profile on p.2015

THE FIRM This group has advised several of the major sports leagues' players' unions in various labor disputes, including recently advising the NHLPA on the NHL lockout. It also practices across other areas of sports law, including broadcasting, where it has acted for ESPN and other Disney companies on a dispute concerning high-definition TV networks.

KEY INDIVIDUALS **James Quinn** (see p.388) is considered to be *"one of the leading trial lawyers in the country,"*

and undertakes sports work as part of his overall litigation practice. Although known for his long-term relationship with the NBPA, he has expanded his practice to include other players' associations, and advised the NHLPA on the recent lockout. **Bruce Meyer** (see p.368) is a *"very, very bright lawyer"* praised for his *"extraordinary capacity to synthesize complex information."* Often working alongside James Quinn, Meyer was involved in the NHLPA representation as well as previous work for the NFLPA and NBPA.

## Other Notable Practitioners

**Howard Jacobs** (see p.339) of Law Offices of Howard L Jacobs is considered one of the top lawyers in the country for representing athletes in cases of alleged doping. Sources *"have such respect"* for Jacobs, who has acted for more than 80 individuals in his career. **Maurice Suh** (see p.414) of Gibson, Dunn & Crutcher LLP represents a variety of individuals and organizations in disputes against governing bodies and leagues concerning a range of issues, including sponsorship and anti-doping. He was involved in representing the NFLPA in the legal challenge to the NFL lockout. Labor lawyer **Daniel Nash** (see p.374) of Akin Gump Strauss Hauer & Feld LLP is highlighted for his case strategy skills and preparation, with one source commenting: *"He knows how to strategize a case from the get-go."* Nash has represented the New York Yankees in player-related issues. **Charles Henn** of Kilpatrick Townsend & Stockton LLP focuses his practice on IP-related sports law, particularly the protection of sports brands. He recently represented adidas in litigation concerning its TECHFIT trademark. Another Kilpatrick Townsend attorney, **Alicia Grahn Jones** was part of the team representing Louisiana State University in trademark negotiations with MLB. She was recently made partner at the firm. **Gregory Curtner** of Schiff Hardin LLP is seen as *"the guy"* for collegiate sports law due to his experience of and connections within the NCAA. He has over 40 years' experience as a trial lawyer in antitrust and commercial litigation. **Mark Levinstein** of Williams & Connolly LLP is respected by peers for his sports practice, which includes representing individual athletes in forums such as the Court of Arbitration for Sport. **Denis Braham** (see p.286) of Winstead PC earns client praise for his knowledge and experience as well as his *"business acumen, toughness and attention to detail."* He has undertaken a number of matters related to stadium financing and construction, including a nine-figure project for the Hamilton Tiger-Cats. **Jason Young** (see p.430) of Clifford Chance US LLP continues to impress sources as a *"very fine young player"* who is *"very thorough but also efficient."* He works predominantly on the bankruptcy, securitization and related financial aspects of sports law.

# TAX CONTROVERSY & FRAUD

Controversy p.243; Fraud p.244

Commentary about individuals can be found under their firm's paragraph. If the firm has no paragraph (is not ranked) look at Other Notable Practitioners.

## Tax: Controversy
### Leading Firms

**Band 1**
Baker & McKenzie *
Bingham McCutchen LLP *
Latham & Watkins LLP *
Mayer Brown LLP *
Skadden, Arps, Slate, Meagher & Flom LLP & Affiliates *

**Band 2**
McDermott Will & Emery LLP *
Sutherland Asbill & Brennan LLP

**Band 3**
Caplin & Drysdale *
Chamberlain, Hrdlicka, White, Williams & Aughtry *
Fulbright & Jaworski LLP *
Kostelanetz & Fink LLP
Miller & Chevalier Chartered *
Steptoe & Johnson LLP

**Band 4**
DLA Piper LLP (US) *
Morrison & Foerster LLP *
Pillsbury Winthrop Shaw Pittman LLP *
Vinson & Elkins LLP *
White & Case LLP *

* *Indicates firm with profile.*

## Band 1

### Baker & McKenzie
See profile on p.435

**THE FIRM** This group has a deep and growing bench of experienced tax litigators which, alongside a significant depth of knowledge, positions it as one of the key practices in tax controversy work. Teams in Chicago, Palo Alto and Washington, DC make up this top-tier practice. Its expertise encompasses alternative dispute resolution, litigation, and cross-border controversy matters, and its sector experience incorporates a broad range of arenas, including pharmaceutical and aviation. Notable clients include Boeing, Mattel and Thomson Reuters. **Sources say:** *"They have a very good group of people." "The service was exceptional."* **KEY INDIVIDUALS** Chicago-based **Mark Oates** (see p.378) is a leading trial lawyer with extensive expertise in complex litigation, including tax fraud, criminal defense and international tax matters. **Gregg Lemein** (see p.354) has an impressive knowledge of the federal tax system, and is known for his expertise in both domestic and multijurisdictional tax controversy work. He is also considered a go-to lawyer for inter-company pricing matters. *"He is a tremendous lawyer; I have a great deal of respect for him,"* mentioned a peer. **James O'Brien** (see p.379) is highly

lauded for his experience with international controversy work and his superb corporate litigation skills. He is also highlighted for his expertise with transfer pricing issues. **Duane Webber** (see p.423) is regarded as one of the luminaries in tax controversy. Clients speak highly of his practicality in resolving tax disputes, including in alternative dispute resolution techniques, and his innovative approach. He chairs the North America tax group and the firm's Washington, DC office. Operating out of the firm's Palo Alto office, **John Peterson** (see p.659) boasts an impressive reputation as one of the strongest experts on the West Coast. He is highly regarded for his tax controversy work on behalf of hi-tech companies and startups.

### Bingham McCutchen LLP
See profile on p.1515

**THE FIRM** With its impressive stable of leading lawyers, Bingham McCutchen's controversy team remains one of the foremost players in the arena. It remains a go-to group for an enviable client list, including GE, Dow Chemical and Santander as well as major names from both the domestic and foreign financial services markets. Bringing its superb expertise in cross-border controversy and transfer pricing to the table, it also represents leading names in the real estate, energy and technology sectors, among other areas. The firm also receives increased recognition for its burgeoning West Coast-based capabilities. **Sources say:** *"The quality of work at the firm is unparalleled." "They are highly competent and knowledgeable of the procedures."* **KEY INDIVIDUALS John Magee** (see p.360) is considered a dean of the tax controversy space, and wins acclaim for his tremendous depth of experience. He has a strong reputation in the field of transfer pricing and is considered a *"world-class tax litigator."* His major clients include Dow Chemical and Santander. **Raj Madan** (see p.360) is praised for his ability to bring *"an entrepreneurial, engaged spirit"* to his representations. Highlighted as one of the sector's future stars, he is especially well versed in representing major financial institutions in tax controversy and litigation. **William Nelson** (see p.375) is co-head of the firm's tax group. He is renowned for being both a versatile lawyer and excellent communicator. One client described him as *"steeped in tax law, with extensive deal and litigation experience."* **Sanford Stark** (see p.411) is one of the team's go-to experts in transfer pricing issues and is actively sought after by several Fortune 100 companies. His practice also includes cross-border tax disputes, structures and accounting matters. The tremendously experienced **David Curtin** (see p.300) is renowned for his ability in both civil and criminal trial cases. Within the practice area of tax controversy he is especially sought after for his experience as a former trial attorney in the Department of Justice's tax division.

### Recommended for Client Service Nationwide

| | |
|---|---|
| DLA Piper LLP (US) | Pillsbury Winthrop Shaw Pittman LLP |
| Morrison & Foerster LLP | |

### Recommended for Commercial Awareness Nationwide

McDermott Will & Emery LLP
Morrison & Foerster LLP

### Latham & Watkins LLP
See profile on p.446

**THE FIRM** Latham & Watkins is highlighted for its high success rate in litigation and for devising innovative approaches to dispute resolution. In its dealings with the IRS, and in disputes involving REITs, the firm is praised as having unparalleled expertise. The group is also increasingly recognized for its expanding capabilities in fraud and Fair and Accurate Credit Transactions Act (FACTA) matters. Its recent highlights include representing Shea Homes before the US Tax Court in relation to long-term contract accounting methods used by home builders, a case with claims exceeding $600 million. **Sources say:** *"Latham displays good common sense and a working understanding of the law. Their track record has shown good judgment and wise counsel."* **KEY INDIVIDUALS Miriam Fisher** (see p.313) has in-depth knowledge of both criminal and civil tax actions, and at both a state and federal level. Her ability in highly complicated cases, especially those involving fraud, is often praised. She has an impressive client list from industries including energy and financial services, and has handled matters before the IRS, Department of Justice and state tax authorities. **Gerald Kafka** (see p.342) chairs the firm's tax controversy practice group and its Washington, DC-based tax department. Described as *"a very fine tax litigator,"* his recent highlights include leading in the Shea Homes matter.

### Mayer Brown LLP
See profile on p.1257

**THE FIRM** Mayer Brown's preeminent practice group undertakes all manner of tax controversy work, including transfer pricing, audits and local, state and international controversy matters. The team also has extensive trial and appellate experience. The firm's global scope and its strong working knowledge of international tax matters are especially lauded by market sources. Recent highlights include representing Eaton Corporation in US Tax Court litigation challenging IRS-asserted tax deficiencies in the company's transfer pricing of various Latin American manufactured products. Other key clients include Nestlé, Pepco and Tyco International.

## Tax: Controversy
### Senior Statesmen

**Senior Statesmen: distinguished older practitioners**

| | | |
|---|---|---|
| Goldman William L | McDermott Will & Emery LLP * | |
| Hall Charles | Fulbright & Jaworski LLP * | |

### Leading Individuals

**Band 1**

| | |
|---|---|
| Cohen N Jerold | Sutherland Asbill & Brennan LLP |
| Fisher Miriam L | Latham & Watkins LLP * |
| Gardner Stephen D | Cooley LLP (ONP)† |
| Gideon Kenneth W | Skadden, Arps, Slate, Meagher & Flom * |
| Goldberg Jr Fred T | Skadden, Arps, Slate, Meagher & Flom * |
| Kafka Gerald A | Latham & Watkins LLP * |
| Magee John B | Bingham McCutchen LLP * |
| Oates Mark A | Baker & McKenzie * |
| Quigley Michael | White & Case LLP * |
| Williams Jr B John | Skadden, Arps, Slate, Meagher & Flom * |
| Williamson Joel V | Mayer Brown LLP |

**Band 2**

| | |
|---|---|
| Aughtry David D | Chamberlain, Hrdlicka, White, Williams * |
| Bailey Arthur L | Steptoe & Johnson LLP |
| Borders Thomas | McDermott Will & Emery LLP * |
| Durham Thomas C | Mayer Brown LLP |
| Hill Lawrence | Shearman & Sterling LLP (ONP)† |
| Karter Philip | Chamberlain, Hrdlicka, White, Williams |
| Kenworthy Kevin | Miller & Chevalier Chartered * |
| Lemein Gregg D | Baker & McKenzie * |
| Libin Jerome B | Sutherland Asbill & Brennan LLP |
| Madan Raj | Bingham McCutchen LLP * |
| Nelson William F | Bingham McCutchen LLP * |
| O'Brien James | Baker & McKenzie * |
| Rosenbloom H David | Caplin & Drysdale |
| Taylor Jasper | Fulbright & Jaworski LLP * |
| Webber A Duane | Baker & McKenzie * |

**Band 3**

| | |
|---|---|
| Abbott David F | Mayer Brown LLP |
| Colgin Jr William F | Morgan, Lewis & Bockius LLP (ONP)† * |
| Curtin David | Bingham McCutchen LLP * |
| Desmond Michael J | Law Offices of Michael J. Desmond (ONP)† |
| Faber Peter L | McDermott Will & Emery LLP * |
| Gerachis George Matthew | Vinson & Elkins LLP * |
| Horowitz Alan | Miller & Chevalier Chartered * |

| | |
|---|---|
| Johnston Thomas D | Shearman & Sterling LLP (ONP)† |
| Jones Roger J | McDermott Will & Emery LLP |
| Kaplan Barbara T | Greenberg Traurig, LLP (ONP)† * |
| Langdon Larry R | Mayer Brown LLP |
| Lerner Matthew D | Steptoe & Johnson LLP |
| Odell Herbert | Chamberlain, Hrdlicka, White, Williams |
| Pawlow Jean A | McDermott Will & Emery LLP * |
| Peterson Jr John M | Baker & McKenzie * |
| Reemer Ellis L | DLA Piper LLP (US) * |

**Band 4**

| | |
|---|---|
| Bonano William E | Pillsbury Winthrop Shaw Pittman LLP |
| Frankel Paul H | Morrison & Foerster LLP * |
| Froelich Edward | Morrison & Foerster LLP * |
| Heltzer Harold J | Crowell & Moring LLP (ONP)† * |
| Husseini Richard | Baker Botts LLP (ONP)† |
| Johnson Walker | Steptoe & Johnson LLP |
| Kazaks Julia M | Skadden, Arps, Slate, Meagher & Flom * |
| Kelleher Michael F | McDermott Will & Emery LLP * |
| Kittle-Kamp Thomas L | Mayer Brown LLP |
| Korb Donald L | Sullivan & Cromwell LLP (ONP)† * |
| Maynes Todd F | Kirkland & Ellis LLP (ONP)† * |
| Pakenham Kathleen M | Cooley LLP (ONP)† |
| Porter John | Baker Botts LLP (ONP)† * |
| Rizek Christopher | Caplin & Drysdale |
| Stark Sanford W | Bingham McCutchen LLP * |
| Stewart Scott M | Mayer Brown LLP |
| Swirski Alan J J | Skadden, Arps, Slate, Meagher & Flom * |
| Townsend John A | Townsend & Jones (ONP)† |
| Vasquez Jr Juan F | Chamberlain, Hrdlicka, White, Williams |
| Welty Todd | Dentons (ONP)† * |

**Up-and-coming individuals**

| | |
|---|---|
| Gleicher Brian | White & Case LLP * |
| Keller Natalie | Kirkland & Ellis LLP (ONP)† * |

**Band Star Associate**

| | |
|---|---|
| Matthews Mark E | Caplin & Drysdale |

## Tax: Fraud
### Leading Individuals

**Band 1**

| | |
|---|---|
| Bruton III James A | Williams & Connolly LLP (ONP)† |
| Campagna Larry A | Chamberlain, Hrdlicka, White, Williams |
| Farber Seth | Winston & Strawn LLP (ONP)† * |
| Fink Robert S | Kostelanetz & Fink LLP |
| Fisher Miriam L | Latham & Watkins LLP * |
| Junghans Paula | Zuckerman Spaeder LLP (ONP)† |
| Matthews Mark E | Caplin & Drysdale |
| Michel Scott D | Caplin & Drysdale |
| Namorato Cono R | Caplin & Drysdale |
| Rettig Charles P | Hochman Salkin Rettig Toscher (ONP)† |
| Skarlatos Bryan | Kostelanetz & Fink LLP |

**Up-and-coming individuals**

| | |
|---|---|
| Ciraolo Caroline | Rosenberg Martin Greenberg (ONP)† * |

## Skadden, Arps, Slate, Meagher & Flom LLP & Affiliates

**See profile on p.2008**

**THE FIRM** Skadden continues to lead the pack with its superb capabilities in sophisticated tax litigation and controversy work. Its vast client roster includes major multinationals, financial institutions, governments, estates and individuals, among others. The group tables a tremendous amount of industry experience, with a significant number of its attorneys having been with the IRS or the Treasury. The team has also been increasingly active on inbound lending, particularly from sovereign wealth funds and other foreign investment sources. Recent highlights include representing BNY Mellon in a US Tax Court trial connected with reported foreign tax credits relating to a major cross-border financing.

**Sources say:** *"I use Skadden on tax matters and I find them to be exceedingly competent experts in that area."*

**KEY INDIVIDUALS Kenneth Gideon** (see p.320) is a pre-eminent figure in the tax litigation space, and remains a leading figure in all types of tax controversy and planning representation. He also maintains a sterling transactional tax practice. He recently represented Transocean in successfully securing a concession before going to trial in significant transfer pricing litigation in the US Tax Court. Co-head of the firm's tax group, **Fred Goldberg** (see p.322) wins superb praise from his peers. He has a leading reputation for the most complex of tax controversy issues, and has extensive experience in IRS and administrative dealings. Another of the firm's sector-leading authorities, **John Williams** (see p.426) is a renowned expert in tax litigation and controversy work. *"A terrific litigator,"* he undertakes a range of IRS, administrative and federal court engagements. He has continued his high-profile representation of CIGNA in a precedent-setting US Tax Court trial. Palo Alto-based **Julia Kazaks** (see p.645) is a key figure in the firm's increasingly recognized West Coast practice. She is considered a very strategic and incisive litigator, and acted in the BNY Mellon case alongside Williams and **Alan Swirski** (see p.415). Swirski has an impressive track record

**KEY INDIVIDUALS** Described as *"a big gun"* of the country's tax controversy arena, **Joel Williamson** recently led in the Eaton Corporation matter. In addition to his superb controversy and litigation skills, sources also highlight his expertise in international and cross-border matters. **Thomas Durham** recently assisted in securing a major victory for Consolidated Edison of New York in a case involving leveraged lease transaction tax issues. He has tremendous expertise in tax-related litigation, including foreign tax, tax-advantaged investments and leasing engagements. Working alongside him in the Consolidated Edison of New York case was the *"very successful lawyer"* **David Abbott.** He has a broad-ranging tax practice undertaking both transactional and litigious work. Palo Alto-based **Larry Langdon** is able to combine in-depth experience in the field, having served as an IRS commissioner, with excellent working knowledge of federal tax law. **Thomas Kittle-Kamp** is increasingly recognized as a major player in the nation's tax litigation arenas. With Abbott and Durham he recently represented Union Bank of California in a matter concerning leveraged leases of a major sports entertainment complex. **Scott Stewart** is highlighted as an excellent name in tax disputes and transfer pricing. He recently played a key role on behalf of Tyco International in an appeal of IRS-proposed income adjustments to certain federal tax returns filed prior to its 2007 separation into Tyco, Covidien and TE Connectivity.

in litigation and tax controversy matters, and sees a number of IRS challenges through to success.

## Band 2

### McDermott Will & Emery LLP
See profile on p.1258

THE FIRM McDermott has drastically increased its national tax controversy capabilities with the arrival of a sizable transfer pricing team in Texas. The additions bolster the firm's sterling controversy practice spanning California, Chicago, New York and Washington, DC. The group's expertise covers a range of litigation, audits and appeals, international controversy, and state and local tax issues, among other matters. It recently secured an impressive success for Home Concrete & Supply in a significant IRS dispute in the Supreme Court.
Commercial Awareness "*They provide a lot of good market knowledge.*"

KEY INDIVIDUALS Thomas Borders (see p.285) is described as "*bright, capable and not afraid of a fight.*" He has a superb reputation for expertise in all manner of tax litigation, including federal tax controversy and criminal investigations. Peter Faber (see p.1891) is highly respected as a state and local tax expert, particularly in controversy and tax planning matters. His key clients include Morgan Stanley and Goldman Sachs. Roger Jones is a recent addition to the firm's controversy team from Latham & Watkins. Sources highlight his superb ability to remain "*three steps ahead*" of the competition in a range of major controversy matters on behalf of taxpayers. He was involved in the recent landmark Home Concrete & Supply case in the Supreme Court. Washington, DC-based Jean Pawlow (see p.383) leads the firm's national tax controversy practice group. She is a go-to expert for a range of issues, and recently represented Discover, a large credit card company, in tax controversy matters relating to income from interchange fees. Also based in Washington, DC, Michael Kelleher's (see p.344) solid expertise extends to transfer pricing and particularly complex federal income tax cases. He has continued his role on behalf of Securitas in significant tax court litigation. Senior counsel William Goldman (see p.322) is an incredibly well-respected figure in the country's legal landscape. A highly experienced lawyer with a well-deserved reputation, he has handled all manner of federal and state controversy engagement.

### Sutherland Asbill & Brennan LLP

THE FIRM This firm has a strong national tax controversy practice group, comprising experts in Atlanta, New York and Washington, DC. While offering a broad-ranging controversy and litigation practice, the team is best known for its excellence in state and local controversy matters. The group has also benefited from the arrival of a number of experts from Dewey & LeBeouf. Its impressive client roster includes Coca-Cola Enterprises, Kraft Foods and GM.
KEY INDIVIDUALS Jerold Cohen wins high praise for his extensive experience in domestic and international tax controversy work. He is also much sought after for his

expertise in tax planning. Practice group chair Jerome Libin is an expert in an array of international and domestic tax controversy issues. He is particularly recognized for his knowledge of tax planning and transfer pricing, as well as general corporate taxation matters.

## Band 3

### Caplin & Drysdale
See profile on p.909

THE FIRM This boutique firm has enjoyed an impressive year of expansion, both in its workload and presence, and strengthened its position as a formidable group for a whole host of tax controversy and litigation. Its expertise covers the gamut of international tax controversy, criminal tax and international tax engagements. It also comes highly recommended for its capabilities in fraud.
Sources say: "*The quality of work has been outstanding.*" "*A talented and very good firm.*"
KEY INDIVIDUALS Scott Michel "*is simply the best. Truly exceptional.*" He is a very highly regarded tax controversy and tax fraud lawyer who has received consistent praise from clients. He has also developed an expertise on the voluntary disclosure program offered by the IRS to US citizens with Swiss bank accounts. Cono Namorato is highly regarded as a criminal tax lawyer specializing in tax fraud. He has a reputation for expertise in issues arising on offshore accounts. David Rosenbloom is considered the foremost legal mind in complicated international tax planning and tax controversy matters and has "*been engaged as an expert witness in at least four or five countries including Canada, Australia and India.*" His formidable expertise has led to him being labeled "*his firm's leading light.*" Christopher Rizek is a civil tax dispute expert enjoying a great reputation in tax controversy for both individual and corporate clients. His areas of expertise include transfer pricing, debt tax accounting and the auditing of high net worth individuals. Mark Matthews is described as "*one of the leading minds in criminal tax fraud.*" He has held positions in the IRS, FBI and CIA, and so brings a wealth of experience to clients' issues.

### Chamberlain, Hrdlicka, White, Williams & Aughtry
See profile on p.2432

THE FIRM Operating out of offices in Atlanta, Houston and Philadelphia, this firm has a notable national reputation for tax litigation. Its broad-ranging practice encompasses local, state and federal tax disputes, as well as criminal and civil tax controversy work. The group is also highlighted for occupying a strong niche in tax controversy relating to business-owned aircraft. Its impressive roster of recent clients includes Western Refining, Inamed Corporate and Colorcon.
KEY INDIVIDUALS Houston-based Larry Campagna is a highly respected litigator with in-depth expertise in fraud, state and local tax controversies, as well as general business litigation. He recently led the team acting for Western Refining in a $10 million tax court case relating to

credits connected with upgrading facilities to produce ultra-low-sulfur diesel fuel. In Atlanta, David Aughtry (see p.1075) is lauded as a "*leading practitioner within the tax controversy area.*" He has a solid practice undertaking federal tax litigation and controversy, and "*has more courtroom experience than anyone in Atlanta,*" say sources. Based in the Philadelphia Metro area, the "*very capable*" Philip Karter has strong expertise in tax controversy work, and excellent courtroom skills. He is considered a solid choice for large corporate issues. Herbert Odell is a multitalented controversy lawyer highlighted for his ability to combine both tax controversy and tax planning work. Juan Vasquez is highlighted for his handling of federal, state and local tax controversies. He is also noted as a practitioner with great energy and excellent client focus.

### Fulbright & Jaworski LLP
See profile on p.2435

THE FIRM Fulbright & Jaworski enjoys an excellent reputation for all types of tax law engagements, including state, federal and local. The Texas-based firm is renowned for its expertise in real estate and oil and gas, among other sectors. The tax controversy team undertakes litigation, tax shelter, gift tax, criminal investigations and IRS audits. Its clients include AT&T, the Armand Hammer Foundation, and Prospector Offshore Drilling.
KEY INDIVIDUALS Jasper Taylor (see p.2418) has a nationally recognized tax litigation and controversy practice, acting on behalf of clients from an array of industries, including energy, real estate and telecom. He has experience before both the IRS and the US Tax Court. Of counsel Charles Hall (see p.328) is described as "*a phenomenal tax lawyer,*" and is highly regarded for his tax controversy expertise and impressive record of successful dealings with the IRS.

### Kostelanetz & Fink LLP

THE FIRM New York-based Kostelanetz & Fink has an enviable national reputation for representing a range of major clients in civil and white-collar criminal tax litigation. Market sources continue to highlight the group's expertise with foreign disclosure and offshore disputes, and its excellence in IRS-related litigation.
Sources say: "*They demonstrate a high level of efficiency and expertise.*"
KEY INDIVIDUALS Clients consider Robert Fink to be one of the most responsive legal minds in the practice area. He has a reputation for being incredibly knowledgeable of the intricacies of tax controversy, as well as for his broad civil and criminal tax, and white-collar defense practice. Bryan Skarlatos is able to combine an excellent knowledge base, extensive experience, great contacts and an unparalleled reputation for achieving client goals. He undertakes a diverse range of white-collar, civil and criminal tax and voluntary disclosure issues, among other matters.

### Miller & Chevalier Chartered
See profile on p.923

THE FIRM Operating out of the firm's head office in Washington DC, Miller & Chevalier offers a wide range of legal services in the tax controversy practice area. The firm has established itself as one of the foremost for issues relating to transfer pricing, cross-border transactions, and complex partnership-related matters. Its practice also has an impressive record in criminal tax cases.

**Sources say:** *"They're outstanding lawyers, an excellent law firm, and a pleasure to work with. Quality people. They have a long history of exemplary work in tax and tax controversy."*

**KEY INDIVIDUALS Kevin Kenworthy** (see p.345) is noted as *"a top litigator"* by peers, and has an impressive reputation for particularly complex tax controversy work. **Alan Horowitz** (see p.336) is renowned for his successful federal appellate tax work, and for his ability to take on the IRS and win.

## Steptoe & Johnson LLP

**THE FIRM** Steptoe & Johnson's superb teams in Atlanta and Washington, DC continue to gain recognition for forming a strong and cohesive tax controversy and litigation practice. It handles all manner of administrative and tax shelter controversies, as well as IRS appeals and audits, and has seen particular growth in insurance and foreign tax haven-related controversies. Its recent highlights include representing John Hancock Financial Services in a US Tax Court dispute with the IRS relating to the treatment of certain leveraged leases. Key clients also include Liberty Global, Amazon.com and Eastman Kodak.

**Sources say:** *"They are very skilled at negotiation with the IRS, strategy and tax litigation."*

**KEY INDIVIDUALS Arthur Bailey** is considered an excellent tax litigator. His practice extends to disputes relating to cross-border investments and life insurance. He led in the John Hancock Financial Services matter. **Matthew Lerner** has an excellent practice encompassing complex tax controversy and fraud matters. **Walker Johnson** has a strong practice covering tax controversy and litigation, as well as tax planning. Sources also highlight his expertise in financial, life insurance and investment tax matters.

## Band 4

### DLA Piper LLP (US)
See profile on p.1971

**THE FIRM** DLA Piper enjoys an increasing profile for its capabilities in representing clients at federal, state and local levels. The firm is lauded for its ability in all areas of tax controversy, including appeals, litigation, and audits. The firm is also well regarded for its ability to deal with criminal tax investigations and also to mediate with the IRS.

**Client Service** *"Top quality work, experts in their matter and very good with clients."*

**KEY INDIVIDUALS** New York-based **Ellis Reemer** (see p.391) leads the firm's tax controversy and tax litigation practice group. He is praised by clients for having *"very good business sense – not just straight legal considerations. He balances out business needs in a way that is extremely practical."* He has a stellar reputation for dealing with the IRS on audit matters and mediation.

## Morrison & Foerster LLP
See profile on p.1990

**THE FIRM** Morrison & Foerster has recently seen substantial growth in tax controversy matters relating to bankruptcy. The firm can call upon impressive knowledge relating to complex financial instruments and has extensive experience in tax litigation. Its capabilities are especially lauded in state and local tax controversy issues, as well as in federal engagements. The team's recent highlights include representing the Official Unsecured Creditors' Committee of Ambac in the US tax aspects of the company's high-profile bankruptcy proceedings.

**Client Service** *"There is always someone available to address any problems or issues that might arise. The firm has always been very responsive."*

**Commercial Awareness** *"I would regard their commercial sense as high – they have an excellent understanding of our business and the issues therein."*

**KEY INDIVIDUALS Edward Froelich** (see p.317) is a rising name in the tax controversy arena. He recently played a key role in the firm's representation of the Official Unsecured Creditors' Committee of Ambac. **Paul Frankel** (see p.315) is a nationally renowned practitioner highlighted as a superb attorney in state tax issues. He has an impressive track record in litigation and a very good reputation for both state and local tax controversy.

## Pillsbury Winthrop Shaw Pittman LLP
See profile on p.2000

**THE FIRM** Pillsbury Winthrop maintains an excellent reputation for handling federal, state and local tax disputes. It acts on behalf of a broad variety of multinational corporations and individuals, and remains well known for its expertise in real estate tax issues. Its impressive docket of recent work includes its representation of the Archdiocese of San Francisco in a $22 million tax dispute with the City and County of San Francisco. Other key clients include Amazon, AT&T and Apple.

**Client Service** *"They have excellent timeliness in responding, expertise in the subject matter, relevance to the subject matter, and a professional approach."* *"We have found Pillsbury's client service to be very good."*

**KEY INDIVIDUALS William Bonano** *"is very intelligent and able to elucidate the argument in an articulate, simple manner that makes sense,"* say clients. He is also commended for his knowledge of transfer pricing and relating that to the software industry.

## Vinson & Elkins LLP
See profile on p.2459

**THE FIRM** Vinson & Elkins maintains its enviable strength in tax controversy, and has also earned a reputation for excellence in transfer pricing. The firm is frequently a first choice for offshore drillers, and has a wealth of both expertise and experience in dealing with the IRS on behalf of energy and oil and gas companies. Its recent highlights include acting for Transocean on tax disputes with the IRS relating to the company's 2006-2009 federal income tax returns. Clients also include Halliburton, 7-Eleven and the University of Texas.

**KEY INDIVIDUALS** Based in Houston, **George Gerachis** (see p.2390) leads the firm's tax and employee benefits and executive compensation practice group. Highlighted by peers for his superb tax controversy practice, he enjoys a strong record of success against the IRS and a reputation for navigating particularly complex matters.

## White & Case LLP
See profile on p.451

**THE FIRM** White & Case's tax controversy group has eight tax experts well placed to handle both domestic civil and international tax controversy issues. The firm's global platform makes it an ideal choice for cross-border matters, and it comes highly recommended for transfer pricing.

**Sources say:** *"They are excellent, always very professional, and always keep to their deadlines."*

**KEY INDIVIDUALS** Washington, DC-based **Michael Quigley** (see p.388) leads the firm's tax controversy and litigation practice group. He has been especially active in transfer pricing matters involving Korean clients and jurisdiction. **Brian Gleicher** (see p.321) *"stands out for his efforts to know and understand his clients' businesses and always has a thorough understanding of the issues involved, no matter the situation,"* say sources. He has an excellent international tax practice focusing on transfer pricing and tax treaty work.

## Other Notable Practitioners

The *"outstanding"* **James Bruton** of Williams & Connolly LLP is lauded as one of the country's leading experts in tax fraud. He operates out of the firm's Washington, DC office and has tremendous experience in acting on cases at every stage of the tax litigation process. The up-and-coming **Caroline Ciraolo** (see p.295) of Rosenberg Martin Greenberg, LLP is a well-known name in the tax fraud arena. Her expertise in both civil and criminal tax litigation is matched by her breadth of experience at both a federal and state level. **William Colgin** (see p.297) of Morgan, Lewis & Bockius LLP has an impressive reputation for tax controversy work and IRS audits. He has extensive experience of appeal work arising out of both litigation and audits and has acted for several Fortune 500 clients. **Michael Desmond** of The Law Offices of Michael J. Desmond is a sole practitioner who brings near-unparalleled experience in the field, having worked in the Treasury Department and the IRS. He is a distinguished name in tax controversy work. **Seth Farber** (see p.311) of Winston & Strawn LLP is a versatile litigator with an impressive success record in litigation for tax fraud. He leads the firm's New York-based litigation practice group, and also maintains a strong reputation for white-collar and appellate matters. Leader of the tax controversy practice group at Cooley LLP in New York, **Stephen Gardner** is renowned among fellow practitioners for his great expertise in the field. He recently successfully led on behalf of Entergy in a Fifth Circuit case relating to the company's claim for nearly $250 million in foreign tax credits related to the UK's windfall tax. **Harold Heltzer** (see p.868) leads the tax practice group at Crowell & Moring LLP in Washington, DC.

He is described as *"very knowledgeable and thorough – a go-to person when you are dealing in the audit and appeals process."* He has extensive experience acting before the IRS. **Lawrence Hill** joined the New York office of Shearman & Sterling LLP from Dewey & LeBeouf in 2012. He specializes in IRS controversies and litigation work across the board. His practice also includes white-collar investigations. Houston-based **Richard Husseini** chairs the tax practice group at Baker Botts LLP. He has both a transactional and controversy practice acting for key clients in the oil and gas industries. He is also highlighted for his expertise with new energy sources, including solar, wind and shale gas. Washington, DC-based **Thomas Johnston** of Shearman & Sterling LLP has expertise in tax controversy and the interrelation of foreign tax credits with domestic tax legislation. He remains a key attorney for an impressive list of clients, including Ford. The highly experienced trial lawyer **Paula Junghans** of Zuckerman Spaeder LLP is commended by sources for her superb knowledge of tax litigation and white-collar crime matters, and for her

excellent judgment. She is a *"top-notch"* player in the sector. **Barbara Kaplan** (see p.342) leads the tax practice at Greenberg Traurig, LLP. She is described as *"an expert attorney in international as well as domestic tax fields,"* say sources. Her practice encompasses a range of federal, state and local tax and tax controversy matters, litigation and examinations. **Natalie Keller** (see p.344) of Kirkland & Ellis LLP is applauded for her knowledge of tax controversy and understanding of the litigation process. She has gained a reputation in transfer pricing, IRS audits, and in overcoming issues related to tax compliance. **Donald Korb** (see p.349) splits his time between the Washington, DC and New York offices of Sullivan & Cromwell LLP. He brings a unique level of experience to his representations as a former Chief Counsel for the IRS. He now leads the firm's tax controversy practice group. Chicago-based **Todd Maynes** (see p.1220) of Kirkland & Ellis LLP is described as *"one of those standout individuals in whom you have total faith that he is giving great advice."* His practice is especially active in tax litigation, debt restructuring and bankrupt-

cy matters. **Kathleen Pakenham** in New York chairs Cooley LLP's tax litigation practice. She has in-depth knowledge of tax shelters and a solid reputation for undertaking issues revolving around valuation disputes and foreign taxes. **John Porter** (see p.386) at Baker Botts LLP in Houston is a tremendously experienced tax controversy expert. He comes especially recommended for his strong niche in gift and estate litigation. **Charles Rettig** of California-based Hochman Salkin Rettig Toscher & Perez is highlighted as *"hands-down, the best for litigation"* in the tax space. His practice encompasses a range of general tax litigation, controversies, investigations and audits, among other matters. **Jack Townsend** operates out of the Houston office of the tax boutique Townsend & Jones. He is highly skilled in litigation and negotiations with the IRS, and is lauded by sources as *"a professor as much as a partner"* in the tax controversy space. Dallas-based **Todd Welty** (see p.2421) leads the tax controversy and litigation practice at Dentons. He comes highly recommended for his civil and criminal tax controversy expertise.

# **TAX** CORPORATE & FINANCE

## Band 1

### Cleary Gottlieb Steen & Hamilton LLP
See profile on p.1963

**THE FIRM** This international goliath has a domestic and global reputation for financial products, taxation issues and M&A work, which sees it placed in the very top tier of US corporate tax firms. The group continues to adapt and evolve according to the new challenges presented by ever-changing domestic and international legislation. Particular growth areas in terms of expertise include the firm's bankruptcy and restructuring-related tax work. In recent highlights, the group advised Google on the tax aspects of its $12.5 billion acquisition of Motorola Mobility.
**Sources say:** *"Very good, very proactive. They do excellent work and are very thoughtful, polished lawyers."*
**KEY INDIVIDUALS** Partners operating out of the firm's New York practice include Erika Nijenhuis, William McRae and Leslie Samuels.

### Cravath, Swaine & Moore LLP
See profile on p.1966

**THE FIRM** This preeminent group extends its expertise to every corner of corporate law and related tax work. It is equally renowned for its general tax expertise, as well as its ability to really home in on specific issues and pioneer new problem-solving techniques. Cravath is able to blend its knowledge of real estate issues and tax to become a real leader in Real Estate Excise Tax matters. Its recent highlights include representing Barnes & Noble in the formation of a strategic partnership agreement with Microsoft. The group has also continued its representation of

Starbucks in its continuing investment in its partnership with Square.
**Sources say:** *"We found them excellent – responsive, diligent and thorough. They're very solid in advice."*
**KEY INDIVIDUALS** Stephen Gordon heads the New York-based group.

### Davis Polk & Wardwell LLP
See profile on p.442

**THE FIRM** This world-renowned tax group has an excellent reputation in domestic, international and cross-border tax law. Well known for dealing with particularly complex matters, the group also undertakes cutting-edge and precedent-setting issues. Its expertise in corporate structures, financial products and M&A work is of such a caliber that clients agree it has a well-deserved place as a top-tier firm both in New York and nationwide. Its enviable client roster includes Ford, Credit Suisse and Citi.
**Client Service** *"Top-quality work. They are very time efficient and do their utmost to keep under budget."*
**Commercial Awareness** *"They are good at proactively spotting issues and suggesting solutions. The partners with whom I regularly work have learned a lot about our business model, and they tailor their suggestions accordingly."*
**KEY INDIVIDUALS** The firm's New York office is home to several of the firm's big names, including Po Sit, Harry Ballan and Avishai Shachar.

### Kirkland & Ellis LLP
See profile on p.1254

**THE FIRM** The Kirkland & Ellis tax team has had a busy year, particularly with regards to structuring, private equi-

ty and finance matters. The firm's superb Chicago and New York teams provide it with a breadth of practice that sees it attract big-name clients such as Tronox and NRG Energy, and also ensures that the group maintains its national reputation. The tax practice has great expertise in tax planning, and is also highlighted for its knowledge of restructuring matters.
**Client Service** *"Excellent, and very responsive." "Great customer service."*
**KEY INDIVIDUALS** Todd Maynes heads up the department from the firm's New York office. In Chicago, notable practitioners include Natalie Keller and Jeffrey Sheffield.

### Skadden, Arps, Slate, Meagher & Flom LLP & Affiliates
See profile on p.2008

**THE FIRM** Skadden has a well-deserved reputation for versatility in counseling on every aspect of tax at both a state and local level. The firm has superb expertise in advising on particularly challenging or novel transactional issues. Skadden also brings together experts from diverse backgrounds, boasting a wealth of experience from across its global network of talent and resources. Current practitioners at the firm include former IRS investigators and controversy judges. High-stake complicated tax controversies, especially those with an international element, are a major strength. Key clients include Yahoo!, Amylin Pharmaceuticals, Fortress Investment Group and the Westfield Group.

**Commercial Awareness** *"Really good tax lawyers who understand how the ideas they're proposing fit within the context of the business deal."*

**KEY INDIVIDUALS** Fred Goldberg and Matthew Rosen lead the practice group out of DC and New York, respectively.

## Sullivan & Cromwell LLP
See profile on p.2011

**THE FIRM** Sullivan & Cromwell has enjoyed a busy year in which not only has the firm built upon its preeminent national name, but also reinforced its position as a global leader in corporate finance and tax work. The group is at the forefront of complicated M&A, capital market and international tax planning matters. Its recent highlights include advising LAN Airlines in its business combination with TAM (Brazil), an engagement involving complex cross-border transactional and restructuring issues. The firm also represented Medco Health Solutions in its $29.1 billion merger with Express Scripts.

**KEY INDIVIDUALS** New York-based Ronald Creamer heads the firm's tax and corporate practice groups.

## Wachtell, Lipton, Rosen & Katz
See profile on p.2012

**THE FIRM** Wachtell is widely regarded as a particularly effective firm for M&A matters, especially those with particularly technical or novel elements. Its relatively compact size is offset by its team's deep expertise in the field. The group is also considered an excellent first choice for a range of spin-off, joint venture, real estate, REIT and restructuring engagements.

**Sources say:** *"They are fantastically good." "They would be in my top five."*

**KEY INDIVIDUALS** New York-based Deborah Paul and Jodi Schwartz are key partners in the tax team.

## Band 2

## Bingham McCutchen LLP
See profile on p.1515

**THE FIRM** Bingham McCutchen enjoys an excellent reputation for both domestic and international tax planning, and is particularly respected for dealing with complex matters involving the interface of partnership and international tax rules. Bankruptcy, restructuring and securitization matters are also considered strong practice areas for the firm. The group recently served as the tax counsel for Energy Transfer Equity Partners in its $5.3 billion takeover of Sunoco. Current clients also include General Mills and Marathon Oil.

**Client Service** *"They are exceptional in their attention to detail, the quality and thoughtfulness of their work product, timeliness and responsiveness."*

**KEY INDIVIDUALS** The DC-based Bill McKee and Will Nelson cochair the tax team alongside Anthony Carbone in New York.

## Debevoise & Plimpton LLP
See profile on p.1968

**THE FIRM** This New York-based firm has a superb international practice, with an excellent reputation for cutting-edge tax advice in both domestic and cross-border transactions. It provides tax counsel on a broad range of subjects, including private equity and hedge fund formations, joint ventures and project finance. The firm is currently acting as special aircraft counsel to American Airlines, and also represented The Carlyle Group in its $3.3 billion acquisition of Getty Images. Other key clients include Kelso & Company, Access Industries/Warner Music, and International Paper.

**Sources say:** *"They have terrific tax expertise that is very proactive and very effective."*

**KEY INDIVIDUALS** Practice group chair Burt Rosen is based in New York.

## Fried, Frank, Harris, Shriver & Jacobson LLP
See profile on p.1975

**THE FIRM** This firm maintains a highly respected practice undertaking a broad range of complex tax issues, including planning, bankruptcy and restructuring, corporate, asset management and fund formation. The group has been especially active in the bankruptcy and litigation space, and also on behalf of major financial institutions. Its recent highlights include advising Goldman Sachs on its $1.1 billion agreement to acquire Interline Brands. Thomson Reuters and Merrill Lynch also feature on its enviable client roster.

**Sources say:** *"They advise us on transactions, and the advice they offer is diligent, business-oriented and flawless."*

**KEY INDIVIDUALS** Alan Kaden heads the firm's tax department in DC, while Robert Cassanos is the lead partner in New York.

## Gibson, Dunn & Crutcher LLP
See profile on p.682

**THE FIRM** Gibson Dunn's exceptional depth of expertise sees it undertaking tax counsel for a broad range of clients, ranging from startup entrepreneurs to established multinationals. Its national practice spans both East and West Coasts, and is complemented by regionally renowned offices in Los Angeles, New York, DC and Dallas, overall contributing to a well-deserved national reputation. Its work highlights include acting for Amazon in its $775 million acquisition of Kiva Systems, as well as Hewlett-Packard in its $10.3 billion acquisition of Autonomy. The group also represented Kraft Foods in a $6 billion bond offering and spin-off debt exchange.

**Sources say:** *"Very responsive, technically strong, and their fees are reasonable."*

**KEY INDIVIDUALS** On the West Coast, Hatef Behnia, Paul Issler and Scott Knutson remain key contacts, as does David Sinak in Dallas.

## Latham & Watkins LLP
See profile on p.446

**THE FIRM** This firm has excellent national breadth in the tax sector, with notable teams covering New York, San Francisco, Los Angeles, DC, Boston, Chicago and Houston. International tax issues are a particular forte of the firm, especially with regards to Master Limited Partnerships (MLPs) and REITs. In recent highlights, the team provided tax advice to Energy Transfer Equity in its $9.4 billion acquisition of Southern Union Company. Its New York team also recently took the spotlight with its handling of the tax issues relating to Lucasfilm's acquisition by Disney.

**Client Service** *"Excellent. Easy to work with and responsive to phone calls and e-mails, even on short notice. It's clear they value and appreciate their clients."*

**Commercial Awareness** *"They think ahead very well and adapt to the way we do business."*

**KEY INDIVIDUALS** David Raab is based in New York and chairs the firm's global tax practice group.

## McDermott Will & Emery LLP
See profile on p.1258

**THE FIRM** This firm's formidable national practice extends across Chicago, DC, New York, California and Texas. Its pioneering work in sophisticated corporate tax structures sees the team sought out by many companies, particularly those based in Silicon Valley, such as eBay and Groupon. Key clients also include Tyco, Johnson & Johnson, and Aon.

**Commercial Awareness** *"I value the knowledge base, experience and practical solutions that MW&E bring in this area."*

**KEY INDIVIDUALS** Lowell Yoder is head of the firm's global tax practice group.

## Paul, Weiss, Rifkind, Wharton & Garrison LLP
See profile on p.1997

**THE FIRM** Operating out of New York, Paul Weiss has notable strength in tax issues relating to joint ventures, partnerships, private equity and hedge investment funds, spin-offs and REITs. Its recent highlights include acting for Apollo Global Management in its $7.15 billion agreement to acquire all oil and gas exploration and production assets from El Paso. Other clients include Rockstar Bidco and Oaktree Capital Management.

**Sources say:** *"They have incredible depth across the board and the most talented lawyers imaginable."*

**KEY INDIVIDUALS** The department is cochaired by Richard Bronstein and Jeffrey Samuels out of the firm's New York office.

## Ropes & Gray LLP
See profile on p.1528

**THE FIRM** Ropes & Gray's national tax practice has highly respected attorneys in both its Boston and New York offices. The firm maintains superb expertise in M&A, private and public fund formation, as well as in work with sovereign wealth funds. The group also has an excellent reputation for tax counseling in relation to major construction projects and various types of investment. Work highlights include advising Bain Capital on its $1 billion acquisition of a 30% stake in India-based outsourcing company Genpact. It also acted for TPG in its $3 billion acquisition of J Crew Group.

**Sources say:** *"Very good lawyers who have a lot of experience, know and understand the market, and are business savvy."*

**KEY INDIVIDUALS** Boston-based Christopher Leich heads up the firm's tax department.

## Simpson Thacher & Bartlett LLP
See profile on p.2006

**THE FIRM** Simpson Thatcher is well regarded by clients for its innovative approach to solving complex transactional and financial tax problems. The group is particularly highlighted for its expertise in fund formation and the tax aspects relating to M&A transactions, as well as cross-border finance issues. Its work highlights include representing Microsoft in its $300 million investment in Barnes & Noble's NOOK business, as well as representing Blackstone Real Estate Partners in various issues, including in acquisition and restructuring deals. Other key clients include Accenture and JPMorgan.

**Sources say:** *"They are excellent in every aspect of the service they provide. Brilliant, and very nice to work with."*

**KEY INDIVIDUALS** Steven Todrys heads the practice group from the firm's office in New York.

## Weil, Gotshal & Manges LLP
See profile on p.2015

**THE FIRM** Weil Gotshal remains a preeminent firm in bankruptcy-related tax issues, with a strong team of practitioners operating out of the firm's hubs in Boston and New York. The group is renowned for its expertise in high-level debt restructuring work. It recently represented Lehman Brothers in its $3 billion purchase of a 53% stake in Archstone, thus acquiring Archstone in its entirety. Other high-profile clients include Goldman Sachs and General Electric.

**Sources say:** *"They are very smart." "I use them a lot because they are top-notch."*

**KEY INDIVIDUALS** New York-based Kenneth Heitner, Scott Sontag and Martin Pollack lead the firm's tax practice.

## Band 3

## Baker & McKenzie
See profile on p.435

**THE FIRM** Baker & McKenzie is able to boast a far-reaching national and global presence, with its international offices working closely with each other in a cohesive global tax operation. While best known in the controversy and fraud space, the group is also experienced in corporate tax issues, including planning, M&A, cross-border and joint ventures. Notable clients include Boeing, Hershey and Thomson Reuters.

**Sources say:** *"The firm has long been known in the tax arena for its international reach."*

**KEY INDIVIDUALS** Len Terr leads the firm's US tax practice group.

## Baker Botts LLP
See profile on p.2427

**THE FIRM** This Houston-based giant has long been respected for its expertise in energy transactions. As such,

it is an excellent first choice for advising on tax issues relating to the oil and gas and renewable energy sectors, among others. Its expertise encompasses a range of matters, including MLP, state and local, partnership, M&A and international issues. The group's recent highlights include acting for the Energy and Minerals Group in relation to Tallgrass Energy Partners's acquisition of midstream assets from Kinder Morgan Energy Partners. It also recently represented Marathon Oil in its $3.5 billion acquisition of Hilcorp Resources.

**Sources say:** *"An outstanding service-oriented firm. Collaborative with their clients, and focused on providing quality support and advice."*

**KEY INDIVIDUALS** Houston-based Richard Husseini chairs the firm's tax practice.

## Cadwalader, Wickersham & Taft LLP
See profile on p.438

**THE FIRM** This New York-based group has specialist knowledge across a diverse tax practice arena, including in bankruptcy and structured finance. The team's strengths in M&A, capital markets and fund formation are also highlighted. Its clients have frequently included a large number of Fortune 100 companies.

**KEY INDIVIDUALS** Based in New York, Linda Swartz is chair of the firm's tax practice group.

## Covington & Burling LLP
See profile on p.441

**THE FIRM** This DC-based group has broad expertise within the tax arena. The team is particularly highlighted for its tax treatment of innovative financial products, M&A work and tax planning, especially structural tax planning for large multinational companies. The firm provides tax counsel for major sports leagues, including the NFL, NHL and Major League Baseball. Its prestigious client roster also includes Viacom and PepsiCo.

**Sources say:** *"Excellent. Easy to reach, they get back to you right away and are available when you need them. They communicate well and provide accessible research."*

**KEY INDIVIDUALS** Co-heads of department Dan Luchsinger and Reeves Westbrook are notable names at the firm.

## Mayer Brown LLP
See profile on p.1257

**THE FIRM** Mayer Brown's excellent national tax practice is centered in Chicago and further supported by experts in California and New York. Its expertise covers corporate, individual and partnership taxation matters, and it also enjoys a strong reputation for transactional tax planning and restructuring. High-profile clients include Bank of America, Siemens and Motorola. The firm is also highly regarded for the tax work it undertakes involving the pharmaceutical industry.

**Client Service** *"They combine client advocacy with integrity, and are always there to be of assistance. What impresses me most about the firm is that they are very team-oriented, and have this effervescent desire to collaborate to obtain the best result."*

**KEY INDIVIDUALS** Practice group leaders James Barry and Jason Bazar, in Chicago and New York, respectively, are highly regarded.

## Shearman & Sterling LLP
See profile on p.2005

**THE FIRM** Shearman & Sterling blends national breadth of practice with global scope. Complicated tax-related matters involving cross-border transactions and M&A are particular areas of focus and expertise for the team. The group is also commended for its increasingly strong reputation in minimizing tax costs for companies operating in multiple jurisdictions. The firm recently represented Synthes in its $21.3 billion acquisition by Johnson & Johnson. Key clients also include Dow Chemical, Legg Mason and Marriott International.

**KEY INDIVIDUALS** New York-based Laurence Bambino and DC-based Michael Shulman cochair the practice group. Shulman is also managing partner of the firm's DC office.

## Sidley Austin LLP
See profile on p.1264

**THE FIRM** Sidley's excellent national practice is especially lauded in Chicago and, increasingly, New York. Its expertise covers the full spectrum of M&A, joint ventures, insurance, leveraged buyouts, spin-offs and recapitalizations. The firm is especially recommended for its superb bankruptcy and restructuring-related tax practice, and also has a solid reputation for REIT-related tax work. The team recently acted as primary issuer's counsel for Starwood Property Trust's REIT tax matters.

**Client Service** *"Outstanding – very responsive. They work quickly to meet deadlines, and they're all really quite good."*

**KEY INDIVIDUALS** Sharp Sorensen leads the firm's Chicago-based tax team. He also leads the firm's wider national tax practice alongside Laura Barzilai in New York.

## Sutherland Asbill & Brennan LLP

**THE FIRM** Sutherland Asbill's tax group is highly regarded for its distinguished and sizable state and local tax practice. The team is consistently highlighted for its expertise in complex and large-scale M&A transactions, as well as in international tax issues. Its recent highlights include acting as US tax counsel to TE Connectivity in relation to its EUR1.55 billion acquisition of Deutsch Group SAS. Recent clients also include General Motors, Procter & Gamble and Coca-Cola.

**KEY INDIVIDUALS** DC-based Jerome Libin chairs the firm's tax practice group.

## Vinson & Elkins LLP
See profile on p.2459

**THE FIRM** Texas-based Vinson & Elkins enjoys a strong reputation as one of the foremost practices in relation to all aspects of energy-related tax law. The firm has benefited greatly from an upsurge in energy transactions of late, as well as from its increasing prominence in issues relating to private equity and sovereign wealth funds. The team recently provided tax advice to Caiman Energy on the $2.5

billion sale of its Caiman Eastern Midstream assets to Williams Partners.

**Sources say:** *"They have a national tax practice that is well known and respected."*

**KEY INDIVIDUALS** Based in Houston, George Gerachis leads the firm's tax and employee benefits and executive compensation practice group.

## Band 4

## Alston & Bird LLP
See profile on p.1102

**THE FIRM** Alston & Bird enjoys a superb nationwide reputation for its tax practice, and in the past year has seen a growth in transfer pricing-related engagements. Its expertise encompasses state and local tax, M&A, cross-border transactions and federal income tax issues, among other matters. Its highly respected Atlanta-based group is further supported by experts in New York and DC. Its enviable client roster includes Honda, UPS and Autoliv.

**Sources say:** *"They provide good technical advice and see things from all different directions, not just what we want to hear. They bring other perspectives."*

**KEY INDIVIDUALS** Henry Birnkrant heads the department from the firm's DC office.

## Fenwick & West LLP
See profile on p.680

**THE FIRM** West Coast firm Fenwick & West has a highly respected national tax practice based in California. It enjoys an excellent reputation for tax work involving companies based in Silicon Valley, and is highly recommended for its experience acting on behalf of hi-tech clients, such as Facebook. The group is also well known for its international tax planning and M&A expertise.

**KEY INDIVIDUALS** Based in the firm's Mountain View office, David Forst chairs the department.

## Fulbright & Jaworski LLP
See profile on p.2435

**THE FIRM** Fulbright & Jaworski's Texas-based tax team has a leading name in tax issues involving the energy sector. The practice undertakes tax planning, restructuring, M&A, partnership, state and local, transfer pricing and international tax matters. The group's recent highlights include acting for National Oilwell Varco in its $2.5 billion acquisition of Robins & Myers.

**Sources say:** *"They have a good group with good-quality people."*

**KEY INDIVIDUALS** John Allender leads the tax group from the firm's Houston office.

## Ivins, Phillips & Barker
See profile on p.918

**THE FIRM** This tax boutique firm operates out of DC, and also has an office in Los Angeles. The group is recognized for having strength across all types of tax issues, with particular expertise in federal tax matters and taxation

relating to employee benefits. Its client list includes a number of Fortune 500 companies.

**Sources say:** *"Well-respected and bright tax lawyers."*

**KEY INDIVIDUALS** Stewart Dunn and Carter Hood are both highly regarded at the firm.

## Milbank, Tweed, Hadley & McCloy LLP
See profile on p.448

**THE FIRM** Milbank Tweed is an international firm that earns praise for its innovation in complex tax matters. The New York-based group has expertise in M&A work, financial restructuring, project finance, and tax relating to executive compensation and employee benefits. Its client roster includes Google, Arrow Electronics and Lightsquared.

**Sources say:** *"Excellent service – great responsiveness, depth of knowledge and expertise. They give practical advice and creativity in solving complex questions and structures."*

**KEY INDIVIDUALS** New York-based Bruce Kayle leads the firm's tax practice group.

## Steptoe & Johnson LLP

**THE FIRM** Steptoe & Johnson's DC-based group is consistently highlighted for its international tax prowess, and is increasingly highlighted for undertaking tax restructuring, spin-offs, bankruptcies and work with tax-exempt organizations. Key clients include Eastman Kodak, the Government of Puerto Rico and Dish Network.

**Sources say:** *"They really put the client first. They have a great depth of expertise, and this enables them to handle with ease all the work we send them."*

**KEY INDIVIDUALS** Based in DC, Philip West chairs the firm's tax practice.

## Band 5

## DLA Piper LLP (US)
See profile on p.1971

**THE FIRM** DLA Piper's national tax group continues to gain recognition for its work on behalf of multinational corporations. Its teams in California, Florida and DC form key pillars of its nationwide practice. Its expertise includes private equity and wealth management-related issues, as well as cross-border M&A and transfer pricing matters. Key clients include Nike and Hasbro.

**Sources say:** *"All of the attorneys are stellar. The service received was excellent."*

**KEY INDIVIDUALS** David Colker leads the firm's global tax practice out of its Palo Alto office.

## King & Spalding LLP
See profile on p.445

**THE FIRM** King & Spalding has an unparalleled reputation in Atlanta, as well as an increasingly prominent practice nationally. The group provides excellent services, including in transactional issues, fund formations and restructurings. It is especially commended for its expertise in REIT-related matters.

**Sources say:** *"They have strong legal expertise and they understand our goals as a client."*

**KEY INDIVIDUALS** Abraham Shashy leads the firm's tax practice out of its DC office.

## Sullivan & Worcester LLP
See profile on p.1534

**THE FIRM** Sullivan & Worcester has a strong presence along the East Coast, with teams in New York, DC and Boston. The group boasts a superb international taxation practice, and frequently advises US companies on outbound investments, as well as foreign business with US interests. Its expertise also extends to include mutual funds, tax planning, state and local, and REIT issues. Clients include Iron Mountain, CommonWealth REIT and Teradyne.

**Client Service** *"Excellent client service. I get an immediate high-quality response."*

**KEY INDIVIDUALS** Boston-based Ameek Ashok Ponda leads the firm's tax department.

# TRANSPORTATION AVIATION: FINANCE

Commentary about individuals can be found under their firm's paragraph. If the firm has no paragraph (is not ranked) look at Other Notable Practitioners.

### Transportation: Aviation: Finance
**Leading Firms**

**Band 1**
Milbank, Tweed, Hadley & McCloy LLP *
Vedder Price PC *

**Band 2**
Clifford Chance US LLP *
Holland & Knight LLP *

**Band 3**
Debevoise & Plimpton LLP *
Fulbright & Jaworski LLP *
Hughes Hubbard & Reed LLP *
Pillsbury Winthrop Shaw Pittman LLP *
White & Case LLP *

**Band 4**
Katten Muchin Rosenman LLP *
Kaye Scholer LLP *

*Indicates firm with profile.*
*Alphabetical order within each band. Band 1 is the highest.*

## Band 1

### Milbank, Tweed, Hadley & McCloy LLP
See profile on p.448

**THE FIRM** This firm is a frequent choice of counsel for high-end lender representation, and continues to court market recognition for its astute command of related capital markets work. A raft of prominent names have come to rely on its perceptive and adept counsel, including Goldman Sachs and JPMorgan Chase. Highlights for the practice include acting as purchasing counsel for Sumitomo Mitsui Banking on the $7.3 billion acquisition of RBS Aviation Capital.

**Client Service** *"It just seems that they are always one step ahead of my thoughts. A great team!"*

**KEY INDIVIDUALS** Drew Fine (see p.312) is one of the most well-known and highly respected lawyers in the aviation finance arena, leading sources to describe him as *"the dean of the industry."* Those seeking a *"hard worker who is always available, and an excellent lawyer,"* would do well to consider instructing him. He had a lead role on the aforementioned work for Sumitomo Mitsui. The *"experienced*

*and practical"* **Helfried Schwarz** (see p.403) wins plaudits for his creative commercial approach to aviation finance. His clients include JPMorgan Chase, which he recently represented in relation to the $675 million purchase of US Ex-Im Bank-supported bonds. **Elihu Robertson** (see p.393) chairs the firm's transportation and space group. He is *"strong technically, and he has lots of experience,"* according to sources. He recently represented the underwriters on a high-value enhanced equipment trust certificate (EETC) deal for Continental Airlines.

### Vedder Price PC
See profile on p.1266

**THE FIRM** Sources are quick to point to this firm's prominent aviation finance practice. It counts Nordic Aviation Capital and Southwest Airlines among its key clients, while recent highlights include advising US Ex-Im Bank on export credit financing work, including the financing of six aircraft for Atlas Air.

**Commercial Awareness** *"It has a strong international reach, which is important for any investor that does work across the globe."*

**KEY INDIVIDUALS** Dean Gerber (see p.319) chairs the firm's global transportation finance practice. He acted as lead partner on the US Ex-Im Bank deals. Sources agree he is *"clearly a leader"* in the field, adding that *"he knows the issues, handles them well and is very easy to deal with."* **Ronald Scheinberg** (see p.400) is the lead aviation finance professional in the New York office. His practice includes representation of foreign bank interests in financing transactions. Sources describe him as *"an excellent lawyer."* He acted as lender counsel for Crédit Agricole with respect to a $340 million credit facility for AeroTurbine. **Joshua Gentner** (see p.319) is lauded by sources as an *"outstanding lawyer."* He is prominent for his cross-border work for US Ex-Im Bank, and provides regular input on its export credit financing matters. His broad experience enables him to provide cogent advice on EETCs, securitizations and insolvency. **Geoffrey Kass** (see p.343) is described as an *"excellent leasing lawyer"* and is noted for being *"very good at complex aircraft-backed debt transactions."* His clients include notable financial institutions such as Macquarie. He acted as a lead lawyer for Ansett Worldwide Aviation Services (AWAS) on its $500 million portfolio acquisition

of 12 leased aircraft. New York office managing shareholder **Jeffrey Veber** (see p.420) also had a lead role on the AWAS portfolio acquisition deal. He wins plaudits for his commercial approach, with market commentators noting that *"he gets the deal done."*

### Recommended for Client Service
**Nationwide**
Milbank, Tweed, Hadley & McCloy LLP

### Recommended for Commercial Awareness
**Nationwide**
Clifford Chance US LLP     Vedder Price PC

## Band 2

### Clifford Chance US LLP
See profile on p.439

**THE FIRM** This UK firm's New York office is highly active, and able to handle sophisticated cross-border aviation finance work including securitization matters. It advised Crédit Agricole in a $390 million Willis Engine securitization via senior secured notes. Other marquee clients of the practice include AerCap and BNP Paribas.

**Commercial Awareness** *"A market leader with lots of experience and quality partners and associates."*

**KEY INDIVIDUALS** John Howitt (see p.337) co-heads the Americas asset finance practice. Sources concur that he is *"very smart and capable"* and note that he *"really puts an expert view on things."* He recently advised Milestone Aviation on a $355 million helicopter portfolio financing deal. **Zarrar Sehgal** (see p.403) co-heads the practice alongside Howitt, and also chairs the transport and logistics group. He took the lead role on the Willis Engine securitization matter. Sources laud him as *"an excellent aviation banker: he has strong relationships and strong capital markets skills."* He also advises BNP Paribas. **Geoffrey White** (see p.425) attracts market attention for his skill in handling matters in the Latin American domain. *"His knowledge is unsurpassed, and he is bright and very hard-working,"* relate enthusiastic sources. His highlights include acting for AWAS as the borrower on a $120 million revolving predelivery payments (PDP) facility.

## Holland & Knight LLP
See profile on p.1028

**THE FIRM** This firm has built a respected profile for advising on high-profile matters for airlines, both foreign and domestic. The team is adept at handling all aspects of aviation finance including acquisition, financing and leasing transactions.

Sources say: *"They really know the legal underpinnings that relate specifically to aircraft."*
**KEY INDIVIDUALS William Piels** (see p.384) is one of the firm's best-known partners for aviation finance. He attracts considerable market acclaim for his financing practice, with sources noting that he is *"very strong in operating lease matters."* **John Pritchard** (see p.387) is a much sought-after aviation finance specialist. Sources have *"nothing but good things to say about him,"* and report that he is *"great at managing deals, and in negotiation he is very reasonable and extremely knowledgeable."* Those seeking a *"very smart analytical lawyer"* with a keen eye for detail would do well to consider retaining the services of **Fred Bass** (see p.279), according to sources. Aircraft finance and leasing are the cornerstones of his practice. **MJ Spelliscy** (see p.411) is a partner in the firm's structured finance practice and is known for her prowess in asset-based transactional work. *"She is extremely responsive, and really good at helping us talk through our provisions and what is reasonable,"* report admiring sources. **Phillip Durham**'s (see p.307) recent promotion to partnership confirms his status as one of the rising stars of aviation finance. Sources praise his commercial awareness and widely tip him for a big future.

## Band 3

### Debevoise & Plimpton LLP
See profile on p.1968

**THE FIRM** Domestic airline representation and bankruptcy work form the mainstays of the aviation practice at this firm. The team advised American Airlines on its high-profile Chapter 11 case, a matter that involved restructuring of financing arrangements for more than 1,000 aircraft. Other key clients include Delta Air Lines.
Sources say: *"They do a quality job."*
**KEY INDIVIDUALS Emily DiStefano** has a varied aviation practice including EETC and leveraged finance matters. She acted on the American Airlines restructuring work. Clients describe her as *"measured, thoughtful and insightful."* **John Curry** heads up the firm's aviation practice. His transactional capabilities include secured lending and complex financings in connection with aircraft. He acted as the lead lawyer on the American Airlines restructuring. Sources were quick to describe him as *"a high-quality, intelligent, capable and analytical lawyer."*

### Fulbright & Jaworski LLP
See profile on p.2435

**THE FIRM** This firm's aviation practice is recognized for its work with airlines and lessors. It acts for a number of impressive names, including Jackson Square Aviation, Boeing Capital and Emirates. Highlights include advising Apollo Aviation on a number of transactions in connection with aircraft purchase, lease, disassembly and disposal.
Sources say: *"The work product of all these lawyers is outstanding."*

**KEY INDIVIDUALS Sean Corrigan** (see p.299) is well known for his work in the aviation finance sector. He was lead counsel for Emirates on a $587.5 million EETC transaction, concerning four A380 aircraft. **Marc Latman** (see p.352) is a younger partner who courts praise for his skills and commitment. Sources agree that *"he knows the documents and does the deals, he really understands the industry and has real passion for it."* He acted for AWAS on negotiation of aircraft leasing and debt financing. The *"experienced and practical"* **James Tussing** (see p.419) heads up the equipment finance group. He wins plaudits in the market for his *"tremendous depth of experience"* in areas including restructuring and debt and lease aviation financing. He led for Jackson Square Aviation in the negotiation of a commercial paper conduit facility.

### Hughes Hubbard & Reed LLP
See profile on p.1981

**THE FIRM** This firm continues to impress, acting for some of the most important names in the aviation industry. It has advised on a number of aircraft lease restructurings and secured financings. Highlights for the practice include acting for Continental Airlines in an $892 million public offering in connection with 18 new aircraft.
**KEY INDIVIDUALS John Hoyns** (see p.337) receives special mention for his command of high-value capital markets transactions, with sources noting that he is *"a very experienced practitioner in EETC work and he brings enormous history to the area."* He was lead attorney on the Continental Airlines public offering. **Steven Chung** (see p.295) enjoys a rising profile in the market. Sources say he is *"an excellent lawyer who is thorough and commercial, and brings strong technical and marketing skills."* His highlights include the representation of Wells Fargo Securities concerning a $320 million senior secured financing for AWAS. **Jeffrey Tenen** recently joined the firm from Greenberg Traurig, LLP. Commentators describe him as *"very detail-oriented but flexible enough to get deals done in a timely fashion."*

### Pillsbury Winthrop Shaw Pittman LLP
See profile on p.2000

**THE FIRM** This firm has a dedicated transportation finance practice, and counts both airline and banking entities on its client list. A number of blue-chip companies seek out its services, including Air Asia X, Crédit Agricole and JPMorgan Chase. The group recently advised Willis Lease Finance on a $390 million note issue.
**KEY INDIVIDUALS William Bowers** is known for his lender representation work, and was the lead adviser on the Willis Lease Finance matter. Sources deem him *"very reasonable"* to work with, and note that he is a *"very knowledgeable structured finance lawyer."* **Payson Coleman** leads the firm's equipment finance practice. He is a skilled and effective practitioner whether advising on leases, finance or bankruptcy. His clients include equipment financiers and aircraft leasing companies. **Mark Lessard** currently heads up the transportation finance practice. His broad client base sees him advising manufacturers, lenders and trustees in aviation finance matters. He recently advised Atlas Air

on delivery financings for nine aircraft. **Michael Schumaecker** has acted as counsel to a number of international airlines as well as to lenders and investors. He advised JPMorgan Chase as guaranteed lender on a $700 million aircraft financing for Cathay Pacific Airways. Sources describe him as *"a very seasoned and experienced aviation lawyer."*

## White & Case LLP
See profile on p.451
**THE FIRM** This firm is known in the market for its lender representation. It benefits from the firm's broad international footprint, and has acted on a number of bankruptcy and workout matters with respect to the aviation industry.
**Sources say:** *"It not only has expertise in aviation finance but also the ability to manage a large project over a number of offices with lawyers worldwide."*
**KEY INDIVIDUALS Michael Smith** (see p.409) wins plaudits as a commercially aware transactional lawyer. Sources say that he is *"good to work with and very reasonable,"* and note that *"he is extraordinarily clever at compromises that meet the needs of other parties."* His client list comprises airlines such as Pegasus Airlines and Virgin Blue Airlines. **Richard Smith** (see p.409) is an asset finance expert with an impressive profile in the aviation industry. Clients agree that he is *"not only a good lawyer but can manage large multibillion-dollar projects involving a huge team."* Spanish speaker **Christian Hansen** (see p.330) practices in the Miami office. He elicits positive comments for his adroit handling of equipment leasing, aviation and workout matters. He has experience of lender and borrower representation, and has close connections with the Mexican aviation industry.

## Band 4

### Katten Muchin Rosenman LLP
See profile on p.1253
**THE FIRM** This three-partner aviation practice has a solid reputation for its transactional and bankruptcy work. The group recently advised Embraer in connection with the restructuring of Brazilian Export Credit Agency debt for 216 aircraft following the American Airlines bankruptcy. Other clients include Citibank.
**Sources say:** *"A strong group of aviation professionals."*
**KEY INDIVIDUALS** The *"highly commercial"* **Timothy Lynes** (see p.359) attracts praise for his pragmatic deal-making capabilities. He had a lead role on the American Airlines bankruptcy work for Embraer. **Thomas Healey's** broad experience has seen him act for lenders, governments and airlines. He recently advised Embraer on the restructuring of a 60-aircraft portfolio with Chautauqua Airlines.

### Kaye Scholer LLP
See profile on p.1984
**THE FIRM** This firm's dedicated aviation finance and leasing practice acts on high-level matters, such as advising eight interested parties on negotiations connected with the widely reported American Airlines bankruptcy proceedings. The team has also advised several European export credit agencies (ECA) and related lenders in relation to 14 aircraft financing transactions.

**KEY INDIVIDUALS Michael Mulitz** (see p.372) heads up the practice. Sources laud his pragmatic style, describing him as *"knowledgeable, capable and practical."* He played a lead role on both the aforementioned American Airlines bankruptcy work and the ECA transactions.

## Other Notable Practitioners

**William Callaway** practices with Zuckert, Scoutt & Rasenberger, LLP. He has built an enviable profile for his US Ex-Im Bank-related financing work. Sources delight in his *"great judgment,"* commenting that *"he is really easy to deal with, even in complicated, large structured finance deals."* **Elizabeth Evans** (see p.310) heads up the aviation finance practice at Jones Day. *"Her deep knowledge of the industry has given us good market and business insight, as well as legal insight,"* report satisfied clients. She was lead adviser to Oak Hill Capital Management on a $236 million transaction for two new Boeing 777 aircraft. **Ji Hoon Hong** is of counsel in the Americas capital markets practice at Shearman & Sterling LLP. He is a widely recognized lawyer who wins plaudits for the quality of his aviation capital markets and EETC work. **Alan Brenner** (see p.287) of Simpson Thacher & Bartlett LLP is described as a *"smart and capable"* lawyer with *"impressive negotiation skills."* His highlights include advising a number of aircraft leasing creditors in relation to the American Airlines bankruptcy matter. Senior counsel **Rory Kelleher** (see p.344) of Sidley Austin LLP has a strong reputation for his aviation finance practice. He acts for a number of entities, including manufacturers, leasing companies and lenders.

# TRANSPORTATION AVIATION: LITIGATION

Commentary about individuals can be found under their firm's paragraph. If the firm has no paragraph (is not ranked) look at Other Notable Practitioners.

## Band 1

### Condon & Forsyth LLP
See profile on p.1965
**THE FIRM** Sources recognize this firm for its long-standing prowess in the highest-profile contentious aviation and airline matters, including litigation surrounding the 9/11 atrocity. Its highlights include acting as lead counsel for an entity involved in the February 2009 air crash in Buffalo, New York, while an impressive client list features a number of household names, such as British Airways, TAP Portugal and Air New Zealand.
**Sources say:** *"A great firm."*
**KEY INDIVIDUALS Desmond Barry** handles aviation and product liability disputes. He is admired for his extensive work as a lead counsel on the 9/11 litigation, and described as *"one of the top aviation lawyers"* by impressed sources. **Michael Holland** has built an enviable reputation for advising airline clients on contentious matters and aviation accidents. He is lead counsel for TACA Airlines in litigation stemming from a May 2008 accident in which an aircraft overran a Honduran runway. **Frank Silane** is managing partner of the firm's Los Angeles office, and an experienced trial lawyer. He handles complex, multijurisdictional tort and insurance litigation for airlines, aerospace insurers and aircraft manufacturers. **Stephen Stegich's** practice includes product liability and insurance litigation for aircraft manufacturers and insurers. He is described by

sources as *"a quality and solid guy"* when aviation-related matters turn contentious. He is well known as national counsel for Embraer.

### Perkins Coie LLP
See profile on p.2548
**THE FIRM** This firm's dedicated aviation and aerospace team is a respected subset of its product liability practice. The group's high profile stems in large part from its long and productive relationship with Boeing, though it acts for a host of big aviation names such as Honeywell and BAE Systems. Highlights for the practice include advising Boeing on ongoing high-stakes litigation arising from 9/11.
**KEY INDIVIDUALS Bruce Campbell** maintains a high profile in aviation-related litigation. He advised Boeing on litigation arising out of the August 2005 Helios Airways accident in Athens. Sources agree he can be relied upon for

expertise in high-stakes disputes. **John Dillow** chairs the practice. Sources deem his command of the contentious aviation area highly impressive, noting that he has impressive technical and tactical acumen. He led for Boeing in international litigation surrounding the September 2005 Mandala Airlines crash in Medan, Indonesia. **Steven Bell** is noted for his adroit input on helicopter-related litigation, and has experience of litigation arising from accidents involving military aircraft. He played a lead role for Boeing in a number of contentious matters. **Thomas McLaughlin** previously worked in-house at Boeing as an aerodynamicist, giving him rare insight into the scientific issues surrounding aviation. He has acted as lead counsel on the ongoing Boeing 9/11 litigation. Sources agree he is deserving of recognition for his command of this area. **Joe Silvernale** spends much of his time advising on complex litigation and product liability matters in the aviation sphere. His highlights include advising navigation software provider Jeppesen Sanderson on a number of disputes.

## Band 2

### Clyde & Co US LLP
**See profile on p.440**

**THE FIRM** This firm is distinguished for the number of insurance clients who seek out its services, while it also acts directly for airlines in all aspects of aviation litigation. The group has a long experience of handling disputes arising from aircraft accidents, with a global network of offices ensuring that it can respond quickly and efficiently to any scenario.

**Client Service** *"It offers us good service and we are happy."*

**KEY INDIVIDUALS Andrew Harakas** heads up the firm's US aviation group. He is an established and highly respected figure who wins plaudits as a *"first-class lawyer"* and an astute appellate brief writer. **Diane Westwood Wilson** is a skilled litigator who concentrates her practice on the representation of insurers to the aviation sector. *"Her attention to detail and overall work product is excellent, and meets the very high standard we set for our service providers,"* relates one delighted client.

### Hogan Lovells US LLP

**THE FIRM** This firm's aviation litigation practice is famous for its close relationship with Airbus. Highlights for the practice include advising Airbus on a patent dispute concerning blended winglet technology, as well as litigation arising from the April 2010 AeroUnion crash in Monterrey, Mexico.

**KEY INDIVIDUALS Thad Dameris** heads up the practice. Sources praise his confidence in acting in difficult disputes, with one interviewee commenting that *"he takes on cases that look impossible, and gets results."* He had a lead role on the aforementioned Airbus litigation matters.

### Holland & Knight LLP
**See profile on p.1028**

**THE FIRM** This national firm's aviation practice continues to be recognized for its solid showing in the market. Recent matters include the representation of Air France-KLM in litigation stemming from the June 2009 Flight 447 crash in the Atlantic Ocean. Clients include AerCap, JetBlue Airways and Turkish Airlines.

**Sources say:** *"Every one of them is an excellent lawyer in complex cases with good practical sense in simpler cases."*

**KEY INDIVIDUALS Randal Craft** (see p.299) chairs the aviation group. Sources agree that he is *"a very thorough and diligent attorney, with a lot of experience with aviation accidents."* He advised Turkish Airlines on litigation surrounding the February 2009 crash in Amsterdam. **Christopher Kelly** (see p.344) leads the firm's New York litigation practice. He acted on the Air France-KLM Flight 447 matter, and has also led for JetBlue in contentious work. He ascends the rankings after receiving strong feedback from the market. **Alan Reitzfeld** (see p.391) also played a lead role on the Air France-KLM Flight 447 matter. Sources describe him as *"a very smart guy"* and *"a good brief writer."*

### Morrison & Foerster LLP
**See profile on p.1990**

**THE FIRM** Market observers praise this firm's impressive track record in aviation-related disputes. The team is recognized for its representation of helicopter manufacturers, including Honeywell and MD Helicopters. Recent matters include the high-profile Getz v Honeywell case, arising from a Chinook helicopter crash in Afghanistan. Other clients include Cessna Aircraft and Amlin Aviation.

**Client Service** *"The lawyers mapped out in advance what their strategy was, told us what the key points of law and evidence were, and they were right because it all worked."*

**KEY INDIVIDUALS** The *"articulate and thoughtful"* **Don Rushing** (see p.397) is a respected product liability and trial lawyer. He attracts praise from the market, with one source commenting on his *"first-class papers and good oral advocacy."* He has a lead role on trial and litigation work for Cessna Aircraft. **William O'Connor** (see p.379) acted on the aforementioned Getz v Honeywell matter, and has also advised MD Helicopters. He is described as *"a very good lawyer."*

## Band 3

### Kirkland & Ellis LLP
**See profile on p.1254**

**THE FIRM** This firm has a noted degree of expertise in complex aviation disputes, regularly acting for airlines, aircraft manufacturers and component manufacturers in accident and product liability cases. Clients include Boeing, Delta Air Lines and United Airlines.

**Sources say:** *"Very good analytically; the lawyers are superb writers and very good practical strategists."*

**KEY INDIVIDUALS Craig Primis** is a key contact.

### Schnader Harrison Segal & Lewis LLP

**THE FIRM** This firm has recognized capabilities in product liability and accident disputes pertaining to the aviation industry. It acts for an array of airlines and manufacturers such as Rolls-Royce and US Airways. Recent matters include the representation of Cessna Aircraft and Global Aerospace in a keenly contested product liability dispute arising from the crash of a Cessna aircraft.

**Sources say:** *"They get good results, communicate well with clients, and give good value."*

**KEY INDIVIDUALS Jonathan Stern** cochairs the firm's aviation group. Sources describe him as a *"very skilled lawyer"* who is *"easy to deal with."* He represented Motorola in litigation stemming from the 2009 Air France Flight 447 crash. **Denny Shupe** is praised as an aggressive and effective trial lawyer, with notable experience relating to air accidents and product liability matters. He is *"excellent at protecting the interests of the client,"* according to sources.

## Other Notable Practitioners

**Michael McQuillen** of Adler Murphy & McQuillen LLP is acclaimed for his trial and appellate skills. Sources describe him as *"very good on his feet and with the jury."* **Gary**

**Westerberg** (see p.425) of Locke Lord LLP is an *"excellent lawyer and advocate,"* according to sources. He represents manufacturers and airline operators in all aspects of aviation litigation. **Sheila Sundvall** of Paul Hastings LLP wins plaudits as an *"incisive, commercially savvy and client-friendly"* attorney who *"understands international aviation litigation like very few of her peers."* She was lead counsel for GE in high-value litigation arising from the Air France Flight 447 accident. **John Goetz** (see p.321) heads up Jones Day's aviation practice. His highlights include advising Doncasters Group on a trial and putative damages claim concerning a fatal aviation accident. He has a rising profile for his legal prowess and communication skills, with one source noting that *"he is very good at looking at the big picture and explaining it to the client."* **Robert Ruckman** (see p.396) is Jackson Walker LLP's lead aviation lawyer. He acted for Rolls-Royce in a jury trial in connection with a 2005 pilot fatality in Rio de Janeiro. Observers name him *"a good and experienced trial attorney."* **Patrick Bradley** is the leader of Reed Smith LLP's aviation litigation practice. Sources laud his *"first-rate intellect,"* noting that *"he is a beautiful writer and very skilled at cross-examining experts."* At the same firm, **Oliver Beiersdorf** acted as lead counsel for Continental Airlines on litigation arising out of the Flight 3407 air crash near Buffalo, New York in February 2009. One client notes that he *"does a great job managing our involvement and risk."*

# TRANSPORTATION AVIATION: REGULATORY

Commentary about individuals can be found under their firm's paragraph. If the firm has no paragraph (is not ranked) look at Other Notable Practitioners.

**Transportation: Aviation: Regulatory**
**Leading Firms**

**Band 1**
Crowell & Moring LLP *
Hogan Lovells US LLP

**Band 2**
Garofalo Goerlich Hainbach PC
Holland & Knight LLP *
Pillsbury Winthrop Shaw Pittman LLP *
Squire Sanders (US) LLP *
WilmerHale *

**Band 3**
Zuckert, Scoutt & Rasenberger, LLP

**Transportation: Aviation: Regulatory**
**Senior Statesmen**

**Senior Statesmen: distinguished older practitioners**

| | | |
|---|---|---|
| Carneal George U | Hogan Lovells US LLP | |

**Leading Individuals**

**Band 1**

| | |
|---|---|
| Garofalo Gary B | Garofalo Goerlich Hainbach PC |
| Halloway Lorraine B | Crowell & Moring LLP * |
| Mosner Anita | Holland & Knight LLP * |
| Quinn Kenneth P | Pillsbury Winthrop Shaw Pittman LLP |

**Band 2**

| | |
|---|---|
| Cohn Robert | Hogan Lovells US LLP |
| Donley Charles F | Squire Sanders (US) LLP * |
| Ellett E Tazewell | Hogan Lovells US LLP |
| Faberman Edward P | Wiley Rein LLP (ONP)[†] * |
| Hainbach Don H | Garofalo Goerlich Hainbach PC |
| Heffernan David | WilmerHale * |
| Hunnicutt Charles | Thompson Hine LLP (ONP)[†] * |
| Sinick Marshall S | Squire Sanders (US) LLP * |
| Trock Jennifer E | Pillsbury Winthrop Shaw Pittman LLP |

**Band 3**

| | |
|---|---|
| Benge Malcolm | Zuckert, Scoutt & Rasenberger, LLP |
| Murphy Gerald | Crowell & Moring LLP * |
| Sahr Evelyn | Eckert Seamans Cherin & Mellott (ONP)[†] |
| Trinder Rachel B | Zuckert, Scoutt & Rasenberger, LLP |

**Associates to watch**

| | |
|---|---|
| Rao Naveen C | Jones Day (ONP)[†] * |

\* Indicates firm / individual with profile.

[†] ONP = Other Notable Practitioner.

**Recommended for Client Service**
**Nationwide**

Crowell & Moring LLP      Hogan Lovells US LLP
Garofalo Goerlich Hainbach PC

## Band 1

### Crowell & Moring LLP
See profile on p.910

**THE FIRM** This firm has a strong reputation for regulatory work in the aviation sector. It took a lead role in advising on the multitude of domestic and international regulatory issues arising from the merger of United Airlines and Continental Airlines. The firm's client roster includes a host of leading airlines and trade organizations including SkyWest, Airlines for America and Helicopter Association International.

**Client Service** *"They are knowledgeable and accessible, and have the ability to complete an assignment in a timely fashion, at a reasonable cost."*

**KEY INDIVIDUALS Lorry Halloway** (see p.329) heads up the firm's aviation group. She has an excellent reputation in the industry, with sources praising her *"insightful and clear regulatory advice."* She played a lead role in the aforementioned United Airlines and Continental Airlines matters. **Gerald Murphy**'s (see p.373) practice encompasses corporate, aviation and administrative law. He is acclaimed for his *"broad understanding and knowledge of the aviation industry."* His clients include SkyWest and United Airlines.

### Hogan Lovells US LLP

**THE FIRM** This international firm has a tremendous reputation in the aviation regulatory space. The group has a strong relationship with Atlas Air, advising on regulatory

and compliance matters and acting as principal government relations counsel in Washington, DC. Other marquee clients include Air France, EADS and Honeywell.

**Client Service** *"The level of service and expertise that the firm has provided when we have sought their assistance is incomparable."*

**KEY INDIVIDUALS Robert Cohn** is the practice leader of the firm's aviation group. He advises airlines, airports, aviation investors and other parties in all aspects of regulatory aviation work, and represents clients regularly before all relevant regulatory bodies. **Ted Ellett** handles FAA and Department of Transportation (DOT) regulatory matters for airlines, manufacturers, airports and other entities. He

recently advised the City of Glendale in relation to alleged violations of the FAA Airport Grant Assurances by Glendale Municipal Airport. **George Carneal** is a founder member of the firm's aviation practice and a venerated figure in the aviation regulatory space. He recently counseled the government of the Commonwealth of the Bahamas on airspace regulatory and airline bankruptcy matters.

## Band 2

### Garofalo Goerlich Hainbach PC

**THE FIRM** This compact Washington, DC boutique punches above its weight in the aviation space. It is a respected force in advising clients on FAA, DOT and National Transportation Safety Board work. Clients include international airlines, leasing companies and parts dealers.

**Client Service** *"We have a great working relationship. It is very quick and cost-effective, and it has very transparent billing."*

**KEY INDIVIDUALS** Name partner **Gary Garofalo** is highly recognized in the aviation regulatory arena. Sources report that *"he is outstanding"* and that *"he knows the DOT regulations inside out."* He advises US and foreign airlines and operators on all aspects of aviation-related administrative law. **Don Hainbach** wins high praise for his faultless client service, with one client reporting: *"I cannot think of a reason to give him less than ten out of ten. He has never failed to respond and his accessibility is excellent."* He acts for a number of international airlines in regulatory matters before the FAA and DOT.

### Holland & Knight LLP
See profile on p.1028

**THE FIRM** This firm wins notable market respect for its airline representation. It recently advised Qatar Airways on regulatory provisions relating to its joint venture with FlexJet. Other key clients include Air Canada and Turkish Airlines.

**KEY INDIVIDUALS Anita Mosner** (see p.372) is highly praised by market sources. Sources speak of her as a committed client advocate, noting that *"she looks out for her clients better than anyone."* She represents airlines and airports, and is noted for her knowledge of the startup process for nascent air carriers.

## Pillsbury Winthrop Shaw Pittman LLP
See profile on p.2000

**THE FIRM** Pillsbury Winthrop Shaw Pittman provides regulatory compliance advice for airlines, airports, municipalities, manufacturers and other industry players. The group is particularly noted by market observers for its representation of regional airlines and new air carriers.

**KEY INDIVIDUALS Kenneth Quinn** is co-head of the firm's aviation practice and the recipient of warm market praise. Sources describe him as *"a bright man"* and *"technically terrific."* His clients include US, Canadian and Asian airlines. The *"terrific"* **Jennifer Trock** is recognized for her command of this practice area. She has extensive experience advising on regulatory issues surrounding airports, and has previously advised Virgin America.

## Squire Sanders (US) LLP
See profile on p.2129

**THE FIRM** This firm's aviation practice has built a notable reputation in acting for foreign clients including Latin American and Asian airlines in US regulatory matters. The group is experienced in acting before the DOT, FAA, National Transportation Safety Board and other bodies.

Other clients include trade organizations, airports and tour operators.

**KEY INDIVIDUALS Charles Donley** (see p.305) comes highly recommended for his broad regulatory knowledge. Sources note that *"he knows the issues and is easy to work with."* **Marshall Sinick** (see p.407) is chair of the aviation practice. Interviewees speak of his effective command of DOT-related regulatory work.

## WilmerHale
See profile on p.930

**THE FIRM** This firm advises a highly distinguished list of aviation groups, such as Star Alliance and Airlines for America. It also advises individual airlines such as Lufthansa, which it recently advised in relation to a number of US and EU regulatory matters.

**KEY INDIVIDUALS David Heffernan** (see p.332) is the practice chair. Sources describe him as *"top-notch"* when advising on international aviation regulatory and antitrust matters.

## Band 3

## Zuckert, Scoutt & Rasenberger, LLP
**THE FIRM** This 20-lawyer firm treats aviation law as one of its core practice areas. The group handles regulatory, compliance and licensing matters for US and foreign players in the aviation industry.

**Sources say:** *"Historically strong in transportation matters."*

**KEY INDIVIDUALS** The *"very knowledgeable"* **Rachel Trinder** is noted for her representation of clients in DOT regulatory matters. Her clients include airports, helicopter operators and manufacturers. **Malcolm Benge** is lauded for his pragmatic negotiation style in regulatory matters and commercial transactions. He is widely skilled in DOT and FAA provisions. Interviewees comment that *"he is fantastic to work with."*

## Other Notable Practitioners

**Edward Faberman** (see p.311) of Wiley Rein LLP advises US and foreign airlines and manufacturers in aviation regulatory matters. Sources agree he is *"exceptionally well connected"* and admire his creative approach. **Charles Hunnicutt** (see p.338) is a senior counsel at Thompson Hine LLP. He is described by sources as *"capable and very much a straight shooter,"* with one market observer noting that *"I trust him completely."* His highlights include advising Delta Air Lines in connection with FAA provisions and lease renewals at a busy US airport. **Evelyn Sahr** chairs the aviation practice at Eckert Seamans Cherin & Mellott, LLC. She acts for a number of domestic and foreign airlines, and is described by sources as *"highly competent and cordial. She is not a pushover but is easy to work with."* **Naveen Rao** (see p.389) is a highly rated associate at Jones Day. Sources speak of his *"very good understanding of aviation regulations and constitutional issues."*

# TRANSPORTATION RAIL (FOR RAILROADS)

Commentary about individuals can be found under their firm's paragraph. If the firm has no paragraph (is not ranked) look at Other Notable Practitioners.

| Transportation: Rail (for Railroads) |
| --- |
| **Leading Firms** |
| **Band 1** |
| Sidley Austin LLP * |
| Steptoe & Johnson LLP |
| **Band 2** |
| Covington & Burling LLP * |
| Mayer Brown LLP * |
| **Band 3** |
| Harkins Cunningham LLP * |
| Lathrop & Gage LLP |

*Indicates firm with profile.*
*Alphabetical order within each band. Band 1 is the highest.*

## Band 1

## Sidley Austin LLP
See profile on p.1264

**THE FIRM** Sidley Austin has an outstanding reputation in the rail sector. It has developed a reputation as a go-to firm for high-value matters before the Surface Transportation

Board (STB), the Department of Transportation (DOT) and other bodies, while it also enjoys a powerful reputation for rail-related litigation. Recent highlights include advising RailAmerica on its $1.39 billion acquisition by Genesee & Wyoming. An impressive client list also includes CSX Transportation, Canadian Pacific Railway and Norfolk Southern.

**Client Service** *"They are willing to enter into alternative fee arrangements, depending on productivity and results."*

**KEY INDIVIDUALS Paul Moates** (see p.370) heads the transportation group. He handles both regulatory work and litigation, and is described by sources as a *"very creative and very thorough"* attorney who *"thinks strategically."* He recently advised CSX Transportation on its proposal to reconstruct a 19th-century railroad tunnel. **Paul Hemmersbaugh** (see p.333) handles regulatory matters and litigation for railroad clients. Clients report that he is *"very thoughtful and very energetic"* and name him as a *"super lawyer."* **Terence Hynes** (see p.338) is a *"great name"* for STB work, according to market commentators. Recent highlights include representing Canadian Pacific Railway before the STB in a complaint concerning Class I railroads.

| **Recommended for Client Service** | |
| --- | --- |
| **Nationwide** | |
| Sidley Austin LLP | |

| **Recommended for Commercial Awareness** | |
| --- | --- |
| **Nationwide** | |
| Covington & Burling LLP | Steptoe & Johnson LLP |

## Steptoe & Johnson LLP
**THE FIRM** Steptoe & Johnson handles all aspects of rail litigation and regulatory work, and is widely recognized for its long history of association with the industry. The group handles work for a range of significant industry players including Genesee & Wyoming, the Association of American Railroads and Stagecoach Group. It continues to be active for key client BNSF Railway, for which it serves as lead counsel on a range of regulatory and litigious matters.

**Commercial Awareness** *"Steptoe & Johnson has a dominant STB practice."*

**KEY INDIVIDUALS Samuel Sipe** has an outstanding reputation for STB-related work, and is a considered a go-to lawyer for rail litigation. Sources report: *"He is brilliant –*

## Transportation: Rail (for Railroads)

### Senior Statesmen

**Senior Statesmen:** distinguished older practitioners

| | |
|---|---|
| Christian Betty Jo | Steptoe & Johnson LLP |

### Leading Individuals

**Band 1**

| | |
|---|---|
| Jenkins III Robert M | Mayer Brown LLP |
| Moates G Paul | Sidley Austin LLP * |
| Morgan Linda | Nossaman LLP (ONP)‡ |
| Rosenthal Michael L | Covington & Burling LLP * |
| Sipe Jr Samuel M | Steptoe & Johnson LLP |

**Band 2**

| | |
|---|---|
| Byrne William | Holland & Knight LLP (ONP)† * |
| Cunningham Paul A | Harkins Cunningham LLP |
| Hemmersbaugh Paul A | Sidley Austin LLP * |
| Hynes Terence M | Sidley Austin LLP * |
| LaRocca Anthony J | Steptoe & Johnson LLP |
| Steel Jr Adrian L | Mayer Brown LLP |

*he has complete command of railroad economics."* **Anthony LaRocca** chairs the firm's rail transportation group and works closely with many of the team's key clients. *"He truly understands the industry and how it is regulated, and he has a very good skill set for addressing economic regulation issues,"* sources say. **Betty Jo Christian** is considered *"the dean of the practice"* by industry sources. She acted as lead lawyer on a number of rail transportation matters for the Port of Houston Authority.

### Band 2

#### Covington & Burling LLP
See profile on p.441

**THE FIRM** Covington & Burling has a solid reputation for meeting the litigation and regulatory requirements of rail industry clients. The team is noted for its representation of clients before the STB and DOT, recently handling a number of STB regulatory proceedings on behalf of Union Pacific. Other significant clients include TTX and Consolidated Rail.

**Commercial Awareness** *"They often appear before the STB. They have great knowledge."*

**KEY INDIVIDUALS Michael Rosenthal** (see p.395) heads the transportation department and anchors much of the firm's work for Union Pacific. Sources report: *"He thinks creatively and outside the box to improve the service to his client."*

#### Mayer Brown LLP
See profile on p.1257

**THE FIRM** This firm handles regulatory, transactional and litigious matters for railroad clients. Clients include railway companies, contractors, manufacturers and trade organizations, including the Association of American Railroads.

**KEY INDIVIDUALS** The *"very solid"* **Robert Jenkins** is a senior counsel in the practice. He has a broad practice encompassing regulatory, transactional and trial work, and is described as an *"excellent lawyer"* by impressed sources. **Adrian Steel** is noted for his expertise in administrative and regulatory matters affecting the railroad industry. Sources report: *"He is extremely knowledgeable and hardworking, and works very hard to be available at all hours."*

### Band 3

#### Harkins Cunningham LLP
See profile on p.2244

**THE FIRM** This compact firm continues to punch above its weight in railroad matters. The group is particularly noted for its work on regulatory matters before the STB and DOT. The group also has significant transactional experience, having represented a number of Class I railroads in mergers.

**KEY INDIVIDUALS Paul Cunningham** is commended by market sources for being *"extremely skilled,"* and a *"wise leader in the industry."* He handles administrative law and economic regulations pertaining to the railroad industry.

#### Lathrop & Gage LLP

**THE FIRM** The firm has a long history of association with the railroad industry. The team continues to represent key client BNSF Railway, for which it acts as nationwide trial counsel. The group has proven capabilities in federal and state courts as well as before administrative agencies and regulatory bodies.

**KEY INDIVIDUALS** Douglas Dalgleish is a key contact.

#### Other Notable Practitioners

**Linda Morgan** of Nossaman LLP is praised for her *"great knowledge of legislative matters,"* while sources speak highly of her industry and policy understanding. She recently advised XpressWest Enterprises on a proposed $7 billion high-speed passenger railway. **William Byrne** (see p.291) of Holland & Knight LLP is recognized by clients for his *"wealth of transportation knowledge and tremendous experience in rail transportation,"* while others note that he is *"always ready with a solution to fix the situation."* He counts CSX Transportation among his key clients.

# TRANSPORTATION RAIL (FOR SHIPPERS)

Commentary about individuals can be found under their firm's paragraph. If the firm has no paragraph (is not ranked) look at Other Notable Practitioners.

### Transportation: Rail (for Shippers)
#### Leading Firms

**Band 1**

Slover & Loftus *
Thompson Hine LLP *

**Band 2**

Van Ness Feldman LLP *

\* Indicates individual with profile.
Alphabetical order within each band. Band 1 is the highest.

### Band 1

#### Slover & Loftus
See profile on p.925

**THE FIRM** This firm enjoys an excellent reputation in railroad matters. It has proven experience in representing clients before the Surface Transportation Board (STB), and continues to impress in related appellate work. Highlights for the practice include the appeal of an STB rate reasonableness decision on behalf of Arizona Electric Power Cooperative. Other marquee clients of the practice include Western Fuels Association and Cargill.

**Client Service** *"The lawyers are extraordinarily responsive, a trait not universal among counsel who are in high demand."*

**Commercial Awareness** *"I rank it based on its consistent ability to obtain positive outcomes in a venue in which the railroads have historically had great influence."*

**KEY INDIVIDUALS Michael Loftus** (see p.358) recently advised Intermountain Power Agency on a coal-related rate reasonableness dispute. Sources report: *"I give him ten out of ten. He is very responsive, very knowledgeable, and doesn't have to spend lots of time researching answers to ques-*

*tions as he is experienced enough to know the answers."* **Kelvin Dowd** (see p.306) is noted for his tenacious litigation style and cogent advice. He acted as lead counsel to Southwestern Electric Power on an STB consultation concerning Genesee & Wyoming's proposed acquisition of RailAmerica. Sources attest that he is *"skilled in contract-drafting language, and his negotiation strategies are great too."* The *"incredibly bright"* **Robert Rosenberg** (see p.395) heads the firm's energy practice. He acted as lead counsel

| Transportation: Rail (for Shippers) | |
| --- | --- |
| **Senior Statesmen** | |
| Senior Statesmen: distinguished older practitioners | |
| DiMichael Nicholas J | Thompson Hine LLP * |
| Loftus C Michael | Slover & Loftus * |
| **Leading Individuals** | |
| **Band 1** | |
| McBride Michael F | Van Ness Feldman LLP * |
| Moreno Jeffrey O | Thompson Hine LLP * |
| Wilcox Thomas W | GKG Law (ONP) † |
| **Band 2** | |
| Booth Karyn A | Thompson Hine LLP * |
| Brown Sandra L | Thompson Hine LLP * |
| Dowd Kelvin J | Slover & Loftus * |
| LeSeur John H | Slover & Loftus * |
| Rosenberg Robert | Slover & Loftus * |
| Slover William | Slover & Loftus * |
| Szabo Robert G | Van Ness Feldman LLP * |
| **Up-and-coming individuals** | |
| Pfohl Peter A | Slover & Loftus * |

on the Arizona Electric Power Cooperative matter. Sources report: "*His analytical skills are superb. He respects his adversaries and anticipates their strategies.*" **John LeSeur** (see p.355) is well known in the industry for his astute litigation skills in the legislative and regulatory sphere. He acted as lead counsel to Western Fuels Association and Basin Electric Power Cooperative on an STB dispute concerning rate reasonableness. **William Slover** (see p.408) recently advised Texas Municipal Power on a petition for review of a coal transportation-related matter. He enters the rankings after receiving strong market approval. **Peter**

**Pfohl** (see p.384) is "*incredibly bright, very thorough and very practical*" and "*delightful to work with,*" according to impressed sources. He was a key counsel to Central California Rail Shippers & Receivers on its STB submission regarding Genesee & Wyoming's proposed acquisition of RailAmerica.

## Thompson Hine LLP
See profile on p.2131

**THE FIRM** The dedicated transportation practice at this firm is known for its extensive work for shippers in the rail arena. It counts an impressive array of manufacturing entities on its client list, including DuPont, M&G Polymers and Dow Chemical. The team recently advised The National Industrial Transportation League on a petition regarding competitive switching.

**KEY INDIVIDUALS Jeffrey Moreno** (see p.371) advises clients from a host of sectors on rail-related issues. He had a lead role advising Total and M&G Polymers in high-value regulatory rail rate disputes. Sources agree he is a "*high-quality*" lawyer who does a "*fine job.*" **Karyn Booth** (see p.285) heads the firm's transportation practice group. She is recognized by sources as a "*very experienced shipper lawyer.*" She played a lead role in the competitive switching petition for The National Industrial Transportation League, for which she serves as general counsel. **Sandra Brown** (see p.288) is noted for her skill in advising bulk shippers on a host of transportation issues. Her highlights include acting for Ameren Missouri before the STB on the reasonableness of coal dust mitigation tariff provisions. **Nicholas DiMichael** (see p.305) is lauded as "*a very accomplished lawyer*" who commands respect for his diplomatic and effective approach to resolving disputes. He is also a recognized arbitrator and mediator. He worked closely

with Booth on the competitive switching matter for The National Industrial Transportation League.

## Band 2

### Van Ness Feldman LLP
See profile on p.926

**THE FIRM** Market observers are keen to emphasize the quality of work product at this firm. The transportation group counsels Consumers United for Rail Equity (CURE) on a raft of legislative and regulatory matters. Other highlights include advising the National Corn Growers Association on opposition to the $8.2 billion premium paid by Berkshire Hathaway on its acquisition of BNSF Railway.

**KEY INDIVIDUALS Michael McBride** (see p.364) is widely respected for his representation of shipping clients in the railroad arena. He was lead lawyer on the National Corn Growers Association work. Sources describe him as a "*very knowledgeable and bright practitioner.*" **Robert Szabo** (see p.415) advised CURE on submission of comments regarding policy-making proceedings. Sources admire the extensive political and lobbying expertise he brings to the practice.

### Other Notable Practitioners

**Thomas Wilcox** practices at GKG Law. Sources describe him as "*experienced and highly qualified,*" and respect his enviable track record in rail-related regulatory disputes before federal agencies.

# TRANSPORTATION ROAD (CARRIAGE/COMMERCIAL)

Commentary about individuals can be found under their firm's paragraph. If the firm has no paragraph (is not ranked) look at Other Notable Practitioners.

| Transportation: Road (Carriage/Commercial) |
| --- |
| **Leading Firms** |
| **Band 1** |
| Gibson, Dunn & Crutcher LLP * |
| Hogan Lovells US LLP |
| Holland & Knight LLP * |
| Mayer Brown LLP * |
| Thompson Hine LLP * |

*\* Indicates individual with profile.*
*Alphabetical order within each band. Band 1 is the highest.*

## Band 1

### Gibson, Dunn & Crutcher LLP
See profile on p.682

**THE FIRM** This firm is highly rated for its work in the road transportation arena. The group is routinely relied upon by automotive manufacturers and major commercial carriers for a broad range of litigation and appellate work. It advised the Association of Global Automakers before the United States Court of Appeals in connection with EPA greenhouse gas emissions regulations. The team also acts for Toyota and Nissan.

**KEY INDIVIDUALS Marjorie Lewis** (see p.356) is an accomplished litigator in the transportation space, with sources naming her "*a terrific advocate.*" Clients also note that "*her level of energy and availability has been really high.*" She recently advised Nissan on a $240 million damages claim by a former franchise dealer.

### Hogan Lovells US LLP

**THE FIRM** The Hogan Lovells automotive practice group is noted for its handling of franchise and dealer network issues, while it also advises on litigation and regulatory matters for a number of the industry's leading manufacturers, trade associations and distributors. The team recently advised Hyundai on safety and emissions compli-

Recommended for Commercial Awareness
Nationwide
Holland & Knight LLP

ance issues. Other clients include Ford, Volkswagen and Daimler.

**Sources say:** "*It is an excellent group.*"

**KEY INDIVIDUALS Jacqueline Glassman** enjoys "*a tremendous reputation in the regulatory area,*" according to sources. She had a lead role on the Hyundai work, and also advises on product liability. **Patrick Raher** is an authority on legislative and rulemaking matters at the intersection of environmental and transportation law. He recently advised Mercedes-Benz on environmental and safety compliance in the USA. **Carl Chiappa** heads the firm's automotive industry sector group. Key work includes advising Ford on state franchise law, warranties and regulatory issues. Sources name him "*an excellent lawyer.*"

## Transportation: Road (Carriage/Commercial)
### Leading Individuals

**Band 1**

| | |
|---|---|
| Glassman Jacqueline | Hogan Lovells US LLP |
| Jones Erika Z | Mayer Brown LLP |
| Raher Patrick M | Hogan Lovells US LLP |

**Band 2**

| | |
|---|---|
| Chiappa Carl | Hogan Lovells US LLP |
| Lewis Marjorie | Gibson, Dunn & Crutcher LLP * |

**Band 3**

| | |
|---|---|
| Byrne William | Holland & Knight LLP * |
| Grigorian Christopher | Foley & Lardner LLP (ONP)† |
| Hamilton Lawrence | Holland & Knight LLP * |
| Jacoby Aaron | Arent Fox LLP (ONP)† * |
| McKelvey, Jr. Steven | Nelson Mullins Riley & Scarborough (ONP)† * |

### Holland & Knight LLP
See profile on p.1028

**THE FIRM** This national firm is recognized for its regulatory and litigation capabilities in the road transportation arena, and is particularly noted for its experience pertaining to the trucking industry. The team recently represented transportation and logistics company Landstar on a federal lawsuit concerning accounting, contract and tort claims exceeding $1 million. Other clients include CXS Transportation and Pacer International.

**Commercial Awareness** *"It is a market leader in knowing the industry and shaping legal issues."*

**KEY INDIVIDUALS William Byrne** (see p.291) handles litigation, contractual and regulatory matters for clients such as CSX and Landstar. Sources report: *"He has vast experience in rail, truck and maritime law, and he works very well with internal clients and other outside law firms."* **Larry Hamilton** (see p.329) played a lead role in the Landstar matter. He receives warm praise from the market, with one interviewee noting both his tremendous trial skills and the fact that *"he brings a common-sense approach to the cost-to-benefit ratio at every stage of the case, which is very helpful."*

### Mayer Brown LLP
See profile on p.1257

**THE FIRM** This firm is recognized for its government relations, regulatory and safety work for road transportation clients. The group routinely advises automotive manufacturers, trade associations and other industry bodies on all aspects of litigation and administrative law in the transportation sector.

**Sources say:** *"A key firm in safety matters."*

**KEY INDIVIDUALS Erika Jones** is admired by sources for her transportation safety-related compliance and litigation practice. Sources name her *"a terrific safety lawyer"* who *"has a good sense of where safety defect investigations are going."*

### Thompson Hine LLP
See profile on p.2131

**THE FIRM** This firm maintains a dedicated transportation practice group. Recent highlights include advising the National Industrial Transportation League on rulemaking in relation to federal hours of service for drivers. Other clients include automotive industry heavyweights such as Chrysler and General Motors.

**KEY INDIVIDUALS Karyn Booth** is a key contact.

### Other Notable Practitioners

**Christopher Grigorian** of Foley & Lardner LLP is known for his strengths in regulatory and safety matters, and leads the firm's NHTSA practice group. *"He is an expert in that area of the law, and apprises me of when changes are coming that will affect us,"* reports one interviewee. His clients include Harley-Davidson and Fisker Automotive. **Aaron Jacoby** (see p.339) chairs the automotive industry group at Arent Fox LLP. His practice includes advising on franchising and distributorship disputes. He advised Honda on a class action of more than 4,000 members, concerning motorcycle sales. **Steven McKelvey** (see p.366) of Nelson Mullins Riley & Scarborough LLP represents franchisors and manufacturers in transportation litigation. He garners warm praise from the market, with one interviewee commenting that *"he has become a really trusted adviser because of his breadth of experience in the industry and his knowledge of administrative boards across the country."*

---

# TRANSPORTATION SHIPPING: FINANCE (NEW YORK)

Commentary about individuals can be found under their firm's paragraph. If the firm has no paragraph (is not ranked) look at Other Notable Practitioners.

## Transportation: Shipping: Finance (New York)
### Leading Firms

**Band 1**

Seward & Kissel LLP *

Watson, Farley & Williams (New York) LLP *

**Band 2**

Holland & Knight LLP *

**Band 3**

Blank Rome LLP *

Gilmartin, Poster & Shafto LLP

Vedder Price PC *

\* *Indicates firm / individual with profile.*
*Alphabetical order within each band. Band 1 is the highest.*

### Band 1

### Seward & Kissel LLP
See profile on p.2004

**THE FIRM** This high-profile firm retains its status as one of the premier shipping finance shops in the USA, continuing to close notable finance and capital markets transactions in the shipping and offshore spheres. The team advised Eagle Bulk Shipping on the $1.2 billion restructuring of its obligations to lenders. Other key clients include DNB and First Reserve Capital.

**Sources say:** *"A solid group with a focus on capital markets and finance. Its people are very good."*

**KEY INDIVIDUALS Lawrence Rutkowski** (see p.397) chairs the maritime and transportation finance practice. Sources report: *"He is a very talented fellow – a good negotiator who doesn't waste time on minor points, as he is such a big picture guy."* He led on the Eagle Bulk Shipping matter. **Gary Wolfe** (see p.427) is recognized for the adroit securities and capital markets expertise he brings to the table. His highlights include acting for Ocean Freight on its $357 million merger with Dryships. **Michael Timpone** (see p.417) is described by sources as *"a very good, business-oriented lawyer"* who *"always focuses on his client's business points."* **Robert Lustrin** (see p.359) concentrates his practice on securities and capital markets in the shipping arena. He recently advised Seadrill on a $960 million secondary common share offering.

### Watson, Farley & Williams (New York) LLP
See profile on p.450

**THE FIRM** This firm is well known for its broad international scope. The group regularly acts for investors on a range of financing transactions and is experienced in handling the restructuring of old deals. Clients have included ABN Amro and Crédit Agricole.

**Commercial Awareness** *"It is a major player in the business."*

**KEY INDIVIDUALS Leo Chang** is praised as *"a very intelligent guy and a good lawyer."* Sources respect his *"experienced view based on the knowledge he has gained over the years."* He handles the full range of shipping finance transactions. **Daniel Rodgers** is praised by sources for his authoritative shipping finance practice and tenacious negotiating style. Interviewees report: *"He is a tough lawyer* *and negotiator, but at the end of the day he is able to come to good terms for clients in an efficient manner."*

## Band 2

### Holland & Knight LLP
**See profile on p.1028**

**THE FIRM** Clients report long and productive relationships with this firm's respected ship finance team. The group is noted for its representation of US and foreign banks in ship finance transactions, and is increasingly active in handling shipping group restructurings. The group recently advised Citigroup Global Markets as underwriter on $269 million of ship financing bonds.

**Sources say:** *"Holland & Knight provides a full-service transport desk."*

**KEY INDIVIDUALS Nancy Hengen** (see p.333) is *"a smart lawyer,"* according to sources, one praising her *"correct and good advice"* in particular. She recently advised DNB and Nordea on financing related to the acquisition of 30 vessel-owning single-purpose corporations. **Brad Berman** (see p.282) is commended for his *"practical and sensible approach to legal issues."* He advised DNB as lead bank on a $685 million financing involving 42 vessels. The *"knowledgeable and reliable"* **Jovi Tenev** (see p.416) handles all aspects of shipping finance for financial institutions and other industry players. He was a lead lawyer on the for Citigroup Global Markets matter.

## Band 3

### Blank Rome LLP
**See profile on p.2235**

**THE FIRM** The Blank Rome maritime commercial and transactions team regularly handles matters pertaining to ship financing, M&A, ship mortgages and lease financings. The team recently advised DNB Bank on the billion-dollar financing of offshore oil rigs. Blue-chip clients also include Credit Suisse and the Bank of Scotland.

**KEY INDIVIDUALS Brian Devine** (see p.304) is the firm's lead New York maritime finance partner. *"He impressed us with his ability to offer solid legal advice, while at the same time maintaining a client focus with a view towards efficiently completing the project,"* relates one client.

### Gilmartin, Poster & Shafto LLP

**THE FIRM** This seven-attorney firm is recognized for its handling of a range of maritime deals, including syndicated loans and asset-based financing. The firm regularly acts for buyers, lenders and leasers on the full range of shipping transactions.

**KEY INDIVIDUALS Robert Poster** (see p.386) is a key partner for shipping finance matters. Sources relate that he is *"very solid, very experienced and very business-oriented."*

### Vedder Price PC
**See profile on p.1266**

**THE FIRM** This firm is noted for its solid shipping finance practice. The group recently advised TAL Advantage IV on two secured note offerings totaling $485 million. Marquee clients of the practice also include Bank of America Leasing & Capital and CIT Group.

**Sources say:** *"It is very good in the narrow aspects of shipping, and the lawyers are very bright."*

**KEY INDIVIDUALS Francis Nolan** (see p.377) receives praise from market sources, with one interviewee relating that *"he understands the ultimate goal and is very pragmatic."* He represents US and foreign lenders and borrowers in a range of financing transactions.

### Other Notable Practitioners

**Thomas Hawley** of Burke & Parsons is an admiralty and maritime attorney who is described by sources as a *"solid lawyer."* Sources also note that he is *"very good on the intricacies of US coastguard and maritime regulations that drive the Jones Act."* **Martin Conniff** (see p.298) co-heads the maritime practice at Morgan, Lewis & Bockius LLP. He is described by sources as a *"very savvy practitioner."* He recently represented AP Moller-Maersk in the sale of a subsidiary company. The *"very smart"* **Glen Oxton** is the sole practitioner at Oxton Law. Sources report that *"he comes at things from a very practical, commercial viewpoint. I think he is great lawyer."* His clients include financial institutions, shipowners and shipbuilders.

# TRANSPORTATION SHIPPING: LITIGATION (NEW YORK)

## Band 1

### Blank Rome LLP
**See profile on p.2235**

**THE FIRM** Blank Rome has an excellent reputation for contentious work in the shipping arena. The group recently advised the Angeln Shipping Company on claims arising from the capsizing and subsequent sinking of the cargo vessel 'MV Angeln.' An impressive client list also includes Steamship Mutual Insurance, UK P&I Club and Oldendorff Carriers.

**Sources say:** *"Great shipping litigation capabilities."*

**KEY INDIVIDUALS John Kimball** (see p.346) chairs the firm's international and maritime litigation and ADR practice. He is described as *"a high-quality individual"* by sources. He played a lead role in the 'MV Angeln' matter. **Thomas Belknap** (see p.281) is vice chair of the department. He enjoys a sound reputation in the market for char-

ter party and attachment work. He took the lead for the Clipper Group on an arbitration concerning alleged engine damage and nonpayment of hire. **Jack Greenbaum** (see p.326) is *"a very senior and experienced litigator,"* according to sources. His principal clients include P&I clubs, charterers and oil companies. His practice covers a broad spectrum of litigation, arbitration and advisory work. **Lauren Wilgus** (see p.426) is a highly rated associate who recently acted for Pearl Sea Cruises on the arbitration of a shipbuilding contract dispute.

### Freehill Hogan & Mahar LLP

**THE FIRM** This firm has a fine reputation for P&I club representation and cargo claims work, and is noted for its work in casualty and personal injury matters. The team recently represented a client in a New York arbitration concerning safe berth charter party issues. Key clients include luxury passenger cruise operators, as well as oil and gas entities.

**Sources say:** *"Highly respected in their field."*
**KEY INDIVIDUALS Peter Gutowski** (see p.328) recently advised on a high-stakes LNG supply contract dispute and subsequent arbitration. He is lauded for his effective approach to disputes, which market observers describe as *"good and properly aggressive."* **Wayne Meehan** (see p.366) is noted for his expertise in litigation stemming from major collisions, and recently advised the owners of a tug and barge on claims arising from two deaths following a

collision and sinking. Sources speak highly of **Don Murnane**'s (see p.372) *"calm, deliberative and bright"* litigation style. He had a key role in the New York arbitration concerning safe berth charter party issues. **William Juska** (see p.341) is recognized for his cargo claim work, acting for clients such as commodities traders and insurance companies. He is also a respected arbitrator. **Gina Venezia** (see p.421) is noted for her handling of personal injury and charter party disputes. She recently acted on a trial concerning damage to a dredge following a collision in New York Harbor. The *"very competent"* **Eric Lenck** (see p.354) is noted for his handling of cargo and charter party disputes.

## Band 2

### Burke & Parsons

**THE FIRM** Burke & Parsons continues to have a solid presence in the contentious maritime arena. The group's areas of expertise include marine casualty litigation, cargo claims work and charter party matters. The team is experienced at state, federal and appellate level, and has regularly represented clients in New York maritime arbitrations.
**KEY INDIVIDUALS** The *"very accomplished"* **Raymond Burke** regularly represents shipowners in charter party disputes. Sources report that *"he really keeps up with the law, and knows the trends."* **Keith Heard** is a respected maritime lawyer who is described by market sources as *"very sharp"* and *"top-notch"* for his *"balanced approach to resolving disputes."* He regularly handles cargo damage and maritime casualties.

### Hill Rivkins LLP

**THE FIRM** This firm is noted for its cargo recovery work on behalf of plaintiffs and insurers. Its areas of expertise also include advising on disputes involving charter parties, marine insurance, maritime personal injury and collisions.
**Sources say:** *"An extraordinarily consistent firm."*
**KEY INDIVIDUALS Raymond Hayden** enjoys an enviable reputation as *"a notable cargo lawyer"* and is *"a great name"* in the market, according to sources. **Anthony Pruzinsky** is a trial lawyer with a fine reputation in the shipping arena. He has previously acted as lead counsel for cargo interests following major maritime incidents.

### Holland & Knight LLP
See profile on p.1028
**THE FIRM** This national firm continues to impress in the maritime litigation arena. The team recently acted for a consortium of insurers on enforcing a multijurisdictional judgment of more than $80 million, following a 1988 chemical explosion aboard the 'MV Aconcagua'. An impressive client roster also includes Hanjin Shipping and Bank of Tokyo-Mitsubishi UFJ, in addition to a host of P&I clubs.
**KEY INDIVIDUALS William Honan** (see p.335) calls on *"a world of experience,"* and is *"very solid and careful,"* according to sources. He represents clients in all aspects of maritime litigation and arbitration. He recently represent-

ed ConocoPhillips and Phillips 66 in connection with an estimated $48 million of damages to a jetty. **James Hohenstein** (see p.335) focuses on charter party disputes, cargo claims and maritime bankruptcy matters. He played a lead role for DNB concerning an insolvency related to a $685 million ship financing to the BLT Group. Sources report: *"He is a real advocate for clients. He is a gentleman, and is fair."* **Michael Frevola** (see p.316) is described as *"very cooperative,"* but also *"aggressive and smart"* in his pursuit of client interests. He led for Gunvor in a bankruptcy preference dispute. **James Power** (see p.387) played a lead role on the 'MV Aconcagua' incident. Sources remark that he is *"very good – aggressive and knowledgeable."*

## Band 3

### Marshall, Dennehey, Warner, Coleman & Goggin

**THE FIRM** This defense litigation boutique maintains a dedicated maritime litigation group. Areas of excellence include litigation stemming from marine insurance and reinsurance, cargo recovery, and marine construction. Clients include shipowners, manufacturers and dealerships.
**KEY INDIVIDUALS** The *"top-drawer"* **Edward Radzik** handles all aspects of shipping litigation, including claims arising from cargo loss, collisions, explosions and marine insurance. **Daniel McDermott** is cochair of the maritime litigation practice. He advises regularly on marine personal injury defense and insurance disputes.

## Band 4

### Nicoletti Hornig & Sweeney

**THE FIRM** This compact firm is recognized for its handling of marine insurance and reinsurance disputes. The team frequently represents clients in cargo matters, and has experience with disputes arising from damage to vessels and piers.
**KEY INDIVIDUALS James Sweeney** is well regarded for his admiralty and marine insurance disputes practice. Sources speak well of his pragmatic style, noting that *"he gets things done in a practical way."*

### Nourse & Bowles LLP

**THE FIRM** Nouse & Bowles is recognized for its effective work in charter party disputes, marine casualties, bills of lading disputes and cargo claims. It also has experience advising on marine personal injury and insurance disputes. The group is experienced in acting on behalf of clients in both state and federal courts as well as maritime arbitration panels.
**KEY INDIVIDUALS** The *"very good"* **Armand Paré** has advised on an array of matters from bankruptcy to explosions in the maritime sector. His clients include insurance companies, shipowners and vessel charterers. Firm founder **David Nourse** is considered a *"straight shooter"* in

shipping disputes such as commodity claims and charter party disputes. He commands substantial market respect for his broad practice, and regularly represents clients in maritime arbitrations.

## Other Notable Practitioners

**Lizabeth Burrell** (see p.290) of Curtis, Mallet-Prevost, Colt & Mosle LLP advises on a wide range of matters, including charter party disputes, foreclosures and maritime insurance litigation. Sources report that she is *"one of the most intellectual members of the maritime Bar."* Sole practitioner **David Mazaroli** is described by sources as a *"bright and diligent"* litigator. He is recognized for his handling of cargo claims. **John Woods** practices at Clyde & Co US LLP. He has developed a sound reputation for his marine insurance and reinsurance work. He is praised by

sources as *"a good lawyer and a good guy."* **Patrick Lennon** of Lennon Murphy Caulfield & Phillips LLC is *"a diligent, reliable straight shooter,"* according to sources. He is noted for his handling of Rule B, charter party and maritime personal injury matters. **Michael Chalos** of Chalos O'Connor & Duffy LLP handles all aspects of shipping litigation, including disputes arising from shipping accidents and claims of criminal liability. **Vincent DeOrchis** of Montgomery, McCracken, Walker & Rhoads, LLP is widely admired for his command of cargo recovery and charter party disputes. He is experienced before state and federal courts and the US Supreme Court. *"Excellent lawyer"* **Edward Keane** of Mahoney & Keane LLP is *"knowledgeable and approaches all cases with a practical point of view,"* say sources. His broad shipping litigation practice covers charter party disputes and maritime casualty matters. **Donald Kennedy** of Carter Ledyard & Milburn LLP han-

dles a broad range of shipping litigation, including maritime insurance coverage disputes, casualty and cargo litigation, and the arrest of vessels. Sources attest to his *"good reputation."* **Stanley McDermott** (see p.365) of DLA Piper LLP (US) is *"always prepared, and always produces sound legal product,"* according to sources. He is also an accomplished arbitrator. **Paul Keane** practices at transportation and regulatory boutique Cichanowicz, Callan, Keane, Vengrow & Textor, LLP. Sources describe him as *"a very hard-working, clever, smart lawyer."* His practice includes representing international shipowners in cargo claims and service contracts. **Bruce Paulsen** (see p.383) of Seward & Kissel LLP has built a good name in the market for sound guidance in shipping-related disputes. He recently led for DryShips on a high-profile derivative action in the Supreme Court of the Marshall Islands. His clients also include Eagle Bulk Shipping and Koch Supply & Trade.

# TRANSPORTATION SHIPPING: LITIGATION (OUTSIDE NEW YORK)

Commentary about individuals can be found under their firm's paragraph. If the firm has no paragraph (is not ranked) look at Other Notable Practitioners.

## Transportation: Shipping: Litigation (outside New York)

### Leading Firms

**Band 1**
Holland & Knight LLP *
Keesal, Young & Logan PC
Lau, Lane, Pieper, Conley & McCreadie PA
Moseley Prichard Parrish Knight & Jones
Phelps Dunbar LLP *

**Band 2**
Fowler Rodriguez *
Winston & Strawn LLP *

### Leading Individuals

**Band 1**

| | | |
|---|---|---|
| Cuva Anthony J | Bajo Cuva Cohen & Turkel P.A. (ONP)[†] |
| De Leo Charles G | De Leo & Kuylenstierna P.A. (ONP)[†] |
| Hooper Chester D | Holland & Knight LLP * |
| Lawton David B | Phelps Dunbar LLP |
| McCreadie David W | Lau, Lane, Pieper, Conley & McCreadie PA |
| Moseley Jr James F | Moseley Prichard Parrish Knight & Jones |
| Parrish Robert B | Moseley Prichard Parrish Knight & Jones |
| Walsh II Joseph A | Keesal, Young & Logan PC |

**Band 2**

| | | |
|---|---|---|
| Kavanagh John | Burr & Forman LLP (ONP)[†] |
| Keesal Jr Samuel A | Keesal, Young & Logan PC |
| Kuylenstierna Jan M | De Leo & Kuylenstierna P.A. (ONP)[†] |
| Vafidis Matthew P | Holland & Knight LLP * |

**Band 3**

| | | |
|---|---|---|
| Collier William H | Keesal, Young & Logan PC |
| Giffin John D | Keesal, Young & Logan PC |
| Rodriguez Antonio J | Fowler Rodriguez * |
| Schreck Gordon D | Womble Carlyle Sandridge & Rice (ONP)[†] |
| Sullivan Norman | Fowler Rodriguez * |

* Indicates firm / individual with profile.
[†] ONP = Other Notable Practitioner.

## Band 1

### Holland & Knight LLP
See profile on p.1028

THE FIRM Market observers have a high opinion of this national firm's capabilities in the maritime litigation arena. The team routinely represents clients in shipping accidents, arrests of vessels and allegations of environmental law infractions. The team recently represented Wilh. Wilhelmsen on an appeal in connection with a 2002 collision in the English Channel.
**Sources say:** *"Holland & Knight has the maritime background and breadth."*
**KEY INDIVIDUALS** The *"very knowledgeable"* **Chester Hooper** (see p.336) played a lead role on the Wilh. Wilhelmsen matter. Sources praise his extensive experience and note that he is *"very knowledgeable."* **Matthew Vafidis**

(see p.420) leads the firm's West Coast litigation group. His practice includes representing domestic and foreign clients in high-stakes marine pollution, attachment and cargo matters.

### Keesal, Young & Logan PC

THE FIRM This California-headquartered firm is considered a market leader for shipping-related disputes such as charter party and environmental matters. Key clients include American President Lines, the UK P&I Club and the American Steamship Owners Mutual Protection and Indemnity Association. The firm offers a 24/7 emergency response unit to assist with maritime emergencies.
**Sources say:** *"Keesal is known as a go-to firm on the West Coast."*
**KEY INDIVIDUALS Joseph Walsh** *"has a very strong personality when responding to incidents,"* according to sources. He is an experienced trial lawyer who has handled a number of claims for personal injury, vessel damage and cargo damage. Firm founder **Samuel Keesal** commands solid market respect for his handling of admiralty and maritime disputes as part of a broader litigation practice. Sources note that *"he really knows what he is doing."* **William Collier** heads the firm's trade and transportation group. His practice includes advising on high-value casualty, regulatory and charter party disputes. **John Giffin** acts on marine personal injury, accidents and environmental matters. Sources reserve special praise for his *"extremely effective"* litigation style.

### Lau, Lane, Pieper, Conley & McCreadie PA

THE FIRM This compact Florida firm punches well above its weight in the maritime litigation arena. The ten-lawyer team represents clients with respect to marine collisions, cargo claims, Jones Act regulatory disputes and longshore claims.
**KEY INDIVIDUALS David McCreadie** is highly respected by the market, with one observer commenting that *"he evaluated the case well, knew what he was doing, and worked to get the case resolved in an efficient way, although still in a good way for the client."* He is experienced at both trial and appellate level.

### Moseley Prichard Parrish Knight & Jones

THE FIRM This Florida firm is highly commended for its shipping litigation expertise, handling disputes arising from marine casualties, allegations of environmental infringement and personal injury. The firm offers a round-the-clock emergency response team to handle all types of maritime emergency. Clients include shipowners and maritime insurers.
**Sources say:** *"A very experienced firm and a very good name in the market."*
**KEY INDIVIDUALS James Moseley** is an *"icon of the Bar"* with *"a very good reputation in trial work,"* according to

sources. He handles admiralty and maritime matters in both state and federal court. **Robert Parrish** is an experienced trial lawyer who handles serious shipping disputes such as maritime casualty matters and oil spill litigation. Sources reflect on his tenacious advocacy and remark that he is *"a good guy to have around."*

### Phelps Dunbar LLP
See profile on p.1383

THE FIRM Phelps Dunbar has a highly respected admiralty and maritime practice. The team routinely represents clients in collisions, personal injury defense, cargo claims and marine insurance coverage. Its client base includes ship owners, P&I clubs and marine insurers.
**KEY INDIVIDUALS David Lawton** wins plaudits as a *"very good lawyer and a fabulous writer."* Sources agree that he is *"calm amongst chaos. Nice and easy to get along with, but a good advocate for client interests."* He is experienced at trial and appellate level on a broad range of shipping litigation matters.

## Band 2

### Fowler Rodriguez
See profile on p.1376

THE FIRM This firm's admiralty and maritime practice regularly represents clients in vessel collisions, charter party matters and component manufacturer disputes. Its client base includes entities from the oil and gas and cruise line sectors.
**KEY INDIVIDUALS Antonio Rodriguez** (see p.394) is described by sources as *"a well-regarded and well-liked practitioner."* He has recently acted on high-profile pollution and product liability disputes in the maritime arena. **Norman Sullivan**'s (see p.414) highlights include marine product liability, underwater pipeline damage and personal injury matters. Sources note that *"he always responds within short time limits, and is clearly an expert in litigation."*

### Winston & Strawn LLP
See profile on p.1267

THE FIRM Winston & Strawn enters the rankings this year after receiving strong feedback for its admiralty and maritime practice. Highlights include representing Maher Terminals in federal courts and before the Federal Maritime Commission on alleged breaches of the Shipping Act of 1984. An impressive client list also includes Liberty Maritime Commission and ConocoPhillips.
**Sources say:** *"The firm is consistent, effective and aware of the market situation."*
**KEY INDIVIDUALS Constantine Papavizas** heads the maritime and admiralty practice.

263

## Other Notable Practitioners

**Anthony Cuva** of Bajo Cuva Cohen & Turkel P.A. handles admiralty and maritime disputes as part of a broader litigation practice. He advises on matters involving collisions and personal injury defense. **Charles De Leo** of De Leo & Kuylenstierna P.A. has a broad shipping litigation practice that includes cargo claims, personal injury and collisions.

Sources report that *"he is smart in terms of the law, and knows the direction he will take a case."* At the same firm, **Jan Kuylenstierna** is recognized for his abilities in maritime and insurance work. His key clients include insurers, underwriters, manufacturers and boatyards. **John Kavanagh** is cochair of the transportation and maritime practice at Burr & Forman LLP. His highlights include advising a P&I club and a vessel owner on a $16 million personal injury claim. Sources report: *"His inherent and learned abilities help him mitigate client risk at every step of a crisis."* **Gordon Schreck** of Womble Carlyle Sandridge & Rice, LLP has built an enviable reputation for the quality of his practice. He has advised on an array of maritime work, from charter party disputes and personal injury to cargo claims.

# TRANSPORTATION SHIPPING: REGULATORY (OUTSIDE NEW YORK)

Commentary about individuals can be found under their firm's paragraph. If the firm has no paragraph (is not ranked) look at Other Notable Practitioners.

### Transportation: Shipping: Regulatory (outside New York)

#### Leading Firms

**Band 1**

| | |
|---|---|
| Blank Rome LLP * | |
| Cozen O'Connor * | |
| K&L Gates * | |
| Winston & Strawn LLP * | |

**Band 2**

| | |
|---|---|
| Goodwin Procter LLP * | |

#### Senior Statesmen

**Senior Statesmen: distinguished older practitioners**

| | |
|---|---|
| Basseches Robert T | Goodwin Procter LLP * |
| Sher Stanley O | Cozen O'Connor * |

#### Leading Individuals

**Band 1**

| | |
|---|---|
| Benner C Jonathan | Thompson Coburn LLP (ONP) † |
| Fink Marc J | Cozen O'Connor * |
| Lawrence Jeffrey F | Cozen O'Connor * |
| Papavizas Constantine G | Winston & Strawn LLP * |
| Rouvelas Emanuel L | K&L Gates * |
| Waldron Jonathan K | Blank Rome LLP * |

**Band 2**

| | |
|---|---|
| Black Allen | Winston & Strawn LLP * |
| Blank Jonathan | K&L Gates |
| Cook David B | Goodwin Procter LLP * |
| Dyer T Michael | Blank Rome LLP * |

**Band 3**

| | |
|---|---|
| Dickman David G | Venable LLP (ONP) † * |
| Grasso Jeanne | Blank Rome LLP * |
| Kiern Larry | Winston & Strawn LLP * |
| Rohde Wayne | Cozen O'Connor * |
| Ruge Mark | K&L Gates * |
| Smith Duncan C | Blank Rome LLP * |

**Up-and-coming individuals**

| | |
|---|---|
| Craig Ashley | Venable LLP (ONP) † * |
| Gardner Bryant | Winston & Strawn LLP * |

*\* Indicates firm / individual with profile.*
*† ONP = Other Notable Practitioner.*

## Band 1

### Blank Rome LLP
See profile on p.2235

**THE FIRM** This firm is recognized for its strong lobbying and legislative talents and its authoritative regulatory advice in the shipping arena. Interviewees speak of the group's impressive maritime background and breadth of practice. It advised oil and gas company Furie Operating Alaska on a judicial review of a $15 million penalty under the Jones Act following the movement of a drilling rig from the Gulf of Mexico to Alaska. Key clients include Carnival Corporation and Marine Spill Response Corporation.

**Commercial Awareness** *"We have found it to be very strong on maritime issues, with good contacts and relationships with the US Coast Guard and Congress."*

**KEY INDIVIDUALS Jonathan Waldron** (see p.422) chairs the maritime, international trade and public contracts practice group. He had a lead role on the Furie Operating Alaska matter. One client reports that *"we chose the firm because of the specialized expertise and reputation of one of their partners, Jon Waldron."* **Michael Dyer** (see p.307) wins plaudits from market observers as *"a great lawyer's lawyer."* He has advised on an array of matters, including federal criminal enforcement actions and False Claims Act work. **Jeanne Grasso** (see p.325) receives strong praise from the market, with one source reporting: *"She doesn't just provide the legal review – rather, she works with us to identify the operational options that either meet or exceed regulatory requirements."* She had a lead role advising Carnival Corporation on government hearings related to the highly publicized Costa Concordia disaster. **Duncan Smith** (see p.408) is viewed as *"the right name for heavily legislative work,"* with sources also describing him as a *"very knowledgeable"* attorney who *"understands Coast Guard matters especially well."* He provided input on the Furie Operating Alaska matter.

### Recommended for Client Service

**Nationwide**

| |
|---|
| Winston & Strawn LLP |

### Recommended for Commercial Awareness

**Nationwide**

| | |
|---|---|
| Blank Rome LLP | K&L Gates |
| Cozen O'Connor | |

### Cozen O'Connor
See profile on p.2237

**THE FIRM** This firm is recognized for its robust presence in shipping regulatory matters, such as international, coast guard and Federal Maritime Commission (FMC) work. It recently advised APM Terminals on a series of regulatory and antitrust matters. Other clients include Hamburg Sud and Evergreen Marine.

**Commercial Awareness** *"Because it is such a specialized firm it is extremely efficient. A lot of the stuff the lawyers know off the top of their heads."*

**KEY INDIVIDUALS Jeffrey Lawrence** (see p.353) chairs the transportation and logistics group. He is lauded as a *"professional and high-quality lawyer"* who is *"very good at bringing a complex issue to the layman."* He counts Hanjin Shipping and Consolidated Chassis Management as key clients. **Marc Fink** (see p.313) is described by sources as *"a very measured lawyer with lots of expertise."* He handled the APM Terminals matter. **Wayne Rohde** (see p.394) enjoys a rising profile for the quality of his FMC-related work. Clients report that *"if it is an important issue, you can always count on him."* The highly experienced **Stanley Sher** (see p.405) is recognized for his high-level representation of container and liner companies, including international ocean carriers.

### K&L Gates
See profile on p.2245

**THE FIRM** Interviewees are quick to point to the extensive lobbying talent at this firm's public policy practice, and highlight its strengths in regulatory and government relations work. Clients include Vigor Industrial and GATX. Highlights include advising the American Maritime Partnership on challenges to cabotage regulations.

**Commercial Awareness** "*Its relationships with federal maritime agencies and lawmakers are unparalleled, and its subject matter expertise is equally impressive.*"
**KEY INDIVIDUALS Manny Rouvelas** (see p.396) acted on the American Maritime Partnership matter. Sources report: "*He is a strong strategic thinker with incredible insights on government relations, legislative process, shipping industry and regulatory matters.*" **Jonathan Blank** has experience of representing clients on DOT and FMC matters. His highlights include advising a shipping company on Emission Control Area (ECA) regulation exemptions. **Mark Ruge** (see p.397) is well known for his lobbying work and regulatory expertise. One client reports that "*he is professional, dedicated, well informed, can handle sensitive issues, and can represent the interests of the whole industry.*"

### Winston & Strawn LLP
See profile on p.1267

**THE FIRM** This firm's maritime and admiralty group is widely respected for its regulatory compliance work regarding the shipping industry. It had a lead role in advising Liberty Maritime Corporation on reauthorization of the Maritime Security Program. Key clients of the practice also include Maher Terminals and BP.
**Sources say:** "*They are consistent, effective, aware of the market situation, problem solvers, and experts in their field.*"

**KEY INDIVIDUALS Charlie Papavizas** (see p.381) chairs the maritime and admiralty practice at the firm. Sources describe him as a "*very good and solid lawyer*" with notable talents across contentious and administrative work for domestic and foreign entities. He had a lead role on the Maritime Security Program work for Liberty Maritime Corporation. **Larry Kiern** (see p.346) acted for Maher Terminals on a number of federal court disputes under the Shipping Act of 1984. Sources describe him as a "*very bright*" and "*very active*" presence in maritime matters. **Allen Black** (see p.284) is acclaimed for his "*solid, broad base of knowledge,*" with sources noting that "*his quality is first class and extremely helpful in our daily operational challenges.*" He led for Great Lakes Dredge & Dock Company on an appeal concerning the partial sinking of a dredge vessel. **Bryant Gardner** (see p.318) is a younger partner with "*a bright future*" in the industry, according to market observers. He also acted on the Maher Terminals matter.

### Band 2

### Goodwin Procter LLP
See profile on p.1522

**THE FIRM** Goodwin Procter is a reliable choice for shipping regulatory matters. Its highlights include advising a number of entities, including American President Lines

and APL Logistics, on regulatory compliance relating to alliances, reporting and mergers.
**KEY INDIVIDUALS David Cook** (see p.298) frequently acts on FMC matters, and is described by sources as an "*excellent lawyer.*" His key clients include American President Lines and APL Logistics. **Robert Basseches** (see p.280) is "*highly knowledgeable on the regulatory issues we deal with,*" according to sources. He has advised clients, including American President Lines, on matters such as vessel registry requirements and cargo preference regulations.

### Other Notable Practitioners

**Jonathan Benner** of Thompson Coburn LLP receives warm praise from the market. Sources note that he is "*a very good lawyer.*" **David Dickman** (see p.304) of Venable LLP is considered by sources to be "*an expert in pollution-related matters.*" He had a lead role in advising tug and barge operator Crowley Maritime on federal transportation issues such as cargo and trade restrictions. Also at Venable, **Ashley Craig** (see p.299) handles legislative and regulatory matters for maritime-related companies. His clients include the Port Authority of New York and New Jersey. He recently advised DHL on logistics agreements and associated regulatory work.

# WEALTH MANAGEMENT

Commentary about individuals can be found under their firm's paragraph.  If the firm has no paragraph (is not ranked) look at Other Notable Practitioners.

### Band 1

### McDermott Will & Emery LLP
See profile on p.1258

**THE FIRM** This preeminent practice remains a dominant force thanks to its exceptional team of lawyers spanning New York, Chicago, Silicon Valley and Los Angeles. It earns plaudits from both peers and clients for its outstanding depth and breadth of experience in all aspects of trust and estate. In addition to advising ultra high net worth families and individuals on trust and estate planning and administration, it has strong capabilities in generation-skipping tax law and fiduciary and probate litigation. It is also particularly well positioned to advise on international planning matters.
**Commercial Awareness** "*Their knowledge of the sophisticated estate planning that we require is incredible; they understand the law and can clearly explain what is happening, and their friendliness and professionalism are unsurpassed.*"
**KEY INDIVIDUALS Carlyn McCaffrey** (see p.364) co-heads the New York practice and is one of the most venerated figures in the wealth management arena. She has a tremendous amount of experience, with one source noting: "*They call her a genius for a reason.*" Fellow practice co-

head **Henry Christensen** (see p.294) also heads the international private client group. He has more than 35 years' experience and a phenomenal international reputation, and is frequently sought for complex cross-border work. Chicago-based **Carol Harrington** (see p.330) heads the firm's private client group nationwide and is best known for her expertise in generation-skipping tax law. Market observers say: "*She's very knowledgeable and really knows how to bridge the space between clients and trust companies.*" **Judith McCue** (see p.365) is a highly esteemed practitioner and a go-to figure for complex trust and estate planning and administration thanks to her extensive experience in the industry. **Jonathan Lurie** (see p.651) is based in Los Angeles and predominantly advises on estate planning and post-death administration matters. "*He's just brilliant – he has the breadth of knowledge that is required to be the attorney for very high net worth individuals,*" states an interviewee. **David Baker** (see p.277) debuts in the rankings this year thanks to widespread recognition of his impressive trust and estates litigation practice. "*He has a reputation for being a stupendous trust and estate litigator,*" according to peers. **Richard Lang** (see p.352) is an experienced attorney noted for advising entrepreneurs, venture capital clients and family offices on income tax planning and wealth transfer issues. **David Herpe** (see p.334) is highly rated by

| Recommended for Client Service Nationwide | |
| --- | --- |
| Day Pitney LLP | Pillsbury Winthrop Shaw Pittman LLP |
| Holland & Knight LLP | |
| Loeb & Loeb LLP | Proskauer Rose LLP |
| Mayer Brown LLP | Ropes & Gray LLP |
| McGuireWoods LLP | Sidley Austin LLP |
| Milbank, Tweed, Hadley & McCloy LLP | Sullivan & Cromwell LLP |
| | Willkie Farr & Gallagher LLP |
| Paul, Weiss, Rifkind, Wharton & Garrison LLP | |

| Recommended for Commercial Awareness Nationwide | |
| --- | --- |
| Debevoise & Plimpton LLP | McDermott Will & Emery LLP |
| Greenberg Traurig, LLP | Milbank, Tweed, Hadley & McCloy LLP |
| Holland & Knight LLP | |
| Mayer Brown LLP | Proskauer Rose LLP |

commentators, one of whom states: "*He is not only technically good but is able to give clients a very practical approach – he presents clients with actions that get them where they need to be without it being extremely complicated.*" **Read Moore** (see p.371) is singled out as "*a very sophisticated and experienced lawyer who is very well connected.*" He is especially valued for his expertise in dealing with interna-

| Wealth Management | |
|---|---|
| **Leading Firms** | |
| **Band 1** | |
| McDermott Will & Emery LLP * | |
| McGuireWoods LLP * | |
| **Band 2** | |
| Greenberg Traurig, LLP * | |
| Holland & Knight LLP * | |
| Katten Muchin Rosenman LLP * | |
| Milbank, Tweed, Hadley & McCloy LLP * | |
| Proskauer Rose LLP * | |
| **Band 3** | |
| Day Pitney LLP * | |
| Loeb & Loeb LLP * | |
| Paul, Weiss, Rifkind, Wharton & Garrison LLP * | |
| Pillsbury Winthrop Shaw Pittman LLP * | |
| Schiff Hardin LLP * | |
| Sidley Austin LLP * | |
| Sullivan & Cromwell LLP * | |
| Withers Bergman | |
| **Band 4** | |
| Arnold & Porter LLP * | |
| Carter Ledyard & Milburn LLP * | |
| Debevoise & Plimpton LLP * | |
| Kirkland & Ellis LLP * | |
| Mayer Brown LLP * | |
| Ropes & Gray LLP * | |
| Willkie Farr & Gallagher LLP * | |

* Indicates firm / individual with profile.
†ONP = Other Notable Practitioner.

| Wealth Management: Central Region | |
|---|---|
| **Leading Individuals** | |
| **Band 1** | |
| Handler David A | Kirkland & Ellis LLP * |
| Harrington Carol A | McDermott Will & Emery LLP * |
| McCue Judith W | McDermott Will & Emery LLP * |
| Porter John | Baker Botts LLP (ONP) * |
| **Band 2** | |
| Abendroth Thomas W | Schiff Hardin LLP |
| Bart Susan T | Sidley Austin LLP * |
| Brody Lawrence | Bryan Cave LLP (ONP)† |
| Katzenstein Lawrence P | Thompson Coburn LLP |
| Lang Richard A | McDermott Will & Emery LLP * |
| Redd Charles A | Stinson Morrison Hecker LLP (ONP)† |
| **Band 3** | |
| Baker David A | McDermott Will & Emery LLP * |
| Harrison Louis S | Harrison & Held (ONP)† |
| Herpe David | McDermott Will & Emery LLP * |
| Hodgman David R | Schiff Hardin LLP |
| Klein Jordan A | Sidley Austin LLP * |
| Moore Read M | McDermott Will & Emery LLP * |
| Morgan Donna | Mayer Brown LLP |
| Richman Lawrence I | Neal, Gerber & Eisenberg LLP (ONP)† * |
| **Up-and-coming individuals** | |
| Casey James A | Mayer Brown LLP |
| Dunn Deborah | Ahrens DeAngeli Law Group LLP (ONP)† |
| Rademacher Kurt G | Butler, Snow, O'Mara, Stevens (ONP)† * |

tional trusts and estates matters. *"Rising star"* **Amy Erenrich Heller** (see p.333) is gaining rising prominence in the estate and trusts field. She works closely alongside Carlyn McCaffrey in New York. *"Very smart"* attorney **Julie Kwon** (see p.351) continues to attract recognition from both peers and clients. She is based in the Silicon Valley office, where she is involved in a range of high-profile wealth planning work. **Nicole Pearl** (see p.383) in Los Angeles is also building a strong reputation. A client explained: *"She is very thorough, efficient and clear in her explanations and is able to explain complicated issues in layman's terms."*

## McGuireWoods LLP
See profile on p.2519

**THE FIRM** McGuireWoods earns a spot in the top band this year following widespread recognition of its distinguished team of lawyers and the outstanding quality of work it produces. It represents a strong portfolio of high net worth individuals, and is increasingly sought by banks and trust companies for trust litigation and estate administration matters.
**Client Service** *"It is by far the leading firm to deal with and has a great reputation – I found working with it to be an extremely good experience and it was able to meet all of our needs."*
**KEY INDIVIDUALS** The name **Ronald Aucutt** is synonymous with wealth management in legal circles. He leads

the firm's private wealth services group and is highly sought for his extensive experience. His practice focuses on estate, gift and generation-skipping transfer tax planning and controversies, as well as tax-exempt organizations. **Dennis Belcher** is a prestigious figure who continues to make an important contribution to the firm's success. He is noted for the breadth of his expertise in advising clients on matters ranging from complex estate and business planning to charitable planning and fiduciary litigation. **Charles Fox** is highly respected in the private client sector and chairs the private wealth team. He is noted for his work on trust and estate planning and administration, as well as tax policy counseling. **Michele McKinnon** debuts in the rankings this year following widespread recognition of her specialism in charitable planning and private foundation work. *"She's remarkably knowledgeable and really the go-to person for us,"* says a client. Clients truly enjoy working with **John O'Grady**, who handles a range of estate work and fiduciary litigation. *"He's been terrific – he stays on top of all the changes that have occurred and is always proactive, and I feel really secure that he will stay on top of everything,"* said one interviewee.

## Band 2

### Greenberg Traurig, LLP
See profile on p.1024

**THE FIRM** This respected wealth management practice is singled out for its comprehensive taxation expertise. In the past year it has acted for clients on complex multigenerational succession planning, and advised on a foreign trust dispute.
**Commercial Awareness** *"Unparalleled expertise in the area that we deal with, and brilliant understanding of our business exposures."*
**KEY INDIVIDUALS** **Linda Hirschson** (see p.334) is a well-known name in the field, with a range of tax and estate planning experience. She also handles a significant amount of probate litigation as well as foundation and charitable trusts work. Highly experienced **Diana Zeydel** (see p.1013) is another important member of the team, and chairs the trusts and estates practice. She handles a wide range of matters, including trust disputes, tax planning and estate administration. **Norman Benford** (see p.985) is an esteemed practitioner with extensive experience advising on all aspects of tax and estate planning, including business succession and IRS disputes. **Lawrence Heller** (see p.333) is based in the Los Angeles office and is particularly well regarded for his international expertise in tax and estate planning for families and individuals. **Jonathan Forster** (see p.315) continues to impress clients, one of whom praised *"the combination of his technical ability and his ability to drive creative solutions – he is very pragmatic and practical."* Forster acts for a range of privately held companies and large family offices.

### Holland & Knight LLP
See profile on p.1028

**THE FIRM** This impressive group continues to advise high net worth estates from across the firm's national network of offices. It also fields a litigation team focusing predominantly on fiduciary duties and probate disputes. It has recently handled an increasing quantity of international estate planning matters.
**Client Service** *"I find them available and responsive. What I really like about them is that they work very much as a team, and that's a great help."*
**Commercial Awareness** *"They understand where practical implementation cuts through the theoretical, and can communicate practical options to clients, who can then make informed decisions."*
**KEY INDIVIDUALS** With over four decades of experience, **Bruce Ross** (see p.395) is one of the most well-respected trust and estates litigators in the country. He cochairs the national trust and estates disputes practice from the Los Angeles office. New York-based **Edward Koren** (see p.997) heads the wealth management practice and is a well-known market player. *"There is no question as to the level of sophistication of his work and his knowledge on current tax changes – he is very knowledgeable and a pleasure to work with,"* say clients. **John Dadakis** (see p.300) leads the New York practice and specializes in advising pri-

## Wealth Management: Eastern Region
### Leading Individuals

**Star individuals**

| | | |
|---|---|---|
| McCaffrey Carlyn S | McDermott Will & Emery LLP * | |

**Band 1**

| | |
|---|---|
| Aucutt Ronald D | McGuireWoods LLP |
| Belcher Dennis I | McGuireWoods LLP |
| Christensen III Henry | McDermott Will & Emery LLP * |
| Halperin Alan S | Paul, Weiss, Rifkind, Wharton & Garrison * |
| Harrison Ellen K | Pillsbury Winthrop Shaw Pittman LLP |
| Lawrence III Robert C | Cadwalader, Wickersham & Taft (ONP)† * |
| Rubenstein Joshua | Katten Muchin Rosenman LLP |
| Schneider Pam H | Gadsden Schneider & Woodward (ONP)† |

**Band 2**

| | |
|---|---|
| Fox IV Charles D | McGuireWoods LLP |
| Hirschson Linda B. | Greenberg Traurig, LLP * |
| Kaufman Beth Shapiro | Caplin & Drysdale (ONP)† |
| Koren Edward | Holland & Knight LLP * |
| McBryde Neill G | Moore & Van Allen, PLLC (ONP)† |
| O'Brien Anne | Arnold & Porter LLP * |
| Pratt David | Proskauer Rose LLP |
| Rikoon Jonathan J | Debevoise & Plimpton LLP |
| Rothschild Gideon | Moses & Singer LLP (ONP)† |
| Siegler Douglas L | Sutherland Asbill & Brennan LLP (ONP)† |
| Slade Georgiana J | Milbank, Tweed, Hadley & McCloy LLP * |
| Waxenberg Jay D | Proskauer Rose LLP |
| Whitaker G Warren | Day Pitney LLP * |
| Zeydel Diana SC | Greenberg Traurig, LLP * |
| Zirinis Basil P | Sullivan & Cromwell LLP * |

**Band 3**

| | |
|---|---|
| Benford Norman J | Greenberg Traurig, LLP * |
| Bloostein Marc J | Ropes & Gray LLP |
| Dadakis John D | Holland & Knight LLP * |
| Detzel Lauren | Dean, Mead, Egerton, Bloodworth (ONP)† |
| Frankel Michael I | Carter Ledyard & Milburn LLP |
| Harrington Susan D | Sidley Austin LLP * |
| Harris Arlene | Kaye Scholer LLP (ONP)† * |
| Kozusko Donald | Kozusko Harris Vetter Wareh LLP (ONP)† |
| McCabe David J | Willkie Farr & Gallagher LLP * |
| O'Neil John J | Paul, Weiss, Rifkind, Wharton & Garrison * |
| Rutherfurd Jr Winthrop | White & Case LLP (ONP)† * |
| Sacks Ivan A | Withers Bergman |
| Stoll David J | Milbank, Tweed, Hadley & McCloy LLP * |

**Band 4**

| | |
|---|---|
| Black III James I | Sullivan & Cromwell LLP * |
| Brockway James | Withers Bergman |
| Djuric Nikola R | Sutherland Asbill & Brennan LLP (ONP)† |
| Dowling Charles T | Sullivan & Cromwell LLP * |
| Forster Jonathan M | Greenberg Traurig, LLP * |
| Gortz Albert W | Proskauer Rose LLP |
| Hader Cheryl | Kramer Levin Naftalis & Frankel (ONP)† * |
| Hall Martin | Ropes & Gray LLP |
| Ippolito Loretta A | Willkie Farr & Gallagher LLP * |
| Kavoukjian Michael E | White & Case LLP (ONP)† * |
| Mancini Mary Ann | Loeb & Loeb LLP * |
| McKinnon Michele | McGuireWoods LLP |
| Mosley Daniel L | Cravath, Swaine & Moore LLP (ONP)† * |
| Novogrod John C | Kramer Levin Naftalis & Frankel (ONP)† * |
| O'Grady John | McGuireWoods LLP |
| Perry C Jones | Shearman & Sterling LLP (ONP)† |
| Pfeifer Michael | Caplin & Drysdale (ONP)† |
| Sanna Dina Kapur | Day Pitney LLP * |
| Sligar James S | Milbank, Tweed, Hadley & McCloy LLP * |
| Tescher Donald | Tescher & Spallina PA (ONP)† |
| Twomey Laura M | Simpson Thacher & Bartlett LLP (ONP)† * |
| Wagner Theodore R | Carter Ledyard & Milburn LLP |

**Up-and-coming individuals**

| | |
|---|---|
| Ben-Jacob Michael | Kaye Scholer LLP (ONP)† * |
| Heller Amy Erenrich | McDermott Will & Emery LLP * |
| Macauley Leiha | Day Pitney LLP * |
| Stein David | Withers Bergman |

## Wealth Management: Western Region
### Leading Individuals

**Band 1**

| | |
|---|---|
| Bishop Leah M | Loeb & Loeb LLP * |
| Frimmer Paul N | Loeb & Loeb LLP * |
| Mezzullo Louis A | McKenna Long & Aldridge LLP (ONP)† * |
| Moore Malcolm A | Davis Wright Tremaine LLP (ONP)† |
| Ross Bruce S | Holland & Knight LLP * |

**Band 2**

| | |
|---|---|
| Katzenstein Andrew M | Proskauer Rose LLP (ONP)† |
| Lurie Jonathan C | McDermott Will & Emery LLP * |
| McCall Jennifer Jordan | Pillsbury Winthrop Shaw Pittman LLP |
| Tobisman Stuart P | Loeb & Loeb LLP * |

**Band 3**

| | |
|---|---|
| Heller Lawrence H | Greenberg Traurig, LLP * |
| Sugarman Myron | Cooley LLP (ONP)† |

**Up-and-coming individuals**

| | |
|---|---|
| Kwon Julie K | McDermott Will & Emery LLP * |
| Pearl Nicole M | McDermott Will & Emery LLP * |

\* Indicates individual with profile.
†ONP = Other Notable Practitioner.

**KEY INDIVIDUALS** Esteemed practitioner **Georgiana Slade** (see p.407) leads the firm's wealth management practice. A source revealed: "She's cutting edge and makes sure clients are well situated." "The thing that distinguishes **David Stoll** (see p.413) is that he's proactive and raises things we should be thinking about. He is business-minded and very practical," says a client. Stoll is especially adept at advising private equity and hedge funds principals, and closely-held business owners. **James Sligar** (see p.408) is an experienced partner with a practice that emphasizes estate planning and charitable giving work, as well as advising nonprofit organizations.

### Proskauer Rose LLP
See profile on p.2001
**THE FIRM** This renowned firm is a mainstay of the country's wealth management market, with trust and estates teams in New York, Florida and California. It benefits from a strong corporate and investment funds practice, attracting a significant volume of work representing private equity and hedge fund principals in complex estate transactions and planning. Notable clients include US Trust, Bessemer, Goldman Sachs and Northern Trust.
**Client Service** "They're excellent attorneys and they do an amazing job for their clients."
**Commercial Awareness** "Absolutely wonderful – I can't speak highly enough of them. They have a creative approach and think outside the box, and they follow up and execute in a timely manner."
**KEY INDIVIDUALS David Pratt** is "one of the most advanced estate planning attorneys when it comes to high-end work and clients love him," confirm sources. He heads the Boca Raton office. **Jay Waxenberg** chairs the firm's trust and estates practice from New York. He has a broad range of experience and is noted for his excellent client service. As one source explained, "the most important thing is his great legal advice, but he is also practical and I can get

vate equity and hedge fund principals, entrepreneurs and executives on their wealth planning needs.

### Katten Muchin Rosenman LLP
See profile on p.1253
**THE FIRM** This New York-headquartered practice remains an active player in the market, and is noted for its international expertise. It handles complex matters such as advising the estates of Vladimir Horowitz, Kurt Weill and Wanda Toscanini Horowitz. Notable work includes representing the Rodgers & Hammerstein Organization and the Rodgers family in the organization's sale to Imagem Music Group.
**Sources say:** "They are responsive to client needs and their advise is clear and concise."
**KEY INDIVIDUALS** "First-rate academic and practitioner" **Joshua Rubenstein** heads the firm's trust and estates practice and is considered one of the country's leading experts. He is also well regarded for his international know-how and is praised as "a polymath and a very likable guy – he

travels everywhere over the world but is readily accessible and really knows his stuff."

### Milbank, Tweed, Hadley & McCloy LLP
See profile on p.448
**THE FIRM** This well-known firm continues to be a key player in the trust and estates field, and has been in the thick of things as the market flourished over the past year. Its ten-strong team continues to attract significant estate administration mandates, such as advising the New York public administrator of the estate of Huguette Clark. The impressive client portfolio also includes the Katherine Hepburn estate, the Jacqueline Kennedy Onassis estate and the Rockefeller family.
**Client Service** "They have a very good personal touch; personality counts for a lot and they are very strong in knowing how to communicate and build confidence and trust."
**Commercial Awareness** "A well-run organization – they get back to you promptly, are responsive and show good knowledge of the industry."

him at two in the morning and on weekends." Los Angeles-based **Andrew Katzenstein** has a well-regarded practice focused on tax planning matters. Clients appreciate "not only his knowledge and understanding of the laws, but also his advice about how decisions can impact future generations." "Exceptionally bright and diligent," **Albert Gortz** is a dedicated trust and estates lawyer who is able to offer extensive estate, income and charitable planning experience. He is also adept in advising on charitable organizations.

## Band 3

### Day Pitney LLP
See profile on p.1753

**THE FIRM** This firm has a robust presence in the trust and estates field. It has been particularly active in the domestic market of late, but is also highly sought for its international capabilities. The team handles a considerable volume of structuring and planning work for multinational families, family offices and individuals moving to the USA.
**Client Service** "They are very user-friendly, very technically sound and also quite practical in terms of their advice."
**KEY INDIVIDUALS Warren Whitaker** (see p.425) is the leading figure in the practice and is sought by clients for "his depth of experience and intellect, and his very good grasp of cross-border taxation." **Dina Kapur Sanna** (see p.399) is a key member of the team and continues to make a strong impression on the market. "She's very responsive, manages our expectations, is very timely, reliable and smart, and really knows her stuff," remarked one client. **Leiha Macauley** (see p.360) is establishing a strong reputation with clients, who highlight that "she's incredibly energetic and has branched into all aspects of the practice." She works across trust and estate planning and administration, as well as estate and fiduciary litigation.

### Loeb & Loeb LLP
See profile on p.689

**THE FIRM** This dynamic law firm continues to make inroads in the trusts and estates sector, strengthening its offering in Washington, DC with the addition of four lawyers from Bryan Cave. The team in Los Angeles is especially well recognized in the market, and has advised several charitable foundations on lending major artworks to educational institutions and museums. Further highlights include acting as lead counsel to the executors of the estate of Leona Hemsley, which is valued at over $5 billion and holds an interest in properties such as the Empire State Building.
**Client Service** "Excellent service – they also send out an e-mail newsletter which is very helpful."
**KEY INDIVIDUALS Leah Bishop** (see p.624) attracts widespread praise for her strong contribution to the field. She cochairs the tax-exempt organizations group and specializes in the administration of trusts and gift tax, as well as estate planning. "Fantastic" **Paul Frimmer** (see p.317) is a key member of the team based in Los Angeles. He offers a wealth of experience in probate, trust and estate plan-

ning, as well as tax-exempt organizations. **Stuart Tobisman** (see p.669) is "a fantastic lawyer with a great stable of clients," confirm sources. He focuses on advising individuals on the administration of trusts, as well as tax and estate planning. **Mary Ann Mancini** (see p.361) joined the firm in September 2012 to lead the Washington, DC trust and estates practice. She brings extensive experience and a great reputation in the field.

### Paul, Weiss, Rifkind, Wharton & Garrison LLP
See profile on p.1997

**THE FIRM** This firm's private client group deals with a wide range of matters, including estate and tax planning, business succession, wealth transfers, and trust and estates administration. It is strongly supported by a first-rate litigation team that is on hand to handle complex fiduciary disputes. Clients praise the team's outstanding level of service and solution-oriented advice.
**Client Service** "Their work is excellent and they are totally responsive. If you have a question they will get you an answer right away or very, very quickly."
**KEY INDIVIDUALS Alan Halperin** (see p.329) cochairs the firm's private client practice and remains a preeminent player in the market. "He's very smart, comes up with solutions, and the work is done very meticulously and on time," according to interviewees. Highly experienced **John O'Neil** (see p.380) is the joint leader of the practice and has a broad practice covering trust and estate planning and administration, matrimonial matters, and private foundations. He also represents numerous family offices and a major medical center.

### Pillsbury Winthrop Shaw Pittman LLP
See profile on p.2000

**THE FIRM** This private client group is noted for its broad coverage, acting on everything from tax and estate planning to generation-skipping exemption and business succession planning. It has strong tax capabilities and advises a wide portfolio of clients, including ultra high net worth individuals, multigenerational families, and hedge fund and private equity managers.
**Client Service** "Fantastic, extremely responsive and professional. Everything is taken care of very well."
**KEY INDIVIDUALS** Peers are united in their admiration of **Ellen Harrison**, praising her as "one of the best in the country." She is especially well recognized for her tax expertise, including gift, income and estate tax planning, as well as tax controversy and estate litigation. **Jennifer Jordan McCall** chairs the firm's trusts and estates practice and splits her time between New York and Silicon Valley. She "is extremely smart and on top of everything, gets it done before you can blink an eye, and is always looking out for my best interests," said one client.

### Schiff Hardin LLP

**THE FIRM** This Chicago-based practice has a longstanding reputation in the sector and has bolstered its national offering with the addition of attorneys in its Atlanta and San Francisco offices. The team prides itself on being able to represent a whole range of clients, including owners of

closely-held businesses, large families, entrepreneurs, senior executives, private equity and hedge fund principals, and financial institutions.
**Sources say:** "The turnaround has been good even during this busy period, trust documents are very well written and they provide good advice."
**KEY INDIVIDUALS Thomas Abendroth** is the leading figure in the firm's trust and estates practice. Clients appreciated that "he's calm and patient, explains things very clearly and has a lot of experience." Much-respected partner **David Hodgman** maintains an active practice. He advises clients on probate, estate planning, private foundations and trust disputes.

### Sidley Austin LLP
See profile on p.1264

**THE FIRM** Sidley Austin maintains a strong foothold in the market, with 18 lawyers across its New York, Chicago and San Francisco offices. It is well equipped to represent clients in all aspects of estate planning, trust and estate administration and litigation, as well as private foundations and public charities work.
**Client Service** "We've worked with them for numerous clients – turnaround is very quick and clients really like them."
**KEY INDIVIDUALS Susan Bart** (see p.279) is an esteemed partner based in the Chicago office and is "extremely knowledgeable about the estate and trusts area," say sources. She has a broad trust and estates practice and currently serves as the Illinois state chair of the American College of Trust and Estate Counsel. Sources describe New York-based partner **Susan Harrington** (see p.330) as "a very skilled practitioner" who can "relate to the clients very well, in a down-to-earth manner. Talking about planning can be very technical but she is able to put things into layman's terms and understand their needs." **Jordan Klein** (see p.347) heads the firm's wealth management group. He "is very good with clients, very efficient and very practical, and provides really great client service and follow-up," according to market observers.

### Sullivan & Cromwell LLP
See profile on p.2011

**THE FIRM** This full-service corporate firm has a dedicated team of trusts and estates lawyers. It is particularly adept at handling major corporate transactions for private clients. For example, it acted for The Heyman Family on its $3.2 billion sale of International Specialty Products to Ashland, and advised it on the family trust administration and governance matters. The team also acted for Frank McCourt on his $2.15 billion sale of the Los Angeles Dodgers baseball team to Guggenheim Baseball Management, and his joint venture to acquire the Chavez Ravine property, which surrounds the Dodgers stadium.
**Client Service** "I'm made to feel like the only client they have, which is a very nice touch."
**KEY INDIVIDUALS** "Top-flight lawyer" **Basil Zirinis** (see p.431) receives universal praise for his work in this field, especially with regards to international trust and estate planning matters. He is also particularly adept in trust and

estate litigation, and heads the firm's international private client group. **James Black** (see p.284) receives fulsome praise from clients. A source explained: *"He has tremendous experience and wisdom, is very practical and rational, and knows exactly how to cut to the chase on things."* **Charles Dowling** (see p.306) is fast developing a reputation for his *"unbelievably thorough"* and *"immediately responsive"* service. He has a broad practice encompassing both domestic and international trust and estates planning.

## Withers Bergman

**THE FIRM** This firm has a longstanding reputation in the wealth management field, and is supported by one of the strongest international private client practices in London. It is well recognized for its inbound practice, advising clients moving to the US on all aspects of planning and structuring of assets. It is also particularly well positioned to advise multinational families on the tax-efficient structuring of investments across multiple jurisdictions.

**KEY INDIVIDUALS** Regional senior partner **Ivan Sacks** is a well-recognized practitioner in the market, and is praised for being *"very accessible in adjusting to the way clients want to do business."* **James Brockway** co-heads the firm's global wealth management practice and offers much experience on both domestic and international trust and estate planning. **David Stein** leads the US wealth management department. He has a broad practice covering trust, estate and tax planning, as well as public charities and private foundation work.

## Band 4

### Arnold & Porter LLP
See profile on p.906

**THE FIRM** This respected wealth management practice has had another busy year. In addition to the established Washington, DC team, it recently bolstered its offering in the West with four partners from Howard Rice Nemerovski Canady Falk & Rabkin joining the San Francisco office. The firm covers a broad range of work, and notably advised a major client seeking federal tax refund.

**Sources say:** *"They are excellent – it's been an extremely pleasant experience."*

**KEY INDIVIDUALS** *"Fabulous lawyer"* **Anne O'Brien** (see p.378) is based in Washington, DC and is a very well-respected trust and estates practitioner. Clients say she is *"very easy to work with, very smart and very prompt in getting back to you with an answer."*

### Carter Ledyard & Milburn LLP
See profile on p.1961

**THE FIRM** This firm is a longstanding player in the wealth management space. It is especially focused on domestic trust and estate planning, and is best known for its specialty in tax planning and litigation.

**Sources say:** *"They've always had a wonderful reputation for estate planning."*

**KEY INDIVIDUALS Michael Frankel** is described by sources as a *"very sharp guy."* He has extensive experience in planning as well as litigation, and cochairs the trusts and estates practice. **Theodore Wagner** is a seasoned practitioner with over four decades of experience in the field. He has represented executors in the successful liquidation of a large block of thinly traded public securities.

### Debevoise & Plimpton LLP
See profile on p.1968

**THE FIRM** This New York-headquartered firm houses a busy wealth management team. In addition to a tremendous volume of gift and asset planning work, the team has also been kept busy with significant cases in the Surrogate's Court. In one highlight it represented the New York Public Library in the highly publicized Brooke Astor probate litigation. Sources note the team's extensive experience in representing private equity and hedge fund principals.

**Commercial Awareness** *"I like everything about them – they are meticulous, thorough, well informed and imaginative in the way they structure things and advise us."*

**KEY INDIVIDUALS Jonathan Rikoon** earns plaudits from clients, who appreciate his *"enormous expertise."* He is also praised as being *"articulate and able to engage in any challenge as a puzzle rather than as an impossible task."* He heads the firm's wealth management department.

### Kirkland & Ellis LLP
See profile on p.1254

**THE FIRM** This Chicago-based private client practice earns praise for the high quality of its work. The lean and efficient team focuses on providing high net worth clients with tailored and sophisticated advice. It is strongly supported by one of the country's leading private equity practices, resulting in significant mandates to advise private equity principals on their various asset planning needs. It also currently represents several large families in their respective transactions.

**Sources say:** *"The team has done an excellent job – very thorough, detailed and knowledgeable."*

**KEY INDIVIDUALS David Handler** (see p.329) in Chicago is the firm's leading practitioner in the private client field. He is highly rated by clients, one of whom explains: *"We enjoy working with him – he has a tremendous intellect and great judgment, is very detail and risk-oriented, and has tremendous technical knowledge."*

### Mayer Brown LLP
See profile on p.1257

**THE FIRM** This group has a strong following and is lauded for its client-oriented service and advice. The relatively compact team handles a whole host of matters, including trust and estate planning, complex family disputes, public charities and private foundations. Among its strong portfolio of work, it continues to act as general counsel to The Poetry Foundation.

**Client Service** *"They have an outstanding skill set and knowledge, the promptness of the communication and delivery of work product is notable, and they are extremely pleasant and nice to work with."*

**Commercial Awareness** *"I've found the folks there at all levels to be at the highest level of quality technically, and the way they present their work product is focused on making it understandable for the end client."*

**KEY INDIVIDUALS** Head of trusts and estates **Donna Morgan** earns plaudits for providing clients with *"outstanding service."* Her well-regarded practice has an emphasis on estate planning and nonprofit organizations. **James Casey** *"is very smart and very good at service and communication, and puts the clients' interests first,"* say market observers. He is noted for his broad practice, covering all aspects of trusts, estates and foundations.

### Ropes & Gray LLP
See profile on p.1528

**THE FIRM** This wealth management group is widely recognized for representing private equity clients, and continues to be highly active in that area. The team represents some of the largest private equity firms, such as The Carlyle Group, Bain Capital and TPG Capital. It also represents multigenerational families and family offices, and is currently advising Harvard University on charitable trust and planned giving matters.

**Client Service** *"The whole team is just terrific – delightful to work with, smart and personable. The turnaround is also excellent and they are very collaborative."*

**KEY INDIVIDUALS** Highly regarded lawyer **Marc Bloostein** is best known for representing private equity and hedge fund principals, as well as their firms. *"He is really remarkable in his judgment, experience and ability to add value,"* note clients. **Martin Hall** leads the firm's private client department and joins the rankings having received tremendous praise for his contribution to the field. He is the driving force behind the firm's charitable planning practice.

### Willkie Farr & Gallagher LLP
See profile on p.2016

**THE FIRM** Clients highlight this firm's excellent trust and estates practice, which maintains a solid presence in the market. The team regularly advises high net worth individuals and families on every aspect of trust and estate planning and administration. It is also experienced in representing private foundations, public charities and charitable trusts.

**Client Service** *"Top-level service, great performance, very accommodating to clients and very sophisticated advice."*

**KEY INDIVIDUALS** *"Extremely knowledgeable and very professional,"* **David McCabe** (see p.364) heads the firm's private client practice and is singled out by sources for his *"ability to make complex matters relatively simple for clients."* Younger partner **Loretta Ippolito** (see p.338) continues to impress clients and is especially noted for her *"distinctive understanding of investments and financial mathematics."*

## Other Notable Practitioners

**Michael Ben-Jacob** (see p.282) of Kaye Scholer LLP is an up-and-coming partner who draws praise for both his domestic and international trust and estates planning practice. **Lawrence Brody** of Bryan Cave LLP is known in the market as the go-to lawyer for life insurance matters. He is based in the St Louis office and works closely with the Washington University School of Law and University of Miami School of Law. Florida-based **Lauren Detzel** chairs the trust and estates practice at Dean, Mead, Egerton, Bloodworth, Capouano & Bozarth PA. She earns praise from peers and clients for her outstanding tax planning practice, and is frequently sought for family or closely-held business succession planning. **Nikola Djuric** of Sutherland Asbill & Brennan LLP is continuing to impress commentators with his growing reputation in the market. He is highlighted for his experience and technical expertise, and also garners praise for his ability to keep up-to-date with trends. **Deborah Dunn** of Ahrens DeAngeli Law Group LLP is described as a *"very bright technical lawyer."* She joined the firm in 2012 from Kirkland & Ellis, bringing considerable experience. **Cheryl Hader** (see p.328) co-heads the trust and estates group of Kramer Levin Naftalis & Frankel LLP. Hader earns tremendous praise from clients, who say: *"She's very good – one of the best lawyers in the city technically. She's very efficient, has a deal-like attitude and turns things around quickly."*

**Arlene Harris** (see p.330) is a special counsel at Kaye Scholer LLP and is best known for her trust and estate litigation practice. She is based in New York. **Louis Harrison** of Harrison & Held is based in Chicago and is a well-respected figure in the wealth management sector. He focuses predominantly on tax and estate planning for partnerships, charitable organizations and privately owned businesses, as well as fiduciary litigation. *"Very solid lawyer"* **Lawrence Katzenstein** of Thompson Coburn LLP has a prominent reputation in the market, drawing admiration from peers for his work in this field. **Beth Shapiro Kaufman** of Caplin & Drysdale is especially well recognized for her tax background, having worked with the Treasury Department's Office of Tax Policy for a number of years. *"She's very quick and very efficient, has a beautiful writing style and is able to explain complicated things in a clear and precise manner,"* say sources. **Michael Kavoukjian** (see p.995) chairs the global private client practice at White & Case LLP and splits his time between New York and Florida. He regularly advises families and individuals on all aspects of domestic and international tax and estate planning. The market has a very high regard for **Donald Kozusko**, a founding partner of Kozusko Harris Vetter Wareh LLP. He is especially noted for his extensive experience advising family offices on planning matters. **Robert Lawrence** (see p.353) of Cadwalader, Wickersham & Taft LLP is one of the best-known names in the industry. He specializes in international trust and estate matters. Highly experienced attorney **Neill McBryde** leads the private client group at Moore & Van Allen, PLLC. Tax and estate planning, wealth transfers and estate administration are key strengths within his practice. **Louis Mezzullo** (see p.368) of McKenna Long & Aldridge LLP is a renowned figure in the wealth management field and currently serves as the president of the American College of Trust and Estate Counsel. His practice emphasizes estate and business succession planning. Seattle-based **Malcolm Moore** of Davis Wright Tremaine LLP is one of the most respected practitioners in the country. He frequently advises clients on estate planning issues, including lifetime transfers, gift and estate tax, and post-death transfers.

New York-based **Daniel Mosley** (see p.372) of Cravath, Swaine & Moore LLP has a well-established trust and estates practice and advises numerous nonprofit organizations. **John Novogrod** (see p.378) co-heads the trust and estates group of Kramer Levin Naftalis & Frankel LLP alongside Cheryl Hader. Novogrod is a well-respected practitioner with a strong international estate planning and transfer tax planning practice. *"He's an excellent attorney, a top-notch guy and clients love him,"* say interviewees. **Jones Perry** is the leading figure in Shearman & Sterling LLP's private client department and is noted for his international estate planning and tax practice. He is adept in advising on matters ranging from the establishment of cross-border trusts to expatriation tax planning. **Michael Pfeifer** of Caplin & Drysdale debuts in the rankings this year having earned significant praise from peers and clients. He focuses on cross-border planning and individuals moving out of the USA. *"Michael is one of the most knowledgeable people on taxation for Americans giving up citizenship and expatriation,"* says an interviewee. **John Porter** (see p.386) is a venerated senior partner at Baker Botts LLP who specializes in tax, trust and estates litigation. He represents the various estates of Yvette Bluhdorn, Julian Cohen and John Koons. **Kurt Rademacher** (see p.388) of Butler, Snow, O'Mara, Stevens & Cannada, PLLC is quickly making a name for himself in this space and is praised for his strong international planning practice. **Charles Redd** heads the private client team at Stinson Morrison Hecker LLP and has an enviable reputation in the market. *"He was very efficient and direct, and ultimately got the job done,"* said a client. Redd's practice covers estate planning as well as trust and estate litigation. **Lawrence Richman** (see p.392) is the leading figure in Neal, Gerber & Eisenberg LLP's trust and estates group. Clients are full of praise, with one noting: *"We always feel like he's keeping an eye out for what he needs to advise us on and is keeping ahead of everything."* Another source adds: *"He's fantastic – he speaks in terms that I can understand and balances legal and business considerations in his advice."* *"Extremely knowledgeable"* **Gideon Rothschild** of Moses & Singer LLP is a well-respected figure in the market and is singled out as a go-to expert on estate planning and asset protection.

With over 35 years' experience, **Winthrop Rutherfurd** (see p.397) of White & Case LLP has a well-established practice and is known for representing private clients and the trust departments of numerous financial institutions. **Pam Schneider** is a founding partner of Gadsden Schneider & Woodward LLP and a revered figure in the trust and estates circle. She is held in high regard by the market for her breadth of experience, particularly on generation-skipping tax matters. **Douglas Siegler** is the driving force in Sutherland Asbill & Brennan LLP's private client group. He earns widespread recognition from commentators for both his expertise in the area, and his dedicated client service approach. Based in San Francisco, **Myron Sugarman** is a senior counsel and the leading figure in Cooley LLP's wealth management group. He maintains an active tax planning practice and is praised by clients as being a trusted adviser. **Donald Tescher** of Tescher & Spallina PA has a longstanding reputation in the market and maintains an active tax and estate planning practice in Florida. **Laura Twomey** (see p.419) of Simpson Thacher & Bartlett LLP is a younger partner who has established a strong reputation in the field and earns praise from peers for her work in this area.

# Leaders' Profiles in Nationwide

**AARON, Wayne M**
Milbank, Tweed, Hadley & McCloy LLP, New York
212 530 5284
waaron@milbank.com
*Featured in Financial Services Regulation (Nationwide)*
**Practice Areas:** Mr Aaron is a partner in the firm's Financial Services Regulatory Practice. He advises securities firms on complex sales and trading and other regulatory issues affecting securities markets, representing these clients in inquiries by and enforcement proceedings before the SEC and other regulatory organizations. His practice encompasses the wide-range of regulatory issues affecting institutional investors including, equity and fixed-income trading practices; market structure, order handling and execution issues; audit trail and trade reporting requirements; commission sharing arrangements and directed brokerage programs; short sales and operational compliance; high-frequency trading, market-making, and specialist obligations; capital markets issues; and research practices.

**ABRAMS, Floyd**
Cahill Gordon & Reindel LLP, New York
212 701 3000
fabrams@cahill.com
*Featured in First Amendment Litigation (Nationwide); Media & Entertainment (New York)*
**Practice Areas:** National trial and appellate practice and extensive experience in high-visibility matters, often involving First Amendment, securities law, IP, insurance, public policy and regulatory issues. Has argued frequently in the Supreme Court in cases raising issues as diverse as the scope of the First Amendment, campaign finance issues, the interpretation of ERISA, the nature of broadcast regulation, the impact of copyright law, and the continuing viability of the Miranda rule. Currently representing Standard & Poor's in cases around the nation.
**Publications:** Speaking Freely: Trials of the First Amendment (Viking Press, 2005).
**Personal:** Member, firm's Executive Committee. American Academy of Arts & Sciences. Visiting Professor and Visiting Lecturer at the Columbia Graduate School of Journalism, the Yale Law School and the Columbia Law School for many years. Cornell University, BA, 1956. Yale Law School, JD, 1960.

**ABRAMS, Marc**
Willkie Farr & Gallagher LLP, New York
212 728 8200
mabrams@willkie.com
*Featured in Bankruptcy/Restructuring (Nationwide), Bankruptcy/Restructuring (New York)*
**Practice Areas:** Partner and Co-Chair of Business Reorganization and Restructuring Department. Specializes in advising companies in complex debt restructurings and insolvencies (including out of court and formal proceedings), investors and purchasers seeking investment, acquisition or financing opportunities in troubled companies, lenders and creditors of troubled companies, including official and unofficial groups seeking a broad range of objectives, pension schemes, and foreign governmental units. Substantial cross-border expertise on creditor and company side matters, including multi-lateral restructuring, M&A, financing and exchange transactions. Represents private funds and, on the company-side, clients in automotive, cable, construction, entertainment/recreation, healthcare, high-tech, hospitality, manufacturing, pharmaceutical, retail, telecommunication and transportation industries.
**Professional Memberships:** Chaired Committee on Bankruptcy and Corporate Reorganization of the Association of the Bar of the City of New York. Fellow of American College of Bankruptcy and member of its Board of Regents. Member of International Insolvency Institute. Recipient of 2011 Professor Lawrence P. King Award in recognition of achievements in field of bankruptcy law and for leadership in philanthropy. Serves as contributing editor for Collier on Bankruptcy and Lexis Practice Advisor. Serves on Advisory Board of ABI's annual "Views from the Bench" Conference. Prolific speaker or panelist for major conferences sponsored by ABI, INSOL, TMA, among other industry organisations.
**Personal:** JD, cum laude, Widener University, 1978. BA, cum laude, Villanova University, 1975. See: http://www.willkie.com/MarcAbrams.

**ACKER, Lawrence G**
Van Ness Feldman LLP, Washington, DC
202 298 1915
lga@vnf.com
*Featured in Energy & Natural Resources (Nationwide)*
**Practice Areas:** Litigates major, complex cases before administrative agencies and secures regulatory authorizations for substantial energy projects, including contested applications. Advises senior company officials respecting strategic planning, contract negotiation and corporate compliance with regulatory and enforcement requirements. Assists clients in every phase of the administrative process from case and project planning to document preparation and witness examination through appeals.
**Professional Memberships:** Energy Bar Association.
**Career:** Dewey & LeBoeuf (1984-2012); Bracewell & Patterson (1981-84); Federal Energy Regulatory Commission (1978-81); Acker & Mansfield, Arlington, Virginia (1976-78); Arlington Legal Aid Society (1974-76).
**Personal:** Georgetown University (JD) 1974; Syracuse University (BA) 1971.

**ADAMS, Matthew**
Dentons, San Francisco
415 882 0351
matthew.adams@dentons.com
*Featured in Climate Change (Nationwide)*
**Practice Areas:** Matthew Adams is a partner in legacy Dentons's Energy, Transport and Infrastructure sector. His practice includes environmental, land use and natural resources law, with a particular focus on advising project developers, public agencies, Indian tribes and trade associations on the National Environmental Policy Act (NEPA), the National Historic Preservation Act (NHPA), the California Environmental Quality Act (CEQA) and other environmental impact assessment laws. He also has experience with the full range of land use, water and climate change issues arising in the context of infrastructure and energy projects.
**Personal:** University of California, Berkeley, JD, MCP, and MA; Northwestern University, BA.

**ADDUCCI, Steven**
Venable LLP, Washington, DC
202 344 4361
saadducci@venable.com
*Featured in Energy & Natural Resources (Nationwide)*
**Practice Areas:** Energy, regulatory
**Professional Memberships:** ABA FBA
**Career:** Energy and administrative law, with emphasis on oil and petroleum products, natural gas liquids ("NGLs"), natural gas, and electricity regulatory issues. Advises and represents refiners, oil, petroleum product, and NGL producers and marketers, NGL gatherers and processors, trade associations, pipelines, and a large electricity RTO regarding various rate, complaint, tariff, certificate, compliance, trial, and appellate proceedings before FERC and other State and Federal agencies and courts.
**Personal:** JD, with honors, University of North Dakota School of Law, 1990; BA, summa cum laude, University of North Dakota, 1987

**ADELFIO, Marco**
Goodwin Procter LLP, Washington, DC
202 346 4530
madelfio@goodwinprocter.com
*Featured in Investment Funds (Nationwide)*
**Practice Areas:** Mr Adelfio's investment company clients include open-end and closed-end funds, multi-class funds and master-feeder funds. In addition to ongoing SEC regulatory and registration activities, he handles complex acquisition and reorganization transactions for fund companies and consolidations following mergers of advisers. He has represented several fund companies since their inception and serves as independent counsel to the independent directors of fund companies. A portion of his practice involves advising private equity funds, exchange funds and operating companies on structural and Investment Company Act (1940 Act) matters, including exemptions.
**Personal:** JD, Boston College Law School, 1982; BA, Bucknell University, 1978.

**ADLER, Arthur S**
Sullivan & Cromwell LLP, New York
212 558 3960
adlera@sullcrom.com
*Featured in Real Estate (Nationwide), Capital Markets (Nationwide), Real Estate (New York)*
**Professional Memberships:** ABA; NYSBA; ABCNY.
**Career:** Partner since 1990. Sophisticated commercial real estate expertise, including permanent and construction mortgage and mezzanine financing (for lenders and borrowers) with bank syndicates, securitization lenders and self-sponsored borrower securitizations; preferred equity, joint venture and other structured investments; loan workouts (for borrowers and lenders); lease-backed financings and sales; development and investment JVs; acquisitions/dispositions of improved and unimproved properties; and construction contracting. Clients include Vornado; Goldman Sachs; Toys "R" Us; Bain Capital; OSI (Outback); Bank of America; CA, Inc.; General Growth Properties; and Tisch Family Interests.
**Personal:** Columbia Law School (JD, 1982); Columbia University (AB, 1979).

**ADLER, Howard B**
Gibson, Dunn & Crutcher LLP, Washington, DC
202 955 8589
hadler@gibsondunn.com
*Featured in Corporate/M&A (District of Columbia), Capital Markets (Nationwide)*
See under District of Columbia for profile.

**ADLER, Kenneth A**
Loeb & Loeb LLP, New York
212 407 4284
kadler@loeb.com
*Featured in Outsourcing (Nationwide), Technology (New York)*
See under New York for profile.

**ADLER, Sheldon S**
Skadden, Arps, Slate, Meagher & Flom LLP & Affiliates, New York
212 735 2136
Sheldon.Adler@skadden.com
*Featured in Energy & Natural Resources (Nationwide)*
**Practice Areas:** Primarily responsible for the development of Skadden's utility merger and acquisition practice, a subgroup of the Corporate Practice that handles utility acquisition transactions. Represents a wide variety of clients in merger and other acquisition transactions. Involved in many recent public utility merger transactions. Has also been involved in many recent generation assets divestiture transactions. Clients include Duke Energy Corporation, National Grid plc, CMS Energy Corporation, Northeast Utilities, TECO Energy, Inc. New England Electric System and Edison Mission Energy.
**Career:** JD, Yale Law School, 1979 (Editor, Yale Law Journal); BA, City College of New York, 1976.

## AFTANAS, Richard
Skadden, Arps, Slate, Meagher & Flom LLP & Affiliates, New York
212 735 4112
richard.aftanas@skadden.com
*Featured in Capital Markets (Nationwide)*
**Practice Areas:** Richard B. Aftanas represents investment banks and US, Canadian and other international issuers in a wide variety of public and private finance transactions. Mr Aftanas has worked on numerous initial public offerings and other public and private equity and equity-hybrid securities offerings, as well as high-yield, investment grade and tax-exempt debt offerings. Mr Aftanas also advises US and international clients with respect to corporate and securities law matters, as well as debt tender offers, exchange offers and other refinancing transactions.
**Career:** LLB McGill University, Faculty of Law, 1994 (Member, McGill Law Journal); BA, University of Manitoba, 1991.

## AGNESHWAR, Anand
Arnold & Porter LLP, New York
212 715 1107
Anand.Agneshwar@aporter.com
*Featured in Products Liability (Nationwide)*
**Practice Areas:** Anand Agneshwar co-chairs the firm's product liability litigation practice group. He represents pharmaceutical and consumer product companies as national, strategic, trial and appellate counsel in product liability and related litigation. His experience includes nearly a dozen bench and jury trials, numerous Daubert and Daubert-style hearings, and hundreds of arguments in state and federal trial and appellate courts. He also counsels on litigation risks, US Food and Drug Administration regulatory issues, and the impact of potential legislation. Mr Agneshwar writes frequently on product liability and FDA issues. He also maintains an active pro bono practice protecting civil liberties.

## AGOGLIA, Michael J
Morrison & Foerster LLP, San Francisco
415 268 6057
magoglia@mofo.com
*Featured in Financial Services Regulation (Nationwide)*
**Practice Areas:** Michael Agoglia is a member and former Co-Chair of Morrison & Foerster's Financial Services Litigation Practice and the Managing Partner of the San Francisco office. His practice is concentrated in complex civil litigation relating to financial services companies, particularly the defense of consumer class actions and enforcement actions. He has defended a variety of financial services institutions and other clients in a wide range of litigation, government enforcement, internal investigation, and ADR contexts. He has represented many clients as national coordinating counsel in large, multi-party, and multi-forum cases.
**Personal:** Boston College (AB, 1986); Harvard Law School (JD, 1989).

## AGUILAR-ALVAREZ, Guillermo
King & Spalding LLP, New York
212 556 2145
gaguilar@kslaw.com
*Featured in International Arbitration (Nationwide)*
**Practice Areas:** Handles arbitration procedures under the Rules of the ICC, the AAA, the LCIA, ICSID, the Arbitration Institute of the Stockholm Chamber of Commerce, the Netherlands Arbitration Institute, the Inter American Commercial Arbitration Commission and UNCITRAL. Represents investors and acts as arbitrator in investment disputes arising under Chapter 11 of the North American Free Trade Agreement and other bilateral investment treaties.
**Personal:** JD, Universidad Nacional Autonoma de Mexico (UNAM).

## ALBANO, Jonathan M
Bingham McCutchen LLP, Boston
617 951 8360
jonathan.albano@bingham.com
*Featured in First Amendment Litigation (Nationwide), Litigation (Massachusetts)*
See under Massachusetts for profile.

## ALBERG, James L
Pillsbury Winthrop Shaw Pittman LLP, Washington, DC
202 663 9123
james.alberg@pillsburylaw.com
*Featured in Outsourcing (Nationwide), Technology (District of Columbia)*
**Practice Areas:** Firmwide Leader of Pillsbury's Global Sourcing Practice. Mr Alberg represents customers in strategic large-scale multinational IT and business process outsourcings, software licensing, and related transactions with emphasis on financial services and information industry clients. Before joining Pillsbury, he spent nearly 20 years in-house with GE and Citibank and was Senior Vice President & General Counsel of Dun & Bradstreet Software.
**Professional Memberships:** District of Columbia, New York, and Massachusetts Bars; Registered Foreign Lawyer in England.
**Personal:** JD, Boston University School of Law, 1977; BA (cum laude), Political Science and Computer Science, Union College, 1974.

## ALBERTSON, Terry
Crowell & Moring LLP, Washington, DC
202 624 2635
talbertson@crowell.com
*Featured in Government (Nationwide)*
**Practice Areas:** Partner in Crowell & Moring LLP's Government Contracts Group. Focuses on government procurement law, including contract cost accounting, pricing and termination issues. Has tried numerous important cases concerning defective pricing, Cost Accounting Standards, the allowability of costs, multiple award contracts, terminations and more.
**Career:** Selected by Legal Times as a leading Washington government contracts lawyer.
**Personal:** Received Bronze Star for service in Vietnam War for service in US Army. Bachelor's degree from Georgetown University, magna cum laude,1968; MA from Yale University, 1969; JD from Harvard Law School, cum laude, 1974.

## ALEXANDER, Lee
DLA Piper LLP (US), Washington, DC
202 799 4581
lee.alexander@dlapiper.com
*Featured in Energy & Natural Resources (Nationwide)*
**Practice Areas:** Energy: oil and gas.
**Career:** He focuses his practice on federal regulatory and transactional energy issues and represents interstate natural gas pipelines and storage projects, natural gas and oil producers and marketers, local distribution companies, electric utilities and generators and oil pipelines and shippers involving proceedings before the Federal Energy Regulatory Commission (FERC), and other US federal and state agencies. He also counsels clients with respect to transactional issues regarding the purchase, sale, transportation and storage of natural gas and liquid hydrocarbons.
**Personal:** JD, University of Pittsburgh Law School; BS, Pennsylvania State University.

## ALEXANDER, Richard M
Arnold & Porter LLP, Washington, DC
202 942 5728
Richard.Alexander@aporter.com
*Featured in Financial Services Regulation (Nationwide)*
**Practice Areas:** Richard Alexander's practice involves some of the most significant enforcement, supervisory, and governance matters affecting the financial services industry. Mr Alexander represents financial services companies and their officers and directors, as well as other professionals, in enforcement or investigative proceedings. His practice includes representing financial service companies with respect to a wide range of issues arising out of the supervisory process. He has extensive experience in federal anti-money laundering laws and frequently counsels clients on the bank examination process. Mr Alexander also has significant experience with respect to issues arising out of the conservatorship or receivership of regulated financial service companies. He regularly is called upon to counsel clients with respect to complex corporate governance issues, representing Boards of Directors or their Audit and Special Committees. He has conducted investigations into alleged accounting fraud, legal, ethical, and internal control violations, self-dealing, and other wrongdoings.

## ALEXANDER, Todd E
Chadbourne & Parke LLP, New York
212 408 5269
talexander@chadbourne.com
*Featured in Projects (Nationwide)*
**Practice Areas:** Advises sponsors, private equity groups and lenders to conventional and renewable power projects, as well as biofuels and clean coal facilities. He has represented private equity groups on the acquisition of power plants in the US and Caribbean. He has advised sponsors developing power plants and biofuels facilities in the US, Canada, Europe, South America, and Sub-Saharan Africa and has represented lenders to wind farms and biofuels projects in the US.
**Professional Memberships:** District of Columbia and New York Bars.
**Personal:** University of Illinois, BS, 1991; Approved Certified Public Accountant (CPA), 1991; Georgetown University Law Center, JD, 1994.

## ALEXANDER, Troy
White & Case LLP, New York
212 819 8532
talexander@whitecase.com
*Featured in Latin American Investment (New York), Projects (Nationwide)*
**Career:** To view a comprehensive biography, please visit www.whitecase.com/talexander.

## ALEXANDROV, Stanimir A
Sidley Austin LLP, Washington, DC
202 736 8115
salexandrov@sidley.com
*Featured in International Arbitration (Nationwide)*
**Practice Areas:** Partner, Sidley's Washington, DC office. Co-chairs International Arbitration practice group. Practices investor-state and international commercial arbitration and resolution of WTO disputes. Has represented parties in ICSID, ICC, LCIA, and AAA arbitrations and under the UNCITRAL Rules. Currently or recently served as arbitrator on more than a dozen tribunals, including several as president. Professor for 15 years teaching investment and arbitration courses at The George Washington University Law School.
**Personal:** The George Washington University Law School, SJD, 1994; LLM, 1992; Moscow Institute of International Relations, JD, 1981. Admissions: New York, District of Columbia. Former Deputy Foreign Minister of Bulgaria.

## ALI, Arif H
Weil, Gotshal & Manges LLP, Washington, DC
202 682 7004
arif.ali@weil.com
*Featured in International Arbitration (Nationwide)*
**Practice Areas:** Mr Ali, Co-chair of Weil's International Arbitration Practice, has served as lead attorney or trial counsel in international arbitrations under the rules of all the major arbitral institutions in disputes involving a variety of industries, including oil and gas, energy, infrastructure development, mining, hospitality, technology and the Internet. He is a peer-recognized leader in investor-state dispute resolution, and has also represented parties before intergovernmental claims tribunals and the International Court of Justice.
**Personal:** Adjunct Law Professor, Georgetown Law School. UN Compensation Commission Section Chief and former Senior Legal Counsel at the WIPO Arbitration and Mediation Center. English/Spanish/French/Hindi/Urdu/Bengali.

## ALLEN, Rand L
Wiley Rein LLP, Washington, DC
202 719 7329
rallen@wileyrein.com
*Featured in Government (Nationwide)*
**Practice Areas:** Chairs firm's nationally prominent 40-attorney Government Contracts Practice. The "go-to" counsel for the industry on some of the highest-profile matters, most prominently the successful Boeing Air Force Tanker protest. Named the Washington, DC area's "Top Government Contracts Lawyer" and a "Visionary" by Legal Times. Handles full range of contracting issues, including bid protests, contract claims and disputes litigation, terminations, mergers and acquisitions, procurement fraud/False Claims Act investigations and suspension/debarment.
**Professional Memberships:** American Bar Association, Past-Chair, Section of Public Contract Law.
**Personal:** Georgetown University Law Center (JD); United States Military Academy at West Point (BS).

## ALLERHAND, Joseph S
Weil, Gotshal & Manges LLP, New York
212 310 8725
joseph.allerhand@weil.com
*Featured in Securities (Nationwide), Litigation (New York)*
**Practice Areas:** Joseph Allerhand is a nationally recognized securities litigator and counselor with over 30 years of experience in major shareholder class and derivative actions, M&A litigations, SEC investigations, arbitrations, corporate governance disputes, and busted deal litigations. Equally comfortable in the boardroom and courtroom, he regularly counsels directors and special committees on transactions and internal investigations. He represented Kinder Morgan in its $37.8 billion dollar acquisition of El Paso and currently serves as lead counsel for AIG in the shareholder class action arising from the 2007-08 financial crisis.
**Personal:** Columbia University (BA, 1975); Georgetown University Law Center (JD, 1978).

## ALPERT, Laurent
Cleary Gottlieb Steen & Hamilton LLP, New York
212 225 2340
lalpert@cgsh.com
*Featured in Banking & Finance (Nationwide)*
**Practice Areas:** Mergers, acquisitions and leveraged buyouts, with particular emphasis on cross-border transactions. Bridge financings and permanent financings of acquisition transactions, representing both major US and foreign industrial and financial companies as well as private equity firms. Corporate governance, including advice to boards of directors and board committees.
**Professional Memberships:** Beazer Homes USA, Inc. (Chairman of the Nominating/Corporate Governance Committee, member of the Finance Committee); International Rescue Committee.
**Career:** Joined firm, 1972; became Partner, 1980. Harvard Law School, 1972; Ecole Nationale d'Administration (Diplome du Cycle Etranger), 1968.

## ALPUCHE, Maripat
Simpson Thacher & Bartlett LLP, New York
212 455 3971
malpuche@stblaw.com
*Featured in Financial Services Regulation (Nationwide)*
**Practice Areas:** Corporate Partner, concentrating in financial institution M&A and capital markets. Transactions include some of the industry's largest, including acquisition of IndyMac Bank from the FDIC ($13.9 billion), Bank of New York Mellon merger ($29 billion) and JPMorgan Chase's merger with Bank One ($58 billion). Major credit card program and sale transactions include Target ($5.9 billion), Best Buy ($7 billion) and Macy's ($6.6 billion). Also represents issuers, underwriters and investors, including JPMorgan, The Carlyle Group, TD Bank, Goldman, Sachs and Wells Fargo, in public and private capital raises and M&A transactions.
**Career:** Joined Firm, 1990; Partner, 2002.

## ALTMAN, James B.
Foster, Murphy, Altman & Nickel, PC, Washington, DC
202 822 4103
jaltman@fostermurphy.com
*Featured in International Trade (Nationwide)*
**Practice Areas:** Focuses on international intellectual property disputes at the US International Trade Commission under Section 337 and at Customs and Border Protection.
**Career:** Has represented clients in more than 35 Section 337 cases. Draws on his background in complex economic and technical litigation and in science and technology. Frequently lectures and coordinates conferences and presentations on Section 337, and publishes on IP and ITC issues. Past President, ITC Trial Lawyers Association.
**Personal:** JD, Boalt Hall, University of California, Berkeley; BS and MS, Physics, Massachusetts Institute of Technology; Registered patent attorney.

## ALTSCHULER, Fredric L
Cadwalader, Wickersham & Taft LLP, New York
212 504 6525
fredric.altschuler@cwt.com
*Featured in Real Estate (Nationwide), Real Estate (New York)*
**Practice Areas:** Represents institutional lenders and investment banks in connection with construction, interim and permanent financings of real estate (land assemblages, hotels, regional shopping centers, office buildings, industrial parks, mixed-use projects, residential and commercial condominiums and cooperatives); workouts of non-performing loans, foreclosures and acceptances of deeds in lieu of foreclosure and dispositions of properties acquired in workouts and foreclosures; and the origination, securitization and disposition of commercial mortgage loans, mezzanine loans and preferred equity interests. Counsels investors acquiring performing and non-performing loans and properties, including the financing of such purchases and restructuring and disposition of the purchased assets. Assists

clients in the acquisition, financing, disposition and leasing of commercial real estate.
**Personal:** JD, St John's University; BA, Syracuse University.

## AMAN, David
Cleary Gottlieb Steen & Hamilton LLP, New York
212 225 2262
daman@cgsh.com
*Featured in Financial Services Regulation (Nationwide)*
**Practice Areas:** Broker-dealer regulation under US law, rules of the SEC and the Financial Industry Regulatory Authority, and Federal Reserve Board margin regulations; also the insolvency of broker-dealers, other financial institutions and their counterparties under the Securities Investor Protection Act, the Bankruptcy Code, the Federal Deposit Insurance Act or the Dodd-Frank Act, especially as the regulatory and insolvency regimes affect the structure and documentation of securities contracts, derivatives and other financial products. Clients include the Securities Industry and Financial Markets Association, the Federal Reserve Bank of New York, and numerous large US and international investment banks and financial institutions.

## ANDERSON, Brian
O'Melveny & Myers LLP, Washington, DC
202 383 5309
banderson@omm.com
*Featured in Products Liability (Nationwide)*
**Practice Areas:** Brian Anderson is Of Counsel in O'Melveny's DC office and has over twenty years of experience managing the defense of all forms of aggregated litigation for major corporations in a wide variety of industries and substantive law. Brian has defended more than 400 class actions, mass tort cases, multi-district proceedings, state attorney general lawsuits and investigations, and mass-joinder actions in state and/or federal courts of 39 states and the District of Columbia. Most recently, Brian co-authored The Class Action Playbook, a leading guide to the strategic decisions underlying the pursuit and defense of class actions.

## ANDERSON, James E
WilmerHale, Washington, DC
202 663 6180
james.anderson@wilmerhale.com
*Featured in Investment Funds (Nationwide)*
**Practice Areas:** Chair, Investment Management Practice. Advises and represents investment advisers, broker-dealers, banks, mutual funds and other investment companies on investment adviser, investment company and broker-dealer regulatory and compliance issues; on related issues pertaining to pension plans and other types of retirement accounts; in investigations and proceedings brought by the Securities and Exchange Commission; and in civil litigation.
**Publications:** Co-author, Investment Advisers: Law & Compliance, a leading treatise on investment adviser regulation; contributing author, Mutual Fund Regulation, a treatise on investment company regulation.

**Personal:** Brigham Young University, J Reuben Clark Law School (JD 1992); University of Utah (BA 1988).

## ANDREWS, Jeffrey B
Bracewell & Giuliani LLP, Houston
713 221 1439
jeff.andrews@bgllp.com
*Featured in Outsourcing (Nationwide), Technology (Texas)*
See under Texas for profile.

## ANDRIL, David T
Vinson & Elkins LLP, Washington, DC
202 639 6542
dandril@velaw.com
*Featured in Energy & Natural Resources (Nationwide)*
**Practice Areas:** Practice concentrates on natural gas and liquefied natural gas sales and transportation contracting, and regulation of the natural gas industry before the Federal Energy Regulatory Commission and the Department of Energy.
**Professional Memberships:** Energy Bar Association.
**Career:** Admitted to District of Columbia Bar in 1980. Came to the firm in 1980 and was admitted to the partnership in January 1989.

## ANGIOLILLO, Bruce
Simpson Thacher & Bartlett LLP, New York
212 455 3735
bangiolillo@stblaw.com
*Featured in Securities (Nationwide), Litigation (New York)*
**Practice Areas:** Senior Partner and Head of the Securities Litigation Practice. Areas of concentration are securities litigation, including class actions, derivative actions and contests for corporate control, and complex commercial litigation, including bankruptcy. Representative cases in the securities area include: Blackstone, Morgan Stanley, Equity Office Properties, Freddie Mac, JPMorgan Chase, EnergySolutions, MetroPCS, PXRE, Focus Media, Enron, Westar Energy, Sirius Satellite Radio, Winstar, Bre-X and WPPSS. He also regularly represents major private equity firms in matters arising from their investment activities.
**Career:** Joined the firm in 1980; Partner, 1985.
**Personal:** BA, magna cum laude, Amherst (1974); JD, Columbia Law School (1977).

## ANGLE, Stephen
Vinson & Elkins LLP, Washington, DC
202 639 6565
sangle@velaw.com
*Featured in Energy & Natural Resources (Nationwide)*
**Practice Areas:** Electric utility ratemaking, electric transmission, power markets, regional transmission organizations, FERC Enforcement.
**Professional Memberships:** Energy Bar Association; American Bar Association.
**Career:** Former Assistant General Counsel for Electric Litigation, Federal Energy Regulatory Commission.
**Publications:** 'American Recovery and Reinvestment Act Analysis', Petroleum Economist,

March, 2009; Implications of the Energy Policy Act of 2005', Oil & Gas Journal, September 2005; 'Public Utilities Fortnightly', August 2005; 'Independent Transmission Companies: The For-Profit ISO Alternative in the Quest for Competitive Markets', Energy Law Journal, 19 (2) (1998).
**Personal:** University of Texas Law School (JD, 1974); Texas Christian University (BA, 1971).

## ANSBACHER, Richard I
Fried, Frank, Harris, Shriver & Jacobson LLP, Washington, DC
202 639 7065
Richard.Ansbacher@FriedFrank.com
*Featured in Investment Funds (Nationwide)*
**Practice Areas:** Corporate partner. Practice focuses on the formation and structuring of investment funds and alternative investments. Extensive experience in global private equity funds. Represents sponsors of, cornerstone and other institutional investors in formation of hedge funds, real estate funds, "hybrid" funds, funds-of-funds, and investment management companies.
**Career:** Joined as partner in 1999.
**Personal:** JD, cum laude, University of Florida (1983), Order of the Coif, editor, Law Review; LLM, New York University School of Law (1984); BS, cum laude, University of Florida (1979).

## ANSELL, David L
Dechert LLP, Washington, DC
202 261 3433
david.ansell@dechert.com
*Featured in Financial Services Regulation (Nationwide)*
**Practice Areas:** Mr Ansell advises financial services companies on a wide variety of matters, including mergers and acquisitions; controlling and private equity investments in banks and bank holding companies; reorganizations and recapitalizations of distressed banks; and corporate finance transactions. He has significant experience in matters pending before various federal bank regulatory agencies.
**Professional Memberships:** Member, Pennsylvania and District of Columbia Bars; admitted to practice before the US Supreme Court; member, American Bar Association's Banking Law Committee.
**Personal:** The Wharton School, University of Pennsylvania (B.S., 1976, cum laude); Temple University Beasley School of Law (JD, 1979, member, Law Quarterly).

## ANTHONY, Michael F
McDermott Will & Emery LLP, Chicago
312 984 7635
manthony@mwe.com
*Featured in Healthcare (Illinois), Healthcare (Nationwide)*
**Practice Areas:** Healthcare practice focused on provider affiliations, integrated delivery system development, formation of HMOs and PPOs, health care mergers, acquisitions and affiliations, various joint ventures, joint operating arrangements, reimbursement systems, medical staff matters, Catholic/non-Catholic transactions, medical

group representation and other legal and policy issues.
**Professional Memberships:** Admitted in District of Columbia, Florida and Illinois; fellow, American College of Healthcare Executives; Past president, American Health Lawyers Association.
**Career:** Former senior vice president for legal affairs at American Hospital Association.
**Personal:** University of Baltimore School of Law (JD); Xavier University (MHA, BS).

## APPLEBY, Bethany L
Wiggin and Dana LLP, New Haven
203 498 4365
bappleby@wiggin.com
*Featured in Franchising (Nationwide)*
**Practice Areas:** Trial Lawyer. Co-chair of the Franchise and Distribution Practice. Focus: franchise, commercial and utility litigation. Represents clients in litigation and arbitration, including international arbitration and before regulatory bodies.
**Professional Memberships:** ABA, Forum on Franchising and Section of Public Utility, Communications and Transportation Law; Editor-in-Chief of the ABA Franchise Law Journal.
**Personal:** Yale University, BA (magna cum laude) (1989); University of Connecticut School of Law, JD (with highest honors) (1997) (Connecticut Law Review Notes and Comments editor). Before law school, had a financial planning practice, held the Certified Financial Planning designation.

## ARCELLA, Craig F
Cravath, Swaine & Moore LLP, New York
212 474 1024
carcella@cravath.com
*Featured in Capital Markets (Nationwide)*
**Practice Areas:** Craig F. Arcella is a partner in Cravath's Corporate Department. He represents financial institutions and corporate clients in a wide variety of matters, including initial public offerings and other equity offerings; investment grade, high-yield and convertible debt offerings; leveraged acquisition finance; mergers and acquisitions; and syndicated loan transactions. Mr Arcella regularly advises public companies with respect to governance, public disclosure and other corporate matters. He is also actively involved in the Firm's Latin American capital markets practice.
**Personal:** Columbia Law School (JD, 1998; Harlan Fiske Stone Scholar; Member, Law Review); Duke University (BA, 1995). For more information: http://www.cravath.com/carcella

## ARCHER, Matt
McDermott Will & Emery LLP, Houston
713 653 1709
marcher@mwe.com
*Featured in Projects (Nationwide)*
**Practice Areas:** Focuses on project development and finance and mergers and acquisitions in the energy industry. Active renewable energy practice and regularly advises clients on wind, landfill gas, solar, energy storage and other alternative energy projects. Also represents clients in connec-

tion with the development, structuring, construction, purchase and sale of traditional power projects, midstream oil and gas pipeline projects and other energy infrastructure projects.
**Professional Memberships:** Admitted to practice in Texas; Houston Bar Association; Houston Young Lawyers Association.
**Personal:** University of Pennsylvania Law School, JD (cum laude), 2001; Texas A&M University, BBA (magna cum laude), 1997.

## ARMAS, Oliver J
Chadbourne & Parke LLP, New York
212 408 5399
oarmas@chadbourne.com
*Featured in International Arbitration (Nationwide)*
**Practice Areas:** Oliver Armas is the co-head of the International Arbitration Group. He represents foreign and domestic clients in arbitrations before the ICC, AAA/ICDR, LCIA, ICSID, and other tribunals. Although Mr Armas has handled cases worldwide, because he is fluent in Spanish (and can understand Portuguese), a significant percentage of his practice involves clients in Latin America. Mr Armas has acted as a legal expert on US law in foreign proceedings and has supervised litigation and arbitrations in many foreign countries.
**Personal:** New York University, BA; New York University, MPA; New York University School of Law, JD.

## ARNHOLZ, John
Bingham McCutchen LLP, Washington, DC
202 373 6538
john.arnholz@bingham.com
*Featured in Capital Markets (Nationwide)*
**Practice Areas:** Leader of Bingham's Structured Transactions Group. Represents financial institutions in asset financings, securitizations and investment fund strategies. Has worked with a broad range of financial assets, including loan portfolios, distressed obligations, credit cards, debt obligations, home equity loans, residential mortgage loans, auto loans, franchise loans and trade receivables. Active in structured finance transactions in England, Eastern Europe, Australia, and other markets.
**Publications:** Co-authored the treatise 'Offerings of Asset-Backed Securities'.
**Personal:** Georgetown University Law Center, JD, cum laude, 1985; Bowdoin College, BA, cum laude, 1981.

## ARONZON, Paul S
Milbank, Tweed, Hadley & McCloy LLP, Los Angeles
213 892 4377
paronzon@milbank.com
*Featured in Bankruptcy/Restructuring (California), Bankruptcy/Restructuring (Nationwide)*
See under California for profile.

## AROVAS, Gregory S
Kirkland & Ellis LLP, New York
212 446 4766
greg.arovas@kirkland.com
*Featured in International Trade (Nationwide), Intellectual Property (New York)*
See under New York for profile.

## ARRINGTON, Scott J
McDermott Will & Emery LLP, Houston
713 653 1712
sarrington@mwe.com
*Featured in Projects (Nationwide)*
**Practice Areas:** Focuses on infrastructure development, acquisitions, dispositions and financings in the oil, gas, petrochemical and power industries, particularly those involving cross-border transactions.
**Professional Memberships:** Member, Houston Bar Association and State Bar of Texas; Fellow, Houston Bar Foundation; Life Fellow, Texas Bar Foundation; Member, Association of International Petroleum Negotiators and Houston World Affairs Council; Advisory Board Member, Institute for Energy Law.
**Personal:** BA (cum laude), Rice University (1990); JD, University of Texas (1995). Speaks Mandarin Chinese and Spanish.

## ASHINOFF, Reid
Dentons, New York
212 768 6730
reid.ashinoff@dentons.com
*Featured in Insurance (Nationwide), Insurance (New York)*
**Practice Areas:** Head, legacy Dentons's National Financial and Class Action Litigation practice group; founder and former head of legacy Dentons's New York Litigation practice. Focuses on commercial crises, multi-jurisdiction matters, class actions, consumer fraud, contractual disputes, real estate, securities litigation and counseling, and complex commercial challenges to products and services. Counsels and represents companies, corporate boards and executives in trial and appellate courts and before regulatory agencies throughout US.
**Personal:** Harvard Law School, JD, cum laude; City College of New York, BA, summa cum laude, Phi Beta Kappa.

## ASMUS, David
Morgan, Lewis & Bockius LLP, Houston
713 890 5718
dasmus@morganlewis.com
*Featured in Corporate/M&A (Texas), Energy & Natural Resources (Nationwide), Projects (Nationwide)*
**Practice Areas:** David Asmus is the leader of Morgan Lewis's Energy Transactions Practice. Mr Asmus focuses particularly on oil and gas development projects (including LNG and unconventional resource projects), offshore developments, and integrated field development projects), acquisitions and divestitures, and energy financings. He has served as lead external counsel on various ground-breaking transactions, including the Tangguh and Equatorial Guinea LNG export projects, the Elk Hills privatization in the US and the first unitizations in several jurisdictions and recently represented BHP Billiton in its acquisition of Petrohawk. In 2006 he received Chambers USA's "Award for Excellence" for Energy: Oil and Gas.

**ASTIGARRAGA, José I**
Astigarraga Davis, Miami
305 372 8282
jia@astidavis.com
*Featured in International Arbitration (Nationwide)*
**Practice Areas:** José Astigarraga focuses his practice on international litigation and arbitration, primarily representing multinational companies in disputes emanating from international business transactions.
**Professional Memberships:** All Florida courts; United States Supreme Court; Circuit Courts of Appeal for the Eleventh and Fifth Circuits.
**Career:** Astigarraga, founding shareholder at Astigarraga Davis, has extensive experience in international business disputes acquired during his over 30 year career. He serves as lead litigation counsel in courts in the US and in arbitral tribunals in the US and abroad. Fully bilingual in Spanish, Astigarraga has supervised and managed complex, high profile legal proceedings for multi-national clients throughout Latin America. He is a board member of the new Latin America Arbitration Association, Vice President of the 35-member London Court of International Arbitration and has served as arbitrator, co-arbitrator or chair before the ICC, LCIA and AAA, among others. He has served as Vice-Chair of the International Bar Association's worldwide Arbitration Committee, and chaired its task force on arbitrator conflicts. He is Vice-Chair of the Board of Directors of the National Law Center for Inter-American Free Trade. A frequent speaker at legal conferences, he is also a member of the Executive Council of the American Law Institute, the publisher of the highly-respected Restatements of Law.
**Publications:** Co-author, 'Latin American Insolvency Systems', World Bank 1999.
**Personal:** Fluent Spanish, born July 20, 1953. University of Miami (1975 BBA summa cum laude; 1978 JD magna cum laude).

**ATKINS, Sean**
Alston & Bird LLP, Washington, DC
202 239 3072
sean.atkins@alston.com
*Featured in Energy & Natural Resources (Nationwide)*
**Practice Areas:** Focused on energy and public utility law including federal and state regulation of electric utilities.
**Professional Memberships:** Energy Bar Association, American Wind Energy Association.
**Career:** Has served as counsel to an independent system operator on electricity market issues for over a decade. Represents transmission-owning public utilities in the northeastern United States on transmission planning, regulatory compliance, commercial matters, and rate issues. Advises renewable power developers on a wide range of regulatory issues.
**Personal:** JD (1996), BA (1991), University of Virginia.

**ATKINSON, Kathryn Cameron**
Miller & Chevalier Chartered, Washington, DC
202 626 5957
katkinson@milchev.com
*Featured in International Trade (Nationwide)*
**Practice Areas:** Corporate ethics and compliance, including FCPA and anti-corruption law, export controls and economic sanctions, and anti-money laundering laws; risk assessment, program design, and auditing; merger and acquisition due diligence; and internal and government investigations.
**Career:** Independent Compliance Monitor to KBR, Inc. pursuant to DOJ/SEC FCPA settlements; former member, Transparency International Task Force on Compliance Toolkit for small and medium-sized entities; co-producer, "Comply But Compete," an FCPA training video.
**Personal:** JD, Cornell Law School, 1992; BA, The Johns Hopkins University, 1989.

**ATNIPP, Douglas C**
Greenberg Traurig, LLP, Houston
713 374 3515
AtnippD@gtlaw.com
*Featured in Energy & Natural Resources (Nationwide)*
**Practice Areas:** Energy finance, energy M&A, oil and gas, energy and natural resources, financial institutions, corporate and securities.
**Professional Memberships:** Member: State Bar of Texas; Houston Bar Association; American Bar Association; Texas Tech School of Law Foundation Board. Sustaining Life Fellow: Houston Bar Foundation; Texas Bar Foundation.
**Career:** Leadership Roles: Co-Regional Operating Shareholder for the Texas Region. Co-Managing Shareholder, Houston office. Co-Chair, Global Energy and Infrastructure Practice. Selected: Chambers USA Guide; Chambers Global Guide; Best Lawyers in America; Super Lawyers and Texas Super Lawyers magazine; 'Top 100 Lawyers in the City of Houston', Texas Monthly, 2003-05. Rated, AV® Preeminent™ 5.0 out of 5.
**Personal:** JD, Texas Tech University School of Law; BA, cum laude, Vanderbilt University.

**ATTANASIO, Donna**
White & Case LLP, Washington, DC
202 626 3589
dattanasio@whitecase.com
*Featured in Energy & Natural Resources (Nationwide)*
**Career:** To view a comprehensive biography, please visit www.whitecase.com/dattanasio

**AUERBACH, Reed D**
Bingham McCutchen LLP, New York
212 705 7400
reed.auerbach@bingham.com
*Featured in Capital Markets (Nationwide)*
**Practice Areas:** Co-chair of Bingham's Corporate Area. Represents a broad range of financial institutions, investment funds and issuers in developing innovative liquidity vehicles and the acquisition and disposition of financial companies and assets. Experience advising underwriters and issuers in connection with public and private offerings of asset-backed and mortgage-backed securities, collateralized debt obligations, whole loan purchases, repurchase agreements, and residual financings involving a variety of assets.
**Personal:** Columbia University School of Law, JD, 1985; Columbia University School of International and Public Affairs, MA, 1982; Franklin & Marshall College, BA, magna cum laude, 1980.

**AUGHTRY, David D**
Chamberlain, Hrdlicka, White, Williams & Aughtry, Atlanta
404 658 5486
david.aughtry@chamberlainlaw.com
*Featured in Tax (Georgia), Tax (Nationwide)*
See under Georgia for profile.

**AUSTIN, Christopher E**
Cleary Gottlieb Steen & Hamilton LLP, New York
212 225 2434
caustin@cgsh.com
*Featured in Private Equity (Nationwide), Corporate/M&A (New York)*
See under New York for profile.

**AVERY, Alan**
Latham & Watkins LLP, New York
212 906 1301
alan.avery@lw.com
*Featured in Financial Services Regulation (Nationwide)*
**Practice Areas:** Alan Avery concentrates on federal and state regulation of banking organizations, advising domestic and foreign banking institutions on the impact of US banking laws on their global operations. Mr Avery has represented US and non-US financial institutions with regard to regulatory approval requirements for bank formations, office establishment and licensing, internal reorganizations, and mergers and acquisitions. Mr Avery is actively advising banks on the implementation of the Dodd-Frank Act. He also advises transactional practices worldwide on US bank regulations. Mr Avery has represented sovereign wealth funds and private equity funds with respect to investments in US financial institutions.

**AVIL, Richard**
Jones Day, Washington, DC
202 879 5401
rdavil@jonesday.com
*Featured in Energy & Natural Resources (Nationwide)*
**Practice Areas:** His practice is focused on regulatory counseling and administrative and appellate litigation for natural gas pipelines, local distribution companies, and electric utilities on matters including rates, new services, competition, and regulatory compliance. He helps develop and present industrywide positions on critical energy rulemaking matters and policy inquiries. He is experienced in the regulatory components of mergers, acquisitions, and other transactions in the energy industry. Listed in 'Who's Who' in America, 'Who's Who' in the World, and Chambers Global.
**Professional Memberships:** Energy Bar Association.

**AXELRAD, David M**
Horvitz & Levy LLP, Encino
818 995 0800
daxelrad@horvitzlevy.com
*Featured in Litigation (California), Appellate Law (Nationwide)*
See under California for profile.

**AXELRAD, Jonathan**
Goodwin Procter LLP, Menlo Park
650 752 3111
jaxelrad@goodwinprocter.com
*Featured in Investment Funds (Nationwide), Corporate/M&A (California)*
**Practice Areas:** Mr Axelrad specializes in all aspects of the formation and operation of venture capital and other private equity funds, with a particular emphasis on issues involving partnerships, limited liability companies, tax, ERISA, the Investment Advisers Act and the Freedom of Information Act. He has extensive experience in the areas of international fund structures and 'market' terms and conditions. He has also been engaged as an expert witness in matters concerning the structure and operation of venture capital funds.
**Personal:** JD, Yale Law School, 1987 (Claude R. Lambe Fellowship); BA, Wesleyan University, 1984 (Phi Beta Kappa).

**AYALI, Noam**
Chadbourne & Parke LLP, Washington, DC
202 974 5623
nayali@chadbourne.com
*Featured in Projects (Nationwide)*
**Practice Areas:** Represents energy companies, project developers, multilateral agencies, commercial banks and equity investors on upstream oil and gas projects, pipelines, and gas-related energy infrastructure projects globally. Advises project participants on political risk insurance for international projects. Extensively involved in the renewable energy industry, with a special focus on the geothermal sector. Represents renewable energy companies on US and international acquisitions, project development, bank and capital markets financings and SEC matters.
**Professional Memberships:** American Bar Association, New York Bar Association, District of Columbia Bar Association, Israel Bar Association, Association of International Petroleum Negotiators.
**Career:** Formerly Senior Counsel, International Finance Corporation.

**AYANIAN, John V**
Morgan, Lewis & Bockius LLP, Washington, DC
202 739 5946
jayanian@morganlewis.com
*Featured in Financial Services Regulation (Nationwide)*
**Practice Areas:** John V. Ayanian is a Partner in Morgan Lewis's Securities Industry and Investment Management Practice. Mr Ayanian advises broker-dealer clients on a wide variety of regulatory and transactional matters, including federal and state registration and compliance issues; SRO membership and compliance issues;

mergers and acquisitions and outsourcing arrangements involving broker-dealers; issues involving the trading of fixed-income securities, exchange-traded options, and exchange-traded funds; broker-dealer and investment adviser networking and compensation arrangements; and issues relating to the dissemination of securities analyst research reports. He counsels various market centers on issues involving market structure issues in the equity and options markets.

## AYER, Donald
Jones Day, Washington, DC
202 879 4689
dbayer@jonesday.com
*Featured in Appellate Law (Nationwide)*
**Practice Areas:** The firm's most experienced Supreme Court lawyer (19 arguments). Extensive experience in federal and state appellate courts. Constitutional law, statutory construction issues, business disputes, civil rights, criminal appeals. Adjunct Professor in Supreme Court Advocacy, Georgetown and Duke Law Schools.
**Professional Memberships:** American Academy of Appellate Lawyers (President); Coke Appellate Inn of Court (President); American Law Institute; Fellow of the American Bar Foundation. Georgetown Supreme Court Institute Advisory Board.
**Career:** Deputy Attorney General of the United States; Principal Deputy Solicitor General; US Attorney, E.D. Cal.; AUSA, N.D. Cal; Law Clerk Justice William H. Rehnquist; Judge Malcolm Wilkey (D.C. Cir.).

## AZIZ, Azam
Shearman & Sterling LLP, New York
212 848 8154
aaziz@shearman.com
*Featured in Capital Markets (Nationwide)*
**Practice Areas:** Azam Aziz is a member of Shearman & Sterling LLP's Executive Group and was formerly the Practice Group Leader of the firm's Asset Management Group. His practice focuses on the structuring and documentation of complex over-the-counter derivatives products for banks, collective investment vehicles and other financial market participants. He counsels alternative asset managers regarding regulatory developments, risk management and hedge fund formation. Mr Aziz has experience drafting and negotiating highly structured trading relationships for a wide variety of products.
**Career:** Bar admission: New York
**Personal:** Hofstra University School of Law, State University of New York at Stony Brook.

## AZZOLLINI, Phillip J
Schulte Roth & Zabel LLP, New York
212 756 2285
phillip.azzollini@srz.com
*Featured in Capital Markets (Nationwide)*
**Practice Areas:** Practice focuses on offerings of collateralized loan obligations and securities of other pooled investment vehicles. Represents issuers, placement agents and portfolio managers. Also represents buyers and sellers of financial assets, including in repurchase agreement transactions.

**Career:** SRZ Partner since January 2005; certified public accountant at Coopers & Lybrand LLP (Audit Group), 1988-92.
**Publications:** Co-author, "On the CLO Horizon — Regulations Expected to Impact CLOs," The International Comparative Legal Guide to: Securitisation 2011.
**Personal:** Fordham University School of Law, JD, 1995, Fordham Law Review; Pace University, BBA, cum laude, 1988.

## BABCOCK, Charles
Jackson Walker LLP, Houston
713 752 4210
cbabcock@jw.com
*Featured in First Amendment Litigation (Nationwide), Litigation (Nationwide), Litigation (Texas)*
**Practice Areas:** Chip Babcock is a national trial and appellate lawyer focusing on business, intellectual property and media litigation.
**Career:** Mr Babcock has tried over 100 cases to a jury. He recently defeated a purported nationwide class action in an invasion of privacy / wiretap case in Texas, won an ERISA case in Rhode Island, continued his defense of Dr Phil in a California defamation case, won a defense jury verdict in a five week trial over claimed fraud and breach of a methanol supply contract and successfully argued an appeal for a major financial institution in a case of first impression regarding the rights of beneficial owners of bonds. He is a Fellow of the American College of Trial Lawyers, The International Academy of Trial Lawyers, The American Board of Trial Advocates and The American Law Institute.

## BACCHUS, James
Greenberg Traurig, LLP, Orlando
407 418 2400
BacchusJ@gtlaw.com
*Featured in International Trade (Nationwide)*
**Practice Areas:** Chair, Global Practice. Globalisation and commercialisation; financial institutions; global trade, investment and business.
**Professional Memberships:** Member: American Bar Association; International Bar Association; International Law Association.
**Career:** Former Chairman, Appellate Body of the World Trade Organisation, court of final appeal in international trade in Geneva, Switzerland; former Member, Congress of the United States; former special assistant to the United States Trade Representative in the Executive Office of the President.
**Personal:** JD, high honours, Florida State University College of Law; MA, Yale University; BA, magna cum laude, Vanderbilt University; Honorary Doctorates: Rollins College, Sierra Nevada College, University of Central Florida.

## BACHMAN, Gary
Van Ness Feldman LLP, Washington, DC
202 298 1880
gdb@vnf.com
*Featured in Energy & Natural Resources (Nationwide)*
**Practice Areas:** Engages in an administrative, legislative, and litigation practice, with special

focus on regulation of the electric utility industry. Counsels electric utility clients on the full range of electric utility regulation and transmission issues, compliance planning and auditing, and the transactional, regulatory and environmental issues encountered in project financing, siting, permitting, and construction.
**Professional Memberships:** Energy Bar Association.

## BACKUS, Marcia E
Vinson & Elkins LLP, Houston
713 758 1101
mbackus@velaw.com
*Featured in Energy & Natural Resources (Nationwide)*
**Practice Areas:** Domestic and international energy M&A and joint ventures in all energy industry segments - E&P, power, refineries, pipelines, trading and oilfield service; private equity; project development; corporate law and other energy related transactions. Is head of the firm's global Energy Transactions/Projects Practice Group.
**Professional Memberships:** Chancellor's Council; Co-Founder, Center for Women in Law, University of Texas School of Law.
**Career:** Came to the firm in 1983 and was admitted to the partnership in 1991.
**Personal:** Attended Georgetown University and graduated from University of Texas, BA in 1976 (summa cum laude) and JD in 1983 (Order of the Coif).

## BAECHER, John
Chadbourne & Parke LLP, New York
212 408 5278
jbaecher@chadbourne.com
*Featured in Projects (Nationwide)*
**Practice Areas:** Advises sponsors, lenders and investors on the development and financing of privately-financed independent power projects and project restructurings, corporate financings and asset acquisitions and divestitures. He has assisted several of the largest global independent power companies in the expansion of their US holdings and in their international development and acquisition activities throughout Latin America, the Middle East and the UK. He advises sponsors and lenders on responding to RFPs relating to the acquisition or development of power plants and associated facilities and transmission and distribution systems.
**Professional Memberships:** BA, Hamilton College; JD, Harvard University. Admitted in New York.

## BAECHTOLD, Robert L
Fitzpatrick, Cella, Harper & Scinto, New York
212 218 2213
rbaechtold@fchs.com
*Featured in Life Sciences (Nationwide), Intellectual Property (New York)*
**Practice Areas:** Robert L Baechtold is one of the founding partners of Fitzpatrick, Cella, Harper & Scinto. Over the past 40 years, he has prepared, tried and argued intellectual property cases in the District Courts, the I.T.C. and the Federal Circuit, primarily in the fields of pharmaceuticals,

biotechnology, chemistry and polymeric materials. Mr Baechtold was selected as a top intellectual property law practitioner in the past and current editions of Best Lawyers in America, Euromoney Magazine's Guides to the Best Patent Lawyers, PLC Which Lawyer, Super Lawyers and LMG Life Sciences. He is listed in Chambers Global as "one of the best in the country." Bob was named Seton Hall University School of Law 2009 Distinguished Graduate and named New York Intellectual Property Lawyer of the Year by Best Lawyers.
**Professional Memberships:** Served as a Member of the Advisory Committee of the Court of Appeals for the Federal Circuit, the Board of Directors of the American Intellectual Property Law Association, the Board of Directors of the New York Intellectual Property Law Association, as President of the New Jersey Patent Law Association and as a member of the Board of Directors and President of the Federal Circuit Bar Association. He was elected as a Founding Fellow of the American Intellectual Property Law Association.
**Career:** Research chemist, American Cyanamid Co. (1958-62); patent agent, M&T Chemicals (1962-65); Ward, McElhannon, Brooks and Fitzpatrick, joined 1965, Partner 1969; Fitzpatrick, Cella, Harper & Scinto, Founding Partner, 1971.
**Publications:** What KSR did and did not change about the law of patent obviousness, Benchmark Litigation: The Definitive Guide to America's Leading Litigation Firms & Attorneys, October, 2008.
**Personal:** Rutgers University (BS Chemistry); Seton Hall University School of Law (JD magna cum laude). Married with three children, five grandchildren. Enjoys music, golf, tennis, sailing and travel.

## BAIRD, Bruce
Covington & Burling LLP, Washington, DC
202 662 5122
bbaird@cov.com
*Featured in Securities (Nationwide)*
**Practice Areas:** Co-chair of Covington's White-Collar Defense and Investigations Practice; Co-Head of Securities Enforcement Practice; advises Corporate Boards, public companies, individuals in securities investigations and litigation; leads internal investigations; tries cases; defends antitrust cartel investigations and other federal criminal matters; white-collar practice includes antitrust, foreign trade controls, government regulatory criminal investigations.
**Career:** Chief, Securities and Commodities Fraud Task Force and other positions in Manhattan US Attorney's Office, where he served for nine years. Special assistant to Deputy Attorney General of the US.
**Personal:** Cornell University (BA 1970); New York University (JD 1975), Editor-in-Chief, Law Review; Vanderbilt Medal; US Army (1971-73).

## BAKER, Charles H
DLA Piper LLP (US), New York
212 335 4724
c.baker@dlapiper.com
*Featured in Sports Law (Nationwide)*

**Practice Areas:** Corporate, Sports Law.
**Career:** His practice encompasses all aspects of public and private mergers and acquisitions, corporate finance, restructurings and private equity transactions, with a core focus in the sports, media, entertainment and consumer sectors. He has represented bidders for sports franchises in the National Football League, National Basketball Association, National Hockey League, Major League Baseball, Major League Soccer and many of the European football leagues. He is regularly featured or quoted on sports M&A and finance issues in media publications.

### BAKER, D J (Jan)
Latham & Watkins LLP, New York
212 906 1293
dj.baker@lw.com
*Featured in Bankruptcy/Restructuring (Nationwide), Bankruptcy/Restructuring (New York)*
**Practice Areas:** Represents companies, lenders, acquirers and other parties in connection with restructurings. Regularly advises boards of directors on matters related to corporate governance and fiduciary duty. Restructuring/Chapter 11 Matters include: American Pad & Paper Company; Archstone; Boston Generating; CIR-CLE K Company; The Delaco Company; Diamond M; DRECO Energy Services; FiberMark, Inc.; FoxMeyer Drug Company; GenTek, Inc.; Global Marine Inc.; Graham-Field Health Products, Inc.; Kaneb, Inc.; MCorp.; MicroAge, Inc.; Owens Corning; RCN Corporation; RHI Entertainment; Safety Kleen Systems, Inc.; Spectrum Brands; Sterling Chemicals; Stroh Brewing Company; and Winn-Dixie Stores, Inc.
**Career:** Qualified since 1973. Global Co-Chair of Latham's Insolvency Practice.

### BAKER, David A
McDermott Will & Emery LLP, Chicago
312 984 7597
dbaker@mwe.com
*Featured in Wealth Management (Nationwide)*
**Practice Areas:** Heads the Estate, Trust and Guardianship Controversy Practice Group. Has extensive experience in the areas of estate, trust and guardianship litigation; probate, estate, trust and guardianship administration; and charitable, foundation and exempt organization administration and litigation. Also practices estate planning.
**Professional Memberships:** A fellow of the American College of Estate and Trust Counsel (ACTEC).
**Personal:** Loyola University Chicago School of Law, JD, (cum laude), 1979; University of Illinois at Urbana-Champaign, BA, (with honors), 1976.

### BAKER, Mark
Fulbright & Jaworski LLP, Houston
713 651 7708
mbaker@fulbright.com
*Featured in International Arbitration (Nationwide)*
**Practice Areas:** Arbitration; mediation; litigation.
**Professional Memberships:** Texas State Bar; Chartered Institute of Arbitrators Fellow; Director and arbitrator for numerous panels of the AAA

and ICDR; Former Court Member and arbitrator for the LCIA; Arbitrator for CPR, WIPO, CAM, CAS; Mediator for CEDR and US courts; Member of the ICC Commission.
**Career:** Mark is Co-Head of Fulbright's International Department and also Co-Head of the firm's Arbitration and ADR Practice Group. He has represented clients and acted as an arbitrator in energy contracts, power purchase and sale agreements, construction contracts, project finance and development agreements, joint ventures and complex financial transactions.

### BAKER, Miller
McDermott Will & Emery LLP, Washington, DC
202 756 8233
mbaker@mwe.com
*Featured in Appellate Law (Nationwide)*
**Practice Areas:** Co-heads the firm's Appellate Practice group, and focuses his practice on appellate and constitutional litigation. Has represented or advised clients in more than 50 appeals in federal and state courts involving a broad range of matters. Argued before the US Supreme Court, the US Courts of Appeals for the Second, Fourth, Fifth, Sixth, Seventh, Ninth, and Federal Circuits, and state appellate courts in Maryland and New York.
**Personal:** Tulane University School of Law, JD, 1984; Louisiana State University.

### BAKER, Pamela
Dentons, Chicago
312 876 8989
pamela.baker@dentons.com
*Featured in Employee Benefits & Executive Compensation (Nationwide), Labor & Employment (Illinois)*
See under Illinois for profile.

### BAKER JR, William T
Day Pitney LLP, New York
212 297 2482
wbaker@daypitney.com
*Featured in Energy & Natural Resources (Nationwide)*
**Career:** Mr Baker advises energy and public utility clients, and focuses his practice on corporate matters, particularly those regarding financing, restructuring and corporate governance, as well as regulatory and policy issues. Prior to joining Day Pitney, Mr Baker was senior counsel at a large international law firm. He was previously a partner at Thelen LLP, and its predecessor, Reid & Priest LLP, where he concentrated on energy and utility corporate, regulatory and policy matters and held leadership positions, including chair of the firm and its executive committee. He also served as chair of its Energy Policy and Regulatory group.

### BAKER-SHENK, Philip M.
Holland & Knight LLP, Washington, DC
202 457 7031
Philip.Baker-Shenk@hklaw.com
*Featured in Native American Law (Nationwide)*
**Practice Areas:** Partner in the firm's national Indian Law Practice Group, he has practiced since 1976, representing dozens of Native American

Indian tribal governments plus tribal organizations and companies doing business with Indian tribes. He has extensive experience in the many diverse fields of federal Indian law and policy — gaming, health services, land use and management, taxation, transportation, business operations, energy development, education, judicial, trust resource management, governance, political relations, and legislative drafting. His work includes transactional negotiation, litigation, regulatory/legislative lobbying, and problem resolution. He has helped draft seminal federal laws on tribal self-governance, child welfare, housing, and education.

### BALABAN, Witold
Latham & Watkins LLP, New York
212 906 4550
witold.balaban@lw.com
*Featured in Capital Markets (Nationwide)*
**Practice Areas:** Specialises in equity derivatives and equity-linked products, including convertible and exchangeable bond offerings (both optional and mandatories) and related equity derivatives products (such as call spread overlays and issuer or affiliate borrow facilities), fixed and variable share forward sales and related equity offerings, issuer share repurchase transactions, hedging and monetization transactions (including equity based finance transactions) and structured products distributed publicly and privately.
**Career:** Qualified since 1994.

### BALE, Morgan
Weil, Gotshal & Manges LLP, New York
212 310 8758
morgan.bale@weil.com
*Featured in Banking & Finance (Nationwide)*
**Practice Areas:** Partner in Weil's Banking & Finance practice. Represents financial institutions in domestic and cross-border lending transactions, with a focus on acquisition and other event-driven high grade financings. Also very experienced in leveraged cash-flow and asset-based syndicated financings, restructurings, debtor-in-possession financings and exit financings. Representative clients include Barclays, Citi, Deutsche Bank, Goldman Sachs, JPMorgan and Morgan Stanley.
**Personal:** York University (BA, 1989); College of Law, York (CPE, 1992); College of Law, York (LSF, 1993); University of Virginia (LLM, 2002). Admitted to the New York Bar and a solicitor of the Supreme Court of England & Wales.

### BALL, Corinne
Jones Day, New York
212 326 7844
cball@jonesday.com
*Featured in Bankruptcy/Restructuring (Nationwide), Bankruptcy/Restructuring (New York)*
**Practice Areas:** Co-Head of the New York Office's Business Restructuring and Reorganisation Practice and leads the Firm's distressed M&A efforts. Thirty years of experience in business finance and restructuring with a focus on complex corporate reorganisations and distress acquisitions, both in court-supervised proceedings and through out-of-court restructurings and

recapitalisations. International Women's Insolvency & Restructuring Confederation "Woman of the Year in Restructuring" award winner. Named "Dealmaker of the Year" by The American Lawyer and one of "The Decade's Most Influential Lawyers" by The National Law Journal.
**Professional Memberships:** Director of the American College of Bankruptcy and the American Bankruptcy Institute; ABA.

### BALLENGER, J Scott
Latham & Watkins LLP, Washington, DC
202 637 2145
scott.ballenger@lw.com
*Featured in Appellate Law (Nationwide)*
**Practice Areas:** Appellate and Supreme Court litigation; strategic analysis and briefing in high-stakes trial court litigation.
**Career:** Clerkships with J. Clifford Wallace, Ninth Circuit, and Antonin Scalia, Supreme Court. Has argued cases in the Supreme Court and federal and state appellate courts across the country, including one the Second Circuit called "the largest criminal tax case in American history," and a case FDLI called the most important in the history of food and drug law. One of five "Rising Stars Under 40" chosen by Law360, which noted that the Supreme Court has granted 10 petitions for certiorari he has written.

### BALLON, Ian C
Greenberg Traurig, LLP, Santa Monica
310 586 6575
Ballon@gtlaw.com
*Featured in IT & Outsourcing (California), Privacy & Data Security (Nationwide)*
See under California for profile.

### BARAN, Jan W
Wiley Rein LLP, Washington, DC
202 719 7330
jbaran@wileyrein.com
*Featured in Government (Nationwide)*
**Practice Areas:** Election Law & Government Ethics practice. Named by Washingtonian a "Top Campaign & Elections Lawyer" and one of Washington, DC's "Top 50 Lawyers." Counsels/litigates on campaign finance laws, ethics requirements/lobbying laws, argues before the US Supreme Court. Author: ABA's "Election Law Primer for Corporations."
**Professional Memberships:** ABA, Former Chair, Standing Committee on Election Law; Member, Commission to Evaluate the ABA Model Code of Judicial Conduct.
**Career:** General Counsel, RNC and 1988 Bush for President Committee; Member, President's Commission on Federal Ethics Law Reform; Executive Assistant, FEC.
**Personal:** Vanderbilt University School of Law (JD); Ohio Wesleyan University (BA).

### BARANCIK, Tia S
Sullivan & Cromwell LLP, New York
212 558 4415
barancikt@sullcrom.com
*Featured in Energy & Natural Resources (Nationwide)*
**Practice Areas:** Extensive experience in M&A, investment, financings and credit transactions for

regulated energy companies and public utilities. Also counsels private equity firms, investment banks, investors and financial institutions on strategic corporate and credit transactions and applicable energy regulatory requirements. Advises on energy legislation and regulatory reform.
**Professional Memberships:** ABA; NYCBA (Former Member, Energy Committee).
**Career:** Special counsel since 2006. Previously, partner at King & Spalding and LeBoeuf.
**Publications:** Frequent commentator on corporate/regulatory issues affecting energy companies and on energy legislation/reform.
**Personal:** Vanderbilt University Law School (JD, 1986); Princeton University (BA, 1983).

### BARBASH, Barry
Willkie Farr & Gallagher LLP, Washington, DC
202 303 1201
bbarbash@willkie.com
*Featured in Investment Funds (Nationwide)*
**Practice Areas:** Partner and Co-Chair, Asset Management Group; Member, Executive Committee. Served as Director of Securities and Exchange Commission's Division of Investment Management. Advises mutual fund/private fund clients and their sponsors and directors/trustees on variety of transactional/compliance/regulatory matters. Areas of expertise include mutual fund/private fund formation, operations/regulation; development of investment services and new products; and fund governance. Regularly represents buyers/sellers in asset management M&A transactions and advises asset managers of all types in connection with administrative and court actions brought by securities regulators.
**Personal:** JD, Cornell University Law School, 1978. AB, (summa cum laude), Bowdoin College in 1975. See: http://www.willkie.com/BarryBarbash

### BARBIERE, Janet A
Kaye Scholer LLP, New York
212 836 7506
janet.barbiere@kayescholer.com
*Featured in Capital Markets (Nationwide)*
**Practice Areas:** Janet Barbiere represents issuers, underwriters, originators, loan sellers and investors in mortgage loan securitisations, real estate syndications, origination and servicing programs, the purchase, sale and acquisition of mortgage loans and mortgage securities, transactions in the secondary mortgage market, and other areas of real estate finance. She has also been active in the workout, restructuring and sale of distressed financial assets, including real estate-related debt and syndicated bank loans, and in the representation of creditors in insolvency proceedings. She serves on various ASF and CREFC Committees.

### BARIS, Jay G
Morrison & Foerster LLP, New York
212 468 8053
jbaris@mofo.com
*Featured in Investment Funds (Nationwide)*
**Practice Areas:** Mr Baris represents financial institutions on all aspects of regulation. He advises

investment companies, investment advisers, independent fund directors and broker-dealers in M&A, disclosure, compliance, governance, exemptive applications and other regulatory issues. He is a vice chair of the Committee on Federal Regulation of Securities of the ABA's Business Law Section and was chair of the Subcommittee on Investment Companies and Investment Advisers. He is chair of the Task Force on Investment Company Use of Derivatives and Leverage, member of the Board of Advisors of The Review of Securities & Commodities Regulation and an active speaker and writer.

### BARKER, Christopher B
Goodwin Procter LLP, Boston
617 570 1462
cbarker@goodwinprocter.com
*Featured in Leisure & Hospitality (Nationwide), Real Estate (Massachusetts)*
**Practice Areas:** Mr Barker has particular expertise in representing tax-exempt entities in structuring and implementing debt and equity investments in real estate and in real estate operating companies. He also does a significant amount of work in the hospitality industry. Mr Barker's practice involves representing institutional investors, public and private real estate operating companies and lenders in a wide range of real estate activities. He has represented a number of prominent public REITs in portfolio acquisitions, joint ventures, merger and acquisition transactions and other strategic transactions.
**Personal:** JD, Harvard Law School, 1985; BA, Brown University, 1982 (magna cum laude).

### BARKER, John
Arnold & Porter LLP, Washington, DC
202 942 5328
John.Barker@aporter.com
*Featured in International Trade (Nationwide)*
**Practice Areas:** John Barker's practice focuses on national security matters including export controls (ITAR and EAR), trade sanctions administered by the Office of Foreign Assets Control at the US Treasury (OFAC), compliance with the Foreign Corrupt Practices Act (FCPA) and practice before the Committee on Foreign Investment (CFIUS). He helps companies and institutions establish compliance plans, obtain export authorizations, and provides representation in enforcement proceedings. He came to the firm from the US Department of State, where he served as the Deputy Assistant Secretary for Non-proliferation Controls and, prior to that, as Deputy Assistant Secretary for Export Controls.

### BARLOON, Joseph L
Skadden, Arps, Slate, Meagher & Flom LLP & Affiliates, Washington, DC
202 371 7322
Joseph.Barloon@skadden.com
*Featured in Financial Services Regulation (Nationwide)*
**Practice Areas:** Co-leader of Skadden's Consumer Financial Services Litigation and Enforcement practice. Represents financial institutions in connection with investigations, class action litigation, grand jury proceedings, and

enforcement and administrative actions involving fair lending, unfair and deceptive trade practices, subprime lending, BSA and OFAC, mortgage fraud, redlining, credit card practices and mortgage loan servicing. Regularly assists financial institutions in developing and implementing compliance and risk management programs.
**Career:** JD, Georgetown University Law Center (summa cum laude); MA, University of Pennsylvania; AB, Harvard University (cum laude).

### BARNARD, Kevin
Arnold & Porter LLP, New York
212 715 1020
Kevin.Barnard@aporter.com
*Featured in Financial Services Regulation (Nationwide)*
**Practice Areas:** Has extensive experience advising financial institutions concerning the application of US banking and securities laws to their worldwide activities. He focuses on acquisitions and reorganization plans, governance and risk mitigation, confidential internal investigations, negotiating regulatory enforcement actions, and obtaining regulatory approvals. Currently, he represents Banco do Brasil in its US expansion (recognized in Financial Times 2012 Innovative Lawyers) and represented the Trustees holding voting control of AIG.
**Professional Memberships:** Director, Foreign Policy Association.
**Career:** Deputy Superintendent of Banks and General Counsel of the New York State Banking Department; Attorney for the US Department of Treasury, OCC.

### BARNETT, Benjamin R
Dechert LLP, Philadelphia
215 994 2887
ben.barnett@dechert.com
*Featured in Litigation (Nationwide)*
**Practice Areas:** Mr Barnett serves as co-chair of the firm's complex commercial litigation practice. He also has extensive experience with respect to eDiscovery issues. He has been the lead attorney responsible for coordinating nationwide discovery in several significant matters.
**Professional Memberships:** Member, Pennsylvania, Maryland, and District of Columbia Bars; admitted to practice before multiple federal courts.
**Personal:** Kenyon College, (B.A. 1984); The Catholic University of America Columbus School of Law, (JD, 1993, note and comment editor, Catholic University Law Review).

### BARON, Robert
Cravath, Swaine & Moore LLP, New York
212 474 1422
rbaron@cravath.com
*Featured in Securities (Nationwide), Litigation (New York)*
**Practice Areas:** Commercial litigation and arbitration, including the representation of major domestic and foreign issuers and financial institutions in litigation related to securities offerings and trading, complex structured financing transactions and mergers and acquisitions.

**Professional Memberships:** Admitted in New York, US Supreme Court, US Courts of Appeals for the Second, Third, Ninth and Federal Circuits, and the Southern District of New York.
**Career:** Litigation Managing Partner since September 2010; partner since 1988.
**Personal:** Harvard Law School (JD, cum laude, 1981); Princeton University (AB, cum laude, 1978).

### BARR, Lynne B
Goodwin Procter LLP, Boston
617 570 1610
lbarr@goodwinprocter.com
*Featured in Financial Services Regulation (Nationwide), Banking & Finance (Massachusetts)*
**Practice Areas:** Ms Barr, Chair of the firm's Consumer Financial Services Practice, advises banks, bank holding companies, brokerage concerns, mortgage companies, trade associations and other entities on general corporate matters, including the operation and offering of their products and services, particularly in the context of federal and state regulation of financial institutions and their activities. She has extensive experience in credit and mortgage lending matters, fair lending and equal credit opportunity issues, credit and deposit services, electronic banking and Internet services and insurance products.
**Personal:** JD, George Washington University, 1975 (with honors); BA, George Washington University, 1972.

### BARR, Matthew S
Milbank, Tweed, Hadley & McCloy LLP, New York
212 530 5194
mbarr@milbank.com
*Featured in Bankruptcy/Restructuring (Nationwide), Bankruptcy/Restructuring (New York)*
See under New York for profile.

### BARR, Michael H
Dentons, New York
212 768 6788
michael.barr@dentons.com
*Featured in Insurance (Nationwide), Insurance (New York)*
**Practice Areas:** US Senior Partner. Concentrates on commercial, class action, consumer fraud, professional liability, insurance coverage and securities litigation and related counseling. Litigates before trial and appellate courts and administrative forums throughout the US Experience including securities, consumer fraud, derivatives and securitizations, environmental, insurance coverage, real estate, professional liability and contractual disputes.
**Career:** Joined Dentons in 1990. Former head of legacy Dentons's Litigation & Disputes practice and sector head for Insurance. Member of legacy Dentons's Global Group Board.
**Personal:** Harvard University, JD, cum laude, 1980; Oberlin College, AB, with highest honors, 1977.

**BARRAGATE, Brett**
Jones Day, New York
212 326 3446
bpbarragate@jonesday.com
*Featured in Banking & Finance (Ohio), Banking & Finance (Nationwide)*
See under Ohio for profile.

**BARRINGER, William H**
Curtis, Mallet-Prevost, Colt & Mosle LLP, Washington, DC
202 452 7332
wbarringer@curtis.com
*Featured in International Trade (Nationwide)*
**Professional Memberships:** American Bar Association
**Career:** Mr Barringer, a partner in the International Trade group with over 30 years of experience practicing international trade law, has represented clients in some of the most important trade disputes, including those involving steel, automobiles, film, textiles and various electronic products. Mr Barringer's practice includes defending foreign interests in trade remedy investigations (antidumping, countervailing duty, and safeguard investigations), bilateral disputes, disputes arising under free trade agreements, and disputes under the World Trade Organization dispute settlement mechanism. He has been involved in numerous disputes before the World Trade Organization involving trade remedies, market access, competition policy, investment policy, and matters arising under various of the other WTO agreements. He has also advised foreign governments on WTO negotiations (the Uruguay Round and the Doha Round), bilateral and plurilateral trade negotiations, as well as compliance with obligations under existing agreements.Mr Barringer's clientele includes government and private sector interests in China, Brazil, Vietnam, Japan, Canada, Thailand, Malaysia, Europe and the United States.
**Personal:** Earned an LLM in 1976 and a JD in 1973 from Georgetown University Law Center, and an AB from Brown University in 1970.

**BARROWES, Brooksany**
Baker Botts LLP, Washington, DC
202 639 7887
brooksany.barrowes@bakerbotts.com
*Featured in Energy & Natural Resources (Nationwide)*
**Practice Areas:** Energy-related regulatory litigation and transactional work, including mergers and acquisitions, internal investigations, defending enforcement actions and audits, negotiating power purchase and interconnection agreements, litigating electricity and transmission rate cases, RTO/ISO issues, trading compliance in electricity and natural gas markets. Represents clients before the FERC, state public utility commissions, DOE, CFTC, and federal and state courts.
**Professional Memberships:** District of Columbia Bar, Virginia State Bar.
**Career:** Partner since 2008, Hiring Partner of Washington office (2012-).
**Personal:** JD, University of Chicago Law School, 1999; Editor-in-chief, Chicago Legal Forum; BA, magna cum laude with university honors, Brigham Young University, 1996.

**BARRY, Dennis M**
King & Spalding LLP, Washington, DC
202 626 2959
dbarry@kslaw.com
*Featured in Healthcare (Nationwide), Healthcare (District of Columbia)*
**Practice Areas:** Healthcare, medicare and medicaid, compliance.
**Professional Memberships:** American Health Lawyers Association (AHLA), past-Chair, Medicare and Medicaid Institute, Member Board of Directors; Healthcare Financial Management Association (HFMA).
**Career:** Ohio Wesleyan University, BA Economics, 1972 (Phi Beta Kappa); University of Virginia School of Law, JD, 1975 (co-editor, 'Virginia Journal of International Law').
**Publications:** Dennis Barry's reimbursement advisor, monthly newsletter published by Aspen Publishers; cost reimbursement (AHLA Health Law Practice Guide), Chpt 15 (West 2004); Legal Issues Surrounding Hospital and Physician Relationships, Health Care Fraud and Abuse: Practical Perspectives (ABA & BNA 2007).

**BARSHAY, Lawrence N**
Fried, Frank, Harris, Shriver & Jacobson LLP, New York
212 859 8551
Lawrence.Barshay@FriedFrank.com
*Featured in Investment Funds (Nationwide)*
**Practice Areas:** Corporate partner, head of the Firm's asset management group. Has a diversified transactional corporate practice, specializing in the structuring and representation of investment funds and other alternative investments. Extensive experience in private equity transactions and M&A. Represents a broad range of clients in the asset management sector, including Goldman Sachs Asset Management; Morgan Stanley; EJF Capital; Bank of New York Mellon Asset Management; JP Morgan Asset Management; Neuberger Berman; Blackrock Asset Management; Citadel Alternative Asset Management.
**Career:** Joined in 1991; became partner in 1999.
**Personal:** JD, New York University School of Law (1991); BA, Columbia College (1988).

**BARSHEFSKY, Charlene**
WilmerHale, Washington, DC
202 663 6130
charlene.barshefsky@wilmerhale.com
*Featured in International Trade (Nationwide)*
**Practice Areas:** Chair, International Trade Practice; Senior International Partner. Practice centers on international business transactions, the structuring and negotiation of commercial agreements and the removal of trade and regulatory impediments to exporting to or investing in markets throughout Asia, Europe and Latin America.
**Professional Memberships:** Member, Council on Foreign Relations; member, American Academy of Diplomacy; member the Trilateral Commission; Boards of Directors of American Express Company, The Estee Lauder Companies Inc., Intel Corporation, and Starwood Hotels & Resorts Worldwide, Inc.; Trustee, Howard Hughes Medical Institute.

**Personal:** Catholic University, Columbus School of Law (JD 1975); University of Wisconsin, 1972.

**BART, Susan T**
Sidley Austin LLP, Chicago
312 853 2075
sbart@sidley.com
*Featured in Wealth Management (Nationwide)*
**Practice Areas:** Partner in Sidley's Chicago office practicing in Private Clients, Trusts and Estates. Regent and Illinois State Chair of The American College of Trust and Estate Counsel. Practice includes estate planning, trust and estate administration, charitable planning and fiduciary counsel. She writes and speaks extensively, and has taught at the University of Michigan Law School. Clients include wealthy individuals/families, family business owners, banks and trust companies, and fiduciaries.
**Personal:** University of Michigan Law School, JD, 1985, magna cum laude, Order of the Coif; Grinnell College, BA, 1982, with honors, Phi Beta Kappa.

**BARTFELD, Daniel D**
Milbank, Tweed, Hadley & McCloy LLP, New York
212 530 5185
dbartfeld@milbank.com
*Featured in Latin American Investment (New York), Projects (Nationwide)*
See under New York for profile.

**BARTH, Giselle**
Sidley Austin LLP, New York
212 839 6749
gbarth@sidley.com
*Featured in Capital Markets (Nationwide)*
**Practice Areas:** A partner in the New York office, Ms Barth focuses on general corporate law with a primary emphasis on structured finance. Her structured finance practice includes registered and private term asset-backed securitizations in traditional asset classes such as ABS and mortgage-backed securities as well as CDOs and CLOs. She represents clients on a variety of asset-based lending arrangements, including repurchase agreements, and regularly advises clients on compliance with respect to new and proposed legislation and regulations.
**Personal:** University of California at Los Angeles School of Law, JD, 1996; University of California - Berkeley, BA, 1992.

**BARTLETT, Maurine R**
Cadwalader, Wickersham & Taft LLP, New York
212 504 6218
maurine.bartlett@cwt.com
*Featured in Financial Services Regulation (Nationwide)*
**Practice Areas:** Concentrates in financial services law with emphasis on securities and bank regulatory matters. Provides regulatory advice to broker-dealers, derivatives dealers, hedge funds and investment advisors. Drafts policies and procedures to comply with legal and regulatory requirements. Addresses issues arising under federal securities laws and regulations and FINRA rules. Assists with NYSE, FINRA and SEC enforcement

proceedings, internal compliance reviews, and applications to the Federal Reserve Board. Provides expert witness services in connection with broker-dealer arbitrations involving margin rules and assistance with formation of SEC-registered broker-dealers and investment advisers.
**Publications:** Author, chapter on Glass-Steagall Act and Regulation D, "The Securitization of Financial Assets;" co-author, chapter on asset-backed securities, "The Handbook of Asset-Backed Securities;" co-author, chapter on "Regulation of the Commodities Futures and Options Markets."
**Personal:** JD, Georgetown University Law Center (magna cum laude; Editor, Georgetown Law Journal; Co-Chair, Barristers' Council); BS, University of Michigan (high distinction, Phi Beta Kappa).

**BASILE, Edward**
King & Spalding LLP, Washington, DC
202 626 2903
EBasile@kslaw.com
*Featured in Life Sciences (Nationwide), Healthcare (District of Columbia)*
See under District of Columbia for profile.

**BASON JR, George R**
Davis Polk & Wardwell LLP, New York
212 450 4340
george.bason@davispolk.com
*Featured in Private Equity (Nationwide), Financial Services Regulation (Nationwide), Corporate/M&A (New York)*
**Practice Areas:** Global co-head of Davis Polk's M&A Department. Concentrates primarily in mergers, acquisitions and joint ventures. Has experience in cross-border transactions, restructurings, takeover defenses and corporate governance issues, as well as in providing general corporate and securities law advice. Transactions he has worked on include ExxonMobil's acquisition of XTO Energy; Citigroup's capital realignment program in 2009; CNOOC's proposed $15.1 billion acquisition of Nexen; PepsiCo's $3.8 billion acquisition of Wimm-Bill-Dann and its $7.8 billion acquisition of its two largest anchor bottlers; Gillette's acquisition by Procter & Gamble; Exxon's $81 billion merger with Mobil; management's attempted leveraged buyout of RJR Nabisco.

**BASS, Fred**
Holland & Knight LLP, New York
212 513 3543
Fred.Bass@hklaw.com
*Featured in Transportation (Nationwide), Banking & Finance (Nationwide)*
**Career:** Fred Bass focuses on the representation of lessors, lenders, lessees and borrowers in a wide range of asset-based financings and leasing of aircraft, railcars, renewable energy facilities (solar and wind). satellites, vessels, manufacturing plants and infrastructure assets, as well as a variety of commercial lending, structured finance and cross-border transactions. He has extensive experience in aviation finance transactions, including secured loans, operating and leveraged leases, export credit agency supported financings, purchases and sales

of new and used aircraft, EETC transactions, pre-delivery deposit facilities, transactions with credit and residual support arrangements, and bankruptcy and non-bankruptcy workouts and restructurings.

## BASS, Scott
Sidley Austin LLP, Washington, DC
202 736 8684
sbass@sidley.com
*Featured in Life Sciences (Nationwide), Healthcare (District of Columbia)*
**Practice Areas:** Partner and head of Sidley's Global Life Sciences Team. Experience includes coordinating pharmaceutical, medical device, food and dietary supplement matters in the United States, Europe and Asia. He is ranked internationally among the top authorities on FDA-related enforcement and regulatory issues, and has led audits and investigations involving off-label promotion, pharmacovigilance, PDMA, GMP, and fraud and abuse issues, as well as DEA and FTC matters.
**Personal:** The University of Michigan Law School, JD, 1975, cum laude; New York University, BA, 1972. Admissions: New York, District of Columbia.

## BASSECHES, Robert T
Goodwin Procter LLP, Washington, DC
202 346 4201
rbasseches@goodwinprocter.com
*Featured in Transportation (Nationwide)*
**Practice Areas:** Mr Basseches specializes in the areas of maritime transportation and administrative litigation. He represents carriers, terminals and other maritime interests before the federal maritime agencies and in court. Mr Basseches is a past-president of the Maritime Administrative Bar Association and a past-chair of the American Bar Association Maritime Transport Subcommittee.
**Personal:** LLB, Yale Law School, 1958 (cum laude); BA, Amherst College, 1955 (magna cum laude).

## BASSETT, W Randall
King & Spalding LLP, Atlanta
404 572 3514
rbassett@kslaw.com
*Featured in Products Liability (Nationwide)*
**Practice Areas:** He has over 20 years experience representing foreign and domestic manufacturers in high exposure product liability cases. He has represented product manufacturers such as Brown & Williamson Tobacco Corporation, Brown-Forman Corporation, General Motors, Purdue Pharma LP, Sofamor Danek, and Subaru in the federal and state courts throughout the Southeast and Southwest. He has argued cases in the federal circuit court of appeals for the Fourth, Sixth, and Eleventh Circuits, and has appeared in the appellate courts of Alabama, Florida, Georgia, North Carolina, and Tennessee.
**Personal:** BS, The Citadel, JD, cum laude, University of Georgia.

## BASTA, Paul M
Kirkland & Ellis LLP, New York
212 446 4750
paul.basta@kirkland.com
*Featured in Bankruptcy/Restructuring (Nationwide), Bankruptcy/Restructuring (New York)*
**Practice Areas:** Paul Basta is a partner in Kirkland's Restructuring Group. He represents debtors in Chapter 11 cases, including A&P Supermarkets, MSR Resorts, Charter Communications, Hawaiian Telcom, Reader's Digest and Global Crossing. He provides restructuring advice to numerous private equity funds, including Silverpeak, and often represents creditors, including Six Flags, Mirant and HealthSouth. Paul was named an Outstanding Restructuring Lawyer by Turnarounds & Workouts and one of the 40 Young Rising Stars in New York by Crain's New York Business.
**Personal:** George Washington University Law School, JD, 1992; University of Michigan, BA, 1988.

## BATEMAN, Thomas
Andrews Kurth LLP, Houston
713 220 4270
tbateman@andrewskurth.com
*Featured in Energy & Natural Resources (Nationwide)*
**Practice Areas:** Tom has broad experience in the foreign and domestic upstream, midstream and downstream sectors of the oil and gas industry. His areas of practice include asset and entity acquisitions and energy finance. He is on the Advisory Board for the Institute for Energy Law and was the Co-Chairman of the AIPN Term Sheet Committee.

## BAUMGARDNER, John E
Sullivan & Cromwell LLP, New York
212 558 3866
baumgardnerj@sullcrom.com
*Featured in Investment Funds (Nationwide)*
**Practice Areas:**
**Professional Memberships:** American Bar Association; New York State Bar Association; Former Chair, NYCBA's Investment Management Regulation Committee, and Chair, Investment Committee; Member, Yale School of Music Board of Visitors; Panelist, PLI and Investment Company Institute.
**Career:** Partner since 1983. Corporate/securities matters. Coordinator, Investment Management Group. Member, Financial Institutions, and Alternative Investment Management Groups. Represents funds, advisers or independent directors of US-registered investment companies, including JPMorgan and those sponsored by Fidelity, Pioneer and General American Investors. Has represented private funds and US broker-dealers.
**Personal:** Columbia Law School (JD, 1975); Princeton University (AB, summa cum laude, 1973).

## BAYMAN, Andrew T
King & Spalding LLP, Atlanta
404 572 3583
abayman@kslaw.com
*Featured in Products Liability (Nationwide)*
**Practice Areas:** Bayman is the leader of the firm's Tort and Environmental Litigation Practice. The group, with over 300 lawyers in five offices, is one of the largest practice groups of its kind in the US and is devoted exclusively to defending tort litigation. He is based in Atlanta, and his practice focuses on representation of pharmaceutical, medical device and automotive manufacturers in product liability cases.
**Personal:** Received his JD from Vanderbilt University School of Law where he was a Patrick Wilson Scholar and a member of the Vanderbilt Law Review.

## BEAN, Lori Ann
Clifford Chance US LLP, Washington, DC
202 912 5014
lori.bean@cliffordchance.com
*Featured in Projects (Nationwide)*
**Practice Areas:** Focuses on project finance, representing export credit agencies, multilateral development institutions and other international financial institutions and commercial lenders. Has structured, drafted and negotiated all aspects of the financing for various infrastructure projects. Has particular expertise in airport, energy and petrochemical projects and has played a leading role in many infrastructure projects located in the Americas, Africa, Asia, the Middle East and Europe.
**Career:** Partner at Clifford Chance since 2006. Cornell Law School, JD cum laude, with a specialization in international legal affairs, 1994. Admitted in the District of Columbia, New York and Maryland.

## BEARD, James
DLA Piper LLP (US), Chicago
312 368 2169
james.beard@dlapiper.com
*Featured in Real Estate (Nationwide), Real Estate (Illinois)*
See under Illinois for profile.

## BEATTIE, Richard I
Simpson Thacher & Bartlett LLP, New York
212 455 2635
rbeattie@stblaw.com
*Featured in Private Equity (Nationwide), Corporate/M&A (New York)*
**Practice Areas:** Senior Chairman of the firm. Focuses on governance issues, M&A, LBOs, corporate law and finance. Participated in the mergers of America Online with Time Warner, Wellpoint Health Networks with Anthem, Inc. and JP Morgan Chase & Co.'s $58 billion acquisition of Bank One Corporation.
**Career:** Joined the Firm in 1968. Former General Counsel of Department of Health, Education and Welfare; Director of the Transition and Counsel to the Secretary of Education (1980). Served on the New York City Board of Education. President Clinton's Emissary for Cyprus (1996-97).

**Personal:** BA, Dartmouth College (1961); LLB, University of Pennsylvania Law School (1968). Prior to law school, served four years in the Marine Corps as a jet pilot.

## BEATY, John B
Venable LLP, Washington, DC
202 344 4859
jbeaty@Venable.com
*Featured in Financial Services Regulation (Nationwide)*
**Practice Areas:** Banking and financial services regulation
**Professional Memberships:** Exchequer Club; Women in Housing and Finance; ABA Business Section Banking Law Committee
**Career:** Strategic advice regarding legal and regulatory developments, including Dodd-Frank and Basel capital and liquidity standards; assisting on corporate restructurings, new financial products, mergers and conversions; advising officers and directors regarding risks and opportunities. Previously General Counsel to First American Bank; Assistant GC at FDIC and RTC Professional Liability Section; Assistant GC of FHLBB.
**Publications:** ALI-CLE: Capital in the Bank, July 16, 2012
**Personal:** JD, University of Chicago, 1978; B.S., with highest honors, Michigan State University, 1975.

## BECKER, Daniel
Dechert LLP, Silicon Valley
650 813 4874
daniel.becker@dechert.com
*Featured in Life Sciences (Nationwide)*
**Practice Areas:** Dr Becker handles all aspects of patent counseling in the life sciences area, including patent portfolio development, life cycle management, transactional and financial IP due diligence. He also has substantial foreign patent experience, including prosecution in a wide variety of jurisdictions.
**Professional Memberships:** Member, California Bar; admitted to practice before the US Patent and Trademark Office and the US Court of Appeals for the Federal Circuit.
**Personal:** Harvard College (AB, 1980, magna cum laude); Stanford University School of Medicine (M.D. with research honors, 1987); Postdoctoral research, Wistar Institute and MIT; Stanford Law School (JD, 1995).

## BECKER, David M
Cleary Gottlieb Steen & Hamilton LLP, Washington, DC
202 974 1530
dbecker@cgsh.com
*Featured in Securities (Nationwide)*
**Practice Areas:** securities regulation, corporate governance, securities enforcement, and internal investigations. Represents companies, boards of directors and senior officers in the US and abroad on regulatory issues and potential liabilities under US securities laws.
**Professional Memberships:** Member of the Bars in New York and District of Columbia.
**Career:** General Counsel of US Securities and Exchange Commission (2002-2002 and 2009-

2011); Deputy General Counsel, SEC (1998-1999); Joined firm as partner, 2002; JD, Columbia University School of Law (1973); AB, Columbia College (1968); Law clerk, Judge Harold Leventhal, US Court of Appeals, D.C.(1973-1974), Judge Stanley Reed (retired), US Supreme Court (1974-1975).

### BECKER, Stephan E
Pillsbury Winthrop Shaw Pittman LLP, Washington, DC
202 663 8277
stephan.becker@pillsburylaw.com
*Featured in International Trade (Nationwide)*
**Practice Areas:** Practice focused on government regulation of international trade and investment, international trade agreements and public international law. Advises and represents clients in matters involving export controls and embargoes, customs law compliance, trade remedy proceedings such as anti-dumping investigations, international investment arbitrations under the NAFTA and bilateral investment treaties, dispute settlement under the World Trade Organization agreements, national security reviews by the Committee on Foreign Investment in the United States, and compliance with the Foreign Corrupt Practices Act.
**Professional Memberships:** DC Bar, ABA.
**Publications:** Regular author/presenter on international trade topics.
**Personal:** BA, Yale University,1979; JD, Columbia University, 1982.

### BECKETT, Mark
Chadbourne & Parke LLP, New York
212 408-5226
mbeckett@chadbourne.com
*Featured in International Arbitration (Nationwide)*
**Practice Areas:** Mark Beckett is the co-head of the Firm's International Arbitration Group. He specializes in international commercial arbitration and international investment arbitration, as well as corporate social responsibility and Alien Tort Statute / Torture Victim Protection Act claims. His practice focuses on the resolution of disputes relating to project construction, long-term purchase agreements, complex commercial, acquisition and joint venture disputes, and those involving demand guarantees, corporate guarantees and state undertakings. Mr Beckett arbitrates disputes involving the expropriation of assets by sovereigns giving rise to state responsibility under international law.
**Personal:** JD, Rutgers University School of Law; BA, Drew University.

### BECKWITH, Van
Baker Botts LLP, Dallas
214 953 6505
van.beckwith@bakerbotts.com
*Featured in Food & Beverages (Nationwide)*
**Practice Areas:** National litigation practice focusing on consumer products, class actions and MDL's, commercial, energy and environmental litigation. Served as national counsel in variety of US and cross-border (US and Canada) class actions. Defense of food and beverage consumer and advocate group class actions claims regarding food and beverage labeling and consumer protection. Experience includes media-intensive and bet-the-company claims. Tried lawsuits to verdict in state and federal courts and arbitration panels throughout the country.
**Career:** 20+ years of practice. Firmwide Partner-In-Charge: Recruiting (2012-).
**Personal:** JD, cum laude, Order of Coif, Southern Methodist University, 1990; BBA, finance, University of Texas, 1987.

### BÉDARD, Julie
Skadden, Arps, Slate, Meagher & Flom LLP & Affiliates, New York
212 735 3236
Julie.Bedard@skadden.com
*Featured in International Arbitration (Nationwide)*
**Practice Areas:** Speaks English, French, Spanish, Romanian and Portuguese. Concentrates practice on international litigation and arbitration. Advises international companies on dispute resolution strategy in cross-border transactions and represents clients in complex domestic and international commercial litigations. Serves as counsel and arbitrator in international arbitration proceedings held under the auspices of the ICC, ICDR, UNCITRAL and ICSID in high-stakes commercial and investment disputes.
**Career:** JSD, Columbia University School of Law, 2006 (doctorate in conflicts of laws); LLM, Columbia University School of Law, 2001; LL.B, McGill University Faculty of Law (common law), 1996; BCL, McGill University Faculty of Law (civil law), 1996.

### BEISNER, John H
Skadden, Arps, Slate, Meagher & Flom LLP & Affiliates, Washington, DC
202 371 7410
John.Beisner@skadden.com
*Featured in Products Liability (Nationwide)*
**Practice Areas:** Co-Head of Skadden's Mass Torts and Insurance Litigation Group. Focuses on the defense of purported class actions, mass torts and other complex civil litigation in both federal and state courts. Regularly handles appellate litigations and has appeared in matters before the US Supreme Court. Has defended major US and international corporations in more than 600 purported class actions filed in federal courts and in the courts of 40 states at both trial and appellate levels. Has advised on numerous high-visibility corporate crisis situations.
**Career:** JD, University of Michigan, 1978 (with honors); BA, University of Kansas, 1975 (with honors).

### BELANGER, Richard M
Sidley Austin LLP, Washington, DC
202 736 8335
rbelanger@sidley.com
·*Featured in International Trade (Nationwide)*
**Practice Areas:** Senior Counsel in Sidley's Washington, DC office. He advises companies, industry associations, and governments on international trade issues, particularly customs, export controls, trade remedies, trade policy and related legislation. His practice extends to counseling, administrative proceedings, litigation, and legisla-tive activities. Mr Belanger has developed and helped to implement import/export compliance programs for major multinational companies from a wide range of industry sectors, including heavy equipment, pharmaceuticals, electronics, steel, food products, footwear and apparel.
**Personal:** Boston University School of Law, JD, 1975; University of New Hampshire, BA, 1971. Admissions: District of Columbia, Massachusetts.

### BELKIN, Jeffrey A
Alston & Bird LLP, Atlanta
404 881 7388
jeff.belkin@alston.com
*Featured in Government (Nationwide)*
**Practice Areas:** Co-chair, firm's Construction & Government Contracts Group. Represents contractors and subcontractors in negotiations of prime and subcontracts and in GAO, Board and COFC protests and claims. Advises and defends in internal and FCA investigations and claims by DOJ, IGs, GAO and other federal agencies, with substantial experience in billing, ethics, domestic sourcing, construction and small business issues. On FAR Committee of AGC Federal and Heavy Division, and member of Law360 Government Contracts Advisory Board.
**Career:** Former lead trial and appellate attorney with Commercial Litigation Branch of the DOJ.
**Personal:** JD (1995) University of Virginia; BA (1992) Duke University.

### BELKNAP JR, Thomas H
Blank Rome LLP, New York
212 885 5270
TBelknap@BlankRome.com
*Featured in Transportation (Nationwide)*
**Practice Areas:** Thomas Belknap concentrates his practice in the areas of international commercial and insurance litigation and arbitration, with particular emphasis on the maritime industry. He has been involved in a wide variety of domestic and international maritime, commercial and insurance matters, including: international and domestic commercial contract disputes; marine casualty and collision cases; vessel limitation of liability actions; marine insurance disputes; charterparty disputes; COGSA and multi-modal cargo damage claims; maritime commercial and "treasure" salvage and general average disputes; maritime attachment and vessel arrest actions; and recognition and enforcement of foreign arbitration awards and judgments. For more information: www.BlankRome.com/TBelknap.

### BELL, Crayton L
King & Spalding LLP, New York
212 556 2112
cbell@kslaw.com
*Featured in Energy & Natural Resources (Nationwide)*
**Practice Areas:** Has significant experience advising clients on a wide range of corporate transactions, with a particular focus in the energy sector, including cash and stock mergers and acquisitions, leveraged buyouts and other private equity transactions, corporate reorganizations, joint ventures and strategic alliances. Experience includes transactions throughout the US, Latin America, Europe and the Middle East.
**Professional Memberships:** New York State Bar Association; American Bar Association.
**Personal:** JD, Fordham Law School; MA, Vanderbilt University; BA, University of the South.

### BELL, Jerry
Fulbright & Jaworski LLP, Austin
512 536 4596
jbell@fulbright.com
*Featured in Healthcare (Texas), Healthcare (Nationwide)*
See under Texas for profile.

### BELL, Thomas
Simpson Thacher & Bartlett LLP, New York
Tel+1 212 455 2533
tbell@stblaw.com
*Featured in Investment Funds (Nationwide)*
**Practice Areas:** Partner specializing in investment management. Oversees firm's private funds practice. Advises clients globally on private equity funds, real estate funds, hedge funds, and similar funds. Representative clients: Aquiline, Calera Capital, CapGen Financial, The Carlyle Group, Ferrer Freeman, The J E Robert Companies, J C Flowers & Co., Macquarie, Morgan Stanley, New Mountain Capital, The Sentient Group and Sterling Investment Partners.
**Professional Memberships:** Founder, past Co-Chair annual International Conference on Private Investment Funds.
**Career:** Joined, 1983; Partner, 1992.
**Personal:** Yale Law School (JD 1983); New College, Oxford University (MA 1980); Dartmouth College (BA, summa cum laude, 1978).

### BELLAH MAGUIRE, Jennifer
Gibson, Dunn & Crutcher LLP, Los Angeles
213 229 7986
jbellah@gibsondunn.com
*Featured in Private Equity (Nationwide), Corporate/M&A (California), Corporate/M&A (Southern California)*
See under California for profile.

### BELLER, Alan
Cleary Gottlieb Steen & Hamilton LLP, New York
212 225 2450
abeller@cgsh.com
*Featured in Capital Markets (Nationwide), Securities (Nationwide)*
**Practice Areas:** Advises on complex disclosure, corporate governance, transactional and other securities and corporate matters. Leading clients include Citigroup, Credit Suisse, Deutsche Bank, Activision and Federal Reserve Bank of New York. Expert on Sarbanes-Oxley, legal issues relating to accounting, Board responsibilities and securities offering reform.
**Career:** Joined firm, 1976; rejoined firm, 2006. Director, Division of Corporation Finance of the SEC and Senior Counselor to the Commission, 2002 to 2006, where he led the most extensive reforms in Corporation Finance history. Member, Board of Directors (Audit and Risk Committees),

Travelers Companies, Inc. Outside Expert, Financial Reform Working Group, Group of 30.

## BEN-AMI, Leora
Kirkland & Ellis LLP, New York
212 446 5943
leora.benami@kirkland.com

*Featured in Life Sciences (Nationwide), Intellectual Property (New York)*

**Practice Areas:** Focuses on biotechnology, medical devices, pharmaceuticals and chemistry. Tried many jury trials as lead counsel and extensive appellate experience.

**Professional Memberships:** Board member of the New York Intellectual Property Association; Faculty/Participant for the Sedona Conference for Patent Litigation (2011-2012); Federal Circuit Bar Association; American Intellectual Property Law Association.

**Career:** Formerly Chair of the Americas IP Group at Clifford Chance, former Chair of IP Practice at Kaye Scholer.

**Personal:** JD (cum laude), SUNY Buffalo; BS, SUNY Stony Brook; law clerk to Senior Circuit Judge Philip Nichols, Jr, US Court of Appeals for the Federal Circuit.

## BENEDICT, James
Milbank, Tweed, Hadley & McCloy LLP, New York
212 530 5696
jbenedict@milbank.com

*Featured in Securities (Nationwide), Litigation (New York)*

See under New York for profile.

## BENFORD, Norman J
Greenberg Traurig, LLP, Miami
305 579 0660
BenfordN@gtlaw.com

*Featured in Wealth Management (Nationwide), Tax (Florida)*

See under Florida for profile.

## BEN-JACOB, Michael
Kaye Scholer LLP, New York
212 836 8310
michael.ben-jacob@kayescholer.com

*Featured in Wealth Management (Nationwide)*

**Practice Areas:** Michael Ben-Jacob's practice focuses on counseling high net-worth individuals, their families, family offices and closely held businesses on an array of US-based and cross-border wealth planning and preservation matters. In addition to a strong US-based practice, he assists numerous international families and corporate fiduciaries with connections to Israel, UK, Italy, France, Switzerland, Brazil, the US Virgin Islands, and numerous other jurisdictions in dealing with a host of strategic planning issues.

## BENNETT, Bruce S
Jones Day, Los Angeles
213 243 2382
bbennett@jonesday.com

*Featured in Bankruptcy/Restructuring (California), Bankruptcy/Restructuring (Nationwide)*

**Practice Areas:** Mr Bennett has represented debtors, creditors and business acquirers in many of the largest corporate reorganization cases in the United States. Recently, Mr Bennett represented

the Los Angeles Dodgers in its chapter 11 reorganization case and sale to Guggenheim Baseball Partners and the largest lender group in the Tribune bankruptcy cases, and he currently represents the largest lender group in the MF Global cases. Mr Bennett was also lead debtor's counsel in the country's largest municipal bankruptcy, In re County of Orange, California, which commenced following a $1.7 billion loss in County's investment pools.

## BENUDIZ, P Peter
Milbank, Tweed, Hadley & McCloy LLP, Los Angeles
213 892 4414
pbenudiz@milbank.com

*Featured in Leisure & Hospitality (Nationwide), Real Estate (California)*

**Practice Areas:** Partner and co-leader of the Gaming and Hospitality Group. Mr Benudiz advises global hospitality companies, investment banks, private equity and hedge funds and their CEOs and boards, as well as investors on their most sensitive strategic and structuring issues. Notable engagements include representation of Lehman Brothers Official Creditors' Committee on all real estate and hospitality assets worldwide following Lehman's Chapter 11 filing, the purchase of the Plaza Hotel in NYC, the recapitalization of the Beverly Hilton, and representation of the senior-secured lender of the World Trade Center on the loan restructuring negotiations and insurance claims relating to 9/11.

## BERG, Eric L
White & Case LLP, New York
212 819 8253
eberg@whitecase.com

*Featured in Banking & Finance (Nationwide)*

**Career:** Eric Berg is head of White & Case's Global Banking Practice and formerly served as a member of the Firm's Management Board. His legal practice covers a broad range of finance matters, with a particular focus on the representation of lenders, sponsors and corporate borrowers in domestic and international leveraged finance transactions. He also regularly leads asset-based financings as well as investment and near-investment-grade financings and has handled a wide variety of workout and restructuring transactions. Eric has extensive experience in hostile takeovers as well as negotiated public and private acquisitions and recapitalizations. To view his biography, please visit www.whitecase.com/eberg.

## BERGDOLT, Robert H
DLA Piper LLP (US), Raleigh
919 786 2002
robert.bergdolt@dlapiper.com

*Featured in Capital Markets (Nationwide)*

**Practice Areas:** Corporate, Securities, Capital Markets.

**Career:** He leads the firm's representation of non-traded, publicly offered real estate investment trusts. His practice focuses on securities regulations, corporate governance and mergers and acquisitions for traded and non-traded REITs and is a frequent speaker at conferences focused on the

REIT industry. He serves as managing partner of the firm's Raleigh office.

**Personal:** JD, Yale Law School; AB, Duke University (magna cum laude).

## BERGER, Max W
Bernstein Litowitz Berger & Grossmann LLP, New York
212 554 1400
mwb@blbglaw.com

*Featured in Securities (Nationwide), Litigation (New York)*

See under New York for profile.

## BERINGER, Ashlie
Gibson, Dunn & Crutcher LLP, Palo Alto
650.849.5219
aberinger@gibsondunn.com

*Featured in Privacy & Data Security (Nationwide)*

**Practice Areas:** Extensive experience in defense of class action and regulatory matters involving online and mobile privacy and technology. Defends technology companies in high-stakes FTC, Congressional and attorney general investigations and actions involving data privacy issues. Has obtained several key rulings dismissing claims in privacy and Internet-related class actions. Advises clients in online publishing, social media, mobile and online advertising and data analytics sectors on implementation of privacy and security policies and practices.

**Career:** Co-Chair, Firm's Information Technology and Data Privacy Practice.

**Personal:** JD, Yale University, 1996; BA, University of California - Los Angeles, 1992.

## BERKE, Barry H
Kramer Levin Naftalis & Frankel LLP, New York
212 715 7560
bberke@kramerlevin.com

*Featured in Litigation (Nationwide), Litigation (New York)*

**Practice Areas:** Mr Berke is Co-Chair of Kramer Levin's White-Collar Defense and SEC Regulatory Practice and a Fellow of the American College of Trial Lawyers. He has represented clients in many sensitive and high profile investigations and proceedings involving all aspects of white-collar crime, and has tried dozens of cases before juries and judges. Mr Berke also has represented prominent corporations and individuals in class action and other complex litigation.

**Professional Memberships:** Fellow, American College of Trial Lawyers; Board of Directors, Federal Defenders of NY; NY Council of Defense Lawyers; American Bar Association.

**Career:** American Lawyer's 'Young Litigators Fab Fifty'; Best Lawyers in America; Super Lawyer's 'Top 10 Lawyers in NY'; The National Law Journal 'Five Winning Trial Attorneys for 2011'; Law360's 2011 MVP list; Legal 500 US; Lawdragon 3000; Benchmark Litigation.

**Publications:** Co-author, The Practice of Federal Criminal Law: Prosecution and Defense (2006 Thomson/West); co-author, Managing White Collar Legal Issues: Leading Lawyers on Key Defense Strategies (2008 Aspatore Books).

**Personal:** Chairman, Coalition for the Homeless.

## BERKELEY, Jill B
Neal, Gerber & Eisenberg LLP, Chicago
312 269 8024
jberkeley@ngelaw.com

*Featured in Insurance (Nationwide), Insurance (Illinois)*

See under Illinois for profile.

## BERMAN, Brad L
Holland & Knight LLP, New York
212 513 3371
brad.berman@hklaw.com

*Featured in Transportation (Nationwide)*

**Career:** Brad L Berman has extensive experience in maritime related corporate finance, restructurings and workouts and capital markets transactions, offshore incorporation and the laws of Liberia and the Marshall Island. He previously served as director of the Liberian International Ship and Corporate Registry, the world's second largest ship registry and a 60-plus-year-old corporate registry. He regularly advises ship owners, operators, investors and lenders on corporate ownership structures, financing arrangements and vessel registration.

**Publications:** "The Challenges of Modern Piracy," Shipping International Monthly, October 2012; "The Distressed Shipping Market Attracts Private Equity," Co-Author, Law Journal Network's Equipment Leasing Newsletter, July 2012.

## BERMAN, Stan
Sidley Austin LLP, Washington, DC
206 262 7681
sberman@sidley.com

*Featured in Energy & Natural Resources (Nationwide)*

**Practice Areas:** Partner in Sidley's Washington, DC office. Represents electric utilities and other electric industry participants in complex high-stakes litigation and appeals at FERC, state regulatory commissions, and in the courts. Winning lead counsel in a recent multi-month, multi-billion dollar FERC trial. Provides advice on electric market operation, electric transmission issues, mergers and acquisitions, enforcement and reliability issues, and other electric industry regulatory issues. Former leader of FERC Office of Hydroelectric and Electric Litigation.

**Personal:** Columbia University School of Law, JD, 1988, Harlan Fiske Stone Scholar; California Institute of Technology, BS, 1985, Physics, Honors.

## BERNSTEIN, Donald S
Davis Polk & Wardwell LLP, New York
212 450 4000
donald.bernstein@davispolk.com

*Featured in Bankruptcy/Restructuring (Nationwide), Bankruptcy/Restructuring (New York)*

**Practice Areas:** Partner, Davis Polk & Wardwell. Represents debtors, creditors, receivers and acquirers in restructurings and insolvencies and financial institutions regarding risk and resolution planning. Recent matters include restructurings of Ford, Ambac, Syncora; bankruptcies of Delphi, Tribune, Lehman, C-BASS, Refco, Enron, Conseco, Adelphia, Bethlehem Steel, Polaroid,

McLeodUSA, Dow Corning, Crown Paper and Toshoku America.
**Professional Memberships:** Commissioner, ABI Chapter 11 Reform Commission. Past Director, International Insolvency Institute, American College of Bankruptcy. Past Chair, National Bankruptcy Conference, NYC Bar Association Bankruptcy Committee. Past Treasurer, NYC Bar Association. Board of Editors, 'Collier on Bankruptcy'.
**Personal:** Princeton (AB) and University of Chicago (JD).

### BERNSTEIN, Glen S
Morgan, Lewis & Bockius LLP, Washington, DC
202 739 5994
gbernstein@morganlewis.com
*Featured in Energy & Natural Resources (Nationwide)*
**Practice Areas:** Glen S. Bernstein advises clients on energy policy and regulatory matters. He represents clients in a variety of federal and state proceedings regarding electric utility regulation and deregulation, with emphasis on transmission and interconnection access, transmission planning, electricity markets, and compliance. He also represents clients regarding development of new structures for provision of transmission services and new market mechanisms. He has served as a trial lawyer in federal courts, at the Federal Energy Regulatory Commission, and in state proceedings and has defended companies in enforcement actions. Mr Bernstein also regularly advises clients in all phases of energy transactions.

### BERNSTEIN, Jay L
Clifford Chance US LLP, New York
212 878 8527
jay.bernstein@cliffordchance.com
*Featured in Capital Markets (Nationwide)*
**Practice Areas:** Co-Chair of Clifford Chance's US Capital Markets Practice. Represents sponsors, investors, investment banks, REITs and other real estate, finance and hotel companies in capital raising and merger and acquisition activities in the US and international markets. Since 1997, Mr Bernstein has participated in more than US$25 billion of capital raising and mergers and acquisitions transactions involving real estate, finance and hotel companies in and outside of the US. These transactions include a variety of IPO transactions, public and private offerings of equity and debt securities, strategic investments and mergers and acquisitions.
**Career:** Partner at Clifford Chance since 1995.

### BERNSTEIN, Stephen W
McDermott Will & Emery LLP, Boston
617 535 4062
sbernstein@mwe.com
*Featured in Healthcare (Massachusetts), Healthcare (Nationwide)*
See under Massachusetts for profile.

### BESHAR, Sarah
Davis Polk & Wardwell LLP, New York
212 450 4000
sarah.beshar@davispolk.com
*Featured in Capital Markets (Nationwide)*
**Practice Areas:** Member of Davis Polk's Corporate Department and represents clients in equity, debt and other securities offerings, and advises on corporate governance and general securities and disclosure issues. She has taken a leading role in the initial public offerings and other financing transactions on behalf of many companies, including the $23.1 billion intial public offering of General Motors – the largest IPO in history. Also, has represented investment banks in a variety of roles, including capital markets and structured products transactions and general compliance matters. Advises companies on governance and general corporate issues.

### BEYER, David
Quarles & Brady LLP, Tampa
813 387 0264
david.beyer@quarles.com
*Featured in Franchising (Nationwide)*
**Practice Areas:** Franchise, distribution, licensing and alternative methods of distribution; mergers and acquisitions; general corporate services.
**Professional Memberships:** American Bar Association Forum on Franchising; International Franchise Association; The Florida Bar.
**Career:** Counsels clients in a wide variety of industries on virtually all aspects of franchising, distribution and other aspects of business expansion, including mergers and acquisitions.
**Publications:** Frequent author and speaker for ABA Franchise Forum, and IFA publications, seminars and symposia; and others.
**Personal:** Vanderbilt University (JD, 1982); Tulane University (MBA 1978, BA 1978).

### BIAGINI, Ray
McKenna Long & Aldridge LLP, Washington, DC
202 496 7687
rbiagini@mckennalong.com
*Featured in Government (Nationwide)*
**Career:** Raymond Biagini is widely recognized for his expertise in defending "contractors on the battlefield," establishing ground-breaking legal principles at the federal appellate level which immunize defense contractors from combat related tort liability. Mr Biagini has also successfully defended companies in cases involving the Exxon Valdez; Cell Phone Radiation Hazards; and "Fen-Phen." Finally, following the 9/11 terrorist attacks, Mr Biagini, at the request of industry, conceived and authored the US SAFETY Act, a landmark legislative remedy which incentivizes homeland security companies to deploy anti-terror technology by potentially immunizing them from enterprise-threatening lawsuits arising out of acts of terrorism.

### BIANCHI, Alden J
Mintz Levin Cohn Ferris Glovsky and Popeo PC, Boston
617 348 3057
ajbianchi@mintz.com
*Featured in Employee Benefits & Executive Compensation (Nationwide), Employee Benefits & Executive Compensation (Massachusetts)*
See under Massachusetts for profile.

### BICE, William B
Milbank, Tweed, Hadley & McCloy LLP, New York
212 530 5622
wbice@milbank.com
*Featured in Projects (Nationwide)*
**Practice Areas:** Focuses on the development, financing, acquisition, disposition and restructuring of power generation (conventional and renewable), electric transmission projects and midstream oil and gas projects in the US and Latin America. Clients include developers, lenders, commodity trading firms, asset owners, hedge funds and private equity funds involved in the energy and infrastructure sectors.
**Career:** Partner, Project Finance Group.
**Personal:** JD, University of Pennsylvania School of Law; AB, Duke University.

### BICKS, Peter A
Orrick, Herrington & Sutcliffe LLP, New York
212 506 3742
pbicks@orrick.com
*Featured in Products Liability (Nationwide)*
**Career:** Peter Bicks is the partner-in-charge of Orrick's New York office. He has extensive trial success nationwide in the areas of mass tort, complex commercial contracts, intellectual property, corporate governance, accountant's liability and bankruptcy. Mr Bicks' major engagements include representation of Union Carbide Corporation in a number of high-profile product liability matters. Additionally, he has handled patent infringement cases and several litigations relating to the life settlement industry. He has written and lectured on trial strategy and techniques in high-stakes cases, has been often quoted in the Wall Street Journal and has appeared on Bloomberg Radio and Television.

### BILKIS, David
White & Case LLP, New York
212 819 8413
dbilkis@whitecase.com
*Featured in Banking & Finance (Nationwide)*
**Career:** David Bilkis primarily represents major commercial banks and investment banks as lead arranger and agent in a variety of lending transactions, with an emphasis on acquisition and leveraged financings. Mr Bilkis also represents borrowers in lending transactions. As lead counsel for the arranger/agent lenders, he is involved in all aspects of the deal structure and in the negotiation and documentation of such transactions. In such capacity, Mr Bilkis also addresses issues of fraudulent conveyance, collateral, compliance with margin regulations and the relationships between senior and subordinated lenders. To view a comprehensive biography, please visit www.whitecase.com/dbilkis.

### BIRD, Terry W
Bird, Marella, Boxer, Wolpert, Nessim, Drooks & Lincenberg PC, Los Angeles
310 201 2100
twb@birdmarella.com
*Featured in Litigation (Nationwide), Litigation (California)*
**Practice Areas:** White Collar criminal defense; Internal investigations; Securities, fraud, antitrust and other complex civil litigation.
**Career:** Represents some of the largest corporations in the country, as well as their top executives. Has litigated for and against Fortune 500 corporations. Civil practice includes commercial litigation and class actions involving fraud, RICO, employment, and unfair competition White collar defense matters include securities, mail fraud, tax, customs, government fraud and antitrust cases. Headed several corporate internal investigations to aid prominent companies and/or their boards of directors.
**Personal:** UCLA Law School; Stanford University; Former Assistant United States Attorney, Fraud and Special Prosecutions Unit.

### BIRNBAUM, Sheila L
Skadden, Arps, Slate, Meagher & Flom LLP & Affiliates, New York
212 735 2450
Sheila.Birnbaum@skadden.com
*Featured in Products Liability (Nationwide)*
**Practice Areas:** Co-head of Skadden's Complex Mass Tort and Insurance Group. Practices primarily in the areas of products liability, toxic torts and insurance coverage litigation. Represents corporations in complex mass tort and insurance litigation.
**Career:** Associate Dean of the Graduate Division (1982-84), professor of law (1978-84) and adjunct professor of law (1984-Present), New York University School of Law; professor of law, Fordham University School of Law (1972-78); LLB, New York University School of Law, 1965; MA, Hunter College, 1962; BA, Hunter College, 1960 (cum laude; Phi Beta Kappa).
**Publications:** Co-author, "Practitioner's Guide to Litigating Insurance Coverage Actions."

### BISHOP, Doak
King & Spalding LLP, Houston
713 751 3205
dbishop@kslaw.com
*Featured in International Arbitration (Nationwide), Litigation (Texas)*
**Practice Areas:** Litigation with more than 28 years of experience focusing on international arbitration and litigation of oil and gas, energy, construction, environmental and foreign investment disputes. Board Certified in Civil Trial Law by the Texas Board of Legal Specialization.
**Professional Memberships:** American Bar Association; Dallas Bar Association; State Bar of Texas; Vice Chairman of the Institute of Transnational Arbitration (1990 to present); Member of the US delegation to the NAFTA

Advisory Committee on Private Commercial Disputes.

**Personal:** BA, Southern Methodist University, 1973; JD, University of Texas, 1976.

## BISHOP, Leah M
Loeb & Loeb LLP, Los Angeles
310 282 2353
lbishop@loeb.com
*Featured in Wealth Management (Nationwide), Tax (California)*
See under California for profile.

## BLACK, Allen
Winston & Strawn LLP, Washington, DC
202 282 5821
hblack@winston.com
*Featured in Transportation (Nationwide)*
**Practice Areas:** Maritime litigation, regulatory, compliance, and corporate.
**Professional Memberships:** Maritime Law Association: Piracy (chair), Marine Finance, and Vessel Regulation Committees; DC Propeller Club; Chesapeake Area Professional Captains Association.
**Career:** US Coast Guard (retired); Adjunct Professor (Maritime Law) University of Baltimore Law School.
**Publications:** Frequent conference speaker and author of legal notes, advisories, and papers on maritime issues including LNG terminals, piracy, maritime regulations, admiralty developments; Develop, conduct seminars on environmental compliance for seafarers.
**Personal:** US Coast Guard Academy (BS 1979); William and Mary (JD 1991, Order of the Coif); USCG licensed Master (100 tons motor and sail).

## BLACK, David
Holland & Knight LLP, Tysons Corner
703 720 8600
david.black@hklaw.com
*Featured in Government (Nationwide)*
**Practice Areas:** David Black is a partner in the firm's Northern Virginia office and practices in the area of government contracts counseling and dispute resolution. His practice includes representing contractors in protests, claims under the Contract Disputes Act, responding to government investigations and audits, False Claims Act investigations and litigation, terminations for default and convenience, prime-subcontractor disputes, compliance programs, and counseling on a variety of contract administration and procurement issues.

## BLACK III, James I.
Sullivan & Cromwell LLP, New York
212 558 3948
blackj@sullcrom.com
*Featured in Wealth Management (Nationwide)*
**Professional Memberships:** American Bar Association; New York City Bar Association (Former Secretary, Committee on Trusts, Estates and Surrogate's Courts); New York State Bar Association. Member of Florida State Bar; New York State Bar, US Tax Court.
**Career:** Partner since 1984. Managing Partner, Estates & Personal Group. Represents individuals in all of their personal legal matters, particularly

estate planning, and various charitable organizations. Also involved in estates and trusts administration. Significant real estate experience.
**Personal:** Harvard Law School (JD, 1976); University of Florida (BA, 1973).

## BLACKABY, Nigel
Freshfields Bruckhaus Deringer LLP, Washington, DC
202 777 4519
nigel.blackaby@freshfields.com
*Featured in International Arbitration (Nationwide)*
**Practice Areas:** Nigel is a Partner and Head of the firm's US and Latin America International Arbitration Groups. He has acted as counsel and arbitrator in over 100 investment and commercial arbitrations in English, Spanish and Portuguese, with a focus on Latin America. He is a co-author of the leading text, Redfern and Hunter on International Arbitration (OUP 2009), A Guide to ICSID Arbitration (Kluwer, 2010) and International Arbitration in Latin America (Kluwer, 2003). He is a former President of the IBA Subcommittee on Investment Arbitration and an Adjunct Professor of Arbitration Law at American University in Washington, DC.

## BLAIR, Stephanie
Morgan, Lewis & Bockius LLP, Philadelphia
215 963 5161
sblair@morganlewis.com
*Featured in Litigation (Nationwide)*
**Practice Areas:** Leader, eData Practice. Practice Focuses on data governance and eDiscovery. Nationally recognized thought leader in electronic discovery and developed industry-leading "best practices" designed to provide clients with state-of-the-art discovery services, knowledge management, and data governance. Developed innovative delivery model offering clients fixed fee, all-in services covering the entire legal and technical spectrum of discovery.
**Professional Memberships:** Founder of eDiscovery think-tank; member of The Sedona Conference Working Group on eDiscovery. Regularly lectures on civil procedure and discovery management; has published articles on document management and eDiscovery in law journals nationwide. Serves as Special eDiscovery Master for Federal District Courts.

## BLANCHARD, James J
DLA Piper LLP (US), Washington, DC
202 799 4303
james.blanchard@dlapiper.com
*Featured in Government (Nationwide)*
**Practice Areas:** Government affairs.
**Career:** He is the former governor of Michigan and ambassador to Canada. He co-chairs the firm's Government Affairs Group, consistently ranked as one of the nation's top practices. The group is active in federal and state legislative affairs, regulatory issues, government contracts, international trade, e-commerce and privacy, communications, antitrust and trade regulation, energy, environment, financial services and a wide range of other issues before the federal government, state governments and internationally.

**Personal:** JD, University of Minnesota; MBA, Michigan State University; BA, Michigan State University.

## BLAND, Douglas S
Vinson & Elkins LLP, Houston
713 758 2498
dbland@velaw.com
*Featured in Energy & Natural Resources (Nationwide)*
**Practice Areas:** Domestic and international transactions practice covering development, acquisition, divestiture, joint venture, and financing of energy-related projects, with particular focus on power, renewables, petrochemicals, and upstream and midstream oil and gas.
**Professional Memberships:** Houston Bar Association.
**Career:** Admitted to Texas Bar in 1984. Joined Vinson & Elkins in 1984; admitted to the partnership in January 1992.
**Personal:** Graduated from the University of Virginia, BA with high honors, in 1981 (Phi Beta Kappa), and the University of Michigan, JD cum laude, in 1984 (Order of the Coif).

## BLANKENSTEIN, Paul
Gibson, Dunn & Crutcher LLP, Washington, DC
202 955 8693
PBlankenstein@gibsondunn.com
*Featured in ERISA Litigation (Nationwide)*
**Practice Areas:** Mr Blankenstein's practice focuses on complex commercial litigation, including cases involving Employee Retirement Income Security Act (ERISA), insurance, securities law issues and financial institution matters. Has handled numerous employment benefit cases, ranging from so-called 401(k) stock drop cases, to potential claims of withdrawal liability under the Multiemployer Pension Protection Act, to breach of fiduciary duty cases, ERISA preemption cases, as well as cases involving benefit claims.
**Career:** Civil Division of the Department of Justice as a Trial and Appellate Attorney.
**Personal:** JD, cum laude, Brooklyn Law School; Editor of the Law Review.

## BLATT, Lisa
Arnold & Porter LLP, Washington, DC
202 942 5842
Lisa.Blatt@aporter.com
*Featured in Appellate Law (Nationwide)*
**Practice Areas:** Heads the firm's Appellate and Supreme Court practice. At the end of the Supreme Court's 2012-13 Term, she will have argued 33 cases, prevailing in 30 (2 pending). Since entering private practice in 2009, she has argued five Supreme Court cases and numerous lower court cases. Ms Blatt appears regularly in national print and television media as an expert on the Supreme Court.
**Career:** Assistant to the Solicitor General, US Department of Justice (1996-2009); Law clerk to Hon. Ruth Bader Ginsburg, US Court of Appeals, DC Circuit (1989-90).
**Personal:** University of Texas, JD 1989; BA 1986.

## BLAU, Richard M
GrayRobinson, PA, Tampa
866 382 5132
richard.blau@gray-robinson.com
*Featured in Food & Beverages (Nationwide)*
**Practice Areas:** Chair of GrayRobinson's Alcohol Beverage and Food Department and presides over the firm's Alcohol Industry Team. Concentrates on alcohol industry-specific areas, including: •Administrative practice •Regulatory compliance for M&A transactions •Litigation and dispute resolution •Advertising and promotional law •Importation matters •Supplier/distributor relations •Hospitality industry trade practices. Works closely with representatives of state and federal government, drafting administrative rules and proposed legislation on behalf of clients as well as at the request of regulators. Has represented international importers and domestic manufacturers, statewide wholesaler trade groups and regional distributors and retailers (including multistate restaurant and hotel chains) across the US.
**Professional Memberships:** Member of the District of Columbia Bar, Florida Bar, American Bar Association, Federal Bar Association and American Association for Justice. Admitted to practice in US Supreme Court; US Court of International Trade; US Courts of Appeals for the Eleventh and Federal Circuits; US District Courts for the Middle and Southern Districts of Florida; US Court of Military Appeals; Florida Supreme Court and The District of Columbia Court of Appeals. Elected Member of the American Law Institute.
**Career:** In the area of Alcohol Beverage regulation, successfully litigated on behalf of manufacturers, setting important precedents for the industry in Geary Distributing Company v All Brand Importers, Inc. (imposing constitutional limits on the application of a state beer franchise law) and Jim Taylor Corporation v Guinness Import Company (defining "brand extension" under Florida law). Has served as regulatory counsel in national and international alcohol industry M&A transactions for both buyer and seller.
**Personal:** Georgetown University Law Center, JD, 1982; Brandeis University, BA, 1979.

## BLAUCH, Kevin C
Sidley Austin LLP, New York
212 839 5548
kblauch@sidley.com
*Featured in Capital Markets (Nationwide)*
**Practice Areas:** Partner Kevin Blauch's practice focuses on all aspects of structured finance, with particular emphasis on the representation of various depositors/issuers, underwriters/initial purchasers and originators/sellers of mortgage loans in a wide range of commercial mortgage-backed securities transactions, re-REMICS and A/B mortgage loan structures. He has done extensive work in the commercial mortgage loan workout area; and various bankruptcy and insolvency matters involving real estate and CMBS. He represents parties who face troubled financial issues or investigations, including financial institutions, their management, professional advisors and investors.

**Personal:** American University, Washington College of Law, JD, 1983; George Washington University, BA, 1980.

## BLITTNER, David
Weil, Gotshal & Manges LLP, New York
212 310 8329
david.blittner@weil.com
*Featured in Private Equity (Nationwide)*
**Practice Areas:** A partner of Weil's Corporate Department and Private Equity Practice, David Blittner represents private equity sponsors in connection with acquisitions, dispositions and financings. He has extensive experience with leveraged buyouts and dispositions of public and private companies, as well as with minority investments, public recapitalizations and restructurings. He also counsels clients on general corporate matters, including governance, equity capital markets liquidity events and securities law compliance matters.
**Personal:** SUNY Binghamton (BA, 1988); Columbia University School of Law (JD, 1991).

## BLOCH, Matthew
Weil, Gotshal & Manges LLP, New York
matthew.bloch@weil.com
*Featured in Capital Markets (Nationwide)*
**Practice Areas:** Head of the firm's Capital Markets Practice. Extensive experience representing underwriters and issuers in a wide variety of securities offerings. Represents investment banks including Barclays, Citi, Goldman Sachs, JP Morgan and Morgan Stanley, and corporations including C.R. Bard, DIRECTV, Estée Lauder, General Growth Properties, and Willis Group in investment grade and high-yield debt and equity offerings. Also has experience in overseas public and private acquisitions and related financings, having been resident in the firm's Budapest office for over two years.
**Personal:** Brandeis University (BA, 1977); Boston University (JD, 1984).

## BLOCKER, Mark B
Sidley Austin LLP, Chicago
312 853 6097
mblocker@sidley.com
*Featured in ERISA Litigation (Nationwide)*
**Practice Areas:** Partner in Sidley's Chicago office and one of the global coordinators of the Consumer Class Action practice group. He litigates a wide array of ERISA class action claims, including 401(k) company stock cases, challenges to cash balance plan features, challenges to 401(k) expenses and revenue sharing, claims relating to retiree medical coverage, and changes made to health and welfare plans. He has extensive experience defending financial institutions and insurances companies in ERISA class actions.
**Personal:** Harvard Law School, JD, 1988, cum laude; University of Chicago, BA, 1985, with honors. Admission: Illinois.

## BLOOM, Jerry
Winston & Strawn LLP, Los Angeles
213 615 1756
jbloom@winston.com
*Featured in Projects (Nationwide), Energy & Natural Resources (California)*
**Practice Areas:** As chair of Winston's Energy Practice, Mr Bloom engages in a broad-based regulatory, infrastructure, project development and finance practice, emphasizing the structuring, development, financing and operation of independent energy projects in the US and abroad. Clients include project developers and sponsors, financiers of debt and equity, wholesalers, marketers, end-users and foreign governments. He provides wide-ranging assistance on renewable, cogeneration, fossil-fuel fired and other alternative energy projects. He is a leading advocate on competitive electric markets, market structure and privatization, practicing before local, state and federal regulatory and legislative bodies.
**Career:** Member of Winston & Strawn Executive Committee.

## BLOOM, Mark D
Greenberg Traurig, LLP, Miami
305 579 0537
BloomM@gtlaw.com
*Featured in Bankruptcy/Restructuring (Nationwide), Bankruptcy/Restructuring (Florida)*
See under Florida for profile.

## BOBYS, Matthew
Skadden, Arps, Slate, Meagher & Flom LLP & Affiliates, Washington, DC
202 371 7739
Matthew.Bobys@skadden.com
*Featured in Government (Nationwide)*
**Practice Areas:** Advises on matters relating to government affairs at the federal, state and local levels, with particular emphasis on campaign finance laws, lobby registration and reporting laws, government ethics laws, gift and entertainment laws, and conflict of interest laws. Also advises on "pay-to-play" laws that impose special restrictions on the political activity of companies that have or seek government contracts, as well as their covered employees and directors. Has implemented comprehensive compliance systems covering all corporate government affairs activities and develops procedures in reaction to new laws.
**Career:** JD, Harvard Law School, 2002; BA, Grinnell College, 1999

## BOCH, David C
Bingham McCutchen LLP, Boston
617 951 8485
david.boch@bingham.com
*Featured in Financial Services Regulation (Nationwide), Securities (Nationwide)*
**Practice Areas:** Advises on all aspects of compliance with federal, state and SRO regulations applicable to securities firms, broker-dealers, investment advisers and transfer agents. Practice includes advising clients concerning the design and implementation of supervisory and compliance programs, the review of existing policies and procedures, and the review of special supervisory procedures and registration issues. Conducts

internal investigations on behalf of both management and independent directors and/or trustees. Represents clients from all segments of the securities industry in regulatory proceedings, private litigations and arbitrations.
**Personal:** Suffolk University Law School, JD, 1979; George Washington University, MPA, 1976; Harvard College, BA, 1975.

## BOEHNING, H Christopher
Paul, Weiss, Rifkind, Wharton & Garrison LLP, New York
212 373 3061
cboehning@paulweiss.com
*Featured in International Arbitration (Nationwide)*
**Practice Areas:** Partner in the Litigation Department. Practice includes complex commercial and civil litigation matters, insurance counseling and litigation, regulatory inquiries, internal investigations and international arbitrations. Tapped as a "Future Star" by Benchmark Litigation. Regarded as an authority on e-discovery issues and has spoken at numerous conferences and seminars on such issues. Adjunct professor at the University of Michigan Law School where he lectures on litigation strategy and e-discovery. Regular contributor to The New York Law Journal's Technology column on the topic, and an ongoing participant in The Sedona Conference Working Group Series.

## BOIES, Bill
McDermott Will & Emery LLP, Chicago
312 984 7686
bboies@mwe.com
*Featured in ERISA Litigation (Nationwide)*
**Practice Areas:** Concentrates on business disputes counseling and business litigation throughout the country, including benefits litigation, securities litigation, financial disputes, class actions, alternative dispute resolution, trials and appeals. Represents benefit plan sponsors and fiduciaries in ERISA class action litigation concerning pension plan administration, fiduciary duty, responsibility for asset losses, and changes in pension and welfare benefits. Defends plan sponsors, company officers and corporate fiduciaries in class actions concerning cash balance plans and declining value of employer stock in 401(k) plans and ESOPs.
**Professional Memberships:** Chicago Bar Foundation, American Bar Foundation.
**Personal:** Brown University (BA); University of Chicago Law School (JD).

## BONNIE, Joshua Ford
Simpson Thacher & Bartlett LLP, New York
212 455 3986
jbonnie@stblaw.com
*Featured in Capital Markets (Nationwide)*
**Practice Areas:** Partner in the Firm's Capital Markets Group. Represents issuers and underwriters in public and private offerings of equity and debt securities and regularly advises public companies on general corporate and securities law matters. Representations include advising the issuer on the largest US IPOs of 2007 (Blackstone), 2006 (MasterCard) and 2001 (Accenture), The Carlyle Group on its 2012 IPO,

and Ingersoll Rand on its 2009 reorganization incorporating its parent company in Ireland.
**Career:** Joined Firm, 1996; Partner, 2005.
**Personal:** BA, University of Virginia (1991); JD, University of Virginia School of Law (1995).

## BOOTH, Karyn A
Thompson Hine LLP, Washington, DC
202 263 4108
Karyn.Booth@ThompsonHine.com
*Featured in Transportation (Nationwide)*
**Career:** Karyn leads the Transportation practice group. She represents multinational corporations, trade associations and intermediaries in domestic and international transportation and logistics matters related to freight movement by rail, motor, vessel and air carriers. Karyn is general counsel to The National Industrial Transportation League, a trade association representing more than 600 shippers before federal agencies and Congress. She represents clients' interests in regulatory proceedings involving STB railroad rate and competition matters, rail and ocean regulatory reform, drivers' hours of service rules and rail abandonments. Karyn assists with contracts, hazmat and security compliance and enforcement, and litigation or arbitration of disputes.

## BORDERS, Thomas
McDermott Will & Emery LLP, Chicago
312 984 7552
tborders@mwe.com
*Featured in Tax (Illinois), Tax (Nationwide)*
**Practice Areas:** Focuses on federal tax controversies involving audits, administrative appeals, litigation and criminal investigations. Worked on numerous tax cases involving corporate tax matters, tax shelter investments, transfer pricing and analysis of tax incentive investments, valuation, finance and accounting issues.
**Career:** Former adjunct tax professor in graduate tax program at IIT Chicago Kent; former IRS trial attorney.
**Personal:** St. Louis University (BA); Georgetown University Law Centre (JD); Northwestern University (MBA).

## BOUCHER, Jamie L
Skadden, Arps, Slate, Meagher & Flom LLP & Affiliates, Washington, DC
202 371 7369
Jamie.Boucher@skadden.com
*Featured in Financial Services Regulation (Nationwide)*
**Practice Areas:** Focuses on financial institution mergers and acquisitions, regulatory and enforcement matters. Represents US and non-US banks, thrifts, mortgage lenders, insurance, securities, money service businesses and investment companies. Regularly advises financial institutions on compliance and enforcement matters. Represented clients on various aspects of federal lending, capital and liquidity support programs, including those established pursuant to the Emergency Economic Stabilization Act of 2008. Also advises clients on the implementation of the Dodd-Frank Act and on strategic transactional and compliance responses to the Act.

**Career:** JD, Georgetown University Law Center, 1996 (cum laude); BA, Oberlin College, 1984.

### BOUTROUS JR, Theodore J
Gibson, Dunn & Crutcher LLP, Los Angeles
213 229 7804
tboutrous@gibsondunn.com
*Featured in First Amendment Litigation (Nationwide), Litigation (California), Appellate Law (Nationwide), Products Liability (Nationwide), Media & Entertainment (California)*
See under California for profile.

### BOWE JR, James F
King & Spalding LLP, Washington, DC
202 626 9601
jbowe@kslaw.com
*Featured in Energy & Natural Resources (Nationwide)*
**Practice Areas:** Energy (including energy project development, energy regulatory matters, energy company M&A). Project finance (US, North America, Latin America). Oil and gas law.
**Professional Memberships:** Energy Bar Association. American Bar Association. Member of the Bar of the District of Columbia and the Bars of several federal courts.
**Career:** Admitted to practice 1982, District of Columbia. Private practice since 1982. Partner, Dewey & LeBoeuf, July 1994-present. Adjunct Professor, Oil and Gas Law, Georgetown University Law Center, 1990-95.
**Personal:** Born May 17, 1955. BA, Williams College, 1977. JD, Northwestern University School of Law, 1982.

### BOWMAN, John
King & Spalding LLP, Houston
713 751 3210
JBowman@kslaw.com
*Featured in International Arbitration (Nationwide)*
**Practice Areas:** Engaged in an arbitration and litigation practice representing primarily international oil companies and service companies in commercial and investment disputes.
**Professional Memberships:** Association of International Petroleum Negotiators; College of Commercial Arbitrators, fellow; The Chartered Institute of Arbitrators, fellow, London.
**Publications:** Dispute resolution in the International oil and gas business, Conference on Commercial and Investment Arbitration in Latin America: New Challenges for Governments, Corporations and Practitioners, Quito, November 2007; Stabilization Clauses in International Petroleum Contracts, AIPN/ ICC Conference on International Arbitration in the Oil and Gas Business, Paris, October 2007.
**Personal:** JD (1980) and BA (1974), University of Kansas.

### BOYD, Thomas M
DLA Piper LLP (US), Washington, DC
202 799 4361
tom.boyd@dlapiper.com
*Featured in Government (Nationwide), Privacy & Data Security (Nationwide)*
**Practice Areas:** Government affairs.
**Career:** He is co-chair of the firm's Regulatory and Government Affairs practice and concentrates

on public policy and regulatory matters, counseling and representing clients on privacy, financial services, e-commerce, and other legislative and related regulatory issues. He advises clients on public policy matters before Congress and the Executive Branch, and helps guide them through the increasingly complex regulatory obligations associated with privacy compliance. He is a frequent speaker and writer.
**Personal:** JD, University of Virginia School of Law; BA, Military Institute.

### BOYLE, Brian
O'Melveny & Myers LLP, Washington, DC
202 383 5327
bboyle@omm.com
*Featured in ERISA Litigation (Nationwide)*
**Practice Areas:** Brian Boyle, a partner in O'Melveny's Washington, DC office, represents financial services companies—including banks, insurers, investment managers, mortgage servicers and health care payors—in class action and other litigation seeking to aggregate consumer and other economic injuries. Brian is Chair of the Firm's Financial Services Practice and Co-Chair of the Firm's Health Care and Life Sciences Practice. Brian also is active in the Firm's Appellate Practice. He has been named by Legal 500 as a leading practitioner in the ERISA litigation and health care areas.

### BRADEN, Gregory C
Morgan, Lewis & Bockius LLP, Washington, DC
202 739 5217
gbraden@morganlewis.com
*Featured in ERISA Litigation (Nationwide)*
**Practice Areas:** Gregory C. Braden is a partner in Morgan Lewis's Labor and Employment Practice and co-chair of the ERISA Litigation Practice. He specializes in ERISA litigation and has served as lead defense counsel in virtually every type of ERISA Title I and Title II class action claim, including employer stock/ESOP claims, 401(k) proprietary fund and fees claims, defined benefit plan claims, retiree benefits claims, severance pay claims, and multiple employer welfare arrangement claims. Greg has authored publications and lectured widely on employee benefits litigation.
**Personal:** Attended the University of Wisconsin Law School, JD, University of Wisconsin, BA.

### BRADSHAW, Brian A
Morgan, Lewis & Bockius LLP, Houston
713 890 5770
bbradshaw@morganlewis.com
*Featured in Projects (Nationwide)*
**Practice Areas:** Brian A. Bradshaw is a partner in the Business and Finance Practice and co-chair of the Latin America Team. He has experience in a range of energy and infrastructure transactions and focuses his practice on the development of energy and infrastructure projects (emphasis on oil and gas, LNG, and power projects), acquisitions and divestitures, and domestic and international finance. He has experience with structuring, negotiating, and documenting the full range of project, M&A, and commercial financing docu-

mentation for domestic and international projects, including LNG liquefaction and regasification projects, FPSO and off-shore developments, refineries, cross-border pipelines, and power plants.

### BRAHAM, Denis Clive
Winstead PC, Houston
713 650 2743
dbraham@winstead.com
*Featured in Sports Law (Nationwide)*
**Practice Areas:** Chairman Emeritus Denis Clive Braham is a member of the firm's Real Estate Development & Investments and Corporate, Securities/Mergers & Acquisitions practices, and he chairs Winstead's Sports Business & Public Venues Practice Group. Denis has specific experience in the representation of clients in the sports industry. From venue financing and new stadium development to representing municipalities, sports commissions, and local organizing committees for major sporting events, Denis has worked with clients throughout the country to provide business solutions to complex sports transactions.

### BRAHMST, Oliver
White & Case LLP, New York
212 819 8219
obrahmst@whitecase.com
*Featured in Private Equity (Nationwide)*
**Career:** Oliver Brahmst is the Head of White & Case's Mergers and Acquisitions Practice Group for the Americas and a member of the Firm's Partnership Committee. He concentrates on domestic and cross-border acquisitions and divestitures, and has experience in both public and private transactions. Oliver has particular experience in the representation of private equity houses. To view a comprehensive biography, please visit www.whitecase.com/obrahmst.

### BRAND, Richard L
Arent Fox LLP, Washington, DC
202 857 6427
rbrand@arentfox.com
*Featured in Sports Law (Nationwide)*
**Practice Areas:** Rich Brand leads Arent Fox's Sports group. Rich has represented numerous professional teams, including the Atlanta Hawks, Charlotte Bobcats, Cleveland Cavaliers, DC United, Los Angeles Galaxy, Los Angeles Kings, Los Angeles Lakers, Miami Dolphins, New Jersey Nets, New York Jets, Washington Capitals, and Washington Wizards. Rich's areas of expertise include media rights, naming rights, acquisitions of professional sports franchises, sponsorships, arena/stadium licenses, executive contracts, concession agreements, suite and club seat licenses, and financings for teams and facilities.
**Personal:** University of Pennsylvania Law School, JD (cum laude), 1984; Georgetown University, BSBA, 1981.

### BRANDOW, John M
Davis Polk & Wardwell LLP, New York
212 450 4000
john.brandow@davispolk.com
*Featured in Capital Markets (Nationwide)*
**Practice Areas:** Member of Davis Polk's Corporate Department and heads the Equity Derivatives Group. The group advises a wide variety of market participants - commercial and investment banks, issuers, hedge funds and institutional and individual holders of equity positions - on a complex array of equity-related transactions. Has been actively involved in the design of exchangeable securities containing imbedded options or forward contracts on the underlying equities, the development of mandatory and optional convertible securities that are issued in tax- or accounting-driven capital-raising transactions, and the structuring of public and private hedging transactions using collars and variable prepaid forward contracts.

### BRASHER, Lance T
Skadden, Arps, Slate, Meagher & Flom LLP & Affiliates, Washington, DC
202 371 7402
Lance.Brasher@skadden.com
*Featured in Projects (Nationwide)*
**Practice Areas:** Concentrates in the acquisition, development, financing and restructuring of energy assets and other infrastructure projects in the US and around the world. Has advised clients with respect to numerous renewable energy projects, including solar, wind, geothermal, waste-to-energy and biomass; gas and coal-fired power plants; electricity transmission lines; coal gasification facilities; LNG and natural gas processing facilities; railways; sports facilities; among others. Has led the negotiation of some of the most complex energy transactions and has extensive knowledge with the related key agreements.
**Career:** JD, Harvard Law School, 1990 (cum laude); B.S., United States Naval Academy, 1982 (with distinction).

### BRAVIN, Mark N
Winston & Strawn LLP, Washington, DC
202 282 5938
mbravin@winston.com
*Featured in International Arbitration (Nationwide)*
**Practice Areas:** Co-chair of Winston & Strawn's International Arbitration Practice, Mark Bravin has represented investors and sovereign governments in international arbitration and cross-border litigation in US courts for 30+ years. He also advises clients on compliance with regulations involving Customs, export controls, embargoes (OFAC), FCPA, CFIUS.
**Career:** 2013 treaty claim victory for McKesson against Iran after 27 years of post-arbitration US litigation; 2012 victory for Romania defeating Greek investor's expropriation claims at ICSID; successfully represented numerous parties in ICC, ICDR and other commercial arbitration; assisted Ukraine to resolve several international disputes; helped American investors prevail against Iran at The Hague.

**BREHENY, Brian V.**
Skadden, Arps, Slate, Meagher & Flom LLP
& Affiliates, Washington, DC
202 371 7180
Brian.Breheny@skadden.com
*Featured in Securities (Nationwide)*
**Practice Areas:** Advises clients on various SEC
compliance, transactional and corporate governance matters, including public disclosures, annual meeting and reporting and proxy, beneficial
ownership reporting and tender offer requirements. Mr Breheny formerly served as Chief of
the SEC's Office of Mergers and Acquisitions and
Deputy Director of the Division of Corporation
Finance. While at the SEC, he assisted the
Commission with its consideration of rule
amendments related to shareholder director nominations, tender offers, beneficial ownership
reporting, electronic delivery of proxy materials,
short sale disclosure, and proxy voting and shareholder communications. His career began at
KPMG as a certified public accountant.

**BRENNAN, Michael G**
DLA Piper LLP (US), Chicago
312 368 4048
michael.brennan@dlapiper.com
*Featured in Franchising (Nationwide)*
**Practice Areas:** Franchising and distribution,
mergers and acquisitions, and international arbi-
tration.
**Professional Memberships:** Former
Chairman, Franchising Committee of the
International Bar Association.
**Career:** He concentrates his practice on domestic
and international business, licensing, and fran-
chising matters. He speaks and writes regularly on
topics of domestic and international business law.
**Personal:** JD, DePaul University (Member,
Depaul International Moot Court); BA, University
of Notre Dame (magna cum laude). Universite
Catholique de l'Ouest, Angers, France; Graduate
Institute of International Studies, Geneva,
Switzerland^Goethe Institute in Murnau,
Germany.

**BRENNAN JR, John T**
Crowell & Moring LLP, Washington, DC
202 624 2760
jbrennan@crowell.com
*Featured in Healthcare (Nationwide), Healthcare
(District of Columbia)*
**Practice Areas:** Co-chair of Crowell &
Moring's Health Care Group. Focuses on health-
care fraud and abuse matters, especially relating to
federal false claims, antikickback, and Stark Law
issues. Advises on compliance matters and con-
ducts internal investigations related to potential
fraud and abuse issues.
**Professional Memberships:** American Health
Lawyers Association and American Bar
Association's White-Collar Crime Health Law
Subcommittee; former Chair of the AHLA's
Substantive Law Committee on Fraud and Abuse,
Self-Referrals and False Claims.
**Career:** Voted one of the nation's top healthcare
provider attorneys by Nightingales; former hospi-
tal administrator.

**BRENNER, Alan Gordon**
Simpson Thacher & Bartlett LLP, New York
212 455 3378
abrenner@stblaw.com
*Featured in Transportation (Nationwide)*
**Practice Areas:** Corporate Partner. Regularly
represents aviation finance participants in operating leases, capital leases, mortgage financings, pre-
delivery payment financings, warehouse facilities,
aircraft purchases and other asset based transactions. Noteworthy transactions include representation of Airbus in its record breaking aircraft sale
agreement with American Airlines and the Primus
Capital led consortium in their pending acquisition of ILFC.
**Career:** Partner since 1996; practiced in the
firm's Hong Kong office from 1993 to 1997 and
headed the firm's Singapore office from 1997 to
2003.
**Personal:** AB, University of Michigan (1979); JD,
cum laude, Ohio State University College of Law
(1983).

**BRESLOW, Stephanie R**
Schulte Roth & Zabel LLP, New York
212 756 2542
stephanie.breslow@srz.com
*Featured in Investment Funds (Nationwide)*
**Practice Areas:** Co-head, Investment
Management Group. Investment management,
partnerships and securities, with focus on the formation of liquid-securities funds (hedge funds,
hybrid funds), private equity funds (LBO, mezza-
nine, distressed, real estate, venture), provides reg-
ulatory advice to investment managers and bro-
ker-dealers.
**Professional Memberships:** Founding mem-
ber, NY's Private Investment Fund Forum; Vice-
Chair, Private Investment Funds Subcommittee,
International Bar Association; The Hedge Fund
Journal's "50 Leading Women in Hedge Funds"
list.
**Career:** SRZ Partner since 1996; Member,
Executive Committee.
**Publications:** PLI Private Equity Funds:
Formation and Operation.
**Personal:** Columbia Law School, JD, 1984,
Harlan Fiske Stone Scholar; Harvard University,
BA, cum laude, 1981.

**BREW, John B.**
Crowell & Moring LLP, Washington, DC
202 624 2720
jbrew@crowell.com
*Featured in International Trade (Nationwide)*
**Practice Areas:** Partner in Crowell & Moring's
International Trade Group and focuses his practice in the area of Customs. He has extensive experience in import and export trade regulation, and
he regularly advises corporations, trade associations, foreign governments, and non-governmental organizations on matters involving customs
administration, enforcement, compliance, litigation, legislation and policy. He represents clients
in proceedings at the administrative and judicial
levels, as well as before Congress and the international bureaucracies that handle customs and
trade matters. He advises clients on all substantive

import regulatory issues handled by US Customs
and Border Protection, and Immigration and
Customs Enforcement.

**BRIAN, Brad D**
Munger, Tolles & Olson LLP, Los Angeles
213 683 9280
brad.brian@mto.com
*Featured in Litigation (Nationwide), Litigation
(California)*
See under California for profile.

**BRIGAGLIANO, James**
Sidley Austin LLP, Washington, DC
202 736 8135
jbrigagliano@sidley.com
*Featured in Financial Services Regulation
(Nationwide)*
**Practice Areas:** Partner and a global coordinator of the Securities and Futures Regulatory
Practice area. Advises financial services firms
including investment and commercial banks, broker-dealers and hedge funds regarding regulatory,
enforcement, compliance, and transactional matters. Focuses his practice on SEC and SRO rules
governing trading by broker-dealers and hedge
funds, broker-dealer registration and conduct
rules, and recent Dodd-Frank initiatives. Focuses
on regulations governing short sales (Regulation
SHO), Regulation M, research analyst conflicts,
FINRA advertising, conduct and offering rules,
clearance and settlement, and broker-dealer registration and compliance issues.
**Personal:** Georgetown University Law Center,
JD, 1982; Amherst College, BA, 1979, cum laude.

**BRIGHTBILL, Timothy C**
Wiley Rein LLP, Washington, DC
202 719 3138
tbrightbill@wileyrein.com
*Featured in International Trade (Nationwide)*
**Practice Areas:** Represents clients on all aspects
of international trade law/policy including import
trade remedies (antidumping, countervailing
duty, safeguards), global trade policy/trade negoti-
ations (WTO, free trade agreements), renewable
energy trade issues, customs, Internet and interna-
tional e-commerce.
**Professional Memberships:** ABA International
Law Section: Senior Advisor/Former Chair,
International Trade Committee, Liaison to ITAC
10; Former Division Chair and Council Member.
**Career:** Member, Industry Trade Advisory
Committee on Services and Finance Industries;
Adjunct Professor, International Trade Law and
Regulation, Georgetown University Law Center;
Faculty, Georgetown Law Academy of WTO Law
and Policy.
**Personal:** Georgetown University Law Center
(JD); Northwestern University (BS, with honors).

**BRITTINGHAM IV, Smith R**
Finnegan, Henderson, Farabow, Garrett &
Dunner LLP, Washington, DC
202 408 4158
smith.brittingham@finnegan.com
*Featured in International Trade (Nationwide)*
**Practice Areas:** Focuses on intellectual proper-
ty litigation before the US International Trade
Commission, with additional experience in both

the trial and appellate courts. He has been
involved in over 50 ITC investigations and 20 ITC
trials, as well as trials in US district courts and
appeals before the US Court of Appeals for the
Federal Circuit. Before joining Finnegan, he
served as a senior investigative attorney with the
ITC's Office of Unfair Import Investigations.
**Personal:** Oberlin College (BA, Chemistry and
Government, 1984); Ohio State University School
of Law (JD, with honors, 1987).

**BROCCOLO, Bernadette**
McDermott Will & Emery LLP, Chicago
312 984 6911
bbroccolo@mwe.com
*Featured in Healthcare (Illinois), Healthcare
(Nationwide)*
See under Illinois for profile.

**BROCK, Robert C.**
Covington & Burling LLP, Washington, DC
202 662 5985
mbrock@cov.com
*Featured in Products Liability (Nationwide)*
**Practice Areas:** Chair of Covington's Product
Liability and Mass Torts Practice, Mr Brock's practice focuses on representation of life sciences companies in defending product liability lawsuits. He
served as trial counsel in Merck's Vioxx cases, and
as national trial counsel for a number of major
pharmaceutical companies facing mass tort
claims. He recently served as lead trial counsel for
BP in the Deepwater Horizon litigation.
**Professional Memberships:** American College
of Trial Lawyers, Fellow; American Board of Trial
Advocates (ABOTA), Member.
**Career:** 25 years of trial experience.
**Personal:** University of Alabama School of Law,
JD, 1984; University of Alabama, BS, 1981.

**BROCKLAND, John P**
Weil, Gotshal & Manges LLP, Silicon Valley
john.brockland@weil.com
*Featured in Outsourcing (Nationwide), IT &
Outsourcing (California)*
See under California for profile.

**BROD, Craig B**
Cleary Gottlieb Steen & Hamilton LLP, New
York
212 225 2650
cbrod@cgsh.com
*Featured in Capital Markets (Nationwide)*
**Practice Areas:** General US and international
issuer representation, corporate governance, corporate finance and securities law. Represents corporate issuers, investment banks and investors and
has extensive experience in initial public offerings
for domestic and foreign issuers, public and private debt and equity financings for companies,
and financings related to private equity transactions and corporate restructurings. International
securities practice involves global and cross-border financings and exchange listings for issuers
domiciled in a wide variety of jurisdictions.
Counseling experience also includes assessing
considerations relevant to out-of-court restructuring and bankruptcy filing alternatives.
**Career:** Joined firm, 1980; became Partner, 1989.
JD, Yale Law School (1980). Editor, The Yale Law

Journal. BA, summa cum laude, Phi Beta Kappa, Columbia College (1977). Member, Securities Advisory Committee of the Ontario Securities Commission (1995-99). Admitted in New York and New Jersey; US District Court for Southern District of New York and District of New Jersey.

## BRODY, Melanie
K&L Gates, Washington, DC
202 778 9203
melanie.brody@klgates.com
*Featured in Financial Services Regulation (Nationwide)*

**Practice Areas:** A co-coordinator of the K&L Gates consumer financial services group, Ms Brody concentrates on federal and state enforcement and regulatory compliance matters, primarily for financial services providers. Melanie defends clients in investigations by government agencies, including the United States Department of Justice, Consumer Financial Protection Bureau, Federal Trade Commission, Department of Housing and Urban Development and state attorneys general. She also develops compliance programs, performs regulatory due diligence and provides compliance counseling. Melanie handles a wide variety of issues, with an emphasis on fair lending and servicing, unfair and deceptive trade practices and federal consumer finance regulation.

## BRODY, Ronald S
White & Case LLP, New York
212 819 2600
rbrody@whitecase.com
*Featured in Capital Markets (Nationwide)*

**Career:** Ronald Brody is a partner in White & Case's Capital Markets Practice and is a recognized leading high yield securities lawyer. He has a broad base of experience across all industry areas, in a wide range of corporate financings, with a particular focus on the representation of investment banks in high yield securities transactions. He is involved in all aspects of deal structure, negotiation and documentation. He has extensive experience in private equity transactions, mergers and acquisitions and recapitalizations, and his clients include investment banks as well as both public and private companies. To view his biography, please visit www.whitecase.com/rbrody.

## BROMLEY, James L
Cleary Gottlieb Steen & Hamilton LLP, New York
212 225 2264
jbromley@cgsh.com
*Featured in Bankruptcy/Restructuring (Nationwide), Bankruptcy/Restructuring (New York)*

**Practice Areas:** Bankruptcy, work-out and acquisition advice to debtors, creditors and investors. Substantial experience in international restructurings involving Asia, Europe, the Americas; expertise in distressed M&A. Notable matters: Overseas Shipholding Group Chapter 11, Nortel bankruptcy and asset sales,UAW (Chrysler and GM bankruptcies), Hellman & Friedman's joint bid for Neuberger Berman, Federal Reserve Bank of NY (Lehman bankruptcy), Goldman's acquisition of Litton Loan Servicing and related restructuring of C-BASS, Doral Financial's turn-around, Foamex's and Covanta Energy's reorganizations, recovery of major claims against Refco, SK Networks' $7B restructuring, Daewoo Motors' sale of Korean automotive business, representing major financial institutions in insolvency matters.

## BROSNAHAN, James
Morrison & Foerster LLP, San Francisco
415 268 7189
jbrosnahan@mofo.com
*Featured in Litigation (Nationwide), Litigation (California)*

**Practice Areas:** A lion of the trial bar, James Brosnahan is one of the most respected and recognized trial lawyers in the United States. He has tried more than 140 cases to verdict, including many high-profile cases involving antitrust and competition law, complex commercial litigation, IP and patent litigation, employment law, product liability, and white-collar criminal defense. He also served as special counsel to the California Legislature's Joint Subcommittee on Crude Oil Pricing. He is a Master Advocate on the faculty and member of the Board of Trustees of the National Institute for Trial Advocacy. View his complete biography at www.mofo.com.

## BROWN, Arthur
Kaye Scholer LLP, New York
212 836 8592
arthur.brown@kayescholer.com
*Featured in Products Liability (Nationwide)*

**Practice Areas:** Arthur Brown, Co-Chair of Kaye Scholer's Product Liability Group, represents and advises clients on mass tort and product liability issues, investigations by federal and state authorities, inquiries from Congress and commercial litigation disputes. As part of his practice, Arthur serves as national and regional counsel representing pharmaceutical companies in mass tort product liability actions (he recently served as co-lead national coordinating counsel for AstraZeneca in thousands of product liability lawsuits regarding its atypical antipsychotic drug Seroquel), advises clients on strategic litigation and settlement decisions, and counsels clients on litigation avoidance.

## BROWN, Banks
McDermott Will & Emery LLP, New York
212 547 5488
bbrown@mwe.com
*Featured in Leisure & Hospitality (Nationwide)*

**Practice Areas:** Based in the firm's New York office. He is head of the New York office Trial practice. Focuses his practice on complex commercial litigation and disputes.
**Professional Memberships:** Serves as the General Counsel for the American Hotel & Lodging Association, the Hotel Association of New York City, Inc. and the Travel Business Roundtable.
**Personal:** University of Virginia School of Law, JD, 1977, Harvard University, BA, (cum laude), 1974.

## BROWN, Donald W
Covington & Burling LLP, San Francisco
415 591 7063
dwbrown@cov.com
*Featured in Insurance (Nationwide), Insurance (California)*
See under California for profile.

## BROWN, Loren H
DLA Piper LLP (US), New York
212 335 4846
loren.brown@dlapiper.com
*Featured in Products Liability (Nationwide)*

**Practice Areas:** Litigation, drug and medical device, product liability.
**Career:** He is Co-Chair of the firm's product liability practice. He has an extensive civil litigation practice with a particular concentration in pharmaceutical and mass tort. His business litigation practice includes substantial consumer class action, securities, commercial tort and contract, and intellectual property litigation experience. He has experience in a wide range of white-collar and compliance matters. He speaks and writes on the subjects of evidence, science in the courtroom, products liability and mass tort, and civil trial practice.
**Personal:** JD, Hofstra University, BA, University of Maryland.

## BROWN, Sandra L
Thompson Hine LLP, Washington, DC
202 263 4101
Sandra.Brown@ThompsonHine.com
*Featured in Transportation (Nationwide)*

**Career:** Sandy is a partner in the firm's Transportation group. She represents bulk commodity shippers and other entities that use transportation services including electric utilities, government entities, ports, as well as coal, aggregates, chemicals and plastics shippers. She advises clients on buying, selling and moving coal domestically and internationally. Sandy also provides strategic planning advice for the transportation of bulk commodities designed at establishing or enhancing competitive transportation alternatives, and counsels on rail construction and environmental review, transportation and coal supply contract drafting and negotiating, regulated rate challenges, federal preemption in transportation matters and representation before the Surface Transportation Board.

## BROWN, Sanford M
Bracewell & Giuliani LLP, Dallas
214 758 1093
sanford.brown@bgllp.com
*Featured in Financial Services Regulation (Nationwide)*

**Practice Areas:** Represents financial institutions and specialty finance companies in matters involving state and federal banking laws and regulations and in corporate transactions, such as mergers, acquisitions, securities offerings, Subchapter S corporation elections, and in matters involving privacy and identity theft.
**Career:** Served in the Office of the Comptroller of the Currency from 1987 to 1989. Faculty member of the Southwestern Graduate School of Banking and frequent speaker at regional and national banking seminars and educational programs.
**Personal:** LLM, Banking, Boston University, 1987; JD, with honors, University of Arkansas, 1986; BSBA, Banking & Finance, University of Arkansas, 1983.

## BROWNE, Maureen F
Covington & Burling LLP, Washington, DC
202 662 5038
mbrowne@cov.com
*Featured in International Trade (Nationwide)*

**Practice Areas:** Intellectual property litigation, products liability, commercial law, customs, international trade regulation and unfair competition, with a focus on Section 337 litigation. She has successfully represented both Complainants and Respondents in Section 337 investigations involving a wide range of technologies such as rubber antidegradants, erythropoietin (EPO), Restylane®, personal music players, batteries, educational toys, machine vision systems, flash memory, voltage regulators, integrated circuits, and tungsten metallization.
**Professional Memberships:** International Trade Commission Trial Lawyers Association; Intellectual Property Section of the American Bar Association; Steering Committee, DC Bar Intellectual Property Law Section.
**Personal:** George Washington University Law School (JD, 1992).

## BROWNELL, F William
Hunton & Williams LLP, Washington, DC
202 955 1555
bbrownell@hunton.com
*Featured in Climate Change (Nationwide), Environment (District of Columbia)*

**Practice Areas:** Mr Brownell is currently chair of Hunton & Williams. He previously chaired the firm's Administrative Law Group and co-chaired its environmental and climate change practices. Mr Brownell and his team have decades of experience representing clients around the globe on a broad range of environmental litigation, regulatory, legislative, transactional, and compliance matters. These representations include proceedings on greenhouse gas emissions, defense of public nuisance and enforcement litigation, international climate change negotiations, and compliance counseling on clean air, chemical and waste issues. Mr Brownell and team also advise on carbon transactions and licensing of large infrastructure projects.

## BRUCH, Gregory S
Willkie Farr & Gallagher LLP, Washington, DC
202 303 1205
gbruch@willkie.com
*Featured in Securities (Nationwide), Litigation (District of Columbia)*
See under District of Columbia for profile.

**BRUEMMER, Russell**
WilmerHale, Washington, DC
202 663 6804
Russell.Bruemmer@wilmerhale.com
*Featured in Financial Services Regulation (Nationwide)*
**Practice Areas:** Chair, Financial Institutions Group. Focus: corporate and financial services areas; regulatory advice; acquisitions, divestitures, and financing transactions; corporate governance and corporate structuring matters; national security issues.
**Professional Memberships:** Former Chair of two ABA banking law subcommittees, former Vice-Chair of subcommittee corporate compliance; Board of Regents of Luther College (Iowa).
**Career:** CIA General Counsel; Special Counsel to Director of Central Intelligence; Chief Counsel-Congressional Affairs, Special Assistant to the Director of the FBI.
**Personal:** JD, University of Michigan Law School; BA, Luther College.

**BRUNO, Frank P.**
Sidley Austin LLP, New York
212 839 5540
fbruno@sidley.com
*Featured in Investment Funds (Nationwide)*
**Practice Areas:** Partner in Sidley's New York office. Has worked on various corporate and securities transactions including equity and debt offerings by industrial, utility, financial institution, investment company and REIT issuers. Extensive experience in matters related to the Investment Company Act of 1940 and has worked on transactions of and offerings by open-end and closed-end investment companies as both fund and underwriters' counsel, including IPOs, rights offerings, preferred stock offerings, debt offerings, asset acquisitions and mergers.
**Personal:** Harvard Law School, JD, 1979, cum laude; Columbia Business School, MBA, 1976; Columbia University, BA, 1974, summa cum laude. Admission: New York.

**BRUNO, Philippe M**
Greenberg Traurig, LLP, Washington, DC
202 331 3193
BrunoP@gtlaw.com
*Featured in International Trade (Nationwide)*
**Practice Areas:** Global trade and investment; governmental affairs; intellectual property.
**Career:** Selected: Chambers USA Guide, 2010-13; Chambers Global, 2012-13; Guide to the World's leading International Trade Lawyers, 2010. Awarded, French Government Scholarship for completion of doctorate thesis. Rated, AV® Preeminent™ 5.0 out of 5.
**Personal:** LLM, International and Comparative Law, Georgetown University Law Center, 1984; PhD, cum laude, European and International Law, University of Grenoble Law School, 1982; LLM, European Integration, University of Grenoble Law School, 1978; JD, Civil Law, University of Grenoble Law School, 1977.

**BUCHANAN, John**
Covington & Burling LLP, Washington, DC
202 662 5366
JBuchanan@cov.com
*Featured in Insurance (Nationwide), Insurance (District of Columbia)*
See under District of Columbia for profile.

**BUCHMAN, Emil**
Fried, Frank, Harris, Shriver & Jacobson LLP, New York
212 859 8298
Emil.Buchman@FriedFrank.com
*Featured in Banking & Finance (Nationwide)*
**Practice Areas:** Corporate partner. Advises financial institutions and corporations on a wide variety of leverage finance and project finance transactions. Has substantial experience in representing both lenders and borrowers in connection with the financings of mergers and acquisitions, leveraged buyouts, recapitalizations and restructurings.
**Career:** Joined in 1996; became partner in 2005.
**Personal:** JD, summa cum laude, Brooklyn Law School (1996), member, Law Review; BA, summa cum laude, Azerbaijan Civil Engineering Institute in Baku (1986). Fellow, American College of Investment Counsel.

**BUCK, Willis**
Sidley Austin LLP, Chicago
312 853 7819
wbuck@sidley.com
*Featured in Capital Markets (Nationwide)*
**Practice Areas:** Partner in Sidley's Chicago office, focusing in securitization and structured finance since 1985. His practice includes term and conduit executions involving a variety of assets, including automobile loans and leases, floorplan loans, student loans, credit card receivables and other consumer assets. Other areas of focus include syndicated and asset-based lending, regulatory developments affecting structured finance, the UCC and legal opinion practice. Transaction structures have included direct asset purchases, master trusts and master note trusts (including de-linked structures).
**Personal:** The University of Chicago Law School, JD, 1984; Yale University, MPhil, 1979; Oxford University, BA, 1975; Williams College, BA, 1973.

**BUCKHOLZ JR, Robert E**
Sullivan & Cromwell LLP, New York
212 558 3876
buckholzr@sullcrom.com
*Featured in Capital Markets (Nationwide)*
**Professional Memberships:** ABA; ABCNY (Chair, Securities Regulation Committee); NYSBA.
**Career:** Partner since 1987. Co-coordinator, Corporate and Finance Group, focusing on capital markets transactions. Has handled a wide range of public/private debt and equity financings for US/non-US issuers and their underwriters, including IPOs, privatizations, and investment grade and high-yield financings. Also has extensive experience advising on corporate governance and disclosure matters. Co-Author, "The Public Company Deskbook" (PLI). Selected debt and

equity offerings: American International Group, Bank of Nova Scotia, Black Diamond, Canadian National Railway, Enbridge, GNC Holdings, Vulcan Materials Corp.
**Personal:** Columbia Law School (JD, 1979); Dartmouth College (AB, 1976).

**BUCKLEY, Jeremiah S**
BuckleySandler LLP, Washington, DC
202 349 8010
jbuckley@buckleysandler.com
*Featured in Financial Services Regulation (Nationwide)*
**Practice Areas:** Mr Buckley, a founding partner of BuckleySandler, assists clients with strategic counsel and advice on business formations and acquisitions, risk management, and enforcement matters involving federal and state regulators. He also represents and counsels financial services companies and their trade associations in connection with legislative and regulatory initiatives by state and federal agencies and Congress.
**Professional Memberships:** General Counsel of the Electronic Signatures and Records Association; Former Chair, RESPA Subcommittee of the ABA Consumer Financial Services Committee; Counsel to the State Attorney General Enforcement Network (STAGE) and Board Member, Exchequer Club.
**Publications:** Introduction to Mortgage Lending, 3rd Edition (American Bankers Association 2009). The Law of Electronic Signatures and Records (West Group 2011). How Do You Rate Your Fairness Awareness? (American Banker, 2011). State Attorneys General Are the New Bank Regulators (American Banker, 2012).

**BUCKLEY, Kevin J**
Hunton & Williams LLP, Richmond
804 788 8616
kbuckley@hunton.com
*Featured in Capital Markets (Nationwide)*
**Practice Areas:** Mr Buckley is Co-Head of Hunton & Williams' nationally-prominent Structured Finance and Securitization Practice. His practice focuses on mortgage-backed and asset-backed securitizations, structured financings and other capital markets transactions. He represents issuers, underwriters, trustees, master servicers, insurers, and other securitization and capital markets participants. Mr Buckley has served as issuer's counsel in connection with the design and implementation of securitization programs involving unique asset types and innovative securities structures, including the first REMIC program backed by a full faith and credit guarantee of the US and the first public securitization of reperforming government-guaranteed loans.

**BUDOFSKY, Daniel**
Davis Polk & Wardwell LLP, New York
212 450 4000
daniel.budofsky@davispolk.com
*Featured in Capital Markets (Nationwide)*
**Practice Areas:** Member of Davis Polk's Derivatives Group. He advises US and foreign financial institutions an issuers on over-the-counter derivatives with particular focus on equity, fund-linked and credit derivatives. He has also

advised on complex equity finance and capital market transactions, including novel convertible and exchangeable offerings (such as the first registered borrow facility). His practice also includes equity-linked, fixed income, currency and commodity-linked structured products, as well as structured products linked to algorithmic and managed trading strategies.

**BUENTE, David**
Sidley Austin LLP, Washington, DC
202 736 8111
dbuente@sidley.com
*Featured in Products Liability (Nationwide), Environment (District of Columbia)*
See under District of Columbia for profile.

**BUERSTETTA, Grant E**
Blank Rome LLP, New York
212 885 5454
GBuerstetta@BlankRome.com
*Featured in Banking & Finance (Nationwide)*
**Practice Areas:** Grant Buerstetta represents clients in structured financings including complex structured and asset-backed securities, collateralized loan obligations and other securitizations; alternative investment fund formation; and lending and capital market executions of those structures. He has significant experience in analyzing and structuring asset-backed securities in cash flow, synthetic and hybrid transactions. He has been involved in the analysis, assessment, restructuring, liquidation and litigation of numerous distressed transactions emerging from the credit crisis. Mr Buerstetta's representation of alternative funds, hedge funds and asset managers is complimented by his broad background in domestic and international securities markets. For more information: www.BlankRome.com/GBuerstetta.

**BURCHFIELD, Bobby R**
McDermott Will & Emery LLP, Washington, DC
202 756 8003
bburchfield@mwe.com
*Featured in Government (Nationwide), Litigation (District of Columbia)*
**Practice Areas:** Member of trial department and head of firm's complex litigation group. Serves on firm's executive committee and management committee. Co-partner-in-charge of Washington, DC office. Expertise includes jury and bench trials, appeals, arbitrations, antitrust, securities, class actions, commercial disputes, constitutional litigation.
**Professional Memberships:** Federalist Society; American Bar Association; George Washington Law School Dean's Advisory Board; Board of Trustees, Wake Forest University; Board of Georgetown Pediatric Center.
**Personal:** George Washington Law School (JD, high honors); Wake Forest University (BA, cum laude).

## BURKE, Timothy P
Bingham McCutchen LLP, Boston
617 951 8620
timothy.burke@bingham.com
*Featured in Securities (Nationwide)*
**Practice Areas:** Co-chair of Bingham's Financial Services Area. Handles a wide variety of securities regulatory and litigation matters. Has represented broker-dealers, investment advisers, registered representatives, senior management, compliance officials and others in connection with private and public investigations and enforcement proceedings brought by the SEC, FINRA and other self-regulatory organizations, as well as numerous state regulators. Experience also includes civil litigation matters and arbitration proceedings relating to securities issues. Has handled matters across the US and cases involving transactions in Europe, Latin America and the Middle East.
**Personal:** Fordham University School of Law, JD, 1991; Boston College, BA, 1988.

## BURMEISTER, Edward
Baker & McKenzie, San Francisco
415 576 3029
edward.burmeister@bakermckenzie.com
*Featured in Employee Benefits & Executive Compensation (Nationwide), Employee Benefits & Executive Compensation (California)*
See under California for profile.

## BURNETT, Henry Guy
King & Spalding LLP, New York
212 556 2201
hburnett@kslaw.com
*Featured in International Arbitration (Nationwide)*
**Practice Areas:** As an experienced trial lawyer, Mr Burnett concentrates on international commercial and investor-state arbitration matters and ADR proceedings generally as well as general domestic and international litigation in state and federal courts. handling inbound litigation matters for foreign clients, many from Latin America, and international arbitration disputes including arbitrations under ICDR, ICC, JAMS International, UNCITRAL and CPR Rules as well as investor-state arbitrations involving claims under ICSID, Bilateral Investment Treaties, the Energy Charter Treaty, multi-lateral investment instruments and local investment laws.
**Personal:** Fluent in Spanish and Portuguese.

## BURNETT, Mark
Goodwin Procter LLP, Boston
617 570 1031
mburnett@goodwinprocter.com
*Featured in Private Equity (Nationwide), Corporate/M&A (Massachusetts), Private Equity (Massachusetts)*
See under Massachusetts for profile.

## BURNS, Caleb P
Wiley Rein LLP, Washington, DC
202 719 7451
cburns@wileyrein.com
*Featured in Government (Nationwide)*
**Practice Areas:** Advises federal officeholders, political candidates and committees, ideological organizations, trade associations, Fortune 50 corporations and private individuals on all aspects of political law including campaign finance, government ethics and lobbying law compliance. Also represents clients before the Federal Election Commission, other federal and state administrative agencies and in federal and state courts.
**Professional Memberships:** Vice-Chair, ABA, Section on Administrative Law & Regulatory Practice, Committee on Legislative Process & Lobbying.
**Career:** Member, Lawyers for Bush-Cheney; Outstanding Scholar Program, US Department of Justice, Antitrust Division.
**Personal:** New York University School of Law (JD); Duke University (BA, cum laude).

## BURNS, Stephen L
Cravath, Swaine & Moore LLP, New York
212 474 1146
sburns@cravath.com
*Featured in Capital Markets (Nationwide)*
**Practice Areas:** Stephen L. Burns is a partner in Cravath's Corporate Department. His practice focuses on representing issuers and investment banking firms in connection with public and private offerings of securities. He also represents various corporations on general corporate matters, including corporate governance and M&A matters. His clients have included Crown Castle International Corp., Flowserve Corporation, Stanley Inc., Time Warner, Time Inc., Turner Broadcasting, Credit Suisse, Goldman Sachs and JPMorgan.
**Personal:** University of Texas School of Law (JD, with Honors, 1990; Associate Editor, Law Review; Member, Chancellor's Honor Society); University of Oklahoma (BBA, with Distinction, 1987). For more information:
http://www.cravath.com/sburns.

## BURRELL, Lizabeth L
Curtis, Mallet-Prevost, Colt & Mosle LLP, New York
212 696 6995
lburrell@curtis.com
*Featured in Transportation (Nationwide)*
**Career:** Ms Burrell has over 30 years experience in domestic and international law affecting shipping and commerce, including arbitration, litigation, and drafting maritime and commercial contracts as well as general terms and conditions for international trading. Formerly a member of Burlingham Underwood, Ms Burrell was the first female president of The Maritime Law Association of the United States and is now the MLA's Co-Opted Delegate to the BIMCO Documentary Committee. She was appointed to the US Secretary of State's Advisory Committee on Private International Law in 2009. For her contributions as advisor to the US delegation to IMO Legal Committee and in facilitating communications between industry stakeholders and the US government, the US Coast Guard conferred on her the Meritorious Public Service Award. Ms Burrell lectures on shipping topics in the US and abroad and has published many articles in top professional journals and treatises, like Moore's Federal Practice and Lexis/Nexis Expert Commentaries. She is an Associate Editor of American Maritime Cases and Benedict's Maritime Bulletin and a Titulary member of the Comité Maritime International.
**Personal:** JD, New York University School of Law; M Phil., with distinction, MA, with honors, Columbia University; BA, cum laude, Swarthmore College.

## BURSKY, Daniel J
Fried, Frank, Harris, Shriver & Jacobson LLP, New York
212 859 8428
Daniel.Bursky@FriedFrank.com
*Featured in Capital Markets (Nationwide)*
**Practice Areas:** Corporate partner. Concentrates his practice in corporate finance and US securities law, representing both issuers and underwriters in a variety of financing transactions, including equity offerings, convertible securities, high-yield debt, Eurobonds and private placements. Often represents investment banks and private equity firms with respect to acquisition financings, including bank, mezzanine and high-yield debt. Active in restructurings and special situations.
**Career:** Joined in 1993; became partner in 2001.
**Personal:** JD, Columbia University Law School (1993), Harlan Fiske Stone Scholar; BA, Yale University (1990).

## BURTON, Richard A
Greenberg Traurig, LLP, McLean
703 749 1324
BurtonR@gtlaw.com
*Featured in Capital Markets (Nationwide)*
**Practice Areas:** Real estate investment trusts (REITs), tax, real estate joint ventures.
**Professional Memberships:** Former Co-Chair, NAREIT Government Relations and Tax Committee; member, Real Estate Roundtable Tax Policy Committee.
**Career:** Listed: Chambers USA Guide, 2006-13; Chambers Global Guide, 2009-13.
**Publications:** Author, The Constitutionality of an Apportioned Value Added Tax, Tax Notes, Tax Analyst, Vol 49, No 1, October 1990; author, Retroactivity and Internal Inconsistency - How Far Extended, Tax Notes, Tax Analyst, Vol. 49, No 8, P 901, November 1990.
**Personal:** LLM, Boston University School of Law; JD, University of Utah College of Law; BA, University of Utah.

## BUSEY, Brian
Morrison & Foerster LLP, Washington, DC
202 887 1504
gbusey@mofo.com
*Featured in International Trade (Nationwide)*
**Practice Areas:** Brian Busey's practice focuses on complex intellectual property matters, especially those before the US International Trade Commission (ITC) and in federal district courts. In addition to litigating more than 30 Section 337 cases, Mr Busey is highly experienced in cross-border intellectual property disputes in a variety of areas, including patents, trademarks, and trade secrets. He also has counseled clients concerning intellectual property licensing and has substantial experience in alternative dispute resolution. Mr Busey is a leader in the ITC Bar, and was the 2011 President of the International Trade Commission Trial Lawyers Association.

## BUSH, Derek M
Cleary Gottlieb Steen & Hamilton LLP, Washington, DC
202 974 1526
dbush@cgsh.com
*Featured in Financial Services Regulation (Nationwide)*
**Practice Areas:** US bank regulatory matters affecting domestic and international financial institutions and foreign sovereigns. Corporate transactions involving financial institutions, including FDIC-assisted transactions, mergers and acquisitions, asset sales, privatizations and capital markets transactions. Internal investigations and enforcement proceedings by the US federal banking agencies, including representation of financial institutions, their boards of directors, employees and shareholders.
**Professional Memberships:** Member of the Bar in the District of Columbia. Previous co-chair, ABA Banking Law Subcommittee on International Banking.
**Career:** Joined firm, 1995; became partner, 2003. JD, with honors, Law Review comment editor, University of Chicago (1994); AB, cum laude, Princeton University (1989).

## BUTLER JR, John Wm
Skadden, Arps, Slate, Meagher & Flom LLP & Affiliates, Chicago
312 407 0730
jack.butler@skadden.com
*Featured in Bankruptcy/Restructuring (Nationwide), Bankruptcy/Restructuring (Illinois)*
**Practice Areas:** Advises companies and their stakeholders with respect to complex business reorganizations, troubled-company M&A, debt restructurings and financing matters, including advising directors and officers on corporate governance, fiduciary duty and strategic matters. Acted on behalf of global businesses in restructurings outside the US, executing cross-border financing and privatization transactions and divesting various business lines and entities. Currently advising the Official Committee of Unsecured Creditors in the AMR Corp. (American Airlines) Chapter 11 reorganization and merger with US Airways Group, Inc. Twice recognized as one of The American Lawyer's Dealmakers of the Year (most recently for work on the US automotive industry restructuring as counsel for Delphi Corporation and previously for the Kmart Corporation, US Airways Group, Inc. and Xerox Corporation restructurings). Named one of the decade's most influential lawyers by The National Law Journal in 2010, and one of ten lawyers profiled for delivering "creative solutions" to clients during the credit crisis in the Financial Times' inaugural "US Innovative Lawyers" report. Inducted into the M&A Advisors Hall of Fame and the inaugural class of the Turnaround, Restructuring and Distressed Investing Industry Hall of Fame. Joined Skadden as a lateral partner in 1990 to help found the firm's corporate restructuring and distressed

M&A practice, and has been active in firm management, serving as a practice leader for 22 years. Listed as a leader in the corporate restructuring and insolvency field in the current editions of The International Who's Who of Business Lawyers, Who's Who Legal USA, The Best Lawyers in America, Euromoney and Legal Media Group's Best of the Best and Expert Guide to the World's Leading Insolvency and Restructuring Lawyers, IFLR 1000 and The Lawdragon 500. Included regularly in the K&A Restructuring Register, the peer group listing of the top restructuring attorneys and financial advisors in the United States, and the most frequently named individual to Turnarounds & Workouts' annual ranking of the outstanding restructuring lawyers in America.
**Professional Memberships:** Fellow, American College of Bankruptcy and International Insolvency Institute; past Director, American Bankruptcy Institute; past Chair and Director, American Board of Certification; past Associate General Counsel, Commercial Finance Association; past Chair, Governing Board, Commercial Finance Association Education Foundation; Founder, INSOL's Group of 36; Director, New York Institute of Credit; past Chair and Director, Turnaround Management Association; Member, American Health Lawyers Association, Association for Corporate Growth, Association for Insolvency and Restructuring Accountants, Executive Club of Chicago, Insolvency Lawyers Association (United Kingdom).
**Career:** JD, University of Michigan Law School, 1980; AB, Princeton University, 1977 (magna cum laude).
**Personal:** Awarded the Ellis Island Medal of Honor, which is given to Americans who exemplify outstanding qualities in both their personal and professional lives. Also recipient of the Albert Schweitzer Award (Hugh O'Brien Youth Leadership) and Celtic Medal of Honor (Irish Chamber of Commerce in the United States). Outside of the law, in addition to serving in leadership positions with numerous civic and charitable organizations, officiated high school and college football for 25 years and is a lifetime member of the American Football Coaches Association.

### BYRD, Michael
Baker & McKenzie, Houston
713 427 5021
michael.byrd@bakermckenzie.com
*Featured in Energy & Natural Resources (Nationwide)*
**Practice Areas:** North America Oil and Gas Practice Chair. Represents clients in all phases of oil and gas acquisitions and divestitures, joint ventures, and exploration activities.
**Professional Memberships:** Advisory Board Member, Institute for Energy Law ; Member, Houston Producers' Forum; Member, American Association of Professional Landmen.
**Career:** Admitted in Texas, Louisiana and Pennsylvania. Board Certified in Oil, Gas, and Mineral Law by the Texas Board of Legal Specialization.

**Publications:** Authored articles on energy matters, including for State Bar of Texas Oil, Gas and Energy Resources Law Section Report and Landman.
**Personal:** University of Texas School of Law , JD 1987.

### BYRNE, William
Holland & Knight LLP, Jacksonville
904 798 5408
william.byrne@hklaw.com
*Featured in Transportation (Nationwide)*
**Practice Areas:** Mr Byrne is admitted in New York (1979) and Florida (1999) with extensive experience in road, rail, intermodal and ocean transportation matters, including regulatory concerns. He has extensive experience in transactions involving shared freight and passenger rail corridors, rail line transfers and complex transportation related contracts and dispute resolution on behalf of motor carriers and all classes of rail carriers. His commercial experience also includes serving as CEO of a New York based logistics agency. Mr Byrne is certified as a Circuit Court mediator in Florida and has served as a commercial arbitrator in New York maritime arbitrations.

### CACCIA, John
Skadden, Arps, Slate, Meagher & Flom LLP & Affiliates, New York
212 735 7826
john.caccia@skadden.com
*Featured in Investment Funds (Nationwide)*
**Practice Areas:** John Caccia represents a range of sponsor and investor clients in the formation, negotiation and capitalization of private investment vehicles, including private equity funds, hedge funds, hybrid funds and managed accounts. He advises on compliance matters, establishing investment management platforms, financings, joint ventures, portfolio transactions and other significant strategic initiatives.
**Career:** B.C.L., Oxford University, 1991; BA, Oxford University Jurisprudence, 1990; LLB, Dalhousie University, 1992; BA, University of Toronto, 1988 (honors with high distinction) Rhodes Scholar, 1988, Chancellor's Medalist, 1988. Mr Caccia lectures on private funds as part of the Oxford University Masters in Law and Finance program.

### CADWALADER, Lynn K
Holland & Knight LLP, San Francisco
415 743 6981
lynn.cadwalader@hklaw.com
*Featured in Leisure & Hospitality (Nationwide)*
**Practice Areas:** Lynn K. Cadwalader is the Co-Chair of Holland & Knight's Global Hospitality Resort and Timeshare Group and is a Partner in the firm's San Francisco office. Ms Cadwalader represents clients investing in, acquiring, repositioning and developing hotels and mixed-use projects in the United States and internationally. She is recognized as an industry expert in negotiating and documenting hotel management agreements and license agreements for both owners and operators, and is known for her creative and strategic thinking. Ms Cadwalader is also active in

representing foreign clients investing in the United States lodging and resort markets.

### CALDWELL, Charles
Vinson & Elkins LLP, Houston
713 758 4518
ccaldwell@velaw.com
*Featured in Energy & Natural Resources (Nationwide)*
**Practice Areas:** Partner in Energy Regulatory Practice. Practice consists primarily of representation of oil pipelines before regulators and appellate courts, compliance counseling, and energy transactions involving regulated assets.
**Professional Memberships:** Member, Energy Bar Association (past Chair, Oil Pipeline Committee); past President, Energy Bar Association - Houston Chapter.
**Career:** Regular speaker: continuing education and client compliance programs. Law clerk to Hon George P Kazen, US District Court, Southern District of Texas (1990-91).
**Publications:** Co-editor, Gas Regulation 2003, Co-editor USA, Oil Regulation 2008 and 2009 (Global Competition Review).
**Personal:** Rice University, BA 1985; University of Virginia, JD 1990.

### CALLCOTT, W Hardy
Bingham McCutchen LLP, San Francisco
415 393 2310
hardy.callcott@bingham.com
*Featured in Financial Services Regulation (Nationwide)*
**Practice Areas:** Concentrates on regulatory counseling concerning securities market and regulatory issues for broker-dealers, investment advisers, mutual funds and others in the financial services industry. Provides securities enforcement defense before the SEC, Department of Justice, FINRA, and other SRO and state regulators for members of the financial services industry, public companies, and officers and directors. Conducts internal investigations and defends securities litigation.
**Career:** Served as senior vice president and general counsel at Charles Schwab & Co. Inc.
**Personal:** Stanford Law School, JD, with distinction, 1986; Yale University, BA, summa cum laude, with honors, 1983.

### CAMPION, Kevin
Sidley Austin LLP, Washington, DC
202 736 8084
kcampion@sidley.com
*Featured in Financial Services Regulation (Nationwide)*
**Practice Areas:** Partner in Sidley's Washington, DC office and co-head of the firm's Broker-Dealer Regulatory practice. Advises a wide array of financial services firms, broker-dealers and hedge funds on a broad variety of regulatory, enforcement, compliance, and transaction matters. Practice focuses on regulations governing short sales (Regulation SHO), short interest reporting, Regulation M, research analyst conflicts, FINRA advertising rules, clearance and settlement, prime brokerage, and Section 13/16 beneficial ownership

reporting. Worked for over 4 years with the SEC before joining Sidley.
**Personal:** The Catholic University of America, Columbus School of Law, JD, 1997; Providence College, BA, 1994, magna cum laude.

### CAMPION, Thomas
Drinker Biddle & Reath LLP, Florham Park
973 549 7300
Thomas.Campion@dbr.com
*Featured in Products Liability (Nationwide), Litigation (New Jersey)*
See under New Jersey for profile.

### CANFIELD, Peter C
Dow Lohnes PLLC, Atlanta
770 901 8857
pcanfield@dowlohnes.com
*Featured in First Amendment Litigation (Nationwide)*
**Practice Areas:** Extensive experience counseling and representing print and electronic publishers, broadcasters, advertisers and others, including lawyers and law firms, with respect to libel, privacy and other publication related claims; rights to access and distribute news, data and other information; and the protection and licensing of intellectual property.
**Professional Memberships:** Director, Georgia First Amendment Foundation; Chair, Georgia Bar Media & Judiciary Conference; Georgia Next Generation Courts Commission; Advisory Committee, Atlanta Chapter, Federal Bar Association. Past: Defense Counsel President, Media Law Resource Center; Governing Committee, ABA Forum on Communications Law; Co-Chair, Newspaper Association of America and National Association of Broadcasters Biannual Media Law Conference.

### CANNON JR, George D
Akin Gump Strauss Hauer & Feld LLP, Washington, DC
202 887 4527
ccannon@akingump.com
*Featured in Energy & Natural Resources (Nationwide)*
**Practice Areas:** Focuses on energy regulatory and commercial matters, concentrating on the production and delivery of electricity and related products from renewable resources. Represents clients on interconnection and transmission issues and Smart Grid programs. Assists clients with acquisitions, divestitures and financings of energy projects. Experienced in FERC enforcement.
**Professional Memberships:** Energy Bar Association.
**Career:** Represents clients before FERC, DOE, federal courts and state regulatory commissions.
**Personal:** JD, George Washington University Law School, cum laude, 1994; BA, Tulane University, cum laude, Phi Beta Kappa, 1988.

### CANTERO, Raoul
White & Case LLP, Miami
305 371 2700
rcantero@whitecase.com
*Featured in Litigation (Florida), Appellate Law (Nationwide)*
See under Florida for profile.

**CAPELOUTO, Richard**
Simpson Thacher & Bartlett LLP, Palo Alto
650 251 5060
rcapelouto@stblaw.com
*Featured in Private Equity (Nationwide), Corporate/M&A (Northern California), Corporate/M&A (California)*
See under California for profile.

**CAPLAN, Gordon**
Willkie Farr & Gallagher LLP, New York
212 728 8266
gcaplan@willkie.com
*Featured in Private Equity (Nationwide), Technology (New York)*
See under New York for profile.

**CAPLAN, Stuart A**
Dentons, New York
212 398 8450
stuart.caplan@dentons.com
*Featured in Energy & Natural Resources (Nationwide)*
**Practice Areas:** Stu Caplan is handling some of the highest profile cases affecting energy companies. His practice spans the electric and natural gas industries, transactions, litigation and investigations. Stuart handles the energy market and regulatory aspects of M&A, project development and financings. Stuart litigates FERC electric market and gas pipeline cases and works with electric utilities, generators, merchant transmission and energy trading companies in ISO/RTO markets. Stuart has for years held numerous leadership positions in the energy bar and is a frequent speaker and author.

**CAPUTE, Courtney G**
Venable LLP, Baltimore
410 244 7531
cgcapute@venable.com
*Featured in Leisure & Hospitality (Nationwide)*
**Practice Areas:** Leisure & hospitality, transactional real estate, CMBS special servicing.
**Professional Memberships:** MD Bar, ABA, ABF.
**Career:** Leads Venable's Leisure and Hospitality practice, representing brand owners, management companies and hotel owners in all aspects of hotel development, acquisition and sale, with a particular focus on hotel management agreements. Maintains transactional real estate and CMBS special servicing practice as a longtime member of Venable's Special Servicing group. Special servicing work focuses on the workout of troubled CMBS loans, including complex restructurings, note sales and disposition of REO property.
**Personal:** JD, University of Maryland, 1986; BA, Ohio Wesleyan University, 1977.

**CÁRDENAS, M. Cristina**
Astigarraga Davis, Miami
305 372 8282
ccardenas@astidavis.com
*Featured in International Arbitration (Nationwide)*
**Practice Areas:** Cristina Cárdenas focuses her practice on international litigation and arbitration.
**Professional Memberships:** International Law Section of the American Bar Association.

**Career:** Colombian-born Cristina Cárdenas is a native Spanish speaker whose experience includes the representation of US and Latin American corporate clients in a variety of business related disputes, including disputes involving distributorship, manufacturing and other commercial agreements. Cárdenas has been named a 2011 and 2012 "Florida Rising Star" by Latin Lawyer 250 and by Super Lawyers; she was also named in "20 Under 40" by Poder 360, which highlighted 20 people under age 40 who have exerted influence over the arts, business, education and media in Miami. Most recently, Cárdenas Co-Chaired the ABA's Section of International Law 2012 Fall Meeting, and is Co-Chair of the Section's Latin American and Caribbean Committee. She is on the Steering Committee for the 2014 ICCA Congress.
**Personal:** Fluent in Spanish; University of North Carolina at Chapel Hill (BA with a double major in Political Science and Latin American Studies); University of Florida (JD); University of Florida University of Miami (LLM in International Law).

**CAREY, Jason**
McKenna Long & Aldridge LLP, Washington, DC
202 496 7711
jcarey@mckennalong.com
*Featured in Government (Nationwide)*
**Career:** Jason Carey represents clients in a wide range of government contracts matters, including compliance counseling, litigation with both the government and private parties, and investigations by federal and state governments. Mr Carey regularly represents government contractors in bid protests before the Government Accountability Office and the Court of Federal Claims. He has litigated more than 50 bid protests involving defense, biotechnology, telecommunications, information technology, and healthcare procurements, among others. He also regularly counsels clients regarding organizational conflicts of interest, and advises biotechnology and other high-technology firms regarding intellectual property issues specific to government contracts.

**CARLSON, R J**
Sidley Austin LLP, New York
212 839 6730
rcarlson@sidley.com
*Featured in Capital Markets (Nationwide)*
**Practice Areas:** R.J. Carlson's practice focuses on asset-backed and mortgage-backed securitizations of all types. He has represented issuers, underwriters and credit enhancement providers in a variety of structured finance transactions, encompassing both public and private offerings of securities in domestic and cross-border transactions. His experience also includes the representation of financial institutions in connection with secured lending and other financing transactions. He regularly advises clients on the application of the Uniform Commercial Code to a broad range of financings.
**Personal:** New York University School of Law, JD, 1998; Arizona State University, BS, 1994.

**CARLSON, Scott A**
Seyfarth Shaw LLP, Chicago
312 460 5946
scarlson@seyfarth.com
*Featured in Litigation (Nationwide)*
**Practice Areas:** E-discovery
**Career:** Founded and chairs Seyfarth's dedicated ten-lawyer E-Discovery and Information Governance Practice and is nationally known in this area. His practice is devoted to e-discovery and information governance issues from both the consulting and litigation perspective. Represents clients in the myriad issues related to e-discovery, computer forensics, records retention, information security and information technology.
**Publications:** Developed and continues to teach the first law school course on e-discovery in the US Writes and lectures extensively on a broad range of e-discovery topics throughout the country.
**Personal:** BS, University of Illinois; JD, Southern Illinois University School of Law.

**CARRUZZO, Fabien**
Kramer Levin Naftalis & Frankel LLP, New York
212 715 9203
fcarruzzo@kramerlevin.com
*Featured in Capital Markets (Nationwide)*
**Practice Areas:** Mr Carruzzo represents and advises hedge funds, mutual funds, investment banks, commodity traders and other market participants on regulatory and transactional derivatives matters in the full spectrum of derivatives and structured products. This includes prime brokerage, repos, securities lending, securities forwards, futures, clearing, custodial and similar arrangements, derivatives in cash and synthetic securitizations, as well as complex bespoke derivatives transactions and swaps with embedded financing. He assists clients in developing and negotiating innovative financial products that cross over banking, insurance and bankruptcy laws and in assessing and mitigating the liquidity, credit and insolvency risks inherent in trading financial products. He also advises clients on the implementation of Dodd-Frank and other regulatory reforms affecting the derivatives and futures industry.

**CARTER, James H**
WilmerHale, New York
212 230 8822
james.carter@wilmerhale.com
*Featured in International Arbitration (Nationwide)*
**Practice Areas:** Senior counsel in the firm's International Arbitration Practice Group. More than 40 years of experience as arbitrator or counsel in more than 140 arbitration cases involving joint ventures, international trade and investment disputes.
**Career:** Mr Carter, former Chairman of the American Arbitration Association Board and American Society of International Law President, has represented clients and served as arbitrator in cases worldwide. Has particular experience in joint venture, investor-state, mergers and acquisitions, investment banking and other financial

services, project finance and energy. Has extensive experience as counsel in US litigation involving commercial, corporate, antitrust, securities and intellectual property matters.

**CARVIN, Michael A**
Jones Day, Washington, DC
202 879 7643
macarvin@jonesday.com
*Featured in Appellate Law (Nationwide)*
**Practice Areas:** Specializes in constitutional, appellate, civil rights, and civil litigation against the federal government. He has argued numerous cases in the US Supreme Court and in virtually every federal appeals court. These include decisions about the constitutionality of the recent Affordable Care Act, overturning the plan to statistically adjust the census, awarding hundreds of millions in damages in contract cases against federal government, and preventing the Justice Department from seeking monetary relief against the tobacco industry under RICO. He was one of the lead lawyers, arguing before the Florida Supreme Court, for Bush in the 2000 Florida recount controversy.

**CASCIARI, Mark**
Seyfarth Shaw LLP, Chicago
312 460 5855
mcasciari@seyfarth.com
*Featured in ERISA Litigation (Nationwide)*
**Practice Areas:** ERISA Litigation.
**Professional Memberships:** Fellow, American College of Employee Benefits Counsel; Fellow, College of Labor and Employment Lawyers; ABA Labor and Employment Section, Employee Benefits Committee; Federal Bar Association; Seventh Circuit Bar Association.
**Career:** Focus on ERISA litigation and other complex employee benefits and employment litigation, including class action litigation; represents employers, plan sponsors, plans, plan administrators, fiduciaries, and independent fiduciaries in courts throughout the United States.
**Publications:** Frequent writer/speaker on ERISA litigation.
**Personal:** JD, Boston College Law School; BA, University of Southern California; Phi Beta Kappa; Adjunct Faculty, Northwestern University School of Law, Trial Advocacy.

**CASIELLO JR, Nicholas**
Fox Rothschild LLP, Atlantic City
609 572 2234
ncasiello@foxrothschild.com
*Featured in Gaming & Licensing (Nationwide)*
**Practice Areas:** Chair, Gaming Practice. 30+ years of experience in all aspects of gaming law in domestic & international jurisdictions.
**Professional Memberships:** International Association of Gaming Advisors (former trustee), NJ State Bar Association Casino Law Section (former officer/director). Co-founder/director: International Masters of Gaming Law (former officer).
**Career:** Clients include casinos, gaming equipment manufacturers & technology providers, private equity firms & other investors. Frequent lecturer & author on gaming law.

**Publications:** Author, "Gaming Developments in the Northeast;" "JAMAICA: The Legalization of Resort Style Casino Gambling," Casino Lawyer
**Personal:** JD, Seton Hall Law Center, 1978; BA, Drew University, 1975.

### CATALANO, Richard
Clifford Chance US LLP, New York
212 878 8421
richard.catalano@cliffordchance.com
*Featured in Capital Markets (Nationwide), Tax (New York)*
**Practice Areas:** Focuses on tax law with an emphasis on partnership and corporate tax planning and the taxation of real estate collective investment vehicles, including REITs and investment funds. Represents REITs and underwriters in various merger, disposition, and acquisition transactions as well as public debt and equity offerings, including IPOs. Advises sponsors and investors in connection with the formation and structuring of real estate funds and investment acquisitions structured as limited partnerships, limited liability companies, and private REITs, including the impact of UBTI on tax-exempt investors and FIRPTA on foreign investors.
**Career:** Partner at Clifford Chance since 2000.

### CAVIANI PEASE, Ann M
Dechert LLP, Silicon Valley
650 813 4851
ann.pease@dechert.com
*Featured in Life Sciences (Nationwide)*
**Practice Areas:** Dr Pease is co-chair of Dechert's intellectual property practice and chair of the patent practice. She works with companies in the biotechnology, pharmaceutical, and life sciences industries on global patent portfolio development, value maximization, opinions and assessments, and evaluating IP portfolios. She develops enforcement and defense strategies in patent infringement suits and USPTO proceedings.
**Professional Memberships:** Member, California Bar; admitted before the USPTO and US Court of Appeals for the Federal Circuit
**Personal:** University of Wisconsin-Madison (B.S., with honors, 1985); University of California, Berkeley (PhD, Biophysical Chemistry, 1990); Stanford University (JD, 1995); National Institutes of Health (post-doctoral fellowship).

### CAYNE, Howard N
Arnold & Porter LLP, Washington, DC
202 942 5656
Howard.Cayne@aporter.com
*Featured in Financial Services Regulation (Nationwide)*
**Practice Areas:** Howard Cayne counsels financial and other institutions on a broad range of regulatory, compliance, and transactional issues. He has litigated many significant enforcement, supervisory, and liability issues facing institutions, and their officers and directors. He has played a prominent role in much of the most significant federal banking litigation of the past three decades, and served as Trial Counsel in a number of cases resulting in hundreds of millions of dollars in total judgments against the United States.

**Career:** He served as senior attorney in the Enforcement and Compliance Division of the Comptroller of the Currency.

### CEREGHINI, Paul G
Bowman and Brooke LLP, Phoenix
602 643 2400
paul.cereghini@bowmanandbrooke.com
*Featured in Products Liability (Nationwide)*
**Practice Areas:** Paul Cereghini leads a very active trial practice representing manufacturers in product liability cases involving automobiles, all-terrain vehicles, motorcycles, other motorized vehicles and other products. He has defended his clients to verdict in more than three dozen catastrophic injury and wrongful death trials. In his cases, he frequently deals with mechanical engineers, computer scientists, accident re-constructionists, biomechanics and other technical experts.
**Career:** Admitted to practice in Arizona, California and Nevada, Mr Cereghini has personally defended cases in over 40 states; trying cases in places as diverse as Providence, RI; San Diego, CA; Tampa Bay, FL and Nome, AK. Mr Cereghini is a member of his firm's six person Executive Committee.
**Publications:** His trial success has been recognized numerous times by both clients and national publications, including the Wall St. Journal and The National Law Journal. He is also a frequent and requested speaker at legal and industry conferences all over the Southwest and nationwide.
**Personal:** Product Liability Advisory Council (PLAC), Arizona State University, College of Law, JD, magna cum laude, Order of the Coif.

### CHAFFETZ, Peter
Chaffetz Lindsey LLP, New York
212 257 6961
Peter.Chaffetz@chaffetzlindsey.com
*Featured in Insurance (Nationwide), Insurance (New York)*
**Practice Areas:** Commercial litigation and insurance/reinsurance dispute resolution.
**Career:** Peter Chaffetz co-founded Chaffetz Lindsey in May 2009. Previously he was the global head of Clifford Chance's litigation group and a member of their Management Committee. Peter has broad commercial litigation experience, representing US and multinational clients in complex disputes across the US. He has also focused on reinsurance and insurance insolvency since the 1980s. Peter has first chaired more than 30 trials and arbitrations. He speaks and publishes regularly on current legal issues.
**Personal:** BA, Harvard College (1974); JD, The University of Chicago Law School (1978). Admitted in New York and California.

### CHANIN, Leonard
Morrison & Foerster LLP, Washington, DC
(202) 887-8790
lchanin@mofo.com
*Featured in Financial Services Regulation (Nationwide)*
**Practice Areas:** Recognized expert in the field of consumer financial protection with extensive experience in regulation of the myriad statutes affecting retail banking. He counsels financial

institutions on consumer financial services law issues. Mr Chanin served as the Assistant Director of the Office of Regulations of the Consumer Financial Protection Bureau. Prior to that position, he was Deputy Director of the Consumer and Community Affairs Division at the Federal Reserve Board.

### CHAO, Cedric
DLA Piper LLP (US), San Francisco
415 836 2534
cedric.chao@dlapiper.com
*Featured in International Arbitration (Nationwide)*
**Practice Areas:** Experienced trial lawyer and international arbitration specialist. Lead counsel in significant disputes before US juries, judges, and major arbitration tribunals (ICC, UNCITRAL, ICDR, AAA and JAMS). Approved CIETAC and SIAC international commercial arbitrator.
**Professional Memberships:** US representative to the ICC Commission on Arbitration; Adviser, ALI's Restatement of the Law Project (the US Law of International Commercial Arbitration); Past President, Northern California International Arbitration Club.
**Career:** Clerk, Hon. William Orrick (USDC, N.D. Cal.). Federal prosecutor (1978-81).
**Personal:** BA, Stanford University; JD, Harvard Law School.

### CHAPMAN, Drew G L
WilmerHale, New York
212 295 6320
drew.chapman@wilmerhale.com
*Featured in Investment Funds (Nationwide)*
**Practice Areas:** Head, Alternative Investment Group. Focuses on corporate and securities law, with emphasis on complex business transactions for alternative investment, asset management, and financial services industries. Broad experience in transactional, structuring, formation and operation of hedge funds, private equity funds, and real estate funds. Counsels clients on crucial and complex policy, governance and regulatory issues, investigations, litigation and adversarial situations, and on transactions of all types, including mergers, acquisitions, dispositions, spin-offs and spin-outs, secondary transactions, and restructurings. Clients include financial institutions, investment banks, hedge funds, private equity funds, broker-dealers, asset management firms, and sovereign wealth funds.

### CHARLES, Scott K
Wachtell, Lipton, Rosen & Katz, New York
212 403 1202
skcharles@wlrk.com
*Featured in Bankruptcy/Restructuring (Nationwide), Bankruptcy/Restructuring (New York)*
**Practice Areas:** Practice focuses on the areas of commercial transactions, distressed mergers and acquisitions and bankruptcy and has represented many institutional lenders, creditors committees and distressed securities investors in various troubled debt situations. His recent matters have included creditor and/or acquiror representations in ATP Oil & Gas Corporation, Boston Generating, LLC., Innkeepers USA Trust,

Blockbuster, Inc., Lyondell Chemicals, Getty Petroleum Marketing, Inc, Dynegy Holdings, DS Water, Mach Gen, MSR Resorts, Graceway Pharmaceuticals, Terrestar Corp., Lifecare Holdings, Inc., Trident Exploration, General Growth Properties, Atrium Corporation, Station Casinos, Riviera Hotel & Casino, Filene's/Syms and Circuit City.
**Career:** Partner in the Restructuring and Finance Department of Wachtell, Lipton, Rosen & Katz since 1991. Has frequently lectured at various seminars conducted by the Practicing Law Institute, Turnaround and Management Association, the Continuing Legal Education and the American Bankruptcy Institute.
**Publications:** Has authored and co-authored several articles and outlines involving distressed mergers and acquisitions, prepackaged plans of reorganization, debtor-in-possession financing, the rights of secured and unsecured creditors both inside and outside of bankruptcy, and various aspects of the Chapter 11 process.
**Personal:** Graduated from Wharton School of Business, University of Pennsylvania in 1981 (BS in Economics) and from Harvard Law School in 1984 (JD); Member of Beta Alpha Psi, Beta Gamma Sigma and Phi Beta Kappa.

### CHARNESS, Michael
Vinson & Elkins LLP, Washington, DC
202 639 6780
mcharness@velaw.com
*Featured in Government (Nationwide)*
**Practice Areas:** Government contracts.
**Career:** University of Pennsylvania, BA, 1976; Georgetown University, JD, 1979. Admitted to practice: District of Columbia, 1979; District Court of Maryland; US Court of Federal Claims; US Courts of Appeal for the District of Columbia and the Federal Circuit. Extensive experience with domestic and international government claims and disputes; due diligence in mergers and acquisitions; bid protests; defense of Qui Tam actions; and internal investigations involving false claims and statements and Foreign Corrupt Practices Act violations.
**Publications:** Numerous articles on government contracts, privatization and outsourcing, and construction law. Frequent lecturer on government and international procurement issues.

### CHATMAN THOMSEN, Linda
Davis Polk & Wardwell LLP, Washington, DC
202 962 7125
linda.thomsen@davispolk.com
*Featured in Securities (Nationwide)*
**Practice Areas:** Ms Thomsen, who was the first woman to serve as the Director of the Division of Enforcement at the Securities and Exchange Commission, is a partner in Davis Polk's Litigation Department and practices in the Washington DC office. Her practice concentrates in matters related to the enforcement of the federal securities laws. She has represented clients in SEC enforcement investigations and inquiries, in enforcement matters before other agencies, including the Department of Justice (various US Attorneys Offices) and the Commodities Futures

Trading Commission, in investigations and inquiries from self-regulatory agencies, including FINRA, and in internal investigations.

## CHATTERJEE, Whitney
Sullivan & Cromwell LLP, New York
212 558 4000
chatterjeew@sullcrom.com
*Featured in Financial Services Regulation (Nationwide)*
**Professional Memberships:** ABA; BADC; NYCBA, Private Investment Funds Committee.
**Career:** Co-head, Alternative Investment Management Group; Member, Financial Institutions Group. Practice focuses on advising hedge fund managers, private equity funds and financial services companies on a wide variety of matters, including transactional, regulatory, compliance and corporate governance issues. Recent examples include acquisitions and sales of strategic interests in hedge fund managers and private equity funds, advising on bank regulatory matters affecting banks and investment funds and procedures relating to conflicts of interest, material non-public information and other compliance matters.
**Personal:** Columbia Law School (JD 2001), Hamilton College (BA 1997).

## CHAUDHRY, Rohit
Chadbourne & Parke LLP, Washington, DC
202 974 5655
rchaudhry@chadbourne.com
*Featured in Projects (Nationwide)*
**Practice Areas:** Specialises in project finance, sales and acquisitions, and restructurings in the energy and independent power industry. Has worked on numerous complex and innovative transactions in the US, Asia, the Middle East and Latin America. Represents commercial lenders, institutional investors, developers and multilateral/bilateral agencies on domestic and cross-border transactions. Co-head of the Project Finance Group.
**Professional Memberships:** New York State Bar and American Bar Associations; The Law Society in England; Delhi Bar Association.
**Personal:** Delhi University, Hindu College, BA, 1989; Delhi University, Faculty of Law, LLB, 1992; Harvard Law School, LLM, 1993; Adjunct Professor, American University Law School (2006-08).

## CHEEK, Marney
Covington & Burling LLP, Washington, DC
202 662 5267
mcheek@cov.com
*Featured in International Arbitration (Nationwide)*
**Practice Areas:** Ms Cheek represents clients in complex international commercial and investment treaty arbitrations across a range of jurisdictions and industries, including oil and gas, mining, and life sciences. Ms Cheek is also vice-chair of Covington's International Trade practice and an expert in international trade disputes.
**Professional Memberships:** Council on Foreign Relations; American Society of International Law; Advisory Board Southwestern Institute for International and Comparative Law

(Dispute Resolution); CAFTA-DR dispute settlement roster of arbitrators.
**Career:** Associate General Counsel, Office of the US Trade Representative (2003-2005).
**Personal:** Harvard Law School, JD (1998); Princeton University, MPA (2000); Stanford University, AB (1994).

## CHEFFO, Mark S
Skadden, Arps, Slate, Meagher & Flom LLP & Affiliates, New York
212 735 2183
Mark.Cheffo@skadden.com
*Featured in Products Liability (Nationwide)*
**Practice Areas:** Represents defendants in products liability, insurance and mass torts litigation, serving as national coordinating and trial counsel in both large, complex matters and individual cases. Has represented pharmaceutical and medical device manufacturers, designers of bioengineered agricultural products, and sellers of consumer and industrial products. Has handled insurance sales practices cases and numerous toxic and environmental exposure suits. Frequent lecturer on products liability issues. Involved in pro bono efforts.
**Career:** JD, Boston University School of Law, 1990 (Paul J. Liacos Scholar; Editor-in-Chief, American Journal of Law & Medicine); BA, State University of New York at Stony Brook, 1987.

## CHESLER, Evan R
Cravath, Swaine & Moore LLP, New York
212 474 1243
echesler@cravath.com
*Featured in Antitrust (New York), Life Sciences (Nationwide), Litigation (Nationwide), Intellectual Property (New York), Litigation (New York)*
**Practice Areas:** Broad litigation experience in areas including securities, intellectual property, general commercial and antitrust. Extensive trial and appellate practice in federal and state courts. Represents companies and their management in virtually every industry including technology, pharmaceutical, manufacturing and financial services.
**Professional Memberships:** ABA; NYSBA; NYCBA; Dwight Opperman Institute of Judicial Administration (President); American College of Trial Lawyers; New York Bar Foundation.
**Career:** Chairman; Presiding Partner (2007-2012); partner since 1982. Clerkship: Hon. Inzer B. Wyatt (US District Court for the Southern District of New York).
**Publications:** Numerous articles on legal topics. Chapter in 'Inside the Minds of Leading Litigators'.

## CHESTER, Jeffrey A
Kaye Scholer LLP, Los Angeles
310 788 1156
jeffrey.chester@kayescholer.com
*Featured in Projects (Nationwide)*
**Practice Areas:** Jeffrey Chester focuses on renewable energy development and project finance representing developers, sponsors, lenders and investors. He regularly works on capital raising transactions at the enterprise and project levels, including project debt, tax equity, private equi-

ty, M&A, and international and strategic joint ventures. Jeffrey has closed over 70 wind power deals throughout the US, including negotiating a 1,500 wind power purchase agreement with Southern California Edison (the largest wind PPA ever signed), as well as advising Bank of America in over 685 MWs of tax equity investments.

## CHILDRESS, Tyrone R
Jones Day, Los Angeles
213 243 2422
tchildress@jonesday.com
*Featured in Insurance (Nationwide), Insurance (California)*
**Practice Areas:** Ty Childress is one of the country's leading insurance recovery lawyers and chairs the Insurance Recovery Group at Jones Day. Ty serves as lead counsel for corporate policyholders in pursuing claims and litigation across the US He has been involved in complex insurance coverage claims relating to a variety of matters, including major product liability claims, mass tort claims, and catastrophic property losses. Ty also has extensive experience in complex business and tort litigation, with an active commercial litigation practice in areas including railroad, antitrust, product defect, real estate, environmental, toxic tort, contract, fraud, and indemnity disputes.

## CHIPERFIELD, Robert N
Weil, Gotshal & Manges LLP, New York
212 310 8701
robert.chiperfield@weil.com
*Featured in Capital Markets (Nationwide)*
**Practice Areas:** Partner in Structured Finance/Derivatives Practice. Represents issuers, underwriters, collateral managers, monoline insurers and investors in structured finance and derivatives transactions, both in the United States and abroad. Has participated in the securitization of a wide variety of asset types, including credit card receivables, residential and commercial mortgage loans, home equity loans, and auto loans, with a focus on CLOs/CDOs, asset-backed commercial paper conduit transactions and credit derivative transactions. Extensive experience with distressed securitization sponsors/vehicles and derivatives counterparties, including in bankruptcy proceedings.
**Personal:** Brown University (BA, 1986); New York University (JD, 1989).

## CHRISTENSEN, Larry E
Miller & Chevalier Chartered, Washington, DC
202 626 1469
lchristensen@milchev.com
*Featured in International Trade (Nationwide)*
**Practice Areas:** Concentrates on export controls, sanctions, and embargoes under ITAR, EAR, and various regulations issued by OFAC. Focuses on pre-acquisition due diligence, CFIUS reviews of foreign direct investment, defense of enforcement cases, as well as compliance processes, assessments, and audits.
**Career:** He is an adjunct professor of Export Controls and Trade Sanctions at the Georgetown University Law Center. Served in the US Department of Commerce for 11 years in the

Office of Chief Counsel of Export Administration and as Director of the Regulatory Policy Division.
**Personal:** JD, Duke University School of Law; BA, University of South Dakota.

## CHRISTENSEN III, Henry
McDermott Will & Emery LLP, New York
212 547 5658
hchristensen@mwe.com
*Featured in Wealth Management (Nationwide)*
**Practice Areas:** Heads private client practice in New York, and the firm's international private client practice. More than 35 years experience in private client and estate planning work. Well known in area of international estate planning. Represents some of the wealthiest individuals and families in the United States and around the world.
**Professional Memberships:** President of the International Academy of Trust and Estate Counsel; member of Board of Regents of the American College of Trust & Estate Counsel (ACTEC).
**Personal:** Harvard Law School, JD, 1969; Yale University, BA, 1966.

## CHRISTIANSEN, Brian D.
Skadden, Arps, Slate, Meagher & Flom LLP & Affiliates, Washington, DC
202 371 7852
Brian.Christiansen@skadden.com
*Featured in Financial Services Regulation (Nationwide)*
**Practice Areas:** Counsels banks, thrifts, investors and other financial services firms in connection with transactions, regulatory, compliance and enforcement matters. Advises financial institution clients on the Dodd-Frank regulatory reform legislation and related rulemaking. Represents clients before all of the major financial services regulatory agencies, including the Federal Reserve, FDIC, OCC and Department of the Treasury, as well as securities regulators.
**Career:** JD, The George Washington University, 2002 (with honors; Member, The George Washington Law Review); B.S., University of Virginia, 1999 (McIntire School of Commerce, Finance).

## CHRISTY JR, David S
Thompson Hine LLP, Washington, DC
202 263 4172
David.Christy@ThompsonHine.com
*Featured in International Trade (Nationwide)*
**Career:** David advises companies and governments on market access issues, including trade disputes and negotiations. The first private counsel to argue a member's case in a WTO dispute, David also represented Saudi Arabia in its WTO accession. He has represented governments and industries in Argentina, Brazil, Canada, Indonesia, Jamaica, Japan, Korea, Poland, St. Lucia, Taiwan, Thailand and the United States. He also advises on trade policy issues before Congress and executive branch agencies, as well as on international arbitration, customs and trade remedy matters, and related court proceedings. David publishes frequently and teaches international trade at Georgetown University Law Center.

**CHU, Morgan**
Irell & Manella, Los Angeles
310 203 7000
mchu@irell.com
*Featured in Litigation (Nationwide), Intellectual Property (California)*
See under California for profile.

**CHUNG, Ernest**
Blank Rome LLP, New York
212 885 5447
EChung@BlankRome.com
*Featured in Projects (Nationwide)*
**Practice Areas:** Ernest Chung concentrates his practice in the areas of project finance and development, both domestically and internationally. He advises financial institutions, sponsors, governments and multilateral institutions in the development and financing of major infrastructure, energy and natural resources projects. Recently, he has been particularly active advising clients in connection with a variety of renewable energy projects and on the development and financing of pipelines and other midstream energy infrastructure. Internationally, he has significant experience representing clients in emerging markets, including the countries of the former Soviet Union, Latin America, the Middle East, Africa and Asia. More information:
www.BlankRome.com/EChung.

**CHUNG, Steven**
Hughes Hubbard & Reed LLP, Washington, DC
202 721 4749
chungs@hugheshubbard.com
*Featured in Transportation (Nationwide)*
**Practice Areas:** Mr Chung represents sponsors, lenders, export credit agencies and commercial banks in connection with a broad spectrum of international financial and corporate transactions, including acquisitions, joint ventures, domestic and cross border secured and unsecured financings, leveraged leasing, structured financings, restructurings and credit enhancements. He has extensive experience in a wide variety of aircraft and other structured equipment financings, including aircraft acquisitions and dispositions; leveraged lease transactions; securitizations; syndicated credit facilities; PDP and warehouse facilities; and joint venture transactions.
**Professional Memberships:** Member, State Bars of NY and Washington, D.C.
**Personal:** JD, New York University School of Law; undergraduate, Georgetown University.

**CHURCHILL, David A**
Jenner & Block LLP, Washington, DC
202 639 6056
dchurchill@jenner.com
*Featured in Government (Nationwide)*
**Career:** David A. Churchill is Co-Chair of the Government Contracts Practice. His practice includes litigation of disputes involving the award, performance and termination of federal contract disputes, including the Court of Federal Claims, the agency boards of contract appeals, and the Government Accountability Office. He has an active counseling practice in contract award-related matters and on issues arising during performance of government contracts and subcontracts. He also counsels in matters involving international public contracts under the US Foreign Military Sales and Foreign Military Finance programs. He served as chair of the Public Contract Law Section of the American Bar Association.

**CIERI, Richard M**
Kirkland & Ellis LLP, New York
212 446 4770
richard.cieri@kirkland.com
*Featured in Bankruptcy/Restructuring (Nationwide), Bankruptcy/Restructuring (New York)*
**Practice Areas:** Mr Cieri's practice involves representing financially challenged companies, debtors, boards of directors, creditors' committees and creditors in out-of-court and in-court restructurings; providing advice in connection with fiduciary duties, legacy liabilities (including environmental, retiree, pension tort and product liability claims facing a debtor), and technology and intellectual property issues; structuring of secured and commercial transactions (including advice related to fraudulent conveyance, corporate spin-offs and related securities issues); and the acquisition of and lending to financially troubled companies.
**Personal:** University of Michigan Law School, JD, cum laude, 1981; State University of New York at Buffalo, BA, 1978.

**CIRAOLO, Caroline**
Rosenberg Martin Greenberg, LLP, Baltimore
410 547 7852
cciraolo@rosenbergmartin.com
*Featured in Tax (Nationwide)*
**Professional Memberships:** Fellow and Regent, American College of Tax Counsel; Vice-Chair, ABA Tax Section, Civil & Criminal Tax Penalties Committee; Chair, MD State Bar Tax Section (2008-09); Thomson West Tax Advisory Board; Advisory Board, CCH Journal of Tax Practice & Procedure.
**Publications:** Criminal Tax Workshop: The Basics (2012); Tax Controversy Training for Pro Bono Lawyers (2012); What You Need to Know About FBAR and International Information Returns Including Defending Against and Litigating the Penalties (2009).
**Personal:** Best Lawyers, Lawyer of the Year 2012, Litigation and Controversy – Tax, Baltimore, MD; Maryland Super Lawyers (Tax) (2009-13), Top 10 Maryland Attorneys (2013).

**CIRESI, Michael V**
Robins, Kaplan, Miller & Ciresi LLP, Minneapolis
612 349 8500
mvciresi@rkmc.com
*Featured in Products Liability (Nationwide), Litigation (Minnesota)*
See under Minnesota for profile.

**CIVIDANES, Emilio W**
Venable LLP, Washington, DC
202 344 4414
EWCividanes@Venable.com
*Featured in Privacy & Data Security (Nationwide)*
**Practice Areas:** Milo Cividanes counsels technology and consumer product companies regarding compliance with privacy, data security, consumer protection and e-commerce regulations. Defends companies in litigation and government investigations. Advises trade associations and companies regarding policy and legislative strategies. Participated in drafting of nearly every federal privacy regulation implemented over past 25 years.
**Professional Memberships:** International Association of Privacy Professionals; Fellow, American Bar Foundation.
**Career:** Among the nation's first privacy lawyers. Counsel to the Technology and the Law Subcommittee of US Senate Judiciary Committee. Former Adjunct Professor, Georgetown University Law Center.
**Personal:** JD, University of Pennsylvania, 1983; BA, Haverford College, 1979.

**CLARK, Barton B**
Latham & Watkins LLP, Washington, DC
202 637 1009
barton.clark@lw.com
*Featured in Investment Funds (Nationwide)*
**Practice Areas:** Focuses on private equity capital formation, investment structuring and related transactions. Represents private equity funds and their sponsors and advisers, as well as other market participants, both internationally and within the US. Advises sponsors of private investment funds on registration, compliance and transactional matters under the Investment Advisers Act of 1940 and the Investment Company Act of 1940.
**Professional Memberships:** Member, District of Columbia and New York State bars.
**Career:** Co-Chair, Investment Funds Group.
**Personal:** JD, with honors, University of Chicago Law School, 1994; BA, magna cum laude, Harvard University, 1990.

**CLARK, James**
Cahill Gordon & Reindel LLP, New York
212 701 3849
jclark@cahill.com
*Featured in Banking & Finance (Nationwide), Capital Markets (Nationwide)*
**Practice Areas:** Represents major commercial and investment banks and corporations in capital market transactions, including debt and equity offerings and bank financings, as well as merger and acquisition transactions and debt restructurings.
**Personal:** Member, firm's Executive Committee. Stonehill College, BS, 1976. Albany Law School, JD, 1979, Editor-in-Chief, Albany Law Review.

**CLARK, James**
Sidley Austin LLP, Chicago
312 853 7776
jclark@sidley.com
*Featured in Banking & Finance (Illinois), Banking & Finance (Nationwide)*
See under Illinois for profile.

**CLARK, Matthew J**
Arent Fox LLP, Washington, DC
202 828 3435
matthew.clark@arentfox.com
*Featured in International Trade (Nationwide)*
**Practice Areas:** Matt's practice focuses on adversarial international trade proceedings and international arbitrations. His practice also covers import and export regulatory matters, including penalty proceedings, investigations, and sanctions. Matt's clients are major international corporations and governments, who he represents in matters arising under the antidumping and countervailing duty laws of the United States, the WTO Agreements, and the NAFTA, among other bodies of law. In addition to an active global dispute resolution practice, Matt is Arent Fox's Managing Partner and a long-serving member of the Firm's Executive Committee.

**CLARK, Peter B**
Cadwalader, Wickersham & Taft LLP, Washington, DC
202 862 2448
peter.clark@cwt.com
*Featured in International Trade (Nationwide)*
**Practice Areas:** Represents clients in all aspects of criminal investigations and litigation, including those involving the Foreign Corrupt Practices Act, as well as in complex civil litigation. Handled hundreds of voluntary disclosures of illicit corporate payments and securities enforcement matters while at the SEC and the DOJ, and successfully prosecuted the Department's first transnational bribery cases. Played an important role in the enactment and subsequent amendments to the Foreign Corrupt Practices Act (FCPA), and was the principal negotiator of the Organisation for Economic Co-operation and Development's (OECD) anti-bribery convention and the Council of Europe Criminal Law Convention.
**Career:** Former Deputy Chief, Fraud Section, Criminal Division, US Department of Justice (DOJ); Former Special Counsel, Division of Enforcement, Securities and Exchange Commission (SEC).
**Publications:** Frequent speaker, lecturer and author of numerous articles and publications.
**Personal:** JD, University of Pennsylvania Law School; AB, Brown University.

**CLARK, Timothy**
Sidley Austin LLP, New York
212 839 5797
tclark@sidley.com
*Featured in Investment Funds (Nationwide)*
**Practice Areas:** Partner in New York. Represents private fund clients on a global basis including (i) sponsors of buyout/growth equity funds, energy funds, bank/financial services funds, secondary funds, real estate funds, RMB-denominated funds, credit opportunity funds and venture capital funds, (ii) managers in spin-outs from financial institutions, (iii) buyers, sellers and other participants in secondary/structured secondary transactions and (iv) institutional clients investing in, or co-investing alongside, private funds.

**Personal:** New York University School of Law, JD, 1988, cum laude, Order of the Coif; Wesleyan University, BA, 1985, Phi Beta Kappa, Heideman Award Community Service.

## CLARY, Richard W
Cravath, Swaine & Moore LLP, New York
212 474 1227
rclary@cravath.com
*Featured in Litigation (Nationwide), Securities (Nationwide), Litigation (New York)*
**Practice Areas:** Securities, antitrust, patent, trade secret, trademark, bankruptcy and commercial litigation (trials and appeals). International and domestic arbitrations.
**Professional Memberships:** ABA; NYSBA; NYCBA.
**Career:** Partner since 1985; Head of Litigation (2005-2010). Clerkships: Hon. Thurgood Marshall (US Supreme Court), Hon. Walter R. Mansfield (US Court of Appeals, Second Circuit).
**Publications:** PLI's annual 'Bet the Company Litigation' conference (Chair).
**Personal:** Harvard Law School (JD, magna cum laude, 1978; Law Review; Sears Prize); Amherst College (BA, magna cum laude, 1975; Phi Beta Kappa). NYCBA: Vice President (2011-2012); Legal Aid Society: Vice Chair (2003-2007), Board of Advisors; Harvard Law School: Lecturer of Law.

## CLAYTON, Jay
Sullivan & Cromwell LLP, New York
212 558 3445
claytonwj@sullcrom.com
*Featured in Capital Markets (Nationwide)*
**Professional Memberships:** American Bar Association; Lecturer in Law at University of Pennsylvania Law School (2009-2013); Chairman New York City Bar Committee on International Business Transactions (since 2010).
**Career:** Experience in domestic and cross-border mergers and acquisitions and capital markets transactions, including various matters involving financial institutions. Regularly represents several high net worth families and private companies. Also has advised various multinational companies and their boards in connection with corporate investigations and regulatory matters.
**Personal:** University of Pennsylvania Law School (JD, 1993); Cambridge University (BA/MA, Economics, 1990); University of Pennsylvania (BS Engineering, 1988).

## CLAYTON, Lewis R
Paul, Weiss, Rifkind, Wharton & Garrison LLP, New York
212 373 3215
lclayton@paulweiss.com
*Featured in ERISA Litigation (Nationwide)*
**Practice Areas:** Co-Chair of Intellectual Property and ERISA Litigation Groups. Has tried major cases and counseled clients in a broad range of complex commercial litigation matters. Represents major banks, financial institutions and private equity and investment management firms in commercial disputes; advises on fiduciary responsibilities and corporate governance issues. Also focuses on intellectual property litigation and counseling and ERISA, benefits and pension liti-

gation. Extensive experience counseling clients in a broad range of patent, copyright, trademark and advertising matters. Intellectual property litigation columnist for The New York Law Journal and The National Law Journal.

## CLEARY, John
Seward & Kissel LLP, New York
212 574 1255
cleary@sewkis.com
*Featured in Investment Funds (Nationwide)*
**Practice Areas:** Investment management; private funds; investment advisers; regulatory investigations and enforcement.
**Professional Memberships:** Mr Cleary is a member of the New York State Bar Association.
**Career:** Mr Cleary is a partner in Seward & Kissel's Investment Management Group. John has practiced at the firm since 1984, and has been a partner since 1993. Mr Cleary specializes in the formation and representation of private investment partnerships, various offshore investment vehicles, the registration of investment advisers and related regulatory compliance, the formation and CFTC registration of commodity pools, commodity pool operators and commodity trading advisors, and general securities and general tax matters.
**Personal:** Mr Cleary received a BA degree from Fairfield University, magna cum laude, in 1981, a JD degree from Fordham University School of Law, cum laude, in 1984, and a LLM degree in Tax from New York University School of Law in 1988.

## CLEARY, John J
Goodwin Procter LLP, Boston
617 570 1199
jcleary@goodwinprocter.com
*Featured in Employee Benefits & Executive Compensation (Nationwide), Employee Benefits & Executive Compensation (Massachusetts)*
See under Massachusetts for profile.

## CLEMENTS, William L
Miller & Chevalier Chartered, Washington, DC
202 626 1495
wclements@milchev.com
*Featured in International Trade (Nationwide)*
**Career:** Former member of the National Security Council Staff, and former Office Director at the Bureau of Export Administration, US Department of Commerce. Served as Corporate Counsel, International Trade Regulation, for the General Electric Company as the principal trade controls lawyer. Former member of the US Department of State, Defense Trade Advisory Group.
**Personal:** LLM (International and Comparative Law), Georgetown University Law Center, 1983; JD, Suffolk University Law School, cum laude, 1976; BS, Engineering, Cornell University, 1970.

## CLINTON, William J
White & Case LLP, Washington, DC
202 626 3620
wclinton@whitecase.com
*Featured in International Trade (Nationwide)*
**Career:** William J. Clinton concentrates in resolving cross-border trade and investment problems. His clients include multinational corpora-

tions, trade associations and sovereign governments facing issues raised by the complex rules that govern international commerce. Mr Clinton has handled disputes in virtually every aspect of the import trade and investment laws of the United States and numerous other jurisdictions worldwide. He is a recognized authority on legal developments related to the World Trade Organization (WTO), the North American Free Trade Agreement and other multilateral trade arrangements. To view a comprehensive biography, please visit www.whitecase.com/wclinton.

## COBERLY, Linda T
Winston & Strawn LLP, Chicago
312 558 8768
lcoberly@winston.com
*Featured in Appellate Law (Nationwide)*
**Career:** A founding member of Winston's Appellate and Critical Motions Practice, Ms Coberly has argued appeals in five federal circuits and various state courts across the country. She counsels clients on strategic issues at all stages of litigation, from trial through proceedings before the Supreme Court. She is well known for her expertise in corporate fraud litigation – specifically, defending auditors and others following the disclosure of corporate fraud. She served as a law clerk to Justice Breyer of the Supreme Court and to Judge Douglas Ginsburg of the DC Circuit.

## COCCI, Meghan
Dentons, Phoenix
602 508 3903
meghan.cocci@dentons.com
*Featured in Leisure & Hospitality (Nationwide)*
**Practice Areas:** Hotels and Leisure. Represents hotel owners and operators in the management, acquisition and development of hotels, resorts, spas, golf courses and mixed use hotel and leisure projects around the world. Primary focus on management and license agreements for hotels and leisure facilities in the upscale and luxury sectors. Also negotiates golf, spa, food and beverage management, access, use and licensing arrangements. Works with clients around the world to provide hotel industry expertise and creative ideas for structuring of hotels with serviced residences, condo-hotels and other mixed-use leisure projects to meet client's business objectives.

## COCHRAN, Martha L
Arnold & Porter LLP, Washington, DC
202 942 5228
Martha.Cochran@aporter.com
*Featured in Government (Nationwide)*
**Practice Areas:** Martha Cochran is a partner in Arnold & Porter LLP's legislative and public policy practice group. She has represented numerous public corporations, financial institutions, private funds, accounting firms, trade associations, and individuals in legislative matters and oversight investigations before the US Senate and House of Representatives. She advises on government ethics, lobbying, and federal election law compliance and represents clients before the Federal Election Commission. Ms Cochran also practices in the firm's financial institutions group, conducts internal investigations, counsels on the implemen-

tation of compliance programs, and represents clients before the Securities and Exchange Commission and other financial regulators.

## COCO, Joseph A
Skadden, Arps, Slate, Meagher & Flom LLP & Affiliates, New York
212 735 3050
Joseph.Coco@skadden.com
*Featured in Private Equity (Nationwide), Corporate/M&A (New York)*
**Practice Areas:** Focuses his practice on acquisition and disposition transactions, restructurings and financings for both public and private companies. Leads negotiated and hostile acquisitions, IPOs and public and private financings as borrower's, issuer's or underwriters' counsel. M&A specialist across numerous major industries, including many of the largest and most complex REIT matters. Represents private equity sponsors in connection with acquisitions, dispositions and financings. Counsels portfolio companies of private equity sponsors on a wide range of corporate matters, including governance.
**Career:** JD, Fordham University School of Law, 1981 (Member, Fordham Law Review); BBA, Finance, Iona College, 1978 (summa cum laude).

## COGAN, Sarah E
Simpson Thacher & Bartlett LLP, New York
212 455 3575
scogan@stblaw.com
*Featured in Investment Funds (Nationwide)*
**Practice Areas:** Head of Investment Management Practice Group. Advises clients on corporate and securities law, including investment management and M&A matters. Represents closed-end and open-end funds, investment advisers, underwriters and independent directors of funds.
**Professional Memberships:** Association of the Bar of the City of New York and former member Committee on Investment Management Regulation; New York State and American Bar Associations.
**Career:** Joined firm, 1981; Partner, 1989.
**Publications:** "The Fund Board of Directors and the Fund's Relationship with the Adviser" chapter in ABCs of Mutual Funds, PLI 2009.
**Personal:** BA, Yale University (1978); JD, Georgetown University Law Center (1981).

## COGUT, Charles 'Casey'
Simpson Thacher & Bartlett LLP, New York
212 455 2550
ccogut@stblaw.com
*Featured in Private Equity (Nationwide), Corporate/M&A (New York)*
**Practice Areas:** Active in STB's M&A and private equity practices. In 2012 represented Eaton Corporation in its acquisition of Cooper Industries; in 2011 represented Microsoft in its acquisition of Skype and the Mosaic Company in its split off from Cargill. Specialises in domestic, international and cross-border M&A transactions. Advises boards of directors on corporate governance and responsibilities of directors.
**Career:** Joined firm, 1973; Partner, 1980.

**Personal:** BA, summa cum laude, Lehigh University (1969); JD, University of Pennsylvania Law School (1973). Member of Adjunct Faculty of University of Pennsylvania Law School. Member of the Board of Cold Spring Harbor Laboratory.

## COHEN, Charles W
Hughes Hubbard & Reed LLP, New York
212 837 6856
cohen@hugheshubbard.com
*Featured in Products Liability (Nationwide)*

**Practice Areas:** Litigation, both domestic and international, with an emphasis on complex, often multi-jurisdictional litigation and products liability; Co-Chair, eDiscovery Practice Group.
**Professional Memberships:** Member (and former Chair 2010-2012), New Jersey Defense Association Products Liability Committee; Member, Defense Research Institute E-Discovery Committee; Member, American Bar Association, Section of Litigation; Member, International Bar Association, Litigation Committee.
**Career:** Partner since 2005; Co-Chair of the firm's Technology Committee.
**Personal:** Georgetown University Law Center, JD, 1995 (cum laude); Brooklyn College, BA, 1992 (magna cum laude); Phi Beta Kappa.

## COHEN, David
Vinson & Elkins LLP, New York
dcohen@velaw.com
*Featured in Energy & Natural Resources (Nationwide), Corporate/M&A (New York)*

**Practice Areas:** David's practice focuses primarily on corporate work, including mergers and acquisitions, joint ventures and project development. David's clients include publicly-traded energy companies, private equity funds, portfolio companies, and financial services companies. David advises these clients in connection with their acquisition, development, financing and disposition of energy and infrastructure assets in the US and internationally.
**Career:** David was admitted to New York Bar in 2008 and the District of Columbia Bar in 1989. He was admitted to the partnership in 1991.
**Personal:** Graduated from The University of Texas School of Law, JD, 1983; The University of Texas, BA, 1980.

## COHEN, H Rodgin
Sullivan & Cromwell LLP, New York
212 558 4000
cohenhr@sullcrom.com
*Featured in Financial Services Regulation (Nationwide), Corporate/M&A (New York)*

**Career:** Senior Chairman since 2010; Chairman, 2000-2009. Acquisitions, regulatory, corporate governance and securities law matters for US/non-US financial institutions/trade associations. Counseled global financial institutions in connection with global financial crisis, including AIG, Fannie Mae, GS, JPMorgan Chase, Lehman, MUFG, Wachovia. Works on wide-ranging regulatory and investigative matters with various governmental agencies. Involved in most major US bank acquisitions and significant cross-border and non-US acquisitions and investments, including Hudson City-M&T, BlackRock-BGI, Bank of

Montreal-M&I, Wells Fargo-Wachovia, PNC-National City, Toronto Dominion-Commerce, BONY-Mellon, MUFG-Morgan Stanley, MUFG-UnionBanCal. Member of the FDIC Systemic Resolution Advisory Committee.
**Personal:** Harvard Law (1968); Harvard (1965).

## COHEN, Lewis
Clifford Chance US LLP, New York
212 878 3144
lewis.cohen@cliffordchance.com
*Featured in Capital Markets (Nationwide)*

**Practice Areas:** Focuses on securitization, representing issuers, credit enhancers and underwriters, including investment banks, commercial banks and other financial institutions, in cross-border securitizations and other structured finance transactions. Has been involved in public and private transactions in the securitization of a wide variety of assets, including bank and private label credit card receivables, trade receivables and equipment leases, and 'future flow' securitizations of assets including oil and maritime freight receivables. Has worked on structured financings involving domestic US assets, as well as assets originated in Europe, Asia and South America.
**Career:** Partner at Clifford Chance since 1997.

## COHEN, Lori G
Greenberg Traurig, LLP, Atlanta
678 553 2385
CohenL@gtlaw.com
*Featured in Products Liability (Nationwide), Litigation (Georgia)*
See under Georgia for profile.

## COHEN, Robin L
Kasowitz, Benson, Torres & Friedman LLP, New York
212 506 1770
rcohen@kasowitz.com
*Featured in Insurance (Nationwide), Insurance (New York)*

**Practice Areas:** Head of the insurance practice, Robin Cohen is a preeminent insurance trial attorney, representing policyholders in complex insurance coverage and insurer bad-faith matters throughout the country. She litigates significant, cutting-edge cases involving asbestos, product liability, toxic tort, environmental, D&O, first-party, employee dishonesty and employment coverage matters. She has recovered over one billion dollars for Fortune 500 clients.
**Career:** Recognized by The National Law Journal as one of the "50 Most Influential Women Lawyers in America," and by Business Insurance as a "Woman to Watch," as well as in several publications as one of the nation's leading insurance litigators.

## COHEN, Steven N
Cadwalader, Wickersham & Taft LLP, Charlotte
704 348 5176
steven.cohen@cwt.com
*Featured in Banking & Finance (Nationwide)*

**Practice Areas:** Resident in New York, NY and Charlotte, NC. Represents domestic and foreign commercial banks, investment banks, funds and other financial institutions in a wide variety of

financing transactions, including leveraged finance and other syndicated bank loan transactions, power plant and renewable energy financings, commodity finance transactions, the financing of financial assets, structured finance transactions, cross-border financings, hedge fund financings, credit enhancement transactions, workouts and debtor-in-possession financings, the trading of distressed debt and bankruptcy claims, and various innovative financing transactions. Serves as a member of Cadwalader's Legal Opinions Committee.
**Professional Memberships:** American Bar Association (including the Section of Business Law).
**Personal:** JD, New York University School of Law (Note and Comment Editor, New York University Law Review); Baccalauréat, Lyceé Classique Mixte, Saintes, France (high honors); Wesleyan University (magna cum laude).

## COHEN, Susan
Mintz Levin Cohn Ferris Glovsky and Popeo PC, Boston
617 348 4468
SJCohen@mintz.com
*Featured in Immigration (Nationwide)*

**Practice Areas:** Founder/Chairperson, Immigration Section.
**Professional Memberships:** American Immigration Lawyers Association (AILA), 8-term Co-chair Immigration Subcommittee of ABA Section of International Law. ABA liaison to USDOL.
**Career:** Best Lawyers in America, International Who's Who of Corporate Immigration, Martindale-Hubbell "AV" rating, Chambers Global.
**Publications:** Frequent writer on immigration issues. AILA Editorial Review Board Member; Contributed to USCIS regulations implementing the US Immigration Act of 1990; DOL regulations implementing PERM; Co-Editor in Chief, David Stanton Manual on Labor Certification; Editor, ABA's Immigration and Nationality Law Newsletter.
**Personal:** BA, magna cum laude, Brandeis University JD, cum laude, Cardozo Law School. Law Review Member.

## COHEN (FORMERLY FLOWE), Carol Connor
Arent Fox LLP, Washington, DC
202 857 6054
carol.cohen@arentfox.com
*Featured in ERISA Litigation (Nationwide)*

**Practice Areas:** Carol Connor Cohen re-joined Arent Fox in 1995 after eight years at the Pension Benefit Guaranty Corporation, the last six as General Counsel. Her nationally-recognized ERISA practice emphasizes trial court and appellate litigation, and representing employers and fiduciaries in fiduciary matters and government investigations. She successfully argued two ERISA cases in the Supreme Court and has been lead counsel in numerous ERISA class actions, including employer "stock drop" cases, technical challenges to cash balance plans and other forms of

defined benefit plans, ESOP matters, disability and other benefit claims, and complex corporate transactions.

## COLAIZZI, Roger
Venable LLP, Washington, DC
202 344 8051
racolaizzi@Venable.com
*Featured in Advertising (Nationwide)*

**Practice Areas:** Roger Colaizzi chairs Venable's National IP Litigation and Advertising Litigation Group. He has significant trial experience litigating IP Rights, false advertising, unfair competition and other Lanham Act, state deceptive trade practices, counterfeiting and class action claims. Mr Colaizzi has tried numerous jury and nonjury cases, and has successfully brought and defended against dozens of preliminary injunction motions and requests for TROs in advertising and brand protection litigation. Mr Colaizzi represents clients before the FTC and state AGs as well as self-regulatory bodies (i.e. ERSP, NAD).
**Personal:** JD, Delaware Law School, 1983; BA, Dickinson College, 1980.

## COLE, Christopher
Crowell & Moring LLP, Washington, DC
202 624 2701
ccole@crowell.com
*Featured in Advertising (Nationwide)*

**Practice Areas:** Co-chair of Crowell & Moring's Advertising & Product Risk Management Group. Practices complex commercial litigation and regularly advises regarding the development, substantiation, approval, and defense of advertising campaigns. Frequently represents companies that have complex product development, reputational, and marketing concerns that require overlapping and multifaceted solutions. Has represented some of the world's leading companies in industries such as food and beverages, media and telecommunications, and consumer products.
**Personal:** Boston University School of Law: JD, magna cum laude, 1992; Articles Editor, Law Review. University of Miami: MS, 1989; Rosenstiel Fellowship. Yale University: BS, 1987.

## COLEMAN, Ira
McDermott Will & Emery LLP, Miami
305 347 6556
icoleman@mwe.com
*Featured in Healthcare (Florida), Healthcare (Nationwide)*

**Practice Areas:** Partner-in-charge of Miami office and Head of Miami Health Department. Concentrates on health care M&A, health care private equity and formation of cutting-edge delivery systems. Has served as counsel in connection with the development and operation of numerous corporate compliance programs for health care clients.
**Professional Memberships:** Board-certified in health law by Florida Bar; Florida Bar; American Bar Association; American Health Lawyers Association; Florida Academy of Healthcare Attorneys; American College of Healthcare Executives.

**Personal:** Nova Southeastern University, Shepard Broad Law Center, JD, 1986; University of Miami School of Law, LLM, 1987; State University of New York-Albany, BA, 1983.

## COLGIN JR, William F
Morgan, Lewis & Bockius LLP, San Francisco
415 442 1347
wcolgin@morganlewis.com
*Featured in Tax (Nationwide), Tax (California)*
**Practice Areas:** William F. Colgin, Jr., a partner in Morgan Lewis's Tax Practice, represents corporate clients in all phases of civil tax controversy and litigation. He has successfully litigated complex cases in the Tax Court, federal courts and state courts, and represents clients before the IRS and state taxing authorities. Client industries include technology and financial services, and issues include transfer pricing and SALT. His broad controversy experience includes administrative rulings, pre-filing agreements, audit and examination defense, administrative appeals/settlements, voluntary disclosures and extensive negotiations. Previously, he was a trial attorney in the Tax Division of the DOJ.

## COLLETTA, Anthony J
Sullivan & Cromwell LLP, New York
212 558 4608
collettaa@sullcrom.com
*Featured in Real Estate (Nationwide), Capital Markets (Nationwide), Real Estate (New York)*
**Career:** Partner since 1997. Concentrates in commercial real estate, private equity fund formation and transactional work, financings, loan workouts and restructurings, JVs, general corporate matters. Works on formation and fund-raising of private equity funds focused on real estate and related assets and represents these funds, as well as hedge funds, in investing/financing activities. Transactional experience includes purchase, development and disposition of real estate assets and companies, purchase of distressed loans, structuring of senior and mezzanine financings (secured and unsecured), workout and restructuring of troubled credits and of JVs.
**Personal:** St. John's University Law School (JD, 1988); Fordham (BA, 1985).

## COLLEY, Mark
Arnold & Porter LLP, Washington, DC
202 942 5720
Mark.Colley@aporter.com
*Featured in Government (Nationwide)*
**Practice Areas:** Chair's the firm's Government Contracts Practice Group. Mr Colley litigates substantial bid protests, as well as government and commercial contract disputes. He provides counsel on regulatory compliance and data rights matters, conducts internal investigations, and defends False Claims Act and suspension/debarment actions. His projects frequently involve highly complex technology and sophisticated services (including classified programs), and include state government and commercial item procurements.
**Professional Memberships:** ABA Public Contract Law Section, Chair; past Chair, Bid Protest Committee.

**Career:** Represents The Humane Society of the United States on wildlife protection projects.

## COLLIN, Thomas J
Thompson Hine LLP, Cleveland
216 566 5509
Tom.Collin@ThompsonHine.com
*Featured in Franchising (Nationwide), Litigation (Ohio)*
See under Ohio for profile.

## COLLINS, Daniel
Munger, Tolles & Olson LLP, Los Angeles
213 683 9125
Daniel.Collins@mto.com
*Featured in Appellate Law (Nationwide)*
**Practice Areas:** Practice focuses on appellate and complex civil litigation. Has argued more than 33 cases in the Ninth Circuit, including two en banc cases. Recent arguments include: Native Village of Kivalina v. ExxonMobil Corp., 696 F.3d 849 (9th Cir. 2012) (Shell Oil); Boeing Satellite Systems International, Inc. v. ICO Global Communications (Operations) Ltd., 2012 WL 1238508 (Cal. App. Apr. 13, 2012) (Boeing).
**Career:** Partner at the firm. Department of Justice, associate deputy attorney general; law clerk to Justice Antonin Scalia.
**Personal:** Stanford Law School (with distinction); Harvard College (AB, summa cum laude).

## CONLAN, James F
Sidley Austin LLP, Chicago
312 853 6890
jconlan@sidley.com
*Featured in Bankruptcy/Restructuring (Nationwide), Bankruptcy/Restructuring (Illinois)*
See under Illinois for profile.

## CONNALLY IV, John B
Vinson & Elkins LLP, Houston
713 758 3316
jconnally@velaw.com
*Featured in Energy & Natural Resources (Nationwide)*
**Practice Areas:** Domestic and international mergers and acquisitions, project development and finance transactions, private equity investments, joint ventures and a variety of energy matters.
**Professional Memberships:** Association of International Petroleum Negotiators (AIPN) Board of Directors.
**Career:** Admitted to the Texas Bar in 1997 and New York Bar in 2008. Admitted to the Vinson & Elkins partnership in 2006. Member of the firm's Management Committee.
**Personal:** Graduated from The University of Texas School of Law, JD high honors, 1997 (Chancellors; Order of the Coif; Texas Law Review); Vanderbilt University, BA, 1994 (Phi Beta Kappa; Founder's Medal).

## CONNELLY, Warren E
Akin Gump Strauss Hauer & Feld LLP, Washington, DC
202 887 4046
wconnelly@akingump.com
*Featured in International Trade (Nationwide)*
**Practice Areas:** Warren Connelly is well known for his representation of clients in proceedings

before the Department of Commerce, International Trade Commission, Office of the US Trade Representative, US Customs and Border Protection, Court of International Trade, and US Court of Appeals for the Federal Circuit. Handles a wide variety of import- and export-related matters, including trade policy, trade legislation, unfair trade litigation, WTO dispute resolution proceedings, NAFTA Chapter Eleven arbitrations, safeguards, and customs law. Has been extensively involved in a variety of general administrative and civil court litigation.
**Personal:** AB, Dartmouth College (1968); JD, Georgetown University Law Center (1973).

## CONNIFF, Martin
Morgan, Lewis & Bockius LLP, New York
212 309 6835
mconniff@morganlewis.com
*Featured in Transportation (Nationwide)*
**Practice Areas:** Martin F. Conniff, a partner in Morgan Lewis's Business & Finance practice, represents leading international companies and their US affiliates in the container shipping, marine container terminal, shipbuilding and oil and gas sectors, as well as international banks lending to the maritime industry. His practice includes complex cross border mergers and acquisitions, joint ventures and financing transactions, frequently involving citizenship, national security and other regulatory considerations relating to foreign investment in the US He advises clients on a wide range of issues encountered by maritime industry participants, including government investigations and disputes under charter parties and shipbuilding contracts.

## CONWAY JR, William B
Skadden, Arps, Slate, Meagher & Flom LLP & Affiliates, Washington, DC
202 371 7135
William.Conway@skadden.com
*Featured in Energy & Natural Resources (Nationwide)*
**Practice Areas:** Focuses on the representation of independent power producers, financial investors and utilities in a wide variety of regulatory, transactional and merger-related matters. From 1985 to 1993, served as minority counsel and then senior counsel to the US Senate Committee on Energy and Natural Resources. Was the principal staff architect of Title VII of the Energy Policy Act of 1992, which effectively made possible competition in wholesale electric markets. Recently co-authored article titled "Sun Shines on Independent Transmission," Project Finance International.
**Career:** JD, Louisiana State University-Paul M. Herbert Law Center; AB, Dartmouth College.

## COOK, David B
Goodwin Procter LLP, Washington, DC
202 346 4189
dcook@goodwinprocter.com
*Featured in Transportation (Nationwide)*
**Practice Areas:** Mr Cook specializes in counseling and litigation on behalf of companies involved in maritime and intermodal transportation, including international container carriers

and marine terminal operators. He provides advice on a wide range of legal issues relating to business planning, agreements and disputes, and handles a variety of matters before the federal agencies dealing with maritime and intermodal transportation, including the Federal Maritime Commission, the Surface Transportation Board and the US Maritime Administration, as well as before federal district and appellate courts.
**Personal:** JD, Yale University Law School, 1971; BA, Princeton University, 1968 (Phi Beta Kappa).

## COOPER, Elizabeth A
Simpson Thacher & Bartlett LLP, New York
212 455 3407
ecooper@stblaw.com
*Featured in Financial Services Regulation (Nationwide)*
**Practice Areas:** Partner in Corporate Department, focusing on mergers and acquisitions for financial institution clients. Significant transactions include Carlyle's acquisition of the TCW Group, acquisition of optionsXpress by The Charles Schwab Corporation, Mellon Financial's merger with The Bank of New York, multiple acquisitions by People's United Financial and the US Treasury's $250 billion TARP capital investment program; also represented financial institutions and private equity firms, including KKR, Blackstone, Corsair Capital and Oak Hill Capital, in public and private capital raises and investments.
**Career:** Joined Firm, 2001; Partner, 2011.
**Personal:** BA, cum laude, Harvard College (1997); JD, Columbia Law School (2001).

## COOPER, James D
Cravath, Swaine & Moore LLP, New York
212 474 1326
jcooper@cravath.com
*Featured in Banking & Finance (Nationwide)*
**Practice Areas:** James D. Cooper is a partner in Cravath's Corporate Department. He represents and advises banking clients in a wide variety of domestic and international financing transactions, including financings of mergers, acquisitions, recapitalizations and spin-offs, working capital financings and various special-purpose financings. Mr Cooper also counsels corporate borrowers negotiating financing arrangements with banks and other financial institutions.
**Personal:** Yale Law School (JD, 1979); University of Chicago (AB, summa cum laude, 1976; Phi Beta Kappa). For more information: http://www.cravath.com/jcooper.

## COOPER, Robert E
Gibson, Dunn & Crutcher LLP, Los Angeles
213 229 7179
rcooper@gibsondunn.com
*Featured in Litigation (Nationwide), Antitrust (California)*
**Practice Areas:** Partner, firm's Antitrust and Trade Regulation Practice Group. Extensive experience trying major antitrust and business cases to a verdict before a jury. Achieved a series of trial victories in antitrust cases for major companies such as Pfizer, American Airlines, and Hewlett-Packard. Other representative clients include Intel,

Ticketmaster, Northrop, Allergan, Callaway Golf and Sempra Energy.
**Professional Memberships:** Fellow, American College of Trial Lawyers.
**Publications:** Frequent lecturer on antitrust laws and trial of complex litigation.
**Personal:** LLB, Yale University School of Law, 1964, Order of the Coif, Article and Book Review Editor, Yale Law Journal.

### COPEN, Robert A
Skadden, Arps, Slate, Meagher & Flom LLP & Affiliates, New York
212 735 3536
Robert.Copen@skadden.com
*Featured in Banking & Finance (Nationwide)*
**Practice Areas:** Advises financial institutions, corporate acquirers, corporate targets, boards of directors, private equity firms and corporate borrowers on the terms, conditions and risks associated with complex, "bet-the-company" and other high-stakes corporate and debt transactions. Has represented lenders such as Bank of America, Bear Stearns, BNP, Credit Suisse, DLJ, Goldman Sachs, JPMorgan and Morgan Stanley; and corporate clients including AES, Apax, BTG Pactual, Joh. A. Benckiser, Pfizer, Rite Aid and Valeant Pharmaceuticals.
**Professional Memberships:** Admitted in New York and Connecticut.
**Career:** JD, New York University School of Law, 1989; BA, Tufts University, 1986 (magna cum laude).

### COPENHEFER, Lea Anne
Bingham McCutchen LLP, Boston
617 951 8515
leaanne.copenhefer@bingham.com
*Featured in Investment Funds (Nationwide), Investment Funds (Massachusetts)*
**Practice Areas:** Practice focuses primarily on the representation of funds and independent directors. Fund clients include the Legg Mason Fixed Income Funds, Pioneer Funds and Transamerica Funds. Independent director clients include the directors of AXA Equitable Funds and the Allianz Funds. Represents a number of the American Funds and their independent directors and a number of other mutual fund boards. Co-led the legal team that reorganized more than 100 mutual funds, including a redomiciliation of the funds.
**Personal:** University of Chicago Law School, JD, 1985; Yale University, BA, summa cum laude, with honors, 1982.

### CORRIGAN, Sean F
Fulbright & Jaworski LLP, New York
212 318 3096
scorrigan@fulbright.com
*Featured in Transportation (Nationwide)*
**Practice Areas:** Aircraft finance; banking; equipment financing.
**Career:** Corrigan, a partner in Fulbright & Jaworski LLP's New York office, practices in the firm's Equipment Financing Department. His legal practice focuses on the representation of airlines, lenders, lessors and manufacturers in aircraft financing matters, including leveraged and cross-

border leasing, secured lending transactions, private and public debt placements and syndicated loan facilities. He has also represented regional carriers in connection with their code share and capacity purchase arrangements.
**Personal:** JD, University of Virginia (1984); BA, summa cum laude, Iona College (1981).

### COSBY, Cameron
Hunton & Williams LLP, Richmond
804 788 8604
ccosby@hunton.com
*Featured in Capital Markets (Nationwide)*
**Practice Areas:** Federal income tax practice focuses on real estate capital markets, including real estate investment trusts, private equity funds, real estate-related tax credits, energy projects, venture capital, partnerships and joint ventures, and mergers and acquisitions.
**Professional Memberships:** Member, Tax Section of American Bar Association, National Association of Real Estate Investment Trusts, and Virginia State Bar.
**Career:** Joined Hunton & Williams upon graduation from law school in 1990. Before law school, he was a certified public accountant for Arthur Andersen & Co in Washington, DC.
**Personal:** JD, William & Mary School of Law, 1990. BS, University of Virginia, Commerce, 1985.

### COVIT, Barrie B
Simpson Thacher & Bartlett LLP, New York
212 455 3141
bcovit@stblaw.com
*Featured in Investment Funds (Nationwide)*
**Practice Areas:** Focuses on private funds and other facets of "alternative asset management." Has represented some of the largest and most well known sponsors of private equity funds including The Carlyle Group, Kohlberg Kravis Roberts, First Reserve Corporation, J.C. Flowers & Co. and Lexington Partners. Mr Covit represented the United States Treasury Department in connection with the establishment of its $30 billion Public-Private Investment Program to purchase legacy assets from financial institutions.
**Career:** Joined firm, 1998; Partner, 2007.
**Personal:** Columbia Law School (JD 1998); Harlan Fiske Stone Scholar; McGill University (BC 1995); James McGill Scholar.

### COWAN, Cameron
King & Spalding LLP, Washington, DC
202 626 5576
ccowan@kslaw.com
*Featured in Capital Markets (Nationwide)*
**Practice Areas:** Serves as counsel to financial institutions, corporations and government agencies in complex financings in the United States, Europe and Asia and as an advisor on financial markets regulation. Cam also helps lead the Social Sector Finance practice at Orrick, serving microfinance and impact investment clients.
**Personal:** JD, University of Virginia MBA, Columbia University B.S., magna cum laude, Syracuse University.

### COX, Brian
Alston & Bird LLP, Charlotte
704 444 1328
brian.cox@alston.com
*Featured in Capital Markets (Nationwide)*
**Practice Areas:** Represents financial institutions which provide corporate trust, custody, loan agency, reporting and administrative services in capital markets transactions, including transactions involving the issuance of CMBS/RMBS, ABS and CDO/CLO securities, project finance transactions and corporate and municipal bond transactions. Represents all types of participants in structured finance transactions, including issuers, underwriters, trustees, servicers and master servicers. Counsels corporate trust groups in connection with the issuance of new capital market products and compliance with existing and new regulatory rules and statutes and the resolution of disputed transactions.
**Personal:** Duke University (AB, 1991) (MAT, 1992); University of Virginia (JD, 1998).

### COZEN, Stephen A
Cozen O'Connor, Philadelphia
215 665 2020
scozen@cozen.com
*Featured in Insurance (Nationwide)*
**Practice Areas:** Steve is an accomplished litigator and counselor focusing on appellate matters, multidistrict litigation, complex torts, insurance corporate and regulatory matters, insurance coverage claims and litigation, professional liability, and reinsurance matters. He has been involved in major financial transactions, including one of the largest national sports deals in recent history.
**Professional Memberships:** American College of Trial Lawyers; International Academy of Trial Lawyers.
**Career:** Steve is the founder and chairman of Cozen O'Connor. Under his leadership, the firm has grown from four attorneys to more than 550 attorneys.
**Publications:** Insuring Real Property
**Personal:** University of Pennsylvania, BA, 1961; LLB, 1964.

### CRAFT, Randal Robert
Holland & Knight LLP, New York
212 513 3411
randal.craft@hklaw.com
*Featured in Transportation (Nationwide)*
**Practice Areas:** Partner in the Litigation Section, his practice's primary focus is providing advice and conducting litigation concerning aviation, product liability, mass disaster, and insurance matters. He has been lead counsel to airlines and manufacturers of aircraft, especially in numerous major air crash cases and NTSB investigations. He also has extensive experience as lead counsel in product liability cases, including mass disaster cases, for manufacturers of various products, including industrial machinery, chemicals, railroad cars, electrical equipment, engines, and consumer products. Additionally, he has advised and represented insurers on the interpretation of policies, coverage issues, and claims settlement procedures.

### CRAIG, Ashley
Venable LLP, Washington, DC
202 344 4351
awcraig@Venable.com
*Featured in Transportation (Nationwide)*
**Practice Areas:** Legislative and Government Affairs, International Trade and Customs, Homeland Security, Privacy and Data Security, Foreign Corrupt Practices Act/Anti-Corruption, Transportation and Transportation Infrastructure, Maritime
**Career:** Ashley Craig maintains a diverse practice advising clients on various domestic and international legislative, regulatory and policy matters. He counsels US and foreign interests on transactional matters, cross-border regulatory and policy concerns and advises clients on homeland and transportation security initiatives. He regularly appears before Executive Branch agencies and congressional committees with oversight of foreign policy, transportation and economic regulation.
**Personal:** JD, Catholic University, Columbus School of Law; Certificate, Comparative and International Law.

### CRIMMINS, Stephen J
K&L Gates, Washington, DC
202 778 9440
stephen.crimmins@klgates.com
*Featured in Securities (Nationwide)*
**Practice Areas:** Steve Crimmins defends clients in enforcement investigations and litigation by the SEC and other financial services regulators, as well as in private securities litigation. He also leads internal investigations and counsels on a broad range of SEC-related issues. He is recognized as a leader in the SEC defense bar and previously served eight years as a senior executive of the SEC's Enforcement Division and co-head of its trial unit.

### CROCKER, Thomas E
Alston & Bird LLP, Washington, DC
202 239 3318
thomas.crocker@alston.com
*Featured in International Trade (Nationwide)*
**Practice Areas:** Regulatory and legislative aspects of international business. Specializes in sanctions, export controls, foreign direct investment reviews by the Committee on Foreign Investment in the United States (CFIUS), anti-money laundering, Foreign Corrupt Practices Act (FCPA) and technology cooperation issues. Has particular expertise in the Office of Foreign Assets Control (OFAC) regulations, Export Administration Regulations (EARs) and the International Traffic in Arms Regulations (ITAR).
**Professional Memberships:** Co-chair, ABA Committee on National Security and Defense; Former member, President's Export Council Subcommittees on Export Administration and Encryption.
**Career:** US Department of State (1976-81).
**Personal:** AB (1971) Princeton University; JD (1974) Columbia University.

## CROSBY, Lisa A
Sidley Austin LLP, Washington, DC
202 736 8754
lcrosby@sidley.com
*Featured in International Trade (Nationwide)*

**Practice Areas:** Partner in Sidley's Washington, DC office. Concentrates in sanctions, export controls and customs law. Advises companies on NAFTA origin requirements, tariff classification of imported goods and sanctions administered by the Office of Foreign Assets Control (OFAC). Counsels companies on compliance with international trade rules and represents clients in export control enforcement proceedings and on licensing matters.
**Professional Memberships:** American Bar Association, International Section; Customs and International Trade Bar Association.
**Personal:** Georgetown University Law Center, JD, 1995, magna cum laude, Order of the Coif; Purdue University, MA, 1986; Linfield College, BA, 1984, magna cum laude. Admission: District of Columbia.

## CROSS, James
Simpson Thacher & Bartlett LLP, New York
212 455 3386
jcross@stblaw.com
*Featured in Private Equity (Nationwide), Banking & Finance (Nationwide)*

**Practice Areas:** Partner in the firm's Corporate Department, where he concentrates on debt financing with emphasis on debt capital commitments and bank and bridge facilities for leveraged acquisitions. Recent transactions include representation of HCA Inc. in new debt facilities, First Data Corporation in its debt refinancings, Cogeco Cable in its acquisition of Atlantic Broadband, KKR in its investment in Fotolia, Sealy in its sale to Tempur-Pedic, and Engility Corporation in the financing of its spin-off from L-3 Communications.
**Career:** Became Partner in 1999.
**Personal:** BA, Princeton University (1986); JD, University of Virginia School of Law (1990).

## CROST, Katharine I
Orrick, Herrington & Sutcliffe LLP, New York
212 506 5070
kcrost@orrick.com
*Featured in Capital Markets (Nationwide)*

**Career:** Katharine Crost's practice involves advising issuers, underwriters, servicers and institutional purchasers in connection with the securitization of a variety of assets, including mortgages, tax liens, tobacco litigation settlement funds and utility stranded costs. Her mortgage-backed experience has involved seasoned mortgage loans and reverse mortgage loans. She represents financial institutions, private companies, governmental agencies and municipalities and has advised clients on innovative transactions and proposals that address issues arising from the financial crisis and housing and financial regulatory reform. Her experience also includes establishing joint ventures, financing of assets, acquisitions of assets and litigation support and advice.

## CULHANE, Stephen
Kaye Scholer LLP, New York
212 836 7035
stephen.culhane@kayescholer.com
*Featured in Investment Funds (Nationwide)*

**Practice Areas:** A Partner in Kaye Scholer's Investment Funds group, Stephen Culhane's practice focuses on representing sponsors of, and select institutional investors in, private equity funds, real estate funds, special situation and distressed investment funds, hedge funds and funds of funds with respect to the structuring, formation and operation of such fund products. Recent matters include LBO and growth equity funds, and RE opportunity funds on behalf of global financial institutions and leading private fund managers; complex secondary transactions; and investment management industry regulatory matters.
**Career:** Previously at Linklaters, King & Spalding, and Goldman, Sachs & Co.

## CULLEN, William J
Kaye Scholer LLP, New York
212 836 7511
william.cullen@kayescholer.com
*Featured in Capital Markets (Nationwide)*

**Practice Areas:** William "Butch" Cullen focuses on securities and corporate finance, with an emphasis on the securitisation of financial assets, particularly commercial mortgage assets. He is also significantly involved in the workout and restructuring of defaulted real estate loans and securities, the sale and liquidation of distressed financial assets, including a sale to governmental authorities on behalf of financial institutions, and the sale of servicing platforms and investment advisory businesses.

## CULOTTA, Kenneth S
King & Spalding LLP, Houston
713 276 7374
kculotta@kslaw.com
*Featured in Projects (Nationwide)*

**Practice Areas:** Advises US and non-US clients in domestic and international oil, gas, LNG, power and natural resources transactions, including mergers and acquisitions, joint ventures, project development and finance, energy management services and other direct and indirect investment transactions. Experienced with industry documentation, including concession, production sharing, joint operating, power purchase, tolling, fuel supply, O&M, construction, gas and electricity transportation and distribution, marketing and other agreements. Languages: German; Spanish.
**Professional Memberships:** Association of International Petroleum Negotiators; Houston Bar Association; State Bar of Texas.
**Personal:** BA University of Texas 1979; JD 1985; Albert Ludwigs-Universität, Freiburg, Germany (DAAD Fellow 1980-81).

## CUMMINS, J Gerard
Sidley Austin LLP, New York
212 839 5374
jcummins@sidley.com
*Featured in Capital Markets (Nationwide)*

**Practice Areas:** Jerry Cummins is a partner in Sidley's New York office and serves as a chair of the firm's REIT industry team. His practice focuses on securities offerings, corporate matters and funds, with an emphasis on real estate-related transactions, primarily REITs and real estate funds. He represents issuers and underwriters in a variety of industries in public and private debt and equity transactions, including IPOs. Mr Cummins represents fund managers in fund and GP formation as well as institutional investors in their investments into private funds.
**Personal:** Fordham University School of Law, JD, 1990; Fordham University, BS, 1987.

## CURNIN, Paul C
Simpson Thacher & Bartlett LLP, New York
212 455 2519
pcurnin@stblaw.com
*Featured in Securities (Nationwide), Litigation (New York)*

**Practice Areas:** Co-head of the Litigation Department. Represents clients in class and derivative actions, takeover litigation, government investigations, particularly involving the SEC, internal investigations, and other matters. Selected prior representations include AIG, WorldCom Inc., Travelers, KKR as well as numerous directors, officers and other individuals.
**Career:** Joined the firm in 1990; Partner since 1995.
**Personal:** BA, Dartmouth College (1983); JD, Fordham University School of Law (1987).

## CURRIER, Maria
Holland & Knight LLP, Miami
305 374 8500
maria.currier@hklaw.com
*Featured in Healthcare (Florida), Healthcare (Nationwide)*
See under Florida for profile.

## CURTIN, David
Bingham McCutchen LLP, Washington, DC
202 373 6669
david.curtin@bingham.com
*Featured in Tax (Nationwide)*

**Practice Areas:** Practice encompasses all aspects of federal tax controversy and litigation matters. Over 35 years of experience in handling tax cases, first as a trial attorney in the Tax Division of the Department of Justice and thereafter in private practice. Particularly recognized for work in preparation and trial of large cases, and has tried both civil and criminal tax matters. Also has tried non-tax cases in both federal and state courts.
**Career:** Fellow, American College of Trial Lawyers.
**Personal:** St. Louis University School of Law, JD, with honors, 1972; St. Louis University, BA, with honors, 1969.

## CURTIS, Philip
Arnold & Porter LLP, New York
212 715 1100
Philip.Curtis@aporter.com
*Featured in Products Liability (Nationwide)*

**Practice Areas:** Philip Curtis leads the national defense of lead pigment product liability litigation for Atlantic Richfield Company. He is a leader in the Firm's smoking and health litigation and climate change litigation, and has been involved in the defense of cases alleging property damage and personal injury from radiation and MTBE product liability litigation. His practice has included individual personal injury and property damage cases, class actions, novel theories of aggregate liability and complex multi-jurisdictional disputes. He has experience defending antitrust class actions and other complex commercial disputes.
**Personal:** JD, Columbia Law School, 1971; BA, Yale University, 1968.

## CURTIS, Susan M
Skadden, Arps, Slate, Meagher & Flom LLP & Affiliates, New York
212 735 2119
Susan.Curtis@skadden.com
*Featured in Capital Markets (Nationwide)*

**Practice Areas:** Co-head of Structured Finance Group. Represents investment managers, issuers, investment banks and other financial institutions in structured financial transactions. Recent experience includes representation of funds and other investment vehicles investing in corporate loans, mortgage loans and other financial assets; restructuring of asset backed securities vehicles and bank risk exposures; and securitizations of US and foreign auto loans and leases. Experienced also with other consumer and structured asset securitizations, including CLOs and CDOs and other structures with exposure to credit derivatives.
**Career:** JD, Vanderbilt University, 1981; BA, University of Tennessee, 1977 (summa cum laude; Phi Beta Kappa).

## CURTIS JR, Charles G
Arnold & Porter LLP, Washington, DC
608 257 1922
Charles.Curtis@aporter.com
*Featured in Native American Law (Nationwide), Litigation (Wisconsin)*
See under Wisconsin for profile.

## CYMROT, Mark A
Baker & Hostetler LLP, Washington, DC
202 861 1677
mcymrot@bakerlaw.com
*Featured in International Arbitration (Nationwide)*

**Career:** A member of the Panel of Arbitrators of the International Centre for Dispute Resolution and London Court of International Arbitration, and chair of the Washington, D.C., Chapter of Chartered Institute of Arbitrators, Mark Cymrot's international litigation and arbitration cases involve commercial and financial matters, including fraud, securities, corporate investigations, antitrust, RICO, banking and real estate, among others. Mark won a $197 million jury verdict against several defendants for an international conspiracy to manipulating silver prices. He defended a South American government in lawsuits brought by international banks seeking repayment of $10 billion in commercial debt lawsuits.

### CZARNIAK, Julia A
Skadden, Arps, Slate, Meagher & Flom LLP & Affiliates, New York
212 735 4194
Julia.Czarniak@skadden.com
*Featured in Projects (Nationwide)*
**Practice Areas:** Ms Czarniak concentrates on project finance and development. She has extensive experience in export credit and multilateral agency financings and in pipeline projects, restructurings and expansions in the United States, Asia, the Middle East and Russia. Ms Czarniak also works on general financing matters, including specialized structured financings, acquisition facilities, Rule 144A bond financings, and secured and unsecured letters of credit and loan facilities.
**Career:** JD, Georgetown University Law Center, 1997; MA, Yale University Graduate School, 1993; BA, Moscow State University, 1990.

### DADAKIS, John D
Holland & Knight LLP, New York
212 513 3354
John.Dadakis@hklaw.com
*Featured in Wealth Management (Nationwide)*
**Practice Areas:** Wealth Management.
**Professional Memberships:** American Bar Association, Attorneys for Family-Held Enterprises, Family Firm Institute.
**Career:** Mr Dadakis concentrates in representing high net worth individuals. He acts as "Personal General Counsel" for numerous Fortune 500 executives and successful private business entrepreneurs. His practice focuses on asset protection, tax minimization, and wealth transference, and he has developed individual client mission statement programs to help clients manage and achieve these goals. He also works with financial advisers and financial institutions to devise and implement wealth preservation strategies.
**Publications:** "529 Plans: Sophisticated Planning with Simple Devices," Co-Author, ABA Trust Letter, December 2012

### DADY, J Michael
Dady & Gardner, PA, Minneapolis
612 359 3500
jmdady@dadygardner.com
*Featured in Franchising (Nationwide)*
**Practice Areas:** Franchise.
**Career:** Founding Member of Dady & Gardner. He and his partners have successfully represented franchisees and dealers in more than 400 different franchise and dealer systems, and they serve as counsel to more than 30 different national franchisee and dealer associations. He has obtained multi-million dollar settlements and judgments, while obtaining precedent-setting rulings that are the foundation of this developing area of law.
**Personal:** University of MN (JD, 1975); St. John's University (BA, 1971).

### DALIERE, Mark
Dentons, Phoenix
602 508 3902
mark.daliere@dentons.com
*Featured in Leisure & Hospitality (Nationwide)*
**Practice Areas:** International hotels and leisure practice representing hotel owners, developers, third-party operators, hospitality brands, and lenders in development and operation of hotel/leisure facilities worldwide. Negotiation of management, licensing, and technical services arrangements for hotels, resorts, spas, golf courses, restaurants, and other recreational facilities. Leads transactions involving acquisition, disposition and development of hospitality properties and portfolios. Focus on financing, emphasizing needs of hotel/resort properties as to SNDAs and cash management arrangements. Counsels hotel developers on residential and mixed-use components, including rental programs. Working with local counsel, acts as primary counsel to hotel brands on mixed-use projects worldwide.

### DALLAS, Bruce
Davis Polk & Wardwell LLP, Menlo Park
650 752 2000
bruce.dallas@davispolk.com
*Featured in Capital Markets (California), Capital Markets (Nationwide)*
See under California for profile.

### DANISH, Kyle W
Van Ness Feldman LLP, Washington, DC
202 298 1876
kwd@vnf.com
*Featured in Climate Change (Nationwide), Environment (District of Columbia)*
**Practice Areas:** Advises energy, manufacturing, and financial sector clients on corporate climate strategy, Clean Air Act regulation and permitting, energy projects, and emissions trading-related transactions. Counsel to the Coalition for Emission Reduction Policy. Frequent speaker on climate change, emissions trading, and carbon finance. Authored several commissioned research papers on climate change and energy policy.
**Professional Memberships:** International Emissions Trading Association. Environmental Markets Association.

### DANTI, Anthony M
Fulbright & Jaworski LLP, Washington, DC
202 662 4520
adanti@fulbright.com
*Featured in Energy & Natural Resources (Nationwide)*
**Practice Areas:** Energy.
**Career:** Anthony has assisted clients in several transactions in the past year, most notably the sale by subsidiaries of Sumitomo Corporation of a 300MW gas-fired generating facility, the acquisition of an approximately 150MW wind-generation facility in California by affiliates of Brookfield Renewable Energy Partners and several distributed and utility scale investments by clients in solar generation assets.
**Personal:** Georgetown University, BS, 1992; JD, 2001.

### DAVENPORT, Kirk A
Latham & Watkins LLP, New York
212 906 1284
kirk.davenport@lw.com
*Featured in Capital Markets (Nationwide)*
**Practice Areas:** Represents underwriters and issuers in public and private high yield, convertible note and equity offerings in many industries.
**Career:** Co-Chair of firm's global Capital Markets practice group and member of firm's Executive Committee.
**Publications:** Contributing editor for the Latham & Watkins - The Book of Jargon which is also available as a free iPhone application. Other works include: "Cheap Stock: An IPO Survival Guide" (Latham & Watkins Client Alert 2010), "Upsizing and Downsizing Your IPO" (Latham & Watkins Client Alert 2010) and "Giving Good Guidance — What Every Public Company Should Know" (Latham & Watkins Client Alert 2007).

### DAVIDOW, Charles E
Paul, Weiss, Rifkind, Wharton & Garrison LLP, Washington, DC
202 223 7380
cdavidow@paulweiss.com
*Featured in Securities (Nationwide)*
**Practice Areas:** Partner in the Litigation Department and Co-chair of the Securities Litigation and Enforcement Group. Focuses practice on securities enforcement proceedings, corporate internal investigations and private securities litigation and arbitration. Extensive experience representing board committees, institutions and individuals in connection with investigations, litigation and SEC enforcement proceedings. Speaks regularly on topics relating to corporate governance, on regulatory and litigation aspects of the credit market crisis, and on lessons to be drawn from the corporate scandals of recent years. Recognized by Chambers USA and The Best Lawyers in America as one of the country's leading lawyers in Securities Regulation/Enforcement.

### DAVIDSON, Douglas E
Morgan, Lewis & Bockius LLP, New York
212 309 6280
douglas.davidson@morganlewis.com
*Featured in Energy & Natural Resources (Nationwide)*
**Practice Areas:** Douglas E. Davidson is a Partner in Morgan Lewis's Business and Finance Practice. Mr Davidson focuses his practice on energy finance and regulation, project development and finance, corporate and securities law, and acquisitions and divestitures. His M&A practice includes auction and other sales of electric generation assets and portfolios, while his finance practice focuses on capital markets and project finance. Mr Davidson's clients include investor-owned utility systems, independent power producers, wind and solar power companies, private equity and underwriting firms.

### DAVIDSON, Gordon K
Fenwick & West LLP, Mountain View
650 988 8500
gdavidson@fenwick.com
*Featured in Investment Funds (Nationwide), Capital Markets (California), Corporate/M&A (Northern California), Corporate/M&A (California)*
See under California for profile.

### DAVIDSON, Gregory
Gibson, Dunn & Crutcher LLP, Palo Alto
650 849 5350
gdavidson@gibsondunn.com
*Featured in Investment Funds (Nationwide), Corporate/M&A (California)*
**Practice Areas:** Represents venture capitalists, corporate strategic investors and angel investors, as well as companies, in connection with private placements of equity and debt. Extensive experience in mergers and acquisitions, private equity, joint ventures, corporate finance and general business law matters. Also advises start-up and emerging growth companies in all aspects of their corporate legal requirements. Regularly counsels public company clients in connection with SEC filings, public disclosure, corporate governance and other securities laws matters.
**Professional Memberships:** American Bar Association.
**Personal:** JD, University of California at Berkeley (Boalt Hall) 1988. BA, Stanford University 1985.

### DAVIDSON, Joshua
Baker Botts LLP, Houston
713 229 1527
joshua.davidson@bakerbotts.com
*Featured in Capital Markets (Texas), Energy & Natural Resources (Nationwide)*
See under Texas for profile.

### DAVIES, Patrick S
Covington & Burling LLP, Washington, DC
202 662 5274
pdavies@cov.com
*Featured in Products Liability (Nationwide)*
**Practice Areas:** Pat Davies advises and represents pharmaceutical companies, multinational corporations, and trade associations in mass tort, product liability, and class action lawsuits. He has represented pharmaceutical and other companies in civil, criminal, and congressional inquiries and investigations, has substantial experience representing clients with interests in Latin America, and has represented clients in insurance coverage and general commercial litigation. He has served as co-chair of the firm's Product Liability Practice.
**Career:** Hon John Butzner, Jr, US Court of Appeals, Fourth Circuit, 1987-88.
**Personal:** Notre Dame Law School (JD 1987), Universidad Catolica de Chile (1984), University of Scranton (BS 1983).

## DAVIS, Gary Scott
McDermott Will & Emery LLP, Miami
305 347 6520
gsdavis@mwe.com
*Featured in Healthcare (Florida), Healthcare (Nationwide)*

**Practice Areas:** Concentrates on managed care, emerging health benefit plans, strategic acquisitions, divestitures, restructurings and reorganizations, hospital-physician joint ventures and related transactional, regulatory and reimbursement issues.

**Career:** Florida Bar Board Certified in Health Law; awarded the prestigious David J Greenburg Service Award (AHLA, 2000), member inaugural class of Fellows (AHLA, 2005); recipient of the Follmer Bronze Merit Award for Outstanding Service (HFMA, 1993).

**Personal:** The George Washington University Law School (JD, Honors); Binghamton University (BA, Honors, Phi Beta Kappa).

## DAVIS, George A
Cadwalader, Wickersham & Taft LLP, New York
212 504 6797
george.davis@cwt.com
*Featured in Bankruptcy/Restructuring (Nationwide), Bankruptcy/Restructuring (New York)*

See under New York for profile.

## DAVIS, Mark G
Weil, Gotshal & Manges LLP, Washington, DC
202 682 7258
mark.davis@weil.com
*Featured in International Trade (Nationwide), Intellectual Property (District of Columbia)*

**Practice Areas:** Mark Davis, Head of Weil's ITC Practice, focuses on litigating intellectual property rights and related antitrust issues and has acted as lead counsel in numerous matters before the International Trade Commission, district courts throughout the country, and the United States Court of Appeals for the Federal Circuit. Representative clients include Apple, Microsoft, Renesas, Samsung, and Hitachi.

**Personal:** Catholic University of America (BA, cum laude), George Washington University Law School (JD).

## DAVIS, Michael W
Sidley Austin LLP, Chicago
312 853 7731
mdavis@sidley.com
*Featured in Products Liability (Nationwide)*

**Practice Areas:** Partner in Sidley's Chicago office, head of Firm's Products Liability practice, secretary of the Executive Committee. Focuses on nationwide defense of product liability claims involving pharmaceuticals, chemicals, consumer and food products. Practice includes complex multiparty and class action litigation. Served as national coordinating counsel in pharmaceutical, food products, and chemical litigation.

**Professional Memberships:** National Judicial College's Complex Litigation Advisory Committee; American, Chicago, Illinois State Bar Associations; Defense Research Institute, International Association of Defense Counsel.

**Personal:** Northwestern University School of Law, JD, 1975, cum laude; State University of New York - Binghamton, BA, 1972, magna cum laude. Admission: Illinois.

## DAVIS, Richard F
Greenberg Traurig, LLP, Santa Monica
310 586 7710
DavisR@gtlaw.com
*Featured in Leisure & Hospitality (Nationwide)*

**Practice Areas:** Regional Coordinator of California, Real Estate Practice. Co-Chair, Hospitality Group.

**Professional Memberships:** Member: American Bar Association, Real Property and International Law Sections; California Bar Association, Real Property and International Sections; Urban Land Institute; US-Mexico Chamber of Commerce. Trustee, American Resort and Residential Development Association

**Career:** Selected: Super Lawyers magazine, 2007, 2009; Chambers USA Guide, 2007-13. Team Member, a Law360 'Real Estate Practice Group of the Year', 2011-12.

**Publications:** Author, 'The Luxury Market's Basic Issues,' American Resort Development Association, 2007.

**Personal:** JD, University of California, Los Angeles, School of Law; AB, Political Science, University of California at Los Angeles.

## DAVIS, Trayton M
Milbank, Tweed, Hadley & McCloy LLP, New York
212 530 5349
tdavis@milbank.com
*Featured in Capital Markets (Nationwide)*

**Practice Areas:** Mr Davis is a partner and chair of the firm's Alternative Investments Practice and a former member of the firm's Executive Committee. He regularly advises leading players in securitizing both financial and hard assets and in other domestic and international structured transactions. His recent areas of particular focus include: (i) innovative uses of structured finance techniques in alternative energy, traditional energy and commodities trading businesses; (ii) complex investment fund structures; (iii) structured investments by distressed and private equity investors; and (iv) cross border structured investments.

## DAVIS VARNER, Chilton
King & Spalding LLP, Atlanta
404 572 4789
cvarner@kslaw.com
*Featured in Litigation (Nationwide), Products Liability (Nationwide), Litigation (Georgia)*

**Practice Areas:** Thirty years of courtroom experience defending corporations in product liability, commercial and civil disputes. Trial and Appellate Counsel for large automotive, pharmaceutical and medical device manufacturers in mass tort litigation, class actions and MDL litigation, including att

## DEAN, Richard N
Baker & McKenzie, Washington, DC
202 452 7009
richard.dean@bakermckenzie.com
*Featured in International Trade (Nationwide)*
**Practice Areas:** FCPA and related legislation, including US money laundering laws and their application to the activities of global companies in high-risk emerging markets, including advising on compliance issues, conducting investigations and defending companies before regulatory bodies.
**Professional Memberships:** US - Russia Business Council - Member of the Board of Directors and of the Executive Committee; Russian-American Institute in Moscow – Trustee; EndPoverty.org - Member, Board of Directors
**Career:** Admitted in DC (1995) and New York (1981).
**Publications:** Frequent writer and speaker on FCPA and anti-corruption compliance topics.
**Personal:** JD and MA, University of Virginia, (1980); BA, Vanderbilt University, 1977.

## DEARMENT, Roderick
Covington & Burling LLP, Washington, DC
202 662 5900
rdearment@cov.com
*Featured in Government (Nationwide)*
**Practice Areas:** Senior member of the Public Policy and Government Affairs practice group and has a broad-based practice handling legislative and regulatory matters for clients in areas including tax, financial services, employee benefits, healthcare, labor law, and international trade.
**Career:** US Department of Labor, Deputy Secretary of Labor (1989-91). Office of the US Senate Majority Leader, Chief of Staff (1985-86). US Senate Committee on Finance, Chief Counsel and Staff Director (1983-85); Deputy Chief Counsel (1979-82).
**Personal:** University of Virginia School of Law, JD, 1973 (Virginia Law Review; Order of the Coif); Trinity College, BA, 1970 (Phi Beta Kappa).

## DEBOLT, Paul A
Venable LLP, Washington, DC
202 344 8384
padebolt@venable.com
*Featured in Government (Nationwide)*
**Practice Areas:** Government contracts, life sciences
**Career:** Assists companies and individuals on issues involving business with the federal government, including civil fraud. Experienced in the competitive source selection process, defending or prosecuting bid protests, issuing advice concerning compliance with government regulations and laws, and helping resolve disputes and claims during contract performance or termination. Counsels clients on the Service Contract Act, False Claims Act, joint ventures and teaming agreements, prime-subcontractor disputes, internal investigations, mandatory disclosures and data rights issues.
**Personal:** JD, The Ohio State University, Michael E. Moritz College of Law, 1989; BA, John Carroll University, 1986.

## DEBUSK, F Amanda
Hughes Hubbard & Reed LLP, Washington, DC
202 721 4790
debusk@hugheshubbard.com
*Featured in International Trade (Nationwide)*
**Practice Areas:** Chair, International Trade & Customs Department: international trade, export controls, sanctions, customs, FCPA, white-collar crime, and corporate compliance.
**Career:** Former Commerce Department Assistant Secretary for Export Enforcement; Appointed to the US Department of State's Advisory Committee on International Economic Policy: Sanctions Subcommittee; Provided expert testimony on international trade issues for two Senate committees; Former counsel of the Chair of the President's Advisory Committee on Trade Policy & Negotiations; Former commissioner, Federal Interagency Commission on Crime and Security in US Seaports; Member, Hughes Hubbard's Executive Committee.
**Personal:** University of Richmond, BA, summa cum laude; Harvard Law School, JD

## DECELLE, Arthur J
McDermott Will & Emery LLP, Washington, DC
Adecelle@mwe.com
*Featured in Food & Beverages (Nationwide)*
**Practice Areas:** Focuses his practice on alcohol beverage regulation at all levels of government and on legal and public policy challenges facing heavily regulated industries.
**Career:** Prior to joining McDermott, he was the general counsel of the Beer Institute for 16 years. From 1981 to 1984, Art held senior staff positions in the US House of Representatives and worked on several federal political campaigns.
**Personal:** George Mason University School of Law, JD, 1987, St. John's University, BA, 1978.

## DECKER, John S
Vinson & Elkins LLP, Washington, DC
202 639 6599
jdecker@velaw.com
*Featured in Energy & Natural Resources (Nationwide)*
**Practice Areas:** Practice concentrates on regulation of electric power and natural gas industries before the Federal Energy Regulatory Commission and the Department of Energy and on domestic and international transactions involving the production, transportation, and sale of natural gas, LNG, and electricity, the development of power plants, and the sale or acquisition of electric power and natural gas assets.
**Career:** Duke University, AB, 1991; University of Virginia, JD, 1994, Order of the Coif. Admitted to practice: Maryland, 1994, District of Columbia, 1996; US Court of Appeals for the District of Columbia. Joined Vinson & Elkins in 1994.

## DECONTI, Elizabeth A
GrayRobinson, PA, Tampa
813 273 5000
elizabeth.deconti@gray-robinson.com
*Featured in Food & Beverages (Nationwide)*
**Practice Areas:** Shareholder in Alcohol Beverage and Food Department. Concentrates on alcohol industry litigation, regulatory compliance, marketing, trade practices, and intra-industry relations/tied house issues. Special focus on promotions in traditional, digital, and social media platforms. Experience representing US and international clients in all three tiers of the alcohol beverage industry, as well as marketing agencies and promotions companies before state and federal courts and administrative agencies.
**Professional Memberships:** Member: Florida Bar, Connecticut Bar, American Bar Association, Federal Bar Association. Admitted US Supreme Court; US Court of Appeals for the Eleventh Circuit; US District Courts for the Northern, Middle and Southern Districts of Florida; Florida Supreme Court; Florida state courts; Connecticut state courts.
**Career:** Successfully litigated on behalf of alcohol beverage manufacturers' disputes involving franchise issues, brand rights, and trademark infringement. Regularly counsels manufacturers, retailers, and marketing companies on national loyalty programs, contests and sweepstakes, incentives, and other consumer-focused marketing programs involving compliance with federal and multi-state laws and regulations.
**Personal:** Judicial Clerk to the Honorable Antoinette L Dupont, Connecticut Appellate Court, 1996-97; University of Miami School of Law, JD (cum laude, 1996); University of Miami, Harvey T. Reid Scholar 1993-96; Yale University, BA Renaissance Studies (cum laude with Distinction, 1993).

## DEDYO, John
Weil, Gotshal & Manges LLP, New York
212 310 8938
john.dedyo@weil.com
*Featured in Capital Markets (Nationwide)*
**Practice Areas:** John J. Dedyo has extensive experience in securitization and other structured products. He has worked with a broad range of asset types, including auto loans, rental cars, credit cards, trade receivables, factoring receivables, commercial loans, high-yield bonds, equipment leases, healthcare receivables, mortgages, future flows, lottery prizes, structured settlements, life settlements, repurchase agreements and residual interests. He has structured commercial paper conduits and term vehicles. He has restructured asset-backed securities, commercial mortgage-backed securities and other structured finance transactions and has advised RMBS originators regarding their mortgage loan put-back exposures.
**Personal:** University of Pennsylvania (BA); Stanford Law School (JD).

## DEGNAN, Frederick H
King & Spalding LLP, Washington, DC
202 626 3742
fdegnan@kslaw.com
*Featured in Food & Beverages (Nationwide)*
**Practice Areas:** Focuses on food and pharmaceutical law. In particular, he handles a wide array of food safety, biotechnology, good manufacturing practice and labeling issues as well as CPSC-related issues.
**Career:** From 1980-88, Mr Degnan served as FDA's associate Chief Counsel for Foods and as an Associate Chief Counsel for Enforcement.
**Publications:** Degnan, Fred H, FDA's Creative Application of the Law: Not Merely A Collection Of Words (2000) FDLI; Second Edition (2006).
**Personal:** BA, cum laude, College of the Holy Cross; JD, Georgetown University.

## DELANEY, John
Morrison & Foerster LLP, New York
212 468 8040
jdelaney@mofo.com
*Featured in Outsourcing (Nationwide), Technology (New York)*
See under New York for profile.

## DEMARCO, Joseph V
DeVore & DeMarco LLP, New York
212 922 9499
jvd@devoredemarco.com
*Featured in Privacy & Data Security (Nationwide)*
**Practice Areas:** Data privacy and security; cybercrime data breach investigations and response; information security audits and assessments; records retention; theft of trade secrets investigations and litigation; intellectual property litigation; iGaming.
**Professional Memberships:** International Bar Association (Technology Section); New York State Bar Association, Commercial and Federal Litigation Section (Co-chair, Internet and IP Committee); Board Member, Fordham Law School Center for Law and Information Policy
**Career:** Associate, Cravath, Swaine & Moore (1993-1997); Assistant US Attorney, Southern District of New York (Coordinator of Cybercrime Program) (1997-2007); DeVore & DeMarco (2007-present).
**Publications:** Member, Professional Editorial Board, Computer Law and Security Review; numerous publications

## DEMMO, Nicholas G
Wachtell, Lipton, Rosen & Katz, New York
212 403 1381
NGDemmo@wlrk.com
*Featured in Financial Services Regulation (Nationwide)*
**Practice Areas:** Practice focuses on transactions involving banks, asset management firms and other financial institutions, and has a broad range of experience in complex mergers and acquisitions, securities, regulatory and other corporate and compliance matters. Has worked on numerous public and private company acquisitions, securities offerings, public and private company investments, corporate control contests, corporate governance matters, bank regulatory matters and joint venture transactions.
**Career:** Joined Wachtell, Lipton, Rosen & Katz in 1997 and was elected partner in 2004.
**Personal:** Graduated from Yale University (BA) in 1993 and from The University of Pennsylvania (JD) in 1996; served on the Journal of International Economic Law; member of the Order of the Coif. Clerked for the Honorable

Dean D Pregerson of the US District Court for the Central District of California.

## DENENBERG, Alan
Davis Polk & Wardwell LLP, Menlo Park
650 752 2000
alan.denenberg@davispolk.com
*Featured in Capital Markets (California), Capital Markets (Nationwide), Corporate/M&A (Northern California)*
See under California for profile.

## DENNY, Otway
Fulbright & Jaworski LLP, Houston
713 651 5588
odenny@fulbright.com
*Featured in Products Liability (Nationwide), Litigation (Texas)*
See under Texas for profile.

## DERINGER, Joshua
Drinker Biddle & Reath LLP, Philadelphia
215 988 2959
Joshua.Deringer@dbr.com
*Featured in Investment Funds (Nationwide)*
**Practice Areas:** Partner in the Investment Management Group. Josh counsels a wide range of national and international financial service companies involved in all aspects of investment management, including registered investment companies, hedge funds and other alternative investment vehicles, as well as investment advisers. Josh is a frequent speaker and writer, and he regularly comments on investment management industry topics.
**Professional Memberships:** Member of the New York and Pennsylvania Bar Associations; the Managed Funds Association; the Hedge Fund Association and the Mid-Atlantic Hedge Fund Association.
**Personal:** University of Pennsylvania, BA, 1996; Fordham University School of Law, JD, 2000, Fordham Law Review.

## DERMAN, Andrew B
Thompson & Knight LLP, Dallas
214 969 1307
Andrew.Derman@tklaw.com
*Featured in Energy & Natural Resources (Nationwide)*
**Practice Areas:** With a concentration on oil and gas investment projects and cross-border transactions, Andy Derman focuses on providing legal and commercial support in connection with acquisitions, divestments, trades, and mergers; strategic commercial and business advice; large infrastructure projects, including LNG, GTL, and refineries; nationalization/expropriation; anti-corruption (FCPA) and sanction advice; unitizations; boundary disputes; exploration, development, and production operations; production sharing contracts; negotiations; and dispute resolution (litigation, arbitration, expert testimony). He has assisted clients in more than 50 countries on six continents.
**Career:** Andy worked for nearly 20 years for Sun Oil Company and its successor, Oryx Energy Company.

## DESANTIS, Victor J
White & Case LLP, Washington, DC
202 626 3607
vdesantis@whitecase.com
*Featured in Projects (Nationwide)*
**Career:** To view a comprehensive biography, please visit www.whitecase.com/vdesantis.

## DETERMANN, Lothar
Baker & McKenzie, San Francisco
650 856 5533
lothar.determann@bakermckenzie.com
*Featured in IT & Outsourcing (California), Privacy & Data Security (Nationwide)*
See under California for profile.

## DEVECCHIO, W Jay
Jenner & Block LLP, Washington, DC
202 639 6893
jdevecchio@jenner.com
*Featured in Government (Nationwide)*
**Career:** W. Jay DeVecchio is Co-Chair of the Government Contracts Practice and a member of the Firm's Management Committee. Clients from the aerospace, technology, and health care sectors seek his representation in all facets of government procurement law, from bid protests to complex claims and disputes through suspension and debarment. He represents clients in related issues such as criminal and civil fraud, qui tam actions, and internal investigations. His litigation practice encompasses the largest defective pricing appeal tried and the leading case on latent defects. He is a recognized leader in the field of intellectual property rights in government contracts.

## DEVINE, Brian
Blank Rome LLP, New York
212 885 5275
BDevine@BlankRome.com
*Featured in Transportation (Nationwide)*
**Practice Areas:** Brian Devine focuses on the representation of financial institutions and borrowers, with a particular emphasis on maritime-related assets. Mr Devine counsels clients both domestically and internationally in areas such as: finance and security arrangements; mergers, acquisitions, and divestitures; debt and equity offerings; sale and purchase; international commercial transactions, restructurings and disputes; corporate governance and structure issues. For more information, see:
www.BlankRome.com/BDevine.

## DEVLIN, Roderick N.
Greenberg Traurig, LLP, New York
212 801 6997
DevlinR@gtlaw.com
*Featured in Projects (Nationwide)*
**Practice Areas:** Roddy Devlin practices in the areas of project finance, public private partnerships (P3s) and energy and natural resources. He has represented project sponsors, lenders, institutional investors, construction companies, governmental municipalities and monoline insurers in a wide variety of sectors, including transportation, energy, water, sports facilities, marine infrastructure projects and casino/resort developments. He has been actively involved in many of the significant US P3 projects of recent years, including the Ohio River Bridges Project in Indiana, the Northwest Corridor Project in Georgia, the Knik Arm Bridge project in Alaska and the Presidio Parkway project in California. He has published widely in the area of project finance and has spoken at key industry events, including the ABA/World Bank March 2012 Washington DC symposium on the 'Legal Implications of the Sovereign Debt Crisis in Europe and America.'
**Publications:** Mr Devlin's publications include: Public Private Partnerships in the US Airport Sector: The Landing Lights Are On, Project Finance International, February 2013, US PPPs: Trends and Developments from the Second Quarter of 2012 and Beyond, Practical Law Journal, August 2012; US P3: Has The Long Awaited Surge Arrived?, Practical Law Journal, April 2012; US Airport P3s: Preparing For Flight?, Project Finance International, March 2012; US P3: Has The Long Awaited Surge Arrived?, Practical Law, March 2012.

## DI MARTINO, Rose F
Willkie Farr & Gallagher LLP, New York
212 728 8215
rdimartino@willkie.com
*Featured in Investment Funds (Nationwide)*
**Practice Areas:** Counsels SEC-registered open-end and closed-end investment companies on organizational/operational matters. Advises funds and their boards on compliance matters, contract approvals, disclosure issues and M&A. Advises investment advisers on regulation, strategic alliances, and acquisitions. Counsels closed-end funds and their boards on tenders, share repurchases, managed distributions and other strategies to address discount at which fund shares trade. Recent work: Gabelli Equity Trust, preferred stock rights offering; Aberdeen Closed End Funds and Credit Suisse High Yield Fund, at-the-market offerings; AQR Funds, organization of cutting edge "alternative" mutual funds; various Closed-End fund, tender offers/share buybacks.
**Personal:** JD, St. John's University, 1981. MA, Fordham University, 1977. BA, Catholic University of America, 1974.
See:http://www.willkie.com/RoseDiMartino.

## DI ROSA, Paolo
Arnold & Porter LLP, Washington, DC
202 942 5060
Paolo.DiRosa@aporter.com
*Featured in International Arbitration (Nationwide)*
**Practice Areas:** International arbitration/litigation; public international law. Experience: investor-State arbitration and disputes under bilateral investment treaties. Extensive experience in sovereign representation.
**Professional Memberships:** Member, IBA; ILA; ASIL; ABA; IABA; DC Bar Association.
**Career:** Former Head, Office of Legal Adviser for Western Hemisphere Affairs, US State Department.
**Publications:** Frequent speaker at conferences sponsored by major international arbitral institutions; various articles on international arbitration (in English and Spanish).

**Personal:** Harvard Law School, JD cum laude (1991); Harvard College, BA magna cum laude (1987). Languages: English (native); Spanish (native); Portuguese & French (reading ability).

## DIBERNARDO, S James
Morgan, Lewis & Bockius LLP, Palo Alto
650 843 7560
jdibernardo@morganlewis.com
*Featured in Employee Benefits & Executive Compensation (Nationwide), Employee Benefits & Executive Compensation (California)*
See under California for profile.

## DIBLASI, Gandolfo V
Sullivan & Cromwell LLP, New York
212 558 3836
diblasig@sullcrom.com
*Featured in Securities (Nationwide), Litigation (New York)*
**Professional Memberships:** Director, Legal Aid Society; Trustee, Federal Bar Foundation; ABA; ABCNY; NYSBA; FBC.
**Career:** Partner since 1985. Extensive experience in securities/commodities class actions, derivatives suits. Represents clients in litigation arising from mortgage-related securities, liquidity concerns and auction rate securities. Lead counsel in major investigations, including: market timing of mutual funds; alleged "back dating" of options; pay-to-play investigations in the municipal securities market; various Enron-related matters; IPO and research analyst practices; and investigations/litigation in CDO and related markets. Has handled numerous SEC, NYSE, NASD and CBOE investigations, including trials.
**Personal:** Yale Law School (JD, 1978); Yale University (BA, 1975).

## DICARLO, Patrick
Alston & Bird LLP, Atlanta
404 881 4512
pat.dicarlo@alston.com
*Featured in ERISA Litigation (Nationwide)*
**Practice Areas:** Defense of litigation, and counseling clients on regulatory compliance issues with an emphasis on ERISA and securities issues surrounding the development and sale of financial products in the retirement plan context.
**Professional Memberships:** American Bar Association's Employee Benefits Committee and the Subcommittee on Reporting and Disclosure.
**Career:** Faculty lecturing on employment law at University of Georgia School of Law and Emory Law School.
**Personal:** AB (1991), JD, cum laude, (1994) - University of Georgia.

## DICKMAN, David G
Venable LLP, Washington, DC
202 344 8026
dgdickman@Venable.com
*Featured in Transportation (Nationwide)*
**Practice Areas:** Transportation, maritime, international trade, environmental, homeland security.
**Career:** David Dickman represents clients on issues involving environmental, marine safety, vessel documentation, port security, and transportation laws and regulations, covering international,

criminal, civil, and administrative law aspects. He regularly addresses maritime, environmental and transportation matters on behalf of clients before Executive agencies and Congress.

**Publications:** Co-Author, "Maritime Security," Benedict on Admiralty; Author, "Oil and Hazardous Substance Spills: Section 311," The Clean Water Act Handbook (American Bar Association).

**Personal:** US Coast Guard (Ret.); JD, St. Louis University School of Law; BS, US Coast Guard Academy.

### DIENELT, John F
Quarles & Brady LLP, Washington, DC
202 372 9510
john.dienelt@quarles.com
*Featured in Franchising (Nationwide)*
**Practice Areas:** Franchise, Litigation.
**Career:** A litigator with more than 35 years experience, concentrating in complex litigation, including class actions, in franchising and related commercial fields, he has tried or arbitrated more than 75 cases and argued more than 25 appeals in various courts, including the Supreme Court. He teaches franchise law at Georgetown and Virginia law schools and is a past chair of the ABA Forum on Franchising. He serves as a court-appointed mediator in Washington and is managing partner of the firm's office there.
**Personal:** LLB, Yale; MA, Fletcher School of Law & Diplomacy; BA, University of Virginia.

### DIETDERICH, Andrew G
Sullivan & Cromwell LLP, New York
212 558 3830
dietdericha@sullcrom.com
*Featured in Bankruptcy/Restructuring (Nationwide),*
*Bankruptcy/Restructuring (New York)*
**Career:** Partner since 2004. Head, Restructuring and Bankruptcy Practice. Focuses on large transactions involving US bankruptcies. Recent representations: Eastman Kodak Chapter 11 case and pending restructuring; Fiat in Chrysler acquisition; Ares Management/Ontario Teachers Private Capital in Simmons acquisition; Pershing Square and Fairholme in General Growth Properties bankruptcy; CIT board of directors in its restructuring; New Chrysler with insolvent suppliers; RR Donnelly in Quebecor bid; Allianz in The Hartford rescue investment; Pershing Square in Borders Group rescue investment. Extensive personal experience in bankruptcy/non-bankruptcy M&A, financial restructuring, equity/debt capital markets, derivatives and JVs.
**Personal:** Harvard Law (JD, 1995); Harvard (AB, 1991).

### DIMICHAEL, Nicholas J
Thompson Hine LLP, Washington, DC
202 263 4103
Nick.DiMichael@ThompsonHine.com
*Featured in Transportation (Nationwide)*
**Career:** Nick assists companies in satisfying domestic and international transportation needs and complex transportation-related litigation. He represents utilities and industrial concerns, including companies in the chemical, steel, forest products, automobile, mining, recycling, and

other industries, as well as agricultural interests. Nick serves as counsel to The National Industrial Transportation League, the nation's largest association representing shippers, and is transportation counsel to The Fertilizer Institute and other trade associations. He has participated in numerous proceedings before the Surface Transportation Board, Department of Transportation, Federal Maritime Commission, and other agencies; in international transportation negotiations; and in litigation and arbitration on transportation matters.

### DIZENGOFF, Ira S
Akin Gump Strauss Hauer & Feld LLP, New York
212 872 1096
idizengoff@akingump.com
*Featured in Bankruptcy/Restructuring (Nationwide),*
*Bankruptcy/Restructuring (New York)*
**Practice Areas:** Practice focuses on corporate restructurings, with an emphasis on creditors' committees and bondholder committees in large, complex cases both out of court and in Chapter 11. Represents bondholders, noteholders, institutional investors, hedge funds and debtors in possession, post-petition lenders and acquirers of distressed assets.
**Professional Memberships:** Admitted to practice, New York, New Jersey, US District Courts, Southern and Eastern Districts of New York, District of New Jersey.
**Career:** 'Outstanding Young Bankruptcy Lawyer', Turnarounds & Workouts, 2003.
**Personal:** BA, magna cum laude, Brandeis University; JD, Benjamin N Cardozo School of Law; Member, Cardozo Law Review.

### DOCKSEY, Ross
Dentons, Chicago
312 876 8171
ross.docksey@dentons.com
*Featured in Outsourcing (Nationwide), Technology (Illinois)*
See under Illinois for profile.

### DODD, Jan E
Fulbright & Jaworski LLP, Los Angeles
+1 213 892 9272
jdodd@fulbright.com
*Featured in Products Liability (Nationwide)*
**Practice Areas:** Litigation; Pharmaceutical and Medical Devices; Product Liability; Mass Tort; Toxic Tort and Environmental Litigation
**Career:** Jan Dodd joined the Los Angeles office of Fulbright & Jaworski L.L.P. as a partner in February 2011. Jan has successfully tried lawsuits throughout the country in both state and federal courts including New York, Illinois, Missouri, Kansas, Arizona and California. Her trial experience includes product liability- pharmaceuticals, medical devices and mass torts, as well as catastrophic personal injury cases.
**Personal:** JD, University of Missouri, Kansas City (1988); BJ, BA, University of Missouri, Columbia (1985).

### DOKE JR, Marshall J
Gardere Wynne Sewell LLP, Dallas
214 999 4733
mdoke@gardere.com
*Featured in Government (Nationwide)*
**Practice Areas:** Government contracts counseling and litigation.
**Professional Memberships:** State Bar of Texas, American Bar Association [Chair, Standing Committee on Audit], US Court of Federal Claims Bar Association [Advisory Council and former President], Federal Circuit Bar Association [former Board of Governors], Board of Contract Appeals Bar Association [Board of Governors and former President], Federal Acquisition Advisory Panel.
**Career:** Marshall Doke represents clients in counseling and litigation regarding disputes and claims under government contracts including procurement protests, changes claims, breach of contract, suspension/debarment, default terminations, and defective pricing, as well as issues related to the Foreign Corrupt Practices Act, the Buy American Act, export controls, and the False Claims Act. Mr Doke was appointed by the Administrator of the OMB's Office of Federal Procurement Policy to the Acquisition Advisory Panel composed of recognized experts in government acquisition law and policy as required by the Services Acquisition Reform Act. He has testified before the US Senate Homeland Security Committee's Subcommittee on Contracting Oversight regarding interagency contracting methods. He has also testified before several Committees of the US House of Representatives regarding government contracts.
**Personal:** LLB, Southern Methodist University School of Law, with high honors, 1959; BA, Hardin Simmons University, magna cum laude, 1956.

### DOKOS, Daniel S
Weil, Gotshal & Manges LLP, New York
212 310 8576
daniel.dokos@weil.com
*Featured in Banking & Finance (Nationwide)*
**Practice Areas:** Daniel Dokos is Head of Weil's global Finance Practice and a member of the firm's Management Committee. He has extensive experience in all areas of bank financing, with a particular focus on acquisition finance and cross-border lending. Mr Dokos represents both financial institutions and corporate borrowers in connection with leveraged acquisition and recapitalization transactions, syndicated lending, investment grade lending, cash flow lending and asset-based lending, as well as loan restructurings, debtor in possession financings and exit financings.
**Personal:** Dartmouth College (AB, 1979); University of Virginia (JD, 1982).

### DOLIN, Mitchell F
Covington & Burling LLP, Washington, DC
202 662-5219
mdolin@cov.vom
*Featured in Insurance (Nationwide), Insurance (District of Columbia)*

**Practice Areas:** Represents corporate policyholders in litigation, arbitration, and mediation of complex disputes over insurance for mass torts, D&O and E&O liabilities, and a wide array of other high-value insurance claims. Serves as chair of Covington's global insurance recovery practice.
**Professional Memberships:** American Law Institute; CPR International Institute for Dispute Resolution (Regional Panel of Neutrals).
**Personal:** Tufts University, BA, 1978; New York University School of Law, JD, 1981; law clerk to Chief Judge Charles Clark, US Court of Appeals for the 5th Circuit (1981-82); with Covington since 1982.

### DONAHUE, Douglas
Cadwalader, Wickersham & Taft LLP, New York
212 504 6511
douglas.donahue@cwt.com
*Featured in Capital Markets (Nationwide)*
**Practice Areas:** Focuses on credit derivatives, fixed income derivatives, and structured financial products. Represents both buy and sell-side institutions, including some of the foremost dealers, banks, and hedge funds, in connection with the development, structuring, negotiation and documentation of a wide variety of financial products, including total return swaps, swap intermediations, credit derivatives, interest rate swaps, commodity swaps, currency swaps, and other funded and unfunded structured financial products. Extensive experience with hybrid products that combine securitization and/or project finance techniques and derivatives. Has (i) developed documentation for derivative transactions with high net worth individuals, and (ii) experience in the use of derivatives and financial products in the municipal markets, including interest rate swaps, rate locks, credit default swaps, total return swaps, forward delivery agreements, forward bond purchase agreements, and gas prepay financings.
**Personal:** JD, New York University School of Law; BS, St. Francis College.

### DONLEY, Charles F
Squire Sanders (US) LLP, Washington, DC
202 626 6840
charles.donley@squiresanders.com
*Featured in Transportation (Nationwide)*
**Practice Areas:** Practice focuses on representing US and non-US airlines, aviation industry manufacturers and service providers, tour operators, airports, airline trade groups, travel agent industry associations, aircraft brokers and foreign governments. Represents clients before the Department of Transportation, FAA, DHS, Department of State, DOJ and other federal agencies. Has extensive experience in aviation licensing, enforcement and operating matters, and advises senior client management on issues involving codesharing, international route authority, bilateral negotiations, foreign investment, strategic alliances and partnering agreements, aviation safety and security, and regulatory aspects of commercial and general aviation aircraft registration, ownership and leasing.

**DONOVAN, John M**
White & Case LLP, New York
212 819 8530
jdonovan@whitecase.com
*Featured in Capital Markets (Nationwide)*
**Career:** John Donovan has an active securities and commercial finance practice with an emphasis on securitization transactions and structured financings. In the asset securitization area, Mr Donovan has represented issuers, underwriters and credit enhancers in connection with the issuance of securities backed by a wide range of assets, including bank loans, high yield bonds, commercial real estate loans, bank and private label credit card receivables, vehicle loan and lease receivables, warehouse loans to residential mortgage bankers, equipment leases, gold ore sales payments, television licensing payments and franchisee loans. To view a comprehensive biography, please visit www.whitecase.com/jdonovan.

**DOOT, David T**
Day Pitney LLP, Hartford
860 275 0102
dtdoot@daypitney.com
*Featured in Energy & Natural Resources (Nationwide)*
**Career:** David Doot is chair of the firm's Energy and Utility Law department and practices in the areas of public utility and energy law. Dave participates in mergers, acquisitions, and related business realignments, and has assisted in the development of generation and transmission projects nationwide. He assists industry participants in compliance-related efforts before federal and state agencies; represents clients in enforcement investigations before the Federal Energy Regulatory Commission; negotiates and documents energy arrangements among industry participants; and counsels businesses concerning wholesale and retail arrangements for the purchase and sale of electricity. Dave is past president of the Energy Bar Association.

**DORN, Joseph W**
King & Spalding LLP, Washington, DC
202 626 5445
jdorn@kslaw.com
*Featured in International Trade (Nationwide)*
**Practice Areas:** International trade regulation, customs law and complex business litigation. Substantial experience in trade remedy actions on behalf of US industries against imports from other countries. Extensive experience in NAFTA and WTO dispute settlement proceedings, appeals before the US Court of International Trade and the US Court of Appeals for the Federal Circuit.
**Professional Memberships:** American Bar Association; ITC Trial Lawyers Association; International Bar Association; State Bar of Georgia; The District of Columbia Bar; US Court of International Trade, US Court of Appeals for the Federal Circuit.
**Personal:** BA, University of North Carolina, 1970; JD, University of Virginia, 1973.

**DORRIS, Malcolm S**
Dechert LLP, New York
212 698 3519
malcolm.dorris@dechert.com
*Featured in Capital Markets (Nationwide)*
**Practice Areas:** Mr Dorris works on public and private transactions spanning many asset types, including auto loans and leases; rental cars; credit card, equipment lease and trade receivables; mortgage loans; and middle-market corporate loans. He also handles esoteric asset types, such as 12b-1 mutual fund fees and healthcare receivables.
**Professional Memberships:** Member, New York Bar; admitted to practice before the State of New York Court of Appeals.
**Personal:** Colgate University (AB, 1976); Washington and Lee University School of Law (JD, 1980, executive editor of the Washington and Lee University Law Review).

**DOUGHERTY, Thomas J**
Skadden, Arps, Slate, Meagher & Flom LLP & Affiliates, Boston
617 573 4820
Dougherty@skadden.com
*Featured in Securities (Nationwide), Litigation (Massachusetts)*
See under Massachusetts for profile.

**DOUGLASS, Duncan B**
Alston & Bird LLP, Atlanta
404 881 7768
duncan.douglass@alston.com
*Featured in Financial Services Regulation (Nationwide)*
**Practice Areas:** Heads Alston & Bird's payment systems practice and focuses on transactions, product development and regulatory issues related to retail and wholesale payment systems and products. He represents clients across the payments industry, including financial institutions, network operators, service providers, financial technology providers, and retailers.
**Career:** Featured in the Fulton County Daily Report as one of only 14 'On the Rise – Rising Lawyers Under 40'. He was recognized for his expertise in the mobile payment systems arena.
**Personal:** JD (2000) Duke University (Summa Cum Laude); MPH (1997) University of South Florida; BA (1995) Cornell University.

**DOWD, Kelvin J**
Slover & Loftus, Washington, DC
202 347 7170
kjd@sloverandloftus.com
*Featured in Transportation (Nationwide)*
**Practice Areas:** Mr Dowd is a Partner with over 30 years' experience providing strategic counseling and transactional and litigation representation to clients in the transportation and energy fields. Clients include electric utilities and other major consumers of freight transportation service, and public and private entities with interests in surface transportation infrastructure. Mr Dowd's experience extends to the negotiation of rail transportation, commodity supply and infrastructure construction contracts, and the representation of clients in litigation and arbitration in disputes arising from these relationships.

**Personal:** BA, University at Albany, 1978; JD, Washington College of Law, American University, 1981.

**DOWLING, Charles T**
Sullivan & Cromwell LLP, New York
212 558 3845
dowlingc@sullcrom.com
*Featured in Wealth Management (Nationwide)*
**Professional Memberships:** ABA; ABCNY (former member, Committee on Trusts, Estates & Surrogate's Courts); NYSBA; Society of Trusts and Estates Practitioners.
**Career:** Partner since 2002. Represents wealthy individuals and families in many aspects of their personal and business affairs, including sophisticated tax and estate planning, the structuring of private business and investment vehicles, trust and estate administration, charitable planning, and a broad range of personal legal matters. Serves as an advisor to or trustee of many large family trusts, charitable foundations and family offices.
**Personal:** Columbia Law School (JD, 1993); Harvard University (AB, 1989).

**DOWNES, Robert W**
Sullivan & Cromwell LLP, New York
212 558 4312
downesr@sullcrom.com
*Featured in Capital Markets (Nationwide)*
**Career:** Partner since 2000. Managing Partner, Corporate and Finance Group; Co-head, General Practice Group; former Co-coordinator, High Yield Financing Group. Extensive experience advising issuers/underwriters in public/private offerings of debt/equity securities, including IPOs and high-yield and structured finance transactions. Counsels US and non-US clients in JVs and M&A. Advises domestic issuers on corporate governance matters. Recent representations: AMC Networks; Cablevision; General Growth Properties; Goldman Sachs; HOVENSA; Madison Square Garden; Morgans Hotel Group; Mitsubishi UFJ Financial Group; NorthStar Realty; Popular, Inc.; and R.R. Donnelley.
**Personal:** George Washington University Law School (JD, 1991); University of Virginia (BS, 1985). Board Member, ArtsConnection.

**DOYLE, Patrick**
Arnold & Porter LLP, Washington, DC
202 942 5949
Patrick.Doyle@aporter.com
*Featured in Financial Services Regulation (Nationwide)*
**Practice Areas:** Patrick Doyle, who headed the firm's financial services practice group from 1993 to 2013, regularly counsels bank holding companies, foreign banks, savings institutions, insurance companies, securities firms, and other non-bank companies on a variety of regulatory matters, including acquisitions, strategic planning, complex regulatory issues, and legislation. Since the passage of the Dodd Frank Act, he has advised a significant number of banks, insurance companies, mutual fund complexes, and other financial industry participants on the implications of the financial reform legislation. During the financial crisis, he represented FHFA in connection with

the conservatorship of Fannie Mae and Freddie Mac.

**DRAKE, Stuart AC**
Kirkland & Ellis LLP, Washington, DC
202 879 5094
stuart.drake@kirkland.com
*Featured in Climate Change (Nationwide), Environment (District of Columbia)*
**Practice Areas:** Stuart Drake represents companies whose products are subject to federal, state and local air pollution and energy controls. His work includes litigation challenging such controls, the defense of enforcement actions brought by the federal and state governments, rulemaking, strategic planning and work in legislative forums.
**Personal:** Yale College, BA, 1977. Cambridge University, MLitt, 1981. Yale Law School, JD, 1981.

**DUBBS, Thomas**
Labaton Sucharow LLP, New York
212 907 0871
tdubbs@labaton.com
*Featured in Securities (Nationwide), Litigation (New York)*
See under New York for profile.

**DUFFELL, David K**
Weil, Gotshal & Manges LLP, Providence
401 278 4710
david.duffell@weil.com
*Featured in Private Equity (Nationwide), Corporate/Commercial (Rhode Island)*
See under Rhode Island for profile.

**DUGAN, John C**
Covington & Burling LLP, Washington, DC
202 662 5051
jdugan@cov.com
*Featured in Financial Services Regulation (Nationwide)*
**Practice Areas:** Advises on legal matters affected by significantly increased regulatory requirements resulting from the financial crisis, including implementation of the Dodd-Frank Act; financial institution mergers, acquisitions, and investments; litigation and enforcement issues; international financial regulation; and legislative and government relations issues.
**Professional Memberships:** DC Bar.
**Career:** Chair, Financial Institutions Group at Covington & Burling LLP. From 2005-2010, US Comptroller of the Currency; Director, Federal Deposit Insurance Corporation; Member, Basel Committee on Banking Supervision; Chair, Joint Forum of Banking, Securities, and Insurance Supervisors; and participant on Financial Stability Board. Directed OCC's actions during financial crisis; actively participated in negotiation of Basel III agreement; and led agency efforts to help shape Dodd-Frank Act provisions on systemic risk regulation; federal preemption; new capital regulation; the Consumer Financial Protection Bureau; derivatives regulation; and the "Volcker Rule." Previously, Partner, Covington & Burling (bank regulatory practice); Assistant Treasury Secretary for Domestic Finance; and Minority General Counsel, US Senate Committee on Banking, Housing, and Urban Affairs.

**Personal:** Harvard Law School, JD, 1981. University of Michigan, AB, 1977.

**DUKES, David E**
Nelson Mullins Riley & Scarborough LLP, Columbia
803 255 9451
david.dukes@nelsonmullins.com
*Featured in Litigation (South Carolina), Products Liability (Nationwide)*
See under South Carolina for profile.

**DUMONT, Edward C**
WilmerHale, Washington, DC
202 663 6910
edward.dumont@wilmerhale.com
*Featured in Appellate Law (Nationwide)*
**Practice Areas:** Partner, Appellate and Supreme Court Group. Focuses on Supreme Court and appellate litigation, dispositive motion practice in lower courts, and advising clients with respect to complex or novel legal issues and the special Supreme Court litigation process. Matters have dealt with a variety of substantive areas, including antitrust, class-action arbitration, federal Indian law and Indian gaming, tax, financial transactions, patent, trademark, administrative law, and constitutional questions.
**Career:** Served as Assistant to the Solicitor General at the US Department of Justice, and Associate Deputy Attorney General. Has argued more than 18 cases before the US Supreme Court.

**DUNCAN, J Kelly**
Jones Walker LLP, New Orleans
504 582 8218
kduncan@joneswalker.com
*Featured in Gaming & Licensing (Nationwide), Gaming & Licensing (Louisiana), Banking & Finance (Louisiana)*
See under Louisiana for profile.

**DUNHAM, Edward Wood**
Wiggin and Dana LLP, New Haven
203 498 4327
edunham@wiggin.com
*Featured in Franchising (Nationwide), Litigation (Connecticut)*
**Practice Areas:** Trial lawyer. For over thirty years has represented businesses in complex litigation and arbitration. Handles a broad variety of matters; special concentration in franchise and distribution disputes. Formerly Chair, firm Executive Committee.
**Professional Memberships:** Fellow of the American College of Trial Lawyers; formerly Chair, American Bar Association Forum on Franchising; formerly Editor-in-Chief, ABA Franchise Law Journal.
**Personal:** Law Clerk to Judge Robert A Ainsworth, Jr., of the US Court of Appeals for the Fifth Circuit (1978-79); New York University School of Law (law review editorial board) (1978); Trinity College (Phi Beta Kappa) (1975).

**DUNN, Christopher A**
Curtis, Mallet-Prevost, Colt & Mosle LLP, Washington, DC
202 452 7325
cdunn@curtis.com
*Featured in International Trade (Nationwide)*
**Professional Memberships:** DC Bar Association; American Bar Association
**Career:** Mr Dunn is a partner in the International Trade group. He focuses his practice on international trade law. Mr Dunn represents clients in matters related to antidumping, subsidies, and safeguards, as well as customs and foreign sanctions controls. His client base is composed of companies in Asia and Latin America, as well as US importers and exporters. He has represented these clients before the US Department of Commerce, US International Trade Commission, US Court of International Trade and US Court of Appeals for the Federal Circuit, as well as presenting several claims before the World Trade Organization. Prior to his legal career, Mr Dunn served on the staff of the general counsel's office of the US Agency for International Development (1974-1975).Following graduation from law school he clerked for then Chief Judge Wilson Cowen of what is now the US Court of Appeals for the Federal Circuit.
**Publications:** Mr Dunn is the co-author of a regularly updated treatise on US trade disputes law, International Trade Practice, as well as numerous articles.
**Personal:** Georgetown University Law Center (JD 1975), served as student Editor-In-Chief of The Tax Lawyer; Brown University (AB 1972).

**DUNN, Martin**
O'Melveny & Myers LLP, Washington, DC
202 383 5418
mdunn@omm.com
*Featured in Securities (Nationwide)*
**Practice Areas:** Marty Dunn is a partner in O'Melveny's Washington, DC office and a member of the Capital Markets Practice. Marty provides guidance on securities law compliance to private and publicly traded companies, counsels on corporate governance and disclosure best practices, advises investors in public companies, guides companies through the public offering process, including compliance with SEC requirements and responses to SEC comments, and provides equity derivatives advice. Marty spent 20 years in various positions at the SEC, most recently as Deputy Director, and former Acting Director, of the Division of Corporation Finance.

**DUNNE, Dennis**
Milbank, Tweed, Hadley & McCloy LLP, New York
212 530 5770
ddunne@milbank.com
*Featured in Bankruptcy/Restructuring (Nationwide), Bankruptcy/Restructuring (New York)*
**Practice Areas:** Co-leader of the Financial Restructuring Group. He has extensive experience representing debtors and creditors in reorganization cases and out-of-court workouts, including exchange and tender offers, and acquirors of financially distressed companies. Mr Dunne's

engagements range across an array of industries, including automotive, airline, apparel, cable and broadcasting, chemical, construction, gambling, healthcare, housing development, manufacturing, pharmaceutical, project finance, retail, shipping, telecommunications, and textile. He assists prospective providers of high risk and debtor-in-possession financing in structuring, documenting and obtaining approval for such loans and regularly advised boards of directors of public companies on corporate governance and fiduciary duty matters.

**DUNNER, Donald R**
Finnegan, Henderson, Farabow, Garrett & Dunner LLP, Washington, DC
202 408 4062
don.dunner@finnegan.com
*Featured in Appellate Law (Nationwide), Intellectual Property (District of Columbia)*
See under District of Columbia for profile.

**DUPLER, Mitchell S**
Cleary Gottlieb Steen & Hamilton LLP, Washington, DC
202 974 1630
mdupler@cgsh.com
*Featured in Capital Markets (Nationwide)*
**Practice Areas:** Corporate, finance — structured financings, related regulatory advice—transactions backed by mortgages, other financial assets. Handled over $2 trillion of mortgage-backed securities since 2001. Executed many "firsts" – first FHLMC REMIC, first public offering of securities combining interests in a swap and a fixed-rate MBS, first FHLMC Reference REMIC, first FNMA Benchmark REMIC, first "synthetic treasuries", first Euromarket CMO. Recent key role in securitization, loan servicing and origination related acquisitions and matters relating to Federal support of financial institutions.
**Career:** Harvard (JD 1979, AB 1976).
**Publications:** Widely published on structured finance and securities law; co-edited 1995 text International Asset Securitization.

**DUPREE JR, Thomas**
Gibson, Dunn & Crutcher LLP, Washington, DC
202 955 8547
TDupree@gibsondunn.com
*Featured in Appellate Law (Nationwide)*
**Practice Areas:** Experienced trial and appellate advocate in federal and state courts. Argued more than 60 appeals, including in all thirteen federal circuits and before five en banc courts. Expertise in cases involving punitive damages, class actions, product liability, arbitration, intellectual property, securities, employment, and constitutional challenges to federal and state statutes. Succeeded in overturning many multimillion-dollar jury verdicts.
**Career:** Deputy Assistant Attorney General, US Department of Justice (2007-2009). Law clerk to Judge Jerry E. Smith, US Court of Appeals for the Fifth Circuit.
**Personal:** JD with honors, University of Chicago Law School, 1997; Editor, University of Chicago Law Review.

**DURHAM, Phillip**
Holland & Knight LLP, New York
212 513 3381
phillip.durham@hklaw.com
*Featured in Transportation (Nationwide)*
**Professional Memberships:** Vice Chair of the American Bar Association Aircraft Financing Subcommittee; ISTAT; Wings Club
**Career:** Mr Durham represents aircraft operating lessors, international financial institutions, US domestic airlines and engine lessors in a broad range of domestic and cross-border transactions, including aircraft operating leases, senior and subordinated secured loans, aircraft purchase and sale transactions, portfolio securitizations, secured bond offerings, commercial jet and corporate jet manufacturer purchase transactions, engine leasing and financing transactions, spare parts leasing and financing transactions and repossessions and foreclosures. Mr Durham has a particular focus on aircraft financing transactions in Latin America.

**DURLING, James P**
Curtis, Mallet-Prevost, Colt & Mosle LLP, Washington, DC
202 425 7328
jdurling@curtis.com
*Featured in International Trade (Nationwide)*
**Professional Memberships:** DC Bar Association
**Career:** Mr Durling, a partner in the International Trade group at Curtis, defends foreign governments and companies in antidumping, countervailing duty, and other trade-remedy investigations. He also advises on parties' obligations under World Trade Organization agreements, and has significant experience litigating WTO disputes and other trade policy disputes. He has significant experience in customs law, including valuation, classification, and customs audits. He has also worked on transfer pricing issues, and the intersection of transfer pricing rules and other regulatory rules on pricing. Mr Durling has also developed a focus on the intersection of trade law and antitrust laws, including the anticompetitive consequences of trade law remedies. He has also worked on issues involving the international regulation of intellectual property, and the intersection of rules on intellectual property, antitrust, and international trade. He has worked with clients on a wide range of high-profile trade policy disputes, including the trade policy battles over automobiles, semiconductors, and color film, and has been actively involved in the related WTO proceedings arising out of these trade policy battles.
**Personal:** NYU School of Law (JD 1984), articles editor of NYU Law Review; Princeton University (MPA 1984); Haverford College (BA 1980), Phi Beta Kappa.

**DWORKIN, Adam**
Cahill Gordon & Reindel LLP, New York
212 701 3131
adworkin@cahill.com
*Featured in Banking & Finance (Nationwide)*
**Practice Areas:** Practice is focused in leveraged finance. Has significant experience representing

arrangers in secured cash flow credit facilities, asset based credit facilities and high yield offerings in leveraged buyout, refinancing and restructuring transactions involving companies in a wide variety of industries. Also represents several companies as borrowers under secured credit facilities. **Personal:** Binghamton University, BA, 1992. George Washington University Law School, JD, 1995.

## DYE, Alexander M
Willkie Farr & Gallagher LLP, New York
212 728 8642
adye@willkie.com
*Featured in Insurance (Nationwide), Insurance (New York)*
**Practice Areas:** Specializes in M&A and capital markets transactions in the insurance industry. Represents strategic and financial buyers, sellers and financial advisers. Advises on public and private acquisitions, auctions, asset acquisitions, activists, hostile takeovers, proxy contests, demutualizations and strategic investments. Advises boards on defensive measures, including shareholder rights plans, charter and by-law provisions and regulatory defenses. Also represents issuers and underwriters in public and private offerings of debt, equity, surplus notes and convertible securities. **Personal:** JD, University of Michigan, 1981. AB, magna cum laude, Brown University, 1978. See: http://www.willkie.com/Alexander_Dye.

## DYER, T Michael
Blank Rome LLP, Washington, DC
202 772 5990
Dyer@BlankRome.com
*Featured in Transportation (Nationwide)*
**Practice Areas:** A skilled strategist and negotiator, T. Michael ("Mike") Dyer counsels clients on a variety of transactional and regulatory issues, both strategically and in crisis-management situations. After more than thirty years of practice in Washington, DC, Mr Dyer's legislative and regulatory experience includes working with Congress, the Administration, and executive agencies on issues such as transportation and maritime regulations; international trade, customs, and foreign-trade regulations; national and homeland security; and congressional investigations and criminal enforcement actions. Mr Dyer is co-chairman of Blank Rome LLP and a principal and director for Blank Rome Government Relations LLC. For more information: www.BlankRome.com/Dyer.

## DYKSTRA, Paul H
K&L Gates, Chicago
312 781 6029
paul.dykstra@klgates.com
*Featured in Investment Funds (Nationwide)*
**Practice Areas:** Paul Dykstra has represented mutual funds or their boards throughout the country for more than 30 years. He also counsels independent fund directors involved in corporate reorganizations and internal or SEC investigations. A frequent speaker and author on mutual fund and independent director issues, he co-authored The Fund Director's Guidebook for the American Bar Association and, along with K&L

Gates' Chicago partner Paulita Pike, was named "Independent Counsel of the Year" by Fund Directions in 2008. Mr Dykstra and Ms Pike also teach a course on mutual fund regulation at Northwestern University Law School.

## EASTMENT, Thomas
Baker Botts LLP, Washington, DC
202 639 7717
tom.eastment@bakerbotts.com
*Featured in Energy & Natural Resources (Nationwide)*
**Practice Areas:** Represents producers, refiners and other shippers in oil and gas pipeline transportation and enforcement matters before FERC and federal trial and appellate courts; represents producers regarding royalty matters before the Department of the Interior and in state and federal courts; represents project owners regarding FERC certificate applications for pipeline projects; and represents electric generation and other clients on gas supply and transportation contract matters. **Professional Memberships:** District of Columbia Bar; New York Bar; Energy Bar Association. **Personal:** JD from the University of Michigan Law School, 1975; BChE from Manhattan College, 1972.

## EATON, Maja C
Sidley Austin LLP, Chicago
312 853 7123
meaton@sidley.com
*Featured in Products Liability (Nationwide)*
**Practice Areas:** Partner in Sidley's Chicago office, practicing in Products Liability and Mass Tort group. Handles pharmaceutical and medical device cases and trials, and toxic tort litigation. Experience includes defense and trial of complex mass torts involving multiple defendants and various scientific and legal issues. Utilizes her science background in developing trial themes, and in working with defense expert witnesses in many medical and scientific specialties. **Professional Memberships:** Firmwide co-chair of the Committee for the Retention and Promotion of Women. **Personal:** University of Iowa College of Law, JD, 1984, with high honors; University of Iowa, BA, 1977. Admission: Illinois.

## ECCLES, Bob
O'Melveny & Myers LLP, Washington, DC
202 383 5363
beccles@omm.com
*Featured in ERISA Litigation (Nationwide)*
**Practice Areas:** Bob Eccles is Of Counsel in O'Melveny's Washington, DC office. His practice focuses on ERISA litigation pertaining to Title I of ERISA and other statutes affecting employee benefit plans. He provides advice and handles litigation under ERISA and related statues for a broad range of clients in the financial, healthcare, automotive, and telecommunications sectors. He also represents clients of the Firm in dealings with federal ERISA agencies and provides advice to corporations, employee benefit plans, and financial institutions. He appears regularly in federal dis-

trict and appellate courts throughout the country and has argued before the US Supreme Court.

## ECKLAND, William S
Sidley Austin LLP, Washington, DC
202 736 8267
weckland@sidley.com
*Featured in Financial Services Regulation (Nationwide)*
**Practice Areas:** Partner in Sidley's Washington, DC office. Focuses primarily on financial institutions, with particular emphasis on federal regulatory issues governing the operations of depository institutions and their holding companies. A key aspect of his practice relates to the development of new products and services for financial services entities. His practice involves the representation of diversified or nontraditional financial services holding companies. He also counsels foreign banking entities regarding their US operations. **Personal:** The George Washington University Law School, JD, 1979, with honors, Order of the Coif; University of Maryland, BA, 1976. Admissions: District of Columbia, New York.

## ECKSTEIN, Kenneth H
Kramer Levin Naftalis & Frankel LLP, New York
212 715 9229
keckstein@kramerlevin.com
*Featured in Bankruptcy/Restructuring (Nationwide), Bankruptcy/Restructuring (New York)*
**Practice Areas:** Partner and Co-Chairman of Kramer Levin Naftalis & Frankel LLP's Corporate Restructuring and Bankruptcy Department. He has practiced in the area of corporate reorganization and bankruptcy since 1979. Practice includes both in and out-of-court restructurings of financially distressed businesses on behalf of debtors, creditor's committees, major secured and unsecured creditors, bondholders, trustees, examiners, and third parties seeking to acquire the assets or businesses of financially troubled companies. **Professional Memberships:** A frequent lecturer and author in the areas of bankruptcy and corporate reorganization. He is a Member of the Section on Corporation, Banking and Business Law of the American Bar Association. He is also a former Member of the Committee on Bankruptcy and Corporate Reorganization of the Association of the Bar of the City of New York. **Career:** Co-chairs a department of 11 partners and 32 associates and has played a prominent role in many of the largest and most complex Chapter 11 reorganization cases over the past 30 years. Representations include the official creditor committees of Residential Capital LLC, General Motors, Chrysler, Cooper-Standard, Magna Entertainment, Leap Wireless, Big V, SGL Carbon Corp., Cityscape Financial, Olympia & York, Integrated Resources, SLM International, Financial News Network, PSNH, Eastern Airlines and Texaco. Mr Eckstein also has represented the debtors in the bankruptcies of General Maritime, Saint Vincent Catholic Medical Centers, Bally Total Fitness, Molecular Insight Pharmaceuticals, Ascendia Brands, Malden Mills, MicroWarehouse, Berry-Hill Galleries, Elite Models, Cross Media

and The Wiz, Inc. His other representations include the Dewey & Leboeuf Lenders, Adelphia/FrontierVision Bondholders, Owens Corning Bank Group, Calpine Canada bondholders and the Dow Corning Claimants Committee. He has represented bank groups, bondholders, acquirors and other major creditors in Washington Mutual, Tribune Company, Charter Communications, Steve & Barry's, Calpine Corporation, Northwest Airlines, PTS, Enron, Warnaco, NTL, Twin Lab, Amerco, Mediq, PacCoin, Big City Radio, Jitney Jungle, LTV, New Valley, Herman's Sporting Goods, Tucson Electric and Farley Industries. He has led his firm's representation of Deloitte LLP for the purchase of assets of BearingPoint's Public Services practice, the Examiner in Bruno's Inc. and the Independent Restructuring Advisor in Coram Healthcare. He has also represented the Trustee in Island Mortgage and in Sharp International. **Personal:** Received a JD degree from New York University in 1979 and a BA degree cum laude from the University of Pennsylvania in 1976.

## EDELMAN, Scott
Milbank, Tweed, Hadley & McCloy LLP, New York
212 530 5149
sedelman@milbank.com
*Featured in Securities (Nationwide), Litigation (New York)*
**Practice Areas:** Mr Edelman is the Chairman of Milbank. His litigation practice focuses on complex commercial and securities litigation, as well as criminal and regulatory matters.In addition, Mr Edelman provides advice to corporate clients and boards of directors on corporate governance and related issues. Prior to joining Milbank, he served as an Assistant United States Attorney in the Southern District of New York from 1990 to 1994.

## EDGAR, George L
Morgan, Lewis & Bockius LLP, Washington, DC
202 739 5459
gedgar@morganlewis.com
*Featured in Energy & Natural Resources (Nationwide)*
**Practice Areas:** George L. Edgar is senior counsel in Morgan Lewis's Energy Practice. Mr Edgar's practice focuses on representing nuclear industry clients before the Nuclear Regulatory Commission (NRC) and related litigation in the federal courts. The range of matters has included financing and restructuring of nuclear projects, performance assessments of nuclear management and organizations, defense of discrimination claims arising under Section 211 of the Energy Reorganization Act, and commercial transactions involving nuclear equipment, services, and fuel.

## EDWARDS, Christine A
Winston & Strawn LLP, Chicago
312 558 5571
cedwards@winston.com
*Featured in Financial Services Regulation (Nationwide)*

**Practice Areas:** Ms Edwards represents clients in the financial services industry-particularly in banking and securities—in areas of regulation, regulatory defense and policy issues. She is recognized as an expert on corporate governance matters. Ms Edwards represents Boards of Directors, Audit, Risk and Special Committees of Boards in matters relating to corporate governance, regulatory enforcement and transactional matters.
**Professional Memberships:** Ms Edwards serves on the boards of The Chicago Network, The Chicago Finance Exchange and the US Chamber Center for Capital Markets Leadership Board. She has been active with the ABA and Corporate Counsel Associations.
**Career:** Capital Partner, Winston & Strawn 2003-Present. EVP and CLO, Bank One Corporation 2000-2003. EVP and CLO, ABN AMRO, US. 1999-2000. EVP and CLO, Morgan Stanley (and predecessor companies) 1990-1999.
**Publications:** ABA Corporate Counsel publication, Corporate Governance: "The In-house Counsel Essential Toolbox." Co-Author-Chapter on Lobbying: "Successful Partnering Between Inside and Outside Counsel." Ms Edwards is a frequent author and speaker on corporate governance, compliance and risk management issues.
**Personal:** Board Member, Risk and Human Resources Committees: BMO Financial Group (TSE, NYSE: "BMO"). Board Member, Chair Audit Committee and member Executive Committee: Rush University Medical Center. Chair, Board of Visitors: University of Maryland School of Law.

**EGAN III, John J**
Goodwin Procter LLP, Boston
617 570 1514
jegan@goodwinprocter.com
*Featured in Investment Funds (Nationwide), Corporate/M&A (Massachusetts), Private Equity (Massachusetts)*
See under Massachusetts for profile.

**EGGLESTON, W Neil**
Kirkland & Ellis LLP, Washington, DC
202 879 5016
neil.eggleston@kirkland.com
*Featured in Securities (Nationwide), Litigation (District of Columbia)*
See under District of Columbia for profile.

**EID, Troy A**
Greenberg Traurig, LLP, Denver
303 572 6521
EidT@gtlaw.com
*Featured in Native American Law (Nationwide), Natural Resources (Colorado)*
**Practice Areas:** Principal Shareholder (Litigation); Co-Chair, American Indian Law Practice Group; environmental; global energy and infrastructure; regulatory and administrative law.
**Professional Memberships:** Chair, National Indian Law and Order Commission; Chair, Navajo Nation Bar Association-Training Committee; Adjunct Professor, American Indian Law Program, University of Colorado School of Law; Adjunct Professor, Natural Resources Law Program, University of Denver College of Law;

Board of Visitors Member, University of Denver Graduate School of Social Work; Member, American Law Institute; admitted to practice in the US Supreme Court; the US Courts of Appeals for the Fifth, Ninth, Tenth and District of Columbia Circuits; and the Navajo Nation Supreme Court.
**Career:** United States Attorney for the District of Colorado, 2006-09. Selected, Chambers USA Guide, 2005-06, 2010-13.
**Publications:** Co-Author, 'Separate But Unequal: The Federal Criminal Justice System in Indian Country', University of Colorado Law Review, Fall 2010.
**Personal:** JD, University of Chicago Law School, 1991; AB, Stanford University, 1986; Law Clerk to the Honorable Edith H. Jones, Chief Judge, US Court of Appeals for the Fifth Circuit, 1991-92; 'Colorado Lawyer of the Year Award,' Law Week Colorado, 2011.

**EILAND, Gary**
King & Spalding LLP, Houston
713 751 3207
geiland@kslaw.com
*Featured in Healthcare (Texas), Healthcare (Nationwide)*
See under Texas for profile.

**EISENBIEGLER, Frederick F**
Bingham McCutchen LLP, New York
212 705 7745
frederick.eisenbiegler@bingham.com
*Featured in Banking & Finance (Nationwide)*
**Practice Areas:** Co-chair of Bingham's Financial Services Area and of its Banking and Leveraged Finance Group. Has extensive experience representing first and second lien senior lenders, mezzanine investors, and equity sponsors and borrowers in senior debt, mezzanine and private equity financing arrangements. Areas of focus include acquisition, recapitalization and other leveraged financings; cash flow and asset-based financings; debtor-in-possession and exit financings; cross-border financings; first lien, second lien and mezzanine financings; and restructurings, workouts and bankruptcies.
**Personal:** Boston College Law School, Juris Doctor, Magna Cum Laude, 1982; The Colorado College, Bachelor of Arts, Magna Cum Laude, 1978.

**EISENHOFER, Jay W**
Grant & Eisenhofer PA, Wilmington
302 622 7050
jeisenhofer@gelaw.com
*Featured in Securities (Nationwide), Chancery (Delaware), Litigation (New York)*
See under Delaware for profile.

**EISENSTAT, Larry**
Dickstein Shapiro LLP, Washington, DC
202 420 2224
eisenstatl@dicksteinshapiro.com
*Featured in Energy & Natural Resources (Nationwide)*
**Practice Areas:** Energy, regulatory, transactional, administrative agency and judicial litigation, compliance and enforcement matters, and strategic planning and energy infrastructure initiatives.

Counsels utilities, independent power producers, marketers, lenders, investors, and customers on matters concerning transmission, interconnection, market design and operation, trading and power procurement, and project development and planning issues, particularly to develop, finance, construct, and operate fossil fuel, renewable, and nuclear generation and transmission.
**Career:** Partner, Head of Energy Practice.
**Publications:** Written and lectured on electric transmission, generation development, renewable power, industry restructuring and competition, and state and federal energy policy.
**Personal:** University of Chicago (JD, 1985; BA, 1982).

**EISERT, Richard**
Davis & Gilbert LLP, New York
212 468 4863
reisert@dglaw.com
*Featured in Advertising (Nationwide)*
**Practice Areas:** Advertising, marketing and promotions.
**Career:** Mr Eisert has extensive experience in the new media area, advising on contracts related to online advertising and commerce, as well as multimedia, software, digital music and technology licensing. He counsels clients on legal/regulatory issues affecting advertising and e-commerce, including privacy and the enforceability of electronic transactions. Mr Eisert has substantial experience advising clients on claim substantiation, false advertising and related issues, as well as negotiating and drafting agency/client agreements, media buying agreements, sponsorship agreements and strategic alliances. In the intellectual property arena, he advises on the protection, enforcement, and licensing of copyrights, trademarks, trade secrets and privacy/publicity rights. Mr Eisert has been recognized in The Legal 500 US for advertising and marketing law.

**EITEL, Mitchell S**
Sullivan & Cromwell LLP, New York
212 558 4960
eitelm@sullcrom.com
*Featured in Financial Services Regulation (Nationwide), Corporate/M&A (New York)*
**Professional Memberships:** ABA; Fellow, ABF; Co-chair, PLI's annual "Guide to Financial Institutions"; Co-chair, NY City Bar/Penn State M&A Conference; General Counsel, Archaeological Institute of America.
**Career:** Partner since 1996. Financial services M&A, securities, regulatory matters; private equity. Recent representations: Regions Financial in its sale of Morgan Keegan to Raymond James; HSBC in its pending business unit sales to Capital One and First Niagara; JPMorgan in; BMO in its acquisition of M&I; US Bancorp in failed bank acquisitions from FDIC; Warburg Pincus in Webster Financial and Sterling investments.
**Personal:** Columbia Law (JD, 1987); Columbia (AB, 1984).

**EIZENSTAT, Stuart E**
Covington & Burling LLP, Washington, DC
202 662 5519
seizenstat@cov.com
*Featured in International Trade (Nationwide)*
**Practice Areas:** Heads Covington's International Practice.
**Career:** Ambassador to the EU; Deputy Treasury Secretary; Under Secretary of State; Under Secretary of Commerce (1993-2001); Chief Domestic Policy Adviser to President Carter (1977-81). During the Clinton Administration, he negotiated the New Transatlantic Agenda; EU agreements regarding Helms-Burton Act and Iran-Libya Sanctions Act; Japan Port Agreement; Kyoto Protocol; Seven honorary PhDs, awards from France, Germany, Austria, Belgium, Israel, and US. Legal Times "Best International Trade Lawyer" (2007); book author and writer in leading papers.
**Personal:** Harvard Law; University of North Carolina (Phi Beta Kappa, cum laude). Serves on UPS, Blackrock, Alcatel, Boards.

**ELLENBERG, Mark C**
Cadwalader, Wickersham & Taft LLP, Washington, DC
202 862 2238
mark.ellenberg@cwt.com
*Featured in Bankruptcy/Restructuring (Nationwide), Bankruptcy/Restructuring (District of Columbia)*
See under District of Columbia for profile.

**ELLIS, Emmett N**
Hunton & Williams LLP, New York
212 309 1064
ellisb@hunton.com
*Featured in Energy & Natural Resources (Nationwide)*
**Practice Areas:** Works with both regulated and non-regulated entities in the global power markets. Represents energy companies and investment banks in public and private capital markets transactions. Also represents corporate clients in the acquisition and divestiture of energy companies and energy assets in the United States and the United Kingdom.
**Professional Memberships:** American Bar Association, Chairman, Finance, Mergers and Acquisitions Committee of the Section of Public Utility, Communications and Transportation Law.
**Personal:** BA, University of Oklahoma, 1975. JD, Yale Law School, 1978.

**ELRIFI, Ivor R**
Mintz Levin Cohn Ferris Glovsky and Popeo PC, Boston
617 348 1747
IRElrifi@mintz.com
*Featured in Life Sciences (Nationwide), Intellectual Property (Massachusetts)*
**Practice Areas:** Ivor co-chairs Mintz Levin's Intellectual Property Section and advises pharmaceutical, biotechnology, life sciences and medical device companies, universities, research institutions and hospitals in the US and worldwide on global patent strategies, patent prosecution, licensing and enforcement, litigation, arbitration and transactions.

**Career:** Patent and later General Counsel, CytoTherapeutics, Inc. Patent Counsel, Modex Therapeutics. Admitted in Massachusetts, California, New York and Ontario and before the US Patent and Trademark Office.

**Publications:** Frequent author in leading legal and scientific publications; speaker at international conferences.

**Personal:** BSc and PhD in Biology, Queen's University. JD, Osgoode Hall Law School.

## ELROD, Eugene R
Sidley Austin LLP, Washington, DC
202 736 8206
eelrod@sidley.com
*Featured in Energy & Natural Resources (Nationwide)*

**Practice Areas:** Partner in Sidley's Washington, DC office and co-head of Firm's Global Energy practice. Focuses on federal and state regulation of production, transmission and distribution of natural gas, crude oil, petroleum products and electric energy. Has represented oil and gas producers, pipelines, distribution and storage companies, electric utilities, and large end-users of natural gas and electric energy. Has appeared before the Federal Energy Regulatory Commission, state courts and state regulatory commissions, Canada's National Energy Board, and handles related matters in federal and state appellate courts.

**Personal:** Emory University School of Law, JD, 1974; Dartmouth College, AB, cum laude, 1971.

## ELWOOD, John
Vinson & Elkins LLP, Washington, DC
202 639 6518
jelwood@velaw.com
*Featured in Appellate Law (Nationwide)*

**Practice Areas:** Considerable experience before the Supreme Court of the United States (briefed or argued more than twenty-four merits cases; briefed more than 130 cases at the certiorari stage), and the federal courts of appeals (appearances before Fourth, Fifth, Seventh, Eighth, Ninth, and Eleventh Circuits). Substantial knowledge of constitutional, criminal, administrative, and environmental law.

**Career:** Senior Deputy Assistant Attorney General, Office of Legal Counsel, Department of Justice, 2005-2009;Assistant to the Solicitor General, 2002-2005; Law clerk to Associate Justice Anthony M. Kennedy, 1996-1997.

**Personal:** Yale Law School, JD; King's College, MA with distinction; Princeton University, AB summa cum laude.

## ELY JR, Clausen
Covington & Burling LLP, Washington, DC
202 662 5152
cely@cov.com
*Featured in Food & Beverages (Nationwide)*

**Practice Areas:** Clausen Ely focuses on food and drug law, pesticide regulation, and representation of trade associations. He represents clients in FDA and FTC regulations, approval of food additives and contact materials, EPA regulation of pesticides, USDA and FDA regulation of biotechnology in food.

**Career:** Counsel to Starlink corn matter; successful challenge to Massachusetts law requiring public disclosure of tobacco product formulas; represented canned tuna industry in successful pre-emption challenge to California consumer warning requirement; defense of EPA challenges to pesticide label claims.

**Personal:** University of Alabama School of Law, JD, 1972, Order of the Coif; Huntingdon College, BA, 1967.

## EMMERICH, Adam O
Wachtell, Lipton, Rosen & Katz, New York
212 403 1234
aoemmerich@wlrk.com
*Featured in Capital Markets (Nationwide), Corporate/M&A (New York)*
See under New York for profile.

## ENGLE, Craig
Arent Fox LLP, Washington, DC
202 775 5791
craig.engle@arentfox.com
*Featured in Government (Nationwide)*

**Practice Areas:** Craig Engle is the founder of the Arent Fox Political Law Group. Craig joined the firm after a distinguished career on Capitol Hill where he was General Counsel to the NRSC, and acted as counselor to Members of the US Senate, campaign committees, and candidates on all aspects of election and office-holder laws, including FEC, FCC, IRS, lobbying, ethics, incorporation and insurance laws. He has advised presidential campaigns, political committees, ideological groups, and corporations on legal, legislative, political and communications issues, and those facing congressional investigations. Craig's clients include a broad range of political organizations, Fortune 500 companies, trade associations, candidates, and other lawyers and law firms. In 2013 Craig devised the legal theory and technology path to allow political committees to receive contributions via text messaging – reversing a two-year ban imposed by the Federal Election Commission. In 2010, Craig created one of the first Super PACs and in 2003 he was chosen by 14 state governments to author a Supreme Court amicus brief in the controversial McCain-Feingold litigation. Craig is a frequent spokesman for clients and media analyst on election law matters.

## EPSTIEN, Jay
DLA Piper LLP (US), Washington, DC
202 799 4100
jay.epstien@dlapiper.com
*Featured in Real Estate (Nationwide), Real Estate (District of Columbia)*

**Practice Areas:** Real Estate

**Professional Memberships:** Fellow of the American College of Real Estate Lawyers; Member, Anglo American Real Property Institute; Member, ICSC Law Conference Program Committee

**Career:** He is a member of the firm's US Executive Committee, chair of the US Real Estate practice and co-chair of the Global Real Estate practice. He represents local and national owners, developers and users in all aspects of real estate transactions involving urban office buildings,

shopping centers and multifamily residential projects.

**Personal:** JD, Cornell Law School, magna cum laude; BS, Case Western Reserve University

## ESCUE, Michael T
Sullivan & Cromwell LLP, New York
212 558 3721
escuem@sullcrom.com
*Featured in Financial Services Regulation (Nationwide)*

**Career:** Partner since 2007. His practice focuses on banking regulation and supervision. Advises US and non-US banks and financial institutions regarding US banking laws and regulations, including those related to investments, activities and M&A; initial entry into the US by non-US banks; affiliate transactions; and enforcement matters. Recent representations include Goldman Sachs, American Express, Allianz, UBS and Bank of New York Mellon.

**Personal:** West Virginia University Law School (JD, 1998); West Virginia University (BS, 1992).

## ESDORN, Joerg
Gibson, Dunn & Crutcher LLP, New York
212 351 3851
jesdorn@gibsondunn.com
*Featured in Banking & Finance (Nationwide)*

**Practice Areas:** He focuses on the representation of providers of capital and issuers/borrowers in leveraged finance transactions, convertible debt offerings and restructurings. His experience includes leveraged loans, high yield notes, mezzanine debt, preferred stock offerings as well as exchange offers and consent solicitations, DIP loans and exit financings.

**Professional Memberships:** Trust Indentures Committee of the American Bar Association.

**Career:** Co-Chair, Global Finance Group.

**Personal:** JD, University of Chicago, 1985. Diplom Engineer, Technical University of Munich, 1981.

## ESTES III, John N
Skadden, Arps, Slate, Meagher & Flom LLP & Affiliates, Washington, DC
202 371 7950
John.Estes@skadden.com
*Featured in Energy & Natural Resources (Nationwide)*

**Practice Areas:** Focuses on complex FERC litigation, enforcement and appellate matters, often involving organized power markets—particularly capacity market issues. Has defended most of the FERC market manipulation cases that have become public, including Energy Transfer Partners, HQ Energy, DB Energy Trading, JP Morgan Ventures Energy, Barclays Bank, Rumford Paper, and Lincoln Paper and Tissue. Played a lead role in major FERC trials, including the "New England LICAP Case" the "California Refund Case," and the "California Long-Term Contract Case." Has argued 24 cases in the US courts of appeals.

**Career:** JD, Louisiana State University, 1983; BA Tulane University, 1979.

## ESTRADA, Miguel A
Gibson, Dunn & Crutcher LLP, Washington, DC
202 955 8257
mestrada@gibsondunn.com
*Featured in Appellate Law (Nationwide)*

**Practice Areas:** Represented clients in federal/state courts and international arbitrations. Handled numerous matters before United States Supreme Court, under False Claims Act, patent, bankruptcy and criminal law, RICO, and ERISA. Extensive Supreme Court experience includes lead counsel (LabCorp v. Metabolite, Aetna v. Davila, Conrad Black v. United States, Comcast v. Behrend) and part of team (Bush v Gore).

**Professional Memberships:** Trustee of Supreme Court Historical Society.

**Career:** Former Supreme Court Law Clerk; former Assistant, Solicitor General of US; former Assistant, US Attorney and Deputy Chief of Appellate Section, US Attorney's Office, Southern District of New York.

## ETH, Jordan
Morrison & Foerster LLP, San Francisco
415 268 7126
jeth@mofo.com
*Featured in Securities (Nationwide), Litigation (California)*
See under California for profile.

## ETTELSON, Bruce I
Kirkland & Ellis LLP, Chicago
312 862 2326
bruce.ettelson@kirkland.com
*Featured in Investment Funds (Nationwide)*

**Practice Areas:** Bruce Ettelson leads Kirkland's Private Funds Group. His practice focuses on structuring and forming premier private equity funds and their management companies, including funds for AEA, American Capital Strategies, Energy Capital Partners, Golden Gate Capital, Madison Dearborn Partners, Marlin Equity Partners, Nautic Partners, Paul Capital Partners, Summit Partners, Thoma Bravo and Vestar Capital Partners. Mr Ettelson has represented more than 100 private equity firms in the formation of over 300 private equity funds. He also represents sponsors and participants in secondary market transactions.

**Personal:** University of Chicago (JD, 1989); Wharton School of the University of Pennsylvania (BSE, 1986).

## EVANS, David
Clifford Chance US LLP, Washington, DC
202 912 5062
david.evans@cliffordchance.com
*Featured in Projects (Nationwide)*

**Practice Areas:** Co-Head of Clifford Chance's Americas Energy and Infrastructure Group. Mr Evans specialises in project finance, utility regulation and commercial contracts predominantly on behalf of developers and sponsors in both Latin America and globally. His practice involves extensive cross-border financing of international projects on a non-recourse or limited recourse basis.

**Career:** Partner at Clifford Chance since 1998. Former Staff Counsel for the Nuclear Regulatory

Commission and Vice President and General Counsel for KMR Power Corporation. University of Maine, JD, cum laude. Boston University, BS, summa cum laude. Admitted in Maine and the District of Columbia.

### EVANS, Elizabeth H
Jones Day, New York
212 326 7830
ehevans@jonesday.com
*Featured in Transportation (Nationwide)*
**Practice Areas:** Concentrates her practice in aviation, project, and satellite finance as well as in equipment leasing and related transactional work, including private placements of debt and equity, and structured finance arrangements. Liz has represented financial institutions, credit capital corporations, equity investors, export credit agencies, and leasing companies in complex aircraft finance transactions, satellite financings, air traffic control financings, equipment leases, airport development transactions and other asset-based financings. She has represented a variety of domestic and foreign passenger and cargo airlines in a wide range of areas, including aircraft sales and leasing matters, FAA and DOT compliance, and restructuring matters.

### EWAN, Christopher
Fried, Frank, Harris, Shriver & Jacobson LLP, New York
212 859 8875
Christopher.Ewan@FriedFrank.com
*Featured in Private Equity (Nationwide)*
**Practice Areas:** Corporate partner. Concentrates his practice in private equity transactions and mergers and acquisitions representing private equity firms and public and private corporations.
**Career:** Joined in 1994; became partner in 2000.
**Personal:** Masters in Law, New York University (2000); LLB, University of Edinburgh (1989); Bachelor of Commerce degree, with honors, University of Cape Town (1987).

### EYBERG, Doug
Gardere Wynne Sewell LLP, Houston
713 276 5704
deyberg@gardere.com
*Featured in Energy & Natural Resources (Nationwide)*
**Practice Areas:** Doug Eyberg serves clients in domestic and international mergers and acquisition (M&A), acquisitions and divestitures of assets and entities, joint ventures, project development, corporate matters, private equity and other transactions. Mr Eyberg represents clients in all principal energy sectors: upstream (oil and gas), midstream (pipelines and facilities), downstream (refineries), power (generation and transmission), renewables (wind, solar, other) and energy services.
**Professional Memberships:** State Bar of Texas, American and Houston Bar Associations, Texas Business Law Foundation.
**Career:** Mr Eyberg chairs Gardere's energy group, and serves on the Firm's Management Committee. He is a member of the Energy

Industry Team, Private Equity Team, and Chemical and Refining Industry Team.
**Personal:** JD, Southern Methodist University, 1976; AB, Duke University, cum laude, 1973.

### EZRING, Gregory
Paul, Weiss, Rifkind, Wharton & Garrison LLP, New York
212 373 3458
gezring@paulweiss.com
*Featured in Banking & Finance (Nationwide), Capital Markets (Nationwide)*
**Practice Areas:** A Partner in the Corporate Department, co-head of the firm's Finance Practice Group and co-head of the firm's North American Capital Markets and Securities Practice Group, Greg focuses his practice on representation of private equity funds and corporations in leverage finance transactions (including both high yield bonds and leveraged loans), IPOs and other financing transactions. Greg also represents many leading alternative asset managers in connection with a broad range of debt and equity investments in distressed and other special situations.

### FABENS, Andrew
Gibson, Dunn & Crutcher LLP, New York
212 351 4034
AFabens@gibsondunn.com
*Featured in Capital Markets (Nationwide)*
**Practice Areas:** Advises companies on long-term and strategic capital planning, representing issuers and underwriters in public and private corporate finance transactions. Experience encompasses IPOs, follow-on equity offerings, investment grade, high-yield and convertible debt offerings and offerings of preferred, hybrid and derivative securities. Regularly advises companies and investment banks on corporate and securities law issues, including M&A financing, spin-off transactions, liability management programs, disclosure and reporting obligations under US securities laws, corporate governance and stock exchange listings. Public company clients include Capital One, GE, HP and Mondelez International.
**Career:** JD, Columbia Law School (2000); BA, University of Michigan (1989).

### FABER, Peter L
McDermott Will & Emery LLP, New York
212 547 5585
pfaber@mwe.com
*Featured in Tax (Nationwide), Tax (New York)*
See under New York for profile.

### FABERMAN, Edward P
Wiley Rein LLP, Washington, DC
202 719 7402
efaberman@wileyrein.com
*Featured in Transportation (Nationwide)*
**Practice Areas:** Co-chairs Aviation Practice. Represents aviation clients including carriers, airport authorities, communities, news helicopters and travel agencies on domestic and international issues.
**Professional Memberships:** Executive Director, Air Carrier Association of America; American Association of Airport Executives; Airport Council International.

**Career:** Recipient, Presidential Award from President Reagan for restructuring air traffic control system and FAA Award for investigating DC-10 accident (1979); Deputy Chief Counsel/Assistant Chief Counsel, FAA (1970-1988); Assistant General Counsel/Vice President of Government Affairs, American Airlines (1988-1996); TSA award recipient (2003); Executive Director, Air Carrier Association of America.
**Personal:** St. John's University School of Law (JD); American University (BS).

### FAGA, Scott
Ashurst, Washington, DC
202 912 8001
scott.faga@ashurst.com
*Featured in Capital Markets (Nationwide)*
**Practice Areas:** Scott is Managing Partner of the US and a partner in the Securities and Derivatives Group in Washington DC. His practice covers securitization and structured finance. Scott represents issuers and underwriters in collateralized loan obligation transactions and other asset-backed securities transactions. He also represents investment banks and others in connection with credit derivative and other swap transactions, distressed asset workouts and asset repackaging programs.
**Personal:** Scott attended George Mason University School of Law (JD) and the College of William and Mary (BA).

### FAGAN, David N
Covington & Burling LLP, Washington, DC
202 662 5291
dfagan@cov.com
*Featured in International Trade (Nationwide), Privacy & Data Security (Nationwide)*
**Practice Areas:** Mr Fagan's practice covers national security, international trade and investment, and privacy and data security. On investment issues, he represents foreign and domestic clients in various industries before the Committee on Foreign Investment in the United States (CFIUS), and he frequently handles matters related to the mitigation of foreign ownership, control or influence (FOCI) under applicable national industrial security regulations. On privacy and data security, he provides transactional and regulatory advice related to the transfer and protection of personal and other sensitive data, and specialises counseling clients in responding to cyber and data security breaches.

### FAGAN, Joseph H
Day Pitney LLP, Washington, DC
202 218 3901
jfagan@daypitney.com
*Featured in Energy & Natural Resources (Nationwide)*
**Career:** Mr Fagan practices in the area of natural gas and electric infrastructure project development, and counsels clients on the regulatory, enforcement and commercial issues involved with such projects. He advises natural gas companies and public utilities on regulatory, litigation and legislative matters, and on project development, market enforcement, rate-making, corporate compliance, asset acquisitions and other industry-spe-

cific issues. Mr Fagan also counsels clients on FERC compliance program design and implementation, and provides on-site regulatory training. He has represented clients in federal, appellate and district court litigation, and before the Federal Energy Regulatory Commission in a range of matters.

### FAHEY, Sean P
Pepper Hamilton LLP, Philadelphia
215 981 4296
faheys@pepperlaw.com
*Featured in Products Liability (Nationwide)*
**Practice Areas:** Partner. Focuses practice in products liability and health care litigation, with a primary emphasis on the defense of pharmaceutical and medical device entities in multidistrict litigation. Experience includes serving as national and regional coordinating counsel for litigation involving prescription pharmaceuticals and medical devices; counsel for pharmaceutical entities responding to Department of Justice subpoenas and other government investigations; counsel for pharmaceutical and medical device entities regarding marketing, promotional activities, recalls and document preservation issues; counsel for health care providers on a broad range of health care issues.
**Personal:** JD 1994 Villanova University School of Law; BA 1991 Villanova University.

### FAHEY, Thomas M
Ungaretti & Harris LLP, Chicago
312 977 4376
tmfahey@uhlaw.com
*Featured in Healthcare (Illinois), Healthcare (Nationwide)*
See under Illinois for profile.

### FARBER, Seth
Winston & Strawn LLP, New York
sfarber@winston.com
*Featured in Tax (Nationwide)*
**Career:** Mr Farber is a Partner in the Litigation Department. He has tried numerous federal cases to juries and is an experienced appellate advocate who has argued both civil and criminal appeals in federal Circuit courts around the county. His practice includes white collar criminal defense and corporate internal investigations, SEC investigations, securities litigation, corporate governance litigation and litigation associated with mergers and acquisitions. He also provides pro bono representation to indigent criminal defendants as a member of the Criminal Justice Act Panel in the Southern District of New York.
**Personal:** JD, Harvard Law School, 1989. AB, Harvard University, 1986.

### FAULKNER, Andrew M
Skadden, Arps, Slate, Meagher & Flom LLP & Affiliates, New York
212 735 2853
Andrew.Faulkner@skadden.com
*Featured in Capital Markets (Nationwide)*
**Practice Areas:** Represents issuers, underwriters, credit-enhancers and lenders in asset-backed securities transactions and credit-enhanced securities issuances. Broad securitization practice with emphasis on credit card transactions and work on

structured products including exchange traded funds. Helped establish credit card master trusts for major issuers, and has represented issuers and underwriters of securities backed by bank VISA and MasterCard and retailer private label credit card receivables. Has worked on restructuring securitization transactions, acquisition financing, consumer loan portfolio sales and structured securities products.

**Career:** JD, Columbia University School of Law, 1985 (Harlan Fiske Stone Scholar); BA, Cornell University, 1981 (magna cum laude).

### FECHNER, Holly
Covington & Burling LLP, Washington, DC
202 662 5475
hfechner@cov.com
*Featured in Government (Nationwide)*
**Practice Areas:** Holly Fechner is Vice Chair of Covington's global Public Policy & Government Affairs practice. She manages a team that handles public policy, government affairs and regulatory matters for clients in Washington, DC, Brussels and around the world. With over two decades of legal, legislative and public policy experience in the public and private sectors, Ms Fechner focuses on pensions, healthcare, intellectual property, tax, energy and education.
**Career:** US Senator Edward M. Kennedy, Policy Director; Senate Health, Education, Labor & Pensions Committee, Chief Labor & Pensions Counsel.
**Personal:** University of Michigan Law School, JD; Oberlin College, AB.

### FEE, Jon
Alston & Bird LLP, Washington, DC
202 239 3387
jon.fee@alston.com
*Featured in International Trade (Nationwide)*
**Practice Areas:** Focuses his practice on customs and international trade matters, with a particular emphasis on preferential trade programs, free trade agreements and US trade legislation. Extensive experience in trade issues affecting textiles, apparel, aircraft, heavy equipment and electronics.
**Professional Memberships:** Member, American, Georgia and Washington, D.C. Bar Associations. Chair, firm's Washington, DC Pro Bono Committee.
**Career:** Licensed customs broker and teaches preparation courses for the national customs broker exam. Speaks frequently in the United States, Asia, Central America and Africa on US trade policy and free trade agreements.
**Personal:** Emory University (JD, 1974); University of Pennsylvania (BS, 1971).

### FEHER, David G
Winston & Strawn LLP, New York
*Featured in Sports Law (Nationwide)*
**Practice Areas:** Mr Feher is one of the leading sports lawyers in the country. He is one of the negotiators of the free agency systems and CBAs in the NFL and NBA, and has litigated numerous high profile matters. Those cases include, among others, representing Oakley in its endorsement contract suit against Rory McIlroy and Nike, and

the New Orleans Saints Bounty case. He also represents the player board representatives of the WTA, and has negotiated endorsement contracts on behalf of both athletes and companies.
**Personal:** AB, magna cum laude, Georgetown University, 1980. JD, Duke University School of Law, 1984.

### FEIMAN, Ronald
Kramer Levin Naftalis & Frankel LLP, New York
212 715 9550
rfeiman@kramerlevin.com
*Featured in Investment Funds (Nationwide)*
**Practice Areas:** Mr Feiman advises clients on regulatory and compliance issues affecting investment companies and investment advisers and related corporate and securities matters. Mr Feiman represents investment companies, investment advisers and investment company independent directors, as well as unregistered domestic and offshore debt and equity funds. He also advises service providers rendering distribution, custody and transfer agent services to registered and unregistered funds. His securities experience includes public and private offerings of equity and debt securities, proxy solicitations, and broker-dealer regulation and compliance. Mr Feiman's corporate experience includes mergers and business combinations; stock and asset acquisitions; and recapitalizations, management buy-outs, and finance and venture capital transactions.

### FEIRMAN, Steven
Nixon Peabody LLP, Washington, DC
202 585 8395
sfeirman@nixonpeabody.com
*Featured in Franchising (Nationwide)*
**Practice Areas:** Franchising, distribution, antitrust.
**Career:** Legal advisor and strategic business advisor to emerging and mature franchise companies in broad spectrum of industries, including restaurants, hospitality, financial services, travel, real estate, personal services, business services, retail, technology, and health care. He focuses on US and international franchising and distribution, including development of multi-tier franchise structures, franchise disclosure documents, supply and distribution arrangements, franchise company acquisitions, and related antitrust and pricing issues. Served as senior trial attorney with Federal Trade Commission. Speaks and writes extensively on franchise related topics.
**Personal:** Washington University, JD; Colgate University (magna cum laude), AB.

### FELDMAN, Elliot J
Baker & Hostetler LLP, Washington, DC
202 861 1679
efeldman@bakerlaw.com
*Featured in International Trade (Nationwide)*
**Career:** Elliot Feldman advises governments, international organizations, American and foreign corporations and individuals on matters of trade policy and international law and litigates on their behalf in all forums in the US and foreign countries. He frequently advises the Government of Canada in WTO cases and represents clients in

Europe, Latin America, Australia and Asia. Elliot is a regular contributor to BakerHostetler's China-US Trade Law blog and principal author and editor of BakerHostetler's treatise, Mergers & Acquisitions in the United States: A Practical Guide for Non-US Buyers, published in English and Mandarin by Wolters Kluwer.

### FELDMAN, Glenn M.
Dickinson Wright Mariscal Weeks, Phoenix
602 285 5138
gfeldman@dickinsonwright.com
*Featured in Native American Law (Nationwide)*
**Practice Areas:** Practices exclusively in the areas of Federal Indian Law, with heavy emphasis on Indian gaming and reservation economic development activities. He is counsel to a number of Indian tribes, tribal casinos and tribal business ventures in Arizona, California and other western states.
**Professional Memberships:** Arizona State Bar, Past Chair, Indian Law Section.
**Personal:** JD, Georgetown University Law Center.

### FELDMAN, Matthew A
Willkie Farr & Gallagher LLP, New York
212 728 8651
mfeldman@wilkie.com
*Featured in Bankruptcy/Restructuring (Nationwide),*
*Bankruptcy/Restructuring (New York)*
See under New York for profile.

### FELLAS, John
Hughes Hubbard & Reed LLP, New York
212 837 6075
fellas@hugheshubbard.com
*Featured in International Arbitration (Nationwide)*
**Practice Areas:** International arbitration and litigation. Acts as counsel, and arbitrator in cases across the world. Represents foreign clients in litigation in US courts and advises foreign and US clients on global litigation strategy.
**Professional Memberships:** American Law Institute; Board of the American Arbitration Association.
**Career:** Admitted in NY; Solicitor of Supreme Court of England and Wales.
**Publications:** Numerous publications on issues on international arbitration and litigation, including, International Commercial Arbitration in New York (Oxford University Press 2010) (co-editor).
**Personal:** University of Durham, BA (Hons) (Law), 1983; Harvard Law School, LLM, 1985; SJD 1989.

### FELSENTHAL, David
Clifford Chance US LLP, New York
212 878 3452
david.felsenthal@cliffordchance.com
*Featured in Capital Markets (Nationwide)*
**Practice Areas:** Focuses on structured securities and derivatives transactions. His recent experience includes work on securities linked to credit derivatives and other financial assets, and on collateralized debt obligations and other securities. He has extensive expertise in a wide range of derivatives and other trading transactions, including equity, credit, foreign exchange and interest rate derivatives and repos and securities lending.

**Career:** Partner at Clifford Chance since 1997. Princeton University, BA. Harvard Law School, JD.

### FERNICOLA, Gregory
Skadden, Arps, Slate, Meagher & Flom LLP & Affiliates, New York
212 735 2918
gregory.fernicola@skadden.com
*Featured in Capital Markets (Nationwide)*
**Practice Areas:** Gregory A. Fernicola represents issuers, investors and investment banks in a variety of domestic and cross-border capital markets matters, including investment grade and high-yield debt financings, equity and equity derivative product financings, hybrid securities transactions, leveraged buyouts, exchange offers and debt restructurings, recapitalizations and spin-offs. In addition to handling many IPOs, follow-on equity offerings and debt financings, he has worked on many exotic financing structures, including equity unit, trust preferred, capital securities, and debt/equity hybrid securities transactions.
**Career:** JD, Georgetown University, 1985 (cum laude); MBA, Rutgers University, 1980; BS, St Francis University, 1978; CPA, New York, 1981.

### FIELDS, Henry M
Morrison & Foerster LLP, Los Angeles
213 892 5275
hfields@mofo.com
*Featured in Financial Services Regulation (Nationwide)*
**Practice Areas:** Broad financial services practice, including international banking regulation, mergers and acquisitions, private equity investment in financial institutions, capital issuance, holding company regulation, corporate governance; trust activities, compliance; enforcement and margin regulations.
**Professional Memberships:** California, New York and New Jersey bars; Board, International Bankers Association of California; Executive Committee, The Starlight Children's Foundation.
**Career:** Various international and domestic rankings in Financial Services and Financial Institutions Mergers & Acquisitions, including Best Lawyers' Lawyer of the Year designation in Financial Services Regulation for 2012.
**Publications:**
**Personal:** Yale Law School, JD; Managing Editor, Yale Law Journal; Harvard College, BA, magna cum laude, Phi Beta Kappa.

### FIFE, Lori R
Weil, Gotshal & Manges LLP, New York
212 310 8318
lori.fife@weil.com
*Featured in Bankruptcy/Restructuring (Nationwide),*
*Bankruptcy/Restructuring (New York)*
**Practice Areas:** Lori Fife's practice covers domestic and international debt restructurings, crisis management and corporate governance. She represents companies, banks, acquirers, bondholders, secured and unsecured creditors. She leads the firm's representation of Lehman Brothers and its affiliates in their chapter 11 cases and also represented MCI/WorldCom, Loral Space, Sunbeam, Texaco, Bruno's, Best Products and Macy's in their restructurings. She has also

represented major lender interests in restructurings and chapter 11 cases including K-V Pharma, Equa-Chlor, Prostar, Lionel, American Home Mortgage, ACA Capital, Herbst Gaming, and Donald J. Trump and affiliates.
**Personal:** University of Pennsylvania (BA); Cardozo School of Law (JD).

### FINE, Drew S
Milbank, Tweed, Hadley & McCloy LLP, New York
212 530 5940
dfine@milbank.com
*Featured in Transportation (Nationwide), Banking & Finance (Nationwide)*
**Practice Areas:** Mr Fine is a member of the firm's Global Executive Committee, the Chair of the Finance Practice Groups and the former Practice Group Leader of the Transportation and Space Group. Mr Fine has extensive experience in a wide variety of international financial and corporate transactions, including public offerings and private placement of securities, acquisitions, leveraged leasing, secured and unsecured lending, structured financings and workouts. He also has particular expertise in financings and corporate transactions involving aircraft, rolling stock and vessels. Mr Fine has worked on several of the most significant EETCs and securitizations involving aircraft.

### FINGERET, Kevin
Latham & Watkins LLP, New York
212 906 1237
kevin.fingeret@lw.com
*Featured in Capital Markets (Nationwide)*
**Practice Areas:** Represents banks and other financial institutions, issuers, bond insurers and others in a wide variety of structured finance and securitization transactions. Experience includes securitisations of aircraft leases and debt (including EETCs), rental car fleet leases, wireless cell towers, automobile loans, credit card receivables, equipment leases and music royalties. Also has substantial experience representing lenders in structured loan transactions and structured credit and liquidity facilities, as well as issuers, underwriters and other parties in CLO transactions.
**Career:** Qualified since 1994. Co-Chair of Latham's Structured Finance and Securitizations Practice.

### FINK, Marc J
Cozen O'Connor, Washington, DC
202 463 2503
mfink@cozen.com
*Featured in Transportation (Nationwide)*
**Practice Areas:** Marc represents companies and organizations in the maritime industry before courts, arbitration panels, boards of contract appeals, federal agencies and Congress. He has broad experience on regulatory issues and the application of antitrust/competition laws to international transportation activities. Marc also litigates cases involving complex commercial disputes and advises companies on laws pertaining to US government contracts.

**Professional Memberships:** Maritime Administrative Bar Association, Association of Transportation Law Professionals.
**Publications:** Co-authored a chapter titled 'Undertaking the Bid Protest Process' and law review article titled 'The Redundant Foreign Shipping Practices Act of 1988'.
**Personal:** George Washington University, JD, 1973 SUNY-Fredonia, BA, 1967

### FINKEL, Robert
WilmerHale, New York
212 295 6555
robert.finkel@wilmerhale.com
*Featured in Outsourcing (Nationwide), Technology (New York)*
**Practice Areas:** Partner in the Corporate Practice Group. He has more than 20 years of experience in private practice representing leading international corporations and financial institutions in complex commercial transactions with a particular focus on technology and outsourcing. He has represented clients in more than 100 major outsourcing transactions, across a wide variety of industries on information technology and business process outsourcing, joint ventures and strategic alliances, software and technology licensing, venture capital, and technology and service company acquisition and finance.
**Professional Memberships:** Member, Stanford Law School Board of Visitors.
**Personal:** Adjunct Professor, New York Law School.

### FIRESTONE, Frederic
McDermott Will & Emery LLP, Washington, DC
202 756 8031
rfirestone@mwe.com
*Featured in Securities (Nationwide)*
**Practice Areas:** Head of the firm's SEC defense practice. Practice focused on investigations and enforcement proceedings by the Division of Enforcement of the US Securities and Exchange Commission (SEC), federal criminal authorities, Financial Industry Regulatory Authority (FINRA), the Public Company Accounting Oversight Board (PCAOB) and state securities regulators.
**Professional Memberships:** Admitted in District of Columbia and Maryland.
**Career:** Formerly Associate Director of the SEC's Division of Enforcement. Was responsible for the supervision of numerous, complex investigations and enforcement actions.
**Personal:** Washington University in St. Louis, JD, 1986; Washington University in St. Louis, BA, (cum laude), 1982.

### FISCHER, L Richard
Morrison & Foerster LLP, Washington, DC
202 887 1566
lfischer@mofo.com
*Featured in Financial Services Regulation (Nationwide), Privacy & Data Security (Nationwide)*
**Practice Areas:** Advises financial institutions and other companies on the full range of financial services, payment system, and retail banking issues. Special emphasis on privacy, payment

cards, e-commerce, technology, and joint venture issues.
**Professional Memberships:** Former President of the American College of Consumer Financial Services Lawyers and winner of its 2013 Life Time Achievement Award.
**Career:** Named one of Washington's top banking and privacy lawyers by the Washingtonian magazine and a Best Lawyer in America in banking law.
**Publications:** Author, 'The Law of Financial Privacy' (AS Pratt & Sons, Third Edition).
**Personal:** BA, University of San Francisco; JD, University of California, Hastings College of the Law.

### FISCHER, Nancy A
Pillsbury Winthrop Shaw Pittman LLP, Washington, DC
202 663 8965
nancy.fischer@pillsburylaw.com
*Featured in International Trade (Nationwide)*
**Practice Areas:** Practice focuses on international trade law and international dispute resolution including compliance and litigation matters related to export controls and embargoes, foreign investment national security reviews under Committee on Foreign Investment in the US and the Defense Security Service, Foreign Corrupt Practices Act, trade remedy laws, customs law, and WTO and NAFTA disputes.
**Professional Memberships:** ABA, DC Bar Association, Trade Policy Forum, Women In International Trade, Society for International Affairs, Society for Satellite Professionals International.
**Career:** Admitted: New York and DC.
**Personal:** JD, Syracuse University Law School 1992, magna cum laude; BBA, University of Georgia, 1989, cum laude.

### FISHER, Lane
Fisher Zucker, LLC, Philadelphia
215 825 3131
lfisher@fisherzucker.com
*Featured in Franchising (Nationwide)*
**Practice Areas:** In private practice since 1989, Lane currently represents more than 75 franchise brands in business transactions and complex franchise litigation.
**Professional Memberships:** Lane is admitted to practice in Pennsylvania and New Jersey and serves on the franchise law committee of the New Jersey State Bar Association, the Philadelphia Bar Association and the American Bar Association's forum committee on franchising. In addition to chairing its membership committee since 2005, Lane serves as a member of the International Franchise Association's Board of Directors and is a past member of its executive committee and a past chair of the executive committee of the Supplier Forum Advisory Board. Lane also is a former chair of the Legal Symposium Task Force and serves on the FranPAC advisory board.
**Career:** Lane is a graduate of American University's Washington College of Law (JD 1989). Lane also holds a BBA in finance (1985) and an MBA in international business (1986) from George Washington University.

**Publications:** Lane is a frequent speaker at franchise conferences and has written extensively on many aspects of franchising. Every year since 2004, Philadelphia Magazine has identified Lane as a Pennsylvania SuperLawyer and Franchise Times identified Lane in the "Top 100 Franchise Attorneys", earning its Legal Eagle designation. Since 2010, Lane has earned the distinction of "Awesome Attorney" in Suburban Life magazine. Lane has published more than 30 articles and given more than 25 presentations on franchising-related issues at conferences and served as a frequent commentator and contributor to such media as CNN-fn, ABC/Live Well!, CN8, INC. Magazine, Franchise Times, Franchise Update, Franchising World, Franchise Law Journal, and The Franchise Lawyer.

### FISHER, Miriam L
Latham & Watkins LLP, Washington, DC
202 637 2178
Miriam.Fisher@lw.com
*Featured in Tax (District of Columbia), Tax (Nationwide)*
**Practice Areas:** Miriam Fisher is a partner in Latham & Watkins' Tax Practice. She handles high-stakes tax litigation, administrative tax disputes and criminal tax matters. She has obtained excellent results in tax controversies affecting domestic and multinational businesses, as well as high net worth taxpayers. A frequent speaker on tax policy and ethics, Ms Fisher was advisor to the Assistant Attorney General, US Department of Justice Tax Division, adjunct tax professor at Georgetown Law, DC Bar Taxation Section Chair and ABA Tax Section Council Director and Committee Chair. She is a Fellow of the prestigious American College of Tax Counsel.

### FISHER, Todd A
K&L Gates, Dallas
214 939 5793
todd.fisher@klgates.com
*Featured in Outsourcing (Nationwide), Technology (Texas)*
See under Texas for profile.

### FITZGERALD, Edmond
Davis Polk & Wardwell LLP, New York
212 450 4000
edmond.fitzgerald@davispolk.com
*Featured in Employee Benefits & Executive Compensation (Nationwide), Employee Benefits & Executive Compensation (New York)*
**Practice Areas:** As a partner in Davis Polk's Executive Compensation and Employee Benefits Practice Group, Mr FitzGerald counsels clients on matters involving senior executive compensation and benefits, both in the ordinary course of clients' business and in the context of mergers and acquisitions, new ventures, and restructurings. He has extensive experience in structuring employment agreements, equity compensation, performance incentives, deferred compensation, change in control protections, and management participation in buyouts and new ventures. Mr FitzGerald also advises clients in structuring investment products, financial services and investment funds

offered to large pension plans and similar institutional investors.

## FITZGERALD, Peter F
Chadbourne & Parke LLP, Washington, DC
202 974 5712
pfitzgerald@chadbourne.com
*Featured in Projects (Nationwide)*
**Practice Areas:** Represents multilateral and bilateral agencies, lenders and developers in domestic and international project financings. Negotiates project financings involving multilateral and bilateral loans, investments and guarantees for conventional and renewable power, infrastructure, mining, petrochemical and industrial projects in the emerging markets and nuclear projects. Represents sponsors, commercial and agency political risk insurers in investment disputes and political risk matters, including political risk insurance and contract claims.
**Career:** Previously served as Chief Counsel for project finance and political risk insurance matters at the Overseas Private Investment Corporation.
**Personal:** University of Notre Dame, BA; Rutgers University School of Law, JD

## FITZPATRICK, James C
Hughes Hubbard & Reed LLP, New York
212 837 6582
fitzpat@hugheshubbard.com
*Featured in Products Liability (Nationwide)*
**Practice Areas:** General litigation and trial practice, with extensive experience in pharmaceutical products litigation and music licensing litigation. Counseling of pharmaceutical clients has included work in connection with Congressional and other governmental inquiries, media, and international litigation.
**Career:** Partner Hughes Hubbard & Reed LLP since 2005.
**Personal:** Harvard College, AB (1993); New York University School of Law, JD (1996); Clerkship for Hon. Hayden W Head, US District Judge S.D. Tex (1996-97).

## FITZPATRICK, John
Wheeler Trigg O'Donnell LLP, Denver
303 244 1874
fitzpatrick@wtotrial.com
*Featured in Products Liability (Nationwide), Litigation (Colorado)*
See under Colorado for profile.

## FITZPATRICK JR, Michael F
Hunton & Williams LLP, New York
212 309 1071
mfitzpatrick@hunton.com
*Featured in Energy & Natural Resources (Nationwide)*
**Practice Areas:** Mr Fitzpatrick has extensive experience representing issuers and underwriters in capital markets transactions, principally in the utility and energy area. These transactions involve both taxable and tax-exempt securities, including "hybrid" securities. He has represented underwriters and electric and natural gas utilities in connection with stranded cost securitizations. He advises companies on general corporate and securities law matters, including continuing advice regarding

compliance with the Sarbanes-Oxley Act and aspects of corporate governance.
**Professional Memberships:** American Bar Association, American Institute of Certified Public Accountants.
**Career:** Energy, Corporate Finance.
**Personal:** JD, Fordham University School of Law, 1990. BS, Villanova University, 1983.

## FLANAGAN, Peter L
Covington & Burling LLP, Washington, DC
202 662 5163
pflanagan@cov.com
*Featured in International Trade (Nationwide)*
**Practice Areas:** Focuses on international trade compliance matters, specifically export controls, economic sanctions constraints, defense trade limitations, and implications of related international regulatory requirements. Clients include leading oil and gas companies, defense contractors, diversified manufacturers, financial institutions, pharmaceutical and biotechnology concerns, software developers, and research laboratories.
**Career:** Member of Covington's Management Committee; former Vice-Chair of International Trade and Finance Group. Federal Reserve Board's International Finance Division (1987-1989).
**Personal:** Former Term Member of the Council on Foreign Relations. NYU (JD, 1993, magna cum laude, Order of the Coif); Princeton University (MPA, 1993); and University of Wisconsin (BA, 1987, with distinction).

## FLANNERY, Anne C
Morgan, Lewis & Bockius LLP, New York
212 309 6370
aflannery@morganlewis.com
*Featured in Securities (Nationwide)*
**Practice Areas:** Focuses on a variety of securities enforcement and litigation matters, including investigations by the US Securities and Exchange Commission (SEC), FINRA and state securities regulators for potential securities fraud, trading and sales practice violations and related supervisory issues.
**Professional Memberships:** Board of Trustees for Marymount Manhattan College; Co-Chair, SRO Subcommittee, ABA Litigation Section Securities Committee
**Career:** SEC: Senior Official in the Washington, D.C. and New York offices. Merrill Lynch: Office of General Counsel – First Vice President and General Counsel for Global Regulatory Affairs, and Global Head of Compliance.

## FLASCHEN, Evan D
Bracewell & Giuliani LLP, Hartford
860 256 8537
evan.flaschen@bgllp.com
*Featured in Bankruptcy/Restructuring (Nationwide), Bankruptcy/Restructuring (New York)*
See under New York for profile.

## FLEDER, Robert C
Paul, Weiss, Rifkind, Wharton & Garrison LLP, New York
212-373-3107
rfleder@paulweiss.com
*Featured in Employee Benefits & Executive Compensation (Nationwide), Employee Benefits & Executive Compensation (New York)*
See under New York for profile.

## FLEISCHMAN, Dana G
Latham & Watkins LLP, New York
212 906 1220
dana.fleischman@lw.com
*Featured in Financial Services Regulation (Nationwide)*
**Practice Areas:** Ms Fleischman, a partner in Latham & Watkins' NY office, focuses on matters involving the regulation of broker-dealers and securities markets, including in connection with public and private offerings, mergers and acquisitions and cross-border transactions. She assists financial institutions in connection with internal investigations and enforcement matters and counsels firms and trade associations with respect to significant regulatory initiatives and rule-making proposals.
**Professional Memberships:** Ms Fleischman is Chair of the ABA's Trading and Markets Subcommittee and a member of SIFMA's Compliance and Legal Division.
**Personal:** BA (high honors) Emory University (1986); JD, Yale Law School (1989).

## FLEISHMAN, Robert S
Covington & Burling LLP, Washington, DC
202 662 5523
rfleishman@cov.com
*Featured in Energy & Natural Resources (Nationwide)*
**Practice Areas:** Robert Fleishman represents and advises clients on regulatory, enforcement, compliance, commercial, legislative, dispute resolution, and public policy matters involving energy and climate issues.
**Professional Memberships:** Energy Law Journal, Editor-in-Chief; Energy Bar Association: Chairman of Compliance and Enforcement Committee, President (1999-2000); former Chairman, ADR Committee (2004-06); CPR International Institute Energy Panel; Project Director and Co-Chairman of the Energy ADR Forum.
**Career:** Constellation Energy Group and its predecessor, Baltimore Gas & Electric Co. (1985-2002) - Vice President of Legislative and Regulatory Policy (2002); Vice President of Corporate Affairs and General Counsel (1997-2001); Federal Energy Regulatory Commission (1979-1985).

## FLEMING, Joseph R
Dechert LLP, Boston
617 728 7161
joseph.fleming@dechert.com
*Featured in Investment Funds (Nationwide), Investment Funds (Massachusetts)*
**Practice Areas:** Mr Fleming, co-chair of Dechert's financial services group and member of

the firm's policy committee, represents investment/mutual fund companies, investment managers, banks, insurance companies, broker-dealers, hedge funds, and other financial institutions in securities and corporate matters.
**Professional Memberships:** Member, Massachusetts, New York, and Rhode Island Bars; member, Securities and Commodities Law Committees, American Bar Association; member, Federal Bar Association.
**Career:** Formerly an attorney with the SEC
**Personal:** Vanderbilt University (B.S., 1976, cum laude); Suffolk University Law School (JD, 1983); Georgetown University Law Center (LLM, securities regulation, 1988).

## FLORACK, James A
Davis Polk & Wardwell LLP, New York
212 450 4000
james.florack@davispolk.com
*Featured in Latin American Investment (New York), Banking & Finance (Nationwide)*
**Practice Areas:** Member of Davis Polk's Corporate Department and co-head of the global Credit Group. Advises clients on a range of corporate finance transactions, including leveraged loans and high-yield debt offerings; distressed debt investments, exchange offers and restructurings; and structured finance transactions. Practice includes transactions both in the US and in international markets, particularly Latin America. Clients include a number of financial institutions, including JPMorgan Chase, Morgan Stanley, Bank of America, Citigroup and Goldman Sachs, as well as many corporate clients.

## FLORIN, Kenneth R
Loeb & Loeb LLP, New York
212 407 4966
kflorin@loeb.com
*Featured in Advertising (Nationwide)*
**Practice Areas:** Represents Fortune 500 companies, media companies, advertising and promotions agencies, sports leagues and teams, and new media and interactive ventures, advising on the development of their advertising and promotion strategies, online communities and technology-related products and services.
**Professional Memberships:** Board of Directors, Promotion Marketing Association.
**Career:** Partner since 2000. Advanced Media and Technology Department Co-Chair; Digital Media Chair.
**Publications:** Authored several articles for publications such as Advertising Age, PROMO Magazine, and Corporate Counsel Magazine, among others.
**Personal:** Columbia University (JD, Harlan Fiske Stone Scholar, 1992); University of Michigan (BA, 1988).

## FOGG, William V
Cravath, Swaine & Moore LLP, New York
212 474 1131
wfogg@cravath.com
*Featured in Capital Markets (Nationwide)*
**Practice Areas:** William V. Fogg is the Managing Partner of Cravath's Corporate Department. His practice focuses on representing

issuers and investment banking firms in connection with public and private offerings of securities. Mr Fogg also advises companies on corporate governance and general corporate and disclosure matters. Mr Fogg's clients have included J.P. Morgan Securities, Credit Suisse, UAL, Jones Apparel, Burlington Northern, Home Depot, Cincinnati Bell, Alliant Energy and Pepsi Bottling. **Personal:** Columbia Law School (JD, 1991; Harlan Fiske Stone Scholar; Managing Editor, Journal of Law and Social Problems); Brown University (AB, magna cum laude, 1988). For more information: http://www.cravath.com/wfogg.

### FONTANA, Angela L
Weil, Gotshal & Manges LLP, Dallas
214 746 7895
angela.fontana@weil.com
*Featured in Banking & Finance (Texas), Banking & Finance (Nationwide)*
See under Texas for profile.

### FORD, Christopher D
Morrison & Foerster LLP, Washington, DC
202 887 1512
cford@mofo.com
*Featured in Outsourcing (Nationwide), Technology (District of Columbia)*
**Practice Areas:** Focuses on the full life cycle of complex information technology and business process outsourcing transactions. In addition, advises clients on sophisticated card processing and payments transactions, telecommunications transactions, joint ventures, ERP and other systems integration, software development and large-scale licensing transactions.
**Professional Memberships:** State Bar of Georgia; District of Columbia Bar.
**Career:** Chair, Global Sourcing Group. Frequent speaker on outsourcing and technology-related legal issues.
**Publications:** Authored numerous articles in numerous publications.
**Personal:** BS, University of Virginia (1987); JD, Emory University (1993).

### FORD, Gary M
Groom Law Group, Washington, DC
202 857 0620
gford@groom.com
*Featured in Employee Benefits & Executive Compensation (Nationwide), Employee Benefits & Executive Compensation (District of Columbia)*
**Practice Areas:** Represents many of the nation's largest plan sponsors, service providers, multiemployer plans, and fiduciaries in various areas, including litigation, planning, and advice. Leading expert on issues relating to the treatment of employee benefit plans in bankruptcy.
**Professional Memberships:** Admitted: Massachusetts and the District of Columbia. Charter Fellow, American College of Employee Benefits Counsel.
**Career:** ERISA Counsel, US Senate Committee on Labor and Human Resources, 1980-81. General Counsel, Pension Benefit Guaranty Corporation, 1987-89. Pro bono President/CEO of MicroCredit Enterprises, which funds microloans to women in the developing world.

**Personal:** JD, Boston University. AB, magna cum laude, Harvard University.

### FORMAN, Daniel R
Crowell & Moring LLP, Washington, DC
202 624 2504
dforman@crowell.com
*Featured in Government (Nationwide)*
**Practice Areas:** Partner in Crowell & Moring's Government Contracts Group. His practice focuses on a wide variety of government procurement law, including bid protests, FCA and qui tam litigation, investigations of potential civil and criminal matters, ethics and compliance, contract claims and disputes, GSA schedule contracting, and small disadvantaged business contracting. Also experienced in negotiating and drafting teaming agreements and subcontracts, providing counseling on the interpretation of FAR clauses and solicitations. Focuses on state and local procurement matters, including State FCA issues, lobbying and contingency payment compliance. Has been involved in bid protest litigation in six states and DC.

### FORSTER, Jonathan M
Greenberg Traurig, LLP, McLean
703 903 7504
ForsterJ@gtlaw.com
*Featured in Wealth Management (Nationwide)*
**Practice Areas:** Chair, National Wealth Management Group. Co-Chair, Insurance Regulatory and Transactions Practice. Tax.
**Professional Memberships:** Special Task Force ABA, Committee for Developing Ethics Rules; Chairman, National Capital Business Ethics Award; Board Member: Northern Virginia Life Underwriters Association, Suburban Maryland Life Underwriters Association, and District of Columbia Life Underwriters Association.
**Career:** Selected: Chambers USA Guide, 2006-13; 'They Know Money 2012: Estate Attorneys', Washingtonian magazine, November 2012. Rated, AV® Preeminent™ 5.0 out of 5.
**Publications:** Co-Author, 'Current Opportunities in Life Insurance Planning', ForumFacts, September 2011.
**Personal:** JD, George Mason University School of Law; BS, Finance, University of Maryland.

### FORT, Jeffrey
Dentons, Chicago
312 876 2380
jeffrey.fort@dentons.com
*Featured in Climate Change (Nationwide), Environment (Illinois)*
See under Illinois for profile.

### FOSTER, F David
Foster, Murphy, Altman & Nickel, PC, Washington, DC
202 822 4101
dfoster@fostermurphy.com
*Featured in International Trade (Nationwide)*
**Practice Areas:** Focuses on international intellectual property litigation, representing both complainants and respondents in litigating patent and other IP disputes under Section 337 of the Tariff Act.

**Career:** Has represented clients in more than 70 Section 337 cases. Formerly in the General Counsel's Office of the US International Trade Commission (where he helped draft the modern Section 337 and implementing regulations), and later assistant to the Chairman; then International Trade Counsel to the Senate Finance Committee, with oversight of trade negotiations and passage of implementing legislation. Founding member and past President, ITC Trial Lawyers Association.

### FOSTER, Hope S
Mintz Levin Cohn Ferris Glovsky and Popeo PC, Washington, DC
202 661 8758
HSFoster@mintz.com
*Featured in Healthcare (Nationwide), Healthcare (District of Columbia)*
See under District of Columbia for profile.

### FOTIS, Stephen C
Van Ness Feldman LLP, Washington, DC
202 298 1908
scf@vnf.com
*Featured in Climate Change (Nationwide)*
**Practice Areas:** Provides advice and representation in legislative matters, agency rulemakings, and appellate litigation under the Clean Air Act and other federal environmental statutes. Advises clients on global climate change, air permitting, environmental regulatory compliance, and policy and regulatory issues related to advanced electric generation and pollution control technologies. Provides legislative drafting assistance and strategic counseling on federal environmental laws, climate change, technology, and related policies. Clients include electric generation, manufacturers, oil and gas, and mineral exploration companies, governmental entities, industry coalitions, trade associations, and think tanks.
**Personal:** JD, American University, Washington College of Law, 1986; BA, Dartmouth College, 1977.

### FOURNARIS, Dean
Wiggin and Dana LLP, New Haven
215 988 8311
cfournaris@wiggin.com
*Featured in Franchising (Nationwide)*
**Practice Areas:** Franchise and distribution lawyer. Represents public and private franchisors, licensors, manufacturers, distributors and developers in matters across the country. Focuses practice on developing, structuring and maintaining franchise and distribution networks, transactions and contracts involving franchise and distribution systems, operating systems and standards, and related regulatory and transactional matters. Advises franchise and distribution system clients in connection with all aspects of their operations and relationships. Prosecutes and defends cases before state and federal courts and arbitration panels on behalf of franchisors, manufacturers and distributors.
**Personal:** Graduated from Franklin & Marshall College (BA 1988) and Cornell Law School (JD 1991).

### FOWLER, Jeffrey
O'Melveny & Myers LLP, Los Angeles
jfowler@omm.com
*Featured in Litigation (Nationwide)*
**Practice Areas:** Jeff Fowler, a litigation partner, is one of the founders and leaders of the O'Melveny's Electronic Discovery and Document Retention Practice. Jeff is one of the longest serving eDiscovery litigators in the country and one of the few whose practice is entirely dedicated to eDiscovery issues. For close to fifteen years, Jeff has contributed his expertise to well over 200 litigation matters in all areas of practice. Jeff is a well-known speaker (over 50 MCLE presentations), author (BNA book), and commentator (LA Times, California Lawyer, Reuters, American Lawyer) on eDiscovery issues.

### FOWLER, Mark D.
DLA Piper LLP (US), East Palo Alto
650 833 2048
mark.fowler@dlapiper.com
*Featured in International Trade (Nationwide)*
**Practice Areas:** International Trade: Intellectual Property (Section 337).
**Career:** He focuses on patent infringement litigation and has experience in handling trials, binding arbitrations, trial preparation and counseling (including litigation avoidance). His patent infringement litigation experience includes cases before the International Trade Commission and the Federal Circuit, as well as District Courts in California, Texas, Virginia, Wisconsin, Delaware, Washington, Utah, Florida, Illinois and Ohio. His experience also encompasses years of working on trade secret and other complex business litigation.
**Personal:** JD, Stanford University; Harvard University; AB, University of California at Berkeley..

### FOX, Paul W
Bracewell & Giuliani LLP, Seattle
206 204 6222
paul.fox@bgllp.com
*Featured in Energy & Natural Resources (Nationwide)*
**Practice Areas:** Managing partner of the firm's Seattle office. Represents domestic and foreign electric and natural gas companies on matters dealing with cross-border trade, competition, open access to transmission, enforcement and investigations, ratemaking, rulemakings, restructuring and regulatory compliance. Has more than 35 years of experience litigating complex, multiparty proceedings before the Federal Energy Regulatory Commission, the Department of Energy, the Bonneville Power Administration, federal trial and appellate courts and arbitration tribunals in the US and Canada.
**Personal:** JD, The University of Texas School of Law, 1972; BA, Harvard University, 1970.

**FRANK, Richard L**
Olsson Frank Weeda Terman Matz PC,
Washington, DC
202 518 6363
rfrank@ofwlaw.com
*Featured in Food & Beverages (Nationwide)*
**Practice Areas:** Food and drug regulation, agriculture law.
**Career:** Rick Frank is a founder (1979) and senior principal of OFW Law, and an expert on the labeling, advertising, inspection and safety of food, drug, and alcohol products regulated by the FDA, USDA, FTC, and TTB. He has testified many times before the US Congress. He is recognized often as a leading food and drug lawyer (2012 peer awarded Top Attorneys – Washington, D.C.; 2012 Super Lawyers List; 2012 Best Lawyers in America; 2011 Martindale-Hubbell Peer Review Ratings awarded AV® Preeminent™).
**Personal:** BA, University of Michigan summa cum laude 1972; JD, University of Michigan 1976, Law Review.

**FRANKEL, Paul H**
Morrison & Foerster LLP, New York
212 468 8000
pfrankel@mofo.com
*Featured in Tax (Nationwide), Tax (New York)*
**Practice Areas:** Senior counsel in the firm's State + Local Tax Group. Member of the New York Bar, the New Jersey Bar, the Virginia Bar, and the Monmouth County (NJ) Bar Association. Has represented taxpayers in major tax controversies in nearly all of the fifty states. Has negotiated settlements in hundreds of cases. Has won significant state Supreme Court cases in Kansas, Kentucky, New Mexico, North Carolina, Minnesota, Massachusetts, Missouri, and Maryland. Has continually fought for due process for industry – particularly for the replacement of internal hearing officer systems with independent, prepayment state tax court.

**FRANKEL, Roger**
Orrick, Herrington & Sutcliffe LLP,
Washington, DC
202 339 8513
rfrankel@orrick.com
*Featured in Bankruptcy/Restructuring (Nationwide), Bankruptcy/Restructuring (District of Columbia)*
See under District of Columbia for profile.

**FRANKLIN, Jonathan S**
Fulbright & Jaworski LLP, Washington, DC
202 662 0466
jfranklin@fulbright.com
*Featured in Appellate Law (Nationwide)*
**Practice Areas:** Litigation, appellate, US Supreme Court.
**Career:** A partner in Fulbright's Washington, DC office, he is head of the Supreme Court and Appellate practice. Franklin has argued seven cases before the US Supreme Court; has litigated numerous other cases before the court at the certiorari and merits stages; has argued and briefed other cases in federal and state courts at trial and appellate levels. His cases have involved constitutional law, administrative law and procedure, intellectual property, contract, tort, insurance, civil

rights, antitrust, labor, telecommunications and international law.
**Personal:** JD, Yale Law School (1990); and AB, Harvard College (1986).

**FRANTZ, Steven P**
Morgan, Lewis & Bockius LLP, Washington, DC
202 739 5460
sfrantz@morganlewis.com
*Featured in Energy & Natural Resources (Nationwide)*
**Practice Areas:** Steven P. Frantz is a partner in Morgan Lewis's Energy Practice. Mr Frantz represents and counsels electric utilities, manufacturers of reactors, and materials licensees on the regulation and licensing of nuclear power plants, as well as other facilities regulated by the Nuclear Regulatory Commission (NRC) and the Department of Energy (DOE). Mr Frantz has been an industry leader in the certification and licensing of new nuclear power plants. He has devoted a substantial part of his practice to assisting utilities in developing strategies for helping nuclear plants obtain permission to resume construction or operation following NRC enforcement action.

**FREDERICK, Thomas**
Winston & Strawn LLP, Chicago
312 558 5983
tfrederick@winston.com
*Featured in Products Liability (Nationwide)*
**Practice Areas:** Tom Frederick's practice includes product liability and commercial litigation, as well as white-collar criminal defense and internal corporate investigation matters.
**Career:** Mr Frederick is the managing partner of Winston & Strawn's Chicago office. His clients include Philip Morris USA Inc., State Farm Mutual Automobile Insurance Company, and Verizon Wireless. Mr Frederick has broad civil and criminal litigation experience, including product liability, antitrust, arbitrations, and grand jury investigations.

**FREDMAN, Steven J**
Schulte Roth & Zabel LLP, New York
212 756 2567
steven.fredman@srz.com
*Featured in Investment Funds (Nationwide)*
**Practice Areas:** Co-Head, Investment Management Group. Practices in the areas of investment funds (domestic and offshore); investment advisers and broker-dealers; acquisitions and related financings of investment management firms; securities regulation; and structuring and organizing private investment partnerships and offshore funds.
**Career:** SRZ partner 1990-, associate 1986-90; Rubin Baum Levin Constant & Friedman associate, 1981-86; Miami Federal District Court Judge William Hoeveler, law clerk, 1980-81.
**Publications:** Co-author, "The Consent Conundrum: Changing Control of US Alternative Investment Advisers," Bloomberg Law.
**Personal:** Georgetown University Law Center, JD, editor, Law and Policy in International

Business; Columbia University, BA, Phi Beta Kappa.

**FREEDMAN, Jonathan L**
Sidley Austin LLP, New York
212 839 6782
jfreedman@sidley.com
*Featured in Insurance (Nationwide), Insurance (New York)*
**Practice Areas:** Partner in Sidley's New York office, practicing in the Insurance, M&A and Private Equity, and Securities groups. He focuses on transactional matters in the insurance industry, including capital markets transactions, mergers and acquisitions and securitizations involving insurance companies. He recently represented the initial purchasers in the largest offering of surplus notes by an insurance company in history. He has also been involved in many of the most innovative transactions recently completed in which insurance company cash flows are securitized.
**Personal:** Georgetown University Law Center, JD, 1981; Columbia University, AB, 1978, magna cum laude. Admission: New York.

**FREEDMAN, Linn F**
Nixon Peabody LLP, Providence
401 454 1108
lfreedman@nixonpeabody.com
*Featured in Privacy & Data Security (Nationwide)*
**Practice Areas:** Linn Freedman is leader of the firm's Privacy & Data Protection Group, chairs the HIPAA Compliance Team and the Health Information Technology Team. Linn's practice focuses on data privacy and security, responses to data breaches and compliance with federal and state privacy and security laws and breach notification laws. Linn is experienced in development and implementation of Regional Health Information Organizations and privacy and security issues related to interoperability of electronic health records. Linn has litigated complex cases, including privacy cases, in state, federal, and appellate courts and serves as general counsel of the Rhode Island Quality Institute.

**FREEMAN, D Reed**
Morrison & Foerster LLP, Washington, DC
202 887 6948
rfreeman@mofo.com
*Featured in Privacy & Data Security (Nationwide)*
**Practice Areas:** Focuses on consumer protection, including privacy, data security, and breach notification; advertising review and competitor challenges; online behavioral advertising and online tracking; privacy regulation regarding mobile apps and social media; and direct marketing. Represents clients in FTC investigations and in investigations with state attorneys general and in private civil disputes.
**Professional Memberships:** Editor of IAPP Privacy Tracker Legislative and Regulatory Service.
**Career:** Formerly staff attorney in FTC's Bureau of Consumer Protection and adjunct professor of Advertising Law at George Mason University School of Law.
**Publications:** Co-author of CCH's Advertising Law Guide and CCH's Privacy Law for Marketers.

**FREEMAN JR, David F**
Arnold & Porter LLP, Washington, DC
202 942 5745
David.Freeman@aporter.com
*Featured in Financial Services Regulation (Nationwide)*
**Practice Areas:** Represents banks, investment managers, and broker-dealers on banking and securities regulatory issues, legislation, mergers and acquisitions, private investment funds, and product development. Has represented clients in acquisition or creation of bank holding companies, banks, trust companies, joint ventures, broker-dealers, and investment advisers.
**Career:** Joined firm as associate, 1987. Partner since 1995. JD and MBA, 1987, University of Virginia.
**Publications:** 'Duty To Supervise,' 'Supervision of Outside Business Activities,' and 'Bank Exemptions from Broker-Dealer Regulation,' Chapters 4, 6 and 9 in Broker-Dealer Regulation (PLI, 2012 with annual updates); 'The Fair Valuation Mess' in The Journal of Investment Compliance (Summer, 2003).

**FREVOLA, Michael J**
Holland & Knight LLP, New York
212 513 3200
michael.frevola@hklaw.com
*Featured in Transportation (Nationwide)*
**Practice Areas:** Partner in the firm's Litigation Section, he has extensive courtroom and arbitration experience, including disputes regarding charter parties, vessel sales/construction, collisions, cargo, bunkers, and crew and penalty wages. He also specializes in arresting or attaching vessels or other assets nationwide to secure or enforce clients' claims. He has represented numerous creditors in maritime bankruptcy proceedings and advised on Liberian law for crew, labor, limitation and maritime lien issues. He has conducted shipboard and overseas investigations concerning both maritime litigation and owners' due diligence. Former US Navy officer: 1988 to 1992 (active) and 1992 to 1999 (reserve).

**FREY, Manuel**
Paul, Weiss, Rifkind, Wharton & Garrison LLP, New York
212 373 3127
mfrey@paulweiss.com
*Featured in Capital Markets (Nationwide)*
**Practice Areas:** Partner, Corporate Department. Focuses on a broad-based cross-border OTC derivatives, structured products and hedge fund practice. Closely involved in the structuring, negotiation and execution of derivative, synthetic and financing products and structures and the resolution of related credit, regulatory, legal and risk management issues. Represents banks, investment funds and corporate end-users in the design and negotiation of OTC derivatives products in all major asset classes (credit, equity, FX, rates and commodities), as well as derivatives-based structured financings. Regularly assists M&A, capital markets, litigation, bankruptcy and finance teams with derivatives aspects of acquisitions, financing transactions and corporate restructurings.

## FRIED, Douglas M
Chadbourne & Parke LLP, New York
212 408 5124
dfried@chadbourne.com
*Featured in Projects (Nationwide)*
**Practice Areas:** Douglas Fried represents sponsors, equity investors and lenders in transportation, infrastructure and energy projects in the US and abroad, including Latin America, the Middle East and India. His practice includes representing such entities in public-private partnerships, the development and financing of new projects, privatizations, workouts of troubled projects, and sales and acquisitions.
**Publications:** Publishes the "Toll Road and Infrastructure Update" on these industries in the US and globally.
**Personal:** Holds a JD from Fordham University School of Law, where he was a member of the Law Review, and a BS in finance, magna cum laude, from SUNY Albany.

## FRIEDLAND, Paul
White & Case LLP, New York
212 819 8917
pfriedland@whitecase.com
*Featured in International Arbitration (Nationwide)*
**Career:** Paul Friedland is global head of the White & Case International Arbitration practice group. He has served as counsel or arbitrator in numerous international arbitrations, both commercial and investor/state. Mr Friedland holds leadership positions at the American Arbitration Association and the International Bar Association, and formerly at the LCIA, and is repeatedly ranked by industry publications among the top arbitration practitioners. To view a comprehensive biography, please visit www.whitecase.com/pfriedland.

## FRIEDMAN, David M
Kasowitz, Benson, Torres & Friedman LLP, New York
212 506 1740
dfriedman@kasowitz.com
*Featured in Bankruptcy/Restructuring (Nationwide), Bankruptcy/Restructuring (New York)*
**Practice Areas:** Name Partner and Head of Creditors' Rights and Bankruptcy Group, Mr Friedman represents debtors-in-possession, commercial lenders, committees of creditors and equity security holders, hedge funds, high-yield mutual funds, trustees, and acquirers of distressed businesses. Recent representations include Borders Group, Inc., and the Official Committee of Unsecured Creditors of Adelphia Communications Corporation. He is ranked in Chambers as a "Leading Individual" in Bankruptcy/Restructuring.
**Career:** He is recognized in Lawdragon as one of the 500 leading lawyers in America, Avenue Magazine's "Legal Elite," Best Lawyers in America, and has been named as a "local litigation star" by Benchmark Litigation 2013.

## FRIEDMAN, Ellen S
Nixon Peabody LLP, New York
212 940 3053
efriedman@nixonpeabody.com
*Featured in Projects (Nationwide)*
**Practice Areas:** Ellen's practice focuses on the financing, development, acquisition and disposition of domestic and international conventional and renewable energy and infrastructure projects. She has counseled a wide variety clients, including equity investors, developers, commercial lenders, financial guarantors, underwriters, purchasers and sellers with respect to deal structure, partnership and joint venture matters, hedging, intercreditor arrangements, restructuring, risk assessment, security arrangements and due diligence. Ellen has significant experience negotiating complex credit documentation, joint venture/partnership arrangements, disclosure materials, hedges and project agreements.
**Personal:** JD, Fordham University Law School, 1989, cum laude; BA, Cornell University, 1984.

## FRIEDMAN, Lawrence
Barnes, Richardson & Colburn, Chicago
312 297 9554
lfriedman@barnesrichardson.com
*Featured in International Trade (Nationwide)*
**Practice Areas:** US customs and export law with an emphasis on import compliance including tariff classification, valuation, origin, free trade agreements (e.g., NAFTA, US-CAFTA-DR, US-Australia, etc.), penalties, and litigation before the US Court of International Trade and the US Court of Appeals for the Federal Circuit.
**Professional Memberships:** Customs and International Trade Bar Association (Secretary); American Bar Association, Section of International Law, Customs Law Committee (Past Co-Chair).
**Career:** Barnes, Richardson & Colburn 1991-Present; Law Clerk to the Honorable Dominick L. DiCarlo, US Court of International Trade 1989-91; Adjunct Professor of Law, John Marshall Law School Center for International Law 1995-Present.
**Publications:** Customs Law (Carolina Academic Press 2011)(Co-author); What is Persuasive? Pushing World Customs Organization Materials through the Skidmore Sieve," Tulane Journal of International and Comparative Law, Vol. 17, Issue No. 2, Page 515; "The Administrative Procedure Act and Judicial Review in Customs Cases at the Court of International Trade," University of Pennsylvania Journal of International Economic Law, Vol. 28, Issue No. 1, Page 1, 2007; Challenging Customs Denial of Prior Disclosure, Georgetown University Law Center International Trade Update 2011.
**Personal:** University of Illinois at Urbana-Champaign, BA Political Science 1986; John Marshall Law School, JD 1989; John Marshall Law School, LLM (Intellectual Property Law) 2001.

## FRIEDRICH, Laura S
Shearman & Sterling LLP, New York
212 848 7411
laura.friedrich@shearman.com
*Featured in Investment Funds (Nationwide)*
**Practice Areas:** Laura Friedrich is a partner in the Investment Funds Group, with a concentration in private fund formation, structuring and compliance matters. She has extensive experience working with US and international private equity funds and their sponsors with investments in the United States, Europe, Latin America, Asia, Africa, India and the Middle East. Ms Friedrich has led fund raising efforts for large and middle market, regional and sector-specific funds, with focuses including real estate, energy, infrastructure, debt, transportation and media.
**Career:** Bar admission: New York.
**Personal:** Personal: University of Pennsylvania Law School, Unversity of California, Berkeley.

## FRIES, Elizabeth Shea
Goodwin Procter LLP, Boston
(617) 570-1559
efries@goodwinprocter.com
*Featured in Investment Funds (Nationwide), Investment Funds (Massachusetts)*
See under Massachusetts for profile.

## FRIES, Richard S
Bingham McCutchen LLP, New York
212 705 7312
richard.fries@bingham.com
*Featured in Real Estate (Nationwide), Real Estate (New York)*
**Practice Areas:** Co-chair of Bingham's Real Estate Practice Group. Represents US and global institutional lenders, investment bankers, owners and developers in distressed loan workouts and restructurings, mortgage foreclosure, distressed portfolio and asset sales, property disposition, creditors' rights and insolvency, origination of real estate loans, asset-based and structured finance, loan participations and syndications, and private equity joint ventures and restructures. Has chaired and lectured at PLI, state and city bar association programs and written extensively on real estate and financing cases.
**Personal:** New York University School of Law, JD, 1977; Brooklyn College, BA, 1974.

## FRIESEN, Connie M
Sidley Austin LLP, New York
212 839 5507
cfriesen@sidley.com
*Featured in Financial Services Regulation (Nationwide)*
**Practice Areas:** Partner in Sidley's New York office. She provides regulatory and transactional advice to domestic and international financial institutions including commercial banks and bank holding companies, trust companies, internet banks, securities firms and insurance companies. She counsels clients on the development of new financial services and the implications of various domestic and international bank regulatory considerations affecting them. She provides advice to international banks on the establishment of branches, agencies and subsidiaries, broker-dealers and finance companies.
**Personal:** Yale Law School, JD, 1978; Harvard University, PhD, 1972; Concordia College - Moorhead, BA, 1967, summa cum laude. Admissions: Connecticut, New York.

## FRIMMER, Paul N
Loeb & Loeb LLP, Los Angeles
310 282 2383
pfrimmer@loeb.com
*Featured in Wealth Management (Nationwide), Tax (California)*
**Practice Areas:** Specializes in estate planning, wills and trusts, probate and trust administration, postmortem tax planning, probate litigation, art law, charitable giving and tax-related issues.
**Professional Memberships:** Authored/co-authored over 50 publications on estate planning and related areas. Frequent speaker at NYU Tax Institute, USC Tax Institute, the University of Miami Estate Planning Institute, ALI-ABA seminars, the USC Probate and Trust Institute and the UCLA Estate Planning Institute.
**Personal:** Fordham University School (JD, 1969, cum laude); Queens College (BS, 1966).

## FRISCHLING, Carl
Kramer Levin Naftalis & Frankel LLP, New York
212 715 7520
cfrischling@kramerlevin.com
*Featured in Investment Funds (Nationwide)*
**Practice Areas:** Mr Frischling is Co-Head of the Financial Services Group. His practice focuses on financial services law and regulation, investment company law, and mutual funds. Mr Frischling counsels clients in the legal facets that impact financial services firms, including acquisitions and sales of investment management companies. He is a pioneer in the field of bank-related mutual funds. He also advises mutual funds and their independent directors/trustees on their fiduciary obligations under federal securities laws. In 2007, Mr Frischling received the Inaugural Independent Counsel of the Year Award and in 2013, he also received the Lifetime Achievement Award from Institutional Investor's magazine Fund Directions. He serves as a Director of the Mutual Fund Directors Forum.

## FROELICH, Edward
Morrison & Foerster LLP, Washington, DC
202 778 1646
efroelich@mofo.com
*Featured in Tax (Nationwide)*
**Practice Areas:** Represents clients in audit and litigation on all Federal tax issues. Former trial attorney of the Department of Justice Tax Division, where he litigated numerous cases, including complex corporate cases; in the US Court of Federal Claims. Some of the recent issues he has handled include employment tax and worker classification issues, subpart F and ECI issues, accounting method issues, section 482 issues, deductibility of legal fees, estate tax penalties, offshore asset issues and privilege and work product issues.

**FRUMKIN, Joseph B**
Sullivan & Cromwell LLP, New York
212 558 4101
frumkinj@sullcrom.com
*Featured in Energy & Natural Resources (Nationwide), Corporate/M&A (New York)*
**Career:** Partner since 1994. Managing Partner, M&A Group. Recent representations: AT&T in numerous transactions; Borealis and Teachers' in Express Pipeline sale to Spectra Energy; Southern Union in ETE sale; Jo-Ann Stores in Leonard Green sale; Dynegy in proposed Blackstone and Icahn sales; E.ON in sale of US power and gas business to PPL; Sempra in sales of RBS Sempra Commodities businesses; UST in Altria sale; TXU in its LBO; Macquarie-led investor group in Duquesne Light acquisition; Endesa in acquisition by Enel and Acciona; Telewest in NTL sale.
**Personal:** U Penn Law (JD, 1985); Georgetown (BA, 1980).

**FRYER, Judith D**
Greenberg Traurig, LLP, New York
212 801 9330
FryerJ@gtlaw.com
*Featured in Capital Markets (Nationwide)*
**Practice Areas:** Co-Chair, Real Estate Investment Trusts (REIT). Corporate and securities; mergers, acquisitions.
**Professional Memberships:** Past President, Women's Forum; Past Member, Executive Committee and of Board of Governors of the National Association of Real Estate Investment Trusts, Inc. (NAREIT); Board Member, Investment Program Association (IPA); Former Co-chair, Women's Executive Circle; Past Board Member, UJA Federation of New York.
**Career:** Fellow, American Bar Foundation (1/3 of 1% of lawyers per state). Listed: Chambers Global, 2009, 2011-13; Chambers USA Guide, 2007-13; Super Lawyers, 2006-12.
**Personal:** JD, Hofstra University School of Law (Recent Developments Editor, Law Review); BS, Washington University in St Louis.

**FULLENWEIDER, Keith**
Vinson & Elkins LLP, Houston
713 758 3838
kfullenweider@velaw.com
*Featured in Corporate/M&A (Texas), Energy & Natural Resources (Nationwide)*
See under Texas for profile.

**FURLETTI, Mark J.**
Ballard Spahr LLP, Philadelphia
215 864 8138
furlettim@ballardspahr.com
*Featured in Financial Services Regulation (Nationwide), Banking & Finance (Pennsylvania)*
**Practice Areas:** Mark J. Furletti is an associate in the Business and Finance Department and a member of the Consumer Financial Services and Bank Regulatory and Supervision Groups. His practice focuses on advising banks and non-bank lenders regarding compliance with federal and state consumer lending and payments laws.
**Career:** Judicial Clerkship, Hon. Franklin S. Van Antwerpen, US Court of Appeals for the Third Circuit Admissions: Pennsylvania.

**Personal:** Education Temple University James E. Beasley School of Law, JD, cum laude Loyola College in Maryland, BBA, cum laude.

**GAJER, Paul**
Dentons, New York
212 398 5293
paul.gajer@dentons.com
*Featured in Investment Funds (Nationwide)*
**Practice Areas:** Co-Chair legacy Dentons's Private Equity and Investment Funds Practice. Concentrates on representing private equity, buy-out and venture capital funds, including funds focused on the business services, media, telecommunications and technology sectors and SBIC funds, and their portfolio companies. Focuses on structuring investment, buy-out, joint venture and roll-up transactions, and the related senior and mezzanine financing aspects of such transactions, as well as management equity and incentive programs. Significant portion of practice focused on fund formation, follow-on offerings and fund restructurings.
**Personal:** Georgetown University Law Center, JD, summa cum laude; Editor, Georgetown Law Review; State University of NY at Stony Brook, BA.

**GALARDI, Gregg M**
DLA Piper LLP (US), New York
212 335 4640
gregg.galardi@dlapiper.com
*Featured in Bankruptcy/Restructuring (Nationwide), Bankruptcy/Restructuring (Delaware)*
See under Delaware for profile.

**GALE, Kelley**
Latham & Watkins LLP, San Diego
619 236 1234
kelley.gale@lw.com
*Featured in Projects (Nationwide)*
**Practice Areas:** Kelley Michael Gale serves as chair of the firm's Project Finance Practice Group and co-chair of the Air Quality and Climate Change Practice Group. His practice centers on the representation of private and public sector clients in the development, regulation and financing of renewable energy and capital intensive infrastructure projects. He represents major project lenders and developers in connection with cogeneration projects and small power production projects, including geothermal, wind, solar, biomass, waste-to-energy and hydroelectric. His environmental and energy law expertise includes a broad range of work in the air, energy regulation, hazardous waste and land use areas.

**GALLAGHER, James J**
McKenna Long & Aldridge LLP, Los Angeles
213 243 6165
jgallagher@mckennalong.com
*Featured in Government (Nationwide)*
**Practice Areas:** Jay Gallagher is a nationally renowned litigator who has been representing government contractors, including the largest aerospace companies, for more than three decades. His experience includes the full range of government contract financial issues, including civil and criminal fraud investigations and litiga-

tion, defective pricing, terminations, claims, breach of contract and cost allowability.

**GALVAN, Ramon P**
Orrick, Herrington & Sutcliffe LLP, Los Angeles
213 612 2383
rgalvan@orrick.com
*Featured in Native American Law (Nationwide)*
**Career:** Ramon Galvan is a partner in the Los Angeles office and a member of Orrick's Banking and Debt Capital Markets Group. He represents a variety of lending institutions in complex commercial finance transactions, both secured and unsecured. He has a wide range of experience in financings involving Native American tribes and tribal entities, including financings for new casino construction projects and expansions.

**GALVIS, Sergio J**
Sullivan & Cromwell LLP, New York
212 558 4740
galviss@sullcrom.com
*Featured in Latin American Investment (New York), Projects (Nationwide)*
See under New York for profile.

**GAMBRO, Michael S**
Cadwalader, Wickersham & Taft LLP, New York
212 504 6825
michael.gambro@cwt.com
*Featured in Capital Markets (Nationwide)*
**Practice Areas:** Co-Chair, Capital Markets Department. Advises financial institutions and funds in the financing, purchase and sale, and securitization of financial assets, such as commercial mortgage loans, residential mortgage loans, and other consumer assets, trade receivables, pharmaceutical receivables, and insurance policy-backed loans. Has represented some of the world's largest companies in noteworthy securitisation transactions, including acting as lead counsel in the largest single borrower commercial mortgage-backed securities transaction ever completed.
**Personal:** JD, Columbia (Harlan Fiske Stone Scholar); BS, Tufts University, (summa cum laude, Phi Beta Kappa).

**GANDHI, Samir A**
Sidley Austin LLP, New York
212 839 5684
sgandhi@sidley.com
*Featured in Capital Markets (Nationwide)*
**Practice Areas:** Partner in Sidley's New York office, a member of the firm's Executive Committee and co-chair of the firm's Marketing and Practice Development Committee. He focuses on private equity transactions and capital markets offerings. He represents issuers, underwriters and selling shareholders on IPOs as well as equity and debt capital markets transactions. Also, he represents domestic/foreign fund sponsors, investment banks and private investors in private equity and venture capital activities and represents investors, including private investment funds, in foreign direct investment transactions oriented towards Asia.

**Personal:** The George Washington University Law School, JD, 1993; University of Chicago, AB, 1990.

**GARDINER, John L**
Skadden, Arps, Slate, Meagher & Flom LLP & Affiliates, New York
212 735 2442
John.Gardiner@skadden.com
*Featured in International Arbitration (Nationwide)*
**Practice Areas:** Co-head of Skadden's International Litigation and Arbitration Group. Represents clients in disputes before all major international arbitration tribunals. Disputes include failed mergers and post-closing adjustments, integrated power development projects, energy project-related issues, partnership and joint venture issues. Also acts as arbitrator and mediator in complex business disputes. Also represents clients before federal and state courts in cases involving fraud, breach of contract, trade secrets, takeovers and class actions.
**Professional Memberships:** Admitted: New York, 1988; Roll of Solicitors, Republic of Ireland, 1988; Roll of Solicitors, England and Wales; LLB, University College, Dublin, 1984.

**GARDNER, Bryant**
Winston & Strawn LLP, Washington, DC
202 282 5893
bgardner@winston.com
*Featured in Transportation (Nationwide)*
**Practice Areas:** Federal regulatory practice specializing in the maritime industry; Federal Maritime Comission Shipping Act compliance; maritime and logistics government contracts counselling and litigation; US flag issues and Jones Act cabotage compliance.
**Professional Memberships:** President, Propeller Club, Port of Washington, D.C.; Maritime Law Association; Maritime Administrative Bar Association.
**Publications:** "Window on Washington" Benedict's Maritime Bulletin (2009-present); "Is the Jones Act Redundant?" USF Mar LJ (2009).
**Personal:** Tulane College (BA 1996 summa cum laude); Tulane Law School (JD 2000 cum laude) (Certificated in Admiralty); Phi Beta Kappa; Editor-in-Chief, Tulane Maritime Law Journal (1999-2000).

**GARDNER, Ronald K**
Dady & Gardner, PA, Minneapolis
612 359 3501
rkgardner@dadygardner.com
*Featured in Franchising (Nationwide)*
**Practice Areas:** Franchise.
**Career:** Represented businesses in virtually all fifty states, including both single-owner and multi-unit franchisees. He has handled issues of unlawful termination, encroachment, and the franchisor's failure to comply with requirements of the FTC and state governments. He is also a nationally known speaker on franchise law and the Immediate Past Chair of the ABA's Forum on Franchising.
**Personal:** Hamline University (JD, cum laude with honors, 1994); Mankato State University (BA, magna cum laude, 1991).

**GARFIELD, Gerald**
Day Pitney LLP, Hartford
860 275 0182
ggarfield@daypitney.com
*Featured in Energy & Natural Resources (Nationwide)*
**Career:** Gerald Garfield's work in the public utility area has included regulatory matters involving the Nuclear Regulatory Commission, the Federal Energy Regulatory Commission, the Environmental Protection Agency, and other federal and state agencies having jurisdiction over the siting, construction, and operation of power plants. Gerry's practice has also included procurement and financing matters involving fossil and nuclear generating facilities; representation of developers, contractors, and equity investors in domestic and international power development fields; and advising utilities and other investors on mergers and acquisitions. Recently, his practice has focused on counseling clients regarding commercial and regulatory arrangements for nuclear "new build."

**GARFINKEL, Barry H**
Skadden, Arps, Slate, Meagher & Flom LLP & Affiliates, New York
212 735 2500
Barry.Garfinkel@skadden.com
*Featured in International Arbitration (Nationwide)*
**Practice Areas:** Senior member of International Arbitration practice. As advocate leads major international arbitrations. Arbitrates/chairs ICC, UNCITRAL and AAA arbitrations. Advises major US and foreign companies on transnational arbitrations.
**Professional Memberships:** Former president, College of Commercial Arbitrators; former chairman and trustee, Practising Law Institute; Advisory Committee, Institute for Transnational Arbitration; International Arbitration Committee, American Arbitration Association (Complex Cases), LCIA and ICC; International Arbitration Club of New York; Fellow, American College of Trial Lawyers.
**Career:** LLB, Yale University, 1955 (Managing Editor, Yale Law Journal); BSS, College of the City of New York, 1950; Law Clerk to US District Judge Edward Weinfeld.

**GARIBALDI, Oscar M**
Covington & Burling LLP, Washington, DC
202 662 5624
ogaribaldi@cov.com
*Featured in International Arbitration (Nationwide)*
**Practice Areas:** International arbitration (investment and commercial).
**Professional Memberships:** ICSID Panel of Conciliators (2002-07); ICDR Neutrals (current).
**Career:** For over 30 years, Mr Garibaldi has drawn on his triple training in the common law, civil law, and public international law to represent clients in complex international disputes. He specializes in international arbitration (investment and commercial) as both counsel and arbitrator. He also represents clients in international litigation and trade disputes.
**Personal:** University of Buenos Aires Law School (Procurador [LLB], 1971, Abogado [JD], 1972,

Diploma de Honor); Harvard Law School (LLM, 1975); studied at Harvard towards SJD.

**GARRE, Gregory**
Latham & Watkins LLP, Washington, DC
202 637 2207
gregory.garre@lw.com
*Featured in Appellate Law (Nationwide)*
**Practice Areas:** Appellate and Supreme Court; argued 38 cases before Supreme Court, including winning arguments in Ashcroft v. Iqbal, United States v. Home Concrete & Supply, and Monsanto v. Geertson Seed Farm; successfully argued numerous cases in appellate courts across country; recognized as leading advocate by Chambers USA, Legal 500, and Best Lawyers in America; named to American Lawyer's "Fab 50" top litigators under 45 (2006).
**Career:** Global Chair, Latham & Watkins Supreme Court and Appellate Practice, 2009-present; US Solicitor General, 2008-2009; Principal Deputy Solicitor General, 2005-2008; Assistant to the Solicitor General, 2000-2004; law clerk to Honorable William H. Rehnquist.

**GARRETT, Robert A**
Arnold & Porter LLP, Washington, DC
202 942 5444
Robert.Garrett@aporter.com
*Featured in Sports Law (Nationwide), Media & Entertainment (District of Columbia)*
See under District of Columbia for profile.

**GARTNER, Steven J**
Willkie Farr & Gallagher LLP, New York
212 728 8222
sgartner@willkie.com
*Featured in Private Equity (Nationwide)*
**Practice Areas:** Co-Chairman, Willkie Farr & Gallagher. Specialises in private equity, mergers and acquisitions and corporate governance matters. Served for two years in firm's London office and continues to be active in firm's international practice. Actively involved in representing private equity funds and their portfolio companies including numerous leveraged buyouts and sales of public and private companies. M&A experience includes going-private transactions, stock and asset sales, and privately negotiated and hostile transactions. Corporate governance experience includes advising special committees regarding interested director transactions and general advice as to fiduciary duties of directors.
**Personal:** JD, magna cum laude, St. John's University School of Law, 1984; member, St. John's Law Review. BSBA, Georgetown University, 1981.
See: http://www.willkie.com/Steven_Gartner.

**GARWOOD, Suzanne**
Venable LLP, Washington, DC
202 344 8046
sgarwood@Venable.com
*Featured in Financial Services Regulation (Nationwide)*
**Practice Areas:** Financial services, consumer finance, regulatory, CFPB
**Professional Memberships:** Past President, Women in Housing & Finance; Fellow, American College of Consumer Financial Services Lawyers.

**Career:** Focuses on laws regarding consumer credit and financial services. Assists mortgage lenders, installment lenders, and banks and thrifts with issues arising under the Truth in Lending Act, Real Estate Settlement Procedures Act, Equal Credit Opportunity Act, and anti-predatory and fair lending laws. Represents clients in the financial services industry (credit counselors, mortgage lenders, credit card issuers).
**Personal:** JD, with distinction, Ohio Northern University, Claude W. Pettit College of Law, 1997; B.S., Bryant University, 1993.

**GATTI, Steven**
Clifford Chance US LLP, Washington, DC
202 912 5095
steven.gatti@cliffordchance.com
*Featured in Financial Services Regulation (Nationwide)*
**Practice Areas:** Concentrates on securities enforcement and counseling, with a focus on broker-dealer and investment management regulation, and issues unique to cross-border, multinational financial services clients. Represents US and international financial institutions, including broker-dealers, banks, and investment advisers in regulatory, enforcement, and commercial matters. Practice includes strategic counseling on financial markets and trading regulation, investment management compliance, trading systems, distribution issues, new products, and mergers and acquisitions in the financial institutions sector. Years of experience conducting internal investigations involving potential securities law violations, and financial fraud, and in conducting internal compliance audits.

**GEDANKEN, Lynne E**
Chadbourne & Parke LLP, Washington, DC
202 974 5646
lgedanken@chadbourne.com
*Featured in Projects (Nationwide)*
**Practice Areas:** Has over 30 years' experience in the electricity sector. She advises developers and lenders on the full range of corporate, project, equity and finance agreements for structuring, developing and financing renewable, conventional and nuclear power projects. She has worked on projects in over 35 countries, focusing on the US, Middle East and Africa. She advises companies and governmental entities on utility privatizations and tenders for existing companies, assets and greenfield projects. She has worked on transactions involving private sector financing as well as financing provided by US governmental entities, multilateral institutions, export credit agenies and development finance institutions.

**GELFOND, Stuart H**
Fried, Frank, Harris, Shriver & Jacobson LLP, New York
212 859 8272
Stuart.Gelfond@FriedFrank.com
*Featured in Capital Markets (Nationwide)*
**Practice Areas:** Corporate partner. Concentrates his practice in corporate finance transactions, including representation of issuers and underwriters, domestic and international high-yield, investment-grade and convertible debt

offerings, acquisition financings, and initial public offerings. Represents debtors and creditors in restructurings. Has experience serving as counsel to corporations and broker-dealers on securities, corporate governance and other regulatory issues.
**Career:** Joined in 1986; became partner in 1993.
**Personal:** JD, New York University School of Law (1986), Order of the Coif and articles editor of Law Review; BS, magna cum laude, Wharton School of the University of Pennsylvania (finance and accounting) (1983).

**GELMAN, Bruce L**
Kirkland & Ellis LLP, Chicago
312 862 2370
bruce.gelman@kirkland.com
*Featured in Capital Markets (Nationwide)*
**Practice Areas:** Tax partner with extensive experience advising fund sponsors and investors (both offshore and domestic). Concentrates in the organization and structuring of real estate, infrastructure and other alternative-asset investment funds. Significant experience representing offshore investors in the US property and infrastructure markets. Maintains a broad tax planning practice representing REITs and other investors in real estate.
**Professional Memberships:** NAREIT; AFIRE.
**Personal:** University of Detroit School of Law (JD, summa cum laude, 1992; Editor, Law Review); Boston College (BA, 1990).

**GENTNER, Joshua D**
Vedder Price PC, Chicago
312 609 7887
jgentner@vedderprice.com
*Featured in Transportation (Nationwide), Banking & Finance (Nationwide)*
**Practice Areas:** Shareholder and member of the firm's Global Transportation Finance team. Represents clients in a wide variety of debt, equity and lease financings, including US and cross-border leveraged leases, mortgage financings, operating leases, export credit agency-supported financings and securitizations including EETCs and pass-through certificates. Experience includes financing of aircraft, rolling stock, vessels and other machinery and equipment, with extensive experience in cross-border leasing transactions including those on behalf of the Export-Import Bank of the United States. Also represented commercial airlines in bankruptcy proceedings and restructuring transactions.
**Personal:** JD, cum laude, Order of the Coif, Northwestern University; BA, Indiana University.

**GENZ, Peter**
King & Spalding LLP, Atlanta
404 572 4935
pgenz@kslaw.com
*Featured in Tax (Georgia), Capital Markets (Nationwide)*
See under Georgia for profile.

**GEORGE, Peter R**
Baker & McKenzie, Chicago
312 861 6587
peter.george@bakermckenzie.com
*Featured in Outsourcing (Nationwide), Technology (Illinois)*
See under Illinois for profile.

**GERACHIS, George Matthew**
Vinson & Elkins LLP, Houston
713 758 1056
ggerachis@velaw.com
*Featured in Tax (Nationwide), Tax (Texas)*
See under Texas for profile.

**GERBER, Dean N**
Vedder Price PC, Chicago
312 609 7638
dgerber@vedderprice.com
*Featured in Transportation (Nationwide), Banking & Finance (Illinois), Banking & Finance (Nationwide)*
**Practice Areas:** Member of the firm's Executive Committee, Shareholder and Chair of the Global Transportation Finance team. Extensive experience as special counsel representing lessees, equity participants, lenders, credit enhancers, underwriters and governmental agencies on aircraft, railcar and equipment finance transactions. Acts for parties involved in leasing transactions, securitizations and financing transactions. Has significant experience developing and structuring financings involving export credit agencies.
**Professional Memberships:** Vice Chair, Legal Advisory Panel to the Aviation Working Group; Member, Board of Directors, ISTAT.
**Career:** Admitted (IL) 1985; C.P.A.
**Publications:** Co-Author, "Practitioners' Guide to the Cape Town Convention and the Aircraft Protocol" (2012).
**Personal:** C.P.A.; JD, University of Illinois.

**GERBER, Toby L**
Fulbright & Jaworski LLP, Dallas
214 855 7171
tgerber@fulbright.com
*Featured in Bankruptcy/Restructuring (Texas), Bankruptcy/Restructuring (Nationwide)*
See under Texas for profile.

**GERGEN, Michael**
Latham & Watkins LLP, Washington, DC
202 637 2188
michael.gergen@lw.com
*Featured in Energy & Natural Resources (Nationwide)*
**Practice Areas:** Represents entities involved in the electric, natural gas and other network industries. Mr Gergen represents entities involved with electric generation, transmission and distribution, natural gas transportation, storage and distribution, electric and natural gas marketing and trading, and finance, as well as international governments and financial institutions. Mr Gergen also assists clients regarding public financing support and incentive programs for clean energy technologies, products and services.
**Professional Memberships:** Member, District of Columbia and New York bars.
**Personal:** JD, New York University School of Law, 1992; MS, Applied Economics, Univ. of

California, Santa Cruz, 1987; BA, Antioch College, 1982.

**GERLACH, C. Andrew**
Sullivan & Cromwell LLP, New York
212 558 4789
gerlacha@sullcrom.com
*Featured in Financial Services Regulation (Nationwide)*
**Practice Areas:** Advises on M&A, joint ventures, securities offerings and similar transactions. Also advises on regulatory, takeover defense and corporate control, and strategic and corporate governance matters. Represents US and non-US public and private financial institutions, including banks, insurance companies, private equity and hedge funds, investment advisers and broker-dealers. Advises on regulatory matters involving federal and state bank regulatory agencies, the SEC, the FINRA and other governmental agencies on behalf of financial institutions.
**Professional Memberships:** Vice Chair, M&A Subcommittee of the Banking Law Committee, ABA; NYCBA Banking Committee.
**Personal:** Boston University Law School (JD); George Mason University (BA).

**GERSTENZANG, Michael A**
Cleary Gottlieb Steen & Hamilton LLP, New York
212 225 2096
mgerstenzang@cgsh.com
*Featured in Investment Funds (Nationwide)*
**Practice Areas:** Forming and advising private investment funds including private equity funds, credit opportunity funds, international funds, hedge funds, and other 'alternative asset' investment vehicles. Regularly represents TPG, Credit Suisse, KKR, Victoria Capital Partners and Unitas Capital.
**Professional Memberships:** Admitted in New York. Member of the Private Investment Fund Forum, the Private Investment Funds subcommittee of the International Bar Association, and the Committee on Private Investment Funds of the Bar Association of the City of New York.
**Career:** JD, Columbia University (Stone Scholar) (1989); BSFS, magna cum laude, Georgetown University (1986).

**GESSNER, Douglas C**
Kirkland & Ellis LLP, Chicago
312 862 2140
douglas.gessner@kirkland.com
*Featured in Private Equity (Nationwide), Corporate/M&A (Illinois)*
**Practice Areas:** Doug Gessner is a partner in the Chicago office of Kirkland & Ellis LLP, where he concentrates on representing private equity and venture capital sponsors in all aspects of private equity and venture capital investment activity, including leveraged buyouts of public and private companies, recapitalisations of private companies, growth equity investments in public and private companies, start-up investments, and formation of private equity funds.
**Personal:** Mr Gessner received his undergraduate degree from the University of Michigan, highest honors, and his JD from Harvard Law School,

magna cum laude, where he was an editor of the Harvard Law Review.

**GIANVECCHIO, Natasha**
Latham & Watkins LLP, Washington, DC
202 637 1079
natasha.gianvecchio@lw.com
*Featured in Energy & Natural Resources (Nationwide)*
**Practice Areas:** Represents entities involved in electric generation, transmission and distribution, electric and gas marketing and trading, and gas transportation and distribution on a variety of regulatory and market matters including with respect to project development and commercialization, market design, mergers/acquisitions and affiliate issues. Negotiates project agreements in association with development or restructuring of energy facilities; including relating to US regional electricity markets. Advises on federal and state energy regulations and related matters before FERC, DOE, DOJ, CFTC and state public utility commissions.
**Professional Memberships:** Member, DC bar.
**Personal:** JD, University of Chicago Law School, 2001; BA, Yale University, 1998.

**GIBBS, Kirstin E**
Bracewell & Giuliani LLP, Washington, DC
202 828 5878
kirstin.gibbs@bgllp.com
*Featured in Energy & Natural Resources (Nationwide)*
**Practice Areas:** Represents natural gas pipelines, traders, marketers, local distribution companies, and end-users in matters related to natural gas and oil transportation and storage issues. Advises clients on Federal Energy Regulatory Commission compliance and enforcement issues, as well as rate, policy, and legislative matters involving natural gas and oil. Also provides regulatory and transactional advice to major oil producers and pipeline companies located in the US and operating in the Gulf of Mexico. Counsels global and US-based clients in connection with liquefied natural gas issues.
**Personal:** JD, Catholic University of America, Columbus School of Law, 1997; BA, LeMoyne College, 1990.

**GIBBS, Robin C**
Gibbs & Bruns LLP, Houston
713 751 5217
rgibbs@gibbsbruns.com
*Featured in Litigation (Nationwide), Litigation (Texas)*
See under Texas for profile.

**GIBLIN JR, Thomas P**
Morgan, Lewis & Bockius LLP, New York
212 309 6277
tgiblin@morganlewis.com
*Featured in Energy & Natural Resources (Nationwide)*
**Practice Areas:** Thomas P. Giblin, Jr. is a Partner in Morgan Lewis's Business and Finance Practice. Mr Giblin's practice focuses on capital markets transactions, particularly in the energy and utility field. He acts as corporate and securities counsel for several energy and utility clients in the United States. Recent transactions include first

mortgage bond and other debt offerings, hybrid security financings, equity units and common stock offerings. Mr Giblin also advises on capital and liability management transactions such as tender offers, exchange offers, consent solicitations, stock buybacks and accelerated share repurchase programs.

**GIBSON, Douglas G**
Covington & Burling LLP, Washington, DC
202 662 5483
dgibson@cov.com
*Featured in Sports Law (Nationwide)*
**Practice Areas:** Corporate counsel to leading US professional sports leagues and teams, and current and aspiring owners, including the NFL, NHL, MLB, USTA, UFC and the Chicago Cubs. Advise with respect to M&A, finance, governance and media matters, including team sales, league-wide financing arrangements, stadium financing, media agreements and sponsorship arrangements. Also represents corporate and private equity clients, including Fortune 100 companies, in broad array of M&A, finance and governance matters.
**Career:** Former General Counsel and Member of Executive Committee of Bacardi Limited.
**Personal:** JD, cum laude, Harvard Law School (1990); BS with honors, The Johns Hopkins University (1987).

**GIDDENS, James W**
Hughes Hubbard & Reed LLP, New York
212 837 6810
kiplok@hugheshubbard.com
*Featured in Bankruptcy/Restructuring (Nationwide), Bankruptcy/Restructuring (New York)*
See under New York for profile.

**GIDEON, Kenneth W**
Skadden, Arps, Slate, Meagher & Flom LLP & Affiliates, Washington, DC
202 371 7540
Kenneth.Gideon@skadden.com
*Featured in Tax (District of Columbia), Tax (Nationwide)*
**Practice Areas:** Represents clients before the US Department of the Treasury and IRS; seeking guidance on novel transactions; and on issues of federal tax law, tax controversy and tax planning. Experience includes appearances in US Tax Court, Federal District Court and the US Court of Federal Claims. Also advises on corporate mergers, acquisitions and restructurings, particularly when the transaction may require a ruling or discussions with the IRS.
**Professional Memberships:** ABA Board of Governors (2012-Present); Chair, ABA Section of Taxation (2004-05).
**Career:** Assistant Secretary for Tax Policy, Treasury Department; Chief Counsel, IRS. JD, Yale University Law School; BA, Harvard University.

**GILBERG, David J**
Sullivan & Cromwell LLP, New York
212 558 4680
gilbergd@sullcrom.com
*Featured in Capital Markets (Nationwide)*
**Career:** Partner since 1996. His practice involves a broad range of derivatives and trading-related

matters, including regulation of derivative products and market participants, registration, compliance and regulation under the Dodd-Frank Act, development of clearing systems, exchanges and electronic trading facilities for the trading of derivatives; regulation of hedge funds and other private funds and managed vehicles, development of financial indices and indexed products and related matters.
**Personal:** Harvard Law School (JD, 1981); University of Pennsylvania (BA, MA, 1978).

### GILL, Sartaj
Davis Polk & Wardwell LLP, New York
212 450 4000
sartaj.gill@davispolk.com
*Featured in Banking & Finance (Nationwide)*
**Practice Areas:** Member of Davis Polk's Corporate Department. Advises borrowers as well as financial institutions on a wide range of corporate finance transactions, with special emphasis on acquisition and other leveraged financing transactions. He has worked on numerous complex domestic and international financing transactions.

### GIPS, Robert
Drummond Woodsum & MacMahon, Portland
207 772 1941
rgips@dwmlaw.com
*Featured in Native American Law (Nationwide)*
**Practice Areas:** National practice representing Indian tribal governments, authorities and enterprises, and businesses working with tribes, including lenders, investors and developers. Expertise in Indian gaming, complex business transactions, development projects and financings.
**Professional Memberships:** Maine Bar Association, Federal Bar Association. Listed in Best Lawyers in America and New England Super Lawyers for Native American law.
**Career:** Clerk, Chief Justice Robert Wilentz, New Jersey Supreme Court. Has focused on Native American law since 1983. Joined Drummond Woodsum as special counsel in 1999.
**Personal:** Yale Law School, JD 1982; Yale School of Management, MBA, 1982; Harvard College (cum laude) 1976.

### GITLIN, David
Greenberg Traurig, LLP, Philadelphia
215 988 7850
GitlinD@gtlaw.com
*Featured in Investment Funds (Nationwide), Corporate/M&A (Pennsylvania)*
**Practice Areas:** David Gitlin practices M&A, venture capital and technology development. He has an extensive practice representing foreign clients doing business in the United States and US clients doing business abroad. He has handled more than 200 M&A transactions, including over 100 cross-border transactions. His representation of US clients has included transactions in more than 15 countries. Mr Gitlin has handled more than 100 venture funding transactions representing both issuers and investors.
**Career:** Listed, Chambers USA, 2007-13.

**Personal:** LLM, with honors, University of Pennsylvania Law School, 1981; LLB, with honors, Tel Aviv University, Faculty of Law, 1979.

### GITOMER, Deborah
Fulbright & Jaworski LLP, Houston
713 651 3636
dgitomer@fulbright.com
*Featured in Energy & Natural Resources (Nationwide)*
**Practice Areas:** Oil, gas and energy transactions.
**Professional Memberships:** Houston Bar Association; State Bar of Texas.
**Career:** Deborah's practice is concentrated in transactions related to the acquisition and disposition of oil and gas reserves, pipelines, gas processing plants, refineries, petrochemical facilities and storage facilities, whether structured as asset or entity acquisitions, as well as joint ventures, partnerships and other joint ownership or participation arrangements in the oil, gas and energy areas.
**Personal:** BA, Trinity University (1979); JD, St. Mary's University (1982). She was admitted to practice in Texas in 1982.

### GIUFFRA JR, Robert J
Sullivan & Cromwell LLP, New York
212 558 3121
giuffrar@sullcrom.com
*Featured in Securities (Nationwide), Litigation (New York)*
**Practice Areas:** Head, Securities Litigation Practice. Member, Management Committee. Complex securities, white-collar, commercial, class-action, insurance, banking, tax litigation, including trials, arbitrations, appeals, investigations (SEC, DOJ, NYSE, IRS, Congress). Clients include leading financial institutions, industrial, technology, healthcare, real estate companies, hedge and private equity funds, corporate executives, lawyers, public officials.
**Career:** Partner since 1998. President, Federal Bar Council. Commissioner, 2008-2010, NYS Public Integrity and Ethics Commissions, 1998-2009. Chief Counsel, US Senate Banking Committee, 1995-1996. Clerk: Chief Justice William Rehnquist, US Supreme Court, 1988-1989; Judge Ralph Winter, US Ct. App., Second Circuit, 1987-1988.
**Personal:** Princeton (AB, 1983); Yale Law (JD, 1987).

### GLAD, Paul E B
Dentons, San Francisco
415 882 5001
paul.glad@dentons.com
*Featured in Insurance (Nationwide), Insurance (California)*
**Practice Areas:** Highly experienced litigator and head of Appellate practice. Successfully participated in over 60 published insurance related appellate cases. Matters include appellate law, insurance coverage issues, bad faith claims, class actions and insolvency issues. Frequent author and publisher including law reviews in Insurance Litigation Reporter and California Insurance Law and Regulation; and chapters in New Appleman

Insurance Law Practice Guide. Experienced Expert Witness.
**Personal:** UCLA Law School, JD; Stanford University, BA, with distinction.

### GLANCZ, Ronald R
Venable LLP, Washington, DC
202 344 4947
rglancz@Venable.com
*Featured in Financial Services Regulation (Nationwide)*
**Practice Areas:** Financial Services Group Chair, focuses on FDIC, OCC, Federal Reserve, CFPB and Treasury regulation, enforcement, directors' and officers' liability, Bank Secrecy Act compliance and fair lending.
**Professional Memberships:** Formerly Chancellor, Exchequer Club, Washington, DC; formerly Vice-Chair, Banking Law Committee, American Bar Association (Frank Simpson II Award).
**Career:** Assistant General Counsel and Acting Deputy General Counsel, Federal Deposit Insurance Corporation; Director, Litigation Division, Office of the Comptroller of the Currency; Assistant Director, Civil Division, US Department of Justice.
**Publications:** Published over 40 financial services regulation articles.
**Personal:** JD, University of Michigan Law School, 1968; BA, University of Michigan, 1964.

### GLAZER, Edward
Goodwin Procter LLP, Boston
617 570 1170
eglazer@goodwinprocter.com
*Featured in Capital Markets (Nationwide)*
**Practice Areas:** Mr Glazer specializes in structuring and implementing tax-oriented commercial transactions of all types, including real estate and venture capital transactions, mergers and acquisitions, pension investments in real estate involving issues of unrelated business taxable income, leveraged financings, and workout and debt restructurings. He regularly advises clients in structuring collective investment vehicles, in structuring real estate securitizations, in forming and operating public and private REITs and in forming real estate funds.
**Personal:** JD, Harvard Law School, 1971 (magna cum laude); BS, Wharton School of the University of Pennsylvania, 1968 (magna cum laude).

### GLAZER, Michael
Bingham McCutchen LLP, Los Angeles
213 680 6646
michael.glazer@bingham.com
*Featured in Investment Funds (Nationwide)*
**Practice Areas:** Represents investment advisers and companies in all aspects of their organization, registration, operation, acquisition and liquidation. Serves as counsel to independent directors of investment companies. Frequent lecturer on securities matters. Advises clients on situations such as manager acquisitions and terminations, complex reorganizations, regulatory investigations, fee challenges, and other litigation.

**Career:** Former chairman, Executive Committee of the Los Angeles County Bar Association, Business and Corporation Law Section.
**Personal:** UCLA School of Law, JD, 1967; Harvard University, MBA, 1964; Stanford University, BS, 1962.

### GLAZER, Michael H
Goodwin Procter LLP, Boston
617 570 1420
mglazer@goodwinprocter.com
*Featured in Real Estate (Nationwide), Real Estate (Massachusetts)*
See under Massachusetts for profile.

### GLEICHER, Brian
White & Case LLP, Washington, DC
202 626 3601
bgleicher@whitecase.com
*Featured in Tax (Nationwide)*
**Career:** Brian S. Gleicher focuses on international tax issues with an emphasis on transfer pricing and tax treaty issues. He routinely represents multinational companies in transfer pricing matters, including advance pricing agreements, with the Internal Revenue Service and foreign tax authorities. He also advises taxpayers on proceedings before the US and foreign Competent Authorities on a broad range of issues, including double taxation, residency and permanent establishment questions. To view a comprehensive biography, please visit www.whitecase.com/bgleicher.

### GLICK, Anna H.
Cadwalader, Wickersham & Taft LLP, New York
212 504 6309
anna.glick@cwt.com
*Featured in Capital Markets (Nationwide)*
**Practice Areas:** Concentrates in securitization of commercial mortgage loans, structuring mezzanine debt and other financings of mortgage-related assets, federal securities laws issues particular to securitizations, compliance issues, registration of public securities, and financings matters. Represents issuers, underwriters and institutional investors active in the primary and secondary capital markets, and special servicers and others in advising regarding legacy securitizations and distressed assets.
**Personal:** JD, New York University School of Law (Member, Law Review and Order of the Coif); BA, Brooklyn College.

### GLICKSTEIN, Steven
Kaye Scholer LLP, New York
212 836 8485
steven.glickstein@kayescholer.com
*Featured in Products Liability (Nationwide)*
**Practice Areas:** Steven Glickstein, formerly Chair of the firm's Product Liability Group, has over 36 years experience in product liability mass torts and class actions. He has been national counsel in a number of high-profile cases involving pharmaceuticals (Rezulin, Viagra, Trovan and hormone therapy), medical devices (heart valves, penile prostheses, hip implants, incontinence devices and stents), blood products (Sandoglobulin), agricultural pesticides

(Galecron), construction materials (Chinese dry-wall), and fire alarms (San Juan Dupont Plaza hotel fire).

**Professional Memberships:** Board of Editors, Product Liability Law and Strategy; American Bar Association (formerly Co-Chair of Class Action Subcommittee, Product Liability Committee, Litigation Section).

### GOEBEL, Teresa
Goodwin Procter LLP, San Francisco
415 733 6052
TGoebel@goodwinprocter.com
*Featured in Leisure & Hospitality (Nationwide)*
**Practice Areas:** Ms Goebel's practice encompasses a broad range of commercial real estate matters, including hotel transactions, joint ventures, financings and real property sales and acquisitions. She represents hotel operators and investors in acquisitions, development, financing, management and sales of hotel, resort and fractional ownership properties. She negotiates, structures and documents management agreements and equity and debt investments for hotels, resorts and other mixed use hospitality projects from New York City to Paris to Macau.
**Personal:** JD, The University of Chicago Law School, 1999 (high honors, Order of the Coif); AB, Brown University, 1994 (magna cum laude, Phi Beta Kappa).

### GOETZ, John D.
Jones Day, Pittsburgh
412 394 7911
jdgoetz@jonesday.com
*Featured in Transportation (Nationwide)*
**Practice Areas:** John Goetz is a first-chair trial lawyer with more than 20 years of experience defending companies in business, tort, and aviation litigation. As a licensed pilot, he leads Jones Day's airlines and aviation industry practice. John is also a recognized authority in transportation litigation.
**Career:** He has represented multinational companies such as Doncasters, Parker Hannifin, Penske Automotive, Pilatus Aircraft, R.J. Reynolds, Textron, U. S. Steel, and Yamaha in trial and appellate courts across the US and in Canada.
**Publications:** John has published articles on litigation strategy, and is a frequent speaker at aviation and other seminars.

### GOFFMAN, Jay M
Skadden, Arps, Slate, Meagher & Flom LLP & Affiliates, New York
212 735 2120
Jay.Goffman@skadden.com
*Featured in Bankruptcy/Restructuring (Nationwide),*
*Bankruptcy/Restructuring (New York)*
**Practice Areas:** Global leader of Skadden's Corporate Restructuring Group. Has led numerous multi-billion-dollar, high-profile and record-setting out-of-court, prepackaged, prearranged and traditional Chapter 11 restructurings worldwide. Numerous awards including: one of the five Most Influential Restructuring Lawyers of the Past Decade (National Law Journal), one of the Most Innovative Lawyers in the World (Financial Times), and a Dealmaker of the Year (American

Lawyer). Internationally recognized as a pioneer in prepackaged restructurings and as a leader in the field.
**Career:** JD with Honors, University of North Carolina, 1983 (Law Review); BS, SUNY Binghamton, 1980.

### GOLD, Martin
Covington & Burling LLP, Washington, DC
202 662 5405
mgold@cov.com
*Featured in Government (Nationwide)*
**Practice Areas:** Martin Gold co-chairs Covington's Government Affairs practice. He has forty years of legislative experience, in government and the private sector. He is a leading expert on congressional procedures. He has presented hundreds of seminars on Senate rules and practices for Congressional, academic, and private sector audiences.
**Career:** Floor Counsel to Majority Leader Bill Frist and Majority Leader Howard Baker. Counsel to Senator Mark Hatfield.
**Publications:** Author, Senate Procedure and Practice (2004, 2008); The Grand Institution: A Profile of the United States Senate (2011); Forbidden Citizens: Chinese Exclusion and the US Congress (2012).
**Personal:** American University, JD, MPA, BA.

### GOLD, Richard M
Holland & Knight LLP, Washington, DC
202 955 3000
rich.gold@hklaw.com
*Featured in Government (Nationwide)*
**Practice Areas:** Leader of the firm's Public Policy & Regulation Practice Group, practices in the areas of legislative and environmental law, emphasizing strategy development, lobbying, and legislative and regulatory counseling. Gold leads the firm's Federal Funding Team which has been successful in achieving federal funding for a wide variety of projects ranging from biotechnology research to major transportation and environmental infrastructure projects. He has been significantly involved in all major environmental and energy legislation before Congress over the last 20 years and has played a central advocacy role for manufacturing clients on significant regulations before the US Environmental Protection Agency.

### GOLDBERG, Michael S
Baker Botts LLP, Houston
713 229 1401
michael.goldberg@bakerbotts.com
*Featured in International Arbitration (Nationwide)*
**Practice Areas:** Senior Litigation Partner. Co-Chair of firm's International Dispute Resolution Practice.
**Career:** Recent representative matters include claims in excess of $100 billion before arbitral panels constituted under the ICC, LCIA, AAA, ZCC, PCA and SCC. His practice includes both investor-State and commercial disputes in areas including construction, energy, environmental, finance, joint venture and tax. Frequent international dispute resolution presenter at conferences and commentator in national publications.

Featured in the cover story of Focus Europe (Summer 2007).
**Personal:** JD (with honors), University of Texas, 1982; BA (magna cum laude and Phi Beta Kappa), Rice University, 1979. Adjunct International Arbitration Professor.

### GOLDBERG, Stephen
Dickstein Shapiro LLP, Los Angeles
310 772 8325
goldbergs@dicksteinshapiro.com
*Featured in Insurance (Nationwide), Insurance (California)*
**Practice Areas:** Represents insureds in a wide range of matters, including claims involving bad faith; first party business interruption and property damage losses; D&O; E&O; asbestos; environmental; and product liabilities in litigations ranging into the billions of dollars. He represented the lender to the World Trade Center lessee in the property damage and business interruption lawsuits following 9/11.
**Professional Memberships:** ABA (Torts/Insurance Practice Section; Litigation Section; Litigation Section's Committee on Insurance Coverage Litigation); State Bar of California.
**Personal:** Yale Law School (JD, 1970); University of Michigan (BA, cum laude, 1967).

### GOLDBERG JR, Fred T
Skadden, Arps, Slate, Meagher & Flom LLP & Affiliates, Washington, DC
202 371 7110
Fred.Goldberg@skadden.com
*Featured in Tax (District of Columbia), Tax (Nationwide)*
**Practice Areas:** Co-head of the firm's Tax Group and global co-chair of the firm's Diversity Committee. Advises clients as special tax counsel on sensitive matters, and represents clients on tax controversies and administrative and regulatory proceedings before the Internal Revenue Service (IRS) and US Department of Treasury. Has directed compliance and management reviews on behalf of senior executives and boards of directors. Clients include businesses, tax-exempt organizations and individuals.
**Career:** Assistant Secretary for Tax Policy, US Department of the Treasury (1992); IRS Commissioner (1989-92); IRS Chief Counsel (1984-86). JD, Yale University, 1973; BA, Yale University, 1969.

### GOLDEN, Adam
Kaye Scholer LLP, New York
212 836 8673
adam.golden@kayescholer.com
*Featured in Life Sciences (Nationwide)*
**Practice Areas:** Adam Golden is Co-Chair of Kaye Scholer's Corporate Department and Head of the Life Sciences Transactions group. His practice focuses on mergers and acquisitions, securities offerings, intellectual property licenses, joint ventures and other corporate partnering transactions. He has represented companies in the pharmaceutical and biotechnology, private equity, infrastructure, chemicals, consumer products, technology, software, healthcare services, medical devices, defense, finance and alternative asset management

industries. His practice is international in scope and clients range in size from multibillion-dollar global businesses to emerging-stage companies.

### GOLDEN, Daniel H
Akin Gump Strauss Hauer & Feld LLP, New York
212 872 8010
dgolden@akingump.com
*Featured in Bankruptcy/Restructuring (Nationwide), Bankruptcy/Restructuring (New York)*
**Practice Areas:** Daniel Golden's practice primarily consists of representing creditors' committees and bondholder committees in large, complex out-of-court restructurings and Chapter 11 cases. He served as lead committee counsel in numerous high profile restructurings and Chapter 11 cases, including WorldCom, Delta Air Lines, Chemtura, TOUSA Homes, Loral Space & Communications, Solutia Inc. and XO Communications. Most recently he has led the restructuring effort in the Lyondell Chemical Chapter 11 cases on behalf of Apollo. He is also a frequent lecturer on bankruptcy/restructuring issues.
**Personal:** BA, University of Wisconsin-Madison; JD, SUNY at Buffalo Law School.

### GOLDFEIN, Shepard
Skadden, Arps, Slate, Meagher & Flom LLP & Affiliates, New York
212 735 3610
Shepard.Goldfein@skadden.com
*Featured in Antitrust (New York), Sports Law (Nationwide)*
**Practice Areas:** Global practice leader, Competition Group. Handles a variety of litigation from antitrust class actions to antitrust criminal investigations. Advises on antitrust issues (compliance programs and antitrust patent licensing issues), and counsels and litigates professional sports league issues (team ownership transfers, collective bargaining, team relocation and intellectual property).
**Professional Memberships:** Chairman, Sports Law Committee, Association of the Bar of the City of NY (1996-99).
**Career:** JD, Rutgers University, 1975 (editor, Rutgers Law Review); MA, Political Science, University of Chicago, 1977; AB, Rutgers University, 1970 (Phi Beta Kappa).
**Publications:** Co-author, monthly trade regulation column, New York Law Journal (1983-present).

### GOLDMAN, Geoffrey B
Shearman & Sterling LLP, New York
212 848 4867
geoffrey.goldman@shearman.com
*Featured in Capital Markets (Nationwide)*
**Practice Areas:** Geoff Goldman focuses on derivatives and structured products, with extensive experience structuring and documenting over-the-counter derivative transactions, particularly credit and equity derivatives. He represents clearinghouses and other infrastructure providers for derivative transactions as well as industry groups in developing industry-standard documentation for derivative products. Mr Goldman advises on commodities, securities and other reg-

ulatory issues related to derivative products and has advised on structuring public and private commodity pools. He also represents issuers and underwriters of synthetic and cash-flow collateralized debt obligation transactions.
**Career:** Bar Admission: New York, 1997. Partner since 2008.
**Personal:** Attended Columbia Law School, Stanford University.

### GOLDMAN, Michael P
Sidley Austin LLP, Chicago
312 853 4665
mgoldman@sidley.com
*Featured in Insurance (Nationwide), Insurance (Illinois)*
See under Illinois for profile.

### GOLDMAN, Michael S
Cravath, Swaine & Moore LLP, New York
212 474 1929
mgoldman@cravath.com
*Featured in Banking & Finance (Nationwide)*
**Practice Areas:** Michael S. Goldman is a partner in Cravath's Corporate Department and serves as the Leader of its Commercial Banking practice. His practice includes complex syndicated loan transactions, acquisition and leveraged finance, asset-based lending and securities offerings for both US and international clients.
**Personal:** Fordham University School of Law (JD, cum laude, 1987; Member, Law Review); University of Pennsylvania (BA, cum laude, 1984). For more information:
http://www.cravath.com/mgoldman

### GOLDMAN, Richard A
Bingham McCutchen LLP, Boston
617 951 8851
rich.goldman@bingham.com
*Featured in Investment Funds (Nationwide), Investment Funds (Massachusetts)*
See under Massachusetts for profile.

### GOLDMAN, William L
McDermott Will & Emery LLP, Washington, DC
202 756 8305
wgoldman@mwe.com
*Featured in Tax (Nationwide)*
**Practice Areas:** Practices in federal and state tax controversy matters, including administrative representation and litigation. Has emphasized appellate litigation, and argued more than 50 cases in courts of appeals, including federal circuit courts, state supreme courts, and the US Supreme Court. Handled a range of corporate issues, including valuation issues and worked extensively on unitary tax issues, including the taxation of payments from unitary subsidiaries and the state tax implications of the federal tax provisions applicable to multi corporate groups.
**Personal:** Harvard Law School (LLB, cum laude); Cornell University, (BA).

### GOLDSCHMIDT, David J
Skadden, Arps, Slate, Meagher & Flom LLP & Affiliates, New York
212 735 3574
David.Goldschmidt@skadden.com
*Featured in Capital Markets (Nationwide)*

**Practice Areas:** Represents investment banks and companies in a wide variety of financing matters, including IPOs and other public and private offerings of equity and debt securities. Active in representing and advising REITs. Extensive experience with technology companies, including Israeli companies, and industrial companies. Also advises private equity firms and their portfolio companies in financing and other matters. Involved in developing new products, such as hybrid securities. Regularly advises on corporate governance and general corporate matters.
**Career:** JD, New York University School of Law, 1987 (Member, Review of Law and Social Change); BA, New York University, 1984 (magna cum laude).

### GOLDSMITH, Barry
Gibson, Dunn & Crutcher LLP, New York
212 351 2440
BGoldsmith@gibsondunn.com
*Featured in Securities (Nationwide)*
**Practice Areas:** Co-Chair Securities Enforcement Practice Group. Represents broker-dealers, corporations, hedge funds, investment advisers, and individuals in government enforcement investigations and related litigation. Conducts internal investigations and advises clients, including boards and audit committees, on a broad range of regulatory and compliance issues and risk strategies.
**Career:** Formerly EVP and Head of Enforcement NASD (now FINRA); SEC Chief Litigation Counsel, in charge of all SEC enforcement litigation nationwide.
**Publications:** Authored numerous articles on securities and regulatory enforcement; frequent chair/speaker at industry conferences.
**Personal:** JD, Georgetown University; BSE (Magna Cum Laude), Wharton School of Finance and Commerce, University of Pennsylvania.

### GOLDSTEIN, David A
DLA Piper LLP (US), New York
212 335 4570
david.goldstein@dlapiper.com
*Featured in Investment Funds (Nationwide)*
**Practice Areas:** Investment Funds.
**Career:** He focuses on the establishment and representation of private investment funds including both domestic and international private equity and hedge funds. He represents merchant banking and LBO funds, real estate opportunity and value funds, international real estate funds and emerging markets funds with management teams around the world. He helps managers create investment products and platforms and has structured and closed numerous seed and stake deals.
**Personal:** JD, New York University School of Law; MS, Accounting, State University of New York at Binghamton; BS, State University of New York at Oneonta.

### GOLDSTEIN, Marcia
Weil, Gotshal & Manges LLP, New York
212 310 8214
marcia.goldstein@weil.com
*Featured in Bankruptcy/Restructuring (Nationwide), Bankruptcy/Restructuring (New York)*

**Practice Areas:** Chair of the Business Finance and Restructuring Department. Practice encompasses all aspects of domestic and international debt restructurings, crisis management and corporate governance. Ms Goldstein is currently counsel for RDA Holding, the Special Administrators of MF Global UK, and Citibank and Barclays as arrangers for a debtor-in-possession facility for Patriot Coal. Recent representations include: AIG on various aspects of their restructuring; lead counsel for General Growth Properties, and Extended Stay Hotels. She also counsels hedge funds, private equity funds, financial institutions and other creditors in connection with major restructurings.
**Personal:** Cornell Law School (AB); Cornell University (JD).

### GOLDSTEIN, Maura
Baker Botts LLP, Washington, DC
202 639 7720
maura.goldstein@bakerbotts.com
*Featured in Projects (Nationwide)*
**Practice Areas:** Project development and finance.
**Professional Memberships:** District of Columbia Bar, New York State Bar.
**Career:** Represents sponsors and lenders on development and financing of energy and transportation infrastructure projects worldwide, with particular experience in the power (renewables, gas and coal fired power plants and energy storage projects), rail and road PPP, and LNG sectors. Extensive experience in structuring equity and debt investment in limited and non-recourse project entities and in negotiation of power purchase agreements and other offtake, tolling and availability arrangements.
**Personal:** JD, University of Virginia School of Law, 1995; BA, economics, international studies, American University, 1986.

### GOLDSTEIN, Stuart N
Cadwalader, Wickersham & Taft LLP, Charlotte
704 348 5258
stuart.goldstein@cwt.com
*Featured in Capital Markets (Nationwide)*
**Practice Areas:** Concentrates in asset securitization, structured products, and fund formation, representing issuers, underwriters, collateral managers, and institutional investors in public and private transactions; fund managers in structuring, organising and financing hedge funds, debt and opportunity funds, funds of funds, and other investment vehicles; and parties in developing, negotiating, and documenting financial products. Experience in analyzing and structuring asset- and mortgage-backed securities, CDOs, and other instruments; structuring transactions involving interest rate swaps, caps, floors and other derivative instruments; and work-outs of non-performing commercial mortgage loans in CMBS transactions. Represents clients in the purchase and sale of commercial and multifamily mortgage loans, mezzanine debt, subordinate debt, and residential first- and second- mortgage loans in whole loan and participation structures.

**Professional Memberships:** Member, American Bar Association; New York State Bar Association.
**Personal:** JD, Boalt Hall School of Law, University of California at Berkeley; BS, Cornell University.

### GOLUMBIC, Lars
Groom Law Group, Washington, DC
202 861 6615
lgolumbic@groom.com
*Featured in ERISA Litigation (Nationwide)*
**Practice Areas:** Represents plan fiduciaries with respect to ERISA litigation, preemption, and fiduciary issues, as well as Department of Labor and Internal Revenue Service investigations. Also represents plan fiduciaries on matters related to plan funding, withdrawal liability, and termination.
**Publications:** Writes and speaks frequently on ERISA employer stock and 401(k) issues and service provider litigation.
**Personal:** Judicial Clerk, Honorable Robert G Doumar, US District Court for the Eastern District of Virginia, 1998-99; JD, University of Pennsylvania, 1998; MA, University of North Carolina, 1994; BA, Phi Beta Kappa, Northwestern University, 1990.

### GONZALES O'KELLY, Cathy
Vedder Price PC, Chicago
312 609 7657
cokelly@vedderprice.com
*Featured in Investment Funds (Nationwide)*
**Practice Areas:** Shareholder, member of the firm's Board of Directors and Investment Services group. Represents mutual funds and their boards, money managers, broker-dealers, banks, insurance companies and other financial institutions regarding investment company, investment adviser, broker-dealer and insurance product matters.
**Professional Memberships:** Member, Chicago Bar Association; Trustee, John Marshall Law School and College of William and Mary Foundation.
**Career:** Admitted (IL) 1989; District of Columbia, 1978; Virginia, 1978.
**Publications:** Co-author of "Soft Dollars and Other Traps for the Investment Adviser: An Analysis of Brokerage Placement Practices," DePaul Business Journal.
**Personal:** JD University of Virginia; AB, College of William and Mary.

### GOOD, John A
Bass, Berry & Sims PLC, Memphis
901 543 5901
jgood@bassberry.com
*Featured in Corporate/M&A (Tennessee), Capital Markets (Nationwide)*
**Practice Areas:** Focuses on securities offerings and other corporate finance matters, mergers and acquisitions, corporate governance and counseling boards of directors of public companies, as well as representing underwriters in public securities offerings. Primary industry emphases are REITs and business development companies.
**Professional Memberships:** American Bar Association (Business Law Section, Corporate Governance Committee, Federal Regulation of

Securities Committee and Securities Registration Subcommittee); National Association of Real Estate Investment Trusts (Government Relations Committee).

**Career:** Joined firm in 1999 as Founding Managing Partner, Memphis office.

**Personal:** BBA (1980), magna cum laude, University of Memphis; JD with honors (1987), University of Memphis.

### GOODE, Jason
Alston & Bird LLP, Atlanta
404 881 7986
jason.goode@alston.com
*Featured in Capital Markets (Nationwide)*

**Practice Areas:** Public and private securities offerings, mergers and acquisitions, corporate governance, securities law compliance and other complex business transactions. Member of firm's REIT team and represents numerous REITs and real estate funds.

**Professional Memberships:** Member of NAREIT, the Legal Committee of the Investment Program Association (IPA); the Southern Capital Forum and ACG.

**Career:** Frequent speaker on securities and corporate governance issues.

**Personal:** AB, Duke University; JD, Duke University School of Law.

### GOODELL JR, Charles P
Goodell, DeVries, Leech & Dann, LLP, Baltimore
410 783 4001
cpg@gdldlaw.com
*Featured in Products Liability (Nationwide)*

**Practice Areas:** Mr Goodell has 40 years of experience in litigation and litigation management on a national, regional and local level. He has counseled clients on various aspects of individual and mass litigation. He has served as National Counsel on matters such as pacemaker leads, tainted blood products used by hemophiliacs, statins for treatment of cholesterol, PPA and lung injuries claimed from talc. He has been a member of national trial teams for companies making drugs to treat diabetes, heart valves, COX-2 pain medications and hormone replacement therapy. He has tried complex pharmaceutical and other cases in various jurisdiction in the US, including Florida, Pennsylvania, Missouri, Maryland, Rhode Island and Indiana. He has also served as Regional Counsel in the southeast, the midwest and the mid-Atlantic US for litigation involving contraception, diabetes medication and hormone replacement therapy. His representative clients include Pfizer Inc, Bayer Corporation and Wyeth.

**Professional Memberships:** Fellow of the American College of Trial Lawyers (ACTL); American Bar Association; Advocate, National Board of Trial Advocates; Maryland State Bar Association; Federal Bar Association; Defense Research Institute(DRI); National Institute of Trial Advocacy; Product Liability Advisory Council (PLAC); International Association of Defense Counsel (IADC).

**Career:** Goodell, DeVries, Leech & Dann, LLP, 1988-present. One of the founding partners of law firm devoted to representation of clients in litigation and litigation management. Semmes, Bowen & Semmes, 1972-88, Partner and Associate in Litigation Department of large, full-service law firm.

**Publications:** "Keys to Winning" Network of Trial Law Firms, 2003: 'Preventing Litigation'; Network of Trial Law Firms, 2003: 'Lesson for Mass Tort Litigation'; Judicial Institute of Maryland, 1995: 'Theories of Recovery and Proof of Causation in Cases Involving Exposure to Hazardous Substances'; Defense Research Institute, February 1994: 'Electromagnetic Fields'; Defense Research Institute, May 1993: 'The Concept of Acceptable Risk'; Defense Research Institute, November 1992: Maryland Judicial Institute, 1991: 'Warnings in Product Liability'; Regulatory Affairs Professional Society Annual Meeting, 1989: 'Products Liability'; Defense Research Institute 1988 Product Liability Seminar: 'Recalls in Products Liability'.

**Personal:** Johns Hopkins University (BA, 1969); George Washington University (JD, with Honors, 1972).

### GOODISON, Eric
Paul, Weiss, Rifkind, Wharton & Garrison LLP, New York
212 373 3292
egoodison@paulweiss.com
*Featured in Banking & Finance (Nationwide)*

**Practice Areas:** Partner in the Corporate Department and member of the firm's Finance Practice. Represents domestic and international clients in their borrowing and lending and other financing transactions. Has significant experience in structuring, negotiating and consummating leveraged financings for borrowers across many industries, with particular strength in complex leveraged transactions. Eric has also recently been advising clients across the spectrum of investors and borrowers in dealing with the opportunities and risks in the robust leverage markets inspired by the global search for yield.

### GOODMAN, Amy
Gibson, Dunn & Crutcher LLP, Washington, DC
202 955 8653
AGoodman@gibsondunn.com
*Featured in Securities (Nationwide)*

**Practice Areas:** Co-chair of the Securities Regulation and Corporate Governance practice, she advises on securities law disclosure and regulatory issues and corporate governance matters, including representing board committees.

**Professional Memberships:** Former President, Association of SEC Alumni; former chair ABA Committee on Director & Officer Liability and Subcommittee on Shareholder & Investor Relations.

**Career:** Former Associate Director and Chief of the Office of Disclosure Policy SEC Division of Corporation Finance, Legal Assistant and Special Counsel to SEC Chairman Harold Williams.

**Publications:** Editor-in-Chief of INSIGHTS and numerous treatises; frequent speaker.

**Personal:** JD, cum laude, Boston University Law School; LLM, Georgetown University Law Center.

### GOODMAN, Jeffrey H
Fulbright & Jaworski LLP, Washington, DC
202 662 4730
jgoodman@fulbright.com
*Featured in Projects (Nationwide)*

**Practice Areas:** Global infrastructure, structured and project finance, energy, banking and business, real estate, joint ventures, construction.

**Professional Memberships:** American Bar Association; District of Columbia Bar; International Bar Association.

**Career:** Goodman heads the Energy and Real Property Department in the Washington office. His practice focuses on international project finance, including projects relating to power, renewable energy, oil and gas, manufacturing, ports, water, transportation, banking and commercial real estate as well as on various domestic project developments, including a downtown sports arena in Washington, D.C.

**Personal:** JD, with honors, University of Michigan Law School (1979); BA, cum laude, Amherst College (1974).

### GOODMAN, Ronald
Foley Hoag LLP, Washington, DC
202 261 7372
rgoodman@foleyhoag.com
*Featured in International Arbitration (Nationwide)*

**Practice Areas:** Dr Ronald Goodman is a partner in the firm's Washington office and co-chairs the firm's international litigation and arbitration practice. His practice in international arbitration is focused on commercial, investor-state and commercial matters. He represents clients in ICSID, ICSID Additional Facility, ICC, LCIA, AAA, UNCITRAL and other fora. He is a member of the ICC Task Force for the Revision of the Arbitration Rules and is admitted to the Bars of New York, Washington, D.C., the US Court of International Trade, various US federal district courts and courts of appeal, and the Paris Bar (not currently on the Roll). He is also an Adjunct Professor of Law at American University Law School, where he teaches Investor-State Dispute Resolution.

**Personal:** Cornell University, BA, cum laude; Princeton University, PhD; Columbia University, JD.

### GOODMAN III, Will
Watkins & Eager PLLC, Jackson
601 965 1998
wgoodman@watkinseager.com
*Featured in Products Liability (Nationwide), Litigation (Mississippi)*

**Practice Areas:** Represents pharmaceutical and chemical companies in complex commercial and personal injury litigations.

**Professional Memberships:** Mississippi Bar; American Bar Association; International Association of Defense Counsel; Defense Research Institute.

**Career:** State, regional, and national trial counsel; admitted pro hac vice in numerous states; Best Lawyers in America (2012, Commercial Litigation, Mass Tort Litigation, and Product Liability Litigation); Mid-South Super Lawyers (2012, Class Action/Mass Torts); The International Who's Who of Product Liability Defense Lawyers, 2012; 2012 Benchmark Litigation.

**Personal:** Millsaps College (BA, cum laude, 1974); University of Mississippi (JD, 1977).

### GOODWIN, David B
Covington & Burling LLP, San Francisco
415 591 7074
dgoodwin@cov.com
*Featured in Insurance (Nationwide), Insurance (California)*

**Practice Areas:** Represents policyholders in all types of insurance disputes, including major errors and omissions, fidelity, and D&O claims, property and business interruption losses, mortgage and financial guarantee insurance, and products liability and environmental matters. Also assists clients in insurance claims and underwriting disputes. Clients include BP, LyondellBasell Industries, UnitedHealth, and Wells Fargo.

**Publications:** Chapter on insurance in McCarthy on Trademarks and Unfair Competition, chapter on property insurance in Appleman on Insurance, chapter on business interruption insurance in the CEB property insurance treatise.

**Personal:** JD, Stanford Law School, 1982; BA, Oxford University, 1976. Taught insurance law at Berkeley Law School.

### GOODWIN, Michael
Arnold & Porter LLP, Washington, DC
202 942 5558
Michael.Goodwin@aporter.com
*Featured in Leisure & Hospitality (Nationwide), Real Estate (District of Columbia)*

See under District of Columbia for profile.

### GOOLSBY, Bryan L
Locke Lord LLP, Dallas
214 740 8550
bgoolsby@lockelord.com
*Featured in Capital Markets (Nationwide)*

**Practice Areas:** Chairs Firm's Real Estate Investment Trust Practice Group and Finance Committee. Facilitates debt and equity offerings on behalf of REITs. Represents boards and board committees, corporations and underwriters in public and private offerings of debt and equity securities, and purchasers and sellers of both public and private entities.

**Professional Memberships:** NAREIT (Associate Member, Board of Governors); Pension Real Estate Association; ABA; Certified Public Accountant-Texas.

**Career:** Serves as Executive Chairman of the Firm. Partner since 1984.

**Personal:** The University of Texas School of Law (JD, with honors, 1977); Texas Tech University (BBA, with honors, 1973).

**GORDON, David A**
Latham & Watkins LLP, New York
212 906 1251
david.gordon@lw.com
*Featured in Projects (Nationwide)*
**Practice Areas:** Represents banks, financial institutions, private equity and other private companies in all phases of the development, purchase, sale, financing and restructuring of energy, telecommunications and other infrastructure and industrial projects. Practices extensively in the development, financing and restructuring of private power projects, including fossil fuel-fired power projects, biomass projects, municipal solid waste projects and other alternative energy projects. Activities include the structuring of projects and the related financing, due diligence and coordination and negotiation of project and financing agreements.
**Career:** Qualified since 1986. Former Managing Partner of Latham's New York office.

**GORDON, Eric B**
McDermott Will & Emery LLP, Los Angeles
310 551 9315
egordon@mwe.com
*Featured in Healthcare (California), Healthcare (Nationwide)*
See under California for profile.

**GORELICK, Jamie**
WilmerHale, Washington, DC
202 663 6500
jamie.gorelick@wilmerhale.com
*Featured in Government (Nationwide)*
**Practice Areas:** Chair, Defense, National Security and Government Contracts Practice. A litigator whose career has spanned the legal, policy and corporate landscape. Represents diverse interests in complex civil and criminal litigation, internal corporate investigations and counsels on issues at the intersection of law, policy and governance.
**Professional Memberships:** Co-Chair of the American Bar Association's Commission on Legal Ethics 20/20.
**Career:** Deputy Attorney General, US Department of Justice; General Counsel, US Department of Defense; Member of 9/11 Commission; special assistant to Secretary of Energy; Vice-Chair, Fannie Mae.
**Personal:** Harvard School of Law (JD 1975); Harvard University (BA 1972).

**GOURLEY, Sara J**
Sidley Austin LLP, Chicago
312 853 7694
sgourley@sidley.com
*Featured in Products Liability (Nationwide)*
**Practice Areas:** Partner in Sidley's Chicago office and member of the Firm's Executive Committee. She has substantial experience in pharmaceutical, medical device, and blood products liability litigation. Her practice is concentrated in pharmaceutical and medical device defense, especially multi-jurisdictional coordination and defense of class actions. She is national counsel for a producer of blood products in AIDS and Hepatitis C litigation and national counsel for a

major pharmaceutical company defending a widely-used diabetes medication.
**Personal:** University of Illinois College of Law, JD, 1980, Law Review, 1978-80; Ripon College, AB, 1977, cum laude, with honors in English. Admission: Illinois.

**GOWAN, Thomas W**
Skadden, Arps, Slate, Meagher & Flom LLP & Affiliates, New York
212 735 2444
thomas.gowan@skadden.com
*Featured in Sports Law (Nationwide)*
**Practice Areas:** Tom Gowan is a corporate and bank finance lawyer concentrating in commercial financings, workouts and restructurings, private equity and sports. His sports experience includes ownership transfers, team and league financings, and licensing and sponsorship arrangements. He has represented sponsors, corporate borrowers and financial institutions in secured and unsecured financings; corporate recapitalizations; and acquisition, tender offer and leveraged financings. He has represented corporate borrowers and institutional lenders in connection with prebankruptcy workouts and debtor-in-possession and Chapter 11 exit financings.
**Career:** JD, New York University School of Law, 1991 (cum laude); B.S., Fordham University, 1986 (summa cum laude).

**GRABAR, Nicolas**
Cleary Gottlieb Steen & Hamilton LLP, New York
212 225 2414
ngrabar@cgsh.com
*Featured in Latin American Investment (New York), Capital Markets (Nationwide)*
See under New York for profile.

**GRAFTON, Susan**
K&L Gates, Washington, DC
202 778 9498
susan.grafton@klgates.com
*Featured in Financial Services Regulation (Nationwide)*
**Practice Areas:** K. Susan Grafton advises broker-dealers and investment advisers on a broad range of registration, business, and regulatory issues. She assists clients in registering with the Securities and Exchange Commission and the states, and becoming members of the Financial Industry Regulatory Authority. She also counsels clients on a wide variety of sales, trading, financial and operational compliance issues. In addition, Ms Grafton represents clients in SEC and self-regulatory organization examinations, investigations and enforcement matters. She also counsels clients and advocates their views on legislation and rule-making. Ms Grafton is a prior chair of the ABA's Trading and Markets Subcommittee.

**GRAHAM, Daniel P**
Wiley Rein LLP, Washington, DC
202 719 7433
dgraham@wileyrein.com
*Featured in Government (Nationwide)*
**Practice Areas:** Counsels government contractors on bid protests; claims preparation/litigation; subcontracts/teaming agreements; mergers &

acquisitions; compliance with ethics, conflict of interest and procurement integrity laws; internal investigations; and suspension/debarment.
**Professional Memberships:** Council Member, ABA Section of Public Contract Law; Co-Chair, ABA Health Care Contracting Committee; Board of Governors, Federal Circuit Bar Association; Associate Editor, Public Contract Law Journal.
**Career:** Adjunct Professor, George Mason University School of Law; Law clerk, US Court of Appeals, Third Circuit (Smith) & Court of Federal Claims (Miller).
**Personal:** William & Mary School of Law (JD; Order of the Coif); Johns Hopkins University (BA).

**GRALA, Bronislaw E**
Cadwalader, Wickersham & Taft LLP, New York
212 504 6466
bronislaw.grala@cwt.com
*Featured in Employee Benefits & Executive Compensation (Nationwide), Employee Benefits & Executive Compensation (New York)*
**Practice Areas:** Focuses on ERISA and other employee benefit matters, particularly ERISA fiduciary responsibilities and obligations, including the ERISA and tax implications of various plan investments and investment formats. Serves as ERISA counsel to third-party plan asset managers, broker-dealers, investment bankers and others seeking to provide services, or develop and sell investment products, to employee benefit plans. Extensive experience in dealings with the Employee Benefits Security Administration in the US Department of Labor.
**Professional Memberships:** New York State Bar Association (Section on Taxation); Association of the Bar of the City of New York; Charter Fellow, American College of Employee Benefits Counsel.
**Publications:** Frequent public speaker and author of numerous articles and publications.
**Personal:** JD, New York University School of Law (cum laude) (Editor, NYU Law Review; Member, the Order of the Coif and Founder's Day Scholar); BA, Fordham University (cum laude).

**GRANT, Stuart M**
Grant & Eisenhofer PA, Wilmington
302 622 7070
sgrant@gelaw.com
*Featured in Securities (Nationwide), Chancery (Delaware), Litigation (New York)*
See under Delaware for profile.

**GRASSO, Jeanne**
Blank Rome LLP, Washington, DC
202 772 5927
Grasso@BlankRome.com
*Featured in Transportation (Nationwide)*
**Practice Areas:** Jeanne Grasso focuses her practice on maritime, international, and environmental law, counseling vessel owners and operators, charterers, and facilities. Her practice involves: regulatory compliance counseling related to the US Coast Guard, EPA, US Customs and Border Protection, and Maritime Administration, among other agencies. Jeanne handles internal and grand

jury investigations and defense of administrative, civil, and criminal enforcement actions; counsels clients on risk mitigation strategies related to pollution incidents; advises on environmental compliance, pollution incident response, and coastwise trade; and conducts training seminars. She is also involved with identifying administrative and legislative solutions to industry compliance challenges. www.BlankRome.com/Grasso

**GRAY, Elizabeth P.**
Willkie Farr & Gallagher LLP, Washington, DC
202 303 1207
egray@willkie.com
*Featured in Securities (Nationwide)*
**Practice Areas:** Partner, Litigation Department. Represents international accounting firms and their partners, public companies and their directors, hedge funds, broker-dealers and other institutions and individuals in connection with securities law enforcement, compliance and litigation. Represents clients before SEC, PCAOB, FINRA and DOJ. Extensive experience handling matters arising under federal securities laws, including internal investigations, defense of potential accounting and auditing irregularities, FCPA violations, market manipulation and insider trading. Advises clients with respect to corporate governance and compliance programs, and has expertise in counseling Indian companies.
**Personal:** JD, University of Virginia School of Law, 1983. AB, Dartmouth College, 1980. See: http://www.willkie.com/ElizabethGray.

**GRAY, William**
Ashurst, New York
212 205 7010
william.gray@ashurst.com
*Featured in Capital Markets (Nationwide)*
**Practice Areas:** Bill is Head of the US Offices and a partner in the Securities and Derivatives Group in New York. His practice covers credit and equity derivatives and derivative products, credit-and equity-linked notes, repackagings, structured credit (cash and synthetic CLOs), structured products and structured financings involving numerous asset classes. In addition, Bill advises on regulatory matters relating to these and other activities engaged in by banks, financial institutions and end users.
**Personal:** Bill attended the University of Pennsylvania Law School (JD cum laude) and Dartmouth College (AB summa cum laude).

**GRAZIANO, Salvatore J**
Bernstein Litowitz Berger & Grossmann LLP, New York
212 554 1538
sgraziano@blbglaw.com
*Featured in Securities (Nationwide), Litigation (New York)*
See under New York for profile.

**GREANEY, William**
Covington & Burling LLP, Washington, DC
202 662 5486
wgreaney@cov.com
*Featured in Insurance (Nationwide), Insurance (District of Columbia)*

**Practice Areas:** Represents policyholders in insurance coverage disputes before federal and state courts, and international and domestic arbitrations. Experience includes disputes over liability insurance coverage for asbestos, environmental, directors and officers, securities, product liability, construction defects, errors and omissions and intellectual property claims; disputes involving coverage under first-party property policies of business interruption, contingent business interruption, extra expense and physical damage losses from hurricanes, eathquakes, tornados, nuclear accidents and other incidents; and disputes arising under crime/fraud, fidelity and builders risk policies. Has an active counseling practice negotiating structured settlements of insurance disputes.
**Personal:** JD, Harvard University; BA, University of Maryland.

## GREEN, Allen B.
McKenna Long & Aldridge LLP, Washington, DC
202 496 7523
agreen@mckennalong.com
*Featured in International Arbitration (Nationwide)*
**Career:** Allen Green has engaged in extensive litigation and counseling on a wide range of international matters. He represents clients in international arbitration and court litigation, focusing on those involving governmental parties. Mr Green counsels and represents clients before federal agencies concerning the US government's regulation of exports, including, in particular, US export controls, the Foreign Corrupt Practices Act ("FCPA") and trade embargoes. He has testified before the Congress on FCPA amendments and has worked on all aspects of international government contracting over the years, including foreign military sales, direct "FMF" sales and US AID contracts and regulations.

## GREEN, Jonathan
Milbank, Tweed, Hadley & McCloy LLP, New York
212 530 5056
jgreen@milbank.com
*Featured in Banking & Finance (Nationwide), Projects (Nationwide)*
**Practice Areas:** Mr Green is a partner and co-chair of the firm's Project Finance Group. Mr Green has extensive experience representing lenders and borrowers in a wide range of international and domestic transactions, including greenfield project financings, acquisitions and leveraged financings, and Public Private Partnerships, in the energy, power, mining & metals, and transportation industries.

## GREEN, Thomas C
Sidley Austin LLP, Washington, DC
202 736 8069
tcgreen@sidley.com
*Featured in Litigation (Nationwide), Litigation (District of Columbia)*
**Practice Areas:** Senior counsel in Washington, DC office. Mr Green highly regarded trial lawyer who has tried countless complex criminal and civil cases and managed Sidley's Federal and State Investigation and White Collar Defense practice

group. Counsels corporate officials on crisis management, conducts internal investigations of alleged corporate wrongdoing, also advising on the implementation of compliance and anti-fraud programs.
**Career:** Fellow of American College of Trial Lawyers; Past president of Assistant United States Attorneys Association; Served as artillery officer attached to the 1st Air Cavalry Division during the Vietnam War.
**Personal:** Yale Law School, LLB, 1965; Dartmouth College, BA, 1962.

## GREENBAUM, Jack A
Blank Rome LLP, New York
212 885 5284
JGreenbaum@BlankRome.com
*Featured in Transportation (Nationwide)*
**Practice Areas:** Jack Greenbaum represents clients in the areas of maritime and international commercial law, arbitration, and general litigation. He has established a reputation as both advocate and arbitrator. Mr Greenbaum's clients include protection and indemnity associations, shipowners, operators, charterers, brokers, and commodity traders, in areas including: charter-party and bill-of-lading disputes; commodity contracts; letters of credit; and general commercial disputes. For more information see: www.BlankRome.com/JGreenbaum.

## GREENBAUM, Jeffrey A
Frankfurt Kurnit Klein & Selz, New York
212 826 5525
jgreenbaum@fkks.com
*Featured in Advertising (Nationwide)*
**Practice Areas:** Managing Partner of the firm and Partner in the firm's Advertising, Marketing, and Public Relations Group. Represents advertisers, advertising agencies, media companies, and production companies on advertising, intellectual property, consumer privacy, and branded entertainment matters. Executive Committee of the Board of the Promotion Marketing Association. Executive Committee of the Global Advertising Lawyers Alliance. Member (and former Chair) of the Committee on Consumer Affairs of the New York City Bar. Chairs the New York City Bar's annual 'Hot Topics in Advertising' program. Member, INTA Nontraditional Marks Committee. Frequent speaker at FTC and other events. Author of the advertising compliance chapter in Corporate Compliance Practice Guide: The Next Generation of Compliance (LexisNexis, 2010). Former Adjunct Faculty Member, Parsons School of Design. Also recognized in Best Lawyers in America, Legal 500, and Super Lawyers.

## GREENBERG, Gordon A
McDermott Will & Emery LLP, Los Angeles
310 551 9398
ggreenberg@mwe.com
*Featured in Litigation (Nationwide), Litigation (California)*
See under California for profile.

## GREENE, Nathan J
Shearman & Sterling LLP, New York
212 848 4668
ngreene@shearman.com
*Featured in Investment Funds (Nationwide)*
**Practice Areas:** Nathan Greene is a partner in the Asset Management Group advising on all regulatory aspects of fund and investment advisory operations. His practice includes the formation and representation of US and foreign investment companies, their sponsors, advisers, directors and marketers. Mr Greene has lectured and written on a broad range of asset management topics, participating as a speaker or panelist at industry conferences sponsored by such organizations as the Global Association of Risk Professionals, Institutional Investor, Investment Company Institute, MAR Hedge and the Regulatory Compliance Association.
**Career:** Bar admission: New York.
**Personal:** Georgetown Law, University of Maryland.

## GREENWALD, John D
Cassidy Levy Kent LLP, Washington, DC
202 567 2306
jgreenwald@cassidylevy.com
*Featured in International Trade (Nationwide)*
**Practice Areas:** Represents clients in matters arising under trade laws of US, Commission of European Communities and other foreign jurisdictions. Advises and represents various clients on trade legislation in Congress and/or trade policy issues under review in Executive branch of US government.
**Career:** Attorney, Office of US Trade Representative from 1974, then served as Deputy General Counsel. From 1980-81 served as first Head of Import Administration at Department of Commerce, responsible for administration of US anti-dumping and countervailing duty laws.
**Personal:** Columbia University School of Law (JD; Editor-in-Chief, Columbia Journal of Transnational Law; Stone Scholar; International Fellow); University of North Carolina at Chapel Hill (BA).

## GRIFFITHS, Sean P.
Gibson, Dunn & Crutcher LLP, New York
212 351 3872
sgriffiths@gibsondunn.com
*Featured in Private Equity (Nationwide)*
**Practice Areas:** Co-Chair of the Firm's Private Equity Practice Group. Specializes in representing private equity firms and their portfolio companies in mergers and acquisitions, dispositions, and minority investments and companies in complex carve out and spin off transactions and acquisitions. Also has extensive experience in corporate finance in both public and private capital markets and troubled company representation (crisis management). Represents CVC Capital Partners, Investcorp, Littlejohn, Whitney and a number of other financial sponsors and companies in a variety of industries.
**Career:** Member, New York and California State Bars.

**Personal:** JD, University of Virginia, 1986; BS, Purdue University, 1983.

## GRINER, G Christopher
Kaye Scholer LLP, Washington, DC
202 682 3619
christopher.griner@kayescholer.com
*Featured in International Trade (Nationwide)*
**Practice Areas:** Co-Chair of the National Security, Government Contracts and Regulatory Compliance Department and the National Security/CFIUS group. Represents clients in acquisitions involving US national security, including sensitive technologies, export controls (International Traffic in Arms Regulations (ITAR) / Export Administration Regulations (EAR)), classified activities, and FINSA/Exon-Florio reviews before the Committee on Foreign Investment in the United States (CFIUS). Counsels clients on government intervention in connection with proposed acquisitions, joint ventures, corporate reorganizations and establishment of foreign ownership, control or influence (FOCI) mitigation arrangements under the National Industrial Security Program Operating Manual (NISPOM) involving the Departments of Defense, Energy and Treasury.

## GROFMAN, Udi
Paul, Weiss, Rifkind, Wharton & Garrison LLP, New York
212 373 3918
ugrofman@paulweiss.com
*Featured in Investment Funds (Nationwide)*
**Practice Areas:** Corporate Department Partner, co-head of the firm's Private Funds Practice Group and a member of the Investment Management Practice Group. Practice emphasizes investment funds, securities law and regulatory compliance. Experience includes structuring financial services and investment management firms, hedge funds, private equity funds and hybrid funds and scalable platforms for fund sponsors and negotiating seed and strategic relationships. Regularly advises investment management firms and their principals on regulatory compliance, crisis and risk management and other operational issues. Also advises on mergers, acquisitions and reorganizations of investment management firms.

## GROLL, Michael
Willkie Farr & Gallagher LLP, New York
212 728 8616
mgroll@willkie.com
*Featured in Insurance (Nationwide), Insurance (New York)*
**Practice Areas:** He has expertise in the area of corporate and securities law, specifically public and private securities offerings, merger and acquisitions, and other transactions in the insurance industry. He has represented underwriters, insurance companies and lenders in such transactions. He has also represented investors, companies and investment banks in the formation, private financing and acquisition of insurance companies as well as many insurers and investment banks in connection with structured financial product transactions and credit derivative transactions

involving both domestic and off-shore insurance and reinsurance companies.
**Personal:** JD, Columbia University, 1978; BA, Boston University, 1975. See: http://www.willkie.com/MichaelGroll.

### GROSKAUFMANIS, Karl A
Fried, Frank, Harris, Shriver & Jacobson LLP, Washington, DC
202 639 7314
Karl.Groskaufmanis@FriedFrank.com
*Featured in Securities (Nationwide)*
**Practice Areas:** Litigation partner, member of white collar criminal defense and securities enforcement practice group and securities enforcement and regulation practice. Practice includes United States Securities and Exchange Commission enforcement investigations, insider trading inquiries, internal investigations and related securities litigation. Also advises public companies and institutional investors on the application of the securities laws to their businesses. Frequent speaker, author on securities laws issues.
**Career:** Joined in 1988; became partner in 1995.
**Personal:** JD, University of Pennsylvania (1988), editor, University of Pennsylvania Law Review; LLB, University of Toronto Law School (1987); BS, with honors, Cornell University (1984).

### GROSS, Edward K.
Vedder Price PC, Washington, DC
202 312 3330
egross@vedderprice.com
*Featured in Banking & Finance (Nationwide)*
**Practice Areas:** Shareholder, Global Transportation Finance team. Over 25 years of experience representing bank-affiliated and large, independent equipment financing companies in all aspects of equipment finance transactions. Handles all types of equipment finance matters and structures, including single-investor, leveraged financings, true/tax-motivated leases, synthetic leases, TRAC leases, "bundled" and other vendor-originated financings, and domestic and cross-border financings.
**Professional Memberships:** Chair, Air, Rail and Marine Subcommittee, ELFA; Member (UCC Committee; Subcommittees on Secured Transactions, Leasing and Airfinance; Air and Space Law Forum), ABA.
**Career:** Admitted (MD) 1982, (DC) 1983
**Personal:** JD, University of Baltimore School of Law; BA, University of Maryland.

### GROSS, Kenneth A
Skadden, Arps, Slate, Meagher & Flom LLP & Affiliates, Washington, DC
202 371 7007
Kenneth.Gross@skadden.com
*Featured in Government (Nationwide)*
**Practice Areas:** Leads Skadden's Political Law practice and is an authority on federal and state campaign laws, gift and gratuity rules, lobby registration provisions, and "pay-to-play" laws including those regulating investment advisory services and municipal securities and various state contracting transactions. Counsels major corporations and political candidates at the state and federal level on matters relating to compliance, and

advises political appointees facing Senate confirmation in matters concerning compliance with ethics laws.
**Career:** Associate General Counsel, Federal Election Commission (1980-86). JD, Emory University School of Law; BA, University of Bridgeport (cum laude).
**Publications:** Co-author, PLI 'Corporate Political Activities.'

### GROSSHANDLER, Seth
Cleary Gottlieb Steen & Hamilton LLP, New York
212 225 2542
sgrosshandler@cgsh.com
*Featured in Capital Markets (Nationwide)*
**Practice Areas:** Creditors' rights, derivative products, clearing, living wills, securities transactions, financial institutions and structured finance, with particular emphasis on risks to counterparties and investors in the event of insolvency.
**Professional Memberships:** Member of the Bar in New York.
**Career:** Joined firm, 1983; became partner, 1992. JD, 'Law Review' editorial board member, cum laude, Order of the Coif, Northwestern University School of Law (1983); BA, Phi Beta Kappa, Reed College (1979).
**Publications:** Mr Grosshandler lectures and is widely published on various aspects of creditors' rights and derivative products and securities transactions.

### GROSSI, Peter
Arnold & Porter LLP, McLean
703 720 7051
Peter.Grossi@aporter.com
*Featured in Products Liability (Nationwide)*
**Practice Areas:** Former Chair, firm's Litigation Department. Adjunct Professor teaching products liability law at Harvard, Penn and UVA Law. Served as National Counsel in a number of pharmaceutical mass tort cases, including Wyeth in its Diet Drug Cases; tried more cases and obtained more defense verdicts than any other attorney in those cases. Extensive involvement representing Philip Morris in product liability cases, including as lead counsel in its successful effort in the US Supreme Court to invalidate FDA's assertion of jurisdiction over the tobacco industry.
**Personal:** JD, Yale Law School, 1973. Clerked for J. Joseph Smith, USCA Second Circuit.

### GROSSMAN, Marshall B
Bingham McCutchen LLP, Santa Monica
310 255 9118
marshall.grossman@bingham.com
*Featured in Litigation (Nationwide), Litigation (California), Media & Entertainment (California)*
See under California for profile.

### GROSSMAN, Maura
Wachtell, Lipton, Rosen & Katz, New York
212 403 1391
MRGrossman@wlrk.com
*Featured in Litigation (Nationwide)*
**Practice Areas:** Practice focuses on advising lawyers and clients on legal, technical, and strategic issues involving electronic discovery and infor-

mation management; expert in search and technology-assisted review.
**Professional Memberships:** Member of the Steering Committee of The Sedona Conference® Working Group 1 on Best Practices for Electronic Document Retention and Production. Serves on the Advisory Boards of the Georgetown Advanced E-Discovery Institute and Bloomberg BNA's Digital Discovery & e-Evidence Report.
**Career:** After a career as a clinical psychologist, joined Wachtell, Lipton, Rosen & Katz in 1999 as a litigation associate; appointed counsel in 2007. Serves as co-chair of the E-Discovery Working Group advising the New York State Unified Court System, and as a member of the Attorney Advisory Group to the Judicial Improvements Committee of the United States District Court for the Southern District of New York. Involved in various initiatives to provide training on e-discovery to federal and state court judges, and has served as a court-appointed e-discovery expert and mediator. Served as coordinator of the Legal Track of the National Institute of Standards and Technology's Text Retrieval Conference ("TREC") from 2009 to 2011. Teaches e-discovery at Columbia Law School, and has taught e-discovery at Rutgers School of Law–Newark and Pace Law School.
**Publications:** Selected publications include: Preservation, Search Technology, and Rulemaking, 30 THE COMPUTER & INTERNET LAWYER 20 (2013); The Grossman-Cormack Glossary of Technology-Assisted Review, with Foreword by John M. Facciola, US Magistrate Judge, 7 FED. COURTS L. REV. 1 (2013); Inconsistent Assessment of Responsiveness in E-Discovery: Difference of Opinion or Human Error?, 32 PACE L.R. 267 (2012); Some Thoughts on Incentives, Rules, and Ethics Concerning the Use of Search Technology in E-Discovery, 12 THE SEDONA CONFERENCE J. 89 (2011); Technology-Assisted Review in E-Discovery Can Be More Effective and More Efficient Than Exhaustive Manual Review, XVII RICH. J.L. & TECH. 11 (2011).

### GROSSMAN, Shukie
Weil, Gotshal & Manges LLP, New York
212 310 8655
shukie.grossman@weil.com
*Featured in Investment Funds (Nationwide)*
**Practice Areas:** Mr Grossman represents private investment fund sponsors in structuring and negotiating terms of domestic and offshore private investment funds. He also negotiates employment/economic sharing arrangements among private investment fund sponsors, represents institutional investors in investing in prominent private investment funds, and advises asset managers generally regarding federal securities laws. He spent several years at the Division of Investment Management at the US Securities and Exchange Commission and is an adjunct Professor at Columbia Law School.
**Professional Memberships:** Member of the Private Investment Fund Forum and the New York Private Funds Committee.
**Personal:** Yeshiva University (BA); Fordham University (JD).

### GROSSMAN, Theodore
Jones Day, Cleveland
216 586 7268
tgrossman@jonesday.com
*Featured in Products Liability (Nationwide), Litigation (Ohio)*
See under Ohio for profile.

### GUAY, Joseph
Holland & Knight LLP, New York
212 513 3226
joe.guay@hklaw.com
*Featured in Leisure & Hospitality (Nationwide)*
**Practice Areas:** Head of Holland & Knight's Real Estate Section, Joe Guay focuses his practice in the area of real estate law with a strong emphasis in hotel and resort development and hospitality law. Joe's hospitality practice includes hotel acquisitions and dispositions, restructuring and workouts of distressed lodging assets, development and finance, mixed-use development projects, hotel management agreements, branded residential projects, restaurant agreements and general hotel operation matters throughout North and South America. Joe's hospitality clients include international brand management companies, hotel company owners, pension fund advisors and investment funds, real estate development companies, institutional lenders and investment banks.

### GUEDRY, David N
K&L Gates, Dallas
214 939 5402
david.guedry@klgates.com
*Featured in Outsourcing (Nationwide), Technology (Texas)*
**Practice Areas:** Internationally recognized for more than 25 years of thought leadership in the outsourcing industry, David Guedry works with buyers of goods and services on their complex sourcing relationships, joint ventures and distribution arrangements, and he regularly advises leading global service providers, including assisting with developing overall legal and business strategies. He has excellent relationships with the leading third party advisory firms and regularly consults with them on market trends that affect his clients. He is skilled at advising clients on structuring their business relationships, and then translating strategy into the negotiation of successful relationships.

### GUERRERA, Sal
Skadden, Arps, Slate, Meagher & Flom LLP & Affiliates, New York
212 735 3910
Sal.Guerrera@skadden.com
*Featured in Banking & Finance (Nationwide)*
**Practice Areas:** Represents banks and other financial institutions in domestic and international financings, including financings of tender offers, mergers and acquisitions generally; financings of recapitalizations and spin-offs; first lien/second lien financings; working capital and asset-based financings; subordinated debt, bridge and mezzanine financings; restructurings and work-outs; and special-purpose financings. While primarily representing financial institutions, including Credit Suisse AG, BNP Paribas, UBS

and Jefferies Finance, Mr Guerrera also represents borrowers and issuers, including Devon Energy Corporation and AEP Industries Inc.

**Career:** JD, University of Pennsylvania School of Law, 1987; BA, Fairfield University, 1984 (summa cum laude).

### GUGGENHEIM, Miriam J
Covington & Burling LLP, Washington, DC
202 662 5235
mguggenheim@cov.com

*Featured in Food & Beverages (Nationwide)*

**Practice Areas:** Miriam Guggenheim counsels food and dietary supplement companies in achieving their marketing goals while minimizing regulatory and litigation risks. She advises clients on all aspects of product development and marketing, from formulation and manufacturing to labeling and advertising. In recent years, she has become a leading expert on the new Food Safety Modernization Act and evolving substantiation standards governing health benefit claims. Her work for a broad range of global companies and major trade associations includes regulatory advice, advocacy before regulators, courts and legislative bodies, and strategic counseling in light of overarching public health and nutrition policy considerations.

### GULLAND, Eugene D
Covington & Burling LLP, Washington, DC
202 662 5504
egulland@cov.com

*Featured in International Arbitration (Nationwide)*

**Practice Areas:** Eugene Gulland's practice includes arbitration and litigation in domestic and international courts and tribunals. He has broad experience in US trial and appellate litigation, which is an unusual and valuable qualification among advocates who also appear in international arbitration proceedings. He has many cases currently pending before courts and arbitration tribunals including Exxon Mobil Corp. v. Venezuela (ICSID); Exxon Mobil Corp. v. PDVSA (ICC); other investment arbitrations (representing both claimants and states) and large international commercial arbitrations.

**Personal:** Yale Law School, JD, 1972 , Princeton University, AB, 1969.

### GULLIKSON, Rosemary L
Dentons, Chicago
312 876 8963
rosemary.gullikson@dentons.com

*Featured in Outsourcing (Nationwide), Technology (Illinois)*

See under Illinois for profile.

### GUMBS, Keir D
Covington & Burling LLP, Washington, DC
202 662 5500
kgumbs@cov.com

*Featured in Securities (Nationwide)*

**Practice Areas:** Keir Gumbs is a corporate and securities lawyer who specializes in capital markets, disclosure and corporate governance matters. His clients include Fortune 500 companies, institutional investors and non-profits.

**Career:** Before Covington Mr Gumbs served as a Special Counsel in the Division of Corporation

Finance at the SEC and as Counsel to an SEC Commissioner.

**Personal:** MrGumbs was named a "2011 Rising Star of Corporate Governance" by the Millstein Center for Corporate Governance and one of the "People to Watch" for the 2011 and 2012 NACD "Directorship 100," which lists the most influential people in corporate governance.

### GUNN, Brian
Drinker Biddle & Reath LLP, Washington, DC
202 230 5172
Brian.Gunn@dbr.com

*Featured in Native American Law (Nationwide)*

**Practice Areas:** Represents tribal clients on a wide variety of federal Indian law and policy issues, with emphasis on legislative and regulatory matters before the US Congress and federal agencies. Specializes in matters related to federal budget and appropriations process, energy development and natural resources, taxation, and Indian health. Works closely with federal agencies and national and regional Indian organizations on policy and legal issues related to federal government's administration of tribal trust funds and trust resources.

**Personal:** University of Washington, JD; Washington State University, BA; member of the Confederated Tribes of the Colville Reservation.

### GUSSACK, Nina M
Pepper Hamilton LLP, Philadelphia
215 981 4950
gussackn@pepperlaw.com

*Featured in Products Liability (Nationwide), Litigation (Pennsylvania)*

**Practice Areas:** Partner; Chair, Health Effects Litigation Practice Group; Past Chair, Executive Committee. Experienced in defense of pharmaceutical and medical device companies regarding marketed products, investigational drugs, medical devices and over-the-counter drug products; serves as national coordinating/trial counsel and as regional counsel in pharmaceutical litigation, including class actions and multi-district litigation.

**Professional Memberships:** Product Liability Advisory Council; International Association of Defense Counsel; Member and former Chair, Drug and Medical Device Committee, Defense Research Institute; Board of Directors, Greater Philadelphia Chamber of Commerce.

**Personal:** JD 1979 Villanova University School of Law; MS and BA, magna cum laude, 1976 University of Pennsylvania.

### GUTIERREZ, Jay M
Morgan, Lewis & Bockius LLP, Washington, DC
202 739 5466
jgutierrez@morganlewis.com

*Featured in Energy & Natural Resources (Nationwide)*

**Practice Areas:** Jay M. Gutierrez is a partner in Morgan Lewis's Energy Practice. For more than 30 years, his practice has focused on representing companies and governments in a variety of matters involving the ownership, operation, and regulation of nuclear power plants. These representa-

tions have involved coordination of such diverse issues as developing nuclear regulatory programs; operating plant performance and related management issues; responding to government investigations, including wrongdoing investigations; counseling on new plant initiatives in the United States, the United Kingdom, Europe, and the Middle East in countries with emerging nuclear programs; and addressing corporate governance and co-owner considerations.

### GUTMAN, Olga
Simpson Thacher & Bartlett LLP, New York
212 455 3522
ogutman@stblaw.com

*Featured in Investment Funds (Nationwide)*

**Practice Areas:** Corporate Partner specializing in hedge funds, private equity funds and investment management matters. Has represented sponsors of private equity and hedge funds including AlpInvest, Breeden Capital Management, Brummer & Partners, CIFC Corp., Citigroup Alternative Investments, Coatue Management, CVC Credit Partners, Goshen Investments, Intermediate Capital Group, MatlinPatterson Global Advisers, Palladium Equity Partners, Pendragon Capital, SkyBridge Capital, Spring Mountain Capital, Tiger Management, and TSG. Also advised on numerous strategic investments and M&A transactions involving asset management firms.

**Career:** Joined firm, 2001; Partner in 2008.

**Personal:** BA, Yeshiva University (1994); JD, Cornell Law School (1997); LLM, Cornell Law School (2001).

### GUTOWSKI, Peter
Freehill Hogan & Mahar LLP, New York
212 425 1900
gutowski@freehill.com

*Featured in Transportation (Nationwide)*

**Practice Areas:** Areas of expertise include litigation and arbitration of charter party, COA and commodities disputes; cargo damage and contamination claims; commodities and international sales disputes; vessel casualty claims; vessel sale and purchase documentation and sales disputes; provisional remedies (including arrest and attachment of assets) domestic and foreign; international enforcement of judgments and awards. Has tried cases in New York State and Federal courts and elsewhere, argued/handled appeals in the 2nd, 3rd and 9th Circuit Courts of Appeal, filed appeals in the US Supreme Court, and has handled multiple arbitration proceedings in New York and elsewhere.

**Professional Memberships:** Maritime Law Association of the United States; New York Bar Association.

**Career:** Joined Freehill, Hogan & Mahar as an associate in 1981 and became a Partner in 1988.

**Personal:** Born 1956, New Jersey; Columbia University, BA, 1978; Tulane University, JD, cum laude, 1981.

### GUYNN, Randall
Davis Polk & Wardwell LLP, New York
212 450 4239
randall.guynn@davispolk.com

*Featured in Financial Services Regulation (Nationwide)*

**Practice Areas:** Head of Davis Polk's Financial Institutions Group. He has long been considered one of the top bank regulatory lawyers in the world. He has been recognised as one of the most widely consulted lawyers during the financial crisis and on financial regulatory reform by The American Lawyer. He represents many of the world's leading banks and has often been asked to advise the US and UK governments, and the Financial Stability Board on a variety of matters. His practice focuses on providing advice on financial reform, M&A including troubled bank acquisitions, capital markets transactions, credit risk and collateral management, enforcement actions, and clearing and settlement systems.

### HADER, Cheryl
Kramer Levin Naftalis & Frankel LLP, New York
212 715 9245
chader@kramerlevin.com

*Featured in Wealth Management (Nationwide)*

**Practice Areas:** Ms Hader's practice focuses on domestic and international estate planning, probate, estate and trust administration, prenuptial matters, private foundations and public charities. She advises clients on sophisticated estate, gift and income tax planning, including such planning in connection with closely-held business interests, private equity funds, hedge funds and the disposition and administration of intellectual property rights. Ms Hader is a frequent lecturer on trusts and estates topics. She has been quoted often in national publications, including The New York Times and The Wall Street Journal. She is the author of Estate Planning and Chapter 14: Understanding the Special Valuation Rules.

### HADJIS, Alexander J
Morrison & Foerster LLP, Washington, DC
202 887 1560
ahadjis@mofo.com

*Featured in International Trade (Nationwide), Intellectual Property (District of Columbia)*

**Practice Areas:** Focuses on complex litigation, including cases involving interface between IP and antitrust and involving technology standards. Experienced lead trial counsel before federal district courts and the US ITC on patent, antitrust and breach of contract cases involving semiconductor, optical storage media, telecommunications, medical device, software and chemical sectors. Clients include Hitachi, Huawei, Spansion, Evapco, MAKO Surgical and International Game Technology.

**Career:** Chair of the ITC practice. Law clerk to Honorable Wilson Cowen, US Court of Appeals for the Federal Circuit.

**Personal:** Ohio State University, BSEE, 1990; University of Pittsburgh, JD, 1993; George Washington University Law School, LLM, 1996.

**HADLEY, Joseph P**
Davis Polk & Wardwell LLP, New York
212 450 4000
joseph.hadley@davispolk.com
*Featured in Projects (Nationwide)*
**Practice Areas:** Member of Davis Polk & Wardwell's Corporate Department. Advises corporations, financial institutions and governmental agencies on a wide variety of corporate and financing matters, with special emphasis on international joint venture and project and leveraged financings. Has extensive experience advising clients raising financing in the telecommunications, power and oil and gas sectors from the debt capital markets, syndicated loan market and governmental and multi-lateral financing sources.

**HAFF, Jeffery S.**
Dady & Gardner, PA, Minneapolis
612 359 3514
jhaff@dadygardner.com
*Featured in Franchising (Nationwide)*
**Practice Areas:** Franchise and distribution.
**Career:** A Partner at Dady & Gardner, Jeff has sucessfully resolved, through litigation and arbitration, hundreds of contract and business disputes on behalf of his clients resulting in millions of dollars of settlements and awards for wronged dealers, distributors and franchisees. Honored with numerous accolades within the area of franchise law, he is also a regular speaker at the ABA Forum on Franchising's annual Legal Symposium.
**Personal:** Duke University (JD, with honors, 1989); State University of New York at Albany (BA, summa cum laude, 1986).

**HALL, Charles**
Fulbright & Jaworski LLP, Houston
713 651 5268
chall@fulbright.com
*Featured in Tax (Nationwide), Tax (Texas)*
**Practice Areas:** Tax litigation; tax law; corporate law.
**Career:** Charles W Hall is the firm's senior tax practitioner. His legal practice involves extensive court room practice involving numerous large and complex tax controversies, and federal, state and local taxation matters, including corporate, estate planning, and business issues. He has represented many of the largest corporations and wealthiest individuals in a variety of complex tax matters in and out of court including major tax case trials in all federal forums.
**Personal:** LLM, Taxation, Southern Methodist University (1959); JD, Southern Methodist University School of Law (1954); BA, University of the South (1951).

**HALL, Joseph A**
Davis Polk & Wardwell LLP, New York
212 450 4000
joseph.hall@davispolk.com
*Featured in Capital Markets (Nationwide)*
**Practice Areas:** Member of Davis Polk's Corporate Department. His practice includes advising issuers and underwriters on capital markets transactions; advising SEC-regulated entities on regulatory matters; and advising on securities, corporate and governance matters, generally. He

returned to the firm in 2005 following completion of his service at the US Securities and Exchange Commission as Managing Executive for Policy under Chairman William H. Donaldson. As a member of Chairman Donaldson's senior management team, Mr Hall assisted in directing the Commission's policy-making and enforcement activities. From 1994 to 1996, he was corporate counsel to Reuters America Inc.

**HALLOWAY, Lorraine B**
Crowell & Moring LLP, Washington, DC
202 624 2538
lhalloway@crowell.com
*Featured in Transportation (Nationwide)*
**Practice Areas:** Partner in Crowell & Moring's Aviation and International Trade groups. Specializes in aviation law and export control matters. In aviation practice, represents airlines/air freight forwarders/charter operators/aviation manufacturers/ shippers/aviation trade associations in proceedings before the Department of Transportation/Federal Aviation Administration/Transportation Security Administration/federal courts/foreign governments. In international practice, represents clients before the Department of Commerce/Directorate of Defense Trade Controls (State Department)/Office of Foreign Assets Control (Treasury Department)/Department of Homeland Security. Advises on licensing and embargo issues/drafts export control compliance programs/conducts audits/prepares voluntary disclosures. Represents clients in enforcement proceedings involving alleged violations of customs/export control/embargo laws/regulations.

**HALPERIN, Alan S**
Paul, Weiss, Rifkind, Wharton & Garrison LLP, New York
212 373 3313
ahalperin@paulweiss.com
*Featured in Wealth Management (Nationwide)*
**Practice Areas:** Partner and Co-Chair of Personal Representation Department. Counsels clients on estate planning and related tax work, estate and trust administration, tax and succession planning for family corporations and partnerships and charitable giving. Works closely with entrepreneurs, fiduciaries, corporate executives, investment bankers, real estate developers, family offices and philanthropists to provide creative, pragmatic advice. Lectures and writes on estate planning. Adjunct professor at NYU School of Law. Fellow of the American College of Trust and Estate Counsel. Co-chair of the Estate and Gift Taxation Committee of the Tax Section of the New York State Bar.

**HALPERT, James J**
DLA Piper LLP (US), Washington, DC
202 799 4441
jim.halpert@dlapiper.com
*Featured in Privacy & Data Security (Nationwide)*
**Practice Areas:** E-commerce and privacy.
**Career:** He counsels technology and content companies on legal issues concerning new technologies, including advising copyright owners, ISPs, and equipment manufacturers regarding

anti-piracy, infringement, and copy protection technology strategies, and advising a wide range of companies regarding privacy and computer security issues. Interested in the evolution of new law in the technology area, he has helped negotiate and draft many of the federal laws that govern e-commerce and use of the internet.
**Personal:** JD, Harvard Law School (cum laude); D.E.A., École de Hautes Etudes en Sciences Sociales/École Normale Supérieure; BA, Yale University (magna cum laude).

**HAMILTON, Lawrence**
Holland & Knight LLP, Jacksonville
904 798 5454
larry.hamilton@hklaw.com
*Featured in Transportation (Nationwide)*
**Practice Areas:** Mr Hamilton is the practice group leader of the firm's North Florida Litigation Group and on the firm's Directors Committee. He has broad experience, including representation of publicly traded nationwide providers of motor, rail, logistics and intermodal transportation services. Mr Hamilton's trial accomplishments include complex class actions, commercial lawsuits, and arbitrations, including the successful defense of a motor carrier class action lawsuit with industry-wide ramifications. He is certified as a Circuit Court Mediator (Florida), on the Executive Committee of the Chester Bedell Inn of Court and has held leadership positions within multiple state and local bar organizations.

**HAMMES, Jeffrey C**
Kirkland & Ellis LLP, Chicago
312 862 2476
jeffrey.hammes@kirkland.com
*Featured in Private Equity (Nationwide), Corporate/M&A (Illinois)*
See under Illinois for profile.

**HAMMOND, Denise**
Hammond Immigration Law, P.C., Rockville
301 917 6901
Denise@HammondImmigration.com
*Featured in Immigration (Nationwide), Immigration (District of Columbia)*
See under District of Columbia for profile.

**HAMMOND, Steven A**
Hughes Hubbard & Reed LLP, New York
212 837 6253
hammond@hugheshubbard.com
*Featured in International Arbitration (Nationwide)*
**Practice Areas:** Specializes in international arbitration and litigation, serving as counsel or arbitrator in international arbitration under ICC, ICSID, UNCITRAL,ICDR, AAA, and IACAC rules, including proceedings conducted in English, Spanish, and French. Also experienced in transnational litigation and mediation.
**Professional Memberships:** Fellow, College of Commercial Arbitrators; UIA (President d'Honneur); IBA, ABA.
**Career:** Partner since 1986.
**Publications:** Work has appeared in The Journal of International Arbitration, Pratical Lawyer and Revista de Arbitragem e Mediação.

**Personal:** Free University of Brussels (LLM, 1979); Maine Law School (JD, 1977); Bowdoin College (AB, 1974). Fluent in French, Spanish.

**HAND, Lloyd**
King & Spalding LLP, Washington, DC
202 626 2931
lhand@kslaw.com
*Featured in Government (Nationwide)*
**Practice Areas:** Practice includes providing counsel to US Fortune 500 companies, foreign governments, and institutional clients regarding legislative, administrative, regulatory, and international trade issues, as well as contract negotiations relating to defense and aerospace matters.
**Professional Memberships:** District of Columbia Bar Association; Texas Bar Association; Treasurer and Board member of the Blair House; Council on Foreign Relations; Center for Strategic and International Studies; Council of American Ambassadors; Executive Council of Diplomacy, Ambassador's Advisory Committee; The Atlantic Council of the United States; Alfalfa Club.
**Personal:** University of Texas (LLB); University of Texas (BA, 1952); University of Texas (JD, 1957).

**HANDLER, David A**
Kirkland & Ellis LLP, Chicago
312 862 2477
david.handler@kirkland.com
*Featured in Wealth Management (Nationwide)*
**Practice Areas:** Extensive experience in estate, tax and charitable planning, business succession, and estate administration, especially closely held businesses and principals of private equity, venture capital and hedge funds.
**Professional Memberships:** ACTEC; NAEPC Estate Planning Hall of Fame, Editorial Advisory Board of Tax Management Estates, Gifts and Trusts; professional advisory committees of several non-profits.
**Publications:** 'Tax Law Update' column in Trusts & Estates Magazine. Estate planning treatise, 'Drafting the Estate Plan: Law and Forms.' Articles in estate planning and taxation journals. Lectures extensively at professional seminars.
**Personal:** Northwestern University School of Law, JD; University of Illinois, BS, Finance, highest honors.

**HANESSIAN, Grant**
Baker & McKenzie, New York
212 891 3986
grant.hanessian@bakermckenzie.com
*Featured in International Arbitration (Nationwide)*
**Practice Areas:** Co-Chair, Baker & McKenzie International Arbitration Group; counsel or arbitrator in more than 75 international arbitrations concerning investment, energy, construction, commodities, financial services and other matters.
**Professional Memberships:** Vice Chairman, Arbitration & ADR Committee, US Council for International Business (US national committee of International Chamber of Commerce Court of Arbitration); member, ICC Commission on Arbitration, ICC Task Force on Arbitration Involving States or State Entities, AAA-ICDR International Advisory Committee, International

Bar Association Arbitration Committee, New York City Bar International Law Committee, New York State Bar Association Task Force on International Arbitration, International Arbitration Club of New York, Arbitration Committee of the International Institute for Conflict Prevention and Resolution, Club Español del Arbitraje, North American Advisory Council, London Court of International Arbitration.

**Publications:** Editor, ICDR Awards and Commentaries (Juris, 2012); co-editor, Comparison of International Arbitration Rules (ABA Section of International Law, 2013), International Arbitration Checklists (Juris, 2d ed., 2009), Gulf War Claims Reporter (Kluwer/ILI, 1998), Baker & McKenzie International Arbitration Yearbook (Juris, 2010, 2011, 2012), bi-monthly electronic "Baker & McKenzie International Litigation & Arbitration Newsletter"; numerous articles and presentations on international arbitration and litigation topics.

**Personal:** Columbia University, LLM; New York University Law School, JD; University of Pennsylvania, BA.

### HANKS, JR, James J
Venable LLP, Baltimore
410 244 7500
jhanks@Venable.com
*Featured in Corporate/M&A (Maryland), Capital Markets (Nationwide)*

**Practice Areas:** Jim Hanks practices general corporation and securities law, mergers and acquisitions, and corporate governance, with emphasis on Maryland corporate law affecting operating companies, real estate investment trusts and investment companies. Serves as independent counsel to boards and board committees, and as an expert witness in connection with major transactions, conflicts of interest, shareholder litigation and corporate governance, and advises governments in revising their corporate and securities laws.

**Publications:** Maryland Corporation Law (Supp., 2012); Co-author, Legal Capital (3rd ed., 1990; 4th ed., forthcoming 2013)

**Personal:** LLM, Harvard University, 1969; LLB, University of Maryland, 1967; AB, Princeton University, 1964.

### HANRAHAN, Marc P
Milbank, Tweed, Hadley & McCloy LLP, New York
212 530 5306
mhanrahan@milbank.com
*Featured in Banking & Finance (Nationwide)*

**Practice Areas:** Mr Hanrahan concentrates on representing lenders in acquisition financings, including leveraged buyouts, tender offers and other going private transactions. He has handled major transactions for financial institutions such as Bankers Trust Company, Barclays Bank PLC, The Chase Manhattan Bank, Credit Suisse, Goldman Sachs Credit Partners L.P., HSBC and The Royal Bank of Scotland. Mr Hanrahan is ranked a "Star Individual" for Banking and Finance in Chambers USA.

**Career:** Practice Group Leader, Global Leveraged Finance Group.

**Personal:** JD, University of Texas, 1980 (cum laude, Order of the Coif); BA, University of California at Santa Barbara, 1977 (summa cum laude).

### HANSEN, Christian W
White & Case LLP, Miami
305 995 5272
chansen@whitecase.com
*Featured in Transportation (Nationwide), Latin American Investment (Florida)*

**Career:** To view a comprehensive biography, please visit www.whitecase.com/chansen.

### HANSEN, Edward J
Baker & McKenzie, New York
212 626 4508
Ed.Hansen@bakermckenzie.com
*Featured in Outsourcing (Nationwide), Technology (New York)*

See under New York for profile.

### HANSEN, Kenneth W
Chadbourne & Parke LLP, Washington, DC
202 974 5656
khansen@chadbourne.com
*Featured in Projects (Nationwide)*

**Practice Areas:** Represents project developers and multilateral, bilateral, and commercial lenders in structuring, negotiating and implementing US and international project financings. His experience includes international debt workouts and investment disputes, including the resolution of political risk insurance claims. He is extensively involved in agency guarantees for conventional, renewable and innovative energy projects. He lectures and publishes on international project finance and international investment law.

**Career:** Formerly General Counsel, Export-Import Bank of the United States; Associate General Counsel, OPIC; Adjunct Professor: Georgetown University Law Center and the John Hopkins University School of Advanced International Studies.

### HANSON, Vivian L
Morrison & Foerster LLP, New York
212 506 7393
vhanson@mofo.com
*Featured in Outsourcing (Nationwide), Technology (New York)*

**Practice Areas:** Specializes in information technology and business process outsourcing, as well as domestic and cross-border transactions involving the transfer of intellectual property rights. Has extensive experience in software and technology licensing, joint ventures, strategic alliances, and mergers and acquisitions; advises clients in a variety of industries, including media, entertainment, information technology, information services, financial services, transportation, biotech, and pharmaceuticals. Fluent in Japanese.

**Career:** Co-Head of the firm's US Sourcing Practice; partner, Technology Transactions Group. Frequent speaker on outsourcing and licensing issues.

**Personal:** BA, University of Hawaii, 1982; JD, Columbia Law School, 1986.

### HARBURG, Stephen J
Skadden, Arps, Slate, Meagher & Flom LLP & Affiliates, Washington, DC
202 371 7470
Stephen.Harburg@skadden.com
*Featured in Products Liability (Nationwide)*

**Practice Areas:** Focuses on complex civil litigation, particularly the defense of mass torts, multidistrict litigation proceedings, and product liability and consumer fraud class actions. Has been involved in numerous mass torts, multidistrict litigation proceedings and class actions in the automobile, medical products, oil and gas and welding industries. Briefed and argued class certification motions, Daubert motions and dispositive motions in state and federal courts at both the trial and appellate levels.

**Career:** Law Clerk, Hon. Donald W. Van Artsdalen, US District Court, Eastern District of Pennsylvania. JD, University of Pennsylvania, 1985; BA, Yale University, 1982.

### HARDIN, Elizabeth
Milbank, Tweed, Hadley & McCloy LLP, New York
212 530 5037
ehardin@milbank.com
*Featured in Capital Markets (Nationwide)*

**Practice Areas:** Concentrates on secured finance transactions and has extensive experience in securitizing financial and hard assets in both domestic and cross-border transactions representing issuers, underwriters, swap counterparties, institutional investors and structuring agents. She has comprehensive expertise in asset-backed debt obligations, structured/special situation lending transactions, derivatives, international securities transactions, mortgage-based obligations, public/private auto loan and auto lease receivable securitizations and managed funds. She also specializes in collateralized loan obligations and regularly acts as purchasers' special counsel in private placement transactions.

**Career:** Partner, Alternative Investments Practice.

**Personal:** JD, Marshall-Wythe School of Law; BA, College of William & Mary.

### HARIDI, Samaa
Weil, Gotshal & Manges LLP, New York
212 310 8998
samaa.haridi@weil.com
*Featured in International Arbitration (Nationwide)*

**Practice Areas:** As a partner in the International Arbitration Practice in Weil's New York office, Ms Haridi's practice focuses on international commercial and investor-state arbitration proceedings involving a variety of industries. She represents corporations and financial institutions from around the world, and has handled proceedings under the arbitration rules of the ICSID, ICC, AAA/ICDR, LCIA, and UNCITRAL. She has particular experience in international disputes with connections to the Middle East.

**Personal:** Sorbonne University (D.E.A., 1998). Fluent in French and Arabic and also conversant in Spanish. Admitted in the US (New York and California), England and Wales.

### HARMAN, Thomas
Bingham McCutchen LLP, Washington, DC
202 373 6725
thomas.harman@bingham.com
*Featured in Investment Funds (Nationwide)*

**Practice Areas:** Practice focuses on investment management matters involving investment advisers, mutual funds, closed-end funds, private investment companies and exchange-traded funds. Serves as counsel to the board of directors of several fund families. Has conducted internal reviews on behalf of fund advisers and on behalf of independent boards.

**Career:** Former chief counsel, Securities and Exchange Commission's Division of Investment Management. Frequent speaker on investment management issues and has authored or co-authored numerous articles on industry issues.

**Personal:** University of Virginia School of Law, Juris Doctor, 1982; Georgetown University Law Center, Master of Laws, 1988; Duke University, Bachelor of Arts, 1979.

### HARMS, David B
Sullivan & Cromwell LLP, New York
212 558 3882
harmsd@sullcrom.com
*Featured in Capital Markets (Nationwide)*

**Professional Memberships:** Past co-chairman, PLI's Annual Institute on Securities Regulation (2003-2007).

**Career:** Partner since 1992. Co-coordinator of the Firm's Securities Law and Broker-Dealer Practices. Securities and corporate law practice focused on public offerings, private investments, SEC disclosures, corporate governance, securities trading and research practices and equity derivatives. Represents broker-dealers in SEC, FINRA and NYSE inquiries and on registration and compliance matters.

**Personal:** NYU Law School (JD, 1984; Editor-in-Chief, NYU Law Review); SUNY Purchase (BA, 1978).

### HARRINGTON, Carol A
McDermott Will & Emery LLP, Chicago
312 984 7794
charrington@mwe.com
*Featured in Wealth Management (Nationwide)*

**Practice Areas:** Head of private client department. Advises clients on a variety of matters, including estate, gift and generation-skipping transfer tax issues, trust and estate administration, and contested trust and tax matters. As a national authority on federal generation-skipping transfer tax, has advised attorneys, tax professionals, executors, trustees and other individuals nationwide on this issue.

**Publications:** Co-author of a tax treatise, Generation-Skipping Transfer Tax (Harrington, Plaine & Zaritsky) and published many articles on federal generation-skipping transfer tax.

**Personal:** University of Illinois College of Law (JD, summa cum laude with University Honors Bronze Table); University of Illinois (BS, summa cum laude).

### HARRINGTON, Susan D
Sidley Austin LLP, New York
212 839 8740
sharrington@sidley.com
*Featured in Wealth Management (Nationwide)*
**Practice Areas:** Partner in Sidley's New York office, focusing her practice on international estate and tax planning for US and non-US individuals and for multinational families. She has lectured on US tax aspects of foreign trust and international estate planning for conferences on offshore trusts, and given seminars to major trust companies and financial institutions.
**Professional Memberships:** Co-Founder and former chair, New York branch of UK-based Society of Trusts and Estate Practitioners.
**Personal:** Fordham University School of Law, JD, 1973; Vassar College, AB, 1969. Admission: New York.

### HARRIS, Adam C
Schulte Roth & Zabel LLP, New York
212 756 2253
adam.harris@srz.com
*Featured in Bankruptcy/Restructuring (Nationwide), Bankruptcy/Restructuring (New York)*
See under New York for profile.

### HARRIS, Arlene
Kaye Scholer LLP, New York
212 836 8816
arlene.harris@kayescholer.com
*Featured in Wealth Management (Nationwide)*
**Practice Areas:** Arlene Harris has over forty years of experience in the areas of estate and trust litigation and planning, probate and administration of estates and trusts, and pre- and post-nuptial agreements. She is also an author/lecturer on estate matters.
**Professional Memberships:** The American College of Trust and Estate Counsel; Executive Committee, Trusts and Estates Law Section of the New York State Bar Association (former Chair); OCA Advisory Committee, the Surrogate's Courts (former Chair); Surrogate's Court Committee, the City Bar Association (former member); the International Academy of Estate and Trust Law; the UJA-Federation Trusts & Estates Specialty Group (former Chair).

### HARRIS, Gregg
Fulbright & Jaworski LLP, Washington, DC
202 662 4694
gharris@fulbright.com
*Featured in Projects (Nationwide)*
**Practice Areas:** Structured and project finance, energy projects, debt restructurings/workouts.
**Career:** Gregg Harris has significant experience representing clients in domestic and international transactions in a variety of sectors, including numerous projects in the power sector and has worked on independent power project financings around the world. A substantial part of Harris' practice focuses on debt restructurings, including a wide range of domestic and international restructurings. He has been recognized for his expertise in numerous publications.
**Personal:** JD, Northwestern University (1984); BA, cum laude, Williams College (1981);

Admitted: Illinois, 1984; District of Columbia, 1985.

### HARRIS, Philip H
Skadden, Arps, Slate, Meagher & Flom LLP & Affiliates, New York
212 735 3805
Philip.Harris@skadden.com
*Featured in Investment Funds (Nationwide)*
**Practice Areas:** Philip H. Harris represents a broad range of issuers, underwriters and investment advisors in both registered and private offerings of various types of funds and fund structures, including corporations, partnerships, LLCs, LDCs and trusts. He focuses primarily on private funds, including US as well as international hedge funds, registered funds, private equity funds and customized offshore products. He also provides ongoing regulatory advice related to these entities and their activities in the capital markets.
**Career:** JD, Western New England College School of Law, 1985 (summa cum laude); Bachelor of University Studies, University of New Mexico, 1982.

### HARRIS GUTIERREZ, Franca
WilmerHale, Washington, DC
202 663 6557
franca.gutierrez@wilmerhale.com
*Featured in Financial Services Regulation (Nationwide)*
**Practice Areas:** Ms Gutierrez maintains a broad financial institutions regulatory, transactional, enforcement and counseling practice. She represents domestic and international institutions on a wide range of US regulatory matters. Experience includes representing clients before the Federal Reserve Board, Federal Reserve Banks, the Office of the Comptroller of the Currency, the FDIC, the CFPB and state regulators.
**Professional Memberships:** American Bar Association and the Association of the Bar of the City of New York.
**Career:** Formerly an attorney in the Office of the Comptroller of the Currency. Prior to that she served in the OCC's Northeastern District in New York.

### HARRISON, Donald
Gibson, Dunn & Crutcher LLP, Washington, DC
202 955 8560
dharrison@gibsondunn.com
*Featured in International Trade (Nationwide)*
**Practice Areas:** Don Harrison has a broad practice representing companies and associations in trade remedy and other proceedings before the Commerce Department, International Trade Commission and US Trade Representative's office, as well as advising companies on a range of customs issues, including customs classification and value, specialized areas such as NAFTA, and customs penalty proceedings. He is also actively involved in advising on trade policy issues and litigation in the Court of International Trade and the Court of Appeals for the Federal Circuit.
**Personal:** JD magna cum laude, Harvard University, Editor, Harvard Law Review; BA magna cum laude, Harvard College.

### HARRISON, Todd
Venable LLP, Washington, DC
202 344 4724
taharrison@Venable.com
*Featured in Advertising (Nationwide)*
**Practice Areas:** FDA, FTC, and other federal, state and international consumer protection agencies governing rules and regulations for drugs, foods, dietary supplements, homeopathic remedies, medical devices and cosmetics
**Career:** Mr Harrison chairs Venable's FDA Group and has experience in matters related to the marketing of foods and dietary supplements, and has developed strategies for companies to communicate information about their products without running afoul of FDA and FTC regulatory requirements. He has a successful track record of defending against FTC advertising complaints, enforcement actions and prosecutions, and defending against competitor challenges in court and other forums.
**Publications:** Columnist, Nutraceuticals World.

### HARTNETT, Daniel J
Kaye Scholer LLP, Chicago
312 583 2380
daniel.hartnett@kayescholer.com
*Featured in Capital Markets (Nationwide)*
**Practice Areas:** Daniel Hartnett, head of the Chicago Structured Finance group, represents managers, servicers, trustees, issuers and investors in securitisation and investment fund transactions, involving residential and commercial real estate, farm credit loans, aircraft, synthetic assets and credit default swaps. He has been involved in global CLO/CDO/CFO, trade receivable and tax lien securitisation and investment transactions. Daniel is currently working on transactions involving mortgage programs, investment funds, receivable conduits, CLOs and credit default swaps. He serves on the Advisory Board of Northwestern University's Kellogg School of Management and the Board of Directors of the National Disability Institute.

### HARTNETT, William M
Cahill Gordon & Reindel LLP, New York
212 701 3847
whartnett@cahill.com
*Featured in Banking & Finance (Nationwide), Capital Markets (Nationwide)*
**Practice Areas:** Advises leading commercial and investment banking firms and public and private companies in a broad range of domestic and cross-border capital markets and lending transactions, including leveraged bank financings, out-of-court restructurings, mergers, acquisitions and debt and equity-linked securities offerings. Serves as outside corporate counsel to a number of public and private companies and has extensive experience representing special committees of the boards of directors of public companies in connection with strategic transactions and related compliance matters.
**Personal:** Chairman of firm's Executive Committee. Rider University, BA, 1976, cum laude. Fordham University School of Law, JD, 1979, cum laude.

### HARVEY, Christopher P
Dechert LLP, Boston
617 728 7167
christopher.harvey@dechert.com
*Featured in Investment Funds (Nationwide), Investment Funds (Massachusetts)*
See under Massachusetts for profile.

### HARVEY, James A
Alston & Bird LLP, Atlanta
404 881 7328
jim.harvey@alston.com
*Featured in Outsourcing (Nationwide)*
**Practice Areas:** On the transactional side, Jim's practice is comprised of enterprise-wide sourcing and technology initiatives. On the counseling and pre-litigation side, Jim's practice focuses on privacy and security and data breach/network intrusion response. When company networks and data are breached, he works with multi-disciplinary teams on everything from legally required notification of the affected individuals under various privacy laws, to e-discovery and litigation preparedness, to internal investigations and law enforcement issues.
**Professional Memberships:** Secretary and former chair, Technology Section of the State Bar of Georgia.
**Personal:** The University of North Carolina (JD, 1988); University of Arkansas (BA, 1983).

### HARVEY, Jeffrey L
Hunton & Williams LLP, Richmond
804 788 8505
jharvey@hunton.com
*Featured in Outsourcing (Nationwide)*
**Practice Areas:** Mr Harvey's practice focuses on large-scale, global business process and IT outsourcing transactions, including related technology transactions. Recent deals include IT infrastructure, Software as a Service (SaaS), cloud computing, ERP implementation, service desk, application development/maintenance, internet hosting, call center, and content management outsourcing transactions for Global 2000 companies across a variety of industries. Mr Harvey advises clients throughout the lifecycle of the typical outsourcing transaction, from the RFP stage, through the down-selection of vendors, negotiations, and execution / post-execution (including change management).

### HASKELL, Mark R
Morgan, Lewis & Bockius LLP, Washington, DC
202 739 5766
mhaskell@morganlewis.com
*Featured in Energy & Natural Resources (Nationwide)*
**Practice Areas:** Mark R. Haskell is a partner in Morgan Lewis's Energy Practice. Mr Haskell's practice focuses on Federal Energy Regulatory Commission (FERC) matters, including FERC investigations, litigation and related court appeals, as well as Commodity Futures Trading Commission (CFTC) investigations affecting the energy industry. A seasoned energy lawyer, Mr Haskell has represented natural gas and power marketers, local distribution companies, end

users, producers, industrial consumers, LNG and shale gas developers in energy regulatory matters.

## HASKO, Judith A
Latham & Watkins LLP, Silicon Valley
650 463 3065
judith.hasko@lw.com
*Featured in Life Sciences (Nationwide), Life Sciences (California)*

**Practice Areas:** Advises companies developing biotechnology, pharmaceutical, medical device, clean technology and diagnostic products, and investors in such companies, in technology-based commercial transactions, including corporate partnering, joint venture, asset purchase, revenue stream sales, spin-out, licensing, distribution, manufacturing, co-development, profit-sharing and co-promotion deals. She is registered to practice before the US PTO and is a certified licensing professional.
**Professional Memberships:** Licensing Executives Society
**Career:** Prior to law school, she earned a master's degree in neurobiology and did cardiovascular research at Genentech Inc.
**Personal:** JD, University of Wisconsin Law School, 1994; M. Phil., University of Sussex, 1988; BA, Vassar College, 1986.

## HASTINGS, Douglas A
Epstein Becker & Green PC, Washington, DC
202 861 1807
dhastings@ebglaw.com
*Featured in Healthcare (Nationwide), Healthcare (District of Columbia)*

**Practice Areas:** Chair of the firm's Board of Directors; Member of the Firm, Health Care and Life Sciences Practice. Mr Hastings provides a wide range of health care organizations with strategic and transactional legal guidance in responding to the legal challenges and opportunities of the rapidly changing US health care system. He has become recognized as one of the nation's leading resources on accountable care, value-based payment, and health care delivery system reform.
**Professional Memberships:** American Health Lawyers Association, Health Insights Foundation, Institute of Medicine.
**Personal:** JD, University of Virginia, Order of the Coif; BA, Duke University.

## HATCHELL, Mike A
Locke Lord LLP, Austin
512 305 4752
mahatchell@lockelord.com
*Featured in Appellate Law (Nationwide), Litigation (Texas)*
See under Texas for profile.

## HAUETER, Eric S
Sidley Austin LLP, San Francisco
415 772 1231
ehaueter@sidley.com
*Featured in Capital Markets (California), Capital Markets (Nationwide)*
See under California for profile.

## HAWKE JR, John D
Arnold & Porter LLP, Washington, DC
202 942 5908
John.Hawke@aporter.com
*Featured in Financial Services Regulation (Nationwide)*

**Practice Areas:** Financial services.
**Career:** Mr Hawke, a Partner at Arnold & Porter since 1967, was General Counsel to the Federal Reserve Board, 1975-78; Under Secretary of the Treasury for Domestic Finance, 1995-98; and Comptroller of Currency, 1998-2004. He served on the Basel Committee on Banking Supervision, the Board of Directors of the FDIC, and the Federal Financial Institutions Examination Council.
**Publications:** Mr Hawke has published extensively on issues of financial regulation.
**Personal:** LLB, Columbia University School of Law, 1960. He has taught banking regulation at Georgetown University Law Center, Columbia Law School and Boston University Law School.

## HAWKINS, Ann A
Skadden, Arps, Slate, Meagher & Flom LLP & Affiliates, Houston
713 655 5104
ann.hawkins@skadden.com
*Featured in Energy & Natural Resources (Nationwide)*

**Practice Areas:** Ann A. Hawkins concentrates in the areas of development, financing, acquisition and disposition of energy projects, including gas, coal, renewables and nuclear power projects. She represents developers, investors, power purchasers, fuel suppliers, traders, contractors and financial institutions. Ms Hawkins has extensive experience structuring transactions and drafting and negotiating asset purchase agreements, power purchase agreements, tolling agreements, joint venture agreements, fuel supply agreements, operation and maintenance agreements, shared services agreements, construction contracts and loan and collateral documentation.
**Career:** JD, Tulane University Law School, 1994; BA, Newcomb College, Tulane University, 1991.

## HEALY, Peter
O'Melveny & Myers LLP, San Francisco
415 984 8833
phealy@omm.com
*Featured in Capital Markets (California), Capital Markets (Nationwide)*

**Practice Areas:** Peter T Healy is a partner in O'Melveny's San Francisco office and a member of the Capital Markets Practice. He has extensive experience representing companies and underwriters in public offerings, private placements, mergers and acquisitions, going-private transactions, and public and private debt offerings. Peter also has recent experience in fund formation, private equity and hedge fund activities. He frequently advises boards of directors and independent committees in connection with various capital market and M&A transactions.

## HECHT, James C
Skadden, Arps, Slate, Meagher & Flom LLP & Affiliates, Washington, DC
202 371 7370
James.Hecht@skadden.com
*Featured in International Trade (Nationwide)*

**Practice Areas:** Extensive experience with complex trade litigation and related policy advice, concentrating on trade remedy issues, anti-dumping and countervailing duty investigations, safeguard proceedings, and international dispute settlement. Counsels clients regarding wide spectrum of legislative and executive branch initiatives relating to trade and manufacturing policy, as well as trade aspects of climate change regulation. Substantial experience with trade negotiations in connection with WTO and other multilateral and bilateral agreements.
**Career:** Chief Counsel for Senate Majority Leader Trent Lott (1999-2000). JD, Yale Law School, 1991; BA, University of Virginia (Echols Scholar) 1988 (with distinction).

## HEEG, Peggy A
Fulbright & Jaworski LLP, Houston
713 651 8443
pheeg@fulbright.com
*Featured in Energy & Natural Resources (Nationwide)*

**Practice Areas:** Corporate; energy.
**Professional Memberships:** Advisory Board Member, National Association of Corporate Directors Texas; Member ABA DirectWomen
**Career:** Heeg is co-chair of Fulbright's Corporate Governance Practice Group and is an authority on energy regulation and corporate governance. Heeg uses her knowledge to solve complex regulatory, governance, business and enforcement matters. She has experience in CFTC and FERC regulation and in conducting internal investigations related to corporate malfeasance, market manipulation and regulatory compliance.
**Personal:** JD, The University of Louisville School of Law, 1986; BA, Political Science, The University of Louisville, 1983.

## HEFFERNAN, David
WilmerHale, Washington, DC
202 663 6360
david.heffernan@wilmerhale.com
*Featured in Transportation (Nationwide)*

**Practice Areas:** Partner; Chair, Aviation Practice. Represents clients, including major US and foreign air carriers (both passenger and cargo), regarding aviation-related corporate transactions, applications for economic authority, code-share authority, international routes and antitrust immunity. Advises clients on US laws, regulations, legislation and DOT/FAA/TSA policies regarding: airline alliances and joint ventures, computer reservations systems, licensing and certification, taxes and fees, airport slots, rates and charges, advertising and consumer enforcement policies, aviation security and competition policy.
**Personal:** JD, summa cum laude, Catholic University of America, Columbus School of Law, Washington, DC; MBS, University College Dublin, Ireland; BA, Trinity College, Dublin, Ireland.

## HEFFERON, Thomas M
Goodwin Procter LLP, Washington, DC
202 346 4029
thefferon@goodwinprocter.com
*Featured in Financial Services Regulation (Nationwide)*

**Practice Areas:** Mr Hefferon specializes in general civil litigation, with particular emphasis on the defense of financial institutions in the consumer financial services industry in both administrative proceedings and in the courtroom. Mr Hefferon is also Chair of the firm's Consumer Financial Services Litigation Practice and frequently provides compliance advice and litigation risk analysis to industry clients. He has been sole or joint lead counsel in the trial of cases in federal and state courts in Massachusetts, Connecticut, New York, Texas and Illinois.
**Personal:** JD, University of Chicago, 1986 (magna cum laude); BA, Trinity College, 1982 (magna cum laude).

## HEIDELBERGER, Brian L
Winston & Strawn LLP, Chicago
312 558 5897
bheidelberger@winston.com
*Featured in Media & Entertainment (Illinois), Advertising (Nationwide)*
See under Illinois for profile.

## HEIL, Joseph B
Dechert LLP, San Francisco
415 262 4510
joseph.heil@dechert.com
*Featured in Real Estate (Nationwide), Real Estate (California)*

**Practice Areas:** Mr Heil, co-chair of Dechert's finance and real estate practice, focuses on securitized lending, workouts, restructurings, commercial mortgage servicing, debt funds, mezzanine debt, preferred equity, and private equity transactions.
**Professional Memberships:** Member, California Bar; member, Mortgage Bankers Association of America; member, American College of Real Estate Lawyers.
**Career:** Helped develop the criteria used in rating CMBS transactions. Chief legal officer, Capital America/Nomura Asset Capital Corporation
**Personal:** University of Notre Dame (BA, 1983, with honors); University of California, Berkeley (MA, 1985); UCLA School of Law (JD, 1988, Order of the Coif).

## HEIM, Robert C
Dechert LLP, Philadelphia
215 994 2570
robert.heim@dechert.com
*Featured in Products Liability (Nationwide), Litigation (Pennsylvania)*
See under Pennsylvania for profile.

## HEIMAN, David G
Jones Day, Cleveland
216 586 7175
dgheiman@jonesday.com
*Featured in Bankruptcy/Restructuring (Nationwide), Bankruptcy/Restructuring (Ohio)*
See under Ohio for profile.

**HEINTZ, John**
Dickstein Shapiro LLP, Washington, DC
202 420 5373
heintzj@dicksteinshapiro.com
*Featured in Insurance (Nationwide), Insurance (District of Columbia)*
**Practice Areas:** John Heintz leads the firm's Insurance Coverage Group. He has secured billions of dollars in coverage for asbestos, lead, environmental contamination, class-action discrimination, directors' and officers' liabilities, and property and business interruption losses arising out of the 9/11 attacks and other catastrophic events. In the course of these representations, Mr Heintz has obtained favorable rulings for his clients in numerous landmark appellate cases in both state and federal courts.
**Personal:** Cornell University (BA, 1970), Princeton University (M.P.A., 1974), New York University School of Law (JD, 1977).

**HEINZELMAN, Kris F**
Cravath, Swaine & Moore LLP, New York
212 474 1336
kris.heinzelman@cravath.com
*Featured in Capital Markets (Nationwide)*
**Practice Areas:** Kris F. Heinzelman is a partner in Cravath's Corporate Department and serves as Chair of its Securities practice. His practice consists primarily of domestic and international corporate finance transactions, including public and private offerings of debt and equity securities. A significant portion of his practice is devoted to representing investment banking firms, which have included Credit Suisse, Goldman Sachs, J.P. Morgan Securities, Morgan Stanley and others. He has also represented corporate clients, including Cummins, Naspers and Olin.
**Personal:** Yale Law School (JD, 1976); Brown University (MA, AB, magna cum laude, 1973; Phi Beta Kappa). For more information: http://www.cravath.com/krisheinzelman.

**HELLER, Amy Erenrich**
McDermott Will & Emery LLP, New York
212 547 5584
aheller@mwe.com
*Featured in Wealth Management (Nationwide)*
**Practice Areas:** Advises clients in connection with domestic and international tax and estate planning matters.
**Professional Memberships:** Adjunct professor at New York University School of Law, teaching Advanced Income Taxation of Trusts & Estates. Chair of Generation-Skipping Transfer Tax Committee of the American Bar Association's Section of Real Property, Trust & Estate Law.
**Personal:** Harvard University (BA); Harvard Law School (JD); NYU Law School (LLM, Tax).

**HELLER, Lawrence H**
Greenberg Traurig, LLP, Santa Monica
310 586 7709
HellerL@gtlaw.com
*Featured in Wealth Management (Nationwide)*
**Practice Areas:** Tax; trusts and estates; wealth management; domestic and international estate planning; income tax planning for individuals;

private foundations and family business succession planning; certified tax specialist.
**Career:** Selected: Super Lawyers Magazine, 2004-13; The Best Lawyers in America, 2008-13; Top 100 Lawyers, The Los Angeles Business Journal, 2009; 'Top 5 Trusts and Estates Lawyers', The Los Angeles Business Journal, 2009; Chambers USA Guide, 2007-09; 2011-12. Rated, AV® Preeminent™ 5.0 out of 5.
**Personal:** LLM, Taxation, New York University, 1970; JD, University of Colorado School of Law, 1969.

**HELM, Robert W**
Dechert LLP, Washington, DC
202 261 3356
robert.helm@dechert.com
*Featured in Investment Funds (Nationwide)*
**Practice Areas:** Mr Helm focuses his practice in the financial services area. His clients include registered investment companies, private funds, UCITS, and traditional and alternative investment funds organized in other jurisdictions offered on a public and private basis. He is deputy chairman of the firm and a member of the policy committee and is also responsible for the firm's international activities.
**Professional Memberships:** Member and former chair, International Bar Association's Investment Funds Committee; member, advisory committees of the Mutual Fund Directors Forum and the Independent Directors Council
**Personal:** Stanford University (AB, 1979, with distinction); Stanford Law School (JD, 1982).

**HELMS, Shawn C**
K&L Gates, Dallas
214 939 5599
shawn.helms@klgates.com
*Featured in Outsourcing (Nationwide), Technology (Texas)*
See under Texas for profile.

**HELTZER, Harold J**
Crowell & Moring LLP, Washington, DC
202 624 2565
hheltzer@crowell.com
*Featured in Tax (District of Columbia), Tax (Nationwide)*
See under District of Columbia for profile.

**HEMMERSBAUGH, Paul A**
Sidley Austin LLP, Washington, DC
202 736 8538
phemmersbaugh@sidley.com
*Featured in Transportation (Nationwide)*
**Practice Areas:** Partner in Sidley's Washington, DC office practicing in Transportation. His practice concentrates on the representation of rail carriers and other transportation industry clients in a variety of regulatory proceedings, rate cases, acquisitions and consolidations, and litigation in federal and state courts. In addition to his representation of transportation clients in regulatory, litigation, and transactional matters, he has extensive experience representing other clients in regulatory and commercial litigation and appeals, and he frequently represents clients in litigation involving complex scientific, engineering, and economic issues and disputes.

**Career:** He serves as outside General Counsel to the District of Columbia Bar.

**HENDERSON JR, Donald B**
Willkie Farr & Gallagher LLP, New York
212 728 8262
dhenderson@willkie.com
*Featured in Insurance (Nationwide), Insurance (New York)*
**Practice Areas:** Partner in Corporate and Financial Services Department. Focuses on merger and acquisition transactions in the insurance industry, complex reinsurance transactions, and general corporate and regulatory matters for insurance clients. Practice includes advising clients in the purchase and sale of businesses, including both stock and asset transactions, and purchases and sales of specific blocks of business. Advises clients in connection with alternative risk transfer arrangements, life settlements and premium finance.
**Personal:** LLM, New York University, 1976. JD, University of Alabama Law Center, 1974. BS, University of Alabama, 1971. See: http://www.willkie.com/Donald_Henderson_Jr_

**HENDLER, Clifford B**
Crowell & Moring LLP, Washington, DC
202 624 2928
chendler@crowell.com
*Featured in Insurance (District of Columbia), Insurance (Nationwide)*
See under District of Columbia for profile.

**HENEGAR, Matthew**
Latham & Watkins LLP, New York
212 906 1814
matthew.henegar@lw.com
*Featured in Projects (Nationwide)*
**Practice Areas:** Represents financial institutions, developers and private equity sponsors in all phases of the development, financing and restructuring of power, renewable energy, oil and gas and other infrastructure projects. Has worked extensively on projects involving a wide range of financing structures, as well as complex intercompany asset sharing and intercreditor arrangements. Experience also includes work on highly structured asset-lien-based commodity hedging transactions and related intercreditor arrangements, as well as extensive involvement with federal and state guarantee and incentive programmes for renewable and alternative energy projects (including the DOE loan guarantee programmes and related applications).
**Career:** Qualified since 2000.

**HENES, Jonathan S**
Kirkland & Ellis LLP, New York
212-446-4927
jonathan.henes@kirkland.com
*Featured in Bankruptcy/Restructuring (Nationwide), Bankruptcy/Restructuring (New York)*
See under New York for profile.

**HENGEN, Nancy L**
Holland & Knight LLP, New York
212 513 3255
nancy.hengen@hklaw.com
*Featured in Transportation (Nationwide), Banking & Finance (Nationwide)*

**Practice Areas:**
**Career:** Nancy Hengen represents clients in sophisticated finance transactions and structuring focused on vessels, offshore drilling rigs and other offshore facilities, aircraft and rail equipment. Her extensive background encompasses commercial vessel finance, including loans, leasing, ship mortgages, Title XI financing, related security documentation and Jones Act issues. She represents both United States and foreign banks, financial institutions and other investors, as well as borrowers and lessees. She also has experience in Marshall Islands, Liberia and Vanuatu laws. Her clients have included major oil companies and other shipping companies as well as the financial institutions that finance them.

**HENGESBAUGH, Brian**
Baker & McKenzie, Chicago
312 861 3077
brian.hengesbaugh@bakermckenzie.com
*Featured in Technology (Illinois), Privacy & Data Security (Nationwide)*
**Practice Areas:** Regulatory and transactional issues, including privacy and data protection, data security and breach notification, electronic contracting, outsourcing, social media and online privacy.
**Professional Memberships:** Certified Information Privacy Professional (CIPP) for the International Association of Privacy Professionals; ABA International Law Section Member.
**Career:** Formerly Special Counsel to the General Counsel of the US Department of Commerce, negotiated the US-EU Safe Harbor Privacy Arrangement. Admitted to Indiana in 1995 and Illinois in 2004.
**Publications:** Frequent writer and speaker about US and global privacy and data protection issues.
**Personal:** JD, cum laude, University of Minnesota Law School; AB, Economics, Washington University.

**HENNIGAN, J Michael**
McKool Smith, Los Angeles
213 694 1200
hennigan@mckoolsmithhennigan.com
*Featured in Litigation (Nationwide), Litigation (California)*
**Practice Areas:** Complex commercial litigation
**Professional Memberships:** Fellow, American College of Trial Lawyers; American Law Institute; American Board of Trial Advocates; Board of Visitors, University of Arizona College of Law; Trustee, Los Angeles County Bar Association; Chair, Litigation Section, Los Angeles County Bar Association, 1998-99; Member, California Judicial Council Task Force on Complex Civil Litigation.
**Career:** Mr Hennigan has been lead counsel in more than 45 major jury trials in state and federal court. As lead trial counsel for plaintiffs, he has litigated judgments and settlements of more than $8 billion for his clients. Before entering private practice, Mr Hennigan was a trial attorney with the Antitrust Division of the United States Department of Justice, and was a lecturer in research and writing at the University of Arizona College of Law in 1973.

**Personal:** University of Arizona College of Law (JD, with distinction, Order of the Coif, 1970); University of Arizona (BA, 1966).

## HENSLEY, Dennis C
Sidley Austin LLP, Washington, DC
202 736 8163
dhensley@sidley.com
*Featured in Financial Services Regulation (Nationwide), Securities (Nationwide)*
**Practice Areas:** Senior counsel and former head of Sidley's Securities and Futures Regulatory practice. He has over 30 years of experience in securities regulatory and enforcement matters. He advises financial services firms – including investment and commercial banks, broker-dealers and hedge funds – on a broad variety of regulatory, enforcement, compliance, and transaction matters. Mr Hensley has advised broker-dealer clients on the creation and restructuring of major business units, strategic corporate transactions including mergers and acquisitions of broker-dealers, cross-border transactions and the creation of new business units overseas, and the defense of SEC, FINRA and NYSE enforcement actions and investigations.

## HENZE II, William F
Jones Day, New York
212 326 3603
wfhenze@jonesday.com
*Featured in Energy & Natural Resources (Nationwide)*
**Practice Areas:** Represents integrated oil and gas companies, pipelines, oilfield equipment and services companies, local distribution companies, electric utilities, nonregulated electricity producers, and energy traders. A frequent speaker and author of numerous articles, he is listed in The Best Lawyers in America, Chambers USA, and Law and Politics' New York Super Lawyers. Recognised for superior client service capabilities by BTI Consulting Group.
**Professional Memberships:** Member of the drafting committee for the EEI Master Power Purchase and Sale Agreement. Energy Bar Association. State Bars of Texas and Arizona.

## HERLIHY, Edward D
Wachtell, Lipton, Rosen & Katz, New York
212 403 1207
edherlihy@wlrk.com
*Featured in Financial Services Regulation (Nationwide), Corporate/M&A (New York)*
**Practice Areas:** Practice focuses on the largest and most complex bank and financial institution mergers and acquisitions and recapitalizations throughout the United States and is often called upon to represent companies involved in takeover battles and proxy contests, including investment banking firms in connection with a wide variety of financial institution matters.
**Career:** Partner at Wachtell, Lipton, Rosen & Katz. Serves as co-chairman of the firm's Executive Committee.
**Publications:** Writes and lectures regularly on issues involving banking and financial matters.

## HERLIHY, Scott C
Latham & Watkins LLP, Washington, DC
202 637 2277
scott.herlihy@lw.com
*Featured in Capital Markets (Nationwide)*
**Practice Areas:** Focuses on public and private securities offerings, mergers and acquisitions, and general corporate governance and securities matters for both public and private companies. Has extensive experience advising public real estate investment trusts.
**Professional Memberships:** Member, District of Columbia and Virginia State bars.
**Career:** Co-Chair, Public Company Representation Practice (2007-2012); Co-Chair, Corporate Governance Task Force; Adjunct professor (corporate governance), Georgetown Law Center (2007-2012).
**Personal:** JD, University of Notre Dame, 1991; BBA, College of William and Mary, 1985.

## HERMAN, Jason
Simpson Thacher & Bartlett LLP, New York
212 455 2000
jherman@stblaw.com
*Featured in Investment Funds (Nationwide)*
**Practice Areas:** Corporate Partner focusing on private fund formation and other facets of alternative asset management. Mr Herman represents some of the largest and most well known sponsors of private funds, including Apax, AllianceBernstein, A&M Capital, GSO/Blackstone, KKR, Lightyear, Morgan Stanley, Northwood Partners, Square Mile Capital, The Carlyle Group and Tiger Management.
**Career:** Joined Firm, 2001; Partner, 2012.
**Personal:** Harvard Law School (JD, 2001); University of Michigan (BA,1997 with highest distinction, Phi Beta Kappa).

## HERPE, David
McDermott Will & Emery LLP, Chicago
312 984 7656
dherpe@mwe.com
*Featured in Wealth Management (Nationwide)*
**Practice Areas:** Partner in firm's Chicago office. Counsels families, family offices, business owners, executives and individuals on all aspects of sophisticated estate and wealth transfer planning. Experience includes the preparation, administration and construction of wills and trusts, charitable gift planning, formation and operation of private foundations, formation and reorganization of closely held corporations, partnerships and LLCs, complex insurance planning, leveraged wealth transfer techniques and family-owned business succession.
**Personal:** University of Chicago Law School, JD (cum laude, Order of the Coif), 1978; University of Illinois at Urbana-Champaign, BA (magna cum laude), 1975.

## HERSHMAN, Stuart
DLA Piper LLP (US), Chicago
312 368 2164
stuart.hershman@dlapiper.com
*Featured in Franchising (Nationwide)*
**Practice Areas:** Franchise and distribution.
**Career:** He focuses his practice in the franchising, general dealership and distribution, and antitrust areas. He has structured, documented, and helped implement hundreds of franchise programs, dealership and distribution relationships, and intellectual property licensing arrangements. He also has engaged in antitrust counseling, particularly in pricing, supply, and other dealership and distribution matters, for public and private companies.
**Personal:** JD, University Michigan (cum laude); BA, University of Michigan (with high honors).

## HESTER, Theodore M
King & Spalding LLP, Washington, DC
202 626 2901
thester@kslaw.com
*Featured in Government (Nationwide)*
**Practice Areas:** Represents clients before Congress and executive agencies, and he has developed particular expertise representing clients being investigated by congressional committees and the Government Accountability Office.
**Professional Memberships:** Mr Hester is a Member of the Boards of Directors of the Ethics Resource Center and the Appleseed Foundation. He is a Member of the William & Mary Washington Council.
**Career:** From 1971-72, Mr Hester was a legislative assistant to US Senator David H Gambrell.
**Personal:** Mr Hester is a graduate of Harvard Law School (JD 1969) and the University of Georgia (AB 1966).

## HINER, Thomas Y
Hunton & Williams LLP, New York
212 309 1302
thiner@hunton.com
*Featured in Capital Markets (Nationwide)*
**Practice Areas:** Mr Hiner represents borrowers, lenders, investors and entrepreneurial companies on a variety of corporate finance transactions with particular focus in the last decade on representing loan servicers and their lenders and investors, and other housing market participants in financing and M&A transactions, including arranging secured financing in securitised structures. Mr Hiner has led acquisition and venture capital transactions, and a wide range of public and private equity and debt offerings and placements, representing issuers, underwriters and investors.
**Professional Memberships:** New York State Bar; Virginia State Bar.
**Personal:** BA, University of Virginia, 1986; JD, Duke University, 1989.

## HINMAN JR, William H
Simpson Thacher & Bartlett LLP, Palo Alto
650 251 5000
whinman@stblaw.com
*Featured in Capital Markets (California), Capital Markets (Nationwide)*
See under California for profile.

## HINSON, H Douglas
Alston & Bird LLP, Atlanta
404 881 7590
doug.hinson@alston.com
*Featured in ERISA Litigation (Nationwide)*
**Practice Areas:** Led defense of numerous Fortune 500 clients in ERISA class actions, including 401(k)/employer stock and fees, welfare benefit termination, defined benefit calculation and cutback, private ESOP, white collar and severance matters. Concentrates on ERISA litigation; also securities, complex commercial and insurance class action defense.
**Professional Memberships:** American Bar Association (Past Chair, Employee Benefits Committee, Tort, Trial and Insurance Practice Section; Member Joint Committee on Employee Benefits).
**Career:** Co-chair, firm's Compensation, Benefits & ERISA Litigation Group. Frequent lecturer and author on ERISA Litigation topics.
**Personal:** BA, magna cum laude, Emory University (1982); JD, cum laude, Georgetown University (1986).

## HIRSCHSON, Linda B.
Greenberg Traurig, LLP, New York
212 801 9342
HirschsonL@gtlaw.com
*Featured in Wealth Management (Nationwide)*
**Practice Areas:** Chair, NY Estate Planning Group. Tax; wealth management.
**Professional Memberships:** American College of Trust and Estates Counsel (ACTEC) (Former Regent; Former New York Downstate Chair; Past chair, Transfer Tax Study Committee); Past chair, Trusts and Estates Law Section, New York State Bar Association. Chair, Metropolitan Museum of Art, Professional Advisory Council. Member, N.Y. EPTL-SCPA.
**Career:** Listed: Best Lawyers in America, 1998-2013; Super Lawyers magazine, 2006-12. Rated, AV® Preeminent™ 5.0 out of 5.
**Publications:** Co-author; 'The American Taxpayer Relief Act: The End to Estate Planning Cliffhangers?, Warren's Heaton Legislative & Case Digest, February 2013.

## HIRSH, Robert M
Paul, Weiss, Rifkind, Wharton & Garrison LLP, New York
212 373 3108
rhirsh@paulweiss.com
*Featured in Investment Funds (Nationwide)*
**Practice Areas:** A Partner in the Corporate Department and Chair Emeritus of the Private Funds Group, Mr Hirsh focuses on the organization, operation and restructuring of private investment funds, including buyout funds, hybrid funds and venture capital funds. Mr Hirsh has handled organizational work for numerous buyout sponsors. He has acted as advisor with regard to the preparation of the funds' offering materials and fund raising strategies, and the preparation and negotiation of the definitive organizational documents. He has also handled transactional work involving funds, including employment

arrangements and multi-billion dollar private equity spin-outs and restructurings.

## HIRSHMAN, Neil S
Kirkland & Ellis LLP, Chicago
312 862 2493
neil.hirshman@kirkland.com
*Featured in Outsourcing (Nationwide), Technology (Illinois)*

**Practice Areas:** Neil's practice focuses on intellectual property and technology related transactions, including outsourcing (business process and information technology), software development, licensing, telecommunications, and strategic alliances. In his outsourcing work, Neil has represented both customers and providers, domestically and internationally, in the outsourcing of functions including IT, human resources, F&A, procurement, learning and call centers, among others. Neil also advises clients on intellectual property and technology issues that arise in mergers, acquisitions, divestitures and bankruptcies.
**Professional Memberships:** Chair, Chicago Chapter, International Association of Outsourcing Professionals.
**Personal:** University of Illinois at Urbana-Champaign (BSEE, 1987); Harvard Law School (JD, 1990).

## HJELM, Lars-Erik A
Akin Gump Strauss Hauer & Feld LLP, Washington, DC
1 202 887 4175
lhjelm@akingump.com
*Featured in International Trade (Nationwide)*

**Practice Areas:** Represents Fortune 500 companies whose imports and exports are regulated by the Department of Homeland Security agencies of Customs and Border Protection (CBP) and Immigration and Customs Enforcement (ICE), as well as other federal agencies.
**Career:** Assistant chief counsel and managing lawyer for Customs Service in the mid-Atlantic. Was principal legal advisor to the customs ports of Baltimore, Philadelphia and Washington, D.C. and customs Special-Agent-in-Charge. Lawyer in the Office of the Chief Counsel and the Office of the General Counsel of the Department of the Treasury.
**Personal:** BA with honors, University of Pennsylvania, 1985; JD, Emory University, 1989.

## HO, Allyson N
Morgan, Lewis & Bockius LLP, Dallas
713 890 5000
aho@morganlewis.com
*Featured in Appellate Law (Nationwide), Litigation (Texas)*
See under Texas for profile.

## HOBEL, Lawrence
Covington & Burling LLP, San Francisco
415 591 7028
lhobel@cov.com
*Featured in Insurance (Nationwide), Insurance (California)*

**Practice Areas:** Representation of policyholders in first and third party coverage disputes under all policy types, including mass tort, errors and omissions, construction defect, and catastrophic business interruption and property damage claims. Additionally, Mr Hobel represents clients in environmental matters. Clients include Aerojet-General Corporation, Bondex International, Freeport-McMoRan Copper & Gold, Inc., Sierra Pacific Industries.
**Personal:** University of California, Berkeley (AB, 1973); Phi Beta Kappa; University of California, Berkeley, Boalt Hall School of Law (JD, 1976).

## HOCHBERG, Kevin J
Sidley Austin LLP, Chicago
312 853 2085
khochberg@sidley.com
*Featured in Capital Markets (Nationwide)*

**Practice Areas:** Partner in Sidley's Chicago office. Focuses on structured finance, asset securitization, merger and acquisition financing, restructurings and bankruptcies, and other secured and unsecured lending transactions. Regularly represents issuers, monoline insurance companies, underwriters and investors in both public and private offerings of asset-backed securities, including commercial paper conduit transactions, Rule 144A and public offerings. Practice involves workouts and bankruptcies as well as new issuances and has covered a range of asset classes, including trade receivables, student loans, auto loans, equipment leases, rental car fleets, shipping containers, container chassis, railcars, utility stranded costs, whole business securitizations and relocation company receivables.

## HODARA, Fred S
Akin Gump Strauss Hauer & Feld LLP, New York
212 872 8040
fhodara@akingump.com
*Featured in Bankruptcy/Restructuring (Nationwide), Bankruptcy/Restructuring (New York)*

**Practice Areas:** Chair, Financial Restructuring Practice Group. Represents creditors' committees in Chapter 11 cases and out-of-court and cross-border restructurings, with emphasis on committees comprised of diverse creditor constituencies. Represents hedge funds, insurance companies, bank lenders and other institutional investors and trade creditors. Failed financial institutions specialist in bankruptcies of brokerages and failed banks and cross-border bankruptcy specialist.
**Professional Memberships:** INSOL International; American College of Investment Counsel; Turnaround Management Association.
**Personal:** BA, State University of New York at Binghamton (1977); JD, New York University (1981). Named among 'America's Top 100 Restructuring Professionals'.

## HOFFMAN, Michael K
Skadden, Arps, Slate, Meagher & Flom LLP & Affiliates, New York
212 735 3406
michael.hoffman@skadden.com
*Featured in Investment Funds (Nationwide)*

**Practice Areas:** Michael Hoffman is a member of the firm's Investment Management Group. He represents public and private investment funds, business development companies and real estate investment trusts and their investment advisers, underwriters and investment banks in the structuring and distribution of financial products in domestic and cross-border transactions. Mr Hoffman counsels investment funds and their boards of directors, advisory boards and investment advisers in connection with transactional, regulatory and compliance issues.
**Career:** JD, Duke University, 1989 (Duke Law Journal); BA, University of Notre Dame, 1986 (cum laude).

## HOFFMANN, Thomas
Ballard Spahr LLP, Washington, DC
202 661 2215
hoffmannrt@ballardspahr.com
*Featured in Projects (Nationwide)*

**Practice Areas:** Mr Hoffmann is the Practice Co-Leader of the Energy and Project Finance Group. He concentrates on energy industry transactions, including project development, investments, finance, and acquisitions. He frequently represents developers and investors in development and financing of solar, wind, and biomass projects, and gas and cogeneration projects. He is a recognized expert in structuring public-private partnerships for energy deals.
**Career:** Admissions: District of Columbia Maryland.
**Publications:** Co-author, "Public-Private Partnerships for Solar Development: Notes from the Field," Solar Industry Magazine.
**Personal:** New York University School of Law, JD Root-Tilden Scholar Oxford University, Law BA Georgetown University, BA.

## HOHENSTEIN, James
Holland & Knight LLP, New York
212 513 3213
jim.hohenstein@hklaw.com
*Featured in Transportation (Nationwide)*

**Practice Areas:** National Practice Group Leader of the Maritime Group and partner in the firm's Litigation Section, his practice focuses in the areas of maritime and commercial litigation, including charter parties, cargo damage actions, maritime liens, maritime bankruptcies and workouts, the impact of piratical acts as well as marine casualty and insurance issues. He has participated in a wide variety of arbitrations and litigations, both in the US and abroad, and has appeared in actions in New York and other maritime jurisdictions in the United States. He has extensive trial experience in commercial and maritime cases, including bankruptcy actions.

## HOLCOMB, Ryan S
Bracewell & Giuliani LLP, Houston
713 221 1282
ryan.holcomb@bgllp.com
*Featured in Projects (Nationwide)*

**Practice Areas:** Represents clients in a wide variety of transactions in the electric power, commodity trading, and oil and gas industries. Represents energy companies, financial institutions, commodity trading businesses and private equity investors in a wide variety of energy transactions and financings. Experience includes acquisition and divestiture transactions involving power generation facilities, commodity trading portfolios and other energy assets, power purchase and tolling agreements and structured commodity trading arrangements.
**Personal:** JD, Baylor University School of Law, 1998; BBA, The University of Texas at Austin, 1994.

## HOLLAND, Mark
Goodwin Procter LLP, New York
212 459 7152
mholland@goodwinprocter.com
*Featured in Securities (Nationwide), Litigation (New York)*

**Practice Areas:** Mr Holland is a Partner in the firm's Litigation Department and a member of its Securities Litigation and SEC Enforcement Practice. He has over 30 years experience defending securities class actions and shareholder derivative suits. He focuses on defending underwriters in public offering litigation and defending investment advisers and mutual funds in litigation under the Investment Company Act of 1940. Mr Holland has appeared as counsel of record for defendants in many of the major securities litigations of the past decade.
**Personal:** JD, Cornell Law School, 1981 (with honors); BA, Colgate University, 1978 (cum laude).

## HOLMES, Hillary H.
Baker Botts LLP, Houston
713 229 1508
hillary.holmes@bakerbotts.com
*Featured in Energy & Natural Resources (Nationwide)*

**Practice Areas:** Capital markets, corporate law, and mergers & acquisitions in the energy industry. Extensive knowledge of US securities laws. Counsel to corporations, master limited partnerships (MLPs) and underwriter investment banks. Regular counsel to public companies, including Exchange Act reporting, stock exchange compliance and corporate governance.
**Professional Memberships:** State Bar of Texas, Women in the Profession Committee; Houston Young Lawyers Association; Houston Bar Association; Texas Bar Foundation; Houston Young Lawyers Foundation
**Personal:** JD, University of Pennsylvania Law School; Certificate in Public Policy and Management, Wharton School; BA (cum laude), public policy studies and women's studies, Duke University.

## HOLMSTEAD, Jeffrey R
Bracewell & Giuliani LLP, Washington, DC
202 828 5852
jeff.holmstead@bgllp.com
*Featured in Climate Change (Nationwide), Environment (District of Columbia)*

**Practice Areas:** Advises clients in an increasingly complex regulatory, legal and public relations landscape, drawing on experience in policy development, administrative and legislative advocacy, litigation and strategic communications. Works with clients on issues related to climate change, Clean Air Act policy and enforcement, and energy policy — including development of new coal-

fired power plants, refineries, renewable energy sources, and electric transmission infrastructure.
**Career:** Former Associate Counsel to President George HW Bush (1989-93), environmental policy; Former Assistant Administrator, Air and Radiation, US EPA (2001-05).
**Personal:** JD, Yale Law School, 1987; BA, Brigham Young University, 1984.

### HOLTZER, Gary T
Weil, Gotshal & Manges LLP, New York
212 310 8463
gary.holtzer@weil.com
*Featured in Bankruptcy/Restructuring (Nationwide), Bankruptcy/Restructuring (New York)*
See under New York for profile.

### HOMMER, Scott
Venable LLP, Tysons Corner
703 760 1658
shommer@Venable.com
*Featured in Government (Nationwide)*
**Practice Areas:** Government Contracts.
**Career:** Scott Hommer co-heads Venable's Government Contracts Group. His practice includes business counseling and litigation focusing on government contractors and technology companies. He represents clients locally, nationally and internationally on negotiating contracts, acquisitions, protecting intellectual property rights, and litigating successfully. He has experience counseling clients doing business with Federal, state and local governments and represents clients on contract administration, contract claims and disputes, bid protests, contract terminations, teaming agreements, conflicts of interest, False Claims Act matters, intellectual property rights, and small business programs.
**Personal:** JD, Georgetown University Law Center, BA, with high distinction, Pennsylvania State University.

### HONAN, William J
Holland & Knight LLP, New York
212 513 3200
bill.honan@hklaw.com
*Featured in Transportation (Nationwide)*
**Practice Areas:** William Honan is the Executive Partner of Holland & Knight's New York office. He has more than 40 years experience in all forms of maritime contracts as a draftsman, negotiator and interpreter and has handled more than 100 maritime arbitrations to conclusion. He is vice-chairman of the Documentary Committee of Intertanko, an entity that represents most of the privately owned tanker owners in the world. He is also a member of: Arbitration Committee of the ABA Section of Dispute Resolutions; Committee on Arbitration and ADR of the International Bar Association; and Committee on Maritime Arbitration - Maritime Law Association.

### HONG, Ki P
Skadden, Arps, Slate, Meagher & Flom LLP & Affiliates, Washington, DC
202 371 7017
Ki.Hong@skadden.com
*Featured in Government (Nationwide)*
**Practice Areas:** Advises major corporations from a wide range of industries on political law

issues they face when engaging in government affairs or government procurement activity. Issues include federal and state campaign finance, lobbying, ethics and conflict-of-interest laws. Also advises clients on "pay-to-play" laws imposing restrictions on corporate and individual employee political activities applicable when companies have or seek government contracts. A Washingtonian Top Lawyer for Ethics and Election Law.
**Career:** JD, Harvard Law School, 1992 (cum laude); BA, Cornell University, 1989 (cum laude).
**Publications:** Co-Author, PLI Corporate Political Activities. Co-Author, Ethics Handbook for Entertaining and Lobbying Public Officials.

### HOOD, John T
Morgan, Lewis & Bockius LLP, New York
212 309 6281
jhood@morganlewis.com
*Featured in Energy & Natural Resources (Nationwide)*
**Practice Areas:** John T. Hood is a Partner in Morgan Lewis's Business and Finance Practice. Mr Hood focuses his practice on corporate finance, securities law, corporate governance, mergers and acquisitions, joint ventures, and general corporate matters. He primarily focuses on the energy and utility industry. He has been involved in a wide variety of financial transactions, including debt and equity offerings, private placements, public offerings, structured finance, and bank lending transactions. Mr Hood also has experience on project financing and leveraged lease transactions of utility facilities, including nuclear power plants, coal-fired generating stations, combustion turbines, cogeneration facilities, and stand-by reservoirs.

### HOOPER, Chester D
Holland & Knight LLP, Boston
617 854 1472
chester.hooper@hklaw.com
*Featured in Transportation (Nationwide)*
**Practice Areas:** Of Counsel in the Maritime Litigation Section. More than 40 years of practice involving vessel casualty, cargo loss and damage, advice on bills of lading and other shipping documents. Past president of The Maritime Law Association of the United States (1994-96) and a Titulary member of the Comité Maritime International. He was a member of the US delegation to the United Nations Commission on International Trade Law Working Group III that drafted the Rotterdam Rules to govern international carriage of goods that includes an international sea leg. He teaches Admiralty Law at the Boston University School of Law.

### HOOPER, James E.
Wheeler Trigg O'Donnell LLP, Denver
303 244 1849
hooper@wtotrial.com
*Featured in Products Liability (Nationwide)*
**Practice Areas:** Helps businesses defend complex, scientific and technically challenging lawsuits. As national counsel, has litigated cases ranging from products liability to civil RICO and federal land use. Practice centers on high-profile,

large-exposure, and expert-intensive cases involving challenges to design, risk and safety profiles and marketing of pharmaceuticals, medical devices, and building materials. Has obtained judicial rulings favorable to business in the areas of expert scientific evidence, product safety warnings, and medical causation.
**Professional Memberships:** Pfizer Legal Alliance Roundtable, DRI Drug and Medical Device Section.
**Personal:** JD, University of Michigan, 1992; B.S., Physics, US Military Academy West Point, 1984.

### HOPKINSON, R Ronald
Cadwalader, Wickersham & Taft LLP, New York
212 504 6789
ron.hopkinson@cwt.com
*Featured in Private Equity (Nationwide)*
**Practice Areas:** Chair, Private Equity Group. Focuses on mergers and acquisitions, private equity, and complex corporate transactions. Involved in some of the largest leveraged buyouts and high profile private equity transactions consummated in the marketplace on behalf of large private equity firms and consortiums. Works with leading corporations in major acquisitions, joint ventures, and corporate restructurings. Representations include counsel to Quest Software, Inc. Chairman and CEO Vincent Smith; the US Treasury in the sale of its remaining equity interests in Chrysler Group, and in the General Motors and Chrysler restructurings; a consortium formed by The Carlyle Group and Welsh Carson in connection with the $7 billion acquisition of QwestDex; a consortium formed by The Blackstone Group, The Carlyle Group, Hellman & Friedman LLC, Kohlberg Kravis Roberts & Co. L.P. and Thomas H. Lee Partners, L.P. in the $12 billion acquisition of VNU, Inc.
**Personal:** JD, Harvard University; BA, Harvard University.

### HORD, Charles
Chadbourne & Parke LLP, New York
212 408 5353
chord@chadbourne.com
*Featured in Energy & Natural Resources (Nationwide)*
**Practice Areas:** Charles Hord's practice is primarily related to corporate and finance law. During his career, he has advised a number of companies and financial institutions concerning a broad range of transactions, including mergers and acquisitions involving both public and private companies, domestic and foreign joint ventures, public offerings and private placements of securities, institutional and bank lending, restructurings, leveraged recapitalizations and buy-outs, leasing and structured financings. These transactions have involved a broad range of businesses, including energy, manufacturing, retailing, technology, life insurance, publishing and telecommunications.
**Professional Memberships:** New York State Bar Association.

### HORKOVICH, Robert M
Anderson Kill & Olick, P.C., New York
212 278 1322
rhorkovich@andersonkill.com
*Featured in Insurance (Nationwide), Insurance (New York)*
**Practice Areas:** Robert M. Horkovich has obtained over $5 billion in settlements and judgments from insurance companies for corporate and government policyholders over the past decade. As lead trial counsel for the State of California, he won a major jury verdict securing coverage for the clean-up of the Stringfellow Acid Pits that was upheld on issues of core interest to policyholders by the State Supreme Court in 2012, at which point recovered gross settlements exceeded $130 million plus $58 million in defense payments (the underlying jury verdict was the largest in the US in insurance in 2005). In Fuller-Austin, he won a jury verdict of over $188 million against numerous insurance companies in an asbestos insurance coverage case (the 9th largest verdict in the US in 2003). His victories also include six landmark state Supreme Court Decisions, two ground breaking Court of Appeal decisions, eight jury verdicts and eight bench trial decisions in favor of policyholders. He presently is lead insurance counsel for the WCI Trust in the Chinese Drywall multi-district litigation and serves on the insurance work-group for the plaintiffs' steering committee in the Deepwater Horizon (BP) multi-district litigation. He has also been engaged on several projects as insurance counsel to the United Nations.
**Publications:** Mr Horkovich frequently lectures and writes on insurance recovery issues. He is co-editor of the book, The Policyholder Advisor, published by Juris Publishing.

### HORN, Charles M
Morrison & Foerster LLP, Washington, DC
202 887 1555
charleshorn@mofo.com
*Featured in Financial Services Regulation (Nationwide)*
**Practice Areas:** Practice focuses on banking and financial services matters. Represents domestic and global financial services firms on regulatory, compliance and transactional issues affecting their organization, structure, governance, management, operations and business activities. Advises banks and other financial services firms on federal and state financial regulation, supervision, enforcement, and compliance matters affecting corporate, institutional, and retail business activities. Extensive experience in capital markets, asset management and other financial products and services, and cross-sector (banking, securities, insurance) financial services activities.

### HOROWITZ, Alan
Miller & Chevalier Chartered, Washington, DC
202 626 5839
ahorowitz@milchev.com
*Featured in Tax (Nationwide)*
**Practice Areas:** US Supreme Court and appellate litigation, with special emphasis on tax litigation.

**Career:** Mr Horowitz has argued 28 cases in the US Supreme Court, plus many others in federal courts of appeals. He has represented major corporations and other clients at all levels of federal court litigation. He served 11 years in the Solicitor General's Office at the Department of Justice, where he briefed and argued some of the most significant tax cases of that period, plus other cases addressing various constitutional, statutory, and criminal issues.

**Personal:** JD, Columbia University, 1977; SB, Massachusetts Institute of Technology, 1974.

### HOROWITZ, Douglas S.
Cahill Gordon & Reindel LLP, New York
212 701 3036
dhorowitz@cahill.com
*Featured in Capital Markets (Nationwide)*

**Practice Areas:** Represents leading investment banks, commercial banks and public and private corporations in leveraged finance transactions involving both new issuance of secured and unsecured high yield debt securities, syndicated institutional loans and asset based loans and out-of-court restructurings. Also represents investment banks and corporations in connection with initial public offerings and other equity securities offerings. Works on both the high-yield bond and bank sides of acquisition financings and refinancings and has practiced in a variety of industries including technology, media and telecommunications, automotive, healthcare and natural resources.

**Personal:** JD, Cornell Law School; MBA, Cornell University; BA, Columbia University.

### HOROWITZ, Gary I
Simpson Thacher & Bartlett LLP, New York
212 455 7113
ghorowitz@stblaw.com
*Featured in Private Equity (Nationwide), Corporate/M&A (New York), Insurance (New York)*

**Practice Areas:** Corporate Partner concentrating on M&A for private equity firms and corporations, joint ventures and corporate finance matters, with an emphasis on asset management, insurance, healthcare and media. Advises corporations and appears before their boards regarding general corporate, disclosure and corporate governance matters. Represents Kohlberg Kravis Roberts & Co., CVC Capital Partners, Dillards, Axis Financial, The Phoenix Companies, Ameriprise Financial, The Carlyle Group and the major investment banks.

**Career:** Joined firm, 1982; Partner, 1989.

**Personal:** BS, Cornell University, 1978; JD, Columbia Law School, 1981, Harlan Fiske Stone Scholar; Columbia Law Review, Editor, 1980-1981.

### HOROWITZ, Steven G
Cleary Gottlieb Steen & Hamilton LLP, New York
212 225 2580
shorowitz@cgsh.com
*Featured in Real Estate (Nationwide), Real Estate (New York)*

**Practice Areas:** Real estate, mortgage finance, joint ventures, capital markets, M&A. Clients:

TPG Capital, Genting, YOTEL, Catellus, Citigroup, Goldman Sachs, Home Depot, Irvine Company, Istithmar, Kindred Healthcare, McDonald's, Neiman Marcus, Nortel, Open Space Institute, Starwood Hotels, Tom Ford, Zegna, Family Dollar.

**Professional Memberships:** American College of Real Estate Lawyers; Anglo-American Real Property Institute.

**Career:** Partner, 1989. Lecturer-in-Law, Columbia Law (2003 - present); Hill & Barlow (1981-1987); US District Court Monitor (1979-1981); Judicial Clerk, Joseph Tauro (1978-1979). JD, cum laude, Harvard Law (1978); MPP, cum laude, Kennedy School (1978); BA, magna cum laude, Yale (1972).

**Publications:** Lecturer/author, ALI-ABA, PLI, CLE seminars.

### HORTON, Michel Yves
Morgan, Lewis & Bockius LLP, Los Angeles
213 612 7300
mhorton@morganlewis.com
*Featured in Insurance (Nationwide), Insurance (California)*

**Practice Areas:** Co-Chair of firm's worldwide Insurance practice. Practice concentrates on insurance counseling and dispute resolution, including complex litigation in federal and state courts involving insurance coverage for toxic torts, product liability, environmental property damage and personal injury, medical devices, product recall, and financial losses. Also assists clients in drafting specialty market insurance policies, particularly in connection with future environmental and toxic tort exposures, through domestic insurers and offshore captives. Has tried bench and jury trials in courts throughout the country, including in California, Delaware, Illinois and Iowa.

### HOSKING, James
Chaffetz Lindsey LLP, New York
212 257 6963
james.hosking@chaffetzlindsey.com
*Featured in International Arbitration (Nationwide)*

**Practice Areas:** International arbitration, business litigation, international law.

**Career:** One of the founding partners of Chaffetz Lindsey, James Hosking focuses on international arbitration and commercial litigation. His current cases cover complex contracts, JVs, licensing, investment protection and sovereign immunity issues across the energy, telecommunications and construction sectors. He was previously a partner with Clifford Chance in New York and earlier practiced in New Zealand. He teaches, speaks and publishes widely on international arbitration.

**Publications:** Co-author of A Guide to the ICDR International Arbitration Rules (OUP, 2011).

**Personal:** BA & LLB (Honors) University of Auckland (1990-1994); LLM Harvard Law School (2000). Admitted in New York.

### HOWARD, Nigel L
Covington & Burling LLP, New York
212 841 1020
nhoward@cov.com
*Featured in Outsourcing (Nationwide), Technology (New York)*

**Practice Areas:** Focuses on technology, outsourcing, privacy and IP issues. Represents clients in complex technology transactions, including outsourcing, licensing, corporate partnering, and online advertising transactions, during IP property purchases and sales, and in reviews of IP portfolios in relation to corporate financing and M&A transactions. Experience includes cross-border technology transfers, development and testing arrangements, distribution channels, technology deployment, data licenses and electronic commerce as well as privacy laws with regard to electronic databases and online services.

**Professional Memberships:** AIPLA, Law Society of England and Wales.

**Personal:** University of London (LLM, 1991), Lancaster University, England (LLB, 1987).

### HOWE, Joseph
Arnold & Porter LLP, Washington, DC
202 942 5230
Joseph.Howe@aporter.com
*Featured in Tax (District of Columbia), Capital Markets (Nationwide)*

**Practice Areas:** Joseph Howe, the Head of the Tax Practice at Arnold & Porter, is an experienced tax and business lawyer with a concentration in the representation of REITs and structuring funds, complex real estate, partnership and business transactions in the US, Europe, and Asia. With the globalization of REITs, he has been active in representing REITs in operations outside the US and exploring the use of foreign REIT structures. Mr Howe has extensive experience in cross-border transactions involving multiple tax systems and parties from different countries in structuring tax efficient operations.

### HOWELL, John E
K&L Gates, Dallas
214 939 5461
john.howell@klgates.com
*Featured in Outsourcing (Nationwide), Technology (Texas)*

**Practice Areas:** Since 1975, John Howell has represented clients in structuring, negotiating, and documenting a wide variety of outsourcing and similar service agreements, as well as other complex business arrangements, with a primary focus on technology-based businesses. He represents both service providers and customers in outsourcing transactions and is keenly aware of their specialized legal needs. His professional associations include memberships in the Computer & Technology Section of the State Bar of Texas and the Computer Law Section of the Dallas Bar Association.

### HOWELL III, George C
Hunton & Williams LLP, Richmond
804 788 8793
ghowell@hunton.com
*Featured in Capital Markets (Nationwide)*

**Practice Areas:** Mr Howell's practice focuses on the federal income tax aspects of REITs, private investment funds, securitizations, financial products, and specialty finance companies.

**Professional Memberships:** American Bar Association, Section of Taxation; American College of Tax Counsel.

**Career:** Partner and Head of the firm's Tax and ERISA Team.

**Personal:** Mr Howell received his AB in Economics from Princeton University in 1978, graduating magna cum laude and Phi Beta Kappa. He received his JD in 1981 from the University of Virginia, where he was a Member of the Law Review and the founding editor-in-chief of the Virginia Tax Review.

### HOWITT, John P
Clifford Chance US LLP, New York
212 878 8250
john.howitt@cliffordchance.com
*Featured in Transportation (Nationwide), Banking & Finance (Nationwide)*

**Practice Areas:** Co-Head of the Americas Asset Finance Practice, focusing on aircraft finance, including leveraged lease transactions, operating leases (domestic and cross-border), new and used aircraft purchases (including portfolio acquisitions), sales (including portfolio sales) and sale-leasebacks, securitizations, restructurings and manufacturer support arrangements.

**Career:** Partner at Clifford Chance since 2006. UCLA, BA, magna cum laude, Phi Beta Kappa, 1975. UCLA, JD, Order of the Coif, 1978.

### HOYNG, Charles F
Latham & Watkins LLP, Silicon Valley
650 463 3040
charles.hoyng@lw.com
*Featured in Life Sciences (Nationwide), Life Sciences (California)*

See under California for profile.

### HOYNS, John K
Hughes Hubbard & Reed LLP, New York
212 837 6767
hoyns@hugheshubbard.com
*Featured in Transportation (Nationwide), Banking & Finance (Nationwide)*

**Practice Areas:** Aviation industry matters, including debt and lease financings, public and private securities offerings, enhanced equipment trust certificates, securitizations, purchases and sales of aircraft, new aircraft orders, maintenance agreements, cross-border transactions, workouts, reorganizations and recapitalizations.

**Professional Memberships:** Member, American Bar Association and the Bar of the City of New York.

**Career:** Partner, New York since 1986.

**Publications:** Author or co-author of three chapters in treatise 'Securities Law Techniques' and various other articles. Lectures at Practising Law Institute and other seminars.

**Personal:** Colgate University (BA, 1976, cum laude); University of Michigan (JD, 1979, magna cum laude).

## HUEBNER, Marshall S
Davis Polk & Wardwell LLP, New York
212 450 4099
marshall.huebner@davispolk.com
*Featured in Bankruptcy/Restructuring (Nationwide), Bankruptcy/Restructuring (New York)*
**Practice Areas:** Co-heads Insolvency and Restructuring Group. One of only five lawyers to have been twice-named a "Dealmaker of the Year" by The American Lawyer. Represents financial institutions, companies and boards in complex restructurings. Lead counsel to Delta Air Lines, Patriot Coal, Pinnacle Airlines, Star Tribune and Frontier; lead counsel to the US Treasury and NY Federal Reserve on AIG; lead US counsel to Lehman UK. Lead DIP Lender counsel in Kodak, A&P, NewPage, Enron, Lyondell and Adelphia. Advises purchasers, companies and boards of directors in non-public distressed matters; provides risk and bankruptcy advice on derivatives and other complex transactions.

## HUIZINGA, James A
Sidley Austin LLP, Washington, DC
202 736 8681
jhuizinga@sidley.com
*Featured in Financial Services Regulation (Nationwide)*
**Practice Areas:** Partner in Sidley's Washington, DC office, and serves as one of the firmwide global coordinators of the Consumer Class Action (Financial Practices) practice area. He has been active in financial services litigation, working with clients in cases in federal and state courts across the country. Mr Huizinga has provided litigation and pre-litigation advice relating to the Truth in Lending Act, Fair Credit Reporting Act, the Real Estate Settlement Procedures Act, false advertising, unfair and deceptive trade practices, federal preemption of state consumer protection laws, credit discrimination and debt collection practices.

## HUMPHREY, Thomas P
Crowell & Moring LLP, Washington, DC
202 624 2633
thumphrey@crowell.com
*Featured in Government (Nationwide)*
**Practice Areas:** Partner in Crowell & Moring LLP's Government Contracts Group. Represents clients in a wide variety of government contracts matters, including bid protests/False Claims Act/qui tam litigation/investigations of potential criminal matters. Specializes in handling computer, telecommunications, and healthcare bid protest litigation before the GAO and various trial and appellate courts.
**Professional Memberships:** Active in the Bid Protest Committee of the Public Contract Law Section of the American Bar Association; served for many years as a Vice-Chair of a committee of the Litigation Section of the American Bar Association.

## HUNGAR, Thomas
Gibson, Dunn & Crutcher LLP, Washington, DC
202 955 8558
thungar@gibsondunn.com
*Featured in Appellate Law (Nationwide)*
**Practice Areas:** Co-Chair, Appellate and Constitutional Law Practice Group. He has presented oral argument before the Supreme Court of the United States in 25 cases, including some of the most important patent, antitrust, securities, and environmental law decisions in recent years, and he has also appeared before numerous lower federal and state appellate courts.
**Career:** Deputy Solicitor General of the United States (2003-2008); Assistant to the Solicitor General (1992-1994); Law Clerk to Justice Anthony M. Kennedy, US Supreme Court (1988-1989) and Judge Alex Kozinski, Ninth Circuit (1987-1988).
**Personal:** JD, Yale Law School, 1987; Senior Editor, Yale Law & Policy Review.

## HUNNICUTT, Charles
Thompson Hine LLP, Washington, DC
202 263 4148
Charles.Hunnicutt@ThompsonHine.com
*Featured in Transportation (Nationwide)*
**Career:** Charles is senior counsel in the Transportation practice group. He focuses his practice on all aspects of transportation and logistics, with emphasis on government regulatory matters and international policy. His background includes extensive experience in transportation policy and international trade, having served with the US Department of Transportation, the US International Trade Commission and the US Department of Commerce. Charles is admitted to practice in the District of Columbia, Georgia, the US Supreme Court, the US Court of International Trade, the US Court of Appeals for the District of Columbia and the US Court of Appeals for the Federal Circuit.

## HUNT, Paul J
Latham & Watkins LLP, Washington, DC
202 637 2241
paul.hunt@lw.com
*Featured in Projects (Nationwide)*
**Practice Areas:** Project development and financing and sale/purchase of energy and infrastructure projects, including: renewable energy (solar, wind, biomass, geothermal), carbon capture and sequestration, IGCC, fossil fuel-fired and cogeneration; mining; water; transportation; pipelines; and transmission. Represents energy companies, developers/sponsors, private equity investors, banks and financial institutions and off-takers in all phases of the development, financing and sale/acquisition of US and international projects. Activities include structuring of projects and negotiation of project agreements, loan and equity investment documentation and purchase and sale agreements.
**Professional Memberships:** Member, DC bar.
**Personal:** JD, University of Virginia School of Law, 1991; BA, Bucknell University, 1988.

## HURVITZ, John A
Covington & Burling LLP, Washington, DC
202 662 5319
jhurvitz@cov.com
*Featured in Life Sciences (Nationwide)*
**Practice Areas:** John Hurvitz is a trusted adviser to many leading pharmaceutical, biotechnology, and smaller, emerging companies, which he counsels on a range of corporate, commercial, partnering, and advisory matters. He has extensive experience structuring, negotiating, and documenting sophisticated, multidisciplinary, cross-border collaborations, and M&A transactions, for clients in the US, Europe, and Asia. He also provides strategic advice in enhancing performance management, dispute resolution, and identifying industry best practices in connection with transactional matters. He co-chairs Covington's Life Sciences Industry Group and is vice-chair of its Corporate Group.
**Personal:** Yale Law School, JD, 1991.

## HURWITZ, Ann
Baker Botts LLP, Dallas
214 953 6997
ann.hurwitz@bakerbotts.com
*Featured in Franchising (Nationwide)*
**Practice Areas:** Franchising; hospitality and leisure.
**Career:** Chairs the Franchise & Distribution Section. For over 25 years she has counseled franchisors in the hotel, restaurant, and retail industries on international expansion, system acquisitions, dispositions, and restructuring, and domestic transactional and regulatory issues. She is listed in Chambers USA America's Leading Lawyers for Business; Who's Who Legal: The International Who's Who of Business Lawyers and Franchise Lawyers; and has been named repeatedly in Franchise Times as one of the top franchise lawyers in the US and Canada.
**Personal:** JD, University of North Carolina at Chapel Hill; BA University of South Carolina.

## HUTCHINGS, Julie
Pillsbury Winthrop Shaw Pittman LLP, Houston
713 276 7730
julie.hutchings@pillsburylaw.com
*Featured in Projects (Nationwide)*
**Practice Areas:** Commercial transactions related to the financing, development, acquisition and divestiture of domestic and international energy and infrastructure projects, particularly in the areas of oil and natural gas (including LNG), electric power, utilities and renewable energy.
**Professional Memberships:** Association of International Petroleum Negotiators, Energy Bar Association.
**Career:** Admitted: Texas (2005); US Court of Appeals, District of Columbia Circuit (2012).
**Personal:** The University of Texas School of Law, JD, 2005; Emory University, MPH, 2002; Emory University, BA, 2001.

## HUTT, Peter Barton
Covington & Burling LLP, Washington, DC
202 662 5522
phutt@cov.com
*Featured in Food & Beverages (Nationwide), Healthcare (District of Columbia)*
See under District of Columbia for profile.

## HUVELLE, Jeffrey
Covington & Burling LLP, Washington, DC
202 662 5526
JHuvelle@cov.com
*Featured in ERISA Litigation (Nationwide)*
**Practice Areas:** Jeffrey Huvelle has won significant victories in ERISA class actions for Verizon, IBM, UTC and GE. These include the successful defense of cash balance plans in two circuits, a Seventh Circuit victory for Verizon correcting a billion dollar scrivener's error in a penson plan, and a Second Circuit victory in a dispute over the reasonableness of fees of a 401(k) plan. He has also won 15 consecutive employment discrimination suits tried to a verdict before a jury or the court.
**Personal:** Columbia Law School (JD); Harvard College (BA).

## HYNES, Terence M
Sidley Austin LLP, Washington, DC
202 736 8198
thynes@sidley.com
*Featured in Transportation (Nationwide)*
**Practice Areas:** Senior counsel in Sidley's Washington, DC office. Focuses his practice primarily in matters involving the transportation industry. Practice includes representation of railroads, ocean shipping companies, and private equity firms in connection with mergers and acquisitions, asset-based transactions, arbitrations, commercial, regulatory and appellate litigation, homeland security and safety issues, and bankruptcy proceedings. Counsels buyers, sellers and lenders in connection with rail line sale transactions, carrier co-production arrangements, and both freight and passenger rail corridor development projects. Represented clients in connection with nearly all of the railroad mergers and consolidations that have taken place over the past three decades.

## IBRAHIM, Ray
Davis Polk & Wardwell LLP, New York
212 450 4000
ray.ibrahim@davispolk.com
*Featured in Capital Markets (Nationwide)*
**Practice Areas:** Partner in Davis Polk's Corporate Department, practicing in the Derivatives and Structured Products Group. He has extensive experience in the development and execution of complex, new and innovative financial products across all asset classes, twice receiving IFLR's Deal of the Year Award. In addition, Mr Ibrahim represents Citigroup in its issuances of retail structured products. He has also been closely involved in the many regulatory initiatives and industry responses relevant to derivatives and other financial products, such as implementation of the Dodd-Frank Act and various reforms to equity short sales.

**ICHEL, David W**
Simpson Thacher & Bartlett LLP, New York
212 455 2000
dichel@stblaw.com
*Featured in Products Liability (Nationwide), Litigation (New York)*
See under New York for profile.

**INDEK, Ben**
Morgan, Lewis & Bockius LLP, New York
212 309 6109
bindek@morganlewis.com
*Featured in Securities (Nationwide)*
**Practice Areas:** Focuses on representing broker-dealers and their employees in governmental, self-regulatory organization, and state securities commission investigations and disciplinary proceedings as well as conducting internal investigations for financial services firms. Also provides counsel to broker-dealers on regulatory and compliance issues, including the development and implementation of written compliance and supervisory procedures and new rules and regulations.
**Professional Memberships:** FINRA-Independent Dealer/Insurance Affiliate Committee.
**Career:** Former Compliance Officer at E.F. Hutton & Co.

**INGIS, Stuart P**
Venable LLP, Washington, DC
202 344 4613
singis@Venable.com
*Featured in Privacy & Data Security (Nationwide)*
**Practice Areas:** A nationally recognized attorney and thought leader in privacy, marketing, advertising, e-commerce and Internet law. Represents media, communications, information services, financial services, advertising and retail companies. Serves as lead counsel in FTC and state consumer protection authority investigations. General Counsel to the Direct Marketing Association, and counsel to the Interactive Advertising Bureau and the Digital Advertising Alliance. Represents companies in a broad range of federal and state laws governing email, telemarketing, privacy, children's privacy, data security and breach notification. Represents clients in testimony before Congress, congressional investigations and crisis management situations.
**Personal:** JD, Villanova University, BA, Hamilton College.

**IPPOLITO, Loretta A**
Willkie Farr & Gallagher LLP, New York
212 728 8680
lippolito@willkie.com
*Featured in Wealth Management (Nationwide)*
**Practice Areas:** Co-Chair and partner Private Clients Group; member Executive Committee. Experienced in all estate planning and administration areas, including comprehensive estate, gift and income tax advice for high net worth individuals and multinational families; domestic trust planning and lifetime wealth transfer; tax and foreign trust planning for non-US persons with US contacts; tax-efficient transfer of closely held family business interests; liquidity issues; and management succession. Also expert in charitable giving,

use of private foundations, and charitable split-interest trusts.
**Personal:** JD, cum laude, Harvard Law School, 1989. BA (Mathematics), Amherst College, 1985, Phi Beta Kappa. See: http://www.willkie.com/LorettaIppolito.

**IRELAND, Oliver I**
Morrison & Foerster LLP, Washington, DC
202 778 1614
oireland@mofo.com
*Featured in Financial Services Regulation (Nationwide)*
**Practice Areas:** Focuses on all aspects of federal bank regulation and retail financial services, including electronic commerce, and deposit account and payment systems.
**Professional Memberships:** Member, American College of Consumer Financial Services Lawyers. Past Chair, Deposit Products and Payment Systems Subcommittee, American Bar Association.
**Career:** Previously served as Associate General Counsel of the Board of Governors of the Federal Reserve System. Named one of Washington's top banking and privacy lawyers by the Washingtonian magazine and a Best Lawyer in America in banking law.
**Personal:** BA, Yale University, 1970; JD, The University of Texas School of Law, 1974.

**IRVIN, Kenneth W**
Cadwalader, Wickersham & Taft LLP, Washington, DC
202 862 2315
ken.irvin@cwt.com
*Featured in Energy & Natural Resources (Nationwide)*
**Practice Areas:** Represents clients on federal and state commodity and energy (electricity, natural gas, oil, alternative energy and emissions) matters, including hedging and credit risks, contract structuring and disputes, arbitrations, bankruptcy or non-performing assets, and regulatory issues involving energy and commodities trading.
**Professional Memberships:** Member, Energy Bar Association; member, District of Columbia and New York bars; admitted to practice before US Supreme Court, and US Court of Appeals for the District of Columbia; practices before the Federal Energy Regulatory Commission.
**Publications:** Frequent speaker, lecturer and author of numerous articles and publications. Contributing author, Cadwalader's Energy & Commodities Resource Center (www.energy-lawresourcecenter.com).
**Personal:** JD, Syracuse University College of Law (magna cum laude); BSEE, Clarkson University.

**IRVIN, Michael P**
Fulbright & Jaworski LLP, Houston
713 651 3705
mirvin@fulbright.com
*Featured in Energy & Natural Resources (Nationwide), Projects (Nationwide)*
**Practice Areas:** Oil, gas and energy transactions; project development and finance.
**Career:** As Head of Fulbright's Energy and Real Property Department, Irvin focuses on domestic

and international oil, gas and energy transactions related to the acquisition and disposition of upstream oil and gas properties, pipeline systems, gas processing plants, refining and petrochemical facilities and electric power generating facilities. He negotiates drilling, development and marketing ventures in the oil, gas and electric power industries. Irvin also handles mortgage financings relating to oil, gas and other energy related properties.
**Personal:** BA, The University of Texas (1972); JD, University of Houston (1975).

**IRWIN, Donald P**
Hunton & Williams LLP, Richmond
804 788 8357
dirwin@hunton.com
*Featured in Energy & Natural Resources (Nationwide)*
**Practice Areas:** Energy: nuclear.
**Professional Memberships:** American Bar Association, District of Columbia and Virginia Bars; Nuclear Energy Institute Lawyers' Committee.
**Career:** 39 years experience before USNRC in nuclear reactor licensing and related enforcement issues, discrimination/SCWE issues, materials license and transportion issues (including USDOT); nuclear liability issues under Price-Anderson Act and international conventions; Yucca Mountain licensing proceeding before USNRC.
**Publications:** Misc speeches and articles.
**Personal:** Born October 15, 1944, New York, NY; AB Princeton University 1965; JD and MA Yale University 1971; US Navy 1965-67; Hunton & Williams 1971- (Partner since 1978).

**ISELIN, Harold N**
Greenberg Traurig, LLP, Albany
518 689 1415
IselinH@gtlaw.com
*Featured in Healthcare (New York), Healthcare (Nationwide)*
See under New York for profile.

**IVANHOE, Robert J**
Greenberg Traurig, LLP, New York
212 801 9333
IvanhoeR@gtlaw.com
*Featured in Real Estate (Nationwide), Real Estate (New York)*
**Practice Areas:** Chair, Global Real Estate Practice. Co-chair, National REIT Practice. Co-Chairman, New York Office
**Professional Memberships:** The Real Estate Roundtable; American College of Real Estate Lawyers, Urban Land Institute; National Association of REITs, Real Estate Lawyers Division of UJA Federation.
**Career:** Consistently selected as one of the most powerful in New York real estate by The New York Observer; Recipient of the Israel Peace Medal; Annual contributing author to Euromoney and the Bureau of National Affairs. Team Member, Law360 'Real Estate Practice Group of the Year', 2011-12.
**Personal:** JD, American University Washington College of Law; BA, Johns Hopkins University.

**IVENER, Mark**
Ivener & Fullmer LLP, Los Angeles
310 477 3000
mark@usworkvisa.com
*Featured in Immigration (California), Immigration (Nationwide)*
See under California for profile.

**JACKSON, Charles C**
Morgan, Lewis & Bockius LLP, Chicago
312 324 1156
charles.jackson@morganlewis.com
*Featured in ERISA Litigation (Nationwide), Labor & Employment (Illinois)*
**Practice Areas:** Chuck is a partner in Morgan Lewis's Labor and Employment Practice. Chuck is co-chair of the Employee Benefits Litigation Practice. He represents plan sponsors, employers and service providers in complex employee benefits (ERISA) litigation, and in labor and employment litigation. He has extensive class action and jury trial experience and has handled dozens of ERISA and other employment cases before federal and state appellate courts, including the US Supreme Court.
**Personal:** Northwestern University School of Law, 1977, JD, Cum Laude; Bethel College, 1974, BA.

**JACOB, Valerie Ford**
Fried, Frank, Harris, Shriver & Jacobson LLP, New York
212 859 8158
Valerie.Jacob@FriedFrank.com
*Featured in Capital Markets (Nationwide)*
**Practice Areas:** Corporate partner, Firm's chairperson, and head of global capital markets group. Acts as counsel to both issuers and underwriters in domestic and international financings and represents her clients in all types of securities offerings, including initial public offerings, secondary offerings, high-yield offerings, mezzanine and bridge financings, investment-grade debt offerings, acquisition financings, and recapitalizations. Also counsels corporations on corporate governance and securities regulation.
**Career:** Joined in 1978; became partner in 1986.
**Personal:** JD, Cornell University (1978); BS, Boston University (1975).

**JACOBS, Charles P**
Nixon Peabody LLP, New York
212 940 3170
cjacobs@nixonpeabody.com
*Featured in Investment Funds (Nationwide)*
**Practice Areas:** Charles Jacobs' practice concentrates on private equity and venture capital fund formation and investments. He represents a number of leading institutional investors in their alternative investment activities, including funds of funds, public pension funds and university endowments and is viewed as a leader in the field of investor-side representation. He has represented clients in over 1000 investments in various venture capital and private equity partnerships, both domestically and internationally. He regularly speaks on private equity matters in a variety of domestic and international settings, including at

conferences sponsored by Dow Jones, Thompson Reuters and the International Bar Association.

## JACOBS, Howard L
Law Offices of Howard L Jacobs, Westlake Village
805 418 9892
howard.jacobs@athleteslawyer.com
*Featured in Sports Law (Nationwide)*
**Practice Areas:** Sports law. Work includes the representation of athletes in all types of disputes, with a particular focus on the defense of athletes charged with doping offenses. Has represented professional athletes, Olympic athletes and amateur athletes in disputes involving doping, endorsements, unauthorized use of name and likeness, salary issues, team selection issues, and other matters.
**Publications:** "Taking Matters Into Their Own Hands: Athlete Lawsuits Against Supplement Companies Following Positive Drug Tests," 25 Entertainment and Sports Lawyer No. 4 (2008); "A Successful Challenge to the IOC's Osaka Rule: An Insider's Look at a Landmark Sports Arbitration," 29 Entertainment and Sports Lawyer No. 3 (2011). In addition, regularly quoted in major newspapers and sports magazines on current issues in sports.

## JACOBS, Ronald
Venable LLP, Washington, DC
202 344 8215
rmjacobs@Venable.com
*Featured in Government (Nationwide)*
**Practice Areas:** State and federal campaign finance, lobbying disclosure, gifts, ethics, tax.
**Career:** Mr Jacobs represents corporations, trade associations, nonprofits, independent expenditure committees, and lobbying firms on all aspects of political activity. Implemented nationwide compliance programs, defended clients before the Federal Election Commission and Office of Congressional Ethics, and assisted clients with organizing high-profile events to comply with ethics rules.
**Publications:** Frequently publishes articles and speaks, and is the author of a forthcoming treatise on political law for the Law Journal Press.
**Personal:** JD, George Washington University Law School, with high honors; BA, George Washington University, cum laude.

## JACOBY, Aaron
Arent Fox LLP, Los Angeles
213 443 7568
aaron.jacoby@arentfox.com
*Featured in Transportation (Nationwide)*
**Practice Areas:** Aaron Jacoby is Chair of the firm's Automotive Industry Practice Group. He focuses his practice on class actions and consumer litigation, unfair competition, federal and state regulatory matters and government investigations affecting the automotive industry. Aaron's industry focus and broad-based litigation and business experience enable him to counsel clients on a wide variety of operational, regulatory, and litigation avoidance issues and to offer pragmatic solutions to the legal challenges they face. Aaron was

twice recognized by the Daily Journal as one of the "Top 100 Lawyers" in California.

## JAFFE, Kenneth G
Alston & Bird LLP, Washington, DC
202 239 3154
kenneth.jaffe@alston.com
*Featured in Energy & Natural Resources (Nationwide)*
**Practice Areas:** Regulatory matters affecting participants in restructured competitive energy markets. Extensive experience in utility mergers and asset transactions, the development and operations of regional transmission system operators, and regulatory litigation. Represents clients before the Federal Energy Regulatory Commission on a variety of matters, including applications for approval of innovative transmission and market structures, transmission incentive rate applications, rate proceedings, compliance and enforcement matters, and disputes arising under power purchase, interconnection, and transmission agreements.
**Personal:** Harvard University (JD, 1981); State University of New York (BA, 1978).

## JAFFE, Marc D
Latham & Watkins LLP, New York
212 906 1281
marc.jaffe@lw.com
*Featured in Capital Markets (Nationwide)*
**Practice Areas:** Represents issuers, investment banking firms and investors in public and private debt and equity offerings and lending transactions in a broad range of industries, including: entertainment, financial services, gaming, hospitality, manufacturing, energy, media and telecommunications, technology and retail. Also represents investment banks, companies and investors in all manners of other engagements including: exchange offers, tender offers and consent solicitations, restructurings, bridge lending and loan commitments and other financing transactions.
**Professional Memberships:** Serves on the Securities Regulation Committee of the Bar of the City of New York.
**Career:** Qualified since 1994. Is Vice-Chair of the firm's global Corporate Department.

## JALINOUS, Farhad
Kaye Scholer LLP, Washington, DC
202 682 3581
farhad.jalinous@kayescholer.com
*Featured in International Trade (Nationwide)*
**Practice Areas:** Co-Chair of the National Security, Government Contracts and Regulatory Compliance Department and the National Security/CFIUS practice group. Represents international clients and their US affiliates in the regulatory aspects of investing in the United States. Focuses on Exon-Florio reviews before the Committee on Foreign Investment in the United States (CFIUS), including extensive experience with complex CFIUS mitigation requirements, as well as Team Telecom reviews and foreign ownership, control or influence (FOCI) mitigation matters before the US Departments of Defense and Energy under the applicable national industrial security regulations. Fluent in French and Farsi.

## JANICK III, Herbert F
Bingham McCutchen LLP, Portland
207 780 8270
herb.janick@bingham.com
*Featured in Securities (Nationwide)*
**Practice Areas:** Conducts a general securities regulatory and enforcement defense practice. Conducts internal investigations and reviews, provides advice concerning compliance systems and controls, and represents broker-dealers, other financial service firms, public companies and senior corporate officers in connection with investigations by the SEC, FINRA, and other self-regulatory bodies and state regulators. Has served as an independent compliance consultant in connection with major SEC enforcement actions involving mutual fund market timing, mutual fund administration and over-the-counter market making.
**Personal:** University of North Carolina School of Law, JD, high honors, 1984; Fairfield University, BA, summa cum laude, 1981.

## JANKOWSKY, Joel
Akin Gump Strauss Hauer & Feld LLP, Washington, DC
202 887 4082
jjankowsky@akingump.com
*Featured in Government (Nationwide)*
**Practice Areas:** Mr Jankowsky is one of three Senior Executive Partners and chaired the firm's Policy Practice for almost 30 years. He represents numerous clients on a variety of public policy matters. In 2010, the Bryce Harlow Foundation honored him with the Bryce Harlow Business-Government Relations Award for significant contributions to the advocacy profession.
**Professional Memberships:** Chairman, Board of Directors, Close Up Foundation; Member, Board of Directors, National Rehabilitation Hospital; Member, Board of Advisors, Carl Albert Center, University of Oklahoma; Sustaining Director, Prevent Cancer Foundation.
**Personal:** BBA, University of Oklahoma (1965); JD, University of Oklahoma Law School (1968).

## JARVIS, Thomas L
Finnegan, Henderson, Farabow, Garrett & Dunner LLP, Washington, DC
202 408 4093
tom.jarvis@finnegan.com
*Featured in International Trade (Nationwide)*
**Practice Areas:** Litigated over 50 ITC Section 337 cases in the past 25 years, logging more than 100 trial days as lead trial counsel, and conducting extensive discovery and motions practice, both domestically and abroad. Cases have involved a full range of computer technology, including electronic design automation tools, system architectures, microprocessors, digital signal processors, parallel processing technology, memory devices, subsystem controllers, networking equipment, and semiconductors.
**Personal:** University of North Carolina, Chapel Hill (BA, Chemistry & Communications, 1978); University of North Carolina Law School (JD, 1985).

## JEDREY, Christopher M
McDermott Will & Emery LLP, Boston
617 535 4405
cjedrey@mwe.com
*Featured in Healthcare (Massachusetts), Healthcare (Nationwide)*
See under Massachusetts for profile.

## JOHNSON, David R
Vinson & Elkins LLP, Washington, DC
202 639 6706
drjohnson@velaw.com
*Featured in Government (Nationwide), International Trade (Nationwide)*
**Practice Areas:** Federal, state and local government contract counseling, bid protests, investigations, and litigation. US export controls counseling, compliance and enforcement defense work involving International Traffic in Arms Regulations (ITAR), Export Administration Regulations (EAR), and Office of Foreign Assets Control (OFAC) sanctions. Represents companies in defense, IT, and energy sectors in government contracts disputes and in export compliance/economic sanctions matters.
**Professional Memberships:** ABA (International Section; Public Contracts Section); DC Bar; Virginia State Bar.
**Career:** Partner.
**Publications:** Written and lectured extensively on US export controls and economic sanctions.
**Personal:** College of William & Mary (JD, 1989); University of Virginia (BA, 1986).

## JOHNSON, Dixie L
Fried, Frank, Harris, Shriver & Jacobson LLP, Washington, DC
202 639 7269
Dixie.Johnson@FriedFrank.com
*Featured in Securities (Nationwide)*
**Practice Areas:** Co-head of securities enforcement and regulation practice and white collar criminal defense and securities enforcement practice group. Focuses on securities enforcement, regulation and disclosure. Represents businesses and business leaders in governmental and quasi-governmental investigations, most frequently federal securities law matters. Counsels on regulatory and disclosure obligations, assists in developing policies and procedures to deter violations, conducts internal investigations.
**Career:** Joined in 1986; became partner in 1993. Chair Elect, ABA Business Law Section.
**Personal:** JD, University of New Mexico School of Law (1986); MBA, New Mexico Highlands University (1983); BA, Oklahoma Baptist University (1977).

## JOHNSON, Jeffrey R
Bingham McCutchen LLP, Washington, DC
202 373 6626
jeffrey.johnson@bingham.com
*Featured in Capital Markets (Nationwide)*
**Practice Areas:** Concentrates his practice in the areas of structured finance and securitization. Has advised financial institutions, finance companies, government agencies, government-sponsored entities and investment banking firms on numerous transactions, including asset-backed securities

issuances, resecuritization of financial assets, net interest margin transactions, whole loan sales and related regulatory matters. Also has significant experience in transactions involving numerous asset types and receivables, including single-family and multifamily residential mortgage loans, commercial mortgage loans, automobile and recreational vehicle loans and leases.
**Personal:** Georgetown University Law Center, JD, 1993; University of Vermont, BS, magna cum laude, 1988.

## JOHNSON, W Stanfield
Crowell & Moring LLP, Washington, DC
202 624 2520
wjohnson@crowell.com
*Featured in Government (Nationwide)*
**Practice Areas:** Served four times as Crowell & Moring's chairman. A senior member of the firm's Government Contracts Group, focusing on counseling/litigation/resolution of contract issues. Helped secure a victory in the 'Great Engine War', a dispute between United Technologies Corp's Pratt & Whitney and the Air Force over a jet engine contract awarded in the 1980s. Negotiated settlements of numerous government claims - cost disallowances/defective pricing/false claims allegations. Counseled and represented a substantial portion of the defense industry and other contractors.
**Personal:** Undergraduate with great distinction, Stanford University,1960; JD, Harvard Law School, 1963. Member of Phi Beta Kappa.

## JOHNSTONE, Debbi M
Fulbright & Jaworski LLP, Houston
713 651 5335
djohnstone@fulbright.com
*Featured in Healthcare (Texas), Healthcare (Nationwide)*
See under Texas for profile.

## JOLLY, Ieuan
Loeb & Loeb LLP, New York
212 407 4810
ijolly@loeb.com
*Featured in Privacy & Data Security (Nationwide)*
**Practice Areas:** Extensive international experience in privacy/technology, with emphasis on regulatory issues such as multi-media marketing/data security. Provides strategic direction on maximizing value and use from data and information across interactive media platforms; and development/implementation of effective information security programs and risk mitigation strategies in outsourcing jurisdictions. Advises on complex technology transactions and sourcing arrangements, systems integration and telecommunications procurement.
**Career:** Heads the Privacy, Security and Data Optimization Practice.
**Personal:** College of Law (London, England), Higher Rights of Audience Advocacy, 2001; Nottingham Law School, Legal Practice Course, 1998; University of Bristol School of Law, LLB, 1997, with Honours.

## JONES, Christy D
Butler, Snow, O'Mara, Stevens & Cannada, PLLC, Ridgeland
601 985 4523
christy.jones@butlersnow.com
*Featured in Litigation (Nationwide), Products Liability (Nationwide), Litigation (Mississippi)*
**Practice Areas:** drug and medical device litigation; product liability; professional liability; mass torts.
**Professional Memberships:** Product Liability Advisory Council; International Association of Defense Counsel; Defense Counsel Trial Academy; Trial Attorneys of America; American Bar Association; Mississippi Bar; Mississippi Defense Lawyers Association.
**Career:** Chair, Firm's Litigation Department; American College of Trial Lawyers (District 6 Regent and Fellow); American Bar Association Foundation (Fellow); Best Lawyers in America (Personal Injury Litigation); Top 6 Product Liability Lawyers in World (Expert Guides); Who's Who Among International Product Liability Lawyers; Defense Research Institute.
**Personal:** University of Arkansas, JD, high honors, 1977; BA, 1974.

## JONES, Laura Ellen
Hunton & Williams LLP, Richmond
804 788 8746
ljones@hunton.com
*Featured in Projects (Nationwide)*
**Practice Areas:** Practice focuses almost exclusively on energy tax credit matters, including tax credit transactions involving the development, purchase and sale and financing of solar, landfill gas, wind, open-loop biomass, geothermal, waste-to-energy, and refined coal facilities. Advises on obtaining private letter rulings and public guidance from the IRS on energy tax credit transactions and issues, and in connection with IRS audits, federal legislative matters and Congressional investigations relating to energy tax credits.
**Professional Memberships:** Board of Directors, Solar Energy Industries Association; Chair, Solar Energy Industries Association's Solar Services and Consumers Division; American Bar Association, Tax Section; Virginia Bar Association.

## JONES, Robert C
Alston & Bird LLP, Washington, DC
202 239 3903
bob.jones@alston.com
*Featured in Government (Nationwide)*
**Practice Areas:** Leads firm's Legislative and Public Policy Group. Counsels business, association and not-for-profit clients on legislative, regulatory and policy matters. Represents clients before all levels of the federal government on a range of federal policy matters, including with regard to budget/appropriations, transportation, financial services, energy, real estate/land use, education, defense and agriculture issues.
**Professional Memberships:** D.C. Bar, State Bar of Virginia.
**Career:** Counsel to Senate Appropriations Committee; Appropriations Counsel to Senator Barbara Mikulski (D-MD).

**Personal:** JD (1986) University of Mississippi, BA (1983) Virginia Polytechnic Institute.

## JONES, Thomas M
McDermott Will & Emery LLP, Chicago
312 984 7536
tjones@mwe.com
*Featured in Insurance (Nationwide), Insurance (Illinois)*
See under Illinois for profile.

## JORDAN, Nora
Davis Polk & Wardwell LLP, New York
212 450 4000
nora.jordan@davispolk.com
*Featured in Investment Funds (Nationwide)*
**Practice Areas:** Head of Davis Polk's Investment Management Group. Advises clients on collective investment vehicles, including hedge funds, mutual funds, closed-end funds, and private equity funds. Acts as Counsel to the adviser, the fund or the independent directors, depending on the client. Many of her matters involve advising clients concerning compliance with the Investment Advisers Act and the Investment Company Act. Also provides exemptive advice concerning the Investment Company Act and the Advisers Act to operating companies, banks, insurance companies and other financial institutions. Has worked on a number of acquisitions, reorganisations and structurings of asset managers.

## JOSEFFER, Daryl
King & Spalding LLP, Washington, DC
202 626 2388
djoseffer@kslaw.com
*Featured in Appellate Law (Nationwide)*
**Practice Areas:** Head of King & Spalding's national appellate practice.
**Career:** Mr Joseffer joined King & Spalding in 2009 after serving as the Principal Deputy Solicitor General and, previously, an Assistant to the Solicitor General. Successfully handled some of the government's most sensitive cases in the courts of appeals. In the Supreme Court, Mr Joseffer argued major patent, pharmaceutical, environmental, and energy cases.
**Personal:** Harvard University (JD, magna cum laude, 1995); Stanford University (AB, 1992).

## JOSEPH, Matthew P
Bingham McCutchen LLP, New York
212 705 7333
matthew.joseph@bingham.com
*Featured in Capital Markets (Nationwide)*
**Practice Areas:** Practice focuses on structured finance transactions. Represents issuers and underwriters in public offerings and private placements of asset-backed securities. Is often involved in structuring innovative transactions with new asset types or unique tax and cash-flow structures, utilizing various forms of credit enhancement and derivatives. Has structured the securitization of a broad range of financial assets, including automobile loans and leases, church loans and bonds, commercial loans, equipment leases, home equity loans and HELOCs, litigation settlement fees, recreational vehicles, and student loans.

**Personal:** University of Pennsylvania Law School, JD, cum laude, 1994; Cornell University, BS, 1991.

## JOSEPH, Robert T
Dentons, Washington, DC
202 408 9181
robert.joseph@dentons.com
*Featured in Franchising (Nationwide)*
**Practice Areas:** Over 40 years' litigation and counseling experience in antitrust, franchising and distribution matters, many with complex and challenging issues. Counsels and represents franchisors and suppliers in disputes involving claims such as resale price fixing, tying, price discrimination and breach of contract.
**Career:** Joined Dentons in 1976. From 1971-76, was a staff attorney at the headquarters of the Federal Trade Commission's Bureau of Competition. Lectures at ABA Section of Antitrust Law programs and before the ABA Forum on Franchising, where he was a Member of the Governing Board.
**Personal:** University of Michigan, JD; Xavier University, AB.

## JOSEPH, Roger P
Bingham McCutchen LLP, Boston
617 951 8247
roger.joseph@bingham.com
*Featured in Investment Funds (Nationwide), Investment Funds (Massachusetts)*
See under Massachusetts for profile.

## JOYCE, David E
White & Case LLP, New York
212 819 8332
djoyce@whitecase.com
*Featured in Banking & Finance (Nationwide)*
**Career:** Mr Joyce's practice covers a broad range of finance matters, with a particular focus on the representation of lenders, sponsors and borrowers in domestic and international leveraged finance transactions and a wide variety of workout and restructuring transactions. He has experience representing lenders and borrowers involving a wide range of industries, with a particular emphasis on the shipping and offshore industry. To view a comprehensive biography, please visit www.whitecase.com/djoyce.

## JULIN, Thomas R
Hunton & Williams LLP, Miami
305 810 2516
tjulin@hunton.com
*Featured in First Amendment Litigation (Nationwide)*
**Practice Areas:** Tom heads his firm's First Amendment team. In 2011, he won the landmark Supreme Court case Sorrell v. IMS Health, recognizing First Amendment protection of data mining.
**Professional Memberships:** Former Chair, Florida Media & Communications Law Committee; Chair, Florida Review of Supreme Court First Amendment Decisions.
**Career:** Partner, Hunton & Williams LLP (2000 - Date); Steel Hector & Davis (1981-2000).
**Publications:** The Dog That Did Bark: First Amendment Protection of Data Mining, 36 Vt. L. Rev. 881 (2012); The Inevitability of Electronic

Media Access to Federal Courts, 1983 Det C L Rev 1303 (1983).
**Personal:** Born 7/10/1957.

## JUSKA JR, William L
Freehill Hogan & Mahar LLP, New York
212 381 3002
juska@freehill.com
*Featured in Transportation (Nationwide)*
**Practice Areas:** Experienced in maritime litigation and arbitration. Areas of expertise are all types of cargo claims, charter party and COA disputes. Also has considerable experience in oil pollution, marine contracts, regulatory matters, commodities contracts and provisional remedies, such as arrest and attachment. Extensive experience advising on trade sanctions and OFAC issues. Bar Admission: New York.
**Professional Memberships:** Maritime Law Association of the United States; New York State Bar Association.
**Career:** Joined Freehill Hogan & Mahar as an associate in 1969 and became a Partner in 1976.
**Personal:** Born 1944, New Jersey; College of the Holy Cross, AB, 1966; Fordham University School of Law, JD, 1969.

## KADLICK, Richard F
Skadden, Arps, Slate, Meagher & Flom LLP & Affiliates, New York
212 735 2716
Richard.Kadlick@skadden.com
*Featured in Capital Markets (Nationwide)*
**Practice Areas:** Co-head of Skadden's Structured Finance Group. Represents underwriters, financial institutions, banks and borrowers in mortgage-backed and asset-backed transactions, and credit enhancers in credit-enhanced issuances and purchasers and sellers of companies issuing such securities. Acts as counsel in a variety of public offerings, private placements and transactions in which structured securities instruments are backed by single-family and commercial mortgage loans, credit card receivables, non-performing assets, home equity and auto loan receivables, federal agency securities, auto and equipment leases and various other assets.
**Career:** JD, Georgetown University, 1982; BA, Hamilton College, 1979 (summa cum laude; Phi Beta Kappa).

## KADZIELSKI, Mark A
Fulbright & Jaworski LLP, Los Angeles
213 892 9306
mkadzielski@fulbright.com
*Featured in Healthcare (California), Healthcare (Nationwide)*
See under California for profile.

## KAFKA, Gerald A
Latham & Watkins LLP, Washington, DC
202 637 2198
gerald.kafka@lw.com
*Featured in Tax (District of Columbia), Tax (Nationwide)*
**Practice Areas:** Tax Controversy.
**Career:** Global Chair, Tax Controversy Practice; Local Chair, Tax Department; Trial Attorney, Tax Division, US Department of Justice (Outstanding Attorney Award); Adjunct Professor, Georgetown

University Law Center (Tax Practice and Procedure - Litigation); ABA Section of Taxation (chair: Committee on Court Procedure; Committee on Appointments to the Tax Court).
**Publications:** Litigation of Federal Civil Tax Controversies (two-volume treatise published by Warren Gorham and Lamont, with semi-annual supplements).
**Personal:** Recognized by the US Supreme Court (Ballard v. Commissioner, 125 S. Ct. 1270, 1282 n. 13 (2005).

## KAGAN, Stewart
Cadwalader, Wickersham & Taft LLP, New York
212 504 6885
stewart.kagan@cwt.com
*Featured in Private Equity (Nationwide)*
**Practice Areas:** Represents private equity and hedge funds, borrowers, bondholders and financial institutions regarding debt financings, private equity investments and general corporate matters. Recent transactions include representation of ad hoc bondholder group of Homer City Funding in connection with the exchange of approximately $650 million of secured notes pursuant to a prepackaged chapter 11 case; a $200 million credit facility for AngioDynamics, Inc. in connection with its acquisition of Navilyst Medical; various financings for Ceva Logistics, including over $2 billion of bank, bridge and high yield financing for its acquisition of EGL, Inc.; Lyondell Chemical Company's $2.6 billion 8% Senior Secured Notes, $3.25 billion 11% Senior 3rd Lien Notes and $8 billion debtor in possession credit facilities; various financings for Metals USA, Inc., including its $500 million asset backed credit facility; and Xerium Technologies' restructuring of approximately $600 million of debt.
**Personal:** JD, Yale Law School; BA, Harvard University.

## KAHALE III, George
Curtis, Mallet-Prevost, Colt & Mosle LLP, New York
212 696 6036
gkahale@curtis.com
*Featured in International Arbitration (Nationwide)*
**Professional Memberships:** Oxford Energy Policy Club; American Society of International Law; American Bar Association; The Association of the Bar of the City of New York.
**Career:** Mr Kahale has acted as lead counsel in some of the world's largest and most publicized transactions and infrastructure projects in the international petroleum industry, representing energy ministries and national oil corporations in many oil and gas producing countries. He also has been acting as lead counsel in several of the world's largest international arbitrations. Mr Kahale's practice was the subject of a feature article in the June 2008 issue of The American Lawyer. In October 2008, The American Lawyer named him a "Dealmaker of the Week." In February 2009, Latin Lawyer announced that a series of financing transactions on which the Curtis project team was led by Mr Kahale was awarded Restructuring Deal of the Year. In April

2009, The American Lawyer named Mr Kahale one of its "Dealmakers of the Year." Mr Kahale was Curtis' Managing Partner for approximately 15 years until 2008. Since that time, he has served as the firm's Chairman.
**Publications:** Mr Kahale has written many articles on topics of international interest, such as sovereign immunity, the act of state doctrine, international arbitration and international petroleum contracts, including: "Is Investor-State Arbitration Broken?" (Transnational Dispute Management, October 2012); "The New Dutch Sandwich: The Issue of Treaty Abuse" (Columbia FDI Perspective No. 48 –October 2011); "The Venezuelan Operating Service Agreements: Trying To Fit A Square Peg In A Round Hole" (Middle East Economic Survey – 2011); "The Uproar Surrounding Petroleum Contract Renegotiations" (Oxford Energy Forum – August 2010); "A Problem in Investor/State Arbitration" (Transnational Dispute Management – March 2009); "Legal Issues Relating to a Restructuring of the Iraqi Petroleum Industry, Issue 55" (Oxford Energy Forum – November 2003)
**Personal:** New York University School of Law, JD; City University of New York, Hunter College, BA.

## KAHN, Benita A
Vorys, Sater, Seymour and Pease LLP, Columbus
614 464 6487
bakahn@vorys.com
*Featured in Privacy & Data Security (Nationwide)*
**Practice Areas:** Partner specializing in privacy, information management, data security and consumer issues. Expertise in data breach response, privacy law compliance and assisting clients with PCI DSS, information security programs, incident response policies and marketing programs in compliance with various state and federal consumer protection laws.
**Professional Memberships:** American Bar Association, Ohio State Bar Association, Columbus Bar Association, International Association of Privacy Professionals, Certified International Privacy Professional.
**Career:** Admitted to Ohio Bar, 1982.
**Personal:** The Ohio State University College of Law, JD, summa cum laude, Order of the Coif, 1982; University of Akron, BA, cum laude, 1970.

## KALICKI, Jean E
Arnold & Porter LLP, Washington, DC
202 942 6155
Jean.Kalicki@aporter.com
*Featured in International Arbitration (Nationwide)*
**Practice Areas:** Experienced in international arbitration as both arbitrator and counsel, she has served as Chair, sole arbitrator and co-arbitrator in commercial and investment disputes, and as counsel to both sovereign governments and private companies on five continents. Ranked by Global Arbitration Review among the "Top 30" women in arbitration worldwide and named one of the "Best Lawyers in America" in her field, she is an Adjunct Professor at both Georgetown and American University law schools.

**Professional Memberships:** Board of Directors, American Arbitration Association; Member, ICC Commission on Arbitration (US National Committee); Chair, DC Bar International Dispute Resolution Committee.

## KALISH, Paul W
Crowell & Moring LLP, Washington, DC
202 624 2644
pkalish@crowell.com
*Featured in Insurance (District of Columbia), Insurance (Nationwide)*
See under District of Columbia for profile.

## KALLOS, Chris P
Kirkland & Ellis LLP, Chicago
312 862 2146
chris.kallos@kirkland.com
*Featured in Investment Funds (Nationwide)*
**Practice Areas:** Chris Kallos is a senior partner in the Private Funds Group. His practice primarily focuses on advising leading and emerging private equity fund sponsors in connection with forming and operating their funds and management companies. He has formed, or is in the process of forming, more than $50 billion of funds for private equity firm sponsors, ranging in size from under $100 million to more than $6 billion. He also advises limited partner investors in making and monitoring substantial private equity fund investments.
**Personal:** Harvard Law School, JD, 1994; University of Virginia, McIntire School of Commerce, B.S., 1989.

## KALLSTROM, D Ward
Seyfarth Shaw LLP, San Francisco
415 732 1107
wkallstrom@seyfarth.com
*Featured in ERISA Litigation (Nationwide), Employee Benefits & Executive Compensation (California)*
See under California for profile.

## KANTER, Jane A
Dechert LLP, Washington, DC
202 261 3302
jane.kanter@dechert.com
*Featured in Investment Funds (Nationwide)*
**Practice Areas:** Ms Kanter concentrates her practice in the regulation and counseling of investment advisers, mutual funds, closed-end funds, fund directors, and private investment funds. She also has significant experience in federal and state securities law matters.
**Career:** Attorney, Office of the Solicitor, Plan Benefits Security Division, US Department of Labor; special counsel, US Securities and Exchange Commission's Division of Investment Management; vice president and legal counsel, T. Rowe Price Associates, Inc.
**Personal:** Queens College (BA, 1970, honors); Brooklyn Law School (JD, 1973, member, Brooklyn Law Review); Washington University School of Law (LLM in Taxation, 1978).

## KANTER, Stacy J
Skadden, Arps, Slate, Meagher & Flom LLP & Affiliates, New York
212 735 3497
Stacy.Kanter@skadden.com
*Featured in Capital Markets (Nationwide)*

**Practice Areas:** Co-head of Skadden's global Corporate Finance practice. Represents corporate clients, investment banks and private equity firms in public and private offerings of equity and debt, exchange offers, consent solicitations, restructurings, and mergers and acquisitions. Has advised on numerous IPOs, including two of the largest recent US IPOs. Counsels clients on general corporate matters. Co-chair of global Diversity Committee.
**Career:** JD, Brooklyn Law School, 1984 (cum laude; Managing Editor, Brooklyn Law Review); BS, State University of New York at Albany, 1979 (magna cum laude); Law Clerk, Honorable Raymond Dearie, United States District Court, Eastern District of New York (1986-1987).

### KAPLAN, Barbara T
Greenberg Traurig, LLP, New York
212 801 9250
KaplanB@gtlaw.com
*Featured in Tax (Nationwide), Tax (New York)*
**Practice Areas:** Chair, NY Tax Practice. Tax compliance counseling; sensitive audits; promoter audits; offshore accounts and voluntary disclosure; preparer penalties; civil tax controversies; complex tax litigation; criminal tax investigations; tax penalties; tax procedure; circular 230 violations.
**Professional Memberships:** Member: Tax Sections, American and New York State Bar Associations; The Association of the Bar of the City of New York; American Association for Justice; The National Association of Criminal Defense Lawyers.
**Career:** Fellow of the American College of Tax Counsel. Listed: Best Lawyers in America, 2006-13; Super Lawyers magazine, 2006-12. Rated, AV® Preeminent™ 5.0 out of 5.
**Personal:** LLM, Taxation, New York University School of Law, 1979; JD, cum laude, Brooklyn Law School, 1975; MA, Northwestern University, 1972; BA, University of Wisconsin-Madison, 1970.

### KAPLAN, Donald
K&L Gates, Washington, DC
202 661 6266
don.kaplan@klgates.com
*Featured in Energy & Natural Resources (Nationwide)*
**Practice Areas:** Mr Kaplan concentrates his practice in litigation and representation before courts and administrative agencies, with particular emphasis on antitrust, economic regulation, energy, and competition and pricing issues in regulated industries. He has developed an extensive practice before the FERC. He has been active in a wide variety of issues, including electric utility restructuring and reorganization; mergers and asset acquisitions; Regional Transmission Organization structure and wholesale markets; transmission incentive and formula rates, cost allocation and open access; market power and market-based rates; and federal wholesale and state retail competition.

### KAPLAN, Gilbert
King & Spalding LLP, Washington, DC
202 737 0500
gkaplan@kslaw.com
*Featured in International Trade (Nationwide)*
**Practice Areas:** International trade and trade policy issues focusing on antidumping (price discrimination), countervailing duties (subsidies), Section 337, (intellectual property infringement), and other trade matters. Substantial experience with international transactions, market access, trade negotiation, export matters, and legislative and trade policy matters. Extensive work in connection with WTO matters.
**Professional Memberships:** Massachusetts Bar Association; District of Colombia Bar Association.
**Personal:** BA, Harvard College, 1973; JD, Harvard Law School, 1977.

### KAPLAN, Michael
Davis Polk & Wardwell LLP, New York
212 450 4000
michael.kaplan@davispolk.com
*Featured in Capital Markets (Nationwide)*
**Practice Areas:** Co-head of Davis Polk's Capital Markets Practice and member of Davis Polk's Corporate Department. Regularly works on offerings by US and non-US issuers, representing both issuers and underwriters, in a variety of capital markets and leveraged finance transactions, including initial public offerings, follow-on offerings and offerings of high-yield debt. Regularly advises investment banking clients on securities law-related matters and corporate clients on securities law and corporate governance related matters.

### KAPLAN, Steven M
K&L Gates, Washington, DC
202 778 9204
steven.kaplan@klgates.com
*Featured in Financial Services Regulation (Nationwide)*
**Practice Areas:** Mr Kaplan is a co-leader of K&L Gates' financial services practice area and a member of the firm's management committee. He concentrates his practice in regulatory compliance, enforcement and transactional matters related to consumer financial products and services, including consumer loans, mortgage loans, prepaid cards, and consumer payment systems. His practice includes: (i) counseling clients on the application of federal and state laws; (ii) defending companies in investigations, enforcement actions, and supervisory matters; (iii) performing regulatory diligence and reviews, including in connection with transactions; (iv) structuring transactions and developing new consumer products, and (iv) assisting in litigation matters.

### KAPLINSKY, Alan S
Ballard Spahr LLP, Philadelphia
215 864 8544
kaplinsky@ballardspahr.com
*Featured in Financial Services Regulation (Nationwide); Banking & Finance (Pennsylvania)*
**Practice Areas:** Alan S. Kaplinsky is Practice Leader of the Consumer Financial Services Group. He devotes his practice to counseling financial

institutions on bank regulatory and transactional matters, particularly consumer financial services law, and defending them in individual and class action lawsuits and government investigations and lawsuits.
**Professional Memberships:** American Bar Association, past Chair, Consumer Financial Services Committee of Section of Business Law American College of Consumer Financial Services Lawyers, first President Co-Chair, Practicing Law Institute Consumer Financial Services Institute (17 years) Consumer Bankers Association, Lawyers Committee.
**Career:** Admissions: Pennsylvania.
**Publications:** The Business Lawyer, annual article on Consumer Arbitration Developments.

### KAROTKIN, Stephen
Weil, Gotshal & Manges LLP, New York
212 310 8350
stephen.karotkin@weil.com
*Featured in Bankruptcy/Restructuring (Nationwide), Bankruptcy/Restructuring (New York)*
**Practice Areas:** Concentrates practice in chapter 11 reorganizations, debt restructurings, debtor and creditors' rights and financing transactions. Mr Karotkin currently represents American Airlines and its affiliates in their pending chapter 11 cases. He has represented numerous chapter 11 debtors including General Motors Corporation, Armstrong World Industries and Blockbuster as well as lenders and borrowers in out-of-court restructuring transactions. He was named Dealmaker of the Year 2010 by The American Lawyer and one of America's "Top 25 Pre - Eminent Insolvency Lawyers" by The Best of the Best USA 2010.
**Personal:** Union College (BS); New York University School of Law (JD).

### KARP, Brad S
Paul, Weiss, Rifkind, Wharton & Garrison LLP, New York
212 373 3316
bkarp@paulweiss.com
*Featured in Financial Services Regulation (Nationwide), Securities (Nationwide), Litigation (New York)*
**Practice Areas:** Chair of the firm; Partner in Litigation Department. Achieved national prominence as litigator and corporate adviser. Extensive experience representing financial institutions and corporations in bet-the-company litigations and regulatory matters. Successfully represented Citigroup in series of multi-billion-dollar jury trials (Terra Firma, Parmalat) and arbitrations (ADIA, Sturm). Current representative matters include: Lead counsel for Citigroup in defense of Subprime, Credit-Crisis, RMBS, Parmalat, Failed Investment and Research Analyst litigations and regulatory matters; lead counsel for JPMorgan in litigations and regulatory matters arising out of Bear Stearns' collapse; lead counsel for Wall Street underwriting syndicates in securities class actions arising out of AIG, Ambac, American Home Mortgage securities offerings; lead counsel for National Football League in concussion-related litigations. Current representative clients include: Citigroup, JPMorgan, Bank of America, Wells

Fargo, Morgan Stanley, HSBC, Bank of New York Mellon, UBS, Apollo, Deloitte, the National Football League, MacAndrews & Forbes, ING, Ericsson, Newmont Mining, Citco, Merck, SICPA, BB&T, Eton Park, OneWest Bank, CIM Group, Fortress, Zurich Capital, Aurora Bank and KKR, among others, in significant securities, commercial and regulatory matters.

### KARPF, Jeffrey D
Cleary Gottlieb Steen & Hamilton LLP, New York
212 225 2864
jkarpf@cgsh.com
*Featured in Capital Markets (Nationwide)*
**Practice Areas:** Corporate and financial transactions; corporate governance. Represents investment banks and issuers in IPOs; public and private debt, equity and convertibles offerings; liability management transactions. Advises on securities regulatory and corporate governance matters. Develops financial instruments and structured derivatives products. Recent transactions: AIG's re-IPO and US Treasury's public offering of AIG common stock (underwriters' counsel); Citigroup's capital realignment exchanges and other offerings; Southern California Edison Company's registered offerings; rue21 and Primerica IPOs.
**Professional Memberships:** NY Bar
**Career:** Joined firm, 1994. JD, Order of the Coif, Stanford University Law School (1994); BA, Political Science, magna cum laude, Yale University (1989).

### KASHATUS, Jennifer
DLA Piper LLP (US), Washington, DC
202 799 4448
jennifer.kashatus@dlapiper.com
*Featured in Privacy & Data Security (Nationwide)*
**Practice Areas:** Privacy & Data Security
**Career:** She routinely advises companies in all industry sectors on privacy and data protection issues. She assists companies in developing internal controls to safeguard customer and employee data and works with companies to navigate the myriad state, federal and international privacy regulations. She regularly works with companies that have experienced a data breach, negotiates vendor agreements and obtains safe harbor certification for multinational companies.
**Personal:** JD, Case Western University School of Law, cum laude; BA, Colgate University.

### KASNER, Jay B
Skadden, Arps, Slate, Meagher & Flom LLP & Affiliates, New York
212 735 2628
Jay.Kasner@skadden.com
*Featured in Securities (Nationwide), Litigation (New York)*
See under New York for profile.

### KASS, Geoffrey R
Vedder Price PC, Chicago
312 609 7553
gkass@vedderprice.com
*Featured in Transportation (Nationwide)*
**Practice Areas:** Shareholder and member of the firm's Global Transportation Finance team.

Counsels and represents clients in corporate and securities matters with particular emphasis on structured financings. Has represented manufacturers, borrowers, lessees, lessors, equity participants and lenders in various financing structures, including portfolio and company acquisitions and divestitures, secured loans, US and cross-border leveraged leases, operating leases, municipal and cross-border structured financings, public and private securities offerings and debt restructurings. He has extensive experience in commercial and private aircraft, railcar, bus, telecommunications, miscellaneous equipment and various facility financings.
**Career:** Admitted (IL) 1989
**Publications:** 'Journal of Air Law and Commerce'.
**Personal:** JD, Northwestern University; BA, Williams College

### KAUFMAN, Christopher L
Latham & Watkins LLP, Silicon Valley
650 463 2606
christopher.kaufman@lw.com
*Featured in Investment Funds (Nationwide), Corporate/M&A (Northern California), Corporate/M&A (California)*
**Practice Areas:** Mergers and acquisitions; corporate finance and corporate governance for primarily high technology companies. Public and private securities offerings representing issuers, underwriters, and venture capital entities.
**Career:** Served as Chairman of the Board of Directors of the PRO Corporation and Rexall Corporation and on the Boards of Directors of Qantel Corporation, Liposome Technology, Inc., and Applied ImmunoSciences, Inc. Presently member of Board of Directors of FP International, Inc.
**Personal:** Harvard Law Review; Clerk to Wilfred Feinberg, US Court of Appeals for Second Circuit.

### KAUFMAN, David
Morrison & Foerster LLP, New York
212 468 8237
dkaufman@mofo.com
*Featured in Capital Markets (Nationwide)*
**Practice Areas:** Concentrates on derivatives and commodities transactions, working closely with financial institutions clients in the equity, commodities and credit derivatives markets. Assists clients in designing new products and evaluating the securities and commodities law issues implicated by hedging and monetization techniques associated with these products. Also works closely with commodities trading firms, focusing in particular on transactions involving energy, precious and base metals and currencies. Assists clients in assessing and mitigating the credit and trading risks inherent in derivatives and commodities issues. Participates actively in several bar and derivatives industry groups.
**Personal:** BA, University of Rochester, JD, Harvard University.

### KAVOUKJIAN, Michael E
White & Case LLP, Miami
212 819 8403
mkavoukjian@whitecase.com
*Featured in Wealth Management (Nationwide), Tax (Florida)*
See under Florida for profile.

### KAWATA, Yukako
Davis Polk & Wardwell LLP, New York
212 450 4000
yukako.kawata@davispolk.com
*Featured in Investment Funds (Nationwide)*
**Practice Areas:** Member of Davis Polk's Investment Management Group. Advises clients on the formation and operation of US and non-US private investment funds pursuing a broad range of strategies, including private equity funds, real estate funds, hedge funds, private bank platforms and fund of funds. Advises funds and fund sponsors on the regulatory issues that apply to their operations, including considerations under the US Investment Advisers Act, other US securities laws and the Volcker Rule. Also advises clients on the formation and operation of various types of carried interest plans and employee investment arrangements.

### KAYUKOV, Edward V
Milbank, Tweed, Hadley & McCloy LLP, Los Angeles
213 892 4682
ekayukov@milbank.com
*Featured in Projects (Nationwide)*
**Practice Areas:** Mr Kayukov is a partner in the Project Finance Group. He has extensive experience in infrastructure and energy project financings, representing both lenders and developers in the US and internationally. Mr Kayukov has particular expertise on financing transactions in the renewable energy sector (including wind, solar, biomass, hydroelectric and geothermal).

### KAZAKS, Julia M
Skadden, Arps, Slate, Meagher & Flom LLP & Affiliates, Palo Alto
650 470 4640
Julia.Kazaks@skadden.com
*Featured in Tax (Nationwide), Tax (California)*
See under California for profile.

### KEATING, David C
Alston & Bird LLP, Atlanta
404 881 7355
david.keating@alston.com
*Featured in Privacy & Data Security (Nationwide)*
**Practice Areas:** Privacy & Security Practice (Co-Chair); Technology Practice. Focuses on developing and implementing compliance initiatives and enabling transactions that raise complex privacy and security issues. Represents public and private corporations in matters involving privacy and security laws in the United States, the European Union, Canada, the Asia-Pacific region and Latin America.
**Professional Memberships:** Board of Directors, Business & Technology Alliance; Board of Directors, Southeastern Software Association; Chair, Technology Law Section, State Bar of

Georgia; Member, IAPP. Admitted to practice: District of Columbia, Georgia.
**Personal:** JD (1995) Emory University (with distinction); BA (1991) University of Massachusetts at Amherst (cum laude).

### KEHOE, Edward
King & Spalding LLP, New York
212 556 2246
ekehoe@kslaw.com
*Featured in International Arbitration (Nationwide)*
**Practice Areas:** Commercial litigation / arbitration matters (international and domestic). Focuses on energy, professional services liability, construction and insurance. Provides strategic advice for effective and efficient resolution at early stages of a dispute. Conducts internal investigations when necessary.
**Professional Memberships:** Fellow of the Litigation Counsel of America, Trial Lawyer Honorary Society; Sits as an arbitrator and is listed as an arbitrator on the Panel of Neutrals for the American Arbitration Association's International Centre for dispute resolution (AAA/ICDR); Advisory Board Representative to the Institute for Transnational Arbitration.
**Personal:** BS, Lehigh University, 1987; JD, cum laude, St John's Law School, 1990.

### KEISLER, Peter
Sidley Austin LLP, Washington, DC
202 736 8027
pkeisler@sidley.com
*Featured in Appellate Law (Nationwide)*
**Practice Areas:** Co-chair of Sidley's Appellate practice. Successfully represented some of the country's largest companies in the telecommunications, transportation, energy and healthcare industries, as well as national trade associations, providing extensive insight and experience gained from his more than 25 years of private and public sector experience. Represents clients before the United States Supreme Court, federal courts of appeals and federal district courts, including the leading role in the following important energy lawsuits: AEP v. Connecticut, EME Homer City Generation LP v. EPA, and United States v. Cinergy Corp.
**Career:** Former Acting Attorney General of the United States.

### KELLEHER, Michael F
McDermott Will & Emery LLP, Washington, DC
202 756 8230
mkelleher@mwe.com
*Featured in Tax (Nationwide)*
**Practice Areas:** Partner in the tax department. Focuses primarily on the representation of corporations in complex federal income tax controversies. Represents clients in pre-audit planning, audits, appeals, competent authority and litigation. Special areas of expertise include transfer pricing, foreign tax credits, and insurance company tax matters.
**Personal:** Georgetown University Law Center (JD); University of Notre Dame (BA, summa cum laude).

### KELLEHER, Rory
Sidley Austin LLP, New York
212 839 7385
rkelleher@sidley.com
*Featured in Transportation (Nationwide), Banking & Finance (Nationwide)*
**Practice Areas:** Senior counsel resident in Sidley's New York office. His practice focuses on finance matters, including aircraft finance, equipment leasing and structured finance. In the equipment financing area, Mr Kelleher has represented major manufacturers of aircraft, aircraft engines and rail transportation products and US finance and leasing companies in both domestic and international finance transactions, single investor, leveraged and cross-border lease transactions, other structured financings and securitizations.
**Personal:** Columbia University School of Law, JD, 1972, Harlan Fiske Stone Scholar, Managing Editor, Columbia Journal of Law and Social Problems; Fordham University, BA, 1969. Admission: New York.

### KELLER, Natalie
Kirkland & Ellis LLP, Chicago
312 862 2229
natalie.keller@kirkland.com
*Featured in Tax (Illinois), Tax (Nationwide)*
**Practice Areas:** Natalie Keller's practice focuses on all aspects of tax controversies, including audits, appeals and litigation. She has litigated cases in the US Tax Court, Court of Federal Claims, district and bankruptcy courts and courts of appeal. She also advises US and foreign multinational clients on intercompany transfer pricing planning and compliance, resolution of transfer pricing audits and competent authority. Her transfer pricing experience includes significant cases in the automotive, consumer electronics and pharmaceutical industries.
**Personal:** University of Utah, S.J. Quinney College of Law, JD, Order of the Coif, 1997; University of Montana, BS, with high honors, 1992.

### KELLEY, Thomas
Levine Sullivan Koch & Schulz LLP, Denver
303 376 2410
tkelley@lskslaw.com
*Featured in First Amendment Litigation (Nationwide)*
**Practice Areas:** Over 35 years experience representing media clients in libel, invasion of privacy, copyright and related First Amendment cases. Represented press covering Oklahoma City bombing cases, JonBenet Ramsey murder case, Kobe Bryant rape prosecution, and Aurora, Colorado movie theatre massacre case. Has tried 20 cases to verdict, including 10 media cases.
**Professional Memberships:** Past-Chair, ABA Forum on Communications Law; past-President, Media Law Resource Center Defense Counsel Section; President, Colorado Freedom of Information Council.
**Career:** Previously a partner in Faegre & Benson, LLP.
**Personal:** Born 27 January 1947. Graduate of Amherst College and the University of Denver College of Law.

## KELLMAN, Sandra Y
DLA Piper LLP (US), Chicago
312 368 4082
sandra.kellman@dlapiper.com
*Featured in Leisure & Hospitality (Nationwide)*
**Practice Areas:** Leisure & Hospitality.
**Professional Memberships:** International Society of Hospitality Consultants.
**Career:** Global Co-Chair of the Hospitality and Leisure practice, her work encompasses complex commercial real estate development and finance, particularly acquisition, development, and financing of hotels, power generation facilities, air cargo facilities, and office buildings, representing borrowers and lenders in multi-party, multi-property transactions. She represents owners and managers negotiating hotel management agreements and landlords and tenants in office and industrial leasing, speculative and build-to-suit industrial development, and land use law.
**Personal:** JD, Northwestern University School of Law (cum laude); BA, University of Illinois at Urbana-Champaign (with high honors).

## KELLY, Christopher G
Holland & Knight LLP, New York
212 513 3264
christopher.kelly@hklaw.com
*Featured in Transportation (Nationwide)*
**Practice Areas:** Christopher G. Kelly defends airlines and manufacturers and their insurers in suits brought throughout the US, and he has particular experience in the defense of mass tort, toxic tort, and complex commercial claims. He has handled accidents due to fuel exhaustion, fuel starvation, passenger claims for emergency landings, airport construction contracts and state attorney general investigations into the conduct of airlines. He was the lead counsel for an airline in its nationwide privacy class-action litigations. Mr Kelly has also represented multiple equipment lessors and guarantors in the successful resolution of secured claims involving aviation equipment.

## KELLY, Suedeen G.
Akin Gump Strauss Hauer & Feld LLP, Washington, DC
202 887 4526
skelly@akingump.com
*Featured in Energy & Natural Resources (Nationwide)*
**Practice Areas:** Co-chair of the firm's energy regulatory practice. Represents clients in the electric and natural gas industries on business, regulatory, litigation, enforcement and policy matters such as electricity and gas markets, renewable energy, electricity transmission, hydro licensing, natural gas infrastructure, LNG, electricity reliability standards, carbon emissions, smart grid, energy efficiency and other issues.
**Career:** Commissioner, Federal Energy Regulatory Commission (2003-2009). Legislative Aide, Sen. Jeff Bingaman (D-NM) (1999. Chair and Commissioner, New Mexico Public Service Commission (1983-1986). National Institute of Standards and Technology, Smart Grid Advisory Committee (2010-present).

## KELLY, T Mark
Vinson & Elkins LLP, Houston
713 758 4592
mkelly@velaw.com
*Featured in Corporate/M&A (Texas), Capital Markets (Texas), Capital Markets (Nationwide)*
See under Texas for profile.

## KELNER, Robert K
Covington & Burling LLP, Washington, DC
202 662 5503
rkelner@cov.com
*Featured in Government (Nationwide)*
**Practice Areas:** Robert Kelner chairs Covington's Election and Political Law practice group and provides political law compliance advice to a range of clients. His practice focuses on campaign finance, lobbying disclosure, pay-to-play, and government ethics laws. Mr Kelner regularly advises corporations on instituting political law compliance programs and conducts compliance training for senior executives and lobbyists. He has extensive experience conducting internal investigations and regularly defends clients in investigations by the Federal Election Commission, the Department of Justice, and various Congressional committees.
**Personal:** University of Virginia School of Law, JD, 1997; Princeton University, AB, 1989.

## KENEALLY, Walter S
Bracewell & Giuliani LLP, Houston
713 221 1423
walter.keneally@bgllp.com
*Featured in Projects (Nationwide)*
**Practice Areas:** Represents and counsels developers, investors, utilities, and contractors in all legal aspects of domestic and international energy and industrial project development, finance, and acquisitions and divestitures. Has experience in the development, acquisition and sale of merchant coal, gas, biomass, hydro and wind power plants, cogeneration facilities, refining and chemical plants, water treatment facilities, and pipeline and storage facilities.
**Personal:** JD, University of Houston Law Center, 1991; BA, Rice University, 1986.

## KENNEDY, John
Vinson & Elkins LLP, Houston
713 758 2550
jkennedy@velaw.com
*Featured in Energy & Natural Resources (Nationwide)*
**Practice Areas:** Practice consists primarily of representing oil pipelines in proceedings before the Federal Energy Regulatory Commission and state commissions and in appeals from decisions of those commissions and providing regulatory advice to oil pipelines.
**Professional Memberships:** Energy Bar Association; American Bar Association; Houston Bar Association.
**Career:** Admitted to practice: Texas, 1971; United States Supreme Court; US Court of Appeals for the Fifth Circuit; US Court of Appeals for the District of Columbia Circuit.

**Personal:** Graduated from Harvard College, AB cum laude in 1968; Harvard Law School, JD magna cum laude in 1971.

## KENNEDY, John B
Wiggin and Dana LLP, Stamford
*Featured in Outsourcing (Nationwide)*
**Practice Areas:** Transactions, litigation, and counseling in intellectual property, outsourcing and offshoring, licensing, technology transfer, information privacy, information security, and electronic commerce. Clients include Fortune 500 companies as well as emerging companies in widely-varying industries. Has negotiated cross-border and domestic outsourcing and licensing transactions, complex licenses and joint ventures, and settlements involving contested intellectual property, licenses and services agreements.
**Professional Memberships:** Co-Chair, Practising Law Institute Privacy and Data Security Annual Institute, 2000-present.
**Personal:** Wiggin and Dana, Partner, Technology and Outsourcing; Privacy and Information Security practice groups.

## KENNEDY, John C
Paul, Weiss, Rifkind, Wharton & Garrison LLP, New York
212 373 3025
jkennedy@paulweiss.com
*Featured in Capital Markets (Nationwide)*
**Practice Areas:** Partner in the Corporate Department and co-head of the North American Capital Markets and Securities Practice Group who focuses primarily on corporate finance and securities transactions. He has represented both issuers and underwriters in a broad range of public and private securities offerings. John has significant experience in initial public offerings and high yield transactions. John has handled many complex securities and financing transactions, such as exchange offers, debt tender offers, consent solicitations and debt restructurings. He also regularly counsels his public clients on corporate governance and securities compliance issues.

## KENNEDY, Robert
Jones Day, New York
212 326 3835
rfkennedy@jonesday.com
*Featured in Private Equity (Nationwide)*
**Practice Areas:** Partner, Private Equity Group. Advises private equity funds and their portfolio companies in leveraged buyouts, private investment and general business matters. Also represents strategic buyers and sellers in acquisitions and dispositions, and public and private businesses in other matters, including Securities Exchange Act reporting matters, general corporate governance issues and directors' fiduciary duties.
**Professional Memberships:** Corporation Law Committee, New York City Bar Association.
**Personal:** JD, University of Virginia, 1993. BA, Amherst College, 1987.

## KENNEY, John H
Latham & Watkins LLP, San Francisco
415 395 8007
john.kenney@lw.com
*Featured in Projects (Nationwide)*
**Practice Areas:** Mr Kenney represents banks, insurance companies, multilateral agencies, leasing companies and developers in all phases of infrastructure project development and finance transactions. His experience encompasses various energy projects including geothermal, wind, low sulfur fuel oil, solar, waste coal, waste coal gasification, biomass, landfill gas and natural gas, and other industrial facilities, such as paper recycling and gas manufacturing. He has worked for lenders, including in multi-tranche transactions, utilities, and developers, from early development and structuring, through contracting, financing and construction.
**Personal:** JD, University of California, Berkeley, Boalt Hall School of Law, 1986; BA, University of California, Berkeley, 1983.

## KENT, Rachael D
WilmerHale, Washington, DC
202 663 6976
rachael.kent@wilmerhale.com
*Featured in International Arbitration (Nationwide)*
**Practice Areas:** Partner, Litigation/Controversy Department; vice chair of International Arbitration Group. Represents clients in a wide variety of commercial and investment disputes in arbitration proceedings under numerous substantive and procedural governing laws. Experience includes ad hoc and institutional arbitrations sited in both common law and civil law jurisdictions including Bermuda, Geneva, Hong Kong, London, New York, Paris, Vienna and Zurich. Has represented clients in telecommunications, energy, insurance, joint venture, mergers and acquisitions, and intellectual property disputes.
**Personal:** Duke University (JD, magna cum laude); Georgetown University (BA). Teaches International Arbitration at the Duke University School of Law.

## KENT, Ronald D
Dentons, Los Angeles
213 892 5030
ronald.kent@dentons.com
*Featured in Insurance (Nationwide), Insurance (California)*
See under California for profile.

## KENWORTHY, Kevin
Miller & Chevalier Chartered, Washington, DC
202 626 5848
kkenworthy@milchev.com
*Featured in Tax (Nationwide)*
**Practice Areas:** Federal income tax controversy emphasizing tax litigation as well as IRS appeals and other administrative procedures.
**Career:** He represents large and mid-sized multinational clients in a variety of federal tax disputes before the courts and the IRS on a range of international and domestic tax issues.
**Publications:** Writes and speaks frequently on tax practice and procedure. Quoted in numerous

publications on a variety of tax topics, including privilege and IRS administrative practices.
**Personal:** JD, Southern Methodist University School of Law, Order of the Coif, 1985; BA, University of Oklahoma, with distinction, 1982.

### KENYON, Geoffrey
Dechert LLP, Boston
617 728 7126
geoffrey.kenyon@dechert.com
*Featured in Investment Funds (Nationwide), Investment Funds (Massachusetts)*
See under Massachusetts for profile.

### KEOUGH, Christopher L
Akin Gump Strauss Hauer & Feld LLP, Washington, DC
202 887 4038
ckeough@akingump.com
*Featured in Healthcare (Nationwide), Healthcare (District of Columbia)*
**Practice Areas:** Focuses on Medicare and Medicaid reimbursement and compliance. Regularly represents hospitals before the Provider Reimbursement Review Board and in the federal court in matters involving reimbursement for disproportionate share hospitals, and other payment issues.
**Professional Memberships:** American Health Lawyers Association; Healthcare Financial Management Association; American Bar Association.
**Career:** Law clerk, US District Court for the District of Columbia (1991-92).
**Publications:** Healthcare Financial Management; Dennis Barry's reimbursement advisor (Aspen); BNA Medicare Reporter.
**Personal:** George Washington University, JD, 1991 (Notes Editor, Law Review); Franklin & Marshall College, BA, Economics, 1987.

### KERR, William D
Sidley Austin LLP, Chicago
+1 312 853 2140
wkerr@sidley.com
*Featured in Investment Funds (Nationwide)*
**Practice Areas:** Partner in Sidley's Chicago office, co-head of the firm's Investment Funds, Advisers and Derivatives practice and a member of the firm's Executive Committee. Represents clients in securities and derivatives-related corporate and regulatory matters, including organization and operation of US and offshore hedge funds, funds of funds, commodity pools, real estate funds and private equity funds, organization and operation of investment advisers, commodity pool operators and commodity trading advisors, fund restructurings, structured products, and derivatives documentation and regulation.
**Personal:** Harvard Law School, JD, 1983; Yale University, BA, 1980, cum laude.

### KERSH, Candice
Frankfurt Kurnit Klein & Selz, New York
212 826 5562
ckersh@fkks.com
*Featured in Advertising (Nationwide)*
**Practice Areas:** Partner in the Advertising, Marketing, and Public Relations Group. Represents leading advertising agencies as well as

some of the largest US advertisers on all areas of advertising and marketing law, including in connection with emerging technology transactions and platforms, branded entertainment, agency-client agreements, advertising copy review, network clearance, sponsorship and celebrity endorsement agreements, talent, music, and license agreements, SAG and AFTRA union issues, user-generated content, advertising challenges, sweepstakes and promotions, and copyrights and trademarks. Has acted as production counsel on independent feature films, and negotiated agreements for writers, directors and performers. First lawyer included in Advertising Age 'Women to Watch' list. Member of Best Lawyers in America. Named a New York-area 'Super Lawyer' for First Amendment, Media, and Advertising (2007-11), and Intellectual Property (2006), by Law and Politics magazine.

### KESSLER, David
Fulbright & Jaworski LLP, New York
212 318 3382
dkessler@fulbright.com
*Featured in Litigation (Nationwide)*
**Practice Areas:** Litigation; E-discovery and Information Governance; Information Technology; Records Management Solutions; Data Privacy.
**Career:** As co-head of Fulbright's E-Discovery and Information Governance Practice, David works with Fulbright's litigation group on e-discovery, information management, data privacy, international discovery and cyber-security matters. David focuses not only on tactical e-discovery issues in particular cases, but advises clients regarding strategic e-discovery portfolio management and data governance. David is an active member of the Sedona Conference and teaches "E-Discovery" at the University of Pennsylvania and Temple Law Schools.
**Personal:** JD, University of Pennsylvania (1997); MS, Fels School (1997); BS, Massachusetts Institute of Technology (1994).

### KESSLER, Jeffrey L
Winston & Strawn LLP, New York
212 294 4698
jkessler@winston.com
*Featured in Antitrust (New York), Sports Law (Nationwide)*
**Practice Areas:** Chair, Antitrust/Competition Practice; Co-Chair, Sports Law Practice. Extensive experience as lead counsel for global clients in some of the most complex antitrust, sports law, IP and other litigation, including major jury trials, and criminal and civil investigations in the antitrust, trade and FCPA areas.
**Professional Memberships:** International Academy of Trial Lawyers, ABA Antitrust Law Section, Board Member of Legal Aid Society and New York International Arbitration Center.
**Career:** Lecturer-in-Law, Columbia Law School.
**Publications:** International Trade and US Antitrust Laws (2nd Ed. 2006).
**Personal:** BA, summa cum laude, Columbia University, 1975. JD, Law Review, Columbia Law School, 1977.

### KESSLER, Judd
Porter Wright Morris & Arthur LLP, Washington, DC
202 778 3080
jkessler@porterwright.com
*Featured in International Arbitration (Nationwide)*
**Career:** Mr Kessler has acted as tribunal chairman, arbitrator and counsel in more than 40 significant institutional and ad hoc arbitration proceedings, including investor-state and complex commercial disputes. He is fluent in Spanish and has substantial experience in Latin America, Europe, Africa and the Middle East. For a complete listing of notable case experience, see Mr Kessler's bio at www.porterwright.com. As an arbitrator or mediator, Mr Kessler draws on broad experience as private counsel and senior US government counsel in investment, infrastructure, construction and energy projects, contracts for services, agency and distribution agreements, and political risk insurance.

### KHOURY, Paul F
Wiley Rein LLP, Washington, DC
202 719 7346
pkhoury@wileyrein.com
*Featured in Government (Nationwide)*
**Practice Areas:** Counsels and represents government contractors in solicitation review, multiple award schedule contracting, state and local procurements, subcontracting, teaming agreements, corporate transactions, bid protests, contract disputes litigation, compliance reviews, inspector general investigations, FCA actions and suspension/debarment proceedings. Handles matters before the GAO, US Court of Federal Claims, Boards of Contract Appeals, and in Federal district courts and state courts.
**Professional Memberships:** ABA, Section of Public Contract Law: Co-Chair, General Interest Division; Vice-Chair, Bid Protest Committee; Vice-Chair, Acquisition Reform and Emerging Issues Committees.
**Personal:** George Washington University (JD, Order of the Coif); Dartmouth College(BA).

### KHURI, Walid
Fried, Frank, Harris, Shriver & Jacobson LLP, Washington, DC
202 639 7013
Walid.Khuri@FriedFrank.com
*Featured in Investment Funds (Nationwide)*
**Practice Areas:** Corporate partner. Practice focuses primarily on fund-related work, including the structuring and offering of hedge funds, funds-of-funds, and other alternative investment products. Also regularly advises hedge funds and other clients on trading and operational issues, including advice regarding swaps and other derivative products.
**Career:** Joined in 2000; became partner in 2005.
**Personal:** JD, with honors, George Washington University (1996), editor, Law Review; BA, Brown University (1991).

### KIERN, Larry
Winston & Strawn LLP, Washington, DC
202 282 5811
LKiern@winston.com
*Featured in Transportation (Nationwide)*
**Practice Areas:** Larry Kiern concentrates his practice in litigation, arbitration, maritime, environmental, legislative, and regulatory matters. He focuses on complex litigation matters, both in arbitrations and the federal courts, involving the Federal Maritime Commission, Department of Justice, Coast Guard, EPA, and the Department of Transportation; and diverse legislative matters on Capitol Hill and regulatory matters before the agencies. He also has extensive experience investigating and litigating major marine casualties, and has represented clients in major maritime environmental criminal investigations. His broad client base includes ship owners, ship managers, charterers, shippers, port authorities, terminal operators, pollution underwriters, OSROs, and P&I Clubs.

### KIESELSTEIN, Marc
Kirkland & Ellis LLP, San Francisco
212 446 4665
marc.kieselstein@kirkland.com
*Featured in Bankruptcy/Restructuring (Nationwide), Bankruptcy/Restructuring (New York)*
See under New York for profile.

### KIESSLING, B Robbins
Cravath, Swaine & Moore LLP, New York
212 474 1500
bkiessling@cravath.com
*Featured in Banking & Finance (Nationwide)*
**Practice Areas:** B. Robbins Kiessling is a partner in Cravath's Corporate Department and serves as the Chair of its Financial Institutions practice. His practice encompasses a broad range of finance, banking, financial institution and related matters, including mergers and acquisitions, syndicated bank financings, leveraged finance, workouts and restructurings, and capital markets transactions. His clients have included JPMorgan Chase, Citigroup, Bank of America, State Street Corporation and other commercial and investment banks.
**Personal:** New York University School of Law (JD, cum laude, 1976; Order of the Coif; Articles Editor, Law Review); Yale College (BA, cum laude, 1973). For more information: http://www.cravath.com/bkiessling.

### KILBERG, William J
Gibson, Dunn & Crutcher LLP, Washington, DC
202 955 8573
wkilberg@gibsondunn.com
*Featured in ERISA Litigation (Nationwide), Employee Benefits & Executive Compensation (District of Columbia), Labor & Employment (District of Columbia)*
See under District of Columbia for profile.

**KIM, Richard K**
Wachtell, Lipton, Rosen & Katz, New York
212 403 1354
RKim@wlrk.com
*Featured in Financial Services Regulation (Nationwide)*
**Practice Areas:** Practice focuses on representing banks, insurance companies and other financial institutions in connection with regulatory matters, mergers and acquisitions and governmental enforcement actions.
**Professional Memberships:** Member of the Association of the Bar of the City of New York and the American Bar Association where he previously served as chair of the Mergers and Acquisitions Subcommittee of the Banking Law Committee. Also a member of the board of directors of the Asian American Legal Defense and Education Fund, the board of trustees of the Rye Country Day School, the advisory board of the Asian American Bar Association of New York and a former trustee of The Stanwich School.
**Career:** Partner in the Corporate Department at Wachtell, Lipton, Rosen & Katz. Previously, he was a staff attorney with the Board of Governors of the Federal Reserve System where he worked on a wide range of regulatory matters, including mergers and acquisitions involving bank holding companies, banks and investment banks. He was also assistant general counsel with NationsBank Corporation.
**Personal:** Graduated from Stanford University (AB, 1983) and from Columbia Law School (JD, 1986).

**KIMBALL, John D**
Blank Rome LLP, New York
212 885 5259
JKimball@BlankRome.com
*Featured in Transportation (Nationwide)*
**Practice Areas:** John Kimball chairs Blank Rome's International and Maritime Litigation and ADR practice. He concentrates his practice in maritime law and commercial litigation. He has more than 30 years' experience both domestically and internationally and counsels clients regarding maritime matters, including maritime casualties; charterparty disputes; insurance; creditors' rights; bankruptcy and insolvency; mass tort litigation; maritime environmental law; and commercial litigation. He is an Adjunct Professor at NYU Law School and is a co-author of Time Charters, Voyage Charters, and The Law of Salvage, 3A Benedict on Admiralty. He was honored by Chambers with a 'Star Individual' ranking.
www.BlankRome.com/JKimball.

**KING, Brian**
Freshfields Bruckhaus Deringer US LLP, New York
212 277 4020
brian.king@freshfields.com
*Featured in International Arbitration (Nationwide)*
**Practice Areas:** Brian is a partner in the International Arbitration Group in the firm's New York office. His practice centers on acting as counsel or arbitrator in investment and commercial arbitrations under the ICSID, ICC, SCC, UNCITRAL and other sets of rules. As counsel in invest-

ment arbitrations, Brian has acted for investors and states in some of the largest cases to date. With respect to both investment and commercial cases, Brian's areas of expertise include energy sector, post-M&A and construction disputes. Brian regularly lectures and publishes on arbitration-related topics. He speaks English and Dutch and reads French and Spanish.

**KING, C Randall**
Porter Hedges LLP, Houston
713 226 6603
rking@porterhedges.com
*Featured in Energy & Natural Resources (Nationwide)*
**Practice Areas:** Randy King represents upstream and midstream clients domestically and internationally in a wide range of energy-related projects. His work includes acquisitions and divestitures of conventional and unconventional oil and gas properties, gathering systems and pipelines. For exploration and production companies, he handles joint operating, exploration and development, and production sales agreements, drilling contracts and derivatives. For midstream companies, he is involved with natural gas, crude oil condensate and liquids gathering, transportation, storage and marketing agreements. Prior to becoming a lawyer, he spent 13 years practicing as a petroleum landman and has been a Certified Professional Landman since 1984.

**KING, Christopher Q**
Dentons, Chicago
312 876 8224
christopher.king@dentons.com
*Featured in Litigation (Nationwide)*
**Practice Areas:** Regularly advises large and midsize companies on all aspects of information governance, including electronic discovery, litigation readiness and records and information management. Litigated electronic discovery issues in numerous federal and state courts. Securities litigation and arbitration, consumer fraud, antitrust and other class actions, director and officer fiduciary and shareholder litigation, including a number of appeals.
**Professional Memberships:** Subcommittee Chair, Seventh Circuit Electronic Discovery Pilot Program, Working Group 1, The Sedona Conference.
**Career:** Clerk to Robert Murphy, Chief Judge, Court of Appeals of Maryland, 1983-84; Dentons 1984 - present
**Personal:** Vanderbilt University, 1983, JD; Northwestern University, 1980, BA

**KING, Deanna E**
Bracewell & Giuliani LLP, Austin
512 494 3612
deanna.king@bgllp.com
*Featured in Energy & Natural Resources (Nationwide)*
**Practice Areas:** Concentrates on representation and counsel of domestic and foreign energy-industry clients in regulatory compliance, hearings, disputes, and associated litigation. Appears on behalf of clients before the Federal Energy Regulatory Commission and other state and fed-

eral agencies, in federal and state courts, and in mediation and arbitration proceedings. Practice involves matters related to competition, market behavior and market design, enforcement and compliance, open access, restructuring, and transnational issues related to foreign participation in US energy markets.
**Personal:** JD, The University of Texas School of Law, 1998; MEd, The University of Texas at Austin, 1988; BS, Baylor University, 1986.

**KINGHAM, Richard F**
Covington & Burling LLP, Washington, DC
202 662 5268
rkingham@cov.com
*Featured in Life Sciences (Nationwide), Healthcare (District of Columbia)*
**Practice Areas:** Food and drug, European Union.
**Professional Memberships:** District of Columbia Bar, registered foreign lawyer in England and Wales.
**Career:** Regulatory counsel to PhRMA and Consumer Healthcare Products Association, served on committees of Institute of Medicine, NIH, and WHO. Adjunct Professor, Georgetown University Law Center.
**Publications:** Co-author, 'FDLI Practical Handbook of Food and Drug Law and Regulation', 'Global Pharmacovigilance: Laws and Regulations'; articles in professional journals.
**Personal:** BA. 1968, GW University; JD 1973, University of VA.

**KIRCHHOEFER, Gregg**
Kirkland & Ellis LLP, Chicago
312 862 2177
gregg.kirchhoefer@kirkland.com
*Featured in Outsourcing (Nationwide), Technology (Illinois)*
See under Illinois for profile.

**KIRKPATRICK, Deanna**
Davis Polk & Wardwell LLP, New York
212 450 4000
deanna.kirkpatrick@davispolk.com
*Featured in Capital Markets (Nationwide)*
**Practice Areas:** Partner in Davis Polk's Corporate Department. As a senior member of the firm's Capital Markets Group, her practice includes public equity, equity-linked, debt and other securities offerings by US issuers. She has regularly worked for issuers and underwriters in connection with capital markets transactions, including initial public offerings, as well as convertible and exchangeable securities offerings. Ms Kirkpatrick has worked on offerings for issuers over a broad spectrum of industries, including financial institutions, health care, oil and gas, retail, media, utilities and special-purpose acquisition companies.

**KIRSCH, Mark**
Gibson, Dunn & Crutcher LLP, New York
212 351 2662
mkirsch@gibsondunn.com
*Featured in Securities (Nationwide), Litigation (New York)*
See under New York for profile.

**KIRSON, Sarah E**
Kirkland & Ellis LLP, Chicago
312 862 2278
sarah.kirson@kirkland.com
*Featured in Investment Funds (Nationwide)*
**Practice Areas:** Sarah is a senior partner in the Private Funds Group who focuses on advising fund sponsors on the structuring and formation of private funds across a variety of investment strategies, including leveraged buyouts, energy, growth equity, venture capital, secondaries and mezzanine. She has represented sponsors in forming funds ranging in size from under $100 million to several billion dollars. Sarah also represents investors in making investments in private funds, secondary market sales and other complex business transactions and operational events.
**Personal:** Harvard Law School, JD, cum laude, 1994; University of Illinois, BS, Finance, highest honors, bronze tablet, 1991.

**KITCHENS, Dean**
Gibson, Dunn & Crutcher LLP, Los Angeles
213 229 7416
dkitchens@gibsondunn.com
*Featured in Securities (Nationwide), Litigation (California)*
**Practice Areas:** Member of Litigation and Securities Litigation Groups. Practice focuses on complex business and commercial litigation with an emphasis on securities litigation and auditor liability matters. Represents companies, accounting firms, underwriters, audit committees and individuals in connection with a broad range of matters, including investigations by the SEC, Department of Justice and other governmental agencies.
**Professional Memberships:** Fellow, American College of Trial Lawyers.
**Career:** Member, firm's Executive and Management Committees.
**Publications:** Contributor, Practicing Law Institute's Securities Litigation: A Practitioner's Guide.
**Personal:** JD, UCLA, 1978, Article Editor, 'Law Review', Order of the Coif.

**KLASMEIER, Coleen**
Sidley Austin LLP, Washington, DC
202 736 8132
cklasmeier@sidley.com
*Featured in Life Sciences (Nationwide), Healthcare (District of Columbia)*
**Practice Areas:** Partner in Sidley's Washington, DC office, leads the firm's product regulatory practice within the Global Life Sciences team. Manages matters on behalf of the world's leading biopharmaceutical, medical technology, and food and consumer product companies. Concentrates her practice on regulatory strategy and risk management, and on FDA litigation and dispute resolution. Involved as FDA regulatory counsel in defending off-label marketing investigations, as well as in product liability, consumer fraud, Hatch-Waxman, criminal, and appellate matters on behalf of life sciences industry clients.

**Career:** Previously worked in the Office of the Chief Counsel at the Food and Drug Administration.

## KLAUBERG, John G
Bracewell & Giuliani LLP, New York
212 938 6400
John.Klauberg@bgllp.com
*Featured in Energy & Natural Resources (Nationwide)*

**Practice Areas:** Provides advice transactions in the electric and gas sectors, including: mergers and restructurings of regulated utilities; acquisitions and dispositions of power plants and leases of generating and transmission facilities and similar "utility-type" properties; formation and restructurings of independent power project partnerships, including the negotiation and structuring of power purchase and sale agreements; and large-scale structured wholesale and retail power purchase and sale transactions.
**Personal:** LLM, New York University School of Law, 1984; JD, Georgetown University Law Center, 1981; BA, Hamilton College, 1978.

## KLEIN, Allen
Latham & Watkins LLP, Washington, DC
202 637 1029
allen.klein@lw.com
*Featured in Outsourcing (Nationwide), Technology (District of Columbia)*
See under District of Columbia for profile.

## KLEIN, Frederick L
DLA Piper LLP (US), Washington, DC
202 799 4101
frederick.klein@dlapiper.com
*Featured in Real Estate (Nationwide), Real Estate (District of Columbia)*

**Practice Areas:** Real estate.
**Career:** He practices in all areas of commercial real estate law, representing construction and permanent lenders, domestic and foreign banks, life insurance companies, local and national developers, and owners and developers of office buildings, multifamily projects, shopping centers, and urban and suburban office buildings. He has handled the acquisition, disposition, and financing of commercial projects in the mid-Atlantic region and elsewhere throughout the United States.
**Publications:** Co-author, 'American Bar Association's Real Property Tax Deskbook', chapter on District of Columbia real property taxation.
**Personal:** JD, University of Miami (cum laude); AB, Duke University.

## KLEIN, Jordan A
Sidley Austin LLP, Chicago
312 853 7302
jklein@sidley.com
*Featured in Wealth Management (Nationwide)*

**Practice Areas:** Partner in Sidley's Chicago office, head of the Chicago Private Clients, Trusts & Estates group and national team leader of the Trusts, Estates and Not-for-Profits practice. His practice encompasses the full range of estate planning, trust and estate administration and settlement, wealth transfer, philanthropy and fiduciary counseling services. His clients include corporate executives, families with dynastic wealth, private-

ly-held business owners (and former privately-held business owners who have experienced a liquidity event), professionals, fund managers, family offices, private foundations and others. Mr Klein has significant experience designing creative solutions to achieve client estate planning objectives and address client concerns.

## KLEINFELD, George
Clifford Chance US LLP, Washington, DC
202 912 5126
george.kleinfeld@cliffordchance.com
*Featured in International Trade (Nationwide)*

**Practice Areas:** Focuses on international economic regulation and foreign investment matters. Extensive experience counselling clients on all aspects of US international trade rules and economic sanctions and embargoes, including investigation and resolution of OFAC and other regulatory compliance matters. Particular experience in notifications under the Exon Florio Amendment and proceedings before the Committee on Foreign Investment in the United States.
**Career:** Partner at Clifford Chance since 2009. US Treasury Department, 1984-85.

## KLEPPER, Martin
Skadden, Arps, Slate, Meagher & Flom LLP & Affiliates, Washington, DC
202 371 7120
Martin.Klepper@skadden.com
*Featured in Projects (Nationwide)*

**Practice Areas:** Co-head of the Energy and Infrastructure Projects Group. Specializes in developing, financing, acquiring and selling energy, transportation and other large infrastructure projects throughout the world. Has handled major transactions related to privatizations and restructurings within the electric and gas industry, and has extensive experience in financing sports stadiums and teams. Has represented project developers, sponsors, lenders and investors in more than 100 major transactions totaling more than $20 billion. A consultant to federal and state governments.
**Career:** Adjunct Professor, Georgetown Law School (2002-07); JD, Rutgers Law School (1973); B.S., University of Pennsylvania, Wharton School (1969).

## KLINGENBERG, Erik D
Dentons, New York
212 768 6843
erik.klingenberg@dentons.com
*Featured in Capital Markets (Nationwide)*

**Practice Areas:** Practice involves all aspects of structured finance and securitization, including the sale, financing and servicing of all types of financial assets. Represents issuers, underwriters and other capital market participants in a wide variety of domestic, off-shore and cross-border transactions, including CMBS, RMBS, ABS, CP conduits, master trusts and credit, repurchase and structured warehouse facilities.
**Professional Memberships:** New York State Bar Association; CRE Finance Council; American Securitization Forum.

**Personal:** St. John's University School of Law, magna cum laude, JD; Hofstra University, Marketing, BA.

## KLUBES, Benjamin B
BuckleySandler LLP, Washington, DC
202 349 8002
bklubes@buckleysandler.com
*Featured in Financial Services Regulation (Nationwide)*

**Practice Areas:** Mr Klubes, Co-Managing Partner of BuckleySandler, represents financial services companies and individuals in enforcement agency investigations and litigation, private civil and class action litigation, independent counsel investigations, and grand jury proceedings. Specifically, he represents clients in investigations by the CFPB, DOJ, FTC, HUD, state attorneys general, and in fair lending-related and other class action litigation concerning the Fair Housing Act, ECOA, Civil Rights Act, unfair and deceptive trade practices, and privacy law claims. He also represents clients in FCPA and False Claims Act matters, conducts internal investigations, and advises on compliance issues and programs.

## KNIGHT, James T
Simpson Thacher & Bartlett LLP, New York
212 455 7123
jknight@stblaw.com
*Featured in Banking & Finance (Nationwide)*

**Practice Areas:** Partner in the firm's Corporate Department. Mr Knight's practice focuses on banking matters and the representation of lenders and borrowers in acquisitions and other leveraged transactions. His principal clients include J.P. Morgan Securities LLC, JPMorgan Chase Bank, N.A. and The Blackstone Group and its portfolio companies.
**Career:** Joined the firm in 1979; became Partner in 1986.
**Personal:** Harvard Law School (JD, cum laude, 1979); Dartmouth College (BA, summa cum laude, 1976); Member of Phi Beta Kappa.

## KNOWLES, Jeffrey
Venable LLP, Washington, DC
202 344 4860
jdknowles@Venable.com
*Featured in Advertising (Nationwide)*

**Practice Areas:** Mr Knowles leads Venable's Advertising, Marketing and New Media practice, the nation's largest and best-known advertising practice. Nationally recognized as one of the top attorneys in the advertising industry, he represents leading brands, direct marketers, and Internet and new media companies around the World. He represents clients before the FTC, FDA, CFPB, state AGs and self-regulatory bodies adjudicating advertising disputes. In 1990, Knowles founded, chaired and was general counsel of the Electronic Retailing Association, the largest international trade group for the direct-response industry.
**Personal:** BA, Columbia University, 1971; JD, New York Law School, 1975.

## KOBUS III, Theodore J
Baker & Hostetler LLP, New York
212 271 1504
tkobus@bakerlaw.com
*Featured in Privacy & Data Security (Nationwide)*

**Career:** Ted Kobus is Co-Chair of BakerHostetler's Privacy and Data Protection Team. He focuses his practice on privacy, data protection and information security. Ted advises clients regarding data security and privacy risk management, compliance programs, breach response strategies, litigation and regulatory actions affecting organizations. He has led more than 400 breach responses and he counsels clients regarding state and federal laws, international laws and other regulations and requirements. Ted has earned a trusted relationship status with many regulators, which is why clients seek his advice regarding compliance, regulatory response and breach response issues.

## KOENIGSBERG, Benjamin Y
Chadbourne & Parke LLP, New York
212 408 8021
bkoenigsberg@chadbourne.com
*Featured in Projects (Nationwide)*

**Practice Areas:** Ben Koenigsberg focuses on project development, financings, hedge transactions, acquisitions and sales relating to complex power, transportation, natural gas and other infrastructure projects. He represents international lenders, lead arrangers and underwriters, sponsors, private equity funds and other investors in limited recourse financings, debt restructurings, privatizations, and structured equity investments. His work in power ranges from conventional to renewables, such as wind, biomass and solar. He has worked on projects throughout the US, Brazil, Colombia and Israel.
**Personal:** Holds a BA, magna cum laude, from the University of Maryland and a JD from the Fordham University School of Law.

## KOEPPEL, John
Nixon Peabody LLP, New York
716 853 8137
jkoeppel@nixonpeabody.com
*Featured in Investment Funds (Nationwide), Corporate/M&A (New York)*

**Practice Areas:** John Koeppel is Chair of Nixon Peabody's Private Equity and Investment Funds Practice, ranked by the Dow Jones Private Equity Analyst as the 3rd most active practice among US law firms. John Koeppel's primary areas of practice are private equity investments and fund formation; mergers, acquisitions and divestitures; venture capital financings; private offerings; and cross-border transactions. Working from the firm's New York City and Buffalo, New York offices, John has led or worked extensively on over 250 significant deals for various US and foreign clients (ranging in deal size from $1 million to over $1 billion).

## KOESTLER, Mark D
Kramer Levin Naftalis & Frankel LLP, New York
212 715 9385
mkoestler@kramerlevin.com
*Featured in Immigration (Nationwide), Immigration (New York)*
See under New York for profile.

## KOHN, Arthur H
Cleary Gottlieb Steen & Hamilton LLP, New York
212 225 2920
akohn@cgsh.com
*Featured in Employee Benefits & Executive Compensation (Nationwide), Employee Benefits & Executive Compensation (New York)*
**Practice Areas:** Executive compensation, including disclosure, governance, taxation, design and negotiation of agreements and arrangements; pension investment and ERISA fiduciary; benefits issues in mergers and acquisitions and private equity; and employment law and related matters.
**Professional Memberships:** Member of the Bar of New York.
**Career:** Joined firm, 1986; became partner, 1995. JD, Columbia University School of Law (1986); BA, Columbia University (1986).

## KOLAR, Joseph M
BuckleySandler LLP, Washington, DC
202 349 8020
jkolar@buckleykolar.com
*Featured in Financial Services Regulation (Nationwide)*
**Practice Areas:** Mr Kolar counsels banks, mortgage lenders, servicers and insurers, investors, trade associations, and others in understanding and navigating consumer financial services laws and regulations affecting the home mortgage and consumer credit industries. Particular areas of focus include: disclosures, prohibitions, practice restrictions, and product and arrangement structuring under RESPA, TILA, HOEPA, Dodd-Frank Act, ECOA, the National Housing Act, HMDA, FCRA, FACTA, FDCPA, S.A.F.E., FIRREA and other federal and state laws regulating the origination, servicing, default management, and collection of mortgage and other consumer loans, fair and responsible lending and servicing, appraisals and appraisal management, credit reporting, fee limitations, unfair, abusive and deceptive acts and practices, privacy, electronic signatures and records, escrows, and licensing.

## KOLKEY, Daniel M
Gibson, Dunn & Crutcher LLP, San Francisco
415 393 8240
dkolkey@gibsondunn.com
*Featured in Litigation (California), Appellate Law (Nationwide)*
See under California for profile.

## KOLYER, Steven
Clifford Chance US LLP, New York
212 878 8473
steven.kolyer@cliffordchance.com
*Featured in Capital Markets (Nationwide)*
**Practice Areas:** Extensive experience in structured capital markets, investment fund formations and conventional securities offerings, including continuously-offered products. Also experienced in credit-linked notes, funded derivatives and synthetics, and in commercial lending and credit transactions. Mr Kolyer's experience over the years has been highlighted by transactions involving innovation and structured solutions in the capital markets. In this regard, he played a lead role in the development of a number of securitization products dating back to the origins of that market, in the US and offshore.
**Career:** Partner since 1991. Cornell Law School, JD, Law Review, 1981. Middlebury College, BA, 1978.

## KONVISSER, Joshua B
Pillsbury Winthrop Shaw Pittman LLP, New York
212 858 1027
joshua.konvisser@pillsburylaw.com
*Featured in Outsourcing (Nationwide), Technology (New York)*
See under New York for profile.

## KORB, Donald L
Sullivan & Cromwell LLP, Washington, DC
202 956 7675
korbd@sullcrom.com
*Featured in Tax (District of Columbia), Tax (Nationwide)*
**Career:** Head, Tax Controversy practice. Partner since January 2009. Previously IRS Chief Counsel since 2004. Developed litigation strategy behind Government's successful tax shelter litigation and served as lead negotiator in landmark transfer pricing dispute, resulting in largest single payment ever made to resolve an IRS tax dispute. Earlier IRS service includes leading IRS's involvement in legislative process that resulted in landmark Tax Reform Act of 1986. Significant private sector experience, most recently at Thompson Hine, developing its tax controversy practice.
**Personal:** Georgetown Law School (LLM, 1977); Case Western Reserve Law School (JD, 1973); John Carroll University (BA, 1970).

## KOREN, Bennet S
McGlinchey Stafford PLLC, New Orleans
504 596 2732
bkoren@mcglinchey.com
*Featured in Financial Services Regulation (Nationwide)*
**Practice Areas:** CFPB and FTC representation; Bank regulation, mortgage lending, motor vehicle lending, manufactured housing finance, student lending, consumer financial services, internet lending, e-commerce and insurance regulatory law.
**Professional Memberships:** American Bar Association, Business Law Section - Consumer Financial Services Committee, American College of Consumer Financial Services Attorneys, Mortgage Bankers Association, Conference on Personal Finance Law, Consumer Bankers Association Lawyers Committee, Louisiana Bankers Association Lawyers Committee.
**Career:** Chairman of McGlinchey Stafford's national consumer financial services practice group; concentrates on bank regulatory and consumer financial services law; frequent speaker at national programs on consumer finance regulations and compliance; listed for the last 17 consecutive years as one of Woodward White's Best Lawyers in America.
**Publications:** "Louisiana Supreme Court Confirms Yield Spread Premiums Are Not Included in HOEPA", Consumer Finance Law Quarterly, Spring 2011; "Suitability" Consumer Finance Law Quarterly, Spring 2008; Chapter on "High Cost Mortgage Loans", Law of Truth in Lending, 2000-2010.

## KOREN, Edward
Holland & Knight LLP, Tampa
813 227 8500
ed.koren@hklaw.com
*Featured in Wealth Management (Nationwide), Tax (Florida)*
See under Florida for profile.

## KORFF, Joshua N
Kirkland & Ellis LLP, New York
212 446 4943
joshua.korff@kirkland.com
*Featured in Capital Markets (Nationwide)*
**Practice Areas:** Joshua Korff has a broad corporate practice focused on private equity and leveraged acquisition transactions and public and private financings. He has extensive experience in connection with high yield, bridge and syndicated loan financings, as well as initial public offerings. He was named one of The American Lawyer's Dealmakers of the Year for representing Clearwire Corporation in a $14.5 billion merger. Other representative clients include Apax Partners, Avis, Bain Capital, Burger King, Goldman Sachs and Vestar Capital Partners.
**Personal:** New York University School of Law, JD, 1993. Dartmouth College, AB, 1990.

## KORFF, Phyllis G
Skadden, Arps, Slate, Meagher & Flom LLP & Affiliates, New York
212 735 2694
phyllis.korff@skadden.com
*Featured in Capital Markets (Nationwide)*
**Practice Areas:** Represents US and international issuers and investment banks in a variety of financing matters. Has worked on equity and debt financings, both investment grade and high-yield, in the US and international markets. Has worked on numerous initial public offerings and other offerings registered with the Securities and Exchange Commission, as well as offerings exempt from SEC registration pursuant to Rule 144A and Regulation S. Has extensive experience in representing Israeli and Canadian companies.
**Career:** JD, New York University School of Law, 1981 (Notes Editor, NY University Law Review); EdM, Boston University, 1967; BA, Brooklyn College, 1964.

## KORMAN, Paul
Van Ness Feldman LLP, Washington, DC
202 298 1830
pik@vnf.com
*Featured in Energy & Natural Resources (Nationwide)*
**Practice Areas:** Experienced in complex litigation before FERC and courts. Advises clients on all aspects of natural gas regulation including litigating interstate pipeline rate cases. Litigated a FERC rule before the Fifth Circuit Court of Appeals and succeeded in having the rule vacated. Represents companies and investors in complaints and confidential enforcement investigations before FERC and other regulatory agencies involving natural gas and electricity. Provides compliance training to regulated entities.
**Professional Memberships:** Energy Bar Association. American Bar Association.
**Career:** Assistant to Commissioner George Hall, FERC, 1977-1979. Special Assistant, Federal Power Commission, 1975-1977.

## KORNBERG, Alan W
Paul, Weiss, Rifkind, Wharton & Garrison LLP, New York
212 373 3209
akornberg@paulweiss.com
*Featured in Bankruptcy/Restructuring (Nationwide), Bankruptcy/Restructuring (New York)*
**Practice Areas:** Chair of Bankruptcy and Corporate Reorganization Department. Past Chair of New York City Bar's Bankruptcy and Corporate Reorganization Committee and Second Circuit Regent of the American College of Bankruptcy. Handles chapter 11 cases, out-of-court restructurings, cross-border insolvency matters, and bankruptcy-related investments and acquisitions. Recent clients include the senior lenders to Australia's Nine Entertainment, Quiznos, Silver Point (in the Hostess Brands chapter 11 case), Houghton Mifflin Harcourt, and Oaktree Capital (in the Aleris International chapter 11 case and other matters).

## KORNBLAU, David
Covington & Burling LLP, New York
212 841 1084
dkornblau@cov.com
*Featured in Securities (Nationwide)*
**Practice Areas:** Co-chairs Covington's Securities Enforcement Practice; represents companies and individuals in complex investigations by the SEC, CFTC, FINRA, DOJ, state attorneys general and regulatory authorities; specializes in subprime mortgage trading and securitization, insider trading, high frequency trading, market manipulation, retail brokerage, revenue recognition and other accounting issues; speaks/writes frequently on securities enforcement.
**Career:** Chief Litigation Counsel and Trial Counsel, SEC Enforcement Division (1995-2005); MD and Head, Global Regulatory Affairs, Merrill Lynch (2005-2009).
**Personal:** Princeton (AB, cum laude, physics, 1983); Harvard (JD, cum laude, 1986); Harvard Law Review; Clerk, Hon. Charles Merrill, US Court of Appeals, San Francisco (1986-87).

## KORZENOWSKI, Scott E
Dady & Gardner, PA, Minneapolis
612 359 5486
sekorzenowski@dadygardner.com
*Featured in Franchising (Nationwide)*
**Practice Areas:** Franchise and distribution.

**Career:** A Partner at Dady & Gardner since 2001, Scott has devoted his efforts to helping the "little guys" enforce their rights against the "big guys". He has helped franchisee associations negotiate more reasonable franchise agreements system-wide (including a negotiation that was publicized in the 'Wall Street Journal'), and has stopped several unlawful terminations. A former full-time radio talk show host, Scott hosts a once a week radio show and is a regular speaker on franchise law.
**Personal:** University of MN (JD, magna cum laude, 1996); University of MN (BA, 1983).

**KOSCHIK, David N**
White & Case LLP, New York
212 819 8241
dkoschik@whitecase.com
*Featured in Banking & Finance (Nationwide)*
**Career:** David Koschik is a member of White & Case's Executive Committee and the former head of the Firm's Americas Banking Section. Mr Koschik's practice focuses on the representation of major commercial and investment banks in lending transactions, and in acquisition and highly-leveraged financings in particular. He has served as senior bank lenders' counsel in connection with many acquisitions and highly leveraged financing transactions. Mr Koschik also represents lenders and borrowers in workouts and restructurings. To view a comprehensive biography, please visit www.whitecase.com/dkoschik.

**KRAIEM, Rubén**
Covington & Burling LLP, New York
212 841 1002
rkraiem@cov.com
*Featured in Climate Change (Nationwide), Latin American Investment (New York)*
**Practice Areas:** Latin America Investment, Clean Energy and Climate.
**Career:** Mr Kraiem has over 25 years' experience working with financial institutions, investors and industry leaders in Latin America, and is the Chair of Covington's Latin American transactional practice. Representative clients in recent transactions include Grupo Financiero Banorte, Raízen Energia, GlaxoSmithKlein, UCB, Brysam Global Partners, Citigroup, British United Provident Association (BUPA) and One Equity Partners. Mr Kraiem also has a history of active engagement on environmental policy issues and is the co-Chair of Covington's Clean Energy and Climate Group. He advises the Coalition for Rainforest Nations, having participated on its behalf in UN climate change negotiations, and works on carbon market policy and transactional matters. He was a Distinguished Scholar in Residence at the New York University Law School (2002-2003) and an Adjunct Professor at the Fordham Law School on Climate Change Law and Policy (2005-2009).He is a Director of Resources for the Future, an Honorary Trustee of the Natural Resources Defense Council and a member of the governing committee of the Cyrus R. Vance Center for International Justice.
**Personal:** Harvard Law School, cum laude (1981); Articles Editor, Harvard International Law Journal; Yale University, BA, summa cum laude (1978).

**KRAMER, Barry J**
Fenwick & West LLP, Mountain View
650 335 7278
bkramer@fenwick.com
*Featured in Investment Funds (Nationwide), Corporate/M&A (California)*
**Practice Areas:** Barry J. Kramer is a partner in the Corporate Group of Fenwick & West LLP. Mr Kramer represents a wide range of technology and life science companies,from privately held start-ups to publicly traded companies as well as prominent venture capital funds.
**Career:** Mr Kramer is recognized as one of the top 25 Venture Capital lawyers in the US by Chambers USA and as one of the top 100 Business/Corporate lawyers in California by Law & Politics magazine.
**Publications:** Mr Kramer speaks on business and legal topics and is the author of a quarterly venture capital survey.

**KRAMER, Daniel J**
Paul, Weiss, Rifkind, Wharton & Garrison LLP, New York
212 373 3020
dkramer@paulweiss.com
*Featured in Securities (Nationwide), Litigation (New York)*
**Practice Areas:** Co-Chair, Litigation and Enforcement Group. Recent matters include representation of Bank of America, AIG, Merck, UBS, Credit Suisse, Citigroup, Schering-Plough, Kohlberg Capital, Swiss Re, Ericsson, JPMorgan, SAC Capital and Hollinger International (now Sun Times Media Group) in complex litigation and securities matters. Represented special board committees of Fannie Mae, Adecco and Hampshire in internal investigations. Lectures and writes extensively on securities litigation and corporate governance issues, and is co-author of Corporate Internal Investigations: An International Guide, and Federal Securities Litigation: A Deskbook for the Practitioner and Regulation of Market Manipulation.

**KRAMER, Howard L**
Willkie Farr & Gallagher LLP, Washington, DC
202 303 1208
hkramer@willkie.com
*Featured in Financial Services Regulation (Nationwide)*
**Practice Areas:** Partner, Asset Management Group. Specializes in securities regulatory law, with particular emphasis on broker-dealer, market structure and compliance matters. Counsels clients on regulatory compliance and also represents clients in regulatory investigations/inquiries/examinations. Practice focuses on trading rules, derivatives, alternative trading systems, and broker-dealer regulatory and compliance issues. Clients have included major securities firms, equity and options market-making desks, securities and derivatives markets, electronic/Internet-based trading systems and hedge funds. Served as independent consultant for several entities with respect to their enforcement settlements with SEC.
**Personal:** JD, University of Michigan Law School, 1981. MA, University of Michigan, 1979. BA, University of Michigan, 1977. See: http://www.willkie.com/HowardKramer.

**KRAMER, Samuel**
Baker & McKenzie, Chicago
312 861 7960
samuel.kramer@bakermckenzie.com
*Featured in Outsourcing (Nationwide), Technology (Illinois)*
See under Illinois for profile.

**KRANTZ, Stefan**
Hogan Lovells US LLP, Washington, DC
*Featured in Energy & Natural Resources (Nationwide)*
**Practice Areas:** Energy: Oil & Gas
**Career:** He represents diverse energy companies before the US Federal Energy Regulatory Commission. With an understanding of the rapidly changing gas markets, including the dramatic rate and infrastructure impacts of the increasing shale production, he represents clients in natural gas certificate proceedings, Section 4 and 5 rate litigation, compliance and enforcement proceedings, all proceedings involving negotiated rate and service issues, credit-related issues and rate and discrimination cases under the Natural Gas Act.
**Personal:** JD, American University; BA, Cornell University, cum laude, with honors.

**KRASKE, Paul S**
Skadden, Arps, Slate, Meagher & Flom LLP & Affiliates, Washington, DC
+1.202.371.7234
Paul.Kraske@skadden.com
*Featured in Projects (Nationwide)*
**Practice Areas:** Represents clients in connection with the development, financing and acquisition of energy and infrastructure projects in the US and abroad. Has extensive experience preparing and negotiating all forms of relevant documentation, including joint development and ownership agreements, construction contracts, power purchase agreements, credit and investment documentation, and sale and purchase agreements.
**Career:** Worked in Mumbai, India as the general counsel of the Dabhol Power Project. JD, Harvard Law School, 1996 (cum laude); MSc, International Relations, London School of Economics and Political Science, 1993; BA, History, Yale University, 1992 (cum laude).

**KRAVETZ, Jonathan**
Mintz Levin Cohn Ferris Glovsky and Popeo PC, Boston
617 348 1674
JLKravetz@mintz.com
*Featured in Life Sciences (Nationwide), Corporate/M&A (Massachusetts)*
**Practice Areas:** Chair, Securities Practice Group; represents clients in public and private financings under Securities Act of 1933; counsels public companies on reporting and compliance issues under Securities Exchange Act of 1934; represents issuers and underwriters in initial and follow-on public offerings of equity and debt securities underwritten by major national and international investment banking firms; represents public and private companies in merger and acquisition transactions, venture capital financings, and other strategic transactions; advises boards and board committees on fiduciary duties and corporate governance matters.
**Professional Memberships:** BoD, Audit & Finance Committee, National Consumer Law Center.
**Personal:** Stanford University, JD.

**KRIESER, Jason D**
K&L Gates, Dallas
214 939 5423
jason.krieser@klgates.com
*Featured in Outsourcing (Nationwide), Technology (Texas)*
See under Texas for profile.

**KRIMMINGER, Michael**
Cleary Gottlieb Steen & Hamilton LLP, Washington, DC
202 974 1720
mkrimminger@cgsh.com
*Featured in Financial Services Regulation (Nationwide)*
**Practice Areas:** Regulatory matters affecting domestic and international financial institutions. Having played a leading role in the FDIC's policy and regulatory response to the financial crisis, he provides focused advice on the policy and legal components of statutory and regulatory requirements.
**Professional Memberships:** Member of DC, California, Virginia Bars. Served as co-chair of Basel Committee's Cross Border Resolutions Group.
**Career:** Joined firm as partner, 2012. More than 20 years with FDIC in senior leadership positions, including as Deputy to the Chairman and General Counsel. JD, Duke University School of Law (1982). BA, Phi Beta Kappa, University of North Carolina (1979).

**KROENER, William F**
Sullivan & Cromwell LLP, Washington, DC
202 956 7095
kroenerw@sullcrom.com
*Featured in Financial Services Regulation (Nationwide)*
**Professional Memberships:** American Bar Association; American Bar Foundation; American Law Institute; Federal Bar Association; Law Society of England and Wales; New York City Bar Association; New York State Bar Association; Former Chair of the Legal Advisory Committee of the FFIEC.
**Career:** Counsel since 2006. Focuses on supervision/regulation of banks and other regulated financial institutions and advisers; encompasses domestic and international activities, acquisitions, financings and other transactions. Widely recognized as a leading practitioner in financial services law. Served as general counsel, FDIC, 1995-2006.
**Personal:** Stanford Law School (JD 1971), Stanford University (MBA 1971), Yale University (BA 1967).

**KROMER, John**
BuckleySandler LLP, Washington, DC
202 349 8040
jkromer@buckleysandler.com
*Featured in Financial Services Regulation (Nationwide)*
**Practice Areas:** Mr Kromer, Co-Managing Partner of BuckleySandler, advises banks and non-banks on compliance with state and federal laws applicable to commercial and consumer credit, including mortgage, student, auto, and personal loans, as well as alternative financial services. He regularly assists clients prepare for and respond to regulatory examinations by the CFPB and other federal and state agencies. Additionally, he helps clients develop compliance management systems and structure and negotiate joint ventures and outsourcing arrangements. Mr Kromer also assists financial and strategic purchasers of financial services firms and assets with pre-transaction regulatory due diligence, deal structuring, and regulatory approvals.

**KROUPA, Sharon A**
Venable LLP, Baltimore
410 244 7509
skroupa@Venable.com
*Featured in Capital Markets (Nationwide)*
**Practice Areas:** Sharon Kroupa counsels clients, including many listed and non-listed real estate investment trusts (REITs), on a wide range of matters, including mergers and acquisitions, several valued at more than $1 billion; private and public equity and debt offerings, including multiple initial public offerings; and corporate governance matters, with particular emphasis on Maryland corporation law as it affects corporations and REITs. She regularly serves as independent counsel to boards and board committees in connection with significant transactions, conflicts of interest, corporate governance and stockholder litigation.
**Personal:** JD, with honors, Boston College Law School, 1982; BA, Loyola College, 1979

**KRUGMAN, Edward P**
Cahill Gordon & Reindel LLP, New York
212 701 3506
ekrugman@cahill.com
*Featured in Insurance (Nationwide), Insurance (New York)*
**Practice Areas:** From a broad business litigation background, has focused for more than 25 years on litigating insurance matters, structuring insurance transactions, and providing strategic advice to insurers. Represents ceding companies and reinsurers in numerous contested reinsurance matters, involving massive financial exposure, litigates high profile coverage issues, and advises on every aspect of the business of insurance and the business of insurance companies.
**Personal:** City College of New York, BS, 1971. New York University, PhD, Mathematics, 1975. Yale Law School, JD, 1978, Note Editor, Yale Law Journal.

**KUDENHOLDT, Stephen S**
Dentons, New York
212 768 6847
steve.kudenholdt@dentons.com
*Featured in Capital Markets (Nationwide)*
**Practice Areas:** Chair of legacy Dentons's US Capital Markets practice. Areas of practice include residential and commercial mortgage-backed securities and other asset-backed securities, primarily focusing on residential mortgage loan securitization and resecuritization transactions involving various classes of mortgage-backed securities. Has helped develop many transaction structures and formats that have become industry standards, including shifting interest subordination techniques. Represents issuers, underwriters, loan sellers and other entities in public offerings and private placements. Steve is a frequent writer and public speaker on regulatory developments affecting securitizations.
**Personal:** University of Michigan Law School, cum laude, JD; University of Illinois, BA.

**KURNIT, Rick**
Frankfurt Kurnit Klein & Selz, New York
212 826 5531
rkurnit@fkks.com
*Featured in Advertising (Nationwide)*
**Practice Areas:** 35 years representing advertisers, marketing services companies and their owners and executives in forming, running, and selling them. Rick has handled key cases defining the application of intellectual property law to advertising and marketing communications, including defendants in the Vanna White, Woody Allen, and Jackie Onassis look-alike cases; Nelson DeMille, Terry McMillan, and others defending libel claims based on fiction; Prodigy in the Stratton Oakmont case defining online liability; John Deere in defining use of trademarks in comparative advertising; and 'Gone With The Wind' in defining parody and copyright infringement. Named Best Lawyers' 2011 New York Media Lawyer of the Year, Chambers' Star Advertising Lawyer, a Legal 500 Leading Advertising Lawyer, and Best Lawyers in Advertising, Entertainment, Intellectual Property, Trademark, and Media. Columbia AB Magna Cum Laude, Phi Beta Kappa, Harvard JD Cum Laude, 30 years teaching advertising and intellectual property law.
**Professional Memberships:** Board Member of The Art Directors Club; The Miami Ad School; The Advertising Compliance Service.

**KURUCZA, Robert M**
Goodwin Procter LLP, Washington, DC
202 346 4515
rkurucza@goodwinprocter.com
*Featured in Investment Funds (Nationwide)*
**Practice Areas:** Mr Kurucza is Chair of the firm's Financial Services Group and is recognized as a leading expert on legal issues concerning the financial service industry. Named by American Banker as one of the 125 most influential people in Washington, DC on financial service matters, he has represented major banks, mutual fund complexes, thrifts, insurance companies, securities firms, and financial planning firms in new prod-

uct and service programs and inter-industry expansion initiatives and issues arising under the federal banking and securities laws and related federal laws.
**Personal:** JD, University of Pennsylvania Law School, 1973; BA, University of Pennsylvania, 1970.

**KUTZSCHBACH, George**
Fulbright & Jaworski LLP, Houston
713 651 3702
gkutzschbach@fulbright.com
*Featured in Energy & Natural Resources (Nationwide)*
**Practice Areas:** Energy.
**Professional Memberships:** Houston Bar Association; State Bar of Texas.
**Career:** Kutzschbach has extensive experience in a broad range of energy transactions. He focuses his practice on domestic and international transactions related to the exploration, acquisition, disposition, development and financing of (and joint venture, operational, transportation and marketing activities concerning) oil, gas, petrochemical and energy companies, properties, pipelines, plants, refineries and other energy assets.
**Personal:** He received a BBA in 1969 and a JD in 1972 from The University of Texas at Austin.

**KWON, Julie K**
McDermott Will & Emery LLP, Menlo Park
312 984 7725
jkwon@mwe.com
*Featured in Wealth Management (Nationwide)*
**Practice Areas:** Focused on advising clients regarding a broad range of estate planning issues, including estate, gift and generation-skipping transfer tax issues; charitable planning and exempt organization compliance; trust and estate administration; contested trust and tax matters; and construction and reformation of wills and trusts.
**Career:** Formerly the philanthropic advisor for Stanford University, where she collaborated with the Office of General Counsel and other members to resolve legal and tax issues.
**Personal:** Yale Law School, JD, 1996; Stanford University, BA (with distinction), 1993.

**KYRWOOD, Jason**
Davis Polk & Wardwell LLP, New York
212 450 4000
jason.kyrwood@davispolk.com
*Featured in Banking & Finance (Nationwide)*
**Practice Areas:** Partner in Davis Polk's Corporate Department, practicing in the Credit Group. He regularly advises financial institutions and borrowers on a wide range of corporate finance transactions, focusing on leveraged and investment-grade acquisition financings including LBOs, dividend recapitalizations and bridge facilities. His clients include financial institutions, including Bank of America, Citibank, Credit Suisse, Goldman Sachs, JPMorgan and Morgan Staley, and corporate clients, including Comcast, Aetna and Warner Chilcott.

**LADNER, Mark P**
Morrison & Foerster LLP, New York
212 468-8035
mladner@mofo.com
*Featured in Antitrust (New York), Financial Services Regulation (Nationwide)*
**Practice Areas:** Mark Ladner is a member and former Co-Chair of the Morrison & Foerster's Financial Services Litigation Practice, and a member of the Antitrust and Competition Practice. He has over 30 years of experience representing banks and other financial institutions in the areas of antitrust and other complex business litigation. In particular, he handles a variety of class actions challenging the structure and practices of the payment card industry, the setting of credit card fees, and the disclosure and setting of charges to holders of credit cards.

**LAFIURA, Dennis R**
Day Pitney LLP, Parsippany
973 966 8068
dlafiura@daypitney.com
*Featured in Franchising (Nationwide), Litigation (New Jersey)*
See under New Jersey for profile.

**LAFOLLETTE, Christine B**
Akin Gump Strauss Hauer & Feld LLP, Houston
713 220 5896
clafollette@akingump.com
*Featured in Corporate/M&A (Texas), Energy & Natural Resources (Nationwide)*
See under Texas for profile.

**LAHLOU, Yasmine**
Chaffetz Lindsey LLP, New York
212 257 6958
yasmine.lahlou@chaffetzlindsey.com
*Featured in International Arbitration (Nationwide)*
**Practice Areas:** International arbitration and commercial litigation.
**Career:** Yasmine Lahlou joined Chaffetz Lindsey shortly after it was founded in 2009. She was previously an Associate at Clifford Chance in New York and Castaldi Mourre & Partners in Paris. Yasmine has broad experience advising and representing private and sovereign clients in international arbitration and litigation proceedings.
**Publications:** Mealey's International Arbitration Report, International Law Office Newsletter and Revue de Droit des Affaires Internationale.
**Personal:** JD, University of Texas; MD, Paris X – Nanterre University. Co-Chair of the Middle East Committee of the ABA Section of International Law. Fluent in English, French and Italian.

**LAMB, William S**
Baker Botts LLP, New York
212 408 2557
bill.lamb@bakerbotts.com
*Featured in Energy & Natural Resources (Nationwide)*
**Practice Areas:** Mergers and Acquisitions, Committee Representation, Corporate Governance and Compliance, Cross-Border Transactions, Capital Markets and Securities Offerings, Downstream, Energy Regulatory, Joint Ventures, Power and Venture.

**Career:** Mr Lamb advises both public and private companies in mergers, acquisitions and divestitures, as well as financings. He represents bidders and targets in both negotiated and unsolicited mergers and acquisitions; and acts as counsel to issuers and underwriters in major financings.

**Personal:** JD, New York University School of Law, 1983; Order of the Coif, Executive Editor, New York University Law Review; BS (magna cum laude), New York University, 1977.

## LAMKEN, Jeffrey A
MoloLamken LLP, Washington, DC
202 556-2010
jlamken@mololamken.com
*Featured in Appellate Law (Nationwide)*

**Practice Areas:** Jeffrey Lamken has argued 21 cases before the US Supreme Court, and many before the courts of appeals, on matters as diverse as administrative law, bankruptcy, civil rights, constitutional separation of powers, criminal law and procedure, energy law, intellectual property, and telecommunications law.

**Professional Memberships:** Edward Coke Appellate Inn of Court; American Academy of Appellate Lawyers; District of Columbia Bar; California Bar.

**Career:** Founding partner, Molo Lamken LLP (2009-present); Head of Supreme Court practice, Baker Botts LLP (2003-09); Assistant to the Solicitor General, US Department of Justice (1997-2003); Kellogg, Huber (1993-97); Law clerk to Associate Justice Sandra Day O'Connor (1992-93), and to Judge Alex Kozinski, US Court of Appeals for the Ninth Circuit (1990-91).

**Personal:** JD, Stanford Law School, 1990 (Order of the Coif, Nathan Abbott Scholar); BA (magna cum laude), political science, Haverford College, 1986.

## LAMM, Carolyn B
White & Case LLP, Washington, DC
202 626 3605
clamm@whitecase.com
*Featured in International Arbitration (Nationwide)*

**Career:** Carolyn B. Lamm's practice concentrates on international dispute resolution through international arbitration, litigation and international trade proceedings. She has substantial experience with ICSID and its Additional Facility, NAFTA and other international arbitral proceedings involving States, as well as commercial arbitral fora including AAA/ICDR, ICC, Vienna Centre, Stockholm Chamber, Swiss Chamber, and in federal court litigation. She is involved primarily in the representation of foreign corporate clients and foreign sovereigns. Ms Lamm has been recognized repeatedly for her professional expertise in international dispute resolution and leadership in the profession by numerous sources. To view a comprehensive biography, please visit www.whitecase.com/clamm.

## LANDA, Leor
Davis Polk & Wardwell LLP, New York
212 450 4000
leor.landa@davispolk.com
*Featured in Investment Funds (Nationwide)*

**Practice Areas:** Partner in Davis Polk's Investment Management Group. Advises clients on structuring, marketing and operating private investment funds, including private equity funds, hedge funds, hybrid funds, real estate funds, secondary funds and funds of funds. Advises private fund managers in connection with their formation and operation and in connection with compensation and investment arrangements. Represents clients in structuring and executing private equity investments and in acquisitions of investment advisers. Advises private fund clients on various regulatory and compliance matters arising under US securities laws. Also represents clients investing in private funds.

## LANDAU, Christopher
Kirkland & Ellis LLP, Washington, DC
202 879 5087
christopher.landau@kirkland.com
*Featured in Appellate Law (Nationwide)*

**Practice Areas:** Chris Landau is the head of the Firm's Appellate Litigation Practice. He has handled appeals involving a wide range of subject matters in courts across the country, including the US Supreme Court, every one of the federal courts of appeals, and many state appellate courts. Chris served twice as a law clerk at the US Supreme Court, first to Justice Antonin Scalia (1990-91) and then to Justice Clarence Thomas (1991-92).

**Personal:** Harvard University, AB, 1985; Harvard Law School, JD, 1989.

## LANDY, Douglas J
Milbank, Tweed, Hadley & McCloy LLP, New York
212 530 5234
dlandy@milbank.com
*Featured in Financial Services Regulation (Nationwide)*

**Practice Areas:** Acknowledged expert in US financial services regulation and has been at the forefront of the financial services practice during the recent credit crisis. He represents many of the leading US and international financial institutions.

**Professional Memberships:** Member of the Board of Editors for The Banking Law Journal and a member of the Advisory and Editorial Board of the International Financial Regulation Review.

**Career:** Partner, Global Leveraged Finance Group.

**Personal:** JD, Boston College Law School in 1993 where he graduated cum laude. BA from the University of Pennsylvania in 1989.

## LANE, Brian
Gibson, Dunn & Crutcher LLP, Washington, DC
202 887 3646
blane@gibsondunn.com
*Featured in Securities (Nationwide)*

**Practice Areas:** Counsels companies on issues relating to corporate governance and the federal securities laws, including: novel and complex disclosure and accounting issues, filings with the SEC (such as public offers, proxies and interpretive requests), activist shareholders, board investigations and resolving inquiries from the SEC. He represents companies such as: AOL, Eastman Kodak, First American, Pitney Bowes, and Towers Watson.

**Career:** Sixteen years inside the SEC: Counsel to the Chairman, and the Director of the Division of Corporation Finance.

**Publications:** Nationally recognized as expert in field as author, media commentator, conference speaker.

## LANG, Richard A
McDermott Will & Emery LLP, Chicago
312 984 7583
rlang@mwe.com
*Featured in Wealth Management (Nationwide)*

**Practice Areas:** Focuses on delivering a wide array of legal services to the nation's wealthiest individuals and families. Among specialties are wealth transfer and income tax planning for venture capital and entrepreneurial clients, as well as counseling for family offices. Maintains offices in Chicago and Silicon Valley with frequent visits to New York.

**Professional Memberships:** Fellow of The American College of Trust and Estate Counsel (ACTEC).

**Personal:** John Marshall Law School (JD), Boston University School of Law, (LLM), Harvard University (BA cum laude).

## LANGLOIS, Jack J
DLA Piper LLP (US), Houston
713 425 8419
jack.langlois@dlapiper.com
*Featured in Energy & Natural Resources (Nationwide)*

**Practice Areas:** Energy, corporate, and private equity.

**Career:** He has significant experience in mergers, acquisitions, and dispositions of assets and stock of energy companies, acquisitions of exploration rights from sovereigns, joint ventures and investments in and financings of energy projects, including mineral exploration and development projects, production sharing agreements, concessions, licenses, pipelines, refineries, power plants and drilling rigs. His clients include leaders in the energy industry.

**Personal:** JD, Lousiana State University Law Center; BA, University of Southwestern Louisiana (with honors); Studied international and comparative law, Faculte de droit d'Aix-en-Provence, France.

## LAPUSHCHIK, Tatiana
Cravath, Swaine & Moore LLP, New York
212 474 1442
tlapushchik@cravath.com
*Featured in Banking & Finance (Nationwide)*

**Practice Areas:** Tatiana Lapushchik is a partner in Cravath's Corporate Department. Her practice focuses on representing the leading financial institutions, as well as corporate borrowers, in domestic and cross-border bank financings across a variety of industries, including healthcare, oil and gas, retail, technology, media and manufacturing. Ms Lapushchik's bank financing practice is broad, and includes financings of acquisitions, recapitalizations and spin-offs, asset-based financings, investment grade commercial paper backstop facilities, liability management transactions and debt restructurings.

**Personal:** Harvard Law School (JD, cum laude, 2000); Barnard College (BA, summa cum laude, 1997). For more information: http://www.cravath.com/tlapushchik

## LAROSE, Cynthia
Mintz Levin Cohn Ferris Glovsky and Popeo PC, Boston
617 348 1732
CJLarose@mintz.com
*Featured in Privacy & Data Security (Nationwide)*

**Practice Areas:** Member of the Corporate Practice, Chair of the Privacy and Security Practice, and a Certified Information Privacy Professional; extensive experience in dealing with the international, federal and state regulations related to the use and transfer of information, behavioral advertising, data security breach compliance, incident response and response planning, and data transfers in the context of mergers and acquisitions and technology transactions.

**Professional Memberships:** International Association of Privacy Professionals; ITECH Law Association

**Publications:** Editor - Privacy and Security Matters Blog, privacyandsecuritymatters.com

**Personal:** MS and JD, Boston University.

## LATMAN, Marc D
Fulbright & Jaworski LLP, New York
212 318 3108
mlatman@fulbright.com
*Featured in Transportation (Nationwide)*

**Practice Areas:** Equipment financing; Lending and leasing; Aviation; Transportation; Global Infrastructure; Structured and Project Finance; Bankruptcy and Insolvency.

**Career:** Marc Latman advises on equipment financings (with an emphasis on aircraft financings), infrastructure financings, project financings, public private partnerships (P3) and secured and unsecured lending transactions. His clients include lenders, borrowers, equity participants, operators, lessors and lessees. Marc's experience also includes general lending work on behalf of both lenders and borrowers. He currently serves as the Chair of the American Bar Association's Aircraft Financing Subcommittee.

**Personal:** JD, Hofstra University School of Law (1997); BA; University of Michigan (1994).

## LAURIA, Thomas E
White & Case LLP, Miami
305 995 5282
tlauria@whitecase.com
*Featured in Bankruptcy/Restructuring (Nationwide), Bankruptcy/Restructuring (Florida), Bankruptcy/Restructuring (New York)*

**Career:** Thomas Lauria is the Global Head of the Financial Restructuring and Insolvency Group at White & Case, which comprises more than 130 lawyers located in over 20 countries around the world. Mr Lauria has led White & Case teams in efforts to restructure more than US$100 billion of debt in some of the largest and most complex restructurings in history, including Washington Mutual Inc., Visteon Corp., Six Flags Amusement Parks, Chrysler, WCI Communities, Delphi Corporation, Adelphia Communications Corporation, Mirant Corporation, Corporación Durango, PhyAmerica Physician Group, The Williams Companies and Williams Communications Group. To view a comprehensive biography, please visit www.whitecase.com/tlauria.

### LAVELLE JR, John P
Morgan, Lewis & Bockius LLP, Philadelphia
215 963 4824
jlavelle@morganlewis.com
*Featured in Products Liability (Nationwide), Litigation (Pennsylvania)*
See under Pennsylvania for profile.

### LAWRENCE, Carmen J
Fried, Frank, Harris, Shriver & Jacobson LLP, New York
212 859 8411
Carmen.Lawrence@FriedFrank.com
*Featured in Securities (Nationwide), Litigation (New York)*
**Practice Areas:** Partner. Co-head of white collar criminal defense and securities enforcement practice group and securities enforcement and regulation practice. Focuses on representing parties in investigations and litigations conducted primarily by the SEC, DOJ, self-regulatory organizations and state securities regulators, conducting internal investigations, providing crisis management advice to public and private companies and counseling public companies and regulated entities on their obligations under the federal securities laws.
**Career:** Joined as partner in 2000. Regional Director for the SEC's Northeast Regional Office, 1996-2000.
**Personal:** JD, University of Michigan Law School (1981); BA, Cornell University (1978).

### LAWRENCE, Gregory
Cadwalader, Wickersham & Taft LLP, New York
212 504 6171
greg.lawrence@cwt.com
*Featured in Energy & Natural Resources (Nationwide)*
**Practice Areas:** Focuses on the electricity and natural gas industries, with extensive experience before the Federal Energy Regulatory Commission (FERC) and multiple state utility commissions regarding regulatory proceedings, compliance and enforcement, transaction structuring and negotiations, market design and trading, jurisdictional asset and ownership transfers, regulated rate setting and services, and governmental affairs. Involved in numerous precedent setting and market-leading matters. Clients include financial institutions and funds, wholesale and retail marketers, physical and financial traders, renewable and other generation and transmission project developers, municipal and investor-owned utilities, and large energy consumers.

**Professional Memberships:** Member, Energy Bar Association; member, Inter-Pacific Bar Association.
**Career:** Former counsel, Massachusetts Department of Public Utilities.
**Publications:** Frequent speaker, lecturer and author of numerous articles and publications. Contributing author, Cadwalader's Energy & Commodities Resource Center (www.energy-lawresourcecenter.com).
**Personal:** JD, New England School of Law; BA, Trinity College.

### LAWRENCE, Jeffrey F
Cozen O'Connor, Washington, DC
202 463 2504
jlawrence@cozen.com
*Featured in Transportation (Nationwide)*
**Practice Areas:** Jeff is chairman of the Transportation and Logistics Group. His primary practice areas are corporate, regulatory, joint ventures, and competition law. Jeff represents US and foreign companies and associations engaged in the maritime, intermodal transportation and offshore energy industries. He regularly represents clients before US federal agencies in Washington, D.C., as well as before national governments and international organizations outside the US.
**Professional Memberships:** Maritime Administrative Bar Association Maritime Law Association.
**Career:** Chair, Cozen O'Connor Transportation and Logistics Group.
**Personal:** University of Pennsylvania, BA, 1973 Rutgers University School of Law—Newark, JD, 1977.

### LAWRENCE III, Robert C
Cadwalader, Wickersham & Taft LLP, New York
212 504 6211
robert.lawrence@cwt.com
*Featured in Wealth Management (Nationwide)*
**Practice Areas:** Former Chairman, Private Client Department. Leading authority in international and domestic tax, trust, estate, and personal planning matters. Advises wealthy individuals on international and domestic tax-efficient structures for US and global family businesses and holdings with emphasis on minimization of taxation, management of holdings, succession planning and philanthropic structuring.
**Professional Memberships:** International Academy of Estate and Trust Law (Past President); American College of Trust and Estate Counsel (International Estate Planning Committee); Society of Trust and Estate Practitioners (International Committee); ABA Tax Section (past Chair, International Estate Planning Subcommittee); NY State Bar Association (International Estate and Tax Planning Committee); Editorial Board, Journal of International Trust and Corporate Planning.
**Publications:** Author, International Tax and Estate Planning: A Practical Guide for Multinational Investors, Practising Law Institute (3rd Ed., 1996); editor and contributor,

International Tax Planning Encyclopedia (Tottel Publishing).
**Personal:** LLB, LLM (Taxation), New York University School of Law; BA, Cornell University.

### LEAKE, Paul
Jones Day, New York
212 326 3482
pdleake@jonesday.com
*Featured in Bankruptcy/Restructuring (Nationwide), Bankruptcy/Restructuring (New York)*
**Practice Areas:** Head of the firm-wide Business Restructuring and Reorganization Practice and Head of the New York Office's Corporate Practice. His practice is focused on US and transnational business reorganizations, including chapter 11 reorganizations and liquidations, out-of-court restructurings, refinancings, distressed acquisitions, and investments in troubled companies. He has represented all of the major constituencies in restructurings, including debtors, bank groups, bondholder committees, official creditors' committees, unsecured creditors, and distressed investors. Principal debtor representations include Independence Air, Globalstar, Olympia & York, Drexel Burnham Lambert, Marvel Entertainment, and Levitz Furniture.
**Personal:** Columbia University School of Law (JD, 1988); Amherst College (BA, 1985).

### LEATHERBURY, Thomas S
Vinson & Elkins LLP, Dallas
214 220 7792
tleatherbury@velaw.com
*Featured in First Amendment Litigation (Nationwide)*
**Practice Areas:** Co-Chair, V&E Appellate Practice Group. Experience in state and federal appeals and trials, including commercial, tort, intellectual property, and healthcare litigation, and class actions. Represents publishers and broadcasters in all aspects of media litigation.
**Professional Memberships:** American Law Institute; American Bar Association; Media Law Resource Center, Defense Counsel Section; Editorial Board, Communications Lawyer.
**Career:** Admitted to practice, Texas, 1979. Joined Vinson & Elkins, 1992.
**Personal:** Yale College, BA History, 1976 (Summa cum laude); Yale Law School, JD, 1979; clerk to Robert M Hill, US District Judge for the Northern District of Texas, Dallas, 1979-80.

### LEAVITT, Jeffrey M
DLA Piper LLP (US), New York
404 736 7818
jeffrey.leavitt@dlapiper.com
*Featured in Investment Funds (Nationwide)*
**Practice Areas:** Investment Funds: Venture Capital.
**Career:** He works with emerging growth companies, venture and growth capital investment entities and mature technology companies. He is a graduate of the Kauffman Fellows Program, a highly competitive national fellowship akin to a Rhodes Scholarship for venture capital professionals. Kauffman Fellows receive two years of specialized training in venture capital investment techniques and develop an extensive network throughout the private equity industry. He was

the first JD ever accepted into the program and the only practicing attorney in the country to have completed it.
**Personal:** JD, University of Pennsylvania 1997; BA, Duke University.

### LEBEY, Daniel M
Hunton & Williams LLP, Richmond
804 788 7366
dlebey@hunton.com
*Featured in Capital Markets (Nationwide)*
**Practice Areas:** Mr LeBey represents issuers and underwriters in public and private equity and debt offerings, with a particular focus in the real estate and specialty finance industries where he represents equity and mortgage REITs and a variety of other real estate related businesses and other permanent capital vehicles. Mr LeBey's practice also includes M&A, joint ventures and general corporate, securities and corporate governance advice.
**Personal:** AB in English from Princeton University in 1987. JD from the University of Georgia School of Law in 1992, and a Member of the Editorial Board of the Georgia Law Review.

### LEBOVITZ, James A
Dechert LLP, Philadelphia
215 994 2510
james.lebovitz@dechert.com
*Featured in Capital Markets (Nationwide), Corporate/M&A (Pennsylvania)*
See under Pennsylvania for profile.

### LECLAIRE, John R
Goodwin Procter LLP, Boston
617 570 1144
jleclaire@goodwinprocter.com
*Featured in Private Equity (Nationwide), Private Equity (Massachusetts)*
See under Massachusetts for profile.

### LEDIG, Robert H
Dechert LLP, Washington, DC
202 261 3454
robert.ledig@dechert.com
*Featured in Financial Services Regulation (Nationwide)*
**Practice Areas:** Mr Ledig advises financial institutions on corporate, regulatory, enforcement, and litigation issues.
**Professional Memberships:** Member, New Jersey and District of Columbia Bars; adjunct faculty member, George Mason University Law School.
**Career:** Attorney in the Office of the General Counsel of the Federal Home Loan Bank Board.
**Personal:** State University of New York at Binghamton, Harpur College (BA, 1979, with honors); George Washington University Law School (JD, 1982, with honors).

### LEE, Judith
Gibson, Dunn & Crutcher LLP, Washington, DC
202 887 3591
jalee@gibsondunn.com
*Featured in International Trade (Nationwide)*
**Practice Areas:** International trade regulation, including USA Patriot Act compliance, economic sanctions/embargoes, commercial/military export

controls, customs, international privacy issues, and international intellectual property issues. 1992: licensed by Department of Treasury as customshouse broker, receiving country's highest score on customshouse broker's examination, administered by US Customs Service.
**Professional Memberships:** International Bar Association – Export Controls, Sanctions and Anti-Corruption Subcommittee (Chair); ABA Customs Committee (prior chair); ABA Export Controls - Economic Sanctions Committee (prior co-chair); Customs - International Trade Bar Association (prior board member).
**Publications:** Author, numerous articles. Participant, legal/business conferences.
**Personal:** JD, William and Mary College, 1987.

### LEE, Ronald D
Arnold & Porter LLP, Washington, DC
202 942 5380
Ronald.Lee@aporter.com
*Featured in Privacy & Data Security (Nationwide)*
**Practice Areas:** Experienced in national security, cybersecurity, and technology law and policy; represents clients on strategic, sensitive, and novel matters in data security, encryption, security breaches, information privacy, security and liability aspects of computer systems and networks, electronic surveillance including FISA and ECPA, Exon-Florio (CFIUS) national security review of foreign investments in the US; IP and IT issues, including legislation, regulation, and enforcement.
**Career:** General Counsel, US National Security Agency; Associate Deputy Attorney General, US Department of Justice; Chief of Staff, Director of CIA.
**Personal:** JD, Yale Law School, 1985; MPhil, Oxford University, 1982; AB, Princeton University, 1980. Rhodes Scholar.

### LEE, William F
WilmerHale, Boston
617 526 6556
william.lee@wilmerhale.com
*Featured in International Trade (Nationwide), Life Sciences (Nationwide), Litigation (Nationwide), Intellectual Property (Massachusetts)*
**Practice Areas:** Partner in the Litigation/Controversy and Intellectual Property Departments. Former co-managing partner, a position which he held for seven years. He was a managing partner of Hale and Dorr from 2000 to 2004 and chaired the firm's Litigation Department for four years.
**Career:** Mr Lee concentrates his practice primarily on intellectual property and commercial litigation. His trial and appellate experience is extensive. Mr Lee has tried more than 100 patent cases, both jury and jury waived, to judgment and argued more than 50 appeals before the Court of Appeals for the Federal Circuit and other Courts of Appeals.

### LEE, Yoon-Young
WilmerHale, Washington, DC
202 663 6720
yoon-young.lee@wilmerhale.com
*Featured in Financial Services Regulation (Nationwide)*
**Practice Areas:** Chair, Broker-Dealer Compliance and Regulation Practice; Partner, Securities Department; Member, Derivatives and Futures Practice; Member, Management Committee; practice emphasis on broker-dealer regulation and securities compliance policies and procedures. Her practice includes providing advice regarding information barriers, research analyst independence, insider trading, sales practices, capital markets trading issues, electronic communications, supervision and surveillance measures.
**Professional Memberships:** Member, National Asian Pacific American Bar Association, the Women's Bar Association and the DC Bar Association.
**Personal:** Harvard Law School (JD, cum laude); Johns Hopkins University (BA).

### LEFKOWITZ, David S
Weil, Gotshal & Manges LLP, New York
212 310 8850
david.lefkowitz@weil.com
*Featured in Capital Markets (Nationwide)*
**Practice Areas:** Senior securities lawyer with over 25 years of experience in the field who led Weil's Capital Markets Practice for 10 years. Has a diverse corporate finance practice, including representing issuers and investment banks in a variety of public and private equity and debt offerings and bridge financings with aggregate proceeds in excess of $60 billion. Also frequently represents corporations and boards in a variety of securities, disclosure and corporate governance matters and has been active in representing corporations in matters related to the 2008 collapse of the residential mortgage market.
**Personal:** Northwestern University (BS, 1982); Georgetown University (JD, 1986).

### LEGGETTE, Poe
Fulbright & Jaworski LLP, Denver
303 801 2746
pleggette@fulbright.com
*Featured in Energy & Natural Resources (Nationwide)*
**Practice Areas:** Litigation; energy.
**Professional Memberships:** Trustee, Rocky Mountain Mineral Law Foundation.
**Career:** Leggette is Co-Chair of Fulbright's Energy Practice Group and heads the Western Lands and Energy Practice. He focuses on judicial and administrative litigation concerning natural resources development, and has been involved in many significant cases at the trial, appellate and Supreme Court levels regarding ownership of mineral rights, royalty disputes and compliance with environmental statutes. Prior to private practice, Leggette served as assistant solicitor for the US Department of the Interior.

**Personal:** BA, magna cum laude, Tufts University (1974); JD, University of Virginia (1977).

### LEHFELDT, Richard
Dickstein Shapiro LLP, Washington, DC
202 420 2215
lehfeldtr@dicksteinshapiro.com
*Featured in Energy & Natural Resources (Nationwide)*
**Practice Areas:** Represents companies in electricity industry, with matters such as complex acquisitions, development and financing of competitive power projects, regulatory and environmental law, corporate communications, and federal and state legislation.
**Professional Memberships:** Former Board Member and Chair of Legislative Committee of Electric Power Supply Association.
**Career:** Counsel to US House Energy and Commerce Committee; Assistant General Counsel, Edison Mission Energy; Senior Vice President - External Affairs, TECO Energy.
**Personal:** Harvard Law School (JD, cum laude), Kennedy School of Government (MPP), University of Michigan (BA, Phi Beta Kappa).

### LEHRER, Jeffrey K
DLA Piper LLP (US), Reston
703 773 4182
jeff.lehrer@dlapiper.com
*Featured in Investment Funds (Nationwide), Corporate/M&A (Northern Virginia)*
See under Virginia for profile.

### LEICHT, Eric F
White & Case LLP, New York
212 819 8796
eleicht@whitecase.com
*Featured in Banking & Finance (Nationwide)*
**Career:** Eric Leicht is head of White & Case's Americas Banking Section. Eric represents major commercial and investment banks in a variety of lending transactions, with an emphasis on acquisition and leveraged financings. As counsel for the agent banks, he is involved in all aspects of deal structure and in the negotiation and documentation of such financings, including the negotiation of intercreditor relationships among senior and junior creditors. He has experience representing lenders in financing transactions involving borrowers in a wide variety of industries, including manufacturing, hotel, retail, consumer products, investment funds and communications. To view his biography, please visit www.whitecase.com/eleicht.

### LEMEIN, Gregg D
Baker & McKenzie, Chicago
312 861 8013
Gregg.Lemein@bakermckenzie.com
*Featured in Tax (Illinois), Tax (Nationwide)*
**Practice Areas:** US federal income taxation of corporations, with emphasis on international tax issues. Extensive experience in international tax planning, transfer pricing and tax controversies before the IRS and in court.
**Professional Memberships:** American Bar Association Tax Section.

**Career:** Joined Baker & McKenzie in 1976 and became a Partner in 1983.
**Publications:** Numerous published articles.
**Personal:** Northwestern University Law School, JD, magna cum laude, Order of the Coif; Kellogg Graduate School of Management, Northwestern University, MM, with distinction; and University of Illinois, BS, with high honors.

### LENAS, Elizabeth
Cleary Gottlieb Steen & Hamilton LLP, New York
212 225 2612
elenas@cgsh.com
*Featured in Investment Funds (Nationwide)*
**Practice Areas:** Forming and advising private investment funds, including private equity funds, debt funds, hedge funds, co-investment funds and other alternative asset investment vehicles. Clients include TPG, KKR, Blackstone and Unitas Capital.
**Professional Memberships:** Member of the Bar in New York.
**Career:** Became counsel, 2009; became partner, 2013. Columbia University School of Law (JD, James Kent Scholar); New York University (BA, University Scholar).

### LENCK, Eric
Freehill Hogan & Mahar LLP, New York
212 381 3004
lenck@freehill.com
*Featured in Transportation (Nationwide)*
**Practice Areas:** Litigation including cargo claims, charter party disputes, maritime fraud, bankruptcy, and marine insurance coverage; drafting all types of maritime contracts, including bills of lading, service contracts, charter parties, VSA's, ship construction, agency agreements, repair contracts, management agreements, stevedore and terminal contracts. Head of firm's transactions department, including ship sale and purchase, financing, asset purchase, company start-ups, and corporate matters.
**Personal:** BA Yale University, 1969; JD University of Michigan Law School 1973; Associate Editor of Michigan Law Review; Speaker and Author on various maritime topics; fluent in Swedish.

### LENHARD, Robert
Covington & Burling LLP, Washington, DC
202 662 5940
rlenhard@cov.com
*Featured in Government (Nationwide)*
**Practice Areas:** Election & Political Law.
**Career:** Robert Lenhard advises corporations, trade associations, not-for-profit organizations, and high-net-worth individuals on compliance with federal and state campaign finance, lobbying, and government ethics laws. Mr Lenhard assists clients in establishing and operating federal and state PACs, compliance programs associated with campaign finance and pay-to-play laws; advises advocacy groups and their donors; conducts trainings and audits of federal and state lobbying and political programs; and counsels clients on compliance with congressional gift and travel rules.
**Personal:** Federal Election Commission, Commissioner; University of California at Los

Angeles School of Law, JD; Johns Hopkins University, BA.

**LENNON, Daniel**
Latham & Watkins LLP, Washington, DC
202 637 2347
dan.lennon@lw.com
*Featured in Private Equity (Nationwide), Corporate/M&A (District of Columbia)*
See under District of Columbia for profile.

**LENNON JR, Michael P**
Baker Botts LLP, Houston
713 229 1867
mike.lennon@bakerbotts.com
*Featured in International Arbitration (Nationwide)*
**Practice Areas:** International Arbitration and Dispute Resolution, Energy Litigation, Construction Litigation, Complex Business Litigation, Intellectual Property Litigation.
**Professional Memberships:** Institute for Transnational Arbitration of The Center for American and International Law, Advisory Board; Institute for Energy Law of The Center for American and International Law, Advisory Board; London Court of International Arbitration; International Bar Association; American Bar Association; Bar Association of the Fifth Federal Circuit; Houston Bar Association.
**Career:** Energy, construction, intellectual property and commercial arbitration and litigation.
**Personal:** JD (with high distinction), University of Iowa College of Law, 1991; BS (with honors), political science, University of Iowa, 1988.

**LENNOX, Heather**
Jones Day, New York
212 326 3837
hlennox@jonesday.com
*Featured in Bankruptcy/Restructuring (Nationwide), Bankruptcy/Restructuring (New York), Bankruptcy/Restructuring (Ohio)*
See under Ohio for profile.

**LEON, Norman**
DLA Piper LLP (US), Washington, DC
312 368 2192
norman.leon@dlapiper
*Featured in Franchising (Nationwide)*
**Practice Areas:** Franchising.
**Career:** He represents franchisors in federal and state courts and alternative dispute resolution forums throughout the United States. He has extensive experience dealing with franchisee terminations and the enforcement of post-termination covenants, and regularly prosecutes motions for temporary restraining orders and preliminary injunctions.
**Personal:** JD, Brooklyn Law School; BA, Boston University.

**LEONARD, Emily I**
Covington & Burling LLP, San Francisco
650 632 4721
eleonard@cov.com
*Featured in Life Sciences (Nationwide), Life Sciences (California)*
**Practice Areas:** Life sciences, corporate, intellectual property.
**Career:** Emily Leonard is vice chair of Covington's Life Sciences Industry Group and res-

ident in the firm's Silicon Valley office. She concentrates in transactions for pharmaceutical, biotechnology, and other life sciences clients from early-stage ventures to large public and private companies. She has extensive experience in handling complex strategic partnering and collaboration agreements, joint ventures, licensing, and other technology transfer arrangements.
**Personal:** George Washington University Law School, JD, 1994, with honors; Catholic University of America, BA, 1990, magna cum laude; Covington & Burling 1994-present (Partner since 2003).

**LERNER, Arthur N**
Crowell & Moring LLP, Washington, DC
202 624 2820
alerner@crowell.com
*Featured in Healthcare (Nationwide), Healthcare (District of Columbia)*
See under District of Columbia for profile.

**LERNER, Jonathan J**
Skadden, Arps, Slate, Meagher & Flom LLP & Affiliates, New York
212 735 2550
jlerner@skadden.com
*Featured in Securities (Nationwide), Litigation (New York)*
**Practice Areas:** Securities, corporate, commercial and international litigation and arbitration. Lead Trial Counsel in DaimlerChrysler, AG victory over Kirk Kerkorian's multi-billion dollar securities action named National Law Journal's 'Top Defense Win of 2005'. Led defense of three of the largest securities class actions ever litigated: Cendant Corporation, McKesson HBOC and DaimlerChrysler Securities Litigation. Recently won dismissals in Second Circuit of both Star Gas Securities Litigation, and antitrust and RICO claims against Jakks Pacific, Inc. Has tried 'bet the company' arbitrations against major companies, including Marriott International and Johnson & Johnson.
**Career:** JD, St. John's University, 1973 (magna cum laude).

**LESEUR, John H**
Slover & Loftus, Washington, DC
202 347 7170
jhl@sloverandloftus.com
*Featured in Transportation (Nationwide)*
**Practice Areas:** Mr LeSeur is a Partner with over 30 years experience in administrative law, civil litigation, arbitration, and appellate work with a focus on railroad transportation. He has been lead counsel for a wide-variety of rail shippers in numerous administrative adjudications, arbitrations, and court appeals in various matters involving rail rates, fuel surcharges, rail build-outs, rail abandonments, and unreasonable rail practices. Mr LeSeur has regularly counseled clients on all phases of rail transportation contracts, coal supply contracts, railcar leases, and other commercial arrangements.
**Personal:** BA, summa cum laude, Dartmouth College, 1974; JD, Georgetown University Law Center, 1979.

**LEVANDER, Andrew J**
Dechert LLP, New York
212 698 3683
andrew.levander@dechert.com
*Featured in Litigation (Nationwide), Securities (Nationwide), Litigation (New York)*
See under New York for profile.

**LEVI, Stuart D**
Skadden, Arps, Slate, Meagher & Flom LLP & Affiliates, New York
212 735 2750
Stuart.Levi@skadden.com
*Featured in Outsourcing (Nationwide), Technology (New York)*
See under New York for profile.

**LEVIN, Richard**
Cravath, Swaine & Moore LLP, New York
212 474 1978
rlevin@cravath.com
*Featured in Bankruptcy/Restructuring (Nationwide), Bankruptcy/Restructuring (New York)*
**Practice Areas:** Richard Levin is a partner in Cravath's Corporate Department and serves as the Chair of its Restructuring practice. His practice focuses on creditors' rights, insolvency, reorganization and bankruptcy. He has negotiated and structured complex domestic and international transactions involving distressed or insolvent companies and guided corporate debtors, creditors and acquirers through Chapter 11 and out-of-court restructurings in negotiated resolutions and in litigation.
**Personal:** Yale Law School (JD, 1975; Editor, Yale Law Journal); Massachusetts Institute of Technology (SB, 1972). For more information: http://www.cravath.com/rlevin

**LEVIN, Timothy W**
Morgan, Lewis & Bockius LLP, Philadelphia
215 963 5037
tlevin@morganlewis.com
*Featured in Investment Funds (Nationwide)*
**Practice Areas:** Timothy W. Levin is a partner in Morgan Lewis's Investment Management and Securities Industry Practice. Mr Levin's practice focuses on advising investment advisers and other financial services firms in connection with design, development and management of pooled investment vehicles and investment advisory programs. Mr Levin represents many types of registered investment companies, such as mutual funds and registered funds of hedge funds, and funds focused on alternative investment strategies, and he counsels managers of funds in connection with organization, registration and ongoing regulatory compliance. He also represents managers of unregistered pooled investment vehicles, including managers and sponsors of private funds, and companies seeking exemption from investment company status.

**LEVINE, David J**
McDermott Will & Emery LLP, Washington, DC
202 756 8153
dlevine@mwe.com
*Featured in International Trade (Nationwide)*

**Practice Areas:** International trade and related regulatory matters. Counsels clients on export controls, sanctions, customs, import relief (AD, CVD, safeguards), market access, FTAs, WTO, FCPA, and antiboycott. Has successfully represented clients in numerous import relief cases; export licensing and disclosure actions; customs audits, disputes and rulings; legislative and rulemaking procedures; trade negotiations; FCPA matters; and trade compliance, including policy development, training and internal reviews.
**Professional Memberships:** Advisory Board, Washington University Global Studies Law Review; NAFTA Chapter 19 Panelists Roster.
**Personal:** Washington University School of Law (JD); University of Denver Graduate School of International Studies (MA); Colorado College (BA).

**LEVINE, Jerome L**
Holland & Knight LLP, Los Angeles
213 896 2400
jerry.levine@hklaw.com
*Featured in Native American Law (Nationwide)*
**Practice Areas:** Partner in the firm's Los Angeles office and director of the firm's national Indian Law Practice Group. For more than 20 years, he has been a leading attorney nationally in the field of Indian law, advising on tribally-based projects throughout the country in a wide range of matters, including complex project financing, constitutional and governance issues, fee to trust matters, economic development, natural resource protection and development, sacred sites protection, and gaming and hotel development and regulation. He also has a broad range of experience in complex business, commercial and government litigation, regulation, and alternative dispute resolution.

**LEVINE, Lee**
Levine Sullivan Koch & Schulz LLP, Washington, DC
202 508 1110
llevine@lskslaw.com
*Featured in First Amendment Litigation (Nationwide), Media & Entertainment (District of Columbia)*
**Practice Areas:** Founding Partner of LSKS. Adjunct professor, Georgetown University Law Center. Over 30 years experience representing media clients in libel, invasion of privacy, copyright and First Amendment cases. In the US Supreme Court, argued Harte-Hanks Communications v Connaughton and Bartnicki v Vopper.
**Professional Memberships:** Past-Chair, ABA Forum on Communications Law; past-President of Media Law Resource Center Defense Counsel Section.
**Publications:** Co-author, "Newsgathering and the Law."
**Personal:** Born 20 November 1954. Graduate of The Yale Law School and Managing Editor of The Yale Law Journal. Law clerk to the Honorable Irving Kaufman, US Court of Appeals for the Second Circuit.

## LEVINSON, Marc A
Orrick, Herrington & Sutcliffe LLP, Sacramento
916 329 4910
malevinson@orrick.com
*Featured in Bankruptcy/Restructuring (California), Bankruptcy/Restructuring (Nationwide)*
See under California for profile.

## LEVITAN, Steve
Bingham McCutchen LLP, New York
212 705 7325
steve.levitan@bingham.com
*Featured in Capital Markets (Nationwide)*
**Practice Areas:** Experienced in structuring highly complex securitization transactions backed by collateral encompassing a broad range of asset types, including student loans, auto loans, Australian mortgage loans, automobile and equipment leases, credit card account receivables, residential mortgage loans, home equity loans, financed insurance premiums, residual interests in pre-existing special purpose entities, and the resecuritization of previously issued asset- and mortgage-backed securities. Clients have ranged from leading investment banks, commercial banks and Fortune 500 companies to boutique finance lenders.
**Personal:** The University of Chicago Law School, JD, 1986; The University of Chicago, MBA, 1986; Dartmouth College, BA, 1982.

## LEVITT, Michael
Fried, Frank, Harris, Shriver & Jacobson LLP, New York
212 859 8735
Michael.Levitt@FriedFrank.com
*Featured in Capital Markets (Nationwide)*
**Practice Areas:** Corporate partner. Practice focuses on the representation of companies, investment banks, private equity firms and selling stockholders in public and private debt and equity securities offerings and related capital markets and financing transactions, including IPOs, high-yield debt offerings, acquisition financings, convertible debt issuances, rights offerings, tender offers, and secured debt financings. Has extensive experience with corporate governance, board of directors and compliance matters.
**Career:** Joined in 1993; became partner in 2001.
**Personal:** JD, Harvard Law School (1993); AB, Harvard University (1990).

## LEVY, Gregg
Covington & Burling LLP, Washington, DC
202 662 5292
glevy@cov.com
*Featured in Sports Law (Nationwide)*
**Practice Areas:** He has extensive experience with complex, multi-party litigation, including trial-level, appellate, and arbitral proceedings, and substantial expertise with respect to legal issues affecting professional sports leagues.
**Career:** He has been the NFL's principal outside counsel for nearly twenty years and played a lead role in each of the NFL's major trial and appellate victories during that period, including Brown v Pro-Football, Inc, decided by the US Supreme Court, Brady v. NFL, upholding the NFL's 2011 player lockout, and Clarett v NFL, upholding the NFL's draft eligibility rules.
**Personal:** Harvard Law School (JD, 1977); Harvard College (AB, 1974).

## LEVY, Jack A
Cassidy Levy Kent LLP, Washington, DC
202 567 2313
jlevy@cassidylevy.com
*Featured in International Trade (Nationwide)*
**Practice Areas:** Government affairs
**Career:** He advises companies and trade associations on all aspects of international economic regulation and trade policy. He has substantial experience litigating before the US Department of Commerce, US International Trade Commission, US Court of International Trade, NAFTA panels, and the World Trade Organization. He represents individual companies and associations on trade legislation in the Congress and trade policy issues under review by the executive branch of the United States government.
**Personal:** JD, Georgetown University Law Center; MSFS, Walsh School of Foreign Service, Georgetown University (with honors); Fulbright Scholar, Paraguay; BA, Johns Hopkins University (with honors).

## LEVY, Neil L
King & Spalding LLP, Washington, DC
202 626 5452
nlevy@kslaw.com
*Featured in Energy & Natural Resources (Nationwide)*
**Practice Areas:** He is well-known for his work representing independent power producers on cutting-edge energy issues. In addition, Mr Levy represents electric power and natural gas marketers, natural gas and oil pipelines, and local distribution companies before the Federal Energy Regulatory Commission, state public utility commissions, and the federal courts. Focuses on regulatory, litigation, and commercial issues arising under the Federal Power Act, the Natural Gas Act, the Public Utility Holding Company Act of 2005, and the Public Utility Regulatory Policies Act of 1978.
**Personal:** The George Washington University (BA, 1987, with special honors); Ohio Northern University (JD, 1990).

## LEW, Darryl
White & Case LLP, Washington, DC
202 626 3674
dlew@whitecase.com
*Featured in International Arbitration (Nationwide)*
**Career:** Darryl Lew focuses his practice on dispute resolution through arbitration and litigation, and on white collar and compliance matters. He has substantial experience representing and advising private parties and state entities in domestic and international arbitrations, including before the International Centre for Settlement of Investment Disputes (ICSID). Mr Lew's arbitrations have included disputes related to concessions, joint ventures, privatizations and construction. To view a comprehensive biography, please visit www.whitecase.com/dlew.

## LEWCZAK, Joseph J
Davis & Gilbert LLP, New York
212 468 4909
jlewczak@dglaw.com
*Featured in Advertising (Nationwide)*
**Practice Areas:** Advertising, marketing and promotions.
**Career:** Mr Lewczak has considerable experience in the areas of games of chance, complex skill contests, telemarketing, direct mail and charitable solicitations. He represents multi-national, national and local advertising agencies, promotions agencies, advertisers, direct marketers, and telemarketers in connection with all aspects of advertising, promotions, marketing, direct marketing and telemarketing. Mr Lewczak regularly counsels clients on issues relating to intellectual property, including copyright and rights of privacy and publicity, and also advises clients on advertising copy content and telemarketing scripts, the review and drafting of rules for sweepstakes and skill contests, and the negotiation of complex agreements relating to the advertising, marketing and promotions industry. He is recognized in The Best Lawyers in America for advertising law and The Legal 500 US for advertising and marketing law.

## LEWIS, David
Pillsbury Winthrop Shaw Pittman LLP, Washington, DC
202 663 8474
david.lewis@pillsburylaw.com
*Featured in Energy & Natural Resources (Nationwide)*
**Practice Areas:** Energy Section Leader. Involved in all aspects of nuclear plant regulation, including siting, initial licensing, licence renewal, decommissioning, investigations and enforcement, and whistleblower proceedings. Involved in reactor design certifications, early site permitting, applications for combined construction permit and operating licences, and international new build. Advises on nuclear business and organisational transactions, including nuclear plant acquisitions, formation of operating companies, and approvals related to utility deregulation.
**Professional Memberships:** American Nuclear Society; ASME BNCS TG-RE; NEI's COL Task Force and Financial Issues Task Force.
**Personal:** JD, George Washington University Law School, 1982; BS, Massachusetts Institute of Technology, 1979.

## LEWIS, Jeffrey S
Cleary Gottlieb Steen & Hamilton LLP, New York
212 225 2510
jlewis@cgsh.com
*Featured in Latin American Investment (New York), Projects (Nationwide)*
See under New York for profile.

## LEWIS, Marjorie
Gibson, Dunn & Crutcher LLP, Los Angeles
213 229 7462
mlewis@gibsondunn.com
*Featured in Transportation (Nationwide)*
**Practice Areas:** Commercial litigator focusing on representation of automobile manufacturers in disputes in state and federal court and before administrative agencies, and lenders exercising remedies with respect to distressed collateral.
**Career:** Named one of California's Top Women Litigators in 2008, 2009, 2010 and 2012. Served from 1998–2007 as co-Partner-in-Charge of the firm's 230-lawyer Los Angeles and Century City offices. Was a member of the firm's Executive Committee from 1996–2000, and of both the Executive Committee and Management Committee from 1999–2000.
**Personal:** JD, New York University, where she was a member of the New York University Law Review.

## LEWIS, Mark K
Bracewell & Giuliani LLP, Washington, DC
202 828 5834
mark.lewis@bgllp.com
*Featured in Energy & Natural Resources (Nationwide)*
**Practice Areas:** Managing partner of the firm's Washington, DC office and serves on the firm-wide management committee. Concentrates on energy-related projects, transactions and controversies. Clients include oil and gas producers and marketers; pipeline developers, owners, operators and investors; gas distributors; and large industrial energy consumers. Handles US and global oil and gas pipeline development projects - project structuring, contracting and governmental approvals. Represents regulated pipelines, pipeline ownership interests regarding pipeline management issues, clients in acquisition of pipeline companies and pipeline assets, and shippers contracting with pipelines.
**Personal:** JD, Georgetown University Law Center, 1990; BS, University of Maryland College Park, 1987.

## LIAZOS, Andrew C
McDermott Will & Emery LLP, Boston
617 535 4038
aliazos@mwe.com
*Featured in Employee Benefits & Executive Compensation (Nationwide), Employee Benefits & Executive Compensation (Massachusetts)*
See under Massachusetts for profile.

## LICHTENBAUM, Peter
Covington & Burling LLP, Washington, DC
202 662 5557
plichtenbaum@cov.com
*Featured in International Trade (Nationwide)*
**Practice Areas:** Co-chair of the International Trade and Finance practice group. Broad experience in international regulatory compliance and trade matters and specialized experience in the aerospace/defense and homeland security industries.
**Career:** Assistant Secretary of Commerce for Export Administration; Acting Under Secretary of Commerce for Industry and Security; VP, Regulatory Compliance and International Policy, BAE Systems, Inc.
**Publications:** Co-authored: "Sanctioning Clarity," European Lawyer (Jan./2012); "The Transatlantic Defence Industry and the Arms Trade Treaty," Chatham House (June/2011);

"Lessons in Mediating for Dairy Warriors," *Financial Times* (4/20/2011); "Investigating and Disclosing Export Control Violations," Georgetown University (March/2011).
**Personal:** Princeton (AB); Harvard (JD); Harvard (MPP).

## LIEBERMAN, David M
Simpson Thacher & Bartlett LLP, New York
212 455 3545
dlieberman@stblaw.com
*Featured in Energy & Natural Resources (Nationwide), Projects (Nationwide)*
**Practice Areas:** Partner in the firm's Corporate Department and Chair of the firm's Energy and Infrastructure Practice Group. Representative clients include Barclays, Blackstone, Energy Capital Partners, NextEra Energy, Macquarie, PPL, Royal Bank of Canada, and Stonepeak Partners.
**Professional Memberships:** New York State Bar Association.
**Career:** Joined firm, 1989; Partner, 1998.
**Personal:** Received his BA magna cum laude from Columbia University in 1986 where he was a member of Phi Beta Kappa. Earned his JD with high honours from Duke Law School in 1989 and was elected to the Order of the Coif.

## LIEBMANN, Jeff S
Sidley Austin LLP, New York
212 839 6775
jliebmann@sidley.com
*Featured in Insurance (Nationwide), Insurance (New York)*
**Practice Areas:** Partner in Sidley's New York office. For over thirty years, he has practiced exclusively in the insurance, corporate, restructuring and insolvency areas. He has represented insurance companies, insurance holding companies, investment banks, financial advisers, commercial banks, private equity funds, financial guarantors, insurance agencies and brokers, credit card companies, insurance markets, insurance regulators, guaranty associations, insurance company receivers and creditor committees in a broad array of insurance matters. These matters include insurance company mergers and acquisitions; sales of insurance blocks of business; reinsurance transactions of all types; closed block, triple-X and embedded value securitizations; and insurance company restructurings.

## LIFSET, Marc
McGlinchey Stafford PLLC, Albany
518 432 8335
mlifset@mcglinchey.com
*Featured in Financial Services Regulation (Nationwide)*
**Practice Areas:** Banking law; consumer financial services; commercial litigation.
**Professional Memberships:** ABA, Consumer Financial Services Committee; Conference on Consumer Finance Law, Governing Committee; American College of Consumer Financial Services Lawyers; Manufactured Housing Institute, Finance Lawyers Committee, Chair; National Association of Residential Construction Lenders; National Mortgage Bankers Association; New York

State Bar Association, Consumer Financial Services Committee.
**Career:** Advises banks and financial institutions on matters involving consumer financial services; licensing; regulatory compliance; and manufactured housing, construction and home improvement lending. Primary drafter and proponent of Manufactured Housing Title Acts in Alaska, Maryland, Missouri, New York and North Dakota.
**Personal:** Cornell University, JD (1978); Hamilton College, BA, cum laude (1974).

## LIGHTHIZER, Robert E
Skadden, Arps, Slate, Meagher & Flom LLP & Affiliates, Washington, DC
202 371 7770
Robert.Lighthizer@skadden.com
*Featured in International Trade (Nationwide)*
**Practice Areas:** Leads the firm's International Trade Department. Extensive experience in trade litigation representing large US corporations and coalitions before domestic agencies and courts, as well as WTO dispute and NAFTA binational panels. Counsels clients with interests affected by bilateral and multilateral international negotiations and domestic legislation and policy issues. Advises companies regarding economic sanctions/export control, transaction due diligence, compliance, and enforcement actions.
**Professional Memberships:** Council on Foreign Relations.
**Career:** Deputy US Trade Representative, rank of Ambassador, Regan Administration (1983-85); Chief of Staff, US Senate Committee on Finance (1978-83). JD, Georgetown University Law Center, 1973; BA, Georgetown University, 1969.

## LILIEN, Warren H
Latham & Watkins LLP, New York
212 906 1787
warren.lilien@lw.com
*Featured in Projects (Nationwide)*
**Practice Areas:** Represents borrowers, issuers and private equity sponsors, and banks, in complex finance transactions, including project financings, acquisition financings, leveraged leases, and credit enhancement facilities. Practice focuses on the energy, infrastructure, telecommunication and industrial sectors. Also represents independent energy companies in all phases of the development and administration of energy projects.
**Career:** Qualified in California since 1990 and New York since 2001.
**Publications:** Has authored articles published in Infrastructure Investor, Project Finance International and Independent Energy.
**Personal:** Attended U.C. Berkeley: BA 1987 and JD (Boalt Hall) 1990.

## LILYESTROM, John
Hogan Lovells US LLP, Washington, DC
202 637 5600
*Featured in Energy & Natural Resources (Nationwide)*
**Practice Areas:** Energy: Electricity.
**Career:** He focuses on electric utility regulation and its competitive and commercial consequences. He represents electric utility companies,

electric power marketers and independent power producers before the Federal Energy Regulatory Commission and before state regulatory agencies and federal and state courts. He has represented utilities in merger proceedings, in proceedings related to the alleged exercise of generation market power, in transmission and wholesale service rate cases and in cases involving the application of standards and codes of conduct.
**Personal:** JD, University of Maryland School of Law; BA, Harvard University.

## LIM, Stephanie
King & Spalding LLP, Atlanta
202 626 8991
slim@kslaw.com
*Featured in Energy & Natural Resources (Nationwide)*
**Practice Areas:** Senior attorney in the Global Transactions practice group at King and Spalding.
**Publications:** "A Deal is Still a Deal: Morgan Stanley Capital Group v. Public Utility District No. 1," 2007-2008 Cato Supreme Court Review 285 (2008) (co-author); "Applying the Mobile-Sierra Doctrine to Market-Based Rate Contracts," 26 Energy Law Journal 437 (2005) (co-author) en.
**Personal:** JD, Duke University MA, Duke University BA English, Amherst College.

## LIN, Raymond Y
Latham & Watkins LLP, New York
212 906 1369
raymond.lin@lw.com
*Featured in Private Equity (Nationwide)*
**Practice Areas:** Represents private equity firms in M&A such as Apollo Global Management and BC Partners domestically and in complex cross-border transactions such as the acquisition of Intelsat and the sale of Unitymedia. Also represents private equity portfolio companies in capital market transactions (including debt offerings and IPO's); and has represented sponsors and lenders in REITS and gaming development transactions.
**Professional Memberships:** Board of Visitors of Columbia Law School and Board of Directors of the Appleseed Foundation.
**Career:** Qualified since 1986. Has been a partner of the firm since 1991 and is the Co-Chair of the US Private Equity Practice.

## LINCER, Richard S
Cleary Gottlieb Steen & Hamilton LLP, New York
212 225 2560
rlincer@cgsh.com
*Featured in Projects (Nationwide)*
**Practice Areas:** International project financings (ASUR and Highstar Capital in SJU Airport privatization, port facilities for DP World and Highstar Capital, Bahia Pulp project in Brazil, toll roads in Mexico and Chile); debt restructurings (UAW and VEBA trust in GM and Chrysler bankruptcies, Istithmar in Loehmann's Chapter 11, Apex Silver Mines, Daewoo); corporate and asset acquisitions (acquisition of Ports America by Highstar, Dexter Corporation by Ahlstrom); joint ventures; leveraged, acquisition finance transactions (Kindred Healthcare/RehabCare, Alkermes/Elan); as well as investment funds.

**Personal:** Joined firm, 1979; became Partner, 1986. JD, Columbia Law School (1978); BA, Yale University (1975). Trustee, Cooper Union.

## LINDAUER, Erik D
Sullivan & Cromwell LLP, New York
212 558 3548
lindauere@sullcrom.com
*Featured in Banking & Finance (Nationwide)*
**Professional Memberships:** ABA; ABCNY; NYSBA.
**Career:** Partner since 1989. Transactional banking, leveraged finance, commercial law (UCC), corporate reorganizations (including DIP financings) and bankruptcy. Complex secured and unsecured financings. Strategic advice on acquisition of assets from troubled companies, including airline, satellite, telecommunications, utility, computer, cable TV and media projects. Recent assignments include bankruptcy financing for Eastman Kodak, restructuring, refinancing and troubled asset collection and sale matters for Goldman Sachs, JPMorgan Chase, Philips Electronics and British Airways.
**Personal:** SUNY Buffalo Law School (JD, 1981); SUNY Albany (BA, 1978).

## LINDSEY, David
Chaffetz Lindsey LLP, New York
212 257 6966
david.lindsey@chaffetzlindsey.com
*Featured in International Arbitration (Nationwide)*
**Practice Areas:** International arbiration, commercial litigation.
**Career:** David Lindsey co-founded Chaffetz Lindsey in 2009. Previously he led the Americas international arbitration group at Clifford Chance in New York. He is lead counsel on a broad range of disputes dealing with joint venture, licensing, IP, international law, and sovereign immunity issues in the energy, telecommunications, and construction sectors across the Americas, Asia, Middle East and Europe.
**Publications:** "International Arbitration in Latin America" (2003); "International Arbitration in New York" Chapter One Applicable Law (2010).
**Personal:** BA, University of Texas (Honors) (1985); JD, Florida State Law (Honors)(1988). Admitted in New York, Florida, District of Columbia.

## LIPSEY, Charles E
Finnegan, Henderson, Farabow, Garrett & Dunner LLP, Reston
571 203 2755
charles.lipsey@finnegan.com
*Featured in Intellectual Property (Northern Virginia), Life Sciences (Nationwide)*
**Practice Areas:** Concentrates on intellectual property litigation, particularly patent infringement litigation, in US district courts and the US Court of Appeals for the Federal Circuit. He has handled cases involving mechanical, chemical, and electrical technologies, with emphasis on biotechnology and pharmaceutical chemistry. Mr Lipsey has also handled numerous patent arbitration proceedings and patent interferences.
**Personal:** Georgia Institute of Technology (B.S., Chemical Engineering, 1972); George Washington

University National Law Center (JD, 1977; LLM, Patent and Trademark Regulation Law, 1981).

## LIPSON, Kevin J

Hogan Lovells US LLP, Washington, DC

*Featured in Energy & Natural Resources (Nationwide)*

**Practice Areas:** Energy: Oil & Gas (Regulatory & Litigation).

**Career:** He has participated in every phase of the energy practice, including representation of clients before the Federal Energy Regulatory Commission (FERC), the Commodity Futures Trading Commission (CFTC) and other federal and state regulatory authorities. Among his clients are investor-owned electric utility companies, interstate natural gas pipeline companies, local distribution companies, midstream operations, financial institutions, energy commodity trading operations and non-traditional energy providers. He has successfully resolved numerous FERC enforcement cases, including some of the most significant in the industry.

**Personal:** JD, Washington University; BA, The George Washington University.

## LITTLE, Kathleen C

Vinson & Elkins LLP, Washington, DC

202 639 6663

klittle@velaw.com

*Featured in International Trade (Nationwide)*

**Practice Areas:** Export controls (ITAR and EAR), OFAC sanctions, FCPA, Foreign Military Sales and Foreign Military Financed Direct Sales, Government Contracts. Work includes criminal and civil enforcement matters, compliance, counseling, training and audits. Represents both domestic and foreign companies.

**Professional Memberships:** ABA, SIA.

**Career:** Partner since 1988.

**Publications:** Has lectured and written extensively on Export Controls and related topics.

## LIU, Gilbert

Kramer Levin Naftalis & Frankel LLP, New York

212 715 9460

gliu@kramerlevin.com

*Featured in Capital Markets (Nationwide)*

**Practice Areas:** Mr Liu practices mainly in the area of securitization and structured finance. He represents issuers, underwriters, borrowers, lenders and service providers on private and public structured finance and securitization transactions involving a wide variety of asset classes. These include collateralized loan obligations, timeshare loans, commercial mortgage loans, clean energy receivables, residential mortgage loans, distressed assets, auto loans, government energy contract receivables, student loans, equipment leases, trademark and licensing rights, music royalties, municipal tax liens and insurance related assets.

## LOBRANO, John D

Simpson Thacher & Bartlett LLP, New York

212 455 2890

jlobrano@stblaw.com

*Featured in Capital Markets (Nationwide)*

**Practice Areas:** Partner in Capital Markets Group. Represents leading underwriters and issuers in domestic and international securities offerings, with particular experience in offerings of convertible securities and high yield securities. These activities are complemented by his representation of dealer managers and issuers in tender offers, exchange offers and consent solicitations.

**Professional Memberships:** American Bar Association, New York Bar Association, NYC Bar Association, the TriBar Opinion Committee.

**Career:** Partner since 1990.

**Personal:** BA, magna cum laude, Amherst College (1979); JD, New York University School of Law (1983).

## LOESER, Julius

Winston & Strawn LLP, Chicago

jloeser@winston.com

*Featured in Financial Services Regulation (Nationwide)*

**Practice Areas:** Bank regulation.

**Professional Memberships:** American Bar Association; Lawyers Council of the Financial Services Roundtable; Lawyers Committee of the Consumer Bankers Association.

**Career:** Special Counsel, Cadwalader, Wickersham & Taft LLC, New York (2009-2010) Deputy General Counsel,Comerica Bank, Detroit, Michigan (1999-2009) Chief Regulatory Counsel, Wells Fargo Bank, N. A., Los Angeles (1984-1999) Associate, Pope, Ballard, Sheppard & Fowle, Chicago (1980-1984) Associate, Rothgerber, Apple & Powers, Denver (1978-1980) Senior Attorney, Federal Reserve Board, Washington, D.C. (1971-1978).

## LOEWINGER, Andrew P

Nixon Peabody LLP, Washington, DC

202 585 8855

aloewinger@nixonpeabody.com

*Featured in Franchising (Nationwide)*

**Practice Areas:** Domestic and international franchising. He has handled numerous outbound and inbound franchise transactions in over 85 countries and represented hundreds of franchisors in the United States.

**Professional Memberships:** Chair, International Franchising Committee, International Bar Association; Governing Committee member (and First Director, International Franchise and Distribution Division), American Bar Association Forum on Franchising.

**Publications:** Author and co-editor of treatise International Franchise Sales Laws, ABA Forum on Franchising (publisher). Authored or presented more than 50 articles, book chapters, and speeches on franchising.

**Personal:** Georgetown University Law Center, JD; Columbia School of International Affairs, MA; Colorado College, BA, magna cum laude.

## LOFCHIE, Steven

Cadwalader, Wickersham & Taft LLP, New York

212 504 6700

steven.lofchie@cwt.com

*Featured in Capital Markets (Nationwide), Financial Services Regulation (Nationwide)*

**Practice Areas:** Co-Chair, Financial Services Department. Represents broker-dealers, public and private funds, investment advisors, banks, CEA-regulated entities, exchanges and clearing corporations. Advises on registration requirements and exemptions; employee issues; cash market, sales and trading; compliance and supervisory procedures; satisfaction of margin, capital, and recordkeeping requirements; SRO rules; M&A of financial organizations; cross-border transaction procedures; anti-money laundering; privacy; and insider trading. Transactional practice includes over-the-counter derivatives, securities financing, prime brokerage (both cash market and derivatives); electronic trading; licensing and membership agreements. Advises clients with respect to Advisers Act, Commodity Exchange Act, and Dodd-Frank. Works for various securities industry organizations including ISDA, MFA, and SIFMA.

**Publications:** Author, Lofchie's Guide to Broker-Dealer Regulation (4th ed 2011). Develops web-based electronic tools for those engaged in compliance and derivatives practices.

**Personal:** JD, Yale Law School (Member, Yale Law Journal); MBA, Columbia Business School (General Motors Fellow); BA, Sarah Lawrence College.

## LOFTIS, James

Vinson & Elkins RLLP, London

020 7065 6027

jloftis@velaw.com

*Featured in International Arbitration (Nationwide)*

**Practice Areas:** Arbitration of international commercial and investment disputes, particularly state contracts, foreign investment laws and investment treaties. Has handled arbitrations under all major arbitration rules and in most major arbitral venues. Experience in disputes involving all facets of oil and gas, energy, construction/technology, infrastructure/project finance, and environmental obligations.

**Professional Memberships:** ICC Commission on Arbitration; LCIA; Chartered Institute of Arbitrators; Chair, International Law Section, Texas Bar (2006).

**Career:** Partner since 2000. Senior Legal Officer, Energy Sector Panel, UN Compensation Commission, Geneva, 1997-2000; Adjunct professor, University of Texas School of Law.

**Publications:** Co-editor, International Litigation Quarterly; executive editor, International Arbitration News.

## LOFTUS, C Michael

Slover & Loftus, Washington, DC

202 347 7170

cml@sloverandloftus.com

*Featured in Transportation (Nationwide)*

**Practice Areas:** Mr Loftus is a Partner with over 35 years experience dealing with transportation and fuel matters, primarily for electric utility clients. He specializes in litigation before administrative agencies and federal and state courts; appellate advocacy; and alternative dispute resolution, both as an advocate and an arbitrator. Mr Loftus has broad experience in negotiating and administering rail transportation and fuel supply contracts, and in counseling clients on numerous rail and fuel related matters.

**Personal:** BS, Wheeling College, 1968; JD, Columbus School of Law at the Catholic University of America, 1973 (Editor-in-Chief, Catholic University of America Law Review).

## LONCAR, Ivan

Cadwalader, Wickersham & Taft LLP, New York

212 504 6339

ivan.loncar@cwt.com

*Featured in Capital Markets (Nationwide)*

**Practice Areas:** Focuses on fixed income and credit derivatives and structured financial products. Represents dealers, banks, and other financial institutions in connection with interest rate swaps, currency swaps, credit derivatives, commodity swaps, structured notes (including credit-linked notes), synthetic CDOs and other unfunded and funded derivative products. Broad experience with other structured financial products that combine securitization techniques and derivative products. Extensive involvement in the development and use of derivatives and financial products in the primary and secondary municipal markets, including interest rate swaps, rate locks, credit default swaps, total return swaps, forward delivery agreements, forward bond purchase agreements, bond warrant agreements, liquidity facilities, and various forms of credit enhancement.

**Personal:** LLM, Columbia University School of Law; LLB, University of Belgrade School of Law.

## LONG JR, Robert A

Covington & Burling LLP, Washington, DC

202 662 5612

rlong@covington.com

*Featured in Appellate Law (Nationwide)*

**Practice Areas:** Robert Long chairs the firm's Appellate and Supreme Court Litigation Group. Mr Long has argued 17 cases before the US Supreme Court and has played a substantial role in the briefing or oral argument of more than 150 cases in federal and state appellate courts. He was a law clerk to Justice Lewis F. Powell, Jr, of the US Supreme Court and Judge John Minor Wisdom of the US Court of Appeals for the Fifth Circuit. From 1990 to 1993, he served as an Assistant to the Solicitor General of the United States.

## LOPEZ, David

Cleary Gottlieb Steen & Hamilton LLP, New York

212 225 2632

dlopez@cgsh.com

*Featured in Capital Markets (Nationwide)*

**Practice Areas:** Capital markets, corporate finance transactions and securities law, including initial public offerings, public and private debt, convertible, investment grade and high yield debt, equity financings, structured securities and equity derivatives. Liability management, including issuer tender offers, public and private exchanges offers related to corporate restructurings, acquisitions, and consent solicitations. Corporate governance and general corporate advice.

**Professional Memberships:** Member of the Bar in New York.

**Career:** Joined firm, 1989; became partner, 1998. JD, University of Chicago (1989); AB, cum laude, Cornell University (1986).

**Publications:** Contributing author to "Securities Law Techniques," a treatise by Matthew Bender.

### LOPEZ JR, Jorge

Akin Gump Strauss Hauer & Feld LLP, Washington, DC
202 887 4385
jlopez@akingump.com

*Featured in Healthcare (Nationwide), Healthcare (District of Columbia)*

See under District of Columbia for profile.

### LOWELL, Bret

DLA Piper LLP (US), Reston
703 773 4242
bret.lowell@dlapiper.com

*Featured in Franchising (Nationwide)*

**Practice Areas:** Franchising, international franchising and distribution.

**Career:** He is an internationally recognized leader in franchise and distribution law and has counseled and represented clients across a broad spectrum of industries, including restaurants and food service, car rental, hotel and motel, healthcare, financial services, hi-tech, real estate, and retail. He speaks and writes extensively on franchise related topics in a variety of forums.

**Personal:** JD, Georgetown University Law Center; BA, State University of New York (magna cum laude).

### LOWELL, Frederick K

Pillsbury Winthrop Shaw Pittman LLP, San Francisco
415 983 1585
frederick.lowell@pillsburylaw.com

*Featured in Government (Nationwide)*

**Practice Areas:** Leader of the firm's Political Law Group. Advises on federal, state and local campaign finance, lobbying and ethics laws, legislation, ballot initiatives, reapportionment and political law enforcement litigation.

**Professional Memberships:** Past President, California Political Attorneys Association; Past Chair, Lincoln Club of Northern California; California delegate to the 1992, 1996, 2000 and 2004 National Republican Conventions; Volunteer California counsel, Bush-Cheney 2000 and 2004 campaigns.

**Career:** Author of numerous articles and lectures on political law regulation. He has also debated campaign reform issues on radio and television.

**Personal:** JD, University of Virginia School of Law, 1975; BA, Columbia University, 1971.

### LOWENTHAL, Mitchell

Cleary Gottlieb Steen & Hamilton LLP, New York
212 225 2760
mlowenthal@cgsh.com

*Featured in Securities (Nationwide), Litigation (New York)*

**Practice Areas:** Corporate and securities litigation. Has represented issuers, directors and officers, underwriters, lending institutions and professional advisors in complex civil litigation involving the capital formation process, mergers and acquisitions, derivative and shareholder disputes.

**Professional Memberships:** Member of the Bar in New York. Chair, Urban Justice Center, Former Chair, Committee on Securities Litigation, City of New York Bar Association; Former member, NYSBA Committee on Professional Ethics.

**Career:** Cornell University (JD, 1981; AB, 1978). Law Clerk, Hon. Edward Weinfeld (SDNY, 1982-83). Chair, Urban Justice Center.

### LOWTHER, Frederick M

Dickstein Shapiro LLP, Washington, DC
202 420 2208
lowtherf@dicksteinshapiro.com

*Featured in Energy & Natural Resources (Nationwide)*

**Practice Areas:** Fred Lowther is a partner in Dickstein Shapiro's Energy Practice. Mr Lowther devotes his career primarily to the development of large energy and natural resource projects in the United States and abroad. He focuses his practice on domestic and international energy, water supply projects and transactions, and general counseling of energy companies in all sectors of the industry. His work on water supply issues involves both structuring projects and litigating over water rights. He also focuses his practice on counseling companies in the energy technology sector.

**Personal:** Yale Law School (JD, 1968), Brown University (BA, 1965).

### LUCE, Gregory M

Skadden, Arps, Slate, Meagher & Flom LLP & Affiliates, Washington, DC
202 371 7310
Greg.Luce@skadden.com

*Featured in Healthcare (Nationwide), Healthcare (District of Columbia)*

**Practice Areas:** Handles civil and criminal litigation and regulatory matters involving the health care industry. Has represented health systems, pharmaceutical and medical device manufacturers, and other health care providers in litigation involving fraud and abuse enforcement, False Claims Act defense, and Medicare and Medicaid reimbursement. Advises clients on the design and implementation of compliance programs.

**Professional Memberships:** American Health Lawyers Association (Board of Directors, 1995-2001; fellow, elected 2005); ABA Health Law Section; Virginia State Bar Health Law Section (Chair, 1990-91).

**Career:** Assistant Attorney General, Commonwealth of Virginia (1978-81). JD, University of Richmond (1977); BA, University of Virginia, with distinction (1974).

### LUDWISZEWSKI, Raymond B

Gibson, Dunn & Crutcher LLP, Washington, DC
202 955 8665
rludwiszewski@gibsondunn.com

*Featured in Climate Change (Nationwide), Environment (District of Columbia)*

See under District of Columbia for profile.

### LUEDKE IV, William T

Bracewell & Giuliani LLP, Houston
713 221 1336
will.luedke@bgllp.com

*Featured in Financial Services Regulation (Nationwide)*

**Practice Areas:** Focuses on mergers and acquisitions, corporate finance and regulatory and enforcement matters for financial institutions. Represents buyers and sellers in mergers and acquisitions. Also represents financial institutions and underwriters in initial public offerings, private placement of debt and equity securities, and trust preferred securities issuances and pools. Has experience chartering de novo financial institutions, Subchapter S elections, bank holding company formations and enforcement matters. Advises boards of directors regarding fiduciary duties, Sarbanes-Oxley and other corporate governance issues, and has overseen internal corporate investigations related to financial institutions.

**Personal:** JD, Vanderbilt University Law School, 1978; AB, Williams College, 1974.

### LUM, Dale

Sidley Austin LLP, San Francisco
415 772 1299
dlum@sidley.com

*Featured in Capital Markets (Nationwide)*

**Practice Areas:** Partner in Sidley's San Francisco office. He has an international practice focused on corporate and structured finance, with particular emphasis on securitizations and the use of structured financings in mergers and acquisitions and hedge fund and private equity transactions. Mr Lum has been at the forefront of securitizations and structured financings in the US, Europe and Asia. Mr Lum is a leading lawyer in the development of motor vehicle lease securitizations and has worked on a number of ground-breaking transactions, including the first automobile lease-secured note issuance and the first mortgage-backed medium-term note program.

### LUMISH, Wendy F

Carlton Fields, P.A., Miami
305 539 7266
wlumish@carltonfields.com

*Featured in Litigation (Florida), Products Liability (Nationwide)*

See under Florida for profile.

### LURIE, Jonathan C

McDermott Will & Emery LLP, Los Angeles
310 284 6169
jlurie@mwe.com

*Featured in Wealth Management (Nationwide), Tax (California)*

See under California for profile.

### LUSTIGMAN, Andrew B

Olshan Frome Wolosky LLP., New York
212 451 2258
alustigman@olshanlaw.com

*Featured in Advertising (Nationwide)*

**Practice Areas:** Head of the Advertising, Marketing & Promotions Group. Represents advertising, interactive, promotion agencies; marketers, businesses and industry suppliers. Advises on clearance of direct/Internet advertising, sweepstakes and promotional materials. Defends federal and state regulatory inquiries and litigation brought by FTC, FCC, USPS and attorneys general. Handles competitor disputes before NAD and federal/state litigation.

**Professional Memberships:** American Bar Association(Past Chair, Special Committee on Promotion and Marketing Law; Consumer Protection), Association of the Bar of the City of New York (Consumer Affairs), Promotion Marketing Association (Legal Affairs).

**Publications:** "Legal Considerations For Promotions Involving User Generated Content,"ABA, The Practical Lawyer, June, 2008.

### LUSTRIN, Robert E

Seward & Kissel LLP, New York
212 574 1420
lustrin@sewkis.com

*Featured in Transportation (Nationwide)*

**Practice Areas:** Corporate finance; maritime and transportation finance; capital markets and securities; business transactions (M&A/private equity; investment management).

**Career:** Robert E Lustrin is a partner in Seward & Kissel's Corporate Securities and Capital Markets Group. He focuses his practice on corporate and securities law related primarily to capital markets activities of shipping companies. Mr Lustrin represents foreign and domestic issuers, underwriters, promoters and money managers in connection with a variety of securities offerings, including registered public offerings, Rule 144A, high-yield debt offerings, convertible bond offerings, "PIPE" transactions, and project finance vehicles. He also represents clients in connection with consent solicitations, exchange offers, mergers, tender offers, and restructurings. Mr Lustrin works with many of the firm's US-listed shipping companies in connection with disclosure and securities law compliance matters, is a frequent speaker at shipping industry conferences and seminars on the subject of United States securities law and regulation, and has published articles on issues relating to United States securities offering rules and project financings. Recent speaking engagements include the 14th Annual Marine Money Greek Ship Finance Conference in October 2012; and Informa Maritime Events, Risk Management in Shipping Conference in September 2011 in London, England.

**Personal:** Mr Lustrin received a BS in Economics from the Wharton School of the University of Pennsylvania in 1985 and a JD from Boston University School of Law in 1988.

## LYNES, Timothy J
Katten Muchin Rosenman LLP, Washington, DC
202 625 3686
timothy.lynes@kattenlaw.com
*Featured in Transportation (Nationwide), Banking & Finance (Nationwide)*
**Practice Areas:** Aviation Practice Chair, Mr Lynes has represented manufacturers, lenders, lessors, airlines and their insurers for over 25 years. His practice involves aircraft sale agreements, cross-border and tax leases, loans, chattel mortgages, residual value and credit support agreements and aviation insurance policies. He also regularly advises clients on DOT and FAA regulatory issues. Mr Lynes is a frequent speaker and author on current industry topics.
**Career:** Admitted to New Jersey, Virginia, Maryland, New York and District of Columbia Bars.
**Personal:** JD, Gonzaga University School of Law (1984); associate editor, Gonzaga Law Review; BA Fairfield University (1981).

## LYNN, David
Morrison & Foerster LLP, San Francisco
202 887 1563
dlynn@mofo.com
*Featured in Securities (Nationwide)*
**Practice Areas:** David Lynn is a highly respected securities advisory counsel who provides guidance to clients, from the Fortune 500 to newly-public, on securities law compliance, as well as counseling on corporate governance and executive compensation disclosure. He guides companies through the public offering process, which includes compliance with SEC requirements and responses to SEC comments. He serves as Vice-Chair of the ABA Business Law Section's Federal Regulation of Securities Committee.
**Career:** Chief Counsel of the SEC's Division of Corporation Finance (2002-2007).
**Publications:** Co-editor, TheCorporateCounsel.net, a widely-read blog on securities and governance matters.

## LYONS, Christopher
Sidley Austin LLP, Washington, DC
202 736 8990
clyons@sidley.com
*Featured in Energy & Natural Resources (Nationwide)*
**Practice Areas:** Partner in Sidley's Washington, D.C. office, and member of its Energy practice. He advises oil and petroleum products pipelines, electric utilities, and financial institutions involved in the energy industry. In his oil pipeline practice, he has represented clients in litigated FERC proceedings, including proceedings related to the Trans Alaska Pipeline System and market-based rate proceedings. He counsels pipeline companies on cost of service ratemaking, market-based rates, indexing, prorationing and other tariff policies, transportation contracts with shippers, and capacity expansions. He has represented clients in arbitrations arising from contract disputes concerning oil royalties and sales of liquefied natural gas.

## MABBITT, Stanley
Ballard Spahr LLP, Phoenix
602 798 5456
mabbitts@ballardspahr.com
*Featured in Financial Services Regulation (Nationwide)*
**Practice Areas:** Stanley D Mabbitt is of counsel in the Business and Finance Department and a member of the Consumer Financial Services and Mortgage Banking Groups. Mr Mabbitt counsels financial institutions on compliance with state and federal statutes and regulations, and implementation of lending and deposit programs. He also counsels mortgage bankers and brokers regarding compliance with state and federal statutes and regulations.
**Professional Memberships:** American College of Consumer Financial Services Lawyers, Founding Member American Bar Association State Bar of California.
**Career:** Admissions: Arizona, California, Washington DC.
**Personal:** Education: Loyola Law School Los Angeles (JD 1977) Occidental College (AB 1970).

## MACAULEY, Leiha
Day Pitney LLP, Boston
617 345 4602
lmacauley@daypitney.com
*Featured in Wealth Management (Nationwide)*
**Career:** Leiha Macauley practices in the areas of trust and estate administration, estate planning, and trust, estate, and fiduciary litigation. Her practice also involves advising clients on achieving philanthropic goals through private foundations and charitable trusts. Leiha serves as an executor or trustee for her clients, and regularly counsels traditional and nontraditional families. Leiha developed and co-directs the Child Health Advocacy Partnership, which teams doctors with attorneys to provide legal information and advocacy to underprivileged families. She is a trustee of the Boston Bar Foundation and the Massachusetts Women's Bar Foundation, and member of a number of other civic organizations.

## MACCOBY, Matthew F
Arnold & Porter LLP, Los Angeles
213 243 4213
Matthew.Maccoby@aporter.com
*Featured in Outsourcing (Nationwide), IT & Outsourcing (California)*
See under California for profile.

## MACKINNON, John A
Sidley Austin LLP, New York
212 839 5534
jmackinnon@sidley.com
*Featured in Investment Funds (Nationwide)*
**Practice Areas:** Partner in Sidley's New York office and co-head of the firm's Investment Funds, Advisers and Derivatives practice. He practices securities law with an emphasis on investment management clients. He has worked on matters involving numerous investment companies in the United States and internationally, and has experience with the registration and exemptive provisions of the Investment Company Act of 1940 and the Investment Advisers Act of 1940. He repre-

sents major investment banks in offerings by public and private funds and advises investment advisers around the globe concerning US securities laws. He also represents independent directors of US investment companies.

## MACKINTOSH, Trip
Holland & Hart LLP, Denver
303 295 8186
tmackintosh@hollandhart.com
*Featured in International Trade (Nationwide)*
**Career:** Mackintosh has defended domestic and foreign parties in administrative and criminal actions brought under US export controls and trade sanctions (ITAR, EAR, OFAC), as well as federal laws affecting anti-corruption (FCPA), money laundering, Customs fraud, securities, environmental controls, and health care. He has led defense efforts and multi-jurisdictional criminal investigations around the globe. Mackintosh and his team served as lead counsel for two of the three 2010 Department of State published resolutions of Arms Export Control Act (ITAR) enforcement actions.
**Personal:** JD, Georgetown University Law Center; MA, Korbel School of International Studies, University of Denver.

## MACLEOD, Scott R
Holland & Knight LLP, Orlando
407 244 5239
scott.macleod@hklaw.com
*Featured in Investment Funds (Nationwide)*
**Career:** Scott MacLeod has spent 100 percent of his practice over the last 22 years forming and representing investment funds, investment advisers and related investment management clients. He has formed and represented a wide spectrum of investment funds and investment advisers including hedge funds, mutual funds, private equity and real estate funds, offshore funds, commodity pools, and bank collective and common trust funds. Mr MacLeod has also represented investment advisers, banks and their trust and investment departments, and institutional investors including government pension plans.
**Personal:** CFTC Rescinds Key Exemption From CPO Registration for 3(c)(7) Funds," Financial Institutions, Alert - 2/22/2012.

## MADAN, Raj
Bingham McCutchen LLP, Washington, DC
202 373 6681
raj.madan@bingham.com
*Featured in Tax (District of Columbia), Tax (Nationwide)*
**Practice Areas:** Practice concentrated in the area of federal tax controversy and litigation, with a focus on the representation of financial institutions. Has represented numerous clients in all stages of IRS administrative practice, Federal District Court litigation and Tax Court litigation. Experience includes a wide range of complex tax issues in foreign tax credits, transfer pricing, life insurance, investment tax credits and business purpose/economic substance.
**Career:** Former trial attorney, Internal Revenue Service.

**Personal:** George Washington University Law School, JD, 1992; New York University, BA, 1990.

## MADDEN, Thomas J
Venable LLP, Washington, DC
202 344 4803
tmadden@Venable.com
*Featured in Government (Nationwide)*
**Practice Areas:** Mr Madden assists a broad array of clients in all aspects of government contracts. Areas of concentration include intellectual property rights, fraud/false claims investigations, protests and dispute resolution.
**Professional Memberships:** Vice-Chair, Procurement Round Table; past Chair, ABA Section of Public Contract Law; past President, Court of Federal Claims Bar Association.
**Career:** Recommended for Government Contracts, Chambers USA 2005-12. Recognized by Legal Times as a "leading" Government Contracts Lawyer. Recognized as a top Washington lawyer by Washingtonian magazine.
**Personal:** JD, with honors, Catholic University of America, Columbus School of Law, 1968; B.Elec.Engr., Villanova University, 1964.

## MAGANUCO, Robert J
Sidley Austin LLP, Chicago
312 853 7598
rmaganuco@sidley.com
*Featured in Leisure & Hospitality (Nationwide)*
**Practice Areas:** Partner in Sidley's Chicago office. His practice focuses in the real estate and real estate finance areas. He has substantial experience in a wide variety of real estate transactions, including construction loans, term loans and other real estate financing, real estate workouts and restructurings and other transactions involving distressed assets, and the acquisition, disposition, leasing and development of real estate. Mr Maganuco has represented Wells Fargo Bank, JPMorgan Chase Bank (and its predecessors, Bank One, and The First National Bank of Chicago), and other financial institutions in numerous financing transactions.

## MAGEE, John B
Bingham McCutchen LLP, Washington, DC
202 373 6229
john.magee@bingham.com
*Featured in Tax (District of Columbia), Tax (Nationwide)*
**Practice Areas:** Focuses on tax controversy and international tax issues, including transfer pricing. More than 30 years of experience in all aspects of income tax planning, Internal Revenue Service administrative proceedings and tax litigation. Has tried cases in the US Tax Court, the US Court of Federal Claims, and the US District Courts and argued in the US Court of Appeals. Speaks extensively in a variety of tax forums.
**Career:** Adjunct Professor, Graduate Tax Program of the Georgetown Law Center.
**Personal:** Georgetown University Law Center, LLM; University of Washington School of Law, JD; Pomona College, BA.

**MAGUIRE, William R**
Hughes Hubbard & Reed LLP, New York
212 837 6000
maguire@hugheshubbard.com
*Featured in Securities (Nationwide), Litigation (New York)*
**Practice Areas:** Partner, New York since 1993. Chair of the Litigation Department, Co-Chair of the Securities Litigation and Chair of the Professional Liability Practice Groups. Concentrates on securities and commercial litigation and trial work.
**Career:** Hughes Hubbard & Reed since 1983. Member of firm's Executive Committee.
**Personal:** Born December 5, 1961. Trinity College Dublin, Foundation Scholar, 1981, BA Leg. Sc., 1983 (first class honors); Hon. Soc. of Kings Inns, Dublin, Barrister-at-Law, 1985.

**MAHONEY, Colleen P**
Skadden, Arps, Slate, Meagher & Flom LLP & Affiliates, Washington, DC
202 371 7900
Colleen.Mahoney@skadden.com
*Featured in Securities (Nationwide)*
**Practice Areas:** Heads the firm's Securities Enforcement and Compliance practice. Represents corporations and their officers, directors and employees in SEC and other law enforcement investigations. Assists management and boards of directors performing internal investigations. Advises public companies, financial services firms and financial institutions on preventive and remedial measures before and after securities-related issues arise.
**Career:** JD, American University, 1981 (summa cum laude); BA, American University School of Government and Public Administration, 1978 (magna cum laude).

**MAHONEY, Maureen**
Latham & Watkins LLP, Washington, DC
202 637 2250
maureen.mahoney@lw.com
*Featured in Appellate Law (Nationwide)*
**Practice Areas:** Leading appellate and US Supreme Court advocate, argued 21 cases in the Supreme Court with winning upsets such as Grutter v. Bollinger and Arthur Andersen; recognized by Washingtonian Magazine as one of the top five lawyers in D.C., identified by The National Law Journal as one of the nation's 100 most influential lawyers, named runner-up for "Lawyer of the Year," and recognized in 2010 as one of the "Decade's Most Influential Lawyers."
**Professional Memberships:** American College of Trial Lawyers; American Academy of Appellate Lawyers.
**Career:** United States Deputy Solicitor General, 1991-1993; Law Clerk to the Honorable William Rehnquist.

**MAIZEL, Jonathan**
Milbank, Tweed, Hadley & McCloy LLP, Washington, DC
202 835 7565
jmaizel@milbank.com
*Featured in Projects (Nationwide)*

**Practice Areas:** Mr Maizel is a partner and heads the firm's Washington DC-based Project Finance Group. Mr Maizel focuses mainly on representing parties in the development and financing of oil and gas, independent power, nuclear fuel cycle, airport, transportation-sector, natural resource and other infrastructure projects. He has particular expertise in multi-sourced financings, especially those involving official credit agencies (including multilateral, export credit and development financing agencies), commercial banks and capital markets lenders.

**MAKICH, Ann**
Cahill Gordon & Reindel LLP, New York
212 701 3699
amakich@cahill.com
*Featured in Banking & Finance (Nationwide)*
**Practice Areas:** Practice is focused on leveraged financings for acquisitions, recapitalizations and going-private transactions, as well as debt exchanges, securities offerings and general corporate advice. Clients include leading investment banking firms, commercial banks and investment funds. Represents underwriters, placement agents and initial purchasers in public and private high-yield and equity offerings and secured bank loans in a wide range of industries.
**Personal:** Rice University, BA, 1991. Columbia Law School, JD, 1996.

**MALEDON, William J**
Osborn Maledon PA, Phoenix
602 640 9331
wmaledon@omlaw.com
*Featured in Litigation (Nationwide), Litigation (Arizona)*
See under Arizona for profile.

**MALLOY, Michael**
Drinker Biddle & Reath LLP, Philadelphia
215 988 2978
Michael.Malloy@dbr.com
*Featured in Investment Funds (Nationwide)*
**Career:** Partner and chair of the Investment Management Practice Group, Mike Malloy counsels open- and closed-end investment companies, their independent directors and trustees, private funds, investment advisors, broker-dealers and other financial institutions on organizational, operational, regulatory and fiduciary matters. He regularly advises investment companies and advisors on strategic alliances and acquisitions.
**Personal:** Boston College, BA, summa cum laude; Boston College Law School, JD, cum laude, law review. Mike serves on the Advisory Board of the Mutual Fund Directors Forum.

**MALYSHEV, Peter**
Latham & Watkins LLP, Washington, DC
202 637 2200
*Featured in Capital Markets (Nationwide)*
**Practice Areas:** Focuses on regulatory, compliance and transactional issues relating to commodities, securities and derivatives products markets. Assists clients with Dodd Frank and CFTC compliance in connection with derivatives trading. Represents financial companies as well as physical commodity traders in front of the CFTC and the SEC.

**Professional Memberships:** Chairman and Founder, DC Bar Committee on Derivatives and Futures; member, Board of Editors of the Futures and Derivatives Law Report; adjunct professor, George Washington University.
**Personal:** LLM, Georgetown University Law Center, 2002; JD, University of the Pacific McGeorge School of Law, 1996, With Distinction; MA, California State University, Sacramento, 1992.

**MANCINI, Mary Ann**
Loeb & Loeb LLP, Washington, DC
202 618 5006
mmancini@loeb.com
*Featured in Wealth Management (Nationwide)*
**Practice Areas:** Advise high net worth families and individuals residing in the US and internationally. Clients include leaders of Fortune 100 companies, as well as families whose wealth is more privately held and, in many cases, based on real estate ownership. Counsels clients on matters that affect their estates, including the structuring and formation of entities, the creation of irrevocable "dynasty" trusts, tax planning for families and the entities they own, and the protection and preservation of their assets.
**Personal:** Georgetown University (LLM, 1992); Catholic University of America, Columbus School of Law (JD, 1984); Washington College (BA, 1980).

**MANCINO, Douglas M**
Hunton & Williams LLP, Los Angeles
dmancino@hunton.com
*Featured in Healthcare (California), Healthcare (Nationwide)*
See under California for profile.

**MANGINO, Brian**
Fried, Frank, Harris, Shriver & Jacobson LLP, Washington, DC
202 639 7258
Brian.Mangino@FriedFrank.com
*Featured in Private Equity (Nationwide), Corporate/M&A (District of Columbia)*
See under District of Columbia for profile.

**MANN, Christopher L**
Sullivan & Cromwell LLP, New York
212 558 4625
mannc@sullcrom.com
*Featured in Latin American Investment (New York), Projects (Nationwide)*
**Professional Memberships:** Former Chair, Project Finance Committee (ABCNY); ABA.
**Career:** Partner since 1998. Acts for sponsors, lenders, private equity funds in investments in oil/gas, mining, power, infrastructure and other sectors in US, Latin America, Africa, elsewhere. Key assignments: Anglo American's pending sale of 70% interest in Amapá iron-ore operation; CPPIB 49.9% acquisition of Chilean toll roads; Chrysler financing for Ducato vehicles production in Mexico; Sincor's Venezuelan extra-heavy oil project and restructuring; and major mining projects in Argentina, Chile, Brazil, Venezuela.
**Personal:** Harvard Law (JD, 1989); Cambridge (MPhil, 1987); Harvard (AB, 1985). Clerk, Hon. Ralph K. Winter, US.Ct.App., 2d Circuit, 1989-90.

**MANOS, Karen L**
Gibson, Dunn & Crutcher LLP, Washington, DC
202 955 8536
kmanos@gibsondunn.com
*Featured in Government (Nationwide)*
**Practice Areas:** Extensive experience on the full range of government contracts issues, including complex claims preparation/ litigation, civil and criminal fraud investigations/litigation, qui tam suits under the False Claims Act, defective pricing, cost allowability, the Cost Accounting Standards, suspension and debarment, bid protests, corporate compliance.
**Professional Memberships:** Past Chair, ABA Public Contract Law Section and National Defense Industrial Association Procurement Division. Editor-in-Chief, 'Public Contract Law Journal' and 'Cost, Pricing & Accounting Report.'
**Publications:** 'Government Contract Costs & Pricing' (Thomson-Reuters 2009), over 40 government contract articles.
**Personal:** JD (highest honors), Duke University School of Law, 1986, Note Editor, 'Duke Law Journal.'

**MARIGO, Noiana Paula**
Freshfields Bruckhaus Deringer US LLP, New York
212 277 4000
noiana.marigo@freshfields.com
*Featured in International Arbitration (Nationwide)*
**Practice Areas:** Noiana is Counsel in Freshfields' international arbitration group based in New York. She acts as counsel in variety of commercial and investment treaty arbitrations, specializing in Latin America. Noiana has represented Latin American corporations and foreign investors in the region in arbitrations under the auspices of ICSID, ICC and UNCITRAL, both in English and Spanish, involving sectors as diverse as oil, mining, electricity, gas, water, sovereign debt, steel plants and airport services. Noiana currently represents several investors in their arbitrations against Argentina, Bolivia, Venezuela and Ecuador, as well as the Republic of Guatemala in two ICSID claims.

**MARKEL, Gregory A**
Cadwalader, Wickersham & Taft LLP, New York
212 504 6112
greg.markel@cwt.com
*Featured in Securities (Nationwide), Litigation (New York)*
**Practice Areas:** Co-Chairman, Litigation Department. Concentrates practice in securities, antitrust and complex commercial litigation. Extensive experience in securities litigation, including class action defense, derivative actions, and private securities litigation; antitrust; accountants defense; complex tax; director and officer liability; trade secret; intellectual property; internet; insurance coverage; banking; and RICO litigation. Years of experience representing accounting firms and the AICPA and has handled numerous securities cases involving accounting issues. Played an important role in litigation relating to Enron, WorldCom, Tyco, Adelphia, IPO Allocation,

Martha Stewart, AIG, Bally, and many other major litigations.
**Professional Memberships:** American Bar Association - Litigation and Antitrust; Federal Bar Council; City Bar Committee on Securities Litigation; Securities Industry Association; New York State Bar Association, Commercial Litigation, Fellow of the New York Bar Foundation, and Board of Directors of the Legal Aid Society.
**Personal:** JD, Yale Law School; MBA, University of Michigan; BA, Columbia College.

## MARKS, Allan T
Milbank, Tweed, Hadley & McCloy LLP, Los Angeles
213 892 4376
amarks@milbank.com
*Featured in Projects (Nationwide)*
**Practice Areas:** Mr Marks is a partner in the Project Finance Group and Latin America Practice Group. He routinely represents developers, investors, lenders, and underwriters in the development and financing of complex infrastructure projects worldwide, with special expertise in the energy, infrastructure and transportation sectors. Mr Marks has participated in numerous project financings, acquisitions, restructurings, securities offerings and private placements for a variety of sophisticated institutional clients. He speaks and publishes frequently on renewable energy, public-private partnerships, cross-border financing issues, infrastructure investments, deregulation and emerging markets. Mr Marks has worked on transactions throughout Asia, Europe and the Americas.

## MARLATT, Jerry
Morrison & Foerster LLP, New York
212 468 8024
jmarlatt@mofo.com
*Featured in Capital Markets (Nationwide)*
**Practice Areas:** Represents issuers and underwriters in the debt and equity capital markets transaction in public, 3(a)(2) and 144A offerings of senior debt, covered bonds, surplus notes, securities of structured investment and specialized operating vehicles, and securities repackagings. Representative transactions include the first SEC registered covered bond program, the first covered bond program for a US financial institution, the first covered bond program for a Canadian bank, surplus notes and common stock for a US monoline insurance company, eurobond offerings for US issuers.

## MARLETTE, Cynthia A.
Akin Gump Strauss Hauer & Feld LLP, Washington, DC
202 887 4531
cmarlette@akingump.com
*Featured in Energy & Natural Resources (Nationwide)*
**Practice Areas:** Ms Marlette focuses her practice on energy matters, including Federal Energy Regulatory Commission regulation and related energy laws and policies.
**Career:** Served for six years as the Federal Energy Regulatory Commission's general counsel and was

responsible for providing legal and policy advice in all areas of the agency's regulation. In addition to twice serving as general counsel, held a number of other positions at the agency including principal deputy general counsel, associate general counsel and legal advisor to the chairman.
**Personal:** JD, American University, Washington College of Law, 1979. BA, University of South Florida, with honors, 1971.

## MARMARO, Richard
Skadden, Arps, Slate, Meagher & Flom LLP & Affiliates, Los Angeles
213 687 5480
richard.marmaro@skadden.com
*Featured in Litigation (Nationwide), Litigation (California)*
**Practice Areas:** Heads West Coast SEC Enforcement and White-Collar Defense Practice. Successfully defended William Ruehle, former Broadcom CFO, in the largest stock options backdating case by obtaining dismissals of criminal, SEC and civil cases. Successfully defended individuals and corporations in all phases of complex civil, criminal and regulatory matters involving allegations of securities fraud. Conducted internal investigations for Fortune 500 companies on FCPA, securities and other issues.
**Career:** JD, New York University School of Law, 1975; BA, George Washington University, 1972 (magna cum laude, Phi Beta Kappa). Law clerk, SDNY; Assistant US Attorney, CD Cal; Assistant Chief, Criminal Division.

## MARPLE, J D
Latham & Watkins LLP, Silicon Valley
650 328 4600
jd.marple@lw.com
*Featured in Outsourcing (Nationwide), IT & Outsourcing (California)*
See under California for profile.

## MARQUARDT, Paul
Cleary Gottlieb Steen & Hamilton LLP, Washington, DC
202 974 1648
pmarquardt@cgsh.com
*Featured in Corporate/M&A (District of Columbia), International Trade (Nationwide)*
**Practice Areas:** Wide range of cross-border transactional and regulatory matters including domestic and international private equity and joint ventures, cross-border regulatory issues (Exon-Florio, sanctions, FCPA, and export controls), and enforcement matters. Representative clients include BBVA Compass, BNP Paribas, Deutsche Telekom, GlaxoSmithKline, Nortel Networks, OneWest Bank, TPG, and VeriSign.
**Professional Memberships:** Michigan and DC Bars.
**Career:** Joined firm, 1995; became partner, 2004; JD and MA, Yale University (1994); BA, with highest distinction, University of Michigan (1990); Law clerk, James B. Loken of the US Court of Appeals for the Eighth Circuit (1994-5).

## MARSH, David
Arnold & Porter LLP, Washington, DC
202 942 5068
David.Marsh@aporter.com
*Featured in Life Sciences (Nationwide), Intellectual Property (District of Columbia)*
**Practice Areas:** Dr Marsh co-chairs the Intellectual Property practice. He focuses extensively on IP counseling, PTO inter partes matters, interferences and patent procurement, predominantly in the mechanical, chemical, medical device, pharmaceutical, and biotechnology areas. He has argued multiple matters before the US Patent and Trademark Office's Patent Trial and Appeal Board. He is an American Arbitration Association neutral arbitrator, a World Intellectual Property Organization neutral arbitrator, and an adjunct professor at Georgetown Law School.
**Personal:** JD, NYU School of Law, 1995; CPE, Nottingham Law School, 1992; PhD, Institute of Plant Science Research, 1989; BSc, University of London, 1985.

## MARSHALL, Steve
Venable LLP, Baltimore
410 244 7407
semarshall@venable.com
*Featured in Products Liability (Nationwide)*
**Practice Areas:** Product liability and mass torts, healthcare, litigation, insurance, pharmaceuticals.
**Career:** For over 15 years, he has concentrated on litigation involving medical, scientific and technology issues. He has participated in several trials involving pharmaceuticals, medical diagnostic assays and technology used by the financial industry. He has been lead counsel in more than 15 trials. He has argued numerous appeals at the federal and state level. Within the last 3 years, he argued and won 4 appeals to Maryland's highest appellate court.
**Personal:** JD, William and Mary Marshall-Wythe School of Law, 1989; BA, cum laude, Wheeling Jesuit University, 1986.

## MARTEL, Jonathan
Arnold & Porter LLP, Washington, DC
202 942 5470
Jonathan.Martel@aporter.com
*Featured in Climate Change (Nationwide), Environment (District of Columbia)*
**Practice Areas:** His practice concentrates on Clean Air Act matters, environmental litigation and counseling. His recent work includes representation of electric utilities, consumer products, automotive, off-road equipment, chemical, petroleum and other diversified manufacturers in Clean Air Act regulatory, permitting and enforcement matters, with substantial focus on greenhouse gas monitoring, reporting and regulation in the United States and internationally. He served for three years at the Office of General Counsel of EPA, where he was involved in the implementation of the Clean Air Act Amendments of 1990.
**Publications:** Writes frequently about environmental, clean air, climate change and administrative law matters.

## MARTELLA, Roger
Sidley Austin LLP, Washington, DC
202 736 8097
rmartella@sidley.com
*Featured in Climate Change (Nationwide), Environment (District of Columbia)*
**Practice Areas:** Partner in Sidley's Environmental practice. His practice focuses on three primary areas. First, he advises companies on developing strategic approaches to achieve their goals in light of rapidly developing demands to address climate change, promote sustainability, and utilize clean energy. Second, he handles a broad range of environmental and natural resource litigation and mediation. Third, he advises multinational companies on compliance with environmental laws in the United States, China, the European Union, and other nations.
**Career:** Mr Martella recently rejoined Sidley after serving as the General Counsel of the United States Environmental Protection Agency.

## MARTIN, David
Covington & Burling LLP, Washington, DC
202 662 5128
dmartin@cov.com
*Featured in Corporate/M&A (District of Columbia), Securities (Nationwide)*
**Practice Areas:** David Martin, Co-Head of the firm's Securities and Capital Markets practice, advises clients in corporate governance, securities regulation and transactional matters, including corporate finance, business combination transactions, internal investigations and corporate compliance issues.
**Career:** Mr Martin has seven years of service with the SEC, including as Director of the Division of Corporation Finance and special Counsel to the Chairman.
**Personal:** He had four years of service in the US Navy and received his JD from the University of Virginia Law School, where he was managing editor of the law review, and his BA from Yale University.

## MARTIN, John
Baker Botts LLP, Dallas
214 953 6757
john.martin@bakerbotts.com
*Featured in Outsourcing (Nationwide), Technology (Texas)*
See under Texas for profile.

## MARTIN, Keith
Chadbourne & Parke LLP, Washington, DC
202 974 5674
kmartin@chadbourne.com
*Featured in Projects (Nationwide)*
**Practice Areas:** Keith Martin is a transactional lawyer whose principal areas of practice are tax and project finance. He acted for 157 companies last year and worked on transactions in the United States and eight foreign countries. He also lobbies Congress and the Treasury Department on policy issues. He is co-head of the Chadbourne project finance group.
**Career:** Former Counsel to Senator Daniel Patrick Moynihan (D-NY) and a legislative assistant to Senator Henry M Jackson (D-Wash).

**Personal:** Wesleyan University, BA, 1974; George Washington University, JD, 1977; The London School of Economics, MSc, 1978.

## MARTIN, Renwick
Sidley Austin LLP, New York
212 839 5319
rmartin@sidley.com
*Featured in Capital Markets (Nationwide)*
**Practice Areas:** Partner in Sidley's New York office and a member of the firm's Executive Committee. Mr Martin has worked in the mortgage-backed area since 1977 when he participated in the Bank of America pass-through transaction, which was the first publicly-offered conventional pass-through transaction. Since 1984, he has concentrated on mortgage-backed and asset-backed financings of all types.
**Personal:** Harvard Law School (JD, 1972); Stanford University (AB, 1969). Admission: New York.

## MARTINO, Paul G
Alston & Bird LLP, Washington, DC
202 239 3439
paul.martino@alston.com
*Featured in Privacy & Data Security (Nationwide)*
**Practice Areas:** Represents businesses and trade associations before Congress, federal departments and agencies on privacy, data security, e-commerce, telecommunications, financial services and intellectual property issues. Featured speaker on privacy and technology policy issues.
**Career:** Co-Leader of firm's Privacy & Security Task Force. Partner in Legislative & Public Policy Group in Washington. Former majority Counsel to US Senate Commerce Committee and principal advisor on privacy and e-commerce to Chairman John McCain. Prior to Washington practice, corporate and securities attorney in Silicon Valley. Member, California and District of Columbia bars.
**Personal:** JD, University of California, Berkeley; A.B., magna cum laude, Georgetown University.

## MASON, Richard G
Wachtell, Lipton, Rosen & Katz, New York
212 403 1252
rgmason@wlrk.com
*Featured in Bankruptcy/Restructuring (Nationwide), Bankruptcy/Restructuring (New York)*
**Practice Areas:** Partner in Wachtell, Lipton, Rosen & Katz's Restructuring and Finance Department, representing bank and bondholder groups and significant shareholders, creditors and acquirers in many large bankruptcy cases and out-of-court restructurings in the United States, as well as other countries, including, over the past five years, the Hawker Beechcraft, Kerzner, Washington Mutual, Lyondell, Fontainebleau Las Vegas, Spectrum Brands, Masonite Corporation, FairPoint Communications, Chrysler and Delphi Corporation matters. Also represents borrowers in leveraged buyouts, mergers and other complex financing transactions.
**Professional Memberships:** Immediate past co-chair of the International Secured Transactions & Insolvency Committee of the ABA Section of International Law, fellow in the American College of Bankruptcy and vice-chair of the Bankruptcy and Reorganization Group of the UJA - Federation of New York's Lawyers Division.
**Career:** Partner at Wachtell, Lipton, Rosen & Katz since 1994. Has given numerous seminars on bankruptcy subjects for Practising Law Institute, the Canadian Institute, the American Bankruptcy Institute/New York University School of Law Bankruptcy and Business Reorganization Workshop, the NYU Pollack Center for Law & Business, Columbia University Business School, Columbia University Law School, LUISS Guido Carli (Rome) and other prominent organisations. Listed in the K&A Restructuring Register as one of the top 100 restructuring advisors in the United States.
**Publications:** Co-author of Chapter 90 of 'Collier's Bankruptcy Practice Guide'.
**Personal:** Graduated magna cum laude from Virginia Commonwealth University in 1983 (BS, Economics) where he was inducted into the Phi Kappa Phi honour fraternity; and cum laude from New York University in 1987 (JD) where he became a Member of the Order of the Coif and was on the staff of the 'Annual Survey of American Law'. Member of the Executive Committee of the Board of Trustees of the Boy Scouts of America's Greater New York Councils and recipient of the Scouts' Silver Beaver Award. Founded (along with his wife and children) the Mason Family Civic League, a 501(c)(3) charity dedicated to providing educational, art and civic support in Hoboken, New Jersey and beyond.

## MASOTTI, Marco
Paul, Weiss, Rifkind, Wharton & Garrison LLP, New York
212 373 3034
mmasotti@paulweiss.com
*Featured in Investment Funds (Nationwide)*
**Practice Areas:** A member of the firm's Management Committee, Marco Masotti is regarded as a leading fund formation lawyer. Recently featured by The Deal as one of the 'Movers & Shakers' in the industry who has played a vital role in transformative transactions. Focuses on the organization and operation of a wide variety of private investment funds, including buyout, hedge, hybrid, distressed, mezzanine, seed capital, venture capital, co-investment funds and funds of funds. Has significant experience in all types of investment funds organized by alternative asset managers and represents a diverse group of sponsors. Advises on the full spectrum of investment management M&A transactions, including acquisitions, divestitures, majority and minority stake investments and spin-outs. Clients include Apollo, Avenue Capital, Bass/Oak Hill, BlackRock, Blackstone/GSO, General Atlantic, Harvest, Reservoir, Sageview and Wellspring. Former Chair of the Committee on Private Investment Funds of the New York City Bar.

## MASSEY, William L
Covington & Burling LLP, Washington, DC
202 662 5322
wmassey@cov.com
*Featured in Energy & Natural Resources (Nationwide)*
**Practice Areas:** Handles high-profile matters before FERC, Congress, and state commissions/legislatures. Advises foreign/domestic clients including investment firms, SWFs, utilities, generators, project developers, DR aggregators, customers, and marketers on M&A, market structure and tariff rules, transmission/infrastructure investment, and FERC enforcement investigations.
**Career:** Currently is Chair of Covington's Energy Regulatory Group. FERC Commissioner (1993-2003). Adjunct Professor, Georgetown University Law Center (2006-2013); US Senator Dale Bumpers (D-AR), Chief Counsel (1980-89); Judge Richard S. Arnold, US Court of Appeals for the 8th Circuit, Law Clerk (1978-80).
**Personal:** Georgetown University Law Center, LLM; University of Arkansas, Fayetteville, JD.

## MASTERS, Lorelie S
Jenner & Block LLP, Washington, DC
202 639 6076
lmasters@jenner.com
*Featured in Insurance (Nationwide), Insurance (District of Columbia)*
See under District of Columbia for profile.

## MATHENY, Richard
Goodwin Procter LLP, Washington, DC
202 346 4130
rmatheny@goodwinprocter.com
*Featured in International Trade (Nationwide)*
**Practice Areas:** Mr Matheny heads the firm's National Security & Foreign Trade Regulation Practice. He represents clients on matters relating to the Export Administration Regulations (EAR) and the Antiboycott Regulations of the Commerce Department; the International Traffic in Arms Regulations (ITAR) of the State Department; the economic sanctions administered by the Office of Foreign Assets Control (OFAC) of the Treasury Department; national security reviews conducted by the Committee on Foreign Investment in the United States (CFIUS); and the Foreign Corrupt Practices Act (FCPA).
**Personal:** JD, University of Pennsylvania Law School, 1999; MA, University of California, 1996; BA, Duke University, 1991.

## MATTHEWS, John E
Morgan, Lewis & Bockius LLP, Washington, DC
202 739 5524
jmatthews@morganlewis.com
*Featured in Energy & Natural Resources (Nationwide)*
**Practice Areas:** John E. Matthews is a partner in Morgan Lewis's Energy Practice. Mr Matthews has successfully assisted clients in obtaining NRC regulatory approvals for "first of its kind" commercial transactions involving nuclear power plants. He advises clients regarding commercial issues relating to nuclear power plants and other nuclear assets, nuclear export controls, certain government contracts matters, NRC's review of license transfers, decommissioning funding issues, and insurance and liability issues associated with the ownership and operation of nuclear assets. He also has directed litigation teams in contested licensing proceedings before the NRC and in complex commercial litigation involving nuclear assets.

## MAY JR, Henry S
Vinson & Elkins LLP, Houston
713 758 2554
hmay@velaw.com
*Featured in Energy & Natural Resources (Nationwide)*
**Practice Areas:** Extensive experience in the regulatory, policy and transactional aspects of the natural gas and electric industries. Has represented clients before federal and state agencies and courts, and assisted in the development of energy policy initiatives, and participated in the structuring and negotiation of domestic and international energy transactions.
**Career:** Attended: The University of Texas (BA with honors, 1969); The University of Texas School of Law (JD with honors 1971); Admitted to practice (Texas, 1972); US Supreme Court; Courts of Appeals of the District of Columbia Circuit, Fifth Circuit, and Eleventh Circuit.

## MAYER, Theodore VH
Hughes Hubbard & Reed LLP, New York
212 837 6888
mayer@hugheshubbard.com
*Featured in Products Liability (Nationwide)*
**Practice Areas:** Mr Mayer is Managing Partner of Hughes Hubbard and maintains an active litigation practice including defense of some of the most active and well-publicized individual and class action product liability litigations pending in the United States.
**Publications:** Co-author with Robb W Patryk of the treatise Product Liability (Law Journal Seminars-Press); numerous published articles on product liability and complex litigation topics.
**Personal:** Harvard Law School (JD, 1977); Yale College (BA, Magna Cum Laude 1974).

## MAYER, Thomas Moers
Kramer Levin Naftalis & Frankel LLP, New York
212 715 9169
tmayer@kramerlevin.com
*Featured in Bankruptcy/Restructuring (Nationwide), Bankruptcy/Restructuring (New York)*
**Practice Areas:** Mr Mayer is Co-Chairman of the Corporate Restructuring and Bankruptcy Department, and specializes in representing investors in claims against, and interests in, financially distressed businesses.
**Professional Memberships:** Mr Mayer is a fellow of the American College of Bankruptcy and a member of the National Bankruptcy Conference.
**Career:** Recent assignments include the Official Creditors Committees in GM, Chrysler, Patriot Coal, Hostess, Smurfit Stone and the Trustee of Lehman Brothers' Dutch financing subsidiary.

**Publications:** He has been the leading scholar on trading claims and taking control of corporations in chapter 11, publishing six papers on that topic since 1988.

## MAYER, William P
Goodwin Procter LLP, Boston
617 570 1534
wmayer@goodwinprocter.com
*Featured in Financial Services Regulation (Nationwide), Banking & Finance (Massachusetts)*
See under Massachusetts for profile.

## MAYESH, Jay
Kaye Scholer LLP, New York
212 836 7606
jay.mayesh@kayescholer.com
*Featured in Products Liability (Nationwide)*
**Practice Areas:** Jay Mayesh is a noted defense lawyer who has defended clients against product liability claims for over 40 years. He has extensive jury trial experience, including serving as trial counsel to The Upjohn Company in DES litigation, Baxter Healthcare in silicone breast implant litigation, Pfizer in pharmaceutical litigation, Warner-Lambert in Rezulin litigation, and DaimlerChrysler in automotive litigation. Most recently, he served as lead counsel for Knauf in the Chinese drywall litigation. Jay is a Lecturer in Forensic Psychiatry at Columbia University, College of Physicians and Surgeons and a Fellow of the American Bar Foundation.

## MAYNARD, Deanne
Morrison & Foerster LLP, Washington, DC
202 887 8740
dmaynard@mofo.com
*Featured in Appellate Law (Nationwide)*
**Practice Areas:** Deanne Maynard is chair of the firm's Appellate and Supreme Court practice. She has argued 13 cases in United States Supreme Court and many more in various federal courts of appeals throughout the country in intellectual property, bankruptcy, securities, antitrust, and other matters. Her Supreme Court arguments include RadLAX Gateway Hotel, LLC v. Amalgamated Bank, MedImmune v. Genentech, and Pacific Bell Telephone Company v. linkLine Communications. From 2004-2009, she served as Assistant to the Solicitor General at the US Department of Justice.

## MAYNES, Todd F
Kirkland & Ellis LLP, Chicago
312 862 2485
todd.maynes@kirkland.com
*Featured in Tax (Illinois), Tax (Nationwide)*
See under Illinois for profile.

## MAZAWEY, Louis T
Groom Law Group, Washington, DC
202 861 6608
LMazawey@groom.com
*Featured in Employee Benefits & Executive Compensation (Nationwide), Employee Benefits & Executive Compensation (District of Columbia)*
**Practice Areas:** Employee benefits; executive compensation; pension and profit sharing; tax law; ERISA.
**Professional Memberships:** Charter Fellow, American College of Employee Benefits Counsel.

Adjunct Professor, Georgetown University Law Center, 2000-05.
**Career:** Thirty eight years of experience on tax aspects of employee benefits for Fortune 200, institutional and state and local governmental clients. Expertise with all forms of benefit plans and compensation arrangements, including tax-favored retirement plans, IRAs, ESOPs, executive compensation, retiree medical, plan terminations, mergers and spinoffs, and life insurance and annuity programs.
**Personal:** Admitted 1975, District of Columbia. JD, Georgetown University Law Center, 1974. BA, New York University, 1971.

## MAZIN, George J
Dechert LLP, New York
212 698 3570
george.mazin@dechert.com
*Featured in Investment Funds (Nationwide)*
**Practice Areas:** Mr Mazin advises clients on the structuring and restructuring of domestic and off-shore private funds, private placements of securities, structured products, private equity investing, and broker-dealer and investment adviser compliance. He has assisted clients in Europe and Asia.
**Professional Memberships:** Member, New York and New Jersey Bars; member, Managed Funds Association Lawyers Advisory Committee; former chair, Private Funds Committee, Bar of the City of New York; member, Advisory Board, Regulatory Compliance Association.
**Personal:** Queens College, The City University of New York (BA, 1972, magna cum laude); Cornell University (M.R.P., 1974); Rutgers University School of Law (JD, 1981).

## MAZZUCHI, Michael A
Cleary Gottlieb Steen & Hamilton LLP, Washington, DC
202 974 1572
mmazzuchi@cgsh.com
*Featured in Capital Markets (Nationwide)*
**Practice Areas:** Corporate and securities matters, particularly domestic and international structured finance and derivatives matters. Has extensive experience in mortgage and asset securitizations, collateralized bond obligation transactions, synthetic debt securities and repackagings, credit derivative transactions and interest rate, currency and equity derivatives.
**Professional Memberships:** Member of the Bar in the District of Columbia.
**Career:** Joined firm, 1992; became Partner, 2001. JD, magna cum laude, member of Law Review's editorial board, University of Michigan Law School (1992); BA, Political Science, Phi Beta Kappa, University of Michigan (1989).

## MCANELLY III, W James
Bracewell & Giuliani LLP, Houston
713 221 1194
james.mcanelly@bgllp.com
*Featured in Energy & Natural Resources (Nationwide)*
**Practice Areas:** Heads the firm's oil & gas practice. Represents oil, gas and energy industry clients in a variety of oil and gas transactions, including purchase, sale and/or financing of exploration and

producing properties, processing plants, production and storage facilities and pipeline systems, and day-to-day operational representation. Also assists in the formation of joint ventures and partnerships for the funding, acquisition, operation and development of energy projects. Has represented investors and lenders to coal mining operations and development projects.
**Personal:** JD, The University of Texas School of Law, 1993; BBA, The University of Texas at Austin, 1990.

## MCBRIDE, Michael F
Van Ness Feldman LLP, Washington, DC
202 298 1989
mfm@vnf.com
*Featured in Transportation (Nationwide)*
**Practice Areas:** Counsel to railroad customers involved in litigation at the Surface Transportation Board and in arbitration and court cases concerning transportation of coal, chemicals and other commodities. Also counsels on commercial matters.
**Professional Memberships:** Association of Transportation Law Professionals (President, 1994-95, 2004-05).
**Career:** Oak Ridge National Laboratory, Environmental Sciences Division, Research Associate 1972; Special Assistant Attorney General, Commonwealth of Massachusetts, 1988-92.
**Publications:** "Is The Price-Anderson Act An Appropriate Model For The Railroads?" 76 J. Transp. L. Logist. & Pol'y 93 (First Qtr. 2009).
**Personal:** JD, University of Wisconsin, Madison; M.S., California Institute of Technology; B.S., University of Wisconsin, Milwaukee.

## MCCABE, David J
Willkie Farr & Gallagher LLP, New York
212 728 8723
dmccabe@willkie.com
*Featured in Wealth Management (Nationwide)*
**Practice Areas:** Chair of Private Clients Group. Specializes in all aspects of estate planning and administration, with emphasis on development of sophisticated plans for high-net-worth individuals and their families. Practice includes preparation of complex wills, trust agreements and related instruments, representation of clients in estate tax and gift tax audits, and general counseling of clients in all phases of administration of decedents' estates. Represents non-resident aliens regarding US tax aspects of their plans as well as US persons establishing trusts off shore. Represents banks and trust companies and counseled bank trust departments on trusts and estates matters. Advises fiduciaries and beneficiaries in estate and trust litigation matters in Surrogate's Courts and Supreme Court of State of New York. Representation includes national public charities, private foundations and charitable trusts. Has advised directors and trustees of eleemosynary organizations on variety of corporate and tax issues and formed numerous private foundations and public charitable entities.
**Personal:** JD, Fordham University School of Law, 1983. BA, magna cum laude, Economics,

Iona College, 1980. See:
http://www.willkie.com/DavidMcCabe

## MCCAFFREY, Carlyn S
McDermott Will & Emery LLP, New York
212 547 5324
cmccaffrey@mwe.com
*Featured in Wealth Management (Nationwide)*
**Practice Areas:** Co-head of private client practice in firm's New York office. Practice focus is tax and estate planning for high net worth individuals.
**Professional Memberships:** Admitted in New York and before US Tax Court; American College of Trust & Estate Counsel; American College of Tax Counsel; International Academy of Trust & Estate Counsel; adjunct professor at New York University School of Law and Miami Law School.
**Publications:** Co-author of "Structuring the Tax Consequences of Marriage and Divorce".
**Personal:** New York University School of Law, LLM, 1974; New York University School of Law, JD, 1967; George Washington University, BA, 1963.

## MCCALEB, Scott M
Wiley Rein LLP, Washington, DC
202 719 3193
smccaleb@wileyrein.com
*Featured in Government (Nationwide)*
**Practice Areas:** Represents contractors in bid protests, contract disputes and termination litigation, government investigations, fraud claims, mergers/acquisitions, and misappropriation and intellectual property disputes.
**Professional Memberships:** Former Co-Chair, Current Member, US Court of Appeals for the Federal Circuit Advisory Council; Member, US Court of Federal Claims Advisory Council; Past President, Federal Circuit Bar Association; Board Member, Court of Federal Claims Bar Association.
**Career:** Adjunct Professor, George Washington University and George Mason University Schools of Law; Law Clerk, US Court of Appeals for the Federal Circuit.
**Personal:** Georgetown University Law Center (JD); Brown University (BA).

## MCCARTHY, Catherine
Clifford Chance US LLP, Washington, DC
202 912 5057
catherine.mccarthy@cliffordchance.com
*Featured in Projects (Nationwide)*
**Practice Areas:** Has many years of experience representing commercial banks, multilateral finance institutions, export credit agencies and project sponsors in international project finance, export finance and other cross-border finance transactions. Has experience in a wide range of financial transactions, including project finance facilities, secured and unsecured syndicated facilities, A/B loans and export credits.
**Career:** Law degree with first class honors from Oxford University and her LLM from Harvard Law School. Previously practiced in the firm's New York and London offices, and is qualified to practice law in New York, England and the District of Columbia.

## MCCARTHY, Catherine
Bracewell & Giuliani LLP, Washington, DC
202 828 5839
cathy.mccarthy@bgllp.com
*Featured in Energy & Natural Resources (Nationwide)*
**Practice Areas:** Has represented clients on energy regulation and policy matters for almost two decades. She has experience with obtaining Federal Energy Regulatory Commission (FERC) and state authorizations for major projects and transactions; FERC compliance matters; FERC transmission and centralized markets issues; and rate, tariff and refund matters. She also represents energy clients before the Department of Energy, the Federal Communications Commission and the Nuclear Regulatory Commission.
**Personal:** JD, Georgetown University Law Center, 1993; BA, Yale University, 1989.

## MCCARTY, Joyce
Cleary Gottlieb Steen & Hamilton LLP, Washington, DC
202 974 1574
jmccarty@cgsh.com
*Featured in Capital Markets (Nationwide)*
**Practice Areas:** Corporate and financial transactions, particularly collateralized loan obligations and other structured finance products. Extensive experience as counsel for issuers, placement agents and collateral managers in CLO transactions, repackagings and other types of structured finance transactions.
**Professional Memberships:** Member of the Bar in the District of Columbia.
**Career:** Joined firm, 1987; became Counsel, 2008. JD, editor-in-chief of the University of Hawaii Law Review, William S. Richardson School of Law at the University of Hawaii (1986); BA, cum laude, Thiel College (1972). Law clerk, Honorable Samuel P. King of the US District Court for the District of Hawaii.

## MCCLURE, Daniel M
Fulbright & Jaworski LLP, Houston
713 651 5159
dmcclure@fulbright.com
*Featured in Energy & Natural Resources (Nationwide), Litigation (Texas)*
See under Texas for profile.

## MCCORMALLY, Brian C
Arnold & Porter LLP, Washington, DC
202 942 5141
Brian.McCormally@aporter.com
*Featured in Financial Services Regulation (Nationwide)*
**Practice Areas:** Brian McCormally, a Partner in the Financial Institutions Practice, has over 20 years of regulatory experience in senior positions in the enforcement and compliance areas at two federal banking agencies, the Office of the Comptroller of the Currency and the Office of Thrift Supervision. He has extensive knowledge of bank and thrift operations, corporate structures and activities, lending and marketing practices, regulatory compliance, and corporate governance issues. He represents diversified financial holding companies, financial institutions, service providers

and their respective boards of directors in regulatory compliance matters, and in enforcement and investigative proceedings by federal or state agencies.

## MCCUE, Judith W
McDermott Will & Emery LLP, Chicago
312 984 7515
jmccue@mwe.com
*Featured in Wealth Management (Nationwide)*
**Practice Areas:** Member of the private client department; focuses on estate planning and trust and estate administration.
**Professional Memberships:** Past president of American College of Trust and Estate Counsel (2005-06) and Past Chair of College's State Laws Committee and Elder Law Committee; past president of Chicago Estate Planning Council; chaired Chicago Bar Association's Probate Practice Committee and Estate and Gift Tax Division of its Federal Tax Committee.
**Personal:** Harvard Law School, JD, 1972; University of Pennsylvania, BA (cum laude), 1969.

## MCCULLOUGH, James J
Fried, Frank, Harris, Shriver & Jacobson LLP, Washington, DC
202 639 7130
James.McCullough@FriedFrank.com
*Featured in Government (Nationwide)*
**Practice Areas:** Litigation partner. Head of the government contracts practice. Practice includes pre-award litigation and counseling on contract formation issues, post-award disputes and litigation and representation of government contractors in civil proceedings, including Procurement Integrity and Freedom of Information Act disputes, and enforcement matters involving mandatory disclosure, suspension and debarment.
**Career:** Joined in 1980; became partner in 1985. Past Chair of National Defense Industrial Association's Procurement Division; vice-chair ABA Public Contract Law Battlespace Committee and member of Section Council; Advisory Board of The Government Contractor.
**Personal:** JD, University of Virginia School of Law (1976); BA, cum laude, Villanova University (1969).

## MCCULLOUGH, Kim
Ballard Spahr LLP, Denver
303 299 7318
mcculloughk@ballardspahr.com
*Featured in Franchising (Nationwide)*
**Practice Areas:** Kim I. McCullough is practice leader of the Franchise and Distribution Group. She focuses her practice on representing franchisors regarding compliance with franchise registration and disclosure laws, franchisor-franchisee relations, international expansion, mergers and acquisitions, general business matters, and trademark issues.
**Professional Memberships:** American Bar Association, Forum Committee on Franchising; Colorado Bar Association, Franchise Law Section; Denver Bar Association.
**Career:** Admissions: Colorado; US District Court for the District of Colorado; US Court of Appeals for the Tenth Circuit.

**Personal:** University of Colorado Law School (JD 1981); University of Oregon (BS 1977).

## MCDERMOTT III, Stanley
DLA Piper LLP (US), New York
212 335 4790
stanley.mcdermott@dlapiper.com
*Featured in Transportation (Nationwide)*
**Practice Areas:** Litigation.
**Career:** Co-chair of the Commercial Litigation practice in New York and has a widespread national and international litigation and arbitration practice that focuses on the litigation and arbitration of a wide range of sophisticated commercial disputes. He has appeared before the United States Supreme Court, numerous US Circuit Courts of Appeals, and many US district courts across the country. He frequently advises international clients concerning cross-border litigations in courts in the US and other countries.
**Personal:** JD, Tulane University; BA, Dartmouth College (magna cum laude).

## MCGAAN, Andrew R.
Kirkland & Ellis LLP, Chicago
312 862 2183
andrew.mcgaan@kirkland.com
*Featured in Products Liability (Nationwide)*
**Practice Areas:** Veteran trial lawyer with deep experience representing clients in complex product liability and restructuring matters. Has tried and won a wide variety of jury and non-jury cases throughout the United States in areas involving tobacco, refineries, securities fraud, non-competition and trade secret, as well as major litigation matters, including fraudulent conveyance claims, in bankruptcy cases. Profiled in National Law Journal's "Winning," annual survey of "the nation's best litigators".
**Professional Memberships:** American Bar Association; International Association of Defense Counsel.
**Personal:** Cornell University, JD, 1986 magna cum laude, Order of the Coif; Phi Kappa Phi; Cornell University, AB, 1983.

## MCGINN, Stacie E.
Simpson Thacher & Bartlett LLP, New York
212 455 2250
smcginn@stblaw.com
*Featured in Financial Services Regulation (Nationwide)*
**Practice Areas:** Financial Services Regulation. Broad experience includes: M&A (represented TD Bank in Target credit card acquisition, Bank of America in MBNA and Countrywide acquisitions, Travelers in Citicorp merger); private equity (represented Silver Lake in Dell acquisition, Carlyle and Oak Hill in FNB United recapitalization); capital markets (securities offerings for domestic and foreign banks); financial services enforcement (negotiated multi-state mortgage settlement with state attorneys general, fair lending and UDAP settlements); and compliance (advise on Dodd-Frank, Volcker, resolutions, AML, capital, Basel III, privacy, data security, payments, fair lending and consumer protection).
**Personal:** JD - Georgetown; BBA (economics and finance) - Baylor.

## MCGLONE, William M
Latham & Watkins LLP, Washington, DC
202 637 2202
william.mcglone@lw.com
*Featured in International Trade (Nationwide)*
**Practice Areas:** Focuses on legal, policy and enforcement issues arising under United States export controls, trade and economic sanctions, and other laws governing cross border transactions. Areas of expertise include the International Traffic in Arms Regulations (ITAR), the Export Administration Regulations (EAR), sanctions administered by the Treasury Department's Office of Foreign Assets Control (OFAC), US antiboycott laws, the Foreign Corrupt Practices Act (FCPA) and multilateral trade controls.
**Professional Memberships:** Member, District of Columbia; New York State bars.
**Career:** Former Chair, Export Controls and Economic Sanctions Committee, American Bar Association (International Section).
**Personal:** JD, Georgetown University, 1987; BA, Harvard University, 1982.

## MCGOWAN, Patricia
Venable LLP, Baltimore
410 244 7539
pmcgowan@venable.com
*Featured in Corporate/M&A (Maryland), Capital Markets (Nationwide)*
**Practice Areas:** Corporate, corporate finance and securities, Maryland corporate law.
**Professional Memberships:** Vice Chair, Business Law Section, Maryland State Bar Association; ABA, Business Law Section.
**Career:** Represents publicly and privately held companies, including many REITs, in mergers, spin-offs, restructurings, securities offerings and other financing transactions. Also represents companies in formation, sale and dissolution transactions. Regularly serves as counsel to boards of directors and board committees of REITs and other major US corporations regarding significant transactions, stockholder litigation, conflicts of interest and corporate governance issues.
**Personal:** JD, with honors, University of Maryland School of Law, 1995; BA, Johns Hopkins University, 1992.

## MCGRANE, John D
Morgan, Lewis & Bockius LLP, Washington, DC
202 739 5621
jmcgrane@morganlewis.com
*Featured in Energy & Natural Resources (Nationwide)*
**Practice Areas:** John D. McGrane is a partner in Morgan Lewis's Energy Practice. Mr McGrane has more than 30 years of experience representing electric utilities and other participants in the electric power industry. He advises clients on all facets of electric regulation and structure. Mr McGrane has been heavily involved in representing utilities in audits and investigations by the Federal Energy Regulatory Commission's Office of Enforcement, NERC and regional reliability entities. He also has been active in the areas of mandatory reliability standards; electric transmission issues; restructuring; mergers, acquisitions, and asset transactions;

affiliate issues; and power purchase sales and agreements.

## MCGUIRE, W John
Bingham McCutchen LLP, Washington, DC
202 373 6799
john.mcguire@bingham.com
*Featured in Investment Funds (Nationwide)*
**Practice Areas:** Concentrates on investment company and investment adviser regulatory issues and related issues affecting broker-dealers and transfer agents. Assists clients with the formation or acquisition of investment companies and investment advisers, in addition to providing them with ongoing representation. Handles matters involving the establishment, representation and counseling of exchange traded investment companies (ETFs), their advisers and listing markets.
**Career:** Has authored/co-authored articles covering securities regulatory issues and the book Mutual Fund Regulation and Compliance Handbook.
**Personal:** Washburn University School of Law, Juris Doctor, 1986; Wichita State University, Master of Public Administration 1986; Wichita State University, Bachelor of Arts, 1980.

## MCINERNEY, William P
Cadwalader, Wickersham & Taft LLP, New York
212 504 6118
william.mcinerney@cwt.com
*Featured in Real Estate (Nationwide), Real Estate (New York)*
**Practice Areas:** Represents commercial and investment banks, and other investors in real estate debt and equity transactions. Advises lenders in all aspects of construction and permanent financings with emphasis on capital markets real estate finance. Counsels clients in restructuring problem loans and selling REO assets. Engaged in sale of commercial mortgage and mezzanine loans in the secondary market. Handled large single borrower hotel transactions and complex cross-border transactions in Latin America. Interacts frequently with rating agencies in their review and analysis of commercial mortgage and mezzanine loan transactions.
**Publications:** Co-author "From Bankruptcy-Remote to Risk-Remote: Reframing the Single-Purpose Entity in the CMBS Finance," NYLJ.
**Personal:** JD, Fordham University School of Law; BA, Catholic University of America, (summa cum laude, Phi Beta Kappa).

## MCISAAC, Christopher
Clifford Chance US LLP, Washington, DC
202 912 5020
chris.mcisaac@cliffordchance.com
*Featured in Projects (Nationwide)*
**Practice Areas:** Co-Head of Clifford Chance's Americas Energy and Infrastructure Group. Represents multilateral development institutions, export credit agencies and commercial lenders in a variety of infrastructure project finance transactions across a wide range of industry sectors around the world, particularly oil and gas, power generation and other energy projects.

**Career:** Partner at Clifford Chance since 2006. University of North Carolina, BA, with highest honors, Phi Beta Kappa, 1982. Morehead Scholar, University of Virginia School of Law, JD, 1985, Dillard Fellow.

## MCKELVEY, JR., Steven
Nelson Mullins Riley & Scarborough LLP, Columbia
803 255 9573
steve.mckelvey@nelsonmullins.com
*Featured in Transportation (Nationwide)*
**Practice Areas:** Mr McKelvey represents automobile manufacturers, distributors, and automobile manufacturer trade associations throughout the US in a range of matters, including add points, relocations, terminations, licensing, vehicle allocations, warranty reimbursements, incentives, facilities, financing, and other manufacturer-related issues concerning dealers and state/federal regulatory bodies. His experience also extends to heavy trucks, light commercial vehicles, motorcycles, and recreational vehicles.

## MCKINSTRY JR, Robert B
Ballard Spahr LLP, Philadelphia
215 864 8208
mckinstry@ballardspahr.com
*Featured in Climate Change (Nationwide), Environment (Pennsylvania)*
See under Pennsylvania for profile.

## MCKOOL, Mike
McKool Smith, Dallas
214 978 4000
mmckool@mckoolsmith.com
*Featured in Litigation (Nationwide), Intellectual Property (Texas), Litigation (Texas)*
See under Texas for profile.

## MCLAUGHLIN, Joseph
Sidley Austin LLP, New York
212 839 5312
jmclaughlin@sidley.com
*Featured in Securities (Nationwide)*
**Practice Areas:** Senior counsel in Sidley's New York office. His practice areas include: public and private US and international securities offerings; US disclosure obligations of public companies; US broker-dealer regulation, including SEC and SRO rules relating to electronic communication, research, financial responsibility, securities credit, short sales, manipulation, misuse of nonpublic information, compliance and supervisory obligations, and activities of offshore broker-dealers.
**Publications:** Mr McLaughlin is the co-author (with Charles J. Johnson, Jr.) of Corporate Finance and the Securities Laws (4d ed. 2006, supplemented 2012) (Aspen Law & Business).
**Personal:** Mr McLaughlin has been recognized with the IFLR Lifetime Achievement Award.

## MCLUCAS, William
WilmerHale, Washington, DC
202 663 6622
william.mclucas@wilmerhale.com
*Featured in Securities (Nationwide)*
**Practice Areas:** Chair, Securities Department; practice focuses on securities enforcement, regulation and litigation matters. Represents public companies, investment banks, accounting firms

and advisors to mutual funds facing SEC investigation. Led numerous audit committee and special committee inquiries, has also represented a number of corporate executives in connection with SEC investigations.
**Career:** Director of Enforcement, US Securities and Exchange Commission's Division of Enforcement for eight years. While at the SEC, received the National Public Service Award, the Tom C Clark Outstanding Lawyer Award, and the President's Award for Distinguished Executive Service.
**Personal:** Pennsylvania State University (BA 1972); Temple University (JD 1975).

## MCNICHOLAS, Edward R
Sidley Austin LLP, Washington, DC
202 736 8010
emcnicholas@sidley.com
*Featured in Privacy & Data Security (Nationwide)*
**Practice Areas:** Partner in Sidley's Washington, D.C. office and a global coordinator of its Privacy, Data Security, and Information Law practice. His practice focuses on clients facing complex information technology, constitutional and privacy issues in civil and white-collar criminal matters. Concentrates his practice on trial and appellate representations of technologically-sophisticated clients including telecommunications carriers, electronic service providers, financial services companies, pharmaceutical manufacturers and other companies facing complex personal information issues. He is an experienced counselor, public policy advocate and internal investigator.
**Career:** Former Associate Counsel to President Clinton. Former clerk to Hon Paul Niemeyer, US Court of Appeals, Fourth Circuit.

## MCSLOY, Steven
Dentons, New York
212 768 6915
steven.mcsloy@dentons.com
*Featured in Native American Law (Nationwide)*
**Practice Areas:** Partner in the Dentons Indian Law and Tribal Representations practice. He advises Native, banking and developer clients on Native American law, gaming, corporate finance, management contracts and joint ventures.
**Career:** Previously General Counsel, Oneida Indian Nation of New York, Turning Stone Casino Resort; Professor of American Indian Law.
**Publications:** Articles on American Indian Law appear in Indian Country Today, American Indian Law Review, Harvard Civil Rights-Civil Liberties Law Review and NYU Journal of International Law and Politics, among others.
**Personal:** Harvard Law School JD (1988, cum laude; New York University BA (1985; Phi Beta Kappa, magna cum laude).

## MECHANIC, Jonathan L
Fried, Frank, Harris, Shriver & Jacobson LLP, New York
212 859 8222
Jonathan.Mechanic@FriedFrank.com
*Featured in Real Estate (Nationwide), Real Estate (New York)*
See under New York for profile.

## MEDVINSKY, Larry
Clifford Chance US LLP, New York
212 878 8149
larry.medvinsky@cliffordchance.com
*Featured in Capital Markets (Nationwide)*
**Practice Areas:** Partner in the Capital Markets Practice of Clifford Chance. Mr Medvinsky's practice encompasses a broad range of corporate transactions including real estate securities, public and private capital markets transactions, mergers and acquisitions, corporate divestitures and other corporate finance and general corporate transactions. Mr Medvinsky has done extensive work in connection with REITs and privately held funds formed for the purpose of investing in real estate.
**Career:** Partner at Clifford Chance since 2002. University of Florida, BS, cum laude, 1990. New York University School of Law, JD, 1993.

## MEEHAN, Wayne D
Freehill Hogan & Mahar LLP, New York
212 425 1900
meehan@freehill.com
*Featured in Transportation (Nationwide)*
**Practice Areas:** Areas of expertise are collisions and all types of marine casualties, including groundings, allisions, sinkings, explosions and fires. Is well-versed in casualty-related issues such as limitation of liability, general average and navigation. Holds US Coast Guard Unlimited Chief Mate's license. Has considerable experience in cargo loss and damage cases and in charter party disputes. Has tried cargo, collision and total loss cases in various Federal Courts. Bar Admissions: New York and New Jersey.
**Professional Memberships:** Maritime Law Association of the United States; Association of Average Adjusters of the United States; New York State Bar Association.
**Career:** Joined Freehill Hogan & Mahar as an associate in 1984 and became a Partner in 1992.
**Personal:** Born 1954, New York; United States Merchant Marine Academy at Kings Point, BS, With Honors, 1976; Boston University, JD, 1984.

## MEHTA, Prakash
Akin Gump Strauss Hauer & Feld LLP, Washington, DC
202 887 4248
pmehta@akingump.com
*Featured in Investment Funds (Nationwide)*
**Practice Areas:** Represents some of the world's most prominent sponsors and investors in the structuring, formation and operation of complex international private equity and hedge funds. Advises clients on manager-level transactions such as seed investments in private investment fund managers, creation of asset managers through joint ventures and spin-outs of existing asset management teams (including proprietary trading desks). Handles cross-border or otherwise complex transactions with a particular focus on emerging markets. Evaluates, structures and negotiates private equity-style investments (minority and control), exit transactions (strategic sale, recapitalization, IPO) and M&A transactions (joint ventures, stock and asset sales).

**MELBY, Barbara Murphy**
Morgan, Lewis & Bockius LLP, Philadelphia
215 963 5053
bmelby@morganlewis.com
*Featured in Outsourcing (Nationwide)*
**Practice Areas:** Barbara Melby co-leads Morgan Lewis' Outsourcing, Technology and Commercial Transactions Practice, focusing on IT and business process outsourcing, strategic alliance and commercial transactions. Ms Melby regularly counsels clients in structuring, negotiating, re-aligning and terminating outsourcing relationships, as well as developing contracting and governance strategies for outsourcing and general commercial transaction portfolios. Ms Melby is a thought leader in addressing legal issues arising with emerging service models, including cloud, SaaS and IaaS solutions. Ms Melby represents a diverse client base and has handled many of the leading outsourcing transactions, including for life sciences, financial, energy, health, and retail clients.

**MELICHAREK JR, John**
Baker & Hostetler LLP, Orlando
407 649 4086
jmelicharek@bakerlaw.com
*Featured in Leisure & Hospitality (Nationwide)*
**Career:** Chair of BakerHostetler's nationwide Hospitality practice, John Melicharek advises on business and transactional matters with emphasis on resorts, hotels and the travel and leisure industry. John counsels clients regarding hotel and resort acquisitions and dispositions, joint ventures, complex financing transactions, raising capital, franchising, leasing, licensing and securities matters. He has substantial experience in hotel and timeshare resort development, drafting and negotiating franchise, license and management agreements, and mixed use project structuring. He assists with construction and working capital financing and negotiates exchange company agreements, vacation club affiliation agreements, and participates in product development and transaction structuring for hospitality industry clients.

**MELTZER, Ronald**
WilmerHale, Washington, DC
202 663 6389
ronald.meltzer@wilmerhale.com
*Featured in International Trade (Nationwide)*
**Practice Areas:** All aspects of US export control and economic sanctions law, including transaction advice, due diligence reviews, regulatory audits, compliance programs, internal investigations, licensing matters and enforcement cases. Extensive experience dealing with OFAC, BIS and DDTC. Advises clients on extraterritorial reach of US export control and sanctions law and applicable US and non-US compliance requirements.
**Professional Memberships:** Member, Washington Council of Human Rights First and Washington Leadership Board of SUNY/Buffalo Law School. Admitted to DC and NY Bars.
**Personal:** JD, SUNY/Buffalo, summa cum laude; PhD, Columbia University, John W Burgess

Distinguished Fellow; and BA, Ohio University, summa cum laude.

**MENDELSOHN, Mark F.**
Paul, Weiss, Rifkind, Wharton & Garrison LLP, Washington, DC
202 223 7377
mmendelsohn@paulweiss.com
*Featured in International Trade (Nationwide)*
**Practice Areas:** Partner in the Litigation Department, Chair of the FCPA Group, and member of the White Collar Crime and Regulatory Defense, Internal Investigations, and Securities Litigation Practice Groups. Prior to joining Paul, Weiss, Mr Mendelsohn served as the deputy chief of the Fraud Section of the Criminal Division of the DOJ, and is internationally acknowledged and respected as the architect and key enforcement official of DOJ's modern Foreign Corrupt Practices Act enforcement program. Mr Mendelsohn regularly represents clients in corruption-related internal investigations, designing and evaluating compliance programs, transactional diligence, and defending against government investigations, prosecutions, and trials.

**MENDELSON, Alan C**
Latham & Watkins LLP, Silicon Valley
650 463 4693
alan.mendelson@lw.com
*Featured in Life Sciences (Nationwide), Corporate/M&A (California), Life Sciences (California)*
**Practice Areas:** Representation of emerging and public growth companies, with emphasis in the life sciences industry. Has managed major business transactions, including venture capital financings, private placements and public offerings, mergers and acquisitions and other strategic joint ventures.
**Professional Memberships:** Member, Board of Directors of BayBio; Member, Board of Trustees, UC Berkeley Foundation and The Scripps Research Institute; Member, Board of Regents, University of California.
**Career:** Secretary and Acting General Counsel, Amgen; Acting General Counsel, Cadence Design Systems; Member, Board of Directors, Biotechnology Industry Organization; President, California Alumni Association.
**Personal:** AB, UC Berkeley; JD, Harvard Law School.

**MENDELSON, Barbara R**
Morrison & Foerster LLP, New York
212 468 8118
bmendelson@mofo.com
*Featured in Financial Services Regulation (Nationwide)*
**Practice Areas:** Financial services: advising international and domestic financial institutions in complex regulatory matters, including acquisitions, sales, new products, applications for business expansion, Bank Secrecy Act and AML matters, and trading and investing in various instruments and derivatives.
**Professional Memberships:** Association of the Bar of the City of New York, Vance Center Committee; New York County Lawyers Association, Banking Law Committee.

**Career:** Began career in Federal Reserve Bank of New York Legal Department; joined firm as partner 1995, Financial Services Group Head 2002-2010.
**Personal:** University of Michigan Law School, JD, 1981; Rensselaer Polytechnic Institute, B.S., 1976.

**MENDELSON, Robert C**
Morgan, Lewis & Bockius LLP, New York
212 309 6303
rmendelson@morganlewis.com
*Featured in Financial Services Regulation (Nationwide)*
**Practice Areas:** Robert C. Mendelson is a Partner in Morgan Lewis's Investment Management Practice and a member of the firm's Financial Services Transactions Group. Mr Mendelson is a recognized authority on securities law, having served on the blue-ribbon IPO Process Committee, the NASD's Corporate Finance Committee and the NASD's Legal Advisory Committee. Mr Mendelson's practice focuses on securities and derivatives markets, broker-dealer regulation and enforcement defense, public offerings, and private placements. He handles all aspects of broker-dealer regulation, representing bulge bracket investment banks in derivatives and securities trading as well as securities offerings and general commercial issues.

**MENDEZ, Mark**
Davis Polk & Wardwell LLP, New York
212 450 4000
mark.mendez@davispolk.com
*Featured in Capital Markets (Nationwide)*
**Practice Areas:** Mr Mendez is a Partner in Davis Polk's Corporate Department, practicing in the Derivatives and Structured Products Group. He advises corporations, investment banks, private equity funds and hedge funds in the structuring, negotiation and execution of equity derivative transactions, high-yield debt, margin loans and other structured financial products, including over-the-counter derivatives (including equity swap, call spread, capped call, accelerated share repurchase transactions and "stake-building" derivatives) and hedging transactions (including puts, calls, collars and forwards), registered and Rule 144A mandatory and optional exchangeable and convertible securities, share lending agreements and variance and correlation swaps.

**MENNA, Gilbert G**
Goodwin Procter LLP, Boston
617 570 1433
gmenna@goodwinprocter.com
*Featured in Capital Markets (Nationwide), Corporate/M&A (Massachusetts)*
**Practice Areas:** Mr Menna is nationally recognized for representing some of the nation's leading publicly traded real estate operating companies in connection with their corporate finance, corporate governance and merger and acquisition transactions. He has extensive knowledge of the industry, and significant experience representing real estate investment managers in connection with their fund formation, portfolio acquisition and merger and acquisition transactions.

**Professional Memberships:** Board of Directors, NYU Real Estate Institute's REIT Center; Board Associate Member, NAREIT; Member, Real Estate Roundtable.
**Personal:** JD, Georgetown University Law Center, 1982; MLT, Georgetown University Law Center, 1983; BA, Syracuse University, 1978 (magna cum laude).

**MENSIK, Michael S**
Baker & McKenzie, Chicago
312 861 8941
michael.mensik@bakermckenzie.com
*Featured in Outsourcing (Nationwide), Technology (Illinois)*
**Practice Areas:** Outsourcing; information technology; data protection; privacy; e-commerce. Advises on business in a global environment, physically and electronically, particularly intellectual property protection and compliance issues. Counsels on structuring sourcing arrangements, from ITO to BPO and supply chain, and creating background to vendor-to-vendor strategic alliances that support such offerings.
**Professional Memberships:** Inducted into the Outsourcing Hall of Fame by the International Association of Outsourcing Professionals (2009). Named a leading outsourcing professional by the PLC (2010).
**Career:** Admitted in Illinois (1980).
**Publications:** Frequent writer, moderator and speaker about global outsourcing and IT issues.
**Personal:** Stanford University (BA), UCB Boalt Hall (JD/MS).

**MENTING, Mark J**
Sullivan & Cromwell LLP, New York
212 558 4859
mentingm@sullcrom.com
*Featured in Financial Services Regulation (Nationwide)*
**Professional Memberships:** ABA; NYCBA; NYSBA.
**Career:** Partner, 1994. M&A, securities, corporate, regulatory and strategic matters for US/non-US financial institutions. Recent Representations: ING in sale of ING Direct US to Capital One, and sale of ING Bank Canada to Scotiabank; M&T Bank in US Treasury's sale of M&T's TARP preferred; Emigrant Bank in sale of its NY Metropolitan area branches; EverBank in its acquisition of GECC's business property lending division; Fiserv in its acquisition of CashEdge; and The Rock Creek Group in its sale of a minority interest to Wells Fargo.
**Personal:** Wisconsin (BS, 1979); U Pennsylvania Law (JD, 1983).

**MERMELSTEIN, Joshua**
Fried, Frank, Harris, Shriver & Jacobson LLP, New York
212 859 8137
Joshua.Mermelstein@FriedFrank.com
*Featured in Real Estate (Nationwide), Real Estate (New York)*
**Practice Areas:** Real estate partner. Practice includes the representation of financial institutions, owners, developers, family offices and offshore investors in connection with financings,

joint ventures, acquisitions and dispositions, development and fund formations. Clients include Brookfield Office Properties, Brookfield Asset Management, RXR Realty, China Investment Corporation, Millennium & Copthorne Hotels, Firmdale Hotels and Atria Assisted Living.
**Career:** Joined in 1980; became partner in 1986. Executive Committee of the Lawyers Division of UJA-Federation of New York. Board of Directors, Selfhelp Community Services, Inc.
**Personal:** JD, Columbia University Law School (1980), Harlan Fiske Stone Scholar; AB, Columbia University (1977).

## MERRIGAN, John A
DLA Piper LLP (US), Washington, DC
202 799 4310
john.merrigan@dlapiper.com
*Featured in Government (Nationwide)*
**Practice Areas:** Federal affairs and legislative.
**Career:** He has extensive political and legal experience. He has played a leading role in building one of the nation's premier law and lobbying practices, formulating and executing successful strategies to advance or protect clients' interests. These clients include numerous Fortune 100 corporations, domestic and foreign governments, and other entities. He provides strategic planning that integrates the firm's capabilities in the legislative, regulatory, judicial, and political arenas.
**Personal:** JD, Loyola University Chicago (cum laude); AB, Georgetown University 1970.

## MERRILL, Susan
Bingham McCutchen LLP, New York
212 705 7705
susan.merrill@bingham.com
*Featured in Financial Services Regulation (Nationwide)*
**Practice Areas:** Head of Bingham's New York Securities Enforcement Practice. Assists broker-dealers, investment advisers, financial institutions and Fortune 500 companies in internal investigations, investigations before the SEC and FINRA, and in enforcement matters. Advises clients on regulatory compliance matters.
**Career:** Former head of enforcement at FINRA.
**Personal:** University of Maryland, BA, cum laude, 1979; Brooklyn Law School, JD, summa cum laude, 1986.

## MESERVE, Richard
Covington & Burling LLP, Washington, DC
202 662 5304
rmeserve@cov.com
*Featured in Energy & Natural Resources (Nationwide)*
**Practice Areas:** Focused on issues at the intersection of law, science, and technology.
**Career:** Former Chairman of the United States Nuclear Regulatory Commission where he was the principal government official with responsibility for regulating nuclear power plants and the use of nuclear materials. Currently serves as President of the Carnegie Institution for Science. He is also Chairman of the International Nuclear Safety Group, which is chartered by the International Atomic Energy Agency.
**Publications:** Numerous policy studies.

**Personal:** Stanford University, Ph.D. in applied physics; Harvard Law School, JD

## MEYER, Bruce S
Weil, Gotshal & Manges LLP, New York
212 310 8013
bruce.meyer@weil.com
*Featured in Sports Law (Nationwide)*
**Practice Areas:** Bruce Meyer, partner in Weil's Litigation Department, in addition to trying complex commercial cases across the country, has represented the players' unions in football, hockey and basketball. In addition to representing the NHLPA in its recently resolved dispute with the NHL, he also played a prominent role in litigation over the NFL's 2011 lockout, and the negotiation sessions for the NBA players that resulted in a final agreement to lift the NBA's 2011 lockout. He is the co-author of the three-volume treatise, International Sports Law and Business.
**Personal:** University of Pennsylvania (BA); Boston University Law (JD).

## MEYER, Lindsay
Venable LLP, Washington, DC
202 344 4829
lbmeyer@Venable.com
*Featured in International Trade (Nationwide)*
**Practice Areas:** International Trade and Customs, Foreign Corrupt Practices Act and Anti-Corruption, Homeland Security, Anti-Counterfeiting, Regulatory.
**Professional Memberships:** Washington District Export Council.
**Career:** Ms Meyer is Venable's Co-Managing Partner. For 25 years, she has provided International Trade and Customs advice at Venable. She concentrates on all aspects of cross border trade matters, regularly advising companies on their compliance with import and export control laws and regulations, and appearing before numerous regulatory authorities.
**Personal:** JD, George Washington University Law School; B.S., cum laude, University of Connecticut; Diplôme d'Études Françaises, Université de Rouen, Rouen, France.

## MEYER, Paul
Clifford Chance US LLP, New York
212 878 8176
paul.meyer@cliffordchance.com
*Featured in Insurance (Nationwide), Insurance (New York)*
See under New York for profile.

## MEYERSON, Lee
Simpson Thacher & Bartlett LLP, New York
212 455 2000
lmeyerson@stblaw.com
*Featured in Financial Services Regulation (Nationwide), Corporate/M&A (New York)*
**Practice Areas:** Head of M&A Group and Financial Institutions Practice. Representations include Petrohawk in $15.1 billion acquisition by BHP Billiton; JPMorgan in $58 billion merger with Bank One; Mellon in $16.8 billion merger with Bank of New York; Toronto-Dominion Bank in $8.5 billion Commerce Bancorp acquisition; US Treasury in $250 billion TARP capital investment program; Schwab in $1 billion

optionsXpress acquisition; Carlyle acquisition of TCW ($138 billion AUM). Capital markets practice includes IPOs and capital securities offerings for financial institutions.
**Career:** Partner, 1989.
**Personal:** BA, magna cum laude, Duke University (1977); JD, NYU Law School (1981), editor of Law Review.

## MEZZULLO, Louis A
McKenna Long & Aldridge LLP, Rancho Santa Fe
858 381 8014
lmezzullo@luce.com
*Featured in Wealth Management (Nationwide)*
**Practice Areas:** Louis Mezzullo focuses his practice on Taxation, Estate and Business Succession Planning, and Employee Benefits. In 2012, Mr Mezzullo was elected to the National Association of Estate Planners & Councils (NAEPC) Estate Planning Hall of Fame as an Accredited Estate Planner. He frequently serves as an expert witness in matters related to estate, tax, and business planning and trust administration, including malpractice matters on behalf of defendant attorneys. Mr Mezzullo is President of the American College of Trust and Estate Counsel and former Chair of the American College of Tax Counsel.
**Professional Memberships:** Immediate Past Chair, American College of Tax Counsel; Fellow, American Bar Foundation; Fellow, Virginia Law Foundation; Fellow and Vice President, American College of Trust and Estate Counsel; Charter Fellow, American College of Employee Benefits Counsel; and Academician and Vice President, International Academy of Estate and Trust Law.
**Personal:** Former member of the faculty of the University of Miami School of Law Graduate Program in Estate Planning. JD, University of Richmond; MA and BA, University of Maryland.

## MICHAELS, Joel
McDermott Will & Emery LLP, Washington, DC
202 756 8375
jmichaels@mwe.com
*Featured in Healthcare (Nationwide), Healthcare (District of Columbia)*
**Practice Areas:** Partner-in-charge of Washington health practice. Experience in healthcare insurance and delivery system organization, financing and regulation. Assists in state and federal licensing, and regulatory issues governing managed care plans, as well as the design and implementation of prescription drug benefit plans. Counsels on federal law issues, including Medicare, False Claims Act, Federal Anti-Kickback Statute, ERISA, and HIPAA. Works on complex litigation matters in the health insurance industry, including payment and claims processing disputes involving health plans and providers, as well as disputes related to pharmacies and payors.
**Personal:** American University-Washington College of Law (JD); George Washington University (BA).

## MICHALCHUK, Daniel J
Milbank, Tweed, Hadley & McCloy LLP, New York
212 530 5079
dmichalchuk@milbank.com
*Featured in Projects (Nationwide)*
**Practice Areas:** Mr Michalchuk is a partner in the Project Finance Group. He has represented project sponsors and financial institutions (including both commercial lenders and export credit agencies) in numerous domestic and international project financings and in infrastructure projects across various industries, including power, oil and gas, petrochemicals, LNG, satellites and telecom.

## MIDVIDY, David H
Skadden, Arps, Slate, Meagher & Flom LLP & Affiliates, New York
212 735 2089
david.midvidy@skadden.com
*Featured in Capital Markets (Nationwide)*
**Practice Areas:** Mr Midvidy has advised issuers, underwriters and foreign and domestic financial institutions in a variety of transactions including securitizations of whole businesses (restaurant and non-restaurant), pharmaceutical royalties and other non-financial assets and consumer finance assets. He has also represented sellers and purchasers of portfolios of securitized and unencumbered financial assets on a servicing released and servicing retained basis. He has substantial experience with titling trusts and other titling entities and led the team that developed the exchange note structure used in auto-lease securitizations.
**Career:** JD, Tulane University Law School, 1990; BSC, McGill University, 1977; MA, McGill University, 1983.

## MIERZEWSKI, Michael B
Arnold & Porter LLP, Washington, DC
202 942 5995
Michael.Mierzewski@aporter.com
*Featured in Financial Services Regulation (Nationwide)*
**Practice Areas:** Michael Mierzewski's practice focuses on financial institutions and corporate and securities law. He routinely counsels clients on bank mergers and acquisitions, fair lending, Community Reinvestment Act, payment systems, enforcement and general regulatory issues. He frequently conducts internal investigations on behalf of Boards of Directors, Audit Committees and other special purpose committees. Named 2012 Best Lawyer, Banking and Finance, Washington, DC.
**Professional Memberships:** Mr Mierzewski is past Vice-Chair of American Bar Association's Section of Antitrust Law Committee on Financial Markets and Institutions.
**Publications:** He is a frequent author and lecturer on bank regulatory and bank antitrust issues.

**MIGDAL, Nelson F**
Greenberg Traurig, LLP, Washington, DC
202 331 3180
MigdalN@gtlaw.com
*Featured in Leisure & Hospitality (Nationwide), Real Estate (District of Columbia)*
**Practice Areas:** Co-Chair, Hospitality Group. Hotel management, branding, operations.
**Professional Memberships:** Vice President, Academy of Hospitality Industry Attorneys. Member: ULI Hotel Development Council; International Society of Hospitality Consultants.
**Career:** Selected: Best Lawyers in America, 2007-13. Team Member, 'Best USA Law Firm For Real Estate & Environment', The International Legal Alliance Summit, 2011; a Law360 'Real Estate Practice Group of the Year', 2011-12. Rated, AV® Preeminent™ 5.0 out of 5.
**Publications:** Author: 'Hospitalitylawcheckin.com', Blog about hospitality industry; 'Issues and Opportunities for the Hospitality Industry', Trend Report, July 2012.
**Personal:** JD, cum laude, Albany Law School; BA, cum laude, Hofstra University.

**MILES, Craig**
King & Spalding LLP, Houston
713 751 3259
cmiles@kslaw.com
*Featured in International Arbitration (Nationwide)*
**Practice Areas:** His practice focuses on representing foreign investors in disputes with host governments, primarily before the World Bank's International Centre for Settlement of Investment Disputes (ICSID), and private parties in commercial disputes before the International Chamber of Commerce (ICC), the American Arbitration Association (AAA), and other domestic and international arbitral institutions. Mr Miles has first- or second-chaired dozens of arbitral hearings involving disputes throughout North and South America, Europe, Asia, Africa and the Middle East, with particularly strong experience in bilateral investment treaty (BIT) disputes.
**Personal:** JD University of Houston AB Cornell University.

**MILES, Steven**
Baker Botts LLP, Washington, DC
202 639 7951
steven.miles@bakerbotts.com
*Featured in Projects (Nationwide)*
**Practice Areas:** Heads firmwide Energy Sector Committee and 50+ attorney LNG practice. Practice emphasis on LNG, natural gas, electric power and renewable and alternative energy industries worldwide, including experience with 100+ major LNG transactions.
**Professional Memberships:** Association of International Petroleum Negotiators (AIPN) Board of Directors 2010-, Co-Chair LNG Committee 2005-; American Bar Association, Committee on International Energy and Resources, Vice Chair, 2001; Saudi Arabia Country Coordinator, 1996.
**Career:** Founded Saudi Arabia office; managed Middle East practice.

**Personal:** JD, Cornell Law School, 1984 (editor, Cornell Law Review); MBA, Cornell University, 1984; BA (summa cum laude), Union College, 1980.

**MILLARD, Alden**
Simpson Thacher & Bartlett LLP, New York
212 455 2871
jmillard@stblaw.com
*Featured in Banking & Finance (Nationwide)*
**Practice Areas:** Partner in the firm's Corporate Department, where he concentrates on the representation of financial sponsors and other borrowers in acquisition financings and other leveraged transactions. His principal clients include The Blackstone Group, First Reserve Corporation and their respective portfolio companies.
**Career:** Joined firm, 1996; Partner, 2004.
**Personal:** AB, cum laude, Harvard University (1991); JD, Columbia Law School (1996).

**MILLER, Brett**
Morrison & Foerster LLP, New York
212 468 8051
bmiller@mofo.com
*Featured in Bankruptcy/Restructuring (Nationwide), Bankruptcy/Restructuring (New York)*
**Practice Areas:** Mr Miller is the Managing Partner of Morrison & Foerster's New York office, a partner in the Business Restructuring & Insolvency Group, and Co-chair of the Distressed Real Estate Group. He handles chapter 11 cases, out-of-court restructurings, bankruptcy-related acquisitions and litigation, and cross-border insolvency matters, across various industries such as real estate, transportation, retail, manufacturing, oil and gas, and media. Mr Miller's clients include official and ad hoc creditors' committees, bank groups, individual lenders, court-appointed fiduciaries, debtors, and investors that focus on distressed situations.
**Personal:** BA, Columbia University, 1988; JD, Georgetown University Law Center, 1991.

**MILLER, Charles G**
Bartko, Zankel, Tarrant & Miller, PLC, San Francisco
415 956 1900
cmiller@bztm.com
*Featured in Franchising (Nationwide)*
**Practice Areas:** Complex business litigation, including franchise matters, class actions, and ADR. He has also served as a neutral arbitrator and mediator in a number of franchise disputes.
**Professional Memberships:** State Bar of California (Franchise Law Committee, Franchise & Distribution Law Advisory Commission), American Bar Association (Sections of Litigation, Antitrust, Forum Committee on Franchising), American Arbitration Association (Commercial Neutral Panel, Franchising), and US District Court, N.D. Cal, Early Neutral Evaluation and Mediation Panel.
**Career:** Franchise litigation and arbitration since early 1970's. Served as neutral arbitrator and mediator in franchise disputes.
**Publications:** Numerous articles in LJN's Franchising Business & Law Alert, ABA Franchise Law Journal, and IFA Annual Legal Symposium.

**MILLER, Evan**
Jones Day, Washington, DC
202 879 3840
emiller@jonesday.com
*Featured in ERISA Litigation (Nationwide), Employee Benefits & Executive Compensation (District of Columbia)*
**Practice Areas:** ERISA litigation, fiduciary counseling, health and welfare plans. Represents companies in private-party fiduciary, retiree health, and plan design litigation, and benefit-related investigations conducted at the regional and national level by the US Department of Labor. Specialized experience in stock drop, cash balance, and accrued benefits class action litigation, as well as multiemployer plan matters, retiree health VEBAs, and pension de-risking.
**Professional Memberships:** ABA: 2003-05, Co-Chair, Employee Benefits Committee, Labor and Employment Section; Member, American College of Employee Benefits Counsel.
**Publications:** Former Co-chair, Board of Senior Editors, 'Employee Benefits Law' (BNA Books) (2001-07).

**MILLER, Harvey R**
Weil, Gotshal & Manges LLP, New York
212 310 8500
harvey.miller@weil.com
*Featured in Bankruptcy/Restructuring (Nationwide), Bankruptcy/Restructuring (New York)*
**Practice Areas:** Mr Miller created and developed the firm's Business Finance & Restructuring Department specializing in reorganizing distressed business entities and representing creditors, investors and purchasers of distressed businesses and assets. From September 2002 to March 2007, he was Managing Director and Vice Chairman of Greenhill & Co., LLC, an international investment banking firm.
**Career:** Adjunct Professor of Law, New York University Law School; Lecturer in Law and Member, Dean's Council Columbia University School of Law; Member, National Bankruptcy Conference; Fellow, American College of Bankruptcy; Fellow of the American Bar Foundation; Trustee, Committee on Economic Development.
**Personal:** Brooklyn College (AB); Columbia University (LLB).

**MILLER, Jessica Davidson**
Skadden, Arps, Slate, Meagher & Flom LLP & Affiliates, Washington, DC
202 371 7850
Jessica.Miller@skadden.com
*Featured in Products Liability (Nationwide)*
**Practice Areas:** Broad experience in the defense of mass torts, purported class actions and other complex civil litigation, focusing on product liability matters, multidistrict litigation proceedings and appellate litigation. Has defended major corporations in consumer-fraud, breach-of-contract and medical-monitoring class actions at both trial and appellate levels. Serves as counselor to organizations dedicated to civil justice reform.
**Career:** Worked for US Senator Frank Lautenberg; former US Senator Bob Graham; the Federal Trade Commission, Office of General

Counsel. JD, Georgetown University Law Center (magna cum laude; Order of the Coif); M.S., Columbia University; BA, Columbia University (magna cum laude; Phi Beta Kappa).

**MILLER, Rod**
Milbank, Tweed, Hadley & McCloy LLP, New York
212 530 5022
rdmiller@milbank.com
*Featured in Capital Markets (Nationwide)*
**Practice Areas:** Mr Miller is a partner and a member of the firm's Global Securities Group. His practice focuses on a wide range of finance, securities and other corporate transactions, particularly in the context of complex acquisition financings and leveraged buyouts. He has extensive experience representing investment banking firms, corporate issuers and investors in public and private debt and equity offerings and other financing and related transactions, including high yield and investment grade debt offerings, initial public offerings, follow-on and secondary equity offerings, equity-linked securities offerings, restructurings and tender and exchange offers.

**MILLER, William**
Cahill Gordon & Reindel LLP, New York
212 701 3836
wmiller@cahill.com
*Featured in Banking & Finance (Nationwide)*
**Practice Areas:** Practice is focused on representing leading investment banks, commercial banks and public and private corporations in debt and equity capital markets transactions and syndicated institutional loans and asset based loans. Works on the bank and high-yield bond sides of acquisition financings, as well as initial public and follow-on equity offerings.
**Personal:** College of the Holy Cross, BA, 1993. Yale University, MA, 1996. Fordham University School of Law, JD, 1999.

**MILLETT, Patricia A**
Akin Gump Strauss Hauer & Feld LLP, Washington, DC
202 887 4450
pmillett@akingump.com
*Featured in Appellate Law (Nationwide)*
**Practice Areas:** Chair Supreme Court and Appellate Practice. Has argued 31 cases before the Supreme Court & approximately 40 in federal and state courts of appeals. Her expertise includes statutory construction; administrative law; federalism & congressional power; religion; civil rights; Americans with Disabilities Act; access to information; Fourth Amendment; national security; and immigration law.
**Career:** Assistant to the Solicitor General, US Department of Justice; Appellate Staff, Civil Division, US Department of Justice; law clerk, US Court of Appeals, 9th Circuit.
**Personal:** BA, summa cum laude, with highest distinction, University of Illinois; JD, magna cum laude, Harvard Law School.

## MILLOCK, Peter J
Nixon Peabody LLP, Albany
518 427 2651
pmillock@nixonpeabody.com
*Featured in Healthcare (New York), Healthcare (Nationwide)*

See under New York for profile.

## MILMOE, J Gregory
Skadden, Arps, Slate, Meagher & Flom LLP & Affiliates, New York
212 735 3770
Gregory.Milmoe@skadden.com
*Featured in Bankruptcy/Restructuring (Nationwide), Bankruptcy/Restructuring (New York)*

**Practice Areas:** Corporate Restructuring Group. Experience includes in-court and out-of-court restructurings, hostile and negotiated mergers and acquisitions, leveraged buyouts, and corporate financings (including IPOs). Draws on experience from various legal disciplines to develop pragmatic, sometimes novel solutions to complex problems. Has played a leading role in restructurings of Long Term Capital, Refco, CIT, Aurora Foods, Genuity, Interstate Bakeries, Vlasic, Realogy, and ITC DeltaCom among others, and in numerous distressed acquisitions, including the recent acquisition of the Phoenix Coyotes by the National Hockey League.
**Career:** JD, Fordham University, 1975 (articles editor, Fordham Law Review); AB, Cornell University, 1970.

## MINESINGER, Kenneth M
Greenberg Traurig, LLP, Washington, DC
202 530 8572
MinesingerK@gtlaw.com
*Featured in Energy & Natural Resources (Nationwide)*

**Practice Areas:** Co-Chair, Global Energy and Infrastructure Practice. Energy regulation; energy project development; antitrust and trade regulation; litigation.
**Career:** Listed: Chambers USA Guide, 2007-13; Chambers Global, 2011-13.
**Publications:** Author, 'Power Struggle: The Amaranth Case Represents the Potentially Broad Scope of FERC's New Authority', The Deal, September 2007; Co-Author, 'Energy Law and Transactions', chapter addressing settlements of FERC proceedings; Co-Author, 'A New Broad Brush: Trying to Clean Up Market Behavior, New FERC Rules Raise More Confusion', Legal Times, August 16, 2004.
**Personal:** JD, cum laude, The George Washington University Law School; BA, cum laude, University of Maryland, Phi Beta Kappa.

## MINOR, William
DLA Piper LLP (US), Washington, DC
202 799 4312
william.minor@dlapiper.com
*Featured in Government (Nationwide)*

**Practice Areas:** Government affairs.
**Career:** He counsels corporations, associations, and professional firms on compliance with federal lobbying statutes and rules, including the Lobbying Disclosure Act of 1995, the Honest Leadership and Open Government Act of 2007, the Foreign Agents Registration Act and the congressional and Executive Branch gift and travel rules.
**Publications:** He is the author of Bureau of National Affairs (BNA) portfolio on the regulation of corporate lobbying, part of the BNA Corporate Practice Series.
**Personal:** JD, Columbia University School of Law; BA, Tufts University (magna cum laude); London School of Economics and Political Science.

## MINSK, Alan
Arnall Golden Gregory LLP, Atlanta
404 873 8690
alan.minsk@agg.com
*Featured in Life Sciences (Nationwide)*

**Practice Areas:** Food and Drug; Government and Regulatory; Israel Business.
**Professional Memberships:** Regulatory Affairs Professionals Society Focus, Editorial Advisory Board; Georgia Biomedical Partnership; Food and Drug Law Institute; American-Israel Chamber of Commerce—Medical Committee, Southeast Region; Center for Communication Compliance Advisory Board; Product Liability Law and Strategy, Editorial Board.
**Publications:** FDA Issues Guidance on Enrichment Strategies for Drug and Biologic Clinical Trials, AGG bulletin, January 2013; Star Power - The Highs and Lows of Celebrity Drug Endorsements, Public Relations Strategist, Winter 2012.
**Personal:** Georgetown University Law Center, 1992; Brandeis University, Bachelor of Arts, 1989, Summa Cum Laude, Highest Honors in Politics.

## MIRVIS, Theodore N
Wachtell, Lipton, Rosen & Katz, New York
212 403 1204
tnmirvis@wlrk.com
*Featured in Securities (Nationwide), Litigation (New York)*

**Practice Areas:** Focuses on litigation involving corporate governance and complex securities and securitization matters, and directors' fiduciary duties in mergers and acquisitions.
**Professional Memberships:** American Law Institute; Planning Committee, Tulane Corporate Law Institute; Advisory Board, Harvard Law School Program on Corporate Governance.
**Career:** Partner at Wachtell, Lipton, Rosen & Katz since 1982, and during that time, has litigated some of the landmark cases regarding corporate governance issues, mergers and acquisitions, stockholder's rights and numerous other matters involving corporate and securities litigation. He is an expert on corporate defense. Prior to joining Wachtell Lipton, Mr Mirvis was a law clerk to the Honorable Henry J Friendly, United States Court of Appeals for the Second Circuit, 1976 term.
**Publications:** Author of numerous articles on corporate governance; and co-author, Wachtell & Mirvis, New York Practice under the CPLR. Regularly lectures at Harvard Business School and Harvard Law School.
**Personal:** Graduated summa cum laude from Yeshiva College in 1973 (BA) and magna cum laude from Harvard Law School in 1976 (JD). While at Harvard Law School, he was editor of 'Harvard Law Review', vol 88, and case editor of 'Harvard Law Review', vol 89.

## MISHKIN, Jeffrey A
Skadden, Arps, Slate, Meagher & Flom LLP & Affiliates, New York
212 735 3230
jeffrey.mishkin@skadden.com
*Featured in Sports Law (Nationwide)*

**Practice Areas:** All aspects of sports law, including antitrust, intellectual property, labor and a wide range of trial and appellate litigation. Formerly its Chief Legal Officer, now serves the NBA as its chief outside counsel. Has participated in every major legal decision that has affected the NBA in the past 35 years. Has acted as lead litigation counsel in numerous major sports cases and advises the NHL, NFL, MLB, PGA Tour, USTA and many other sports organizations.
**Career:** JD, Cornell Law School, 1972; BA, State University of New York at Albany, 1969.

## MITCHELL, David S
Fried, Frank, Harris, Shriver & Jacobson LLP, New York
212 859 8292
David.Mitchell@FriedFrank.com
*Featured in Capital Markets (Nationwide)*

**Practice Areas:** Corporate partner. Concentrates on commodities, futures and derivatives. Practice includes providing advice in connection with product development, structuring funds and other investment vehicles, establishment of electronic trading facilities and clearing solutions for swaps and derivatives, and compliance, investigations and enforcement matters relating to futures, swaps and derivatives. Member, Board of Editors of Futures & Derivatives Law Report; Director, Futures Industry Association.
**Career:** Joined as partner in 2006.
**Personal:** JD, magna cum laude, New York Law School (1979), member, Law Review; LLM, New York University (1980); BA, summa cum laude, City College (1976), Phi Beta Kappa.

## MITCHELL, Michael H
Chapman and Cutler LLP, Washington, DC
202 478 6446
mitchell@chapman.com
*Featured in Capital Markets (Nationwide)*

**Practice Areas:** Mike Mitchell is a partner in Chapman and Cutler's Banking Department and Asset Securitization Group. He serves as counsel to financial institutions in capital markets and debt financing transactions and provides expertise on application of the federal securities laws in the structured finance market. Mr Mitchell has served on the Board of Directors of the American Securitization Forum (ASF) and regularly serves as outside counsel to the ASF in connection with Dodd-Frank and independent SEC rule-making initiatives.

## MIXTER, Christian J
Morgan, Lewis & Bockius LLP, Washington, DC
202 739 5575
cmixter@morganlewis.com
*Featured in Securities (Nationwide)*

**Practice Areas:** Focuses on securities litigation, including SEC, SRO, and state enforcement proceedings and investigations, and shareholder class actions. Has represented public companies, broker-dealers, investment advisors, and individuals associated with those entities in a wide variety of matters.
**Professional Memberships:** American Bar Association, Business Law and Litigation Sections; Association of the Bar of the City of New York; District of Columbia Bar Association; Securities Industry Association; Order of the Coif; Articles Editor- Duke Law Journal.
**Career:** Former Chief Litigation Counsel for the SEC's Division of Enforcement; Served in the Office of Independent Counsel under Lawrence E. Walsh during Iran/Contra.

## MOATES, G Paul
Sidley Austin LLP, Washington, DC
202 736 8175
pmoates@sidley.com
*Featured in Transportation (Nationwide)*

**Practice Areas:** Partner and head of Sidley's Transportation practice. Represents several of the largest freight railroads in the United States and the railroad industry's national trade association. Tried contract and antitrust cases in the federal courts, argued appeals of decisions of federal regulatory agencies in the United States Court of Appeals, represented various railroad clients in rate cases and other commercial disputes, and has served as lead litigation counsel before the Interstate Commerce Commission (now the Surface Transportation Board of the Department of Transportation).
**Personal:** The University of Chicago Law School, JD, 1975; Amherst College, BA, 1969, cum laude.

## MOELLER, Elizabeth V
Pillsbury Winthrop Shaw Pittman LLP, Washington, DC
202 663 9159
elizabeth.moeller@pillsburylaw.com
*Featured in Government (Nationwide)*

**Practice Areas:** Head of Pillsbury's Public Policy Group. Manages federal policy matters involving energy, the environment, transportation, water and other issues. Strong Washington network includes key personnel in Congress, the executive branch and the press. Advises Fortune 500 companies, utilities, and non-profits. Directs federal funding efforts that have secured millions for R & D, economic development, and technology initiatives. Represents clients in high-profile congressional investigations.
**Professional Memberships:** State Bar of: California and DC.
**Career:** Partner with Patton Boggs, LLP before joining Pillsbury Winthrop Shaw Pittman.
**Personal:** BA, U.C. Berkeley, 1992 (highest honors, Phi Beta Kappa); JD, U.C.L.A., 1996.

## MOFFATT, J Curtis
Van Ness Feldman LLP, Washington, DC
202 298 1885
jcm@vnf.com
*Featured in Energy & Natural Resources (Nationwide)*

**Practice Areas:** Represents energy companies regulated by the Federal Energy Regulatory Commission. Over 30 years of experience in corporate and strategic counseling on corporate business plans and regulatory impact. Also involved in major energy infrastructure development. Provides strategic business advice to publicly-traded and early-state energy companies and investment funds. Member of Leaf Clean Energy Board of Directors.
**Professional Memberships:** District of Columbia Bar Association, North Carolina Bar Association, Energy Bar Association.
**Career:** Legal Assistant to the Chairman, Federal Energy Regulatory Commission, 1977-79.
**Personal:** JD, University of North Carolina at Chapel Hill, 1975; A.B., Duke University, 1973.

## MOONEY CARROLL, Katherine
Cleary Gottlieb Steen & Hamilton LLP, Washington, DC
202 974 1584
kcarroll@cgsh.com
*Featured in Financial Services Regulation (Nationwide)*

**Practice Areas:** US bank regulatory matters, including Dodd-Frank regulatory reforms such as the Volcker Rule, heightened prudential requirements and preparation of "living wills", regulatory aspects of bank M&A, investments by and in banking organizations, and compliance with US sanctions and anti-money laundering laws. Advises financial institutions in investigations and enforcement matters involving federal banking agencies and OFAC.
**Professional Memberships:** Member of the Bars in New York and District of Columbia.
**Career:** Became Partner, 2012; worked in firm's Hong Kong office, 2001-2002; previously Executive Director of the Open Society Institute in Uzbekistan; JD, Yale Law School (2001); A.B., magna cum laude, Harvard College (1992).

## MOORE, Charles A
Morgan, Lewis & Bockius LLP, Houston
713 890 5730
cmoore@morganlewis.com
*Featured in Energy & Natural Resources (Nationwide)*

**Practice Areas:** Internationally recognized authority in the field of energy industry regulation and litigation. Held a number of high level government positions in this field. In private practice, he has been involved in numerous international and domestic transactions in the energy sector.
**Professional Memberships:** American Bar Association (Litigation Section); Energy Bar Association; Maritime Law Association of the United States.
**Career:** Joined Dewey & LeBoeuf in 2002; Chairman, Energy and Converging Industries, Akin, Gump, Strauss, Hauer & Feld, LLP; General

Counsel, US Federal Energy Regulatory Commission (1981-83).
**Personal:** University of Houston (JD magna cum laude) 1975; University of Houston (BA) 1972.

## MOORE, Harold F
Skadden, Arps, Slate, Meagher & Flom LLP & Affiliates, New York
212 735 3252
Harold.Moore@skadden.com
*Featured in Projects (Nationwide)*

**Practice Areas:** Co-head of Skadden's Energy and Infrastructure Projects Group. He has been the lead lawyer in more than 160 US and international project and corporate financings, representing underwriters, banks and issuers in some of the most complex transactions financed in recent years.
**Career:** JD, Notre Dame, 1980 (summa cum laude; articles editor, Notre Dame Law Review; Thomas J White Scholarship; Peters Scholarship; Farabaugh Prize for High Scholarship in Law); PhD, Fordham University, 1971; MA, Fordham University, 1970; BS, Fordham University, 1968.

## MOORE, Margaret
Van Ness Feldman LLP, Washington, DC
202 298 1847
mam@vnf.com
*Featured in Energy & Natural Resources (Nationwide)*

**Practice Areas:** Advises developers, owners, investors, and financiers on energy trading, power purchases and sales, acquisition of electric generation and transmission projects, and development of renewable and fossil fuel-fired generation and merchant transmission projects. Areas of concentration include merchant electric generation and transmission projects and renewable energy transactions involving wind, solar, geothermal, and biomass energy projects.
**Professional Memberships:** Energy Bar Association.
**Career:** Staff Attorney, Office of General Counsel, Electric Rates and Corporate Regulation, Federal Energy Regulatory Commission, 1982-85.

## MOORE, Read M
McDermott Will & Emery LLP, Chicago
312 984 75 76
mmoore@mwe.com
*Featured in Wealth Management (Nationwide)*

**Practice Areas:** Focused on all aspects of estate planning, estate and trust administration, and tax-exempt charitable organizations. Considerable experience in the international aspects of the private client practice, including foreign trusts, planning for foreigners residing in the United States and US citizens residing abroad.
**Professional Memberships:** Fellow of The American College of Trust and Estate Counsel, and member of its International Estate Planning Committee; International Academy of Estate and Trust Law; active member of bars in Illinois, California, Oregon and Washington.
**Personal:** University of Virginia School of Law, JD, 1990; Rice University, BA, (Phi Beta Kappa|magna cum laude), 1987.

## MOORE, Rodney L
Weil, Gotshal & Manges LLP, Dallas
214 746 8102
rodney.moore@weil.com
*Featured in Energy & Natural Resources (Nationwide)*

**Practice Areas:** Mr Moore has more than 20 years of experience advising private equity firms and public and private companies in acquisition, divestiture and joint venture transactions. He has significant experience representing clients in every type of upstream and midstream oil and gas transactions, including shale gas transactions. His clients have included: BlackBrush TexStar LP; Magnetar Capital; EIG Global Energy Partners; GSO Capital Partners; Approach Resources; EXCO Resources; Kinder Morgan; Lindsey Goldberg; Pioneer Natural Resources; Wildcat Midstream Partners; Natural Gas Partners; and Regency Energy Partners.
**Personal:** Austin College (BA, 1984); Washington & Lee University School of Law (JD, cum laude, 1987).

## MOORE, Thomas J
Baker Botts LLP, Houston
713 229 1137
thomas.moore@bakerbotts.com
*Featured in Energy & Natural Resources (Nationwide)*

**Practice Areas:** Co-Head of Energy Mergers and Acquisitions Practice. Leading role in many major energy assignments in the US and worldwide. Representation of high profile clients in mergers and acquisitions and power, pipeline, petrochemical and LNG projects. Strong presence in the international arena, leading the firm's representation in client development of foreign investment initiatives and natural gas based economic expansion.
**Professional Memberships:** Colorado Bar; Texas Bar.
**Career:** Joined the firm in 1994; Faegre & Benson (1974-77, 1979-94); University of Minnesota, Associate Professor of Law (1977-79).
**Personal:** University of Minnesota Law School (JD) 1974; University of California at Berkeley (AB) 1971.

## MOORE III, Thomas O
Bracewell & Giuliani LLP, Houston
713 221 1409
thomas.moore@bgllp.com
*Featured in Projects (Nationwide)*

**Practice Areas:** Represents and counsels clients in commercial public and private project development and finance transactions, and mergers and acquisitions, with a particular focus on infrastructure and energy. He has experience representing US-based and global companies in public private partnerships and the acquisition, development, financing, operation, restructuring and sale of all types of commercial and industrial facilities, including transportation projects, sports stadiums, electric power plants, LNG plants, chemical plants, water plants, and entertainment facilities.
**Personal:** JD, The University of Texas School of Law, 1973; BE, Vanderbilt University, 1969.

## MOOREHEAD, Paul
Drinker Biddle & Reath LLP, Washington, DC
202 230 5174
paul.moorehead@dbr.com
*Featured in Native American Law (Nationwide)*

**Practice Areas:** Indian tribal energy development; water settlements and natural resources; land into trust and gaming; housing, infrastructure and community development; taxation and project finance; healthcare; appropriations; tribal self-governance; and international indigenous affairs.
**Career:** 1997-2005 chief counsel and staff director to the Senate Committee on Indian Affairs. Before 1997, counsel and government affairs director to the National Congress of American Indians.
**Publications:** Editor, 'Tribal Business Journal;' Running the 2006 Federal Appropriations Marathon; Improving Native Health Through Emerging Technologies; Cigars and Kachinas: Enforcing the Indian Arts and Crafts Act.
**Personal:** Temple University Beasley School of Law, JD; University of Delaware, BA.

## MOOT, John S
Skadden, Arps, Slate, Meagher & Flom LLP & Affiliates, Washington, DC
202 371 7890
John.Moot@skadden.com
*Featured in Energy & Natural Resources (Nationwide)*

**Practice Areas:** Represents energy companies in a broad range of high-profile matters, including enforcement cases concerning reliability, market manipulation and tariff matters; mergers and acquisitions; federal preemption litigation; transmission access and rate cases; transmission infrastructure development; market power and market design cases; stranded cost litigation; and RTO entry and exit cases.
**Career:** FERC, General Counsel (2005-07) and Chief of Staff (2007-08). JD, American University, 1988 (cum laude); BA, St. Lawrence University, 1983.
**Publications:** A leading author on energy regulation, with influential articles on reliability regulation, enforcement policy and compliance programs, transmission access reform and merger policy reform.

## MORAN, Charles R
Ballard Spahr LLP, Baltimore
410 528 5689
moran@ballardspahr.com
*Featured in Corporate/M&A (Maryland), Capital Markets (Nationwide)*
See under Maryland for profile.

## MORENO, Jeffrey O
Thompson Hine LLP, Washington, DC
202 263 4107
Jeff.Moreno@ThompsonHine.com
*Featured in Transportation (Nationwide)*

**Career:** Jeff is a partner in the firm's Transportation Practice Group, where he handles both commercial and regulatory issues involving transportation by rail and truck. Jeff represents major utility, petrochemical, mining, agricultural, metals, automotive and other industrial interests. He advises shipper clients and transportation intermediaries on transportation contract matters, rail rate and service issues, loss and damage claims, hazardous materials liability, rail line purchase and construction, rail abandonments, rail car leases, and a host of related transportation issues. Jeff has extensive experience in matters before the Surface Transportation Board and agencies within the Department of Transportation.

## MOREY, Richard J.
DLA Piper LLP (US), Chicago
312 368 7088
richard.morey@dlapiper.com
*Featured in Franchising (Nationwide)*
**Practice Areas:** Franchise.
**Career:** His practice focuses on working with both experienced and start-up franchise companies, helping them structure new franchise programs and determine the most appropriate methods of single- and multi-unit franchising. He counsels franchisors on everyday compliance and other franchise-related issues and works extensively on international franchising and licensing transactions in Asia, Europe, Central America, the Middle East and the Caribbean. He has contributed to numerous articles covering franchise law.
**Personal:** JD, University of Pennsylvania; BA, University of Illinois at Urbana-Champaign (magna cum laude).

## MORGAN II, Kirk D
Bracewell & Giuliani LLP, Washington, DC
202 828 5854
kirk.morgan@bgllp.com
*Featured in Energy & Natural Resources (Nationwide)*
**Practice Areas:** Focuses on energy-related projects, transactions and controversies. Advises clients in contract negotiations involving operating, transportation, and gas purchase and sales agreements, and advises clients regarding regulatory aspects of contract, tariff, compliance, and enforcement matters before the Federal Energy Regulatory Commission and various state regulatory agencies. Prepares and participates in pipeline rate cases on behalf of clients and advises clients on obtaining certificates and authorizations for interstate pipelines and storage facilities, as well as non-jurisdictional facilities.
**Personal:** JD, Catholic University of America, Columbus School of Law, 2001; BA, Catholic University of America, 1998.

## MORRIELLO, Henry G
Kaye Scholer LLP, New York
212 836 7170
henry.morriello@kayescholer.com
*Featured in Capital Markets (Nationwide)*
**Practice Areas:** Henry Morriello, Chair of the Finance Department and the Structured Finance Group, represents clients in term securitisation and commercial paper conduit transactions involving residential/commercial mortgage loans, equipment leases, student loans, aircraft loans/leases, auto paper, trade receivables, home

equity loans, intellectual property royalties and esoteric assets. He has represented global financial institutions in groundbreaking governmental financial assistance transactions and troubled financial asset portfolio sales and liquidations. He has been active in forming investment funds to purchase distressed assets which, in certain cases, have utilized government debt/equity programs. He has extensive experience in restructuring failed SIVs/SIV Lites and mortgage conduits.

## MORRISON, Kenneth P
Kirkland & Ellis LLP, Chicago
312 862 2347
kenneth.morrison@kirkland.com
*Featured in Capital Markets (Nationwide)*
**Practice Areas:** Ken leads Kirkland's Asset Finance and Securitisation Practice. Ken takes an active role in tracking and shaping developments in the regulatory process. Ken represents many active issuers and managers. Since 1990, he has handled securitisations and principal finance matters involving diverse asset classes including auto finance, timeshare, security alarm contracts, film finance, charge-offs and cell sites. Ken is the lead author of numerous comment letters submitted by the Vehicle ABS Sponsors, AFSA and the ABA.
**Personal:** Boston University School of Law, JD, magna cum laude, 1983; Massachusetts Institute of Technology, MBA, 1983; Yale University, BA, 1977.

## MORRISON, Stephen G
Nelson Mullins Riley & Scarborough LLP, Columbia
803 255 9410
steve.morrison@nelsonmullins.com
*Featured in Litigation (South Carolina), Products Liability (Nationwide)*
See under South Carolina for profile.

## MOSER, Eric K
Milbank, Tweed, Hadley & McCloy LLP, New York
212 530 5388
emoser@milbank.com
*Featured in Capital Markets (Nationwide)*
**Practice Areas:** Mr Moser is a partner and a member of the firm's Alternative Investments Practice. He represents banks, hedge funds and other market participants in the area of complex financing transactions, much of that focusing on structured finance transactions and derivatives. Mr Moser has experience representing investors in failed structured investment vehicles (SIVs) and CLOs, as well as in the workout of the swap, derivative and securitization portfolios of large insolvent financial institutions. He represents issuers, underwriters, lenders and agents in domestic and cross-border financial transactions, as well as on domestic and cross-border workouts and restructurings.

## MOSER, Joel H
Kaye Scholer LLP, New York
212 836 8425
joel.moser@kayescholer.com
*Featured in Projects (Nationwide)*
**Practice Areas:** Joel Moser, Head of the firm's Energy & Infrastructure group, focuses his prac-

tice on the planning, development, acquisition, financing, refinancing, operation and sale of energy and infrastructure assets around the world. He represents investment funds, developers, industrial sponsors, banking and investment firms, governments and agencies in investments and transactions in range of industries that includes oil and gas, transportation, power, water, renewables, professional athletics facilities and education. Joel is an adjunct professor at Columbia University's School of International and Public Affairs and a member of the Council on Foreign Relations.
**Career:** Founding editor, "Global Infrastructure," 2008 - present.

## MOSLEY, Daniel L
Cravath, Swaine & Moore LLP, New York
212 474 1696
dmosley@cravath.com
*Featured in Wealth Management (Nationwide)*
**Practice Areas:** Daniel L. Mosley is a partner in Cravath's Trusts and Estates Department. He is Chairman of the Board of Directors of Greenwich Hospital, and is on the board of various New York City not-for-profit organizations, including the Madison Square Boys & Girls Club, the William S. Paley Foundation, the Pinkerton Foundation, the Edward John Noble Foundation and the Thomas J. Watson Foundation, and also the William E. Simon Foundation in Morristown.
**Personal:** New York University (LLM, 1981); University of Alabama (JD, summa cum laude, 1980; Order of the Coif); University of Alabama (BS, 1977). For more information: http://www.cravath.com/dmosley

## MOSNER, Anita
Holland & Knight LLP, Washington, DC
202 419 2604
anita.mosner@hklaw.com
*Featured in Transportation (Nationwide)*
**Practice Areas:** Partner and Deputy Chair of the Firm's Aviation Team, Mosner practices in the areas of aviation law, competition law, and public policy and regulation, focusing on the commercial aviation industry. She has negotiated and secured regulatory approval and antitrust immunity for several airline alliances. She handles airline mergers and cross-border airline investments. She also handles complex airline licensing matters as well as enforcement and compliance matters before agencies such as Customs, TSA, FAA and DOT. Mosner provides competition law advice and training. Her practice also encompasses issues relating to airport access and development, as well as asset privatizations.

## MOTLEY, Warren
Davis Polk & Wardwell LLP, New York
212 450 4000
warren.motley@davispolk.com
*Featured in Capital Markets (Nationwide)*
**Practice Areas:** Member of Davis Polk's Corporate Department and the Derivatives and Structured Products Group. Focused primarily on domestic and international securities offerings of structured products since 1994. He has extensive experience in the development of new financial products, including various types of synthetic

exchangeable securities and other equity-, index-, commodity- and currency-linked products for both retail and institutional investors and in the related regulatory issues.

## MOYER JR, Homer E
Miller & Chevalier Chartered, Washington, DC
202 626 6020
hmoyer@milchev.com
*Featured in International Trade (Nationwide)*
**Practice Areas:** FCPA, anti-corruption law, compliance, internal investigations, litigation, international trade and investment disputes, export controls and sanctions.
**Career:** Firm Vice-Chair, Policy Committee Chair; Founder, International Department; GC, Department of Commerce (1980-81); Chair, International Law Section, ABA (1990-91); past Chair, IBA Anti-Corruption Committee; Co-founder, Central European and Eurasian Law Initiative (1990-2000); Founder/Chair, CEELI Institute (Prague); ABA's International Law Section Lifetime Achievement Award; Chambers Award: Contribution to the Legal Profession.
**Publications:** Anti-Corruption Regulation (editor); Export Controls as Instruments of Foreign Policy; Justice and the Military; The R.A.T. (Real-World Aptitude Test).
**Personal:** LLB, Yale Law School, 1967; BA, Emory University, 1964.

## MULITZ, Michael C
Kaye Scholer LLP, New York
212 836 7532
michael.mulitz@kayescholer.com
*Featured in Transportation (Nationwide)*
**Practice Areas:** Michael Mulitz, Chair of the Aviation Finance and Leasing group, concentrates on commercial and private jet aircraft transactions, with experience in the structuring, drafting and negotiation of financing and leasing transactions and portfolio sales (including tax-based leveraged and cross-border leasing, operating leases, PDP financings, portfolio securitisations and EXIM Bank/ECA supported financings) on behalf of banks, leasing companies, private equity funds and investment companies. He advises on fleet financing, acquisitions and leasing of private jet aircraft, fractional interest ownership and timeshare programs. Professional Memberships: Legal Advisory.
**Professional Memberships:** Legal Advisory Panel to the Aviation Working Group for the Cape Town Convention, ABA, ISTAT.

## MULLEN, Kevin
Jenner & Block LLP, Washington, DC
202 639 6024
kmullen@jenner.com
*Featured in Government (Nationwide)*
**Career:** Kevin Mullen has broad experience in procurements, claims, terminations, subcontracting, and due diligence for mergers and acquisitions. He has handled more than 150 bid protests before administrative and judicial bodies. In 2012, he successfully represented a contractor protesting a contract award at GAO and then helped defend the agency's corrective action against a protest by

the awardee at the U.S. Court of Federal Claims. He is a member of the Board of Governors of the Court of Federal Claims Bar Association and Co-Chair of the Contract Claims and Disputes Resolution Committee of the ABA's Public Contract Law Section.

## MULLER, Scott
Davis Polk & Wardwell LLP, New York
212 450 4359
scott.muller@davispolk.com
*Featured in International Trade (Nationwide), Litigation (New York)*
**Practice Areas:** Leads Davis Polk's Global Investigations, Enforcement and Compliance practice with broad civil litigation and criminal experience. A former federal prosecutor, he served as General Counsel of the Central Intelligence Agency from October 2002 through July 2004. He pioneered the use of the corporate "deferred prosecution" and has handled numerous internal and multi-jurisdictional investigations ranging from money laundering, corruption and sanctions to securities, tax, antitrust and environmental. He represented Siemens AG snd Morgan Stanley in their high profile FCPA corruption matters and is currently representing a number of clients in significant tax, accounting, OFAC and corruption cases.

## MUMMERY, Daniel
Gibson, Dunn & Crutcher LLP, Palo Alto
650.849.5318
dmummery@gibsondunn.com
*Featured in Outsourcing (Nationwide), IT & Outsourcing (California)*
See under California for profile.

## MURASHIGE, Kate H
Morrison & Foerster LLP, San Diego
858 720 5112
kmurashige@mofo.com
*Featured in Life Sciences (Nationwide), Life Sciences (California)*
**Practice Areas:** Focus on IP and patent issues within pharmaceuticals and healthcare, including drafting and prosecution of patent applications, re-examinations, opinions of validity and infringement, due diligence, and freedom-to-operate opinions. A recognized industry pioneer, clients include companies and universities working on cutting-edge biological advancements.
**Professional Memberships:** Member, SDIPLA, AIPLA, and LES. Former Member, AAAS Committee on Scientific Freedom and Responsibility. Former Member, National Biotechnology Policy Board for the NIH. Former Chair, Biotechnology Committee for the AIPLA. Advised the OTA on gene patenting.
**Personal:** BA, Washington University (St. Louis); PhD, UCLA; JD, Santa Clara University School of Law.

## MURNANE, Don P
Freehill Hogan & Mahar LLP, New York
212 425 1900
murnane@freehill.com
*Featured in Transportation (Nationwide)*
**Practice Areas:** Areas of expertise are maritime litigation and arbitration of contractual and tort

disputes including cargo, charter party, collisions and casualties. Has significant experience with cases involving bulk and product tanker disputes including product contamination and loss. Has also handled major cases involving vessel purchase and sale, liner service contract disputes and issues involving U.S. military and U.S. AID cargoes and electronic bills of lading. Has served as an arbitrator in proceedings conducted before the International Centre for Dispute Resolution.
**Professional Memberships:** Maritime Law Association of the United States (Arbitration Committee Member); Society of Maritime Arbitrators - MLA Liaison Committee (Chairman); New York State Bar Association. Bar Admissions: New York (State and Federal); District of Columbia.
**Career:** Joined Freehill Hogan & Mahar as a Partner in 1997 having been associated with Haight, Gardner, Poor & Havens from 1986-97.
**Personal:** Born 1960; United States Merchant Marine Academy at Kings Point, BS, 1982 (Salutatorian); Georgetown University Law Center, JD, 1986.

## MURPHY, Barbara A
Foster, Murphy, Altman & Nickel, PC, Washington, DC
202 822 4102
bmurphy@fostermurphy.com
*Featured in International Trade (Nationwide)*
**Practice Areas:** ITC Section 337 Litigation; Intellectual Property Litigation; International Trade Regulation; Antidumping; Customs Border Enforcement.
**Career:** Involved in over 60 Section 337 investigations, handling all aspects, from preparation of complaints through appellate review and customs enforcement. Represents both domestic and foreign companies pursuing and defending against Section 337 relief, in cases involving patent, trademark and copyright infringement, trade secret misappropriation and gray market goods. Her experience covers an array of technologies and products, from tools and machinery to flash memory devices and chemicals. Active in bar leadership.
**Personal:** JD, George Washington University Law School, 1982; BA, Dartmouth College, 1979.

## MURPHY, Brian
Frankfurt Kurnit Klein & Selz, New York
212 826 5577
bmurphy@fkks.com
*Featured in Advertising (Nationwide)*
**Practice Areas:** Partner in the firm's Advertising, Marketing, and Public Relations Group. Counsels advertising agencies, advertisers, and entertainment companies as they develop and exploit advertising and entertainment properties across all media, with a focus on digital and social media. Advises clients on copyright, trademark, right of publicity/privacy, false advertising, and unfair competition issues. Practice includes negotiating and structuring app development agreements, branded entertainment deals, celebrity talent agreements, product placements, sponsorship arrangements, content licenses, and agency-client

contracts. Frequent speaker at bar and industry association events. Named a New York-area "Super Lawyer" for First Amendment, Media, and Advertising law by Law and Politics magazine and listed by Best Lawyers as a top advertising lawyer.
**Professional Memberships:** Member, Copyright Society of the U.S.A.; Promotion Marketing Association; American Bar Association Intellectual Property Section's Special Committee on Promotions and Marketing Law.

## MURPHY, Gerald
Crowell & Moring LLP, Washington, DC
202 508 8855
gmurphy@crowell.com
*Featured in Transportation (Nationwide)*
**Practice Areas:** Partner in Crowell & Moring's Aviation, Corporate, and Administrative Law/Regulatory practice groups. His experience includes advising clients in aviation regulatory matters and commercial aviation transactions. He represents clients, ranging from major US and foreign air carriers to individual and corporate aircraft owners, in a variety of licensing and enforcement proceedings before the U.S. Department of Transportation (DOT) and the Federal Aviation Administration (FAA) and routinely advises clients on Transportation Security Administration (TSA) security requirements.
**Personal:** Loyola University Chicago, BA,Catholic University of America, Columbus School of Law, JD

## MURPHY, Jack W
Dechert LLP, Washington, DC
202 261 3303
jack.murphy@dechert.com
*Featured in Investment Funds (Nationwide)*
**Practice Areas:** Mr Murphy provides legal advice to registered mutual funds and investment advisers in connection with all aspects of their operations.
**Professional Memberships:** Member, District of Columbia and New York Bars.
**Career:** Associate General Counsel of PaineWebber/Mitchell Hutchins Asset Management, Inc. (1991-1994); Associate Director and Chief Counsel of Securities and Exchange Commission Division of Investment Management (1994-1997).
**Personal:** State University of New York at Albany (BA, 1980); Boston College Law School (JD, 1983).

## MURPHY, Kathleen
Drinker Biddle & Reath LLP, Chicago
312 569 1690
Kathleen.Murphy@dbr.com
*Featured in International Trade (Nationwide)*
**Practice Areas:** Counsels clients on maximizing trade benefits, making informed procurement decisions, and developing international trade compliance programs based on risk management principles. Plans and implements periodic tracking and monitoring programs intended to foster self-governance. Represents clients in transfer price reviews and government audits and investigations involving cross-border product flows.

**Professional Memberships:** Board of Governors, American Association of Exporters and Importers; Professional Development Committee, Midwest Global Trade Association; and past vice-chair, Customs and U.S. Trade Law Committee, American Bar Association.
**Personal:** Loyola University Chicago, MA and JD; St. Xavier College, BA with honors, Political Science.

## MURPHY, Michael
Baker & McKenzie, Washington, DC
202 452 7069
ted.murphy@bakermckenzie.com
*Featured in International Trade (Nationwide)*
**Practice Areas:** Customs compliance; particularly relating to international trade agreements, customs valuation matters, internal customs compliance programs, voluntary trade programs, prior disclosures, US Customs and Border Protection/US Immigration and Customs Enforcement audits and investigations.
**Professional Memberships:** Industry Trade Advisory Committee on Customs Matters and Trade Facilitation (ITAC 14); US Council of International Business Customs & Trade Facilitation Committee, ABA - International Law and Practice Section.
**Career:** Admitted in DC (1998) and Pennsylvania (1997).
**Publications:** Frequent speaker on customs compliance-related topics in the US and abroad.
**Personal:** JD, University of Pennsylvania, 1996; BA, College of the Holy Cross, 1993.

## MURPHY, Michael
Pillsbury Winthrop Shaw Pittman LLP, San Francisco
415 983 1303
michael.murphy@pillsburylaw.com
*Featured in Outsourcing (Nationwide), IT & Outsourcing (California)*
**Practice Areas:** Outsourcing, IT law, procurement. Michael develops outsourcing relationships that improve a company's performance by advising on all aspects of the outsourcing lifecycle (strategy, selection, contracting, restructuring). He helps clients acquire and implement disruptive technologies, with a focus on risk management, cost control and speed to value. His clients include Fortune 100 companies in some of the largest and most transformational projects in their industries.
**Professional Memberships:** Member: New York Bar, California Bar, American Bar Association.
**Publications:** 'What Happens on the Outsourcer's Insolvency: A Comparison of Relevant Insolvency Principles in the US, India and China' (PLC Outsourcing Handbook, 2010); 'Structuring Outsourcing Technology Relationships: Customer Concerns, Strategies and Processes' (International Journal of Law and Information Technology, Vol. 4 No. 2); 'Optimizing the Tax Function Through Strategic Sourcing,' Journal of Corporate Tax Automation, Spring 2004.

## MUSOFF, Scott
Skadden, Arps, Slate, Meagher & Flom LLP & Affiliates, New York
212 735 7852
Scott.Musoff@skadden.com
*Featured in Securities (Nationwide), Litigation (New York)*
**Practice Areas:** Represents financial institutions, corporations and individuals in federal and state trial and appellate courts, as well as in arbitration proceedings. Has extensive experience in securities and other complex commercial litigation. Handles subprime-related and other matters for Bank of American/Merrill Lynch, Societe Generale, and Canadian Imperial Bank of Commerce. Has also advised issuers and underwriters in securities litigation around the country and counsels clients in a variety of other litigation matters.
**Career:** JD, New York University, School of Law, 1994 (Order of the Coif); BA, Tufts University, 1991.

## MYERS, Linda K
Kirkland & Ellis LLP, Chicago
312 862 2322
linda.myers@kirkland.com
*Featured in Banking & Finance (Illinois), Banking & Finance (Nationwide)*
See under Illinois for profile.

## NADEL, Steven B
Seward & Kissel LLP, New York
212 574 1234
nadel@sewkis.com
*Featured in Investment Funds (Nationwide)*
**Practice Areas:** Investment Management Private Funds Investment Advisers Broker-Dealers and Other Regulated Entities.
**Professional Memberships:** Mr Nadel is a member of the American Bar Association and the New York State Bar Association. Steve also sits on the Boards of Directors of the charities Hedge Funds Care and the RBaby Foundation.
**Career:** Mr Nadel is a partner in Seward & Kissel's Investment Management Group. He joined the Firm in 1997. He is also the founding editor of The Private Funds Report and The Private Funds Bullet Report, two Group newsletters. Mr Nadel has extensive experience in issues relating to the establishment and ongoing operation of hedge funds, funds of funds (US and off-shore), private equity funds, separate accounts, registered investment advisers, commodity pool operators and commodity trading advisors, as well as related matters, including management company structuring, fund marketing, employment agreements, solicitation agreements, joint ventures, seed capital arrangements, regulatory compliance and general organizational matters. Through his large network, Mr Nadel is able to source practical industry trends, which he seeks to impart in addition to his legal guidance. He represents a wide variety of clients ranging from start-up entrepreneurs to very large, well known institutions, and he is considered by the various services providers in the space (including accountants and brokers) to be one of the premier attorneys in the alternative investment management arena.

**Publications:** Mr Nadel wrote a chapter on US private investment fund regulation for the book entitled The Capital Guide to Alternative Investment, as well as for The Review of Securities & Commodities Regulation. He has also authored the following investment management articles: Foresight for Established Managers, Law 360, June 2010; The Expansion of Hedge and Private Equity Funds, Law 360, May 2010; How to Reinvigorate Investment in Hedge Funds, HedgeWorld.com, July 2009; Hedge Funds Affected by New Rules, 2009 Hedge Fund Industry Report; State Level Investment Adviser Registration, Private Investment Forum, Fourth Quarter 2001; The Principal Elements of Private Equity, Private Asset Management, May 3, 1999; An Accountant's Guide to the Major Legal Issues Affecting Hedge Funds, The CPA Journal, October 1998; and Becoming an SEC-Registered Investment Adviser: Understanding What's Really Involved, Hedge Views, Summer 1998. Steve is a sought after lecturer who speaks regularly on various investment management topics, and who is also often quoted in many leading business and legal publications, including the New York Times, the Wall Street Journal and Bloomberg. He previously taught a course at the New York Institute of Finance titled, "How to Start a Hedge Fund."
**Personal:** Mr Nadel received his JD from Brooklyn Law School, magna cum laude, in 1991 and his BS from New York University's Leonard N. Stern School of Business, magna cum laude, in 1988.

## NADLER, David
Dickstein Shapiro LLP, Washington, DC
202 420 2281
nadlerd@dickstienshapiro
*Featured in Government (Nationwide)*
**Practice Areas:** Dave Nadler is a partner at Dickstein Shapiro in Washington, DC, and a recognized authority on government contracting matters. His practice focuses on bid protests, government audits and investigations, the False Claims Act, government cost, accounting, and pricing issues, the GSA Schedule, the Foreign Corrupt Practices Act,and government compliance matters. Mr Nadler also serves as the National Judge Advocate of the Navy League of the United States.
**Personal:** Mr Nadler received his BA, summa cum laude, from Brooklyn College (1978) and his JD from Temple University School of Law (1981).

## NAEVE, Clifford M
Skadden, Arps, Slate, Meagher & Flom LLP & Affiliates, Washington, DC
202 371 7070
Mike.Naeve@skadden.com
*Featured in Energy & Natural Resources (Nationwide)*
**Practice Areas:** Leads the firm's Energy Practice Group and is Head of the Washington, DC office. Involved in a broad range of energy policy and regulatory matters. Represents clients in federal and state regulatory proceedings.
**Professional Memberships:** Member, Electricity Advisory Board to the Secretary of

Energy (2002-08); Board of Directors, Ontario Independent Electricity System Operator (2006-08).
**Career:** Commissioner, FERC (1985-88); Legislative Director, Office of Senator Lloyd Bentsen (1978-80). JD, George Washington University, 1984 (highest honors, Order of the Coif); M.P.A., L.B.J. School of Public Affairs, The University of Texas, 1972; B.S., Mechanical Engineering, The University of Texas, 1970.

## NAFTALIS, Gary P
Kramer Levin Naftalis & Frankel LLP, New York
212 715 9253
gnaftalis@kramerlevin.com
*Featured in Litigation (Nationwide), Litigation (New York)*
See under New York for profile.

## NAGEL, Trevor
White & Case LLP, Washington, DC
202 626 3616
tnagel@whitecase.com
*Featured in Outsourcing (Nationwide), Technology (District of Columbia)*
**Career:** Dr. Nagel is the chair of the Sourcing and Technology Transactions Group. He advises both public and private sector clients on legal and commercial issues of large-scale global outsourcing and complex technology transactions. Dr. Nagel represents clients in structuring, negotiating and implementing information technology, off-shore application development and management, managed network services and business process outsourcing transactions, joint ventures, strategic alliances and co-marketing arrangements. To view a comprehensive biography, please visit www.whitecase.com/tnagel.

## NAGER, Glen
Jones Day, Washington, DC
202 879 5464
gdnager@jonesday.com
*Featured in Labor & Employment (District of Columbia), Appellate Law (Nationwide)*
**Practice Areas:** Chairs the firm's Issues and Appeals Practice. He has argued 13 cases before the US Supreme Court. He has argued appeals in such areas as antitrust, IP, government contracts, and environmental cases. His substantive specialty is employment law, doing jury trials, class action litigation, and counseling, with particular emphasis on discrimination and employee benefits. Named one of the top 12 employment lawyers in Washington, DC. Adjunct Professor at Georgetown University Law Center teaching administrative law and constitutional law.
**Professional Memberships:** Member of the Edward Coke Appellate American Inn of Court. ABA. District of Columbia Bar.

## NAHRA, Kirk J
Wiley Rein LLP, Washington, DC
202 719 7335
knahra@wileyrein.com
*Featured in Privacy & Data Security (Nationwide)*
**Practice Areas:** Chairs and co-chairs the firm's Privacy and Health Care Practices, respectively. Specializes in health care, privacy, information

security and compliance programs/False Claims Act issues for the health care and insurance industries and others facing legal obligations on these issues. Served as co-chair of Confidentiality, Privacy and Security Workgroup of the American Health Information Community (AHIC).
**Professional Memberships:** Editorial Board, Bloomberg BNA Privacy & Security Law Report (2009-Present); Editor, The Privacy Advisor (2002-Present); Board of Directors, International Association of Privacy Professionals (2003-Present).
**Personal:** Harvard Law School (JD, cum laude); Georgetown University (BA, magna cum laude).

## NAIMON, Jeffrey
BuckleySandler LLP, Washington, DC
202 349 8030
jnaimon@buckleysandler.com
*Featured in Financial Services Regulation (Nationwide)*
**Practice Areas:** Mr Naimon provides regulatory, enforcement, and transactional advice to bank and non-bank lenders and servicers. He advises on the entire panoply of banking and consumer finance statutes including fair lending laws, unfair, deceptive and abusive acts and practices laws, the Dodd-Frank Act, the National Bank Act, TILA, RESPA, FCRA, the Fair Debt Collection Practices Act, the Gramm-Leach-Bliley Act, and state laws governing lending, servicing, and collections. He assists with CFPB and other examinations and investigations.

## NASH, Bernard
Dickstein Shapiro LLP, Washington, DC
202 420 2209
nashb@dicksteinshapiro.com
*Featured in Government (Nationwide)*
**Practice Areas:** Bernard Nash leads the firm's State Attorneys General Practice, where he represents clients in complex state and federal legal and legislative matters. Mr Nash's work typically involves cases of first impression, matters having public policy implications and/or a governmental interest, and complex litigation. He routinely counsels major private sector clients on a wide range of matters involving State Attorneys General and also has represented states in significant policy disputes.
**Publications:** Editor of State AG Monitor, stateagmonitor.com.
**Personal:** Brooklyn Law School, cum laude, JD, 1966); City College of the City University of New York (BBA, 1963).

## NASH, Daniel L
Akin Gump Strauss Hauer & Feld LLP, Washington, DC
202 887 4067
dnash@akingump.com
*Featured in Labor & Employment (District of Columbia), Sports Law (Nationwide)*
**Practice Areas:** Represents clients in federal and state courts and before various administrative agencies such as the National Labor Relations Board, the Equal Employment Opportunity Commission and the US Department of Labor. Represents employers in class and complex

employment litigation and arbitrations. Clients include employers in the retail, publishing and professional sports industries.

**Career:** Extern law clerk, Honorable Stanley Mosk, California Supreme Court.

**Personal:** BS, cum laude, State University of New York at Cortland (1976); JD, magna cum laude, University of California, Hastings College of Law, Note and Comment editor, Hastings Law Journal, Order of the Coif.

### NASH, Glenn
Sidley Austin LLP, Palo Alto
650 565 7113
gnash@sidley.com
*Featured in Outsourcing (Nationwide), IT & Outsourcing (California)*
See under California for profile.

### NASSAU, Henry N
Dechert LLP, Philadelphia
215 994 2138
henry.nassau@dechert.com
*Featured in Private Equity (Nationwide), Corporate/M&A (Pennsylvania)*
See under Pennsylvania for profile.

### NAZARETH, Annette
Davis Polk & Wardwell LLP, Washington, DC
202 962 7000
annette.nazareth@davispolk.com
*Featured in Financial Services Regulation (Nationwide), Securities (Nationwide)*
**Practice Areas:** Ms Nazareth leads Davis Polk's Trading and Markets Practice. She advises on a broad range of securities regulatory matters. Her clients include major international banks, broker-dealers, swap dealers, securities exchanges, central counterparties and financial industry trade associations. She also works closely with Davis Polk's SEC enforcement practice, counseling non-financial sector corporations that are subject to government regulatory and enforcement actions.

### NEAHER JR, Ned
White & Case LLP, Washington, DC
202 626 3622
eneaher@whitecase.com
*Featured in Projects (Nationwide)*
**Career:** To view a comprehensive biography, please visit www.whitecase.com/eneaher.

### NEALE, Margery
Willkie Farr & Gallagher LLP, New York
212 728 8297
mneale@willkie.com
*Featured in Investment Funds (Nationwide)*
**Practice Areas:** Specializes in counseling investment companies, their advisers and independent directors. Advises on the creation and operation of registered open-end and closed-end investment companies, including ETFs, and business development companies, and on M&A and other transactions. Assists investment advisers on various matters including regulatory compliance, new product development, advisory programs involving mutual funds and other wrap fee programs, and internal investigations.
**Personal:** JD, Yale Law School, 1983. AB, magna cum laude, Phi Beta Kappa, Smith College, 1980.
See: http://www.willkie.com/MargeryNeale

### NEDZBALA, Michael
Hunton & Williams LLP, Charlotte
704 378 4703
mnedzbala@hunton.com
*Featured in Capital Markets (Nationwide)*
**Practice Areas:** Mr Nedzbala's practice focuses on structured finance, securitization and other capital markets transactions. He is Co-Head of the firm's Structured Finance and Securitisation Group and a Member of the Corporate Team and previously served as Co-Chairman of the American Securitization Forum's Outside Counsel Subforum.

### NEELY, Wilson S
Simpson Thacher & Bartlett LLP, New York
212 455 7063
wneely@stblaw.com
*Featured in Private Equity (Nationwide)*
**Practice Areas:** Corporate Partner practicing primarily in the mergers and acquisitions area and also in the capital markets area. Has worked on many private equity transactions, including leveraged buyouts, recapitalizations and strategic partnerships between private equity funds and corporate partners, as well as strategic M&A transactions. Has also overseen a number of initial public offerings, involving both common stock and high yield securities.
**Career:** Joined firm in 1982; became Partner in 1991.
**Personal:** BA, cum laude, Dartmouth College (1978); JD, with honors, University of Texas Law School (1982).

### NELSON, Cynthia
Gardere Wynne Sewell LLP, Dallas
214 999 4884
cnelson@gardere.com
*Featured in Leisure & Hospitality (Nationwide)*
**Practice Areas:** Hospitality, real estate.
**Professional Memberships:** State Bar of Texas, Dallas Bar Association, Dallas Real Estate Council.
**Career:** Cindy Nelson practices in the Gardere Real Estate Practice Group and is on the Hospitality Industry Team. She has vast experience in sophisticated and complex real estate and finance transactions, including representing owners, REITs, opportunity funds, and developers in acquiring, disposing, leasing, financing, and managing significant and/or high profile commercial enterprises such as shopping centers, multi and single family housing developments, hotels and mixed use developments, office buildings, industrial properties, and unimproved land with a particular emphasis on lodging properties and the hospitality industry. Ms Nelson's representation includes senior and mezzanine financing, complex workout and debt restructure, joint ventures, management agreements, franchise agreements, buying, selling, developing and ground leasing of all types of real estate products including hotels, mixed use developments, and fractional and time share products. She also assists investors with recapitalization of distressed borrowers and purchasers of troubled assets. Ms Nelson's practice is both domestic and foreign.

**Personal:** JD, St. Mary's University School of Law, 1991; BBA, The University of Texas at Austin, 1988.

### NELSON, Edward D
Gibson, Dunn & Crutcher LLP, New York
212 351 2666
enelson@gibsondunn.com
*Featured in Investment Funds (Nationwide)*
**Practice Areas:** Represents a wide variety of private investment funds, including buyout funds, venture capital funds, real estate funds, secondary funds, distressed funds, international funds and hedge funds. Also represents institutional investors in their private investment fund and other alternative investment activities; and has significant experience in issues relating to the Securities Act, the Investment Company Act and the Investment Advisers Act.
**Professional Memberships:** Committee on Private Investment Funds of the Association of the Bar of the City of New York.
**Personal:** JD, Harvard University, 1994; MPP Harvard University 1994; MPhil, Cambridge University, 1990; BA Dartmouth College, 1989.

### NELSON, Howard L
Greenberg Traurig, LLP, Washington, DC
202 331 3163
NelsonH@gtlaw.com
*Featured in Energy & Natural Resources (Nationwide)*
**Practice Areas:** Litigation; energy and natural resources; government litigation.
**Professional Memberships:** Member: Energy Bar Association; DC Bar Association; Maryland Bar Association; American Bar Association.
**Career:** Selected: Chambers USA Guide, 2007-13. Team Member, Law360 'Appellate Practice Group of the Year', 2010.
**Publications:** Author, 'Victims' Suits Against Government Entities and Officials for Reckless Release', 29 Am. UL Rev 595, 1980.
**Personal:** JD, American University Washington College of Law; BA, cum laude, State University of New York at Buffalo; BS, cum laude, State University of New York at Buffalo.

### NELSON, Timothy G
Skadden, Arps, Slate, Meagher & Flom LLP & Affiliates, New York
212 735 2193
tim.nelson@skadden.com
*Featured in International Arbitration (Nationwide)*
**Practice Areas:** Mr Nelson represents clients in international disputes, including arbitration before ICSID, ICC, ICDR, and UNCITRAL. He has conducted and argued some of the larger recent Bilateral Investment Treaty (BIT) arbitrations before ICSID and UNCITRAL involving expropriation and unfair treatment of investors by host states, as well as high-profile United States litigation involving international law and arbitration. Mr Nelson also has an active international commercial arbitration practice.
**Career:** BA, University of New South Wales, Australia, 1990; LLB, University of New South Wales Law School, Australia, 1990; BCL,

University of Oxford, 1997 (John Morris Prize for Conflict of Laws).

### NELSON, William F
Bingham McCutchen LLP, Washington, DC
202 373 6782
william.nelson@bingham.com
*Featured in Tax (District of Columbia), Tax (Nationwide)*
**Practice Areas:** Co-leader of Bingham's Tax Group. Practice encompasses all areas of federal taxation, with a special emphasis on partnership taxation and tax controversy and litigation matters. One of the founding partners of McKee Nelson, which joined Bingham in 2009. Has written articles on tax law for numerous journals and institutes. Frequent lecturer at various tax institutes.
**Career:** Former chief counsel, Internal Revenue Service.
**Publications:** Co-author, 'Federal Taxation of Partnerships and Partners;' Co-author, 'Structuring and Drafting Partnership Agreements: Including LLC Agreements.'
**Personal:** University of Virginia School of Law, JD, 1972; Mississippi State University, BS, high honors, 1969.

### NESTER, Brian
Sidley Austin LLP, Washington, DC
202 736 8017
bnester@sidley.com
*Featured in International Trade (Nationwide)*
**Practice Areas:** Partner in Sidley's Washington, D.C. office. He focuses his practice on patent and trade secret litigation and has extensive experience before the U.S. International Trade Commission. His practice emphasizes patent litigation involving high-technology and consumer electronics. He has broad experience in electrical technologies including telecommunications, Flash, DRAM, photolithography, DMA technology, Linux code, LCD and plasma technologies disk drives, magnetic media, cooling systems, optical communication, Ethernet networks, video and graphics processing, flat panel displays and scalers, and power supplies.
**Personal:** The George Washington University Law School, JD, 1996, with honors; Temple University, BA in Biology, 1990, magna cum laude.

### NEUHAUS, Joseph E
Sullivan & Cromwell LLP, New York
212 558 4000
neuhausj@sullcrom.com
*Featured in International Arbitration (Nationwide)*
**Professional Memberships:** Vice-chair, Institute for Transnational Arbitration; member and former chair, NYSBA Professional Ethics Committee; chair, NYSBA Committee on Standards of Attorney Conduct; member, ABCNY International Commercial Disputes Committee.
**Career:** Partner since 1992. International commercial litigation in arbitral and court settings, with emphasis on Latin American matters. Co-coordinator of Firm's Arbitration Practice and has served as counsel and arbitrator in arbitral proceedings administered by the International

Chamber of Commerce and the American Arbitration Association, as well as in investment treaty disputes. Also acts as counsel in arbitration-related litigation in courts.

**Personal:** Columbia Law School (JD, 1982); Dartmouth College (AB, 1979).

## NEWCOMB, Danforth
Shearman & Sterling LLP, New York
212 848 4184
dnewcomb@shearman.com
*Featured in International Trade (Nationwide)*

**Practice Areas:** Danforth Newcomb started the anti-corruption practice at Shearman & Sterling LLP and is founding editor of its FCPA Digest. Mr Newcomb has served as a UN expert on ethics and compliance and a DOJ and SEC sanctioned compliance monitor. His FCPA engagements include: Nokia in a multi¬-jurisdictional review about Siemens and investigations related to Oil for Food, ABB, Norsk Hydro/Statoil, Titan, Daimler Chrysler, Bonny Island Nigeria, Faro Technologies and Oil States International. He is a member of the Board of Advisers to the FCPA Reporter. He also advises on AML and Economic Sanctions matters.

## NEWCOMB, Richard
DLA Piper LLP (US), Washington, DC
202 799 4434
richard.newcomb@dlapiper.com
*Featured in International Trade (Nationwide)*

**Practice Areas:** International trade.
**Career:** He is chair of the firm's International Trade practice and has considerable international experience dealing with target governments, front-line states, like-minded allies, multilateral organizations, financial and business communities worldwide and others who are responsible for compliance with asset controls and economic sanctions and embargo programs. He is adept at handling regulatory procedures relating to international transactions.
**Personal:** JD, Case Western Reserve University School of Law; BA, Kenyon College.

## NEWKIRK, Thomas
Jenner & Block LLP, Washington, DC
202 639 6099
tnewkirk@jenner.com
*Featured in Securities (Nationwide)*

**Career:** Thomas C Newkirk co-chairs the Securities Litigation and Enforcement Practice and is a member of the Securities Practice and Subprime Litigation Task Force. He represents some of America's largest companies, CEOs, boards, committees, directors and hedge funds in Securities and Exchange Commission and confidential investigations involving accounting, disclosure, insider trading, Foreign Corrupt Practices Act and other issues. He counsels boards and committees on corporate governance and compliance, conducts internal investigations and defends class and derivative securities actions. He writes and lectures on SEC enforcement matters. Before joining the firm, he spent 19 years in senior positions with the SEC.

## NEWMAN, Bruce H
WilmerHale, New York
212 230 8835
bruce.newman@wilmerhale.com
*Featured in Financial Services Regulation (Nationwide)*

**Practice Areas:** Member, Broker-Dealer Compliance and Regulation, Futures and Derivatives, and FinTech Groups. Practice focuses in the areas of securities law, broker-dealer issues, policies and compliance, membership applications, restructurings involving broker-dealers, trading advice and market structure.
**Career:** Former Director of Equities Compliance and Executive Director at UBS Warburg, Director of Capital Markets Compliance at PaineWebber and Branch Chief of Broker-Dealer Enforcement Division of the SEC. Admitted, New York Bar, 1991. Joined firm, 2001.
**Personal:** Yeshiva University, Benjamin N Cardozo School of Law (JD , magna cum laude); Rutgers University (BA).

## NEWMAN, Karol Lyn
McDermott Will & Emery LLP, Washington, DC
202 756 8405
knewman@mwe.com
*Featured in Energy & Natural Resources (Nationwide)*

**Practice Areas:** Worked in the energy area for over 30 years, counseling and advising natural gas producers, marketers, local distribution companies and end-users. Advises on regulatory issues associated with asset acquisitions, infrastructure development, and the negotiation of commercial agreements related to the purchase, sale, and transportation of natural gas. Regularly represents clients in litigated and ADR proceedings before the FERC. Also a seasoned appellate lawyer, having argued numerous cases in the US Courts of Appeals.
**Professional Memberships:** Admitted in District of Columbia and Maryland.
**Personal:** University of Maryland School of Law, JD, (with honors), 1973; University of Maryland, BA, 1971.

## NEWMAN, Michael B
Holland & Knight LLP, San Francisco
415 743 6989
michael.newman@hklaw.com
*Featured in Food & Beverages (Nationwide)*

**Practice Areas:** Partner located in San Francisco and Head of the Alcohol Beverage Team. Newman counsels industry clients on national and international regulatory, contract, legislative, and licensing matters, advertising and promotional law, intellectual property rights, importation matters, trade practices, and inter-tier relations. He represents clients before the federal Alcohol & Tobacco Tax & Trade Bureau, the California Department of Alcoholic Beverage Control and State Board of Equalization, and other state alcohol beverage agencies. He has experience representing all three tiers of the alcohol beverage industry and has worked with international importers, suppliers and exporters,

domestic manufacturers, regional and local distributors.

## NEWMAN, Philip
Goodwin Procter LLP, Boston
617 570 1558
pnewman@goodwinprocter.com
*Featured in Investment Funds (Nationwide), Investment Funds (Massachusetts)*
See under Massachusetts for profile.

## NEWTON, Peter B
Neal, Gerber & Eisenberg LLP, Chicago
312 269 8027
pnewton@ngelaw.com
*Featured in Products Liability (Nationwide)*

**Practice Areas:** Represents clients in complex commercial litigation in state and federal courts throughout the country. Also represents a variety of clients in products liability defense cases on products ranging from pharmaceuticals to liquid petroleum gas valves and regulators. Serves as national products liability counsel for a propane gas equipment manufacturer and as a US counsel for a Canadian telecommunications equipment designer and manufacturer. Served as lead trial counsel in jury cases in various jurisdictions across the country.
**Career:** Partner; Litigation Practice Group.
**Personal:** Columbus College (BS, 1979); Chicago-Kent College of Law (JD, 1983).

## NIBLEY, Stuart B
K&L Gates, Washington, DC
202 778 9428
stu.nibley@klgates.com
*Featured in Government (Nationwide)*

**Practice Areas:** Mr Nibley focuses his practice on both counseling and dispute resolution on behalf of government contractors. His experience includes representation of defense and civilian contractors before Boards of Contract Appeals, federal and state courts, administrative agencies, and international arbitration forums relative to the procurement process, from contract negotiation and proposal preparation through claims and dispute resolution. He has particular experience in representing clients in bid protests; preparing, litigating, and resolving claims against the government and disputes between prime contractors and subcontractors; and assisting clients with government contracts compliance work, including internal investigations, and mandatory and voluntary disclosures.

## NICELY, Matthew
Hughes Hubbard & Reed LLP, Washington, DC
202 721 4750
nicely@hugheshubbard.com
*Featured in International Trade (Nationwide)*

**Practice Areas:** International Trade
**Career:** Matt advises clients on risks and opportunities presented by US and international trade regulatory regimes. He has represented multiple industries in trade remedy proceedings (antidumping, safeguards, countervailing duties) before administrative agencies, in appeals to US courts, and in WTO dispute settlement. Matt also counsels clients on compliance with day-to-day

regulation of goods, services, and investment moving across borders, including customs, export controls, economic sanctions, anti-boycott, and anti-bribery laws. Matt teaches international trade law at American University.
**Personal:** American University Law School, JD (1991, cum laude); Oberlin College, BA (1987).

## NICKEL, David F
Foster, Murphy, Altman & Nickel, PC, Washington, DC
202 822 4104
dnickel@fostermurphy.com
*Featured in International Trade (Nationwide)*

**Practice Areas:** ITC Section 337 Litigation; Customs and International Trade; Intellectual Property Litigation.
**Career:** He has successfully represented clients based in the United States, Europe, and Asia in more than 50 Section 337 investigations involving patents, trademarks, copyrights, and trade secrets covering various technologies, including chemicals, medical devices, batteries, ink cartridges, computers, telecommunication devices, global positioning systems, semiconductors, power management controllers, bulk welding wire, and televisions. He has also handled several enforcement issues related to Section 337 exclusion orders before U.S. Customs and Border Protection.
**Personal:** JD, George Washington University School of Law, 2000; BA, Princeton University, 1997.

## NICOLAS, Stephanie
WilmerHale, London
202 663 6825
stephanie.nicolas@wilmerhale.com
*Featured in Financial Services Regulation (Nationwide)*

**Practice Areas:** Partner in the Securities Department, and a member of the Broker-Dealer Compliance and Regulation and Futures and Derivatives Practice Groups. Works with major investment banking firms, broker-dealers and other financial institutions to develop comprehensive compliance and supervisory procedures for a range of broker-dealer activities, including research activities; firm-wide supervision; information barriers; and surveillance procedures, trading issues and sales practice issues.
**Career:** JD, magna cum laude, Georgetown University Law Center, 1999, Order of the Coif; BA, Brown University, 1994.

## NIEBRUEGGE, Michael E
Cadwalader, Wickersham & Taft LLP, Houston
713 343 7560
michael.niebruegge@cwt.com
*Featured in Banking & Finance (Texas), Banking & Finance (Nationwide)*
See under Texas for profile.

## NISHAWALA, Vipul N
Pillsbury Winthrop Shaw Pittman LLP, New York
+1 212 858 1021
vipul.nishawala@pillsburylaw.com
*Featured in Outsourcing (Nationwide), Technology (New York)*

See under New York for profile.

### NISSENBAUM, David
Schulte Roth & Zabel LLP, New York
212 756 2227
david.nissenbaum@srz.com
*Featured in Investment Funds (Nationwide)*
**Practice Areas:** Corporate, bank regulation and securities matters, primarily focusing on representing institutional and entrepreneurial investment managers, financial services firms and private investment funds in all aspects of their business, including fund structuring, transactions, regulatory, compliance, management of conflicts of interest, succession planning and US banking laws.
**Professional Memberships:** New York City Bar Association, Banking Law Committee, 1998-2001; American Bar Association; Alternative Investment Financial Executives Association, Advisory Board, 2007-present.
**Career:** SRZ Partner since 2003; Member, Executive Committee.
**Publications:** Lectures and writes extensively on alternative investments and banking regulation.

### NOCCO, Frank
Weil, Gotshal & Manges LLP, New York
212 310 8918
frank.nocco@weil.com
*Featured in Capital Markets (Nationwide)*
**Practice Areas:** Head of the firm's Structured Finance/Derivatives Practice. Works closely with counterparts in London and in other offices worldwide. Represents issuers, underwriters, collateral managers and credit enhancers in structured securities offerings (including asset-backed securities and CLOs) and derivatives transactions, and restructuring work related thereto. Has participated in the securitization of a wide variety of assets including commercial loans, mortgage loans, credit card receivables, trade receivables, auto loans, equipment (including aircraft) and vehicle leases, student loans, insurance premium finance contracts and intellectual property rights.
**Personal:** Columbia University (BA, magna cum laude, 1985); Columbia University School of Law (JD, 1988).

### NOEL, Gregg A
Skadden, Arps, Slate, Meagher & Flom LLP & Affiliates, Los Angeles
213 687 5234
gregg.noel@skadden.com
*Featured in Capital Markets (California), Capital Markets (Nationwide)*
See under California for profile.

### NOLAN, Matthew
Arent Fox LLP, Washington, DC
202 857 6013
matthew.nolan@arentfox.com
*Featured in International Trade (Nationwide)*
**Practice Areas:** Matthew Nolan's international trade and business regulation practice encompasses trade counseling, investigations, and disputes covering a range of areas, including customs rules, focused assessments, import investigations, US export controls and trade sanctions, NAFTA and WTO, foreign investment, trade policy and the Foreign Corrupt Practices Act. He has worked extensively on issues pertaining to trade and investment in the Americas, Europe, South Africa, Turkey and other countries. Matt also has experience in international commercial transactions, disputes and arbitrations. Matt has worked extensively in Canada and Mexico (for both government and private sector clients) on issues related to the North American Free Trade Agreement and WTO disputes; and has worked for major US and foreign corporations on export control and sanctions matters; antidumping, countervailing duty, safeguards and section 301 investigations; customs audits; NAFTA verification audits by US, Mexico and Canadian authorities; civil and criminal investigations on export, import and FCPA issues; development, implementation and audits of internal compliance programs; and advising on trade policy initiatives. He has also worked with companies in a range of industries, including softwood lumber, steel, oil exploration and production, chemical products, food and beverages, computer electronics, defense, airlines, textiles, tobacco, banking, telecommunications, and insurance.

### NOLAN, Michael D
Milbank, Tweed, Hadley & McCloy LLP, Washington, DC
202 835 7524
mnolan@milbank.com
*Featured in International Arbitration (Nationwide)*
**Practice Areas:** Partner in Washington, DC office. Has served as counsel or arbitrator in cases under AAA, ICC, ICSID, UNCITRAL and other rules. Represents companies and states in court proceedings involving sovereign immunity, act of state, and recognition and enforcement of foreign judicial and non-judicial awards. Writes frequently on transnational disputes and co-edited collection of determinations in political risk insurance disputes (Oxford University Press). Adjunct professor of law, Georgetown University; member, AAA Board of Directors; member, Panel of ICSID Arbitrators; General Counsel, Intellectual Property Owners Association. Harvard, AB (1988); Univ. of Chicago, JD (1991).

### NOLAN, Thomas J
Skadden, Arps, Slate, Meagher & Flom LLP & Affiliates, Los Angeles
213 687 5000
tnolan@skadden.com
*Featured in Litigation (Nationwide), Litigation (California)*
**Practice Areas:** Chair of Skadden's West Coast Litigation Practice, he is widely recognized as one of the nation's leading trial attorneys and has extensive experience representing corporations and individuals in complex civil and criminal litigation. Has won over $1 billion in trial verdicts for corporate plaintiffs and beat back more than $2 billion in claims against corporate defendants. A former federal prosecutor, he served as Chief of Fraud and Special Prosecutions in the Los Angeles US Attorney's Office, and has been a member of the defense bar since 1979.
**Career:** JD, Loyola University, 1975; BBA, Loyola University, 1971.

### NOLAN, III, Francis X
Vedder Price PC, New York
212 407 6950
fnolan@vedderprice.com
*Featured in Transportation (Nationwide)*
**Practice Areas:** Shareholder, Global Transportation Finance team. Experience in financing of transportation assets and projects, including all types of vessels, drill rigs, locomotives and rolling stock and containers. Assists clients with a wide range of transactions, including operating leases and leveraged and synthetic leasing structures and cross-border transactions.
**Professional Memberships:** Fellow, American College of Commercial Finance Lawyers; Chair, Marine Financing Committee; Board of Directors, Maritime Law Association of the United States.
**Career:** Admitted (NY) 1975, (CA) 1976.
**Publications:** Author, "The Financing of Vessels" chapter in 'Equipment Leasing' (Matthew Bender, 2012).
**Personal:** JD, Syracuse University; A.B., University of Notre Dame.

### NORDAHL, Stephen D
Gibson, Dunn & Crutcher LLP, New York
212 351 2442
snordahl@gibsondunn.com
*Featured in Outsourcing (Nationwide), Technology (New York)*
**Practice Areas:** Practice focuses on information technology, business process and asset management outsourcing transactions, commercial and other technology related transactions, as well as patent acquisitions and licensing, joint ventures and strategic alliances, in each case, focusing on complex international transactions. Works with clients on a wide range of legal and business issues relating to complex outsourcing and technology transactions, including structuring, negotiating and documenting both large and small scale ITO and BPO transactions and assisting clients with complex licensing and systems implementations. Also, represents clients on outsourcing lift-outs, acquisitions and disputes.
**Personal:** JD, Fordham University, 1994; BS, Lehigh University, 1991.

### NORDHAUS, Robert
Van Ness Feldman LLP, Washington, DC
202 298 1910
rrn@vnf.com
*Featured in Energy & Natural Resources (Nationwide)*
**Practice Areas:** Provides strategic counsel on federal electric, natural gas, and environmental regulation, encompassing legislative, regulatory, and transactional work, alternative dispute resolution, and administrative and appellate litigation. Represents electric utilities, independent power producers, end users of natural gas and electricity, and state and local governments, and has served as neutral and party-appointed arbitrator in electric and natural gas arbitration proceedings.
**Professional Memberships:** Energy Bar Association.
**Career:** General Counsel, DOE, 1993-97; General Counsel, FERC, 1977-80; Assistant Administrator, Federal Energy Administration, 1977; Counsel, Committee on Interstate and Foreign Commerce, U.S. House of Representatives, 1975-76.

### NORMAN, James M
Holland & Knight LLP, Fort Lauderdale
954 468 7888
jim.norman@hklaw.com
*Featured in Leisure & Hospitality (Nationwide)*
**Practice Areas:** Co-Chair of Holland & Knight's Global Hospitality, Resort and Timeshare Group. His client responsibilities include owners, operators, licensors and developers of hotels, resorts and mixed-use projects. His practice focuses on all aspects of the development of hotel, resort and mixed-use projects, including the structure and documentation of hospitality industry development ventures and the permitting, design, construction and management and licensing for hotel and resort developments throughout the United States, the Caribbean and Central America. He is a frequent author and lecturer on topics relating to hospitality industry issues and trends, and serves as a mediator of industry disputes.

### NORRIS, Trenton H
Arnold & Porter LLP, San Francisco
415 471 3303
Trent.Norris@aporter.com
*Featured in Environment (California), Food & Beverages (Nationwide)*
See under California for profile.

### NORTON, Lawrence H
Venable LLP, Washington, DC
202 344 4541
lhnorton@Venable.com
*Featured in Government (Nationwide)*
**Practice Areas:** Political Law (Campaign Finance, Lobbying Registration and Disclosure, and Government Ethics); Nonprofit Organizations and Associations; Regulatory.
**Professional Memberships:** Former Member, Maryland Office of Attorney General Campaign Finance Task Force.
**Career:** Partner and Co-Chair, Venable's Political Law Group; General Counsel, Federal Election Commission; Associate Director, Division of Enforcement, Commodity Futures Trading Commission; Assistant Director, Bureau of Consumer Protection, Federal Trade Commission; Maryland Assistant Attorney General, Civil Litigation Division.
**Personal:** JD, University of Maryland School of Law, 1983; BA, magna cum laude, University of Maryland, 1980.

### NORTON IV, Floyd L
Morgan, Lewis & Bockius LLP, Washington, DC
202 739 5620
fnorton@morganlewis.com
*Featured in Energy & Natural Resources (Nationwide)*
**Practice Areas:** Floyd L. Norton, IV is a partner in Morgan Lewis's Energy Practice. His practice focuses on electric utility issues, with an emphasis on regulation and competition. He has a broad background in market power issues and investiga-

tions, mergers and acquisitions, and wholesale power and transmission rates and services. Mr Norton has represented numerous clients in investigations of electric trading and transmission access practices and has advised on development of regional transmission organizations, on regional markets, and on reliability requirements. He also has performed project development and regulatory work for a number of generation projects, particularly renewable energy facilities.

## NORWOOD JR, Colvin G
McGlinchey Stafford PLLC, New Orleans
504 596 2707
wnorwood@mcglinchey.com
*Featured in Products Liability (Nationwide)*

**Practice Areas:** Products liability, business litigation, class action defense, intellectual property, professional liability.
**Professional Memberships:** American, Louisiana State and New Orleans Bar Associations, American Bar Foundation, American College of Trial Lawyers, Defense Research Institute, International Association of Defense Counsel, Louisiana Association of Defense Counsel, Louisiana Bar Foundation, Louisiana Supreme Court Historical Society, New Orleans Association of Defense Counsel, New Orleans Pro Bono Project, Product Liability Advisory Council, Tulane University Dean's Council, Board of Trustees, Xavier University of Louisiana.
**Career:** Practice focuses on defense of products liability litigation; represents Fortune 100 clients as lead counsel in jury cases throughout the United States; cases handled involve heavy equipment, electrical generation and transmission systems, industrial plant design, helicopter accidents, automotive design, medical devices, marine propulsion systems, heavy truck design, and electronic control systems; invited to lecture on advanced concepts in product liability law, product liability trial technique, expert witness examination, and law practice management for professional organizations including the Louisiana Association of Defense Counsel, and the continuing legal education programs of both Tulane University and Louisiana State University law schools; selected for inclusion in Best Lawyers in America and named one of the ten best Louisiana litigators by the National Law Journal.

## NOVETSKY, Terry D
Kaye Scholer LLP, New York
212 836 8590
terry.novetsky@kayescholer.com
*Featured in Capital Markets (Nationwide)*

**Practice Areas:** Terry Novetsky represents US and international banks and other financial institutions in a variety of leveraged finance and structured finance transactions. He also represents several money center banks in global trade finance transactions, many of which involve international companies and cross-border issues. Terry has significant experience in healthcare finance transactions, representing one of the largest lenders in that sector in its financing program and commercial loans. He has also represented numerous senior lender groups in restructurings.
**Career:** Prior to joining Kaye Scholer, Terry was an investment banker, concentrating on energy-related project finance and leveraged leasing.

## NOVICK, Robert T
WilmerHale, Washington, DC
202 663 6140
robert.novick@wilmerhale.com
*Featured in International Trade (Nationwide)*

**Practice Areas:** Co-Managing Partner; Member, Management Committee, Represents clients doing business globally in investment, market access, negotiation, regulatory, government affairs and dispute resolution matters, including clients like Cisco, Google, HP, ExxonMobil and Boeing.
**Career:** Former Counselor and General Counsel, USTR, Executive Office of the President. Among the leadership team that developed US trade policy; was a principal negotiator of the US-China WTO accession agreement and established and implemented the Administration's enforcement and WTO litigation policies.
**Personal:** JD, cum laude, American University, Washington College of Law, Executive Editor, Law Review; BA, Bucknell University.

## NOVIKOFF, Harold S
Wachtell, Lipton, Rosen & Katz, New York
212 403 1249
hsnovikoff@wlrk.com
*Featured in Bankruptcy/Restructuring (Nationwide), Bankruptcy/Restructuring (New York)*

**Practice Areas:** Specialises in creditors' rights, bankruptcy, debt restructurings, and financial markets transactions. Recent representations include US Treasury in Fannie Mae and Freddie Mac rescues, JPMorgan (the largest secured creditor) in the Lehman Brothers and MF Global bankruptcies, and major creditors of Thornburg Mortgage, American Home Mortgage, Collins & Aikman, KKR Atlantic and Pacific, Axon Financial, Victoria Finance, Ottimo, Northwest Airlines, Blockbuster, Meridian Automotive, HealthSouth, 360networks, Independent Wireless One, Looking Glass Networks, National Century Financial Enterprises, American Business Financial Services and Navigator Gas.
**Professional Memberships:** Commissioner on the American Bankruptcy Institute to Study Chapter 11 Reform, former chair of the Committee on Bankruptcy and Corporate Reorganisation of the Association of the Bar of the City of New York; Capital Markets Committee and Rethinking Chapter 11 Committee of the National Bankruptcy Conference; fellow of the American College of Bankruptcy; member of the Steering Committee of the Board of Visitors of Columbia Law School; member of the Law Review at Columbia University School of Law.
**Career:** Partner at Wachtell, Lipton, Rosen & Katz since 1981. Chair of the Restructuring and Finance Practice Group. Has extensive experience in representing the principal lenders, bondholders and underwriters in Chapter 11 cases and out-of-court debt restructurings of a wide range of public and private companies; purchasers of and investors in major financially-distressed companies; and major dealers and other market participants in connection with derivatives, repurchase agreements, securities loans and other financial market transactions. Winner of 2006 Chambers Shield of Excellence in Bankruptcy. Has chaired and taught numerous continuing legal education and professional programs on a broad spectrum of financial, creditors' rights and bankruptcy-related topics, including Chapter 11 plans and disclosure statements, valuation of companies in Chapter 11, bankruptcy-remote vehicles, special protections for financial market transactions in bankruptcy, structuring of loans and other credit transactions, lender liability, and pension claims in bankruptcy.
**Publications:** Contributing author to 'Collier on Bankruptcy' and author of numerous published articles and outlines on bankruptcy-related topics.
**Personal:** Graduated with distinction from Cornell University in 1972 (BS) and from Columbia University Law School in 1975 (JD).

## NOVOGROD, John C
Kramer Levin Naftalis & Frankel LLP, New York
212 715 9327
jnovogrod@kramerlevin.com
*Featured in Wealth Management (Nationwide)*

**Practice Areas:** Complex foreign and domestic estate planning; trust and estate administration; closely-held business, asset protection, and charitable planning and administration.
**Professional Memberships:** American Bar Association, New York State Bar Association, Association of the Bar of the City of New York.
**Publications:** "Federal Transfer Tax Consequences of an Irrevocable Self-Settled Trust Governed by New York Law" (BNA Tax Management, November 1993); "Private Settlements of Fiduciary Accounts: A Prescription For Achieving Finality" (Trusts & Estates Magazine Dec 2000); "The BIG Issues: Confronting Built-in Gains In Transfer Tax Valuations" (New York Law Journal, February 22, 2008); "Estate Planning with Venture Capital Interests"; "Charitable Organizations in the Administrations of Estates and Trusts"; "Law and Vietnam" (Oceana Publications 1968); "Owning Up: The Accountability of a Fiduciary Holding a Controlling Interest in a Corporation" (New York Law Journal, January 31, 2011); "An Estate Planner's Guide to Client Representation" (New York Law Journal, January 30, 2012).

## NOWAK, Gregory J
Pepper Hamilton LLP, Philadelphia
215 981 4893
nowakg@pepperlaw.com
*Featured in Investment Funds (Nationwide)*

**Practice Areas:** Partner. Concentrates practice in securities law, particularly in representing investment management companies and others on matters arising under the Investment Company Act of 1940 and related Investment Advisers Act of 1940. Handles mergers and acquisitions, corporate and regulated investment company tax work. Represents broker-dealers and CTAs/CPOs regarding matters under the Securities Exchange Act of 1934 and the Commodity Exchange Act.
**Publications:** Hedge Fund Disclosure Documents Line by Line – A User's Guide to Confidential Private Placement Memoranda for Funds Formed as Limited Liability Companies. Hedge Fund Agreements Line by Line – A User's Guide to LLC Operating Contracts.

## NUGENT, Eileen T
Skadden, Arps, Slate, Meagher & Flom LLP & Affiliates, New York
212 735 3176
Eileen.Nugent@skadden.com
*Featured in Private Equity (Nationwide), Corporate/M&A (New York)*

**Practice Areas:** Global co-head of corporate transactional practices and co-head of Private Equity Group. Concentrates in M&A, including leveraged buyout transactions. Has worked on a wide variety of acquisitions and dispositions of companies, subsidiaries and divisions, both public and private, hostile and negotiated, in the United States and around the world, representing a wide variety of parties. The breadth of her experience has resulted in her being increasingly regarded as a senior legal, business and strategic advisor to her clients, particularly in the areas of corporate governance and conflict-of-interest situations.
**Career:** JD, Brooklyn Law School, 1978; AB, Cornell University, 1975.

## NUSSBAUM, Bernard W
Wachtell, Lipton, Rosen & Katz, New York
212 403 1266
bwnussbaum@wlrk.com
*Featured in Litigation (Nationwide), Litigation (New York)*

**Practice Areas:** Practice focuses on corporate and securities litigation.
**Professional Memberships:** Admitted to practice in the United States District Courts for the Southern and Eastern Districts of New York, the United States Court of Appeals for the Second Circuit, and the United States Supreme Court; and Member of the Association of the Bar of the City of New York (Vice President from 1984-85), the New York State Bar Association, the American Bar Association, and the Federal Bar Council (President from 1990-92).
**Career:** Partner at Wachtell, Lipton, Rosen & Katz. Has served in both the public and private sectors throughout career, working as an assistant attorney in the United States Attorney's Office for the Southern District of New York after graduating from law school, as senior associate counsel to the United States House of Representatives Judiciary Committee's impeachment inquiry in 1974 regarding President Richard Nixon and as Counsel to the President during the Clinton Administration in 1993 and 1994. Has been a lecturer at Columbia University Law School.
**Personal:** Graduated from Columbia University in 1958 (BA), where he was a member of Phi Beta Kappa, from Harvard Law School in 1961 (LLB), where he was notes editor of Harvard Law Review,

and awarded a Harvard University Sheldon Travelling Fellowship, and was awarded an honorary LLD from George Washington University National Law Center in 1993.

### NYHAN, Lawrence
Sidley Austin LLP, Chicago
312 853 7710
lnyhan@sidley.com
*Featured in Bankruptcy/Restructuring (Nationwide), Bankruptcy/Restructuring (Illinois)*
**Practice Areas:** Co-chair of Sidley's Corporate Reorganization and Bankruptcy practice and member of the firm's Management and Executive Committees.
**Career:** Representative public engagements include: Adelphia Communications; AM Cosmetics, Inc.; AmeriServe Food Distribution, Inc.; Bethlehem Steel Company; Birch Telecommunications; Boston Chicken, Inc.; Budget Group, Inc.; Centennial Coal Company; Choice One Communications; Columbia Gas Transmission Corporation; Devon Convenience Stores, Inc.; Communications Corporation of America; Einstein/Noah Bagel Corp.; Fairchild Aircraft Corporation; Federal Mogul Corporation; Heartland Publications, Inc.; Hilex Poly Co. LLC; Integrated Electrical Services, Inc.; JL French; LaClede Steel Company; Lee Enterprises, Inc.; London Fog Industries, Inc.; and Lone Star Steel Company.

### OATES, Mark A
Baker & McKenzie, Chicago
312 861 7594
Mark.Oates@bakermckenzie.com
*Featured in Tax (Nationwide)*
**Practice Areas:** Tax litigation, federal tax controversies, white-collar criminal defense. Mr Oates is former Chair of the North American Tax Litigation Practice. His practice focuses on large case tax litigation, including domestic and international tax issues.
**Professional Memberships:** American College of Tax Counsel, National Institute of Trial Advocacy, American, Federal, Illinois, Colorado, Chicago, and Denver Bar Associations.
**Career:** JD (cum laude), University of Michigan. MBA and BS (magna cum laude) in Finance, Indiana University.
**Publications:** Mr Oates has published and served on Advisory Boards for the International Tax Journal, Journal of Global Transactions and Journal of Global Transfer Pricing.

### O'BRIEN, Anne
Arnold & Porter LLP, Washington, DC
202 942 6080
Anne.O'Brien@aporter.com
*Featured in Wealth Management (Nationwide)*
**Practice Areas:** She has experience in international and domestic estate planning, trust and estate administration, family governance matters, charitable tax planning, and related areas of federal and state tax law involving transfers of family wealth to succeeding generations. She concentrates on advising wealthy individuals regarding the structure of their US and global holdings and

the transfer of those holdings to family members, trusts, other entities, and charitable organizations.
**Professional Memberships:** Fellow of the American College of Trust and Estate Counsel where she chaired the International Estate Planning Committee and Academician of the International Academy of Estate and Trust law.

### O'BRIEN, James
Baker & McKenzie, Chicago
312 861 8602
James.M.O'Brien@bakermckenzie.com
*Featured in Tax (Nationwide)*
**Practice Areas:** Tax controversies, international tax planning, and transfer pricing. He has tried cases on behalf of Microsoft, Symantec, Compaq Computer, Perkin-Elmer, Union Carbide and Sundstrand. Regularly represents US and foreign multinationals in competent authority and IRS administrative proceedings.
**Career:** Graduated from the Harvard Law School (magna cum laude) and has spent his entire career with Baker & McKenzie LLP. He is a past Chair of the North American Tax Practice Group.
**Publications:** Mr O'Brien is the lead author of US Corporations Doing Business Abroad (RIA), now in its ninth edition. He has written over 40 tax articles.

### O'BRIEN, Peter
Hunton & Williams LLP, New York
212 309 1024
pobrien@hunton.com
*Featured in Energy & Natural Resources (Nationwide)*
**Practice Areas:** Mr O'Brien has extensive experience in domestic and international capital markets transactions, with emphasis on financings by regulated and unregulated power companies. He is underwriters counsel to several large utility systems, has served as products counsel to investment banks and acted as US securities counsel for distribution and supply companies in Australia and the UK.
**Career:** Partner, Dewey & LeBoeuf. Energy, corporate finance, tax exempt finance. Admitted to practice, 1992, New York.
**Personal:** JD, Washington & Lee University School of Law, 1991. BA, The College of Holy Cross, 1988.

### O'BRIEN, Vincent
Nixon Peabody LLP, New York
212 940 3139
vobrien@nixonpeabody.com
*Featured in Food & Beverages (Nationwide)*
**Practice Areas:** Vincent "Vince" O'Brien has extensive experience in beverage alcohol law, representing beer, wine, and spirits industries clients globally. He is member of the US delegation to the International Federation of Wines and Spirits, an advisor to the Laws and Regulations Working Group of the International Wine Office (OIV), and a founding member of the International Wine Law Association. Mr O'Brien has been honored by wine societies in France and Hungary and is a recipient of France's Chevalier de l'Ordre Mérite Agricole. He previously served as general

counsel, executive VP, and director of Joseph E. Seagram & Sons, Inc.

### O'BRIEN, William
McKenna Long & Aldridge LLP, Washington, DC
202 496 7107
wobrien@mckennalong.com
*Featured in International Arbitration (Nationwide)*
**Career:** William O'Brien focuses on international arbitration and litigation in complex government contracts and commercial disputes. Mr O'Brien has extensive experience litigating before numerous major international arbitral institutions and US courts involving among other issues, breach of contract disputes, cross-border enforcement of arbitration awards, treaty issues, foreign sovereign immunity, defense against allegations of fraud or corruption, and handling of multi-jurisdictional matters. In addition, he actively counsels clients and conducts investigations on matters concerning U.S. Export Laws and Regulations and the Foreign Corrupt Practices Act ("FCPA") involving audits, compliance programs, classification and licensing issues, voluntary disclosures, and governmental actions.

### O'CONNOR, James
Sidley Austin LLP, New York
212 839 8613
joconnor@sidley.com
*Featured in Capital Markets (Nationwide)*
**Practice Areas:** Partner in Sidley's New York office. He represents both issuers and underwriters in a wide variety of corporate and securities matters and capital markets transactions. His experience includes public and private offerings of all types, including IPOs and other common equity transactions, preferred stock offerings and secured and unsecured debt transactions (registered and 144A). In addition to securities transactions, his practice includes consultation with clients regarding corporate governance matters and public company reporting obligations.
**Personal:** Albany Law School of Union University, JD, 1991, cum laude, Albany Law Review, Note and Comment Editor; Georgetown University, BA, 1986.

### O'CONNOR, William
Morrison & Foerster LLP, San Diego
858 720 7932
woconnor@mofo.com
*Featured in Transportation (Nationwide)*
**Practice Areas:** Mr O'Connor handles aviation, product liability, commercial, and IP litigation. He has tried jury cases to verdict in federal and state court. He has represented airlines, aerospace manufacturers, and airports in cases involving commercial airline crashes, and military and civilian helicopter and business jet accidents.
**Professional Memberships:** Leadership Development Committee, Association of Business Trial Lawyers, SD Chapter; Barrister, Honorable J. Clifford Wallace Chapter, American Inns of Court; and Lawyer Pilots Bar Assn.
**Career:** Pilot; secondment to the Group General Counsel of Amlin, PLC (a Lloyd's insurer).

**Personal:** BA, University of California, San Diego. JD, Georgetown University Law Center.

### ODONER, Ellen J
Weil, Gotshal & Manges LLP, New York
212 310 8438
ellen.odoner@weil.com
*Featured in Securities (Nationwide)*
**Practice Areas:** As Head of Weil's Public Company Advisory Group, Ellen Odoner advises US public companies and US-listed foreign private issuers, as well as boards of directors and audit and other independent committees, on SEC disclosure, corporate governance, financial restatements and internal control matters. She is one of the leaders of the firm's high-stakes corporate counseling team. She also specializes in merger and acquisition and securities transactions, particularly those with cross-border elements, and has extensive experience representing non-US companies in the US.
**Personal:** Yale University (BA, magna cum laude); Harvard University (JD).

### O'DONNELL, Earle
White & Case LLP, Washington, DC
202 626 3582
eodonnell@whitecase.com
*Featured in Energy & Natural Resources (Nationwide)*
**Career:** To view a comprehensive biography, please visit www.whitecase.com/eodonnell.

### O'DONNELL, G Daniel
Dechert LLP, Philadelphia
215 994 2762
daniel.odonnell@dechert.com
*Featured in Private Equity (Nationwide), Corporate/M&A (Pennsylvania)*
See under Pennsylvania for profile.

### OELMAN, David
Vinson & Elkins LLP, Houston
713 758 3708
doelman@velaw.com
*Featured in Corporate/M&A (Texas), Capital Markets (Texas), Capital Markets (Nationwide)*
See under Texas for profile.

### O'GORMAN, Kevin
Fulbright & Jaworski LLP, Houston
713 651 3771
kogorman@fulbright.com
*Featured in International Arbitration (Nationwide)*
**Practice Areas:** International arbitration and litigation.
**Professional Memberships:** Vice Chair, Energy Arbitrators List; Past Chair, Disputes Division and International Arbitration Committee of ABA International; Member, ICDR, AAA and HMAA Rosters of Arbitrators; Former Team Leader & Senior Legal Secretary, Claims Resolution Tribunal for Dormant Accounts in Switzerland; Admitted Texas, New York and England & Wales (Solicitor).
**Career:** Kevin represents clients in energy, commercial, investor-state and construction disputes and serves as arbitrator.
**Personal:** JD, cum laude, University of Michigan Law School; University of Bonn; BA, magna cum laude, University of Houston.

## O'HANLON, John V
Dechert LLP, Boston
617 728 7111
john.ohanlon@dechert.com
*Featured in Investment Funds (Nationwide), Investment Funds (Massachusetts)*
**Practice Areas:** Mr O'Hanlon represents investment managers, investment funds and their boards of directors, and other financial institutions in corporate, regulatory, compliance, and enforcement matters.
**Professional Memberships:** Member, Massachusetts Bar; member, American Bar Association Federal Securities Law Committee; co-chair, Boston Bar Association Investment Companies and Investment Advisers Committee.
**Career:** Mr O'Hanlon served on the staff of the U.S. Securities and Exchange Commission's Division of Investment Management for five years.
**Personal:** Georgetown University (B.S.F.S., 1984); Georgetown University Law Center (JD, 1989, cum laude).

## OLD, Gareth
Clifford Chance US LLP, New York
212 878 8539
gareth.old@cliffordchance.com
*Featured in Capital Markets (Nationwide)*
**Practice Areas:** Concentrates on regulation and trading of commodity and derivatives, including cleared and uncleared derivative transactions. Advising major sell-side and buy-side clients on regulatory matters, including capital, margin and netting, clearing and exchange-trading, reporting, documentation and the implementation of compliant trading and business conduct systems. Significant experience in bilateral and synthetic securities transactions involving commodities, rates, FX and credit derivatives, repurchase agreements and securities lending, and in the resolution of derivatives exposures.
**Career:** Before coming to New York, worked with Clifford Chance in London, Hong Kong and Frankfurt. Admitted in England and Wales and New York.

## O'LEARY, Michael
Andrews Kurth LLP, Houston
713 220 4360
moleary@andrewskurth.com
*Featured in Corporate/M&A (Texas), Capital Markets (Texas), Energy & Natural Resources (Nationwide)*
See under Texas for profile.

## OLSHAN, Regina
Skadden, Arps, Slate, Meagher & Flom LLP & Affiliates, New York
212 735 3963
regina.olshan@skadden.com
*Featured in Employee Benefits & Executive Compensation (Nationwide), Employee Benefits & Executive Compensation (New York)*
See under New York for profile.

## OLSON, John
Gibson, Dunn & Crutcher LLP, Washington, DC
202 955 8522
jolson@gibsondunn.com
*Featured in Securities (Nationwide)*
**Practice Areas:** Identified in surveys as one of the nation's foremost authorities on securities law, corporate governance and M&A. Advises boards and committees of leading companies including General Electric, Coca Cola, BP plc, Marriott, Textron, ConEd, and MGIC. Leads independent internal investigations.
**Professional Memberships:** Executive Council, Securities Law Divison, Federal Bar Association; Former Chair, ABA Committees on Corporate Governance and Federal Regulation of Securities.
**Career:** Distinguished Visitor from Practice, Georgetown Law School; formerly taught, Northwestern and Cornell Law Schools.
**Publications:** Over 100 articles; several books.
**Personal:** JD, Harvard, cum laude, 1964; BA, University of California, Berkeley, with highest honors, 1961.

## OLSON, Theodore B
Gibson, Dunn & Crutcher LLP, Washington, DC
202 955 8668
tolson@gibsondunn.com
*Featured in Appellate Law (Nationwide)*
**Practice Areas:** One of the nation's premier appellate and US Supreme Court advocates, argued 59 cases in the Supreme Court (including Bush v Gore cases). Practice encompasses constitutional law, appellate, media, commercial disputes and crisis management.
**Professional Memberships:** American College of Trial Lawyers; American Academy of Appellate Lawyers.
**Career:** US Solicitor General, 2001-2004; Assistant US Attorney General, Office of Legal Counsel, 1981-1984; private counsel to Presidents Ronald Reagan and George W. Bush; Visiting Scholar, National Constitution Center, 2007; Council Member, Administrative Conference of the United States.
**Personal:** JD, University of California - Berkeley, 1965.

## O'NEIL, John J
Paul, Weiss, Rifkind, Wharton & Garrison LLP, New York
212 373 3379
joneil@paulweiss.com
*Featured in Wealth Management (Nationwide)*
**Practice Areas:** Partner and Co-Chair of Personal Representation Department. Concentrates on international and domestic estate planning, trusts and estates administration and related tax work, matrimonial matters including divorce and premarital agreements, private foundations and planning for partnerships and closely held corporations. Has extensive experience in representing the development offices of two major medical centers and a large number of family offices. Member of the Association of the Bar of the City of New York, New York State Bar

Association and the American Bar Association. Fellow of the American College of Trust and Estate Counsel.

## O'NEIL, John R
Kirkland & Ellis LLP, New York
212 446 4991
john.oneil@kirkland.com
*Featured in Investment Funds (Nationwide)*
**Practice Areas:** Mr O'Neil concentrates his practice on representing both domestic and international sponsors of leading private equity, venture capital, hedge and other private investment funds. Mr O'Neil has represented sponsors in numerous billion dollar private equity fund formations, as well as assisted clients with a wide range of on-going operational as well as extraordinary events involving private investment funds including "key person" events, investor defaults, strategic investments in fund sponsors and other significant transactions.
**Personal:** Northwestern University School of Law, JD, cum laude, 1998; University of Wisconsin, B.B.A, Management Information Systems, 1991.

## O'NEILL, Brian D
Van Ness Feldman LLP, Washington, DC
202 298 1983
bdo@vnf.com
*Featured in Energy & Natural Resources (Nationwide)*
**Practice Areas:** Advises clients on energy projects, privatizations and regulatory matters. Clients include major natural gas and oil pipelines, LNG companies, and electric utilities. Experienced litigator in regulatory proceedings involving complex tariff and ratemaking issues, multi-million dollar construction projects, transportation and supply contract matters.
**Professional Memberships:** ABA; Energy Bar Association; Florida Bar; DC Bar.
**Career:** Dewey & LeBoeuf (1980-2012); Farmer, Shibley, McGuinn & Flood (1975-1980); Federal Power Commission, Trial Attorney (1972-75); Military Service: US Air Force (1971-72).
**Publications:** Contributing author, Energy Law and Transactions; Energy Law Journal; Natural Gas & Electricity.
**Personal:** Florida State University (JD) 1971, (BA) 1968.

## ORAVA, Stephen J
King & Spalding LLP, Washington, DC
202 661 7937
sorava@kslaw.com
*Featured in International Trade (Nationwide)*
**Practice Areas:** Advises clients on a wide range of international trade, market access, investment and other regulatory matters, as well as related litigation and enforcement actions, including antidumping, countervailing duty (anti-subsidy) and safeguard proceedings in the United States, the European Union, China, Mexico, India and other countries.
**Personal:** Georgetown University (JD, 1993); Southern Methodist University (BS, magna cum laude, 1990); London School of Economics and Political Science, UK (Legal Studies, 1989).

## ORDWAY, Eric
Weil, Gotshal & Manges LLP, New York
212 310 8609
eric.ordway@weil.com
*Featured in International Arbitration (Nationwide)*
**Practice Areas:** Eric Ordway is a leading member of Weil's International Arbitration Group. He specializes in international commercial and investor-state arbitration, representing companies and foreign governments in disputes concerning various sectors, such as nuclear power, oil and gas, real estate, financial services and banking. He has handled international arbitrations before the ICC, AAA, International Arbitration Center of The Austrian Federal Economic Chamber, Arbitration Court of Hungarian Chamber of Commerce, ICSID, and investor-state arbitrations under UNCITRAL rules.
**Personal:** Institut d'Etudes Politiques (CEP, 1970); Princeton University (AB, 1971); New York University (MA, 1982); Brooklyn Law School (JD, cum laude, 1986).

## ORINGER, Andrew L
Dechert LLP, New York
212 698 3571
andrew.oringer@dechert.com
*Featured in Employee Benefits & Executive Compensation (Nationwide), Employee Benefits & Executive Compensation (New York)*
**Practice Areas:** Mr Oringer, co-chair of Dechert's ERISA and Executive Compensation group, leads the firm's national fiduciary practice. He counsels clients on employee benefit plans and programs, benefits-related tax matters and fiduciary issues in connection with the investment of employee benefit plan assets.
**Professional Memberships:** Co-chair, New York State Bar Association Tax Section's Employee Benefits Committee; Chair, ABA Section of Taxation's Fiduciary/Investments Subcommittee of the Employee Benefits Committee; Fellow, American College of Employee Benefits Counsel; Adjunct Professor, Hofstra University School of Law.
**Personal:** Duke University (A.B., 1980); Adelphi University (MBA., 1984) Hofstra University School of Law (JD, 1984).

## ORTELERE, Brian T
Morgan, Lewis & Bockius LLP, Philadelphia
215 9635150
bortelere@morganlewis.com
*Featured in ERISA Litigation (Nationwide)*
**Practice Areas:** Brian T. Ortelere is a partner in Morgan Lewis's Labor and Employment Practice, resident in New York and Philadelphia, and is co-chair of the ERISA Litigation Practice. Brian's practice covers the full range of ERISA litigation matters, including numerous class actions. He defends class action claims challenging the administration of defined benefit pension plans, 401(k) savings plans, cash balance plans, and ESOPs. Brian is a former law clerk to the Hon. William D. Hutchinson of the United States Court of Appeals for the Third Circuit.
**Personal:** Attended College of William & Mary, 1986, JD; Muhlenberg College, 1983, A.B.

**OSBORN, John W**
Skadden, Arps, Slate, Meagher & Flom LLP & Affiliates, New York
212 735 3270
John.Osborn@skadden.com
*Featured in Capital Markets (Nationwide)*
**Practice Areas:** Head of Skadden's Derivative Financial Products Group. In his OTC derivatives practice, represents banks and other dealers, as well as major corporations, private funds and other end-users. He has analyzed, developed, negotiated and documented full range of equity, credit and other transactions. In his securities-related financial products practice, represents issuers, banks and other parties in wide range of convertible securities, equity securities units and other complex debt, equity and structured securities. Strong new product development focus. Significant involvement in restructurings and litigations.
**Career:** SEC, 1975-1979; JD, University of Pennsylvania School of Law, 1975; BA, Michigan State University, 1972.

**OSENDARP, Joanne**
Hughes Hubbard & Reed LLP, New York
212 837 6165
osendarp@hugheshubbard.com
*Featured in International Trade (Nationwide)*
**Practice Areas:** Joanne Osendarp advises and represents governments, industry associations, export credit agencies and companies in international trade and investment matters, including dispute settlement proceedings under the NAFTA and WTO, international arbitrations, bilateral and regional negotiations, and trade law investigations before the Department of Commerce and the ITC. She previously served as senior trade counsel with the Government of Canada and played key roles in the negotiation and drafting of NAFTA, the Agreement on Internal Trade and the Softwood Lumber Agreement.
**Personal:** York University BA, MA; University of Ottawa LLB.

**OSHINSKY, Jerold**
Jenner & Block LLP, Los Angeles
213 239 5156
joshinsky@jenner.com
*Featured in Insurance (Nationwide), Insurance (California)*
**Career:** Co-chair of the Insurance Litigation & Counseling Practice, Jerold Oshinsky represents policyholders in complex and significant insurance coverage matters in federal and state courts. Mr Oshinsky's coverage practice involves representing policyholders in major coverage disputes ranging from products and environmental claims to emerging areas involving directors and officers, universities, hospitals, law firms and more traditional Fortune 500 clients. He leads the firm insurance teams representing Duke University in the lacrosse player claims and Pennsylvania State University in the claims stemming from the Gerald Sandusky affair. He frequently lectures and publishes on a variety of insurance law topics.

**OSTERMAN, Jeffrey D**
Weil, Gotshal & Manges LLP, New York
212 310 8155
jeffrey.osterman@weil.com
*Featured in Outsourcing (Nationwide), Technology (New York)*
See under New York for profile.

**OSTRAGER, Barry R**
Simpson Thacher & Bartlett LLP, New York
212 455 2655
bostrager@stblaw.com
*Featured in Insurance (Nationwide), Litigation (Nationwide), Insurance (New York), Litigation (New York)*
**Practice Areas:** Senior Litigation Partner. Tried scores of cases and argued dozens of appeals in U.S. Circuit Courts. Prominently involved in many high profile cases. Successfully argued before the United States Supreme Court twice. Lead trial Counsel in five multi-billion dollar cases that resulted in successful trial verdicts, and many centi-million dollar cases.
**Professional Memberships:** American Bar Association, City Bar Association, Federal Bar Council
**Career:** Partner since 1980.
**Publications:** Co-author: 'Handbook on Insurance Coverage Disputes' (Wolters Kluwer Law & Business, 16th Ed 2012).
**Personal:** New York University (JD 1972); City College of New York (BA 1968; MA 1973).

**OWENS, Andre**
WilmerHale, Washington, DC
202 663 6350
andre.owens@wilmerhale.com
*Featured in Financial Services Regulation (Nationwide)*
**Practice Areas:** Partner, Securities Department; member, Broker-Dealer Compliance and Regulation Practice Group; Co-Chair D.C. Diversity Committee; Member, D.C. Recruiting Committee. Practice focuses on broker-dealer and investment adviser activities including counseling clients on compliance with SEC, FINRA and NYSE rules including: Regulation M and Regulation NMS; Regulation ATS; short sale and other trading rules; and sales practice and order handling matters. Also counsels clients on acquisitions of securities broker-dealers and investment advisers.
**Career:** Member of SEC's Office of General Counsel 1992-1994; Counsel to SEC Commissioner 1994-1997.
**Personal:** Harvard Law School (JD); Providence College (BA, summa cum laude).

**OWREN-WIEST, Nicole J**
Wiley Rein LLP, Washington, DC
202 719 7430
nowrenwiest@wileyrein.com
*Featured in Government (Nationwide)*
**Practice Areas:** Represents government contractors on bid protests; DCAA audits, CAS and cost allowability; data rights/IP; OCIs; REAs; CDA claims, disputes and appeals; subcontract and teaming agreements; and terminations.

**Professional Memberships:** ABA Section of Public Contract Law: Editor-in-Chief, The Procurement Lawyer; Vice-Chair, Accounting Cost and Pricing Committee; Research and Development and Intellectual Property Committee; Advisory Board, Government Contract Costs Pricing & Accounting Report; National Defense Industrial Association, Procurement Division, Procurement Planning & Contract Finance Committees; Federal Circuit Bar Association, Vice-Chair, Government Contracts Committee.
**Career:** Counsel, Boeing Commercial Airplanes (2004-2005).
**Personal:** Willamette University College of Law (JD); Minnesota State University (BS).

**PALMA, Laura**
Simpson Thacher & Bartlett LLP, New York
212 455 2000
lpalma@stblaw.com
*Featured in Capital Markets (Nationwide)*
**Practice Areas:** Corporate Partner primarily concentrating on structured finance transactions, including esoteric structured finance transactions, such as rental car and rental truck fleet financings, franchise royalty securitizations, intellectual property securitizations, cell tower securitizations, aircraft portfolio securitizations and timeshare loan securitizations, and auto, truck and equipment loan and lease securitizations, dealer floorplan securitizations and other receivables financings.
**Career:** Partner since 1995.
**Personal:** BA, magna cum laude, Dartmouth College (1980), Phi Beta Kappa; JD, Columbia Law School (1983).

**PALMER, Christopher E**
Goodwin Procter LLP, Washington, DC
202 346 4253
cpalmer@goodwinprocter.com
*Featured in Investment Funds (Nationwide)*
**Practice Areas:** Mr Palmer focuses his practice on securities, investment management and insurance matters. He represents mutual funds, investment advisers, insurance companies and broker-dealers on the development, regulatory approval, sale and administration of a variety of investment products, including mutual funds and variable and fixed life insurance and annuity contracts. He advises companies on securities law matters, including reporting and corporate governance matters, and represents companies in financial services litigation, SEC inspections and enforcement actions, and before state insurance departments.
**Personal:** JD, Georgetown University Law Center, 1986 (magna cum laude); BA, St John's University (Minnesota), 1982 (egregia cum laude).

**PANAGAKIS, George N**
Skadden, Arps, Slate, Meagher & Flom LLP & Affiliates, Chicago
312 407 0638
george.panagakis@skadden.com
*Featured in Bankruptcy/Restructuring (Nationwide), Bankruptcy/Restructuring (Illinois)*
See under Illinois for profile.

**PANOVKA, Robin**
Wachtell, Lipton, Rosen & Katz, New York
212-403-1352
rpanovka@wlrk.com
*Featured in Capital Markets (Nationwide), Real Estate (New York)*
See under New York for profile.

**PANTALEO, Peter V**
Simpson Thacher & Bartlett LLP, New York
212 455 2220
ppantaleo@stblaw.com
*Featured in Bankruptcy/Restructuring (Nationwide), Bankruptcy/Restructuring (New York)*
**Practice Areas:** Partner in and head of the Firm's Bankruptcy Department. Exclusively involved in major workouts and reorganisations representing agent banks, lending syndicates, buyers and distressed investors. Actively involved in all areas of the practice, including court proceedings, drafting, negotiating, counseling, chairing meetings, writing and lecturing. Experience in many industries, including healthcare, energy, steel, retail, real estate, textile, telecom, automotive, financial institutions and media and entertainment.
**Career:** Joined Firm as a Partner in 2001. Member, American College of Bankruptcy.
**Personal:** New York University School of Law (JD 1982); Columbia College (BA 1978).

**PANTANO, Paul**
Cadwalader, Wickersham & Taft LLP, Washington, DC
202 862 2410
paul.pantano@cwt.com
*Featured in Capital Markets (Nationwide), Energy & Natural Resources (Nationwide)*
**Practice Areas:** Head, Energy & Commodities Group. Represents energy companies, commodity and swap dealers, brokerage firms, trade associations and financial industry professionals in a variety of transactional, regulatory, legislative and litigation matters. Represents clients before the Commodity Futures Trading Commission, Federal Energy Regulatory Commission, and other governmental agencies. Experience negotiating and drafting structured commodity and derivative transactions.
**Professional Memberships:** Past Chair, ABA Committee on Regulation of Futures & Derivative Instruments; Member, Futures Industry Association, Inc. Law & Compliance Division, Energy Bar Association, and District of Columbia Bar Association.
**Career:** Former trial attorney, Division of Enforcement, Commodity Futures Trading Commission (CFTC).
**Publications:** Frequent speaker, lecturer and author of numerous articles and publications. Contributing editor, Cadwalader's Energy & Commodities Resource Center (www.energy-lawresourcecenter.com).
**Personal:** JD, Duke University School of Law; BA, Trinity College.

## PAPARELLA, Christopher
Hughes Hubbard & Reed LLP, New York
212 837 6644
paparella@hugheshubbard.com
*Featured in International Arbitration (Nationwide)*
**Practice Areas:** International arbitration, business litigation.
**Professional Memberships:** Contributor, Yearbook of Commerical Arbitration.
**Career:** Partner, Hughes Hubbard & Reed since 2006; previously a Partner at Nixon Peabody in New York.
**Personal:** St. John's University School of Law, JD, 1987; University of Scranton, BA, 1983, magna cum laude; University of Amsterdam (courses in international law, European Communities law, international relations, and economics).

## PAPARELLI, Angelo
Seyfarth Shaw LLP, Los Angeles
213 270 9797
apaparelli@seyfarth.com
*Featured in Immigration (California), Immigration (Nationwide)*
See under California for profile.

## PAPAVIZAS, Constantine G
Winston & Strawn LLP, Washington, DC
202 282 5732
cpapavizas@winston.com
*Featured in Transportation (Nationwide)*
**Practice Areas:** Foreign investment in US maritime industry/Jones Act, maritime finance, maritime litigation, US regulatory and legislative.
**Professional Memberships:** Editorial Board, J Maritime Law & Commerce (2003-); Governors, DC Propeller Club (1996-2002); frequent conference speaker.
**Publications:** Publications include: 'Does the Jones Act Apply to Offshore Alternative Energy Projects?' Tulane Maritime LJ (Summer 2010); 'Is the Jones Act Redundant' USF Maritime LJ (2008-09); 'US-Flag Vessel Financing and Citizenship Requirements' Tulane Maritime LJ (Winter 2007); '2009-2010 US Maritime Legislative Developments', J Maritime Law & Commerce (July 2011).
**Personal:** Georgetown (BA, 1978); Columbia (MIA, 1981); George Washington (JD, 1984 with honors).

## PAPSON, Thomas C
McKenna Long & Aldridge LLP, Washington, DC
202 496 7639
tpapson@mckennalong.com
*Featured in Government (Nationwide)*
**Career:** Tom Papson is an experienced litigator and bid protest lawyer, focusing on business litigation relating to government contracts. His practice includes conflict of interest and ethics matters, contract disputes, trade secret misappropriation and unfair competition claims, Administrative Procedure Act and Freedom of Information matters, contract and tort claims against the United States, and protests of both state and federal government contract awards. Mr Papson has prosecuted and defended major bid protest cases involving telecommunications, information tech-

nology, healthcare, and aerospace/defense procurements in the federal courts and before the Government Accountability Office.

## PARISI, Donna
Shearman & Sterling LLP, New York
212 848 7367
dparisi@shearman.com
*Featured in Capital Markets (Nationwide)*
**Practice Areas:** Donna Parisi is Co-Practice Group Leader of the Asset Management Group and a former member of the firm's Executive Group. Her practice focuses on derivatives and structured products, assisting in the development and structuring of new financial products and in the negotiation and documentation of OTC derivative transactions. Ms Parisi has developed, documented and implemented risk management strategies and policies for clients in both the OTC and exchange-traded derivatives markets and has been actively advising market participants regarding global financial regulatory reform.
**Career:** New York Bar, 1994. Partner since 2001.
**Personal:** Boston College Law School, Vassar College.

## PARK, William W
William W Park - Sole Practitioner, Boston
617 353 3149
wwpark@bu.edu
*Featured in International Arbitration (Nationwide)*
**Practice Areas:** Arbitrator in commercial, BIT and ad hoc proceedings in English and French. Foreign investment, joint ventures, insurance, acquisitions, LNG price adjustment, taxation, construction and finance.
**Professional Memberships:** President, London Court of International Arbitration; General Editor, Arbitration International ; Panel of Arbitrators, International Centre for the Settlement of Investment Disputes (ICSID); NAFTA Chapter 14 Financial Services Roster; Member, International Council for Commercial Arbitration (ICCA); Chartered Arbitrator; Fellow, College of Commercial Arbitrators.
**Career:** Professor of Law, Boston University (1979-present ); Director, Boston University Center for Banking and Financial Law Studies (1990-93); Appeals Tribunal, International Commission on Holocaust Era Insurance Claims (2001-06); Arbitrator, Claims Resolution Tribunal for Dormant Accounts in Switzerland (1998-2002); Counsel, Rope & Gray, Boston (1990-2005); law practice, Paris (1972-79). Visiting Academic Appointments include Cambridge University, Fletcher School of Law and Diplomacy, University of Geneva, University of Dijon, University of Hong Kong, University of Auckland.
**Publications:** Works include ARBITRATION OF INTERNATIONAL BUSINESS DISPUTES (2006; Second Ed. 2012); INTERNATIONAL CHAMBER OF COMMERCE ARBITRATION (1984; Third Edition, 2000), with Craig & Paulsson; INTERNATIONAL FORUM SELECTION (1995); INTERNATIONAL COMMERCIAL ARBITRATION (1997), with Reisman, Craig & Paulsson; INCOME TAX TREATY ARBITRATION (2004), with Tillinghast.

**Personal:** Yale, BA; Columbia, JD, Cambridge, MA. Admitted to Bar, Massachusetts and District of Columbia.

## PARKER, Bruce
Venable LLP, Baltimore
410 244 7400
brparker@venable.com
*Featured in Products Liability (Nationwide)*
**Practice Areas:** Product liability and mass torts; litigation pharmaceuticals; drugs, medical devices and biologics; consumer products and services; nanotechnology; life sciences.
**Professional Memberships:** Fellow, American College of Trial Lawyers, Past President, International Association of Defense Counsel, Past Board member, DRI.
**Career:** Practice focuses primarily on product liability and toxic tort litigation, in particular, pharmaceutical and medical device product liability litigation. Clients include: Boehringer Ingelheim Pharmaceuticals, Inc.; LabCorp; Takeda Pharmaceuticals; Johnson & Johnson; Georgia Pacific; Navistar International, Inc.; and Vulcan Materials Company.
**Personal:** JD, Valedictorian, Catholic University of America, Columbus School of Law, 1978; BA, with honors, Johns Hopkins University, 1975.

## PARKER, C Allen
Cravath, Swaine & Moore LLP, New York
212 474 1765
aparker@cravath.com
*Featured in Banking & Finance (Nationwide)*
**Practice Areas:** C. Allen Parker is Cravath's Presiding Partner. He has extensive experience in a broad range of finance, banking and related matters, including syndicated loan transactions, acquisition financings and leveraged recapitalizations, as well as extensive experience in a broad range of corporate advisory matters. Mr Parker's clients have included JPMorgan Chase, Citigroup, Covenant House, DreamWorks Animation, DreamWorks Studios, Kissinger Associates and Permira.
**Personal:** Columbia Law School (JD, magna cum laude, 1983; Harlan Fiske Stone Scholar; Notes and Comments Editor, Law Review); University of Chicago (MA, 1980); Duke University (BA, magna cum laude, 1977). For more information:
http://www.cravath.com/aparker

## PARKER, Kimberly
WilmerHale, Washington, DC
202 663 6987
kimberly.parker@wilmerhale.com
*Featured in International Trade (Nationwide)*
**Practice Areas:** Partner, Litigation/Controversy Department; member, Investigations and Criminal Litigation Practice; Co-Chair, Pro Bono/Community Service Committee. Practice focuses on white-collar matters and internal and congressional investigations. Significant experience in Foreign Corrupt Practices Act matters. Recent FCPA cases include representing Armor Holdings and Helmerich & Payne in their settlements with the SEC and DOJ.

**Publications:** Co-author of the leading treatise, "Complying with the Foreign Corrupt Practices Act" (Matthew Bender, 7th ed. 2010).
**Personal:** Named to the The American Lawyer's list of "45 Under 45;" Harvard Law School (JD, magna cum laude); Princeton University (AB, magna cum laude).

## PARKER, Steve
Arnold & Porter LLP, McLean
703.720.7006
Steve.Parker@aporter.com
*Featured in Intellectual Property (Northern Virginia), Life Sciences (Nationwide)*
See under Virginia for profile.

## PARKS, Randall S
Hunton & Williams LLP, Richmond
804 788 7375
rparks@hunton.com
*Featured in Outsourcing (Nationwide)*
**Practice Areas:** Randy Parks leads the firm's Global Technology and Sourcing Group. His practice focuses on complex commercial transactions, particularly business process and information technology outsourcing, licensing, systems acquisition, development and integration agreements and joint ventures. Mr Parks and his team have negotiated and documented multiple large-scale, global outsourcing transactions valued at billions of dollars for numerous Global 2000 firms.

## PASICH, Kirk A
Dickstein Shapiro LLP, Los Angeles
310 772 8305
pasichk@dicksteinshapiro.com
*Featured in Insurance (Nationwide), Insurance (California)*
**Practice Areas:** Represents insureds in complex coverage matters, including trial and appellate matters. Provides strategic insurance advice in business transactions. Substantial experience in all lines of insurance and industries, including the entertainment industry, and in resolving a wide range of disputes.
**Publications:** Mr Pasich is the author of more than 400 articles and columns. He writes insurance law columns for the Los Angeles Daily Journal and the San Francisco Daily Journal.
**Personal:** BA, cum laude, from the University of California, Los Angeles (1977) and JD, cum laude, from Loyola Law School in Los Angeles, California (1980).

## PASSANNANTE, William G
Anderson Kill & Olick, P.C., New York
212 278 1328
wpassannante@andersonkill.com
*Featured in Insurance (Nationwide), Insurance (New York)*
**Practice Areas:** A leading lawyer for corporations seeking insurance recovery, William G. Passannante has represented policyholders in major precedent-setting cases tried in courts throughout the country. In recent years he has successfully pursued claims for clients including a foreign manufacturer seeking defense and indemnification for a large number of asbestos claims; Princeton University in a claim on its D&O liability insurance policy; and franchisees of a major

food chain in a business income recovery matter stemming from alleged food-borne illness. He also has represented a number of large financial institutions, as well as chemical companies, telecommunications companies, and healthcare-related organizations in multi-million dollar insurance recovery efforts. Earlier in his career, Mr Passannante represented Weyerhaeuser Company in its precedent-setting insurance recovery case.
**Publications:** Mr Passannante frequently writes on insurance recovery issues in publications including National Underwriter, University Business, The International Bar Association (IBA) Newsletter, Risk Management Magazine, Marketwatch, The Brief, Corporate Counsel Magazine, The Corporate Counselor, Corporate Board Member, and American Banker. He is also the editor of the book, The Policyholder Advisor, published by Juris Publishing.

### PASTUSZENSKI, Brian E
Goodwin Procter LLP, Boston
617 570 1094
bpastuszenski@goodwinprocter.com
*Featured in Securities (Nationwide), Litigation (Massachusetts)*
See under Massachusetts for profile.

### PATRICK, Kathy
Gibbs & Bruns LLP, Houston
713 751 5253
kpatrick@gibbsbruns.com
*Featured in Securities (Nationwide), Litigation (Texas)*
See under Texas for profile.

### PATRIKIS, Ernest T
White & Case LLP, New York
212 819 8200
epatrikis@whitecase.com
*Featured in Financial Services Regulation (Nationwide)*
**Career:** Ernest (Ernie) T. Patrikis is a partner in White & Case's New York office its firmwide Bank and Insurance Regulatory Practice. Mr Patrikis is one of the few lawyers in private practice who has extensive experience in both the banking and insurance industries, having served in senior positions for 30 years at the Federal Reserve Bank of New York and for eight years at AIG. To view a comprehensive biography, please visit www.whitecase.com/epatrikis.

### PATTON, David
Locke Lord LLP, Houston
713 226 1254
dpatton@lockelord.com
*Featured in Energy & Natural Resources (Nationwide)*
**Practice Areas:** Co-chairs the Firm's Energy Practice Group. He has over 30 years of experience in various legal aspects of the oil and gas industry, including acquisitions and sales of assets or equity interests, drafting and negotiating leases, contracts and agreements related to field, pipeline and plant operations.
**Professional Memberships:** Rocky Mountain Mineral Law Foundation; State Bar of Texas; Center for American and International Law; Houston Bar Association; The College of the State Bar of Texas.

**Career:** Partner since 1983.
**Personal:** University of Houston Law Center (JD, 1977); The University of Texas at Austin (BA, 1973).

### PAULSEN, Bruce G.
Seward & Kissel LLP, New York
212 574 1533
paulsen@sewkis.com
*Featured in Transportation (Nationwide)*
**Practice Areas:** Commercial, maritime and international litigation and arbitration.
**Professional Memberships:** Mr Paulsen is a member of the Committees on Commercial Litigation and Business Litigation of the American Bar Association, the Litigation Committee of the International Bar Association, is a Proctor member of the Maritime Law Association, and a member of the faculty of the Tulane Admiralty Law Institute.
**Career:** Mr Paulsen is a partner in Seward & Kissel's Litigation Group and has been a partner since 2002. Described as a notable litigator (Chambers 2012) Mr Paulsen specializes in handling complex commercial, maritime and international disputes including contract and other business disputes, securities, fraud, insurance, reinsurance, investment funds, trade claims, commodities, derivatives, international disputes (including international arbitration), banking, real estate, bankruptcy, regulatory disputes, and others. He handled the first piracy of a ship owned by an American-based shipping company and has been involved in over forty live piracies since then. Mr Paulsen also handles finance-related shipping disputes. He has represented bondholders, bond issuers as well as secured lenders in matters arising from some of the most significant financing defaults in the shipping business. Mr Paulsen has successfully defended securities claims brought against publicly financed shipping companies brought in the United States and in offshore jurisdictions. Further, he has acted for shipowners, charterers, lenders, borrowers, marine insurers, shipyards and others in litigations and arbitrations involving more traditional maritime disputes, including environmental matters. Further information is available at www.sewkis.com.
**Publications:** Mr Paulsen co-authored the following recent articles: "Republic of Argentina v BG Group, PLC: US appellate court vacates International investment award for failure to comply with condition precedent." International Bar Association Arbitration News, September 2012; "Marine kidnap and ransom coverage: who needs it?" Insurance Day, July 26, 2012; "US Court of Appeals for the Second Circuit decides that courts have the power to stay arbitration under the Federal Arbitration Act." Newsletter of the Arbitration Committee of the Legal Practice Division of the International Bar Association, April 2012; "Targeting the Shipping Industry." Maritime Risk International, March 2012; "The Risks of Mergers." Maritime Risk International, February 2012; Mr Paulsen is also the co-editor of, "Out of the Fog: The Sinking of Andrea Doria." Schiffer Publishing, 2003, winner of the U.S. Maritime Literature Award.

**Personal:** Mr Paulsen received a BA from Columbia University in 1980 and a JD from Tulane University School of Law, cum laude, in 1985.

### PAWLOW, Jean A
McDermott Will & Emery LLP, Washington, DC
202 756 8297
jpawlow@mwe.com
*Featured in Tax (Nationwide)*
**Practice Areas:** Chair of the federal tax controversy practice, and member of the US & international tax practice group. Has been involved in significant tax litigation matters for over 20 years, including litigation concerning credit card interchange and original issue discount, shrinkage estimates, and the telecommunications excise tax. Has represented clients in disputes before the US Tax Court, the Court of Federal Claims, US District Courts, US Courts of Appeal, the Internal Revenue Service Appeals Division and the Internal Revenue Service National Office.
**Personal:** Harvard Law School, JD (cum laude), 1988; University of California-Berkeley, BS (with high honors), 1985.

### PEARL, Nicole M.
McDermott Will & Emery LLP, Los Angeles
310 551 9359
npearl@mwe.com
*Featured in Wealth Management (Nationwide)*
**Practice Areas:** Focuses her practice on estate planning, wealth transfer planning, marital property agreements, business succession planning and post-death administration. Her work involves helping high net worth individuals pass wealth to the next generation, while minimizing their tax burden. To that end, she creates estate plans and charitable giving programs designed to meet her clients' family succession and wealth management objectives.
**Personal:** University of California, Berkeley, School of Law, JD, 1998, University of Illinois at Urbana-Champaign, BA, (cum laude), 1994.

### PELTA, Eleanor
Morgan, Lewis & Bockius LLP, Washington, DC
202 739 5050
epelta@morganlewis.com
*Featured in Immigration (Nationwide), Immigration (District of Columbia)*
See under District of Columbia for profile.

### PEMBERTON, Alan
Covington & Burling LLP, Washington, DC
202 662 5642
apemberton@cov.com
*Featured in Government (Nationwide)*
**Practice Areas:** Co-Chair, Government Contracts practice group. Bid protests, claims and other litigation before GAO, agency boards, courts and ADR tribunals. Advises clients about the full range of government proposal, performance, compliance, regulatory, transactional, suspension and debarment, and legislative issues. Chair, Public Service Committee.
**Professional Memberships:** Adjunct Professor, Georgetown University Law Center; Life Fellow,

ABA Foundation; Boards of Directors, Bread for the City, Inc., Children's Law Center, Indigent Civil Litigation Fund, Inc.; Member, Committee on Pro Se Litigation, D.C.D.C.
**Personal:** University of Michigan Law School, JD; University of Michigan, MA; The University of Chicago, BA; winner, M55-59 Boston Marathon 2009.

### PENZER, Michèle
Latham & Watkins LLP, New York
212 906 1245
michele.penzer@lw.com
*Featured in Banking & Finance (Nationwide)*
**Practice Areas:** Member of the firm's Finance Department and Banking and Project Finance practice groups. Practice focuses primarily on the representation of commercial and investment banks, as well as borrowers and issuers, in leveraged finance transactions, including acquisition financings, project financings, other senior secured lending transactions and restructurings.
**Career:** Qualified since 1994. Global Co-Chair of the Banking Practice. Former member of the firm's Executive Committee and former chair of the firm's Diversity Committee and Associates Committee. Member of the State Bar of New York, the New York State Bar Association and the American Bar Association.

### PEPONIS, Margaret S
Cleary Gottlieb Steen & Hamilton LLP, New York
212 225 2822
mpeponis@cgsh.com
*Featured in Banking & Finance (Nationwide)*
**Practice Areas:** Leveraged buyout, acquisition and distressed financing. Has recently represented Sabre, Neiman Marcus, Biomet, Crossmark, Consolidated Precision Products, Endurance International Group, Bausch & Lomb, Rural/Metro Corporation, RegionalCare Hospital Partners, Valerus Compression Services in a number of acquisition financings and refinancing transactions. Has also represented Vertafore, Lehman Brothers Holdings (as debtor in possession), Alltel, Alpha Natural Resources, Harrahs, Vale and Targa Resources in financing and acquisition financing transactions.

### PEREGRINE, Michael W
McDermott Will & Emery LLP, Chicago
312 984 6933
mperegrine@mwe.com
*Featured in Healthcare (Illinois), Healthcare (Nationwide)*
See under Illinois for profile.

### PEREZ, Alfredo R
Weil, Gotshal & Manges LLP, Houston
212 310 8510
alfredo.perez@weil.com
*Featured in Bankruptcy/Restructuring (Texas), Bankruptcy/Restructuring (Nationwide)*
See under Texas for profile.

**PEREZ, Tania**
Fulbright & Jaworski LLP, New York
212 318 3147
tperez@fulbright.com
*Featured in Energy & Natural Resources (Nationwide)*
**Practice Areas:** Energy.
**Professional Memberships:** New York City Bar, Energy Committee; Energy Bar Association.
**Career:** Perez's practice focuses on transactions involving the development of energy infrastructure (such as natural gas storage and pipelines, LNG terminals, power plants, and renewable energy projects). She participates in proceedings before the FERC involving the siting, construction and operation of energy projects and the Department of Energy involving LNG imports and exports. She also provides advice on compliance matters including affiliate issues, and energy trading and risk assessment.
**Personal:** JD, Fordham University School of Law (2002); BA, Economics and Political Science, Columbia College (1998).

**PERKINS, Nancy L**
Arnold & Porter LLP, Washington, DC
202 942 5065
Nancy.Perkins@aporter.com
*Featured in Privacy & Data Security (Nationwide)*
**Practice Areas:** Privacy and security regulation of medical, financial, and other personal data, including online, especially under HIPAA, the HITECH Act; Gramm-Leach-Bliley Act, Fair Credit Reporting Act, Children's Online Privacy Protection Act, Drivers License Protection Act, Videotape Privacy Protection Act, and federal and state data breach notification laws. Global data protection regulation, particularly under the EU Data Protection Directive and the related US-EU "Safe Harbor."
**Professional Memberships:** American Law Institute; American Bar Association; American Society of International Law.
**Personal:** JD, Harvard Law School, 1987; MPP, Harvard University, John F. Kennedy School of Government, 1987; AB, Harvard College, 1979.

**PERLIS, Mark**
Dickstein Shapiro LLP, Washington, DC
202 420 4703
perlism@dicksteinshapiro.com
*Featured in Energy & Natural Resources (Nationwide)*
**Practice Areas:** Mark Perlis focuses his broad federal regulatory and litigation practice on energy, biotechnology, and environmental matters with electric utility, industry restructuring, and global warming emphasis. He represents clients in Federal Energy Regulatory Commission adjudicatory and rulemaking proceedings. Counsels on commercial energy agreements, compliance matters, and tradable environmental allowances.
**Professional Memberships:** Environmental Markets Association; Energy Bar Association; ABA.
**Personal:** Harvard Law School (JD, 1977), editor, Harvard Law Review; Yale College (BA, 1974).

**PERRY, Mark A**
Gibson, Dunn & Crutcher LLP, Washington, DC
202 887 3667
mperry@gibsondunn.com
*Featured in Appellate Law (Nationwide)*
**Practice Areas:** Represents clients in class actions and other complex commercial disputes, including securities, employment, and patent cases. Emphasis on the appellate aspects of such litigation, with principal responsibility for many cases in federal and state supreme courts and courts of appeals.
**Career:** Teaches upper-level course on Class Action Law and Procedure at Georgetown University Law Center. Former Justice Department attorney and law clerk to the Supreme Court and Ninth Circuit. JD with high honors, University of Chicago Law School (1991).
**Publications:** Authored multiple articles on securities litigation, class actions, arbitration, and civil justice reform.

**PESCH, Ellen**
Sidley Austin LLP, New York
212 839 5569
epesch@sidley.com
*Featured in Capital Markets (Nationwide)*
**Practice Areas:** Partner in Sidley's New York office, and co-head of the firm's OTC Derivatives cross-practice area team. She concentrates in the representation of capital market participants with respect to structuring and execution of derivatives and structured financial products, as well as restructuring and working out challenged transactions. She represents participants in a wide variety of transactions, including interest rate swap and cap agreements, swaptions, total return swaps, credit default swaps, weather, catastrophic, and mortality and longevity related swaps, and the complex regulatory issues related to such products.

**PETERS, William J**
Gibson, Dunn & Crutcher LLP, Los Angeles
213 229 7515
wpeters@gibsondunn.com
*Featured in Outsourcing (Nationwide), IT & Outsourcing (California)*
**Practice Areas:** Co-Chair of Gibson Dunn's Strategic Sourcing and Technology Transactions Practice. Counsels Fortune 1000 companies on strategic outsourcing and technology transactions. His experience includes structuring and negotiating agreements for business process and IT outsourcing, cloud computing, software development and licensing, and complex systems integration and offshore sourcing arrangements. These transactions have involved clients in the automotive, biotech, energy, entertainment, financial services, logistics, retail sales, telecommunications and technology industries.
**Career:** Joined Gibson Dunn in 2008. Previously Chair of Transactional IP Practice at O'Melveny & Myers LLP.
**Personal:** Loyola Law School, JD, 1994. University of California, Los Angeles, BA, 1990.

**PETERSON JR, John M**
Baker & McKenzie, Palo Alto
650 856 5538
John.Peterson@bakermckenzie.com
*Featured in Tax (Nationwide), Tax (California)*
See under California for profile.

**PETROSKY, Edward F**
Sidley Austin LLP, New York
212 839 5455
epetrosky@sidley.com
*Featured in Capital Markets (Nationwide)*
**Practice Areas:** Partner in Sidley's New York office and global coordinator of the firm's Securities practice. Represents both issuers and underwriters in corporate and securities matters, and has extensive experience providing legal advice to clients under the Securities Act of 1933 and the Securities Exchange Act of 1934. Currently serves as designated underwriter's counsel and company counsel for more than 15 companies, with an emphasis on REITs, financial institutions and energy companies. Practice focuses on IPOs, as well as public and private offerings of convertible and exchangeable securities, trust preferred securities, structured debt products and senior and subordinated debt securities.

**PFOHL, Peter A**
Slover & Loftus, Washington, DC
202 347 7170
pap@sloverandloftus.com
*Featured in Transportation (Nationwide)*
**Practice Areas:** Mr Pfohl is a Partner specializing in railroad transportation law. He actively participates in Surface Transportation Board proceedings and in the courts. Mr Pfohl represents a variety of clients on railroad economic regulatory issues, and in railroad acquisition, abandonment, and related administrative/transactional work, along with preemption and railroad/customer liability issues. Mr Pfohl has been actively involved in railroad legislative issues; he previously worked as a legislative assistant on Capitol Hill covering transportation, energy, and other issues.
**Personal:** BA, University of Notre Dame, 1989; JD, cum laude, Columbus School of Law at the Catholic University of America, 1997.

**PHELAN, Rod**
Baker Botts LLP, Dallas
214 953 6609
rod.phelan@bakerbotts.com
*Featured in Litigation (Nationwide), Litigation (Texas)*
See under Texas for profile.

**PHILLIPS, Carter G**
Sidley Austin LLP, Washington, DC
202 736 8270
cphillips@sidley.com
*Featured in Telecommunications (District of Columbia), Appellate Law (Nationwide)*
**Practice Areas:** Co-Chair of Sidley's Executive Committee and was the managing partner of its Washington, D.C. office from 1995 to 2012. Since joining Sidley, Carter has argued 67 cases in the Supreme Court. His 76 arguments before that Court are the most of any lawyer currently in private practice. Carter also has argued more than 100 cases in United States courts of appeals, including at least one in every Circuit in the country, and 25 in the Court of Appeals for the Federal Circuit.

**PHILLIPS, Thomas R**
Baker Botts LLP, Austin
512 322 2565
tom.phillips@bakerbotts.com
*Featured in Appellate Law (Nationwide), Litigation (Texas)*
See under Texas for profile.

**PHLEGER, Peter M**
Morgan, Lewis & Bockius LLP, San Francisco
415 442 1096
pphleger@morganlewis.com
*Featured in Investment Funds (Nationwide)*
**Practice Areas:** Peter Phleger is a partner in Morgan Lewis's Private Investment Funds Group. His practice focuses on the formation of private investment funds, including venture and private equity funds, fund-of-funds, and secondary funds, representing both sponsors and institutional and corporate investors. He advises sponsors in their operation and investment activities, with focus on secondary transactions. Mr Phleger represents both multi-billion dollar partnerships and early-stage venture capital firms. His skills include the structure, formation, governance, and investing activities of private investment funds, including partnership agreement terms and conditions, public disclosure issues, securities law compliance, investor relations, and general partner separations.

**PIELS, William**
Holland & Knight LLP, San Francisco
415 743 6930
william.piels@hklaw.com
*Featured in Transportation (Nationwide), Banking & Finance (Nationwide)*
**Professional Memberships:** American Bar Association Subcommittee on Aircraft Finance and Contracts; International Registry Advisory Board, alternate member designate for the American Bar Association; Aviation Working Group Legal Advisory Panel; American College of Commercial Finance Lawyers.
**Career:** William Piels leads the Structured Finance Group in Holland & Knight's San Francisco office. His clients are among the world's largest aircraft operating lessors and international financial institutions, and include major international airlines and US domestic airlines. He has more than 25 years' experience in asset-based aviation financing, representing parties in a variety of domestic and cross-border transactions, securitizations, operating leases, workouts and repossessions.

**PIERCE, John V H**
WilmerHale, New York
212 230 8829
john.pierce@wilmerhale.com
*Featured in International Arbitration (Nationwide)*
**Practice Areas:** Has a diverse practice focusing on the arbitration and litigation of international disputes.
**Professional Memberships:** IBA, ASA, ABCNY, ABA.

**Publications:** 'The Haitian Crisis and the Future of Collective Enforcement of Democratic Governance,' 27 Law and Policy in International Business 477 (1996); co-author, Trade Finance Fraud: Understanding the Threats and Reducing the Risk, ICC Commercial Crime Services, April 2002; co-author, International Commercial Arbitration in New York (Oxford Press 2010).
**Personal:** Georgetown University Law Center (JD 1996); Ecole Polytechnique (Programme Jean Monnet 1993); Georgetown University, School of Foreign Service (BSFS 1992); Institut d'Etudes Politiques (CEP 1991).

**PIERCE, Kenneth J**
Hughes Hubbard & Reed LLP, Washington, DC
2020 721 4690
piercek@hugheshubbard.com
*Featured in International Trade (Nationwide)*
**Practice Areas:** International Trade.
**Professional Memberships:** International Trade Steering Committee, ABA; U.S. Court of International Trade; Trade and Investment Committee, U.S. Council for International Business.
**Career:** Over 29 years of experience advising clients in the full range of US international trade actions, including antidumping and countervailing, safeguards, customs, WTO, GSP, trade agreements (market access), and non-US trade investigations. Clients include manufacturers, governments, and importers.
**Personal:** JD (cum laude), Cornell Law School (1984); editor, Cornell International Law Journal; Earl Warren Prize; BA (magna cum laude), University of Vermont (1978), scholastic awards (Phi Beta Kappa). LA to US Senator Patrick Leahy (1978-81).

**PIGOTT, Ginger**
Greenberg Traurig, LLP, Santa Monica
310 586 7760
PigottG@gtlaw.com
*Featured in Products Liability (Nationwide)*
**Practice Areas:** Vice-Chair, Pharmaceutical, Medical Device & Health Care Litigation Group. Litigation.
**Professional Memberships:** ABA; Defense Research Institute; LA County Bar Association.
**Career:** Selected: Chambers USA Guide, 2011-13; Legal 500 US, 2008-10; Super Lawyers Rising Stars, 2004, 2006-07.
**Publications:** Co-Author, Top 20 Food and Drug Cases, 2012 & Cases to Watch, 2013, Bowdrie v. Sun Pharmaceutical Industries, Food and Drug Law Institute, April 2013; 'Top Food & Drug Cases, 2011 & Cases to Watch, 2012, Degelmann v. Advanced Medical Optics, Inc.', FDLI, April 2012.
**Personal:** JD, honors, Loyola University Chicago School of Law, 1992; BA, honors, University of Michigan, 1989.

**PILLION, Michael L**
Morgan, Lewis & Bockius LLP, Philadelphia
215 963 5554
mpillion@morganlewis.com
*Featured in Outsourcing (Nationwide)*

**Practice Areas:** Michael Pillion is the founding partner of the Global Outsourcing, Technology, and Commercial Transactions Practice at Morgan Lewis. Mr Pillion's practice focuses on information technology and business process outsourcing transactions, as well as other complex technology and commercial transactions, including system implementation, licensing, SaaS, strategic alliances, cloud computing, mobility and agreements in support of sourcing and supply chain operations. Mr Pillion counsels clients on structuring outsourcing relationships, as well as the renegotiation, termination and realignment of existing transactions. Mr Pillion represents a large and diverse client base, including in the health, life sciences, energy and financial institution industries.

**PINEDO, Anna**
Morrison & Foerster LLP, New York
212 468 8179
apinedo@mofo.com
*Featured in Capital Markets (Nationwide)*
**Practice Areas:** Concentrates on securities and derivatives, representing issuers, investment banks and financial intermediaries in financings, including public and private offerings of equity and debt securities, as well as structured products and innovative financial products. In the derivatives area, counsels financial institutions acting as dealers and participants in the derivatives markets. Advises on structuring issues, as well as on regulatory issues and hedging techniques. Speaks and writes regularly on financial instruments and other securities laws issues. Active participant in various bar and other professional associations.
**Personal:** BSFS, Georgetown University, 1990; University of Chicago Law School, 1993. Bar admission: New York.

**PINKERTON, Glenn**
Sidley Austin LLP, Houston
713 495 4505
gpinkerton@sidley.com
*Featured in Projects (Nationwide)*
**Practice Areas:** Partner in Sidley's Houston office. He has extensive experience in project development and finance, mergers and acquisitions and international transactions. In particular, he has experience in all facets of the energy business, including upstream, pipelines, LNG, refining and chemicals, power generation and transmission and retail. Mr Pinkerton has experience with many types of transactions, including mergers and acquisitions, joint ventures development, construction, long-term contracting, financing, investments and privatizations. Given the commercial similarity to large scale, long term off-take agreements, Mr Pinkerton has maintained an active practice in corporate headquarters and other large scale office leasing transactions.

**PINKUSIEWICZ, Tomer**
Gibson, Dunn & Crutcher LLP, New York
212 351 2630
TPinkusiewicz@gibsondunn.com
*Featured in Projects (Nationwide)*
**Practice Areas:** Focuses on capital markets and infrastructure financings, with substantial and

particular experience in project bonds, Latin America-related transactions and all types of debt financings. Represents sponsors and project companies in respect of complex infrastructure projects, spanning a wide array of asset classes. Represents both issuers and underwriters in a full range of transactions, including public offerings, Rule 144A/Regulation S offerings and private placements. Has also represented banks in all types of financings to Latin American companies.
**Personal:** JD, Boston University School of Law, 1998, magna cum laude. Fluent in Spanish.

**PINOVER, Eugene**
Willkie Farr & Gallagher LLP, New York
212 728 8254
epinover@willkie.com
*Featured in Real Estate (Nationwide), Real Estate (New York)*
**Practice Areas:** Co-Chair, Real Estate Department. Specializes in representing domestic and foreign real estate companies and institutional clients in acquisitions, sales, restructuring and sophisticated financings and development projects throughout United States. Practice includes representing public real estate investment trusts, underwriters and investors in equity offerings and debt securitizations and working on real estate aspects of merger and acquisition transactions. Work-outs of sophisticated financing and partnership structures has become an area of increasing focus over the past several years.
**Personal:** JD, cum laude, New York University School of Law, 1973. BA, cum laude, Dartmouth College, 1969. See:
http://www.willkie.com/EugenePinover

**PISA, Albert**
Milbank, Tweed, Hadley & McCloy LLP, New York
212 530 5319
apisa@milbank.com
*Featured in Capital Markets (Nationwide)*
**Practice Areas:** Advises clients on structured financings, leveraged lending and workouts/debt restructurings, both in and out of bankruptcy. He has extensive experience in structured financings of esoteric and "off-the-run" assets and structured financings using credit, energy and other derivative products. Mr Pisa also has extensive experience in the workout of troubled structured finance transactions having represented creditors and bondholder committees in the bankruptcies of Enron, NCFE and several subprime mortgage lenders.
**Career:** Partner and Practice Group Leader, Alternative Investments Practice.
**Personal:** JD (cum laude), The University of Pennsylvania Law School; BBA-Finance (magna cum laude), University of Notre Dame.

**PISA, Regina M**
Goodwin Procter LLP, Boston
617 570 1525
rpisa@goodwinprocter.com
*Featured in Financial Services Regulation (Nationwide)*
**Practice Areas:** Ms Pisa serves as Chairman of Goodwin Procter LLP. Her practice focuses on the

financial services area. She concentrates on mergers and acquisitions of banks and financial institutions, and represents banks and financial institutions on a wide variety of other matters, including corporate and board governance issues, capital raising, and general corporate and securities law issues.
**Professional Memberships:** Boys and Girls Club of America: Board of Trustees; Simmons College: Board of Trustees; Massachusetts Business Round Table: Board of Directors.
**Personal:** JD, Georgetown University Law Center; BA, MA, Oxford University, St Hilda's College; AB, Harvard University.

**PITTS, Andrew J**
Cravath, Swaine & Moore LLP, New York
212 474 1620
apitts@cravath.com
*Featured in Capital Markets (Nationwide)*
**Practice Areas:** Andrew J. Pitts is a partner in Cravath's Corporate Department. He is a generalist corporate lawyer who advises on a broad range of corporate issues and has a significant corporate finance practice. He regularly represents clients in connection with liability management transactions, including debt tender and exchange offers and consent solicitations. Mr Pitts's advisory work covers, among other things, corporate governance, public company disclosure obligations and director and officer liability issues.
**Personal:** Boston University (MBA, with High Honors, 1995); Boston University (JD, summa cum laude, 1994; Notes Editor, Law Review); Trinity College (BA, 1988). For more information: http://www.cravath.com/apitts

**PLATT, Laurence E**
K&L Gates, Washington, DC
202 778 9034
larry.platt@klgates.com
*Featured in Financial Services Regulation (Nationwide)*
**Practice Areas:** Mr Platt has a national practice, concentrating in a range of matters related to real estate finance, mortgage banking and consumer finance in both the primary and secondary markets. This includes representing purchasers and sellers of mortgage-related companies and assets, counseling clients on federal and state consumer credit laws, defending companies with governmental investigations and enforcement proceedings, assisting in defense of consumer class action lawsuits, and representing clients with Congress and executive agencies on public policy issues related to consumer credit issues.

**PLAUT, Christopher R**
Latham & Watkins LLP, New York
212 906 1262
chris.plaut@lw.com
*Featured in Banking & Finance (Nationwide)*
**Practice Areas:** Practice focuses primarily on the representation of commercial and investment banks in leveraged finance transactions, including acquisition financings, asset-based facilities, and debtor-in-possession and exit financings. Also devotes a portion of his practice to the workout of troubled loans and to the representation of

issuers/borrowers in connection with their financing needs.

**Career:** Qualified since 1989. Member of firm's Finance Committee. Has served as a member of the Banking Law Committees of the New York State Bar Association and the New York County Lawyers Association.

## PLESNARSKI, Rob
O'Melveny & Myers LLP, Washington, DC
202 383 5149
rplesnarski@omm.com
*Featured in Securities (Nationwide)*

**Practice Areas:** Rob Plesnarski is a partner in O'Melveny's Washington, DC office and a member of the Capital Markets Practice. He represents public and private companies, independent board and committee members, investment banks, private equity funds, and other clients in US Securities and Exchange Commission regulatory, corporate governance and transactional matters. Rob represents a number of public companies as outside corporate counsel, advising them on SEC registration and reporting requirements, corporate governance, stock option and other employee benefit matters and general corporate matters. Prior to joining O'Melveny, Rob was Deputy Chief Counsel for the SEC's Division of Corporation Finance.

## PLOTKIN, Mark E
Covington & Burling LLP, Washington, DC
202 662 5656
mplotkin@cov.com
*Featured in Financial Services Regulation (Nationwide), International Trade (Nationwide), Privacy & Data Security (Nationwide)*

**Practice Areas:** Represents clients before US and foreign government agencies in connection with major transactions, as well as significant enforcement and regulatory matters. Counsels foreign and domestic banks, investment firms, technology companies, manufacturers and governmental entities on financial services regulation, bank secrecy, privacy, national security and technology issues.

**Career:** Clients have included American Express, AOL, BAE, Bank of America, Brown Brothers Harriman, BT, CIC, CNOOC, Deutsche Börse, Expedia, Facebook, JPMorgan Chase, GE, IBM, Microsoft, Mubadala, NFL, Northrop Grumman, Patagonia, Procter & Gamble, Raiffeisen, Temasek, others.

**Publications:** Numerous books/articles.

**Personal:** Yale (BA, summa cum laude, Phi Beta Kappa), Harvard (JD, honors).

## POHL, Paul M
Jones Day, Pittsburgh
412 394 7900
pmpohl@jonesday.com
*Featured in Products Liability (Nationwide), Litigation (Pennsylvania)*

**Practice Areas:** Mickey Pohl is the Head of Jones Day's Business and Tort Litigation practice ("BATL-USA"), the nation's largest civil litigation practice. He is a Fellow of The American College of Trial Lawyers, Chairman of the Rand Corporations's Institute for Civil Justice, named in

The Best Lawyers in America in three categories and has been named by the BTI Consulting Group to it's Client Service All Star Team. He handles "Bet the Company" product liability and commercial litigation matters across the country and around the world.

**Publications:** Contributing author to 'Conflicts of Interest - A Trial Lawyer's Guide', (ABA).

## POHLEN, Patrick A
Latham & Watkins LLP, Silicon Valley
650 463 3067
patrick.pohlen@lw.com
*Featured in Investment Funds (Nationwide), Capital Markets (California), Corporate/M&A (California)*
See under California for profile.

## POLE, Debra E
Sidley Austin LLP, Los Angeles
213 896 6623
dpole@sidley.com
*Featured in Products Liability (Nationwide)*

**Practice Areas:** Partner in Sidley's Los Angeles office, a global coordinator of firm's Products Liability practice, member of the firm's Executive Committee, member of the firm's West Coast Accounting and Finance Committee. A seasoned trial lawyer with experience in multi-district litigation (MDL), class actions, and products liability litigation. Extensive jury trial experience in both federal and state courts involving mass tort litigation, class actions, complex litigation, and Daubert proceedings. Supervised numerous defense law firms, both domestically and internationally, that were involved in complex pharmaceutical and medical device litigation, and has had responsibility for national financial management of mass tort litigation.

## POLEBAUM, Elliot E
Fried, Frank, Harris, Shriver & Jacobson LLP, Washington, DC
202 639 7067
Elliot.Polebaum@FriedFrank.com
*Featured in International Arbitration (Nationwide)*

**Practice Areas:** Litigation partner. Leads Fried Frank's international arbitration practice; chair of the Washington, DC litigation department. Concentrates in international arbitration (cases throughout the world) and complex civil litigation in US courts. Also serves as arbitrator in disputes administered by, among others, the ICC and ICDR, and in ad hoc cases.

**Career:** Joined in 1986; became partner in 1989. Adjunct Professor of Law at Georgetown, teaching International Commercial Arbitration. Law clerk to Supreme Court Justice William J. Brennan, Jr.

**Personal:** JD, cum laude, New York University School of Law; MPA, Harvard University; AB, magna cum laude, Middlebury College.

## POLKES, Jonathan
Weil, Gotshal & Manges LLP, New York
212 310 8881
jonathan.polkes@weil.com
*Featured in Securities (Nationwide), Litigation (New York)*

**Practice Areas:** Jonathan Polkes, Co-chair of Weil's Securities Litigation Practice Group, is recognized as a top securities lawyer in the US. He

supervises investigations, regulatory and criminal matters, and securities litigation for financial services and other public companies. A former federal prosecutor, he was lead counsel to many high-profile companies involved in the financial crisis, including AIG, Lehman Brothers, and WaMu, and currently represents a number of global companies in matters relating to the Facebook IPO, the Tribune Company LBO and bankruptcy, and the Archstone-Smith LBO.

**Personal:** Haverford College (BA, 1981); New York University School of Law (JD, 1984).

## POLLACK, Richard A
Sullivan & Cromwell LLP, New York
pollackr@sullcrom.com
*Featured in Private Equity (Nationwide)*

**Career:** Partner since 1997. Co-heads the Firm's Private Equity Group. Was previously co-head of the Firm's General Practice Group from January 2006 to February 2012. Has extensive experience in cross-border mergers and acquisitions and public and private equity and debt securities offerings by US and non-US issuers. Recent clients include American Express, Aquiline Capital, Canada Pension Plan Investment Board, China Investment Corporation, Ripplewood Holdings, Rhône Capital, Silver Lake Partners and York Capital Management.

**Personal:** NYU School of Law (JD, 1988); Columbia (AB, 1984).

## POLONSKY, Alex
Morgan, Lewis & Bockius LLP, Washington, DC
202 739 5830
apolonsky@morganlewis.com
*Featured in Energy & Natural Resources (Nationwide)*

**Practice Areas:** Alex Polonsky is a partner in Morgan Lewis's Energy Practice, focusing on energy and environmental law. His energy practice includes advising on Nuclear Regulatory Commission (NRC) licensing and litigation, including license renewal, power uprates, decommissioning, and enforcement proceedings. He is co-author of Fundamentals of Nuclear Regulation in the US and an experienced litigator before the NRC's Atomic Safety and Licensing Boards. Mr Polonsky also advises on clients in nuclear export-related matters before federal agencies. His environmental law practice includes advising clients on shale gas development and on litigation and enforcement related to CERCLA and NEPA.

## POMERANTZ, Mark F
Paul, Weiss, Rifkind, Wharton & Garrison LLP, New York
212 373 3010
mpomerantz@paulweiss.com
*Featured in Litigation (Nationwide), Litigation (New York)*
See under New York for profile.

## POMPEO, Paul E
Arnold & Porter LLP, Washington, DC
202 942 5723
Paul.Pompeo@aporter.com
*Featured in Government (Nationwide)*

**Practice Areas:** Paul Pompeo counsels a wide range of contractors in all phases of contract formation, performance, and closeout and compliance matters. He litigates bid protests/overrides, claims, appeals and ADR. Much of Paul's work focuses on accounting, cost and pricing:CAS, TINA, cost principles, and DCAA audits. He has experience with FMS and international matters. He also counsels clients on mergers & acquisitions, financing, appropriations and contract negotiations. Paul also conducts internal and ethics investigations.

**Professional Memberships:** ABA Public Law Section; NDIA.

**Career:** VP & GC of Johnson Controls Inc., Government Division.

**Publications:** Government Contractor, frequent author and Advisory Board Member.

## PONDA, Ameek Ashok
Sullivan & Worcester LLP, Boston
617 338 2443
aponda@sandw.com
*Featured in Capital Markets (Nationwide), Tax (Massachusetts)*
See under Massachusetts for profile.

## PONGRACE, Donald R
Akin Gump Strauss Hauer & Feld LLP, Washington, DC
202 887 4466
dpongrace@akingump.com
*Featured in Native American Law (Nationwide)*

**Practice Areas:** Chair of Akin Gump's American Indian Law and Policy Practice; advises and represents tribal clients on complex private, and government-to-government negotiations, including land and water claims, gaming compacts, development projects, transportation infrastructure and rights of way, among others; represents clients in negotiations, federal, state and tribal courts, and before federal agencies and the U.S. Congress.

**Professional Memberships:** District of Columbia Bar.

**Personal:** BA (magna cum laude and Phi Beta Kappa), Bates College (1979); JD (magna cum laude), American University (1985); law clerk, Honorable HE Widener Jr, US Court of Appeals for the 4th Circuit (1985-86).

## PORTER, Daniel L
Curtis, Mallet-Prevost, Colt & Mosle LLP, Washington, DC
202 452 7340
dporter@curtis.com
*Featured in International Trade (Nationwide)*

**Professional Memberships:** DC Bar Association; American Bar Association.

**Career:** Mr Porter is a partner in the International Trade group. He focuses his practice on international trade law. He counsels clients on the myriad of US laws that affect the cross-border shipment of goods, including trade remedy provi-

sions (e.g. antidumping and subsidy), export controls, and Customs regulations. Mr Porter has assisted and defended numerous clients with exporting operations in China, Canada, Japan, Korea, Brazil, Indonesia and Vietnam. Mr Porter has also been active in several WTO disputes across a range of issues. He also advises companies making submissions to CFIUS, and confronting international trade regulatory issues in their cross border M&A transactions. Mr Porter has particular expertise in assisting companies that need to import products from China. Working with Curtis' mandarin-speaking attorneys and local Chinese counsel, Mr Porter helps client maintain uninterrupted access to the US and other markets. He is admitted to practice in the U.S. Supreme Court, U.S. Court of Appeals for the Federal Circuit and the U.S. Court of International Trade.
**Publications:** A Business Guide to US Trade Remedy Laws (2d 2006).
**Personal:** Cornell Law School (JD 1985), editor of the Cornell International Law Journal; Columbia University (BA 1982).

### PORTER, John
Baker Botts LLP, Houston
713 229 1597
john.porter@bakerbotts.com
*Featured in Tax (Nationwide), Wealth Management (Nationwide), Tax (Texas)*
**Practice Areas:** Federal tax litigation, controversy, including gift, estate, income tax disputes with IRS; fiduciary litigation. Represents clients in tax cases in US Tax Court, US District Courts, Court of Federal Claims, Federal Circuit Courts of Appeals, and in IRS audits and administrative appeals.
**Professional Memberships:** ABA Real Property, Probate and Trust Section (Former Chair, Tax Controversy Committee; Supervisory Council Member); American College of Trust and Estate Counsel (Former Regent).
**Publications:** Frequent speaker, author regarding federal tax controversy issues, including business valuation, limited partnership issues.
**Personal:** JD (cum laude), Baylor Law School, 1986, BBA, accounting, Texas A&M University, 1982.

### PORTNOY, Lawrence
Davis Polk & Wardwell LLP, New York
212 450 4000
lawrence.portnoy@davispolk.com
*Featured in Securities (Nationwide), Litigation (New York)*
See under New York for profile.

### POSTER, Robert L
Gilmartin, Poster & Shafto LLP, New York
212 425 3220
rlposter@lawpost-nyc.com
*Featured in Transportation (Nationwide)*
**Practice Areas:** Ship and equipment financing, sales, and leasing.
**Career:** Past Chair, Admiralty Committee, The Association of the Bar of the City of New York; Past Chair, Subcommittee on US Coast Guard Documentation, US Citizenship and Related

Matters, Marine Finance Committee, Maritime Law Association of the United States.
**Publications:** 'The Uniform Commercial Code and Bankruptcy', 59 Tulane Law Review, No 5 and 6, p1361; 'Case Note, Shipping Statutes', Journal of Maritime Law and Commerce, Vol 27, No 3, July, 1996; principal author, 'Unnecessary Citizenship Requirements Imposed on Maritime Industries', by the Committee on Admiralty, The Record, Association of Bar of City of New York, Vol 49, No 6.
**Personal:** AB Princeton University 1962, JD Harvard Law School 1965, LLM Harvard Law School 1966.

### POWELL, Benjamin
WilmerHale, Washington, DC
202 663 6770
ben.powell@wilmerhale.com
*Featured in International Trade (Nationwide)*
**Practice Areas:** Practice focuses on advising companies on structuring international investments and acquisitions, including issues related to the Committee on Foreign Investment in the United States (CFIUS), issues related to data security and cyber security, including responses to data breaches and litigation, national security, investigations, litigation and regulatory issues.
**Career:** Confirmed by the US Senate as General Counsel to the first three Directors of National Intelligence. Served as Special Assistant to the President and Associate White House Counsel; Counsel to software company in Silicon Valley; Tried largest antitrust jury verdict case in US history; Former Air Force officer.

### POWER, James H
Holland & Knight LLP, New York
212 513 3494
james.power@hklaw.com
*Featured in Transportation (Nationwide)*
**Practice Areas:** James Power focuses generally on marine casualties, cargo cases, charter party disputes, maritime liens, government bid protests, marine pollution, seamen's claims and variety of other maritime and non-maritime matters. He has extensive experience handling large complex litigation cases and is presently Senior Counsel on the multi-billion dollar oil pollution spill case involving the vessel Prestige on behalf of the Kingdom of Spain. He has argued motions in numerous Federal and State Courts and has represented clients in federal mediation and in maritime arbitrations. He has conducted numerous onboard investigations for both civil and criminal claims against vessel interests.

### POWERS, Richard
Venable LLP, Washington, DC
202 344 4360
repowers@Venable.com
*Featured in Energy & Natural Resources (Nationwide)*
**Practice Areas:** Chairs Venable's Energy Practice. Has over 35 years of experience on a broad range of administrative, judicial and transactional matters, primarily in the oil and gas industry. Provides legislative, administrative and corporate counsel to crude oil, natural gas, and

renewable energy projects. Has handled transactional and regulatory compliance and trial proceedings in the energy industry. Counsels airlines, oil and natural gas companies, propane companies, refiners, trade associations and other oil and natural gas pipeline shippers and users with respect to rates, regulated practices, and business opportunities. Has advised clients, including foreign governments, on international energy laws and projects.

### POZZERLE, Sergio A
Sidley Austin LLP, Houston
713 495 4507
spozzerle@sidley.com
*Featured in Projects (Nationwide)*
**Practice Areas:** As partner in Sidley's Houston office, Sergio focuses his global practice on projects, corporate finance and M&A. He has a very active renewable energy practice and also advises on co-generation and other conventional power projects, LNG terminals, drilling rigs and other energy and infrastructure projects. He handles every stage of project development and finance, from joint venture formation to acquisition/divestiture to equipment supply/construction (EPC) to fuel/feedstock procurement to offtake/marketing arrangements to debt/equity financing, and has a particularly deep knowledge of the major electricity markets. Sergio is fluent in Spanish and Portuguese and has extensive experience in international transactions.

### PRAME, Michael
Groom Law Group, Washington, DC
202 861 6633
mprame@groom.com
*Featured in ERISA Litigation (Nationwide)*
**Practice Areas:** As Chair of Groom's Litigation Practice Group, Mike counsels plan sponsors, administrators and trustees on ways to minimize litigation risk and defends the plan fiduciaries in the event litigation is commenced. He also represents recordkeepers, actuaries and other plan professionals in litigation and Department of Labor investigations. In addition, Mike counsels clients on retiree health issues, employee benefit issues arising in bankruptcy, and ERISA compliance issues.
**Publications:** Mike has written and spoken often on ERISA litigation matters, including 401(k) fee and employer securities lawsuits.
**Personal:** BS, summa cum laude, LeMoyne College (1990); JD, Georgetown University (1993).

### PRESSMAN, Arthur L
Nixon Peabody LLP, Boston
617 345 1158
apressman@nixonpeabody.com
*Featured in Franchising (Nationwide)*
**Practice Areas:** Leading franchise lawyer representing franchisors. Represents world leaders in franchising and retail distribution, hotel, real estate, and consumer services. Handles litigation and dispute resolution for clients throughout the United States and its territories.
**Professional Memberships:** American Bar Association Forum on Franchising (Governing Committee 1997-2000; Chair, Litigation and

Dispute Resolution Division 1995-97); Named Top 100 franchise lawyers in the country by Franchise Times; Best Lawyers in America; MA Super Lawyer.
**Personal:** Temple University, JD; University of Pennsylvania, BA.

### PREZIOSO, Giovanni
Cleary Gottlieb Steen & Hamilton LLP, Washington, DC
202 974 1650
gprezioso@cgsh.com
*Featured in Financial Services Regulation (Nationwide), Securities (Nationwide)*
**Practice Areas:** SEC enforcement and regulatory matters, internal investigations, corporate governance. Clients include Bank of America, SIFMA, Goldman Sachs and major corporations, auditors, and boards of directors.
**Professional Memberships:** Member of the Bar in the District of Columbia; Co-Chair of the ABA Presidential Task Force on Financial Markets Regulatory Reform; Member (Chairman 2006-10) of the Executive Council of the Federal Bar Association Securities Law Committee.
**Career:** Joined firm, 1982; became partner, 1991. General Counsel of the United States Securities and Exchange Commission, 2002-06. JD, magna cum laude, Harvard Law School (1982); AB, magna cum laude, Harvard College (1979).

### PRICE, Alan H
Wiley Rein LLP, Washington, DC
202 719 3375
aprice@wileyrein.com
*Featured in International Trade (Nationwide)*
**Practice Areas:** Chair, International Trade Practice. 25+ years experience handling high-profile/complex trade regulatory matters, including litigation involving public/government relations issues. Leads the antidumping/countervailing duty practice. Represents clients in connection with bilateral/multilateral agreements, WTO dispute resolution, trade legislation, customs regulation, escape clause investigations and Section 301 cases. Expert in trade rules governing raw materials, trade, investment issues related to State Owned Enterprises and US-China trade issues. Testifies before Congress.
**Professional Memberships:** President, Committee to Support U.S. Trade Laws (2012-2014).
**Personal:** George Washington University Law School (JD, with honors); State University of New York at Stony Brook (BA, with high honors).

### PRINS, Richard T
Skadden, Arps, Slate, Meagher & Flom LLP & Affiliates, New York
212 735 2790
richard.prins@skadden.com
*Featured in Investment Funds (Nationwide)*
**Practice Areas:** Richard T. Prins heads Skadden's Investment Management Group, which includes the firm's investment advisory, investment company, business development company and broker-dealer practices. He actively participates in the firm's merger and acquisition and corporate finance practices in those industries and

the development of new investment products in conjunction with other practice groups. Mr Prins also handles a wide variety of general securities and corporate matters for financial services companies.
**Career:** JD, University of Michigan, 1977 (cum laude); BA, Calvin College, 1972 (summa cum laude).

### PRITCHARD, John F
Holland & Knight LLP, New York
212 513 3200
john.pritchard@hklaw.com
*Featured in Transportation (Nationwide), Banking & Finance (Nationwide)*
**Professional Memberships:** Aviation Working Group, Legal Advisory Panel, Former Chairman; American College of Commercial Finance Lawyers.
**Career:** John F Pritchard, with over 20 years' experience in aircraft, equipment and facility finance, is knowledgeable in all areas of asset-based financing and has concentrated on representing lessees, lessors, lenders, borrowers, and government guarantors in domestic and cross-border financings, securitizations, workouts and foreclosures.
**Publications:** Chapter on United States, Aircraft Finance: Registration, Security and Enforcement, Longmans; Chapter on Aircraft Leasing, Equipment Leasing, Matthew Bender; Chapter on United States, Aircraft Liens and Detention Rights, Sweet & Maxwell; Chapter on Aviation Workouts, Business Workouts, Warren, Gorham & Lamont.

### PROCTOR, Shemin
Andrews Kurth LLP, Washington, DC
202 662 3052
sproctor@andrewskurth.com
*Featured in Energy & Natural Resources (Nationwide)*
**Practice Areas:** Shemin has broad energy expertise that combines regulatory representations before the Federal Energy Regulatory Commission in Washington, DC with legal advice to major energy companies in Houston and other energy centers. Her clients include pipeline, midstream, gathering, local distribution and storage companies, as well as publicly traded partnerships (master limited partnerships). Shemin has counseled clients in numerous rate, restructuring, tariff, certificate, complaint and enforcement matters in natural gas, oil and electric proceedings before the FERC, other agencies and federal courts. Shemin has significant experience advising clients on regulatory considerations in public offerings and mergers and acquisitions transactions.

### PRUITT, Laura
Alston & Bird LLP, Washington, DC
202 239 3618
laura.pruitt@alston.com
*Featured in Financial Services Regulation (Nationwide)*
**Practice Areas:** Counsels broker-dealers, alternative trading systems, investment advisers, and other market participants on securities law and market regulation issues, with particular emphasis

on broker-dealer registration and compliance, trading rules, market structure issues, investment adviser regulation, transfer agent rules and anti-money laundering rules. Also represents clients before the Securities and Exchange Commission and Self-Regulatory Organizations in connection with regulatory exams, investigations and enforcement actions, and she has conducted independent compliance reviews in connection with the settlement of several enforcement actions.
**Personal:** AB (1984) Harvard University; JD (1987) Columbia Law School.

### PTASHEK, Jay M
Kirkland & Ellis LLP, New York
212 446 4747
jay.ptashek@kirkland.com
*Featured in Banking & Finance (Nationwide)*
**Practice Areas:** Jay focuses on syndicated senior debt and bridge loan financings, primarily in the leveraged acquisition finance area. His experience also includes significant high-yield, corporate finance and restructuring engagements. Representative clients include financial sponsors such as Apax Partners, Bain Capital and 3G Capital, as well as large financial institutions and a multitude of private equity portfolio companies and corporate borrowers, including Alcatel-Lucent, Burger King and Prestige Brands.
**Career:** Kirkland & Ellis LLP, 2009-present. Simpson Thacher & Bartlett LLP, 1992-2009.
**Personal:** New York University School of Law, JD, cum laude, 1992; University of Michigan, BBA, with high distinction, 1989.

### PULLEY III, J Waverly
Hunton & Williams LLP, Richmond
804 788 8783
wpulley@hunton.com
*Featured in Projects (Nationwide)*
**Practice Areas:** Waverly Pulley's practice focuses on public-private infrastructure projects, capital finance and complex commercial lending and equipment leasing transactions. He chairs Hunton & Williams' Transportation Infrastructure Group and has been involved with PPP statutory reform legislation and complex infrastructure projects, including highways, bridges, tunnels, seaports and toll roads, in the United States representing sponsors, governmental entities, concessionaires, investors, lenders and construction companies for more than 15 years.

### PURETZ, Jeffrey S
Dechert LLP, Washington, DC
202 261 3358
jeffrey.puretz@dechert.com
*Featured in Investment Funds (Nationwide)*
**Practice Areas:** Mr Puretz concentrates on investment management matters for mutual funds, mutual fund boards, investment advisers, and insurance companies.
**Professional Memberships:** Member, District of Columbia Bar; member, ABA Federal Regulation of Securities Committee and Securities Activities of Insurance Companies Subcommittee; member, Board IQ Consulting Board; member, Mutual Fund Directors Forum Advisory Board;

member, Insured Retirement Institute Regulatory Affairs Committee.
**Career:** Former staff attorney, SEC Division of Investment Management.
**Personal:** University of Maryland (BA, 1976); The Catholic University of America Columbus School of Law (JD, 1981).

### QUIGLEY, Michael
White & Case LLP, Washington, DC
202 626 3593
michaelquigley@whitecase.com
*Featured in Tax (Nationwide)*
**Career:** Michael Quigley resolves tax disputes by negotiation and also litigation before court. To achieve negotiated settlements, he works with IRS agents and field personnel to resolve disputes at early as possible. He has appeared before the IRS Office of Appeals and represented clients in appeals conferences, fast-track mediations and post-appeals mediations. Michael is a leading authority on intercompany transfer pricing and tax issues affecting multinational corporations. He has negotiated advance pricing agreements with the IRS and the tax authorities of foreign jurisdictions, obtaining some of the first APAs between the US, Japan and Korea. To view his biography, visit www.whitecase.com/michaelquigley.

### QUINN, James W
Weil, Gotshal & Manges LLP, New York
212 310 8385
james.quinn@weil.com
*Featured in Litigation (Nationwide), Sports Law (Nationwide), Litigation (New York)*
**Practice Areas:** James Quinn is an accomplished trial lawyer who specializes in high-stakes commercial matters across all areas of litigation and alternative dispute resolution, including antitrust, securities, false advertising, sports, patent, IP, product liability and insurance. Recent representations include: advising Simon & Schuster on the resolution of government antitrust investigations into the e-book industry and related private class actions; obtaining the dismissal, affirmed on appeal, for CBS and certain of its officers of a multi-billion dollar securities class action; representing Exxon as lead trial counsel in a high-profile matter regarding the use of MTBE in gasoline; and representing the NFL players, NBA players, and NHL players in the resolution of high-profile lockout disputes with, respectively, the NFL, NBA, and NHL.
**Professional Memberships:** American College of Trial Lawyers; International Academy of Trial Lawyers; The New York Bar Foundation; Committee Chair, The American Bar Association and The New York City Bar Association; Member, Advisory Board of the National Judicial College, the Panel of Distinguished Neutrals of the Center for Public Resources, and the International Society of Barristers.
**Personal:** University of Notre Dame (AB); Fordham University (LLB).

### QUINN, Patrick T
Cadwalader, Wickersham & Taft LLP, New York
212 504 6067
pat.quinn@cwt.com
*Featured in Capital Markets (Nationwide)*
**Practice Areas:** Co-Chair, Capital Markets Department. Practices primarily in the area of structured products and finance, representing issuers, underwriters, and investors in securities and financing transactions. Represents lenders in real estate structured credit transactions and in the acquisition, disposition and financing of structured real estate debt instruments. Regularly advises clients with respect to the restructuring or liquidation of non-performing real estate debt instruments and structured products.
**Personal:** JD, University of Virginia School of Law; BA, Fordham University.

### QUINTER, Peter
GrayRobinson, PA, Miami
305 416 6960
Peter.Quinter@Gray-Robinson.com
*Featured in International Trade (Nationwide)*
**Practice Areas:** Chair of Customs and International Trade Law Group. Resolve seizure, penalty, audit, tariff classification and other import, export, and international trade related cases with U.S. Customs and Border Protection (CBP), U.S. Food and Drug Administration (FDA), U.S. Department of Homeland Security (DHS), Transportation Security Administration (TSA), Office of Foreign Assets Control (OFAC), and Bureau of Industry and Security (BIS).
**Professional Memberships:** U.S. Court of International Trade; The Florida Bar; American Bar Association; U.S. District Court, Southern District of Florida; Florida Customs Brokers and Forwarders Association, Inc. (FCBF); Customs and International Trade Bar Association (CITBA); Council of Supply Chain Management Professionals; National Customs Brokers and Forwarders Association of America, Inc. (NCB-FAA).
**Career:** Board Certified in International Law by the Florida Bar since 1999. Florida Trend magazine repeatedly recognized him among its "Legal Elite" in the area of International Law. Appointed to the Florida District Export Council by U.S. Secretary of Commerce. Rated "superb" by Avvo Ratings. Annually included in the top 5% of Florida lawyers by Florida Super Lawyer magazine, and recognized in "Best Lawyers in America" in the area of FDA Law. Editor of www.GRCustomsLaw.com blog.
**Personal:** Cornell University, B.S. (1986); The American University, Washington College of Law, JD (1989).

### RACITI-KNAPP, Melissa
Freshfields Bruckhaus Deringer US LLP, New York
212 277 4000
melissa.raciti@freshfields.com
*Featured in Projects (Nationwide)*
**Practice Areas:** Melissa is a member of Freshfields' finance group and is co-head of their Latin America practice. She has considerable

experience in the Americas, including financings and purchase and sale of projects in the US, Argentina, Bolivia, Brazil, Chile, Colombia, the Dominican Republic, Mexico, Panama, Peru, Trinidad and Venezuela. Sector experience includes mining, power, oil and gas, infrastructure, water and telecoms.
**Career:** Received her JD from Columbia University (Harlan Fiske Stone scholar, Senior Editor of Columbia Law Review) and her BA, magna cum laude, from Columbia College.
**Publications:** Speaks Spanish fluently and has a working knowledge of Portuguese.

### RADCLIFFE, Mark F
DLA Piper LLP (US), East Palo Alto
650 833 2266
mark.radcliffe@dlapiper.com
*Featured in Outsourcing (Nationwide), IT & Outsourcing (California)*
See under California for profile.

### RADEMACHER, Kurt G
Butler, Snow, O'Mara, Stevens & Cannada, PLLC, Ridgeland
601 985 4548
kurt.rademacher@butlersnow.com
*Featured in Wealth Management (Nationwide)*
**Practice Areas:** Private client and wealth management; estate and trust planning; international taxation.
**Professional Memberships:** Mississippi Bar; American Bar Association; Society of Trust and Estate Practitioners.
**Career:** Chambers Asia, Leader in the Fields of Private Client and Wealth Management; Chambers USA, Leader in the Field of Wealth Management: Central Region, 2011 (National); Fellow, American College of Trust and Estate Counsel.
**Personal:** University of Mississippi, B.Accy., magna cum laude, 1995, M.Tax., 1996; University of Notre Dame, JD, cum laude, 1999; New York University, LL.M., 2000.

### RADKE, Kirk A
Kirkland & Ellis LLP, New York
212 446 4940
kirk.radke@kirkland.com
*Featured in Private Equity (Nationwide)*
**Practice Areas:** Kirk Radke is a corporate partner in Kirkland & Ellis' New York office where he is a member of the private equity practice. Mr Radke has over 25 years experience in various types of corporate and private equity transactions. He has advised domestic and foreign clients in private and public offerings of debt and equity securities, credit facilities, venture capital and private equity investments, fund formation, acquisitions and divestures and other complex transactions. He is regularly recognized by numerous publications and participates in various legal and financial seminars.

### RAFF, Joshua E
Orrick, Herrington & Sutcliffe LLP, New York
212 506 5090
jraff@orrick.com
*Featured in Capital Markets (Nationwide)*

**Career:** Joshua Raff, a partner in the New York office, advises issuers, underwriters, investment funds, institutional investors, fund sponsors, investment advisors and other financial institutions on a variety of complex financing and capital markets transactions, as well as asset purchases and sales, asset- and mortgage-backed securities, fund formation, corporate transactions with respect to asset management entities and platforms, and related matters. Mr Raff has participated in the development of innovative structures on behalf of a wide array of participants in the financial markets. He currently serves on the Advisory Board of the Capital Markets Law Journal.

### RAFTE, G Alan
Bracewell & Giuliani LLP, Houston
713 221 1411
alan.rafte@bgllp.com
*Featured in Banking & Finance (Texas), Energy & Natural Resources (Nationwide), Projects (Nationwide)*
**Practice Areas:** Co-chairs the firm's business and regulatory practice. Serves clients in transactions that involve upstream oil and gas projects; gas and liquids pipelines and facilities; merchant electric generation facilities; electric utilities; and energy commodity trading. Represents utilities, private equity investors, financial institutions and commodity trading businesses in transactions that include acquisitions and divestitures of assets and companies, joint venture arrangements, structured finance, leveraged finance, project development and project finance.
**Personal:** JD, Emory University School of Law, 1979; BA, Syracuse University, 1976.

### RAIM, David
Chadbourne & Parke LLP, Washington, DC
202 974 5625
draim@chadbourne.com
*Featured in Insurance (District of Columbia), Insurance (Nationwide)*
**Practice Areas:** Co-Chair, Reinsurance and Insurance Group. Has represented parties in hundreds of reinsurance arbitrations and litigations on wide range of issues, including property/ casualty and life/ health reinsurance, finite reinsurance, London Market matters, MGAs, allocation issues, rescission claims, 'fronting' issues, surety, clash and catastrophe covers. Additionally, provides advice to clients in the reinsurance and insurance industry on wide range of subject matters, including commutations, contract wordings, inspections and insolvencies.
**Professional Memberships:** ARIAS-US; District of Columbia Bar - Chairman, Members Benefits Committee (1988-94).
**Personal:** Yale University, BA, cum laude, 1975; University of Pennsylvania Law School, JD, cum laude, 1978.

### RAIN, John W
Thompson & Knight LLP, Dallas
214 969 1644
John.Rain@tklaw.com
*Featured in Banking & Finance (Texas), Energy & Natural Resources (Nationwide)*
See under Texas for profile.

### RAINERO, Julian
Bracewell & Giuliani LLP, New York
212 508 6142
julian.rainero@bgllp.com
*Featured in Financial Services Regulation (Nationwide)*
**Practice Areas:** Head of the firm's broker-dealer practice. Advises broker-dealers and alternative trading systems on compliance with SEC, self-regulatory organization (SRO) and Federal Reserve Board rules. Practice involves all aspects of broker-dealer regulation, with particular concentration in correspondent clearing, prime brokerage, net capital, margin, securities lending, customer protection and NYSE and NASDAQ trading practices.
**Professional Memberships:** Member of the NASDAQ market operations review committee and serves on the best-execution committees of several major broker-dealers.
**Personal:** JD, American University, Washington College of Law, 1998; BA, Dickinson College, 1994.

### RAISLER, Kenneth M
Sullivan & Cromwell LLP, New York
212 558 4675
raislerk@sullcrom.com
*Featured in Capital Markets (Nationwide)*
**Professional Memberships:** ABA (Section on Corporation, Banking & Business Law), (Vice Chairman, Futures and Derivatives Committee); NYCBA (Chairman, Committee on Futures Regulation, 1988-1991); Board of Directors, Futures Industry Association.
**Career:** Partner since 1994. Coordinator, Commodities, Futures and Derivatives Group, which renders regulatory, transactional and litigation advice in derivatives, commodities, futures, securities, banking areas to brokerage, hedge fund, investment banking, banking, commercial clients.
**Personal:** New York University School of Law (JD, 1976); Yale University (BS, 1973). Judicial Clerk to Hon. Lee P. Gagliardi, US District Court (SDNY) (1976-1977). Assistant US Attorney, DC, Criminal and Civil Divisions (1977-1982). General Counsel, CFTC (1983-1987).

### RAMAN, Anand S
Skadden, Arps, Slate, Meagher & Flom LLP & Affiliates, Washington, DC
202 371 7019
Anand.Raman@skadden.com
*Featured in Financial Services Regulation (Nationwide)*
**Practice Areas:** Co-leader of Consumer Financial Services Litigation and Enforcement practice. Represents financial institutions in connection with investigations, class action litigation, enforcement and administrative actions involving fair lending, unfair and deceptive trade practices, subprime lending, mortgage fraud, redlining, credit card practices and mortgage loan servicing. Regularly assists financial institutions in analyzing lending data and with respect to compliance and risk management programs.
**Career:** Law Clerk to the Honorable Patricia Wald, U.S. Court of Appeals for the D.C. Circuit (1995-96); Legislative Assistant, Congressman Jim Cooper (1990-92). JD, Yale Law School, 1995 (edi-

tor, Yale Law Journal); A.B., Statistics, University of Chicago, 1990.

### RANAWAKE, Jerome
Freshfields Bruckhaus Deringer US LLP, New York
212 277 4000
jerome.ranawake@freshfields.com
*Featured in Capital Markets (Nationwide)*
**Practice Areas:** Jerome is a partner in Freshfields Bruckhaus Deringer's New York-based Finance Practice Group. He specializes in structured finance transactions, advising bank, broker-dealer and hedge fund clients on US and cross-border securitization transactions (including cash and synthetic CLO and CDO transactions, trade receivables securitizations and other asset monetizations), prime brokerage and related trading documentation, complex derivatives (including TRS, CDS, equity and commodity derivatives), repos and securities lending, and other fund financing structures.

### RANCE, Brian
Freshfields Bruckhaus Deringer US LLP, New York
212 277 4000
brian.rance@freshfields.com
*Featured in Capital Markets (Nationwide)*
**Practice Areas:** Brian is a finance partner based in the firm's New York office. He represents commercial and investment banks, insurance companies, managed investment funds and other financial institutions in a variety of domestic and international financial and corporate transactions. Brian's practice focuses on structured financings (particularly collateralized debt obligation funds), commercial bank and other private financings (including highly-leveraged loans and merchant banking investments), derivative transactions (including fixed income, credit, equity and commodity derivatives), institutional private placements and debt to equity conversions. Brian is also an expert on laws affecting the financial industry, including bank regulatory and insolvency laws.

### RAO, Naveen C
Jones Day, Washington, DC
202 879 3708
ncrao@jonesday.com
*Featured in Transportation (Nationwide)*
**Practice Areas:** Advises air carriers, aerospace firms, and other companies on regulatory matters involving the Federal Aviation Administration, the U.S. Secretary of Transportation and foreign regulators.
**Career:** Served as General Counsel of Naverus, Inc. (2008-2009) Served with the U.S. Department of Transportation in the following positions: Counselor to the Assistant Secretary for Aviation and International Affairs (2006-2008) and Regulations Attorney, Federal Aviation Administration, Office of the Chief Counsel (2001-2003 and 2005-2006) As a Mike Mansfield Fellow, assigned to the Japan Civil Aviation Bureau and the Japan Fair Trade Commission (2004-2005). Assistant Editor of the ABA's The Air & Space Lawyer.

## RAPISARDI, John J
Cadwalader, Wickersham & Taft LLP, New York
212 504 5585
john.rapisardi@cwt.com
*Featured in Bankruptcy/Restructuring (Nationwide), Bankruptcy/Restructuring (New York)*
See under New York for profile.

## RAPPAPORT, Louis
Blank Rome LLP, Philadelphia
215 569 5647
Rappaport@BlankRome.com
*Featured in Investment Funds (Nationwide)*
**Practice Areas:** Louis Rappaport concentrates his practice on business and corporate matters, with specific emphasis on venture and private equity backed businesses. Mr Rappaport represents both private equity firms - buyout and venture capital - and business operators with respect to mergers and acquisitions and investment transactions. Mr Rappaport advises clients in a wide range of industries in mergers and acquisitions; venture capital and private equity funding transactions; securities offerings; corporate finance matters; strategic alliances and joint ventures; intellectual property/technology licensing and transfer matters; executive employment and compensation matters; and business formation and planning. For more information: www.BlankRome.com/Rappaport

## RASHKOVER, Barry
Sidley Austin LLP, New York
212 839 5850
brashkover@sidley.com
*Featured in Securities (Nationwide), Litigation (New York)*
See under New York for profile.

## RAUL, Alan Charles
Sidley Austin LLP, Washington, DC
202 736 8477
araul@sidley.com
*Featured in Privacy & Data Security (Nationwide)*
**Practice Areas:** Partner, and a global coordinator of Sidley's Privacy, Data Security and Information Law practice. Broad litigation and counseling practice covering privacy, data protection, cybersecurity, consumer protection, Internet and information law. Represents clients in connection with global compliance programs, international data transfers, FTC and State AG investigations, class actions, e-Commerce, and cyberlaw. Also handles matters involving government enforcement, corporate compliance and administrative law. Served as Vice Chairman of the White House Privacy and Civil Liberties Oversight Board.
**Personal:** Yale Law School, JD, 1980; Harvard University, MPA, 1977; Harvard College, AB, 1975, magna cum laude. Admissions: DC, New York.

## RAYIS, John D
Skadden, Arps, Slate, Meagher & Flom LLP & Affiliates, Chicago
312 407 0778
john.rayis@skadden.com
*Featured in Tax (Illinois), Capital Markets (Nationwide)*

**Practice Areas:** Handles various tax matters, including complex partnership transactions, real estate investment trusts, debt offerings and restructurings, mergers and acquisitions, entertainment joint ventures and financings, Section 1031 like-kind exchanges, project financings, sale/leaseback transactions and tax-exempt financings. Advises on foreign investments in the United States involving the Foreign Investment Real Property Tax Act and issues involving tax-exempt organizations. Tax adviser for various partnerships, investment companies, REITs and foreign governments. Frequently featured in articles discussing REITs and tax law.
**Career:** LLM, University of Michigan, 1980; JD, Wayne State University, 1979 (cum laude); BS and BA, Michigan State University, 1977 (with Honors).

## RAYSMAN, Richard
Holland & Knight LLP, New York
212 513 3469
richard.raysman@hklaw.com
*Featured in Outsourcing (Nationwide), Technology (New York)*
See under New York for profile.

## REA, Anne E
Sidley Austin LLP, Chicago
312 853 7156
area@sidley.com
*Featured in ERISA Litigation (Nationwide)*
**Practice Areas:** Global coordinator of Sidley's ERISA Litigation practice area team. Concentrates in complex class action litigation with a focus on ERISA and fiduciary lawsuits as well as corporate, securities, and tax matters. Represents companies, plans and fiduciaries in ERISA class action lawsuits challenging the design and administration of employee benefit plans. Represents companies in securities fraud class action, derivative suits, and other complex litigation. Member of the firm's Management and Executive Committees.
**Personal:** The University of Chicago Law School, JD, 1984; Brown University, AB, 1981, magna cum laude. Member, American Law Institute. Admission: Illinois.

## REAMER, David C
Skadden, Arps, Slate, Meagher & Flom LLP & Affiliates, Los Angeles
213 687 5052
david.reamer@skadden.com
*Featured in Banking & Finance (California), Banking & Finance (Nationwide)*
See under California for profile.

## REARDON, Marc A
Bingham McCutchen LLP, Boston
617 951 8297
marc.reardon@bingham.com
*Featured in Projects (Nationwide)*
**Practice Areas:** Co-chair of Bingham's Energy and Project Finance Group. Focuses on development, construction, financing and transfer of electric generating facilities and other infrastructure, including industrial, transportation, recycling and waste disposal facilities. Has represented developers, financial institutions, equity investors and contractors in connection with numerous domes-

tic and international power and infrastructure projects.
**Career:** His work representing Astoria Energy was named 2009 Americas Power Deal of the Year by 'Project Finance International Magazine.'
**Personal:** Georgetown University Law Center, JD; Harvard College, BA.

## REASONER, Harry M
Vinson & Elkins LLP, Houston
713 758 2358
hreasoner@velaw.com
*Featured in Antitrust (Texas), Litigation (Nationwide), Litigation (Texas)*
**Practice Areas:** Complex civil litigation. Lead Counsel in trials, arbitrations, and appeals involving antitrust, securities, energy, insurance, contract, media, and tort claims.
**Professional Memberships:** Fellow: American College of Trial Lawyers; International Academy of Trial Lawyers; International Society of Barristers; American Law Institute; American Board of Trial Advocates; Former Chair, ABA Section of Antitrust Law.
**Career:** Admitted to practice: Texas, District of Columbia, New York. Partner, Vinson & Elkins.
**Publications:** With C A Wright, "Procedure: The Handmaid of Justice."
**Personal:** Rice University, BA; University of Texas Law School, JD; Rotary Foundation Fellow, University of London; law clerk, USCA, 2d Cir.

## RECTOR, Richard P
DLA Piper LLP (US), Washington, DC
202 799 4400
richard.rector@dlapiper.com
*Featured in Government (Nationwide)*
**Practice Areas:** Government contracts, aerospace and defense, homeland security.
**Career:** He chairs the firm's Government Contracts group, and focuses on federal and state procurement issues. He has litigated contract actions and bid protests before various courts and other jurisdictions and has represented prime contractors and subcontractors in breach-of-contract and protest actions, as well as prepared contract claims and requests for equitable adjustment.
**Personal:** JD, University of Maryland; BA, University of Maryland.

## REDGRAVE, Jonathan
Redgrave LLP, Washington, DC
202 603 1497
jredgrave@redgravellp.com
*Featured in Litigation (Nationwide)*
**Practice Areas:** Jonathan Redgrave is internationally recognized for his work in the areas of eDiscovery and Information Governance. His practice at Redgrave LLP focuses exclusively on Information Law, providing Fortune 500 companies and AmLaw 100 law firms with the legal and technical advice, business strategy and legal representation needed to support their legal, regulatory and operational requirements. Jonathan's practice areas include competencies such as National and International Discovery Counsel, Litigation Readiness, Information Governance and Data Privacy, as well as serving in the roles of Expert Witness and Special Master.

**Professional Memberships:** Jonathan Redgrave helped found, was the first Chair of and is currently Chair Emeritus of the renowned Sedona Conference Working Group on Electronic Document Retention and Production. His professional memberships also include serving as a founding member of the Advisory Board of the acclaimed Georgetown University Law School eDiscovery Institute and as a Member of the Advisory Committee on the Electronic Records Archives for the United States National Archives and Records Administration. Jonathan is also an approved eDiscovery Special Master for the United States District Court for the Western District of Pennsylvania. He is also a member of several bar associations and professional organizations including ARMA International, AIIM, and IAPP. Jonathan Redgrave helped found, was the first Chair of and is currently Chair Emeritus of the renowned Sedona Conference Working Group on Electronic Document Retention and Production. His professional memberships also include serving as a founding member of the Advisory Board of the acclaimed Georgetown University Law School eDiscovery Institute and as a Member of the Advisory Committee on the Electronic Records Archives for the United States National Archives and Records Administration. Jonathan is also an approved eDiscovery Special Master for the United States District Court for the Western District of Pennsylvania. He is also a member of several bar associations and professional organizations including ARMA International, AIIM, and IAPP.
**Publications:** Using Contract Terms to Get Ahead of Prospective eDiscovery Costs and Burdens in Commercial Litigation (Rich. J. L. & Tech., June 2012) (with Jay Brudz) Managing the Emerging Business and Legal Realities of Social Media in Corporate America (ACC Docket, November 2011) (with Vincent Catanzaro) Discovery of Electronic Information in the third edition of the treatise Business and Commercial Litigation in Federal Courts (Thompson Reuters) (December 2011) (with Hon. Shira A. Scheindlin) Co-Editor, The Sedona Conference ®Commentary on Legal Holds: The Trigger & The Process (2010 Version), The Sedona Conference Journal, Volume 11 (Fall 2010) (published by The Sedona Conference® Working Group on Best Practices for Electronic Document Retention & Production (WG1)) (with Thomas Y. Allman and Conor R. Crowley) Asserting and Challenging Privilege Claims in Modern Litigation: The Facciola-Redgrave Framework (Federal Court Law Review, Volume 1, Issue 1 (2009)) (with Hon. John M. Facciola) Special Masters and E-Discovery: The Intersection of Two Recent Revisions to the Federal Rules of Civil Procedure (Cardozo Law Review, Volume 30, Issue 2. November 2008) (with Hon. Shira A. Scheindlin) E-Discovery: Technology Requires Greater Care in Preserving Evidence (ABA Journal, April 2008) (with Hon. Shira A. Scheindlin) Editor-in-Chief, The Sedona Principles (Second Edition): Best Practices Recommendations & Principles for Addressing Electronic Document Production (2007

Annotated Version) (published by The Sedona Conference® Working Group on Best Practices for Electronic Document Retention & Production (WG1)) Editor-in-Chief, The Sedona Principles (Second Edition): Best Practices, Recommendations and Principles for Addressing Electronic Document Production (July 2007) (published by The Sedona Conference® Working Group on Best Practices for Electronic Document Retention & Production (WG1)) Co-Editor-in-Chief, The Sedona Guidelines: Best Practices Guidelines and Commentary for Managing Information and Records in the Electronic Age (September 2005) (with Charles R. Ragan and Lori Ann Wagner) Editor-in-Chief, The Sedona Principles: Best Practices Recommendations & Principles for Addressing Electronic Document Production (2005 Annotated Version) (published by The Sedona Conference® Working Group on Best Practices for Electronic Document Retention & Production (WG1)) The Evolution and Impact of the New Federal Rule Governing Special Masters (51 The Federal Lawyer 34, February 2004) (with Hon. Shira A. Scheindlin) Editor-in-Chief, The Sedona Principles: Best Practices, Recommendations and Principles for Addressing Electronic Document Production (January 2004; rev ed. July 2005) (published by The Sedona Conference® Working Group on Best Practices for Electronic Document Retention & Production (WG1)) Revisions in Federal Rule 53 Provide New Options for Using Special Masters in Litigation (76 New York State Bar Journal 18, January 2004) (with Hon. Shira A. Scheindlin) Fishing in the Ocean: A Critical Examination of Discovery in the Electronic Age (The Sedona Conference Journal, Vol. II, Fall 2001) (with Ted. S. Hiser) Juror Investigation on the Internet – Implications for the Trial Lawyer (The Sedona Conference Journal, Vol. II, Fall 2001) (with Jason J. Stover) Unplugging Jurors from the Internet (48 The Federal Lawyer 19, July 2001) Litigation and Technology: How the Internet is Changing the Practice (47 The Federal Lawyer 25, January 2000) The Blue Oval Blues: Trade Secrets and the Internet (Bench & Bar of Minnesota, November 1999) (with Brian L. McMahon) Insurance Coverage and Internet Transactions (Bench & Bar of Minnesota, April/May 1999) Civil Discovery and the Data Practices Act (Bench & Bar of Minnesota, October 1995) (with Mary K. Martin).

**REDLICK, David E**
WilmerHale, Boston
617 526 6434
david.redlick@wilmerhale.com
*Featured in Life Sciences (Nationwide), Corporate/M&A (Massachusetts)*
**Practice Areas:** Co-Chair of WilmerHale's Life Sciences Group. Practice focuses on corporate and securities law, with an emphasis on public offerings, corporate collaborations, mergers and acquisitions, and venture capital transactions.
**Professional Memberships:** Overseers Committee, Brigham and Women's Hospital; guest lecturer, Harvard Business School, Kellogg School of Management at Northwestern

University, Harvard Law School, and Sloan School of Management at MIT.
**Career:** Admitted to Massachusetts Bar. Joined the firm in 1975.
**Personal:** Harvard Law School (JD, cum laude); University of Wisconsin (BA, Class Valedictorian, Phi Beta Kappa).

**REED, Glen**
King & Spalding LLP, Atlanta
404 572 3393
gareed@kslaw.com
*Featured in Healthcare (Georgia), Healthcare (Nationwide)*
See under Georgia for profile.

**REEDER III, Robert W**
Sullivan & Cromwell LLP, New York
212 558 4000
reederr@sullcrom.com
*Featured in Capital Markets (Nationwide)*
**Career:** Robert Reeder is co-coordinator of S&C's Corporate group and Commodities, Futures and Derivatives practice group and is a member of the Firm's Broker/Dealer and Executive Compensation and Benefits Groups. Mr Reeder is also Head of the Firm's Pro Bono Committee. Mr Reeder has experience in a wide array of general corporate and securities matters.
**Personal:** Partner since 1993. Ohio State University, JD 1984, Youngstown State University, B.S. 1981.

**REEMER, Ellis L**
DLA Piper LLP (US), New York
212 335 4980
ellis.reemer@dlapiper.com
*Featured in Tax (Nationwide)*
**Practice Areas:** Tax Controversy
**Career:** He heads the Tax Controversy and Tax Disputes practice and has more than two decades of experience in tax controversy, tax disputes and tax litigation matters. He concentrates in representing clients in complex federal, state and local tax controversies and tax litigation and has represented both public and privately held corporations, as well as partnerships, estates, trusts and individuals. He regularly represents accounting firms and accountants in matters involving their obligations under federal and state tax laws.
**Personal:** LLM, Taxation, New York University; JD, St. John's University (cum laude); BA, Hunter College.

**REESE, Michael T.**
Pillsbury Winthrop Shaw Pittman LLP, New York
212 858 1411
michael.reese@pillsburylaw.com
*Featured in Projects (Nationwide)*
**Practice Areas:** Concentrates in the development and financing of power generation (conventional, renewable and nuclear), electric transmission, toll road and other infrastructure projects. Experience in every stage of project life, from joint venture formation to acquisition/divestiture. Also represents parties in corporate financings in energy and related industries. Represents sponsors, financial institutions, investors, utilities and gov-

ernment agencies in transactions in the US, Europe, Asia and the Middle East.
**Career:** Admitted: State of New York.
**Personal:** JD, University of Texas School of Law, 2001 (Townes-Rice Scholar); MA, University of Texas at Austin, 1995; BA, University of Dallas, 1991.

**REGER JR, Robert J**
Morgan, Lewis & Bockius LLP, New York
212 309 6282
rreger@morganlewis.com
*Featured in Energy & Natural Resources (Nationwide)*
**Practice Areas:** Robert J. Reger, Jr. is a partner in Morgan Lewis's Business and Finance Practice. Mr Reger focuses his practice on corporate finance, SEC-related matters, corporate governance, and general corporate matters. He advises investor-owned utilities and underwriting firms with respect to securitizations built around statutorily mandated ratepayer charges, as well as SEC registered, Rule 144A, and private issuances of debt and equity securities, including first mortgage bonds, pollution control revenue bonds, collateral trust bonds, debentures, unsecured debt, secured facility bonds, trust originated preferred securities, preferred stock, common stock, equity units, and other hybrid instruments.

**REIDY, Andrew**
Dickstein Shapiro LLP, Washington, DC
202 420 2535
reidya@dicksteinshapiro.com
*Featured in Insurance (Nationwide), Insurance (District of Columbia)*
See under District of Columbia for profile.

**REIDY, Daniel E**
Jones Day, Chicago
312 269 4140
dereidy@jonesday.com
*Featured in Litigation (Nationwide), Litigation (Illinois)*
See under Illinois for profile.

**REIFF, Laura Foote**
Greenberg Traurig, LLP, McLean
703 749 1372
ReiffL@gtlaw.com
*Featured in Immigration (Nationwide), Immigration (District of Columbia)*
See under District of Columbia for profile.

**REILLY, Michael J**
Bingham McCutchen LLP, New York
212 705 7763
michael.reilly@bingham.com
*Featured in Bankruptcy/Restructuring (Nationwide), Bankruptcy/Restructuring (New York)*
**Practice Areas:** Co-head of Bingham's global Financial Restructuring Group and former deputy chair of the Financial Services Area. More than 30 years of experience representing public and private bondholders and lenders in financial restructurings in a wide array of industries in the US, UK/Europe and Latin America. Frequent speaker and lecturer at industry seminars on workouts and bankruptcy.
**Career:** Fellow, American College of Bankruptcy and the American College of Investment Counsel.

**Personal:** University of Connecticut School of Law, JD, 1976; University of Connecticut, BA, 1973.

**REINDEL, F William**
Fried, Frank, Harris, Shriver & Jacobson LLP, New York
212 859 8189
F.William.Reindel@FriedFrank.com
*Featured in Banking & Finance (Nationwide)*
**Practice Areas:** Corporate partner. Represents private equity sponsors, investment banks, hedge funds and public and private companies on a broad range of leveraged financing transactions. Practice includes advising sponsors, corporations and lenders on syndicated senior facilities, second lien facilities, US and European mezzanine financings, private placements and commodities hedge financings, as well as assisting private equity and mezzanine funds in raising fund level financings.
**Career:** Joined in 1978; became partner in 1986.
**Personal:** JD, University of Minnesota Law School (1978), editor, Law Review; BA, magna cum laude, Amherst College (1975), Phi Beta Kappa.

**REISER, Bert C**
Latham & Watkins LLP, Washington, DC
202 637 1026
bert.reiser@lw.com
*Featured in International Trade (Nationwide)*
**Practice Areas:** Represents complainants and respondents in the litigation and trial of international intellectual property disputes before the US International Trade Commission (ITC) under Section 337 of the Tariff Act of 1930. Also represents patentees and defendants in patent litigation before federal district courts.
**Professional Memberships:** Member, DC and Virginia state bars.
**Career:** Current head of ITC litigation practice at Latham & Watkins; former attorney advisor to Chief Administrative Law Judge of the ITC; former head of Section 337 practice at Howrey LLP.
**Personal:** JD, American University, Washington College of Law, 1990; BA, Central College of Iowa, 1985.

**REISNER, Carl L**
Paul, Weiss, Rifkind, Wharton & Garrison LLP, New York
212 373 3017
creisner@paulweiss.com
*Featured in Private Equity (Nationwide)*
**Practice Areas:** Co-head of North American Mergers and Acquisitions Group. Has diverse M&A practice, providing counsel to a varied and long-standing client base, especially private equity firms and their portfolio companies. He has represented enterprises through all stages of the corporate life cycle, including start-up companies, growing companies in a wide variety of acquisitions, and restructurings of financially troubled enterprises. Principal private equity clients include CI Capital Partners, KPS Capital Partners, Oak Hill Capital Partners, Straus Capital Group and Beowulf Energy. Broad experience in manufacturing, distribution, health care, defense and power industries.

**REISS, John**
White & Case LLP, New York
212 819 8247
jreiss@whitecase.com
*Featured in Private Equity (Nationwide),*
*Corporate/M&A (New York)*
See under New York for profile.

**REITER, Glenn M**
Simpson Thacher & Bartlett LLP, New York
212 455 3358
greiter@stblaw.com
*Featured in Latin American Investment (New York),*
*Capital Markets (Nationwide)*
**Practice Areas:** Of counsel focusing on capital markets transactions, including US and cross-border securities offerings and other financings. Experienced in M&A transactions. Represents US and non-US corporations, government entities and investment banks in equity offerings (including IPOs and follow-on offerings), debt offerings (including investment grade, high-yield and sovereign bond offerings), structured financings, liability management transactions, M&A transactions and other transactions. Transactions involve the US, Latin America, the Caribbean, Canada and Europe.
**Career:** Partner 1984-2012; Of counsel 2013-.
**Personal:** BA, summa cum laude, Phi Beta Kappa, Yale College (1973); JD, Yale Law School (1976).

**REITZFELD, Alan D**
Holland & Knight LLP, New York
212 513 3200
alan.reitzfeld@hklaw.com
*Featured in Transportation (Nationwide)*
**Practice Areas:** Alan D Reitzfeld is a partner in the firm's Litigation Practice Group. For over 30 years, he has played a leading role in defending US and foreign airlines in multi-district litigation arising out of major domestic and foreign commercial jet airline crashes and other incidents involving death or serious personal injuries. He has briefed and argued aviation case appeals in various appellate courts across the country. Mr Reitzfeld has extensive experience with alternative dispute resolution procedures in the aviation litigation context. In addition, he has handled high technology disputes involving software and hardware and various intellectual property matters.

**REPKA, David A**
Winston & Strawn LLP, Washington, DC
202 282 5726
drepka@winston.com
*Featured in Energy & Natural Resources (Nationwide)*
**Practice Areas:** Regulation of nuclear power, nuclear fuel cycle facilities, and industrial and medical uses of radiological materials. Extensive experience in: Nuclear Regulatory Commission licensing and administrative hearings, including initial licenses, license renewals, and license transfers; NRC regulatory compliance and enforcement matters; federal and internal investigations including employee protection matters; and federal court appeals.

**Professional Memberships:** District of Columbia Bar.
**Career:** Partner since 1991.
**Publications:** Co-author 'A Dose of History: Nuclear Energy Cases That Shaped Environmental Law,' Natural Resources & Environment, Summer 2010.
**Personal:** Northwestern University, BA, Physics, 1978; Georgetown University Law Center, JD, 1981.

**RESSA, Gregory J**
Simpson Thacher & Bartlett LLP, New York
212 455 7430
gressa@stblaw.com
*Featured in Leisure & Hospitality (Nationwide), Real Estate (Nationwide), Real Estate (New York)*
**Practice Areas:** Greg Ressa is Head of the firm's Real Estate Department and a member of the firm's Executive Committee. His practice involves all aspects of the real estate industry with emphasis on representation of real estate opportunity funds, real estate mergers and acquisitions and real estate finance. Has handled transactions involving The Blackstone Group, AIG Global Real Estate, Barclays Capital, Hilton Worldwide, Och-Ziff, Centerbridge Partners and Northwood Investors on a wide variety of both domestic and international transactions.
**Career:** Joined firm, 1987; Elected Partner, 1995.
**Personal:** BA, Tufts University (1984); JD, Fordham University School of Law (1987).

**REYNOLDS III, John B**
Davis Polk & Wardwell LLP, Washington, DC
202 962 7000
john.reynolds@davispolk.com
*Featured in International Trade (Nationwide)*
**Practice Areas:** Advises corporations, financial institutions and defense, technology and consumer products companies on privacy, security and regulatory issues including inward/outward foreign investment transactions, economic sanctions, export controls, anti-boycott compliance and FCPA compliance. Represents clients before the US Departments of State, Treasury, Commerce, Defense and Homeland Security and the Office of the US Trade Representative.
**Professional Memberships:** ABA: Former Chair, Committee on Export Controls and Economic Sanctions; Former Co-Chair, Committee on Senior International Appointments; Former Co-Chair, Committee on National Security and International Law.
**Career:** Attorney-Adviser, US Department of State.
**Personal:** Yale Law School (JD); Williams College (BA, magna cum laude).

**RICCIARDI, Walter G**
Paul, Weiss, Rifkind, Wharton & Garrison LLP, New York
212 373 3350
wricciardi@paulweiss.com
*Featured in Securities (Nationwide)*
**Practice Areas:** Partner in the Securities Litigation and Enforcement Group. Extensive experience defending a broad variety of investigations conducted by the SEC and other regulatory

authorities, and in conducting internal investigations for public companies and directors, including investigations related to allegations of accounting and financial fraud and compliance with the Foreign Corrupt Practices Act. Prior to joining Paul, Weiss in June 2008, Walter was the Deputy Director of the SEC's Division of Enforcement, where he supervised many of the Commission's most significant investigations related to financial fraud, FCPA, insider trading and broker-dealer and mutual fund compliance issues.

**RICE, James**
Sidley Austin LLP, Houston
713 495 4504
jrice@sidley.com
*Featured in Energy & Natural Resources (Nationwide)*
**Practice Areas:** Partner in Sidley's Houston office, Mr Rice's practice focuses principally on transactions for energy industry participants, including companies engaged in oil and gas exploration and production, midstream activities, petroleum refining, petrochemicals processing, oilfield services and electric power generation. He has significant experience in mergers, acquisitions and divestitures; private equity investments; bank financings; structured financings; and debt restructurings, with primary emphasis on the energy sector.
**Personal:** Tulane University Law School, JD, 1983, Tulane Law Review; Tulane University, BA, 1979.

**RICH, Frederic C**
Sullivan & Cromwell LLP, New York
212 558 3981
richf@sullcrom.com
*Featured in Projects (Nationwide)*
**Professional Memberships:** Director, U.S. Council for International Business; ABA (Former Chair, Committee on Privatization); ASIL; IBA.
**Career:** Partner since 1989. Coordinator, Project Development and Finance Group. More than 30 years' experience representing sponsors, investors and lenders in major international projects, including landmark oil and gas, metals and mining, and infrastructure transactions in Argentina, Australia, Azerbaijan, Chile, China, Indonesia, Kazakhstan, Kyrgyzstan, Panama, Papua New Guinea, Russia, Tanzania, Turkey, US, Venezuela and Zimbabwe. Extensive experience in global capital markets and international privatization transactions.
**Personal:** University of Virginia Law School (JD, 1981); King's College, Cambridge (Keasbey Fellow, 1978); Princeton University (AB, 1977).

**RICH, Randall S**
Pierce Atwood LLP, Washington, DC
202 470 6424
rrich@pierceatwood.com
*Featured in Energy & Natural Resources (Nationwide)*
**Practice Areas:** Randy represents all segments of the energy and utility industries before the FERC, the U.S. Department of Energy, and state public utility commissions.

**Professional Memberships:** Energy Bar Association, 1986-present; Board of Directors, 2004-2007; Member, Compliance & Enforcement, Natural Gas Regulation, 2012; American Bar Association, 1986- present; Independent Oil & Gas Association of West Virginia, Inc., 1986-present.
**Career:** Leads the firm's Energy Practice and serves as Partner-In-Charge of the Washington, DC office.
**Personal:** Washington University, JD, (1980); Brandeis University, BA, magna cum laude, (1977).

**RICHARDS, Eric A S**
O'Melveny & Myers LLP, Los Angeles
213 430 6552
erichards@omm.com
*Featured in Projects (Nationwide)*
**Practice Areas:** Eric Richards is a Partner in O'Melveny's Los Angeles office and a member of its Project Development and Finance Practice. His practice focuses on project finance and infrastructure investment and development, both in the United States and abroad. Eric represents sponsors, developers, financial institutions, investors, and others in a range of financing, development and investment-related transactions involving infrastructure assets. He is particularly experienced in transactions involving transportation assets (including airports, ports, rail, and surface transportation projects), various types of energy projects, social infrastructure and public-private partnerships.

**RICHARDSON, Bruce L**
King & Spalding LLP, Washington, DC
202 626 5510
brichardson@kslaw.com
*Featured in Energy & Natural Resources (Nationwide)*
**Practice Areas:** Mr Richardson focuses his practice on energy law. He represents and advises independent power producers, merchant transmission developers, electric power marketers, energy asset managers, private equity firms involved in the energy sector, and generation-owning industrial companies in connection with a broad range of transactional issues, administrative litigation, regulatory matters, and project issues. Transactional matters include electric power contracts, interconnection, and mergers and acquisitions. Regulatory matters include issues arising under the Federal Power Act, and the Public Utility Regulatory Policies Act of 1978.
**Personal:** JD, with honors George Washington University BA University of Chicago.

**RICHMAN, Lawrence I**
Neal, Gerber & Eisenberg LLP, Chicago
312 269 8070
lrichman@ngelaw.com
*Featured in Wealth Management (Nationwide)*
**Practice Areas:** Advises entrepreneurs, tax-exempt organizations, fiduciaries and high net worth families on estate, gift and charitable planning issues, including business succession, tax-efficient ownership structures, sophisticated tax-exempt structures, trust and estate administration,

executive benefits, life insurance and international estate planning issues.

**Professional Memberships:** American College of Trust and Estate Counsel (fellow); Chairman, Trust Law Committee, Chicago Bar Association; named to Worth magazine's 2006, 2007 and 2008 "100 Top Attorneys" nationwide list.

**Career:** Partner; Private Wealth Services Chair.

**Publications:** Author, commentator and lecturer on various private wealth management topics.

**Personal:** University of Chicago Law School (JD, 1977); Columbia University (BA, 1974).

---

### RIDINGS, Donald
Covington & Burling LLP, Washington, DC
202 662 5357
dridings@cov.com
*Featured in International Trade (Nationwide)*

**Practice Areas:** Don Ridings is co-chair of the firm's Anti-Corruption Practice Group. He counsels clients on proposed investment transactions, helps companies strengthen their anti-corruption compliance programs, leads internal investigations, and represents clients before enforcement authorities. Mr Ridings has advised companies in virtually every major industry, including agriculture, automotive, consumer products, energy, finance, gaming, life sciences, manufacturing, medical devices, mining, pharmaceuticals, private equity, professional services, software, technology, and transportation. Mr Ridings also maintains an active civil litigation and international arbitration practice.

**Personal:** Harvard University, BA; The George Washington University Law School, JD.

---

### RIPPEY, Edward
Covington & Burling LLP, Washington, DC
202 662 5171
erippey@cov.com
*Featured in Litigation (Nationwide)*

**Practice Areas:** Edward Rippey — who is Chair of Covington & Burling's E-Discovery Practice Group — litigates, advises, and speaks worldwide on legal and technical e-discovery issues. Mr Rippey routinely handles the e-discovery component of complex litigations in numerous fields for such global corporations as Procter & Gamble, AstraZeneca, Warner Chilcott, and Northrop Grumman. In addition, Mr Rippey has a robust e-discovery advisory practice that focuses on thorny issues for such clients as the New York Stock Exchange, eBay, Merck, Chiquita, and the National Football League. His other significant e-discovery activities include publishing articles in journals worldwide, sitting on national industry advisory boards, leading webinars and panels, and providing a comprehensive annual desk book for clients and potential clients.

**Personal:** Harvard University, A.B., summa cum laude and phi beta kappa (1991). Harvard Law School, JD, cum laude (1994).

---

### RISMAN, Clifford J
Gardere Wynne Sewell LLP, Dallas
214 999 4287
crisman@gardere.com
*Featured in Leisure & Hospitality (Nationwide), Real Estate (Texas)*

**Practice Areas:** Hospitality, real estate.

**Professional Memberships:** International Society of Hospitality Consultants (ISHC), Academy of Hospitality Industry Attorneys (AHIA), Global Alliance of Hospitality Attorneys (GAHA), Hospitality Industry Bar Association [Director] (HIBA), State Bar of Texas, American and Dallas Bar Associations.

**Career:** Cliff Risman chairs the Gardere Hospitality Industry Team and has a comprehensive business and real estate practice, with a particular emphasis on the global hospitality industry. He advises clients in the development, acquisition, financing, and operation of hotel, resort, and mixed-use properties throughout the United States and internationally; the structuring of domestic and foreign equity investments and the formation of equity investment entities; debt financings, recapitalizations and restructurings; the negotiation of management, franchise, development, technical services, and design agreements; the structuring, development, and marketing of various whole and fractional residential ownership products and related rental program arrangements; and the structuring of management, license, use, and access agreements for golf, spa, and residential project components. Mr Risman regularly publishes and speaks on hospitality industry, real estate, and finance topics and is also a member of Gardere's Private Equity Team.

**Personal:** JD, Syracuse University College of Law, magna cum laude, 1984; BS, Syracuse University, magna cum laude, 1980.

---

### RIZZO, Sandra E
Bracewell & Giuliani LLP, Washington, DC
202 828 5858
sandra.rizzo@bgllp.com
*Featured in Energy & Natural Resources (Nationwide)*

**Practice Areas:** Head of the firm's energy regulatory practice. Clients include electric utilities, power marketers, independent power producers, and investment and hedge funds. Assists clients in litigated proceedings before the Federal Energy Regulatory Commission and state and federal courts; advocates regarding the development of and changes to federal regulatory policies, regulations and rules applicable to the electric industry; and advises clients regarding regulatory compliance and enforcement issues, including compliance with the North American Electric Reliability Corporation's reliability standards.

**Personal:** JD, The College of William and Mary, Marshall-Wythe School of Law, 1992; BA, George Washington University, 1989.

---

### ROBBINS, Brian D
Simpson Thacher & Bartlett LLP, New York
212 455-3090
brobbins@stblaw.com
*Featured in Employee Benefits & Executive Compensation (Nationwide), Employee Benefits & Executive Compensation (New York)*

See under New York for profile.

---

### ROBERTS, Michele A
Skadden, Arps, Slate, Meagher & Flom LLP & Affiliates, Washington, DC
202 371 7250
Michele.Roberts@skadden.com
*Featured in Litigation (Nationwide), Litigation (District of Columbia)*

**Practice Areas:** Focuses on complex civil and white collar criminal litigation before state and federal courts and in administrative proceedings. Tried more than 100 cases to jury verdicts, representing clients in a variety of areas, including products liability, white collar, racketeering, securities regulation violations, Title VII issues and premises liability. A frequent presenter to the bench and bar on litigation and trial practice topics.

**Career:** Chief of Trial Division, Public Defender Service for the District of Columbia. Adjunct Member, Faculty at Harvard Law School. JD, Boalt Hall School of Law (University of California at Berkeley), 1980; BA, Wesleyan University, 1977.

---

### ROBERTSON, Elihu
Milbank, Tweed, Hadley & McCloy LLP, New York
212 530 5187
ERobertson@milbank.com
*Featured in Transportation (Nationwide), Banking & Finance (Nationwide)*

**Practice Areas:** Mr Robertson is the leader of the Transportation and Space Group. He has extensive experience representing underwriters, lenders, lessors and airlines in aircraft finance matters including syndicated and Ex-Im Bank supported loans, EETC transactions, acquisition financings, aircraft portfolio securitizations, airline bankruptcies and domestic and cross-border leases. Mr Robertson's experience also includes financings of aircraft engines and flight simulators and other extensions of credit to the airline sector.

---

### ROBFOGEL, Susan S
Nixon Peabody LLP, New York
212 940 3116
srobfogel@nixonpeabody.com
*Featured in Healthcare (New York), Healthcare (Nationwide)*

**Practice Areas:** Practice includes extensive experience in preventive labor relations, labor negotiations, employee/executive recruitment, compensation and retention policies, substance abuse, supervisory training and human rights matters. Has wide and varied corporate experience in the healthcare industry in general. Has lectured widely on employment/healthcare topics across the country.

**Professional Memberships:** Mrs Robfogel has handled cases before all New York State courts, in various federal district courts, the Second Circuit Court of Appeals and the US Supreme Court. Fellow of the College of Labor and Employment Lawyers.

**Personal:** Cornell Law School, JD; Smith College, BA, cum laude.

---

### ROBINSON, Arthur D
Simpson Thacher & Bartlett LLP, New York
212 455 7086
arobinson@stblaw.com
*Featured in Capital Markets (Nationwide)*

**Practice Areas:** Partner representing clients in initial public offerings, high yield issuances, restructurings and corporate governance issues. Transactions include offerings to finance the acquisitions of NBC Universal, Burger King, Pharmaceutical Product Development and Realogy; high yield offerings for Virgin Media, Smithfield Foods, Brunswick Corporation, Neustar, Endo Pharmaceuticals, and Air Lease Corporation and offerings to finance Mirant Corporation's and Reader's Digest's emergences from bankruptcy; IPOs of Realogy and Pike Electric.

**Career:** Joined, 1988; Partner, 1997.

**Personal:** University of Virginia School of Law (JD 1988); Wharton School of the University of Pennsylvania, (BSE summa cum laude, 1983).

---

### ROBINSON, Frederick
Fulbright & Jaworski LLP, Washington, DC
202 662 4534
frobinson@fulbright.com
*Featured in Healthcare (Nationwide), Healthcare (District of Columbia)*

**Practice Areas:** Health law, criminal law, and litigation.

**Professional Memberships:** American Health Lawyers Association; ABA Health Law Section.

**Career:** Rick Robinson represents a wide variety of corporations and their officers in government investigations and white-collar criminal cases, particularly in the health care industry. His cases cover all phases of trial and appellate practice in criminal and civil cases, including qui tam and 'whistle blower' lawsuits under the federal False Claims Act. He also advises clients on compliance program operations, internal investigations and voluntary disclosure matters.

**Personal:** BA Duke University (1979); JD Duke University (1982).

---

### ROBINSON, Patricia
Wachtell, Lipton, Rosen & Katz, New York
212 403 1127
parobinson@wlrk.com
*Featured in Financial Services Regulation (Nationwide)*

**Professional Memberships:** Member of the District of Columbia Bar and the American Bar Association.

**Career:** Of counsel at Wachtell, Lipton, Rosen & Katz. Prior to joining the firm in 2011, was an assistant general counsel in the Legal Division of the Board of Governors of the Federal Reserve System, managing the Legal Division's evaluation of merger and acquisition applications subject to Federal Reserve Board review under the Bank Holding Company Act, Bank Merger Act, Change in Control Act or Federal Reserve Act, and other applications and interpretive issues under these statutes. Previously was an associate at Sidley & Austin in the firm's financial institutions regulatory practice in its Washington, D.C. office.

**Publications:** Has participated on a number of panels at seminars and conferences on bank regulatory issues and served as an instructor at the American Bar Association's Banking Law II course.

**Personal:** Received her JD from Georgetown University Law Center in 1987. Prior to going to law school, was a teacher in middle school and for homebound students and a meeting and convention manager.

## ROBINSON, Robert J
Sidley Austin LLP, New York
212 839 5762
rrobinson@sidley.com
*Featured in Capital Markets (Nationwide)*

**Practice Areas:** Practice focuses on OTC derivatives and bank-sponsored risk transfers and synthetic CLOs, covering portfolios of loans to internationally-active or emerging market corporates and other businesses and mortgage loan portfolios. Works with arbitrage synthetic and hybrid CDOs. Experience includes disputes over CDO, OTC derivative and structured credit transactions and defaults and restructurings of such transactions. Cross-border practice emphasis. Advises on Dodd- Frank Act concerns.

**Professional Memberships:** New York State Bar Association, derivatives and structured products law committee.

**Personal:** Harvard Law School, JD, 1987; Swarthmore College, BA, 1982, with high honors. Admission: New York.

## ROCK, Neil L
Skadden, Arps, Slate, Meagher & Flom LLP & Affiliates, New York
212 735 3787
Neil.Rock@skadden.com
*Featured in Capital Markets (Nationwide), Real Estate (New York)*

**Practice Areas:** Mr Rock is head of the New York real estate practice. He advises clients with respect to acquisition, disposition, financing, restructuring, development, sale/leaseback and roll-up transactions with respect to portfolios and strategic assets including hotels, office buildings, shopping centers, residential properties, skilled nursing and assisted living facilities, hospitals, independent living communities, stadiums and arenas. His clients have included public and private companies, REITs, funds and governmental entities. He also has an active leasing practice.

**Career:** JD, Fordham University School of Law, 1988 (cum laude, Member, Fordham Law Review); BA, Brandeis University, 1985 (cum laude).

## ROCKETT, James M
Bingham McCutchen LLP, San Francisco
415 393 2025
james.rockett@bingham.com
*Featured in Financial Services Regulation (Nationwide)*

**Practice Areas:** Co-chair of Bingham's Financial Institutions Corporate and Regulatory Group. More than 30 years experience representing banking and financial services clients ranging from large national financial institutions to community banks and thrifts. Experience includes regulatory enforcement, mergers and acquisitions, corporate governance and bank regulation, regulatory compliance and operations, and de novo bank and holding company formation.

**Personal:** University of San Francisco School of Law, JD, 1969; University of San Francisco, BA, 1966.

## ROCKWELL, Alan
White & Case LLP, New York
212 819 7888
arockwell@whitecase.com
*Featured in Banking & Finance (Nationwide)*

**Career:** Alan Rockwell is a Partner in White & Case's New York Bank Finance Practice. Alan is dual-qualified in New York and England and Wales and has acted on a wide range of transactions for banks and borrowers, including leveraged and investment grade acquisition finance, real estate finance, general syndicated finance, DIP lending, restructuring, cash management, asset finance and structured finance, and has worked on a wide range of cross-border multi-jurisdiction secured financings and workouts (involving Borrowers and Guarantors in the US, the UK, Belgium, France, Germany, Luxembourg, Netherlands, Spain and Italy). To view a comprehensive biography, please visit www.whitecase.com/arockwell.

## ROCKWELL, Clinton
Buckleysandler LLP, Santa Monica
310 424 3901
crockwell@buckleysandler.com
*Featured in Financial Services Regulation (Nationwide)*

**Practice Areas:** Mr Rockwell is the Managing Partner of BuckleySandler's California offices. He advises financial services clients, including: banks, mortgage companies, secondary market loan purchasers, commercial lenders, and securities broker-dealers regarding regulatory, licensing, enforcement, compliance, and transactional matters. He also leads the firm's Federal Housing Administration practice, representing clients in connection with the regulatory aspects of audits, Mortgage Review Board actions, and related litigation and enforcement matters.

**Professional Memberships:** State Bar of California Consumer Financial Services Committee; American Bar Association's Consumer Financial Services Committee; University of London Post Graduate Law Society; Bentham Society at University College, London.

## RODGERS, Greg
Latham & Watkins LLP, New York
212 906 2918
greg.rodgers@lw.com
*Featured in Capital Markets (Nationwide)*

**Practice Areas:** Mr Rodgers represents investment banks, issuers and investors (including private equity) in public and private equity, debt and hybrid capital markets transactions, commercial lending transactions, restructurings and other financing transactions, with a particular focus on equity linked securities and high yield securities.

**Career:** Qualified in California since 1997 and in New York since 2008.

## RODRIGUEZ, Antonio J
Fowler Rodriguez, New Orleans
504 595 5170
ajr@frfirm.com
*Featured in Transportation (Nationwide)*

**Practice Areas:** Antonio Rodriguez has extensive experience in all aspects of maritime law, with particular emphasis on shipping casualties, pollution incidents and environmental regulation. He represents shipowners and charterers, Protection & Indemnity associations, marine and other insurers, and major energy companies. Mr Rodriguez is highly acclaimed in the fields of marine and environmental law. He has long served as Adjunct Professor at Tulane University School of Law. He is a renowned author of treatises and numerous maritime and oil pollution articles. Mr Rodriguez, a Naval Academy graduate, served as an officer at sea and holds the rank of Captain, USN(Ret.).

## RODRIGUEZ, Carlos A
Sidley Austin LLP, New York
212 839 5857
crodriguez@sidley.com
*Featured in Capital Markets (Nationwide)*

**Practice Areas:** Partner in Sidley's New York office, member of the firm's executive committee, practicing in securitizations and structured finance. Represents banks, fund advisors, insurance companies, other companies and government entities in the US and Latin America in structuring and investing in complex structured financial instruments, including CLOs, CMBS, RMBS, derivatives, repurchase contracts and warehouse facilities. He also advises US and Latin American clients in connection with domestic and cross-border financings and securities offerings.

**Personal:** Columbia University School of Law, JD, 1985; Harvard University, AB, 1982. Admission: New York.

## ROGERS JR, William P
Cravath, Swaine & Moore LLP, New York
212 474 1270
wrogers@cravath.com
*Featured in Capital Markets (Nationwide)*

**Practice Areas:** William P. Rogers Jr. is a partner in Cravath's Corporate Department. His practice encompasses the representation of both corporate and financial institution clients in a wide variety of matters, including international securities offerings, corporate governance and SEC compliance matters, mergers and acquisitions, and derivative financial products. Mr Rogers regularly advises a wide variety of the Firm's clients including Royal Dutch Shell plc, Bacardi Limited, INEOS Group Limited, Polygon Investment Partners, Costamare Inc., Morgan Stanley, Citigroup and Goldman Sachs.

**Personal:** Case Western Reserve University School of Law (JD, 1978); Union College (BA, 1972). For more information: http://www.cravath.com/wrogers

## ROH, Charles E
Weil, Gotshal & Manges LLP, Washington, DC
202 682 7100
chip.roh@weil.com
*Featured in International Trade (Nationwide)*

**Practice Areas:** Chip Roh focuses on international trade and international investment matters, advising companies, associations and governments in dispute settlement proceedings, arbitrations and negotiations. He has served as party counsel in seven investor-state treaty arbitrations and in more than 25 dispute settlement proceedings under the WTO and GATT. He counsels businesses regarding US laws pertaining to economic sanctions, export controls, national security, anti-bribery, and anti-boycott. Among his senior government official roles, he served as Assistant US Trade Representative, and was deputy chief negotiator of the NAFTA for the US.

**Personal:** Princeton University (BA, 1969); Harvard Law School (JD, 1973).

## ROHDE, Wayne
Cozen O'Connor, Washington, DC
202 463 2507
wrohde@cozen.com
*Featured in Transportation (Nationwide)*

**Practice Areas:** Wayne represents international transportation companies with respect to both regulatory and commercial matters. He advises on regulatory compliance, and represents clients in administrative audits, investigations and litigation. He has extensive experience advising on a wide variety of agreements, contracts, charters, and leases. He also advises clients on antitrust issues.

**Professional Memberships:** Association of Transportation Law Professionals; Maritime Administrative Bar Association.

**Publications:** "Government Regulation of Ocean Transportation" (with J. Lawrence and A. Mickey), included in Schoenbaum, Admiralty and Maritime Law, 4th ed. (2004).

**Personal:** Georgetown University, JD, 1989 Georgetown University, M.S., 1989 Middlebury College, M.A. 1985 Lake Forest College, BA, 1984.

## ROMANO, Robert M
Morgan, Lewis & Bockius LLP, New York
212 309 7083
rromano@morganlewis.com
*Featured in Securities (Nationwide)*

**Practice Areas:** Focuses on a variety of securities regulatory litigation matters, including the defense of individuals and companies in the financial services industry in investigations and/or litigation by the Securities and Exchange Commission (SEC), FINRA, and state securities regulators for securities fraud, trading and sales violations, and related supervisory issues. Also has handled numerous matters involving financial and accounting fraud, including individuals, companies, and accounting firm personnel in investigations and litigation with securities regulators, and has worked on white collar criminal defense matters, including the representation of individuals and companies in investigations by federal and state prosecutors for business-related crimes.

**ROMATOWSKI, Peter J**
Jones Day, Washington, DC
202 879 7625
pjromatowski@jonesday.com
*Featured in Securities (Nationwide), Litigation (District of Columbia)*
See under District of Columbia for profile.

**ROSEN, Edward J**
Cleary Gottlieb Steen & Hamilton LLP, New York
212 225 2820
erosen@cgsh.com
*Featured in Capital Markets (Nationwide)*
**Practice Areas:** Structuring and regulatory analysis of complex securities and derivatives transactions and US securities and commodities law regulation. Clients include SIFMA, ISDA, FIA, The Bond Market Association, major commercial and investment banks, exchanges, and clearinghouses.
**Professional Memberships:** Member ISDA Regulatory Advisory Committee, FIA Board of Directors, CFTC Technology Advisory Committee. Chair, Practicing Law Institute Annual Conference on Swaps and Derivatives, Advisory Board, Oxford University Press Capital Markets Law Journal.
**Career:** JD, Columbia University School of Law (1982) (Stone Scholar); BA, MA (Hon), Oxford University (1975).
**Publications:** Co-author "US Regulation of the International Securities and Derivatives Markets" (eighth edition, 2005).

**ROSEN, Richard**
Paul, Weiss, Rifkind, Wharton & Garrison LLP, New York
212 373 3305
rrosen@paulweiss.com
*Featured in Securities (Nationwide), Litigation (New York)*
**Practice Areas:** Litigation Partner with extensive experience in civil litigation in state and federal courts in the fields of securities, directors' and officers' liability, mergers and acquisitions, derivatives and other complex business disputes. Co-Chair of firm's Securities Litigation and Enforcement Group. Has represented public companies and underwriting syndicates in securities fraud class action litigations, and issuers and investment banking firms in a variety of other securities matters. Has defended many class actions involving open and closed-end funds and limited partnerships. Appears on behalf of directors and officers in derivative suits alleging breaches of fiduciary duty. Frequently lectures and publishes articles.

**ROSENBERG, Andrew N**
Paul, Weiss, Rifkind, Wharton & Garrison LLP, New York
212 373 3158
arosenberg@paulweiss.com
*Featured in Bankruptcy/Restructuring (Nationwide), Bankruptcy/Restructuring (New York)*
**Practice Areas:** Partner in Bankruptcy and Corporate Reorganization Department. Primarily practices in corporate restructuring and bankruptcy; additional focus in representing lenders providing financing to highly leveraged companies. Official and unofficial committee restructuring representations include General Motors, CIT, GMAC, Dynegy Inc., Nortek, Inc., Calpine Corporation, Armstrong World Industries and Quebecor chapter 11 cases. American Lawyer "Dealmaker of the Year" for representation of CIT. Represented bondholder groups in many of the largest out of court exchanges, including GMAC, Tyco and Equity Office Properties. Debtor's chapter 11 counsel in Spectrasite, Top-Flite Golf and Cone Mills. Represented numerous companies in acquisition of chapter 11 debtors.

**ROSENBERG, Ezra D**
Dechert LLP, Princeton
609 955 3222
ezra.rosenberg@dechert.com
*Featured in Products Liability (Nationwide), Litigation (New Jersey)*
See under New Jersey for profile.

**ROSENBERG, Marc S**
Cravath, Swaine & Moore LLP, New York
212 474 1676
mrosenberg@cravath.com
*Featured in Securities (Nationwide)*
**Practice Areas:** Marc S. Rosenberg is a partner in Cravath's Corporate Department and serves as Co-Chair of its Corporate Governance and Board Advisory practice. His practice includes counseling boards of directors, board committees and senior management in connection with SEC investigations, governance issues and other special situations, as well as securities work and mergers and acquisitions.
**Personal:** Harvard Law School (JD, magna cum laude, 1983; Sears Prize; Editor, Law Review); Princeton University (AB, summa cum laude, 1980; Phi Beta Kappa). For more information: http://www.cravath.com/mrosenberg

**ROSENBERG, Robert**
Slover & Loftus, Washington, DC
202 347 7170
rdr@sloverandloftus.com
*Featured in Transportation (Nationwide)*
**Practice Areas:** Mr Rosenberg is a Partner with over 25 years experience in administrative law, regulation, and litigation in transportation and energy, including railroad and electric power matters and analysis of damages and other economics issues. Mr Rosenberg has represented shippers in rate cases and rulemakings at the Surface Transportation Board, including proceedings involving the railroad cost of capital and productivity.
**Personal:** AB, magna cum laude, Brown University, 1978; JD, Harvard Law School, 1981.

**ROSENBLATT, Brett P**
Latham & Watkins LLP, San Diego
619 236 1234
brett.rosenblatt@lw.com
*Featured in Leisure & Hospitality (Nationwide)*
**Practice Areas:** Brett Rosenblatt was a founding co-chair of Latham & Watkin's Hospitality, Gaming and Leisure industry group. He represents public and private sector clients, including financial institutions, in connection with a broad array of domestic and international gaming, hotel, hospitality and leisure interests. His practice focuses on leveraged, mezzanine, acquisition and project financings, Indian gaming, development and operation of (and investment in) gaming, hotel, hospitality and leisure projects, acquisitions and dispositions, joint venture and other development/management relationships and representations in connection with 144A offerings and private placements.
**Personal:** JD, University of California, Berkeley; BA, University of California, Los Angeles.

**ROSENBLUM, Jeremy T**
Ballard Spahr LLP, Philadelphia
215 864 8505
rosenblum@ballardspahr.com
*Featured in Financial Services Regulation (Nationwide), Banking & Finance (Pennsylvania)*
**Practice Areas:** Jeremy T. Rosenblum is Practice Leader of the Consumer Financial Services Group. His practice focuses on federal and state lending and consumer practices laws and involves product development, structuring, and documentation; litigation defense and avoidance; and interaction with regulatory agencies.
**Professional Memberships:** American Bar Association Section of Business Law, Consumer Financial Services Committee American College of Consumer Financial Services Lawyers, Fellow Conference on Consumer Finance Law, Governing Committee Consumer Financial Services Law Report, Financial Services Advisor.
**Career:** Admissions: Pennsylvania Illinois.
**Personal:** Yale Law School (JD 1979) Stanford University (A.B 1975).

**ROSENTHAL, Barry P**
Bingham McCutchen LLP, Washington, DC
202 373 6078
barry.rosenthal@bingham.com
*Featured in Real Estate (Nationwide), Real Estate (District of Columbia)*
See under District of Columbia for profile.

**ROSENTHAL, Edward H**
Frankfurt Kurnit Klein & Selz, New York
212 826 5524
erosenthal@fkks.com
*Featured in Advertising (Nationwide)*
**Practice Areas:** Chair of firm's Intellectual Property group and co-chair of its Litigation Group. Focuses on intellectual property and civil litigation, emphasizing trademark, copyright, right of publicity, privacy and publishing matters. Represents high-profile businesses and individuals in the media, advertising, publishing, sports and entertainment fields. Listed in Best Lawyers in America. Named a New York-area "Super Lawyer" for Intellectual Property Litigation by Law and Politics magazine for six consecutive years.
**Professional Memberships:** Co-chair, Publicity, Privacy and Media Committee of the New York State Bar Association's Entertainment Arts and Sports Law Section. Member Copyright Society of the U.S.A.; International Trademark Association.

**ROSENTHAL, Jeffrey**
Cleary Gottlieb Steen & Hamilton LLP, New York
212 225 2086
jrosenthal@cgsh.com
*Featured in International Arbitration (Nationwide)*
**Practice Areas:** General commercial, international arbitration, litigation. Tried/arbitrated cases concerning contract, international joint venture, bilateral investment treaty disputes, financial products, intellectual property, maritime, bankruptcy, tort, insurance, sports law.
**Professional Memberships:** Bar admissions: New York, New Jersey. Member, International Arbitration Club of NY; Former Chair, Entertainment, Arts and Sports Law Section, New York State Bar Association; Member, International Commercial Disputes Committee, Association of the Bar of City of New York; Founding Director, NY International Arbitration Center; taught sports law, New York Law School and Rutgers Law School (adjunct).
**Personal:** Harvard Law School (JD, magna cum laude); Dartmouth College (A.B., cum laude).

**ROSENTHAL, John J**
Winston & Strawn LLP, Washington, DC
202 282 5785
jrosenthal@winston.com
*Featured in Litigation (Nationwide)*
**Practice Areas:** John Rosenthal is a litigation Partner in Winston & Strawn LLP's Washington, DC office, representing clients across the globe in complex antitrust and litigation matters. Mr Rosenthal is one of the most experienced practitioners in the United States of e-discovery. He counsels the Fortune 500 on record retention programs, e-discovery risk reduction programs, privacy and cross border and privacy issues. He is National Counsel to several major corporations on e-discovery. Mr Rosenthal also lectures and write extensively on the issues of e-discovery and record retention programs.

**ROSENTHAL, Michael L**
Covington & Burling LLP, Washington, DC
202 662 5448
mrosenthal@cov.com
*Featured in Transportation (Nationwide)*
**Practice Areas:** Michael Rosenthal is chair of the firm's Transportation practice group and a member of the Litigation and Antitrust practice groups. He represents railroads and other rail-industry clients in regulatory proceedings, including mergers, rate cases, unreasonable practice cases, abandonment proceedings, and rulemakings before the Surface Transportation Board. He also represents both railroads and non-rail clients in litigation and appeals in federal and state courts, in arbitration proceedings, and before antitrust and other regulatory agencies, and he advises them on transportation and competition law.
**Personal:** Harvard Law School, JD, 1993; Cornell University, BS, 1990.

## ROSENTHAL, Thorn
Cahill Gordon & Reindel LLP, New York
212 701 3823
trosenthal@cahill.com
*Featured in Insurance (Nationwide), Insurance (New York)*
See under New York for profile.

## ROSENWASSER, Michael
Vinson & Elkins LLP, New York
212 237 0019
mrosenwasser@velaw.com
*Featured in Energy & Natural Resources (Nationwide)*
**Practice Areas:** Capital markets and securities and mergers and acquisitions.
**Professional Memberships:** American Bar Association.
**Career:** Practicing for over 40 years, Mike has worked on more than 200 public financings and 100 M&A transactions. His focus is on transactions with a relatively high degree of tax structuring. Mike has participated in developing several unique financing techniques including the development of master limited partnerships. He has worked on several gas pipeline projects in the United States and South America.
**Personal:** Graduated from The University of Texas, BBA, summa cum laude, 1968; The University of Texas, JD, magna cum laude, 1971.

## ROSH, Kenneth I
Fried, Frank, Harris, Shriver & Jacobson LLP, New York
212 859 8535
kenneth.rosh@friedfrank.com
*Featured in Investment Funds (Nationwide)*
**Practice Areas:** Corporate partner, head of the Firm's Private Equity Funds group. Represents clients in a broad range of corporate transactions, specializing in private equity fund formation, investments and secondary transactions; securities and capital markets; cross-border transactions and general corporate matters. Clients include Goldman, Sachs; Highbridge Principal Strategies; JP Morgan; Fortress; Sankaty; Audax; StepStone; Televisa; Coach; Generali.
**Career:** Joined in 1988; became partner in 1996.
**Personal:** JD, Boston University School of Law (1988), G. Joseph Tauro Distinguished Scholar, editor-in-chief, Annual Review of Banking Law; Board of Advisors, Northwestern Journal of International Law and Business; BA, Tufts University (1985).

## ROSNER, David S
Kasowitz, Benson, Torres & Friedman LLP, New York
212 506 1726
drosner@kasowitz.com
*Featured in Bankruptcy/Restructuring (Nationwide), Bankruptcy/Restructuring (New York)*
See under New York for profile.

## ROSS, Bruce S
Holland & Knight LLP, Los Angeles
213 896 2527
bruce.ross@hklaw.com
*Featured in Wealth Management (Nationwide)*
**Professional Memberships:** Regent Emeritus and past President, American College of Trust and Estate Counsel; former Chair, Executive Committee California State Bar Trusts & Estates Section.
**Career:** Bruce S Ross is Chair of Holland & Knight's National Private Wealth Dispute Resolution Team. A nationally recognized trial lawyer with over 40 years' experience litigating trust, estate and conservatorship matters, he has appeared pro hac vice in many states to handle such litigation and has consulted overseas on cases involving international succession matters. He is also Chair of Holland & Knight's Mickey Rooney Elder Abuse Pro Bono Program.

## ROSS, Richard F
Dentons, Phoenix
602 508 3901
rick.ross@dentons.com
*Featured in Leisure & Hospitality (Nationwide)*
**Practice Areas:** Global head of legacy Dentons's Hotels and Leisure practice. Widely recognized global industry leader in advising owners, operators and investors on the acquisition, development, financing and operation of hospitality/leisure properties across the world, including hotels, resorts, hotels with serviced residential condominiums, condo hotels, spas, golf courses and other complex mixed-use projects. Counsels clients as to management agreements, technical services and license agreements, shared services and facility access agreements as to hotel and leisure properties, as well as identifying, structuring and negotiating the capitalization of these projects; debt and equity (joint ventures). Assists clients on their company's corporate-level policies, practices and procedures.

## ROSSETTI, Michael
Akin Gump Strauss Hauer & Feld LLP, Washington, DC
202 887 4311
mrossetti@akingump.com
*Featured in Native American Law (Nationwide)*
**Practice Areas:** Advises tribal clients regarding economic development, Indian gaming, and tribal governance issues. Also lobbies on a broad range of tribal, non-tribal and business concerns, works on litigation matters and the settlement of Indian water rights, and works closely with state attorneys general.
**Career:** Personal counselor to the secretary of the Department of the Interior; Assistant county attorney in Buffalo, NY; Executive deputy and General counsel to New York State's Office of the Advocate for Persons with Disabilities; chief deputy to the New York attorney general; assistant US attorney.
**Personal:** BA, University of Buffalo; JD, Cleveland-Marshall College of Law.

## ROTH, Paul N
Schulte Roth & Zabel LLP, New York
212 756 2450
paul.roth@srz.com
*Featured in Investment Funds (Nationwide)*
**Practice Areas:** Chair of Investment Management Group. Over 40 years experience representing hedge funds, private equity funds, offshore funds, investment advisers and broker-dealers in connection with securities regulation and compliance, fund formation, M&A and financial transactions.
**Professional Memberships:** Special Advisor, Board of Directors of Managed Fund Association; Advisor, Alternative Investment Management Association; Chair, Subcommittee on Hedge Funds of American Bar Association's Committee on Federal Securities Regulation; Member, Advisory Board of RAND Center for Corporate Ethics and Governance.
**Personal:** Fulbright Fellowship; Harvard Law School, JD, cum laude; Harvard College, AB, magna cum laude, Phi Beta Kappa; fellow, New York Bar Foundation.

## ROTHERMEL, Sarah
WilmerHale, Boston
617 526 6512
sarah.rothermel@wilmerhale.com
*Featured in Investment Funds (Nationwide), Private Equity (Massachusetts)*
See under Massachusetts for profile.

## ROTHWELL, James T
Davis Polk & Wardwell LLP, New York
212 450 4000
james.rothwell@davispolk.com
*Featured in Capital Markets (Nationwide)*
**Practice Areas:** Member of Davis Polk & Wardwell's Corporate Department. Advises dealers, corporations and funds regarding structured equity derivative transactions and securities offerings of convertible and equity-linked securities. Has been involved in the original design of many innovative transaction structures that have become staples of the equity derivatives marketplace.

## ROTTER, Irving L
Sidley Austin LLP, New York
212 839 5456
irotter@sidley.com
*Featured in Projects (Nationwide)*
**Practice Areas:** Partner in Sidley's New York office. He represents sponsors, lenders, and equity participants in project finance, buyers and sellers in M&A and financial institutions in banking and corporate finance. His clients include acquirors and sellers in domestic and cross-border transactions in the energy, power infrastructure, telecommunications, technology, media, paper and food industries. He represents lenders and borrowers in senior and mezzanine financings involving the energy, power, infrastructure, media and manufacturing industries.
**Personal:** Columbia University School of Law, JD, 1980 (Stone Scholar); Yeshiva University, MS, 1980; Yeshiva University, BA, 1974, magna cum laude. Admission: New York.

## ROUVELAS, Emanuel L
K&L Gates, Washington, DC
202 661 6262
manny.rouvelas@klgates.com
*Featured in Government (Nationwide), Transportation (Nationwide)*
**Practice Areas:** Mr Rouvelas engages in a wide-ranging federal counseling and lobbying practice, and has acted as Lead Counsel advising and representing Fortune 500 companies and trade associations in the transportation, telecommunications, high technology, hospitality, and manufacturing industries regarding their Washington, DC activities and strategies. He has also served as lead government affairs counsel for major companies in transnational acquisitions, mergers, and corporate reorganizations. He is a recognized authority in ocean shipping law and for three decades has traveled globally to advise the CEOs of many of the world's leading shipping companies.

## ROWEN, Andrew S
Sullivan & Cromwell LLP, New York
212 558 3896
rowena@sullcrom.com
*Featured in Insurance (Nationwide), Insurance (New York)*
See under New York for profile.

## RUBEL, Eric
Arnold & Porter LLP, Washington, DC
202 942 5749
Eric.Rubel@aporter.com
*Featured in Products Liability (Nationwide)*
**Practice Areas:** Eric Rubel is Co-Head of the firm's Product Liability Litigation Group. He is experienced in product safety matters and related litigation, including evaluating the need for and implementing recalls, defending CPSC enforcement actions and class action litigation, and helping companies comply with CPSC regulations and the CPSIA. His product safety experience includes representing manufacturers, distributors and retailers of consumer products, and pharmaceutical drugs and cosmetics.
**Career:** General Counsel to the US Consumer Product Safety Commission, 1994-97.
**Personal:** JD, George Washington University Law School, 1985; BA, Middlebury College, 1982.

## RUBENSTEIN, William S
Skadden, Arps, Slate, Meagher & Flom LLP & Affiliates, New York
212 735 2642
William.Rubenstein@skadden.com
*Featured in Financial Services Regulation (Nationwide)*
**Practice Areas:** Co-head of Skadden's Financial Institutions Group. Advises on all kinds of transactions involving financial institutions. Extensive experience in negotiated and contested mergers and acquisitions, proxy fights, privately negotiated investments and restructuring transactions.
**Career:** JD, Benjamin N. Cardozo School of Law, 1981 (cum laude; Note and Comment Editor, Cardozo Law Review); BA, Fairleigh Dickinson University, 1978.

**RUBIN, James I**
Butler Rubin Saltarelli & Boyd LLP, Chicago
312 696 4443
jrubin@butlerrubin.com
*Featured in Insurance (Nationwide), Insurance (Illinois)*
See under Illinois for profile.

**RUBINOFF, Edward L**
Akin Gump Strauss Hauer & Feld LLP, Washington, DC
202 887 4288
erubinoff@akingump.com
*Featured in International Trade (Nationwide)*
**Practice Areas:** Mr Rubinoff 's national security trade controls practice covers export controls, economic sanctions, antiboycott regulations, the Foreign Corrupt Practices Act and the Committee on Foreign Investment in the United States. He counsels domestic and foreign companies on compliance with US laws, conducts internal investigations and audits, designs and assesses internal control programs, handles CFIUS reviews of foreign investments in the US, and represents clients in enforcement cases. He served on the President's Export Council Subcommittee on Export Administration and held several positions with the ABA Section of International Law.
**Personal:** BA, University of Pennsylvania; JD, George Washington University.

**RUBY, Allen J**
Skadden, Arps, Slate, Meagher & Flom LLP & Affiliates, Palo Alto
650 470 4590
allen.ruby@skadden.com
*Featured in Litigation (Nationwide), Litigation (California)*
**Practice Areas:** Mr Ruby is recognized as one of the nation's leading trial attorneys. His state and federal court trial practice includes a variety of high-profile, complex commercial and intellectual property cases, as well as white collar criminal matters. He has represented chief executives and technology companies in landmark Silicon Valley litigation, including cases involving Avant!, SanDisk, Microsoft, Fujitsu and Hynix Semiconductor. Other clients have included: Major League Baseball star Barry Bonds; Facebook, Inc.; Hewlett-Packard Co.; Bank of America; and the National Football League.
**Career:** JD Stanford Law School, 1969; BA Michigan State University, 1965.

**RUCKMAN, Robert**
Jackson Walker LLP, Dallas
214 953 6024
rruckman@jw.com
*Featured in Transportation (Nationwide)*
**Practice Areas:** Robert F Ruckman's practice primarily involves representation of airlines, aircraft or aircraft component part manufacturers and aviation insurers or individuals involved in aviation or related businesses.
**Career:** Mr Ruckman has extensive trial experience, with numerous jury and non-jury trials in state and federal courts, as well as appeals in both state and federal courts. He has served as lead counsel in complex multidistrict air carrier and product liability litigation. Mr Ruckman is Board Certified in Texas in both Civil Trial Law and Personal Injury Trial Law.

**RUDDER, Richard D**
Kramer Levin Naftalis & Frankel LLP, New York
212 715 9470
rrudder@kramerlevin.com
*Featured in Capital Markets (Nationwide)*
**Practice Areas:** Mr Rudder is Counsel in Kramer Levin's Banking and Finance Group. His practice focuses on solar energy finance, intellectual property and whole business transactions, structured settlements, lottery receivables, tobacco settlements, time share interests, equipment leases, and other esoteric assets.
**Professional Memberships:** American Bar Association and Commercial Real Estate Finance Council.
**Career:** He is admitted to practice in the States of New York and Connecticut.
**Personal:** Graduated from Lafayette College (1963), received LLB from New York University School of Law (1966), and MBA from Bernard M. Baruch School of Business (1971).

**RUDMAN, Jeffrey**
WilmerHale, Boston
617 526 6912
jeffrey.rudman@wilmerhale.com
*Featured in Securities (Nationwide), Litigation (Massachusetts)*
See under Massachusetts for profile.

**RUDMAN, Samuel**
Robbins Geller Rudman & Dowd LLP, Melville
631 367 7100
srudman@rgrdlaw.com
*Featured in Securities (Nationwide), Litigation (New York)*
See under New York for profile.

**RUDNICK, Amy G**
Gibson, Dunn & Crutcher LLP, Washington, DC
202 955 8210
arudnick@gibsondunn.com
*Featured in Financial Services Regulation (Nationwide)*
**Practice Areas:** Assists banks, broker-dealers, insurance companies, money services businesses, other financial institutions, and businesses in developing and implementing anti-money laundering programs and complying with AML laws and regulations, including the Bank Secrecy Act. Represents clients in criminal and regulatory BSA and AML enforcement actions and in responding to regulatory examinations. Conducts due diligence reviews and internal investigations.
**Career:** Former Member, Treasury Department, BSA Advisory Group; Director, Office of Financial Enforcement, Treasury Department; Trial Attorney, Narcotic & Dangerous Drug Section, Justice Department; Law Clerk, U.S. District Court Judge Ellen Bree Burns.
**Personal:** Stanford University, BA; George Washington University, JD.

**RUGE, Mark**
K&L Gates, Washington, DC
202 661 6231
mark.ruge@klgates.com
*Featured in Transportation (Nationwide)*
**Practice Areas:** A co-coordinator of K&L Gates public policy and law group, Mr Ruge focuses his practice on the federal government, representing clients on policy matters before Congress, regulatory issues before the federal agencies/departments, and administrative disputes in the federal courts. He is closely involved in a broad range of maritime issues and issues related to his home state of Michigan. He also serves as counsel to the American Maritime Partnership, the largest coalition in the history of the US maritime industry, and represents numerous other maritime clients on federal policy issues.

**RUSHING, Don**
Morrison & Foerster LLP, San Diego
858 720 5145
DRushing@mofo.com
*Featured in Transportation (Nationwide)*
**Practice Areas:** Mr Rushing is a recognized authority on bet-the-company litigation with more than 30 years of trial experience. He focuses on aviation, product liability, toxic tort, and commercial litigation.
**Professional Memberships:** American College of Trial Lawyers; American Board of Trial Advocates; American Law Institute; IADC; American Inns of Court; NBTA (Certified Civil Trial Advocate); NITA (Faculty); PLAC (Sustaining Member); SMU Air Law Symposium (Board of Advisors).
**Career:** USAFA (BS, 1970); USC (MBA, 1973); UCLA (JD, 1978); Former U.S. Air Force officer, Air Force Systems Command. Former co-chair, Product Liability practice.
**Personal:** Private pilot.

**RUTHBERG, Miles**
Latham & Watkins LLP, New York
212 906 1688
miles.ruthberg@lw.com
*Featured in Securities (Nationwide), Litigation (New York)*
**Practice Areas:** Represents major companies in their most important litigation, including securities law, class actions, and accounting issues.
**Professional Memberships:** Member, State Bars of New York, California, and District of Columbia.
**Career:** Former Global Chair of Latham's Litigation Department; former clerk for US Supreme Court Justice Thurgood Marshall. Has won complete defense victories at trial on claims totaling more than US$3 billion, and has obtained dismissal of numerous multi-billion dollar cases. Widely recognized as a leading strategist in high-stakes litigation.
**Personal:** JD, Harvard Law School, magna cum laude (Law Review); BA, Yale University, summa cum laude; 1st in Class.

**RUTHERFURD JR, Winthrop**
White & Case LLP, New York
212 819 8700
wrutherfurd@whitecase.com
*Featured in Wealth Management (Nationwide)*
**Career:** Mr Rutherfurd practices in the trusts and estates department, advising individuals and families in all aspects of estate planning, including charitable giving, tax-motivated transfers of property and the taxation of estates and trusts. He also advises charitable organizations and trusts and has extensive experience in audit and appellate proceedings with federal and state taxing authorities. He has considerable experience in advising fiduciaries in connection with the administration of estates and trusts. In advising both individual and corporate fiduciaries, he has extensive experience of contested proceedings involving the administration of complex estates and trusts. To view his biography, visit www.whitecase.com/wrutherfurd.

**RUTHIZER, Theodore**
Kramer Levin Naftalis & Frankel LLP, New York
212 715 9421
truthizer@kramerlevin.com
*Featured in Immigration (Nationwide), Immigration (New York)*
See under New York for profile.

**RUTKOWSKI, Lawrence**
Seward & Kissel LLP, New York
212 574 1206
rutkowski@sewkis.com
*Featured in Transportation (Nationwide)*
**Practice Areas:** Maritime and Transportation Finance, Corporate Finance, Structured Finance and Asset Securitization, and Business Transactions (M&A/Private Equity).
**Professional Memberships:** Mr Rutkowski is a Member of the Association of the Bar of the City of New York, the American Bar Association (the Air and Space Law Forum, Business Law Section, International Law and Practice Section) and the Maritime Law Association of the United States (Maritime Finance Committee).
**Career:** Mr Rutkowski is head of the Firm's Maritime and Transportation Finance Group, a cross section of attorneys within the firm from the Corporate Finance, Corporate Securities, Litigation and Tax departments with expertise on matters of interest to clients in the transportation industry and is a member of the Firm's Business Transactions Group. In such capacity, Mr Rutkowski has worked on matters ranging from the formation of joint ventures, asset finance transactions, secured and unsecured lending, registered and unregistered securities transactions, mergers and acquisitions and cross border leases to restructurings and bankruptcy. In addition to representing clients in the transportation and financial services industries, Mr Rutkowski's practice has included considerable experience in equipment finance and in the energy and mining fields. Mr Rutkowski has been featured on CNN and appeared on both the Fox News and Fox Business networks as an authority on the impact

on the shipping business of piracy off the coast of Somalia.

**Personal:** Mr Rutkowski received a BA Degree from College of the Holy Cross in 1975, and a JD Degree from Columbia Law School in 1978.

## RYAN, Antony
Cravath, Swaine & Moore LLP, New York
aryan@cravath.com
*Featured in Securities (Nationwide), Litigation (New York)*

**Practice Areas:** Handles a wide variety of litigation, with a particular focus on accountants' liability and securities litigation. Regularly represents accounting firms and companies in federal and state courts around the country, as well as in SEC and Department of Justice investigations and enforcement matters. His work has led to important rulings for professional services firms on issues such as imputation, in pari delicto and personal jurisdiction.
**Career:** Partner since 2003. Clerkship: Hon. Judith W. Rogers (US Court of Appeals, DC Circuit).
**Personal:** Harvard Law School (JD, magna cum laude, 1995); Yale University (BA, summa cum laude, 1992).

## RYAN, Michael L
Cleary Gottlieb Steen & Hamilton LLP, New York
212 225 2520
mryan@cgsh.com
*Featured in Private Equity (Nationwide), Corporate/M&A (New York)*

**Practice Areas:** Longtime counsel to Texas Pacific Group, previously to Robert M. Bass; active in restructuring/private equity since 1988. Significant experience counseling senior executives and corporate boards in M&A, financial, governance, restructuring matters. Represents acquirors, targets and corporate boards. Substantial industry expertise in banking/financial institutions, restructuring, aviation, private equity/hedge funds. Broad experience in financial institution restructuring and development of financial products (including the first CMO). Prior career in book publishing as Senior Editor E.P. Dutton; published critically-acclaimed books including Almanac of American Politics.
**Career:** BA, Harvard College (1973); JD, New York University School of Law (1978).

## RYAN, Patrick J
Simpson Thacher & Bartlett LLP, New York
212 455 3463
pryan@stblaw.com
*Featured in Banking & Finance (Nationwide)*

**Practice Areas:** Partner in the Firm's Corporate Department and head of the Firm's Banking and Credit Practice Group. Practice focuses on the representation of large financial institutions and borrowers in connection with the arrangement and syndication of leveraged and investment grade financings, including leveraged and investment grade acquisition and bridge financings. Recent transactions include the representation of arrangers in the financing of the acquisition of Citadel by Cumulus, Collective Brands by

Wolverine World Wide, NetSpend by TSYS and Phadia by Thermo-Fisher.
**Career:** Partner, 1998.
**Personal:** Manhattan College (BA, magna cum laude, 1985); Fordham University (JD, cum laude, 1989).

## RYAN, Priscilla E
Sidley Austin LLP, Chicago
312 853 7072
pryan@sidley.com
*Featured in Employee Benefits & Executive Compensation (Nationwide), Labor & Employment (Illinois)*
See under Illinois for profile.

## SABATER, Aníbal Martin
Fulbright & Jaworski LLP, Houston
713 651 5548
asabater@fulbright.com
*Featured in International Arbitration (Nationwide)*

**Practice Areas:** International Arbitration and Disputes.
**Professional Memberships:** Member of several arbitrator rosters (ICDR, SIAC, etc.); LCIA; ITA (Executive Committee, Advisory Board); Spanish Royal Academy of Jurisprudence and Law (corresponding member); American Branch of International Law Association (Executive Committee, and International Commercial Arbitration Committee Chairman).
**Career:** Counsel in numerous ICC, ICDR, ICSID, and UNCITRAL arbitration cases. Significant experience as arbitrator, including under IACAC, ICC, and ICDR rules. Practice involves disputes around the globe. Licensed in: California, Washington DC, Spain, and England and Wales.
**Personal:** JD, first in the class, Universidad Complutense (Madrid, 1997); Ph.D., cum laude, Universidad Complutense (Madrid, 1999).

## SABEL, Bradley K
Shearman & Sterling LLP, New York
212 848 8410
bsabel@shearman.com
*Featured in Financial Services Regulation (Nationwide)*

**Practice Areas:** Brad Sabel joined Shearman & Sterling in 1994 after spending 18 years at the Federal Reserve Bank of New York. He advises domestic and foreign clients on bank regulation and represents them before the Federal Reserve and other agencies. He is a co-leader of Shearman & Sterling's Financial Institutions Advisory group and advises on the full range of Federal Reserve and other regulatory agencies' requirements and guidance, including the continuing issuance of proposals to implement the Dodd-Frank Act.
**Career:** Bar Admission: New York. Partner since 1997.
**Personal:** Columbia Business School, Cornell Law School, and Vanderbilt University.

## SABIN, Jeffrey S
Bingham McCutchen LLP, New York
212 705 7747
jeffrey.sabin@bingham.com
*Featured in Bankruptcy/Restructuring (Nationwide), Bankruptcy/Restructuring (New York)*

**Practice Areas:** Co-head of Bingham's global Financial Restructuring Group. Co-head of Bingham's Task Force on Dodd-Frank Financial Reforms. Focuses on creditors' rights, bankruptcy, debt restructuring and financial transactions. More than 30 years of professional experience representing public companies, lenders, committees of secured and unsecured creditors, boards of directors, investors, and acquirers in numerous Chapter 11 cases and out-of-court restructurings.
**Career:** Fellow, American College of Bankruptcy. Recent chair, New York City Bar Association's Subcommittee on Fraudulent Conveyance Law.
**Personal:** Boston College Law School, JD, cum laude, 1977; Cornell University, BA/BS, 1974.

## SACHS, John
Latham & Watkins LLP, Washington, DC
202 637 2264
john.sachs@lw.com
*Featured in Projects (Nationwide)*

**Practice Areas:** Represents sponsors, investors, lenders, governments and national utilities worldwide in connection with all phases of the development, financing, acquisition and divestiture of infrastructure projects, including power projects, oil and gas projects, water projects and transportation projects. Particularly focuses on the development and project financing of private power projects, including a wide variety of renewable energy and conventional power projects. Also has extensive experience in the privatization of the power sector and the creation of related regulatory frameworks.
**Professional Memberships:** Member, District of Columbia Bar.
**Personal:** JD, Harvard Law School, 1980; BA, Yale University, 1976.

## SACKHEIM, Michael
Sidley Austin LLP, New York
212 839 5503
msackheim@sidley.com
*Featured in Capital Markets (Nationwide)*

**Practice Areas:** Partner in Sidley's New York office, Mr Sackheim focuses on futures and derivatives regulatory, transactional and enforcement matters. He was appointed by a federal court as receiver in one of the largest foreign currency fraud cases ever brought by the government. He has represented a Dubai trading entity in a federal court injunctive action brought by the U.S. Commodity Futures Trading Commission and in a civil forfeiture action brought by the Department of Justice.
**Personal:** NYU School of Law, LLM, 1979; Brooklyn Law School, JD, 1974; New School University, MA, 1972; CUNY - Queens College, BA, 1969.

## SACKS, Robert A
Sullivan & Cromwell LLP, Los Angeles
310 712 6640
sacksr@sullcrom.com
*Featured in Securities (Nationwide), Litigation (California)*
See under California for profile.

## SACKS, Russell
Shearman & Sterling LLP, New York
212 848 7585
rsacks@shearman.com
*Featured in Financial Services Regulation (Nationwide)*

**Practice Areas:** Russell Sacks, a partner in the Financial Institutions Advisory & Financial Regulatory Group, provides advice to market participants on a worldwide basis with respect to regulatory, transactional, trading and markets issues. He has particular experience in the formation, acquisition, registration, licensing and expansion of securities broker-dealers and investment banks, clearing agencies, alternative trading systems, and other electronic communications and trading networks, in providing advice regarding retail brokerage and private banking issues, and in assisting market participants with investigations and enforcement actions.
**Career:** Bar admissions: New York.
**Personal:** University of Toronto, Faculty of Law; Columbia College.

## SAFIR, Peter O
Covington & Burling LLP, Washington, DC
202 662 5162
psafir@cov.com
*Featured in Life Sciences (Nationwide), Healthcare (District of Columbia)*
See under District of Columbia for profile.

## SAGER, David S
Lowenstein Sandler LLP, Roseland
973 597 2528
dsager@lowenstein.com
*Featured in Franchising (Nationwide)*

**Practice Areas:** David Sager has been representing large corporations in commercial disputes throughout the United States for over 20 years. He has extensive experience litigating and arbitrating complex matters involving franchise issues, mergers and acquisitions, consumer class actions, and contract actions. He gains an in-depth understanding of his clients' businesses which helps him effectively counsel clients on avoiding and resolving disputes when possible.
www.lowenstein.com/dsager

## SALAMAN, Christian A
Pillsbury Winthrop Shaw Pittman LLP, San Diego
858 509 4046
christian.salaman@pillsburylaw.com
*Featured in Leisure & Hospitality (Nationwide)*

**Practice Areas:** Corporate/M&A; leisure and hospitality. His practice focuses on the buying, selling and financing of businesses, as well as governance issues, operational matters and strategic relationships. For leisure and hospitality matters, he represents owners, operators, lenders, asset managers, receivers and others. This includes negotiating management agreements, condominium marketing agreements and technical services agreements and handling acquisitions and dispositions of properties, portfolios and companies, joint ventures and financings.
**Career:** Admitted to Practice: State of California; State of Illinois.

**Personal:** JD, Northwestern University School of Law, 1999; BSFS, Georgetown University, 1996.

## SALCIDO, Robert S
Akin Gump Strauss Hauer & Feld LLP, Washington, DC
202 887 4095
rsalcido@akingump.com
*Featured in Healthcare (Nationwide), Healthcare (District of Columbia)*
**Practice Areas:** Represents companies and individuals in responding to governmental investigations, in conducting internal investigations, and in defending False Claims Act and wrongful retaliation lawsuits brought by alleged whistleblowers, and provides counseling regarding the application of healthcare fraud and abuse laws. He has authored a treatise on the False Claims Act and lectured extensively on defenses to False Claims Act actions, healthcare coding compliance and fraud and abuse laws and voluntary disclosures.
**Personal:** BA, Claremont McKenna College; JD, Harvard Law School.

## SALEHI, Nader H
Bingham McCutchen LLP, New York
212 705 7230
nader.salehi@bingham.com
*Featured in Securities (Nationwide)*
**Practice Areas:** Conducts a general securities regulatory and enforcement defense practice. Represents broker-dealers, investment advisers, hedge funds and other financial services firms in connection with investigations by the SEC, FINRA, and other SROs and federal and state regulators. Practices internal investigations and reviews and regulatory counseling.
**Career:** Former staff attorney at SEC Division of Enforcement.
**Personal:** University of Richmond School of Law, JD, 1995; University of Richmond, MBA, 1995; University of Virginia, BA, 1992.

## SALLEMI, Kelli
Fulbright & Jaworski LLP, New York
212 318 3141
ksallemi@fulbright.com
*Featured in Banking & Finance (Nationwide)*
**Practice Areas:** Equipment Finance; Global Infrastructure; Corporate; Structured and Project Finance.
**Professional Memberships:** American Bar Association, Business Law Section and Commercial Finance Committee; New York State Bar Association; New York City Bar Association.
**Career:** As an associate in the Equipment Finance, Global Infrastructure and Corporate groups, Kelli's practice focuses on equipment financing (with an emphasis on transportation equipment), secured lending transactions and other global infrastructure and corporate matters.
**Personal:** JD, magna cum laude, New York Law School (2009); B.S., Pennsylvania State University (2006). During law school, Kelli was honored as a John Marshall Harlan Honors Scholar.

## SALOMON, Claudia T
Latham & Watkins LLP, New York
212 906 1230
claudia.salomon@lw.com
*Featured in International Arbitration (Nationwide)*
**Practice Areas:** International Arbitration and Public International Law.
**Career:** Ms Salomon focuses her practice on complex international disputes. She is a leading practitioner in significant investor treaty arbitration and international commercial arbitration cases under the AAA/ICDR, ICC, ICSID, LCIA, Stockholm, UNCITRAL and Vienna rules, around the world, under a wide variety of governing laws. She has handled all phases of US federal and state court litigation, including evidentiary hearings, motion practice, emergency relief, appellate practice and ADR proceedings.
**Personal:** JD, Harvard University (cum laude); BA, Brandeis University (summa cum laude, with honors).

## SALZMAN, Jerrold E
Skadden, Arps, Slate, Meagher & Flom LLP & Affiliates, Chicago
312 407 0718
jerrold.salzman@skadden.com
*Featured in Capital Markets (Nationwide)*
**Practice Areas:** Concentrates in futures regulation and litigation. Has served as the principal outside counsel to the Chicago Mercantile Exchange since 1968. Successfully counseled/defended the CME in numerous antitrust, employment, contract, patent and other matters. Has represented clients in disciplinary proceedings before federal agencies and self-regulatory organizations in addition to a securities, commercial litigation and arbitration practice.
**Career:** LLB, Harvard Law School, 1965 (cum laude; editor, Harvard Law Review); BA, University of Michigan, 1962 (with high distinction; Phi Beta Kappa).
**Publications:** "SEC/CFTC Merger - Is It Still the Same Debate?", Futures & Derivatives Law Report, January 2008.

## SANCHEZ, Vincent
DLA Piper LLP (US), Chicago
312 368 3420
vincent.sanchez@dlapiper.com
*Featured in Outsourcing (Nationwide), Technology (Illinois)*
See under Illinois for profile.

## SANDFORD, H Neal
Goodwin Procter LLP, Boston
617 570 1632
nsandford@goodwinprocter.com
*Featured in Capital Markets (Nationwide), Tax (Massachusetts)*
See under Massachusetts for profile.

## SANDLER, Andrew L
BuckleySandler LLP, Washington, DC
202 349 8001
asandler@buckleysandler.com
*Featured in Financial Services Regulation (Nationwide)*
**Practice Areas:** Mr Sandler, Chairman and Executive Partner of BuckleySandler LLP, is a rec-ognized leader in financial services litigation, enforcement, regulation, and compliance. He is strategic legal advisor to banks, the mortgage industry, auto lenders, and consumer finance companies. Mr Sandler has been the lead defense counsel in more than 80 class action cases and has represented financial services companies in complex commercial litigation and in civil and criminal investigations by federal and state enforcement and bank regulatory agencies, often involving fair lending, UDAP, AML/BSA, mortgage fraud, and False Claims Act issues. Mr Sandler has been named one of 30 D.C. "Superstar" lawyers by Washingtonian Magazine and a "Star of the Bar" in Banking and Financial Services. In June 2010, Legal Times named him a "Legal Visionary" for his role in founding BuckleySandler.
**Professional Memberships:** American Association of Bank Directors, Board of Advisors; numerous leadership positions in ABA Litigation Section and ABA Banking Law Committee; American College of Consumer Finance Lawyers.
**Career:** University of Pennsylvania Law School (1982); MBA, University of Pennsylvania Wharton School (1983); M.A., University of Warwick (UK) Rotary Foundation Fellow (1984).

## SANDLER, Richard J
Davis Polk & Wardwell LLP, New York
212 450 4000
richard.sandler@davispolk.com
*Featured in Capital Markets (Nationwide)*
**Practice Areas:** A leader of Davis Polk's Global Capital Markets Practice and Co-Head of Davis Polk's Corporate Governance Group. He has extensive experience advising on all aspects of public and private securities offerings, including initial public offerings, high-yield debt securities, derivatives, spinoffs, restructurings and new financial products. He also advises frequently on corporate governance and securities regulatory matters, and served on the NYSE Commission on Corporate Governance. Has regularly represented Aetna, Campbell Soup, Citigroup, Goldman Sachs, JP Morgan Chase, Morgan Stanley, PartnerRe and Verisk Analytics, as well as representing other corporate and investment banking clients on domestic and international matters.

## SANFORD, Bruce W
Baker & Hostetler LLP, Washington, DC
202 861 1626
bsanford@bakerlaw.com
*Featured in First Amendment Litigation (Nationwide), Media & Entertainment (District of Columbia)*
**Career:** Described by 'American Journalism Review' as one of the most accomplished press lawyers in the nation, Bruce Sanford has represented most of the leading national news media and book publishers including: E.W. Scripps, Tribune Co., Hearst Corporation, ABC, NBC, Fox Television, AOL/Time Warner, National Geographic and Random House. Bruce has represented President Clinton in negotiation and publication of a book; won libel and copyright cases brought against First Lady Barbara Bush and John Grisham, respectively; defended 'The New York Times' in a seminal libel case; won five-year lawsuit for 'Esquire' brought by former White House National Security Adviser Robert McFarlane.

## SANNA, Dina Kapur
Day Pitney LLP, New York
212 297 2455
dksanna@daypitney.com
*Featured in Wealth Management (Nationwide)*
**Career:** Dina Kapur Sanna, partner in the Individual Clients department, practices in the area of US federal tax planning for high net worth individuals with property interests and/or heirs in more than one country. Dina has considerable experience developing wealth management structures for residents and nonresidents of the US, and has significant exposure to federal income and transfer tax issues affecting US residents with non-US assets and income and nonresidents with US assets and income. Dina is a frequent speaker at international tax and estate planning seminars, and is a fellow of the American College of Trusts and Estate Counsel.

## SANSONETTI, Thomas L
Holland & Hart LLP, Cheyenne
307 778 4250
tlsansonetti@hollandhart.com
*Featured in Native American Law (Nationwide)*
**Practice Areas:** Represents clients in the areas of Indian law, air quality, geothermal development, water rights, water quality, endangered species, surface mining, natural resource damage assessments, takings, public lands management, Superfund, and other areas of natural resources law.
**Professional Memberships:** Colorado, Wyoming, and District of Columbia Bar Associations.
**Career:** Formerly Chair of the firm's Natural Resources Department. Assistant Attorney General, Environment and Natural Resources Division, U.S. Department of Justice (2001-2005). Solicitor, U.S. Department of the Interior (1990-93).
**Personal:** Washington & Lee University (JD 1976); University of Virginia (MBA 1973; BA 1971).

## SANTA MARIA, Michael E
Baker & McKenzie, Dallas
214 978 3016
michael.santamaria@bakermckenzie.com
*Featured in Franchising (Nationwide)*
**Practice Areas:** Mr Santa Maria has an extensive corporate practice with a focus on representing companies in cross-border business transactions. Mr Santa Maria's practice includes an emphasis on international franchising transactions in which he helps clients analyze, structure, negotiate and implement cross-border franchise development transactions via direct investment, joint venture, and master franchise or development agreements.
**Professional Memberships:** American Bar Association; Texas Bar Association; International Franchise Association.
**Career:** Mr Santa Maria previously practiced with Thompson & Knight and DLA Piper.

**Personal:** Mr Santa Maria is happily married to his wife, Allison, and has three children, Nick, Adam and Caitie.

### SANTENS, Ank A
White & Case LLP, New York
212 819 8599
asantens@whitecase.com

*Featured in International Arbitration (Nationwide)*

**Career:** Ank Santens is a partner in the international arbitration group of White & Case. She has served as counsel or arbitrator in commercial, investment, construction and sports arbitrations under all major international arbitration rules (ICC, ICDR/AAA, ICSID, LCIA, UNCITRAL, Court of Arbitration for Sport), as well as in ad hoc arbitrations and arbitrations under the rules of several regional centers. Ms Santens has extensive experience in infrastructure, construction and energy, and she has also handled significant disputes in the insurance, telecommunications, metals and mining, maritime, pharmaceutical, financial services, logistics and consumer goods industries. To view her biography, please visit www.whitecase.com/asantens.

### SANTUCCI, Ettore A
Goodwin Procter LLP, Boston
617 570 1531
esantucci@goodwinprocter.com

*Featured in Capital Markets (Nationwide), Corporate/M&A (Massachusetts)*

**Practice Areas:** Mr Santucci's practice focuses on public and private securities offerings, mergers and acquisitions, corporate governance, securities law compliance and cross-border transactions. His specific experience includes representing public and private issuers, underwriters, financial advisers and institutional investors in offerings of a broad range of debt and equity securities, including investment grade and high yield bonds, and sophisticated convertible and exchangeable securities with a wide spectrum of economic, structural and tax-sensitive features.

**Personal:** JD, Boston College Law School, 1985 (summa cum laude); JD, Faculty of Jurisprudence of the University of Bologna, Italy, 1982 (summa cum laude); BA, Manhattanville College, 1981.

### SANZO, Kathleen M
Morgan, Lewis & Bockius LLP, Washington, DC
202 739 5209
ksanzo@morganlewis.com

*Featured in Life Sciences (Nationwide), Healthcare (District of Columbia)*

**Practice Areas:** Kathleen Sanzo, leader of Morgan Lewis' FDA Practice Group, focuses her practice on all regulatory and compliance matters of the FDA relating to bulk and finished prescription and OTC drug and biologic manufacture, approval, marketing, and distribution; pre-clinical and clinical testing; drug and device promotional and labeling issues; food additive and dietary supplement matters; regulatory and enforcement matters of the Office of Inspector General of the Department of Health and Human Services and the Centers for Medicare and Medicaid Services; and regulatory and compliance matters of the Consumer Product Safety Commission and related state enforcement agencies.

### SARNO, Glenn R
Simpson Thacher & Bartlett LLP, New York
212 455 2706
gsarno@stblaw.com

*Featured in Investment Funds (Nationwide)*

**Practice Areas:** Corporate Partner focusing on private investment funds and other facets of alternative asset management. Has represented domestic and international fund sponsors on a global basis, including Carlyle, CVC Credit Partners, KKR, BTG Pactual, Citigroup, Tiger, SteelRiver, A&M Capital, Brown Brothers, Cherokee, CSFB and Cypress in a wide variety of asset classes and product types. Also represents sponsors of hedge fund products, employee securities companies, spin-outs and house-team arrangements.

**Career:** Joined Firm, 1993; Partner, 2001.

**Personal:** Duke University (JD, with honors, 1992); University of Connecticut (BA, summa cum laude, University Scholar, Phi Beta Kappa); Judicial Clerkship.

### SARRAILLE, William A
Sidley Austin LLP, Washington, DC
202 736 8195
wsarraille@sidley.com

*Featured in Healthcare (Nationwide), Healthcare (District of Columbia)*

See under District of Columbia for profile.

### SASSOWER, Edward O
Kirkland & Ellis LLP, New York
212 446 4733
edward.sassower@kirkland.com

*Featured in Bankruptcy/Restructuring (Nationwide), Bankruptcy/Restructuring (New York)*

**Practice Areas:** Edward represents debtors, creditors and distressed or special situation investors in bankruptcy cases, out-of-court restructurings and acquisitions. Company-side representations include MSR Resorts, Sbarro, Horizon Lines, Majestic Star, Calpine, Constellation Energy, NRG Energy, Muzak and Leiner. Represented ad hoc committees in the restructurings of Capmark Financial Group, Lyondell Chemical Company, AbitibiBowater, Mirant, Avecia and other large Chapter 11 cases. Represents private equity and hedge funds in acquisitions of companies in distress such as recently representing Oaktree Capital Management as plan sponsor in General Maritime's Chapter 11 cases.

**Personal:** Duke University School of Law, JD, 1998; Duke University, BA, 1995.

### SATHY, Anup
Kirkland & Ellis LLP, Chicago
312 862 2046
anup.sathy@kirkland.com

*Featured in Bankruptcy/Restructuring (Nationwide), Bankruptcy/Restructuring (Illinois)*

See under Illinois for profile.

### SAWYERS, Al B
Orrick, Herrington & Sutcliffe LLP, New York
212 506 5041
asawyers@orrick.com

*Featured in Capital Markets (Nationwide)*

**Career:** Al Sawyers serves as Chair of the Structured Finance Group. He focuses on the creation of structured financial products and repackaged asset-backed, corporate and municipal securities. He represents issuers and underwriters on complex financial transactions, including the issuance of a wide variety of fixed income securities, including credit-linked notes and synthetic securities. Mr Sawyers also works with clients on money market eligible products. He focuses on derivative transactions including interest rate, credit default, currency and equity swap agreements, securities lending agreements and repurchase agreements. Mr Sawyers previously served as co-head of Orrick's worldwide Finance Practice.

### SAWYIER, David R
Sidley Austin LLP, Chicago
312 853 7261
dsawyier@sidley.com

*Featured in Investment Funds (Nationwide)*

**Practice Areas:** Partner in Sidley's Chicago office, member of the Investment Products and Derivatives Group. Advises and represents clients in investment advisory, hedge fund and futures-related corporate and regulatory matters, including the organization and offering of interests in hedge funds and commodity pools and investments in advisory and trading firms.

**Career:** Clerkship: US Court of Appeals, DC Circuit, George McKinnon, 1977-78.

**Personal:** Cambridge University, Diploma in Law, 1979; Harvard Law School, JD, 1977; Oxford University, MA, 1974; Harvard University, AB, 1972. Admissions: District of Columbia, Illinois. Captain of the Harvard and Oxford Crews, US Champion 1971; Munich Olympics 1972.

### SCALLET, Edward
Groom Law Group, Washington, DC
202 861 5422
tscallet@groom.com

*Featured in ERISA Litigation (Nationwide)*

**Practice Areas:** Trial practice (investment prudence, ESOP, actuarial malpractice, and class actions generally); Appellate Litigation (Party and Amicus Curiae); Preemption; Benefits Financing (Captive Insurance Transactions); MEWAs.

**Career:** Joined Groom in 2000 after almost twenty years in private practice, following eight years in government, including service as the Assistant Counsel for Litigation in the Department of Labor's ERISA program.

**Publications:** Editorial Board, Benefits Law Journal; Former Editor in Chief, HealthSpan; 'New Class Action Lawsuits Aimed at Revenue Sharing and Company Stock'; "Captive Benefit Transactions: Has the Time Finally Come?'

**Personal:** Washington University (JD, 1975). Harvard University (BA, magna cum laude, 1972).

### SCAVONE, Arthur A
White & Case LLP, New York
212 819 8710
ascavone@whitecase.com

*Featured in Projects (Nationwide)*

**Career:** To view a comprehensive biography, please visit www.whitecase.com/ascavone.

### SCHACTER, Ira J
Cadwalader, Wickersham & Taft LLP, New York
212 504 6035
ira.schacter@cwt.com

*Featured in Capital Markets (Nationwide)*

**Practice Areas:** Creates and structures complex financial solutions and advises on the formation, acquisition, and capital raising activities of businesses that issue, underwrite, trade or invest in financial products. Develops unique financial solutions for corporate and financial institutions that bridge traditional finance with structured finance. Involved in all aspects of structured finance and with almost every type of securitization, including insurance risk, whole-company and CDOs, and with assets from the traditional to the varied, including corporate loans, swap receivables, repo and other financial assets. Experience with many other unique assets, such as franchise royalties and shipping containers. Counsels monoline insurers.

**Personal:** JD, Nova Center for the Study of Law; LLM, New York University School of Law; BA, State University of New York at Stony Brook.

### SCHAEFER, Georgette A
Morgan, Lewis & Bockius LLP, New York
212 309 6607
gschaefer@morganlewis.com

*Featured in Investment Funds (Nationwide)*

**Practice Areas:** Georgette A. Schaefer is a member of the firm's Private Investment Funds Practice and focuses her practice on private equity, venture, hedge, real estate, and infrastructure funds, and customized separate accounts.Ms Schaefer represents many of the largest pension funds in the US, banks, investment managers, insurance companies, and universities with respect to their investment programs. Ms Schaefer is frequently invited to speak on investment matters and has presented at meetings of the Institutional Limited Partner Association (ILPA), the National Association of Public Pension Attorneys, the American College of Investment Counsel, and the Private Equity Women Investor Network.

### SCHAFFZIN, Jonathan A
Cahill Gordon & Reindel LLP, New York
212 701 3380
jschaffzin@cahill.com

*Featured in Banking & Finance (Nationwide), Capital Markets (Nationwide)*

**Practice Areas:** Practice includes a range of financing, private equity transactions, mergers, acquisitions and out-of-court debt restructurings. Has represented leading banking firms and borrowers and issuers, in leveraged, mezzanine and equity financings, including IPOs; represented private equity firms and their portfolio companies in acquisitions of private and public companies, mezzanine investments, PIPEs and other investments. Actively representing financial institutions in their capacities as advisors, dealer managers and/or creditors in large debt-for-debt and debt-for-equity swaps, as well as other restructuring efforts.

**Personal:** Member, firm's Executive Committee. Northwestern University, BA, 1982. Columbia Law School, JD, 1985, Harlan Fiske Stone Scholar.

## SCHANER, Lawrence
Jenner & Block LLP, Chicago
312 923 2689
lschaner@jenner.com
*Featured in International Arbitration (Nationwide)*
**Career:** Lawrence S. Schaner, co-chair of the International Arbitration Practice, focuses on complex commercial disputes in courts and before arbitral tribunals. He is a fellow of the Chartered Institute of Arbitrators and Adjunct Professor of Law at Northwestern University School of Law, where he teaches international arbitration. He is a vice-chair of the IBA Arbitration Committee, member of the ICC Commission on Arbitration, chair of the USCIB Midwest Arbitration Committee and the editor of Dispute Resolution International. He regularly serves as an arbitrator and is a member of numerous arbitration panels. Stanford Law School, JD, 1986; Duke University, BA, 1982.

## SCHECHTER, Ronald A
Arnold & Porter LLP, Washington, DC
202 942 5160
Ronald.Schechter@aporter.com
*Featured in Government (Nationwide)*
**Practice Areas:** Ronald Schechter is a partner in Arnold & Porter LLP's Government Contracts practice group. He has served as lead attorney in litigation involving government contracts, enforcement actions, and administrative law before the US Court of Federal Claims, federal district courts; courts of appeals; and alternative dispute resolution forums. Prior to joining Arnold & Porter, he served as a Trial Attorney for the US Department of Justice, Commercial Litigation Branch. He has extensive experience in bid protests, claims litigation, False Claims Act cases, and fraud investigations by the Department of Justice, the Central Intelligence Agency and various other agencies.

## SCHEINBERG, Ronald
Vedder Price PC, New York
212 407 7730
rscheinberg@vedderprice.com
*Featured in Transportation (Nationwide), Banking & Finance (Nationwide)*
**Practice Areas:** Shareholder and member of the firm's Global Transportation Finance team. Concentrates his practice on corporate finance with a special focus on equipment and commercial bank finance. Represents underwriters, insurance companies, manufacturers and airlines in the financing of aircraft, railcars and other equipment. Represented financial institutions in purchase agreements and in the financing of simula-

tors, satellites, industrial production facilities, cars and trucks, and office buildings.
**Career:** Admitted (NY) 1984.
**Publications:** "LIBOR: A Finance Lawyer's Assessment," The Banking Law Journal (February 2013).
**Personal:** JD, cum laude, Harvard University; BA, magna cum laude, Brown University.

## SCHEINFELD, Steven G
Fried, Frank, Harris, Shriver & Jacobson LLP, New York
212 859 8475
Steven.Scheinfeld@FriedFrank.com
*Featured in Capital Markets (Nationwide)*
**Practice Areas:** Vice-chair of corporate department and co-head of corporate real estate transactions group. Represents real estate companies and other financial institutions in connection with public and private securities offerings, mergers and acquisitions, fund formations, strategic partnerships, corporate governance matters and financings. Clients include: AREA Properties, Essar Holdings, Goldman Sachs, Green Oak, GTIS Partners, L&M Developers, Meritage Properties, Morgan Stanley Real Estate, Onex Real Estate, REIS, Inc., SL Green Realty Corp., Terex Corporation, Thomson Reuters, Tradeweb and Vodafone.
**Career:** Joined as partner in 1998.
**Personal:** JD, Brooklyn Law School (1985), managing editor, Law Review; BA, Hobart College (1982).

## SCHELER, Brad Eric
Fried, Frank, Harris, Shriver & Jacobson LLP, New York
212 859 8019
Brad.Scheler@FriedFrank.com
*Featured in Bankruptcy/Restructuring (Nationwide), Bankruptcy/Restructuring (New York)*
See under New York for profile.

## SCHERMAN, William S
Gibson, Dunn & Crutcher LLP, Washington, DC
*Featured in Energy & Natural Resources (Nationwide)*
**Practice Areas:** Provides strategic, commercial, regulatory, legislative and litigation advice regarding US and international energy markets. At FERC, played a key role in many major pro-competitive policy initiatives. Helped guide FERC's efforts to foster greater competition in the electric utility industry, contributed to the development of the Energy Policy Act of 1992 and testified before Congress on numerous occasions with regard to legislation and other energy policy-related matters.
**Career:** General Counsel, FERC; Chief of Staff and Senior Legal and Policy Advisor, FERC. JD, University of Louisville School of Law, 1984; BA, George Washington University, 1980.

## SCHETMAN, Richard M
Cadwalader, Wickersham & Taft LLP, New York
212 504 6906
richard.schetman@cwt.com
*Featured in Capital Markets (Nationwide)*

**Practice Areas:** Co-Chair, Financial Services Department. Concentrates in derivatives advisory work, funded derivatives, asset financing structures, securitization structures and hedge fund investments in ABS and structured products as well as hedge fund derivatives, insurance products, and equity derivatives. Extensive experience in credit products, synthetic CDOs, credit derivatives and vehicles for repackaging corporate, asset-backed, and non-US securities. Represents underwriters, issuers, institutional investors, and swap counterparties in a wide range of matters, including hedge fund investments, prime brokerage, FX products, commercial paper vehicles, credit-linked and, life settlements notes, the securitization and financing of cash flows from such assets as credit card receivables, mortgage loans and hedge fund interests.
**Professional Memberships:** American Bar Association; Association of the Bar of the City of NY.
**Publications:** Frequent speaker on structured products, derivatives, CDOs, and other securitization issues.
**Personal:** JD, The University of Pennsylvania School of Law (cum laude; Moot Court Board member); BA, Brown University.

## SCHEVE, Stephen
Baker Botts LLP, Houston
713 229 1659
steve.scheve@bakerbotts.com
*Featured in Products Liability (Nationwide)*
**Practice Areas:** Products liability and toxic tort litigation, with emphasis on pharmaceuticals and medical devices.
**Professional Memberships:** International Association of Defense Counsel; past-President Missouri Organization of Defense Lawyers; International Who's Who of Product Liability Defense Lawyers (2002-11); International Who's Who of Life Sciences Lawyers (2010-11).
**Career:** Mr Scheve is a Senior Partner at Baker Botts, LLP, and serves as Practice Group Leader for the firm's Pharmaceutical Litigation Group. National counsel on multiple pharmaceutical product litigations.
**Personal:** JD, University of Kansas School of Law, Kansas Law Review, Order of the Coif, 1981; BS, University of Kansas, 1978.

## SCHIAVONE, Michael J
O'Melveny & Myers LLP, New York
212 326 2277
mschiavone@omm.com
*Featured in Capital Markets (Nationwide)*
**Practice Areas:** Michael J. Schiavone is a partner in O'Melveny's New York office and a Co-Chair of the Firm's Capital Markets Practice. Michael has broad experience in public and private securities transactions, representing underwriters and issuers in a wide variety of equity, debt and convertible securities offerings. He also has extensive experience in acquisition finance, debt restructuring and liability management transactions.

## SCHLAGER, Ivan A
Skadden, Arps, Slate, Meagher & Flom LLP & Affiliates, Washington, DC
202 371 7810
Ivan.Schlager@skadden.com
*Featured in Telecommunications (District of Columbia), International Trade (Nationwide)*
**Practice Areas:** Head of the firm's CFIUS practice. Represents telecommunication providers, media companies, technology companies, private equity firms, manufacturing companies and defense companies. Assisted in the development of successful legislative and regulatory strategies for a number of major M&A transactions. Has experience representing clients in Exon/Florio reviews before the Committee on Foreign Investment in the United States.
**Career:** Senior Advisor, Senator John F. Kerry (D-Ma), 2004 presidential campaign; Democratic Chief Counsel and State Director, U.S. Senate Committee on Commerce, Science and Transportation.

## SCHLOENDORN, Daniel
Willkie Farr & Gallagher LLP, New York
212 728 8265
dschloendorn@willkie.com
*Featured in Investment Funds (Nationwide)*
**Practice Areas:** Investment management, hedge funds and private equity funds. Formation and operation of US and offshore hedge funds, funds of funds and private equity funds, the organisation of and ongoing advice to, management companies, including compliance matters, seed capital arrangements, employment and joint venture matters; acquisitions of investment managers; advice to institutional investors and family offices relating to investments in private investment funds; and status issues under the Investment Company Act of 1940.
**Personal:** JD, New York University School of Law, 1973. Editor, Law Review. BA, cum laude, Fordham University, 1970. See: http://www.willkie.com/DanielSchloendorn

## SCHMIDT, Donald R
Carlton Fields, P.A., Tampa
813 229 4319
dschmidt@carltonfields.com
*Featured in Healthcare (Florida), Healthcare (Nationwide)*
See under Florida for profile.

## SCHMIDT, Paul W
Covington & Burling LLP, Washington, DC
202 662 5272
pschmidt@cov.com
*Featured in Products Liability (Nationwide)*
**Practice Areas:** Paul Schmidt has a wide-ranging trial and appellate practice, with a particular specialty in pharmaceutical litigation. His recent trial work includes serving as trial counsel for Hoffmann-La Roche in two Accutane trials; trial counsel for the NFL in first-of-their-kind trials involving labor and television carriage disputes; and representing Genentech in the only FDA hearing to occur over the withdrawal of accelerated approval for a medication. He has also success-

fully argued pharmaceutical appeals before state and federal courts around the country.
**Personal:** New York University School of Law (JD 1998), University of British Columbia (BA 1992).

## SCHMIDTBERGER, Michael J
Sidley Austin LLP, New York
212 839 5458
mschmidtberger@sidley.com
*Featured in Investment Funds (Nationwide)*
**Practice Areas:** Global co-head of Investment Funds, Advisers and Derivatives group, managing partner of the NY office and member of the Management and Executive Committees. Practices securities and futures-related funds and corporate transactions, including related regulatory matters. Represents clients in domestic and international offerings of hedge funds, fund of funds, public and private commodity pools and structured derivative and principal-protected transactions. Counsels clients in fund restructurings and work-out situations.
**Personal:** Columbia University School of Law, JD, 1985, Editor-in-Chief, Columbia Human Rights Law Review; Columbia College, BA, 1982, cum laude, Phi Beta Kappa, Bennett Cerf Prize in English. Admission: New York.

## SCHNEIDER, Lawrence
Arnold & Porter LLP, Washington, DC
202 942 5694
Lawrence.Schneider@aporter.com
*Featured in International Trade (Nationwide)*
**Practice Areas:** Lawrence Schneider is a Senior Partner who heads the firm's International Trade Practice. He represents clients in a full range of international trade, customs, legislative, and policy issues, including disputes under various import laws. Mr Schneider has 30 years of experience representing companies, trade associations, and governments in antidumping, countervailing duty, and other international trade proceedings before administrative agencies, courts, and international dispute settlement panels.
**Professional Memberships:** Served as President and member of the Board of Directors of the Washington Council of Lawyers.
**Personal:** JD, Harvard Law School, 1974, cum laude; BA, Yale University, 1971, cum laude.

## SCHNEIDER, Lisa
Fried, Frank, Harris, Shriver & Jacobson LLP, New York
212 859 8784
Lisa.Schneider@FriedFrank.com
*Featured in Investment Funds (Nationwide)*
**Practice Areas:** Practice focuses primarily on investment management matters, with an emphasis on hedge funds, hybrid funds, managed accounts and bespoke products. Advises major financial institutions and fund sponsors on the establishment of management companies, the structuring and offering of funds and managed accounts, and related transactional matters, including the seeding of management companies and investment funds.
**Career:** Joined in 2002; became partner in 2010.

**Personal:** JD, New York University School of Law (2002); BA, Emory University (1999).

## SCHNEIDER, Richard A
King & Spalding LLP, Atlanta
404 572 4889
dschneider@kslaw.com
*Featured in Products Liability (Nationwide), Litigation (Georgia)*
See under Georgia for profile.

## SCHNEIROV, Allison R
Skadden, Arps, Slate, Meagher & Flom LLP & Affiliates, New York
212 735 4138
Allison.Schneirov@skadden.com
*Featured in Private Equity (Nationwide)*
**Practice Areas:** Ms Schneirov is a partner in Skadden's M&A Department and is co-head of the Private Equity Group. She has extensive experience in mergers and acquisitions, private equity, securities and general corporate matters. She represents public and private companies, private equity firms and hedge funds, as well as investment banks and financing sources in a variety of domestic and international transactions.
**Career:** JD, The New York University School of Law, 1991 (cum laude); BA, University of Pennsylvania, 1988 (magna cum laude).

## SCHONBERGER, Mark
Goodwin Procter LLP, New York
212 813 8842
MSchonberger@goodwinprocter.com
*Featured in Capital Markets (Nationwide)*
**Practice Areas:** Mr Schonberger is a member of the firm's Real Estate, REITs & Real Estate Capital Markets Group and participates in the firm's M&A/Corporate Governance, Capital Markets and Private Investment Funds Practices. He specializes in corporate and securities law, with particular expertise in real estate companies, real estate-related matters and fund formation. He has extensive transactional experience representing publicly and privately held entities in acquisitions, joint ventures, ongoing management, public and private securities offerings, and fund formation transactions.
**Personal:** JD, Boston University School of Law, 1979; BA, Wesleyan University, 1975 (cum laude).

## SCHONHOLTZ, Margot
Willkie Farr & Gallagher LLP, New York
212 728 8258
mschonholtz@willkie.com
*Featured in Bankruptcy/Restructuring (Nationwide), Bankruptcy/Restructuring (New York)*
See under New York for profile.

## SCHOON, Eugene A
Sidley Austin LLP, Chicago
312 853 7279
eschoon@sidley.com
*Featured in Products Liability (Nationwide)*
**Practice Areas:** Partner in Sidley's Chicago office. Focuses on product liability defense, particularly pharmaceutical products and medical devices, and consumer class actions. Extensive experience in defending cases involving anticoagulant drugs, cholesterol lowering drugs, antifibrinolytics, antipsychotics, plasma derivatives,

implants, oral contraceptives, nutritional supplements and other medical products. Handled several major matters for healthcare clients including False Claims Act Defense, medical liability and tort reform cases. He has argued appeals in several federal courts of appeal and state appellate courts.
**Personal:** Valparaiso University School of Law, JD, 1980, with highest distinction, Indiana State University, MA, 1977, Calvin College, BA, 1975. Admission: Illinois.

## SCHOONOVER, Martha J
Greenberg Traurig, LLP, McLean
703 749 1374
SchoonoverM@gtlaw.com
*Featured in Immigration (Nationwide), Immigration (District of Columbia)*
See under District of Columbia for profile.

## SCHROEDER, Jeff
Hunton & Williams LLP, Washington, DC
202 955 1599
jschroeder@hunton.com
*Featured in Projects (Nationwide)*
**Practice Areas:** Practice focuses on project development and finance (both domestic and international), tax equity transactions, acquisitions and disposition of projects and portfolios and related financings.
**Professional Memberships:** Member, District of Columbia Bar.
**Publications:** Co-author: 'Regulatory Considerations for Cross-Border Power Plant Development' (Project Finance, September 2001).
**Personal:** BA, University of Virginia; JD, Washington and Lee (cum laude).

## SCHULMAN, Phillip
K&L Gates, Washington, DC
202 778 9027
phil.schulman@klgates.com
*Featured in Financial Services Regulation (Nationwide)*
**Practice Areas:** Mr Schulman, a partner in the consumer financial services practice, concentrates on a range of matters related to real estate finance, mortgage banking and consumer finance in both the primary and secondary markets. He has vast experience representing companies in the mortgage lending, title insurance and real estate industries in connection with administrative and regulatory compliance matters; defending companies in connection with governmental audits, investigations and enforcement proceedings, class action and litigation matters and developing and analyzing proposed business plans, and drafting the related agreements and disclosures, based upon applicable federal and state laws, regulations and rules.

## SCHULZ, David A
Levine Sullivan Koch & Schulz LLP, New York
212 850 6103
dschulz@lskslaw.com
*Featured in First Amendment Litigation (Nationwide), Media & Entertainment (New York)*
**Practice Areas:** Thirty years experience in access, libel, privacy, and First Amendment litigation. Visiting Lecturer/Co-Director, Media Freedom and Information Access Clinic, Yale Law

School; Lecturer, Columbia Law School. Represented press in Guantanamo access cases, Martha Stewart prosecution, Hatfill libel claims.
**Professional Memberships:** N.Y. City Bar, Chair, Intellectual Property Council, Past-Executive Committee and Past-chair, Media Law Committee; International Bar Association, Chair, Media Law Committee; MLRC, Past-President, Defense Counsel Section.
**Career:** Past-Partner in Rogers & Wells; Clifford Chance.
**Publications:** Co-author, "Internet Jurisdiction, Choice of Law Issues, ISP Immunity and Anonymous On-Line Speech."
**Personal:** Born 30 March 1952. JD, Masters (economics), Yale University.

## SCHUMAN, Ian
Latham & Watkins LLP, New York
212 906 1894
ian.schuman@lw.com
*Featured in Capital Markets (Nationwide)*
**Practice Areas:** Represents issuers and underwriters in capital market transactions in a broad array of industries, including initial public offerings, high-yield debt offerings, public and private equity offerings, debt exchange offers and tender offers and consent solicitations. Mr Schuman also represents companies with respect to general corporate and securities matters, including corporate governance issues, periodic and current filings with the Securities and Exchange Commission and the satisfaction of requirements set forth by the New York Stock Exchange and Nasdaq.
**Career:** Qualified since 2001. Deputy Office Managing Partner of the New York office.

## SCHWARTZ, David L
Latham & Watkins LLP, Washington, DC
202 637 2125
david.schwartz@lw.com
*Featured in Energy & Natural Resources (Nationwide)*
**Practice Areas:** Represents entities in electric generation, transmission and distribution; electric and gas marketing/trading; and gas transportation and distribution on energy regulatory and markets matters, including mergers/acquisitions, RTO markets, rates, siting, development and affiliate issues. Negotiates structured energy transactions relating to electric and gas products. Leads administrative litigation before federal and state regulators. Advises on federal/state energy legislation and regulations, and matters before FERC, DOE, state commissions, and CFTC.
**Career:** Global Chair, Energy Regulatory and Markets Practice; Co-chair, Global Energy - Power Industry Group.
**Personal:** JD, American University, Washington College of Law, 1989; AB, Bowdoin College, 1986.

## SCHWARTZ, Erich T
Skadden, Arps, Slate, Meagher & Flom LLP & Affiliates, Washington, DC
202 371 7660
Erich.Schwartz@skadden.com
*Featured in Securities (Nationwide)*
**Practice Areas:** Represents public companies, public accounting firms, broker-dealers and

investment advisers, their officers, directors and employees in investigations by the SEC and other regulatory authorities. He also conducts internal investigations of conduct that may raise potential regulatory issues and counsels his clients on strategies for avoiding such issues. Experienced in complex representations that involve parallel investigations by the SEC, Department of Justice, state regulators or FINRA as well as related private litigation.
**Career:** JD, George Washington University Law School (with honors), 1983; BA, University of Maryland (with honors in history), 1980.

### SCHWARTZ, Jordan M
Cadwalader, Wickersham & Taft LLP, New York
212 504 6136
jordan.schwartz@cwt.com
*Featured in Capital Markets (Nationwide)*
**Practice Areas:** Has served as lead counsel in hundreds of public and private securitization transactions involving securities and a wide array of asset classes, with clients including major mortgage banks, investment banks, commercial banks, insurance companies and institutional investors. Over 30 years experience as corporate lawyer and business advisor with participation in a variety of corporate transactions, including mergers and acquisitions, leveraged buyouts, initial public offerings, leveraged aircraft leasing, computer hardware and software development, acquisition and licensing arrangements, and entertainment and brand licensing.
**Professional Memberships:** Member, Executive Committee and Board of Directors of The American Securitization Forum; American Bar Association; Mortgage Bankers Association (Secondary and Capital Markets Committee).
**Personal:** JD, University of Chicago Law School; BA, Stanford University.

### SCHWARTZ, Lanny
Davis Polk & Wardwell LLP, New York
212 450 4000
lanny.schwartz@davispolk.com
*Featured in Financial Services Regulation (Nationwide)*
**Practice Areas:** Member of the firm's Trading and Markets practice. Mr Schwartz advises on securities and derivatives compliance, regulatory and transactional matters, and his clients include major international banks, broker-dealers, securities exchanges and consulting firms. Prior to joining Davis Polk. Mr Schwartz was Executive Vice President and General Counsel of the Philadelphia Stock Exchange and a Managing Director at Bankers Trust Company, concentrating in bank and broker-dealer regulation and investment banking. Mr Schwartz has been a leading figure in counseling clients on the Dodd-Frank Act, including in the areas of OTC derivatives reform, municipal advisors and the Volcker Rule.

### SCHWARTZ, Max J
Sullivan & Cromwell LLP, New York
212 558 3936
schwartzma@sullcrom.com
*Featured in Employee Benefits & Executive Compensation (Nationwide), Employee Benefits & Executive Compensation (New York)*
**Practice Areas:** Former Co-Managing Partner, Executive Compensation and Benefits Practice. Broad-based experience in securities, tax, labor laws affecting executive compensation/employee benefits. Advises clients regularly and in context of corporate transactions and IPOs.
**Professional Memberships:** ABA (Employee Benefits Committee, Tax Section); NYSBA (former Co-Chair, Employee Benefits Committee); Charter Member, American College of Employee Benefits Counsel; Co-Chair, ALI-ABA Annual Executive Compensation Program; Employee Benefits Advisory Committee, Practising Law Institute.
**Career:** Joined firm in 1998 as Of Counsel. Partner since 2000.
**Personal:** University of Michigan Law School (JD, 1973); Institut d'Etudes Politiques (BA equivalent, 1970).

### SCHWARTZ, Steven
Locke Lord LLP, New York
212 812 8312
sschwartz@lockelord.com
*Featured in Insurance (Nationwide), Insurance (New York)*
**Practice Areas:** Devotes most of his practice to reinsurance litigation and arbitration. He has also represented clients in litigation relating to mergers and acquisitions of reinsurance companies, and in other disputes arising out of the use of reinsurance in corporate transactions.
**Professional Memberships:** ABA; The Association of the Bar of the City of New York.
**Career:** Partner at Locke Lord since 2009.
**Publications:** Author of "Reinsurance Law: An Analytic Approach," a comprehensive treatise published by Law Journal Press.
**Personal:** Columbia Law School (JD, Harlan Fiske Stone Scholar, 1984); Princeton University (AB, cum laude, 1981).

### SCHWARZ, Helfried
Milbank, Tweed, Hadley & McCloy LLP, New York
212 530 5434
hschwarz@milbank.com
*Featured in Transportation (Nationwide), Banking & Finance (Nationwide)*
**Practice Areas:** Mr Schwarz is a partner and a member of the firm's Transportation and Space Group. He focuses mainly on aircraft and other structured equipment financings. He has particular expertise in domestic and cross-border leveraged lease transactions; pre-delivery payment and warehouse facilities; aircraft acquisitions and dispositions; enhanced equipment trust certificate offerings; aircraft portfolio securitizations; airline bankruptcies and restructurings; and export credit agency-supported financings.

### SCHWECHTER, Melvin S
Baker & Hostetler LLP, Washington, DC
202 861 1559
mschwechter@bakerlaw.com
*Featured in International Trade (Nationwide)*
**Career:** Melvin Schwechter is a Partner in BakerHostetler's Washington, D.C., office and is the firm's National Team Leader for its International Trade – Compliance Practice. He represents manufacturing, distribution and financial institution clients on customs, export control, trade/financial sanction and embargo and CFIUS matters. His work includes performing internal investigations and compliance audits/assessments, defending clients in governmental audits/enforcement matters, minimizing clients' penalty exposure through the preparation and submission of self-disclosures, and creating/improving clients' trade compliance and recordkeeping programs. He is a Past President of the Customs & International Trade Bar Association and is currently Chair of its Export Committee.

### SCHWED, Robert
WilmerHale, New York
212 937 7276
robert.schwed@wilmerhale.com
*Featured in Private Equity (Nationwide)*
**Practice Areas:** Represents private equity firms and portfolio companies in corporate finance transactions including intial public offerings, venture capital and buyout firms and other institutional investors in equity and debt investments, public and private buyout transactions, recapitalizations and other restructurings. Leveraged buyout experience includes the acquisition of business units from major industrial, financial services, healthcare, retailing, media and communications companies, and the acquisition of public companies in the computer, data processing, healthcare and communications industries.
**Professional Memberships:** Adjunct Professor, George Washington University Law School, venture capital law.
**Personal:** Harvard Law School (JD, 1974); Williams College (BA, 1971).

### SCHWEITZER, Lisa M
Cleary Gottlieb Steen & Hamilton LLP, New York
212 225 2629
lschweitzer@cgsh.com
*Featured in Bankruptcy/Restructuring (Nationwide), Bankruptcy/Restructuring (New York)*
See under New York for profile.

### SCHWENKEL, Robert C
Fried, Frank, Harris, Shriver & Jacobson LLP, New York
212 859 8167
Robert.Schwenkel@FriedFrank.com
*Featured in Private Equity (Nationwide)*
**Practice Areas:** Partner, chair of global corporate department and global head of M&A and private equity practice. Diverse transactional practice focused on private equity and M&A. Clients include Goldman Sachs Group Inc. and private investment funds managed by Goldman, Sachs & Co.; Permira Advisors LLC; Appaloosa

Management LP; and Citadel Investment Group. Also represents private equity portfolio companies and private equity sponsors in "club" transactions.
**Career:** Joined in 1982; became partner in 1989. Adjunct professor of law at Hofstra Law.
**Personal:** JD, magna cum laude, University of Buffalo (1982); articles editor, Law Review; BA, cum laude, University of Buffalo (1974).

### SCHWOLSKY, John
Willkie Farr & Gallagher LLP, New York
212 728 8232
jschwolsky@willkie.com
*Featured in Insurance (Nationwide), Insurance (New York)*
See under New York for profile.

### SEALE, Daniel
Latham & Watkins LLP, New York
212 906 1341
daniel.seale@lw.com
*Featured in Banking & Finance (Nationwide)*
**Practice Areas:** Complex syndicated loan transactions, primarily in the context of acquisition financings, leveraged buyouts and recapitalizations; capital markets transactions; project financings; and work-outs and restructurings.
**Career:** Qualified since 1996. Clerkship: Hon Ronald Lagueux (US District Court for the District of Rhode Island), 1995.

### SEEGERS, James D
Vinson & Elkins LLP, Houston
713 758 2939
jseegers@velaw.com
*Featured in Energy & Natural Resources (Nationwide)*
**Practice Areas:** Partner in Energy Regulatory Practice Group. Represents natural gas pipelines, storage providers and shippers before the Federal Energy Regulatory Commission and other regulators. Advises clients regarding rate, certificate, complaint, compliance, enforcement/audit, gas quality, import/export and rulemaking matters, as well as appellate litigation and energy transactions involving regulated assets.
**Professional Memberships:** Energy Bar Association; American Bar Association.
**Career:** Partner since 2002.
**Personal:** South Texas College of Law, JD 1993; Southern Methodist University, BBA 1985.

### SEFF, James M
Pillsbury Winthrop Shaw Pittman LLP, San Francisco
415 983 7441
james.seff@pillsburylaw.com
*Featured in Food & Beverages (Nationwide)*
**Practice Areas:** Leader, Beverage Practice; Co-Chair, Restaurant, Food and Beverages Team; Advises US and international supplier, retailer and investor clients on all aspects of beverage law including licensing, trade practices, tied house, trademarks, labeling, international trade, taxes, real estate, M&A, litigation, legislation; special liquor counsel to numerous law firms; practices before federal and state courts and regulatory agencies.
**Professional Memberships:** California and Hawaii bars; US Supreme Court; Former chair,

ABA Alcoholic Beverage Practice Committee; International Wine Lawyers; American Society for Enology and Viticulture (Honorary Research Lecturer). Adjunct Lecturer in Wine Law, UC Berkeley Law, Fall, 2012.
**Career:** Pillsbury Partner since 1986; former Chief Counsel, Wine Institute, SF Bar (President), CA State Bar (VP).
**Publications:** Chapters in Wine in America: Law & Policy; University of California/Sotheby Book of California Wine; Successful Wine Marketing; California CEB Wine Law Coursebooks, Flinders Journal of Law Reform, among others.
**Personal:** U of Mich (AB, 1963); U of California (Berkeley Law) (JD, 1966); Captain, USNR (Ret.).

**SEGAL, Michael J**
Wachtell, Lipton, Rosen & Katz, New York
212 403 1000
MJSegal@wlrk.com
*Featured in Employee Benefits & Executive Compensation (Nationwide), Employee Benefits & Executive Compensation (New York)*
See under New York for profile.

**SEHGAL, Zarrar**
Clifford Chance US LLP, New York
212 878 3409
zarrar.sehgal@cliffordchance.com
*Featured in Transportation (Nationwide), Banking & Finance (Nationwide)*
**Practice Areas:** Co-Head of the Americas Asset Finance Practice with extensive experience representing underwriters, lenders, lessors and governmental agencies in a wide variety of asset finance transactions, including portfolio securitizations, acquisition financing, leveraged leasing, EETC transactions, secured lending, structured financing and credit enhancements.
**Career:** Partner at Clifford Chance since 2006. Boston University, BA, 1994. Georgetown University Law Center, JD, 1997.

**SEIDEL, Stuart**
Baker & McKenzie, Washington, DC
202 452 7088
stuart.seidel@bakermckenzie.com
*Featured in International Trade (Nationwide)*
**Practice Areas:** Customs classification, valuation and compliance, country of origin and free trade agreements.
**Professional Memberships:** Customs and International Trade Bar Association, Customs Lawyers Association, ABA.
**Career:** Spent 32 years as a lawyer with the US Customs Service in senior roles including Assistant Commissioner, Assistant Chief Counsel for Enforcement and Operations and Director of International Trade Compliance.
**Publications:** Frequent speaker on customs and free trade, and the co-author of a chapter in the ABA Deskbook, US Customs Practitioner's Guide to Principles, Processes and Procedures.
**Personal:** JD, Brooklyn Law School, 1969; BA, Hunter College - City University of New York, 1967.

**SEIDER, Mitchell A**
Latham & Watkins LLP, New York
212 906 1200
mitchell.seider@lw.com
*Featured in Bankruptcy/Restructuring (Nationwide), Bankruptcy/Restructuring (New York)*
See under New York for profile.

**SEIFE, Howard**
Chadbourne & Parke LLP, New York
212 408 5361
hseife@chadbourne.com
*Featured in Bankruptcy/Restructuring (Nationwide), Bankruptcy/Restructuring (New York)*
See under New York for profile.

**SELBY, Timothy P**
Alston & Bird LLP, New York
212 210 9494
tim.selby@alston.com
*Featured in Investment Funds (Nationwide)*
**Practice Areas:** Structure securities- and futures-based alternative investment funds. Advise institutional and independent fund managers on forming hedge funds, funds of funds, commodity pools, and private equity funds. Advise clients regarding compliance with SEC and CFTC rules.
**Professional Memberships:** President, NY Hedge Fund Roundtable; Immediate preceding Chair, Futures and Derivatives Regulation Committee of the NYC Bar Association; member of the Private Investment Funds Committee of the NYC Bar Association; member, Futures Industry Association; member, Lawyer's Advisory and CPO/CTA Committees of the Managed Funds Association.
**Personal:** JD (1993) St. John's University; MBA (1990), BBA (1987) Iona College; licensed CPA in NY.

**SELDEN, Andrew**
Briggs and Morgan, Minneapolis
612 977 8485
aselden@briggs.com
*Featured in Franchising (Nationwide)*
**Practice Areas:** Franchising, antitrust.
**Career:** Andy has a nationally pre-eminent practice advising associations of franchisees. He also represents franchisors, franchisees, and purchasing and advertising cooperatives. He advises franchisors in the development, conversion and operation of franchise systems in numerous industries; negotiating international franchise, joint ventures and licenses; formation and operation of regional and national purchasing and advertising cooperatives; and counseling franchisors and franchisee associations in connection with renegotiation of system franchise agreements and other contracts.
**Personal:** JD, magna cum laude, University of Minnesota Law School.

**SELDEN, David W**
Fried, Frank, Harris, Shriver & Jacobson LLP, New York
212 859 8775
David.Selden@FriedFrank.com
*Featured in Investment Funds (Nationwide)*
**Practice Areas:** Corporate partner. Practice includes investment management and securities law matters, with emphasis on private investment vehicles including hedge funds, private equity funds, real estate funds, hybrid funds and funds-of-funds. Advises major financial institutions, fund sponsors, institutional investors, investment advisors and commodity trading advisors on commercial, securities and compliance matters relating to the formation and offering of funds, management company structure, bespoke products, managed accounts and related matters.
**Career:** Joined in 2005; became partner in 2009.
**Personal:** JD, magna cum laude, University of Minnesota Law School (2001), editor, Minnesota Law Review; BA, University of Virginia (1996).

**SELIGMAN, Terri**
Frankfurt Kurnit Klein & Selz, New York
212 826 5580
tseligman@fkks.com
*Featured in Advertising (Nationwide)*
**Practice Areas:** Co-Chair of the firm's Advertising, Marketing and Public Relations Group. Counsels clients on legal issues concerning the creation and distribution of advertising and promotional materials in all media. Practice covers review of claims and substantiation, compliance with marketing laws, and representation of clients before the National Advertising Division, broadcast networks and government agencies. Practice also covers legal compliance for social media programs and marketing devices such as gift cards, rewards and rebates. Transactional work includes celebrity talent, sponsorship, licensing and media agreements. Has been a featured speaker at Association of National Advertisers, National Advertising Division, Promotion Marketing Association, The Media Law Resource Center and other national conferences. Named one of the "Top 50 Women" lawyers in New York by Super Lawyers magazine and recognized in The Legal 500.

**SEYMOUR, Karen Patton**
Sullivan & Cromwell LLP, New York
212 558 3196
seymourk@sullcrom.com
*Featured in Financial Services Regulation (Nationwide), Litigation (New York)*
See under New York for profile.

**SEYMOUR, Samuel W**
Sullivan & Cromwell LLP, New York
212 558 3156
seymours@sullcrom.com
*Featured in Financial Services Regulation (Nationwide), Litigation (New York)*
See under New York for profile.

**SHACKELFORD, Richard L**
King & Spalding LLP, Atlanta
404 572 4995
rshackelford@kslaw.com
*Featured in Healthcare (Georgia), Healthcare (Nationwide)*
See under Georgia for profile.

**SHAFFERMAN, Howard H**
Ballard Spahr LLP, Washington, DC
202 661 2205
hhs@ballardspahr.com
*Featured in Energy & Natural Resources (Nationwide)*
**Practice Areas:** Howard H. Shafferman is a partner in the Business and Finance Department and Practice Leader of the Energy and Project Finance Group. He advises and represents clients on all aspects of federal and state regulation of electric, hydroelectric, and gas facilities and services.
**Professional Memberships:** Ballard Spahr's Board, North American Energy Standards Board, Energy Bar Association.
**Career:** Admissions: District of Columbia.
**Publications:** "Three Disciplines for Serving Energy Clients," Energy Law Client Strategies: Leading Lawyers on Litigation, Negotiations, and Industry Regulations, Aspatore Books, 2007.
**Personal:** Education: University of Virginia School of Law (JD 1978) Princeton University (A.B. 1975).

**SHAPIRO, David**
Wachtell, Lipton, Rosen & Katz, New York
212 403 1314
DEShapiro@wlrk.com
*Featured in Capital Markets (Nationwide), Corporate/M&A (New York)*
See under New York for profile.

**SHAPIRO, David I**
Fried, Frank, Harris, Shriver & Jacobson LLP, New York
212 859 8039
David.Shapiro@FriedFrank.com
*Featured in Investment Funds (Nationwide), Tax (New York)*
See under New York for profile.

**SHAPIRO, Hal S**
Akin Gump Strauss Hauer & Feld LLP, Washington, DC
202 887 4053
hshapiro@akingump.com
*Featured in International Trade (Nationwide)*
**Practice Areas:** Advises multinational companies, trade associations and foreign governments on international trade policy and agreements, international-related legislation, litigation of disputes before the World Trade Organization (WTO) and other international dispute-resolution bodies, import/export and customs matters, CFIUS/national security policy issues and a wide range of financial and investment issues.
**Career:** Senior advisor for International Economic Affairs and Senior Counselor to the Director, National Economic Council at the White House; Associate General Counsel, Office of the U.S. Trade Representative; Trial Attorney, U.S. Department of Justice.
**Personal:** BA, summa cum laude, Phi Beta Kappa, Columbia College, 1988; JD, Columbia Law School, 1991.

**SHAPIRO, Howard**
Van Ness Feldman LLP, Washington, DC
202 298 1884
hes@vnf.com
*Featured in Energy & Natural Resources (Nationwide)*
**Practice Areas:** Represents clients in litigation, including appellate proceedings, on matters involving power sales contracts, railroad antitrust

issues, and provides insight on complex environmental questions arising in federal hydropower licensing and under the Clean Air Act, Indian rights, regulatory takings, judicial review, statutory pre-emption, and federal state disputes under the Commerce Clause.
**Professional Memberships:** Supreme Court Institute of the Georgetown University Law Center.
**Career:** Deputy General Counsel, Federal Trade Commission, 1980-85; Solicitor, Federal Energy Regulatory Commission, 1978-80; U.S. Department of Justice: Assistant to the Solicitor General, 1975-78; Chief of Appellate Section, Antitrust Division, 1968-75; Attorney, 1955-68.

**SHAPIRO, Robert**
Chadbourne & Parke LLP, Washington, DC
202 974 5670
rshapiro@chadbourne.com
*Featured in Energy & Natural Resources (Nationwide)*
**Practice Areas:** Robert Shapiro's practice involves legal representation of industrial firms, investors and developers (and their lenders) that build, finance, own, operate, sell and use the energy output from renewable energy and conventional power facilities in the US and abroad. He has extensive knowledge of regulatory schemes in numerous countries, including Latin America and Africa. He regularly advises on negotiation and defense of long-term power contracts, operation, maintenance, transmission and fuel contracts, as well as mergers and acquisitions of utility assets. He also has extensive experience before US federal and state regulatory agencies and in US courts on energy matters.

**SHAPIRO, Robyn**
Drinker Biddle & Reath LLP, Milwaukee
414 221 6056
Robyn.Shapiro@dbr.com
*Featured in Life Sciences (Nationwide)*
**Practice Areas:** Chair, Life Sciences; Regional Partner in Charge, Milwaukee; practice focuses on research compliance, including regulatory requirements, fraud & abuse, conflicts of interest, and privacy.
**Professional Memberships:** Council, ABA Health Law Section; Chair, ABA Special Committee on Bioethics and the Law; appointed member NIH Recombinant DNA Advisory Committee Biosafety Working Group; Consultant, FDA Drug Safety & Risk Management Advisory Committee.
**Career:** Formerly, 25+ year tenure as Director, Medical College of Wisconsin Bioethics Center and Professor of Bioethics.
**Publications:** Authored 60+ peer-reviewed articles and book chapters.
**Personal:** Harvard Law School, J.D; University of Michigan, BA, summa cum laude, Highest Distinction.

**SHARF, Jesse**
Gibson, Dunn & Crutcher LLP, Los Angeles
310 552 8512
JSharf@gibsondunn.com
*Featured in Real Estate (Nationwide), Real Estate (California)*
**Practice Areas:** Co-Chair, Real Estate Practice. Experience includes representation of funds and other investors, lenders, servicers and operators/developers in all real estate and finance matters including: loan and partnership workouts, restructurings, receiverships and remedies; bankruptcies; acquisition, sale and financing of loan portfolios; forming ventures; mortgage, preferred equity and mezzanine financing; structured finance; real estate M&A; commercial development; acquisitions and sales of assets and operating companies; leasing; and structuring and resolving multi-tranched debt and equity structures.
**Publications:** Frequent lecturer on workouts, remedies, funds, entity formation, financing, acquisition and development.
**Personal:** JD, NYU Law School, Editor, 'Law Review'; BA, University of Pennsylvania.

**SHARP, Richard T**
Milbank, Tweed, Hadley & McCloy LLP, New York
212 530 5209
rsharp@milbank.com
*Featured in Financial Services Regulation (Nationwide)*
**Practice Areas:** Mr Sharp is a partner and a member of the Litigation & Arbitration Group. He is a leading practitioner representing major US and foreign broker-dealers, investment advisers, and investment partnerships in connection with a broad range of regulatory issues, SEC and self-regulatory organization enforcement investigations and proceedings, and corporate transactions. He has counseled almost all of the major US securities firms and many foreign broker-dealers on various regulatory matters, with a particular focus on trading issues under the Securities Exchange Act of 1934 and the rules and regulations of the Financial Services Regulatory Authority and other self-regulatory organizations.

**SHARPE, Ralph E**
Venable LLP, Washington, DC
202 344 4344
resharpe@Venable.com
*Featured in Financial Services Regulation (Nationwide)*
**Practice Areas:** Banking and Financial Services Regulation.
**Professional Memberships:** American Bar Association, Federal Bar Association, Women in Housing and Finance.
**Career:** Mr Sharpe heads Venable's Financial Services Group Risk Management and Compliance Team. His 26 years of experience with the Office of the Comptroller of the Currency make him intimately familiar with financial services regulation. Mr Sharpe has represented numerous financial institutions, officers and directors in enforcement and regulatory matters involving issues ranging from BSA and OFAC

compliance to corporate applications and structural issues.
**Publications:** See http://www.venable.com/Professionals/Bio.aspx?Bio=96d50ad1-25a0-4c9b-80aa-fa85cfca56d5&view=pubs
**Personal:** JD, University of Wisconsin Law School, BA, University of Wisconsin.

**SHAW-LORELLO, Loretta**
Covington & Burling LLP, New York
212 841 1073
lshawlorello@cov.com
*Featured in Investment Funds (Nationwide)*
**Practice Areas:** Vice Chair of Covington's Private Funds Practice. Ms Shaw-Lorello represents a broad range of investment fund clients (both sponsors and investors) with a focus on sponsor representations in the formation of private equity funds across various asset classes (including buyout, growth equity, real estate, distressed debt, and venture capital), private bank and other feeder funds and joint ventures. She also advises clients in connection with manager formation and structuring carried interest and other compensation arrangements.
**Personal:** JD, cum laude, Fordham University Law School (1993), Order of the Coif, Member Fordham Law Review. BA, Yale University (1985).

**SHEEHAN, Bartholomew**
Sidley Austin LLP, New York
212 839 8652
bsheehan@sidley.com
*Featured in Capital Markets (Nationwide)*
**Practice Areas:** Partner Bartholomew Sheehan focuses on the representation of issuers and underwriters of publicly and privately offered debt and equity securities, with an emphasis on companies in the energy and real estate industries, particularly real estate investment trusts ("REITs"). In addition to securities offerings, his practice includes consultation with clients regarding corporate governance matters and public company reporting obligations. Mr Sheehan is also active in representing pooled investment entities, such as hedge funds and private equity partnerships and their sponsors.
**Personal:** New York University School of Law, JD, 1995; Georgetown University, BA, 1991, summa cum laude.

**SHELLEY, Anthony**
Miller & Chevalier Chartered, Washington, DC
202 626 5924
ashelley@milchev.com
*Featured in ERISA Litigation (Nationwide)*
**Practice Areas:** Litigates employee benefits, health care, and pension issues before federal and state courts and administrative agencies; including litigation involving ERISA and FEHBA.
**Career:** Firm Chair. Defends companies and plans in class actions and individual suits concerning challenges to benefits denials, exclusions from coverage, eligibility, fiduciary duties, and subrogation and reimbursement matters. Deals frequently with issues of federal jurisdiction and the preemption of state law. Represents entities

and classes of individuals aggrieved by plan terminations before and against the Pension Benefit Guaranty Corporation. Has argued before the US Supreme Court.
**Personal:** JD, Harvard Law School; BA, Canisius College.

**SHENBERG, Michael**
White & Case LLP, New York
212 819 8200
mshenberg@whitecase.com
*Featured in Energy & Natural Resources (Nationwide)*
**Career:** Michael Shenberg is a partner in White & Case's Mergers and Acquisitions Practice Group in the New York office. A recognized leader in his field, he focuses on energy M&A, capital markets and financing transactions for the Firm. Mr Shenberg has represented financial and strategic investors in numerous transactions involving the purchase or sale of energy assets, including large portfolios, single-asset deals and joint ventures. Additionally, he advises on financings including restructurings, and corporate and commercial matters for energy company clients. To view a comprehensive biography, please visit www.whitecase.com/mshenberg.

**SHENKER, Joseph C**
Sullivan & Cromwell LLP, New York
212 558 3768
shenkerj@sullcrom.com
*Featured in Capital Markets (Nationwide), Real Estate (New York)*
See under New York for profile.

**SHER, Stanley O**
Cozen O'Connor, Washington, DC
202 463 2501
ssher@cozen.com
*Featured in Transportation (Nationwide)*
**Practice Areas:** Stanley Sher represents international ocean carriers and other clients before Federal and State courts, U.S. Congress, and government agencies. Stan has participated in virtually every recent major legislative initiative and judicial proceeding affecting the regulatory and competition laws governing international shipping.
**Career:** In 2010, Stan was inducted into the International Maritime Hall of Fame, also named in the Best Lawyers' 2011 Washington, D.C., Maritime Lawyer of the Year, and in 2011 was given the Lifetime Achievement Award by the Containerization & Intermodal Institute.
**Personal:** University of Wisconsin, B.S., 1956, Phi Beta Kappa; Harvard Law School, JD, 1959.

**SHERIDAN, Mark F**
Holland & Hart LLP, Santa Fe
505 954 3671
msheridan@hollandhart.com
*Featured in Native American Law (Nationwide), Native American Law (New Mexico)*
See under New Mexico for profile.

**SHEYKA, Joseph W**
DLA Piper LLP (US), Chicago
312 368 4022
joseph.sheyka@dlapiper.com
*Featured in Franchising (Nationwide)*

**Practice Areas:** Franchising, international franchising, and antitrust.

**Professional Memberships:** ABA; Illinois Bar Association; Chicago Bar Association; ABA Forum on Franchising; Franchising Committee, Antitrust Section of the ABA; International Franchising Committee, Business Law Section of the International Bar Association.

**Career:** He concentrates in the field of franchising and distribution law. He is a frequent lecturer on franchising and distribution topics.

**Publications:** Co-author of General Franchising Considerations, published by the Illinois Institute for Continuing Legal Education, and Franchising in the United States, a Canadian Franchise Guide.

**Personal:** JD, Northwestern University School of Law; BA, University of Illinois at Urbana-Champaign.

## SHIM, Paul J
Cleary Gottlieb Steen & Hamilton LLP, New York
212 225 2930
pshim@cgsh.com
*Featured in Private Equity (Nationwide), Corporate/M&A (New York)*

**Practice Areas:** M&A and leveraged buyouts. Represented TPG (Savers, Primedia, Creative Artists Agency, Vertafore, Alltel, Sabre, Harrah's and other investments); Dollar Thrifty (Hertz); Nortel Networks (Section 363 bankruptcy sale of residual patent assets, sale of CDMA and GSM wireless infrastructure assets); American Express (Loyalty Partner, Ameriprise spin-off, GE's Corporate Payment Services acquisition, travel acquisitions); Bank of America (sale of non-US wealth management business to Julius Baer Group and Columbia Management business to Ameriprise Financial, China Construction Bank investment, , Fleet Financial acquisition).

**Career:** Joined firm (1987); partner (1996). JD, cum laude, NYU (1987). BS, MS (Chem. E.), MIT (1984).

## SHIRAZI, Ray
Cadwalader, Wickersham & Taft LLP, New York
212 504 6666
ray.shirazi@cwt.com
*Featured in Capital Markets (Nationwide)*

**Practice Areas:** Practice encompasses full range of derivatives products and related issues from cash trading and related regulatory issues to OTC equity derivatives, registered and privately-placed structured products, and hedge fund derivatives. Advises on structures, execution of credit derivatives, asset swaps, convertible arbitrage products, and fixed income derivatives. Covers equity, rate and commodity-linked notes, warrants, certificates, CD's and assists in development and execution of variety of hedge-fund structured products (and OTC counterparts) including principal-protected notes, warrants, and certificates. Advises on related hedge fund financing transactions including credit facilities, secured loans, and collateralized financial obligations. Represents investment banks, domestic and foreign commercial banks, asset managers, and hedge funds on transactional and trading regulatory issues.

**Professional Memberships:** ISDA North American Committee on Equity Derivatives and Equity Derivatives Drafting Committee.

**Personal:** JD, University of California Los Angeles School of Law (Managing Editor UCLA Law Review); BS, University of California Riverside (cum laude).

## SHOEMATE, Steven R
Gibson, Dunn & Crutcher LLP, New York
212 351 3879
sshoemate@gibsondunn.com
*Featured in Private Equity (Nationwide), Corporate/M&A (New York)*

**Practice Areas:** Public and private mergers and acquisitions and other strategic transactions including leveraged buyouts, joint ventures, cross border, industry roll-ups, tender and exchange offers, go private transactions and preferred equity investments. Mr Shoemate has extensive experience in a variety of industries, including financial institutions, healthcare, mining, construction, consumer and retail.

**Career:** Co-Partner-in-Charge of the New York office; Co-Chair of the Private Equity Practice.

**Personal:** JD, Duke University, 1988, Member of the Duke Law Journal and the Duke chapter of the Order of the Coif.

## SHONEMAN, Charles H
Bracewell & Giuliani LLP, Washington, DC
202 828 5860
charles.shoneman@bgllp.com
*Featured in Energy & Natural Resources (Nationwide)*

**Practice Areas:** Counsels major energy industry participants in federal and state energy regulatory matters and represents them before the Federal Energy Regulatory Commission, Department of Energy, state public utility commissions, and in the appellate courts. Practice involves project authorization, ratemaking and tariff, compliance, regulatory litigation and enforcement matters. Advises clients with respect to the energy regulatory aspects of: commercial contracting; structured transactions; mergers, acquisitions and sales of assets; financings; natural gas and liquefied natural gas projects; and gas imports and exports.

**Personal:** JD, The George Washington University Law School, 1972; BA, Duke University, 1969.

## SHOR, Michael T
Arnold & Porter LLP, Washington, DC
202 942 5732
Michael.Shor@aporter.com
*Featured in International Trade (Nationwide)*

**Practice Areas:** Michael Shor has 30 years experience representing private companies, trade associations, and foreign governments in international trade matters, including anti-dumping and countervailing duty investigations, reviews and appeals, sunset reviews, WTO disputes, and US Customs investigations and compliance matters. Mr Shor also has extensive experience with appeals of trade cases, including involvement as counsel in some 50 decisions issued by courts and binational panels. He has also assisted foreign governments in dispute settlement proceedings before the World Trade Organization.

**Career:** Legal Assistant, Iran-United States Claims Tribunal, 1984-86.

**Personal:** JD, Harvard Law School, 1983; AB, Dartmouth College, 1980.

## SHORTZ, Richard
Morgan, Lewis & Bockius LLP, Los Angeles
213 612 2526
rshortz@morganlewis.com
*Featured in Projects (Nationwide)*

**Practice Areas:** Richard A. Shortz is a Partner in Morgan Lewis's Business and Finance Practice. Mr Shortz practices in the corporate area with an emphasis on energy and project finance; corporate mergers, acquisitions, and other business combinations; renewable energy; oil and gas; corporate securities and general representation of publicly held companies. Mr Shortz currently serves as the Vice Chairman of the Energy and Infrastructure Finance Group of the firm and is the Practice Group Leader of the Business and Finance Group in Los Angeles.

## SHOYER, Andrew W
Sidley Austin LLP, Washington, DC
202 736 8326
ashoyer@sidley.com
*Featured in International Trade (Nationwide)*

**Practice Areas:** Partner, chairs Sidley's International Trade and Dispute Resolution practice. Focuses on implementation and enforcement of international trade and investment agreements. Advises companies, trade associations and governments on the use of WTO, FTA, and other treaty-based trade and investment rules to open markets and resolve disputes. Works with clean tech manufacturers and telecom service providers, WTO compliance in Asia, and on protection of intellectual property in bilateral and regional free trade negotiations.

**Personal:** Georgetown University Law Center, JD, 1986; Georgetown University School of Foreign Service, MS in Foreign Service, 1986; University of Pennsylvania, BA, 1981. Admission: District of Columbia.

## SIBBISON, V Heather
Dentons, Washington, DC
202 408 6439
heather.sibbison@dentons.com
*Featured in Native American Law (Nationwide)*

**Practice Areas:** Heather serves as chair of legacy Dentons's Native American Law and Policy Group. Heather's practice is primarily focused on Indian lands issues, including trust acquisitions, Indian lands opinions, Carcieri and Patchak issues, land claim settlement issues, and compliance with the Indian Gaming Regulatory Act and the Natural Environmental Policy Act. Heather served in the Office of the Secretary at the Department of the Interior, and at the Department of Justice.

**Personal:** Tufts University 1983, Columbia Law School, 1988.

## SIEGEL, David
Irell & Manella, Los Angeles
310 203 7129
dsiegel@irell.com
*Featured in Securities (Nationwide), Litigation (California)*
See under California for profile.

## SILBERG, Jay
Pillsbury Winthrop Shaw Pittman LLP, Washington, DC
202 663 8063
jay.silberg@pillsburylaw.com
*Featured in Energy & Natural Resources (Nationwide)*

**Practice Areas:** Senior Partner in firm's Energy Section. Represents electric utilities, nuclear suppliers, industry associations, nuclear waste facilities and others on the regulatory, litigation, transactional and other aspects of their nuclear-related projects and enterprises. Has appeared on behalf of these clients before the Nuclear Regulatory Commission, the Department of Energy, state regulatory agencies, the courts, and Congress in all phases of nuclear licensing, regulation, enforcement, and litigation. Advises US and international clients on nuclear-related transactions. Has led industry-wide litigation on key nuclear issues, including leading nuclear waste cases.

**Personal:** JD, Harvard Law School, 1966; BA, Amherst College, 1963 (cum laude).

## SILBERMAN, Alan H
Dentons, Chicago
312 876 8103
alan.silberman@dentons.com
*Featured in Franchising (Nationwide), Antitrust (Illinois)*

**Practice Areas:** Chair emeritus, Antitrust, Competition Franchising and Marketing practice. Over 45 years' experience in antitrust, franchising, general commercial litigation, counseling, and related transactions. Represents franchisors in negotiated, litigated, and arbitrated disputes with franchisees and third parties and domestic and international activities. Has acted for McDonald's, Pella Corporation, Purina Animal Nutrition, InterContinental Hotels and other franchisors and manufacturers.

**Career:** Joined Dentons in 1966. 1964-66 law clerk to Honorable Hubert L Will, US District Judge (Northern District of Illinois). Frequent speaker on antitrust topics, including marketing, distribution, franchising, litigation and insurance.

**Personal:** Yale University, LLB; Northwestern University, BA, with distinction.

## SILVERMAN, Donald J
Morgan, Lewis & Bockius LLP, Washington, DC
202 739 5502
dsilverman@morganlewis.com
*Featured in Energy & Natural Resources (Nationwide)*

**Practice Areas:** Donald J. Silverman is a partner in Morgan Lewis's Energy Practice. Mr Silverman represents utilities, fuel cycle companies, and industrial and medical materials licensees before the Nuclear Regulatory

Commission (NRC), as well as in related proceedings before other agencies and the federal courts. He has also represented the Department of Energy on the NRC's Yucca Mountain licensing proceeding. Mr Silverman's practice focuses on both the "front end" of the fuel cycle (fuel fabrication, enrichment) and the "back end" of the fuel cycle (radioactive waste disposition, including storage, recycling, and permanent disposal).

### SILVERMAN, Eric
Milbank, Tweed, Hadley & McCloy LLP, New York
212 530 5648
esilverman@milbank.com
*Featured in Projects (Nationwide)*
**Practice Areas:** Mr Silverman is a partner and co-chair of the Project Finance Group. He has experience in project development and financing of major oil and gas, power/renewables and infrastructure projects in the US and overseas. He represents multinational corporations, PE funds, banks and ECAs in greenfield projects and acquisitions/restructuring/recapitalization transactions. He has advised hedge funds, bondholders and other investors in connection with acquisitions and divestitures of energy and infrastructure assets and distressed companies in the energy, telecoms and natural resources sectors. His financing experience includes multi-source financing, project bonds, securitizations, private equity funds, project leasing and other financing structures.

### SILVERMAN, Leslie N
Cleary Gottlieb Steen & Hamilton LLP, New York
212 225 2380
lsilverman@cgsh.com
*Featured in Capital Markets (Nationwide)*
**Practice Areas:** Domestic and international capital markets, particularly cross-border offerings and development of new financial products, and counseling regarding compliance with the Sarbanes-Oxley and Dodd-Frank legislation and related corporate governance matters.
**Professional Memberships:** Member of the Bar in New York. Admitted to practice before US Court of Appeals (Second Circuit) and US District Court (Southern District of New York).
**Career:** Joined firm, 1974; became partner, 1982. JD, Law Journal Editor, Yale Law School (1973); BS, summa cum laude, Wharton School of the University of Pennsylvania (1969).
**Publications:** Chair of Legal Advisory Group for "Interim Report of the Committee on Capital Markets Regulation" (November 2006) and Member of the Committee on Capital Markets Regulation; Co-author of "US Regulation of the International Securities and Derivatives Markets" (Tenth edition, 2011); "PLI's Guide to the Securities Offering Reforms" (Practising Law Institute 2005); "The Sarbanes-Oxley Act: Analysis and Practice" (2003).

### SIMMONS, Rebecca J
Sullivan & Cromwell LLP, New York
212 558 3175
simmonsr@sullcrom.com
*Featured in Capital Markets (Nationwide)*
**Professional Memberships:** ABA; FIA; SIA; NYCBA; NYSBA (Immediate Past Chair, Business Law Section).
**Career:** Partner since 2000. Member of the Firm's Corporate & Finance and Financial Institutions Groups. Practice areas: securities; banking and commodities laws and regulation; insolvency and restructuring; and structured finance. Transactions: CIFG restructuring (IFLR Restructuring Deal of the Year); AIG's $500 million contingent liquidity facility; UBS's $15 billion rights offering; GS conversion to bank holding company. Developed first synthetic AAA-rated derivatives program for an insured US bank; first synthetic swap receivables securitization.
**Personal:** Columbia Law School (JD, 1984); Harvard University (AB, 1991).

### SIMON, Norman
Kramer Levin Naftalis & Frankel LLP, New York
212 715 7816
nsimon@kramerlevin.com
*Featured in Advertising (Nationwide)*
**Practice Areas:** Norman C Simon has litigation experience in several areas, including advertising; employment; electronic discovery; criminal and regulatory investigations; licensing and contract disputes; trademark and copyright infringement; and general commercial matters. As part of his diverse practice, Mr Simon has significant expertise in advertising law. He has litigated many false advertising disputes under the Lanham Act, and frequently represents clients in challenges before the National Advertising Division. He regularly counsels clients on prospective claims, and also has experience with consumer fraud and false advertising class actions.

### SIMPSON, Aaron P.
Hunton & Williams LLP, New York
212 309 1126
asimpson@hunton.com
*Featured in Privacy & Data Security (Nationwide)*
**Practice Areas:** Aaron Simpson is a partner with Hunton & Williams LLP, resident in the New York office. He is well-known as a top privacy professional and has been recognized by The Legal 500, New York Super Lawyers and Computerworld magazine. Aaron advises clients on a broad range of complex privacy and cybersecurity matters, including state, federal and international requirements, as well as the remediation of large-scale cybersecurity incidents. He is a sought-after media resource on privacy and cyber issues and has been quoted in publications such as Bloomberg, Businessweek Magazine and DataGuidance.

### SIMPSON, Linda A
Davis Polk & Wardwell LLP, New York
212 450 4000
linda.simpson@davispolk.com
*Featured in Capital Markets (Nationwide)*
**Practice Areas:** Member of Davis Polk's Corporate Department, practicing in the Derivatives and Structured Products Group. She advises clients on securities matters, specifically structuring, documentation and regulatory issues for over-the-counter and public market transactions involving derivatives. She has participated in the design of a number of innovative products involving securities and derivatives, and is currently advising financial institutions with respect to their issuance of structured notes linked to a variety of reference assets, including commodities, currencies, equities and rates.

### SINGER, Louis H
Morgan, Lewis & Bockius LLP, New York
212 309 6603
lsinger@morganlewis.com
*Featured in Investment Funds (Nationwide)*
**Practice Areas:** Chair of the firm's Global Private Investment Funds Practice. Represents domestic and international clients in regard to virtually every type of private investment fund, including buyout, venture capital, real estate, hedge, distressed assets, energy, infrastructure and credit funds. Very active in the formation of funds-of-funds, feeder funds and single-investor funds, in co-investments and in secondary transactions involving fund interests.
**Professional Memberships:** American College of Investment Counsel (President and Trustee); Association of Life Insurance Counsel (Board of Governors); NAPPA; Private Investment Funds Forum.
**Personal:** Stanford (JD, Law Review); Cambridge University (LLB, First Class); University of Pennsylvania (BA).

### SINGER, Roger
Clifford Chance US LLP, New York
212 878 3288
roger.singer@cliffordchance.com
*Featured in Investment Funds (Nationwide)*
**Practice Areas:** Head of the US Private Funds Group at Clifford Chance. Focuses on private equity fund formation (for sponsors and investors) and related investments. Fund types include real estate, funds of funds, buyout and debt, and clients range from institutional sponsors to first time funds. Extensive experience in international funds.
**Career:** Partner at Clifford Chance since 2006. Princeton University, AB, 1993. Columbia University School of Law, JD, 1996.

### SINGER, Steven
Bernstein Litowitz Berger & Grossmann LLP, New York
212 554 1413
steven@blbglaw.com
*Featured in Securities (Nationwide), Litigation (New York)*
See under New York for profile.

### SINGER, Steven D
WilmerHale, New York
212 295 6307
steven.singer@wilmerhale.com
*Featured in Life Sciences (Nationwide)*
**Practice Areas:** Chair of WilmerHale's Transactional Department; Co-Chair of Life Sciences Group; Chair of Technology Transactions and Licensing Group. Has served as counsel for public and private companies in the life sciences sector, including biotechnology, medical device and pharmaceutical companies. Practice focuses on joint ventures and strategic alliances, corporate and securities laws, public offerings and venture capital transactions.
**Professional Memberships:** American Bar Association; Massachusetts Biotechnology Council; Biotechnology Industry Organization.
**Career:** Admitted to Massachusetts Bar and New York Bar. Joined the firm in 1979.
**Personal:** Harvard Law School (JD, magna cum laude); Tufts University (BA, summa cum laude).

### SINGER, Toby G
Jones Day, Washington, DC
202 879-4654
tgsinger@jonesday.com
*Featured in Healthcare (Nationwide), Healthcare (District of Columbia)*
See under District of Columbia for profile.

### SINGERMAN, Paul Steven
Berger Singerman, Miami
305 714 4343
psingerman@bergersingerman.com
*Featured in Bankruptcy/Restructuring (Nationwide), Bankruptcy/Restructuring (Florida)*
See under Florida for profile.

### SINHA, Pankaj K
Skadden, Arps, Slate, Meagher & Flom LLP & Affiliates, Washington, DC
202 371 7307
Pankaj.Sinha@skadden.com
*Featured in Corporate/M&A (District of Columbia), Energy & Natural Resources (Nationwide)*
**Practice Areas:** Practice leader of the firm's Mergers and Acquisitions Group. Focuses on M&A, corporate finance, and general corporate and securities matters and has represented purchasers, sellers and their financial advisors in public and private acquisitions and divestitures, negotiated and contested public acquisitions, auctions, privatizations, proxy fights, initial public offerings and joint ventures. In addition, he advises clients on distressed M&A transactions, securities law compliance, disclosure issues, stock repurchase programs and corporate governance matters.
**Career:** JD, Georgetown University Law Center, 1990; MBA, Georgetown University, 1990; A.B., Columbia College, Columbia University, 1986.

### SINICK, Marshall S
Squire Sanders (US) LLP, Washington, DC
202 626 6651
marshall.sinick@squiresanders.com
*Featured in Transportation (Nationwide)*
**Practice Areas:** Leads Squire Sanders' Aviation Practice Group. Represents clients before the US Departments of Transportation, State and Justice;

Federal Aviation Administration; US Senate and House of Representatives; and various federal and state courts. Advises on commercial and corporate matters including antitrust investigations, marketing alliances, codeshare agreements, acquisitions, route sales and GDS issues. Defends airlines and aviation-related businesses in commercial litigation and administrative enforcement proceedings and counsels on global aviation issues involving the US and non-US governments. Frequent speaker at IATA Legal Symposia and ABA Aviation Law Forum.

### SKIDMORE, Jonathan B
Fulbright & Jaworski LLP, Dallas
214 855 8038
jskidmore@fulbright.com
*Featured in Products Liability (Nationwide)*
**Practice Areas:** Pharmaceutical and medical devices; mass torts; general civil litigation.
**Professional Memberships:** American Bar Association; State Bar of Texas.
**Career:** Skidmore serves on the firm's Executive Committee after leading the Dallas litigation group for 10 years. He focuses on pharmaceutical and medical device litigation, with an emphasis on mass torts. He handles class actions, commercial litigation, professional malpractice, and has represented Fortune 100 companies in venues across the state of Texas. Recognized as a 'Texas Super Lawyer', 2003-2012.
**Personal:** JD, with honors, The University of Texas School of Law (1983); BA, Accounting, The University of Texas at Austin (1980).

### SKINNER, William P
Covington & Burling LLP, Washington, DC
202 662 5470
wskinner@cov.com
*Featured in Insurance (Nationwide), Insurance (District of Columbia)*
**Practice Areas:** Areas include advising policyholders and negotiating, arbitrating, and litigating complex insurance coverage disputes. Extensive experience with the following types of insurance policies: directors and officers, employment practices liability, errors and omissions, fiduciary liability, general liability, products liability, and property and business interruption policies. Clients include Fortune 100 and 500 policyholders, including bank holding companies, financial services companies, mutual funds, manufacturers, pharmaceutical companies, retailers and utilities. Has also represented both offshore and domestic group captive insurance companies.
**Personal:** JD, Harvard Law School, 1975, magna cum laude; BA, Harvard College, 1972.

### SLADE, Georgiana J
Milbank, Tweed, Hadley & McCloy LLP, New York
212 530 5616
GSlade@milbank.com
*Featured in Wealth Management (Nationwide)*
**Practice Areas:** Ms Slade has extensive experience in estate and tax planning, charitable planning, estate and trust administration/litigation, art law, interfamily dispute resolution.

**Professional Memberships:** NYSBA (Vice Chair – Life Insurance and Employee Benefits Committee, Trusts and Estates Section); ACTEC (Fellow); Duke University Estate Planning Council.
**Career:** Partner, Leader Trusts and Estates Practice.
**Publications:** Tax Management Portfolio 210-4th, Personal Life Insurance Trusts, Portfolio 836, Partial Interests - GRATs, GRUTs, QPRTs (Section 2702); Practical Guide to Estate Planning, Generation-Skipping Transfer Tax Planning Chapter 9.
**Personal:** JD, Harvard; BA (Phi Beta Kappa, summa cum laude), Duke.

### SLATER, Valerie A
Akin Gump Strauss Hauer & Feld LLP, Washington, DC
202 887 4112
vslater@akingump.com
*Featured in International Trade (Nationwide)*
**Practice Areas:** Chair, International Trade Practice. Represents clients before the U.S. Department of Commerce, U.S. International Trade Commission and the Office of the U.S. Trade Representative. Has extensive experience with antidumping and countervailing duty cases, and other types of unfair trade litigation, including "safeguard" cases and various types of proceedings under the Generalized System of Preferences. Also advises clients on WTO and trade policy matters.
**Professional Memberships:** Member, Advisory Committee on Rules, US Court of International Trade.
**Career:** Legal Times' Top Ten Trade Lawyers, 2007.
**Personal:** BA, Allegheny College (magna cum laude, Phi Beta Kappa); JD, Catholic University of America.

### SLIGAR, James S
Milbank, Tweed, Hadley & McCloy LLP, New York
212 530 5839
JSligar@milbank.com
*Featured in Wealth Management (Nationwide)*
**Practice Areas:** Mr Sligar specializes in estate planning and trusts and estates law, and in representing charitable organizations.
**Professional Memberships:** Association of the Bar of the City of New York (serving on the Committee on Not-for-Profit Corporations), the New York State Bar Association, the American Bar Association.
**Career:** Partner, Trusts and Estates Practice.
**Personal:** JD from Harvard Law School (member of the Harvard International Law Journal); summa cum laude and Phi Beta Kappa graduate of Dartmouth College. Member of Union Theological Seminary, and Family Care International, Inc.

### SLONAKER, Norman
Sidley Austin LLP, New York
212 839 5356
nslonaker@sidley.com
*Featured in Capital Markets (Nationwide)*

**Practice Areas:** Senior Counsel in Sidley's New York office, practising in corporate securities. Previously, he had been a partner at the firm since 1973. He has extensive experience in a variety of transactions with particular emphasis on structured securities, investment grade debt securities, medium-term note programmes, Rule 144A offerings and convertible and exchangeable securities.
**Professional Memberships:** Former chair, Financial Reporting Committee of the NYC Bar; Former member, ABA Task Force on Sellers' Due Diligence and Similar Defenses under Federal Securities Laws.
**Personal:** Harvard Law School, LLB, 1965; University of Washington, BS, 1962. Admission: New York.

### SLOTKIN, David P
Morrison & Foerster LLP, Washington, DC
202 887 1554
dslotkin@mofo.com
*Featured in Capital Markets (Nationwide)*
**Practice Areas:** Represents publicly and privately held companies in mergers and acquisitions, equity, debt, and other public and private securities offerings. Advises on general securities, corporate governance and compliance issues. Represents investment banking firms in connection with domestic and international securities offerings. Recent experience includes advising companies in initial public offerings, compliance program implementation and corporate governance matters, and representing companies in various industries in securities offerings.
**Career:** Private practice for over 15 years; previously general counsel at a multinational, publicly-traded telecommunications company.
**Personal:** Benjamin Cardozo School of Law (JD, 1995); Wharton School of the University of Pennsylvania (BS, 1992).

### SLOVER, William
Slover & Loftus, Washington, DC
202 347 7170
wls@sloverandloftus.com
*Featured in Transportation (Nationwide)*
**Practice Areas:** Mr Slover is the nation's most experienced practitioner of surface transportation law. He has enjoyed a highly successful and distinguished career representing a broad range of clients in transportation and energy law engagements. He has won numerous cases before courts, regulatory agencies, and arbitral tribunals. He remains active in selected engagements.
**Personal:** Yale University, A.B., 1959, Columbia University, LLB, 1962.

### SMEDINGHOFF, Thomas J
Edwards Wildman Palmer, Chicago
312 201 2021
tsmedinghoff@edwardswildman.com
*Featured in Technology (Illinois), Privacy & Data Security (Nationwide)*
See under Illinois for profile.

### SMIT, Robert H
Simpson Thacher & Bartlett LLP, New York
212 455 7325
rsmit@stblaw.com
*Featured in International Arbitration (Nationwide)*

**Practice Areas:** Partner in the Firm's Litigation Department, where he Co-Chairs the International Arbitration and Dispute Resolution Practice. He specializes in international commercial and investment arbitration and international litigation.
**Career:** Adjunct Professor of International Arbitration, Columbia Law School; US Member, ICC International Court of Arbitration (2002-2009), Chair, ICC Task Force on Production of Electronic Documents in Arbitration. Chair, New York City Bar Association International Commercial Disputes Committee. Adviser, ALI Restatement (Third) on International Arbitration.
**Personal:** Universite de Paris I, Pantheon Sorbonne (DEA, 1987); Columbia Law School (JD 1986); Cornell University (BA 1981).

### SMITH, Andrew M
Morrison & Foerster LLP, Washington, DC
202 887 1558
asmith@mofo.com
*Featured in Privacy & Data Security (Nationwide)*
**Practice Areas:** Andrew Smith concentrates his practice on retail financial services, credit reporting, privacy, technology and e-commerce issues. He assists banks, insurers, non-bank lenders, credit bureaus, technology companies, and their vendors with regulatory compliance, litigation and transactional matters. Mr Smith often represents clients before federal and state agencies—particularly the FTC and CFPB—in law enforcement and rulemaking proceedings.
**Career:** Prior to joining Morrison & Foerster, Mr Smith served in senior policy-making and supervisory positions at the Federal Trade Commission and the Securities and Exchange Commission.

### SMITH, Bradley Y
Davis Polk & Wardwell LLP, New York
212 450 4000
bradley.smith@davispolk.com
*Featured in Banking & Finance (Nationwide)*
**Practice Areas:** Partner in Davis Polk 's Credit Group. A recognised leader of the finance bar for a generation. Practice in recent years has focused on acquisition finance and a broad range of secured credit transactions, from traditional leveraged acquisition structures to complex debt restructurings. During 2012 he represented JPMorgan, Bank of America Merrill Lynch, Citigroup and other lead arrangers with respect to more than $25 billion of financing for a broad range of borrowers.

### SMITH, Colin P
Holland & Knight LLP, Chicago
312 263 3600
colin.smith@hklaw.com
*Featured in Products Liability (Nationwide)*
**Practice Areas:** Mr Smith is a Partner in the firm's Litigation Section and is the leader of its Product Liability Team. He practices in the areas of product liability, toxic tort and commercial litigation. Smith has represented clients in Illinois and throughout the United States as both trial counsel and national or regional coordinating counsel in both individual matters and complex, consolidated, and class action litigation. He has

also extensively counseled clients in loss prevention and litigation management matters across a broad spectrum of issues.

### SMITH, Douglas
Van Ness Feldman LLP, Washington, DC
202 298 1902
dws@vnf.com
*Featured in Energy & Natural Resources (Nationwide)*
**Practice Areas:** Advises regulated companies on FERC policy and regulatory matters; represents utilities on FERC audits and investigations; provides strategic advice on clean air and clean energy matters; counsels clients on advanced energy technology issues including carbon capture and sequestration; represents equipment manufacturers on product efficiency regulation; advises clients pursuing innovative energy and environmental policies; advises clients seeking federal support for infrastructure investment.
**Career:** General Counsel, FERC; Deputy General Counsel for Energy Policy, DOE; Assistant General Counsel for Legal Policy and Analysis, DOE.
**Personal:** JD, Yale Law School; S.B., Massachusetts Institute of Technology.

### SMITH, Duncan C
Blank Rome LLP, Washington, DC
202 772 5956
Smith-D@BlankRome.com
*Featured in Transportation (Nationwide)*
**Practice Areas:** Duncan Smith engages primarily in a legislative and administrative practice, representing clients in connection with a variety of issues, including transportation, infrastructure, and public facilities; maritime, including yachts and recreational vessels; environment; defense and homeland security; federal appropriations and budgetary matters; economic and natural resources development; government contracting; public finance; nonprofits; and election, lobbying, and ethics compliance. He was a staff counsel to the House Merchant Marine and Fisheries Committee and a congressional advisor on a US delegation to the International Maritime Organization regarding oil pollution matters. He is also a retired Coast Guard Reserve Rear Admiral. www.BlankRomegr.com/Smith-D

### SMITH, Edwin E
Bingham McCutchen LLP, Boston
617 951 8615
edwin.smith@bingham.com
*Featured in Bankruptcy/Restructuring (Massachusetts), Banking & Finance (Nationwide), Banking & Finance (Massachusetts)*
See under Massachusetts for profile.

### SMITH, Jason
Weil, Gotshal & Manges LLP, New York
212 310 8914
jason.smith@weil.com
*Featured in Capital Markets (Nationwide)*
**Practice Areas:** Partner in the Structured Finance/Derivatives Practice. Extensive experience structuring rental car fleet financings, equipment and vehicle lease and loan financings, collateralized bond and loan obligations (including dis-

tressed debt), as well as a range of synthetic/derivative products including credit default and total return swaps and credit-linked notes. Has participated in the securitization of commercial loans, student loans, equipment loans, credit card receivables, trade receivables, as well as royalty receivables and intellectual property in the term and commercial paper markets as well as numerous restructurings involving the foregoing.
**Personal:** Columbia College (BA, 1993); New York University (JD, 1996).

### SMITH, Jeffrey
Arnold & Porter LLP, Washington, DC
202 942 5115
Jeffrey.Smith@aporter.com
*Featured in Government (Nationwide)*
**Practice Areas:** Jeffrey Smith heads Arnold & Porter LLP's national and homeland security practice, which regularly counsels both US and foreign companies on a wide range of national security issues. His practice includes advising major defense and aerospace companies and representing major media organizations and individuals with respect to First Amendment issues and unauthorized disclosures of classified information. He has frequently represented prominent individuals in congressional investigations and federal prosecutions. Mr Smith is a former General Counsel of the Central Intelligence Agency (CIA) and also served as the General Counsel of the Senate Armed Services Committee.

### SMITH, Jeffrey
Crowell & Moring LLP, New York
212 895 4260
JASmith@crowell.com
*Featured in Climate Change (Nationwide), Environment (New York)*
See under New York for profile.

### SMITH, Jeffrey Q
Bingham McCutchen LLP, New York
212 705 7566
jq.smith@bingham.com
*Featured in Securities (Nationwide), Litigation (New York)*
**Practice Areas:** Co-chair of Bingham's Securities and Financial Institutions Litigation Group. Over three decades of experience handling complex financial cases in federal and state courts throughout the US. Proficient in various forms of alternative dispute resolution. Maintains active counseling practice designed to help clients avoid and/or minimize litigation risks. Represents financial services companies, including banks, broker-dealers, hedge funds, insurance companies, investment advisers and other market participants, in litigation and regulatory matters involving CDOs, asset- and mortgage-backed securities, swaps, and other complex financial products.
**Personal:** New York University School of Law, JD, cum laude, 1977; Yale University, BA, cum laude, 1974.

### SMITH, Jennifer M
Baker Botts LLP, Houston
713 229 2065
jennifer.smith@bakerbotts.com
*Featured in International Arbitration (Nationwide)*

**Practice Areas:** Represents claimants and respondents in significant international disputes, both ad hoc and administered arbitrations. She recently obtained an arbitral award in favor of a vertically integrated Asian power company against a leading ship operator in a Singapore arbitration. She frequently acts for companies in disputes arising out of joint venture agreements.
**Professional Memberships:** Qualified Solicitor, England and Wales; Texas Bar; LCIA; IBA; ABA; Advisory Board Institute for Energy Law; Advisory Board Institute for Transnational Arbitration.
**Career:** Deputy Head- Litigation Department.
**Personal:** JD (with honors), University of Texas School of Law, 1990; BA (magna cum laude), Wellesley College, 1987.

### SMITH, Joel H
Bowman and Brooke LLP, Columbia
803.726.7422
joel.smith@bowmanandbrooke.com
*Featured in Litigation (South Carolina), Products Liability (Nationwide)*
See under South Carolina for profile.

### SMITH, Joseph A
Schulte Roth & Zabel LLP, New York
212 756 2250
joseph.smith@srz.com
*Featured in Investment Funds (Nationwide)*
**Practice Areas:** Focuses on representing private equity fund sponsors and institutional investors in connection with fund formation, acquisition of portfolio investments and implementation of exit strategies; advises on securities, governance, ERISA, Investment Advisers Act, structural issues. Extensive experience with all alternative asset classes, (venture capital and later-stage growth equity investments, leveraged buyouts, mezzanine investments, real estate ventures and opportunity funds, secondary investments, funds-of-funds and hedge funds).
**Career:** SRZ Partner (current); Global Chair of Private Equity, Dewey LeBoeuf; Chair of Private Equity and Real Estate Groups, Dewey Ballantine.
**Personal:** New York University School of Law, JD; Columbia University, AB.

### SMITH, Leslie M
Kirkland & Ellis LLP, Chicago
312 862 2141
leslie.smith@kirkland.com
*Featured in Products Liability (Nationwide)*
**Practice Areas:** Leslie concentrates her practice on products liability, mass torts, class actions, and antitrust litigation. In July 2001, Leslie was selected as one of "40 Illinois Attorneys Under 40" to Watch by The Law Bulletin Publishing Company. In April 2004, Leslie was listed as one of 21 rising women litigators in "A Woman's Place is in the Courtroom," which appeared in Diversity & the Bar magazine.
**Professional Memberships:** Chair, Legal Aid Society of the Legal Aid Bureau of Metropolitan Family Services.
**Personal:** Georgetown University, BA, 1984. Georgetown University Law Center, JD, magna cum laude, Order of the Coif, 1987.

### SMITH, Michael W
White & Case LLP, New York
212 819 8968
msmith@whitecase.com
*Featured in Transportation (Nationwide), Banking & Finance (Nationwide)*
**Career:** To view a comprehensive biography, please visit www.whitecase.com/mismith.

### SMITH, Paul M
Jenner & Block LLP, Washington, DC
202 639 6060
psmith@jenner.com
*Featured in First Amendment Litigation (Nationwide), Appellate Law (Nationwide), Media & Entertainment (District of Columbia)*
**Career:** Paul M. Smith is Chair of the Appellate and Supreme Court Practice; Co-Chair of the Media and First Amendment, and Election Law and Redistricting Practices; and member of the Content, Media & Entertainment Practice. Mr Smith has had an active Supreme Court practice for nearly three decades, including oral arguments in fourteen Supreme Court cases, including Schwarzenegger v. Entertainment Merchants Association (First Amendment); LULAC v. Perry, and Vieth v. Jubelirer (redistricting); Lawrence v. Texas (landmark gay rights case); U.S. v. American Library Association (First Amendment challenge to the Children's Internet Protection Act) and Mathias v. WorldCom (Eleventh Amendment).

### SMITH, Robert A
Wiley Rein LLP, Washington, DC
202 719 4481
rsmith@wileyrein.com
*Featured in Franchising (Nationwide)*
**Practice Areas:** Chairs the firm's Franchise Practice. Represents franchisors, licensors and investors domestically and internationally in connection with all legal issues arising in franchised and licensed networks. Included in "The International Who's Who of Business Lawyers" in the Franchise category (2005-2013) and Best Lawyers in America (2013).
**Professional Memberships:** ABA, Forum on Franchising; International Franchise Association: Advisory Board, Supplier Forum (1999-2005); Planning Task Force, Annual Legal Symposium (2004-2005, 2010-2012).
**Career:** Corporate Counsel, Marriott International (1984-1987).
**Personal:** Columbus School of Law, The Catholic University of America (JD, graduated first in class); The Catholic University of America (BS, summa cum laude).

### SMITH, Russell L
Willkie Farr & Gallagher LLP, New York
202 303 1116
rsmith@willkie.com
*Featured in Government (Nationwide)*
**Practice Areas:** Specializes in variety of federal relations areas, including legislative matters, congressional investigations, and Executive Branch and independent agency proceedings involving foreign direct investment in United States (including Exon-Florio and CFIUS), international trade laws and policy, trade embargoes, anti-money

laundering, consumer products, financial services, foreign boycotts, nuclear power, defense contracting, federal and state campaign finance law, and federal lobbying and gift rules. Clients include major manufacturing/services corporations, multinational businesses, financial services, pharmaceutical, insurance, and automobile manufacturing companies, trade associations, and prominent individuals.

**Personal:** JD, with honors, University of Georgia School of Law, 1972. BA, Vanderbilt University, 1968. See: http://www.willkie.com/RussellSmith

## SMITH, Tyson
Winston & Strawn LLP, San Francisco
415 591 6874
trsmith@winston.com
*Featured in Energy & Natural Resources (Nationwide)*

**Practice Areas:** With a blend of technical and legal experience, Tyson represents clients regarding nuclear safety regulations and environmental statutes. He has been extensively involved in the licensing, construction, and regulation of new nuclear facilities in the US, including power reactors, uranium enrichment facilities, and uranium mines. Tyson counsels on license extensions for existing nuclear units and works closely with state and federal agencies to resolve safety and environmental issues at those facilities. He also assists clients in enforcement matters involving nuclear facilities and materials. His clients range from small public utilities to the largest nuclear companies in the world.

## SMITH JR, Richard K
White & Case LLP, Los Angeles
213 620 7788
rsmith@whitecase.com
*Featured in Transportation (Nationwide), Banking & Finance (Nationwide)*

**Career:** To view a comprehensive biography, please visit www.whitecase.com/rsmith.

## SMUTNY, Abby Cohen
White & Case LLP, Washington, DC
202 626 3608
asmutny@whitecase.com
*Featured in International Arbitration (Nationwide)*

**Career:** Abby Cohen Smutny is recognized as a leading expert in international arbitration. She represents clients in international commercial arbitration, in investment treaty arbitration, and in international disputes before US courts. She has represented clients in disputes involving numerous industries, including banking, financial services, oil & gas, mining, electric power, real estate development, water supply, retail, pharmaceuticals, construction, tobacco, railroads, telecommunications, and manufacturing. She represents clients in arbitrations before all major arbitral forums and handles disputes arising under bilateral investment treaties (BITs), the Energy Charter Treaty, the NAFTA, the DR-CAFTA, and the ASEAN treaty. To view her biography, visit www.whitecase.com/asmutny.

## SNIPES, James C
Covington & Burling LLP, San Francisco
415.591.7071
jsnipes@cov.com
*Featured in Life Sciences (Nationwide), Life Sciences (California)*
See under California for profile.

## SNYDER, Jeffrey L
Crowell & Moring LLP, Washington, DC
202 624 2790
jsnyder@crowell.com
*Featured in International Trade (Nationwide)*

**Practice Areas:** Partner and chair of Crowell & Moring's International Trade Group. Practice concentrates on the US regulation of international trade. His experience includes export controls and other outbound regulations, including the EAR, the ITAR, and the FCPA. He has worked extensively developing approaches for multinationals to manage the impact of US extraterritorial regulations, such as the sanctions administered by the Office of Foreign Assets Control, and the scope of ISA and Helms-Burton. Also advises on Customs law, antidumping law, and other import laws.

## SOBEL, Gerald
Kaye Scholer LLP, New York
212 836 8515
gerald.sobel@kayescholer.com
*Featured in Life Sciences (Nationwide), Intellectual Property (New York)*

**Practice Areas:** Gerald Sobel, Special Counsel, has litigated many complex cases in over 40 years of practice. His trials include landmark wins in cases of exceptional complexity and novel legal issues; for example, representing Xerox on antitrust-patent issues in the longest federal civil jury trial, Xoma in the longest biotech patent trial (also to a jury), and Pfizer in the Celebrex patent infringement case on summary judgment and then on appeal at the Federal Circuit. He has represented a substantial number of companies in varied industries among the Fortune Global 200, as well as start-ups, one-product companies and major universities.

## SOBIN, Sturgis M
Covington & Burling LLP, Washington, DC
202 662 5040
ssobin@cov.com
*Featured in International Trade (Nationwide)*

**Practice Areas:** Mr Sobin has represented clients in more than 45 ITC Section 337 investigations and related district court litigation, and served as lead trial counsel in complex trials covering a range of technologies and commercially valuable IP rights. He has assisted clients with 337 enforcement issues before U.S. Customs and the U.S. Court of International Trade, served as global coordinating counsel for IP disputes spanning multiple countries, and represented clients in all major areas of international trade regulation, including Section 337, antidumping, Section 301, and WTO proceedings.

**Personal:** American University, Washington College of Law (JD 1983).

## SOLDO, Linda J
Cleary Gottlieb Steen & Hamilton LLP, Washington, DC
202 974 1640
lsoldo@cgsh.com
*Featured in Financial Services Regulation (Nationwide)*

**Practice Areas:** Financial institution regulatory matters, including supervisory and enforcement matters involving banks and bank holding companies and their officers and directors. Financial transactions, including structured finance products. Advises on regulatory matters involving federal banking agencies.

**Professional Memberships:** Member of the DC and Maryland Bars. Admitted, U.S. Supreme Court; U.S. Court of Appeals for the District of Columbia Circuit; and U.S. District Court for the District of Columbia.

**Career:** Joined firm, 1981; became partner, 1990. JD, highest academic average, Columbus School of Law, Catholic University of America (1981); AB, Manhattanville College (1972).

## SOLER, Jonathon G
Weil, Gotshal & Manges LLP, New York
212 310 8278
jonathon.soler@weil.com
*Featured in Investment Funds (Nationwide)*

**Practice Areas:** Mr Soler regularly represents sponsors of private investment funds in connection with the organization and operation of such funds. He also advises private fund managers in connection with their formation and operation and counsels investment firms on the sale of majority and minority interests in their businesses. Additionally, he represents sponsors and investors in connection with "non-fund" investment arrangements and represents institutional investors in connection with their investments in private funds. Clients include American Securities, CCMP Capital, Genstar Capital and Lindsay Goldberg.

**Personal:** Queens University School of Business (BComm, Honours, 1995); Columbia University School of Law (JD, 1998).

## SOLOMON, Adam
Olshan Frome Wolosky LLP., New York
212 451 2306
asolomon@olshanlaw.com
*Featured in Advertising (Nationwide)*

**Practice Areas:** Partner in Advertising, Marketing & Promotions Group. Represents numerous advertising agencies, promotions agencies, Internet marketers, direct marketers, start-ups in connection with all aspects of advertising, promotions, marketing, and compliance. Has considerable experience in a broad range of advertising, direct marketing, and promotions matters, including sweepstakes, complex skill contests, telemarketing, Internet marketing, and direct mail including representing marketers in connection with federal/state regulatory inquiries.

**Professional Memberships:** Promotion Marketing Association, Direct Marketing Association, New York Direct Marketing Association.

**Publications:** "Legal Considerations For Promotions Involving User Generated Content," ABA, The Practical Lawyer, June 2008.

## SOLOMON, Ronni
King & Spalding LLP, Atlanta
404 572 3547
rsolomon@kslaw.com
*Featured in Litigation (Nationwide)*

**Practice Areas:** Head of the firm's E-Discovery Practice. Focuses practice on the management of major discovery matters. Serves as National E-Discovery Counsel for large corporations providing guidance on e-discovery issues, including both litigation preparedness and discovery strategy in active litigation.

**Career:** Prior to joining King & Spalding, Ms Solomon was a corporate discovery specialist for one of the largest e-discovery companies in the industry where she advised and consulted with in-house counsel of large corporations on electronic discovery strategies.

**Personal:** JD, Yeshiva University BA, SUNY at Binghamton.

## SONG, Wayne W
Morgan, Lewis & Bockius LLP, Los Angeles
213 612 7385
wsong@morganlewis.com
*Featured in Projects (Nationwide)*

**Practice Areas:** Mr Song's practice focuses on project finance, corporate finance, project development, and mergers and acquisitions in the energy and infrastructure sectors. He has worked on numerous renewable energy project developments, acquisitions, and financings. Mr Song has a background in a wide range of energy and infrastructure project developments and has represented energy industry participants in the negotiation of commercial project contracts such as construction contracts, power purchase agreements, equipment supply contracts, and operations and maintenance agreements.

**Personal:** JD, University of Southern California School of Law; BS, United States Military Academy.

## SOPHER, Edward D
Gibson, Dunn & Crutcher LLP, New York
212 351 4000
esopher@gibsondunn.com
*Featured in Investment Funds (Nationwide)*

**Practice Areas:** Private investment funds, including private equity, hedge, real estate and distressed investment funds, and funds of funds in their organization, operation and investment activities. Represents investment managers and sponsors of these funds, institutional and seed investors, placement agents and joint venture partners. Also active in secondary transactions involving fund interests and M&A, financing and other transactions involving investment management firms. Regulatory counseling, including Investment Advisers Act and Dodd-Frank (including Volcker Rule).

**Professional Memberships:** New York Bar; Solicitor, England & Wales; Association of the Bar of New York City.

**Personal:** BA, Cambridge University, 1982; MA, Cambridge University, 1985.

---

**SORINI, Marc**
McDermott Will & Emery LLP, Washington, DC
202 756 8284
msorini@mwe.com
*Featured in Food & Beverages (Nationwide)*
**Practice Areas:** Heads the firm's alcohol beverages and products group. Regulatory practice covers licensing, labeling, advertising, trade practices, import-export, product formulation and excise taxation. Distribution practice includes supplier-wholesaler and importer-supplier disputes, distribution structuring and strategies, distribution agreements and the distribution aspects of mergers and acquisitions. Represents alcohol beverage suppliers before federal and state courts, the Alcohol & Tobacco Tax & Trade Bureau, the Federal Trade Commission and state alcohol beverage control agencies.
**Personal:** Georgetown University Law Center (JD); Lehigh University (BA).

---

**SOSLAND, Martin**
Weil, Gotshal & Manges LLP, Dallas
214 746 7730
martin.sosland@weil.com
*Featured in Bankruptcy/Restructuring (Texas),*
*Bankruptcy/Restructuring (Nationwide)*
See under Texas for profile.

---

**SOTTO, Lisa J**
Hunton & Williams LLP, New York
212 309.1223
lsotto@hunton.com
*Featured in Privacy & Data Security (Nationwide)*
**Practice Areas:** Lisa Sotto, head of the firm's Privacy and Information Security Practice and Managing Partner of the New York office, is consistently ranked the top lawyer in her field. She was rated 'No. 1 privacy expert' in Computerworld magazine's three most recent surveys and was named one of Ethisphere Magazine's 100 '2012 Attorneys Who Matter.' She assists clients in identifying, evaluating and managing privacy and cybersecurity risks. She is a regular speaker and author on privacy issues and is the Chair of the Department of Homeland Security's Data Privacy and Integrity Advisory Committee. Ms Sotto is the author of Aspen Publishers' Privacy and Data Security Law Deskbook.

---

**SOUSSLOFF, Andrew D**
Sullivan & Cromwell LLP, New York
212 558 3681
soussloffa@sullcrom.com
*Featured in Capital Markets (Nationwide)*
**Practice Areas:** Domestic/international capital markets, M&A and corporate experience representing clients from US, Latin America, Canada and Europe in hundreds of transactions. Represents corporations, financial institutions, private equity firms and sovereign governments in capital-raising and M&A activities in US and international markets. Advisor to listed companies on disclosure, corporate governance, securities law and other regulatory and compliance issues.

**Professional Memberships:** IBA (Legal Practice Division Council, 2004-2006; Chair, Capital Markets Forum, 2005-2006; Chair, Securities Law Committee, 2000-2003).
**Career:** Partner since 1986. Former Managing Partner, General Practice Group.
**Personal:** University of Pennsylvania (JD cum laude, 1979; BA magna cum laude, MA, 1975).

---

**SPAK, Gregory J**
White & Case LLP, Washington, DC
202 626 3641
gspak@whitecase.com
*Featured in International Trade (Nationwide)*
**Career:** Gregory Spak practices primarily in the area of international trade regulation, advising governments, exporters, and importers on a variety of trade-related proceedings. He has extensive experience with administrative, judicial and arbitral proceedings related to the implementation of trade remedy laws in the United States and in other jurisdictions. He also counsels private companies on compliance with the laws and regulations related to customs, export control, and economic sanctions. Mr Spak is an active advisor on disputes before the World Trade Organization ("WTO"), in which he has been lead counsel in multiple phases of proceedings. To view his biography, visit www.whitecase.com/gspak.

---

**SPAK, Walter J**
White & Case LLP, Washington, DC
202 626 3606
wspak@whitecase.com
*Featured in International Trade (Nationwide)*
**Career:** Mr Spak is the head of the International Trade Group at White & Case. During his nearly 30 years of international practice in the trade area, Mr Spak has handled legal issues in virtually every aspect of the import trade laws. His practice emphasizes the United States and third country trade proceedings, customs issues, bilateral and multilateral trade negotiations, dispute resolution under NAFTA and the WTO and sector specific trade policy issues. To view a comprehensive biography, please visit www.whitecase.com/wspak.

---

**SPEIER, Anthony**
Baker Botts LLP, Houston
713 229 1819
anthony.speier@bakerbotts.com
*Featured in Energy & Natural Resources (Nationwide)*
**Practice Areas:** Speier's practice focuses on mergers, acquisitions and divestitures, including the sale of oil and gas properties, midstream assets, crude oil refineries, and business units and subsidiaries of energy companies. He also has advised clients on a broad range of sophisticated transactional matters including project development, joint ventures, farmout and participation agreements to develop oil and gas properties, oil and gas transportation and gathering agreements, natural gas processing and fractionation agreements, and other commercial transactions concerning the development of oil and gas properties.
**Personal:** JD (summa cum laude), Tulane University, 2005; BA (cum laude), sociology, Tulane University, 1997.

---

**SPELLISCY, M J**
Holland & Knight LLP, New York
212 513 3237
mj.spelliscy@hklaw.com
*Featured in Transportation (Nationwide)*
**Career:** M.J. Spelliscy's practice focuses on domestic and cross-border asset-based financing, leasing, sales and acquisitions. Asset types include rail cars, vessels, real estate, manufacturing facilities and satellites, with particular emphasis on commercial aircraft, corporate jets and fractional shares. She has represented participants in all roles in a wide variety of transactions, including loans, sale and leasebacks, operating and finance leases, pre-delivery payment financing, receivables financing, portfolio acquisitions, leveraged and synthetic leases, warehousing facilities and manufacturer financing. She also has experience in restructurings, workouts and bankruptcies.

---

**SPIEGEL, John**
Munger, Tolles & Olson LLP, Los Angeles
213 683 9152
John.Spiegel@mto.com
*Featured in Securities (Nationwide), Litigation (California)*
See under California for profile.

---

**SPIES, Charles**
Clark Hill PLC, Washington, DC
202 572 8663
cspies@clarkhill.com
*Featured in Government (Nationwide)*
**Practice Areas:** Political Law Government & Public Affairs Tax Exempt Organizations Advocacy White Collar Criminal Defense.
**Professional Memberships:** Next Generation Society of the United States Holocaust Memorial Museum, Board Member Resurgent Republic, Legal Advisory Board.
**Career:** Charles R. Spies is the leader of Clark Hill's national Political Law practice, as well as the Member in Charge of the Washington D.C. office. Charlie has over a decade of experience providing strategic counsel at the highest levels in Washington D.C. and nationwide. He counsels a broad range of corporations, organizations, candidates and individuals confronting challenges and opportunities at the intersection of political and issue campaigns, government ethics, law and public policy. Mr Spies serves as counsel to multiple super PACs, trade associations, and organizations, including co-founding and serving as counsel to Restore Our Future, the largest super PAC in history. As Chief Financial Officer and Counsel for Governor Mitt Romney's 2008 Presidential campaign, Mr Spies developed and managed the national campaign's budget and systems for legal compliance with Federal Election Commission, IRS and various state regulations, as well as record-keeping and accounting. During the 2005 and 2006 election cycles, Mr Spies served as General Counsel and Chief Financial Officer for the Republican Governors Association. At the RGA, he developed the legal and budgeting strategy for the association's participation in governors' races in thirty-eight states. During the 2004 Presidential election cycle, Mr Spies served as

Election Law Counsel for the Republican National Committee, where he focused on federal and state election law compliance for the national party, as well as policy and litigation issues involved in campaign finance reform and "527 organizations." His tenure at the RNC began with the Bush-Cheney administration in 2001, and continued under four Chairmen. Mr Spies previously served as legal and policy advisor to FEC Chairman Darryl R. Wold, where he counseled the Chairman on a wide range of issues regarding the administration of the Federal Election Campaign Act.
**Personal:** JD, Georgetown University Law Center, 1998 BA, University of Michigan, 1995.

---

**SPIVAK, Mark**
Vinson & Elkins LLP, Washington, DC
202 639 6664
mspivak@velaw.com
*Featured in Projects (Nationwide)*
**Practice Areas:** Practice focuses primarily in the project development and finance, infrastructure, restructuring, and mergers and acquisitions areas. Represents developers, financial institutions, infrastructure funds, private equity firms, and institutional investors in developing, financing, restructuring, acquiring, and selling infrastructure projects, including power generation projects (including thermal and renewable projects), electric transmission projects and LNG projects, in the U.S. and abroad.
**Professional Memberships:** DC Bar Association.
**Career:** Admitted to District of Columbia Bar in 1984. Joined V&E in 1994 as a Partner.
**Personal:** Muhlenberg College, BA magna cum laude (1980), Georgetown University, JD (1983).

---

**SPRADLING, Mark**
Vinson & Elkins LLP, Houston
713 758 2828
mspradling@velaw.com
*Featured in Projects (Nationwide)*
**Practice Areas:** Partner in the firm's Corporate Section specializing in energy transactions and projects. Extensive experience in project development and finance, joint venture developments and structured finance.
**Career:** Admitted to Texas Bar, 1980. Clerked for Judge Robert A. Ainsworth, U.S. Court of Appeals for the Fifth Circuit, 1980-81. Joined V&E in 1981, admitted to the partnership, January 1988.
**Publications:** Frequent speaker and writer on project development, finance, and bankruptcy remote structures.
**Personal:** Dartmouth College, AB, 1977 (Phi Beta Kappa; summa cum laude; with highest distinction in major); Stanford University, JD, 1980 (Order of the Coif; Associate Editor, Stanford Law Review).

---

**SPRAYREGEN, James HM**
Kirkland & Ellis LLP, Chicago
312 862 2481
james.sprayregen@kirkland.com
*Featured in Bankruptcy/Restructuring (Nationwide),*
*Bankruptcy/Restructuring (Illinois),*
*Bankruptcy/Restructuring (New York)*

**Practice Areas:** Extensive experience representing major US and international debtors, creditors, committees, buyers/sellers of assets and boards of directors both in and out of court in complex restructuring and distressed situations. Representative clients include General Growth, Hawker Beechcraft, Japan Airlines, United Airlines, Visteon, Lear, The Great Atlantic & Pacific Tea Company, Edison Mission Energy and Reader's Digest.
**Professional Memberships:** VP and Member of the Executive Committee of the Board of Directors of INSOL International.
**Career:** Kirkland & Ellis 1990-2006; Goldman Sachs 2006-2008; Kirkland & Ellis 2008-Present.
**Personal:** University of Illinois College of Law, JD, 1985; University of Michigan, BA, 1982.

### SPULAK, Thomas
King & Spalding LLP, Washington, DC
202 661 7948
tspulak@kslaw.com
*Featured in Government (Nationwide)*
**Practice Areas:** Drawing upon his extensive knowledge of Congress and its internal processes, Spulak assists clients in the development and execution of legislative and executive branch strategies for a wide array of issues that include tax, health, energy, aerospace and appropriations.
**Career:** Prior to entering private practice, he served as Democratic staff director and general counsel of the House Committee on Rules, and as general counsel to the U.S. House of Representatives.
**Personal:** University of Miami (BA, 1977); Florida State University (JD, 1982).

### STADLER, Brian M
Simpson Thacher & Bartlett LLP, New York
212 455 3765
bstadler@stblaw.com
*Featured in Private Equity (Nationwide)*
**Practice Areas:** Represents corporations, private equity firms and financial advisors in merger and acquisition transactions. Has advised Blackstone in numerous transactions, including acquisitions of Hilton Hotels, Equity Office Properties, Apple REIT Six and Centro Properties' US business, sale of Extended Stay Hotels and investments in Capital Trust, Patria and General Growth Properties; Hellman & Friedman in acquisitions of Internet Brands and Getty Images; and the Special Committee of IAC in a transaction with Liberty Media.
**Career:** Joined firm 1990; became Partner 1998.
**Personal:** Columbia Law School (JD 1990); Wharton School of the University of Pennsylvania (BS, summa cum laude, 1987).

### STAMER, Michael S
Akin Gump Strauss Hauer & Feld LLP, New York
212 872 1025
mstamer@akingump.com
*Featured in Bankruptcy/Restructuring (Nationwide), Bankruptcy/Restructuring (New York)*
See under New York for profile.

### STARK, Sanford W
Bingham McCutchen LLP, Washington, DC
202 373 6678
sanford.stark@bingham.com
*Featured in Tax (Nationwide)*
**Practice Areas:** Focuses on federal tax controversy and litigation matters. Represents clients in a variety of industries and in all aspects of the controversy process, including pre-audit, audit, appeals, competent authority, and the federal trial and appellate courts. Has experience in a broad range of areas, including transfer pricing, cross-border structures, debt/equity, economic substance and business purpose, tax accounting, and procedural considerations.
**Career:** Former trial attorney, Tax Division, U.S. Department of Justice.
**Personal:** Duke University School of Law, JD, with high honors, 1991; Yale University, BA, cum laude, 1988.

### STEIN, Craig
Schulte Roth & Zabel LLP, New York
212 756 2390
craig.stein@srz.com
*Featured in Capital Markets (Nationwide)*
**Practice Areas:** Co-Head, Structured Products & Derivatives Group. Practice focuses on CLOs and other structured products, derivatives, including fund linked products, loan total return swaps and credit derivatives, and other trading agreements, including prime brokerage arrangements, repurchase agreements and custody arrangements.
**Professional Memberships:** American Bar Association, New York State Bar Association, MFA, ASF, LSTA, SIFMA, ISDA Credit Derivatives Market Practice Committee.
**Career:** SRZ partner since 2001, associate, 1995-2001; Rogers & Wells associate, 1992-95.
**Personal:** University of Pennsylvania Law School, JD, cum laude; Colgate University, BA, cum laude.

### STEINHARDT, Brian
Simpson Thacher & Bartlett LLP, New York
212 455 3802
bsteinhardt@stblaw.com
*Featured in Banking & Finance (Nationwide)*
**Practice Areas:** Partner in the Firm's Corporate Department, where he regularly represents private equity sponsors and their portfolio companies and other companies in connection with a broad range of corporate finance transactions, including bank and bridge loan financings and acquisition financings, and energy-related finance transactions, including project and oil and gas bank financings. His principal clients include Hellman & Friedman, KKR, TPG Capital, Apax Partners, Eaton Corporation, SiriusXM Radio and Weight Watchers International.
**Career:** Joined firm, 1999; Partner, 2008.
**Personal:** University of Michigan Law School (JD, cum laude, 1998); McGill University (BA, with great distinction, 1994).

### STENGEL, James L
Orrick, Herrington & Sutcliffe LLP, New York
212 506 3775
jstengel@orrick.com
*Featured in Products Liability (Nationwide)*
**Career:** Jim Stengel represents clients in large, complex, and multi-party class action litigation. He has handled significant actions involving the chemical, tobacco, and medical device industries. Mr Stengel serves as national counsel for Union Carbide in asbestos litigation, has represented The Dow Chemical Company in litigation relating to silicone breast implants, and has served as the company's lead litigation counsel in the Dow Corning Corporation reorganization. Mr Stengel has written and lectured on complex litigation, and mass tort subjects at a variety of law schools and seminars.

### STENGEL, Scott
King & Spalding LLP, Washington, DC
202 626 2936
sstengel@kslaw.com
*Featured in Financial Services Regulation (Nationwide)*
**Practice Areas:** Specializes in banking law. Provided regulatory counsel to global and domestic financial institutions in connection with strategic investments, acquisitions and divestitures, debt issuances, internal restructurings, affiliate transactions, commercial lending programs, government investigations, consumer-protection laws, and regulatory capital requirements.
**Career:** Played an active role in the securitization industry and in the development of a covered-bond market in the United States, including as outside counsel to the American Securitization Forum and as a member of the Steering Committee for SIFMA's U.S. Covered Bond Council.
**Personal:** JD, magna cum laude, University of Notre Dame BA, summa cum laude, University of Notre Dame.

### STEPHENS, Robert
Cadwalader, Wickersham & Taft LLP, Houston
713 343 7575
Robert.Stephens@cwt.com
*Featured in Energy & Natural Resources (Nationwide)*
**Practice Areas:** Focuses on representing energy companies, financial institutions, project sponsors, and private investors in energy transactions and financings. Has handled multi-billion dollar secured financings involving public and private secured debt, bankruptcy remote structured transactions, project developments and financings, and merger and acquisition transactions in the energy sector.
**Personal:** JD, with honors, The University of Texas School of Law; MBA, Finance, University of Wisconsin School of Business; BBA, Marketing and Management Information Systems, University of Wisconsin School of Business (Beta Gamma Sigma).

### STERN, Akiba
Loeb & Loeb LLP, New York
212 407 4235
astern@loeb.com
*Featured in Outsourcing (Nationwide), Technology (New York)*
**Practice Areas:** Concentrates his practice on outsourcing, technology-enabled business transactions, e-commerce, technology transfers, licensing, intellectual property and joint ventures. Also specializes in transactions involving the commercialization of intellectual property. Helps clients with outsourcing transactions and strategic alliances, as well as with structuring, negotiating and implementing commercial strategies, alliance structures, pricing models, governance arrangements, change management protocols, contract administration and supplier compliance strategies.
**Career:** Previously with Pillsbury and Morgan Lewis. Joined Loeb as Partner in 2010.
**Personal:** Boston University (MBA, 1980); Boston University School of Law (JD, 1979); Yeshiva University (BA, 1976).

### STERN, Gary
Sidley Austin LLP, Chicago
312 853 7267
gstern@sidley.com
*Featured in Capital Markets (Nationwide)*
**Practice Areas:** Partner in Sidley's Chicago office, practicing in domestic and international finance transactions. Focuses on representing lenders, investors and borrowers in film financing transactions and other deals involving financing of intellectual property royalties and revenue streams. Extensive work in financing and securitization representing lenders, investors, borrowers and issuers in transactions involving a variety of asset classes such as auto loans, equipment leases, trade receivables, mortgage loans, servicer advances and timeshares.
**Professional Memberships:** American Bar Association; Chicago Bar Association.
**Personal:** Northwestern University School of Law, JD, 1982, cum laude, Order of the Coif; University of Michigan, BA, 1979. Admission: Illinois.

### STEUBER, David W
Jones Day, Los Angeles
213 243 2457
dsteuber@jonesday.com
*Featured in Insurance (Nationwide), Insurance (California)*
**Practice Areas:** Dave Steuber represents insureds in disputes with their insurers and is an undisputed leader in his field. When critical insurance disputes arise anywhere, insureds consistently look to him for representation. Prior to joining Jones Day in 2011, Dave handled bet-your-company matters that are among the most cutting edge, high-profile, and dollar-intensive - from the Coordinated Asbestos Insurance Proceeding (reputed to be the largest judicial proceeding ever in California) to seminal environmental coverage matters involving FMC, Southern Pacific, Montgomery Ward, and SoCal Gas to insurance

representation of WorldCom in its bankruptcy proceedings and to more recent stock option backdating matters.

### STEVENS, Mark C
Fenwick & West LLP, Mountain View
650 335 7257
mstevens@fenwick.com
*Featured in Investment Funds (Nationwide), Corporate/M&A (California)*

**Practice Areas:** Mark C Stevens is a partner in the Corporate and Intellectual Property Groups of Fenwick & West LLP. He represents companies ranging from newly formed startup teams to mature public companies, venture capitalists and investment banks involved in the information technology industries, with particular focus on complex transactions. He has led teams handling merger, acquisition and divestiture transactions with total announced value well in excess of $25 billion. He has directed dozens of IPOs and hundreds of strategic alliance transactions.
**Career:** Mr Stevens is listed in the AlwaysOn Power Players West list as one of the top attorneys who support the Global Silicon Valley's entrepreneurs, in Best Lawyers in America for corporate law, leveraged buyouts and private equity, in Euromoney's Legal Expert Guides as one of the top M&A attorneys in California and is named by Chambers USA and Chambers Global as one of the top corporate attorneys in California, in Legal 500 as one of the top attorneys in the US for Interactive Entertainment and in Law & Politics as one of northern California's "Super Lawyers".

### STEVENS III, N L (Larry)
Gardere Wynne Sewell LLP, Houston
713 276 5774
lstevens@gardere.com
*Featured in Energy & Natural Resources (Nationwide)*

**Practice Areas:** Energy and energy services, mergers and acquisitions (M&A), global projects, executive compensation.
**Professional Memberships:** State Bar of Texas, American and Houston Bar Associations.
**Career:** Larry Stevens' practice includes a broad spectrum of corporate, securities, energy, energy services, and international transactions. He represents private and public companies, private equity funds, and large individual investors in mergers and acquisitions and all forms of debt and equity financings. He advises executive management groups and boards of directors of public and private companies on governance and executive compensation matters. He also provides counsel to private investors, senior executives, large private trusts, private limited partnerships, and public companies on a myriad of corporate matters. He is a current member of several of Gardere's specialty practice areas, including the Energy Industry Team and the International/Project Finance Group. Mr Stevens is a member of Gardere's compensation committee and a former member of Gardere's Management Committee. He also serves on the Board of Directors of the Houston chapter of the Texas General Counsel Forum.

**Personal:** LLM in Taxation, New York University School of Law, 1977; JD, Southern Methodist University Dedman School of Law, 1976; BBA, Southern Methodist University Cox School of Business, 1972 (accounting and finance).

### STEWART, Dan
Vinson & Elkins LLP, Dallas
214 220 7761
dstewart@velaw.com
*Featured in Bankruptcy/Restructuring (Texas), Bankruptcy/Restructuring (Nationwide)*
See under Texas for profile.

### STOCK, Stuart C
Covington & Burling LLP, Washington, DC
202 662 5384
sstock@cov.com
*Featured in Financial Services Regulation (Nationwide)*

**Practice Areas:** Represents financial institutions regarding governance matters, financial services regulation, regulatory enforcement, litigation, and mergers and acquisitions.
**Career:** Law clerk, US Supreme Court Justice Marshall; and law clerk, Chief Judge Friendly, US Court of Appeals, Second Circuit.
**Publications:** 'Federal and State Regulation of Insurance after the Gramm-Leach-Bliley Act', The Review of Banking & Financial Services; 'Barnett Bank Opens New Opportunities for Banks', Int'l Financial Law Review 21; and 'The Reigle-Neal Interstate Banking and Branching Efficiency Act of 1994', 9J. Int'l Banking Law 402.
**Personal:** JD, magna cum laude, Harvard Law School; BS in Engineering, with highest distinction, Purdue University.

### STOCKER II, Robert W
Dickinson Wright PLLC, Lansing
517 487 4715
rstocker@dickinsonwright.com
*Featured in Gaming & Licensing (Nationwide)*

**Practice Areas:** Gaming Law with hearing practice before the Michigan Gaming Control Board; drafting Referendum Approved Amendment to Michigan Constitution; legislative amendments to the Michigan Compiled Laws; international emerging jurisdiction gaming laws and related regulations; opinion memoranda in diverse areas of gaming, alternative insurance coverage, regulatory, general and commercial business matters.
**Professional Memberships:** Member, State Bar of Michigan; Founding Member and Past President, International Masters of Gaming Law; Editorial Board Member, Gaming Law Review and Economics; Member, International Association of Gaming Advisors; Chair, Gaming Law Committee of American Bar Association Adjunct Professor, The Thomas M Cooley Law School.
**Publications:** Co-author, Chapter 11 Proceedings Involving Casino Businesses, Collier's Guide to Chapter 11 Practice; Co-author, Gambling with Bankruptcy: Navigating a Casino through Chapter 11 Bankruptcy Proceedings, 2008; 'Remedying the Lose-Lose Game of Compulsive Gambling: Voluntary Exclusions,

Mandatory Exclusions, or an Alternative Method?' The John Marshall Law Review, Volume 40, Summer 2007; Co-author, The Child Protection Registry Acts: Feel Good Legislation Run Amok, 2007; Author, Michigan Detroit Casino Supplier and Occupational Licensing Process, 2007; Chair of the ABA Annual Program on Gaming Enforcement, The Gaming Law Minefield, 2006-20013; Author of Captive Insurance Manual.
**Personal:** JD, University of Michigan Law School; BA, Denison University.

### STODDARD, Marshall C
Morgan, Lewis & Bockius LLP, New York
212 309 6350
mstoddard@morganlewis.com
*Featured in Banking & Finance (California), Banking & Finance (Nationwide)*
See under California for profile.

### STOLL, David J
Milbank, Tweed, Hadley & McCloy LLP, New York
212 530 5880
dstoll@milbank.com
*Featured in Wealth Management (Nationwide)*

**Practice Areas:** Mr Stoll represents clients in complex estate planning, trust and estate administration, pre-nuptial agreements and charitable giving.
**Professional Memberships:** NYC Bar (Estate & Gift Tax Committee); NYS Bar Association (Committee on Estate Planning, Trusts and Estates Section; Committee on Estates and Trusts, Tax Section).
**Personal:** JD, Yale; BA, Columbia. Following Yale, Mr Stoll clerked for the Hon. Samuel A. Alito, Jr., US Court of Appeals. Member of the Professional Advisory Councils of Metropolitan Museum, Central Park Conservancy, Memorial Sloan-Kettering, and Columbia University Medical Center. Mr Stoll is a Visiting Lecturer in Law at Yale Law School.

### STONE, Steven W
Morgan, Lewis & Bockius LLP, Washington, DC
202 739 5453
sstone@morganlewis.com
*Featured in Financial Services Regulation (Nationwide)*

**Practice Areas:** Steve Stone leads Morgan Lewis's Investment Management Practice and focuses on broker and investment adviser regulation and enforcement defense. Steve represents major investment banks, brokers and advisers in wide ranging matters, including development of innovative products, separately managed accounts, hedge funds, trading issues affecting brokers and advisers, soft dollars, SEC and FINRA investigations and enforcement matters, deals, "no-action" letter requests, and insider trading. Steve is listed in US Legal 500 and Chambers USA. Chambers named Steve as a leading US lawyer for investment management and broker-dealer law and recognized him as "one of the best in the field."

### STONE, Susan
Sidley Austin LLP, Chicago
312 853 2177
sstone@sidley.com
*Featured in Insurance (Nationwide), Insurance (Illinois)*

**Practice Areas:** Partner, co-head of the global Insurance and Financial Services group, combines deep understanding of the insurance industry with extensive first-chair trial and arbitration skills. A former federal prosecutor, she has extensive trial experience in federal and state courts. Practices insurance and reinsurance disputes, while maintaining a general international commercial arbitration and litigation practice.
**Career:** Past Chairperson of ARIAS; Law clerk for Judge William J Orrick of the Northern District of California; Former Adjunct Professor, DePaul University College of Law.
**Personal:** Harvard Law School, JD, 1987, cum laude; Yale University, BA, 1983, summa cum laude, Phi Beta Kappa.

### STRAIN, Paul
Venable LLP, Baltimore
410 244 7717
pfstrain@Venable.com
*Featured in Products Liability (Nationwide), Litigation (Maryland)*
See under Maryland for profile.

### STRAUSS, Stuart
Dechert LLP, New York
212 698 3529
stuart.strauss@dechert.com
*Featured in Investment Funds (Nationwide)*

**Practice Areas:** Mr Strauss advises investment companies and their independent directors, banks, and other financial institutions on matters pertaining to US securities laws, particularly the Investment Company Act of 1940 and the Investment Advisers Act of 1940. He has experience in the area of exchange-traded fund (ETFs) and represents ETF sponsors and ETF fund complexes.
**Professional Memberships:** Member, New York Bar.
**Career:** Mr Strauss worked for three years as an attorney for the U.S. Securities and Exchange Commission.
**Personal:** University of Pennsylvania Wharton School of Business (BA, 1975); St. John's University (JD, 1978); Georgetown University (LLM, Taxation, 1981).

### STRINGFELLOW, James S
Skadden, Arps, Slate, Meagher & Flom LLP & Affiliates, New York
212 735 3405
James.Stringfellow@skadden.com
*Featured in Capital Markets (Nationwide)*

**Practice Areas:** Represents issuers, underwriters, placement agents, lenders, agents, managers, investment advisers, investors and other participants in public and private structured finance transactions. Experience includes credit card, auto and other receivable securitizations and financings; financial asset portfolio restructurings and financings; collateralized debt obligation issuances (including cash flow, market value and synthetic transactions); sales of investment managers and management contracts; leveraged investment funds; commercial and residential mortgage loan securitizations; asset-backed commercial paper transactions; and resecuritizations and repackagings of various securities and other financial assets and derivative products.

**Career:** JD, New York University School of Law, 1987; AB, Columbia College, 1983.

## STROMFELD, Lary
Cadwalader, Wickersham & Taft LLP, New York
212 504 6291
lary.stromfeld@cwt.com
*Featured in Capital Markets (Nationwide)*

**Practice Areas:** Concentrates in OTC fixed income products, credit derivatives, and municipal finance. Represents numerous commercial banks, bond insurers, derivative product companies, broker-dealers, hedge funds, and other financial institutions. Develops, negotiates and documents wide variety of complex financial products and other complex financings, as well as related advisory matters arising from disputes, close-outs and bankruptcies. Extensively involved in developing and utilizing financial products in the primary and secondary municipal markets. Advising ISDA on the revisions of its documents necessitated by the Dodd-Frank related regulatory requirements. Also advises SIFMA.

**Professional Memberships:** National Association of Bond Lawyers; Securities Law and Disclosure Committee; Municipal Legal Advisory Committee of SIFMA.

**Publications:** Frequent speaker, lecturer and author.

**Personal:** JD, University of Pennsylvania Law School; BA, Brandeis University.

## STRUBECK, Lou
Fulbright & Jaworski LLP, Dallas
214 855 8040
lstrubeck@fulbright.com
*Featured in Bankruptcy/Restructuring (Texas), Bankruptcy/Restructuring (Nationwide)*
See under Texas for profile.

## STUCKER, Robert J
Vedder Price PC, Chicago
312 609 7606
rstucker@vedderprice.com
*Featured in Employee Benefits & Executive Compensation (Nationwide), Labor & Employment (Illinois)*
See under Illinois for profile.

## STURC, John
Gibson, Dunn & Crutcher LLP, Washington, DC
202 955 8243
jsturc@gibsondunn.com
*Featured in Securities (Nationwide)*

**Practice Areas:** Focuses on securities and financial institution enforcement matters before SEC, FINRA, DOJ, CFTC, PCAOB and banking agencies; internal investigations, criminal and civil litigation. Represents corporations, officers, accountants, brokers, investment fund managers,

lawyers, and other market participants in securities law matters.

**Professional Memberships:** ABA Sections of Business Law, Litigation, Criminal Justice; National Advisory Board, SEC Institute, Inc.; Legal Advisory Board, NASD; Executive Council, Federal Bar Association Securities Law Section; Association of SEC Alumni; Legal/Compliance Division, Securities Industry and Financial Markets Association.

**Career:** Former SEC Associate Director of Division of Enforcement, SEC Deputy Chief Litigation Counsel, Assistant U.S. Attorney in D.C.

**Publications:** Frequent author/speaker.

## STYLES, Angela B
Crowell & Moring LLP, Washington, DC
202 624 2500
astyles@crowell.com
*Featured in Government (Nationwide)*

**Practice Areas:** Partner and chair of Crowell & Moring's Government Contracts Group focusing on federal procurement law and litigation. Represents contractors before the US Court of Federal Claims and the United States Court of Appeals for the Federal Circuit.

**Career:** Served in two key procurement positions in the Bush Administration: appointed to General Services Administration January 2001; subsequently appointed Administrator for Federal Procurement Policy within the Office of Management and Budget (OMB) at the White House. Also Chaired Federal Acquisition Regulatory Council; Federal Acquisition Council; Cost Accounting Standards Board.

**Personal:** University of Virginia, BA; University of Texas Law School, JD.

## SUAREZ ANZORENA, Ignacio
Clifford Chance US LLP, Washington, DC
202 912 5185
ignacio.suarezanzorena@cliffordchance.com
*Featured in International Arbitration (Nationwide)*

**Practice Areas:** Ignacio Suarez Anzorena focuses his practice in international arbitration and investor-state disputes resulting from the application of bilateral investment treaties. Mr Suarez Anzorena has acted and given advice with regard to disputes before the most relevant arbitral institutions including the ICC, AAA, LCIA, and particularly ICSID. He has been involved in disputes related to Brazil, Argentina, Paraguay, Peru, Ecuador, Uruguay, Venezuela, Bolivia, Honduras, El Salvador, Panama and Spain.

**Professional Memberships:** Harvard Law School, LLM, 1998; University of Buenos Aires, Law Degree, Diploma de Honor, Secretary to Law Review, 1995. Admitted in Argentina and New York.

## SUCHAROW, Lawrence
Labaton Sucharow LLP, New York
212 907 0860
lsucharow@labaton.com
*Featured in Securities (Nationwide), Litigation (New York)*
See under New York for profile.

## SUH, Maurice
Gibson, Dunn & Crutcher LLP, Los Angeles
213 229 7260
MSuh@gibsondunn.com
*Featured in Sports Law (Nationwide)*

**Practice Areas:** Represents top sports organizations, teams and athletes on issues relating to sponsorship, licensing, strategic planning, anti-doping and crisis-management. Represented top athletes in landmark cases involving use of anabolic steroids and related issues in US courts, arbitration panels and before the International Olympic Committee and the International Court for Arbitration of Sport (CAS). Clients include the National Football League Players Association, Olympic Committees and various elite athletes, including cyclists Floyd Landis and Alexandre Vinokourov, Rashid Ramzi and sprinter Justin Gatlin.

**Personal:** JD, Columbia Law School of Columbia University, 1989. BA, Columbia College of Columbia University, 1986, summa cum laude.

## SULLIVAN, Diane P
Weil, Gotshal & Manges LLP, Princeton
212 310 8897
diane.sullivan@weil.com
*Featured in Products Liability (Nationwide), Litigation (New Jersey)*

**Practice Areas:** Diane Sullivan is a nationally acclaimed trial attorney and a partner in Weil's Litigation Department. She focuses on complex commercial, class action, consumer fraud, product liability, and mass torts litigation for companies in a variety of industries, including pharmaceuticals, consumer products, medical devices, and chemicals. She has been recognized for her successful trial work by prominent legal and trade publications, and is a frequent author/speaker on topics relating to litigation and trial issues.

**Professional Memberships:** New Jersey Bar; admitted to practice before several federal courts.

**Personal:** Fairfield University (BA, 1984); University of Pennsylvania Law School (JD, 1987).

## SULLIVAN, Jeffrey
Hunton & Williams LLP, Raleigh
919 899 3094
jsullivan@hunton.com
*Featured in Capital Markets (Nationwide)*

**Practice Areas:** Securities, M&A, corporate governance.

**Career:** He concentrates on securities law, mergers and acquisitions, corporate governance matters and general corporate law. He focuses primarily on the real estate industry, particularly exchange-listed real estate investment trusts (REITs). He regularly advises investment banks, public companies, including boards of directors, and private funds and other businesses on capital raising, investment and other strategic transactions.

**Personal:** JD, Vanderbilt University Law School; BA, University of North Carolina at Chapel Hill.

## SULLIVAN, Michael D
Levine Sullivan Koch & Schulz LLP, Washington, DC
202 508 1116
msullivan@lskslaw.com
*Featured in First Amendment Litigation (Nationwide), Media & Entertainment (District of Columbia)*

**Practice Areas:** Founding Partner of LSKS. Over 30 years experience representing media clients in libel, privacy, copyright and First Amendment cases. Cases include Anderson v Liberty Lobby, and trial victories in Towler v Sayles, Stokes v WCCO-TV and Kendall v Daily News Publishing. Has taught media law at Georgetown University Law Center and University of Maryland College of Journalism.

**Publications:** "Developments in West Virginia Insurance Bad Faith Law—Where Do We Go from Here?"; Maryland MLRC Privacy Survey.

**Personal:** Born 16 September 1955. Graduate of Georgetown University Law Center; Case & Note Editor, Georgetown Law Journal.

## SULLIVAN, Michael J
Greenberg Traurig, LLP, Orlando
407 418 2376
SullivanM@gtlaw.com
*Featured in Leisure & Hospitality (Nationwide), Real Estate (Florida)*
See under Florida for profile.

## SULLIVAN, Neal E
Bingham McCutchen LLP, Washington, DC
202 373 6159
neal.sullivan@bingham.com
*Featured in Financial Services Regulation (Nationwide), Securities (Nationwide)*

**Practice Areas:** Co-chair of Bingham's Financial Services Area. Leader of the firm's Broker-Dealer Group and co-managing partner of the Washington office. Conducts comprehensive securities regulatory practice with particular focus on broker-dealer and investment adviser matters. Represents clients before the SEC, FINRA, and other self-regulatory organizations and state securities agencies, frequently concerning emerging regulatory issues, private and public investigations, and enforcement proceedings. Represents clients in all of the SEC's major Wall Street investigations.

**Career:** Appears regularly on industry and legal panels that address issues of concern to the securities industry.

**Personal:** Suffolk University Law School, JD, 1990; Stonehill College, BA, 1982.

## SULLIVAN, Norman
Fowler Rodriguez, New Orleans
504 595 5110
nsullivan@frfirm.com
*Featured in Transportation (Nationwide)*

**Practice Areas:** Norman Sullivan is a partner in Fowler Rodriguez's New Orleans office. He received the 2012 Distinguished Maritime Lawyer Award of the Year from the New Orleans Bar Association. He is engaged in a comprehensive litigation practice and focuses his practice on maritime litigation, with emphasis on products liability, contract and insurance law, and construction disputes. He is a member of the New Orleans, California, Louisiana and American Bar Associations and the Maritime Law Association, the International Association of Defense Counsel, the Association of Average Adjusters of the United States and the Southeastern Admiralty Law Institute (Chairman 1998).

### SULLIVAN, Robert J
Skadden, Arps, Slate, Meagher & Flom LLP & Affiliates, New York
212 735 2930
Robert.Sullivan@skadden.com
*Featured in Insurance (Nationwide), Insurance (New York)*

**Practice Areas:** Robert Sullivan co-heads the firm's worldwide Financial Institutions Group, and has over 35 years of experience representing insurance and reinsurance companies, both in the United States and internationally, in the life and annuities, property/casualty, financial guaranty, health and reinsurance fields. His practice focuses on mergers and acquisitions, corporate transactions, insurance regulatory matters, reinsurance matters and restructurings involving insurance and reinsurance companies. His practice also involves the formation of insurance and reinsurance companies in connection with both their onshore and offshore operations and expansion.
**Career:** JD, New York Law School, 1974; BA, Fordham University, 1971.

### SULLIVAN, T J
Drinker Biddle & Reath LLP, Washington, DC
202 230 5157
TJ.Sullivan@dbr.com
*Featured in Healthcare (Nationwide), Healthcare (District of Columbia)*

**Practice Areas:** Partner, healthcare and tax practice which covers complex regulatory and transactional issues.
**Professional Memberships:** Fellow, AHLA; AHLA Board of Directors (1995-2001); Co-Chair, Health Care Subcommittee, Committee on Exempt Organizations, ABA Tax Section.
**Career:** Formerly Special Assistant (Healthcare) to IRS Assistant Commissioner, focus: tax treatment of hospitals, HMOs, other exempt organizations; coordinated development of Service positions on healthcare matters, advised agents during examinations; White House Task Force on Health Reform (1993).
**Publications:** Frequent author, lecturer.
**Personal:** George Washington University, JD, 1985 (Honors); Georgetown University Law Center, LLM, 1991, (Distinction); West Virginia University, MPA, 1979; Salem College, BA, 1977.

### SUNDBACK, Mark
Andrews Kurth LLP, Washington, DC
202 662 2755
msundback@andrewskurth.com
*Featured in Energy & Natural Resources (Nationwide)*

**Practice Areas:** Since 1981, Mark has counseled over a dozen pipelines and numerous shippers across a wide array of issues under the Natural Gas Act, the Interstate Commerce Act, the Outer Continental Shelf Lands Act and other relevant federal and state statutes. He has counseled and represented before the Federal Energy Regulatory Commission, and other tribunals, pipelines applying for or subject to agency action, or competing with other pipelines, and shippers, on matters involving rates, other tariff provisions, certificates, accounting, and enforcement as well as issues regarding agency jurisdiction. His work frequently requires integration of transactional and regulatory goals.

### SUSKO, A Richard (Brick)
Cleary Gottlieb Steen & Hamilton LLP, New York
212 225 2410
bsusko@cgsh.com
*Featured in Employee Benefits & Executive Compensation (Nationwide), Employee Benefits & Executive Compensation (New York)*

**Practice Areas:** Employee benefits and executive compensation, including fiduciary and tax aspects of pension fund investments, golden parachutes, stock options, and other executive incentive compensation plans. Extensive experience in benefits aspect of mergers and acquisitions, ESOPs, plan terminations, and bankruptcy. He taught executive compensation at New York University and Yale Law School.
**Professional Memberships:** Member of the Bar in New York; Charter Member, American College of Employee Benefits Counsel.
**Career:** Joined firm, 1974; became partner, 1982. LLM in taxation, New York University School of Law (1980); JD and MBA, Stanford University (1974); BS (Mathematics), Union College (1969).

### SUTTON, Kathryn M
Morgan, Lewis & Bockius LLP, Washington, DC
202 739 5738
ksutton@morganlewis.com
*Featured in Energy & Natural Resources (Nationwide)*

**Practice Areas:** Kathryn M. Sutton leads the Morgan Lewis Energy Practice. As a partner, Ms Sutton represents clients with respect to the full panoply of issues involving operation of the current fleet of commercial nuclear reactors. She also routinely advises clients regarding NRC's license renewal regulations, including attendant NEPA obligations, CZMA requirements, and adjudicatory matters. Furthermore, she is actively involved in licensing new nuclear power plants in the US, serving as counsel to clients in matters involving the issuance of design certifications, combined operating licenses, early site permits, limited work authorizations, and initial Part 50 operating licenses.

### SWAPP, Russell
Seyfarth Shaw LLP, Boston
617 946 4800
rswapp@seyfarth.com
*Featured in Immigration (Nationwide)*

**Practice Areas:** Managing Partner, Boston Office; Co-Chair Immigration Practice. Represents multinationals, and education, medical and financial institutions in employment and investment related immigration matters. Architects customized service delivery models by combining principles of Lean Six Sigma, knowledge and process management, with alternative fee structures.
**Professional Memberships:** Member, American Immigration Lawyers Association ("AILA"); Member, Immigration Subcommittee, U.S. Chamber of Commerce; Past Chair, MA Bar Association's Committee on Immigration; Liaison, U.S. DOL, NE Chapter of AILA.
**Publications:** MESQUITA BARROS – 2012 and 2010 Global Mobility Handbook.
**Personal:** JD, Franklin Pierce Law Center; Executive Leadership Program, Kellogg School of Management, Northwestern University.

### SWEET JR, William J
Skadden, Arps, Slate, Meagher & Flom LLP & Affiliates, Washington, DC
202 371 7030
William.Sweet@skadden.com
*Featured in Financial Services Regulation (Nationwide)*

**Practice Areas:** Head of the firm's Financial Institutions Regulatory and Enforcement Group. Concentrates in financial institution merger and acquisition, regulatory and enforcement matters. Represents US and non-US banks, thrifts, insurance, securities and investment companies in connection with the acquisition of banks, thrifts, investment managers, securities firms, credit card issuers and other financial institutions.
**Professional Memberships:** Vice-Chairman, Banking Committee, American Bar Association (2005-2011); Chairman, Mergers and Acquisitions Subcommittee, Banking Committee, American Bar Association (1998-2003).
**Career:** Attorney, Board of Governors, Federal Reserve System (1978-81). JD, Georgetown University Law Center, 1978; BA, Bucknell University, 1974.

### SWIRSKI, Alan J J
Skadden, Arps, Slate, Meagher & Flom LLP & Affiliates, Washington, DC
202 371 7610
Alan.Swirski@skadden.com
*Featured in Tax (Nationwide)*

**Practice Areas:** Focuses his practice on tax litigation before the federal courts, including the U.S. Tax Court, the U.S. Court of Federal Claims and US district courts, as well as federal tax controversy matters before the IRS. In 2012, Mr Swirski was co-trial counsel in Massachusetts Mutual Life Insurance Company v. United States, which was tried before the U.S. Court of Federal Claims and decided in the taxpayer's favor.
**Professional Memberships:** Interview Editor, ABA Tax Section; D.C. Bar Taxation Section.
**Career:** U.S. Department of Justice, Tax Division (1995-99). JD, Georgetown University Law Center, 1988; BA, Boston College, 1985.

### SZABO, Robert G.
Van Ness Feldman LLP, Washington, DC
202 298 1920
rgs@vnf.com
*Featured in Transportation (Nationwide)*

**Practice Areas:** Counsels and advocates to the Congress and the Executive Branch agencies and departments on behalf of firm clients in the areas of federal energy, environmental, land and water, public policy, and freight railroad transportation law.
**Career:** Senior Legislative Assistant, Senator J. Bennett Johnston, (D-LA), U.S. Senate, 1975-1978 Law Clerk, Justice John A. Dixon, Jr., Supreme Court of Louisiana, 1972-1973.
**Personal:** JD, Louisiana State University Law School, 1972 (Associate Editor, Louisiana Law Review) B.S., Louisiana State University, 1970.

### TABAK, Jeffrey E
Weil, Gotshal & Manges LLP, New York
212 310 8343
jeffrey.tabak@weil.com
*Featured in Investment Funds (Nationwide)*

**Practice Areas:** Mr Tabak is a founding partner in Weil's Private Funds Practice and represents both sponsors of private investment funds in connection with their organization and institutional investors. Mr Tabak has also been involved in many acquisitions and sales of money management firms.
**Professional Memberships:** Vice Chairman, ABA Subcommittee on Hedge Funds; Member, Private Investment Funds Forum.
**Career:** Trustee and counsel: Museum of Jewish Heritage; counsel to Board of National 9/11 Memorial and Museum and HIPPY USA.
**Personal:** Duke University (BA, 1979; JD, 1982). Phi Beta Kappa.

### TABOR, Bert
Vinson & Elkins LLP, Houston
713 758 2620
btabor@velaw.com
*Featured in Energy & Natural Resources (Nationwide)*

**Practice Areas:** Practice counseling clients in the pipeline transportation area on both strategic and tactical levels mainly related to the formation, construction, acquisition, financing, sale, regulation, and operation of oil pipelines and products pipelines, and representing clients in administrative litigation before federal and state regulatory agencies. He has represented clients in pipeline ventures throughout the United States, including extensive experience in Alaska.
**Professional Memberships:** Member: Energy Bar Association (Served, Executive Committee; Past Chair, Oil Pipeline Committee).
**Career:** Joined the firm in 1973; admitted to the partnership in January 1976.
**Personal:** Ohio State University, BS, 1961; JD, 1964 (Phi Delta Phi).

### TAFT, Kingsley L
Goodwin Procter LLP, Boston
617 570 1222
ktaft@goodwinprocter.com
*Featured in Life Sciences (Nationwide)*

**Practice Areas:** Mr Taft is co-chair of the firm's Life Sciences Practice. He represents biotechnology, pharmaceutical and medical device companies in all aspects of their businesses and legal affairs, including venture capital financings, mergers and

acquisitions, strategic alliances and business transactions. He works with clients ranging in size from start-ups to public companies and has extensive experience with corporate partnering in the life sciences field. He represents venture capital and private equity groups investing in life sciences companies.
**Personal:** JD, Harvard Law School, 1997 (magna cum laude); PhD, Massachusetts Institute of Technology, 1993; BS, Yale University, 1989 (magna cum laude).

## TAGLIABUE, Paul
Covington & Burling LLP, Washington, DC
202 662 5100
ptagliabue@cov.com
*Featured in Sports Law (Nationwide)*
**Practice Areas:** Paul Tagliabue advises clients on strategic matters in the communications, technology, and international sectors. Mr Tagliabue served as NFL Commissioner from 1989-2006. During his tenure, the League grew from 28 to 32 teams, secured the largest television contracts in entertainment history, and supported the construction of more than 20 NFL stadiums.
**Professional Memberships:** Georgetown University Board of Directors; U.S. Olympic Committee; Graduate Institute of International Relations and Commerce of the State University of New York; Council on Foreign Relations.
**Personal:** New York University School of Law, JD, with honors.

## TAHYAR, Margaret
Davis Polk & Wardwell LLP, New York
212 450 4000
margaret.tahyar@davispolk.com
*Featured in Financial Services Regulation (Nationwide)*
**Practice Areas:** Member of Davis Polk's Financial Institutions Group, providing strategic bank regulatory and financial regulatory reform advice and advising on bank M&A and recapitalisations and capital markets transactions where the target or issuer is a financial institution. Advises on living wills, corporate governance and securities settlement systems and payment systems. Recently, worked closely with US and foreign financial institutions providing regulatory, legislative reform and resolution planning advice. From 1997-2009, worked in the Paris and London offices. Frequently advises on the international aspects of transactions and regulatory reform.
**Professional Memberships:** Member of Paris, New York and District of Columbia Bars.

## TANENBAUM, James
Morrison & Foerster LLP, New York
212 468 8163
jtanenbaum@mofo.com
*Featured in Capital Markets (Nationwide)*
**Practice Areas:** Mr Tanenbaum is the Chair of the firm's Capital Markets Practice. He concentrates on corporate finance, structuring domestic and international capital markets transactions. He represents issuers, including some of the nation's largest financial institutions, underwriters and other financial intermediaries, in securities offerings. He has developed some of the most widely

used hybrid techniques for placing and distributing securities. Mr Tanenbaum works closely with leading investment banks to formulate innovative financial products. He is a frequent lecturer on capital markets topics.
**Personal:** SA, Lehigh University; MA, Fletcher School of Diplomacy of Tufts and Harvard Universities; JD, University of Pennsylvania.

## TANENBAUM, William A
Kaye Scholer LLP, New York
212 836 7661
william.tanenbaum@kayescholer.com
*Featured in Outsourcing (Nationwide), Technology (New York)*
See under New York for profile.

## TARUN, Robert W
Baker & McKenzie, San Francisco
415 591 3220
Robert.Tarun@bakermckenzie.com
*Featured in International Trade (Nationwide)*
**Practice Areas:** Trial lawyer with more than 50 federal trials and 25 years of experience in business litigation, internal investigations and white collar crime. Represented corporations and executives in sensitive matters in 50 countries and before the DOJ and SEC.
**Professional Memberships:** Fellow (and Regent); American College of Trial Lawyers, 1992 - present.
**Career:** Executive Assistant US Attorney (Chicago) 1982-85; AUSA 1976-82. Lecturer in Law, University of Chicago Law School.
**Publications:** Author, FOREIGN CORRUPT PRACTICES ACT HANDBOOK (ABA 3d 2013); Co-author, CORPORATE INTERNAL INVESTIGATIONS, Law Journal Press (1993-2013).
**Personal:** MBA, University of Chicago; JD, DePaul University; BA, Stanford University.

## TATO, Joseph A
DLA Piper LLP (US), New York
212 335 4975
joseph.tato@dlapiper.com
*Featured in Projects (Nationwide)*
**Practice Areas:** Projects.
**Career:** He represents independent power producers, equity investors, project sponsors, financial institutions and governments in the development and financing of power, oil and gas, LNG, water and wastewater, telecommunications, waste management and other infrastructure projects in the US, Africa, Latin America and Europe. He also represents sponsors and financial institutions in mergers and acquisitions, restructurings and workouts in the energy and infrastructure areas.
**Personal:** JD, New York University School of Law; BA, Columbia University, magna cum laude, Phi Beta Kappa.

## TAVSS, John
Seward & Kissel LLP, New York
212 574 1261
tavss@sewkis.com
*Featured in Investment Funds (Nationwide)*
**Practice Areas:** Investment management, private funds, investment advisers, and regulatory investigations and enforcement.

**Professional Memberships:** New York State Bar Association (Tax Section); International Bar Association (Private Funds Section).
**Career:** Mr Tavss advises clients on a wide variety of securities, tax and business law matters relating to the investment management business. Mr Tavss has significant expertise in the investment management area including the representation of "hedge funds," other private investment vehicles (both onshore and offshore) and private equity funds. Mr Tavss is a frequent speaker on "hedge fund" and other private investment fund issues. Mr Tavss is actively involved with Hedge Funds Care, a not-for-profit organization supported by the hedge fund industry dedicated to the prevention and treatment of child abuse.
**Personal:** Mr Tavss received a BA Degree (with honors) from University of Virginia in 1976, a JD Degree from Vanderbilt University School of Law in 1979, and an LLM Degree in Taxation from New York University School of Law. He has practiced at Seward & Kissel since 1979, and has been a Partner since 1988.

## TAVZEL, Erik R
Cravath, Swaine & Moore LLP, New York
212 474 1796
etavzel@cravath.com
*Featured in Capital Markets (Nationwide)*
**Practice Areas:** Erik R. Tavzel is a partner in Cravath's Corporate Department. His practice covers a variety of areas, including board representations, mergers and acquisitions, and general corporate matters. A substantial portion of Mr Tavzel's practice involves representing financial institutions, or their boards of directors, in connection with significant corporate transactions. Mr Tavzel also represents foreign public companies in connection with US mergers and acquisitions and securities matters. He has particular experience representing large Canadian public companies.
**Personal:** University of Michigan (JD, cum laude, 1998); Massachusetts Institute of Technology (SB, 1993). For more information: http://www.cravath.com/etavzel

## TAYLOR, James D
Loeb & Loeb LLP, New York
212 407 4895
jtaylor@loeb.com
*Featured in Advertising (Nationwide)*
**Practice Areas:** Provides transactional/regulatory counsel to advertisers, advertising and promotion agencies, entertainment and media companies. Expertise includes strategic partnerships; agency and sponsorships/branded content agreements; mobile platform contracts; talent and music agreements; guild disputes; content, software/ technology licensing; copyright and trademark protection; publicity/privacy; data collection; sweepstakes, contests and other promotions.
**Career:** Partner since 1995. Advanced Media and Technology Department Co-Chair; Advertising and Promotions Law Practice Group Chair.
**Publications:** Frequent speaker on advertising and promotions, branded entertainment, intellectual property and media topics.

**Personal:** Brooklyn Law School (JD, 1987); University of Illinois, Urbana-Champaign (BS, 1979).

## TAYLOR, Jasper
Fulbright & Jaworski LLP, Houston
713 651 5670
jtaylor@fulbright.com
*Featured in Tax (Nationwide), Tax (Texas)*
See under Texas for profile.

## TEITELBAUM, David E
Sidley Austin LLP, Washington, DC
202 736 8683
dteitelbaum@sidley.com
*Featured in Financial Services Regulation (Nationwide)*
**Practice Areas:** Partner in Sidley's Washington, DC office. He has a broad regulatory practice for all types of entities involved in our financial and payment systems, including insured depository institutions and their holding companies, securities, insurance and finance companies, technology providers, payment processors and systems and retailers. He assists these companies in the wide range of regulatory issues that impact their business by providing a combination of regulatory guidance, transactional assistance and legislative planning.
**Personal:** Stanford Law School, JD, 1986, Order of the Coif; Amherst College, BA, 1983, cum laude, Phi Beta Kappa. Admission: District of Columbia.

## TENEV, Jovi
Holland & Knight LLP, New York
212 513 3200
jovi.tenev@hklaw.com
*Featured in Transportation (Nationwide)*
**Career:** Jovi Tenev has extensive experience representing financial institutions, investment banks, foreign and domestic companies and airlines in a wide variety of transactions. He practices in all corporate and finance areas, including projects in the US and international aerospace, energy, alternative energy, shipping, offshore drilling, rail, utilizing capital markets, complex syndicated loan, leveraged and single-investor leasing structures, acquisitions, investigations, work-outs and enforcement. In 2012 and 2013, he represented leading international banks and a national export credit agency in financing deepwater drillships, leading lenders in international shipping workouts and insolvencies, and foreign and US private equity funds investing in various assets.

## TERRELL, Irv
Baker Botts LLP, Houston
713 229 1231
irv.terrell@bakerbotts.com
*Featured in Litigation (Nationwide), Litigation (Texas)*
**Practice Areas:** Trial practice in Texas, Arizona, California, Delaware, Florida, Illinois, New Mexico, Louisiana, New York, and Pennsylvania: takeover suits, contract disputes, intellectual property claims, and business torts, including such matters as tortious interference, antitrust, fiduciary duty, securities fraud, and fraudulent transfer. Trial Counsel for President Bush in the 2000

Florida election contest against Vice - President Gore.

**Career:** National Law Journal's Co-Lawyer of The Year in 2000; 40 years in practice.

**Personal:** JD, cum laude, The University of Texas School of Law, 1972; Order of the Coif; Phi Delta Phi; BA, cum laude, The University of Texas, 1968.

## TEWKSBURY, David
King & Spalding LLP, Washington, DC
202 626 5454
dtewksbury@kslaw.com
*Featured in Energy & Natural Resources (Nationwide)*

**Practice Areas:** Represents independent power producers, electric power marketers, trade associations and others in connection with a wide range of regulatory and transactional matters. Regulatory matters include issues arising under various federal and state laws, including the Federal Power Act, the Natural Gas Act, the Public Utility Regulatory Policies Act of 1978, the Public Utility Holding Company Act of 2005 and the Energy Policy Act of 2005. Transactional matters include electric power and natural gas supply contracts, and interconnection agreements.

**Personal:** JD, magna cum laude, Washington and Lee University School of Law, Order of the Coif, BA, economics, Williams College.

## THATCH, David
White & Case LLP, New York
212 819 8342
dthatch@whitecase.com
*Featured in Capital Markets (Nationwide)*

**Career:** David Thatch is a member of White & Case's Securitization Practice, where he focuses on advising clients in connection with domestic and international structured finance transactions. Mr Thatch has particular expertise in "esoteric" securitizations, leveraged investment funds and complex financial transactions and structures that require highly customized analysis, structuring and documentation. To view a comprehensive biography, please visit www.whitecase.com/dthatch.

## THOMAS, C William
Gibson, Dunn & Crutcher LLP, Washington, DC
202 887 3735
WThomas@gibsondunn.com
*Featured in Investment Funds (Nationwide)*

**Practice Areas:** Experience in the formation and operation of domestic and international private investment funds, including hedge funds, private equity funds, real estate funds and funds of funds. Represents fund managers and sponsors, as well as institutional investors and joint venture partners.

**Professional Memberships:** Board Member of the Society for Latin American Justice.

**Publications:** "SEC Finalizes Investment Adviser Registration Exemptions and Grants Extension to New Registrants," in BNA: Securities Regulation & Law Report (July 2011).

**Personal:** JD, Harvard University, 1998, magna cum laude. MA, Fletcher School of Law &

Diplomacy, Tufts University. Dartmouth College, 1992, summa cum laude.

## THOMAS, Jeane
Crowell & Moring LLP, Washington, DC
202 624 2877
jthomas@crowell.com
*Featured in Litigation (Nationwide)*

**Practice Areas:** Partner in Crowell & Moring's Antitrust Group and the co-chair of the E-Discovery Practice. Engaged in all types of antitrust representations including mergers and joint ventures, class and individual civil litigation, and civil and criminal government investigations. Counsels clients on a broad range of antitrust issues, including intellectual property and licensing issues, trade association law, the Hart Scott Rodino Act, and pricing and distribution issues. Focuses extensively on the telecommunications, technology, chemicals and healthcare/pharmaceuticals industries. In her role with the E-Discovery practice, she has managed many types of e-discovery matters in both government investigations and private litigation.

## THOMAS, Robert
Porter Hedges LLP, Houston
713 226 6636
bthomas@porterhedges.com
*Featured in Energy & Natural Resources (Nationwide)*

**Practice Areas:** Bob Thomas is a partner and leader of the Energy Transactions section at Porter Hedges. His practice principally consists of the representation of domestic and international oil and gas companies in all phases of the energy business with emphasis on the upstream and midstream segments of the industry. In addition, his practice includes representation of energy companies involved in complex energy cases, whether mediation, arbitration or litigation. Prior to joining Porter Hedges, Mr Thomas was Division Attorney for Mesa Petroleum Co. in Houston, Texas and in-house counsel for Gulf Oil Corporation in Midland, Texas and New Orleans, Louisiana.

## THOMAS, Scott
Dickstein Shapiro LLP, Washington, DC
202 420 2601
thomasscott@dicksteinshapiro.com
*Featured in Government (Nationwide)*

**Practice Areas:** Head of the Political Law Practice. Focuses his practice on campaign finance, ethics, and lobbying law. With more than 30 years of experience in this field, he assesses current compliance issues and suggests best practices to ensure adherence to the rules. Given the ever-changing law and its interpretations by regulatory bodies, he provides up-to-date advice that enables businesses, associations, PACs, and others to work successfully with government representatives at the federal, state, or local level.

**Personal:** Stanford University (BA, 1974), Georgetown University Law Center (JD, 1977).

## THOMAS, William L
Willkie Farr & Gallagher LLP, Washington, DC
202 303 1210
wthomas@willkie.com
*Featured in Climate Change (Nationwide), Environment (District of Columbia)*

**Practice Areas:** Advises companies, financiers, developers and other enterprises on environmental law matters, including transactions, projects, and formulation of management and legal compliance strategy. Handles litigation and disputes involving environmental, health and safety concerns, as well as climate change and other matters of international environmental law and policy. Regularly counsels clients on matters with foreign/global environmental dimension, including risks and opportunities arising under regional and international environmental agreements, emerging EHS legal regimes and related international standards and codes of conduct, and legal aspects of sustainability and corporate social responsibility.

**Personal:** JD, Georgetown University, 1989. BA, St. Olaf College, 1986. See: http://www.willkie.com/WilliamThomas

## THOMASCH, Daniel J
Gibson, Dunn & Crutcher LLP, New York
212 351 3800
DThomasch@gibsondunn.com
*Featured in Products Liability (Nationwide), Intellectual Property (New York)*
See under New York for profile.

## THOMPSON, Chet M
Crowell & Moring LLP, Washington, DC
202 624 2655
cthompson@crowell.com
*Featured in Climate Change (Nationwide), Environment (District of Columbia)*

**Practice Areas:** Co-chair of Crowell & Moring's Environment, Energy & Resources Group. Focuses on counseling, litigation, and regulatory and legislative representation of a variety of clients under major environmental statutes, including the Clean Air Act, the Resource Conservation and Recovery Act, the Comprehensive Environmental Response, Compensation, Liability, and Recovery Act.

**Career:** Former Deputy General Counsel and associate Deputy General Counsel of the US Environmental Protection Agency. Oversaw the Agency's air and radiation law office and the legal aspects of several hallmark CAA initiatives.

**Publications:** Boston College, BA - cum laude; Catholic University of America, Columbus School of Law, JD.

## THOMPSON, Dahl
Andrews Kurth LLP, Houston
713 220 4376
dahlthompson@andrewskurth.com
*Featured in Projects (Nationwide)*

**Practice Areas:** Dahl has extensive experience representing clients in a range of domestic and international project development and financing transactions, with a particular emphasis on energy infrastructure projects, including wind and solar power facilities and gas-fired power plants. He

primarily represents developers in all major aspects of the structuring, development, financing, acquisition and disposition of such projects, including the negotiation and drafting of financing and security agreements, credit support arrangements, joint development agreements, shareholder, partnership and LLC agreements, power purchase agreements, construction agreements, major equipment supply agreements, and stock and asset purchase and sale agreements.

## THOREN-PEDEN, Deborah S
Pillsbury Winthrop Shaw Pittman LLP, Los Angeles
213 488 7320
deborah.thorenpeden@pillsburylaw.com
*Featured in Privacy & Data Security (Nationwide)*

**Practice Areas:** Advises on issues related to privacy, data mining, and information use for marketing purposes. Handles a range of privacy matters, including collection and usage of information strategies; preparing policies and procedures; establishing compliance programs; training; responding to law enforcement and government requests for information; addressing international capture, processing and cross-border information sharing; information safeguarding strategies; and preparing for and handling security breaches.

**Professional Memberships:** Bank Operations Counsel Association; NACHA Council for Electronic Billing and Payment; Western Payment Alliance Association Board; National Branded Prepaid Card Assoc.

**Career:** Admitted: California.

**Personal:** JD, USC School of Law; BA, University of Michigan.

## THORPE, Jane F
Alston & Bird LLP, Atlanta
404 881 7822
jane.thorpe@alston.com
*Featured in Food & Beverages (Nationwide), Products Liability (Nationwide)*

**Practice Areas:** Serves as national counsel and science counsel in mass tort and class actions involving foods and beverages, consumer products, chemicals, pharmaceuticals and medical devices. Her work on scientific evidence issues has led to a string of important Daubert decisions. She defends the food and beverage industry before the FTC and against claims brought by states' attorney generals and under state consumer protection acts.

**Career:** Former member of firm's management committee. Lectures and writes extensively on mass torts and class actions.

**Personal:** BA (1976) and JD (1979) University of Georgia.

## THURBER, Mark
Andrews Kurth LLP, Houston
713 220 4338
markthurber@andrewskurth.com
*Featured in Projects (Nationwide)*

**Practice Areas:** Mark has prepared and negotiated a wide variety of infrastructure-related agreements in the areas of thermal generation, wind farm development, coal to liquids and LNG, including construction, equipment purchase, fuel supply and transportation, power purchase, and operation and maintenance agreements. He also has represented a range of development companies in negotiating private equity and debt arrangements at all stages of project development. Mark has represented a variety of financial institutions, including lenders, investment banks, and other capital providers and arrangers, with financing numerous infrastructure projects and acquisitions.

### THURSTON, Rosemarie A
Alston & Bird LLP, Atlanta
404 881 4417
rosemarie.thurston@alston.com
*Featured in Capital Markets (Nationwide)*
**Practice Areas:** Represents REITs, real estate funds and business development companies in fund formation, public securities offerings, private placements, mergers and acquisitions, joint ventures, roll-ups, corporate governance and securities law compliance. Frequent speaker at national industry conferences.
**Professional Memberships:** Member, National Association of Real Estate Investment Trusts (NAREIT), serving on Associate Board of Governors; Member, Investment Program Association (IPA), serving on Board of Trustees.
**Career:** Leads REITs and Real Estate Funds Team.
**Personal:** JD – Vanderbilt University; BS – University of Kentucky.

### TIMPERIO, John M
Dechert LLP, Charlotte
704 339 3180
john.timperio@dechert.com
*Featured in Capital Markets (Nationwide)*
**Practice Areas:** Mr Timperio advises commercial and investment banks, financial guarantors, and others on securitization and various types of restructurings. He focuses on asset-backed securitization (ABS), collateral manager merger and acquisitions, structured lending, workouts, and collateral loan obligation (CLO) transactions. He is also very involved in the development of the middle-market CLO sector.
**Professional Memberships:** Member, North Carolina Bar.
**Personal:** University of Pennsylvania (BA, magna cum laude, 1988); Georgetown University Law Center (JD, 1991).

### TIMPONE, Michael
Seward & Kissel LLP, New York
212 574 1342
timpone@sewkis.com
*Featured in Transportation (Nationwide)*
**Practice Areas:** Maritime and Transportation Finance, Corporate Finance, and Business Transactions (M&A/Private Equity).
**Professional Memberships:** Mr Timpone is a member of the Association of the Bar of the City of New York, the American Bar Association and the Maritime Law Association of the United States.
**Career:** Mr Timpone is a partner in the Corporate Finance Group at Seward & Kissel. He devotes most of his time to the activities of the

firm's Transportation Finance Group, a cross section of attorneys within the firm from the Corporate Finance, Corporate Securities, Litigation and Tax Departments with expertise on matters of interest to clients in the transportation industry. Mr Timpone is also part of the firm's Business Transactions Group. In such capacities, Mr Timpone's work includes the formation of joint ventures, mergers and acquisitions, asset finance transactions, registered and unregistered securities transactions and restructurings.
**Personal:** Mr Timpone received a BA Degree, with honors, from Rutgers College, in 1995, and a JD Degree, from Fordham University School of Law in 2000. Mr Timpone has spent his entire legal career at Seward & Kissel.

### TOBIN, Charles D
Holland & Knight LLP, Washington, DC
202 955 3000
charles.tobin@hklaw.com
*Featured in First Amendment Litigation (Nationwide), Media & Entertainment (District of Columbia)*
**Practice Areas:** Chair, National Media Practice Team. Former journalist, Tobin appears for media clients in state and federal courts throughout the country. He conducts pre-publication review for newsrooms; represents the media in libel and privacy litigation, access and freedom of information matters; and advises commercial clients on unfair competition claims. Tobin was former in-house counsel at Gannett Co., Inc., a prominent national multimedia company ('USA TODAY' publishers). He is senior editor of the ABA publication 'LITIGATION', Immediate Past Chair of ABA's Forum on Communications Law and a PEN USA Award of Honor recipient for his service to the First Amendment.

### TOBISMAN, Stuart P
Loeb & Loeb LLP, Los Angeles
310 282 2323
stobisman@loeb.com
*Featured in Wealth Management (Nationwide), Tax (California)*
See under California for profile.

### TOLLEY III, Edward P
Simpson Thacher & Bartlett LLP, New York
212 455 3189
etolley@stblaw.com
*Featured in Capital Markets (Nationwide)*
**Practice Areas:** Corporate Partner representing financial sponsors, including Blackstone, KKR, First Reserve, TPG and THLee in connection with high yield/bridge financings such as Samson Resources, TXU, SunGard, HCA, TPC Group, Summit, Mid-States, Apria, PGI, American Tire, Warner Music, Travelport, Nalco, Foundation Coal, Team Health and Houghton-Mifflin. Equity experience includes Issuer's Counsel for the IPOs of Team Health, Dresser-Rand, Warner Music and Celanese. Has represented underwriters in multiple IPOs, including the IPO of Kraft Foods.
**Career:** Joined Firm, 1990; Partner, 1999.
**Personal:** University of Virginia School of Law (JD 1990); Dartmouth College (BA, magna cum laude, 1984); Phi Beta Kappa.

### TOMASZCZUK, Alex
Pillsbury Winthrop Shaw Pittman LLP, Los Angeles
213 488 7110
alex.tomaszczuk@pillsburylaw.com
*Featured in Government (Nationwide)*
**Practice Areas:** Litigates disputes and bid protests at the U.S. Courts of Appeals and District Courts, the U.S. Court of Federal Claims, and the Government Accountability Office involving complex govenrnment contracts in the energy, defense, real property leasing and government services sectors; manages internal investigations/audit responses.
**Professional Memberships:** ABA, FBA.
**Career:** U.S. Department of State, 1987-90 (Superior Honor Award); Former Chair, Government Contracts Section, Federal Bar Association, 1995-96. Admitted: California, Virginia, DC and Missouri.
**Publications:** Author/presenter on government ethics, bid protests, government leasing.
**Personal:** LLM, Columbia University, 1987; JD, University of Missouri, 1981 (law review editor); BA, Stanford University, 1977.

### TONER, Michael E
Wiley Rein LLP, Washington, DC
202 719 7545
mtoner@wileyrein.com
*Featured in Government (Nationwide)*
**Practice Areas:** Election Law & Government Ethics practice. Advises candidates, corporations, trade associations, campaign committees, political party committees and individuals on federal and state election laws, federal and state lobbying laws and ethics and gift restrictions, Office of Congressional Ethics matters and congressional investigations. Named a Washingtonian magazine "Best Lawyer."
**Career:** FEC Chairman (2006) and Commissioner (2002-2007); RNC Chief Counsel (2001-2002) and Deputy Counsel (1997-1999); General Counsel, Bush-Cheney Transition Team in Washington, DC and Bush-Cheney 2000 Presidential Campaign; Counsel, Dole-Kemp Presidential Campaign (1996).
**Personal:** Cornell Law School (JD, cum laude); Johns Hopkins University (MA); University of Virginia (BA, with distinction).

### TONERY, Lisa
Fulbright & Jaworski LLP, New York
212 318 3009
ltonery@fulbright.com
*Featured in Energy & Natural Resources (Nationwide)*
**Practice Areas:** Energy; corporate.
**Professional Memberships:** District of Columbia Bar; New York Bar; Energy Bar Association.
**Career:** Practice focuses on advising clients on regulatory strategy and compliance as well as securing all required authorizations for major energy projects, including obtaining the first authorization issued by the Department of Energy to export domestic natural gas as LNG to all trading partners and representation of first bi-directional LNG terminals proposed in the US in pro-

ceedings before the Federal Energy Regulatory Commission. Practice also focuses on transactional matters involving the energy industry.
**Personal:** BA, Catholic University (1984); JD, Catholic University (1989).

### TORTORIELLO, Robert L
Cleary Gottlieb Steen & Hamilton LLP, New York
212 225 2390
rtortoriello@cgsh.com
*Featured in Financial Services Regulation (Nationwide)*
**Practice Areas:** Bank capital markets; compliance, internal investigations/enforcement; mergers, acquisitions, joint ventures, restructurings; derivative products; activity expansion. Regulatory counseling to US and foreign banks and industry participants concerning Dodd-Frank Act, Gramm-Leach-Bliley Act, Bank Holding Company Act, National Bank Act, International Banking Act. Clients include: Bank of America, BNP Paribas, Commerzbank, Credit Suisse, Goldman Sachs, ING, Natixis, HSBC, Sherman Financial.
**Career:** Joined firm, 1974; partner, 1982. JD, magna cum laude, Harvard (1974); BA, summa cum laude, St. Peter's College (1971).
**Publications:** Guide to Bank Underwriting, Dealing and Brokerage Activities (Thomson West, 17th edition, 2012). Scholarly and professional journals.

### TOTTENHAM, Terry O
Fulbright & Jaworski LLP, Austin
512 536 4555
ttottenham@fulbright.com
*Featured in Products Liability (Nationwide)*
**Practice Areas:** Healthcare.
**Professional Memberships:** President, State Bar of Texas; American Board of Trial Advocates (president, Austin chapter); American College of Trial Lawyers (fellow); International Academy of Trial Lawyers (fellow); International Society of Barristers (fellow).
**Career:** Tottenham handles complex litigation in both federal and state courts, and is certified by the Texas Board of Legal Specialization in Personal Injury and Civil Trial Law and the National Board of Trial Advocacy.
**Personal:** LLM, George Washington University (1973); JD, with honors, The University of Texas School of Law (1970); Registered Pharmacist (1967); BS, magna cum laude, The University of Texas (1967).

### TOUMEY, Donald J
Sullivan & Cromwell LLP, New York
212 558 4077
toumeyd@sullcrom.com
*Featured in Financial Services Regulation (Nationwide)*
**Practice Areas:** Financial institutions, M&A, securities/corporate governance. Advised numerous major bank mergers/acquisitions, as well as bank acquisitions of investment management/investment banking firms and joint ventures in the financial services industry. Handles banking and broker-dealer regulatory

and enforcement matters, including with respect to Volcker Rule, AML/BSA and OFAC issues. Advises US/non-US financial institutions on numerous matters with federal banking agencies and on securities offerings.

**Professional Memberships:** ABA; Federalist Society; LeGaL; NYCBA.

**Career:** Partner since 1990. Former Special Assistant to General Counsel, US Department of Treasury.

**Personal:** Yale Law School (JD, 1981); Williams College (BA, 1978).

### TOWNSEND, John M
Hughes Hubbard & Reed LLP, Washington, DC
202 721 4640
townsend@hugheshubbard.com
*Featured in International Arbitration (Nationwide)*

**Practice Areas:** Partner; Chair, Arbitration and ADR Group.

**Professional Memberships:** Chairman of the Board 2007-2010, American Arbitration Association; US Member,ICSID Panel of Arbitrators, 2008-2014; Chair of Privilege Task Force, Member, Arbitration and Competition Law Committees, US council for International Business; Chair 2005-06, Mediation Committee,International Bar Association; Challenge Review Board, CPR Institute; College of Commercial Arbitrators; American Law Institute.

**Career:** Hughes Hubbard & Reed since 1971, New York, Paris, Washington. Admitted NY 1972; DC 1990.

**Publications:** Complete list at www.hugheshubbard.com

**Personal:** BA Yale University 1968; JD Yale University 1971.

### TRACTENBERG, Craig R
Nixon Peabody LLP, New York
212 940 3722
ctractenberg@nixonpeabody.com
*Featured in Franchising (Nationwide)*

**Practice Areas:** Franchise development, licensing, and enforcement. Injunction, termination, nonrenewal, fraud litigation and arbitration. Protecting trade secrets, trademarks and restrictive covenants, restructuring and acquiring franchise and distribution companies. Counsel to Republic of Turkey before the International Court of Commerce in Geneva and ICSID in Washington, DC.

**Professional Memberships:** Leader of firm's Franchise and Distribution team, recognized as Law Firm of the Year–Franchise Law and as NYC-Lawyer of the Year–Franchise Law by U.S. News. ABA Forum on Franchising member; PA Bar Association Franchise Chair; NY Bar Association, Board, Business Law Section; Franchise Times Top 100 Franchise Lawyers; SuperLawyer; IFA Supplier Member.

### TRAGER, Michael D
Arnold & Porter LLP, Washington, DC
202 942 6976
Michael.Trager@aporter.com
*Featured in Securities (Nationwide)*

**Practice Areas:** Senior Partner; Chairs Securities Enforcement and Litigation Practice. Defends investigations conducted by SEC, DOJ, Congress, FINRA, PCAOB, and other regulators. Conducts and defends internal investigations and independent reviews, defends securities litigation, and counsels on compliance, crisis management, corporate governance, and securities and market matters. Maintains global practice involving high profile engagements. Clients include public companies, broker-dealers, banks, financial services firms, investment advisers, hedge funds, private equity firms, accounting and law firms, boards, directors, officers, and other individuals. Previously served in SEC's Division of Enforcement in Washington.

**Personal:** JD, Boston University School of Law, 1985; BA, Wesleyan University, 1981.

### TREVINO, Marc R
Sullivan & Cromwell LLP, New York
212 558 4239
trevinom@sullcrom.com
*Featured in Employee Benefits & Executive Compensation (Nationwide), Employee Benefits & Executive Compensation (New York)*
See under New York for profile.

### TRIGG, John
Wheeler Trigg O'Donnell LLP, Denver
303 244 1860
trigg@wtotrial.com
*Featured in Products Liability (Nationwide)*

**Practice Areas:** National litigation practice focuses on complex business litigation, product liability, and class actions. Represents major corporate defendants, such as Crocs, Toyota, and Anheuser-Busch as national or regional trial counsel and has tried cases to juries in many state and federal courts. Also focuses on risk-management and design and analysis of document retention and control programs. Handles large and frequent claims arising out of alleged recurrent design, manufacturing defects, or recall problems.

**Professional Memberships:** Fellow, American College of Trial Lawyers.

**Personal:** JD, University of Denver College of Law; 1963, B.S., University of Colorado, 1961.

### TRIPODORO, John A
Cahill Gordon & Reindel LLP, New York
212 701 3505
jtripodoro@cahill.com
*Featured in Capital Markets (Nationwide)*

**Practice Areas:** Practice is principally focused on capital market transactions, including debt and equity offerings and bank financings. John has represented financing sources in many acquisitions, including the leverage buyouts of Clear Channel Communications, Harrah's Entertainment, Berry Plastics, Intelsat, VNU/Nielsen and SunGard Data Systems. Also represents leading banking firms and financial advisors in out of court debt restructurings.

**Personal:** Co-Administrative Partner. Pace University, BBA, 1986, magna cum laude. Fordham University School of Law, JD, 1989, Dean's List.

### TROOBOFF, Peter D
Covington & Burling LLP, Washington, DC
202 662 5512
ptrooboff@cov.com
*Featured in International Trade (Nationwide)*

**Practice Areas:** Foreign trade including export controls and economic sanctions; international litigation and arbitration.

**Professional Memberships:** Curatorium, Hague Academy of International Law (1991-); lecturer, General Course on Private International Law (2008); American Society of International Law, President (1990-92); American Journal of International Law, honorary editor (2007-); Theberge Award, ABA International Law Section (2010).

**Career:** US delegation, Hague Conference on Private International Law (1992-2005; 2013).

**Publications:** National Law Journal, regular columns (2001-).

**Personal:** Harvard University (LLB, cum laude); London School of Economics (LLM); Hague Academy of International Law, (Diploma, cum laude); Columbia University (AB, cum laude); Institut d' Études Européennes.

### TROPP, Paul D
Fried, Frank, Harris, Shriver & Jacobson LLP, New York
212 859 8933
Paul.Tropp@FriedFrank.com
*Featured in Capital Markets (Nationwide)*

**Practice Areas:** Corporate partner. Focuses practice on capital markets transactions, including the representation of issuers and underwriters in domestic and international public and private debt and equity securities offerings and related transactions. Frequently represents investment banks in connection with acquisition financings and with clients on corporate governance matters. Clients include BofA Merrill Lynch, Citi, Deutsche Bank Securities, UBS Investment Bank, Morgan Stanley, Credit Suisse, Goldman, Sachs & Co. and J.P. Morgan.

**Career:** Joined in 2001; became partner in 2005.

**Personal:** JD, New York University School of Law (1996); BA, Harvard University (1993).

### TRUESDELL, Richard D
Davis Polk & Wardwell LLP, New York
212 450 4000
richard.truesdell@davispolk.com
*Featured in Capital Markets (Nationwide)*

**Practice Areas:** Mr Truesdell is co-head of Davis Polk's Global Capital Markets Group. He represents clients in US and international capital markets transactions and advises on corporate governance and securities market regulation. He regularly represents investment banks, including Banc of America, Citigroup, Credit Suisse, Goldman Sachs, JP Morgan Chase and Morgan Stanley, and a variety of corporate clients. Mr Truesdell has extensive experience with a wide variety of both public and private debt and equity offerings, including initial public offerings, convertible offerings, high-yield and investment grade debt financings and exchange offers and other restructurings.

### TSE, Marian A
Goodwin Procter LLP, Boston
617 570 1169
mtse@goodwinprocter.com
*Featured in Employee Benefits & Executive Compensation (Nationwide), Employee Benefits & Executive Compensation (Massachusetts)*
See under Massachusetts for profile.

### TUCKER, Hugh
Baker Botts LLP, Houston
713 229 1656
hugh.tucker@bakerbotts.com
*Featured in Energy & Natural Resources (Nationwide)*

**Practice Areas:** Practice includes oil and gas, chemical, real estate, energy and infrastructure transactions, particularly acquisitions and divestitures, project development, joint ventures, equity investments and financing. Primary focus has been in the upstream, midstream and downstream sectors, including conventional and unconventional resources, alternative fuels, refining and petrochemicals.

**Professional Memberships:** State Bar of Texas, District of Columbia Bar; Houston Bar Association, Institute for Energy Law, Advisory Board, Association of International Petroleum Negotiators, Rocky Mountain Mineral Law Foundation.

**Personal:** JD, Southern Methodist University School of Law, 1982 (Order of the Coif); BA, economics and business administration, Vanderbilt University, 1979.

### TUSSING, James D
Fulbright & Jaworski LLP, New York
212 318 3024
jtussing@fulbright.com
*Featured in Transportation (Nationwide), Banking & Finance (Nationwide)*

**Practice Areas:** Aviation; equipment finance; infrastructure.

**Professional Memberships:** Advisory Board, Cape Town International Aircraft Registry; American Bar Association, Chair, Aircraft Finance Subcommittee (2003-06); International Bar Association, Vice Chair, Aviation Committee; Fellow, American College of Finance Lawyers; Fellow, American Bar Foundation.

**Career:** Head of Fulbright's Equipment Finance Group and Co-Head of its Global Infrastructure Group, Tussing represents financial institutions, leasing companies and airlines in US and cross border equipment financing and leasing transactions and related joint ventures, mergers and acquisitions, reorganizations and litigation. He has over 35 years of experience in aircraft financing.

### TWOMEY, Laura M
Simpson Thacher & Bartlett LLP, New York
212 455 3120
ltwomey@stblaw.com
*Featured in Wealth Management (Nationwide)*

**Practice Areas:** Partner in Personal Planning Department. Her practice includes estate planning, estate administration, trust administration and charitable planning. Expertise includes estate freezing techniques, planning with private equity and hedge fund interests, family business succession planning, planning with real estate interests, modifying trusts, and migrating trusts for tax and non-tax purposes.

**Professional Memberships:** Co-Chair of Gift and Estate Tax Committee of NYSBA Tax Section. Fellow of American College of Trusts and Estates Counsel. NYCBA, Estate and Gift Tax Committee.

**Personal:** Boston College BA (1994) JD (1997), New York University School of Law LLM in Taxation (2003).

### UMANOFF, Adam S.
Akin Gump Strauss Hauer & Feld LLP, Los Angeles
213 892 2055
aumanoff@akingump.com
*Featured in Projects (Nationwide)*

**Practice Areas:** Adam Umanoff co-chairs Akin Gump's global project finance practice. His practice focuses on the development, financing, operation, disposition and acquisition of renewable energy projects and renewable energy companies. He represents project sponsors and developers, lenders, equity investors, manufacturers, technology companies and other participants in the sector and has substantial experience in the wind, solar and geothermal industries.

**Career:** Served as Senior Vice President/General Counsel, then President and CEO, Zond Corp./Enron Wind Corp.

**Personal:** Holds a BS from Cornell University and a JD from Columbia Law School, where he was a Harlan Fiske Stone Scholar.

### UNGER, Timothy
Andrews Kurth LLP, Houston
713 220 4370
tunger@andrewskurth.com
*Featured in Projects (Nationwide)*

**Practice Areas:** In recent years, Tim's practice has focused on project development, financing, and mergers and acquisitions primarily in the energy (upstream, midstream and downstream) and chemical business both domestic and international. His projects include mergers and acquisition of oil and gas reserves and companies, oil field service companies, chemical facilities and electric generating facilities, as well as development and financing of oil and gas reserves, pipelines, LNG facilities, power generating facilities, petrochemical facilities, and renewable energy projects including wind, solar and geothermal projects.

### URBACH, Ronald R
Davis & Gilbert LLP, New York
212 468 4824
rurbach@dglaw.com
*Featured in Advertising (Nationwide)*

**Practice Areas:** Advertising, marketing and promotions.

**Career:** Chairman and Co-Chair of the Advertising, Marketing & Promotions Practice Group. Regarded as one of the leading advertising and marketing lawyers in the country, Mr Urbach counsels clients on all aspects of the law governing the creation, production and distribution of advertising across multi-platform media channels.

His practice involves appearing before the FTC, state Attorneys General, and other federal and local regulatory agencies that have jurisdiction over advertising, marketing and promotions. Mr Urbach has handled many of the most critical advertising and marketing practice cases in recent years, a number of which were joint FTC and/or multi-state actions. He is recognized in The Best Lawyers in America for advertising law, The Legal 500 U.S. for advertising and marketing law and selected as a Super Lawyer by New York Metro Super Lawyers.

### URGENSON, Laurence A
Kirkland & Ellis LLP, Washington, DC
202 879 5145
laurence.urgenson@kirkland.com
*Featured in International Trade (Nationwide)*

**Practice Areas:** Laurence Urgenson is a partner whose practice focuses on the Foreign Corrupt Practices Act, the False Claims Act and internal investigations. Larry is the former Acting Deputy Assistant Attorney General and Chief of the Fraud Section for the Criminal Division of the Department of Justice, and is a former Chief Assistant US Attorney for the Eastern District of New York.

**Professional Memberships:** Chairman and Board of Editors, Business Crimes Bulletin.

**Personal:** City University of New York, City College, BBA, 1968; Brooklyn Law School, JD, 1975 (cum laude, National Moot Court Team, Senior Editor of the Brooklyn Law Review).

### URIS, Harvey R
Skadden, Arps, Slate, Meagher & Flom LLP & Affiliates, New York
212 735 2212
Harvey.Uris@skadden.com
*Featured in Real Estate (Nationwide), Real Estate (New York)*

**Practice Areas:** Leads global real estate practice. Specializes in capital markets and syndicated loan transactions; CMB loan origination and securitizations, public and private REITs, bondable and other credit tenant transactions: sale-leasebacks; acquisitions, financings, sales, exchanges and other dispositions of property; multi-property and multi-state mortgage financings; mezzanine and preferred equity senior and subordinated secured financings; partnerships; LLCs; US/non-US joint ventures; workouts and restructurings of secured loans and credit facilities for single asset and/or operating companies and enforcement actions; formation of investment vehicles by domestic, offshore and cross-border private equity funds.

**Career:** JD, 1979 (cum laude), BA, 1979 (cum laude) Boston University.

### URQUHART, Douglas
Weil, Gotshal & Manges LLP, New York
212 310 8001
douglas.urquhart@weil.com
*Featured in Banking & Finance (Nationwide)*

**Practice Areas:** Co-head of US Banking & Finance Practice. Represents lenders, private equity sponsors and borrowers on leveraged, asset-based and investment grade financing and

restructuring transactions, including acquisition facilities, event-driven bridge loans, mezzanine and second lien financings and DIP and exit facilities. He is the co-author of chapters in Reorganizing Failing Businesses (American Bar Association) and The Law and Practice of Restructuring the UK and US (Oxford University Press). Board member of ACCION East, Inc., the largest provider of microfinance in the United States.

**Personal:** University of Leicester (LLB, 1985); College of Law, Guildford (LSF, 1986).

### UTLEY, Frederick
Clifford Chance US LLP, New York
212 878 8356
frederick.utley@cliffordchance.com
*Featured in Capital Markets (Nationwide)*

**Practice Areas:** Since founding Clifford Chance's US structured finance group in the 1980s, Mr Utley has structured transactions involving nearly every type of security, mortgage and receivable securitized to date, both domestically and in cross-border markets. He regularly represents all types of market participants - issuers, underwriters, investment managers, insurers and investors.

**Career:** Harvard Law School, JD. Cambridge University, MA. Yale University, BA, magna cum laude.

### UZZI, Gerard
Milbank, Tweed, Hadley & McCloy LLP, New York
212 530 5670
guzzi@milbank.com
*Featured in Bankruptcy/Restructuring (Nationwide), Bankruptcy/Restructuring (New York)*

See under New York for profile.

### VACKETTA, Carl Lee
DLA Piper LLP (US), Washington, DC
202 799 4402
carl.vacketta@dlapiper.com
*Featured in Government (Nationwide)*

**Practice Areas:** Government affairs, government contracts, aerospace and defense.

**Career:** With more than 40 years of experience in government contracts law, he has represented companies selling information technology, telecommunications equipment, and professional and technical services to the government. He has led teams of attorneys, accountants, and engineers in the investigation and preparation of multimillion-dollar claims for major shipyards, aerospace, power generating, electronics, and telecommunication companies. He has in depth experience in the General Services Administration's Multiple Award Schedule Contract (MASC) program.

**Personal:** JD, University of Illinois at Urbana-Champaign; BS, University of Illinois at Urbana-Champaign (with honors).

### VACURA, Richard J
Morrison & Foerster LLP, McLean
703 760 7764
rvacura@mofo.com
*Featured in Government (Nationwide)*

**Practice Areas:** Co-Chair of firm's Government Contracts practice and experienced trial lawyer

involving major weapon and space systems, software development, communications systems, prime/subcontract disputes, bid protests, injunctive suits, procurement fraud, FOIA actions and Federal Tort Claims Act cases. Has in-depth experience conducting internal investigations involving false claims and Foreign Corrupt Practices Act violations, and defending suspension and debarment actions. Named a Top Government Contracts Lawyer by the Washington Business Journal.

**Career:** Admitted to practice in Minnesota, Virginia, and the District of Columbia.

**Personal:** BA, University of Texas; JD, William Mitchell College of Law; LLM, The George Washington University.

### VAFIDIS, Matthew P
Holland & Knight LLP, San Francisco
415 743 6900
matthew.vafidis@hklaw.com
*Featured in Transportation (Nationwide)*

**Practice Areas:** Partner in the Litigation Section and leader of the firm's West Coast Litigation Group. Mr Vafidis, who is also a qualified English barrister, has practiced commercial, admiralty and international litigation in San Francisco for over 32 years. He is experienced in a wide range of complex commercial litigation, international arbitration and mediation, representing both foreign and US companies; he serves as a mediator and concentrates in commercial and admiralty litigation, particularly environmental, marine pollution and casualties, and regularly provides advice upon matters of international trade and transportation.

### VALUKAS, Anton R
Jenner & Block LLP, Chicago
312 923 2903
avalukas@jenner.com
*Featured in Litigation (Nationwide), Litigation (Illinois)*

See under Illinois for profile.

### VANCE, Janet
Gibson, Dunn & Crutcher LLP, New York
212 351 3854
jvance@gibsondunn.com
*Featured in Banking & Finance (Nationwide)*

**Practice Areas:** Experience includes representation of private equity sponsors, funds, public and private corporate borrowers and lenders with respect to secured and unsecured lending transactions, senior and subordinated debt financings, first lien/second lien transactions, mezzanine loans, high yield notes, loan syndications, restructurings and other credit and banking matters.

**Career:** Clerk, Judge Richard Gadbois, Jr., U.S. District Court for the Central District of California.

**Personal:** JD, Columbia University School of Law, 1987, Harlan Fiske Stone Scholar. BA, University of Pennsylvania, 1984, with honors.

### VARDELL III, James C
Cravath, Swaine & Moore LLP, New York
212 474 1900
jvardell@cravath.com
*Featured in Banking & Finance (Nationwide)*

**Practice Areas:** James C. Vardell, III is a partner in Cravath's Corporate Department. His practice includes a broad range of corporate finance transactions, primarily focusing on syndicated bank financings, including acquisition financings, leveraged buyouts and recapitalizations, debtor-in-possession financings and other complex secured transactions, as well as more conventional financings, such as commercial paper back-up and other revolving credit facilities, multicurrency facilities and letter of credit facilities. Mr Vardell also has experience in project financings, equipment financings, leveraged lease financings, synthetic leases and vendor financings.
**Personal:** Yale Law School (JD, 1980); Washington and Lee University (BA, 1977). For more information: http://www.cravath.com/jvardell

### VARTANIAN, Thomas
Dechert LLP, Washington, DC
202 261 3439
Thomas.Vartanian@dechert.com
*Featured in Financial Services Regulation (Nationwide)*
**Practice Areas:** Mr Vartanian advises clients on matters including mergers and acquisitions; private equity investments; FDIC receiverships; D&O liability; enforcement; contests for control of financial institutions, reorganizations and recapitalizations of distressed banks; securitizations and structured finance; and matters involving government sponsored enterprises (GSEs).
**Professional Memberships:** Member, District of Columbia and New York Bars; admitted before the U.S. Supreme Court.
**Career:** General Counsel, Federal Home Loan Bank Board.
**Publications:** Co-author, American Bankers Association's published analysis of the Dodd-Frank Wall Street Reform and Consumer Protection Act of 2010.
**Personal:** Cathedral College, (BA, 1971, cum laude); Brooklyn Law School, (JD, 1976, cum laude).

### VÁZQUEZ-AZPIRI, A James
Morgan, Lewis & Bockius LLP, San Francisco
415 442 1343
ajvazquez@morganlewis.com
*Featured in Immigration (California), Immigration (Nationwide)*
See under California for profile.

### VEBER, Jeffrey T
Vedder Price PC, New York
212 407 7728
jveber@vedderprice.com
*Featured in Transportation (Nationwide)*
**Practice Areas:** Managing Shareholder of the firm's New York office and a member of the Board of Directors and Global Transportation Finance team. Over 15 years' experience representing lenders, export-credit agencies, lessors, finance companies and other parties in tax-motivated structured financings, mortgage financings, operating lease financings and asset purchase agreements involving commercial aircraft, corporate

jets, rolling stock and vessels. Well recognized within the industry for his work with the Export-Import Bank of the United States (Ex-Im Bank) in cross-border lease financings.
**Career:** Admitted (IL) 1992, (NY) 2005.
**Personal:** JD, Northwestern University; BA, Colgate University.

### VEBMAN, Yossi
Skadden, Arps, Slate, Meagher & Flom LLP & Affiliates, New York
212 735 3719
yossi.vebman@skadden.com
*Featured in Capital Markets (Nationwide)*
**Practice Areas:** Yossi Vebman is a member of Skadden's Corporate Finance and Derivative Financial Products practices, representing major corporations, investment banks, funds and others. Representation includes convertible, trust preferred and hybrid securities; equity derivatives, including accelerated share repurchase plans, forward contracts and call spread transactions; credit derivatives; and a broad range of over-the-counter derivatives. He also has significant experience with traditional corporate financing transactions and securitization transactions.
**Career:** LLM, NYU School of Law, 1996; LLB, Hebrew University, 1994 (with honors; Dual Honors Degree in Law and Economics; Member of the Editorial Board of the Law Review).

### VENEZIA, Gina
Freehill Hogan & Mahar LLP, New York
212 381 3018
venezia@freehill.com
*Featured in Transportation (Nationwide)*
**Practice Areas:** Areas of expertise are maritime litigation and arbitration of contractual and tort disputes including cargo, charter party, and major causalities, as well as litigation and arbitration of general commercial matters. Has significant experience with cases involving major casualties including casualties involving the carriage of hazardous cargoes. Has also handled major cases involving long-term COAs, vessel purchase and sale, liner service contracts, and issues involving US military cargoes and electronic bills of lading. Also has extensive experience in providing advice on OFAC matters.
**Professional Memberships:** Maritime Law Association of the United States; Marine Insurance and Claims Association (Board Member); New York State Bar Association. Bar admissions: New York (state and federal); Louisiana (state and federal); District of Columbia.
**Career:** Joined Freehill Hogan & Mahar as an associate in 2000 having previously been associated with Chaffe, McCall, Phillips, Toler & Sarpy in New Orleans, Louisiana. Became a partner with Freehill Hogan & Mahar in 2003.
**Personal:** Born 1969; Louisiana State University, BS, 1991; Loyola University School of Law, JD, 1994 (Salutatorian); New York University School of Law, LLM, 2000.

### VERONEAU, John K
Covington & Burling LLP, Washington, DC
202 662 5034
jveroneau@cov.com
*Featured in International Trade (Nationwide)*
**Practice Areas:** International trade and investment.
**Professional Memberships:** District of Columbia and Maryland Bar Associations.
**Career:** Partner, Covington & Burling; Deputy United States Trade Representative (USTR); General Counsel, USTR; Assistant Secretary of Defense.
**Publications:** "U.S. Trade and Investment Policy," Council on Foreign Relations (2011); Testimony: Trade Agenda, U.S. Senate Finance Committee (2011); "Sign the Colombia Trade Pact," The Washington Times (2/7/2011); Testimony: WTO Consistency of Section 211, U.S. House Committee on the Judiciary (2010); "Asian Investors Beware," Wall Street Journal (3/10/2006); "A High Bar for US Safeguards," China Business Review (2006).
**Personal:** University of Maine School of Law, JD.

### VERRILL JR, Charles Owen
Wiley Rein LLP, Washington, DC
202 719 7323
cverrill@wileyrein.com
*Featured in International Trade (Nationwide)*
**Practice Areas:** Chairman Emeritus, International Trade Practice. Counsels on trade law and policy including import/export regulation, WTO agreements, trade remedies, international bilateral/multilateral negotiations, commercial disputes mediation and regulation of foreign investments in the US and abroad. Acts as Counsel in disputes rising under investment agreements before international arbitration tribunals. Represents clients before the ITC, U.S. Department of Commerce, Court of International Trade, U.S. Federal Circuit Court of Appeals and arbitration tribunals.
**Career:** Senior Lecturing Fellow, International Business Transactions, Duke University School of Law; Adjunct Professor, International Trade Law and Regulations, Georgetown University Law Center.
**Personal:** Duke University(JD); Tufts University (BA).

### VETA, D Jean
Covington & Burling LLP, Washington, DC
202 662 5294
jveta@cov.com
*Featured in Financial Services Regulation (Nationwide)*
**Practice Areas:** Financial institutions civil and regulatory enforcement matters, including safety and soundness, accounting, anti-money laundering, lending discrimination, and other government investigations; white-collar crime; and internal corporate and congressional investigations. Selected "Litigator of the Week" by The Am Law Litigation Daily.
**Career:** Deputy Associate Attorney General, US DOJ; Deputy GC, US Dept of Education; Law

clerk, Hon Harold H Greene, US District Court (DC); Member of the DC Bar.
**Personal:** Tulane Law School (magna cum laude, Order of the Coif); Editor-in-Chief, Tulane Law Review; Thomas J Watson Fellowship; Tulane University Newcomb College (summa cum laude, Phi Beta Kappa, with honors).

### VINCE, Clinton A
Dentons, Washington, DC
202 408 8004
clinton.vince@dentons.com
*Featured in Energy & Natural Resources (Nationwide)*
**Practice Areas:** Leads legacy Dentons's award winning Energy, Transport and Infrastructure sector team ranked by Law360 as third-largest globally and "one of the world's strongest," which includes lawyers and professionals in more than 60 locations. Directed the expansion of legacy Dentons's energy team into a premier global practice, offering a full range of services to energy clients. Experience involves major project development, public policy and regulatory counsel for public and private clients, and top-tier track record for handling high profile litigation and appellate cases including US Supreme Court advocacy.
**Personal:** Georgetown University Law Center, JD; Trinity College of Hartford Connecticut, BA.

### VINE, Stephen M
Akin Gump Strauss Hauer & Feld LLP, New York
212 872 1030
svine@akingump.com
*Featured in Investment Funds (Nationwide)*
**Practice Areas:** For the past 30 years, Steve Vine has advised some of the largest and most prominent private investment funds and fund managers in connection with their fund formation and capital raising activities in investment disciplines including distressed investments, private equity, emerging markets, and domestic and foreign real estate. In addition, he provides advice on planning and execution of portfolio investment and financing transactions, and on formation and operation of investment management firms and related service companies, including seed capital, carry plan and monetization transactions. He also assists fund managers with regulatory compliance.
**Personal:** AB, JD, Harvard University.

### VITALE, Joseph P
Schulte Roth & Zabel LLP, New York
212 756 2485
joseph.vitale@srz.com
*Featured in Financial Services Regulation (Nationwide)*
**Practice Areas:** Representation of financial institutions and money service businesses with respect to: chartering; regulatory compliance; financial transactions; mergers, acquisitions and reorganizations; responses to formal and informal regulatory actions; litigations and claims; and legislative and regulatory developments.
**Professional Memberships:** American Bar Association, Banking Law Committee; American

Bankers Association; Institute of International Banks; Network Branded Prepaid Card Association.

**Career:** SRZ partner since 2008.

**Publications:** Writes and speaks extensively on issues related to the banking industry. Frequently quoted in the national media regarding banking law issues.

**Personal:** Georgetown University Law Center, JD; College of the Holy Cross, AB.

---

### VIZCARRONDO JR, Paul
Wachtell, Lipton, Rosen & Katz, New York
212 403 1208
pvizcarrondo@wlrk.com
*Featured in Securities (Nationwide), Litigation (New York)*

**Practice Areas:** Practice focuses on corporate and securities litigation and regulatory and white collar criminal matters.

**Professional Memberships:** Served on several committees of the Association of the Bar of the City of New York, including the Criminal Law and Federal Courts Committees, and currently is a member of the Securities Litigation Committee; has been a master of the Federal Bar Council's Inn of Court, is a member of the Columbia Law School Board of Visitors and of the American Bar Foundation, and a fellow of The New York Bar Foundation.

**Career:** Partner at Wachtell, Lipton, Rosen & Katz since 1981. Has tried significant cases in courts throughout the United States. Worked as law clerk to the Honorable Edward Weinfeld, United States District Judge for the Southern District of New York (1973-74) and as an assistant United States attorney in the Southern District of New York (1974-78). Awarded the Department of Justice's Special Achievement Award for his work in the Securities and Commodities Fraud Unit of the United States Attorney's Office. Has taught trial practice as an adjunct assistant professor of law at New York University School of Law and as a faculty member at the National Institute for Trial Advocacy; has lectured on United States federal securities laws for the Practising Law Institute; and has lectured on litigation issues as a Member of numerous continuing legal education panels.

**Publications:** Wrote the chapter on 'RICO' in Obermaier & Morvillo's 'White Collar Crime; Business and Regulatory Offenses'.

**Personal:** Graduated from Cornell University in 1970 (BS) and from Columbia University School of Law in 1973 (JD) where he was a Harlan Fiske Stone Scholar and Articles and Book Reviews Editor of Columbia Law Review.

---

### VOORHEES JR, Theodore
Covington & Burling LLP, Washington, DC
202 662 5236
tvoorhees@cov.com
*Featured in Products Liability (Nationwide)*

**Practice Areas:** Ted Voorhees has represented clients in software, mining, medical devices, sports, construction equipment, pharmaceutical, chemical, food, and beverage alcohol industries. He has advised on product recalls and served as national coordinating counsel for clients involved in multi-district tort litigation over chemical exposures, welding fumes exposures, beverage alcohol products and hip implants. Representative past and current clients include: Air Products & Chemicals Co., American Chemistry Council, Distilled Spirits Council, General Mills, Patagonia, Topps and The Toxicology Forum.

**Personal:** Ted received his AB Degree in 1971 from Harvard University and his JD Degree in 1974 from Catholic University.

---

### VYSKOCIL, Mary Kay
Simpson Thacher & Bartlett LLP, New York
212 455 3093
mvyskocil@stblaw.com
*Featured in Insurance (Nationwide), Insurance (New York)*

**Practice Areas:** Commercial litigation, insurance/reinsurance, securities and financial services. Represents insurers in complex coverage and reinsurance litigations (including jury trials) and arbitrations in the US, UK and Bermuda. Successfully represented Equitas against antitrust claim by Gerling; Bench trial resulting in verdict for JPMorganChase; represented Paramount in Paramount-Viacom-QVC takeover litigation; represented Matsushita in MCA v Epstein, successfully argued in the US Supreme Court; Represents SwissRe in 9/11 cases, including successful jury trial against Silverstein.

**Professional Memberships:** Chair of ARIAS-U.S.; Exec Comm & Chair of 2nd Circuit Courts Comm of Federal Bar Council.

**Publications:** Modern Reinsurance Law & Practice (Glasser LegalWorks).

---

### WACHEN, Kimberly
Arent Fox LLP, Washington, DC
202 775 5749
kimberly.wachen@arentfox.com
*Featured in Leisure & Hospitality (Nationwide), Real Estate (District of Columbia)*
See under District of Columbia for profile.

---

### WACHSBERGER, Chaim
Chadbourne & Parke LLP, New York
212 408 5232
cwachsberger@chadbourne.com
*Featured in Projects (Nationwide)*

**Practice Areas:** Senior Partner in Chadbourne's Project Finance Practice. Represents financing sources and sponsors in connection with domestic and international renewable and conventional energy, transportation and other industrial and infrastructure projects. Work includes acquisitions, portfolio financings, and development and project financing of greenfield projects. Works with sponsors on different types of debt and equity and construction contracts, fuel supply, off-take agreements, and other project-related agreements. Representations involve complex structures, multilateral and/or export credit agency involvement and political risk insurance products.

**Professional Memberships:** New York State Bar Association; American Bar Association (Section on Corporation, Banking and Business Law).

---

### WACHTELL, Herbert M
Wachtell, Lipton, Rosen & Katz, New York
212 403 1216
hmwachtell@wlrk.com
*Featured in Litigation (Nationwide), Litigation (New York)*

**Practice Areas:** Practice focuses on major, complex case litigation.

**Professional Memberships:** Fellow, American College of Trial Lawyers, American Bar Association; Member, American Law Institute, American Bar Association, Association of the Bar of the City of New York, New York County Lawyers.

**Career:** Partner at Wachtell, Lipton, Rosen & Katz and predecessor, 1958 to date; assistant US attorney, Southern District of New York, 1955-57.

**Publications:** Author: 'New York Practice under the CPLR', First Edition, 1963, Second Edition, 1966, Third Edition, 1970, Fourth Edition, 1973, Fifth Edition, 1976, Sixth Edition, 1986, Practicing Law Institute.

**Personal:** Graduated from New York University in 1952 (BS), from New York University in 1954 (LLB) where he was decisions editor, New York University Law Review, Order of the Coif and Root-Tilden Scholar, and from Harvard University in 1955 (LLM). Recipient of the Chambers Lifetime Achievement Award in Litigation in 2006.

---

### WADZINSKI, Kevin
Drinker Biddle & Reath LLP, Washington, DC
202 230 5144
kevin.wadzinski@dbr.com
*Featured in Native American Law (Nationwide)*

**Practice Areas:** Counsels tribes and gaming companies on all aspects of Indian gaming, including management contracts; casino development; financing; tribal and federal licensing; NIGC submissions; tribal gaming commission compliance; and compact negotiations. Advises tribal clients on economic development, business structures and employment law. Represents tribal governments before Congress and federal agencies.

**Professional Memberships:** Native American Bar Association, Washington, DC (Founding Member); Wisconsin State Bar Association Indian Law Section; Wisconsin Law Foundation Fellow.

**Publications:** Unionization: Is Your Tribe Prepared?; Board Rules National Labor Relations Act Applies to Indian Tribal Casinos.

**Personal:** University of Wisconsin, JD cum laude; University of Wisconsin, BA.

---

### WALD, Peter A
Latham & Watkins LLP, San Francisco
415 395 8009
peter.wald@lw.com
*Featured in Securities (Nationwide), Litigation (California)*

**Practice Areas:** Mr Wald has extensive trial and appellate experience in complex securities and professional liability matters. Practice highlights include numerous dismissals, summary judgments, trial, arbitration, and appellate victories in multi-billion dollar lawsuits against the world's leading accounting, professional services, financial services, and technology firms.

**Career:** Chair, Latham & Watkins Global Litigation Department (2004-10).

**Personal:** JD, Harvard Law School, 1977, Magna cum laude. Notes Editor, Harvard Law Review; AB, Brown University, 1974, Magna cum laude.

---

### WALDRON, Jonathan K
Blank Rome LLP, Washington, DC
202 772 5964
Waldron@BlankRome.com
*Featured in Transportation (Nationwide)*

**Practice Areas:** Jonathan Waldron chairs Blank Rome's Maritime practice. He focuses his practice in regulatory and legislative issues related to maritime, international, and environmental law. He counsels clients, both domestically and internationally, in areas such as citizenship and manning issues; coastwise trade; criminal defense; environmental maritime compliance and pollution response; maritime security compliance; LNG licensing; and vessel/facility operations. For more information see: www.BlankRome.com/Waldron

---

### WALKER, Helgi C
Wiley Rein LLP, Washington, DC
202 719 7349
hwalker@wileyrein.com
*Featured in Telecommunications (District of Columbia), Appellate Law (Nationwide)*
See under District of Columbia for profile.

---

### WALL, Christopher R
Pillsbury Winthrop Shaw Pittman LLP, Washington, DC
202 663 9250
cwall@pillsburylaw.com
*Featured in International Trade (Nationwide)*

**Practice Areas:** Mr Wall is the firm's senior International Trade Partner. He served as Assistant Secretary of Commerce for Export Administration during 2008-09. His practice includes export licensing (commercial and defense), compliance and enforcement; OFAC economic sanctions; CFIUS reviews and investigations; anti-boycott compliance and enforcement; Foreign Corrupt Practices Act compliance and investigations; import relief proceedings; market access; bilateral investment treaties; NAFTA and WTO disputes; complex Customs matters; trade, investment, export control and technology transfer policy; and legislation.

**Personal:** BA, Yale College, 1974 (Summa cum laude, Phi Beta Kappa); BA, Oxford University, 1976; JD, University of Virginia Law School, 1979.

---

### WALLACH, Kenneth
Simpson Thacher & Bartlett LLP, New York
212 455 3352
kwallach@stblaw.com
*Featured in Capital Markets (Nationwide)*

**Practice Areas:** Corporate Partner representing private equity sponsors, including Apax, Invus, JLL and TDR Capital, in connection with high yield and bridge financings such as Cengage Learning, Algeco Scotsman, MultiPlan and Bumble Bee. Regularly advises corporate clients including Weight Watchers, Drummond, Mars/Wrigley, Tesoro and Cooper-Standard.

Equity experience includes Issuer's Counsel for the IPOs of Weight Watchers and AGA Medical. Also represents underwriters in high yield debt offerings, including Cinemark and MEG Energy.
**Career:** Joined Firm in 1993; Partner, 2004.
**Personal:** BA, magna cum laude, Duke University, Phi Beta Kappa (1990); JD, University of Virginia School of Law (1993).

### WALSH, Linda
Hunton & Williams LLP, Washington, DC
202 955 1526
lwalsh@hunton.com
*Featured in Energy & Natural Resources (Nationwide)*
**Practice Areas:** Advises on regulatory matters affecting the electric utility industry, particularly transmission rates, administrative litigation, reliability compliance, and financial transactions. Serves as FERC Counsel to transmission companies, investor-owned utilities and independent generators. Represents clients in NERC and FERC compliance investigations, transmission rate proceedings, generator interconnection issues, Section 203 applications, and provides general regulatory advice on generation, transmission and operational issues.
**Professional Memberships:** Chair, Energy Bar Association, System Reliability, Planning and Compliance Committee, 2008-09; Board of Directors, EBA Charitable Foundation, 2008-09; President, EBA Charitable Foundation, 2007-08.
**Career:** Trial attorney, Federal Energy Regulatory Commission, OGC/Office of Electric Litigation, 1991-97.
**Personal:** Syracuse University College of Law, JD, cum laude, 1987; University of Hartford, MA, Economics, 1984, University of Connecticut, BA, 1982.

### WALTERS, Neal
Ballard Spahr LLP, Cherry Hill
856 761 3438
waltersn@ballardspahr.com
*Featured in Products Liability (Nationwide), Litigation (New Jersey)*
See under New Jersey for profile.

### WALTHER-MEADE, Carolina
Milbank, Tweed, Hadley & McCloy LLP, New York
212 530 5238
cwalther-meade@milbank.com
*Featured in Projects (Nationwide)*
**Practice Areas:** Partner in the Project Finance Practice Group and Latin America Practice Group. She has experience in cross-border financings and international project finance and development in Latin America, with an emphasis on oil and gas, infrastructure, mining and energy projects throughout the Latam region. Ms Walther-Meade's practice includes representation of commercial bank syndicates, multilateral and export credit agencies and other lenders, as well as corporate developers and industrial groups, particularly in Mexico, Brazil, Peru and Chile. She is a native Spanish speaker and is fluent in Portuguese. She spends a significant amount of time in our São Paulo office.

### WARD, Sarah M
Skadden, Arps, Slate, Meagher & Flom LLP & Affiliates, New York
212 735 2126
Sarah.Ward@skadden.com
*Featured in Banking & Finance (Nationwide)*
**Practice Areas:** Co-head of Skadden's Banking Group. Represents lenders and borrowers in leveraged finance transactions, including acquisition financings by private equity groups and public companies, project financings and other secured lending transactions, as well as restructurings and workouts.
**Career:** JD, Fordham University School of Law, 1986; AB, Princeton University, 1981.

### WARE JR, Paul F
Goodwin Procter LLP, Boston
617 570 1280
pware@goodwinprocter.com
*Featured in Litigation (Nationwide), Intellectual Property (Massachusetts), Litigation (Massachusetts)*
See under Massachusetts for profile.

### WARIN, Joseph
Gibson, Dunn & Crutcher LLP, Washington, DC
202 887 3609
fwarin@gibsondunn.com
*Featured in International Trade (Nationwide), Securities (Nationwide), Litigation (District of Columbia)*
**Practice Areas:** Chair, Washington, DC Office's Litigation Department of 140 lawyers; Co-chair, White-Collar Defense and Investigations Practice Group, and Executive Committee member. Expertise includes white collar crime, securities enforcement – Foreign Corrupt Practices Act investigations, False Claims Act cases, audit committee and special committee representations, compliance counseling and complex civil litigation. He handles complex litigation in federal courts, achieving dismissals of securities class action cases. He defends clients, including accounting firms against class actions and regulatory investigations.
**Career:** Assistant U.S. Attorney, Washington, D.C. (1976-1983).
**Personal:** JD, Georgetown University Law Center (1975); Editor, Law and Policy in International Business.

### WARNER, Douglas
Weil, Gotshal & Manges LLP, New York
212 310 8751
doug.warner@weil.com
*Featured in Private Equity (Nationwide)*
**Practice Areas:** Douglas Warner is Head of Weil's US Private Equity Group and has represented private equity sponsors in connection with acquisitions, dispositions and financings for more than 20 years. He has extensive experience in leveraged buyouts and dispositions of both public and private US and European companies, as well as minority investments and restructurings. Current clients include Centerbridge, Credit Suisse, CVC, Lee Equity, Oak Hill Capital, The Public Sector Pension Investment Board and Snow Phipps Group.

**Personal:** University of Puget Sound (BA, 1981); Boston University School of Law (JD, 1986).

### WARNER, E Waide
Davis Polk & Wardwell LLP, New York
212 450 4000
waide.warner@davispolk.com
*Featured in Projects (Nationwide)*
**Practice Areas:** Member of Davis Polk's Corporate Department, heads the firm's Project Finance Group and is active in acquisition finance, structured finance and distressed credits. Has been involved for more than 30 years in a wide range of US and international financings, debt and equity capital markets transactions and joint ventures, including project financings in the oil and gas, infrastructure, petrochemical, mining, power and telecommunications sectors in every region of the world.

### WARNER, Margaret H
McDermott Will & Emery LLP, Washington, DC
202 756 8228
mwarner@mwe.com
*Featured in Insurance (District of Columbia), Insurance (Nationwide)*
See under District of Columbia for profile.

### WATERS, Jennifer N
Crowell & Moring LLP, Washington, DC
202 624 2715
jwaters@crowell.com
*Featured in Energy & Natural Resources (Nationwide)*
**Practice Areas:** Partner in Crowell & Moring's Environment, Energy & Resources Group. Represents clients in a variety of energy regulatory and transactional matters. Focuses on energy law, having participated in the restructurings and transformations of the natural gas/electric industries that have occurred in the last two decades. Clients include natural gas distribution companies and municipal utility systems providing gas/electric service. Has practiced extensively before the Federal Energy Regulatory Commission, the Courts of Appeals, and the US Congress. Expertise includes FERC's and the appellate courts' rules of procedure. Has negotiated and prepared the contractual documents for many energy transactions.

### WATKISS, Jeffrey D
McDermott Will & Emery LLP, Washington, DC
202 756 8144
dwatkiss@mwe.com
*Featured in Energy & Natural Resources (Nationwide)*
**Practice Areas:** Represents clients in energy and related industries, including power companies; exploration, production and mid-market companies; natural gas pipelines; power and liquefied natural gas project developers; lenders; governments; and regulators. Areas of practice focus on antitrust and competition issues, and counseling power and natural gas companies on designing and implementing best-in-class legal and regulatory compliance programs. Represents clients in transactions, investigations, complex litigation and appeals in state and federal courts, and before

administrative agencies, arbitral panels, the US Congress and the executive branch.
**Personal:** JD, University of Utah School of Law, 1980; AB, Stanford University, 1975.

### WATTERSON, Paul N
Schulte Roth & Zabel LLP, New York
212 756 2563
paul.watterson@srz.com
*Featured in Capital Markets (Nationwide)*
**Practice Areas:** Co-Head, Structured Products & Derivatives Group. Structured product and derivative transactions, formation and representation of credit funds, capital markets regulation.
**Career:** SRZ Partner, 1984-; Law Clerk, Judge Leonard I. Garth, U.S. Court of Appeals, Third Circuit; Assistant, Mayor of the City of New York.
**Publications:** Frequent speaker and widely published. Articles appearing in Alternative Investment Quarterly, Futures and Derivatives Law Report, Derivatives Week, Credit, International Financial Law Review. Co-authored U.S. Chapter in The International Comparative Legal Guide to: Securitisation 2012.
**Personal:** Harvard Law School, JD, magna cum laude, editor of Harvard Law Review; Princeton University, AB, cum laude.

### WAXMAN, Seth
WilmerHale, Washington, DC
202 663 6800
seth.waxman@wilmerhale.com
*Featured in Appellate Law (Nationwide)*
**Practice Areas:** Broad litigation and counseling practice, with emphasis on challenges involving governments or public policy issues. Delivered over 60 US Supreme Court oral arguments. Clients range from financial institutions to technology, consumer, industrial and media companies.
**Professional Memberships:** Director and Fellow of several professional, educational and cultural institutions, including American College of Trial Lawyers, American Academy of Appellate Lawyers, American Bar Foundation, American Law Institute, Supreme Court Institute and Supreme Court Historical Society.
**Career:** US Solicitor General from 1997-2001.
**Publications:** Lectures and writes frequently on topics related to litigation, constitutional history/doctrine, First Amendment, intellectual property and Supreme Court.

### WEBB, Dan K
Winston & Strawn LLP, Chicago
312 558 5856
dwebb@winston.com
*Featured in Antitrust (Illinois), Litigation (Nationwide), Products Liability (Nationwide), Litigation (Illinois)*
See under Illinois for profile.

### WEBB, Robert J
Baker & Hostetler LLP, Orlando
407 649 4060
rwebb@bakerlaw.com
*Featured in Leisure & Hospitality (Nationwide)*
**Career:** Rob Webb maintains a diverse real estate and hospitality law practice emphasizing international resort and mixed-use developments, time-

shares, hotels and condominium hotels, as well as cruise ship and residence vessel programs. He was instrumental in the creation, design and development of many of today's leading international timeshare plans and serves as the treasurer of ARDA, the US timeshare trade association. Rob is Board Certified in Real Estate Law by The Florida Bar, has a strong background in commercial real estate development and title insurance law, and served as president of timeshare development company Island One, Inc., in 2000.

### WEBBER, A Duane
Baker & McKenzie, Washington, DC
202 452 7040
duane.webber@bakermckenzie.com
*Featured in Tax (Nationwide)*
**Practice Areas:** Tax controversy and litigation, transfer pricing, and international tax planning. Mr Webber has litigated cases on behalf of AIG, AOL, Apple Computer, Bausch & Lomb, Boeing, Cigna, Compaq Computer, Electronic Arts, Guardian Industries, HP, RadioShack, Sun Microsystems, Yamaha, Zurich Insurance, among others, and has negotiated resolutions through Appeals, APAs, and other ADR techniques for numerous companies. Issues include FTCs, Subpart F, transfer pricing, research credits, and others.
**Career:** JD, Georgetown University (magna cum laude); Chair, Global Tax Dispute Resolution Group; former Chair, North American Tax Group, Baker & McKenzie.
**Publications:** Numerous articles in tax journals and other publications.

### WEBER, Paul L
Chadbourne & Parke LLP, New York
212 408 5344
pweber@chadbourne.com
*Featured in Projects (Nationwide)*
**Practice Areas:** Paul Weber is a project finance attorney who has worked on a broad range of matters related to project financings and privatisations, internationally and in the United States. Mr Weber has represented developers, lenders, equity participants, equipment suppliers and others in the development and financing and the acquisition and disposition of infrastructure projects in more than 20 counties. His work includes transactions in the power, renewables, oil and gas, petrochemical and transport sectors.
**Personal:** Columbia University, Columbia College, BA, cum laude, 1981; University of Michigan Law School, JD, cum laude, 1984.

### WEBSTER, Susan
Cravath, Swaine & Moore LLP, New York
212 474 1660
swebster@cravath.com
*Featured in Securities (Nationwide)*
**Practice Areas:** Susan Webster is a partner in Cravath's Corporate Department and leads the Firm's General Corporate practice. She represents public companies in a wide variety of corporate matters and has extensive experience counseling senior management and boards of directors in connection with corporate and board governance, crisis management, compliance, and public

reporting obligations. She has advised clients on financial statement restatements and accounting-related disclosure issues and has substantial experience negotiating significant complex transactions.
**Personal:** Fordham University School of Law (JD, cum laude, 1984; Editor-in-Chief, Law Review); New York University (MS, 1978); Wesleyan University (BA, 1977). For more information: http://www.cravath.com/swebster

### WEDDLE, Jennifer H
Greenberg Traurig, LLP, Denver
303 572 6565
WeddleJ@gtlaw.com
*Featured in Native American Law (Nationwide)*
**Practice Areas:** Co-Chair, National American Indian Law Practice. Environmental; global energy and infrastructure; litigation; consumer finance.
**Professional Memberships:** Chair, Federal Bar Association Indian Law Section, 2011-13; Board Member, Colorado Conservation Trust; Chair, Center for Legal Inclusiveness, 2010-12; President, Colorado Indian Bar Association, 2009-12.
**Career:** Selected: 'Forty Under 40', Denver Business Journal, 2010; Super Lawyers Magazine—Rising Star, 2010-12; Best Lawyers in America, 2010-13. Adjunct Faculty, University of Colorado School of Law, 'American Indian Economic Development', Spring 2012; National Congress of American Indians, Colorado Election Protection Coordinator, 2004-13.
**Personal:** JD, Harvard Law School, 2000; BA, Classical Languages, University of Michigan, 1997.

### WEIGEL, Kenneth
Alston & Bird LLP, Washington, DC
202 239 3431
Ken.Weigel@alston.com
*Featured in International Trade (Nationwide)*
**Practice Areas:** Over thirty years advising US and foreign companies on all aspects of international trade regulatory issues—export controls and sanctions, imports, trade remedy proceedings, and trade policy. Represents companies in civil and criminal investigations and audits, provides counseling and assists in compliance programs.
**Career:** Regularly appears before US government agencies, including the U.S. Departments of Commerce, Treasury, Justice and State, the U.S. International Trade Commission, U.S. Customs & Border Protection and the Office of the United States Trade Representative.
**Personal:** The George Washington University (JD, 1979) with highest honors; University of Michigan (BA Economics with distinction, 1976).

### WEIL, Alan S
Sidley Austin LLP, New York
212 839 5315
aweil@sidley.com
*Featured in Leisure & Hospitality (Nationwide), Real Estate (New York)*
**Practice Areas:** Partner in Sidley's New York office and Head of the New York Real Estate Group. He represents banks and borrowers in permanent and construction loan originations secured by real estate and finance transactions. His lending practice involves securitized loans and

structured finance transactions and the acquisition of distressed debt on real estate. He also focuses in development, acquisition and disposition of commercial properties, commercial lease transactions, formation of real estate joint ventures and partnerships and real estate loan workouts.
**Personal:** The University of Chicago Law School, JD, 1982; Tufts University, BA, 1979, magna cum laude. Admission: New York.

### WEINBERGER, Harold P
Kramer Levin Naftalis & Frankel LLP, New York
212 715 9132
hweinberger@kramerlevin.com
*Featured in Advertising (Nationwide)*
**Practice Areas:** Harold Weinberger is recognized as one of the country's leading lawyers in the litigation of false advertising cases under the Lanham Act. Over the last several decades he has been lead counsel in many of the most significant cases in the field. Mr Weinberger is also a Lecturer in Law at Columbia Law School, where he teaches a Seminar in False Advertising Law. Mr Weinberger has spoken at many conferences on various aspects of false advertising law and has authored numerous published articles in the field. He is a fellow of the American College of Trial Lawyers.

### WEINGRAD, Howard
Davis & Gilbert LLP, New York
212 468 4829
hweingrad@dglaw.com
*Featured in Advertising (Nationwide)*
**Practice Areas:** Advertising, marketing and promotions.
**Career:** Mr Weingrad advises advertising and media companies in all aspects involving the creation, production and distribution of advertising campaigns. He is one of the country's leading experts in matters involving the provisions and implications of the Screen Actors Guild and other advertising and entertainment industry collective bargaining agreements. He also handles a wide array of music and talent matters, social media, copyright, rights of privacy and publicity, and other intellectual property issues. A significant portion of Mr Weingrad's practice is devoted to advertising production matters and negotiating and structuring agreements governing the use of celebrity talent. He is recognized in The Best Lawyers in America for advertising law, and The Legal 500 U.S. for advertising and marketing law.

### WEINSTEIN, Martin J
Willkie Farr & Gallagher LLP, Washington, DC
202 303 1122
mweinstein@willkie.com
*Featured in International Trade (Nationwide)*
**Practice Areas:** Represents organisations and individuals in internal investigations and foreign business practices, compliance, and white-collar matters, including Foreign Corrupt Practices Act (FCPA). Recent FCPA representations include Alcatel, Pride, Daimler and Tyco in settlements with SEC and DOJ; ongoing counsel for numer-

ous global energy/communications/health care/manufacturing companies.
**Personal:** JD, University of Virginia Law School, 1984. BA, cum laude, honors in government, Dartmouth College, 1981. Named by Ethisphere Magazine (2009-11) as one of "Attorneys Who Matter" and as one of the "100 Most Influential People in Business Ethics for 2007." President's Leadership Council, Dartmouth College. See: http://www.willkie.com/MartinWeinstein

### WEISSER, Michael E
Weil, Gotshal & Manges LLP, New York
212 310 8249
michael.weisser@weil.com
*Featured in Private Equity (Nationwide)*
**Practice Areas:** Michael Weisser represents private equity sponsors and portfolio companies in connection with acquisitions, dispositions and general corporate matters. He has extensive experience with leveraged buyouts, going private transactions and minority investments and frequently counsels clients on a variety of securities law, corporate governance and strategic matters. He regularly represents American Securities, CVC Capital Partners, HIG/Bayside, HM Capital Partners, Irving Place Capital, The Jordan Company, Lindsay Goldberg, Ontario Teachers' Pension Plan Board and Providence Equity Partners and their portfolio companies.
**Personal:** University of Pennsylvania (BA, 1995); Columbia University School of Law, (JD, 1998).

### WELCH, Richard J
Bingham McCutchen LLP, Los Angeles
213 229 8510
rick.welch@bingham.com
*Featured in Private Equity (Nationwide), Corporate/M&A (California)*
See under California for profile.

### WELLER, David L
WilmerHale, Washington, DC
202 663 6544
david.weller@wilmerhale.com
*Featured in International Trade (Nationwide)*
**Practice Areas:** Partner, Regulatory and Government Affairs Department; member, International Trade, Investment and Market Access Practice Group; China Practice. Represents clients regarding trade and regulatory impediments to accessing foreign markets, in international dispute settlement proceedings at the WTO and elsewhere, and on trade and investment policy issues, including US legislation and trade agreement negotiations.
**Career:** Served as Deputy Assistant US Trade Representative for China, Hong Kong and Taiwan and USTR Assistant General Counsel, where he was USTR's chief legal advisor on China trade issues.
**Personal:** Columbia Law School (JD, Columbia Law Review); Harvard University (BA, cum laude). Proficient in Mandarin.

**WELLS JR, Theodore V**
Paul, Weiss, Rifkind, Wharton & Garrison LLP, New York
212 373 3089
twells@paulweiss.com
*Featured in Litigation (Nationwide), Litigation (New York)*
**Practice Areas:** Co-Chair of Litigation Department. Extensive experience defending corporations and corporate executives in bet-the-company jury trials and federal regulatory investigations. Particular focus on complex civil and corporate litigation, including massive securities and product liability class actions, SEC regulatory work, health care fraud and FCPA matters. Representative engagements: successfully defended Citigroup in two multi-billion dollar civil fraud jury trials that went to verdict; lead trial counsel for Bank of America in class action litigations relating to the bank's acquisition of Merrill Lynch & Co.; lead trial counsel for Merck in SEC and DOJ investigations arising from the sale and marketing of Vioxx. In 2010, The National Law Journal named Ted one of "The Decade's Most Influential Lawyers" and over the years has repeatedly selected him as one of the 100 most influential lawyers in America, including naming Ted as the Lawyer of the Year in 2006. Fellow of American College of Trial Lawyers, and recognized as one of the outstanding jury trial lawyers in the United States.

**WELSHIMER, Mark J**
Sullivan & Cromwell LLP, New York
212 558 3669
welshimerm@sullcrom.com
*Featured in Capital Markets (Nationwide)*
**Professional Memberships:** Commercial Law Committee, ABA.
**Career:** Partner since 1983. Coordinator, Structured Finance Group; Deputy, Financial Institutions Group. Broad banking and securities practice, particularly structured capital raising transactions and asset-based finance, with a focus on new products. He has represented issuers/underwriters in numerous firsts, including the development of hybrid capital instruments and, earlier, the first securitizations of a public automobile loan, public commercial real estate loan, funded C&I loan, and life insurance policy, and first public good bank/bad bank transaction. Advises financial institutions in commercial and regulatory matters.
**Personal:** Harvard Law School (JD, 1976); Harvard College (BA, 1973).

**WELTY, Todd**
Dentons, Dallas
214 259 0953
todd.welty@dentons.com
*Featured in Tax (Nationwide), Tax (Texas)*
See under Texas for profile.

**WERNER, Kathleen L**
Clifford Chance US LLP, New York
212 878 8526
kathleen.werner@cliffordchance.com
*Featured in Capital Markets (Nationwide)*

**Practice Areas:** Partner in the Capital Markets Practice of Clifford Chance. Ms Werner primarily represents companies and investment banks in capital markets and mergers and acquisitions transactions.
**Career:** Partner with the firm since 2000. St Joseph's University, BA, cum laude, 1988. Georgetown University Law Center, JD, cum laude, 1991.

**WESELY, Marissa C**
Simpson Thacher & Bartlett LLP, New York
212 455 7173
mwesely@stblaw.com
*Featured in Banking & Finance (Nationwide)*
**Practice Areas:** Corporate Partner specializing in domestic and international financing, with an emphasis on leveraged acquisition finance and recapitalization transactions, principally advising equity sponsors and corporate borrowers. Recent representations include: Algeco Scotsman in a multi-jurisdictional ABL facility as part of its global recapitalization; Affinia Group in the financing of the spin-off of its brake business; Peabody Energy in the financing of its acquisition of MacArthur Coal; and Sealed Air in the financing of its acquisition of Diversey.
**Career:** Partner since 1989.
**Personal:** BA, magna cum laude, Williams College (1976); JD, cum laude, Harvard Law School (1980).

**WEST, Glenn D**
Weil, Gotshal & Manges LLP, Dallas
214 746 7780
gdwest@weil.com
*Featured in Private Equity (Nationwide), Corporate/M&A (Texas)*
See under Texas for profile.

**WEST, Joseph D**
Gibson, Dunn & Crutcher LLP, Washington, DC
202 955 8658
jwest@gibsondunn.com
*Featured in Construction (District of Columbia), Government (Nationwide)*
See under District of Columbia for profile.

**WEST, Lawrence**
Latham & Watkins LLP, Washington, DC
lawrence.west@lw.com
*Featured in Securities (Nationwide)*
**Practice Areas:** Represents entities and individuals in SEC, PCAOB and other enforcement matters. Conducts internal investigations. Counsels corporations, officers and boards regarding disclosure, corporate compliance, insider trading, FCPA and whistleblower issues. Clients include public companies, accounting firms, broker-dealers, financial services firms, investment advisers, hedge funds, private equity firms and individuals. Maintains global practice.
**Career:** Former senior member of the SEC's Enforcement Division. Former Adjunct Professor, George Washington University Law School.
**Personal:** JD, Yale Law School, 1991; AB, Harvard College, 1988.

**WEST, Paul**
Baker, Donelson, Bearman, Caldwell & Berkowitz, PC, Baton Rouge
225 381 7018
PWest@bakerdonelson.com
*Featured in Gaming & Licensing (Nationwide), Gaming & Licensing (Louisiana)*
See under Louisiana for profile.

**WESTERBERG, Gary W**
Locke Lord LLP, Chicago
312 443 0245
gwesterberg@lockelord.com
*Featured in Transportation (Nationwide)*
**Practice Areas:** Former chair of the firm's Aviation Section. His practice primarily involves defense of aircraft product manufacturers, airlines, aircraft leasing companies, general aviation operators in crash litigation and the representation of aviation insurers in connection with complex insurance coverage issues.
**Professional Memberships:** ABA; International Bar Association; Lawyer-Pilots Bar Association; Aviation Insurance Association.
**Career:** Of Counsel with Locke Lord.
**Personal:** Southern Methodist University School of Law (JD, 1971), Order of the Coif; Cornell College (BA, Economics, 1968). He is a former aircraft owner and instrument rated commercial pilot with more than 4,000 hours of flight experience in land and seaplanes.

**WHEELER, Malcolm**
Wheeler Trigg O'Donnell LLP, Denver
303 244 1870
wheeler@wtotrial.com
*Featured in Litigation (Nationwide), Products Liability (Nationwide), Litigation (Colorado)*
**Practice Areas:** Complex business litigation and product liability litigation, especially nationwide pattern litigation, class actions, and appeals. National coordinating trial counsel for Fortune 100 clients in pharmaceuticals, automotive, and consumer products industries. Defended manufacturers at trial in several highly publicized cases and argued before U.S. Supreme Court.
**Professional Memberships:** Fellow, International Academy of Trial Lawyers; Fellow, American College of Trial Lawyers; Product Liability Advisory Council Lifetime Achievement Award.
**Publications:** Numerous articles in law reviews and other publications, including seminal article on constitutional arguments for providing substantive and procedural safeguards in punitive damages proceedings.
**Personal:** JD, Stanford, 1969; S.B., MIT, 1966.

**WHELAN III, William J**
Cravath, Swaine & Moore LLP, New York
212 474 1644
wwhelan@cravath.com
*Featured in Capital Markets (Nationwide)*
**Practice Areas:** Bill Whelan is a partner in Cravath's Corporate Department and serves as the Leader of its Securities practice. He is a generalist corporate lawyer who advises on a broad range of corporate issues, including corporate governance and public company disclosure obligations. Since

1993, he has devoted a substantial amount of his time to representing issuers and investment banks in initial public offerings, high-yield and investment grade debt offerings and follow-on equity offerings.
**Personal:** Fordham University School of Law (JD, cum laude, 1983; Managing Editor, Fordham Law Review); University of Virginia (BA, with Distinction, 1980). For more information: http://www.cravath.com/wwhelan

**WHITAKER, G Warren**
Day Pitney LLP, New York
212 297 2468
gwwhitaker@daypitney.com
*Featured in Wealth Management (Nationwide)*
**Career:** G. Warren Whitaker, member of Day Pitney's Executive Board and partner in the Individual Clients Department, focuses on complex domestic and international estate planning and related planning for high net worth individuals and multinational families. Warren is the former US chair of the Society of Trusts and Estates Practitioners (STEP) and a member of STEP's Worldwide Council. He is a fellow of the American College of Trusts and Estates Counsel and its International Estate Planning Committee and a member of the Estate and Gift Tax Committee of the Association of the Bar of the City of New York.

**WHITAKER, Mark**
DLA Piper LLP (US), New York
703 773 4183
mark.whitaker@dlapiper.com
*Featured in Sports Law (Nationwide)*
**Practice Areas:** Sports Law.
**Career:** He has a multi-faceted transactional practice with an emphasis on financings involving sports properties. He represents financial institutions, investors and borrowers, sellers and prospective purchasers of Major League Baseball, National Basketball Association, National Hockey League and Major League Soccer franchises and has been instrumental in a number of high-profile financings for new stadiums and arenas for National Football League, National Basketball Association and Major League Baseball teams.
**Personal:** JD, Yale Law School; AB, Duke University (magna cum laude) Phi Beta Kappa.

**WHITE, Geoffrey**
Clifford Chance US LLP, New York
212 878 8098
geoffrey.white@cliffordchance.com
*Featured in Transportation (Nationwide), Banking & Finance (Nationwide)*
**Practice Areas:** Specialises in asset financing, banking, leasing and M&A. Has extensive experience structuring and documenting aircraft finance transactions for financiers, operating lessors and airlines around the world. Particular expertise in export credit agency-supported financings, including European ECA aircraft financings, US Ex-Im Bank backed aircraft financings and JBIC and Export Development Corporation.
**Career:** The Hutchins School, Hobart, Tasmania. University of Melbourne, LLB Honors and B Comm. Southern Methodist University, LLM.

Qualified in Melbourne Victoria, England and Japan.

## WHITE, John W
Cravath, Swaine & Moore LLP, New York
212 474 1732
jwhite@cravath.com
*Featured in Capital Markets (Nationwide), Securities (Nationwide)*
**Practice Areas:** John W White is a partner in Cravath's Corporate Department and serves as Co-Chair of its Corporate Governance and Board Advisory practice. He served as Director of the Division of Corporation Finance at the SEC from 2006-2008. His practice focuses on representing public companies on a wide variety of matters, including corporate governance matters, public reporting obligations, public financings and restatements and other financial crises.
**Personal:** New York University School of Law (JD, magna cum laude, 1973; Order of the Coif; Managing Editor, Law Review); University of Virginia (BS, with Honors, 1970). For more information: http://www.cravath.com/jwhite

## WHITE, Peter C
DLA Piper LLP (US), New York
212 335 4555
peter.white@dlapiper.com
*Featured in Sports Law (Nationwide)*
**Practice Areas:** Sports Law, Corporate, Finance
**Career:** He has over 20 years of experience in the professional sports business, representing various parties in commercial and financing transactions involving the world's major sports leagues, including Major League Baseball, the National Basketball Association, the National Football League, the National Hockey League and the Barclays Premier League. He has developed an expertise representing teams, owners, banks, investors and other parties in the financing of sports properties, including leagues, clubs, media interests, stadiums, arenas, concessions and related assets.
**Personal:** JD, St. John's University School of Law; BA, Adelphi University.

## WHITESELL, Anne Marie
Dechert LLP, Washington, DC
202 261 3469
annemarie.whitesell@dechert.com
*Featured in International Arbitration (Nationwide)*
**Practice Areas:** Ms Whitesell, former secretary general of the ICC International Court of Arbitration, is a member of Dechert's international resolution and dispute resolution practice. Based in Washington. D.C., she works closely with the firm's Paris office.
**Professional Memberships:** Member, New York and District of Columbia Bars; admitted to practice before the U.S. District Courts for the Southern and Eastern Districts of New York; director, Alternative Dispute Resolution Center, International Law Institute.
**Personal:** University of Virginia School of Law (JD); Université de Paris I, Panthéon-Sorbonne (Doctorate in Law); Smith College (A.B.).

## WHITESTONE, David
Holland & Knight LLP, Washington, DC
202 457 7080
david.whitestone@hklaw.com
*Featured in Government (Nationwide)*
**Practice Areas:** Partner in the Public Policy & Regulation Practice Group and oversees the provision of legal and legislative counsel services to firm clients. He is the chairman of the firmwide Transportation Industry practice and a member of the firm's Directors Committee. He practices in the areas of transportation, homeland security, defense and appropriations. Prior to entering private practice, he served on the U.S. House Appropriations Committee as associate staff where he focused on aviation, transit, highway, rail and public infrastructure matters. Representative clients include Fortune 500 companies, municipalities, not-for-profits and professional sports leagues.

## WIDER, Jedd H
Morgan, Lewis & Bockius LLP, New York
212 309 6605
jwider@morganlewis.com
*Featured in Investment Funds (Nationwide)*
**Practice Areas:** Jedd H Wider is a Partner in Morgan Lewis's Private Investment Funds Practice in New York. Mr Wider represents many of the world's leading hedge funds, private equity funds and institutional investors in connection with the structuring and formation of and investment in global private investment funds, particularly hedge funds, private equity funds, secondary funds, venture capital funds, funds-of-funds, and captive funds and in their subsequent investment and regulatory activities. Mr Wider regularly speaks at international private fund conferences and is often cited in many of the most prestigious international publications on investment fund and regulatory issues.

## WIECZOREK, Dennis E
DLA Piper LLP (US), Chicago
312 368 4087
dennis.wieczorek@dlapiper.com
*Featured in Franchising (Nationwide)*
**Practice Areas:** Franchising, international franchising and distribution, antitrust.
**Professional Memberships:** Past Chair of the American Bar Association Forum on Franchising.
**Career:** He chairs the firm's Franchise and Distribution Group. He concentrates in US and international franchising, licensing, antitrust, and distribution. He has spoken at numerous seminars and symposia for lawyers, executives, accountants, and government regulators, and has written for a wide variety of legal and business publications. He has testified before the US Congress on the subject of franchise legislation.
**Personal:** JD, Duke University School of Law; BA, Washington University in St Louis (magna cum laude).

## WIEMAN, Lawrence E
Davis Polk & Wardwell LLP, New York
212 450 4000
lawrence.wieman@davispolk.com
*Featured in Banking & Finance (Nationwide)*

**Practice Areas:** Member of Davis Polk's Credit Group. Represents borrowers and lenders in secured and unsecured financings for US and non-US transactions. Advises lenders and financially distressed borrowers on workouts and debt restructurings, various lender, borrower and acquiror clients on senior and subordinated financing for contested and friendly acquisitions, and financial institutions and other clients regarding credit risks involved in domestic and cross-border securities and derivatives transactions, structured products and related collateral arrangements.

## WIESEN, Jeffrey M
Mintz Levin Cohn Ferris Glovsky and Popeo PC, Boston
617 348 1759
JWiesen@mintz.com
*Featured in Life Sciences (Nationwide), Corporate/M&A (Massachusetts)*
**Practice Areas:** Chair, Life Sciences Practice; involved in formation of some of the industry's largest companies, structuring and negotiating their strategic alliances, VC financings, and public offerings; counsels clients (start-ups to large public companies; domestic and international) on private and public finance, M&A, strategic alliances and joint ventures, and technology transfer and cross-transfer agreements; has successfully structured, coordinated, and negotiated technology-based collaborations and acquisitions with numerous world-wide pharmaceutical and chemical companies.
**Professional Memberships:** Advisory Council, Harvard-MIT Division of Health Sciences and Technology; Board, HST Biomedical Enterprise Program; BoD, Biomedical Science Careers Program; Former GC, Massachusetts Biotechnology Council.
**Personal:** Yale Law School, JD.

## WIGGINS, Dena E
Ballard Spahr LLP, Washington, DC
202 661 2225
wigginsd@ballardspahr.com
*Featured in Energy & Natural Resources (Nationwide)*
**Practice Areas:** Dena E. Wiggins is a partner in the Business and Finance Department. She focuses her practice on federal regulatory matters involving natural gas transportation and storage, crude oil, petroleum products, and hydropower. She has participated in numerous natural gas and oil pipeline rate proceedings and in rulemakings affecting the Federal Energy Regulatory Commission's (FERC) regulation of those commodities. She also advises clients on FERC enforcement and compliance.
**Professional Memberships:** American Bar Association Section of Environment, Energy and Natural Resources.
**Career:** District of Columbia.
**Personal:** Georgetown University Law Center (JD 1988) University of Richmond (BA 1977, magna cum laude).

## WILGUS, Lauren
Blank Rome LLP, New York
212 885 5348
LWilgus@BlankRome.com
*Featured in Transportation (Nationwide)*
**Practice Areas:** Lauren Wilgus practices in the areas of international and maritime litigation and alternate dispute resolution. Ms Wilgus represents clients in a wide range of domestic and international matters, including: charterparty disputes; cargo damage claims; marine insurance disputes; shipbuilding contract disputes; oil spills and maritime casualties; salvage and general average; general commercial litigation; and international and domestic commercial contract disputes. She is active in the Maritime Law Association. For more information see: www.BlankRome.com/LWilgus

## WILKINSON, Phoebe A
Chadbourne & Parke LLP, New York
212 408 1157
pwilkinson@chadbourne.com
*Featured in Products Liability (Nationwide)*
**Practice Areas:** Ms Wilkinson has handled disputes matters around the country and abroad, for domestic and international clients. She specializes in products liability and commercial disputes, with a focus on class action and other consolidated litigation defense matters, as well as regulatory and risk management counseling. Ms Wilkinson has significant experience before international arbitration tribunals operating under the auspices of all the major arbitration institutions. In the products liability arena, Ms Wilkinson serves clients in the pharmaceutical, medical device, and durable goods industries.
**Personal:** Brown University (1988); Brooklyn Law School (1993).

## WILLIAMS, Mark C
Bingham McCutchen LLP, Washington, DC
202 373 6181
mark.williams@bingham.com
*Featured in Energy & Natural Resources (Nationwide)*
**Practice Areas:** Counsels clients on energy regulatory and utility holding company matters. Plans transactions subject to regulatory oversight and leads energy regulatory and restructuring initiatives. Works with project developers and financial institutions on energy projects and documenting secured lending and direct equity positions in the energy sector.
**Career:** Sole lawyer in Federal Energy Regulatory Commission's Division of Corporate Applications, advising on merger, divestiture, financing, independent power and transmission matters. Adviser to House of Representatives' Subcommittee on Regulatory Reform and Paperwork Reduction in 1998 oversight hearings on electric utility regulation.
**Personal:** New York Law School, JD, 1990; Columbia University, BA, 1987.

## WILLIAMS, William A
Sidley Austin LLP, Washington, DC
202 736 8767
bill.williams@sidley.com
*Featured in Energy & Natural Resources (Nationwide)*

**Practice Areas:** Partner in Sidley's Washington, DC office, practicing in energy regulatory. He focuses on the representation of interstate gas and oil pipelines and other clients before the Federal Energy Regulatory Commission. He advises clients involved in litigation or commercial transactions with regulated companies and represents clients in FERC enforcement proceedings. He currently represents TransCanada's Keystone oil pipeline project, the Alaska Pipeline Project sponsored by TransCanada and ExxonMobil, Alliance Pipeline, National Fuel Gas Supply Corp and Empire Pipeline.
**Personal:** University of Virginia, JD, 1977; George Mason University, BS, 1974. Admission: District of Columbia.

## WILLIAMS JR, B John
Skadden, Arps, Slate, Meagher & Flom LLP & Affiliates, Washington, DC
202 371 7080
BJohn.Williams@skadden.com
*Featured in Tax (District of Columbia), Tax (Nationwide)*

**Practice Areas:** Represents clients in federal tax controversy and litigation matters, from Internal Revenue Service (IRS) examinations and administrative appeals through trial and appeal in the federal courts.
**Professional Memberships:** American College of Tax Counsel, American Law Institute, American Bar Association's Tax Section.
**Career:** Formerly Chief Counsel for the IRS. Also served as judge on the U.S. Tax Court, Deputy Assistant Attorney General in the Tax Division of the Justice Department and Special Assistant to the Chief Counsel of the IRS. JD, George Washington University Law School, 1974 (with distinction); BA, George Washington University, 1971 (with honors).

## WILLIAMS JR, William J
Sullivan & Cromwell LLP, New York
212 558 3722
williamsw@sullcrom.com
*Featured in Capital Markets (Nationwide)*
**Professional Memberships:** ABA; former member, NASD Legal Advisory Board and NYSE Legal Advisory Committee.
**Career:** Of Counsel since 2005. Partner, 1969-2004. Extensive experience in international securities offerings by European, Japanese and Latin American issuers. Major role in developing SEC Regulation S, Rule 15a-6, Regulation M, and Securities Act and public offering reforms. Represented Securities Industry Association in SEC's consideration of fixed price offerings, shelf registration, Securities Act Concept Release, "Aircraft Carrier" and Regulation FD.
**Personal:** NYU Law School (LLB, 1961); College of Holy Cross (AB, 1958).

## WILSON, Anita
Vinson & Elkins LLP, Washington, DC
202 639 6776
awilson@velaw.com
*Featured in Energy & Natural Resources (Nationwide)*

**Practice Areas:** Federal and state energy regulation and energy transactions. Represents natural gas pipelines, storage providers and shippers in proceedings before the Federal Energy Regulatory Commission, Department of Energy, Department of State, and USCG/MARAD. Advises clients regarding certificate, rate, compliance, import/export, presidential permit, complaint, enforcement/audit, and rulemaking matters, as well as appellate litigation and due diligence review of pipeline, storage and LNG terminal assets.
**Professional Memberships:** American Bar Association; Energy Bar Association.
**Career:** Partner since 1999.
**Personal:** University of Virginia (JD 1990) (President of Law School Class); College of William and Mary (BS 1986) (Phi Beta Kappa).

## WILSON, Bruce S
Covington & Burling LLP, Washington, DC
202 662 5400
bwilson@cov.com
*Featured in Sports Law (Nationwide)*
**Practice Areas:** Practice includes corporate finance, M&A, joint ventures, sponsorships and media rights transactions. He advises the NFL, NHL, NBA, NASCAR, MLB, other sports leagues, owners and prospective owners on team acquisitions, investors and sponsors on facility finance, media development, sponsorships, entity structuring, corporate governance, commercial matters.
**Career:** Joined Covington in 1987. 1993-97, General Counsel, Bacardi Limited. 1986-87, law clerk to Judge Pasco M Bowman, US Court of Appeals for the Eighth Circuit. 1981-83, legislative assistant to Rep Steven L Neal, US House of Representatives.
**Personal:** University of Virginia, JD, (1986), Order of the Coif; BA (1981), Phi Beta Kappa.

## WIMMER, Kurt A
Covington & Burling LLP, Washington, DC
202 662 5278
kwimmer@cov.com
*Featured in First Amendment Litigation (Nationwide), Media & Entertainment (District of Columbia)*
**Practice Areas:** U.S. Chair of firm's global privacy and data security practice; co-chair, Media, Internet and Technology group. Represents Microsoft, Facebook, CBS, Viacom, General Mills, Newsweek and others on privacy, data protection, data security, IP and digital media issues.
**Professional Memberships:** Vice-chair, Privacy and Informatino Security Committee of American Bar Association Antitrust Division; c-chair, Privacy Committee, Federal Communications Bar Association.
**Career:** 2006-2009, SVP and GC of Gannett Co., Inc.; Managing Partner, London office of firm, 2000-2003.
**Personal:** Syracuse University, JD, M.A., 1985.

## WINBURNE, Blake H
McDermott Will & Emery LLP, Houston
713 653 1740
bwinburne@mwe.com
*Featured in Projects (Nationwide)*
**Practice Areas:** Head of firm's global energy advisory practice, based in the Houston office. A transactional lawyer focusing on the downstream and midstream energy sectors. Advises clients on the development, structuring and financing of large-scale energy projects and on energy sector mergers, acquisitions, dispositions and joint ventures, both in the United States and abroad.
**Professional Memberships:** New York State Bar; State Bar of Texas; The Institute for Energy Law.
**Personal:** LLM (with honors), international and comparative law, Georgetown University Law Center, 1997; JD, George Mason University School of Law, 1995; BBA, University of Texas, 1991.

## WINK, Stephen
Latham & Watkins LLP, New York
212 906 1229
stephen.wink@lw.com
*Featured in Financial Services Regulation (Nationwide)*
**Practice Areas:** Mr Wink advises investment banks, hedge funds, private equity firms, proprietary trading firms and other financial institutions on regulation of broker-dealers and investment advisors, market regulation and compliance and enforcement matters. He provides commentary on regulatory initiatives and rule-making proposals on behalf of clients and trade associations, and frequently obtains no-action relief and interpretive guidance on behalf of clients from various regulatory bodies. Wink is a former member of the Securities Industry and Financial Markets Association's Federal Regulation Committee, the New York Stock Exchange's Compliance Advisory Committee and was Chair of the Bond Market Association's Municipal Legal Advisory Committee.

## WINTER, John D
Patterson Belknap Webb & Tyler LLP, New York
212 336 2836
jwinter@pbwt.com
*Featured in Products Liability (Nationwide)*
**Practice Areas:** John Winter has focused his practice on the defense of pharmaceutical and medical device cases. A member of Patterson Belknap since 1990, Mr Winter has tried or argued the appeal of more than 40 product liability cases in state and federal courts throughout the United States. Mr Winter also has acted as national counsel for pharmaceutical, consumer product, and medical device manufacturers in consolidated proceedings in state and federal courts. In addition, Mr Winter has published articles on regulatory and evidentiary issues concerning pharmaceutical and medical devices Mr Winter has substantial experience litigating commercial matters for Patterson Belknap clients including tax-exempt organizations, governmental entities, privately held companies as well as pharmaceutical, cosmetic, and medical device companies.

**Professional Memberships:** Member, Product Liability Advisory Council; International Association of Defense Counsel; Member, New York State Bar Association (Co-Chair, Committee on the Federal Judiciary of the Commercial and Federal Litigation Section).
**Career:** Prior to joining Patterson Belknap, Mr Winter served as Law Clerk to the Hon. John M. Cannella, U.S. District Judge for the Southern District of New York.
**Personal:** JD, 1981, Fordham University School of Law, Editor-in-Chief, Fordham Urban Law Journal; M.A., 1978, University of Pennsylvania, Government Affairs; BA, 1978, University of Pennsylvania, cum laude.

## WISEMAN, Kenneth L
Andrews Kurth LLP, Washington, DC
202 662 2715
kwiseman@andrewskurth.com
*Featured in Energy & Natural Resources (Nationwide)*

**Practice Areas:** Litigates complex energy cases, including enforcement proceedings, before FERC and state public utility commissions. Has argued appeals of energy decisions before Federal and state courts of appeal and state supreme courts. Provides strategic advice to senior company executives on all aspects of electric and gas regulation and related commercial undertakings. Has represented major interstate natural gas pipelines since 1986. Has represented electric generators since early 1990s. Served as lead counsel in numerous cases, including arbitrations, to increase generator compensation in various organized markets, including New York and New England electric capacity markets.

## WISEMAN, Michael M
Sullivan & Cromwell LLP, New York
212 558 3846
wisemanm@sullcrom.com
*Featured in Financial Services Regulation (Nationwide)*

**Professional Memberships:** Former Chair, Banking Law Committee, ABCNY; Member, Banking Law Committee, NYSBA; Member, Council on Foreign Relations; Member, American Law Institute; Reporter, Capital Markets Lawyers Group on guidelines for OTC transactions.
**Career:** Managing Partner, Financial Institutions Group. Broad experience in US and international banking and finance, including transactional, regulatory, enforcement, M&A, legislative and corporate governance matters. Client Representations include: AIG, including matters related to the government's assistance and exit; BONY; GS, including conversion to bank holding company; Moody's; the Clearing House; Barclays; JPMC; and UBS in diverse matters.
**Personal:** Harvard Law School (JD, 1978); Harvard University (AB, 1975).

## WISHNIA, Jonathan C
Lowenstein Sandler LLP, Roseland
646 414 6797
jwishnia@lowenstein.com
*Featured in Capital Markets (Nationwide)*

**Practice Areas:** Jonathan C. Wishnia is a capital markets attorney who advises on mortgage and structured finance matters, including trading and financing whole loans and servicing rights; mortgage loan servicing; and securitization of various asset classes. Jon additionally counsels clients on secured and unsecured credit facilities, asset purchases and sales, mergers and acquisitions and other general corporate and finance matters. Jon also heads the capital markets litigation group's transactional team assisting the litigation and restructuring of mortgage- and asset-backed securities, collateralized obligations, asset-backed commercial paper conduits, structured investment vehicles, derivatives and other distressed debt. www.lowenstein.com/jwishnia

## WITTEN, Roger M
WilmerHale, New York
212 230 8850
Roger.Witten@wilmerhale.com
*Featured in International Trade (Nationwide)*

**Practice Areas:** Partner, Litigation/Controversy Department. Practice emphasizes complex international and domestic litigation, internal corporate investigations, law enforcement matters and Foreign Corrupt Practices Act matters. Leads a group of 45 lawyers who specialize in FCPA enforcement and counseling issues.

**Career:** Admitted to New York and District of Columbia Bar. Served as Assistant Special Prosecutor of the Watergate Special Prosecution Force 1973 and 1974; law clerk to Hon Harrison L Winter, US Court of Appeals for the Fourth Circuit 1972-1973.

**Publications:** Witten & Parker, Complying with the FCPA (LexisNexis).

**Personal:** Harvard Law School (JD, cum laude); Dartmouth College (AB, magna cum laude).

## WOLF, Barry M
Weil, Gotshal & Manges LLP, New York
212 310 8209
barry.wolf@weil.com
*Featured in Investment Funds (Nationwide)*

**Practice Areas:** Mr Wolf is Weil's Executive Partner and Chair of the 16-member Management Committee. He provides commercial advice and tax advice to private investment funds and their sponsors in their organization and operation, and institutional investors investing in private equity funds. Mr Wolf's background as a Tax partner provides a unique combination of skills for advising clients on fund formation.

**Personal:** State University of New York at Albany (BA, summa cum laude); University of Michigan Law School (JD, cum laude); and New York University School of Law (LLM, tax).

## WOLFE, Gary J
Seward & Kissel LLP, New York
212 574 1274
wolfe@sewkis.com
*Featured in Transportation (Nationwide)*

**Practice Areas:** Corporate finance, maritime and transportation finance, capital markets and securities, business transactions (M&A/private equity).

**Professional Memberships:** Mr Wolfe has been Chair of the Admiralty and Maritime Law Committee of the New York County Lawyers Association, a member of the Admiralty and Maritime Law Committee of the Association of the Bar of the City of New York and President of the U.S. Business Council for Southeastern Europe, an organization of American businesses with trade and investment interests in Slovenia, Croatia and the rest of the Balkan region.

**Career:** Mr Wolfe specializes in corporate securities and capital markets transactions. He represents foreign and domestic issuers and investment banks and money managers in private placements, initial and secondary United States and offshore public offerings and consent solicitations, private equity transactions, mergers and acquisitions, joint ventures, commercial transactions, and investors and issuers in restructurings to limit environmental liability risk. Mr Wolfe has acted as counsel to issuers and underwriters in groundbreaking offerings by companies in the international transportation industry involving structured transactions, equity offerings, debt placements, cross-border mergers, global listings, master limited partnerships and establishment and termination of American Depositary Receipt programs. Mr Wolfe's transactions included the first initial public offering by way of a warrants offering and the first initial public offering by a passive foreign investment company. Mr Wolfe has spoken at industry conferences, and has published papers on United States domestic and offshore securities offerings by international transportation and emerging market companies, high-yield offerings by issuers, mergers, going private transactions and the United States oil pollution laws. Mr Wolfe has been named one of the 10 most influential lawyers in the shipping industry, the only American on the list when he was named (Lloyd's List 2010 Top 100).

**Personal:** Mr Wolfe received an AB Degree from Cornell University in 1971, Phi Beta Kappa, and a JD Degree in 1975 from Yale Law School. He was a Post-Doctoral Fulbright Scholar at the University of Ljubljana and University of Belgrade and was a recipient of an IREX Fellowship. His languages are English, Croatian, Slovenian and Russian.

## WOLFF, Alan Wm
McKenna Long & Aldridge LLP, Washington, DC
202 496 7337
awolff@mckennalong.com
*Featured in International Trade (Nationwide)*

**Practice Areas:** Ambassador Alan Wm. Wolff is a leading member of the International Trade Practice. The practice specializes in improving the international competitive position of major clients.

**Professional Memberships:** Wolff is Chairman of the Board of the National Foreign Trade Council (NFTC); chairs the Committee of Comparative Innovation Policies of the National Academies; is a member of the Advisory Committee of the Peterson Institute for International Economics, the Science Technology

and Economic Policy (STEP) Board of National Academies, and Chairman of the Board of the Institute for Trade and Commercial Diplomacy.

**Personal:** JD Columbia Law School; BA Harvard University.

## WOLFSON, Paul RQ
WilmerHale, Washington, DC
202 663 6390
paul.wolfson@wilmerhale.com
*Featured in Appellate Law (Nationwide)*

**Practice Areas:** Mr Wolfson's practice focuses on Supreme Court and appellate litigation, and on advising clients on complex issues of federal law, especially constitutional law. He has argued 19 cases in the United States Supreme Court and has also argued before six federal courts of appeals. Active in pro bono matters.

**Career:** Assistant to the Solicitor General, 1994-2002. Law clerk to US Supreme Court Justice Byron R. White, 1989-90, and to Judge Phyllis Kravitch, US Court of Appeals for the Eleventh Circuit, 1987-88.

**Personal:** Yale Law School (JD); University of Cambridge, Trinity College (MPhil); Harvard University (AB).

## WOLITZER, Michael
Simpson Thacher & Bartlett LLP, New York
212 455 2000
mwolitzer@stblaw.com
*Featured in Investment Funds (Nationwide)*

**Practice Areas:** Partner focusing on private fund formation and other facets of "alternative asset management." Represents some of the largest and most well known sponsors of private investment funds, such as Apax, Blackstone, Centerbridge, Lexington, JPMorgan/One Equity Partners, Patria and Silver Lake Partners. Involved in many acquisitions of, and investments in, private investment firms.

**Professional Memberships:** Executive Committee/former Chairman of the Private Investment Fund Forum; served as Co-Chairman of the Sub-Committee on Private Funds of the IBA and on the advisory boards of the Private Equity CFO Association and the Private Equity Investment Guidelines Group.

**Career:** Partner, 1998.

## WOLK, Michael D
Bingham McCutchen LLP, Washington, DC
202 373 6249
michael.wolk@bingham.com
*Featured in Securities (Nationwide)*

**Practice Areas:** Focuses practice on SEC, exchange and FINRA compliance and enforcement matters, particularly on equity and fixed income trading, marketplace and conduct rules, and their application to broker-dealers, associated persons and investment advisers. Represents firms and associated persons in regulatory investigations and counsels on regulatory and compliance issues. Frequent speaker at financial industry seminars.

**Career:** Served as vice president and chief counsel of the Market Regulation Department at the NASD (now FINRA). Served as branch chief of the Division of Enforcement at the SEC.

**Personal:** Thomas M Cooley School of Law, JD, 1984; University of Maryland, BA, 1980.

## WONG, Karen
Milbank, Tweed, Hadley & McCloy LLP, Los Angeles
213 892 4419
kwong@milbank.com
*Featured in Projects (Nationwide)*

**Practice Areas:** Ms Wong is a partner in the Project Finance Group. She represents sponsors, financing parties, tax equity investors, and contractors in the energy and infrastructure sector. She has been recognized as a leading lawyer in the renewable energy sector having led numerous transactions involving wind, solar, geothermal, biomass, hydroelectric, and waste energy projects. Ms Wong has established an expertise in developing coal gasification projects and poly-generation plants. Ms Wong led numerous development, financing and acquisition cutting edge transactions across the energy sector in North America and Asia involving a broad range of technologies often involving innovative financing structures.

## WOODS, Will K
Baker Botts LLP, Dallas
214 953 6996
will.woods@bakerbotts.com
*Featured in Franchising (Nationwide)*

**Professional Memberships:** Texas State Bar; Dallas Bar Association.

**Career:** Counsels franchisors in the hotel, restaurant and retail industries on international and domestic franchise transactions, system evaluation and development, franchise registration and disclosure matters, system re-structuring and related relationship issues and acquisitions and dispositions. Franchise Times named him a leading franchise lawyer; Law & Politics listed him as a Texas Rising Star; and D Magazine named him one of the "best lawyers" in Dallas. He serves on the Governing Committee of the ABA Forum on Franchising.

**Personal:** JD (cum laude), Baylor Law School, 1998; BBA, Baylor University, 1994.

## WRIGHT, Andrew
Kirkland & Ellis LLP, New York
212 446 4793
andrew.wright@kirkland.com
*Featured in Investment Funds (Nationwide)*

**Practice Areas:** Andrew advises leading sponsors of private investment funds, including both private equity and hedge funds, in connection with the formation and operation of their funds. Andrew has advised clients on numerous billion-dollar fund-raisings, and has formed and provided ongoing advice to sponsors of some of the largest and most complex private equity funds ever raised. He represents US and international sponsors of a broad range of types of funds, including LBO funds, hedge funds, credit investment funds and "hybrid" funds. Andrew's clients also include institutional investors, placement agents, investment professionals and other constituents in the alternative assets industry.

**WRIGHT, Corey**
Cahill Gordon & Reindel LLP, New York
212 701 3165
cwright@cahill.com
*Featured in Banking & Finance (Nationwide)*
**Practice Areas:** Principally focused on representing arrangers of asset based and cash-flow bank financings, underwriters in offerings of high yield debt securities and dealer managers and financial advisors in out-of-court debt restructurings, including exchange offers and tender offers.
**Personal:** Western New England College, BA, 1997. Columbia Law School, JD, 2000.

**WRIGHT, David C**
Hunton & Williams LLP, Richmond
804 788 8638
dwright@hunton.com
*Featured in Capital Markets (Nationwide)*
**Practice Areas:** Mr Wright's practice focuses on capital markets transactions, in particular, for equity REITs and mortgage REITs, real estate operating companies and companies in the hospitality industry, and specialty finance companies. Mr Wright regularly advises companies and leading investment banks on public and private issuances of debt and equity securities and M&A transactions. He heads the firm's Real Estate Capital Markets Group, which has handled over 500 capital markets transactions for more than 165 public and private real estate companies, including more than 120 IPOs and Rule 144A equity offerings, in recent years.
**Personal:** BA, JD University of Virginia.

**WUGMEISTER, Miriam**
Morrison & Foerster LLP, New York
212 506 7213
mwugmeister@mofo.com
*Featured in Privacy & Data Security (Nationwide)*
**Practice Areas:** Privacy and Data Security. Assists multinational organizations with complex global compliance efforts, assist in negotiating strategic deals, and defend regulatory and litigation matters relating to privacy and data security in the US and internationally including: data security breach issues; global collection, use, sharing of employee, customer, vendor and consumer personal information; ediscovery/monitoring conflicts; social media issues; and cloud computing deals, as well as on developing data security policies and procedures and cybersecurity preparedness and response plans.
**Career:** Chair, Global Privacy and Data Security Group.
**Publications:** Editor, 'Global Employee Privacy and Data Security Law, Second Edition' (BNA Books, 2011).

**WULFF, Erik B**
DLA Piper LLP (US), Washington, DC
202 799 4271
erik.wulff@dlapiper.com
*Featured in Franchising (Nationwide)*
**Practice Areas:** Franchise and distribution.
**Career:** He has a broad-based practice in franchising law, business law and international business transactions and has extensive experience in all aspects of representing franchising and distri-

bution companies, including domestic and international expansion. He is a former member of the board of directors of a New York stock exchange-listed company, and, as president of its international division, was instrumental in developing its business abroad.
**Personal:** JD, Indiana University, cum laude; BS, Indiana University, with distinction.

**WUSLICH, Raymond**
Winston & Strawn LLP, Washington, DC
202 282 5725
rwuslich@winston.com
*Featured in Energy & Natural Resources (Nationwide)*
**Practice Areas:** Mr Wuslich advises electric and natural gas clients on matters before the Federal Energy Regulatory Commission, including transactional and regulatory counseling and litigation. He represents utilities, generators, transmission companies, banks, private equity, hedge funds and trade organizations on regulatory strategy, structuring transactions, filings, rate and transmission incentives proceedings, mergers and acquisitions, FERC investigations and show cause proceedings.
**Professional Memberships:** DC Bar, PA Bar, Energy Bar Association.
**Career:** Partner since 1999.
**Personal:** University of Pittsburgh, BA (1981) and MPIA (1986); American University, JD (1988).

**WYMAN, Kenneth**
Simpson Thacher & Bartlett LLP, New York
212 455 7435
kwyman@stblaw.com
*Featured in Projects (Nationwide)*
**Practice Areas:** Corporate Partner specializing in energy and infrastructure finance. Recent representations include KKR Infrastructure Fund in purchase with Google of Recurrent Energy solar energy projects; Barclays and Credit Suisse in Essential Power refinancing; Citibank and Barclays in Terra-Gen's Alta II-V wind energy leveraged lease project financing; Mizuho in Exelon's Clean Horizons solar project financing; Credit Agricole and Union Bank in Alta 6/8 wind energy project financing and First Reserve in the Longview Power project financing.
**Career:** Partner, 1997.
**Personal:** University of Pennsylvania School of Law (JD 1987); Wharton School of the University of Pennsylvania (BS 1984).

**WYNNE, Richard**
Jones Day, Los Angeles
213 243 2548
rlwynne@jonesday.com
*Featured in Bankruptcy/Restructuring (California), Bankruptcy/Restructuring (Nationwide)*
See under California for profile.

**XU, Joyce Y.**
Simpson Thacher & Bartlett LLP, New York
212 455 3680
jxu@stblaw.com
*Featured in Capital Markets (Nationwide)*
**Practice Areas:** Corporate Partner and Head of the firm's derivatives practice group. Advises financial institutions, corporations and funds on

the structuring, negotiation and documentation of a broad range of equity, fixed income, fx and commodity derivative transactions and prime brokerage and trading documentation and also on Dodd-Frank and other derivatives regulatory and compliance matters. Recent representations include Apax, Credit Suisse, Blackstone, KKR, First Reserve, Goldman Sachs, Morgan Stanley, Barclays, Microsoft, Teleflex and Best Buy.
**Professional Memberships:** ISDA Equity Derivatives Committee, NYSBA Derivatives and Structured Products Association, NYCBA Committee on Futures and Derivatives Regulation.
**Personal:** JD, Columbia Law School.

**XU, Tao**
DLA Piper LLP (US), Washington, DC
703 773 4181
Tao.xu@dlapiper.com
*Featured in Franchising (Nationwide)*
**Practice Areas:** Franchise.
**Career:** He devotes his practice to franchising and distribution matters, especially international franchising, licensing and distribution transactions. He counsels a broad range of clients in their international expansions, including master franchising, multi-unit licensing, area development, single-unit licensing and direct investment (both joint venture and wholly foreign owned). He provides clients with legal background briefing, general corporate advice, contract drafting, negotiation and other services. He has helped clients in countries and regions all over the world and has been deeply involved in franchising activities in China.
**Personal:** JD, Tulane University (cum laude); BA, Beijing Foreign Studies University.

**YAFFE, Joseph M**
Skadden, Arps, Slate, Meagher & Flom LLP & Affiliates, Palo Alto
650 470 4650
joseph.yaffe@skadden.com
*Featured in Employee Benefits & Executive Compensation (Nationwide), Employee Benefits & Executive Compensation (California)*
See under California for profile.

**YANG, Grace**
GrayRobinson, PA, Tampa
813 273 5000
grace.yang@gray-robinson.com
*Featured in Food & Beverages (Nationwide)*
**Practice Areas:** Shareholder in the Alcohol Beverage and Food Department. Practice includes compliance issues for alcohol beverage and food vendors; alcohol, hotel, restaurant and other retail licensing work; representation of alcohol and hospitality industry members before local, state and federal administrative agencies; land use issues, including alcohol-related conditional or special use permitting and variance issues; drafting and negotiating various types of agreements; alcohol tax issues; and other matters affecting hospitality industry members.
**Personal:** Cornell Law School, JD (1997; Cornell Journal of Law and Public Policy, Managing Editor (1996-97); General Editor (1995-96); Phi

Alpha Delta, Wilson Chapter Justice (1995-97); Yale University, BA Political Science (cum laude and with Distinction in the Major, 1994).

**YANNI, Palma**
Dickstein Shapiro LLP, Washington, DC
202 420 2275
yannip@dicksteinshapiro.com
*Featured in Immigration (Nationwide), Immigration (District of Columbia)*
See under District of Columbia for profile.

**YANNUCCI, Thomas D**
Kirkland & Ellis LLP, Washington, DC
202 879 5056
thomas.yannucci@kirkland.com
*Featured in First Amendment Litigation (Nationwide), Litigation (District of Columbia), Media & Entertainment (District of Columbia)*
See under District of Columbia for profile.

**YANOS, Alexander**
Freshfields Bruckhaus Deringer US LLP, New York
212 277 4000
alex.yanos@freshfields.com
*Featured in International Arbitration (Nationwide)*
**Practice Areas:** Alex is a partner in the International Arbitration Group and a member of the Energy and Natural Resources and Latin America Groups. He has spent 18 years litigating and arbitrating treaty-based, commercial and financial disputes, particularly in the energy sector. Alex specializes in disputes involving sovereigns, handling arbitrations on behalf of claimants against Algeria, Argentina, Bolivia, Ecuador, Libya, Russia, the United States, Venezuela and Vietnam before the ICC, ICSID and the ICJ, while representing Lithuania and Pakistan in ICSID arbitrations and Paraguay in US courts. Alex also focuses on multijurisdictional disputes involving securities, banking, antitrust and insurance.

**YARETT, Jordan**
Paul, Weiss, Rifkind, Wharton & Garrison LLP, New York
212 373 3126
jyarett@paulweiss.com
*Featured in Capital Markets (Nationwide)*
**Practice Areas:** Co-head of Finance Group. Handles innovative structured finance deals, including restaurant royalties, billboards, nonperforming loans, CMBS and timeshare. Named a 'Dealmaker of the Year' in 2007 by The American Lawyer for his representation of Lehman Brothers Inc., lead underwriter for Dunkin' Brands Inc. in its complex $1.7 billion whole-business securitization. Represented Barclays Capital and J.P. Morgan in their 2012 $1.6 billion whole business securitization of the assets of Domino's Pizza. Has acted for several leading banks and funds in the restructuring of many significant structured finance and collateralized debt transactions.

**YEATES, Marie**
Vinson & Elkins LLP, Houston
713 758 4576
myeates@velaw.com
*Featured in Appellate Law (Nationwide), Litigation (Texas)*
See under Texas for profile.

## YELENICK, Mary T
Chadbourne & Parke LLP, New York
212 408 5493
myelenick@chadbourne.com
*Featured in Products Liability (Nationwide)*
**Practice Areas:** Chadbourne & Parke Litigation Partner Mary T Yelenick has focused her practice on complex products liability litigation, counseling, and compliance for nearly thirty years. She has served as national or international counsel in the pharmaceutical, distilled spirits, durable goods, tobacco, and over-the-counter-products industries. Her representations include trial and appellate work in federal and state courts; class-action defense, attorney-general lawsuits, and third-party economic recoupment actions; domestic and international regulatory and risk-management counseling, and international compliance investigations. Ms Yelenick is the author of numerous published articles and is actively involved in pro bono social-justice advocacy.

## YERES, David
Clifford Chance US LLP, New York
212 878 8075
david.yeres@cliffordchance.com
*Featured in Capital Markets (Nationwide)*
**Practice Areas:** Represents, among others, trading companies, banks, and funds with regard to related internal investigations and contentious matters. Has over 35 years experience in government and private practice with Commodity Exchange Act matters. Heads the US commodities and derivatives enforcement practice. Was counsel to the Chairman of the Commodity Futures Trading Commission and served on the Commission's Financial Products Advisory Committee. Was also the Deputy Associate Attorney General of the United States as well as a federal criminal prosecutor. Former chairman of the New York State Bar Association Committee on Commodities Law.

## YINGLING, Ed
Covington & Burling LLP, Washington, DC
202 662 5029
eyingling@cov.com
*Featured in Financial Services Regulation (Nationwide)*
**Practice Areas:** Edward Yingling advises financial institutions and trade associations on regulatory and legislative matters, M&A, and enforcement, emphasizing the implementation of the Dodd-Frank Act. Mr Yingling was formerly President and CEO of the American Bankers Association. During his 26 years with the ABA, he was involved in virtually every major regulatory and legislative issue facing the industry. He played a lead role in debates that culminated in the enactment of the Dodd-Frank Act. Before becoming working with the ABA, he was in charge of the ABA's legislative, legal, regulatory, tax, and policy development activities.
**Personal:** Stanford Law School, JD

## YOON, Andrew J
Weil, Gotshal & Manges LLP, New York
212 310 8689
andrew.yoon@weil.com
*Featured in Banking & Finance (Nationwide)*
**Practice Areas:** Partner in the US Banking & Finance Practice. Represents borrowers, private equity sponsors and financial institutions on a wide variety of bank financing transactions, including acquisition financing, cross-border finance, middle market financing, asset-based lending, debtor-in-possession and exit financings and workouts and restructurings. Representative clients include Providence Equity Partners, Avista Capital Partners, Berkshire Partners, THL Partners, DIRECTV and Sotheby's.
**Personal:** Bard College (BA, 1994); Vermont Law School (JD, 1999).

## YOST, Nicholas C
Dentons, San Francisco
415 882 2440
nicholas.yost@dentons.com
*Featured in Native American Law (Nationwide), Environment (California)*
**Practice Areas:** Partner practicing under all environmental and Indian laws; obtaining environmental authorizations; representation of clients before federal and state agencies; and litigation. Assists tribal entities facing a range of regulatory matters.
**Professional Memberships:** Bars of California, District of Columbia and US Supreme Court; American Bar Association; US Delegation to the Rio Earth Summit.
**Career:** Joined Dentons in 1994. As General Counsel of the President's Council on Environmental Quality, drafted federal government's environmental impact assessment (NEPA) regulations. American Bar Association 2010 award for Distinguished Achievement in Environmental Law and Policy.
**Personal:** University of California, Berkeley, LLB; Princeton University, AB.

## YOUNG, Jason
Clifford Chance US LLP, New York
212 878 8519
jason.young@cliffordchance.com
*Featured in Sports Law (Nationwide)*
**Practice Areas:** Partner in the Banking & Finance practice. His practice focuses mainly on representing major domestic and foreign financial institutions and corporate borrowers in secured and unsecured financing transactions, including syndicated lending, acquisition and leveraged financing, refinancing and restructuring, bankruptcy workouts, asset financing, structured financing and other financing transactions. His experience covers a full array of domestic and cross-border transactions and a variety of industries, including professional sports, real estate, telecommunications, information technology, financial institutions and insurance.
**Career:** Partner at Clifford Chance since 2010. Tulane University, BS, 1996, summa cum laude, Phi Beta Kappa; Harvard Law School, JD, 1999.

## YOUNG, Michael
Willkie Farr & Gallagher LLP, New York
212 728 8280
myoung@willkie.com
*Featured in Securities (Nationwide), Litigation (New York)*
See under New York for profile.

## YOUNGWOOD, Jonathan K
Simpson Thacher & Bartlett LLP, New York
212 455 2000
jyoungwood@stblaw.com
*Featured in Securities (Nationwide), Litigation (New York)*
See under New York for profile.

## YUFFEE, Michael
Fried, Frank, Harris, Shriver & Jacobson LLP, Washington, DC
202 639 7075
michael.yuffee@friedfrank.com
*Featured in Energy & Natural Resources (Nationwide)*
**Practice Areas:** Corporate partner, head of Firm's energy practice. Focuses on regulatory, enforcement defense and transactional matters relating to the wholesale energy markets. Experience leading the energy due diligence and Federal Energy Regulatory Commission and Commodity Futures Trading Commission aspects of M&A and financing transactions, representing clients in energy regulatory proceedings and conducting energy-related litigations and investigations. Assists clients with the development of energy regulatory compliance programs and represents clients in public and non-public investigations and enforcement actions.
**Career:** Joined as partner in 2012.
**Personal:** JD, cum laude, Washington University St. Louis School of Law (1994); BA, Boston University (1991).

## ZAELKE, Edward W
Akin Gump Strauss Hauer & Feld LLP, Los Angeles
213 254 1234
ezaelke@akingump.com
*Featured in Projects (Nationwide)*
**Practice Areas:** Edward Zaelke co-chairs Akin Gump's global project finance practice. Mr Zaelke focuses his practice on project development and finance, with a particular emphasis on representing companies engaged in the development, financing and operation of wind power, solar power and other alternative energy projects. His clients include many of the top renewable energy developers and investors in the United States.
**Professional Memberships:** Past President, American Wind Energy Association (board member since 2002); American Wind Energy Foundation (board member).
**Personal:** California State University, Long Beach, BA; University of California, Los Angeles School of Law, JD.

## ZALENSKI, Walter E
Weil, Gotshal & Manges LLP, Washington, DC
212 310 8878
walter.zalenski@weil.com
*Featured in Financial Services Regulation (Nationwide)*
**Practice Areas:** Walter Zalenski specializes in bank regulation, consumer financial services, housing finance, privacy law, and counseling on M&A transactions involving a wide variety of financial services companies. He defends financial services providers against class action claims under consumer credit protection laws and against governmental enforcement actions. He has lectured and written on a wide variety of issues including private equity investments in banks, fair lending laws, electronic consumer finance, privacy laws, arbitration, credit disclosures, money transmitter regulation, and the impact of tax laws on consumer credit.
**Personal:** George Washington University (BA, 1981 with Distinction and Special Honors); (JD, 1984).

## ZALESIN, Steven A
Patterson Belknap Webb & Tyler LLP, New York
212 336 2110
sazalesin@pbwt.com
*Featured in Advertising (Nationwide)*
**Practice Areas:** Steven Zalesin is a nationally recognized trial lawyer with extensive experience in intellectual property and complex commercial matters. He has successfully tried numerous false advertising and other cases in courts throughout the United States. For more than 25 years, Mr Zalesin has represented the manufacturers of several of the nation's best-selling nonprescription medicines in a series of landmark false advertising cases that have shaped the law in this area, and helped to preserve and grow the markets for our clients' products. In 2009, he successfully defended the world's largest beverage company against an attempt by its primary competitor to halt the launch advertising for an improved sports drink. In 2010, Mr Zalesin obtained summary judgment on behalf of the world's largest health care, computer software and beverage companies, in each instance defeating claims by key rivals. Most recently in 2011, he successfully represented the manufacturer of the nation's best-selling mouthwash in a multi-district litigation, obtaining dismissal of all claims. And in 2012, he obtained a landmark ruling from the 9th Circuit that affirmed the dismissal of a suit against a major juice manufacturer and set an important precedent concerning the intersection between the Lanham Act and the Food, Drug and Cosmetic Act. Mr Zalesin has substantial experience defending consumer class actions, and handles a variety of general commercial matters, including licensing and other contract disputes.
**Professional Memberships:** Member, Editorial Advisory Board, Advertising Compliance Service; American Bar Association (Litigation and Patent, Trademark and Copyright Law Sections); New York State Bar Association.

**Personal:** JD, 1985, University of Pennsylvania Law School, cum laude; Editor, University of Pennsylvania Law Review; B.S., 1982, Syracuse University, S.I. Newhouse School of Public Communications, magna cum laude.

### ZASLOWSKY, David
Baker & McKenzie, New York
212 891 3518
david.zaslowsky@bakermckenzie.com
*Featured in International Arbitration (Nationwide)*
**Practice Areas:** Has spent 28 years at Baker & McKenzie litigating and arbitrating a wide range of complex commercial disputes, often involving international aspects (including long-term contract, financial services, insurance and intellectual property disputes).
**Professional Memberships:** ICC Task Force on Decision on Costs, International Arbitration Club of New York, American Bar Association, NY City Bar, New York State Bar Association.
**Publications:** Editor of bi-monthly electronic 'International Litigation & Arbitration Newsletter'; Co-author New York Law Journal, 'International Litigation' column; Co-author 'Litigating International Commercial Disputes' (West Group).
**Personal:** Brooklyn College, BS computer science, summa cum laude (1981); Yale Law School, JD (1984).

### ZEIDMAN, Philip F
DLA Piper LLP (US), Washington, DC
202 799 4272
philip.zeidman@dlapiper.com
*Featured in Franchising (Nationwide)*
**Practice Areas:** International Franchising.
**Career:** He focuses on domestic franchising law and the rapidly growing field of international distribution, licensing and franchising law. He is counsel to a number of US and foreign companies and trade associations. He has been retained to advise a number of international governmental organizations on the subject of franchising as a technique for international development. He is a frequent writer and speaker on both domestic and internation distribution, licensing, franchising matters, and the antitrust aspects of franchising for the Practicing Law Institute.
**Personal:** LLB, Harvard Law School; BA, Yale University (cum laude).

### ZELBO, Howard
Cleary Gottlieb Steen & Hamilton LLP, New York
212 225 2452
hzelbo@cgsh.com
*Featured in International Arbitration (Nationwide)*
**Practice Areas:** International arbitration and commercial and international litigation. Represents financial institutions, sovereigns and state-owned entities in international arbitrations governed by public international law and laws of numerous countries. Recent clients: Citigroup, Nortel, Goodyear, Governments of Russia, Argentina, Dominican Republic and Ivory Coast, Bank of America, the Federal Reserve Bank of New York, Interpublic Group, Pluspetrol S.A., Kookmin Bank, Vale S.A. and Finmeccanica.

**Professional Memberships:** New York and Connecticut Bars; former Chair, Committee on Securities Litigation, NYCBA.
**Career:** JD, summa cum laude, valedictorian, Cornell Law School (1985); Law Clerk, Hon. John E. Sprizzo (SDNY 1985-87), became partner at CGSH (1994).

### ZERN, Peter
Covington & Burling LLP, Washington, DC
202 662 5679
pzern@cov.com
*Featured in Sports Law (Nationwide)*
**Practice Areas:** Represents many of the firm's sports clients, including the Big East Conference, MLB, NASCAR, the NBA, NFL, NHL and US Olympic Committee, in addition to individual teams and owners. Sports practice includes advice on corporate, ownership, finance and media matters, including stadium financings, ownership transfers and team acquisitions, sports networks, television contracts and new media matters. He also has significant experience advising clients on a broad range of debt and equity financings and M&A transactions.
**Personal:** Georgetown University Law Center, JD, 1998, magna cum laude, Order of the Coif; Dartmouth College, AB, 1995.

### ZEVNIK, Paul A
Morgan, Lewis & Bockius LLP, Washington, DC
202 739 5755
pzevnik@morganlewis.com
*Featured in Insurance (Nationwide), Insurance (District of Columbia)*
**Practice Areas:** Insurance coverage advice, litigation and alternative dispute resolution, with an emphasis on environmental, asbestos, toxic tort, and product liability coverage disputes. Sophisticated transactional experience, including insurance-related derivatives, structured settlements, I.R.C. § 468B qualified settlement funds, captives, restructuring and bankruptcy proceedings. Directors and officers, fiduciary, and errors and omissions policy procurement, advice and counseling, and dispute resolution.
**Professional Memberships:** District of Columbia Bar, State Bar of California, Pennsylvania Bar Association, United States Supreme Court Bar.
**Career:** Founding and Managing Partner, Zevnik Horton LLP (1993-2003); Partner, Kaye Scholer (1987-1993), Paul Hastings (1983-1987); Co-Founder and Lead Director, Entravision Communications Corporation (NYSE:EVC).

### ZEYDEL, Diana S.C.
Greenberg Traurig, LLP, Miami
305 579 0575
ZeydelD@gtlaw.com
*Featured in Wealth Management (Nationwide), Tax (Florida)*
See under Florida for profile.

### ZIEGLER, Richard F
Jenner & Block LLP, New York
212 891 1680
rziegler@jenner.com
*Featured in International Arbitration (Nationwide)*

**Career:** Richard F. Ziegler is Managing Partner of Jenner & Block's New York office and co-chairs the firm's International Arbitration Practice. He was general counsel of the 3M Company from 2003-07, and before that headed the New York litigation practice at a leading international firm. Mr Ziegler focuses his practice on complex commercial disputes, international arbitration, corporate governance and compliance matters. He serves on the ICDR and CPR panels of neutrals. He is a graduate of Yale University, summa cum laude, and Harvard Law School, magna cum laude, where he was an editor of the Harvard Law Review.

### ZIMAN, Kenneth S
Skadden, Arps, Slate, Meagher & Flom LLP & Affiliates, New York
212 735 3310
ken.ziman@skadden.com
*Featured in Bankruptcy/Restructuring (Nationwide), Bankruptcy/Restructuring (New York)*
**Practice Areas:** A deputy practice leader of Corporate Restructuring Group. Represents clients in connection with out-of-court restructurings and Chapter 11 cases, primarily representing troubled companies and debtholders through all aspects of the restructuring process. Often provides advice in connection with the formulation and development of out-of-court restructurings (including credit agreement amendments and/or exchange offers), Chapter 11 plans, debtor-in-possession financing and exit financing. Also represents acquirers of financially distressed companies and significant individual creditors in Chapter 11 cases and advises on the structuring of corporate transactions.
**Career:** JD, University of Pennsylvania, 1990; BA, Colgate University (magna cum laude) 1987.

### ZIRINIS, Basil P
Sullivan & Cromwell LLP, New York
212 558 4000
zirinisb@sullcrom.com
*Featured in Wealth Management (Nationwide)*
**Professional Memberships:** NYCBA, NYSBA.
**Career:** Partner since 1994. Leads the Firm's international private client practice. Represents individuals, fiduciaries and family-controlled businesses throughout the world in estate and trust planning, family business governance and transition, and estate and trust administration and litigation. Speaks regularly at international conferences regarding cross-border tax and estate planning. Extensive experience in US and offshore trust and estate litigation, including highly publicized litigation involving the Pritzker family in the US and Bahamas, and the America's Cup trust litigation.
**Personal:** Columbia Law School (JD, 1985); Bowdoin College (AB, 1980).

### ZIRINSKY, Bruce R
Greenberg Traurig, LLP, New York
212 801 9222
ZirinskyB@gtlaw.com
*Featured in Bankruptcy/Restructuring (Nationwide), Bankruptcy/Restructuring (New York)*
**Practice Areas:** Co-Chair, Business Reorganisation and Financial Restructuring

Practice. Chair, Global Business Solutions Group. Restructurings; reorganisations; financial transactions; bankruptcy litigation; mergers and acquisitions.
**Career:** Selected: Super Lawyers magazine, 2006-12; one of the Lawdragon 3000 Leading Lawyers in America, Lawdragon.com, 2010; Chambers USA Guide, 2009-13; a Dealmaker of the Year, The American Lawyer, 2008; Chambers Global, 2011-13; Best Lawyers in America; 'PLC Which Lawyer?', 2009 Yearbook; America's Top 100, K&A Restructuring Register, 2011; Legal 500 US, 2011-12.
**Personal:** JD, New York University School of Law, 1972; BS, Cornell University, 1969.

### ZOBITZ, George (Jed) E
Cravath, Swaine & Moore LLP, New York
212 474 1996
jzobitz@cravath.com
*Featured in Banking & Finance (Nationwide)*
**Practice Areas:** Jed Zobitz is a partner in Cravath's Corporate Department. He works in all areas of the Firm's corporate practice. Currently, his practice focuses on complex syndicated loan transactions, including acquisition and leveraged finance and asset-based lending, as well as securities, mergers and acquisitions, and general corporate representations.
**Personal:** New York University School of Law (JD, cum laude, 1995); Franklin & Marshall College (BA, 1991). For more information: http://www.cravath.com/jzobitz

### ZOCHOWSKI, T Robert
Paul, Weiss, Rifkind, Wharton & Garrison LLP, New York
212 373 3762
rzochowski@paulweiss.com
*Featured in Capital Markets (Nationwide)*
**Practice Areas:** Corporate Department partner; extensive experience in innovative and specialized asset-backed financing structures, such as whole-company and operating-asset securitizations as well as project financings, involving esoteric assets such as films, patent royalties and other IP, power plants and hydrocarbon reserves.Clients include Citigroup, Barclays Capital, Jefferies, Goldman Sachs, Credit Suisse, UBS, the U.S. Department of Energy, Ambac, Paramount Studios and Marvel Entertainment. Transactions include entertainment-asset securitizations, production financings and risk participations for Universal Studios, Twentieth Century Fox, Paramount, Sony Pictures, Miramax, Marvel Studios and The Weinstein Company; pharmaceutical-product R&D private equity investments; U.S. Government loan programs; and power-plant financings.

### ZORNOW, David M
Skadden, Arps, Slate, Meagher & Flom LLP & Affiliates, New York
212 735 2890
david.zornow@skadden.com
*Featured in Securities (Nationwide), Litigation (New York)*
See under New York for profile.

**ZUBKOFF, Daniel J**
Cahill Gordon & Reindel LLP, New York
212 701 3466
dzubkoff@cahill.com
*Featured in Banking & Finance (Nationwide)*
**Practice Areas:** Practice is principally focused on a range of capital markets and lending transactions including bank financings, debt and equity securities offerings and out-of-court debt restructurings. Represents leading domestic and international banking firms in bank financings, exchange offers and other debt restructurings, high yield and investment grade debt offerings, equity and equity-linked securities offerings, including initial public offerings, preferred stock issuances and convertible debt offerings, tender offers and other banking transactions.
**Personal:** Member, firm's Executive Committee. Cornell University, AB, 1979 magna cum laude, phi beta kappa. Harvard Law School, JD, 1982, cum laude.

**ZUTZ, Robert**
K&L Gates, Washington, DC
202 778 9059
robert.zutz@klgates.com
*Featured in Investment Funds (Nationwide)*
**Practice Areas:** A partner in the Washington, DC, office of K&L Gates, Mr Zutz has over 30 years of experience as a securities lawyer. His practice focuses on the representation of investment companies, their independent directors and trustees, investment advisers, and broker-dealers with respect to regulatory and fiduciary matters. Prior to joining K&L Gates in 1983, he was a member of the Securities and Exchange Commission staff for more than five years, including service in the Division of Investment Management and as Legal Counsel to a Commissioner.

**ZWEIFACH, Lawrence J.**
Gibson, Dunn & Crutcher LLP, New York
212 351 2625
lzweifach@gibsondunn.com
*Featured in Securities (Nationwide), Litigation (New York)*
See under New York for profile.

# ALLEN & OVERY LLP

www.allenovery.com **tel:** 212 610 6300 **fax:** 212 610 6399

**Managing Partners:** David Krischer (US), Barbara Stettner (Washington, DC)
Number of partners: 42 (US), 470+ (Global)
Number of lawyers: 175 (US), 2,800 (Global)
Languages: *(spoken in the US)* Arabic, Cantonese, Dutch, English, French, German, Greek, Italian, Japanese, Korean, Mandarin, Portuguese, Russian, Spanish and Yiddish.

### Firm Overview:

Allen & Overy LLP is a premier international legal practice with more than 5,000 staff, including more than 470 partners, working in 42 major business centers worldwide. The New York and Washington, DC offices are the core of the firm's global US practice with more than 175 of the US qualified lawyers based there. The firm's attorneys handle the most sophisticated and complex domestic and cross-border transactions and cases for their US and non-US clients. As more than 65% of the firm's work involves more than two countries, the US practice is fully integrated with its offices in Europe, Asia, South America, the Middle East, Australia and Africa to provide international and domestic clients with seamless solutions and a global reach that is unmatched by any other US firm.

### Main Areas of Practice:

**Banking & Corporate Finance:**
Allen & Overy has a strong finance practice that can seamlessly lead the most complex cross-border transactions. The Leveraged Finance Team works closely with the Private Equity Group, advising private equity houses on debt financing issues and advising debt arranging banks on private equity deal issues. It also has a leading asset finance practice, with experience advising on a number of different capital assets including aviation, rail, infrastructure, renewable energy, satellites, ship and equipment. The Project Finance Team is recognized domestically and globally for its high profile work in all areas of project finance including public-private partnerships, infrastructure, power and oil and gas.

**Corporate/M&A:**
The corporate and M&A practice in New York has advised on multi-billion dollar transactions over the last few years for clients such as Novartis, GE, Tyco, SAP and Thomson Reuters. The firm advises on all types of public and private M&A transactions.

**International Capital Markets:**
The firm represents underwriters, arrangers and US domestic and foreign issuers on the full range of debt and equity capital market transactions, including SEC-registered offerings, Rule 144A and Regulation S offerings, American and Global Depositary receipts offerings, convertible bonds and equity warrants, with a particular focus on Latin America and the Caribbean region.

**Litigation & Arbitration:**
The litigation practice brings together lawyers with enormous experience handling and resolving many of the major headline financial and commercial disputes both internationally and in the United States. This group includes four former Assistant United States Attorneys for the Southern District of New York, two former Chiefs of that office's Securities and Commodities Fraud Task

Force and the former President of the New York City Bar Association.

**Financial Services Restructuring & Insolvency:**
The Financial Services Restructuring Group has extensive experience in US-based and multi-jurisdictional restructurings, both in bankruptcy court proceedings and out-of-court restructurings. The group represents issuers, financial institutions, holders of public debt and debtors, as well as acquirers of businesses or assets of financially distressed companies.

**Financial Services Regulatory (FSR):**
Allen & Overy's FSR practice has bases in New York and Washington, DC, as well as Europe and Asia. Allen & Overy has over 160 US qualified lawyers practicing in international offices outside the US who provide advice to clients on particular US FSR issues across all the world's principal financial markets. The practice offers a distinctive international US regulatory practice that is unmatched by its competitors, as it is able to provide US regulatory advice to globally active financial institutions on an international basis.

**Real Estate:**
The real estate practice primarily involves real estate debt and equity investment throughout the United States for domestic and international institutions and funds. The practice is capital markets and private equity fund focused, and includes primarily large loan, mezzanine, A/B and preferred equity origination, securitization, the sponsorship and investment in real estate investment funds, secondary market debt acquisitions, loan workouts, real estate mergers and acquisitions, joint venture structuring and complex real estate acquisitions.

**Tax:**
The tax practice advises clients on issues across a broad range of sectors and types of transaction. It provides clients with comprehensive US tax advice, whether it relates to strategic tax planning for multinational operations,

expanding their business into Europe from the US, or seeking to raise or invest funds in or outside of the US.

**China Practice:**
The firm advises corporations and financial institutions investing in China and Chinese enterprises investing in the Americas. The group focuses on project financing, foreign direct investment, M&A, private equity, real estate and environmental law.

**Latin America Practice:**
In conjunction with the São Paulo office, this highly integrated group of attorneys focuses on corporate finance, including projects, capital markets, banking, derivatives, securitization, M&A, restructuring and insolvency. The practice has worked on some of the most high profile transactions and international arbitrations in Latin America.

**Recent Work:**
- RBC Capital Markets, as dealer, on the first ever registration of a covered bond program with the SEC for Royal Bank of Canada
- Elster Group, the NYSE-listed provider of "smart" gas, electricity and water meters, on the USD2.3 billion tender offer for all its shares by Melrose
- Thomson Reuters on its announced sale of its corporate services business to NASDAQ OMX for USD390 million
- International Finance Corporation (IFC), Inter-American Development Bank (IDB), Export Development Canada (EDC), SACE, BNDES, Bancomex and Nafin on the USD4.5 billion financing of the Etileno XXI Petrochemical Project in Mexico sponsored by Braskem S.A. and Grupo Idesa

## ALLEN & OVERY

**OFFICES**

NEW YORK

**NEW YORK:** 1221 Avenue of the Americas, NY 10020
Tel: 212 610 6300   Fax: 212 610 6399

DISTRICT OF COLUMBIA

**WASHINGTON DC:** 1301 K Street NW, 9th Floor,
East Tower, DC 20005
Tel: 202 683 3800   Fax: 202 683 3999

**INTERNATIONAL OFFICES**

Casablanca, New York, São Paulo, Washington, DC, Bangkok, Beijing, Hanoi, Ho Chi Minh City, Hong Kong, Jakarta*, Perth, Shanghai, Singapore, Sydney, Tokyo, Amsterdam, Antwerp, Athens**, Belfast, Bratislava, Brussels, Bucharest*, Budapest, Düsseldorf, Frankfurt, Hamburg, Istanbul, London, Luxembourg, Madrid, Mannheim, Milan, Moscow, Munich, Paris, Prague, Rome, Warsaw, Abu Dhabi, Doha, Dubai, Riyadh*

* Associated offices   ** Representative office

# ASHURST LLP

**www.**ashurst.com **tel:** 212 205 7000 **fax:** 212 205 7020

**Head of US:** William Gray
**US Managing Partner:** Scott Faga
Number of partners: 400
Number of lawyers: 1,700

## Firm Overview:

Ashurst is a leading international law firm advising corporations, financial institutions and governments worldwide. With 24 offices in 14 countries and over 400 partners and 1,700 lawyers in total, Ashurst offers the international insight of a global network combined with local market knowledge.

**Ashurst US:** With over 40 attorneys in the US, the firm's core business includes structured products (CLOs/CDOs, municipals, and derivatives), tax, financial regulatory, corporate and capital markets, leveraged finance and energy, transportation and infrastructure.

## Main Areas of Practice:

### Securitization:

Ashurst offers specialist advice across a range of securitized products. The firm is uniquely placed to offer an integrated service in securitization and securitization restructurings, drawing on the strengths of the Ashurst network and other market-leading tax and regulatory groups. It is a market leader in the CLO area. Products covered include: CLOs, whole business securitization, consumer finance securitization, mortgage-backed securities, receivables based financings, and repackagings (in each case, using synthetic and funded structures). Ashurst also has extensive experience in derivatives, including bespoke credit and equity derivatives transactions, and working with distressed securitizations, including CDOs and CLOs.

### Municipal Finance:

Ashurst's team has over 100 years of experience in all areas of municipal finance. Lawyers have advised on transactions with borrowers and counterparties in over half the states in the US and Puerto Rico. The firm understands the demands of the US municipal market and the objectives of all participant groups having acted for issuers, underwriters, lenders, credit enhancers, liquidity providers, and swap providers for Private Activity Bond financings for transportation, housing, hospitals and other healthcare facilities, higher education, other non-profit organizations and other types of exempt facilities. Ashurst has assisted clients with the development of innovative new products and structures, as well as the restructuring of existing transactions and programs to address recent disruptions in the capital markets.

### Banking & Corporate:

Ashurst's lending practice handles a variety of cash-flow and asset-based loan transactions, including senior secured, mezzanine and subordinated financings, repurchase agreement facilities, fund-financing and capital call facilities, derivative financing transactions, reinsurance facilities and the equity aspects of loan transactions. Clients include the world's largest banks and commercial finance companies, as well as borrowers, issuers, equity investors, sponsors, financial advisors, asset managers, funds, governments and governmental entities. When combined with Ashurst's market-leading, worldwide corporate lending practice, the firm brings the expertise, market-knowledge and experience to handle virtually any type of lending transaction. Within the US, the firm also advises on private M&A transactions and funds-related work.

### Tax:

Ashurst focuses primarily on the US federal income tax aspects of, among other things, domestic and cross-border financial products and fixed income and equity derivatives; US and non-US originated structured products transactions, including structured notes, CLOs, REMICs, and other securitization vehicles; US and non-US sponsored hedge funds, private equity funds and other investment vehicles; US and non-US originated debt and equity securities offerings and transactions; offshore entities including PFICs and CFCs; and traditional bank loans. In addition, the practice also provides tax planning for banks and securities dealers; product development of tax sensitive financial products; and audit and litigation support for other law and accounting firms in need of expertise in securitization and derivatives taxation.

### Regulatory/ERISA:

Ashurst's US financial regulatory practice is concentrated on counseling investment advisers, broker-dealers and other financial institutions on all matters relating to the development and offering of investment products and services. Clients include global asset management firms, broker-dealers, banks, insurance companies as well as specialized firms servicing high net worth, institutional or other unique clients. The practice encompasses all aspects of the investment management and broker-dealer business, including product design and distribution, compliance programs, sales practices and compensation arrangements. The firm also advises on the regulatory issues associated with private investment companies. It concentrates on ERISA and tax aspects of various structured finance and capital market products including CLOs, CDOs, hedge funds, private equity funds, loans and derivatives as well as asset-backed and mortgage-backed securities.

### Energy, Transportation & Infrastructure:

Ashurst's global energy, transportation and infrastructure team consists of over 100 lawyers, with six out of 28 partners based in the New York and Washington DC offices. The US practice focuses on the Americas markets and the growth of P3s in the infrastructure and transportation sectors, leveraging off international experience and knowledge coupled with in-depth understanding of federal, state and local municipal funding. Ashurst acts for sponsors, funders and authorities/issuers while local capability includes experience with roads, rail, social infrastructure (schools, hospitals, courts, etc.), stadiums, waste management, airports, prisons and renewables (including offshore wind transmission, biomass, waste to energy, etc).

## PRACTICE AREAS

Banking & Corporate
Energy, Transportation & Infrastructure
Municipal Finance
Regulatory/ERISA
Securitization
Tax

## OFFICES

NEW YORK

**NEW YORK:** 7 Times Square, 42nd Floor, NY, NY 10036
Tel: 212 205 7000  Fax: 212 205 7020
Email: william.gray@ashurst.com

DISTRICT OF COLUMBIA

**WASHINGTON, DC:** 1875 K Street, N.W. Suite 750,
Washington, DC 20006
Tel: 202 912 8000  Fax: 202 912 8050
Email: scott.faga@ashurst.com

## INTERNATIONAL OFFICES

The firm also has offices in Australia, Belgium, China, France, Hong Kong SAR, Indonesia (associated office), Italy, Japan, Papua New Guinea, Singapore, Spain, Sweden, United Arab Emirates and United Kingdom.

# BAKER & MCKENZIE

www.bakermckenzie.com **tel:** +1 312 861 8000 **fax:** +1 312 861 8823

**Chairman of the Executive Committee:** Eduardo C Leite
**North American Managing Partner:** Philip F Suse
Number of lawyers worldwide: 4,000+

## Firm Overview:

For more than 60 years, Baker & McKenzie has provided sophisticated advice and legal services to many of the world's most dynamic and successful organizations. Helping clients thrive in diverse legal, political, social and economic systems made Baker & McKenzie one of the world's largest law firms and the first to be truly global. With more than 4,000 locally qualified, internationally experienced lawyers in 45 countries, the firm has the fluency to deliver a broad scope of quality legal services – consistently, with confidence and sensitivity for cultural, social and legal practice differences. The firm now has about 100 lawyers in each of these three offices: NY, London and Hong Kong, and more than 150 in Tokyo. No other law firm has as substantial a presence in all of these key financial centers. The nearly 10,000 professionals of Baker & McKenzie share common values of integrity, personal responsibility and tenacity in an enthusiastic client-service culture. The firm is still guided by the entrepreneurial spirit and demanding standards of its founders and works to forge close personal relationships among its professionals in order to foster the responsiveness and accountability clients rightfully expect. The firm has a diverse and welcoming culture. Its lawyers and other professionals are citizens of more than 60 countries and are admitted to practice in nearly 250 jurisdictions. They speak more than 75 languages, with English in common. They have offices in 72 locations worldwide, including in 26 of the world's 30 largest economies. The firm's advanced technology and management systems include a single, shared global technology platform for client intake, email and billing systems; global practice standards; a quality audit program; and a worldwide conflicts policy based on the standards of the American Bar Association.

## Main Areas of Practice:

### Clients:

Baker & McKenzie serves more than half of the world's largest public companies as well as a broad spectrum of regional and local organizations. With its diverse capabilities and experience, the firm advises leading clients in most major industries, from aviation to water and wastewater. It has particular experience in clothing, household and consumer products; banking and financial services, chemicals and petrochemicals; construction; energy and utilities; entertainment and media; insurance; mining; oil and gas; pharmaceuticals and healthcare products; professional services; real estate; technology; telecommunications; tourism; and transport and infrastructure.

### International Recognition:

Baker & McKenzie is frequently acknowledged as a preeminent provider of legal services by leading publications, professional organizations and research institutions. In 2012, Baker & McKenzie was recognized as Firm of the Year in Europe and Southeast Asia by Chambers. The Acritas sharplegal® Global Elite Brand Index has named Baker & McKenzie the world's No. 1 law firm brand for three consecutive years. The firm has been one of Corporate Board Member magazine's

Most Admired Law Firms since the survey began in 2001 and has been a member of BTI Consulting's Client Service A-Team in four of the past five years. Baker & McKenzie also has been cited as Asian Counsel's Most Responsive International Firm of the Year for China, Hong Kong, Indonesia, Japan, Singapore and Thailand.

### Social Commitment:

Baker & McKenzie invests in communities where its people live and work, and is a pioneer in teaming with its clients on corporate social responsibility efforts worldwide. The firm leverages its global network and legal skills to work on complex, cross-border pro bono projects that meaningfully advance fundamental rights and opportunities for people in need throughout the world. As the first truly global law firm, Baker & McKenzie embraces diversity among its lawyers, staff and clients – and the resulting variety of backgrounds and perspectives that lead to practical solutions and innovation. And as a pioneer in climate change law, the firm's respect for the environment extends to how it does business. Its commitment to sustainability is reflected in efforts to reduce its environmental footprint through initiatives like recycling, alternative energy use and carbon offsets.

## PRACTICE AREAS

Antitrust & Competition
Banking & Finance
Dispute Resolution
Employment
Environment & Climate Change
Intellectual Property
IT/Communications
Energy, Mining & Infrastructure
Mergers & Acquisitions
Pharmaceuticals & Healthcare
Private Equity
Real Estate
Securities
Tax
Trade & Commerce

## OFFICES

### ASIA PACIFIC
Bangkok, Beijing, Hanoi, Ho Chi Minh City, Hong Kong, Jakarta, Kuala Lumpur, Manila, Melbourne, Shanghai, Singapore, Sydney, Taipei and Tokyo

### EUROPE, MIDDLE EAST & AFRICA
Abu Dhabi, Almaty, Amsterdam, Antwerp, Bahrain, Baku, Barcelona, Berlin, Brussels, Budapest, Cairo, Casablanca, Dusseldorf, Frankfurt, Geneva, Istanbul, Johannesburg, Kyiv, London, Luxembourg, Madrid, Milan, Moscow, Munich, Paris, Prague, Riyadh, Rome, St. Petersburg, Stockholm, Vienna, Warsaw and Zurich

### NORTH & SOUTH AMERICA
Bogota, Brasilia, Buenos Aires, Caracas, Chicago, Dallas, Guadalajara, Houston, Juarez, Lima, Mexico City, Miami, Monterrey, New York, Palo Alto, Porto Alegre, Rio de Janeiro, San Francisco, Santiago, Sao Paulo, Tijuana, Toronto, Valencia, and Washington, DC

**BAKER & MCKENZIE**

# BARNES & THORNBURG LLP

www.btlaw.com **tel:** 317 236 1313 **fax:** 317 231 7433

**Chairman:** Alan A Levin
**Managing Partners:** David C Allen (Los Angeles); D Randall Brown (Fort Wayne); Philip J Faccenda, Jr (South Bend); Robert T Grand (Indianapolis); Stuart C Johnson (Atlanta); Tracy T Larsen (Grand Rapids); Karen A McGee (Washington); William A Nolan (Columbus); Peter J Ekberg (Minneapolis); Mark E Rust (Chicago); J Scott Troeger (Elkhart)
Number of partners: 329 Number of other attorneys: 227

## Firm Overview

With more than 600 attorneys and other legal professionals, Barnes & Thornburg LLP is one of the largest US firms and provides legal services to a diverse group of clients ranging from entrepreneurial growth companies to *Fortune* 500 corporations. Attorneys represent clients in many industries, including financial services, technology, international business, life sciences, healthcare, government, higher education, renewable energy, manufacturing, and non-profit organizations and foundations, among others.

## Main Areas of Practice:

### Corporate Transactions & Counseling:

The firm's Corporate Group has experience in merger, acquisition, joint venture, and capital raising transactions of all types, and in working with entrepreneurial companies. Attorneys counsel corporate clients in the areas of governance, shareholder relations, antitrust planning, distribution, tax and securities matters. Transactional attorneys handle matters that include public and private equity and debt placement, conventional and asset-based lending, commercial real estate finance, structured and asset-backed financing and securitization, and leveraged ESOPs, as well as industrial revenue bonds.

### Environmental:

Attorneys assist clients with compliance counseling, obtaining and negotiating permits, business transactions and planning, facility cleanups, and administrative adjudication before federal and state agencies, among other activities.

### Finance, Insolvency & Restructuring:

Attorneys handle all aspects of representation of secured and unsecured creditors, borrowers, guarantors, trustees and creditors' committees, including negotiating and drafting loan agreements, negotiable instruments, and other commercial transactions. They also represent creditors and obligors nationally in out-of-court workouts and refinancings, as well as in various state and federal courts.

### Governmental Services & Finance:

Firm attorneys regularly represent government issuers and underwriters in government bond financings and many other public finance projects in several states. Attorneys also assist a variety of clients at the local, state, and national levels through lobbying and public affairs efforts. The firm serves clients on business, government and trade association issues and in regulatory and administrative matters, including licensing, rate, finance, contracting with the federal government and complaint proceedings before federal regulatory agencies.

### Healthcare:

The firm represents physicians, medical groups, managed care organizations, hospitals, nursing homes, and national healthcare-related associations. Attorneys deliver guidance on long-term care facilities, managed care networks, medical staff issues, Medicare and Medicaid, mergers and acquisitions, physician-hospital contracting, physician practice groups, provider, joint ventures, reimbursement disputes and audits and tax exemption issues.

### Intellectual Property:

The firm has experience in several facets of IP law, from patent and trademark prosecution to franchising, from antitrust and unfair trade practices to technology development and deployment, and from life sciences and biotechnology to 'bet the company' patent infringement litigation.

### Labor & Employment:

Attorneys routinely defend clients against claims of wrongful discharge, harassment, discrimination, workplace defamation, breach of contract, invasion of privacy, ERISA violations, illicit drug testing and other federal and state law claims, and enforce non-competition and non-solicitation agreements. The firm's extensive traditional labor practice encompasses defending against unfair labor practice charges and union-organizing campaigns, negotiating and administrating union contracts, and coaching and training on lawful union-avoidance techniques.

### Litigation:

The firm's litigators have represented businesses in controversies in all 50 states and before most of the US federal courts, as well as before various international and multi-jurisdictional tribunals. The firm has key practices in white-collar criminal defense, insurance recovery, construction, and product liability, among others.

### Real Estate Services:

The firm's services include rezoning and land-use planning; negotiation of financing; project development; organization of owners' associations and development of architectural standards; leasing, sale, or tax-free exchange of the completed project; and any other matters, including litigation, which may be encountered before, during, and after the completion of a project.

## OFFICES

### CALIFORNIA

**LOS ANGELES:** 2049 Century Park East, Suite 3550, CA 90067
Tel: 310 284 3880  Fax: 310 284 3894

### DELAWARE

**WILMINGTON:** 1000 N. West Street, Suite 1500, DE 19801-1058
Tel: 302 300 3434  Fax: 302 300 3456

### DISTRICT OF COLUMBIA

**WASHINGTON, DC:** 1717 Pennsylvania Avenue, N.W., Suite 500, DC 20006-4623
Tel: 202 289 1313  Fax: 202 289 1330

### GEORGIA

**ATLANTA:** Prominence in Buckhead, Suite 1700, 3475 Piedmont Road NE, GA 30305-2954
Tel: 404 846 1693  Fax: 404 264 4033

### ILLINOIS

**CHICAGO:** One North Wacker Drive, Suite 4400, IL 60606-2833
Tel: 312 357 1313  Fax: 312-759 5646

### INDIANA

**ELKHART:** 121 W. Franklin Street, Suite 200, IN 46516-3200
Tel: 574 293 0681  Fax: 574 296 2535

**FORT WAYNE:** 600 One Summit Square, 110 E. Wayne Street, IN 46802-3119
Tel: 260 423 9440  Fax: 260 424 8316

**INDIANAPOLIS:** 11 South Meridian Street, IN 46204-3535
Tel: 317 236 1313  Fax: 317 231 7433

**SOUTH BEND:** 600 1st Source Bank Center, 100 North Michigan, IN 46601-1632
Tel: 574 233 1171  Fax: 574 237 1125

### MICHIGAN

**GRAND RAPIDS:** 171 Monroe Avenue N.W., Suite 1000, MI 49503-2694
Tel: 616 742 3930  Fax: 616 742 3999

### MINNESOTA

**MINNEAPOLIS:** 225 South Sixth Street, Suite 2800, , MN 554020-4662
Tel: 612 333 2111  Fax: 612 333 6798

### OHIO

**COLUMBUS:** 41 S. High Street, Suite 3300, OH 43215-6104
Tel: 614 628 0096  Fax: 614 628 1433

# BROWN RUDNICK LLP

www.brownrudnick.com **tel:** 617 856 8200 **fax:** 617 856 8201

**Managing Partner:** Joseph F Ryan, Chief Executive Officer
**Managing Director, Corporate & Capital Markets:** Samuel P Williams
**Managing Director, Litigation & Corporate Restructuring:** William R Baldiga
**Administrative Partner:** Andrew P Strehle
Number of lawyers: Over 200

### Firm Overview:
Brown Rudnick is an international law firm with offices in the United States and Europe. Representing clients from around the world, the firm provides business-focused solutions that address today's ever-changing, ever-demanding competitive marketplace. Founded more than 60 years ago, Brown Rudnick has over 200 lawyers providing advice and services across key areas of the law.

### Main Areas of Practice:

**Bankruptcy & Corporate Restructuring:**
The firm's Bankruptcy and Corporate Restructuring Group is well-known for successes in the 'hard cases', and is credited with helping to reshape the dynamics of insolvency and financial distress. The breadth of the firm's practice includes a wide range of clients including bondholders, distressed funds, equity funds and other opportunistic investors in restructurings and bankruptcy cases, with hedge funds being a primary focus.

**Complex Litigation:**
Brown Rudnick's Litigation Department specializes in resolving substantial, complex business disputes in the areas of bankruptcy and corporate restructuring, construction, creditors rights, energy, finance and securities, insurance, intellectual property, international arbitration, mass torts, real estate, wage and hour, and white-collar defense and government investigations.

**Corporate & Transactional:**
With a reputation as deal makers, Brown Rudnick's Corporate Department works with companies at all stages of development, including start-ups, emerging growth companies and established,multi-national public companies. The Corporate Team also represents and works closely with members of the underwriting community, venture capital, private equity and hedge funds and large private institutional businesses. Corporate attorneys have counseled clients on hundreds of deals involving billions of dollars.

**Energy, Renewables & Cleantech:**
The Energy Practice at Brown Rudnick handles matters involving complex electric generation, transmission and distribution, natural gas transmission and distribution, renewable energy project development and finance, emissions reduction schemes, cleantech and alternative energy sources.

**Finance:**
Brown Rudnick's Finance Group provides an extensive array of services to finance companies, private and institutional investors, insurance companies and other financial institutions. The Group serves clients with a focus on three primary areas: bankruptcy and corporate restructuring, commercial finance and structured finance.

**Government Contracts:**
The Government Contracts team represents clients in the defense, energy, environment, technology, healthcare, real estate and construction industries. The Group prosecutes and defends bid protests before the Government Accountability Office (GAO), asserts and defends claims before courts and boards of contract appeals, and investigates and defends civil and criminal fraud accusations.

**Government Law & Strategies:**
The Government Law and Strategies Team provides legal, political and strategic counsel to members of the private, public and non-profit sectors. The team helps clients strengthen their competitive profile by addressing and managing difficult challenges, and helps protect and advance clients' interests with federal, state and local government entities.

**Patents & Intellectual Property:**
Brown Rudnick's Intellectual Property (IP) Practice Group combines legal, business and technical backgrounds to help global clients maximize their intellectual property assets worldwide. The group offers perspective and experience in patents, trademarks, trade secrets and copyrights, including the technology development, transactions and litigation related to these assets.

**Real Estate:**
The Real Estate Group addresses the full range of contemporary real estate issues, including development and construction, environmental, zoning, and land use, leasing, acquisitions and dispositions, financing, and retail and shopping centers. Brown Rudnick has focused most recently on applying its capabilities to assist real estate investors and developers faced with a restructuring or bankruptcy.

## PRACTICE AREAS
Bankruptcy & Corporate Restructuring
Finance
Complex Litigation
Corporate & Transactional
Patents & Intellectual Property
Emerging Technologies
Cleantech & Energy
Real Estate
Tax
Government Contracts
Government Law & Strategies
White-Collar & Criminal Defense

## OFFICES
**MASSACHUSETTS**
**BOSTON:** One Financial Center, MA 02111
Tel: 617 856 8200   Fax: 617 856 8201

**NEW YORK**
**NEW YORK:** Seven Times Square, NY 10036
Tel: 212 209 4800   Fax: 212 209 4801

**CONNECTICUT**
**HARTFORD:** 185 Asylum Street, CT 06103
Tel: 860 509 6500   Fax: 860 509 6501

**RHODE ISLAND**
**PROVIDENCE:** 10 Memorial Boulevard, RI 02903
Tel: 401 276 2600   Fax: 401 276 2601

**DISTRICT OF COLUMBIA**
**WASHINGTON, DC:** 601 Thirteenth Street NW, Suite 600, DC 20005
Tel: 202 536 1700   Fax: 202 536 1701

## INTERNATIONAL OFFICES
The firm also has offices in London and Dublin.

### International Work:
Brown Rudnick has an extensive international practice, offering the full breadth of its M&A, project and leveraged finance, equity and debt capital markets, bankruptcy and corporate restructuring, arbitration and litigation services to a global client base. The firm's corporate experience includes advising businesses on cross border expansion, acquisitions or divestments and assisting those seeking public and private equity and debt capital and investors providing such financing. The firm's European corporate insolvency and litigation teams are recognized for their work on behalf of hedge fund clients. Most notably, the London teams are leading the firm's involvement in Eurozone bank restructuring matters, including those related to Anglo Irish, Allied Irish Bank and Bank of Ireland. Brown Rudnick is also a founding member of the International Law Firm Network, an association of law firms with affiliates in more than 40 countries.

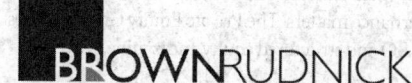

# CADWALADER, WICKERSHAM & TAFT LLP

**www.**cadwalader.com **tel:** 212 504 6000 **fax:** 212 504 6666

**Chairman:** W Christopher White
**Deputy Chairman:** James C Woolery
Number of partners: 101   Number of lawyers: 334

**Firm Overview:**
Established in New York in 1792, Cadwalader is a leading global advisor to corporations and financial institutions, offering innovative solutions to complex legal issues.

## Main Areas of Practice:

### Antitrust:
Represents clients in merger, monopolization and price-fixing matters before the DOJ, FTC, state attorneys general, foreign antitrust authorities, trial and appellate courts in the US, and before European courts. Knowledgeable in merger review, including HSR, commercial arrangements, antitrust compliance programs, joint ventures, distribution arrangements, pricing policies, standard-setting organizations, trade associations, joint purchasing alliances, R&D collaborations and IP.
**Contact:** Charles (Rick) Rule  **Tel:** +1 202 862 2420
**Email:** rick.rule@cwt.com

### Business Fraud:
Handles significant civil, criminal and administrative disputes, and enforcement actions in federal and state proceedings and litigation, as well as in congressional investigations and hearings for financial institutions, major corporations, their boards, audit committees, directors and officers. Advises on corporate compliance, governance, internal investigations, and audits of US and foreign operations.
**Contact:** Raymond A Banoun  **Tel:** +1 202 862 2426
**Email:** ray.banoun@cwt.com
**Contact:** Kenneth L Wainstein **Tel:** +1 202 862 2474
**Email:** ken.wainstein@cwt.com

### Capital Markets:
Experienced in traditional fixed income and equity capital markets, structured finance, synthetic products, hybrid products and derivatives. Develops new products and structures; devises cross-border structures and assist in managing risks caused by subperforming securitized loans and troubled financial products.
**Contact:** Michael S Gambro  **Tel:** +1 212 504 6825
**Email:** michael.gambro@cwt.com
**Contact:** Patrick T Quinn  **Tel:** +1 212 504 6067
**Email:** pat.quinn@cwt.com

### Corporate:
The M&A and Securities Group advises on IPOs, exchange and secondary offerings, private placements, workouts, convertible debt and equity, hybrid securities and distressed M&A. They also advise on mergers, acquisitions, recapitalizations, spin-offs, dispositions and governance matters. The Private Equity Group focuses on LBO and structured equity, mezzanine, real estate, venture growth capital and funds' investments. The Finance Group addresses all areas of debt finance, including secured and unsecured commercial lending, mortgage banking and real estate investment, acquisitions, sales, exchanges, development and workouts.
**Contact:** James C Woolery **Tel:** +1 212 504 6200
**Email:** james.woolery@cwt.com
**Contact:** Louis J Bevilacqua **Tel:** +1 212 504 6057
**Email:** louis.bevilacqua@cwt.com
**Contact:** William P McInerney **Tel:** +1 212 504 6118
**Email:** william.mcinerney@cwt.com

### Energy & Commodities:
Experienced in complex transactional, litigation, regulatory and compliance matters. Counsel to financial institutions and investors; oil, power and gas companies, producers and developers; industrial and commercial customers; trade associations; hedge funds; commodity marketers; exchanges; and clearing organizations.
**Contact:** Paul J Pantano Jr  **Tel:** +1 202 862 2410
**Email:** paul.pantano@cwt.com

### Financial Restructuring:
Represents debtors, secured and unsecured lenders, bondholders, creditors' committees, borrowers, asset purchasers and other distressed entities. Broad capabilities in transactions and litigation, developing bankruptcy sensitive products, and structuring deals to preserve and enhance value.
**Contact:** John J Rapisardi **Tel:** +1 212 504 5585
**Email:** john.rapisardi@cwt.com
**Contact:** George A Davis  **Tel:** +1 212 504 6797
**Email:** george.davis@cwt.com

### Financial Services:
Expertise in financial law related statutory and regulatory requirements, including those governing broker-dealers, securities and futures exchanges, banks, investment advisers and funds. Advises clients on OTC derivatives, structured products, hedge fund derivatives and hybrid transactions. Structures and develops investment products, funds and services for and with domestic and offshore hedge funds; funds of funds; commodity pools; acquisition, venture capital, real estate and structured product funds; and investment advisers and management firms.
**Contact:** Steven D Lofchie  **Tel:** +1 212 504 6700
**Email:** steven.lofchie@cwt.com
**Contact:** Richard M Schetman  **Tel:** +1 212 504 6906
**Email:** richard.schetman@cwt.com

### Health Care/Not-for-Profit:
Counsels on corporate governance, corporate finance, government regulation, Medicare/Medicaid, restructuring, labor relations, litigation, risk management, securities, capital markets and tax. Represents charitable and tax-exempt entities, including religious organizations, educational institutions, museums, social service agencies, foundations and trade associations.
**Contact:** Kathy Hirata Chin **Tel:** +1 212 504 6542
**Email:** kathy.chin@cwt.com
**Contact:** Paul Mourning **Tel:** +1 212 504 6216
**Email:** paul.mourning@cwt.com

### Intellectual Property:
The IP team handles trials and litigation in complex patent and trade secret matters in federal courts, and in ITC and WIPO proceedings. The team also enforces and defends claims; provides expert opinions; secures rights; evaluates, sells, or licenses IP; and conducts due diligence.
**Contact:** Christopher Hughes **Tel:** +1 212 504 6891
**Email:** christopher.hughes@cwt.com

### Litigation:
Litigators handle disputes for financial institutions, major corporations, and their officers and directors in state and federal courts throughout the US and in the UK, as well as in proceedings before administrative and regulatory agencies and international tribunals. In addition to antitrust, business fraud and intellectual property, the practice focuses on commercial, complex financial products, insurance, international and securities disputes.
**Contact:** Gregory A Markel **Tel:** +1 212 504 6112
**Email:** greg.markel@cwt.com
**Contact:** Louis M Solomon  **Tel:** +1 212 504 6600
**Email:** louis.solomon@cwt.com

### Tax & Private Wealth:
The Tax Group pioneers innovative tax structures that drive complex deals and maintains a tax controversy practice for US and non-US corporations and financial institutions. The Private Wealth team provides personal, financial, charitable and tax planning for individuals and closely-held family companies.
**Contact:** Linda Z Swartz **Tel:** +1 212 504 6062
**Email:** linda.swartz@cwt.com
**Contact:** Robert C Lawrence, III  **Tel:** +1 212 504 6211
**Email:** robert.lawrence@cwt.com

---

**OFFICES**
NEW YORK
**NEW YORK:** One World Financial Center NY 10281
Tel: 212 504 6000 Fax:  212 504 6666

Additional US locations: Charlotte, NC; Washington, DC; Houston, TX

International: London, Brussels, Beijing and Hong Kong

# CLIFFORD CHANCE US LLP

**www.**cliffordchance.com **tel:** 212 878 8000 **fax:** 212 878 8375

Number of partners: 73
Number of other attorneys: 186

## Firm Overview:

US and global organizations require the highest quality US legal capability coupled with seamless international service. Clifford Chance offers a comprehensive and nationally recognized practice, backed by top-ranked practices in the world's major financial and business centers. Through a single, worldwide partnership and a client-focused approach, the firm delivers consistent, commercially oriented advice wherever its clients do business. In the US, Clifford Chance's practice is dedicated to complex corporate and financial transactions and high-stakes dispute resolution. The firm regularly advises the leading international financial institutions and US and international corporations, as well as governments and multilateral agencies.

## Main Areas of Practice:

### Corporate/M&A:

Clifford Chance has a long history of advising in landmark US and cross-border transactions. Clients include public and private corporations, investment banks and financial institutions, and private equity sponsors. The firm advises clients on the full spectrum of M&A transactions, including those related to public M&A, distressed M&A, private equity investment, insurance transactions and fund formation. In addition, the firm regularly handles US inbound foreign direct investment work for non-US clients.

Clifford Chance's team has also been at the forefront of developing a wide array of structured products. The firm's lawyers represent clients of all types across a broad spectrum of securitization and other structured capital markets products, and in derivative products, in the US and internationally. They advise on complex on balance sheet structured financings; structured debt, real estate related and other debt funds (including TALF/PPIP); fund-linked and other alternative investment products; traditional asset-backed securities offerings; CMBS and other real estate securitizations; cash flow and market value CDOs; structured ABCP conduits; synthetic CDOs and CLNs; restructuring and workouts of complex financial products and capital market transactions; "future-flow" and other cross-border securitizations; covered bonds; Islamic finance; insurance-linked securitizations; credit opportunity funds; credit-linked notes and other derivative products.

**Contacts:** John Healy, Brian Hoffmann, Steven Kolyer

### Capital Markets:

The firm's Domestic Securities Practice is industry-focused, with significant experience in real estate, leisure, hospitality, specialty finance, healthcare, industrial manufacturing, mutual funds and municipal bonds. The Domestic Practice has earned an outstanding reputation for developing innovative solutions in the expanding area of specialty finance (i.e. permanent capital vehicles, alternative REIT structures, etc). Product coverage includes: IPOs, secondary equity, private placements, preferred equity, equity-linked products, debt and high-yield offerings. The firm's Funds Group represents numerous investment banks as underwriters of securities issued by closed-end funds and is also engaged in fund creation work for US registered open-end and closed-end funds, exchange-traded funds, offshore funds and hedge funds. The Cross-Border Securities Practice focuses principally on Latin America and has a market leading reputation in Brazil and significant experience in Mexico, Argentina and other Latin American countries.

**Contacts:** Jay Bernstein, Alex Camacho

### Banking & Finance:

The firm's Banking and Finance Practice focuses on the representation of financial institutions in complex national and multinational insolvency and restructuring proceedings. In addition, sophisticated lenders and borrowers call on the firm for acquisition finance, bank lending, asset finance, equipment leasing and debt trading. The firm also boasts a Financial Services Regulatory Group that works hand-in-hand with the firm's global network. The firm is among the most active in the world in project finance, representing lenders, sponsors and developers, particularly in the oil and gas, telecom and petrochemical sectors.

**Contact:** Evan Cohen

### Litigation:

Clifford Chance offers a pre-eminent national Litigation Practice, combining market leading local capability in the US with a unique ability to work efficiently with firm colleagues across its global network. The firm helps clients resolve complex disputes in a manner that promotes their business objectives and develop compliance programs to assist in minimizing future risks. The firm has trial expertise in all manners of civil and criminal cases before juries and judges in multiple jurisdictions, and in appellate practice before national and international courts and tribunals. Clifford Chance offers an experienced team of securities litigators in the US, with extensive experience in defending complex and high-risk securities class actions, combined with a prestigious regulatory and white-collar capability. The firm's Antitrust Practice has been involved in many of the most significant antitrust and fair trade cases before the courts in the US. Clifford Chance's approach emphasizes practical understanding of its clients' business problems with experience across every segment of the corporate and financial world.

**Contact:** David DiBari

### Real Estate:

Clifford Chance advises clients in the execution of real estate acquisitions and dispositions, leasing transactions and development arrangements. The Real Estate Group also counsels sophisticated borrowers and lenders on complex real estate finance matters that originate through both traditional sources and the capital markets (public and private), including mezzanine financing, and construction and warehouse lending. The firm is a leader in both real estate securities and real estate investment funds transactions.

**Contact:** Douglas Wisner

### Tax, Pensions & Employment:

The firm's TPE Group provides advice on US and international taxation, covering corporate and commercial transactions, equity and debt offerings, real estate and private equity funds and investments, financing and securitization transactions, tax efficient structured transactions, insurance taxation, charitable organizations and the resolution of tax disputes. The firm offers an in-depth understanding of US rules, combined with the knowledge of international tax systems and how the systems interlink. The firm's ERISA and Executive Compensation Practice structures and negotiates benefits and compensation packages. In addition, the firm provides advice on a wide range of ERISA fiduciary and other related issues. The firm has a market-leading practice regarding a number of compensation issues and ERISA issues relating to the establishment and operation of investment funds.

**Contact:** Richard Catalano

**OFFICES**

NEW YORK

**NEW YORK:** 31 W 52nd Street, NY 10019
Tel: 212 878 8000   Fax: 212 878 8375
Email: info@cliffordchance.com

DISTRICT OF COLUMBIA

**WASHINGTON DC:** 2001 K Street NW, DC 20006 1001
Tel: 202 912 5000   Fax: 202 912 6000

# CLYDE & CO US LLP

**www.**clydeco.com **tel:** 212 710 3900 **fax:** 212 710 3950

**US Managing Partners:** Bill Casey, Michael Knoerzer, Daren McNally
Number of partners: 290
Total number of fee earners: 1,400

## Firm Overview:

Clyde & Co is a global law firm with a pioneering heritage. With over 1,400 lawyers operating from 30 offices in six continents, the firm advises corporations, financial institutions, private individuals and governments. Widely recognised as a market leader in insurance and international trade, the firm has a particularly strong track record in complex cross-jurisdictional disputes and transactional matters. Having expanded rapidly in recent years, the firm also has an unrivalled reputation for its work in aviation, marine, energy and infrastructure. By combining sector specialism with legal excellence, Clyde & Co provides the most commerically valuable solutions to its clients' needs. Wholly committed to the industries and markets they serve, the growing practices in New York, San Francisco and New Jersey play a key role in Clyde & Co's global legal offering.

## Main Areas of Practice:

### Insurance/Reinsurance:

The firm boasts one of the leading insurance and reinsurance litigation practices in the world. Benefiting from a favourable conflicts environment, Clyde & Co has been able to attract talented attorneys from some of the largest and best known US law firms. These include Michael Knoerzer, Paul Koepff, William Casey, Daren McNally, Joan D'Ambrosio, Peter Whelan, Stephen Kennedy, Robert Priestley and Andrew Wagner. Robert Ansehl heads up the corporate insurance group. The US offices boast a team of more than 40 experienced insurance and reinsurance litigators, comprising one of the largest such insurance focused litigation groups in the US. The attorneys in the firm routinely handle some of the largest and most complex insurance and reinsurance matters litigated in the United States.

### Aviation:

The firm has one of the world's foremost aviation practices, serving a wide range of leading market participants with respect to all legal aspects of the aviation and aerospace industry, including insurance, accidents, liability, passenger and cargo claims, aircraft sale, purchase, leasing and financing, commercial contracts, regulatory/competition matters and non-contentious work. The defense of aviation mass disasters is one of the core strengths of the firm's US team, which is headed up by Andrew Harakas and includes Diane Westwood Wilson, Chris Carlsen and Kevin Sutherland.

### Litigation & Arbitration:

The firm has acted on many high profile cases and offers comprehensive litigation, arbitration and mediation services in all major jurisdictions. The firm has one of the largest commercial dispute resolution practices of any international law firm. Clyde & Co's

New York and New Jersey partners are leading litigators, each with over 20 years of experience. They handle all types of litigation in state and federal courts throughout the US. The US team also has extensive experience in the defense of product manufacturers located in Europe, Asia and the US. The firm's lawyers have broad experience advising companies in the US and all over the world, providing clients with a seamless global service.

### Maritime:

The firm has long been a world leader in shipping matters and expanded its well-regarded US maritime practice by adding noted New York practitioner John Keough, who joins team leader John Woods. Clyde & Co acts in many of the largest and most complex marine matters, working closely with attorneys across the firm's global network.

### Professional Liability:

The firm specializes in the representation of professionals and their insurers and reinsurers, providing both litigation and insurance counselling services. The firm's experience encompasses claims involving: attorneys; architects, engineers and other design professionals; directors and officers; real estate professionals; technology, media and communications companies; insurance brokers and adjusters; employers; physicians and related medical and healthcare professionals; and nursing homes. The Professional Liability Group's experience also extends to aviation risks (including space and satellite exposures), cargo and transportation, sports and entertainment management, film and music industry risks, and the insurance products associated with each of these fields. Ned Kirk leads this practice in New York and Bill Casey, Kim West and Joan D'Ambrosio lead this practice in San Francisco.

## OFFICES

### NEW YORK

**NEW YORK:** The Chrysler Building, 405 Lexington Avenue, NY 10174
Tel: 212 710 3900   Fax: 212 710 3950
Email: info@clydeco.us

### CALIFORNIA

**SAN FRANCISCO:** 101 Second Street, 24th Floor, CA 94105
Tel: 415 365 9800   Fax: 415 365 9801
Email: info@clydeco.us

### NEW JERSEY

**FLORHAM PARK:** 200 Campus Drive, Suite 300, NJ 07932
Tel: 973 210 6700   Fax: 973 210 6701
Email: info@clydeco.us

## INTERNATIONAL OFFICES

Abu Dhabi, Caracas, Dar Es Salaam*, Doha, Dubai, Guildford, Hong Kong, London, Montreal, Moscow, Mumbai*, Nantes, New Delhi*, Paris, Perth, Piraeus, Rio De Janeiro*, Riyadh*, Shanghai, Singapore, St Petersburg*, Sydney, Toronto, Tripoli

\* Associated Offices

## International Work:

The firm advises businesses in more than 120 countries and has extensive experience handling complex, multi-party, multi-jurisdictional issues before litigation and protecting client interests in the event of litigation. Clyde & Co has one of the largest international networks of foreign correspondent law firms, comprising over 500 firms. The firm's lawyers are qualified in 17 jurisdictions and fluent in over 50 languages. International clients include airlines, a broad spectrum of multinational corporations, insurance, reinsurance and trading companies, credit insurers, ship owners and salvors, P&I Clubs and trade and energy companies.

# COVINGTON & BURLING LLP

www.cov.com

**Management Committee Chair:** Timothy C Hester
Number of partners worldwide: 262
Number of lawyers worldwide: 895

## Firm Overview:

From its offices in Beijing, Brussels, London, New York, San Diego, San Francisco, Seoul, Shanghai, Silicon Valley and Washington, Covington practices as one firm, holding closely to core values: a deep commitment to its clients and the high quality of its work on their behalf. The firm emphasizes teamwork among its lawyers and other professionals and believes in the obligation of lawyers to make legal services available to all who need them.

## Main Areas of Practice:

### Corporate:

Covington was ranked among the top 25 firms nationally by corporate directors and general counsel in Corporate Board Member's America's Best Corporate Law Firms. With more than 200 lawyers practicing in the corporate, securities, finance, venture capital, bankruptcy, real estate, tax, and employee benefits areas, Covington provides a full range of transactional and advisory services from offices in the US, UK, EU, and Asia.

**Bankruptcy & Restructuring:** Covington handles all facets of bankruptcy and restructuring practice, from non-judicial consensual restructurings to contentious bankruptcy proceedings. The firm represents debtors, financial creditors, trade creditors, indenture trustees, and official committees in Chapter 11 cases.

**Financial Institutions:** The additions in January of 2011 of the most recent US Comptroller of the Currency and the long-time head of the American Bankers Association have significantly strengthened this Chambers top-rated practice.

**M&A:** In the past few years, the firm has advised on more than 200 mergers and acquisitions, with an aggregate value of more than $300 billion. The firm's clients include Global 100 companies, private equity firms, and investment banks as well as venture backed companies who depend on the firm's industry knowledge to support their formative transactions.

**Securities:** Co-headed by a former Director of the SEC's Division of Corporation Finance, Covington's Securities Practice integrates transactional skills and understanding of corporate financing techniques and practices with a deep understanding of securities and related business laws. Covington's attorneys have handled significant public and private offerings of equity, debt and derivative securities, representing issuers, financial institutions, and investors.

### Litigation:

Recognized as one of the top litigation firms by The American Lawyer magazine in its Litigation Department of the Year awards, Covington's Litigation Practice of more than 450 attorneys covers virtually every important area of civil and criminal law. The firm handles important and high-stakes legal disputes in federal and state courts, arbitral tribunals, and administrative agencies throughout the US, as well as in international forums and selected European courts.

**Antitrust:** Co-chaired by the two recent heads of the Department of Justice's Antitrust Division, Covington attorneys play leading roles in the fields of antitrust and consumer litigation. The firm represents clients in both private antitrust litigation and before the FTC and the DOJ, and has been named to Global Competition Review's Global Elite, a listing of top 20 competition practices worldwide.

**Insurance–Policyholder:** Chambers recognized Covington as the world's pre-eminent Insurance Coverage Practice by presenting the group with the first ever Award of Excellence for Insurance in 2007, an award the group received again in 2009, 2010 and 2012. Covington's International Insurance Practice focuses on the representation of corporate policyholders globally and has helped clients recover more than $15 billion.

**Intellectual Property:** Covington's IP practice has been recognized for excellence by Managing Intellectual Property, Best Lawyers in America, and WORLDLeaders International IP Awards. Covington handles a wide range of intellectual property matters across the US and internationally, including patent, trademark, trade secret, copyright, privacy, and anti-piracy disputes.

**International Arbitration:** Recognized by Chambers for the ability to "present extremely complicated matters lucidly and persuasively," Covington's lawyers have handled matters in virtually all major arbitral bodies operating in the world today. Covington's practice in arbitration and other forms of alternative dispute resolution covers the field from complex international disputes that span the globe to domestic matters in specific industries conducted under specialized rules.

**White-Collar:** Recognized by Chambers, Legal 500, and others, Covington's White-Collar Practice is lauded not only for litigating and winning high profile criminal cases, but also for devising creative legal strategies to resolve cases long before they draw public scrutiny. The firm has a long-standing record of excellence in the areas of regulatory enforcement, internal investigations, and ethics inquiries.

**Regulatory:**
Covington's 150+ regulatory lawyers are recognized as experts in their fields and regularly combine their talents on behalf of the world's top energy, financial services, pharmaceutical and life sciences companies, telecommunications and technology companies, utilities, railroads, sports leagues, and consumer goods companies, among others.

**Foreign Trade & Controls:** Recipient of the 2011 Chambers Award of Excellence for International Trade, the firm has broad expertise handling advisory and enforcement matters involving foreign trade controls, including export controls, economic sanctions, anti-boycott requirements, and anti-bribery prohibitions. The firm also represents international and domestic clients before CFIUS agencies often involving high stakes commercial investments.

**Life Sciences:** Ranked 1st in PLC's Life Sciences Regulatory Super Leagues for four years running, Covington's Life Sciences Practice is a cross-disciplinary and cross-border powerhouse. The firm provides a full range of litigation, regulatory, and transactional services to pharmaceutical, biotechnology, medical device, veterinary, and agricultural companies in the US and abroad.

### OFFICES

DISTRICT OF COLUMBIA
**WASHINGTON DC:** 1201 Pennsylvania Avenue NW, DC 20004-2401
Tel: 202 662 6000   Fax: 202 662 6291

CALIFORNIA
**SAN FRANCISCO:** One Front Street, CA 94111
Tel: 415 591 6000   Fax: 415 591 6091

**SAN DIEGO:** 9191 Towne Centre Drive, 6th Floor, CA 92122-1225
Tel: 858 678 1800   Fax: 858 678 1600

**REDWOOD SHORES:** 333 Twin Dolphin Drive, Suite 700, CA 94065-1418
Tel: 650 632 4700   Fax: 650 632 4800

NEW YORK
**NEW YORK:** The New York Times Building, 620 Eighth Avenue, NY 10018-1405
Tel: 212 841 1000   Fax: 212 841 1010

### INTERNATIONAL OFFICES

The firm also has offices in London, Brussels, Beijing, Seoul and Shanghai.

# COVINGTON

COVINGTON & BURLING LLP

# DAVIS POLK & WARDWELL LLP

**www.**davispolk.com **tel:** 212 450 4000 **fax:** 212 701 5800

**Managing Partner:** Thomas J Reid
Number of partners worldwide: 160
Number of other lawyers worldwide: 651
Languages: *Collectively, Davis Polk lawyers speak more than 50 languages.*

**Firm Overview:**

Davis Polk is a global law firm based in New York City. For over 160 years, the firm has advised many of the world's leading companies and financial institutions as they face complex legal and business challenges.
With over 800 lawyers, Davis Polk is one of the world's premier law firms. Lawyers in the firm's corporate practice advise companies and financial institutions on the full range of domestic and global transactions. Their litigators lead the profession in such areas as securities litigation and compliance, white collar criminal defense, products liability and mass torts, global enforcement, antitrust, intellectual property litigation and insolvency and restructuring. Lawyers in their tax practice work on intricate and novel taxation issues associated with transactions and corporate structures, as well as all types of tax controversy matters.

**Main Areas of Practice:**

**Corporate:**

Davis Polk's Corporate Department encompasses a broad range of practice areas, including capital markets, mergers and acquisitions, credit, insolvency and restructuring, intellectual property, investment management/funds, financial regulatory, executive compensation and employee benefits, environmental and real estate. These groups are widely recognized as being among the preeminent practices worldwide.
Davis Polk lawyers have been involved in a number of the most important recent corporate transactions, including advising:

- The U.S. Treasury, as selling shareholder, on the $20.7 billion SEC-registered common stock offering of AIG. This was the largest common stock offering in US history.
- Grupo Financiero Santander México on its $4.1 billion IPO and global share offering. This is the largest equity offering in Latin America in 2012 and the largest-ever IPO by a Mexican issuer.
- CNOOC on its $15.1 billion acquisition of Nexen
- Heinz on its $28 billion acquisition by Berkshire Hathaway and 3G Capital
- ConAgra Foods on its $6.8 billion acquisition of Ralcorp
- Lehman Brothers International (Europe) ("LBIE") on the settlement in principle of $38 billion in claims between LBIE and Lehman Brothers

**Litigation:**

Companies from around the world in every industry, as well as their executives and directors, retain Davis Polk lawyers for their most significant litigation matters. The firm's 201 litigators, based in its New York, Washington DC and Menlo Park offices, routinely represent clients in trials, criminal and regulatory investigations, congressional inquiries, arbitrations, hearings, appeals and crisis management situations. The firm's broad-

based practice encompasses matters involving securities litigation and enforcement, antitrust, white collar crime, FCPA, intellectual property litigation, mass tort and products liability, acquisition-related litigation, banking litigation, insolvency and restructuring, directors' and officers' liability, professional liability, commercial arbitration and tax controversy.

**Tax:**

Davis Polk's tax lawyers are at the leading edge of innovation, working closely with clients on complex transactions and corporate structures, as well as first-of-their-kind derivatives and other financial products. Davis Polk's Tax Controversy Group has prevailed in a number of significant tax matters and is frequently sought out by companies to handle their most sensitive tax disputes, including most recently on behalf of PepsiCo in a significant case regarding the appropriate tax treatment of important inter-company financial instruments created in the 1990s to facilitate the company's international growth.

**Clients:**

The firm's clients include Aetna, Altria, Angie's List, Arcos Dorados, AstraZeneca, Baidu, Banco Santander, Bank of America, BBVA, Bertelsmann, Campbell Soup, Cigna, Citigroup, CNOOC, Cobalt International Energy, Comcast, ConAgra Foods, Credit Suisse, CSX, CVS Caremark, Delphi Automotive, Delta Air Lines, Deutsche Bank, Digicel, Emerson, E*TRADE, ExxonMobil, Facebook, FedEx, Ford, Freeport-McMoRan Copper & Gold, Goldman Sachs, Grupo Aval, Heinz, Ingram Micro, JPMorgan Chase, KPMG, Limited Brands, Lloyds TSB, LVMH, Mexichem, Morgan Stanley, NBCUniversal, NYSE Euronext, Oracle, Pandora, PepsiCo, Pfizer, PIMCO, Prada, Ralph Lauren, Roche, RBS, Siemens, Sodexo, Telefónica, Texas Instruments, VF, Warner Chilcott and Yahoo!.

**PRACTICE AREAS**

CORPORATE
Capital Markets
Corporate Governance
Credit
Environmental
Executive Compensation & Employee Benefits
Financial Institutions
Insolvency & Restructuring
Intellectual Property
Investment Management
Mergers & Acquisitions
Real Estate
Trading & Markets
LITIGATION
Antitrust & Competition
Bankruptcy Litigation
Board of Directors Litigation & Strategic Counseling
Commercial Dispute & Contract
Compliance & Advisory
Congressional Investigations
Consumer Class Action
Economic Sanctions & National Security
Foreign Corrupt Practices Act
Intellectual Property Litigation
Internal Investigations
International & Domestic Arbitration
International Litigation & Enforcement
Investment Funds Litigation & Investigations
M&A-Related Litigation
Mass Torts & Products Liability
Professional Liability
Securities Litigation
Securities Enforcement
White Collar Criminal Defense
TAX
Financial Products
International Tax
Investment Funds
Tax M&A
Tax Insolvency & Restructuring
Tax Controversy & Advisory Services

**OFFICES**

NEW YORK
**NEW YORK:** 450 Lexington Avenue, NY 10017
Tel: 212 450 4000 Fax: 212 701 5800

CALIFORNIA
**MENLO PARK:** 1600 El Camino Real, CA 94025
Tel: 650 752 2000 Fax: 650 752 2111

DISTRICT OF COLUMBIA
**WASHINGTON DC:** 901 15th Street, NW, DC 20005
Tel: +1 202 962 7000 Fax: +1 202 962 7111

**INTERNATIONAL OFFICES**

Beijing, Hong Kong, London, Madrid, Paris, São Paulo, Tokyo

# FRESHFIELDS BRUCKHAUS DERINGER

www.freshfields.com

**Senior Partner:** William Lawes
**Managing Partner:** Ted Burke
**US Managing Partner:** Julian Pritchard

**OFFICES**

NEW YORK

**NEW YORK:** 601 Lexington Avenue, NY 10022
Tel: 212 277 4000  Fax: 212 277 4001

DISTRICT OF COLUMBIA

**WASHINGTON:** 701 Pennsylvania Avenue, NW, Suite 600,
DC 20004
Tel: 202 777 4500  Fax: 202 777 4555

## Firm Overview:

Freshfields is a leader among international law firms, providing business law advice of the highest quality throughout the US, Europe, Asia, Latin America and the Middle East. With more than 2,500 lawyers in 28 key business centers around the world, the firm provides a comprehensive service to national and multinational corporations, financial institutions and governments.

In the US, Freshfields provides integrated and proactive legal counsel to clients seeking local or international advice. The firm's US practice is a key part of its international network; it has more than 170 lawyers based in the US and more than 200 US-qualified lawyers working in its offices around the world.

## Main Areas of Practice:

### Antitrust, Competition & Trade:

The Washington, DC-based US Antitrust Group has an extensive background in US antitrust enforcement. The firm's lawyers have strong ties to the US enforcement agencies, having both worked for and represented many clients in front of the US Department of Justice and the Federal Trade Commission. The combined experience of its lawyers includes dozens of Second Request merger investigations, full-phase civil conduct investigations, and litigation of major antitrust cases in federal courts. The firm regularly advises on mergers and acquisitions, joint ventures, intellectual property licensing, and distribution and supply agreements. Additionally, the group advises on related international trade issues that might arise in connection with a national security review such as the Foreign Corrupt Practices Act (FCPA) and embargoes and sanctions administered by the Office of Foreign Asset Control.

### Corporate:

In the US, the Corporate Practice is almost entirely involved in cross-border work, either in-bound or out-bound, helping to deliver the firm's network to its US-based clients. The firm's New York-based Corporate Group advises on a wide range of transactional, commercial and general corporate matters. It regularly advises clients in connection with mergers and acquisitions, private equity transactions, spin-offs, joint ventures and securities offerings.

### Finance:

The New York-based Finance Practice consists predominately of work in project finance, structured finance, asset finance, acquisition and property finance and private placements.

The Project Finance Team in the Americas represents project sponsors and investors, commercial banks, institutional lenders, international financial institutions, export credit agencies, underwriters, public authorities and governmental agencies on projects across the full spectrum of the industry, including the transportation, energy and social infrastructure sectors. The US-based Structured Finance Team advises on and develops complex tax-driven products, derivative-based transactions, collateralized debt obligation funds, capital raising and arbitrage transactions, and securitizations (including synthetic securities, repackagings, conduits, and future flow transactions). Clients include major financial institutions, asset originators, asset purchasers, asset managers, insurers, rating agencies and other market participants.

### Litigation:

The firm's Litigation Group comprises sophisticated civil litigation, white-collar defense and international arbitration practices. It represents public companies, financial institutions, foreign governments and other entities – as well as corporate executives and directors – in grand jury and regulatory enforcement investigations and in complex civil litigation. It also has extensive experience handling clients' US-based domestic litigation challenges. Freshfields represents financial institutions, public companies and government entities in complex civil litigation and has significant trial experience in the event a case cannot be resolved by negotiation. The firm also routinely conducts internal corporate investigations for corporate clients, audit committees and board special committees and defends clients in government investigations in cases involving allegations of financial accounting and other securities fraud, insider trading, stock options backdating, cartel and other anti-competitive activity, possible violations of the FCPA and the off-label promotion of pharmaceutical products and devices. The US-based members of its international arbitration group represent national and international corporations, financial institutions and governments in major arbitrations. In particular, the team is the world leader in arbitrations involving Latin America and handles most of the world's largest energy disputes. The firm's pre-eminence in the field of international arbitration is acknowledged worldwide, given its unrivalled track record of conducting UNCITRAL, ICC, LCIA, ICSID, AAA and ad hoc international arbitrations in the US, established European venues and elsewhere.

### Tax:

Its US tax lawyers focus on corporate and financial transactions, with an emphasis on cross-border acquisitions and restructuring, private equity and financial products. Working closely with the firm's tax teams in other countries, the team advises on major corporate transactions, such as mergers and international group restructuring, and on private equity structures that enhance returns from multinational portfolio investments. The team also provides tax advice on structured finance matters ranging from securitizations to derivatives and other complex structured products.

### International Work:

The firm's international approach is founded on strong local capabilities and experience, offering clients multidisciplinary teams from a number of jurisdictions. The firm's lawyers, many of whom are multilingual, work effectively across disciplines, cultures and time zones to provide clients with integrated commercial, business and practical advice. Freshfields actively monitors developments and identifies trends in the US, Europe, Asia, Latin America and the Middle East, as well as within industry sectors, enabling it to understand the issues that are important to its clients' businesses.

 **Freshfields Bruckhaus Deringer**

# HAYNES AND BOONE, LLP

www.haynesboone.com **tel:** 214 651 5000 **fax:** 214 651 5940

**Managing Partner:** Terry Conner
Number of partners: 220  Number of other lawyers: 300
Languages: *American Sign, Arabic, Armenian, Chinese (Cantonese, Mandarin, Shanghainese, Toisan), Dutch, Filipino, French, German, Hebrew, Indian (Gujarati, Hindi, Hurdu, Malayalam, Urdu), Indonesian, Italian, Japanese, Korean, Latin, Persian, Portuguese, Romanian, Russian, Serbo-Croatian, Spanish, Taglog, Taiwanese, Thai and Vietnamese*

## Firm Overview:

Haynes and Boone, LLP is an international corporate law firm representing global businesses in a full range of sophisticated legal matters. With more than 520 lawyers in 11 offices across Texas, New York, California, Washington, DC and Mexico City, Haynes and Boone is ranked among the largest law firms in the US by The National Law Journal.

## Main Areas of Practice:

### Corporate/Securities/M&A:
More than 105 lawyers assist clients with the full spectrum of corporate and capital market needs, serving a range of clients, from multinational corporations and financial institutions to start-ups.
**Key Clients:** AMR Corp., AT&T Inc., Halliburton.
**Contact:** Greg Samuel
**Email:** greg.samuel@haynesboone.com
**Contact:** Steven Buxbaum
**Email:** steven.buxbaum@haynesboone.com

### Litigation:
Approximately 186 attorneys handle all aspects of business litigation including IP, insurance coverage, environmental and appellate.
**Key Clients:** Shell Oil Company, Hess Corporation, AT&T Inc., Marvel Entertainment.
**Contact:** David Harper
**Email:** david.harper@haynesboone.com
**Contact:** Anne Johnson
**Email:** anne.johnson@haynesboone.com

### Bankruptcy/Restructuring:
Nationally ranked and one of the largest and most experienced business reorganization groups, their lawyers assist debtors and creditors in all aspects of insolvency – in and out of court.
**Key Clients:** AMR Corporation, Midland Loan Service, Credit Agricole Corporate and Investment Bank.
**Contact:** Stephen Pezanosky
**Email:** stephen.pezanosky@haynesboone.com

### Energy:
Comprised of more than 125 attorneys and industry professionals, this group knows the domestic and international physical and financial energy markets.
**Key Clients:** Shell, InterOil Corporation, EV Energy Partners, EDP Renewables.
**Contact:** Buddy Clark
**Email:** buddy.clark@haynesboone.com

### Banking & Finance:
The team helps companies secure capital market access through complex combinations of debt, equity and securitized financing.
**Key Clients:** Bank of America Merrill Lynch, Citibank.
**Contact:** Scott Night
**Email:** scott.night@haynesboone.com

### Franchise:
Internationally recognized, the franchise lawyers assist clients in domestic and international regulatory, expansion, government contract, work out, dispute resolution, arbitration and litigation matters.
**Key Clients:** Krispy Kreme Doughnut Corporation, Radio Shack Corporation, T.G.I. Friday's.
**Contact:** Joyce Mazero
**Email:** joyce.mazero@haynesboone.com

### Intellectual Property/Technology Law:
More than 77 attorneys assist clients in the development, use, preservation and defense of IP rights, helping clients in structuring, negotiating, documenting and closing a wide variety of commercial transactions involving technology and IP.
**Key Clients:** AT&T Inc., eBay, Inc., Cisco Systems, Inc.
**Contact:** Randall Brown
**Email:** randall.brown@haynesboone.com
**Contact:** David McCombs
**Email:** david.mccombs@haynesboone.com

### International:
The firm has one of the largest Latin America-wide practices of any US-based law firm, anchored by its 18-attorney Mexico City office.
**Key Clients:** Sumitomo Mitsui Banking Corporation, Natixis Real Estate Capital, Credit Agricole Corporate and Investment Bank, FMC Corporation.
**Contact:** Larry Pascal
**Email:** larry.pascal@haynesboone.com

### Labor & Employment:
The firm handles all aspects of complex labor and employment matters that face domestic and international businesses such as counseling management, labor union issues and employment litigation.
**Key Clients:** ASARCO, The Home Depot, United

### OFFICES

#### TEXAS
**DALLAS:** 2323 Victory Avenue, Suite 700, TX 75219
Tel: 214 651 5000  Fax: 214 651 5940

**HOUSTON:** 1221 McKinney Street, Suite 2100, TX 77010
Tel: 713 547 2000  Fax: 713 547 2600

**AUSTIN:** 600 Congress Ave., Suite 1300, TX 78701
Tel: 512 867 8400  Fax: 512 867 8470

**SAN ANTONIO:** 112 East Pecan St., Suite 1200, TX 78205
Tel: 210 978 7000  Fax: 210 978 7450

**FORT WORTH:** 201 Main St., Suite 2200, TX 76102
Tel: 817 347 6600  Fax: 817 347 6650

**RICHARDSON:** 2505 N. Plano Road, Suite 4000, TX 75082
Tel: 972 739 6900  Fax: 972 680 7551

#### DISTRICT OF COLUMBIA
**WASHINGTON DC:** 1615 L Street, NW, Suite 800, DC 20036-5610
Tel: 202 654 4500 Fax: 202 654 4501

#### CALIFORNIA
**IRVINE:** 18100 Von Karman Ave., Suite 750, CA 92612
Tel: 949 202 3000 Fax: 949 202 3001

**SAN JOSE:** 2033 Gateway Place, Suite 300, CA 95110
Tel: 408 660 4120 Fax: 408 660 4121

#### NEW YORK
**NEW YORK:** 30 Rockefeller Plaza, 26th Floor, NY 10112
Tel: 212 659 7300 Fax: 212 918 8989

### INTERNATIONAL OFFICES
The firm also has an office in Mexico.

*Working under a cooperation agreement with MMA Lawyers in Rio de Janeiro. Available by appointment with MMA Lawyers. Haynes and Boone, LLP and MMA Lawyers operate as independent firms.

Rentals.
**Contact:** Melissa Goodman
**Email:** melissa.goodman@haynesboone.com

### Real Estate:
One of the largest and most experienced real estate practices in the nation, attorneys represent clients in every facet of buying, selling, developing, operating, leasing, capitalizing and financing real estate for operators, investors and users for US and foreign clients.
**Key Clients:** Hillwood Alliance Services, SL Green Realty Corp., USAA Real Estate Company.
**Contact:** Matthew Schindel
**Email:** matthew.schindel@haynesboone.com
**Contact:** Walter Schleimer
**Email:** walter.schleimer@haynesboone.com

### White-Collar Criminal Defense/Antitrust:
The firm represents Fortune 500 companies worldwide in defending and prosecuting competition cases.
**Key Clients:** American Airlines, ExxonMobil, AT&T Inc.
**Contact:** Ron Breaux
**Email:** ron.breaux@haynesboone.com

*haynesboone*
Setting precedent.

# KING & SPALDING LLP

**www.kslaw.com tel:** 404 572 4600 **fax:** 404 572 5100

**Chairman:** Robert D Hays

## Firm Overview:

Celebrating more than 125 years of service, King & Spalding is an international law firm that represents a broad array of clients, including half of the *Fortune Global* 100, with 800 lawyers in 17 offices in the United States, Europe, the Middle East and Asia. The firm has handled matters in over 160 countries on six continents and is consistently recognized for the results it obtains, uncompromising commitment to quality and dedication to understanding the business and culture of its clients.

## Main Areas of Practice:

### Antitrust:
Tries cases to verdict and defends clients against criminal investigations, opt-out group actions, class actions, appellate matters and other antitrust litigation.

### Business Litigation:
Experienced in issues of antitrust, product liability, mass tort, patents and trademarks, class action certification, securities law, franchise law, white-collar defense and consumer fraud.

### Corporate, Public & Private Finance:
More than 50 lawyers located in offices across the United States, Europe and Middle East represent lenders, investors, funds and borrowers in finance and other commercial transactions.

### Employee Benefits & Exec. Comp:
Advises on employee benefit plans and executive compensation programs and the related funding vehicles.

### E-Discovery:
Serves as lead national discovery counsel for *Fortune* 50 companies in the banking, energy, pharmaceutical, medical device, telecommunications, chemical, manufacturing, and tobacco industries.

### Energy:
Informs clients on a spectrum of transactional, regulatory, litigation and arbitration matters in the oil and gas, power and mining industries.

### Environmental:
Assists clients with virtually every type of environmental issue – including regulatory and compliance advice, permit appeals, enforcement actions, and property damage claims.

### FDA & Life Sciences:
Represents pharmaceutical, medical device, biotechnology, healthcare technology companies and food manufacturers, in a range of regulatory, compliance, policy, and litigation matters.

### Financial Restructuring:
Directs on reorganizations, including in court and out-of-court debt restructurings, bankruptcy and insolvency litigation, and distressed asset mergers and acquisitions.

### Global Transactions:
Counsels clients through the entire project development process, from concept to ribbon-cutting, with particular emphasis in the energy and transportation sectors.

### Government Advocacy & Public Policy:
Supports clients in managing their interactions with the federal government including congressional investigations, international, and ethics and election law.

### Healthcare:
As one of the largest practices in the country, the firm is praised for its excellence in transactional, litigation and regulatory representation of clients across the spectrum of healthcare.

### Intellectual Property:
Aids clients with the development and strategic planning needed to handle patent and trademark prosecution and intellectual property litigation matters that stretch across borders.

### International Arbitration:
Highly experienced in handling cases before major arbitral institutions such as the ICSID, ICC, LCIA, and AAA, as well as under UNCITRAL and other ad hoc rules.

### International Trade & WTO:
Over 40 lawyers and consultants, handling a wide range of international trade and customs matters for US and non-US clients.

### Labor & Employment:
Provides labor and employment services to employers ranging from preventive advice and training to litigation and representation under federal and state labor and employment laws.

### Mergers & Acquisitions:
Covers acquisitions of public and private companies, tender offers, joint ventures and partnering arrangements, purchases and sales of divisions, and takeover preparation and defense.

### Pharmaceutical, Biotechnology & Medical Devices:
More than 125 of the firm's lawyers and professionals devote all or a substantial portion of their practices to clients in these industries, with specialized experience at every stage of the product life cycle.

### Private Equity & Investment Funds:
Draws on the lawyers' extensive experience in fund formation, mergers and acquisitions, leveraged finance, Islamic finance, securities offerings, tax and restructuring.

### Real Estate:
Provides advice on a complete range of commercial real estate transactions. The practice is known for creative structuring of mergers and acquisitions and complex equity and debt financing transactions.

### Special Matters:
Represents corporations and individuals in complex federal and state criminal investigations, internal investigations and congressional investigations.

### Tax:
Covers range of federal income tax issues, with particularly extensive experience in the corporate, partnership and international practice areas.

### Tort Litigation:
Offers large-firm litigation resources and lawyers who have tried high-exposure tort cases, including some of the most plaintiff-friendly jurisdictions in the US.

## OFFICES

**GEORGIA**
**ATLANTA:** 1180 Peachtree Street NE, Atlanta, GA 30309
Tel: 404 572 4600  Fax: 404 572 5100

**CALIFORNIA**
**SAN FRANCISCO:** 101 Second Street, Suite 2300, San Francisco, CA 94105
Tel: 415 318 1200  Fax: 415 318 1300

**REDWOOD SHORES:** 333 Twin Dolphin Drive, Suite 400, Redwood Shores, CA 94065
Tel: 650 590 0700  Fax: 650 590 1900

**NEW YORK**
**NEW YORK:** 1185 Avenue of the Americas, New York, NY 10036
Tel: 212 556 2100  Fax: 212 556 2222

**NORTH CAROLINA**
**CHARLOTTE:** 100 N. Tryon Street, Suite 3900, Charlotte, NC 28202
Tel: 704 503 2600  Fax: 704 503-2622

**TEXAS**
**HOUSTON:** 1100 Louisiana Street, Suite 4000, Houston, TX 77002
Tel: 713 751 3200  Fax: 713 751 3290

**AUSTIN:** 401 Congress Avenue, Suite 3200, Austin, TX 78701
Tel: 512 457 2000  Fax: 512 457 4000

**DISTRICT OF COLUMBIA**
**WASHINGTON, DC:** 1700 Pennsylvania Avenue, N.W., Washington, DC 20006
Tel: 202 737 0500  Fax: 202 626 3737

## INTERNATIONAL OFFICES
Abu Dhabi, Dubai, Frankfurt, Geneva, London, Moscow, Paris, Riyadh (affiliated) and Singapore.

# KING & SPALDING

# LATHAM & WATKINS

www.lw.com

**Chair & Managing Partner:** Robert M Dell
Number of partners worldwide: more than 600
Number of lawyers worldwide: more than 2,000

**OFFICES**
For more information visit www.lw.com

**INTERNATIONAL OFFICES**
The firm also has offices in Asia, the Middle East and Europe

## Firm Overview:

Latham & Watkins is a leading global law firm serving multinational companies, start-ups, investment banks, private equity funds, venture capital firms, sovereign wealth funds, governments and other organizations from its 31 offices across Asia, Europe, the Middle East and the US. The firm is internationally recognized for its practices, and has received recognition for its handling of landmark matters. Latham offers unrivalled legal and strategic thinking to provide clients with innovative solutions to complex business and legal matters.

## Main Areas of Practice:

### Antitrust/Competition:
Latham's Antitrust and Competition Practice provides integrated service to clients facing issues relating to in-country and cross-border merger clearance and cartel defense. The team offers skills in litigation, government investigations and private antitrust matters.

### Banking:
Latham's Banking Practice handles financing and funding transactions for lenders, borrowers and purchasers. The firm represents market-leading financial institutions and financial services providers, including banks, commercial finance lenders, leasing concerns, funds and insurance companies.

### Capital Markets:
Latham represents corporate and partnership issuers, underwriters, placement agents and initial purchasers in hundreds of offerings of equity, equity-linked and debt securities for US and international clients.

### Corporate/M&A:
Latham garners market recognition in the US and around the globe for its involvement in cross-border M&A and corporate transactions, handling enterprise-transforming deals for a wide range of clients. The firm provides clients with unique resources and expertise when executing complex, multijursidictional transactions, and day to day advice on corporate governance and compliance issues.

### Climate Change:
This multijurisdictional and multidisciplinary group has expertise is all aspects of the climate change landscape, including clean technology and clean energy development, greenhouse gas trading mitigation and global carbon dioxide trading markets.

### Environmental:
Latham has one of the most respected environmental and resources practices in the US, with experience in all aspects of environmental, energy, land use and natural resource law. Latham lawyers have been at the forefront of the most significant environmental and resource litigation and regulatory developments.

### Restructuring, Insolvency & Workouts:
Latham is a leading global adviser in complex corporate insolvencies, restructurings and workouts. A roster of experienced practioners advise debtors, sponsors, creditors and creditor's committees on some of the most significant and innovative restructurings across a wide range of industries and jurisdictions.

### Intellectual Property:
Latham's intellectual property experience, resources and geographic reach combine to assist clients as they acquire, manage, license, develop and defend their intellectual property rights in all forms. The firm has significant experience in intellectual property counseling, transactions and litigation.

### Litigation:
Latham's renowned litigation practice is known for its ability to try complex cases with multibillion dollar exposures, and is frequently retained in the late stages of litigation to do just that. Latham provides sound preventative advice and effective crisis management. The team has the US and global footprint and cross-disciplinary and multijurisdictional expertise that clients require.

### Private Equity:
Latham advises on investments, deal structuring and financing, as well as exit strategies for large and middle market private equity funds and their portfolio companies. The group is fully integrated with attorneys specializing in competition, executive compensation, tax and employee benefits covering numerous sectors.

### Project Development & Finance:
The firm's global team of project finance lawyers has the knowledge and experience to advise on structuring, documenting and negotiating a vast array of development and financing agreements, as well as the related issues, from commercial, energy and environmental issues to tax, banking and real estate law.

### Tax:
Latham lawyers regularly handle tax matters of all types, including planning for multinational corporations, structuring inbound and outbound business and real estate investments or handling tax controversies before the US IRS and other tax authorities. The group also carries out specialized tax planning related to complex transactions.

### Supreme Court & Appellate:
The internationally renowned lawyers of Latham's Appellate practice handle a variety of cases before the US Supreme Court, US federal circuits and state appellate courts.

### White Collar Defense & Investigations:
Many of Latham's team have previous prosecutorial experience, enabling them to secure the best possible outcome for clients facing civil and criminal investigations, and in compliance matters.

### Clients:
With clients in more than 75 countries, Latham lawyers are immersed in the issues that affect its clients' enterprises, in numerous industries including: aerospace and defense; cleantech; communications; energy, in particular in the oil, gas and power sectors; financial institutions; healthcare; hospitality and gaming; industrials and manufacturing; information technology; life sciences and pharmaceutical; real estate; REITS and semiconductors.

### International Work:
Latham advises clients on the international aspects of high profile and enterprise-transforming matters. At the heart of the firm is its collaborative approach; across jurisdictions, practices and industries, the firm draws upon its deep subject matter expertise, its abiding commitment to teamwork and its tradition of providing creative counsel and strategic commercial thinking.

# LATHAM&WATKINS

# LINKLATERS LLP

www.linklaters.com  **tel:** 212 903 9000  **fax:** 212 903 9100

**Senior Partner:** Robert Elliott
**Managing Partner:** Simon Davies
**Americas Co-Managing Partners:** Jeff Norton, Conrado Tenaglia
Number of lawyers worldwide: 2,529
Number of US lawyers worldwide: 199
Number of lawyers in US: 124

**OFFICES**

**NEW YORK:** 1345 Avenue of the Americas, NY 10105
Tel: 212 903 9000  Fax: 212 903 9100

**WASHINGTON, DC:** 601 Thirteenth Street N.W., Suite 800
North, DC 20005
Tel: 202 737 0657  Fax: 212 903 9100

The firm also has international offices in Abu Dhabi,
Amsterdam, Antwerp, Bangkok, Beijing, Berlin, Brussels,
Dubai, Düsseldorf, Frankfurt, Hong Kong, Lisbon, London,
Luxembourg, Madrid, Milan, Moscow, Munich, Paris, Rome,
São Paulo, Shanghai, Singapore, Stockholm, Tokyo,
Warsaw.

## Firm Overview:

Linklaters LLP is a leading global law firm, supporting clients in achieving their strategies wherever they do business. The firm's US based lawyers are located in New York and Washington, DC. This group advises clients on a wide range of domestic and cross-border transactions, regulatory matters and complex litigation. In addition to this strong core team in the US, the firm boasts an additional 75 US qualified lawyers across its international offices who regularly advise on US issues for clients across a variety of sectors, including automotive; financial; chemicals; energy and utilities; food and beverages; healthcare; industrials; infrastructure and transport; insurance; investment managers; IT, business services and media; mining; private equity and sovereign wealth funds; real estate and leisure; retail; and telecommunications.

The New York office also boasts a strong cross-practice team who advise leading corporates and financial institutions on a broad range of transactions in many Latin American countries, including: Argentina, Bolivia, Brazil, Chile, Colombia, Ecuador, Mexico, Peru, Uruguay and Venezuela.

## Main Areas of Practice:

### Antitrust:

The US antitrust team advises clients on the antitrust implications of mergers, acquisitions and joint ventures. Notably, they regularly get proposed deals approved by the FTC and the US DOJ. They also defend clients in international price-fixing investigations and represent them in civil antitrust litigation.

### Banking:

The US banking team has significant experience representing market-leading financial institutions, financial sponsors, mezzanine providers, funds and public and private companies in complex domestic and cross-border financing transactions.

### Capital Markets:

The US capital markets team focuses on equity, debt and convertible bonds traded on the major US and international exchanges, initial public offerings, high-yield debt offerings, SEC-registered offerings and non-registered offerings made pursuant to Rule 144A and Regulation S, liability management transactions involving debt tender offers and exchange offers and cross-border listings by US and US-sponsored issuers.

### Corporate/M&A:

The US corporate/M&A team represents a wide range of leading US and international corporations, financial institutions and private equity funds. The US team has extensive experience with both public and private domestic and cross-border transactions.

### Executive Compensation:

The US executive compensation team advises on all aspects of compensation and benefits, including corporate, securities and tax laws, stock exchange listing requirements and ERISA. They represent both US and non-US based companies in the context of corporate transactions, restructurings and initial public offerings.

### Financial Regulation:

The US financial regulation team advises domestic and international banking organizations on a wide variety of bank regulatory matters, including mergers and acquisitions involving banks and their holding companies, private equity investment in the banking sector, capital markets transactions, capital adequacy and bank-sponsored private investment funds.

### Investment Management:

The US investment management team, in conjunction with Linklaters' tax and ERISA lawyers, have assisted clients in raising capital for a broad range of private equity, real estate, special situations, credit opportunity and hedge funds. They have extensive experience with complex secondary transactions, the purchase and sale of minority and controlling interests in investment management firms, and advise select institutional investors with respect to participation in private funds.

### Litigation & Arbitration:

The US litigation/arbitration team advises and defends clients with significant exposure in cross-border and US litigation. The team has extensive trial and appellate experience before federal and state courts, bankruptcy courts, governmental agencies and other tribunals.

### Restructuring & Insolvency:

The US restructuring and insolvency team advises lending institutions, investment funds, financial advisors and global companies in all phases of in-court and out-of-court restructurings and workouts. They focus on distressed or insolvent companies, restructurings and recapitalizations, capital structure arbitrage, public/private exchanges and Section 363 sale and other distressed M&A matters, US and cross-border bankruptcy proceedings, derivatives/structured finance transactions, and bankruptcy litigation.

### Structured Finance & Derivatives:

The US structured finance and derivatives team focuses on domestic and international securitizations, distressed transactions, hedge fund-linked and hedge fund finance products, repackagings and other structured products, risk-based capital and balance sheet relief transactions, transactions involving commodity-, carbon-, equity-, and insurance-linked exposures, repos and securities lending, treatment of derivatives under the US insolvency regime, regulatory advice, and assorted other structured products.

### Tax:

The US tax team counsels clients in M&A transactions, spin-offs and other divestitures, internal restructurings, consolidated return matters and workouts, as well as transactions involving REITs, partnerships and other pass-through entities. They also advise clients on a broad range of global tax matters, and all types of debt and equity offerings. Their clients include public, private, domestic, and multinational companies. They represent acquiring and acquired corporations and their shareholders, investors and their investment vehicles, underwriters and all categories of lenders.

# Linklaters

# MILBANK, TWEED, HADLEY & MCCLOY LLP

www.milbank.com  **tel:** 212 530 5000  **fax:** 212 530 5219

**Chairman:** Scott A Edelman
Number of US partners: 112   Number of other US lawyers: 326

**Firm Overview:**
For nearly 150 years Milbank, a pre-eminent global law firm, has provided innovative legal solutions in many of the world's largest, most complex, 'first-ever' corporate transactions and litigation. Milbank's clients range from prominent multinational financial, industrial and commercial enterprises to governments and institutions.

## Main Areas of Practice:

**Banking & Finance:**
Milbank represents banks and other institutional investors in transactions such as acquisition and leveraged buyout finance, debt restructurings and workouts, trade finance, cross-border financing, debt arbitrage and equity investments by financial institutions.

**Capital Markets:**
This practice represents sellers, purchasers and financial intermediaries in international debt / equity offerings, derivatives / synthetic products, public utility financings, banks and other financial institution financings, project financing in the capital markets and domestic and foreign government financings.

**Communications:**
Milbank distinguishes itself globally with its deep understanding of the communications industry. The firm counsels clients in transactions involving wireless, fixed-line, satellites, submarine cables and cable TV, intellectual property and regulatory issues.

**Corporate/M&A:**
This group counsels clients on negotiated and hostile transactions in mergers and consolidations, stock / asset acquisitions and dispositions, strategic alliances, joint ventures, proxy contests / tender offers, leveraged / management buyouts, restructurings / bankruptcy reorganizations and corporate governance and executive compensation matters.

**Executive Compensation & Employee Benefits:**
This practice advises on corporate transactions and financial restructurings.

**Financial Restructuring:**
Milbank's track record of chapter 11 cases and corporate restructurings includes some of the largest, highest profile bankruptcy and restructuring matters in the world, such as the representation of major stakeholders in the Lehman Brothers, Kodak, Enron, Satélites Mexicanos, Refco and Global Crossing proceedings.

**Gaming & Hospitality:**
Milbank has worked on transactions involving some of the world's most well known names in gaming and hospitality, in areas such as private equity, restructuring, bankruptcy, private/public financings, joint ventures and long-term management deals.

**Global Leveraged Finance:**
Milbank advises financial institutions, companies and private equity clients on all aspects of leveraged transactions, including senior, subordinated/mezzanine debt transactions, bridge financings and high yield bond offerings. The firm has extensive experience in structuring complex debt instruments utilized in a wide variety of leveraged loan and high yield financing transactions.

**Intellectual Property:**
This group handles complex, multiparty litigation, difficult prosecution of patent, trademark and copyright applications, and multi-million dollar core technology and trademark licenses.

**Latin America:**
Milbank's Latin American transactions include project financings, capital markets, privatizations, M&A, debt-for-equity conversions, corporate / public sector restructurings and banking / financial services.

**Litigation & Arbitration:**
Milbank's litigators serve as lead counsel in some of the largest, most significant and high profile disputes in the world. They represent clients in cases ranging from multi-jurisdiction securities litigations to white-collar/regulatory investigations to complex disputes involving intellectual property, insurance, mergers / acquisitions, antitrust and other commercial litigation.

**Mutual Fund Litigation:**
Milbank has unrivalled experience in mutual fund class action and derivative litigation and has handled and tried more 1940 Act cases than any law firm in the country, including most of the seminal cases.

**Power, Energy & Utilities:**
This group combines a breadth and depth of industry knowledge with project finance expertise, corporate transaction experience and specialized regulatory skills to implement the strategies necessary to be an integral component of a client's team.

**Private Equity:**
Milbank represents participants in private equity investing and assists in structuring, negotiating, executing and financing private equity transactions, including leveraged and management buyouts, 'going-private', recapitalizations and exit transactions.

**Project Finance:**
Milbank lawyers have pioneered the application of limited recourse project finance techniques for over 25 years. In the past three years, Milbank closed over 140 project financings worldwide, which raised more than $125 billion for energy and power, natural resources and other infrastructure projects.

**Real Estate:**
Milbank attorneys play key roles in complex and creative financings and are involved in the debt restructuring of numerous high profile real estate developers.

**Securitization & Structured Finance:**
Milbank is an international leader in creating and applying innovative structured finance and securitization techniques to meet the capital needs of issuers in the US, the EEC and emerging international markets. This group represents issuers, sponsors, underwriters, structuring advisors, collateral managers, credit enhancers and investors in structured finance and securitization transactions.

**Tax:**
Milbank lawyers create and implement acquisition and financing arrangements and advise corporations and senior management on executive compensation and employee benefits issues.

**Technology, Communications & Outsourcing:**
A global leader in information technology and business process outsourcing, Milbank has represented clients in more than 400 transactions in over 90 countries, with a combined deal value in excess of $100 billion.

**Transportation & Space:**
A premier provider of legal services to the aviation and space industries, this group's transactions are routinely singled out for originality and prominence.

**Trusts & Estates:**
Milbank serves individual and institutional clients in estate planning, trusts and estate administration and charitable giving.

# Milbank

# DENTONS (PREVIOUSLY SNR DENTON)

www.dentons.com **tel:** 212 768 6700 **fax:** 212 768 6800

**Global Chief Executive:** Elliott Portnoy
**Global Chair:** Joe Andrew
**US Chief Executive:** Peter Wolfson
**US Managing Partner:** Mike McNamara
Number of global partners: 944
Number of global lawyers/professionals: 2,580

## Firm Overview:

Established in 2013 through the combination of international law firm Salans, Canadian law firm Fraser Milner Casgrain (FMC) and international law firm SNR Denton, Dentons is a new global firm driven to provide clients with a competitive edge in an increasingly complex, interconnected and global marketplace. Dentons connects clients to top-tier, innovative and integrated legal talent across Africa, Asia Pacific, Canada, Europe and Central Asia, the Middle East, the UK and the US. The firm's 2,500 lawyers and professionals in 79 locations across 52 countries are dedicated to providing clients with consistent high-quality service wherever they do business. As diverse and multifaceted as its global client base, Dentons is truly polycentric, forgoing a headquarters and dominant culture in favor of being able to offer clients solutions that are tailored to their business regions and legal needs.

## Main Areas of Practice:

Dentons delivers client service through lawyers and professionals grounded in the following practice disciplines:

- Aboriginal (Canada)
- Arbitration
- Banking and Finance
- Capital Markets
- Competition and Antitrust
- Corporate
- Corporate Governance
- Employment and Labor
- Energy
- Environmental and Natural Resources
- Franchising and Distribution
- Healthcare
- Immigration
- Insurance
- Intellectual Property and Technology
- Life Sciences
- Litigation and Dispute Resolution
- Mergers and Acquisitions
- Mining
- Native American Law and Policy
- Notary Services (Germany)
- Pensions, Benefits and Executive Compensation
- Privacy and Security
- Private Equity
- Project Development
- Public International Law
- Public Law
- Public Policy and Regulation
- Real Estate
- Restructuring, Insolvency and Bankruptcy
- Securities and Corporate Finance
- Tax
- Trade, WTO and Customs
- Transportation
- Trusts, Estates and Wealth Preservation
- Venture Technology and Emerging Growth Companies

The firm's industry focus includes the following representative sectors:

**Energy; Mining; Transportation; Infrastructure & PPP:**
These award-winning teams have seen substantial growth in areas such as environmental and natural resources, oil and gas, project finance and energy trading.

**Financial Institutions:**
Several hundred lawyers and professionals worldwide offer expertise and depth to financial institutions and funds of every size, focus and geography, with capabilities in each of the firm's global locations—including the world's leading financial and commercial centers of London, New York, Paris, Toronto, Frankfurt, Hong Kong, Moscow, Dubai, Chicago, Shanghai and Singapore.

**Government:**
For governmental bodies, regulatory agencies, public sector contractors, multilateral institutions and nonprofit institutions, Dentons offers counsel shaped by the experience of lawyers and professionals who have served in governments worldwide.

**Life Sciences & Healthcare:**
Dentons helps clients meet the rigors of a competitive marketplace and find solutions amid dramatic scientific and medical advances, healthcare reform, regulatory uncertainty, limitations on intellectual property protection and unstable financial markets.

**Insurance:**
Dentons services numerous clients in this sector, anticipating issues and providing creative and comprehensive solutions to today's global challenges.

**Manufacturing:**
With a focus on understanding clients' business models and industries, Dentons services numerous manufacturing clients.

**Real Estate; Retail; Hotels & Leisure:**
Whether it's offering strategic counsel to a hotel investor on key business and legal issues for a complex long-term management agreement, advising an online retailer with regard to product liability issues, or representing a major commercial real estate developer on environmental land use issues, Dentons comprises a core team of internationally respected lawyers who focus exclusively on these three key industries.

**Technology; Communications; Media, Entertainment & Sports:**
With a multidisciplinary team around the globe of several hundred lawyers and professionals operating at the convergence of innovation, strategy, finance and law, Dentons represents clients ranging from Fortune 500 and emerging growth companies to venture capital firms, private equity firms and investment banks.

Additional sector expertise includes automotive; aviation and aerospace; construction; defense; forest products and agribusiness; gaming; luxury, fashion and beauty; private equity; and professional services.

# WATSON, FARLEY & WILLIAMS

www.wfw.com **tel:** 212 922 2200

**Chairman:** Frank Dunne
**Managing Partner:** Michael Greville
Heads of Office: London: Michael Greville and Liz Buchan; New York: Daniel Rodgers; Paris: Laurence Martinez-Bellet; Hamburg: Lothar Wegener; Munich: Lothar Wegener and Simon Preisenberger; Frankfurt: Ivana Mikešić; Rome: Eugenio Tranchino; Milan: Eugenio Tranchino; Madrid: María Pilar García; Athens: George Paleokrassas and Virginia Murray; Piraeus: George Paleokrassas; Singapore: Mei Lin Goh; Bangkok: Steven Burkill; Hong Kong: Loretta Lau.
Number of partners: 130 Number of other fee-earners: 288
Languages: *English, French, German, Spanish, Portuguese, Greek, Italian, Russian, Norwegian, Armenian, Cantonese, Mandarin, Thai*

**Firm Overview:**
Watson, Farley & Williams is a leading international law firm with a presence in major financial centres in Europe, Asia and the USA.

**Main Areas of Practice:**
Watson, Farley & Williams offers its clients services of the highest quality through expertise in the sectors it knows best: finance and investment, maritime, energy, natural resources, transport, real estate and ICT. The firm makes use of specialist skills and experience to provide effective, commercially focused advice across a broad range of corporate, finance, dispute resolution and tax matters as well as employment and regulatory issues.

**Finance & Investment:**
Watson, Farley & Williams ranks among the leading international practices advising banks and investors on financing transactions in Europe, North America, the Middle East and Asia. It advises on the full spectrum of general banking matters, leasing, securitisation, international capital markets, private equity, workouts, insolvency and restructuring.

**Maritime:**
Watson, Farley & Williams has the largest team of dedicated ship finance specialists of any law firm worldwide and its client base collectively dominates global shipping markets. With offices in the world's major ship finance centres it offers fully integrated advice on every aspect of domestic and international transactions including newbuilding and second-hand acquisitions, domestic and cross-border finance, structured financing, credit enhancement structures, commercial contracts, sale and purchase, workouts, restructuring and insolvency.
Head of Maritime: Chris Lowe

**Energy:**
Watson, Farley & Williams advises on domestic and cross-border financings, project development, M&A and associated financial and legal issues in conventional and renewable energy, both onshore and offshore. It has advised on power generation transactions in virtually every fuel category: coal, biomass, oil, LNG, natural gas, waste, hydroelectric, geothermal, nuclear, waste to energy, solar and wind. It is a European leader in the renewable energy sector, known for innovative and sophisticated use of financing.
Head of Energy: Evan Stergoulis

**Natural Resources:**
Watson, Farley & Williams advises on exploration and production, financing, servicing and trading in natural resources, including oil and gas, mining and metals and all forms of soft commodities. The firm's natural resources team deals with all aspects of work in the sector worldwide, particularly equity investment, construction; operation and maintenance; project, commodity and export finance; M&A; capital markets; offtake and trading arrangements; and transport.
Head of Natural Resources: Jan Mellmann

**Transport:**
Watson, Farley & Williams' transport practice acts for banks, lessors, export credit agencies, operators, owners, and manufacturers, as well as advising on major infrastructure investments in the transport sector. Its expertise includes aircraft and rolling stock finance and leasing, as well as corporate and commercial aspects of the aviation and railway sectors.

The firm also advises ports, terminals and logistics developers, investors, operators and managers.
Head of Transport: Rex Rosales

**Real Estate:**
Watson, Farley & Williams' Real Estate Practice acts for developers, domestic and overseas occupiers, investors and lenders on investment, development, finance, construction of commercial real estate, as well as hotels and leisure. It deals with all aspects of commercial property matters – often working with the firm's tax and corporate lawyers – and has particular experience with international financial institutions and investment banks.
Head of Real Estate: Mark Prevezer

**Information & Communications Technology (ICT):**
Watson, Farley & Williams' ICT lawyers specialise in the converging areas of IT, internet, telecoms, satellite communications, multimedia, media and entertainment. They advise on a full spectrum of legal and commercial issues from regulatory, M&A and finance/commercial contracts to content creation and provision, competition law and litigation.

Watson, Farley & Williams

# WHITE & CASE LLP

**www**.whitecase.com **tel:** +1 212 819 8200 **fax:** +1 212 354 8113

**Managing Partner:** Hugh Verrier
Number of partners worldwide: 423
Total lawyers worldwide: 1900

**Firm Overview:**
White & Case is a global law firm, ideally positioned to help its clients achieve their ambitions in today's G20 world. The firm's cross-border expertise and unrivalled depth of local, US and English-qualified lawyers help clients navigate some of the most complex domestic and multijurisdictional deals and disputes. White & Case's commitment to its clients' immediate needs and long-term interests helps create enduring partnerships.

**Main Areas of Practice:**

**Antitrust:**
Clients throughout the world seek the advice of White & Case antitrust lawyers. They count on the firm's extensive experience in litigation against governmental authorities or private parties, counseling on delicate questions and comprehensive worldwide coverage of merger control regimes.

**Asset Finance:**
White & Case is a recognised leader in global leasing, asset-based financing and structured financial transactions and has pioneered many of the tax, legal and financial structures used in countries around the world.

**Banking:**
Since White & Case's founding, banking has been at the core of the firm's practice. Today, it represents major banks worldwide, including many of the largest. The firm provides guidance related to acquisition finance, commercial lending, project finance, bankruptcy and debt restructurings and regulatory advice.

**Capital Markets:**
White & Case has a formidable reputation in the field of international securities and finance. Clients benefit from the firm's capabilities in equity and debt offerings, sovereign issues, high-yield debt, securitisations, derivatives, investment funds and regulatory and broker-dealer matters.

**Commercial Litigation:**
Clients entrust White & Case with their "must-win" matters – disputes in which huge sums, invaluable patents and brands, and even out-and-out company survival are at stake. The firm has won major trials and appeals for clients in an array of industries, including financial services, pharmaceuticals, technology, sports media and entertainment and consumer products.

**Financial Restructuring & Insolvency:**
Representing clients in all aspects of restructurings, workouts and insolvency matters, including transactional and litigation matters, White & Case has the global resources and experience necessary for

handling transactions in multiple jurisdictions and a wide range of industries. The firm has played key roles in many of the most complex and high-profile restructuring matters of recent years, including many of the largest Chapter 11 filings in the United States as well as the Greek sovereign debt restructuring.

**Intellectual Property:**
White & Case was one of the first full-service firms to develop an intellectual property practice. Its lawyers protect and defend clients' innovations, creative works and brands around the world, offering advice related to patents, copyrights and designs, IP audits and due diligence, licensing and merchandising, sourcing and technology, and privacy and data protection.

**International Arbitration:**
White & Case is the only leading global law firm with large and long-established international arbitration teams in New York, Washington, DC, London, Paris and Stockholm. With more than 150 specialist arbitration practitioners across 20 of its 39 offices, White & Case offers unsurpassed breadth and depth of resources worldwide.

**Mergers & Acquisitions:**
White & Case offers market-leading expertise regarding strategic and private equity transactions and cross-border transactions. It has devised creative deal structures, designed acquisition programs and planned and implemented strategies for both acquirers and potential acquisition targets in domestic and cross-border transactions around the world.

**Pro Bono:**
White & Case has a long history of pro bono and is one of the largest providers of pro bono legal services in the world. The firm places pro bono on a par with its commercial practices in the leadership, focus and management that it brings to bear for its clients' benefit.

**Project Finance:**
White & Case is an innovator in project finance, energy and infrastructure law. The firm offers market-leading advice on cross-border project structuring and

development, financing, government regulation, M&A, and construction and other contract issues across several sectors, including oil and gas, power, infrastructure, telecommunications and mining and metals.

**Tax:**
White & Case's tax lawyers and advisors are strategically located in financial centers and government capitals worldwide to provide timely, effective advice on evolving tax law and policies. The practice has provided clients with innovative, practical approaches to minimise tax liabilities on issues ranging from mergers and acquisitions to financings and investment fund transactions.

**Trade:**
White & Case helps clients manage the risks and maximise the opportunities associated with the increasing regulation of international trade in goods and services. The firm has an interdisciplinary, full-service global trade practice that is one of the world's largest and most active in trade remedies and in the law of the World Trade Organization.

**White-Collar:**
White & Case helps clients deal with government investigations and enforcement matters. In addition to years of front-line prosecutorial experience, the firm has substantial experience defending clients through all phases of investigations, as well as criminal and civil enforcement proceedings. Clients include large corporations, as well as individuals prominent in business and political affairs.

**PRACTICE AREAS**
Antitrust
Asset Finance
Banking
Capital Markets
Commercial Litigation
Financial Restructuring & Insolvency
Intellectual Property
International Arbitration
Mergers & Acquisitions
Pro Bono
Project Finance
Tax
Trade
White-Collar

**OFFICES**
Abu Dhabi, Almaty, Ankara, Beijing, Berlin, Bratislava, Brussels, Bucharest, Budapest, Doha, Düsseldorf, Frankfurt, Geneva, Hamburg, Helsinki, Hong Kong, Istanbul, Johannesburg, London, Los Angeles, Madrid, Mexico City, Miami, Milan, Monterrey, Moscow, Munich, New York, Paris, Prague, Riyadh, São Paulo, Shanghai, Silicon Valley, Singapore, Stockholm, Tokyo, Warsaw and Washington, DC.

STATE RANKINGS AND COMMENTARY

## How lawyers are ranked

Every year we carry out thousands of in-depth interviews with clients in order to assess the reputations and expertise of business lawyers worldwide. The qualities we look for (and which determine rankings) include technical legal ability, professional conduct, client service, commercial awareness/astuteness, diligence, commitment, and other qualities most valued by the client. For details of our research team, see p.5.

# BANKING & FINANCE

Commentary about individuals can be found under their firm's paragraph. If the firm has no paragraph (is not ranked) look at Other Notable Practitioners.

### Banking & Finance
### Leading Firms

**Band 1**
Balch & Bingham LLP *
Bradley Arant Boult Cummings LLP *

**Band 2**
Burr & Forman LLP *
Maynard, Cooper & Gale, P.C. *

**Band 3**
Johnston Barton Proctor & Rose LLP
Jones Walker LLP *
Sirote & Permutt PC *
Wallace, Jordan, Ratliff & Brandt, LLC

## Band 1

### Balch & Bingham LLP
See profile on p.475

**THE FIRM** Balch & Bingham's team has been strengthened by the incorporation of the firm Presley, Burton & Collier, increasing the firm's already considerable expertise, most notably on public finance matters. The firm's regulatory practice is also particularly recognized. The group advises banks and financial institutions on both a state and regional-wide basis on federal and state banking laws and regulations, as well as other issues including ERISA, bond, securities and fiduciary matters.

**Sources say:** *"They are meticulous, thorough, have great expertise and we have unbelievable trust in them. They understand not only Alabama law but other states' laws as well."*

**KEY INDIVIDUALS** Hampton Boles continues to enjoy an outstanding reputation for his representation of banks, insurance companies and real estate developers. He is general counsel for the Alabama Bankers Association and is regarded as *"an authority when it comes to banking law in*

### Banking & Finance
### Senior Statesmen

**Senior Statesmen: distinguished older practitioners**

| | |
|---|---|
| Carmody Richard P | Adams and Reese LLP (ONP)[†] * |

### Leading Individuals

**Band 1**

| | |
|---|---|
| Compton Paul | Bradley Arant Boult Cummings LLP |
| Dresher J David | Bradley Arant Boult Cummings LLP |
| Lowry Kris | Maynard, Cooper & Gale, P.C. * |
| Vinson Laurence D | Bradley Arant Boult Cummings LLP |

**Band 2**

| | |
|---|---|
| Bains Kay K | Bradley Arant Boult Cummings LLP |
| Brandt Michael | Wallace, Jordan, Ratliff & Brandt, LLC |
| Gibbons Ray D | Gibbons Graham, LLC (ONP)[†] |
| Mixson Dwight | Burr & Forman LLP |
| Morrow Randall | Maynard, Cooper & Gale, P.C. * |

**Band 3**

| | |
|---|---|
| Jones Haskins W | Johnston Barton Proctor & Rose LLP |
| Mills Gail L | Burr & Forman LLP |
| Price Jr Joel A | Burr & Forman LLP |
| Sharff Dawn Helms | Bradley Arant Boult Cummings LLP |
| Shevin Maurice L | Sirote & Permutt PC * |
| Taylor III George M | Burr & Forman LLP |

**Up-and-coming individuals**

| | |
|---|---|
| Gambino Lucas | Maynard, Cooper & Gale, P.C. * |

*Alabama – what makes him good is the years of experience he has and the background of knowledge."* **Foster Clark** *"is smart, has good judgment, wants to get a transaction done and is easy to work with on a personal level,"* according to one enthusiastic interviewee. **Hobson Presley** is extremely well regarded in the market and his public finance practice only adds to the firm's expertise in this area. He is described as *"easy to work with and oriented toward the transaction – you know the answer you get from him will*

### Banking & Finance: Mainly Regulatory
### Leading Individuals

**Band 1**

| | |
|---|---|
| Boles H Hampton | Balch & Bingham LLP |
| Compton Paul | Bradley Arant Boult Cummings LLP |
| Vinson Laurence D | Bradley Arant Boult Cummings LLP |

**Band 2**

| | |
|---|---|
| Miller T Kurt | Johnston Barton Proctor & Rose LLP |
| Pearson Richard | Balch & Bingham LLP |

**Band 3**

| | |
|---|---|
| Waters Michael | Jones Walker LLP * |

### Banking & Finance: Public Finance
### Leading Individuals

**Band 1**

| | |
|---|---|
| Birchall James L | Jones Walker LLP * |
| Bolt Preston | Hand Arendall (ONP)[†] |
| Clark J Foster | Balch & Bingham LLP |
| Presley J Hobson | Balch & Bingham LLP |

**Band 2**

| | |
|---|---|
| Burton Jr John H | Balch & Bingham LLP |
| Hosch Heyward C | Maynard, Cooper & Gale, P.C. * |
| Smith Jodie | Maynard, Cooper & Gale, P.C. * |
| Zeigler Alan K | Bradley Arant Boult Cummings LLP |

**Up-and-coming individuals**

| | |
|---|---|
| Kanter Rod | Bradley Arant Boult Cummings LLP |

* Indicates firm / individual with profile.
[†] ONP = Other Notable Practitioner.

*always be right."* **John Burton** comes recommended for his public finance work, particularly in the healthcare and education sectors. Sources describe him as *"easy to work with, knowledgeable and someone whose judgment you can trust."* **Richard Pearson** is a new addition to the rankings and a well-respected regulatory attorney. He draws praise for his ability to *"take complicated legal concepts, explain* *them in normal English and translate them into practical advice for the client."*

## Bradley Arant Boult Cummings LLP
See profile on p.476

**THE FIRM** This sizable practice offers impressive coverage across all areas of banking and finance law. It has been particularly active advising clients on US federal regulatory compliance, distressed loan sales and tax credit lending issues. Highlights include representing Regions Bank in the ongoing sale of distressed loans to national investors, as well as representing Campus Crest Communities on all of its financing matters.

**KEY INDIVIDUALS Laurence Vinson** is described by one source as *"the Godfather of the banking Bar in Alabama"* and is renowned for his legal abilities throughout the state. He is an expert in the UCC in Alabama and has significant expertise in federal regulatory law. **Kay Bains** *"is a strong negotiator and her ability to manage large-scale projects has been incredible,"* notes one impressed source. She played a leading role in the aforementioned matter for Regions Bank. **Paul Compton** has particular expertise advising banks on tax credit cases, particularly with regard to affordable housing, and as one source observed, *"he has vast knowledge of this industry, and his advice is always sound and well thought out."* **David Dresher** is well versed in regulatory, compliance and transactional matters and is also noted for his real estate lending work. *"He is experienced, practical, helpful in decision-making and focused on the client's best interest,"* asserts one impressed commentator. **Alan Zeigler** is particularly respected for his public school finance expertise and also comes recommended for his work with utilities companies. *"He understands the market and provides excellent guidance,"* notes one observer, who goes on to add: *"He has a great deal of patience and offers thoughtful perspective."* **Dawn Helms Sharff** has a strong transactional practice, most notably representing banks on real estate lending matters. She impresses sources with her *"depth and breadth of knowledge, tireless work ethic, and genial and positive disposition."* **Rod Kanter** is well-regarded name in the market, with one interviewee commenting: *"He has an extraordinary breadth of knowledge of municipal finance laws and has all the required skills to negotiate complex agreements."*

## Band 2

## Burr & Forman LLP
See profile on p.477

**THE FIRM** The reputation of this firm is derived from its traditionally strong commercial and industrial lending practice both in Alabama and regionally. The group acts for major banking clients such as Wells Fargo and Synovus and is particularly active advising such clients in the healthcare and senior housing arenas. Highlights include representing a lender on a $25 million revolving line of credit of a regional department store chain in California.

**Sources say:** *"They are very knowledgeable, easy to deal with, and they don't overstep their bounds with regard to the business part of the deal."*

**KEY INDIVIDUALS Gail Mills** works primarily on real estate lending matters and receives particular praise for her knowledge of the healthcare sector. One source singles her out as *"easy to deal with, outgoing and clients love her."* The highly regarded **Joel Price** has a traditional lending practice primarily on asset-based transactions. He was the lead partner on the aforementioned $25 million revolving line of credit. **Dwight Mixson** has extensive experience advising on real estate lending matters and also comes recommended for his healthcare lending work. *"He's professional to deal with and efficient in getting the deal done,"* notes one impressed peer. **George Taylor** regularly represents lenders in transactional work and capital financing, perhaps most notably in the healthcare sector. He was the lead partner in representing the issuer and developer in a $20 million assisted living facility transaction.

## Maynard, Cooper & Gale, P.C.
See profile on p.483

**THE FIRM** This strong group is praised by clients for its strength across all banking and finance areas. In addition to an accomplished transactional and regulatory practice the firm is particularly well known for its representation of community banks. A key client is Regions Bank, for whom it has been very active, not least in arranging multiple credit facilities for Scotch & Gulf Lumber. The firm also has a strong reputation for its public finance capabilities and frequently advises universities and public schools on bond issues.

**Sources say:** *"They are very knowledgeable and very accessible. They guide us and give us excellent legal advice."*

**KEY INDIVIDUALS Kris Lowry** (see p.470) has extensive experience advising both lenders and borrowers in secured and unsecured transactions. Sources praise his *"depth of knowledge and ability to take the lead and see a project through to completion."* **Jodie Smith** (see p.473) is highly regarded for his strength on securities matters and is also a fine choice of counsel to advise clients on tax-exempt, tax credit and tax-advantaged financings. *"He has a wide range of knowledge, is very accessible and very good at helping clients through complex processes,"* asserts one impressed source. **Heyward Hosch** (see p.470) recently acted for the Board of School Commissioners of Mobile County on the issuance of tax-exempt warrants for school construction. *"He is well respected because of his insightful counsel and solutions-based approach. He has the maturity, experience, intellect and business understanding to facilitate a timely and successful closing,"* reports one enthusiastic interviewee. **Randall Morrow** (see p.471) is particularly adept at advising clients on commercial lending transactions and also comes recommended by sources for his strength in the healthcare sector. **Lucas Gambino** (see p.469) has a strong lending practice and is singled out as *"a fountain of knowledge of different deal structures and a pleasure to do business with."*

## Band 3

## Johnston Barton Proctor & Rose LLP

**THE FIRM** This team represents financial institutions and borrowers across a range of financing transactions. The firm has a particular strength advising clients on syndicated loan transactions and sources point to its capabilities in both the real estate and healthcare sectors.

**KEY INDIVIDUALS** The highly regarded **Kurt Miller** specializes in working for banks, financial institutions and insurance companies on corporate and commercial lending, as well as securities matters. **Haskins Jones** has notable experience advising both lenders and developers in the real estate, senior housing and healthcare arenas. *"I trust him implicitly and love having him in my corner,"* reports one impressed client.

## Jones Walker LLP
See profile on p.1378

**THE FIRM** This practice continues to develop its already strong regulatory practice and receives particular praise for its effectiveness in this area. The firm's public finance team also comes highly regarded for its adept bond counsel work on behalf of a diverse mix of public companies. Additionally, the group is able to leverage off its offices in other states to provide its banking clients with quality support on a regional and national basis.

**KEY INDIVIDUALS James Birchall** (see p.468) is much noted for his experience acting as bond counsel for municipalities, counties, utilities and healthcare organizations, as well as boards of education. He also advises clients in relation to tax incentives for business development. Sources reserve particular praise for his client care skills. **Michael Waters** (see p.473) is a new addition to the rankings and recently joined the firm from Balch & Bingham. His experience and expertise on regulatory matters is much respected as are his strengths in banking M&A and securities issues. *"He understands clients' needs from start to finish,"* a source affirms.

## Sirote & Permutt PC
See profile on p.484

**THE FIRM** This strong team comes recommended for expertise with regard to loans, leases and purchase agreements, and also maintains a fine track record in taxable and tax-exempt finance transactions. It has much experience representing financial institutions such as ServisFirst Bank, Frontier Bank and JPMorgan Chase and is also noted for its strength in real estate-related matters.

**KEY INDIVIDUALS Maurice Shevin** (see p.472) is a new entry into the rankings and is particularly well regarded in the market for his expertise in consumer finance and regulatory matters.

## Wallace, Jordan, Ratliff & Brandt, LLC

**THE FIRM** The firm maintains a strong reputation for its work on behalf of financial institutions in financing transactions and also represents a fine choice of counsel for matters concerning state and federal banking laws and regulations. It frequently acts as local counsel for banks in other states.

**KEY INDIVIDUALS** The *"very efficient"* **Michael Brandt** has a strong real estate and asset-based commercial lending practice. Sources are quick to celebrate his ability to keep things simple in a matter and also praise his cooperative approach to work.

## Other Notable Practitioners

**Ray Gibbons** of Gibbons Graham, LLC is *"particularly sharp on the commercial lending and bank lending sides,"* notes one impressed commentator. The *"very knowledgeable"* **Preston Bolt** at Hand Arendall draws praise for the strength of his public finance practice in south Alabama.

Adams and Reese LLP's **Richard Carmody** (see p.468) continues to provide much valued experience in complex commercial banking transactions and general banking advice.

# BANKRUPTCY/RESTRUCTURING

Commentary about individuals can be found under their firm's paragraph. If the firm has no paragraph (is not ranked) look at Other Notable Practitioners.

| Bankruptcy/Restructuring Leading Firms | |
| --- | --- |
| **Band 1** | |
| Bradley Arant Boult Cummings LLP * | |
| Burr & Forman LLP * | |
| **Band 2** | |
| Baker, Donelson, Bearman, Caldwell & Berkowitz, PC * | |
| Balch & Bingham LLP * | |
| Maynard, Cooper & Gale, P.C. * | |

| Senior Statesmen | |
| --- | --- |
| Senior Statesmen: distinguished older practitioners | |
| Carmody Richard P | Adams and Reese LLP (ONP)† * |
| Denaburg Charles L | Najjar Denaburg (ONP)† |

| Leading Individuals | |
| --- | --- |
| **Band 1** | |
| Darby Patrick | Bradley Arant Boult Cummings LLP |
| Hall Michael L | Burr & Forman LLP |
| Lamar Jayna Partain | Maynard, Cooper & Gale, P.C. * |
| Lupinacci Timothy M | Baker, Donelson, Bearman, Caldwell * |
| **Band 2** | |
| Bender Jay R | Bradley Arant Boult Cummings LLP |
| Hartley Jeffrey J | Helmsing, Leach, Herlong, Newman (ONP)† * |
| Joseph Joe A | Burr & Forman LLP |
| Vogtle Jr. Jesse S. | Balch & Bingham LLP |
| Watson Clark | Balch & Bingham LLP |
| **Band 3** | |
| Carson D Christopher | Burr & Forman LLP |
| Glenos Chris | Bradley Arant Boult Cummings LLP |
| Gray Kevin | Maynard, Cooper & Gale, P.C. * |
| Meek Derek | Burr & Forman LLP |
| Pruitt Eric | Baker, Donelson, Bearman, Caldwell * |
| Sparks Daniel | Christian & Small LLP (ONP)† |
| Stewart Donald | Cabaniss, Johnston, Gardner (ONP)† * |
| Wright Richard | Jones Walker LLP (ONP)† * |

| Up-and-coming individuals | |
| --- | --- |
| Hahn W Patton | Baker, Donelson, Bearman, Caldwell * |
| Ray Eric | Balch & Bingham LLP |

* Indicates firm / individual with profile.
† ONP = Other Notable Practitioner.

## Band 1

### Bradley Arant Boult Cummings LLP
See profile on p.476

**THE FIRM** This large firm continues to be a dominant player in the market, primarily representing creditors, but it also maintains a strong debtor-side and bankruptcy litigation practice. As well as the firm's continued representation of Jefferson County in its Chapter 9 bankruptcy case, it is also representing HealthSouth in a $2.9 billion multistate collection effort against the company's former CEO. **Sources say:** *"A well-rounded practice."*

**KEY INDIVIDUALS** The *"first-rate"* **Patrick Darby** is esteemed by peers for work on all bankruptcy-related matters, in particular his ongoing work in the aforementioned Jefferson County Chapter 9 matter. Sources describe him as *"a very creative, outside-the-box thinker who is good for complex situations."* **Chris Glenos** is a creditors' rights attorney who has particular expertise advising on consultancy litigation matters. He is a *"skilled and confident lawyer who doesn't take a scorched earth policy to matters,"* notes one impressed commentator. **Jay Bender** is *"an excellent lawyer with a good temperament,"* note interviewees. He has particular expertise representing clients on Chapter 11 and Chapter 9 bankruptcy cases. In a recent highlight, he represented CLK Longview in its distressed acquisition of five multifamily housing properties.

### Burr & Forman LLP
See profile on p.477

**THE FIRM** This highly rated team is well known for its creditors' rights work both in Alabama and throughout the Southeast and champions the use of receiverships as an alternative to traditional Chapter 11 bankruptcy proceedings. This includes representing Tatonka Capital in seeking receivership over a telecommunication and internet service provider. In addition to this work the firm is increasingly representing debtors and is acting as lead debtor's counsel for the Chapter 11 debtor Adams Produce, a distributor of fruit and vegetables.

**Sources say:** *"They were detailed, creative, thorough, sharp and excellent in the courtroom."*

**KEY INDIVIDUALS** The *"extremely talented"* **Michael Hall** leads the firm's bankruptcy and restructuring team and draws praise from peers and clients alike. He took a leading role in the aforementioned matter for Tatonka Capital. **Joe Joseph** often acts as a lead secured lender for

the firm's banking clients and is described as *"someone who works hard for the client and has a realistic grasp of what's possible."* **Christopher Carson** is noted for the breadth of his practice and, in a recent highlight, he acted as lead partner representing Wells Fargo in a lawsuit against the owner of a student housing complex. **Derek Meek** is *"a good negotiator, delivers succinct analysis and makes sure our interests are protected,"* notes one impressed client.

## Band 2

### Baker, Donelson, Bearman, Caldwell & Berkowitz, PC
See profile on p.2313

**THE FIRM** The team continues to expertly represent its stable of financial institution clients and CMBS special servicers on defaulted loans. This includes advising clients on acquiring and servicing portfolios of troubled loans from banks.

**Sources say:** *"It is a good firm and was good at handling problem loans, workouts and bankruptcy issues for us."*

**KEY INDIVIDUALS** Chair of the practice group **Timothy Lupinacci** (see p.470) predominantly represents special servicers throughout the nation and is described by a satisfied client as *"creative, hard-working and responsive to our needs."* **Eric Pruitt** (see p.471) primarily represents banking and financial institutional clients in commercial loan transactions and receives warm praise from clients for his thoughtful approach to matters. **Patton Hahn** (see p.469) focuses on bankruptcy and insolvency litigation and is noted as *"a very capable and tough adversary who does a good job for his clients."*

### Balch & Bingham LLP
See profile on p.475

**THE FIRM** A full-service bankruptcy and creditors' rights firm, this team has been particularly active advising banks and creditors on troubled lending portfolios. Highlights include representing Cadence Bank on a $1.8 billion bad debt portfolio as well as advising BBVA Compass Bank on a multimillion-dollar workout and refinance of a retail franchise. The firm also supplements its strength in Alabama with offices in Mississippi, Georgia and Washington, DC, providing clients with regional capabilities.

**Sources say:** *"They take a holistic and outcome-based approach. We've been very pleased all around. They are attentive to our needs and go above and beyond."*
**KEY INDIVIDUALS Clark Watson** is described as *"a fine bankruptcy lawyer who knows how to get the job done."* He has acted as lead bankruptcy counsel to Blue Cross and Blue Shield in Chapter 11 and Chapter 7 cases. **Jesse Vogtle** heads the firm's bankruptcy and creditors' rights practice and draws praise for being a *"practical lawyer with a calming presence"* who is *"very good in the courtroom."* The experienced **Eric Ray** continues to be highly regarded for his work representing utility companies on bankruptcy cases.

### Maynard, Cooper & Gale, P.C.
See profile on p.483
**THE FIRM** The group maintains a fine track record advising secured lenders and other creditors on insolvency issues. The firm continues to advise Regions Bank on judicial foreclosure proceedings to recover a $20 million outstanding loan balance through the liquidation of property

developer D&H property. The firm also represented Bank of the West in the foreclosure and subsequent litigation concerning a loan secured by a hotel under the America's Best Value Inn brand. Other key clients include PNC Bank and Synovus.
**Sources say:** *"They have a good bankruptcy group – very responsive and very cost-conscious."*
**KEY INDIVIDUALS Jayna Partain Lamar** (see p.470) has a diverse practice and is well respected for the work she does on complex restructuring files. One source notes: *"She has got a way about her that instills confidence in clients and judges."* Hunstville-based **Kevin Gray** (see p.469) draws praise for client care skills and is also singled out by sources as *"efficient, conscientious and very knowledgeable on the bankruptcy code."*

### Other Notable Practitioners

A *"go-to lawyer in Mobile,"* **Jeffrey Hartley** (see p.469) of Helmsing, Leach, Herlong, Newman & Rouse, PC works predominantly on the creditors' side, although he is also

well respected for the work he does representing both debtors and trustees as well. Christian & Small LLP's **Daniel Sparks** is a new entry into the rankings. He is particularly respected for the work he does on bankruptcy matters and receives praise from peers for having *"a good knack of taking a matter, analyzing it and getting to a right resolution."* **Donald Stewart** (see p.473) of Cabaniss, Johnston, Gardner, Dumas & O'Neal primarily acts as local counsel for various creditors. He is based in Mobile, and one source describes him as a *"smart and seasoned lawyer who judges think a lot of."* Najjar Denaburg's **Charles Denaburg** is an extremely seasoned practitioner and continues to enjoy a stellar reputation in the market. He is noted for his expertise in secured transactions, creditors' rights matters and foreclosures. **Richard Wright** (see p.474) of Jones Walker LLP has both a banking as well as a bankruptcy practice and maintains a fine track record on restructuring deals as well as commercial lending transactions. **Richard Carmody** (see p.468) of Adams and Reese LLP is regarded as a seasoned practitioner with a fine track record for his representation of creditors.

## CORPORATE/COMMERCIAL

Commentary about individuals can be found under their firm's paragraph. If the firm has no paragraph (is not ranked) look at Other Notable Practitioners.

| Corporate/Commercial | |
| --- | --- |
| **Leading Firms** | |
| **Band 1** | |
| Bradley Arant Boult Cummings LLP * | |
| Burr & Forman LLP * | |
| Maynard, Cooper & Gale, P.C. * | |
| **Band 2** | |
| Baker, Donelson, Bearman, Caldwell & Berkowitz, PC | |
| Balch & Bingham LLP * | |
| **Band 3** | |
| Johnston Barton Proctor & Rose LLP | |
| Sirote & Permutt PC * | |

## Band 1

### Bradley Arant Boult Cummings LLP
See profile on p.476
**THE FIRM** This highly respected team is particularly valued for its strength in depth and has a significant presence in the healthcare market, advising clients on M&A deals. The group maintains an office in Huntsville, as well as Birmingham, and comes particularly recommended for representing family-owned businesses and financial institutions, as well as technology-focused companies, in the Huntsville area. Recent highlights include representing Molpus Woodlands Group in the formation of a joint venture with Hancock timber to acquire a 1.88 million acre timberland portfolio from Forest Partner Timberland. The firm also represented Regions Financial in the sale of its broker-dealer and investment banking subsidiary to Morgan Keenan.

**Sources say:** *"The firm has a long-standing reputation of working effectively on transactions and is superb at coordinating all of the different aspects of a deal."*
**KEY INDIVIDUALS Harold Kushner** is described by one source as *"incredibly bright, knowledgeable and thorough."* He has a broad practice and was the lead attorney on the aforementioned Molpus Woodlands Group deal. **Denson Franklin** has much experience advising on M&A and other corporate transactions. He recently represented Ready Mix USA Inc. in the sale of its interests in Ready Mix USA LLC and CEMEX Southeast. *"He is an excellent attorney – a smart, likable guy, who is easy to get along with,"* notes one enthusiastic source. **James Childs** is particularly noted for his work with technology startups, especially within the healthcare sector. *"He has built a fine practice and is a very experienced transactional attorney,"* asserts one impressed interviewee. **John Molen** is a particularly seasoned securities lawyer who comes particularly recommended for his technical abilities. He recently served as securities and borrower's counsel for Energen in the financing of ongoing operations. **Paul Ware** focuses on securities matters within the banking sector. He is singled out by one commentator as *"unflappable, knowledgeable and good to work with."* **John Grenier** maintains a fine track record in M&A and finance matters and is regarded by sources as *"a great corporate transactional attorney."*

### Burr & Forman LLP
See profile on p.477
**THE FIRM** The team at this regional firm continues to enjoy a distinguished reputation particularly on economic development and M&A transactions. Highlights include acting as lead counsel for ProAssurance in its $153.7 mil-

| Corporate/Commercial | |
| --- | --- |
| **Leading Individuals** | |
| **Band 1** | |
| Curran Gregory S | Maynard, Cooper & Gale, P.C. * |
| Kushner Harold | Bradley Arant Boult Cummings LLP |
| **Band 2** | |
| Brockman Richard J | Johnston Barton Proctor & Rose LLP |
| Christian Edward R | Burr & Forman LLP |
| Cooper John H | Sirote & Permutt PC * |
| Drew Mark | Maynard, Cooper & Gale, P.C. * |
| Franklin III Denson N | Bradley Arant Boult Cummings LLP |
| Grenier John B | Bradley Arant Boult Cummings LLP |
| Harmon Christopher B | Maynard, Cooper & Gale, P.C. * |
| Minisman Jr B G | Baker, Donelson, Bearman, Caldwell * |
| Molen John K | Bradley Arant Boult Cummings LLP |
| Price Gene | Burr & Forman LLP |
| Simonetti D J | Baker, Donelson, Bearman, Caldwell * |
| Stephenson Jack | Burr & Forman LLP |
| Thuston Lee | Burr & Forman LLP |
| Tracy Timothy J | Balch & Bingham LLP * |
| Ware Paul | Bradley Arant Boult Cummings LLP |
| **Band 3** | |
| Childs Jr James W | Bradley Arant Boult Cummings LLP |
| Crawford Roy J | Cabaniss, Johnston, Gardner (ONP)† |
| Gregg Timothy W. | Maynard, Cooper & Gale, P.C. * |
| Rose Jr J William | Johnston Barton Proctor & Rose LLP |
| Sklar Bradley J | Sirote & Permutt PC * |
| Taylor III George M | Burr & Forman LLP |

* Indicates firm / individual with profile.
† ONP = Other Notable Practitioner.

lion acquisition of Medmarc Mutual Insurance and in the purchase of the Independent Nevada Doctors Insurance Exchange. The firm also has a strong presence in the automotive industry representing key clients such as Honda and Mercedes-Benz.

**Sources say:** "*The firm is practical, business-oriented and tries to find solutions rather than identify problems that prolong the negotiation or settlement process.*"

**KEY INDIVIDUALS** The highly regarded **Lee Thuston** is the firm's managing partner and is particularly active in driving the firm's much-admired economic development practice. **Edward Christian** has particular expertise on private equity matters. In a recent highlight, he was lead partner representing AMG Holding in the sale of stock of visual merchandising company Array Canada. "*He is a great lawyer who is very practical in his approach,*" asserts one impressed source. **Gene Price** focuses on general corporate, securities and M&A deals. He has extensive experience particularly in the renewable energy, environmental and biotech arenas. **Jack Stephenson** maintains a strong securities practice, working with both private and public companies. He was lead counsel on the aforementioned ProAssurance transactions. **George Taylor** dedicates a substantial part of his practice to debt and equity financing deals. He also has a robust M&A practice and recently represented educational material distributor, Budgetext, in its asset sale to Follet Corporation.

## Maynard, Cooper & Gale, P.C.
See profile on p.483

**THE FIRM** This corporate, tax and securities group continues to be a market leader in the state, and has a particularly strong name advising clients on private equity, fund formation and healthcare M&A-related deals. The firm advised a number of investors on a joint venture to form Battle Plan Capital, a real estate private investment fund. The firm also acted for Protective Life in two public offerings of subordinated debentures worth a total of $437.5 million.

**Sources say:** "*Their expertise is phenomenal and their interaction and promptness have been superb.*"

**KEY INDIVIDUALS Gregory Curran** (see p.468) has been particularly active on private equity and M&A-related matters, and was lead lawyer on the Battle Plan Capital fund formation deal mentioned above. "*He has the intellectual skills to do complex transactional work and works extremely well with all manner of lawyers – he has the personality and legal technical skills that clients love,*" notes one enthusiastic interviewee. **Mark Drew** (see p.468) is managing partner at the firm and is primarily a transaction lawyer for the firm's manufacturing clients. Sources are

quick to single out his ability to "*streamline processes and not waste time negotiating superfluous issues.*" **Christopher Harmon** (see p.469) is "*an experienced attorney with good insight.*" He has a strong M&A and public securities practice and has particular expertise advising healthcare clients. **Timothy Gregg** (see p.469) is chair of the firm's securities regulation practice and also advises public companies on corporate governance and public reporting obligations. "*He has done an exceptional job for us,*" reports one satisfied client.

## Band 2

### Baker, Donelson, Bearman, Caldwell & Berkowitz, PC
See profile on p.2313

**THE FIRM** This group continues to enjoy a strong reputation for the corporate and securities assistance it offers clients. It maintains a fine track record for its work in the healthcare arena and also represents a excellent choice of counsel to advise businesses in the food sector.

**Sources say:** "*You get quality lawyers and advice for a very good price.*"

**KEY INDIVIDUALS B G Minisman** (see p.471) comes recommended for his securities work on behalf of a range of public companies and has also been particularly active of late advising clients in the medical device arena. "*He is methodical, smart and thorough – he does meticulous work and raises the right issues with clients,*" asserts one enthusiastic interviewee. **D J Simonetti** (see p.472) has a wide-ranging general corporate practice and is routinely sought after to advise on matters concerning the heathcare sector. "*He is an excellent lawyer who does an excellent job for his clients,*" notes one source.

### Balch & Bingham LLP
See profile on p.475

**THE FIRM** This team advises on a wide range of corporate and securities matters, including tax and corporate governance, and enjoys a fine track record for its work in the energy, healthcare and financial services sectors, advising private equity funds, healthcare institutions, construction companies and multifamily housing developers.

**Sources say:** "*We regularly work with them and they have a very good team.*"

**KEY INDIVIDUALS Timothy Tracy** has a lot of experience working with private equity funds, in particular, and is singled out by one commentator as "*extremely hardworking – he works on complex transactions and gets them done.*"

## Band 3

### Johnston Barton Proctor & Rose LLP

**THE FIRM** This practice is known for the quality advice and assistance it offers across a wide range of corporate and business law, including securities, economic development and corporate finance. The group is an especially fine choice of counsel for clients in the healthcare and financial services sectors.

**KEY INDIVIDUALS William Rose** is noted for his significant experience in tax-related work in particular. "*He brings a lot of savviness to a transaction and is good to work with,*" affirms one source. **Richard Brockman** is chair of the healthcare practice and focuses a large portion of his practice on work concerning long-term care, retirement communities and assisted living facilities.

### Sirote & Permutt PC
See profile on p.484

**THE FIRM** This group has a strong focus advising on corporate formation, tax planning and tax controversy. On the transactional side the firm represents healthcare providers, such as UAB Medical West, as well as real estate companies and financial institutions. Highlights include representing Corporate Realty Development in its joint venture with Brasfield & Gorrie, in connection with the development and assemblage of property to relocate a minor league baseball team to Birmingham.

**KEY INDIVIDUALS John Cooper** (see p.468) is the managing partner of the firm and comes recommended for his in-depth securities expertise. **Bradley Sklar** (see p.472) has extensive experience working on real estate and tax planning matters, and is routinely sought after to advise limited liability companies. In addition to acting as lead lawyer on the aforementioned Corporate Realty matter, he represented Equity Resources in the real estate development of multifamily and commercial properties.

## Other Notable Practitioners

**Roy Crawford** of Cabaniss, Johnston, Gardner, Dumas & O'Neal is noted for his tax planning and litigation work, in addition to his general corporate expertise. "*He is a very well-respected tax lawyer who does a really good job for his clients,*" note sources.

# LABOR & EMPLOYMENT

Commentary about individuals can be found under their firm's paragraph. If the firm has no paragraph (is not ranked) look at Other Notable Practitioners.

## Labor & Employment
### Leading Firms

**Band 1**
Burr & Forman LLP *
Lehr Middlebrooks & Vreeland, P.C.
Littler Mendelson, PC *
Maynard, Cooper & Gale, P.C. *

**Band 2**
Balch & Bingham LLP *
Ogletree, Deakins, Nash, Smoak & Stewart, PC *

**Band 3**
Baker, Donelson, Bearman, Caldwell & Berkowitz, PC *
Bradley Arant Boult Cummings LLP *
Constangy, Brooks & Smith, LLP
Jackson Lewis LLP *

## Senior Statesmen

**Senior Statesmen:** distinguished older practitioners

| | |
|---|---|
| Ingram Fredric J | Burr & Forman LLP |
| Lacy Jr Peyton | Ogletree, Deakins, Nash, Smoak & Stewart * |
| Mitchell Chris | Maynard, Cooper & Gale, P.C. * |
| Nelson Carol Sue | Maynard, Cooper & Gale, P.C. * |

## Leading Individuals

**Band 1**

| | |
|---|---|
| Lehr Richard | Lehr Middlebrooks & Vreeland, P.C. |
| Middlebrooks David J | Lehr Middlebrooks & Vreeland, P.C. |
| Singer Fern H | Watterson & Singer PC (ONP)[†] |
| Smith David M | Maynard, Cooper & Gale, P.C. * |
| St Clair Jay D | Littler Mendelson, PC * |

**Band 2**

| | |
|---|---|
| Brown Stephen E | Maynard, Cooper & Gale, P.C. * |
| Coleman John | Burr & Forman LLP |
| Davis Thomas A | Jackson Lewis LLP * |
| Lucas Michael L | Burr & Forman LLP |
| Miller Carole G | Maynard, Cooper & Gale, P.C. * |
| Pennington James C | Ogletree, Deakins, Nash, Smoak & Stewart * |
| Powell IV Charles A | Littler Mendelson, PC * |
| Starling III M Jefferson | Balch & Bingham LLP |
| Umbach III Arnold W | Starnes Davis Florie LLP (ONP)[†] * |
| Vreeland Albert L | Lehr Middlebrooks & Vreeland, P.C. |

**Band 3**

| | |
|---|---|
| Baker Tammy L | Jackson Lewis LLP * |
| Brown Richard | Constangy, Brooks & Smith, LLP |
| Debruge Marcel | Burr & Forman LLP |
| Frazier Jr Sydney F | Cabaniss, Johnston, Gardner, Dumas (ONP)[†] |
| Hancock William K | Adams and Reese LLP (ONP)[†] * |
| Hargrove John | Bradley Arant Boult Cummings LLP |
| Kauffman Douglas B. | Balch & Bingham LLP |
| Miller T Matthew | Bradley Arant Boult Cummings LLP |
| Sharp Lisa J | Balch & Bingham LLP |
| Somerville III William G | Baker, Donelson, Bearman, Caldwell * |
| Spotswood Robert | Spotswood Sansom & Sansbury (ONP)[†] |
| Stiles Matthew | Lehr Middlebrooks & Vreeland, P.C. |
| Thrasher Dana | Constangy, Brooks & Smith, LLP |
| Yuengert Anne | Bradley Arant Boult Cummings LLP |

**Up-and-coming individuals**

| | |
|---|---|
| Ahnert Janell M. | Maynard, Cooper & Gale, P.C. * |
| Hattaway Ashley | Burr & Forman LLP |
| Metheny Bryance | Burr & Forman LLP |
| Yelling Tamula | Constangy, Brooks & Smith, LLP |

\* Indicates firm / individual with profile.
[†]ONP = Other Notable Practitioner.

## Band 1

### Burr & Forman LLP
See profile on p.477

THE FIRM This comprehensive practice is extremely well regarded for its advice across all labor and employment issues. It has notable expertise in matters involving union-organizing campaigns, decertification campaigns and collective bargaining matters, and its employment practice has been particularly active in employment discrimination cases as well as in policy review and labor relations work. The team has a fine track record for acting for manufacturing companies in the automotive industry, and is also recommended for its counsel to clients in the healthcare and retail sectors. Recent highlights include acting for Honda Manufacturing of Alabama on getting an FLSA collective action of over 600 plaintiffs decertified.
Sources say: *"They are excellent to work with, thorough and effective, and take the time to understand our business."*
KEY INDIVIDUALS John Coleman is particularly noted for his representation of manufacturing clients, and was one of the attorneys advising on the aforementioned Honda case. He elicits particular praise for his written analysis. Labor and employment practice chair Marcel Debruge is similarly noted for his work with manufacturing clients, and recently advised RockTenn before the NLRB on the successful decertification of an existing union. Michael Lucas has notable experience in discrimination and wage and hour cases, and successfully represented Mercedes-Benz in an overtime entitlement case brought by 86 employees. Ashley Hattaway focuses on employment discrimination, OSHA and wage and hour disputes. *"She is extremely knowledgeable and extremely smart, and her clients are very happy with her work,"* asserts one interviewee. Fredric Ingram is highly regarded for his legal abilities and continues to offer invaluable support to the firm. Bryance Metheny focuses on representing clients in the service industry and is described as *"a creative thinker who offers practical solutions."*

### Lehr Middlebrooks & Vreeland, P.C.

THE FIRM This labor and employment boutique is active in a number of areas, and is particularly recommended for its employer rights work. The group continues to be highly sought after for its advice on disability discrimination claims and employee benefits, and also has a strong reputation for labor contract negotiations and union avoidance campaigns. Additionally, the group is regarded as a fine choice of counsel for clients in the energy, manufacturing and healthcare sectors. In a recent highlight, it acted for a subsidiary of O'Neal Steel in a lawsuit brought by an executive, concerning alleged discrimination.
Sources say: *"One of the standout labor and employment firms in the state."*
KEY INDIVIDUALS The *"preeminent"* Richard Lehr draws much praise from the market, and is singled out for his *"knowledge, calm demeanor and ability to support clients."* He is particularly active in the consultation and negotiation of complex labor issues across the country. David Middlebrooks recently defended Hyundai in a retaliatory discharge claim relating to the Alabama's Workers' Compensation Act. Sources are quick to commend his thoughtful approach and strong advocacy skills. Matthew Stiles is noted for his assistance on labor issues, primarily providing strategic advice on union-avoidance campaign work and the defense of employment claims. *"He is calm and easy to work with; he understands clients very well and what they are trying to achieve,"* asserts one impressed source. The *"pragmatic, bright and knowledgeable"* Albert Vreeland represents plaintiffs and defendants across a wide range of complex litigation matters, including business litigation and whistle-blowing claims. He recently defended Williams, a division of Global Power & Equipment, in a whistle-blower case under the Energy Reorganization Act.

### Littler Mendelson, PC
See profile on p.688

THE FIRM This high-quality practice is particularly noted for its strengths in wage and hour cases, and its considerable trial expertise. It represents employers almost exclusively, most notably in the manufacturing and construction sectors as well as in the service industry. A notable highlight was defending Santa Fe Protective Services against 17 plaintiffs in an age and race discrimination case concerning the application process for positions as security guards at an army base.
KEY INDIVIDUALS Jay St Clair (see p.473) maintains an excellent reputation in the market, particularly for his litigation capabilities. He recently successfully defended Infosys Technologies in a high-profile harassment case brought by the plaintiff, Jack Palmer, claiming that harassment had begun following a report he filed with the company's whistle-blower team. He also led in the aforementioned matter for Santa Fe Protective Services. Charles Powell (see p.471) comes recommended for his work on wage and hour cases and, as one enthusiastic source

asserts, *"has super analytical skills, is a good communicator, and can manage a case and explain it in a way the client can understand."*

## Maynard, Cooper & Gale, P.C.
See profile on p.483

**THE FIRM** This practice is active across a diverse range of both labor and employment matters, including employment discrimination, EEOC, class action and FLSA collective action cases. The group has a varied client base, which includes financial services and energy companies. Among its recent work, it is defending Clayton Manufactured Housing in a class action regarding the Worker Adjustment and Retraining Notification Act (WARN), which is pending in Texas Federal Court.

**Sources say:** *"Top-notch advocacy."*

**KEY INDIVIDUALS David Smith** (see p.473) primarily represents employers in areas such as EEOC defense, employment discrimination, and mine safety cases. *"He is a good all-around lawyer: he's smart and experienced, and knows and understands cases and how to handle them,"* reports one interviewee. **Carole Miller** (see p.471) focuses on representing employers across a wide range of employment matters, particularly in the securities industry. *"She is an extremely shrewd legal tactician with a wealth of experience from which to draw her recommendations. She is creative, diligent and responsive."* **Stephen Brown** (see p.468) is a hugely experienced attorney primarily representing employers and management. He is currently defending Clayton Manufactured Housing in the aforementioned WARN class action. **Chris Mitchell** (see p.471) lends the firm considerable experience and expertise, especially with regards to union and labor relations law. **Carol Sue Nelson** (see p.471) has a strong reputation in the market, particularly for employment disputes, and represents a fine choice of counsel for clients in the financial services, healthcare and manufacturing sectors. **Janell Ahnert** (see p.467) is well regarded for representing clients in discrimination cases. In a recent highlight, she defended Tyson Foods against Leeth in a case concerning race discrimination and sexual harassment.

## Band 2

## Balch & Bingham LLP
See profile on p.475

**THE FIRM** Balch & Bingham advises a number of large clients, not least in the energy and utilities arenas, and is also routinely sought after by banks and financial institutions. The team is particularly recognized for its expertise in FLSA collective action and wage and hour cases, and has further expertise in immigration compliance issues. A recent highlight involved defending the Personnel Board of Jefferson County in regards to the withholding of merit-based pay increases to three plaintiffs and a police fraternal organization.

**Sources say:** *"They are very sound in their guidance and diligent in their processes. The consistency in the quality of their advice really impresses me."*

**KEY INDIVIDUALS Jefferson Starling** has a particular focus on federal and state employment litigation and labor relations matters, and has recently handled a series of discrimination and retaliation cases for Fresenius Medical Group North America. Sources reserve particular praise for his *"practical approach"* to matters. **Lisa Sharp** principally handles employment disputes and has recently represented Southern Nuclear Operating in employment discrimination and labor relations matters. *"She provides good advice and is very thorough,"* asserts one satisfied client. **Douglas Kauffman** has a diverse employment law practice, but frequently works for the firm's banking and energy clients. *"He is dependable and responsible and evaluates all of the risks,"* according to one impressed interviewee.

## Ogletree, Deakins, Nash, Smoak & Stewart, PC
See profile on p.1110

**THE FIRM** This highly respected boutique continues to be very active in employment litigation, particularly in wage and hour, discrimination and employee benefits cases. The group also has expertise in defending clients in workers' compensation and toxic tort class actions, as well as FLSA-related cases. Its client roster is drawn from a diverse field, ranging from banking and insurance to mining and manufacturing. Recent highlights include defending Blue Cross and Blue Shield of Alabama against a putative cross-border class action of chiropractors.

**Sources say:** *"They approach legal issues on a proactive basis, which is invaluable. What is really impressive is their nimbleness to respond to legal issues."*

**KEY INDIVIDUALS** Practice head **James Pennington** (see p.471) recently acted for the Drummond Company on a longstanding fraud, unjust enrichment and breach of contract file relating to the closing of one of its lines of business. According to one impressed source, *"he takes a practical approach to law, he approaches a case thinking about what's best for the client, and he won't waste time and clients' money on something pointless."* **Peyton Lacy** (see p.470) brings huge experience to the firm, handling a mix of traditional labor work and employment matters. He is described as *"an exceptionally good lawyer with good judgment – a high-quality guy."*

## Band 3

## Baker, Donelson, Bearman, Caldwell & Berkowitz, PC
See profile on p.2313

**THE FIRM** This group has a substantial reputation for handling harassment and discrimination cases, and is also frequently sought after to advise on a wealth of traditional labor issues. It regularly defends FLSA collective action and EEOC cases brought against its clients, and is well versed in matters concerning enforcement of noncompete and non-solicitation agreements. The firm recently defended Koch Foods against allegations of sex and race discrimination and RICO violations, in connection with the alleged hiring of illegal aliens.

**KEY INDIVIDUALS William Somerville** (see p.473) is particularly noted for his expertise in wage and hour matters, and is a fine choice of counsel for clients in the healthcare sector.

## Bradley Arant Boult Cummings LLP
See profile on p.476

**THE FIRM** This firm has a substantial presence in Alabama and offers an array of labor and employment services to clients, particularly in the financial services and healthcare sectors. It has been especially active of late defending clients against EEOC charges, as well as other employment litigation. Recent work has included defending Jim Walter Resources against an instituted disability discrimination EEOC charge.

**KEY INDIVIDUALS John Hargrove** is recommended for his representation of clients in manufacturing and mining, and recently defended Southland Tube in a race discrimination class action. He commands much respect from the market, not least for his wealth of trial experience. **Matthew Miller** draws praise from clients and peers alike for his considerable expertise in wage and hour cases. *"He is extremely knowledgeable, responsive and a good litigator,"* notes one enthusiastic source. **Anne Yuengert** has much experience working in the healthcare sector and with government contractors. Commentators are quick to commend her excellent advice and sound judgment.

## Constangy, Brooks & Smith, LLP

**THE FIRM** This nationwide litigation boutique represents employers across the full range of labor and employment matters, and maintains a fine employee benefits practice. The group is noted for its work concerning EEOC and ERISA matters, and is also well versed in traditional labor issues. It remains a fine choice of counsel for clients in the manufacturing sector.

**KEY INDIVIDUALS Richard Brown** is noted for his strength on both the traditional labor side and in employment matters, and is frequently sought after to handle work on behalf of healthcare, manufacturing and financial services-based clients. The *"superb"* **Dana Thrasher** is regarded as one of the best employee benefits attorneys in the state and is noted for her extensive ERISA knowledge. *"Clients really value her work,"* asserts one interviewee. **Tamula Yelling** is much in demand as an employment dispute specialist. According to one enthusiastic source, *"she is great at research: she knows how to take information and use it to our advantage."*

## Jackson Lewis LLP
See profile on p.1982

**THE FIRM** Jackson Lewis's Birmingham office has a particularly active employment litigation practice and is recognized for its representation of clients in the insurance, manufacturing and automotive sectors. In addition, the group has a fine track record for affirmative action matters and has noteworthy experience managing large-scale ERISA cases. It also maintains a highly recommended traditional labor law practice.

KEY INDIVIDUALS **Thomas Davis** (see p.468) earns the respect of his peers for his wealth of litigation expertise, and has particular experience advising retail companies throughout the region. **Tammy Baker** (see p.467) continues to be an accomplished litigator and is a fine choice of counsel on complex class actions.

## Other Notable Practitioners

**Sydney Frazier** of Cabaniss, Johnston, Gardner, Dumas & O'Neal is described by sources as *"diligent, punctual, succinct and responsive."* He has defended Norfolk Southern on several whistle-blower cases of late. Adams and Reese LLP's **William Hancock** (see p.469) is regarded by peers as an *"extremely practical and no-nonsense lawyer."* **Fern Singer** of Watterson & Singer PC receives widespread praise for her mediation and arbitration expertise. She is described as *"the go-to private mediator in Birmingham"*

and elicits particular praise for her ability to render complicated matters simply and clearly. **Arnold Umbach** (see p.473) at Starnes Davis Florie LLP *"understands what clients are looking for and delivers the desired results in a timely manner and on budget."* He maintains a robust disputes practice, frequently handling discrimination and noncompete cases. **Robert Spotswood** of Spotswood Sansom & Sansbury LLC is well versed in complex commercial and wage and hour matters. One impressed source says: *"He is extremely quick on his feet, can appeal to many different types of people and is very, very thorough."*

# LITIGATION

Mainly Plaintiff p.463; Medical Malpractice Defense p.463

Commentary about individuals can be found under their firm's paragraph. If the firm has no paragraph (is not ranked) look at Other Notable Practitioners.

## Litigation: General Commercial
### Leading Firms

**Band 1**
Bradley Arant Boult Cummings LLP *
Lightfoot, Franklin & White, LLC *

**Band 2**
Balch & Bingham LLP *
Burr & Forman LLP *
Helmsing, Leach, Herlong, Newman & Rouse, PC *
Maynard, Cooper & Gale, P.C.
McDowell Knight Roedder & Sledge LLC
Starnes Davis Florie LLP *

**Band 3**
Bainbridge, Mims, Rogers & Smith, LLP
Lanier Ford Shaver & Payne P.C.
Rushton, Stakely, Johnston & Garrett

**Band 4**
Christian & Small LLP *
Huie, Fernambucq & Stewart, LLP
Sirote & Permutt PC *
Spotswood Sansom & Sansbury LLC *

## Litigation: Construction
### Leading Individuals

**Band 1**

| | | |
|---|---|---|
| Meyerson Edward P | Baker, Donelson, Bearman, Caldwell (ONP)† | |
| Rogers E Mabry | Bradley Arant Boult Cummings LLP | |

\* Indicates firm / individual with profile.
†ONP. = Other Notable Practitioner.

*The editorial is in alphabetical order by firm name.*

## Bainbridge, Mims, Rogers & Smith, LLP

**THE FIRM** This long-standing practice is highly regarded by peers for the strength of its attorneys and for its expertise in complex business litigation. The team is equally

adept at representing both plaintiffs and defendants in civil and commercial litigation. Its client base is drawn from a wide variety of sectors including construction, environment and financial services.
KEY INDIVIDUALS **Bruce Rogers** has a very strong reputation for representing clients in general business, shareholder and contract disputes. One source said: *"He has good common sense, and pays lots of personal attention to cases. He is confident and clients like him."*

## Balch & Bingham LLP
See profile on p.475

**THE FIRM** This robust team acts for clients in heavily regulated sectors such as energy, healthcare and financial services on large, high-stakes disputes, and maintains a fine reputation for its work in personal injury and employment cases. It has also developed a strong presence in the manufacturing sector. The firm recently represented Blue Cross & Blue Shield of Alabama before the Supreme Court of Alabama in relation to the reimbursement of skilled nursing facilities services for Medicare Part C enrollees.
**Sources say:** *"They are fine litigators."* *"They have a very deep bench and a lot of quality attorneys."*
KEY INDIVIDUALS **Michael Edwards** is an extremely experienced business litigator often representing healthcare and financial institution clients. One source said: *"He is good at handling complex matters and is a lawyer you look for if you have a case you have to win."* *"Intelligent and hardworking"* **David Boyd** practices out of Birmingham and Montgomery. Highly regarded by sources for his appellate work, he also has extensive experience advising on business and employment litigation. He recently acted for pulp and paper manufacturer Parsons & Whittemore on a complex commercial dispute. **Alan Rogers** has extensive experience handling cases for clients in the energy and financial services sectors. *"He is a high-quality litigator, very organized and a great presence,"* said one source. **Michael Freeman**

enjoys a fine reputation handling environmental disputes. He recently acted for Alabama Power in relation to a civil enforcement action by the government in relation to alleged violations of the CAA. **Allen Estes** is described as *"very dedicated and motivated – he deals well with clients and is a very good communicator."* He maintains a strong track record in energy, personal injury and complex commercial litigation.

## Beasley, Allen, Crow, Methvin, Portis & Miles, PC

**THE FIRM** This large, Montgomery-based plaintiffs' team enjoys a prominent position in the state and is very highly regarded for its wide-ranging expertise. The firm continues to advise on many cases relating to the pharmaceutical industry, in particular representing clients on Medicaid fraud or average wholesale price litigation. The firm is equally adept at advising on personal injury and product liability, among others, and is also an excellent choice for class actions.
KEY INDIVIDUALS Hugely experienced **Jere Beasley** is noted for his *"history of substantial results in court"* and represents clients across a number of areas including product liability, consumer fraud and personal injury cases.

## Bradley Arant Boult Cummings LLP
See profile on p.476

**THE FIRM** This premier practice operates not only throughout the state but often represents clients in multi-state and nationwide cases. The team is particularly well known for handling product liability, pharmaceutical and financial services litigation and has an especially strong construction litigation practice. Highlights include representing Ally Financial, Residential Capital and GMAC Mortgage in a robo-signing investigation and Attorney General/DOJ settlement.

*The editorial is in alphabetical order by firm name.*

## Litigation: General Commercial
### Leading Individuals

**Band 1**

| | |
|---|---|
| Atchison W Michael | Burr & Forman LLP |
| Christian Thomas W | Christian & Small LLP |
| Edwards Michael L | Balch & Bingham LLP |
| Franklin Samuel H | Lightfoot, Franklin & White, LLC |
| Gewin James | Bradley Arant Boult Cummings LLP |
| McGivaren Jr Crawford S | Cabaniss, Johnston, Gardner (ONP)† |

**Band 2**

| | |
|---|---|
| Boyd David R | Balch & Bingham LLP |
| Marsh David H | Marsh, Rickard & Bryan P.C |
| Novak Tabor | Ball, Ball, Matthews & Novak (ONP)† |
| Prater Harlan | Lightfoot, Franklin & White, LLC |
| Rediker J Michael | Haskell Slaughter Young & Rediker (ONP)† |
| Rogers Alan T | Balch & Bingham LLP |
| Rogers Bruce F | Bainbridge, Mims, Rogers & Smith, LLP |

**Band 3**

| | |
|---|---|
| Bains Jr Lee E | Maynard, Cooper & Gale, P.C. * |
| Cavender C Paul | Burr & Forman LLP |
| Ezelle Jay | Starnes Davis Florie LLP * |
| Florie Michael A | Starnes Davis Florie LLP * |
| Gill Richard | Copeland, Franco, Screws & Gill (ONP)† |
| Haston Tripp | Bradley Arant Boult Cummings LLP |
| Knight Michael D | McDowell Knight Roedder & Sledge LLC |
| McDowell Jerry | McDowell Knight Roedder & Sledge LLC |
| Pennington Michael | Bradley Arant Boult Cummings LLP |
| Porter Maibeth | Maynard, Cooper & Gale, P.C. * |
| Rodgers W Stanley | Lanier Ford Shaver & Payne P.C. |
| Tozzi Rik S | Burr & Forman LLP |

**Band 4**

| | |
|---|---|
| Babington Joseph | Helmsing, Leach, Herlong, Newman * |
| Baugh Robert R | Sirote & Permutt PC * |
| Childs Larry | Waller Lansden Dortch & Davis (ONP)† * |
| Dukes Carter H | Scott Dukes & Geisler, PC (ONP)† * |
| Freeman Michael D | Balch & Bingham LLP |
| Huckaby Jr James C | Christian & Small LLP |
| Leach Jr John N | Helmsing, Leach, Herlong, Newman * |
| Mulvaney Michael | Maynard, Cooper & Gale, P.C. * |
| Sansom Kenneth D | Spotswood Sansom & Sansbury LLC |
| Scott John W | Scott Dukes & Geisler, PC (ONP)† * |
| Spotswood Robert | Spotswood Sansom & Sansbury LLC |
| Thomas Alan D | Huie, Fernambucq & Stewart, LLP |

### Up-and-coming individuals

| | |
|---|---|
| Estes Allen | Balch & Bingham LLP |
| Maddox Robert | Bradley Arant Boult Cummings LLP |

**Sources say:** *"They are smart, practical and effective in court."*

**KEY INDIVIDUALS** The highly regarded **James Gewin** is a hugely experienced attorney who comes recommended for his defense work on behalf of clients in mass tort and antitrust cases. **Mabry Rogers** is much admired for his construction practice. A sources says of him: *"You want him in your corner – he analyzes things deeply and thoroughly."* **Tripp Haston** is described as a *"very knowledgeable, diligent, reliable and service-oriented lawyer."* In a recent highlight, he acted as co-lead defense for Pfizer on a product liability claim concerning the medicine Chantix.

## Litigation: Mainly Plaintiff
### Leading Firms

**Band 1**

Beasley, Allen, Crow, Methvin, Portis & Miles, PC
Cunningham Bounds, LLC
Hare, Wynn, Newell & Newton LLP *
Marsh, Rickard & Bryan P.C

### Leading Individuals

**Band 1**

| | |
|---|---|
| Ashford Leon | Hare, Wynn, Newell & Newton LLP |
| Beasley Jere L | Beasley, Allen, Crow, Methvin, Portis |
| Cunningham Robert | Cunningham Bounds, LLC |
| Marsh David H | Marsh, Rickard & Bryan P.C |

**Band 2**

| | |
|---|---|
| Breedlove Gregory B | Cunningham Bounds, LLC |

## Litigation: Medical Malpractice Defense
### Leading Firms

**Band 1**

Starnes Davis Florie LLP *

### Leading Individuals

**Band 1**

| | |
|---|---|
| Florie Michael A | Starnes Davis Florie LLP * |
| Keene Thomas | Rushton, Stakely, Johnston & Garrett |
| Sellers Randal H | Starnes Davis Florie LLP * |

**Band 2**

| | |
|---|---|
| Bates Walter W | Starnes Davis Florie LLP * |
| Frazer A Danner | Frazer, Greene, Upchurch & Baker (ONP)† |
| Rodgers W Stanley | Lanier Ford Shaver & Payne P.C. |
| Waldrop Jr Norman E | Armbrecht Jackson LLP (ONP)† |

\* Indicates firm / individual with profile.
†ONP = Other Notable Practitioner.

**Michael Pennington** is particularly active in advising on commercial disputes and mass tort litigation. He is currently acting for Pharmacia, defending a nationwide class action in relation to printed circuit boards in fluorescent light ballasts manufactured before 1979. **Robert Maddox** led on the aforementioned robo-signing investigation and is described as *"an excellent attorney who is very organized and has the ability to work through a lot of information very quickly."*

### Burr & Forman LLP
See profile on p.477

**THE FIRM** This talented team has significant expertise handling product liability, financial services and general commercial litigation. It also continues to act on an increasing number of medical malpractice and healthcare-related cases. In a recent highlight, the group defended ST Aerospace in claims brought by plaintiffs over neurological injuries caused by contaminated cabin air.
**Sources say:** *"They are very responsible and look at the cost-benefit of each part of the case and act accordingly."*
**KEY INDIVIDUALS** *"Wonderful trial lawyer"* **Michael Atchison** is head of the litigation team and has a diverse practice, which includes defending clients on medical mal-

practice, product liability, securities class actions and commercial disputes. **Paul Cavender** has over three decades' worth of experience in product liability matters. *"The way he thought through the case and the suggestions he made to best defend us"* were particularly valued by one satisfied client. **Rik Tozzi** has significant expertise defending banks and financial institutions and is also sought after for his strengths in class actions.

### Christian & Small LLP
See profile on p.479

**THE FIRM** This group is particularly active in product liability disputes and class actions and has notable expertise advising clients in the healthcare, manufacturing, technology and insurance arenas. Among its recent highlights, it defended Clayton College of Natural Health in a breach of contract, fraud and conversion lawsuit.
**KEY INDIVIDUALS** *"Outstanding and hard-working trial lawyer"* **Thomas Christian** has a diverse litigation practice and comes much recommended by clients, who especially value his wealth of experience in disputes. **James Huckaby** has notable expertise advising on financial services and insurance litigation, as well as securities and antitrust defense. He is currently defending Wright Pharmaceutical in several nutritional supplement lawsuits.

### Cunningham Bounds, LLC

**THE FIRM** This preeminent plaintiffs' firm continues to be particularly active on class action, product liability and professional negligence cases. The firm was recently successful in a $15 million medical negligence suit against Springhill Hospitals.
**KEY INDIVIDUALS** According to commentators, **Gregory Breedlove** *"does a great job representing his clients."* He advises clients across a broad range of areas including class actions, personal injury and product liability. **Robert Cunningham** is currently part of the 15-member Plaintiffs Steering Committee appointed to manage, direct and control all cases filed against BP and other defendants in connection with the Deepwater Horizon disaster. He is highly respected in the market, with one well-placed source saying: *"I hear nothing but good things about him."*

### Hare, Wynn, Newell & Newton LLP
See profile on p.480

**THE FIRM** This superb team continues to be a dominant force in the state. It maintains a fine track record on multiparty and multiplaintiff cases concerning pharmaceutical and medical device cases, and is also known for its government representation. The firm recently represented more than 2,500 rice farms against Bayer CropScience, in a case related to the contamination of rice crops, with one of the trials resulting in a successful $48 million verdict.
**KEY INDIVIDUALS** **Leon Ashford** is particular active in single-event litigation and has a strong record in medical malpractice and product liability cases. *"He is an outstanding attorney – smart and well prepared."*

# Alabama Litigation

*The editorial is in alphabetical order by firm name.*

## Helmsing, Leach, Herlong, Newman & Rouse, PC
See profile on p.481

**THE FIRM** This compact and very effective firm maintains an excellent reputation in the Mobile market, primarily handling litigation relating to product liability and medical malpractice. It is also regularly sought after for its expertise in general commercial cases.

**KEY INDIVIDUALS Joseph Babington** (see p.467) has a strong general commercial, medical device and product liability practice. *"He is a very good lawyer and he knows how to manage big cases,"* reports one well-placed source. **John Leach** (see p.470) has extensive experience representing clients across a wide variety of high-profile commercial disputes.

## Huie, Fernambucq & Stewart, LLP

**THE FIRM** A new entry into the rankings this year, this boutique is renowned for its expertise in product liability litigation, most notably in the automotive and manufacturing arenas. It also comes recommended for its strong medical malpractice work. Major clients include Ford, which it is defending in multiple cases across the country.

**KEY INDIVIDUALS Alan Thomas** is well regarded for his representation of motor companies and is described by one source as *"a very accomplished trial lawyer – very capable, very smart and hands-on."*

## Lanier Ford Shaver & Payne P.C.

**THE FIRM** This experienced Huntsville team provides clients with representation across the full range of business and civil litigation matters. It is also well versed in practicing before state and federal appellate courts.

**KEY INDIVIDUALS** The seasoned **Stanley Rodgers** is highly regarded for his expertise in medical malpractice suits. A well-placed source says: *"He is one of the finest trial lawyers you will see."*

## Lightfoot, Franklin & White, LLC
See profile on p.482

**THE FIRM** This excellent boutique maintains a strong presence in Alabama and is well known for its skill in product liability, pharmaceutical and medical device-related cases. Its client base includes manufacturers and financial services institutions and, while primarily noted for its defendant-side representation, it is also frequently sought after to handle plaintiffs' work. The team is representing GE over alleged improper sterilization equipment at a hospital.

**Sources say:** *"It is one of the foremost litigation firms in Alabama."*

**KEY INDIVIDUALS Harlan Prater** counts Hyundai Motors among his key clients and has recently acted for the company in a personal injury case in Virginia. He is also increasingly active in pharmaceutical defense work. An interviewee says: *"He is easy to work with, has a very good trial practice and handles his practice very well. His clients have a lot of faith in him."* **Samuel Franklin** has a diverse practice but is particularly adept on large financial cases. *"He is just a tremendous litigator: he is able to take complex issues and simplify them. He also has the ability to put folks at ease, even in a high-stakes case. He does a great job of thinking through the case and seeing the end game,"* reports one enthusiastic source.

## Marsh, Rickard & Bryan P.C

**THE FIRM** This group receives strong praise for its expertise in personal injury and professional negligence work. It is also commended for its adept handling of product liability cases.

**KEY INDIVIDUALS David Marsh** comes recommended for representing clients in personal injury cases. A source comments: *"He is very bright and articulate, he works hard, is incredibly effective and great to work with."*

## Maynard, Cooper & Gale, P.C.
See profile on p.483

**THE FIRM** This group has a fine reputation for its expertise in the financial services sector, where it defends clients on securities litigation and other banking-related cases. It is also adept at representing manufacturing clients, most notably in product liability, contractual disputes and environmental claims. Highlights include representing Colonial Pipeline in a commercial dispute arising out of the coal mining industry, and representing the company in a toxic tort case brought by a local church. It also represented Regions Financial in a securities class action in relation to financial performances during the credit crisis.

**Sources say:** *"We really like them, they are very knowledgeable and really involved."*

**KEY INDIVIDUALS Lee Bains** (see p.467) has particular expertise in class action and appellate work. He successfully defended Life of the South Insurance in striking a plaintiff's class action. **Maibeth Porter** (see p.471) maintains a strong reputation for her banking and insurance litigation practice and was one of the lead attorneys on the Regions Financial securities class action. A source is quick to praise her as *"excellent: she is involved in big-dollar litigation and gets great results."* **Michael Mulvaney** (see p.471) concentrates on defending clients in insurance and financial services. One happy client said: *"He was brilliant: we got a good outcome and he was able to communicate the case very well and made our points crystal-clear to the jury."*

## McDowell Knight Roedder & Sledge LLC

**THE FIRM** This Mobile-based boutique has been particularly active defending clients in personal injury, professional and medical malpractice and product liability cases. The firm has also recently handled a discrimination case where it defended Austal USA against 23 plaintiffs in race discrimination and hostile work environment lawsuits.

**Sources say:** *"The manner in which they have handled themselves with us, our clients and other attorneys has been really great. They get results, which is the most important thing."*

**KEY INDIVIDUALS Michael Knight** enjoys a fine track record defending clients on product liability cases and is also noted for his experience in complex business litigation. He is identified by one well-placed source as a *"really fine lawyer who is very, very good in the courtroom."*

**Jerry McDowell** has an extensive litigation practice and comes particularly recommended for his expertise in railroad and other transportation litigation. *"He is very thorough and very good with juries,"* reports one impressed interviewee.

## Rushton, Stakely, Johnston & Garrett

**THE FIRM** Sources particularly single out this Montgomery firm's expertise in medical malpractice defense work, but it is also recognized for its strengths in a broad range of other areas, including insurance and product liability disputes.

**KEY INDIVIDUALS Thomas Keene** is renowned for his wealth of courtroom experience, and is also applauded for his judgment and advocacy abilities.

## Sirote & Permutt PC
See profile on p.484

**THE FIRM** A new addition to the rankings, Sirote & Permutt is recognized for its robust mortgage banking and real estate disputes practice, and is also highly sought after for its expertise in business and product liability cases as well.

**KEY INDIVIDUALS Robert Baugh** (see p.467) heads the firm's litigation department and is particularly active in insurance, business and product liability disputes. He is noted as *"a big-picture guy who is able to give practical and sound legal advice."*

## Spotswood Sansom & Sansbury LLC
See profile on p.485

**THE FIRM** This litigation boutique has notable expertise advising clients in the financial services arena and also has a fine track record acting on behalf of companies in the aviation sector. Highlights include defending Stryker against Applied Surgical and The University of Alabama in regards to the alleged theft of the IP of a surgical device.

**KEY INDIVIDUALS Kenneth Sansom** is described as *"an extremely bright and capable litigator, who is very meticulous regarding his research and very articulate in presenting the case."* Sources regard **Robert Spotswood** as *"a lawyer's lawyer: extremely capable and effective in the courtroom."*

## Starnes Davis Florie LLP
See profile on p.486

**THE FIRM** This firm is well known for having one of the preeminent medical malpractice groups in the state and also maintains a formidable commercial litigation practice. The team also enjoys a fine reputation for securities and banking and finance disputes. It has been particularly active of late defending ProAssurance in several medical-related cases, and is also representing KKR in a lawsuit arising from the leveraged recapitalization of Bruno's.

**Sources say:** *"The firm is extremely responsible, competent, responsive and knowledgeable. They demonstrated a level of caring beyond what you would expect, which made you feel that you had the best representation possible."*

**KEY INDIVIDUALS** *"Fine trial lawyer"* **Michael Florie** (see p.469) is particularly recognized for his medical malpractice work, but also comes recommended for his strong

*The editorial is in alphabetical order by firm name.*

commercial litigation practice as well. In particular, he works extremely closely with key client ProAssurance. **Randal Sellers** (see p.472) is highly regarded by peers for his vast experience and expertise in medical malpractice cases. In addition, he is routinely sought after to handle complex IP and commercial disputes. **Jay Ezelle** (see p.469) focuses on complex high-risk litigation. He was lead partner in the aforementioned KKR leveraged recapitalization lawsuit. Sources are particularly impressed with his strategic approach to matters. The highly regarded **Walter Bates** (see p.467) is head of the medical malpractice defense team and has an impressive practice covering all healthcare-related disputes. He recently represented ProAssurance in a medical malpractice and wrongful death case against a cardiologist.

## Other Notable Practitioners

**Crawford McGivaren** of Cabaniss, Johnston, Gardner, Dumas & O'Neal is described as *"a savvy, experienced litigator who has a good grasp of the 'big picture' in cases but is able to argue the finer points as well."* He has wide-ranging experience across commercial litigation, personal injury and punitive damages cases. Mobile-based **Danner Frazer** of Frazer, Greene, Upchurch & Baker, L.L.C. is an adept litigator who has broad-ranging experience across many contentious areas, but comes particularly recommended for his medical malpractice defense work. **Tabor Novak** of Ball, Ball, Matthews & Novak has a diverse litigation practice but places a particular emphasis on medical malpractice matters, for which he is highly regarded by peers. Sources also point to his charisma in the courtroom as one of his strengths. Armbrecht Jackson LLP's **Norman Waldrop** draws praise for his courtroom experience, with one impressed source commenting: *"He does a great job, works extremely hard and is a very good trial lawyer in the courtroom."* **Richard Gill** is the senior partner at Copeland, Franco, Screws & Gill and is noted for his experience on both the plaintiff and defendant side in matters including securities fraud and complex business litigation. **Michael Rediker** of Haskell Slaughter Young & Rediker has experience representing both plaintiffs and defendants in areas such as securities and product liability disputes. **Larry Childs** (see p.468) of Waller Lansden Dortch & Davis primarily represents financial institutions in bankruptcy as well as professional liability cases. Scott Dukes & Geisler, PC's **Carter Dukes** (see p.469) concentrates on professional liability, commercial and employment litigation. A commentator reports: *"He is a very effective lawyer – resourceful, creative and cost-effective."* At the same firm, **John Scott** (see p.472) enjoys a broad commercial litigation practice and has much experience representing banks and other financial institutions. The excellent **Edward Meyerson** (see p.471) of Baker, Donelson, Bearman, Caldwell & Berkowitz, PC continues to be regarded as one of the leading construction disputes-oriented attorneys in the state.

# REAL ESTATE

Zoning/Land Use p.466

Commentary about individuals can be found under their firm's paragraph. If the firm has no paragraph (is not ranked) look at Other Notable Practitioners.

| Real Estate Leading Firms |
| --- |
| **Band 1** |
| Baker, Donelson, Bearman, Caldwell & Berkowitz, PC * |
| Balch & Bingham LLP * |
| Bradley Arant Boult Cummings LLP * |
| Burr & Forman LLP * |
| Maynard, Cooper & Gale, P.C. * |
| **Band 2** |
| Leitman, Siegal, Payne & Campbell, P.C. |
| Rushton, Stakely, Johnston & Garrett |
| Sirote & Permutt PC ** |

*\* Indicates firm with profile.*

## Band 1

### Baker, Donelson, Bearman, Caldwell & Berkowitz, PC
See profile on p.2313

**THE FIRM** This premier group continues to enjoy a fine reputation for its wealth of real estate expertise and maintains a particular strength in its development and transactional practices. The team is especially adept at advising on retail, multifamily, senior living and medical-related real estate matters and benefits from its regional footprint to provide clients with a multistate platform on both the lender or borrower side. Key clients include Bayer Properties and the Medical Properties Trust.

**Sources say:** *"They are good lawyers, they are very practical in resolving issues and I enjoyed working with them and will continue to use them."*
**KEY INDIVIDUALS Murphy McMillan** (see p.470) is noted for his real estate development experience and has been particularly active of late advising private equity groups on acquiring distressed commercial real estate loans and property. *"He is a smart lawyer, easy to work with and represents his clients well,"* notes one observer. **William Sylvester** (see p.473) enjoys a strong reputation in the market and comes much recommended for his work on multifamily matters. **Denise Killebrew** (see p.470) often represents senior living and multifamily developers and has a strong reputation for her work on leasing and development. *"I found her easy to work with. She knows what she's doing and I'd have a lot of confidence sending clients to her,"* remarked one impressed peer. **Chervis Isom** (see p.470) is described as the *"grandaddy of real estate in Alabama,"* and continues to add significant value to the Baker Donelson team with his extensive experience in the real estate arena.

### Balch & Bingham LLP
See profile on p.475

**THE FIRM** Peers are quick to highlight this firm's lending-based real estate practice and also single out the firm's impressive client base. The group continues to represent BBVA Compass Bank on commercial and industrial real estate financings, as well as tax-exempt financings of municipal and county facilities. It also represented Southern Company in transactions to acquire land and other property for power generation, transmission and distribution.

**Sources say:** *"It's great to have a firm with the experience and expertise to help us."*
**KEY INDIVIDUALS Randolph Lanier** is heavily involved in real estate finance transactions and comes much recommended for his expertise on workout and loan sales of distressed assets. According to one client, *"he is an outstanding attorney – his knowledge, experience and the ease of doing a deal with him are particular positives."* Montgomery-based **James Edwards** continues to represent Jim Wilson & Associates in an enhanced use lease development of a US Army property to a private developer. *"He has a wealth of knowledge, he pushes to get the deal done and he is good to work with,"* reports one source. **Felton Smith** handles much of the firm's Southern Company work. *"He is a great draftsman, he pays attention to detail and his work is always excellent,"* asserts one impressed commentator. **John Pickering** is primarily a transactional lawyer and has a fine track record acting on behalf of banks and financial institutions. *"I feel fortunate to have access to his real estate expertise,"* notes one satisfied client.

### Bradley Arant Boult Cummings LLP
See profile on p.476

**THE FIRM** This impressive team is one of the largest in the state and has been especially active advising financial institutions on distressed real estate files. The firm also continues to have particularly strong development and land use practices. Recent highlights include representing a publicly traded REIT, Campus Crest Communities, on the purchase, financing, development, management and leasing of a portfolio of student housing projects nationwide. **Sources say:** "*It is an outstanding firm that does top-drawer work.*"

**KEY INDIVIDUALS Charles Beavers** enjoys a strong reputation for his expertise on transactional matters as well as zoning and land use. "*He has a fine reputation,*" asserts one commentator. **Stephen Monk** is particularly well regarded for his real estate development practice. According to one impressed interviewee, "*he is very good – he is a technically proficient and practical lawyer.*" The highly regarded **Kay**

---

**Bains** has been particularly active representing Regions Bank in all its corporate real estate work and recently has helped the bank in the sale of over 60 foreclosed properties, valued at over $50 million. **William Byrd** has experience advising both lenders as well as developers and has been particularly active on mixed-use development cases. One source said: "*He knows his stuff and I've always found him very good to work with.*" **David Dresher** has a fine reputation in the state for his work with developers on the acquisition, sale, leasing and financing of properties, and also comes recommended for his work with clients raising investment funds for acquisitions. **Dawn Helms Sharff** is a new entry into the rankings this year and is playing a leading role on the aforementioned Campus Crest Communities matter. "*She is a gifted attorney, who is detail-oriented, logical and pragmatic,*" remarked one enthusiastic interviewee.

### Burr & Forman LLP
See profile on p.477

**THE FIRM** This regional firm draws praise from peers for its high-quality lending practice as well as for its strong commercial real estate offering, and maintains a fine reputation for mixed-use or healthcare-related projects. The firm has been particularly active advising clients on shopping center acquisitions and currently serves as lead counsel for the Bristol Development Group-PGM Properties joint venture concerning the $85 million Twickenham Square mixed-use urban redevelopment project.
**Sources say:** "*It is an excellent firm and one of the best in Alabama.*"
**KEY INDIVIDUALS John De Buys** is highly regarded for his expertise on planning and zoning issues and also comes recommended for property rights dispute resolution. "*He is wonderful, has so much experience and gets good results,*" reports one enthusiastic commentator. **Gail Mills** focuses on development issues including the purchase and sale of shopping centers. She was the lead lawyer on the aforementioned Twickenham Square project. Sources describe her as "*a great lawyer: she is practical, will protect the client and won't waste time on unnecessary issues.*" The much-respected **Dwight Mixson** has over three decades' worth of real estate experience, acting on behalf of both lenders and developers on projects ranging from office buildings and shopping centers to apartments, condominiums and hotels. **Fred Powell** has, according to one source, "*one of the best grasps of real estate and knows how to close a transaction.*"

### Maynard, Cooper & Gale, P.C.
See profile on p.483

**THE FIRM** This leading firm has offices in both Birmingham and Huntsville and combines a strong commercial real estate practice with expertise on lending matters including workouts and foreclosures. The group is particularly noted for its work on behalf of clients in the healthcare and natural resources arenas. A notable highlight saw it act as counsel to the mayor of the City of Birmingham, advising on matters concerning the development of a baseball stadium.

---

**Sources say:** "*I like them because of their efficiency and demeanor: they are always looking at ways to solve problems.*"
**KEY INDIVIDUALS** The highly respected **Thomas Clark** (see p.468) has a diverse practice encompassing the acquisition, development and financing of real estate. He continues to represent Evson on joint venture arrangements, financing and property sales in connection with redevelopment of a shopping center and apartment complex in Mountain Brook. **Robert Sexton** (see p.472) has expertise across all areas of real estate and took a leading role in the aforementioned baseball stadium deal. According to one enthusiastic interviewee, "*his ability to comprehend the smallest details in a very complex project with a number of moving parts is very impressive.*" **Mary Beth O'Neill** (see p.471) has particular expertise advising clients in the natural resources sector. "*She is smart, practical and pleasant to work with, and does a really good job for her client,*" asserts one impressed peer. **Stephen Stallcup** (see p.473) acted as lead counsel to the Education Corporation of America in the purchase, development and leasing of a series off-college campus facilities throughout the country. According to one commentator, "*he does a really good job of understanding the transaction from different sides of the table and tries to get a workable solution that suits all parties.*" **Lee Sheppard** (see p.472) primarily represents lenders and, according to one source, "*gets how a lawyer can bring value to a deal, is responsive and stays on top of things.*"

## Band 2

### Leitman, Siegal, Payne & Campbell, P.C.

**THE FIRM** This practice is primarily engaged in commercial real estate matters with a distinct focus on multifamily developments. Its clients include both lenders and developers, as well as title and mortgage companies. A notable highlight includes advising Colonial Properties Trust on the sale of shopping centers and the acquisition of multifamily assets.
**KEY INDIVIDUALS Phillip Stutts** is particularly noted for his work with title companies, and combines this with a substantial state tax law work practice, which covers a range of real estate issues. **Don Siegal** is a seasoned figure and has over 40 years of experience in real estate finance and development.

### Rushton, Stakely, Johnston & Garrett

**THE FIRM** This highly-regarded Montgomery-based team has significant experience advising lenders and developers on a wide variety of real estate matters from retail to residential. The firm regularly acts as local counsel to out-of-state lenders and borrowers and also maintains a fine track record acting on behalf of lenders in commercial and residential foreclosure proceedings.
**KEY INDIVIDUALS Jeffrey Blitz** draws particular praise for his all-around capabilities and is a well-respected member of the firm. One impressed source says: "*He does a really good job for his client. He is fair, he knows what is needed and gets it accomplished.*"

## Sirote & Permutt PC
See profile on p.484

**THE FIRM** In addition to a traditional commercial development practice, Sirote & Permutt has a dedicated mortgage banking and real estate foreclosure practice, representing mortgage lenders and government agencies on all creditor-related work. This typically involves handling litigation through the bankruptcy courts, in which the firm has extensive experience. On real estate development, a recent highlight saw it represent Equity Resources in a variety of acquisitions, financings and development of multi-family and commercial properties across the region.
**KEY INDIVIDUALS** Steven Brickman (see p.468) principally represents clients in commercial real estate development and is described as "*a very practical, smart and cordial attorney*" who is able to be both "*a hard negotiator and a true gentleman.*" **Jerry Held** (see p.469) is particularly adept at representing mortgage lenders, servicers and government agencies and heads the firm's mortgage banking group. **Adam Sigman** (see p.472) is a traditional real estate transaction attorney and regularly represents investors in acquiring real estate and developing projects.

### Other Notable Practitioners

**Jesse Evans** divides his time between the Birmingham and Montgomery office of Haskell Slaughter Young & Rediker and predominantly focuses on litigation matters. He is particularly singled out for his knowledge and expertise on eminent domain and condemnation matters. **Haskins Jones** of Johnston Barton Proctor & Rose LLP is particularly active in healthcare lending as well as real estate development work. He elicits much praise from peers, one of whom says: "*He does a very good job on a technical level, as well as from a service standpoint.*" **Warren Herlong** (see p.470) of Helmsing, Leach, Herlong, Newman & Rouse, PC enjoys an extremely strong reputation, predominantly representing owners on eminent domain and condemnation issues. "*He is a very effective communicator, he really thinks about strategy and, at the bottom line, he is very good at negotiating,*" asserts one highly impressed commentator.

# Leaders' Profiles in Alabama

### AHNERT, Janell M.
Maynard, Cooper & Gale, P.C., Birmingham
205 254 1202
jahnert@maynardcooper.com
*Featured in Labor & Employment (Alabama)*
**Practice Areas:** Ms Ahnert's practice encompasses all facets of employment law. She has extensive and successful experience in obtaining summary judgment. In addition, Ms Ahnert has considerable trial, arbitration and appellate experience.
**Professional Memberships:** ABA & Alabama Bar L&E and Women Sections, National Association of Women Lawyers.
**Career:** Alabama Super Lawyers, Alabama Top 25 Women; Martindale Hubbell AV Preeminent Rating; admitted to United States Supreme Court and Eleventh Circuit.
**Personal:** University of Virginia School of Law (JD, 1999); Virginia Journal of Social Policy and Law, Editorial Board; University of South Alabama (BA, 1991), cum laude, Omicron Delta Kappa.

### BABINGTON, Joseph
Helmsing, Leach, Herlong, Newman & Rouse, PC, Mobile
251 434 0874
jpb@helmsinglaw.com
*Featured in Litigation (Alabama)*
**Practice Areas:** General civil trial and appellate practice. Product Liability defense. Mass Tort, multi-district, class action complex litigation. Commercial and insurance disputes. Successfully argued for petitioners in Kumho Tire Co. v. Carmichael, 526 U.S. 137 (1999).
**Professional Memberships:** Federation of Defense & Corporate Counsel; Defense Research Institute; Trial Attorneys of America; Alabama Defense Lawyers' Association.
**Career:** University of Notre Dame, BA 1981 (with highest honors) Phi Beta Kappa; University of Virginia School of Law, JD 1984. Admitted to practice in the United States Supreme Court and all federal and state courts in Alabama and Louisiana.

### BAINS JR, Lee E
Maynard, Cooper & Gale, P.C., Birmingham
205 254 1022
lbains@maynardcooper.com
*Featured in Litigation (Alabama)*
**Practice Areas:** Mr Bains' practice focuses primarily on complex civil litigation with an emphasis on class action litigation, punitive damages litigation, life insurance litigation, business tort and commercial litigation, antitrust litigation, and post-trial and appellate litigation.
**Professional Memberships:** American Bar Association; Alabama State Bar Association, former Chairman of the Business Torts and Antitrust Law Section; Birmingham Bar Association.
**Career:** Admitted to practice in Alabama in 1980. Joined Maynard Cooper when it started in 1984. Martindale-Hubbell AV Rating (since 1988, after seven years of practice).
**Personal:** Harvard University (AB, 1977 cum laude); Harvard Law School (JD, 1980 cum laude).

### BAKER, Tammy L
Jackson Lewis LLP, Birmingham
205 332 3106
BakerT@jacksonlewis.com
*Featured in Labor & Employment (Alabama)*
**Practice Areas:** Litigation includes Title VII, Age Discrimination in Employment Act, Equal Pay Act, ADA, FMLA, FLSA. Counsels employers, conducts management training on workplace issues.
**Professional Memberships:** Alabama and Mississippi State Bars; Birmingham Bar; Society for Human Resource Management.
**Career:** Law Clerk to Honorable Sharon Lovelace Blackburn, Northern District of Alabama, 1993-1994; Constangy, Brooks & Smith, 1994-2007; Jackson Lewis LLP, 2007–present.
**Publications:** Contributor, Employment Discrimination Law (2d. Supp. 1999); Contributor, HR Alabama, May 2011 and May 2012.
**Personal:** University of Alabama School of Law, JD, magna cum laude, 1993; University of Alabama at Birmingham, BS, magna cum laude, 1990.

### BATES, Walter W
Starnes Davis Florie LLP, Birmingham
205 868 6059
bbates@starneslaw.com
*Featured in Litigation (Alabama)*
**Practice Areas:** He has been lead defense counsel in a wide variety of civil trials and appeals spanning over 30 years of practice. He has tried in excess of 120 complex civil cases to a jury verdict, including the defense of physicians, hospitals and product manufacturers.
**Professional Memberships:** Fellow, American College of Trial Lawyers; Diplomate, American Board of Trial Advocates (President of Alabama State Chapter 2007-08); Member, Birmingham, Alabama, and American Bar Associations. Selected by his peers for inclusion in The Best Lawyers in America; selected for inclusion in Alabama Super Lawyers; and named a Litigation Star by Benchmark Litigation.
**Career:** Admitted to the Bar in 1981, Alabama; Partner at Starnes Davis Florie LLP for 25 years; Managing Partner of Starnes Davis Florie LLP since 2006.
**Publications:** He is a regular speaker on trial advocacy and litigation tactics.
**Personal:** Born October 22, 1956. The University of Alabama, BS Finance (1978); Cumberland School of Law, JD (1981).

### BAUGH, Robert R
Sirote & Permutt PC, Birmingham
205 930 5307
rbaugh@sirote.com
*Featured in Litigation (Alabama)*
**Practice Areas:** Chair, Litigation Practice Group. Represents clients in insurance, business, and product liability litigation. Advises businesses and business owners on intellectual property matters, as well as labor and employment law.
**Professional Memberships:** President, Birmingham Bar Association, 2013. Member of the American, Alabama, Georgia and Mississippi Bar Associations. Fellow of the Alabama Law Foundation, and the Birmingham Bar Foundation. Member, International Association of Defense Counsel. Faculty Member, 2012 IADC Trial Academy. Member, Litigation Counsel of America. Member of the Defense Research Institute, Alabama Defense Lawyers Association and Birmingham Inns of Court.
**Career:** JD, University of Alabama School of Law, 1982 (Alabama Law Review). Martindale-Hubbell AV rated. Best Lawyers in America for Commercial Litigation and Personal Injury Litigation. Alabama Super Lawyers for Business Litigation. Best of US for Intellectual Property, Insurance, Employment and Arbitration.
**Publications:** Published Opinion, Nihon Rufuto v. Nidek Medical, 437 Fed. Appx. 782, 2011 WL 3505211 (C.A. 11 (Ala.)). Published Opinion, Maciasz V. Fireman's Fund Ins. Co., 988 So. 2d 991 (Ala. 2008) Published Opinion, Verchot v. General Motors Corp., 812 So. 2d 296 (Ala. 2001)
**Personal:** BS, The University of Alabama, 1979. Legal Counsel and Board of Directors, Birmingham International Festival. Member of the Downtown Kiwanis Club and the Newcomen Society.

## BIRCHALL, James L
Jones Walker LLP, Birmingham
205 244 5222
jbirchall@joneswalker.com
*Featured in Banking & Finance (Alabama)*
**Practice Areas:** Banking and financial services; public finance.
**Professional Memberships:** Alabama State Bar; American Bar Association; American College of Bond Counsel (Fellow); Birmingham Bar Association; National Association of Bond Lawyers.
**Career:** Mr Birchall is a Partner in the firm's Business and Commercial Transactions Practice Group. His practice has included both municipal and public finance for more than 30 years.

## BRICKMAN, Steven A
Sirote & Permutt PC, Birmingham
205 930 5171
sbrickman@sirote.com
*Featured in Real Estate (Alabama)*
**Practice Areas:** Shareholder in the firm's Business and Real Estate Law Group. Represents clients in commercial real estate development, including land acquisition, financing, leasing and planning. Handles the acquisition and sale of businesses. Represents clients in general business matters.
**Professional Memberships:** Birmingham and American Bar Associations; Alabama and Georgia State Bars.
**Career:** JD, University of Virginia School of Law, 1974. Joined Sirote & Permutt, P.C. in 1982 as a Shareholder. Martindale Hubbell AV Rated. Best Lawyers in America for Real Estate and Banking Law. Alabama Super Lawyers for Real Estate.
**Personal:** Born February 11, 1949. BS with High Distinction, University of Virginia, 1971, Phi Beta Kappa. Member: Leadership Alabama, Class XII; President's Advisory Council, Birmingham Southern College. Former Member: UAB Leadership Council; National Executive Committee, AIPAC. Past President: Birmingham Jewish Foundation; Birmingham Jewish Federation; Crisis Center. Past Board Member: Partnership Assistance to the Homeless; Birmingham Jewish Community Center; Temple Beth-El Synagogue; N. E. Miles Jewish Day School; Jewish Family Services. Former Executive Committee and Regional Chairman: National Conference of Community and Justice (NCCJ); 2001 Brotherhood and Sisterhood Award. Former Co-Chair: United Way Campaign, Leadership Division; Birmingham Jewish Federation, Israel NOW Campaign. Former Program Chair: Leadership Birmingham. Recipient: Tikkun Olam Community Service Award, 2007. Recipient: Declaration of Independence Award, Israel Bonds, 2004.

## BROWN, Stephen E
Maynard, Cooper & Gale, P.C., Birmingham
205 254 1023
sbrown@maynardcooper.com
*Featured in Labor & Employment (Alabama)*
**Practice Areas:** Since 1974, Mr Brown has represented management in labor and employment litigation in both federal and state courts and before various federal and state administrative agencies. Mr Brown chairs the firm's Labor and Employment Practice Group.
**Professional Memberships:** American Bar Association; Alabama State Bar; Birmingham Bar Association; Fellow, College of Labor and Employment Attorneys; Business Council of Alabama.
**Career:** Admitted US Supreme Court; 11th and 4th U. S. Circuit Courts of Appeal; Northern, Middle and Southern Districts of Alabama; all Alabama State Courts.
**Personal:** Dartmouth College (AB, 1971); Tulane School of Law (JD, 1974).

## CARMODY, Richard P
Adams and Reese LLP, Birmingham
205 250 5000
richard.carmody@arlaw.com
*Featured in Bankruptcy/Restructuring (Alabama), Banking & Finance (Alabama)*
**Practice Areas:** Partner: commercial restructuring and bankruptcy, banking and finance, forestry law, construction, real estate, contracts.
**Professional Memberships:** American Bankruptcy Institute, American Board of Certification, Alabama Law Institute, Alabama Appleseed, Board of Directors.
**Career:** Represents clients in difficult financial situations, including secured lenders in documenting loans and working out troubled loans, unsecured creditors in bankruptcy proceedings, debtors in bankruptcy reorganizations, trustees in special bankruptcy litigation matters and purchasers of assets in bankruptcy proceedings.
**Personal:** JD, Vanderbilt University Law School, 1975, BA, University of Illinois, 1964 (Finance).

## CHILDS, Larry
Waller Lansden Dortch & Davis, Birmingham
205 226 5701
larry.childs@wallerlaw.com
*Featured in Litigation (Alabama)*
**Practice Areas:** More than 30 years' experience representing financial institutions, manufacturers and other clients in complex litigation, including lender liability lawsuits, shareholder derivative lawsuits, securities and ERISA class actions, cases under the Uniform Commercial Code, consumer products class actions and industrial accidents. Serves as Co-Practice Group Leader for Litigation and Dispute Resolution.
**Professional Memberships:** Birmingham, Alabama and American Bar Associations; Business Entities Committee of the Alabama Law Institute.
**Career:** Licensed in Alabama since 1977, in Tennessee since 2006. Joined Waller in 2005.
**Personal:** JD, Order of the Coif, 1977, University of Virginia; BA, magna cum laude, 1974, University of Alabama.

## CLARK III, Thomas C
Maynard, Cooper & Gale, P.C., Birmingham
205 254 1072
tclark@maynardcooper.com
*Featured in Real Estate (Alabama)*
**Practice Areas:** Real estate; commercial lending; economic development and incentives; general corporate. Mr Clark's practice focuses on all aspects of the representation of buyers, sellers, developers, landlords and tenants in all types of real estate matters, including acquisition, development, financing, and leasing matters. In addition, Mr Clark focuses on all aspects of the representation of lenders and borrowers in secured and unsecured transactions and multi-state transactions.
**Professional Memberships:** American Bar Association; Alabama State Bar Association; Birmingham Bar Association.
**Career:** Admitted in Alabama.
**Personal:** Duke University (BS, 1988 cum laude); University of Pennsylvania School of Law (JD, 1991).

## COOPER, John H
Sirote & Permutt PC, Birmingham
205 930 5108
jcooper@sirote.com
*Featured in Corporate/Commercial (Alabama)*
**Practice Areas:** CEO of Sirote & Permutt, P.C.; Shareholder in the firm's Corporate Law, Corporate Finance and Tax Law Group. Advises businesses on the planning, structuring and negotiating of mergers and acquisitions; corporate reorganizations and purchases and sales of businesses; the structuring of business organizations with respect to ownership, financial, and tax planning issues; venture capital transactions; and public and private securities transactions in diverse industries, such as technology, health care, pharmaceutical, real estate and retail.
**Professional Memberships:** Birmingham and American Bar Associations; Alabama State Bar; Alabama Ethics Commission, Former Chair.
**Career:** JD, University of Alabama School of Law, 1978 (Order of the Coif, Top 10 percent). LLM in Taxation, New York University, 1980. Joined Sirote & Permutt in 1980. Serves as the firm's Chief Executive Officer. Adjunct Professor of Advanced Corporate Tax, University of Alabama Law School (1982-2008). Former Adjunct Professor of Partnership Taxation, Cumberland School of Law, Samford University. Martindale-Hubbell AV rated. Ranked by Chambers USA for Corporate and Commercial Law. Best Lawyers in America for Securities Law and Tax Law. Alabama Super Lawyers for Tax. Birmingham Magazine Top Attorney for Tax. Corporate Counsel Magazine Top Rated Lawyer for Tax Law. Best of US Best of Class in Tax. Birmingham Business Journal "Best of the Bar."
**Personal:** Born Jan. 11, 1953. BA, University of Alabama in Huntsville, 1975. Board of Directors: Birmingham Business Alliance, John Carroll Catholic High School, Greater Birmingham Habitat for Humanity. Advisory Board: Alabama Arthritis Foundation. Board of Trustees: Holy Family Cristo Rey High School. Former President: Vestavia Hills Board of Education.

## CURRAN, Gregory S
Maynard, Cooper & Gale, P.C., Birmingham
205 254 1098
gcurran@maynardcooper.com
*Featured in Corporate/Commercial (Alabama)*
**Practice Areas:** Corporate governance/compliance; mergers/acquisitions; venture capital/private equity investment; securities regulation/corporate finance; private investment fund formation; emerging businesses; executive compensation. Mr. Curran represents clients in business acquisitions, venture capital/private equity transactions and corporate finance transactions. He also provides legal and strategic advice to companies, their boards and management regarding corporate governance, crisis response, dispute resolution, strategic planning and communications.
**Career:** Recognized in Chambers USA; Best Lawyers in America, 2010-2011 Birmingham Corporate Lawyer of the Year; Alabama Super Lawyers; Firm Executive Committee; Chairman of Firm Corporate Practice Group.
**Personal:** Vanderbilt University (BA, 1985); University of Alabama School of Law (JD, 1989).

## DAVIS, Thomas A
Jackson Lewis LLP, Birmingham
205 332 3101
DavisT@jacksonlewis.com
*Featured in Labor & Employment (Alabama)*
**Practice Areas:** Workplace litigation emphasis on class action and multi-plaintiff litigation (including non-compete). Preventative strategies to avoid employment claims. Particular emphasis on retail clients.
**Professional Memberships:** American Employment Law Council; American, Alabama and Birmingham Bar Associations; Super Lawyer 2007- present, Best Lawyers 2007-present, Chambers 2007 - present; Top 40 under 40 (2006); Sunrise Rotary (1994 -present), Retail Industry Leaders Association (2009 - present).
**Career:** Judicial Law Clerk, U.S. District Court Judge Robert B. Propst (1992-1993); Constangy, Brooks & Smith (1993-2007); Jackson Lewis (Managing Partner Birmingham, 2007-present)
**Personal:** Emory University BA (1989); Samford University, Cumberland School of Law JD (1992)

## DREW, Mark
Maynard, Cooper & Gale, P.C., Birmingham
205 254 1031
mdrew@maynardcooper.com
*Featured in Corporate/Commercial (Alabama)*
**Practice Areas:** Mergers and acquisitions; venture capital and private equity investment; emerging businesses; financial institutions; general corporate. Mr Drew focuses primarily in the areas of mergers and acquisitions, venture capital financings, joint ventures and related corporate activities and transactions. He regularly represents both public and private companies in a variety of matters and also has significant experience representing financial institutions.
**Career:** Recognized in Chambers USA, The Best Lawyers in America, Alabama Super Lawyers; Firm Executive Committee; Current Managing Partner of Maynard Cooper.
**Personal:** Wake Forest University (BS, 1983); Wake Forest University School of Law (JD, 1988).

**DUKES, Carter H**
Scott Dukes & Geisler, PC, Birmingham
205 244 2502
cdukes@scottdukeslaw.com
*Featured in Litigation (Alabama)*
**Practice Areas:** Employment law; commercial litigation; general civil litigation; mass and complex litigation; and professional and fiduciary liability litigation. Mr Dukes's practice focuses on the representation of business and management in a variety of matters.
**Professional Memberships:** Defense Research Institute; Alabama Defense Lawyers Association; Member of the Alabama, Georgia, and American Bar Associations.
**Career:** Admitted in Alabama (1990) and Georgia (1994). Founding Member of Scott Dukes & Geisler, P.C. (2000).
**Personal:** Born 16 July 1965 in Opelika, Alabama; JD Emory University School of Law (1990), Articles Editor, Emory Law Journal; BA David Lipscomb College (1987).

**EZELLE, Jay**
Starnes Davis Florie LLP, Birmingham
205 868 6025
jezelle@starneslaw.com
*Featured in Litigation (Alabama)*
**Practice Areas:** Jay has worked on a broad variety of litigation matters, concentrating on complex, high-risk litigation. He has represented major financial institutions in numerous matters involving securities fraud in federal and state courts as well as multidistrict litigations. He has also represented numerous Fortune 500 companies in a variety of litigation, including national class actions. He has represented the Board of Trustees of the University of Alabama in a variety of high-profile litigation, including patent and trademark infringment actions.
**Professional Memberships:** Member, Birmingham, Alabama, and American Bar Associations; Member, Alabama Defense Lawyers Association; Selected as a "Future Star" for the state of Alabama in Benchmark Litigation; Listed in Alabama Super Lawyers; Named one of Birmingham's "Top 40 Under 40" for 2012 by the Birmingham Business Journal.
**Career:** Admitted to the Alabama Bar and joined Starnes Davis Florie LLP in 1999; Previously served as the Head of Recruiting for Starnes Davis Florie LLP.
**Personal:** Rhodes College, BS in Biochemistry (1995); The University of Alabama School of Law, summa cum laude (1999).

**FLORIE, Michael A**
Starnes Davis Florie LLP, Birmingham
205 868 6045
mflorie@starneslaw.com
*Featured in Litigation (Alabama)*
**Practice Areas:** In 36 years devoted entirely to civil litigation, he has had extensive trial experience in medical malpractice defense, and has been Lead Counsel in cases involving securities, aviation, pharmaceutical, railroad and product liability. Mike has tried over 175 complex civil cases to

jury verdict, throughout the State of Alabama and the Southeastern United States.
**Professional Memberships:** Fellow, American College of Trial Lawyers; Diplomate, American Board of Trial Advocates (Alabama State President, 2002); Member, Birmingham, Alabama, Louisiana and American Bar Associations. Mike has been selected by his peers for inclusion in The Best Lawyers in America for 18 consecutive years and named by that publication as medical malpractice lawyer of the year for 2010 and 2012; named to Benchmark's Litigation Stars; selected for inclusion in Alabama Super Lawyers; and named to Who's Who in Healthcare in Birmingham.
**Career:** Bar admissions: Alabama, 1976; Louisiana, 1977; associate, Phelps Dunbar (New Orleans), 1977-78; Partner, Burge & Florie (Birmingham), 1978-85; Senior Partner, Starnes Davis Florie (Birmingham), 1985 to present.
**Personal:** Born April 27, 1950. Tulane University, BA, 1972; Tulane University Law School, JD, 1976.

**GAMBINO, Lucas**
Maynard, Cooper & Gale, P.C., Birmingham
205 254 1219
lgambino@maynardcooper.com
*Featured in Banking & Finance (Alabama)*
**Practice Areas:** Commercial lending; corporate finance; financial institutions; real estate. Mr. Gambino's experience includes representation of lenders and borrowers in various secured and unsecured structured-finance, asset-based, multistate and syndicated loan transactions, spanning manufacturing, healthcare, retail and many other industries.
**Professional Memberships:** American, Alabama and Birmingham Bar Associations
**Career:** Admitted in Alabama (1999); Listed in Alabama 'Super Lawyers'
**Publications:** Financing Alternative Becoming Popular, Birmingham Business Journal, Vol. 21, No. 25 (6/18/2004)
**Personal:** University of Alabama at Birmingham, high honors (BA, 1995); University of Alabama School of Law, high honors (JD, 1999)

**GRAY, Kevin**
Maynard, Cooper & Gale, P.C., Huntsville
256 512 0112
kgray@maynardcooper.com
*Featured in Bankruptcy/Restructuring (Alabama)*
**Practice Areas:** Bankruptcy, Workouts and Creditors' Rights; Insurance and Financial Services Litigation; Real Estate; Complex Litigation. Mr. Gray's practice focuses on representing financial institutions, commercial lenders, landlords, and other secured and unsecured creditors in workouts, commercial litigation, chapters 7, 11 and 13 bankruptcy cases and adversary proceedings.
**Professional Memberships:** American Bar Association; American Bankruptcy Institute; Alabama and Tennessee State Bar Associations; Martindale-Hubbell AV Preeminent Rating.
**Career:** Recognized in Chambers USA, The Best Lawyers in America and Alabama Super Lawyers. Admitted in Alabama and Tennessee.

**Personal:** The University of Memphis School of Law (JD, 1996); David Lipscomb University (BA, 1993).

**GREGG, Timothy W.**
Maynard, Cooper & Gale, P.C., Birmingham
205 254 1212
tgregg@maynardcooper.com
*Featured in Corporate/Commercial (Alabama)*
**Practice Areas:** Securities regulation, corporate finance; corporate governance; mergers and acquisitions; venture capital and private equity financings. Mr Gregg represents publicly traded and privately held companies on numerous corporate and securities matters, including public and private securities offerings. He also advises public companies and their boards regarding corporate governance, internal investigations and crisis response matters.
**Professional Memberships:** American, Alabama, and Birmingham Bar Associations
**Career:** Chair of Firm's Securities Regulation Practice Area; Co-Chair of Corporate Practice Group. Admitted in Alabama, Washington, DC and Maryland.
**Personal:** University of North Carolina at Chapel Hill (BA, 1992); Vanderbilt University School of Law (JD, 1999).

**HAHN, W Patton**
Baker, Donelson, Bearman, Caldwell & Berkowitz, PC, Birmingham
205 250 8366
phahn@bakerdonelson.com
*Featured in Bankruptcy/Restructuring (Alabama)*
**Practice Areas:** Patton concentrates his practice in complex commercial litigation, bankruptcy and creditors' rights litigation, litigation involving corporate governance and control, and construction law.
**Professional Memberships:** Listed: Best Lawyers in America. Member: American Bankruptcy Institute, American Bar Association, the Turnaround Management Association and the Construction Suppliers Association
**Career:** Licensed: Alabama; Alabama Supreme Court; U.S. Court of Appeals, Eleventh Circuit; U.S. District Courts and U.S. Bankruptcy Courts: Northern, Middle and Southern Districts of Alabama; U.S. Court of Federal Claims
**Personal:** University of Alabama School of Law, JD; Colgate University, BA.

**HANCOCK, William K**
Adams and Reese LLP, New Orleans
205 250 5000
will.hancock@arlaw.com
*Featured in Labor & Employment (Alabama)*
**Practice Areas:** Partner: Special Business Services Practice Group; labor and employment; management counseling.
**Professional Memberships:** Alabama Bar Association; American Bar Association.
**Career:** Represents management in the labor and employment field and has handled ERISA litigation matters since 1989, assisting healthcare, telecommunications, poultry processing and other clients plan, implement, and defend employment policies and procedures.

**Personal:** JD, Cumberland School of Law, Alabama, 1989, Dean's Scholar and editor of the Cumberland Law Review; BA, University of the South, Sewanee, Tennessee,1986.

**HARMON, Christopher B**
Maynard, Cooper & Gale, P.C., Birmingham
205 254 1090
charmon@maynardcooper.com
*Featured in Corporate/Commercial (Alabama)*
**Practice Areas:** Securities regulation, corporate finance; mergers and acquisitions; health care; executive compensation; corporate governance and compliance; antitrust; financial institutions; venture capital, private equity investment; intellectual property and technology. Mr Harmon handles mergers and acquisitions, private equity, general corporate and securities matters for private and publicly held companies with a non-exclusive concentration in transactions relating to healthcare and financial institutions. His practice also involves advising companies on corporate governance.
**Professional Memberships:** American, Alabama and Birmingham Bar Associations; Certified Public Accountant (inactive status).
**Career:** Admitted in Alabama.
**Personal:** University of Alabama (BS, 1985); University of Alabama School of Law (JD, 1991).

**HARTLEY, Jeffrey J**
Helmsing, Leach, Herlong, Newman & Rouse, PC, Mobile
251 432 5521
jjh@helmsinglaw.com
*Featured in Bankruptcy/Restructuring (Alabama)*
**Practice Areas:** Bankruptcy; creditors rights; debtor rights; insolvency litigation; commercial transactions; mediation.
**Professional Memberships:** Alabama State Bar (Former Chairman of Bankruptcy and Commercial Law Section); American Bankruptcy Institute; Federal Panel of Neutrals.
**Career:** Spring Hill College, BS; University of Alabama School of Law, JD; Law Clerk to Honorable Margaret A. Mahoney, US Bankruptcy Court, Southern District of Alabama, 1994-96; Majority Counsel, US Senate, Committee on the Judiciary, 1990-93; Senate Liaison, National Commission on Judicial Discipline and Removal, 1992-93; Member, National Bankruptcy Review Commission, 1995-97. Admitted in Alabama state and federal courts and US District Court for Northern District of Florida.

**HELD, Jerry**
Sirote & Permutt PC, Birmingham
205 930 5151
jerryheld@sirote.com
*Featured in Real Estate (Alabama)*
**Practice Areas:** Chair, Mortgage Banking Practice Group. Represents national mortgage lenders, servicers, and government agencies in the areas of mortgage banking law, real estate litigation, default servicing, and title insurance law. Negotiates and handles commercial real estate and loan transactions. Frequent speaker at nationwide industry conferences. Hosts client seminars and

training sessions at client offices across the country.

**Professional Memberships:** USFN, America's Mortgage Banking Attorneys, Member of the Commercial/Multi-Family, Audit, Finance, and Advisory committees of the USFN; Mortgage Bankers Association of America (MBA); Mortgage Bankers Association of Alabama (MBAA); American Legal & Financial Network (ALFN); American Bar Association, Foreclosure & Related Remedies Committee, and Real Property, Probate & Trust Section; American Arbitration Association, certified mediator.

**Career:** JD, Emory University School of Law, 1974. Joined Sirote & Permutt, P.C. in 1976 and became a Shareholder in 1978. Currently serves on the firm's Board of Directors/Management Committee. Martindale Hubbell AV rated. Best Lawyers in America for Mortgage Banking Foreclosure Law, Real Estate Law and Banking & Finance Law, 2010-13. Alabama Super Lawyers for Real Estate, 2012-13.

**Publications:** Contributing author, National Mortgage Servicer's Reference Directory (NMSRD), 1999-2013. Panelist and contributor to written materials at USFN Default Servicing Seminars, 1999-2013.

**Personal:** Born October 15, 1949. BS, Commerce & Business Administration, University of Alabama, 1971. President as of May 2013, Board of Directors, Executive Committee, Vice President of Fundraising, and Chair of Annual Campaign, Birmingham Jewish Federation; Board of Directors, Temple Emanuel Synagogue; Past President, Birmingham Jewish Community Center; Past Board Member and Vice President of Fundraising, Crohn's & Colitis Foundation of America, Alabama Chapter; Past Board Member, Collat Jewish Family Services. Leisure interests include golf and travel.

### HERLONG, Warren
Helmsing, Leach, Herlong, Newman & Rouse, PC, Mobile
wch@helmsinglaw.com
*Featured in Real Estate (Alabama)*

**Practice Areas:** Condemnation, Eminent Domain, Land Valuation Litigation.

**Professional Memberships:** Fellow, American College of Real Estate Lawyers; Alabama representative and Board Member, Owner's Counsel of America; former Co-Chairman, American Bar Association, Section of Litigation's Condemnation, Zoning and Land Use Committee.

**Career:** University of Alabama, BS; University of Virginia School of Law, JD; (Winner, William Minor Lyle Moot Court Competition); University of Edinburgh, Scotland, Diploma of Roman Law; Admitted to practice in the United States Supreme Court and all federal and state courts in Alabama. Practiced with same law firm for 34 years.

### HOSCH, Heyward C
Maynard, Cooper & Gale, P.C., Birmingham
205 254 1855
hhosch@maynardcooper.com
*Featured in Banking & Finance (Alabama)*

**Practice Areas:** Mr Hosch practices in the area of public and commercial finance including representation as bond counsel in Alabama for public bodies and private organizations; representation of commercial banks, underwriters, and placement agents in public financings in southeastern United States; and counsel in Alabama to public bodies for incentives for economic development, levy of taxes and assessments, and preparation of legislation and constitutional amendments.

**Professional Memberships:** American, Alabama State and Birmingham Bar Associations; National Association of Bond Lawyers; American College of Bond Counsel.

**Career:** Admitted in Alabama.

**Personal:** Vanderbilt University (BA, 1976); Vanderbilt University School of Law (JD, 1982).

### ISOM, Chervis
Baker, Donelson, Bearman, Caldwell & Berkowitz, PC, Birmingham
205 250 8302
cisom@bakerdonelson.com
*Featured in Real Estate (Alabama)*

**Practice Areas:** Former Chair of firm's Real Estate Group. Emphasis on development, leasing, financing and disposition of real estate including retail, office, industrial, residential and mixed use properties.

**Professional Memberships:** Member, American College of Mortgage Attorneys; Member, American, Alabama and Birmingham Bar Associations; Associate Member, International Council of Shopping Centers.

**Career:** Joined Berkowitz, Lefkovits, 1967; Partner, 1972; merged, Baker Donelson, 2003. Forty-six years with same firm. Practice concentrated in real estate, development and finance. Best Lawyers in America since 1987. Alabama Super Lawyer.

**Personal:** Birmingham-Southern College, BA, 1962. Cumberland School of Law, Samford University, JD, 1967, Curia Honoris.

### KILLEBREW, Denise
Baker, Donelson, Bearman, Caldwell & Berkowitz, PC, Birmingham
205 250 8320
dkillebrew@bakerdonelson.com
*Featured in Real Estate (Alabama)*

**Practice Areas:** Denise Killebrew has over 20 years of experience in the acquisition, development and financing of real estate, as well as in land use planning, financial structuring and restructuring, public/private partnerships and public policy matters.

**Professional Memberships:** Birmingham and American Bar Associations. Alabama State Bar, Virginia State Bar. Associate Member, International Council of Shopping Centers.

**Career:** Licensed in Alabama and Virginia. Listed in The Best Lawyers in America and Alabama Super Lawyers in Real Estate Law.

**Personal:** University of Alabama School of Law, JD, 1985. Mary Baldwin College, BA, 1980.

### LACY JR, Peyton
Ogletree, Deakins, Nash, Smoak & Stewart, PC, Birmingham
205 328 1990
peyton.lacy@ogletreedeakins.com
*Featured in Labor & Employment (Alabama)*

**Practice Areas:** Represents employers in labor and employment law - trial and appeal of cases before state and federal courts, agencies, arbitration advocacy, contract negotiations, and strike injunctions.

**Professional Memberships:** Alabama, American and District of Columbia Bar Associations; various US Courts of Appeals; National Association, College & University Counsel.

**Career:** Trial attorney, NLRB; labor and employment counsel, Fortune 500 paper company; private practice, labor and employment law since 1981; Adjunct Professor, labor law, University of Alabama.

**Publications:** Papers for L & E Law conferences; Co-author, Alabama Employers Handbook.

**Personal:** University of Alabama (BA Jn, 1962), School of Law (LLB, 1965).

### LAMAR, Jayna Partain
Maynard, Cooper & Gale, P.C., Birmingham
205 254 1048
jlamar@maynardcooper.com
*Featured in Bankruptcy/Restructuring (Alabama)*

**Practice Areas:** Bankruptcy, workouts and creditors' rights. Ms Lamar regularly represents banks, financial institutions, other lenders and creditors in commercial bankruptcy or reorganization proceedings, loan workouts, foreclosures and debt restructuring efforts. She also handles large commercial collections, defends lender liability allegations, and litigates commercial, contractual and intercreditor disputes, preference defenses and fraudulent conveyance actions in bankruptcy proceedings and in state and federal courts.

**Professional Memberships:** American, Alabama and Birmingham Bar Associations; American Bankruptcy Institute; Turnaround Management Association; IWIRC

**Career:** Admitted in Alabama.

**Personal:** University of Alabama (BA, 1985 summa cum laude); Vanderbilt University School of Law (JD, 1988).

### LEACH JR, John N
Helmsing, Leach, Herlong, Newman & Rouse, PC, Mobile
251 432 5521
jnl@helmsinglaw.com
*Featured in Litigation (Alabama)*

**Practice Areas:** Commercial disputes, business litigation and professional liability.

**Professional Memberships:** Member of the American, Alabama and Mobile Bar Associations (past President of Mobile Bar Association); Fellow of the American College of Trial Lawyers (past Chair of its State Committee as well as the American Board of Trial Advocates); Fellow of the Alabama Law Foundation.

**Career:** Vanderbilt University, BA in 1963 (cum laude); University of Virginia School of Law, JD in 1966. Law Clerk for US District Judge Virgil Pittman in the Southern District of Alabama 1966-1968.

**Personal:** Born in Gadsden, Alabama in 1941.

### LOWRY, Kris
Maynard, Cooper & Gale, P.C., Birmingham
205 254 1041
klowry@maynardcooper.com
*Featured in Banking & Finance (Alabama)*

**Practice Areas:** Commercial lending; corporate finance. Mr Lowry's experience includes representation, at various times, of lenders and borrowers in the negotiation and documentation of a variety of secured and unsecured transactions, including structured finance transactions, multistate transactions, and syndicated transactions. He has extensive knowledge of the UCC, particularly Article 9 (Secured Transactions).

**Professional Memberships:** American, Alabama and Birmingham Bar Associations.

**Career:** Admitted in 1987. Practice group leader for firm's Finance and Real Estate Group. Listed in The Best Lawyers in America and Alabama Super Lawyers.

**Personal:** University of Tennessee at Martin, highest honors (1984); Vanderbilt University School of Law (1987).

### LUPINACCI, Timothy M
Baker, Donelson, Bearman, Caldwell & Berkowitz, PC, Birmingham
205 244 3835
tlupinacci@bakerdonelson.com
*Featured in Bankruptcy/Restructuring (Alabama)*

**Practice Areas:** Represents special servicers, banks, financial institutions and asset-based lenders in sophisticated and complex loan workouts and insolvency. Emphasis on creative restructuring of problem loans, including healthcare defaults. Extensive experience with workouts and bankruptcies involving defaulted CMBS loans.

**Professional Memberships:** Birmingham and American Bar Associations (Section of Business Law Council). American Bankruptcy Institute. CRE Finance Council (formerly CMSA).

**Career:** Licensed in Alabama. Listed in Best Lawyers in America since 2004 (Bankruptcy and Creditor-Debtor Rights Law). Contributing editor, Norton Bankruptcy Law & Practice 3d.

**Personal:** Vanderbilt University School of Law, JD, 1991. The University of Montevallo, BA, 1988, cum laude.

### MCMILLAN, Murphy
Baker, Donelson, Bearman, Caldwell & Berkowitz, PC, Birmingham
205 244 3825
mmcmillan@bakerdonelson.com
*Featured in Real Estate (Alabama)*

**Practice Areas:** Shareholder in the Real Estate/Finance group who focuses on helping clients acquire, finance and develop real estate and infrastructure projects, including distressed real estate and loans secured by real estate. Many projects involve alternative financing, such as public private partnerships.

**Professional Memberships:** Member: Birmingham, Alabama and American Bar

Associations. Fellow: American Bar Foundation. Associate Member: International Council of Shopping Centers (ISCS). Member: ISCS Alliance Advisory subcommittee. Co-founder: Alabama Retail Alliance.
**Career:** Alabama, 1995.
**Personal:** University of Alabama Law School, JD, 1995.

### MEYERSON, Edward P
Baker, Donelson, Bearman, Caldwell & Berkowitz, PC, Birmingham
205 250 8334
emeyerson@bakerdonelson.com
*Featured in Litigation (Alabama)*
**Practice Areas:** Leader of the Construction Practice Group, concentrates his practice in the areas of construction law, litigation and mediation and arbitration.
**Professional Memberships:** Member, American and Birmingham Bar Associations. Board of Directors, American College of Construction Lawyers. Member, National Panel of Arbitrators and Mediators, American Arbitration Association. Steering Committee Board Member, American Bar Association Forum on Construction. Member, Board of Bar Commissioners for the Tenth Judicial Circuit, Place No 5.
**Career:** Licensed in Alabama and Florida since 1969.
**Personal:** Cumberland School of Law of Samford University, JD, 1969. University of Tampa, BA, 1964.

### MILLER, Carole G
Maynard, Cooper & Gale, P.C., Birmingham
205 254 1096
cmiller@maynardcooper.com
*Featured in Labor & Employment (Alabama)*
**Practice Areas:** Ms Miller represents employers with regard to a wide variety of employment-related claims, specializing in financial institutions and the securities industry. She regularly appears before FINRA and courts throughout the country. She also conducts training, drafts policies and handbooks, and counsels employers with respect to various employment issues.
**Professional Memberships:** Chambers USA; Best Lawyers of America; Alabama Super Lawyers as a Top 50 Lawyer; Member - Securities Industry & Financial Markets Assoc., Compliance and Legal Society.
**Personal:** Samford University (BS, 1992); The University of Alabama School of Law (JD, 1995), both summa cum laude; AV rated- Martindale Hubbell.

### MINISMAN JR, B G
Baker, Donelson, Bearman, Caldwell & Berkowitz, PC, Birmingham
205 250 8305
bminisman@bakerdonelson.com
*Featured in Corporate/Commercial (Alabama)*
**Practice Areas:** Practice concentrated in corporate, securities and health law. Extensive experience in mergers and acquisitions and representing public companies, including compliance with proxy solicitation and periodic reporting require-

ments, tender offers, corporate governance and going-private transactions. Practice also includes representation of a variety of closely-held companies, including healthcare companies.
**Professional Memberships:** Member, American, Alabama and Birmingham Bar Associations. Member, Order of the Coif.
**Career:** Licensed in Alabama since 1970.
**Personal:** University of North Carolina, BA, 1967. Emory University School of Law, JD, 1970, with distinction.

### MITCHELL, Chris
Maynard, Cooper & Gale, P.C., Birmingham
205 254 1160
cmitchell@maynardcooper.com
*Featured in Labor & Employment (Alabama)*
**Practice Areas:** Mr Mitchell represents management in a wide variety of labor, EEO and employment matters. His experience includes advising management on union organizing issues, negotiating union contracts and handling labor-management arbitrations. In addition, he has tried over 30 employment discrimination cases to successful jury verdicts and has extensive experience in appellate courts.
**Career:** Admitted to practice before Federal and State courts in Alabama and Georgia, the US Supreme Court, and numerous Federal Courts of Appeals.
**Personal:** Georgia Tech (BS, 1970 summa cum laude); University of Alabama School of Law (JD, 1973).

### MORROW, Randall
Maynard, Cooper & Gale, P.C., Birmingham
205 254 1047
rmorrow@maynardcooper.com
*Featured in Banking & Finance (Alabama)*
**Practice Areas:** Commercial lending; real estate; financial institutions; energy and natural resources. Mr Morrow's commercial lending practice focuses on the representation of lenders and borrowers in secured and unsecured transactions, structured financing transactions and multistate transactions. His real estate practice focuses on the representation of sellers and purchasers in real estate acquisitions, development, financing and leasing matters.
**Professional Memberships:** American, Alabama and Birmingham Bar Associations; American College of Mortgage Attorneys, Fellow.
**Career:** Admitted in Alabama (1988). Listed in 'The Best Lawyers in America' and Alabama 'Super Lawyers'.
**Personal:** Vanderbilt University (BA, 1985); Vanderbilt University School of Law (JD, 1988).

### MULVANEY, Michael
Maynard, Cooper & Gale, P.C., Birmingham
205 254 1076
mmulvaney@maynardcooper.com
*Featured in Litigation (Alabama)*
**Practice Areas:** Insurance Practice and bad faith litigation; class action and complex litigation; product liability litigation; wrongful death litigation; general commercial litigation. Mr Mulvaney has a national trial practice, focusing on the defense of complex claims against the insurance

and financial services industry. He has been involved in the litigation of a broad range of cases as well as specializing in insurance fraud, bad faith, product liability, and personal injury cases.
**Career:** Admitted in Alabama and Mississippi.
**Personal:** Auburn University (BA, 1987); The University of Alabama School of Law (JD, 1990).

### NELSON, Carol Sue
Maynard, Cooper & Gale, P.C., Birmingham
205 254 1119
cnelson@maynardcooper.com
*Featured in Labor & Employment (Alabama)*
**Practice Areas:** Ms Nelson handles employment litigation and advises clients on employment issues. She counsels clients in the healthcare, insurance and financial industries, as well as manufacturing entities and municipalities on EEO, FMLA, ADA, FLSA, and affirmative action issues. She handles arbitrations and represents clients in administrative matters before the EEOC and the OFCCP.
**Professional Memberships:** American, Alabama, and Birmingham Bar Associations; Litigation Counsel of America, Fellow; Alabama Supreme Court Committee on Rules of Conduct and Canons of Judicial Ethics.
**Career:** Chambers USA; Best Lawyers; Martindale-Hubbell AV Preeminent Rating
**Personal:** Auburn University (BA, 1974); Cumberland School of Law (JD, 1977).

### O'NEILL, Mary Beth
Maynard, Cooper & Gale, P.C., Birmingham
205 254 1093
boneill@maynardcooper.com
*Featured in Real Estate (Alabama)*
**Practice Areas:** Real Estate; Energy and Natural Resources (comprehensive representation of owners, landlords, tenants and developers; acquisition, development, financing, land use planning and leasing; significant experience in mineral and mining transactions, medical and commercial office transactions, and hospital and medical facility transactions); Intellectual Property & Technology (intellectual property licensing and complex contracting; significant experience with financial institutions and healthcare entities); General Corporate.
**Career:** Recognized in Chambers USA, The Best Lawyers in America, Alabama Super Lawyers; Martindale-Hubbell AV Preeminent Rating.
**Personal:** Auburn University (BA, 1985); University of Alabama School of Law (JD, 1988).

### PENNINGTON, James C
Ogletree, Deakins, Nash, Smoak & Stewart, PC, Birmingham
205 714 4430
james.pennington@ogletreedeakins.com
*Featured in Labor & Employment (Alabama)*
**Practice Areas:** Labor and employment law, education law, class action defense, benefits litigation. Represents management in court and administrative proceedings. Develops policies, procedures and programs for avoiding labor and employment legal problems.
**Professional Memberships:** ABA (Labor and Employment Law), Alabama State Bar (Labor and

Employment Law), National Association of College and University Attorneys, SHRM.
**Career:** Shareholder Ogletree Deakins since 1997. Previously partner Lange, Simpson, Robinson & Somerville. Admitted in U.S. Supreme Court, Alabama Courts, U.S. Court of Appeals (Eleventh Circuit), U.S. District Court (All Alabama Districts).
**Personal:** Vanderbilt School of Law (JD, 1990); Birmingham Southern College (BA, cum laude, 1987).

### PORTER, Maibeth
Maynard, Cooper & Gale, P.C., Birmingham
205 254 1049
mporter@maynardcooper.com
*Featured in Litigation (Alabama)*
**Practice Areas:** Commercial litigation; insurance litigation; banking and fiduciary litigation; products liability litigation; appellate work.
**Professional Memberships:** American Bar Association, Alabama State Bar, Birmingham Bar Association, International Academy of Trial Lawyers, Litigation Counsel of America.
**Career:** Admitted in Alabama.
**Personal:** University of the South (Sewanee) (BA, 1977); Vanderbilt University School of Law (JD, 1980).

### POWELL IV, Charles A
Littler Mendelson, PC, Birmingham
205 421 4700
cpowell@littler.com
*Featured in Labor & Employment (Alabama)*
**Practice Areas:** Discrimination and Harassment Litigation and Jury Trials Wage and Hour Competition and Trade Secret Law Training Compliance, Ethics, Leadership
**Professional Memberships:** Member, Labor and Employment Law Section - American Bar Association Member, Equal Employment Opportunity Committee - American Bar Association Member, Railway and Airline Labor Law Committe - American Bar Association Member, Employer Council - American Bar Association 2009-2013 Co-chair, EEO Committee Government Liaison Program - American Bar Association, 2001-present Member, Labor and Employment Law Section - Alabama State Bar Member, Labor and Employment Law Section - Florida Bar Member, Birmingham Bar Association Fellow, American Bar Association Chair, McWane Science Center Secretary/ founding board member, Cultural Alliance of Greater Birmingham
**Personal:** University of Alabama School of Law, JD, 1992; MPA, 1989 Vanderbilt University, BA, 1987 Eagle Scout

### PRUITT, Eric
Baker, Donelson, Bearman, Caldwell & Berkowitz, PC, Birmingham
205 244 3836
epruitt@bakerdonelson.com
*Featured in Bankruptcy/Restructuring (Alabama)*
**Practice Areas:** Represents banks, CMBS special servicers and lenders in bankruptcy and real estate matters, particularly in restructuring and workouts of commercial loan transactions. Experienced in healthcare loan workouts, as well

as in maximizing value for creditors through loan sales and foreclosure, collateral recovery and the subsequent disposition of assets (REO).
**Professional Memberships:** Member: American Bar Association, American Bankruptcy Institute, Commercial Real Estate Finance Council, Turnaround Management Association (Alabama Chapter, Board Member)
**Career:** Alabama, 1998.
**Personal:** University of Alabama School of Law, JD, 1998. New York University School of Law, LLM in Taxation, 2011.

### SCOTT, John W
Scott Dukes & Geisler, PC, Birmingham
205 244 2501
jscott@scottdukeslaw.com
*Featured in Litigation (Alabama)*
**Practice Areas:** Banking and financial services; commercial litigation; toxic tort and environmental liability; class actions; professional and fiduciary liability; insurance coverage litigation. Mr Scott's practice focuses on the defense of business and management.
**Professional Memberships:** Defense Research Institute; The Conference on Consumer Finance Law (Member of Governing Committee); Alabama Defense Lawyers Association; ACA International.
**Career:** Admitted in Alabama (1996) and the District of Columbia (1989). Founding Member of Scott Dukes & Geisler, P.C. (2000).
**Personal:** Born 24 April 1960 in Birmingham, Alabama; JD Tulane University School of Law (1989), Order of the Coif; BA University of Virginia (1982).

### SELLERS, Randal H
Starnes Davis Florie LLP, Birmingham
205 868 6019
rsellers@starneslaw.com
*Featured in Litigation (Alabama)*
**Practice Areas:** Over 30 years of experience dedicated to civil litigation in state and federal courts, including complex commercial litigation, intellectual property, healthcare, professional medical liability, and long-term care.
**Professional Memberships:** Fellow, American College of Trial Lawyers; Diplomate, American Board of Trial Advocates; Member, Defense Lawyers Association; Member, Birmingham, Alabama and American Bar Associations. Randy has been selected by his peers for inclusion in The Best Lawyers in America; named to Benchmark's Litigation Stars; and selected for inclusion in Alabama Super Lawyers.
**Career:** Admitted to the Alabama Bar in 1981. Randy is a Senior Partner at Starnes Davis Florie, LLP and has tried more than 175 complex civil cases to a jury verdict.
**Personal:** Graduated from Vanderbilt University, cum laude, with a BA degree in 1978. Graduated from Vanderbilt University Law School in 1981.

### SEXTON, Robert R
Maynard, Cooper & Gale, P.C., Birmingham
205 254 1032
rsexton@maynardcooper.com
*Featured in Real Estate (Alabama)*

**Practice Areas:** Commercial lending; real estate. Mr Sexton's lending practice focuses on representing lenders in loan transactions secured primarily by real estate. His Real Estate Practice focuses on representing sellers and purchasers in the acquisition, development, financing and leasing of income producing properties.
**Professional Memberships:** American, Alabama State and Birmingham Bar Associations; American College of Mortgage Attorneys, Fellow.
**Career:** Admitted in Alabama. Listed in Best Lawyers in America® since 1995 in real estate. Listed in Chambers since 2003 in real estate. Listed in Alabama Super Lawyers.
**Personal:** Birmingham-Southern College (BA, 1971); University of Alabama School of Law (JD, 1974).

### SHEPPARD, Lee
Maynard, Cooper & Gale, P.C., Birmingham
205 254 1185
lsheppard@maynardcooper.com
*Featured in Real Estate (Alabama)*
**Practice Areas:** Real estate; commercial lending; construction. Mr. Sheppard represents clients in commercial real estate matters including the acquisition, development and disposition of real estate, including office buildings, industrial sites, undeveloped land, and other commercial properties. In addition, Mr Sheppard represents lenders and borrowers in secured, structured and unsecured commercial lending transactions. He also advises owners, developers, contractors and design professionals in commercial construction matters.
**Professional Memberships:** American, Alabama, Florida and Birmingham Bar Associations.
**Career:** Alabama Super Lawyers.
**Personal:** Auburn University (BA, 1996); University of Alabama School of Law (JD, 2002 Magna Cum Laude, Editor in Chief Alabama Law Review).

### SHEVIN, Maurice L
Sirote & Permutt PC, Birmingham
205 930 5149
mshevin@sirote.com
*Featured in Banking & Finance (Alabama)*
**Practice Areas:** Banking and Finance Law; Corporate Law and Financial Services. Shareholder in the firm's Business and Financial Services Practice Group. Serves as counsel for trade associations, financial institutions and business clients. Advises numerous local, regional and national real estate, finance and consumer credit clients with respect to federal and state consumer credit protection laws and regulations.
**Professional Memberships:** Member, American, Alabama and Birmingham Bar Associations. Fellow of the American College of Consumer Financial Services Lawyers.
**Career:** JD, University of Alabama School of Law, 1977 (Hugo L. Black Scholar). Martindale-Hubbell AV rated. Best Lawyers in America for Banking, Corporate, Mergers & Acquisitions and Securities Law. Alabama Super Lawyers for Consumer Law, Real Estate and Business/Corporate Law. Birmingham Magazine

Top Attorney for Consumer Finance. Best of US for Real Estate, Insurance and Commercial Litigation Law. Birmingham Business Journal "Birmingham's Best Lawyers." General Counsel to the Alabama Lenders Association and Modern Financial Services Association. Member, Conference on Consumer Finance Law. Adjunct Professor, Consumer Protection, University of Alabama School of Law 2012 and 2013.
**Publications:** Author, "Increased Government Regulations on the Banking Industry," Birmingham Business Journal. Author, "What to Expect From Financial Reform," Birmingham Business Journal. Author, "What RESPA Servicers Need to Know About Qualified Written Requests," Insight: Mortgage Law. Author, "Mortgage Market Meltdown and its Consequences," The Counselor. Chapter Author, "The Real Estate Settlement Procedures Act," Basic Mortgage Law Cases and Materials, Second Edition. Author, "Exotic Loans Roundtable," Mortgage Originator, 2006. Author, "Doing What's Right," Legal Outlook, Equity Magazine. Author, "Keeping an Eye on the States," Legal Outlook, Equity Magazine.
**Personal:** BA, Washington University, 1973. JD, University of Alabama School of Law, 1977. Member, Alabama Holocaust Commission and the Alabama Advisory Committee to the United States Commission on Civil Rights. Former Chair, Jewish Community Relations Committee. Former President, Temple Beth-El. Former Vice President, Birmingham Jewish Federation. Former Board Member of the Cahaba Girl Scout Council, Childcare Resources, Anti-Defamation League—Southeast Region, and Levite Jewish Community Center.

### SIGMAN, Adam J
Sirote & Permutt PC, Birmingham
205 930 5755
asigman@sirote.com
*Featured in Real Estate (Alabama)*
**Practice Areas:** Real estate development, leasing and finance, and business and tax planning for closely held businesses and real estate companies. Attorney in the firm's Corporate Tax Group. Focuses on real estate and project finance, representing developers and investors in connection with retail, office, industrial, hotel, multi-family and mixed-use properties. Extensive experience with acquisitions, land use planning, leasing, financing, public incentives and negotiating with anchor tenants.
**Professional Memberships:** American Bar Association (Chairman, Ethics Committee, RPTE Section), Alabama State Bar Association, Birmingham Bar Association, International Council of Shopping Centers.
**Career:** University of Southern California Gould School of Law, (JD, 1998). Vanderbilt University (BA, 1995, magna cum laude, Phi Beta Kappa). Admitted in Alabama (1998). Martindale Hubbell AV rated. Best Lawyers in America for Real Estate Law (2008-12), Alabama Super Lawyers for Real Estate (2011-12) and a 2010 Alabama Rising Star in Real Estate. Birmingham Business Journal's Top 40 Under 40, 2006.

**Publications:** Presenter, "Hot Topics from the Ethics Corner," ABA/RPTE Spring Symposium, 2012. Presenter, "Ethics for the Real Estate Lawyer," Samford University Cumberland School of Law seminar: Trends in Commercial Real Estate, 2010. Author and Editor, "The Ethics Corner," Property & Probate Magazine (a publication of ABA/RPTE) 2010-2011. Presenter, "Acquisition and Development Due Diligence," Lorman Education Services: Strategic Planning for Shopping Centers and the Commercial Lease in Alabama, 2003-04.
**Personal:** Board of Directors, Urban Development Group, 2010-11; Board of Directors, Camp Smile-A-Mile, 2003-08; Board of Directors, Zoning Board of Adjustment of the City of Birmingham, 2002-04. Member, Temple Emanu-El, 1998-present.

### SIMONETTI, D J
Baker, Donelson, Bearman, Caldwell & Berkowitz, PC, Birmingham
205.250.8311
djsimonetti@bakerdonelson.com
*Featured in Corporate/Commercial (Alabama)*
**Practice Areas:** D. J. Simonetti concentrates his practice in the areas of corporate and business law, employee benefits and executive compensation.
**Professional Memberships:** Birmingham and American Bar Associations.
**Career:** Licensed in Georgia and Alabama. Listed in The Best Lawyers in America since 1995 in corporate law and employee benefits law.
**Personal:** Vanderbilt University, JD, 1979. Wharton School of the University of Pennsylvania, BS (cum laude), 1975.

### SKLAR, Bradley J
Sirote & Permutt PC, Birmingham
205 930 5152
bsklar@sirote.com
*Featured in Corporate/Commercial (Alabama)*
**Practice Areas:** Current Board Member and Shareholder of Sirote & Permutt, P.C. Past co-chair of the Firm's Corporate and Tax Practice Group. Focuses on tax, entity and business planning transactions, including mergers, acquisitions, sales of businesses, real estate fundings, raising capital and navigation of state and local tax issues. Counsels clients in tax and business planning, succession planning and entity formations for development and business structuring. Co-ordinates planning of transactions to maximize tax benefits, reduce risk and comply with tax law at local, state and federal levels, including incentive and economic development opportunities.
**Professional Memberships:** Member, Alabama State Bar, Tax Section, Past Chair, 1997-98
**Career:** JD, University of Alabama School of Law, 1987. LLM in Taxation, New York University, 1988. Joined Sirote & Permutt, P.C. in 1988 and became a Shareholder in 1992. Currently serves on the firm's Board of Directors. Martindale Hubbell AV rated. Birmingham Magazine, Top Attorney, Tax Law. Best Lawyers in America, Tax Law. Best of US, Real Estate & Tax Law. Corporate Counsel Magazine, Best Lawyers in America, Tax

Law. Alabama Super Lawyers, Tax Law. Birmingham Business Journal's, Best of the Bar, Corporate and Securities. Alabama Law Foundation, Fellow - 2012. American Institute on Federal Taxation, Trustee and named Co-Chair in 2013. Birmingham Business Alliance Trustee; Chair, Finance and Taxation Committee 2011-2012; Federal Tax Clinic, Board Member and Chair, 2009. Birmingham Tax Forum, President 1999-00. Birmingham School of Law, Adjunct Professor of Taxation, 1990-97.

**Publications:** Co-Reporter and Principal Draftsperson for the Alabama Limited Liability Company Act (passed 1993); Has served for 20 years on the Alabama Law Institute Drafting Committee for Alabama Business Entity Statutes. Author, "The Alabama Limited Liability Act," Alabama Law Review VOL 45, No. 1 Author, "Limited Liability Companies, Alabama Society of Certified Public Accountants," The Alabama CPA Newsletter VOL III, No.12 Author, "The Alabama Limited Liability Act: A New Entity Choice," Journal of Commercial Lending Author, "The Alabama Limited Liability Act: A New Entity Choice," The Alabama Lawyer VOL 54, No. 4 Author, "The Limited Liability Company: A New Type of Borrowing Entity," The Journal of Commercial Lending VOL 76, No. 7 Author, "Limited Liability Company Update. 'Happy' Birthday," The Alabama Lawyer, Fall Edition

**Personal:** BBA in Accounting from the University of Texas, 1984 JD, University of Alabama School of Law, 1987. LLM in Taxation, New York University, 1988. Board Member: Mountain Brook Board of Education; American Cancer Society (Corporate Chair; 2009 Hope Gala); REV Birmingham/Operation New Birmingham. Board Member and Past Vice President: Birmingham Jewish Federation, recipient Joanie Plous Bayer Young Leadership Award, 2002; Past Member of Birmingham Jewish Foundation Board. Past Board Member, Executive Committee, and Building Committee: Temple Emanu-El; Grafman Endowment Fund Board Member. Community Leadership Activities: United Way Tocqueville Campaign 2012; Leadership Alabama (2009-10); Leadership Birmingham (2000-2001); Project Corporate Leadership (1998); Birmingham Chamber of Commerce, Leadership Development (1992); Monday Morning Quarterback Club; Leadership Birmingham (2001).

## SMITH, David M
Maynard, Cooper & Gale, P.C., Birmingham
205 254 1059
dsmith@maynardcooper.com
*Featured in Labor & Employment (Alabama)*

**Practice Areas:** Mr Smith is a labor and employment litigator, representing management. He has 31 years of experience and is a Practice Group Leader of the firm's 20-lawyer L&E group. Mr. Smith handles major cases against private plaintiffs and the US Department of Labor in discrimination, FLSA, mine/workplace safety and other labor-related subjects. During 2009-2010, he was in three FLSA jury trials for 22 weeks.

**Professional Memberships:** ABA (Labor Section) and Alabama Bar.
**Career:** Law clerk, US District Judge Robert B Propst, 1982-83.
**Personal:** Birmingham-Southern College (BA, 1979 Phi Beta Kappa); Vanderbilt University School of Law (JD, 1982).

## SMITH, Jodie
Maynard, Cooper & Gale, P.C., Birmingham
205 254 1109
jodie.smith@maynardcooper.com
*Featured in Banking & Finance (Alabama)*

**Practice Areas:** Mr Smith's practice focuses on public finance, securities, healthcare, and general corporate. His practice includes work on public offerings and private placements of securities, restructuring securities previously issued, and tax-advantaged financings such as deals eligible for New Markets Tax Credits. Mr Smith also advises clients on corporate governance, mergers and acquisitions, corporate reorganizations, and joint ventures and partnerships.

**Professional Memberships:** American, Alabama, Georgia, and Birmingham Bar Associations; National Association of Bond Lawyers (Chair, Securities Law and Disclosure Committee); American Health Lawyers Association.
**Personal:** Birmingham-Southern College (BA, 1989); University of North Carolina School of Law (JD, 1995).

## SOMERVILLE III, William G
Baker, Donelson, Bearman, Caldwell & Berkowitz, PC, Birmingham
205 250 8375
wsomerville@bakerdonelson.com
*Featured in Labor & Employment (Alabama)*

**Practice Areas:** Practice concentrated in litigation, employment law and gaming law. Defends employers in matters ranging from class action discrimination cases to wage and hour investigations. Handles a variety of complex and commercial cases on behalf of corporate litigants.
**Professional Memberships:** Birmingham, Alabama and American Bar Associations. Listed in Best Lawyers in America (L&E and Commercial Litigation).
**Career:** Licensed in Alabama. AV Peer Review Rated by Martindale-Hubbell. Law Clerk to Hon. Seybourn H. Lynne, U.S. District Court, N.D. Ala., 1986-87.
**Personal:** University of Alabama School of Law, JD, 1986 (Editor in Chief, Alabama Law Review, 1985-86). Harvard College, BA, 1983.

## ST CLAIR, Jay D
Littler Mendelson, PC, Birmingham
205 421 4700
jstclair@littler.com
*Featured in Labor & Employment (Alabama)*

**Practice Areas:** Complex Litigation and Jury Trials; Appellate Practice; Wage and Hour; Labor Management Relations; Workplace Safety and Health (OSHA & MSHA)
**Professional Memberships:** Fellow, College of Labor and Employment Lawyers; Former Chair, Alabama State Bar, Labor and Employment Law

Section; Adjunct Professor, Cumberland School of Law; Member, Alabama Bar
**Personal:** JD, Yale Law School, 1983; BA, University of Tennessee, 1980 Office Managing Shareholder

## STALLCUP, Stephen
Maynard, Cooper & Gale, P.C., Birmingham
205 254 1053
sstallcup@maynardcooper.com
*Featured in Real Estate (Alabama)*

**Practice Areas:** Real estate; commercial lending. Mr Stallcup's practice focuses on all aspects of the representation of buyers, sellers, developers, landlords and tenants in all types of real estate matters, including acquisition, development, financing and leasing matters as well as all aspects of the representation of lenders in secured, unsecured and multistate transactions.
**Professional Memberships:** ICSC; Recognized in Best Lawyers of America for Real Estate, Banking and Finance.
**Personal:** University of Alabama (BS, 1993); Jasons Senior Honor Society; University of Alabama School of Law (JD, 1996); AV rated by Martindale Hubbell.

## STEWART, Donald
Cabaniss, Johnston, Gardner, Dumas & O'Neal, Mobile
251 415 7303
djs@cabaniss.com
*Featured in Bankruptcy/Restructuring (Alabama)*

**Practice Areas:** Bankruptcy and Creditor-Debtor Rights Law, Municipal Law, Zoning and Land Use Planning.
**Professional Memberships:** American Bankruptcy Institute; the Section of Bankruptcy and Commercial Law of the Alabama Bar; International Municipal Lawyers Association, the Section of State and Local Government Law of the American Bar Association;& the Alabama Association of Municipal Attorneys.
**Career:** Listed in the Municipal Law Section of The Best Lawyers in America, and in Best Lawyers' as their 2011 "Mobile Banking Lawyer of the Year." He is also named by Super Lawyers magazine as a top attorney in Alabama.

## SYLVESTER, William
Baker, Donelson, Bearman, Caldwell & Berkowitz, PC, Birmingham
205 250 8372
bsylvester@bakerdonelson.com
*Featured in Real Estate (Alabama)*

**Practice Areas:** Shareholder with focus in commercial real estate and related tax law. Recent transactions involving multifamily, office and retail properties, securitized finance, tax planning, structuring the acquisition disposition of troubled properties and conservation easement transactions.
**Professional Memberships:** American Bar Association; Alabama State Bar (Real Estate Section President, 1998); Birmingham Bar Association; American Colleage of Real Estate Lawyers; Land Trust Alliance; International Council of Shopping Centers; Forum on the Construction Industry.

**Career:** Licensed in Alabama, 1978.
**Personal:** Degrees from Alabama, Georgia Tech and University of Virginia School of Law.

## UMBACH III, Arnold W
Starnes Davis Florie LLP, Birmingham
205 868 6072
tumbach@starneslaw.com
*Featured in Labor & Employment (Alabama)*

**Practice Areas:** Trip's practice focuses primarily in labor and employment law. He chairs the firm's Labor and Employment Practice Group. Trip represents both public and private employers in all types of labor and employment litigation in state court, federal court, and before administrative agencies.
**Professional Memberships:** Served as Vice-President, Legal and Legislative Affairs, Birmingham Society for Human Resource Management; listed: Best Lawyers in America; Alabama Super Lawyers.
**Career:** Clerked for the Honorable Patrick E Higginbotham, United States Supreme Court of Appeals for the Fifth Circuit, 1992-93.
**Publications:** Co-author, Alabama Supreme Court Clarifies Enforceability of No-Hire Agreements, Alabama Defense Lawyers Association Journal, October 2007; Author, Discrimination Law Developments in the Supreme Court: Sexual Harassment, Statute of Limitations for Race Claims, Age Discrimination, Americans with Disabilities Act, and the Eleventh Amendment, Employment Law Update, 2005, at 1; Co-author, Using Rule 23 to Define FLSA Class Actions: A Solution to the "Similarly Situated" Debate, Employment Law Update, 2002, at 117.
**Personal:** Born in Auburn, Alabama, 1966. Education: University of Virginia (BA 1988); University of Alabama School of Law (JD 1992).

## WATERS, Michael
Jones Walker LLP, Birmingham
205 244 5210
mwaters@joneswalker.com
*Featured in Banking & Finance (Alabama)*

**Practice Areas:** De Novo Banking; Bank and Bank Holding Company Regulatory, Compliance & Operations; Banking & Financial Services; Community Banking; Corporate & Securities; Corporate Governance; Equity & Debt Financing; Insurance Business, Regulatory & Government Relations Practice; Investment Management Legal Services.
**Professional Memberships:** Alabama Law Institute (Member, 1989 to date; Chairman, Task Force on the Revised Alabama Uniform Securities Act, 2004–2005); Farrah Law Society (Board of Trustees, 1992 to date); University of North Carolina School of Law Center for Banking & Finance (Member, Board of Advisors)
**Career:** Mr Waters is a Partner in the firm's Banking and Financial Services Practice Group and also serves as a member of its board of directors. He has practiced corporate and securities law, primarily in the financial institutions area, for more than 30 years. He has advised both buyers and sellers in approximately 80 bank mergers and acquisitions, ranging from small community

banks to the acquisition of a $34-billion holding company. He also advises banks regarding regulatory issues, examination, compliance, and enforcement proceedings.

**Personal:** Since 1994, he has served as an adjunct professor of law at The University of Alabama School of Law, where he teaches courses in banking law and corporate mergers and acquisitions.

### WRIGHT, Richard
Jones Walker LLP, Mobile
251 439 7573
rwright@joneswalker.com
*Featured in Bankruptcy/Restructuring (Alabama)*

**Practice Areas:** Banking and financial services; bankruptcy, restructuring and creditors-debtors rights; business and commercial litigation; commercial lending and finance; real estate: land use, development and finance.

**Professional Memberships:** Alabama State Bar; American Bar Association; Mobile Bar Association.

**Career:** Richard Wright's focus has been in representing financial institutions in the areas of commercial collections, mortgage foreclosures, bankruptcy, loan closings, workouts, loan restructuring, bank operations and bank regulatory matters, particularly those regarding impaired and special assets.

**Personal:** The University of Alabama School of Law, JD, 1982; The University of Alabama, BA, 1978, cum laude.

# BALCH & BINGHAM LLP

www.balch.com **tel:** 205 251 8100 **fax:** 205 226 8799

**Managing Partner & Chairman, Executive Committee:** Alan T Rogers
Number of partners: 151  Number of lawyers: 243

## Firm Overview:

Balch & Bingham LLP is a corporate law firm with offices in Birmingham and Montgomery, Alabama; Jacksonville, Florida; Atlanta, Georgia; Gulfport and Jackson, Mississippi; and Washington, DC. The firm is recognized for its deep experience serving clients in regulated industries, including energy, financial services and healthcare, and established practices in business, environmental, government relations, labor and employment and litigation. The firm's professional, collegial culture is inspired by nationally ranked attorneys who combine business intelligence and industry leadership with high-quality legal counsel to anticipate and respond to corporate challenges both creatively and proactively. They manage client partnerships with efficient processes and transparencies that result in an uncommon, efficient client experience. Balch & Bingham was founded in 1922.

## Main Areas of Practice:

### Litigation:

The firm's Litigation Practice manages a wide variety of disputes and has extensive experience appearing in state and federal courthouses, before arbitration panels and throughout a series of industries across the country. The attorneys are experienced in almost every area of law from complex commercial litigation to personal injury and products liability. This group supports the litigation needs of the firm's other practice groups, including banking, healthcare, ERISA and managed care litigation, environmental, labor and commercial disputes.
**Contact:** J Russ Campbell

### Financial Industries:

Balch & Bingham provides comprehensive services to banks, trust companies, insurance carriers, investment firms, broker-dealers and other financial institutions at the state, regional and national level. The firm represents developers, owners and mortgage lenders in commercial real estate development and has played a significant role in major real estate acquisition and sale transactions in the Southeast. The firm's Bankruptcy Practice is devoted to creditors' rights, debt restructuring, workouts, debt collection and bankruptcy.
**Contact:** Richard L Pearson

### Energy:

For over 90 years, Balch & Bingham attorneys have included some of the industry's leading practitioners representing clients before state public utility commissions, the Federal Energy Regulatory Commission and the Nuclear Regulatory Commission. The firm represents clients in matters involving the creation and operation of electric generating companies and the licensing, construction, purchase or sale of generating assets, including hydroelectric, fossil and nuclear powered facilities. The practice is also involved in the procurement of fuel and other services for these various forms of generation. They regularly represent clients in connection with the use of electric transmission and distribution systems and in transactions involving the purchase or sale of generating capacity and energy. Attorneys actively are involved in the drafting and evaluating of proposed federal and state legislation and regulations.
**Contact:** Dan H McCrary

### Business:

Balch & Bingham is actively engaged in the formation of business entities and in advising clients in a wide variety of corporate transactions, financings, and corporate law matters. Lawyers in the firm represent clients in all facets of their corporate work, including economic development and tax, estate planning, public finance, antitrust and intellectual property. The firm also regularly advises public companies with respect to Securities Exchange Act compliance and reporting responsibilities, listing and maintenance requirements for the New York and American Stock Exchanges and NASDAQ. Attorneys have advised boards of public corporations in many areas of corporate governance. The practice is also recognized for its robust healthcare industry experience including healthcare compliance, transactional, operational and regulatory legal issues.
**Contact:** J Foster Clark

### Labor & Employment

Balch & Bingham's Labor and Employment Practice offers comprehensive knowledge and a collaborative, multi-disciplinary approach to complex and routine employment matters. This group represents clients in administrative proceedings, elections, arbitrations and jury and non-jury trials in state and federal forums. Industries served include utility, construction, manufacturing, retail, banking and financial organizations as well as municipalities, school boards and universities.
**Contact:** M Jefferson Starling, III

### Environmental & Natural Resources

The Environmental & Natural Resources Practice at Balch & Bingham successfully resolves complex matters covering a wide range of federal, state and local environmental issues. With the largest environmental practice in Alabama and one of the largest in the Southeast, firm attorneys are experienced in matters involving work permitting, water law, transactions, federal compliance, endangered species and environmental litigation. Firm lawyers are actively engaged in both state and federal legislative processes impacting environmental and natural resources issues.
**Contact:** Steven G McKinney

### Government Relations:

Since its inception over 90 years ago, Balch & Bingham has been involved in politics, government relations and lobbying. The firm's attorneys and lobbyists have developed relationships with members of Congress and Administration officials over the years that have served its clients well.
**Contact:** Robin G Laurie and Tim Ford

### International Work:

The firm assists its clients as needed in transactions in foreign countries.

BALCH
& BINGHAM LLP

# BRADLEY ARANT BOULT CUMMINGS LLP

**www.**babc.com   **tel:** 205 521 8000   **fax:** 205 521 8800

**Chairman & Managing Partner:** John B Grenier
Number of partners: 257
Number of lawyers: 440
Languages: *Arabic, Bulgarian, Chinese, French, German, Hebrew, Hungarian, Macedonian, Romanian, Spanish, Vietnamese*

## Firm Overview:

With more than 440 attorneys, Bradley Arant Boult Cummings is a regional law firm with a global practice. It is not uncommon to find a Bradley Arant Boult Cummings attorney working for a major construction company in Europe or Asia, for a multinational pharmaceutical company in New York or California, for a national tire manufacturer in Tennessee and Georgia, or for a national hospital system across the country. The firm frequently serves as national coordinating counsel, regional counsel, and statewide counsel for numerous clients in various industries.

Whether the firm is helping its clients acquire real property, defend lawsuits, raise capital, comply with regulatory requirements, enter new markets, obtain and defend intellectual property rights, develop and distribute products and services, or merge or divest businesses, it treats its clients' goals as its own. When its clients are faced with disputes, the firm assembles diverse, multi-disciplinary, and industry-specific teams trained to identify and pursue the fastest and most effective solutions.

The firm is focused on providing service that incorporates clear communication, leveraging technology such as a secure client-customizable extranet to ensure project efficiency and transparency; and partnering with clients to structure fixed-fee arrangements which incentivize efficiency and promote risk management. The firm's history is one of lasting alliances with its clients which are based on quality legal work, superior value, and outstanding service.

## Clients:

Bradley Arant Boult Cummings LLP represents a diverse client base ranging from individuals to emerging business enterprises to established regional, national, and international companies, including nearly 100 of the Fortune 500 companies. The firm's attorneys serve clients operating in a variety of industries, including:

- Accounting
- Automotive
- Banking and finance
- Biotechnology
- Construction
- Education
- Emerging business
- Energy
- Equipment leasing
- Forest products
- Health care
- Insurance
- Manufacturing
- Materials and aggregate production
- Media and communications
- Mining
- Municipal and public finance
- Oil and gas
- Pharmaceuticals and medical devices
- Public utilities
- Real estate
- Retail
- Steel
- Technology
- Telecommunications
- Textiles
- Transportation
- Venture capital

## PRACTICE AREAS

Antitrust & Competition
Appellate
Banking & Financial Services
Bankruptcy, Restructuring & Distressed Investing
Class Action
Construction & Procurement
Corporate & Securities
Economic Development
Emerging Growth Companies
Employee Benefits & Executive Compensation
Energy
Environmental
Financial Services Litigation
Government Contracts
Governmental Affairs
Health Care
Immigration
Insurance
Intellectual Property
International Arbitration
Labor & Employment
Life Sciences
Litigation
Media & Entertainment
Public Finance
Real Estate
Tax
Telecommunications & Utilities
White-Collar Crime & *Qui Tam* Defense

## OFFICES

### ALABAMA
**BIRMINGHAM:** One Federal Place, 1819 Fifth Avenue North, AL 35203
Tel: 205 521 8000   Fax: 205 521 8800

**HUNTSVILLE:** 200 Clinton Avenue West, Suite 900, AL 35801-4900
Tel: 256 517 5100   Fax: 256 517 5200

**MONTGOMERY:** Alabama Center for Commerce, 401 Adams Avenue, Suite 780, AL 36104
Tel: 334 956 7700   Fax: 334 956 7701

### DISTRICT OF COLUMBIA
**WASHINGTON DC:** 1615 L. Street N.W., Suite 1350, DC 20036
Tel: 202 393 7150   Fax: 202 347 1684

### MISSISSIPPI
**JACKSON:** One Jackson Place, 188 E. Capitol Street, Suite 400, MS 39201
Tel: 601 948 8000   Fax: 601 948 3000

### NORTH CAROLINA
**CHARLOTTE:** Bank of America Corporate Center, 100 N. Tryon Street, Suite 2690, NC 28202
Tel: 704 332 8842   Fax: 704 332 8858

### TENNESSEE
**NASHVILLE:** Roundabout Plaza, 1600 Division Street, Suite 700, TN 37203
Tel: 615 244 2582   Fax: 615 252 6380

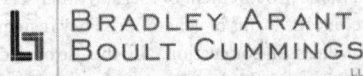

# BURR AND FORMAN LLP

**www.**burr.com   **tel:** 800 GET BURR

**Chairman:** Lee Thuston
Managing Partners: 9   Number of partners: 178   Number of lawyers: 288

**Firm Overview:**

Burr & Forman is a full service law firm with a long history of serving clients in Alabama, Florida, Georgia, Mississippi and Tennessee. The firm's forward-thinking approach allows it to provide legal solutions appropriate to the needs of its clients. With nearly 300 attorneys, Burr & Forman offers a wide range of business and litigation services to diverse clients with local, national and international interests.

**Main Areas of Practice:**

**Automotive:**
Represents automotive dealerships in claims associated with franchise agreements, breach of contract, sales and acquisitions, non-competes and wrongful termination.

**Banking & Finance:**
Represents lenders of all types in lending and financial transactions for working capital needs, refinancings, specific personal and real property asset acquisitions and development and company acquisitions in the middle and large corporate markets.

**Commercial Litigation:**
Represents financial institutions, businesses and officers and directors in complex commercial disputes and securities litigation.

**Corporate & Tax:**
Represents businesses and not-for-profits of all sizes and in all stages of development in complex business matters, mergers and acquisitions, capital raises and regulatory compliance issues.

**Creditors' Rights & Bankruptcy:**
Represents financial services institutions, asset-based lenders and local, regional and national banks in significant and complex bankruptcy proceedings.

**Construction:**
Represents owners, contractors, suppliers and design professionals in all construction-related transactional matters and in the litigation or dispute resolution of all construction claims.

**Economic Development:**
Leading economic development firm in the Southeast. Projects reflect a diversity of industries and represent over $16 billion of capital investment and over 25,000 new jobs created.

**Environmental:**
Represents industries, developers, financial institutions and individuals in environmental matters related to business strategy, permitting and regulatory compliance, litigation, sustainability, and administrative proceedings.

**Financial Services Litigation:**
Represents banks, mortgage, finance and credit card companies in all types of litigation involving deceptive loan origination, predatory lending, wrongful foreclosure, mortgage fraud and statutory violation claims.

**Health Care:**
Represents all types of health care organizations in a variety of litigation, regulatory, compliance, licensure and corporate law matters.

**Insurance Regulatory:**
Represents all types of businesses and insurance entities in connection with structuring solutions to their business insurance needs and maintaining regulatory compliance.

**Labor & Employment:**
Represents employers of all sizes in matters ranging from drafting policies and handbooks to defending against the entire gamut of employment-related claims.

**Maritime & Transportation:**
Represents clients whose businesses are in, around or near navigable waters with all types of litigation claims, financing activities, contract negotiations, employment matters and other regulatory issues.

**Products Liability:**
Represents clients in all industries with products and premises liability, personal injury, industrial and construction site accidents, pharmaceuticals, medical devices, mass torts and toxic tort cases.

**Real Estate:**
Represents commercial real estate development companies in land planning, entitlement and development, governmental incentives, title matters, acquisition and disposition and performing and distressed assets.

**Securities Litigation:**
Represents broker-dealers and investment bankers in disputes, such as mutual-fund class-actions, derivative contracts trials, government enforcement actions and constitutional challenges to municipal securities rules.

**Technology:**
Represents businesses in protection of, and licensing strategies for, intellectual property, contract negotiation, growth, investment and acquisition strategies.

## OFFICES

**ALABAMA**

**BIRMINGHAM:** 420 North 20th Street, Suite 3400, AL 35203
Tel: 205 251 3000   Fax: 205 458 5100

**MOBILE:** RSA Tower, 11 North Water Street, Suite 22200, AL 36602
Tel: 251 344 5151   Fax: 251 344 9696

**MONTGOMERY:** RSA Tower, 201 Monroe Street, Suite 1950, AL 36104
Tel: 334 241 7000   Fax: 334 262 0020

**FLORIDA**

**FT. LAUDERDALE:** Las Olas Centre I, 450 East Las Olas Boulevard, Suite 700, FL 33301
Tel: 954 414 6200   Fax: 954 414 6201

**ORLANDO:** 200 South Orange Avenue, Suite 800, FL 32801
Tel: 407 540 6600   Fax: 407 540 6601

**TAMPA:** One Tampa City Center, Suite 3200, FL 33602
Tel: 813 221 2626   Fax: 813 221 7335

**GEORGIA**

**ATLANTA:** 171 17th Street, NW Suite 1100, GA 30363
Tel: 404 815 3000   Fax: 404 817 3244

**MISSISSIPPI**

**JACKSON:** The Heritage Building, 401 E Capitol Street, Suite 100, MS 39201
Tel: 601 355 3434   Fax: 601 355 5150

**TENNESSEE**

**NASHVILLE:** 700 Two American Center, 3102 West End Avenue, TN 37203
Tel: 615 724 3200   Fax: 615 724 3290

**Clients:**

American Cast Iron Pipe Company; ADTRAN; American Suzuki Motor Corporation; Assuranceforeningen Gard-gjensidig; Bank of America; Bank of Tampa; Brasfield and Gorrie General Contractors; Brice Building Company; Budgetext; Capital One; Charles Schwab & Co., Inc.; Circle K; Citibank; City of Tampa; Coastal Forest Products; Coca-Cola Enterprises; CVS Caremark; Daniel Realty Company; Dillard's; East Alabama Medical Center; First American; Founders Insurance Company; Gray Construction; HealthSouth Corporation; Laboratory Corporation of America; Mercedes-Benz U.S. International, Inc.; M/I Homes; Millard Maritime; Morgan Keegan & Co.; National Steel Car; Nissan Motors of America, Inc.; Nutech Medical Inc.; Nu Tech Spine, Inc.; ProAssurance; RockTenn Company; Rinnai; Standard Insurance; Southpace Properties; SunTrust Mortgage; Synovus Bank; Tacala; Tenet Healthcare Corporation; Guardian Life; ThyssenKrupp; Time Insurance Company; TriNovus Capital, LLC; UAB Health Services Foundation; United States Steel; Wells Fargo Bank; Wells Fargo Advisors; Whirlpool

# CABANISS, JOHNSTON, GARDNER, DUMAS & O'NEAL LLP

www.cabaniss.com **tel:** 205 716 5200 **fax:** 205 716 5389

**Management Committee:** Crawford S McGivaren, Jr, Sydney F Frazier, Jr, Roy J Crawford

Number of partners: 28
Number of other lawyers: 8

## Firm Overview:

Recognized as the oldest continuous law practice in Birmingham and one of the oldest continuous practices in Alabama, the firm of Cabaniss, Johnston, Gardner, Dumas & O'Neal LLP has a distinguished history. The origins of the firm, which began in Birmingham in 1887, can be traced back to the firm's first lawyer, E H Cabaniss, who left the small Alabama town of Union Springs traveling to Birmingham to capitalize on the growth of industry and business in the rapidly growing southern town. There he formed Cabaniss & Banks. A merger in 1920 produced Cabaniss, Johnston, Cocke & Cabaniss. 'Cabaniss Johnston' has been a familiar and respected name in Alabama legal circles ever since.

## Main Areas of Practice:

Practice areas include bankruptcy and corporate reorganization; corporate matters including banking and financial services, contract negotiation, incorporations, joint ventures and partnerships, and mergers and acquisitions; environmental law and litigation; healthcare law; labor and employment; general litigation including antitrust, biotechnology, business torts, commercial, construction, consumer finance, contracts, employment, ERISA, franchising, fraud, insurance, intellectual property, maritime, medical malpractice, personal injury, product liability, professional liability, securities, toxic torts, trade regulation, trust and workers compensation; municipal law; real estate and timber transactions; taxation; wills, estates and trusts.

## Clients:

AAA Cooper Transportation, ABB Environmental Systems, Access Insurance Company, Air Ambulance Card, LLC, Alabama Maternity, Inc., Alabama Poultry & Egg Association, Alabama Orthopedic, Spine & Sports Medicine Associates, Alcoa, Inc., Allied Worldwide, Amsher Financial Services, Auburn University, Billy Barnes Enterprises, Birmingham Motorcycle Company, LLC, Blue Cross and Blue Shield of Alabama, Boehringer Ingelheim Pharmaceuticals, Inc., Boise Cascade Corporation, Books-A-Million, BP America, Inc., Castrol Industrial North America, Inc., CBI Services, Inc., Cemex, Inc., City of Mobile, Alabama, Clayton Homes, Inc., The Coca-Cola Company, Colsa Corporation, Coregis Insurance Company, DataBank Business Services, Inc., Dillard Department Stores, Diolen Industrial Fibers Europe, Inc., The Dixie Group, Inc.,The Doctors Company, Doster Construction Company, Inc., Dun & Bradstreet, Inc., Eastern Health System, Inc., Employers Reinsurance Corporation, First Specialty Insurance Corporation, Four Seasons Solar Products LLC, Georgia Crown, Gorrie Regan & Associates, Hillcrest Behavioral Health Systems, Holmes Oil Company, Inc., Howard Miller Clock Company, Imaging Business Machines, LLC, International Paper Company, Jasper Lumber Company, J.H. Berry & Gilbert, Inc., JP Morgan Chase Bank, Lamont Trading Advisor, Inc., Liberty Mutual Insurance Company, Liberty National Life Insurance Company, Lyondell Chemical Company, Inc., Masland Carpets, LLC, McElroy Truck Lines, Inc., McWane, Inc., Medical Center Blount, Medical Center East, Miller and Company, Milo's Tea Company, The Mitchell Company, Momma Goldberg's, MP3 Fibre, Inc., Nalco Company, Noland Health Services, Inc., Norfolk Southern Corporation, Northrop Grumman Corporation, Norwood Clinic, Inc., OfficeMax, O'Neal Steel, Inc., Parade Homebuilders, Inc., PetroNova, LLC, Plains Marketing, L.P., Providence Hospital, Red Diamond, Inc, Research Solvents and Chemicals, Inc., Resting S. Ranch, Inc., Rex Alabama, Inc., Rheem Manufacturing Company, Russo Corporation, Shoe Corporation, Sodexo Services, Inc, Southeast Physician Network, P.C., Southeast Wood Treating, Inc., Southern Energy Homes, Inc., Southern ENT & Sinus Center, P.C., Southside Surgical Specialists, St. Clair Regional Hospital, St. Vincent's Health System, SunTrust Banks, Inc., Superior Bank, Swiss Reinsurance America Corporation, Troy University , UAB Medical West, University of Montevallo, UOP , West Ellis Investment Management, Inc., West Oil, Inc., Westport Insurance Corporation, Weyerhaeuser Packaging, Inc.

## OFFICES

**ALABAMA**

**BIRMINGHAM:** 2001 Park Place North, Suite 700, AL 35203
Tel: 205 716 5200   Fax: 205 716 5389
Email: info@cabaniss.com

**MOBILE:** 63 South Royal Street, Suite 700, AL 36602
Tel: 251 415 7300   Fax: 251 415 7350

# Cabaniss Johnston
**CABANISS, JOHNSTON, GARDNER, DUMAS & O'NEAL LLP**

# CHRISTIAN & SMALL LLP

**www.csattorneys.com**

**Managing Partner:** Deborah Alley Smith
Number of partners: 30
Number of other lawyers: 9

## Firm Overview:

Christian & Small is committed to superior performance that creates value through collaboration among internal and external partners in the areas of litigation, business and tax. The firm represents a diverse clientele throughout Alabama, the southeast and across the nation. Founded in July 2000 by partners Thomas W Christian and Clarence M Small, formerly with Rives & Peterson, the firm has a solid foundation and an impressive history. Five partners are Fellows of the American College of Trial lawyers; four are Fellows of the International Academy of Trial Lawyers; four are members of the American Board of Trial Advocates; four are Fellows of the American Bar Foundation; two have served as President of the Alabama State Bar; eighteen are included in the Best Lawyers in America; and twenty are recognised as Alabama Super Lawyers. Each of the firm's lawyers is committed to providing the most vigorous, effective and cost-efficient representation available, with a continual focus on building enduring client relationships and exceeding client expectations. Christian & Small has proven itself as a leader among Alabama law firms, offering the high quality of legal representation expected from the larger firms and the client focused attention that distinguishes the best boutique firms. The firm's team approach, recruitment of top level lawyers, and investment in the most advanced technology enhances their success and efficiency. Zealous client advocacy tempered by a commitment to the highest ethical standards has secured the superior reputation in every representation the firm undertakes. These guiding principles have earned Christian & Small a distinguished place among Alabama's elite law firms.

## Main Areas of Practice:

Christian & Small's diverse practice enables the firm to provide the broad range of capabilities that clients expect from a full-service law firm. By working in practice teams, the lawyers are able to deliver innovative solutions to the legal and business problems facing their clients. The firm's practice groups are primarily divided into the areas of litigation, business and tax.

## Litigation:

Christian & Small's trial lawyers have an impressive history of earning defense verdicts. Extensive experience in a variety of state and judicial forums nationwide combined with the firm's reputation for creative and zealous client advocacy has earned Christian & Small a distinguished place in Alabama's Trial Bar. The firm matches highly experienced litigators with specific client needs so that the most innovative, effective and efficient solutions can be achieved. The firm assists clients in all stages of litigation from preventative strategies to avoid potential liability, pre-transaction counseling, alternative dispute proceedings, trial and, if necessary, appeal. Christian & Small's litigation practice encompasses virtually every area of the law including: labor and employment; medical/professional malpractice defense; product liability; business and commercial; transportation, including trucking and aviation; bankruptcy; environmental and toxic tort;

construction; white-collar criminal defense; securities; insurance and first party insurance defense; bad faith and fraud; briefing and appellate.
**Contact:** Thomas W Christian
**Email:** twc@csattorneys.com

## Business & Tax Transactions:

The corporate and business lawyers at Christian & Small handle all aspects of a business' operations through all stages of development, including real estate acquisition. They also have substantial experience managing the legal needs of individuals with small business, estate planning and tax needs. The firm's corporate and business lawyers routinely handle legal matters in the following areas: business and tax planning; business organization and reorganization; corporate and business transactions; contract disputes; employer/employee relationship agreements; real estate; wills, estate and trust planning.
**Business Contact:** Richard E Smith
**Email:** res@csattorneys.com
**Tax Contact:** Steven A Benefield
**Email:** sab@csattorneys.com

## Alternative Dispute Resolution:

The firm also has several attorneys who routinely participate in ADR proceedings as mediators and arbitrators. Consistently recognized by their peers for the strength and effectiveness of their mediation skills, the firm's attorney mediators' comprehensive knowledge of litigation, claims and the judicial process allows them to provide meaningful insight and assessment to the involved parties throughout the negotiation.
**Contact:** Kenneth O Simon
**Email:** kos@csattorneys.com

## Clients:

Christian & Small represents a diverse clientele, ranging from individuals and closely held businesses to *Fortune500* corporations. The firm's list of clients includes manufacturers, banks and financial institutions, hospitals, nursing homes and assisted living facilities, physicians, accountants, retail companies, technology companies, insurance companies, trucking companies and construction companies.

**PRACTICE AREAS**

Litigation
Business
Tax
Alternative Dispute Resolution

**OFFICES**

ALABAMA
**BIRMINGHAM:** 505 North 20th Street, Suite 1800, AL 35203
Tel: 205 795 6588 Fax: 205 328 7234

**Christian & Small**
ATTORNEYS AND COUNSELORS

# HARE, WYNN, NEWELL & NEWTON, LLP

www.hwnn.com **tel:** 205 328 5330  **fax:** 425 324 2165

**Managing Partner:** Leon Ashford
Number of partners: 10
Number of attorneys: 16
Languages: *English*

## Firm Overview:

In its second century of practice, Hare Wynn is one of the most respected plaintiffs' litigation firms in the country. The firm's success has come as a result of the unique opportunity its attorneys have had to become experienced, successful trial lawyers, as well as legal tacticians. Built on a legacy of representing ordinary people involved in significant litigation, Hare Wynn continues to build on more than a century of successful trial experience in its representation of individuals, Fortune 500 companies, small business, and government entities. In an age when fewer and fewer cases go to trial, Hare Wynn's lawyers are still arguing to juries on a regular basis. In just the last two years, ninety percent of Hare Wynn's lawyers were involved in jury trials. The verdicts in those trials exceeded $100 million.

## Main Areas of Practice:

### Aviation Crashes:

The firm actively engages in all areas of aviation law involving personal injuries and wrongful death, including litigation against the major airlines, military, general aviation, the United States government, and all aircraft manufacturers. In one of the few cases to overrule the Warsaw Convention pact, which limited damages obtainable in international airline crashes, the firm successfully demonstrated that an Aeromexico airline crew was guilty of "willful misconduct" under Alabama Law. The court ruled the state's legal definition of willful misconduct was the same under the Warsaw Convention – thereby clearing the way to overturn the pact's limitation on damages.

### Commercial & Business Litigation:

Hare Wynn represents small businesses and individuals in a variety of business litigation. This area of practice includes representation of 2,500 commercial rice farmers in a $750 million settlement against Bayer CropScience in 2011 and on behalf of HealthSouth Corporation, a derivative claim against former CEO, Richard M Scrushy, resulting in a $2.87 billion award - believed to be the largest derivative verdict against an individual in the history of American jurisprudence.

### Dangerous & Defective Drugs:

The firm has a long history of representing consumers who suffer serious injuries or death resulting from dangerous and defective drugs placed on the market by pharmaceutical companies. Hare Wynn is also heavily involved in the representation of States in their efforts to recover damages against drug manufacturers like Merck for unlawful and illegal marketing practices aimed at increasing profits. The firm currently represents the Commonwealth of Kentucky, the State of Montana, and the State of Alaska against Merck. These cases involve violations of the states' Consumer Protection Acts with respect to Merck's deceptive, false and misleading trade practices in the marketing of its controversial pain killer drug Vioxx. The firm regularly works in conjunction with the state's Attorney General's office in prosecuting these claims.

### Defective Products:

Hare Wynn has handled numerous noteworthy and groundbreaking products liability cases – both in state and federal courts. The firm recently obtained a $19.1 million dollar verdict against Ford Motor Company in the United States District Court for the Eastern District of Arkansas in Jonesboro, Arkansas, for a young man who was paralyzed in the course of a rollover of his Ford vehicle. This is believed to be a record-setting verdict for the inadvertent unlatching of a seat belt.

### False Claims / Qui Tam / Whistleblower:

Hare Wynn has battled on behalf of whistleblowers in federal district courts around the country, as well the United States Supreme Court and the Sixth, Eleventh and DC Circuit Courts of Appeal. To date, the firm has recovered and returned more than $1 billion to the United States Department of Treasury, including $422.5 million from Novartis to settle criminal and civil investigations into the marketing of the anti-seizure medicine Trileptal and five other drugs.

### Medical Malpractice:

The firm is recognized nationally for its work on behalf of injury victims and families whose medical provider has breached the standard of care in diagnosing or treating a medical condition. In 2012 alone, Hare Wynn successfully represented clients in recoveries totaling more than $20 million in medical malpractice cases.

### Motor Vehicle Accidents:

Hare Wynn has handled hundreds of automobile/trucking accident cases throughout Alabama and around the Southeast. The firm's investigators have law enforcement experience and are well trained and knowledgeable in interviewing witnesses, locating evidence, and reconstructing what occurred in a motor vehicle automobile collision. They are available at a moment's notice in these cases.

### Nursing Home Abuse & Neglect:

Hare Wynn's lawyers take great pride in handling these cases on behalf of families whose loved ones have been harmed. Hopefully, such efforts will force the nursing home industry to clean up its act and provide the level of care, treatment and staffing their residents deserve. In 2012, a Hare Wynn client was awarded a jury verdict of $8 million in a nursing home abuse and neglect case in Kentucky.

### Wrongful Death:

Hare Wynn has a long and highly successful track record of representing clients in wrongful death cases at trial. The firm recently tried a personal injury case under Alabama's Dram Shop Act, which prohibits the unlawful sales of alcohol to minors. The jury returned a $3.75 million verdict in favor a teenager who was injured in a motor vehicle collision after the underage driver had made multiple purchases of alcohol at a local convenience store.

## PRACTICE AREAS

Aviation Crashes
Catastrophic Personal Injury
Commercial & Business Litigation
Dangerous & Defective Drugs
Defective Products
False Claims Act / Qui Tam / Whistleblower
Medical Malpractice
Motor Vehicle Accidents
Nursing Home Abuse & Neglect
Securities Fraud
Wrongful Death

## OFFICES

**ALABAMA**
**BIRMINGHAM:** The Historic Massey Building
2025 Third Avenue North, Suite 800, AL 35203
Tel: 205 328 5330  Toll Free: 800 568 5330
Fax: 205 324 2165

**ARKANSAS**
**LITTLE ROCK:** 2226 Cottondale Lane, Suite 210, AR 72202
Tel: 501 225 5500  Toll Free: 877 225 6312
Fax: 501 225 5501

**KENTUCKY**
**LEXINGTON:** 200 West Vine Street, Suite 700, KY 40507
Tel: 859 550 2900  Toll Free: 855 202 2628
Fax: 859 550 2902

# HARE | WYNN
### NEWELL & NEWTON

# HELMSING, LEACH, HERLONG, NEWMAN & ROUSE LLP

**www.**helmsinglaw.com **tel:** 251 432 5521 **fax:** 251 432 0633

**Managing Partner:** Jim Newman
Number of partners: 15  Number of lawyers: 18

**Firm Overview:**
Founded in 1976 when successful partners from larger firms joined together to create a small firm offering a diverse array of legal services, the firm has maintained its small firm personality along with its large firm capabilities. While primarily devoted to handling litigation matters, the firm also has extensive experience in several other areas of law.

## Main Areas of Practice:

**Alternative Dispute Resolution (ADR):**
**Contact:** Jim Newman **Tel:** 251 432 5521
**Email:** jbn@helmsinglaw.com

**Appellate:**
▪ State and federal court brief writing and appeals
**Contact:** Jim Newman **Tel:** 251 432 5521
**Email:** jbn@helmsinglaw.com

**Banking & Finance:**
▪ Counsel for borrowers and lenders in all types of financing arrangements
**Contact:** Robert Rouse **Tel:** 251 432 5521
**Email:** rhr@helmsinglaw.com

**Bankruptcy/Creditor's Rights:**
▪ Creditor's rights, workouts and insolvency litigation
▪ Representation of asset-based lenders and financial service institutions
▪ Representation of bankruptcy trustees, examiners and other fiduciaries
▪ Creditor and corporate debtor business insolvencies
**Contact:** Jeffery Hartley **Tel:** 251 432 5521
**Email:** jjh@helmsinglaw.com

**Corporate/Mergers & Acquisitions:**
▪ Create, maintain, reorganize, liquidate and dissolve corporations, partnerships, limited liability companies, joint ventures, professional corporations and associations
▪ Corporate acquisitions and mergers
**Contact:** Charlie Mixon **Tel:** 251 432 5521
**Email:** crm@helmsinglaw.com

**Eminent Domain/Condemnation:**
▪ Representation of landowners and condemning agencies throughout the State of Alabama
▪ Direct and inverse condemnation actions
**Clients:** Alabama Power Company; Florida Gas Transmission Company; landowners
**Contact:** Warren Herlong **Tel:** 251 432 5521
**Email:** wch@helmsinglaw.com

**Employment & Labor:**
**Contact:** Jim Newman **Tel:** 251 432 5521
**Email:** jbn@helmsinglaw.com

**Healthcare Law:**
▪ Administrative and regulatory compliance
▪ Medicare and Medicaid fraud defense
**Contact:** Alan Alexander **Tel:** 251 432 5521
**Email:** raa@helmsinglaw.com

**Insurance:**
▪ Representation of insurance companies in coverage disputes and extra-contractual litigation
▪ Insurance defense of insureds
**Clients:** State Farm, Baldwin Mutual
**Contact:** Jim Newman **Tel:** 251 432 5521
**Email:** jbn@helmsinglaw.com

**Land Use & Zoning:**
**Contact:** Casey Pipes **Tel:** 251 432 5521
**Email:** jcp@helmsinglaw.com

**Litigation – Aviation:**
**Contact:** Jim Newman **Tel:** 251 432 5521
**Email:** jbn@helmsinglaw.com

**Litigation – Commercial:**
▪ Bet-the-company litigation experience
**Clients:** Hunt Petroleum; Parsons & Whittemore Enterprise Corporation
**Contact:** Jim Newman **Tel:** 251 432 5521
**Email:** jbn@helmsinglaw.com

**Litigation – Construction:**
▪ Representation of contractors, developers, engineers and suppliers in all phases of construction including environmental issues
▪ Enforcement and defense of construction liens
**Clients:** Sherwin Williams, Thompson Engineering
**Contact:** Russell Buffkin **Tel:** 251 432 5521
**Email:** rcb@helmsinglaw.com

**Litigation – Medical Malpractice Defense:**
▪ Representation of hospitals, nurses, and medical professionals in malpractice claims
**Clients:** Infirmary Health, Providence Hospital, Ascension Health
**Contact:** Alan Alexander **Tel:** 251 432 5521
**Email:** raa@helmsinglaw.com
**Contact:** Win Stuardi **Tel:** 251 432 5521
**Email:** aes@helmsinglaw.com

**PRACTICE AREAS**
Banking & Finance
Bankruptcy/Creditor's Rights
Corporate/M&A
Insurance
Litigation
Real Estate/Eminent Domain

**OFFICES**
ALABAMA
**MOBILE:** PO Box 2767, AL 36652
Tel: 251 432 5521   Fax: 251 432 0633

**Litigation – Products Liability:**
▪ Aircraft, automobiles, boats, household appliances, power tools, pharmaceutical products, medical devices, surgical supplies, tires, motor homes, paper-making machinery, wire rope, heavy machinery, engines, and other types of products
▪ Representation of manufacturers and distributors of products in toxic tort cases and class actions
▪ Represented Kumho Tire at trial and on appeal in the case where the United States Supreme Court clarified the admissibility of expert witness opinions - Kumho Tire Co. v Carmichael, 119 S.Ct.1167 (1999)
▪ National and state counsel in multi-district litigation
▪ Served on national, state and science teams for pharmaceutical and medical device companies
**Contact:** Joe Babington **Tel:** 251 432 5521
**Email:** jpb@helmsinglaw.com

**Municipal Law:**
▪ Representation of cities and municipal entities
▪ Representation of contractors, developers and owners before municipal entities
**Contact:** Casey Pipes **Tel:** 251 432 5521
**Email:** jcp@helmsinglaw.com

**Real Estate Law:**
▪ Residential and commercial transactions
▪ Landlords and tenants
▪ Condominiums and Developers
▪ Title insurance claims and defense
**Contact:** John Dukes **Tel:** 251 432 5521
**Email:** jtd@helmsinglaw.com

**Tax, Trust, Estate & Probate:**
▪ Individual and corporate tax advice, estate planning, trusts and all aspects of Probate proceedings
**Contact:** Robert Rouse **Tel:** 251 432 5521
**Email:** rhr@helmsinglaw.com

**White-Collar Criminal Defense:**
**Contact:** Patrick Finnegan **Tel:** 251 432 5521
**Email:** pcf@helmsinglaw.com

# LIGHTFOOT, FRANKLIN & WHITE LLC

www.lightfootlaw.com **tel:** 205 581 0700 **fax:** 205 868 6099

**Managing Partner:** Adam Peck
Number of partners: 33
Number of other attorneys: 26

## Firm Overview:

Lightfoot, Franklin & White, LLC was founded on January 15, 1990, and presently has over 50 lawyers. The firm's size allows it to provide for clients the best of all worlds – the resources and technology of a nationwide firm, and the efficiency and individuality of a regional firm.

In order to concentrate on what the firm does best, its attorneys focus solely on civil litigation matters, with the exceptions of also assisting clients with environmental compliance advice, issues concerning white-collar crime, NCAA compliance matters, and conducting internal investigations. The firm handles all types of civil litigation in state and federal courts across the United States, and its primary areas of practice include commercial disputes, product liability, antitrust, consumer fraud, appeals, intellectual property, catastrophic personal injury and death, environmental/toxic torts, class actions, professional malpractice, securities fraud, employment and communications.

## Main Areas of Practice:

**Appellate:**
Contact: Chris King

**Business Litigation:**
Contact: Sam Franklin

**Catastrophic Injury:**
Contact: Lee Hollis

**Environmental & Mass Torts:**
Contact: Johnny Johnson

**Medical Malpractice:**
Contact: Mike Bell

**NCAA Compliance:**
Contact: William King

**Pharmaceuticals, Medical Devices & Healthcare:**
Contact: Harlan Prater

**Product Liability:**
Contact: Adam Peek

## Clients:

Lightfoot, Franklin & White represents numerous *Fortune* 500 clients in a broad range of industries. The firm's clients have interests spanning the globe, comprising some of the largest corporations in the United States and abroad as well as universities across the country. The firm's clients are involved in industries as diverse as product, chemical, and pharmaceutical manufacturing, communications and media, insurance and financial services, healthcare, and energy, and they rely on the firm to be there when it matters. Some representative clients include: Chartis Inc. (formerly AIG), BASF Corporation, Bristol-Myers Squibb Company, Deere & Company, E.I. du Pont de Nemours & Company, Emerson Electric Co., ExxonMobil Corporation, General Electric Company, Hyundai Motor Company, and JPMorgan Chase & Company.

LIGHTFOOT
LIGHTFOOT FRANKLIN WHITE LLC
TRIAL & APPELLATE COUNSEL

# MAYNARD, COOPER & GALE, P.C.

www.maynardcooper.com

**Managing Partner:** Mark L Drew
Number of Partners: 140  Number of other attorneys: 88

## Firm Overview:

Founded in 1984, Maynard, Cooper & Gale, P.C., is a full-service law firm with over 220 attorneys, one of the largest law firms in the State of Alabama. The firm's client base ranges from numerous *Fortune* 500 companies to a broad range of closely held companies, partnerships, professional associations, charities and individuals. Maynard Cooper attorneys have held numerous leadership positions in varying professional organizations. At the national level, two of the firm's partners have served as president of the 400,000 member American Bar Association, (2008-09 and 1996-97), three are former Chairs of the 74,000 member Litigation Section of the ABA and one is past chair of the ABA's Criminal Justice Section. In addition, one Maynard Cooper shareholder is a past-President of the American College of Trust and Estate Counsel. At the state and local levels, Maynard Cooper's attorneys include a former Chief Justice of the Alabama Supreme Court and a special counsel to the current Governor of Alabama. In addition, one of the firm's attorneys is the 2013-14 President of the Alabama State Bar, and three of the firm's current and former attorneys have served as President of the Birmingham Bar Association.

## Main Areas of Practice:

### Banking & Finance:

Maynard Cooper regularly advises banks, bank holding companies, and other financial institutions on a wide range of matters. The firm represents banks and financial institutions of all sizes – from large regional holding companies to smaller publicly held and closely-held bank holding companies and community banks.
**Key Clients:** Regions Bank, National Bank of Commerce, IberiaBank
**Contact:** Kris Lowry  **Tel:** 205 254 1041
**Email:** klowry@maynardcooper.com

### Bankruptcy/Restructuring:

Maynard Cooper's Bankruptcy, Workouts and Creditors' Rights group primarily represents creditors (including banks and other secured lenders, trade creditors, judgment creditors and creditors' committees) in bankruptcy matters and work-out situations. However, the firm also represents borrowers in debt restructurings and workouts, and debtors in complex bankruptcy and insolvency proceedings on a select basis.
**Key Clients:** Regions Bank; PNC Bank, National Association
**Contact:** Jayna P Lamar  **Tel:** 205 254 1048
**Email:** jlamar@maynardcooper.com

### Corporate/Commercial:

Maynard Cooper's corporate attorneys assist clients in the structuring, formation and financing of a wide range of public and private companies. The firm regularly advises clients on the negotiation of mergers, acquisitions, joint ventures and divestitures of their business interests. Maynard Cooper has significant experience in private equity fund formation and private equity financing, mergers and acquisitions. The firm frequently acts as outside general counsel and assists clients with business planning, succession planning, ownership and management issues, corporate governance, incentive compensation and commercial law matters. Several of the firms attorneys specialize in international corporate transactions.
**Key Clients:** McWane, Inc., Baptist Health System, Inc., Torchmark Corporation
**Contact:** Christopher B Harmon  **Tel:** 205 254 1090
**Email:** charmon@maynardcooper.com

### Employment:

Devoted exclusively to the representation of management in all aspects of labor and employment law, Maynard Cooper's Labor and Employment Group is one of the largest and most experienced in the Southeast. The firm's attorneys regularly assist clients with employment litigation and arbitration, administrative proceedings, preventive counseling and compliance assistance, labor relations and compliance with federal and state employment laws.
**Key Clients:** Baptist Health System, Inc., Tyson Foods, Inc., Walter Energy, Inc.
**Contact:** Stephen E Brown  **Tel:** 205 254 1023
**Email:** sbrown@maynardcooper.com

### Litigation:

Maynard Cooper represents clients before state and federal courts and arbitration panels throughout the United States with regard to: antitrust and trade regulation; appellate and post-verdict; class action; complex litigation; environmental; insurance sales practice; intellectual property and technology; product liability; securities litigation; and other general litigation matters.
**Key Clients:** Regions Financial Corporation, Protective Life Corporation, Clayton Homes, Inc.
**Contact:** John Bolus  **Tel:** 205 254 1025
**Email:** jbolus@maynardcooper.com

### PRACTICE AREAS

Appellate Litigation
Banking
Bankruptcy
Class Action Litigation
Commercial Lending & Project Finance
Corporate
Economic Development & Incentives
Employee Benefits & Exec. Compensation
Environmental
ERISA & Group Insurance Litigation
Estates & Trusts
Government Contracts
Governmental & Regulatory Affairs
Healthcare
Insurance & Financial Services Litigation
Intellectual Property & Technology
International Trade Regulation
Labor & Employment
Litigation
Mergers & Acquisitions
Private Equity & Venture Capital
Product Liability
Public Finance
Real Estate
Securities
Securities Litigation
Tax
White-Collar Criminal Practice

### OFFICES

**ALABAMA**
**BIRMINGHAM:** 1901 Sixth Avenue North, 2400 Regions / Harbert Plaza, AL 35203-2618
Tel: 205 254 1000  Fax: 205 254 1999

**HUNTSVILLE:** 655 Gallatin Street, AL 35801
Tel: 256 551 0171  Fax: 256 512 0119

**MOBILE:** 11 N. Water Street, Suite 27000, AL 36602
Tel: 251 432 0001  Fax: 251 432 0007

**MONTGOMERY:** RSA Union Building, 100 North Union Street, Suite 650, AL 36104
Tel: 334 262 2001  Fax: 334 262 2043

### Real Estate:

The attorneys in Maynard Cooper's Real Estate group regularly represent clients regarding virtually every aspect of real estate and real estate development. The firm's real estate practice includes representation of clients in the following types of transactions: acquisition and development of commercial and residential property; land use; mining; leasing; financing; tax planning and other incentives; timber law; and other related services.
**Key Clients:** Harbert Management Corporation, Johnson Development, LLC, Education Corporation of America
**Contact:** Thomas C Clark III  **Tel:** 205 254 1072
**Email:** tclark@maynardcooper.com

# SIROTE & PERMUTT, P.C.

www.sirote.com **tel:** 205 930 5100 **fax:** 205 930 5101

**CEO:** John H Cooper
Shareholders: 76
Other Attorneys: 34

## Firm Overview:

Sirote & Permutt is a full-service law firm focused on serving its clients in the business and financial services industries. It represents clients throughout the United States from its offices in Birmingham, Huntsville and Mobile, Alabama and Fort Lauderdale and Pensacola, Florida.

Since its founding in 1946, Sirote attorneys have held numerous leadership positions in professional organizations. In 2013, four shareholders were inducted into the Fellows of the Birmingham Bar Foundation, and another shareholder was chosen as a Fellow of the Alabama Law Foundation. Three attorneys have served as President of the Birmingham Bar Association, and a shareholder currently serves as 2013 President. The law firm is recognized as a Best Law Firm by the 'Best Lawyers in America 2013', which also selected 42 Sirote attorneys for legal excellence.

Sirote has developed strong client relationships by providing quality, sophisticated legal services.

## Main Areas of Practice:

The law firm's 115 attorneys in 15 practice areas handle corporate transactions, business and financial services, estate planning and litigation on behalf of *Fortune* 500 companies, family-owned businesses, charities and high net-worth individuals.

**Appellate Law:**
Thomas A Woodall

**Banking & Financial Services:**
Steven A Brickman

**Business & Corporate Services:**
Joseph T Ritchey

**Mortgage Banking:**
Jerry E Held

**Estates, Wills & Trusts:**
Craig M Stephens

**Health Care:**
Lenora W Pate

**Litigation:**
Robert R Baugh
J Rushton McClees

**Mediation & Arbitration:**
Marty Van Tassel

## Clients:

Sirote & Permutt is one of the largest full-service law firms in the Southeast. Sirote offers a diversified practice to an equally diversified client base of small and emerging businesses, publicly traded companies, individuals, trusts, estates and charitable institutions. Firm clients include financial institutions, developers and builders, securities underwriters, municipalities, physician groups, hospitals, professional services, insurers, manufacturers and trade associations.

## International Work:

Sirote & Permutt is Alabama's only member of the Law Firm Alliance, an international association of more than 50 law firms, which by membership gives the firm access to high quality local experts throughout the world.

## PRACTICE AREAS

Appellate Litigation
Banking & Finance
Bankruptcy & Reorganization
Business & Corporate Services
Commercial Transactions & M&A
Conservation Easements
Construction Law
Consumer Finance & Creditors' Rights
Corporate & Regulatory Compliance
Economic Development
Elder Care Law
ERISA & Bad Faith Insurance
Estate & Tax Planning
Health Care Law
Incentive Planning
Intellectual Property
Labor & Employment
Legislative & Governmental Affairs
Litigation
Mediation & Arbitration
Mortgage Banking
Nonprofits & Trade Associations
Privacy & Data Security
Probate, Estate & Trust Litigation
Real Estate Law
Regulatory Compliance
Securities & Corporate Governance
Special Needs Planning
Tax – Federal, State and Local
White Collar Criminal Defense

## OFFICES

### ALABAMA

**BIRMINGHAM:** 2311 Highland Avenue South, AL 35205
Tel: 205 930 5100   Fax: 205 930 5101
Email: bham@sirote.com

**HUNTSVILLE:** 305 Church Street, Suite 800, AL 35801
Tel: 256 536 1711   Fax: 256 518 3681
Email: huntsville@sirote.com

**MOBILE:** One St. Louis Centre, Suite 1000, AL 36602
Tel: 251 432 1671   Fax: 251 434 0196
Email: mobile@sirote.com

### FLORIDA

**FORT LAUDERDALE:** 200 East Broward Blvd. Suite 900, FL 33301
Tel: 954 828 1100   Fax: 954 828 1101

**PENSACOLA:** 1115 East Gonzalez Street, FL 32503
Tel: 850 462 1500   Fax: 850 462 1599
Email: pensacola@sirote.com

# SPOTSWOOD SANSOM & SANSBURY LLC

**www.**spotswoodllc.com **tel:** 205 986 3620 **fax:** 205 986 3639

**Managing Partner:** Robert K. Spotswood
Number of partners: 4
Number of lawyers: 7
Languages: English

## Firm Overview:

Spotswood Sansom & Sansbury is a boutique law firm specializing in complex, business litigation. Since its founding in 2001, Spotswood Sansom has taken on some of the most important legal issues facing business in America, litigating class actions in Southern Illinois, punitive damages awards in Oregon, and wage-and-hour suits in California. It has represented clients in the US Supreme Court, seven of the thirteen US Courts of Appeal, and in state appellate courts across the country. In its home state of Alabama, Spotswood Sansom has been involved in virtually every high-profile, complex litigation matter in recent years. Spotswood Sansom offers clients a comprehensive approach to complex business litigation, considering the big picture and creating effective strategies to meet its clients' need – whether that need is early resolution, cost-effective litigation, or vindication of important legal principles.

## Main Areas of Practice:

### Complex Litigation:

- Obtained $64 million jury verdict in federal court based on allegations of tortious interference with contractual and business relations. The verdict was #38 on list of the Top 100 Verdicts of 2012 by the National Law Journal
- Obtained summary judgment for the defendant on federal overtime claims in a putative nationwide class and collective wage-and-hour action involving temporary employees. The outcome turned on innovative arguments regarding the scope of the Motor Carrier Act exemption and the result provided valuable precedent for motor carriers nationwide
- Developed a national litigation strategy for wage-and-hour class and collective actions asserting joint-employment theories. Obtained precedential opinions from several different courts, which eliminated potentially viable class liability theories
- Obtained judgment in federal district court on five of six counts and on punitive damages in a multi-million dollar business dispute using preemption defenses available to the transportation industry. Remainder of case was dismissed on appeal
- Defeated request in federal district court for preliminary injunction on behalf of an out-of-state manufacturer of hybrid batteries for the automobile industry
- Obtained pre-certification dismissal of a putative nationwide ERISA class action and putative New England state law class action alleging that a motor carrier jointly employed certain drivers who worked for independent transportation services contractors
- Extensive experience in litigation of complex intellectual property claims, especially involving misappropriation of trade secrets.

**Contact:** Robert K Spotswood **Tel:** 205 986 3621
**Email:** rks@spotswoodllc.com
**Contact:** Michael T Sansbury **Tel:** 205 986 3623
**Email:** msansbury@spotswoodllc.com

### Appellate Practice:

- Representing amicus curiae in a case now pending before the US Supreme Court that involves preemption issues affecting both the air and ground transportation industries
- Representing the Commodity Markets Oversight Coalition as amicus curiae before the US Court of Appeals for the DC Circuit in support of rules establishing position limits in commodities futures markets
- Representing National Conference of State Legislatures as amicus curiae before the US Court of Appeals for the Eleventh Circuit regarding legislative privilege
- Represented a group of intellectual property law professors as amicus curiae before the US Court of Appeals for the Eleventh Circuit in a case involving "fair use" copyright issues
- Appeal in Oregon state court resulted in precedent-setting opinion that reduced a $7 million punitive damages award to $1.05 million
- Successfully petitioned for writ of certiorari to the US Supreme Court to review a Second Circuit decision regarding what constitutes the "charge" that must be submitted by an employee before he or she can sue under the Age Discrimination in Employment Act
- Briefed the First Circuit and the US Supreme Court, on behalf of amicus curiae, on important issues of federal preemption under the Federal Aviation Authorization Administration Act (FAAAA). The First Circuit and the Supreme Court both adopted the position advocated by the firm
- Obtained a writ of mandamus on novel jurisdiction and venue theories that forced a trial court in a "judicial hellhole" to transfer the case to a more appropriate venue. Case was dismissed shortly thereafter

**Contact:** Kenneth D Sansom **Tel:** 205 986 3622
**Email:** ksansom@spotswoodllc.com
**Contact:** Emily J Tidmore **Tel:** 205 986 3625
**Email:** etidmore@spotswoodllc.com

## PRACTICE AREAS

Antitrust & Competition
Banking & Finance
Commercial Litigation
Constitutional Claims
Contract Disputes
Derivative Litigation & Shareholder Disputes
Director & Officer Liability
Insurance
Intellectual Property & Trade Secrets
Internal Investigations
Labor & Employment
Partnership Dissolution
Racketeer Influenced & Corrupt Organizations Act (RICO) Claims

## OFFICES

ALABAMA
**BIRMINGHAM:** One Federal Place, 1819 Fifth Avenue North, Suite 1050, 35203
Tel: 205 986 3620  Fax: 205 986 3639
Email: rks@spotswoodllc.com

# STARNES DAVIS FLORIE LLP

**www.**starneslaw.com **tel:** 205 868 6000 **fax:** 205 868 6099

**Managing Partner:** Walter W Bates
Number of partners: 44
Number of other attorneys: 16

### Firm Overview:

Since 1975 Starnes Davis Florie LLP has grown to be one of the largest firms in Alabama devoted exclusively to litigation. With 60 attorneys, the firm continues to commit itself to a diverse civil litigation practice. With its principal office in Birmingham and a second office in Mobile, the firm regularly handles litigation matters throughout the United States. Its attorneys try to verdict a high number of complex jury trials and rank among the most experienced litigators in the South. Four of the firm's partners are Fellows of the American College of Trial Lawyers, seven of its partners are members of the American Board of Trial Advocates, seventeen of its attorneys are listed in the Best Lawyers in America, and twenty-two of its attorneys are listed in Alabama Super Lawyers. From healthcare to consumer finance, from product liability to telecommunications, Starnes Davis Florie's capabilities span virtually every area of complex litigation.

### Clients:

Abercrombie & Fitch; ACE USA; ADS Construction, Inc.; Alabama Municipal Insurance Corp.; ALAS; Allianz – Life; Allied Home Mortgage Capital Corp.; Altec Industries, Inc.; American Contractors Insurance Group; American Equity Underwriters, Inc.; American Family Insurance Group; American Longshore Mutual Association Ltd.; American Southern Insurance Company; Arch Insurance Co.; Ascension Health Care; Asset Acceptance LLC; Atlantic United Construction Co.; Autry Greer & Sons, Inc.; Ball Healthcare Corp.; Banks Finley White & Co., P.C.; Bass Underwriters; Behavioral Health Systems; Berkley Regional Insurance Company, Inc.; Books-A-Million; Buffalo Rock Co.; Carl Warren & Company; Central State Bank; Chartis; Chubb Group Insurance; Cincinnati Insurance Company; Citigroup Global Markets Inc.; Citigroup Financial Products Inc; CitiMortgage Inc.; Citigroup Mortgage Loan Trust Inc.; Citicorp Mortgage Securities Inc.; CNA Insurance Co.; CNA Surety; Cohen Carnaggio Reynolds; Cooper Marine and Timberlands; Cooper/T Smith Corp; Correctional Medical Services, Inc.; Corizon, Inc; Crowne Management, LLC; Danaher Corporation; Deutsche Bank AG; Diversicare; Document and Packaging Brothers, Inc.; Dollar Tree Stores, Inc.; Drummond Co., Inc.; Farmers Insurance Co.; Feld Entertainment, Inc.; Fidelity and Deposit Co. of Maryland; Fidelity and Guaranty Insurance Co.; Fleet Securities, Inc.; Food Giant Supermarkets, Inc.; Gallagher Bassett Services; Gates Corporation; GE Capital Corporation; GE Healthcare Financial Services, Inc.; Gentiva Health Services; Georgia Pacific Corporation; GlaxoSmithKline Plc.; Goldman, Sachs & Co.; Golden Living; Gorrie-Regan & Associates, Inc.; Great American Insurance Co.; Guarantee Insurance Company; Hanover Insurance Co.; Harbert Management Corporation; Hart & Cooley, Inc.; Hartford Insurance; Hek Manufacturing BV; Hendon & Huckestein Architects, PC; Hennessy Industries, Inc.; Herrington Architects; Hibbett Sports, Inc.; Homeowners Loan Corp.; Hudson Advisors; Iberia Bank; Independent Marine Consultants; Insurance Company of the West; Jackson-Renfro & Associates; Jim Barnes Enterprises, Inc.; J.P. Morgan Securities Inc.; Kemper Insurance Co.; Kohlberg, Kravis, Roberts & Co.; Liberty Mutual; Liberty Mutual Surety; Lifeguard Transportation Service, Inc.; Live Nation; Marcus & Millichap Real Estate Investment Services, Inc.; Markel Insurance Co.; Marshall Bankfirst Corp.; Marshall Financial Inc.; Marshall Investments Corporation; Meadowbrook ASI Insurance Group; Mediacom Southeast, Inc.; Millenium Risk Managers; Mobile Fixture & Equipment Company, Inc.; Mortgage Contracting Services, LLC; Mr. Appliance Corp.; Murphy Oil USA, Inc.; NationsBanc Montgomery Securities LLC; National Bank of Commerce; National Healthcare Association, Inc.; NBC Securities, Inc.; NHS Management, LLC; North American Coal Co.; Ohio Casualty; Old Republic Surety Co.; Patriot National Insurance Group; Phoenix America Insurance; PNC Bank, National Association; ProAssurance, Inc.; ProAssurance Indemnity Co.; Research Solvents & Chemicals, Inc.; RLI Insurance Company; Robinson-Adams; RSUI; Saad's Healthcare Services; Scottsdale Insurance Company; Sherwin-Williams Company; Sony Computer Entertainment America, Inc.; St. Paul/Travelers; St. Vincent's Health System; State Farm Insurance Co.; Stonebridge Life Insurance Co.; Syncora Guarantee Inc.; The Marshall Group; Thermasys Corporation; Timberline Homes; T-Mobile; Travelers Insurance Co.; Twin Pines Coal Co., Inc.; UBS Securities, LLC; Ullico Casualty Company; University of Alabama; University of Alabama at Birmingham; University of Alabama Health Services Foundation; Verizon; Verizon Wireless; Vinson Guard Service, Inc.; Walter Energy, Inc.; Warren Averett, LLC; Western Heritage Insurance Company; Western Surety Co.; Westfield Insurance Group; Winn-Dixie Stores, Inc.; Zurich Insurance Co.

## PRACTICE AREAS:

Civil Defense Litigation:
Admiralty & Maritime Litigation
Alternative Dispute Resolution (Arbitration & Mediation)
Appellate & Written Advocacy
Aviation
Banking & Financial Services
Biotechnology & Pharmaceutical
Business Litigation
Class Actions & Mass Torts
Collegiate Sports (NCAA Compliance & Investigations and Collegiate Sports Licensing)
Complex Insurance Litigation
Construction Litigation
Dram Shop / Liquor Liability Litigation
Energy & Natural Resources
Environmental Litigation & Regulatory Compliance
Federal Black Lung Litigation
Fidelity & Surety Litigation
General Civil Litigation
Governmental & Public Litigation
Hospitality & Retail Litigation
Intellectual Property
Labor & Employment
Legal Malpractice
Long Term Care & Nursing Home Litigation
Long Term Care & Other Healthcare Regulatory Compliance
Medical Malpractice Defense
Mining & Mineral Law
Product Liability & Consumer Litigation
Professional Liability
Professional Licensing Defense
Securities Litigation
Telecommunications
Toxic Torts
Workers' Compensation

## OFFICES

ALABAMA

**BIRMINGHAM:** 100 Brookwood Place, 7th floor, PO Box 598512, AL 35259
Tel: 205 868 6000   Fax: 205 868 6099

**MOBILE:** RSA Battle House Tower, 11 North Water Street, Suite 20290, PO Box 1548, AL 36633
Tel: 251 433 6049   Fax: 251 433 5901

## How lawyers are ranked

Every year we carry out thousands of in-depth interviews with clients in order to assess the reputations and expertise of business lawyers worldwide. The qualities we look for (and which determine rankings) include technical legal ability, professional conduct, client service, commercial awareness/astuteness, diligence, commitment, and other qualities most valued by the client. For details of our research team, see p.5.

### Contents:

# CORPORATE/M&A

Commentary about individuals can be found under their firm's paragraph. If the firm has no paragraph (is not ranked) look at Other Notable Practitioners.

### Corporate/M&A
### Leading Firms

**Band 1**
Birch, Horton, Bittner & Cherot
Davis Wright Tremaine LLP *
Dorsey & Whitney LLP *

**Band 2**
Durrell Law Group, PC

### Leading Individuals

**Band 1**

| | |
|---|---|
| Black Kathryn A | Birch, Horton, Bittner & Cherot * |
| Blumstein Philip | Landye Bennett Blumstein LLP (ONP) † |
| Dawson Jon S | Davis Wright Tremaine LLP |
| Durrell Brian | Durrell Law Group, PC |
| Reece Joseph | Davis Wright Tremaine LLP |
| Rosston Richard | Dorsey & Whitney LLP |
| Sneed Spencer | Dorsey & Whitney LLP |

**Band 2**

| | |
|---|---|
| Kraft Barbara Simpson | Davis Wright Tremaine LLP |
| Mills Michael | Dorsey & Whitney LLP |
| Parise Michael J | Lane Powell PC (ONP) † * |
| Tindall John H | Tindall Bennett & Shoup PC (ONP) † |
| Turner Terrance A | Turner & Mede, PC (ONP) † |

### Corporate/M&A: Bankruptcy
### Leading Individuals

**Band 1**

| | |
|---|---|
| Bundy David H | David H Bundy PC (ONP) † |
| Christianson Cabot | Christianson & Spraker (ONP) † |
| Mills Michael | Dorsey & Whitney LLP |
| Parise Michael J | Lane Powell PC * |
| Siemers John C | Burr, Pease & Kurtz, PC (ONP) † |
| Sneed Spencer | Dorsey & Whitney LLP |

\* Indicates firm / individual with profile.
† ONP = Other Notable Practitioner.

## Band 1

### Birch, Horton, Bittner & Cherot

**THE FIRM** During its 40 years of activity, this firm has developed significant expertise in general corporate and M&A matters. Combining a deep knowledge of Alaska law with nationwide expertise, the team often assists firms in other states on local laws. A recent notable transaction involved its representation of a major communications company.

**KEY INDIVIDUALS Kathryn Black** (see p.492) mainly represents financial institutions, and covers every aspect of the sector from bankruptcy to real estate financing and banking law. She also specializes in business and resource development.

### Davis Wright Tremaine LLP
See profile on p.2544

**THE FIRM** This versatile team represents public utilities, healthcare clients, native corporations, mining companies and various fishing companies, among others. The diversity of its client base lends the firm an added level of broad-ranging expertise. The team's recent highlights include its role on behalf of Chugach, Alaska in relation to breach of fiduciary duty claims.

**Sources say:** *"A solid firm with broad service capacity. Knowledgeable and effective."*

**KEY INDIVIDUALS Jon Dawson** is particularly experienced in commercial transactions, M&A, real estate, IP matters and civil litigation. One impressed client said: *"He has valuable insight into our operations; we do not risk the loss of his knowledge and expertise on legal matters."* Among his most recent work is a complex transaction for marine bulk fuel supplier Vitus Marine. **Joseph Reece** specializes in commercial, corporate and real estate law. Clients describe him as *"efficient and quick, with a very impressive background."* They also add that *"he is a man of tremendous integrity, and he has so much experience in this field."*

**Barbara Simpson Kraft** has a superb reputation in the corporate and finance law areas. She is also involved in real estate development and land use law, and has considerable experience representing healthcare companies.

### Dorsey & Whitney LLP
See profile on p.1583

**THE FIRM** Dorsey & Whitney is able to provide interdisciplinary advice due to the team's varied experience and far-reaching capabilities, and it offers counsel for all types of M&A transactions. Among its recent highlights is an M&A transaction for Cruz Holdings.

**Sources say:** *"The firm is professional and dedicated."*

**KEY INDIVIDUALS Michael Mills** is a renowned corporate and bankruptcy lawyer. He recently represented Bristol Bay Native Corporation in an M&A mission lodge acquisition, and also acted for Chenega Corporation in a complicated stock purchase transaction. **Richard Rosston** is described by peers as a *"great practitioner with a lot of knowledge of finance and corporate transactions."* He is a recognized expert in the field and has led major financing transactions as well as a number of M&A matters. **Spencer Sneed** is a top name in the field. He focuses on financing transactions as well as commercial and gas and oil litigation. He recently represented Alaska Central Express in an aircraft acquisition and financing transaction.

## Band 2

### Durrell Law Group, PC

**THE FIRM** This expanding practice attracts a range of clients from various corporations and nonprofit organizations. The main areas of focus of the firm are business law and estate planning.

**KEY INDIVIDUALS Brian Durrell** is the founder of the firm. In addition to his solid expertise in business law, he has the added knowledge of estate and gift tax matters.

## Other Notable Practitioners

**Philip Blumstein** of Landye Bennett Blumstein LLP is an established name in the field. He represents various private and public entities in commercial and real estate transactions, and works extensively with municipalities. **David Bundy** of David H Bundy PC focuses on business law and is widely renowned for his bankruptcy expertise, representing both debtors and creditors, within Alaska and further afield. **Michael Parise** (see p.493) of Lane Powell PC undertakes M&A, commercial law, business litigation and loan transactions. He also handles oil and gas exploration financing, mining lease matters and timber sale contracts. **John Siemers** of Burr, Pease & Kurtz, PC is a commercial law expert and litigator focusing predominantly on bankruptcy. He has notable experience in tax issues, especially in the oil industry, as well as a deep knowledge of real estate and personal property financing. **John Tindall** of Tindall Bennett & Shoup PC is a well-established attorney specializing in real estate and corporate work. Peers did not hesitate to recommend him. **Terrance Turner** of Turner & Mede, PC is described as a *"very powerful and effective corporate lawyer"* who *"knows client businesses very well."* He works mainly in the corporate, institutional and government areas and deals with financings, M&A and business formations. **Cabot Christianson** of Christianson & Spraker is recognized as a superb bankruptcy expert due to his broad knowledge and excellent results in the field. He is also known for his experience of M&A transactions.

# ENVIRONMENT, NATURAL RESOURCES & REGULATED INDUSTRIES

Commentary about individuals can be found under their firm's paragraph. If the firm has no paragraph (is not ranked) look at Other Notable Practitioners.

| Environment, Natural Resources & Regulated Industries | |
| --- | --- |
| **Leading Firms** | |
| **Band 1** | |
| Ashburn & Mason, PC | |
| Guess & Rudd PC | |
| Perkins Coie LLP | |
| **Band 2** | |
| Crowell & Moring LLP * | |
| Stoel Rives LLP | |

| **Senior Statesmen** | |
| --- | --- |
| Senior Statesmen: distinguished older practitioners | |
| Mason III Julian L | Ashburn & Mason, PC |

| **Leading Individuals** | |
| --- | --- |
| **Band 1** | |
| Fjelstad Eric B | Perkins Coie LLP |
| Perkins Jr Joseph J | Stoel Rives LLP |
| Veerman Louis R | Guess & Rudd PC |
| **Band 2** | |
| Grovier Tina M | Birch, Horton, Bittner & Cherot (ONP)[†] * |
| Keithley Bradford G | Perkins Coie LLP |
| Linxwiler James | Guess & Rudd PC |
| Lyle George R | Guess & Rudd PC |
| Reeves Susan | Reeves Amodio LLC (ONP)[†] |
| Rozell William B | Sole Practitioner (ONP)[†] |
| Saupe A William | Ashburn & Mason, PC |
| Serdahely Douglas J | Patton Boggs LLP (ONP)[†] |

| **Up-and-coming individuals** | |
| --- | --- |
| Thompson Dean D | Kemppel, Huffman and Ellis, P.C. (ONP)[†] |

\* Indicates firm / individual with profile.
[†]ONP = Other Notable Practitioner.

## Band 1

### Ashburn & Mason, PC

**THE FIRM** With tremendous experience in the field, this firm offers superior knowledge and great versatility. It has a strong gas and oil practice, and represents major public utilities in Alaska, as well as handling regulatory issues and sales negotiations.
**Sources say:** *"Smart, strong lawyers with a good reputation in litigation."*
**KEY INDIVIDUALS William Saupe** is head of the public utility and regulatory practices within the firm. He handles administrative as well as judicial procedures, and deals with general civil litigation. **Julian Mason** is a leading name in the public utility area and has been practicing for over three decades. As a litigator, he has carried out several cases in state and federal courts in Alaska, and he has been awarded various recognitions throughout the years.

### Guess & Rudd PC

**THE FIRM** Guess & Rudd is renowned for its broad natural resources practice, which caters for a variety of clients including mining companies, financial institutions and native corporations. Its most prominent area of expertise remains oil and gas, and due to its long experience the team is able to handle virtually any type of transaction relating to this area.
**KEY INDIVIDUALS Louis Veerman** is involved in administrative law as well as litigation, and peers acknowledge his *"great reputation"* in the field. **James Linxwiler** has a wealth of experience in the natural resources arena, and is considered *"a great, level-headed lawyer and a good guy"* by clients. His clients include oil and mining companies, and electric utilities. **George Lyle** is a standout lawyer with a broad practice covering oil and gas, environmental and natural resources laws, among others. Interviewees state that he is *"good to work with,"* and are impressed with his *"good judgment."*

### Perkins Coie LLP
See profile on p.2548

**THE FIRM** Perkins Coie is highly active in the mining and oil and gas sectors, where it acts for impressive clients such as BP and Statoil. It has been involved in large mining projects of late, as well as gas pipeline work. The considerable size of the team, backed by the firm's strong national network of resources, contributes to the wealth of expertise it offers.
**KEY INDIVIDUALS Eric Fjelstad** is one of the top lawyers in the field. He recently successfully represented Teck Alaska in litigation before the EPA and the Ninth Circuit Court of Appeals, and defended Usibelli coal mine in another successfully resolved case. Practice area veteran **Bradford Keithley** mainly focuses on oil and gas matters. Clients praise his high levels of subject matter expertise and astute understanding of the related political issues.

## Band 2

### Crowell & Moring LLP
See profile on p.910

**THE FIRM** Crowell & Moring operates a sterling practice in the environment and natural resources sector, and works extensively with high-profile clients such as Shell and Marathon. Its recent highlights include representing Buccaneer Energy in its acquisition of a jack-up drilling rig for use in oil and gas exploration drilling in Alaskan waters.
**Sources say:** *"Excellent client service; key team members are always available at any time, and they back each other up very effectively."*
**KEY INDIVIDUALS Kyle Parker** is a key partner in the firm's Anchorage energy and natural resources group.

### Stoel Rives LLP

**THE FIRM** Stoel Rives has expertise in a variety of industries, including agriculture, energy facilities, irrigation districts, pulp and paper, mining and oil and gas. Its key clients include Shell, BP Exploration (Alaska) and Millrock Resources.

**KEY INDIVIDUALS Joseph Perkins** is a recognized expert in complex questions involving mining and oil and gas laws.

### Other Notable Practitioners

**Tina Grovier** (see p.492) of Birch, Horton, Bittner & Cherot has a solid practice covering various aspects of nat-

ural resources law. She has expertise in mineral leases and surface use agreements, among other areas, and frequently represents public utilities. **Susan Reeves** of Reeves Amodio LLC is a *"very experienced lawyer"* focused on environmental law. She is particularly well versed in drafting applications and handling permits for natural resource projects. Peers agree that *"she is a strong lawyer and is well regarded in the community."* **Douglas Serdahely** of Patton Boggs LLP is particularly well known for his expertise in civil litigation involving environmental matters. Peers declare that

*"he is a very good litigator – one of the top in Anchorage."* **Dean Thompson** of Kemppel, Huffman and Ellis, P.C. benefits from his past experience as a utility economist in representing major corporate and business clients, including electric and telecommunications utilities. Sole practitioner **William Rozell** practices in Juneau and has many years of experience in the field. He is particularly active in the oil and gas sector.

# LABOR & EMPLOYMENT

Commentary about individuals can be found under their firm's paragraph. If the firm has no paragraph (is not ranked) look at Other Notable Practitioners.

| Labor & Employment Leading Firms | |
| --- | --- |
| **Band 1** | |
| Davis Wright Tremaine LLP * | |
| Perkins Coie LLP | |
| **Band 2** | |
| Sedor, Wendlandt, Evans & Filippi, LLC | |

| Leading Individuals | |
| --- | --- |
| **Band 1** | |
| Daniel Thomas M | *Perkins Coie LLP* |
| Evans William J | *Sedor, Wendlandt, Evans & Filippi, LLC* |
| Mede William | *Turner & Mede, PC (ONP)[†]* |
| **Band 2** | |
| Colbo Kimberlee A | *Hughes Gorski Seedorf Odsen (ONP)[†]* |
| Juliussen James H | *Davis Wright Tremaine LLP* |
| Limeres Amy | *Birch, Horton, Bittner & Cherot (ONP)[†] \** |
| Parker Doug | *Littler Mendelson PC (ONP)[†] \** |
| Stewart Robert K | *Davis Wright Tremaine LLP* |
| **Band 3** | |
| Dunne Kim | *Landye Bennett Blumstein LLP (ONP)[†]* |
| Fisher Gregory | *Davis Wright Tremaine LLP* |
| Johnson Linda | *Clapp Peterson & Stowers LLC (ONP)[†]* |
| Partnow Peter C | *Lane Powell PC (ONP)[†] \** |

\* *Indicates firm / individual with profile.*
[†] *ONP = Other Notable Practitioner.*

## Band 1

### Davis Wright Tremaine LLP
See profile on p.2544
**THE FIRM** This superb team is highly active in the healthcare, communications and broadcast sectors, among others. It deals with everything from class actions and litigation to labor relations work. Recent highlights include representing a major Alaskan community mental healthcare

provider in delicate negotiations, and acting for a large electric utility in defending a lawsuit.
**Sources say:** *"It is the overall high quality and practicality of the firm's work, advice and counsel that ensure its growing client base."*
**KEY INDIVIDUALS James Juliussen** is an experienced litigator with a particular focus on employee policy. He recently represented Chenega Commercial Holdings in collective bargaining negotiations. **Robert Stewart** offers counsel in several areas of labor and employment, and has been praised for his *"outstanding skills in litigation, and commercial, transactional and regulatory work."* **Gregory Fisher** is known for his excellent commercial litigation practice and vast experience in jury trials and appeals.

### Perkins Coie LLP
See profile on p.2548
**THE FIRM** Perkins Coie continues to represent leading businesses, including Fortune 100 names, as well as local companies. The team has developed special expertise in dealing with native Alaskan corporations and advises the likes of the Southcentral Foundation. It has also recently concluded a challenging case for the University of Alaska.
**KEY INDIVIDUALS Thomas Daniel** is one of the most prominent names in this area. He deals with both counseling and litigation, and has been very active in cases covering virtually every aspect of labor and employment. Peers consider him an outstanding lawyer.

## Band 2

### Sedor, Wendlandt, Evans & Filippi, LLC
**THE FIRM** A growing name in the field, this group offers high-quality services to a broad range of clients, including private sector businesses, healthcare companies and public institutions.

**KEY INDIVIDUALS William Evans**'s strong litigation practice has made him *"a real heavyweight in the labor and employment field in Alaska,"* sources say. He has wide-ranging experience in employment-related matters.

### Other Notable Practitioners

Well regarded by peers, **Kim Dunne** of Landye Bennett Blumstein LLP acts as counsel to many public institutions, such as hospitals and housing authorities on a full range of employment needs. **Kimberlee Colbo** of Hughes Gorski Seedorf Odsen & Tervooren, LLC has a strong practice advising management on employment issues and also represents clients on matters concerning insurance, product liability and general civil litigation. **Amy Limeres** (see p.492) of Birch, Horton, Bittner & Cherot is particularly active in handling employee benefits, tax and retirement plans. She is also involved in the healthcare sphere. Peers have *"a very high regard"* for **Linda Johnson** of Clapp Peterson & Stowers LLC. She litigates in state and federal courts, taking up defense cases as well as acting for plaintiffs. Her practice deals with private companies as well as municipalities. **Peter Partnow** (see p.493) of Lane Powell PC focuses on complex litigation and dispute resolution, and is highly recommended for labor and employment issues. He is *"well known, well respected and well liked"* by peers. **Doug Parker** (see p.493) of Littler Mendelson PC has a broad-ranging practice covering various labor and employment matters such as class actions and discrimination claims. He has particular experience in arbitrations and labor negotiations, and counts ENSTAR Natural Gas, Northern Air Cargo and Alaska Communications Systems as key clients. **William Mede** of Turner & Mede, PC is considered an *"outstanding, first-class"* labor and employment lawyer. He represents a range of public and private sector employers, and his experience stretches over 25 years.

# LITIGATION

## Litigation: General Commercial
### Leading Firms

**Band 1**
Birch, Horton, Bittner & Cherot
Dorsey & Whitney LLP *
Feldman Orlansky & Sanders

**Band 2**
Ashburn & Mason, PC
Atkinson, Conway & Gagnon
Patton Boggs LLP
Stoel Rives LLP

**Band 3**
Lane Powell PC *
Perkins Coie LLP

## Litigation: General Commercial
### Senior Statesmen

**Senior Statesmen: distinguished older practitioners**

| | |
|---|---|
| Ashburn Mark | *Ashburn & Mason, PC* |
| Bankston William M | *Bankston, Gronning, O'Hara, PC (ONP)[†]* |
| Bundy Robert C | *Dorsey & Whitney LLP* |
| Gagnon Bruce | *Atkinson, Conway & Gagnon* |

### Leading Individuals

**Band 1**

| | |
|---|---|
| Feldman Jeffrey M | *Feldman Orlansky & Sanders* |
| Oesting David W | *Davis Wright Tremaine LLP (ONP)[†]* |
| Orlansky Susan | *Feldman Orlansky & Sanders* |
| Petumenos Timothy J | *Birch, Horton, Bittner & Cherot *^ |
| Serdahely Douglas J | *Patton Boggs LLP* |
| Torgerson James | *Stoel Rives LLP* |

**Band 2**

| | |
|---|---|
| Gilmore Patrick | *Atkinson, Conway & Gagnon* |
| Jamieson Brewster | *Lane Powell PC *^ |
| Sanders Eric | *Feldman Orlansky & Sanders* |
| Sneed Spencer | *Dorsey & Whitney LLP* |

**Band 3**

| | |
|---|---|
| Coughlin Jennifer | *K&L Gates (ONP)[†]*^ |
| Crosby Dani | *Ashburn & Mason, PC* |
| Cutler Louisiana | *K&L Gates (ONP)[†]*^ |
| Dawson Jon S | *Davis Wright Tremaine LLP (ONP)[†]* |
| Hutchings Stephen H | *Birch, Horton, Bittner & Cherot *^ |
| Peterson Matthew | *Clapp Peterson & Stowers LLC (ONP)[†]* |

* Indicates firm / individual with profile.

[†]ONP = Other Notable Practitioner.

## Litigation: Construction
### Leading Individuals

**Band 1**

| | |
|---|---|
| Dickson Robert J | *Atkinson, Conway & Gagnon* |
| Hutchings Stephen H | *Birch, Horton, Bittner & Cherot *^ |
| Kreger Michael E | *Perkins Coie LLP* |
| Watts Grant | *Holmes Weddle & Barcott (ONP)[†]* |

**Up-and-coming individuals**

| | |
|---|---|
| Holden-Davis Julia | *Garvey Schubert Barer (ONP)[†]* |

## Band 1

### Birch, Horton, Bittner & Cherot

**THE FIRM** This team combines arbitration and mediation skills with a great reputation in complex litigation. It represents several important organizations in the region and is particularly proficient in anticipating and considering all possibilities during the pre-litigation stages. Its broad litigation practice also encompasses class actions and appellate matters.
**Sources say:** *"One of the best in the area."*
**KEY INDIVIDUALS Stephen Hutchings** (see p.492) is deemed a *"wonderful guy and a great business lawyer – the go-to guy on complicated business law claims."* He has a strong commercial litigation practice, and is highlighted in particular for his expertise in construction-related disputes. **Timothy Petumenos** (see p.493) is an expert in big-scale litigation and has represented numerous native corporations over the years. Peers maintain that he is *"a very capable litigator who can see the big picture and can put together all the pieces to present the picture."*

### Dorsey & Whitney LLP
See profile on p.1583
**THE FIRM** Dorsey & Whitney's strong litigation practice has a preeminent position in handling complex commercial disputes. The team has expertise in oil and gas and aviation disputes in particular, and maintains long-standing relations with a number of important clients such as Bristol Bay Native Corporation and Alaska Airlines. The firm recently represented ConocoPhillips in a complicated case against the State of Alaska in connection with contract and regulatory issues relating to oil and gas unit leases.
**Sources say:** *"They did a great job and we enjoyed working with them."*
**KEY INDIVIDUALS** The highly reputed **Spencer Sneed** has a diverse practice covering oil and gas commercial litigation as well as transactional finance work. He recently led in the aforementioned case on behalf of ConocoPhillips. *"A fine lawyer"* and *"an excellent litigator,"* **Robert Bundy** handles various types of litigation, from

civil to criminal. In addition to his experience in healthcare and environmental matters, he is also a white-collar specialist. His recent highlights include representing Southcentral Foundation, Safeway and Fred Meyer Stores in defense of a qui tam case alleging Medicaid fraud.

### Feldman Orlansky & Sanders
**THE FIRM** An established litigation practice dealing with both civil and criminal matters, this team endeavors to resolve disputes in the early stages but also boasts a broad expertise in trials. Areas of focus include constitutional matters, professional negligence, contract disputes and antitrust claims.
**Sources say:** *"At the top of the game."*
**KEY INDIVIDUALS** The widely recognized **Jeffrey Feldman** has extensive trial and appellate experience. His rounded practice is further enriched by numerous public and professional appointments. Peers maintain that he is *"effective at whatever he does"* and assert that he is a *"very good lawyer with many high-profile clients."* **Susan Orlansky** has an excellent civil and criminal litigation practice, and is *"one of the best appellate attorneys in the state,"* according to sources. She is primarily engaged in complex litigation and has been described as *"an excellent attorney"* and a *"strong writer."* **Eric Sanders** works extensively in mediations and arbitrations and has also been

lauded as a very *"good litigator"* in relation to a wide range of civil litigation.

## Band 2

### Ashburn & Mason, PC
**THE FIRM** Ashburn & Mason's team possesses exceptional litigation capabilities across a range of complex commercial litigation types, including in environmental and natural resources-related disputes. The group's recent highlights include acting for the State of Alaska in the high-profile Alaska Supreme Court case relating to the Point Thomson oil fields.
**Sources say:** *"A fine firm; high-level and respected."*
**KEY INDIVIDUALS Dani Crosby** has a strong practice covering all manner of business, oil and gas, and employment disputes. Competitors deem her a *"very capable"* lawyer. **Mark Ashburn** is a well-regarded litigator with many years of experience in the field. He is mostly active in civil litigation and is involved in oil and gas matters.

### Atkinson, Conway & Gagnon
**THE FIRM** This well-regarded group possesses in-depth expertise in commercial disputes, and is known for the broad-ranging nature of its remit, covering everything from professional malpractice defense to fraud and theft.
**KEY INDIVIDUALS Robert Dickson** has strong expertise in construction litigation and healthcare law, as well as in a variety of commercial matters, and he represents a number of major engineering firms and healthcare providers. Peers agree that he is *"very experienced and has a good reputation."* **Patrick Gilmore** undertakes commercial litigation and is skilled in an array of lender liability, taxation and employment issues, among other things. Competitors regard him highly and affirm that he is a *"very good commercial litigator."* **Bruce Gagnon** has wide-ranging expertise covering commercial and construction litigation and transactional business assignments.

### Patton Boggs LLP
**THE FIRM** This global firm boasts a solid litigation practice in its Anchorage office, encompassing a wide range of areas and representing local and national clients.
**KEY INDIVIDUALS Douglas Serdahely** is a prominent name in the area. Within his complex civil litigation prac-

tice, he handles antitrust issues and represents various companies in the environmental sector. Peers praise him unanimously, stating that he is *"a very effective and smart litigator."*

### Stoel Rives LLP

**THE FIRM** Stoel Rives has an excellent business litigation practice. The group is comprised of experts in construction, employment law and tax matters, among other things. The firm's enviable client list includes the likes of BP Exploration (Alaska) and Shell.

**KEY INDIVIDUALS James Torgerson** is a respected commercial litigator and trial attorney. His practice covering several sectors ranging from employment to real property and environmental matters.

## Band 3

### Lane Powell PC
See profile on p.2547

**THE FIRM** Lane Powell has a solid litigation practice spanning numerous industries, including mining, oil and gas, fisheries and tourism. Its recent work includes successfully representing A-1 Timber Consultants in a breach of contract claim relating to the termination of a timber harvesting contract.

**KEY INDIVIDUALS** The sterling **Brewster Jamieson** (see p.492) litigates across a diverse range of fields and is particularly known for his expertise in maritime litigation.

### Perkins Coie LLP
See profile on p.2548

**THE FIRM** Perkins Coie is increasingly recognized for the excellent commercial litigation services it offers, backed by the firm's extensive nationwide network of resources. The group is especially noted for its strength in construction litigation. Key clients include Alaska Gold and RIM Architects.

**KEY INDIVIDUALS Michael Kreger** earns praise for his depth of understanding and subject knowledge. He is best known for his construction litigation expertise.

### Other Notable Practitioners

**William Bankston** of Bankston, Gronning, O'Hara, PC has a wealth of experience in civil litigation and is well regarded by peers. He is primarily involved in commercial law and construction law. **Matthew Peterson** of Clapp Peterson & Stowers LLC is mainly known for his insurance defense work and for handling medical malpractice cases. **David Oesting** of Davis Wright Tremaine LLP has a broad practice encompassing an array of commercial litigation, and he frequently handles bankruptcy proceedings. **Jon Dawson**, also of Davis Wright Tremaine LLP, focuses on complex litigation. His experience stretches over three decades, and he has a strong line in representing national banks, television networks and manufacturers. **Grant Watts** of Holmes Weddle & Barcott, A Professional Corporation is noted in particular for his construction law expertise. **Jennifer Coughlin** (see p.492) of K&L Gates is particularly active in complex business litigation and also works extensively in medical malpractice and employment cases. Peers agree that she is *"very smart and effective."* **Louisiana Cutler** (see p.492) of K&L Gates is recognized for her work in the environmental field and her expertise in oil and gas issues. She has been active in complex litigation for over 20 years. **Julia Holden-Davis** of Garvey Schubert Barer is deemed *"smart and capable"* by her peers. Her central area of expertise is construction litigation, and she also has extensive experience in government contracts.

# REAL ESTATE

Commentary about individuals can be found under their firm's paragraph. If the firm has no paragraph (is not ranked) look at Other Notable Practitioners.

| Real Estate Leading Firms |
| --- |
| **Band 1** |
| Ashburn & Mason, PC |
| Davis Wright Tremaine LLP * |
| Dorsey & Whitney LLP * |
| **Band 2** |
| Atkinson, Conway & Gagnon |
| Birch, Horton, Bittner & Cherot |

## Band 1

### Ashburn & Mason, PC

**THE FIRM** Ashburn & Mason's real estate practice covers all the major areas of the field, including developer and landlord representations, and is noted in particular for its recent work involving condemnation disputes.

**KEY INDIVIDUALS Donald McClintock** has been lauded as *"one of the very best real estate lawyers in town"* by interviewees. He has a vast experience representing commercial landlords, developers and various businesses. Peers *"think very, very highly"* of him.

### Davis Wright Tremaine LLP
See profile on p.2544

**THE FIRM** This large team has significant national presence and handles real estate issues across the board, including leasings, purchases, sales and zoning. Its recent work includes representing Sears in a complicated condemnation matter.

**Sources say:** *"The firm relates very well to the needs of the client and their services are always rendered in a timely manner. Their lawyers are both smart and practical."*

**KEY INDIVIDUALS** The highly respected **Jon Dawson** has a wide-ranging practice covering corporate transactions, IP, litigation and of course real estate. Sources praise his *"deep knowledge"* and his superb ability to *"view matters from a client perspective."* His recent highlights include negotiating leases for Crowley Petroleum Distribution. **Barbara Simpson Kraft** is considered an *"expert in matters of corporate organization and governance"* in relation to real estate, say sources. She recently represented GEO Group in an entitlements case, and also advised Trident Seafoods on various issues. **Joseph Reece** handles various real estate transactions for an array of clients. He acted as lead partner in the Sears case, and represented Natives of Kodiak in relation to timber sale contracts.

| Real Estate Leading Individuals | | |
| --- | --- | --- |
| **Band 1** | | |
| Black Kathryn A | Birch, Horton, Bittner & Cherot | * |
| Cherot Suzanne | Birch, Horton, Bittner & Cherot | * |
| Durrell Brian | Durrell Law Group, PC (ONP) | † |
| McClintock Donald | Ashburn & Mason, PC | |
| McCollum James | Law Offices of James McCollum (ONP) | † |
| Rosston Richard | Dorsey & Whitney LLP | |
| **Band 2** | | |
| Dawson Jon S | Davis Wright Tremaine LLP | |
| Gilmore Patrick | Atkinson, Conway & Gagnon | |
| Kraft Barbara Simpson | Davis Wright Tremaine LLP | |
| Reece Joseph | Davis Wright Tremaine LLP | |
| Tindall John H | Tindall Bennett & Shoup PC (ONP) | † |
| Travostino Joan | K&L Gates (ONP) | † * |

\* Indicates firm / individual with profile.
† ONP = Other Notable Practitioner.

### Dorsey & Whitney LLP
See profile on p.1583

**THE FIRM** Dorsey & Whitney has a leading name in the commercial real estate space, and represents major clients in the area, such as Royal Bank of Canada and Morrison Investments. The team recently represented Doyon in the negotiating, drafting and restructuring of a lease with Alyeska Pipeline Service.

**KEY INDIVIDUALS** The leading **Richard Rosston** has a broad-ranging corporate, real estate, M&A, finance, telecom and securities practice. He recently represented Holiday Alaska in litigation concerning environmental and easement matters.

## Band 2

### Atkinson, Conway & Gagnon

**THE FIRM** This team is experienced in dealing with real estate transactions, often advising lenders, and regularly carries out property sales and purchases, among other things.

**KEY INDIVIDUALS Patrick Gilmore** has a wide practice covering commercial litigation as well as transactional work. His peers consider him "*a fine lawyer.*"

### Birch, Horton, Bittner & Cherot

**THE FIRM** This group works with a variety of clients and represents several private corporations and banks in the region. The team is also particularly adept in managing conveyance documents and advising lenders.

**KEY INDIVIDUALS Suzanne Cherot** (see p.492) is an established name in the real estate field. She deals with many commercial clients in complex transactions. **Kathryn Black** (see p.492) is well regarded by peers and she is currently highly active in the oil and gas, healthcare and environmental sectors, and represents a number of native corporations.

## Other Notable Practitioners

**Brian Durrell** of Durrell Law Group, PC has a solid practice covering several areas of real estate. Competitors view him as a strong attorney. Solo practitioner **James McCollum** of Law Offices of James McCollum LLC has a strong reputation in the real estate field. He specializes in public land law and handles common ownership work. **John Tindall** of Tindall Bennett & Shoup PC combines his real estate work with expertise in corporate law. **Joan Travostino** (see p.493) of K&L Gates mainly deals with commercial transactions, including in real estate finance.

# Leaders' Profiles in Alaska

## BLACK, Kathryn A
Birch, Horton, Bittner & Cherot, Anchorage
907 276 1550
kblack@bhb.com
*Featured in Real Estate (Alaska), Corporate/M&A (Alaska)*

**Practice Areas:** Banking, finance, corporate, real estate, business, M&A, complex real estate transactions, represents lenders in complex oil and gas transactions and financings, commercial loans, secured transactions, real estate financings, bankruptcies, collections, and repossessions.
**Professional Memberships:** Alaska State Bar (1980); American Bar Association (1980); admitted US Supreme Court; US District Court/Alaska.
**Career:** Joined Birch Horton Bittner & Cherot 1984; Managing Shareholder 2011 to present.
**Publications:** Co-author: 'When Worlds Collide: Alaska Native Corporations and the Bankruptcy Code', Alaska Law Review, 1989.
**Personal:** JD (magna cum laude), University of Santa Clara, Santa Clara, California (1979); BA, Anthropology, University of Colorado, Boulder, Colorado (1973).

## CHEROT, Suzanne
Birch, Horton, Bittner & Cherot, Anchorage
907 276 1550
scherot@bhb.com
*Featured in Real Estate (Alaska)*

**Practice Areas:** Real estate and corporate. Extensive experience in representing sellers, purchasers and developers in complex real estate transactions, including purchases, sales, financings and leasing of commercial buildings, medical buildings, residential subdivisions, condominium developments, mobile home parks, and in the organization of corporations and limited liability companies.
**Professional Memberships:** Alaska Bar Association (1972).

**Career:** Joined Birch, Horton, Bittner and Cherot in 1973; Managing shareholder 1995-97 and 1999-2008. JD, University of Kansas (1972); BA, University of Kansas (1970).
**Personal:** Anchorage Economic Development Corporation Board of Directors; Member of the Anchorage ATHENA Society.

## COUGHLIN, Jennifer
K&L Gates, Anchorage
907 777 7632
jennifer.coughlin@klgates.com
*Featured in Litigation (Alaska)*

**Practice Areas:** Partner Jennifer Coughlin focuses primarily on litigation, handling complex business litigation in addition to medical malpractice and employment cases. Her commercial case experience includes a recent arbitration on behalf of a royalty owner that resulted in a $245 million award, in addition to contract disputes and real property litigation. She has handled medical malpractice cases involving issues relating to hospital employees, and employment law cases representing and counseling employers on discrimination and wage and hour issues in state and federal court, and before administrative agencies.

## CUTLER, Louisiana
K&L Gates, Anchorage
907 865 2475
louisiana.cutler@klgates.com
*Featured in Litigation (Alaska)*

**Practice Areas:** Louisiana Cutler has more than 20 years of experience as a litigator focusing on complex litigation involving environmental issues and oil and gas taxation and royalties. She has litigated such matters in Alaska trial and appellate courts, as well as in administrative hearings and arbitrations. She also advises clients on oil and gas related legislation, ordinance drafting and constitutional law questions. She has been involved in a series of administrative and court appeals on large oil and gas tax matters.

## GROVIER, Tina M
Birch, Horton, Bittner & Cherot, Anchorage
907 276 1550
tgrovier@bhb.com
*Featured in Environment (Alaska)*

**Practice Areas:** Natural resources law including oil, gas and mining; negotiates mineral leases, easements, and surface use agreements; assists with permits and government approvals; represents pipelines, public utilities and other entities before the Regulatory Commission of Alaska.
**Professional Memberships:** Alaska Bar Association; Alaska Legal Services Corp., Alternate Board Member; Anchorage Youth Court, Volunteer Legal Advisor; National Institute of Trial Advocacy, NITA Seminar Graduate, Ft. Lauderdale, Florida (1997).
**Career:** JD from Washington University School of Law in 1993 (Order of the Coif); Law Clerk for Chief Judge of the Court of Appeals, Alexander Bryner from 1993-1994, admitted to practice Alaska 1994.

## HUTCHINGS, Stephen H
Birch, Horton, Bittner & Cherot, Anchorage
907 276 1550
shutchings@bhb.com
*Featured in Litigation (Alaska)*

**Practice Areas:** Senior Litigation Shareholder; corporate law and commercial and construction litigation; general corporate counsel to Alaska Native corporations.
**Professional Memberships:** Alaska Bar Association (1976); US District Court for Alaska (1986); Ninth Circuit Court of Appeals (1986); Alaska Bar Association Board of Law Examiners.
**Career:** Iowa Bar (1976); Alaska Bar (1977); Assistant DA, Anchorage; District Attorney Bethel and Sitka, Alaska; Instructor Alaska State Trooper Academy; Lead trial counsel AG's Office, Torts and Special Litigation Section; Birch, Horton, Bittner and Cherot (1989).

**Personal:** BA, Grinnell College (1971); JD, Washington University, St Louis, Missouri (1976). Fluent Spanish.

## JAMIESON, Brewster
Lane Powell PC, Anchorage
907 264 3325
jamiesonb@lanepowell.com
*Featured in Litigation (Alaska)*

**Practice Areas:** Commercial litigation, professional negligence defense, admiralty and maritime law, ERISA defense, insurance coverage and bad faith litigation, medical products liability litigation and employment litigation. Has received favorable verdicts in a wide variety of maritime, construction, aviation, commercial and professional negligence matters.
**Professional Memberships:** International Association of Defense Counsel; The Maritime Law Association of the United States; ABA, Torts and Insurance Practice Section.
**Career:** Shareholder since 1991. Law Clerk, Alaska Supreme Court, 1984-85.
**Personal:** Willamette University (JD, magna cum laude, 1984; BS, 1980).

## LIMERES, Amy
Birch, Horton, Bittner & Cherot, Anchorage
907 263 7203
alimeres@bhb.com
*Featured in Labor & Employment (Alaska)*

**Practice Areas:** Amy Limeres focuses on employee benefits and employment law advice. Her emphasis is on the regulation of qualified retirement, welfare benefit and executive compensation plans; and advising employers concerning employee benefits compliance, correction and taxation issues. She routinely represents plans and employers in plan correction and other proceedings before the DOL and IRS. She advises employers regarding best employment practices.

**PARISE, Michael J**
Lane Powell PC, Anchorage
907 264 3322
PariseM@LanePowell.com
*Featured in Corporate/M&A (Alaska)*
**Practice Areas:** Business law, mergers and acquisitions, secured lending, mineral exploration finance, Alaska oil and gas tax credits, mining, timber sales and logging, bankruptcy, Uniform Commercial Code, financial institution litigation, maritime transactions, ship mortgage foreclosures.
**Professional Memberships:** Equipment Leasing & Finance Association. Practice groups include Financial Institutions, Business Transactions, Canada Practice, Creditors Rights.
**Career:** Representative clients include KeyBank, Wells Fargo, Union Bank, K2 Principal Fund, Brinker International, Renaissance Minerals (Australia), Gruma International Foods, AFD Petroleum, A-1 Timber, Horizon Lines of Alaska, Alaska Maritime Documentation SMS Equipment.
**Personal:** BA, cum laude, Williams College; Phi Beta Kappa. JD, Boston University.

**PARKER, Doug**
Littler Mendelson PC, Anchorage
503 221 0309
DParker@littler.com
*Featured in Labor & Employment (Alaska)*
**Practice Areas:** Labor Management Relations; Complex Litigation and Jury Trials; Wage and Hour; Discrimination and Harassment; ERISA and Benefit Plan Litigation.
**Professional Memberships:** Chairman: Employment Law Section - Alaska Bar Association, 1987–1988; Member: Oregon State Bar, Labor Law Section; Washington State Bar Association; American Bar Association, Labor and Employment Law Section; Federal Bar Association; American Employment Law Council, 1993–present; and Alaska State Bar.
**Career:** The office founder in Anchorage, Doug has represented employers in Alaska and throughout the Pacific Northwest in all aspects of labor and employment law for more than 25 years. Prior to joining Littler in 2007, Doug chaired the labor and employment practice at another law firm.
**Publications:** "Laws Influence How Entities Can Help Employees in Need," Portland Business Journal, January 2006; "Kirchowski v. Weyerhaeuser: Strict Scrutiny of 'Decisional Unit'-Based Disclosure Requirements for ADEA Waivers," Employee Relations Law Journal, Vol. 32, No. 2, Autumn 2006; "Employer Advice From the Perspective of Years of Labor and Employment Claims Defense Work," Inside the Minds: Resolving Employee Disputes & Litigation, October 2006.
**Personal:** JD, Willamette University College of Law, 1981; BA, Oregon State University, with honors, 1976.

**PARTNOW, Peter C**
Lane Powell PC, Anchorage
907 277 9511
partnowp@lanepowell.com
*Featured in Labor & Employment (Alaska)*
**Practice Areas:** Practice emphasizes litigation and dispute resolution in employment and labor disputes, ERISA defense, public procurement, contract claims and other complex litigation.
**Professional Memberships:** Admitted Alaska Bar, Ninth Circuit Court of Appeals and United States Supreme Court; Member, Alaska Bar Association, Labor and Employment Section Executive Committee; Fee Arbitrator, Alaska Bar Association; Form Alaska Attorney Representative, Ninth Circuit Judicial Conference.
**Career:** Served as General Counsel, Anchorage School District and as Chief of the Civil Section, Alaska Attorney General's Anchorage Office.
**Personal:** University of Chicago (JD); Bowdoin College (BA, magna cum laude, Phi Beta Kappa); Board Member/Secretary, Anchorage Concert Association.

**PETUMENOS, Timothy J**
Birch, Horton, Bittner & Cherot, Anchorage
907 276 1550
tpetumenos@bhb.com
*Featured in Litigation (Alaska)*
**Practice Areas:** Litigation; jury trials; plaintiff and defendant.
**Professional Memberships:** American Law Institute. Certified Faculty, National Institute for Trial Advocacy (NITA). Advocate, American Board of Trial Advocates. Alaska Bar Association, 1976; US District Court/Alaska; Ninth Circuit; US Supreme Court.
**Career:** JD, Georgetown University Law Center, Washington DC (1976). Assistant District Attorney; attorney-Office of Special Prosecutions; Joined Birch Horton Bittner and Cherot (1983).
**Personal:** Fluent Spanish.

**TRAVOSTINO, Joan**
K&L Gates, Anchorage
907 777 7608
joan.travostino@klgates.com
*Featured in Real Estate (Alaska)*
**Practice Areas:** Partner Joan Travostino practices primarily in the areas of real estate, commercial transactions and finance. As an outgrowth of real estate and financing, she also has represented a number of creditors in various types of bankruptcy proceedings. Her real estate experience includes representing sellers and buyers and advising on commercial building leases, while her commercial transactions work includes representing buyers and sellers of businesses and separate assets within businesses. Because Alaska's economy largely is based on natural resources, she also has commercial experience with mining and fishing transactions.

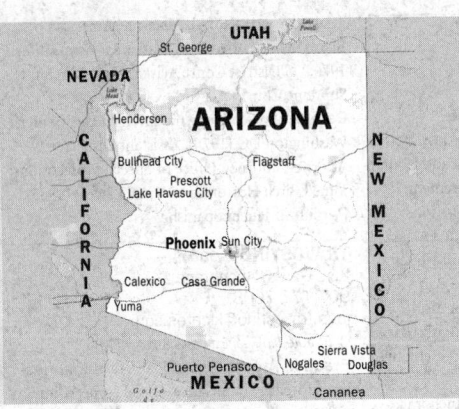

## How lawyers are ranked

Every year we carry out thousands of in-depth interviews with clients in order to assess the reputations and expertise of business lawyers worldwide. The qualities we look for (and which determine rankings) include technical legal ability, professional conduct, client service, commercial awareness/astuteness, diligence, commitment, and other qualities most valued by the client. For details of our research team, see p.5.

### Contents:

# CORPORATE/M&A

Commentary about individuals can be found under their firm's paragraph. If the firm has no paragraph (is not ranked) look at Other Notable Practitioners.

### Corporate/M&A
### Leading Firms

**Band 1**
DLA Piper LLP (US) *
Greenberg Traurig LLP *
Osborn Maledon PA *
Snell & Wilmer LLP *
Squire Sanders (US) LLP *

**Band 2**
Ballard Spahr LLP *
Fennemore Craig

**Band 3**
Quarles & Brady LLP *

**Band 4**
Bryan Cave LLP
Gallagher & Kennedy PA
Perkins Coie LLP
Polsinelli PC *

* Indicates firm with profile.
Alphabetical order within each band. Band 1 is the highest.

## Band 1

### DLA Piper LLP (US)
See profile on p.1971
THE FIRM This international powerhouse continues to prove its strong credentials in this practice area. It is capable of handling matters for large, established businesses in the region, and for smaller startups. Recent large matters include representing DriveTime Automotive in its $1.8 billion sale of a consumer finance receivables portfolio to Santander Consumer USA, and in selling more than 100 reconditioning facilities and dealerships to a newly formed entity financed by several private equity firms.
Sources say: "A firm like this will always be at the top."
KEY INDIVIDUALS Co-managing partner of the Phoenix office, **Steven Pidgeon** (see p.510) receives warm praise for his "professional and respectful performance at board meetings. He's knowledgeable on both the legal and business side." In addition to being the joint lead partner on

the DriveTime Automotive deal, he also advised Isola Group on its $100 million IPO and $350 million debt refinancing. **Greg Hall** (see p.508) is renowned for his skill at handling international matters and recently handled a $900 million cross-border deal advising Mobile Mini on its revolving credit facility. He is praised for his effectiveness and "can handle big and small deals." **David Lewis** (see p.509) is known for his business acumen and is respected by peers as someone who can take on important deals. He recently represented Isagenix Worldwide in its recapitalization by Cyprium Partners, as well as being joint lead partner on the DriveTime Automotive matter.

### Greenberg Traurig LLP
See profile on p.1024
THE FIRM The Phoenix office of this national firm continues to be recognized as one of the best in the state for its work advising private equity firms and public companies on corporate matters. In addition to general corporate law and M&A, it advises businesses on venture capital, strategic investments and public offerings. One of its more significant deals of late was representing LifeLock in its $141 million IPO.
Sources say: "This firm provides superior representation, and is extremely reliable in critical areas, such as price efficiency and responsiveness."
KEY INDIVIDUALS Head of the Phoenix corporate and M&A team, **Robert Kant** (see p.509) is regarded as "an icon" and "a dean of securities in Arizona." He was joint lead partner advising LifeLock on its IPO, and also represented Synaptics in its purchase of Integrated Device Technology's video display operations business and the Pacinian Corporation. **Bruce Macdonough** (see p.509) is lauded by clients as "an excellent, outstanding lawyer – very strong." He represented Roadrunner Transportation Systems in seven business combinations and acquisitions totaling $162 million. **Brian Blaney** (see p.507) continues to distinguish himself and retains the respect of his peers. In addition to being the joint lead partner on the LifeLock IPO, he represented Rentokil Initial in its $114.6 million acquisition of the Western Exterminator Company, a cross-border

deal between the USA and the UK. **Quinn Williams** (see p.512) has more than two decades' experience representing investment funds, private companies and public companies, and is noted by peers as being active in assisting start-up businesses. He also has experience in handling significant cross-border matters.

### Osborn Maledon PA
See profile on p.514
THE FIRM This firm prides itself on its ability to handle clients of any size, from small venture capital entities and angel-backed startups to large public businesses. It differentiates itself from other firms of similar size by staying transaction-oriented. One notable example of its work was advising FireHost on the sale of Series C convertible preferred stock for $10 million.
Sources say: "They're superb. They've just been an excellent business partner for our legal, human resources and strategic work."
KEY INDIVIDUALS Practice co-head **Thomas Curzon** (see p.507) is praised by peers for "representing clients zealously, yet in a gentlemanly manner," and by clients as "a wise sage who deals with complex issues." He led on the FireHost deal. Fellow co-head **William Hardin** (see p.508) also continues to uphold his reputation as a leading lawyer in the field. Clients appreciate his "insight and thoroughness." **Andrew Kelly** (see p.509) is praised for his intelligence and is a strong choice for corporate matters. He remains an experienced member of the Greater Phoenix Economic Council. Another attorney greatly valued by clients is **Christopher Stachowiak** (see p.511), who "is very thorough and thoughtful, and can step back and take a high-level view of the situation and break down problems."

### Snell & Wilmer LLP
See profile on p.517
THE FIRM With one of the largest corporate law groups in Arizona, this firm offers a wide variety of services to its clients, including corporate organization and governance, securities offerings and fund formation. Of late, it has advised On Semiconductor as borrower's counsel on a

$325 million senior revolving credit facility, and represented DriveTime Automotive in its 2012 issue of $482 million asset-backed notes.

**Sources say:** *"A very good firm. They're good at coming forward with ideas and solutions – I have no hesitation in relying on them."*

**KEY INDIVIDUALS** Group cochair **Matthew Feeney** remains one of the most prominent attorneys in the field and is *"particularly good at handling high-level work advising boards and committees."* Peers praise him as *"a very impressive, first-rate lawyer."* Fellow practice leader **Jon Cohen** is regarded by peers as *"a dean of corporate law in Arizona."* His strong reputation is built on decades of experience handling corporate matters. **Terry Roman**, also a practice group leader, is *"excellent in the M&A area, espe-*

cially the sale of business assets."* She is also known for her work in contract negotiations, venture capital and healthcare. Joint practice group leader **Michael Donahey** is considered *"terrific"* by peers, and clients praise his ability to do *"quality corporate work."* Among other things, he handles matters related to corporate governance, restructurings, and public offerings. Highly rated by his peers, **Daniel Mahoney** frequently represents businesses in the telecom, life sciences, biotech and manufacturing industries. He represents both large companies and smaller startups.

## Squire Sanders (US) LLP
See profile on p.2129

**THE FIRM** A global firm with a strong presence in Arizona, Squire Sanders is highly praised by clients for its ability to handle cross-border work, its corporate structuring and management work, and its ability to take on large deals. It counts private and publicly listed companies, private equity houses and entrepreneurs in its expansive client base. One notable recent deal was representing Rural Metro in its acquisition of PMT Ambulance and related entities, which involved refinancing, labor, tax and antitrust elements.

**Sources say:** *"The firm is first-rate. They are responsive and timely, and helped us think critically through any issues or pitfalls that may have come up."*

**KEY INDIVIDUALS** With more than 30 years' experience, **Christopher Johnson** (see p.509) is highly regarded by peers and clients, one of whom notes that *"he's never let me down on getting things closed."* He recently advised Brookfield on the sale of its US real estate franchise business to HomeServices of America and their subsequent joint venture. *"A very pragmatic and experienced lawyer,"* **Frank Placenti** (see p.510) is chair of the firm's corporate finance and governance practice group, and is highly regarded by clients, who appreciate his knowledge and expertise in handling cross-border matters. He recently advised Avnet on its acquisition of the assets of Hartford Computer and Nexicore Services. **Joseph Crabb** (see p.507) is praised by clients as being *"outstanding, professional and articulate,"* and his strong understanding of his clients' businesses and culture is also highly appreciated. In addition to advising Rural Metro on the PMT Ambulance acquisition, he also advised it on the issuance of senior discount notes and the refinancing of a credit facility.

## Band 2

## Ballard Spahr LLP
See profile on p.2234

**THE FIRM** A well-respected name in the Arizona market, this firm completed more than 40 transactions in 2012. Major deals include representing Alerion Capital Group in its $26 million acquisition of Apex Microtechnology. Other major clients include Avnet, Republic Services and Barna Broadcasting.

**Sources say:** *"They're spectacular. In particular, we appreciate the responsiveness and thoroughness provided. They give pragmatic advice and are very business-oriented."*

**KEY INDIVIDUALS Karen McConnell** (see p.510) leads the M&A and private equity practice at the firm, and was the lead partner on the Alerion Capital deal. *"She is extremely professional, very bright and, more than anything, she becomes like a partner to us in the transaction,"* reports one impressed source. Clients also note that she *"is very practical and really helps to get the deals done."* **Adrienne Wilhoit** (see p.512) has a great deal of experience representing blue-chip businesses in mergers, joint ventures and capital markets transactions. She has experience in handling extremely large, nationwide matters.

## Fennemore Craig

**THE FIRM** This well-respected regional firm prides itself on being able to advise local and national clients on significant matters across a broad spectrum of corporate law, including governance, franchise law, securities offerings and commercial finance. It represents clients such as Rosemont Copper, the Arizona Sports & Tourism Authority and Freeport-McMoRan Copper & Gold. A recent highlight representing Special Devices in its acquisition by Daicel, a cross-border deal involving Japan.

**Sources say:** *"They do an excellent job and I get an excellent product. The billing and rates are very reasonable."*

**KEY INDIVIDUALS** A director of the firm, **Sarah Strunk** is well thought-of by peers and is appreciated by clients for her ability to carry out complex transactions. She acts for many clients in the renewable energy and natural resources sectors, and recently represented Drake Cement in matters arising from the opening of its $300 million cement factory, involving permitting, financing and land acquisition aspects. **Susan Wissink** chairs the firm's business and finance department, and represents both buyers and sellers in a number of large and complicated transactions, including mergers, corporate reorganizations and stock and asset-based sales and acquisitions. Clients appreciate her depth of experience. She recently advised Climatec on the sale of its membership interests in itself and its affiliates to Pegasus.

## Band 3

## Quarles & Brady LLP
See profile on p.2593

**THE FIRM** This national firm has two offices in Arizona – in Phoenix and Tucson – and has a great deal of local expertise in the state. It focuses its M&A practice particularly on the healthcare, education and technology sectors, as well as frequently advising emerging companies. It recently represented Fox Restaurant Concepts in a joint venture with the Hard Rock Cafe and Casino in Las Vegas. It also advised Sentinel Partners as franchise counsel on the sale of the Massage Envy franchise system to Roark Capital's Atlanta branch.

**KEY INDIVIDUALS Steven Emerick** (see p.508) is greatly respected by peers for his strong ability to handle securities work. He represents clients in a wide range of industries, including airlines, manufacturing and biotech. **Christian Hoffmann** (see p.509) is appreciated by clients for his depth of experience. He focuses primarily on assisting emerging growth businesses, particularly in the software, financial services, pharmaceutical and restaurant sectors.

## Band 4

### Bryan Cave LLP

**THE FIRM** This international firm has a significant amount of experience taking on matters for fast growth companies, and represents a number of angel, private equity and venture capital funds in both organizing and investing capital. It is able to advise on cross-border matters, with a particular focus on business and finance issues pertaining to Mexico. It recently acted as local counsel to Omega Healthcare Investors on the initial sale of $400 million senior notes, and a subsequent exchange offer.
**KEY INDIVIDUALS David Beauchamp** is liked by clients thanks to his insight and expertise in private equity and securities law. In addition to leading on the Omega Healthcare Investors deal, he assisted Trendline Management as underwriter's counsel with structuring the private placement of $38.5 million in notes.

### Gallagher & Kennedy PA

**THE FIRM** This regional firm is well known for advising both public and private businesses on large, capital intensive investments, often relating to infrastructure. It represents clients from a wide spectrum of industries, with a particular focus on healthcare, sports, and tourism; it also has a strong reputation for handling corporate matters for mining companies. Clients include Laser Options, Grand

Canyon Resort, the Arizona Cardinals and the Arizona Diamondbacks.
**KEY INDIVIDUALS** Head of the corporate and M&A department **Terence Thompson** is well regarded by peers for the depth of his experience, and is described as *"an excellent lawyer – very detail-oriented and responsive."*

### Perkins Coie LLP
See profile on p.2548

**THE FIRM** Perkins Coie has an impressive network across the West and around the country. It is best known in Arizona for handling corporate organization and governance work and complex IP matters, and for representing companies in midmarket M&A deals. It represents clients such as PetSmart, ams AG, and Freeport-McMoRan Copper & Gold.
**KEY INDIVIDUALS Judith Weiss** has a great deal of expertise in handling M&A, public and private offerings, and joint ventures. In addition, she receives a great deal of praise from clients for her expertise in complex IP work.

### Polsinelli PC
See profile on p.1641

**THE FIRM** The Arizona-based corporate team of this national firm prides itself on handling matters connected with the healthcare, technology and mining industries. It is able to take on a diverse range of matters, including joint ventures, M&A, LBOs and stock and asset purchases and sales. One of its major recent deals was representing Karlsson in the collateralization of carryback financing with mining rights and real property in the sale of its 50% stake in American West Potash to Prospect Global Resources, a $225 million deal.

**KEY INDIVIDUALS** Acting for clients ranging from emerging growth businesses to large global companies, **Phillip Guttilla** is well regarded by clients for his expertise in securities and tax law, and is also an accomplished private equity and hedge fund attorney. **Brian Moll** is also able to advise clients from startups to multinationals, and works across a diverse range of sectors, including defense, restaurants, manufacturing and banking.

## Other Notable Practitioners

**Joseph Richardson** of Gammage & Burnham, PLC is regarded by peers as *"very smart and well known in the securities area."* He has considerable experience handling IPOs, secondary offerings and private placements. **Scott DeWald** of Lewis and Roca LLP is respected among peers for his M&A and corporate abilities, and has recently been active in drafting new Arizona legislation governing partnerships, limited liability companies and corporations. **Robert Hackett** of Ridenour, Hienton & Lewis PLLC practices in the fields of corporate finance, public offerings, private placements and M&A. Peers recognize the depth of his expertise in these areas, and admire the length of his experience. **James Brophy** of Ryley Carlock & Applewhite has been practicing at the firm since 1974 and is thought of by peers as a *"very sophisticated lawyer."* In addition to deep knowledge of securities law, he is experienced at handling M&A on both the buy and sell side. He is also experienced in business transactions and labor and employment. As well as being able to handle securities and public and private offering matters, **Steven Lawrence** of Milligan Lawless, P.C. is known as a standout lawyer for handling healthcare-related M&A work, in addition to being skilled in the IP field.

# ENVIRONMENT (INCLUDING WATER RIGHTS)

Water Rights p.497

Commentary about individuals can be found under their firm's paragraph. If the firm has no paragraph (is not ranked) look at Other Notable Practitioners.

## Band 1

### Fennemore Craig

**THE FIRM** One of the strongest firms in the region, Fennemore Craig receives fine praise for its environmental practice and is particularly noted for its deep bench. It serves clients in the agribusiness, mining and life sciences sectors, covering water law, the Endangered Species Act and toxic torts. It recently represented DMB Associates, Sunbelt Holdings, Robson Communities and Douglas Ranch El Dorado Holdings in ensuring a mechanism for acquiring water supplies for future growth for the Central Arizona Project to supply water to Pinal, Pima and Maricopa counties.
**Sources say:** *"The firm is very responsive, obviously has a lot of knowledge of Maricopa county regulations and keeps very up to date on any changes."*

**KEY INDIVIDUALS Norman James** is praised by clients for his communication skills, with one source saying: *"Lots of these issues are difficult to communicate, but his writing abilities are excellent – he writes clear, concise work."* James recently advised the Rosemont Copper Company on, and successfully opposed, a preliminary injunction which would have stopped the release of its environmental impact statement for the opening of its new copper mine. **Robert Anderson** has a focus on water-related work and particular experience in dealing with wetlands, assured water supply and Groundwater Code compliance water quality. Peers respect his skill in this subject and interviewees reveal that *"he's excellent. He knows his stuff very well, is a good communicator and is very responsive."* He led on the Central Arizona Project matter. **Phillip Fargotstein** is an environmental and toxic tort litigator and has deep expertise in the field of air quality, having helped to draft the 1992 Arizona Comprehensive Air Quality Act.

According to clients, *"his customer service is top-notch."* **Lauren Caster** works in the water rights area, and recently advised a number of parties on an appeal against a Special Master's decision to deny the Arizona State Government's claim to a federal reserved water right on approximately 8.8 million acres of state trust land. Peers regard **Maggie Gallogly** as a strong water rights lawyer, and clients are enthusiastic about her communication skills. She recently assisted Robert Anderson with the Central Arizona Project matter.

## Gallagher & Kennedy PA

**THE FIRM** This Phoenix-based firm has deep local roots and maintains its reputation as one of Arizona's top choices for environmental work. It offers a wide range of environmental services and advice, including pesticide regulation, NEPA and Superfund exposure and liability. It represents clients such as the Arizona Mining Association, Freeport-McMoRan Copper & Gold and the Fertilizer Institute. It notably advised Energy Fuel Resources on obtaining permits to open three uranium mines.

**Sources say:** *"They provide very comprehensive service. The lawyers have a high level of expertise and understand the status of industry in many areas."*

**KEY INDIVIDUALS Stanton Curry** has an emphasis on Superfund and air quality work, and was recently involved in advising Freeport-McMoRan Copper & Gold on the supervision and coordination of remediation matters on more than 100 sites across the USA. **David Kimball** heads the firm's environmental and natural resources practice, and has experience representing clients in local, state and federal courts. He was the lead attorney on the Energy Fuel Resources and Freeport-McMoRan Copper & Gold matters. **Chris Leason** is lauded by sources as being *"among the very few who are specialists for the Resource Conservation and Recovery Act,"* and is known for working on a national level. He recently advised the Fertilizer Institute on advocacy strategy and challenges to final EPA rules. **James Derouin** has over four decades of experience handling environmental issues, and has particular skill in remediation cases. He recently assisted with the Freeport-McMoRan Copper & Gold matter.

## Polsinelli PC
See profile on p.1641

**THE FIRM** Polsinelli earns praise from peers and clients for the quality of its work, especially in the area of remediation and regulation. Among its environmental attorneys, it has three policy advisers who focus specifically on environmental policy and legislation. The team represents clients such as BHP Billiton, Nord Resources and Dolphin Industries. It has been providing compliance counseling and enforcement defense to EPCOR relating to Superfund liability negotiations concerning a contamination release by others.

**Sources say:** *"Really solid work; they have great regulatory attorneys."*

**KEY INDIVIDUALS** Chair of the firm's environmental and natural resources practice, **Lucas Narducci** has a wealth of experience handling environmental law, and sources reveal he has *"a good concept of balancing legal issues with those of business and reputation."* He recently represented BHP Copper in regulatory, permit and licensing issues relating to the reopening of a copper pit mine after years of disuse. **Barton Day** advises on regulatory matters, and permitting and compliance. He recently advised the Hearth, Patio & Barbecue Association on an appeal against the US Department of Energy's imposition of energy conservation standards. **Margaret LaBianca** centers her practice around environmental requirements and standards, including NEPA, water supply, endangered species and natural resource damage. Sources reserve particular praise for her responsiveness. She was joint lead partner on the BHP Copper deal.

## Quarles & Brady LLP
See profile on p.2593

**THE FIRM** This firm is well regarded among clients for the breadth of its environmental practice. The attorneys have deep knowledge of many different aspects of environmental law, including alternative energy, clean water, environmental insurance and brownfield development. The team represents clients such as Chevron Mining, the Maricopa Association of Governments and the Gila River Indian Community. A notable recent case involved acting for Univar on 30 groundwater well projects under Superfund provisions.

**Sources say:** *"They really stand out. They're really solid, with lots of good attorneys who have expertise in many different areas."*

**KEY INDIVIDUALS Joseph Drazek** (see p.508) is recommended by peers as being *"on the cutting-edge"* of environmental law, and focuses primarily on litigation and regulation. In addition to leading on the Univar case, he has also represented Crane in a number of negotiations with municipal stakeholders and private parties concerning alleged impacts and complication to groundwater wells due to migration of a contamination plume. **Roger Ferland** (see p.508) has huge stature in the Arizona environmental law community, commanding the respect of peers thanks to the quality of his work and the depth of his experience.

## Squire Sanders (US) LLP
See profile on p.2129

**THE FIRM** This group has the reputation and ability to act for large blue-chip clients such as Procter & Gamble, the City of Phoenix and Boeing. Clients are particularly impressed with the attorneys' depth of knowledge, while peers acknowledge the advantages afforded by the firm's wider international network of offices. It recently represented Johnson Utilities in its opposition to the development of an in situ leach copper mine, and upgradient of the drinking water aquifer for the town of Florence.

**Sources say:** *"I thought the work was very thorough and insightful, and the lawyers were very responsive."*

**KEY INDIVIDUALS Christopher Thomas** (see p.511) is highly regarded by peers, who highlight him as *"an attorney with a reputation for getting things done."* In addition to representing Johnson Utilities, he also defended the City of Phoenix against a Superfund suit alleging contamination of drinking water. **Peter Culp's** (see p.507) clients praise him as *"the person to go to when there are water issues."* He represents The Nature Conservancy as continuing counsel in its Colorado River Basin Initiative to allocate water in Colorado among seven states, including Arizona.

## Band 2

### Ballard Spahr LLP
See profile on p.2234

**THE FIRM** This team represents industrial, municipal and commercial clients at the local, state and federal level. It deals primarily with complex litigation, regulatory and transactional issues. A prime example of its recent work is its representation of the Salt River Project Agricultural Improvement and Power District, which is currently involved in Superfund litigation alleging contamination of groundwater wells.

**KEY INDIVIDUALS Lee Storey** (see p.511) represents clients in matters relating to water use, entitlements and resource management within county, state and federal jurisdictions. Peers are enthusiastic about her work in the water rights field, particularly her assistance with resolving complicated situations to obtain for clients the rights for developments. **David Armstrong** (see p.507) is an environmental litigator, praised by peers for his litigation ability and regulatory knowledge. He was the lead attorney on the Salt River Project Agricultural Improvement and Power District case.

### Lewis and Roca LLP

**THE FIRM** This is a well-known regional firm whose environmental practice also spans Nevada and New Mexico. It represents energy, utility and mining companies in both transactional and regulatory matters, such as permitting and planning, resource planning and responses to alleged regulatory violations. It recently conducted extensive due diligence for SAMSUNG on the regulatory, permitting and regulatory issues relating to its Florence copper recovery project.

**Sources say:** *"Top-quality work. Broad coverage of regulatory, energy and tax issues in Arizona."*

**KEY INDIVIDUALS Carla Consoli** leads the energy, natural resources, environmental, regulatory, government relations and Indian affairs group, and earns peer praise for her work as both an environmental generalist and a water rights specialist. She led on the SAMSUNG project, and also advised Allied Tube & Conduit on an investigation it is undertaking on an alleged release of contaminants.

### Maguire & Pearce, PLLC

**THE FIRM** This Phoenix-based firm specializes in water rights and serves clients in the real estate development, conservation, mining and water supply sectors. It advises on such topics as water quality and water transfer law, water management and land use planning, and the planning and development of infrastructure.

**KEY INDIVIDUALS Rita Maguire** is a former director of the Arizona Department of Water Resources, a role she performed for eight years. Her experience on both the public and private sides of water rights law gives her a depth rightly praised by her peers. **Michael Pearce** is well known among peers as a *"really good water lawyer,"* and is a former chief legal counsel to the Arizona Department of Water Resources, where he represented Arizona in both interstate and international water matters.

### Ryley Carlock & Applewhite
See profile on p.515

**THE FIRM** This regional firm has a good reputation in the environmental law community for its solid water rights capabilities. Its water-related work includes storm water permits and water quality standards development. It also has a good generalist environmental practice, advising clients on matters relating to environmental real estate permitting, Superfund and Water Quality Assurance Revolving Fund work.

**Sources say:** *"A longstanding firm with experience of local Arizona water laws."*

**KEY INDIVIDUALS Sheryl Sweeney** chairs the water, energy, resources and environment practice group, and is particularly praised by peers for her skill in water work. She represents land developers, irrigation districts and golf courses, among other clients. **Fredric Bellamy** focuses on environmental litigation, including toxic torts and the environmental aspects of corporate succession.

### Salmon Lewis & Weldon
See profile on p.516

**THE FIRM** This well-known local firm is praised for its sterling work in the field of water rights. It has been involved in some of the most complex Superfund and Water Quality Assurance Revolving Fund work in Arizona, acting for clients on sites contaminated by solvents, asbestos, metals and other substances. It represents both small and large businesses, real estate developers and public entities.

**KEY INDIVIDUALS** Peers highlight **John Weldon** as *"the resident water expert."* He advises the largest water users' association in Arizona, an Arizona municipality and an agricultural improvement and power district, on water rights issues. He has been counsel for the Salt River Project in the Gila River and Little Colorado River general stream adjudications since 1977. **Van Wolf**'s practice includes environmental transaction due diligence, regulatory compliance and defense against environmental claims at the local, state and federal levels. In particular, he focuses on CERCLA laws, water quality and hazardous waste.

### Snell & Wilmer LLP
See profile on p.517

**THE FIRM** With offices in both Phoenix and Tucson, this regional firm is one of the oldest in Arizona and is known for the diversity of its environmental practice. It handles matters relating to renewable energy, toxic tort defense, permitting and water rights. It advises clients such as Freeport McMoRan, Cole Real Estate Investments, LPMP and Dial Corporation. It recently acted for the Bank of Tokyo-Mitsubishi UFJ as Arizona counsel on compliance with zoning, land use and environmental permit requirements of Arizona's largest wind project, a $300 million deal.

**KEY INDIVIDUALS Patrick Paul** focuses on toxic tort litigation, including mold, pollution and asbestos claims. He was lead partner on the Bank of Tokyo-Mitsubishi UFJ deal. Peers are highly impressed by **William Staudenmaier**, who is primarily known for his work involving water rights, including rights transfer negotiations, general stream adjudications and settlement negotiations of Indian water rights claims.

## Other Notable Practitioners

**Karen Gaylord** of Jennings, Haug & Cunningham LLP is extremely well regarded among peers, with one commenting: *"She would be my first point of call in a conflict."* Gaylord has counseled individuals, municipalities, businesses and water providers. **Michelle De Blasi** (see p.508) of Greenberg Traurig LLP has a strong reputation among peers, especially for her work in alternative energy, with solar power and air quality being particular areas of note.

# LABOR & EMPLOYMENT

Commentary about individuals can be found under their firm's paragraph. If the firm has no paragraph (is not ranked) look at Other Notable Practitioners.

## Band 1

### Jackson Lewis LLP
See profile on p.1982

**THE FIRM** This national boutique has gained a strong reputation in Arizona, which has been reflected in the recent expansion of the team and the increased time the firm is devoting to labor matters. It has experience across many areas of labor and employment law, and is particularly strong in matters relating to discrimination, harassment and retaliation. It recently successfully defended Hanger in a complex case involving harassment and retaliation. Other clients include Best Western International, City of Apache Junction and Southwest Risk Services.

**Sources say:** *"The service they gave me was fantastic, with good strategy and planning."*

**KEY INDIVIDUALS Richard Cohen** (see p.507) advises public and private businesses on any type of employment law, with a particular focus on discrimination. He also advises clients on everyday issues relating to sexual harassment, disability accommodation, and employee terminations and discipline. One source says: *"He is very responsive to clients; he kept me involved and in the loop at all times. We worked closely together developing strategy."* Former office managing partner **Amy Gittler** (see p.508) is particularly skilled at defending large firms in wage and hour, sexual harassment, wrongful termination and employment discrimination cases. Clients admire her ability to win in difficult, complex cases.

### Ogletree, Deakins, Nash, Smoak & Stewart, PC
See profile on p.1110

**THE FIRM** A nationwide firm with offices in Phoenix and Tucson, Ogletree has one of the strongest full-service labor and employment specialist teams in Arizona, handling employment litigation, appeals and representation before administrative agencies. It represents clients of all sizes, and recently defended Boeing Laser Technical Services against a $500,000 claim by a former employee.

**Sources say:** *"Not only is the work of high quality, but the responsiveness is incredible." "It's my go-to firm."*

**KEY INDIVIDUALS Joseph Clees** (see p.507) is head of the firm's practice in Phoenix and is regarded by clients as *"savvy, smart and practical – and he has a good business focus."* He has particular expertise in discrimination, labor relations and wrongful termination matters. He recently successfully defended Advanced Call Center Technologies against a $5 million wrongful dismissal lawsuit. Head of department at the Tucson office, **Tibor Nagy** (see p.510) represents clients across a broad spectrum of labor and employment laws, including labor-management relations, wage and hour, and employment handbooks and contracts. Clients praise him for giving *"comprehensive analysis that is applicable and realistic."* **Mark Kisicki** (see p.509) has over 20 years of experience representing clients,

including in union-avoidance campaigns, litigation under the False Claims Act and complicated IP theft cases. Sources note: *"He's fantastic, an excellent lawyer – diligent, responsive and creative."*

### Steptoe & Johnson LLP

**THE FIRM** This team prides itself on its ability to provide a full service to clients, and on its ability to successfully argue complex matters before federal agencies, such as the NLRB and the EEOC, and the US Supreme Court. It has in-depth experience taking on union-organizing campaigns and is skilled at defending employers against breach of contract, civil rights and wrongful termination cases. It recently defended Red Door Spa Holdings against an 18-plaintiff case, including claims of discrimination.

**Sources say:** *"They're very good. We were very happy with the conclusion."*

**KEY INDIVIDUALS Lawrence Katz** is head of the firm's labor relations and employment law department, and has deep experience handling union-related issues, including litigation. He also litigates in both state and federal court on common law employment rights and employment discrimination statutes and contracts. Peers refer to him as *"the dean of labor and employment."* **Stephanie Quincy** is rated by peers as *"a wonderful labor and employment lawyer,"* and is respected for the depth of her experience. She recently defended Banner Health against a $10 million claim including allegations of religious discrimination, breach of contract and a violation of the False Claims Act. **Steven Wheeless** has a national practice and often advises clients in the Eastern USA. He acts on matters relating to NLRB representations, arbitration and collective bargaining.

## Band 2

### Fennemore Craig

**THE FIRM** The labor and employment team at this strong regional firm defends and advises on virtually all aspects of employment law. Its clients range from small businesses to large utilities and mining companies. It recently defended Southwest Airlines against a claim that it violated employees' rights under the FMLA. It also serves as benefits counsel to ASARCO, and assists with employee retirements plans, including any restating of, and amendments to, plans.

**Sources say:** *"The advice we have received on personnel matters has been timely and on the mark."*

**KEY INDIVIDUALS** Cochair of the firm's labor and employment practice, **Ronald Stolkin** is well versed in advising management on discrimination and harassment matters. He is considered a top trial lawyer, and referred to as a *"dynamite attorney."* Fellow cochair **Donald Gilbert** advises clients on HR matters, such as reviewing changes to employee policies. His abilities are respected by peers, and clients appreciate that he becomes *"part of the team and fabric."* Tucson-based **Erwin Kratz** focuses on employee benefits law and ERISA. He acts on a number of benefits cases nationally and is the lead attorney advising ASARCO.

## Ryley Carlock & Applewhite
See profile on p.515

**THE FIRM** This regional firm has a diverse labor practice and is able to advise clients on collective bargaining and union representation, counseling employers on their rights and obligations under local and federal employment and employee benefits laws. It represents clients in a diverse range of sectors, such as manufacturing, banking, technology and healthcare. Its client list includes Bank of America, Intel, Thames Water and Freeport McMoRan Copper & Gold.

**Sources say:** *"The firm is very thoughtful with its legal advice, very accessible, and willing to take the time to assure that all aspects of the matter at hand are fully addressed in a cost-effective manner."*

**KEY INDIVIDUALS** Former head of the firm's labor and employment practice, **Michael Moberly** has over 20 years' experience in the field and is considered by peers to be an *"exceedingly talented lawyer."* **Nathan Niemuth** advises employers on matters of government contractor, labor relations, wage and hour and equal opportunity laws at both the state and federal levels. He is described as a *"high-quality"* labor lawyer.

## Snell & Wilmer LLP
See profile on p.517

**THE FIRM** From its offices in Phoenix and Tucson, Snell & Wilmer is capable of taking clients through all phases of employment and labor litigation, and helps them avoid litigation where possible. Among other things, it advises clients on matters relating to the Equal Pay Act, age discrimination and wrongful termination. It also has a strong cross-border labor practice, with Mexico labor matters being a particular area of accomplishment.

**KEY INDIVIDUALS John Lomax** frequently advises clients on union-related matters. Peers recommend him as a *"dynamite employment attorney,"* and clients appreciate his litigation skills. **Rebecca Winterscheidt** is cochair of the firm's labor and employment practice, and takes clients' cases all the way from administration through discovery and finally to trial. She has handled jury trials in both state and federal court, and has nearly 30 years' experience defending against discrimination cases. Fluent Spanish speaker **Gerard Morales** advises on Hispanic labor force and cross-border employment, compliance and

wage and hour laws before both state and federal regulatory bodies.

## Band 3

### Coppersmith Schermer & Brockelman PLC

**THE FIRM** This Phoenix-based firm prides itself on having good relationships with local organizations and has become very well known in Arizona for its work in the employment field. It advises management on compliance with federal and state laws, internal investigations and the preparation and review of employment policies.

**Sources say:** *"Good rate structures."*

**KEY INDIVIDUALS Kent Brockelman** serves as the primary outside counsel to a number of businesses in Arizona, and can represent clients in state and federal court, in addition to advising on day-to-day employment issues. Peers note that he is a top choice for conflict referrals. **Kimberly Fatica** is *"very experienced and talented."* She represents clients before administrative agencies as well as in state and federal courts. Peers also use her as an investigator on labor matters.

### Littler Mendelson, PC
See profile on p.688

**THE FIRM** The Phoenix office of this national labor and employment specialist is praised for its strong local knowledge of the businesses and professional bodies in Arizona. It advises companies of all standings and statures, from Fortune 500 firms to local small businesses. It is capable of taking on NLRA, collective action and discrimination matters. It recently successfully defended the City of Phoenix in a class action suit alleging denial of benefits and constructive fraud.

**Sources say:** *"They're very responsive and cost-conscious, and do all they can to make good economic decisions for our company."*

**KEY INDIVIDUALS Shawn Oller** (see p.510) is a trial lawyer who defends employers in arbitration, mediation and litigation. Clients say *"he's as good a guide as Virgil"* and *"balances a company's need to be prepared for litigation against all relevant costs."* In addition to leading on the City of Phoenix case mentioned above, Oller also defended the City of Surprise against a $1 million wrongful termination claim.

### Quarles & Brady LLP
See profile on p.2593

**THE FIRM** This firm maintains a strong presence throughout Arizona. It has a strong labor practice, in addi-

tion to established ability in employment law, giving its team great depth. It offers a full range of services, including ERISA litigation, affirmative action requirements, training programs for managers and supervisors, and OSHA matters.

**KEY INDIVIDUALS** Chair of the firm's labor and employment practice group, **Jon Pettibone** (see p.510) is thought of as *"a stalwart"* and *"a really fine lawyer."* His knowledge of the NLRA earns particular praise, and he often represents management in collective action matters.

## Other Notable Practitioners

**Lawrence Rosenfeld** (see p.511) of Squire Sanders (US) LLP has been practicing employment law, as well as health and administrative law, for over 35 years and peers are very enthusiastic about the quality of his work. He recently represented a number of groups and individuals in the healthcare sector in a series of contract negotiations and employment disputes. Former NLRB attorney **Daniel Pasternak** (see p.510), also of Squire Sanders, represents employers before state and federal administrative agencies and courts in the areas of class action, discrimination and retaliation. **John Doran** of Sherman & Howard LLC is singled out for his strong presence in court. He recently successfully defended loanDepot against restrictive covenants attempted to be enforced on several employees by a rival. Said by sources to be *"even-keeled yet tenacious,"* **Scott Rodgers** (see p.511) heads the employment law practice at Osborn Maledon PA. He defends management against a range of allegations, such as contract violations, and regularly advises corporations on employment law. **David Selden** (see p.511) of The Cavanagh Law Firm is described by clients as *"incredibly diligent, very thoughtful and strategic. He's a pleasure to work with."* He represents management in a number of employment cases, including breach of contract, discrimination and unfair competition. He recently represented Pinal County in a federal investigation of its sheriff's office, alleging illegal political activities. **Lonnie Williams** of Stinson Morrison Hecker LLP focuses on civil litigation, particularly as it relates to employment matters. He recently represented Service Corporation International in decertifying a previously conditionally certified class action. **Michael Berman** of Perkins Coie LLP has a strong employment practice, in addition to being an accomplished litigator and alternative dispute resolution attorney. Peers *"think the world"* of **Mary Ellen Simonsen** of Lewis and Roca LLP, and clients are impressed with her communicative style. She has nearly three decades of experience handling litigation and counseling businesses on labor and employment matters.

# LITIGATION

Commentary about individuals can be found under their firm's paragraph. If the firm has no paragraph (is not ranked) look at Other Notable Practitioners.

## Litigation: General Commercial

### Leading Firms

**Band 1**
Osborn Maledon PA *
Snell & Wilmer LLP *

**Band 2**
Lewis and Roca LLP
Perkins Coie LLP

**Band 3**
Bryan Cave LLP
Fennemore Craig
Gallagher & Kennedy PA
Steptoe & Johnson LLP

**Band 4**
Dickinson Wright Mariscal Weeks *
Polsinelli PC *
Quarles & Brady LLP *

### Senior Statesmen

**Senior Statesmen: distinguished older practitioners**

| Harrison Mark I | Osborn Maledon PA * |

### Leading Individuals

**Star individuals**

| Maledon William J | Osborn Maledon PA * |

**Band 1**

| Birnbaum Gary L | Dickinson Wright Mariscal Weeks * |
| Bouma John Jacob | Snell & Wilmer LLP |
| Eckstein Paul F | Perkins Coie LLP |
| Mais Joseph E | Perkins Coie LLP |
| Rosenbaum David | Osborn Maledon PA * |

**Band 2**

| Beus Leo R | Beus Gilbert PLLC (ONP)[†] |
| Cabot Howard Ross | Perkins Coie LLP |
| Martin Don P | Quarles & Brady LLP * |
| Scarborough Lawrence G | Bryan Cave LLP |

**Band 3**

| Bienstock Floyd P | Steptoe & Johnson LLP |
| Bivens Donald | Snell & Wilmer LLP |
| Cohen Ronald Jay | Cohen Kennedy Dowd & Quigley PC (ONP)[†] |
| Condo James | Snell & Wilmer LLP |
| Danneman Dale | Lewis and Roca LLP |
| Federhar Andrew M | Fennemore Craig |
| Harper Marty | Polsinelli PC |
| Hirsch Steven A | Bryan Cave LLP |
| Kennedy Michael K | Gallagher & Kennedy PA |
| McKirgan Robert H | Lewis and Roca LLP |
| Nadeau Mark A | DLA Piper LLP (US) (ONP)[†] * |
| O'Malley Kevin E | Gallagher & Kennedy PA |
| Rusing Michael J | Rusing Lopez & Lizardi PLLC (ONP)[†] |
| Thomason Timothy | Dickinson Wright Mariscal Weeks * |

**Band 4**

| DeWulf John E. | Roshka DeWulf & Patten (ONP)[†] |
| Iurino John N | Lewis and Roca LLP |
| Northup Douglas C | Fennemore Craig |

## Litigation: White-Collar Crime & Government Investigations

### Leading Firms

**Band 1**
Gallagher & Kennedy PA
Osborn Maledon PA *
Perkins Coie LLP
Piccarreta Davis PC

### Senior Statesmen

**Senior Statesmen: distinguished older practitioners**

| Green Jordan | Perkins Coie LLP |

### Leading Individuals

**Band 1**

| Belanger James J | Coppersmith Schermer & Brockelman (ONP)[†] |
| Hammond Larry A | Osborn Maledon PA * |
| Henze Tom | Gallagher & Kennedy PA |
| Mitchell Barry D | Gallagher & Kennedy PA |
| Novak Edward F | Polsinelli PC |
| Piccarreta Michael L | Piccarreta Davis PC |
| Stein Lee | Perkins Coie LLP |

**Band 2**

| Butler III A Bates | A. Bates Butler Law (ONP)[†] |
| Charlton Paul | Gallagher & Kennedy PA |
| Kimerer Michael | Kimerer & Derrick, P.C. (ONP)[†] |
| Nash Walter | Nash & Kirchner (ONP)[†] |

**Band 3**

| Cabou Jean-Jacques | Perkins Coie LLP |
| Ryan James A | Quarles & Brady LLP |

* Indicates firm / individual with profile.
[†] ONP = Other Notable Practitioner.

*The editorial is in alphabetical order by firm name.*

## Bryan Cave LLP

**THE FIRM** The Arizona office of Bryan Cave combines the resources of an international firm with the regional knowledge of well-known local attorneys to provide an optimal litigation team for its clients. It particularly excels in the class action, utility, antitrust and real estate areas, and acts for companies of all sizes, from smaller local business to large clients such as One World Enterprises, JPMorgan Chase and Fender Musical Instruments. It recently successfully defended UnitedHealthcare against two class action suits and up to 80 individual suits as a result of a hepatitis C outbreak.

**KEY INDIVIDUALS Lawrence Scarborough** is considered an outstanding lawyer, particularly with regards to class actions. He represents clients across the defense, semiconductor, medical device and computer industries, among others. In addition to representing UnitedHealthcare in the two class actions, he also successfully defended Sey Pet against tort, contract and Interstate Land Sales Act claims. **Steven Hirsch** has been involved in trials concerning land use regulation, real estate valuation,

contract and lease disputes and eminent domain, among other matters. Clients praise his sector knowledge and his ability to convey complex issues in easy-to-understand terms. He recently represented Conair in seeking $14 million in damages relating to an airport clear zone affecting the company's future growth area.

## Fennemore Craig

**THE FIRM** With a strong local base and enviable regional presence, this firm represents clients from Arizona and the Western USA in both state and federal courts. It handles litigation related to utilities regulation, e-discovery and data contracts, securities, and tort and insurance. It recently represented BNSF Railway in the Arizona Court of Appeals, overturning a previous collective bargaining decision.

**Sources say:** *"The firm has a lot of depth, and devoted a great deal of resources to our work."*

**KEY INDIVIDUALS** A director at the firm, **Douglas Northup** focuses on complex tort, commercial and professional liability litigation. Sources confirm that he delivers *"excellent results on a consistent basis."* **Andrew Federhar** is a director in the Phoenix and Tucson offices, and is praised by clients as being *"highly experienced, with a broad knowledge of commercial litigation. His communication and cooperation are great."* He has deep experience in the telecom and healthcare sectors.

## Gallagher & Kennedy PA

**THE FIRM** This commercial litigation team maintains high standards and prides itself on the number of attorneys it fields with trial experience. The group also goes to great lengths to assess each client's situation and decide when it is and is not appropriate for a client to take its matter to court. It is highly experienced in commercial litigation matters such as product liability, anticompetitive conduct, public contracting and professional malpractice. It recently defended SSP America against an injunction to prevent the award of a contract worth $700 million over ten years. In addition, its government investigation and white-collar crime litigation team continues to uphold its strong reputation in the field, with sources noting the strength of the group's preparation when it comes to trial argument. It represents both corporate and individual clients at the state and federal level.

**Sources say:** *"They're timely and did an exceptional job. We were fortunate to work with them." "The work is excellent. The attorneys are thorough, diligent, and easy to work with."*

**KEY INDIVIDUALS Barry Mitchell** focuses on criminal, administrative and regulatory matters, and is thought of by many as *"the first port of call at the firm."* Peers praise his detail-oriented style, his sense of judgment and his proactive approach. **Tom Henze** works on white-collar prosecutions and commercial matters at both a federal and state level, and is well known as an influential figure in Arizona. Peers cite the depth of his experience and superb trial ability as his major strengths, and note him as *"a dean of criminal defense in Arizona."* **Paul Charlton**, who focuses his practice on white-collar defense and internal compliance, is a former US Attorney praised by sources as being *"very professional and well prepared."* He works with both the commercial litigation and white-collar crime teams, and led on the SSP America case. A founding partner of the firm, **Michael Kennedy** handles general civil litigation and is regarded by his peers as *"a fabulous deal-maker"* and *"a very persuasive, powerful presence."* He recently defended Swift Transportation against four national class action suits alleging, unjust enrichment, breach of contract and negligence, among others. **Kevin O'Malley** is head of the litigation department and is praised by peers as *"a lawyer's lawyer."* Recently, he represented D.R. Horton in arbitration involving a dispute over whether other parties in a joint development agreement paid their share of funding for offsite improvements relating to the construction of a sewer system.

## Lewis and Roca LLP

**THE FIRM** This is a strong regional firm with offices in both Phoenix and Tucson, and provides strong coverage across the entirety of Arizona. It is active across a wide range of sectors, and is especially strong in the area of real estate litigation. As well as a strong trial group, the firm is also noted for its accomplishments at the appellate level. It recently defended Morgan Stanley Private Bank and Morgan Stanley Smith Barney against an antideficiency claim.

**Sources say:** *"The lawyers write exceptionally well. The research and analysis is all very good."*

**KEY INDIVIDUALS** Phoenix-based **Dale Danneman** is experienced at handling breach of contract, racketeering, antitrust litigation and fraud matters. He has extensive experience, owing to his time spent as an Assistant United States Attorney in the District of Arizona for the Fraud Section, of dealing with land fraud. He is praised by peers for his skill at representation. **John Iurino** has three decades' experience handling trials and appellate cases, particularly in the real estate sphere. He is well regarded in the Tucson market by peers. Practicing mainly within the fields of bankruptcy and business litigation, **Robert McKirgan** is a former public accountant who has a great deal of experience litigating in the specific areas of commercial torts, breach of fiduciary duty and breach of contract. Sources note that *"for complex cases, including those for local big healthcare companies, he's great."*

## Dickinson Wright Mariscal Weeks
See profile on p.1561

**THE FIRM** This team from the newly combined Dickinson Wright and Mariscal, Weeks, McIntyre & Friedlander has experience representing clients before state and federal agencies and courts, and in taking on litigation involving antitrust, land use and insurance. The group recently completed a number of eminent domain cases.

**KEY INDIVIDUALS** **Gary Birnbaum** (see p.507) is known for handling high-profile mediation work as well as insurance, real estate and eminent domain litigation. Peers

are highly impressed with his work, singling him out as a *"top-notch advocate."* **Timothy Thomason** (see p.512) is considered *"one of the most experienced trial lawyers in Arizona,"* and *"a top-flight malpractice attorney."* His litigation work focuses on representing financial institutions in commercial disputes, professional liability and escrow matters.

## Osborn Maledon PA
See profile on p.514

**THE FIRM** The commercial litigation team at Osborn Maledon, one of the top regional firms, continues to be recognized as one of Arizona's strongest, excelling in complicated business litigation. The team recently represented the Arizona Independent Redistricting Commission in two cases each in state and federal courts, relating to state and federal constitutionality, respectively. The white-collar crime group is known for the breadth of its practice in internal and government investigations, and continues to receive plaudits from peers and clients for its work. It advised corporate clients on investigations and responses to government inquiries for a number of different matters, including healthcare fraud, employee misconduct, and corporate governance.

**Sources say:** *"They positioned us in the litigation very well by thinking ahead."* *"The firm brings two important and elusive qualities: vast experience and good judgment."*

**KEY INDIVIDUALS** **William Maledon** (see p.509) is regarded as one of the top commercial litigators in Arizona, with peers saying: *"He really stands out – a bet-the-company kind of guy."* He recently represented AstraZeneca as one of 45 clients in a class action suit against numerous pharmaceutical companies for an alleged price-fixing scheme, a $100 million matter. He also acted as liaison counsel for all the defendants and coordinated the defense of all the parties generally. **Larry Hammond** (see p.508) heads the white-collar crime department and has over three decades of experience litigating in the private sector. He is regarded by peers as a *"terrific"* lawyer, with *"dignity and gravitas."* He is also the founder of the Arizona Justice Project, an organization that assists wrongfully convicted criminals. **David Rosenbaum** (see p.511) is singled out by peers for his skill at securities litigation and is described as *"very good and practical, with sound judgment and sound advice,"* while clients laud him as *"a phenomenal, creative lawyer and a great advocate."* He recently represented the Apollo Group and its current and former directors and executives in a number of shareholder derivative and securities fraud class action suits. **Mark Harrison** (see p.509) is a highly respected, *"extraordinary"* attorney and is seen as *"a dean in Arizona for representing lawyers in disciplinary matters."* He also has a fine reputation for appellate work.

## Perkins Coie LLP
See profile on p.2548

**THE FIRM** As part of a national firm with a wealth of resources, this Arizona commercial litigation team is noted for its depth and strength in the local market. It represents a number of national and multinational clients across a

broad range of commercial litigation, including product liability, corporate governance and business tort litigation. The Phoenix office also houses a respected white-collar crime practice, highly experienced in both investigations and defense work, with a particularly strong focus on FCPA matters. It recently advised Dennis Burke on his testimony before Congress and government investigations relating to the Fast and Furious investigation.

**KEY INDIVIDUALS** Head of commercial litigation throughout the firm, **Joseph Mais** has a reputation as a leading litigator for high stakes and bet-the-company disputes. Cochair of the firm's investigations and white-collar defense group, **Lee Stein** is another attorney who wins praise from peers. Stein has represented several clients in cases related to RICO, fraud and money laundering, as well as public officials accused of corruption. **Howard Ross Cabot** takes on various kinds of litigation, including class actions, securities and antitrust. His experience extends to defense and representation in both state and federal courts. **Jean-Jacques Cabou** has a focus on government investigations and criminal defense, with particular expertise in racketeering and civil forfeiture in both federal and state courts. **Paul Eckstein** often acts as a mediator or arbitrator in addition to his practice in commercial litigation. He is considered by peers to be one of Phoenix's strongest lawyers. **Jordan Green** has represented businesses and individuals in matters relating to OSHA, FCPA, antitrust and environmental allegations. He is known in Arizona as one of the most sought-after criminal lawyers.

## Piccarreta Davis PC

**THE FIRM** This Tucson-based firm has a strong reputation and deep roots in southern Arizona, and frequently defends clients against allegations of white-collar crimes including tax evasion, embezzlement, and various types of fraud. The firm is singled out for its ability to allocate large amounts of resources and time to the cases it receives.

**KEY INDIVIDUALS** Peers consider **Michael Piccarreta** to be *"the best criminal lawyer in Tucson,"* and he is *"in high demand – they don't come any better."* He focuses specifically on representing individuals and businesses in criminal defense, including environmental, fraud and securities litigation.

## Polsinelli PC
See profile on p.1641

**THE FIRM** This firm represents corporate clients and individuals in the transport, condemnation, retail and hospitality and professional liability sectors. It recently represented a number of airline pilots in a class action suit regarding the use of a seniority list which their union refused to include in a new collective bargaining agreement.

**Sources say:** *"They take a pragmatic approach to cases. They're always looking to prevail legally, but also constantly monitor as to the practical solution for businesses."*

**KEY INDIVIDUALS** **Edward Novak** is *"very sought after"* and *"does a great job at reaching resolution."* He has deep experience dealing with government investigations and complex civil litigation, and has particular expertise in the healthcare arena. The vice-chair of Polsinelli Shughart's commercial litigation practice group, **Marty Harper** has nearly 40 years of experience handling complex commercial litigation matters, and is described as *"a talented trial attorney."* He recently represented Red Mountain Machinery, Owen Cowing and Linda Cowing in seeking between $20 million and $40 million in damages for wrongful conduct against the company's former CFO, primary bank and investment bank.

## Quarles & Brady LLP
See profile on p.2593

**THE FIRM** This commercial litigation team has deep benches in Phoenix and Tucson, and impresses clients with its attorneys' communication skills and incisiveness. It represents clients from a number of different sectors, and is particularly well known for representing banks and other financial institutions. It recently succeeded in defending Massage Envy against its former software vendor in a suit seeking $95 million in outstanding license fees and late fees, punitive damages and costs.

**Sources say:** *"They are consistently giving us outstanding results and the quality of writing is excellent."*

**KEY INDIVIDUALS Don Martin** (see p.510) is based in the firm's Phoenix office, and works on complex commercial litigation and real estate litigation. Peers agree that he *"knows his stuff,"* and respect his ability to handle complex cases. Also in Phoenix, **James Ryan** takes on litigation involving direct sales contracts, commercial litigation and civil racketeering litigation, among other matters. He recently successfully defended Stearns Bank against state and federal level racketeering claims, and related tort claims at the state level.

## Snell & Wilmer LLP
See profile on p.517

**THE FIRM** An Arizona-based firm with one of the deepest benches in the state, Snell & Wilmer earns praise for its ability to provide quality work on a large number of cases. It represents clients at both trial and appellate level, and handles litigation relating to business torts, real estate, public utilities and telecommunications, among other matters. It represents a number of high-profile corporations and individuals, and recently acted for Insight Enterprises in the Ninth Circuit Court of Appeals on a shareholder derivative suit.

**Sources say:** *"One of the best in town for many reasons, not least its size, depth and level of sophistication."*

**KEY INDIVIDUALS Donald Bivens** is known among peers as a highly effective litigator, who *"really understands the litigation business and knows how to get things done."* He has previously tried cases relating to environmental liability, trade secrets, patent infringements and discrimination. **James Condo** is cochair of the firm's commercial litigation practice group, and litigates on both the regional and national stage. Peers praise him as an *"outstanding lawyer."* Firm chairman **John Bouma** commands the highest respect of his peers, who consider him to be a *"major community mover."* He recently represented the State of Arizona and Governor Jan Brewer in a number of federal suits relating to the S.B.1070 Act regarding illegal immigration.

## Steptoe & Johnson LLP

**THE FIRM** This team receives praise for its ability to handle complex and specialized work. It represents clients in both state and federal court, and has been noted for its ability to take on cases of national importance. It is well known for handling financial fraud matters, and for the defense of insurance companies accused of acting in bad faith. It recently successfully defended the National Union Fire Insurance Company of Pittsburgh against a multimillion-dollar claim relating to a directors and officers liability policy.

**KEY INDIVIDUALS Floyd Bienstock** is the leader of the firm's insurance coverage and bad faith group, and is admired for his specialty in complex bad faith insurance. In addition to leading on the National Union Fire Insurance Company of Pittsburgh matter, he also represented Casualty Insurance and Metropolitan Group Property in reducing punitive damages from a tortious breach case from a 4:1 ratio to a 1:1 ratio.

## Other Notable Practitioners

**Leo Beus** of Beus Gilbert PLLC is a greatly admired litigator, mainly focusing on representing plaintiffs. Peers say he *"thrives on huge cases. If you want someone who'll get results, he's the man."* He heads the litigation department at the firm and recently represented Karl and June Eller in a case against PwC, concerning the sale of a financial product that was deemed by the IRS to be a fraudulent tax shelter.

Former US Attorney for Arizona **Bates Butler** of A. Bates Butler Law defends individuals and companies under investigation by state or federal regulatory or law enforcement agencies, and also represents witnesses and victims in legal proceedings. Lauded by his peers, **James Belanger** of Coppersmith Schermer & Brockelman PLC has been defending individuals and organizations for 25 years against regulatory and criminal charges, including allegations of antitrust conspiracy, securities violations, predatory lending and fraud. **Michael Kimerer** of Kimerer & Derrick, P.C. specializes in criminal defense matters and centers his practice around environmental and white-collar crime. Peers note that *"he is often called on to assist with cases, particularly those that require in-depth knowledge in court."* He is licensed to practice in Arizona, California, and several federal courts, including the United States Supreme Court. Co-managing partner of DLA Piper LLP (US)'s Phoenix office, **Mark Nadeau** (see p.510) is well known for handling complex litigation matters in the region, and throughout the USA. Clients praise him as being a *"very reliable source on tactics, litigation and arbitration on an international scale."* He recently successfully defended Nautic Partners in a $20 million case following disputes arising as a result of fund investments in the healthcare industry. Founding member of Cohen Kennedy Dowd & Quigley PC, **Ronald Cohen** handles a significant amount of commercial litigation from the plaintiff side. Market sources regard him highly, saying: *"He's got a great reputation nationally."* A trial lawyer in Tucson since 1971, **Walter Nash** of Nash & Kirchner focuses on criminal law and is said by peers to be *"among the most senior and highly regarded criminal defense lawyers."* Tucson-based **Michael Rusing** is head of Rusing Lopez & Lizardi PLLC's litigation section, and has a strong reputation among peers as one of the strongest lawyers in southern Arizona. He has tried over 100 cases in state and federal courts, covering areas such as legal and medical malpractice, breach of fiduciary duty, ERISA and insurance coverage cases. **John DeWulf** of Roshka DeWulf & Patten is *"a seasoned lawyer"* and *"very talented."* He has a broad practice within litigation and has represented local, regional and multinational clients in trade secret, real estate, business tort and securities litigation.

# REAL ESTATE

Commentary about individuals can be found under their firm's paragraph. If the firm has no paragraph (is not ranked) look at Other Notable Practitioners.

## Real Estate
### Leading Firms

**Band 1**

Fennemore Craig
Dickinson Wright Mariscal Weeks *
Quarles & Brady LLP *
Snell & Wilmer LLP *

**Band 2**

Greenberg Traurig LLP *
Lewis and Roca LLP

**Band 3**

Osborn Maledon PA *
Perkins Coie LLP
Ryley Carlock & Applewhite *

*The editorial is in alphabetical order by firm name.*

## Real Estate
### Leading Individuals

**Band 1**

| | |
|---|---|
| Fathe Fred C | Dickinson Wright Mariscal Weeks * |
| Haller Diane | Quarles & Brady LLP * |
| Hanks Gregg | Fennemore Craig |
| Kramer Jay S | Fennemore Craig |
| Lansky David | Dickinson Wright Mariscal Weeks * |
| Mast Gregory | Mast Law Firm, PC (ONP) [†] |
| Pokorski Jody | Snell & Wilmer LLP |
| Storey Lesa J | Greenberg Traurig LLP * |

**Band 2**

| | |
|---|---|
| Biskind Neil | Biskind Hunt, PLC (ONP) [†] |
| Burnham Rebecca Lynne | Greenberg Traurig LLP * |
| Lisker Steven L | Squire Sanders (US) LLP (ONP) [†] * |
| Lowe Ronald E | Perkins Coie LLP |
| Sorenson Derek L | Quarles & Brady LLP * |
| Van Winkle, Jr Kenneth | Lewis and Roca LLP |
| Wright Joyce | Snell & Wilmer LLP |

**Band 3**

| | |
|---|---|
| Broadfoot Alexander L | Gallagher & Kennedy PA |
| Hink John | Lewis and Roca LLP |
| Irwin R Neil | Bryan Cave LLP (ONP) [†] |
| King Charles M | Fennemore Craig |
| Osborn II Jones | Osborn Maledon PA * |
| Robinson Robert P | Fennemore Craig |
| Stokes Randall | Lewis and Roca LLP |
| Tiffany Michael E. | Tiffany & Bosco, PA (ONP) [†] * |
| Williams Craig K | Snell & Wilmer LLP |
| Winkler Peter | Dickinson Wright Mariscal Weeks * |

**Band 4**

| | |
|---|---|
| Curley Michael | Earl, Curley & Lagarde, PC |
| Hettinger Kyle | Perkins Coie LLP |
| Irvine Thomas | Polsinelli PC (ONP) [†] |
| Mehr Matthew | Quarles & Brady LLP * |
| Ripp Michael | Ryley Carlock & Applewhite |
| Schorr Andrew D | Lewis and Roca LLP |
| Shein David E | Chester & Shein (ONP) [†] * |
| Wiley Jay | Snell & Wilmer LLP |

* Indicates firm / individual with profile.

[†] ONP = Other Notable Practitioner.

## Real Estate: Zoning/Land Use
### Leading Firms

**Band 1**

Berry & Damore LLC
Beus Gilbert PLLC
Burch & Cracchiolo
Earl, Curley & Lagarde, PC
Gammage & Burnham, PLC
Snell & Wilmer LLP *

**Band 2**

Fennemore Craig
Gallagher & Kennedy PA
Withey Morris PLC

**Band 3**

Lewis and Roca LLP

### Senior Statesmen

**Senior Statesmen: distinguished older practitioners**

| | |
|---|---|
| Gammage Jr Grady | Gammage & Burnham, PLC |

### Leading Individuals

**Band 1**

| | |
|---|---|
| Bangs Frank | Lazarus, Silvyn & Bangs, P.C. (ONP) [†] |
| Berry John V | Berry & Damore LLC |
| Bull Edwin | Burch & Cracchiolo * |
| Earl Stephen | Earl, Curley & Lagarde, PC |
| Gilbert Paul E | Beus Gilbert PLLC |
| Lazarus Larry S | Lazarus, Silvyn & Bangs, P.C. (ONP) [†] |
| Withey Michael B | Withey Morris PLC |

**Band 2**

| | |
|---|---|
| Phalen Michael | Fennemore Craig |
| Stagg Belknap Dana | Gallagher & Kennedy PA |
| Wood Nicholas J | Snell & Wilmer LLP |

**Band 3**

| | |
|---|---|
| Allison William | Gallagher & Kennedy PA |
| Anderson Stephen W | Gammage & Burnham, PLC |
| Morris Jason | Withey Morris PLC |
| Silvyn Keri | Lazarus, Silvyn & Bangs, P.C. (ONP) [†] |

### Associates to watch

| | |
|---|---|
| Ray Brennan | Burch & Cracchiolo |

## Berry & Damore LLC

**THE FIRM** This compact boutique firm has a focus on helping clients through all aspects of the processes of real estate workout, entitlement and development. It is praised by peers as the top firm for land use and zoning in the Scottsdale area.

**Sources say:** *"A very good firm."*

**KEY INDIVIDUALS John Berry** is well known around the state for his focus on zoning. Peers give very positive feedback on his practice, saying he is a top referral choice in Scottsdale.

## Beus Gilbert PLLC

**THE FIRM** Beus Gilbert maintains its reputation as one of the strongest zoning and land use firms in the state, with experience in handling matters at the litigation, administrative and legislative levels. It recently represented Macerich in an infrastructure reimbursement agreement for a master planned community of 3,000 acres, a deal valued at $200 million.

**KEY INDIVIDUALS** Peers praise **Paul Gilbert** as *"a dean of zoning lawyers in the Phoenix metro area,"* and clients are enthusiastic about his approachability. In addition to leading on the Macerich case above, he also advised Southwest Value Partners on successfully opposing the construction of a copper mine near a 6,000-acre master planned community in Florence, Arizona.

## Burch & Cracchiolo

**See profile on p.513**

**THE FIRM** This Phoenix-based firm has been involved in the development of several local landmarks, and has a distinguished pedigree in the field of zoning and land use. Clients and peers alike praise the depth of experience that the firm has built over the years. It represents clients such as Camelot Homes, Red Development and Fulton Homes, and recently advised Investment Property Associates on a complex multifamily site planning and zoning variances matter.

**Sources say:** *"They're attentive to our needs and have a great grasp of the market and how we need to flow and adapt."*

**KEY INDIVIDUALS** President of the firm **Edwin Bull** (see p.507) is admired by clients for his thoroughness and for the depth of his knowledge in the zoning field. He was recently lead partner on the Investment Property Associates matter, and also advised Red Development on obtaining approvals in downtown Phoenix for electronic offsite commercial signage. **Brennan Ray** is an associate at the firm and is praised for his close attention to detail and ability to work well with many parties. He assisted with the Red Development matter and also assisted Bull with a design review for a multifamily apartment in the town of Gilbert.

## Earl, Curley & Lagarde, PC

**THE FIRM** A zoning and land use specialist, this Phoenix-based firm receives very strong feedback from peers for the depth of its experience throughout the valley. It assists clients on such matters as the development review process, rezoning, use permits and variances and signage and wireless communication entitlements. Clients include the

Chinese Culture Center, Four Seasons Resort and McDonald's.

Sources say: *"They're excellent – knowledgeable and responsive, and have a high success rate."*

KEY INDIVIDUALS Peers consider **Stephen Earl** to be one of the best zoning lawyers in Arizona, and clients report that he is *"very intelligent – a fantastic negotiator who is able to balance our zoning budget with the tactics he takes."* He has nearly three decades of experience handling zoning matters. **Michael Curley** has more than 20 years' experience handling land use matters and has particularly deep knowledge of land use planning law. Clients mark him out as a top land use lawyer, saying: *"He's very skilled and highly experienced, especially in Phoenix."*

## Fennemore Craig

THE FIRM A well-known regional firm with offices in Phoenix, Tucson and Nogales, Fennemore Craig has one of the most positively regarded real estate teams in the state. Peers admire the breadth of service the real estate practice provides, and note that it is adept at taking on complex matters for large clients. It recently represented ML Manager in the sale of 18 parcels of property, including retail, apartment, hotel and office real estate, for an aggregate $74 million. The firm also has a solid reputation in the land use and zoning field, and clients appreciate the strength of the team's regional knowledge and its close cooperation with other groups at the firm. The zoning team recently represented Roles Inn of America in a $5 million deal to purchase land from the Arizona State Land Department, which it had previously been leasing for 30 years.

Sources say: *"The firm is very strong and has lots of breadth."* *"They certainly have a lot of local knowledge and I appreciate the depth of the firm."*

KEY INDIVIDUALS **Gregg Hanks**'s real estate practice centers around joint ventures and syndications, and he also has a great deal of tax law experience to assist with any taxation issues which may arise. He recently represented an individual and related entities in the redemption of partnership interests which involved multiple real property distributions. **Jay Kramer**'s peers give very positive feedback once again, with one source reporting: *"I can only say wonderful things about my experience with him."* Kramer recently worked on a joint venture between an affiliate of Trammell Crow and its equity partner in the $79 million sale of a six-story class A office building in Scottsdale to a REIT in Canada. He chairs the firm's real estate practice. **Michael Phalen** has a broad practice covering commercial ground leasing, signage, rezoning and development. He was the lead attorney on the Roles Inn of America deal. **Charles King** handles a wide range of real estate matters, and is noted for his strength in transactional work. *"He's very knowledgeable, experienced and prompt. I give him high marks,"* said one interviewee. **Robert Robinson** chairs the real estate finance practice at the firm and has more than 40 years of experience in this area. He recently assisted with the ML Manager matter.

## Gallagher & Kennedy PA

THE FIRM Based in Phoenix, this firm is well known for its work in land use and zoning, and is often involved in drafting planning and land use legislation for the state of Arizona, as well as local zoning rules. The firm is noted for handling big-ticket Arizona work. It recently represented the Ak-Chin Indian Community in the City of Maricopa's annexation of property held by the community, and the subsequent transferring of that land to Trust status.

Sources say: *"We're very happy with the work they did. They're able to see the realistic side of what we want, and able to make the other side see when it is being unreasonable."*

KEY INDIVIDUALS **William Allison** is a former city planner for the City of Phoenix and is praised for his *"very client-oriented"* approach to matters. He successfully represented D&T Property Leasing in a complex rezoning matter. **Dana Belknap** is head of the firm's zoning and land use department, and is respected by peers as *"one of the strongest development agreement lawyers in Arizona."* She is also praised by clients as being *"forthright, practical, timely and insightful."* She recently assisted Freeport-McMoRan Copper & Gold with the acquisition of nearly 9,100 acres of Arizona State Land Trust for a new tailings impoundment. Real estate generalist **Alexander Broadfoot** is highly regarded by his peers. He is experienced at handling matters between sellers and buyers, and landlords and tenants.

## Gammage & Burnham, PLC

THE FIRM Based in Phoenix, this firm is able to handle a broad range of land use and zoning-related work, including referendum and zoning opposition, land use litigation and development and incentive agreements. It often undertakes development entitlements for large master plan communities, specialized PPPs and urban high rises.

KEY INDIVIDUALS **Stephen Anderson** has 20 years' experience handling land use matters and is described as a *"go-to"* land use lawyer. **Grady Gammage** is a land use and zoning specialist who has been practicing for nearly 35 years. He was a principal author of the Urban Land Act in Arizona and has represented several clients in deals relating to state trust land.

## Greenberg Traurig LLP
See profile on p.1024

THE FIRM The real estate team in this national firm's Phoenix office is known for its work on real estate transactions and finance, and has a particularly strong track record in matters relating to bank loans. It recently represented Synaptics in the fast track purchase of a three-building office industrial project, a $12 million deal.

KEY INDIVIDUALS Well respected by her peers, **Rebecca Lynne Burnham** (see p.507) specializes in representing real estate developers in acquisition, infrastructure and use agreements of development interests. She was the lead attorney on the Synaptics matter. **Lesa Storey** (see p.511) also represents development interests and is praised by peers for her work in the residential sector. She is said to be *"top quality"* by peers, and interviewees reveal that *"even as opposing counsel, she's great to work with."*

## Lewis and Roca LLP

THE FIRM The real estate team in the Phoenix office of this national firm excels at representing clients in large matters and is experienced at handling a wide range of transactions. Clients are enthusiastic about the firm's responsiveness and business sense. The Tucson office also has a noted zoning and land use team, which wins praise for its strength in the southern Arizona region.

Sources say: *"They've been superb. They're always on time and on budget, and have a good understanding of clients' needs."*

KEY INDIVIDUALS Managing partner **Kenneth Van Winkle** is well regarded as *"thoughtful, pragmatic, and responsive"* by clients, and receives praise for his work from peers. **Randall Stokes**'s practice has a focus on commercial and mixed-use communities, shopping centers and planned residential projects, and on representing home builders. With a focus on commercial real estate transactions, **John Hink** is described by sources as *"detailed and congenial. He gets to the bottom of issues and gets results."* He recently advised Maricopa County on lease agreements, vendor contracts and risk documents for the construction of a new $300 million court tower facility. **Andrew Schorr** is known for working for blue-chip clients and is experienced at handling large-scale office building projects from beginning to end.

## Dickinson Wright Mariscal Weeks
See profile on p.1561

THE FIRM Formed through the recent merger of Mariscal, Weeks, McIntyre & Friedlander and Dickinson Wright's office in Phoenix, this firm now combines extensive local experience with the resources of a national firm. It has a diverse client base, representing governments, corporations, contractors and developers, and focuses on financing, leasing and acquisition, development and sales. Peers single out its strength in representing public bodies.

KEY INDIVIDUALS **Fred Fathe**'s (see p.508) peers consider him *"top-quality"* and *"extremely knowledgeable, reasonable and responsible."* He receives enthusiastic feedback for his work in real estate finance. **David Lansky** (see p.509) is praised by peers as *"a first-rate lawyer,"* especially for leasing and office building real estate work. **Peter Winkler** (see p.512) advises on lending and development, landlord and tenant law, and commercial real estate law. Peers also praise him for his skill at handling arbitration matters.

## Osborn Maledon PA
See profile on p.514

THE FIRM This regional firm's real estate team covers all aspects of real estate law and has expertise in acquisitions, leasing and Indian land matters. It represents clients such as Wells Fargo, the Salt River Pima-Maricopa Indian Community and Westdale Capital, and recently represented the Hopi Tribe in a $4 million land acquisition.

Sources say: *"The attorneys have a lot of deep knowledge and are good at translating legal terminology into everyday speech."*

*The editorial is in alphabetical order by firm name.*

**KEY INDIVIDUALS** Founder of the firm and head of the real estate department **Jones Osborn** (see p.510) is remarked on by clients as having a talent for *"balancing risks inherent in contracts to make sure we understand those risks, allowing us to make the best decisions."* He recently worked with Courtland Homes on the negotiation and document preparation of a $40 million sale of lots.

## Perkins Coie LLP
See profile on p.2548

**THE FIRM** This is a national firm with all the resources that entails, and its real estate team in Phoenix prides itself on handling complex, high-value matters for blue-chip clients. It has a broad focus, and frequently represents clients doing work outside Arizona.

**KEY INDIVIDUALS Ronald Lowe** has a focus on real estate transaction and securities work. Clients are quick to praise his responsive approach and extensive depth of subject matter expertise. Sources praise **Kyle Hettinger's** responsive and efficient approach. Peers note that he is skilled at taking on work for clients concerning mortgages which have been foreclosed on.

## Quarles & Brady LLP
See profile on p.2593

**THE FIRM** With offices in both Phoenix and Tucson, this national firm is well placed to provide real estate coverage to clients across Arizona. It is highly praised for its work in the areas of real estate finance, and lauded by clients for its commercial sensibilities. It represents clients such as JPMorgan Chase Bank, the Yavapai Prescott Indian Tribe and Liberty Property Trust. It recently advised the Solanna Group, which is comprised of several individual Native American landowners, on obtaining a business master lease of federally allotted Indian trust land.

**Sources say:** *"They're fantastic from both a legal and business perspective."*

**KEY INDIVIDUALS** Peers consider **Derek Sorenson** (see p.511) to be very strong, and clients praise his practicality and business understanding. The firm's national real estate and land use practice chair **Diane Haller** (see p.508) is praised by clients for her creativity. Peers describe her as a *"wonderful lawyer."* She has recently handled several significant projects for national companies. **Matthew Mehr** (see p.510) focuses on the documentation and negotiation of real estate finance deals. In particular, he has experience advising on loan transactions.

## Ryley Carlock & Applewhite
See profile on p.515

**THE FIRM** This regional firm has a solid presence in Arizona and its real estate team is singled out by peers as doing strong work. It combines the strength of its real estate team with its environmental, tax and natural resources groups in order to provide a full service to clients.

**KEY INDIVIDUALS Michael Ripp** represents insurance companies and banks in real estate loan transactions, enforcement and workouts. He is also experienced at handling residential subdivisions, master planned communities and redevelopment matters.

## Snell & Wilmer LLP
See profile on p.517

**THE FIRM** A regional mainstay with offices in Phoenix and Tucson, this firm maintains an enviable reputation for real estate work. It can provide service across the transactional real estate spectrum, whether simple or complex, concerning land or properties. It recently represented Scottsdale Healthcare in an $81 million sale and partial leaseback of eight medical office buildings. It is also strong in the area of land use and zoning, and interviewees are grateful for the efficiency with which the work is done. It recently advised Marriott on the rezoning of the Indian Bend Golf Course, a matter made complex by neighboring residents who initially opposed the plans.

**Sources say:** *"Probably one of the broadest benches in Arizona."* *"They really did an amazing job. The attorneys know how to get things done efficiently and with as little stress as possible."*

**KEY INDIVIDUALS Jody Pokorski** focuses on real estate finance and transactions. Peers are enthusiastic about her skill and clients are grateful that *"she has the ability to distill very complex issues to a very understandable format."* She recently advised on acquisitions for a student housing development in Tempe. **Joyce Wright** is a practice group leader for real estate, commercial finance, environmental and energy at the firm, and is greatly respected by peers, while clients enthuse that she is *"very, very thorough."* She recently acted as Arizona counsel to Prospect Global on its purchase of 50% of American West Potash from The Karlsson Group. Peers are enthusiastic about **Craig Williams's** skill, particularly in the area of real estate finance. He recently assisted Joyce Wright with the Prospect Global matter. The widely respected **Jay Wiley** is of counsel at the firm. Peers are impressed with his extensive experience in transactional real estate. **Nicholas Wood** has been working in the zoning and land use area for 27 years and in that time has built a reputation as being among the strongest in the state. Clients say he is *"very knowledgeable and practical."* He recently represented Rockefeller Group Development in a $20 million rezoning of 160 acres of land to accommodate multifamily, light industrial and business park development.

## Withey Morris PLC

**THE FIRM** This Phoenix-based real estate boutique has a good reputation for representing clients before municipal, county and state commissions, councils and boards for land use and zoning matters. It acts for residential, commercial, industrial and master planned developers.

**Sources say:** *"They practice throughout the valley, across over a dozen cities, each with different zoning requirements. A very good firm."*

**KEY INDIVIDUALS** Founding partner **Michael Withey** handles complex rezonings and negotiating development and redevelopment agreements with municipalities and counties in Arizona. Fellow founding partner **Jason Morris** takes on land use cases for property owners against municipalities in Arizona. He represents clients such as national retailers, industrial land owners and Fortune 100 companies.

## Other Notable Practitioners

**Neil Biskind** is a principal of real estate boutique Biskind Hunt, PLC, and is described by peers as being *"A+."* He represents several real estate developers in the Southwest, and has extensive experience in the acquisition, development and disposal of real estate. **David Shein** (see p.511) of Chester & Shein has a background in finance and accounting, and can call on sophisticated technical skills to assist clients with real estate acquisition. Peers also note his ability to tackle litigation work. Clients of **Gregory Mast** of Mast Law Firm PC are grateful for his *"experience, intelligence, tenacity and great business sense,"* and note that he puts as much effort into smaller real estate matters as could be expected in larger projects. **Thomas Irvine** of Polsinelli PC is highly regarded by peers for real estate transaction and litigation work. Well known among peers for his work on master planned communities, **Steven Lisker** (see p.509) of Squire Sanders (US) LLP represents regional and national builders and developers in the planning, financing, review, development, sale and regulatory aspects of real estate projects. Managing attorney at his firm, **Michael Tiffany** (see p.512) of Tiffany & Bosco, PA is known as a specialist in HUD financing and is praised by sources as *"one of the best lawyers in Phoenix. He doesn't rest until the desired outcome is achieved."* He recently represented Trillium Residential in its $81.8 million refinancing of three separate apartment projects, all HUD-insured. **Neil Irwin** of Bryan Cave LLP has previously worked as in-house counsel for a real estate developer and earns praise from peers for his work. He recently represented the Desert Viking Group and related entities in a multiblock redevelopment project in the City of Chandler, a $75 million deal. **Larry Lazarus** of Lazarus, Silvyn & Bangs, P.C. has over 30 years' experience of working as a land use lawyer in Phoenix, and has worked as a driving force to develop community centers, golf courses, light industrial centers and luxury high-rise condominiums, among other things. **Frank Bangs** recently left Lewis & Roca to begin a real estate boutique, Lazarus, Silvyn & Bangs, P.C., and is praised as an *"excellent lawyer"* by his peers, especially for work in Tucson. Also formerly of Lewis & Roca, **Keri Silvyn** of Lazarus, Silvyn & Bangs, P.C. represents private developers and local governments in zoning and land use planning.

# Leaders' Profiles in Arizona

**ARMSTRONG, David J**
Ballard Spahr LLP, Phoenix
602 798 5412
armstrongd@ballardspahr.com
*Featured in Environment (Arizona)*
**Practice Areas:** David J Armstrong is a partner in the Litigation Department who counsels clients on environmental risks and liabilities in corporate and real estate transactions and regulatory compliance. He assists clients in the defense of administrative and civil proceedings involving permitting and enforcement matters at the federal and state levels. Mr Armstrong regularly litigates environmental matters for clients nationwide. He also conducts environmental due diligence, and advises on environmental issues, agreements, and policies in a variety of transactions.
**Career:** Admissions: Arizona, Pennsylvania.
**Personal:** Temple University James E. Beasley School of Law (JD 1992) College of Charleston (BA 1985).

**BIRNBAUM, Gary L**
Dickinson Wright Mariscal Weeks, Phoenix
602 285 5009
gbirnbaum@dickinsonwright.com
*Featured in Litigation (Arizona)*
**Practice Areas:** Practices principally in the areas of commercial and real estate litigation, legal malpractice defense, and eminent domain and valuation disputes. Also serves as a private mediator and arbitrator in commercial, valuation, construction and other cases.
**Professional Memberships:** Fellow, American College of Trial Lawyers; Fellow, Litigation Counsel of America; Fellow, College of Law Practice Management; Member, National Academy of Distinguished Neutrals; Member, American Society of Counsellors of Real Estate (CRE); Member, Panel of Commercial Arbitrators and Mediators, American Arbitration Association; Selected Phoenix, Arizona "Lawyer of the Year" by Best Lawyers in America in "Bet the Company Litigation" (2009), Alternative Dispute Resolution (2010), Condemnation and Eminent Domain Law (2012), and Legal Malpractice-Defense (2013).
**Publications:** Contributing author: The Law of Eminent Domain - 50-State Survey (2012); Nichols on Eminent Domain (1994); Arizona Commercial Real Estate Transactions Practices Manual (1989). Presentations at more than 50 professional seminars and author of various law journal and bar journal articles.
**Personal:** JD magna cum laude, Indiana University School of Law (Order of the Coif); BA summa cum laude, State University of New York at Binghamton (Highest Honors; Phi Beta Kappa). Adjunct Professor of Law at Arizona State University and The University of Arizona. Former Associate Dean at the Sandra Day O'Connor College of Law at ASU.

**BLANEY, Brian H**
Greenberg Traurig LLP, Phoenix
602 445 8322
BlaneyB@gtlaw.com
*Featured in Corporate/M&A (Arizona)*
**Practice Areas:** Corporate and securities; mergers and acquisitions.
**Professional Memberships:** Board of Directors, Desert Voices Oral Learning Center; Past Chairman of Awards Selection Committee, Governor's Celebration of Innovation; Past Planning Committee Member, Invest Southwest (f/k/a Arizona Venture Capital Conference); State Bar of Arizona, Past Chairman, Securities Regulation Section, Member, Securities Regulation Section and Business Law Section.
**Career:** Listed: Best Lawyers in America, 2010-13; Chambers USA Guide, 2006-13; Southwest Super Lawyers magazine, 2007-12. (Among others).
**Personal:** JD, magna cum laude, University of Notre Dame Law School; BBA, University of Michigan.

**BULL, Edwin**
Burch & Cracchiolo, Phoenix
602 234 9913
ebull@bcattorneys.com
*Featured in Real Estate (Arizona)*
**Practice Areas:** Real estate law, land use and zoning, real estate transactions, administrative law.

**BURNHAM, Rebecca Lynne**
Greenberg Traurig LLP, Phoenix
602 445 8251
BurnhamR@gtlaw.com
*Featured in Real Estate (Arizona)*
**Practice Areas:** Real estate; retail; sports facilities and entertainment venues; land development.
**Professional Memberships:** Member: Urban Land Institute (Community Development Council - Green; Arizona District Council); ASU Economic Club; ASU Foundation Women and Philanthropy Program. Boards of Directors: Teach For America (Arizona); Crisis Nursery Foundation; Blue Cross Blue Shield of Arizona, Inc.
**Career:** Listed: Chambers USA Guide, 2005-13; Best Lawyers in America, 1998-2013; Lawdragon 3000 'Leading Lawyers in America', 2006, 2008-2011; Southwest Super Lawyers magazine, 2007-12. Rated, AV® Preeminent™ 5.0 out of 5.
**Personal:** JD, University of California-Los Angeles, School of Law; BS, magna cum laude, Arizona State University.

**CLEES, Joseph T**
Ogletree, Deakins, Nash, Smoak & Stewart, PC, Phoenix
602 778 3701
joe.clees@ogletreedeakins.com
*Featured in Labor & Employment (Arizona)*
**Practice Areas:** Labor and Employment, State, Federal and Tribal.

**Professional Memberships:** Past Chair, Arizona State Bar Labor Section; Board, Metro Phoenix Human Resources Association (SHRM).
**Career:** "100 Most Powerful Employment Lawyers", HR Executive Magazine; "Number 1" tier, Chambers USA; Best Lawyers in America; "Top 50 Southwest Super Lawyers"; "Southwest Super Lawyers"; "The Legal 500"; Top Attorneys of Arizona, Arizona Business Magazine; Best Lawyers in the United States; "Best of the Bar", Phoenix Business Journal. AV Rated.
**Publications:** Arizona Employment Law Handbook (Editor); Arizona Labor Letter (Member, Editorial Board).
**Personal:** Dickinson College (BA, Magna cum laude 1981), Villanova University (JD, 1984).

**COHEN, Richard S**
Jackson Lewis LLP, Phoenix
602 714 7062
CohenR@jacksonlewis.com
*Featured in Labor & Employment (Arizona)*
**Practice Areas:** Employment, Class Action, Systemic Litigation, OFCCP, Diversity Planning, Litigation Avoidance, Non-competition, and Trade Secrets. Practices before federal and state courts, EEOC, and other administrative agencies.
**Professional Memberships:** American Bar Association, EEO Litigation Subcommittee Member; Arizona State Bar, Fair Employment Practices Committee; American Employment Law Council; U.S. Chamber of Commerce, Labor & Employment Law Committee; College of Labor and Employment Lawyers
**Career:** Partner 1978-2007, Lewis and Roca, Partner 2007-2009, Ford & Harrison; Joined 2010.
**Publications:** Contributor, Arizona Employment Law Letter.
**Personal:** George Washington University, JD, with Honors, 1971; Rutgers University, BA, 1968.

**CRABB, Joseph**
Squire Sanders (US) LLP, Phoenix
602 528 4084
joseph.crabb@squiresanders.com
*Featured in Corporate/M&A (Arizona)*
**Practice Areas:** Partner focusing on corporate finance and securities matters including M&A transactions, public and private securities offerings, corporate reorganizations and restructurings, venture capital financings and 1934 Act compliance. Has significant experience with a wide variety of transaction structures across a broad range of industries for both public and private clients. Frequent speaker on corporate governance and securities matters. Listed in The Best Lawyers in America 2009 to 2012. Selected as a Southwest Super Lawyer and as one of bizAZ magazine's Up & Comers.

**CULP, Peter W**
Squire Sanders (US) LLP, Phoenix
602 528 4063
peter.culp@squiresanders.com
*Featured in Environment (Arizona)*

**Practice Areas:** Partner focusing on water and natural resources law, environmental law, and federal Indian law. Represents private, public and nonprofit entities in matters involving surface water rights, groundwater rights, state and federal water policy and the Law of the Colorado River; industrial and municipal clients with facility siting, permitting, regulatory compliance and environmental cleanup matters under federal and state law; tribal interests and entities doing business in Indian country on various federal Indian law issues; and private and public clients in matters involving land development, urban planning, and management, planning and conservation of public lands and state trust lands.

**CURZON, Thomas H**
Osborn Maledon PA, Phoenix
602 640 9308
tcurzon@omlaw.com
*Featured in Corporate/M&A (Arizona)*
**Practice Areas:** Serves as outside general counsel to emerging, growth-oriented companies; entrepreneurial transactions, including venture capital and other private placements of securities, entity formation and transaction structuring, mergers, acquisitions and divestitures, initial public offerings, corporate governance, licensing and distribution of software and other products, employee matters, and executive compensation.
**Career:** Partner, Osborn Maledon, PA (and predecessor firm) since 1986; recognitions include: Chambers USA, America's Leading Business Lawyers, 2003-13; The Best Lawyers in America'®, editions 1995-2012; Phoenix Best Lawyers Mergers & Acquisitions Lawyer of the Year, 2011; Phoenix Best Lawyers, Corporate Lawyer of the Year, 2013 and 2009; 2008 Centers of Influence Award: Honoring Arizona's Most Influential Accountants, Bankers & Lawyers; Best of the Bar (Business Journal), 2004.
**Publications:** Arizona Legal Forms, Business Organizations (Corporations), Volumes eight and nine, West Publishing, Second Edition, 2001-02; Presenter: "The Good, the Bad or the Ugly: Crowdfunding Update" (2012 AZ Entrepreneurial Conference); Presenter: "Ridin' the Storm Out - Some Thoughts on the Angel and Venture Markets in AZ" (2011 AZ State Bar Conv.); Presenter: "Corporate Governance Issues in Our Troubled Times" (2009 AZ State Bar Conv.); Presenter: "Lecture on Hot Topics in Securities Laws" (W.P. Carey School of Business, 2004); Presenter: "Show Me the Money: Lecture on Intellectual Property in Business Models" (Thunderbird, the Garvin School of International Management, 2004); Presenter: "Venture Capital Financing Recent Trends and Developments" (Enterprise Network Business Seminar Series, 2003); Presenter: "Venture Capital Financing - Standard Terms and Recent Developments" Financial Executives Institute, 2002); Presenter: "Getting Ready for the Dance: Preparing to Raise Venture Capital - A Coaching Primer" (The Seminar Group, 2001).

**Personal:** JD, magna cum laude, University of Texas, 1979; BA, summa cum laude, University of Kansas, 1976; fourth degree black belt, Taekwon-do (ITF).

## DE BLASI, Michelle A
Greenberg Traurig LLP, Phoenix
602 445 8485
DeBlasiM@gtlaw.com
*Featured in Environment (Arizona)*
**Practice Areas:** Energy and natural resources; environmental.
**Professional Memberships:** Co-Chair, Arizona Energy Consortium, Arizona Technology Council; Environment Chair, Real Estate Litigation, ABA; Past Chair, Grand Canyon Chapter, Air & Waste Management Association; Executive Committee, Board of Directors, Past Chair: Energy Committee, Valley Forward.
**Career:** Listed: The Best Lawyers in America, Energy Law; Environmental Law, 2013; 'Top 25 Women in Business', Phoenix Business Journal, 2012; Chambers USA Guide, National - Environmental Law, 2011-12.
**Personal:** JD, University of Washington School of Law, Certificate of Emphasis in Environmental Law; BS, magna cum laude, Arizona State University.

## DRAZEK, Joseph A
Quarles & Brady LLP, Phoenix
602 229 5335
joe.drazek@quarles.com
*Featured in Environment (Arizona)*
**Practice Areas:** Environmental.
**Professional Memberships:** Arizona Technology Council, Board of Directors; Consortium for Business and the Environment, Board of Directors; State Bar of Arizona; Former Chair (Environmental and Natural Resources Law Section); Former Chair, Phoenix Environmental Quality Commission; Member: Maricopa County Bar Association; American Bar Association (Natural Resources and Administrative Law Sections); Member: State Bar of California (Natural Resources Subsection).
**Career:** Partner since 2000.
**Personal:** DePaul University College of Law (JD, 1981); University of Chicago (MS, 1978); University of Michigan (BS, 1976).

## EMERICK, Steven P
Quarles & Brady LLP, Phoenix
602 230 5517
steve.emerick@quarles.com
*Featured in Corporate/M&A (Arizona)*
**Practice Areas:** Corporate finance, public and private offerings of debt and equity, securities law compliance for domestic and foreign private issuers, corporate governance, including compliance with Sarbanes-Oxley Act, Dodd-Frank and exchange listing rules, private and public company mergers and acquisitions, private equity and venture capital, commercial financial services, equipment finance.
**Professional Memberships:** State Bar of Arizona; State Bar of Wisconsin; Maricopa County Bar Association; American Bar Association.

**Career:** Partner since 1991.
**Personal:** Lewis & Clark College (JD, cum laude, 1984); Oregon State University (BS, highest honors, 1981).

## FATHE, Fred C
Dickinson Wright Mariscal Weeks, Phoenix
602 285 5012
ffathe@dickinsonwright.com
*Featured in Real Estate (Arizona)*
**Practice Areas:** Focuses practices on real estate transactions; banking (primarily real estate and corporate finance); Uniform Commercial Code matters; tax-exempt financing; and corporate and LLC acquisitions, restructurings and mergers. He is a Certified Specialist, Real Property Law, State Bar of Arizona Board of Legal Specialization.
**Professional Memberships:** American Bar Association, Member; Real Property Section; Arizona State Bar (past Member, Business Law Section Council; past Chair and current Member, Real Property Section; past Chair and current Member, Business Law Section). Frequent lecturer respecting real property and finance issues at seminars, presentations and conventions sponsored by the State Bar of Arizona and others.
**Personal:** BA, Chemistry and Physics, Wittenberg University (Magna Cum Laude); JD, University of Michigan Law School (Magna Cum Laude; Order of the Coif).

## FERLAND, Roger
Quarles & Brady LLP, Phoenix
602 229 5607
roger.ferland@quarles.com
*Featured in Environment (Arizona)*
**Practice Areas:** Environmental.
**Professional Memberships:** State Bar of Arizona; Chair, Arizona Association of Industries (Air Quality Subcommittee); former Chair, Governor's Air Quality Strategies Task Force; former Chair, Arizona Chamber of Commerce Air Quality Subcommittee; State Bar of Arizona (Administrative Law Committee); Board Chair, Audubon Arizona.
**Career:** Partner since 1984.
**Publications:** "The Development of the Gila River Indian Community Tribal Air Quality Implementation Plan," Natural Resources & Environment, American Bar Association, Publication, Winter 2007, Volume 21, Issue 3.
**Personal:** Duke University (JD, with distinction, 1974); Lewis & Clark College (BA, magna cum laude, 1968).

## GITTLER, Amy J
Jackson Lewis LLP, Phoenix
602 714 7044
GittlerA@jacksonlewis.com
*Featured in Labor & Employment (Arizona)*
**Practice Areas:** Employment counseling and litigation, sexual harassment, discrimination, wage and hour; non-competes, trade secrets and labor (NLRB).
**Career:** Opened Phoenix office Jackson Lewis December 2007. Prior: Frazer Ryan Goldberg Arnold & Gittler; member Brown & Bain, P.A. (Perkins Coie); Executive Director, Arizona Center for Law in the Public Interest.

ArizonaGoverningCommittee v Norris, 463 U.S. 1073 (1983)
**Publications:** Co-author, Arizona Employment Law Handbook, The ADA and Rehabilitation Act of 1973 (1995).
**Personal:** Oberlin College (BA, 1972); Northwestern University (JD, 1977). Best Lawyers in America®, 2010-present; Southwest Superlawyer; ranked one of top 500 litigators in US by Lawdragon 2006.

## HALL, Greg R
DLA Piper LLP (US), Phoenix
480 606 5128
greg.hall@dlapiper.com
*Featured in Corporate/M&A (Arizona)*
**Practice Areas:** Corporate/M&A, securities.
**Career:** He concentrates on domestic and international mergers and acquisitions, joint ventures, venture capital and private equity transactions, restructurings, and securities transactions, including public and private offerings of equity and debt, tender offers and exchange offers. He represents issuers, underwriters and placement agents in their underwriting, investment, and advisory activities. He counsel clients in securities law compliance, corporate governance and general corporate matters, including employment agreements, stock option plans, warrant agreements, and management and service arrangements.
**Personal:** JD, University of Arizona (cum laude); BS, University of Kansas.

## HALLER, Diane
Quarles & Brady LLP, Phoenix
602 229 5625
diane.haller@quarles.com
*Featured in Real Estate (Arizona)*
**Practice Areas:** Real estate.
**Professional Memberships:** Member: State Bar of Arizona; Maricopa County Bar Association; American Bar Association; United States District Court.
**Career:** Partner since 1993.
**Publications:** CoreNet Global "Advanced Lease Analysis," 2008; "Regulations and Laws Relating to Homebuilding," Arizona State University, Del E. Webb School of Construction, 2006; 'Breach of a Real Estate Contract,' Arizona Journal of Real Estate and Business, 1995; contributing editor to Commercial Real Estate Transactions Practice Manual, Arizona State Bar Association, 1988-89 (first edition).
**Personal:** University of Notre Dame (JD, cum laude, 1986); University of Utah (BS, magna cum laude, 1983).

## HAMMOND, Larry A
Osborn Maledon PA, Phoenix
602 640 9000
lhammond@omlaw.com
*Featured in Litigation (Arizona)*
**Practice Areas:** Criminal defense (including white-collar, internal investigations, and major felony - especially capital defense); also engages in complex commercial litigation and False Claims Act litigation.
**Professional Memberships:** American College of Trial Lawyers; President, American Judicature

Society (2003-05); Chair, Justice Project of Arizona Attorneys for Criminal Justice (Arizona's project related to questions of actual innocence); Chair, Arizona State Bar Indigent Defense Task Force; Board Member, Arizona Capital Representation Project.
**Career:** Mr Hammond has practiced law for 42 years; five of those years were spent with the United States Department of Justice both as an Assistant Watergate Special Prosecutor and as the First Deputy Assistant Attorney General in the Office of Legal Counsel during the Carter Administration. His practice has always included both complex commercial litigation and criminal defense. Throughout his career he has devoted substantial time to cases, projects and programs designed to improve the administration of justice. Mr Hammond has been honored to have a scholarship named after him by the University of Arizona's James E. Rogers College of Law and also to have received the 2008 Justice Award from the American Judicature Society - that organization's highest career public service award. In 2010, he received Morris Dees Justice award at a ceremony in New York sponsored by the University of Alabama School of Law and the law firm of Skadden Arps. In 2013, the Litigation Section of the American Bar Association has selected Mr Hammond to receive its John Minor Wisdom Award in recognition of his career-long commitment to public service.
**Publications:** Mr Hammond has written extensively on issues associated with convictions of the wrongfully accused. A sampling of his numerous publications can be found at the website for Osborn Maledon.
**Personal:** Mr Hammond is one of the founders of Osborn Maledon, and values highly the firm's ability to attract and retain extraordinary lawyers. He is also extremely proud to be able to say that all of his children have devoted their careers to public service; his eldest daughter works with victims of abuse; his son is a Phoenix police officer; and his youngest daughter after returning from the Peace Corps obtained her Law Degree at the University of Colorado and has spent the last five years as a public defender in Colorado.

## HARDIN, William M
Osborn Maledon PA, Phoenix
602 640 9322
whardin@omlaw.com
*Featured in Corporate/M&A (Arizona)*
**Practice Areas:** Business transaction practice, including outside general counsel services, mergers and acquisitions, venture capital and private equity financings, intellectual property transactions and executive compensation matters.
**Professional Memberships:** State Bar of Arizona.
**Career:** Partner, Osborn Maledon, PA (and predecessor firm) since 1988. Board of Directors, Arizona Economic Resource Organization (AERO); Governor's Council on Innovation and Technology, 2004-08 (Co-Chair, 2005-06). Recognitions include: Chambers USA, America's Leading Business Lawyers, 2003-12; The Best Lawyers in America®, editions 1995-2012. Law

Clerk to Judge Thomas Gibbs Gee, United States Court of Appeals for the Fifth Circuit, 1982-83.
**Publications:** Arizona Legal Forms, Business Organizations, (Corporations), Volumes 8 and 9, West Publishing, 2nd Edition, 2001-02. Presenter: 'Venture Capital Financing Recent Trends and Developments' (Enterprise Network Business Seminar Series); Presenter: 'Venture Capital Financing - Standard Terms and Recent Developments', (Financial Executives Institute); Presenter: 'Getting Ready for the Dance: Preparing to Raise Venture Capital - A Coaching Primer' (The Seminar Group).
**Personal:** JD, with honors, University of Chicago Law School, 1982; associate editor, University of Chicago Law Review; Order of the Coif.

### HARRISON, Mark I
Osborn Maledon PA, Phoenix
602 640 9324
mharrison@omlaw.com
*Featured in Litigation (Arizona)*
**Practice Areas:** Professional ethics and professional liability; consulting and testifying as an expert in matters involving legal and judicial ethics, professional liability and law firm risk management; appellate litigation; complex commercial and tort litigation; service as a mediator and arbitrator.
**Professional Memberships:** Member and past President, State Bar of Arizona and Arizona Bar Foundation; Member and past President, Maricopa County Bar Association; Member and past President, Association of Professional Responsibility Lawyers; Fellow and past President, American Academy of Appellate Lawyers; ABA Member and Chair, Standing Committees on Professional Discipline and Professionalism; Member, Standing Committee on Ethics; Chair, American Bar Association Commission to Evaluate the Code of Judicial Conduct.
**Career:** Law clerk to former Chief Justice Lorna E Lockwood, Supreme Court of Arizona; Harrison, Harper, Christian & Dichter (and predecessor firms), 1966-93; Partner, Bryan Cave LLP (1993-2004); Member, Osborn Maledon, PA (2004-present).
**Publications:** Co-author, Arizona Appellate Practice; 'An Overview: The New Arizona Rules of Professional Conduct', 20 Arizona Bar Journal 8 (1985); 'LLPs Are Just Another Star Wars!' 39 S Tex LR 633 (1998); co-author, 'Ethical Implications of Partnerships and Other Associations Involving American and Foreign Lawyers', 22 Penn State Internat'l LR 639 (Spring 2004); co-author, 'On the Validity and Vitality of Arizona's Judicial Merit Selection System: Past, Present, and Future', XXXIV, No 1 Fordham Urb LJ 239 (2007); 'The 2007 ABA Model Code of Judicial Conduct: Blueprint for a Generation of Judges,' Vol 28 The Justice Journal, No 3 (2007); Extrajudicial Comments Concerning Pending Cases: The New Code's Controversial Self-Defense Exception, 64 N.Y.U. ANN. SURV. AM. L. (2009); 'Can We Allow Justice To Become a Saleable Commodity?', 30 Yale L. & Pol'y Rev. Inter Alia, p.29 2012).

**Personal:** Adjunct Professor University of Arizona College of Law (1994-97), Arizona State University Law School (Legal Ethics), 2000-present; Antioch College (BA 1957); Harvard Law School (LLB, 1960).

### HOFFMANN, Christian
Quarles & Brady LLP, Phoenix
602 229 5336
chris.hoffmann@quarles.com
*Featured in Corporate/M&A (Arizona)*
**Practice Areas:** Corporate services, corporate finance/securities, mergers and acquisitions, private equity/venture capital. Client concentration in advising public and private emerging growth companies and structuring real estate syndications.
**Professional Memberships:** State Bar of Arizona (Securities Law Section); American Bar Association; Maricopa County Bar Association; District of Columbia Bar; Director, Economic Club of Phoenix, 1997-present; Member of Board of Regents, Georgetown University (2006-2012); Chairman of the Board, Catholic Community Foundation of Phoenix, 2012-present.
**Career:** Partner since 1979.
**Personal:** Georgetown University (JD, 1973); Georgetown University (BSBA, magna cum laude, 1969).

### JOHNSON, Christopher D
Squire Sanders (US) LLP, Phoenix
602 528 4046
christopher.johnson@squiresanders.com
*Featured in Corporate/M&A (Arizona)*
**Practice Areas:** Partner with more than more than 30 years' experience in the corporate and securities areas, with significant experience in initial and subsequent public offerings, private placements, M&A, corporate reorganizations and restructurings, public company securities law compliance, venture capital finance and corporate governance. Named Phoenix Corporate Lawyer of the Year in The Best Lawyers in America 2012. Frequent author and lecturer on corporate and securities law topics.
**Professional Memberships:** State Bar of Arizona, Securities Regulation Section, Executive Council 1979-1995, chair 1994-1995; Arizona Chapter of Association for Corporate Growth; Phoenix CEO/CFO Group.

### KANT, Robert S
Greenberg Traurig LLP, Phoenix
602 445 8302
KantR@gtlaw.com
*Featured in Corporate/M&A (Arizona)*
**Practice Areas:** Corporate and securities; mergers and acquisitions; public offerings; private placements; venture capital; corporate finance.
**Professional Memberships:** Member, State Bar of Arizona, Small Business Capital Formation Subcommittee.
**Career:** Rated, AV® Preeminent™ 5.0 out of 5. Selected: Chambers USA Guide, 2003-13; Best Lawyers in America, 2003-13; Southwest Super Lawyers magazine, 2007-12; one of the 'Lawdragon 3000 Leading Lawyers in America', Lawdragon.com, 2006; 'Best of the Bar', Corporate

Law, Phoenix Business Journal, 2003; 'Best of the Bar', Securities Law, Phoenix Business Journal, 2004; 'Best Lawyer in Valley', Phoenix Business Journal, 2005.
**Personal:** JD, Villanova University School of Law; BA, University of Pennsylvania.

### KELLY, Andrew P
Osborn Maledon PA, Phoenix
602 640 9329
akelly@omlaw.com
*Featured in Corporate/M&A (Arizona)*
**Practice Areas:** Commercial transactions practice including mergers and acquisitions, entity formation, employment matters, securities and general counsel services with an emphasis on transactional and regulatory aspects of Indian gaming.
**Professional Memberships:** State Bar of Arizona; Maricopa County Bar Association; Greater Phoenix Economic Council Ambassador Steering Committee, 2004-present.
**Career:** Osborn Maledon, PA since 1996.
**Personal:** JD, magna cum laude, Arizona State University, 1994; Arizona State Law Journal, editor, 1993-94; Order of the Coif; BA, cum laude, History, Williams College, 1988.

### KISICKI, Mark G
Ogletree, Deakins, Nash, Smoak & Stewart, PC, Phoenix
602 778 3700
mark.kisicki@ogletreedeakins.com
*Featured in Labor & Employment (Arizona)*
**Practice Areas:** Successfully represented employers in ULP trials and union avoidance campaigns, corporate campaigns, decertification efforts and collective bargaining negotiations. Also counseled clients and handled numerous employment cases involving allegations of discrimination, harassment and/or retaliation. Additional employment-related litigation experience includes complex cases involving the theft of intellectual property and trade secrets, and litigation under the False Claims Act.
**Career:** Admitted to practice in Arizona, California
**Publications:** Written and spoken extensively on a variety of labor and employment topics.
**Personal:** University of California, Los Angeles (BA, 1987), Pepperdine University (JD, 1990)

### LANSKY, David
Dickinson Wright Mariscal Weeks, Phoenix
602 285 5130
dlansky@dickinsonwright.com
*Featured in Real Estate (Arizona)*
**Practice Areas:** Practices in the areas of acquisition, development, disposition, financing and leasing of improved and unimproved real properties, individually and as portfolios.
**Professional Memberships:** Member, State Bar of Arizona; Member, International Council of Shopping Centers.
**Personal:** JD, Sandra Day O'Connor College of Law; BA, Northwestern University.

### LEWIS, David P
DLA Piper LLP (US), Phoenix
480 606 5126
david.lewis@dlapiper.com
*Featured in Corporate/M&A (Arizona)*
**Practice Areas:** Corporate/M&A, private equity, and capital markets.
**Career:** He focuses on mergers and acquisitions, securities offerings and compliance issues, private equity and venture capital transactions, corporate governance and other general corporate matters. His experience covers a number of different industries, including technology, financial services, consumer products, for-profit education, and media. His clients are public and private companies, investment banks, and private equity and venture capital firms.
**Personal:** JD, Duke University School of Law; MA, Duke University; BA, Dartmouth College.

### LISKER, Steven L
Squire Sanders (US) LLP, Phoenix
602 528 4023
steven.lisker@squiresanders.com
*Featured in Real Estate (Arizona)*
**Practice Areas:** Represents real estate developers and builders in the review, planning, acquisition, development, financing, sale, leasing and regulatory compliance of real estate projects. Clients include national and regional developers and home builders of master planned communities, residential subdivisions, condominiums, mixed-use developments and golf courses. Represents companies in the sale and purchase of home building businesses and partially completed residential and mixed-use projects. Also represents clients in the disposition of distressed projects.
**Career:** Certified Specialist in Real Property Law, State Bar of Arizona.

### MACDONOUGH, Bruce E
Greenberg Traurig LLP, Phoenix
602 445 8305
MacdonoughB@gtlaw.com
*Featured in Corporate/M&A (Arizona)*
**Practice Areas:** Corporate and securities; mergers and acquisitions; public and private equity and debt offerings; periodic SEC reporting; board and special committee advice, including corporate governance counsel; start-up and venture capital transactions.
**Career:** Rated, AV® Preeminent™ 5.0 out of 5. Selected, Chambers USA Guide, 2006-13; Southwest Super Lawyers magazine, 2007-12; Best Lawyers in America, 2009-13; Arizona's Finest Lawyers, 2011; Legal 500 US, 2009-10.
**Personal:** JD, University of Virginia School of Law; AB, Stanford University.

### MALEDON, William J
Osborn Maledon PA, Phoenix
602 640 9331
wmaledon@omlaw.com
*Featured in Litigation (Nationwide), Litigation (Arizona)*
**Practice Areas:** Complex commercial litigation, with an emphasis on antitrust, trade regulation, securities, product liability, insurance bad faith, and sports litigation.

**Professional Memberships:** Fellow, American College of Trial Lawyers. Fellow, Litigation Counsel of America. A member of various state and federal Bar Associations, a Founding Fellow of the Arizona Bar Foundation and a Life Member of the American Bar Foundation, a former Chairman of the Antitrust Section of the Arizona State Bar, and a member of various Arizona State Bar Committees. Member of the Ninth Circuit Advisory Board. Member of the Maricopa County Bar Association's Hall of Fame.
**Career:** University of Notre Dame (JD, 1972); Editor-in-Chief, Notre Dame Law Review; law clerk to the Honorable William J Brennan, Jr, United States Supreme Court (1972-73).
**Publications:** Has lectured extensively on trade regulation matters, complex litigation, and jury trial reform issues.
**Personal:** Adjunct Professor of Sports Law, Arizona State University Law School.

## MARTIN, Don P
Quarles & Brady LLP, Phoenix
602 229 5700
don.martin@quarles.com
*Featured in Litigation (Arizona)*
**Practice Areas:** Complex commercial litigation; financial institution litigation; professional liability defense of law and accounting firms, federal and state agency disputes, and real estate litigation.
**Professional Memberships:** American Bar Association (Litigation Section, Corporate Counsel and Professional Liability Committees); Federal Bar Association; Arizona State Bar Association; Chairman of Board of Directors, Meridian Bank N.A.; Board of Trustees and past President, Phoenix Art Museum; Counsel to Greater Phoenix Leadership, 2001-2003.
**Career:** Partner since 1980; former National Chair of firm's Litigation Section.
**Personal:** University of Virginia School of Law (JD, with honors, 1975); University of Virginia (BA, with honors, 1972).

## MCCONNELL, Karen C
Ballard Spahr LLP, Phoenix
602 798 5403
mcconnellk@ballardspahr.com
*Featured in Corporate/M&A (Arizona)*
**Practice Areas:** Karen C. McConnell is a partner in the Business and Finance Department and Practice Leader of the Mergers and Acquisitions/Private Equity Group. She concentrates her practice in the areas of corporate and securities law, with emphasis on mergers and acquisitions and private equity investment transactions.
**Career:** Admissions: Arizona.
**Publications:** Author and speaker, Corporate Counsel Roundtable, "Trends in Mergers and Acquisitions" (November 2010) and "Conducting Internal Investigations" (March 2010).
**Personal:** University of Notre Dame Law School (JD 1984) Ohio University (BBA 1981).

## MEHR, Matthew
Quarles & Brady LLP, Phoenix
602 229 5288
matthew.mehr@quarles.com
*Featured in Real Estate (Arizona)*
**Practice Areas:** Financial institutions, commercial lending, real estate finance, real estate.
**Professional Memberships:** Member, State Bar of Arizona; Member, Maricopa County Bar Association.
**Career:** He focuses on real estate and commercial financing transactions. His practice emphasizes the representation of financial institutions in construction loans, permanent loans, leasehold financing, secured revolving lines of credit, asset based financing, lines of credit secured by multiple properties and collateral in multiple states, syndicated loans, tax-exempt bond financing, loan modifications, workouts and forebearance agreements.
**Personal:** University of Arizona James E. Rogers College of Law (JD, with highest distinction); The University of Vermont (BA).

## NADEAU, Mark A
DLA Piper LLP (US), Phoenix
480 606 5110
mark.nadeau@dlapiper.com
*Featured in Litigation (Arizona)*
**Practice Areas:** Corporate/M&A, international arbitration.
**Career:** He is co-managing partner of the firm's Phoenix office. He has a very active litigation practice in the United States, and his international arbitration practice spans Europe, Asia and South America. He is widely recognized as a leading commentator and has chaired numerous symposia on international dispute resolution. He is a published author with articles concerning trade competition, product liability and dispute resolution for transfers of technology.
**Personal:** JD, University of Pittsburgh School of Law; BA, University of Colorado.

## NAGY JR, Tibor
Ogletree, Deakins, Nash, Smoak & Stewart, PC, Tucson
520 575 7422
tibor.nagy@ogletreedeakins.com
*Featured in Labor & Employment (Arizona)*
**Practice Areas:** Labor & Employment Law and Employment Litigation.
**Professional Memberships:** State Bar of Arizona–Labor and Employment Law Section (past Chairman), American Bar Association, Pima County Bar Association, Arizona Theater Company–Board of Directors (1998-2004), Fox Tucson Theatre Foundation (2005-2007).
**Career:** Best Lawyers 2012 "Lawyer of the Year," Employment Law-Management (Tucson); 2013 "Lawyer of the Year," Litigation L&E (Tucson); Southwest Super Lawyer; Admitted: Arizona; U.S. District Court (Arizona), Ninth Circuit Court of Appeals; U.S. Supreme Court.
**Publications:** Arizona Employment Law Handbook (Editor/Writer); Arizona Labor Letter (Editorial Review Board Member).

**Personal:** University of Arizona (BA, 1979 and JD, 1982).

## OLLER, Shawn
Littler Mendelson, PC, Phoenix
602 474 3608
soller@littler.com
*Featured in Labor & Employment (Arizona)*
**Practice Areas:** Discrimination and Harassment; Training - Compliance, Ethics, Leadership; Transportation; Complex Litigation and Jury Trials; Healthcare
**Career:** Trial lawyer representing management and companies in all aspects of employment litigation arbitration, and mediation; Counsels on day-to-day personnel matters and practices and compliance; Conducts in-house training on employment-related topics; Certified by the New Mexico Board of Specialization in employment and labor law; Member of Littler's Associates Committee, the firm's Diversity & Inclusion Council and the Good Business Practices Committee
**Publications:** "New Mexico Charge of Discrimination Form Creates Trap for the Unwary," February 27, 2012
**Personal:** JD, Baylor University School of Law, 1995; BS, Northeastern University, 1992

## OSBORN II, Jones
Osborn Maledon PA, Phoenix
602 640 9338
josborn@omlaw.com
*Featured in Real Estate (Arizona)*
**Practice Areas:** Commercial real estate including transactions, leasing, secured transactions, financing, foreclosures and entitlements; entity formation and joint ventures; development; construction and general corporate and business law.
**Career:** Founding Partner, Osborn Maledon, PA; Member, Phoenix Planning Commission, 1981-85; Chairman, City of Phoenix Peripheral Planning Committee, 1986-88; and member and past President of CoreNet Arizona (organization of corporate real estate executives).
**Publications:** Author of book, Arizona Real Estate Law; and numerous articles in various business and legal publications.
**Personal:** Adjunct Professor, Commercial Real Estate Law, Arizona State University Law School 2005-09; University of Arizona (JD, 1970); law clerk to Justice James Duke Cameron, Arizona Supreme Court (1970-71).

## PASTERNAK, Daniel B
Squire Sanders (US) LLP, Phoenix
602 528 4187
daniel.pasternak@squiresanders.com
*Featured in Labor & Employment (Arizona)*
**Practice Areas:** Labor and employment; employment litigation and counseling; traditional labor law; workplace training.
**Professional Memberships:** American Bar Association (Committee on Development of the Law Under the National Labor Relations Act); Society for Human Resource Management; Arizona Labor & Employment Relations Association; Maricopa County Bar Association (Bar Counsel; 2005-present).

**Publications:** Co-Editor, 'GT LE Blog: National Developments in Labor & Employment Law' http://www.gtleblog.com/. Contributing Editor, The Developing Labor Law, American Bar Association 4th and 5th eds.; 2004-11 Cumulative Supplements.
**Personal:** JD, cum laude, University of Illinois College of Law, 1994; BS, University of Illinois at Urbana-Champaign, 1991.

## PETTIBONE, Jon E
Quarles & Brady LLP, Phoenix
602 230 5572
jon.pettibone@quarles.com
*Featured in Labor & Employment (Arizona)*
**Practice Areas:** Jon Pettibone is Managing Partner of the Quarles Phoenix Office, recent chair of the firm's Labor & Employment Group and 3-time chair of the Arizona State Bar's Employment & Labor Section. He represents management in healthcare, energy, mining, construction, transportation, manufacturing and other industries. He has successfully handled over 400 hearings, trials and arbitrations and achieved notable successes in collective bargaining, organizing campaigns and before trial and appellate courts in discrimination, harassment, wrongful discharge and ERISA cases.
**Personal:** Arizona State University (JD, 1976; BS, high distinction, 1973). Married 1974, 3 children; flyfisher.

## PIDGEON, Steven D
DLA Piper LLP (US), Phoenix
480 606 5124
steven.pidgeon@dlapiper.com
*Featured in Corporate/M&A (Arizona)*
**Practice Areas:** Corporate/M&A, capital markets, private equity
**Career:** He is co-managing partner of the Phoenix office. His practice concentrates on securities offerings, mergers and acquisitions, recapitalizations, and private equity and venture capital investments. His clients operate in a wide variety of industries, including technology, sports and entertainment, financial services, healthcare, manufacturing, transportation, homebuilding, franchising, and consumer goods. He represents underwriters, investors, venture capital firms, and financial intermediaries in their underwriting, investment, and advisory activities.
**Personal:** JD, University of Miami School of Law (magna cum laude); BA, University of Miami (magna cum laude).

## PLACENTI, Frank
Squire Sanders (US) LLP, Phoenix
602 528 4004
frank.placenti@squiresanders.com
*Featured in Corporate/M&A (Arizona)*
**Practice Areas:** Chair, Squire Sanders' corporate finance/governance practice. Represents special committees in internal investigations, change of control and other settings. Focuses on M&A, PE, corporate governance, securities law, antitakeover and shareholder relations issues. Represents public companies, PE firms, portfolio companies and brokers/dealers in capital formation, securities/corporate law, regulatory compli-

ance and recapitalizations. Assists clients, special committees and audit committees with internal investigations, and SEC and stock exchange investigatory matters. Listed in The Best Lawyers in America and Lawdragon 500. Recommended in Arizona for corporate matters and M&A by PLC Which Lawyer? Yearbook 2009.
**Professional Memberships:** Vice-chair, ABA Corporate Governance Committee.

### RODGERS, Scott W
Osborn Maledon PA, Phoenix
602 640 9344
srodgers@omlaw.com
*Featured in Labor & Employment (Arizona)*
**Practice Areas:** Employment law representing employers. Practice includes litigation involving issues of discrimination, wrongful termination, and other employment claims. Extensive experience with disputes over restrictive covenants (non-competition and non-solicitation) and theft of trade secrets. Regularly counsels clients on risk avoidance best practices, employment policies, compensation plans, and employment agreements.
**Career:** Partner since 1995.
**Publications:** Frequent lecturer on employment-related topics.
**Personal:** University of Utah (JD, 1989; BS 1986 magna cum laude, Phi Beta Kappa).

### ROSENBAUM, David
Osborn Maledon PA, Phoenix
602 640 9345
drosenbaum@omlaw.com
*Featured in Litigation (Arizona)*
**Practice Areas:** Complex commercial litigation in US federal and state courts. He has represented public companies and their officers and directors in numerous securities fraud class actions and represented Fortune 50 companies in a wide range of complex commercial litigation. He has handled intellectual property and antitrust litigation and large sales and use tax disputes.
**Professional Memberships:** ABA; AZBA; DAZ; 9thCir; US Supreme Court; former President, Federal Bar Association Phoenix Chapter; Fellow, American Bar Foundation; Charter Fellow, former President, Foundation of Federal Bar Association; former Chair, Fellows of the Foundation of Federal Bar Association.
**Career:** Partner since 1990.
**Publications:** He lectures frequently on litigation topics.
**Personal:** Georgetown Law School (JD, 1983); University of Pennsylvania (BA 1979).

### ROSENFELD, Lawrence
Squire Sanders (US) LLP, Phoenix
602 528 4886
lawrence.rosenfeld@squiresanders.com
*Featured in Labor & Employment (Arizona)*
**Practice Areas:** Employment; litigation; administrative; health.
**Professional Memberships:** Fellow, College of Labor and Employment Lawyers.
**Career:** '100 Most Powerful Employment Attorneys in America', Lawdragon/Human Resources Executive Magazine, 2010-11; 2009

Justice Harry A. Blackmun Award for Extraordinary Achievement. Southwest Super Lawyers Magazine, 2007-11, and Top 50 (Arizona), 2007, 2009-11; Arizona's Finest Lawyers, 2011; International Who's Who of Management Labour and Employment Lawyers, 2010-11; Marquis Who's Who in American Law, 2011-12; Best Lawyers in America, 2003-12; Chambers USA, 2005-12. Rated AV® Preeminent™ 5.0 out of 5.
**Personal:** JD, Yale Law School; BA, magna cum laude, City University of New York-Queens College.

### SELDEN, David A
The Cavanagh Law Firm, Phoenix
602 322 4009
dselden@cavanaghlaw.com
*Featured in Labor & Employment (Arizona)*
**Practice Areas:** Labor; Employment; Trial, Appellate Litigation; OSHA, EEOC, NLRB, DOL, Davis-Bacon, I-9 Audits, E-Verify; Non-Compete Agreements and Litigation, Human Resources, Handbooks, Investigations; Governmental Affairs.
**Professional Memberships:** Arizona Chamber of Commerce Board, General Counsel, Employment Committee (Chair, 1990- ); Phoenix Symphony Board, General Counsel; Management Labor/Employment Roundtable; Litigation Counsel of America.
**Career:** Authored several Arizona employment laws curtailing wrongful termination litigation; Congressional aide, 1971-82; Adjunct Professor of Employment Law.
**Publications:** Editor, 'Arizona Human Resources Manual'; 'Model Policies and Forms for Arizona Employers'; 'Employment Verification-Employer's Guide to Immigration, Form I-9 and E-Verify'; Author, 'Legal Briefs on Immigration from 25 Top Legal Minds in the Country'.
**Personal:** BA, MA, George Washington University (1973, 1976); JD, magna cum laude, Georgetown University (1982).

### SHEIN, David E
Chester & Shein, Scottsdale
480 922 3933
dshein@cslawyers.com
*Featured in Real Estate (Arizona)*
**Practice Areas:** Real estate acquisition, development, financing and secured lending; commercial leasing; mergers and acquisitions; entity formation; and business and tax planning.
**Professional Memberships:** Real estate specialist, certified by the State Bar of Arizona – Board of Legal Specialization; Judge Pro Tem, Maricopa County Superior Court.
**Career:** 25 years as a leading Arizona commercial practitioner focusing on the representation of established and emerging companies and financial institutions in all facets of real estate acquisition, development and financing, including asset based lending, development planning and entitlement, venture formation, due diligence, strategic business planning, capital acquisition and financing, complex contract negotiations and mergers and acquisitions.
**Personal:** Bachelor of Science - University of Arizona (with honors), double major in account-

ing and corporate finance; JD - Arizona State University College (cum laude), emphasis in tax and commercial transactions.

### SORENSON, Derek L
Quarles & Brady LLP, Phoenix
602 229 5320
derek.sorenson@quarles.com
*Featured in Real Estate (Arizona)*
**Practice Areas:** Real estate development and finance; joint ventures; land use; mining.
**Professional Memberships:** Member, Arizona State Bar Association; Valley Partnership.
**Career:** Partner since 1992.
**Personal:** University of Minnesota (JD, cum laude, 1985); Colgate University (BA, magna cum laude, 1982). Phi Beta Kappa.

### STACHOWIAK, Christopher S
Osborn Maledon PA, Phoenix
602 640 9353
cstachowiak@omlaw.com
*Featured in Corporate/M&A (Arizona)*
**Practice Areas:** Chris focuses primarily on serving as outside general counsel to emerging, growth-oriented companies and represents public and private companies in securities law compliance, corporate governance and business transactions, including mergers, acquisitions, angel and venture capital financings, public and private securities offerings, strategic relationships, technology licensing and distribution, executive employment and equity-based compensation plans.
**Professional Memberships:** State Bar of Arizona, Securities Regulation Section: Chair, 2005-06; Member since 1998. Invest Southwest Capital Conference: Co-Chair of Presenting Company Committee, 2006-07. Greater Phoenix Chamber of Commerce Arizona Angels Investor Conference: Co-Chair of Investor Summit, 2005; Mentor Team Leader 2004. Greater Phoenix Chamber of Commerce Arizona Venture Capital Conference: Mentor Team Leader 2003, Member, 1997-2002. The Enterprise Network, Board Member, 2005-06. Arizona Corporation Commission, Securities Division, Rules Committee Member, 1997-98.
**Career:** Osborn Maledon, PA, Partner (2002-present); associate (1997-2002); Husch Blackwell Sanders LLP, associate (1993-97).
**Publications:** 'Dodd-Frank Act Effect on Smaller Reporting Companies and Foreign Private Issuers, Private Securities Offerings and Corporate Governance', Arizona State Bar Convention, 2011. 'Dodd-Frank Financial Reform Legislation Discussion', Arizona State Bar Securities Regulation Section, 2010. 'Securities Offering Reform and Accounting Issues for Smaller Public Companies', Arizona State Bar Convention, 2006. 'Becoming an Angel: Its a Wonderful Life', Greater Phoenix Chamber of Commerce Arizona Angel Investment Conference, November 30, 2005. 'Ethical Issues in Securities Representations; Attorney Liability', Arizona State Bar Convention, 2005. 'Representing the Arizona Business', State Bar of Arizona CLE, October 24, 2003. 'Business Law Contracts', Honeywell Notifier Annual

Conferences, September 30, 2003. 'Review of Recent Changes to Section 16 Rules', In-House Corporate Counsel Seminar, 1996.
**Personal:** JD, University of Kansas, 1993; The Kansas Law Review; Order of the Coif; Robert E Edmonds Prize for Outstanding Achievement.

### STOREY, Lee
Ballard Spahr LLP, Phoenix
602 798 5443
storeyl@ballardspahr.com
*Featured in Environment (Arizona)*
**Practice Areas:** Lee A. Storey is a partner in the Litigation Department and leads the firm's water law practice, providing consultation and litigation services for municipalities, water districts, industries, and developers regarding water use, resource management, Indian law, and entitlements under federal, state, and county regulatory programs.
**Professional Memberships:** American Bar Association; State Bar of Arizona, Indian Law Section; Ambassadors For Change, Chair.
**Career:** Admissions: Arizona; U.S. District Court for the District of Arizona; U.S. Supreme Court.
**Personal:** University of California, Berkeley, School of Law (JD 1987); University of California, Los Angeles (MA 1984,; BA 1982).

### STOREY, Lesa J
Greenberg Traurig LLP, Phoenix
602 445 8239
StoreyL@gtlaw.com
*Featured in Real Estate (Arizona)*
**Practice Areas:** Real estate.
**Professional Memberships:** Chair, The Heather Farr Golf Tournament. Member: Executive Women's Golf Association; Valley Partnership; Phoenix Field and Obedience Club; Arizona State University Sandra Day O'Connor College of Law Council of 100.
**Career:** Selected: Chambers USA Guide, 2005-13; Best Lawyers in America, 2000-13; Southwest Super Lawyers magazine, 2007-12; Arizona's Finest Lawyers, 2011. Rated, AV® Preeminent™ 5.0 out of 5. Team Member, a Law360 'Real Estate Practice Group of the Year', 2011-12.
**Personal:** JD, cum laude, Arizona State University College of Law; BS, magna cum laude, Miami University.

### THOMAS, Christopher D
Squire Sanders (US) LLP, Phoenix
602 528 4044
christopher.d.thomas@squiresanders.com
*Featured in Environment (Arizona)*
**Practice Areas:** Partner focusing on environmental litigation, mediation and counseling. Practice concentrates on hazardous substances, hazardous waste, groundwater contamination, industrial compliance, environmental permitting for new and expanded facilities, and the environmental aspects of real estate and corporate transactions, and covers the major federal environmental statutes including CERCLA, RCRA, the Clean Water Act and the Clean Air Act, as well as numerous state counterparts and tort theories. Has defended or prosecuted cases under CERCLA, RCRA, and parallel state law and tort theories pertaining to more than 30 sites throughout

the US. Listed in The Best Lawyers in America 2012.

## THOMASON, Timothy
Dickinson Wright Mariscal Weeks, Phoenix
602 285 5026
tthomason@dickinsonwright.com
*Featured in Litigation (Arizona)*

**Practice Areas:** Practice focuses primarily on litigation involving professional liability, real property, financial institutions, trust and estate litigation, commercial disputes, title insurance and escrow. Heavy emphasis on trial practice.
**Professional Memberships:** Fellow, American College of Trial Lawyers; Fellow, Litigation Counsel of America; Judge Pro Tem, Maricopa County Superior Court; American Arbitration Association Commercial Arbitrator; Former Co-Chair of the Trial Practice Committee and the Health Care Law Litigation Committee of the ABA's Section of Litigation.
**Publications:** "Logerquist – Anything Goes in Arizona," American Bar Association Section of Litigation Annual Meeting, May 2001; "Key Evidentiary Issues in Health Care Cases," American Bar Association Section of Litigation Annual Meeting, April 2002; "How Juries Decide Cases," American Bar Association Section of Litigation Annual Meeting, April 2003; Contributing Author: Arizona Tort Law Handbook, State Bar of Arizona, 2012.

**Personal:** BA, Creighton University; JD, University of Iowa.

## TIFFANY, Michael E.
Tiffany & Bosco, PA, Phoenix
602 255 6001
met@tblaw.com
*Featured in Real Estate (Arizona)*

**Practice Areas:** Corporate, business planning and formations, financing and HUD insured loans, real estate, and telecommunications.
**Professional Memberships:** State Bar of Arizona and Maricopa County Bar Association.
**Career:** Built a large diversified real estate practice, including HUD insured loans, representing borrowers with loans in excess of $2.6 billion for more than 200 multi-family housing projects and healthcare facilities nationwide.
**Publications:** Real Estate Financing: Current Trends and Opportunities, An Attorney's Role in Commercial Transactions, Broken Priority May Cause Delay in Construction, and HUD Insured Loans - A Preferred Source of Funds for Multi-Housing Projects.

## WILHOIT, Adrienne W.
Ballard Spahr LLP, Phoenix
602 798 5414
wilhoita@ballardspahr.com
*Featured in Corporate/M&A (Arizona)*

**Practice Areas:** Adrienne W Wilhoit is a partner in the Mergers and Acquisitions/Private Equity and Securities Groups. She practices in the areas of mergers and acquisitions, securities, general corporate law, and commercial lending, representing public and private companies with asset and stock acquisitions and dispositions, as well as mergers and other business reorganizations.
**Professional Memberships:** State Bar of Arizona, Securities Section and Business Law Section Maricopa County Bar Association, Corporate Counsel Division.
**Career:** Admissions: Arizona California.
**Personal:** University of California, Los Angeles, School of Law (JD) University of California, San Diego (BA).

## WILLIAMS, Quinn
Greenberg Traurig LLP, Phoenix
602 445 8343
WilliamsQ@gtlaw.com
*Featured in Corporate/M&A (Arizona)*

**Practice Areas:** Corporate and securities; mergers, acquisitions, recapitalization; private, public equity and debt financings; technology licensing, joint venture transactions; franchising, intellectual property compliance; board of directors (corporate governance).
**Professional Memberships:** Director's Emeritus, Arizona Technology Council, 2008-present; Board Member, Scottsdale Chamber of Commerce. Founding Chair Governor's Business Executive Council, Founder AZ Venture Capital Conference.
**Career:** Selected: Chambers USA, 2005-13; Best Lawyers in America, 1995-2013; Arizona's Finest Lawyers, 2011; Southwest Super Lawyers, 2007-12; Top 50 Super Lawyers in Arizona, 2007-08, 2010, 2012. AV® Preeminent™ 5.0 out of 5.
**Personal:** JD, University of Arizona James E. Rogers College of Law; BBA, University of Wisconsin-Madison.

## WINKLER, Peter
Dickinson Wright Mariscal Weeks, Phoenix
602 285 5107
pwinkler@dickinsonwright.com
*Featured in Real Estate (Arizona)*

**Practice Areas:** Practices in the areas of commercial real estate, lending and development, landlord and tenant law, and general commercial and secured lending transactions. Certified by the Arizona State Bar Board of Legal Specialization as a specialist in real estate law.
**Professional Memberships:** Maricopa County Bar Association; State Bar of Arizona; American Bar Association.
**Personal:** BA, State University of New York at Stony Brook; JD, New York University.

# BURCH & CRACCHIOLO, P.A.

**www.**bcattorneys.com **tel:** 602 274 7611 **fax:** 602 234 0341

**Managing Partners:** Edwin C Bull
Number of partners: 27
Number of lawyers: 42
Languages: *English, Finnish, Portuguese, Spanish*

### Firm Overview:

Serving corporate, governmental and individual clients throughout the Southwest and nationally, Burch & Cracchiolo is known for outstanding and cost-effective representation that emphasize client objectives. Founded in 1970, the firm currently has 42 attorneys. The firm has offices in Phoenix, Arizona; Las Vegas, Nevada; and Orange County, California. A number of its lawyers are recognized in Best Lawyers in America, Super Lawyers of the Southwest, Arizona's Finest Lawyers, Chambers USA, National Trial Lawyers and more. The firm has been recognized as one of the Best Places to Work in Arizona. In order to better serve clients Burch & Cracchiolo is a member of Primerus, an international alliance of 170 law firms from 120 cities around the world.

### Main Areas of Practice:

#### Business & Corporate:

Burch & Cracchiolo offers business and corporate law services in a variety of areas, from forming and maintaining a business entity, to overseeing the legal aspects of business transactions, to effective representation if a matter reaches litigation. The firm's attorneys represent clients before a wide array of government agencies at all levels.

#### Commercial Litigation:

Burch & Cracchiolo prides itself in offering among the most comprehensive services available in this area. Attorneys provide advisory services designed to find alternative solutions in order to prevent litigation and a number of its attorneys are experienced arbitrators and mediators, as well as skilled advocates in the alternative dispute resolution process.

#### Construction:

The team of lawyers deals with the entire range of construction issues, including contract drafting and negotiation, bid disputes, claims preparation, delay claims, defect litigation, design issues, surety claims, Registrar of Contractor complaints, specification interpretations, mechanic's and materialmen's liens and job site injuries

#### Creditors' Rights/Bankruptcy:

The team of bankruptcy litigators provides the unique combination of specialized knowledge of the bankruptcy process with experience in complex multi-party litigation disputes. Burch & Cracchiolo attorneys represent secured and unsecured lenders and lender groups, as well as landlords, trade creditors and bondholders.

#### Estate & Wealth Preservation Planning:

Burch & Cracchiolo has extensive experience in all aspects of estate planning, succession planning and probate. The firm's attorneys represent clients in a broad range of trust, estate and tax matters, structuring of executive compensation and employee benefits plans and assist in drafting buy-sell agreements, forming partnerships, corporations, ESOPS and limited liability companies and devising strategies for family succession planning

#### Family:

Burch & Cracchiolo attorneys handle a wide variety of matters in family law, emphasizing dissolution issues including divorce representation and mediation, property division issues and child custody, support and paternity. The family law practice area includes issues that may arise in the family context, such as prenuptial agreements, grandparents' rights, annulments, legal separations, paternity, in loco parentis, guardianships and adult adoptions.

#### Insurance Defense/Personal Injury Litigation:

Burch & Cracchiolo attorneys have successfully resolved cases involving bodily injury and property damage claims, including, but not limited to automobile, trucking and motor carrier liability, and commercial vehicles; premises liability; professional liability; dram shop/liquor liability; property damage, including construction defect, fire and casualty losses; construction site injuries; product liability; general liability, aviation accidents and environmental torts. Burch & Cracchiolo attorneys represent government and public entities, self-insured companies and Native American tribal governments and enterprises.

#### Labor & Employment

The firm's labor and employment lawyers help our clients understand and comply with the more than 180 federal laws administered and enforced by the Department of Labor (DOL), the National Labor Relations Board (NLRB), the Equal Employment Opportunity Commission (EEOC) and state agencies. These laws cover workplace safety and health, union activity, equal employment opportunity, family and medical leave, plant closings, and layoffs. The firm's attorneys are adept at negotiating and drafting all types of employment agreements and contracts.

#### Real Estate:

Burch & Cracchiolo has an extensive history representing clients in all facets of real estate transactions and related litigation. The firm is experienced in acquisition, development and zoning of large commercial, residential and planned development projects, as well as build out and lease up of shopping centers, commercial and industrial facilities and office buildings. The firm is also skilled in representing local and national lending institutions in the negotiation, preparation and enforcement of financial documentation for large commercial transactions.

#### Tax Controversy

The firm's attorneys represent individuals, corporations, trusts and estates in civil and criminal tax litigation with the Internal Revenue Service and the Department of Justice and in the United States Tax Court, United States District Courts and United States Courts of Appeal, as well as in litigation with the State of Arizona and Arizona Department of Revenue.

## PRACTICE AREAS

Business/Corporate
Commercial Litigation
Construction
Creditor's Rights/Bankruptcy
Estate/Wealth Preservation Planning
Family
Insurance Defense/Personal Injury Litigation
Labor & Employment
Real Estate
Tax Controversy

## OFFICES

**ARIZONA**
**PHOENIX:** Burch & Cracchiolo, P.A., 702 E. Osborn Road, Suite 200, AZ. 85014
Tel: 602 274 7611  Fax: 602 234 0341
Email: clong@bcattorneys.com

**CALIFORNIA**
Santa Ana: Burch & Cracchiolo, P.C., 400 N. Tustin Avenue, Suite 370, CA. 92705
Tel: 714 542 0852  Fax: 714 542 0530
Email: sdana-kobey@bcattorneys.com

**NEVADA**
Las Vegas: Burch & Cracchiolo, P.A., 401 N. Buffalo Drive, Suite 202, NV. 89145
Tel: 702 331 7600  Fax: 702 331 7601
Email: tmacbeth@bcattorneys.com

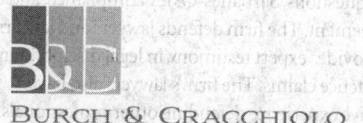

# OSBORN MALEDON, P.A.

www.omlaw.com **tel:** 602 640 9000 **fax:** 602 640 9050

**Managing Partner:** Scott Rodgers
Number of Members: 37 Number of other lawyers: 15

## Firm Overview:

A leading law firm in Phoenix, Arizona, Osborn Maledon is recognized by its clients and peers for its smart and creative litigation, business and general counsel solutions to complex problems. The firm represents a wide range of clients from sophisticated international companies in major litigation and transactions to start-up enterprises requiring efficient counsel in launching a new venture.

## Main Areas of Practice:

### Administrative & Regulatory:

Osborn Maledon has extensive experience in administrative and regulatory work involving the electric utility, telecommunications and cable industries.

### Antitrust & Trade Regulation:

The firm provides comprehensive antitrust litigation and counseling services to its clients and has been heavily involved in a majority of the significant antitrust and trade regulation cases in Arizona, as well as important cases throughout the US.

### Bankruptcy:

The firm's restructuring practice ranges from complex loan restructurings to acquisitions and sales in the bankruptcy courts. The firm's bankruptcy lawyers have extensive experience in a variety of industries ranging from all types of retail and commercial real estate to agricultural, technology and media based enterprises as well as construction, manufacturing, aerospace, hospitality and healthcare businesses.

### Corporate/Mergers & Acquisitions:

Osborn Maledon serves clients ranging from venture capital-backed start-ups to publicly-held corporations. The firm has made a significant commitment to assist emerging ventures in the technology, life sciences and media industries in the Southwest and has extensive experience in software and digital media. The firm provides advice and general counsel services in the areas of corporate governance, public and private equity financing, venture capital and angel financings, debt financing, mergers, acquisitions and strategic transactions, technology licensing, compliance with state and federal securities laws, public and private securities offerings, equity compensation and executive employment, compensation and severance agreements.

### Ethics & Professional Liability:

The firm counsels clients in matters relating to complex ethics questions, Sarbanes-Oxley compliance, and risk management. The firm defends lawyers and law firms and provides expert testimony in legal discipline and malpractice claims. The firm's lawyers also have extensive experience defending other professionals including physicians, psychologists and accountants.

### Indian Law:

The firm represents Indian tribes in litigation, employment, business, and real estate and development matters. The Indian law practice also assists non-Indian clients in business dealings with Indian tribes.

### Intellectual Property & Technology:

Osborn Maledon assists clients in acquiring, exploiting and transferring proprietary assets and businesses, and in aggressively defending proprietary positions.

### Labor & Employment:

The firm defends employers and executives in litigation involving a wide variety of employment issues before administrative agencies such as the EEOC and in state and federal court. The firm has an extensive employment counseling practice focusing on preventative practices.

### Litigation & Appellate:

The firm represents clients throughout the country in complex litigation in individual class actions and multi-district matters in state and federal court and before regulatory agencies. Appellate services include pre-trial counsel on surviving appellate scrutiny, special action petitions and appeals in state and federal courts, including the United States Supreme Court.

### Real Estate:

The firm's real estate lawyers provide extensive real estate services involving real estate transactions, development, financing, zoning and land use regulations, joint ventures, leasing, brokerage, taxation and public and Indian lands.

### Securities Litigation:

The firm has extensive experience in all aspects of litigation involving private and publicly issued securities. The firm regularly defends companies, officers, directors, accountants and attorneys in actions pending in federal and state courts, including shareholder derivative and class actions. Osborn Maledon also has a broad range of experience in regulatory investigations and enforcement proceedings conducted by the federal and state authorities, including the Department of Justice, the Securities and Exchange Commission, the Public Company Accounting and Oversight Board and the Arizona Corporation Commission.

### White-Collar Criminal:

Osborn Maledon represents corporations, directors, employees and other individuals in matters involving securities fraud, cyber-crime, racketeering, civil and criminal forfeiture, healthcare fraud, industrial accidents, environmental crimes and financial frauds in federal and state criminal investigations, grand jury inquiries and in all manner of pre-trial, trial and appellate proceedings. The firm also conducts internal investigations for corporate clients.

## PRACTICE AREAS

Administrative & Regulatory
Antitrust & Trade Regulation
Bankruptcy
Corporate/Mergers & Acquisitions
Ethics & Professional Liability
Indian Law
Intellectual Property & Technology
Labor & Employment
Litigation & Appellate
Real Estate
Securities Litigation
White-Collar Criminal

## OFFICES

ARIZONA
**PHOENIX:** 2929 North Central Avenue, 21st Floor,
AZ 85012-2794
Tel: 602 640 9000 Fax: 602 640 9050
Email: webmaster@omlaw.com

## Clients:

21st Century® HealthCare, Inc.; AAA Arizona, Inc; AAM, LLC; Apollo Group, Inc.; Arizona Public Service Co; Arizona State University; Banner Health; Brain State Technologies LLC; Chartis, Inc.; Contatta Inc.; Cox Communications; EmpowHER; FireHost, Inc.; Gila River Indian Community; Grayhawk Venture Partners; HelmsBriscoe International; Heska Corporation; Honeywell International Inc.; Hopi Indian Tribe; iMemories, Inc.; Informative Graphics Corporation; Infusion Software, Inc.; Insight Enterprises, Inc.; Intesource, Inc.; Inventure Foods, Inc.; IPRO Tech, Inc.; Lowell Observatory; Medicis Pharmaceutical Corporation; Microchip Technology, Inc.; Next Generation Insurance Group, LLC; PGA Tour, Inc.; Pinnacle West, Inc.; Salt River Pima-Maricopa Indian Community; SNTech, Inc.; Southwest Solar Technologies, Inc.; ST Microelectronics, Inc.; The Boeing Co; Trax Technologies, Inc.; W.L. Gore & Associates; Wells Fargo Bank; Western Union.

# RYLEY CARLOCK & APPLEWHITE

**www.rcalaw.com  tel:** 602 258 7701  **fax:** 602 257 9582

**Executive Committee Chairman:** Rodolfo Parga, Jr

Number of shareholders: 51

Number of other lawyers: 85

**OFFICES**

ARIZONA

**PHOENIX:** One North Central Avenue, Suite 1200,
AZ 85004-4417
Tel: 602 258 7701  Fax: 602 257 9582

COLORADO

**DENVER:** 1700 Lincoln Suite 3500, CO 80203
Tel: 303 863 7300 Fax: 303 595 3159

## Firm Overview:

Ryley Carlock & Applewhite (RC&A) provides clients a rock solid, 66-year track record of providing legal solutions in the West. With practices concentrated in areas of highest legal demand for the region, the firm has flourished as it focuses on key geographic centers and on providing the highest level of value to clients, even in eras of economic uncertainty. In 2011, the firm doubled the size of its Denver Offices by adding the leadership of the former Isaacson Rosenbaum law firm – a 50-year old powerhouse. That acquisition gave the firm a substantial practice in corporate and securities, real estate, IP and litigation to compliment its league-leading environmental and water practice. The firm is a leader in representing banks and the financial sector, mining, technology, and real estate industries. The firm rivals large law firms with top notch talent, but holds its costs low and manages the firm aggressively, providing a value added alternative for virtually all segments of the business community, from large corporations and banks, to start-up ventures in emerging growth areas with associated intellectual property, employment and regulatory concerns. In addition to full service traditional law offerings, Ryley Carlock lives up to its "The Business of Solutions" trademark by providing one of the US's best e-Discovery practices – dubbed the Document Control Group. This group not only services the *Fortune* 500 in their large scale litigation services need (including review of terabytes of information), but also serves the world's leading law firms as 'review counsel', helping them to avoid the trap and potential liability of using staffing agencies. RC&A lawyers strive to understand the client's business and its present business objectives; and work in partnership to meet those objectives in the most practical, creative and professional manner possible, taking into account both the short-term and the long-term impacts and interests for the client. This formula is time tested and has been shaped by the experience of many of the firm's lawyers who have served as in-house counsel. Appreciating the demands on a client's time and budget, RC&A has become a leader in creative and effective solutions.

## Main Areas of Practice:

### Corporate and Securities:

Banks, investors, funds, corporations, municipalities, partnerships, and high-wealth individuals turn to RC&A for advice on business planning, formation, financing, mergers, acquisitions, securities, bonds, estate planning, wills, taxation, and intellectual property matters. The firm also has an active practice in all aspects of public finance and municipal law.

### Creditors' Rights & Bankruptcy:

RC&A represents a wide array of creditors, creditors committees, and trustees in bankruptcy matters. Financial institutions regularly tap into the firm's broad experience in defaults, restructuring, liquidations and reorganizations.

### Water, Energy, Resources & Environment:

The firm's Water, Energy, Resources and Environmental Practice is among the premier practices in the West. RC&A provides services ranging from assistance with regulatory compliance and permitting issues associated with the handling and use of hazardous materials, water quality, hazardous and solid waste disposal and underground storage tanks to contamination cleanup, asbestos abatement and environmental real estate due diligence. RC&A has extensive experience in all aspects of water law, and is involved in water rights litigation, transactions, legislation and rule-making efforts in Arizona, Colorado and throughout much of the Southwest.

### Labor & Employment:

RC&A is recognized as a leading counselor to employers and a leading defender of companies in workplace and employment law matters. Its lawyers write and lecture extensively on employment matters and advise employers and management throughout the Southwest and nationally on a comprehensive range of labor and employment law issues.

### Litigation:

The firm's litigation practice is devoted primarily to complex commercial disputes and other matters involving business interests. The diverse backgrounds of the firm's litigators result in a diversity of substantive expertise and industry knowledge. The bulk of RC&A's trial practice is in complex litigation, with an emphasis on intellectual property, business torts and complex business transactions.

### Document Control Group:

The Document Control Group at Ryley Carlock is among the leading such practices in the country, assisting *Fortune* 500 clients, law firms, and accounting firms in the management of millions of electronic and hard-copy documents for purposes of litigation support, litigation prevention and compliance with various federal and state statutes. The group has teamed with cutting-edge software companies to combine privileged and sophisticated review and decision making with precision management and control.

### Real Estate & Lending:

RC&A is actively involved in the commercial real estate industry, historically a key driver of the economy in the West. The firm provides comprehensive legal services in all aspects of real estate development, ownership, construction and financing. RC&A is vastly experienced in all relevant federal, state and local laws and regulations affecting real estate, including those relating to water, mineral and other property rights, commercial leases, land use controls, condemnation, duties and liabilities of landlords and real property owners, subdivisions and lot sales, business planning and ownership, entity structuring, federal, state and local taxation, environmental issues, construction law, and title insurance.

### Clients:

The firm's clients include: Wells Fargo, Bank of America, Banner Health Arizona, Safeway, Freeport-McMoran, Intel Corporation, Knight Transportation, State Farm, Pulte Homes, and The Industrial Authority of the County of Maricopa.

# SALMON LEWIS & WELDON PLC

www.slwplc.com **tel:** 602 801 9060 **fax:** 602 801 9070

**Management Committee Members:** John B Weldon, Elizabeth M Behnke, Mark A McGinnis
Number of members: 8
Number of other lawyers: 7

**OFFICES**

ARIZONA

**PHOENIX:** 2850 East Camelback Road, Suite 200, AZ 85016
Tel: 602 801 9060  Fax: 602 801 9070
Website: www.slwplc.com

## Firm Overview:

Salmon, Lewis & Weldon, P.L.C. (SLW) is located in Phoenix, Arizona. Built on a dedication to providing practical solutions to clients, the firm represents clients with interests primarily in the industries of natural resources/water law, environmental regulation and commercial transactions including real estate. In addition, it offers counsel on insurance coverage and defense, civil litigation, Indian law, municipal law, government relations and public utility law. The firm's clients range in size from large companies to individuals and include one of Arizona's largest utilities, irrigation and electrical districts, municipalities, water providers, manufacturing companies, food and drink processors, national retailers, shopping center owners and families and individuals. The firm's success has been based on providing value, efficiency and flexibility to its clients with a focus on solving problems. Its attorneys are adept at working with clients, in-house counsel, consultants and other parties to creatively and efficiently resolve disputes and achieve solutions in a wide range of matters, including multiparty negotiations, collaborative working groups and litigation.

## Main Areas of Practice:

### Natural Resources & Water:

SLW's Natural Resources and Water Group is one of the most respected in the region. Its practice covers all facets of water law in Arizona, including litigation, settlement negotiations, Colorado River issues and matters arising under Arizona's Groundwater Code. Several of SLW attorneys have been involved for decades in the state court proceedings relating to the Gila and Little Colorado River General Stream Adjudications. SLW attorneys also have been actively involved in the negotiated settlement of numerous water right disputes and assisting clients with Arizona Groundwater Code compliance and obtaining Certificates of Assured Water Supply.

### Environmental:

SLW's attorneys practicing in the environmental area combine in-depth knowledge of often complex areas of the law with a focus on sensible and cost-effective solutions. Excellent working relationships with local, state and federal regulators and other environmental counsel facilitate their ability to resolve problems efficiently and effectively. The Environmental Practice Group provides a wide range of assistance to their clients, including obtaining favorable permit conditions; negotiating settlements of regulatory violations and compliance issues; successfully obtaining alternative water supplies and other protections for injured water providers and well owners; and handling wastewater treatment and reuse matters.

### Commercial Transactions:

The Commercial Transactions Group at SLW has experienced attorneys assisting developers, lenders, landlords, tenants and business owners in many business and transactional areas. The practice group covers all aspects of real estate investment, including acquisitions and dispositions of real estate, due diligence matters, development issues, debt and mezzanine financing and refinancing for vacant land, condominiums, hotels, office buildings, shopping centers, golf courses, multi-family housing developments, industrial parks and other commercial projects. Additionally, SLW counsels clients in connection with retail, office, restaurant and commercial leasing and lease administration. The Commercial Transactions Group also offers its clients assistance in structuring business entities, investment deals, joint ventures and preferred equity transactions.

### Civil Litigation:

SLW's Litigation Practice focuses on assisting clients to ascertain their objectives, evaluate suitable options and pursue favorable results. The firm's seasoned attorneys have experience primarily in complex commercial disputes, ranging from water rights, administrative permits, contract disputes, insurance matters and environmental liability. SLW is familiar with working closely with our clients' staffs, boards of directors and technical consultants on litigation matters, all within a budget in order to control litigation expenses.

### Insurance Coverage & Defense:

SLW attorneys have advised insurers on matters of policy interpretation and duty to defend under a wide array of policies, including comprehensive general liability insurance, excess insurance, reinsurance, director and officer liability insurance, property insurance, accident and health insurance, life insurance and marine insurance. In addition, they have assisted clients with litigation involving insurance coverage claims in both state and federal court and defense of claims against insureds and prosecution of subrogation claims, including those involving bodily injury and wrongful death, personal injury, hazardous waste disposal and toxic torts, professional errors and omissions, securities fraud, product liability and construction disputes.

### Electric Power & Utilities:

SLW has substantial involvement in power issues. The firm's attorneys have been involved in negotiating and drafting power contracts, in the siting of electrical generating and distribution facilities, and in locating rights-of-way and easements. SLW has particular expertise in drafting and negotiating fuel supply contracts, arbitrating and litigating price disputes and addressing labor and right-of-way issues.

### Special Districts & Utility Law:

The attorneys at SLW have a long history of representing special governmental districts, water and power providers and municipalities. This representation has provided the firm with a unique understanding of the problems and challenges such entities face. SLW has substantial experience in performing the tasks that are required of general counsel for such entities, including working cooperatively as a team with the board of directors, staff and technical consultants. The firm's experience representing cities and special districts has allowed us to develop particular knowledge of the state's open meeting and public records laws, labor issues, municipal services, rights-of-way and election law.

### Clients:

The firm represents regional and national clients, including manufacturing companies, one of Arizona's largest utilities, special governmental districts, real estate developers, lenders, business owners, insurance companies, municipalities, water providers, food and drink processors, national retailers and shopping center owners.

# SNELL & WILMER L.L.P.

**www.**swlaw.com **tel:** 602 382 6000 **fax:** 602 382 6070

**Chairman:** John J Bouma
Number of partners: 209
Number of lawyers: 417
Languages: *Armenian, Chinese (Cantonese), Chinese (Mandarin), English, Farsi, Finnish, French, German, Greek (Ancient Greek), Guarani, Gujrati, Hebrew, Hindi, Italian, Japanese, Korean, Latin, Persian, Polish, Portuguese, Romanian, Russian, Spanish, Swedish, Taiwanese, Ukrainian*

### Firm Overview:

Founded in 1938, Snell & Wilmer is a full-service business law firm with more than 400 attorneys practicing in nine locations throughout the western United States and in Mexico, including Phoenix and Tucson, Arizona; Los Angeles and Orange County, California; Denver, Colorado; Las Vegas and Reno, Nevada; Salt Lake City, Utah; and Los Cabos, Mexico. The firm represents clients ranging from large, publicly traded corporations to small businesses, individuals and entrepreneurs. Since its inception, it has been dedicated to providing superior client service. As a result, it has earned a reputation for providing clients with what they value – exceptional legal skills, quick response and practical solutions delivered with the highest level of professional integrity.

### Main Areas of Practice:

- AgriFinance
- Alternative Dispute Resolution
- Antitrust
- Appellate
- Bankruptcy & Reorganization
- Business & Finance
- Commercial Finance
- Commercial Litigation
- Construction
- Data Center
- Education
- Election Law
- Emerging Business
- Employee Benefits & Compensation
- Energy & Utilities
- Environmental
- Financial Services Litigation
- Franchise Litigation
- Franchise Services
- Gaming
- Government Relations
- Health Care
- Immigration
- Indian
- Infrastructure Development & Project Finance

- Insurance
- Intellectual Property & Technology
- Internal Investigations & Regulatory Compliance
- International
- Labor & Employment
- Mergers & Acquisitions
- Mining Industry Services
- Oil & Gas
- Pharmaceuticals & Medical Devices
- Privacy & Data Protection
- Product Liability Litigation
- Professional Liability Litigation
- Public Utilities
- Real Estate & Commercial Finance
- Renewable Energy
- Retail & Franchising
- Safety & Health
- Securities Litigation & Investigations
- Tax-General Federal
- Tax-State & Local
- Trusts & Estates
- Venture Capital & Private Equity
- Water Law
- White Collar Defense & Investigations
- Zoning & Land Use

## OFFICES

**ARIZONA**

**PHOENIX:** One Arizona Center, 400 East Van Buren Street, Suite 1900, AZ 85004
Tel: 602 382 6000  Fax: 602 382 6070
Email: info@swlaw.com

**TUCSON:** One South Church Avenue, Suite 1500, AZ 85701
Tel: 520 882 1200  Fax: 520 884 1294

**CALIFORNIA**

**LOS ANGELES:** Two California Plaza, 350 South Grand Avenue, Suite 2600, CA 90071
Tel: 213 929 2500  Fax: 213 929 2525

**ORANGE COUNTY:** Plaza Tower, 600 Anton Boulevard, Suite 1400, CA 92626
Tel: 714 427 7000  Fax: 714 427 7799

**COLORADO**

**DENVER:** Tabor Center, 1200 Seventeenth Street, Suite 1900, CO 80202
Tel: 303 634 2000  Fax: 303 634 2020

**NEVADA**

**LAS VEGAS:** Hughes Center, 3883 Howard Hughes Parkway, Suite 1100, NV 89169
Tel: 702 784 5200  Fax: 702 784 5252

**RENO:** 50 West Liberty Street, Suite 510, NV 89501
Tel: 775 348 5940  Fax: 775 348 6074

**UTAH**

**SALT LAKE CITY:** Gateway Tower West, 15 West South Temple, Suite 1200, UT 84101-1531
Tel: 801 257 1900  Fax: 801 257 1800

## INTERNATIONAL OFFICES

San Jose del Cabo, Mexico

## How lawyers are ranked

Every year we carry out thousands of in-depth interviews with clients in order to assess the reputations and expertise of business lawyers worldwide. The qualities we look for (and which determine rankings) include technical legal ability, professional conduct, client service, commercial awareness/astuteness, diligence, commitment, and other qualities most valued by the client. For details of our research team, see p.5.

## CORPORATE/COMMERCIAL

Commentary about individuals can be found under their firm's paragraph. If the firm has no paragraph (is not ranked) look at Other Notable Practitioners.

### Corporate/Commercial
### Leading Firms

**Band 1**
Friday, Eldredge & Clark, LLP *
Kutak Rock LLP *
Mitchell, Williams, Selig, Gates Woodyard, PLLC *

**Band 2**
Rose Law Firm
Wright, Lindsey & Jennings LLP *

**Band 3**
Gill Ragon Owen, P.A.
Quattlebaum, Grooms, Tull & Burrow PLLC *
Williams & Anderson PLC *

### Band 1

#### Friday, Eldredge & Clark, LLP
See profile on p.530

THE FIRM This market-leading, full-service firm is renowned for its excellent corporate practice and particularly its work in public bonds, large transactions and tax. Work highlights include bond issuances for several public institutions and school districts. Clients benefit from the firm's deep bench and wide range of expertise.

**Sources say:** *"They do things in a timely manner, they do it right, and they're very responsive. Their work is by far the best in our state."*

**KEY INDIVIDUALS Shepherd Russell** (see p.528) is widely regarded as one of the state's most accomplished public finance professionals. He frequently acts on behalf of higher education institutions, while one client remarks: *"I would give him the highest marks and recommendations."*
**Robert Beach** (see p.525) specializes in municipal bonds and is particularly experienced in acting on behalf of entities in the education sector. One source says: *"He's been*

### Senior Statesmen

**Senior Statesmen: distinguished older practitioners**
Selig John S — Mitchell, Williams, Selig, Gates Woodyard, PLLC

### Leading Individuals

**Band 1**
| | |
|---|---|
| Buford Jr C Douglas | Mitchell, Williams, Selig, Gates Woodyard |
| Burns Kevin | Rose Law Firm |
| Ebel Walter | Friday, Eldredge & Clark, LLP * |
| Gregory H Watt | Kutak Rock LLP * |

**Band 2**
| | |
|---|---|
| Benham III Paul B | Friday, Eldredge & Clark, LLP * |
| Gardner Price C | Friday, Eldredge & Clark, LLP * |
| Grooms Timothy W | Quattlebaum, Grooms, Tull & Burrow * |
| Hatch M Sean | Wright, Lindsey & Jennings LLP * |
| Heard Daniel L | Kutak Rock LLP * |
| Jack Jr Donald | Jack, Nelson, Jones, Fink, Jiles (ONP)† |
| May Walter | Mitchell, Williams, Selig, Gates Woodyard |
| Smith James | Smith Hurst PLC |

**Band 3**
| | |
|---|---|
| Burrow Patrick | Quattlebaum, Grooms, Tull & Burrow * |
| Campbell Frederick K | Mitchell, Williams, Selig, Gates Woodyard |
| Goodwin T Daniel | Gill Ragon Owen, P.A. |
| Joyce Jeb | Quattlebaum, Grooms, Tull & Burrow * |
| Kooistra John | Williams & Anderson PLC |
| Lovell D Nicole | Mitchell, Williams, Selig, Gates Woodyard |
| Ragon III Heartsill | Gill Ragon Owen, P.A. |
| Rosenthal Brian | Rose Law Firm |

**Up-and-coming individuals**
| | |
|---|---|
| Brooks Steven L | Friday, Eldredge & Clark * |

\* Indicates firm / individual with profile.
Alphabetical order within each band. Band 1 is the highest.

*doing it for a long time and has a great reputation in public finance."* **Price Gardner** (see p.526) has considerable expertise in advising clients on tax issues and one client notes that they would *"recommend him highly."* He is also

### Corporate/Commercial: Municipal Bonds
### Senior Statesmen

**Senior Statesmen: distinguished older practitioners**
Williams W Jackson — Williams & Anderson PLC

### Leading Individuals

**Star individuals**
| | |
|---|---|
| Russell III J Shepherd | Friday, Eldredge & Clark, LLP * |

**Band 1**
| | |
|---|---|
| Beach Jr Robert B | Friday, Eldredge & Clark, LLP * |
| Dickey M Jane | Rose Law Firm |
| Menz David F | Williams & Anderson PLC |
| Spivey III John William | Wright, Lindsey & Jennings LLP * |
| Wilbourn Gordon | Kutak Rock LLP * |

**Band 2**
| | |
|---|---|
| Allgood Michele S | Mitchell, Williams, Selig, Gates Woodyard |
| Bohannon C Tad | Wright, Lindsey & Jennings LLP * |
| Hathaway III James E | Kutak Rock LLP * |
| Parker Anne S | Mitchell, Williams, Selig, Gates Woodyard |
| Tisdale John R | Wright, Lindsey & Jennings LLP * |

**Band 3**
| | |
|---|---|
| Bowman Ryan | Friday, Eldredge & Clark, LLP * |

### Corporate/Commercial: Tax
### Senior Statesmen

**Senior Statesmen: distinguished older practitioners**
Eiseman Byron — Friday, Eldredge & Clark, LLP *

### Leading Individuals

**Band 1**
| | |
|---|---|
| Gardner Price C | Friday, Eldredge & Clark, LLP * |
| Tisdale John R | Wright, Lindsey & Jennings LLP * |

**Band 2**
| | |
|---|---|
| Bohannon C Tad | Wright, Lindsey & Jennings LLP * |
| Owen Charles | Gill Ragon Owen, P.A. |
| Smith James | Smith Hurst PLC (ONP)† |

active in merger and asset purchase and sale transactions, as part of his wider corporate practice. **Walter Ebel** (see p.526) is *"absolutely brilliant and very, very accommodating,"* according to one source. His broad corporate practice includes mergers and acquisitions, restructurings and tax matters. **Ryan Bowman** (see p.525) is recognized for his expertise in the municipal bonds arena, and is often active in deals that have a significant tax element. One satisfied client reports: *"The manner in which Ryan prepares and processes all the necessary documents is outstanding."* **Byron Eiseman** (see p.526) is one of the market's most seasoned and respected corporate attorneys. He is highly regarded as an authority on tax matters. Rogers-based **Steven Brooks** (see p.525) is an up-and-coming professional, who impresses clients and peers alike with his sound corporate advice. Areas of focus include private equity, fund formation and M&A. **Paul Benham** (see p.525) acts on behalf of some of the state's largest corporate clients, and is recognized for his skill with banking and securities work.

### Kutak Rock LLP
See profile on p.1670

**THE FIRM** This national firm serves clients from offices in Little Rock and Fayetteville, and is highly regarded for its corporate and transactional practices and its impressive capability in municipal finance. The team has extensive experience in providing clients with commercial and regulatory advice, as well as acting on a range of mergers and acquisitions and bond transactions.

**KEY INDIVIDUALS Watt Gregory** (see p.526) is renowned for his market-leading expertise in securities law and his extensive experience with private and public entities. He enjoys a sterling reputation among his peers as a *"top-notch"* lawyer. **Gordon Wilbourn** (see p.529) specializes in municipal finance and bond transactions, for which he has an *"A+ reputation"* in the market. Based in the firm's Little Rock office, he is well regarded as a leader in the field. **James Hathaway** (see p.527) is recognized for his work in the arena of public finance and bonds. Specific areas of expertise include asset and stock acquisitions and dispositions and student loan finance. **Daniel Heard** (see p.527) advises a number of the firm's largest clients on a range of issues, particularly with regard to securities matters. Sources consider him *"a good young partner with a good future ahead of him."*

### Mitchell, Williams, Selig, Gates Woodyard, PLLC
See profile on p.531

**THE FIRM** This firm draws plaudits for the impressive scope of its corporate and commercial expertise, advising clients on a broad spectrum of matters, including advising clients on insurance, public finance and tax. The firm serves clients from two Little Rock offices, and can call on resources from a further two out-of-state offices in New York and Texas.

**Sources say:** *"It is growing by leaps and bounds. A good firm coming on strong."*

**KEY INDIVIDUALS John Selig** is renowned in the Little Rock market as an authority on banking, finance and secu-

rities matters. Sources describe him as a *"very, very talented"* attorney. **Douglas Buford** does *"excellent securities and publicly traded company work,"* according to sources. He garners praise for his strength in transactional work and experience in brokering deals. **Walter May** has a broad corporate practice, including limited liability company formations and mergers and acquisitions. He is recognized in the market for his extensive expertise in securities filings and matters. **Anne Parker** is an experienced practitioner and a well-established presence in the bond market. Her practice extends to advising clients on mergers and acquisitions, as well as securities matters. **Michele Allgood** is part of a team that joined the firm from Williams & Anderson in 2012. She specializes in municipal finance, and has considerable experience representing state and city bodies and institutions. **Nicole Lovell** also joined the firm from Williams & Anderson. She garners praise for her *"strong securities practice,"* with sources noting that she is *"very knowledgeable in her area."* **Frederick Campbell** is well respected in the market for his expertise in insurance work. He has considerable experience of niche regulatory compliance issues.

## Band 2

### Rose Law Firm

**THE FIRM** The corporate team at this Little Rock firm serves clients in a variety of matters, and fully warrants its strong reputation in tax and municipal finance. This well-established player in the Arkansas market recently acted as bond counsel to the Arkansas Development Finance Authority (ADFA), and as special counsel to the Arkansas National Resources Commission in the issuance of a $57 million capital improvement bond.

**KEY INDIVIDUALS Kevin Burns** advises clients on complex corporate issues and high-profile acquisitions, and is well respected by his peers in the market. One source notes that *"he does a very good job on the corporate side. A very good general corporate practice."* **Jane Dickey** has a proven track record and considerable expertise in the bonds market. She was lead partner on the ADFA transaction noted above, and has acted on numerous multimillion-dollar bonds this year. **Brian Rosenthal** provides corporate and transactional advice to his clients, and has considerable experience in environmental matters.

### Wright, Lindsey & Jennings LLP
See profile on p.534

**THE FIRM** This firm advises clients on a broad range of transactions from offices in Little Rock and Rogers. The group is highly regarded for its considerable expertise in the areas of municipal finance and tax, and has substantial experience in representing public institutions in bond matters. Clients include Arkansas Blue Cross Blue Shield, Central Arkansas Water and Irwin Partners.

**KEY INDIVIDUALS Bill Spivey** (see p.529) is praised as one of the state's *"preeminent"* municipal finance attorneys, and has a proven track record in the public bonds arena. He recently served as bond counsel to the City of

Maumelle in an $8 million bond issuance. **John Tisdale** (see p.529) has a broad expertise in corporate law and is highly regarded for his work in municipal bonds. Tisdale has an active tax practice, of which one source notes: *"He is probably the best tax person in Arkansas."* **Tad Bohannon**'s (see p.525) practice incorporates both tax and bonds work, particularly for public bodies and water companies. He also advises clients on regulatory compliance matters. **Sean Hatch** (see p.527) advises on corporate and commercial matters for a number of companies, including Rector Phillips Morse and is held in high regard by his peers.

## Band 3

### Gill Ragon Owen, P.A.

**THE FIRM** This solid corporate practice offers clients expertise in a broad spectrum of transactional, banking and tax matters. The team advises financial institutions, energy companies and property developers on a range of issues including regulatory compliance, refinancing and contract matters. Clients include Delta Bank, Regions Bank and American Electric Power.

**KEY INDIVIDUALS Charles Owen** is an experienced practitioner with more than four decades experience as a tax attorney in Arkansas. He is highly regarded by peers for his expertise in the field. **Daniel Goodwin** acts for clients such as financial institutions and investors in a number of corporate and commercial real estate transactions. He has an impressive client roster that includes Centennial Bank and Methodist Family Health. The *"very practical"* **Heartsill Ragon** has a broad practice that includes real estate transaction, municipal finance and corporate and regulatory work. He frequently acts as local counsel in high-value corporate financings.

### Quattlebaum, Grooms, Tull & Burrow PLLC
See profile on p.532

**THE FIRM** This firm represents clients on mergers and acquisitions, banking, and a variety of other corporate issues. Recent matters include advising Simmons First National on its acquisition of substantial assets of Truman Bank before the latter's closure.

**Sources say:** *"They do the research appropriately and they come up with novel ideas."*

**KEY INDIVIDUALS Timothy Grooms** (see p.526) is held in high esteem for his work in mergers and acquisitions. He is popular with peers and clients alike, with one source reporting: *"Tim is a very, very bright individual. He is pragmatic and good to work with."* **Patrick Burrow** (see p.526) represents financial institutions in loan and M&A transactions. He represented Simmons First National in the transaction described above. Clients appreciate his thoroughness and *"wide knowledge base."* Springdale-based **Jeb Joyce** (see p.527) enjoys a good reputation for his broad transactional practice. He advises clients on both real estate and corporate matters, and is well regarded by the market.

## Williams & Anderson PLC

See profile on p.533

**THE FIRM** This well-established firm remains active in bond, securities and M&A matters among other corporate transactions. The team has considerable experience advising clients in both the public and private sector.

**KEY INDIVIDUALS** Founding partner **David Menz** receives praise from market sources for his expertise in public finance and bonds. He is particularly associated with financing work for public utilities, and is noted by sources for his work with water utilities. **John Kooistra** acts for clients on a number of issues from the corporate and banking arenas. He is popular among his peers for his collaborative approach to negotiations, while sources say he is *"a fantastic lawyer."* **Jackson Williams** remains a significant authority in the market, renowned for his expertise in municipal bonds and various finance transactions.

## Other Notable Practitioners

**Donald Jack** of Jack, Nelson, Jones, Fink, Jiles & Gregory, PA has *"been an A+ business transaction lawyer forever,"* according to one commentator. Peers note his *"good sense of how to accomplish the goals."* **James Smith** of two-partner firm Smith Hurst PLC is highly regarded by his peers for his skill as a tax attorney. Market sources also consider him to be a *"very good business lawyer."*

# LABOR & EMPLOYMENT

Employee Benefits & Compensation p.521

Commentary about individuals can be found under their firm's paragraph. If the firm has no paragraph (is not ranked) look at Other Notable Practitioners.

| Labor & Employment |
|---|
| **Leading Firms** |
| **Band 1** |
| Cross, Gunter, Witherspoon & Galchus, PC |
| Wright, Lindsey & Jennings LLP * |
| **Band 2** |
| Friday, Eldredge & Clark, LLP * |
| Littler Mendelson * |
| Mitchell, Williams, Selig, Gates Woodyard, PLLC * |
| Rose Law Firm |
| **Band 3** |
| Williams & Anderson PLC * |

## Band 1

### Cross, Gunter, Witherspoon & Galchus, PC

**THE FIRM** This labor and employment boutique enjoys a superlative reputation for its expertise in contentious and regulatory compliance issues. The firm defends clients against a variety of accusations, including wrongful dismissal and race or age discriminations. The firm also advises clients on how to avoid future labor and employment disputes.

**Sources say:** *"They offer a lot of quality education on employment issues."*

**KEY INDIVIDUALS** *"Top-notch attorney"* **Russell Gunter** is praised by clients and peers alike for his breadth of experience and sound judgment in matters of employment and traditional labor disputes. **Bruce Cross** is highly regarded for his work with the National Labor Relations Board (NLRB) and labor unions. One interviewee remarks that he *"does an excellent job representing management"* in labor disputes. **Donna Galchus** advises clients on a wide range of contentious and noncontentious employment matters. She is highly regarded for her expertise in immigration law. One source remarks that **Carolyn Witherspoon** is *"very effective in the courtroom,"* while others praise her for her *"calm demeanor and years of experience."* She represents employers in the public and private sectors in a range of employment-related litigation. The *"detail-oriented and very sharp"* **Benjamin Shipley** is based in the firm's Fort Smith offices, and receives praise for his work in both employment and traditional labor matters. **Melissa Duke** is considered a rising star in labor, employment and immigration law. Interviewees remark that *"she is very good with dealing with wage and hour claims and has a strong future ahead."*

### Wright, Lindsey & Jennings LLP

See profile on p.534

**THE FIRM** The impressive labor and employment team at this full-service firm offers a broad range of expertise, including employee discrimination defense and traditional labor matters. Recent work highlights include handling a sensitive investigation into allegations of harassment at The Oxford American magazine. Other clients include Mercy Health and Walgreens.

**Sources say:** *"We were in very good hands. They are very experienced. I came away feeling very impressed with the firm and their professionalism."*

**KEY INDIVIDUALS** **John Davis** (see p.526) has a broad range of expertise including acting as general employment counsel and in employee benefits matters. His clients include Central Arkansas Radiation Therapy Institute, for whom he provides counsel on a range of employment matters. **Stuart Jackson** (see p.527) leads the firm's labor and employment department, and is described by one interviewee as *"terribly knowledgeable and particularly effective in court."* He was part of the team that advised The Oxford American. **Lee Muldrow**'s (see p.528) areas of excellence include employee benefits matters and discrimination defense litigation. One client says: *"He is very thorough and very easy to work with."* **Michelle Kaemmerling** led the investigations into the allegations of harassment at The Oxford American. Sources report that her *"attention to detail is a real strength."* Senior of counsel **John Lile** continues to enjoy a strong reputation for contentious matters in the employment law sphere. Highly rated associate **Jane Kim** (see p.527) worked closely with senior colleagues Jackson and Kaemmerling on The Oxford American investigation. She defends employers in litigation at state and federal level.

| Labor & Employment | | |
|---|---|---|
| **Senior Statesmen** | | |
| Senior Statesmen: distinguished older practitioners | | |
| Lile John G | Wright, Lindsey & Jennings LLP | |
| **Leading Individuals** | | |
| **Star individuals** | | |
| Kaplan Philip | Williams & Anderson PLC | |
| **Band 1** | | |
| Boe Tim | Rose Law Firm | |
| Davis John D | Wright, Lindsey & Jennings LLP * | |
| Freeland Byron | Mitchell, Williams, Selig, Gates Woodyard | |
| Graves Kathlyn | Mitchell, Williams, Selig, Gates Woodyard | |
| Gunter Russell | Cross, Gunter, Witherspoon & Galchus, PC | |
| Herrington Daniel | Friday, Eldredge & Clark, LLP * | |
| Martin David | Rose Law Firm | |
| Robinson Spencer | Ramsay, Bridgforth, Harrelson (ONP)[†] | |
| Witherspoon Carolyn B | Cross, Gunter, Witherspoon & Galchus, PC | |
| **Band 2** | | |
| Cross J Bruce | Cross, Gunter, Witherspoon & Galchus, PC | |
| Jackson William Stuart | Wright, Lindsey & Jennings LLP * | |
| Jones Michael R | Gilker and Jones PA (ONP)[†] | |
| Madison Eva | Littler Mendelson * | |
| Moore Michael | Friday, Eldredge & Clark, LLP * | |
| Pulliam Janet | Watts, Donovan & Tilley, P.A. (ONP)[†] | |
| **Band 3** | | |
| Chiles IV E B (Chip) | Quattlebaum, Grooms, Tull (ONP)[†] * | |
| Donovan David M | Watts, Donovan & Tilley, P.A. (ONP)[†] | |
| Galchus Donna Smith | Cross, Gunter, Witherspoon & Galchus, PC | |
| Kaemmerling Michelle M | Wright, Lindsey & Jennings LLP | |
| Muldrow Lee J | Wright, Lindsey & Jennings LLP * | |
| Shipley III Benjamin H | Cross, Gunter, Witherspoon & Galchus, PC | |
| Yeargan Leigh-Anne | Mitchell, Williams, Selig, Gates Woodyard | |
| **Up-and-coming individuals** | | |
| Duke Melissa M | Cross, Gunter, Witherspoon & Galchus, PC | |
| Potts Dylan | Gill Ragon Owen, P.A. (ONP)[†] | |
| Vandiver Brian | Mitchell, Williams, Selig, Gates Woodyard | |
| **Associates to watch** | | |
| Kim Jane | Wright, Lindsey & Jennings LLP * | |
| * Indicates firm / individual with profile. | | |
| [†] ONP = Other Notable Practitioner. | | |

## Band 2

### Friday, Eldredge & Clark, LLP
See profile on p.530

**THE FIRM** This eight-attorney labor and employment practice has a wealth of experience representing employers in the healthcare, education, utilities and manufacturing sectors. The firm's impressive stable of clients includes Entergy Arkansas, Arkansas Children's Hospital and the City of Little Rock. The firm handles employment discrimination and employee compensation and benefits litigation, as well as noncontentious matters.
**Sources say:** *"The client service is impeccable. We got great value."*
**KEY INDIVIDUALS Daniel Herrington** (see p.527) *"sets a high bar for employment law,"* and receives praise for his breadth of knowledge and exceptional standards of client service. He defended Entergy Arkansas as lead counsel in allegations of discrimination and retaliation. **Wyckliff Nisbet** (see p.528) is a well-established player in the market. His focus is on employee benefits, complex tax and benefits matters. Experienced partner **Michael Moore** (see p.528) draws plaudits for his skills as a litigator and substantial knowledge base on employment discrimination matters. **Joseph Hurst** (see p.527) specializes in employee benefits and compensation issues, both contentious and noncontentious. Clients applaud his *"attention to detail,"* and say they are *"very satisfied"* with his service.

### Littler Mendelson
See profile on p.688

**THE FIRM** This national labor and employment boutique serves clients on a broad range of issues from its offices in Fayetteville. The firm has substantial experience in employee discrimination litigation, federal labor investiga-

tions and regulatory compliance matters. The firm is also active in a number of putative wage and hour class action cases.
**KEY INDIVIDUALS Eva Madison** (see p.528) earns client praise for her responsiveness and commercial awareness. Madison is experienced in handling a wide range of employment discrimination and class action litigations.

### Mitchell, Williams, Selig, Gates Woodyard, PLLC
See profile on p.531

**THE FIRM** Mitchell Williams handles a broad range of matters including EEOC investigations, wage and hour litigation, and ERISA and employee benefits issues. The firm maintains a presence across the state from offices in Little Rock and Rogers, and also offers counsel on NLRB and traditional labor matters.
**KEY INDIVIDUALS** Experienced practitioner **Byron Freeland** enjoys an impressive reputation for his skills as a litigator and has extensive experience representing employers in a number of contentious matters. Sources describe him as *"an excellent attorney."* Clients value **Kathlyn Graves**'s talents as both an impressive litigator and trusted adviser. Her practice includes both employment disputes and traditional labor matters. Rogers-based **Leigh-Anne Yeargan** frequently works with large companies and corporations on employment regulatory compliance matters and handling of employee disputes. Up-and-comer **Brian Vandiver** is described by peers as *"very knowledgeable and very effective."* He works closely with colleague Yeargan on a broad range of matters.

### Rose Law Firm

**THE FIRM** The labor and employment practice at this full-service firm continues to be a significant player in the market. The firm represent employers in a number of areas, particularly Occupational Health & Safety Administration (OSHA) and wage and hour matters. Current clients include Nucor Corporations, Roller Funeral Homes and Cooper Communities.
**Sources say:** *"They have a presence in the market and do good work."*
**KEY INDIVIDUALS Tim Boe**'s *"deep understanding and experience in labor law is tremendous,"* notes one interviewee. His practice also includes OSHA compliance matters, and defending employers against allegations of discrimination or wrongful dismissal. The highly experienced **David Martin** is *"everything you'd want in an employment lawyer,"* say sources. He is a respected trial lawyer and han-

dles a number of contentious and noncontentious OSHA-related matters. **Bryant Cranford** specializes in employee benefits and compensation work, and clients benefit from his background and knowledge in tax.

## Band 3

### Williams & Anderson PLC
See profile on p.533

**THE FIRM** This solid labor and employment practice is respected in the market for its representation of both employers and plaintiffs in a range of discrimination and wrongful dismissal cases. The firm has experienced a number of personnel changes this year, but continues to be a presence in the market.
**KEY INDIVIDUALS** *"Terrific lawyer"* **Philip Kaplan** is considered the firm's leading light for employment law matters, and enjoys an outstanding reputation in the market for employee discrimination litigation.

## Other Notable Practitioners

**Michael Jones** of Gilker and Jones PA is highly regarded in the market for his extensive experience and expertise in traditional labor matters. He serves clients from the firm's Mountainburg office. **Dylan Potts** of Gill Ragon Owen, P.A. is active in both contentious and regulatory matters in the employment arena, including EEOC investigations and wage and hour disputes. **Spencer Robinson** of Ramsay, Bridgforth, Harrelson & Starling LLP is well respected for his representation of clients in the Pine Bluff region. His broad practice includes wage and hour and discrimination litigation. The *"tenacious and intelligent"* **Janet Pulliam** of Watts, Donovan & Tilley, P.A. is highly regarded for her expertise in employment and healthcare work. Peers remark on her skill as a litigator and deep knowledge of the law. **Chip Chiles** (see p.526) heads the department at Quattlebaum, Grooms, Tull & Burrow PLLC and is well regarded as an effective trial attorney. His practice includes both commercial and employment litigation. **Craig Westbrook**'s practice at Overbey, Strigel, Boyd & Westbrook, PLC is noted for his handling of employee benefits matters, pensions and ERISA claims. **David Donovan** of Watts, Donovan & Tilley, P.A. represents employers in a number of employee discrimination disputes, as part of a wider litigation practice.

# LITIGATION

Commentary about individuals can be found under their firm's paragraph. If the firm has no paragraph (is not ranked) look at Other Notable Practitioners.

## Litigation: General Commercial
### Leading Firms

**Band 1**
Friday, Eldredge & Clark, LLP *
Quattlebaum, Grooms, Tull & Burrow PLLC *
Williams & Anderson PLC *
Wright, Lindsey & Jennings LLP *

**Band 2**
Mitchell, Williams, Selig, Gates Woodyard, PLLC *
Rose Law Firm

**Band 3**
Wilson, Engstrom, Corum & Coulter

## Litigation: Environmental
### Leading Individuals

**Band 1**

| | |
|---|---|
| Gates Allan | Mitchell, Williams, Selig, Gates Woodyard |
| Nestrud Charles | Chisenhall, Nestrud & Julian, PA (ONP)[†] |
| Perkins G Alan | Perkins & Trotter PLLC (ONP)[†] |
| Rosenthal Brian | Rose Law Firm |

### Band 1

#### Friday, Eldredge & Clark, LLP
See profile on p.530

**THE FIRM** This firm's market-leading litigation department has a wealth of experience in multiple areas, including class action defense, medical malpractice, commercial litigation and bankruptcy. The firm typically represents pharmaceutical companies, hospitals, financial institutions and insurance providers, among others. Recent work highlights include defending Johnson & Johnson against allegations of deceptive trade practices and Medicare fraud.
**Sources say:** *"This firm stands above the rest."*
**KEY INDIVIDUALS** Laura Smith (see p.529) is widely regarded as *"one of the best lawyers in the state."* She heads the firm's medical malpractice and medical device defense team and handled the aforementioned matters for Johnson & Johnson. **Kevin Crass** (see p.526) is highly respected throughout the market for his expertise in complex commercial litigation and class action cases. Peers commend his first-rate legal mind, commenting that he is *"a great writer"* and highlighting his aptitude for *"intellectual heavy lifting."* **William Waddell** (see p.529) draws praise for his handling of complex business and class action litigation. One client reports: *"He has a practical, common-sense approach to understanding our business concerns as well as the legal issues involved."* **Michelle Ator** (see p.525) specializes in medical malpractice defense work, typically representing major hospitals across the state. Clients note that she is an important member of the firm's impressive malpractice defense team. *"Excellent trial lawyer"* **James Simpson** (see p.529) leads the firm's business litigation

## Litigation: General Commercial
### Senior Statesmen

**Senior Statesmen:** distinguished older practitioners

| | |
|---|---|
| Anderson Philip S | Williams & Anderson PLC |
| Lile John G | Wright, Lindsey & Jennings LLP |

### Leading Individuals

**Band 1**

| | |
|---|---|
| Allen William | Allen Law Firm (ONP)[†] |
| Crass Kevin | Friday, Eldredge & Clark, LLP * |
| Everett John | Everett Law Firm (ONP)[†] |
| Kaplan Philip | Williams & Anderson PLC |
| Lowther Jr Edwin L | Wright, Lindsey & Jennings LLP * |
| Matthews David R | Matthews, Campbell, Rhoads, McClure (ONP)[†] |
| Quattlebaum Steven W | Quattlebaum, Grooms, Tull & Burrow * |
| Rather Jr Gordon S | Wright, Lindsey & Jennings LLP * |
| Shemin Kenneth R | Shemin Law Firm, PLLC (ONP)[†] |
| Tull III John E | Quattlebaum, Grooms, Tull & Burrow * |
| Waddell Jr William A | Friday, Eldredge & Clark, LLP * |

**Band 2**

| | |
|---|---|
| Chiles IV E B (Chip) | Quattlebaum, Grooms, Tull & Burrow * |
| Coleman Charles T | Wright, Lindsey & Jennings LLP * |
| Coulter Nate | Wilson, Engstrom, Corum & Coulter |
| Donovan Richard T | Rose Law Firm |
| Henry Judy | Wright, Lindsey & Jennings LLP * |
| Kumpe Peter G | Williams & Anderson PLC |
| Powell David M | Williams & Anderson PLC |
| Pruitt Lyn P | Mitchell, Williams, Selig, Gates Woodyard |
| Simpson James | Friday, Eldredge & Clark, LLP * |

**Band 3**

| | |
|---|---|
| Askew III Jess | Williams & Anderson PLC |
| Baker John K | Mitchell, Williams, Selig, Gates Woodyard |
| Bartley Sherry P | Mitchell, Williams, Selig, Gates Woodyard |
| Elrod John R | Conner & Winters, LLP (ONP)[†] |
| Engstrom Stephen | Wilson, Engstrom, Corum & Coulter |
| Goss Patrick | Rose Law Firm |
| Miller Marie-Bernarde | Williams & Anderson PLC |
| Schlumberger Charles L | Quattlebaum, Grooms, Tull & Burrow * |
| Shults Steven | Shults & Brown LLP (ONP)[†] |
| Stewart Amy Lee | Rose Law Firm |

**Band 4**

| | |
|---|---|
| Brenner Benjamin | Mitchell, Williams, Selig, Gates Woodyard |
| Lancaster Stephen R | Wright, Lindsey & Jennings LLP * |
| Miller Lance R | Mitchell, Williams, Selig, Gates Woodyard |
| Wilcox Tony | Wilcox & Lacy PLC (ONP)[†] |
| Wilson David D | Friday, Eldredge & Clark, LLP * |

team. He has recently handled matters for pharmaceutical companies and natural gas providers, acting alongside Ms Smith in the Johnson & Johnson matter. Experienced trial lawyer **David Wilson** (see p.529) handles a broad range of commercial and business litigation. One client commends him for being *"prompt and on point"* and for his *"creativity in achieving results."* Rising star **Jason Hendren** (see

## Litigation: Medical Malpractice Defense
### Leading Individuals

**Star individuals**

| | |
|---|---|
| Smith Laura | Friday, Eldredge & Clark, LLP * |

**Band 1**

| | |
|---|---|
| Beard III RT | Mitchell, Williams, Selig, Gates Woodyard |
| Cox Walter B | Cox, Cox & Estes PLLC (ONP)[†] |
| McNeill Paul D | Womack, Phelps & McNeill (ONP)[†] |

**Band 2**

| | |
|---|---|
| Ator Michelle | Friday, Eldredge & Clark, LLP * |
| Cauley Michelle | Mitchell, Williams, Selig, Gates Woodyard |
| Hopkins Mariam T | Anderson, Murphy & Hopkins LLP (ONP)[†] |
| Lowther Jr Edwin L | Wright, Lindsey & Jennings LLP * |
| Pruitt Lyn P | Mitchell, Williams, Selig |
| Waddell Paul | Waddell Cole & Jones (ONP)[†] |

**Up-and-coming individuals**

| | |
|---|---|
| Hendren Jason | Friday, Eldredge & Clark * |

* Indicates firm / individual with profile.
[†]ONP = Other Notable Practitioner.

p.527) is part of the firm's deep bench specializing in medical malpractice defense.

#### Quattlebaum, Grooms, Tull & Burrow PLLC
See profile on p.532

**THE FIRM** This impressive team earns plaudits for its depth of experience and proven track record. The firm is highly regarded for its broad commercial practice and is particularly active in product liability defense and real estate litigation. Recent work highlights include acting for Mercedes-Benz in a case alleging a defective seatbelt.
**Sources say:** *"They are judicious in the work they do, the best bang for my buck."*
**KEY INDIVIDUALS** Head of department **Steven Quattlebaum** (see p.528) is *"down to earth, a straight shooter and relates well to the jury,"* say sources. He is highly regarded for his expertise in product liability defense and his meticulous pre-trial preparation. **John Tull** (see p.529) has a broad litigation practice including real estate and environmental disputes. Recent work highlights include representing Arkansas Realtors Association in a breach of contract litigation. **Chip Chiles** (see p.526) specializes in handling appellate cases as part of a broad litigation practice that includes general commercial and product liability disputes. He recently acted for American Greetings in a negligence case following an electrical incident. **Charles Schlumberger** (see p.529) is active in a wide range of areas including complex commercial litigation, antitrust matters and First Amendment litigation.

#### Williams & Anderson PLC
See profile on p.533

**THE FIRM** This firm's litigation team is primarily engaged in defending financial institutions and insurance companies in a variety of cases including class actions. The team also has experience handling construction and professional liability litigation and appellate work.

**KEY INDIVIDUALS** The *"very experienced"* Philip Kaplan is *"a go-to guy for litigation,"* says one market source. His broad experience includes appellate and class action cases. Sources commend **Jess Askew** as *"a good cross-examiner,"* and relate that *"on any given day he's the smartest guy in the building."* His deep trial expertise encompasses business, media and appellate litigation. **Peter Kumpe** has a practice focused on appellate, IP and complex business litigation. Sources note his good team management. Commentators note **David Powell**'s skill in construction and professional liability defense cases. He is also experienced in handling arbitration cases. **Marie-Bernarde Miller** has a broad practice with experience in commercial, retail and employment law. *"Elder statesman"* **Philip Anderson** is held in high esteem in the market for his proven track record in business litigation and appellate work.

## Wright, Lindsey & Jennings LLP
See profile on p.534

**THE FIRM** This premier team demonstrates considerable expertise in a vast range of civil litigation matters including complex commercial litigation, insurance coverage disputes and IP litigation. The firm can count Bank of America, Baptist Health and Ford among its impressive client roster. Recent matters include representing Bayer CropScience in litigation surrounding genetically modified rice.

**Sources say:** *"Wright, Lindsey & Jennings distinguishes itself in providing great comfort that assignments will be properly handled in terms of technical expertise as well as in an economic manner."*

**KEY INDIVIDUALS** The *"astounding"* **Edwin Lowther** (see p.527) is *"absolutely excellent in a courtroom,"* according to his peers. He is renowned for his skills in product liability cases, including medical devices liability. Head of the firm's business litigation department **Gordon Rather** (see p.528) is *"a splendid trial lawyer"* who is *"always extremely well prepared,"* say sources. He is well regarded in the market for his expertise in commercial disputes and bankruptcy. **Judy Henry** (see p.527) is *"very responsive and thorough, both as an advocate and as a counselor."* Recent matters include acting for SunTrust Mortgage in two cases filed respectively under the Arkansas Deceptive Trade Act and Arkansas Statutory Foreclosure Act. **Charles Coleman** (see p.526) specializes in Chapter 11 and insurance disputes. He typically represents creditors and trustees in complex bankruptcy matters. **Stephen Lancaster** (see p.527) has a broad litigation practice that includes title insurance litigation, breach of contract litigation and general commercial litigation. Senior of counsel **John Lile** handles employment litigation as part of a wider trial practice that extends to commercial disputes. He enjoys an impressive reputation in the market.

## Band 2

### Mitchell, Williams, Selig, Gates Woodyard, PLLC
See profile on p.531

**THE FIRM** This accomplished team of trial lawyers offers clients a range of expertise including medical malpractice, environmental and business tort defense. Key clients come from the insurance, healthcare and financial services sectors.

**KEY INDIVIDUALS** Experienced practitioner **RT Beard** heads the firm's medical malpractice defense team and has a *"long-standing"* reputation for work in the field. He receives praise for his strength as a trial lawyer. **Allan Gates** has experience in a broad range of environmental issues, including air pollution, hazard waste and toxic tort litigation and environmental real estate work. **Michelle Cauley** specializes in medical malpractice defense, product liability and general insurance defense. She is popular with clients for her tenacity in contentious matters. *"Accomplished trial lawyer"* **Lyn Pruitt** garners praise for her work in product liability defense. She services clients from the healthcare and pharmaceutical industries. Clients describe **John Baker** as a *"very impressive litigator who is very well informed."* He offers a broad practice including business tort, real estate and class actions. *"Excellent courtroom lawyer"* **Sherry Bartley** is highly regarded for a broad practice that focuses on toxic tort and insurance defense work. **Benjamin Brenner** recently arrived from Williams & Anderson and focuses on commercial and corporate litigation and business tort. Market observers name him *"a fine young lawyer."* **Lance Miller** is head of the firm's business disputes group and frequently represents financial institutions in bankruptcy litigation and arbitration. Sources attest that he is *"a solid, solid lawyer."*

### Rose Law Firm

**THE FIRM** The litigation practice at this firm handles a broad range of commercial litigation, including significant experience in product liability defense, class actions and IP. Recent work highlights include acting as co-counsel representing Monte Carlo Aviation in a $40 million dispute concerning the manufacture and sale of a corporate jet.

**KEY INDIVIDUALS Brian Rosenthal** handles environmental litigation as a part of a broader environmental practice including transactional and regulatory matters. **Richard Donovan** handles a variety of commercial disputes and led the team that acted for Monte Carlo Aviation. He is well regarded for his strength as a trial lawyer. **Patrick Goss** concentrates on product liability law and received summary judgment for Hawker Beechcraft in the defense of a multiple-death wrongful death trial. **Amy Lee Stewart** is widely respected for her expertise in antitrust, privacy and breach of contract disputes. She has experience handling class action and appellate work.

## Band 3

### Wilson, Engstrom, Corum & Coulter

**THE FIRM** This litigation boutique is active in a number of areas including personal injury, employment, real estate and land use and zoning disputes. The firm's four-partner team operates from its base in Little Rock.

**KEY INDIVIDUALS Nate Coulter** receives recognition from peers for a sharp legal mind and has experience of a broad range of commercial litigation including insurance and real estate work. Interviewees claim that **Stephen Engstrom** is a *"master of detail – nothing gets past him."* Engstrom has significant experience in professional liability matters as part of a wider commercial litigation practice.

### Other Notable Practitioners

**John Everett** of Everett Law Firm is highly regarded as *"a superb trial lawyer, well prepared, quick-witted and good on his feet."* **Alan Perkins** of Perkins & Trotter PLLC specializes in environmental issues, particularly disputes in the oil, gas and mining industries. *"Very good trial lawyer"* **Kenneth Shemin** of litigation boutique Shemin Law Firm, PLLC *"has a personality that plays well for a jury, very smart and likable,"* say sources. **Charles Nestrud** of Little Rock firm Chisenhall, Nestrud & Julian, PA has a highly regarded practice focused on contentious and noncontentious environmental law. He also has experience with commercial litigation. The *"very well-respected"* **Walter Cox** of Cox, Cox & Estes PLLC is an experienced medical malpractice defense attorney based in Fayetteville. Key clients include hospitals and pharmaceutical companies. Experienced trial lawyer **David Matthews** of Rogers-based firm Matthews, Campbell, Rhoads, McClure, Thompson & Fryauf is described by peers as *"quick-witted"* and *"very accomplished."* His practice include personal injury litigation, insurance defense and utilities work. **William Allen** is the principal at Allen Law Firm and is active in a number of insurance defense and class action litigations. He is renowned in the market as a talented advocate and experienced trial counsel. *"Premier medical malpractice defense attorney"* **Paul McNeill** of Womack, Phelps & McNeill. A Professional Association is highly regarded for work in both professional and product liability disputes in the healthcare industry. Jonesboro-based **Paul Waddell** of Waddell Cole & Jones is highly regarded for his medical malpractice and insurance defense practice. **Mariam Hopkins** of Anderson, Murphy & Hopkins LLP is *"extremely well respected"* for her work in medical malpractice defense and general insurance defense, according to market sources. Fayetteville-based **John Elrod** of Conner & Winters, LLP is a seasoned trial advocate who is active in a broad range of commercial litigation and dispute resolution matters. **Steven Shults** of Shults & Brown LLP has a broad litigation practice, with significant expertise in handling complex commercial disputes, bankruptcy and business tort. **Tony Wilcox** of Jonesboro firm Wilcox & Lacy PLC advises clients on a wide range of contentious matters, including personal injury and franchise disputes.

# REAL ESTATE

Commentary about individuals can be found under their firm's paragraph. If the firm has no paragraph (is not ranked) look at Other Notable Practitioners.

## Real Estate
### Leading Firms

**Band 1**
Friday, Eldredge & Clark, LLP *
Mitchell, Williams, Selig, Gates Woodyard, PLLC *
Quattlebaum, Grooms, Tull & Burrow PLLC *
Wright, Lindsey & Jennings LLP *

**Band 2**
Kutak Rock LLP *
Rose Law Firm
Williams & Anderson PLC *

**Band 3**
Gill Ragon Owen, P.A.

### Leading Individuals

**Star individuals**

| | | |
|---|---|---|
| Grooms Timothy W | Quattlebaum, Grooms, Tull & Burrow * | |

**Band 1**

| | |
|---|---|
| Barrier W Christopher | Mitchell, Williams, Selig, Gates Woodyard |
| Hamlin Harold W | Mitchell, Williams, Selig, Gates Woodyard |
| Saxton James | Friday, Eldredge & Clark, LLP * |
| Spivey III John William | Wright, Lindsey & Jennings LLP * |
| Taylor Jay | Friday, Eldredge & Clark, LLP * |

**Band 2**

| | |
|---|---|
| Frazier Randal B | Kutak Rock LLP * |
| Gardner Price C | Friday, Eldredge & Clark, LLP * |
| Goodwin T Daniel | Gill Ragon Owen, P.A. |
| Lewis John Alan | Mitchell, Williams, Selig, Gates Woodyard |
| McKinney II J Cliff | Quattlebaum, Grooms, Tull & Burrow * |
| Pool Terry W | Kutak Rock LLP * |

**Band 3**

| | |
|---|---|
| Bohannon C Tad | Wright, Lindsey & Jennings LLP * |
| Hankins Stuart | Hankins Law Firm PA (ONP)† |
| Kooistra John | Williams & Anderson PLC |
| Tisdale John R | Wright, Lindsey & Jennings LLP * |

**Associates to watch**

| | |
|---|---|
| Childers Michael B | Friday, Eldredge & Clark, LLP * |

\* Indicates firm / individual with profile.
†ONP = Other Notable Practitioner.

## Real Estate: Zoning/Land Use
### Leading Individuals

**Band 1**

| | |
|---|---|
| Frazier Randal B | Kutak Rock LLP * |
| Giles Stephen R | Stephen R Giles PA (ONP)† |

## Band 1

### Friday, Eldredge & Clark, LLP
See profile on p.530

THE FIRM Clients appreciate this impressive firm's experienced bench and commendable levels of service. The team has significant experience in representing lenders and investors in large-scale real estate transactions. The firm's stable of real estate clients includes Region's Bank, Arkansas Children's Hospital and Bank of the Ozarks.
**Sources say:** *"They have the depth of experience and they provide very good value service."*
**KEY INDIVIDUALS** Practice group head **James Saxton** (see p.528) receives praise for his collaborative approach to negotiations. He enjoys a strong reputation in the market and is experienced in dealing with tax issues relating to real estate transactions. Sources describe *"talented"* partner **Jay Taylor** (see p.529) as *"responsive and thorough."* He represents financial institutions and real estate developers in a range of matters including the sale, purchase, financing or leasing of commercial real estate. Clients of the *"very capable"* **Price Gardner** (see p.526) benefit from his extensive tax background in relation to real estate matters. Gardner has a broad practice that also includes corporate advice and transactional work. Associate **Michael Childers** (see p.526) impresses sources with his awareness of client needs and *"timely"* responses to queries and documents. He is noted for his handling of a range of real estate transactions.

### Mitchell, Williams, Selig, Gates Woodyard, PLLC
See profile on p.531

THE FIRM This firm handles the full range of real estate matters including transactions, financing, zoning and tax. The team has a strong market presence with attorneys based in both the central and north west regions of the state. Clients include real estate investors, developers, owners and lenders.
**KEY INDIVIDUALS** The *"outstanding"* **Christopher Barrier** is revered in the state for his extensive experience and authoritative knowledge base. He is head of the firm's real estate and land use practice and described by one interviewee as *"the dean of real estate lawyers in the state."* Sources remark on **Harold Hamlin's** talent in closing real estate transactions. Hamlin is the firm's managing partner and has extensive experience of representing real estate developers and property managers. Rogers-based **John Lewis** is active representing developers and investors in a variety of real estate transactions including financings.

### Quattlebaum, Grooms, Tull & Burrow PLLC
See profile on p.532

THE FIRM This market-leading firm has an impressive stable of clients including banks and real estate developers. Recent work highlights include representing Moses Tucker Real Estate in the development of the $13.8 million mixed-use Arcade Building Project in downtown Little Rock. The firm operates from offices in Little Rock and Springdale.
**Sources say:** *"The attorneys are knowledgeable, responsive and provide their services at reasonable fees."*
**KEY INDIVIDUALS** **Timothy Grooms** (see p.526) is *"widely known in the market as one of its most expert attorneys on commercial real estate,"* notes one commentator. He led the team representing Moses Tucker Real Estate and heads the firm's real estate practice. **Cliff McKinney** (see p.528) is active in a broad range of real estate transactions and environmentally friendly building projects. He receives praise for his depth of knowledge and his efficient and responsive service to his clients.

### Wright, Lindsey & Jennings LLP
See profile on p.534

THE FIRM The impressive real estate practice at this firm handles the full range of real estate matters including regulatory matters, financing and a broad range of transactions. The team provides counsel to Bearskin Farms in all matters relating to the acquisition and financing of agricultural property. Other clients include Central Arkansas Water and Fairwood Capital.
**Sources say:** *"High-quality individuals who are extremely professional in how they conduct their business."*
**KEY INDIVIDUALS** **Bill Spivey** (see p.529) has extensive experience in real estate transactions and complex zoning work, particularly for the timber industry. Clients value his straightforward and accurate counsel, responsiveness and diligence. *"I would highly recommend him to anyone needing counsel,"* remarks one impressed client. **Tad Bohannon** (see p.525) has an impressive stable of clients in the water and utilities sector. He is active in both contentious and noncontentious real estate matters including acquisitions, land use and real estate litigation. **John Tisdale** (see p.529) is active advising a broad range of clients on acquisitions and financings. Clients benefit from his additional expertise in tax and public finance matters.

## Band 2

### Kutak Rock LLP
See profile on p.1670

THE FIRM This national firm acts for clients on a wide range of real estate issues including acquisitions, financing, land use and litigation from offices in the north west and center of the state. The team can draw on support from across the firm's 16 nationwide offices.
**KEY INDIVIDUALS** Sources describe **Randal Frazier** (see p.526) as *"very experienced"* and *"very competent"* in zoning regulatory matters. Frazier advises clients on land use law as part of a broader practice that includes financings and transactional work. Fayetteville-based **Terry Pool** (see p.528) is well regarded in the market. He has a broad real estate practice including acquisitions, tax issues and a variety of financing matters. One interviewee describes him as *"very responsive, diligent and thorough."*

### Rose Law Firm

THE FIRM This well-established, five-partner real estate practice has extensive experience in a variety of financing and refinancing transactions, including stock and tax credit-related matters. The firm can count Mountaire

Corporation, The Stephens Groups and Welspun Tubular among its client roster.

**KEY INDIVIDUALS** Garland Garrett is a key contact.

## Williams & Anderson PLC

**See profile on p.533**

**THE FIRM** This firm is known for its depth of experience in a broad range of transactional matters. The Little Rock-based team enjoys a good reputation for its representation of real estate owners, developers and financial institutions. The team also advises clients on contentious real estate matters.

**KEY INDIVIDUALS** *"Fantastic lawyer"* **John Kooistra** has a broad practice advising clients on both corporate and real estate matters. He is particularly active in representing clients on the lender side of real estate deals.

## Band 3

### Gill Ragon Owen, P.A.

**THE FIRM** This firm represents a number of clients from the banking sector in real estate-connected lending and financing matters. The firm, which enters the rankings for the first time this year, can count Centennial Bank and Delta Trust & Bank among its client roster. The group is also active in real estate transactions and contentious matters.

**Sources say:** *"A very solid and respected firm."*

**KEY INDIVIDUALS** **Daniel Goodwin** *"is very strong in contracts, personal relationships and negotiations,"* enthuses one client. He is noted for his representation of banks and institutional lenders such as Centennial and Delta Bank & Trust.

## Other Notable Practitioners

**Stephen Giles** of Stephen R Giles PA specializes in zoning and land use matters and is a popular choice for those needing expertise in this niche area. **Stuart Hankins** of Hankins Law Firm PA has a general real estate practice and is well regarded for his experience in the field. Sources say he is *"a very capable real estate lawyer"* who produces *"high-quality work."*

# Leaders' Profiles in Arkansas

### ATOR, Michelle
Friday, Eldredge & Clark, LLP, Little Rock
501 370 3319
mator@fridayfirm.com
*Featured in Litigation (Arkansas)*
**Practice Areas:** Medical Malpractice Defense.
**Professional Memberships:** Appointed to Arkansas Supreme Court Committee on Civil Practice; American, Arkansas and Pulaski County (currently serving as President) Bar Associations; American Inns of Court (Past Inn President, Master of the Bench); Arkansas Association of Defense Counsel; DRI.
**Career:** Joined firm in 2001; Partner since 2006; Previously served as Division Chief, Prosecuting Attorney's Office.
**Personal:** University of Colorado, BA Political Science, 1989; University of Arkansas at Little Rock School of Law (JD, with Honors), 1995, Associate Casenotes Editor, UALR Law Journal, Recipient of Arkansas Bar Foundation Award for Excellence in Legal Writing.

### BEACH JR, Robert B
Friday, Eldredge & Clark, LLP, Little Rock
501 376 2011
beach@fridayfirm.com
*Featured in Corporate/Commercial (Arkansas)*
**Practice Areas:** Municipal Bonds and public finance. Has extensive experience (over 1,800 transactions) with financings for school districts. Has worked with almost all Arkansas school districts.

**Professional Memberships:** American, Arkansas and Pulaski County Bar Associations; National Association of Bond Lawyers.
**Career:** Practiced law since 1985; Partner since 1990.
**Personal:** Baylor University (BBA, summa cum laude); University of Arkansas, Leflar Law Center, Fayetteville (JD, with honors).

### BENHAM III, Paul B
Friday, Eldredge & Clark, LLP, Little Rock
501 370 1517
benham@fridayfirm.com
*Featured in Corporate/Commercial (Arkansas)*
**Practice Areas:** Focuses on banking and corporate finance law representing both lenders and borrowers in private and public transactions and in sophisticated, non-traditional project finance transactions. Advises clients with respect to state regulatory and legislative matters. Experienced in the areas of mergers and acquisitions, public utility finance and regulation, municipal finance and real estate law.
**Professional Memberships:** American, Arkansas and Pulaski County Bar Associations.
**Career:** Admitted to Arkansas Bar in 1971; joined the firm in 1972; Partner since 1977.
**Personal:** Vanderbilt University (BA 1968); University of Arkansas, Fayetteville, Leflar Law Center (JD 1971).

### BOHANNON, C Tad
Wright, Lindsey & Jennings LLP, Little Rock
501 212 1362
ctbohannon@wlj.com
*Featured in Corporate/Commercial (Arkansas), Real Estate (Arkansas)*
**Practice Areas:** Municipal corporations, municipal finance, real estate, land use, taxation, business and franchise law. General counsel to water and wastewater commissions. Teaches local government at local law school.
**Professional Memberships:** American Water Works Association, Arkansas Water Works Association, National Association of Bond Lawyers.
**Career:** Admitted to practice, Arkansas (1992) and Texas (1993).
**Personal:** Hendrix College, BA; UALR School of Law, JD; Washington University, LLM. Arkansas State Chamber of Commerce, Director; Leadership Greater Little Rock, Class XVI; Leadership Arkansas, Class II; Chairman, Leadership Arkansas, Class IV, V, VI & VII; Chariman, Little Rock Zoo Board of Governors; St James UMC.

### BOWMAN, Ryan
Friday, Eldredge & Clark, LLP, Little Rock
501 370 1597
rbowman@fridayfirm.com
*Featured in Corporate/Commercial (Arkansas)*
**Practice Areas:** All aspects of public finance; municipal law.

**Professional Memberships:** Arkansas and Pulaski County Bar Associations; National Association of Bond Lawyers.
**Career:** Joined firm in 2000; partner since 2007.
**Publications:** "Grayson v. Bank of Little Rock: The Battle Between an Attorney's Lien and a Security Interest," 52 Ark. L. Rev. 827 (1999).
**Personal:** Harding University, BS, Public Administration, summa cum laude, 1997; University of Arkansas School of Law, JD, magna cum laude, 2000.

### BROOKS, Steven L
Friday, Eldredge & Clark, Rogers
479 695 2116
sbrooks@fridayfirm.com
*Featured in Corporate/Commercial (Arkansas)*
**Practice Areas:** Mergers and acquisitions; private equity and venture capital; corporate/commercial transactions; real estate; commercial lending; and taxation of business enterprises.
**Professional Memberships:** American, Arkansas, Benton County and Washington County Bar Associations; American Institute of CPA's; Arkansas Society of CPA's.
**Career:** Practiced as a CPA from 1996 to 2003; joined firm in 2003; partner since 2010.
**Publications:** "The Venture Capital Investment Act of 2001, Arkansas's Vision for Economic Growth," 56 Ark. L. Rev. 397, 2003.
**Personal:** University of Arkansas, BSBA in Accounting, 1995; University of Arkansas School of Law, JD, cum laude, 2003.

**BURROW, Patrick**
Quattlebaum, Grooms, Tull & Burrow PLLC, Little Rock
501 379 1715
pburrow@QGTB.com
*Featured in Corporate/Commercial (Arkansas)*
**Practice Areas:** Primary areas of practice include banking, mergers and acquisitions, securities, taxation, commercial transactions, entity creation and governance.
**Professional Memberships:** American, Arkansas, and Pulaski County Bar Associations.
**Career:** Admitted to Arkansas (1981) and Tennessee (1978) Bars. A founding and Managing Member of Quattlebaum, Grooms, Tull & Burrow PLLC. Recognized by Chambers and Partners since 2012 and The Best Lawyers in America since 2007.
**Personal:** JD, Vanderbilt University School of Law (1978); LLM, Taxation, New York University (1981); BS (with honors), University of Central Arkansas (1975).

**CHILDERS, Michael B**
Friday, Eldredge & Clark, LLP, Little Rock
501 370 3394
mbchilders@fridayfirm.com
*Featured in Real Estate (Arkansas)*
**Practice Areas:** All aspects of commercial real estate transactions, including development, financing, acquisition, disposition and leasing of commercial real estate projects; oil and gas law; broad range of general commercial transactions.
**Professional Memberships:** Arkansas and Pulaski County Bar Associations.
**Personal:** University of Arkansas (BA) and University of Arkansas School of Law (JD, magna cum laude).

**CHILES IV, E B (Chip)**
Quattlebaum, Grooms, Tull & Burrow PLLC, Little Rock
501 379 1734
cchiles@QGTB.com
*Featured in Labor & Employment (Arkansas), Litigation (Arkansas)*
**Practice Areas:** Primary areas of practice include complex business litigation, appellate practice, class action litigation, product liability litigation, employment litigation, and ERISA litigation.
**Professional Memberships:** American Law Institute; Defense Research Institute; International Association of Defense Counsel; Litigation Counsel of America; Bar Association of the United States Court of Appeals for the Eighth Circuit; William R. Overton Inn of Court; American Bar Association; Arkansas Bar Association; Pulaski County Bar Association; Arkansas Bar Foundation.
**Career:** Admitted to Arkansas (1996) and Tennessee (1998) Bars. A Managing Member of Quattlebaum, Grooms, Tull & Burrow PLLC. Law Clerk to Hon. G. Thomas Eisele, USDC, Eastern District of Arkansas (1996-98). Recognized by Chambers and Partners since 2005; The Best Lawyers in America since 2007; Mid-South Super Lawyers since 2006; Benchmark Litigation 2012.

**Publications:** A Hand to Rock the Cradle: Transracial Adoption, the Multiethnic Placement Act, and a Proposal for the Arkansas General Assembly, 49 Ark. L. Rev. 501 (1996).
**Personal:** JD (cum laude), Harvard Law School (1996); BA (summa cum laude and with distinction), Hendrix College (1993).

**COLEMAN, Charles T**
Wright, Lindsey & Jennings LLP, Little Rock
501 212 1276
ccoleman@wlj.com
*Featured in Litigation (Arkansas)*
**Practice Areas:** Commercial litigation, primarily in the area of bankruptcy and debtor/creditor issues, including representation of creditors, creditors committees, trustees and debtors in business cases.
**Professional Memberships:** Fellow, American College of Bankruptcy; fellow, Litigation Counsel of America; American Bar Association; Arkansas Bar Association; Pulaski County Bar Association (past President 2004-05); Debtor-Creditor Bar of Central Arkansas (past President 2004); US Bankruptcy Court, Eastern District of Ark. Advisory Committee (Member 2003-07).
**Career:** Wright, Lindsey and Jennings LLP (1980-present).
**Publications:** Coleman and Henry, 'Bankruptcy 101-Starting Over', The Arkansas Lawyer, Vol 40, No 4, Fall 2005.
**Personal:** University of Arkansas (BSBA 1977) (JD 1980).

**CRASS, Kevin**
Friday, Eldredge & Clark, LLP, Little Rock
501 370 1592
crass@fridayfirm.com
*Featured in Litigation (Arkansas)*
**Practice Areas:** Business litigation, class actions, securities fraud, ERISA, business torts, trade secrets, products liability, patent and trademark litigation, toxic torts.
**Professional Memberships:** American, Arkansas and Pulaski County Bar Associations; International Association of Defense Counsel; Defense Research Institute; United States District Courts; United States Supreme Court; Eighth Circuit Court of Appeals.
**Career:** Head of Class Action and Business Litigation Practice Group.
**Personal:** Ouachita Baptist University (BA); University of Arkansas, Little Rock (JD); Special Justice, Supreme Court of Arkansas; Personal counsel to former Governor of Arkansas, Michael Huckabee.

**DAVIS, John D**
Wright, Lindsey & Jennings LLP, Little Rock
501 212 1373
jddavis@wlj.com
*Featured in Labor & Employment (Arkansas)*
**Practice Areas:** Representation of management in all areas of labor and employment law and workers' compensation defense.
**Professional Memberships:** American Bar Association (Labor and Employment Law section); Arkansas Bar Association; Pulaski County

Bar Association; Arkansas Human Resources Association.
**Career:** Engaged in the practice of labor and employment law and workers' compensation defense since 1980. Listed in Chambers USA (2006-2012), The Best Lawyers in America (1997-2012) and Mid-South Super Lawyers (2010-2011).
**Personal:** University of Arkansas School of Law (JD 1980); Auburn University (BS 1975).

**EBEL, Walter**
Friday, Eldredge & Clark, LLP, Little Rock
501 370 1557
ebel@fridayfirm.com
*Featured in Corporate/Commercial (Arkansas)*
**Practice Areas:** Mergers and acquisitions and other business transactions; corporate law, taxation; horseracing law.
**Professional Memberships:** Arkansas and Pulaski County Bar Associations; Arkansas Society of Certified Public Accountants.
**Career:** Joined firm in 1984; Head of Mergers and Acquisitions Practice Group.
**Personal:** University of Arkansas, Fayetteville, 1980 (BSBA, with high honors); University of Texas School of Law, Austin, 1983 (JD, with high honors), Order of the Coif, Chancellors; New York University School of Law, 1984 (LLM in Taxation); Certified Public Accountant (Inactive).

**EISEMAN, Byron**
Friday, Eldredge & Clark, LLP, Little Rock
507 370 1546
eiseman@fridayfirm.com
*Featured in Corporate/Commercial (Arkansas)*
**Practice Areas:** Business transactions, taxation and estate planning.
**Professional Memberships:** American, Arkansas and Pulaski County Bar Associations; Fellow, American College of Tax Counsel, American College of Trust and Estate Counsel and American Bar Foundation.
**Career:** Head of firm's business and taxation practice 1977-2004; Managing Partner 2005-11.
**Personal:** University of Tennessee (BS and JD); New York University (LLM in Taxation); Certified Public Accountant; Adjunct professor of taxation at University of Arkansas at Little Rock School of Law; serve on boards of several non-profit civic and charitable organizations.

**FRAZIER, Randal B**
Kutak Rock LLP, Little Rock
501 975 3000
randy.frazier@kutakrock.com
*Featured in Real Estate (Arkansas)*
**Practice Areas:** Partner, Corporate Group. Represents banks, lending institutions, real estate developers and wireless communication companies in transactional and litigation matters. Has extensive experience in commercial lending, real estate acquisition, real estate finance, land use and zoning matters and is counsel to numerous financial institutions, real estate developers and corporate clients. Handles commercial and real estate lending as well as complex workouts and foreclosures.

**Professional Memberships:** American Bar Association; Arkansas Bar Association; Pulaski Bar Association.
**Career:** Education: BA, Olivet Nazarene University (1981); JD, University of Oklahoma School of Law (1984).

**GARDNER, Price C**
Friday, Eldredge & Clark, LLP, Little Rock
501 370 1543
gardner@fridayfirm.com
*Featured in Corporate/Commercial (Arkansas), Real Estate (Arkansas)*
**Practice Areas:** Mergers and acquisitions; corporate law; taxation; real estate and healthcare.
**Professional Memberships:** American and Arkansas Bar Associations; Fellow, Arkansas Bar Foundation; American Institute of Public Accountants, Arkansas Society of Public Accountants.
**Career:** Joined Firm in 1989; Partner 1995; Head, Healthcare Practice Group; Vice Chairman of the Firm since 2012.
**Personal:** Arkansas State University (BS in Accounting); University of Arkansas at Little Rock Bowen School of Law (JD), University of Florida Levin College of Law (LLM in Taxation); Certified Public Accountant (inactive).

**GREGORY, H Watt**
Kutak Rock LLP, Little Rock
501 975 3000
watt.gregory@kutakrock.com
*Featured in Corporate/Commercial (Arkansas)*
**Practice Areas:** Partner, corporate group. Has served as issuer's and underwriter's counsel in initial and secondary public offerings and private offerings of equity and debt securities, and as purchaser's and seller's counsel in merger and acquisition transactions. Provides public and private company general corporate, securities and governance representation in numerous areas of business, science and industry, including banking, information management, health care, life science, medical technology and other emerging ventures.
**Professional Memberships:** Accelerate Arkansas (Board of Directors and Past Chairman).
**Career:** Education: BA, Vanderbilt University (1963); LLB, University of Arkansas at Little Rock School of Law (1966).

**GROOMS, Timothy W**
Quattlebaum, Grooms, Tull & Burrow PLLC, Little Rock
501 379 1713
tgrooms@QGTB.com
*Featured in Corporate/Commercial (Arkansas), Real Estate (Arkansas)*
**Practice Areas:** Primary areas of practice include banking law, real estate, mergers and acquisitions, commercial transactions and financing. Serves as General Counsel to the Arkansas REALTORS® Association, Arkansas Homebuilders Association, and the Arkansas Community Bankers.
**Professional Memberships:** American, Arkansas, and Pulaski County Bar Associations; American College of Real Estate Lawyers;

International Council of Shopping Centers; Fellow, American College of Mortgage Attorneys. **Career:** Admitted to the Arkansas Bar (1984). A founding and Managing Member of Quattlebaum, Grooms, Tull & Burrow PLLC. Arkansas Licensed Real Estate Broker, 1979 - present (inactive). Recognized by Chambers and Partners since 2002; The Best Lawyers in America since 1995; Mid-South Super Lawyers since 2006. **Personal:** JD (with high honors), University of Arkansas at Little Rock, (1984); BA (magna cum laude), University of Arkansas at Little Rock, (1981).

### HATCH, M Sean
Wright, Lindsey & Jennings LLP, Little Rock
501 212 1305
mshatch@wlj.com
*Featured in Corporate/Commercial (Arkansas)*
**Practice Areas:** Mr Hatch practices primarily in the areas of mergers and acquisitions, corporate and project finance, and corporate strategy and governance. He regularly serves as counsel to private and public companies, issuers, and investors. **Professional Memberships:** American Bar Association (Business Law Section); Arkansas Bar Association; Pulaski County Bar Association. **Personal:** Education: Hendrix College (BA 1993); University of Arkansas at Little Rock (JD 1996, High Honors), Executive Editor, UALR Law Journal (1995-96).

### HATHAWAY III, James E
Kutak Rock LLP, Little Rock
501 975 3000
James.HathawayIII@KutakRock.com
*Featured in Corporate/Commercial (Arkansas)*
**Practice Areas:** Partner, Public Finance Group. Focuses on public finance, energy, banking, securities and real estate matters. Has extensive experience in student loan finance, university financings, single-family housing bonds, electric generation financings and business acquisitions and dispositions. Experience includes working on legislation with respect to highway bonds, tobacco bonds, tax increment financing and electric energy deregulation. **Professional Memberships:** National Association of Bond Lawyers; Energy Bar Association. **Career:** Education: BA, Vanderbilt University (1979); JD, with high honors, University of Arkansas at Little Rock School of Law (1986).

### HEARD, Daniel L
Kutak Rock LLP, Little Rock
501 975 3000
Daniel.Heard@KutakRock.com
*Featured in Corporate/Commercial (Arkansas)*
**Practice Areas:** Partner, Corporate Group. Primarily represents public companies in corporate, securities and merger and acquisition transactions. Clients represent a wide range of industries, including telecommunications, information technology and food processing. Has experience in proxy contests, negotiating, structuring and consummating mergers and acquisitions, public offerings of debt and equity securities and other corporate finance transactions. Also provides his

clients advice regarding compliance with federal securities laws and NYSE and NASDAQ listing standards. **Professional Memberships:** Arkansas Bar Association, Securities Law Section. **Career:** Education: BA, University of Central Arkansas (1997); JD, with honors, University of Arkansas School of Law (2000).

### HENDREN, Jason
Friday, Eldredge & Clark, Rogers
479 695 6053
hendren@fridayfirm.com
*Featured in Litigation (Arkansas)*
**Practice Areas:** Medical malpractice defense, general insurance defense, analysis of coverage issues. Frequent speaker on medical malpractice issues. **Professional Memberships:** American Bar Association, United States Supreme Court Bar Association, Arkansas Bar Association, Benton County Bar Association, Arkansas Association of Defense Counsel (President Elect, 2012-13), American Inns of Court, DRI, Mid-South Super Lawyers (2011 and 2012). **Career:** Practiced since 1997, and a Partner since 2003. **Personal:** University of Arkansas, BA with honors; UALR (now William H. Bowen) School of Law, JD with honors. William H. Bowen School of Law Alumni Association Board of Directors (President Elect, 2012-13), Bentonville Public Schools Foundation.

### HENRY, Judy
Wright, Lindsey & Jennings LLP, Little Rock
501 212 1391
jhenry@wlj.com
*Featured in Litigation (Arkansas)*
**Practice Areas:** Litigation (commercial, bankruptcy, banking); NFLPA Certified Contract Advisor. **Professional Memberships:** Litigation Counsel of America (Fellow); American Bar (Bus Law Sec); AR Bar (former Chair DR-CR, former Chair Bus Law); Pulaski Co Bar; AR Bar Foundation (Fellow); Debtor-Creditor Bar of Central AR (past Pres); AR Judicial Discipline and Dis Comm (Alt Member, 2001-14); AR Professional Practicum (Charter Faculty); Special Justice to AR Sup Ct. **Career:** Partner. **Personal:** University of Arkansas (JD 1984, ME 1981); University of Central Arkansas (BSE 1980). Best Lawyers in America, 2005-current; Mid-South SuperLawyers (Bus Lit 06-12, Top 50 Arkansas 06&12, Top 50 Mid-South Women 11&12).

### HERRINGTON, Daniel
Friday, Eldredge & Clark, LLP, Little Rock
501 370 1571
herrington@fridayfirm.com
*Featured in Labor & Employment (Arkansas)*
**Practice Areas:** Representing management in all areas of labor and employment law, including discrimination defense, immigration, ADA, FMLA, FLSA, NLRA, drug testing, sexual harassment, privacy, contract, wrongful discharge, non-

competition covenants, trade secrets and ERISA litigation. **Professional Memberships:** American, Arkansas (former Chair, Labor and Employment Section) and Pulaski County Bar Associations; SHRM; Arkansas SHRM State Council (General Counsel); Former Adjunct Law Professor; Chapter Author, Employment Discrimination Lawsuits (Aspatore 2008). **Personal:** Arkansas State University (BS, with honors); University of Arkansas at Little Rock (JD, with high honors); Executive Editor, Law Review.

### HURST JR, Joseph B
Friday, Eldredge & Clark, LLP, Little Rock
501 370 1590
hurst@fridayfirm.com
*Featured in Labor & Employment (Arkansas)*
**Practice Areas:** The design, implementation and administration of tax-qualified plans (defined benefit, profit sharing, 401(k) and ESOP), non-qualified deferred compensation plans and welfare plans for all types of entites. Counsel to plan sponsors and fiduciaries with respect to ERISA transactions and controversies. **Professional Memberships:** American and Arkansas Bar Associations. **Career:** Partner since 1986; Head of Employee Benefits Practice Group. **Personal:** Vanderbilt University (BA 1977, cum laude); University of Arkansas, Leflar Law Center, Fayetteville (JD 1980, with honors); New York University School of Law (LLM in Taxation, 1981).

### JACKSON, William Stuart
Wright, Lindsey & Jennings LLP, Little Rock
501 371 0808
wjackson@wlj.com
*Featured in Labor & Employment (Arkansas)*
**Practice Areas:** Defends clients in federal/state court litigation, including claims under Title VII, ADA, FMLA, ADEA, GINA, FLSA and 42 USC Sec 1983, and state law claims involving trade secrets, non-compete agreements and the Ark. Civil Rights Act. Assists clients on a variety of other issues, including day-to-day employment issues and the creation of personnel policies and employment agreements. **Professional Memberships:** American, Arkansas and Pulaski County Bar Associations. **Career:** Served as a Special Supreme Court Justice in ADC v Williams in 2009. **Personal:** Duke Law School (JD 1992); Hendrix College (BA 1989, magna cum laude with distinction).

### JOYCE, Jeb
Quattlebaum, Grooms, Tull & Burrow PLLC, Little Rock
479 444 5202
jjoyce@QGTB.com
*Featured in Corporate/Commercial (Arkansas)*
**Practice Areas:** Primary areas of practice include real estate financing, real estate acquisitions, securities law, banking law, and commercial transactions.

**Professional Memberships:** American, Arkansas, and Washington County Bar Associations; W. B. Putman Inn of Court. **Career:** Admitted to the Arkansas Bar (1997). A Member of Quattlebaum, Grooms, Tull & Burrow PLLC. Recognized by Chambers and Partners since 2012 and by The Best Lawyers in America since 2011. **Personal:** JD, University of Arkansas at Little Rock School of Law (1997); LLM, Securities and Financial Regulation, Georgetown University Law Center (2001); BA, University of Arkansas (1993).

### KIM, Jane
Wright, Lindsey & Jennings LLP, Little Rock
501 371 0808
jkim@wlj.com
*Featured in Labor & Employment (Arkansas)*
**Practice Areas:** Defends clients in federal/state court litigation, including claims under Title VII, ADA, FMLA, and ADEA, and state law claims involving non-compete agreements and other employment and general litigation. Assists clients on a variety of other employment matters including preparation of handbooks, day to day personnel issues, and training. **Professional Memberships:** American, Arkansas, and Pulaski Bar Associations; National Asian Pacific American Bar Association; Arkansas Association of Defense Counsel. **Publications:** Tort Law Desk Reference, A Fifty State Compendium, Arkansas chapter. **Personal:** University of Arkansas-Fayetteville (JD 2007); University of Missouri-Columbia (BJ 2002, summa cum laude); Mid-South Super Lawyers "Rising Star" (2010-2012).

### LANCASTER, Stephen R
Wright, Lindsey & Jennings LLP, Little Rock
501 212 1238
slancaster@wlj.com
*Featured in Litigation (Arkansas)*
**Practice Areas:** General commercial litigation practice, primarily in areas of trust litigation, engineer and architect defense, gaming regulation, and general commercial dispute resolution. **Professional Memberships:** Arkansas Supreme Court, Committee on Model Jury Instructions – Civil; Best Lawyers in America in Commercial Litigation, Trusts & Estates Litigation, and Construction Litigation; Mid-South Super Lawyers in Business Litigation; American, Arkansas, and Pulaski County Bar Associations. **Career:** Partner. Chief Operating Officer. **Personal:** University of Texas at Austin (JD 1992)(MBA 1986); University of Arkansas (BSBA 1984); American Red Cross of Greater Ozarks Blood Region; American Red Cross of Greater Arkansas, past board chairman.

### LOWTHER JR, Edwin L
Wright, Lindsey & Jennings LLP, Little Rock
501 371 0808
elowther@wlj.com
*Featured in Litigation (Arkansas)*
**Practice Areas:** General litigation (including products liability), class action and multidistrict

litigation, commercial litigation, legal and medical malpractice litigation.

**Professional Memberships:** American Bar Association (Tort and Insurance Practice and Litigation Sections); Arkansas Bar Association; Pulaski County Bar Association; American College of Trial Lawyers; American Board of Trial Advocates; Arkansas Association of Defense Counsel; International Association of Defense Counsel; Arkansas Bar Foundation; American Bar Foundation-Arkansas Chapter.

**Career:** Partner since 1987. Managing Partner (2005-present).

**Personal:** Ouachita Baptist University (BA1975, cum laude); University of Arkansas at Little Rock (JD 1981, with honors); UALR Law Journal (1980-81).

### MADISON, Eva
Littler Mendelson, Fayetteville
479 582 6102
emadison@littler.com

*Featured in Labor & Employment (Arkansas)*

**Practice Areas:** Discrimination and Harassment; Training - Compliance, Ethics, Leadership; Complex Litigation and Jury Trials; Alternative Dispute Resolution; Appellate Practice.

**Professional Memberships:** Justice of the Peace, Washington County, Arkansas, elected 2010; Labor and Employment Law Section - Arkansas Bar Association; Oklahoma Bar Association; Washington County Bar Association; Barrister, W.B. Putman Inn of Court.

**Career:** Adjunct professor at the University of Arkansas School of Law since 2004; Prior to joining Littler Mendelson, practiced law with prestigious firms in Tennessee and Arkansas. Worked in-house in the area of employment litigation for a Fortune 50 company.

**Personal:** JD, summa cum laude, University of Arkansas, 1998; BS magna cum laude, Vanderbilt University.

### MCKINNEY II, J Cliff
Quattlebaum, Grooms, Tull & Burrow PLLC, Little Rock
501 379 1725
cmckinney@QGTB.com

*Featured in Real Estate (Arkansas)*

**Practice Areas:** Primary areas of practice include real estate, green building, land use and business transactions.

**Professional Memberships:** American, Arkansas, Pulaski County, Mississippi Bar Associations and State Bar of Texas; American Society for Public Administration; International Council of Shopping Centers; Christian Legal Society.

**Career:** Admitted to Arkansas (2002), Texas (2003), Mississippi (2004), and Missouri (2011) Bars. A Member of Quattlebaum, Grooms, Tull & Burrow PLLC. Recognized by Chambers and Partners since 2010; Mid-South Super Lawyers since 2008. LEED® Accredited Professional.

**Publications:** Adverse Possession and Boundary by Acquiescence in Arkansas: Some Suggestions for Reform, with Prof. Lynn Foster, 33 U. Ark. Little Rock L. Rev. 199 (2011). Deed Covenants of

Title and the Preparation of Deeds: Theory, Law, and Practice in Arkansas, with Prof. Lynn Foster, 34 U. Ark. Little Rock L. Rev. 53 (2011). Arkansas, in Implementing Institutional Controls at Brownfields and Other Contaminated Sites 223 (Amy L. Edwards ed., American Bar Association 2012).

**Personal:** JD (cum laude), University of Arkansas School of Law (2002); LLM, emphasizing Real Estate Financing, Southern Methodist University, (2003); MPA, University of Arkansas, (2002); BA, Baylor University, (1999).

### MOORE, Michael
Friday, Eldredge & Clark, LLP, Little Rock
501 370 1526
mmoore@fridayfirm.com

*Featured in Labor & Employment (Arkansas)*

**Practice Areas:** Labor and Employment law.

**Professional Memberships:** American, Arkansas and Pulaski County Bar Associations; Chairman, Arkansas Judges and Lawyers Assistance Program.

**Career:** Practiced with Friday, Eldredge & Clark since 1982.

**Personal:** University of Arkansas (BSBA 1979 and JD 1982); Arkansas Bar Commission on Diversity; Former Vice President, Arkansas Judges and Lawyers Assistance Program Foundation; Former Member, Little Rock Racial and Cultural Diversity Commission.

### MULDROW, Lee J
Wright, Lindsey & Jennings LLP, Little Rock
501 371 0808
lmuldrow@wlj.com

*Featured in Labor & Employment (Arkansas)*

**Practice Areas:** General litigation to include representation of employers, self-insured employers, insurance carriers and third-party administrators in defense of workers' compensation claims.

**Professional Memberships:** American, Arkansas and Pulaski County Bar Associations; International Association of Defense Counsel; Arkansas Association of Defense Counsel; fellow, Arkansas Bar Foundation; American Law Firm Association (Workers' Compensation National Steering Committee); Defense Research Institute.

**Career:** Partner since 1984.

**Personal:** Georgetown University (AB 1968); University of Oklahoma (MA 1973); University of Arkansas at Little Rock (JD 1979, with highest honors); UALR Law Journal, research editor (1978-79); The Best Lawyers in America (1995-present).

### NISBET, JR, A Wyckliff
Friday, Eldredge & Clark, LLP, Little Rock
501 370 1544
nisbet@fridayfirm.com

*Featured in Labor & Employment (Arkansas)*

**Practice Areas:** Employee benefits. Significant experience in handling matters relating to qualified and nonqualified retirement plans and welfare benefit programs for private, non-profit and governmental employees. Frequent speaker on ERISA issues.

**Professional Memberships:** American, Arkansas and Pulaski County Bar Associations; American College of Tax Counsel.

**Career:** Practiced law since 1974 and has been a Partner since 1979.

**Personal:** University of Arkansas, Fayetteville, Leflar Law Center (JD, with honors); Georgetown Law Center (LLM in Taxation, with honors).

### POOL, Terry W
Kutak Rock LLP, Fayetteville
479 973 4200
Terry.Pool@KutakRock.com

*Featured in Real Estate (Arkansas)*

**Practice Areas:** Partner, corporate group. Concentrates his practice in real estate and commercial transactions, including acquisition, disposition, leasing and development and related taxation, lending, loan restructuring and workouts, and equity financing of commercial and residential real estate-based transactions. Has extensive experience in structuring complex commercial transactions to address tax, liability, operational and exit strategy issues with investors and lenders.

**Professional Memberships:** Arkansas Bar Association; Oklahoma Bar Association; Texas Bar Association.

**Career:** Education: BS, Central State University (1991); JD, University of Arkansas (1994); Certified Public Accountant (Oklahoma — inactive).

### QUATTLEBAUM, Steven W
Quattlebaum, Grooms, Tull & Burrow PLLC, Little Rock
501 379 1707
quattlebaum@QGTB.com

*Featured in Litigation (Arkansas)*

**Practice Areas:** Primary areas of practice include business litigation, complex commercial litigation, product liability litigation, environmental litigation, and toxic tort litigation.

**Professional Memberships:** International Academy of Trial Lawyers; Litigation Counsel of America; American Board of Trial Advocates; Product Liability Advisory Council; International Association of Defense Counsel; Arkansas Association of Defense Counsel; Defense Research Institute; American Academy of Trial Counsel; Fellow of the American Bar Foundation; William R. Overton Inn of Court; American, Arkansas, and Pulaski County Bar Associations.

**Career:** Admitted to Arkansas Bar (1984). A founding and Managing Member of Quattlebaum, Grooms, Tull & Burrow PLLC. Recognized by Chambers and Partners since 2003; The Best Lawyers in America since 2001; Benchmark Litigation since 2008; Benchmark Plaintiff 2012; Lawdragon 500 Leading Lawyers in America 2007-2010, 2012; Mid-South Super Lawyers since 2006; Who's Who Legal since 2009.

**Publications:** 'Defending the Institution of Trial by Jury', Voir Dire, Fall 2001; 'Effective Video Presentations at Trial', Arkansas Lawyer, Spring and Summer 1993.

**Personal:** JD, University of Arkansas School of Law, (1983); BA, Western State College of Colorado, (1981).

### RATHER JR, Gordon S
Wright, Lindsey & Jennings LLP, Little Rock
501 371 0808
grather@wlj.com

*Featured in Litigation (Arkansas)*

**Practice Areas:** Litigation (including product liability, toxic tort, commercial issues, and maritime defense).

**Professional Memberships:** American Board of Trial Advocates (National President 1996; President, Arkansas Chapter 1987-88); American College of Trial Lawyers (Fellow); International Academy of Trial Lawyers (Fellow and State Chair); Arkansas Association of Defense Counsel; Maritime Law Association of the United States (Proctor); American Bar Association (Litigation Section); Arkansas Bar Association; Pulaski County Bar Association; Arkansas Bar Foundation (Fellow); Arkansas Chapter of The Fellows of the American Bar Foundation.

**Career:** Partner since 1972.

**Personal:** Vanderbilt University (BA 1961, cum laude), Phi Beta Kappa; Duke University (JD 1968).

### RUSSELL III, J Shepherd
Friday, Eldredge & Clark, LLP, Little Rock
501 376 2011
russell@fridayfirm.com

*Featured in Corporate/Commercial (Arkansas)*

**Practice Areas:** All aspects of public finance including financings for industrial development, housing, higher education, healthcare and utilities. Clients include state and local governments, underwriters, trustees and conduit borrowers.

**Professional Memberships:** Arkansas and Pulaski County Bar Associations; National Association of Bond Lawyers.

**Career:** Partner since 1983; Head of Public Finance Practice Group; Managing Partner since 2012.

**Personal:** University of North Carolina, Chapel Hill (BA 1975); University of Arkansas, Fayetteville, Leflar Law Center (JD 1978).

### SAXTON, James
Friday, Eldredge & Clark, LLP, Little Rock
501 370 1586
saxton@fridayfirm.com

*Featured in Real Estate (Arkansas)*

**Practice Areas:** Real estate transactions, business transactions, leasing, commercial development and financing, like-kind exchanges, pass through entities, state and local tax and property tax matters. Representative real estate services include: multistate sales of land in excess of 250 sites, acquisitions, all categories of financing and analysis and drafting of reciprocal easements.

**Professional Memberships:** American, Arkansas and Pulaski County Bar Associations.

**Career:** Head of Real Estate/Commercial Practice Group.

**Personal:** University of Alabama (BS in Business Administration); University of Arkansas, Fayetteville, Leflar Law Center (JD), Arkansas Law Review, Associate Editor; Georgetown University Law Center (LLM in Taxation).

## SCHLUMBERGER, Charles L
Quattlebaum, Grooms, Tull & Burrow PLLC, Little Rock
501 379 1762
cschlumberger@QGTB.com
*Featured in Litigation (Arkansas)*

**Practice Areas:** Primary areas of practice include complex commercial litigation, antitrust and trade practices, newspaper and media law, constitutional law, intellectual property litigation, regulatory and governmental relations, and alternative dispute resolution.
**Professional Memberships:** Member of American, Arkansas, and Pulaski County Bar Associations; Member, Panel of Arbitrators, American Arbitration Association.
**Career:** Admitted to Arkansas Bar (1979). A Managing Member of Quattlebaum, Grooms, Tull & Burrow PLLC. Recognized by Chambers and Partners since 2010; The Best Lawyers in America since 2005; Mid-South Super Lawyers since 2006.
**Personal:** JD, Vanderbilt University School of Law, (1979); BA, Cornell University, (1976).

## SIMPSON, James
Friday, Eldredge & Clark, LLP, Little Rock
501 370 1520
simpson@fridayfirm.com
*Featured in Litigation (Arkansas)*

**Practice Areas:** Business litigation and personal injury litigation including business torts, products liability, toxic torts, class actions and drug and medical devices.
**Professional Memberships:** American College of Trial Lawyers; American Board of Trial Advocates; International Association of Defense Counsel; International Academy of Trial Lawyers; DRI; Arkansas Bar Association; Arkansas Association of Defense Counsel; American Bar Association; Pulaski County Bar Association.
**Career:** Head of General Litigation Practice Group.
**Publications:** Insurance: The Products Hazard Exclusion Arkansas Law Review, Vol. 30, Fall, 1976.
**Personal:** University of Arkansas School of Law, JD, 1977; University of Arkansas at Little Rock, BA, cum laude, 1974.

## SMITH, Laura
Friday, Eldredge & Clark, LLP, Little Rock
501 370 1537
smith@fridayfirm.com
*Featured in Litigation (Arkansas)*

**Practice Areas:** Medical malpractice defense with special expertise in catastrophic injury cases and birth injury cases; drug and medical device product liability defense.
**Professional Memberships:** Arkansas and Pulaski Bar Associations; FDCC; ABOTA.
**Career:** Joined Firm in 1981, Partner 1986; Head of Medical Malpractice Practice Group and member of firm Management Committee.
**Personal:** Southern Methodist University, BS, 1977; University of Arkansas, Fayetteville, Leflar

Law Center, 1981 (JD, with honors), Arkansas Law Review, University of Arkansas Supreme Court; Honor Council; married, two children in college; active in lake activities.

## SPIVEY III, John William
Wright, Lindsey & Jennings LLP, Little Rock
501 212 1310
jspivey@wlj.com
*Featured in Corporate/Commercial (Arkansas), Real Estate (Arkansas)*

**Practice Areas:** Banking and finance, commercial real estate, zoning and land use, acquisitions, municipal bonds, and property tax appeals.
**Professional Memberships:** American Bar Association (Urban, State and Local Government Law and Real Property Sections); Arkansas Bar Association; National Association of Bond Lawyers; fellow, American College of Mortgage Attorneys.
**Career:** Partner since 1983.
**Personal:** Hendrix College Alumni Loyalty Fund (past Chair); Hendrix College Alumni Association (past Member, Board of Governors); Arkansas Territorial Restoration Foundation (past President, Board Member); Camp Aldersgate, Inc. (past Treasurer, Board of Directors); Board Member, City Parks Conservancy; Board Member, Camp Aldersgate Foundation.

## TAYLOR, Jay
Friday, Eldredge & Clark, LLP, Little Rock
501 370 1485
jtaylor@fridayfirm.com
*Featured in Real Estate (Arkansas)*

**Practice Areas:** Commercial real estate finance (including new markets and low income housing tax credits), acquisitions, sales, and leasing, and banking law. Serves as counsel to numerous state, regional and national financial institutions and real estate development companies.
**Professional Memberships:** American, Arkansas, Georgia and Pulaski County Bar Associations.
**Personal:** University of Arkansas, Little Rock (BA, summa cum laude); Emory University School of Law, Atlanta (JD); America's Leading Business Lawyers, 2004-2010; Arkansas Business, Top 40 Under 40; Leadership Greater Little Rock, Class XX; Leadership Arkansas, Class III.

## TISDALE, John R
Wright, Lindsey & Jennings LLP, Little Rock
501 212 1256
jtisdale@wlj.com
*Featured in Corporate/Commercial (Arkansas), Real Estate (Arkansas)*

**Practice Areas:** Taxation (including tax-exempt financing, corporate and partnership issues), corporate law, health law and real estate.
**Professional Memberships:** American Bar Association (Taxation and Business Law Sections); Arkansas Bar Association; Pulaski County Bar Association; National Association of Bond Lawyers; Fellow, Arkansas Bar Foundation.

**Career:** Partner since 1980.
**Personal:** Rhodes College (BA 1968, with honors); Washington University (JD 1975), Managing Editor, Washington University Law Quarterly (1974-75). Chancellor, Episcopal Diocese of Arkansas; Moderator American Institute of Certified Public Accountants seminars; advisor, Tobacco Settlement Task Force-Arkansas House of Representatives.

## TULL III, John E
Quattlebaum, Grooms, Tull & Burrow PLLC, Little Rock
501 379 1705
jtull@QGTB.com
*Featured in Litigation (Arkansas)*

**Practice Areas:** Primary areas of practice include complex commercial litigation, newspaper and media law, and product liability.
**Professional Memberships:** Fellow, American College of Trial Lawyers; American Board of Trial Advocates; International Association of Defense Counsel; Arkansas Association of Defense Counsel; Defense Research Institute; Libel Defense Resource Center; American, Arkansas and Pulaski County Bar Associations; William R. Overton Inn of Court.
**Career:** Admitted to Arkansas Bar (1984). A founding and Managing Member of Quattlebaum, Grooms, Tull & Burrow PLLC. Recognized by Chambers and Partners since 2004; The Best Lawyers in America since 2003; Benchmark Litigation since 2008; Benchmark Plaintiff 2012; Mid-South Super Lawyers since 2006.
**Personal:** JD (with high honors), University of Arkansas School of Law, (1984); BA, Vanderbilt University, (1980).

## WADDELL JR, William A
Friday, Eldredge & Clark, LLP, Little Rock
501 370 1510
waddell@fridayfirm.com
*Featured in Litigation (Arkansas)*

**Practice Areas:** Litigation, including business torts, lender liability, class actions, qui tam defense, business torts, franchise litigation and trade secrets; banking and insurance regulation.
**Professional Memberships:** American, Arkansas and Pulaski County Bar Associations; Fellow, American College of Trial Lawyers; former Chair of Arkansas Supreme Court Model Jury Instructions Committee; former Chair, Financial Law Section; Commissioner, Arkansas Access to Justice Commission.
**Career:** Head of Commercial Litigation and Regulation Practice Group.
**Personal:** University of Central Arkansas, 1978 (BA, summa cum laude); University of Arkansas, Little Rock, 1984 (JD, with honors); legal advisor to the Council of Bishops of the United Methodist Church.

## WILBOURN, Gordon
Kutak Rock LLP, Little Rock
501 975 3000
gordon.wilbourn@kutakrock.com
*Featured in Corporate/Commercial (Arkansas)*

**Practice Areas:** Partner, public finance group. Represents a variety of clients in tax-exempt and taxable public finance transactions. Experience serving as counsel in hospital, general obligation, utility revenue, sales and use tax, exempt facility, higher education, multifamily and industrial development issues. Clients include state agencies and authorities, cities, counties, local governments, public and private corporations, health care providers, universities and colleges and underwriters.
**Professional Memberships:** National Association of Bond Lawyers.
**Career:** Education: BSBA, University of Arkansas at Fayetteville (1983); MBA, Southern Methodist University (1984); JD, University of Arkansas School of Law (1987); also a certified public accountant.

## WILSON, David D
Friday, Eldredge & Clark, LLP, Little Rock
wilson@fridayfirm.com
*Featured in Litigation (Arkansas)*

**Practice Areas:** Commercial Litigation, Contract Disputes, Covenants not to Compete, Energy & Natural Resources Litigation, Tort, Insurance & Personal Injury Litigation, Trade Secrets, Intellectual Property Litigation.
**Professional Memberships:** American, Arkansas and Pulaski County Bar Associations.
**Career:** Practiced law since 1990, Partner with Friday, Eldredge & Clark since 1995.
**Personal:** University of Arkansas at Little Rock School of Law, JD, with honors, 1990; Ouachita Baptist University, BA cum laude, 1987.

# FRIDAY, ELDREDGE & CLARK, LLP

www.fridayfirm.com **tel:** 501 376 2011 **fax:** 501 376 2147

**Managing Partner:** J Shepherd Russell III
Number of partners: 62 Number of lawyers: 87

**OFFICES**

ARKANSAS

**LITTLE ROCK:** 400 West Capitol, Suite 2000, AR 72201
Tel: 501 376 2011   Fax: 501 376 2147

**FAYETTEVILLE:** 3425 North Futrall Drive, Suite 103,
AR 72703
Tel: 479 695 2011   Fax: 479 695 2147

**ROGERS:** 600 S. 52nd Street, Suite 200, AR 72758
Tel: 479 695 2011   Fax: 479 845 4363

## Firm Overview:

Friday, Eldredge & Clark serves business, non-profit, governmental and individual clients in Arkansas and throughout the United States. Since the 1950s, the firm has continuously been Arkansas' largest law firm. Although Friday is respected for its rich history, it is committed to further growth and improvement of its expertise so that long-term clients as well as new clients can trust it with their future. The firm can attribute its continuous success and excellent results for clients to its strong internal leadership and the early development of practice groups. Friday provides clients single-source convenience by offering a range of services in a variety of practice areas. Friday is proud of its past success and current standing within the legal, professional, business and civic communities. It looks forward to even greater achievement and stands ready to meet future legal challenges.

## Main Areas of Practice:

### Litigation:

Friday has some of the most experienced trial lawyers in the state who represent its clients on both a regional and national basis. The firm has represented individuals and businesses in a wide array of disputes. Major practice areas include: personal injury defense, professional malpractice defense, commercial litigation, railroad litigation, worker's compensation and class actions.
**Contacts:** General Litigation: James M Simpson; Medical Malpractice: Laura H Smith; Class Action & Business Litigation: Kevin A Crass; Commercial Litigation & Regulation: William A Waddell Jr; Railroad: Scott H Tucker

### Business & Tax:

Friday's business and tax practice lawyers provide advice in a wide variety of areas, including entity law matters, individual and corporate income tax planning, and corporate finance. The firm's clients in the business and tax area range from individuals and small closely-held professional businesses to publicly traded corporations, including large retailers, manufacturers, financial institutions, investment managers, public utilities, hospitals and public and private universities.
**Contacts:** Walter M Ebel, Price C Gardner

### Labor & Employment:

Friday's labor and employment lawyers have a working knowledge of the complex network of federal and state laws and regulations that control how employers must treat employees, former employees and applicants for employment. They have experience in class action litigation, labor arbitration, litigation under federal and state statutes, downsizing, severance and compensation issues, and many other labor areas.
**Contact:** Elizabeth R Murray

### Mergers & Acquisitions:

In the mergers and acquisitions area, Friday handles transactions which deal with fundamental changes in business ownership that often involve debt or equity financing and structural changes to an existing business entity or the formation of a new entity. The firm's attorneys who practice in this area have backgrounds in corporate finance and securities, accounting, income taxation, commercial lending and management, giving them the ability to understand not only the legal aspects of a deal, but also what is at stake from a business perspective.
**Contact:** Walter M Ebel

### Public Finance:

Friday combines experience, tax expertise, resources, innovation and reputation to provide sophisticated financial structures tailored to each client and transaction. The firm's wide range of services includes bond counsel for state and local bonds, underwriter's, trustee's and issuer's counsel services, formation of improvement districts and university and college financings.
**Contact:** J Shepherd Russell III

### Estate Planning:

Friday provides estate planning and estate tax dispute resolution services to a wide range of clients, including individuals, executives, professionals, business owners, farmers and ranchers and forest landowners. The estate planning area focuses on helping clients achieve comprehensive estate planning goals, from the most traditional level of estate planning to the most advanced level of tax-saving strategies.
**Contact:** William T Baxter

### Employee Benefits & Executive Compensation:

Friday's lawyers practicing in the employee benefits area have a wealth of experience in designing and drafting plans for all types and sizes of employers, and in giving practical and understandable legal advice about operating and maintaining the plans to achieve their business objectives and to comply with applicable laws. This area of the firm's practice represents clients in profit, non-profit and governmental sectors. Clients range from small closely-held professional businesses to publicly traded corporations, including large retailers, manufacturers, financial institutions, investment managers, public utilities, hospitals and public and private universities.
**Contact:** Joseph B Hurst, Jr

### Real Estate:

Friday works with developers, owners, property managers, tenants, financial institutions and investors in all types of transactions from routine purchase agreements to complicated development plans and multi-state sales, acquisition and financing. This area of practice includes acquisition, disposition, leasing and operation of real property, debt and equity financing, partnerships, joint ventures, new markets tax credits and other investment vehicles, and land use, brokerage and management agreements.
**Contact:** James M Saxton

### Healthcare:

Friday provides representation to the dynamic healthcare industry covering the full spectrum of healthcare delivery and payment systems.
**Contact:** Price C Gardner

### Insolvency & Restructuring:

Friday works on complex, sophisticated and distressed financial situations representing financial institutions, businesses, landlords, creditors, debtors and other parties.
**Contact:** William A Waddell Jr

### Clients:

Friday serves a wide-ranging array of clients, including Acxiom Corporation, Arkansas Children's Hospital, Arkansas Mutual, Baptist Health, CDI Contractors, CNA Insurance Company, Deltic Timber Corporation, Dillard's, Inc, Entergy Corporation, Liberty Mutual Insurance Company, Little Rock School District, Micro Flo Company, Murphy Oil Corporation, Oaklawn Jockey Club, Regions Bank, St. Paul Travelers, State Volunteer Mutual Insurance Company, Stephens Inc, Tyson Foods, Inc and Union Pacific Railroad Company.

FRIDAY | ELDREDGE & CLARK LLP
Client focused every day

# MITCHELL, WILLIAMS, SELIG, GATES & WOODYARD, P.L.L.C.

www.MitchellWilliamsLaw.com **tel:** 501 688 8800 **fax:** 501 688 8807

**Managing Partner:** R T Beard, III
Number of partners: 49  Number of other lawyers: 35

## Firm Overview:

Providing strategic counsel on a variety of sophisticated legal matters since 1954, Mitchell Williams combines decades of diverse professional experience with extensive relationships to offer clients across the United States the most comprehensive services possible.

## Main Areas of Practice:

The firm is a full-service law firm organized into three areas of service – business, regulated business and litigation. Each area consists of specialty practices designed to provide the firm's clients with customized solutions to best meet their legal needs.

## Business:

Health provider business; banking finance; public and bond finance; real estate; tax controversy and litigation; taxation and estate planning intellectual property and technology; business restructuring and bankruptcy; bank regulatory; corporate/M&A; securities; sustainability.

## Regulated Business:

Insurance regulatory; health regulatory; environmental; governmental affairs and lobbying; petroleum marketing; sustainability; utility; energy and alternative fuels.

## Litigation:

Business litigation; business and insurance defense; construction litigation; creditor rights; environmental litigation; labor and employment; healthcare provider litigation; product liability/drug and medical device; professional liability defense litigation; information management and security; government investigations, enforcement and white-collar crime.

**Bank & Finance:**
Contact: Harold W Hamlin

**Bank Regulatory:**
Contact: Walter E May

**Commercial Restructuring & Bankruptcy:**
Contact: Stan D Smith

**Corporate/Mergers & Acquisitions:**
Contact: C Douglas Buford, Jr

**ERISA & Employee Benefits:**
Contact: Tod Yeslow

**Intellectual Property & Technology:**
Contact: Hermann Ivester

**Physician Practice / Business Arrangements:**
Contact: John Alan Lewis

**Real Estate & Land Use:**
Contact: W Christopher Barrier

**Securities:**
Contact: C Douglas Buford, Jr

**Taxation & Estate Planning & Probate Administration:**
Contact: Steve Bauman

**Environmental:**
Contact: Allan Gates

**Governmental Affairs & Lobbying:**
Contact: T Ark Monroe

**Insurance Regulatory:**
Contact: Jeffrey H Thomas

**Business Tort & Insurance Defense:**
Contact: Stuart P Miller

**Construction Litigation:**
Contact: Byron L Freeland

**Creditor Rights:**
Contact: Lance R Miller

**Environmental & Toxic Tort Litigation:**
Contact: Sherry P Bartley

**Labor & Employment:**
Contact: Leigh Anne Yeargan

**Product Liability/Drug & Medical Device Defense:**
Contact: Lyn P Pruitt

**Tax Controversy & Litigation:**
Contact: Anton L Janik, Jr

## International Work:

Recent significant international work includes: complex litigation involving a major European company; Vendors and suppliers with manufacturing operations in China; and representation of international manufacturers of wind blades and turbines. Additionally, Mitchell Williams is the exclusive Arkansas member of TerraLex®, one of the largest global networks of independent law firms. Members make up a worldwide network of 15,000 attorneys in more than 155 top independent law firms located in 100 countries and 44 states. The firm's membership in TerraLex® enables it to better serve its clients' international interests from Canada to China and all points between.

## OFFICES

**ARKANSAS**

**LITTLE ROCK:** 425 West Capitol Avenue, Suite 1800, AR 72201-3525
Tel: 501 688 8800   Fax: 501 688 8807

**ROGERS:** 5414 Pinnacle Point Drive, Suite 500, AR 72758-8131
Tel: 479 464 5650   Fax: 479 464 5680

**TEXAS**

**AUSTIN:** 106 East Sixth Street, Suite 300, TX 78701-3661
Tel: 512 480 5100   Fax: 512 322 0301

**NEW YORK**

**NEW YORK:** 5 Penn Plaza, , Suite 1900, NY 10121-1590
Tel: 212 896 3856   Fax: 212 292 4894

## Clients:

Tenenbaum Recycling Group; ALCOA; Ameriprise Financial Inc.; Arcadian Health Plan, Inc; Arkansas Electric Cooperative; Arkansas Oil Marketers Association; Arvest Bank; Ash Grove Cement Company; BancorpSouth Bank; Bank of America; Baptist Health; Beverly Enterprises/Golden Ventures; C N A; Connecticut General Life Insurance; Conseco, Inc.; Coulson Oil Company, Inc.; Deltic Timber Corp.; E-Z Mart Stores, Inc.; Farmers Group, Inc.; First Electric Cooperative Corp.; Helena Chemical Company; Home Banchares, Inc.; International Paper Company; J. B. Hunt Transportation Services, Inc.; Little Rock Advertising & Promotion Comm.; Medical Associates of Northwest Arkansas; Medical Assurance; Merrill Lynch; Metropolitan Life Insurance Company; Minnesota Mining and Manufacturing, Co.; Peterson Industries, Inc.; Regions Bank; Reliance Health Care Management; State Farm Insurance Companies; Bank of the Ozarks; The Prudential Insurance Company; Transamerica Life Insurance Company; UnitedHealth Group; USAA; Wyeth Pharmaceuticals.

MITCHELL ‖ WILLIAMS

# QUATTLEBAUM, GROOMS, TULL & BURROW PLLC

**www.QGTB.com tel:** 501 379 1700 **fax:** 501 379 1701

**Managing Partners:** Steven W Quattlebaum, Timothy W Grooms, John E Tull III, Patrick A Burrow, E B (Chip) Chiles IV, Thomas G Williams, Charles L Schlumberger, Michael N Shannon
Number of partners: 15
Number of lawyers: 32
Languages: *English*

## Firm Overview:

Quattlebaum, Grooms, Tull & Burrow PLLC provides a full range of business-related legal services. The firm represents individuals, sole proprietorships, partnerships, limited liability companies, corporations, and government organizations. Its practice encompasses a wide variety of transactions, litigation, regulatory work, and estate planning.

## Main Areas of Practice:

**Litigation:**
11 Partners; 21 fee earners

- The firm serves as a member of the multi-district litigation defense team for Johnson & Johnson in product liability litigation alleging defective artificial hip implants
- The firm represents Koppers, Inc., Beazer East, Inc., Honeywell International, Inc., Ashland Chemical Co., and United States Steel in a number of claims alleging chemicals used in aluminum smelting caused bladder cancer in the plaintiffs
- The firm represents a greeting card company in a negligence case in which three municipal employees were seriously injured during an electrical arc flash while servicing a transformer at one of the company's facilities
- The firm represented Hortica-Florists' Mutual Insurance Company in a bad faith insurance claim. Following trial, the trial court granted the insurance company's motion for summary judgment as a matter of law, finding that there was no basis to support the claims of negligence and bad faith
- The firm represents several manufacturers and distributors of HVAC equipment in a matter alleging violation of the Arkansas Franchise Practices Act and violation of the Arkansas Deceptive Trade Practices Act
- The firm represents Live Nation Entertainment, Inc., and Ticketmaster, L.L.C., in defense of a putative class action in which plaintiffs claim that service fees charged on concert and event tickets violate Arkansas law
- The firm represents Vanderbilt Mortgage and Finance, Inc., and CMH Homes, Inc., in multiple lawsuits against a title insurance agent and a company retained by the agent to perform title searches and issue title reports
- The firm successfully represented a defendant on appeal in a product liability case in which a jury awarded the plaintiff $2.5 million. In a unanimous decision, the Arkansas Supreme Court reversed and dismissed as to the firm's client, Yanmar Co., Ltd.
- The firm represents Tyson Foods, Inc., in defense of a case claiming arsenic in chicken litter allegedly used as fertilizer on fields planted with rice resulted in concentrations of arsenic in rice that caused a reduction in the price of rice

**Key Clients:** Yanmar Co., Ltd.; Johnson & Johnson; AstraZeneca Pharmaceuticals, LP; Hortica Insurance; Johnson Controls; Tyson Foods, Inc.; Osmose, Inc., Verizon Wireless.
**Contact:** Steven W. Quattlebaum **Tel:** 501 379 1707
**Email:** quattlebaum@QGTB.com

**Real Estate:**
3 Partners; 7 fee earners

- The firm represents multiple financial institutions in numerous financing transactions
- The firm represented a national retailer in multiple acquisitions of land for development of multiple locations in Arkansas and Texas
- The firm assists Verizon Wireless with the disposition of corporate property, including one $10.5 million project
- The firm represented Moses Tucker Real Estate, Inc., in two mixed-use development projects in downtown Little Rock, Arkansas, one of which was the first redevelopment project in the state of Arkansas to utilize both New Markets Tax Credits and Historic Tax Credits as part of its financing structure
- The firm assisted a client in the successful purchase of assets of a concrete company, hardware store, mineral quarry and truss plant, with assets and inventory located in eight locations in three counties. Transaction involved financing from two private lenders, as well as the Arkansas Development Finance Authority

**Key Clients:** Arkansas REALTORS® Association; Verizon Wireless; U.S. Bank; First Security Bank; IBERIABANK; Heartland Bank; Moses Tucker Real Estate, Inc.
**Contact:** Timothy W Grooms **Tel:** 501 379 1713
**Email:** tgrooms@QGTB.com

**Banking & Finance:**
3 Partners; 5 fee earners

- The firm represents Arkansas banks, both large and small, in merger and acquisition transactions, real estate, general lending transactions, problem loan workouts, bankruptcies, and litigation
- The firm represents lenders and developers in federal program transactions, including Low Income Housing apartments and transactions involving private and public developers utilizing New Markets Tax Credits
- The firm regularly represents banking clients in corporate governance matters including transactions with affiliates, directors, and officers

**Key Clients:** Simmons First National Bank; U.S. Bank; IBERIABANK; First Security Bank; Heartland Bank; First National Bankers Bank.
**Contact:** Patrick A Burrow **Tel:** 501 379 1715
**Email:** pburrow@QGTB.com

**Corporate, Tax & Estates:**
3 Partners; 5 fee earners

- The firm represents numerous companies in real estate acquisitions, franchise issues, and general corporate matters
- The firm regularly assists clients with estate and gift tax planning, life insurance planning, nonprofit organizations, charitable giving, wills and trusts, estate administration, and asset protection

**Key Clients:** Wilkerson Jewelers; Medical Assets Holding Company; Baptist Health.
**Contact:** Timothy W Grooms **Tel:** 501 379 1713
**Email:** tgrooms@QGTB.com

## PRACTICE AREAS

Appellate
Banking
Bankruptcy
Business & Complex Commercial Litigation
Business Transactions
Electronic Discovery & Document Management
Employee Benefits (ERISA) Law
Employment Law
Environmental & Regulatory Practice
Governmental Organizations
Insurance Coverage & Defense
Land Use
Legislative Advocacy
Media Law & Defamation
Products Liability
Real Estate
Secured Transactions
Securities Regulation
Taxation & Estate Planning
Tax Increment Financing
Tort Litigation
Toxic Torts & Environmental Litigation

## OFFICES

**ARKANSAS**
**LITTLE ROCK:** 111 Center Street, Suite 1900, AR 72201
Tel: 501 379 1700   Fax: 501 379 1701

**SPRINGDALE:** 4100 Corporate Center Drive, Suite 310, AR 72762
Tel: 479 444 5200   Fax: 479 444 6647

# WILLIAMS & ANDERSON PLC

**www.**williamsanderson.com **tel:** 501 372 0800 **fax:** 501 372 6453

**Managing Partner:** Peter G Kumpe
Number of partners: 9
Number of lawyers: 19
Languages: *English*

**Firm Overview:**

Williams & Anderson PLC provides the highest level of legal services with discretion, loyalty and dedication to their clients. The firm represents large and small, traditional and emerging businesses and state and local government agencies. It is known for finding creative and efficient solutions to difficult legal problems.

**Main Areas of Practice:**

**Banking, Finance & Real Estate:**
6 Partners; 10 fee earners
▪ General counsel for Metropolitan National Bank
▪ Counsel for regional and national banks in numerous loan and finance workouts
▪ Trustee counsel for numerous regional and national trust offices
▪ Counsel in foreclosure of well-known golf course in 2011
▪ Arkansas counsel for Harland Clarke Financial Forms, the nation's leading financial form provider
▪ Bond counsel for Arkansas Student Loan Authority, Arkansas Development Finance Authority and numerous local water districts
**Key Clients:** Metropolitan National Bank, Arkansas Student Loan Authority, Arkansas Development Finance Authority
**Contact:** W Taylor Marshall  **Tel:** 501 396 8427
**Email:** tmarshall@williamsanderson.com

**Business Litigation, Class Actions & Appeals:**
6 Partners; 15 fee earners
▪ State and national class action defense counsel for world's largest retailer
▪ Successfully prosecuted state's largest foreclosure case for Metropolitan National Bank in 2011
▪ Counsel in many of state's highest profile appeals, including reversal of $5 million jury verdict for personal liability against the corporate officer of nursing home (Bedell v. Williams, 2012 Ark. 75) and successful reversal of order to produce confidential documents and trade secrets (Cooper Tire & Rubber Co. v. Phillips County Circuit Court, 2011 Ark. 183)
▪ Employment counsel in nationwide race discrimination class action for world's largest retailer
▪ Employment counsel for AT&T in on-going litigation
▪ Employment counsel in wrongful discharge and termination claims, benefits litigation, contract and labor disputes, unfair competition and trade secrets, employment discrimination and sexual harassment

▪ Counsel for developers, builders, lenders and professionals in broad spectrum of construction litigation
▪ Registered counsel with American Arbitration Association
**Key Clients:** World's largest retailer, AT&T
**Contact:** Jess Askew III  **Tel:** 501 372 0800
**Email:** jaskew@williamsanderson.com
**Contact:** Peter G Kumpe  **Tel:** 501 372 0800
**Email:** pkumpe@williamsanderson.com

**Corporate, Securities & Emerging Companies:**
4 Partners; 6 fee earners
▪ Outside counsel to Baldor Electric Company, including employment matters, real estate transactions, contract review and general corporate advice
▪ Securities counsel for publicly traded oil and gas company
▪ Securities counsel for bank in complex, uniquely-structured private offering involving numerous parties
▪ Securities counsel for numerous public and private companies, broker-dealers, investors, accountants and other participants in business transactions, securities and regulatory matters, including public and private offerings, advising with regard to terms, structure and mechanics of registered and exempt offerings, resale registration and alternatives to registration
▪ Counsel in mergers, acquisitions, restructurings and similar transactions involving assets and ownership interests
▪ Counsel for open-enrollment public charter schools
▪ Non-profit counsel for Heifer International
▪ Sponsor counsel for an association of emerging companies and their coworking facility
**Key Clients:** Baldor Electric Company, Heifer International
**Contact:** Jamie Fugitt  **Tel:** 501 396 8818
**Email:** jfugitt@williamsanderson.com

**Media & Intellectual Property:**
3 Partners; 6 fee earners
▪ General counsel to the Arkansas Democrat-Gazette, a newspaper of statewide circulation
▪ General counsel to WEHCO Media and Video
▪ IP counsel for the University of Arkansas system
▪ Technology licensing counsel for biotechnology, healthcare, chemical processes and software matters
**Key Clients:** Arkansas Democrat-Gazette, University of Arkansas
**Contact:** Philip S Anderson  **Tel:** 501 372 0800
**Email:** psanderson@williamsanderson.com
**Contact:** Harold J Evans  **Tel:** 501 396 8461
**Email:** hevans@williamsanderson.com

**Wealth & Estate Management & Tax Planning:**
1 Partner; 2 fee earners
▪ Counsel for estate management and succession planning for closely-held companies
▪ Tax planning counsel for public and private businesses, non-profits, tax-exempt organizations, colleges and universities, families and individuals
▪ Probate counsel for high net worth individuals
**Contact:** Terry Mathews  **Tel:** 501 372 0800
**Email:** tmathews@williamsanderson.com

# WRIGHT, LINDSEY & JENNINGS LLP

www.wlj.com **tel:** 501 371 0808 **fax:** 501 376 9442

**Managing Partner:** Edwin L Lowther, Jr
Number of partners: 41   Number of lawyers: 66
Languages: *English, Spanish, French, Korean*

## Firm Overview:

Wright, Lindsey & Jennings LLP is a full-service law firm with offices in Little Rock and Rogers, Arkansas. Founded in 1900, the firm now consists of some 66 lawyers. Interaction among the practice groups enables the firm's members to address legal issues while remaining sensitive to the business considerations inherent in every legal matter. The firm strives to understand each client's particular needs and to address them in a cost-efficient and timely manner.

## Main Areas of Practice:

### Banking & Finance:
- The firm handles a variety of financing and funding transactions for both lenders and borrowers
- Represent financial institutions in regulatory and corporate matters, acquisitions, enforcement proceedings and litigation

**Key Clients:** Bank of America, N.A.; First Arkansas Bank & Trust; Malvern National Bank.
**Contact:** Judy Simmons Henry **Tel:** 501 212 1391
**Email:** jhenry@wlj.com
**Contact:** M Sean Hatch **Tel:** 501 212 1305
**Email:** mshatch@wlj.com

### Bankruptcy:
- Represent debtors in Chapter 11 reorganization and liquidation cases
- Represent secured and unsecured creditors in all chapters of bankruptcy cases and adversary proceedings
- Serve as counsel to Chapter 7 trustees and to Chapter 11 creditor committees

**Key Clients:** Bank of America, N.A., Caterpillar Financial Services Corp., Deutsche Bank National Trust Company.
**Contact:** Charles T Coleman **Tel:** 501 212 1276
**Email:** ccoleman@wlj.com
**Contact:** Judy Simmons Henry **Tel:** 501 212 1391
**Email:** jhenry@wlj.com

### Corporate & Securities:
- Represent clients in mergers, acquisitions, financings, and joint ventures
- Represent clients in public and private offerings of equity and debt securities
- Serve as outside counsel to established and emerging companies

**Key Clients:** Lion Oil Corporation; Ritter Crop Services, Inc.
**Contact:** John R Tisdale **Tel:** 501 212 1256
**Email:** jtisdale@wlj.com
**Contact:** M Sean Hatch **Tel:** 501 212 1305
**Email:** mshatch@wlj.com

### Intellectual Property:
- Handle patent, trademark, copyright, trade secret, unfair competition, and technology matters, along with related licensing issues
- Litigate intellectual property cases in state and federal courts, and before the relevant administrative bodies

**Key Clients:** Acxiom Corporation, Entergy Corporation, the University of Arkansas, William J. Clinton Foundation.
**Contact:** J Charles Dougherty **Tel:** 501 212 1383
**Email:** jdougherty@wlj.com

### Labor & Employment:
- Counsel for CARTI on employment matters, including the assimilation of new employees
- Defended EEOC charges filed against major Health System alleging age discrimination and a related federal court lawsuit

**Key Clients:** CARTI; Chubb Group of Insurance Companies; CNA; The Price Companies; QualChoice/QCA; Sedgewick CMS
**Contact:** Stuart Jackson **Tel:** 501 212 1358
**Email:** wjackson@wlj.com
**Contact:** John D Davis **Tel:** 501 212 1373
**Email:** wjddavis@wlj.com

### Litigation:
- Serve as Arkansas counsel for Bayer CropScience in litigation over genetically-modified rice
- Won dismissal of a class action against Bayer Corporation alleging false advertising in marketing
- Obtained a substantial judgment for an Arkansas bank in a dispute over a life insurance policy

**Key Clients:** Bank of America, N.A., Baptist Health, Bayer Corporation, Chubb Group of Insurance Companies.
**Contact:** Gordon S Rather, Jr **Tel:** 501 212 1267
**Email:** grather@wlj.com
**Contact:** Judy Simmons Henry **Tel:** 501 212 1391
**Email:** jhenry@wlj.com

### Municipal Finance:
- Serve as Bond Counsel in connection with municipal obligations of various types
- Serve as Underwriter's Counsel for state and regional bond issues
- Serve as Issuer's Counsel and Trustee's Counsel

**Key Clients:** City of Little Rock, Arkansas Development Finance Authority, Stephens Inc., numerous cities/counties throughout the State.
**Contact:** John William Spivey III **Tel:** 501 212 1310
**Email:** jspivey@wlj.com;

**Contact:** C Tad Bohannon **Tel:** 501 212 1362
**Email:** ctbohannon@wlj.com

### Products Liability:
- Successfully defended Ford Motor Company in Arkansas products liability cases, including a post-collision fire case
- Represent Hyundai Motor Company in Arkansas products liability rollover case
- Obtained summary judgment for Gillingham Best, Inc. in a wrongful death action

**Key Clients:** Bayer Corporation, Chubb Group of Insurance Companies, Ford Motor Company, Hyundai Motor Company.
**Contact:** Gordon S Rather, Jr **Tel:** 501 212 1267
**Email:** grather@wlj.com
**Contact:** Edwin L Lowther, Jr **Tel:** 501 212 1294
**Email:** elowther@wlj.com

### Real Estate:
- Represent Deltic Timber Corporation in zoning and land use matters
- Represent Flis Enterprises in acquisition, siting and financing of restaurant locations
- Represent Central Arkansas Library System in acquisition, financing, and construction of branches

**Key Clients:** Deltic Timber Corporation, Rector Phillip Morse Inc., Irwin Partners, and Flis Enterprises.
**Contact:** John William Spivey III **Tel:** 501 212 1310
**Email:** jspivey@wlj.com
**Contact:** C Tad Bohannon **Tel:** 501 212 1362
**Email:** ctbohannon@wlj.com

### Tax Practice:
- Representation of Arkansas based health insurance company in creation of holding company
- Representation of a government-owned hospital in its conversion to a 501(c)(3) tax exempt entity
- Representation of a company with diversified holdings in the divestiture of certain agricultural and oil subsidiaries

**Key Clients:** QualChoice of Arkansas, Inc.; CARTI; E. Ritter & Company; Drew Memorial Hospital.
**Contact:** John R Tisdale **Tel:** 501 212 1256
**Email:** jtisdale@wlj.com
**Contact:** P Delanna Padilla **Tel:** 479 986 3278
**Email:** dpadilla@wlj.com

## OFFICES

**ARKANSAS**

**LITTLE ROCK:** Bank of America Plaza, 200 West Capitol Avenue, Suite 2300, AR 72201-3699
Tel: 501 371 0808   Fax: 501 376 9442

**ROGERS:** 3333 Pinnacle Hills Parkway, Suite 510, AR 72758-8960
Tel: 479 986 0888   Fax: 479 986 8932

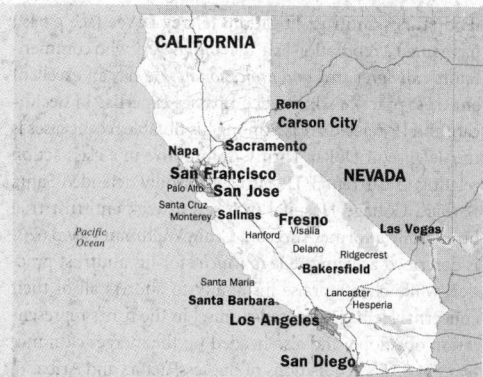

## How lawyers are ranked

Every year we carry out thousands of in-depth interviews with clients in order to assess the reputations and expertise of business lawyers worldwide. The qualities we look for (and which determine rankings) include technical legal ability, professional conduct, client service, commercial awareness/astuteness, diligence, commitment, and other qualities most valued by the client. For details of our research team, see page 5.

# ANTITRUST

Mainly Plaintiff p.536

Commentary about individuals can be found under their firm's paragraph.  If the firm has no paragraph (is not ranked) look at Other Notable Practitioners.

| Antitrust |
| --- |
| **Leading Firms** |

**Band 1**
Gibson, Dunn & Crutcher LLP *
Latham & Watkins LLP *

**Band 2**
Jones Day *
Munger, Tolles & Olson LLP *
O'Melveny & Myers LLP *

**Band 3**
Bingham McCutchen LLP *
Davis Polk & Wardwell LLP *
Morrison & Foerster LLP *
Orrick, Herrington & Sutcliffe LLP *

**Band 4**
Arnold & Porter LLP *
Fenwick & West LLP *
Paul Hastings LLP *
Sheppard, Mullin, Richter & Hampton LLP
Sidley Austin LLP *

\* Indicates firm with profile.
Alphabetical order within each band. Band 1 is the highest.

## Band 1

### Gibson, Dunn & Crutcher LLP
See profile on p.682

**THE FIRM** Gibson, Dunn & Crutcher is indisputably one of the leading antitrust firms for litigation in California. Peers and clients alike see it as a powerhouse in the area, with a seemingly endless list of high-quality lawyers at all levels. Although it has great expertise across the civil antitrust space, including in class action defense, the firm is best known for its cartel defense practice, led by Gary Spratling. Among its work highlights is achieving an extremely favorable settlement for Intel against the State of New York in an alleged monopolization case, as well as the ongoing defense of UBS in a class action case concerning alleged fixing of the LIBOR inter-bank rate.

**Sources say:** *"Their intelligence and professionalism is at a different level."*

**KEY INDIVIDUALS** *"The master of the cartel leniency program in the US,"* **Gary Spratling** (see p.667) is world-renowned and has *"instant credibility"* in the criminal defense arena. He is able to *"bring something unique to the process,"* no doubt in part due to his 28 years' experience as a DOJ prosecutor. He is co-lead counsel in the UBS LIBOR case. **Joel Sanders** (see p.664) is *"one hell of a lawyer"* according to sources, who praise him for his intelligence and *"great interpersonal skills."* He maintains a broad antitrust practice, which includes expertise in such diverse areas as shipping and technology. His notable work of late includes representing Micron in the defense and settlement of a price-fixing claim brought by Oracle. One commentator described the *"fabulous"* **Daniel Swanson** (see p.668) as *"head and shoulders above most other antitrust lawyers,"* pointing in particular to his PhD in economics,

while another called him *"the guy you'd want in a super-sensitive meeting with the government."* A highly adept trial lawyer, he was lead counsel for Cox Communications in defeating a class action brought on behalf of cable and satellite TV subscribers, and won dismissal with prejudice for Dole Food in the fresh and process potatoes litigation. **Robert Cooper** (see p.298) is, in the words of one commentator, *"one of the best lawyers I've ever seen."* He has almost 50 years' experience in the fields of antitrust and commercial litigation and was involved in the representation of Intel against the State of New York.

### Latham & Watkins LLP
See profile on p.446

**THE FIRM** This group is a giant in this sector, with a depth of experience across the board that few can match, and a presence in all the big cases. Sources praise not only the strength of the practice, but also the diversity of the work it undertakes, with all the bases including criminal and civil litigation and merger clearance well covered. It represented National Semiconductor in the investigation of its $6.5 billion merger with Texas Instruments, and also acted for Oracle in a case filed by Hewlett-Packard claiming anticompetitive practices.

**Sources say:** *"With their deep, deep bench and ability to do all aspects of antitrust, they're the real deal."*

**KEY INDIVIDUALS** The *"phenomenal"* **Daniel Wall** (see p.671) is *"a big player"* in the antitrust arena, say commentators. He is seen as a *"rounded antitrust practitioner"* and this combination of breadth and depth of experience is evident from the number and variety of cases he has undertaken lately. Among these is the representation of Nuance Communications in the investigation into its acquisition of SVOX and Loquendo, and acting for Wells Fargo Bank on the ATM antitrust litigation. Another antitrust all-rounder, **Alfred Pfeiffer** (see p.659) has got *"every aspect of an outstanding antitrust lawyer"* according to one source, with another pointing out that he and Daniel Wall make *"a pretty powerful pair."* This partnership was on display in the Oracle case mentioned above, while Pfeiffer also represented Lundbeck in successfully defending against a challenge to a completed merger brought by the FTC and the State of Minnesota. **Karen Silverman** (see p.666) works mainly on the transactional side of antitrust and in matters involving government agencies, where she is described as *"a really superb"* and *"very prominent"* practitioner. Among her recent work is advising Avery Dennison on its $550 million sale to 3M and representing Singapore Airlines in a global cartel investigation. **Niall Lynch** (see p.651) is continuing to build his practice, having arrived at Latham in January 2011. Already a *"well-liked and respected"* attorney, sources say that he will be *"a strong contender over the coming years,"* with his prior experience at the DOJ especially notable. He focuses on cartel defense within the antitrust sphere in addition to undertaking white-collar criminal work.

### Band 2

#### Jones Day
See profile on p.919

**THE FIRM** Jones Day's California antitrust practice builds on the profile and successes of the firm nationwide to deliver excellent results for its clients, which include a number of blue-chip companies. With a fairly even split between litigation and transactional work, it can handle with ease most antitrust work referred to it, helped by a strong team of partners at both the senior and junior levels. It represented Adobe and Intuit in a high-profile class action brought by former employees against some of the largest technology companies in California.
**Sources say:** *"What you get from a firm like Jones Day is responsiveness from the partners and tremendous support behind them."*
**KEY INDIVIDUALS Robert Mittelstaedt** (see p.655) is seen by sources as an *"all-purpose litigator"* who is *"one of the finest trial lawyers in the state."* He is adept in a wide array of areas and within antitrust is noted in particular for his skill in class action litigation. He worked on matters for Adobe and Intuit as well as acting for Apple in the

iPod/iTunes antitrust litigation. **Jeffrey LeVee** (see p.649) has gained a reputation as a *"terrific lawyer"* who commentators call *"prepared and professional."* He has an excellent antitrust practice which encompasses expertise in healthcare and IP-related areas. Among his notable recent cases is the defense of Dollar Thrifty Automotive in a class action relating to car rental. He also successfully defended Santa Barbara Cottage Hospital in a seven-week antitrust trial brought by a former surgeon. **Craig Waldman** (see p.670) is described as being *"one to watch"* for his antitrust practice, while clients praise his ability to address all of their concerns. He has been lead counsel in the firm's representation of Adobe, and also headed up the merger clearance team in SAP's acquisitions of SuccessFactors and Ariba.

#### Munger, Tolles & Olson LLP
See profile on p.691

**THE FIRM** This strong antitrust group has two offices in California, where its entire operation is based. It excels across a variety of areas including pharmaceuticals, technology and entertainment. Although traditionally recognized for the litigation aspects of its practice, the firm has expertise in transaction-related work, as exemplified by its representation of Universal Music in the FTC review of its widely publicized $1.9 billion merger with EMI. On the litigation side, clients have included LG Display in the LCD antitrust litigation and Fox Entertainment in a lawsuit alleging a conspiracy in the cable and satellite TV market.
**Sources say:** *"They are very responsive, very commercially savvy and have a wealth of practical experience."*
**KEY INDIVIDUALS Glenn Pomerantz** (see p.660) is back in the firm's employ having briefly transferred to the DOJ to be co-counsel on the high-profile investigation into the proposed merger of AT&T and T-Mobile. This stint, as one source put it, *"shows you how well respected he is."* Commentators are full of praise, describing him as *"very analytical and aware of commercial realities."* He has a wealth of experience representing clients in the entertainment industry. **Bradley Phillips** (see p.659) is an *"extraordinarily talented lawyer,"* according to one source, while another called him *"outstanding."* His complex civil litigation practice takes in a great deal more than just antitrust work, including having argued a constitutional case in the US Supreme Court. In the antitrust arena he was recently part of the team involved in the AT&T/T-Mobile proposed merger. **Jeffrey Weinberger** (see p.671) is described as a *"top litigator"* who is *"very strong in antitrust and IP."* Noted particularly for his pharmaceuticals expertise, he acted for Abbott Laboratories in a complaint brought by the FTC concerning a so-called 'pay for delay' agreement.

#### O'Melveny & Myers LLP
See profile on p.693

**THE FIRM** Known principally for its prowess in the courtroom, O'Melveny & Myers handles the full panoply of litigation matters. With five offices in the state and superb nationwide coverage, this team is frequently seen by peers on many of the biggest cases in California. This has included a significant victory for Hynix Semiconductor in a claim brought by Rambus concerning an alleged computer memory conspiracy. Other notable clients include Apple in the e-books antitrust litigation and US Airways in a case relating to travel agents.

**Sources say:** "*They are a significant player on a national level.*"

**KEY INDIVIDUALS Michael Tubach** has an excellent reputation for his criminal antitrust and white-collar defense work, although he is also an active practitioner on the civil side. Described as a "*leader in the field*" and a "*phenomenal lawyer*," he is noted for his ability to work well with defendants in cartel cases. He has played an active role in the Apple and Hynix cases mentioned above. **Kenneth O'Rourke** (see p.658) is described as being an "*all-purpose antitrust lawyer*" with an "*excellent practice*" in antitrust and intellectual property. In addition to being lead counsel in the Hynix Semiconductor case, he also co-led with Michael Tubach the representation of Ranbaxy Pharmaceuticals against an allegation of collusion made by several California pharmacies. **Chuck Diamond** is a noted trial lawyer at the firm who has substantial expertise in the antitrust, intellectual property and technology sectors. He led the firm's representation in the US Airways case against Sabre Airways and others.

## Band 3

### Bingham McCutchen LLP
See profile on p.1515

**THE FIRM** This group continues to be well regarded for its litigation ability, with particular aptitude and experience working with technology companies. It has solid bench strength, with a number of younger partners becoming more prominent. Bingham continues its relationship with Intel, representing it in several cases including the hi-tech employees antitrust case. Other work for top clients includes acting for SanDisk on a Sherman Act case relating to flash memory, and assisting Sharp with the TFT-LCD antitrust litigation.

**Sources say:** "*They've been amazingly good at thinking creatively and the work they produce is phenomenal.*"

**KEY INDIVIDUALS** Sources call **Donn Pickett** (see p.659) a "*first-rate first chair trial lawyer*" who "*exudes credibility.*" His trial expertise encompasses IP and securities in addition to antitrust. He has been the leading attorney in the firm's representation of Intel, including a case relating to the alleged monopolization of the market for x86 microprocessors. **Frank Hinman** (see p.642) is held in "*high regard*" by peers for his antitrust and appellate practice. He cochairs the firm's antitrust and competition practice group, and was involved in the SanDisk and Intel hi-tech employees cases. **Brian Rocca** (see p.662) is quickly gaining a reputation as one to watch in the coming years across the antitrust and complex commercial litigation space. Clients have been "*very impressed*" by his willingness to "*roll up his sleeves and really dive in deep to understand the case,*" as well as his strategic mindset. He led the firm's representation of Ricoh Americas in a case relating to purported anticompetitive practices by Ricoh's subsidiary, IKON Office Solutions.

### Davis Polk & Wardwell LLP
See profile on p.442

**THE FIRM** The team at Davis Polk & Wardwell has been involved in cases for clients across a range of media and technology-related industries. These include representing Chimei Innolux in the LCD antitrust litigation and acting for Comcast on a DOJ investigation into dealings involving GE and NBCUniversal. It is active on both the litigation and transactional fronts and also counsels organizations such as the United States Golf Association.

**Sources say:** "*One of the best firms I've worked with.*"

**KEY INDIVIDUALS** The "*really talented*" **Arthur Burke** (see p.626) is respected by peers for the strength of his antitrust litigation practice. He has regularly represented Comcast in various matters and has also acted for LoopNet in an FTC investigation into its acquisition by CoStar Group. He splits his time between Menlo Park and New York. **Christopher Hockett** (see p.642) is a "*tremendous trial lawyer*" according to commentators, who also point out his excellent negotiation skills. His practice covers a wide range of litigation areas in addition to antitrust, including IP and securities. His recent clients include T-Mobile, which he has represented in a number of matters, including multidistrict litigation concerning text messaging rates.

### Morrison & Foerster LLP
See profile on p.1990

**THE FIRM** This group's focus is on the intersection between technology, IP and antitrust, an increasingly relevant and important part of the California antitrust market. Its clients include several major names in these areas such as Verizon, which it represented on a policy matter, and Nikon Metrology, for which it acted in a case involving antitrust matters in relation to patents. Its two California offices undertake antitrust litigation, counseling and transactional work.

**Sources say:** "*Substantive expertise is a given – what differentiates them is that their partners are very practical and business-oriented problem solvers.*"

**KEY INDIVIDUALS Penelope Preovolos** is held in high regard by sources, who call her a "*very bright and successful lawyer.*" Her antitrust expertise covers areas such as consumer class action defense and product liability, with an emphasis on technology matters.

### Orrick, Herrington & Sutcliffe LLP
See profile on p.1994

**THE FIRM** With significant strength in technology and IP-related antitrust work, the team at Orrick is noted for the experience and skill of its antitrust bench in those fields. It has a very good presence in California, with five offices across the state. Lately, it has undertaken multiple representations for Microsoft, as well as acting for Sony Electronics in the LCD antitrust litigation, and representing Apple in a matter before the ITC.

**Sources say:** "*They're excellent lawyers and tacticians and have a very good way of interacting with the client.*"

**KEY INDIVIDUALS** Senior counsel **Stephen Bomse** is a "*fantastic antitrust lawyer*" who has around 45 years' experience in the field. He is also an accomplished appellate lawyer, appearing in several cases before the US Supreme Court. He led Orrick's representation of Sony in the LCD antitrust litigation. Clients call **Robert Rosenfeld** "*a fantastic substantive adviser – brilliant but approachable and easy to work with.*" A highly experienced litigator, he has a long-standing relationship with Microsoft, representing the software and technology giant in several matters recently. He is chair of the firm's antitrust group. **Laurence Popofsky** is an "*incredible lawyer*" who remains an active presence at the firm in a senior counsel role. He is a seasoned litigator in a wide range of antitrust and intellectual property matters.

## Band 4

### Arnold & Porter LLP
See profile on p.906

**THE FIRM** This firm's experienced bench is adept across a broad spectrum of antitrust litigation, including government investigations on both the civil and criminal side, and civil class actions. Recent representations include representing LG Electronics in the cathode ray tube antitrust litigation, and BP in a number of actions contending claims of vertical price-fixing and other anticompetitive practices.

**Sources say:** "*They were responsive and the lawyers were very knowledgeable in their field.*"

**KEY INDIVIDUALS** The "*excellent*" **Ronald Redcay** (see p.661) is a lawyer with a "*great practical perspective,*" according to sources. Undertaking both litigation and counseling work, he has been practicing in antitrust for almost 40 years. Of late he has been co-lead in the defense of BP against allegations relating to the sale of gasoline. **Robert Taylor** (see p.668) practices in antitrust and intellectual property, and is lauded for his wealth of litigation experience. He is also an active antitrust counselor, undertaking work for a number of firms.

### Fenwick & West LLP
See profile on p.680

**THE FIRM** The antitrust group at Fenwick & West is recognized for its expertise in merger clearance and related transactional matters, although it also undertakes litigation work in a variety of antitrust areas. The firm is particularly prominent for its presence in the technology and life sciences arenas.

**KEY INDIVIDUALS Tyler Baker** (see p.621) is praised by commentators as a "*very impressive*" attorney who is both "*smart and capable.*" He is co-chair of the firm's antitrust practice group, and a litigator with expertise in both antitrust and intellectual property. **Mark Ostrau** (see p.658) assists clients with the antitrust aspects of mergers and acquisitions, with a particular focus on those linked to intellectual property. Sources note his strength in technology-related matters.

## Paul Hastings LLP
### See profile on p.1996

**THE FIRM** This team has been boosted by the addition of two partners well regarded for their expertise in the antitrust arena, which has served to give its nascent California office an increased profile in this area. It practices in both the litigation and transactional aspects of antitrust, with notable matters including advising SAMSUNG on the sale of its hard disk drive business to Seagate, and acting as co-counsel for defendants LG Display in the LCD antitrust litigation.

**Sources say:** *"A firm we see and respect, and their recent additions are a boost to the practice."*

**KEY INDIVIDUALS** The *"very incisive"* **Holly House** is described as a *"really down-to-earth lawyer who gives very practical, very sound advice."* Her expertise in antitrust is complemented by experience in IP, and she represents both plaintiffs and defendants. She recently brought her experience to bear for LG Display in the LCD consumer class action. **Thomas Brown**'s niche expertise in payment systems technology makes him *"stand out from the crowd"* according to sources. Lately, he has worked extensively with eBay on litigation and counseling matters.

## Sheppard, Mullin, Richter & Hampton LLP

**THE FIRM** With eight offices in California, Sheppard Mullin is an active and busy presence in the state. The antitrust team undertakes a range of work, including criminal cartel cases, civil litigation and class actions. It has a long-standing relationship with MasterCard, which it represents in two antitrust cases, and has also represented Samsung SDI in the LCD and CRT litigations.

**KEY INDIVIDUALS Gary Halling** has over 35 years' experience as a litigator, with antitrust being his primary focus. He is particularly adept at defending clients against criminal cartel cases brought by government agencies. **James McGinnis** is another practitioner with a criminal focus, and he undertakes white-collar criminal work in addition to his antitrust practice. He also has particular experience coordinating defendants in class action cases.

## Sidley Austin LLP
### See profile on p.1264

**THE FIRM** Sidley Austin's antitrust practice covers a broad range of areas and industries, with clients ranging from electronics firms to insurance companies. One of its strengths is in the pharmaceuticals sector, where it represented AstraZeneca against an allegation of conspiracy among major manufacturers. The team also represented Johnson & Johnson in a case alleging collusion with a nursing home provider.

**Sources say:** *"They provide a unique combination of substantive legal advice with experience in the regulatory world."*

**KEY INDIVIDUALS Marie Fiala** (see p.635) is a litigator specializing in complex commercial cases, with a practice covering antitrust and energy. She has 35 years' experience in the field. Senior counsel **Samuel Miller** (see p.655) is a *"knowledgeable and reliable"* practitioner who has a broad litigation practice including white-collar, securities and antitrust work. He has continued his relationship with Microsoft as a counsel on antitrust matters, and also lectures at Berkeley Law School.

## Other Notable Practitioners

**Robert Pringle** (see p.660) of Winston & Strawn LLP is *"very well-respected in the antitrust field"* and has *"a strong presence on the West Coast"* according to sources. A highly experienced antitrust litigator, of late he has undertaken cases for NEC in the SRAM, DRAM and optical drive cases. **Allison Davis** of Davis Wright Tremaine LLP is an attorney who *"goes the extra mile"* for clients and has a *"no-nonsense, practical"* approach. She has an active transactional practice, including acquisitions and Hart-Scott-Rodino filings. On the litigation side, she recently represented SANYO in the LCD antitrust class action. **Anita Stork** (see p.668) of Covington & Burling LLP is a respected attorney with a wealth of experience in government investigations and counseling in addition to antitrust litigation. She is currently representing S-Y Systems Technologies in the automotive wire harness litigation.

**Geraldine Alexis** of Perkins Coie LLP undertakes a wide range of antitrust matters in both the litigation and transactional arenas. She is also an active antitrust counselor and has a particular expertise on payments matters. Sources say **Megan Dixon** of Hogan Lovells US LLP is *"a tremendous lawyer."* She is a criminal antitrust specialist, with a particular focus on criminal cartel investigations. Of late, she has represented Appliance Components Companies in the defense of a cartel case relating to alleged price-fixing of refrigerator compressors. **Roxane Polidora** of Pillsbury Winthrop Shaw Pittman LLP is head of Pillsbury's antitrust practice team, although she practices in a diverse range of areas including IP, energy and healthcare. Sources compliment her direct and efficient approach. **Joseph Alioto** of Alioto Law Firm is one of California's highest profile plaintiff lawyers and is consistently involved in many of the largest antitrust matters in the state. **Francis Scarpulla** of Zelle Hofmann Voelbel & Mason LLP is described as *"one of the deans of the antitrust Bar"* for his plaintiff-side practice, which focuses mainly on class actions. He is a respected and well-liked figure, earning recognition from peers on both sides. **Bruce Simon** of Pearson, Simon, Warshaw & Penny, LLP is also noted for his plaintiff antitrust work, although he also undertakes consumer fraud and securities cases. He has substantial experience in class action cases and is currently one of the lead lawyers in the DRAM antitrust litigation. Several sources call **Maxwell Blecher** of Blecher & Collins *"the top plaintiffs' antitrust lawyer in California"* and a *"unique and superb"* litigator. Vastly experienced, he has practiced in California for almost six decades and continues to represent plaintiffs in a plethora of antitrust matters. Another seasoned litigator is **Eugene Crew** of Kilpatrick Townsend & Stockton LLP, who is described as a *"heavy hitter"* for his antitrust practice. A senior counsel at the firm, he continues to represent clients on both the plaintiff and defense side.

# BANKING & FINANCE

Commentary about individuals can be found under their firm's paragraph. If the firm has no paragraph (is not ranked) look at Other Notable Practitioners.

| Banking & Finance |
| --- |
| **Leading Firms** |

**Band 1**
Latham & Watkins LLP *
Skadden, Arps, Slate, Meagher & Flom LLP & Affiliates *

**Band 2**
Bingham McCutchen LLP *
Gibson, Dunn & Crutcher LLP *
Paul Hastings LLP *

**Band 3**
Buchalter Nemer *
Orrick, Herrington & Sutcliffe LLP *
Proskauer Rose LLP *

**Band 4**
Kirkland & Ellis LLP *
McDermott Will & Emery LLP *
Morrison & Foerster LLP *
Sidley Austin LLP *

## Band 1

### Latham & Watkins LLP
See profile on p.446

**THE FIRM** This practice maintains its reputation as a major powerhouse in the California finance market. The team boasts substantial breadth and depth which, when paired with a high activity in market-leading deals and an impressive range of services across the full spectrum of financial transactions, allows the firm to offer clients concise, high-quality and on-the-pulse representation. In recent work it represented UBS in a $1.25 billion term B loan and revolving credit facility for the acquisition of EMI Music Publishing Group.
**Sources say:** *"Their lawyers are the smartest of the smart. They're bright, competent and actively involved in transactions that are setting the trends."*
**KEY INDIVIDUALS** Well respected by market observers, **John Jameson** is praised for being *"an intelligent, proactive problem solver."* Sources frequently laud the *"superb"* **Gregory Robins**, whose practice focuses on representing large investment banks like Goldman Sachs, which he recently advised on a $480 million term loan and credit facility for WireCo WorldGroup during its purchase of Koninklijke Lankhorst-Euronete Group. **Glenn Collyer** is experienced in both public and private finance transactions, from structuring to documenting and exit financings.

### Skadden, Arps, Slate, Meagher & Flom LLP & Affiliates
See profile on p.2008

**THE FIRM** Skadden's banking and finance team is recognized as one of the major players in the market. It is adept at handling a wide variety of transactions such as syndicat-

| Senior Statesmen | |
| --- | --- |
| **Senior Statesmen:** distinguished older practitioners | |
| Hisert George A | *Bingham McCutchen LLP* * |

| **Leading Individuals** | |
| --- | --- |

**Star individuals**
| Hilson John F | *Paul Hastings LLP* |
| --- | --- |

**Band 1**
| Reamer David C | *Skadden, Arps, Slate, Meagher & Flom* * |
| Weise Steven O | *Proskauer Rose LLP* |

**Band 2**
| Benjamin Alan | *Orrick, Herrington & Sutcliffe LLP* * |
| Carson Peter H | *Bingham McCutchen LLP* * |
| Cummings Neil | *Proskauer Rose LLP* |
| Curtis Linda | *Gibson, Dunn & Crutcher LLP* * |
| Dunn K Kristine | *Skadden, Arps, Slate, Meagher & Flom* * |
| Jameson John | *Latham & Watkins LLP* |
| Kilb Brian D | *Liner Grode Stein Yankelevitz (ONP)[†] * |
| Kirkham Christopher | *Kirkland & Ellis LLP* * |
| Kitchen David | *Skadden, Arps, Slate, Meagher & Flom* * |
| Matichak Jill | *Chapman and Cutler LLP (ONP)[†]* |
| Montgomery Cromwell | *Gibson, Dunn & Crutcher LLP* * |
| Robins Gregory | *Latham & Watkins LLP* |
| Sherman Steven E | *Shearman & Sterling LLP (ONP)[†]* |
| Stoddard Marshall C | *Morgan, Lewis & Bockius LLP (ONP)[†] * |
| Yount Jennifer S | *Paul Hastings LLP* |

**Band 3**
| Baxter Tom | *O'Melveny & Myers LLP (ONP)[†]* |
| Burke Peter S | *Paul Hastings LLP* |
| Callobre Anthony R | *Buchalter Nemer* * |
| Davidson Robert J | *Buchalter Nemer* * |
| Good Samantha | *Kirkland & Ellis LLP* * |
| Hudson Jeff R | *Gibson, Dunn & Crutcher LLP* * |

| Leventhal F Daniel | *Morrison & Foerster LLP* * |
| --- | --- |
| Mansfield Melainie K | *Milbank, Tweed, Hadley & McCloy (ONP)[†] * |
| Martinson Pamela J | *Sidley Austin LLP* * |
| Rosenbaum Gary B | *McDermott Will & Emery LLP* * |
| Samson Gary D. | *McGuireWoods LLP (ONP)[†]* |
| Spitzer Mark | *Bingham McCutchen LLP* * |
| Stevens Pauline M | *Allen Matkins Leck Gamble Mallory (ONP)[†] * |

**Band 4**
| Alker Susan C | *Reed Smith LLP (ONP)[†]* |
| Berrios Ariel | *Buchalter Nemer* * |
| Collyer Glenn | *Latham & Watkins LLP* |
| Crawford Bradley C | *Bingham McCutchen LLP* * |
| Hellman Dolph | *Orrick, Herrington & Sutcliffe LLP* * |
| Kupietzky Moshe J | *Sidley Austin LLP* * |
| Montgomery Sandra Lee | *Bingham McCutchen LLP* * |
| Newhouse Brian E | *Mayer Brown LLP (ONP)[†]* |
| Reimer Eric R | *O'Melveny & Myers LLP (ONP)[†]* |
| Rust Neil | *McGuireWoods LLP (ONP)[†]* |
| Schoenholz William | *Buchalter Nemer* * |

**Up-and-coming individuals**
| Gregson Gabriel F | *Weil, Gotshal & Manges LLP (ONP)[†] * |
| Hildebrandt Jennifer B | *Paul Hastings LLP* |
| Lim Glen | *Proskauer Rose LLP* |

**Associates to watch**
| Barshop Melissa | *Gibson, Dunn & Crutcher LLP* * |
| Bell Katherine E. | *Paul Hastings LLP* |
| Finley Zachary S | *Orrick, Herrington & Sutcliffe LLP* * |

ed loans, acquisition financings, bridge loans, restructurings and workouts. The firm works in a broad range of industries including telecommunications, real estate, gaming and retail. Key clients include lenders such as Credit Suisse and BNP Paribas as well as private equity firms such as TPG and Calera Capital.
**Sources say:** *"A firm with in-depth legal knowledge and experience, and a strong client-service attitude."*
**KEY INDIVIDUALS David Reamer** (see p.661) is described by interviewees as being *"very commercial but equally a good advocate who is reliable and trustworthy."* This year he represented Penn National Gaming, an owner and operator of horse-racing tracks, casinos and hotels, in $2.5 billion of new senior secured credit facilities. **Kristine Dunn** (see p.633) is widely respected by market observers for her strong representation of private equity clients in large financial transactions. She frequently works with companies including Metro-Goldwyn-Mayer, US Airways

and Quicksilver. **David Kitchen** (see p.646) is praised for being *"very tenacious in negotiations on your behalf, without being overbearing."* He handles financial transactions in various spheres including entertainment, media, retail and real estate, as well as cross-border matters.

## Band 2

### Bingham McCutchen LLP
See profile on p.1515

**THE FIRM** This 25-strong group offers high-quality representation across the region. It skillfully handles a gamut of financial transactions including work in asset-based lending, syndicated finance and private placement lending. The practice has experience in many industries including transportation, technology and REITs. Key clients include Wells Fargo, PNC Bank and GE Capital.

Sources say: *"Their attorneys are always strong and effective advocates."*

KEY INDIVIDUALS Peter Carson (see p.627) is viewed favorably by interviewees who say that *"he always puts an appropriate priority on legal and business issues knowing which to prioritize and when."* He is situated in San Francisco and his practice involves representing clients in all aspects of secured and unsecured debt financings. Mark Spitzer (see p.667) is described as *"a very sharp attorney who is easy to work with. He has a great ability to translate complex issues into easily digestible facts."* This year he worked with regular client PNC Bank on a number of syndicated credit facility matters. Sandra Lee Montgomery (see p.655) focuses on acquisition, mezzanine and structured finance work. She is experienced in handling deals with both a nationwide and cross-border scope. Bradley Crawford (see p.630) *"has exceptionally strong knowledge and a deep understanding of clients' goals."* Recent highlights include advising Prudential Capital Group in a $1.27 billion corporate reorganization. George Hisert (see p.642) is well respected by market observers for his wealth of experience in commercial loan and credit transactions as well as regulatory issues.

## Gibson, Dunn & Crutcher LLP
See profile on p.682

THE FIRM With a well-deserved reputation as a leading borrowers' counsel, this practice continues to see substantial work from a wide variety of clients. It has recently been involved in a great number of credit facility deals including representing Del Monte Foods in a $3.45 billion term loan and asset-based revolving credit facility. The firm continues to develop its lender-side practice, building relationships with institutions such as Wells Fargo.

Sources say: *"They are a valuable firm because of their knowledge, efficiency and thoroughness."*

KEY INDIVIDUALS Linda Curtis (see p.630) wins the praise of interviewees who note her value, saying: *"When a deal starts to unravel she can solve problems that look unsolvable. She is very smart and very practical and does an amazing job."* Jeff Hudson (see p.643) has done significant work in the acquisition finance space, alongside his traditional debt finance practice. This year he worked with private investment firm Aurora Capital on a revolving credit facility to finance the purchase of Industrial Container Service. Cromwell Montgomery's (see p.655) reputation continues to advance. Sources say: *"He is a terrific lead partner for us. He is pragmatic, efficient and has a great memory."* Associate Melissa Barshop (see p.622) attracts commendation from clients, one of whom states: *"She does an outstanding job – she works so hard for us and is just absolutely stellar."*

## Paul Hastings LLP
See profile on p.1996

THE FIRM Paul Hastings's California group does a high volume of work in both the asset-based lending space and in leveraged buyout transactions. It is well respected for its strength as lenders' counsel, with institutions such as RBC Capital Markets, Morgan Stanley and GE Capital among key clients. This year the firm continued to work with Wells Fargo on a variety of matters including representation of the bank in a $1.14 billion revolving loan facility.

Sources say: *"They have the resources and capabilities to handle deals with an international angle. They always produce thorough and thoughtful work."*

KEY INDIVIDUALS Chair of the finance and restructuring practice, John Hilson is widely respected for his vast market knowledge and experience with asset-based lending. Sources say: *"When he is on your team, you have the smartest guy in the room."* Peter Burke is praised as a *"very logical, thoughtful and direct attorney."* His recent work includes representing regular client City National Bank as a lender in a $2 billion senior credit facility for Health Care REIT. Jennifer Yount is revered by clients, who say that *"she has incredibly deep knowledge and is an excellent communicator with a great ability to home in on what is important to us."* Highlights of late include the representation of Wells Fargo in the aforementioned loan transaction. Described as *"a very detail-oriented, hard-working and technically excellent"* lawyer, Jennifer Hildebrandt earns significant respect from market observers. Katherine Bell stands out to clients as a talented associate who *"consistently provides us with great work and an amazing service."*

## Band 3

## Buchalter Nemer
See profile on p.676

THE FIRM Recognized for its proficiency as lenders' counsel, this banking and finance team attracts an increasing volume of work from some of the largest national and regional financial institutions, as well as several foreign credit providers who are active in the market. The firm's expertise spans a range of business sectors including film finance, gaming, healthcare and intellectual property.

Sources say: *"They are very skillful and have an aptitude to get the deal done. Their documentation will stand up to any test and they do their business in a timely and efficient way."*

KEY INDIVIDUALS Anthony Callobre (see p.626) is recognized as having a *"wide breadth of knowledge and a very strong, confident style."* His practice includes a full range of services in commercial lending. Robert Davidson (see p.631) is appreciated for *"his invaluable ability not just to know the law and protect clients, but to build strong working relationships."* He has ample experience working in asset-based lending, syndicated loan transactions and acquisition finance. William Schoenholz (see p.664) is described as *"a knowledgeable, technically strong and extremely thorough attorney."* This year he represented HSBC as administrative agent in a credit facility that involved several foreign subsidiaries. Clients say Ariel Berrios (see p.623) *"knows*

the law well and is strong at protecting our interests."* He is well versed in a range of banking, commercial and bankruptcy matters.

## Orrick, Herrington & Sutcliffe LLP
See profile on p.1994

THE FIRM Orrick boasts one of the best public finance practices in the state and is also a particularly strong option for acquisition finance. The group is active in the gaming space and advises in the niche area of Native American finance. The firm recently represented Wells Fargo Gaming Capital in a term loan facility made available to the Mohegan Tribal Gaming Authority which owns and operates several casinos.

Sources say: *"They are smart, strategic and to the point in negotiations."*

KEY INDIVIDUALS Alan Benjamin (see p.623) is praised by sources who say that *"he is a true counselor and really understands the business side of a deal."* His practice focuses on complex financial transactions and restructuring. He is one of the firm's leading experts on the gaming industry and was the lead attorney in the aforementioned deal. Senior associate Zachary Finley (see p.635) is a valued team member in many of the firm's highlight deals this year. He is experienced in a range of commercial transactions and his clients include both lenders and borrowers. Highlighted by interviewees, Dolph Hellman (see p.641) is respected as being *"smart, hard-working, rational and very creative in reaching solutions."* He represented Equinix in obtaining a $750 million syndicated credit facility led by Bank of America.

## Proskauer Rose LLP
See profile on p.2001

THE FIRM This firm is acknowledged for its expertise in bank finance. The group handles complex and sophisticated transactions and clients note the seamless, full-service representation across various offices and practices. Standout deals this year include the representation of Ares Management in its $1.6 billion acquisition of 99¢ Only Stores and the related $950 million financing.

Sources say: *"I value their depth and scope of knowledge as well as their tremendous attention to our needs as a business."*

KEY INDIVIDUALS Steven Weise is doubtless one of the most respected lawyers in the California market. Observers say: *"He is a giant in this field and continues to educate us all."* His impressive intellect can be demonstrated in all manner of areas, including structured finance, workouts, letters of credit and investment securities. Neil Cummings' ability to *"always find practical solutions to issues"* paired with his *"very solid and fundamental understanding of the law and the market"* ensure he is highly valued by clients. He was the lead finance attorney on the Ares Management deal mentioned above. A fairly recent addition to the team, senior counsel Glen Lim wins praise for being a *"very knowledgeable, diligent and highly efficient individual with immense technical skills."* He represents both lenders and borrowers in domestic and international financings.

## Band 4

### Kirkland & Ellis LLP
See profile on p.1254

THE FIRM This expanding California group displays particular strength in representing private equity clients and their portfolio companies in a diverse range of debt finance matters. The firm's standout transactions have included a number of acquisition financings, restructurings, dividend recapitalizations and refinancings. Clients of the firm include Oaktree Capital Management, Huntsmen Gay Global Capital and Golden Gate Capital.

Sources say: *"A highly responsive firm which offers good quality advice. The attorneys achieve the right balance between business and legal matters."*

KEY INDIVIDUALS **Christopher Kirkham** (see p.646) is noted by interviewees who observe: *"He has experienced a lot of deals and his knowledge and insight are very valuable."* His abilities span the field of corporate finance, with notable strengths to be found in secured and unsecured debt finance, workouts and restructurings. **Samantha Good** (see p.638) has taken a lead role in a number of noteworthy transactions, including a $4 billion out-of-court restructuring for Kerzner International, which owns and manages the Atlantis and One & Only holiday resorts.

### McDermott Will & Emery LLP
See profile on p.1258

THE FIRM This banking and finance team remains focused on representing both lenders and borrowers in middle and upper-middle market deals. The group has done significant work with private equity firm H.I.G Capital, including several acquisition-related deals and credit facility transactions. Other major clients of the group include GE Capital, JPMorgan and US Bank.

Sources say: *"Their attorneys are responsive and proactive and they efficiently move transactions along."*

KEY INDIVIDUALS Finance practice head **Gary Rosenbaum** (see p.663) is described by sources as a *"self-starter who knows our business and makes appropriate decisions that suit us well."* He is regularly seen representing GE Capital in its West Coast activities.

### Morrison & Foerster LLP
See profile on p.1990

THE FIRM Clients single out Morrison & Foerster's banking and finance team for the excellence of its debt work, and the firm has built up a strong foothold in cleantech financing as well. The group continues to represent Boyd Gaming Corporation, advising it on several significant matters, including obtaining commitments for financing the purchase of Peninsula Gaming.

Sources say: *"Their work is always strong. They are pragmatic and have the ability to prioritize properly between business and legal issues."*

KEY INDIVIDUALS **Daniel Leventhal** (see p.649) splits his time between California and London. Sources say: *"He is good to work with and builds strong relationships with in-house counsel. Has an excellent delivery and is always timely."* He is well versed in cross-border deals, including syndicated and asset-based lending matters.

### Sidley Austin LLP
See profile on p.1264

THE FIRM Sidley Austin's LA-based branch frequently works with regional and national banks that are actively involved in commercial lending. Established clients include Silicon Valley Bank, which the firm represented in a number of matters including a $72.5 million senior secured credit facility for Francisco Partners' recapitalization of T-System. Other key clients include Merrill Lynch, Citi and BNP Paribas.

Sources say: *"Their attorneys have great expertise. A valuable and standout team."*

KEY INDIVIDUALS Recognized by observers for her strength in commercial lending, **Pamela Martinson** (see p.652) has worked for decades on the West Coast and has developed an especially strong relationship with Silicon Valley Bank, which she represented in the matter listed above. Practice head **Moshe Kupietzky** (see p.648) is widely praised for his tremendous intelligence and market experience. He frequently leverages off his strong corporate practice to act as borrowers' counsel to clients such as ROM Corporation, which he advised on tens of millions of dollars in loans and facilities recently.

## Other Notable Practitioners

**Pauline Stevens** (see p.667) of Allen Matkins Leck Gamble Mallory & Natsis LLP has been a strong addition to the firm. She is praised by clients for *"possessing a very broad knowledge of the banking and finance field. She is passionate when representing us and great at understanding what matters to our company."* San Francisco-based **Jill Matichak** of Chapman and Cutler LLP is well versed in a variety of transactions and is known for her strong relationships with leading financial institutions. She is particularly highly praised for her acquisition finance expertise. **Steven Sherman** of Shearman & Sterling LLP continues to divide his time between New York and San Francisco. Interviewees note his *"solid intellect and driven character."* This year he continued to represent regular client Bank of America in several transactions in the asset-based finance sphere. Although he divides his time between New York and Los Angeles, **Marshall Stoddard** (see p.667) of Morgan, Lewis & Bockius LLP remains a significant presence in the California market. Sources say: *"His strengths are his industry knowledge, his work ethic and his ability to streamline complex issues,"* paired with his *"rare ability to protect clients with precise documentation on the one hand and a win-win discussion style on the other."* **Tom Baxter** of O'Melveny & Myers LLP is viewed by market observers as a strong asset to his firm. This year he represented Western Digital Corporation in connection with its $2.8 billion of unsecured loan facilities. Chair of the corporate finance practice **Eric Reimer** of O'Melveny & Myers LLP represents clients from both sides of the financial transaction. He recently worked with Avenue Capital in a refinancing and recapitalization of $1.2 billion in notes related to a merger. **Brian Kilb** (see p.646) of Liner Grode Stein Yankelevitz Sunshine Regenstreif & Taylor LLP is noted for his *"stellar reputation and penetrating intellect."* He has some of the broadest and deepest financing expertise in the state. **Susan Alker** of Reed Smith LLP is acknowledged by sources as being *"very hands-on – she gets to know her clients and tailors agreements accordingly. She's great at business development and focusing on what the company needs."* Regular clients include Toyota Motor Credit Company and Wells Fargo. **Brian Newhouse** of Mayer Brown LLP is seen by market observers as a significant lawyer in this field and a strong addition to the rankings. He follows the trend of several others in dividing his practice between New York and Los Angeles, and is particularly strong in representing financial institutions in leveraged finance transactions. **Neil Rust** recently joined McGuireWoods LLP from White & Case. He has experience in a broad range of financial transactions as well as M&A. He has recently advised several leading banks including JPMorgan and Wells Fargo. **Melainie Mansfield** (see p.652) of Milbank, Tweed, Hadley & McCloy LLP is especially active in acquisition finance and works in a number of industries including telecommunications, technology and entertainment. Sources describe her as *"absolutely wonderful to work with."* Well-respected **Gary Samson** of McGuireWoods LLP is acknowledged for his strength in lender-side representation. Clients appreciatively note that he is *"very experienced in asset-based lending"* and laud his *"very keen business sense."* One client calls him *"the best-balanced lawyer I've seen. He makes opposing counsel feel like they're working to a common goal."* Market observers praise Silicon Valley-based **Gabriel Gregson** (see p.639) of Weil, Gotshal & Manges LLP for his expertise in sponsor-side work. His impressive client roster includes numerous private equity firms including Summit Partners, The Gore Group and Technology Crossover Ventures.

# BANKRUPTCY/RESTRUCTURING

Commentary about individuals can be found under their firm's paragraph. If the firm has no paragraph (is not ranked) look at Other Notable Practitioners.

## Bankruptcy/Restructuring
## Leading Firms

### Band 1
Jones Day *
Klee, Tuchin, Bogdanoff & Stern LLP *
Latham & Watkins LLP *
Milbank, Tweed, Hadley & McCloy LLP *
Pachulski Stang Ziehl & Jones LLP *

### Band 2
Gibson, Dunn & Crutcher LLP *
O'Melveny & Myers LLP *
Orrick, Herrington & Sutcliffe LLP *
Sidley Austin LLP *
Stutman, Treister & Glatt Professional Corporation

### Band 3
Buchalter Nemer *
Peitzman Weg LLP *
Sheppard, Mullin, Richter & Hampton LLP
Winston & Strawn LLP *

### Band 4
Felderstein Fitzgerald Willoughby & Pascuzzi LLP
Irell & Manella *
Katten Muchin Rosenman LLP *
Levene, Neale, Bender, Yoo & Brill LLP
Skadden, Arps, Slate, Meagher & Flom LLP & Affiliates *
White & Case LLP *

## Band 1

### Jones Day
#### See profile on p.919

**THE FIRM** Jones Day has one of the biggest bankruptcy and business restructuring offerings in the state. This follows the arrival of a highly regarded team, led by Bruce Bennett, from Dewey & LeBoeuf. The team is further aided by the wider firm's deep network of experts that spans many jurisdictions and areas of law. The team has experienced a number of highlights in the past year, including its ongoing representation of an ad hoc group of lenders with an interest in $850 million of debt and bonds in the MF Global Chapter 11 bankruptcy. The team is also acting for FGIC as cochair of the official creditors' committee during the Chapter 11 proceedings of Residential Capital (ResCap). The addition of the team from Dewey & LeBoeuf also adds considerably to Jones Day's Chapter 9 municipal bankruptcy expertise.

**Sources say:** *"The Jones Day team has been extremely responsive. It possesses extensive substantive expertise and experience and has provided legal advice that takes into account the specific issues related to our industry."*

**KEY INDIVIDUALS Richard Wynne** (see p.672) is a leading member of the firm's Los Angeles business restructuring department. Respondents admire his far-reaching strategic guidance, adding that *"he is all over the country*

## Senior Statesmen

**Senior Statesmen: distinguished older practitioners**

| | | | | |
|---|---|---|---|---|
| Greenfield Robert A | Stutman, Treister & Glatt | | Peitzman Lawrence | Peitzman Weg LLP * |

## Leading Individuals

### Band 1

| | | | | |
|---|---|---|---|---|
| Aronzon Paul S | Milbank, Tweed, Hadley & McCloy LLP * | | Hagle Jennifer | Sidley Austin LLP * |
| Bennett Bruce S | Jones Day * | | Holden Jr Frederick D | Orrick, Herrington & Sutcliffe LLP * |
| Bogdanoff Lee R | Klee, Tuchin, Bogdanoff & Stern LLP | | Jones Evan M | O'Melveny & Myers LLP |
| Gilhuly Peter | Latham & Watkins LLP | | Keller Tobias S | Jones Day * |
| Klee Kenneth N | Klee, Tuchin, Bogdanoff & Stern LLP | | Levinson Sidney P | Jones Day * |
| Levinson Marc A | Orrick, Herrington & Sutcliffe LLP * | | Lunt Gregory O | Latham & Watkins LLP |
| Logan III Ben H | O'Melveny & Myers LLP | | Millet Craig H | Gibson, Dunn & Crutcher LLP * |
| Pachulski Richard M | Pachulski Stang Ziehl & Jones LLP | | Minnick M David | Pillsbury Winthrop Shaw Pittman (ONP) † * |
| Tuchin Michael L | Klee, Tuchin, Bogdanoff & Stern LLP | | Rafatjoo Hamid | Venable LLP (ONP) † * |
| Wynne Richard | Jones Day * | | Rogers Randy | Winston & Strawn LLP * |
| | | | Samuels Joel G | Sidley Austin LLP * |

### Band 2

| | | | | |
|---|---|---|---|---|
| Ahrens Michael | Sheppard, Mullin, Richter & Hampton LLP | | Schochet Harvey | Davis Wright Tremaine LLP (ONP) † |
| Bender Ron | Levene, Neale, Bender, Yoo & Brill LLP | | Steinberg Howard | Greenberg Traurig LLP (ONP) † * |
| Benvenutti Peter J | Jones Day * | | Uhland Suzzanne | O'Melveny & Myers LLP * |
| Cohen Marc S | Kaye Scholer LLP (ONP) † * | | Walper Thomas | Munger, Tolles & Olson LLP (ONP) † * |
| Davidson Jeffrey | Stutman, Treister & Glatt | | Warren Steve | O'Melveny & Myers LLP |
| Durrer II Van C | Skadden, Arps, Slate, Meagher & Flom * | | Zohn Martin S | Proskauer Rose LLP (ONP) † |
| Garza Oscar | Gibson, Dunn & Crutcher LLP * | | | |
| Havel Richard W | Sidley Austin LLP * | | **Band 4** | |
| Johnston James O | Jones Day * | | Averch Craig H | White & Case LLP * |
| Klyman Robert | Latham & Watkins LLP | | Bollinger Bernard | Buchalter Nemer * |
| Kreller Thomas R | Milbank, Tweed, Hadley & McCloy LLP * | | Chenetz Sara L | Blank Rome LLP (ONP) † * |
| Lobel William N | The Lobel Firm, LLP (ONP) † | | Eisenberg Joe | Jeffer, Mangels, Butler & Mitchell (ONP) † |
| Moore Robert | Milbank, Tweed, Hadley & McCloy LLP * | | Fiero John D | Pachulski Stang Ziehl & Jones LLP |
| Neely Sally S | Sidley Austin LLP * | | Fredericks John | Winston & Strawn LLP * |
| Pachulski Isaac M | Stutman, Treister & Glatt | | Freeman William B | Katten Muchin Rosenman LLP |
| Patterson Thomas E | Klee, Tuchin, Bogdanoff & Stern LLP | | Grassgreen Debra | Pachulski, Stang, Ziehl, Young, Jones |
| Pomerantz Jeffrey N | Pachulski Stang Ziehl & Jones LLP | | Krause Jeffrey | Gibson, Dunn & Crutcher LLP * |
| Reisner Jeffrey M | Irell & Manella * | | Lantry Kevin T | Sidley Austin LLP * |
| Sagerman Eric E | Winston & Strawn LLP * | | Neale David L | Levene, Neale, Bender, Yoo & Brill LLP |
| Shinderman Mark | Milbank, Tweed, Hadley & McCloy LLP * | | Newman Samuel A | Gibson, Dunn & Crutcher LLP * |
| Webster Pamela K | Buchalter Nemer * | | Shemano David B | Peitzman Weg LLP * |
| Weg Howard J | Peitzman Weg LLP * | | Shenson Jonathan | Shenson Law Group PC (ONP) † |
| | | | Simonds David | Akin Gump Strauss Hauer & Feld (ONP) † * |

### Band 3

| | | | | |
|---|---|---|---|---|
| Barbarosh Craig A | Katten Muchin Rosenman LLP | | Soref Randye | Polsinelli PC (ONP) † |
| Bjork Jeffrey E | Sidley Austin LLP * | | Spiegel Bennett | Jones Day * |
| Bray Gregory A | Milbank, Tweed, Hadley & McCloy LLP * | | Weiss Sharon Z. | Bryan Cave LLP (ONP) † |
| Cohen Cynthia M | Paul Hastings LLP (ONP) † | | Winston Eric | Quinn Emanuel Urquhart & Sullivan (ONP) † |
| Felderstein Steven H | Felderstein Fitzgerald Willoughby | | | |
| Fenning Lisa Hill | Arnold & Porter LLP (ONP) † * | | **Up-and-coming individuals** | |
| Gautier Scott F | Peitzman Weg LLP * | | Holt Whitman | Klee, Tuchin, Bogdanoff & Stern LLP |
| | | | Katz Ori | Sheppard, Mullin, Richter & Hampton LLP |
| | | | Kurth Mette | Arent Fox LLP (ONP) † * |
| | | | Rawlins Justin | Winston & Strawn LLP * |

\* Indicates firm / individual with profile.
† ONP = Other Notable Practitioner.

*and is an excellent lawyer; I would trust him on my cases."* He is currently representing over $1 billion of debt on behalf of FGIC, a cochair of the official creditors' committee in the ResCap bankruptcy. The *"brilliant and very effective"* **Bruce Bennett** (see p.282) is a high-profile new addi-

tion to the Jones Day team. Commentators note that he is *"certainly a key player in the whole state."* He is experienced across the breadth of bankruptcy-related matters, acting for both debtors and creditors in high-profile restructurings. He led the team acting for the ad hoc group of lenders in the MF Global bankruptcy. **Peter Benvenutti** (see p.623) is one of the more experienced members of Jones Day's team. Clients have been quick to sing his praises, noting that *"in addition to being talented and professional he is just a pleasure to deal with and a consummate professional."* He acts for a range of clients, including debtors, committees, lenders and distressed asset acquirers. **James Johnston** (see p.644) is another ex-Dewey & LeBoeuf partner. He has enjoyed a successful year that included acting for US Bank as indenture trustee of $1 billion of senior secured notes in the bankruptcy of American Airlines. Clients describe Johnston as *"very bright, incredibly dedicated and productive; he is good about client satisfaction, keeping us in the loop and returning calls swiftly."* **Tobias Keller** (see p.645) is acknowledged as a *"very smart and talented"* attorney. He is regularly praised for vision and tactics during negotiations. He is the lead lawyer in the firm's ongoing representation of ground beef processing business AFA Foods and related companies during their ongoing Chapter 11 bankruptcies. **Sidney Levinson** (see p.650) arrives from Dewey & LeBoeuf with an exemplary reputation, both in court and during negotiations. Clients note that it *"helps to have someone of huge stature on the case; he has given us credibility immediately."* He is praised for his litigation expertise and for regularly acting for clients with a wide range of interests. **Bennett Spiegel** (see p.666) receives recognition for his thorough analysis and technical know-how. He plays a key role in the firm's representation of an ad hoc group of lenders in the MF Global Chapter 11 bankruptcy.

### Klee, Tuchin, Bogdanoff & Stern LLP
See profile on p.687

**THE FIRM** This nationally recognized boutique practice is regularly seen alongside large, multinational firms in some of the country's largest bankruptcy matters. The firm has particularly distinguished itself at the forefront of Chapter 9 municipal bankruptcy matters. It has been engaged by a number of municipal debtors in recent years, including the ongoing $4 billion Jefferson County, Alabama bankruptcy, and more recently advising the town of Mammoth Lakes, California, on its Chapter 9 case.

**Sources say:** *"Incredibly knowledgeable on the bankruptcy statutes and they are very strategic thinkers."* *"They are always able to come up with unique approaches and multiple methods of solving problems."*

**KEY INDIVIDUALS** The firm's joint managing partner **Lee Bogdanoff** is admired for his *"excellent strategizing in negotiations and counter-arguments."* He is currently acting for a large group of former Dewey & LeBoeuf partners on that firm's highly publicized bankruptcy. Bogdanoff manages the firm alongside **Kenneth Klee**, who is respected by peers as *"one of the smartest guys around."* He is an expert in municipal bankruptcies and continues to advise Jefferson County and Mammoth Lakes on their respective Chapter 9 bankruptcies. Clients have been quick to note that he is *"incredibly resourceful and creative; he gets his hands dirty and is very effective."* **Michael Tuchin** is also a founding member of the firm. *"He's someone who gets the respect of everybody,"* note enthusiastic interviewees, who add: *"Michael in particular is exceptional in the courtroom."*

Recent highlights for Tuchin include his advice to national sports retailer Pacific Sunwear of California during its successful out-of-court restructuring. **Thomas Patterson** has a diverse practice spanning the full range of bankruptcy and restructuring-related issues. He is an expert in the healthcare bankruptcy sector. Patterson recently led for the firm as special appellate counsel in Thorpe Insulation's mass asbestos Chapter 11 bankruptcy proceedings and related litigation. **Whitman Holt** continues to be considered a superb rising star by commentators. He is currently playing a prominent part in the firm's role as counsel to Jefferson County in its Chapter 9 municipal bankruptcy. Sources are impressed with his quick turnaround and effectiveness.

### Latham & Watkins LLP
See profile on p.446

**THE FIRM** Latham & Watkins takes a leading position in the rankings on the strength of a highly successful year. The firm's national reach has resulted in the Los Angeles-based team being able to offer expertise across a broad range of insolvency and restructuring matters. It continues to gain recognition as a powerhouse in representing secured lenders, and the firm regularly acts for clients like GE, Yucaipa, Saban, Guthy-Renker and other private equity and hedge funds. The team has also gained strong praise from commentators for its company representation. An example of this can be found in its acting for New United Motors Manufacturing (NUMMI) on a large-scale out-of-court wind-down and various insolvency issues.

**Sources say:** *"An excellent firm which has stayed very busy."* *"One of the top firms in the country; the bankruptcy lawyers I've dealt with are all brilliant."*

**KEY INDIVIDUALS Peter Gilhuly** is chair of Latham's West Coast insolvency practice. He is highly regarded nationally and acts for a wide range of debtor and secured creditor clients. One respondent has remarked that Gilhuly is a *"fantastic lawyer and in terms of who I'd be looking to hire it'd be Peter."* He counts GE as a regular client and is the lead attorney in representing both NUMMI and Traffic Control and Safety. **Robert Klyman** represents a wide range of clients, many of whom note that he is an expert bankruptcy litigator who presents his clients' positions in court effectively. He recently acted for Ship Finance Management as the largest creditor of Horizon Lines Shipping on its cross-border out-of-court restructuring. **Gregory Lunt** is adept in representing both debtors and creditors in matters ranging from distressed business acquisitions to complex corporate restructurings. He garners praise from interviewees, who describe him as a *"straight shooter, and you can take his word."*

### Milbank, Tweed, Hadley & McCloy LLP
See profile on p.448

**THE FIRM** This team plays an integral part in Milbank's nationally reputed financial restructuring group. It benefits from a deep bench of highly regarded attorneys who practice across the spectrum of bankruptcy-related matters. While traditionally recognized for acting for bondholders and creditor committees, the team is increasingly

acclaimed for its excellence in debtor-side representation. The group recently acted for Franklin Advisors on more than $1 billion in bonds in the Dynegy Chapter 11 bankruptcy. Milbank is also currently representing Midland Loan Services as special servicer of a $1 billion mortgage loan to MSR Resort Hotel.

**Sources say:** *"A top-drawer practice."* *"I think they are a good mix of counsel who can help in negotiating consensual transactions but who are also effective in litigation and trial strategy; regardless of the direction, you know you are in good hands."*

**KEY INDIVIDUALS** Department head **Paul Aronzon** (see p.620) is also co-leader of Milbank's national financial restructuring group. Commentators note: *"He has a deep knowledge of the law and process,"* adding that *"he has a great ability to evaluate cases and figure out the issues; a very fine strategic thinker."* He is currently representing Franklin Advisors in the Dynegy matter. **Robert Moore** (see p.655) is revered by peers as a *"fantastic lawyer with a fantastic practice,"* while clients add that *"he brings a certain gravitas and commands respect which is very helpful to clients."* He recently acted for the Chapter 11 trustee of Las Vegas-area developer South Edge during its bankruptcy proceedings. **Mark Shinderman** (see p.665) is the lead lawyer in Milbank's representation of Midland Loan Services in the MSR Resort Hotel matter. His strengths are described as *"practical and responsive; very intelligent and doesn't miss the forest for the trees."* **Thomas Kreller** (see p.648) is *"calm and measured but will advance your cause,"* according to satisfied clients, many of whom *"found him to be very effective in front of judges."* His diverse practice is evidenced in his acting for bondholder Franklin Advisors in the Dynegy matter, as well as debtor Silver Legacy Resort Casino in its Chapter 11 bankruptcy. **Gregory Bray** (see p.625) is acclaimed for his *"knowledge of the Bankruptcy Code and legal precedents; he also brings a very professional approach, is always available throughout the day and gives us a quick turnaround."* He is currently acting as counsel to an ad hoc committee of senior noteholders representing some $500 million in claims in the bankruptcy of aircraft manufacturer Hawker Beechcraft.

### Pachulski Stang Ziehl & Jones LLP
See profile on p.694

**THE FIRM** This leading boutique's California offices are the base of the firm's nationally recognized bankruptcy practice; they are backed by teams in Delaware and New York. While winning significant praise from sources for its superb expertise in debtor-side cases, the team brings in-depth talent to all aspects of bankruptcy and restructuring work. In recent highlights, the firm represented air carrier group Mesa Air and affiliated companies in their Chapter 11 proceedings.

**Sources say:** *"A fantastic firm."* *"They know everyone and are the ultimate in professionalism."*

**KEY INDIVIDUALS** A leading specialist in the state and nationally, **Richard Pachulski** is *"by far one of the most prolific attorneys,"* say sources, many of whom also praise him as an immensely *"effective negotiator and lawyer."* He appears in many of the state's most significant bankruptcies, adding a name that *"brings instant credibility to any situation you are discussing."* **Jeffrey Pomerantz** is increasingly lauded for developing a practice *"of the highest quality."* He is particularly recognized for his creditor-side expertise, but is also active in company-side representations. These have recently included acting for technology services company CyberDefender in its Chapter 11 proceedings. The *"incredibly smart and effective"* **John Fiero** is cochair of the firm's creditors' committee practice group. While best known for his representations of committees, he also manages a significant debtor-side practice. Peers and clients *"have a lot respect for"* new entry **Debra Grassgreen**. She is frequently seen assisting Richard Pachulski in some of the firm's most significant cases.

## Band 2

### Gibson, Dunn & Crutcher LLP
See profile on p.682

**THE FIRM** Gibson, Dunn & Crutcher's versatile bankruptcy attorneys are admired both locally and nationally. The California team leverages a hefty national network of expertise to provide thorough solutions to both company and creditor-side clients. This is particularly so in relation to bankruptcy litigation, where the firm is singled out for praise by commentators. The team is also developing a commanding presence in cross-border bankruptcies, and has been acting for Bahrain-based investment bank Arcapita Bank BSC and five Cayman Island subsidiaries on Arcapita's New York-based Chapter 11 proceedings.
**Sources say:** *"The team can marshal resources in big cases. It is dedicated and hardworking. They are all good, up and down the line."*
**KEY INDIVIDUALS** The highly experienced **Oscar Garza** (see p.637) is regularly singled out as a *"brilliant restructuring attorney; very pragmatic and thorough."* He is currently representing the Chandler Trusts and several former directors of Tribune in litigation arising out of Tribune's bankruptcy. Orange County-based **Craig Millet** (see p.655) is cochair of Gibson's national business restructuring and reorganization practice. He is adept across the bankruptcy spectrum and harbors expertise in cross-border and international matters. *"He is a down-to-earth guy; very practical,"* say sources. **Samuel Newman** (see p.657) provides wide-ranging bankruptcy experience to clients. Of late, he has acted on a number of Section 363 asset acquisitions, including representing Contec in its acquisition of all the assets of PowerBalance. **Jeffrey Krause** (see p.647) is praised for his intelligence and strong demeanor during negotiations. He joined Gibson Dunn from Stutman Treister in 2012. He is the lead lawyer acting as debtor's counsel for RE Loans during its prominent Chapter 11 bankruptcy.

### O'Melveny & Myers LLP
See profile on p.693

**THE FIRM** O'Melveny's solid national practice sees a broad range of restructuring and insolvency matters, both domestic and international. The team is especially renowned for its prominence in lender representation. In recent highlights, the group has been representing an ad hoc committee of holders of second lien debt issued by AMF Bowling, the world's largest operator of bowling centers. High-profile clients also include Oaktree Capital Management, Cerberus, Bank of America, Samsung Electronics and Gottschalks.
**Sources say:** *"Thoughtfulness in providing strategic advice, attention to detail, clear communication with the client regarding options and timelines."*
**KEY INDIVIDUALS** The *"extremely talented"* **Ben Logan** is a seasoned and highly respected authority in the bankruptcy field. A key figure in a number of the firm's most significant bankruptcy cases, he recently led the team on behalf of the ad hoc committee in the AMF Bowling bankruptcy. **Evan Jones** is best known for his sterling work on behalf of major financial institutions and banks. Chair of the firm's restructuring practice group **Suzzane Uhland** (see p.670) played a key part in the AMF Bowling bankruptcy matter on behalf of the ad hoc committee. **Steve Warren** receives high praise from clients: *"Steve has been a pleasure to work with, giving sound counsel and timely feedback,"* mentioned one happy source.

### Orrick, Herrington & Sutcliffe LLP
See profile on p.1994

**THE FIRM** Orrick Herrington's California-based bankruptcy group has experienced a successful year on the back of developing niche expertise in a number of distressed industries. While handling work across the bankruptcy spectrum, the team has also flourished in the municipal bankruptcy space, the most recent such representation being for the city of Stockton, California, the largest US city to file for Chapter 9 protection. Orrick has also been very active in the solar energy sector, in which it has recently represented both debtors and creditors in various distressed situations, and also harbors significant expertise in cross-border matters, particularly relating to Asia.
**Sources say:** *"The firm is staffed by veteran attorneys who are forthright and imaginative in their assessment of our options"*
**KEY INDIVIDUALS** **Marc Levinson** (see p.650) is the driving force behind the firm's municipal bankruptcy expertise, with sources noting that he is *"emerging as a national expert in Chapter 9 cases"* and *"he has really cornered that market."* He is currently representing the city of Stockton in its high-profile bankruptcy proceedings. **Frederick Holden** (see p.642) is immensely experienced and highly regarded for his cross-border expertise. He represents an extensive range of debtor and lender clients. He is also heavily involved in the solar energy sector, in which again he acts on both the company and lender-sides of distressed situations.

### Sidley Austin LLP
See profile on p.1264

**THE FIRM** Sidley Austin's California-based corporate reorganization and bankruptcy team covers the gamut of bankruptcy-related representation. The group is able to draw on the firm's global network of offices, from Chicago to London, all of which work collaboratively to achieve the desired solutions for clients. As an example, Sidley has been acting as debtor's counsel to Dynegy Holdings during its highly publicized New York-based bankruptcy. The team is also representing building company Flintkote in its bankruptcy.
**Sources say:** *"They are extremely responsive; we feel like we are a priority for them and it makes a difference. What we like is they are not just technical, they have that rare business judgment as well; they come up with business solutions."*
**KEY INDIVIDUALS** **Richard Havel** (see p.641) is one of the most senior members of the team. He is regularly singled out for his even-keeled manner and technical knowhow in complicated situations. He is particularly adept in bankruptcy matters that relate to real estate. **Sally Neely** (see p.656) has over 30 years' bankruptcy law experience. She garners tremendous respect amongst peers and clients for intelligent, thorough analysis. She acts for a range of different interests in restructurings and reorganizations. **Jeffrey Bjork** (see p.624) has played a significant role in the debtor representations of Dynegy and Flintkote. He has developed a strong following in Chapter 9 municipal bankruptcies. Interviewees are quick to emphasize that *"Jeff is creative, passionate and extremely service-oriented."* **Jennifer Hagle** (see p.639) acts across the spectrum of bankruptcy and restructuring mandates, and has particular expertise in representing lenders. As one impressed source put it: *"She is technically top-notch and represents us very well in a group setting; in dealing with investors, companies and creditors she takes control of meetings and expresses our viewpoints."* Impressed commentators single out **Joel Samuels** (see p.664) for praise, noting that *"he is one of the smartest people I've met; he knows the Bankruptcy Code inside and out."* He is regularly identified as an expert in acting for secured creditors and in conducting bankruptcy litigation. **Kevin Lantry** (see p.648) is praised for his contributions to the Tribune and Dynegy debtor representations, an area where he is particularly adept. Interviewees appreciate his foresight in implementing strategic objectives.

### Stutman, Treister & Glatt Professional Corporation

**THE FIRM** This prominent bankruptcy boutique maintains a robust reputation in the region across a broad range of restructuring and insolvency issues. While best known for its excellent debtor-side representations, the group undertakes a broad swath of bankruptcy matters, acting for creditors and committees, companies, and sellers and purchasers of distressed assets.
**KEY INDIVIDUALS** *"Terrific attorney"* **Jeffrey Davidson** has a superb practice covering all manner of creditor and debtor representation. Peers have uniformly *"been impressed with his ability."* The *"absolutely brilliant"* and

"*super-smart*" **Isaac Pachulski** is an immensely experienced bankruptcy practitioner in an array of reorganization and distressed company issues. **Robert Greenfield** is a seasoned authority in the region's bankruptcy arena, and has a multitude of major insolvencies and restructurings to his name.

## Band 3

### Buchalter Nemer
See profile on p.676

**THE FIRM** Buchalter Nemer's highly respected insolvency practice maintains an eminent reputation for bankruptcy work across a wide range of creditor and debtor representations. However, it is for its prominence and expertise in creditor-side matters that the group wins most praise. The group took the spotlight recently with its representation of Ron Tutor, the president and CEO of Tutor Perrini, in the high-profile ThinkFilm bankruptcy matters.

**Sources say:** "*They know what they are doing and do it well.*"

**KEY INDIVIDUALS** The "*very bright and very practical*" **Pamela Webster** (see p.671) is particularly renowned for handling bankruptcy issues occurring in the healthcare, insurance and financial services industries, among others. Practice group chair **Bernard Bollinger** (see p.624) has been particularly active in real estate-related bankruptcies over the past year, including acting for the joint equity committee of investors on the bankruptcies of Real Estate Partners and its affiliates.

### Peitzman Weg LLP
See profile on p.695

**THE FIRM** Peitzman Weg is a renowned Los Angeles-based bankruptcy boutique with a sterling reputation in a host of regional creditor and debtor-side representations. However, the group has geographical reach belying this reputation. Indicative of this was its recent representation of fast food franchise owner Wagstaff Minnesota in a dozen Chapter 11 cases filed in Minneapolis.

**Sources say:** "*Rapid response and excellent service.*"

**KEY INDIVIDUALS** **Howard Weg** (see p.671) appears in a significant proportion of the firm's most significant cases, and is widely considered one of the most experienced practitioners in the region. He and **Scott Gautier** (see p.637) led in the Wagstaff Minnesota bankruptcies. **David Shemano** (see p.665) is "*a good lawyer who is really coming on strong*" in the sector, say peers. His recent highlights include acting for premiere boutique gym operator Club Ventures Investments in a $70 million debt restructuring. Seasoned bankruptcy authority **Lawrence Peitzman** (see p.658) has been especially active, alongside Weg, Shemano and Gautier, in representing film studios and producers in numerous bankruptcy issues, including matters concerning MGM's bankruptcy.

### Sheppard, Mullin, Richter & Hampton LLP

**THE FIRM** This adaptable bankruptcy and restructuring team represents both debtor and creditor clients in a wide range of matters. Drawing on the firm's extensive network of experts and resources allows it to meet the requirements of clients in most distressed situations. Recent highlights include its continued representation of the official committee of unsecured creditors during the asbestos bankruptcy of Plant Insulation. At the other end of the spectrum, the team also acted for Peak Broadcasting and various affiliates in their pre-packaged Chapter 11 restructurings.

**Sources say:** "*I think they have been very efficient and responsive; they have served the company well and steered us in the right direction.*"

**KEY INDIVIDUALS** The "*well-connected and well-respected*" **Michael Ahrens** is based in the firm's San Francisco office. He undertakes a wide range of mandates, with clients praising his "*breadth of knowledge, experience and responsiveness.*" **Ori Katz** enters the rankings on the back of a stellar year and glowing praise. Interviewees are quick to point out that he "*is really making a name for himself as a top-notch debtor-side restructuring lawyer,*" while others add that "*he was insightful, knowledgeable and able to get up to speed on a new industry very quickly.*"

### Winston & Strawn LLP
See profile on p.1267

**THE FIRM** Winston & Strawn's wide-ranging bankruptcy abilities come particularly lauded for its excellence in the creditors' rights space. Work highlights include its high-profile representation of the official committee of unsecured creditors of People's Choice Home Loan, which was followed by the firm's role on behalf of the liquidating trustee. The team similarly took the spotlight with its representation of the unsecured creditors committee, and subsequently the liquidating trustee, of Touch America Holdings.

**Sources say:** "*The combined team was incredible.*"

**KEY INDIVIDUALS** The experienced **Randy Rogers** (see p.662) undertakes an array of complex bankruptcy issues. Given the contentious nature of many bankruptcy issues, many clients "*find him to be the voice of reason in these situations.*" **Eric Sagerman** (see p.663) is chair of the firm's restructuring and insolvency practice, and managing partner of its Los Angeles office. According to sources, he is "*responsive, knowledgeable, pragmatic and effective.*" Sagerman is particularly lauded for his expert handling of creditor and committee representations. Based in San Francisco, **John Fredericks** (see p.636) handles the full array of creditor and debtor representations, as well as distressed M&A matters. He recently led on behalf of Medley Capital in three separate lawsuits involving an investor. Rising star **Justin Rawlins** (see p.661) played a key role in the People's Choice matter, and has been active in a number of significant cross-border assignments.

## Band 4

### Felderstein Fitzgerald Willoughby & Pascuzzi LLP

**THE FIRM** Felderstein Fitzgerald is a Sacramento-based bankruptcy boutique renowned for its effective handling of local and regional bankruptcy and restructuring assignments. The group manages a broad practice representing all manner of creditors, debtors, trustees and committees.

**Sources say:** "*They have a lock on the Sacramento market; they are terrific attorneys.*"

**KEY INDIVIDUALS** The "*fantastic*" **Steven Felderstein** is the firm's managing partner. He continues to gain particular acclaim for his role on behalf of the unsecured creditors committee in the bankruptcy of law firm Heller Ehrman.

### Irell & Manella
See profile on p.686

**THE FIRM** Irell & Manella's bankruptcy, reorganization and creditors' rights group is an established player in many of the state's more significant bankruptcies. The team acts for a full range of clients and has recently seen an upturn in instructions capitalizing on Irell's notable expertise in bankruptcy litigation. Notable examples include the group's recent representation of Carmel Land & Cattle in alleged claims arising out of the failure of the Lake Las Vegas resort project. The team also acts for a special litigation trust that includes the US Department of Justice, the US Environmental Protection Agency, and more than a dozen states and others, who are together seeking $25 billion in damages from Anadarko Petroleum.

**Sources say:** "*Extremely satisfied with their performance from beginning to end. Given that they are a large firm, they tend to know a lot of the judges and have a good idea of how judges will respond. Highly competent technically*"

**KEY INDIVIDUALS** **Jeffrey Reisner** (see p.661) "*is technically one of the best I've ever seen; he is very imaginative and comes up with some great ideas,*" mentioned one impressed interviewee. He is responsible for Irell's representation in the Carmel Land litigation on the failed Lake Las Vegas resort project. Reisner is head of Irell & Manella's bankruptcy, reorganization and creditors' rights group.

### Katten Muchin Rosenman LLP
See profile on p.1253

**THE FIRM** Katten Muchin enters the rankings on the back of extremely strong praise for its expertise in representing major financial institutions and creditors, and the impressive recent growth of its Californian bankruptcy team. In highlights, the group acted for BNY Mellon in the restructuring of $143 million of mortgage notes secured by Silver Legacy Resort Casino and issued by a joint venture between Circus (MGM) and Eldorado.

**Sources say:** "*Our experience has been fantastic; their strength is their experience.*"

**KEY INDIVIDUALS** **Craig Barbarosh** led a team joining Katten Muchin from Pillsbury in 2012. As sources note, he "*handles very large cases; his ability to manage large complex matters is impressive.*" He divides his time between the firm's Orange County and New York offices. The Los

Angeles-based **William Freeman** is another arrival from Pillsbury. According to interviewees, *"he's very well respected; very solution-oriented, and can work with everybody."* He is especially recommended for his work on behalf of creditors, lenders, financial institutions and committees.

## Levene, Neale, Bender, Yoo & Brill LLP

**THE FIRM** This is a Los Angeles-based bankruptcy boutique renowned as a go-to group for mid-market insolvencies and restructurings. While best known for its company-side roles, the team also handles committee, creditor, debtor and trustee representations, and undertakes a variety of complex distressed M&A assignments.

**KEY INDIVIDUALS Ron Bender** plays a key role in a large proportion of the group's most significant bankruptcy matters, and has a wide-ranging, highly respected practice. Founder and co-managing partner **David Neale** is especially lauded for his superb bankruptcy litigation expertise.

## Skadden, Arps, Slate, Meagher & Flom LLP & Affiliates

See profile on p.2008

**THE FIRM** Skadden's West Coast bankruptcy team, based in Los Angeles, forms a key pillar supporting the firm's pre-eminent international practice. The team's recent highlights include representing mechanical printing paper manufacturer Catalyst Paper in its $650 million debt restructuring. The group also took the spotlight with its role on behalf of MGM.

**KEY INDIVIDUALS** The *"very respected"* **Van Durrer** (see p.633) leads the firm's West Coast bankruptcy practice group, and he is credited as a superb driving force behind its strength in the region.

## White & Case LLP

See profile on p.451

**THE FIRM** White & Case's compact Los Angeles-based financial restructuring and insolvency team integrates admirably with the firm's wider nationwide network of experts. The team is traditionally identified as a creditor-based practice, but it has been successful in expanding its practice to company-side matters also. Recent highlights include acting for Otero County Hospital during its Chapter 11 bankruptcy and related litigation.

**KEY INDIVIDUALS Craig Averch** (see p.621) leads the bankruptcy practice's Los Angeles presence. He is skilled across a wide range of financial restructuring and insolvency matters, and is particularly well regarded for his

bankruptcy litigation expertise. He has recently acted as debtor's counsel for Otero County Hospital.

## Other Notable Practitioners

Los Angeles-based **David Simonds** (see p.666) of Akin Gump Strauss Hauer & Feld LLP *"has the ability to look at the broader context and view things from a business perspective,"* according to market sources, many of whom add that *"he understands the business drivers and applies the law to that; something that is quite rare."* He recently acted for the official committee of unsecured creditors in the bankruptcy of Imperial Capital Bancorp. Former judge **Lisa Fenning** (see p.635) of Arnold & Porter LLP is described as *"very clear and easy to understand; she is able to respond in a way that doesn't leave you scratching your head as a non-bankruptcy lawyer."* She is highly experienced and harbors particular expertise within the healthcare and real estate sectors. **Sara Chenetz** (see p.628) of Blank Rome LLP has wide-ranging bankruptcy expertise, and regularly represents secured lenders and debtors-in-possession. *"She is very bright, has a calm personality and is well attuned to clients' needs,"* notes one happy client, while another adds: *"I love that she keeps me informed regularly and is so knowledgeable about bankruptcy."* **Sharon Weiss** of Bryan Cave LLP is praised for her analytical skills in distressed situations, and for her commercial awareness. She acts for clients on a wide range of bankruptcy issues. The *"thoughtful and creative"* **Mette Kurth** (see p.648) is a partner in the bankruptcy and financial restructuring group of Arent Fox LLP. *"She's very direct, has a plan of action and goes on the attack with it,"* say sources. Others are *"impressed with her knowledge of the law and personal skills."* **Harvey Schochet** heads Davis Wright Tremaine LLP's bankruptcy and creditors' rights practice in California. His practice often involves credit recovery, bankruptcy and financing transactions, and representing financial institutions. He is particularly adept within the real estate, agricultural and investment sectors. **Howard Steinberg** (see p.667) recently arrived at Greenberg Traurig LLP from Irell & Manella. *"I use and trust him because he treats business matters like his own money is at stake,"* says one impressed client. He is especially commended for his bankruptcy litigation expertise. **Joe Eisenberg** is based in the Los Angeles office of Jeffer, Mangels, Butler & Mitchell LLP. According to sources, he *"is a terrific practitioner with a high-level practice."* He is accomplished in all aspects of bankruptcy law and receives particular praise for his work on company-side matters. **Marc Cohen** (see p.629) is chair of the Los

Angeles bankruptcy and restructuring department of Kaye Scholer LLP. His lender and bondholder experience is especially highly regarded, as is his litigation expertise. Impressed sources note that *"he is honest, creative, responsive, and always looks for ways to resolve things amicably."* **Thomas Walper** (see p.671) of Munger, Tolles & Olson LLP has a developing reputation as *"an excellent strategist, tactician and scholar."* Peers go on to praise him as *"very effective in court and totally versatile; a good creditors and debtors lawyer."* **Cynthia Cohen** is of counsel in the Los Angeles office of Paul Hastings LLP, where she specializes in bankruptcy litigation. She is also an expert in antitrust matters. **David Minnick** (see p.655) of Pillsbury Winthrop Shaw Pittman LLP is the firm's national insolvency and restructuring practice leader. He is immensely experienced in representing lenders, investors and general creditors in bankruptcy matters, and counts Bank of America, Bank of the West and Wells Fargo as regular clients. The *"thorough and professional"* **Martin Zohn** heads Proskauer Rose LLP's California bankruptcy and restructuring offering. Market sources commend him as *"a keen strategist who knows how to advocate for his client but is capable of reaching a practical solution."* **Eric Winston** of Quinn Emanuel Urquhart & Sullivan, LLP represents a wide variety of clients in bankruptcy-related situations, and has particular expertise in litigation. He recently advised the official committee of equity interest holders in the Chapter 11 bankruptcy of Trident Microsystems. **William Lobel** of The Lobel Firm, LLP is an immensely experienced bankruptcy and restructuring practitioner who garners tremendous respect among market commentators. He has in recent times been highly active on matters related to distressed real estate, although he has over 40 years of wide-ranging bankruptcy expertise. Venable LLP partner **Hamid Rafatjoo** (see p.660) has a practice covering the gamut of bankruptcy and restructuring representations. *"He is good with strategy and is very results-driven; also well connected and respected,"* say happy clients. Other interviewees have noted that Rafatjoo is *"adept at seeking consensus on issues where it is possible; with aggressive advocacy where consensus cannot be reached."* **Jonathan Shenson** recently left Klee, Tuchin, Bogdanoff & Stern in order to form Shenson Law Group PC. He remains well regarded and commentators are eager to see him in action with his new practice. **Randye Soref** recently joined Polsinelli PC in Los Angeles as of counsel from Buchalter Nemer. Clients laud her as a *"very good, responsive attorney who knows the bankruptcy courts and the practice very well."*

# CAPITAL MARKETS DEBT & EQUITY

Commentary about individuals can be found under their firm's paragraph. If the firm has no paragraph (is not ranked) look at Other Notable Practitioners.

## Capital Markets: Debt & Equity
### Leading Firms

**Band 1**
Davis Polk & Wardwell LLP *
Latham & Watkins LLP *
Simpson Thacher & Bartlett LLP *
Skadden, Arps, Slate, Meagher & Flom LLP & Affiliates *
Sullivan & Cromwell LLP *
Wilson Sonsini Goodrich & Rosati *

**Band 2**
Cooley LLP
Fenwick & West LLP *
Gibson, Dunn & Crutcher LLP *
Sidley Austin LLP *

**Band 3**
Goodwin Procter LLP *
O'Melveny & Myers LLP *
Orrick, Herrington & Sutcliffe LLP *
Paul Hastings LLP *
Pillsbury Winthrop Shaw Pittman LLP *

## Leading Individuals

| Band 1 | |
| --- | --- |
| Dallas Bruce | Davis Polk & Wardwell LLP * |
| Davidson Gordon K | Fenwick & West LLP * |
| Denenberg Alan | Davis Polk & Wardwell LLP * |
| Fore John A | Wilson Sonsini Goodrich & Rosati |
| Hinman Jr William H | Simpson Thacher & Bartlett LLP * |
| Noel Gregg A | Skadden, Arps, Slate, Meagher & Flom * |
| Saper Jeff | Wilson Sonsini Goodrich & Rosati |
| Sonsini Larry W | Wilson Sonsini Goodrich & Rosati |
| Wilson John | Shearman & Sterling LLP (ONP)[†] |

| Band 2 | |
| --- | --- |
| Brown Patrick S | Sullivan & Cromwell LLP * |
| del Calvo Jorge | Pillsbury Winthrop Shaw Pittman LLP |
| Haueter Eric S | Sidley Austin LLP * |
| Hodgkins Scott | Latham & Watkins LLP |
| Kennedy Kevin P. | Simpson Thacher & Bartlett LLP * |
| Layne Jonathan K | Gibson, Dunn & Crutcher LLP * |
| Pohlen Patrick A | Latham & Watkins LLP * |
| Ressler Alison S | Sullivan & Cromwell LLP * |
| Smith Douglas D | Gibson, Dunn & Crutcher LLP * |
| Stegemoeller Mark | Latham & Watkins LLP |
| Wolfe Scott N | Latham & Watkins LLP * |

| Band 3 | |
| --- | --- |
| Brentani William B | Simpson Thacher & Bartlett LLP * |
| Fleck Casey T | Latham & Watkins LLP |
| Healy Peter | O'Melveny & Myers LLP * |
| Ivey Thomas J. | Skadden, Arps, Slate, Meagher & Flom * |
| Jensen Eric | Cooley LLP |
| Kennedy Shayne | Latham & Watkins LLP * |
| Lehot Louis | Cooley LLP |
| Martin Katharine A | Wilson Sonsini Goodrich & Rosati |
| McDowell Stewart L | Gibson, Dunn & Crutcher LLP * |
| Muto Fred | Cooley LLP |
| Savva John L | Sullivan & Cromwell LLP * |
| Snyder David R | Pillsbury Winthrop Shaw Pittman LLP * |
| Stokdyk Steven B | Latham & Watkins LLP |
| Vetter Jeffrey R | Fenwick & West LLP * |
| Woronoff Michael A | Proskauer Rose LLP (ONP)[†] |

| Up-and-coming individuals | |
| --- | --- |
| Flanagan Sharon R | Sidley Austin LLP * |

* Indicates firm / individual with profile.
[†] ONP = Other Notable Practitioner.

## Band 1

### Davis Polk & Wardwell LLP
See profile on p.442

**THE FIRM** This outstanding team earns the respect of the business community for its representation of leading investment banks and corporates on capital markets offerings of complexity and high value. Recent highlights include advising Morgan Stanley, Credit Suisse Securities, JPMorgan Securities and others as joint book-running managers on the IPO of Splunk. The team also works with leading names like Comcast/NBC Universal, Equinix and E*TRADE Financial.
**Sources say:** *"I would describe the services our company has received as of the highest quality that can be provided." "They have a massive amount of expertise in anything you can come up with."*
**KEY INDIVIDUALS Bruce Dallas** (see p.630) gives clients *"world-class, current knowledge and expertise both from a commercial side and a legal side,"* impressed clients say. He recently represented Texas Instruments in its $3.5 billion SEC-registered debt offering. The *"highly knowledgeable"* **Alan Denenberg** (see p.631) is *"thorough but congenial," "really gets things done"* and is *"incredibly business-savvy,"* sources note. He heads the Menlo Park office and recently advised Citigroup Global Markets, Goldman Sachs and others as joint book-running managers on a $5 billion SEC-registered debt offering by Intel.

### Latham & Watkins LLP
See profile on p.446

**THE FIRM** This superb team earns strong market endorsement for its high-quality representation of issuers and underwriters on a range of substantial debt and equity offerings. Recent highlights include representing Amgen on multitranche senior notes offerings in the USA, Europe and the UK with a value of $12 billion. Other notable clients include Spirit Airlines and Intermolecular.
**Sources say:** *"They have a unique way of explaining complicated issues which is useful to the nonlawyer." "They do not manage the client to their timeline, rather they manage themselves to meet our timeline."*

**KEY INDIVIDUALS** The *"terrific"* **Mark Stegemoeller** is *"one of the deans of the high-yield market,"* sources say. He frequently advises both investment banks and corporate clients on a wide array of debt and equity offerings. Market sources describe **Scott Hodgkins** as *"exceedingly practical and highly bright and experienced."* He has notable expertise advising clients in the consumer products, real estate and life sciences industries. **Scott Wolfe** (see p.672) represents companies and investment banks in public offerings and debt offerings with a focus on the life sciences and hi-tech spheres. He heads the North San Diego office. The *"bright and highly creative"* **Casey Fleck** recently joined the Los Angeles office. He has a formidable reputation for his advice to clients on IPOs, convertible debt offerings, high-yield bonds and investment-grade bonds. **Shayne Kennedy** (see p.645) is a *"great lawyer and businessperson"* who is *"good at taking a practical approach,"* according to commentators. He advised Banc of America Securities on Gilead Sciences' recent multitranche senior notes offering and Skullcandy on its IPO on the NASDAQ. **Steven Stokdyk** is *"highly knowledgeable and has a steady hand,"* interviewees note. He is the global cochair of the firm's public company representation practice. **Patrick Pohlen** (see p.659) recently represented Intermolecular on its IPO. He has particular expertise advising financial institutions and companies in the technology, life sciences and clean technology arenas.

### Simpson Thacher & Bartlett LLP
See profile on p.2006

**THE FIRM** This team maintains its excellent profile for advising top companies on IPOs, high-yield bonds, investment-grade bonds and convertible debt offerings, with a particular focus on the technology sector. Its client list includes names like Oaktree Capital Management, Hellman & Friedman and Goldman Sachs. Recent highlights include advising the underwriters on the high-profile Facebook IPO and advising KKR Financial Holdings on two senior notes offerings.
**Sources say:** *"Their people are very good across the board."*
**KEY INDIVIDUALS William Hinman** (see p.642) represented the underwriters in Avago's two recent secondary offerings. Commentators regard him as an *"outstanding securities lawyer"* who has a *"fantastic mix of technical expertise and strategic thinking."* **William Brentani** (see p.625) is *"highly technically knowledgeable," "great to work with"* and *"our needs are his needs,"* impressed clients say. He recently represented JPMorgan as initial purchaser in the $1 billion senior notes issuance by Air Lease. **Kevin Kennedy** (see p.645) represented the underwriters led by Goldman Sachs and Barclays Capital on the IPO of Ceres. Sources say he has *"great depth of experience in all facets of capital markets."*

## Skadden, Arps, Slate, Meagher & Flom LLP & Affiliates
See profile on p.2008

THE FIRM This stellar team is exalted by market sources for its prowess in representing private and public companies, investment banks and government entities on the full range of debt and equity transactions. It recently represented Sara Lee in its division into two pure-play publicly traded companies. Other key clients include Westfield Group, Farmers Insurance Exchange and Merrill Lynch. **Sources say:** *"Skadden anticipated the legal issues, worked proactively to resolve them and patiently explained to third parties all over the world the complexities of this deal."* **KEY INDIVIDUALS Gregg Noel** (see p.657) is *"insightful"* and *"has an encyclopedic memory for the terms and conditions in our deals."* He recently represented a group of initial purchasers led by Merrill Lynch and others on a $700 million high-yield offering by Fidelity National Information Services. Commentators describe **Thomas Ivey** (see p.644) as a *"highly accomplished and skillful lawyer."* His recent highlights include advising Broadcom on its $500 million public offering of 2.7% senior notes.

## Sullivan & Cromwell LLP
See profile on p.2011

THE FIRM This team is a frequent and highly respected option for significant issuers and underwriters to advise on IPOs, follow-on offerings and bond issuances. It recently advised Mattel on its $600 million SEC-registered offering of 5.450% and 2.5% senior unsecured notes. The team also advises underwriters including Barclays Bank and First Republic Bank. **Sources say:** *"They are highly prompt and thorough; practical as well as creative."* **KEY INDIVIDUALS Alison Ressler** (see p.661) enjoys a fine reputation for her work on a range of capital markets transactions. She recently represented Citigroup Global Markets as representative of the underwriters in the SEC-registered follow-on offering of Penny Mac Investment Trust valued at $200 million in aggregate. **Patrick Brown** (see p.626) is *"highly practical," "down to earth, approachable and works hard,"* sources say. He recently represented the underwriters on the $380 million IPO of Oaktree Capital Management. **John Savva** (see p.664) is *"creative, practical and thorough."* He recently advised CNH Capital on its $500 million of high-yield senior unsecured notes.

## Wilson Sonsini Goodrich & Rosati
See profile on p.700

THE FIRM This team excels at advising issuers, underwriters and sellers in a range of equity and debt transactions, with an impressive presence in the technology sector. Its underwriter clients include big names like JPMorgan Securities and it frequently advises growing corporates on IPOs including recently advising Jive Software on its $161.3 million IPO. **Sources say:** *"They really know the drill and work very well as a team."* **KEY INDIVIDUALS** The *"highly talented"* **John Fore** is head of the corporate finance practice. He is well known in the market for his representation of technology companies

in debt transactions and recently represented Micron in its $1 billion convertible senior notes offering. **Jeff Saper** is *"hands-on"* and does *"outstanding work,"* impressed sources note. His recent highlights include representing Splunk in its $229.5 million IPO. **Katharine Martin** advised LinkedIn on its $621.5 million follow-on offering. Sources particularly recommend her expertise in 1934 Act matters. **Larry Sonsini** is *"a leading light in Silicon Valley,"* market sources say. He recently represented Tesla Motors in its $152 million follow-on offering.

## Band 2

## Cooley LLP

THE FIRM This team has a superb reputation for representing issuers in the technology and life sciences sectors on equity offerings. It recently advised Zynga on its $1 billion IPO and the underwriters on the $93.6 million IPO of Vocera Communications. Other notable clients include Ardea Biosciences, Amylin Pharmaceuticals and Jazz Pharmaceuticals.

**KEY INDIVIDUALS Eric Jensen** is praised for his pragmatic and knowledgeable approach to matters. He recently advised Morgan Stanley on LinkedIn's follow-on offering. **Fred Muto** is highly valued by sources for his experience in the field. His recent work includes assisting Yelp on its IPO. **Louis Lehot** recently joined the team from Sheppard, Mullin, Richter & Hampton. Lehot is applauded for his strong negotiation skills and experience in working with a range of parties, including the SEC.

## Fenwick & West LLP
See profile on p.680

THE FIRM This team is highly recommended for its work advising technology companies at all stages of their growth and underwriters on the full range of debt and equity transactions. It receives particular acclaim for its representation of clients in IPOs. Recent highlights include representing Facebook in its $18.4 billion IPO. Silver Spring Networks, Exponential Interactive and Proofpoint are other leading clients of this team. **Sources say:** *"They are an incredibly impressive group of people."* **KEY INDIVIDUALS Gordon Davidson** (see p.631) has a *"terrific skill set," "is really tied in to the top companies in Silicon Valley"* and has a *"highly balanced approach and a tremendous amount of experience,"* impressed sources say. He recently represented the cloud computing company ServiceNow on its IPO. **Jeffrey Vetter** (see p.670) advised Morgan Stanley on the IPO of Jive. Sources highly commend the excellence of his drafting skills.

## Gibson, Dunn & Crutcher LLP
See profile on p.682

THE FIRM Sources commend this team for its wide market knowledge and astute advice on a range of debt and equity transactions. Recent highlights include representing Intel in its $5 billion senior notes public offering. Other key

clients include Bally Technologies, Eros International and Pixelworks.

**Sources say:** *"They are incredibly hard-working, thoughtful and quick to provide us with whatever the situation demands."* **KEY INDIVIDUALS** The highly regarded **Jonathan Layne** (see p.649) advised Ameristar Casinos on a Rule 144A offering of 7.50% senior notes. He has a good reputation for his debt and equity work among peers in the field. **Douglas Smith** (see p.666) is *"thoughtful, totally engaged and really took the time to understand the issues and develop his own opinions about things,"* asserted one impressed client. His recent highlights include advising Wells Fargo on the establishment of a $100 billion global note program for Wells Fargo Bank. The *"thoughtful and knowledgeable"* **Stewart McDowell** (see p.653) is a *"creative lawyer who is good at solving problems,"* enthusiastic clients say. She recently represented Wells Fargo Securities on the public offering of floating-rate notes by Wells Fargo & Company.

## Sidley Austin LLP
See profile on p.1264

THE FIRM This team is held in high esteem for its representation of corporates and underwriters on an array of capital markets transactions including IPOs, offerings of convertible debt, and investment-grade and high-yield debt offerings. The firm represents names like Barclays Capital, eBay and SMART Technologies. Recent highlights include representing Corsair Components on its $97 million IPO. **Sources say:** *"I am impressed with the level of service and quick response time."* **KEY INDIVIDUALS Eric Haueter** (see p.640) is *"able to overcome issues easily as he has a great breadth of knowledge,"* avers one impressed source. He represents underwriters and issuers in a range of transactions including recently acting for the underwriters in the $600 million offering of notes by Sempra Energy. **Sharon Flanagan** (see p.635) is *"highly practical and thoughtful about the issues"* and is commended by interviewees for her technical expertise. She recently represented the underwriters in a $359 million offering of common stock and a $450 million offering of senior notes by HCP.

## Band 3

## Goodwin Procter LLP
See profile on p.1522

THE FIRM This team enters the rankings this year due to strong market endorsement for its work advising underwriters and corporates on IPOs and debt offerings. The group has excellent presence throughout the state, operating out of offices in Los Angeles, San Diego, San Francisco and Silicon Valley.

**KEY INDIVIDUALS Richard Kline** is the main contact in the Menlo Park office.

## O'Melveny & Myers LLP
See profile on p.693

THE FIRM This team represents a balanced array of high-profile companies and underwriters on the full array of debt and equity transactions. Recent highlights include representing Merrill Lynch and Citigroup Global Markets as joint managers and co-managers on the $35 million IPO of Synacor. Other notable clients include Cell Therapeutics, Lions Gate Entertainment and Sabra Health Care.

**KEY INDIVIDUALS** The highly regarded **Peter Healy** (see p.332) recently represented the underwriters in AvalonBay Communities' $725.4 million common stock offering.

### Orrick, Herrington & Sutcliffe LLP
See profile on p.1994

**THE FIRM** This team is recognized for its broad experience in capital markets transactions and its notable international capabilities. It represents clients on transactions including IPOs, follow-on offerings, investment-grade, medium-term and convertible notes offerings.

**KEY INDIVIDUALS** Brett Cooper is a key contact in the San Francisco office.

### Paul Hastings LLP
See profile on p.1996

**THE FIRM** This team maintains a good reputation for its representation of underwriters and issuers on equity and debt offerings, and has notable expertise in high-yield debt financings. It recently represented Goldman Sachs as lead underwriters on the $70 million IPO of Envivio. Other clients include ROTH Capital Partners, Stifel Nicolaus Weisel and Kratos Defense & Security Solutions.

**KEY INDIVIDUALS** Jeff Hartlin is a key contact at the firm and divides his time between the Palo Alto and San Diego offices.

### Pillsbury Winthrop Shaw Pittman LLP
See profile on p.2000

**THE FIRM** This team has noted expertise in advising companies on the full sweep of capital markets transactions, with particular strength in representing emerging companies from inception to IPO. It recently represented Envivio on its IPO. Other key clients include AmeriGas and Banco Latinoamericano de Comercio Exterior.

**KEY INDIVIDUALS** *"Prolific company-side lawyer"* **Jorge del Calvo** is *"highly knowledgeable"* and *"calming and methodical."* He recently represented Cafepress in its $85.5 million IPO. **David Snyder** (see p.666) advised Petco Animal Supplies on its $1.8 billion leveraged recapitalization transaction. He frequently acts as lead counsel on equity and debt offerings.

### Other Notable Practitioners

**Michael Woronoff** of Proskauer Rose LLP *"puts you in a position to make a good decision,"* a satisfied client attests. He recently represented GNC Holdings in its $655 million secondary offering of common stock. Shearman & Sterling LLP's **John Wilson** is recognized by market sources as a leading light in the field. He recently advised Merrill Lynch and others as joint book-running managers on Amgen's registered offering of $3 billion of investment-grade notes.

# CONSTRUCTION

Mediators p.550

Commentary about individuals can be found under their firm's paragraph. If the firm has no paragraph (is not ranked) look at Other Notable Practitioners.

| Construction |
| --- |
| **Leading Firms** |
| **Band 1** |
| Farella Braun + Martel LLP |
| Watt, Tieder, Hoffar & Fitzgerald, LLP * |
| **Band 2** |
| Allen Matkins Leck Gamble Mallory & Natsis LLP * |
| Gibbs Giden Locher Turner Senet & Wittbrodt LLP. * |
| Hanson Bridgett LLP |
| Jones Day * |
| Monteleone & McCrory, LLP |
| **Band 3** |
| Alston & Bird LLP * |
| Atkinson, Andelson, Loya, Ruud & Romo |
| Peckar & Abramson, P.C. * |
| Pillsbury Winthrop Shaw Pittman LLP * |
| Sheppard, Mullin, Richter & Hampton LLP |
| **Band 4** |
| Crowell & Moring LLP * |
| Duane Morris LLP * |
| Gordon & Rees, LLP |
| Sedgwick LLP * |

* *Indicates firm with profile.*
*Alphabetical order within each band. Band 1 is the highest.*

## Band 1

### Farella Braun + Martel LLP

**THE FIRM** This market-leading practice undertakes a broad range of construction work for its high-profile client base, both in the USA and abroad. The team is known for its ability to handle highly complex matters relating to energy, health, utilities, infrastructure and commercial and residential developments. The firm currently advises the Port of Oakland on a range of construction and insurance matters, including a retrofit project at Oakland Airport. Other key clients represented by the firm include Trane US, BP Solar and AECOM.

**Sources say:** *"The attorneys were extremely professional and committed to doing the right thing for their client."*

**KEY INDIVIDUALS Charles Sink** is known for the breadth of his practice, and represents a variety of owners and contractors in the private and public sectors. According to sources, he *"provides excellent strategy advice"* and is *"very focused and easy to deal with."* He also regularly sits as an arbitrator. **Jeffrey Sykes** is a very well-respected practitioner who has a particularly strong reputation for his work representing contractors. *"He's very good, very smart, tenacious, represents his clients well and is a formidable adversary,"* commentators say. The eminent **Alan Harris** brings a wealth of construction law experience to his top-level work as a mediator. The highly regarded **Deborah Ballati** enjoys an excellent reputation for her work on construction and insurance. *"She does an extraordinary job and is clearly a top construction lawyer,"* sources say. **Carl Switzer** is well respected as a litigator, and also has extensive experience in methods of alternative dispute res-

olution such as mediation and arbitration. He undertakes a variety of work for his client base of public and private owners, developers and design professionals.

### Watt, Tieder, Hoffar & Fitzgerald, LLP
See profile on p.2522

**THE FIRM** This firm is recognized as one of the top names in California for construction law. The team has expertise across a full spectrum of contentious and noncontentious matters, such as public works construction, public-private partnerships, infrastructure developments and litigation. The firm represents a number of major insurers, contractors and other construction professionals, including Arch Insurance, DPR Construction, URS and the Travelers Casualty and Surety Company of America. Currently, the firm is acting for the Traylor-Shea Joint Venture on claims in excess of $60 million relating to a high-value public works project.

**Sources say:** *"They have very good lawyers, they're extremely thorough and they are bright and creative."*

**KEY INDIVIDUALS Michael Long** (see p.650) is known for his great experience in preparing and defending claims, and he also advises on contract documents and various methods of alternative dispute resolution. According to sources, he is *"a very professional and sharp attorney. He knows his stuff and works with the other side to get a resolution."* Observers highlight **Bennett Lee** (see p.649) as *"a solid litigator with a very good understanding of the contractor surety side of the construction business."* Sources also say: *"He has the ability to combine solid business strategy and business sense with his legal advice."* He is also well-respected for his work as a mediator. Contentious specialist

## Construction
### Senior Statesmen

| Senior Statesmen: distinguished older practitioners | |
| --- | --- |
| Harris Alan | Farella Braun + Martel LLP |

### Leading Individuals

| Band 1 | |
| --- | --- |
| Ashcraft Howard W | Hanson Bridgett LLP * |
| Ballati Deborah S | Farella Braun + Martel LLP |
| Buoncristiani David | Jones Day |
| Duffy Patrick J | Monteleone & McCrory, LLP |
| Heisse II John R | Pillsbury Winthrop Shaw Pittman LLP |
| Long Michael G | Watt, Tieder, Hoffar & Fitzgerald, LLP * |
| O'Neal Stephen V | Jones Day * |
| Sink Charles | Farella Braun + Martel LLP |
| Thum Robert B | Pillsbury Winthrop Shaw Pittman LLP * |
| Turner III Glenn E | Gibbs Giden Locher Turner Senet * |

| Band 2 | |
| --- | --- |
| Gadbois Barbara | Gibbs Giden Locher Turner Senet * |
| Hanover John D | Peckar & Abramson, P.C. * |
| Lee Bennett J | Watt, Tieder, Hoffar & Fitzgerald, LLP * |
| McMillan Daniel D | Jones Day * |
| Minchella Michael F | Monteleone & McCrory, LLP |
| Roux G Christian | Alston & Bird LLP * |
| Sykes Jeffrey A | Farella Braun + Martel LLP |
| Zovickian Stephen | Bingham McCutchen LLP (ONP)† * |

| Band 3 | |
| --- | --- |
| Baker Michael J | Atkinson, Andelson, Loya, Ruud & Romo * |
| Buddie Raymond M | Allen Matkins Leck Gamble Mallory * |
| Dukellis Gregory J | Watt, Tieder, Hoffar & Fitzgerald, LLP * |
| Ippolito Peter J | McKenna Long & Aldridge LLP (ONP)† * |
| McKeeman Michael T | Seyfarth Shaw LLP (ONP) * |
| Ortmann Dale | Hunt Ortmann Palffy Nieves Lubka (ONP)† |
| Salamone Mary | Atkinson, Andelson, Loya, Ruud & Romo * |
| Strong Kenneth F | Gordon & Rees, LLP |
| Truax Tim | Law Offices of Timothy M Truax (ONP)† |

| Band 4 | |
| --- | --- |
| Barron Anthony | Nixon Peabody LLP (ONP)† * |
| Bressler Todd N | Peckar & Abramson, P.C. * |
| Curtis Kenneth W | Allen Matkins Leck Gamble Mallory * |
| Diwik James | Sedgwick LLP |
| Hack Marion T | Gibbs Giden Locher Turner Senet * |
| Hamersmith Harold | Sheppard, Mullin, Richter & Hampton LLP |
| Hendrickson Robert C | Duane Morris LLP |
| Holmes Lock | Duane Morris LLP |
| Klinger Marilyn | Sedgwick, Detert, Moran & Arnold LLP * |
| Kovacich Thomas | Atkinson, Andelson, Loya, Ruud & Romo * |
| McInerney Tim | McInerney & Dillon (ONP)† |
| Niesley Robert | Watt, Tieder, Hoffar & Fitzgerald, LLP * |
| Pierce Timothy | K&L Gates (ONP)† * |
| Switzer Carl | Farella Braun + Martel LLP |
| Wittbrodt Richard J | Gibbs Giden Locher Turner Senet * |

**Gregory Dukellis** (see p.633) wins praise from commentators for being *"a strong litigator who knows the law and applies it well."* He is currently representing a general contractor in a high-value breach of contract action against the City of Los Angeles. Highly regarded construction practitioner **Robert Niesley** (see p.657) regularly acts on construction claims relating to lost productivity, delay and

## Construction: Mediators
### Senior Statesmen

| Senior Statesmen: distinguished older practitioners | |
| --- | --- |
| Harris Alan | Farella Braun + Martel LLP |

### Leading Individuals

| Star individuals | |
| --- | --- |
| Wulff Randall W | Wulff, Quinby & Sochynsky (ONP)† |

| Band 1 | |
| --- | --- |
| Gibbs Kenneth C | JAMS (ONP)† |
| Ippolito Peter J | McKenna Long & Aldridge LLP (ONP)† * |

| Band 2 | |
| --- | --- |
| Calkins II George D | JAMS (ONP)† |
| Erickson Randall L | Crowell & Moring LLP * |

\* Indicates individual with profile.

†ONP = Other Notable Practitioner.

differing site conditions. His current clients include American Motorists.

### Band 2

#### Allen Matkins Leck Gamble Mallory & Natsis LLP
See profile on p.674

**THE FIRM** This highly regarded construction offering represents high-profile universities, hospitals, developers and construction companies. The team regularly handles construction disputes, and recent highlights include acting for the owners of a biofuel facility on a $10 million claim made against them by a contractor. The firm is also active on high-value transactional matters, and recently represented DPR Construction on the construction elements of an $800 million medical center project. Other major clients represented by the team include the California Institute of Technology, Concert Realty Partners, Skanska and the White Memorial Hospital.

**KEY INDIVIDUALS** Clients value **Raymond Buddie** (see p.626) for his *"high intellect and sound business instincts."* He represents major names in construction in a variety of transactional matters and disputes. **Kenneth Curtis** (see p.630) is *"an outstanding construction lawyer who is pragmatic, very client-focused and efficient,"* according to market commentators. He has particular experience advising on public and private works construction.

#### Gibbs Giden Locher Turner Senet & Wittbrodt LLP.
See profile on p.681

**THE FIRM** This California construction practice is known for its prowess in litigation. Recently, the team successfully acted for the City of Victorville on a claim relating to design faults of a $60 million power plant project. The group represents a number of major construction names, such as Swinerton Builders and Layron Construction, and other key clients include the City of Glendale and the City of Huntingdon Beach. The firm also has an increasing presence in the energy sector, and is currently retained by

a number of key solar manufacturers, such as Suntech Power Holdings and SunWize.

**Sources say:** *"The firm has done outstanding work at a reasonable price, and has achieved excellent results."*

**KEY INDIVIDUALS** Department head **Glenn Turner** (see p.670) enjoys an impressive reputation for his work on insurance-related construction matters. He wins applause from sources for being *"practical in his approach and effective in the courtroom."* The well-respected **Barbara Gadbois** (see p.637) acts for a number of major developers on various residential projects in San Francisco and Los Angeles. She is known for her negotiation skills. **Marion Hack** (see p.639) offers expertise in a range of transactional construction matters and disputes. She receives high praise from market commentators, who find that she *"always knows what the facts are and always puts together a very practical solution. She is clearly going to be a star."* **Richard Wittbrodt** (see p.672) is a well-known construction practitioner and has recently advised on the construction of a $200 million regional medical center. *"He is brilliant, very good at analysis and does an excellent job representing his client,"* sources say.

#### Hanson Bridgett LLP

**THE FIRM** This impressive boutique practice continues to do high-level construction work in a number of fields. Its forte is public works construction projects, and the team recently acted on a number of major infrastructure projects. It currently represents the Modesto Irrigation District on a high-value claim relating to a large-scale regional water treatment plant. The team also has expertise in matters relating to health, insurance and HUD financing. The firm acts for a varied client base, which includes ProLogis, MaineGeneral Health, Roebbelen Contracting and Sutter Healthcare.

**KEY INDIVIDUALS** Howard Ashcraft (see p.621) heads the construction team at Hanson Bridgett and currently acts for such key clients as Harder Mechanical Construction. *"He is a very clear-headed attorney who is the country's leading authority on alternative project delivery models in construction,"* sources say.

#### Jones Day
See profile on p.919

**THE FIRM** An international firm with a strong California presence, Jones Day undertakes a broad range of work for its high-profile clients. The team is active on large-scale transactions and disputes both in the USA and overseas, with recent highlights including representing the contractor on a $2.2 billion solar thermal installation project in California. The group also represents the Los Angeles Unified School District in a complex multiparty litigation relating to breach of contract and design defects. Jones Day also has significant expertise incorporating alternative dispute resolution methods into resolving construction disputes.

**Sources say:** *"An outstanding resource for our company that has added value to many different matters for us over the years."*

KEY INDIVIDUALS **Stephen O'Neal** (see p.658) is hailed by commentators as *"a very impressive guy and a very worthy adversary in litigation."* He is acting for MGM Resorts International in a dispute relating to the design and construction of the $8.5 billion CityCenter project. *"Superstar"* **David Buoncristiani** (see p.626) enjoys a top reputation for his construction practice. He regularly acts on highly sensitive matters, and is currently advising PB Americas on a high-value radar facility being constructed for the government of Taiwan. **Daniel McMillan** (see p.654) has considerable expertise acting on construction disputes and wins particular praise for his written work. *"He is an extremely valuable counselor who offers a commercial perspective based upon his experience as a construction litigator,"* according to clients.

## Monteleone & McCrory, LLP

THE FIRM This is a well-regarded regional firm with an excellent reputation for its work representing subcontractors. The experienced team acts on a range of disputes and transactional work in both the public and the private spheres. The team currently advises on the California earthquake retrofit campaign and a range of other high-profile highway and water projects.
Sources say: *"They're a top-notch firm who do sophisticated work and are very able advocates."*
KEY INDIVIDUALS The impressive **Patrick Duffy** regularly advises on disputes relating to transport, industrial plants and wastewater facilities. *"He is extremely professional, keeps to his word and is a thorough litigator,"* according to sources. **Michael Minchella** is a highly experienced construction practitioner who acts for a range of major contractors, subcontractors, owners and design professionals on complex litigations. He also sits as a mediator and arbitrator.

## Band 3

## Alston & Bird LLP
See profile on p.1102

THE FIRM This strong construction offering acts for clients on all stages of the construction process, from planning and contract negotiation to the eventual resolution of disputes. Its client base includes contractors, subcontractors, owners and program managers. One key area of focus for the firm is public infrastructure, and the team has expertise in projects relating to utilities, energy, health, education and transportation. Recently, the team represented Tenet Healthsystem Hospitals, Seville Construction Services and Miller Brothers Investments.
KEY INDIVIDUALS Observers highlight **Christian Roux** (see p.663) as *"an excellent litigator who is firm but fair."* He currently represents such clients as OnisLiving and Gateway Science and Engineering.

## Atkinson, Andelson, Loya, Ruud & Romo

THE FIRM Well known for its strength in the public sector, this firm represents owners and contractors on a variety of transactional matters and disputes. The team has

particular experience advising clients on labor and employment issues that relate to construction, as well as regularly acting on matters in the education sector. Its key clients include a number of schools and colleges, including Cerritos Community College District, Rio Hondo Community College District and Fullerton Joint High School District.
KEY INDIVIDUALS **Michael Baker** (see p.621) has extensive experience working on school and college districts. He has recently handled a high-value dispute for the Los Angeles Community College District. The highly regarded **Mary Salamone** (see p.663) currently represents a major mechanical subcontractor in a dispute relating to a $100 million hospital in California. Sources describe her as *"super sharp and very pleasant to deal with."* **Thomas Kovacich** (see p.647) heads the firm's construction department. He wins high praise from sources for his experience in construction and employment matters: *"He is not only extremely knowledgeable in this area of law but also very well respected by the entire labor community, which is very useful for resolving issues."*

## Peckar & Abramson, P.C.
See profile on p.1998

THE FIRM This strong construction practice has particular prowess acting for general contractors and construction managers. The firm has extensive experience acting on complex litigations, and recently it successfully represented a national construction management firm in a dispute relating to the San Diego New Central Library. Other recent highlights include disputes relating to the construction of a hotel, a luxury resort, a highway and a skilled nursing facility.
Sources say: *"I am impressed with all of the attorneys. They are well-seasoned veterans in the construction industry and understand how to minimize risk."*
KEY INDIVIDUALS **John Hanover** (see p.640) has extensive experience in construction litigation. Recently, he represented an international design and engineering firm in a high-value dispute with the Nevada Department of Transportation. **Todd Bressler** (see p.625) is an experienced construction practitioner who has recently acted for a national general contractor in a dispute with a major international hotel chain. *"He is articulate and handles himself well under pressure, knowing when to back off and work towards compromise positions,"* clients say.

## Pillsbury Winthrop Shaw Pittman LLP
See profile on p.2000

THE FIRM This construction group is going from strength to strength, and continues to attract high praise for its dispute resolution capabilities. It also offers considerable transactional expertise, enhanced by the construction group's ties with the firm's energy and infrastructure projects groups. The team currently advises Stanford University on construction, construction management and engineering agreements, which includes acting on the Graduate School of Business.
Sources say: *"A firm with fantastic attorneys."*

KEY INDIVIDUALS The *"outstanding"* **John Heisse** enjoys a top-tier reputation for his work in construction law, and has particular expertise in dispute resolution. *"He's a very good, straight-shooting, no-nonsense practitioner and a really good counselor in managing and avoiding disputes,"* commentators say. **Robert Thum** (see p.669) brings in-depth construction knowledge to his handling of complex construction disputes and wins praise from observers for being *"very talented and experienced."*

## Sheppard, Mullin, Richter & Hampton LLP

THE FIRM This construction practice has a strong presence in California, and is experienced in handling both transactional work and disputes. The team advises on the negotiation and drafting of construction documentation, as well as having capabilities in the area of California mechanic's lien law. The group also regularly acts on litigations and methods of alternative dispute resolution. High-profile clients represented by the firm include Picerne Construction Group, County of Orange and John Wayne airport.
KEY INDIVIDUALS Observers highlight **Harold Hamersmith** as *"someone who is very focused on achieving efficient solutions."* He is currently advising an international resort development client on a multibillion-dollar resort development in the Bahamas.

## Band 4

## Crowell & Moring LLP
See profile on p.910

THE FIRM The Crowell & Moring construction offering represents a broad range of clients, including engineers, contractors, subcontractors, design professionals and owners. The team regularly undertakes public and private matters on a national and regional scale, and has extensive experience in litigation, mediation and arbitration. Recently, the firm has acted on litigations relating to delay, termination and differing site conditions.
Sources say: *"A very impressive firm known for their good work on high-stakes litigation."*
KEY INDIVIDUALS **Randall Erickson** (see p.634) wins praise for his knowledge of public contracting and construction documentation, as well as his exensive experience in various methods of alternative dispute resolution. *"He's great. He's been around a long time and he really knows his stuff,"* according to sources.

## Duane Morris LLP
See profile on p.2239

THE FIRM This team undertakes a variety of transactional construction matters and disputes, with extensive experience in litigation and methods of alternative dispute resolution. Recent work highlights include acting for a major telecommunications installation contractor on a delay claim. The team also advises on government contracts, public-private partnerships and agreements with government agencies.

**Sources say:** "*A significant player in the construction business.*"

**KEY INDIVIDUALS Robert Hendrickson** is a very well-established construction practitioner who enjoys an excellent reputation for his work representing contractors in construction disputes. **Lock Holmes** is an experienced attorney who wins praise for his practical approach. His expertise lies in government contracts and the negotiation of construction documentation.

## Gordon & Rees, LLP

**THE FIRM** This firm is widely recognized for its experience in insurance-related work, though it also undertakes a variety of other construction matters. The team acts for developers, owners and general contractors on a full spectrum of insurance matters, including the prevention of litigation. It also advises clients on labor and employment issues.

**KEY INDIVIDUALS Kenneth Strong** is an expert in advising on claims relating to insurance. He is described by market sources as "*very professional, competent, practical, helpful – he tries to find simple solutions to complex issues.*"

## Sedgwick LLP
See profile on p.698

**THE FIRM** The focus of the substantial Sedgwick construction group is litigation, and the team regularly undertakes complex disputes for its contractor client base. The group also has expertise in insurance-related matters, and recently acted for Arch Insurance Company on a high-value claim against its bond principal, Mitchell Engineering. Other major names represented by the firm include Pacific Gas and Electric Company, Superior Wall Systems and Vance Brown.

**Sources say:** "*A very professional and high-quality firm with an excellent work product, which meets clients' needs.*"

**KEY INDIVIDUALS** Clients value **James Diwik** for his understanding of federal government projects and California law. "*He is extremely knowledgeable and understands surety extremely well,*" sources say. The impressive **Marilyn Klinger** (see p.647) heads the Sedgwick construction team. Sources say she is "*very responsive, able to give us insight into different strategies and has the resources to always get us answers.*"

## Other Notable Practitioners

The eminent **Randall Wulff** of Wulff, Quinby & Sochynsky enjoys a formidable reputation as a construction mediator. According to commentators, "*he walks on water in California. He is by far the most respected mediator in the state.*" Sources also say: "*He's very bright, very measured, very patient and has the ability to deal with very nuanced issues.*" **Peter Ippolito** (see p.643) of McKenna Long & Aldridge LLP is very highly regarded for his work on litigations and mediations. He represents a very broad client base that includes developers, public agencies, owners, contractors and design professionals. **George Calkins** of JAMS wins high praise for his work as a mediator: "*He is excellent, hard-working, insightful, has a winning personality and gets cases settled.*" The highly regarded **Kenneth Gibbs** of JAMS regularly acts on high-profile construction mediations. Observers applaud him for being "*excellent, efficient and a terrific mediator who gets things done.*" At Bingham McCutchen LLP, **Stephen Zovickian** (see p.673)

acts for a number of major owners on construction matters, including advising Stanford University on construction documentation for the multibillion-dollar New Stanford Hospital Project. **Dale Ortmann** of Hunt Ortmann Palffy Nieves Lubka Darling & Mah, Inc. is well-known for his prowess as a litigator and his in-depth understanding of construction law. The well-regarded **Tim Truax** of Law Offices of Timothy M Truax handles a broad range of construction matters, from transactional work to litigations and methods of alternative dispute resolution. He wins praise from observers for his knowledge of construction law and hard-working approach. At Seyfarth Shaw LLP, **Michael McKeeman** (see p.653) acts on complex construction disputes for such major names as Skanska and the Oakley Union School District. "*I would use him for project-related issues with subcontractors or owners that require someone who knows how to get the job done,*" sources say. According to sources, **Timothy Pierce** (see p.659) of K&L Gates "*knows construction very well and is a very good litigator.*" He advises on all stages of construction matters, from contract negotiation to disputes. Widely recognized as "*a very tough competitor in the legal arena,*" **Anthony Barron** (see p.622) of Nixon Peabody LLP is described by market sources as "*quick, clean, fast, precise and doesn't waste anyone's time.*" He is currently advising Constellation Wines on high-value disputes relating to a series of solar projects. **Tim McInerney** of McInerney & Dillon wins praise from sources for his knowledge of the construction industry and experience as a litigator. Clients also benefit from his in-depth understanding of methods of alternative dispute resolution, such as mediation and arbitration.

# CORPORATE/M&A

Commentary about individuals can be found under their firm's paragraph. If the firm has no paragraph (is not ranked) look at Other Notable Practitioners.

*The editorial is in alphabetical order by firm name.*

## Bingham McCutchen LLP
See profile on p.1515

**THE FIRM** From its offices in Los Angeles, Orange County and Palo Alto, this firm acts for a range of strategic players, midmarket private equity firms and the portfolio companies they own. Its private equity clients include Platinum Equity, Freeman Spogli & Co and The Gores Group. On the company side, Bingham represents the likes of Oracle, Citrix Systems and Mitsui & Co. Recently, the firm represented Mitsui & Co's US entity in the sale of its portfolio company, Cornerstone Research & Development, to Sun Capital Partners.

**Sources say:** "*All the attorneys at Bingham have the same characteristics: they are respectful and professional, and know what they're doing.*"

**KEY INDIVIDUALS** "*An extraordinarily experienced transactions lawyer,*" **Richard Welch** (see p.672) joins the

rankings for private equity this year. Clients say he is an "*extraordinarily attentive*" attorney with a "*poised*" and unflappable demeanor. In recent highlights, he represented Freeman Spogli & Co in a number of transactions, including the sale of the Sur La Table restaurant franchise and the acquisition of specialty retailer Boot Barn.

## Cooley LLP

**THE FIRM** Cooley has an impressive market share in the emerging companies sphere, where it is considered a market leader. In IT and software, the firm acts for clients such as Zynga, NVIDIA and Quest Software, while its life sciences and cleantech practices advise clients such as Power Integrations and Jazz Pharmaceuticals. In 2012, Cooley added a team in Santa Barbara to its existing offices in San Diego, San Francisco and Palo Alto. Recent highlights for the firm include representing Israeli 3D printing company Objet in its $1.4 billion merger with Stratsys.

**KEY INDIVIDUALS** Venture capital practice head **Craig Dauchy** is held in high regard for his experience in this area. His recent highlights include advising Institutional Venture Partners on its GBP200 million Series B investment in Dropbox. **Mark Tanoury** garners praise for his pragmatic and business-minded approach to transactions. Recent work includes advising Madrone Partners on a $60 million investment in Sunrun. **Fred Muto** chairs the firm's business department, and has worked with clients from a wide range of industries. He offers notable experience in the venture capital space. Based in San Diego, **Barbara Borden** heads the Cooley M&A practice. She recently led a cross-office Cooley team representing Micromet in its all-cash $1.16 billion acquisition by Amgen. Recent highlights for Palo Alto M&A lawyer **Jennifer Fonner DiNucci** include advising Jazz Pharmaceuticals on its $700 million bid to acquire EUSA Pharma and, separately, on the $475 million purchase of Dublin-based Azur Pharma. Among this year's significant lateral hires, **David Hernand** joined

*The editorial is in alphabetical order by firm name.*

## Corporate/M&A: Northern California
### Leading Firms

**Band 1**
Latham & Watkins LLP *
Skadden, Arps, Slate, Meagher & Flom LLP & Affiliates *
Wilson Sonsini Goodrich & Rosati *

**Band 2**
Davis Polk & Wardwell LLP *
Fenwick & West LLP *
Weil, Gotshal & Manges LLP *

**Band 3**
Cooley LLP
Gibson, Dunn & Crutcher LLP *
Morrison & Foerster LLP *
Shearman & Sterling LLP *
Simpson Thacher & Bartlett LLP *

**Band 4**
DLA Piper LLP (US) *
Pillsbury Winthrop Shaw Pittman LLP *

**Band 5**
Goodwin Procter LLP *
Jones Day *
O'Melveny & Myers LLP *
Orrick, Herrington & Sutcliffe LLP *
Sidley Austin LLP *

## Corporate/M&A: Deals in Asia
### Leading Individuals

**Band 1**
| Chao Howard | O'Melveny & Myers LLP |
| Gisser Michael | Skadden, Arps, Slate, Meagher & Flom * |

**Band 2**
| King Kenton J | Skadden, Arps, Slate, Meagher & Flom * |
| Townsend Robert S | Morrison & Foerster LLP * |

**Band 3**
| Chang Carmen I | Covington & Burling LLP (ONP)†* |

* Indicates firm / individual with profile.
† ONP = Other Notable Practitioner.

## Corporate/M&A: Northern California
### Leading Individuals

**Star individuals**
| Sonsini Larry W | Wilson Sonsini Goodrich & Rosati |

**Band 1**
| Climan Richard | Weil, Gotshal & Manges LLP * |
| Davidson Gordon K | Fenwick & West LLP * |
| Flaum Keith A | Weil, Gotshal & Manges LLP * |
| King Kenton J | Skadden, Arps, Slate, Meagher & Flom * |

**Band 2**
| Camahort Steve L | Shearman & Sterling LLP * |
| Cogen Douglas N | Fenwick & West LLP * |
| Denenberg Alan | Davis Polk & Wardwell LLP * |
| Hansen Russell C | Gibson, Dunn & Crutcher LLP * |
| Kelly William | Davis Polk & Wardwell LLP * |
| Kerman Peter F | Latham & Watkins LLP * |
| Korman Martin W | Wilson Sonsini Goodrich & Rosati |
| Ringler Michael S | Wilson Sonsini Goodrich & Rosati * |

**Band 3**
| Capelouto Richard | Simpson Thacher & Bartlett LLP * |
| del Calvo Jorge | Pillsbury Winthrop Shaw Pittman LLP |
| Dorf Michael | Shearman & Sterling LLP * |
| Frankle Diane H | Kaye Scholer LLP (ONP)† * |
| Kaufman Christopher L | Latham & Watkins LLP * |
| King Leif | Skadden, Arps, Slate, Meagher & Flom * |
| O'Bryan Michael | Morrison & Foerster LLP * |
| Razzak Amr | Skadden, Arps, Slate, Meagher & Flom * |
| Tonsfeldt Steven | O'Melveny & Myers LLP |
| Townsend Robert S | Morrison & Foerster LLP * |

**Band 4**
| Adas Craig | Weil, Gotshal & Manges LLP * |
| Dillon Christopher D | Gibson, Dunn & Crutcher LLP * |
| DiNucci Jennifer Fonner | Cooley LLP |
| Grover Gavin B | Morrison & Foerster LLP * |
| Krpata Kyle C | Weil, Gotshal & Manges LLP * |
| Lesser Henry | DLA Piper LLP (US) * |
| Mitz Daniel R. | Jones Day * |
| Zuklie Mitchell | Orrick, Herrington & Sutcliffe LLP * |

**Up-and-coming individuals**
| Deibert Edward | Arnold & Porter LLP (ONP)† * |
| Flanagan Sharon R | Sidley Austin LLP * |
| Gersich Bradley J | DLA Piper LLP (US) * |
| McCusker Anthony | Goodwin Procter LLP * |
| Ross Jane | Weil, Gotshal & Manges LLP * |
| Wellington Martin | Davis Polk & Wardwell LLP |

**Associates to watch**
| Rolston Chad G. | Latham & Watkins LLP * |

## Corporate/M&A: Private Equity
### Leading Firms

**Band 1**
Kirkland & Ellis LLP *
Latham & Watkins LLP *
Simpson Thacher & Bartlett LLP *

**Band 2**
Proskauer Rose LLP *
Skadden, Arps, Slate, Meagher & Flom LLP & Affiliates *

**Band 3**
Bingham McCutchen LLP *
Gibson, Dunn & Crutcher LLP *
Milbank, Tweed, Hadley & McCloy LLP *
Ropes & Gray LLP *
Weil, Gotshal & Manges LLP *

### Leading Individuals

**Band 1**
| Capelouto Richard | Simpson Thacher & Bartlett LLP * |
| Kerman Peter F | Latham & Watkins LLP * |
| Weissenbach John A | Kirkland & Ellis LLP * |
| Woronoff Michael A | Proskauer Rose LLP |

**Band 2**
| Bellah Maguire Jennifer | Gibson, Dunn & Crutcher LLP * |
| Breach David A | Kirkland & Ellis LLP * |
| Cohen Jeffrey H | Skadden, Arps, Slate, Meagher & Flom * |
| Haber Scott R | Latham & Watkins LLP * |
| Kemp J Hovey | Goodwin Procter LLP * |
| Ressler Alison S | Sullivan & Cromwell LLP * |
| Simpson William | Paul Hastings LLP |

**Band 3**
| Baronsky Kenneth | Milbank, Tweed, Hadley & McCloy LLP * |
| Kennedy Mike | Shearman & Sterling LLP * |
| Shilling Monica J | Proskauer Rose LLP |
| Welch Richard J | Bingham McCutchen LLP * |

**Up-and-coming individuals**
| Dixon David L | Kirkland & Ellis LLP * |
| Madden Rick C | Skadden, Arps, Slate, Meagher & Flom |

---

Cooley as the managing partner of the firm's new Santa Monica office. He was formerly at Gibson Dunn, and is praised for his dedicated approach to client service. **Eric Jensen** heads the firm's capital markets department and is praised for his strong public company practice. He recently advised Zynga on its $1 billion IPO and $593 million follow-on offering. He also advises on M&A.

### Davis Polk & Wardwell LLP
**See profile on p.442**
**THE FIRM** This national heavyweight has a great reputation for transactional and advisory work in Northern California, and earns praise for its ability to provide innovative solutions in difficult negotiations. Oracle, Symantec and Symphony Technology Group all feature on its enviable roster of clients. Recent highlights include advising Vector Capital on its acquisition of Gerber Scientific and its subsequent divestiture of Spandex, one of Gerber's business units.

**Sources say:** "*The firm is highly business-oriented and efficient in what it does. I would not do another deal, regardless of size, without this team.*" "*One of the deeper M&A benches in the Valley.*"
**KEY INDIVIDUALS** Menlo Park office head **Alan Denenberg** (see p.631) is "*impressive for his business acumen and savvy.*" Sources say he has a "*well-deserved, great reputation*" and that he "*combines great knowledge not only of the law but also of how to apply it and its practical implications.*" Recent highlights include advising SMART Modular Technologies on its $645 million sale to Silver

Lake. **William Kelly** (see p.645) advised web security firm Blue Coat Systems on its $1.3 billion acquisition by a group of investors led by Thoma Bravo. Commentators say his name "*provides credibility on a deal*" and that his history as an in-house lawyer affords him both an even keel and a pragmatic sensibility. The up-and-coming **Martin Wellington** "*knows what he's doing,*" interviewees say. One client added: "*He sees solutions where other lawyers see problems.*" Recent highlights include advising Corel on its acquisition of Roxio.

### DLA Piper LLP (US)
**See profile on p.1971**
**THE FIRM** DLA Piper maintains a practice in both Northern and Southern California which is respected for its involvement in high-quality technology and life sciences transactions. Notable highlights include representing Scripps Networks Interactive in the $394 million acquisition of Virgin Media's 50% stake in UKTV, the British cable and satellite network.

*The editorial is in alphabetical order by firm name.*

## Corporate/M&A: Southern California
## Leading Firms

**Band 1**
Gibson, Dunn & Crutcher LLP *
Latham & Watkins LLP *
Skadden, Arps, Slate, Meagher & Flom LLP & Affiliates *

**Band 2**
Munger, Tolles & Olson LLP *
Sullivan & Cromwell LLP *

**Band 3**
Milbank, Tweed, Hadley & McCloy LLP *
Proskauer Rose LLP *
Sheppard, Mullin, Richter & Hampton LLP

**Band 4**
DLA Piper LLP (US) *
Morgan, Lewis & Bockius LLP *
O'Melveny & Myers LLP *
Paul Hastings LLP *

**Band 5**
Morrison & Foerster LLP *
Sidley Austin LLP *

**Sources say:** *"They are very client service-oriented, and very willing to address our needs, create innovative fee structures and sign on to those."*

**KEY INDIVIDUALS** A San Diego partner and cochair of the firm's global corporate practice, **Jay Rains** (see p.661) is seen by commentators as a *"really impressive"* transactional lawyer. Recent highlights include advising PF Chang's China Bistro on its $1.1 billion merger with Centerbridge Partners. Senior counsel **Henry Lesser** (see p.649) also has an esteemed practice, as has **Curtis Mo** (see p.655), who in the words of one client is *"extremely dedicated and extremely hard-working"* as well as *"willing to go the extra mile."* Up-and-comer **Bradley Gersich** (see p.637) impressed sources this year with his *"incredible work ethic"* and growing practice. He recently represented Aeris Capital in its Series E financing of Nanosolar.

### Fenwick & West LLP
See profile on p.680

**THE FIRM** Fenwick & West is one of the venture capital world's leading firms, representing a range of IT, software and online businesses from its headquarters in Silicon Valley. Its strong investor-side and startup practice is complemented by a formidable transactional team, which advises the likes of Cisco Systems, Twitter and Symantec. The firm attracted global headlines with its recent representations of Facebook, first in a $1 billion deal to acquire mobile photography app Instagram and subsequently in its record-breaking $18.4 billion IPO.

**Sources say:** *"Their ability to translate a command of the rules into practical business advice is the most critical element for why we keep them. We give them more because they deliver great results." "They've done a fabulous job in the social networking space and have penetrated that market extremely well."*

**KEY INDIVIDUALS** Department head **Gordon Davidson** (see p.631) is hailed by commentators as a *"leader,"* a

## Leading Individuals

**Star individuals**

| | |
|---|---|
| McCarthy Brian J | *Skadden, Arps, Slate, Meagher & Flom* * |

**Band 1**

| | |
|---|---|
| Layne Jonathan K | *Gibson, Dunn & Crutcher LLP* * |
| Ressler Alison S | *Sullivan & Cromwell LLP* * |
| Ruck Charles K | *Latham & Watkins LLP* * |
| Tosetti Paul | *Latham & Watkins LLP* |

**Band 2**

| | |
|---|---|
| Braun Lawrence M | *Sheppard, Mullin, Richter & Hampton LLP* |
| Denham Robert E | *Munger, Tolles & Olson LLP* * |
| Knauss Robert B | *Munger, Tolles & Olson LLP* * |
| Woronoff Michael A | *Proskauer Rose LLP* |

**Band 3**

| | |
|---|---|
| Baronsky Kenneth | *Milbank, Tweed, Hadley & McCloy LLP* * |
| Cohen Jeffrey H | *Skadden, Arps, Slate, Meagher & Flom* * |
| Gisser Michael | *Skadden, Arps, Slate, Meagher & Flom* * |
| Hartigan John F | *Morgan, Lewis & Bockius LLP* * |
| Le Sage Jeffrey | *Gibson, Dunn & Crutcher LLP* * |
| Rains Jay | *DLA Piper LLP (US)* * |
| Sadler Thomas C | *Latham & Watkins LLP* |
| Waters Martin | *Wilson Sonsini Goodrich & Rosati* |

**Band 4**

| | |
|---|---|
| Bellah Maguire Jennifer | *Gibson, Dunn & Crutcher LLP* * |
| Borden Barbara | *Cooley LLP* |
| Kupietzky Moshe J | *Sidley Austin LLP* * |
| Meyer Bruce D | *Gibson, Dunn & Crutcher LLP* * |
| Miller Robert | *Paul Hastings LLP* |
| Reddick C N Franklin | *Akin Gump Strauss Hauer & Feld (ONP)* †* |
| Sanchez Carl R | *Paul Hastings LLP* |
| Sanders Michael | *Reed Smith LLP (ONP)* † |
| Shilling Monica J | *Proskauer Rose LLP* |

**Up-and-coming individuals**

| | |
|---|---|
| Kim Mark | *Munger, Tolles & Olson LLP* * |
| Todd Mary Ann | *Munger, Tolles & Olson LLP* * |

**Associates to watch**

| | |
|---|---|
| Domzalski Shawn | *Gibson, Dunn & Crutcher LLP* * |

* *Indicates firm / individual with profile.*
† *ONP = Other Notable Practitioner.*

*"major player"* and *"a huge figure"* in the Silicon Valley M&A market, particularly in relation to emerging companies. One client said: *"There's a reason why he's one of the top lawyers in America. His ability to counsel us at the board level and engage tactically if necessary is incredible."* **Douglas Cogen** (see p.628) represented Facebook in its $550 million purchase of a portion of the patent portfolio Microsoft acquired from AOL. Other highlights include advising Cisco Systems on its $5 billion acquisition of NDS Group. Sources say he *"understands strategy"* and is *"an incredible negotiator"* who *"sees the big picture." "Balanced, fair and easy to deal with,"* **Mark Stevens** (see p.412) also receives high praise. He has a strong practice in the electronic gaming sector. Operating in the life sciences and technology space, **Barry Kramer** (see p.350) represents a range of venture funds. His client list includes BitTorrent, Centaur Pharmaceuticals and Versant. The *"terrific"* **Jeffrey Vetter** (see p.670) has a respected securities and M&A

practice, and was a key figure on Facebook's landmark $18.4 billion IPO. One source enthused: *"He is the best corporate lawyer I've worked with on public company matters."*

### Gibson, Dunn & Crutcher LLP
See profile on p.682

**THE FIRM** This fine practice group is noted for its diverse M&A activity across the state, particularly in Los Angeles where its business transactions group counts among the very best. In addition to a company transactional practice, its scope encompasses work in private equity and venture capital, with a strong investor-side practice. Recent highlights include representing Morgan Stanley as financial adviser to Ariba regarding its $4.3 billion sale to SAP.

**Sources say:** *"Preeminent in Southern California." "You get top-quality talent and resources, and broad-based assets across the globe, which is important to us because we do business all over the world."*

**KEY INDIVIDUALS** LA-based **Jonathan Layne** (see p.649) is *"very impressive in terms of his experience, knowledge and demeanor. We rely heavily on his advice, which is very balanced and thoughtful,"* say clients. He cochairs the M&A practice group, and recently advised Goldman Sachs on its role as financial adviser to Beckman Coulter in its $6.8 billion acquisition of Danaher. Palo Alto partner-in-charge **Russell Hansen** (see p.640) advised Intel on the $1.25 billion sale of IM Flash Technologies and related assets to Micron Technology. **Jeffrey Le Sage** (see p.649) advised OnX Enterprise Solutions on its $64 million acquisition of Agilysys' Technology Solutions division. Sources say the LA-based lawyer is *"fantastic, responsive and incredibly bright,"* with *"a broad base of knowledge"* and *"off-the-chart"* client service skills. Private equity fund formation lawyer **Jennifer Bellah Maguire** (see p.623) is also widely recommended. She recently represented Leonard Green & Partners in the formation of Green Equity Investors VI, a $6.25 billion new LP private equity fund. **Bradford Weirick** (see p.671) cochairs the firm's emerging technologies practice alongside **Gregory Davidson** (see p.301). Weirick recently advised Idealab! on its $640 million sale of Internet Brands to a Hellman & Friedman affiliate. Davidson acted for Shazam Entertainment on a $35 million investment by Kleiner Perkins, DN Capital and Institutional Venture Partners. **Bruce Meyer** (see p.654) has a long history of top-notch transactions to his name, several of which stem from his strong relationship with Aurora Capital and its portfolio companies. The *"smart, personable and highly responsive"* **Christopher Dillon** (see p.632) was counsel to financial advisers Morgan Stanley in relation to Ariba's acquisition by SAP and RightNow's acquisition by Oracle. Associate **Shawn Domzalski** (see p.632) is singled out by clients as being *"incredibly smart, very thorough and detailed"* in his approach. Others highlight his strong communication skills and *"willingness to do whatever it takes to get the job done."*

### Goodwin Procter LLP
See profile on p.1522

**THE FIRM** Goodwin Procter's entry into the Silicon Valley venture capital market is seen by sources as having been

*The editorial is in alphabetical order by firm name.*

## Corporate/M&A: Venture Capital
### Leading Firms

**Band 1**
Cooley LLP
Fenwick & West LLP *
Gunderson Dettmer Stough Villeneuve Franklin & Hachigian
Wilson Sonsini Goodrich & Rosati *

**Band 2**
Latham & Watkins LLP *

**Band 3**
Gibson, Dunn & Crutcher LLP *
Goodwin Procter LLP *
Morrison & Foerster LLP *
Orrick, Herrington & Sutcliffe LLP *
Pillsbury Winthrop Shaw Pittman LLP *
Sheppard, Mullin, Richter & Hampton LLP

highly successful, and the practice is complemented by strong transactional and capital markets teams. In highlights, the team represented Pensco Trust in its acquisition of Lincoln Trust. Other key clients include Guidewire Software, NetSuite and Rovio.

**Sources say:** *"Their team is very intelligent and also very business-savvy. It's a group with interesting prospects in the Valley."*

**KEY INDIVIDUALS Jonathan Axelrad** (see p.275) is *"a leading practitioner in venture capital fund formation,"* say sources. He heads Goodwin Procter's private investment funds practice in California. Recent work includes advising on the restructuring of $2 billion of Sequoia Capital India funds from Cayman Islands to Mauritius entities. **Hovey Kemp** (see p.645) relocated to San Francisco in December 2011, bringing an excellent pedigree. Previously, he led the firm's private equity practice in DC and was regarded as one of that market's most prolific and respected players. Venture capital practice head **Anthony McCusker** (see p.653) is *"absolutely a player"* in the emerging companies market, and a *"smart, practical guy"* with *"really good relationships around the Valley."* Recent highlights include representing Altassian in its acquisition of HipChat.

## Gunderson Dettmer Stough Villeneuve Franklin & Hachigian

**THE FIRM** This firm has a fantastic reputation for the scale, output and quality of its emerging companies practice. It also has a tremendous track record for advising on the sale of promising startups to some of the technology market's most prolific acquirers. Examples of its recent work in this space include representing Ariba in its $4.3 billion acquisition by SAP, and acting on the $99 million sale of BNI Video to Cisco Systems.

**Sources say:** *"They've built a strong reputation in this sector." "They do more venture deals than anybody else in the USA."*

**KEY INDIVIDUALS Scott Dettmer** recently advised Southwall Energy Technologies on its $113 million acquisition by Solutia. Other highlights include his involvement in teams counseling OMGPOP on its acquisition by Zynga and, separately, Efficient Frontier on its acquisition by

### Leading Individuals

**Star individuals**

| | |
|---|---|
| Davidson Gordon K | *Fenwick & West LLP* * |

**Band 1**

| | |
|---|---|
| Dauchy Craig | *Cooley LLP* |
| del Calvo Jorge | *Pillsbury Winthrop Shaw Pittman LLP* |
| Dettmer Scott | *Gunderson Dettmer Stough Villeneuve* |
| Franklin Steven R | *Gunderson Dettmer Stough Villeneuve* |
| Kaufman Christopher L | *Latham & Watkins LLP* * |
| Mendelson Alan C | *Latham & Watkins LLP* * |
| Tanoury Mark | *Cooley LLP* |

**Band 2**

| | |
|---|---|
| Axelrad Jonathan | *Goodwin Procter LLP* * |
| Gunderson Bob | *Gunderson Dettmer Stough Villeneuve* |
| Muto Fred | *Cooley LLP* |
| Saper Jeff | *Wilson Sonsini Goodrich & Rosati* |
| Stevens Mark C | *Fenwick & West LLP* * |

**Band 3**

| | |
|---|---|
| Bochner Steven | *Wilson Sonsini Goodrich & Rosati* |
| de Groot Jay | *Morrison & Foerster LLP* * |
| Latta Bob | *Wilson Sonsini Goodrich & Rosati* |
| McGlynn Casey | *Wilson Sonsini Goodrich & Rosati* |
| Pohlen Patrick A | *Latham & Watkins LLP* * |
| Sands David H | *Sheppard, Mullin, Richter & Hampton LLP* |
| Voxman W. Alex | *Latham & Watkins LLP* * |
| Weirick Bradford P | *Gibson, Dunn & Crutcher LLP* * |
| Yee Bennett | *Gunderson Dettmer Stough Villeneuve* |
| Zuklie Mitchell | *Orrick, Herrington & Sutcliffe LLP* * |

**Band 4**

| | |
|---|---|
| Bautista John | *Orrick, Herrington & Sutcliffe LLP* * |
| Bushnell Laura | *King & Spalding LLP (ONP)* † * |
| Davidson Gregory | *Gibson, Dunn & Crutcher LLP* * |
| Hernand David | *Cooley LLP* |
| Jensen Eric | *Cooley LLP* |
| Kramer Barry J | *Fenwick & West LLP* * |
| Lazarow Warren T | *O'Melveny & Myers LLP* |
| Mo Curtis L | *DLA Piper LLP (US)* * |
| Thau Stephen B | *Morrison & Foerster LLP* * |
| Vetter Jeffrey R | *Fenwick & West LLP* * |

**Up-and-coming individuals**

| | |
|---|---|
| Glaser Michael | *Perkins Coie (ONP)* † |
| McCusker Anthony | *Goodwin Procter LLP* * |

**Associates to watch**

| | |
|---|---|
| Zeppa Stephanie | *Dentons (ONP)* † * |

* *Indicates firm / individual with profile.*
†*ONP = Other Notable Practitioner.*

Adobe. **Steven Franklin** is *"an excellent lawyer and a very bright guy,"* whose practice emphasizes venture capital fund formation. **Bob Gunderson** is *"a tremendous name"* in the world of venture capital, sources say. Recent highlights include representing Tealeaf and DemandTec in their acquisitions by IBM. **Bennett Yee** is very well regarded within the Valley, with one peer saying: *"If I had to think of a young partner with a great practice, who is very smart and has a good attitude, then Bennett is on my list."*

## Jones Day
See profile on p.919

**THE FIRM** Jones Day joins the rankings this year having been recognized by clients and peers for its increasing prominence in the Northern California M&A market. Its corporate team operates in a wide market space within biotech and technology, and benefits from the firm's network of offices across the globe. Prominent clients include German multinational software company SAP, which the firm represented in a number of high-profile transactions in 2012. Other notable highlights include advising Lam Research on its $3.3 billion acquisition of Novellus Systems.

**Sources say:** *"A very credible force." "They've built up a very substantial practice in Northern California."*

**KEY INDIVIDUALS** M&A department head and new entrant **Daniel Mitz** (see p.655) is *"a very tough lawyer"* who is *"very good technically."* He represented SAP in its acquisitions of Ariba and SuccessFactors for $4.4 billion and $3.4 billion respectively.

## Kirkland & Ellis LLP
See profile on p.1254

**THE FIRM** This firm is admired for the depth of its capabilities in transactions for private equity funds and their portfolio companies. Its immersion in this space allows the firm to deliver sophisticated advice on all manner of private equity transactions, including LBOs. Oaktree Capital Management, Shamrock Capital Advisors and The Carlyle Group are all clients of the firm, and its recent highlights include representing Singapore-based Flextronics International in its acquisition of Stellar Microelectronics.

**Sources say:** *"The team brings an incredible quality of work product and ethic to the table that is head and shoulders above other firms with which I have worked." "We are at a distinct advantage when we are represented by Kirkland."*

**KEY INDIVIDUALS** *"An extremely talented lawyer and a very skilled negotiator,"* **John Weissenbach** (see p.672) is singled out by clients in the private equity world as someone with *"great business instincts."* Recently, he advised Oaktree Capital Management on its acquisition of Osmose Holdings. **David Breach** (see p.625) is *"an outstanding professional and an expert in investments, divestments and M&A."* Sources say: *"His devotion to client service is spectacular – he goes out of his way to be available and to gather the right resources within or outside of the firm to answer any question."* **David Dixon** (see p.632) *"plays the role of quarterback on deals,"* said one source. Another added: *"He is solution-oriented and does a nice job of moving negotiations forward with little need for supervision."*

## Latham & Watkins LLP
See profile on p.446

**THE FIRM** This practice group has an undisputed reputation across the state for its representation of major organizations in high-end transactions. The firm is recognized for its extremely deep and talented bench of partners across its Silicon Valley, San Francisco, Los Angeles, Orange County and San Diego offices. Clients include AMD, Mattel and US Airways. Representative recent highlights

*The editorial is in alphabetical order by firm name.*

include advising Lucasfilm on its $4.05 billion sale to Disney.

**Sources say:** *"They continue to have a really premier position and their brand is widely recognized." "You get real top-tier partners with a depth of experience. The people I have met there are of extremely high quality across the board."*

**KEY INDIVIDUALS Christopher Kaufman** (see p.343) is widely regarded as a highly robust and effective negotiator. Based in Menlo Park, he has a long history of advising Silicon Valley hi-tech clients on substantial transactions. He also played the role of lead partner on Lucasfilm's sale to Disney. Also in Silicon Valley, **Peter Kerman** (see p.646) recently acted for Allos Therapeutics on its $206 million acquisition by Spectrum Pharmaceuticals. He also represented Prometheus Laboratories in its acquisition by Nestlé Health Science. In the same office, **Alan Mendelson** (see p.367) is *"a tremendous company-side lawyer"* who is *"very client-focused. He'll do anything for his clients,"* sources say. His highlights include representing KAI Pharmaceuticals in its $315 million acquisition by Amgen. Based in Orange County, **Charles Ruck** (see p.663) is *"an excellent lawyer,"* sources say. He acted for Complete Production Services on its $6.2 billion acquisition by Superior Energy Services. LA partner **Paul Tosetti** has a *"very deep, broad knowledge of high-yield offerings: unparalleled experience."* He was recently co-lead on URS's $1.25 billion acquisition of Flint Energy Services. San Francisco partner **Scott Haber** (see p.639) advised Genstar Capital on a $400 million deal to acquire and take eResearchTechnology private. Other deals include representing Genstar portfolio company Woods Equipment in its $185 million acquisition by Blount International. **Patrick Pohlen** (see p.659) is *"incredibly well connected"* around Silicon Valley. Clients benefit from his consummate *"operational experience"* as a former businessman, which assists him in being *"super practical at solving problems."* Recent work includes handling a $35.5 million Series E financing for Delivery Agent. **Thomas Sadler** is *"both intellectually brilliant and practical,"* clients say. *"He finds a solution to every problem, no matter how difficult. He is able to bring parties together with disparate interests, build consensus and get deals done without ruffling any feathers along the way."* In Los Angeles, **Alex Voxman** represented Demand Media in its acquisition of online advertising platform IndieClick. **Chad Rolston** (see p.662) is a *"rising star"* in this market, according to interviewees. *"He's everything you'd want in an experienced law firm associate. He's a superstar."*

## Milbank, Tweed, Hadley & McCloy LLP
See profile on p.448

**THE FIRM** This firm is well regarded for its transactional practice in Southern California. Its nine-partner team has a commendable presence in the gaming, hospitality and energy sectors, and has also made a name for itself in the world of private equity. Its diverse list of clients includes Google, Station Casinos and RealMex Restaurants. In a recent deal for Google and Kohlberg Kravis Roberts, the team advised on the acquisition of a majority stake in four

solar utility-scale projects in Sacramento from Recurrent Energy.

**Sources say:** *"Milbank compares extremely favorably to other firms we have tried. We would not work with anyone else on our joint venture and investor transactions. In addition, the talent and breadth of people who are top flight in their respective areas has been impressive. Milbank feels like a local boutique, yet is full service."*

**KEY INDIVIDUALS** LA managing partner **Kenneth Baronsky** (see p.622) has deep expertise in energy, and observers further highlight his *"very strong gaming practice."* He advised Station Casinos on a number of M&A transactions in 2012, totaling in the vicinity of $3.2 billion.

## Morgan, Lewis & Bockius LLP
See profile on p.2246

**THE FIRM** This Los Angeles-based corporate group has an esteemed presence in the Southern California M&A market. In addition to its buy and sell side practice, clients also benefit from its strong ESOP and executive compensation offerings. Recent highlights include representing Driverside in an $11.8 venture financing and in its subsequent $18.25 million acquisition by an affiliate of Advance Auto Parts.

**Sources say:** *"The firm offers experience, responsiveness, attention to detail and a broad purview of counsel."*

**KEY INDIVIDUALS John Hartigan** (see p.640) is regarded as *"an incredible lawyer."* Notable work highlights include handling the sale of a privately held insurance company with assets valued at $5 billion.

## Morrison & Foerster LLP
See profile on p.1990

**THE FIRM** With a firm grounding in technology and life sciences, Morrison & Foerster continues to be a strong contender in the California corporate market. It has been involved in a number of important deals across the state, and the Northern California team continues to act on acquisitions for Intel and its new subsidiary, Intel McAfee. Other significant clients include Novellus, Hitachi, Clorox and Visa. In Southern California, recent highlights include representing Raymond James Financial in its $1.2 billion acquisition of Florida-headquartered Morgan Keegan.

**Sources say:** *"I like that the team is responsive and able to address issues practically with experience-based solutions. The expansive global platform from which they operate gives us access to most of the specific expertise that is likely to become necessary."*

**KEY INDIVIDUALS** San Francisco-based global M&A cochair **Robert Townsend** (see p.669) *"is highly responsive and provides great client service,"* say sources. One market observer comments that he is a *"highly tactical"* M&A lawyer with deep expertise in Asian deals. Highlights include advising Novellus on its $3.3 billion sale to Lam Research. San Diego partner **Jay de Groot** (see p.631) continues to represent SKINIT, most recently in its $8 million Series E financing. In San Francisco, **Michael O'Bryan** (see p.657) cochairs the firm's international M&A group. Since advising a special board of directors on taking 99 Cents Only Stores private in 2011, he has continued to advise the

committee on potential deals in Northern California. **Stephen Thau** (see p.668) has a strong life sciences practice, and recently acted on a $27 million Series B financing for TOPICA Pharmaceuticals. **Gavin Grover** (see p.639) is *"diligent and thoughtful,"* sources say, and offers *"a great balance between providing the right legal counsel alongside practical business considerations."* His highlights include representing healthy snack business popchips! in the sale of a majority interest to Belgian investment firm Verlinvest.

## Munger, Tolles & Olson LLP
See profile on p.691

**THE FIRM** Munger, Tolles & Olson continues to impress sources with its high-quality transactions team in Los Angeles. Its star clients include Berkshire Hathaway, Yucaipa and Universal Music Group, and as a department it excels across the gaming, media and entertainment industries. One feature of the team is its experience in going-private transactions, which of late has included deals for Wesco and Playboy Enterprises. Notably, the firm also represented the Yahoo! board of directors in connection with the company's sale of its stake in Alibaba.

**Sources say:** *"They have an extraordinary quality of lawyers from top to bottom." "The lawyers at MTO have an incredible work ethic, always going the extra mile to get things done and done well."*

**KEY INDIVIDUALS Robert Denham** (see p.631) *"brings a unique perspective to any corporate problem, that of an insider – his kind of advice and counsel cannot be found anywhere else,"* said one source. Clients say that his experience as both CEO and general counsel of a major corporation affords him great creativity and inventiveness when faced with difficult transactions. Department head **Robert Knauss** (see p.647) is also well regarded by clients and other sources in this market, and is regarded as a *"thoughtful, focused"* deal attorney. He represented the Yahoo! board of directors in relation to its aforementioned $7 billion staged exit liquidity deal with Alibaba. The *"excellent, knowledgeable"* **Mark Kim** (see p.646) wins high praise from clients, who say *"he understands the corporate world really well."* His recent highlights include working on the team that represented Berkshire Hathaway in its $5 billion investment in Bank of America. **Mary Ann Todd** (see p.669) continues to attract notice from peers in this market, and clients say she is *"terrific."* She worked alongside Denham and Kim on Berkshire Hathaway's Bank of America investment, and also represented the company in a $2.5 billion deal to acquire the remaining 19.9% of Wesco's common stock.

## O'Melveny & Myers LLP
See profile on p.693

**THE FIRM** O'Melveny & Myers has a noteworthy reputation across the state for its handling of significant deals for companies of all sizes, with much of its public company work coming out of its Los Angeles office. This group is held in high regard by many entrepreneurs and CEOs due to its leading reputation for providing outside primary business counsel. The firm also advises a strong stable of technology clients in Newport Beach and Silicon Valley. In highlights, it acted for Alta Partners on its $111 million sale of Taligen Therapeutics to Alexion Pharmaceuticals.

**Sources say:** *"They are able to handle major corporate transactions and securities matters." "A solid practice."*

**KEY INDIVIDUALS** A senior partner in the firm's Asia practice, **Howard Chao** works out of the firm's Menlo Park and Hong Kong offices. Sources say in relation to his China specialty: *"He's a fantastic guy, no question about it – a really strong player."* M&A practice head **Steven Tonsfeldt** is *"very smart and able,"* sources say. Notable work highlights include representing Dell in its purchase of Clerity Solutions. **Warren Lazarow** has a vast presence in the Valley, according to interviewees. He chairs the firm's transactions department, and recently advised Apache Design Solutions on its $310 million acquisition by ANSYS.

## Orrick, Herrington & Sutcliffe LLP
### See profile on p.1994

**THE FIRM** This firm had a tremendous year in Northern California, particularly in work for venture growth companies. It has notable strength in acting for IT, software and online companies, and also has a sizable energy practice. Key clients include Taiwanese computer hardware company Acer, communications giant Telenor and online commenting service Disqus. Among other examples of its rising profile, the firm stood out for representing Instagram in its $1 billion acquisition by Facebook.

**Sources say:** *"It's a strong team. They strongly advocate for their clients and they understand practical results. They will ask what the business is trying to accomplish and are able to translate a concern under the law into why it matters to you."*

**KEY INDIVIDUALS** Sources say the firm's resident cleantech and biotech expert **Mitchell Zuklie** (see p.673) is *"terrific."* Interviewees describe him as *"a very solid all-around lawyer"* and *"a good source of common sense and general business judgment."* He recently represented Nanosolar in its $70 million Series E financing. The *"extremely well-regarded"* **John Bautista** (see p.622) is noted by sources as a highly capable deal attorney with vast connections in the emerging companies space. He heads the corporate department, and recently advised photo-sharing site Posterous on its sale to Twitter.

## Paul Hastings LLP
### See profile on p.1996

**THE FIRM** Paul Hastings continues to be highly regarded for its transactional practice in Southern California. Its expertise covers deals in the engineering, life sciences and aerospace and defense industries, among others. In highlights, the team represented Ardea Biosciences in its $1.27 billion acquisition by AstraZeneca. Other notable clients include Samsung Electronics and CounterPoint Capital Partners.

**Sources say:** *"An easy firm to work with. Cradle to grave, they shine all the way through."*

**KEY INDIVIDUALS William Simpson** is an *"experienced and calm deal strategist"* who *"has a very level head, is really creative and really shines when the situation reaches an impasse."* He recently advised Western-themed clothing retailer Boot Barn on its sale to Freeman Spogli & Co. Based in San Diego, global M&A chair **Carl Sanchez** advised SRS Labs on its $148 million acquisition by DTS. He also acted for Samsung Electronics on the sale of its hard disk operation assets to Seagate Technology. The *"very talented"* **Robert Miller** advised CounterPoint Capital Partners on its acquisition of Qualy-Pak Specialty Foods.

## Pillsbury Winthrop Shaw Pittman LLP
### See profile on p.2000

**THE FIRM** This firm has a strong reputation in the Northern California market, and is recognized for its work for venture growth companies. Recent highlights include acting for Zecco Holdings on its acquisition by TradeKing, and representing Vista Applied Technology Group in its sale to Aerostar International. Other notable clients include Envivio, Cloud.com and 3E.

**Sources say:** *"Tremendous value without sacrificing quality."*

**KEY INDIVIDUALS Jorge del Calvo** *"not only has exceptionally deep industry experience, he also has tremendous presence and preserve. He doesn't throw ideas out lightly – he's creative but very much grounded in business reality. He is the ideal outside counsel because he can think like an in-house lawyer."* He represented LitePoint in its $600 million acquisition by Teradyne.

## Proskauer Rose LLP
### See profile on p.2001

**THE FIRM** This Los Angeles M&A practice group provides an extremely high caliber of service to its strategic and private equity clients. Many of the firm's transactions have attracted considerable publicity of late, including its representation of Bed Bath & Beyond in its proposed $580 million buyout of Cost Plus. Other key clients include Ares Management and Ares Capital, GNC Holdings and The Gores Group.

**Sources say:** *"They have taken that LA office to a new level." "They're doing a marvelous job in the private equity sector."*

**KEY INDIVIDUALS** Clients say **Michael Woronoff** *"is not just a good technical lawyer, but has a keen insight for business and financial issues. He's brilliant."* Sources say his counsel *"puts you in a position to make a good decision."* Representative work highlights include representing Ares in the acquisition of Potomac Fusion by its portfolio company, Sotera Defense Solutions. **Monica Shilling** is *"a solid performer and an excellent lawyer, and she understands private equity like only a handful of people do."* Peers also characterize her as being *"highly creative and skilled at negotiating, structuring and completing complex M&A transactions."*

## Ropes & Gray LLP
### See profile on p.1528

**THE FIRM** The firm has taken advantage of its longstanding East Coast private equity practice by transplanting two of its Boston private equity partners to San Francisco, and market sources have already begun to note its activity in this market. Recent highlights include advising Genstar Capital on a series of acquisitions of insurance software solutions businesses. Other clients include Silver Lake Partners, Huntsman Gay Global Capital and Altamont Capital Partners.

**Sources say:** *"They have a personal, relationship-driven approach, which is refreshing."*

**KEY INDIVIDUALS** Key contacts in San Francisco include Howard Glazer and Todd Boes.

## Shearman & Sterling LLP
### See profile on p.2005

**THE FIRM** The San Francisco and Palo Alto-based M&A group at Shearman & Sterling has a strong reputation for its activity across a broad swathe of industries, including financial services, technology, automotive and life sciences. Its active clients include Amyris, Francisco Partners and Twitter. In a recent engagement, the firm advised Microsemi on its acquisition of Maxim Integrated Products' timing, synchronization and synthesis business unit.

**KEY INDIVIDUALS** M&A and corporate governance lawyer **Steve Camahort** (see p.626) has a fine practice, as evidenced by his recent transactions. These include representing Symphony Technology Group in its acquisition of Source Healthcare Analytics, which it then went on to combine with ImpactRx. He also advised VMWare on its acquisitions of SocialCast, Cetas Software and others, alongside **Michael Dorf** (see p.632). **Mike Kennedy** (see p.645) is *"a very smart guy,"* market observers comment. He represented White Oak Resources alongside Dorf in relation to a $69.5 million initial investment from Alliance Resource Partners.

## Sheppard, Mullin, Richter & Hampton LLP

**THE FIRM** This practice group represents a diverse array of companies in the financial services, healthcare, entertainment and technology sectors on complex, midmarket M&A deals. Examples of recent transactions include representing The adidas Group and its TaylorMade-adidas golf subsidiary in a $70 million merger with Adams Golf. Other highlights include advising DaVita on its acquisition of ModernMed.

**Sources say:** *"They are very meticulous and work to a very high caliber." "The team was very good: highly experienced with a tremendous amount of expertise, because of which there's very little they haven't seen before."*

**KEY INDIVIDUALS Lawrence Braun** has *"a very fine reputation in Los Angeles,"* sources say. *"He is just so experienced,"* said one interviewee, *"that you get the feeling of confidence from him."* Recent transactions include representing Arcadian Management Services in its $157 million sale to Humana. *"A terrific lawyer"* and *"a good problem-solver,"* **David Sands** gives clients an advantage with his *"even-keeled"* approach. He advised DEKRA on its acquisition of safety consulting firm Behavioral Science Technology.

## Sidley Austin LLP
### See profile on p.1264

**THE FIRM** This M&A group maintains a definitive presence across the state, with deal activity centered around its offices in San Francisco, Palo Alto and Los Angeles. In a

*The editorial is in alphabetical order by firm name.*

recent cross-border highlight, the team represented Synopsys in its acquisition of Japanese company Inventure. In another significant deal, the team advised eBay on its acquisition of mobile payment service Zong. Other clients include Century Park Capital Partners, Roche and Genentech.

**Sources say:** *"A powerful team that I would recommend without reservation to anyone. They understand my priorities, are cost-effective and always have my back."*

**KEY INDIVIDUALS** The *"very bright"* **Moshe Kupietzky** (see p.648) recently represented ROM Holdings in its acquisition of Prime Design, and acted for Berkley Operations on the sale of its agricultural thermoforming subsidiary to bakery packaging manufacturer Peninsula Packaging. **Sharon Flanagan** (see p.635) is *"an absolute rock star of a corporate attorney."* Clients say she *"provides solid, pragmatic business law guidance and is incredibly responsive and also a pleasure to deal with. She is the person you want to call to achieve your business objectives."*

## Simpson Thacher & Bartlett LLP
See profile on p.2006

**THE FIRM** Simpson Thacher is rated among the very best for private equity transactions in California. Representative deals include representing Datatel and its equity holder, Hellman & Friedman, in their $1.775 billion acquisition of SunGuard Higher Education. The firm's corporate practice extends outside the scope of private equity M&A, and recent highlights saw it represent Universal Studios Japan in its acquisition of the rights to the Wizarding World of Harry Potter theme park. Other clients include Silver Lake, Elevation Partners and Blum Capital Partners.

**Sources say:** *"They are knowledgeable, responsive and highly competent on complex transactions." "Undoubtedly a leader in this area."*

**KEY INDIVIDUALS** Clients say **Richard Capelouto** (see p.627) is *"highly effective on bigger, complex deals,"* and peers comment on his *"tremendous market share."* He is lauded for his experience in private equity, where recent highlights include advising Silver Lake on its acquisition of a minority interest in William Morris Endeavor Entertainment. One client enthused: *"Richard is a great lawyer and a great businessman."*

## Skadden, Arps, Slate, Meagher & Flom LLP & Affiliates
See profile on p.2008

**THE FIRM** This nationwide giant has a considerable presence in both Northern and Southern California, and is also acknowledged as a serious player with respect to private equity and corporate finance. It is seen as a firm of choice for complex, high-profile matters, particularly those with multijurisdictional aspects. Deals out of its Los Angeles office include representing Nationwide Health Properties in its $7.4 billion sale to Ventas, and advising Disney on its $4.05 billion acquisition of Lucasfilm. From Palo Alto, the firm advised Broadcom on its $3.7 billion acquisition of NetLogic MicroSystems.

**Sources say:** *"If it's a really big deal with all sorts of complexities, Skadden's the safe choice – they can deliver the best professionals within specialty areas." "They're uniquely suited to big, complicated cross-border deals."*

**KEY INDIVIDUALS Brian McCarthy** (see p.653) is perhaps the most esteemed corporate attorney operating in Southern California, described by sources as *"an absolute superstar."* A don of the Los Angeles M&A market, his practice shows no signs of slowing down. Recent megadeals include the Ventas and Disney transactions mentioned above, both of which attracted significant media commentary. Splitting his time between Shanghai and Los Angeles, **Michael Gisser** (see p.638) heads the firm's Asia-Pacific practice. Recent highlights include representing leading Chinese video streaming service Youku in its $1.1 billion merger with chief competitor Tudou. **Kenton King** (see p.646) is hailed as *"an incredible and efficient M&A lawyer."* Sources appreciate his depth of experience in cross-border deals, particularly in Asia, and that *"he speaks Japanese, which is particularly helpful."* In work examples, he represented Japanese company Advantest in its $1.1 billion unsolicited takeover of Singapore-based Verigy. LA-based corporate group leader **Jeffrey Cohen** (see p.628) is *"very good at taking the law and applying it to business situations."* He is well versed in transactions for private equity funds as well as strategics, and sources say his high degree of expertise in M&A and securities means he delivers speedy results to tricky legal questions. Recent highlights for **Amr Razzak** (see p.661) in Palo Alto include representing storage drive manufacturer Hitachi Global Storage Technologies in its $4.8 billion acquisition by Western Digital Corporation. He also acted on Advantest's acquisition of Verigy alongside Kenton King. **Leif King** (see p.646) was part of a team representing Yahoo! in its $7.1 billion sale of a 40% stake in Alibaba. He also acted on a $4 billion deal concerning the relationship between Alibaba and its former subsidiary Alipay. Los Angeles partner **Rick Madden** is *"always available and highly pragmatic."* A good indication of his impressive private equity practice is his representation, with Michael Gisser, of real estate developer Centro Properties in a $9.4 billion auction sale of its US shopping centers to The Blackstone Group.

## Sullivan & Cromwell LLP
See profile on p.2011

**THE FIRM** Sullivan & Cromwell continues to be a force to be reckoned with in Southern California, and had another year of superb high-end M&A deals. Its diverse client roster features Amgen, Barclays Bank, Billabong, Ares Management and AT&T, among other household names. Notably, the team represented real estate tycoon Frank McCourt in the $2.15 billion sale of the Los Angeles Dodgers to Guggenheim Baseball Management.

**Sources say:** *"It is clearly an outstanding firm." "A super high-quality firm that we view as a peer."*

**KEY INDIVIDUALS** *"A very good lawyer with a very strong client following,"* **Alison Ressler** (see p.661) is regarded by market sources as *"a vigorous advocate for her clients"* and *"a real deal M&A lawyer."* One source enthused: *"She's tough as nails."* 2012 highlights include representing the

chairman and CEO of Savers in its $1.72 billion sale to TPG and Leonard Green & Partners.

## Weil, Gotshal & Manges LLP
See profile on p.2015

**THE FIRM** This highly regarded corporate M&A team continues to draw great strength from the firm's celebrated bankruptcy and IP groups, and has benefited from the recent arrival of Dewey & LeBoeuf's star M&A team, led by Richard Climan and Keith Flaum. Prior to this, the firm already counted the likes of The Gores Group, Getty Images and GenStar Capital among its clients. New clients include Silver Lake Partners, Summit Partners and Technology Crossover Ventures.

**Sources say:** *"The Weil team really cares about the success and health of the company. It is viewed as part of the family, part of our team."*

**KEY INDIVIDUALS** The arrival of **Richard Climan** (see p.628) and **Keith Flaum** (see p.635) has not gone unnoticed in the legal market, with one peer saying: *"It's certainly a game-changer for 2012."* Another market source said: *"Climan and Flaum are a destination practice. Everywhere they go their business will go with them, so to me they're the top of the field."* Climan is hailed by clients as *"the dean of M&A,"* and Flaum is *"great technically, as well as business-practical enough to know the real concerns."* Managing partner **Craig Adas** (see p.620) recently represented Symantec in its $115 million acquisition of LiveOffice Holdings. Sources say he is *"impressive with respect to his calm, reassuring style as well as his knowledge and expertise. He never gets rattled even under the most pressured circumstances and is always a voice of reason."* **Kyle Krpata** (see p.648) is seen by clients as a *"highly commercial," "thoughtful"* and *"efficient"* M&A lawyer who has strong ties with Valley-based technology corporations. He represented Lehman Brothers Holdings in its $1.6 billion acquisition of the remaining 26.5% of Archstone Enterprise's shares. Up-and-comer **Jane Ross** (see p.663) is another of the firm's recent transplants from Dewey, and as an acolyte of Climan and Flaum – as well as a deal lawyer in her own right – she commands a considerable degree of respect from clients and peers. Clients say she is *"an incredibly hard worker: patient, dogged and persistent in negotiations."*

## Wilson Sonsini Goodrich & Rosati
See profile on p.700

**THE FIRM** This respected Silicon Valley practice is one of the most successful firms operating in Northern California, and is regarded as a leader in the venture capital market statewide. Its illustrious client roster features such big names in technology as Google, Electronic Arts and LinkedIn, as well as a range of major Wall Street financial institutions. Recent highlights include acting on LinkedIn's $118 million acquisition of SlideShare, Taleo's $1.9 billion acquisition by Oracle and Electronic Arts' $750 million purchase of PopCap Games.

**Sources say:** *"A tremendous Bay Area presence." "The firm keeps its clients' goals in mind when providing legal advice."*

**KEY INDIVIDUALS** *"A force of nature"* in Silicon Valley, founding partner and firm chairman **Larry Sonsini** is

*The editorial is in alphabetical order by firm name.*

widely regarded as a *"highly effective"* attorney and *"a great lawyer and trusted business adviser"* to a number of significant area companies. He recently represented Seagate in its acquisition of SAMSUNG's HDD operations. Sources say vice chairman and *"IPO head honcho"* **Jeff Saper** is *"really an impressive lawyer."* He advised Splunk on its $229.5 million IPO, and recently acted alongside Ringler for The Go Daddy Group on a partnership agreement with Silver Lake Partners, KKR and Technology Crossover Ventures. Also held in very high esteem is the *"solid"* **Steven Bochner**, who stepped down as the firm's CEO in 2012 in order to focus on his practice. He recently represented MapR Technologies in a $20 million Series B financing, and acted for the underwriters on InvenSense's $75 million IPO. *"Semiconductor industry specialist"* **Bob Latta** also maintains a fine practice, and recently handled Ubiquiti Networks' $105.6 million IPO. He is also well versed in cleantech, software and e-commerce. Splitting his time between the firm's offices in Palo Alto and San Diego, growth technology expert **Casey McGlynn** is a highly respected attorney, particularly in life sciences. He is considered a market leader in medical devices transactional work, with sources saying: *"He knows everyone in life sciences; he's very experienced."* San Diego partner **Marty Waters** is a *"diligent, creative"* lawyer. Sources say: "He

knows what the rules of the game are and understands what the goals are and has a high level of interest in getting it right without browbeating the other side." Recent highlights include representing Concerro in its sale to API Healthcare. **Marty Korman** leads the firm's M&A practice and recently represented Electronic Arts in its $750 million acquisition of PopCap Games. He works out of the firm's San Francisco and Palo Alto offices. **Michael Ringler** (see p.662) has a superb reputation in M&A work. Peers say he is straight-talking, highly intelligent and *"focused on practical solutions."*

## Other Notable Practitioners

Senior counsel **Carmen Chang** (see p.627) of Covington & Burling LLP maintains an active practice, and has been involved in a number of transactions in Asia and the Pacific of late. Additionally, market sources highlight her representation of Chinese entrepreneurs in respect of their US operations. Since leaving DLA Piper in 2011 to head up the corporate group at Kaye Scholer LLP, **Diane Frankle** (see p.636) has overseen a steadily growing practice. Clients describe her as *"outstanding," "brilliant"* and *"incredibly intelligent."* Interviewees further emphasize her *"wealth of information as it relates to M&A and governance*

issues,"* and her *"ability to frame issues and drive a win-win situation."* **Laura Bushnell** (see p.626) of King & Spalding LLP continues to be esteemed in the Valley. Sources say she is *"solid"* and has an impressive track record, which includes work for Citi Ventures, Gatekeeper Pharmaceuticals and MFG.com. Clients say Reed Smith LLP corporate and securities department head **Michael Sanders** is highly responsive to clients' needs and *"extremely knowledgeable about all manner of transactions,"* and provides business-conscious advice on how to structure deals. **Frank Reddick** (see p.661) heads the transactional group at Akin Gump Strauss Hauer & Feld LLP, and is seen as someone who *"understands all the issues"* and *"really helps to get things done."* In recent work, he represented VCA Antech in a series of acquisitions of veterinary businesses. At Arnold & Porter LLP, market sources single out **Edward Deibert** (see p.631) as an up-and-comer in the M&A market. Clients say he is *"knowledgeable and efficient"* as well as an *"excellent drafter and negotiator."* Palo Alto emerging companies lawyer **Michael Glaser** of Perkins Coie LLP wins commendation from peers as a rising star. Clients laud his practical approach. **Stephanie Zeppa** (see p.673) of Dentons is described by clients as *"a very solid ally on your team," "a very logical and fast thinker"* and *"an excellent negotiator"* with a *"broad understanding of issues."*

# EMPLOYEE BENEFITS & EXECUTIVE COMPENSATION

Commentary about individuals can be found under their firm's paragraph. If the firm has no paragraph (is not ranked) look at Other Notable Practitioners.

## Employee Benefits & Executive Compensation
### Leading Firms

**Band 1**
Baker & McKenzie *
Latham & Watkins LLP *
Morgan, Lewis & Bockius LLP *

**Band 2**
Gibson, Dunn & Crutcher LLP *
O'Melveny & Myers LLP *
Paul Hastings LLP *
Skadden, Arps, Slate, Meagher & Flom LLP & Affiliates *
Trucker Huss PC
Wilson Sonsini Goodrich & Rosati *

**Band 3**
Cooley LLP
Fenwick & West LLP *
Gunderson Dettmer Stough Villeneuve Franklin & Hachigian
Morrison & Foerster LLP *
Orrick, Herrington & Sutcliffe LLP *

## Senior Statesmen

**Senior Statesmen:** distinguished older practitioners

| Johnson Robert K | Munger, Tolles & Olson LLP * |
| Trucker Lee A | Trucker Huss PC |

## Leading Individuals

**Star individuals**

| Barrall James | Latham & Watkins LLP |

**Band 1**

| Burmeister Edward | Baker & McKenzie * |
| DiBernardo S James | Morgan, Lewis & Bockius LLP * |
| Lipsig Ethan | Paul Hastings LLP |
| Spector Scott | Fenwick & West LLP * |
| Yaffe Joseph M | Skadden, Arps, Slate, Meagher & Flom * |

**Band 2**

| Aguirre John E | Wilson Sonsini Goodrich & Rosati |
| Baker James P | Baker & McKenzie * |
| Borden Paul | Morrison & Foerster LLP |
| Diamond Valerie H | Baker & McKenzie * |
| Fackler Stephen W | Gibson, Dunn & Crutcher LLP * |
| Frank Michael T | Morrison & Foerster LLP |
| Hendricks Sharon J | Gunderson Dettmer Stough Villeneuve |
| Huss R Bradford | Trucker Huss PC |
| Jacobsen Wayne | O'Melveny & Myers LLP |
| Kallstrom D Ward | Seyfarth Shaw LLP (ONP)† * |
| Ocker Jonathan M | Orrick, Herrington & Sutcliffe LLP |
| Stern Roger D | Wilson Sonsini Goodrich & Rosati |

**Band 3**

| Blumling Sheldon J | Fisher & Phillips LLP (ONP)† * |
| Brown Tristan | Simpson Thacher & Bartlett LLP (ONP)† * |
| Chen Nancy | Orrick, Herrington & Sutcliffe LLP |
| Davis Wendy | Jones Day (ONP)† * |
| Diller Nicole A | Morgan, Lewis & Bockius LLP * |
| Harris Stephen H | Paul Hastings LLP |
| Poonja Zaitun | Morgan, Lewis & Bockius LLP * |
| Storke Charles A | Trucker Huss PC |
| Walbridge Jeffrey | O'Melveny & Myers LLP |
| Webb Elizabeth | Gunderson Dettmer Stough Villeneuve |

**Up-and-coming individuals**

| Feller Sean C | Gibson, Dunn & Crutcher LLP * |
| Klementz Barbara | Baker & McKenzie * |

\* Indicates firm / individual with profile.
†ONP = Other Notable Practitioner.

## Band 1

### Baker & McKenzie
See profile on p.435

THE FIRM This 20-strong team handles a range of employee benefits, executive compensation and ERISA litigation matters, but is praised in particular for its strength advising multinational employers on the design and implementation of equity-based compensation packages. It often advises companies in relation to IPOs and M&A.
**Sources say:** *"They really invest in their clients and have good continuity."*
**KEY INDIVIDUALS** The *"excellent"* **Edward Burmeister** (see p.626) is a seasoned practitioner who is a leading force in the realm of private equity. He frequently advises domestic companies on expanding their private equity plans to other countries. **Valerie Diamond** (see p.631) similarly focuses on opening companies' equity compensation to international employees. **James Baker** (see p.621) impresses on an array of ERISA, employee benefits and executive compensation issues. He is particularly noted for his expertise on matters with international elements. **Barbara Klementz**'s (see p.647) expertise in American and German law makes her a good choice for multinationals. Much like her colleagues, she focuses largely on enacting equity compensation programs across the globe.

### Latham & Watkins LLP
See profile on p.446

THE FIRM This Golden State group deftly provides a mix of transactional and counseling advice and routinely advises clients in relation to company buyouts and other transactions based domestically and abroad. The team recently handled the employee benefits and executive com-

pensation aspects of Mattel's $680 million acquisition of HIT Entertainment.
**Sources say:** *"The group is excellent, knowledgeable and responsive."*
**KEY INDIVIDUALS** Peers consider **James Barrall** to be *"a real star."* He is based in the firm's Los Angeles office and handles a range of executive compensation, employee benefits and corporate governance matters.

### Morgan, Lewis & Bockius LLP
See profile on p.2246

THE FIRM Morgan Lewis has an impressive geographical reach in California, with offices in Los Angeles, Irvine, Palo Alto and San Francisco, and lays claim to a state-leading employee benefits and executive compensation team, as well as a distinct ERISA litigation group. Its impressive list of clients includes major pharmaceuticals companies and shipping businesses. Recently, the team advised Hawaii-based Alexander & Baldwin following a corporate reorganization that required the restructuring of equity incentive awards.
**KEY INDIVIDUALS James DiBernardo** (see p.632) sits on the group's employee benefits and executive compensation team. *"He is very seasoned and knows his subject area. I rely on his advice,"* notes a client. DiBernardo advised Alexander & Baldwin on the matter above. **Zaitun Poonja** (see p.660) similarly focuses on employee benefits and executive compensation matters. She advises public and private companies based domestically and abroad. **Nicole Diller** (see p.632) is an adroit litigator who focuses largely on ERISA and other employee benefit claims. Her clients include insurance carriers, financial institutions, employers and other third parties.

## Band 2

### Gibson, Dunn & Crutcher LLP
See profile on p.682

THE FIRM This group acts for substantial public and private companies on an array of incentive, deferred compensation and executive compensation plans. It also often advises companies on compensation and benefits matters spinning out of IPOs and M&A. Clients include substantial corporates in the technology, retail and pharmaceutical sectors.
**Sources say:** *"The lawyers are very good – I have a lot of time for them."*
**KEY INDIVIDUALS Sean Feller** (see p.635) deftly advises companies on incentive, particularly equity, benefits. He also handles executive compensation and termination matters. **Stephen Fackler** (see p.635) brings nearly 30 years of experience to employee benefits and executive compensation matters. He recently advised on Transatlantic Holdings' incentives compensation program when the company was acquired by Alleghany Corporation.

### O'Melveny & Myers LLP
See profile on p.693

THE FIRM This practice is known for its comprehensive counseling to major companies spanning sectors such as technology and manufacturing. It neatly complements O'Melveny's transactional work, and provides compensation and benefits advice in the wake of shifting corporate structures. ERISA litigation also forms a substantial portion of the team's work.

**KEY INDIVIDUALS Jeffrey Walbridge** is hailed as an excellent practitioner by market sources. He concentrates predominantly on incentives, deferred compensation and severance packages. **Wayne Jacobsen** is based in Newport Beach and focuses on stock ownership and option plans, welfare plans, employment agreements and severance arrangements.

## Paul Hastings LLP
See profile on p.1996

**THE FIRM** Paul Hastings's employee benefits and executive compensation division is situated within its labor and employment practice, thereby providing a rounded and integrated service to employers. It counsels on pension and other benefits plans and also handles audits by government agencies and ERISA litigation. Recently, the group has represented UPS in ERISA litigation relating to its benefit plans.

**Sources say:** *"They always give us analytical, commercial and legally sound advice. I like them for the broad perspective they bring."*

**KEY INDIVIDUALS Ethan Lipsig** is a leader on employee benefits and employment matters. *"He understands the practical implications of highly technical things,"* sources note. In the past year, he has been representing the San Diego City Employees' Retirement System in its litigation with the City of San Diego, in which the latter is seeking to force the former to charge city employees half the cost of making up the losses made as a result of the 2008 market crash. **Stephen Harris** divides his time between litigious and counseling matters. He recently advised American Airlines on the compensation, benefits and ERISA elements of bankruptcy-related union negotiations. A client said: *"When he handles a case for us, he does not just bring value – he never lets us down."*

## Skadden, Arps, Slate, Meagher & Flom LLP & Affiliates
See profile on p.2008

**THE FIRM** Executive compensation matters associated with M&A deals are the bread and butter for this team, although it also advises on the employee benefit aspects of corporate transactions. It recently advised Nationwide Health Properties on executive compensation matters relating to its acquisition by Ventas.

**Sources say:** *"The intensity they bring to problems is highly valued by us."*

**KEY INDIVIDUALS Joseph Yaffe** (see p.673) has a formidable presence in Northern California. He is highly adept at the securities and tax issues that accompany equity compensation.

## Trucker Huss PC

**THE FIRM** This boutique firm enjoys an enviable market share of California's employee benefits and ERISA work. Its specialized focus and sophisticated work product attract the full range of clients, from small companies to some of the nation's largest employers. Noted areas of

expertise are health and welfare plans, ERISA consulting and litigation, and equity and executive compensation.

**KEY INDIVIDUALS Bradford Huss** continues to impress for his ERISA mediation and litigation skills, although he also handles government audits, long-term benefits plans and fiduciary responsibility issues. **Charles Storke** places an emphasis on advising on pension, health and welfare plans. He is highly adept at advising on the tax and regulatory implications of pension plans. **Lee Trucker** is often retained by corporates, venture capital firms, other law firms and employee benefits organizations. His practice is a mix of ERISA advice and employee benefits litigation.

## Wilson Sonsini Goodrich & Rosati
See profile on p.700

**THE FIRM** This sizable group neatly complements the firm's corporate and transactional work in other departments. Although it advises a range of companies, the bulk of its clients are technology corporates, many of which are based in Silicon Valley. It handles both executive compensation and employee benefits matters, including equity compensation, employment and severance agreements and tax-qualified retirement plans. Recent clients include Cypress Semiconductor, Atmel and Coherent.

**Sources say:** *"I am thoroughly satisfied and rate them highly across the board."*

**KEY INDIVIDUALS John Aguirre** is widely regarded for his advice to technology, financial services and semiconductor companies, among others. He recently handled executive compensation and employee benefits planning for Applied Materials during its acquisition of Varian Semiconductor. *"He is a very careful and practical lawyer, and also has very good business judgment,"* notes a source. The *"very impressive"* **Roger Stern** places particular emphasis on growth and startup companies. He recently represented Microchip Technology during its acquisition of Standard Microsystems, and handled the new executive compensation and employee benefits plans.

## Band 3

## Cooley LLP

**THE FIRM** Cooley's 16-strong group advises a diverse range of public and private companies on compensation and benefits plans. The group is particularly active in technology company IPOs and M&A. Areas of expertise include equity and cash bonus plans, distressed company retention and compliance with new regulations.

**KEY INDIVIDUALS Tom Reicher** heads the compensation and benefits practice from San Francisco.

## Fenwick & West LLP
See profile on p.680

**THE FIRM** Within this nationally recognized life science and technology firm is situated a strong Californian employee benefits and executive compensation team. With two offices, one in Silicon Valley and the other in San Francisco, the group is able to advise a range of clients, from those in the retail industries to technology startups

and venture capital firms. It focuses heavily on executive and equity compensation.

**KEY INDIVIDUALS** The *"fantastic"* **Scott Spector** (see p.666) is expert at equity and executive compensation arrangements. He often advises clients regarding IPOs and M&A.

## Gunderson Dettmer Stough Villeneuve Franklin & Hachigian

**THE FIRM** This group spans offices in San Diego and Silicon Valley, and is a top choice among businesses, venture capital firms and other industry managers. It handles a broad mix of executive and employment matters, from equity compensation plans to employee severance packages. The group often acts in connection with M&A, venture capital financings and IPOs.

**KEY INDIVIDUALS Elizabeth Webb** operates from the firm's Silicon Valley office, and is well positioned to advise a range of public and startup companies. She handles both executive compensation and employee benefits planning. **Sharon Hendricks** has a focus on representing technology and other emergent companies. She often advises clients on executive and equity compensation, as well as employment and severance packages.

## Morrison & Foerster LLP
See profile on p.1990

**THE FIRM** This compact team comprises two California partners and is split between offices in Palo Alto and San Francisco. Its forte lies in advising firms on employee benefits, executive compensation and ERISA matters arising out of sizable corporate transactions. The group is also developing a specialty advising clients on compliance with new healthcare laws. The team recently acted for Novellus System in its merger with Lam Research, a deal valued at $3.3 billion.

**KEY INDIVIDUALS Paul Borden** represents clients from a variety of industries, including aerospace, finance and technology. *"He is really outstanding,"* states a market commentator. **Michael Frank** is particularly active during M&A deals and attendant transactions. He recently represented Novellus System when it merged with Lam Research.

## Orrick, Herrington & Sutcliffe LLP
See profile on p.1994

**THE FIRM** This team, drawn from the firm's Silicon Valley and San Francisco offices, is perhaps best known for its employee benefits work. Areas of focus include pensions and employee stock purchase plans. It also has notable global equity and executive compensation capabilities. While it has a wide spread of clients, it is particularly touted for its work with emerging growth companies.

**KEY INDIVIDUALS Nancy Chen** is expert at equity compensation, but also dedicates a sizable portion of her practice to employment and severance agreements. A market source notes that she is *"very, very solid."* **Jonathan Ocker** is an adept executive and equity compensation specialist. He typically advises clients from the technology, communication and financial services sectors.

## Other Notable Practitioners

Seyfarth Shaw LLP's **Ward Kallstrom** (see p.645) is based in the firm's San Francisco office and divides his practice between counseling and litigation. He places heavy emphasis on ERISA matters, although he also counsels on other employee benefits and employment matters. At Fisher & Phillips LLP, **Sheldon Blumling** (see p.624) is praised for being *"extremely smart, outcome-oriented and client-friendly."* Although he advises on a range of employee benefits and executive compensation matters, a unique area of focus is healthcare reform advice. **Tristan Brown** (see p.626) of Simpson Thacher & Bartlett LLP impresses with his advice to companies going through M&A and IPOs. Clients value him for being *"incredibly intelligent and highly responsive."* **Robert Johnson** (see p.644) of Munger, Tolles & Olson LLP is considered to be a *"fantastic lawyer."* His broad practice encompasses employee benefits, executive compensation and tax matters. **Wendy Davis** (see p.631) of Jones Day specializes in equity and executive compensation. At her former firm Cooley, she acted during Zynga's acquisition of OMGPop.

# ENERGY

Commentary about individuals can be found under their firm's paragraph. If the firm has no paragraph (is not ranked) look at Other Notable Practitioners.

## Energy: State Regulatory & Litigation
### Leading Firms

**Band 1**
Davis Wright Tremaine LLP *
Ellison, Schneider & Harris L.L.P.
Goodin, MacBride, Squeri, Day & Lamprey LLP
Orrick, Herrington & Sutcliffe LLP *
Winston & Strawn LLP *

**Band 2**
Morrison & Foerster LLP *
Munger, Tolles & Olson LLP *
Pillsbury Winthrop Shaw Pittman LLP *

### Leading Individuals

**Band 1**

| | |
|---|---|
| Bloom Jerry | Winston & Strawn LLP * |
| Ellison Christopher T | Ellison, Schneider & Harris L.L.P. |
| Greenwald Steven | Davis Wright Tremaine LLP |
| Malkin Joseph | Orrick, Herrington & Sutcliffe LLP * |
| Weissmann Henry | Munger, Tolles & Olson LLP * |

**Band 2**

| | |
|---|---|
| Carroll Michael | Latham & Watkins LLP (ONP)[†] * |
| Day Michael | Goodin, MacBride, Squeri, Day & Lamprey |
| Gray Jeffrey | Davis Wright Tremaine LLP |
| Hanschen Peter | Morrison & Foerster LLP * |
| Harris Jeffery D | Ellison, Schneider & Harris L.L.P. |
| Karp Joseph | Winston & Strawn LLP * |
| O'Neill Edward | Davis Wright Tremaine LLP |

**Band 3**

| | |
|---|---|
| Cottle Lisa A | Winston & Strawn LLP * |
| Hindus Michael | Pillsbury Winthrop Shaw Pittman LLP |
| Huard David | Manatt Phelps & Phillips LLP (ONP)[†] |
| Kissinger William D | Bingham McCutchen LLP (ONP)[†] * |
| Leslie John W | McKenna Long & Aldridge LLP * |
| Read Charles | Jones Day (ONP)[†] * |
| Squeri James D | Goodin, MacBride, Squeri, Day & Lamprey |
| Weiner Peter H | Paul Hastings LLP (ONP)[†] |

* Indicates firm / individual with profile.
[†] ONP = Other Notable Practitioner.

## Band 1

### Davis Wright Tremaine LLP
See profile on p.2544

**THE FIRM** This standout San Francisco practice retains its strong reputation in the energy regulatory and transactional sphere, acting on behalf of utilities, power companies and energy consumers. Its activity in front of the California Public Utilities Commission (CPUC) has continued recently with the representation of Chevron Pipe Line Company in rates issues. The group has also acted for California Pacific Electric Company in a range of regulatory issues, while also handling matters for public sector clients including San Francisco Bay Area Rapid Transit District and the City of Long Beach.

**Sources say:** *"Competent, reliable and conscientious legal counsel."*

**KEY INDIVIDUALS** *"Solid practitioner"* **Steven Greenwald** is a lead member of the team in California. He is a go-to expert for the likes of California Pacific Electric in a range of energy issues. **Jeffrey Gray** has continued to handle a range of sophisticated regulatory issues on behalf of Calpine. He has recently represented the company before the CPUC in relation to resource adequacy contracts and energy procurement policies. *"Good, solid lawyer,"* **Edward O'Neill** is held in high regard by his clients. His recent highlights include representing the City of Long Beach in CPUC proceedings.

### Ellison, Schneider & Harris L.L.P.

**THE FIRM** This highly regarded boutique has continued to be prominent in licensing cases for significant solar projects. The team regularly acts before regulatory bodies such as the California Energy Commission (CEC) in a range of issues, particularly focusing on electricity. Clients benefit from the deep expertise provided by a group of dedicated energy practitioners supplemented by environmental experts.

**Sources say:** *"A boutique firm that has for many years represented power producers effectively."*

**KEY INDIVIDUALS Christopher Ellison** regularly acts for clients in front of all of California's key regulatory bodies. He is deeply experienced in representing energy suppliers and customers, as well as assisting trade associates with their energy issues. His practice also incorporates related transactions and arbitrations. **Jeffery Harris** has extensive expertise in sophisticated permitting issues on behalf of energy clients. He has also been involved in power plant siting work and continues to be a player in environmental matters relating to the California Environmental Quality Act (CEQA).

### Goodin, MacBride, Squeri, Day & Lamprey LLP

**THE FIRM** This compact San Francisco firm concentrates its energy focus on public utility regulation. The group's broad expertise and wealth of experience before regulatory bodies enables it to assist clients from the full range of sectors including providers of natural gas and other utilities and telecommunications and transportation companies.

**Sources say:** *"A firm with great experience in regulatory work before the CEC."*

**KEY INDIVIDUALS Michael Day** is a leading expert in both natural gas and electricity regulatory proceedings. He has also developed a strong niche in wireless telecommunications, and regularly acts on such issues before the CPUC. The respected **James Squeri** focuses largely on telecoms and energy matters involving the CPUC. On the utilities side, he handles a range of issues relating to natural gas, electricity and oil.

### Orrick, Herrington & Sutcliffe LLP
See profile on p.1994

**THE FIRM** Orrick's prominent 25-partner team continues to be known for its representation of California's leading utilities, thanks in particular to its longstanding association with PG&E. The team has also recently been involved in ongoing matters before the CPUC on behalf of Chevron in proceedings against Shell relating to a crude oil pipeline between the San Joaquin Valley and the Bay Area.

**Sources say:** *"A phenomenal firm with capability in renewable energy finance."*

**KEY INDIVIDUALS Joseph Malkin** (see p.651) *"is one of the leading lights of the energy regulatory Bar in California,"* according to commentators. He has taken a lead role in many of the firm's most prominent and high-value energy matters.

## Winston & Strawn LLP
See profile on p.1267

**THE FIRM** The California team at this established national firm is well-positioned to offer clients a full service energy practice with deep expertise in all kinds of energy including renewables and greenhouse gas issues. The group has been particularly active in the solar energy sphere having represented First Solar, Soitec Solar and Solar Reserve in their power purchasing agreements. The team also appears regularly before major California regulatory bodies.

**Sources say:** *"One of the best in this market."*

**KEY INDIVIDUALS Jerry Bloom** (see p.285) heads the firm's energy, project development and finance group. He is known for his expertise in energy regulatory work and has recently been involved in a series of matters relating to solar and renewable energy. **Joseph Karp** (see p.645) is lauded as *"very intelligent, creative, responsive and well respected in the industry."* He earns particular praise from clients for his regulatory expertise and negotiation skill in power purchase agreements. Well-regarded partner **Lisa Cottle** (see p.629) has recently been advising NextEra Energy Resources on a range of transactional and regulatory issues before the CPUC. She focuses on the development and financing of various energy projects.

## Band 2

## Morrison & Foerster LLP
See profile on p.1990

**THE FIRM** Morrison & Foerster's energy and environment practice earns high market praise, with clients particularly praising its regulatory expertise before the Federal Energy Regulatory Commission (FERC). In recent high-

lights, the group has been advising enXco, a renewable energy project development and management company, on a variety of regulatory, siting and environmental issues relating to wind and solar energy.

**Sources say:** *"They provide outstanding representation and service in a cost-efficient manner."*

**KEY INDIVIDUALS** Senior counsel **Peter Hanschen** (see p.640) is an experienced energy specialist who is described as an *"excellent lawyer."* He has recently acted for Verizon Wireless in the CPUC's investigation into utility pole failure relating to the 2007 Malibu Canyon fire.

## Munger, Tolles & Olson LLP
See profile on p.691

**THE FIRM** This firm's broad energy practice incorporates the full range of regulatory issues as well as remaining a prominent player for energy-related litigation. It regularly acts for major industry organizations including Shell Oil and Transocean, which it has represented in a series of disputes arising from the 2012 Deepwater Horizon oil spill in the Gulf of Mexico. The group's regulatory element has represented clients in various proceedings before the CPUC.

**KEY INDIVIDUALS** Market sources think very highly of **Henry Weissmann** (see p.672). He is a leading expert in regulatory proceedings and major energy class actions. He has played a key part in the group's representation of Transocean.

## Pillsbury Winthrop Shaw Pittman LLP
See profile on p.2000

**THE FIRM** Pillsbury's healthy presence in California is bolstered by a significant presence in San Francisco and Los Angeles. The energy practice's experience across the full range of energy issues is exemplified by its varied client

base, which includes organizations such as ExxonMobil, AES Solar Power and Teck Metals. The team is also experienced across all aspects of regulatory work.

**KEY INDIVIDUALS Michael Hindus** takes a lead in many of the group's most significant matters, such as the representation of AES Solar Power in a project acquisition.

### Other Notable Practitioners

**Michael Carroll** (see p.627) is cochair of the energy and infrastructure project siting and defense practice group at Latham & Watkins LLP. He handles a range of high-value permitting matters, such as the representation of Hydrogen Energy California on a $4 billion project. **David Huard** co-leads the energy, environment and natural resources practice group at Manatt Phelps & Phillips LLP. He also leads the firm's climate change solutions and its renewables projects teams. The *"very highly thought of"* **William Kissinger** (see p.646) of Bingham McCutchen LLP represents a number of major energy clients. He recently represented Competitive Power Ventures in relation to the Sentinel energy project in Riverside County. **John Leslie** (see p.649) of McKenna Long & Aldridge LLP focuses on natural gas and electricity regulation. He is known among peers as a prominent player in the field. **Charles Read** (see p.661) of Jones Day is experienced in acting before regulatory bodies on behalf of a broad range of energy clients. His recent highlights include acting for NRG Energy in relation to the $688 million financing of a power plant in El Segundo. **Peter Weiner** leads the environmental and energy group at Paul Hastings LLP. He has recently acted for First Solar in a series of major utility projects valued at a total of $10 billion.

# ENVIRONMENT

Commentary about individuals can be found under their firm's paragraph. If the firm has no paragraph (is not ranked) look at Other Notable Practitioners.

## Band 1

## Bingham McCutchen LLP
See profile on p.1515

**THE FIRM** This market-leading environment group handles a broad range of litigation, permitting, compliance and transactional matters for its high-profile client base. The team has been closely involved in advising K Road Power on re-permitting and defending the approvals for a $1 billion solar project. Other highlights include acting for Quail Brush Genco on the development of a 100 MW electric power plant in San Diego. Other major clients represented by the firm include Chevron, Mitsui and Anadarko Petroleum.

**Sources say:** *"They do an outstanding job for their clients."*

**KEY INDIVIDUALS** The eminent **James Dragna** (see p.633) is a leading light of California environment law. *"He has a keen ability to organize the team, set the strategic course*

*for proceedings and to work seamlessly with the company and the other parties involved,"* relates one impressed source. Observers highlight **Rick Rothman** (see p.663) as *"very meticulous in his thought processes,"* and *"knowledgeable, responsive and accurate."* He has recently advised the Imperial County Air Pollution Control District on regulations of dust emissions. Clients value **Ella Foley Gannon** (see p.636) for her *"impressive knowledge of California and federal environmental laws and permitting processes, thoughtful advice and ability to forge strong relationships with regulators."* She recently led the team in its successful defense of K Road Power, the owners of the Calico Solar Project, against two California Environmental Quality Act (CEQA) challenges in the California Supreme Court.

## Latham & Watkins LLP
See profile on p.446

**THE FIRM** The highly regarded Latham & Watkins environmental offering is particularly well known for its prowess in air quality and water quality work. The team also has strong capabilities in the energy field, recently advising Hydrogen Energy California on a $4 billion power project in Kern County. Other key matters for the team include representing the City of San Diego and the La Jolla Community Fireworks Foundation in groundbreaking litigation on the possible impact of fireworks on the environment.

**Sources say:** *"Top-notch lawyers, well versed in the field and worthy adversaries."*

**KEY INDIVIDUALS** Global practice chair **Robert Wyman** is a very well-respected practitioner with extensive experience advising on a broad range of matters, including air quality, energy and climate change. According to market

## Environment
## Leading Firms

### Band 1
Bingham McCutchen LLP *
Latham & Watkins LLP *

### Band 2
Alston & Bird LLP *
Farella Braun + Martel LLP
Gibson, Dunn & Crutcher LLP *
Morrison & Foerster LLP *

### Band 3
Allen Matkins Leck Gamble Mallory & Natsis LLP *
Barg Coffin Lewis & Trapp LLP
Paul Hastings LLP *
Pillsbury Winthrop Shaw Pittman LLP *

### Band 4
Arnold & Porter LLP *
Best Best & Krieger LLP
Brownstein Hyatt Farber Schreck, LLP *
Fulbright & Jaworski LLP *
Greenberg Glusker Fields Claman & Machtinger LLP *
Nossaman LLP *
Sheppard, Mullin, Richter & Hampton LLP

\* Indicates firm / individual with profile.
†ONP = Other Notable Practitioner.

## Leading Individuals

### Band 1
| | |
|---|---|
| Barr Michael R | Pillsbury Winthrop Shaw Pittman LLP * |
| Bruen James | Farella Braun + Martel LLP |
| Corash Michèle B | Morrison & Foerster LLP * |
| Dennis Patrick W | Gibson, Dunn & Crutcher LLP * |
| Dragna James J | Bingham McCutchen LLP * |
| Rubalcava Sharon | Alston & Bird LLP * |
| Wyman Jr Robert | Latham & Watkins LLP |

### Band 2
| | |
|---|---|
| Barg John F | Barg Coffin Lewis & Trapp LLP |
| Coffin Richard C | Barg Coffin Lewis & Trapp LLP |
| Hernandez Jennifer L | Holland & Knight LLP (ONP)† * |
| Lucero Gene | Latham & Watkins LLP |
| McTigue Martin | O'Melveny & Myers LLP (ONP)† |
| Norris Trenton H | Arnold & Porter LLP * |
| Schmall Deborah J | Paul Hastings LLP |
| Steel Michael | Morrison & Foerster LLP * |
| Weaver Elizabeth | Fulbright & Jaworski LLP * |
| Weiner Peter H | Paul Hastings LLP |
| Zischke Michael H | Cox Castle & Nicholson LLP (ONP)† |

### Band 3
| | |
|---|---|
| Cermak Jr John F | Baker & Hostetler LLP (ONP)† * |
| Cooke David | Allen Matkins Leck Gamble Mallory * |
| Dintzer Jeffrey D | Gibson, Dunn & Crutcher LLP * |
| Donnelly Thomas M | Jones Day (ONP)† * |
| Hines Robert L | Farella Braun + Martel LLP |
| Howard Robert | Latham & Watkins LLP * |
| Landfair Stan | McKenna Long & Aldridge LLP (ONP)† |
| Margulies Jeffrey Brian | Fulbright & Jaworski LLP * |
| Nardi Karen | Arnold & Porter LLP * |
| Nyquist Peter A | Alston & Bird LLP * |
| Praitis Judith | Sidley Austin LLP (ONP)† * |
| Riff Lawrence P | Steptoe & Johnson LLP (ONP)† |

| | |
|---|---|
| Rosegay Margaret | Pillsbury Winthrop Shaw Pittman LLP |
| Rothman Rick R | Bingham McCutchen LLP * |
| Slater Scott S. | Brownstein Hyatt Farber Schreck, LLP |
| Thompson Jocelyn | Alston & Bird LLP * |
| Visser Randolph C | Sheppard, Mullin, Richter & Hampton LLP |

### Band 4
| | |
|---|---|
| Amantea Chris M | Squire Sanders (US) LLP (ONP)† * |
| Andes Pamela | Allen Matkins Leck Gamble Mallory * |
| Benshoof Ward L | Alston & Bird LLP * |
| Carlin Norman | Pillsbury Winthrop Shaw Pittman LLP |
| Chen Patricia J | PC Law Group (ONP)† |
| Cranston David | Greenberg Glusker Fields Claman * |
| Farabee David R | Pillsbury Winthrop Shaw Pittman LLP * |
| Foley Gannon Ella | Bingham McCutchen LLP * |
| Gilhuly Morgan | Barg Coffin Lewis & Trapp LLP * |
| Hart Gordon E | Paul Hastings LLP |
| Hedgpeth Tiffany R | Edgcomb Law Group (ONP)† |
| Hsiao Peter | Morrison & Foerster LLP * |
| Lally Amy | Sidley Austin LLP (ONP)† * |
| Leslie Michael R | Caldwell Leslie & Proctor, PC (ONP)† |
| Locke Chris | Farella Braun + Martel LLP |
| McHenry Thomas J.P. | Gibson, Dunn & Crutcher LLP * |
| McNevin Chris | Pillsbury Winthrop Shaw Pittman LLP * |
| Meeder James | Allen Matkins Leck Gamble Mallory * |
| Nichols Sandi | Allen Matkins Leck Gamble Mallory * |
| Parker Jeffrey | Sheppard, Mullin, Richter & Hampton LLP |
| Poloncarz Kevin | Paul Hastings LLP |
| Roberts Gary M | Dentons (ONP)† * |
| Schussman Barbara J | Perkins Coie LLP (ONP)† |
| Thornton Robert D | Nossaman LLP |
| Uram Robert J | Sheppard, Mullin, Richter & Hampton LLP |
| van Aelstyn Nicholas | Beveridge & Diamond PC (ONP)† |
| Yost Nicholas C | Dentons (ONP)† * |

commentators he is "one of the most influential environmental lawyers in the country." **Gene Lucero**, of counsel, continues to be recognized as a significant force in matters concerning superfunds and environmental enforcement. According to one impressed source: "Gene has an extraordinary knowledge base and ability to craft solutions to difficult remediation-related problems. He also has a background as a former EPA regulator, which gives him a particularly valuable perspective on environmental questions." **Robert Howard** (see p.642) is recognized for his work on clean water matters, product liability cases, toxic tort and enforcement actions. Observers describe him as "extremely hard-working and a first-class strategist."

## Band 2

### Alston & Bird LLP
See profile on p.1102
**THE FIRM** This strong environment practice is well regarded for its expertise in the fields of green chemistry, infrastructure and energy. Recently, the team advised Fortune 500 company Sempra Energy on a large-scale sediment cleanup project and the development of renewable power generation projects. The firm's client base includes a number of high-profile names, including Occidental Petroleum, Southern California Edison and the Federal Realty Investment Trust.
**Sources say:** "A terrific group of lawyers, no question about that."
**KEY INDIVIDUALS Sharon Rubalcava** (see p.663) is known for her prowess as an air quality attorney. Market sources consider her "probably one of the best in this arena.

She's down to earth, liked by regulators and very good at explaining situations to her clients. She continues to impress." **Jocelyn Thompson** (see p.669) has extensive experience advising clients on CEQA and the National Environmental Policy Act (NEPA). She handles work relating to hazardous waste, clean air and clean water legislation and coastal development. The impressive **Peter Nyquist** (see p.657) recently acted for DIRECTV on a number of environmental matters, including the planned acquisition and development of a new headquarters on a former brownfield site. He is described by sources as "extremely reasonable and results-oriented." **Ward Benshoof** (see p.623) enjoys an excellent reputation for his strengths as a litigator and his experience of matters relating to the CEQA. "He is tenacious and really knowledgeable in the field," interviewees say.

### Farella Braun + Martel LLP
**THE FIRM** This well-regarded practice covers a broad spectrum of environmental matters for such clients as Monsanto, Novartis Pharmaceuticals, GE and First Solar. The strong team of litigators, regulatory lawyers and compliance counselors advise on matters including water quality, air quality and climate change, natural resources law and worker health and safety. Currently, the team is representing Union Pacific Railroad in complex tort litigation

involving a large number of plaintiffs which arises from issues of groundwater contamination and vapor intrusion. **Sources say:** "One of the best environmental litigation firms that I have dealt with. They performed superbly and I would recommend them without hesitation to anyone."
**KEY INDIVIDUALS** Clients benefit from **James Bruen**'s extensive experience in environmental matters. "He is one of the best trial lawyers I know: very well prepared, very polished, and someone you would want to be using for a bet-the-company kind of a case," relates one impressed observer. **Robert Hines** has decades of experience practicing environmental law and wins high praise for his skills as an advocate. Clients find that "his work is always expert, practical and cost-effective." **Chris Locke** is a highly experienced environmental practitioner with in-depth knowledge of federal and state regulation, including the Clean Air Act, the Clean Water Act and Proposition 65. "He is a pleasure to work with due to how thorough and consistently well prepared he is. He is an excellent advocate for his client," according to market sources.

### Gibson, Dunn & Crutcher LLP
See profile on p.682
**THE FIRM** This firm enjoys an excellent reputation for its work on high-profile environmental litigation. The team

has a strong record for handling government enforcement actions, and is currently advising the Tesoro Refining and Marketing Company on an appeal against a groundbreaking OSHA citation, as well as defending it in a wrongful death action following an industrial accident. The firm acts for a number of major names on environmental questions, including Intel, Southern California Gas, Climate Action Reserve and MidAmerican Energy Holdings.

**Sources say:** *"They did a great job. They're very detail-oriented, results-oriented and service-oriented, and very good at communicating their points to clients and government agencies."*

**KEY INDIVIDUALS Patrick Dennis** (see p.631) is currently representing Intel in a series of cases arising from allegations of birth defects. Observers consider him *"a prominent and thoughtful lawyer who is very focused and intellectual. First rate."* Clients value **Jeffrey Dintzer** (see p.632) for being *"intelligent, thorough, persistent, aggressive when necessary and responsive."* He has extensive expertise acting on high-stakes class actions and toxic tort litigation. **Thomas McHenry** (see p.653) wins praise from sources for his negotiating skills and expertise in the hazardous waste and air quality arenas. *"There's very little environmental law he doesn't know, but it's his business sense that stands out the most,"* commentators say.

## Morrison & Foerster LLP
See profile on p.1990

**THE FIRM** The environment group at Morrison & Foerster is known for its strength across the full spectrum of environmental matters, and is particularly active in the renewable energy sector. It currently provides environmental advice to enXco on its wind and solar developments, and on such matters as compliance with the California Endangered Species Act and the CEQA. The team also handles high-value litigation arising from a broad range of federal and state environmental statutes, including chemical regulation relating to consumer products and food and drink.

**Sources say:** *"I wouldn't use anyone else – they're unbelievable! They can handle a lot of technical issues and I know of no better lawyers for air quality issues." "They're a big player and we use them when we need the heavy guns."*

**KEY INDIVIDUALS** Market-leading environmental attorney **Michèle Corash** (see p.629) has a top reputation as a *"brilliant strategist"* with excellent knowledge of Proposition 65 regulation. **Michael Steel** (see p.667) wins applause from market sources for being *"very responsive, very insightful and very engaged – he had a good intuition for the government agency we were dealing with and what our organization was ultimately trying to achieve."* He has been closely involved in advising Union Pacific Railroad on compliance issues for the modernization of an intermodal rail yard. According to sources, **Peter Hsiao** (see p.643) is *"an amazing lawyer who is really good at advocating your position in a professional way. He is a great strategist who has never steered me wrong."* Clients also value his technical understanding provided by a background in chemical engineering.

## Band 3

### Allen Matkins Leck Gamble Mallory & Natsis LLP
See profile on p.674

**THE FIRM** This firm has a strong presence in the California market and undertakes a range of environmental litigation and transactions for its clients. The team currently represents the City of San Diego Unified Port District in high-value litigation relating to the Oil Pollution Control Act and CERCLA. The group is also active on permitting work, and is assisting Gregory Canyon in obtaining a permit for a new solid waste landfill. Other major names advised by the team include California American Water, Imperial Irrigation District and IDE Americas.

**Sources say:** *"First class. Very good attorneys who work hard and well for their clients."*

**KEY INDIVIDUALS David Cooke**'s (see p.629) abilities as a litigator receive high praise from sources, who describe him as *"terrific and top-flight."* The highly-regarded **Sandi Nichols** (see p.657) regularly acts on groundwater contamination matters in California. Observers highlight her as *"very impressive"* and *"a very good environmental litigator."* The impressive **Pamela Andes** (see p.620) specializes in transactional matters. *"She knows the law, how to work with the government agencies and how to get the job done,"* according to clients. **James Meeder** (see p.654) has experience advising on a broad range of state and federal environmental statutes, including Proposition 65, CERCLA, CEQA and NEPA. According to market sources, *"he's smart, careful and can think outside the box."*

### Barg Coffin Lewis & Trapp LLP

**THE FIRM** This respected boutique is known for its team of strong litigators, who handle toxic torts, natural resource damages, citizen suits and enforcement actions. In addition, the group has extensive expertise in Proposition 65, CEQA, NEPA and other environmental statutes, and is well known for its strong focus on insurance-related work. The firm also wins praise for offering excellent value for money.

**Sources say:** *"A very good boutique firm."*

**KEY INDIVIDUALS** The well-regarded **John Barg** regularly acts on litigation relating to the Clean Air Act, the Clean Water Act, Superfund and environmental insurance coverage. He wins applause from peers for being *"a terrific lawyer – great to work with, a good writer and a good analyst."* A strong presence in California environmental law, **Richard Coffin** has in-depth knowledge of Proposition 65 environmental insurance-related claims. According to commentators, he is *"phenomenally insightful and a very, very bright lawyer."* **Morgan Gilhuly** (see p.637) is highly respected as a litigator, and is known for his work on contaminated properties. *"He is knowledgeable and a pleasure to work with,"* sources say.

## Paul Hastings LLP
See profile on p.1996

**THE FIRM** The Paul Hastings environmental offering handles a variety of matters, including brownfield redevelopment, permitting for renewable energy projects, greenhouse gas regulation and litigation relating to endangered species, and the CEQA, NEPA and CERCLA. The team recently advised Calpine, California's largest power producer, on the development of a groundbreaking new program to regulate greenhouse gases. Other highlights include advising Facebook on entitlements and CEQA compliance for a large-scale employee accommodation project.

**KEY INDIVIDUALS** The *"phenomenal"* and highly experienced **Deborah Schmall** has an excellent reputation among an expansive client base that includes universities, life science companies, developers and transport companies. *"She's so bright and so smart! She's absolutely the best around,"* according to one impressed interviewee. The well-respected **Peter Weiner** brings decades of experience to his role as head of the department at Paul Hastings. He has considerable expertise in a range of environmental issues in the public and private sectors, including hazardous waste and hazardous materials. **Gordon Hart** is a strong force in base closure redevelopment work who represents a number of high-profile clients. *"He is a tough negotiator and knows his area of law well. We've been happy,"* clients recall. The *"brilliant"* **Kevin Poloncarz** receives high praise for his work on air quality and greenhouse gas regulation. *"He is very creative in coming up with solutions and his work is tremendous,"* market commentators say.

## Pillsbury Winthrop Shaw Pittman LLP
See profile on p.2000

**THE FIRM** This environmental practice undertakes work in the fields of hazardous waste management, Superfund, endangered species and toxic tort. The team continues to advise such major names as Chevron and ExxonMobil on the defense of enforcement actions brought by such agencies as the US Environmental Protection Agency. Recent work includes advising Homestake Mining Company of California on the closure and reclamation of a mine in Northern California. The group also advises the Institute of Scrap Recycling Industries in California on hazardous waste legislation.

**Sources say:** *"They have really developed a good reputation in the marketplace. They have good lawyers and are very respectable."*

**KEY INDIVIDUALS Michael Barr** (see p.622) is described by sources as *"a guru and a great air quality lawyer."* He has recently advised the Western States Petroleum Association on the implementation of the groundbreaking California Low Carbon Fuel Standard program. **Margaret Rosegay** is a respected practitioner who recently handled the hazardous waste matter for the Institute of Scrap Recycling Industries. **Norman Carlin** has represented the San Francisco Bay Area Rapid Transit District on land use and environmental issues relating to a number of high-value expansion projects. Air quality specialist **David Farabee** (see p.635) regularly advises corporate clients on environmental compliance issues. He has considerable experience advising on CEQA legislation. **Chris McNevin** (see p.654) advises on a broad spectrum of environmental issues and is an experienced litigator. Key highlights for him have included assisting Teck Metals in negotiations for a landmark agreement on trans-border pollution claims.

## Band 4

### Arnold & Porter LLP
See profile on p.906

**THE FIRM** This practice has a considerable presence in California and provides advice on a wide variety of environmental matters for clients in the oil and gas, food and consumer products sectors. The team has considerable expertise in Proposition 65 legislation and green chemistry initiatives, as well as regularly advising on compliance and transactional matters. The firm's strong client base includes McDonald's, PepsiCo, Disney and the Southern California Gas Company.
**Sources say:** *"The lawyers we work with at Arnold & Porter are completely invested in our success. The time, effort and commitment they display has impressed us all."*
**KEY INDIVIDUALS** Market commentators single out **Trenton Norris** (see p.657) as *"one of the best Proposition 65 litigators in the state."* He also regularly advises on other product-related litigation. Clients describe him as *"very well informed on the issues that matter to me, and skilled in identifying new issues that may come to be important to me."* The *"fantastic"* **Karen Nardi** (see p.656) has a very good reputation for her work in areas including water, air quality and health and safety, as well as brownfield development.

### Best Best & Krieger LLP

**THE FIRM** Along with its highly regarded water quality and water rights practice, the solid team at Best Best & Krieger also handles matters relating to the CEQA, NEPA, hazardous waste and endangered species. Work highlights for the team include advising the South Coast Air Quality Management District on air quality issues.
**Sources say:** *"They have some really excellent lawyers."*
**KEY INDIVIDUALS** Steven Anderson heads the firm's Environmental Law & Natural Resources group.

### Brownstein Hyatt Farber Schreck, LLP
See profile on p.725

**THE FIRM** This well-known group has a particular focus on water issues, with recent key matters including acting for Cadiz on a groundbreaking water supply development throughout southern California. The team also represents the San Diego Water Authority, Golden State Water Company and Nestlé Water North America.
**Sources say:** *"They're extremely well versed in the subject matter and you can feel the confidence and competence. There would be no hesitation on my part to recommend them."*
**KEY INDIVIDUALS** Scott Slater is widely recognized for his impressive water law practice and wins high praise

from clients and peers alike. *"His depth of knowledge negotiation skills, strategic planning and transactional abilities are unequaled,"* sources say, adding that *"he's probably one of the most knowledgeable guys for California water issues and is incredibly well connected."*

### Fulbright & Jaworski LLP
See profile on p.2435

**THE FIRM** This group acts on environmental matters for retail, hospitality, commercial, public agency and utilities clients. It currently acts for such major names as Amazon, Shell, the California Retailers Association and ExxonMobil. Climate change is an important part of the practice, and the team has experience advising on renewable energy credits, sequestration, cap-and-trade and carbon capture. Advising on Proposition 65 is another key area of expertise, and the group recently advised Safeway on an enforcement matter on the presence of lead in packaged food.
**KEY INDIVIDUALS** **Elizabeth Weaver** (see p.671) handles a variety of environmental matters and is described by sources as *"solid, unflappable and very experienced."* **Jeffrey Margulies** (see p.652) heads the department. He is known for his knowledge of Proposition 65 legislation, European chemical laws and his skills as a trial lawyer.

### Greenberg Glusker Fields Claman & Machtinger LLP
See profile on p.683

**THE FIRM** This firm is established as a strong player in the fields of environmental insurance coverage and cost recovery, as well as being active on air quality issues. The team's client base includes such names as California Dairies, Walton Street Capital, Northrop Grumman and the Union Pacific Railroad. Recently, the group represented the City of Culver City in landmark litigation against the County of Los Angeles on CEQA issues arising from the proposed expansion of an oil field.
**Sources say:** *"The firm combines broad technical and legal expertise in oil and gas, hazardous waste and other environmental issues with its professional demeanor and dedication to their clients' concerns, making it a high caliber, full-service firm."*
**KEY INDIVIDUALS** **David Cranston** (see p.630) is *"always really well prepared with a great endgame in mind,"* according to clients. *"He is a master strategist and we've had amazingly positive results with him."*

### Nossaman LLP
See profile on p.692

**THE FIRM** The Nossaman team offers a broad range of environmental expertise that covers such areas as air and water quality, endangered species, CEQA and NEPA compliance, climate change and renewable energy. Recent highlights for the group include acting for the Castaic Lake Water Agency in a lawsuit relating to perchlorate groundwater contamination, and securing $100 million in cleanup costs. The firm's impressive client base also includes such key players as the California High Speed Rail

Authority, Chevron, the City and County of San Francisco and the City and County of Honolulu.
**Sources say:** *"High-quality lawyers at a fair price, with deep commitment to and understanding of client concerns."*
**KEY INDIVIDUALS** The highly-regarded **Robert Thornton** wins praise from observers for being *"extremely knowledgeable, creative and easy to work with. He contributes ideas and works out solutions to difficult issues and provides excellent service."*

### Sheppard, Mullin, Richter & Hampton LLP

**THE FIRM** This team regularly acts on hazardous waste, soil and groundwater contamination and air quality work and is experienced in working with such agencies as California Coastal Commission, California State Water Resources and the US Environmental Protection Agency. Recent standout matters for the team include defending an international wood products coating manufacturer in a $90 million claim relating to alleged VOC emissions from noncompliant product violations. The team has also acted for ESCO Corporation on matters arising from the Portland Harbor Superfund Site.
**Sources say:** *"They do good work and we get good value."*
**KEY INDIVIDUALS** Randolph Visser has considerable expertise acting on air quality matters and handles both litigation and regulatory matters. He recently represented California Portland Cement Company in a federal Clean Air Act enforcement action. Sources describe **Jeffrey Parker** as *"a terrific lawyer who meets our needs and is very knowledgeable about our business and about legal issues."* Recently, he acted for Exxon Mobil on a product liability matter. Observers highlight **Robert Uram** as a *"very good lawyer, very tenacious and very knowledgeable."* His clients include CSOLAR Development and Newhall Land and Farming.

## Other Notable Practitioners

**John Cermak** (see p.627) of Baker Hostetler LLP has an impressive reputation for advising on multiparty Superfund matters. *"He's really practical, pragmatic and efficient, which in this day and age is really key,"* clients say. **Nicholas van Aelstyn** of Beveridge & Diamond PC is very experienced in the field of climate change and is hailed as an expert in matters relating to the California Air Resources Board. Clients praise his business acumen and consider him an *"experienced lawyer who is creative and detail-oriented."* The *"very highly regarded"* **Michael Zischke** of Cox Castle & Nicholson LLP is recognized as a leading authority on CEQA legislation. **Michael Leslie** of Caldwell Leslie & Proctor, PC is a highly experienced and well-respected litigator. According to sources, he is *"reasonable, very easy to work with and approaches issues in a smart way."* *"Powerhouse"* **Jennifer Hernandez** (see p.642) of Holland & Knight LLP enjoys a very good reputation for her environmental practice. She regularly advises high-profile clients on endangered species, brownfields redevelopment and wetlands work. **Thomas Donnelly** (see p.632) of Jones Day is valued by clients for being *"knowledgeable and practical with a very quick turnaround."* His clients include major names in the fields of oil and gas, mining, retail, aerospace and financial institutions. **Stan Landfair** of McKenna Long & Aldridge LLP is highly regarded for his work on chemical regulatory matters. According to interview sources, *"he's really top-rate, very knowledgeable and his advice is sought after and valued."* **Martin McTigue** of O'Melveny & Myers LLP is well known for his experience acting in the regulatory arena. Sources describe him as *"top-notch"* and *"very impressive in his knowledge and his approach."* The impressive **Patricia Chen** of PC Law Group handles work relating to green chemistry, hazardous materials, air and water quality and Proposition 65 for such clients as the Southern California Association of Government and the City of Oceanside. *"She is a very experienced environmental lawyer for private firms and public entities. She is smart, pragmatic, detail-oriented and focused on problem solving,"* sources say. **Barbara Schussman** of Perkins Coie LLP earns widespread praise

for her comprehensive understanding of both legal and environmental issues, as well as her negotiation skill and business acumen. The outstanding **Judith Praitis** (see p.660) of Sidley Austin LLP is very well regarded for her expertise in Proposition 65 legislation, though she also handles a variety of other environmental matters. *"She has a very good ability to work with opposing counsel and understand what needs to get done without creating animosity, and she knows how to move the case forwards. She also works well with the Attorney General and is a very, very smart lawyer,"* clients say. **Lawrence Riff** of Steptoe & Johnson LLP is a very highly regarded toxic trial lawyer who is applauded by clients for his *"ability to communicate, his writing skills, trial skills, impeccable judgment and innovation. He's one of the best."* **Nicholas Yost** (see p.430) of Dentons enjoys an excellent reputation for his work on environmental compliance and permitting, and is also a well-respected litigator. His practice places particular focus on NEPA legislation, an

area in which he has strong expertise. **Gary Roberts** (see p.662) of Dentons regularly handles high-stakes environmental litigation and has in-depth understanding of Proposition 65 legislation. According to sources, he is *"a top-flight lawyer, very thoughtful and creative and a good litigator."* **Amy Lally** (see p.648) of Sidley Austin LLP wins praise from clients for being *"really top-notch and very insightful in terms of how to handle the issues."* She is particularly well-known for her Proposition 65 expertise. The well-regarded **Chris Amantea** (see p.620) of Squire Sanders (US) LLP advises high-profile clients on a range of matters including Proposition 65 compliance, Superfund liability, air and water quality and hazardous waste. **Tiffany Hedgpeth** recently joined Edgcomb Law Group from Bingham McCutchen. She has extensive expertise in environmental litigation and represents a variety of municipalities and private companies. Sources describe her as *"very good, very smart, high-energy and thorough."*

# HEALTHCARE

| Healthcare | | |
|---|---|---|
| **Leading Firms** | | |
| **Band 1** | | |
| Hooper Lundy & Bookman PC | | |
| Latham & Watkins LLP * | | |
| McDermott Will & Emery LLP * | | |
| **Band 2** | | |
| Davis Wright Tremaine LLP * | | |
| Manatt Phelps & Phillips LLP * | | |
| **Band 3** | | |
| Foley & Lardner LLP * | | |
| Hanson Bridgett LLP | | |
| Jones Day * | | |
| Paul Hastings LLP * | | |
| Ropes & Gray LLP * | | |
| Sheppard, Mullin, Richter & Hampton LLP | | |
| **Band 4** | | |
| Arent Fox LLP * | | |
| Buchalter Nemer * | | |
| Fulbright & Jaworski LLP * | | |
| Nossaman LLP * | | |

## Band 1

### Hooper Lundy & Bookman PC

**THE FIRM** Hooper Lundy & Bookman's areas of specialty include patient privacy and security law, life sciences, Medicare and Medicaid compliance, and matters relating to reimbursement and payment. This boutique healthcare firm, which has three offices across California, has stepped up to meet the demands of a changing healthcare market by opening a new federal government relations and public policy department in Washington, DC, highlighting the firm's desire to be close to decision makers as healthcare reform is implemented.

| Senior Statesmen | | |
|---|---|---|
| **Senior Statesmen: distinguished older practitioners** | | |
| Weissburg Carl I | *Foley & Lardner LLP* | |
| **Leading Individuals** | | |
| **Band 1** | | |
| Bookman Lloyd A | *Hooper Lundy & Bookman PC* | |
| Dutro James R | *Jones Day* * | |
| Gordon Eric B | *McDermott Will & Emery LLP (ONP)[†] * | |
| Higgins Daniel B | *Manatt Phelps & Phillips LLP* | |
| Hinkley Gerry | *Pillsbury Winthrop Shaw Pittman (ONP)[†]* | |
| Hooper Patric | *Hooper Lundy & Bookman PC* | |
| Kadzielski Mark A | *Fulbright & Jaworski LLP* * | |
| Lundy Robert W | *Hooper Lundy & Bookman PC* | |
| Mancino Douglas M | *Hunton & Williams LLP (ONP)[†] * | |
| Owens James F | *Paul Hastings LLP* | |
| Root Jr George L | *Procopio, Cory, Hargreaves (ONP)[†]* | |
| Thompson Martin J | *Manatt Phelps & Phillips LLP* | |
| **Band 2** | | |
| Chesley John O | *Ropes & Gray LLP* | |
| Demetriou Andrew James | *Credo Law Partners Inc. (ONP)[†]* | |
| Goldman Joel S | *Hanson Bridgett LLP* * | |
| Helvestine William A | *Crowell & Moring LLP (ONP)[†] * | |
| Hirsch Reece | *Morgan, Lewis & Bockius LLP (ONP)[†] * | |
| Lipton M Steven | *Hooper Lundy & Bookman PC* | |
| Olejko Mitchell J | *Buchalter Nemer* * | |
| Peters Gerald | *Latham & Watkins LLP* * | |
| Pimstone Gregory N | *Manatt Phelps & Phillips LLP* * | |
| Rappeport Ira J | *McDermott Will & Emery LLP* * | |
| Schwartz James R | *Manatt Phelps & Phillips LLP* | |
| Settelmayer Daniel K | *Latham & Watkins LLP* | |
| Stanton W Clark | *Hooper Lundy & Bookman PC* | |
| Yood Kenneth J | *Sheppard, Mullin, Richter & Hampton LLP* | |
| **Band 3** | | |
| Brown Lowell C | *Arent Fox LLP* * | |

| | | |
|---|---|---|
| Diaz Dennis S. | *Davis Wright Tremaine LLP* | |
| Girard Robert D | *Davis Wright Tremaine LLP* | |
| Gordon Jill H | *Nixon Peabody LLP* * | |
| Gordon Paul A | *Hanson Bridgett LLP* * | |
| Hellow John R | *Hooper Lundy & Bookman PC* | |
| Keville Terri D | *Davis Wright Tremaine LLP* | |
| Klein Eric A | *Sheppard, Mullin, Richter & Hampton LLP* | |
| Landsberg Barry S | *Manatt Phelps & Phillips LLP* | |
| Lauer Katherine A. | *Latham & Watkins LLP* * | |
| Liset J Robert | *Musick Peeler & Garrett (ONP)[†]* | |
| O'Connell Ann | *Nossaman LLP* | |
| Oppenheim Charles B | *Hooper Lundy & Bookman PC* | |
| Rodriguez Denise Rios | *Foley & Lardner LLP* | |
| Scarano Jr R Michael | *Foley & Lardner LLP* | |
| Tully W Bradley | *Hooper Lundy & Bookman PC* | |
| Waltz Judith A | *Foley & Lardner LLP* | |
| **Band 4** | | |
| Ehrgott Catherine | *Jones Day* * | |
| Gertler Gary B | *McDermott Will & Emery LLP* * | |
| Jeffry Thomas | *Arent Fox LLP* * | |
| Lawrence Paul F | *McDermott Will & Emery LLP* * | |
| Lucas Carol | *Buchalter Nemer* * | |
| Peterson Kurt | *Reed Smith LLP (ONP)[†]* | |
| Schuchard Robert L | *Davis Wright Tremaine LLP* | |
| Smith Paul T | *Hooper Lundy & Bookman PC* | |
| Spohn Richard B | *Nossaman LLP* | |
| Weese Esther Chang | *McDermott Will & Emery LLP* * | |
| **Up-and-coming individuals** | | |
| Gomez Paul A. | *Paul Hastings LLP* | |

| | | |
|---|---|---|
| Westendorf Gayl A | *Paul Hastings LLP* | |

\* *Indicates firm / individual with profile.*

[†]*ONP = Other Notable Practitioner.*

Sources say: "*This is a great LA-based healthcare-focused firm.*" "*Hooper Lundy & Bookman is a clear leader in the field.*"

KEY INDIVIDUALS Lloyd Bookman is particularly renowned for his expertise in Medicare and Medicaid reimbursement. Bookman has significant litigation experience, and has made representations on behalf of hospitals and healthcare providers before a range of venues, including the Provider Reimbursement Review Board, federal and state courts, and state Medicaid agencies. Former Deputy Attorney General, Patric Hooper has an extensive background in healthcare litigation. His client base includes for-profit and nonprofit organizations requiring assistance with matters which relate to licensure, certification and reimbursement. Managing partner Robert Lundy has a particular specialty in assisting healthcare clients with corporate matters, which include M&A, JVs and financing. Steven Lipton primarily represents hospitals, and he maintains a focus on handling matters involving physician contracting, healthcare transactions, regulatory and compliance matters and EMTALA investigations, among other areas. Clark Stanton's practice predominantly concentrates on operational and regulatory matters impacting hospitals, healthcare providers and similar organizations. Stanton is adept at advising clients on issues of privacy and security and general peer review matters, including hearings, investigations and confidentiality. Bradley Tully has a particular focus on fraud and abuse matters relating to Medicare, Medicaid and private payors, in addition to counseling a range of healthcare clients on matters arising out of business transactions. John Hellow's areas of specialty include antikickback measures and defending clients in disputes relating to cost reporting, arising out of the Medicare False Claims Act. Charles Oppenheim is adept at assisting clients with transactional healthcare, in addition to advising on operational and regulatory matters. Oppenheim is also admired by peers for his expertise in Stark-related issues. Paul Smith's particular skills include assisting healthcare clients in matters of regulatory compliance, corporate governance and information privacy and security.

## Latham & Watkins LLP
See profile on p.446

THE FIRM Latham & Watkins's formidable healthcare and life sciences group numbers 60 California-based attorneys, with a wealth of additional worldwide expertise to draw on as required. The team defended HCA alongside other hospitals in healthcare litigation involving a nationwide investigation by the DOJ relating to reimbursement of hospital equipment. Other clients include Watson Pharmaceuticals and Atrium Medical.

Sources say: "*They provide an excellent product and advice, and always do a great job.*"

KEY INDIVIDUALS Gerald Peters's (see p.659) areas of expertise include assisting clients with transactional and regulatory healthcare matters. He has great experience advising on mergers and acquisitions, regulatory compliance, fraud and abuse issues and the development of integrated healthcare systems. Daniel Settelmayer recently

counseled DaVita, one of the largest providers of kidney care in the USA, in relation to the structuring of its $4.4 billion acquisition of HealthCare Partners, which oversees the running of medical groups in California, Nevada and Florida. He is global cochair of the healthcare group. Katherine Lauer (see p.648) cochairs the group alongside Settelmayer, and her specialty is healthcare litigation. She represented TridentUSA Health Services in an unsealed False Claims Act qui tam case, which alleged kickbacks in violation of California Medi-Cal discriminatory pricing rules.

## McDermott Will & Emery LLP
See profile on p.1258

THE FIRM The health industry advisory practice group at McDermott Will & Emery has had a busy year, providing ongoing counsel to Ascension Health in relation to its acquisition of Daughters of Charity Health System, which was the the largest nonprofit acquisition of 2012 in the USA. The firm receives praise for its collaborative and creative approach to working with clients, and the group is noted for both its litigation expertise and its strength handling business and transactional matters, including acquisitions and joint ventures, on behalf of healthcare clients.

Sources say: "*The lawyers are smart and talented, and the partners are collegial.*"

KEY INDIVIDUALS Head of practice Eric Gordon (see p.638) led on McDermott's representation of long-standing client, Vanguard Health Systems, advising on a Securities and Exchange Commission Rule 144A private placement of $350 million to qualified institutional buyers. He is praised for the depth of his subject matter experience and knowledge. Ira Rappeport (see p.661) leads on counseling Ascension Health in relation to the acquisition outlined above, and is appreciated by sources for his understanding of his clients, creativity, and "*willingness to engage in transactions.*" Gary Gertler (see p.637) assisted the Regents of the University of California with a matter relating to the university's San Diego campus, and its execution of a definitive asset purchase agreement to acquire all of the clinical-related assets of the Nevada Cancer Institute. Clients affirm that Gertler "*has done a lot of deals and really knows how to structure and document them with our business needs in mind.*" 2012 saw Paul Lawrence (see p.648) advising Tenet Healthcare on the sale of Creighton University Medical Center to Alegent Health. Esther Chang Weese (see p.671) has worked alongside Lawrence and other members of the team to advise Tenet Healthcare on a wide variety of acquisitions and other transactional matters. Sources say: "*Esther can turn things around quickly. She does a good job and works well in a team.*"

## Band 2

## Davis Wright Tremaine LLP
See profile on p.2544

THE FIRM Davis Wright Tremaine has offices in San Francisco and Los Angeles, which are home to many of the 21 attorneys comprising the healthcare practice group. The

attorneys in the team have broad expertise in this field, and advise on many mergers and acquisitions involving hospitals and health systems. The group also represents providers in relation to government payment programs such as Medicare and Medicaid, and assists faith-based providers with their legal requirements and how this interfaces with their religious principles.

Sources say: "*They're very efficient – they get answers quickly without a lot of cost and delay, and they've been very good for us.*"

KEY INDIVIDUALS Robert Girard impresses clients with his work in the areas of medical staffing and hospital physician contracts. Other matters frequently handled by Girard include service contracts, bioethics, tax, and corporate securities issues affecting healthcare clients. Terri Keville is assisting a number of healthcare providers filing amicus curiae submissions in a high-profile case involving the authority of hospital governing boards in matters relating to peer review. Sources agree that Keville is "*very responsive to client needs.*" Dennis Diaz is praised for his handling of compliance issues, as well as his knowledge of Stark law and antikickback measures. Clients are quick to praise both his expertise and collegial approach: "*Dennis is a knowledgeable attorney, and is quick to respond to any query I might have. If he feels someone else is best suited to answer the question, he lets me know that, with an introduction to the other individual.*" Robert Schuchard is noted for his excellent transactional work for healthcare clients, and he adeptly handles matters relating to contracts, financing, governance and board relations.

## Manatt Phelps & Phillips LLP
See profile on p.690

THE FIRM Manatt Phelps & Phillips has four offices situated across California, which are home to over 50 healthcare attorneys. Sources note the firm's skill at handling litigation matters and government investigations. The group represents a broad range of healthcare clients, including Adventist Health, California Hospital Association and Sun Healthcare Group.

Sources say: "*Their performance is top-notch, and they know healthcare law very well. They supply the government perspective on issues, as many of them have worked for the government in the past.*"

KEY INDIVIDUALS Daniel Higgins leads on high-value transactional work on behalf of healthcare providers. He represented nonprofit healthcare network Sutter Health in relation to bond issuances by the California Health Facilities Financing Authority and the California Statewide Communities Development Authority to the value of $465 million. Martin Thompson received remarkable praise from one particularly impressed client: "*He is truly Mr Healthcare Antitrust – the best in this area.*" Thompson is based in Costa Mesa, and his clients include multi-hospital systems, in addition to other forms of healthcare provider. Gregory Pimstone (see p.659) is well known for his involvement in significant healthcare disputes. Notably, he secured a significant victory on behalf of Blue Shield of California in a case concerning the interpretation of the Mental Health Parity Act, which had a major impact on affordable healthcare in the state. **James Schwartz** is recognized for his expertise in assisting nonprofit healthcare organizations with transactions, with one example being his high-profile work on behalf of Dignity Health, which was previously known as Catholic Healthcare West. Schwartz worked alongside Daniel Higgins on the organizational restructuring to convert the provider to its new incarnation as Dignity Health, including compliance with federal and state laws, in addition to the requirements of the Catholic Church. **Barry Landsberg** is a renowned state litigator, who has experience of representing health industry clients before the California Supreme Court and the California Court of Appeal.

## Band 3

### Foley & Lardner LLP
See profile on p.2588

**THE FIRM** The 23 California-based attorneys in this group receive praise for their collective expertise in healthcare compliance, provider enrollment, subscription program rules and their knowledge of the ambulance industry. The team's clients include the California Association of Public Hospitals, Pacific Alliance Medical Center and the Society Of Critical Care Medicine.

**Sources say:** *"The team undertakes thorough research, and provides solid opinions and great customer service."*

**KEY INDIVIDUALS Denise Rios Rodriguez** has great experience of representing healthcare clients before administrative boards, in addition to state and federal courts. Her areas of specialty include assisting clients with payment issues arising out of Medicare and Medicaid. Sources rate **Michael Scarano** as an industry leader for air medical issues. Clients praise *"his knowledge and accessibility, and the practicality of his thought processes."* **Judith Waltz** is admired by peers, who describe her as a *"great lawyer."* She represented Sierra Vista Hospital in a qui tam matter. She also represented Palm Drive Hospital in relation to disclosures regarding physician arrangements and billing. **Carl Weissburg** remains an impressive figure at Foley & Lardner, due to his extensive experience of healthcare mergers and acquisitions and the negotiation of Medicaid and Medicare contracts.

### Hanson Bridgett LLP

**THE FIRM** This California-focused firm has five offices based in San Francisco, Sacramento, North Bay, Silicon Valley and East Bay, which are home to a total of 31 healthcare-focused attorneys. The team represents well-known names within the industry, such as Fortress Investments, the American Seniors Housing Association and the California Assisted Living Association. The firm receives praise for its skill in representing physicians and medical staff organizations, in addition to handling matters relating to senior care facilities, peer review and litigation.

**Sources say:** *"The firm has a strong healthcare division, with people that really understand regulatory enforcement."*

**KEY INDIVIDUALS Joel Goldman** (see p.638) represented Fortress Investments in a portfolio acquisition of assist-

ed living facilities in three states to the value of $257 million. Observers note that Goldman *"always keeps the best interests of his client in mind – he is collaborative, resourceful and smart."* Clients are full of praise for **Paul Gordon** (see p.638) thanks to his *"intellectual horsepower"* and *"ability to help you think and work through issues."*

### Jones Day
See profile on p.919

**THE FIRM** Jones Day receives much admiration for its substantial transactional work, representing large healthcare clients in bond financings, mergers and acquisitions of healthcare bodies, and transactions involving hospital equipment. The healthcare group is also praised for its handling of enforcement matters, healthcare-related intellectual property, and antitrust issues. Clients include City of Hope, Stanford Hospital and Clinics, John Muir Health and St Jude Children's Research Hospital.

**Sources say:** *"The team is always willing to go the extra mile to ensure the end product is of high quality. They are superb team players."*

**KEY INDIVIDUALS** Clients enjoy working with **James Dutro** (see p.633), and peers affirm that *"he is an excellent lawyer."* His areas of expertise include high-value healthcare mergers and acquisitions. **Catherine Ehrgott** (see p.634) works closely with Dutro on many transactions, including acting for Dignity Health on its acquisition of US Healthworks, a national provider of occupational health and urgent care services. Erhgott also represented the Loma Linda University Medical Center in its acquisition of the membership units of Physicians' Hospital of Murrieta.

### Paul Hastings LLP
See profile on p.1996

**THE FIRM** The healthcare department at Paul Hastings numbers 15 attorneys, and its impressive list of clients includes names such as Cedars-Sinai Health System, Dignity Health, Beecken Petty O'Keefe & Company and Scripps Health. With five offices serving California, Los Angeles, Orange County, Palo Alto, San Diego and San Francisco, the group can provide a rounded service across the state. The team receives particular recognition for its work in litigation.

**Sources say:** *"This is a very strong practice."*

**KEY INDIVIDUALS** Head of department **James Owens** is renowned for his skill in handling matters relating to hospital-physician integration and hospital acquisitions. Sources say: *"He is one of the best lawyers on hospital systems in California. He knows this area like the back of his hand."* Peers have a lot of respect for **Gayl Westendorf**, whose practice remains focused on complex transactions involving healthcare clients, including joint ventures, service agreements and integrated delivery systems. Sources note that **Paul Gomez** is *"doing very well – he's going up in the world."* Gomez worked alongside James Owens to represent MemorialCare Medical Foundation in its affiliation with Greater Newport Physicians Medical Group.

### Ropes & Gray LLP
See profile on p.1528

**THE FIRM** The healthcare group at Ropes & Gray has a particularly strong reputation in San Francisco. The firm continued its longstanding representation of Daughters of Charity Health System, a five-hospital system, in the establishment of a medical foundation, in affiliation negotiations with Ascension Health, and in the design and implementation of electronic health records across the system, among other matters.

**Sources say:** *"The practice is solid and well known in the San Francisco area."*

**KEY INDIVIDUALS John Chesley** leads the group, and is representing West Penn Allegheny Health System in its affiliation with Highmark, for the purpose of establishing an insurer/provider healthcare delivery and financing system.

### Sheppard, Mullin, Richter & Hampton LLP

**THE FIRM** The healthcare team at Sheppard Mullin is respected for its transactional work and its ability to handle associated intellectual property matters on behalf of healthcare clients. The group represented Facey Medical Foundation and Facey Medical Group in an affiliation with Providence Health & Services. The team also counseled One Lambda, a manufacturer of transplant diagnostics, in its $925 million sale to Thermo Fisher Scientific.

**Sources say:** *"The team has terrific involvement in healthcare transactions."*

**KEY INDIVIDUALS Kenneth Yood** provided counsel to DaVita in its $4.4 billion acquisition of HealthCare Partners Holdings. **Eric Klein** is the practice leader, and peers hold him in high regard, describing him as *"a very good and sophisticated lawyer."* He worked alongside Yood on the DaVita transaction, and both also worked together to advise ABQ Health Partners, the largest independent medical group in New Mexico, on an alliance with Blue Cross Blue Shield of New Mexico.

## Band 4

### Arent Fox LLP
See profile on p.905

**THE FIRM** Arent Fox's client base includes a mix of healthcare clients, including Pacific Health, California Hospital Association and the Children's Hospital of Orange County. The firm is praised for its work across a broad range of matters, from bond applications and approvals, mergers, regulatory compliance and complex contracts, to representing clients in specialized civil litigation involving tort claims against government agencies.

**Sources say:** *"They are responsive, willing to think outside the box, and have expertise in the nuances of regulatory enforcement in California."*

**KEY INDIVIDUALS** Clients are enthusiastic about **Lowell Brown**'s (see p.625) work in relation to medical administration and medical staff. One source stated that *"his style just fits in so well – he is very solution-oriented."* **Thomas Jeffry** (see p.644) assisted Kaiser Permanente with coordinating the recovery of a lost hard drive containing sensitive data, and handling breach reporting requirements following the incident.

## Buchalter Nemer
See profile on p.676

**THE FIRM** Buchalter Nemer is well regarded as a firm with particular corporate and finance-related expertise which it draws upon when representing clients within the healthcare industry. Additionally, the group is well known for its counseling of financially troubled healthcare businesses. Notably, the team assisted Success Healthcare with its acquisition of the City of Angels Medical Center, which involved purchase price negotiations and a post-sale Chapter 11 filing by the seller. Other clients of the firm include El Camino Hospital, Emergent Medical Associates and Sun Capital Healthcare.

**Sources say:** *"The lawyers provide timely responses. Their advice is reasonable and practical, and they have a can-do attitude."*

**KEY INDIVIDUALS** Sources admire **Mitchell Olejko**'s (see p.657) *"very helpful, focused, 'get it done' approach to transactional work."* Olejko has experience of designing and organizing healthcare delivery systems for a range of providers, and is adept at counseling clients on contract and regulatory matters. Department head **Carol Lucas** (see p.651) has expertise in healthcare acquisitions, structuring physician-owned entities and ensuring compliance with federal and California healthcare laws. Clients have been impressed with her work: *"Carol is pragmatic, strategic and a true partner to the companies she serves. Her keen insight has been of great benefit in determining our strategic directives."*

## Fulbright & Jaworski LLP
See profile on p.2435

**THE FIRM** Based in Los Angeles, this team has several lawyers with prior experience of working in the healthcare industry. The team caters to the needs of clients requiring assistance with medical staff issues, and is also able to advise on a range of litigation, regulation and transactional matters. Clients include Providence Holy Cross Medical Center, Presbyterian Intercommunity Hospital, Blue Shield of California and Palomar Pomerado Health.

**Sources say:** *"It is a good practice, with a good client base and skilled associates."*

**KEY INDIVIDUALS Mark Kadzielski** (see p.644) leads the Los Angeles health law practice at Fulbright, and sources admire his work in California regulatory and medical staff matters. Kadzielski successfully defended Kaiser Foundation Health Plan and Kaiser Foundation Hospitals in a case in which physicians sought to challenge a process used by California hospitals to review complaints against doctors.

## Nossaman LLP
See profile on p.692

**THE FIRM** Nossaman continued to act for key clients, and one notable mandate was its longstanding representation of HealthCare Partners, counseling the company through its acquisition by DaVita. The firm provides advice on a broad range of healthcare matters, acting for clients ranging from hospitals to research organizations. Clients include Monarch HealthCare, Dignity Health and United Surgical Partners International.

**Sources say:** *"This is a solid firm with a presence in San Francisco."*

**KEY INDIVIDUALS Ann O'Connell** represented California Hospital Association in the filing of an amicus brief to the California Supreme Court, requesting a review of the disposition handed down in El-Attar v Hollywood Presbyterian Hospital. This matter concerned a hospital governing body's authority to act in a situation where a medical executive committee has declined to do so. **Richard Spohn** is admired for his expertise in representing health maintenance organizations. He provides ongoing counsel to the Word & Brown Companies, which sees him advising on the CaliforniaChoice program against the backdrop of extensive federal reforms.

## Other Notable Practitioners

At Pillsbury Winthrop Shaw Pittman LLP, **Gerry Hinkley** assists healthcare organizations with corporate law and matters relating to board governance. Recent highlights include advising hospital clients participating in joint ventures. Co-head of the healthcare practice at Hunton & Williams LLP, **Douglas Mancino** (see p.651) has particular expertise representing tax-exempt organizations, and his case work has helped to determine the limits applicable to tax-exempt organizations involved in healthcare-related joint ventures. **George Root** is leader of the healthcare practice group at Procopio, Cory, Hargreaves & Savitch LLP. Root has vast experience acting as general counsel to specialty hospitals and a number of healthcare organizations, which include OxyHeal Health Group and Alliance Healthcare Foundation. At Credo Law Partners Inc., **Andrew Demetriou**'s expertise in both healthcare and corporate law enables him to provide strategic counseling to a broad range of clients including health plans and hospital systems. **William Helvestine** (see p.641) of Crowell & Moring LLP has specialist expertise representing insurance carriers and health plans in litigation and regulatory matters. Clients are quick to share their appreciation for Helvestine's assistance: *"He has the ability to digest huge amounts of federal law and identify the issues of interest to us. I have been struck by his ability to analyze law so quickly."* Peers report that **Reece Hirsch** (see p.642) is a *"terrific healthcare attorney."* Based in the San Francisco office of of Morgan, Lewis & Bockius LLP, Hirsch has great expertise counseling clients on a range of transactional and regulatory healthcare matters. He is also an accomplished author. **Jill Gordon** (see p.638) is one of the driving forces behind the healthcare practice at Nixon Peabody LLP. Her areas of focus include health law and life sciences, and she has assisted a broad range of clients with mergers and acquisitions, contract negotiation, Stark law and antikickback matters. **Robert Liset** is based in the Los Angeles office of West Coast firm Musick Peeler & Garrett. Liset's specialist areas include administrative litigation, fraud and abuse, medical staff and corporate compliance matters. **Kurt Peterson** of Reed Smith LLP recently acted on behalf of Anthem Blue Cross to successfully resolve a class action concerning rescission brought by all California hospitals. Sources praise Peterson's *"excellent understanding"* of all the parties in a dispute, as well as the intricacies of the courts.

# IMMIGRATION

Commentary about individuals can be found under their firm's paragraph. If the firm has no paragraph (is not ranked) look at Other Notable Practitioners.

## Immigration
### Leading Firms

**Band 1**
Berry Appleman & Leiden LLP
Ivener & Fullmer LLP
Pearl Law Group
Wolfsdorf Immigration Law Group *

**Band 2**
Jackson & Hertogs LLP
Larrabee Mehlman Albi Coker LLP
Mautino & Mautino
Morgan, Lewis & Bockius LLP *
Seyfarth Shaw LLP *
Weaver Schlenger Mazel LLP

**Band 3**
Fragomen, Del Rey, Bernsen & Loewy, LLP *
Litwin & Associates
Tafapolsky & Smith
The Law Offices of Carl Shusterman

## Band 1

### Berry Appleman & Leiden LLP

**THE FIRM** This group's San Francisco office remains a leader for immigration matters in Silicon Valley and the Bay Area, and also benefits from the firm's expanding global presence. Alongside the wide range of visa and green card services provided, the team also excels in establishing and running immigration programs for large national and international corporations.

**Sources say:** *"They're very responsive and of course very bright and knowledgeable in their area of expertise."*

**KEY INDIVIDUALS Warren Leiden** has an *"enormous amount of experience and scope of knowledge,"* according to sources. He is actively involved in government relations and is a seasoned attorney in all areas of corporate immigration law. **Jeff Appleman** is recognized as a knowledgeable attorney who can effectively handle unusual or difficult issues. He has extensive experience in immigration matters and related litigation. Sources comment: *"He is very accommodating with all of our requests and special needs for assistance and consultation."* **David Berry** manages the San Francisco office's global visa practice. Clients gain an advantage from his expertise in international legislation and regulation. He advises large companies on corporate compliance and develops strategies for their global migration needs. The *"extremely talented"* **Susan Wehrer** satisfies a broad range of business immigration needs. Among other matters, she advises employers on compliance and labor certification issues.

### Ivener & Fullmer LLP

**THE FIRM** This full-service firm is highly regarded in the market, particularly in the EB-5 investor category and for

## Leading Individuals

### Star individuals
| | |
|---|---|
| Paparelli Angelo | Seyfarth Shaw LLP * |
| Pearl Julie | Pearl Law Group |
| Wolfsdorf Bernard | Wolfsdorf Immigration Law Group |

### Band 1
| | |
|---|---|
| Gonzalez Josie | Gonzalez & Harris PC (ONP)[†] |
| Haight Catherine L | Haight Law Group, PLC (ONP)[†] |
| Ivener Mark | Ivener & Fullmer LLP * |
| Leiden Warren R | Berry Appleman & Leiden LLP |
| Mehlman Sharon R | Larrabee Mehlman Albi Coker LLP |
| Shusterman Carl | The Law Offices of Carl Shusterman |
| Van Der Hout Marc | Van Der Hout Brigagliano (ONP)[†] |
| Vázquez-Azpiri A James | Morgan, Lewis & Bockius LLP * |

### Band 2
| | |
|---|---|
| Appleman Jeff T | Berry Appleman & Leiden LLP |
| Berry David P | Berry Appleman & Leiden LLP |
| Fullmer David R | Ivener & Fullmer LLP * |
| Litwin Edward R | Litwin & Associates |
| Mautino Kathrin | Mautino & Mautino |
| Mautino Robert A | Mautino & Mautino |
| Schlenger Kirsten | Weaver Schlenger Mazel LLP |
| Tafapolsky Alan | Tafapolsky & Smith |
| Wada Ronald | Tafapolsky & Smith |
| Weaver Mary Jane | Weaver Schlenger Mazel LLP |

### Band 3
| | |
|---|---|
| Albi Fausta M | Larrabee Mehlman Albi Coker LLP |
| Coker Diana Vellos | Larrabee Mehlman Albi Coker LLP |
| Drummond Ilana J | Jackson & Hertogs LLP |
| Khedekar Sameer | Pearl Law Group |
| Lange Cynthia J | Fragomen, Del Rey, Bernsen & Loewy, LLP |
| Lawler Martin J | Lawler & Lawler Law Offices (ONP)[†] |
| Mazel Laura J | Weaver Schlenger Mazel LLP |
| Plotkin Norman C | Jackson & Hertogs LLP |
| Spiegel Lisa | Duane Morris LLP (ONP)[†] |

### Band 4
| | |
|---|---|
| Glucoft Frida P | Mitchell Silberberg & Knupp LLP (ONP)[†] |
| Kunzman Kathleen | Pearl Law Group |
| Nguyen Christy | Pearl Law Group |
| Sostrin Rita | Sostrin Immigration Lawyers, LLP (ONP)[†] |
| Stone Lincoln | Stone & Grzegorek LLP (ONP)[†] |

### Up-and-coming individuals
| | |
|---|---|
| Horne Daniel | Jackson & Hertogs LLP |
| Wehrer Susan K | Berry Appleman & Leiden LLP |

* Indicates firm / individual with profile.
[†]ONP = Other Notable Practitioner.

representing companies and individuals in the entertainment industry. Other areas of expertise include global visas, immigration due diligence and corporate training. The team also has a dedicated website for investor immigration. A network of attorneys around the world enables the group to arrange global immigration services for corporate clients.

**Sources say:** *"Knowledgeable and timely in responding. We have a great relationship with our attorneys."*

**KEY INDIVIDUALS David Fullmer** (see p.637) is recommended for his work obtaining immigrant and nonimmigrant visas for corporate clients and advising on compliance issues. Sources say: *"He brings a wealth of knowledge to help us through our cases."* **Mark Ivener** (see p.643) is *"exceptional, very thoughtful, very inciteful and extremely knowledgeable,"* according to informants. He offers a range of immigration services and is deeply involved in work related to the EB-5 investor category.

### Pearl Law Group

**THE FIRM** This boutique immigration group continues to enjoy a stellar reputation in the field. Lately the group has been busy undertaking increasing amounts of work relating to immigrant investors, I-9 compliance and trusted traveler programs. Alongside the team's global capabilities, Pearl Law Group is also considered to be a leader of technological developments for use by the legal industry and its clients. Major clients include Electronic Arts, LucasFilm Entertainment and Tyco Electronics.

**Sources say:** *"Pearl Law Group is a boutique-style law firm with the sophistication of a big global firm. They are able to provide very hands-on service, with near immediate responses to my requests."*

**KEY INDIVIDUALS Julie Pearl** is commended by sources for being *"innovative, and a forward-thinker".* Observers comment that *"she really knows her stuff."* She is managing partner at the firm and is known for her service-oriented approach. **Sameer Khedekar** is recommended for his well-developed knowledge of employment-based immigration issues. His practice has a truly global outlook as he handles both inbound and outbound immigration cases for clients from a variety of industries. Supervising attorney **Kathleen Kunzman** undertakes a full range of immigrant and nonimmigrant matters for both professionals and corporations. **Christy Nguyen** is praised for her ability to deal with complicated US visa matters. Sources consider her to be *"amazing in terms of handling volume without missing a beat."* Clients appreciate her advice about what to expect at borders and throughout the visa process.

### Wolfsdorf Immigration Law Group
See profile on p.701

**THE FIRM** Wolfsdorf Immigration Law Group enjoys a healthy reputation for effectively handling the full range of immigration services for individuals, corporations and institutions. The team recently advised on and managed a series of issues relating to the entertainment and arts industries, and in the EB-5 investor category. The group also has substantial experience in representing universities and academics, and the firm has a healthy outbound practice and global capability.

**Sources say:** *"Obviously a firm at the top of the profession."*

KEY INDIVIDUALS Longstanding practitioner **Bernard Wolfsdorf** provides a *"sense of reassurance that you are in capable hands."* Observers note that he is exceptionally knowledgeable, and are impressed by his *"work ethic and compassion."* He is highly regarded as an active member of the immigration law community.

## Band 2

### Jackson & Hertogs LLP

THE FIRM This San Francisco-based boutique corporate immigration practice regularly represents technology and biotechnology companies across the country. The group offers services in a range of areas for clients including I-9 compliance, EB-5 investor visas, and global visas. Peers are quick to note the firm as a significant competitor in the West Coast market.

KEY INDIVIDUALS **Norman Plotkin** is well known in the immigration law community and is appreciated for his in-depth knowledge of the law and how to communicate complex matters to his clients. **Daniel Horne** is known as a go-to for the more sophisticated legal issues. Observers say: *"His depth of legal knowledge is among the top of the immigration attorneys."* Managing partner **Ilana Drummond** gains respect among commentators due to her *"excellent attention to detail."* Clients also welcome her compassionate approach when dealing with their cases.

### Larrabee Mehlman Albi Coker LLP

THE FIRM This San Diego team has earned a healthy reputation locally for its work on employment-based immigration matters. The group offers a range of services for immigrant and nonimmigrant petitions, I-9 compliance strategies and immigration concerns during M&A. The firm also has experience in handling family-based immigration matters.

Sources say: *"Outstanding and extraordinary attorneys."*

KEY INDIVIDUALS **Sharon Mehlman** is recognized as an active player by the immigration law community and government agencies. One source describes her as *"a class act and one of the smartest lawyers I know."* The *"extremely talented"* **Fausta Albi** undertakes immigration work for corporate clients, particularly in the technological and scientific industries. **Diana Vellos Coker** is an *"extremely bright"* lawyer according to sources. She focuses on business immigration matters and implementing policies and strategies for corporate clients.

### Mautino & Mautino

THE FIRM This highly-respected boutique handles a wide variety of immigration and nationality cases including immigrant and nonimmigrant visas, citizenship, asylum and deportation. The team is particularly well known for its activity in naturalization cases and is held in high regard by many market competitors as a leading presence in San Diego.

Sources say: *"Really wonderful advocacy and they give back by teaching and mentoring on immigration."*

KEY INDIVIDUALS **Kathrin Mautino** is a *"walking encyclopedia"* according to sources. She is considered an expert on immigration matters, particularly in derived citizenship. **Robert Mautino** is described by one observer as *"one of the smartest immigration attorneys I have ever worked with."* Clients benefit from the wealth of experience he has acquired throughout his career in immigration law.

### Morgan, Lewis & Bockius LLP
See profile on p.2246

THE FIRM Morgan Lewis offers a full immigration service which is integrated with its global labor and employment practice. The group advises companies on their immigration needs and continues to work for a series of household names including Apple, Fujitsu and Samsung Electronics in their respective immigration cases and hiring programs. The firm has recently handled much work relating to labor certification, export control and immigration issues arising during M&A.

Sources say: *"They are experts in the industry and have the depth that we need as a global company."*

KEY INDIVIDUALS Clients are full of praise for **James Vázquez-Azpiri** (see p.670) who *"not only is a subject matter expert, his level of availability at critical and often urgent times continues to make him indispensable."* He advises on a series of business immigration matters including labor certification, intracompany transfers and compliance during corporate M&A.

### Seyfarth Shaw LLP
See profile on p.1262

THE FIRM Seyfarth Shaw's California team undertakes a variety of business immigration and employer defense work and has increasingly handled work in the EB-5 investor category. The group represents individuals and companies from a wide range of backgrounds and industries including electronics, manufacturing, healthcare and universities, among others. Offices in San Francisco and Los Angeles enable the firm to offer considerable West Coast depth to a practice that is nationwide in scope.

KEY INDIVIDUALS Practice head **Angelo Paparelli** (see p.658) is *"very much a force in his field"* and *"one of the most original and creative minds in immigration law,"* according to impressed clients.

### Weaver Schlenger Mazel LLP

THE FIRM This boutique firm focuses on business immigration matters including immigrant and nonimmigrant visas, compliance and counsel on M&A. The group also has leading family-based immigration and naturalization capabilities. It has recently advised clients such as the California Department of Transportation on its immigration strategy, and Blood Systems Research Institute and the Wikimedia Foundation on various immigration cases.

Sources say: *"They take the time to learn the organization in order to make the best cases."*

KEY INDIVIDUALS **Kirsten Schlenger** is described as a *"tremendous advocate"* who *"approaches work with creativity and passion."* She has extensive experience in the full spectrum of business, family, asylum, removal and natural-

ization matters. Client favorite **Mary Jane Weaver** represents startups and other organizations in their various immigration needs including compliance. She also provides counsel on the immigration implications brought about by company reorganizations. The *"focused, reliable and passionate"* **Laura Mazel** specializes in immigrant and nonimmigrant petitions for corporate and research institution clients. She also performs audits, advises on compliance and handles issues arising out of M&A.

## Band 3

### Fragomen, Del Rey, Bernsen & Loewy, LLP
See profile on p.1974

THE FIRM Fragomen has a presence in several locations across California and comes recommended for its ability to handle large volumes of significant immigration cases for corporate clients. The team has expertise in developing compliance strategies and advises on individual cases across a variety of industries.

KEY INDIVIDUALS **Cynthia Lange** specializes in developing corporate compliance programs and in governmental audits. She leads the firm's high-tech practice.

### Litwin & Associates

THE FIRM This immigration firm in the Bay Area provides a full range of business and family-based immigration services. The group assists both individuals and companies, and has particular expertise in developing strategies for corporate immigration compliance.

KEY INDIVIDUALS **Edward Litwin** is an established name in the immigration law community. He focuses his practice on business visa petitions and labor certifications.

### Tafapolsky & Smith

THE FIRM Tafapolsky & Smith concentrates on representing businesses from a variety of industries in their immigration needs. Startups, global companies expanding into the United States and companies concerned with immigration matters during M&A are well served by a team that has extensive experience.

Sources say: *"An extremely good firm."*

KEY INDIVIDUALS San Francisco managing director **Alan Tafapolsky** is a *"sterling practitioner"* who is *"all about developing the most sophisticated legal strategies to service clients,"* according to commentators. He concentrates on advising clients on immigration matters during M&A and restructurings. *"Intellectual giant"* **Ronald Wada** is praised by sources for being *"very wise and someone to go to for in-depth analysis."* He has particular expertise in immigrant visa petitions but clients also benefit from his varied background in a wide range of immigration matters.

### The Law Offices of Carl Shusterman

THE FIRM This respected boutique firm practices in a diverse range of immigration, asylum and naturalization matters, and related litigation. The team has particular expertise in representing clients in the healthcare industry and also has substantial experience in the IT sector.

**KEY INDIVIDUALS Carl Shusterman** is highly regarded for his advocacy and work in the immigration law community. He is deeply established in the industry and is highly experienced in an array of immigration matters including employment and family-based immigration as well as asylum and deportation cases.

### Other Notable Practitioners

**Josie Gonzalez** is managing partner of Gonzalez & Harris PC in Pasadena. She is well known in the field, particularly for I-9 compliance work. **Lisa Spiegel** of Duane Morris LLP has been involved in the representation of startup

companies and individuals in creative industries. While the majority of her work is focused on business immigration, she also maintains an active practice in family immigration and deportation cases. **Catherine Haight** is a founding member of Haight Law Group, PLC in Los Angeles. She handles both employment-based and family immigration matters, and has particular expertise in sports and business immigration. **Martin Lawler** of Lawler & Lawler Law Offices focuses on EB-5 investor cases. He has recently arranged visas for many startup companies, particularly in technology industries. **Frida Glucoft** of Mitchell Silberberg & Knupp LLP has considerable experience representing clients in the entertainment and fashion industries. Commentators say: *"We trust her opinion completely,"* and *"she knows the entertainment industry and understands*

*the sense of urgency."* She also handles work for manufacturing companies and healthcare organizations. **Marc Van Der Hout**, founder of Van Der Hout Brigagliano & Nightingale LLP, is known as an *"immigration litigator par excellence."* Observers praise him for his creativity, especially in deportation matters. **Rita Sostrin** of Sostrin Immigration Lawyers, LLP has notable expertise in immigration matters for individuals of extraordinary ability. She has also developed a niche in the representation of physicians. **Lincoln Stone** of Stone & Grzegorek LLP is considered a prominent practitioner, particularly in the EB-5 immigrant investor category. Sources recommend him for his *"ability to synthesize the legal and economic reality aspects."*

---

# INSURANCE INSURER

Insurer p.573; Reinsurance p.574

Commentary about individuals can be found under their firm's paragraph. If the firm has no paragraph (is not ranked) look at Other Notable Practitioners.

| Insurance: Insurer Leading Firms |
| --- |
| **Band 1** |
| Dentons * |
| Duane Morris LLP * |
| **Band 2** |
| Barger & Wolen LLP |
| **Band 3** |
| Bullivant Houser Bailey PC |
| Gordon & Rees, LLP |
| Horvitz & Levy LLP * |
| O'Melveny & Myers LLP * |
| Sedgwick LLP * |
| **Band 4** |
| Gibson, Dunn & Crutcher LLP * |
| McKenna Long & Aldridge LLP * |
| Nixon Peabody LLP * |
| Troutman Sanders LLP |

*\* Indicates firm with profile.*
*Alphabetical order within each band. Band 1 is the highest.*

## Band 1

### Dentons

See profile on p.449

**THE FIRM** This highly respected global firm is valued by clients for its strong connections to the insurance industry. The California team is recognized by peers for its deep expertise and experience in both disputes and regulatory matters. For example, the group has continued its long-term representation of PacifiCare against allegations of nearly one million separate insurance law violations involving a series of constitutional issues.
**Sources say:** *"A top-notch firm that understands the insurance industry."*

**KEY INDIVIDUALS** According to clients, **Ronald Kent** (see p.646) is *"everything you want in a lawyer"* thanks to *"his calm demeanor and good sense of humor which add to the effectiveness of his thoughtful but aggressive approach to litigation."* **Paul Glad** (see p.321) is viewed by peers as *"an extremely capable and extremely experienced attorney."* He has recently appeared in a number of bad faith claims, regulatory matters and large asbestos coverage disputes. **Kara Baysinger** (see p.622) is regularly retained by life and health insurers and financial services companies in a range of issues, with a particular focus on insurance transactional and regulatory matters.

### Duane Morris LLP
See profile on p.2239

**THE FIRM** This team stands out for its expertise in asbestos and environment-related disputes. Clients particularly praise its effective handling of complex arbitrations. The team has a longstanding practice in general liability matters and deep experience in sophisticated cases. The group has recently represented American Centennial in high-value coverage matters, including a range of issues involving bankruptcy and pollution.
**Sources say:** *"Very bright lawyers whose work is of very high quality."*
**KEY INDIVIDUALS Philip Matthews** is known as a *"terrific lawyer"* who *"commands lots of respect."* His practice encompasses high-value pollution matters, including asbestos coverage cases and complex class action suits. Practice head **Max Stern** is praised for his pragmatic approach and ability to view issues from the client's perspective. He has recently handled large asbestos liability coverage claims of more than $2 billion for American Centennial relating to Thorpe Insulation's bankruptcy. Experienced litigator **Ray Wong** is lauded by peers as *"a gentleman and a scholar."* He has recently been involved in

insurance disputes on behalf of Canadian mining giant Teck Metals. **Andrew Gordon** enjoys a healthy reputation for handling London market matters, including his recent representation of several UK insurers and subsequent work on behalf of CNA. **Richard Seabolt** is regarded by market commentators as a *"fine attorney"* with broad insurance and general commercial litigation expertise.

## Band 2

### Barger & Wolen LLP

**THE FIRM** This firm is held in high regard by peers for its strong insurance regulatory focus. It is recognized for its significant California presence and has a broad focus across the industry. The team is known for its expertise in the life, health and disability areas, as well as dealing with a range of reinsurance, corporate and transactional matters.
**KEY INDIVIDUALS Kent Keller** enjoys a strong reputation among peers for his wide-ranging litigation practice. He deals with a variety of insurance and reinsurance claims, including the representation of financial institutions and life and annuity insurers. *"Excellent lawyer"* **Steven Weinstein** has impressed peers with his deep expertise and experience with complex cases. He specializes in class actions, coverage litigation and bad faith claims, with particular expertise in the regulatory field. **Royal Oakes** is known as one of the most prominent lawyers in the insurance regulatory market. He has been involved in class action claims in the life insurance sector.

**Band 1**

| Crane Steven | Berkes Crane Robinson & Seal, LLP (ONP)[†] |
| Glad Paul E B | Dentons [*] |
| Keller Kent | Barger & Wolen LLP |
| Matthews Philip R | Duane Morris LLP |

**Band 2**

| Casey William J | Clyde & Co LLP (ONP)[†] |
| Cathcart Patrick | Alvarado & Smith LLP (ONP)[†] |
| Goetz Richard | O'Melveny & Myers LLP |
| Gordon Andrew K | Duane Morris LLP |
| Kent Ronald D | Dentons [*] |
| Klee Peter | McKenna Long & Aldridge LLP [*] |
| Oakes Royal F | Barger & Wolen LLP |
| Stern Max | Duane Morris LLP |
| Tilner Mitchell C | Horvitz & Levy LLP [*] |
| Weinstein Steven H | Barger & Wolen LLP |
| Wong Ray L | Duane Morris LLP |

**Band 3**

| Baysinger Kara | Dentons [*] |
| Capell David C | Gordon & Rees, LLP |
| Celebrezze Bruce | Sedgwick LLP |
| Checov Martin S | O'Melveny & Myers LLP |
| Doren Richard J | Gibson, Dunn & Crutcher LLP [*] |
| Downs Andrew | Bullivant Houser Bailey PC |
| Friedman Bruce A | Friedman Mediation (ONP)[†] |
| Millikan Jess | Bullivant Houser Bailey PC |
| Plevin Mark | Crowell & Moring LLP (ONP)[†] [*] |
| Wood Mark | O'Melveny & Myers LLP |

**Band 4**

| Brooks John T | McKenna Long & Aldridge LLP [*] |
| Lewis Robert A | Bingham McCutchen LLP (ONP)[†] [*] |
| Mason Peter H | Fulbright & Jaworski LLP (ONP)[†] [*] |
| McInnis Terrence R | Troutman Sanders LLP |
| Schopf Gregory E | Nixon Peabody LLP [*] |
| Seabolt Richard L | Duane Morris LLP |
| Thorpe Sara | Gordon & Rees, LLP |

**Band 1**

| Bank Jonathan | Locke Lord LLP (ONP)[†] [*] |
| Dakin-Grimm Linda | Milbank, Tweed, Hadley & McCloy (ONP)[†] [*] |
| Weissman Barry L | Edwards Wildman Palmer (ONP)[†] [*] |

[*] Indicates individual with profile.
[†] ONP = Other Notable Practitioner.

**Band 3**

## Bullivant Houser Bailey PC

**THE FIRM** This firm earns recognition from clients for its thoughtful and strategic approach and its analytical strength in litigation. The team has acted on behalf of a number of major insurers both domestically and in the London market, and has recently represented Fireman's Fund in highly contentious bad faith litigation. The practice has the ability to handle a range of sophisticated and unique matters, exemplified by its recent work for Zurich on marine insurance issues arising from the sinking of a dry dock in Guam.

**Sources say:** *"The Bullivant firm is very service-oriented and is quite thorough in its evaluation of cases."*

**KEY INDIVIDUALS** Clients praise **Andrew Downs** for his ability to understand and act upon client needs. His complex coverage practice takes in a range of E&O and bad faith cases. Clients find **Jess Millikan** an *"extremely personable and pragmatic"* lawyer. She has recently been involved in high-value coverage claims relating to major fire damage cases at Arizona State University and Garfield High School.

## Gordon & Rees, LLP

**THE FIRM** Gordon & Rees is held in high regard by clients for its ability to obtain good results in complex coverage matters. The group has represented a number of major insurance industry players including Aetna, Farmers Insurance and Allied World Assurance. Recent highlights include the representation of Rawlings in a class action dispute concerning the reimbursement of medical bills arising from a vehicle accident and injury settlement.

**Sources say:** *"They are very, very thorough in their research, analysis and handling of cases."*

**KEY INDIVIDUALS David Capell** is known among peers for his expertise in the field. He has recently handled appellate matters in insurance bad faith claims. **Sara Thorpe** earns praise as a *"very client-focused"* practitioner. She is known for her expertise in asbestos-related matters and for her strong litigation skills.

## Horvitz & Levy LLP
See profile on p.685

**THE FIRM** Horvitz & Levy's deep expertise in appellate matters ensures both peers and clients identify it as an exceptional firm for insurance appeals. The group has recently been involved in appeals against a variety of coverage and liability dispute decisions on behalf of some of the country's most prominent insurance companies including Chartis, Nationwide and State Farm.

**Sources say:** *"Horvitz & Levy is always on the shortlist in the insurance industry for appellate work – it is the Rolls-Royce of its field."*

**KEY INDIVIDUALS** The *"outstanding"* **Mitchell Tilner** (see p.669) has recently been involved in a number of appeals on behalf of major insurers. For example, he has recently represented Travelers in a Ninth Circuit appeal.

## O'Melveny & Myers LLP
See profile on p.693

**THE FIRM** This national player is identified by clients as a go-to firm for high-severity coverage issues, while peers particularly recognize the practice for its work relating to complex asbestos and insurance bankruptcy cases. The team was recently successful on behalf of Resolute Management in the heavily disputed Thorpe Insulation mass tort bankruptcy. Other major industry clients include ACE and Fireman's Fund.

**Sources say:** *"They are all easy to deal with, strategic and very intelligent."*

**KEY INDIVIDUALS Mark Wood** is valued by clients for his *"very informative"* approach. His practice focuses on product liability disputes involving aviation and aerospace insurance issues. Department head **Richard Goetz** is recognized for his ability to handle complex matters on the West Coast and across the country. Clients find him *"very strategic, thoughtful and bright."* Peers identify **Martin Checov** as an expert in coverage issues. He has been particularly active on a range of asbestos and environmental disputes.

## Sedgwick LLP
See profile on p.698

**THE FIRM** Market commentators recognize Sedgwick for its high-quality insurance dispute work. Clients rely on the team to handle a range of matters including securities class actions, D&O claims and healthcare insurance disputes. The team was recently successful in defending a putative class action relating to premiums connected with workers' compensation schemes on behalf of the State Compensation Insurance Fund of California. The firm has also handled professional liability matters for a number of major insurers.

**Sources say:** *"A terrific group that is cost-effective and results-oriented."*

**KEY INDIVIDUALS** Firmwide insurance head **Bruce Celebrezze** has deep expertise in casualty insurance, IP and class action litigation. According to clients: *"He has a very good way of facilitating a discussion with the other side to move the case forward to a reasonable resolution."*

**Band 4**

## Gibson, Dunn & Crutcher LLP
See profile on p.682

**THE FIRM** This well-established California practice handles a range of complex insurance disputes. The team divides its time between high-exposure actions on behalf of major carriers and sophisticated class actions in the context of environmental, healthcare and employment issues, including ERISA matters. Zurich, Aetna, CIGNA and Gemini feature among the firm's regular clients.

**KEY INDIVIDUALS** Clients are effusive in their praise of **Richard Doren** (see p.632), who is *"wonderfully creative and has a terrific courtroom presence."* He has recently been involved in a series of insurance class actions on behalf of Aetna.

## McKenna Long & Aldridge LLP
See profile on p.922

**THE FIRM** This team has a strong reputation in California for insurance defense litigation across a range of areas. The firm regularly acts for major insurance carriers on disputes including class action litigation, unfair competition and insurance bad faith claims. Major clients include carriers such as Allstate and Travelers, while the group recently defeated an employment class action on behalf of Infinity.

**Sources say:** *"Very high performance and very good advice."*

**KEY INDIVIDUALS** Peers describe **Peter Klee** (see p.646) as a *"great and very, very strong litigator."* He is known for representing carriers in high exposure and complex cases. According to clients, **John Brooks** (see p.625) *"gives good counsel and has good strategic thinking."* He has recently represented clients in insurance bad faith and class action disputes.

### Nixon Peabody LLP
See profile on p.1526

**THE FIRM** The California arm of this established national firm is recognized for its insurance coverage dispute work. The team has worked on a number of bad faith actions for major clients including ACE Global UK and United National Insurance. The group also has expertise and experience in the health insurance and reinsurance areas.

**KEY INDIVIDUALS Gregory Schopf** (see p.664) is described by sources as *"courteous, persistent and willing to be innovative in searching for a path to a solution."* He has recently been involved in a variety of insurance bad faith litigation and mediation matters.

### Troutman Sanders LLP

**THE FIRM** Troutman Sanders's vast nationwide team handles the full range of insurance coverage work. Lawyers

in the San Diego office continue to represent major insurance companies in large coverage litigation cases, while the Orange County team is particularly strong in the field of D&O liability claims.

**KEY INDIVIDUALS Terrence McInnis** is held in high regard for handling complex coverage disputes on behalf of large insurance companies. He has recently been involved in a series of contentious environmental and employment matters.

## Other Notable Practitioners

Representing reinsurers, **Barry Weissman** (see p.672) of Edwards Wildman Palmer is often involved in London market matters. He also advises legislators on the development of new insurance regimes and is recommended by clients for being *"very savvy on regulatory matters."* **Jonathan Bank** (see p.622) of Locke Lord LLP is recognized by peers and clients for his expertise in the reinsurance and transactional insurance fields. Peers describe him as a *"very good deal-maker."* **Linda Dakin-Grimm** (see p.630) of Milbank, Tweed, Hadley & McCloy LLP gains unanimous praise from market commentators, who identify her as an *"incredibly good litigator and definitely an expert in reinsurance."* **William Casey** of Clyde & Co LLP is experienced in coverage and professional liability disputes.

Peers describe him as *"very knowledgeable, very practical and skilled at focusing on the real issues."* **Patrick Cathcart** of Alvarado & Smith LLP is known for his experience in sophisticated commercial disputes. He handles complex multiparty coverage litigation and malpractice claims. **Steven Crane** of Berkes Crane Robinson & Seal, LLP is noted by peers for being an *"excellent lawyer"* with particular expertise in the environmental coverage sector. He has recently appeared in a number of appellate cases. **Robert Lewis** (see p.650) of Bingham McCutchen LLP is known for his knowledge of the insurance industry and his expertise in malpractice actions. Crowell & Moring LLP's **Mark Plevin** (see p.886) has transitioned his practice to San Francisco from the firm's Washington, DC office. He is viewed by insurer clients as their *"go-to guy for bankruptcy-related issues."* **Peter Mason** (see p.652) of Fulbright & Jaworski LLP handles a full range of insurance and project liability claims. He is heavily involved in life insurance matters. **Bruce Friedman** of Friedman Mediation is a highly experienced mediator and litigator. Areas of focus include insurance, reinsurance and insurance regulatory disputes.

# INSURANCE POLICYHOLDER

Commentary about individuals can be found under their firm's paragraph. If the firm has no paragraph (is not ranked) look at Other Notable Practitioners.

| Insurance: Policyholder |
| :--- |
| **Leading Firms** |
| **Band 1** |
| Covington & Burling LLP * |
| **Band 2** |
| Jenner & Block LLP * |
| Reed Smith LLP |
| **Band 3** |
| Dickstein Shapiro LLP * |
| Farella Braun + Martel LLP |
| Jones Day * |
| Latham & Watkins LLP * |
| Morgan, Lewis & Bockius LLP * |

\* Indicates with profile.
Alphabetical order within each band. Band 1 is the highest.

## Band 1

### Covington & Burling LLP
See profile on p.441

**THE FIRM** This national policyholder giant continues to reaffirm its California presence by taking the lead in the most prominent insurance law cases. The firm has recently been involved in a major asbestos coverage action against more than 300 insurers on behalf of ExxonMobil,

while maintaining its activity for key clients such as UnitedHealth and BP. Clients are quick to praise the value they receive from Covington's longstanding experience and extensive knowledge of the insurance market.

**Sources say:** *"An excellent law firm that's got it all: a deep bench and top partners who get the job done."*

**KEY INDIVIDUALS Donald Brown** (see p.625) is held in high esteem by peers who say: *"He makes the opponent's job tougher because he focuses on the real issues."* He is regularly involved in sophisticated disputes, leading on ExxonMobil's $100 million asbestos coverage action and opposing Hartford on behalf of PNC Financial Services in a complex fraud-related fidelity bond claim. The widely respected **David Goodwin** (see p.324) possesses an *"encyclopedic knowledge of insurance law,"* according to one peer. He has recently represented Health Net in a dispute involving a large coverage claim relating to consumer class actions. He has also acted for LyondellBasell on a complex London arbitration. **Lawrence Hobel** (see p.335) handles the full range of coverage claims, with a particular focus on business interruption and toxic tort cases. He has recently represented Sierra Pacific Industries in third party coverage claims.

## Band 2

### Jenner & Block LLP
See profile on p.1252

**THE FIRM** Part of a strong national network, Jenner's Los Angeles office has continued to make its presence felt on the West Coast. The team is involved in a variety of coverage cases from the representation of Pennsylvania State University in sexual misconduct allegations, to suing Allstate on behalf of Tyson Foods on alleged environmental contamination. The team has also recently handled large international arbitrations and professional liability disputes.

**Sources say:** *"They are very skilled and know their business."*

**KEY INDIVIDUALS** The highly-esteemed **Jerold Oshinsky** (see p.380) has been active on a number of recent environmental coverage cases. He has taken the lead for Tyson Foods in its contamination coverage action, and represented M.D.C. Holdings in a claim arising from alleged exposure to radon. According to commentators, **Mary Craig Calkins** (see p.626) has *"subject matter knowledge that is second to none."* She deals with a range of D&O and coverage disputes on behalf of major media and entertainment clients, including the representation of News Corporation in coverage issues arising from the UK phone hacking scandal. **Linda Kornfeld** (see p.647) regularly defends D&O actions arising out of high-profile bank failure coverage suits. Her broad coverage practice includes the representation of Amgen subsidiary Immunex in pharmaceutical matters.

## Reed Smith LLP

**THE FIRM** Reed Smith's West Coast practice remains a key part of the firm's nationwide policyholder group, with activity in professional and general liability, first party property and bankruptcy-related insurance coverage work. Recent highlights include acting for Quicken Loans and Homeward Residential in sophisticated mortgage insurance disputes. Clients value the team's ability to provide the full range of services required when dealing with complex insurance cases.

**Sources say:** "*I get the one-to-one relationship as if they were a small firm, but I know they have an army behind them when it is needed.*"

**KEY INDIVIDUALS David Halbreich** is highly sought by clients, who say: "*There has not been anything that has been thrown at him that he has not been able to approach with an impeccable logic and guided by his experience.*"

## Band 3

### Dickstein Shapiro LLP
See profile on p.911

**THE FIRM** This established nationwide practice deals with the full range of policyholder disputes, from entertainment coverage actions to casualty insurance matters. The team has recently been involved in ongoing coverage issues for San Diego Gas & Electric Company arising from litigation following the 2007 San Diego wildfire. Key entertainment industry clients include Fox, Live Nation and NBCUniversal.

**KEY INDIVIDUALS Kirk Pasich** (see p.382) is regarded by clients as "*one of the best attorneys in town*" He plays a key role in many of the team's most significant cases, including the continued representation of Northrop Grumman in a high-value dispute. **Stephen Goldberg** (see p.322) enjoys a healthy reputation among peers for coverage disputes. He represents both corporations and plaintiffs in insurance recovery matters including D&O, E&O and business interruption. The "*sensational*" **Cassandra Franklin** (see p.636) was recently involved in coverage defense for Universal Music Group. As well as her entertainment practice, she also handles professional liability and general commercial coverage cases.

### Farella Braun + Martel LLP

**THE FIRM** This well-established California firm deals with commercial coverage disputes connected with exposures including environmental, professional and product liability. The team represents clients from a range of industries, and has been particularly active in the technology space with sophisticated work on behalf of clients including Seagate, McAfee and Electronic Arts.

**Sources say:** "*They are very conscious and aware of client needs and are understanding of our issues.*"

**KEY INDIVIDUALS William Friedrich** is an expert in insurance coverage and bad faith matters. He has also been active in professional liability disputes, having represented McAfee in D&O liability claims. Sources describe **Mary McCutcheon** as an "*extremely competent attorney with a great wealth of knowledge.*" Her practice focuses on professional liability, securities fraud and IP disputes.

### Jones Day
See profile on p.919

**THE FIRM** This policyholder practice has a broad case portfolio which covers environmental disaster claims, IP issues, large putative class actions and bad faith matters. The group has also represented clients in significant insurance recovery claims arising from major disasters including 9/11, Hurricane Katrina and the 2011 Japanese tsunami. Significant clients include Adobe Systems, Dell, Chevron and Union Pacific Railroad Company.

**KEY INDIVIDUALS David Steuber** (see p.412) is described by sources as a "*wonderful human being and terrific lawyer.*" He provides the full range of insurance coverage services, ranging from traditional toxic tort claims to large bankruptcy actions. **Tyrone Childress** (see p.294) represents clients from a range of industries including large technology companies and insurance holding groups. He regularly represents Union Pacific Railroad Company in coverage matters. New entry **Martin Myers** (see p.656) joins the rankings following strong feedback from the market. He has recently represented leading software company Adobe Systems in a coverage action.

### Latham & Watkins LLP
See profile on p.446

**THE FIRM** This well-established firm is known for its experience in high-stakes insurance disputes on behalf of major policyholders. The team has recently represented Fluor in a series of disputes involving bodily injury and property damage claims, while also acting for significant organizations from a range of industries including Sempra Energy and the Los Angeles Dodgers. Clients are particularly impressed with the team's extensive knowledge across the insurance industry.

**Sources say:** "*They have experts in everything and we know we can call them at a moment's notice.*"

**KEY INDIVIDUALS Andrew Lundberg** earns plaudits from a series of commentators. According to clients, he is "*a real expert who knows the case law.*" He has played a key role on behalf of the Los Angeles Dodgers in major negotiations with Hartford Life Insurance. **Peter Rosen** has taken a lead role on behalf of URS in a $500 million coverage case. He is also involved in ongoing business interruption actions connected with 9/11.

### Morgan, Lewis & Bockius LLP
See profile on p.2246

**THE FIRM** The California branch of this established national insurance practice has a prominent role in dealing with historical general liability programs for mass torts, with a particular focus on asbestos-related claims. The firm also represents clients in professional liability and bankruptcy coverage issues. Its client portfolio includes Pepsi, Kimberly-Clark and Deutsche Bank.

**KEY INDIVIDUALS** "*Fine attorney*" **Michel Horton** (see p.337) advises and litigates on a wide range of insurance recovery actions. He recently represented ITT Corporation and Goulds Pumps in a $300 million excess policy class action dispute. **Jeffrey Raskin** (see p.661) specializes in large asbestos cases. He has taken the lead on the $1 billion asbestos and bankruptcy coverage representation of Plant Insulation.

## Other Notable Practitioners

**Nancy Cohen** of Proskauer Rose LLP is held in high regard by her peers at the insurance bar. She routinely appears in jury trial cases as well as being experienced in conducting complex negotiations. **Harvey Levine** of Levine & Miller Law Offices maintains his healthy standing in the field as an expert in insurance bad faith matters. Clients praise Munger, Tolles & Olson LLP partner **Cary Lerman** (see p.649) as *"a strong litigator"* with a commercial approach. He handles professional liability and business interruption matters, as well as reinsurance issues. Irell & Manella LLP practice head **Marc Maister** (see p.651) focuses on professional liability and environmental disaster coverage. He is both *"good on his feet and in the courtroom."* **Curtis Porterfield** (see p.660) of Hunton & Williams LLP *"has an innate sense of where the client is and where the client wants to be,"* according to sources. He is experienced in a range of

insurance recovery disputes. **William Shernoff** of plaintiff firm Shernoff Bidart Echeverria LLP is recognized as a leading insurance bad faith lawyer who is *"as good as it gets in that area."* **Michael Bidart** of Shernoff Bidart Echeverria LLP is an experienced healthcare litigator with extensive expertise in disability insurance claims on behalf of plaintiffs. **Reynold Siemens** (see p.665) of Pillsbury Winthrop Shaw Pittman LLP is a popular choice for policyholder clients. He has particular experience in nuclear liabilities and consumer torts. *"He has added value to our organization every time we have engaged him,"* say clients.

Litigator **Barry Levin** of Orrick, Herrington & Sutcliffe LLP is known in the market as a *"very bright, very savvy"* coverage lawyer. He has been involved in a number of matters arising out of the residential mortgage crisis, including a significant victory in monoline insurer cases on behalf of Credit Suisse. Market commentators know Orrick, Herrington & Sutcliffe LLP's **Richard DeNatale** as an experienced expert in coverage law. He was recently retained by Pacific Gas & Electric to pursue coverage in connection with the San Bruno natural gas pipeline explosion.

# INTELLECTUAL PROPERTY

Commentary about individuals can be found under their firm's paragraph.  If the firm has no paragraph (is not ranked) look at Other Notable Practitioners.

| Intellectual Property Leading Firms |
| --- |
| **Band 1** |
| Irell & Manella * |
| Morrison & Foerster LLP * |
| Quinn Emanuel Urquhart & Sullivan, LLP |
| **Band 2** |
| Covington & Burling LLP * |
| Keker & Van Nest LLP * |
| Orrick, Herrington & Sutcliffe LLP * |
| Weil, Gotshal & Manges LLP * |
| **Band 3** |
| Bingham McCutchen LLP * |
| Cooley LLP |
| DLA Piper LLP (US) * |
| Durie Tangri LLP |
| Fish & Richardson PC |
| Gibson, Dunn & Crutcher LLP * |
| Kirkland & Ellis LLP * |
| Latham & Watkins LLP * |
| McDermott Will & Emery LLP * |
| Ropes & Gray LLP * |
| Sidley Austin LLP * |
| Skadden, Arps, Slate, Meagher & Flom LLP & Affiliates * |
| WilmerHale * |
| **Band 4** |
| Arnold & Porter LLP * |
| Fenwick & West LLP * |
| Finnegan, Henderson, Farabow, Garrett & Dunner LLP * |
| Greenberg Traurig, LLP * |
| Jones Day * |
| Knobbe Martens Olson & Bear |
| O'Melveny & Myers LLP * |
| Wilson Sonsini Goodrich & Rosati * |

\* Indicates firm with profile.
Alphabetical order within each band. Band 1 is the highest.

*The editorial is in alphabetical order by firm name.*

## Arnold & Porter LLP
**See profile on p.906**
**THE FIRM** Arnold & Porter's IP practice is led from its offices in Los Angeles, San Francisco and Palo Alto, which represent technology, life sciences, entertainment and new media companies. The team has litigation, prosecution, counseling and transactional capabilities, as well as experience in protecting all types of intellectual property assets. Notable clients include CBS, Google, Boston Scientific and Amazon.com.
**Sources say:** *"They are practical, easy to work with and communicate well. They have good substantive knowledge."*
**KEY INDIVIDUALS Marty Glick** (see p.638) recently represented Amazon in a trademark action brought by Apple, relating to the use of the term 'Appstore'. He has experience in copyright, trademark, trade secret, patent and antitrust litigation. **Thomas Magnani**'s (see p.651) practice encompasses IP counseling, transactional and licensing matters. Clients say he is *"knowledgeable, effective and efficient."* **Ronald Johnston** (see p.644) is cochair of the international IP and technology practice at Arnold & Porter. He focuses on litigation in the IT and entertainment industries. Clients comment: *"If you have a complicated, nuanced copyright issue to which there is no clear answer, Ron is the person who will think creatively and outside the box to try and find the solution."*

## Bingham McCutchen LLP
**See profile on p.1515**
**THE FIRM** The West Coast intellectual property practice of this national, multiservice firm operates out of its San Francisco and Silicon Valley offices. The team offers extensive IP litigation services; transactional and strategic services; and prosecution and counseling across patent, trade-

mark, trade dress, domain names and copyright. Oracle, Yardi Systems and eBay are key clients.
**KEY INDIVIDUALS Geoffrey Howard** (see p.642) is a trial lawyer with expertise in internet, software and telecom matters. He recently acted as co-lead counsel for Oracle in a high-value copyright infringement action against SAP. Sources say he is *"an excellent writer and a superb oral advocate."* One satisfied client adds that *"he understands our business and interacts very well with our executives."*

## Cooley LLP
**THE FIRM** This West Coast-based firm has offices in Palo Alto, Los Angeles, San Francisco and San Diego. Patent litigation is a key focus of the IP practice, alongside the team's patent counseling and protection capabilities and its trademark, copyright and advertising services. Cooley has particular expertise in technology matters, including computer hardware, software and internet-related issues such as e-commerce and domain names. HTC, Facebook and LinkedIn are key clients.
**KEY INDIVIDUALS Thomas Friel** is head of the firm's IP litigation practice and has experience in patent, trademark, copyright and trade secrets litigation. He recently represented NexTag, an online price comparison site, in a patent infringement action brought by LendingTree. Peers praise him as being an expert attorney while clients name him as a go-to for coordinating patent litigation. **Michael Rhodes** enjoys a healthy market reputation for hi-tech and internet-related IP work. He recently acted for Facebook on Yahoo!'s claims that it had infringed 12 social network patents, resulting in a strategic partnership and patent cross-licensing agreement. He is praised by clients for his notable litigation skills. **Anne Peck** chairs Cooley's trademark, copyright and advertising group and has a practice focus on the selection and protection of brand names, domain names and copyrights. Recent work includes rep-

## Intellectual Property: Patent

### Senior Statesmen

**Senior Statesmen: distinguished older practitioners**

| | | | |
|---|---|---|---|
| Anthony William | Orrick, Herrington & Sutcliffe LLP | Martens Don | Knobbe Martens Olson & Bear |

### Leading Individuals

**Star individuals**

| | |
|---|---|
| Chu Morgan | Irell & Manella * |
| Powers Matthew D | Tensegrity Law Group (ONP)† |

**Band 1**

| | |
|---|---|
| Haslam Robert | Covington & Burling LLP * |
| Jacobs Michael A | Morrison & Foerster LLP * |
| McElhinny Harold J | Morrison & Foerster LLP * |
| McMahon Terrence P | McDermott Will & Emery LLP * |
| Van Nest Robert | Keker & Van Nest LLP |
| Verhoeven Charles K | Quinn Emanuel Urquhart & Sullivan, LLP |

**Band 2**

| | |
|---|---|
| Allcock John | DLA Piper LLP (US) * |
| Bobrow Jared | Weil, Gotshal & Manges LLP * |
| Bunsow Henry | Bunsow De Mory Smith Allison LLP (ONP)† |
| Chatterjee I Neel | Orrick, Herrington & Sutcliffe LLP |
| Durie Daralyn J | Durie Tangri LLP |
| Keker John | Keker & Van Nest LLP |
| Krevans Rachel | Morrison & Foerster LLP * |
| Reines Edward R | Weil, Gotshal & Manges LLP * |
| Shulman Ron | Latham & Watkins LLP * |

**Band 3**

| | |
|---|---|
| Barsky Wayne | Gibson, Dunn & Crutcher LLP * |
| Chaikovsky Yar R | McDermott Will & Emery LLP * |
| Elacqua James J | Skadden, Arps, Slate, Meagher & Flom * |
| Flagel Mark A | Latham & Watkins LLP |
| Fram Robert | Covington & Burling LLP * |
| Friel Jr Thomas J | Cooley LLP |
| Gartman John | Gartman Law P.C. (ONP)† |
| Lemley Mark | Durie Tangri LLP |
| Lumish Douglas E | Kasowitz, Benson, Torres (ONP)† * |
| Lutton Katherine | Fish & Richardson PC |
| Ottenweller Chris R | Orrick, Herrington & Sutcliffe LLP |
| Randall Jeff G | Paul Hastings LLP (ONP)† |
| Samuels Mark A | O'Melveny & Myers LLP |
| Selwyn Mark D | WilmerHale * |

| | |
|---|---|
| Stern Claude M | Quinn Emanuel Urquhart & Sullivan, LLP |
| Stone Greg | Munger, Tolles & Olson LLP (ONP)† * |

**Band 4**

| | |
|---|---|
| Abrams William F | King & Spalding LLP (ONP)† * |
| Bettinger Michael | K&L Gates (ONP)† * |
| Bohler William J | Law Office of William Bohler (ONP)† |
| Doyle David C | Morrison & Foerster LLP * |
| Gindler David I | Irell & Manella * |
| Glick Marty | Arnold & Porter LLP * |
| Goldman Robert J | Ropes & Gray LLP |
| Guy III G Hopkins | Baker Botts LLP (ONP)† * |
| Haile Lisa A | DLA Piper LLP (US) * |
| Hansen David | Skadden, Arps, Slate, Meagher & Flom * |
| Hattenbach Benjamin | Irell & Manella * |
| Iancu Andrei | Irell & Manella * |
| Johnson Kevin | Quinn Emanuel Urquhart & Sullivan, LLP |
| Johnson Jr Daniel | Morgan, Lewis & Bockius LLP (ONP)† * |
| Korniczky Stephen S | Sheppard, Mullin, Richter (ONP)† |
| Lehr Matthew | Davis Polk & Wardwell LLP (ONP)† * |
| Malecek Michael | Kaye Scholer LLP (ONP)† * |
| Meeker Heather J | Greenberg Traurig, LLP * |
| Olson Jeffrey M | Sidley Austin LLP * |
| Pasahow Lynn H | Fenwick & West LLP * |
| Plimack Michael | Covington & Burling LLP * |
| Poplawski Edward G | Wilson Sonsini Goodrich & Rosati * |
| Quinn John B | Quinn Emanuel Urquhart & Sullivan, LLP |
| Re Joseph R | Knobbe Martens Olson & Bear |
| Rhodes Michael G | Cooley LLP |
| Thayer M Patricia | Sidley Austin LLP * |
| Thomases Andrew N | Skadden, Arps, Slate, Meagher & Flom LLP * |
| Winters Vernon M | Sidley Austin LLP * |
| Yannuzzi Dan N | Sheppard, Mullin, Richter & Hampton (ONP)† |

**Up-and-coming individuals**

| | |
|---|---|
| Magnani Thomas A | Arnold & Porter LLP * |

## Intellectual Property: Trademark, Copyright & Trade Secrets

### Leading Individuals

**Band 1**

| | |
|---|---|
| Abel Sally | Fenwick & West LLP * |
| Bridges Andrew P | Fenwick & West LLP * |
| Chanin Jeffrey R | Keker & Van Nest LLP |
| Hayes David L | Fenwick & West LLP * |
| Kramer David H | Wilson Sonsini Goodrich & Rosati |
| Nimmer David | Irell & Manella * |
| Page Michael | Durie Tangri LLP |
| Stern Claude M | Quinn Emanuel Urquhart & Sullivan, LLP |
| Viscounty Perry J | Latham & Watkins LLP * |

**Band 2**

| | |
|---|---|
| Howard Geoffrey M | Bingham McCutchen LLP * |
| Hurst Annette | Orrick, Herrington & Sutcliffe LLP |
| Johnston Ronald | Arnold & Porter LLP * |
| Pruetz Adrian | Glaser, Weil, Fink, Jacobs, Howard (ONP)† |
| Weiss Gary E | Orrick, Herrington & Sutcliffe LLP |

**Band 3**

| | |
|---|---|
| Abrams William F | King & Spalding LLP * |
| Grace David W | Loeb & Loeb LLP (ONP)† * |
| Mayer Marc | Mitchell Silberberg & Knupp LLP (ONP)† |
| Peck Anne | Cooley LLP |
| Ransom Rollin A | Sidley Austin LLP * |
| Slafsky John | Wilson Sonsini Goodrich & Rosati |
| Tangri Ragesh K | Durie Tangri LLP |

## Intellectual Property: Patent Prosecution

### Leading Firms

**Band 1**

Knobbe Martens Olson & Bear

**Band 2**

Finnegan, Henderson, Farabow, Garrett & Dunner LLP *

Kilpatrick Townsend & Stockton LLP *

Morrison & Foerster LLP *

\* Indicates firm / individual with profile.
†ONP = Other Notable Practitioner.

resenting TiVo in a trademark dispute in Australia, resulting in the cancellation of the defendant's 'Vivo' mark.

### Covington & Burling LLP
See profile on p.441

**THE FIRM** This firm offers clients an IP practice focused on the hi-tech and life sciences fields. From its offices in Silicon Valley, San Francisco and San Diego, Covington handles litigation and appellate work in computer ware, telecom, pharmaceuticals, medical devices and financial services. Recent work has included smartphone, semiconductor and wireless network technology.

**Sources say:** "They have good trial counsel and a good technical team."

**KEY INDIVIDUALS Robert Haslam** (see p.640) is a "very well-regarded" litigator with experience in patent and trade secrets disputes. Clients hail from the hi-tech and life sciences sectors, with technologies including semiconductor,

software, microprocessor and medical devices. He recently represented Palm in wireless and optical reader patent litigation, securing two appellate victories confirming noninfringement of seven patents. Other clients include Samsung Electronics and Huawei Technologies. **Robert Fram** (see p.636) is experienced in patent, trade secret and licensing litigation, ranging across such technologies as computer, semiconductor and software. He recently worked with Fujitsu in a patent infringement action relating to wireless networking. **Michael Plimack** (see p.659) is chair of the electronics and information technology group and has experience in patent, trademark, copyright and trade secret litigation. He recently acted for Huawei Technologies on ITC disputes relating to 3G wireless technology patents.

### DLA Piper LLP (US)
See profile on p.1971

**THE FIRM** This international firm has offices in Silicon Valley, Los Angeles, San Francisco, San Diego and Sacramento, housing over 70 IP and technology attorneys. The practice covers life sciences technologies as well as electrical engineering, semiconductor, computer system and internet technologies. Key clients include Apple, Samsung Electronics, Pfizer, Motorola and Abbott Laboratories.

**KEY INDIVIDUALS John Allcock** (see p.620) is a well-regarded patent litigator with experience in district court, appellate work, the ITC and arbitration proceedings. Recent work includes acting for Abbott on a patent infringement claim brought against Sandoz's generic high cholesterol drug. **Lisa Haile** (see p.639) has particular expertise in life sciences patent protection, as well as patentability and validity matters. Her practice covers technologies including molecular biology, diagnostics, drug delivery platforms and bioinformatics. Sources say she *"stays current with changes in patent law"* and that *"her reputation in the San Diego community and beyond is stellar."*

## Durie Tangri LLP
### See profile on p.679
**THE FIRM** This streamlined San Francisco-based litigation boutique has a reputation for high-quality IP work in the patent, copyright, trademark and trade secrets arenas. Clients include Genentech, Google and Twitter.
**Sources say:** *"They are becoming a go-to firm for a lot of clients. They're very, very good."*
**KEY INDIVIDUALS Daralyn Durie** is a highly regarded patent litigator whose clients include Genentech and LinkedIn. She recently acted for Google on the settlement of copyright infringement claims relating to its digitization of works for the Google Library Project. Peers name her as *"a real star of the future"* and *"a special lawyer who will be around a long time."* **Mark Lemley** has expertise in computer and internet matters, IP law and antitrust. His practice covers all areas of IP litigation and counseling. Peers praise him as *"very knowledgeable about intellectual property law."* **Ragesh Tangri** has represented IP clients in district court, appellate court and ITC proceedings. Hi-tech is a particular area of activity within his practice. **Michael Page** is an experienced IP litigator with particular experience in trademark and copyright matters. Peers describe him as *"a great litigator and a no-nonsense lawyer"* and note that he *"has been involved in some of the most important copyright cases of the last few years."*

## Fenwick & West LLP
### See profile on p.680
**THE FIRM** This full-service firm has offices in San Francisco and Silicon Valley. The practice covers patent prosecution, litigation and licensing as well as counseling and strategy across copyright, trademark and trade dress. The team is particularly active in the software and new media spheres.
**KEY INDIVIDUALS Lynn Pasahow** (see p.658) is a litigator with experience in electronics, software, life sciences and internet matters. His practice covers patent and other IP cases. **Sally Abel** (see p.620) specializes in trademark and trade name counseling, with particular experience in domain name matters and online trademark rights. She also handles trademark portfolio development and management. **Andrew Bridges** (see p.625) is an experienced trial lawyer with copyright, trademark and trade secret expertise. Clients say: *"He knows the copyright and trademark space and is in touch with the market globally. He is a global player and an excellent strategist."* **David Hayes** (see p.641) chairs the firm's IP practice. He handles counseling, litigation, licensing and transactional work across the gamut of IP matters, with particular experience in copyright issues in new media. Sources say he is *"a major influence in the development of IP work in California."*

## Finnegan, Henderson, Farabow, Garrett & Dunner LLP
### See profile on p.912
**THE FIRM** The Palo Alto office of this national boutique offers the full range of IP services, including patent prosecution and litigation, transactional and strategic counseling, ITC and patent office proceedings, and copyright, trademark and trade secret work. The team recently represented HTC in ITC investigations relating to smartphones, wireless communications and other technologies. The firm also handles patent prosecution and counseling work for Shionogi on its pharmaceutical and diagnostic products.
**Sources say:** *"Finnegan is a fantastic firm and I would highly recommend them to others. I feel very taken care of by the Finnegan attorneys."*
**KEY INDIVIDUALS Erik Puknys** is the managing partner of the Palo Alto office.

## Fish & Richardson PC
**THE FIRM** This national IP boutique has offices in San Diego and Silicon Valley servicing such clients as Microsoft, Allergan and SAP. The practice is particularly recognized for its patent prosecution work across consumer products, chemicals, life sciences, hi-tech and academic research. The firm also offers litigation and counseling services in trademark, copyright and regulatory matters.
**KEY INDIVIDUALS Katherine Lutton** is a well-regarded patent litigator with experience in a variety of technology fields including semiconductor, internet and computer, and telecom.

## Gibson, Dunn & Crutcher LLP
### See profile on p.682
**THE FIRM** Gibson Dunn's West Coast IP practice operates out of offices in Orange County, Palo Alto and Century City. The team has litigation, transactional, regulatory and trademark prosecution capabilities. Recent work includes representing Apple in an eight-patent infringement action brought against Samsung smartphone, tablet and media player products. Other notable clients include Novo Nordisk, Amazon and Allergan.
**KEY INDIVIDUALS Wayne Barsky** (see p.622) is a patent litigator and cochair of the firm's IP practice. His practice encompasses biotech, pharmaceutical and medical device matters as well as new media technology, including social networks. He recently represented Merck Serono, Pfizer and EMD Serono in a high-value patent infringement action brought by Biogen.

## Greenberg Traurig, LLP
### See profile on p.1024
**THE FIRM** This national firm has offices in Los Angeles, Orange County and San Francisco representing such clients as Mozilla, LinkedIn and Demand Media. The practice covers patent, trademark and copyright matters and is particularly known for its strength in entertainment IP. The team recently represented The Pokémon Company in a patent suit relating to the electronic trading cards market.

**Sources say:** *"They're fantastic – completely client-oriented."*
**KEY INDIVIDUALS Heather Meeker** (see p.654) focuses on technology transfer and licensing in the hi-tech, communications and medical devices fields. Clients say she is *"just outstanding. She understands our business, the environment that we work in and is an expert at licensing and technology transactions in general."*

## Irell & Manella
### See profile on p.686
**THE FIRM** Irell & Manella is widely regarded as one of the preeminent IP practices in California, with offices in Los Angeles and Newport Beach. The firm has an excellent reputation for patent litigation in particular, recently representing TiVo in an infringement action against AT&T surrounding DVR technology. Other notable clients include HuLu, BlackBerry and Tessera. The practice also encompasses trademark, copyright and trade secrets matters.
**Sources say:** *"The uniform brightness of these lawyers is remarkable. They have what I call 'talent density'."*
**KEY INDIVIDUALS Morgan Chu** (see p.628) has a stellar reputation in intellectual property litigation and is commended by peers as *"a fabulous trial lawyer."* He recently represented St Jude Medical in a patent infringement action, securing a permanent injunction against AccessClosure in relation to vascular closing device technology. Other representations include Tessera, Skechers and Novellus Systems. **David Gindler** (see p.638) specializes in the life sciences sector and has experience in semiconductor, computer architecture and microprocessor technologies. He recently acted for Ariosa on its prenatal testing technology, striking out a motion for preliminary injunction. Peers say he *"is supersmart, very strategic and writes beautifully."* Patent litigator **Benjamin Hattenbach** (see p.640) has experience in the ITC and USPTO as well as in federal and district courts. He has a background in engineering and recently acted for Tessera on a licensing dispute with Amkor, securing an arbitration award for his client. Sources appreciate that he *"so often finds different ways of approaching an issue."* According to market sources, **Andrei Iancu** (see p.643) is *"enormously sharp and strategic"* and a *"brilliant lawyer."* Iancu's primary focus is on litigation, with experience in patent and trademark prosecution, licensing and due diligence. He recently acted for TiVo on its patent infringement suit against AT&T. Of counsel **David Nimmer** (see p.657) has a practice focus on the entertainment and publishing industries, as well as representing clients in the hi-tech field. He is particularly known for his expertise in copyright matters.

## Jones Day
### See profile on p.919
**THE FIRM** This international firm has a West Coast IP practice spread across offices in Silicon Valley, Irvine, San Francisco and Los Angeles. The practice covers patent strategy and portfolio management, counseling and litigation in patent, copyright, trademark and trade secret matters. The team has worked with clients in a range of industries and technologies, including pharmaceuticals, biotech,

*The editorial is in alphabetical order by firm name.*

software, semiconductor and energy. Celgene and Apple are key clients.

**Sources say:** *"Their patent group is staffed with attorneys with highly technical backgrounds in addition to their excellent legal expertise. They are very responsive and have delivered great work product under intense time pressure."*

**KEY INDIVIDUALS** San Diego partner Anthony Insogna is the firmwide leader of the IP practice.

## Keker & Van Nest LLP

**THE FIRM** This San Francisco-based litigation boutique is renowned for its trial lawyers and handles disputes in patent, trademark, copyright and trade secrets. An impressive client list includes a series of well-known names such as HTC, Genentech, Intel, Twitter and Facebook. The team recently represented Google as lead counsel in a high-value patent infringement and copyright action brought by Oracle against elements of the Android operating system and the use of Java APIs. Both patent and copyright claims were dismissed.

**Sources say:** *"A superb smaller firm. The quality of the lawyering there in patent cases is just excellent."*

**KEY INDIVIDUALS** Highly regarded and well known in the industry, **Robert Van Nest** is *"by all accounts, a first-rate trial lawyer."* He has a wide-ranging trial practice, with experience in patent infringement and trademark litigation. *"If you had a case in Silicon Valley going to trial, you'd be lucky to have John Keker or Robert Van Nest standing right there with you,"* say sources. **John Keker**'s intellectual property work covers patent, copyright, trademark and trade secret matters. Market commentators note that *"he can try a case and try it extremely well."* **Jeffrey Chanin**'s IP practice includes patent infringement and copyright litigation. He has particular experience in trade secrets matters.

## Kilpatrick Townsend & Stockton LLP
See profile on p.1109

**THE FIRM** The San Diego, San Francisco, Silicon Valley and Walnut Creek offices of this firm serve clients in the technology and life sciences arenas. Recent work includes patent preparation, prosecution and counseling for Logitech on a variety of electronics and peripherals. The team also handled patent prosecution and counseling for Oracle on middleware, web server, application interfacing and other products.

**KEY INDIVIDUALS** William Shaffer, managing partner of the Silicon Valley office, is a key practice contact.

## Kirkland & Ellis LLP
See profile on p.1254

**THE FIRM** This full-service national firm has an active IP litigation practice in its Los Angeles, Palo Alto and San Francisco offices. The team's work includes patent, trademark, copyright, internet and trade secrets cases, as well as transactional matters. Intel is a key client of the firm, as are Oracle, Yahoo! and Apple.

**Sources say:** *"They are strong, hard-working lawyers. No stone will be left unturned on any case."*

**KEY INDIVIDUALS** Luke Dauchot is a key practice contact for the West Coast.

## Knobbe Martens Olson & Bear

**THE FIRM** Knobbe Martens is a specialist firm offering services in litigation, licensing, due diligence, strategy and prosecution across all areas of IP. A particular area of strength is the development of clients' patent assets through prosecution and opinion work. The team is experienced in a variety of proceedings at the USPTO.

**Sources say:** *"An outstanding firm."*

**KEY INDIVIDUALS** **Joseph Re** is an experienced IP litigator with expertise in the life sciences arena. His practice covers patent proceedings before district and appellate courts. **Don Martens** is a well-regarded practitioner with extensive patent litigation experience in arbitration and in court. He now serves as arbitrator, mediator or special master in IP disputes. Peers say his is *"a name that always has a lot of luster."*

## Latham & Watkins LLP
See profile on p.446

**THE FIRM** This international firm has West Coast offices in Silicon Valley, San Francisco, San Diego, Orange County and Los Angeles. The team focuses on IP litigation, representing such clients as Adobe, AU Optronics and Cadence Pharmaceuticals in patent disputes, as well as Symantec in trademark infringement matters. The practice also has copyright and trade secrets capabilities.

**KEY INDIVIDUALS** **Ron Shulman** (see p.665) is a *"very sharp"* attorney focusing on patent matters, including prosecution and defending infringement claims. Previous work has included diverse subject matters, including medical devices, semiconductors, chemicals and nuclear fuel technology. **Mark Flagel** is a *"very strategic and very thoughtful"* patent litigator specializing in IT matters. Recent work includes representing Monolithic Power Systems in a patent and breach of contract dispute relating to voltage converters, resulting in a $2 million award that was affirmed at the Federal Circuit. **Perry Viscounty** (see p.670) handles a broad array of IP issues, from patent to trade secrets and domain name disputes. He is particularly experienced in trademark and technology matters, recently acting for Symantec on a trademark infringement action brought against Johns Creek Software relating to domain names and Norton software products.

## McDermott Will & Emery LLP
See profile on p.1258

**THE FIRM** This international, multiservice firm has offices in Orange County, Los Angeles and Silicon Valley, the latter expanding with the addition of nine IP lawyers in early 2012. The practice focuses on IP litigation across patent, trademark, trade secret, trade dress and copyright. Notable clients include Amazon.com, HTC, LinkedIn and Amgen.

**Sources say:** *"They are excellent lawyers and they achieved a tremendous result for us."*

**KEY INDIVIDUALS** Sources name **Terrence McMahon** (see p.653) as *"one of the top courtroom lawyers in California,"* praising his *"ability to make complex technology accessible and easy to understand for judges and juries."* His practice covers a broad range of IP litigation issues,

particularly in the hi-tech arena. **Yar Chaikovsky** (see p.627) is well regarded in the California market and his IP litigation practice is recognized by peers and clients alike. His fields of experience include semiconductor, communications, network and computer technologies. He recently represented HTC in ITC and district court patent infringement cases.

## Morrison & Foerster LLP
See profile on p.1990

**THE FIRM** This multiservice firm has a strong Californian presence, with IP practices in its Los Angeles, San Diego, San Francisco and Palo Alto offices. The team is known for both IP litigation and patent prosecution, particularly in the hi-tech and life sciences fields. Recent work includes assisting Genentech with the development of patent strategy and prosecution. The team also acted for Oracle on a high-profile patent and copyright infringement action against Google.

**Sources say:** *"As big a firm as it is, they're very low key and approachable. The work is great."*

**KEY INDIVIDUALS** **Michael Jacobs** (see p.644) is *"a pillar of the Silicon Valley patent litigation community,"* with expertise in hi-tech and life sciences technologies. He recently represented Novell in long-running software copyright litigation, defeating damages claims of between $115 and $200 million. **Harold McElhinny** (see p.653) focuses his practice on patent, trade secret and copyright litigation in the electronics and life sciences fields. Market commentators identify him as *"a fabulous trial lawyer and a nice guy who has had some major successes."* He recently obtained a summary judgment of invalidity for Nikon in relation to patent infringement claims brought by Anvik. **Rachel Krevans** (see p.648) is a patent litigator with experience in a variety of electronic and life science technologies. Sources say she is *"incredibly bright"* with a *"good reputation"* in the market. She recently represented DISH Network/EchoStar at the Federal Circuit, achieving a summary judgment of invalidity ruling for the client. **David Doyle** (see p.633) focuses on patent disputes in the pharmaceutical, biotechnology and medical device fields. He is also experienced in cases involving electronics. He recently acted for Sandoz in a number of ANDA litigation matters, defending its products against infringement claims made by Allergan and Hospira, among others.

## O'Melveny & Myers LLP
See profile on p.693

**THE FIRM** O'Melveny has offices in Silicon Valley, Los Angeles, Century City and San Francisco and provides IP services to technology and entertainment companies. Clients include Apple, Samsung Electronics, Novartis and Warner Bros. As well as the acquisition and development of IP rights, the team handles patent, trademark, copyright and trade secrets disputes.

**KEY INDIVIDUALS** **Mark Samuels** is a *"strong trial lawyer"* focused on technology litigation. He is particularly praised for his *"ability to take complex legal concepts and translate them for his clients."* He recently represented RealPage, an online property management software company, in litigation and settlement of trade secrets and copyright infringement claims brought by Yardi Systems.

## Orrick, Herrington & Sutcliffe LLP
See profile on p.1994

**THE FIRM** With offices in San Francisco, Sacramento, Silicon Valley, Los Angeles and Orange County, Orrick Herrington & Sutcliffe has a considerable presence in the California IP market. The practice encompasses a broad range of services, including patent prosecution and litigation; trademark, copyright, trade secret and false advertising litigation; technology transfer and transactions; and due diligence and IP counseling. Particular fields of expertise are life sciences, hi-tech and internet matters, and the entertainment industry.

**KEY INDIVIDUALS Neel Chatterjee** cochairs the firm's IP group and focuses his practice on software, computer technology, networks, internet-related litigation and data storage. Sources praise his ability to "*look at the case as a big picture,*" and his "*high-level strategy.*" He recently secured a noninfringement judgment for Apple in ITC proceedings relating to image compression patents, part of the ongoing 'smartphone war'. **Chris Ottenweller** also represented Apple in ITC proceedings, as well as securing a summary judgment of noninfringement for NVIDIA in a patent case brought by BIAX Corporation in early 2012. His practice covers copyright and trade secrets matters in addition to patent work, with cases covering technologies that range from smartphones to semiconductors and operating systems. **William Anthony**'s practice covers semiconductors, computer technology and biotech matters. He focuses on patent litigation. **Annette Hurst** has a trial practice covering patent, trademark, copyright and trade secrets disputes. Recent work includes representing Brocade and Foundry Networks in patent infringement, copyright infringement and trade secret misappropriation actions against A10 Networks and others. Peers praise her as "*a very effective and strong presenter*" as well as "*a really good litigator.*" **Gary Weiss** manages the strategic expansion of the IP group at Orrick and is an experienced trade secrets litigator.

## Quinn Emanuel Urquhart & Sullivan, LLP

**THE FIRM** Intellectual property litigation is the largest practice area at this well-regarded firm, with patent litigation a particular strength. The firm's California presence is spread across offices in Silicon Valley, San Francisco and Los Angeles. Hi-tech and electronics are areas of expertise, with notable clients including Google, Sony, NVIDIA and Broadcom.
**Sources say:** "*Their track record is very successful. They're a huge force in the market.*"
**KEY INDIVIDUALS Charles Verhoeven** is head of the Northern California offices. A litigator with a focus on IP cases, he has particular experience in patent matters. Market sources commend him as "*an incredibly smart attorney*" and note that he is "*excellent at cross-examination.*" He recently represented Cisco, Motorola Mobility, MediaTek, NVIDIA and others in an ITC investigation relating to six DDR memory chip and interface patents.

**Claude Stern** is an experienced intellectual property litigator with expertise in the hi-tech space. His practice covers a range of IP issues, including trade secret misappropriation and patent, copyright and trademark infringement. Clients say he is "*top-notch*" and "*exudes confidence, which engenders the same feeling of confidence in senior business management.*" **Kevin Johnson** has a background in electrical engineering, with clients ranging from household names like HTC and Samsung Electronics to smaller technology companies. Recent work includes acting for 16 defendants, including Sony, on a patent infringement case relating to internal temperature control in electronic goods. Sources say he is an "*outstanding lawyer.*" **John Quinn** is a seasoned trial lawyer who impresses clients with "*his ability to pick things up quickly and identify strong themes.*" He has experience in trade secret and patent cases. Notable clients include Google and NVIDIA.

## Ropes & Gray LLP
See profile on p.1528

**THE FIRM** The Silicon Valley and San Francisco offices of this national firm offer patent prosecution, licensing and IP litigation services. The team represents clients in the life sciences and technology industries, including Google, Pfizer, Vertex Pharmaceuticals and Motorola Mobility.
**KEY INDIVIDUALS Robert Goldman** focuses on litigation across patent, copyright and trade secrets. His practice covers both hi-tech electronics and life sciences, including pharmaceutical products and medical devices. He has acted for Purdue Pharma for a number of years in relation to patent exclusivity of its OxyContin product, recently representing the company in nine actions against proposed generic versions.

## Sidley Austin LLP
See profile on p.1264

**THE FIRM** Sidley Austin's California IP practice operates out of offices in Los Angeles, Palo Alto and San Francisco. The team primarily focuses on patent litigation for plaintiffs and defendants in a range of industries, including e-commerce, computer ware, mobile communications, business methods, biotech and medical devices. Key clients include Apple, AT&T, Deutsche Bank and Genentech.
**Sources say:** "*They're great. They get good results, they're cost-effective, they're very knowledgeable about the law and they're easy to work with.*"
**KEY INDIVIDUALS Jeffrey Olson** (see p.657) is an IP litigator focusing on patent infringement disputes. He also litigates trade secrets and trademark cases. His practice includes counseling on licensing, due diligence and patent procurement. Sources say **Patricia Thayer** (see p.669) is "*very impressive, hard-working, very smart and well thought-of.*" She specializes in patent litigation in life science technologies, including medical devices and biopharmaceuticals. She recently represented Conceptus in a patent infringement case relating to its Essure contraceptive procedure, resulting in a jury award of $18.8 million for her client. **Vernon Winters** (see p.672) joined Sidley Austin's San Francisco office from Weil, Gotshal & Manges in early 2012. Clients say he is "*a very sophisticated and*

smart lawyer, and very responsive.*" He focuses on patent matters in the hi-tech field and Intel is a key client. **Rollin Ransom** (see p.661) has "*extraordinary technical and substantive knowledge*" in trademark and copyright infringement matters. He is focused on internet and entertainment issues. Clients say he is "*a very calm, responsive and intellectual litigator.*"

## Skadden, Arps, Slate, Meagher & Flom LLP & Affiliates
See profile on p.2008

**THE FIRM** The Palo Alto office of this national firm offers copyright and trade secrets litigation services, with patent litigation work a primary focus. The team has particular experience in computing and electronics. Key clients include Medtronic, SanDisk and Hewlett-Packard.
**KEY INDIVIDUALS James Elacqua** (see p.634) heads the firm's patent litigation practice and represents clients in both the technology and life sciences sectors. He recently represented Yahoo! in a dispute involving six patents. Clients say he is "*a very good attorney and very good to work with.*" **David Hansen** (see p.640) is a litigator with experience in patent, trade secret and copyright matters. Recent work includes representing SanDisk at the Federal Circuit, in the Western District of Wisconsin and in the California state court. **Andrew Thomases** (see p.669) focuses on patent and trade secret cases in a variety of technologies, including medical device, wireless and semiconductor. He recently acted for Hewlett-Packard on the settlement of a patent infringement action brought by WiAV Networks relating to WiFi technology.

## Weil, Gotshal & Manges LLP
See profile on p.2015

**THE FIRM** The Silicon Valley office of this multiservice firm is known for its IP litigation practice and, in particular, for patent cases. The team also offers counseling, transactional and strategy services, with a focus on hi-tech IP assets. The firm recently represented Yahoo! and Amazon in an infringement action brought by Eolas, in which previously reexamined and reconfirmed patents relating to internet browser interactivity were ultimately found invalid. Other notable clients include Apple, Cisco Systems, Microsoft and Samsung Electronics.
**Sources say:** "*They are superb on counseling and transactional matters.*"
**KEY INDIVIDUALS Jared Bobrow** (see p.624) specializes in complex patent litigation and has been described by peers as a "*brilliant lawyer.*" His patent litigation practice covers a range of technologies including medical devices, computer architecture, network communications and semiconductors. One client described him as "*probably the finest patent litigator I have ever worked with. He has a keen intellect and a good sense of what will resonate with judges and juries.*" **Edward Reines** (see p.661) is an experienced trial lawyer and "*something of a thought-leader in the patent field.*" He recently acted for NetApp on a patent infringement claim made by Data Network Storage, obtaining a summary judgment of noninfringement for the client.

Sources say: "He really knows patent litigation and he knows how to get it right."

## WilmerHale
### See profile on p.930
**THE FIRM** This national firm has offices in Palo Alto and Los Angeles providing a range of IP services to hi-tech and other clients. The practice is particularly recognized for its patent litigation capabilities, recently representing such clients as Verizon, MediaTek and Cisco Systems.

**KEY INDIVIDUALS** IP litigation practice cochair **Mark Selwyn** (see p.665) has experience in a range of patent matters, from biomedical and business methods to e-commerce and integrated circuits. Sources say: "He's very smart, a very good writer and he gets good results."

## Wilson Sonsini Goodrich & Rosati
### See profile on p.700
**THE FIRM** This multiservice firm has Palo Alto, SoMa, San Francisco and San Diego offices servicing technology and life sciences clients including Pacific Biosciences, Amgen, Google and Broadcom. The team has transactional, counseling and litigation capabilities across patent, trademark, trade secret and copyright matters.

**KEY INDIVIDUALS** David Kramer is "an extraordinarily gifted attorney" specializing in copyright and internet matters. He recently acted for Dropbox in four trademark claims at the USPTO and in the district court in Texas. One client comments: "His litigation skills are as good as they come, but beyond that he understands our business and cares deeply about our success." John Slafsky specializes in trademark, domain name, copyright and advertising matters. A "knowledgeable" attorney, he assists clients with trademark registration and enforcement, copyright clearance, IP licensing and the litigation of trademark, copyright and domain name disputes. **Edward Poplawski** (see p.660) recently joined the firm from Sidley Austin and is described as "an outstanding lawyer" who "really knows what he's doing." He has experience in trademark, copyright and trade secret disputes, and is primarily focused on patent litigation. While at his previous firm he represented eBay/PayPal in a patent infringement dispute relating to a point-of-sale payment system.

## Other Notable Practitioners

**Matthew Powers** of Tensegrity Law Group is a renowned trial lawyer with expertise in both patent and trade secrets litigation. Market commentators recognize him as a "formidable lawyer and a formidable presence" in the court room. **John Gartman** of Gartman Law P.C. has a background in electrical engineering and specializes in hi-tech patent litigation. **Hopkins Guy** (see p.639) of Baker Botts LLP is a "knowledgeable and very good lawyer" specializing in semiconductors, electronics, telecom and computer ware. He has experience in patent and trade secrets law and in ITC, district court and Federal Circuit proceedings. Paul Hastings LLP's global IP practice cochair **Jeff Randall** focuses on patent and trade secret litigation. He has recently represented BlackBerry, IBM, Barclays Bank and AT&T. **Greg Stone** (see p.667) of Munger, Tolles & Olson LLP has particular experience in patent litigation and is named by sources as "a terrific lawyer." His practice covers a range of industries including hi-tech, software, manufacturing and consumer goods. **Michael Bettinger** (see p.623) of K&L Gates is a litigator with experience in the district courts and the ITC. His practice covers both biotech and hi-tech matters. He recently represented Google in a patent infringement action relating to the Android operating system and Android smartphone market. **William Bohler** of Law Office of William Bohler is a patent litigator with expertise in electrical engineering. Sources commend him as "a very smart and very good lawyer." Patent litigator **Daniel Johnson** (see p.644) of Morgan, Lewis & Bockius LLP has particular experience in the hi-tech field, with clients including Sony Computer Entertainment America and SafeNet. Other areas of practice include trade secrets and licensing disputes. **Stephen Korniczky** is cochair of the IP practice group at Sheppard, Mullin, Richter & Hampton LLP. His practice includes trademark, trade secret and copyright counseling, with particular focus on patent litigation. Clients include companies in the e-commerce, life sciences, automotive and hi-tech sectors. **Douglas Lumish** (see p.651) of Kasowitz, Benson, Torres & Friedman LLP is a "highly intelligent and highly organized" patent litigator with particular expertise in the software and internet spheres. Sources say he is "very determined in his approach to litigation." He recently represented Google and YouTube in a high-profile patent infringement case brought by Eolas and the University of California Regents in relation to internet interactivity. **Henry Bunsow** of Bunsow De Mory Smith Allison LLP has experience in ITC proceedings as well as district and Federal Circuit courts. His practice encompasses patent matters relating to electronics, software, biotech and mechanics. Sources say he is "a great lawyer and a great guy." Clients say that Davis Polk & Wardwell LLP IP practice head **Matthew Lehr** (see p.649) is "a terrific trial lawyer" with "the right combination of business savvy and practicality." He focuses on patent litigation in various fields, including life sciences, computer technology and plasma physics. **Adrian Pruetz** is chair of the IP group at Glaser, Weil, Fink, Jacobs, Howard, Avchen & Shapiro, LLP. Her practice covers patent, trademark, trade secret and copyright litigation in the telecom, biotechnology and fashion sectors. **William Abrams** (see p.620) of King & Spalding LLP has a broad practice encompassing patent, trade secrets, copyright and new media matters, as well as technology transfer and licensing. He has experience in the life sciences, computer ware and publishing sectors. **Marc Mayer** of Mitchell Silberberg & Knupp LLP specializes in trademark, copyright and trade secrets matters. His practice covers both entertainment and technology, with market commentators describing him as "incredibly savvy in the digital space." **Dan Yannuzzi** of Sheppard, Mullin, Richter & Hampton LLP is experienced in hi-tech IP matters. His practice includes patent litigation, portfolio development, technology licensing and IP asset transactions. **Michael Malecek** (see p.651) of Kaye Scholer LLP is "a spot-on litigator with great credentials." He focuses on patent litigation, recently representing such companies as Google, Sequenom and Complete Genomics. Clients say: "He brings obvious industry and subject area expertise. He also brings the perspective of an in-house lawyer and a view towards what is best for the business." **David Grace** (see p.638) of Loeb & Loeb LLP primarily focuses on trademark and copyright acquisition, protection and licensing. Recent clients include City National Bank and Duraflame.

# IT & OUTSOURCING

Commentary about individuals can be found under their firm's paragraph. If the firm has no paragraph (is not ranked) look at Other Notable Practitioners.

## IT & Outsourcing
### Leading Firms

**Band 1**
Gibson, Dunn & Crutcher LLP *
Latham & Watkins LLP *
Morrison & Foerster LLP *
Wilson Sonsini Goodrich & Rosati *

**Band 2**
Baker & McKenzie *
Cooley LLP
DLA Piper LLP (US) *
Fenwick & West LLP *
Greenberg Traurig, LLP *

**Band 3**
Arnold & Porter LLP *
Morgan, Lewis & Bockius LLP *
Orrick, Herrington & Sutcliffe LLP *
Pillsbury Winthrop Shaw Pittman LLP *

**Band 4**
Foley & Lardner LLP *
Kirkland & Ellis LLP *
Sheppard, Mullin, Richter & Hampton LLP
Weil, Gotshal & Manges LLP *

## Band 1

### Gibson, Dunn & Crutcher LLP
See profile on p.682

**THE FIRM** This formidable team retains its position as a market leading outsourcing practice. The strategic sourcing and technology transactions practice group draws on the firm's global reach to tackle the most complex ITO, BPO and transformational strategic alliances. Sources note the depth of knowledge and breadth of experience displayed by the group. The team's leading lawyers regularly act on behalf of global heavyweights such as Heineken and KPMG, guiding them through ITO and BPO agreements and the outsourcing of infrastructure services respectively. **Sources say:** *"The main reasons we work with Gibson Dunn are the quality of service and the fact that they are very cognizant of what current market positions are on the issues that are important to us."*
**KEY INDIVIDUALS** *"A recognized authority in the field,"* **Daniel Mummery** (see p.656) is *"one of the very best outsourcing lawyers in the world"* who *"fiercely protects client interests and provides high-value, strategic business and legal advice."* His premier clientele includes McGraw-Hill and Symantec, with the past year seeing him handle a range of outsourcing transactions. Co-heading the practice alongside Mummery, **William Peters** (see p.384) is admired for the extensive expertise that he has accumulated over the years. Commentators note: *"He brings deep subject matter and market knowledge, along with a collaborative working*

*style, in order to achieve optimal results."* He recently handled a series of transactions for Marsh & McLennan.

### Latham & Watkins LLP
See profile on p.446

**THE FIRM** This firm's established technology transactions group is respected for the international scope of its practice. The large team represents companies at every stage of the corporate life cycle, ranging from startups to mature global entities. Latham offers a wealth of expertise to clients from industries including cleantech, semiconductor and software. Peers attest to the caliber of work that the practice attracts, while clients are impressed by the outstanding service provided by the team. The group recently handled several complex matters, such as Seamless Web's acquisition of media assets from Slick City Media, and amendments to Advanced Micro Devices' supply agreement.
**Sources say:** *"Latham is extraordinarily capable in a wide variety of matters. The size of the firm allows them to marshal whatever resources are required to meet a particular objective."*
**KEY INDIVIDUALS** Interviewees are keen to recommend **J D Marple** (see p.652), drawing attention to his expertise in business critical transactions. His attention to detail and recognition of the client's objectives see him lauded for the quality of his work: *"J D has demonstrated the highest levels of professionalism and ability in terms of knowledge, responsiveness and service."* He recently represented Avery Dennison in a series of transactions and outsourcing agreements. **Anthony Klein** (see p.646) is valued for the business-oriented counsel he provides to emerging growth companies and leading service providers. Global cochair of the semiconductor industry group, he is particularly well versed in transactions relating to that field, while also maintaining expertise in other areas including clean technology and medical devices. Recent highlights include advising Tessura Technologies and its subsidiary DigitalOptics on an acquisition of assets from Vista Point Technologies.

### Morrison & Foerster LLP
See profile on p.1990

**THE FIRM** This team of highly esteemed practitioners meets with widespread acclaim. The firm's global sourcing and technology transactions group brings a wealth of expertise to complex deals, and is singled out by interviewees for the intellectual strength that hones its work product. The dedicated team attracts a host of high-profile clients such as Dreamworks Animation and Intel, with the latter instructing lawyers in a series of strategic acquisitions. The firm is particularly well known for its expertise in areas of high activity, such as social media and cloud computing.

### Senior Statesmen

**Senior Statesmen: distinguished older practitioners**

| | |
|---|---|
| Moore Gary H | Cooley LLP |
| Savage Diane | Cooley LLP |
| Stern Michael | Cooley LLP |

### Leading Individuals

**Star individuals**

| | |
|---|---|
| Mummery Daniel | Gibson, Dunn & Crutcher LLP * |
| Nash Glenn | Sidley Austin LLP (ONP)† * |
| Radcliffe Mark F | DLA Piper LLP (US) * |

**Band 1**

| | |
|---|---|
| Bell Suzanne Y | Wilson Sonsini Goodrich & Rosati |
| Brockland John P | Weil, Gotshal & Manges LLP * |
| Hayes David L | Fenwick & West LLP * |
| Kapoor Rahul | Morgan, Lewis & Bockius LLP * |
| Meeker Heather J | Greenberg Traurig, LLP * |
| Peters William J | Gibson, Dunn & Crutcher LLP * |
| Schwartz William | Morrison & Foerster LLP * |
| Villeneuve Tom | Gunderson Dettmer Stough Villeneuve (ONP)† |

**Band 2**

| | |
|---|---|
| Ballack Karen N | Weil, Gotshal & Manges LLP * |
| Ballon Ian C | Greenberg Traurig, LLP * |
| Determann Lothar | Baker & McKenzie * |
| Jahn Paul E | Morrison & Foerster LLP * |
| Klein Anthony | Latham & Watkins LLP * |
| Maccoby Matthew F | Arnold & Porter LLP * |
| Marple J D | Latham & Watkins LLP * |
| Mousavi Nader A | Sullivan & Cromwell LLP (ONP)† * |
| Murphy Michael | Pillsbury Winthrop Shaw Pittman LLP * |
| Pass Brian J | Sheppard, Mullin, Richter & Hampton LLP |
| Sharron Stephanie L | Orrick, Herrington & Sutcliffe LLP * |

**Band 3**

| | |
|---|---|
| Craig Carolyn | Cooley LLP |
| Earl Lisa C | Pillsbury Winthrop Shaw Pittman LLP * |
| Kalyvas James R | Foley & Lardner LLP |
| Karamali Riaz | Sheppard, Mullin, Richter & Hampton LLP |
| Lee Victoria | DLA Piper LLP (US) * |
| Mehra Shailesh (Shaalu) | Sheppard, Mullin, Richter & Hampton |
| Moskatel Ira D | Arnold & Porter LLP * |
| Murphy Michael J | Wilson Sonsini Goodrich & Rosati |
| Overly Michael | Foley & Lardner LLP |
| Rosen Lawrence | Rosenlaw & Einschlag (ONP)† |

**Up-and-coming individuals**

| | |
|---|---|
| Rubin Aaron P. | Morrison & Foerster LLP * |
| Schwartz Tessa | Morrison & Foerster LLP * |
| Surpin Beni | DLA Piper LLP (US) * |
| Yost Daniel | Orrick, Herrington & Sutcliffe LLP * |

**Associates to watch**

| | |
|---|---|
| Siok Jan | Arnold & Porter LLP * |

\* *Indicates firm / individual with profile.*
† *ONP = Other Notable Practitioner.*

**Sources say:** *"They are very attuned to commercial realities and have a wide range of experience that is beneficial to their clients."*

**KEY INDIVIDUALS** The *"excellent"* **William Schwartz** (see p.664) is singled out for his *"encyclopedic knowledge of licensing law and agreements."* An established presence in the field, he has wide-ranging expertise that includes strategic alliances and outsourcing transactions. Sources attribute his success to his *"practical, experienced and really smart"* approach. He has continued to represent Yahoo! in a series of transactions. **Paul Jahn** (see p.644) is *"a very strong strategist and negotiator"* whose pragmatism and tireless dedication in complex deals impresses both peers and clients. Interviewees praise his responsiveness and attention to the commercial realities of business. Recent highlights include advising Intel on its acquisitions of QLogic Corporation's InfiniBand networking assets and Fulcrum Microsystems. Rising star **Aaron Rubin** (see p.663) stands out to market commentators for his ability to explain legal terminology to the layperson. Sources note the *"bright and detail-oriented"* approach that produces *"an excellent work product."* The past year has seen him represent Dreamworks Animation on a joint venture in China. Interviewees praise **Tessa Schwartz's** (see p.664) astute understanding of her clients' business needs. She is *"exceedingly practical and smart about what really matters in a deal."* An impressive breadth of practice sees her handle a range of transactions for both emerging and established clients, such as Catchlight Energy and McAfee.

## Wilson Sonsini Goodrich & Rosati
See profile on p.700

**THE FIRM** This established firm remains a dominant player in the market with a large dedicated technology transactions practice. Its lawyers are best known for their mastery of strategic outsourcing transactions. Market commentators praise the breadth of practice that enables the firm to understand the needs of both emerging and mature businesses. The team represents clients from all corners of the technology industry, including the software, clean technology and digital media arenas. Examples of the team's stellar stable of clients include Google and TiVo.
**Sources say:** *"Outstanding on all fronts."*
**KEY INDIVIDUALS** A longstanding reputation for excellence sees **Suzanne Bell** remain at the top of her game. Leader of the firm's technology transactions and IT group, she focuses on substantial outsourcing deals and strategic transactions. Sources refer to her *"deep, commercial experience,"* and note the benefit of her business sense: *"She is tough enough to be very forceful at the right point in negotiations, but wise enough to know when to let issues go."* Her recent clients include heavy hitters like Polycom and Google. Peers attest to the wealth of experience **Michael Murphy** brings to the complex transactions he regularly handles. He offers highly respected expertise in licensing, intellectual property and technology partnering agreements to clients from a range of industries. He recently represented TiVo in a $500 million patent litigation settlement agreement.

## Band 2

## Baker & McKenzie
See profile on p.435

**THE FIRM** Baker & McKenzie is distinguished by an impressive global footprint. The international abilities of this firm feed into its California IT & outsourcing team, benefiting high-profile clients such as Qualcomm and Ancestry.com. The team regularly advises on a range of technology-related transactions including systems procurement, outsourcing, intellectual property rights and privacy issues.
**Sources say:** *"The lawyers are commercial, easy to deal with and provide sound legal advice."*
**KEY INDIVIDUALS** **Lothar Determann** (see p.631) is a privacy and data security specialist. He is particularly in demand for his international expertise, with a focus on European issues. Over the past year highlights include advising Yelp on the international expansion of its social media site, and representing NetSuite in global data privacy compliance matters.

## Cooley LLP

**THE FIRM** This respected firm is acclaimed as a strong force in the technology sector. The team acts on behalf of an expansive group of clients including emerging business and established entities. Lawyers regularly advise industry leaders on the strategic use and development of technology and the protection of existing assets. Cooley is best known for the depth of its abilities in IT, digital media, e-commerce and alternative energy.
**KEY INDIVIDUALS** **Carolyn Craig's** specialist IP and technology transactions practice is focused on representing clients in their interactions with federal, state and local governing bodies. Clients benefit from her familiarity with a broad range of transactions and background in systems engineering. **Michael Stern** is well regarded for the high-quality work that has characterized his practice. Interviewees refer to his deep knowledge of the transactional life cycle of companies, ranging from startups to international corporations. His expertise stretches across licensing agreements, strategic outsourcing and alliances. **Gary Moore** meets with widespread admiration and is respected for the longevity of his practice. He is an established practitioner with particular expertise in the handling of intricate transactions and business-critical strategic alliances. As founder of the firm's technology transactions group, **Diane Savage** has amassed a wealth of experience that sees her held in the highest regard. Sources note the influential role she has played in the legal community and praise her expertise in the field. She is best known for her extensive experience of advising emerging growth companies.

## DLA Piper LLP (US)
See profile on p.1971

**THE FIRM** DLA Piper's ability to draw on the expertise of its international offices attracts high-profile clients who value the practice's cross-border capabilities. The team guides clients in handling technology assets throughout

their lifecycle. Clients repeatedly refer to the commercial acumen that adds value to the detailed technical advice they receive. Its attorneys are also singled out for their responsiveness to client needs. The team acts for both service providers and their customers, with high-profile clients including eBay and Sony Electronics.
**Sources say:** *"Outstanding on all fronts – a standout on client service."*
**KEY INDIVIDUALS** The highly rated **Victoria Lee** (see p.649) is praised for her *"personable, conscientious and knowledgeable"* manner of delivering expert advice. Market commentators are quick to utilize her skills *"when we need firepower on the technology side."* She is also singled out for the depth of experience that ensures rapid responses to complex issues. Her practice focuses on strategic transactions. **Mark Radcliffe** (see p.660) is revered as a key figure in the field of open source. Described quite simply as *"the gold standard,"* he maintains an enviable position for his thought leadership in a specialized field. Interviewees allude to his strengths in cloud computing, licensing and intellectual property strategy. Newly ranked **Beni Surpin** (see p.668) wins plaudits for his brilliance as a practitioner, and is a growing presence in the legal community. Sources compliment his *"amazing command of the law,"* which *"is blended with practical consideration of what drives business."*

## Fenwick & West LLP
See profile on p.680

**THE FIRM** Fenwick's established technology practice is described as a stalwart of Silicon Valley. Peers attest to the impressive stable of clients the group attracts with its deep-rooted industry knowledge. The dedicated team brings expert guidance to companies undertaking strategic alliances, outsourcing agreements and patent licensing.
**Sources say:** *"A fantastic adviser for emerging technology companies – they really get how this works."*
**KEY INDIVIDUALS** The *"excellent"* **David Hayes** (see p.641) leads the team. Sources praise his broad practice which encompasses transactions ranging from intellectual property protection and patent licensing to strategic acquisitions. His legal expertise is enhanced by his background in electrical engineering.

## Greenberg Traurig, LLP
See profile on p.1024

**THE FIRM** This firm is widely known for its strength in specialist areas such as open source agreements and IP litigation. Greenberg also offers an impressive command of licensing agreements and M&A deals. A host of high-profile clients entrust its lawyers with innovative transactions and substantial disputes. The team continues to work with globally-known names such as Google and Myspace.
**KEY INDIVIDUALS** Co-managing partner **Heather Meeker** (see p.654) maintains her reputation as a *"very accomplished open source lawyer."* She offers an outstanding level of expertise in open source licensing strategies and is also recognized for her prowess in the intellectual property issues surrounding M&A transactions. Seasoned litigator **Ian Ballon** (see p.621) is well known for the depth of

his internet related litigation practice. He is highly adept in the field of copyright, trademark disputes and the defense of privacy class actions. He recently successfully obtained a dismissal for a trio of prominent entities fighting a privacy and behavioral advertising class action.

## Band 3

### Arnold & Porter LLP
See profile on p.906

THE FIRM Arnold & Porter offers an impressive breadth of practice that attracts a stellar clientele. The team represents high-profile names from a range of industries including hospitality and finance. The team is noted for its experience of handling deals from both the service provider and customer perspective.

KEY INDIVIDUALS **Matthew Maccoby** (see p.651) comes highly recommended for his knowledge of the outsourcing cycle and the attendant transactional needs faced by clients. He is also vastly experienced in technology-based disputes. The past year has seen him leading a series of cross-border transactions. An extensive background in technology and engineering gives **Ira Moskatel** (see p.656) a deep understanding of the business needs of clients in the software, publishing and communications market. He is particularly adept when faced with complex licensing agreements, acquisitions and strategic alliances. **Jan Siok** (see p.666) is well regarded for the breadth of her transactional practice. She specializes in guiding clients through the IP and technology elements of M&A deals, and provides expertise in large-scale outsourcings. Sources also refer to her experience in the financial sector, which has given her in-depth knowledge of the technology needs of international banking clients.

### Morgan, Lewis & Bockius LLP
See profile on p.2246

THE FIRM This firm's technology transactions and outsourcing group impresses peers and clients with its breadth of practice and understanding of the concerns of technology companies. The team regularly advises high-end clients on business strategy, technology licensing and asset purchases. Highlights from the past year include acting on behalf of Apollo Group on its purchase of IP assets from Carnegie Mellon University.

Sources say: *"They have a great depth of expertise in a number of areas that impact technology companies."*

KEY INDIVIDUALS Department head **Rahul Kapoor** (see p.645) is singled out for his expertise in structuring complex contracts and patent issues. He is highly respected for his understanding of cutting-edge IP strategy. Market commentators value his *"smart, focused and extremely effective"* approach. He recently represented SanDisk in its agreement to develop a flash memory storage product with the Western Digital and Home Entertainment arms of Twentieth Century Fox and Warner Bros.

### Orrick, Herrington & Sutcliffe LLP
See profile on p.1994

THE FIRM Orrick retains a strong reputation for its work on both the customer and vendor side of transactions. Interviewees draw attention to the high standard of client service provided by members of the team. The outsourcing and technology transactions group represents clients ranging in size from emerging growth to established Fortune 500 companies. Its attorneys offer experience in a wide variety of technology-related transactions such as outsourcing, service agreements, acquisitions and disposals. Current clients include Instagram and the Chrysler Group.

Sources say: *"Great commercial awareness, attuned to the latest general practices in each area served."*

KEY INDIVIDUALS Sources attest to the strength of department cochair **Stephanie Sharron**'s (see p.665) practice, describing her as an *"excellent business lawyer and negotiator."* She remains an active presence and is well known for her depth of experience in Silicon Valley. The past year has seen her represent Chrysler in a series of strategic transactions. **Daniel Yost** (see p.673) heads the practice alongside Sharron and is noted for his skill in working with emerging companies. His *"pleasant, professional and smart"* manner stands out to clients who also praise his dedicated results-oriented approach. Yost led the team advising Instagram on the $1 billion sale of its mobile photo sharing application to Facebook.

### Pillsbury Winthrop Shaw Pittman LLP
See profile on p.2000

THE FIRM This well-known firm is distinguished by its team of sourcing consultants who work alongside the practice's lawyers. Market commentators report that the team displays an exemplary level of industry-focused understanding, and praise the professionalism of the global sourcing practice. The practice is characterized by its focus on strategic transactions across a range of industries. Leading clients include Blue Shield and Federal Home Loan Bank of San Francisco.

Sources say: *"Pillsbury has very strong knowledge and experience in this field. For me, they are a clear firm of choice."*

KEY INDIVIDUALS The highly respected **Michael Murphy**'s (see p.373) practical and knowledgeable approach wins plaudits from both peers and clients. Sources value his *"ability to put the legal issues into context for our business folks"* and that he is *"always thinking of options to solve any point of contention."* He offers expertise in a range of technology transactions such as alliances, joint ventures and outsourcing. **Lisa Earl** (see p.633) is recommended for her excellent drafting and negotiating skills. She is also applauded for her consistent dedication to the particular needs of each client. Clients look to her for expert guidance through international outsourcing transactions from both the service provider and customer perspective.

## Band 4

### Foley & Lardner LLP
See profile on p.2588

THE FIRM Foley & Lardner's IT and outsourcing practice attracts a range of market-leading clients who place value on the breadth of expertise offered by the team. Its lawyers are recognized for their ability to work seamlessly alongside in-house counsel, and are praised for the depth of knowledge that they consistently display. This responsive team regularly represents entities such as Maricopa Integrated Health System and TD Ameritrade in transactions including the acquisition of information systems, outsourcing procurement and legal risk assessment.

Sources say: *"They are knowledgeable about state-of-the-art approaches, strong on client service and practical problem solvers."*

KEY INDIVIDUALS **Michael Overly** stands out to interviewees as *"extremely smart, detail-oriented and responsive."* He is held in high regard by clients who note his ability to understand industry practices and the nuances of each organization. His practice is focused on technology agreements, software licensing and acquisition arrangements. Department chair **James Kalyvas** is singled out for his *"strong vision, leadership, knowledge and client service."* Those who retain his services note: *"He listens well and helps you achieve your goals."* He is well known for his work with emerging technologies and advises on a wide range of matters such as the structuring of complex outsourcing transactions, technology initiatives and the management of technology assets.

### Kirkland & Ellis LLP
See profile on p.1254

THE FIRM Kirkland & Ellis is particularly well established in the field of outsourcing and continues to be singled out for its strength in this area. The team has also developed a breadth of experience across the technology sector, and is recognized for its prowess in investments, acquisitions and associated litigation. Lawyers in the firm's San Francisco and Palo Alto offices regularly act on behalf of established and emerging growth companies.

KEY INDIVIDUALS **Karen Spindler** is a key contact.

### Sheppard, Mullin, Richter & Hampton LLP

THE FIRM Sheppard Mullin's outsourcing and technology practice serves clients from across the IT and computer industries. The team regularly structures an array of outsourcing arrangements covering logistics, employee benefits and data center operations, among others. The group is also recognized for its experience in the handling of acquisition and development transactions on behalf of international clients such as Russell Investments and Cyclos Semiconductor.

Sources say: *"The principals possess a unique depth and breadth of knowledge both on the legal and business matters involved with IT and outsourcing."*

KEY INDIVIDUALS **Brian Pass** is respected as an established presence in the outsourcing sector. Sources value his significant experience in all manner of ITO and BPO transactions. He continues to guide clients such as Conduit through lengthy outsourcing cycles. **Riaz Karamali** continues to be recognized for his cross-border work. His practice is focused on structuring outsourcing agreements for emerging growth companies in the technology sector. Practice leader and firm-wide chair of the technology transactions and outsourcing group, **Shaalu Mehra** specializes in complex multinational outsourcing initiatives. Acting on behalf of leading vendors, he structures large-scale agreements that illustrate *"deep technical knowledge due not only to his legal training and experience but to his earlier career as a technologist."*

### Weil, Gotshal & Manges LLP
See profile on p.2015

**THE FIRM** Weil has undergone significant expansion in its California technology and IP transactions practice. The highly capable team handles work such as strategic alliances, outsourcing and licensing arrangements. Interviewees are quick to praise the firm's client-focused approach, and have confidence in the team's ability to achieve results. Its attorneys have recently worked on substantial transactions for eBay and Yahoo!.

**Sources say:** *"Weil is excellent in every way: client service, responsiveness and business savvy."*

**KEY INDIVIDUALS** *"True professional"* **John Brockland** (see p.625) is singled out for his in-depth understanding of clients' needs. Market commentators note: *"One of his main strengths is his ability to interface effectively with a broad spectrum of deal participants, including business leads, IP specialists and deal lawyers."* He is widely recognized for his breadth of experience in the outsourcing sector and is also well known for the acumen he displays across a range of transactions. **Karen Ballack** (see p.621) *"is a master drafter of technology and other agreements and is one of the most amazing negotiators. She does not blindly advocate her client's position, but listens to the other side, convinces the other side that their story has been heard and then illustrates her client's needs articulately and persuasively."* The past year saw her act for Symantec on its acquisition of LiveOffice Holdings.

### Other Notable Practitioners

Market commentators have *"tremendous respect"* for **Tom Villeneuve** of Gunderson Dettmer Stough Villeneuve Franklin & Hachigian, and regard him as *"an incredibly talented lawyer."* Best known for his work with emerging growth companies, he specializes in licensing, joint ventures and strategic alliances. Sources draw attention to

**Nader Mousavi** (see p.656) of Sullivan & Cromwell LLP, commenting on his active presence in the field of IP transactions. He maintains an interesting breadth of practice and continues to work with clients from industries that range from pharmaceutical to semiconductor. **Lawrence Rosen** of Rosenlaw & Einschlag is respected as an open source expert and *"a very accomplished practitioner."* He remains an attorney of choice for leading technology companies which benefit from his experience in dealing with the full lifecycle of companies. **Glenn Nash** (see p.656) of Sidley Austin LLP is singled out for his outstanding technical abilities and business acumen. Sources are fulsome in their praise, noting: *"Glenn understands the delicate balance between getting a deal done and minimizing your client's legal risks. He also has a clear understanding of our business as well as trends within Silicon Valley."* His practice is focused on IP-related transactions and cross-border strategic alliances.

# LABOR & EMPLOYMENT

Commentary about individuals can be found under their firm's paragraph. If the firm has no paragraph (is not ranked) look at Other Notable Practitioners.

| Labor & Employment |
| --- |
| **Leading Firms** |
| **Band 1** |
| Paul Hastings LLP * |
| **Band 2** |
| Gibson, Dunn & Crutcher LLP * |
| Morgan, Lewis & Bockius LLP * |
| Munger, Tolles & Olson LLP * |
| Orrick, Herrington & Sutcliffe LLP * |
| **Band 3** |
| Jones Day * |
| Littler Mendelson, PC * |
| Mitchell Silberberg & Knupp LLP |
| Morrison & Foerster LLP * |
| O'Melveny & Myers LLP * |
| Proskauer Rose LLP * |
| Seyfarth Shaw LLP * |
| Sheppard, Mullin, Richter & Hampton LLP |
| **Band 4** |
| Akin Gump Strauss Hauer & Feld LLP * |
| Allen Matkins Leck Gamble Mallory & Natsis LLP * |
| Barnes & Thornburg LLP * |
| Davis Wright Tremaine LLP * |
| Jackson Lewis LLP * |
| Manatt Phelps & Phillips LLP * |
| Winston & Strawn LLP * |

*\* Indicates firm with profile.*
*Alphabetical order within each band. Band 1 is the highest.*

## Band 1

### Paul Hastings LLP
See profile on p.1996

**THE FIRM** This 25-partner team has virtually unrivaled strength and depth in California. The group is renowned for its work on highly complex matters, including misclassification and wage and hour class and collective actions. Equally impressive is the practice's traditional labor arm, which often advises major corporations on union contract renegotiations. Recently, the team acted for Sara Lee, and defeated class certification of a claim in which delivery route operators alleged that they were misclassified as independent contractors.

**Sources say:** *"They bring insights you can't find anywhere in books."*

**KEY INDIVIDUALS** The *"brilliant and tenacious"* **Nancy Abell** is a luminary on the California labor and employment scene. She often acts in discrimination, misclassification and wage and hour class actions. A peer comments: *"I have such an appreciation for her; she is amazing."* **Paul Grossman** is described as *"incredibly knowledgeable in a unique way."* His practice encompasses the full run of employment matters, including wage and hour and discrimination claims. **Kirby Wilcox** handles an impressive array of matters, such as wage and hour and equal employment opportunity claims. Clients deem him a *"great resource."* **Paul Cane** is highly regarded for his appellate work, although he does deal with other major motions. He

is known for being *"really helpful and producing really polished work."* A market source states that **Elena Baca** is *"excellent and varied in her expertise."* Of late she represented AIG in a putative worker's compensation class action. **Jeffrey Wohl**'s practice handles employment matters, including single plaintiff claims and class actions. *"He is a great litigator and achieves great results,"* notes a commentator. **Bradford Newman** has developed a strong focus on trade secrets and employee mobility issues.

## Band 2

### Gibson, Dunn & Crutcher LLP
See profile on p.682

**THE FIRM** Gibson Dunn enjoys a growing reputation thanks to recent key hires and an impressive caseload. The group is highly regarded for its work in substantial wage and hour, discrimination and misclassification claims. The group recently acted for the defendant in Wal-Mart v Dukes, in which the Supreme Court overturned a mammoth Title VII class certification.

**Sources say:** *"Customer service is beyond any other firm I have experienced. The lawyers are quick to respond and are very aware of current trends."*

**KEY INDIVIDUALS Catherine Conway** (see p.629) joined the team from Akin Gump this past year, and is making waves with her work in a number of wage and hour and discrimination class actions. *"She is smart, confi-*

## Labor & Employment
### Senior Statesmen

**Senior Statesmen:** distinguished older practitioners

| | | |
|---|---|---|
| Wheeler Raymond | *Morrison & Foerster LLP* * |

### Leading Individuals

**Star individuals**

| | |
|---|---|
| Abell Nancy L | *Paul Hastings LLP* |
| Grossman Paul | *Paul Hastings LLP* |

**Band 1**

| | |
|---|---|
| Hermle Lynne C. | *Orrick, Herrington & Sutcliffe LLP* * |
| Mathiason Garry G | *Littler Mendelson, PC* * |
| Sanchez Terry | *Munger, Tolles & Olson LLP* * |
| Wilcox Kirby | *Paul Hastings LLP* |

**Band 2**

| | |
|---|---|
| Alvarez Fred | *Wilson Sonsini Goodrich & Rosati (ONP)[†]* |
| Berman Jeffrey | *Seyfarth Shaw LLP* * |
| Cane Paul | *Paul Hastings LLP* |
| Cole William | *Mitchell Silberberg & Knupp LLP* |
| Conway Catherine A | *Gibson, Dunn & Crutcher LLP* * |
| Diekmann Jr Gilmore F | *Seyfarth Shaw LLP* * |
| Drapkin Steven | *Law Offices of Steven Drapkin (ONP)[†]* |
| Eisen Rebecca | *Morgan, Lewis & Bockius LLP* * |
| Fabrick Howard | *Barnes & Thornburg LLP* * |
| Howard Jr George S | *Jones Day* * |
| Kadue David | *Seyfarth Shaw LLP* * |
| Kennedy Tracey A | *Sheppard, Mullin, Richter & Hampton LLP* |
| Oncidi Anthony J | *Proskauer Rose LLP* |
| Simmons Richard | *Sheppard, Mullin, Richter & Hampton LLP* |
| Siniscalco Gary | *Orrick, Herrington & Sutcliffe LLP* * |
| Virjee Framroze | *O'Melveny & Myers LLP* |

**Band 3**

| | |
|---|---|
| Armstrong Dwight L | *Allen Matkins Leck Gamble Mallory* * |
| Ashe Brian T | *Seyfarth Shaw LLP* * |
| Baca Elena | *Paul Hastings LLP* |
| Bierman Ivy Kagan | *Loeb & Loeb LLP (ONP)[†]* * |
| Chopra Apalla | *O'Melveny & Myers LLP* |
| Gillette Patricia | *Orrick, Herrington & Sutcliffe LLP* * |

| | |
|---|---|
| Keyes Judith Droz | *Davis Wright Tremaine LLP* |
| Kubin Karen | *Morrison & Foerster LLP* * |
| Levin Adam | *Mitchell Silberberg & Knupp LLP* |
| Petroff Laura R | *Winston & Strawn LLP* * |
| Riechert Melinda S | *Morgan, Lewis & Bockius LLP* * |
| Siegel Robert | *O'Melveny & Myers LLP* |
| Sulzer Kenneth D | *Proskauer Rose LLP* |
| Wohl Jeffrey D | *Paul Hastings LLP* |

**Band 4**

| | |
|---|---|
| Allderdice Linda | *Holland & Knight LLP (ONP)* * |
| Barker Charles F | *Sheppard, Mullin, Richter & Hampton LLP* |
| Bergstrom Rick | *Jones Day* * |
| Birenbaum Charles S | *Winston & Strawn LLP* * |
| Corman Karen L | *Skadden, Arps, Slate, Meagher (ONP)[†]* * |
| Cripps Jr. Jesse A | *Gibson, Dunn & Crutcher LLP* * |
| Friedman Alan | *Munger, Tolles & Olson LLP* * |
| Gallion Michael L | *Sheppard, Mullin, Richter & Hampton LLP* |
| Heinicke Malcolm | *Munger, Tolles & Olson LLP* * |
| Hirschfeld Stephen J | *Curiale Hirschfeld & Kraemer LLP (ONP)[†]* |
| Husar Linda S | *Reed Smith LLP (ONP)[†]* |
| Knopp Gregory W | *Akin Gump Strauss Hauer & Feld LLP* * |
| Kun Michael S | *Epstein Becker & Green PC (ONP)[†]* * |
| Lederman Henry D | *Littler Mendelson, PC* * |
| Liburt Joseph | *Orrick, Herrington & Sutcliffe LLP* * |
| Newman Bradford K | *Paul Hastings LLP* |
| Poon Julian | *Gibson, Dunn & Crutcher LLP* * |
| Tabacopoulos Diana | *Seyfarth Shaw LLP* * |
| Tanenbaum Jeffrey M | *Nixon Peabody LLP (ONP)[†]* * |
| Tichy George | *Littler Mendelson, PC* * |
| Witlin Scott | *Barnes & Thornburg LLP* * |

**Up-and-coming individuals**

| | |
|---|---|
| Forster Katherine M. | *Munger, Tolles & Olson LLP* * |

\* *Indicates individual with profile.*
[†]*ONP = Other Notable Practitioner.*

---

dent and a role model," notes a peer. Los Angeles-based **Julian Poon** (see p.660) is praised for his ability to "*handle unique and novel areas of the law.*" He recently represented the defendant in Tien v Tenet Healthcare, in which a wage and hour class action certification was dismissed. **Jesse Cripps** (see p.630) is a litigator who often focuses on Federal Labor Standards Act (FLSA) and wage and hour issues. He recently acted for Raytheon, and successfully dismissed claims that managers were misclassified as exempt under Californian wage and hour laws.

### Morgan, Lewis & Bockius LLP
**See profile on p.2246**

**THE FIRM** This superb group benefits from a nationwide network of eminent labor and employment practices. The California group is comprised of almost 60 attorneys spread among four offices. Noted areas of expertise include wage and hour, discrimination and wrongful termination

claims. The group attracts clients from a range of industries, including retail, shipping and technology.

**Sources say:** "*They produce fabulous results and guide us through tricky situations.*"

**KEY INDIVIDUALS Rebecca Eisen** (see p.634) focuses her practice on wage and hour disputes, whether they be class, collective or multiplaintiff. "*She is hard-working, gets things done right, and knows the law,*" notes a market commentator. **Melinda Riechert** (see p.662) has a broad-ranging employment practice encompassing wrongful termination, sexual harassment and discrimination claims. Observers praise her and state: "*She knows the intricacies of laws in California.*"

### Munger, Tolles & Olson LLP
**See profile on p.691**

**THE FIRM** This group truly has expertise in the complete spectrum of labor and employment issues. On the traditional labor side, the team deftly represents media and

entertainment entities in collective bargaining negotiations and arbitrations. The group also acts on a range of substantial employment matters, including gender discrimination and overtime pay issues. The team recently represented Warner Bros. in its dispute with Charlie Sheen.

**Sources say:** "*They know how to get things done and have an excellent knowledge of the law.*"

**KEY INDIVIDUALS** Peers state that **Terry Sanchez** (see p.664) "*has a very good reputation and is very high-profile.*" He represented Warner Bros. during the Charlie Sheen matter. **Alan Friedman** (see p.637) is a seasoned attorney who handles both labor and employment disputes and negotiations. San Francisco-based **Malcolm Heinicke** (see p.641) handles both employment and commercial matters. A client notes that "*his oral arguments are outstanding.*" **Katherine Forster** (see p.636) is known as an "*impressive lady.*" She recently acted for 99 Cent Only Stores in a gender discrimination class action concerning female store managers.

### Orrick, Herrington & Sutcliffe LLP
**See profile on p.1994**

**THE FIRM** This group benefits from being housed in a full-service firm with an international reach. The dedicated employment law team wins plaudits for its work in areas including trade secrets, whistle-blower defense, and class actions. The practice's clients come from a variety of industries, including retail, financial services and biotech. The group recently acted for Morgan Stanley in a wage and hour class action concerning financial advisers' entitlement to overtime pay.

**Sources say:** "*They are really high-caliber attorneys. They produce excellent work and have very successful outcomes.*"

**KEY INDIVIDUALS Lynne Hermle** (see p.642) places particular emphasis on representing retail and technology companies in high-stakes employment claims. Sources consider her to be "*a strong lawyer and a very good advocate for her clients.*" She recently represented the defendant in Austin Park v Morgan Stanley. One impressed client commented that **Gary Siniscalco** (see p.666) "*is able to offer a lot of insights to us – he is a font of knowledge.*" He recently acted for Lawrence Livermore National Laboratories in a contract and discrimination case. The "*exceptional*" **Patricia Gillette** (see p.637) deals with employment litigation, including wrongful termination and discrimination claims. She recently represented Bank of America in a Sarbanes-Oxley whistle-blower claim. **Joseph Liburt** (see p.650) dedicates a sizable proportion of his practice to wage and hour matters, although he also handles uniform, harassment, retaliation and discrimination issues. He recently represented Health Net in a charge brought by the National Labor Relations Board (NLRB) concerning an employee being fired after engaging in union-organizing activities.

### Band 3

### Jones Day
**See profile on p.919**

**THE FIRM** This dynamic team has a presence up and down California, with multiple offices and some 20 dedicated lawyers. The group undertakes employment litigation such as wage and hour, trade secret and discrimination claims. The team also has strong labor capabilities, and handles a substantial number of NLRB and collective bargaining matters. The group recently represented a number of nationwide companies, including Verizon Wireless and Avon Products, in wage and hour litigation.

**KEY INDIVIDUALS** Peers consider **George Howard** (see p.643) to be a *"perfect gentleman."* He has a broad employment practice encompassing harassment, trade secret, discrimination and contractual disputes. **Rick Bergstrom** (see p.623) has recently been active in several wage and hour and trade secret cases. *"I have been impressed with him in terms of strategic thinking and judgment,"* a client states.

## Littler Mendelson, PC
See profile on p.688

**THE FIRM** The Californian arm of this national labor and employment boutique impresses with its size and range of services. The 140-odd partners in California are involved in wage and hour, wrongful termination, collective bargaining agreements, and misclassification litigation. In recent highlights, the group acted for Huhtamaki on a single plaintiff, wrongful termination case, and obtained summary judgment.

**Sources say:** *"They are very professional and do an incredible job."*

**KEY INDIVIDUALS** Peers consider **Garry Mathiason** (see p.652) to be *"so creative and analytical."* He is based in the firm's San Francisco office and currently handles a mix of wage and hour and classification issues. **Henry Lederman** (see p.649) divides his time between employment litigation, arbitration and counseling. Sources state: *"He is a really good communicator and trial lawyer."* **George Tichy**'s (see p.669) practice covers an array of labor and employment matters, including collective bargaining and civil rights issues. Clients consider him to be *"very helpful"* and *"cost-sensitive."*

## Mitchell Silberberg & Knupp LLP

**THE FIRM** This group has a sterling reputation for advising clients with media and entertainment interests. While the group does represent studios and networks in union issues, it also has sophisticated employment dispute capabilities. The team often represents employers in wrongful termination, sexual harassment and discrimination claims. It recently represented Desperate Housewives' producer Marc Cherry, Touchstone Pictures and ABC Studios in allegations of wrongful termination, retaliation and battery brought by Nicollette Sheridan.

**Sources say:** *"Their client service is excellent; their lawyers are personable, responsive and always attuned to our needs."*

**KEY INDIVIDUALS** **William Cole** divides his energies between employment and labor matters, including whistle-blower and NLRB hearings. An interviewee notes that *"he is effective because he is brilliant, and has tremendous credibility – not just with his clients, but with the opposing side."* **Adam Levin** similarly handles both labor and employment issues, often for major networks, studios, and

companies with a media bent. *"He has an instinctive understanding of everything legal,"* sources state.

## Morrison & Foerster LLP
See profile on p.1990

**THE FIRM** This compact but effective seven-partner team is dispersed among four offices, and enjoys a growing reputation for its litigation capabilities. Wage and hour class actions form a substantial part of the team's work, but the group also handles trade secrets, misclassification and discrimination matters. The group recently advised Brinker Restaurants on a California Supreme Court case, the ruling of which stated that employers have to provide meal breaks, but do not have to ensure that employees take meal breaks.

**KEY INDIVIDUALS** The *"excellent"* **Karen Kubin** (see p.648) is particularly well regarded for her work in wage and hour class actions, although she is equipped to handle a range of employment issues. She recently acted on the influential Brinker case. **Raymond Wheeler** (see p.672) is considered to be a veteran of the labor and employment space. He has an impressively broad practice encompassing matters such as union organizing and trade secrets issues.

## O'Melveny & Myers LLP
See profile on p.693

**THE FIRM** This group continues to garner praise for its counseling and representation of national and multinational companies across a broad spread of industries. Other noted areas of expertise include wage and hour issues, collective bargaining and external investigations advice. This team also has notable expertise in Railway Labor Act matters. The group recently represented H&R Block in three wage and hour class actions.

**KEY INDIVIDUALS** A peer considers the Los Angeles-based **Framroze Virjee** to be *"an excellent lawyer whom I have no hesitation recommending."* Virjee recently represented Bank of America in a claim concerning charging check-cashing fees to employees without Bank of America accounts. **Apalla Chopra** predominantly focuses on employment litigation concerning discrimination and wrongful discharge, but also advises on traditional labor matters. *"She's a fantastic lady and really something special,"* praises a market commentator. Sources describe **Bob Siegel** as a *"significant lawyer."* He recently represented the defendant in USAPA v US Airways, a case concerning alleged interference with collective bargaining rights.

## Proskauer Rose LLP
See profile on p.2001

**THE FIRM** This five-partner team strikes an effective balance between labor and employment work, and acts for some of California's big-ticket clients. The group offers major employers the full run of labor and employment expertise, from collective bargaining negotiations to high-stakes single plaintiff litigation. The team has continued its work with the Creative Artists Agency, and represented the organization in a discrimination class action and non-compete suit.

**Sources say:** *"I rate their speed of responsiveness, their commercial savvy and all-around service."*

**KEY INDIVIDUALS Anthony Oncidi** has an outstanding reputation acting for entertainment industry clients, among others. A client characterizes him as *"smart, cost-effective, appropriately aggressive and generally fabulous."* **Kenneth Sulzer** joined Proskauer Rose in 2012 from Seyfarth Shaw, and is considered by the market to be a *"terrific addition"* to the team. He recently represented Swissport USA in a Californian class action concerning meal and rest breaks.

## Seyfarth Shaw LLP
See profile on p.1262

**THE FIRM** This group successfully divides its labor and employment practice into ten focused subgroups, thereby helping to ensure that clients receive highly specialized advice. Clients come from a variety of industries, including technology, media, retail and general business. The team acts for employers on issues including discrimination, misclassification and whistle-blower claims. The group recently acted for Mutual of Omaha Insurance in a putative class action concerning the classification of insurance agents as independent contractors.

**Sources say:** *"They provide practical, business-oriented advice and work toward reasonable and practical solutions."*

**KEY INDIVIDUALS Jeffrey Berman** (see p.623) has a diverse practice, and handles both traditional labor negotiations and substantial employment litigation. He recently represented White Memorial Medical Center and Glendale Adventist Hospital in a wage and hour class action. **David Kadue** (see p.644) moves up the rankings thanks to effusive market feedback and an impressive year. He is an employment litigator who typically handles discrimination, wrongful termination and harassment issues. Clients consider **Gilmore Diekmann** (see p.632) to be a *"standout"* practitioner. He is based in the firm's San Francisco office and deals with a range of employment litigation and proceedings with administrative bodies including the EEOC and the NRLB. **Brian Ashe** (see p.621) specializes in employment litigation, although his practice includes traditional labor and employment counseling elements. A client states: *"He helps us assess the risk with various employment actions in a way that is easy to understand, and he does so in an expeditious manner."* The *"smart, responsible and reliable"* **Diana Tabacopoulos** (see p.668) focuses the bulk of her time on wage and hour matters, but has considerable expertise in ERISA, securities and unfair competition issues.

## Sheppard, Mullin, Richter & Hampton LLP

**THE FIRM** This team's labor and employment offering is principally dispersed among its Century City, Orange County and Los Angeles office. It enjoys a robust reputation for its advice to employers and management on human resources issues. The group's impressive roster of clients includes retail, restaurant and healthcare entities. The group is often involved in single plaintiff litigation, but is also active on class and collective actions. The practice recently acted for Whole Foods Market on a single plaintiff retaliation, harassment and wrongful termination claim.

**Sources say:** *"Sheppard Mullin has outstanding client service – the firm always makes you feel like its most important client."*

KEY INDIVIDUALS **Richard Simmons** comes highly recommended for his representation of healthcare bodies, although he represents a range of employers. *"He is amazing and a key resource,"* a commentator lauds. **Tracey Kennedy** impresses with her work on discrimination, retaliation, wrongful termination and wage and hour disputes. Sources praise her abilities, and note: *"She is very good at thinking strategically and is obviously incredibly experienced in an employment law context."* **Charles Barker** divides his time between employment litigation and labor-related negotiations and disputes. He has also represented employers and managers before administrative bodies, including the EEOC, the NLRB and the Department of Labor. **Michael Gallion** has in-depth trade secrets, discrimination and wage and hour expertise. Clients deem him a *"very practical and knowledgeable lawyer."*

## Band 4

### Akin Gump Strauss Hauer & Feld LLP
See profile on p.904

THE FIRM This practice group operates out of the firm's San Francisco and Los Angeles offices, and impresses with its employment litigation capabilities. Sources praise the team for its discrimination, wage and hour and misclassification work. In highlights, the group continued its relationship with Ernst & Young in a wage and hour class action concerning employees being exempt from overtime pay. Sources say: *"The firm is very well known in the labor and employment space."*
KEY INDIVIDUALS **Gregory Knopp** (see p.647) frequently acts on wage and hour, discrimination and harassment claims, as well as other issues, including collective bargaining negotiations and noncompete cases. His peers consider him to be an *"excellent litigator."*

### Allen Matkins Leck Gamble Mallory & Natsis LLP
See profile on p.674

THE FIRM The practice acts for an impressive range of clients, such as food producers, retailers and financial institutions. The team undertakes wage and hour class actions, NLRB proceedings and retaliation claims, among other matters. High-profile clients include Quiksilver, Dole Foods and Wells Fargo.
Sources say: *"They have tremendous knowledge that has proven extremely valuable."*
KEY INDIVIDUALS Orange County-based **Dwight Armstrong** (see p.620) has a practice covering employment litigation and counseling, including discrimination, harassment and employee handbook matters. *"He gives very sound, great advice, and has a calming demeanor,"* notes a source.

### Barnes & Thornburg LLP
See profile on p.436

THE FIRM This team joins the rankings after growing in size and generating market enthusiasm for its work. The group is comprised of four partners and is particularly well regarded for its representation of entertainment industry clients. The practice excels on union-related litigation, organization and negotiations, as well as wage and hour class actions. Its clients include the Flint Group, Relativity Media and Warner Bros.
KEY INDIVIDUALS **Howard Fabrick** (see p.634) moved to Barnes & Thornburg in 2012 from Akin Gump, and continues to be considered a traditional labor guru. Sources note that **Scott Witlin** (see p.672) *"comes to practical solutions and is very focused on being business savvy."* He recently represented major names in the video game industry during a new collective bargaining agreement.

### Davis Wright Tremaine LLP
See profile on p.2544

THE FIRM This group is highly active in single plaintiff cases and class actions. With offices in San Francisco and Los Angeles, the team ably advises clients from a range of industries, including media and entertainment, financial services and technology. The group recently represented Playboy in two gender discrimination class actions concerning fundraising events at the Playboy Mansion.
Sources say: *"They have great technical knowledge and appropriate staffing."*
KEY INDIVIDUALS **Judith Droz Keyes** recently acted on an impressive array of cases, such as representing Verizon Wireless in a sexual harassment claim. *"She is a superb strategist and is very thoughtful,"* notes an interviewee.

### Jackson Lewis LLP
See profile on p.1982

THE FIRM The California offering of this substantial national boutique impresses across the complete spectrum of labor and employment matters. The group excels at matters such as wage and hour, discrimination, harassment and whistle-blower claims. The team recently represented Kinecta Alternative Financial Solutions in a wage and hour class action concerning the company's branch managers.
Sources say: *"They are very knowledgeable about the law, very efficient and practical."*
KEY INDIVIDUALS The Los Angeles-based **Mia Farber** is a key contact.

### Manatt Phelps & Phillips LLP
See profile on p.690

THE FIRM This 20-strong team has had an impressive year, and currently represents big-name clients in a range of employment claims. Recent matters have included trade secrets, wage and hour and discrimination elements. The group recently acted for the Chinese Daily News in a wage and hour class action.
Sources say: *"The firm is always really reassuring."*
KEY INDIVIDUALS **Sandi King** leads the team.

### Winston & Strawn LLP
See profile on p.1267

THE FIRM This group is comprised of 18 attorneys and spans offices in Los Angeles and San Francisco. The group's employment team focuses on wage and hour class actions, trade secrets and discrimination claims. On the traditional labor side, the group has particular expertise advising renewable energy entities during union negotiations and organizing activities. Among the practice's clients are Louis Vuitton, Solar Gen 2 and CHRISTUS Health.
KEY INDIVIDUALS San Francisco-based **Charles Birenbaum** (see p.624) has a superb practice covering traditional labor matters. He frequently advises management and employers on collective bargaining, NLRB proceedings and the labor implications of corporate reorganizations. **Laura Petroff** (see p.659) is an employment specialist praised for her work on wage and hour, discrimination and harassment issues. A market commentator states: *"She is a brilliant attorney – I have an enormous amount of respect for her as a person and as a litigator."*

## Other Notable Practitioners

Clients note that **Fred Alvarez** of Wilson Sonsini Goodrich & Rosati *"comes with a great perspective and a great history of accomplishments."* He recently defended Marvell Technology in a misclassification class action, in which engineering employees were not compensated for missed meal and rest breaks, as well as overtime hours. **Steven Drapkin** of the Law Offices of Steven Drapkin is based in Los Angeles and covers a diverse spread of labor and employment matters. A peer terms Drapkin *"one of the leaders"* in the field. Loeb & Loeb LLP's **Ivy Kagan Bierman** (see p.623) is considered to be *"highly specialized and talented."* She continues to advise Hasbro on union and guild matters in relation to the company's motion picture and television show ventures. At Holland & Knight LLP, **Linda Allderdice** (see p.620) has a robust practice that includes employment litigation and union matters. Sources heap praise on **Karen Corman** (see p.629) of Skadden, Arps, Slate, Meagher & Flom LLP & Affiliates, and note: *"Her advice is clear and sensible, and she focuses on what is important."* At Curiale Hirschfeld & Kraemer LLP, **Stephen Hirschfeld** is praised for *"having a lot of energy and being extremely passionate."* He recently represented Circle Bank in a wrongful termination suit brought by the bank's former CEO. Reed Smith LLP's **Linda Husar** regularly handles whistle-blower, privacy rights, wrongful discharge and discrimination claims. *"She is very analytical, efficient with her time, and fights very hard on behalf of her clients,"* notes an interviewee. The *"persistent and tenacious"* **Michael Kun** (see p.648) of Epstein Becker & Green PC focuses on employment litigation, predominantly wage and hour, discrimination and retaliation claims. He recently represented Aerotek in a putative class action concerning the amount of hours employees worked. **Jeffrey Tanenbaum** (see p.668) of Nixon Peabody LLP is perhaps best known for his OSHA work, but he also acts for clients on other labor and employment matters. Peers characterize him as *"very strong and a great guy."*

# LIFE SCIENCES

Commentary about individuals can be found under their firm's paragraph. If the firm has no paragraph (is not ranked) look at Other Notable Practitioners.

## Life Sciences
### Leading Firms

**Band 1**
Cooley LLP
Latham & Watkins LLP *

**Band 2**
Covington & Burling LLP *
Morrison & Foerster LLP *
Wilson Sonsini Goodrich & Rosati *

**Band 3**
DLA Piper LLP (US) *
Goodwin Procter LLP *
Knobbe Martens Olson & Bear
Pillsbury Winthrop Shaw Pittman LLP *
Stradling Yocca Carlson & Rauth, A Professional Corporation *

**Band 4**
Foley & Lardner LLP *
McDermott Will & Emery LLP *
Perkins Coie LLP
Ropes & Gray LLP *

## Life Sciences: Corporate/Commercial
### Leading Individuals

**Band 1**

| | |
|---|---|
| Clark Kenneth A | Wilson Sonsini Goodrich & Rosati |
| Jones Robert | Cooley LLP |
| Kosacz Barbara | Cooley LLP |
| McGlynn Casey | Wilson Sonsini Goodrich & Rosati |
| Mendelson Alan C | Latham & Watkins LLP * |
| Muto Fred | Cooley LLP |
| Snipes James C | Covington & Burling LLP * |

**Band 2**

| | |
|---|---|
| Hasko Judith A | Latham & Watkins LLP * |
| Hoyng Charles F | Latham & Watkins LLP * |
| Jenett Bruce W | DLA Piper LLP (US) * |
| Leonard Emily I | Covington & Burling LLP * |
| Thau Stephen B | Morrison & Foerster LLP * |
| Wolfe Scott N | Latham & Watkins LLP * |

**Band 3**

| | |
|---|---|
| Campbell John W | Morrison & Foerster LLP * |
| Chandler L Kay | Cooley LLP |
| Clowes Howard | DLA Piper LLP (US) * |
| Cohn Lawrence B | Stradling Yocca Carlson & Rauth |
| Edvalson Ian B | Wilson Sonsini Goodrich & Rosati |
| Hill James W | McDermott Will & Emery LLP * |
| Kamb Barclay | Cooley LLP |
| Levy Seth D | Nixon Peabody LLP (ONP)† * |
| Sanders Michael | Reed Smith LLP (ONP)† |
| Zucker Sam | O'Melveny & Myers LLP (ONP)† |

**Band 4**

| | |
|---|---|
| Snyder David R | Pillsbury Winthrop Shaw Pittman LLP * |
| Toro Amy L | Covington & Burling LLP * |

## Life Sciences: IP/Patent Litigation
### Senior Statesmen

**Senior Statesmen: distinguished older practitioners**

| | |
|---|---|
| Murashige Kate H | Morrison & Foerster LLP * |

### Leading Individuals

**Band 1**

| | |
|---|---|
| Monroy Gladys H | Morrison & Foerster LLP * |
| Norviel Vern | Wilson Sonsini Goodrich & Rosati |

**Band 2**

| | |
|---|---|
| de Bodo Richard | DLA Piper LLP (US) * |
| Dreger Ginger R | Arnold & Porter LLP (ONP)† * |
| Gindler David I | Irell & Manella (ONP)† * |
| Haile Lisa A | DLA Piper LLP (US) * |
| Insogna Anthony M | Jones Day (ONP)† * |
| Polizzi Catherine | Morrison & Foerster LLP * |
| Wise Michael | Perkins Coie LLP |

**Up-and-coming individuals**

| | |
|---|---|
| Wehrli John | Latham & Watkins LLP * |

\* Indicates firm / individual with profile.
†ONP = Other Notable Practitioner.

## Band 1

### Cooley LLP

**THE FIRM** This highly regarded firm is called on by clients across the pharmaceutical and biotech industries, as well as business consultants and specialist life sciences investors. A wide-ranging workload includes corporate, financing, IP, licensing and commercialization issues. The practice is well known for its strength in working with early-stage companies, and peers commend its prolific practice in this arena. Key clients include Onyx Pharmaceuticals, Cypress BioSciences, SciClone Pharmaceuticals and PaxVax.

**KEY INDIVIDUALS Robert Jones**'s practice covers public and private financing, fiduciary issues, securities law and licensing transactions. He is considered an expert adviser, with valuable experience in the biotechnology sector. **Barbara Kosacz** is an experienced corporate attorney focused on strategic partnerships and M&A, as well as private financing, strategic investment and public offerings. She is renowned as a leading attorney in the market, and is well known for her expertise in venture capital work. **Fred Muto** is head of the firm's business department and specializes in the representation of emerging and public clients in corporate and securities work. He is experienced in acting for companies and investors on public offerings, as well as a variety of corporate transactions; biotech and medical devices are key areas of practice. **Kay Chandler** has a broad practice, advising on technology licensing, M&A, collaboration agreements, profit-sharing and co-promotion agreements. She is singled out for her combination of legal skills and technical industry knowledge. **Barclay Kamb** represents clients in corporate, financing and IP matters, and has impressive experience in biotech and medical devices. His workload includes partnership agreements, joint venture agreements, strategic alliances and licensing.

### Latham & Watkins LLP

See profile on p.446

**THE FIRM** This high-caliber firm has offices in Los Angeles, San Francisco, Silicon Valley, San Diego and Orange County, and can also draw on the resources of an extensive international network. Latham represents clients ranging from startups to public companies in corporate matters including M&A transactions, IPOs, financing and strategic alliances. ANDA patent litigation is also a key area of practice. In standout matters, the team assisted Kythera Biopharmaceuticals with a $37.4 million Series D financing, and advised Amgen on its $315 million acquisition of KAI Pharmaceuticals.

**Sources say:** "*Latham is one of the firms that is just head and shoulders above the others.*"

**KEY INDIVIDUALS Alan Mendelson** (see p.367) is a highly experienced and respected practitioner in the life sciences arena. His practice covers M&A, joint ventures and strategic alliances, venture capital financing and public offerings. He acted for Amgen on the KAI Pharmaceuticals acquisition, and for Transcept Pharmaceuticals on a $40.5 million common stock offering. **Judith Hasko** (see p.331) is a corporate and licensing attorney based in the Silicon Valley office, who handles a range of corporate partnership, joint venture, codevelopment and profit sharing arrangements. She attracts enthusiastic praise from clients, who describe her as "*very experienced in licensing, and very hard-working, clear-thinking and practical.*" **Charles Hoyng** (see p.643) splits his time between the Silicon Valley and Boston offices. His practice covers technology licensing as well as development, manufacturing and distribution. He recently acted for ImmuNext on a strategic collaboration agreement with Janssen Biotech relating to the commercialization of a cancer treatment. **Scott Wolfe** (see p.672) represents a wide variety of companies in private placements, public offerings, venture capital financing and M&A transactions. Practice highlights include advising Sunovion Pharmaceuticals on its acquisition of Elevation Pharmaceuticals, a privately held biopharmaceutical company. **John Wehrli** (see p.671) specializes in strategic alliances, M&A, joint ventures and spin-outs, and has impressive knowledge of Asian and European transactions. He acted for Impax Laboratories on a licensing agreement with AstraZeneca relating to the commercialization of the Zomig product.

## Band 2

### Covington & Burling LLP
See profile on p.441

THE FIRM This firm's California practice operates out of offices in San Francisco, Silicon Valley and San Diego, offering clients transactional, litigation, IP and regulatory services. Key clients include Abbott, Amgen, Astellas and Sanofi. In standout matters, the team represented AstraZeneca in the $1.26 billion acquisition of Ardea Biosciences, a San Diego-based biotechnology company. **Sources say:** *"They're very thorough and their work product is excellent. They also have a lot of depth, so if a peculiar issue arises they have always had someone on staff who not only has experience but is probably an expert in the field."* **KEY INDIVIDUALS** San Francisco-based **James Snipes** (see p.666) focuses on transactional and corporate matters, advising clients on collaborations, licensing, M&A and other commercial arrangements. Sources describe him as *"an extremely smart, powerful guy – he's a superstar."* **Emily Leonard** (see p.354) handles both corporate and IP matters for life sciences companies. Partnership and collaboration agreements are key areas of practice, as well as joint ventures, licensing and technology transfer. Clients describe her as *"very responsive"* while peers comment that she *"really knows her stuff."* **Amy Toro** (see p.669) handles a range of collaboration and licensing agreements within the biotechnology and pharmaceutical industries. Clients say she is *"incredibly intelligent, super-responsive, and she really rolls up her sleeves and takes charge of heated situations."*

### Morrison & Foerster LLP
See profile on p.1990

THE FIRM This highly regarded firm advises life sciences clients from its San Diego, Palo Alto and San Francisco offices. The team has an excellent reputation for IP matters, including patent prosecution, enforcement and counseling. As well as an active product liability litigation practice, the firm also has strong corporate capabilities, and can draw on in-depth expertise in early round financings. Key clients include Genentech, Novartis and Sandoz. **Sources say:** *"Morrison & Foerster has a really good reputation in this area."* **KEY INDIVIDUALS** Peers describe **Gladys Monroy** (see p.655) as a *"stateswoman of patent prosecution"* in California. Her practice ranges from strategy and patent portfolio management to interference, reexamination and reissue proceedings. She also undertakes due diligence evaluations and patentability analysis. **Catherine Polizzi** (see p.659) assists clients with portfolio management and patent prosecution, as well as due diligence reviews and opinion work. Her experience takes in a broad spectrum of areas, including biologics, nanotechnology, drug formulation and nucleic acids. **Stephen Thau** (see p.668) is a biotech specialist who offers clients *"outstanding advice and timely follow-up."* He has been highly active in venture financings of late, and also handles strategic alliances, licensing and public offerings. **John Campbell** (see p.627) is a corporate attorney whose practice covers M&A, venture capital financings and public and private securities offerings. His client base

includes various life sciences companies, investors and underwriters. Sources name **Kate Murashige** (see p.372) as an *"extremely distinguished"* practitioner in the California life sciences industry. She represents clients in patent drafting and prosecution, and is seen as a thought-leader in biotechnology litigation.

### Wilson Sonsini Goodrich & Rosati
See profile on p.700

THE FIRM This multiservice firm has a highly regarded life sciences practice which spans its Palo Alto, San Diego, San Francisco and South of Market offices. The group represents clients in corporate transactions, partnership and licensing agreements, and various IP matters. The team is known for its experience in the venture capital arena, and represented Heartflow in its $75 million series C financing. Other clients include Amgen, Astellas Pharma, Bio-Rad and Pacific Biosciences. **Sources say:** *"Wilson is a huge competitor on the West Coast."* **KEY INDIVIDUALS Kenneth Clark** is a *"superb"* corporate attorney working primarily in the biotechnology field. He advises on strategic alliances, financings and technology transactions, and acted for KAI Pharmaceuticals on its $315 million acquisition by Amgen. **Casey McGlynn** is a well-regarded figure in the California life sciences market and is well known for his representation of startup and growth technology companies. He represented Heartflow in its series C financing, and advised ForteBio on its acquisition by Pall Corporation. **Vern Norviel** advises life sciences companies and venture capital firms on patent and strategy matters, and is described as *"an outstanding lawyer who has built a vibrant practice."* **Ian Edvalson** assists companies with IP and product-related transactions such as collaboration and development agreements, technology acquisitions and licensing. Highlights include representing Mylan in an exclusive strategic collaboration with Pfizer to develop, manufacture and commercialize generic products in Japan.

## Band 3

### DLA Piper LLP (US)
See profile on p.1971

THE FIRM This international firm has a strong presence in California, with life sciences specialists in its Silicon Valley, San Francisco, Sacramento, Century City, Golden Triangle and downtown San Diego offices. Its broad-ranging capabilities include a variety of corporate and finance transactions and patent litigation. It is also singled out by peers for its highly active product liability practice. **KEY INDIVIDUALS Bruce Jenett** (see p.644) has a globe-spanning practice representing technology companies and financial clients in the life sciences arena. Areas of expertise include strategic alliances, M&A, equity and debt financing, licensing and distribution. **Howard Clowes** (see p.628) divides his time between the San Francisco and Silicon Valley offices, and focuses on M&A, collaborations and venture finance. Cochair of the patent litigation practice **Richard de Bodo** (see p.631) is highly regarded by

peers, who single him out as *"smart, and a good strategist."* He handles all aspects of IP and is well known for his experience in the life sciences sphere. Clients are enthusiastic in their praise of patent attorney **Lisa Haile** (see p.639). She is *"wonderful in terms of responsiveness,"* and also has a *"strong scientific background,"* which covers molecular biology, diagnostics, host-vector systems and bioinformatics.

### Goodwin Procter LLP
See profile on p.1522

THE FIRM The life sciences practice at Goodwin Procter encompasses patent prosecution, litigation, and corporate and commercial matters, including venture financing, capital markets transactions and M&A. It has a broad presence across the state, with offices in San Diego, San Francisco and Silicon Valley. Mandates include representing Roxane Laboratories in a patent infringement action brought by Genzyme. **Sources say:** *"Very strong in biotechnology."* **KEY INDIVIDUALS Bradley Bugdanowitz** is a key contact based in the firm's San Francisco office.

### Knobbe Martens Olson & Bear

THE FIRM This well-regarded IP boutique has an excellent reputation in the life sciences arena, receiving high praise from peers for strength in patent issues. Its client base features clients in the pharmaceutical, biotech, nanotechnology and medical devices fields. Areas of expertise include patent prosecution, opinion work, appeals, interferences and portfolio management. **Sources say:** *"They dominate medical devices IP in Southern California."* **KEY INDIVIDUALS Ned Israelsen** is managing partner of the San Diego office.

### Pillsbury Winthrop Shaw Pittman LLP
See profile on p.2000

THE FIRM The life sciences practice at this full-service firm operates out of its San Diego, Silicon Valley, Los Angeles and Sacramento offices. The team assists clients with IP protection, litigation, corporate transactions and financing. Work highlights include representing Affymax in a settlement and licensing agreement between Affymax, Johnson & Johnson and Takeda Pharmaceuticals valued at $13 million. Other clients include Arriva Pharmaceuticals and the University of Kansas Center for Research. **KEY INDIVIDUALS David Snyder** (see p.666) is a corporate and finance attorney in the San Diego office with valuable experience in public offerings, public and private M&A transactions and other corporate and commercial agreements.

### Stradling Yocca Carlson & Rauth, A Professional Corporation
See profile on p.699

THE FIRM Stradling Yocca has a strong reputation in life sciences work, which attracts clients ranging from startups to public companies in the medical device, pharmaceutical and biotech industries. The practice focuses primarily on financing and corporate matters, and represented

Endologix in its $40 million public offering. The team also advised Spectrum Pharmaceuticals on its $314 million acquisition of Allos Therapeutics.

**Sources say:** *"A really strong presence in Southern California."*

**KEY INDIVIDUALS Lawrence Cohn** represents life sciences companies in a variety of corporate and financing matters, including M&A, strategic alliances, technology transfers and venture capital funding. He is noted for his background in organic chemistry and his in-house industry experience.

## Band 4

### Foley & Lardner LLP
See profile on p.2588

**THE FIRM** This multiservice firm provides corporate and IP assistance to life sciences clients in various stages of development, and sources are highly impressed by the team's strength in representing startup companies. The practice acts for clients in the pharmaceuticals, medical devices and biologics fields, attracting names such as Anaerobe Systems, Drais Pharmaceuticals and Kythera Biopharmaceuticals. Life sciences specialists are stationed across the state, advising clients from Los Angeles, Sacramento, San Francisco, Silicon Valley and Del Mar.

**KEY INDIVIDUALS** Antoinette Konski and Richard Kaufman are cochairs of the department.

### McDermott Will & Emery LLP
See profile on p.1258

**THE FIRM** This team spans the firm's Silicon Valley, Orange County and Los Angeles offices. The practice is particularly well known for its IP capabilities, which include strategic planning and prosecution, licensing, due diligence reviews, Hatch-Waxman litigation and other patent disputes. The practice also handles corporate transactions, restructuring and financing within the life sciences

industry, and acted for Mature Women's Health Solutions on an initial $2.2 million venture capital investment.

**KEY INDIVIDUALS James Hill** (see p.642), based in the Orange Country office, has a practice focus on IP counseling, due diligence, licensing, and patent prosecution and litigation. He is a qualified medical doctor with expertise in a variety of fields, including ophthalmology, radiology and arteriography. The University of Utah and the University of Rochester are key clients.

### Perkins Coie LLP
See profile on p.2548

**THE FIRM** This full-service firm has boosted its life sciences practice with three lateral hires. The group is based across the team's offices in San Francisco, San Diego, Palo Alto and Los Angeles, and offers IP, corporate and litigation services. The IP team handles patent procurement, patent litigation and interference proceedings, as well as portfolio management. Clients include Sequenom, Cargill and Mylan Pharmaceuticals.

**KEY INDIVIDUALS** Cochair of the life sciences practice **Michael Wise** handles patent portfolio management, due diligence, litigation and interference. His wide range of experience includes biologics, small molecules, medical devices and diagnostics. Clients praise his knowledge of the Chinese market.

### Ropes & Gray LLP
See profile on p.1528

**THE FIRM** The California practice of this national firm operates out of its Silicon Valley and San Francisco offices, representing financiers and investors, as well as medical device, biotech and biopharmaceutical clients. The corporate and transactional team focuses on capital raising, M&A, licensing and collaboration agreements. Notable clients include Sadra Medical, Pfizer and Johnson & Johnson.

**KEY INDIVIDUALS** Ryan Murr is a key contact in the San Francisco office.

## Other Notable Practitioners

**Michael Sanders** of Reed Smith LLP represents startup and growth life sciences companies in capital raising matters. He also assists institutional investors in the life sciences arena, such as Domain Associates and DRI Holdings. Practice highlights include representing Domain Associates in negotiating a partnership with RUSNANO with the aim of investing in around 20 US life sciences companies. **Seth Levy** (see p.650) advises clients from the Los Angeles office of Nixon Peabody LLP. He focuses on patent prosecution, licensing, IP due diligence and IP management for life sciences companies. **Anthony Insogna** (see p.643) is the cochair of Jones Day's IP practice, and represents clients in the IP aspects of transactions, collaborations and financings. Other work includes patent prosecution and litigation, particularly Hatch-Waxman cases. In one standout matter, he defended Celgene and Abraxis Bioscience in a patent infringement claim relating to the Abraxane breast cancer drug. **Ginger Dreger** (see p.633) of Arnold & Porter LLP offers strategic IP counseling to pharmaceutical, biotech and medical devices companies, with a particular focus on patent protection. She recently worked with Tengion on due diligence matters, and the worldwide patent issue for its tissue engineering technology. One satisfied client comments: *"She gives the kind of sophisticated, mature advice that is critical for businesses to be able to make decisions."* **Sam Zucker** of O'Melveny & Myers LLP divides his time between the Silicon Valley and New York offices. His practice focuses on corporate transactions, including M&A, strategic alliances, joint ventures, financings, and securities offerings. He led the team handling CytomX Therapeutics' series B financing round expansions, which brought the equity total of that round to $41 million. **David Gindler** (see p.638) of Irell & Manella handles patent litigation relating to biotechnology and medical devices, and acted for Ariosa Diagnostics on its opposition to a preliminary injunction filed by Sequenom.

# LITIGATION

Commentary about individuals can be found under their firm's paragraph. If the firm has no paragraph (is not ranked) look at Other Notable Practitioners.

*The editorial is in alphabetical order by firm name.*

### Bingham McCutchen LLP
See profile on p.1515

**THE FIRM** This full-service firm has an enviable national and international network, which gives it the breadth to maintain a robust litigation practice. Its capabilities extend to handling securities litigation tailored to serve the needs of accounting firms, hedge funds and leading financial institutions. Obtaining a favorable class action settlement for Pacific Capital Bancorp, and advising Anadarko Petroleum on ongoing matters related to the Deepwater

Horizon oil spill, are among the team's recent undertakings.

**Sources say:** *"I would rate the firm to be at the top for trial capacity, issue identification, written product, pragmatism and negotiating talent."*

**KEY INDIVIDUALS Marshall Grossman** (see p.639) is *"one of the best commercial litigators I have worked with. He can take a complex set of facts and really focus on what is important,"* enthuses a client. He is highly praised for his extraordinary diligence when assisting with complex commercial litigation. He acted for Agudas Chabad on its high-profile victory against the Russian Federation, ordering the return of several religious manuscripts and books confis-

cated during the the Bolshevik Revolution and the Second World War. **Donn Pickett** (see p.659) maintains a respected securities and antitrust-focused practice. He led for Oracle in securing a $1.3 billion victory in a copyright infringement case, and represented Intel in antitrust litigation, among numerous highlights. Distinguished litigator **David Balabanian** (see p.621) brings a wealth of experience when overseeing the most complex, high-profile energy, securities and antitrust disputes. He is hailed by a client as an *"outstanding lawyer and a pleasure to work with."* **Dale Barnes** (see p.622) is a respected securities litigator highly regarded for his ability to handle high-stakes class actions and M&A litigation. He receives praise as a *"responsive,*

## Litigation: General Commercial
### Leading Firms

**Band 1**
Gibson, Dunn & Crutcher LLP *
Keker & Van Nest LLP
Morrison & Foerster LLP *
Munger, Tolles & Olson LLP *
Quinn Emanuel Urquhart & Sullivan, LLP
Skadden, Arps, Slate, Meagher & Flom LLP & Affiliates *

**Band 2**
Latham & Watkins LLP *
O'Melveny & Myers LLP *

**Band 3**
Cooley LLP
Irell & Manella *
Jones Day *
Kirkland & Ellis LLP *
Morgan, Lewis & Bockius LLP *
Orrick, Herrington & Sutcliffe LLP *
Sidley Austin LLP *
Wilson Sonsini Goodrich & Rosati *

**Band 4**
Bingham McCutchen LLP *
Farella Braun + Martel LLP
Hogan Lovells US LLP
Manatt Phelps & Phillips LLP *
McDermott Will & Emery LLP *
Paul Hastings LLP *
Sullivan & Cromwell LLP *
White & Case LLP *

**Band 5**
Caldwell Leslie & Proctor, PC *
Crowell & Moring LLP *
Dechert LLP *
Holland & Knight LLP *
Nixon Peabody LLP *
Reed Smith LLP
Sheppard, Mullin, Richter & Hampton LLP

## Litigation: General Commercial
### Senior Statesmen

**Senior Statesmen: distinguished older practitioners**

| | |
|---|---|
| Balabanian David M | Bingham McCutchen LLP * |

### Leading Individuals

**Star individuals**

| | |
|---|---|
| Brian Brad D | Munger, Tolles & Olson LLP * |
| Keker John | Keker & Van Nest LLP |

**Band 1**

| | |
|---|---|
| Cotchett Joseph | Cotchett, Pitre & McCarthy |
| Grossman Marshall B | Bingham McCutchen LLP (ONP) † * |
| Hennigan J Michael | McKool Smith (ONP) † * |
| Kennedy Raoul | Skadden, Arps, Slate, Meagher & Flom * |
| Neal Stephen C | Cooley LLP |
| Nolan Thomas J | Skadden, Arps, Slate, Meagher & Flom * |
| Petrocelli Daniel | O'Melveny & Myers LLP |
| Quinn John B | Quinn Emanuel Urquhart & Sullivan, LLP |
| Ruby Allen J | Skadden, Arps, Slate, Meagher & Flom * |

**Band 2**

| | |
|---|---|
| Aronson Seth | O'Melveny & Myers LLP |
| Kitchens Dean | Gibson, Dunn & Crutcher LLP * |
| Olson Ronald | Munger, Tolles & Olson LLP * |
| Spiegel John | Munger, Tolles & Olson LLP * |
| Young Douglas R | Farella Braun + Martel LLP |

**Band 3**

| | |
|---|---|
| Dwyer John | Cooley LLP |
| Feldman Larry | Kaye Scholer LLP (ONP) † * |
| Glaser Patricia | Glaser, Weil, Fink, Jacobs, Howard (ONP) † |
| Mittelstaedt Robert A | Jones Day * |
| Price Bill | Quinn Emanuel Urquhart & Sullivan, LLP |
| Sacks Robert A | Sullivan & Cromwell LLP * |
| Urquhart A William | Quinn Emanuel Urquhart & Sullivan, LLP |
| Van Nest Robert | Keker & Van Nest LLP |

**Band 4**

| | |
|---|---|
| Call Gregory | Crowell & Moring LLP |
| González Arturo J | Morrison & Foerster LLP * |
| Hainline III Forrest A | Goodwin Procter LLP * |
| Matthias Michael R | Baker & Hostetler LLP (ONP) † * |
| McKnight Frederick (Rick) | Jones Day * |
| McNamara Michael | Steptoe & Johnson LLP (ONP) † |
| Pickett Donn P | Bingham McCutchen LLP * |
| Schatz Steven | Wilson Sonsini Goodrich & Rosati |
| Schrader David L | Morgan, Lewis & Bockius LLP * |
| Steinberg Michael H | Sullivan & Cromwell LLP * |
| Woods Daniel | Musick Peeler & Garrett (ONP) † |

**Band 5**

| | |
|---|---|
| Barron Anthony | Nixon Peabody LLP * |
| Bayless David | Covington & Burling LLP (ONP) † * |
| Caldwell Christopher | Caldwell Leslie & Proctor, PC |
| Eggleton Keith | Wilson Sonsini Goodrich & Rosati |
| Johnson Edward D | Mayer Brown LLP (ONP) † |
| Kahn Michael A. | Crowell & Moring LLP * |
| Larrabee Matthew L | Dechert LLP * |
| Mallow Michael | Loeb & Loeb LLP (ONP) † * |
| McKane Mark | Kirkland & Ellis LLP * |
| Merryman Bryan A | White & Case LLP * |
| Oxley William W | Dechert LLP * |
| Rhodes Michael G | Cooley LLP |
| Sullivan Douglas | Crowell & Moring LLP * |

**Up-and-coming individuals**

| | |
|---|---|
| Ruhland Christopher | Dechert LLP * |

## Litigation: Mainly Plaintiff
### Leading Firms

**Band 1**
Cotchett, Pitre & McCarthy
Robbins Geller Rudman & Dowd LLP *

* Indicates firm / individual with profile.
†ONP = Other Notable Practitioner.

**KEY INDIVIDUALS Christopher Caldwell** *"sits down and talks to us, listens carefully and helps us find our ultimate goal,"* asserts a client. He is a senior litigator with a reputation to match his years of experience. He recently represented Countrywide Financial Corporation's former president in various investigatory and civil issues.

### Cooley LLP

**THE FIRM** This full-service firm has a far-reaching national network that gives the five California offices the breadth to handle disputes of all complexities. It has seen recent action in the high-profile, $272 million Ernest Rady dispute, which involved alleged breach of contract and share-selling issues. Other notable clients include Facebook, eBay and Google.
**KEY INDIVIDUALS** Based in the Palo Alto office, **Stephen Neal** is cited as a top-notch lawyer by market

## Litigation: Securities
### Leading Firms

**Band 1**
Gibson, Dunn & Crutcher LLP *
Irell & Manella *
Morrison & Foerster LLP *
Skadden, Arps, Slate, Meagher & Flom LLP & Affiliates *
Wilson Sonsini Goodrich & Rosati *

**Band 2**
Latham & Watkins LLP *
Munger, Tolles & Olson LLP *
O'Melveny & Myers LLP *
Orrick, Herrington & Sutcliffe LLP *

**Band 3**
Bingham McCutchen LLP *
DLA Piper LLP (US) *
Goodwin Procter LLP *
Hogan Lovells US LLP
Keker & Van Nest LLP
Paul Hastings LLP *
Sidley Austin LLP *

*thoughtful and intelligent lawyer."* **John Pernick** (see p.658) and **Charlene Sachi Shimada** (see p.665) are two notable additions to this year's rankings. A client states that Pernick is *"bright"* and *"communicates complicated items in an easy to understand way."* Shimada has considerable experience assisting with investigations by the IRS, SEC and DOJ and is highlighted as a *"very experienced lawyer who does well for her clients,"* by one satisfied client.

### Caldwell Leslie & Proctor, PC
See profile on p.677
**THE FIRM** This highly trusted litigation boutique is known for its high-profile appellate and litigation work. Representing Paramount Pictures in a $20 million copyright infringement dispute, and representing Obey Clothing in a high-profile copyright case involving a popular image of Barack Obama, are among its notable recent highlights.
**Sources say:** *"They are very smart and strong litigators, who have a great ability to think outside the box."*

sources. He is a highly experienced litigator with an impressive practice covering the spectrum of commercial litigation. **John Dwyer** is well respected in the community for his experience. He was heavily active litigating on behalf of eBay in a landmark case that held the California Resale Royalty Act unconstitutional. **Michael Rhodes** chairs the firm's litigation department nationally and splits his practice between the San Francisco and San Diego offices. Renowned for his privacy practice, he recently represented Google against a class action claim and also advises heavy hitters such as Sony Computer Entertainment America and Facebook.

## Cotchett, Pitre & McCarthy

**THE FIRM** This dedicated litigation firm stands at the forefront of plaintiff-side litigation. The talented team is skilled in handling complex litigation such as consumer protection, fraud and intellectual property matters.

**KEY INDIVIDUALS Joseph Cotchett** is a highly renowned litigator and, with over 45 years' experience, is considered *"a legend in the state."* He is recognized for his skill in representing a range of clientele including colossal multinationals and smaller local corporations.

## Crowell & Moring LLP
### See profile on p.910

**THE FIRM** Crowell & Moring makes its debut following rapid growth in California over the past few years. Sources praise its strength in managed care issues and class action representations. Among its major recent cases is acting for the Regents of the University of California and Dr Michael Jung in a contract case brought by Medivation concerning the ownership of a new prostate cancer drug.

**Sources say:** *"We hire them when we have a particularly challenging matter and want somebody really good to handle it, somebody that we really trust."*

**KEY INDIVIDUALS** *"Excellent trial lawyer"* **Douglas Sullivan** (see p.668) *"has a tremendous capacity for retaining knowledge and then deploying it,"* according to sources. He defended Enterprise Holdings in complex commercial litigation concerning the use of quick response codes in rented automobiles. Sources hold **Gregory Call** in high regard, lauding him for being *"tenacious and fearless"* and having *"everything you want in a litigator."* He undertakes breach of contract, antitrust and general commercial work and recently acted for a number of major retailers as plaintiffs on a case against Westfield Roseville Galleria. Senior counsel **Michael Kahn** (see p.645) is described as a *"master strategist"* and *"an unbelievably quick assimilator of information."* He acted for the Regents of the University of California on litigation and reviews into the use of pepper spray and batons during the 'Occupy' protests.

## Dechert LLP
### See profile on p.1969

**THE FIRM** This group is able to deploy experienced litigators across a range of industries, including technology and insurance, and is praised by clients for its creative solutions and responsiveness. It acts extensively for DHL Express, representing it in five recent cases, including cases concerning DHL's decision to cease domestic shipping in the US.

**Sources say:** *"The quality of analysis, creativity of thought and depth of research is exceptional."*

**KEY INDIVIDUALS Matthew Larrabee** (see p.648) is an *"excellent strategist, experienced litigator and a valued adviser on all matters related to litigation."* He is a busy securities litigator in addition to taking on more general commercial work. He recently represented Lord Abbett Distributor in a FINRA arbitration concerning an alleged conspiracy with Merrill Lynch during the 2008 financial crisis. **William Oxley** (see p.658) is described by sources as *"a very skilled trial lawyer"* who is a *"gifted cross-examiner."* He recently acted for DHL on the appeal against a trial judgment in a case against Falcon Express. **Christopher Ruhland** (see p.663) gains positive comments from commentators for trial and brief writing skills. He acted for DHL on a federal breach of contract trial in Utah, leading a team of eight lawyers.

## DLA Piper LLP (US)
### See profile on p.1971

**THE FIRM** DLA Piper has impressed clients with its securities practice, which boasts experience across the area, including representing clients before the SEC, FINRA and the DOJ. Of late it has acted for Finisar Corporation on several matters, including shareholder class action litigation.

**Sources say:** *"They've been absolutely outstanding in their approach to strategy, availability and correspondence and, most importantly, the result."*

**KEY INDIVIDUALS Shirli Weiss** (see p.672) represented Finisar in its litigation as well as acting for the former CFO of Countrywide Financial on a case brought by the SEC alleging fraud and negligence. Sources particularly praise her negotiation skills, and describe her as a *"terrific, really tough lawyer."*

## Farella Braun + Martel LLP

**THE FIRM** This firm's client list includes prominent names, such as Dell, Toyota and Google, for which it acted on a number of patent infringement cases. It is seen as a full-service litigation firm but has particular strengths in the technology sector and on intellectual property-related matters. It acts for both plaintiffs and defendants.

**Sources say:** *"They are strategic, have strong juniors and do well in the courtroom."*

**KEY INDIVIDUALS Douglas Young** is a *"really smart guy who gives good, strategic advice"* and has a *"wonderful style in talking to judges, which ensures they're going to listen,"* according to commentators. He represented Dell in the LCD antitrust litigation and regularly acts on white-collar and IP matters.

## Gibson, Dunn & Crutcher LLP
### See profile on p.682

**THE FIRM** Gibson Dunn continues to be one of the most formidable and well-respected litigation groups on the West Coast. It has 65 partners practicing in this area across the full range of litigation matters, including antitrust and securities. On the securities front, it maintains a deep roster and a busy practice, including such recent representations as acting for UBS on a case brought by billionaire

Igor Olenicoff alleging mismanagement. More generally, it successfully defeated a putative class action claim brought against PepsiCo and South Beach Beverage alleging false advertising.

Sources say: *"They are exceptional professionals who really care. They developed an outstanding strategy which worked perfectly as they anticipated and which they executed beautifully. They were rainmakers – amazing."*

KEY INDIVIDUALS Dean Kitchens (see p.347) is an experienced litigator who practices general commercial law with a distinct securities flavor. Sources praise him for his client focus and describe him as a *"terrific and savvy traditional trial lawyer who gets good results."* He led in the UBS matter. Another strong securities litigator, Wayne Smith (see p.666) has *"an enormous amount of trial experience"* and is credited for his ability to *"sort out and simplify the factual areas that can bedevil cases."* He led the firm's successful representation of ITT Educational Services in defending claims of securities fraud in its recruiting practices. Cochair of the securities practice group, Meryl Young (see p.673) is *"incredibly well connected with the judicial system and has a lot of insight into the SEC."* She is co-leading in a case for Citigroup Global Markets in defence of a suit brought by Tri-City Healthcare District relating to the issuing of bonds.

## Goodwin Procter LLP
See profile on p.1522

THE FIRM Goodwin Procter has a busy and well-regarded practice in California, with practitioners noted for their knowledge in the field. It has acted for Countrywide Financial on a number of cases, including matters relating to mortgage-backed securities and other alleged breaches of securities laws.

Sources say: *"They tend to take a holistic approach to representing clients and I like their expertise."*

KEY INDIVIDUALS Forrest Hainline (see p.639) is a *"fierce litigator"* and *"very effective advocate who fully appreciates the business realities of his clients."* He practices across general commercial law and recently acted for Fairmont Raffles Hotel International on a case concerning the early termination of a hotel management agreement. Sources are impressed by Daniel Tyukody's (see p.670) *"detailed knowledge of trends in the securities field and his very sharp analytical skills."* Recently, he represented Apollo Group in a class action relating to alleged financial misstatement and misleading of the market.

## Hogan Lovells US LLP

THE FIRM This team has an effective litigation presence that focuses on product liability and insurance, among other areas. In addition, it has a strong securities practice that often represents Hogan Lovells's numerous pharmaceutical and biotech clients. Among its recent representations was that for VIVUS in a securities class action concerning the drug Qnexa.

Sources say: *"They are always very responsive to our requests. We're very pleased with the results and the working relationship."*

KEY INDIVIDUALS Norman Blears focuses on complex securities litigation, for which *"clients hold him in high regard."* He acts for Dendreon on litigation relating to Provenge, a cancer drug. He heads the California securities practice. The *"very respected"* Douglas Schwab is of counsel at the firm and has over 40 years' experience in securities and general commercial litigation. He recently acted for a number of senior individuals at Cadence Design Systems on a case alleging irregularities in financial statements.

## Holland & Knight LLP
See profile on p.1028

THE FIRM This firm has a nine-partner California litigation group and is well regarded by clients and involved in several significant cases. It practices in a number of commercial litigation areas, including toxic tort and product liability. It recently acted for Twin Anchors Marine on a case concerning an boating incident which resulted in death and personal injury.

Sources say: *"They stand out in my mind as one of the best at keeping their clients informed."*

KEY INDIVIDUALS Matthew Vafidis is the head of the California litigation group. He is based in the firm's San Francisco office.

## Irell & Manella
See profile on p.686

THE FIRM This group has a strong reputation for its litigation work, with a particular emphasis on intellectual property matters and, among other matters, has acted for DIRECTV on a complex government contract. On the securities side, it has a leading practice, led by the inimitable David Siegel. It continues to represent former head of Countrywide Financial, Angelo Mozilo, in a number of suits and has also acted for officers and management directors of MGM Resorts International on litigation brought by shareholders following the financial crisis.

Sources say: *"They have very high-quality lawyers and do top-notch legal work."*

KEY INDIVIDUALS Star attorney David Siegel (see p.665) is *"in a class by himself"* for securities defence and SEC work, according to sources, who point to his *"laser-sharp advocacy"* and *"spectacular strategic insight."* He has represented Angelo Mozilo in various cases and was also the lead lawyer for the officers and directors of MGM Resorts.

## Jones Day
See profile on p.919

THE FIRM Jones Day has a solid litigation presence in California and is able to call upon its excellent national and international network when needed. Accordingly, the group undertakes work for a plethora of major clients. Among its representative matters has been acting for Chevron on alleged environmental liability in Ecuador resulting from Chevron's merger with Texaco. It also represented Yamaha in product liability matters concerning its Rhino SxS vehicle.

Sources say: *"They do excellent work, their attorneys are always prepared and they're ready to go." "They work very hard and are responsive."*

KEY INDIVIDUALS Robert Mittelstaedt (see p.655) is someone who *"gets very good results"* and who clients *"put a lot of trust in."* He is an experienced litigator who is also highly proficient in antitrust law. He represents Chevron in the Ecuador matter. Rick McKnight (see p.653) is credited for his *"great presence in front of a jury"* by commentators, who also point out his trial proficiency. He was the lead lawyer on the Yamaha Rhino SxS matter, achieving a successful outcome.

## Keker & Van Nest LLP

THE FIRM Keker & Van Nest serves as a reminder that biggest is not always best, as this 65-lawyer litigation firm punches well above its weight in the California litigation market. It boasts a very strong bench of litigators, with particular strengths in white-collar matters and securities. In the latter category, it recently represented a former director of Citigroup in a case arising from CDOs sold by Citigroup.

Sources say: *"They're the people you see when a big case with a lot at stake is going to trial. If they're on the other side, you know the other party is serious."*

KEY INDIVIDUALS Superlatives abound when John Keker's name is mentioned, with one source calling him *"the finest lawyer in the US"* and *"a legend in his own right."* In particular, his *"fearlessness"* and strategy as a white-collar counsel are picked out, although he is equally proficient at complex commercial matters. He leads on the CDO case. *"Very accomplished trial lawyer"* Robert Van Nest is described as *"someone you go to with a case that needs to be fought, rather than settled."* He is noted by sources for his prowess in IP-related work. He acted for the Regents of the University of California on a copyright infringement case relating to online video streaming.

## Kirkland & Ellis LLP
See profile on p.1254

THE FIRM This group is another of the major nationwide litigation firms with a presence on the West Coast, with three offices around California. Sources point out its abilities in class action litigation and this expertise has been brought to bear representing Facebook in a multitude of class action and shareholder claims following the company's IPO in 2012. Other clients include UBS and RBS.

Sources say: *"I have enormous confidence when I have them on a case."*

KEY INDIVIDUALS Mark McKane (see p.653) practices across a range of complex commercial disputes and has over 15 years' experience in this area. He acted for the special committee of Green Valley Ranch Gaming in an internal investigation relating to suspected illegal financial activity following a recapitalization.

## Latham & Watkins LLP
See profile on p.446

THE FIRM Latham & Watkins is well regarded by sources for its litigation prowess, which includes complex commercial work, merger litigation and securities matters. It has an extensive roster of some 64 partners in California. It acted for Apple on the AT&T Mobile antitrust litigation and, on the securities side, represented Ernst & Young in a class action arising from the collapse of IndyMac Bank.

**Sources say:** *"The work they have done has been fantastic."*

**KEY INDIVIDUALS** Peter Wald (see p.422) is singled out by sources for his *"extraordinary level of commitment"* as well as his foresight and team management. He is a skilled litigator who is extremely well regarded for his securities work. He recently represented Deloitte & Touche in a case related to the collapse of Washington Mutual, as well as acting on the Ernst & Young matter.

## Manatt Phelps & Phillips LLP
See profile on p.690

**THE FIRM** Within California, this group has a solid and respected litigation practice with expertise across a range of industries, including advertising and healthcare. Its clients include Wal-Mart and Sirius XM Radio, and it also acted for Ticketmaster on a consumer class action case alleging false advertising.

**Sources say:** *"Very good lawyers."*

**KEY INDIVIDUALS** Chad Hummel in its Los Angeles office continues to head the firm's litigation department.

## McDermott Will & Emery LLP
See profile on p.1258

**THE FIRM** This team brings its strong nationwide framework to California with a very capable litigation practice. It handles work in such industries as pharmaceuticals, technology and healthcare. It successfully represented Seagate Technology in a patent and trade secrets case concerning hard disk drives.

**Sources say:** *"They don't just go through the motions. They are willing to go to battle for you and willing to think outside the box."*

**KEY INDIVIDUALS** The leading lawyers for the firm in California are Tom Ryan, Rick Meyer and Dan Alberti.

## Morgan, Lewis & Bockius LLP
See profile on p.2246

**THE FIRM** This firm is well respected in California and beyond for handling a wide range of complex litigation matters. It is representing Hewlett-Packard in a series of disputes stemming from a decrease in its stock price, and assisting property developer Kitchell with a $68 million real estate dispute. The team regularly handles high-profile cases for major clients such as Shell Oil, Cisco Systems and Toyota.

**Sources say:** *"They are really very high-quality litigators, who understand both the litigation in general and the securitization aspect in particular."*

**KEY INDIVIDUALS** David Schrader's (see p.664) *"court manner is very respectful and he is effective at keeping the case on track,"* praises a client. He is particularly noted for his ability to assist clients from the energy, life sciences and manufacturing industries. He is handling two separate complex groundwater contamination cases on behalf of EDO Corporation and ITT Corporation.

## Morrison & Foerster LLP
See profile on p.1990

**THE FIRM** Drawing on excellent national and international resources, this litigation giant is a natural choice for big-ticket commercial and securities litigation. The firm continues to handle complex litigation matters, such as representing Capital One and US Bank in a major overdraft fee class action spanning several jurisdictions, obtaining a $21 million arbitration award on behalf of Marin General Hospital, and handling a $2.5 billion breach of contract dispute on behalf of EchoStar Satellite. It has also assisted clients with impressive securities matters, such as representing a Chinese automotive parts manufacturer in a class action involving insider trading and securities fraud allegations.

**Sources say:** *"Excellent advocates. They demonstrate excellent judgment and a mastery of their subspecialties."*

**KEY INDIVIDUALS** Arturo González (see p.638) is a *"dynamic individual"* praised for *"reading judges well and bonding with the jury."* He cochairs the firm's litigation practice and recently represented International Lease Finance and AIG in their suits alleging breach of fiduciary duty and trade secret theft. Jordan Eth (see p.634) is championed by peers and clients for being *"practical, thorough and experienced in the securities area."* He is renowned for his prestigious securities practice and has a strong track record in advising public companies with SEC investigations and complex derivative matters. He recently handled a high-profile securities class action on behalf of Yahoo! involving Chinese regulations limiting foreign ownership of online payment systems.

## Munger, Tolles & Olson LLP
See profile on p.691

**THE FIRM** This venerable California heavyweight continues to demonstrate impressive abilities in the litigation sphere. The team recently assisted Boeing and Boeing Satellite Systems with a reversal of a $604 million verdict, successfully dismissing class actions against Philip Morris, and handling mortgage-backed securities litigation on behalf of major financial institutions.

**Sources say:** *"What I liked about them was their eagerness to take on tough cases from the beginning. They are hard workers and very trial savvy."*

**KEY INDIVIDUALS** Clients are thoroughly impressed with Brad Brian (see p.625), with one commenting: *"He lives up to his fame and is one of the best trial attorneys."* He enjoys a strong following among large multinational corporations and is considered to be one of the state's top trial lawyers. He was the lead in representing Transocean in various proceedings and investigations stemming from the BP oil spill. Ronald Olson (see p.657) is well thought of as a skilled litigator with a peer stating that they *"have only good things to say about him."* His impeccable business knowledge is a vital asset when handling corporate investigations and complex litigation for financial institutions and a range of private and public companies. A client enthuses that John Spiegel (see p.666) is *"very strategic and a great all-around litigator."* His distinguished practice covers the spectrum of business litigation. He was the lead partner

representing Warner Bros. in Charlie Sheen's termination action, and defending Google founders Larry Page and Sergey Brin in a stockholder class action. Marc Dworsky (see p.633) enters the rankings this year and is highly regarded by clients, with one commenting: *"His quality of work is beyond anyone else."* He was the lead counsel handling $10 billion mortgage-backed securities litigation on behalf of Bank of America, and representing Citigroup Global Markets against Impac Funding in a dispute related to securities law violations.

## Nixon Peabody LLP
See profile on p.1526

**THE FIRM** With a strong bench of litigators in three California offices and a broad international network, this firm is equipped to deal with the full spectrum of complex litigation matters. The firm recently represented TV One in a suit against Northstar Media, Music World Music and BET Networks concerning the broadcast rights of the 2010 Essence Music Festival. The team also handled a high-profile cross-border matter on behalf of the Thyssen-Bornemisza Collection Foundation, securing its rightful ownership of a Camille Pissarro oil painting.

**Sources say:** *"Impressed with the way they explained everything and covered all possibilities."*

**KEY INDIVIDUALS** Anthony Barron (see p.622) serves as the deputy practice leader of the firm's commercial litigation group. He has a broad litigation practice and is noted for his ability to handle cases involving intricate banking, real estate and construction issues. Handling a $25 million dispute on behalf of Scottsdale Insurance, relating to its termination of a relationship with a broker, was a notable recent highlight.

## O'Melveny & Myers LLP
See profile on p.693

**THE FIRM** This Los Angeles-based outfit boasts a deep bench strength and an established commercial litigation practice, most notably within the media and entertainment industry. The talented group also conducts securities litigation on behalf of numerous companies in the financial sector.

**Sources say:** *"They have very good resources and looked at my case from every angle."*

**KEY INDIVIDUALS** Clients single out Daniel Petrocelli for being *"the best in the courtroom, but also the best at keeping you out of the courtroom."* He has a tremendous reputation for his prowess in handling highly publicized litigation and ability to effortlessly tackle disputes spanning a broad spectrum. Seth Aronson is cited as *"excellent"* on account of his highly distinguished practice. He handles every facet of securities litigation, representing directors, officers and corporations in SEC enforcement proceedings, class actions and many other issues.

## Orrick, Herrington & Sutcliffe LLP
See profile on p.1994

**THE FIRM** This firm boasts a well-connected network of West Coast offices that can provide comprehensive advice on virtually any kind of dispute. The group is therefore well equipped to handle varying types of litigation, ranging from securities to IP and commercial. The California teams worked closely with New York in advising DISH Networks on a case against several broadcast networks.

**Sources say:** *"They are exceptional and they get the whole picture."*

**KEY INDIVIDUALS** The *"fantastic"* **Michael Torpey** (see p.669) chairs the securities litigation group and his expertise in SEC investigations and class actions comes highly recommended. One client proclaims: *"He goes in front of the board on a regular basis – they are a tough crowd but he has no problems in dealing with them."* He currently represents Sequans Communications in a securities suit brought by its underwriters and various directors and officers. **James Kramer** (see p.647) enters the rankings for the first time, earned through his impressive and flourishing securities litigation practice. Sources commend his *"amazing presentation abilities,"* which made the opposition *"appear like bumbling idiots."* He recently led the team to victory on behalf of IronPlanet in a two-year dispute regarding the ownership of shares valued at more than $20 million.

## Paul Hastings LLP
### See profile on p.1996

**THE FIRM** Paul Hastings is renowned for tackling sophisticated litigation matters across a broad range of areas including antitrust, employment, IP and securities. The team recently achieved a significant victory for Andersen after almost five years of litigation against Yancy, which sought over $40 million in damages. Other notable clients include Morgan Stanley, L'Oréal USA and Dow Chemicals.

**Sources say:** *"They did a fabulous job. Each lawyer is very capable and hardworking."*

**KEY INDIVIDUALS William Sullivan** is the respected global chair of the firm's litigation department and is praised for being *"ten moves ahead of the opposition"* and his extensive *"knowledge of the law."* Sources also divulge: *"He's very good at planning the long-term strategy for a case."* He recently concluded litigation lasting two years with a dismissal on behalf of Morgan Stanley, after a breach of fiduciary duty and fraud case was brought against it by over 50 plaintiffs in Hawaii.

## Quinn Emanuel Urquhart & Sullivan, LLP

**THE FIRM** This national litigation boutique is widely praised for its breadth of superlative advice, and is well known for representing plaintiffs in securities matters. The team also possesses recognized expertise in IP and financial services litigation. The group recently won a complete defense verdict on behalf of Micron Technology after six years of litigating against Rambus over an alleged antitrust law violation. The case sought over $12 billion in damages.

**Sources say:** *"The team is excellent; aggressive, very smart, creative and a true pleasure to work with."*

**KEY INDIVIDUALS** The *"exceptional"* **John Quinn** heads the commercial litigation department and is regarded by peers as a *"ferocious competitor."* He is a seasoned business litigator who is described as *"enormously talented"* and praised for his *"ability to pick things up quickly and identi-*

fy strong themes." **Bill Price** is described as a *"fantastic"* trial lawyer who specializes in bet-the-company cases. For example, he recently led the team in representing Micron in the $12 billion Rambus dispute. One source revealed: *"He is just devastating in court; he's one to keep your eye out for."* **William Urquhart** has a *"well-deserved"* reputation for his depth and breadth of knowledge in IP litigation matters. As a well-rounded business litigator he also maintains an active practice defending class actions on behalf of various corporations. **Harry Olivar** heads the securities litigation department in Los Angeles and is characterized as *"a true technician and impressive oral advocate"* who *"is really smart, thinks logically and is very client-friendly."* He is currently defending former chairman of Peregrine Systems, John Moores, in a securities appeal. **Molly Stephens** enters the rankings this year amid praise for her *"powerful and impressive"* securities litigation practice. She is also described as *"phenomenally bright, a critical thinker and great listener."*

## Reed Smith LLP

**THE FIRM** This group offers a vast range of services under the commercial litigation umbrella and is highlighted specifically for its dedication to outstanding client service. The team recently acted as co-counsel to help win a product liability class action on behalf of St. Jude Medical following 11 years of litigation. Other clients include Siemens, Forever 21 and the California State Teachers' Retirement System.

**Sources say:** *"They provide high quality and tremendous value."*

**KEY INDIVIDUALS** Los Angeles-based **Lorenzo Gasparetti** is a key contact at the firm. He cochairs the firm's national commercial litigation group.

## Robbins Geller Rudman & Dowd LLP
### See profile on p.696

**THE FIRM** This headline firm is forever at the forefront of defense against corporate securities fraud litigation. Many of its top players are equipped with previous government experience, ensuring clients have access to expert securities knowledge, regardless of case type or industry involved.

**Sources say:** *"They have the tenacity, knowledge, experience and resources to stand up against big corporations."*

**KEY INDIVIDUALS** Securities expert **Patrick Coughlin** (see p.629) is regarded as one of the finest litigators in the state. His impressive background includes handling numerous iconic securities litigation matters. *"Spectacular"* **Darren Robbins** is hailed as a *"sharp plaintiff lawyer,"* by peers. He is a go-to name for securities matters and has extensive experience litigating in federal and state courts.

## Sheppard, Mullin, Richter & Hampton LLP

**THE FIRM** This firm is acknowledged for its strong track record in commercial litigation and impressive Asia connections. It has been busy handling entertainment disputes and class actions relating to privacy, consumer and securities matters. The team has had several recent successes in healthcare disputes. In addition to its strong litigation

presence, the group is often called upon to advise on arbitrations and other ADR methods.

**Sources say:** *"Excellent in the entertainment space."*

**KEY INDIVIDUALS Fred Puglisi** is a key contact and cochairs the firm's Business Trial Practice group.

## Sidley Austin LLP
### See profile on p.1264

**THE FIRM** This firm is equipped with a strong group of litigators renowned for their strength in handling a broad range of disputes. The team is adept at securities matters, notably for its expertise in assisting Chinese companies involved with US securities violations. It enlisted the strength of its national network when handling a series of complex shareholder cases on behalf of SMART Technologies. Goldman Sachs, Citibank, Wilshire Bancorp and China Green are some of the firm's notable clients.

**Sources say:** *"They truly have defined the meaning of going above and beyond."*

**KEY INDIVIDUALS Sara Brody** (see p.625) splits her practice between the San Francisco and Palo Alto offices and serves as the global coordinator for the firm's securities litigation practice. She represented the former CEO of Diamond Foods in various derivatives and securities class action matters and parallel government investigations, and assisted with the SMART Technologies litigation matters.

## Skadden, Arps, Slate, Meagher & Flom LLP & Affiliates
### See profile on p.2008

**THE FIRM** Skadden has risen in the rankings having earned strong praise for its talented litigation team, which is talented at handling a catalog of challenging securities and commercial litigation. It has represented a range of clients including energy and technology companies, special committees and financial institutions in national and international proceedings. It successfully represented international auction house Christie's in a landmark class action related to the California Resale Royalties Act, and handled various federal and state derivative actions and securities class actions on behalf of American Apparel.

**Sources say:** *"They are top of their game in terms of knowledge and expertise."*

**KEY INDIVIDUALS** Palo Alto-based **Raoul Kennedy** (see p.645) is a gifted facilitator of mass tort litigation and cases involving complex RICO matters, and is often described by clients as being *"fantastic."* He represented Fresh Del Monte in a $13 million trademark violation and breach of contract action. **Thomas Nolan** (see p.377) is a celebrated figure who enjoys extensive endorsement from clients as *"one of the best litigators"* and who *"has really good instincts."* A former federal prosecutor and current chair of the firm's West Coast litigation practice, he is highly experienced litigating a wide range of matters in federal and state courts nationally. He is currently involved in the colossal multidistrict litigation on behalf of client Toyota involving claims of faulty throttle control systems. Nolan also successfully represented Wells Fargo in litigation involving claims of race discrimination in pricing consumer mortgages. **Allen Ruby** (see p.396) *"is a legend and* *great in court,"* according to a loyal client. He is widely viewed as being one the leading attorneys in the state and offers a subspecialty in technology-related work. His recent highlights include assisting ConAgra Foods in a public nuisance dispute and handling shareholder derivative suits on behalf of past and present Hewlett-Packard directors. **Eric Waxman**'s (see p.671) *"knowledge is incredible,"* beams a client. He is particularly well known for his experience in handling various tort and contract claims that include partnership disputes, breach of lender liability and loan commitments. He has been in considerable demand for handling M&A-related litigation and recently assisted Cost Plus in disputes involving claims under the Williams Act.

## Sullivan & Cromwell LLP
See profile on p.2011

**THE FIRM** Sullivan & Cromwell houses a talented group of litigators who often handle M&A-related litigation, securities class action matters and a range of other complex commercial disputes. The firm assisted with high-profile matters including representing Standard Chartered Bank in numerous Madoff-related claims and achieving successful resolution of an antitrust case against Microsoft. **Sources say:** *"There is very little in the corporate world that they can't deal with."*

**KEY INDIVIDUALS** Managing partner **Robert Sacks**'s (see p.663) solid reputation is highlighted by a client whose view is that he is *"very strategic in his thinking, tactically oriented and really great on his feet."* His impressive practice encompasses handling complex matters before the SEC, advising on merger reviews and assisting with appeals in courts nationally. He recently represented footwear company Collective Brands in derivatives cases before the Kansas federal and state courts and the Delaware Chancery Court. **Michael Steinberg** (see p.667) *"really understands the law and all its nuances,"* reports a satisfied client. He represented Philips in a major class action related to allegedly defective parts in some of the company's flat screen televisions.

## White & Case LLP
See profile on p.451

**THE FIRM** This impressive litigation group is split between the firm's Los Angeles and Palo Alto offices. The firm acts around the state and also has an established cross-border litigation focus, particularly advising Korean clients. The firm advises Facebook on its overseas disputes and is currently handling a significant volume of important cases across five continents. Other clients include Gerber Products, Nestlé USA and Time Warner Cable. **Sources say:** *"They have a deep substantive knowledge of the law."*

**KEY INDIVIDUALS Bryan Merryman** (see p.654) *"understands issues immediately and always has a solution."* He successfully represented Comcast Corporation in a class action suit that alleged consumer protection law violations.

## Wilson Sonsini Goodrich & Rosati
See profile on p.700

**THE FIRM** Securities litigation is a central plank of this international firm's service. The firm has a pedigree bench to tackle securities class actions, derivative lawsuits and intricate accounting fraud matters. The team recently assisted Occam Networks with a high-profile merger case involving allegations of breaching fiduciary duty. The team has also represented major clients including Expedia, Netflix, McAfee and Hotwire.com in various complex litigation suits. **Sources say:** *"They are a solid firm with lawyers who handle work aggressively in a positive way."*

**KEY INDIVIDUALS** Peers champion senior litigator **Steven Schatz** as one of the smartest practitioners in the market. With a federal prosecutorial background, he is highly sought for his advocacy skills. He has teamed up with **Boris Feldman** on various shareholder derivative matters on behalf of Hewlett-Packard. Peers have the *"utmost respect"* for Feldman, whose esteemed practice is dedicated to challenging securities litigation. He was the driving force successfully representing Stryker in a securities fraud class action. A client applauds securities and commercial litigator **Keith Eggleton** as a *"phenomenally capable lawyer with tremendously good instincts."* He is noted for his focus on advising clients from the technology sector. **Nina Locker** is an experienced securities practitioner and draws praise for her skills in handling shareholder class actions, internal investigations relating to stock options, and insider trading disputes. She and Schatz recently represented Strayer Education in successfully achieving dismissal of a case involving allegations of improper recruitment practices.

## Other Notable Practitioners

**David Bayless** (see p.622) of Covington & Burling LLP is the firm's national chair for the securities and commercial litigation practice group. He enjoys a healthy reputation for his skills before SEC administrative forums and federal and state courts, with peers commenting that they are *"very impressed with him."* He represented the IndyMac Bank's former CEO Michael Perry in several matters, including a securities fraud suit brought by the SEC. **Maxwell Blecher** of Blecher & Collins remains *"one of the iconic"* lawyers in California and is recognized for his antitrust knowledge and handling of high-profile appellate proceedings. He is an extremely distinguished figure with impeccable trial experience gained in federal and state courts, as well as the US Supreme Court. Special counsel **Larry Feldman** (see p.635) of Kaye Scholer LLP is a respected civil litigator whose trial skills are rated very highly by clients. His broad practice includes expertise in the entertainment, real estate and insurance sectors. **Patricia Glaser** of Glaser, Weil, Fink, Jacobs, Howard, Avchen & Shapiro, LLP *"continues to be incredibly impressive,"* asserts a market observer. She is an accomplished litigator lauded for her ability to assist diverse clients such as major movie studios, financial institutions and Fortune 500 companies with complicated high-stakes litigation disputes. *"Creative thinker"* **Michael Hennigan** (see p.333) of McKool Smith is

a prominent and seasoned trial attorney with impressive antitrust and securities fraud litigation knowledge. He successfully obtained an appellate victory at the US Courts of Appeals for the Ninth Circuit on behalf of Connecticut Retirement Plans and Trust Funds in a class action securities suit against Amgen. Clients *"thinks very highly of"* **Edward Johnson** of Mayer Brown LLP, who is highly sought for his expertise in litigation related to antitrust and technology matters. He recently assisted with various class actions on behalf of Google involving unfair competition, violations of California's advertising and competition laws, and allegations of breaching California's consumer protection statutes. **Michael Mallow** (see p.651) of Loeb & Loeb LLP chairs the firm's consumer protection defense group and is rated for his expertise in defending consumer class actions and unfair competition claims. He was instrumental in successfully defeating a class certification motion on behalf of Toyota Motor Sales USA relating to customer complaints about antilock brake systems present in some 2010 car models. A client praises him as *"a fierce advocate and an excellent writer"* and someone who *"is really good at coming up with strategy that works."* **Michael Matthias** (see p.653) of Baker Hostetler *"delivers impeccable service and advice,"* states an impressed client. He is highly experienced in defending securities class actions and in handling complex business litigation. He recently defended Sharp Memorial Hospital and Eisenhower Medical Center in two separate groundbreaking class actions alleging violations of the California Confidentiality of Medical Information Act. **Michael McNamara** of Steptoe & Johnson LLP is applauded by peers for being *"energetic and sophisticated."* He has nearly three decades of litigation experience on the local, national and international stages. He is presently the firm's practice head for the professional liability and legal malpractice defense group and is also well equipped in handling securities, entertainment and antitrust disputes. **Jonathan Shapiro** (see p.665) of WilmerHale is a formidable force in the securities litigation sphere. He frequently concentrates on complex federal securities fraud, major securities class actions and disclosure matters. He represented Frank Quattrone, former head of CSFB's technology group, in securing the dismissal of a securities fraud action brought by Time Warner's shareholders, in addition to other successes. A commentator admires the dedication of **Joseph Tabacco** of Berman DeValerio, remarking that *"he went an extra mile to achieve a fair resolution."* He is noted for his background as a senior trial attorney in the DOJ's antitrust division and is a respected force who regularly litigates landmark commercial high-tech, securities fraud and antitrust matters. National chair of the firm's securities and litigation practice group, **Bruce Vanyo** of Katten Muchin Rosenman LLP enjoys an excellent reputation for his securities litigation practice. Most recently he assisted with several derivatives claims on behalf of Himelsein Mandel and various related entities, and defended DemandTec and its directors against allegations of breaching fiduciary duties. **Daniel Woods** of Musick Peeler & Garrett is a well-respected attorney whose practice concentrates on handling complicated trials and appellate proceedings in federal and state courts. He is noted for his experience assisting with disputes related to real estate and lender liability.

# LITIGATION APPELLATE

Commentary about individuals can be found under their firm's paragraph. If the firm has no paragraph (is not ranked) look at Other Notable Practitioners.

## Band 1

### Gibson, Dunn & Crutcher LLP
See profile on p.682

**THE FIRM** This appellate behemoth continues to justify its position as a market leader in California. Its team members, many of whom sit on California Judicial Council committees, are frequently engaged upon the most complex and high-profile cases, offering a truly unparalleled level of service and expertise. Over the past year, the team remained heavily involved in the landmark Perry v Brown case. After having previously advised the plaintiffs throughout their successful challenge of Proposition 8, the firm continued their representation, subsequently ensuring that a motion for reconsideration was summarily dismissed by the United States Courts of Appeals.

**Sources say:** *"They do terrific work; they're both very thoughtful and very timely in what they do. Outstanding client service."*

**KEY INDIVIDUALS Theodore Boutrous** (see p.624) is universally recognised as the most skilled and experienced appellate lawyer in the state. He is described as being *"thoughtful, very good at looking at the big picture and a very effective strategist,"* while *"his appellate ability is undeniable."* Indeed, one particularly effusive source claimed that *"when you compare somebody to him, everyone's going to come up short."* He was lead partner in the Perry v Brown case and also represented Chevron as it emerged victorious in the Lago Agrio litigation. Former appellate judge **Daniel Kolkey** (see p.647) is, according to sources, an *"outstandingly well-qualified"* attorney who *"deserves his reputation as one of the top appellate lawyers in the country."* He acted on behalf of Commonfund Realty and successfully argued that the $34 million in punitive damages previously levied against the company was excessive, obtaining a $17.6 million reduction in the amount owed.

### Horvitz & Levy LLP
See profile on p.685

**THE FIRM** This firm has carved a highly successful niche for itself as the largest civil appellate boutique in the country. The highly regarded members of its bench have experience working in a variety of practices, offering their specialist appellate services across a wide range of areas of law. Recent substantial matters from which the firm's clients emerged victorious include the O'Neill v Crane Co. product liability appeal and the revocation of the wrongful termination verdict in Gardner v Baby Trend.

**Sources say:** *"Both their writing and advocacy skills are extremely high"*

**KEY INDIVIDUALS** Lead partner **David Axelrad** (see p.621) has recently been active in the toxic tort area, in addition to having been heavily involved in the O'Neill v Crane Co. case. Those surveyed identified his strong behind the scenes work, lauding his *"consistency"* and the quality of his advocacy skills. Sources have commended **Lisa Perrochet**'s (see p.658) aptitude for *"knowing which cases to appeal, which arguments to make and how best to write briefs that will capture the justices' attention."* She was lead partner in Barrese v Murray, a breach of contract case in which her team successfully brought a motion for a new trial. **Jon Eisenberg** (see p.634) recently returned to the firm following the winding-down of his previous firm Eisenberg & Hancock LLP. Market observers consider him a *"recognized expert"* in appellate procedure. **Mitchell Tilner** (see p.669) continues to command the respect of both peers and clients; he has most recently been engaged in the successful reversal of a personal injury ruling in State Farm v Frake.

## Band 2

### Akin Gump Strauss Hauer & Feld LLP
See profile on p.904

**THE FIRM** This large full-service firm benefits from the collaborative potential of its myriad of offices. The appellate practice is particularly strong, with a number of its practitioners able to boast judicial experience and, accordingly, a comprehensive knowledge of the inner machinations of appellate courts. The firm recently acted on behalf of the Brinker Restaurant Corporation and was able to persuade the California Supreme Court to deliver a landmark verdict that significantly alters the criteria for employees bringing class actions pertaining to uninterrupted meal breaks.

**Sources say:** *"They are very thorough and very much on point."*

**KEY INDIVIDUALS Rex Heinke** (see p.641) heads the firm's appellate practice and continues to impress observers. He was lead partner in the Brinker Restaurant case, in addition to heading the team that was successful in Starbucks v Superior Court. He is perhaps best known for his impressive work in the employment appellate arena.

### Arnold & Porter LLP
See profile on p.906

**THE FIRM** This highly regarded appellate practice continues to flourish following its 2011 merger with Howard Rice Nemerovski Canady Falk & Rabin. With the firm's California footprint having grown substantially the team is widely considered to have gained the impetus to ascend to the top tier of appellate practices. Recent clients include Ammari Electronics, DineEquity and ICO Global Communications.

**Sources say:** *"They're very thorough, they've got lots of experience, they've spent lots of time in the arena and are thus able to understand exactly what you need to do."*

**KEY INDIVIDUALS Sean SeLegue** (see p.665) led the appellate team in its representation of the Mannatt, Phelps & Phillips law firm in a putative class action suit in April 2012. In doing so, he was able to draw heavily upon his knowledge of the legal malpractice area, in which he is held in great esteem.

### Greines, Martin, Stein & Richland LLP
See profile on p.684

**THE FIRM** This well-staffed California appellate boutique is most notable for its proficiency in defending insurance companies. The practice is comprised of 14 partners who have all repeatedly demonstrated their state court prowess with a number of impressive and high-profile victories. One such success was obtained in the hugely significant

Howell v Hamilton case; had the Supreme Court rejected the firm's arguments and ruled in favor of the plaintiff, the financial implications for the health insurance industry would have been vast.

**Sources say:** *"I was highly impressed with the Greines team. The client service was top notch – they were responsive, timely and inclusive."*

**KEY INDIVIDUALS Kent Richland** (see p.662) is a well-respected appellate practitioner who can draw on over 30 years' experience. His expertise was recently called upon in Aguilar v Goldstein, in which he was successful in convincing the court that a breach of fiduciary duty had not taken place. **Robin Meadow's** (see p.654) expanding practice is a testament to his aptitude in appellate litigation. He is engaged across a diverse range of practice areas and is regarded by peers as an expert in the technology sector.

## Band 3

### Munger, Tolles & Olson LLP
See profile on p.691

**THE FIRM** This firm enters the rankings for appellate law in California for the first time having received warm praise from the market. The firm's appellate practitioners represent clients in matters involving virtually every major area of law, while its formidable reputation at trial level ensures that clients are able to receive a seamless, high-quality service.

**KEY INDIVIDUALS** Daniel Collins is a key contact.

### Reed Smith LLP

**THE FIRM** Reed Smith's California appellate practice retains its solid reputation, with both the overall standard of litigation and the quality of written documents produced by its attorneys serving as distinguishing factors. The firm has been called upon to represent clients across a sizable number of practice areas, with the highly experienced bench possessing substantial strength in appeals

relating to product liability, healthcare and insurance matters.

**Sources say:** *"Their strategic advice is on point and nuanced, and they regularly provide a clear and concise written product."*

**KEY INDIVIDUALS** Blessed with an ability to draw extensively on her previous experience as a judge, **Margaret Grignon** is recognised as one of the leading practitioners within the field. Clients *"think very highly of her,"* often making reference to her *"calm demeanor"* and her instinctive ability to grasp the most complex elements of technical minutiae. She garnered praise from media outlets when acting as lead partner in Quarry v Doe, a sexual abuse suit.

### Sidley Austin LLP
See profile on p.1264

**THE FIRM** Sidley Austin enters the table having garnered considerable feedback from the market. The Los Angeles office plays an integral role in the firm's highly respected national appellate group, with its California practitioners experienced in cases at state, federal and Supreme Court levels. High-profile matters include the representation of W. Scott Harkonen, former CEO of InterMune, in the highly publicized appeal against his conviction for wire fraud.

**Sources say:** *"Absolutely excellent work. They are extremely responsive and able to focus immediately on the issue. Their drafting skills are superb."*

**KEY INDIVIDUALS Mark Haddad** (see p.639) led the team in the representation of W. Scott Harkonen, and is the global coordinator for the national appellate group. Sources relate that he is *"an excellent speaker who doesn't get rattled in any way."*

## Other Notable Practitioners

**Mary-Christine Sungaila** of Snell & Wilmer LLP continues to enhance her growing reputation as a prodigiously talented appellate attorney. She is described as being *"very*

*articulate," "incredibly professional"* and *"well respected by both the bench and the bar."* **Donald Falk** heads the appellate team at Mayer Brown LLP and is increasingly prominent in the California appellate bar after some stunning successes in recent years. Recent highlights include representing American Honda Motor in its successful appeal against a consumer class action claiming unfair competition, false advertising and unjust enrichment. **Elwood Lui** (see p.651) of Jones Day is a vastly experienced practitioner generally tasked with leading his firm's appellate practice. Sources have cited his intelligence and strong worth ethic as reasons for his success within the field, further praising his capacity to *"identify the relevant issues and tactically prepare the facts and arguments in a case."* He has enjoyed an extremely active year, during which he was engaged in a number of discrimination, freedom of speech and employee negligence appeals. **Miriam Vogel** (see p.670) of Morrison & Foerster LLP is *"highly respected and admired,"* and able to strongly represent her clients in an *"eloquent and intelligent way."* Having served as a Justice in the California Court of Appeal for 18 years, she is aptly described as possessing a *"refined presence"* and being *"incredibly experienced."* She recently appeared in court on behalf of Ralphs Grocery as it successfully fought off an appeal from members of the Missionary Church of the Disciples of Jesus Christ regarding their unconstitutional solicitation of funds from directly outside a grocery store. **Richard Derevan** of Snell & Wilmer LLP is renowned for the cordial yet commanding manner in which he conducts himself in court. Indeed, sources have been vociferous in lauding his courtroom prowess, with one observer maintaining that Derevan is the *"preeminent appellate lawyer"* in the state. **Kevin Fong** of Pillsbury Winthrop Shaw Pittman LLP is recognized by peers as being one of the most talented appellate attorneys in the state. His prestige is exemplified by his recent performance as lead partner on behalf of the Chehalis Tribe in its appeal against property taxes that a county in Washington State sought to levy against it.

# LITIGATION WHITE-COLLAR CRIME & GOVERNMENT INVESTIGATIONS

White-Collar Crime & Government Investigations p.601; Specialist Firms in White-Collar Crime & Government Investigations p.601

Commentary about individuals can be found under their firm's paragraph. If the firm has no paragraph (is not ranked) look at Other Notable Practitioners.

### Litigation: White-Collar Crime & Government Investigations
Band 1

### Gibson, Dunn & Crutcher LLP
See profile on p.682

**THE FIRM** This highly respected firm's California offices often liaise with others around the country, and the firm has a wealth of resources that extend to working in multiple international jurisdictions. Its renowned FCPA practice and deep bench of talented attorneys that have served within the SEC and DOJ secure its position as one of the top California white-collar crime practices. Recent high-

lights include handling an investigation relating to fraud allegations under Medicaid on behalf of a healthcare company and assisting a petroleum product marketer and refiner with a criminal industrial accident investigation brought by the US Chemical and Safety Hazard Investigation Board.

**Sources say:** *"They were able to execute in a beautiful manner. They are a class above everyone else."*

**KEY INDIVIDUALS Debra Wong Yang** (see p.673) receives tremendous praise from a client who praises her *"understanding of the process from the prosecutorial and judicial side, which added to my comfort."* She cochairs the firm's white-collar defense and investigations group and

the crisis management group, and is particularly recommended for her expertise in China-related work. Work highlights include providing advice relating to compliance and FCPA corporate organization. **Nicola Hanna** (see p.640) served as the lead partner on an SEC enforcement action relating to Nigerian bribery charges. A client applauds him for his *"profound insight into the inner workings of the US prosecution system and exceptional ability to interpret the law."*

### Keker & Van Nest LLP

**THE FIRM** This San Francisco white-collar stalwart has continually been at the forefront of handling landmark

## Litigation: White-Collar Crime & Government Investigations
### Leading Firms

**Band 1**
Gibson, Dunn & Crutcher LLP *
Keker & Van Nest LLP
Latham & Watkins LLP *
Munger, Tolles & Olson LLP *
Orrick, Herrington & Sutcliffe LLP *
Quinn Emanuel Urquhart & Sullivan, LLP
Skadden, Arps, Slate, Meagher & Flom LLP & Affiliates *

**Band 2**
Crowell & Moring LLP *
Irell & Manella *
Jones Day *
O'Melveny & Myers LLP *

**Band 3**
Caldwell Leslie & Proctor, PC *
Farella Braun + Martel LLP
Foley & Lardner LLP *
McDermott Will & Emery LLP *

**Band 4**
Arent Fox LLP *
Sidley Austin LLP *

## Litigation: Specialist Firms in White-Collar Crime & Government Investigations
### Leading Firms

**Band 1**
Arguedas, Cassman & Headley, LLP
Swanson & McNamara LLP

**Band 2**
Bird, Marella, Boxer, Wolpert, Nessim, Drooks & Lincenberg *
Clarence Dyer & Cohen, LLP
Scheper Kim & Harris LLP

## Litigation: White-Collar Crime & Government Investigations
### Senior Statesmen

**Senior Statesmen: distinguished older practitioners**

| | | | |
|---|---|---|---|
| Bird Terry W | Bird, Marella, Boxer, Wolpert, Nessim PC * | Marella Vincent J | Bird, Marella, Boxer, Wolpert, Nessim * |
| Brosnahan James | Morrison & Foerster LLP (ONP)† * | Vandevelde John | Crowell & Moring LLP * |

### Leading Individuals

**Star individuals**

| | | | |
|---|---|---|---|
| Arguedas Cristina C | Arguedas, Cassman & Headley, LLP | Handzlik Jan Lawrence | Venable LLP (ONP)† * |
| Greenberg Gordon A | McDermott Will & Emery LLP * | Harris Marc S | Scheper Kim & Harris LLP |
| Keker John | Keker & Van Nest LLP | Hayman Russell | McDermott Will & Emery LLP * |

**Band 1**

| | | | |
|---|---|---|---|
| Asperger James | Quinn Emanuel Urquhart & Sullivan, LLP | McNamara Mary | Swanson & McNamara LLP * |
| Bookin Daniel | O'Melveny & Myers LLP | Peters Elliot | Keker & Van Nest LLP |
| Brian Brad D | Munger, Tolles & Olson LLP * | Proctor Michael J | Caldwell Leslie & Proctor, PC |
| Brown Walt | Orrick, Herrington & Sutcliffe LLP * | Schindler David J | Latham & Watkins LLP |
| Dicanio Jack P | Skadden, Arps, Slate, Meagher & Flom * | Spiegel John | Munger, Tolles & Olson LLP * |
| Hennigan Brian J | Irell & Manella * | Swanson Edward | Swanson & McNamara LLP * |
| Holscher Mark | Kirkland & Ellis LLP (ONP)† * | Williams Bart H | Munger, Tolles & Olson LLP * |
| Hueston John C | Irell & Manella * | Yang Debra Wong | Gibson, Dunn & Crutcher LLP * |
| Levine Janet | Crowell & Moring LLP * | | |
| Little Jan Nielsen | Keker & Van Nest LLP | **Band 3** | |
| Marmaro Richard | Skadden, Arps, Slate, Meagher & Flom * | Bowers Terree | Arent Fox LLP * |
| O'Connell George L | DLA Piper LLP (US) (ONP)† * | Carlucci Thomas F | Foley & Lardner LLP |
| Potter John | Quinn Emanuel Urquhart & Sullivan, LLP | Cline John | Law Office of John D Cline (ONP)† |
| Ruby Allen J | Skadden, Arps, Slate, Meagher & Flom * | Ehrlich Miles F | Ramsey & Ehrlich LLP (ONP)† |
| Scheper David C. | Scheper Kim & Harris LLP | Goodman William M | Kasowitz, Benson, Torres (ONP)† * |
| Sun Brian A | Jones Day * | Hanna Nicola T | Gibson, Dunn & Crutcher LLP * |
| Young Douglas R | Farella Braun + Martel LLP | Johnston Pamela L | Foley & Lardner LLP |
| | | Kubota Carolyn | O'Melveny & Myers LLP |
| **Band 2** | | Lincenberg Gary | Bird, Marella, Boxer, Wolpert, Nessim * |
| Bauer Steven M | Latham & Watkins LLP * | Mansfield Stephen A | Akin Gump Strauss Hauer & Feld (ONP)† * |
| Beck Mark | Orrick, Herrington & Sutcliffe LLP * | Ramsey Ismail | Ramsey & Ehrlich LLP (ONP)† |
| Brewer Jr Robert S | Jones Day * | Robbins Patrick D | Shearman & Sterling LLP (ONP)† |
| Clarence Nanci L | Clarence Dyer & Cohen, LLP * | Shepard Michael J | Hogan Lovells US LLP (ONP)† |
| Corbin Robert L | Corbin & Fitzgerald LLP (ONP)† | Tubach Michael | O'Melveny & Myers LLP |
| Daly Bryan D | Sheppard, Mullin, Richter & Hampton (ONP)† | | |
| Dunne Kimberly A | Sidley Austin LLP * | **Up-and-coming individuals** | |
| | | McConville Tom | Orrick, Herrington & Sutcliffe LLP * |
| | | Rutherford Jeffrey | Crowell & Moring LLP * |

*Also in Star individuals section:*

| | |
|---|---|
| Handzlik Jan Lawrence | Venable LLP (ONP)† * |
| Harris Marc S | Scheper Kim & Harris LLP |
| Hayman Russell | McDermott Will & Emery LLP * |

*Indicates firm / individual with profile.

†ONP = Other Notable Practitioner.

cases. The 65-strong team has unrivaled skill in undertaking complex matters such as misbehavior by securities professionals, accounting and disclosure fraud and handling various securities law enforcement issues. One recent highlight was successfully representing robotic surgery device manufacturer Intuitive Surgical in a class action that alleged it had produced misleading financial prospects and results. The team also defended the former CEO of hedge fund ValueAct Capital in an insider trading dispute. Other high-profile clients this impressive boutique has represented include former Enron CFO Andrew Fastow and KB Home CEO Bruce Karatz.
**Sources say:** *"Very strong group of lawyers, who I would trust with any matter."*
**KEY INDIVIDUALS** *"Superstar"* **John Keker** is highly acclaimed by clients and peers nationally. His experience includes litigating relentlessly on behalf of clients involved in complex business crime matters. Along with **Jan Nielsen Little**, Keker was instrumental in winning a favorable defense verdict for Citigroup executive Brian Stoker. Little has focused her practice on handling highly publicized criminal investigations and complex trials. She wins admiration from clients and peers, who appreciate her as an

*"incredibly smart and talented"* advocate. A peer acknowledges **Elliot Peters** as *"excellent, with a great manner in front of a jury."* Representing a major client in the US food industry against charges of mail fraud, bribery, and antitrust is one Peters' recent highlights.

### Latham & Watkins LLP
See profile on p.446
**THE FIRM** With a team of approximately 30 highly experienced litigators, Latham & Watkins enjoys a noteworthy reputation in the white-collar criminal defense realm. It regularly impresses clients with its ability to assist with investigations and criminal and civil trials that cross international borders. The firm frequently liaises with colleagues based in the Washington, DC office, which provides for tremendous government agency expertise.
**Sources say:** *"They are the smartest of the smart."*
**KEY INDIVIDUALS** Hailed as a *"very fine white-collar lawyer,"* **Steven Bauer** (see p.622) currently serves as the global cochair of the firm's white-collar defense and gov-

ernment investigations practice. Most recently he handled grand jury investigations on behalf of PG&E following a fatal pipeline explosion in San Bruno County. Los Angeles-based **David Schindler** is praised by a client as *"particularly knowledgeable about the healthcare sector."* Most recently he successfully represented a HMO serving 130,000 members in Arizona and California in parallel state and federal civil and criminal investigations relating to allegations that it received overpayments from California's Medi-Cal program. He also has niche expertise in conducting China-based investigations.

### Munger, Tolles & Olson LLP
See profile on p.691
**THE FIRM** This established firm has a well-deserved reputation for its superb white-collar criminal defense practice. The group regularly handles criminal antitrust violations, high-profile corporate investigations and tax fraud issues. The firm has a strong record representing clients against various federal and state agencies that include the

IRS, Federal Trade Commission and the Financial Industry Regulatory Authority.

**Sources say:** *"The lawyers are preeminent and the firm stands out in many respects."*

**KEY INDIVIDUALS Brad Brian** (see p.625) is renowned for his remarkable capacity in effortlessly representing Fortune 500 corporations involved in high-value litigation. His dedicated work ethic is highlighted by a client who praises him as *"very thoughtful, easy to work with and responsive."* He is also well regarded for his great depth of expertise handling claims made under the False Claims Act's qui tam provisions. Former US Supreme Court clerk, **John Spiegel** (see p.666) concentrates his practice on complex investigations and white-collar criminal defense. He regularly appears in state and federal courts and is recognized for being *"top of the practice."* A market source praises **Bart Williams** (see p.672) as *"a trial lawyer at heart who is always great on his feet"* and for his advocacy skills. He has a very strong and varied practice that covers conducting internal corporate investigations for international companies and defending high-profile public figures and politicians in complex public corruption matters.

## Orrick, Herrington & Sutcliffe LLP
### See profile on p.1994

**THE FIRM** This firm continues to maintain its stellar reputation in the white-collar space. The team has extensive trial experience and handles white-collar criminal defense issues, and matters relating to the Foreign Corrupt Practices Act and False Claims Act. It also assists clients with SEC and regulatory investigations. The team is noted for its representation of international clients, particularly in Asia.

**Sources say:** *"Their dedication to a positive outcome is really unbelievable."*

**KEY INDIVIDUALS Walt Brown** (see p.626) is *"a great litigator and very personable,"* states an appreciative client. He is highly experienced handling international corporate investigations, securities fraud and FCPA matters. Most recently he assisted with complex litigation and investigations for a matter involving the SEC, class action plaintiffs, the California Attorney General and various insurers and hedge funds. **Mark Beck** (see p.623) is sought for his unique experience in advising company counsel on crime prevention matters. He is also adept at litigating stock option backdating cases and has assisted clients from the aerospace and maritime, healthcare and financial services sectors. Clients strongly endorse **Tom McConville** (see p.653) as *"phenomenal in front of a jury."* He is a former assistant US Attorney and member of the Computer Crimes and Intellectual Property Unit, and has specialist litigation expertise in a wide range of industries.

## Quinn Emanuel Urquhart & Sullivan, LLP

**THE FIRM** This widely acclaimed firm stands out for its white-collar crime representation. The firm boasts several former federal prosecutors, experts in the pharmaceutical, bankruptcy and accounting fields, and an extensive national and international network that effectively caters to its diverse client base. Representing Kaiser Permanente

in a case involving allegations of medical waste dumping and handling a complex dispute relating to RICO, trafficking and Alien Tort Claims are among its recent work highlights. Other notable clients include Home Depot and Johnson & Johnson.

**Sources say:** *"They have some of the smartest lawyers and their intellectual ability is combined with an understanding of how to address and resolve matters."*

**KEY INDIVIDUALS James Asperger** has an impressive background of having served as a Supreme Court clerk and the Central District of California's Chief of the Major Frauds Section. A client applauds his *"superior intellect"* and says that *"he really knows how to work well with clients."* Most recently Asperger represented Home Depot in a matter alleging violating local environmental regulations. He serves as the firm's cochair of the white-collar and corporate investigations practice along with **John Potter**. Potter draws praise as *"a very good lawyer"* from peers and has a prominent white-collar criminal defense and civil litigation practice. Recent work highlights include representing Johnson & Johnson and its subsidiary, Scios, in a high-profile off-label marketing investigation. He also handled an Economic Espionage Act prosecution for Pangang Group, one of China's largest steel, vanadium and titanium products manufacturers.

## Skadden, Arps, Slate, Meagher & Flom LLP & Affiliates
### See profile on p.2008

**THE FIRM** This international giant houses a top-rated white-collar criminal defense and government enforcement team. Its lawyers are continually recognized as leaders for their handling of state and federal grand jury investigations, environmental crime investigations and regulatory matters on behalf of accounting firms and major financial institutions. Most recently the team successfully achieved dismissal of two whistle-blower lawsuits alleging violations under the False Claims Act on behalf of Kinetic Concepts.

**Sources say:** *"Extremely helpful with giving information and providing timely responses."*

**KEY INDIVIDUALS** Clients say **Jack Dicanio** (see p.632) is *"exceptional"* and *"always gives a timely response."* He and **Richard Marmaro** (see p.362) have been active in handling various matters for KPMG and have been heavily involved in representing Kuwaiti-based Agility Logistics in a government contracting fraud matter, which is valued at billions and is to date the largest government fraud case in history. Marmaro heads the firm's West Coast SEC enforcement and white-collar defense group and splits his practice between the Los Angeles, Palo Alto and New York offices. Peers enjoy working with him and state that he is a *"real warrior."* **Allen Ruby** (see p.396) is a hugely experienced white-collar litigator who is revered for his prowess in the courtroom. Clients consider him to be an *"extraordinary lawyer"* who is *"very versatile."*

## Litigation: White-Collar Crime & Government Investigations
## Band 2

### Crowell & Moring LLP
### See profile on p.910

**THE FIRM** This firm maintains a robust practice and frequently liaises with its sizable white-collar crime team across the country. It leverages its strength in the banking and securities fraud, healthcare and regulatory enforcement arenas and is actively involved in disputes involving the DOJ, SEC and FDA.

**Sources say:** *"They are very generous with their time."*

**KEY INDIVIDUALS** Clients appreciate **Janet Levine** (see p.650) and say that she *"is an exemplary lawyer, who is intelligent, extremely hard-working and meticulous."* She has an impressive litigation track record and chairs the firm's white-collar and regulatory enforcement group nationally. She recently handled complex securities and banking fraud, antitrust and trade secret theft cases. Recent work highlights include handling the reversal of the first-ever conviction of a corporation violating the FCPA, and representing the founder of a California charter school in a political corruption case along with **Jeffrey Rutherford** (see p.663). Rutherford has a dedicated white-collar criminal defense practice and recently served as the lead partner handling a significant antitrust case against the DOJ and SEC. **John Vandevelde** (see p.670) has long been admired as a senior white-collar criminal defense authority. He continues to lend his knowledge to complex matters and is respected for his expertise in handling False Claims Act matters.

### Irell & Manella
### See profile on p.686

**THE FIRM** This Southern California stalwart is highly regarded nationally for its strength across the full range of business, white-collar and securities disputes. It has particularly been active handling antitrust, False Claims Act and price-fixing violations. Additionally, the firm's bench strength is highlighted by the presence of former federal prosecutors, defenders and a federal district court judge.

**Sources say:** *"The attorneys work hard and no stone goes unturned. They bring intellect to cases, which pays off in the quality of their written work product."*

**KEY INDIVIDUALS Brian Hennigan** (see p.641) cochairs the firm's corporate crisis and white-collar criminal defense practice. An interviewee enthuses: *"Hennigan brings unparalleled judgment, courtroom abilities and professionalism to the practice."* He handled a criminal antitrust investigation by the DOJ's Antitrust Division for a client, and an FCPA investigation related to China on behalf of a Fortune 500 company's senior officer. *"Terrific talent"* **John Hueston** (see p.643) is a distinguished go-to adviser for high-profile individuals involved in complex white-collar crime disputes. He maintains an enviable reputation of having been the lead prosecutor in the Enron trial and is recognized for his robust expertise in internal investigations and corporate criminal defense issues. Hueston has represented a Goldman Sachs managing director in the highly publicized Galleon investigations against federal prosecutors and the SEC, handled a criminal investigation alleging mislabeling and material nondisclosures on behalf on Edwards Lifesciences, and served as the lead partner in a highly publicized healthcare fraud investigation.

## Jones Day
See profile on p.919

THE FIRM This firm continues to impress with its robust trial experience. It is noted for its expertise in handling public corruption issues, securities violations and regulatory and internal investigations. Recent work highlights include assisting with an internal investigation involving accounting fraud allegations, defending clients in an FCPA investigation spanning multiple jurisdictions, and representing an international energy company against allegations of violating the Food, Drug and Cosmetic Act and antikickback and other federal laws.

KEY INDIVIDUALS "*Excellent*" **Brian Sun** (see p.668) enjoys a thriving national reputation for his white-collar criminal defense practice. He is a heavyweight lawyer sought for technology transfer violations, government procurement fraud and internal investigations. Representing the former general counsel of a Fortune 500 company in a FCPA investigation brought by the SEC and DOJ, and assisting former employees of a Swiss financial entity with US tax evasion allegations, are two noteworthy highlights. **Robert Brewer Jr** (see p.625) "*had a great grasp of facts and did a terrific job representing us,*" says an impressed client. Brewer is a highly experienced litigator highlighted for his criminal and civil advocacy skills. His recent work includes assisting a title insurance company with a criminal antitrust investigation and handling an FCPA investigation focusing on Mexican business operations.

## O'Melveny & Myers LLP
See profile on p.693

THE FIRM This solid team comes highly recommended for its superb representation of Fortune 500 entities, individuals and government officials in white-collar criminal investigations and complex securities disputes. It has had a particularly busy year handling FCPA-related matters and assisting with healthcare fraud and criminal antitrust issues.

KEY INDIVIDUALS "*Phenomenal lawyer*" **Daniel Bookin** chairs the firm's national white-collar defense and corporate investigations practice. Based in San Francisco, he commands tremendous admiration for representing clients in the financial and healthcare sectors in a wide array of white-collar criminal matters and his depth of litigation experience. **Carolyn Kubota** enters the rankings backed by strong support highlighting her experience assisting international and domestic companies with internal investigations and her strong track record in the courtroom. Sources praise her "*good demeanor and judgment*" and state that "*she is great with clients.*" Former assistant US Attorney **Michael Tubach** is described as "*fantastic*" by market sources. He devotes his practice to handling crimi-

nal antitrust matters as well as parallel SEC proceedings that accompany investigations.

## Litigation: White-Collar Crime & Government Investigations Band 3

### Caldwell Leslie & Proctor, PC
See profile on p.677

THE FIRM This firm has an exceptional team that is praised for its white-collar crime defense prowess. It is regularly mandated to act on high-profile disputes. The team appears in courts around the country and advises on fraud, insider trading, corruption and numerous other white-collar matters. Clients are especially quick to praise the firm's outstanding trial work.

Sources say: "*Good writers, hard workers and very focused.*"
KEY INDIVIDUALS **Michael Proctor** "*has strengths across the spectrum of things important to business.*" He leads on many of the firm's high-profile cases and is called "*a truly gifted litigator.*"

### Farella Braun + Martel LLP

THE FIRM This San Francisco office is well regarded for its strength representing clients before the SEC and expertise in a wide range of areas such as antitrust, money-laundering and securities-related litigation. Advising clients on matters involving insider trading, fraud and FCPA are among the team's areas of expertise.

KEY INDIVIDUALS In addition to being a sought-after litigator in the Bay Area, **Douglas Young** has steadily built an impressive reputation nationally. He commands considerable respect from peers for his track record in handling complex antitrust, securities and white-collar civil and criminal defense cases. Sources describe him as "*superb*" and "*an expert courtroom lawyer.*"

### Foley & Lardner LLP
See profile on p.2588

THE FIRM This superb group has a strong track record for its skillful handling of a broad spectrum of securities and white-collar criminal litigation. Its team is recognized for its valuable experience that includes assisting Latin American clients with FCPA investigations and handling allegations of off-label pharmaceutical marketing. The firm also comes strongly recommended for its dedicated import/export controls practice, which provides guidance on trade laws and policy.

Sources say: "*Foley combines large firm resources with small firm personal care.*"
KEY INDIVIDUALS **Thomas Carlucci** is well versed in acting for clients involved in federal and state tax litigation and tax fraud. An impressed client reports he "*has a keen understanding of what one can reasonably seek to achieve in court.*" **Pamela Johnston** chairs the firm's government enforcement, compliance and white-collar defense practice and is regarded as a "*fantastic lawyer*" by peers. She devotes her practice to healthcare fraud, FCPA actions, government contracting fraud and various business crimes. Most

recently she represented the ex-CFO of a publicly traded company in an SEC enforcement issue.

## McDermott Will & Emery LLP
See profile on p.1258

THE FIRM This firm has an enviable national and international network of litigators who are equipped to tackle complex government investigations, criminal cartel matters and anti-corruption issues. The team recently represented a Fortune 100 health insurance administrator in an FCA case of first impression and assisted the nation's leading provider of administrative services for mobile dental services with various legal matters.

Sources say: "*Extremely professional and perceptive.*"
KEY INDIVIDUALS Clients say **Russell Hayman** (see p.641) is a "*fantastic critical thinker who is quick on his feet.*" He is nationally renowned for his strong healthcare-related practice. **Gordon Greenberg**'s (see p.639) clients note that "*he has the ability to summarize things concisely.*" Greenberg played a pivotal role in the headline-grabbing money laundering case that involved an Antiguan bank and the former Ukrainian Prime Minister.

## Litigation: White-Collar Crime & Government Investigations Band 4

### Arent Fox LLP
See profile on p.905

THE FIRM This team has achieved much success for its high-profile clients in the white-collar crime and government investigations space. The group continues to expand in response to a tremendous increase in its workload. Recent work includes the representation of Colonies Partners in its highly publicized corruption case and playing a central role in gaining a favorable decision for a high-ranking member of the Department of Homeland Security involved in a federal agency corruption charge.

Sources say: "*Their role has been greatly appreciated and they have done a tremendous job.*"
KEY INDIVIDUALS **Terree Bowers** (see p.624) is a respected lawyer with over 30 years of experience. His practice spans white-collar criminal defense, government investigations and complex commercial litigation. A client endorses him as an "*expert at what he does – focused and ruthlessly protective of his clients.*" One recent highlight was handling a RICO and antitrust matter for a large insurance client.

### Sidley Austin LLP
See profile on p.1264

THE FIRM This team is noted for its white-collar criminal defense work. It is able to draw on the firm's extensive national network in successfully representing clients and major corporations. It continues to handle a number of matters such as trade secret thefts, FDA fraud, and FCA and FCPA issues.

Sources say: "*They do not leave any stone unturned.*"

KEY INDIVIDUALS **Kimberly Dunne** (see p.633) cochairs the firm's white-collar practice and has an enviable background of serving as the Chief of the US Attorney Office's Public Corruption and Government Fraud section in the Central District of California. *"She has been very good to work with and she consults me on the right things,"* praises a client. She is especially noted for her recent work in advising on qui tam and FCPA matters.

## Litigation: Specialist Firms in White-Collar Crime & Government Investigations Band 1

### Arguedas, Cassman & Headley, LLP

THE FIRM Arguedas, Cassman & Headley continues to sit at the vanguard of the California white-collar crime and internal investigations market. This nationally renowned litigation boutique has a stronghold in handling securities prosecutions and their parallel civil trials against the SEC, defending corporate officers involved in grand jury investigations and maintaining an active antitrust practice.
**Sources say:** *"Outstanding firm."*
KEY INDIVIDUALS **Cristina Arguedas** is one of the most highly respected litigators in the country. Commentators have ceaseless praise for her, stating that she is *"a superb trial lawyer"* and is *"relentless and extremely effective."*

### Swanson & McNamara LLP

THE FIRM This San Francisco litigation boutique has a strong track record representing corporations and individuals in a broad range of white-collar crime matters. The group regularly assists clients facing various financial offenses such as insider trading and procurement fraud and is also adept at handling complex investigations.
**Sources say:** *"Excellent boutique firm."*
KEY INDIVIDUALS Peers afford much praise to **Mary McNamara** (see p.654), noting she is *"smart"* and *"very impressive."* She devotes her practice to regulatory, white-collar criminal and civil litigation matters, and is recognized for her strong capabilities in antitrust and securities-related matters. Market sources say **Edward Swanson** (see p.668) is *"really solid, a pleasure to deal with and does a terrific job for clients."* With his longstanding appellate and trial experience, he is a trusted litigator on money laundering, tax fraud and securities-related matters.

## Litigation: Specialist Firms in White-Collar Crime & Government Investigations Band 2

### Bird, Marella, Boxer, Wolpert, Nessim, Drooks & Lincenberg PC
See profile on p.675

THE FIRM This Los Angeles firm boasts a talented team of litigators. The group represents organizations and private individuals and excels at white-collar crime defense and handling healthcare fraud and a wide spectrum of alleged

business crimes. It also stands out for its prowess in matters involving the FCPA.
**Sources say:** *"Very solid group of white-collar lawyers."*
KEY INDIVIDUALS **Gary Lincenberg** (see p.650) is noted for his *"significant work and achievements."* He has an active white-collar crime defense practice and continues to impress as the current cochairman of the ABA's National White Collar Crime Committee. **Terry Bird** (see p.283) is a stalwart of California's white-collar criminal litigation sphere. With four decades of experience and a federal prosecution background, peers recognize him as being *"among the best."* Highly respected **Vincent Marella** (see p.652) is considered a leading authority in the white-collar criminal defense sphere. He has over 30 years of experience representing companies and individuals in complex business crime cases.

### Clarence Dyer & Cohen, LLP

THE FIRM This widely respected San Francisco boutique is renowned for its exceptional performance investigating federal crimes and handling antitrust and securities litigation. It combines the solid trial experience and capabilities of a large firm with the attention and care of a small firm in securing numerous victories. It is particularly recognized for representing clients from the mortgage, banking and pharmaceutical arenas.
**Sources say:** *"Outstanding firm."*
KEY INDIVIDUALS **Nanci Clarence** (see p.628) leads some of the firm's significant engagements and draws upon her longstanding experience in white-collar criminal defense work, government investigations and state and federal prosecutions.

### Scheper Kim & Harris LLP

THE FIRM Sources recommend this Los Angeles firm's pedigree bench for its capabilities in representing corporations and high net worth individuals in complex white-collar crime defense work and FCPA-related matters. Peers and clients praise the firm's consistent quality and dedication. The team is particularly sought for its expertise in matters relating to securities and antitrust claims.
KEY INDIVIDUALS Market sources applaud **David Scheper** as a *"premier, go-to lawyer."* He has an extensive white-collar crime practice and enjoys a stellar reputation nationally for his ability to handle criminal antitrust, healthcare fraud and SEC investigations. **Marc Harris**, a former assistant US Attorney, comes highly recommended for his in-depth expertise in securities fraud and tax fraud, and federal and state prosecutions and investigations. Additionally, he has an enviable trial record in federal court and before the Ninth Circuit Court of Appeals. Peers highlight that he is *"very diligent with clients."*

### Other Notable Practitioners

**Stephen Mansfield** (see p.652) of Akin Gump Strauss Hauer & Feld LLP co-leads the firm's white-collar defense and corporate investigations practice. Described as *"smart and capable"* by one source, he has amassed a wealth of experience with prosecutions and investigations on behalf

of defendants. **Mark Holscher** (see p.642) of Kirkland & Ellis LLP is widely respected for his practice and represents a wide variety of clients from the aerospace and defense, financial services and entertainment industries. He most recently liaised with the firm's Washington, DC office in relation to an insider trading investigation. A commentator praises **George O'Connell** (see p.657) of DLA Piper LLP (US) as *"terrifically skilled."* A highly respected and prominent trial lawyer, O'Connell's experience includes serving as a federal prosecutor and a United States Attorney. His expertise spans defending physicians, hospitals and various healthcare providers, trying jury trials and representing clients in complex civil and criminal cases. **William Goodman** (see p.638) of Kasowitz, Benson, Torres & Friedman LLP has an active practice assisting with securities fraud and complex civil and criminal defense matters. He most recently assisted the Kauai Island Utility Cooperative in a matter involving alleged violations of the Endangered Species Act and handled a grand jury investigation focusing on subprime mortgage financing on behalf of significant real estate developers. **John Cline** of Law Office of John D Cline garners praise from the market as being a *"pure white-collar lawyer who is just fantastic."* His impressive practice is noted for handling tax evasion, money laundering and securities fraud matters. According to an impressed source, **Michael Shepard** of Hogan Lovells US LLP possesses *"good tactical and advocacy skills."* In addition to an active internal corporate investigation and white-collar crime and civil litigation practice, Shepard also has expertise assisting cross-border FCPA work. He recently handled a criminal prosecution on behalf of a pharmacist and represented a former Illinois Governor's Chief of Staff in an investigation. **James Brosnahan** (see p.288) of Morrison & Foerster LLP remains a distinguished figure in the white-collar criminal defense realm. He earns glowing praise from several sources, with one prizing him as *"one of the greatest trial lawyers in the country."* **Jan Lawrence Handzlik** (see p.640) of Venable LLP cochairs the firm's anticorruption and FCPA practice and splits his time between the Los Angeles and Washington, DC offices representing individuals and corporations in prosecutions and investigations. A nationally respected litigator, his experience also includes assisting with criminal environmental matters and foreign currency control investigations. A peer admires Handzlik's *"particular aptitude for communicating with juries"* and notes that he is an *"outstanding criminal defense lawyer with a wealth of firsthand trial experience in a whole range of cases."* **Bryan Daly** of Sheppard, Mullin, Richter & Hampton LLP, cochair of the firm's government contracts and white-collar defense, has a reputation for being *"very pragmatic and focused."* A recent highlight saw him assisting GE Aviation with substantial compliance reviews and internal investigations. Clients say **Patrick Robbins** of Shearman & Sterling LLP *"has great judgment and is able to bring a wealth of experience in an effective and valuable way."* He is the current deputy leader of the firm's litigation practice group. He recently won a dismissal for a Taiwanese client accused in a criminal Sherman Act/price-fixing matter. **Miles Ehrlich** of Ramsey & Ehrlich LLP *"manages to accomplish amazing *things and achieves good results for clients,"* according to interviewees. He is renowned for representing clients from the technology, financial services and healthcare sectors across the country. Along with colleague **Ismail Ramsey**, he has a wealth of experience stemming from his days as a federal prosecutor. Ramsey continues to impress with his wide-ranging SEC-defense and criminal practice. **Robert Corbin** of Corbin & Fitzgerald LLP is noted for his rigor- ous preparation of clients. He is a highly experienced advocate who is strong in both white-collar criminal defense work and complex investigations.

# MEDIA & ENTERTAINMENT LITIGATION

Commentary about individuals can be found under their firm's paragraph. If the firm has no paragraph (is not ranked) look at Other Notable Practitioners.

## Media & Entertainment: Litigation — Leading Firms

**Band 1**
Davis Wright Tremaine LLP *
Gibson, Dunn & Crutcher LLP *
Munger, Tolles & Olson LLP *

**Band 2**
Greenberg Glusker Fields Claman & Machtinger LLP *
Lavely & Singer PC
O'Melveny & Myers LLP *
Quinn Emanuel Urquhart & Sullivan, LLP
Sheppard, Mullin, Richter & Hampton LLP

**Band 3**
Bryan Cave LLP
Glaser, Weil, Fink, Jacobs, Howard, Avchen & Shapiro, LLP
Irell & Manella *
Katten Muchin Rosenman LLP *
Kendall, Brill & Klieger LLP
Liner Grode Stein Yankelevitz Sunshine Regenstreif & Taylor
Mitchell Silberberg & Knupp LLP
Robins, Kaplan, Miller & Ciresi LLP *

\* Indicates firm with profile.
Alphabetical order within each band. Band 1 is the highest.

## Band 1

### Davis Wright Tremaine LLP
See profile on p.2544

**THE FIRM** This firm remains a powerhouse in First Amendment litigation. It fields an impressive team of high-quality lawyers, who advise a broad range of traditional and new media clients on a variety of matters, including defamation, privacy, rights of publicity and IP infringement. The team has represented clients in front of the US Supreme Court and appellate courts. The firm has recently defended a number of media entities such as Electronic Arts, Microsoft and Lionsgate against right of publicity claims.

**Sources say:** *"They are extraordinarily responsive, pragmatic and sophisticated."*

**KEY INDIVIDUALS Alonzo Wickers** is lauded by peers and clients alike as *"a calm and thoughtful attorney who is universally admired and liked, even by the most difficult clients."* He is *"very pragmatic," "an amazing collaborator"* and *"ridiculously smart."* He advises clients on trademark, copyright, publicity and access to information issues. **Kelli Sager** is a renowned litigator of the highest quality whose

## Media & Entertainment: Litigation — Senior Statesmen

**Senior Statesmen:** distinguished older practitioners

| | |
|---|---|
| Fields Bertram | Greenberg Glusker Fields Claman |

### Leading Individuals

**Band 1**

| | |
|---|---|
| Edelman Scott | Gibson, Dunn & Crutcher LLP * |
| Frackman Russell | Mitchell Silberberg & Knupp LLP |
| Glaser Patricia | Glaser, Weil, Fink, Jacobs, Howard, Avchen |
| Marenberg Steven | Irell & Manella * |
| Pomerantz Glenn D | Munger, Tolles & Olson LLP * |
| Singer Martin D | Lavely & Singer PC |
| Stein Stanton 'Larry' | Liner Grode Stein Yankelevitz Sunshine * |

**Band 2**

| | |
|---|---|
| Katz Marty | Sheppard, Mullin, Richter & Hampton LLP |
| Kendall Richard B | Kendall, Brill & Klieger LLP |
| Petrich Louis P | Leopold, Petrich & Smith PA (ONP)[†] |
| Petrocelli Daniel | O'Melveny & Myers LLP |
| Schwartz Robert | O'Melveny & Myers LLP |
| Title Gail | Katten Muchin Rosenman LLP |

**Band 3**

| | |
|---|---|
| Bandlow Lincoln | Lathrop & Gage LLP (ONP)[†] |
| Basich Anthony M | Hogan Lovells US LLP (ONP)[†] |
| Contopulos Stephen G | Sidley Austin LLP (ONP)[†] * |
| Eskenazi Bonnie | Greenberg Glusker Fields Claman * |
| Grossman Marshall B | Bingham McCutchen LLP * |
| Lavely Jr John H | Lavely & Singer PC |
| Olson Ronald | Munger, Tolles & Olson LLP * |
| Stone Richard L | Jenner & Block LLP (ONP)[†] * |
| White Andrew M | Kelley Drye & Warren LLP (ONP)[†] |

**Band 4**

| | |
|---|---|
| Charnley Richard | Ropers Majeski Kohn & Bentley (ONP)[†] * |
| Gans Gary E | Quinn Emanuel Urquhart & Sullivan, LLP |
| Halberstadter David | Katten Muchin Rosenman LLP |
| Harris Marcia | Robins, Kaplan, Miller & Ciresi LLP * |
| Hazzard Yakub | Robins, Kaplan, Miller & Ciresi LLP * |
| Jacobs Robert A | Manatt Phelps & Phillips LLP * (ONP)[†] |
| Kinsella Dale F | Kinsella Weitzman Iser Kump & Aldisert (ONP)[†] |
| Rozansky Daniel | Stroock & Stroock & Lavan LLP (ONP)[†] |
| Schulman John A | Mitchell Silberberg & Knupp LLP |
| Steinthal Kenneth | King & Spalding LLP (ONP)[†] * |
| Taylor Joseph | Liner Grode Stein Yankelevitz Sunshine * |
| Thomas Andrew J | Jenner & Block LLP (ONP)[†] * |

particular expertise lies in First Amendment matters. She has been working on the major right of publicity cases

## Media & Entertainment: First Amendment Litigation — Leading Individuals

**Star individuals**

| | |
|---|---|
| Sager Kelli L | Davis Wright Tremaine LLP |

**Band 1**

| | |
|---|---|
| Bostwick Gary L | Bostwick & Jassy LLP (ONP)[†] |
| Boutrous Jr Theodore J | Gibson, Dunn & Crutcher LLP * |
| Wickers IV Alonzo | Davis Wright Tremaine LLP |

**Band 2**

| | |
|---|---|
| Burke Thomas R | Davis Wright Tremaine LLP |
| Carolan Duffy | Davis Wright Tremaine LLP |
| Chadwick James | Sheppard, Mullin, Richter & Hampton LLP |
| Cummins Guylyn | Sheppard, Mullin, Richter & Hampton LLP |
| Matteo-Boehm Rachel E | Bryan Cave LLP |
| Myers Roger | Bryan Cave LLP |

\* Indicates individual with profile.
[†]ONP = Other Notable Practitioner.

mentioned above, as well as for other media giants such as the Los Angeles Times. Sources say: *"She is extremely sharp, one of the best we work with. One of the top entertainment lawyers in LA."* **Duffy Carolan** has a wealth of experience acting for a variety of media entities, particularly news organizations, in libel, privacy and First Amendment matters. She currently acts as newsroom counsel to over two dozen newspapers across the state. **Thomas Burke** has been representing CNN this year on a number of litigation matters. According to sources: *"He has developed a wonderful practice beyond traditional media."*

### Gibson, Dunn & Crutcher LLP
See profile on p.682

**THE FIRM** This longstanding member of the California legal community is admired for its full-service litigation practice. The media team concentrates on the television industry, particularly profit participation, while also tackling copyright infringement claims and contract disputes. The firm can boast an enviable list of top clients, including NBC Universal, FOX Broadcasting and Hard Rock Café. The team recently represented CBS Studios and Warner Bros. in profit participation lawsuits.

**Sources say:** *"Extremely successful, very responsive and proactive."*

**KEY INDIVIDUALS Scott Edelman** (see p.633) is well regarded by peers, with particular commendation for his impressive and highly successful courtroom abilities. He has been involved in a wide array of cases of late, with a particular focus on profit participation litigation. He is currently representing NBC Universal in such litigation brought by producer Glen Larson. **Theodore Boutrous** (see p.624) is cochair of the firm's media and entertainment group and has experience in federal and state appellate courts nationwide. He advises a broad spectrum of clients, including authors and media organizations, on a wide range of matters, from First Amendment and defamation to copyright and news gathering.

## Munger, Tolles & Olson LLP
### See profile on p.691

**THE FIRM** The media and entertainment team at Munger Tolles continues to provide clients with an incredibly diverse legal service in a range of contentious matters. It counsels the biggest names from the motion picture, television and music industries in numerous matters, but can boast a particular wealth of experience battling the ever-increasing threat of internet piracy. The group successfully concluded a case representing six major film studios in a copyright infringement claim against internet service provider Zediva.

**KEY INDIVIDUALS Glenn Pomerantz** (see p.660) is a highly esteemed litigator in his field. He continues to represent media heavyweights such as ABC, Disney, Universal and FOX. He recently acted for Universal Music Group in the FTC's antitrust review of its EMI acquisition. Sources say: *"He is very smart, very strategic, and also very personable."* **Ronald Olson** (see p.657) is a respected litigator with years of experience to draw upon. He is a noted trial lawyer among his peers. Recently he has been working on the successful representation of Dick Clark Productions in a production and distribution lawsuit.

## Band 2

## Greenberg Glusker Fields Claman & Machtinger LLP
### See profile on p.683

**THE FIRM** The entertainment litigation practice at Greenberg Glusker is well known for its strong talent-focused practice in the motion picture and television industries. However, it continues to demonstrate its breadth of expertise dealing with an array of matters, from copyright and trademark infringement to defamation and profit participation, for studios, gaming publishers and musicians. The team has expertise in representing both plaintiff and defendant clients. The team is currently representing Tom Cruise in a defamation lawsuit against the publisher of Life & Style magazine.

**KEY INDIVIDUALS Bonnie Eskenazi** (see p.634) is one of the *"best-connected attorneys in the media and entertainment space."* She advises clients on the entire spectrum of entertainment issues, and is well respected for her ability to take on *"big and powerful studios in dispute resolution cases."* She is currently representing the plaintiff Shahrokh Mireskandari in a case brought against the Daily Mail. **Bertram Fields** is praised by peers and clients as *"the best*

*of the best."* A true senior statesman of the industry, he has years of experience and a wealth of knowledge to draw upon. He represents both plaintiffs and defendants, including the Hollywood elite. He is currently leading on the Tom Cruise defamation matter.

## Lavely & Singer PC

**THE FIRM** This niche entertainment firm continues to be the go-to practice for Hollywood's biggest celebrities. The team represents celebrated directors, actors, producers and artists in a variety of litigation matters, including defamation, IP, privacy and contract disputes.

**KEY INDIVIDUALS Martin Singer** remains *"the go-to guy for talent disputes."* A talent specialist, he represents high-profile clients against tabloids and other media entities. Sources say: *"He is wonderful!"* **John Lavely** has a broad media and entertainment practice covering libel, copyright infringement, privacy and right of publicity.

## O'Melveny & Myers LLP
### See profile on p.693

**THE FIRM** The strong litigation team at O'Melveny continues to work with clients in a diverse range of media and entertainment matters, including film financing, IP, video games and talent. Its impressive client roster includes heavyweights Time and Warner Bros. It recently obtained an impressive win for Warner Bros. in the highly publicized case against the heirs of Joe Shuster, the original illustrator of Superman.

Sources say: *"They are very responsive and proactive."*

**KEY INDIVIDUALS Robert Schwartz** continues to represent top entertainment clients in a variety of media matters, from copyright and First Amendment to defamation and advertising. However, he has recently expanded his practice in the video gaming industry. He is praised and respected by his peers, who dub him *"outstanding!"* Sources note **Daniel Petrocelli**'s excellent trial skills, with one going on to say: *"He is talented and entrepreneurial, he is so skilled and clients love him."* He has been involved in various high-profile cases, taking the lead on the Warner Bros. matter and representing Time in a defamation case brought against it by basketball player Reeves Nelson.

## Quinn Emanuel Urquhart & Sullivan, LLP

**THE FIRM** This talented group of litigators is strongly recommended for its expertise in all forms of intellectual property disputes, from copyright and trademarks to rights of publicity and idea theft. The team tackles a wide range of media and entertainment issues, including film finance arbitration. It represents clients from all corners of the entertainment industry, including recently advising the cast of television show 'Modern Family' on a contract dispute.

Sources say: *"Excellent. The attorneys at the firm are smart, professional and very dedicated to the needs of the client. They know when to be aggressive but also know when to sit back and see how things develop."*

**KEY INDIVIDUALS Gary Gans** is an experienced trial litigator involved in copyright, trade secrets, film financing, production and distribution matters. Recent highlights

include his impressive win in the theft of idea case Benay v Warner Bros. relating to the film 'The Last Samurai'. *"He is a superb lawyer. He is extremely intelligent and has tremendous judgment and good sense. He is an excellent strategist and trial lawyer,"* say sources.

## Sheppard, Mullin, Richter & Hampton LLP

**THE FIRM** The multidisciplinary media and entertainment team at this firm is known for both its litigation and transactional work. It deals with a range of matters including licensing, IP and First Amendment litigation. The group advises renowned clients such as MGM, Businessweek Magazine and the Walt Disney Company. Recent highlights include the team's success representing Dick Clark Productions in the widely publicized case involving the rights to distribute the Golden Globe Awards Show.

Sources say: *"They are constantly thinking outside the box, but still make sure we have mitigated our risk."*

**KEY INDIVIDUALS James Chadwick** has been busy representing various newspapers and other media organizations against libel actions. He provides counsel to a diverse range of media, technology and online entities. **Guylyn Cummins** is a renowned First Amendment litigator who represents a range of media organizations. This year she successfully represented a Clear Channel news reporter in a defamation action. **Marty Katz** is a *"real player"* in this space, and well-known industry litigator. He continues to represent some of the biggest names in the industry, including MGM and the Walt Disney Company, and led the charge on the high-profile Golden Globes case for Dick Clark Productions.

## Band 3

## Bryan Cave LLP

**THE FIRM** This team deals with a broad spectrum of issues from the media and entertainment arena. It has gained particular renown for its strength in First Amendment matters. The group works with impressive and varied media clients, such as Google, Pandora Media and the New York Times Company. The team is currently representing Courthouse News Service in an access to public records case.

**KEY INDIVIDUALS Rachel Matteo-Boehm** is an acclaimed First Amendment advocate, and is currently representing the First Amendment Coalition, made up of 14 media organizations, in the Californian Supreme Court, in filing an amicus brief regarding right of access to electronic mapping records maintained by local government. **Roger Myers** is praised as an extremely intelligent and experienced attorney. Sources particularly highlight his strength in the defense of the First Amendment.

## Glaser, Weil, Fink, Jacobs, Howard, Avchen & Shapiro, LLP

**THE FIRM** This group of experienced trial litigators continues to represent a varied client roster, including directors, producers, writers and recording artists. The team advises on IP and licensing issues, and can offer clients cross-border expertise.

**KEY INDIVIDUALS Patricia Glaser** is, according to sources, a *"name everybody knows"* and *"a go-to lawyer"* in the field. Head of the litigation practice, she is a formidable trial lawyer, representing high-profile companies, motion picture studios and entertainers.

### Irell & Manella
See profile on p.686

**THE FIRM** The media litigation department at Irell & Manella continues to demonstrate its strength in IP litigation, while also covering other matters, from contract disputes to profit-participation. In addition to this, a considerable part of the firm's practice involves arbitration proceedings. Clients include Warner Bros., Hulu and Universal. The team is currently representing the latter in a copyright infringement lawsuit against video-sharing site Veoh.

**Sources say:** *"I have found them to be outstanding lawyers, without exception very smart."*

**KEY INDIVIDUALS Steven Marenberg** (see p.652) is commended for his *"excellent"* trial skills, in particular his *"connection with the jury."* Sources say: *"He can be aggressive without being unpleasant, he is very professional, very smart and willing to think independently and creatively."* He is head of the firm's entertainment litigation practice and works with clients from the music, motion picture and video gaming industries.

### Katten Muchin Rosenman LLP
See profile on p.1253

**THE FIRM** This firm has an impressive bench, and is commended for its teamwork and cohesive approach. It deals with a broad spectrum of media issues, including copyright infringement, profit-participation, theft of ideas and antitrust. Recently the team has been advising NBC Universal on a number of copyright infringement claims.

**Sources say:** *"Excellent! They are very good at what they do. All the lawyers are extremely responsive and great people."*

**KEY INDIVIDUALS Gail Title** is the firm-wide head of Katten's entertainment and media litigation practice. She is particularly adept at contractual disputes and is currently leading for NBC Universal and Pilgrim Films on copyright contractual matters. Sources describe her as *"a real pleasure to work with."* **David Halberstadter** receives praise for his ability to talk to clients and explain issues clearly. He is also *"extremely responsive"* and *"approachable."* His practice focuses on the film and television industries, advising and representing clients on copyright and trademark infringement, defamation and First Amendment issues. He recently represented Summit Entertainment in a First Amendment litigation regarding the film 'The Hurt Locker'.

### Kendall, Brill & Klieger LLP
**THE FIRM** This Los Angeles-based boutique litigation firm has maintained a strong focus on the media and entertainment industry. The media team advises motion picture, advertising, music and video gaming clients on a

number of litigation matters, such as licensing, distribution, copyright, trademark and trade secret disputes.

**KEY INDIVIDUALS Richard Kendall** has over three decades of litigation experience and has argued in federal and state courts, appellate courts and the US Supreme Court. He is an expert in First Amendment and privacy disputes who *"really knows the business."*

### Liner Grode Stein Yankelevitz Sunshine Regenstreif & Taylor LLP
**THE FIRM** The media and entertainment practice group at Liner Grode advises both corporate and talent clients. It has experience working with clients from a range of industries and can boast top names such as Rob Lowe and David Duchovny on its talent roster. Recent work includes advising Summit Entertainment on its sale to Lionsgate.

**KEY INDIVIDUALS Larry Stein** (see p.667) is a highly adept talent litigator and considered *"a worthy adversary"* by his peers. Clients include the glitterati of the music and film world, as well as other corporate media entities. He is currently representing rapper Rick Ross in a right of publicity matter. **Joseph Taylor** (see p.668) represents a broad swath of players from the television and film industries. He deals with a range of matters, including contractual disputes, IP infringement and distribution rights.

### Mitchell Silberberg & Knupp LLP
**THE FIRM** This team is recognized for its work throughout the media and entertainment industries. It maintains an enviable list of prominent media clients, including NBC, EMI Music and Warner Bros. The firm represents clients in arbitration and other mediation procedures as well as litigation matters. It had recent success representing ABC, Touchstone and Marc Cherry against a wrongful termination claim brought by former 'Desperate Housewives' star Nicollette Sheridan.

**Sources say:** *"They are incredibly efficient and responsive. These are lawyers who, if you don't get them on the telephone when you call, will get back to you in less than an hour. You also get incredible results!"*

**KEY INDIVIDUALS Russell Frackman** is lauded by sources as *"the dean of the Bar of entertainment litigators in LA"* and *"an excellent lawyer."* He has particular experience with music industry clients, representing music publishers and record companies. He is currently involved in ongoing litigation against internet site Vimeo for Capitol Records and EMI Music Publishing concerning copyright infringement. **John Schulman** deals in production, distribution and financing matters in television, film and the internet. His wealth of knowledge in this area comes from his invaluable time working in-house at a major studio.

### Robins, Kaplan, Miller & Ciresi LLP
See profile on p.1588

**THE FIRM** This California media and entertainment practice works with clients from film, television, music and advertising, and has a particular reputation for its work in the talent space. The group deals with contract disputes, privacy, defamation, copyright and trademark infringement and licensing disputes.

**KEY INDIVIDUALS** Cochair of the firm's entertainment and litigation practice, **Yakub Hazzard** (see p.641) focuses on rights of publicity and privacy, trademark and copyright infringement and contractual disputes. His expertise lies in the music industry. **Marcia Harris** (see p.640) is *"a true trial lawyer"* with experience in both state and federal courts, as well as alternative dispute resolution sessions. Her particular specialty lies in profit participation disputes within the film and television industries.

### Other Notable Practitioners

According to sources, **Lincoln Bandlow** of Lathrop & Gage LLP represents a wide range of clients from all corners of the media and entertainment industry in copyright infringement, libel, trademark infringement and First Amendment disputes. One source notes: *"He gets claims resolved very quickly, settling when they need to be settled."* **Gary Bostwick** of Bostwick & Jassy LLP is a highly esteemed and *"stellar attorney,"* with a particular focus on First Amendment litigation. He is commended by peers for his trial abilities and, unusually, represents both plaintiffs and defendants in libel disputes. **Stephen Contopulos** (see p.629) of Sidley Austin LLP has impressed clients with his *"tenacity,"* *"exceptional experience and thoughtful legal advice."* He has experience in both federal and state courts representing television stations, magazines, book publishers and newspapers. **Dale Kinsella** of Kinsella Weitzman Iser Kump & Aldisert LLP is an *"effective"* and *"skilled"* litigator. Clients appreciate his ability to cut through legal speak and offer *"big picture strategies."* He has experience in the whole gamut of media issues, from IP infringement to antitrust. **Anthony Basich** of Hogan Lovells US LLP has a broad range of expertise within the entertainment sphere and advises clients from production companies to talent. *"He is a very conscientious lawyer, an outstanding writer and very dedicated to his work. He is a pleasure to work with and knows our business incredibly well,"* says one impressed client. **Marshall Grossman** (see p.639) of Bingham McCutchen LLP is a highly respected and talented trial litigator. *"He can take a complex set of facts and really focus on what is important. He has a big personality and presence, he is a very forceful advocate. He is smart, creative and a great orator,"* say sources. He recently acted for Estée Lauder in a matter regarding a stock purchase. **Andrew Thomas** (see p.669) of Jenner & Block LLP has lots of experience working with clients, from major film studios and newspapers to publishers. He recently acted for Universal on a copyright and trademark lawsuit. **Richard Stone** (see p.667) has recently made the move over to Jenner & Block LLP's media and entertainment litigation team. He litigates copyright, trademark, piracy and antitrust matters. Recent highlights include his successful representation of Fox Sports in its dispute with the LA Dodgers over the planned sale of the team and its assets. He is especially noted for his trial skills: *"I've never seen any lawyer better in deposition or oral argument than Rick."* With over 35 years of experience, **Andrew White** of Kelley Drye & Warren LLP is a seasoned trial attorney. Within the media arena he has a focus on IP and defamation disputes. Sources say: *"He is an experi-*

enced and outstanding lawyer." **Kenneth Steinthal** (see p.667) recently joined King & Spalding from Greenberg Traurig. He is well known for his work within the music industry, particularly regarding copyright disputes and regulatory issues. **Richard Charnley** (see p.627) of Ropers Majeski Kohn & Bentley heads the entertainment litigation department. He has an excellent talent practice, representing some of Hollywood's biggest stars. Recent clients have

included Steven Seagal and Chris Rock. **Daniel Rozansky** of Stroock & Stroock & Lavan LLP focuses on defamation, profit participation, First Amendment and other entertainment matters. He has lately been providing counsel to Screen Capital International in various film financing disputes. **Robert Jacobs** (see p.644) of Manatt Phelps & Phillips LLP has a predominantly music industry-focused practice, dealing with copyright infringement and general

commercial disputes. According to sources his "*litigation work is of the highest level,*" "*he is informed on legal issues surrounding copyright and he is pragmatic, reliable and proactive.*" **Louis Petrich** of Leopold, Petrich & Smith PA is an "*institution*" in California media law. His practice focuses on First Amendment and IP litigation within the television, music and motion picture industries.

# MEDIA & ENTERTAINMENT TRANSACTIONAL

Transactional: Mainly Talent p.609

Commentary about individuals can be found under their firm's paragraph. If the firm has no paragraph (is not ranked) look at Other Notable Practitioners.

## Media & Entertainment: Transactional
### Leading Firms

**Band 1**
Akin Gump Strauss Hauer & Feld LLP *
Loeb & Loeb LLP *
O'Melveny & Myers LLP *
Sheppard, Mullin, Richter & Hampton LLP

**Band 2**
Gibson, Dunn & Crutcher LLP *
Manatt Phelps & Phillips LLP *
Stroock & Stroock & Lavan LLP *

**Band 3**
Davis Wright Tremaine LLP *
Greenberg Traurig, LLP *
Katten Muchin Rosenman LLP *

\* Indicates firm / individual with profile.
Alphabetical order within each band. Band 1 is the highest.

*The editorial is in alphabetical order by firm name.*

## Akin Gump Strauss Hauer & Feld LLP
**See profile on p.904**

**THE FIRM** The entertainment and media group at Akin continues to draw praise for its work with investors in the entertainment industry, gaining particular renown in film financing. The group has a deep bench of talent and experience with cross-border transactions, allowing it to represent top clients from Goldman Sachs and The American Film Institute to foreign governments. Recent highlights include the firm's representation of Hemisphere Capital in a slate financing deal for films including 'The Adventures of Tintin' and 'World War Z'.
**Sources say:** "*They have really taken the practice to a new level. The lawyers are very strong and their product is strong.*"
**KEY INDIVIDUALS John Burke** (see p.626) is head of the firm's media and entertainment practice. He continues to be emblematic of the team's approach, bringing a strong business acumen to media finance. He recently represented established client Union Bank on various domestic and cross-border film financing deals in connection with various blockbusters including 'Snow White', 'The Hunger Games' and 'Limitless'. **Marissa Román Griffith** (see p.662) continues to build a solid reputation in film financing. One interviewee noted: "*She is a great lawyer, a very*

## Media & Entertainment: Transactional
### Leading Individuals

**Band 1**

| | |
|---|---|
| Brearton Christopher | O'Melveny & Myers LLP |
| Calabrese Joseph | O'Melveny & Myers LLP |
| Darwell Robert A | Sheppard, Mullin, Richter & Hampton LLP |
| Frankenheimer John T | Loeb & Loeb LLP * |
| Mayerson Mickey A | Loeb & Loeb LLP * |
| Scharf Stephen | O'Melveny & Myers LLP |

**Band 2**

| | |
|---|---|
| Burke P John | Akin Gump Strauss Hauer & Feld LLP * |
| Cohen Jill | Davis Wright Tremaine LLP |
| Fisher Ruth | Gibson, Dunn & Crutcher LLP * |
| Hobel Michael | Katten Muchin Rosenman LLP |
| Moore Schuyler M | Stroock & Stroock & Lavan LLP |
| Murray Christopher | O'Melveny & Myers LLP |

**Band 3**

| | |
|---|---|
| Black Daniel H | Greenberg Traurig, LLP * |
| Conner Lindsay | Manatt Phelps & Phillips LLP * |
| Edel Scott | Loeb & Loeb LLP * |
| Haymer Robert | O'Melveny & Myers LLP |
| Leo Thomas Glen | Sheppard, Mullin, Richter & Hampton LLP |
| Román Griffith Marissa | Akin Gump Strauss Hauer & Feld LLP * |
| Saltzman Stephen L | Loeb & Loeb LLP * |
| Thompson Matthew C | Stroock & Stroock & Lavan LLP |
| Zuckerman Williams Susan | Loeb & Loeb LLP * |

**Up-and-coming individuals**

| | |
|---|---|
| Logue Kelly | Davis Wright Tremaine LLP |

*good draftsman and works very hard.*" She led the team representing Hemisphere Capital in the slate film financing deal.

## Bloom Hergott Diemer Rosenthal LaViolette & Feldman, LLP

**THE FIRM** This firm is well known for its strong talent-focused practice. Based in Beverly Hills, it continues to offer corporate and general business advice to its high-profile clients across the entertainment industry.
**Sources say:** "*One of the best boutique firms.*"
**KEY INDIVIDUALS Jacob Bloom** is "*one of the best in the business.*" His talent practice is renowned and he represents many of the top names in Hollywood.

## Media & Entertainment: Transactional: Mainly Talent
### Leading Firms

**Band 1**
Gang, Tyre, Ramer & Brown, Inc.
Hansen, Jacobson, Teller, Hoberman, Newman, Warren
Ziffren Brittenham LLP

**Band 2**
Hirsch Wallerstein Hayum Matlof & Fishman
Jackoway Tyerman Wertheimer Austen Mandelbaum Morris
Bloom Hergott Diemer Rosenthal LaViolette & Feldman, LLP

### Leading Individuals

**Band 1**

| | |
|---|---|
| Bloom Jacob A | Bloom Hergott Diemer Rosenthal LaViolette |
| Branca John G | Ziffren Brittenham LLP |
| Brittenham Harry M | Ziffren Brittenham LLP |
| Cooper Jay L | Greenberg Traurig, LLP * |
| Fischer Samuel N | Ziffren Brittenham LLP |
| Hansen Thomas | Hansen, Jacobson, Teller, Hoberman |
| Hirsch Barry L | Hirsch Wallerstein Hayum Matlof & Fishman |
| Nochimson David | Ziffren Brittenham LLP |
| Passman Donald S | Gang, Tyre, Ramer & Brown, Inc. |
| Ramer Bruce | Gang, Tyre, Ramer & Brown, Inc. |
| Ziffren Kenneth | Ziffren Brittenham LLP |

**Band 2**

| | |
|---|---|
| Brown Harold A | Gang, Tyre, Ramer & Brown, Inc. |
| Emanuel Craig A | Loeb & Loeb LLP * |
| Horacek Joseph | Manatt Phelps & Phillips LLP |
| Jackoway James R | Jackoway Tyerman Wertheimer Austen |
| Jacobson Craig | Hansen, Jacobson, Teller, Hoberman |
| Klein Deborah | Jackoway Tyerman Wertheimer Austen |
| Lichter Linda | Lichter Grossman Nicholas Adler (ONP)[†] |
| Newman Jeanne | Hansen, Jacobson, Teller, Hoberman |
| Phillips Lee | Manatt Phelps & Phillips LLP |
| Weissmann Eric | Eric Weissmann (ONP)[†] |

**Up-and-coming individuals**

| | |
|---|---|
| Rosenberg Aaron | Myman Greenspan Fineman Fox (ONP)[†] |

\* Indicates firm / individual with profile.
[†]ONP = Other Notable Practitioner.

## Davis Wright Tremaine LLP
See profile on p.2544

**THE FIRM** The main area of focus for the experienced media and entertainment team at Davis Wright continues to be film finance, although it is gaining strength in the new media arena as well. The team receives a wealth of praise for its work on financial transactions, and recent highlights include its representation of various financial institutions, including City National Bank, in single and slate motion picture financing deals.
**Sources say:** *"Extraordinarily responsive, pragmatic and sophisticated."*
**KEY INDIVIDUALS** Head of the media and entertainment group, **Jill Cohen** continues to secure a wealth of praise for her knowledge and experience, particularly in film finance. *"She is extremely experienced, knowledgeable, practical, hard-working and will do anything within her power to serve the needs of her clients."* This year she has worked on a number of important financial transactions in the film industry. **Kelly Logue** represents a variety of banks, studios and other investors in motion picture and television financial transactions. He recently advised The Jim Henson Company in a note financing deal.

## Gang, Tyre, Ramer & Brown, Inc.
**THE FIRM** The team at Gang Tyre is viewed as the dominant force in the talent space. The group is widely recognized for its excellence in transactional work and its client list is a veritable who's who of the music and film industries.
**KEY INDIVIDUALS** **Donald Passman** is an excellent talent attorney who specializes in the music industry. He represents producers, record labels and recording artists. With decades of experience under his belt he is *"one of the reigning masters of the field."* **Bruce Ramer** is a *"standout,"* excellent entertainment attorney with particular experience representing top film star clients. **Harold Brown** is well known and respected for his thriving entertainment practice advising some of the biggest names in the business.

## Gibson, Dunn & Crutcher LLP
See profile on p.682

**THE FIRM** This firm continues to gain prominence for its high-profile corporate transaction work. Highlights includes joint ventures, M&A and multiyear slate financing deals. Recent work includes single and slate film financing transactions for Paramount Pictures and Twentieth Century Fox.
**Sources say:** *"A really wonderful firm. They understand the media and entertainment industry; they understand its nuances even within M&A."*
**KEY INDIVIDUALS** **Ruth Fisher** (see p.635) is a *"very strong,"* highly experienced corporate lawyer with a focus on media and entertainment. This year she advised top clients Technicolor and Universal Pictures on various acquisitions.

## Greenberg Traurig, LLP
See profile on p.1024

**THE FIRM** This firm covers a wide range of the media and entertainment industry, but has drawn particular praise for its strength in music and talent work. The team works with a variety of clients from industries such as film, television, internet and publishing. It has also continued to increase activity in new media and technology.
**Sources say:** *"Excellent! They are very professional."*
**KEY INDIVIDUALS** **Jay Cooper** (see p.629) is renowned for his strong talent practice at Greenberg. His continued expansion into the television, film and digital arenas has seen his historically strong music-focused practice develop into a broad-based practice crossing the boundaries between media industries. **Daniel Black** (see p.624) is the go-to transactional attorney at the firm. He has experience with traditional and new media matters, representing clients in the film, television and digital industries. Sources find him *"extremely knowledgeable in the field and a wonderful counsel."*

## Hansen, Jacobson, Teller, Hoberman, Newman, Warren & Richman, LLP
**THE FIRM** This Beverly Hills-based firm is an acknowledged leader in the entertainment transaction space. The boutique works with individuals and companies across the television and film industries, but is particularly known for its talent work. The firm works with top writers, producers, directors and actors.
**KEY INDIVIDUALS** A founding partner of the firm, **Thomas Hansen** is adept at representing the gamut of entertainment clients, from directors and producers to actors and writers. **Craig Jacobson** has developed a broad practice dealing with traditional and nontraditional entertainment matters. He represents talent from television and film, while also advising on other areas such as film financing. **Jeanne Newman** continues to have a strong focus on the television industry. She is highly regarded for her work with writers.

## Hirsch Wallerstein Hayum Matlof & Fishman
**THE FIRM** This Los Angeles entertainment boutique specializes in talent representation. The team advises both established and new actors, directors, producers and writers in all transactional entertainment matters.
**KEY INDIVIDUALS** Founding partner **Barry Hirsch** primarily focuses on entertainment law. He represents a whole host of clients including writers, directors and actors from the film and television industries.

## Jackoway Tyerman Wertheimer Austen Mandelbaum Morris & Klein
**THE FIRM** This full-service law firm is renowned for its talent-based work in entertainment law. As well as media and entertainment the practice offers real estate, taxation and corporate expertise.
**KEY INDIVIDUALS** **James Jackoway** is a renowned lawyer with experience in virtually all aspects of the entertainment sphere. He represents an impressive group of clients including David Letterman. **Deborah Klein** is dis-

tinguished for her work with some of the biggest names in Hollywood.

## Katten Muchin Rosenman LLP
See profile on p.1253

**THE FIRM** This full-service law firm continues to advise clients on all manner of media and entertainment issues, from licensing and distribution deals to IP protection and new media content. The group works with top-end clients such as DreamWorks Animation, NBC and Microsoft. Recent work includes the representation of Skype in sponsorship and promotion agreements.
**Sources say:** *"High quality. Attorneys with more specialized knowledge of media and entertainment than the big firms."*
**KEY INDIVIDUALS** **Michael Hobel** impresses clients with his *"practical and timely"* advice and *"strong network, allowing him to get information regarding general approaches and practices that are relevant in the industry."* He is head of the firm's entertainment and media practice, and with over 25 years of experience Hobel is adept at representing a number of media clients in financial transactions, IP rights matters, and production, development and merchandising deals.

## Loeb & Loeb LLP
See profile on p.689

**THE FIRM** The Los Angeles team at this national powerhouse advises on a broad range of media and entertainment matters from licensing and distribution agreements to film financing and talent representation. The firm boasts an enviable list of clients from all corners of the industry, including Warner Music Group, Diana Ross and Bank of America.
**Sources say:** *"They are very thorough, strategic and connected."*
**KEY INDIVIDUALS** **John Frankenheimer** (see p.636) is lauded by peers and clients alike as a *"dominant force,"* with one calling him *"the best in the music business."* This year he advised Revolution Studios on Sony ATV Music Publishing's purchase of Revolution's music publishing assets, and continues to represent huge music stars Diana Ross, Colbie Caillat and Duncan Sheik. **Mickey Mayerson** (see p.653) continues to enjoy a fabulous reputation for his high-profile work in entertainment finance and media matters. Recent highlights include representing Netflix on its acquisition of streaming rights from DreamWorks Animation. **Craig Emanuel** (see p.634) chairs the entertainment department and talent practice at the firm. He has considerable experience within the industry. Clients appreciate that *"he doesn't look to score at the expense of the other party. He makes sure that I have a full understanding of the implications of all I am asking for and the needs of the other party."* **Scott Edel** (see p.633) works with heavy-hitting clients from the film and television industries, such as YouTube and BBC Worldwide. He receives praise for his practicality and his *"client-friendly"* demeanor. **Stephen Saltzman** (see p.664) has extensive experience with international media financing and production deals. He has handled various cutting-edge matters in China this year including advising Beijing-based New Pictures Film on a

whole host of issues including distribution and sales agreements for the film 'The Flowers of War'. **Susan Zuckerman Williams** (see p.673) has been working with a multitude of impressive clients on corporate and financial transactions. She assisted Netflix in the financing and distribution of the series 'Hemlock Grove', and Benaroya Pictures with slate financing deals concerning films such as 'Lawless'.

## Manatt Phelps & Phillips LLP
See profile on p.690

**THE FIRM** This firm advises clients on the full range of matters within this industry, from film finance and labor to music and talent. The team works with many preeminent clients, including Sony Pictures Entertainment, Touchdown Entertainment and Michael Douglas. Manatt is currently representing the International 3D society in its merger with 3D@Home.

**Sources say:** *"They produce excellent, fantastic work; they are good at anticipating problems and looking after our interests. They understand the transaction, the parties and the business."*

**KEY INDIVIDUALS Lee Phillips** is a seasoned talent attorney for a wealth of superstar clients including the Eagles and Tracy Chapman. Recent highlights include negotiating an agreement for Randy Jackson in his role as judge on 'American Idol'. **Lindsay Conner** (see p.629) is a highly respected transactional lawyer who has impressed clients with his sophisticated approach and deep industry experience. *"He is exceedingly clever; the other side respects him – he can hold his own against anyone in the world."* **Joseph Horacek** chairs the firm's motion picture and television department. He has a broad media practice, but is particularly singled out by peers for his strong talent-based work.

## O'Melveny & Myers LLP
See profile on p.693

**THE FIRM** This highly regarded media and entertainment group is a full-service practice, offering clients advice on a range of matters from entertainment finance, M&A and contracts to litigation. This year the team worked with Lionsgate Entertainment on its acquisition of Summit Entertainment.

**Sources say:** *"O'Melveny is certainly one of the top firms I have encountered in my long practice."*

**KEY INDIVIDUALS Christopher Brearton** has quickly risen to the top of the pile of media and entertainment lawyers. Clients describe him as *"very hard-working, com-*mitted to clients, practical and plain-spoken."* He advises clients from all corners of the industry on financial agreements, licensing matters and M&A. This year he worked with Cross Creek Pictures on its distribution deal with Universal Pictures. **Joseph Calabrese** has established a reputation as a *"terrific corporate lawyer"* who *"really knows the industry."* He chairs O'Melveny's entertainment, sports and media practice. *"He is very smart and creative – an old-fashioned good lawyer."* **Christopher Murray** has a wealth of experience over a broad range of media and entertainment areas including film finance, production and distribution, and copyright. He is also particularly well known for his IP work in this industry. Due to his wealth of industry experience **Stephen Scharf** is considered one of the *"leading lawyers in the city"* and is described by one source as *"the godfather of entertainment finance."* He has acted on a number of high-profile investments and acquisitions this year, including advising Falcon Capital on cofinancing arrangements for roughly 100 films over the next three years with StudioCanal. **Robert Haymer** is a prominent corporate and M&A lawyer with considerable media and entertainment experience. He helped lead the team on Lionsgate's purchase of Summit.

## Sheppard, Mullin, Richter & Hampton LLP

**THE FIRM** This established multidisciplinary team is at the top of the media and entertainment field, with increasing cross-border abilities. The firm has worked on various high-profile films including financing for 'The Host' and 'Two Guns', and assisting Lionsgate in its marketing campaign for 'The Hunger Games'.

**Sources say:** *"Very professional and reasonable regarding their advice, which is key in the ever-changing entertainment industry."*

**KEY INDIVIDUALS Robert Darwell** *"is smart, savvy and a tough negotiator."* Sources also say that he is *"very experienced and is not only an expert in almost all aspects of entertainment law, but also has great common sense."* **Thomas Glen Leo** is a partner in the firm's Century City office. He focuses on entertainment finance and commercial law, working with a variety of clients including film studios and production companies.

## Stroock & Stroock & Lavan LLP
See profile on p.2010

**THE FIRM** The entertainment team at the firm's Los Angeles office offers clients a variety of services including advice on production financing, talent, IP and taxation.

The firm counsels a medley of clients, including top investment banks, production companies and talent.

**Sources say:** *"The firm is committed to excellence and client service."*

**KEY INDIVIDUALS Schuyler Moore** is noted by sources for his *"combination of professional brilliance, relentless work ethic and charm!"* His particular strengths lie in corporate and tax issues related to the media and entertainment industry. **Matthew Thompson** advises a range of entertainment clients from producers and directors to distributors and talent, focusing on M&A and financial media deals. Clients find him *"thoughtful, reasonable and practical."*

## Ziffren Brittenham LLP

**THE FIRM** Ziffren Brittenham draws particular praise from peers for its deep bench of talent and entertainment work. The firm works with impressive clients from the music, television and film industries, and is considered one of the best talent practices in California.

**Sources say:** *"Top firm!"*

**KEY INDIVIDUALS** Seen as *"a dean of entertainment lawyers,"* **Kenneth Ziffren** impresses clients with his *"experience, seniority and intellect"* and ability *"to get into the details of a deal."* **John Branca** is lauded by peers and clients as a *"standout"* lawyer who *"dominates the music business."* He is *"highly regarded"* and has worked on major transactions for some of the biggest names in the industry. **Harry Brittenham** has built a reputation as the go-to guy for big entertainment companies. **Samuel Fischer** is a respected and experienced entertainment attorney, known particularly for his work with talent in the television industry. **David Nochimson** maintains a robust talent-based entertainment practice.

## Other Notable Practitioners

**Aaron Rosenberg** of Myman Greenspan Fineman Fox Rosenberg & Light LLP is a young talent lawyer with a promising practice. He currently represents some of the biggest names in music, including Justin Bieber. **Linda Lichter** of Lichter Grossman Nicholas Adler & Goodman continues to work with a wide variety of top clients from the film industry. **Eric Weissmann** recently formed his own practice. He remains a highly regarded attorney, adept at talent representation. *"He is a wonderful guy and a great lawyer."*

# REAL ESTATE

Zoning/Land Use p.612

Commentary about individuals can be found under their firm's paragraph. If the firm has no paragraph (is not ranked) look at Other Notable Practitioners.

## Real Estate
### Leading Firms

**Band 1**
Allen Matkins Leck Gamble Mallory & Natsis LLP *
Cox Castle & Nicholson LLP
Gibson, Dunn & Crutcher LLP *
Paul Hastings LLP *

**Band 2**
DLA Piper LLP (US) *
Goodwin Procter LLP *
Latham & Watkins LLP *
Pircher, Nichols & Meeks
Sidley Austin LLP *
Skadden, Arps, Slate, Meagher & Flom LLP & Affiliates *

**Band 3**
McKenna Long & Aldridge LLP *
Morrison & Foerster LLP *
Orrick, Herrington & Sutcliffe LLP *
Pillsbury Winthrop Shaw Pittman LLP *

**Band 4**
Coblentz, Patch, Duffy & Bass LLP
Dechert LLP *
Farella Braun + Martel LLP
Holland & Knight LLP *
Manatt Phelps & Phillips LLP *
Munger, Tolles & Olson LLP *

\* Indicates firm / individual with profile.
†ONP = Other Notable Practitioner.

## Real Estate
### Senior Statesmen

**Senior Statesmen: distinguished older practitioners**

| | | | |
|---|---|---|---|
| Nellis Noel W | Orrick, Herrington & Sutcliffe LLP * | Pircher Leo | Pircher, Nichols & Meeks |
| Nicholson Phillip R | Cox Castle & Nicholson LLP | Seneker Carl (Kim) | Morrison & Foerster LLP * |

### Leading Individuals

**Band 1**

| | | | |
|---|---|---|---|
| April Rand S | Skadden, Arps, Slate, Meagher & Flom * | Feder Philip | Paul Hastings LLP |
| Arnold Dennis | Gibson, Dunn & Crutcher LLP * | Fischer Bruce | Greenberg Traurig, LLP (ONP)† * |
| Carey Stevens | Pircher, Nichols & Meeks | Gross Jonathan | Gilchrist & Rutter PC (ONP)† |
| Matkins Michael L | Allen Matkins Leck Gamble Mallory * | Hayutin Marc I | Sidley Austin LLP * |
| Meyer Michael E | DLA Piper LLP (US) * | Herr Robert | Pillsbury Winthrop Shaw Pittman LLP |
| Natsis Anton N | Allen Matkins Leck Gamble Mallory * | Mendelson Richard C | Seyfarth Shaw LLP (ONP)† * |
| Nichols Phillip | Pircher, Nichols & Meeks | Murray Jr William G | Orrick, Herrington & Sutcliffe LLP * |
| Sfregola Michael F | Gibson, Dunn & Crutcher LLP * | Richman James D | Arnold & Porter LLP (ONP)† * |
| Sharf Jesse | Gibson, Dunn & Crutcher LLP * | Rishwain James | Pillsbury Winthrop Shaw Pittman LLP * |
| Waldman Ira J | Cox Castle & Nicholson LLP | Teplin Lawrence | Cox Castle & Nicholson LLP |
| Walker Paul | Sidley Austin LLP * | Thornton Charles | Paul Hastings LLP |
| | | Weakland Alan W | Paul Hastings LLP |

**Band 2**

| | | | |
|---|---|---|---|
| Benudiz P Peter | Milbank, Tweed, Hadley & McCloy (ONP)† * | Westreich Benzion | Katten Muchin Rosenman LLP (ONP)† |
| Cowan Stephen A | DLA Piper LLP (US) * | Young Marc D | Morrison & Foerster LLP * |
| Dillon Carol K | Bingham McCutchen LLP (ONP)† * | | |
| Feldman Lewis G | Goodwin Procter LLP * | **Band 4** | |
| Fileti Thomas | Morrison & Foerster LLP * | Booth Susan J | Holland & Knight LLP * |
| Heil Joseph B | Dechert LLP * | Chae Meryl K | Skadden, Arps, Slate, Meagher & Flom * |
| Liever Michael H | Orrick, Herrington & Sutcliffe LLP * | Linder David M | Dechert LLP * |
| Mallory Richard C | Allen Matkins Leck Gamble Mallory * | Masenga Thomas J | Seyfarth Shaw LLP (ONP)† * |
| Miller O'Malley | Munger, Tolles & Olson LLP * | Remensperger Eric | Proskauer Rose LLP (ONP)† |
| Pappas Dean C | Goodwin Procter LLP * | Scull Nancy | McKenna Long & Aldridge LLP * |
| | | Swalwell Chauncey | Stroock & Stroock & Lavan LLP (ONP)† |
| **Band 3** | | Walsh Gerard J | Orrick, Herrington & Sutcliffe LLP * |
| Becket Tom | McGuireWoods LLP (ONP)† | Wyman Mathew A | Cox Castle & Nicholson LLP |
| Berger Donald I | Latham & Watkins LLP | | |
| Cooper M Scott | Sidley Austin LLP * | **Up-and-coming individuals** | |
| Cussen Deborah | Gibson, Dunn & Crutcher LLP * | Flowers Drew C. | Gibson, Dunn & Crutcher LLP * |
| Eatman Louis P | Proskauer Rose LLP (ONP)† | Hamilton Michael D | DLA Piper LLP (US) * |
| Edwards Steve | Manatt Phelps & Phillips LLP | McPhee Scott | Morrison & Foerster LLP * |
| Ehrhart Kevin M | Latham & Watkins LLP | Praw Douglas | Goodwin Procter LLP * |
| | | **Associates to watch** | |
| | | Yearwood Kahlil | Dechert LLP * |

## Allen Matkins Leck Gamble Mallory & Natsis LLP

See profile on p.674

**THE FIRM** This market-leading firm undertakes a broad range of real estate work and enjoys a top reputation for its expertise in leasing. Recent highlights for the team include handling all real estate elements of the $4 billion sale of the Los Angeles Dodgers to Guggenheim Baseball Management. The firm's land use offering is also strong, and it advised on the acquisition of a 2,600 acre master planned community in Santee, California, and the California Environmental Quality Act (CEQA) litigation that followed. The firm acts for a range of high-profile clients, including AT&T, JPMorgan, Wells Fargo and BlackRock.

**Sources say:** *"They're excellent, a really top-notch firm with a deep focus on real estate and the corporate, land use and environmental issues that go alongside that."*

**KEY INDIVIDUALS** Highly regarded leasing expert **Anton Natsis** (see p.656) regularly acts on major high-value real estate matters, including development transactions, commercial office leases and purchase contracts. *"He is very knowledgeable, has been around a long time and knows the industry well,"* says one source. **Michael Matkins**

(see p.652) is applauded by clients as *"loyal, client-focused and a great networking contact."* He is *"excellent, very well respected and gets to the heart of the matter quickly,"* according to market commentators. The eminent **Richard Mallory** (see p.651) wins high praise for his work on leasing and real estate transactions. *"The best thing about him is his practicality. He doesn't waste time, and he also comes with the ability to find a fair result for both sides, given the particular circumstances of the particular transaction,"* says one source. **Jeffrey Chine** (see p.628) enjoys an excellent reputation for his land use practice and represents such key names as the Building Industry Association of San Diego County and the Otay Land Company. According to one client, he offers *"outstanding grasp of the subject matter and*

*excellent relationships with local public officials, government agency staff and local public officials. He is knowledgeable, responsive and a creative problem solver."*

## Coblentz, Patch, Duffy & Bass LLP

**THE FIRM** This highly regarded firm benefits from the close connection between its real estate and land use groups. The team handles a full spectrum of work, from drafting and negotiating leasing and financing transactions to advising on land use issues and obtaining entitlements. Major clients of the firm include the California Academy of Science, TMG, the San Francisco 49ers and the Pacific Gas & Electric Company. Recently, the group has acted on eBay's 2 million sq ft campus expansion and the

1.3 million sq ft high-profile Westfield San Francisco Centre.

**Sources say:** *"The firm seems to really care about its people and I think that's reflected in how they deal with their clients."*

**KEY INDIVIDUALS Pamela Duffy** remains one of the leading names in California for land use, and is currently advising the California Pacific Medical Center on a $2.5 billion rebuilding project over five campuses. According to market sources, *"she has particular expertise in the planning department and has seen it all and done it all."* **Harry O'Brien** regularly handles high-level real estate work for such major names as the California Academy of Sciences. *"He's a smart lawyer with tremendous business sense and a*

great guy to have with you when you're in the middle of a huge, complex, very difficult deal. I can't praise him enough," says one client.

## Cox Castle & Nicholson LLP

**THE FIRM** This impressive full-service real estate firm enjoys an excellent reputation throughout California. The group handles the full spectrum of real estate matters for a client base of landlords, tenants, lenders, investors and developers. It has considerable leasing expertise, with a particularly strong reputation for its work representing landlords. The team offers expertise in the areas of complex industrial, office and retail leasing, with its activity on industrial matters involving issues of hazardous materials and deferred maintenance.

**Sources say:** *"They are extremely competent and represent the finest real estate entrepreneurs."*

**KEY INDIVIDUALS** The well-respected **Ira Waldman** is praised for his commercial outlook and attention to detail. According to clients, he is *"incredibly smart, fantastically practical, hard-working and a delight to work with."* **Mathew Wyman** is applauded by market sources as *"someone who works through things quickly, takes very rational positions and gets deals done."* He handles sales, acquisitions, workouts and restructurings. The eminent **Phillip Nicholson** offers invaluable advice to the team. He brings a wealth of real estate experience to his position at the firm, and during his career has handled a broad range of transactional real estate matters and disputes for market-leading clients. **Michael Zischke** is *"very thorough and a real pleasure to work with,"* according to market sources. He has a highly-regarded land use practice and offers particular expertise in CEQA matters. **Kenneth Bley** is a real estate attorney with extensive experience advising developers on land use entitlements. He also has considerable expertise as a litigator. **Lawrence Teplin** enjoys an excellent reputation for his real estate practice, with a particular focus on litigation. His experience acting on real estate disputes includes work on environmental questions, defect and delay claims and contract claims.

## Dechert LLP

See profile on p.1969

**THE FIRM** This group handles a variety of real estate work for its client base of commercial banks, insurance companies, REITs and real estate funds. The team has particular expertise advising on commercial real estate loans and issues arising from distressed real estate. Recent work highlights include advising a major commercial bank and various other lenders on the origination of $300 million of mortgage and mezzanine loans secured by a number of hotels nationwide. Key clients represented by the firm include Wells Fargo and Standard & Poor's.

**Sources say:** *"They're one of our go-to counsels for complicated work. They're extremely responsive, very sophisticated, and proactive in working with both us and the other side in order to get things done quickly and correctly."*

**KEY INDIVIDUALS** The *"outstanding"* **Joseph Heil** (see p.332) enjoys a top reputation for his work in real estate finance, with particular expertise in CMBS lending. *"He is*

articulate, extremely knowledgeable, responsive and has built a deep bench of experienced commercial real estate professionals," says one source. Key associate **Kahlil Yearwood** (see p.673) wins high praise from market commentators this year: *"He has a great experience level, is very responsive, terrific at dealing with people and keeping things productive and calm during tough negotiating situations,"* according to commentators. Commercial real estate specialist **David Linder** (see p.650) is known among peers for his drafting skills and expertise in securitized lending. Observers highlight him as *"someone who understands the lay of the land for a negotiation and can give you wise counsel, as well as represent you confidently on the technical legal aspects of the matters."*

## DLA Piper LLP (US)

See profile on p.1971

**THE FIRM** An international firm with a strong California presence, DLA Piper handles a broad range of real estate work, although it is best known for its expertise in finance and leasing. The substantial team regularly handles matters on the international stage. Recent highlights include acting for the Bank of China on the $3.5 billion refinancing of the Venetian Macau resort, for which the team liaised with the firm's Hong Kong office. Other high-profile names represented by the firm include Macerich, Citibank and Tishman Speyer Properties.

**Sources say:** *"I had a great impression of the firm, they do top-notch work and are very, very responsive."*

**KEY INDIVIDUALS** Market commentators consider **Michael Meyer** (see p.654) to be a *"great talent"* and *"far and away the giant of the leasing field."* He acted for Guggenheim Baseball Management on the $2 billion acquisition of the Los Angeles Dodgers. **Stephen Cowan** (see p.630) regularly undertakes top-level work for such major clients as Hyatt and Marriott International. *"He is first-rate and very thoughtful,"* say sources. **Michael Hamilton** (see p.640) is a well-regarded real estate practitioner whose recent work highlights have included acting for Macerich on a complex swap transaction which involved liaising with the firm's corporate and tax groups.

## Farella Braun + Martel LLP

**THE FIRM** This well-regarded San Francisco-based team handles a broad range of real estate work for its client base of lenders, asset managers, investors, designers and renewable energy companies. Key names being represented by the firm include Embarcadero Capital Partners, Archstone and San Francisco Waterfront Partners. Recently, the team acted for First Solar on the sale of a 4,000-acre solar photovoltaic facility, advising on real estate, permitting and environmental issues.

**Sources say:** *"Very personable attorneys who are very knowledgeable about real estate and treat their clients well."*

**KEY INDIVIDUALS Steven Vettel** is described by sources as a *"fantastic land attorney who is well connected, very skilled and just knows the law so well."* He has recently represented the San Francisco Museum of Modern Art.

### Gibson, Dunn & Crutcher LLP
See profile on p.682

THE FIRM This very well-respected practice undertakes a wide range of real estate work, including leasing, sales and acquisitions, financings and workouts. Recent major highlights for the team include acting for Tishman Speyer on the sale of 555 Mission Street in San Francisco, and advising Normandy Realty Partners on the $355 million recapitalization of 10 University City Plaza in Los Angeles. The firm's zoning and land use group is also very strong, and acts on a number of high-profile matters in California. It currently advises the NBA team Golden State Warriors on the land use and entitlement issues of its move to a new stadium in San Francisco.

Sources say: *"Seasoned professionals with great bench strength and the ability to address a wide array of issues."*

KEY INDIVIDUALS Clients consider **Michael Sfregola** (see p.665) to be *"one of the most intelligent, flexible, understanding lawyers in the city. He's very practical and responsive, keenly aware of the ins and outs of the matter, not just the legal issues but the nature of the market as well."* His particular expertise lies in the acquisition and financing of hotel, commercial, residential and industrial properties. **Dennis Arnold** (see p.620) is recognized by clients and peers alike as an extremely knowledgeable attorney, and sources describe him as being *"like an Encyclopedia Britannica of law."* He has particular experience advising on mortgage remedies and foreclosures. Market-leading zoning and land use practitioner **Amy Forbes** (see p.636) has extensive experience across a range of project development and construction issues and the processing of entitlements. She wins high praise from clients and peers alike: *"She is extremely intelligent, articulate and responsive. She is an excellent team player and problem solver, and her broad expertise is very valuable in negotiating effective solutions."* Impressive land use attorney **Mary Murphy** (see p.656) has worked on some of San Francisco's most significant public/private development deals. She is lead counsel on the high-profile Treasure Island Community Development, which proposes to build a sustainable San Francisco neighborhood on the island. *"She's an absolute powerhouse and very, very prominent,"* sources say, describing her as *"effective, knowledgeable and practical."* One of the leading figures of California real estate law, **Jesse Sharf** (see p.404) impresses clients as *"a real businessman's lawyer and probably one of the most connected real estate partners that I've come across. He's also extraordinarily practical in terms of closing a deal."* Sources applaud financing expert **Deborah Cussen** (see p.630) for being *"fantastic, incredibly energetic, positive and practical."* *"She's very good at making sure everything gets done, has a lot of experience in the lending phase and is very detail-oriented,"* say clients. **Drew Flowers** (see p.636) regularly handles high-value real estate matters, and recently advised Normandy Realty Partners on a joint venture with Morgan Stanley Real Estate Investing on the recapitalization of an office tower in Los Angeles. Clients praise him as *"spectacular, able to deal with situations thoughtfully and with very good business sense."*

### Goodwin Procter LLP
See profile on p.1522

THE FIRM The impressive Goodwin Procter real estate offering wins high praise for its advice on joint ventures, debt structuring and restructuring and the raising and deployment of capital for major REITs, investment managers and developers. It also handles a broad spectrum of real estate matters across a range of sectors, with particular experience in hospitality and leisure. The team recently acted as lead bonds counsel for the City and County of San Francisco in three series of obligation bonds totaling $331 million.

Sources say: *"They're fantastic, very helpful, thoughtful, detail-oriented and thorough."*

KEY INDIVIDUALS **Dean Pappas** (see p.658) is highly regarded for his in-depth understanding of joint ventures, leasing and loan transactions, and his high-profile clients include the Donahue Schriber Realty Group. *"I am impressed with the thoroughness of his analyses, his breadth of knowledge, negotiation capabilities and responsiveness. He is the attorney that I look to when the most complex deal issues arise,"* says one source. The market-leading practitioner **Lewis Feldman** (see p.635) wins applause from sources for being *"very well respected, very helpful and incredibly responsive."* He has advised Anschutz Entertainment Group on the development of a $1.5 billion event center in Los Angeles. Real estate and public finance specialist **Douglas Praw** (see p.660) handles high-profile matters for clients who include major public equity funds and shopping center developers.

### Holland & Knight LLP
See profile on p.1028

THE FIRM This firm is best known for its prowess in zoning and land use. Its large and experienced team has expertise across the full spectrum of land use issues. The firm's land use group stands out for its integration with the environment practice, and clients benefit from the team's knowledge of the full range of environmental issues, from CEQA and NEPA regulation to wetlands and endangered species. The team currently advises AT&T on permitting for wireline and wireless installations statewide.

Sources say: *"They're fantastic: very helpful, thoughtful, detail-oriented and thorough."*

KEY INDIVIDUALS The impressive **Jennifer Hernandez** (see p.642) is known for her extensive land use expertise and has recently advised Lewis Operating Corporation on permitting matters for a series of high-profile projects across California. *"She is second to none: a superior talent with a great client base, and very versatile,"* say market commentators. The highly regarded **Susan Booth** (see p.624) heads the firm's West Coast real estate practice. She is a capital markets specialist with a background in finance, and clients benefit from her in-depth business knowledge. Observers highlight the *"fantastic"* land use specialist **Tamsen Plume** (see p.659) as *"very responsive, focused, smart and a great deal maker."* She currently acts for such major names as Target Corporation and Regent Properties.

### Latham & Watkins LLP
See profile on p.446

THE FIRM This top real estate practice has a very strong presence in California, with expertise in commercial, industrial and residential developments. The team is known for its strength in real estate finance, working for such major names as Deutsche Bank, Wells Fargo, Credit Suisse and Bank of America. As well as restructurings and loan workouts, loan originations and acquisitions are a key area of focus for the practice. Recent work highlights for the team include acting for Anschutz Entertainment Group on the $275 million financing of a 3.6 million sq ft mixed-use development in Los Angeles. The team also enjoys a strong reputation for its work on California land use issues.

Sources say: *"This firm is by far the most sophisticated and the best at handling large projects."*

KEY INDIVIDUALS Highly regarded attorney **George Mihlsten** is described by market commentators as *"the dean of land use and political relations."* He acts for such major names as Paramount, NBCUniversal and JMB Realty. **Cindy Starrett** *"is extremely qualified, savvy and connected in Los Angeles. Her advice is sound and strategic,"* say clients. She recently advised Westfield on securing entitlements for a large-scale mixed-use development. Clients applaud **Duncan Joseph Moore** for being *"incredibly competent and responsive. His knowledge base is quite impressive, as is his ability to interact with city officials. He has a good sense of nuance and delicacy in dealing with complex matters."* The *"incredibly impressive"* **James Arnone** wins praise for being *"a very good land use litigator and very good at strategy."* According to clients, *"his knowledge of zoning issues and ability to get things done is outstanding."* **Donald Berger** is hailed as *"exceptional"* by clients, who value his *"technical expertise in dealing with complex real estate debt issues, particularly where the capital structure contains multiple complex layers of different debt instruments."* He has recently acted for Deutsche Bank on the $1.5 billion financing for a major shopping center REIT. **Kevin Ehrhart** is a highly regarded real estate attorney who advises a range of developers, public pension funds, joint ventures, partnerships and private equity funds. Commentators say that he is *"solid, gets deals done and is a really great lawyer."*

### McKenna Long & Aldridge LLP
See profile on p.922

THE FIRM This substantial team undertakes work for developers and public agencies, lenders and borrowers, including institutional lenders such as banking associations and insurance companies. The group is experienced in commercial, retail and residential projects, public-private partnerships and mixed-use developments. Recent work highlights for the team include acting for Sudbury Properties on a large-scale, $1 billion master planned community in San Diego. The team's client base includes CityView, KB Home and LNR Property Corporation.

Sources say: *"Good people, well qualified and reasonable."*

KEY INDIVIDUALS **Nancy Scull** (see p.664) *"is the attorney to have in California for homeowner association and* *community-related issues. She's terrific, she thinks things through, is thorough and has a lot of credibility,"* according to commentators. **Timothy Tosta** (see p.669) *"is well connected within the community and knows the lay of the land very well,"* say sources.

## Manatt Phelps & Phillips LLP
See profile on p.690

**THE FIRM** This firm's real estate team has expertise across a range of real estate and land use issues. The group undertakes work relating to sales and acquisitions, development, financing and restructuring of commercial, industrial and residential properties. Recently, the team advised TIAA-CREF on a joint venture to design and build a $150 million luxury apartment complex. The firm also has a highly regarded zoning and land use practice, which has particular experience dealing with municipal law, redevelopment law and coastal development matters. The group recently acted for Alvarez & Marsal on obtaining entitlements for a nine-acre residential development in the City of Dana Point in California.
**Sources say:** *"A very knowledgeable and well-connected firm."*
**KEY INDIVIDUALS** Distinguished land use practitioner **Susan Hori** recently advised Lewis Operating Corporation on the re-entitlement of a 205-acre residential site in Eastvale, California, for commercial and industrial use. **Steve Edwards** is noted for his broad experience in real estate, acting for such clients as Citibank, York Capital and Fortus Property Group. He recently worked on the acquisition of a $100 million multifamily development site and of seven affordable housing projects with a value of $50 million.

## Morrison & Foerster LLP
See profile on p.1990

**THE FIRM** The real estate practice at Morrison & Foerster places particular focus on workouts and restructuring work, representing major banks such as JP Morgan, Wells Fargo and Eurohypo. The group also has strong expertise in loan origination, and recently advised AMB Property Corporation on a $210 million portfolio financing and $160 million loan restructuring, secured by a portfolio of 26 properties in six states. Other key clients represented by the firm include Kaiser Foundation Health Plan, Gramercy Capital and AREA Property Management.
**KEY INDIVIDUALS Thomas Fileti** (see p.635) is experienced in a variety of real estate finance transactions, with emphasis on the lease financing of corporate real estate assets. *"He's a smart, cooperative and knowledgeable lawyer who pursues his clients' interests,"* say clients. **Marc Young** (see p.673) chairs the firm's global real estate group. He undertakes high-profile work for investment banks, capital companies, commercial banks and mezzanine investment funds. According to sources, he is *"a businessman's lawyer,"* and *"very thorough and well respected."* The eminent **Kim Seneker** (see p.665) has extensive experience in California real estate law, from land use matters to complex financing transactions. Sources describe **Scott McPhee** (see p.654) as *"a practical lawyer who gets deals done, with expertise in*

*tricky high-end lending."* He represents investors, lenders, owners and developers on real estate financing matters including joint ventures and ground leases.

## Munger, Tolles & Olson LLP
See profile on p.691

**THE FIRM** The Munger, Tolles & Olson's real estate offering is known for its prowess in litigation, although the team's expertise covers areas ranging from acquisitions, leasing and development projects to workouts and restructurings. Recently, it represented Downtown Properties in the $344 million acquisition of the office building Three First National Plaza in Chicago. The firm has also acted for key names in Los Angeles, including the Los Angeles Metropolitan Transportation Authority and the County of Los Angeles.
**KEY INDIVIDUALS** The *"phenomenal"* **O'Malley Miller** (see p.654) wins applause from peers for being *"exceptionally talented"* and *"very intellectual."* He acted on the acquisition of Three First National Plaza, one of the largest buildings in Chicago.

## Orrick, Herrington & Sutcliffe LLP
See profile on p.1994

**THE FIRM** This prominent real estate group has particular strengths in the area of hospitality, acting on transactions relating to major hotels such as the Four Seasons and Westin in San Francisco, the Ritz-Carlton in Boston and the Huntingdon Hotel. In addition, the firm undertakes work on fund formation and distressed assets. The team is advising Gerding Edlen on the formation of a $250 million value added fund for the acquisition and redevelopment of green multifamily and office properties.
**KEY INDIVIDUALS** According to market commentators, **Michael Liever** (see p.650) *"is extremely pragmatic, does not get bogged down in the minutiae and really keeps his clients' practical interests front and center."* He recently acted for Northern California Industrial Portfolio on the $520 million sale of its 5.3 million sq ft industrial portfolio. **William Murray** (see p.656) is recognized by sources as *"very experienced with a very good reputation"* and *"a legend in San Francisco."* Recently, he represented Swift Realty on the purchase of an office campus from Bank of America for $88 million. **Gerard Walsh** (see p.671) is known for his work in the hospitality sector, with particular experience in distressed debt transactions. *"He was able to get to the core of what was really at stake in the deal without being side-tracked. He is a businessman's lawyer,"* say observers. The eminent **Noel Nellis** (see p.656) offers invaluable advice to the real estate team from his position as consultant at the firm. He brings decades of experience to the role and is currently focused on the firm's development in the Asian market.

## Paul Hastings LLP
See profile on p.1996

**THE FIRM** This leading practice has particular strength in distressed real estate work, both in California and nationwide. Its clients include a number of major real estate private equity funds, developers and financial institutions,

such as Oaktree Capital Management, Morgan Stanley and TPG Capital. Recent work highlights for the firm include advising Dubai World on the refinancing and $2 billion note offering of the City Center project in Las Vegas. Hospitality is another key area of focus, as demonstrated by the team's work for the developer of the $3.5 billion Baha Mar resort in the Bahamas.
**Sources say:** *"Extremely high-quality work, responsiveness, excellent judgment and excellent representation of client interests."*
**KEY INDIVIDUALS Charles Thornton** *"has been doing this forever and is at the top of his game, has a very sophisticated group of clients and always gets the job done well,"* according to observers. **Alan Weakland** is particularly known for his strength in hospitality work, with recent work including representing Chartres Lodging in the acquisition of the Novotel Hotel Times Square. Sources praise him for being *"solid, pragmatic and to the point."* The well-respected **Philip Feder** is described by market commentators as a *"very knowledgeable"* real estate attorney. He recently advised on the restructuring of the financing for a $500 million luxury condominium project in Los Angeles.

## Perkins Coie LLP
See profile on p.2548

**THE FIRM** This firm enjoys an impressive reputation for its zoning and land use practice, which acts on major education, transport, military base reuse, energy and water projects in California. The team is also recognized for its expertise in CEQA legislation. High-profile clients represented by the firm include City of Alameda, Lennar Communities and Rockwood Capital. Currently, the group is lead counsel to Redwood City for the complex and high-profile Saltworks redevelopment in the San Francisco Bay Area.
**KEY INDIVIDUALS Cecily Talbert Barclay** is very highly regarded for her varied zoning and land use practice. Sources praise her detailed and analytical approach. The top-quality land use practitioner **Barbara Schussman** advises a client base that includes such high-profile names as Stanford University. Clients praise her high levels of subject matter expertise.

## Pillsbury Winthrop Shaw Pittman LLP
See profile on p.2000

**THE FIRM** This strong real estate team is active in the areas of leasing, finance, energy and environment, as well as distressed real estate work. The team recently advised on loan modifications and originations, commercial office acquisitions, hotel sales and the construction of schools, handling work both in the USA and overseas. The breadth of the firm's work is demonstrated by its broad client base, which includes the Los Angeles Unified School District, AXA Equitable, the San Francisco Giants and Chevron Mining.
**KEY INDIVIDUALS** The well-respected **Robert Herr** now leads the firm's real estate practice. He undertakes a range of transactional, land use and distressed real estate work for such clients as Spear Street Capital, SKS Investments and Smart Cities International. Partner **James Rishwain**

(see p.662) is a real estate practitioner who undertakes work for a variety of high-profile clients. He acts for Fifth Street Properties, and recently advised them on the takeover of a $1 billion nationwide portfolio of office properties.

## Pircher, Nichols & Meeks

**THE FIRM** A boutique firm with impressive real estate expertise, Pircher, Nichols & Meeks is recognized for its ability to handle a broad range of complex transactions. The team advises on all stages of real estate matters, from land use and environmental issues through leasing to any arising litigation and workouts.

**Sources say:** "*They have a tremendous amount of experience and we have high regard for them.*"

**KEY INDIVIDUALS Stevens Carey** is "*supersmart and so effective in his negotiations it's incredible. He's always calm and he gets everything his client wants,*" according to sources. **Phillip Nichols** wins applause from market commentators, who find that "*his attention to detail is phenomenal*" and consider him to be a "*brilliant and really pragmatic*" attorney. Commercial real estate expert **Leo Pircher** has been a strong presence in the market for decades. His highly regarded practice covers joint ventures, financings, sales and acquisitions.

## Sheppard, Mullin, Richter & Hampton LLP

**THE FIRM** Widely recognized for its zoning and land use prowess, this substantial real estate offering also represents lenders, landowners, builders, investors and developers on a broad range of real estate matters. Recent work highlights for the team include advising NRG on the acquisition and financing of a 66 MW solar project. The firm also recently advised Hong Kong company Chevalier Holdings on the acquisition of three assisted living and memory care facilities in California.

**Sources say:** "*A significant player with a good reputation.*" "*An excellent firm all-around.*"

**KEY INDIVIDUALS** Market sources describe **Robert Thompson** as "*a bright sophisticated lawyer*" with "*a fine legal mind and ability to participate in, and lead when appropriate, business strategy efforts.*" He has expertise advising on California Environmental Quality Act compliance relating to residential and mixed-use development, as well as military base reuse work. **Pamela Westhoff** enjoys an excellent reputation for her real estate work, and has a particular focus on zoning and land use matters. She has acted for a number of radio and television clients on the licensing of broadcast and communications towers.

## Sidley Austin LLP
### See profile on p.1264

**THE FIRM** This is a very well-regarded firm that combines expertise in complex financing transactions with strong litigation capabilities. Clients benefit from the close links maintained between the real estate practice and lawyers from the firm's bankruptcy, tax and environment groups. The team currently advises Credit Suisse on $250 million of syndicated senior debt secured by a ski resort project. It also recently acted for GE Capital on the proposed sale of

a $343 million mezzanine loan. Other major names represented by the firm include Wells Fargo, Bank of America, Deutsche Bank and Oaktree Capital Management.

**Sources say:** "*Their lawyers are insightful, responsive and helpful, and I've been very impressed with them.*"

**KEY INDIVIDUALS** Distressed real estate expert **Paul Walker** (see p.671) wins praise from market sources for being "*rock solid and always having his finger on the pulse.*" "*He is fantastic, extraordinarily knowledgeable in the field and very well respected. He is very focused on details and a great overall practitioner,*" add commentators. The highly regarded **Marc Hayutin** (see p.641) regularly handles a range of high-value financing transactions and disputes. "*I am consistently impressed by how, when new twists and turns come into play, he has a knowledge base of that particular issue. He is also very good at explaining complicated points,*" says one source. Observers highlight **Scott Cooper** (see p.629) as "*a very practical lawyer with a no-nonsense approach.*" "*He is very analytical, very bright, understands his area of expertise very well and gives good sound legal advice,*" according to sources. He is currently advising a major life insurance company on a number of mortgage loans.

## Skadden, Arps, Slate, Meagher & Flom LLP & Affiliates
### See profile on p.2008

**THE FIRM** This well-regarded group is known for its ability to handle sophisticated real estate matters in the domestic and international spheres. Its practice covers sales, acquisitions and financings of commercial, industrial and residential properties, as well as leasings, restructurings and joint ventures. Recently, the firm acted for Nationwide Health Properties in the much-reported $7.4 billion acquisition of Ventas. The team has also advised MPG Office Trust on the $160 million refinancing of a multistory office tower in Los Angeles.

**Sources say:** "*Extremely high-quality work, responsiveness and attention to detail, excellent business as well as legal judgment and excellent representation of client interests.*"

**KEY INDIVIDUALS Rand April** (see p.620) "*has a deep knowledge of real estate and good commonsense, and he's extremely practical and direct,*" say clients. He handles a variety of high-value sales and acquisitions, and regularly undertakes work relating to private and public real estate securities. Peers applaud **Meryl Chae** (see p.627) for being "*a hard worker, enormously persistent and a great drafter who serves her clients very well.*" She advises on sales and acquisitions and enjoys a very good reputation for her REIT expertise.

## Other Notable Practitioners

**Carol Dillon** (see p.632) of Bingham McCutchen LLP is applauded by sources for being "*very smart, strategic and effective*" with "*a deep understanding of clients' needs and interests.*" Recently, she represented Stanford University in the restructuring of five long-term ground leases. The well-regarded land use attorney **Edward Casey** (see p.627) of Alston & Bird LLP is "*an excellent lawyer, a sharp guy*

and very cooperative. He figures out a good way to make the team effective,*" sources say. His clients include various commercial, retail and residential developers and he also has experience on CEQA matters. **James Richman** (see p.662) heads the Arnold & Porter LLP real estate practice in Los Angeles and is recognized by market commentators as "*a knowledgeable attorney.*" He recently acted for the lender on a finance transaction relating to loans of $800 million secured by a portfolio of office buildings. The very highly regarded **Howard Ellman** (see p.634) continues to offer invaluable advice to the team at Buchalter Nemer. His extensive transactional and litigation experience covers a broad spectrum of real estate matters. **Bruce Fischer** (see p.635) of Greenberg Traurig, LLP specializes in real estate funds and investment trusts. Observers consider him to be "*incredibly technically solid with a big practice.*" **Benzion Westreich** of Katten Muchin Rosenman LLP is hailed by market sources as "*a very practical, smart lawyer whose clients adore him.*" He has experience of a wide variety of transactional real estate matters, and recently advised iStar Financial on a loan portfolio of more than $750 million. At Loeb & Loeb LLP, the highly regarded land use attorney **Paul Rohrer** (see p.662) handles matters relating to sales and acquisitions, optioning and leasing, and has experience advising on construction-related agreements, joint development agreements and owner participation agreements.

The "*terrific*" **Louis Eatman** of Proskauer Rose LLP is described by market sources as "*very well known and respected and an excellent attorney.*" He represents private equity funds, commercial property landlords and tenants, life insurance companies, portfolio asset managers and pension funds. Capital markets expert **Eric Remensperger** of Proskauer Rose LLP is valued by clients for his "*intelligence, diligence and good judgment.*" He is "*very good at leading a large team on complicated transactions,*" according to sources. According to commentators, **Jonathan Gross** of Gilchrist & Rutter PC is "*a good attorney who is tough-minded but civil, very creative and doesn't lose sight of the details.*" He undertakes a broad range of commercial real estate work for such key figures as Lend Lease Real Estate, Thomas Development Partners and the Equitable-Nissei Figueroa Company.

Observers highlight **Richard Mendelson** (see p.654) of Seyfarth Shaw LLP as "*probably one of the quickest, smartest attorneys when it comes to examining the real risk, and someone who's always improving.* " He has particular strengths advising on real estate financing transactions, as well as restructuring and workouts. **Chauncey Swalwell** of Stroock & Stroock & Lavan LLP "*has extensive, encyclopedic knowledge of California real estate, particularly joint ventures,*" say clients. "*His background in real estate litigation makes him uniquely valuable in that he understands the endgame better than most. He tells you what he can do and then he executes it, reliably, every time.*" Sources recognize **Peter Benudiz** (see p.282) of Milbank, Tweed, Hadley & McCloy LLP as a "*top-notch hospitality lawyer.*" He undertakes high-profile acquisition, financing and restructuring work for his client base of major private equity funds and financial institutions. **Tom Becket** of McGuireWoods LLP has a varied real estate practice that includes brokerage representations, leasing, development and project finance. He acts for such major clients as Verizon Wireless, South Coast Plaza and McDonald Development. Observers highlight **Thomas Masenga** (see p.652) of Seyfarth Shaw LLP as a "*meticulous*" and "*very knowledgeable and experienced commercial real estate attorney.*"

# TAX

Estate Planning p.617; State & Local p.617

Commentary about individuals can be found under their firm's paragraph. If the firm has no paragraph (is not ranked) look at Other Notable Practitioners.

## Band 1

### Gibson, Dunn & Crutcher LLP
See profile on p.682

**THE FIRM** This team continues to impress sources with its international capabilities and tax skills, especially while handling complex M&A transactions. The 11-lawyer team is notably prominent in Northern California, and beyond transactional work is very active in tax litigation and controversy. Clients include the likes of Kraft, Hewlett-Packard, Intel and Wells Fargo Securities.
**Sources say:** "*Very responsive, technically strong and their fees are reasonable.*"
**KEY INDIVIDUALS** Sources readily praise **Hatef Behnia** (see p.623), saying: "*He is just brilliant,*" and describing him as "*a terrific lawyer and an excellent guy.*" His practice focuses on taxable and tax-free M&A, spin-offs, restructurings, joint ventures, debt and equity financings, and other areas involving complex financial instruments and structures. **Paul Issler**'s (see p.643) practice emphasizes domestic and international corporate, limited liability company

and partnership tax matters. Market commentators describe him as a "*responsive and strong*" lawyer. **Dora Arash** (see p.620) wins widespread recognition among peers and clients alike and is described as "*an excellent practitioner, always available and entirely committed.*"

### Latham & Watkins LLP
See profile on p.446

**THE FIRM** The 32-lawyer team enjoys a strong reputation for its wide range of expertise in tax. Its talented team is able to handle complex transactional tax work, company representation, tax-exempt organizations, benefits and compensation at both the national and international level. Highlights include advising Complete Production Services on its merger with Superior Energy Services, while other clients include Oracle and Spirit Airlines.
**Sources say:** "*A great firm.*" "*They do very substantial work.*"
**KEY INDIVIDUALS Michael Brody** cochairs the firm's REIT industry group, and wins widespread recognition in the tax field, with commentators saying: "*He is the principal expert in real estate trusts in California.*" Sources are ready to praise **John Clair** for his achievements throughout his long career. His practice focuses on corporate taxation and he is particularly active on financial products and M&A. **Laurence Stein** is highly regarded in the tax legal community and peers describe him as a "*great lawyer, very skilled on transactions.*" He is particularly active on transactional tax, including M&A, dispositions, restructurings and tax-free reorganizations. Los Angeles-based partner **Samuel Weiner** chairs the transactional tax practice group. Peers describe him as an "*outstanding lawyer*" and he focuses on federal and state taxation of corporations and partnerships. He acted for AMD on the acquisition of SeaMicro.

## Band 2

### Baker & McKenzie
See profile on p.435

**THE FIRM** This team excels through its extensive experience on transfer pricing, tax assessments for domestic and international clients, tax planning strategies for high net worth individuals and tax controversy cases. It is a popular choice among technology clients and has a strong base in Northern California.
**Sources say:** "*A destination tax practice, a highly respected competitor.*"
**KEY INDIVIDUALS** Palo Alto-based **John Peterson** (see p.659) chairs the firm's global tax practice group. He enjoys

an outstanding reputation for his in-depth knowledge of transfer pricing, structuring of international operations and international tax planning. Sources praise **Gary Sprague**'s (see p.667) international tax knowledge and sophistication. He is the managing partner of the firm's Palo Alto office and chairs the global tax planning and transactions practice groups.

### Fenwick & West LLP
See profile on p.680

**THE FIRM** This team is a primary port of call for technology companies in the state, and its strength in Silicon Valley and across Northern California attracts leading clients. The firm's vibrant M&A practice creates many opportunities for the tax team, which acts for major international companies, mainly in tax planning, joint ventures, transfer pricing and controversy. Notably, the team advised Xilinx on a case that attracted significant media attention.
**Sources say:** "*They stand out in Silicon Valley.*"
**KEY INDIVIDUALS James Fuller** (see p.637) receives widespread recognition and is described as a "*true star*" by market sources. His practice covers a wide range of areas, of which international tax planning, transfer pricing and tax controversy are especially prominent. Tax practice group leader **David Forst** (see p.636) focuses on international corporate and partnership taxation. **Ronald Schrotenboer** (see p.664) heads the M&A tax practice group and was involved in the Xilinx transfer pricing and cost-sharing litigation.

### Loeb & Loeb LLP
See profile on p.689

**THE FIRM** This team provides comprehensive advice across tax areas, including restructuring procedures and tax controversy, but it stands out particularly as one of the primary destinations for real estate management and trust-related work. Clients include high-profile individuals in the entertainment and finance world as well as international corporations. Clients and peers praise the group across the board.
**Sources say:** "*The firm is a key player in high net worth estate planning*"
**KEY INDIVIDUALS** Sources describe **Terence Cuff** (see p.630) as "*a star in the partnership tax area.*" Some of his most prominent clients include REITs, real estate investors, energy companies and financial institutions. **Leah Bishop** (see p.624) continues to impress clients, who remark: "*She comprehends complex legal issues quickly and is very pleasant to work with*" and "*she is incredibly responsive, smart, and most importantly, she is able to effectively communicate*"

## Tax
### Senior Statesmen

**Senior Statesmen: distinguished older practitioners**

| | |
|---|---|
| Hyman Milt | Irell & Manella * |
| Rabinovitz Joel | Irell & Manella * |

### Leading Individuals

**Star individuals**

| | |
|---|---|
| Fuller James P | Fenwick & West LLP * |

**Band 1**

| | |
|---|---|
| Behnia Hatef | Gibson, Dunn & Crutcher LLP * |
| Blashek Robert D | O'Melveny & Myers LLP |
| Brody Michael J | Latham & Watkins LLP |
| Chilton Frederick | McDermott Will & Emery LLP * |
| Clair John J | Latham & Watkins LLP |
| Cuff Terence | Loeb & Loeb LLP * |
| Divola Julie | Pillsbury Winthrop Shaw Pittman LLP |
| Humphreys Ivan H | Wilson Sonsini Goodrich & Rosati |
| Peterson Jr John M | Baker & McKenzie * |
| Rettig Charles P | Hochman Salkin Rettig Toscher & Perez |
| Rose Stephen | Munger, Tolles & Olson LLP * |

**Band 2**

| | |
|---|---|
| Fernhoff Michael | Proskauer Rose LLP |
| Forst David | Fenwick & West LLP * |
| Freier Elliot | Irell & Manella * |
| Iredale Nancy L | Paul Hastings LLP |
| Issler Paul | Gibson, Dunn & Crutcher LLP * |
| Kushman Moshe J | Skadden, Arps, Slate, Meagher & Flom * |
| Langdon Larry R | Mayer Brown LLP (ONP)† |
| Lipton Stuart | Arnold & Porter LLP * |
| Schaaf Douglas A | Paul Hastings LLP |
| Schrotenboer Ronald | Fenwick & West LLP * |
| Sprague Gary D | Baker & McKenzie * |
| Stein Laurence J | Latham & Watkins LLP |
| Weiner Samuel | Latham & Watkins LLP |
| Wisialowski Thomas S | Paul Hastings LLP |
| Wolf George G | Orrick, Herrington & Sutcliffe LLP (ONP)† |

**Band 3**

| | |
|---|---|
| Arash Dora | Gibson, Dunn & Crutcher LLP * |
| Bassett Barton | Morgan, Lewis & Bockius LLP * |
| Bolding Grady | Orrick, Herrington & Sutcliffe LLP (ONP)† |
| Colgin Jr William F | Morgan, Lewis & Bockius LLP * |
| Colker David | DLA Piper LLP (US) * |
| Kaplan Gary P | Sidley Austin LLP * (ONP)† |
| Kazaks Julia M | Skadden, Arps, Slate, Meagher & Flom * |
| Kim Sang | DLA Piper LLP (US) * |
| Kornblith Richard L | Fulbright & Jaworski LLP * (ONP)† |
| Lee Alexander | Paul Hastings LLP |
| Newman David | Mitchell Silberberg & Knupp LLP (ONP)† |
| Presant Sanford C | Greenberg Traurig, LLP (ONP)† * |
| Sczudlo Paul | Law Offices of Paul A Sczudlo (ONP)† |
| Zhu Jonathan | Wilson Sonsini Goodrich & Rosati |

**Up-and-coming individuals**

| | |
|---|---|
| Kleinberg Rachel D. | Davis Polk & Wardwell LLP (ONP)† * |
| Moir Katharine P. | Simpson Thacher & Bartlett LLP (ONP)† * |

*Indicates individual with profile.*

†*ONP = Other Notable Practitioner.*

## Tax: Estate Planning
### Leading Individuals

**Star individuals**

| | |
|---|---|
| Bishop Leah M | Loeb & Loeb LLP * |

**Band 1**

| | |
|---|---|
| Frimmer Paul N | Loeb & Loeb LLP * |
| Loeb Jeffrey M | Loeb & Loeb LLP * |
| Lurie Jonathan C | McDermott Will & Emery LLP * |
| Mooradian George T | Baker & Hostetler LLP (ONP)† |
| Pearson Ronald C | Loeb & Loeb LLP * |
| Streisand Adam F | Loeb & Loeb LLP * |
| Tobisman Stuart P | Loeb & Loeb LLP * |

**Up-and-coming individuals**

| | |
|---|---|
| Pelavin Alyse N | Loeb & Loeb LLP * |

## Tax: State & Local
### Leading Individuals

**Band 1**

| | |
|---|---|
| Coffill Eric J | Morrison & Foerster LLP * |
| Moll Charles J | Winston & Strawn LLP * |
| Vesely Jeffrey M | Pillsbury Winthrop Shaw Pittman LLP * |

**Band 2**

| | |
|---|---|
| Ayoob Richard | Ajalat, Polley, Ayoob & Matarese (ONP)† |
| Roberts Carley A | Sutherland Asbill & Brennan LLP (ONP)† |
| Silverstein Amy | Silverstein & Pomerantz (ONP)† |

**Up-and-coming individuals**

| | |
|---|---|
| Van Dongen Troy | Winston & Strawn LLP * |

with clients who have a nonlegal background." Her practice focuses on estate and gift tax planning for high net worth individuals, and the administration of estates and trusts. **Paul Frimmer** (see p.317) enjoys an excellent reputation in the trusts and estate area. His practice also includes post mortem tax planning, probate litigation, art law and charitable giving. **Ronald Pearson** (see p.658) is highly regarded for his tax planning strategies, and one impressed commentator said: "*He is a lawyer's lawyer, and has certainly impressed me.*" **Adam Streisand**'s (see p.668) litigation capabilities are highly praised by sources. He focuses on private wealth disputes, including litigation involving trusts, estates and conservatorships. He co-represented Michael Jackson's mother in her son's estate. **Stuart Tobisman** (see p.669) wins clients recognition for his "*ability to explain complex concepts in a simple way.*" He specializes in the administration of estates and trusts. **Alyse Pelavin** (see p.658) focuses her practice on estate and gift tax planning and has substantial experience in charitable giving and tax-exempt organizations. Sources described **Jeffrey Loeb** (see p.650) as a "*very exceptional client-handler, and a knowledgeable and pragmatic lawyer.*"

### McDermott Will & Emery LLP
See profile on p.1258

**THE FIRM** This firm's tax department covers a wide range of matters, from tax planning for local and international companies, state and local tax to controversy and litigation. However, its IP-related tax knowledge is one of the key factors attracting clients, mainly in the hi-tech sector.

Key clients include hardware and software companies, web retail companies and financial institutions.

**Sources say:** "*The ability of the attorneys at MW&E to refer to actual experience in support of their ideas sets them apart.*"

**KEY INDIVIDUALS** Sources commend **Frederick Chilton**'s (see p.628) "*ability to simplify complex matters and identify solutions based upon his experience of what works, rather than basing his solutions on theoretical concepts.*" He is highly regarded for his international tax planning knowledge and tax litigation skills. **Jonathan Lurie** (see p.651) focuses on estate planning, and clients praise his "*very broad grasp of international tax concepts.*"

### Paul Hastings LLP
See profile on p.1996

**THE FIRM** This team enjoys a healthy reputation providing advice to clients in the real estate funds, capital markets and private equity sectors regarding business restructurings, investment management, project finance and matters concerning tax-exempt entities. It also has a very active international practice, particularly oriented toward Asian countries, where the team advises on various debt and equity offerings. Highlights include the representation of Wells Fargo Capital Finance in more than 40 financing transactions, and assisting Oaktree Capital Management with issues related to real estate acquisitions.

**KEY INDIVIDUALS** **Nancy Iredale**'s practice sees her advising international and domestic clients on tax ancillary to M&A transactions as well as tax controversy. She successfully led tax litigation brought by Loyola University Health System for a refund of taxes paid on wages to medical residents. Palo Alto office chair **Thomas Wisialowski** continues to impress market sources with his real estate tax capabilities. Clients are especially pleased by his efficiency: "*I value his ability to get to the key issues in a short amount of time.*" His practice focuses on private equity and real estate funds, real estate transactions and corporate venture capital structurings. **Alexander Lee** receives excellent comments from peers, praising his intelligence. He focuses on M&A transactions and capital markets, with a special emphasis on Asian clients. Tax department head **Douglas Schaaf** is commended for his client-oriented approach and technical aptitude. His experience encompasses cross-border transactions, acquisitions, restructurings, real estate tax, tax controversy and compensation arrangements.

### Wilson Sonsini Goodrich & Rosati
See profile on p.700

**THE FIRM** This tax team provides support to the firm's thriving M&A practice, assisting with domestic and international transactions, including public and private acquisitions, corporate restructurings and joint ventures. The three-lawyer group is highly sought by technology companies of the stamp of Kodak, Google and SolarCity.

**Sources say:** "*I value their completeness, which is demonstrated by their knowledgeable stance and strong research background.*"

**KEY INDIVIDUALS** **Ivan Humphreys** enjoys a solid reputation in the tax community and specializes in the formation of partnerships and limited liability companies, acquisitions, disposals, spin-offs, restructurings and financings. Satisfied sources praise **Jonathan Zhu** as a lawyer *"able to discuss any matter with ease and immediately provide potential solutions."* His strong base of knowledge on all matters concerning international taxation also garners praise.

## Band 3

### Arnold & Porter LLP
See profile on p.906

**THE FIRM** The team's recent merger with Howard Rice has strengthened this firm's tax, trusts and estates practice. The five-strong team works on a variety of matters, ranging from domestic and international tax planning to tax controversy. Its list of clients include The Charles Schwab Corporation, University of California, The Grupe Company and The Oakland Raiders.

**KEY INDIVIDUALS Stuart Lipton** (see p.650) is very highly rated, with sources saying: *"His style is extremely analytical; he is a great teacher and has the ability to explain complicated tax concepts in an easy way."* One commentator rated him *"ten out of ten – Stuart is extremely intelligent and really easy to work with."*

### DLA Piper LLP (US)
See profile on p.1971

**THE FIRM** This formidable team provides comprehensive advice to leading local and multinational companies regarding tax planning, restructuring procedures and tax controversy. However, it is its strong transfer pricing practice and advance pricing agreement knowledge that sources are eager to highlight as distinctive strengths. Clients include Evernote, Skechers and Allergan.

**KEY INDIVIDUALS David Colker** (see p.629) earns significant recognition for his proven track record: *"David stands out on the tax litigation side as he has a huge amount of experience dealing with the IRS."* **Sang Kim** (see p.646) is increasingly noted for accumulating *"a lot of experience on the international side, and he is very good at coordinating work with international offices."*

### Hochman Salkin Rettig Toscher & Perez

**THE FIRM** This firm enjoys a solid reputation across the board for complex tax litigation, and sources are ready to point out the firm's prestige in tax fraud cases. In addition, the team offers comprehensive advice in civil and criminal tax litigation at both federal and state level, as well as handling tax controversy, white-collar criminal defense, estate and business planning, probate and tax-exempt organizations.

**Sources say:** *"This firm is a specialist in tax fraud and one of the leaders for such matters."*

**KEY INDIVIDUALS Charles Rettig** receives a raft of positive comments, including assertions that he is *"hands down, the best for litigation"* and *"a star in the controversy area."* His main activities include dealing with criminal tax controversy, general tax litigation, examinations and investigations for individuals, partnerships and corporations.

### Irell & Manella
See profile on p.686

**THE FIRM** This eight-strong team provides comprehensive advice on matters ranging from M&A, debt and equity financings, insolvency workouts and bankruptcy restructurings, to formations of startup companies and federal and state tax controversy representation. Highlights include its advisory role to BlackBerry concerning the creation and funding of the Rockstar Consortium, a joint venture with other leading technology companies (including Apple, Ericsson, Microsoft and Sony) and the subsequent purchase of a significant patent portfolio from Nortel Networks and its worldwide affiliated debtors in bankruptcy.

**KEY INDIVIDUALS Elliot Freier** (see p.637) excels on taxation for corporations, partnerships and individuals, and also handles bankruptcy and workout taxation for debtors and creditors, as well as tax ancillary to M&A transactions. **Milt Hyman** (see p.643) enjoys a solid reputation in the California tax market, especially in complex corporate tax matters. **Joel Rabinovitz** (see p.660) specializes in international tax matters, a subject he has lectured on at UCLA School of Law.

### Morgan, Lewis & Bockius LLP
See profile on p.2246

**THE FIRM** This Northern California-based tax team provides comprehensive advice on most tax matters, ranging from state tax advice to transactional and controversy matters. The 16-lawyer team is particularly sought for its international expertise and transfer pricing knowledge. The client base is testament to this, with major names from the USA, Canada, South America, Europe and Asia using the firm.

**Sources say:** *"It provides good, quality work and has a very cost-effective structure, where we get the most for our money."*

**KEY INDIVIDUALS Barton Bassett** (see p.622) focuses on international tax planning and represents clients in audits and appeals before the Internal Revenue Service. Clients say: *"He has a great overall understanding of the challenges faced by multinational companies – very conscientious."* Sources praise **William Colgin** (see p.297) for his negotiation skills. He specializes in tax controversy and litigation, representing corporate clients in complex disputes.

### Morrison & Foerster LLP
See profile on p.1990

**THE FIRM** This extensive tax team enjoys a solid reputation advising clients on state and local tax matters especially. It also provides comprehensive advice on tax ancillary to funds, real estate and infrastructure, and M&A transactions. Besides a strong local client base, the firm serves many major names, including the likes of General Mills and Toshiba.

**Sources say:** *"The team has excellent communications skills and the lawyers are able to explain highly technical issues within a nonlegal context."*

**KEY INDIVIDUALS Eric Coffill** (see p.628) receives widespread praise thanks to his litigation skills in state and local tax controversy work.

### Munger, Tolles & Olson LLP
See profile on p.691

**THE FIRM** This compact tax team has a solid reputation, particularly in the taxation aspects of complex transactions, including M&A, joint ventures, real estate transactions, venture capital and private equity, restructurings and issues of financial instruments. Highlights include the representation of HealthCare Partners in its acquisition by DaVita for $4.42 billion.

**KEY INDIVIDUALS Stephen Rose** (see p.662) is commended for his in-depth finance and tax structuring knowledge.

### O'Melveny & Myers LLP
See profile on p.693

**THE FIRM** This sizable team covers a vast range of matters, from M&A operations and fund-raising in new markets to restructuring. It is particularly active in the entertainment, sports, media, private equity and hi-tech industries. Clients include Oaktree Capital Management, Coller Capital, Colony Capital and San Diego Padres.

**KEY INDIVIDUALS Robert Blashek** is described as *"a real deal-maker when it comes to tax matters."*

### Pillsbury Winthrop Shaw Pittman LLP
See profile on p.2000

**THE FIRM** This tax team provides comprehensive tax advice in a plethora of contexts, including corporate and business transactions, estates, trusts and tax planning, executive compensation and benefits, tax controversy and litigation, international tax, state and local tax and tax-exempt organizations. Clients especially endorse the team's expertise in real estate tax matters.

**Sources say:** *"Pillsbury is the best for real estate tax litigation because it has the resources and a deep bench."*

**KEY INDIVIDUALS Julie Divola** receives widespread recognition from the market, and sources describe her as *"a nationally known practitioner."* She focuses on corporate taxation with particular emphasis on domestic and international M&A, restructurings, joint ventures and private equity investments. **Jeffrey Vesely** (see p.670) is highly regarded for his state and local practice, particularly for his litigation skills, with satisfied clients calling him *"an excellent and smart litigator."*

### Proskauer Rose LLP
See profile on p.2001

**THE FIRM** This sizable tax team enters the rankings based on strong feedback. The 49-strong group provides a wide range of tax-related advice in M&A, restructurings, cross-border transactions and tax controversy. Clients comment that the team particularly shines in the area of estate planning. Recent highlights include assisting Neuberger Berman with its MBO of the equity Lehman Brothers had in the company.

Sources say: "*Terrific lawyers. They stay on top of the latest changes and their intellectual capital is beyond compare.*" **KEY INDIVIDUALS Michael Fernhoff** continues to impress clients and peers alike, with commentators asserting: "*He has every answer at the tip of his tongue*" and "*he is an extremely smart and constructive tax lawyer.*" He has a great deal of experience in real estate transactions, including M&A, partnerships, joint ventures and tax-related restructurings.

## Skadden, Arps, Slate, Meagher & Flom LLP & Affiliates
See profile on p.2008

**THE FIRM** This California-based tax department focuses on transactional work, including high-end M&A, international tax planning and transfer pricing as well as tax controversy and other work before the IRS. Highlights include advising Hitachi Global Storage Technologies on the tax aspects of its $4.8 billion acquisition by Western Digital.
**Sources say:** "*Their main strengths are high-quality technical analysis, solid opinions and a broad partner network to cross-check difficult technical issues.*"
**KEY INDIVIDUALS Moshe Kushman** (see p.648) is the recipient of increasingly impressive feedback, with some sources describing him as a "*top lawyer.*" He focuses on domestic and international M&A, tax-free spin-offs, restructurings and workouts and international tax planning. He advised Hitachi Global Storage Technologies on the Western Digital transaction. The highly rated **Julia Kazaks** (see p.645) recently relocated to the firm's Palo Alto office from Washington, DC. Sources relate that "*she is thoroughly prepared and has a good strategic sense.*"

## Winston & Strawn LLP
See profile on p.1267

**THE FIRM** This California-based tax team enjoys a healthy practice in state and local issues, which comprise one of the core areas of this practice. Its client base includes local and international names in the pharmaceutical, technology and beverage industries, including the likes of Genentech and Canandaigua Wine.
**KEY INDIVIDUALS Charles Moll**'s (see p.655) most notable area of focus is state and local tax controversy. Clients describe him as a "*responsive, incredibly knowledgeable and confident*" lawyer. **Troy Van Dongen** (see p.670) receives praise for his "*great communication skills.*" He specializes in property taxation.

## Other Notable Practitioners

**Larry Langdon** of Mayer Brown LLP receives widespread recognition thanks to his longstanding career and previous experience as US Internal Revenue Service Commissioner. **George Mooradian** (see p.655) of Baker Hostetler receives widespread recognition from clients, who describe him as "*attentive, direct and pragmatic.*" **Richard Ayoob** of Ajalat, Polley, Ayoob & Matarese wins market praise for his state and local tax work. He focuses on real estate, sales, business and employment taxes. **Carley Roberts** of Sutherland Asbill & Brennan LLP focuses on tax planning and tax controversy. She continues to impress market sources with her expertise in the field. **Amy Silverstein** of Silverstein & Pomerantz specializes in state and local tax controversy but also advises multinational companies on tax planning and transactional work. Impressed peers describe her as "*an excellent lawyer.*" **Gary Kaplan** (see p.645) of Sidley Austin

LLP earns much client praise, and in the words of one source he is "*one of the best tax attorneys I have ever worked with.*" He focuses on international taxation, business transactions, cross-border taxation, M&A and joint ventures. **Richard Kornblith** (see p.647) of Fulbright & Jaworski LLP enjoys a solid reputation, especially for tax controversy and the public law aspects of municipal finance. **David Newman** of Mitchell Silberberg & Knupp LLP is very active in the charitable sector, advising clients on their tax exemption and charitable gift planning programs. He also represents individuals and families on estate planning and tax planning matters. **Sanford Presant** (see p.660) of Greenberg Traurig, LLP chairs his firm's real estate funds practice group and specializes in tax structuring advice for real estate private equity funds and REITs on local and international matters. **Paul Sczudlo** of Law Offices of Paul A Sczudlo operates from Los Angeles, and has more than 30 years' experience in international tax planning, compliance and wealth transfer planning, as well as entertainment taxation. Sources are keen to praise **Rachel Kleinberg** (see p.647) of Davis Polk & Wardwell LLP, calling her "*just brilliant and always fully updated.*" **Katharine Moir** (see p.655) of Simpson Thacher & Bartlett LLP heads the Palo Alto office's tax practice and is described as a "*very thorough, diligent and responsive attorney.*" **George Wolf** of Orrick, Herrington & Sutcliffe LLP is described as "*a leader in his field, very responsive and thoughtful.*" His areas of expertise include tax-exempt bonds, real estate-financing transactions and federal and state tax planning. **Grady Bolding** of Orrick, Herrington & Sutcliffe LLP spends his time in corporate and real estate transactions, including real estate funds, venture capital and hedge funds.

# Leaders' Profiles in California

## ABEL, Sally
Fenwick & West LLP, Mountain View
650 335 7212
sabel@fenwick.com
*Featured in Intellectual Property (California)*
**Practice Areas:** Sally M Abel is Chair of the Trademark Group at Fenwick & West LLP. Her practice focuses on international trademark and trade name counseling, including the development and management of international trademark portfolios and trademark rights on-line.
**Career:** Ms Abel has repeatedly won international, national, state and Silicon Valley accolades as a preeminent trademark lawyer and was most recently named as an honoree for the Chambers USA Women in Law Awards as one of the top 12 women IP lawyers in the US (2012). She was also named to the International Who's Who Legal Trademarks 2010 "Most Highly Regarded Individual", an honor reserved to 15 trademark lawyers, only three of whom are from the United States. For the past three years, Ms Abel has been recognized by The Best Lawyers in America in the area of intellectual property and trademark law.
**Publications:** Sally Abel writes and lectures internationally on trademarks and the Internet and teaches international trademark law and practice at Boalt Hall School of Law (UC Berkeley).

## ABRAMS, William F
King & Spalding LLP, Redwood Shores
650 590 0703
babrams@kslaw.com
*Featured in Intellectual Property (California)*
**Practice Areas:** Specific areas of recent experience include patent infringement, trade secrets and misappropriation, unfair competition and antitrust, technology transfer and licensing, trademarks and advertising, copyright, Internet and media, startup company formation and governance, non-compete and non-disclosure disputes, and First Amendment and defamation.
**Career:** Lectures on children's legal issues and the death penalty at Stanford University.
**Personal:** Santa Clara University School of Law, JD, 1979; Stanford University, BA, 1976.

## ADAS, Craig
Weil, Gotshal & Manges LLP, Silicon Valley
650 802 3020
craig.adas@weil.com
*Featured in Corporate/M&A (Northern California)*
**Practice Areas:** Craig Adas is Managing Partner of Weil's Silicon Valley office. He has over 20 years of experience representing some of the world's most prolific companies and private equity funds in sophisticated transactions, with particular emphasis on leveraged buyouts, private and public acquisitions and dispositions, tender offers, going private transactions, joint ventures and securities offerings. He also regularly serves as counsel to boards of directors and special committees on corporate governance and other strategic matters.

**Personal:** Southern Methodist University (BA, 1987); Northwestern University School of Law (JD, 1991); admitted to practice in California and Texas.

## ALLCOCK, John
DLA Piper LLP (US), San Diego
619 699 2828
john.allcock@dlapiper.com
*Featured in Intellectual Property (California)*
**Practice Areas:** Intellectual property, patent litigation, life sciences.
**Career:** His practice focuses on patent litigation. He has handled patent cases through trial and appeal to the Federal Circuit, and has tried over 30 patent cases. He was lead counsel in excess of 100 arbitrations, and has extensive experience in court trials, International Trade Commission hearings, alternate dispute resolution, and management of complex litigation.
**Personal:** JD, Harvard Law School (cum laude); AB, Boston College (summa cum laude).

## ALLDERDICE, Linda
Holland & Knight LLP, Los Angeles
213 896 2400
linda.allderdice@hklaw.com
*Featured in Labor & Employment (California)*
**Practice Areas:** Linda Auerbach Allderdice leads the firm's Labor, Employment and Benefits group in California and resides in the Los Angeles office. Ms Allderdice represents clients in complex litigation in all aspects of labor and employment law including class actions and appellate court proceedings, advises clients on compliance with state and federal labor and employment laws, and represents companies in proceedings before the NLRB. Her clients are from a wide range of industries, including transportation, hospitality, real estate, manufacturing, electronics and technology, entertainment, healthcare and retail. Ms Allderdice also represents clients in alternative dispute proceedings, including mediation and arbitration.

## AMANTEA, Chris M
Squire Sanders (US) LLP, Los Angeles
213 689 5131
chris.amantea@squiresanders.com
*Featured in Environment (California)*
**Practice Areas:** Partner in the Environmental Practice Group. Focuses on regulatory and judicial proceedings involving toxic substance, air and water quality, land use, climate change, California's Proposition 65, and other environmental matters. Represents clients in complex environmental litigation matters including class action and toxic tort litigation. Trial experience in State and Federal courts, including an en banc argument before the Ninth Circuit Court of Appeals.
**Professional Memberships:** American Bar Association (sections on Litigation and Natural Resources and Environmental Law), Los Angeles County Bar Association, Illinois State bar associa-

tion. Board of Directors of the Legal Aid Foundation of Los Angeles.
**Career:** Admitted to the State Bar of California; the State Bar of Illinois; and Bar of the United States Supreme Court.
**Personal:** Chicago-Kent College of Law (JD)(Order of the Coif), University of California-Davis (BS).

## ANDES, Pamela
Allen Matkins Leck Gamble Mallory & Natsis LLP, Irvine
949 851 5405
pandes@allenmatkins.com
*Featured in Environment (California)*
**Practice Areas:** Pamela Andes has worked on a wide range of complex environmental and real estate projects. Pam's broad-based real estate experience coupled with her specialized focus on environmental law makes her uniquely qualified to work on challenging, environmentally impacted projects from the initial acquisition due diligence and contract negotiation, through insuring, financing and leasing these sites, redeveloping them and ultimately selling them as income investments. Pam has 23 years of experience working with environmental agencies and guiding the work of environmental consultants, litigation experts and public relations consultants on sites challenged with soil, soil vapor and groundwater contamination.

## APRIL, Rand S
Skadden, Arps, Slate, Meagher & Flom LLP & Affiliates, Los Angeles
213 687 5060
rand.april@skadden.com
*Featured in Real Estate (California)*
**Practice Areas:** A real estate partner, his practice includes acquisitions and sales, financings, restructurings, development work, leasing and joint ventures. He regularly advises both US and international clients, including REIT's, private equity funds and institutional investors, in transactions involving a wide variety of asset classes (with particular emphasis on hotels, office and retail). Recent representations include the workout of major office and hotel loans and the sale of interests in a portfolio of significant office properties.
**Career:** JD, Columbia University, 1975 (Harlan Fiske Stone Scholar); BA, Northwestern University, 1972 (Phi Beta Kappa).

## ARASH, Dora
Gibson, Dunn & Crutcher LLP, Los Angeles
213 229 7134
darash@gibsondunn.com
*Featured in Tax (California)*
**Practice Areas:** Ms Arash is a partner in the Los Angeles office of Gibson, Dunn & Crutcher. She has advised clients on the tax consequences of taxable stock and asset acquisitions, tax-free reorganizations, public and private offerings of stock and debt, spin-offs, and joint ventures. She has

also represented clients in a variety of tax controversy matters.
**Career:** Before joining Gibson Dunn, Ms Arash served as attorney-advisor to the Honorable Carolyn Chiechi of the U.S. Tax Court.
**Personal:** Ms Arash received an LLM in Taxation from New York University and received a JD, magna cum laude, from Pepperdine University.

## ARMSTRONG, Dwight L
Allen Matkins Leck Gamble Mallory & Natsis LLP, Irvine
949 851 5424
darmstrong@allenmatkins.com
*Featured in Labor & Employment (California)*
**Practice Areas:** Dwight represents employers and management in matters ranging from wrongful termination and employment discrimination litigation and arbitrations to preventative counseling and advice. His litigation experience includes single-plaintiff cases, complex wage/hour class actions and trade secret matters. He has first chaired cases at both trial (jury and court) and appellate levels in state and federal courts.
**Professional Memberships:** Appointed as neutral arbitrator on Employment Law Panel of American Arbitration Association.
**Career:** Chair of firm's Labor & Employment Law Department.
**Publications:** Has taught classes at the graduate level, including as guest lecturer at USC Law School and UC Irvine.

## ARNOLD, Dennis
Gibson, Dunn & Crutcher LLP, Los Angeles
213 229 7864
darnold@gibsondunn.com
*Featured in Real Estate (California)*
**Practice Areas:** Workouts, debt restructuring/bankruptcy, "front-end" transactional real estate (loans/JV's/acquisitions), foreclosures, mezzanine debt remedies and CMBS loans. Recognized expert in real estate finance, commercial law (Articles 3, 5 & 9/guaranty-suretyship) and California's "one action" and "anti-deficiency" laws.
**Professional Memberships:** American College of Real Estate Lawyers; American College of Commercial Finance Attorneys; American Law Institute; American Bankruptcy Institute.
**Career:** Drafted California Civil Code Section 2856. Advisor, Restatement of Suretyship & Guaranty. Co-drafter California Civil Code Section 2938.
**Personal:** JD, Yale Law School, 1975. Outstanding Real Estate Lawyer 2009-LA County Bar Association; 2010 Los Angeles Real Estate Lawyer of the Year-Best Lawyers.

## ARONZON, Paul S
Milbank, Tweed, Hadley & McCloy LLP, Los Angeles
213 892 4377
paronzon@milbank.com
*Featured in Bankruptcy/Restructuring (California), Bankruptcy/Restructuring (Nationwide)*

**Practice Areas:** Mr Aronzon is a partner and Co-Practice Group Leader of the Financial Restructuring Group. With over 30 years' experience in corporate reorganizations and restructurings, Mr Aronzon is nationally recognized as one of the preeminent attorneys in his field. He has represented debtors, equity holders, creditors, and official and ad hoc committees in many complex reorganization cases and out-of-court workouts, including exchange and tender offers, rights offerings, prepackaged and prearranged reorganizations, as well as acquirors of financially distressed companies or their assets. Mr Aronzon's engagements span a number of industries including, most recently, gaming, energy, broadcasting and financial services.

### ASHCRAFT, Howard W
Hanson Bridgett LLP, San Francisco
415 995 5073
hashcraft@hansonbridgett.com
*Featured in Construction (California)*
**Practice Areas:** Structuring complex construction projects, including Integrated Project Delivery and its variants, Design/Build, P3, Lean Project Delivery and Building Information enabled projects. Project facilitation and consultation regarding project organization and structure. Construction contracting for all project delivery types. Litigating delay and impact cases and significant construction defect matters. Expertise in electronic discovery and management of large scale litigation actions. Fellow of the American College of Construction Lawyers, the American Bar Foundation, Task Group Chair for the National Building Information Modeling Standard, and a prolific author and speaker on project delivery, construction and technology topics.

### ASHE, Brian T
Seyfarth Shaw LLP, San Francisco
415 544 1029
bashe@seyfarth.com
*Featured in Labor & Employment (California)*
**Practice Areas:** Labor and employment.
**Career:** Mr Ashe's practice includes complex employment litigation, employment class actions and counseling. He represents employers in unfair competition litigation, wage and hour matters, trade secret cases, discrimination and wrongful termination actions. He provides creative solutions to various aspects of human resources management, including employee privacy, discipline and termination decisions, employment policies and handbooks, harassment prevention and disability matters.
**Publications:** Mr Ashe speaks widely to management groups, writes frequently on employment matters and is often quoted in newspapers and periodicals.
**Personal:** JD, George Washington University; BA, Boston College.

### AVERCH, Craig H
White & Case LLP, Los Angeles
213 620 7704
caverch@whitecase.com
*Featured in Bankruptcy/Restructuring (California)*

**Career:** Craig Averch leads the Financial Restructuring and Insolvency Practice's Los Angeles-based team. His experience includes workouts and restructurings of problem loans and investments, as well as insolvencies, throughout the United States and Central and Eastern Europe. He counsels clients in a wide range of industries, including transportation, real estate, retail, textile, oil and gas, energy, banking and financial services, healthcare, manufacturing, high-tech and telecommunications. Mr Averch regularly represents bondholders, bank groups, strategic and financial investors, miscellaneous creditor constituencies, sovereigns, and debtors in connection with bankruptcy and restructuring matters. To view a comprehensive biography, please visit www.whitecase.com/caverch.

### AXELRAD, David M
Horvitz & Levy LLP, Encino
818 995 0800
daxelrad@horvitzlevy.com
*Featured in Litigation (California), Appellate Law (Nationwide)*
**Practice Areas:** Civil appellate litigation in a wide range of substantive areas, including toxic torts, products liability, premises liability, insurance bad faith and personal injury.
**Professional Memberships:** Member, California Academy of Appellate Lawyers, American Academy of Appellate Lawyers.
**Career:** California State Bar Certified Appellate Specialist; California Lawyer Attorney of the Year (CLAY) Award (2011).
**Publications:** Editor, Appellate Practice in Federal and State Courts (Law Journal Press 2011); Editor, Chapter 6 (Staying Enforcement During Appeal) California Civil Appellate Practice 3d Edition (CEB 2011).

### AXELRAD, Jonathan
Goodwin Procter LLP, Menlo Park
650 752 3111
jaxelrad@goodwinprocter.com
*Featured in Investment Funds (Nationwide), Corporate/M&A (California)*
See under Nationwide for profile.

### BAKER, James P
Baker & McKenzie, San Francisco
415 591 3232
james.baker@bakermckenzie.com
*Featured in Employee Benefits & Executive Compensation (California)*
**Practice Areas:** Recognized by The National Law Journal, Legal 500, Best Lawyers and Chambers USA as a Leading Lawyer nationally for ERISA litigation. He has successfully obtained dismissals with prejudice in numerous published ERISA class action cases including Spivey v. Southern Company (billion dollar stock drop case) Chapman v. ACF Industries (defeated claim for unchangeable retiree medical coverage); and Strunk v. State of Oregon Public Employees Retirement Board (upheld $9 billion in statutory reforms).
**Professional Memberships:** Fellow of the American College of Employee Benefits Counsel,

Chair of the ERISA Litigation Subcommitee, ABA Business and Corporate Litigation Section.

### BAKER, Michael J
Atkinson, Andelson, Loya, Ruud & Romo, Irvine
949 453 4260
mbaker@aalrr.com
*Featured in Construction (California)*
**Practice Areas:** Michael Baker is defined by his experience in representing public and private owners, design professionals and contractors in business and contractual matters, mediations, arbitrations, and matters before state and federal courts, involving construction projects collectively valued to date in excess of $25 billion. His expertise includes contract performance disputes, construction claims, professional liability, surety bond claims, and the full range of insurance issues involving public and private construction projects, engineering systems and specialized facilities.
**Professional Memberships:** 2012 President of the Southern California Chapter of CMAA. Mr Baker is a member of the State Bar of California, and admitted to practice before the Supreme Court of the United States.
**Publications:** Over 200 articles published locally, nationally and internationally, and numerous lectures related to design and construction law. List of published articles and lectures available upon request.
**Personal:** Completed his bachelor's degree in Business Economics from DePaul University and received his Juris Doctor degree from the Pepperdine University School of Law.

### BAKER, Tyler A
Fenwick & West LLP, Mountain View
650 335 7624
tbaker@fenwick.com
*Featured in Antitrust (California)*
**Practice Areas:** Tyler A. Baker, a partner in the Litigation Group of Fenwick & West, co-chairs the firm's Antitrust and Unfair Competition Group and chairs the Appellate Group. His practice focuses on complex litigation, with an emphasis on antitrust and IP law. He represents plaintiffs and defendants in civil antitrust trials and individuals and companies in state and federal antitrust investigations. He also has significant experience in IP cases.
**Career:** Mr Baker has been involved in several major antitrust developments. He was the law clerk who worked with Justice Powell on the landmark GTE Sylvania case reversing the per se rule against vertical non-price agreements. He was the principal draftsman of the 1982 Merger Guidelines issued by the Department of Justice which have influenced merger analysis for almost 30 years. He represented Leegin Creative Leather Products in the case that led to the 2007 Supreme Court reversal of the long-standing per se rule against vertical price agreements. Mr Baker is recognized as a leading US antitrust lawyer in numerous surveys including: The International Who's Who of Competition Lawyers and Economists, Euromoney Legal Media Group's Guide to the World's Leading Competition and

Antitrust Lawyers and Chambers USA's America's Leading Lawyers for Business.

### BALABANIAN, David M
Bingham McCutchen LLP, San Francisco
415 393 2170
david.balabanian@bingham.com
*Featured in Litigation (California)*
**Practice Areas:** Former co-chair of Bingham's Securities and Financial Institutions Litigation Group. More than 40 years of experience handling complex, high-stakes commercial litigation, including antitrust and securities cases and takeover litigation.
**Career:** Past president of the Bar Association of San Francisco. Teaches continuing legal education courses and writes extensively on many topics, particularly the management of large, complex cases. Former member of the commission that authored the California Judicial Council's 'Deskbook on the Management of Complex Civil Litigation.'
**Personal:** Harvard Law School, LLB, cum laude, 1965; University of Oxford, Bachelor of Philosophy, 1962; Harvard University, BA, magna cum laude, 1960.

### BALLACK, Karen N
Weil, Gotshal & Manges LLP, Silicon Valley
650 802 3120
karen.ballack@weil.com
*Featured in IT & Outsourcing (California)*
**Practice Areas:** Karen N Ballack, a partner in Weil's Silicon Valley office, has extensive experience in technology and intellectual property alliances and transactions. She works with a range of technology companies, particularly in the semiconductor, computer, internet, biotechnology, medical device and pharmaceutical industries. She is regularly engaged to work on complex and sophisticated technology and intellectual property transactions. Representative matters include licensing, R&D collaborations, strategic alliances, joint ventures, intellectual property acquisitions and divestitures, cloud computing arrangements, outsourcing transactions, and manufacture, supply and distribution arrangements.
**Personal:** San Diego State University (BS, summa cum laude, 1981); University of San Francisco (JD, 1986).

### BALLON, Ian C
Greenberg Traurig, LLP, Santa Monica
310 586 6575
Ballon@gtlaw.com
*Featured in IT & Outsourcing (California), Privacy & Data Security (Nationwide)*
**Practice Areas:** Complex Internet and IP litigation, including the defense of data privacy class action suits; privacy and security counseling. Admitted California, Washington, DC, Maryland, US Supreme Court.
**Career:** Recognized as one of the Top 75 IP Litigators and Top 100 lawyers in California by the Daily Journal; 2010 Vanguard Award winner, California State Bar IP section; IAM 250 - The World's Leading IP Strategists, 2009-10. Listed, 'Best Lawyers in America', 2006-13; Variety, 'Legal Impact Report: 50 Game-Changing Attorneys',

2012. Executive Director, Stanford Law School's Center for e-Commerce. Recent court victories: Oracle America Corp. v. Google, Inc., 872 F. Supp. 2d 974 (N.D. Cal. 2012) (copyrightability of software APIs); Ibey v. Taco Bell Corp., 2012 WL 2401972 (S.D. Cal. 2012) (inapplicability of TCPA to text marketing campaign); Inman v. Technicolor USA, Inc., 2011 WL 5829024 (W.D. Pa. 2011) (successful defense of eBay based on federal preemption).

**Publications:** Author, E-Commerce and Internet Law: Treatise With Forms, 2d Edition (volumes, 4-Thomson West, updated annually, www.IanBallon.net); The Complete State Security Breach Notification Compliance Handbook (Thomson West); The Complete CAN-SPAM Act Handbook (Thomson West).

**Personal:** LLM, Georgetown University Law Center; JD, with honors, The George Washington University Law School, 1986; BA, magna cum laude, Tufts University, 1983; CIPP-certified by the International Association of Privacy Professionals.

## BANK, Jonathan
Locke Lord LLP, Los Angeles
213 687 6700
jbank@lockelord.com
*Featured in Insurance (California)*

**Practice Areas:** In his 40+ years of corporate and private practice, has been involved in all phases of reinsurance litigation/arbitration and regulatory transactions, from formation to liquidation. Has spoken at numerous industry conferences and seminars.

**Professional Memberships:** ABA; CA/NY State Bar Associations; AIRROC; ARIAS; IAIR; SOFE; PXRE Reinsurance Company (BOD); Lincoln General Insurance Co. (BOD).

**Career:** Of Counsel at Locke Lord since 2004. Previously, he was the insurance practice leader of PricewaterhouseCoopers' US insurance/reinsurance regulatory/restructuring practice, and then a founding partner of Tawa.

**Personal:** Creighton University School of Law (JD, 1968); University of Oklahoma (BBA, 1965).

## BARNES JR, Dale E
Bingham McCutchen LLP, San Francisco
415 393 2522
dale.barnes@bingham.com
*Featured in Litigation (California)*

**Practice Areas:** Practices securities enforcement and litigation defense, merger and acquisition litigation, corporate governance, class actions, and other complex business litigation. Experience with financial and tax accounting and disclosure issues. Represents clients in federal and state courts and before the SEC, PCAOB and other regulatory agencies. Also has experience assisting clients with investigations and risk management issues.

**Career:** Member of AIG Securities Litigation Panel.

**Personal:** University of Pennsylvania Law School, JD, magna cum laude, 1979; University of Pennsylvania, MBA, with distinction, 1978; Harvard College, BA, 1975.

## BARONSKY, Kenneth
Milbank, Tweed, Hadley & McCloy LLP, Los Angeles
213 892 4333
kbaronsky@milbank.com
*Featured in Corporate/M&A (California), Corporate/M&A (Southern California)*

**Practice Areas:** Mr Baronsky is managing partner and head of the firm's Corporate Group in Los Angeles. He specializes in corporate and securities law with a strong focus on the gaming industry. He represents public and privately-held companies, investment banks, hedge funds and private equity funds in public offerings, private financings, mergers and acquisitions, buyouts, and other complex transactions. Mr Baronsky has extensive experience handling distressed situations, including out-of-court financial restructurings and the corporate aspects of bankruptcies.

## BARR, Michael R
Pillsbury Winthrop Shaw Pittman LLP, San Francisco
415 983 1151
michael.barr@pillsburylaw.com
*Featured in Environment (California)*

**Practice Areas:** Mr Barr is a leader of Pillsbury's Environment, Land Use and Natural Resources Practice Section, a leader of the firm's Energy Team and a Member of the Corporate and Real Estate Sections. He practices in administrative, commercial and corporate law and has extensive experience assisting established and emerging ventures in the transportation, communications, computer, chemical, food products, healthcare, energy, mining and manufacturing industries. Barr focuses on emerging issues and innovative solutions to complex regulatory, commercial and corporate matters.

**Professional Memberships:** ABA SEER.

**Career:** Admitted: California.

**Personal:** JD, Harvard University, 1973; BS, University of Washington at Seattle, 1970.

## BARRON, Anthony
Nixon Peabody LLP, San Francisco
415 984 8309
abarron@nixonpeabody.com
*Featured in Construction (California), Litigation (California)*

**Practice Areas:** Extensive experience in construction, real estate, banking and other complex commercial litigation.

**Career:** Tony is the Deputy Practice Group Leader of Nixon Peabody's Commercial Litigation practice group. He has tried cases in state and federal courts and handled domestic and international arbitrations. He advises on all kinds of construction projects, including residential, commercial, educational, manufacturing, and power generation, both public and private, and both domestically and internationally. His work on such projects ranges from contract negotiations to project counseling and dispute resolution.

**Personal:** UCLA School of Law, JD; Williams College, BA, cum laude.

## BARSHOP, Melissa
Gibson, Dunn & Crutcher LLP, Los Angeles
310 552 8615
mbarshop@gibsondunn.com
*Featured in Banking & Finance (California)*

**Practice Areas:** Corporate finance, including acquisition financings, secured and unsecured corporate credit facilities, Rule 144A transactions, private placements, convertible debt offerings, exchange offers, mezzanine transactions and work-outs and debt restructurings.

**Personal:** JD, Columbia Law School, 2006, Harlan Fiske Stone Scholar. BA, University of California – Berkeley, 2002, Phi Beta Kappa.

## BARSKY, Wayne
Gibson, Dunn & Crutcher LLP, Los Angeles
310 557 8183
wbarsky@gibsondunn.com
*Featured in Intellectual Property (California)*

**Practice Areas:** Co-Chair of the Intellectual Property Practice Group. Practices exclusively in patent litigation area for clients in the biotech, pharmaceutical, internet, computer, software, and medical device industries. Representative clients include Medtronic, Merck-Serono, Novo-Nordisk, Electronic Arts, Turner, Pfizer, and Zynga.

**Professional Memberships:** American Intellectual Property Law Association, Inns of Court, Federal Circuit Bar Association, American Bar Association. Chairperson/Board of Directors, Public Counsel Law Center; Executive Committee, USC Intellectual Property Institute.

**Publications:** Numerous publications and speaking engagements; frequent participant in Practising Law Institute programs on intellectual property and patent trial practice.

**Personal:** BA, SUNY-Binghamton (1979); JD, University of California, Berkeley (1983).

## BASSETT, Barton
Morgan, Lewis & Bockius LLP, Palo Alto
650 843 7576
bbassett@morganlewis.com
*Featured in Tax (California)*

**Practice Areas:** Barton W. S. Bassett is a partner and chair of the firm's Tax Practice. His practice focuses on the tax aspects of international transactions and tax controversy matters. This includes advising corporate taxpayers on structuring mergers and acquisitions, internal restructurings and operations, joint ventures, and external/internal financings. He has a wide range of experience, both at the planning and controversy stages, with respect to transfer pricing issues, subpart F, tax-related aspects of manufacturing supply chains, R&D credit, §199, and tax issues relating to intangible property.

## BAUER, Steven M
Latham & Watkins LLP, San Francisco
415 395 8083
steven.bauer@lw.com
*Featured in Litigation (California)*

**Practice Areas:** Steven Bauer is the Global Co-chair of Latham & Watkins' White Collar Defense and Investigations Practice Group. He has tried nearly 40 cases to verdict and successfully represented dozens of companies and executives in

government investigations in every major area of government regulation in 20 years of private practice.

**Career:** Assistant US Attorney, Los Angeles (1989-1993); Special Prosecutor, Office of Independent Counsel (1996).

**Personal:** Stanford University Law School, 1986, Associate Editor, Stanford Law Review; BA, Duke University, 1983, summa cum laude.

## BAUTISTA, John
Orrick, Herrington & Sutcliffe LLP, Menlo Park
650 614 7652
jbautista@orrick.com
*Featured in Corporate/M&A (California)*

**Career:** Mr Bautista, a partner in the Silicon Valley office, leads Orrick's Emerging Companies Group. Before joining Orrick, he was a co-founder of Venture Law Group and served on the Executive Committee. Mr Bautista focuses on emerging and later-stage companies in many areas, including corporate and securities law, venture capital financings, mergers and acquisitions, public offerings, public company representation, and technology licensing. Clients include: Codecademy, ClariPhy Communications, Crowdtilt, elasticsearch Global BV, Datasift, Heroku (sold to SalesForce), IronPlanet, MemSQL, Meteor, MongoHQ, Optimizely, PagerDuty, RapGenius, Sequans Communications (NYSE: SQNS), Stripe, and ZenPayroll.

## BAYLESS, David
Covington & Burling LLP, San Francisco
415 591 7005
dbayless@cov.com
*Featured in Litigation (California)*

**Practice Areas:** David Bayless is a partner in Covington's San Francisco office. He focuses on SEC enforcement work, internal investigations, and private securities class actions. He has extensive experience involving financial and accounting fraud allegations, FCPA, mortgage-backed securities and insider trading. He represents broker-dealers and investment advisers in SEC and FINRA investigations. Finally, he represents issuers, underwriters and public officials in SEC municipal securities investigations. Mr Bayless is an experienced trial lawyer, having litigated to verdict cases in federal, state and SEC administrative forums.

**Career:** Head of the SEC's San Francisco office.

**Personal:** University of Chicago, JD; Cambridge University, PhD.

## BAYSINGER, Kara
SNR Denton, San Francisco
415 882 2475
kara.baysinger@dentons.com
*Featured in Insurance (California)*

**Practice Areas:** Head of legacy SNR Denton's Global Insurance Sector and Insurance Regulatory Practice. Represents insurers and reinsurers, and insurance-related service companies on compliance, single-state and multi-state market conduct examinations and investigations, government/regulatory relations, privacy, security, e-business, licensing and approvals, transactions, acquisitions, administrative litigation, reinsurance and product development.

**Career:** Joined Dentons in 1998. Managed insurance company compliance, government relations and legal affairs 1988-1997.

**Publications:** Co-author, Courageous Counsel: Conversations with Women General Counsel in the Fortune 500, 2011 Co-author, The Sonnenschein Guide to Insurance Market Regulation, 2008 Co-author, eBusiness and Insurance CCH Publishing, 2001.

**Personal:** Loyola University, JD; University of Michigan, BA; Northwestern University, Women Director's Program.

## BECK, Mark
Orrick, Herrington & Sutcliffe LLP, Los Angeles
213 612 2339
mbeck@orrick.com
*Featured in Litigation (California)*

**Career:** Mark Beck, Chair of Orrick's White Collar Criminal Defense and Corporate Investigations practice, defends corporations and individuals in complex civil, criminal and regulatory matters in the U.S. and abroad. He has extensive experience conducting corporate internal investigations and advising company counsel on governance, compliance and crime prevention matters. He regularly handles matters such as securities and healthcare fraud, corruption, antitrust and FCPA violations. Nationally recognized as a trial lawyer, he was invited to join the American College of Trial Lawyers in 2004. Prior to entering private practice, he was an Assistant Chief in the U.S. Attorney's office, Los Angeles.

## BEHNIA, Hatef
Gibson, Dunn & Crutcher LLP, Los Angeles
213 229 7534
hbehnia@gibsondunn.com
*Featured in Tax (California)*

**Practice Areas:** Specializes in tax aspects of mergers and acquisitions, leveraged buy-outs, spin-offs, debt and equity financings, derivative securities, and partnership transactions. Has successfully represented taxpayers before the Internal Revenue Service in cases involving significant audit adjustments.

**Personal:** JD, University of Southern California, 1981, Order of the Coif, Note and Article Editor, University of Southern California Law Review. MBA, Stanford University graduate School of Business, 1977. BA in mathematics, Reed College, 1975.

## BELLAH MAGUIRE, Jennifer
Gibson, Dunn & Crutcher LLP, Los Angeles
213 229 7986
jbellah@gibsondunn.com
*Featured in Private Equity (Nationwide),*
*Corporate/M&A (California), Corporate/M&A*
*(Southern California)*

**Practice Areas:** Ms Bellah Maguire is co-chair of the firm's Investment Fund Group. Her practice includes general representation for buyout, real estate, clean tech and other funds and investors, and mergers and acquisitions, including public

company transactions and private equity fund formation.

**Career:** Clerked for the 9th Circuit Court of Appeals and has practiced in Gibson Dunn's Los Angeles offices and Paris office.

**Personal:** JD, University of California – Berkeley, 1982, Order of the Coif, BA Bryn Mawr College, Watson Fellow. Ms Bellah Maguire serves on the Boards of Los Angeles Ballet and Otis College of Art and Design.

## BENJAMIN, Alan
Orrick, Herrington & Sutcliffe LLP, Los Angeles
213 612 2431
abenjamin@orrick.com
*Featured in Banking & Finance (California)*

**Career:** Alan Benjamin is a partner in Orrick's Los Angeles office and the co-head of the firm's Banking and Debt Capital Markets Group. Mr Benjamin has been practicing law for more than 30 years. Mr Benjamin concentrates his practice on complex financial transactions and restructurings, including secured and unsecured loan transactions, project financings, leveraged buy-outs and insolvency matters. He has particular experience in lending to the gaming industry, including lending to Native American tribes.

## BENNETT, Bruce S
Jones Day, Los Angeles
213 243 2382
bbennett@jonesday.com
*Featured in Bankruptcy/Restructuring (California),*
*Bankruptcy/Restructuring (Nationwide)*
See under Nationwide for profile.

## BENSHOOF, Ward L
Alston & Bird LLP, Los Angeles
213 576 1108
ward.benshoof@alston.com
*Featured in Environment (California)*

**Practice Areas:** Environmental litigation, including defense of (a) civil penalty actions under state and federal environmental statutes, (b) hazardous waste litigation under CERCLA and RCRA, (c) toxic tort actions arising from environmental releases and (d) challenges under the California Environmental Quality Act.

**Professional Memberships:** Serves on the External Advisory Council to the Director of the California Department of Toxic Substances Control.

**Career:** Active in the development of environmental law in California and is closely involved in the implementation of California's Green Chemistry Initiative.

**Personal:** New York University (JD, 1972); Macalester College (BA, 1968).

## BENUDIZ, P Peter
Milbank, Tweed, Hadley & McCloy LLP, Los Angeles
213 892 4414
pbenudiz@milbank.com
*Featured in Leisure & Hospitality (Nationwide), Real Estate (California)*
See under Nationwide for profile.

## BENVENUTTI, Peter J
Jones Day, San Francisco
415 875 5826
pjbenvenutti@jonesday.com
*Featured in Bankruptcy/Restructuring (California)*

**Practice Areas:** Restructuring and insolvency; bankruptcy litigation.

**Professional Memberships:** State Bar of California; American Bar Association; Bar Association of San Francisco; American College of Bankruptcy.

**Career:** Mr Benvenutti has engaged in a bankruptcy and creditors' rights practice since 1974, representing debtors in possession, committees, institutional and private lenders, reorganization trustees, trade creditors, lessors, asset acquirers and investors, and parties in insolvency-related litigation, with recent focus on asbestos-related reorganizations. He also counsels on insolvency aspects of business transactions.

**Personal:** Harvard College (BA, cum laude, 1971); University of California, Berkeley, Boalt Hall School of Law (JD, 1974); Order of the Coif.

## BERGSTROM, Rick
Jones Day, San Diego
858 314 1118
rjbergstrom@jonesday.com
*Featured in Labor & Employment (California)*

**Practice Areas:** Handles complex employment litigation matters, including wage and hour class actions, trade secret litigation, discrimination class actions and compliance with Title III of the ADA.

**Professional Memberships:** Member, Labor and Employment Law Section, SD County Bar Association; Member, SHRM.

**Career:** Co-Chair, Employment and Labor Group. Testified before Congress concerning US Supreme Court's Garcetti v Ceballos decision. Recognized by PLC Which Lawyer? for his "broad employment litigation practice," and recommended by Best Lawyer and San Diego Super Lawyer.

**Personal:** BS, California State Polytechnic University; JD, Pepperdine University; California Supreme Court Survey Editor, Pepperdine Law Review.

## BERMAN, Jeffrey
Seyfarth Shaw LLP, Los Angeles
310 201 1541
jberman@seyfarth.com
*Featured in Labor & Employment (California)*

**Practice Areas:** Partner in Seyfarth's Century City office, practicing in labor and employment law. His experience includes representing employers in state and federal courts and before the National Labor Relations Board in a variety of industries, including major medical centers, universities, manufacturers, restaurants, trade associations and religious institutions.

**Professional Memberships:** Member, Labor Relations Advisory Committee; Legal Committee of the Employers Group and Chair of its Amicus Committee; Fellow of The College of Labor & Employment Lawyers.

**Personal:** University of California at Los Angeles, JD, 1971; University of California, Santa

Barbara, BA, 1968, with honors. Admission: California.

## BERRIOS, Ariel
Buchalter Nemer, Los Angeles
213 891 5480
aberrios@buchalter.com
*Featured in Banking & Finance (California)*

**Practice Areas:** Represents clients in a variety of industries including national lending and financial institutions, domestic and international technology-based companies, food retailers, pharmaceutical and manufacturing companies. Extensive experience in the areas of asset-based lending, cash flow lending, factoring, acquisition financing, and bridge financing. Additionally works on senior secured debt, second lien, mezzanine and unsecured/unsubordinated debt. Practice also includes expertise in forbearance situations, workouts, repossessions and foreclosures, as well as 363 sales. Advises clients on general corporate transactions such as mergers & acquisitions, corporate restructuring, and various forms of financing.

**Publications:** Co-author, 'Second Lien Financing and Workouts', Business Workouts Manual, Ch. 30.

**Personal:** Fluent in Spanish and Portuguese. Loyola Law School (JD 1997); California State University, San Bernardino (BA, 1989).

## BETTINGER, Michael
K&L Gates, San Francisco
415 882 8002
mike.bettinger@klgates.com
*Featured in Intellectual Property (California)*

**Practice Areas:** Mike Bettinger is the national lead trial counsel for K&L Gates' patent litigation group. He regularly practices in Federal Courts throughout the United States and the International Trade Commission in Washington, D.C. Recent patent trials include jury defense verdicts for Microsoft, Baxter Healthcare, Novatel Wireless, Abercrombie & Fitch and Zmed. Recent ITC cases include wins for Kodak, AMD, STMicroelectronics, Spansion and Nanya. Mr Bettinger has three times been selected as one of the 100 Most Influential Lawyers in California, and twice his jury trial wins have been selected as California defense verdicts of the year.

## BIERMAN, Ivy Kagan
Loeb & Loeb LLP, Los Angeles
310 282 2327
ibierman@loeb.com
*Featured in Labor & Employment (California)*

**Practice Areas:** Counsels entertainment/advertising companies about SAG, AFTRA, DGA, WGA, AFM, Teamsters and IATSE agreements and handles claims arising out of such agreements. Advises clients with respect to guilds' and unions' evolving positions regarding reality television, brand integration and development and exhibition of content over internet and mobile devices. Also provides sexual harassment, discrimination and non-fraternization training to entertainment industry companies with 'edgy' programming content. Regularly defends entertainment companies against labor claims before administrative agencies and in court. Defends entertainment companies against wage and hour class action lawsuits.

**Professional Memberships:** Board of Women in Film; member: Academy of Television Arts & Sciences; Hollywood Radio & Television Society; Anti-Defamation League Entertainment Industry Council.

**Career:** Joined Loeb as Partner in 2006.

**Personal:** Northwestern University School of Law (JD, cum laude, 1984); Duke University (BA, magna cum laude, 1980).

### BIRD, Terry W
Bird, Marella, Boxer, Wolpert, Nessim, Drooks & Lincenberg PC, Los Angeles
310 201 2100
twb@birdmarella.com
*Featured in Litigation (Nationwide), Litigation (California)*

See under Nationwide for profile.

### BIRENBAUM, Charles S
Winston & Strawn LLP, San Francisco
415 591 1403
cbirenbaum@winston.com
*Featured in Labor & Employment (California)*

**Practice Areas:** Traditional labor (management side) and employment law: union negotiations, labor disputes, litigation on employee benefits, noncompetes, wage and hour, government contracting, discrimination, harassment. Broad industry experience including: energy, healthcare, construction, manufacturing, technology, service.

**Professional Memberships:** California Bar Association; Bar Association of San Francisco; Lawyers Club of San Francisco (Board of Governors, Past President); Georgetown Law Center's National Law Alumni Board; former adjunct professor, Santa Clara University Law School; American Arbitration Association, Employment Panel.

**Career:** Executive, Operations, and Partner Compensation Committees.

**Personal:** BA, Government, with honors, Oberlin College (1979); JD, Georgetown University Law Center (1982).

### BISHOP, Leah M
Loeb & Loeb LLP, Los Angeles
310 282 2353
lbishop@loeb.com
*Featured in Wealth Management (Nationwide), Tax (California)*

**Practice Areas:** Focuses on estate and gift tax planning for high net worth individuals and closely held businesses, and in the administration of estates and trusts. Extensive experience in charitable giving and tax exempt organizations.

**Professional Memberships:** Vice President and trustee (Jewish Community Foundation).

**Publications:** Speaker at Western Conference on Tax Exempt Organizations, CPA Foundation, YPO, Blue Ribbon Finance Forum, UCLA, LA County Museum of Art, Beverly Hills Bar Association Committee for the Arts, Skirball Cultural Center, California Community Foundation and Jewish Community Foundation, among others.

**Personal:** Columbia University (JD, 1979); Brandeis University (BA, summa cum laude, 1975).

### BJORK, Jeffrey E
Sidley Austin LLP, Los Angeles
213 896 6037
jbjork@sidley.com
*Featured in Bankruptcy/Restructuring (California)*

**Practice Areas:** Partner in the firm-wide Corporate Reorganization and Bankruptcy group. Mr Bjork has significant experience in representing clients in all aspects of restructuring, including debtors (public company and privately-held), distressed investors, sellers and purchasers of financially-troubled companies, bond insurers, debt syndicates and bondholder groups. He has experience in large-scale cross-border restructurings and insolvencies involving the United States, Canada and Europe and has advised clients in distressed situations across industries, including gaming/hospitality, print media, real estate, manufacturing, casual dining and retail.

**Personal:** Emory University School of Law, JD, 1998, with distinction; Pepperdine University, BA, 1995, magna cum laude. Admission: California.

### BLACK, Daniel H
Greenberg Traurig, LLP, Santa Monica
310 586 7742
BlackD@gtlaw.com
*Featured in Media & Entertainment (California)*

**Practice Areas:** Co-Chair, West Coast Media and Entertainment Practice.

**Professional Memberships:** Co-Chair, Motion Pictures, Television, Cable and Radio Division, Forum on the Entertainment and Sports Industries, American Bar Association. Adjunct Professor, Film and Television Law, University of Southern California Law School. Chair, Board of Overseers, Emerson College.

**Career:** Listed: Southern California Super Lawyers, 2011-13; The Best Lawyers in America, Entertainment Law / Motion Pictures and Television, 2009-13; 'Power Lawyers: Top 100 Most Influential Entertainment Lawyers in America', The Hollywood Reporter, 2007-12.

**Personal:** JD, The George Washington University Law School; AB, cum laude, New York University (Phi Beta Kappa).

### BLOOM, Jerry
Winston & Strawn LLP, Los Angeles
213 615 1756
jbloom@winston.com
*Featured in Projects (Nationwide), Energy & Natural Resources (California)*

See under Nationwide for profile.

### BLUMLING, Sheldon J
Fisher & Phillips LLP, Irvine
949 798 2127
sblumling@laborlawyers.com
*Featured in Employee Benefits & Executive Compensation (California)*

**Career:** Sheldon Blumling is a Partner in the Irvine office and a Member of the firm's Employee Benefits Practice Group. He advises employers with respect to all aspects of employee benefits and executive compensation, including

qualified and nonqualified retirement plans, health and other welfare benefit plans, cafeteria plans, severance plans, equity-based compensation plans, related mergers and acquisitions issues and various other issues arising under ERISA and the Internal Revenue Code. Blumling also advises employers on all types of federal, state and local employment taxes and various issues arising under state insurance laws and HIPAA.

### BOBROW, Jared
Weil, Gotshal & Manges LLP, Silicon Valley
+1 650 802 3034
jared.bobrow@weil.com
*Featured in Intellectual Property (California)*

**Practice Areas:** Jared Bobrow is Head of Weil's Patent Litigation Practice nationwide. Since 1989, he has specialized in trying and litigating complex patent cases. He has successfully first-chaired patent jury trials and has conducted dozens of claim construction, preliminary injunction, and summary judgment hearings. He has served clients in important technology areas, including semiconductor design and processing; semiconductor equipment and metrology; computer hardware and software; networks; telecommunications and mobile devices; and a broad array of medical devices. He has a reputation for leading cases efficiently.

**Personal:** University of Washington (BA, 1983); Columbia University School of Law (JD, 1986).

### BOLLINGER, Bernard
Buchalter Nemer, Los Angeles
213 891 5009
bbollinger@buchalter.com
*Featured in Bankruptcy/Restructuring (California)*

**Practice Areas:** Bernard ("Bo") Bollinger focuses his practice on business bankruptcy matters and workouts, with an emphasis on creditors and acquirers in real estate-related bankruptcy cases, including multiple engagements for one of the largest real estate development companies in Southern California.

**Professional Memberships:** Financial Lawyers Conference; Los Angeles Bankruptcy Forum.

**Career:** Significant recent engagements: Joint debtors in restructuring of $160 million credit facility secured by portfolio of multi-family residential apartment complexes (In re Gulfstream Apt. Portfolio, LLC); Official Committee of Unsecured Creditors (In re Benjamin S. Catlin, IV); Official Committee of Unsecured Creditors (In re Active Wallace Group); Chair, Insolvency and Financial Solutions Practice Group; Member, Buchalter Nemer Board of Directors; Co-Chair, Buchalter Nemer Continuing Legal Education Committee.

**Publications:** Select publications: Could an Increase in Bankruptcy Sales Change the Game?" Commercial Investment Real Estate, January/February 2012; Interview: "6 Questions for Buchalter Nemer's Bo Bollinger," GlobeSt.com, October 14, 2011; "To Serve or Not to Serve? The Creditors' Committee Conundrum," Points & Authorities, Spring 2011.

**Personal:** Loyola Law School, JD, 1987; University of Sourthern California, BA, 1984.

### BOOTH, Susan J
Holland & Knight LLP, Los Angeles
213 896 2540
susan.booth@hklaw.com
*Featured in Real Estate (California)*

**Practice Areas:** Susan Booth is a Partner and heads the firm's West Coast Real Estate Group. She counsels banks, private equity funds, REITs and developers on various real estate matters including acquisitions/dispositions, portfolio and CMBS secured lending transactions (acquisition, development, construction, revolving, permanent, mezzanine and Shari'ah compliant), mortgage loan portfolio sales/acquisitions, workouts and REO management. Her experience includes shopping centers, hotels, condominiums, office buildings, industrial parks, senior-living centers and mixed-use developments. Ms Booth has spoken and written on numerous topics including mortgage loan sales, the development and implementation of strategies to resolve non-performing real estate assets and California's anti-deficiency laws.

### BOUTROUS JR, Theodore J
Gibson, Dunn & Crutcher LLP, Los Angeles
213 229 7804
tboutrous@gibsondunn.com
*Featured in First Amendment Litigation (Nationwide), Litigation (California), Appellate Law (Nationwide), Products Liability (Nationwide), Media & Entertainment (California)*

**Practice Areas:** Co-Chair of Appellate, Crisis Management and Transnational Litigation Groups. Represents clients in federal and state appellate courts throughout the U.S. in wide spectrum of cases, including punitive damages, class action, securities, employment, antitrust, environmental, product liability, civil rights, and constitutional litigation. Responsible for the nationwide appellate strategy for several major companies and has successfully persuaded courts to overturn some of the largest jury verdicts and class actions in history. Also represents media organizations and reporters in First Amendment matters.

**Personal:** JD, University of San Diego School of Law, 1987, summa cum laude, Valedictorian, Editor-in-Chief, Law Review.

### BOWERS, Terree
Arent Fox LLP, Los Angeles
213 443 7573
terree.bowers@arentfox.com
*Featured in Litigation (California)*

**Practice Areas:** Terree Bowers is chair of the White Collar and Investigations Practice Group. His practice focuses on complex commercial litigation, white collar criminal defense, and government enforcement. Terree brings over 30 years of experience in securities fraud, financial institutions, FCPA matters, civil rights actions, political corruption and campaign contribution issues, government contracting, false claims, customs, tax fraud, antitrust issues, and insurance coverage, among others. He previously served as United States Attorney for the Central District of California and Chief Deputy City Attorney for Los Angeles. He is sought after for his significant experience in international criminal law.

**BRAY, Gregory A**
Milbank, Tweed, Hadley & McCloy LLP, Los Angeles
213 892 4470
gbray@milbank.com
*Featured in Bankruptcy/Restructuring (California)*
**Practice Areas:** Mr Bray is a partner in the firm's Financial Restructuring Group. He regularly represents hedge and private equity funds, money center banks, financial institutions, lender syndicates comprised of first and second lien lenders, trustees and receivers, creditors' committees and equity securities holders. Mr Bray advises funds making control investments in, and potential purchasers of, financially distressed companies, both in and out-of-court. He advises lenders in the structuring and documentation of high risk loans and debtor-in-possession loans, and the board of directors of public companies in financial distress with respect to corporate governance and fiduciary duty issues.

**BREACH, David A**
Kirkland & Ellis LLP, San Francisco
415 439 1410
david.breach@kirkland.com
*Featured in Corporate/M&A (California)*
**Practice Areas:** David is a Founding Partner of the corporate group for Kirkland & Ellis' San Francisco office. He also sits on the firm's Global Executive Management Committee. He represents private equity funds in all aspects of their businesses, including formation, acquisitions and divestitures. He serves as lead counsel in structuring and negotiating various strategic and leveraged acquisitions and divestitures, joint ventures, mergers and acquisitions, senior bank financings, subordinated debt financings, equity financings, executive compensation matters, growth equity investments and restructurings and workouts.
**Personal:** University of Michigan Law School, JD, magna cum laude, 1994. Eastern Michigan University, BBA, 1991.

**BRENTANI, William B**
Simpson Thacher & Bartlett LLP, Palo Alto
650 251 5110
wbrentani@stblaw.com
*Featured in Capital Markets (California)*
**Practice Areas:** Corporate Partner. Represents issuers and underwriters in connection with a variety of public and private debt and equity offerings, including high-yield, IPO, mezzanine, convertible debt and cross-border transactions. Regularly represents private equity sponsor clients in connection with acquisition financings and advises clients on corporate governance and securities law-related matters. Fluent in Portuguese.
**Career:** Joined firm, 1989; Partner since 1999.
**Personal:** Tufts University (BA, 1986); Boston University School of Law (JD, 1989).

**BRESSLER, Todd N**
Peckar & Abramson, P.C., Los Angeles
310 228 1075
tbressler@pecklaw.com
*Featured in Construction (California)*
**Practice Areas:** Mr Bressler regularly advises general contractors, construction managers, general engineering contractors, owners, developers and property managers on contract negotiations, risk management and disputes.
**Professional Memberships:** Mr Bressler is a member of the Associated General Contractors of California, the Construction Management Association of America, the Southern California Development Forum and the Los Angeles County Bar Association. He is admitted to practice law in California.
**Career:** Mr Bressler is a Partner in the Los Angeles office.
**Personal:** For more information, please visit: www.pecklaw.com

**BREWER JR, Robert S**
Jones Day, San Diego
858 314 1172
rsbrewer@jonesday.com
*Featured in Litigation (California)*
**Practice Areas:** Represents officers, directors and employees in complex civil and criminal litigation cases including government contract fraud; qui tam claims; securities/shareholder disputes; corporate compliance; internal investigations; and class action defense.
**Professional Memberships:** Fellow, American College of Trial Lawyers; Association of Business Trial Lawyers; Master, Enright Inn of Court (President, 2005-06); Member of Board of Directors of Federal Defenders, Inc. (1996-2006).
**Career:** University of San Diego, JD, 1975; St Lawrence University, BA, 1968; Captain, US Army, Infantry, active duty, 1968-72; Deputy District Attorney, Los Angeles, 1975-77; Assistant US Attorney, Los Angeles, 1977-82.
**Publications:** Numerous re: 'Business Crimes and Evidentiary Issues'.

**BRIAN, Brad D**
Munger, Tolles & Olson LLP, Los Angeles
213 683 9280
brad.brian@mto.com
*Featured in Litigation (Nationwide), Litigation (California)*
**Practice Areas:** One of the premier trial attorneys in the United States, handling civil and criminal matters, including the defense in litigation arising from the largest oil spill in history.
**Professional Memberships:** Board, RAND Civil Justice Institute (past chair).
**Career:** Named a Lawyer of the Year for Bet-the-Company Litigation by Best Lawyers in 2013. Repeatedly named among 100 most influential attorneys in California by the Daily Journal.
**Publications:** The Importance of a Plan in Litigation (Best Lawyers 2013); Co-editor, Internal Corporate Investigations (ABA 3d Ed. 2007.
**Personal:** Harvard Law School (magna cum laude); U.C. Berkeley (member, USA All-Star Baseball Team).

**BRIDGES, Andrew P**
Fenwick & West LLP, San Francisco
415 875 2389
abridges@fenwick.com
*Featured in Intellectual Property (California)*
**Practice Areas:** Andrew P Bridges is a partner in the Litigation and Intellectual Property Groups of Fenwick & West. His global practice is dedicated to trial and appellate litigation, arbitration and strategic counseling in high stakes matters for internet, technology and consumer-focused companies with respect to new business models, media, technologies and communications platforms. Considered a thought leader on cutting-edge legal issues, he has 25 years of complex litigation experience in copyright, trademark, advertising, trade secret, consumer protection, unfair competition, licensing, and other commercial law disputes. Mr Bridges is a strategic advisor to entrepreneurs and companies on their branding and trademark portfolios. He also oversees the management of global portfolios and the coordination of foreign litigation matters for innovators and companies around the globe.
**Career:** Since 2008, Mr Bridges has been listed as one of the top 100 lawyers in California and has repeatedly ranked among the top 75-100 IP litigators in California. He has rankings in Band 1 for IP—Trademark, Copyright, and Trade Secrets by Chambers USA and in Band 1 for Trademark Litigation by World Trademark Review, is listed in Best Lawyers in America and in "Best of the Best" by Legal Media Group for trademark law.

**BROCKLAND, John P**
Weil, Gotshal & Manges LLP, Silicon Valley
john.brockland@weil.com
*Featured in Outsourcing (Nationwide), IT & Outsourcing (California)*
**Practice Areas:** Partner in the Technology and Intellectual Property Transactions Practice Group. Mr Brockland's practice focuses on strategic and commercial transactions involving the development, transfer and licensing of technology assets, and the provision of technology-related services. He has extensive experience representing companies ranging from startups to multinational public companies in the software, semiconductor, Internet, renewable energy, healthcare and other industries.
**Personal:** Trinity University (BA, magna cum laude, 1992) University of Chicago Law School (JD, with honors, 1996).

**BRODY, Sara B.**
Sidley Austin LLP, San Francisco
415 772 1279
sbrody@sidley.com
*Featured in Litigation (California)*
**Practice Areas:** Partner in Sidley's San Francisco office and global co-chair of the Securities Litigation Practice Group. Her practice focuses on defending issuers, officers, directors, underwriters and venture capital firms in shareholder class actions and derivative actions in state and federal courts throughout the United States. She also represents companies and individuals in matters involving Securities and Exchange Commission and self-regulatory organizations.
**Professional Memberships:** State Bar of California; American Bar Association; San Francisco Bar Association.
**Personal:** Emory University School of Law, JD, 1987, Managing Editor, Emory Law Journal; University of California, Berkeley, BA, 1982. Admissions: California, District of Columbia.

**BROOKS, John T**
McKenna Long & Aldridge LLP, San Diego
619 699 2401
jtbrooks@mckennalong.com
*Featured in Insurance (California)*
**Practice Areas:** John Brooks represents insurers in coverage and extra-contractual litigation in both the liability and property insurance context; defends insurers and other businesses in class action litigation; and represents clients in civil writs and appeals. Mr Brooks has represented class action defendants in a variety of fields (including insurance, unfair competition and false advertising, credit card privacy, antitrust, and annuity sales), and has obtained numerous appellate decisions in favor of his clients on insurance and class action issues.
**Professional Memberships:** California Academy of Appellate Lawyers.
**Personal:** JD, Stanford Law School, with distinction; BA, Stanford University, Phi Beta Kappa.

**BROSNAHAN, James**
Morrison & Foerster LLP, San Francisco
415 268 7189
jbrosnahan@mofo.com
*Featured in Litigation (Nationwide), Litigation (California)*
See under Nationwide for profile.

**BROWN, Donald W**
Covington & Burling LLP, San Francisco
415 591 7063
dwbrown@cov.com
*Featured in Insurance (Nationwide), Insurance (California)*
**Practice Areas:** Represents insurance policyholders in complex coverage litigation and arbitration over substantial claims under all policies, including directors and officers liability claims, false advertising and media/advertiser liability claims, consumer fraud and unfair business practices claims, products/mass tort liability, errors and omissions including technology liability, patent infringement, construction defect, fidelity bonds and catastrophic property damage claims. Clients include Fortune 500 companies in financial services, pharmaceuticals, energy, computer and software, new media, manufacturers, and retailers.
**Publications:** Business and Commercial Litigation in Federal Courts (West 2011) ('Insurance' chapter co-author).
**Personal:** JD, Yale Law School, 1978; AB, Ohio University, summa cum laude, 1975.

**BROWN, Lowell C**
Arent Fox LLP, Los Angeles
213 443 7516
lowell.brown@arentfox.com
*Featured in Healthcare (California)*
**Practice Areas:** Lowell is a leading member of the firm's national Health Care Practice Group. He advises hospitals, health systems, long-term care facilities, medical groups, and other health care provider organizations in business, regulatory, and medico-legal matters, emphasizing laws

regarding operational issues, including clinical integration of delivery systems and designing and implementing compliance programs; practitioner credentialing; peer review; disciplinary hearings; Medicare certification; licensing and accreditation issues; and related policies and procedures. Lowell has been a leader in national and state health law associations and is nationally recognized for EMTALA - the federal law prohibiting improper emergency patient transfers by hospitals.

### BROWN, Patrick S
Sullivan & Cromwell LLP, Los Angeles
310 712 6603
brownp@sullcrom.com
*Featured in Capital Markets (California)*

**Career:** Partner since 2005. M&A, securities and general corporate matters. Represents issuers, underwriters and other participants in equity, debt and hybrid securities offerings. Provides general corporate advice, including corporate governance, Sarbanes-Oxley Act, Dodd-Frank and general securities law compliance. Recent representations: SK Hynix in the acquisition of Link_A_Media Devices; Castle Creek Capital and other investors in the recapitalization of Intermountain Community Bancorp;; Mattel and Zions Bancorporation in debt/equity offerings; and underwriters in Oaktree Capital Group, Tilly's, AT&T and Pennymac debt/equity offerings.
**Personal:** UCLA Law School (JD, 1995); UCLA (BA, 1991).

### BROWN, Tristan
Simpson Thacher & Bartlett LLP, Palo Alto
650 251 5140
tbrown@stblaw.com
*Featured in Employee Benefits & Executive Compensation (California)*

**Practice Areas:** Advises clients regarding the compensation and benefits issues arising in mergers, sales, spinoffs, IPOs and other transactions; negotiating employment and separation agreements; the securities law aspects of compensation; and drafting incentive compensation, deferred compensation, and golden parachute plans and agreements. Representative clients include Hellman & Friedman, Silver Lake Partners and Seagate Technology.
**Career:** Clerk, Canada Federal Appeals Court; Joined the firm as partner in 2008.
**Personal:** BA and JD (Toronto), LLM (Georgetown).

### BROWN, Walt
Orrick, Herrington & Sutcliffe LLP, San Francisco
415 773 5995
wbrown@orrick.com
*Featured in Litigation (California)*

**Career:** Walt Brown is the Managing Director of Orrick's five global business units. He is a seasoned trial lawyer who handles white-collar criminal defense, securities matters and business litigation. He represents public and private companies in antitrust, FCPA, health care fraud, public corruption, environmental and tax evasion matters. He is also engaged routinely by companies, and by

audit and special committees of boards of directors, to conduct internal investigations. He is consistently recognized by Chambers USA, and is a former prosecutor in the U.S. Attorney's Office, Los Angeles. He received his JD from the University of Notre Dame Law School.

### BUDDIE, Raymond M
Allen Matkins Leck Gamble Mallory & Natsis LLP, San Francisco
415 8371515
rbuddie@allenmatkins.com
*Featured in Construction (California)*

**Practice Areas:** Mr Buddie practices construction law and represents of some of the largest general contractors in the U.S. He combines his engineering background and hands-on construction experience to benefit his clients. He has handled matters for clients on projects in excess of $1 Billion.
**Professional Memberships:** Member of ASCE, ABA (Construction Industry Forum); DBIA and AGC. Mr Buddie is licensed as a Professional Engineer.
**Career:** Partner and Co-Chair of firm's Construction Law Group and former Mayor of Sausalito, California.
**Personal:** Mr Buddie graduated from the University of Miami (BSCE 1974) and Case Western Reserve University School of Law (1981).

### BUONCRISTIANI, David
Jones Day, San Francisco
415 875 5764
dbuoncristiani@jonesday.com
*Featured in Construction (California)*

**Practice Areas:** More than 40 years of commercial litigation experience with primary emphasis on the construction industry. Dave has represented clients before state and federal courts, arbitration tribunals, and administrative panels, with extensive experience on international construction disputes. He has been involved in numerous mediations that resolved extremely complicated construction disputes.
**Professional Memberships:** He is a Fellow of the American College of Construction Lawyers and a member of the American Bar Association (Forum on the Construction Industry and Public Contracts and Sections), The Bar Association of San Francisco, The Olympic Club, and a U.C. Hastings Foundation Trustee.

### BURKE, Arthur J
Davis Polk & Wardwell LLP, Menlo Park
212 450 4352
arthur.burke@davispolk.com
*Featured in Antitrust (New York), Antitrust (California)*

**Practice Areas:** Member of Davis Polk's Litigation Department and Antitrust Practice Group. Has advised US and international clients in connection with mergers, acquisitions and joint ventures in the cable television, computer hardware and software, chemicals, pharmaceuticals, biotechnology and defense industries. Works closely with attorneys in Davis Polk's technology group in Silicon Valley (where he was based for five years). Has also represented clients in litiga-

tions involving allegations of price-fixing, monopolization, tying and exclusive dealing. Clients include AstraZeneca, Cadence, Citigroup, Comcast, KLA-Tencor and Tyco Electronics. Holds leadership position in ABA Antitrust Section; frequent speaker at antitrust conferences and seminars.

### BURKE, P John
Akin Gump Strauss Hauer & Feld LLP, Los Angeles
310 229 1038
jburke@akingump.com
*Featured in Media & Entertainment (California)*

**Practice Areas:** Represents financial institutions, hedge and equity funds, producers, high net worth individuals, studios and distributors in production, financing and distribution matters, with emphasis on complex financing and co-production arrangements worldwide.
**Professional Memberships:** Officer and Corporate Counsel, American Film Institute; Co-Chair, Advisory Committee, UCLA Entertainment Law Symposium (2002-10); Advisory Board Member, AFI International Film Festival (2000-03); Member, Entertainment Law Section, Beverly Hills Bar Association; Variety's Dealmakers Impact List (2012); Hollywood Reporter's Power Lawyers 100 (2007-12); Chambers USA: America's Leading Lawyers for Business (2004-13).
**Personal:** BA, USC (1973); JD, Southwestern University School of Law (1976), LLM, NYU (1977).

### BURMEISTER, Edward
Baker & McKenzie, San Francisco
415 576 3029
edward.burmeister@bakermckenzie.com
*Featured in Employee Benefits & Executive Compensation (Nationwide), Employee Benefits & Executive Compensation (California)*

**Practice Areas:** Leading advisor on global equity-tax, legal and regulatory. Specializes in creative plan design/tax strategies.
**Professional Memberships:** Best Lawyers in America (15th ed.);San Francisco Benefits Lawyer of the Year (2011); Super Lawyers Corporate Counsel Edition (2012); Northern California Super Lawyers (2012); NASPP Advisory Board/2010 Achievement Award;GEO 2008 Pioneer Award; Past Chairman, State Bar of California-Taxation Section.
**Career:** Partner, Baker & McKenzie LLP 1988-2012; Senior Counsel 2012-present.
**Publications:** Speeches, Webinars, Podcasts for NASPP/GEO/TEI/NCEO. Corporate Taxation (May/June 2011)"Income Tax Issues with Equity Grants to Employees of Foreign Subsidiaries."
**Personal:** Stanford University (AB); Stanford Law School (JD);Order of the Coif; Managing Editor, Stanford Law Review.

### BUSHNELL, Laura
King & Spalding LLP, Redwood Shores
650 590 0713
lbushnell@kslaw.com
*Featured in Corporate/M&A (California)*

**Practice Areas:** Practice focuses on a wide variety of corporate and securities law matters for

public and private companies, investment banks and venture capital firms.
**Career:** Extensive experience in corporate finance and securities law matters, and has represented issuers, investors and financial institutions in numerous capital raising transactions. These transactions include initial public offerings, follow-on and secondary offerings, PIPE financings, venture capital and seed financings, strategic investments and recapitalizations. Served as primary outside corporate counsel to companies in the life sciences and technology industries.
**Personal:** JD Georgetown University, BA Stanford University.

### CALKINS, Mary Craig
Jenner & Block LLP, Los Angeles
213 239 5148
mcalkins@jenner.com
*Featured in Insurance (California)*

**Career:** Mary Craig Calkins is a partner in the Litigation Department and member of the Insurance Litigation and Counseling Practice. A nationally-known litigator, her practice focuses on insurance recovery for policyholders in high-stakes litigation. She has extensive coverage experience in directors and officers liability, entertainment and intellectual property, construction defect, e-commerce/technology claims, and first-party property and business interruption losses. She advises in-house counsel and company management on maximizing insurance protections. She has been named repeatedly as one of the Top Women Lawyers in California, and was national Co-Chair of the American Bar Association Section of Litigation Insurance Coverage Litigation Committee.

### CALLOBRE, Anthony R
Buchalter Nemer, Los Angeles
213 891 5024
acallobre@buchalter.com
*Featured in Banking & Finance (California)*

**Practice Areas:** Member, Bank and Finance Practice Group, Los Angeles and San Francisco. Practices in the areas of commercial lending and corporate finance. Clients include commercial banks, commercial finance companies, hedge funds, private equity groups, business development companies, small business investment companies, and other institutional investors and lenders. Practices across a broad spectrum of the commercial and industrial sector and has considerable experience in syndicated finance, asset-based lending, and acquisition and recapitalization financings. Represents both credit providers and credit takers in the originations of financings and in problem financings, restructurings and workouts.
**Personal:** Boston University School of Law, LLM, 1986; Boston University School of Law, JD, 1985; Brown University, BA, 1982.

### CAMAHORT, Steve L
Shearman & Sterling LLP, San Francisco
415 616 1240
steve.camahort@shearman.com
*Featured in Corporate/M&A (Northern California)*

**Career:** Steve Camahort is a partner in the firm's Mergers and Acquisitions Practice Group. Mr Camahort has extensive experience in mergers and acquisitions and related corporate governance issues. He has worked for corporate clients, private equity funds, and financial advisors in negotiated and hostile transactions in the technology, health care, financial services, entertainment and media, consumer products, aerospace, real estate, and other industries. Mr Camahort also has advised numerous investment banks in their capacity as financial advisor in M&A transactions. He joined the firm as a partner in 2008.

### CAMPBELL, John W
Morrison & Foerster LLP, San Francisco
415 268 7197
jcampbell@mofo.com
*Featured in Life Sciences (California)*
**Practice Areas:** With a focus on life sciences matters, John Campbell concentrates on securities, mergers and acquisitions and general corporate and board representation of issuers, venture capitalists and investment banks. Has represented companies, investors and financial intermediaries in hundreds of equity and debt financing transactions ranging from seed investments in start-up companies to public offerings of equity and debt securities. Has advised on more than 40 public offerings in his career and dozens of other public capital markets transactions.
**Career:** Admitted to practice in California.
**Personal:** BA, Duke University, 1979; JD, Yale Law School, 1982.

### CAPELOUTO, Richard
Simpson Thacher & Bartlett LLP, Palo Alto
650 251 5060
rcapelouto@stblaw.com
*Featured in Private Equity (Nationwide),*
*Corporate/M&A (Northern California),*
*Corporate/M&A (California)*
**Practice Areas:** Corporate Partner. Advises clients in M&A and securities law matters, including leveraged buyouts, joint ventures, public company acquisitions and restructurings. Represents leading private equity firms including Silver Lake, Hellman & Friedman, Elevation Partners and Blum Capital in their investment activities. Also advises technology companies on significant M&A matters including Google in its acquisition of YouTube; Electronic Arts in its bid for Take-Two and Agilent in the sale of its Semiconductor Products Group.
**Career:** Joined the firm in 1986; Partner since 1994.
**Personal:** BA, summa cum laude, Rutgers University (1983); JD, cum laude, Harvard Law School (1986).

### CARROLL, Michael
Latham & Watkins LLP, Costa Mesa
714 755 8105
michael.carroll@lw.com
*Featured in Energy & Natural Resources (California)*
**Practice Areas:** Co-chair of the firm's global Energy and Infrastructure Project Siting and Defense practice. Focuses on permitting, entitlement and environmental review of complex

development projects with an emphasis on energy.
**Career:** Recognized by Chambers USA in 2004-12 as a leading environmental regulatory and litigation attorney and by Who's Who Legal: California 2007 as one of "California's Leading Environmental Practitioners." Named as one of "3000 Leading Lawyers in America" by Lawdragon.
**Personal:** JD, University of Michigan Law School, 1989; BA, University of Michigan, 1986.

### CARSON, Peter H
Bingham McCutchen LLP, San Francisco
415 393 2830
peter.carson@bingham.com
*Featured in Banking & Finance (California)*
**Practice Areas:** Co-chair of Bingham's Healthcare Industry Group and its Pro Bono National committee. Represents domestic and foreign banks, commercial finance lenders, debt funds, and other institutional lenders as well as the firm's company and private equity clients in all aspects of complex secured and unsecured debt financings, including acquisition, senior syndicated, asset-based, mezzanine, second lien, bridge, debtor-in-possession, credit enhancement, private placement, leveraged lease and other financings, recapitalizations, and restructurings.
**Personal:** University of California Berkeley School of Law (Boalt Hall), JD, 1985; University of California, Berkeley, BA, 1980.

### CASEY, Edward J
Alston & Bird LLP, Los Angeles
213 576 1005
ed.casey@alston.com
*Featured in Real Estate (California)*
**Practice Areas:** Represents variety of residential, retail and commercial developers in land use matters, including those arising under the California Environmental Quality Act (CEQA). Practice encompasses every facet of the entitlement process, from pre-acquisition due diligence to permitting. Also represents private landowners and developers in connection with securing sufficient water supplies for projects.
**Career:** Successfully prosecuted and defended CEQA and other land use lawsuits for a number of major development projects.
**Personal:** University of Chicago (JD, 1985); Hofstra University (BA, 1982). Named to Daily Journal's 2011 "California's Top 25 Land Use Leaders" and 2012 "Top 100 Lawyers in California" lists.

### CERMAK JR, John F
Baker & Hostetler LLP, Los Angeles
310 442 8885
jcermak@bakerlaw.com
*Featured in Environment (California)*
**Career:** A former U.S. Department of Justice attorney with the Natural Resources Division, Environmental Defense Section, John Cermak litigates environmental cases, including toxic tort suits, cost recovery actions, common law tort actions and penalty actions in state and federal courts throughout the United States and litigates appellate court challenges to agency rulemakings

and proceedings before federal and state agencies. John counsels on water and air quality, hazardous solid waste, land use, health/safety, Proposition 65 and environmental compliance and handles environmental aspects of the purchase and sale of real property and the environmental due diligence aspects of corporate mergers and acquisitions.

### CHAE, Meryl K
Skadden, Arps, Slate, Meagher & Flom LLP & Affiliates, Los Angeles
213 687 5035
meryl.chae@skadden.com
*Featured in Real Estate (California)*
**Practice Areas:** As leader of the LA office's real estate practice and one of the leaders of Skadden's REIT practice, she advises clients on a wide range of complex real estate and REIT matters including public and private placements of various types of real estate securities, complicated workouts, restructurings and financings, domestic and international partnership and joint venture formations and restructurings, headquarters leasing, trophy property development, and portfolio property sales and acquisitions.
**Career:** JD, University of California Hastings College of the Law, 1994 (Member of the Hastings Law Journal); BA, Tufts University, 1991 (magna cum laude, Phi Beta Kappa).

### CHAIKOVSKY, Yar R
McDermott Will & Emery LLP, Menlo Park
650 798 0330
ychaikovsky@mwe.com
*Featured in Intellectual Property (California)*
**Practice Areas:** Focuses on intellectual property litigation. In addition to appearing in federal courts and the US International Trade Commission, has coordinated multinational offensive and defensive patent actions. Litigates and counsels on matters for companies in all stages of development, from start-ups to established companies, in technology fields as diverse as networking, software, hardware, Internet, communications, video compression, semiconductors, consumer electronics, analog devices and medical devices.
**Professional Memberships:** Fellow, American Bar Foundation.
**Personal:** UCLA Law School, JD; University of Southern California, BS, magna cum laude and Trustees' Scholarship.

### CHANG, Carmen I
Covington & Burling LLP, Redwood Shores
650 632 4713
cchang@cov.com
*Featured in Corporate/M&A (California)*
**Practice Areas:** Carmen Chang is senior of counsel in Covington's Silicon Valley office. Her practice focuses on the representation of public and private technology companies and financial institutions in public offerings, mergers and acquisitions, joint ventures, financings, and other types of transactions in the United States and abroad, particularly in the People's Republic of China, Taiwan, and other Asian countries. Ms Chang is a well-regarded expert in corporate and

securities law and cross-border transactions and a frequent writer and speaker.
**Personal:** JD, with distinction, Stanford Law School; MA, Stanford University; BA, Sarah Lawrence College.

### CHARNLEY, Richard
Ropers Majeski Kohn & Bentley, Los Angeles
213 312 2000
rcharnley@rmkb.com
*Featured in Media & Entertainment (California)*
**Practice Areas:** Entertainment; intellectual property; commercial litigation.
**Professional Memberships:** California State Bar Association; American Bar Association; American Board of Trial Advocates (ABOTA).
**Career:** Currently a Partner in the firm's Los Angeles office, trial attorney Richard Charnley has practiced law for 36 years. He is admitted in all California courts, the United States Supreme Court, the Ninth Circuit, the United States Tax Court, and the United States Court of Claims. He is a member of the American Board of Trial Advocate and peer rated AV® by Martindale-Hubbell. In 2012, Mr Charnley was named by the Hollywood Reporter as one of the 100 Most Powerful Attorneys in the Entertainment Business. He has also been named multiple times by Southern California Super Lawyers® magazine in the area of intellectual property. Mr Charnley's pre-law career was in screenwriting. After graduating from law school and practicing law for eight years, Mr Charnley was awarded a full fellowship to attend the Peter Stark Motion Picture Producers' Program at the University of Southern California School of Cinema Television, where he received his Master of Fine Arts Degree in 1986. Since that time, Mr Charnley's first chair trial expertise has been sought by studios, television networks, producers, insurers and public figures. Mr Charnley has provided legal commentary for The Larry King Show, The Today Show, MS NBC, Entertainment Tonight, Access Hollywood, KNBC (Los Angeles), KABC (Los Angeles), The New York Times, The Wall Street Journal, Variety, Hollywood Reporter, and Vanity Fair. He served for five years on the Board of Directors of the National Graphic Artists Guild. He has been a featured speaker at RIMS International (Entertainment) and has addressed national audiences before the American Bar Association Forum on Entertainment and Sports Industries.
**Publications:** He has published in Variety, Hollywood Reporter, ABA Forum on Entertainment, Sports Industries, Risk Magazine, Insurance Journal, The Los Angeles Daily Journal, The Recorder, Verdicts, and Property & Casualty.
**Personal:** Mr Charnley received his BA from U.C. Irvine in 1970, his JD from Pepperdine University School of Law in 1976 and his MFA from University of Southern California in 1986. Actively involved in his community, Mr Charnley was the charter president of the Los Angeles Westside Sunrise Rotary Club. He is a Paul Harris Fellow and a life member of the National Eagle Scout Association.

## CHENETZ, Sara L
Blank Rome LLP, Los Angeles
424 239 3464
Chenetz@BlankRome.com
*Featured in Bankruptcy/Restructuring (California)*

**Practice Areas:** Sara Chenetz represents clients with varied interests and perspectives in restructuring, bankruptcy, workouts, litigation and related matters. Her clients include first and second lien holders, asset acquirers, official and unofficial committees, debtors-in-possession, bond and equity holders, investment funds, vendors, insurers, landlords, tenants, franchisors, franchisees, employee benefit plans, trustees, examiners, directors and officers, partnerships, limited liability companies, REITS, individuals, assignors, assignees and creditors in assignments for the benefit of creditors, plaintiffs and defendants, all in a myriad of industries. Ms Chenetz also regularly advises clients on doing business with financially trouble companies and is a frequent speaker and author.www.BlankRome.com/Chenetz.

## CHILDRESS, Tyrone R
Jones Day, Los Angeles
213 243 2422
tchildress@jonesday.com
*Featured in Insurance (Nationwide), Insurance (California)*
See under Nationwide for profile.

## CHILTON, Frederick
McDermott Will & Emery LLP, Menlo Park
650 813 5121
fchilton@mwe.com
*Featured in Tax (California)*

**Practice Areas:** Partner in firm's tax department. Focuses on the representation of high technology, biotechnology and other companies on complex tax matters.
**Professional Memberships:** Often speaks and serves as chair for seminars on behalf of the ATLAS, Practicing Law Institute and the Tax Executives Institute.
**Career:** Law clerk for Judge Leo H Irwin, US Tax Court and a Tax Law Specialist in the Foreign Rulings Group of the Internal Revenue Service.
**Personal:** Fresno State College (BA); Hastings College of Law (JD); New York University (LLM).

## CHINE, Jeffrey
Allen Matkins Leck Gamble Mallory & Natsis LLP, San Diego
619 235 1525
jchine@allenmatkins.com
*Featured in Real Estate (California)*

**Practice Areas:** Jeffrey Chine specializes in a wide variety of land use and environmental matters involving the permitting and development of complex projects throughout California. He also represents developers in state and federal courts against environmental groups and opponents of development in CEQA, NEPA, Endangered Species Act, Clean Water Act, Subdivision Map Act, Coastal Act and other challenges to entitlements. Jeff specializes in emerging regulatory issues facing development in California, including water supply, climate change, and stormwater regulation.

**Professional Memberships:** General Counsel for the Building Industry Association of San Diego County and chairs its Legal Action Committee.

## CHU, Morgan
Irell & Manella, Los Angeles
310 203 7000
mchu@irell.com
*Featured in Litigation (Nationwide), Intellectual Property (California)*

**Practice Areas:** Morgan Chu is a partner at Irell & Manella, where he is Chair of the litigation practice group, a member of the Executive Committee and previously served as Managing Partner. Throughout his monumental career, Mr Chu has been lead trial counsel in cases with over $3.2 billion in verdicts, judgments and settlements, including more than $565 million paid to City of Hope and, most recently, more than $1 billion paid to TiVo.
**Personal:** Harvard Law School (JD, magna cum laude); Yale University (MSL); University of California, Los Angeles (BA; MA; PhD).

## CLARENCE, Nanci L
Clarence Dyer & Cohen, LLP, San Francisco
415 749 1800
nclarence@clarencedyer.com
*Featured in Litigation (California)*

**Practice Areas:** Nanci Clarence is a nationally renowned trial lawyer who has defended clients in some of the nation's highest-profile white collar criminal cases. Leading her firm's White Collar practice, Ms Clarence has spent nearly three decades litigating complex commercial, regulatory and criminal cases on behalf of corporations and individuals. Ms Clarence frequently is retained to represent senior officers and executives in sensitive criminal matters, including securities fraud and insider trading violations, antitrust, tax fraud, health care fraud, trade secret violations, public corruption, commercial bribery and environmental crimes.
**Professional Memberships:** Fellow, American College of Trial Lawyers (Chair of the Federal Criminal Procedure Committee and former Chair of the California State Committee (Northern); President, Bar Association of San Francisco (2006-07).
**Career:** Ms Clarence has been recognized repeatedly as one of the top 10 litigators in Northern California and top 75 women litigators in California. She was appointed by U.S. Senator Barbara Boxer to serve on her Federal Judicial Selection Committee and has served on the lawyers advisory committees for the United States Attorney for the Northern District of California. In 2007, she was appointed by Chief Justice Ronald George to serve on the California Supreme Court's Commission for Impartial Courts.
**Publications:** "Employee Privacy After Quon & Jones," ABA CLE Course material (2012); "Private Parts Aren't Private: Florence v. Bd of Chosen Freeholders," Daily Journal (2012); "Borderline Intrusive," Daily Journal (2008); "Computer Searches at the Nations Border: Why All Lawyers

Have a Stake in United States v. Arnold," Forum, California Attorneys for Criminal Justice (CACJ) (2008); "Advising and Defending Corporate Directors and Officers," Continuing Education of the Bar (CEB) (Oct 2006); "Putting the Government to Its Proof Prior to Trial: Tactics for Forcing the Government's Hand in Complex White-Collar Cases," ABA National Institute on White Collar Crime (March 2005); "Finding Your Way Through a Maze: Representing Corporate Officers & Directors in a Criminal Investigation," 17 California Labor & Employment Law Review (Jan 2003).
**Personal:** University of California, Hastings College of the Law (JD, 1985); University of California at Berkeley (BA, Phi Beta Kappa, 1981).

## CLIMAN, Richard
Weil, Gotshal & Manges LLP, Silicon Valley
650 802 3210
richard.climan@weil.com
*Featured in Corporate/M&A (Northern California)*

**Practice Areas:** Mr Climan specialises in domestic and international mergers and acquisitions and related securities and corporate governance matters.
**Professional Memberships:** ABA; Executive Council (and former Chair), Committee on Mergers and Acquisitions; Corporate Laws Committee; adjunct faculty, UC Berkeley School of Law. Chair, Securities Regulation Institute (Northwestern School of Law); Co-chair, Annual Institute on Negotiating Business Acquisitions (ABA).
**Career:** Pettit & Martin (associate 1977-83; partner 1984-94). Cooley Godward (partner 1994-2009). Dewey & LeBoeuf (partner 2009 to 2012). Weil, Gotshal & Manges (partner 2012 to present).
**Personal:** Harvard College (AB); Harvard Law School (JD).

## CLOWES, Howard
DLA Piper LLP (US), East Palo Alto
650 833 2153
howard.clowes@dlapiper.com
*Featured in Life Sciences (California)*

**Practice Areas:** Corporate, M&A, Life Sciences.
**Career:** He concentrates his practice in the representation of public companies, venture finance, M&A and corporate collaborations. He has represented clients in the life sciences, semiconductor, networking, telecommunications and other industries. He has been named a Northern California Super Lawyer in every year since 2005, as the result of a joint research project conducted by Law & Politics and San Francisco magazines. He has also been listed in The Best Lawyers in America.
**Personal:** JD, University of California at Berkely; BA, University of California at Santa Barbara.

## COFFILL, Eric J
Morrison & Foerster LLP, Sacramento
916 325 1324
ecoffill@mofo.com
*Featured in Tax (California)*

**Practice Areas:** Managing Partner of Morrison & Foerster's Sacramento office, and heads the firm's Sacramento State & Local Tax Practice. He

has more than 25 years of experience in state tax matters. His practice focuses on state tax controversies, including administrative and state court litigation; state and local tax aspects of business transactions; personal income tax resident/non-resident and sourcing issues; and taxation of trusts. A large component of his practice is California tax representation before the Franchise Tax Board and the California State Board of Equalization. Mr Coffill is a frequent speaker and has authored more than 70 articles.

## COGEN, Douglas N
Fenwick & West LLP, San Francisco
415 875 2409
dcogen@fenwick.com
*Featured in Corporate/M&A (Northern California)*

**Practice Areas:** Douglas N Cogen is a partner in the Corporate Group and Co-Chair of the Mergers and Acquisitions Group of Fenwick & West LLP. His practice focuses on M&A, strategic and commercial transactions, corporate counseling and financings. Mr Cogen's practice also includes advising publicly traded and privately held companies with respect to corporate, securities, commercial and intellectual property licensing matters generally. His transactional experience includes over $70 billion of completed mergers, acquisitions and divestitures, including cross-border transactions, in the networking, software, life sciences, medical devices, telecommunications, semiconductor, internet, computer hardware and consumer products industries; public company tender offers; and private placements of equity and debt securities.
**Career:** Mr Cogen has received numerous accolades for his achievements and was most recently named by Global M&A Network as "M&A Lawyer of the Year" for 2010. The Los Angeles Daily Journal and San Francisco Daily Journal named him as one of the Top 100 Attorneys in the State of California, one of only five northern California "Dealmakers" included in the list. Mr Cogen is also listed as "Highly Recommended" in M&A and Corporate Finance in PLC Which Lawyer? and is ranked in Corporate Law/M&A by Chambers USA.

## COHEN, Jeffrey H
Skadden, Arps, Slate, Meagher & Flom LLP & Affiliates, Los Angeles
213 687 5288
jeffrey.cohen@skadden.com
*Featured in Corporate/M&A (California), Corporate/M&A (Southern California)*

**Practice Areas:** Leader of the Corporate Group in Skadden's Los Angeles office. Extensive experience in private equity, mergers and acquisitions, securities and corporate governance. Regularly represents a number of leading private equity funds and their portfolio companies in acquisitions, financings and dispositions. Representative clients include: Oaktree Capital Management and its GFI Energy Group; Goldman Sachs; OPI Products; American Apparel; BCBGMaxAzria; Colony Capital; Silver Point Capital; Crimson SV; Dutch, LLC; AdvancePierre Foods; Oakley; TOMS

Shoes; SKBHC Holdings; and the Los Angeles County Museum of Art.
**Career:** JD, UCLA School of Law, 1988; BS, Economics, The Wharton School, University of Pennsylvania, 1985.

### COHEN, Marc S
Kaye Scholer LLP, Los Angeles
310 788 1223
marc.cohen@kayescholer.com
*Featured in Bankruptcy/Restructuring (California)*
**Practice Areas:** Marc Cohen, Chair of the Los Angeles Bankruptcy & Restructuring Department, has over 35 years of experience in corporate reorganization. He represents the California State Controller in disputes with life insurance companies regarding escheat matters, and LAX in connection with American Airlines' Chapter 11. He represents clients in a variety of areas, including state and city agencies, energy, aviation, real estate and entertainment.
**Professional Memberships:** Marc is a Fellow in the American College of Bankruptcy, a lawyer representative to the Ninth Circuit Judicial Conference, and Chairman of the First-In Fire Foundation, which connects citizens with local fire stations.

### COLGIN JR, William F
Morgan, Lewis & Bockius LLP, San Francisco
415 442 1347
wcolgin@morganlewis.com
*Featured in Tax (Nationwide), Tax (California)*
See under Nationwide for profile.

### COLKER, David
DLA Piper LLP (US), East Palo Alto
650 833 2000
david.colker@dlapiper.com
*Featured in Tax (California)*
**Practice Areas:** Tax.
**Career:** Chair of the firm's Global and US Tax practices. He concentrates his practice on tax disputes and tax planning and has more than 30 years experience resolving federal, state and local tax disputes and has successfully represented numerous clients in more than 200 tax cases. He is highly experienced in establishing, improving and evaluating business structures to achieve beneficial tax consequences and has helped clients better prepare for government reviews of their business structures.
**Personal:** JD, Stanford Law Review (Articles Editor); BA, Georgetown University (magna cum laude) Economics, Phi Beta Kappa

### CONNER, Lindsay
Manatt Phelps & Phillips LLP, Los Angeles
310 312 4229
lconner@manatt.com
*Featured in Media & Entertainment (California)*
**Practice Areas:** Conner is co-chair of Manatt's Entertainment & Media Practice, advising clients through the life cycle of film, television and new media assets. He represents film and television clients, as well as financial institutions and hedge funds, in equity and debt finance deals, distribution and licensing deals, and agreements with talent. He has restructured the production and dis-

tribution of a multibillion-dollar television franchise, closed half-billion-dollar feature film finance and distribution deals, and negotiated studio film slate financing deals and international television production and distribution deals, as well as deals for the acquisition of companies and film and television assets.

### CONTOPULOS, Stephen G
Sidley Austin LLP, Los Angeles
213 896 6625
scontopulos@sidley.com
*Featured in Media & Entertainment (California)*
**Practice Areas:** Los Angeles Partner. His practice is civil litigation in federal and state courts, focusing on representing media companies, particularly in the areas of libel, privacy, copyright and trademark. He has represented newspapers, magazines, book publishers, television stations and entertainment companies. His more than 40 years of litigation experience has ranged from defamation, privacy, copyright, theft of idea and trademark to reporter's privileges, access to courtrooms and public records acts. His litigation experience is not only at the trial level, but also the appellate courts.
**Personal:** Loyola Law School, JD, 1971; California State University - Los Angeles, BA, 1967.

### CONWAY, Catherine A
Gibson, Dunn & Crutcher LLP, Los Angeles
213 229 7822
cconway@gibsondunn.com
*Featured in Labor & Employment (California)*
**Practice Areas:** Co-Chair, Labor & Employment Practice. Focuses on complex class actions, with emphasis on class action discrimination cases and wage and hour litigation. Extensive experience in state and federal litigation, including employment discrimination, sexual harassment, wrongful discharge, unfair competition, trade secret and unfair business practice litigation under California Business and Professional Code Section 17200. Appeared before state and federal regulatory bodies, including the Equal Employment Opportunity Commission, the California Department of Fair Employment and Housing and the California Labor Commissioner's Office.
**Professional Memberships:** Member - California, Indiana Bars.
**Personal:** BA, Purdue University (1975); JD, Indiana University School of Law (1978).

### COOKE, David
Allen Matkins Leck Gamble Mallory & Natsis LLP, San Francisco
415 837 1515
dcooke@allenmatkins.com
*Featured in Environment (California)*
**Practice Areas:** Practice concentrated in environmental litigation and environmental regulatory and transactional counseling, with a focus on hazardous waste and contaminated property issues; regulatory, permitting and enforcement issues and actions arising under the Clean Water Act and Clean Air Act; land use and litigation matters under CEQA and NEPA; and environmental issues in regional transportation planning.

**Professional Memberships:** Member of/involved in the American Bar Association, Bar Association of San Francisco, and California Bar—Environmental Law Section.
**Career:** Co-Chair of firm's Environmental and Natural Resources Group.
**Personal:** BA from the University of Virginia, with highest distinction, JD from the University of Virginia.

### COOPER, Jay L
Greenberg Traurig, LLP, Santa Monica
310 586 7888
Cooper@gtlaw.com
*Featured in Media & Entertainment (California)*
**Practice Areas:** Vice-Chair, Global Media/Entertainment Practice. Co-Chair, West Coast Entertainment Division. Music, motion picture, TV, multimedia, IP.
**Professional Memberships:** Formerly: President, The Recording Academy; California Copyright Conference, Chair, ABA Forum Committee, Entertainment and Sports. Co-Chairman: Alliance of Artists & Recording Companies. Board: SoundExchange, Recording Artists Coalition. GC: USA for Africa, Hands Across America.
**Career:** Listed, Best Lawyers in America, 1987-13; Super Lawyers magazine, 2004-13; U.S. News - Best Lawyers 'Law Firm of the Year' in Entertainment Law - Music, 2011-12; Chambers USA Guide, 2004-13. Rated, AV® Preeminent™ 5.0 out of 5.
**Personal:** JD, DePaul University College of Law.

### COOPER, M Scott
Sidley Austin LLP, Los Angeles
213 896 6631
scooper@sidley.com
*Featured in Real Estate (California)*
**Practice Areas:** Partner in Sidley's Los Angeles office, Mr Cooper's practice involves full-range representation of investors, financial institutions, developers and users in all forms of transactions involving real property. Major engagements have included acquisition, disposition, development, leasing, financing, and structuring equity in office buildings, retail centers, malls, hotels, resorts, and large-scale residential projects. He also has served as general counsel to a major national developer of hotels, shopping centers and office buildings.
**Personal:** UCLA School of Law, JD, Order of the Coif, Board of Editors, UCLA Law Review; UCLA, AB.

### COOPER, Robert E
Gibson, Dunn & Crutcher LLP, Los Angeles
213 229 7179
rcooper@gibsondunn.com
*Featured in Litigation (Nationwide), Antitrust (California)*
See under Nationwide for profile.

### CORASH, Michèle B
Morrison & Foerster LLP, San Francisco
415 268 7124
mcorash@mofo.com
*Featured in Environment (California)*
**Practice Areas:** Ms Corash's practice covers environmental issues and toxic exposure claims.

She is a leading expert on California's Proposition 65 and Unfair Competition Laws, having successfully defended hundreds of cases under those statutes.
**Professional Memberships:** American College of Environmental Lawyers (Past President).
**Career:** Formerly: General Counsel, U.S. EPA; Deputy General Counsel, U.S. Dept. of Energy; Assistant to Chairman, U.S. FTC. Recognized as a leading environmental lawyer by Legal 500 US, U.S. Lawyer Rankings, Daily Journal, and The Recorder. Best Lawyers' "2013 Lawyer of the Year" for SF Environmental Litigation.
**Personal:** BA, Mount Holyoke College; JD, NYU School of Law.

### CORMAN, Karen L
Skadden, Arps, Slate, Meagher & Flom LLP & Affiliates, Los Angeles
213 687 5208
karen.l.corman@skadden.com
*Featured in Labor & Employment (California)*
**Practice Areas:** Ms Corman advises clients in labor and employment litigation and corporate matters. She defends employers in federal and state court in individual and class action wage and hour, discrimination, harassment and wrongful termination litigation, as well as in arbitration and mediation, and also advises on issues arising in corporate transactions and bankruptcies. In addition, she negotiates executive officers' departures and settlement of equity interests and investigates and resolves threatened claims, including for disability discrimination and sexual harassment, against executive or high-level employees.
**Career:** JD, Harvard Law School, 1987; BA, University of California at Los Angeles, 1984 (magna cum laude).

### COTTLE, Lisa A
Winston & Strawn LLP, San Francisco
415 591 1579
lcottle@winston.com
*Featured in Energy & Natural Resources (California)*
**Practice Areas:** Lisa Cottle has broad energy project development and regulatory experience. Her project experience includes negotiating wholesale and retail power purchase agreements and other key contracts, obtaining permits and regulatory approvals, and supporting project finance transactions. She regularly appears before state and federal agencies, particularly the California Public Utilities Commission and the California Energy Commission (CEC). She obtains certification from the CEC for large thermal power plant projects, and advises on permitting, environmental, and regulatory issues, including compliance with the California Environmental Quality Act (CEQA).
**Personal:** BA, Colgate University, cum laude (1990); JD, University of Pennsylvania Law School (1993).

### COUGHLIN, Patrick J
Robbins Geller Rudman & Dowd LLP, San Diego
619 231 1058
patc@rgrdlaw.com
*Featured in Litigation (California)*

**Career:** Patrick J. Coughlin is "Of Counsel" to Robbins Geller Rudman & Dowd LLP and has been lead counsel for several major securities matters, including one of the earliest and largest class action securities cases to go to trial, In re Apple Computer Sec. Litig., No. C-84-20148 (N.D. Cal.). Additional prominent securities class actions prosecuted by Mr Coughlin include the Enron litigation, in which $7.3 billion was recovered; the Qwest litigation, in which a $445 million recovery was obtained; and the HealthSouth litigation, in which a $671 million recovery was obtained.

## COWAN, Stephen A
DLA Piper LLP (US), San Francisco
415 615 6000
stephen.cowan@dlapiper.com
*Featured in Real Estate (California)*

**Practice Areas:** Real Estate Capital Markets, Finance.
**Career:** He focuses on real estate, finance, and bankruptcy/workouts, with such clients as developers, investors, insurance companies, and financial institutions. His experience includes acquisitions, dispositions, joint ventures and partnerships, workouts, restructurings, bankruptcies, multifamily and IDB and IRB letter of credit bond transactions, sale leasebacks, synthetic leases, and restructuring of US real estate portfolios with complex inter-creditor issues.
**Personal:** JD, Harvard Law School (cum laude), MBA, University of California at Berkeley; BA, University of California at Berkeley (with distinction).

## CRANSTON, David
Greenberg Glusker Fields Claman & Machtinger LLP, Los Angeles
310 785 6897
DCranston@greenbergglusker.com
*Featured in Environment (California)*

**Career:** David Cranston chairs the firm's Environmental Group and the Climate Change and Sustainability Practice Group. His broad-based experience ranges from the litigation of complex environmental disputes to representation and counseling on regulatory matters. His expertise includes adversarial matters under CERCLA, Clean Air Act, Clean Water Act, CEQA and insurance coverage for environmental liabilities. Dave represents some of the country's largest companies to recover environmental cleanup costs - from responsible parties and insurers - in connection with national portfolios of contaminated properties. He has represented clients at a number of Superfund sites and has served as common or lead counsel for a number of PRP groups. He emphasizes the implementation of strategies for the cost-effective, innovative and favorable resolution of disputed claims through litigation, ADR or other means. Dave provides representation before regulatory agencies; including rule-makings, negotiating fines and penalties and addressing cleanup requirements. He provides environmental support for corporate and real estate acquisitions. Representative clients include Union Pacific Railroad Company, Northrop Grumman Corporation, Eni Oil & Gas, Inc., Realty Income,

Culver City and Dairy Cares (a coalition of California dairy trade associations and related businesses). Mr Cranston emphasizes the implementation of strategies for the cost-effective, innovative and favorable resolution of such claims through litigation, ADR or other means. Mr Cranston has represented his clients in connection with a number of Superfund sites, including defense of U.S. EPA claims of liability and the negotiation of administrative orders, consent decrees and allocation among potentially responsible parties. Mr Cranston has served as common or lead counsel for a number of defense groups in litigated and non-litigated matters. Mr Cranston has substantial expertise in air quality litigation, regulation and counseling on policy and rule-making matters. His litigation experience has resulted in the publication of leading appellate opinions favorable to his clients. The dairy industry in Central California, one of the largest in the world, has exclusively relied on Mr Cranston for providing the legal counseling, representation and litigation necessary to face a dynamic regulatory environment in a region known for significant air quality issues and aggressive challenges by environmental organizations. Mr Cranston has substantial experience in challenging and defending the decisions and documentation required under the California Environmental Quality Act (CEQA). Mr Cranston also advises real estate investors and developers in connection with the acquisition and redevelopment of properties impacted by environmental contamination. He helps direct the due diligence, risk management and regulatory initiatives necessary for a successful project. Mr Cranston has worked with most of the major insurance markets in negotiating manuscripted environmental insurance policies to specifically address environmental risks arising from known and unknown pollution conditions. He has also helped his clients recover claims under such policies and has significant experience under the Clean Water Act.
**Personal:** BA San Diego State University 1981, UC Davis School of Law 1985.

## CRAWFORD, Bradley C
Bingham McCutchen LLP, San Francisco
415 393 2888
brad.crawford@bingham.com
*Featured in Banking & Finance (California)*

**Practice Areas:** Represents insurance companies and other institutional investors, banks, mezzanine funds, commercial finance lenders and other lenders, and issuers and borrowers in a wide range of debt and equity financing transactions. Has extensive experience in traditional private placement financings (both domestic and cross-border), mezzanine and structured equity financings, secured and unsecured syndicated bank financings, and loan restructurings, with many of these transactions having been in the context of tender offers, buyouts and other acquisitions.
**Personal:** University of California, Hastings College of the Law, Juris Doctor, 1995. University of California, Berkeley, Bachelor of Science, Business Administration, 1983.

## CRIPPS JR., Jesse A
Gibson, Dunn & Crutcher LLP, Los Angeles
213 229 7792
jcripps@gibsondunn.com
*Featured in Labor & Employment (California)*

**Practice Areas:** Expertise includes full range of labor and employment matters under federal and state law, specializing in defense of high risk, complex and class action litigation. Representative matters include defense of statewide and nationwide class actions (wage/hour, discrimination), high stakes non-compete and trade secret disputes, and individual discrimination, retaliation and whistleblowing claims. Wide range of courtroom and administrative experience, including state and federal jury trials, and first chair success in the California Court of Appeal and Ninth Circuit Court of Appeals.
**Professional Memberships:** Executive Committee, L.A. County Bar Association, Center for Civic Mediation.
**Personal:** JD, Pepperdine Law, 2002.

## CUFF, Terence
Loeb & Loeb LLP, Los Angeles
310 282 2181
tcuff@loeb.com
*Featured in Tax (California)*

**Practice Areas:** Partnership taxation and real estate taxation.
**Career:** Partner since 1986.
**Personal:** NYU Law School (LLM 1979); USC Law School (JD, 1977); University of California, Santa Cruz (BA, 1974).

## CURTIS, Kenneth W
Allen Matkins Leck Gamble Mallory & Natsis LLP, Irvine
949 851 5493
kcurtis@allenmatkins.com
*Featured in Construction (California)*

**Practice Areas:** Kenneth Curtis specializes almost exclusively in the areas of public and private works construction. Now in his 25th year of practice, Ken has handled a broad array of complex legal matters for owners, contractors, engineers, subcontractors, suppliers and design professionals. He is experienced in all phases of construction – providing start-to-finish advice and counsel on both public and private sector projects. From bid protests to claims resolution, Ken has successfully guided clients through the labyrinth of intricate construction legal issues using the most efficient and effective means possible, including his experience with various forms of alternative dispute resolution.

## CURTIS, Linda
Gibson, Dunn & Crutcher LLP, Los Angeles
213 229 7582
lcurtis@gibsondunn.com
*Featured in Banking & Finance (California)*

**Practice Areas:** Corporate finance, including secured and unsecured corporate credit facilities, acquisition financings, Rule 144A transactions, exchange offers, securitizations, asset-based lending, cross-border financings, mezzanine transactions, preferred stock financings, DIP financings and work-outs and debt restructurings.

**Career:** Trustee and Senior Vice President, LA County Bar Association. Former Chair of Commercial Law and Bankruptcy Section Executive Committee and Business & Corporations Law Section Executive Committee, LA County Bar Association.
**Personal:** JD, Stanford University, 1987; MBA, Stanford University, 1987; BA University of Oxford (Balliol College), 1984; BA Princeton University, 1982. Phi Beta Kappa. Newton-Tatum Scholar and Truman Scholar.

## CUSSEN, Deborah
Gibson, Dunn & Crutcher LLP, San Francisco
415 393 8226
dacussen@gibsondunn.com
*Featured in Real Estate (California)*

**Practice Areas:** Represents lenders, borrowers, institutional and non-institutional investors, developers and managers in all areas of commercial real estate and all asset classes, including acquisition and development loans, construction loans, mezzanine and permanent financing transactions; purchase and repurchase transactions; acquisitions and dispositions; acquisition, sale and financing of loans and loan portfolios; debt restructurings, extensions, workouts, forbearance agreements, foreclosures and other enforcement actions; formation of general and limited partnerships, limited liability companies and other joint ventures; fund formation and private equity work; and resolution of joint venture issues and disputes.

## DAKIN-GRIMM, Linda
Milbank, Tweed, Hadley & McCloy LLP, Los Angeles
213 892 4404
ldakin-grimm@milbank.com
*Featured in Insurance (California)*

**Practice Areas:** Ms Dakin-Grimm is a partner in the Litigation & Arbitration Group. She has successfully handled numerous jury and bench trials, appeals and arbitration proceedings across the US. She represents performing rights organization BMI in disputes over use of copyrighted music. She has won numerous contentious valuation disputes in trial. In 2010, she won a trial, representing a group of secured lenders, a hotly contested "cram-up" fight, defeating both the Debtor and the Creditors' Committee's efforts to reinstate secured debt of Young Broadcasting. She repeatedly wins significant financial victories for property/casualty insurers and reinsurers in confidential arbitration disputes.

## DALLAS, Bruce
Davis Polk & Wardwell LLP, Menlo Park
650 752 2000
bruce.dallas@davispolk.com
*Featured in Capital Markets (California), Capital Markets (Nationwide)*

**Practice Areas:** Member, Davis Polk's Corporate Department and Menlo Park office founder. He advises on corporate finance, equity derivatives, SEC disclosure and corporate governance. His corporate clients include AVG Technologies, Comcast, Masco, NBCUniversal, Oracle, Roper Industries and Texas Instruments and he regularly advises leading underwriters. Recent transactions include $10.0 billion in debt offerings Comcast, Masco, NBCUniversal, Roper Industries and Texas Instruments, $480 million in initial public offerings for AVG, Enphase and Palo Alto Networks, $1.5 billion in equity offerings for Amylin Pharmaceuticals, Jazz Pharmaceuticals, Netflix, Onyx Pharmaceuticals, Palo Alto Networks and Xenoport and a debt exchange offer for Universal Orlando.

### DAVIDSON, Gordon K
Fenwick & West LLP, Mountain View
650 988 8500
gdavidson@fenwick.com
*Featured in Investment Funds (Nationwide), Capital Markets (California), Corporate/M&A (Northern California), Corporate/M&A (California)*
**Practice Areas:** Gordon K Davidson is a partner in the Corporate Group and Chairman of Fenwick & West LLP. He advises high technology companies, clean technology and life sciences companies. Mr Davidson's clients range from start-ups to Fortune 1000 companies as well as investors and investment banks. He has worked on over 50 public offerings and has represented boards of directors, audit committees and executives in numerous special investigations. He has acted as lead counsel on over 100 M&A's valued at more than $50 billion in the aggregate.
**Career:** Mr Davidson has received numerous accolades for his achievements, including recognition by Chambers USA as first tier Corporate/M&A attorney in the US; "Corporate Lawyer of the Year" for Silicon Valley by Best Lawyers magazine (2009 and 2013); San Francisco Area "Securities Lawyer of the Year" by Best Lawyers magazine (2010); one of a dozen lawyers named to the AlwaysOn Power Players West list (2011); one of the Top 25 Biotech Lawyers in California by the Daily Journal (2011) and as one of the 100 best lawyers in Northern California (2004-12) by Super Lawyers magazine.

### DAVIDSON, Gregory
Gibson, Dunn & Crutcher LLP, Palo Alto
650 849 5350
gdavidson@gibsondunn.com
*Featured in Investment Funds (Nationwide), Corporate/M&A (California)*
See under Nationwide for profile.

### DAVIDSON, Robert J
Buchalter Nemer, Los Angeles
213 891 5023
rdavidson@buchalter.com
*Featured in Banking & Finance (California)*
**Practice Areas:** Primarily representing institutional lenders in senior secured and unsecured credit facilities; including asset-based lending, cash flow and recurring revenue lending, acquisition and working capital finance, syndicated loan transactions, cross-border financing, loan portfolio acquisitions and financing, problem loan workouts and restructuring, debtor-in-possession financings, liquidations and foreclosures.
**Career:** Member, Buchalter Nemer Board of Directors; past Co-Chair, Bank and Finance Practice Group

**Personal:** University of Southern California School of Law and Graduate School of Business and Management (JD, MBA); University of Southern California (BS).

### DAVIS, Wendy
Jones Day, Palo Alto
650 739 3920
wdavis@jonesday.com
*Featured in Employee Benefits & Executive Compensation (California)*
**Practice Areas:** Wendy focuses on equity and executive compensation and corporate governance. Her practice addresses the practical design considerations of programs, including the complicated intersection of tax, securities, employment, and corporate laws, as well as shareholder relations issues. Wendy works regularly with clients to develop and maintain their equity and bonus plans, deferred compensation arrangements, and severance and change of control agreements. She is actively involved in the preparation of public company disclosures, including drafting CD&As and proxy proposals. She also works with M&A lawyers to determine equity award treatment, negotiate the definitive agreement, and address other M&A compensation issues.

### DE BODO, Richard
DLA Piper LLP (US), Los Angeles
310 595 3100
richard.debodo@dlapiper.com
*Featured in Life Sciences (Nationwide), Life Sciences (California)*
**Practice Areas:** Patent Litigation.
**Career:** He is co-chair of the firm's Patent Litigation practice and litigates patent, trade secret, copyright, trademark and licensing cases before trial courts, appellate courts, arbitration panels and the International Trade Commission. He has litigated numerous cases for clients in the US, Europe and Asia involving computer hardware and software, Internet technology, broadband communications, consumer electronics, semiconductors and other technologies. He has been recognized as a creative and innovative trial lawyer and an effective and practical problem solver for clients.
**Personal:** JD, Harvard Law School; BA, Harvard University.

### DE GROOT, Jay
Morrison & Foerster LLP, San Diego
858 720 5180
jdegroot@mofo.com
*Featured in Corporate/M&A (California)*
**Practice Areas:** Over 20 years of experience representing public and private companies, VC funds, and underwriters in corporate and securities matters. Has consummated more than $7 billion of M&A transactions across a wide range of industries and technologies. Counsels privately held companies in the life sciences, technology, and cleantech sectors, as well as the funds that finance them. In the last several years, has closed more than 80 venture financings with over $1 billion of aggregate proceeds. Has helped raise over $2 billion in IPO and capital market transactions.

Regularly counsels public companies on corporate governance, reporting, and compliance matters.

### DEIBERT, Edward
Arnold & Porter LLP, San Francisco
415 471 3149
Edward.Deibert@aporter.com
*Featured in Corporate/M&A (Northern California)*
**Practice Areas:** Edward Deibert, a partner in the corporate and securities practice, has broad experience representing individuals, companies, private equity firms, venture capital funds, and investment banks in a variety of transactions and matters. His practice focuses on mergers and acquisitions, and he has been involved in numerous transactions buying and selling privately held and publicly traded businesses. He represents clients in a number of industries, including financial services, technology and consumer products.

### DENENBERG, Alan
Davis Polk & Wardwell LLP, Menlo Park
650 752 2000
alan.denenberg@davispolk.com
*Featured in Capital Markets (California), Capital Markets (Nationwide), Corporate/M&A (Northern California)*
**Practice Areas:** A partner in Davis Polk's Corporate Department and head of the Menlo Park office. He has extensive experience in corporate finance and mergers and acquisitions transactions. His practice includes a broad range of public and private equity and debt financing representing both domestic and foreign issuers and underwriters in a variety of industries, including technology, telecommunications, health care, retail and manufacturing. In the mergers and acquisitions area, he has worked on a number of public and private transactions, representing both acquirer and target companies, as well as private equity firms.

### DENHAM, Robert E
Munger, Tolles & Olson LLP, Los Angeles
213 683 9104
Robert.Denham@mto.com
*Featured in Corporate/M&A (Southern California)*
**Practice Areas:** Mergers and acquisitions, corporate governance, strategic advice. Recent representations: Berkshire Hathaway in its acquisitions of the H.J. Heinz Co., The Lubrizol Corporation, and its $5 billion investment in Bank of America; HealthCare Partners in its sale to DaVita Inc.
**Professional Memberships:** Chairman, Russell Sage Foundation; Vice Chairman, Good Samaritan Hospital of Los Angeles; Boards of: Chevron Corporation; Fomento Economico Mexicano, S.A. de CV (FEMSA); The New York Times Company; Oaktree Capital Group LLC.
**Career:** Partner at the firm; former managing partner.
**Personal:** Harvard Law School (magna cum laude); Harvard University (MA); University of Texas (BA).

### DENNIS, Patrick W
Gibson, Dunn & Crutcher LLP, Los Angeles
213 229 7567
pdennis@gibsondunn.com
*Featured in Environment (California)*

**Practice Areas:** Co-Chair of firm's Environmental Litigation and Mass Tort Practice Group. Represents clients in environmental litigation, toxic tort lawsuits, defense of public and private enforcement actions, private party cleanup cost recovery, diligence/transactional matters with environmental liabilities, and complex permit/entitlement requirements. Extensive experience with administering agencies for air quality, hazardous waste, and water quality. Represents buyers and sellers of major industrial facilities worldwide and contaminated real estate for redevelopment. Lead litigation counsel for numerous cleanup cost recovery, toxic tort, enforcement and Superfund matters, including natural resource damage actions brought by the US.
**Personal:** UCLA, BS, 1976; MS, 1978; JD-MBA, 1982.

### DETERMANN, Lothar
Baker & McKenzie, San Francisco
650 856 5533
lothar.determann@bakermckenzie.com
*Featured in IT & Outsourcing (California), Privacy & Data Security (Nationwide)*
**Practice Areas:** Data privacy, electronic commerce, Software licensing, intellectual property and international commercial law related to technology transactions and outsourcing.
**Publications:** Determann's Field Guide to International Data Privacy Law Compliance (2012), three other books and more than 80 articles and treatise contributions on topics including software licensing, electronic commerce, data protection, and intellectual property.
**Personal:** Admitted in California and Germany; teaches Computer, E-Commerce and Data Privacy Law at UC Berkeley School of Law (Boalt Hall), Freie Universitaet Berlin and Hastings College of the Law.

### DIAMOND, Valerie H
Baker & McKenzie, San Francisco
415 576 3086
valerie.diamond@bakermckenzie.com
*Featured in Employee Benefits & Executive Compensation (California)*
**Practice Areas:** Assists companies in the design and implementation of international executive compensation and employee stock plans. Provides advice on the tax, securities law and exchange control compliance issues that arise when issuer grants options, restricted stock or purchase rights to employees on a global basis.
**Professional Memberships:** Chair of Certified Equity Professionals Advisory Board and member of National Association of Stock Plan Professionals Advisory Board and Global Equity Organization. Member of California State Bar.
**Career:** Top 75 Corporate Lawyer, Daily Journal (2011 and 2012). National Association of Stock Plan Professional Individual Achievement Award (2008).
**Publications:** "Global Plan Design and Compliance Strategies for ESPP" (Workspan Magazine) (September 2012); "Employee Stock Purchase Plans" Guidance, Procedures and Systems, Certified Equity Professional Institute

(2012); "Global Forum: Coping with Legal Obstacles to Granting Equity Awards in Asia-Pacific" (Workspan Magazine) (September 2010); "Current Equity and Employment Challenges for U.S. Multinationals in China" (Daily Journal) (August 2010); "Are Retirement Benefits and Equity a Bad Mix?" (Workspan Magazine) (August 2010); "The Global Side of Option Exchange Programs" (The Bureau of National Affairs, Inc.) (June 2009).
**Personal:** JD from the University of San Francisco School of Law. MA and BA in history from California State University, Sacramento.

## DIBERNARDO, S James
Morgan, Lewis & Bockius LLP, Palo Alto
650 843 7560
jdibernardo@morganlewis.com
*Featured in Employee Benefits & Executive Compensation (Nationwide), Employee Benefits & Executive Compensation (California)*
**Practice Areas:** S James DiBernardo is a senior counsel in Morgan Lewis's Employee Benefits and Executive Compensation Practice. He specializes in all areas of equity compensation and nonqualified deferred compensation programs for both public and private companies. Mr DiBernardo regularly counsels employers on the tax, securities, corporate governance and financial accounting implications of such programs and provides comprehensive advice on employee benefit issues in connection with mergers and acquisitions.
**Personal:** He is a graduate of Columbia University Law School (1973, JD) and Holy Cross College (1967, AB in literature). Mr DiBernardo is admitted to practice in California.

## DICANIO, Jack P
Skadden, Arps, Slate, Meagher & Flom LLP & Affiliates, Los Angeles
213 687 5430
jack.dicanio@skadden.com
*Featured in Litigation (California)*
**Practice Areas:** Represents corporate and individual clients in complex business litigation and criminal and regulatory actions. Specializes in trial practice, internal investigations, Foreign Corrupt Practice Act investigations, federal and state securities litigation, securities regulatory and enforcement proceedings, financial institution fraud, and government procurement fraud.
**Career:** JD, Boston College Law School, 1988; BA, University of Notre Dame, 1985 (magna cum laude). Assistant US Attorney, Central District of California, Deputy Chief, General Crimes Section (1994-2000). Trained federal prosecutors in trial practice and criminal law/procedure. Recipient of the US Attorney General's Distinguished Service Award.

## DIEKMANN JR, Gilmore F
Seyfarth Shaw LLP, San Francisco
415 544 1070
gdiekmann@seyfarth.com
*Featured in Labor & Employment (California)*
**Practice Areas:** Specializes in the defense of complex employment litigation, particularly employment discrimination and wage/hour class actions. Has tried six employment class actions to

judgment, both to judges and juries, in the federal and state courts. Also has tried five single-plaintiff wrongful discharge cases to jury verdicts. Occasionally serves as a professional mediator in complex employment cases. Frequent lecturer/panelist on employment litigation topics.
**Publications:** Numerous papers on employment litigation strategies and tactics.
**Personal:** Northwestern University School of Business (BSBA, 1968) and School of Law (JD, Magna Cum Laude, 1971); Order of the Coif; Best Lawyers in America, 1989 to date.

## DILLER, Nicole A
Morgan, Lewis & Bockius LLP, San Francisco
415 442 1312
ndiller@morganlewis.com
*Featured in Employee Benefits & Executive Compensation (California)*
**Practice Areas:** Nicole Diller is a partner in Morgan Lewis's Labor and Employment Practice. Her practice focuses on ERISA and other employee benefit litigation, fiduciary counseling, and legal aspects of benefits and plan administration. She counsels and defends employers, financial institutions, and non-profits (including religiously-affiliated entities) in class actions, multi-party cases, and individual benefit litigation matters nationwide. Her clients include public and private corporations, nonprofit entities, governmental benefit plans, financial institutions, and multiemployer pension plans.
**Personal:** Attended Stanford Law School, JD; University of Michigan, BGS, with Distinction.

## DILLON, Carol K
Bingham McCutchen LLP, East Palo Alto
650 849 4812
carol.dillon@bingham.com
*Featured in Real Estate (California)*
**Practice Areas:** Managing partner of Bingham's Silicon Valley office. Focuses on complex commercial ground leasing, representation of institutional investors, and acquisition and development of land for renewable energy projects. Practice includes a broad spectrum of real estate matters, including the acquisition, development and disposition of a wide range of properties such as office buildings, shopping centers, agricultural lands and medical facilities. Has represented clients in real estate matters valued at more than $5 billion.
**Career:** Award-winning former reporter and producer of television news programs.
**Personal:** University of California Berkeley School of Law (Boalt Hall), JD, 1982; Stanford University, BA, 1975.

## DILLON, Christopher D
Gibson, Dunn & Crutcher LLP, Palo Alto
650 849 5325
cdillon@gibsondunn.com
*Featured in Corporate/M&A (Northern California)*
**Practice Areas:** Regularly advises public and private corporate and private equity clients in a wide range of mergers and acquisitions (friendly and hostile), divestitures, joint ventures, strategic alliances and capital raising transactions. In addi-

tion, he has extensive experience in counseling boards of directors and senior management teams in connection with corporate governance, public disclosure, SEC filings and other securities laws matters.
**Professional Memberships:** Member, California and New York State Bars.
**Career:** Former Senior Managing Director, Union Square Advisors LLC.
**Personal:** JD Boston College, 1988; BA, Boston College, 1983.

## DINTZER, Jeffrey D
Gibson, Dunn & Crutcher LLP, Los Angeles
213 229 7860
jdintzer@gibsondunn.com
*Featured in Environment (California)*
**Practice Areas:** Co-Chair of the firm's Environment Litigation and Mass Tort Practice Group. Specializes in environmental litigation, involving cost recovery, toxic torts, water rights, and land use entitlements. He has served as lead trial counsel in matters concerning groundwater contamination, and CEQA compliance. Representative clients include Occidental Petroleum, Goodrich, United Technologies, Plains Exploration and Production, and Lockheed Martin.
**Publications:** Co-author, Cleanup Liability and Cost Recovery, 'California Environmental Law and Land Use.
**Personal:** JD, Boston University, 1988, cum laude; former Law Clerk to Judge Alice-Marie Stotler, Central District of California.

## DIXON, David L
Kirkland & Ellis LLP, San Francisco
415 439 1454
david.dixon@kirkland.com
*Featured in Corporate/M&A (California)*
**Practice Areas:** David Dixon is a partner in the San Francisco office of Kirkland & Ellis. He represents private equity firms and their portfolio companies in all aspects of their businesses, with a focus on leveraged and management buyouts, venture and growth capital investments, divestitures, other mergers and acquisitions, equity financings, restructurings and work outs, executive compensation matters, and corporate governance.
**Personal:** University of Florida Fredric G. Levin College of Law, JD, 1999 with honors; University of Florida, BS, 1996 with honors.

## DOMZALSKI, Shawn
Gibson, Dunn & Crutcher LLP, Los Angeles
213 229 7512
sdomzalski@gibsondunn.com
*Featured in Corporate/M&A (Southern California)*
**Practice Areas:** Member of firm's Corporate Department, M&A, Gaming, Media, Entertainment & Technology, Investment Funds, Emerging Technologies, and Private Equity practice groups. Broad experience, including domestic and cross-border mergers and acquisitions, private equity fund formation, going-private transactions, special committee representations, and general business matters. Speak and read Mandarin Chinese; used in client representations.

**Career:** Member, The Soldiers Project Board; advisor, China Enterprise Council; former Chinese-English translator.
**Publications:** Co-author, Due Diligence, Mergers & Acquisitions, LEXIS PRACTICE ADVISOR (2013).
**Personal:** JD, Loyola University, 2006 (Magna Cum Laude, Order of the Coif), Executive Editor, Loyola Law Review; SAIS Hopkins-Nanjing Center, 1989-90.

## DONNELLY, Thomas M
Jones Day, San Francisco
415 875 5880
tmdonnelly@jonesday.com
*Featured in Environment (California)*
**Practice Areas:** Environmental, climate change, and insurance coverage law. Represents clients in environmental litigation and administrative proceedings; provides environmental compliance counseling (including with respect to greenhouse gas emissions and climate change) and due diligence/transactional support; and assists clients in securing defense and indemnity from their liability insurers. Has considerable experience defending environmental litigation matters brought under all major federal and California environmental statutes (including California's Proposition 65) and various common law theories. Represents clients in regulatory enforcement actions (such as cleanup and abatement orders and civil penalty actions), and regularly assists clients in brownfields redevelopment, land use and permitting.

## DOREN, Richard J
Gibson, Dunn & Crutcher LLP, Los Angeles
213 229 7038
rdoren@gibsondunn.com
*Featured in Insurance (California)*
**Practice Areas:** Mr Doren has extensive experience representing managed care companies and insurers in class actions as well as coverage and bad faith litigation. His areas of expertise include commercial and homeowners insurance, as well as health plans in both ERISA and non-ERISA contexts. He represents insurers and claim administrators in commercial disputes and federal and state investigations. He has also represented reinsurers in a wide variety of matters.
**Personal:** JD, University of San Diego, 1986, cum laude, Editor-in-Chief, University of San Diego Law Review.

## DORF, Michael
Shearman & Sterling LLP, San Francisco
415 616 1246
mdorf@shearman.com
*Featured in Corporate/M&A (Northern California)*
**Career:** Michael Dorf is a partner in the firm's Mergers and Acquisitions Practice Group. Mr Dorf has extensive experience in public and private mergers and acquisitions and related corporate governance matters. He has represented strategic and financial buyers and sellers in a wide range of public and private business combination transactions, including mergers, stock and asset acquisitions and divestitures, tender and exchange offers, minority investments, joint ventures and corporate partnering transactions. He also has sig-

nificant experience in cross-border transactions. Mr Dorf joined the firm as a partner in 2008.

### DOYLE, David C
Morrison & Foerster LLP, San Diego
858 720 5139
ddoyle@mofo.com
*Featured in Intellectual Property (California)*
**Practice Areas:** Mr Doyle specializes in patent litigation and licensing disputes for pharmaceutical, biotechnology, and electronics companies. He practices on a nationwide basis and currently serves as lead trial counsel in patent cases pending in Texas, Delaware, New York, New Jersey, and Nevada.
**Professional Memberships:** Mr Doyle is Chairman of San Diego's Kyoto Symposium Organization. He also has led Magistrate Selection and Patent Local Rules committees for the Southern District of California.
**Career:** Admitted to practice in California. Former firmwide Co-Chair of the Intellectual Property Group (2002-06).
**Personal:** BA, University of California, San Diego; JD, UCLA School of Law.

### DRAGNA, James J
Bingham McCutchen LLP, Los Angeles
213 680 6436
jim.dragna@bingham.com
*Featured in Environment (California)*
**Practice Areas:** Represents energy, aerospace and manufacturing clients in a wide range of environmental matters nationwide, including air, water and wastewater enforcement and litigation. Practice also includes the representation of water purveyors in water rights cases and the resolution of environmental claims in bankruptcy proceedings. Serves as group or common counsel to several multiparty Superfund groups, in addition to representing a host of individual clients in over 50 federal or state Superfund matters nationwide.
**Career:** Senior trial counsel, US Department of Justice, Environmental Enforcement Section.
**Personal:** Loyola Law School, JD, 1979; University of California, Irvine, BA, cum laude, 1976.

### DREGER, Ginger R
Arnold & Porter LLP, San Francisco
415 471 3315
Ginger.Dreger@aporter.com
*Featured in Life Sciences (California)*
**Practice Areas:** Ginger Dreger is a partner in the firm's intellectual property practice group. She concentrates her practice on counseling and providing strategic advice to emerging and established public companies in the biotechnology, medical device, and pharmaceutical industries. She advises clients on domestic and international patent matters, including worldwide patent protection and enforcement strategies; freedom-to-operate issues; intellectual property due diligence; and analysis of third-party patents.

### DUKELLIS, Gregory J
Watt, Tieder, Hoffar & Fitzgerald, LLP, Irvine
949 852 6700
gdukelli@wthf.com
*Featured in Construction (California)*

**Practice Areas:** Construction, government contracts.
**Professional Memberships:** American Bar Association.
**Career:** Greg represents general contractors, owners, subcontractors, construction managers and sureties in a broad range of commercial and construction matters. His practice includes preparation and defense of claims, preparation and negotiation of contract documents, advice regarding contract administration, strategies for contract close-out and completion, preparation and defense of bid protests, analysis of false claim issues, analysis of design/build issues, and dispute resolution and litigation on a wide variety of heavy industrial and commercial construction projects.
**Publications:** Greg has authored numerous articles for construction industry trade publications within the United States.

### DUNN, K Kristine
Skadden, Arps, Slate, Meagher & Flom LLP & Affiliates, Los Angeles
213 687 5493
kristine.dunn@skadden.com
*Featured in Banking & Finance (California)*
**Practice Areas:** Represents corporations, equity sponsors and strategic investors as borrowers; and investment banks, commercial banks and other investors as agents and lenders in a broad range of transactions encompassing a wide variety of industries, including real estate, gaming, media, telecommunications, technology, retail and manufacturing. Such transactions have included acquisition financings, leveraged buyouts, bridge loans, asset-based loans, first lien/second lien financings, subordinated debt, mezzanine financings, out-of-court restructurings and other types of complex and traditional financings.
**Career:** JD, University of Minnesota, 1998; BA, Carleton College, 1995.

### DUNNE, Kimberly A
Sidley Austin LLP, Los Angeles
213 896 6659
kdunne@sidley.com
*Featured in Litigation (California)*
**Practice Areas:** Co-chair of White Collar and Government Investigations Group. Extensive experience with internal investigations, False Claims Act litigation, and criminal defense, with focus on regulated industries such as health care, government contracts, and securities. Significant jury trial and appellate experience. Former Chief of Public Corruption and Government Fraud Section in U.S. Attorney's Office in Central District of California.
**Personal:** Harvard Law School, JD, 1989; Harvard Kennedy School - John F. Kennedy School of Government, MPA, 1989; Claremont McKenna College, BA, 1985, magna cum laude, Phi Beta Kappa.

### DURRER II, Van C
Skadden, Arps, Slate, Meagher & Flom LLP & Affiliates, Los Angeles
213 687 5200
van.durrer@skadden.com
*Featured in Bankruptcy/Restructuring (California)*
**Practice Areas:** Leads Skadden's corporate restructuring practice in Western US and Pacific Rim. Represents public and private companies, secured creditors, official and unofficial committees of unsecured creditors, investors and asset-purchasers in troubled company M&A, financing and restructuring transactions, including out-of-court workouts and formal insolvency proceedings. Representative engagements: AmericanWest Bancorporation (buyer); Blue Bird Body Company; Catalyst Paper Corporation; Pierre Foods, Inc. (plan sponsor); Spansion, LLC and Station Casinos (independent director).
**Professional Memberships:** Business Bankruptcy Specialist (American Board of Certification); Board Member, California Bar Association's Insolvency Law Committee.
**Career:** JD, University of Maryland School of Law, 1993; BA, Johns Hopkins University, 1990.

### DUTRO, James R
Jones Day, San Francisco
415 875 5839
jdutro@jonesday.com
*Featured in Healthcare (California)*
**Practice Areas:** James is co-leader of Jones Day's Health Care Practice. His practice focuses on mergers and acquisitions, affiliations, joint ventures and other complex business transactions involving hospitals, health systems and other health care and life sciences companies. James is widely recognized as one of the leading attorneys in California in structuring and implementing accountable care organizations, integrated delivery systems and other hospital-physician alignment arrangements. In addition, James has significant experience advising clients regarding strategies and structures aimed at improving the quality and efficiency of health care delivery.
**Professional Memberships:** American Health Lawyers Association; California Society of Healthcare Attorneys.

### DWORSKY, Marc
Munger, Tolles & Olson LLP, Los Angeles
213 683 9256
Marc.Dworsky@mto.com
*Featured in Litigation (California)*
**Practice Areas:** Practice involves crisis management and high-stakes litigation with an emphasis on the financial sector. Recent experience includes serving as lead national counsel for Wells Fargo in all class and individual litigation by institutional investors in RMBS, and for Bank of America in a wide range of such cases, including a $10 billion lawsuit by AIG.
**Career:** Named to the Daily Journal's 2011 "Top 100" lawyers in California and Lawdragon's "Top 500" lawyers in the U.S.
**Personal:** Harvard Law School (LLM, 1988); Osgoode Hall Law School (LLB, gold medalist,

1986); University of Toronto, York University (BA, with distinction, 1983).

### EARL, Lisa C
Pillsbury Winthrop Shaw Pittman LLP, San Francisco
415 983 1631
lisa.earl@pillsburylaw.com
*Featured in IT & Outsourcing (California)*
**Practice Areas:** Ms Earl is Counsel in Pillsbury's Global Sourcing Practice and has significant experience acting for corporations in the US, the UK and Australia. Her practices focuses on multi-national outsourcing, technology transactions, telecommunications and other complex service and product procurements. In the sourcing area, Ms Earl's experience includes information technology, human resources and other business process outsourcing. Ms Earl's experience in technology transactions includes sophisticated software licensing and commercialization and the sale and acquisition of technology assets.
**Personal:** Grad.Dip, The College of Law, 1993; LLB (Hons), University of Wollongong, 1993; B Com, University of Wollongong, 1990.

### EDEL, Scott
Loeb & Loeb LLP, Los Angeles
310 282 2131
sedel@loeb.com
*Featured in Media & Entertainment (California)*
**Practice Areas:** Handles complex production, distribution and financing transactions involving major motion pictures and independent productions, as well as represents writers, directors and producers. Clients also include television production companies and executive producers, writers and directors in non-scripted and scripted television programming. Additionally, practice consists of significant music component including representation of music composers, songwriters, performers and production and publishing companies.
**Career:** Joined Loeb as Partner in 2008.
**Personal:** University of Southern California, Gould School of Law (JD, 1986); Bucknell University (BA, 1982).

### EDELMAN, Scott
Gibson, Dunn & Crutcher LLP, Los Angeles
310 557 8061
sedelman@gibsondunn.com
*Featured in Media & Entertainment (California)*
**Practice Areas:** Co-Chair Media and Entertainment Practice. Represents major entertainment clients in matters involving antitrust, IP (copyright, trademark, right of publicity, misappropriation of ideas, trade secret), profit participation, film distribution, false advertising, royalty disputes. Significant IFTA experience. Significant first-chair trial experience. Commercial litigation experience includes cross-border commercial disputes, environmental, product liability, employment, sports, professional negligence, RICO, real estate and construction defects. Representative clients: CBS, NBC Universal, Sony Corporation of America and Sony Pictures and SonyBMG, Fox Broadcasting Company, and Mattel.

**Personal:** JD, University of California, Boalt Hall School of Law, 1984. Co-Editor-in-Chief, Ecology Law Quarterly.

## EHRGOTT, Catherine
Jones Day, Los Angeles
213 243 2552
cehrgott@jonesday.com
*Featured in Healthcare (California)*

**Practice Areas:** Represents companies in the healthcare industry in a broad range of transactions, including structuring healthcare networks, ACOs, acquisitions, divestitures, joint ventures and other corporate matters.
**Professional Memberships:** State Bar of California (Business Law Section); American Health Lawyers Association; California Society of Health Lawyers.
**Career:** University of Southern California (BS cum laude 1984); Loyola Law School, Los Angeles (St Thomas More Law Honor Society; editor, International and Comparative Law Journal; JD 1988); Executive Committee of the State Bar Business Law Section, Secretary (2008-2009), CFO (2009-2010); Liason to State Bar Health Law Committee (2008-2010); Vice Chair (2004-2005); Co-Chair (2003-2004).

## EISEN, Rebecca
Morgan, Lewis & Bockius LLP, San Francisco
415 422 1328
reisen@morganlewis.com
*Featured in Labor & Employment (California)*

**Practice Areas:** Rebecca Eisen is a partner in Morgan Lewis's Labor and Employment Practice. Becky chairs the firm's West Coast Wage and Hour Practice and regularly defends employers in wage and hour class actions, multiple-plaintiff, and collective actions brought under California law and the FLSA. Becky also serves on the Legal Board of California's largest employer association, The Employers Group, and serves as a Trustee on the Board of Trustees of the California State University system.
**Personal:** Attended University of San Francisco School of Law, JD, valedictorian; San Francisco State University, MA; University of California, Berkeley, BA.

## EISENBERG, Jon B
Horvitz & Levy LLP, Oakland
510 452 2581
jeisenberg@horvitzlevy.com
*Featured in Litigation (California)*

**Career:** Jon B. Eisenberg is the principal author of the leading treatise on California civil appellate practice, The Rutter Group's "California Practice Guide: Civil Appeals and Writs." His practice, in addition to business-related appeals, has included pro bono work in numerous civil rights cases involving issues such as same-sex marriage, the right to die, affirmative action, and national security. In 2011, he received California Lawyer magazine's "Attorney of the Year" (CLAY) award for Constitutional Law. In 2010, he was featured in the Los Angeles and San Francisco Daily Journal as one of ten "Lawyers Who Helped Shape a Decade."

## ELACQUA, James J
Skadden, Arps, Slate, Meagher & Flom LLP & Affiliates, Palo Alto
650 470 4510
james.elacqua@skadden.com
*Featured in Intellectual Property (California)*

**Practice Areas:** As leader of Skadden's Patent and Technology Litigation and Counseling practice, Mr Elacqua has focused his 35-year career on patent litigation in the computer, electronics, life sciences, and medical device industries, often drawing on his electrical engineering background. He has represented numerous Fortune 500 companies in state and district courts, the Federal Circuit, and the ITC. He also advises general counsel and boards of directors on intellectual property enforcement matters, defensive and litigation strategy, and settlement negotiations.
**Career:** Clarkson University, BSEE, 1972; Ohio Northern University Pettit College of Law, JD, 1976.

## ELLMAN, Howard
Buchalter Nemer, Los Angeles
415 296 1610
hellman@buchalter.com
*Featured in Real Estate (California)*

**Practice Areas:** Zoning, land use, land use litigation, natural resources, real estate transactions, water law.
**Professional Memberships:** State Bar of California, American Bar Association, Bar Association of San Francisco, American College of Real Estate Lawyers.
**Career:** Howard Ellman handles transactions and litigation involving diverse matters such as land use entitlements, natural resource regulations, endangered species, constitutional rights of property owners and others, property transfers, real property security, development joint ventures, and water law. He has served as lead counsel on numerous high-profile entitlement and development projects and presented cases in the United States Supreme Court, the California Supreme Court, the United States Court of Appeal (Ninth Circuit) and the California Courts of Appeal.
**Personal:** JD, Stanford University. An active participant in California's real estate community, he has owned and operated a rice farm in the Sacramento Valley since 1978 and is active in water and conservation issues there. He is also author of the historical novel, The Wayfarers, set in the Thirteenth Century.

## EMANUEL, Craig A
Loeb & Loeb LLP, Los Angeles
310 282 2262
cemanuel@loeb.com
*Featured in Media & Entertainment (California)*

**Practice Areas:** Counsels advertisers and media clients on issues ranging from sponsorship agreements, celebrity placement agreements, matters related to branded entertainment. Represents high level writers, directors, actors and producers in all aspects of motion picture and television transactions, both at studio and independent levels. Counsels on negotiation of strategic distribution relationships with studios including licensing of digital media content.
**Professional Memberships:** LA Film Festival Advisory Committee; Entertainment Symposium, UCLA Law School Advisory Board.
**Career:** Partner since 1989. Entertainment and Talent Chair.
**Personal:** Monash University, Melbourne, Australia (LLB, 1981); Monash University (BA Law, 1979).

## ERICKSON, Randall L
Crowell & Moring LLP, Irvine
949 798 1323
rerickson@crowell.com
*Featured in Construction (California)*

**Practice Areas:** Senior Counsel and chair of Crowell & Moring's Construction group. Has 30+ year experience in the construction industry, specializing in construction claims and construction defect disputes, public contracts and bid disputes, labor law issues, real estate development, and related environment concerns. He has represented clients in arbitrations, trials and mediations.
**Professional Memberships:** Federal Bar Association of Orange County's Board of Directors and serves on the Large and Complex Case panel at the American Arbitration Association.
**Career:** He served as an Infantry Platoon Commander in the United States Marine Corps and has been decorated for combat action.

## ESKENAZI, Bonnie
Greenberg Glusker Fields Claman & Machtinger LLP, Los Angeles
310 553 3610
BEskenazi@greenbergglusker.com
*Featured in Media & Entertainment (California)*

**Practice Areas:** Ms Eskenazi represents plaintiffs and defendants in a variety of litigation matters, primarily focusing on entertainment disputes over issues such as profit participations, copyright ownership, idea theft, contracts, defamation, invasion of privacy, merchandise and licensing, music distribution, and new technology. Ms Eskenazi also handles various entertainment transactional matters as well, and serves as the outside general counsel for the Estate of Bob Marley.
**Professional Memberships:** Founding Member, Board of Directors, The Festival of New American Musicals 2006-present.
**Career:** Recognized by Variety as one of its "Women of Impact" within the Entertainment Industry, by the Recorder as California's Entertainment Lawyer of the Year, by Hollywood Reporter as one of the Top 100 "Power Lawyers" in Hollywood, Los Angeles Daily Journal as one of "California's Top 75 Women Litigators," by the Los Angeles Business Journal as "The Best of the Bar," by Los Angeles Magazine as a "Super Lawyer," Best Lawyers in America and by Chambers & Partners as one of America's leading media and entertainment lawyers. Ms Eskenazi also carries the highest peer-review rating, "AV" by Martindale Hubbell. Ms Eskenazi has represented some of Hollywood's most famous actors, directors, writers, producers, musicians, independent production companies and major studios. Clients have included Marvel Entertainment, MGM, Paramount Pictures, DreamWorks, Jeffrey Katzenberg, Marlon Brando, Mike Tyson, Brett Ratner, Estate of Bob Marley, Hans Zimmer, Estate of J.R.R. Tolkien, Renee Fleming, Joshua Bell, Itzhak Perlman, Harvey Entertainment, DIC Entertainment, Elle Macpherson, Geffen Records and many others. Ms Eskenazi also teaches Entertainment Law at Stanford Law School and appears as a guest lecturer in Entertainment Law at Harvard Law School.
**Personal:** JD, Stanford Law School (1985); BA, University of Virginia with Highest Distinction (1982); clerked for Hon. Donald B. King, First District California Court of Appeal (1985-1986).

## ETH, Jordan
Morrison & Foerster LLP, San Francisco
415 268 7126
jeth@mofo.com
*Featured in Securities (Nationwide), Litigation (California)*

**Practice Areas:** Nationally recognized litigator, representing public companies and their officers and directors in securities class actions, SEC investigations, derivative suits, mergers and acquisitions litigation, and internal investigations. Representations have led to significant victories for defendants, as reflected in numerous published judicial decisions. Represented JDSU and three former executives in a jury trial finding for defendants on all claims in case seeking $20 billion for alleged fraudulent statements and insider trading.
**Career:** Co-Chair of the firm's Securities Litigation, Enforcement, and White-Collar Criminal Defense Group. Admitted to practice in California.
**Personal:** BA, Swarthmore College, 1980; JD, Stanford University Law School, 1985.

## FABRICK, Howard
Barnes & Thornburg LLP, Los Angeles
howard.fabrick@btlaw.com
*Featured in Labor & Employment (California)*

**Practice Areas:** Represents motion picture and television producers with respect to guilds and unions concerning all types of productions including new media, screen credits, residuals and ancillary rights.
**Professional Memberships:** Public Counsel, 1998-2001; California Motion Picture Development Council, 1975-80; Adjunct Professor, USC Peter Stark Producer Program, 1982-91.
**Career:** NLRB Attorney, 1962-64; VP Labor Relations, Columbia Pictures, 1966-71; VP, Assoc. of Motion Picture & Television Producers, 1973-75; Partner, Loeb & Loeb, 1975-81, Proskauer Rose, 1981-99, Akin Gump, 1999-2012, Barnes & Thornburg LLP, 2012-present.
**Publications:** Entertainment Law Review, Loyola Law School, 2001.
**Personal:** BA, Stanford University 1960; JD, Stanford Law School, 1962.

**FACKLER, Stephen W**
Gibson, Dunn & Crutcher LLP, Palo Alto
650 849 5385
sfackler@gibsondunn.com
*Featured in Employee Benefits & Executive Compensation (California)*
**Practice Areas:** Co-Chair of the firm's Executive Compensation and Employee Benefits Group. Advises public and private companies, private equity funds and boards of directors on compensation and benefits matters. Also regularly advises senior executives on employment and severance arrangements, management teams on buy-out compensation and stock ownership terms, and directors on compensation and indemnification arrangements.
**Professional Memberships:** Chairman, Certification Council for the Certified Equity Professional Institute. Outside counsel for Global Equity Organization, the leading international trade association for stock plan professionals.
**Personal:** JD, Stanford University (1984); Honours BA, St. Johns' College, Oxford (1981); BA, Harvard University, Phi Beta Kappa (1979).

**FARABEE, David R**
Pillsbury Winthrop Shaw Pittman LLP, Washington, DC
415 983 1124
david.farabee@pillsburylaw.com
*Featured in Environment (California)*
**Practice Areas:** Air quality and climate (greenhouse gas/AB 32) regulation, including policy and development of federal, state and local legislation and regulations, regulatory compliance, enforcement defense, facility permitting and defense of permit challenges.
**Professional Memberships:** ABA (Environment, Energy and Resources Section); State Bar of California (Environmental Law Section); Bar Association of San Francisco (Environmental and Water Law Section); Air and Waste Management Association.
**Career:** Admitted: California.
**Personal:** JD, University of California, Davis, King Hall School of Law, 1987, Order of the Coif; MPH, Environmental Health, University of California, Los Angeles, 1980; BA, Biology, University of California, Los Angeles, 1977.

**FELDMAN, Larry**
Kaye Scholer LLP, Los Angeles
310 788 1090
larry.feldman@kayescholer.com
*Featured in Litigation (California)*
**Practice Areas:** Larry Feldman, Special Counsel, has been trying jury trials for over 35 years. He focuses on civil litigation with an emphasis in high-stakes entertainment, business, insurance, legal malpractice, real estate and personal injury tort litigation. He has tried over 100 civil jury trials, and obtained millions of dollars in settlements and verdicts for his clients. Larry has been honored twice as Trial Lawyer of the Year, by the Los Angeles Trial Lawyers Association and by Loyola Law School. He has also been elected to the prestigious American College of Trial Lawyers and the International Academy of Trial Lawyers.

**FELDMAN, Lewis G**
Goodwin Procter LLP, Los Angeles
213 426 2688
lfeldman@goodwinprocter.com
*Featured in Real Estate (California)*
**Practice Areas:** Mr Feldman serves as Chair of Goodwin Procter's Los Angeles office and heads the firm's Public/Private Development Practice. He specializes in structuring, entitling and executing large-scale financings for real estate industry participants and the public sector. Mr Feldman has advised clients on more than $75 billion in debt and equity financings for market-rate and affordable apartments, master-planned residential communities, industrial and manufacturing facilities, urban entertainment centers, primary, secondary and university educational facilities, retail malls, and mixed-use projects.
**Personal:** JD, University of California at Davis, 1982; BA, University of California at Santa Cruz, 1978 (with highest honors).

**FELLER, Sean C**
Gibson, Dunn & Crutcher LLP, Los Angeles
213 229 7579
sfeller@gibsondunn.com
*Featured in Employee Benefits & Executive Compensation (California)*
**Practice Areas:** Practice focuses on all aspects executive compensation and employee benefits. Encompasses tax, ERISA, accounting, corporate, and securities law aspects of equity and other incentive compensation plans; securities law disclosures regarding executive compensation; engagement with proxy advisory firms and institutional shareholders; qualified and nonqualified retirement and deferred compensation plans and executive employment and severance arrangements.
**Professional Memberships:** New York Bar; California Bar.
**Personal:** JD, Columbia University, 2000; BS, Cornell University, 1997.

**FENNING, Lisa Hill**
Arnold & Porter LLP, Los Angeles
213 243 4019
Lisa.Fenning@aporter.com
*Featured in Bankruptcy/Restructuring (California)*
**Practice Areas:** Lisa Hill Fenning, a fellow of the American College of Bankruptcy, is a Partner in the Bankruptcy and Corporate Reorganization Practice Group. She advises companies with respect to corporate and financial restructuring, asset acquisitions and mergers in bankruptcy, and bankruptcy and insolvency-related litigation, drawing upon her extensive experience in presiding over thousands of chapter 11 corporate reorganizations as a bankruptcy judge. Ms Fenning also serves as a mediator in bankruptcy-related matters. From 1985 to 2000, Ms Fenning served as a US Bankruptcy Judge for the Central District of California, and then as a mediator with JAMS.

**FIALA, Marie L**
Sidley Austin LLP, San Francisco
415 772 1278
mfiala@sidley.com
*Featured in Antitrust (California)*

**Practice Areas:** Marie Fiala, a partner at Sidley, has a litigation and counseling practice in the federal and state courts with emphasis on complex antitrust, energy and financial issues. She was recently recognized in the 2013 edition of "The Best Lawyers in America" in Antitrust, Commercial Litigation and Energy Law. Ms Fiala has served as lead trial and appellate counsel for Pacific Gas & Electric Company in numerous cases and counseling engagements involving antitrust, preemption, contract, Commerce Clause and other commercial issues.
**Personal:** Stanford Law School, JD, 1977; University of San Francisco, MFA, 2007; Stanford University, BA, 1974.

**FILETI, Thomas**
Morrison & Foerster LLP, Los Angeles
213 892 5276
tfileti@mofo.com
*Featured in Real Estate (California)*
**Practice Areas:** Acquisition, development, financing, operation and disposition of real estate assets and investments, including apartments, shopping centers, office and industrial buildings, hotels, resorts, and portfolios. Emphasizes syndicated financing, A/B financing, mezzanine financing, lease financing, loan sales, joint ventures, and transactions involving REITs. Also, workouts and remedies relating to problem real estate loans and investments.
**Professional Memberships:** Member, National Association of Real Estate Investment Trusts; American College of Real Estate Lawyers.
**Career:** Head, Real Estate Practice Group, Los Angeles office.
**Personal:** AB, with distinction, Cornell University, 1978; JD, cum laude, University of Pennsylvania Law School, 1981. Order of the Coif.

**FINLEY, Zachary S**
Orrick, Herrington & Sutcliffe LLP, San Francisco
415 773 5921
zfinley@orrick.com
*Featured in Banking & Finance (California)*
**Career:** Zach Finley, a senior associate in Orrick's San Francisco office, is a member of the Banking and Debt Capital Markets Group. Mr Finley advises clients on a wide array of commercial finance transactions. His clients include publicly-held and privately-owned companies as borrowers and acquirers in connection with working capital credit facilities, asset-based financings and acquisition financings, as well as financial institutions serving as agent and/or lender in such credit facilities and financings. Mr Finley is a past member and past co-chair of the Uniform Commercial Code Committee of the Business Law Section of The State Bar of California.

**FISCHER, Bruce**
Greenberg Traurig, LLP, Orange County
949 732 6670
FischerB@gtlaw.com
*Featured in Real Estate (California)*
**Practice Areas:** Real Estate; real estate funds; REITS; acquisitions, dispositions; commercial real

estate financing; section 42 tax credits; complex loan restructuring.
**Professional Memberships:** Member, Los Angeles County Bar Association, Real Property Section; Past Co-Chair, Real Estate Finance Subsection for the Real Property Section of the Los Angeles County Bar Association; Past President, Hillel of Orange County; Executive Board, Real Estate Council for Orange County Federation.
**Career:** Selected: Chambers USA Guide, 2008–13. Team Member, a Law360 'Real Estate Practice Group of the Year', 2011-12.
**Personal:** JD, University of Southern California Law School, 1982; BA, University of California at San Diego, 1979.

**FISHER, Ruth**
Gibson, Dunn & Crutcher LLP, Los Angeles
310 557 8057
Rfisher@gibsondunn.com
*Featured in Media & Entertainment (California)*
**Practice Areas:** Co-Chair, Media, Entertainment & Technology Practice, specializing in transactional matters. Represents clients in the film, television, music, interactive gaming, software and technology industries in connection with: mergers and acquisitions, including acquisitions and dispositions of libraries and catalogs; various companies investing in or financing entertainment related entities or entering into joint ventures related to entertainment or technology; and content licensors and licensees in distribution and licensing agreements. Clients include investment banks, DirecTV, Macquarie Capital, Madison Square Garden, Technicolor S.A., THQ Games, Universal Music Group, Universal Studios, and Vivendi S.A.
**Personal:** JD, UCLA, 1980; Comment Editor, UCLA Law Review.

**FLANAGAN, Sharon R**
Sidley Austin LLP, San Francisco
415 772 1271
sflanagan@sidley.com
*Featured in Capital Markets (California), Corporate/M&A (Northern California)*
**Practice Areas:** Managing partner of Sidley's San Francisco office, she practices in the Corporate and Securities group. She represents companies in a broad range of merger and acquisition transactions. Her experience includes public company mergers, tender offers, spin-offs, restructurings, and acquisitions of stock and assets of private and public companies. She has experience representing issuers and underwriters in a variety of securities offerings, including initial public offerings, follow-on offerings, public debt offerings and 144A debt offerings.
**Personal:** Harvard Law School, JD, 1996, cum laude; Columbia University, BA, 1992, summa cum laude, Phi Beta Kappa. Admissions: California, Illinois.

**FLAUM, Keith A**
Weil, Gotshal & Manges LLP, Silicon Valley
650 802 3090
keith.flaum@weil.com
*Featured in Corporate/M&A (Northern California)*

**Practice Areas:** Represents both public and private companies in a wide range of industries, including information technology and life sciences. He has particular expertise in handling acquisitions of publicly traded companies and in cross-border acquisition transactions. Mr Flaum was named one of the 'Top 100 Leading Lawyers' in California by The Daily Journal and named one of a dozen 'Dealmakers of the Year' by The American Lawyer.

**Professional Memberships:** Vice-Chair of the Mergers and Acquisitions Committee of the American Bar Association's Section of Business Law and a Member of the Committee's Task Force on Acquisitions of Public Companies.

### FLOWERS, Drew C.
Gibson, Dunn & Crutcher LLP, Los Angeles
213 229 7885
dlfowers@gibsondunn.com
*Featured in Real Estate (California)*

**Practice Areas:** Represents real estate funds, lenders, developers and institutional and non-institutional investors in the formation and negotiation of joint ventures; structured finance, including preferred and mezzanine financing; workouts, loan restructuring and loan enforcement; the purchase, sale and finance of secured real estate loans; loan participations; acquisition and sale of vacant land, office buildings, apartment buildings, hotels, shopping centers, and other commercial and residential properties; all aspects of real estate development, including contractor, architect, broker and management agreements; commercial leasing; ground leasing and ground leasehold financing.

**Personal:** JD, University of Southern California, 1998.

### FOLEY GANNON, Ella
Bingham McCutchen LLP, San Francisco
415 393 2572
ella.gannon@bingham.com
*Featured in Environment (California)*

**Practice Areas:** Office managing partner of Bingham's San Francisco office and co-chair of the Environmental, Land Use and Natural Resources Practice Group. Focuses her practice on federal and state environmental laws, natural resource permitting, and land use entitlements. Assists developers and landowners who undertake complex development projects, including renewable and traditional energy and transmission projects, as well as residential, commercial, industrial and mixed-use projects. Obtains and defends both land use entitlements and environmental permits.

**Personal:** University of California, Hastings College of the Law, Juris Doctor, 1998. University of Michigan, Bachelor of Arts, 1989.

### FORBES, Amy R
Gibson, Dunn & Crutcher LLP, Los Angeles
213 229 7151
aforbes@gibsondunn.com
*Featured in Real Estate (California)*

**Practice Areas:** Land use, development, California Environmental Quality Act (including litigation), municipal law, redevelopment and public/ private partnerships, eminent domain and

real estate transactions. Representative clients: Stockbridge Real Estate Fund; Madison Square Garden, Fifteen Group, Athens, Rockpoint.

**Professional Memberships:** Member, American College of Real Estate Lawyers.

**Career:** Luce Scholar, Bangkok, Thailand 1988-89. Named among 50 most powerful women lawyers by Los Angeles Business Journal and a 'best and busiest' real estate lawyer by California Law Business.

**Personal:** BSE Civil Engineering (Transportation), Princeton University, 1980. JD, University of Southern California, 1984, Order of the Coif.

### FORST, David
Fenwick & West LLP, San Francisco
650 335 7254
dforst@fenwick.com
*Featured in Tax (California)*

**Practice Areas:** David L. Forst is the Practice Group Leader of the Tax Group at Fenwick & West LLP. Mr Forst's practice focuses on international corporate and partnership taxation.

**Career:** Mr Forst is included in Legal Media Group's Guide to the World's Leading Tax Advisers and he is recognized in Law and Business Research's International Who's Who of Corporate Tax Lawyers (2009 and 2010). He was named one of the top tax advisors in the western U.S. by the International Tax Review, is listed in Chambers USA America's Leading Lawyers for Business (2011-2012), and has been named a Northern California Super Lawyer in Tax by San Francisco Magazine.

**Publications:** Mr Forst is a lecturer at Stanford Law School on international taxation and he is an editor and regular contributor to the Journal of Taxation. He has chaired and spoken at numerous tax seminars, including the NYU Tax Institute, Tax Executives Institute, and the International Fiscal Association.

### FORSTER, Katherine M.
Munger, Tolles & Olson LLP, Los Angeles
213 683 9538
Katherine.Forster@mto.com
*Featured in Labor & Employment (California)*

**Practice Areas:** Represents employers in discrimination and wage and hour class actions and single-plaintiff litigation. Recent representations: Southern California Edison in a putative class action; Harbor Distributing in a putative class action and in a wrongful termination suit; and NBC Universal in settlement of putative class actions.

**Professional Memberships:** Executive Committee, L.A. County Bar: Labor and Employment Section; Women Lawyers Association of Los Angeles (past president); Board, Downtown Women's Center.

**Career:** Partner at the firm; named to the Daily Journal's Top 100 Women Litigators in California, 2009 and 2010.

**Personal:** University of Southern California (JD); Princeton University (AB).

### FRAM, Robert
Covington & Burling LLP, San Francisco
415 591 7025
rfram@cov.com
*Featured in Intellectual Property (California)*

**Practice Areas:** Mr Fram has substantial experience litigating patent, trade secret and licensing cases. His trial experience includes proceedings in federal and state courts, including service as special assistant district attorney, and patent trials in California, New Jersey, Texas and the International Trade Commission. He represents clients in a range of high-tech industries including software, computer and electronic, semiconductor and others.

**Professional Memberships:** Association of Business Trial Lawyers, President, Northern California Chapter (2002).

**Career:** Co-Chair, IP Litigation Practice Group.

**Personal:** Harvard Law School (JD, 1985), magna cum laude, President of the Harvard Law Review.

### FRANKENHEIMER, John T
Loeb & Loeb LLP, Los Angeles
310 282 2135
jfrankenheimer@loeb.com
*Featured in Media & Entertainment (California)*

**Practice Areas:** Advises on acquisition and sale, financing and restructuring of companies, including valuation, securitization and due diligence. Represents record companies and distributors, music publishing companies as well as artists and executives in music industry in connection with talent contracts, licensing, technology, publishing, touring and production. Represents technology and new media companies in intellectual property and content acquisition and licensing agreements. Represents writers, producers and directors in film and television.

**Professional Memberships:** Founding Member/Advisory Board/past Chair of the Entertainment Law Initiative (National Academy of Recording Arts and Sciences); Advisory Board/past Chair Entertainment Law Symposium (UCLA Law School); Executive Board/past Chair Music and Entertainment Chapter and Member of the National Board of Trustees (City of Hope); Board of Governors, Fulfillment Fund.

**Career:** Partner since 1978. Chairman Emeritus of the firm 1998-2011. Named in "Billboard Power 100" list of the most powerful people in the music business, Billboard.biz (2012 and 2013). Named "Los Angeles Music Lawyer of the Year," Best Lawyers (2012). Named "Top Dealmaker" in Variety's "Dealmakers Impact Report" (2009, 2010 and 2012). Received 2011 Entertainment Law Initiative (ELI) Service Award from The GRAMMY Foundation®. Named 'Who's Who in LA Law' by the Los Angeles Business Journal (2007/2009); 'Top Lawyer' in The Hollywood Reporter, ESQ.'s 'Power Lawyers Top 100' list (2007-2012). Honored by The Saban Free Clinic (2009).

**Publications:** Frequent speaker on entertainment law-related topics at law schools, California Copyright Society, NYU State CPA/Entertainment Forum and industry seminars such as the

Billboard Music & Money Symposium and Digital Music Forums.

**Personal:** UCLA School of Law (JD, 1973); Claremont McKenna (BS, 1968).

### FRANKLE, Diane H
Kaye Scholer LLP, Palo Alto
650 319 4518
diane.frankle@kayescholer.com
*Featured in Corporate/M&A (Northern California)*

**Practice Areas:** Diane Holt Frankle concentrates in mergers and acquisitions, corporate governance, disclosure, anti-takeover counseling, internal investigations, public offerings, venture capital financing, new company formation and executive compensation. Her clients include publicly traded and privately held companies engaged in US and cross-border mergers, acquisitions and leveraged buyouts. She represents companies in public and private offerings of equity and debt, technology companies in strategic alliances and joint ventures, and startup companies and venture capitalists in financing transactions. She also advises boards of directors and special committees on corporate governance matters, disclosure issues, and in internal investigations and related party transactions.

### FRANKLIN, Cassandra
Dickstein Shapiro LLP, Los Angeles
310 772 8309
franklinc@dicksteinshapiro.com
*Featured in Insurance (California)*

**Practice Areas:** Cassandra Franklin serves as California Regional Leader in Dickstein Shapiro's Insurance Coverage Group. She represents a wide range of businesses in complex insurance recovery matters. Her insurance recovery experience includes disputes concerning first-party policies, such as property, business interruption, and crime coverage policies, as well as third-party policies, such as directors and officers, errors and omissions, and commercial general liability policies.

**Publications:** Co-author of New Appleman Sports and Entertainment Insurance Law & Practice Guide.

**Personal:** University of Arizona, BA, 1980, with highest distinction. Duke University School of Law, JD, 1985.

### FREDERICKS, John
Winston & Strawn LLP, San Francisco
415 591 1422
jfredericks@winston.com
*Featured in Bankruptcy/Restructuring (California)*

**Practice Areas:** Mr Fredericks regularly represents financial institutions, investment funds and portfolio companies in workouts and restructurings, chapter 11 bankruptcies, state law winddowns, assignments for the benefit of creditors, distressed M&A, foreclosure and creditors' rights, commercial lending, and finance.

**Publications:** Mr Fredericks is an author and lecturer on insolvency-related topics, including intercreditor dynamics, technology company bankruptcies and liquidations, solvent tenant bankruptcies, and out-of-court wind-downs and liquidations.

**Personal:** Mr Fredericks obtained his BA at the University of California at Santa Cruz in 1987 and his JD, cum laude, University of San Francisco in 1993.

### FREIER, Elliot
Irell & Manella, Los Angeles
310 203 7055
efreier@irell.com
*Featured in Tax (California)*

**Practice Areas:** Elliot Freier leads the tax practice of Irell & Manella from its Los Angeles office. Mr Freier specializes in federal and California taxation of corporations, partnerships and individuals, with a focus on taxation of merger and acquisition transactions, bankruptcy and workout taxation for debtors and creditors, and federal and California tax controversy representation. In addition to his work at the firm, Mr Freier has been significantly involved in the American Bar Association Taxation Section and frequently speaks on tax issues.
**Personal:** Yale Law School (JD); University of Virginia (BA, Economics, with highest distinction, Phi Beta Kappa).

### FRIEDMAN, Alan
Munger, Tolles & Olson LLP, Los Angeles
213 683 9169
alan.friedman@mto.com
*Featured in Labor & Employment (California)*

**Practice Areas:** Labor and employment law representing employers in a wide variety of industries; provides general labor and employment advice, negotiations and litigation.
**Professional Memberships:** ABA: Labor and Employment Law Section; Board, Bet Tzedek Legal Services Foundation; Board, Constitutional Rights Foundation; Past member and Chair, Los Angeles Board of Civil Service Commissioners.
**Career:** Labor Relations counsel to the 1984 Los Angeles Olympic Organizing Committee; U.S. Department of Labor, D.C., with extensive work in labor relations and civil rights law.
**Personal:** Georgetown University Law Center (LLM); Case Western Reserve University (LLB); University of Pennsylvania (AB).

### FRIMMER, Paul N
Loeb & Loeb LLP, Los Angeles
310 282 2383
pfrimmer@loeb.com
*Featured in Wealth Management (Nationwide), Tax (California)*

See under Nationwide for profile.

### FULLER, James P
Fenwick & West LLP, Mountain View
650 335 7205
jpfuller@fenwick.com
*Featured in Tax (California)*

**Practice Areas:** James P Fuller is a partner in the Tax Group at Fenwick & West LLP. He is or was counsel in numerous tax cases, including cases for CBS, Limited Brands, Hitachi, Dover, Chrysler, Textron, Del Commercial, Apple and many others. Many involved transfer pricing issues. Mr Fuller was lead in resolving many other transfer pricing cases at the IRS Appeals level and during the IRS examination stage.

**Career:** Mr Fuller is one of the top 25 tax advisors in the world, according to Euromoney's Best of the Best (2012) (one of only two US tax advisors to appear all seven times in Euromoney's top 25). He is the only US tax adviser to receive the Chambers coveted star performer rating, Chambers USA (2012). Mr Fuller is also included in Euromoney's world's leading transfer pricing advisors (2012.
**Publications:** Mr Fuller writes a monthly column in Tax Notes International and has taught an international tax course at Stanford Law School for the past 25 years. He is a frequent speaker at tax seminars.

### FULLMER, David R
Ivener & Fullmer LLP, Los Angeles
310 477 3000
david@usworkvisa.com
*Featured in Immigration (California)*

**Practice Areas:** Immigration: Business.
**Career:** David R Fullmer has over 15 years of experience in immigration law. David received his Juris Doctor degree from Loyola Law School in California and his Bachelor's degree from Brigham Young University. Having lived and worked in Japan, David is fluent in Japanese. David has a broad base of experience in immigration and consular law, having represented a wide spectrum of clients ranging from famous entertainers, corporate executives and international corporations to students, trainees and sole proprietorships. David has special expertise assisting management, in-house counsel and HR Departments at small and large companies with both processing work visas of all types and educating and counseling them on staying in compliance with immigration-related regulations. David also represents major studios and independent producers on obtaining O-1 visas for actors, directors and production staff. He is the co-author of the book, Handbook of Immigration Law (2012) and has written numerous articles on immigration law and visas published in Immigrant Magazine and is a frequent CLE speaker on immigration related topics.

### GADBOIS, Barbara
Gibbs Giden Locher Turner Senet & Wittbrodt LLP., Los Angeles
310 552 3400
bgadbois@ggltsw.com
*Featured in Construction (California)*

**Practice Areas:** Construction and Public Contracts.
**Professional Memberships:** State Bar of California, Los Angeles County Bar Association, American Bar Association, California's Coalition for Adequate School Housing, and the City Attorneys Association of Los Angeles County.
**Career:** Ms Gadbois has been a partner with the firm since 1993. She concentrates her practice in the development and management of construction projects including the drafting and negotiation of bid and contract documents, procurement issues, public works, competitive bidding requirements, bid protest issues, prequalification, project delivery methods, including design-build projects,

risk allocation in contracts, claims avoidance and project closeout. She is also one of the few attorneys in California to be a U.S. Green Building Council LEED AP.
**Publications:** She is an active speaker/author on topics such as, construction disputes, AIA and public contracts, local hire Programs, prevailing wage, and design-build on local and Federal construction projects.
**Personal:** JD, UCLA School of Law, 1985; BA, Northwestern University, 1982. LEED AP 2009.

### GARZA, Oscar
Gibson, Dunn & Crutcher LLP, Irvine
949 451 3849
ogarza@gibsondunn.com
*Featured in Bankruptcy/Restructuring (California)*

**Practice Areas:** Represents corporate debtors (both publicly traded and privately owned), creditors' committees, secured creditors in chapter 11 cases, advises buyers and sellers of the assets of financially distressed companies and represents Bankruptcy Trustees in complex cases. He also has extensive experience advising transnational corporations defending against attempts to recognize and enforce foreign judgments in the U.S and abroad.
**Publications:** Frequent lecturer on bankruptcy law and practice. Co-authored various articles published in the Daily Deal, the California Bankruptcy Journal and the Los Angeles Daily Journal.
**Personal:** JD, University of Arizona College of Law, 1990 (Law Review).

### GAUTIER, Scott F
Peitzman Weg LLP, Los Angeles
310 552 3100
sgautier@peitzmanweg.com
*Featured in Bankruptcy/Restructuring (California)*

**Practice Areas:** Corporate bankruptcies, workouts. Representation of debtors, creditors, committees, equity holders, acquirers. Significant roles in such bankruptcy cases as Allegheny Health Education and Research Foundation, Applause, Bugle Boy, Cimm's, Closet World, Fleming Companies, Halcyon Holding, Mercury Finance, Millennium Pacific Icon, PG&E, Sexy Hair Concepts, Sun World, Wagstaff Management Corp. Served in various roles in out-of-court financial restructuring matters; advises clients on bankruptcy issues in non-bankruptcy matters.
**Professional Memberships:** Director, American Bankruptcy Institute; National Editor, ABI's Volo program; Southern California TMA.
**Publications:** "New Chapter 11 Strategies for Unsecured Creditors Under BAPCPA," California Business Practitioner, vol 21, num 4 (Fall 2006).

### GERSICH, Bradley J
DLA Piper LLP (US), East Palo Alto
650 833 2074
bradley.gersich@dlapiper.com
*Featured in Corporate/M&A (Northern California)*

**Practice Areas:** Corporate/M&A.
**Career:** He advises high-technology, networking and biotechnology companies in venture capital financings, debt financing transactions and general operations; represents venture capital firms in

early and late stage private placement investments; represents purchasing and selling companies in mergers and acquisitions and asset sales; negotiates and drafts executive employment agreements on behalf of companies and high-level executives, and represents companies and underwriters in initial and secondary public offerings, including Rule 144A convertible debt offerings.
**Personal:** JD, Stanford University; BA, University of St. Thomas.

### GERTLER, Gary B
McDermott Will & Emery LLP, Los Angeles
310 551 9328
ggertler@mwe.com
*Featured in Healthcare (California)*

**Practice Areas:** Partner in the Los Angeles Health Law Department. Practice focuses on the representation of hospitals, dialysis providers, surgery centers, imaging companies, physician organizations and other healthcare companies with an emphasis on joint ventures and syndications, mergers and acquisitions, private equity and debt transactions for startup companies, consolidations and reorganizations, healthcare regulatory and licensure issues, and general healthcare corporate matters. Works with investor-owned and nonprofit hospitals and hospital systems, dialysis, surgery center and imaging center companies and developers, management companies and entrepreneurs.
**Personal:** University of Southern California Law School (JD), University of California-Los Angeles (MPH, BS).

### GILHULY, Morgan
Barg Coffin Lewis & Trapp LLP, San Francisco
415 228 5460
rmg@bctlaw.com
*Featured in Environment (California)*

**Practice Areas:** Environmental Law and Environmental Litigation.
**Career:** Morgan Gilhuly is the managing partner of Barg Coffin Lewis & Trapp, LLP. He has 25 years of experience in environmental litigation and environmental compliance counseling. He has represented responsible parties at several Superfund sites in Silicon Valley for over 15 years, and has tried a variety of environmental matters in state and federal trial and appellate courts. He represents semiconductor and industrial companies, utilities, universities, and other businesses in complex environmental matters, including cap-and-trade, environmental enforcement and penalty actions, government and private cost recovery actions, and citizen suits involving federal and state environmental laws. Morgan received his JD from Yale Law School in 1986 and his BA from Amherst College in 1980.

### GILLETTE, Patricia
Orrick, Herrington & Sutcliffe LLP, San Francisco
415 773 5773
pgillette@orrick.com
*Featured in Labor & Employment (California)*

**Practice Areas:** Pat Gillette's practice focuses on all aspects of employment law, including wrongful discharge, discrimination class actions, individual/multi-plaintiff cases in both state and federal court, representation of employers before administrative agencies and counseling and training employers on preventive personnel practices. Ms Gillette is the founder of the Opt-In Project, a nationwide initiative focused on changing the structure of law firms to increase the retention and advancement of women in the workplace. Ms Gillette is a commissioner on the ABA Commission for Women in the Profession and is the Co-Chair of the San Francisco Bar Association's No Glass Ceiling Initiative.

### GINDLER, David I
Irell & Manella, Los Angeles
310 203 7106
dgindler@irell.com
*Featured in Intellectual Property (California), Life Sciences (California)*
**Practice Areas:** David Gindler specializes in complex litigation involving patents, license and technology transfer agreements, and trade secrets. His clients include biotechnology innovators (such as Ariosa Diagnostics and PDL BioPharma), multi-national corporations (such as Aon Corporation) and major academic institutions (such as Columbia University). Mr Gindler's litigation achievements include a $302 million jury verdict, the largest compensatory damage award ever upheld in a published California appellate decision. His work spans a broad array of technologies, including biotechnology, medical devices, computer architecture, advanced semiconductor materials and business methods.
**Personal:** UCLA School of Law (JD); Pomona College (BA, Philosophy and Economics).

### GISSER, Michael
Skadden, Arps, Slate, Meagher & Flom LLP & Affiliates, Los Angeles
213 687 5213
michael.gisser@skadden.com
*Featured in Corporate/M&A (California), Corporate/M&A (Southern California)*
**Practice Areas:** Leads the firm's Asia-Pacific practice from its office in Los Angeles, and also served for six years as senior partner in the firm's Hong Kong office. Actively advises clients throughout Asia and the United States in a range of industries with respect to mergers and acquisitions, corporate and international transactions, as well as major firm clients in the software, online services, technology and entertainment industries.
**Professional Memberships:** Member, Executive Committee, Asia Society Southern California.
**Career:** JD, Stanford Law School, 1982 (Order of the Coif; senior articles editor, Stanford Law Review); AB, Harvard College, 1978 (cum laude).

### GLAD, Paul E B
SNR Denton, San Francisco
415 882 5001
paul.glad@dentons.com
*Featured in Insurance (Nationwide), Insurance (California)*
See under Nationwide for profile.

### GLICK, Marty
Arnold & Porter LLP, San Francisco
415 471 3153
Martin.Glick@aporter.com
*Featured in Intellectual Property (California)*
**Practice Areas:** Marty Glick is a senior litigator with extensive experience in a wide range of complex civil litigation matters, concentrating in intellectual property. He represented Research in Motion in appellate litigation and the highly-publicized settlement of the BlackBerry patent litigation. More recently, he successfully represented Datel Design & Development Ltd. in the settlement of an antitrust action against Microsoft Corp. alleging monopolization of the aftermarket for accessories for the Xbox 360. Mr Glick is currently representing Amazon in its dispute with Apple over Amazon's use of "App Store" in connection with its "Amazon Appstore for Android."

### GOLDBERG, Stephen
Dickstein Shapiro LLP, Los Angeles
310 772 8325
goldbergs@dicksteinshapiro.com
*Featured in Insurance (Nationwide), Insurance (California)*
See under Nationwide for profile.

### GOLDMAN, Joel S
Hanson Bridgett LLP, San Francisco
415 995 5028
jgoldman@hansonbridgett.com
*Featured in Healthcare (California)*
**Practice Areas:** Joel Goldman devotes his practice to representation of an array of developers, owners and operators of senior care communities. His primary focus is on licensure, regulatory, operational and risk management issues affecting assisted living communities, congregate senior communities and continuing care retirement communities. Joel has been a noted presenter at numerous conferences throughout the country for organizations including Assisted Living Federation of America, American Health Lawyers Association, American Seniors Housing Association, and The Erickson School of Aging Studies, UMBC. He is a long-time member of the Board as well as past President of the California Assisted Living Association.

### GONZÁLEZ, Arturo J
Morrison & Foerster LLP, San Francisco
415 268 7020
agonzalez@mofo.com
*Featured in Litigation (California)*
**Practice Areas:** Arturo González is co-chair of Morrison & Foerster's Litigation Department. He is a trial lawyer who specializes in high-stakes, bet-the-company litigation in various substantive areas, including trade secrets, fraud, breach of contract, unfair business practices, and product liability.
**Professional Memberships:** Member, American Board of Trial Advocates; former president, SF Bar Association.
**Career:** Named as one of California's Top 100 leading lawyers by Daily Journal (2006-2012); one of the country's top 30 trial lawyers by Legal 500

(2010-2012); and profiled in The National Law Journal's 2009 "Winning" Special Report.
**Personal:** Harvard Law School (JD, 1985); UC Davis (AB, 1982).

### GOOD, Samantha
Kirkland & Ellis LLP, San Francisco
415 439 1914
samantha.good@kirkland.com
*Featured in Banking & Finance (California)*
**Practice Areas:** Samantha concentrates her practice on debt financing transactions, representing private equity clients and their portfolio companies in acquisition financings, dividend recapitalizations, and refinancings; company clients and ad hoc committees of creditors in out-of-court restructuring transactions and bankruptcy cases; and opportunities funds, hedge funds and mezzanine funds in unsecured, mezzanine and secured lending. She has handled a number of cross-border transactions, out-of-court restructurings, amend-and-extend transactions, and financing transactions for the hospitality industry, film portfolios and FCC-regulated broadcasting companies.
**Personal:** University of California at Hastings, College of the Law, JD, magna cum laude, 1997. Pomona College, BA, Economics, 1994.

### GOODMAN, William M
Kasowitz, Benson, Torres & Friedman LLP, San Francisco
415 421 6140
wgoodman@kasowitz.com
*Featured in Litigation (California)*
**Practice Areas:** Specializing in white-collar criminal defense and related complex civil and administrative litigation, Mr Goodman represents clients in all types of criminal actions, including antitrust, bank fraud, securities fraud, political corruption, environmental and healthcare. He has argued many appeals before the California Supreme Court and federal/state appellate courts.
**Career:** Law Clerk, Chief Justice Donald R. Wright, California Supreme Court, 1974-75; Assistant Federal Public Defender, N.D. Cal., 1975-80; Partner, Topel and Goodman, 1980-07; Partner, Kasowitz, Benson, Torres & Friedman, 2007 – present. Admitted to California State Bar in 1974.
**Personal:** University of California, Boalt Hall School of Law (JD, 1974).

### GOODWIN, David B
Covington & Burling LLP, San Francisco
415 591 7074
dgoodwin@cov.com
*Featured in Insurance (Nationwide), Insurance (California)*
See under Nationwide for profile.

### GORDON, Eric B
McDermott Will & Emery LLP, Los Angeles
310 551 9315
egordon@mwe.com
*Featured in Healthcare (California), Healthcare (Nationwide)*
**Practice Areas:** Heads the firm's California Health Practice and national co-chair of the Academic Medical Center Practice. Represents

national hospital systems, private equity, medical groups, medical device manufacturers, group purchasing organizations, research institutes. Transactional matters include hospital-physician joint ventures, nonprofit affiliations. Academic medical center representation includes: organization of faculty practice plans, AMC restructuring, compliance plan development, HIPAA, fraud and abuse policies, Stark audits, residency affiliations, GME/IME planning and appeals.
**Publications:** Author, 'Faculty Practice Plans' (BNA); Co-author, 'Guide to Stark Physician Self-Referral Rules' (AIS).
**Personal:** JD (UCLA); MD (Brown University); AB (Brown University).

### GORDON, Jill H
Nixon Peabody LLP, Los Angeles
213 629 6175
jgordon@nixonpeabody.com
*Featured in Healthcare (California)*
**Practice Areas:** Jill Gordon is a partner in Nixon Peabody's Health Services practice group. Jill represents hospitals, long-term care facilities, medical groups, accountable care organizations, and other health care entities. She advises on transactional and regulatory matters, including joint venture development; mergers and acquisitions; entity formation and financing; and negotiating physician contracts, leases, management and co-management arrangements, bundled payment relationships, pay for performance and gainsharing programs, and managed care contracts. Jill also represents companies in the health information, medical device, and telemedicine fields.
**Personal:** Washington University in St. Louis, JD and MHA.; Sarah Lawrence College, AB.

### GORDON, Paul A
Hanson Bridgett LLP, San Francisco
415 995 5014
pgordon@hansonbridgett.com
*Featured in Healthcare (California)*
**Practice Areas:** Paul Gordon has been working with seniors housing and care providers since 1975. He authored the book Seniors' Housing and Care Facilities: Development, Business and Operations (Urban Land Institute, 1998), which contains over 600 pages of text, plus a CD-ROM with over 1,000 pages of business forms. He is General Counsel to the American Seniors Housing Association and on its Executive Board, past chair of the Housing for the Elderly Committee of the American Bar Association, and served on the Legal Committee of the American Association of Homes and Services for the Aging (1978-2001; chair 1996-97).

### GRACE, David W
Loeb & Loeb LLP, Los Angeles
310 282 2108
dgrace@loeb.com
*Featured in Intellectual Property (California)*
**Practice Areas:** Handles trademark, copyright, right of publicity, Internet domain name, entertainment, advertising, and patent disputes and litigation. Counsels clients with respect to the acquisition, management and protection of international intellectual property portfolios. Represents

clients in negotiating trademark, copyright, endorsement and entertainment agreements. **Professional Memberships:** International Trademark Association (INTA) and Panel of Neutrals, Member; Chair of Right of Publicity Subcommittee; Co-Chair of 2009 Annual Meeting Team.
**Career:** Partner and Intellectual Property Protection Co-Chair.
**Personal:** University of Virginia School of Law (JD, 1981); George Mason University (BS, With Highest Distinction, 1978).

**GREENBERG, Gordon A**
McDermott Will & Emery LLP, Los Angeles
310 551 9398
ggreenberg@mwe.com
*Featured in Litigation (Nationwide), Litigation (California)*
**Practice Areas:** Partner in trial department with more than 25 years of experience handling a wide range of business crime investigations and trials. Regularly represents clients in civil and criminal investigations, trials and congressional hearings. Often defends clients in high stakes "bet your company" matters.
**Professional Memberships:** Lecturer, Federal Judicial Center; ABA.
**Career:** Previously a federal prosecutor, serving as the Chief of the Financial Investigations Unit in the Los Angeles US Attorney's Office; also a state and special federal prosecutor in Chicago.
**Personal:** Chicago-Kent College of Law, JD (with honors), 1980; University of Illinois at Urbana-Champaign, BA, 1976.

**GREGSON, Gabriel F**
Weil, Gotshal & Manges LLP, Silicon Valley
650 802 3990
gabriel.gregson@weil.com
*Featured in Banking & Finance (California)*
**Practice Areas:** Gabriel Gregson is a banking and finance partner in Weil's Silicon Valley office and specializes in financings for private equity sponsors and corporate borrowers. He represents top-tier private equity firms, portfolio companies and other corporate borrowers in connection with first and second lien credit facilities, ABL facilities, mezzanine loans, LBO financings, exit financings, recapitalizations, restructurings and complex intercreditor arrangements. Gabriel represents clients in sophisticated financing transactions across a variety of industries, including telecommunications, real estate, industrial supply, healthcare, apparel and consumer products.
**Personal:** University of British Columbia (B.Comm., Finance, 1997); New York University School of Law (JD, 2000).

**GROSSMAN, Marshall B**
Bingham McCutchen LLP, Santa Monica
310 255 9118
marshall.grossman@bingham.com
*Featured in Litigation (Nationwide), Litigation (California), Media & Entertainment (California)*
**Practice Areas:** Prosecutes and defends major commercial litigation. Successfully defended Blockbuster in consumer class action litigation as well as patent infringement litigation filed by

Netflix. Successfully prosecuted suit for University of Southern California to terminate long-term lease of University Hospital to Tenet Healthcare. Successfully represented Televisa, the world's largest Spanish language media company, in a three-year litigation against Univision Communications. Counseled JK Rowling, Steven Spielberg, Clint Eastwood, Mariah Carey, Tommy Hilfiger, Erin Andrews and Larry King in selected matters.
**Career:** Past commissioner and chair, State of California Commission on Judicial Performance.
**Personal:** University of Southern California Law School, JD.

**GROVER, Gavin B**
Morrison & Foerster LLP, San Francisco
415 268 7113
ggrover@mofo.com
*Featured in Corporate/M&A (Northern California)*
**Practice Areas:** Mr Grover has completed over 250 merger and acquisition transactions during his career. Specializes in advising growth companies particularly those seeking to grow through acquisitions and alliances. Clients include public and private growth companies across industries including consumer, technology, cleantech and Life Sciences. Advises Boards of Directors and committees of public companies on transactional and other matters. Frequently works with management teams of his clients over a period of many years as they orchestrate growth acquisition programs.
**Career:** Admitted in California. Chair, firm's Global Corporate Practice Group, 1996 - 2004; Co-chair, M&A Group, 2004 to present.

**GUY III, G Hopkins**
Baker Botts LLP, Palo Alto
650 739 7510
hop.guy@bakerbotts.com
*Featured in Intellectual Property (California)*
**Practice Areas:** Hopkins Guy has extensive expertise in patent, trade secrets and commercial contract litigation involving all areas of Web-based telecommunications, electronics and computer technologies. He also provides intellectual property counsel to technology companies from start-up to mature companies, particularly in clean-tech and solar technologies. Mr Guy's patent and trade secrets litigation experience has involved technologies in Web-based payment systems, social networking, wireless data communication equipment and routing, semiconductor processing, packaging and equipment, microprocessors, power semiconductor devices, DIMM memory module technology and solar technologies. Mr Guy's representations have included Acer, Apple, Applied Materials, Intel, Cisco, eBay, PayPal, Powertech and SemiLEDs.

**HABER, Scott R**
Latham & Watkins LLP, San Francisco
415 395 8137
scott.haber@lw.com
*Featured in Corporate/M&A (California)*
**Practice Areas:** Mr Haber has experience representing public and private corporations and private equity firms in mergers and acquisitions and

advising on securities laws compliance and general corporate matters. Mr Haber has represented financial and strategic buyers and sellers in numerous private and public company M&A transactions in a wide variety of industries, including retail, manufacturing and healthcare.
**Career:** Office Managing Partner, Latham & Watkins San Francisco office (2005-2012).
**Personal:** JD, Cornell Law School, 1984; MBA, Cornell University, 1983; BA, Cornell University, 1980.

**HACK, Marion T**
Gibbs Giden Locher Turner Senet & Wittbrodt LLP., Los Angeles
310 552 3400
mhack@ggltsw.com
*Featured in Construction (California)*
**Practice Areas:** Construction Litigation; Construction Law.
**Professional Memberships:** Past President, Southern California Development Forum; ABA, Construction Industry Subsection; CMAA Legal Committee; AGC, Legal Committee.
**Career:** Ms Hack specializes in handling multi-million dollar claim disputes involving high profile, complex construction projects. She recently obtained a $52.1M unanimous jury verdict in favor of the City of Victorville for the failed Foxborough Power Plant Project. Her practice also includes bidding disputes, contract negotiations and drafting, scheduling and delay issues, mechanics lien and claims resolution. She has extensive experience with construction licensing issues and has been asked to be an expert witness in this field.
**Publications:** She is an author and speaker on the topics of construction claims and collection, and licensing requirements affecting contractors and construction managers.
**Personal:** University of the Pacific– McGeorge School of Law – (JD, Dean's List), 1995; University of Southern California – (BS, Business Administration), 1989.

**HADDAD, Mark**
Sidley Austin LLP, Los Angeles
213 896 6604
mhaddad@sidley.com
*Featured in Litigation (California)*
**Practice Areas:** Mark Haddad chairs the Appellate practice in the Los Angeles office and co-chairs Sidley's Global Appellate practice. His matters frequently involve the impact of federal constitutional, statutory, and regulatory provisions on the scope of business liability, across many areas, including administrative, antitrust, and constitutional law, intellectual property, products liability, and professional responsibility.
**Professional Memberships:** Public Counsel - Member, Board of Directors; Town Hall-Los Angeles - Member, Board of Directors
**Personal:** Yale Law School, JD, 1985, Editor-in-Chief, Yale Law Journal; Oxford University, MA, 1980, Rhodes Scholar; Stanford University, AB, 1978, with honors, with distinction.

**HAGLE, Jennifer**
Sidley Austin LLP, Los Angeles
213 896 6015
jhagle@sidley.com
*Featured in Bankruptcy/Restructuring (California)*
**Practice Areas:** Jennifer Hagle is a transactional bankruptcy lawyer with over 25 years of experience representing clients in bankruptcy and out-of-court restructurings. Practice focuses on representing holders of senior secured, mezzanine, subordinated debt in public and private middle market and large cap deals in various industries. Also experienced in corporate finance regarding loan originations and merger and acquisition transactions in non-distressed deals. Clients include banks, hedge funds and other financial institutions.
**Professional Memberships:** Member of Executive Committee, chair of Los Angeles Corporate Transactions group.
**Personal:** University of California, Hastings College of the Law, JD, 1987; UCLA, BA, 1983. Admission: California.

**HAILE, Lisa A**
DLA Piper LLP (US), San Diego
858 677 1456
lisa.haile@dlapiper.com
*Featured in Intellectual Property (California), Life Sciences (California)*
**Practice Areas:** IP, Patent Litigation, Life Sciences.
**Career:** She focuses on patentability, non-infringement, and validity opinions, licensing strategies, FDA counseling, due diligence work in connection with venture capital, private, and public financing, merger and acquisitions in the life sciences industry and strategic counseling for comprehensive life sciences patent portfolio management. She is a member of the firm's Policy Committee and is the author of a weekly blog on biotech issues for the San Diego News Network.
**Personal:** JD, California Western School of Law; PhD, Georgetown University School of Medicine (Microbiology and Immunology); BA, Rollins College (Biology).

**HAINLINE III, Forrest A**
Goodwin Procter LLP, San Francisco
415 733 6065
fhainline@goodwinprocter.com
*Featured in Litigation (California)*
**Practice Areas:** Mr Hainline has tried cases in toxic torts, environment, antitrust, securities, employment issues, false advertising, construction, patent, trademark and media defense. Many of his cases involved the presentation of complex scientific and/or economic evidence. He has been retained as trial counsel in 'crisis litigation' - where a case has been initially handled by others. He has appeared in the Supreme Court of the United States and has argued before seven United States Courts of Appeals.
**Personal:** JD, University of Michigan Law School, 1974; MA, State University of New York at Buffalo, 1971; BA, University of Notre Dame, 1968.

### HAMILTON, Michael D
DLA Piper LLP (US), Los Angeles
213 330 7736
michael.hamilton@dlapiper.com
*Featured in Real Estate (California)*
**Practice Areas:** Real Estate.
**Professional Memberships:** Member, American College of Real Estate Lawyers.
**Career:** He focuses on business transactions with particular emphasis on finance and real estate matters. In addition to addressing the legal and situational risks attendant to any transaction, he is passionate about utilizing existing and creating new systems and processes to enhance internal and external business and legal functions. He writes and lectures extensively on matters pertinent to clients, the industry and the profession.
**Personal:** JD, University of Oregon School of Law; MA, Geology and Geophysics, Rice University; BA and MA, Geology, Hamilton College.

### HANDZLIK, Jan Lawrence
Venable LLP, Los Angeles
310 229 0378
jlhandzlik@Venable.com
*Featured in Litigation (California)*
**Practice Areas:** Litigation; business crime; FCPA; export controls; internal investigations.
**Professional Memberships:** ABA Criminal Justice Section: Governing Council, 2005-11; Chair, National White-Collar Crime Committee, 2003-05; International Bar Association: Vice-Chair, Business Crime, 2010-present.
**Career:** Law Clerk, U.S. District Judge, 1970-71; Assistant U.S. Attorney, 1971-76, Special Prosecutions, 1974-76; FCPA Compliance Monitor, 2005-08.
**Personal:** 2013 Defense Attorney of the Year, Criminal Courts Bar Association, Los Angeles; 2012 "Top 100 Lawyers in California," Daily Journal Corporation; 2012 California Lawyer Attorney of the Year Award (CLAY), criminal law; 2012 White-Collar Defense Award, NACDL; American Lawyer, February 2012; Best Lawyers in America, 1983-2013; JD, UCLA, 1970.

### HANNA, Nicola T
Gibson, Dunn & Crutcher LLP, Irvine
949 451 4270
nhanna@gibsondunn.com
*Featured in Litigation (California)*
**Practice Areas:** Focuses on complex criminal, SEC and regulatory enforcement actions, including healthcare fraud, securities, and financial crimes, money laundering and Bank Secrecy Act violations, Foreign Corrupt Practices Act investigations, False Claims Act defense, and sensitive internal investigations.
**Career:** Inducted in 2009 as a Fellow of the American College of Trial Lawyers. Previously served as Assistant United States Attorney, Central District of California, Los Angeles (1990-1994) and Assistant United States Attorney, Southern District of California, San Diego (1995-1998).
**Personal:** JD, Georgetown University, 1987; BA, UC San Diego, 1984.

### HANOVER, John D
Peckar & Abramson, P.C., Los Angeles
310 228 1075
jhanover@pecklaw.com
*Featured in Construction (California)*
**Practice Areas:** For more than 25 years, Mr Hanover has handled construction claims related to delays, impacts and inefficiencies, lost productivity, defective construction, and disputes related to non-payment.
**Professional Memberships:** Member of the California and Nevada State Bar Associations, the Forum on the Construction Industry and the Construction Section of the American Bar Association. Admitted to practice law in California, Nevada, Colorado, and Tennessee.
**Career:** Mr Hanover is a Partner in the firm's California offices.
**Personal:** For more information, please visit: www.pecklaw.com

### HANSCHEN, Peter
Morrison & Foerster LLP, San Francisco
925 295 3450
phanschen@mofo.com
*Featured in Energy & Natural Resources (California)*
**Practice Areas:** Peter Hanschen is experienced in all types of energy matters, including state and federal regulation, energy-related transactions, arbitrations, and project financings. He has participated in "traditional" utility proceedings before state and federal regulatory commissions and the California Supreme Court. Working with the firm's Cleantech Group, he advises clients affected by regulatory and legislative developments, and clients that wish to take advantage of the unique opportunities offered by California's leadership role in renewable energy and Cleantech. Peter also assists the firm's project finance team in the development and financing of domestic and international energy projects.

### HANSEN, David
Skadden, Arps, Slate, Meagher & Flom LLP & Affiliates, Palo Alto
650 470 4560
David.Hansen@skadden.com
*Featured in Intellectual Property (California)*
**Practice Areas:** More than 25 years experience representing technology and media companies in broad variety of high-stakes patent, copyright, trade secret and related disputes, as well as in a range of IP transactional matters. Representative clients have included SanDisk, Hitachi Global Storage, MGA Entertainment, Yahoo! and Zynga. Lecturer in Stanford University's Computer Science department since 2004; Special Counsel, Intellectual Property, to the Aspen Institute IDEA Project; frequent writer and speaker on a range of IP issues.
**Career:** JD, Illinois Institute of Technology, Chicago-Kent College of Law, 1984 (highest honors; law review); BS, General Engineering, University of Illinois at Urbana-Champaign, 1979.

### HANSEN, Russell C
Gibson, Dunn & Crutcher LLP, Palo Alto
650 8495383
rhansen@gibsondunn.com
*Featured in Corporate/M&A (Northern California)*
**Practice Areas:** Extensive experience in mergers, acquisitions and divestitures for corporate and private equity clients, corporate finance and securities matters, joint ventures and strategic alliances and counseling boards of directors. Clients range from large, global corporations to emerging growth and middle market companies and include private equity and individual private investors. Clients recently represented in transactions include Hewlett-Packard, Intel, AppliedMicro, Convergence.io, O1 Works, Admiralty Partners, Leach Capital, Taylor Farms and the Pritzker Group.
**Career:** Partner-in-Charge of the Palo Alto office.
**Personal:** JD, Stanford University Law School; MBA, Stanford Graduate School of Business, 1980; AB Princeton University (summa cum laude), 1976.

### HARRIS, Marcia
Robins, Kaplan, Miller & Ciresi LLP, Los Angeles
310 552 0130
mjharris@rkmc.com
*Featured in Media & Entertainment (California)*
**Practice Areas:** Entertainment litigation with emphasis on accounting and profit participation disputes in television and motion picture industries, and disputes involving talent agencies.
**Professional Memberships:** Member of the Litigation Counsel of America Trial Lawyer Honor Society, and the Beverly Hills, Century City, Los Angeles County, American Bar Associations.
**Career:** Recognized by the LA Daily Journal among the "Top 75 Women Litigators" (2005). Named WIN Outstanding Woman by the Women's Image Network (2006). Named in The Best Lawyers in America.
**Personal:** University of Missouri School of Journalism (BJ, with honors); Loyola Law School (JD). Member, American Cinematheque and Women in Film.

### HARTIGAN, John F
Morgan, Lewis & Bockius LLP, Los Angeles
213 612 2630
jhartigan@morganlewis.com
*Featured in Corporate/M&A (Southern California)*
**Practice Areas:** Partner in Business and Finance Practice and Co-Chair of the firm's Securities Interdisciplinary Practice Group. Advises companies, financial institutions, boards of directors and independent committees thereof on securities and corporate law matters, mergers and acquisitions, corporate governance, broker-dealer matters, SEC enforcement, internal investigations and corporate finance. Former Assistant Director of the SEC Division of Enforcement; President of the Association of SEC Alumni; Board of Visitors of Georgetown University Law Center; GC of BISA; and a frequent speaker/author on securities law, financial institutions, corporate governance, investigations and broker-dealers.
**Personal:** JD Georgetown University Law Center; BS (Finance) University of Illinois.

### HASKO, Judith A
Latham & Watkins LLP, Silicon Valley
650 463 3065
judith.hasko@lw.com
*Featured in Life Sciences (Nationwide), Life Sciences (California)*
See under Nationwide for profile.

### HASLAM, Robert
Covington & Burling LLP, Redwood Shores
650 632 4702
rhaslam@cov.com
*Featured in Intellectual Property (California)*
**Practice Areas:** Mr Haslam's practice has emphasized trial work involving patent and trade secret litigation. He has represented clients in litigation involving a range of technologies, including semiconductor products and processes, electronic circuits and devices, cellular, wireless and GPS technologies, microprocessors and software products, and cryptography. He has tried cases in District Courts around the country and at the ITC.
**Professional Memberships:** American College of Trial Lawyers, Fellow.
**Personal:** UC Hastings College of the Law (JD, 1976); MIT (BS Aeronautics and Astronautics, 1968).

### HATTENBACH, Benjamin
Irell & Manella, Los Angeles
310 203 7937
bhattenbach@irell.com
*Featured in Intellectual Property (California)*
**Practice Areas:** Ben Hattenbach is a partner at Irell & Manella, where he serves on the firm's Executive Committee. His practice focuses on intellectual property litigation and pre-litigation counseling, with an emphasis on the trial of patent infringement matters. Hattenbach has litigated patent disputes before numerous federal and state courts, as well as the International Trade Commission, United States Patent & Trademark Office and arbitration panels. He also provides strategic guidance regarding patent portfolio management, licensing, prosecution and acquisitions. He is registered to practice in the USPTO.
**Personal:** University of California, Berkeley (Boalt Hall) (JD); Harvey Mudd College (MS/BS, Engineering).

### HAUETER, Eric S
Sidley Austin LLP, San Francisco
415 772 1231
ehaueter@sidley.com
*Featured in Capital Markets (California), Capital Markets (Nationwide)*
**Practice Areas:** Partner in Sidley's San Francisco office. His principal areas of practice include corporate finance and M&A. He has represented underwriters and issuers in a broad range of public and private debt and equity financings, M&A transactions and other matters, including IPOs, add-on stock offerings, PIPEs and registered directs, offerings of convertible debt and other

equity-linked securities, and investment grade and high-yield debt offerings.

**Personal:** Columbia University School of Law, JD, Harlan Fiske Stone Scholar, 1979; Columbia Business School, MBA, Beta Gamma Sigma, 1980; Williams College, BA, Phi Beta Kappa, 1975. Admissions: California, New York.

## HAVEL, Richard W
Sidley Austin LLP, Los Angeles
213 896 6017
rhavel@sidley.com
*Featured in Bankruptcy/Restructuring (California)*

**Practice Areas:** Senior Counsel in Sidley's Los Angeles office and senior member of the firm's Bankruptcy/Corporate Reorganization practice. He represents parties in informal workouts and in Chapter 11 proceedings, and has served as Counsel to creditors' committees, Chapter 11 trustees, debtors and other parties in interest.
**Personal:** Active as a panelist and speaker in continuing education. He has lectured in areas such as: ALI-ABA programs on Lender Liability; frequent presentations on issues relating to bankruptcy and environmental law; and annual appearances at the Bankruptcy Litigation Institute in San Francisco. He was also an adjunct professor at Loyola School of Law.

## HAYES, David L
Fenwick & West LLP, San Francisco
415 875 2411
dhayes@fenwick.com
*Featured in IT & Outsourcing (California), Intellectual Property (California)*

**Practice Areas:** David L Hayes is the Chair of the Intellectual Property Group of Fenwick & West LLP. His practice concentrates on IP counseling, litigation and audits, and technology licensing, distribution and transfer. Mr Hayes counsels high technology companies on establishing and maintaining procedures to protect the company's IP through copyrights, patents, trade secrets, mask works and trademarks, and on avoiding infringing the rights of others. He represents clients on high profile complex open source issues and technology transactions, including patent license transactions and acquisition strategies for both component technologies and turnkey systems. He is a nationally recognized expert on copyright issues related to the Internet and digital media.
**Career:** Mr Hayes has served as counsel in a number of precedent setting software copyright infringement cases, including Lotus Development Corp. v. Borland International, Apple Computer v. Microsoft Corp. and A&M Records v. Napster, Inc.
**Publications:** Over the past decade, Mr Hayes has been recognized more than 75 times as one of the top practitioners in various fields of IP law and strategy by leading publications and ranking organizations. In 2013, he was named "Lawyer of the Year" in Information Technology Law for the Silicon Valley by Best Lawyers.

## HAYMAN, Russell
McDermott Will & Emery LLP, Los Angeles
310 551 9334
rhayman@mwe.com
*Featured in Litigation (California)*

**Practice Areas:** Member of firm's health and trial departments. Experience include compliance programs, corporate internal investigations, voluntary disclosures, grand jury investigations, jury and court trials, and appellate practice. Handled variety of matters involving healthcare fraud and abuse issues.
**Professional Memberships:** Criminal Law Section, American Bar Association; Criminal Law Section, California Bar Association; American Health Lawyer's Association; District of Columbia Bar Association.
**Career:** Served for more than 10 years as a federal prosecutor in Los Angeles and as a senior official of the US Justice Department in Washington, DC.
**Personal:** Yale University Law School, JD, 1982; Duke University, BA, 1979.

## HAYUTIN, Marc I
Sidley Austin LLP, Los Angeles
213 896 6018
mhayutin@sidley.com
*Featured in Real Estate (California)*

**Practice Areas:** Partner in Sidley's Los Angeles Real Estate group, and co-global coordinator for the firm's world-wide Real Estate practice. He has experience in corporate finance, real estate and partnership matters, including residential, hotel, and commercial development and purchase, sale, sale leasebacks, finance and restructuring both inside and outside bankruptcy. His practice has also involved negotiation and restructuring of numerous general and limited partnerships and limited liability companies. He has experience in strategic counseling concerning significant real estate litigation matters, from inception through settlement or trial.
**Personal:** Harvard Law School, JD, 1968, cum laude; Stanford University BA, 1965, with distinction.

## HAZZARD, Yakub
Robins, Kaplan, Miller & Ciresi LLP, Los Angeles
310 552 0130
yhazzard@rkmc.com
*Featured in Media & Entertainment (California)*

**Practice Areas:** Entertainment industry and intellectual property issues, including trademark and copyright infringement, violations of rights of publicity and privacy, and breach of contract.
**Professional Memberships:** Member, Black Entertainment and Sports Law Association. Member of the John Langston Bar Association, the Los Angeles County, Century City, and American Bar Associations.
**Career:** Lecturer at various law schools and continuing education seminars (Harvard, Stanford, USC, LawReviewCLE ).
**Personal:** Stanford University (BA, Public Policy, 1986); UCLA (JD, 1990) Member of the Board of Directors of Public Counsel and Berry Gordy

Family Foundation. Former Member of the Board of Directors of the Fulfillment Fund.

## HEALY, Peter
O'Melveny & Myers LLP, San Francisco
415 984 8833
phealy@omm.com
*Featured in Capital Markets (California), Capital Markets (Nationwide)*
See under Nationwide for profile.

## HEIL, Joseph B
Dechert LLP, San Francisco
415 262 4510
joseph.heil@dechert.com
*Featured in Real Estate (Nationwide), Real Estate (California)*
See under Nationwide for profile.

## HEINICKE, Malcolm
Munger, Tolles & Olson LLP, Los Angeles
415 512 4029
Malcolm.Heinicke@mto.com
*Featured in Labor & Employment (California)*

**Practice Areas:** Practice focuses on class action and employment litigation. Recently obtained significant victories in wage and hour, WARN act and commercial class actions.
**Professional Memberships:** Board member, San Francisco Municipal Transportation Agency; Board member, Bar Association of San Francisco; Board Member, Say Hey Foundation.
**Career:** Partner at the firm. Board member, San Francisco Municipal Transportation Agency. Also served as a Taxicab Commissioner and chair of the San Francisco Human Rights Commission.
**Personal:** Stanford Law School (JD); Harvard University (AB).

## HEINKE, Rex S
Akin Gump Strauss Hauer & Feld LLP, Los Angeles
310 229 1030
rheinke@akingump.com
*Featured in Litigation (California)*

**Practice Areas:** Co-Chair, Supreme Court & Appellate Practice. Has handled hundreds of appeals, writs and substantive motions in state and federal courts throughout the country involving, antitrust, attorneys' fees, bankruptcy, class actions, complex business disputes, constitutional law, contracts, copyrights, defamation, domestic and international arbitrations, environmental law, false advertising, federal preemption, federal securities, personal jurisdiction, reporters' privilege, sovereign immunity, statutory interpretation, tax, trademarks, unfair competition, wage and hour, and wrongful termination.
**Professional Memberships:** Fellow, American & California Academies of Appellate Law; Best Lawyers' 2013 Los Angeles First Amendment "Lawyer of the Year"; California Lawyer magazine's 2013 Attorneys of the Year Award.

## HELLMAN, Dolph
Orrick, Herrington & Sutcliffe LLP, San Francisco
415 773 5678
dolphhellman@orrick.com
*Featured in Banking & Finance (California)*

**Career:** Dolph Hellman, a partner in Orrick's San Francisco office, has a broad range of experience in commercial financing transactions, including secured financings, asset-based financings, venture debt financings, vendor financings, mezzanine financings, subscription credit facilities, project financing, letters of credit, receivables purchase financings and leasing. Mr Hellman's clients include various financial institutions, Fortune 500 companies and numerous start-up companies (the latter group of which he represents in dozens of venture debt financing transactions each year for which he is recognized as one of the leading company-side counsel in the San Francisco Bay Area).

## HELVESTINE, William A
Crowell & Moring LLP, San Francisco
whelvestine@crowell.com
*Featured in Healthcare (California)*

**Practice Areas:** Partner in Crowell & Moring's Health Care Group and concentrates on health care law, regulatory matters and litigation. He primarily represents health plans, insurance carriers, hospital systems, and IPAs. His experience spans all areas of managed care law, including regulatory, transactional, litigation, antitrust and class action matters.
**Professional Memberships:** American Association of PPOs-Pacific Region; American Bar Association; American Health Lawyers Association; California Association of Health Plans; California Bar Association.
**Personal:** JD, Georgetown University, case and note editor, Georgetown Law Journal; BS, University of North Carolina, Physics.

## HENNIGAN, Brian J
Irell & Manella, Los Angeles
310 203 7159
bhennigan@irell.com
*Featured in Litigation (California)*

**Practice Areas:** Brian Hennigan is a partner at Irell & Manella, where he is co-chair of the white collar practice. Hennigan specializes in complex litigation and white collar criminal defense. He represents individuals and corporations in criminal, civil and administrative matters, including complex tax investigations, insider trading and backdated option investigations, and financial frauds. Hennigan also maintains a successful civil litigation practice. He is a Fellow of the American College of Trial Attorneys and was previously an Assistant U.S. Attorney in the Central District of California.
**Personal:** Northwestern University (JD, cum laude; BA).

## HENNIGAN, J Michael
McKool Smith, Los Angeles
213 694.1200
hennigan@mckoolsmithhennigan.com
*Featured in Litigation (Nationwide), Litigation (California)*
See under Nationwide for profile.

## HERMLE, Lynne C.
Orrick, Herrington & Sutcliffe LLP, Menlo Park
650 614 7422
lchermle@orrick.com
*Featured in Labor & Employment (California)*
**Practice Areas:** Lynne Hermle is consistently recognized as one of the best employment lawyers in the country. She has a long track record of wins, including outstanding results in jury trials. Lynne has defended well over 100 employment class actions, with a sterling record of defeating certification, obtaining early dismissal through procedural strategies and winning on the merits. Lynne serves as an Early Neutral Evaluator for the Northern District of California and has been appointed by that court to serve as a mediator in complex class actions. She writes and speaks frequently on employment issues.

## HERNANDEZ, Jennifer L
Holland & Knight LLP, San Francisco
415 743 6900
jennifer.hernandez@hklaw.com
*Featured in Environment (California), Real Estate (California)*
**Practice Areas:** National Environmental Team Co-Chair, leads the West Coast Land Use and Environmental Law Team. Hernandez advises developers, investors, sellers, and agencies in land use and environmental law, emphasizing resolving federal, state and local agency approvals, and securing community and political support for complex development projects, including urban infill and brownfields projects, master planned communities, and other mixed use, retail, industrial and commercial projects. She achieved national prominence in brownfield redevelopment, wetlands and endangered species development project work. She served as co-founder and General Counsel of Landbank, Inc., and as Presidential appointee to San Francisco's Presidio National Park Trust.

## HILL, James W
McDermott Will & Emery LLP, Irvine
949 757 7157
jahill@mwe.com
*Featured in Life Sciences (California)*
**Practice Areas:** Focuses on patent prosecution and litigation, strategic counseling, intellectual property due diligence and licensing in the areas of medical devices, biotechnology, pharmaceuticals, software, and signal and imaging processing.
**Professional Memberships:** California State Bar; US Patent and Trademark Office; American Medical Association; American Bar Association; American Intellectual Property Law Association; Licensing Executives Society.
**Career:** Also Clinical Assistant Professor of Radiology at University of Southern California School of Medicine.
**Personal:** Boston University School of Law, JD (cum laude), 1998; University of Southern California - Keck School of Medicine, MD (with honors), 1986; California State University - Los Angeles, BS, 1982.

## HINMAN, Frank M
Bingham McCutchen LLP, San Francisco
415 393 2462
frank.hinman@bingham.com
*Featured in Antitrust (California)*
**Practice Areas:** Co-chair of Bingham's Antitrust and Trade Regulation Group. Has practiced antitrust law for more than 20 years. Represents clients in public and private antitrust enforcement, including international cartel cases, class actions, merger clearance and civil conduct investigations. Recent antitrust litigation matters involved microprocessors, flash memory, bundled discounts and acquisitions. Also provides day-to-day counseling on antitrust issues, with an emphasis on distribution and acquisition strategies.
**Career:** Past vice-chair of ABA Antitrust Section's Trade, Sports and Professional Associations Committee.
**Personal:** University of California, Hastings College of the Law, JD, 1991; Claremont McKenna College, BA, cum laude, 1988.

## HINMAN JR, William H
Simpson Thacher & Bartlett LLP, Palo Alto
650 251 5000
whinman@stblaw.com
*Featured in Capital Markets (California), Capital Markets (Nationwide)*
**Practice Areas:** Partner in STB's Palo Alto office, concentrating on corporate finance. Active in major debt and equity offerings of high technology, healthcare, and biopharmaceutical companies, and a variety of offerings and general corporate work for a range of issuers and underwriters. Experienced in convertible offerings, derivatives, novel securities, and private placements. Regularly represents boards of directors and their committees on governance matters.
**Career:** Joined as Partner, 2000. Previously Managing Partner of Shearman & Sterling's San Francisco and Menlo Park Offices.
**Personal:** Cornell University Law School (JD, 1980); Editorial Board, Cornell Law Review. Michigan State University (BA, with honours, 1977).

## HIRSCH, Reece
Morgan, Lewis & Bockius LLP, San Francisco
415 442 1422
rhirsch@morganlewis.com
*Featured in Healthcare (California)*
**Practice Areas:** Reece Hirsch focuses his practice on healthcare law regulatory and transactional matters. He counsels and represents hospitals, health plans and insurers, physician organizations, healthcare information technology and life sciences companies on transactional and regulatory matters, including Medicare, fraud and abuse, self-referral, and privacy issues. Mr Hirsch has specific knowledge in data privacy and security, including compliance with HIPAA and the Gramm-Leach-Bliley Act. He has advised clients from virtually all sectors of the healthcare industry on privacy and security compliance matters, including assisting them in developing policies and procedures,

structuring healthcare information technology ventures, and responding to security breaches.

## HISERT, George A
Bingham McCutchen LLP, San Francisco
415 393 2577
george.hisert@bingham.com
*Featured in Banking & Finance (California)*
**Practice Areas:** Co-chair of Bingham's Banking and Leveraged Finance Practice Group. Nearly 40 years of experience representing major banking and financial institutions in commercial loan and credit transactions, letters of credit, and regulatory matters. Practice includes substantial representation of non-financial institutions and borrowers in a broad variety of credit transactions. Significant experience in mergers and acquisitions, general corporate matters, and international business transactions.
**Career:** Fellow, American College of Commercial Finance Lawyers.
**Personal:** University of Chicago Law School, JD, 1970; Brown University, MS and BS, summa cum laude, 1966.

## HOBEL, Lawrence
Covington & Burling LLP, San Francisco
415 591 7028
lhobel@cov.com
*Featured in Insurance (Nationwide), Insurance (California)*
See under Nationwide for profile.

## HOCKETT, Christopher
Davis Polk & Wardwell LLP, Menlo Park
650 752 2009
chris.hockett@dpw.com
*Featured in Antitrust (California)*
**Practice Areas:** Member of Davis Polk's Litigation Department, practicing in the Menlo Park office. Global head of firm's antitrust practice. Handles a broad range of commercial and antitrust matters. Has represented clients as lead counsel in high stakes commercial litigation, including antitrust and unfair competition disputes, securities litigation, patent litigation, consumer class actions and professional liability claims. Also represents clients in connection with government investigations and the antitrust aspects of mergers and acquisitions. Clients have included industry-leading technology and telecommunications companies, as well as prominent firms in a variety of other sectors, including financial services, law, media and entertainment, manufacturing and healthcare.

## HOLDEN JR, Frederick D
Orrick, Herrington & Sutcliffe LLP, San Francisco
415 773 5985
fholden@orrick.com
*Featured in Bankruptcy/Restructuring (California)*
**Career:** Fred Holden's practice has been focused for more than 35 years on restructuring, buying and selling businesses that are facing financial crisis. He represents creditors, debtors, committees, trustees, boards of directors, governmental interests and asset purchasers in Chapter 11 reorganizations, loan restructurings, distressed mergers and acquisitions, financial institution liquidations

and related litigation. Mr Holden has handled numerous cross-border insolvency matters, with an emphasis on reorganizations in China, the Philippines and Singapore, and he is currently advising numerous international companies in the solar energy business on insolvency and related corporate governance issues.

## HOLSCHER, Mark
Kirkland & Ellis LLP, Los Angeles
213 680 8190
mark.holscher@kirkland.com
*Featured in Litigation (California)*
**Practice Areas:** Mark Holscher is a partner and a member of the firm's commercial litigation and white-collar criminal defense groups. Mark has successfully defended individuals and corporations in complex civil, criminal and regulatory matters. He is currently handling multiple insider trading and FCPA matters.

## HORTON, Michel Yves
Morgan, Lewis & Bockius LLP, Los Angeles
213 612 7300
mhorton@morganlewis.com
*Featured in Insurance (Nationwide), Insurance (California)*
See under Nationwide for profile.

## HOWARD, Geoffrey M
Bingham McCutchen LLP, San Francisco
415 393 2485
geoff.howard@bingham.com
*Featured in Intellectual Property (California)*
**Practice Areas:** Co-chair of Bingham's Litigation Area and former co-chair of the firm's Intellectual Property Group. Served as lead trial counsel in a broad range of high-profile commercial and intellectual property litigation, including for Oracle in one of the US's largest copyright infringement and Computer Fraud and Abuse Act cases. Substantive emphasis includes Internet intrusion, software and telecommunications technology. Has prosecuted and defended cases involving claims for copyright infringement, computer fraud, unfair competition, misappropriation of trade secrets, patent and trademark infringement, regulatory issues, business torts, and putative class actions.
**Personal:** Harvard Law School, JD, cum laude, 1991; UCLA, BA, 1988.

## HOWARD, Robert
Latham & Watkins LLP, San Diego
619 236 1234
robert.howard@lw.com
*Featured in Environment (California)*
**Practice Areas:** Chairs San Diego's Environment, Land and Resources Department with 25 environmental litigation attorneys. Tries high-profile federal and state criminal and civil environmental cases. Over two decades expertise in cutting-edge government enforcement, clean air/water, toxic tort, land use, sediment and natural resources damages cases.
**Professional Memberships:** Association of Business Trial Lawyers.
**Career:** Co-Chaired Mass Torts Practice Group with 100 attorneys. Recognized in Chambers, Law360, San Diego publications as leader in field.

**Publications:** Criminal procedure, evidence, torts articles cited by Florida, Michigan, Wisconsin Supreme Courts.
**Personal:** JD/MBA, Duke 1989, BS Mechanical Engineering/Physics, Tufts 1982. Retired military. Enjoys history, alpine sports.

### HOWARD JR, George S
Jones Day, San Diego
858 314 1166
gshoward@jonesday.com
*Featured in Labor & Employment (California)*
**Practice Areas:** Has practiced labor and employment law in San Diego since 1977. He has successfully tried multi-week bench and jury trials, numerous shorter trials, arbitrations, and administrative proceedings. He has extensive experience in union/management relations, as well as all types of employment litigation.
**Professional Memberships:** Member and Past Chair, the Employers Group Legal Committee, a select group of 18 California lawyers who appear as amicus curiae in the appeals of important employment cases in CA. Listed in 'Best Lawyers In America' since 1993.
**Personal:** JD, University of Virginia (1977); BA, University of Virginia (with highest distinction, 1974).

### HOYNG, Charles F
Latham & Watkins LLP, Silicon Valley
650 463 3040
charles.hoyng@lw.com
*Featured in Life Sciences (Nationwide), Life Sciences (California)*
**Practice Areas:** Structuring, drafting and negotiating strategic alliances, joint venture and intellectual property license agreements, counseling universities and public and private life sciences companies in the development, protection, manufacture and distribution of products and technology in the areas of biotechnology, pharmaceuticals, diagnostics, medical devices and healthcare businesses.
**Professional Memberships:** Admitted, State Bar of California, Massachusetts Bar Association, United States Patent and Trademark Office.
**Career:** Post-doctoral research fellow, California Institute of Technology; Assistant Professor, Chemistry, Texas A&M University; held several positions, Genentech, Inc.
**Personal:** JD, UC Berkeley, School of Law (Boalt Hall), 1989; PhD, MIT, 1976; BS, Miami University (Ohio), 1972.

### HSIAO, Peter
Morrison & Foerster LLP, Los Angeles
213 892 5731
phsiao@mofo.com
*Featured in Environment (California)*
**Practice Areas:** Trial attorney and chemical engineer with 28 years of experience in environmental, natural resources and toxic tort litigation. Expertise in clean air and water laws, climate change regulation, hazardous substances, green chemistry, auditing, product manufacturing and safety laws.
**Professional Memberships:** Member, ABA Standing Committee on Environmental Law.

Former chair, California State Bar Environmental Law Section. Board of Directors, LA County Bar Foundation.
**Career:** Department of Justice, Assistant U.S. Attorney. Judge Pro Tem, California Municipal Court.
**Publications:** California Environmental and Natural Resources Law Handbook
**Personal:** University of Utah (BS, 1982); UC Berkeley School of Law (JD, 1985)

### HUDSON, Jeff R
Gibson, Dunn & Crutcher LLP, Los Angeles
213 229 7332
jhudson@gibsondunn.com
*Featured in Banking & Finance (California)*
**Practice Areas:** Practice focuses on debt financing, including acquisition financings, secured and unsecured corporate credits, underwritten debt offerings, Rule 144A financings, private placements, first and second lien notes, mezzanine transactions, convertible debt offerings, debt tender and exchange offers, asset-based lending, structured financings, work-outs and restructurings, and DIP financings.
**Career:** Co-leader of the Global Finance Group. Over 30 years of finance experience at Gibson Dunn.
**Personal:** JD, Harvard Law School, 1978. BA, Claremont McKenna College, 1974.

### HUESTON, John C
Irell & Manella, Los Angeles
310 203 7152
jhueston@irell.com
*Featured in Litigation (California)*
**Practice Areas:** John Hueston is a partner at Irell & Manella, where he is co-chair of the white collar practice and on the Executive Committee. Mr Hueston has extensive jury trial experience serving as lead counsel for Fortune 500 companies and governments in numerous cases, including securities and shareholder class action, patent litigation, trademark infringement and environmental cases, and cases alleging unfair business practices. A former lead prosecutor for the Enron trial of Kenneth Lay and Jeffrey Skilling, his practice focuses on internal investigations, corporate crisis management and white collar criminal defense.
**Personal:** Yale Law School (JD); Dartmouth College (BA).

### HYMAN, Milt
Irell & Manella, Los Angeles
310 203 7145
mhyman@irell.com
*Featured in Tax (California)*
**Practice Areas:** Milton Hyman is a partner emeritus at Irell & Manella, where his practice focuses on complex tax and corporate matters. Mr Hyman specializes in business planning for corporations, limited liability companies and partnerships, handling major acquisitions and combinations. He also handles tax controversies involving federal and state taxation, including corporate and partnership tax matters, California unitary taxation, residency disputes, and property and sales tax controversies. Mr Hyman acts as special tax counsel to debtors in possession, creditors' com-

mittees and major creditors in major corporate reorganizations.
**Personal:** Harvard University (JD, magna cum laude); UCLA (BA, Economics, Phi Beta Kappa).

### IANCU, Andrei
Irell & Manella, Los Angeles
310 203 7537
aiancu@irell.com
*Featured in Intellectual Property (California)*
**Practice Areas:** Andrei Iancu is Managing Partner of Irell & Manella, where his practice focuses on IP litigation. Mr Iancu also has extensive experience with patent and trademark prosecution, due diligence and licensing. He represents clients across the technology spectrum, including those associated with medical devices, genetic testing, multimedia, cell phones and telephony, the Internet, computer software and hardware, and video game systems. An award-winning author, Mr Iancu regularly speaks and writes on patent law and practice. He is registered to practice in the USPTO.
**Personal:** UCLA School of Law (JD); UCLA (MS, Mechanical Engineering); UCLA (BS, Aerospace Engineering).

### INSOGNA, Anthony M
Jones Day, San Diego
858 314 1130
aminsogna@jonesday.com
*Featured in Life Sciences (California)*
**Practice Areas:** Anthony is co-chair of the firm's Global Intellectual Property Practice, which has over 265 professionals in 10 countries. He has over 20 years of experience representing life sciences companies in creating patent portfolios to protect their most important products, as well as enforcing and defending those portfolios throughout the world. Anthony's patent strategies have been tested through patent litigation, due diligence, U.S. patent interferences, oppositions and invalidation proceedings. Anthony has significant experience planning for and handling Hatch-Waxman litigation. Anthony has helped several emerging companies to become the largest and most successful pharma and biotech companies today.

### IPPOLITO, Peter J
McKenna Long & Aldridge LLP, San Diego
619 595 5400
PIppolito@mckennalong.com
*Featured in Construction (California)*
**Practice Areas:** Peter J. Ippolito concentrates his practice on all areas of construction including: architect and engineer malpractice, federal, state and local courts, arbitrations and administrative boards nationwide. He represents public agencies, developers, sureties, general and specialty contractors, vendors and suppliers. He has extensive experience with disputes arising out of the design and construction of hotels, hospitals, dams, roads, bridges, railways, tunnels, pipelines and nuclear power plants. In addition to representing parties in construction disputes he is a mediator and arbitrator.

**Personal:** LLM, George Washington University, 1975; JD, University of Notre Dame, 1966; BA, Virginia Military Institute, 1963.

### ISSLER, Paul
Gibson, Dunn & Crutcher LLP, Los Angeles
213 229 7763
pissler@gibsondunn.com
*Featured in Tax (California)*
**Practice Areas:** Mr Issler's practice emphasis is on domestic and international corporate and partnership tax matters. His practice involves diversified representations of public and private corporations, partnerships/LLCs - including private equity funds — and their investors and executives. He has extensive experience in tax planning for corporate and real estate acquisitions, dispositions, reorganizations and complex joint ventures. His expertise includes taxable and tax-free acquisitions and dispositions, UBTI matters, REITs, venture capital, bankruptcy and insolvency/workouts and executive compensation.
**Personal:** JD, University of Southern California Law Center; Order of the Coif; Managing Editor - Southern California Law Review.

### IVENER, Mark
Ivener & Fullmer LLP, Los Angeles
310 477 3000
mark@usworkvisa.com
*Featured in Immigration (California), Immigration (Nationwide)*
**Practice Areas:** Business immigration law; global mobility.
**Career:** For more than 35 years, Mark A Ivener has exclusively practiced immigration law, advising on immigration due diligence in M&A; global mobility management; professional, investor and entertainment visas; and EB-5 investor Green Cards. He has lectured on US immigration law for organizations such as the World Trade Institute; the California, Federal and International Bar Associations; and the American Immigration Lawyers Association. A leader in his field, Mark Ivener is a founder of the National Consortium of Immigration Law Firms (IMMLAW) and the Alliance of Business Immigration Lawyers (ABIL). He is listed in the Martindale-Hubbell Bar Register of Preeminent Lawyers (Immigration and Naturalization), the International Who's Who of Corporate Immigration Lawyers and Chambers Global and USA. Also, Mark Ivener was the only immigration attorney named in the Top 100 Wealth Advisers and Managers in the Americas by Citywealth Magazine.
**Publications:** His books include Handbook of Immigration Law, Volumes I & II; Doing Business in the USA Under Free Trade; Get the Right Visa; A Complete Guide to Getting An American Visa (in Japanese); and Have You Thought About Immigrating to the U.S.? (in Spanish). In addition, he has authored many articles for such publications as the California International Law Journal, the Canadian-American Bar Association Newsletter, and Business and the Law.

## IVEY, Thomas J.
Skadden, Arps, Slate, Meagher & Flom LLP
& Affiliates, Palo Alto
650 470 4522
thomas.ivey@skadden.com
*Featured in Capital Markets (California)*

**Practice Areas:** Mr Ivey represents public and private companies, investment banks and private equity funds in a range of corporate and securities matters, including public and private offerings of equity and debt securities, mergers, acquisitions, joint ventures, exchange offers, restructurings and general corporate counseling. Transactions include: VMware, Inc. in its $1.1 billion IPO; Hitachi Global Storage Technologies in its $4.3 billion sale to Western Digital Corporation; and Yahoo! Inc. in its $750 million convertible notes offering.

**Career:** JD, UC Berkeley School of Law, 1992; BA, University of California at Los Angeles, 1989 (Honors Collegium).

## JACOBS, Michael A
Morrison & Foerster LLP, San Francisco
415 268 7455
mjacobs@mofo.com
*Featured in Intellectual Property (California)*

**Practice Areas:** Represents leading IT and life sciences companies in highest profile matters. Co-lead counsel in obtaining billion dollar verdict in 2012's "trial of the century." Co-founded firm's intellectual property group and heads firm's life sciences practice group.

**Career:** Admitted to practice in California. Co-founder and co-chair, Intellectual Property Group (1990-2002 and 2008-2010). Firmwide Managing Partner for Operations (1995-97).

**Publications:** Co-author, 'World Intellectual Property Guidebook', United States (1992, Matthew Bender & Company, New York).

**Personal:** BA, Stanford University; U.S. Foreign Service, assignments in Jamaica and Washington, DC; JD, Yale Law School ; Adjunct professor, UC Berkeley School of Law.

## JACOBS, Robert A
Manatt Phelps & Phillips LLP, Los Angeles
310 312 4360
rjacobs@manatt.com
*Featured in Media & Entertainment (California)*

**Practice Areas:** Jacobs is chair of Manatt's Entertainment Litigation Practice and specializes in commercial, copyright and other intellectual property disputes in the entertainment, media and fine art industries. He has represented top-level talent, movie studios, major record labels, music publishers, talent agencies and brands in contract, fraud, tortious interference, fiduciary duty, copyright, idea theft, trademark, right of publicity, unfair competition, labor agreement and royalty actions in federal and state courts and arbitrations. His clients have included entities such as Lions Gate Entertainment, the Richard Avedon Foundation, Warner Music Group, and artists Bruce Springsteen, Usher, and Jay DeMarcus of Rascal Flatts.

## JAHN, Paul E
Morrison & Foerster LLP, San Francisco
415 268 6387
pjahn@mofo.com
*Featured in IT & Outsourcing (California)*

**Practice Areas:** Specializes in transactions involving development, licensing, acquisition, and sale of intellectual property and technology. Transactions typically involve strategic alliances/joint ventures; commercialization/distribution arrangements; BPO/IT sourcing, and resolution of related disputes. Represents clients in adversarial patent license negotiations and portfolio acquisition. Clients generally operate in high technology, life sciences, and financial services industries.

**Career:** Former Co-Chair of firm's Technology Transactions Group. Formerly resident in firm's Tokyo and Brussels offices. Admitted to practice in California.

**Personal:** BA, University of California, Berkeley, 1986; JD, Hastings College of the Law, 1993; Clerk, Hon Claudia Wilken, Northern District of California, 1995-96.

## JEFFRY, Thomas
Arent Fox LLP, Los Angeles
213.443 7520
thomas.jeffry@arentfox.com
*Featured in Healthcare (California)*

**Practice Areas:** Tom Jeffry is a partner in the firm's Health Care and Life Sciences practice groups. His practice is devoted to business and regulatory compliance, including compliance investigations, corporate integrity programs and transactions. Tom represents hospital systems and other providers in many areas, including development and construction of health facilities, joint ventures, mergers and acquisitions, drafting and negotiating contracts, and advising on fraud and abuse issues. He assists clients with governance, nonprofit tax and antitrust issues related to integrated delivery systems, health information technology, bioethics, clinical research, privacy and security, and HIPAA Administrative Simplification regulations.

## JENETT, Bruce W
DLA Piper LLP (US), East Palo Alto
650 833 2321
bruce.jenett@dlapiper.com
*Featured in Life Sciences (California)*

**Practice Areas:** Life sciences, corporate and securities.

**Career:** His practice focuses on the representation of domestic and international high technology business clients, primarily in the life sciences industry. He is experienced in equity and debt financing, licensing and distribution, strategic alliances, joint ventures, and mergers and acquisitions, as well as general counseling issues, representing both start-ups and large multinational corporations. He is a frequent speaker on corporate and finance issues to both business and attorney audiences.

**Personal:** JD, Georgetown University Law Center; BA, Princeton University.

## JOHNSON, Robert K
Munger, Tolles & Olson LLP, Los Angeles
213 683 9109
Robert.Johnson@mto.com
*Featured in Employee Benefits & Executive Compensation (California)*

**Practice Areas:** Specializes in tax, executive compensation and employee benefits. Represents public and private companies, senior executives and consulting firms. Major representations include: Air Lease Corp., Berkshire Hathaway Inc., City National Corp., Edison International and MGM Resorts International.

**Professional Memberships:** Los Angeles County Bar Association Tax Section, Past Chair; California State Bar Tax Section, Past Chair; Fellow of the American College of Tax Counsel and the American College of Employee Benefits Counsel.

**Career:** Served as co-managing partner for six years.

**Personal:** Stanford University (LLB) Harvard University (AB).

## JOHNSON JR, Daniel
Morgan, Lewis & Bockius LLP, San Francisco
415 442 1392
djjohnson@morganlewis.com
*Featured in Intellectual Property (California)*

**Practice Areas:** Focuses on high-stakes complex litigation, including patent cases, trade secret cases, disputes over software structure and source code, license disputes, and unfair competition and false advertisement disputes. He has tried numerous cases in state and federal courts throughout the United States and before the International Trade Commission, the American Arbitration Association, and Judicial Arbitration and Mediation Services.

**Professional Memberships:** American Bar Association, National Bar Association; Member, Inns of Court, Intellectual Property section.

**Career:** 1973-1976, Deputy Attorney General to the State of California.

**Personal:** Yale Law School, 1973, JD; University of California, Berkeley, 1970, AB, With Honors

## JOHNSTON, James O
Jones Day, Los Angeles
213 243 2431
jjohnston@jonesday.com
*Featured in Bankruptcy/Restructuring (California)*

**Practice Areas:** Jim Johnston represents debtors, creditors, creditor groups, indenture trustees, and other parties in interest in chapter 11 cases and out-of-court workouts across the United States.

**Career:** Jim has represented many corporate and municipal debtors in reorganization cases, including Desert Hot Springs California, Kenetech Windpower, Komag, Orange County California, SmarTalk TeleServices, and Weststar Cinemas. He has represented creditors and indenture trustees in proceedings involving, among others, Adelphia Communications, American Airlines, Calpine Corporation, Delta Airlines, Hawaiian TelCom, Northwest Airlines, RBX Corporation, SpectraSite Holdings, the City of Stockton (California),

Tribune Company, Tropicana Las Vegas, and United Airlines.

## JOHNSTON, Ronald
Arnold & Porter LLP, Los Angeles
213 243 4256
Ronald.Johnston@aporter.com
*Featured in Intellectual Property (California)*

**Practice Areas:** Ronald Johnston is a senior litigation partner and has served as a Responsible Partner for the firm's Los Angeles office and its Intellectual Property Group. He represents clients in leading cases in the information technology and entertainment industries at the trial and appellate levels. Substantive areas of his practice include copyright, patent, trade secret, trademark, right of publicity, antitrust and unfair competition law. A leader in the IP bar for over 25 years, he was founder and Chairperson of the University of Southern California's Computer & Internet Law Institute, and is founder/Editor-in-Chief of The Computer & Internet Lawyer.

## KADUE, David
Seyfarth Shaw LLP, Los Angeles
310 201 5211
dkadue@seyfarth.com
*Featured in Labor & Employment (California)*

**Practice Areas:** Labor and employment.

**Professional Memberships:** American Bar Association.

**Career:** Mr Kadue represents management in employment counseling and litigation. His practice emphasizes the defense of individual and class action claims for wage and hour violations and employment discrimination. He also advises employers with respect to prevention of workplace harassment, employment contracts, employment policies, and employee discipline.

**Publications:** Mr Kadue has authored numerous publications relating to California labor law, employee privacy, workplace harassment, wrongful dismissal, and employment discrimination.

**Personal:** JD, University of Minnesota Law School; BA, Yale University.

## KADZIELSKI, Mark A
Fulbright & Jaworski LLP, Los Angeles
213 892 9306
mkadzielski@fulbright.com
*Featured in Healthcare (California), Healthcare (Nationwide)*

**Practice Areas:** Health law.

**Professional Memberships:** American Health Lawyers Association and the California Society for Healthcare Attorneys.

**Career:** Mr Kadzielski is a past Member of the AHLA's Board of Directors and served on the organization's first executive committee. In 2005, he was elected to the AHLA's inaugural class of Fellows, members recognized for their extraordinary contributions to health law in the US. 'Best Lawyer in America' in Health Law for the past 25 years, and Southern California 'Super Lawyer' in Health Law, 2004-13.

**Personal:** AB, magna cum laude, John Carroll University (1968); JD, University of Pennsylvania Law School (1976).

**KAHN, Michael A.**
Crowell & Moring LLP, San Francisco
415 365 7817
mkahn@crowell.com
*Featured in Litigation (California)*
**Practice Areas:** Senior Counsel at Crowell &
Moring and is a member of the Litigation & Trial
Group. Practice involves federal and state court
proceedings throughout the US. He has tried over
twenty cases to verdict with a success rate of over
ninety percent. He has also argued over a dozen
appeals in State Supreme Court and Federal and
State Courts of Appeal and has arbitrated over a
dozen cases to decision.
**Career:** Prior to joining Crowell & Moring, Mr
Kahn was a senior counsel at the San Francisco
firm of Folger Levin & Kahn LLP.

**KALLSTROM, D Ward**
Seyfarth Shaw LLP, San Francisco
415 732 1107
wkallstrom@seyfarth.com
*Featured in ERISA Litigation (Nationwide), Employee
Benefits & Executive Compensation (California)*
**Practice Areas:** ERISA Litigation; Employee
Benefits and Executive Compensation.
**Professional Memberships:** Charter Fellow
and Former Governor, ACEBC; Management
Council Member, ABA Section of L&E Law 2002-
2012; Fellow, College of L&E Lawyers.
**Career:** Mr Kallstrom focuses on employee benefits fiduciary advice and litigation. He has handled
the full panoply of ERISA litigation cases, from fee
and expense, ESOP, and stock-drop litigation to
health care provider fraud and reimbursement
cases, retiree medical and other cutback claims.
He counsels clients, including Taft-Hartley funds,
on fiduciary compliance matters for 401(k),
defined benefit, medical, LTD, and other plans.
**Personal:** JD, Duke Law School.

**KAPLAN, Gary P**
Sidley Austin LLP, San Francisco
415 772 1277
gkaplan@sidley.com
*Featured in Tax (California)*
**Practice Areas:** Partner in Sidley's Tax practice.
Focuses practice on international taxation, representing US and international clients in connection
with cross-border taxation and M&A, joint ventures and other strategic relationships. For multinationals, he has developed tax-efficient international expansion plans, set up holding companies,
established foreign representative offices, branches
and subsidiaries, advised on Subpart F and PFIC
issues and migrated intellectual property rights
through buy-in and cost-sharing agreements. He
represents non-US companies engaged in US
business and investment activities, with a focus on
FIRPTA and treaty interpretation. Also works with
global families on personal tax, business and
investment activities.

**KAPOOR, Rahul**
Morgan, Lewis & Bockius LLP, Palo Alto
650 843 7580
rkapoor@morganlewis.com
*Featured in IT & Outsourcing (California)*

**Practice Areas:** Rahul Kapoor is a partner in
Morgan Lewis's Business and Finance Practice, the
firmwide hiring partner, and a member of the
firm's Advisory Board and Finance Committee.
Mr Kapoor has deep transactional experience in
technology transactions, strategic alliances, joint
ventures, corporate partnering transactions, standards body licensing structures, intellectual property strategic counseling, open source software,
and commercial transactions. Mr Kapoor has an
electrical engineering degree and, prior to practicing law, spent six years as an engineer and project
manager. Mr Kapoor teaches an Intellectual
Property Strategy class at the University of
California – Berkeley Law School.

**KARP, Joseph**
Winston & Strawn LLP, San Francisco
415 591 1529
jkarp@winston.com
*Featured in Energy & Natural Resources (California)*
**Practice Areas:** Energy-regulatory and transactional matters, project development and operations matters for natural gas and electricity concerns, water-utility regulation. Particular expertise
representing electricity generators (renewable and
conventional) in full range of issues affecting electricity revenues, fuel costs and operations. Active
in administrative litigation, contract negotiation,
dispute resolution and compliance advice; regularly represents, among others, the California
Cogeneration Council and California Wind
Energy Association and their members. Also represents clients in wind, solar, geothermal, biomass
and landfill-gas based generation transactions.
**Personal:** JD, cum laude, Harvard Law School,
1989; BA, SUNY Binghamton, 1986 (Foundation
Award for Academic Excellence, Phi Beta Kappa).

**KAUFMAN, Christopher L**
Latham & Watkins LLP, Silicon Valley
650 463 2606
christopher.kaufman@lw.com
*Featured in Investment Funds (Nationwide),
Corporate/M&A (Northern California),
Corporate/M&A (California)*
See under Nationwide for profile.

**KAZAKS, Julia M**
Skadden, Arps, Slate, Meagher & Flom LLP
& Affiliates, Palo Alto
650 470 4640
Julia.Kazaks@skadden.com
*Featured in Tax (Nationwide), Tax (California)*
**Practice Areas:** Represents clients in all phases
of tax controversy and litigation, including federal
court proceedings, IRS audits and appeals, and
alternative dispute resolution venues. Covers a
broad range of issues including transfer pricing,
other international tax matters, employee/contrac-
tor classification, the economic substance and
business purpose doctrines, business and real
estate valuation, partnership taxation, income tax
accounting questions, taxation of stock options,
capitalization principles, transportation excise
taxes and proposed exempt status revocation.
Regularly represents clients in the technology,
financial services, pharmaceutical, energy, and
transportation industries.

**Career:** JD, Georgetown University Law Center;
AB, Political Science and History, Stanford
University.

**KELLER, Tobias S**
Jones Day, San Francisco
415 875 5869
tkeller@jonesday.com
*Featured in Bankruptcy/Restructuring (California)*
**Practice Areas:** Has a diverse corporate practice emphasizing counseling for companies in
transition arising from financing challenges,
uncontrolled litigation, or unanticipated employee
or vendor problems; and the governance problems that often arise in connection with those
challenges. Regularly lectures on corporate and
commercial law topics for organizations including
Stanford Law School and various bar organizations.
**Personal:** Harvard University (BA magna cum
laude 1985); Stanford University (JD 1990).

**KELLY, William**
Davis Polk & Wardwell LLP, Menlo Park
650 752 2000
william.kelly@davispolk.com
*Featured in Corporate/M&A (Northern California)*
**Practice Areas:** Focuses on M&A and strategic
transactions, as well as corporate governance and
securities law compliance, largely for technology
companies. Represented Oracle in hostile takeover
of PeopleSoft and acquisitions of Siebel,
Primavera, Hyperion and others. Other M&A
transactions: KLA-Tencor (ADE); Blue Coat
(Packeteer); Photon Dynamics (sale to Orbotech);
Yahoo! (Inktomi). Represented Comcast in strategic IP arrangements with Microsoft, TV Guide
and TiVo. Corporate clients include Oracle, KLA-
Tencor, Palm, FormFactor, Affymetrix, Apple,
Novellus. A founder of Davis Polk's Menlo Park
office; formerly general counsel and senior business executive at Silicon Graphics (1994-99).

**KEMP, J Hovey**
Goodwin Procter LLP, San Francisco
415 733 6092
hkemp@goodwinprocter.com
*Featured in Corporate/M&A (California)*
**Practice Areas:** Mr Kemp's practice focuses primarily on private equity and financing transactions in connection with middle-market leveraged
buyouts and buildups across a number of industries, including financial services, healthcare, education, business services, information technology,
consumer products, traditional manufacturing
and light industry, as well as the alternative energy
and clean technologies sectors. His practice also
focuses heavily on mergers and acquisitions,
including for a number of public and private
companies which are outside of his private equity
practice.
**Personal:** JD, Georgetown University Law
Center, 1980; AB, Harvard University, 1976
(magna cum laude).

**KENNEDY, Kevin P.**
Simpson Thacher & Bartlett LLP, Palo Alto
650 251 5000
kkennedy@stblaw.com
*Featured in Capital Markets (California)*

**Practice Areas:** Corporate partner, specializing
in securities and corporate governance matters.
Emphasis on IPOs and public financings in the
high technology, consumer products, biopharmaceutical, consulting and staffing industries. Also
has extensive experience working with companies
in these industries on mergers and acquisitions
and representing these companies on general corporate matters. Representative transactions
include the IPOs of Tesla Motors, Demand Media
and eBay and convertible note offerings for Apple
and Amazon.
**Career:** Joined the firm in 2000 as Partner.
**Personal:** BA, with Highest Honors, University
of California, Davis (1988); JD, Boalt Hall School
of Law, University of California, Berkeley (1991).

**KENNEDY, Mike**
Shearman & Sterling LLP, San Francisco
415 616 1248
michael.kennedy@shearman.com
*Featured in Corporate/M&A (California)*
**Career:** Michael Kennedy, a partner in the firm's
Mergers and Acquisitions Practice Group, concentrates in the areas of mergers, acquisitions, divestitures, corporate partnering, joint ventures and
corporate governance, with an emphasis in the
technology, emerging growth, healthcare, biotechnology and media industries. Mr Kennedy has
extensive experience in the private equity and
leveraged buyout industries as well as decades of
experience in other industries. He represents
many major investment banks in their advisory
roles on M&A deals. Mr Kennedy currently serves
as the managing partner of the firm's Bay Area
offices.

**KENNEDY, Raoul**
Skadden, Arps, Slate, Meagher & Flom LLP
& Affiliates, Palo Alto
650 470 4550
raoul.kennedy@skadden.com
*Featured in Litigation (California)*
**Practice Areas:** Lead counsel in 50+ jury and
25+ nonjury trials; argued over 50 appeals in
complex civil matters. Named Daily Journal "Top
100" lawyer. Member State Bar's Trial Lawyer Hall
of Fame. Listed in Best Lawyers in America in:
Appellate Law, Bet-The-Company Litigation,
Commercial Litigation, Insurance.
**Professional Memberships:** Member:
American College of Trial Lawyers, International
Academy of Trial Lawyers, American Board of
Trial Advocates, International Society of
Barristers, American Academy of Appellate
Lawyers.
**Career:** JD, U.C. Berkeley School of Law, 1967;
BA, University of the Pacific, 1964.
**Publications:** Co-author, California Complex
Litigation Manual and California Expert Witness
Guide.

**KENNEDY, Shayne**
Latham & Watkins LLP, Costa Mesa
714 755 8181
shayne.kennedy@lw.com
*Featured in Capital Markets (California)*
**Practice Areas:** Capital markets, general corporate and securities matters and mergers and acqui-

sitions. Regularly represents issuers and underwriters in both public and private securities offerings in various industries, with a particular emphasis in life sciences and retail and consumer products. Advises companies and boards of directors with respect to general and corporate governance matters. M&A transactions include public company mergers, as well as various private company acquisitions and dispositions.
**Career:** Vice-chair of the firm's Associates Committee. Recognized in Chambers USA 2012 legal guide as a "Leading Lawyer."
**Personal:** JD, University of Southern California; BA, Brigham Young University.

## KENT, Ronald D
SNR Denton, Los Angeles
213 892 5030
ronald.kent@dentons.com
*Featured in Insurance (Nationwide), Insurance (California)*
**Practice Areas:** Represents insurance companies in coverage and bad-faith actions, regulatory matters, underwriting and claims-related class actions, environmental, asbestos and toxic tort claims, and general business disputes. Lead trial and appellate experience in state and federal courts across US. Multi-year experience acting as National or Regional Coordinating Counsel for insurer clients' coverage and litigation issues arising from natural and man-made disasters (earthquake, hurricanes, childhood sexual abuse, etc.). More than fifty percent of working days in trial over past five years.
**Personal:** University of California, Berkeley, JD, Order of the Coif; UCLA, BA, summa cum laude, Phi Beta Kappa.

## KERMAN, Peter F
Latham & Watkins LLP, Silicon Valley
650 328 4600
peter.kerman@lw.com
*Featured in Corporate/M&A (Northern California), Corporate/M&A (California)*
**Practice Areas:** Practice centers on mergers and acquisitions, and public company representation. Within M&A, has represented financial buyers, strategic buyers and sellers, special committees and investment banking firms in numerous acquisitions and dispositions of public and private companies. Transactions include tender offers, mergers of equals, carve-outs, unsolicited offers, cross-border, leveraged buy-outs, asset transactions, acquisitions out of bankruptcy and many others. Advised numerous companies in a variety of public and private offerings, corporate governance matters and compliance with federal securities laws.
**Personal:** JD, Harvard Law School, 1984; MS, Stanford University, 1977; BA, Stanford University, 1977.

## KILB, Brian D
Liner Grode Stein Yankelevitz Sunshine Regenstreif & Taylor LLP, Los Angeles
310 500 3584
bkilb@linerlaw.com
*Featured in Banking & Finance (California)*

**Practice Areas:** Partner in the firm's media/entertainment finance group. Represents lenders, studios and production companies in a wide variety of film financings. Also represents private equity and other borrowers, and investment and commercial banks, in leveraged acquisition financings and other secured and unsecured senior, mezzanine and subordinated loan transactions, second-lien financings, asset securitizations and other financing transactions. In addition to media and entertainment, Mr Kilb's finance practice also covers other industries, including gaming, lodging and real estate. Representative clients include Hilton Hotels Corporation, Colony Capital, Bank of America, Union Bank, Comerica, First Republic Bank, MGM and Miramax.
**Personal:** JD, cum laude, Harvard Law School, 1983.

## KIM, Mark
Munger, Tolles & Olson LLP, Los Angeles
213 683 9144
Mark.Kim@mto.com
*Featured in Corporate/M&A (Southern California)*
**Practice Areas:** Corporate (M&A, private equity, securities offerings). Recent transactions: Representing HealthCare Partners in $4.4 billion sale to DaVita Inc.; representing Air Lease Corporation in over $4 billion of securities offerings; representing Berkshire Hathaway in $5 billion investment in Bank of America.
**Professional Memberships:** Co-head of firm's "Kids in Need of Defense" program.
**Career:** Recognized by the Daily Journal in 2011 as a top 20 California attorney under age 40 and named to "Who's Who in L.A. Law" by the L.A. Business Journal.
**Personal:** Yale Law School (JD, 1998); Harvard College (AB, magna cum laude, 1994).

## KIM, Sang
DLA Piper LLP (US), East Palo Alto
650 833 2072
sang.kim@dlapiper.com
*Featured in Tax (California)*
**Practice Areas:** International Tax.
**Career:** Co-managing partner of the firm's Silicon Valley office and is a member of the Executive Committee, as well as the National Diversity and Inclusion Committee. He focuses on international tax and operational structuring, global transfer pricing strategy and documentation, cross-border mergers, acquisitions, dispositions and joint ventures, post-acquisition integration and international tax controversy. He has led over a hundred international expansion and structuring projects for companies across a wide spectrum of industries and jurisdictions.
**Personal:** LLM, New York University School of Law (Taxation); JD, Northwestern University School of Law; BA, Columbia University.

## KING, Kenton J
Skadden, Arps, Slate, Meagher & Flom LLP & Affiliates, Palo Alto
650 470 4530
kenton.king@skadden.com
*Featured in Corporate/M&A (California), Corporate/M&A (Northern California)*

**Practice Areas:** Head of Skadden's Palo Alto office and co-head of global corporate transactions practice. Extensive experience in US and cross-border M&A, corporate and board governance, and capital markets. Representative transactions: Yahoo! in numerous matters, including the unsolicited $45 billion proposal from Microsoft and its sale of a portion of its stake in Alibaba Group Holding Limited (the largest-ever e-commerce M&A transaction); Compaq Computer's $25 billion merger with Hewlett-Packard; and Ascend Communications' $20 billion acquisition by Lucent Technologies.
**Career:** JD, U.C. Berkeley School of Law, 1987 (Editor in Chief, California Law Review; Order of the Coif); BA, Stanford University, 1977.

## KING, Leif
Skadden, Arps, Slate, Meagher & Flom LLP & Affiliates, Palo Alto
650 470 4662
leif.king@skadden.com
*Featured in Corporate/M&A (Northern California)*
**Practice Areas:** Represents clients in corporate transactions, including mergers and acquisitions, private equity transactions, and securities offerings. Advises public and private companies and their stakeholders on corporate and securities law compliance issues. Representative transactions: Yahoo! Inc. in its sale for at least $7.1 billion of a portion of its stake in Alibaba Group Holding Limited (the largest-ever e-commerce M&A transaction); Broadcom Corporation in its $3.7 billion acquisition of NetLogic Microsystems.; and McKesson Corporation in its $2.16 billion acquisition of US Oncology.
**Career:** JD, Georgetown University Law Center, 1996 (magna cum laude, Order of the Coif).

## KIRKHAM, Christopher W
Kirkland & Ellis LLP, San Francisco
415 439 1878
christopher.kirkham@kirkland.com
*Featured in Banking & Finance (California)*
**Practice Areas:** Christopher Kirkham represents private equity sponsors, commercial borrowers and financial institutions in secured and unsecured senior and mezzanine debt financing transactions and related workouts and restructurings. He has particular experience in leveraged acquisition transactions and cross-border financings, as well as structuring distressed acquisition financings and negotiating credit facilities for investment funds. Christopher has represented buyers, targets and financial advisers in both private and public M&A transactions.

## KISSINGER, William D
Bingham McCutchen LLP, San Francisco
415 393 2850
william.kissinger@bingham.com
*Featured in Energy & Natural Resources (California)*
**Practice Areas:** Practice focuses on energy matters in California and across the US, as well as related environmental issues. Energy practice includes representing parties in litigation arising out of the purchase and sale of electricity as well as providing advice on regulatory matters involving the California Independent System Operator,

the California Public Utilities Commission, California Energy Commission and the Federal Energy Regulatory Commission.
**Career:** Former senior deputy legal affairs secretary, California Gov. Gray Davis.
**Personal:** University of California Berkeley School of Law (Boalt Hall), JD, 1987; Princeton University, BA, cum laude, 1982.

## KITCHEN, David
Skadden, Arps, Slate, Meagher & Flom LLP & Affiliates, Los Angeles
213 687 5280
david.kitchen@skadden.com
*Featured in Banking & Finance (California)*
**Practice Areas:** Represents lenders, investors, borrowers and equity investors in a broad range of financing transactions, including leveraged buyouts and recapitalizations, corporate credit facilities, private placements, mezzanine financing, bridge financing, asset-based facilities, debtor-in-possession financing and workouts and restructurings. His broad range of experience encompasses retail, gaming, entertainment and media, real estate, portfolio financings and cross-border transactions.
**Career:** JD, Loyola Marymount University, 1991 (Loyola Law Review); BA, Dartmouth College, 1987.

## KITCHENS, Dean
Gibson, Dunn & Crutcher LLP, Los Angeles
213 229 7416
dkitchens@gibsondunn.com
*Featured in Securities (Nationwide), Litigation (California)*
See under Nationwide for profile.

## KLEE, Peter
McKenna Long & Aldridge LLP, San Diego
619 699 2412
pklee@mckennalong.com
*Featured in Insurance (California)*
**Practice Areas:** Peter Klee's focus is defending insurance companies and their affiliates that are sued in individual actions and class actions for bad faith, fraud, unfair competition and other torts. Mr Klee has handled over 1,000 such cases throughout the country over the past 25 years. No client represented in trial by Mr Klee has ever been held liable for breach of insurance contract, bad faith or any other tort.
**Professional Memberships:** Fellow, American College of Trial Lawyers; Associate, American Board of Trial Advocates.
**Personal:** JD, University of California, Berkeley - Boalt Hall; AB, University of California, Berkeley, Phi Beta Kappa.

## KLEIN, Anthony
Latham & Watkins LLP, Silicon Valley
650 463 2612
anthony.klein@lw.com
*Featured in IT & Outsourcing (California)*
**Practice Areas:** Global Co-chair of Latham & Watkins' Semiconductor Industry Group and Global Co-chair of Latham & Watkins' Technology Transactions Practice Group. Practice focuses on strategic counseling and negotiation of intellectual property and technology-related

transactions worldwide for a wide range of emerging growth and established technology and service companies and their customers, particularly in the fields of semiconductor design and manufacture, medical devices, clean technologies, Internet services, eCommerce and software.
**Professional Memberships:** Member, Board of Directors, Greater Bay Area Chapter of the Juvenile Diabetes Research Foundation.
**Personal:** JD, UCLA School of Law, 1990; AB, Harvard College, 1986.

## KLEINBERG, Rachel D.
Davis Polk & Wardwell LLP, New York
650 752 2000
rachel.kleinberg@davispolk.com
*Featured in Tax (California)*
**Practice Areas:** Partner in Davis Polk's Tax Department, practicing in the Menlo Park office. Her practice focuses on advice to corporate and private equity fund clients on mergers and acquisitions, joint ventures, spinoffs and reorganizations, as well as cross-border restructurings. She also has significant experience in the areas of corporate finance and derivatives.

## KLEMENTZ, Barbara
Baker & McKenzie, San Francisco
415 591 3211
barbara.klementz@bakermckenzie.com
*Featured in Employee Benefits & Executive Compensation (California)*
**Practice Areas:** Ms Klementz focuses her practice on global equity compensation programs, employee benefits and executive compensation. She regularly advises multinational companies on implementing their equity compensation programs worldwide — particularly as it relates to tax and securities law matters and exchange control regulations. Ms Klementz also frequently advises on the treatment of such programs in corporate transactions, as well as on the tax treatment of cross-border employees.
**Professional Memberships:** San Francisco Bar Association; National Association of Stock Plan Professionals; Global Equity Organization; State Bar of California.
**Career:** Admitted in Germany in 1999; Admitted in California in 2001.

## KLINGER, Marilyn
Sedgwick, Detert, Moran & Arnold LLP, London
213 615 8038
marilyn.klinger@sedgwicklaw.com
*Featured in Construction (California)*
**Practice Areas:** Marilyn Klinger is involved in all aspects of construction law on a state and national level. She represents the spectrum of the construction industry, from owners, contractors, subcontractors, and sureties in litigation, arbitration and mediation.
**Professional Memberships:** She serves as chair of AGC of California's Legal Advisory Committee, co-chair of ABA/Construction Forum 2013 Annual Meeting, and incoming chair of ABA/Construction Forum, Division 5 (2013-2014), former chair ABA/FSLC (2003-2004).

**Career:** Chair Emeritus of firmwide Construction Practices Group.
**Personal:** University of California, Hastings College of the Law, JD; University of Santa Clara, BS, cum laude. Admitted to practice in California.

## KNAUSS, Robert B
Munger, Tolles & Olson LLP, Los Angeles
213 683 9137
rob.knauss@mto.com
*Featured in Corporate/M&A (Southern California)*
**Practice Areas:** Practice concentrates on general corporate and partnership law, primarily mergers and acquisitions, private equity, corporate governance and corporate finance. Recent representations include: Guardian Industries in an investment by Koch Industries; Beats' sale of equity to HTC; Hugh Hefner in his going private transaction for 'Playboy.'
**Career:** Clerked for U.S. Supreme Court Justice William H. Rehnquist; Frequent lecturer on corporate topics.
**Personal:** University of Michigan Law School, 1979; Harvard College (AB), 1975.

## KNOPP, Gregory W
Akin Gump Strauss Hauer & Feld LLP, Los Angeles
310 552 6436
gknopp@akingump.com
*Featured in Labor & Employment (California)*
**Practice Areas:** Mr Knopp specializes in complex litigation, including class and collective actions and other high-stakes employment lawsuits. He has extensive experience counseling companies with respect to a wide variety of employment issues, including wage and hour issues, discrimination issues, benefits/ERISA issues, reductions-in-force and communications to employees. He also has experience conducting union collective bargaining, developing strategies for union relationships, conducting labor arbitrations, and advising companies with respect to corporate transactions.
**Personal:** JD, with high honors, Georgetown University Law Center (1996), member of The Georgetown Law Journal; BA, Cornell University (1992).

## KOLKEY, Daniel M
Gibson, Dunn & Crutcher LLP, San Francisco
415 393 8240
dkolkey@gibsondunn.com
*Featured in Litigation (California), Appellate Law (Nationwide)*
**Practice Areas:** Co-chair, firm's Appellate and Constitutional Law Practice Group. Focuses on appellate litigation, California state law/political law/state government litigation, and Indian gaming. Advised four different state governors, including service as Governor Schwarzenegger's lead negotiator for tribal-state compacts under the Indian Gaming Regulatory Act.
**Career:** Former Associate Justice, California Court of Appeal, Third Appellate District; Legal Affairs Secretary and Counsel to Governor Pete Wilson.

**Publications:** Co-editor, Practitioner's Handbook on International Arbitration and Mediation.
**Personal:** JD, Harvard Law School, 1977, magna cum laude. Member, American Law Institute & Pacific Council on International Policy. Board and executive committee member, Pacific Research Institute.

## KORNBLITH, Richard L
Fulbright & Jaworski LLP, Los Angeles
213 892 9312
rkornblith@fulbright.com
*Featured in Tax (California)*
**Practice Areas:** Tax.
**Professional Memberships:** American Bar Association, Taxation Section.
**Career:** Kornblith is head of the Tax Department in Los Angeles, and holds a joint assignment to the Public Law Department. His principal interests in tax include municipal finance and other capital markets transactions, partnership, project finance, asset securitization and intellectual property. He is an active member of the state bars of California, Texas, Pennsylvania and the District of Columbia.
**Personal:** JD, University of Pennsylvania School of Law (1977); PhD, Theoretical Physics, University of Rochester (1976); BA, magna cum laude, Washington University in St. Louis (1969).

## KORNFELD, Linda D
Jenner & Block LLP, Los Angeles
213 239 5176
lkornfeld@jenner.com
*Featured in Insurance (California)*
**Career:** Linda D. Kornfeld is a member of the Insurance Litigation and Counseling Practice. Ms Kornfeld's clients include telecommunications and technical companies, real estate developers, utilities, movie studios, manufacturers, corporate directors and officers, and nonprofits; her experience includes claims involving directors' and officers' liability, business interruption, employee fidelity, errors and omissions, employment, entertainment industry liabilities, intellectual property infringements, construction defects and environmental and product liabilities. She provides strategic counseling on mitigating risk and maximizing recoveries. She is a frequently requested speaker, media resource, and author and recently co-authored A Policyholder's Primer on Insurance, published by the Association of Corporate Counsel.

## KOVACICH, Thomas
Atkinson, Andelson, Loya, Ruud & Romo, Cerritos
562 653 3200
tkovacich@aalrr.com
*Featured in Construction (California)*
**Practice Areas:** Thomas Kovacich is a senior partner in the Cerritos office and chair of the firm's construction practice. Mr Kovacich has represented employers for over 30 years in all aspects of employment law and labor relations matters, and public agencies with respect to all aspects of public works. He has successfully defended contractors before the Department of Industrial

Relations ("DIR") and in private wage and hour class action lawsuits including those related to prevailing wage coverage and apprenticeship claims. Mr Kovacich is an authority in state and federal public works, wage and hour laws, and labor relations, including NLRB elections and arbitrations and has acted as lead counsel in over 50 wage and hour actions.
**Professional Memberships:** Mr Kovacich is a member of the State Bar of California, the American Bar Association, including the Labor Law Section, and the Los Angeles and Orange County Bar Associations. He serves as counsel and on the board of directors to the Southern California Contractors Association (SCCA).
**Personal:** Mr Kovacich has lectured extensively on public works and wage and hour matters and is a contributor to various construction-related periodicals.

## KRAMER, Barry J
Fenwick & West LLP, Mountain View
650 335 7278
bkramer@fenwick.com
*Featured in Investment Funds (Nationwide), Corporate/M&A (California)*
See under Nationwide for profile.

## KRAMER, James
Orrick, Herrington & Sutcliffe LLP, San Francisco
415 773 5923
jkramer@orrick.com
*Featured in Litigation (California)*
**Career:** Jim Kramer, a partner in the San Francisco office, is Chair of the Securities Litigation and Regulatory Enforcement Group. His practice focuses on defending companies, officers and directors in shareholder class actions, derivative suits and regulatory proceedings. Mr Kramer has extensive experience representing companies and individuals in securities class actions, derivative actions, merger and acquisition related litigation, SEC enforcement proceedings and other complex commercial litigation. He also has extensive experience representing board committees in internal investigations, including SEC, SRO and FCPA related investigations.

## KRAUSE, Jeffrey
Gibson, Dunn & Crutcher LLP, Los Angeles
213 229 7995
jkrause@gibsondunn.com
*Featured in Bankruptcy/Restructuring (California)*
**Practice Areas:** Represents debtors, creditors' committees, acquirers of assets from distressed debtors, lessors, and secured and unsecured creditors. Representations include chapter 11 debtors THQ, Inc., Pacific Monarch Resorts, Inc., Falcon Industries, Inc., R. E. Loans, LLC, official committee of unsecured creditors in the Hyatt Regency Waikiki's chapter 11 case, and the investment vehicle that funded Hawaiian Airlines' successful reorganization plan.
**Professional Memberships:** Fellow, American College of Bankruptcy; Past-President, L.A. Bankruptcy Forum; Past-Chair, L.A. County Bar Association Debtor Assistance Pro Bono Program,

Past-Board Member, Financial Lawyers Conference.
**Personal:** JD, University of California Los Angeles, Order of the Coif, UCLA Law Review.

## KRELLER, Thomas R
Milbank, Tweed, Hadley & McCloy LLP, Los Angeles
213 892 4463
tkreller@milbank.com
*Featured in Bankruptcy/Restructuring (California)*
**Practice Areas:** Mr Kreller is a partner in the Financial Restructuring Group, focusing on corporate restructurings and reorganizations. He represents debtors, lenders, equity holders, committees and acquirors in bankruptcy cases and out-of-court workouts. Significant debtor representations include: Dial Global, Silver Legacy, Station Casinos, MacGregor Golf, American Restaurant Group and Bugle Boy Industries. Significant creditor representations include: bondholder groups for Nortel Networks, Nextel International, National Equipment Services and Trump Casinos; lenders to Herbst Gaming, Centaur Gaming, EH/Transeastern LLC and Nellson Neutraceuticals; Franklin Advisors in the Dynegy bankruptcies; and Cerberus Capital Management, Oaktree Capital Management and QUALCOMM as creditors in various matters.

## KREVANS, Rachel
Morrison & Foerster LLP, San Francisco
415 268 7178
rkrevans@mofo.com
*Featured in Intellectual Property (California)*
**Practice Areas:** Focuses on patent litigation. Patent controversy practice includes district court, ITC, and appellate experience, prelitigation, and licensing strategy analysis. Experience in related proceedings, such as reexaminations, interferences, and appeals. Past matters include various life sciences and electrical engineering technologies, such as DVRs, cable and satellite TV, computer-phone interfaces, HIV and cancer treatments, and blood and antibody research. Led the team that won a rare defense jury verdict for client EchoStar in the Eastern District of Texas in 2007.
**Career:** Former Managing Partner of the firm's San Francisco office.
**Personal:** BA, Dartmouth College; JD, UC Davis School of Law.

## KRPATA, Kyle C
Weil, Gotshal & Manges LLP, Silicon Valley
650 802 3093
kyle.krpata@weil.com
*Featured in Corporate/M&A (Northern California)*
**Practice Areas:** Kyle Krpata is a partner in Weil's Silicon Valley office specializing in private equity and mergers and acquisitions. He has a wide ranging practice with particular emphasis on private equity transactions, public and private mergers and acquisitions, dispositions, distressed and bankruptcy acquisitions and venture capital transactions. He represents several leading private equity firms and public and private companies in various industries. He also regularly counsels boards of directors on corporate governance, fidu-

ciary duty, corporate control and other strategic matters.
**Personal:** Stanford University (BA); Southern Methodist University (JD). He is licensed to practice in California and Texas.

## KUBIN, Karen
Morrison & Foerster LLP, San Francisco
415 268 6168
kkubin@mofo.com
*Featured in Labor & Employment (California)*
**Practice Areas:** Karen Kubin defends employers in class actions and other employment litigation alleging wage and hour violations, discrimination, harassment, wrongful discharge, trade secret theft, ERISA violations, and whistleblower retaliation. She has broad jury and bench trial experience.
**Professional Memberships:** Member, ABA, SF Bar Association, and Employment Law Section, California State Bar.
**Career:** Daily Journal named Karen as one of California's Top Women Litigators (2007 – 2008), Top 100 Lawyers (2009), Top Employment Lawyers (2010 – 2012), and Top Women Lawyers (2012). Named a Law360 "Employment MVP" (2012).
**Personal:** BA, University of Washington; JD, UC, Hastings College of the Law.

## KUN, Michael S
Epstein Becker & Green PC, Los Angeles
310 557 9501
mkun@ebglaw.com
*Featured in Labor & Employment (California)*
**Practice Areas:** Member of firm, Labor and Employment Practice; Co-Chairperson of the firm's Wage and Hour, Individual and Collective Actions group and the Hospitality Employment and Labor Law Outreach group (HELLO). Mr Kun represents clients in such diverse industries as hospitality, health care, logistics, housing, and staffing services.
**Publications:** Author, "An Empathetic Approach To Layoffs," Employment Law360; Author, "Disclosure of Identities In Employment Class Actions," Employment Law360. Mr Kun is also a published novelist and sportswriter.
**Personal:** JD, University of Virginia School of Law, 1988; BA, Johns Hopkins University, with honors, 1984.

## KUPIETZKY, Moshe J
Sidley Austin LLP, Los Angeles
213 896 6020
mkupietzky@sidley.com
*Featured in Banking & Finance (California), Corporate/M&A (Southern California)*
**Practice Areas:** Partner in Sidley's Los Angeles office and head of the Los Angeles Corporate and Finance practice. His practice emphasizes mergers and acquisitions, private investments and financing transactions. Represents companies in various corporate acquisition and merger transactions, either as acquisition or target company counsel. Advises Boards of Directors and management on various corporate transactions. Represents investment fund sponsors and private equity groups.

Also represents corporate borrowers and lenders in various credit transactions.
**Personal:** Harvard Law School, LLB, 1968, magna cum laude; City College of the City University of New York, BBA, 1965, cum laude. Admission: California.

## KURTH, Mette
Arent Fox LLP, Los Angeles
213 443 7547
mette.kurth@arentfox.com
*Featured in Bankruptcy/Restructuring (California)*
**Practice Areas:** Mette Kurth is a partner in the bankruptcy and financial restructuring practice. She represents companies, creditor committees and asset purchasers in federal bankruptcy cases as well as out of court workouts and alternatives such as assignments for the benefit of creditors. She has experience across a wide range of industries, including retail, restaurants, health care, real estate, gaming, manufacturing and distribution, imports, agriculture, telecommunications, and multi-level marketing. University of California, Los Angeles, JD, (Order of the Coif), 1996; Trinity University, BA, (cum laude with University Honors), 1990.

## KUSHMAN, Moshe J
Skadden, Arps, Slate, Meagher & Flom LLP & Affiliates, Los Angeles
213 687 5263
mkushman@skadden.com
*Featured in Tax (California)*
**Practice Areas:** Represents clients in a wide range of federal income tax matters, with an emphasis on domestic and international mergers and acquisitions, restructurings and workouts, controlled foreign corporations, and international tax planning. Structures complex private equity and hedge fund partnership ventures, derivative transactions, financial instruments, and develops and structures domestic and cross-border corporate acquisitions and financings.
**Career:** JD, Loyola Law School, 1987; MBT, University of Southern California, 1981; MBA, University of Southern California, 1980; BA, University of California, Los Angeles, 1976.

## LALLY, Amy
Sidley Austin LLP, Los Angeles
213 896 6642
alally@sidley.com
*Featured in Environment (California)*
**Practice Areas:** Partner in Sidley's Los Angeles office. She works in all areas of litigation, including contract dispute litigation, real estate litigation, Proposition 65 litigation and litigation under California's Unfair Business Practices Act, Consumer Legal Remedies Act, and Song Beverly Credit Card Act. She has represented financial institutions, hedge funds, consumer goods retailers, vitamin and dietary supplement companies, pharmaceutical companies, medical device manufacturers, accounting firms, oil and gas companies, and other institutions in a wide variety of civil litigation matters.
**Personal:** Georgetown University Law Center, JD, 1998; Boston College, BA, 1995, summa cum laude, Phi Beta Kappa.

## LANTRY, Kevin T
Sidley Austin LLP, Los Angeles
213 896 6022
klantry@sidley.com
*Featured in Bankruptcy/Restructuring (California)*
**Practice Areas:** Partner in Sidley's Los Angeles office in the Bankruptcy and Corporate Reorganization group. He focuses his practice primarily on business reorganizations, and has represented debtors, secured and unsecured creditors, official unsecured creditors' committees, trustees, purchasers of estate assets, and plaintiffs and defendants in adversary proceedings. He has also represented lenders, borrowers and equity holders in out-of-court workouts and global settlements, and has represented secured creditors in real and personal property foreclosure actions.
**Personal:** University of California, Berkeley School of Law (Boalt Hall), JD, 1991; Loma Linda University, MA, 1982; Pacific Union College, BA, 1980.

## LARRABEE, Matthew L
Dechert LLP, San Francisco
415 262 4579
matthew.larrabee@dechert.com
*Featured in Litigation (California)*
**Practice Areas:** Mr Larrabee has significant experience in financial institutions litigation, securities class actions, consumer class actions, private antitrust cases and other complex commercial litigation. He also utilizes mediation and other alternatives to traditional trial proceedings.
**Professional Memberships:** Member, California Bar; member, American Bar Association; member, American Law Institute; admitted to practice before numerous federal courts
**Personal:** University of California, Davis (BA, 1977, with honors); University of California Hastings College of the Law (JD, 1980, Thurston Honor Society, Order of the Coif, editor-in-chief, Hastings Law Journal).

## LAUER, Katherine A.
Latham & Watkins LLP, San Diego
619 2361234
katherine.lauer@lw.com
*Featured in Healthcare (California)*
**Practice Areas:** Katherine Lauer is a global co-chair of the Latham & Watkins' Health Care and Life Sciences Practice Group. She focuses her practice on healthcare litigation, with emphasis on healthcare fraud defense and has defended some of the country's largest and most high-profile civil and criminal government healthcare fraud investigations and qui tam cases. Ms Lauer has extensive expertise in the federal Anti-kickback Statute, the Stark Laws and the federal False Claims Act.
**Personal:** JD, University of Michigan Law School; BA, University of Michigan.

## LAWRENCE, Paul F
McDermott Will & Emery LLP, Los Angeles
310 551 9329
plawrence@mwe.com
*Featured in Healthcare (California)*
**Practice Areas:** Partner in Los Angeles. Concentrates on mergers, acquisitions, affiliations,

dispositions and complex business transactions involving companies in the healthcare services industry. Developed a particular expertise in representing hospitals, health systems, pharmacy companies, dialysis companies, and private equity firms in the acquisition and divestiture of healthcare services businesses.
**Professional Memberships:** Admitted to practice in California as well as before the US District Court for the Central District of California, the US Court of Appeals for the Ninth Circuit and the US Tax Court.
**Personal:** Harvard Law School, JD, 1991; University of California-Los Angeles, BA (summa cum laude), 1988.

**LAYNE, Jonathan K**
Gibson, Dunn & Crutcher LLP, Los Angeles
310 552 8641
jlayne@gibsondunn.com
*Featured in Capital Markets (California), Corporate/M&A (Southern California)*
**Practice Areas:** Extensive experience in public and private mergers and acquisitions, public offerings of equity (including IPOs) and debt, corporate finance and securities law and board of directors, special board committee and corporate governance representations.
**Career:** Member, firm's Executive Committee. Former member, firm's Management Committee. Member, Board of Directors, California Chamber of Commerce; member Board of Trustees, Emory University.
**Publications:** Frequent lecturer, mergers and acquisitions and securities law topics.
**Personal:** JD, Emory University School of Law, 1979, Order of the Coif, Managing Editor, 'Emory Law Journal'. MBA, Emory University Goizueta Business School, 1979, Beta Gamma Sigma.

**LE SAGE, Jeffrey**
Gibson, Dunn & Crutcher LLP, Los Angeles
213 229 7504
jlesage@gibsondunn.com
*Featured in Corporate/M&A (Southern California)*
**Practice Areas:** Member of firm's Corporate Department, M&A, Gaming, Health Care and Media, Entertainment & Technology Practice Groups. Extensive experience advising boards, management and private equity firms on a broad array of topics including domestic and international mergers and acquisitions, going private transactions, hostile takeovers, public offerings, private placements, distressed transactions, corporate governance, corporate securities and general business law matters.
**Publications:** LexisNexis M&A Practice Guide, 2008-2012 Editions, and the Lexis Practice Advisor California module, 2012 edition.
**Personal:** JD, Loyola University, 1998 (Cum Laude; Order of the Coif); BA, Brown University, 1995 (Business Economics and Organizational Behavior and Management, Resource Allocation).

**LEDERMAN, Henry D**
Littler Mendelson, PC, Walnut Creek
925 932 2468
hlederman@littler.com
*Featured in Labor & Employment (California)*

**Practice Areas:** Alternative Dispute Resolution, Appellate Practice, Discrimination and Harassment.
**Professional Memberships:** California State Bar, District of Columbia Bar, New York State Bar.
**Career:** Mr Lederman's practice has been devoted to employment law litigation and appeals. Mr Lederman appeared before the United States Supreme Court and prevailed on behalf of his client in a matter involving the enforcement of an arbitration agreement that delegated to the arbitrator the issue whether the agreement itself was unconscionable.
**Publications:** Mr Lederman frequently contributes to Littler's ASAP and Insight publications.
**Personal:** JD, New York University School of Law, 1974; BA, University of Maryland, Phi Beta Kappa, 1971.

**LEE, Bennett J**
Watt, Tieder, Hoffar & Fitzgerald, LLP, San Francisco
415 623 7000
blee@wthf.com
*Featured in Construction (California)*
**Practice Areas:** Domestic and international construction, suretyship, government contracts.
**Professional Memberships:** American Bar Association, Asian-Pacific American Bar Association.
**Career:** Bennett Lee represents general contractors, sureties, engineering firms, and owners on a wide variety of issues arising from industrial and commercial construction projects, including power plants, office buildings, hospitals, prisons, schools, dams, mass transit systems, tunnels, pipelines and electrical power systems. He has significant litigation experience before both federal and state courts, as well as domestic and international arbitrations, on a variety of construction and suretyship law issues.
**Publications:** Bennett has authored numerous articles and presented various seminars throughout the US.

**LEE, Victoria**
DLA Piper LLP (US), East Palo Alto
650 833 2091
victoria.lee@dlapiper.com
*Featured in IT & Outsourcing (California)*
**Practice Areas:** Technology, outsourcing, corporate/M&A, venture capital.
**Career:** She concentrates in strategic intellectual property counseling, technology procurements and transfers, manufacturing agreements, distribution and licensing agreements, open source business models and licensing issues, document retention policies, general business counseling, private and venture financing, startup companies. She represents public and private companies in the software, hardware, networking, semiconductor and electronic commerce industries.
**Personal:** JD, University of California at Davis; BA, University of California at Davis.

**LEHR, Matthew**
Davis Polk & Wardwell LLP, New York
212 450 4000
matthew.lehr@davispolk.com
*Featured in Intellectual Property (California)*
**Practice Areas:** Partner in Davis Polk's Litigation Department, practicing in the Menlo Park office. Head of the intellectual property litigation practice, focusing primarily on complex patent litigation matters. Has extensive experience in patent and technology cases. Has served as lead trial counsel in numerous jury and bench trials and has represented clients in complex cases involving trade secrets and commercial litigation, as well as Lanham Act actions in courts across the United States. Has also appeared and argued before the U.S. Court of Appeals for the Federal Circuit.

**LEONARD, Emily I**
Covington & Burling LLP, San Francisco
650 632 4721
eleonard@cov.com
*Featured in Life Sciences (Nationwide), Life Sciences (California)*
See under Nationwide for profile.

**LERMAN, Cary**
Munger, Tolles & Olson LLP, Los Angeles
213 683 9100
cary.lerman@mto.com
*Featured in Insurance (California)*
**Practice Areas:** Represents policyholders and reinsurers in insurance coverage litigation and advises on restructuring corporate insurance programs. Recent representations: Equilon and Motiva, in multiple international arbitrations against insurers for coverage of environmental liabilities; Ameron International Corporation, with regard to coverage for product liability lawsuits.
**Professional Memberships:** LACBA: Judicial Appellate Judges Evaluation Committee; Center for International Legal Studies; ABA: Insurance Coverage Section; ARIAS-US.
**Publications:** Federal Jurisdiction of Insurance and Reinsurance Arbitration (ARIAS Journal, Fall 2011). Binding Non-Parties To An Arbitration Agreement in the United States (Samara State University for Economics, Spring 2008).
**Personal:** UCLA Law School; University of Illinois (BS).

**LESLIE, John W**
McKenna Long & Aldridge LLP, San Diego
619 699 2536
jleslie@mckennalong.com
*Featured in Energy & Natural Resources (California)*
**Practice Areas:** Mr Leslie specializes in energy regulatory litigation and utility/ administrative law, focusing in natural gas and electricity regulation, including the regulatory structures for renewable energy procurement and greenhouse gas emissions reduction programs. He represents energy producers, consumers and marketing and trading companies in proceedings before state and federal agencies addressing barriers to competition, compliance and enforcement of regulatory requirements, ensuring access to utility infrastruc-

ture, rate and service disputes and challenges to anti-competitive utility practices.
**Personal:** JD, University of North Carolina School of Law, with honors, Order of the Coif, 1980 BA, Political Science, Gettysburg College, Phi Beta Kappa, 1977.

**LESSER, Henry**
DLA Piper LLP (US), East Palo Alto
650 833 2425
henry.lesser@dlapiper.com
*Featured in Corporate/M&A (Northern California)*
**Practice Areas:** Corporate/M&A, private equity.
**Career:** He focuses his practice on corporate acquisitions, corporate governance, and restructuring matters, and all aspects of merger and acquisition work involving public and private companies, including hostile tender offers, proxy contests, friendly mergers, leveraged buyouts, stock acquisitions, and asset sales. His clients include a wide variety of bidders, targets, stockholders, and financial advisors.
**Personal:** LLM, Harvard University; MA, Cambridge University; BA, Cambridge University.

**LEVEE, Jeffrey A**
Jones Day, Los Angeles
213 243 2572
jlevee@jonesday.com
*Featured in Antitrust (California)*
**Practice Areas:** Jeff LeVee's practice focuses on complex business and class action litigation, with a particular emphasis in antitrust litigation and health care litigation. He also does a considerable amount of antitrust counseling. His clients include health care providers, pharmaceutical companies, retailers, telecommunications companies, manufacturers, and internet companies. From 2008 to 2011, Jeff was Partner-in-Charge of Jones Day's Silicon Valley Office.
**Professional Memberships:** Member of ABA Antitrust Council, and previous chair of three of its committees.
**Personal:** Northwestern Law School (JD 1984); Duke University (BA 1981).

**LEVENTHAL, F Daniel**
Morrison & Foerster LLP, San Francisco
415 268 6870
dleventhal@mofo.com
*Featured in Banking & Finance (California)*
**Practice Areas:** Based in the London and San Francisco offices, Mr Leventhal specializes in debt financing transactions with substantial expertise in cross-border financings. His extensive experience includes syndicated lending, asset-based lending, private debt placements, debt restructurings, subordinated debt transactions, project finance, acquisition financings, vendor finance and other corporate finance, across a diverse spectrum of industries. He acts for U.S., U.K. and international banks, institutional and other non-bank lenders, and borrowers, private equity funds and other clients in these transactions.
**Personal:** University of California, Berkeley (AB,1976), Boalt Hall School of Law, University of California, Berkeley (JD,1981); Georg-August-Universität, Göttingen, Germany, (1974-75).

## LEVINE, Janet
Crowell & Moring LLP, Los Angeles
213 443 5583
jlevine@crowell.com
*Featured in Litigation (California)*
**Practice Areas:** Chair of Crowell & Moring's Trial Practice and partner in the White Collar and Regulatory Enforcement Group. Experienced trial and appellate attorney, extensive experience in espionage, securities, healthcare, tax, and public corruption matters. Represented politicians, judges, and licensed professionals in myriad industries, providing defenses against governmental accusations of wrongdoing. Clients are local, national, and international and include individuals, entities, and government organizations.
**Career:** Elected to firm's Management Board.
**Personal:** Fromer co-chair of the ABA's White-Collar Crime Committee, and former Chair of the ABA's West Coast Regional Subcommittee on White-Collar Crime. Named California Lawyer's Attorney of the Year 2012.

## LEVINSON, Marc A
Orrick, Herrington & Sutcliffe LLP, Sacramento
916 329 4910
malevinson@orrick.com
*Featured in Bankruptcy/Restructuring (California), Bankruptcy/Restructuring (Nationwide)*
**Career:** Marc A Levinson, a partner in Orrick's Restructuring Group, is nationally recognized for his capabilities in complex reorganizations and restructurings, financially-distressed municipalities, out-of-court workouts and other insolvency matters. He frequently lectures on bankruptcy, insolvency and corporate reorganization topics, and has spoken to numerous bar associations, in-house counsel and industry groups. Mr Levinson served as chief bankruptcy counsel to the City of Vallejo, which filed a chapter 9 case in May 2008. In June 2012, he filed a chapter 9 case for the City of Stockton, the largest California city ever to seek chapter 9 relief.

## LEVINSON, Sidney P
Jones Day, Los Angeles
213 243 2475
slevinson@jonesday.com
*Featured in Bankruptcy/Restructuring (California)*
**Practice Areas:** Bankruptcy, business litigation. Represent debtors, bondholders, lenders, trustees, creditors' committees, trade creditors and other significant parties in complex restructuring and business litigation matters. Recent matters include representation of Los Angeles Dodgers; serving as lead counsel for Hawaiian Airlines against Mesa Air Group in obtaining $80 million judgment; and serving as lead counsel for bondholders in obtaining $11 million judgment for breach of a no-call provision.
**Professional Memberships:** Admitted California (1988), District of Columbia (1989), New York (2009). Co-Chair, ABA Subcommittee on Administration & Courts (2002-present); Member, Board of Directors, Los Angeles Bankruptcy Forum (2007-2011).

## LEVY, Seth D
Nixon Peabody LLP, Los Angeles
213 629 6161
slevy@nixonpeabody.com
*Featured in Life Sciences (California)*
**Practice Areas:** Seth D. Levy is a partner in Nixon Peabody's Patents practice group. With a background in biological engineering, his practice focuses on patent prosecution and intellectual property management, primarily in the life sciences area. In addition to technology-based companies, he has extensive experience working with technology transfer programs at educational and health care institutions. Seth works with clients to procure patents, license these patents, and enforce them against possible infringers. He coordinates complex research arrangements, negotiates commercial transactions involving intellectual property, and resolves related disputes.
**Personal:** University of Southern California Law School, JD Cornell University, BS, cum laude.

## LEWIS, Robert A
Bingham McCutchen LLP, San Francisco
415 393 2328
robert.lewis@bingham.com
*Featured in Insurance (California)*
**Practice Areas:** Trial lawyer whose complex commercial litigation practice emphasizes insurance law, antitrust, trade secrets litigation and professional liability defense. Has extensive trial experience, including numerous trials in federal and state courts throughout California. Active in alternative dispute resolution, both arbitrating many cases and serving as an arbitrator. Has litigated and provided counseling in virtually every facet of insurance law. Routinely represents lawyers, insurance brokers, actuaries and other professionals in malpractice actions, including a recent jury verdict on a reinsurance intermediary malpractice claim.
**Personal:** Harvard Law School, JD, 1978; University of Illinois/Urbana-Champaign, BA, summa cum laude, 1975.

## LIBURT, Joseph
Orrick, Herrington & Sutcliffe LLP, Menlo Park
650 614 7447
jliburt@orrick.com
*Featured in Labor & Employment (California)*
**Practice Areas:** Joe Liburt represents retail, technology and manufacturing clients in the full range of employment litigation. Joe is well-known for collaborating with clients on creative strategies to achieve the best and most efficient result. He has defended dozens of wage class actions, and has extensive experience litigating claims for discrimination, harassment, retaliation, wrongful termination and various torts. Joe also litigates ERISA claims for change-in-control severance benefits after company mergers, disability benefits, breach of fiduciary duty, retaliation and interference with vesting of benefits. Joe advises on a wide range of issues.

## LIEVER, Michael H
Orrick, Herrington & Sutcliffe LLP, San Francisco
415 773 5808
mliever@orrick.com
*Featured in Real Estate (California)*
**Career:** Mr Liever is a partner in the Real Estate group at Orrick. He has extensive involvement in representing both foreign and domestic investors in the acquisition, disposition, development, leasing, financing, and joint venture of office buildings, shopping centers, hotels, industrial parks, and apartments. Mr Liever advises numerous clients throughout California and the U.S., including RREEF America LLC, Morgan Stanley, BlackRock Realty Advisors, Rockwood Capital, New York Life, The Stockbridge Funds, Industrial Income Trust, Broadreach Capital Partners, LACERA, The City and County of San Francisco's Employee's Retirement System, and Alecta Real Estate Funds.

## LINCENBERG, Gary
Bird, Marella, Boxer, Wolpert, Nessim, Drooks & Lincenberg PC, Los Angeles
310 201 2100
gsl@birdmarella.com
*Featured in Litigation (California)*
**Practice Areas:** White collar criminal defense; Internal investigations; Securities, health care and other complex civil litigation.
**Professional Memberships:** Federal Bar Association (former President and current member Board of Directors); American Bar Association(Vice-chair, White Collar Crime Committee and winner of Outstanding National Leadership award).
**Career:** Tried over 35 cases to verdict, and argued over 20 appeals. Regularly recognized among the top white collar defense attorneys in California.
**Publications:** Authored treatises on environmental crimes, election crimes, and conflicts of interest. Authored more than 25 articles on criminal law topics. Frequent lecturer.
**Personal:** Harvard Law School; Former Assistant United States Attorney, Deputy Chief.

## LINDER, David M
Dechert LLP, San Francisco
415 262 4511
david.linder@dechert.com
*Featured in Real Estate (California)*
**Practice Areas:** Mr Linder focuses his practice on commercial mortgage loan servicing, workouts and restructurings, distressed asset trading, and loan origination. He has significant experience in the commercial mortgage capital markets, both as a lawyer and as a large loan banker.
**Professional Memberships:** Member, California and New Jersey Bars; member, Commercial Real Estate Finance Council.
**Career:** Former director at Capital America.
**Personal:** Bucknell University (BS, 1986, cum laude), Drexel University (MS, 1990), Temple University Beasley School of Law (JD, 1995, summa cum laude; editor-in-chief, Temple Law Review).

## LIPTON, Stuart
Arnold & Porter LLP, San Francisco
415 471 3161
Stuart.Lipton@aporter.com
*Featured in Tax (California)*
**Practice Areas:** Stuart Lipton is a Partner in the Tax, Trusts, and Estates Practice Group, where he represents clients ranging from closely held businesses to public companies. He provides comprehensive tax counseling regarding a range of corporate, partnership, financial and work-out transactions, including the development and implementation of creative tax-advantaged strategies for structuring M&A transactions, reorganizations and joint ventures. His practice includes sophisticated tax planning for start-up ventures, mature companies, LLCs, partnerships and "Subchapter S" corporations, as well as family businesses. He also handles tax audit and controversy work, including TEFRA proceedings involving the IRS and the Franchise Tax Board.

## LOEB, Jeffrey M
Loeb & Loeb LLP, Los Angeles
310 282 2266
jloeb@loeb.com
*Featured in Tax (California)*
**Practice Areas:** Provides estate planning, including preparation of revocable living trusts, wills, irrevocable life insurance trusts, irrevocable trusts for children, generation-skipping transfer trusts, private foundations, charitable lead and remainder trusts, sales to grantor trusts, private annuity sales, grantor-retained annuity trusts, family limited partnerships, qualified personal residence trusts, health and education exclusion trusts.
**Career:** Served as probate mediator for Probate Department of LA Superior Court/appellate court mediator for the Second District of the California Court of Appeal. Deputy DA in the Office of the LA County District Attorney (1983–1985).
**Personal:** University of California, Hastings College of Law (JD, 1981).

## LONG, Michael G
Watt, Tieder, Hoffar & Fitzgerald, LLP, Irvine
949 852 6700
mlong@wthf.com
*Featured in Construction (California)*
**Practice Areas:** Construction, government contracts, suretyship.
**Professional Memberships:** American Bar Association, AGC of California, Orange County Bar Association.
**Career:** Mike is Managing Partner of WTHF's Irvine, California office. His practice focus includes construction and engineering issues, representing general contractors, owners, sureties and subcontractors. His practice includes contract litigation, preparation and defense of claims, preparation of contract documents and alternative dispute resolution. Mike has litigated extensively before federal and state courts, arbitration panels and administrative boards of contract appeals.
**Publications:** Mike has authored numerous works and speaks regularly on construction issues within the United States.

## LUCAS, Carol
Buchalter Nemer, Los Angeles
*Featured in Healthcare (California)*
**Practice Areas:** Health Care transactional attorney specializing in mergers and acquisitions, joint ventures, securities, private placements, state and federal regulations, entity formation and corporate representation of both public and private companies in the health care industry. Expert on the establishment and representation of ambulatory surgery centers, med spas, imaging centers and other ancillary providers in a variety of medical specialties, and in the legal and business issues that confront ACOs, foundations, independent practice associations and other physician organizations. Also experienced with Federally Qualified Health Centers including governance requirements and issues raised by hospital sponsorship of FQHCs.
**Professional Memberships:** Chair of the firm's Health Care Practice Group; Former Chair of the California State Bar Business Law Section Executive Committee and Health Law Committee.
**Personal:** New York University School of Law (JD, 1982); University of Rochester (BA, 1979).

## LUI, Elwood
Jones Day, Los Angeles
213 243 2435
elui@jonesday.com
*Featured in Litigation (California)*
**Practice Areas:** Has concentrated his practice in appeals and complex commercial litigation in federal and state courts and has represented major corporations and public entities in trial and appellate matters. He is committed to public service and has served on numerous boards and committees for professional and community groups.
**Professional Memberships:** Fellow in the American Academy of Appellate Lawyers. Member of the California Academy of Appellate Lawyers.
**Career:** Deputy California Attorney General (1969-70); Judge, Los Angeles Municipal Court (1975-80); Judge, Los Angeles Superior Court (1980-81); Associate Justice, California Court of Appeal (1981-87), Jones Day Partner (1987-Present).

## LUMISH, Douglas E
Kasowitz, Benson, Torres & Friedman LLP, Redwood Shores
650 453 5410
dlumish@kasowitz.com
*Featured in Intellectual Property (California)*
**Practice Areas:** Doug Lumish is a seasoned trial lawyer who has defeated more than $1 billion in claims since joining Kasowitz in 2011, including winning a jury verdict for Google and others against Eolas, and summary judgment for Hitachi against MIT and MagSil. Head of the firm's IP group, he focuses on complex patent cases and has amassed numerous precedent-setting victories for industry leaders, including Google, Hitachi, Microsoft, Oracle and Yahoo!
**Career:** Recognized in Chambers USA, Daily Journal's 2012 list of the top 75 patent attorneys

in California, Legal 500, Super Lawyers, and San Jose Business Journal.

## LURIE, Jonathan C
McDermott Will & Emery LLP, Los Angeles
310 284 6169
jlurie@mwe.com
*Featured in Wealth Management (Nationwide), Tax (California)*
**Practice Areas:** Focuses on estate planning and post-death administration, including international estate planning.
**Professional Memberships:** Past executive committee member of the Trust and Probate Committee of the Los Angeles County Bar; past chair of Estate and Gift Tax Committee of the Tax Section of the Los Angeles County Bar; fellow of the American College of Trust and Estate Counsel.
**Personal:** University of Witwatersrand-Johannesburg, South Africa (BA, LLB).

## LYNCH, Niall
Latham & Watkins LLP, San Francisco
415 395 8262
niall.lynch@lw.com
*Featured in Antitrust (California)*
**Practice Areas:** Mr Lynch is a member of the firm's Global Antitrust & Competition and White Collar Defense & Investigations Practice Groups. Having spent 15 years as a prosecutor in the Antitrust Division of the US DOJ, Mr Lynch is able to draw upon his in-depth experience when counseling clients with issues pertaining to international antitrust and competition matters, including cartels, merger review, civil conduct, and criminal investigations.
**Career:** US DOJ, Assistant Chief of the Department of Justice Antitrust Division San Francisco (1996-2010).
**Personal:** JD, University of California, Hastings College of the Law, 1991; BA, Univ. of California, Berkeley, 1986.

## MACCOBY, Matthew F
Arnold & Porter LLP, Los Angeles
213 243 4213
Matthew.Maccoby@aporter.com
*Featured in Outsourcing (Nationwide), IT & Outsourcing (California)*
**Practice Areas:** Matthew Maccoby is experienced in complex business transactions, including outsourcing and other technology transactions, mergers and acquisitions, joint ventures, and strategic alliances. Mr Maccoby represents clients in information technology outsourcing, business process outsourcing, technology services transactions, and the development, purchase, sale, licensing, and distribution of technology. He also counsels clients regarding technology-related disputes.

## MAGNANI, Thomas A
Arnold & Porter LLP, San Francisco
415 471 3162
Thomas.Magnani@aporter.com
*Featured in Intellectual Property (California)*
**Practice Areas:** Tom Magnani focuses primarily on intellectual property licensing and counseling and on structuring technology and commercial transactions for companies and investors in a broad range of industries, including media and

entertainment, e-commerce, life sciences, consumer products, and information technology. He has provided strategic advice to clients in connection with a variety of intellectual property-related transactions, including research and development collaborations, mergers, asset acquisitions, public offerings, venture capital financings, copyright, trademark, and patent licenses, software licenses, distribution and supply arrangements, and sponsorship deals.

## MAISTER, Marc
Irell & Manella LLP, Newport Beach
949 760 5283
mmaister@irell.com
*Featured in Insurance (California)*
**Practice Areas:** Marc Maister is a partner at Irell & Manella, where he is a member of the litigation practice group and chair of the insurance practice. Maister specializes in handling high-profile insurance issues, complex business litigation matters and professional liability defense actions. He has obtained several hundred million dollar recoveries for clients and helps clients, brokers and risk managers analyze and structure insurance programs to maximize coverage. Maister also works with Irell's transactional attorneys on sophisticated insurance matters.
**Personal:** UC Berkeley School of Law (JD, Order of the Coif); University of Witwatersrand (Johannesburg, South Africa) (Bachelor of Commerce).

## MALECEK, Michael
Kaye Scholer LLP, Palo Alto
650 319 4508
michael.malecek@kayescholer.com
*Featured in Intellectual Property (California)*
**Practice Areas:** Michael Malecek, Co-Chair of Kaye Scholer's Intellectual Property Department, represents several leading biotech and technology companies in the US, including Sequenom, Affymetrix, Complete Genomics, Google and salesforce.com. Mike has served as trial counsel in over a dozen jury trials, all of which resulted in victories for his clients. He is currently litigating cases that will likely have a broad public impact, including IP related to non-invasive tests for Down Syndrome and technology that has driven down the cost of sequencing of human genomes. Mike previously served as an AUSA and as chief advocacy counsel for a biotech company.

## MALKIN, Joseph
Orrick, Herrington & Sutcliffe LLP, San Francisco
415 773 5505
jmalkin@orrick.com
*Featured in Energy & Natural Resources (California)*
**Career:** Joe Malkin has over 35 years of experience representing companies in complex commercial litigation of all types. He has tried or settled major cases in state and federal courts as well as before arbitrators, the Federal Energy Regulatory Commission and administrative agencies. He has successfully petitioned the U.S. Supreme Court for certiorari, argued before the Ninth Circuit U.S. Court of Appeals en banc, and in other federal circuit Courts of Appeals and the

California Courts of Appeal. His cases have involved patent, contract, fraud, breach of fiduciary duty, products liability, unfair competition, constitutional claims and intellectual property matters.

## MALLORY, Richard C
Allen Matkins Leck Gamble Mallory & Natsis LLP, Los Angeles
415 837 1515
rmallory@allenmatkins.com
*Featured in Real Estate (California)*
**Practice Areas:** Allen Matkins Founding Partner Rick Mallory represents landlords and tenants in commercial, industrial and retail leasing transactions.
**Professional Memberships:** Fellow of American College of Real Estate Lawyers and Lambda Alpha International; serves on advisory boards of Fisher Center for Real Estate and Urban Economics, Practising Law Institute, Commercial Lease Law Insider, Commercial Tenant's Lease Insider and Georgetown Advanced Commercial Leasing Institute. Member of Board of Directors of Coro Center for Civic Leadership.
**Publications:** Rick has published several articles on commercial leasing issues. Rick is a frequent CLE speaker.

## MALLOW, Michael
Loeb & Loeb LLP, Los Angeles
310 282 2287
mmallow@loeb.com
*Featured in Litigation (California)*
**Practice Areas:** Represents clients in unfair competition, false/deceptive advertising, business torts, entertainment and IP cases. Defend consumer protection actions/investigations initiated by FTC, US DOJ, Consumer Product Safety Commission and FCC; California Attorney General, Department of Corporations, Department of Real Estate and the State Licensing Board, to name some. Defended FTC's first prosecution of National Do-Not-Call registry and was lead trial counsel in dietary supplement case under Section 5 of FTC Act.
**Career:** Partner and Consumer Protection Defense Chair.
**Personal:** George Washington University (JD, 1991, With Honors); State University of New York at Binghamton (BA, 1988).

## MANCINO, Douglas M
Hunton & Williams LLP, Los Angeles
dmancino@hunton.com
*Featured in Healthcare (California), Healthcare (Nationwide)*
**Practice Areas:** Represents nonprofit organizations on tax, business and financial matters; represents organizations and individuals in connection with the formation of nonprofit organizations such as public charities, private foundations, corporate foundations and trade associations, corporate transactions and restructuring of corporate organizations. Extensive experience in audit, appeals and tax controversy matters, served as lead tax counsel in numerous IRS audits.

**Publications:** Author, 'Taxation of Hospitals and Health Care Organizations' and the co-author of 'Taxation of Exempt Organizations'.
**Personal:** Moritz (The Ohio State University) College of Law (JD, summa cum laude); Kent State University (BA, cum laude).

## MANSFIELD, Melainie K
Milbank, Tweed, Hadley & McCloy LLP, Los Angeles
213 8924611
mmansfield@milbank.com
*Featured in Banking & Finance (California)*
**Practice Areas:** Ms Mansfield is a partner in the Corporate Group and a member of the firm's Technology and Communication Practice sub-group. Her practice centers on transactional and general corporate representations. She focuses on secured lending, acquisition finance, troubled debt restructuring, securities financings, and private equity investments, as well as mergers and acquisitions and general corporate matters. Ms Mansfield's clients include investment funds, banks and domestic and foreign companies. She has extensive experience across a broad range of industries, including technology, telecommunications, media, manufacturing, retail and entertainment.

## MANSFIELD, Stephen A
Akin Gump Strauss Hauer & Feld LLP, San Francisco
415 765 9519
smansfield@akingump.com
*Featured in Litigation (California)*
**Practice Areas:** Trial lawyer, represents corporations, officers, directors and employees in trials and government enforcement actions before federal and state courts and administrative agencies. Practice focuses on corporate and government investigations, white-collar criminal defense, complex civil fraud litigation and class action defense. Former federal prosecutor. Heads the San Francisco office and co-chairs the firm's White-Collar Defense Practice Group.
**Professional Memberships:** American Bar Association, White-Collar Crime Committee; California Committee, Human Rights Watch.
**Personal:** BA (summa cum laude), University of Rhode Island (1977); JD, Law Review, University of Maine School of Law (1982).

## MARELLA, Vincent J
Bird, Marella, Boxer, Wolpert, Nessim, Drooks & Lincenberg PC, Los Angeles
310 201 2100
vjm@birdmarella.com
*Featured in Litigation (California)*
**Practice Areas:** White Collar criminal defense.
**Professional Memberships:** Former National Chairman of the American Bar Association's Committee on White Collar Crime.
**Career:** Represented an international corporation and its chief executive officer in the largest federal criminal tax case in the nation. Successfully represented chief executive officers, general counsel, chief financial officers and employees of major corporations in cases involving allegations of securities fraud, antitrust, health

care fraud, customs fraud, embargo violations, as well as tax, mail and wire fraud. Conducted internal investigations, both in the U.S. and abroad, for many publicly held corporations.
**Personal:** Former Assistant United States Attorney.

## MARENBERG, Steven
Irell & Manella, Los Angeles
310 203 7547
smarenberg@irell.com
*Featured in Media & Entertainment (California)*
**Practice Areas:** Steve Marenberg is a litigation partner at Irell & Manella where he is Head of the Entertainment Litigation practice group. Mr Marenberg's practice encompasses a wide range of commercial litigation matters, with particular concentrations in the areas of entertainment, high-technology and intellectual property litigation, and antitrust and business tort disputes. His clients include some of the nation's leading motion picture studios, television networks, independent production companies, music companies, interactive game companies and entertainers, as well as prominent technology firms.
**Personal:** University of Chicago Law School (JD); Wesleyan University (BA).

## MARGULIES, Jeffrey Brian
Fulbright & Jaworski LLP, Los Angeles
213 892 9286
jmargulies@fulbright.com
*Featured in Environment (California)*
**Practice Areas:** Environmental compliance, regulatory, and litigation; climate change; product safety; class actions.
**Professional Memberships:** California State Bar, Los Angeles County Bar Association.
**Career:** Environmental and product safety regulatory, compliance, litigation, and enforcement, including California Proposition 65; REACH, hazardous substances, chemical regulation, and labeling; product defect compliance and enforcement; Clean Air Act implementation and enforcement; site assessment and contamination; groundwater contamination. Leads firm's California Environmental Department and Climate Change practice group. Toxic tort, product liability and class action litigation. Transactional support and compliance auditing.
**Personal:** JD, Villanova University School of Law (1986); BS, Duke University (1982).

## MARMARO, Richard
Skadden, Arps, Slate, Meagher & Flom LLP & Affiliates, Los Angeles
213 687 5480
richard.marmaro@skadden.com
*Featured in Litigation (Nationwide), Litigation (California)*
See under Nationwide for profile.

## MARPLE, J D
Latham & Watkins LLP, Silicon Valley
650 328 4600
jd.marple@lw.com
*Featured in Outsourcing (Nationwide), IT & Outsourcing (California)*
**Practice Areas:** Practice focuses on strategic counseling and negotiation with respect to tech-

nology transactions and outsourcing arrangements. Structures and negotiates strategic alliances, joint ventures, intellectual property asset acquisitions, patent and other intellectual property licenses, manufacturing, supply and distribution agreements, and IT and business processing outsourcing arrangements. Clients range from start-ups to established public companies and their customers worldwide, in the fields of eCommerce, Internet, mobile services, software, hardware, semiconductor design, transportation, retail and related industries.
**Career:** Lobbyist in Washington, DC for the Business Software Alliance and legislative aide to Congressman Joe Moakley.
**Personal:** JD, George Washington University Law School.

## MARTINSON, Pamela J
Sidley Austin LLP, Palo Alto
650 565 7044
pmartinson@sidley.com
*Featured in Banking & Finance (California)*
**Practice Areas:** Partner in Sidley's Palo Alto and Los Angeles offices. She represents major institutional and other lenders, lessors, borrowers and equity sponsors. She possesses extensive experience in complex financings of all kinds, including syndicated and single-bank lending transactions (secured and unsecured), leasing (leveraged and synthetic), asset-based lending, subscription finance, securitizations and structured finance. She regularly handles the debt aspects of leveraged acquisition transactions. Her practice regularly involves cross-border loans and security, international trade finance and lending to technology and growth companies. She develops and updates commercial loan and lease documentation for banks and equipment lessors.

## MASENGA, Thomas J
Seyfarth Shaw LLP, Los Angeles
213 270 9679
tmasenga@seyfarth.com
*Featured in Real Estate (California)*
**Practice Areas:** Real estate, real estate restructuring and loan workouts.
**Career:** Tom Masenga is recognized nationally for structuring and closing complex real estate transactions for institutional investors, including pension funds and their advisors, banks, life insurance companies, private equity funds, and REITs. His finance and capital markets practice has included advising on portfolio, syndicated and mezzanine loan originations, workouts and restructurings, and foreclosures, as well as the acquisition and disposition of performing and non-performing loan portfolios.
**Personal:** JD, Loyola University of Law (cum laude); BA, University of Notre Dame (magna cum laude).

## MASON, Peter H
Fulbright & Jaworski LLP, Los Angeles
213 892 9233
pmason@fulbright.com
*Featured in Insurance (California)*
**Practice Areas:** Insurance and consumer class actions.

**Professional Memberships:** California Bar Association; American Bar Association.
**Career:** Mason is Partner-in-Charge of the Los Angeles office and a member of the firm's Policy Committee. His practice includes complex commercial litigation, unfair competition, insurance coverage and marketing practices and products liability. With more than 30 years of experience, he has tried cases in both state and federal courts. He received the 2010 California Lawyer of the Year award from California Lawyer magazine for a precedent-setting insurance case.
**Personal:** JD, American University (1976); BA, University of California at Berkeley (1973).

## MATHIASON, Garry G
Littler Mendelson, PC, San Francisco
415 433 1940
gmathiason@littler.com
*Featured in Labor & Employment (California)*
**Practice Areas:** Class Actions, Alternative Dispute Resolution, Wage and Hour, Complex Litigation and Jury Trials, Corporate Ethics and Compliance, Robotics Employment Law.
**Professional Memberships:** California State Bar; former Chair, Labor Law Division of the American Bar Association Forum Committee on the Construction Industry.
**Career:** Garry Mathiason is chairman of the board and a senior shareholder of Littler Mendelson. His career as litigator spans four decades, and is recognized as a leading authority on the nation's employment trends. Mr Mathiason is the key relationship attorney for several of the firm's major clients and is consulted on the most difficult cases. Mr Mathiason has personally overseen the firm's attorneys on over 1,000 employment and labor litigation matters while maintaining his own practice representing employers in complex wage and hour and discrimination class action cases. He's recently successfully argued cases in the U.S. and California Supreme Courts.
**Publications:** Mr Mathiason has authored and/or edited 22 employment law books and written over 100 published articles on workplace issues. He has been interviewed and quoted on employment topics in scores of national publications.
**Personal:** JD, Stanford Law School; Member of the Board of Editors and served on the Stanford Law Review; BS, Northwestern University, School of Communication Clarion DeWitt Hardy Scholar.

## MATKINS, Michael L
Allen Matkins Leck Gamble Mallory & Natsis LLP, Los Angeles
213 622 5555
mmatkins@allenmatkins.com
*Featured in Real Estate (California)*
**Practice Areas:** Mike advises institutional investors, owners, and developers in the purchase, sale and financing of real estate projects.
**Professional Memberships:** Member: Council of Advisors of National Geographic Society, Advisory Council of University of Southern California Lusk Center for Real Estate, Board of

Governors of Stanford's Professionals in Real Estate, Board of Advisors of ULI LA, Governor of ULI, Co-Chair of 75th Anniversary Fall Meeting in Los Angeles, California.
**Career:** Mike is a founding Partner of Allen Matkins. He has represented clients in the real estate industry for more than 40 years.

### MATTHIAS, Michael R
Baker & Hostetler LLP, Los Angeles
310 442 8802
mmatthias@bakerlaw.com
*Featured in Litigation (California)*
**Career:** Michael Matthias focuses on business and commercial litigation, handling securities, unfair trade practice, real estate, false advertising, trade secret, privacy, franchise, tax, class action and other complex litigation. His practice includes SEC investigations, civil enforcement defense and investigations conducted by state regulatory authorities and self-regulatory agencies, as well as the defense of class actions in securities, unfair trade practice and privacy areas. Michael has experience in litigation involving financial institutions and the financial services area, including secured transactions, commercial code and lending practice matters, and complex collection-related matters. Michael also has experience in medical devices and other products liability litigation.

### MAYERSON, Mickey A
Loeb & Loeb LLP, Los Angeles
310 282 2165
mmayerson@loeb.com
*Featured in Media & Entertainment (California)*
**Practice Areas:** Acted for clients in connection with more than $3 billion in financing transactions including studio slate financings to funding of single pictures. Established various new companies in entertainment, as well as creation of new mezzanine and equity film funds. Expertise includes project financing, LOC, securitization, co-financing, co-productions and tax-advantaged financing transactions.
**Career:** Partner since 1989. LA Office Managing Partner 2000-present.
**Publications:** Speaker at Paul Kagan's Motion Picture and Finance Seminar, UCLA Entertainment Symposium.
**Personal:** Columbia University Law School (JD, 1981, Harlan Fiske Stone Scholar); Wharton School/University of Pennsylvania (BS in Finance, magna cum laude, 1978).

### MCCARTHY, Brian J
Skadden, Arps, Slate, Meagher & Flom LLP & Affiliates, Los Angeles
213 687 5070
brian.mccarthy@skadden.com
*Featured in Corporate/M&A (Southern California)*
**Practice Areas:** The leader of Skadden's Los Angeles office, he concentrates on corporate and securities matters, with emphasis on mergers, acquisitions, corporate governance, and restructurings. Has acted as counsel to companies, special committees and investment banks, including Walt Disney Company in its acquisition of Lucasfilm; Gen-Probe in its sale to Hologic; Freedom Communications in its acquisition by

2100 Trust; and Cost Plus in its sale to Bed Bath & Beyond.
**Professional Memberships:** Executive Committee, Business and Corporations Law Section, Los Angeles County Bar Association.
**Career:** JD, Fordham University School of Law, 1978; BA, Tufts University, 1975 (magna cum laude).

### MCCONVILLE, Tom
Orrick, Herrington & Sutcliffe LLP, Los Angeles
949 852 7747
tmcconville@orrick.com
*Featured in Litigation (California)*
**Career:** Tom McConville, a partner in Orrick's White Collar Criminal Defense and Corporate Investigations practice, has 20 years of federal prosecutorial and private sector experience, and focuses his practice on white collar criminal defense, internal investigations and complex business litigation. An experienced trial lawyer, Mr McConville has handled cases involving securities fraud, FCPA violations, defense procurement fraud, false claims, intellectual property rights, and commercial contract disputes. Mr McConville represents both private and public companies, officers, directors and partners. Prior to joining Orrick, Mr McConville served 10 years as an assistant United States attorney focusing on fraud and public corruption prosecutions.

### MCCUSKER, Anthony
Goodwin Procter LLP, Menlo Park
650 752 3267
AMcCusker@goodwinprocter.com
*Featured in Corporate/M&A (Northern California), Corporate/M&A (California)*
**Practice Areas:** Mr McCusker is co-chair of the firm's Technology Companies Group. He specializes in all areas of corporate, securities and partnership laws, with a primary focus on the formation and financing of emerging growth companies. His representation of companies spans the entire corporate life-cycle, including pre-incorporation planning, general corporate representation and counseling, venture capital financings, public offerings, joint ventures, and mergers and acquisitions. Mr McCusker works with venture capitalists, private equity investors and investment banks involved in private and public stock offerings.
**Personal:** JD, University of California Hastings College of the Law, 1995; BA, University of California, Berkeley, 1992.

### MCDOWELL, Stewart L
Gibson, Dunn & Crutcher LLP, San Francisco
415 393 8322
SMcDowell@gibsondunn.com
*Featured in Capital Markets (California)*
**Practice Areas:** Co-Chair of the firm's Capital Markets Practice Group. Practice involves the representation of business organizations as to capital markets transactions, M&A, corporate governance and general corporate matters. Represents both underwriters and issuers in a broad range of both debt and equity securities offerings. Also represents both buyers and sellers in connection with

U.S. and cross-border mergers, acquisitions and strategic investments.
**Professional Memberships:** Member, California State Bar and New York Bar Association.
**Personal:** JD University of Virginia, 1995; BA, Princeton University, 1991.

### MCELHINNY, Harold J
Morrison & Foerster LLP, San Francisco
415 268 7265
hmcelhinny@mofo.com
*Featured in Intellectual Property (California)*
**Practice Areas:** Trial lawyer for some of the world's leading companies. Represents plaintiffs and defendants in patent litigation, copyright and trade secret violations, class actions, and enforcement. In 2012, served as lead trial counsel in Apple's victories over Samsung in California and the ITC.
**Professional Memberships:** Fellow, American College of Trial Lawyers; Former President, Northern California Association of Business Trial Lawyers.
**Career:** Former firmwide Managing Partner, IP Group co-chair, and Litigation Department chair.
**Personal:** JD, UC Berkeley School of Law; Law Clerk, Honorable Joseph Blumenfeld, US District Court, Connecticut; Lecturer, Trade Secret law, Stanford University School of Law.

### MCHENRY, Thomas J.P.
Gibson, Dunn & Crutcher LLP, Los Angeles
213 229 7135
tmchenry@gibsondunn.com
*Featured in Environment (California)*
**Practice Areas:** General environmental law with emphasis on air quality, hazardous waste, environmental diligence, land use and energy issues. Represents clients in negotiations with state and federal environmental agencies including air quality management districts, regional water quality control boards, Department of Toxic Substances Control (DTSC) and California and U.S. Environmental Protection Agencies in the context of air quality, soil and groundwater cleanup, California Environmental Quality Act (CEQA) compliance, facility siting, permitting and other environmental and natural resource issues.
**Personal:** JD, New York University, 1983. MFS, Yale School of Forestry & Environmental Studies, 1980. Adjunct Professor of Government, Claremont McKenna College.

### MCKANE, Mark
Kirkland & Ellis LLP, San Francisco
415 439 1473
mark.mckane@kirkland.com
*Featured in Litigation (California)*
**Practice Areas:** Mark McKane is a litigation partner in Kirkland's San Francisco office who focuses on complex commercial matters. He has successfully tried cases in federal and state courts and before arbitration panels throughout the United States. He represents Fortune 500 and private equity clients in antitrust, contract, fraud, energy, mergers and acquisitions, bankruptcy, and securities disputes. Recent representative matters

include the Del Monte bid-rigging antitrust litigation and Ally Financial/Residential Capital veil piercing dispute.
**Personal:** Yale University, BA, Political Science, 1993; Northwestern University School of Law, JD, cum laude, 1997.

### MCKEEMAN, Michael T
Seyfarth Shaw LLP, San Francisco
415 544 1038
mmckeeman@seyfarth.com
*Featured in Construction (California)*
**Practice Areas:** Construction; Real Estate.
**Professional Memberships:** AGC Legal Advisory Committee.
**Career:** Leads Seyfarth's California construction practice and co-chairs the San Francisco Litigation Department. Specializes in construction and real estate transactions and litigation. Significant experience representing owners, contractors, subcontractors and design professionals in every phase of public and private construction, including: contract drafting; project delivery methods; licensing; default, delay, acceleration and extra work claims; defect and warranty claims; and mechanics' lien, stop notice and bond claims.
**Publications:** "State-by-State Guide to Architect, Engineer and Contractor Licensing," California Chapter, Aspen (2009-12).
**Personal:** BS, University of California, Berkeley; JD, Santa Clara University.

### MCKNIGHT, Frederick (Rick)
Jones Day, Los Angeles
213 243 2777
fmcknight@jonesday.com
*Featured in Litigation (California)*
**Practice Areas:** Recognized in 2012 by National Law Journal as Top Litigator. Recognized for obtaining Top Plaintiffs Verdict of 2010. Recently named as one of California's Top 100 lawyers. His practice primarily involves complex business litigation. He has an active trial docket, including successful bench and jury trials of antitrust, contract, securities, oil and gas, healthcare, fraud, intellectual property, business tort, entertainment, product liability, toxic tort, bankruptcy, and environmental cases. He frequently lectures on and writes about trial practice and developments in the law.
**Professional Memberships:** Fellow of the American College of Trial Lawyers.

### MCMAHON, Terrence P
McDermott Will & Emery LLP, Menlo Park
650 815 7501
tmcmahon@mwe.com
*Featured in Intellectual Property (California)*
**Practice Areas:** Concentrates trial practice on patent, copyright, trade secret, trade dress, trademark and other high stakes, "bet the company" litigation. More than 30 years of trial experience representing technology heavyweights.
**Professional Memberships:** Admitted to practice in California, US Court of Appeals for Ninth Circuit, Court of Appeals for the Federal Circuit, US District Courts for Northern and Central Districts of California and Colorado.

**Career:** Adjunct Professor of law, teaching intellectual property litigation at Santa Clara University's Law School.
**Personal:** Santa Clara University School of Law, JD (cum laude), 1976; Santa Clara University, BSC, 1972.

### MCMILLAN, Daniel D
Jones Day, Los Angeles
213 243 2582
ddmcmillan@jonesday.com
*Featured in Construction (California)*
**Practice Areas:** Co-chairs Jones Day's worldwide Construction Practice. Specializes in complex construction litigation, contractual disputes, and claims involving federal and state false claims acts. Substantial trial, law and motion, and appellate experience and extensive experience with all forms of alternative dispute resolution. Served as adjunct Professor at Loyola Law School and is an instructor for the National Institute of Trial Advocacy. Frequent writer and speaker on issues affecting the construction industry and legal profession.
**Professional Memberships:** ABA Forum on the Construction Industry/Steering Committee for Dispute Avoidance and Resolution. Los Angeles Economic Development Corporation/Executive Director. Disputes Review Board Foundation.

### MCNAMARA, Mary
Swanson & McNamara LLP, San Francisco
415 477 3800
mmcnamara@swansonmcnamara.com
*Featured in Litigation (California)*
**Practice Areas:** Ms McNamara focuses on white collar criminal and general litigation practice. Representations include SEC, Export Control Act, tax, fraud, environmental, trade secret and antitrust matters.
**Professional Memberships:** Co-Chair, Lawyer Representatives to the Ninth Circuit 2002; Chair, BASF Judiciary Committee 2005; CJA Fee Review Committee ND California 2006 to present; CJA Representative ND California; Magistrate Judge Merit Selection Committee 2010. Selected as one of the 50 top women lawyers in Northern California 2008 and 2009. Selected as Daily Journal Top 75 Lawyers 2012, US News Best Lawyers 2012 Lawyer of the Year for White Collar Criminal Defense in San Francisco. Martindale-Hubbell AV-rated.
**Career:** Clerk, Hon Thomas Gibbs Gee, Fifth Circuit U.S. Court of Appeals (1989-90); associate, Morrison & Foerster (1990-94); Assistant Federal Public Defender (1994-98).
**Personal:** BA (First Class Hon.) Trinity College, Dublin (1986). JD and LLM (UC Berkeley) (1989).

### MCNEVIN, Chris
Pillsbury Winthrop Shaw Pittman LLP, Los Angeles
213 488 7507
chris.mcnevin@pillsburylaw.com
*Featured in Environment (California)*
**Practice Areas:** Leads Environmental Litigation Team. Focus is on litigation, agency negotiation and counseling relating to soil, groundwater, surface water and sediment contamination, natural resource damages, air and water quality and water rights.
**Professional Memberships:** Admitted: States of California and Texas; U.S. District Courts for California; U.S. Court of Appeals for the 3rd and 9th Circuits. Mr McNevin has offices in Austin, Houston and Los Angeles.
**Personal:** JD, Stanford Law School, 1983; BS, Biology, University of Miami, 1979, summa cum laude.

### MCPHEE, Scott
Morrison & Foerster LLP, San Francisco
213 892 5473
smcphee@mofo.com
*Featured in Real Estate (California)*
**Practice Areas:** Practice covers a broad range of real estate and finance transactions, including first mortgage lending, mezzanine and other subordinate loans, syndicated credit facilities, loan repurchase and warehouse facilities, and construction lending. Represents lenders, investors, mezzanine and equity investment funds, and property owners and developers in connection with the financing, acquisition, disposition, and development of various property types, and also in connection with the work-out of troubled loans and joint ventures. Regularly advises clients in connection with the formation of joint ventures, disposition and development agreements with municipalities, and the financeability of ground leases.

### MEADOW, Robin
Greines, Martin, Stein & Richland LLP, Los Angeles
310 859 7811
RMeadow@gmsr.com
*Featured in Litigation (California)*
**Practice Areas:** Appellate law.
**Professional Memberships:** California Academy of Appellate Lawyers; American Academy of Appellate Lawyers.
**Career:** In addition to almost four decades of handling appeals, Robin Meadow brings to his clients a wide range of experience representing both plaintiffs and defendants in virtually every kind of business dispute, particularly in the areas of entertainment law, intellectual property, real estate, partnerships and legal malpractice. He also has extensive experience in family law, medical malpractice and medical staff privileges disputes. And, unlike most full-time appellate lawyers, he has substantial first-chair trial experience from the first half of his career.

### MEEDER, James
Allen Matkins Leck Gamble Mallory & Natsis LLP, San Francisco
415 273 7471
jmeeder@allenmatkins.com
*Featured in Environment (California)*
**Practice Areas:** Jim has 35 years experience in complex environmental matters; contaminated soil, water, and air, the Clean Water Act, CERCLA, RCRA, nuisance and trespass, land use, NEPA/CEQA, Proposition 65, contract disputes, indemnity claims, toxic torts, civil penalty and criminal prosecutions. He practices before federal and state agencies, trial and appellate courts, and has mediation and settlement experience.
**Career:** University of Illinois, BA (1968); Senior Research Librarian U.S. Supreme Court (1972-1974); Georgetown University Law Center, JD (1974); Law Clerk, Hon. Robert Kelleher, U.S. District Court, Cent. Dist. California; Brobeck, Phleger & Harrison (1974-1991); Beveridge & Diamond (1991-2000); Allen Matkins (2000-).

### MEEKER, Heather J
Greenberg Traurig, LLP, East Palo Alto
650 289 7825
MeekerH@gtlaw.com
*Featured in IT & Outsourcing (California), Intellectual Property (California)*
**Practice Areas:** Chair, Greenberg Traurig IP/IT Licensing and Transactions Group.
**Professional Memberships:** Member: American Law Institute, 2006-Present; Lawyers' Committee for Civil Rights, San Francisco Bay Area, 2006-Present.
**Career:** Co-Managing Shareholder, Silicon Valley Office. Adjunct Professor of Law, Seminar on Software Licensing, University of California-Berkeley School of Law, 2007-10. Named, 'San Francisco Information Technology Law Lawyer of the Year', Best Lawyers®, 2012. Listed: Best Lawyers in America, 2008-13; Chambers USA Guide, 2008-13; 'The IAM Patent 1000', Licensing, IAM Magazine, 2012.
**Personal:** JD, Order of the Coif, University of California-Berkeley School of Law; BA, magna cum laude, Economics, Yale University.

### MENDELSON, Alan C
Latham & Watkins LLP, Silicon Valley
650 463 4693
alan.mendelson@lw.com
*Featured in Life Sciences (Nationwide), Corporate/M&A (California), Life Sciences (California)*
See under Nationwide for profile.

### MENDELSON, Richard C
Seyfarth Shaw LLP, Los Angeles
213 270 9619
rmendelson@seyfarth.com
*Featured in Real Estate (California)*
**Practice Areas:** Real estate, real estate restructuring and loan workouts, hospitality and leisure.
**Career:** Richard has particular knowledge in the areas of acquisitions, joint ventures, and financing transactions, as well as in workouts and restructurings. He has extensive experience in representing real estate funds, both domestic and international insurance companies and banks, public pension funds (and their advisors), and significant family real estate companies in all matters relating to commercial real estate.
**Personal:** JD, University of Pennsylvania (cum laude); AB, Rutgers University.

### MERRYMAN, Bryan A
White & Case LLP, Los Angeles
213 620 7802
bmerryman@whitecase.com
*Featured in Litigation (California)*
**Career:** Bryan A Merryman is the Executive Partner of White & Case's Los Angeles office. Mr Merryman has a national practice handling complex commercial litigation, including class actions, arbitrations involving business disputes and bankruptcy litigation. He obtained one of the largest judgments in Nevada on behalf of a real estate developer after a two-week arbitration hearing and has successfully opposed class certification motions on behalf of Time Warner Cable, Gerber Products Company, and Comcast Corporation. To view a comprehensive biography, please visit www.whitecase.com/bmerryman.

### MEYER, Bruce D
Gibson, Dunn & Crutcher LLP, Los Angeles
213 229 7979
BMeyer@gibsondunn.com
*Featured in Corporate/M&A (Southern California)*
**Practice Areas:** Member of the firm's Corporate Transactions Practice Group. Has extensive experience in representation of private equity clients and in mergers, acquisitions and divestitures of business entities, corporate securities matters, formation of partnerships, joint ventures and strategic alliances and international business transactions. Representative clients include Aurora Capital Partners and Korn/Ferry International.
**Career:** Vice President and Assistant General Counsel of Whittaker Corp of Los Angeles from 1973 to 1979.
**Personal:** JD, University of Illinois School of Law, 1970, Order of the Coif.

### MEYER, Michael E
DLA Piper LLP (US), Los Angeles
213 330 7777
michael.meyer@dlapiper.com
*Featured in Real Estate (California)*
**Practice Areas:** Real estate, landlord leasing.
**Professional Memberships:** ACREL.
**Career:** With a national reputation as one of the pre-eminent leasing attorneys in the United States, he regularly represents many of this country's leading financial institutions, accounting firms, and law firms in major lease transactions throughout the United States. He is one of the leading authorities on Fair Market Rental Rates, the Assignment and Subleasing Provision, the Tenant Improvement Agreement and the Rent Commencement Date. He has been named to the top rank of influential lawyers in numerous publications.
**Personal:** JD, University of Chicago; BA, University of Wisconsin-Madison.

### MILLER, O'Malley
Munger, Tolles & Olson LLP, Los Angeles
213 683 9591
om.miller@mto.com
*Featured in Real Estate (California)*
**Practice Areas:** Represents institutional investors, developers and lenders in connection with real estate projects, including office buildings, planned communities, multi-family projects, regional shopping centers and hotels. Key representations include: Simon Property Group in a $1 billion merger, Oaktree Capital Management and Hines in acquiring and financing a portfolio of office buildings in Las Vegas and Downtown

Properties LLC in the acquisition of 1.3 million square foot Chicago office building.
**Professional Memberships:** Member, American College of Real Estate Lawyers; Real Property Section, Los Angeles County Bar Association.
**Career:** Partner at the firm.
**Personal:** USC Gould School of Law; Stanford University (BA).

### MILLER, Samuel R
Sidley Austin LLP, San Francisco
415 772 7447
srmiller@sidley.com
*Featured in Antitrust (California)*
**Practice Areas:** Senior counsel in the firm's San Francisco office. He focuses his litigation practice in the areas of antitrust, intellectual property, securities law, complex civil litigation and white-collar criminal matters. His clients include major companies in the computer and consumer electronics industries.
**Career:** Mr Miller has extensive experience in handling monopolization cases. He served as lead counsel in the first Department of Justice case of U.S. v Microsoft Corp. He has represented a number of companies in matters relating to the conduct of a dominant firm.
**Personal:** He teaches an antitrust seminar in hi-tech industries at Berkeley Law School.

### MILLET, Craig H
Gibson, Dunn & Crutcher LLP, Irvine
949 451 3986
cmillet@gibsondunn.com
*Featured in Bankruptcy/Restructuring (California)*
**Practice Areas:** Co-Chair, Business Restructuring and Reorganization Practice. Extensive experience in chapter 11 reorganization, complex bankruptcy litigation; cross-border bankruptcy, distressed M&A, crisis management and strategic planning. Counsel to Arcapita Bank in its chapter 11 filing; lead counsel in chapter 11 of Fleetwood Enterprises, Inc. and 49 affiliates; counsel to Fleetwood Liquidating Trust; counsel to Thomas Kinkade in Pacific Metro bankruptcy; special counsel to debtor Solutia; represented debtor FLAG Telecom; represented five major broker/dealers in In re County of Orange chapter 9 proceedings.
**Personal:** JD, Pepperdine University, 1982, summa cum laude, Editor in Chief, Law Review.

### MINNICK, M David
Pillsbury Winthrop Shaw Pittman LLP, San Francisco
415 983 1351
dminnick@pillsburylaw.com
*Featured in Bankruptcy/Restructuring (California)*
**Practice Areas:** Representation of lenders, investors, property owners and other creditors in restructures, enforcement of creditors' rights and bankruptcies. Advising buyers and sellers on commercial law and bankruptcy issues in the buying and selling of businesses or assets, including representation of buyers in bankruptcy sales.
**Professional Memberships:** American Bankruptcy Institute, State Bar of California,

American Bar Association, Bar Association of San Francisco, Bay Area Bankruptcy Forum.
**Career:** State of California, US Supreme Court, Ninth Circuit Court of Appeals, US District Courts - Northern, Eastern and Central Districts of California.
**Personal:** JD University of Michigan Law School; BA University of Michigan.

### MITTELSTAEDT, Robert A
Jones Day, San Francisco
415 875 5710
ramittelstaedt@jonesday.com
*Featured in Antitrust (California), Litigation (California)*
**Practice Areas:** Experienced in trying and arbitrating high profile complex commercial cases, including antitrust, product liability, intellectual property and international law claims under the Alien Tort Statute in a wide range of industries ranging from software and digital music to gasoline and telecommunications. Recognized in California for defense verdict of 2008 in Alien Tort case and for gaining new trial in 2011 in intellectual property case. Partner-in-Charge of the firm's San Francisco Office.
**Professional Memberships:** Served as a director of the Bar Association of San Francisco, the Lawyers' Committee for Civil Rights, and Association of Business Trial Lawyers.

### MITZ, Daniel R.
Jones Day, Palo Alto
650 739 3918
drmitz@jonesday.com
*Featured in Corporate/M&A (Northern California)*
**Practice Areas:** Daniel Mitz represents technology companies in domestic and cross-border merger and acquisition transactions. Recent representative public company transactions include SAP's acquisitions of Sybase, Ariba and SuccessFactors, Zoran's sale to CSR, and Lam Research's acquisition of Novellus.
**Career:** Prior to joining Jones Day, Daniel was vice president of business affairs on Sun Microsystems' business development team in charge of structuring, negotiating, and executing Sun's acquisitions and equity investments.

### MO, Curtis L
DLA Piper LLP (US), East Palo Alto
650 833 2015
curtis.mo@dlapiper.com
*Featured in Corporate/M&A (California)*
**Practice Areas:** Corporate and securities.
**Career:** He is a leading corporate and securities lawyer in Silicon Valley and has represented emerging growth companies, major public companies, investment banks, venture capital and private equity funds in hundreds of public offerings, mergers and acquisitions, buyouts, venture capital financings, and other complex transactions. He has extensive experience in corporate governance matters and regularly acts as general outside counsel to public and private companies at all stages of development, particularly in the technology, life sciences, clean energy technology and consumer sectors.

**Personal:** JD, Columbia Law School; BA, Columbia University.

### MOIR, Katharine P.
Simpson Thacher & Bartlett LLP, Palo Alto
650 251 5035
kmoir@stblaw.com
*Featured in Tax (California)*
**Practice Areas:** Tax Partner and head of firm's Palo Alto tax practice. Focused on federal income tax matters, including mergers, acquisitions, private investment fund formation and capital markets transactions. Experience includes formation of private equity funds for Silver Lake, Centerbridge and Oaktree and numerous buyout transactions for private equity sponsors, including Hellman & Friedman, KKR and Silver Lake.
**Career:** Joined the firm in 1998; became Partner in 2008.
**Personal:** AB, with honors, Princeton University (1992); JD, with honors, University of Chicago (1996).

### MOLL, Charles J
Winston & Strawn LLP, San Francisco
415 591 1582
cmoll@winston.com
*Featured in Tax (California)*
**Practice Areas:** Charles Moll leads the firm's nationwide state and local tax practice. His practice focuses on resolving tax controversies and audits. He appears before state, county, and city tax authorities (including auditors and administrators), and judicial tribunals, on a wide variety of taxes. He also handles tax matters beyond California and federal tax controversies, including at the US Tax Court, the US Supreme Court, and at appellate hearings before the IRS.
**Professional Memberships:** Member, Executive Committee, ABA Section of Taxation State and Local Taxes Committee. Past Chair, California Bar Tax Section and ABA Section of Taxation Environmental Taxes Committee.

### MONROY, Gladys H
Morrison & Foerster LLP, Palo Alto
650 813 5711
gmonroy@mofo.com
*Featured in Life Sciences (California)*
**Practice Areas:** Practices in the areas of patents and technology transfer agreements, strategic counseling, and comprehensive patent prosecution and portfolio management, and IP due diligence studies. Has a wide range of experience in the life science-related areas, as well as special technical expertise in biochemistry, microbiology, molecular biology, immunology, diagnostics, therapeutics, virology, drug delivery systems, high-throughput screening, microarray technology, gene therapy, liposomal technology, small molecules, proteomics, bioinformatics and biomass conversion.
**Professional Memberships:** Admitted to practice in California, the USPTO, and the CAFC.
**Personal:** BA, Hunter College CUNY; MS, New York University; PhD, New York University; JD, University of San Francisco.

### MONTGOMERY, Cromwell
Gibson, Dunn & Crutcher LLP, Los Angeles
310 551 8744
cmontgomery@gibsondunn.com
*Featured in Banking & Finance (California)*
**Practice Areas:** Member of the firm's Global Finance Group. Represents borrowers and various capital providers in a broad variety of secured and unsecured credit transactions, including second lien, mezzanine and subordinated debt transactions, work-outs and other restructuring matters. Practice also includes capital markets transactions.
**Personal:** JD, Boalt Hall School of Law, University of California, Berkeley, 1997.

### MONTGOMERY, Sandra Lee
Bingham McCutchen LLP, Los Angeles
213 680 6641
sandra.montgomery@bingham.com
*Featured in Banking & Finance (California)*
**Practice Areas:** Practices commercial and corporate finance, asset-based lending, subordinated debt finance, other secured and unsecured lending, and related workout transactions, including establishing credit facilities for public and private companies. Industry experience in various business sectors, including retail, technology, transportation, manufacturing, distribution, general industrial, import/export, agriculture and services. Experience in Article 9 of the Uniform Commercial Code and other laws that relate to secured transactions. Handles numerous cross-border transactions.
**Personal:** University of Washington School of Law, JD, 1997; University of California, Berkeley, BA, magna cum laude, 1993.

### MOORADIAN, George T
Baker & Hostetler LLP, Costa Mesa
714 966 8800
gmooradian@bakerlaw.com
*Featured in Tax (California)*
**Career:** Partner-in-Charge of the firm's Costa Mesa office, George Mooradian's practice focuses on tax and estate planning for high-net-worth individuals and the administration of trusts and estates. His clientele includes corporate executives, successful closely held businesses and their owners and corporate trustees. George has substantial experience in the development of sophisticated business succession and estate plans for the owners of closely held businesses. He has advised high-net-worth individuals on personal tax and charitable planning through the use of devices such as charitable remainder trusts, charitable lead trusts, private foundations and supporting organizations.

### MOORE, Robert
Milbank, Tweed, Hadley & McCloy LLP, Los Angeles
213 892 4501
rmoore@milbank.com
*Featured in Bankruptcy/Restructuring (California)*
**Practice Areas:** Mr Moore is a partner in the Financial Restructuring Group. He has practiced bankruptcy and corporate reorganization law for 36 years. Mr Moore has led complex and groundbreaking restructuring engagements for debtors,

equity owners, first and second lien lenders, creditors' committees, private equity, hedge and bond funds, trustees, liquidation and litigation trusts, and asset purchasers in virtually every industry segment. Additionally, Mr Moore has led many complex bankruptcy litigation matters and significant international, chapter 9 municipal, and Native American restructurings, and has been named "Dealmaker of the Year" by American Lawyer and one of California's "Top 100 Lawyers".

## MOSKATEL, Ira D
Arnold & Porter LLP, Los Angeles
213 243 4223
Ira.Moskatel@aporter.com
*Featured in IT & Outsourcing (California)*
**Practice Areas:** Ira Moskatel represents businesses that depend on IP or technology, including computer software and hardware, electronics, semiconductors, optics, entertainment, publishing, communications, and electronic commerce, with emphasis on licensing, M&A, joint ventures, strategic alliances, and technology strategies. In addition, he consults on litigation matters involving issues in the physical sciences as well as information technologies. He is certified as a specialist in taxation law by the Board of Legal Specialization of the State Bar of California and has advised on a wide variety of California and federal tax issues related to technology, intellectual property, and corporate and partnership transactions.

## MOUSAVI, Nader A
Sullivan & Cromwell LLP, Palo Alto
650 461-5600
mousavin@sullcrom.com
*Featured in IT & Outsourcing (California)*
**Professional Memberships:** ABA; BBA; CBA.
**Career:** S&C partner since 2010. Co-head, Intellectual Property Group. Previously partner at WilmerHale. Practice includes advising on intellectual property and technology in diverse corporate and transactional matters, including M&A, joint ventures, spin-outs, financings, licensing, monetization, R&D and commercialization. Extensive intellectual property experience with many different industries, including technology, software, hardware, media, consumer products, pharmaceuticals and financial institutions. Recent clients include Anheuser-Busch InBev, AT&T, Avon Products, Billabong, Collective Brands, Cúram Software, Eastman Kodak, ING, Intel, NXP, Pharmasset, Silver Lake Partners, Skype and VeriFone.
**Personal:** Stanford Law School (JD, 1997); University of California, Los Angeles (BA, 1993).

## MUMMERY, Daniel
Gibson, Dunn & Crutcher LLP, Palo Alto
650 849 5318
dmummery@gibsondunn.com
*Featured in Outsourcing (Nationwide), IT & Outsourcing (California)*
**Practice Areas:** Mr Mummery's practice encompasses a wide range of sourcing and technology transactions matters, with a particular emphasis on complex information technology and business process outsourcing transactions,

including offshore arrangements, outsourcing renegotiations and restructurings, and software licensing and implementation arrangements including cloud-computing. ITO experience includes infrastructure, ADM, end-user computing, help desk and network transactions. BPO experience includes HR, finance and accounting, procurement, claims processing and logistics transactions. In his career, he has represented a broad array of clients in virtually every industry.
**Personal:** JD, Fordham University, 1988; BA, Bowdoin College, 1981.

## MURASHIGE, Kate H
Morrison & Foerster LLP, San Diego
858 720 5112
kmurashige@mofo.com
*Featured in Life Sciences (Nationwide), Life Sciences (California)*
See under Nationwide for profile.

## MURPHY, Mary
Gibson, Dunn & Crutcher LLP, San Francisco
415 393 8257
MGmurphy@gibsondunn.com
*Featured in Real Estate (California)*
**Practice Areas:** Represents developers and investors in large-scale real estate entitlements and transactions, with expertise in historic preservation. Current projects in San Francisco include development of arena for the Golden State Warriors; redevelopment of Treasure Island Naval Station; Parkmerced (city's largest residential development); Brisbane Baylands (700 acres); development of several waterfront and two major cultural institution projects. Completed projects include Presidio/Lucasfilm ground lease; historic rehabilitations (Piers 1.5, 3, 5 and San Francisco Ferry Building); Westfield San Francisco Centre.
**Career:** Two-term appointee, Presidents Clinton and Bush, Presidio Trust Board of Directors.
**Personal:** Harvard JD; Oxford (Rhodes Scholar); Yale BA.

## MURPHY, Michael
Pillsbury Winthrop Shaw Pittman LLP, San Francisco
415 983 1303
michael.murphy@pillsburylaw.com
*Featured in Outsourcing (Nationwide), IT & Outsourcing (California)*
See under Nationwide for profile.

## MURRAY JR, William G
Orrick, Herrington & Sutcliffe LLP, San Francisco
415 773 5807
wmurray@orrick.com
*Featured in Real Estate (California)*
**Career:** Mr Murray is a partner in the Real Estate group at Orrick. His practice focuses on negotiating and documenting acquisitions and financing transactions, acquisition of distressed debt, real estate mergers and acquisitions, fund formation, construction and long-term lending, ground leasing, sale-leaseback financings, synthetic leases, and development transactions. He has advised on numerous significant retail, office, hotel and resort, and industrial complex transactions. Mr Murray has been featured in publications such as

the Best Lawyers in America, Guide to the World's Leading Real Estate Lawyers, Legal 500, Who's Who Legal and Chambers.

## MYERS, Martin H
Jones Day, San Francisco
415 875 5859
mhmyers@jonesday.com
*Featured in Insurance (California)*
**Practice Areas:** Marty Myers is globally recognized for his success obtaining large insurance recoveries for complex losses in many industries, with particular emphasis on the technology sector. He has litigated and arbitrated disputes under all types of policies, including D&O, E&O, EPL, GL, Data Breach, Property/Business Income, Product Recall and Marine Cargo throughout the world, including in Europe and Scandinavia. He is among the world's leading practitioners in Transaction Risk insurance, including Tax Loss, Rep & Warranty and Environmental. Clients include Adobe Systems, BlackRock, Century Aluminum, Chevron, IAC/InterActive.
**Personal:** Miami U. Ohio (BA 1984); U. of Michigan Law (JD 1987).

## NARDI, Karen
Arnold & Porter LLP, San Francisco
415 471 3301
Karen.Nardi@aporter.com
*Featured in Environment (California)*
**Practice Areas:** Karen Nardi is a Partner in the Environmental Practice Group. In her practice she counsels clients on environmental and safety laws, including regulatory compliance, audits, environmental due diligence, site cleanups, redevelopment of contaminated properties, and OSHA matters. She also represents companies in enforcement actions and helps them manage liabilities in business transactions. She is co-author of several books, including the Environmental Law Handbook and Brownfields Law and Practice.
**Personal:** JD, University of California, Boalt Hall School of Law, 1982; MA in Public Policy, University of California, Berkeley, 1981; BA, magna cum laude, Barnard College, Columbia University, 1974.

## NASH, Glenn
Sidley Austin LLP, Palo Alto
650 565 7113
gnash@sidley.com
*Featured in Outsourcing (Nationwide), IT & Outsourcing (California)*
**Practice Areas:** Partner in Sidley's Palo Alto office and global co-head of Sidley's Technology Transactions practice. He has deep experience in the Internet, media, software, hardware and information technology industries. His practice focuses on intellectual property matters and providing strategic counseling to companies establishing and expanding their business and operations domestically and internationally. He handles complex business transactions including technology, content and intellectual property transactions, joint ventures and other strategic collaborations and commercial transactions domestically and internationally for both established and emerging growth companies.

**Personal:** University of Saskatchewan, JD, 1988; Memorial University of Newfoundland, BA, 1984.

## NATSIS, Anton N
Allen Matkins Leck Gamble Mallory & Natsis LLP, Los Angeles
310 788 2400
tnatsis@allenmatkins.com
*Featured in Real Estate (California)*
**Practice Areas:** Development, leasing, purchase/sale, portfolio transactions, fair market value disputes and CAM disputes. Debt, equity and joint venture workouts and purchase of distressed asset and debt.
**Professional Memberships:** American College of Real Estate Lawyers. Chief consultant, California Continuing Education Commercial Leasing Series. Founding Board Member of Ziman Real Estate Center. Adjunct Professor—Loyola Law School.
**Career:** Name Partner, Chairman of the firm's Real Estate Group. In the past decade, closed commercial office leases exceeding 50 million square feet, real estate purchase contracts with total consideration of $30+ billion, and worked on development transactions with total consideration of $25+ billion.

## NEELY, Sally S
Sidley Austin LLP, Los Angeles
213 896 6024
sneely@sidley.com
*Featured in Bankruptcy/Restructuring (California)*
**Practice Areas:** Senior counsel in Sidley's Los Angeles office in the Corporate Reorganization and Bankruptcy practice. She has practiced for more than 30 years in the area of corporate workouts and chapter 11 reorganizations, representing debtors, committees, creditors, contract parties, purchasers, defendants in adversary proceedings, and other interested parties in insolvency proceedings. She regularly works with Congress regarding bankruptcy legislation in her capacity as Chair of the Committee on Legislation of the National Bankruptcy Conference (NBC) and serves on NBC's Executive Committee.
**Personal:** Stanford Law School, JD, 1971, Order of the Coif; Stanford University, BA, 1970, Phi Beta Kappa.

## NELLIS, Noel W
Orrick, Herrington & Sutcliffe LLP, San Francisco
415 773 5806
nnellis@orrick.com
*Featured in Real Estate (California)*
**Practice Areas:** Real Estate, Development and Construction, Leasing, Lending and Financing, Real Estate Investment Funds, Real Estate Investment Trust and Real Estate Operating Company Representation.
**Career:** Mr Nellis, a Senior Counsel in the San Francisco office, focuses his practice on negotiating and documenting transactions in the areas of financing, leasing, development, construction and operation of real property. He has been responsible for the legal aspects of numerous large-scale land development projects such as high-rise office buildings, shopping centers, hotel and resort

properties and industrial buildings. He represents public and private REITs and institutional and pension fund investors and foreign investors.

## NEWMAN, Samuel A
Gibson, Dunn & Crutcher LLP, Los Angeles
213 229 7644
snewman@gibsondunn.com
*Featured in Bankruptcy/Restructuring (California)*
**Practice Areas:** Partner in firm's Business Restructuring and Reorganization Group in Los Angeles Office. Practice involves representing debtors, creditors' committees, and creditors in Chapter 11 cases. Also advises buyers and sellers of financially distressed assets and parties in distressed asset financing transactions. Has been active in cases including Blockbuster, Inc.; Barzel Industries, Inc.; and CCS Medical, Inc.
**Professional Memberships:** Board of Directors Southern California Chapter — Turnaround Management Association; Board of Governors — Financial Lawyers Conference.
**Publications:** Lectures frequently on corporate and bankruptcy law.
**Personal:** JD, Georgetown University, 2001, magna cum laude; BA, Georgetown University, 1992.

## NICHOLS, Sandi
Allen Matkins Leck Gamble Mallory & Natsis LLP, San Francisco
415 273 7454
snichols@allenmatkins.com
*Featured in Environment (California)*
**Practice Areas:** Sandi focuses on counseling and litigation for ports, commercial landowners/developers, industrial and other facilities in matters under the federal Clean Water Act, CERCLA, state statutory schemes, and CEQA. She handles all phases of litigation, from mediation through trial and appeal, in state and federal courts. Sandi also assists clients with environmental due diligence and allocation of responsibility in real estate transactions, environmental remediation, and related insurance issues. Her matters involve contaminated soil, sediments, groundwater, and surface waters; vapor intrusion; mold issues; and storm water permitting compliance.
**Career:** Partner and Co-chair of the Environmental and Natural Resources Group.

## NIESLEY, Robert
Watt, Tieder, Hoffar & Fitzgerald, LLP, Irvine
949 852 6700
rniesley@wthf.com
*Featured in Construction (California)*
**Practice Areas:** Construction and suretyship.
**Professional Memberships:** American Bar Association (Fidelity and Surety Law Committee, Forum on the Construction Industry, and Tort Trial and Insurance Practice Section), Los Angeles County and Orange County Bar Associations.
**Career:** Rob Niesley's litigation practice focuses upon the prosecution of construction affirmative claims against private and public owners throughout the United States. Rob is an expert in handling cases involving differing site conditions, lost productivity and construction delay claims. He has

handled lawsuits involving all types of construction projects.
**Publications:** Rob speaks regularly on surety and construction issues for industry clients.

## NIMMER, David
Irell & Manella, Los Angeles
310 203 7079
dnimmer@irell.com
*Featured in Intellectual Property (California)*
**Practice Areas:** David Nimmer is of counsel to Irell & Manella where he is a member of the intellectual property practice group. He successfully represented Amazon.com in defeating the Google Book Settlement in 2011. Besides client work, he updates and revises Nimmer on Copyright, the standard reference treatise in the field, first published in 1963 by his late father, Professor Melville B. Nimmer. Routinely cited by domestic foreign courts at all levels in copyright litigation, cases within the US have relied on Nimmer on Copyright as authority in over 3500 judicial opinions.
**Personal:** Yale Law School (JD); Stanford University (AB).

## NOEL, Gregg A
Skadden, Arps, Slate, Meagher & Flom LLP & Affiliates, Los Angeles
213 687 5234
gregg.noel@skadden.com
*Featured in Capital Markets (California), Capital Markets (Nationwide)*
**Practice Areas:** Represents issuers, investment banks and financial institutions in corporate transactions including private placements, public offerings, acquisitions, dispositions and corporate restructurings, and has been involved with over 65 IPOs. Represented Sara Lee Corporation in the spin-off of its international coffee and tea business, which created two separately traded public companies: The Hillshire Brands Company (NYSE) and D.E Master Blenders 1753 (Euronext Amsterdam). Co-head of firm's REIT practice and has worked with REITs for over 15 years.
**Career:** JD, Loyola Law School, 1982 (cum laude; St Thomas More Law Honor Society); BBA, BA Loyola Marymount University, 1979 (magna cum laude).

## NOLAN, Thomas J
Skadden, Arps, Slate, Meagher & Flom LLP & Affiliates, Los Angeles
213 687 5000
tnolan@skadden.com
*Featured in Litigation (Nationwide), Litigation (California)*
See under Nationwide for profile.

## NORRIS, Trenton H
Arnold & Porter LLP, San Francisco
415 471 3303
Trent.Norris@aporter.com
*Featured in Environment (California), Food & Beverages (Nationwide)*
**Practice Areas:** Trenton Norris litigates complex scientific and technical disputes in the areas of consumer protection, product liability, product safety, environmental, advertising, and food law. His clients are primarily manufacturers, distribu-

tors, and retailers of everyday products. Mr Norris advises and defends companies regarding federal, state, and local regulation of consumer products and services, including California's unique toxics and labeling law, Proposition 65, and expansive state consumer protection laws. Common issues in Mr Norris' matters are preemption, commercial speech, interstate commerce, citizen enforcement, jurisdiction, and class action requirements.
**Career:** Legislative aide to US Senator Wyche Fowler, Jr. (D-Ga)(1987-89).

## NYQUIST, Peter A
Alston & Bird LLP, Los Angeles
213 576 1142
pete.nyquist@alston.com
*Featured in Environment (California)*
**Practice Areas:** Environmental law, with an emphasis on federal and state contaminated sites, environmental and cost recovery litigation, water quality and NPDES compliance, and brownfield development. Represents clients in connection with CERCLA, RCRA corrective action and sediment cleanup sites and agency proceedings, and facilities under oversight of CalEPA, including the DTSC and RWQCBs.
**Professional Memberships:** Los Angeles County Bar Association (Vice-Chair, Environmental Law Section); California Bar Association (Environmental Law Section).
**Personal:** JD, University of California, Davis, 1995 (Executive Editor, Law Review); BA, University of California, Los Angeles, 1991 (magna cum laude, College Honors).

## O'BRYAN, Michael
Morrison & Foerster LLP, San Francisco
415 268 6352
mobryan@mofo.com
*Featured in Corporate/M&A (Northern California)*
**Practice Areas:** Mr O'Bryan focuses on U.S. and international M&A, divestitures and other strategic transactions, including "going private" and other related party transactions, as well as corporate governance. He has been involved in more than 350 M&A transactions, advising public and private companies, boards and special committees, as well as investment banks, in both negotiated and contested transactions.
**Career:** Co-Chair of firm's Global M&A Group. Prior to joining the firm, Mr O'Bryan worked at a Japanese law firm advising on cross-border deals, financings and joint ventures.
**Personal:** JD, cum laude, Harvard Law School, 1988; BA, University of Michigan 1983.

## O'CONNELL, George L
DLA Piper LLP (US), Sacramento
916 930 3289
george.oconnell@dlapiper.com
*Featured in Litigation (California)*
**Practice Areas:** Litigation: White-Collar Crime & Government Investigations.
**Career:** He focuses on complex civil litigation and sophisticated white collar criminal cases. He has represented clients ranging from some of the biggest companies in the world to politically prominent individuals in the most challenging types of civil and criminal cases. His background

as a former United States Attorney and federal prosecutor has made him particularly well suited to represent corporations and individuals in an extremely wide range of sophisticated matters.
**Personal:** JD, Harvard Law School (cum laude); BA, Purdue University (summa cum laude) Phi Beta Kappa; Phi Kappa Phi.

## OLEJKO, Mitchell J
Buchalter Nemer, San Francisco
415 227 3603
molejko@buchalter.com
*Featured in Healthcare (California)*
**Practice Areas:** Represents healthcare entities in connection with all legal issues from initial program development and ongoing operations through extraordinary transactions such as sales, joint ventures or alliances. With over 25 years' experience in the healthcare field both as a lawyer and as a senior manager, he has assisted companies in meeting the challenges of the ever-changing healthcare environment.
**Career:** California Bar (1998); Oregon Bar (1992); Washington Bar (1977).
**Personal:** JD, Washington University School of Law (1977); AB (History), Boston College (1973).

## OLSON, Jeffrey M
Sidley Austin LLP, Los Angeles
213 896 6041
jolson@sidley.com
*Featured in Intellectual Property (California)*
**Practice Areas:** Mr Olson is a partner in Sidley's Los Angeles Intellectual Property group. He serves as lead counsel in matters involving claims for patent infringement and other forms of intellectual property. Mr Olson represents a broad spectrum of established and emerging technology companies, including those in the biomedical, computer, electronic and telecommunication industries. In addition to having tried numerous cases, Mr Olson counsels clients in all aspects of domestic and international intellectual property law, including patent procurement, licensing, due diligence and audits.
**Personal:** The University of Michigan Law School, JD, 1981; University of Illinois, BS in General Engineering, 1977.

## OLSON, Ronald
Munger, Tolles & Olson LLP, Los Angeles
213 683 9111
Ron.Olson@mto.com
*Featured in Litigation (California), Media & Entertainment (California)*
**Practice Areas:** Major litigation and corporate counseling. Key representations: Berkshire Hathaway matters; Google founders for 2-tier stock structure; Udvar-Házy and Air Lease Corporation to establish new, global airline leasing company; Directors of Yahoo!, in connection with Alibaba transaction, Microsoft's proposed takeover, and proxy contests; Grupo Mexico in resolving $2,5000,000,000 judgment.
**Professional Memberships:** Director of Berkshire Hathaway, Edison International, City National Corp., The Washington Post Co., Western Asset Trusts, RAND Corp., Mayo Clinic and California Institute of Technology.

**Career:** Name partner.

**Personal:** Michigan Law School (JD 1966); Oxford University (Diploma Law 1967); Drake University (BS 1963).

## O'NEAL, Stephen V
Jones Day, San Francisco
415 875 5780
soneal@jonesday.com
*Featured in Construction (California)*

**Practice Areas:** His practice includes construction, real estate, and complex business litigation. He has been involved in projects including energy, building, industrial, pharmaceutical plant, bridge, railway, and highway construction in the United States and throughout the world, working on both private sector and government contract matters. In addition to acting as litigation counsel for parties to bench and jury trials, administrative proceedings, arbitrations, and mediations, Mr O'Neal also has many years of experience as an arbitrator.

**Publications:** Business and Commercial Litigation in Federal Courts. Thomson West (2005). Construction Chapter; Second Edition (2005) and Third Edition (2012). Engineering Evidence. Thomson West (2008). Co-author.

## O'ROURKE, Kenneth R
O'Melveny & Myers LLP, Los Angeles
213 430 7281
korourke@omm.com
*Featured in Antitrust (California)*

**Practice Areas:** Kenneth R. O'Rourke heads O'Melveny's Los Angeles litigation group. His practice focuses on representing established and emerging companies in large, multi-forum civil litigation, including antitrust cases (class actions, monopolization, international cartels, unfair competition), intellectual property lawsuits (patents, trade secrets, standard setting), and other business controversies. Ken was a member of the Hynix trial team that obtained a defense verdict from a San Francisco state court jury in November 2011 in Rambus' multi-billion dollar antitrust lawsuit against Hynix and other chip makers.

## OSHINSKY, Jerold
Jenner & Block LLP, Los Angeles
213 239 5156
joshinsky@jenner.com
*Featured in Insurance (Nationwide), Insurance (California)*

See under Nationwide for profile.

## OSTRAU, Mark S
Fenwick & West LLP, Mountain View
650 335 7269
mostrau@fenwick.com
*Featured in Antitrust (California)*

**Practice Areas:** Mark S. Ostrau is Co-Chair of the Antitrust and Unfair Competition Group, Co-Chair of the Cleantech Group and a partner in the Intellectual Property and Technology Transactions Groups at Fenwick & West LLP. As a member of Fenwick's Technology Transactions Group, his focus is helping cleantech and other high technology companies grow into sustainable businesses by assisting them in acquiring, developing and commercializing their technologies and products. As co-chair of the Antitrust and Unfair

Competition Group, Mr Ostrau advices clients on a wide variety of antitrust issues, including distribution, marketing, M&A and intellectual property.

**Career:** Mr Ostrau is recognized as one of Northern California's "Super Lawyers" (since 2006), and as one of the top antitrust lawyers in California by Chambers USA (2011) and is named to The Best Lawyers in America for antitrust law (since 2009).

## OXLEY, William W
Dechert LLP, Los Angeles
213 808 5712
william.oxley@dechert.com
*Featured in Litigation (California)*

**Practice Areas:** Mr Oxley is a trial lawyer who focuses on products liability and mass tort cases, complex business disputes, and intellectual property matters. He has worked extensively on false advertising, contract, class action and real estate disputes and has also defended nutritional and health product manufacturers and distributors against Proposition 65 claims.

**Professional Memberships:** Member, California and Texas Bars; Los Angeles County Bar Association.

**Personal:** California State University, Sacramento (BA, 1985); University of the Pacific McGeorge School of Law (JD, with distinction, 1988, Order of the Coif).

## PAPARELLI, Angelo
Seyfarth Shaw LLP, Los Angeles
213 270 9797
apaparelli@seyfarth.com
*Featured in Immigration (California), Immigration (Nationwide)*

**Professional Memberships:** Alliance of Business Immigration Lawyers, Founder; American Immigration Council, Trustee Emeritus; Federal Bar Association, Board Member (Los Angeles Chapter).

**Career:** Practicing bi-coastally from offices in Los Angeles and New York City and providing creative solutions to immigration law challenges involving mergers, acquisitions, corporate restructuring, EB-5 Regional Centers, all categories of employment-based immigration, compliance audits, government investigations, global visas and consular practice, and federal court litigation.

**Publications:** Co-authors the New York Law Journal's 'Immigration' column, writes a blog (www.nationofimmigrators.com), co-edited, The Immigration Compliance Book (ILW 2011) and is frequently quoted in leading national publications on immigration law.

## PAPPAS, Dean C
Goodwin Procter LLP, Los Angeles
213 426 2525
dpappas@goodwinprocter.com
*Featured in Real Estate (California)*

**Practice Areas:** Mr Pappas' practice involves structuring, negotiating, drafting and closing various real estate and corporate transactions, including joint venture formation (partnerships and limited liability companies), merger, acquisition and disposition transactions, construction, mort-

gage and mezzanine loan transactions, public contracting, leasing and other various transactions.

**Professional Memberships:** Vice-Chair: American College of Real Estate Lawyers's Investment Entity Committee; Member: USC Gould School of Law – LA County Bar Association's Real Estate Law and Business Forum Planning Committee.

**Personal:** JD, University of Southern California Law School, 1991 (Order of the Coif); BS, University of Southern California, 1988.

## PASAHOW, Lynn H
Fenwick & West LLP, Mountain View
650 335 7225
lpasahow@fenwick.com
*Featured in Intellectual Property (California)*

**Practice Areas:** Lynn H. Pasahow is a partner in the Litigation Group at Fenwick & West LLP, handling complex litigation, principally patent and other intellectual property suits in the software, Internet, hardware and life science industries. He has represented cutting-edge technology companies and universities and their highly innovative inventors in their most important suits.

**Career:** Mr Pasahow is among the leading intellectual property lawyers recognized in The Best Lawyers in America, Chambers Guides and other lawyer surveys.

**Publications:** Mr Pasahow is a co-author of the Federal Judicial Center's patent handbook for judges, the Patent Case Management Judicial Guide (2009), and, with Hon. William W. Schwarzer, of Civil Discovery: A Guide to Efficient Practice.

## PASICH, Kirk A
Dickstein Shapiro LLP, Los Angeles
310 772 8305
pasichk@dicksteinshapiro.com
*Featured in Insurance (Nationwide), Insurance (California)*

See under Nationwide for profile.

## PEARSON, Ronald C
Loeb & Loeb LLP, Los Angeles
310 282 2230
rpearson@loeb.com
*Featured in Tax (California)*

**Practice Areas:** Focuses on estate planning for high net worth individuals, owners of closely-held businesses and in representing corporate and individual fiduciaries in the administration of estates and trusts, including living trusts, gift and insurance trusts, generation-skipping trusts; grantor-retained annuity trusts; qualified personal residence trusts; family limited partnerships; private foundations; charitable trusts and qualified domestic trusts for non-citizen spouses.

**Career:** Became Partner at ReedSmith (formerly Crosby, Heafey) in 1999. Joined Loeb as Partner in 2003.

**Publications:** Commentator, Life-Stage Investing: Turning Real-Estate Malaise into an Estate-Plan Cure, Standard & Poor's MarketScope Advisor (2008).

## PEITZMAN, Lawrence
Peitzman Weg LLP, Los Angeles
310 552 3100
lpeitzman@peitzmanweg.com
*Featured in Bankruptcy/Restructuring (California)*

**Practice Areas:** Business bankruptcies, workouts. Represents Chapter 11 debtors, creditors' committees, secured and unsecured creditors, parties in bankruptcy litigation, asset purchasers, Chapter 7 trustees and Chapter 15 representatives.

**Professional Memberships:** Has been President of Financial Lawyers Conference; Chair of ABA committee on Loan Workouts; Member, Executive Committee, Los Angeles County Bar Association's Commercial and Bankruptcy Section; Fellow, American College of Bankruptcy; Treasurer, American College of Bankruptcy Foundation.

**Publications:** Numerous articles in such publications as American Bankruptcy Law Journal, California Law Review, California Business Law Reporter. Lecturer for such organizations as American Bar Association, Practicing Law Institute, State Bar of California.

## PELAVIN, Alyse N
Loeb & Loeb LLP, Los Angeles
310 282 2298
apelavin@loeb.com
*Featured in Tax (California)*

**Practice Areas:** Focuses on estate and gift tax planning for high net worth individuals and closely held businesses, and in the administration of estates and trusts. Extensive experience in charitable giving and tax exempt organizations. Her estate planning experience includes substantially all aspects of legal matters pertaining to high net worth individuals, including probate court procedures, living trusts, gift and insurance trusts, and sophisticated transfer tax techniques. Her charitable giving and exempt organizations representation involves all aspects of tax and corporate non-profit law.

**Career:** Partner since 2010.

**Personal:** New York University (JD, 2002, cum laude); Northwestern University (BS, 1998).

## PERNICK, John D
Bingham McCutchen LLP, San Francisco
415 393 2544
john.pernick@bingham.com
*Featured in Litigation (California)*

**Practice Areas:** Focuses on complex litigation, securities litigation and broker-dealer work. Represents clients in the finance, technology, energy, insurance and other industries in litigating securities, antitrust, trade regulation, insurance and business tort disputes, including class actions and other representative actions before state and federal courts and agencies.

**Personal:** University of Michigan Law School, Juris Doctor, Cum Laude, 1991. Harvard College, Bachelor of Arts, 1988.

## PERROCHET, Lisa
Horvitz & Levy LLP, Encino
818 995 0800
lperrochet@horvitzlevy.com
*Featured in Litigation (California)*

**Practice Areas:** Lisa Perrochet, a partner at Horvitz & Levy, has specialized in appellate litigation since 1987, and has argued before the California Supreme Court and intermediate appellate courts throughout the state. She defends clients against consumer and punitive damages claims; toxic tort and product liability actions; insurance litigation; and professional liability claims.

**Professional Memberships:** American Academy of Appellate Lawyers (fellow); Association of Southern California Defense Counsel (board member and editor of the organization's law publication, Verdict magazine).

**Career:** California State Bar Certified Appellate Specialist (since the first year specialist certification was offered in 1996).

### PETERS, Gerald
Latham & Watkins LLP, San Francisco
415 395 8160
jerry.peters@lw.com
*Featured in Healthcare (California)*

**Practice Areas:** Mr Peters' practice includes business, transactional, regulatory and compliance matters for health care clients, including health care systems, hospitals, physician organizations, payers and ancillary service providers. His expertise includes mergers, acquisitions, joint ventures, restructurings, medical practice consolidation, regulatory compliance, contract negotiation, tax-exemption, fraud and abuse law, and corporate law. Clients rely upon Mr Peters for his clear communication of strategic options, ability to organize and prioritize business, regulatory and financial considerations, and his judgment as to next steps.

**Personal:** JD, University of California, Hastings College of the Law, 1982; , Univ. of California, Berkeley, 1978.

### PETERS, William J
Gibson, Dunn & Crutcher LLP, Los Angeles
213 229 7515
wpeters@gibsondunn.com
*Featured in Outsourcing (Nationwide), IT & Outsourcing (California)*

See under Nationwide for profile.

### PETERSON JR, John M
Baker & McKenzie, Palo Alto
650 856 5538
John.Peterson@bakermckenzie.com
*Featured in Tax (Nationwide), Tax (California)*

**Practice Areas:** John M Peterson Jr is a Partner in the Palo Alto office of Baker & McKenzie LLP. He practices corporate tax law, with heavy emphasis on structuring of international operations, intercompany transfer pricing, international tax planning generally, high technology tax issues, and federal income tax controversies. Mr Peterson is a former Chair of Baker & McKenzie's Global Tax Practice Group.

**Career:** Received his BBA in Accounting from the University of Notre Dame in 1973 and his JD Degree from Harvard Law School in 1977, graduating cum laude.

**Personal:** Mr Peterson joined Baker & McKenzie in 1977.

### PETROFF, Laura R
Winston & Strawn LLP, Los Angeles
213 615 1736
lpetroff@winston.com
*Featured in Labor & Employment (California)*

**Practice Areas:** Significant complex litigation, including trial, experience representing employers in employment-related litigation and counseling, and defending multi-party and class action litigation, including wage and hour claims. Has handled a broad range of employment-related cases, including sexual and other harassment and discrimination claims, retaliation, wrongful discharge, constructive discharge, and trade secret and non-competition disputes. Uniquely skilled at settling high-stakes cases. Experience also includes negotiations, training, investigations, preparing targeted employment policies and procedures, and negotiating employment contracts, confidentiality agreements, and non-competition agreements. Represents employers in the financial services, technology, manufacturing, fashion, and retail industries, among others.

### PFEIFFER, Alfred
Latham & Watkins LLP, San Francisco
415 395 8898
Al.Pfeiffer@lw.com
*Featured in Antitrust (California)*

**Practice Areas:** Extensive experience with antitrust trials, civil and criminal government antitrust investigations, and competition-related commercial cases and ADR proceedings, including mediations and arbitrations. In addition to trial work, has successfully represented clients in investigations conducted by the US DOJ, Federal Trade Commission and California Attorney General's office and advises companies regarding potential strategic acquisitions, joint ventures and distribution agreements. He has developed a particular focus on claims involving dominant firm conduct and the information technologies and telecommunications arenas.

**Career:** Chair, Latham & Watkins Global Antitrust and Competition Practice.

**Personal:** JD, Yale Law School, 1985; BA, St. Joseph's University, 1982.

### PHILLIPS, Bradley S
Munger, Tolles & Olson LLP, Los Angeles
213 683 9262
brad.phillips@mto.com
*Featured in Antitrust (California)*

**Practice Areas:** Antitrust, unfair competition, constitutional law, civil rights. Antitrust matters include: Texaco, Inc. v. Dagher, 547 U.S. 1 (2006); Rick-Mik Enterprises, Inc. v. Equilon Enterprises LLC, 532 F.3d 963 (9th Cir. 2008); and Aguilar v. Atlantic Richfield Co., 25 Cal.4th 826 (2001).

**Professional Memberships:** Fellow, American Bar Foundation; Former Co-Chair, Lawyers' Committee for Civil Rights Under Law; Former President, Legal Aid Foundation of Los Angeles.

**Personal:** BA, Stanford University; JD, Yale Law School; law clerk to Honorable Wm. Matthew Byrne, Jr.

### PICKETT, Donn P
Bingham McCutchen LLP, San Francisco
415 393 2082
donn.pickett@bingham.com
*Featured in Antitrust (California), Litigation (California)*

**Practice Areas:** Co-chair of Bingham's Litigation Area. Past vice chairman of the firm. Concentrates his work in antitrust, intellectual property and securities litigation and has developed extensive experience in the defense of class actions. Unique case management style emphasizes responsible, lean and effective staffing; extraordinary responsiveness; early attempts to resolve matters especially through mediation; discriminate use of discovery; creative motions practice; avoidance of unnecessary costs; strict budgeting; and close client communications with active in-house participation.

**Career:** Fellow, American College of Trial Lawyers.

**Personal:** Yale Law School, JD, 1976; Carleton College, BA, magna cum laude, 1973.

### PIERCE, Timothy
K&L Gates, Los Angeles
310 552 5058
timothy.pierce@klgates.com
*Featured in Construction (California)*

**Practice Areas:** With a practice focused on legal matters involving the construction industry, Timothy Pierce works with his clients from the inception of a project and the formation of contracts to the resolution of claims in litigation. An experienced litigator, he seeks efficient, cost effective solutions to construction disputes. He has extensive trial experience in construction matters, including as trial counsel in five lengthy jury trials. Noted successes include obtaining a $37 million judgment on behalf of a contractor on a power plant project after a ten week jury trial, one of the year's top ten California jury trial verdicts.

### PIMSTONE, Gregory N
Manatt Phelps & Phillips LLP, Los Angeles
310 312 4133
gpimstone@manatt.com
*Featured in Healthcare (California)*

**Practice Areas:** Pimstone chairs Manatt's national Healthcare Litigation practice. He has been lead counsel in numerous high-profile cases that have established new precedent in the healthcare field. He has represented, at trial and on appeal, managed care health plans, health insurers, trade associations, medical providers and other healthcare companies in RICO, consumer and unfair competition class actions; government criminal and civil audits, investigations and enforcement actions; ERISA suits; fraud and abuse and qui tam actions; bad faith denial of benefits suits and policy rescission investigations and actions; HIPAA and other privacy matters; antitrust disputes; product liability actions; and pharmaceutical litigation.

### PLEVIN, Mark
Crowell & Moring LLP, Washington, DC
415 365 7446
mplevin@crowell.com
*Featured in Bankruptcy/Restructuring (District of Columbia), Insurance (California)*

See under District of Columbia for profile.

### PLIMACK, Michael
Covington & Burling LLP, San Francisco
415 591 7002
mplimack@cov.com
*Featured in Intellectual Property (California)*

**Practice Areas:** Mr Plimack has litigated patent infringement and trade secret cases for 25 years. He has served as lead counsel in patent infringement trials in the U.S. District Court and the International Trade Commission and has briefed and argued appeals before the U.S. Court of Appeals for the Federal Circuit.

**Career:** Chair, Electronics & Information Technology Industry Group; Board of Governors, Association of Business Trial Lawyers.

**Personal:** University of California, Berkeley School of Law (JD, 1986); Brown University (AB, 1983). California Law Review, Senior Articles Editor. Law Clerk to Hon. James R. Browning, U.S. Court of Appeals, Ninth Circuit.

### PLUME, Tamsen
Holland & Knight LLP, San Francisco
415 743 6941
tamsen.plume@hklaw.com
*Featured in Real Estate (California)*

**Practice Areas:** Tamsen Plume is a partner in Holland & Knight's West Coast Land Use and Environment Group. Her practice concentrates on land use and environmental law. She represents project proponents in land use and environmental permitting, compliance, and due diligence matters for complex land use, development and redevelopment projects throughout California.

### POHLEN, Patrick A
Latham & Watkins LLP, Silicon Valley
650 463 3067
patrick.pohlen@lw.com
*Featured in Investment Funds (Nationwide), Capital Markets (California), Corporate/M&A (California)*

**Practice Areas:** Represents public and private companies primarily in the technology, cleantech and life science industries, and the financial institutions (venture capitalists and investment banks) that finance them. Practice focuses on general corporate counseling, corporate governance, private finance, public offerings, securities and mergers & acquisitions.

**Professional Memberships:** Member, New York, California and Missouri Bar; Member, Corporate Laws Committee, ABA.

**Career:** Ran a venture-backed technology company prior to joining Latham & Watkins.

**Personal:** JD, University of Iowa College of Law, 1984; BA Iowa State University, 1981.

### POLIZZI, Catherine
Morrison & Foerster LLP, San Francisco
650 813 5651
cpolizzi@mofo.com
*Featured in Life Sciences (California)*

**Practice Areas:** Helps emerging and established companies to obtain patents, providing strategic, effective portfolio counseling and management primarily in biotechnology and pharmaceutical industries. Develops valuable, strategic portfolios around breakthrough therapies in a variety of areas, including cancer, personalized medicine, autoimmune diseases, and neurodegenerative diseases. Significant experience in a wide spectrum of technology areas. Also conducts due diligence evaluation and counseling in the context of venture investment assessments and corporate transactions, and devises strategies with a business and value-oriented perspective.

**Career:** Former chair, firmwide Patent Prosecution & Counseling Group and former co-chair, firmwide IP Group.

### POMERANTZ, Glenn D
Munger, Tolles & Olson LLP, Los Angeles
213 683 9132
pomerantzgd@mto.com
*Featured in Antitrust (California), Media & Entertainment (California)*

**Practice Areas:** Practice focuses on counseling and litigation in antitrust, copyright and commercial disputes. Recent representations: Universal Music Group in obtaining regulatory approval to acquire EMI; successfully defended ABC in copyright and trade secret action by CBS relating to competing reality programs; major record companies in copyright action against LimeWire.

**Professional Memberships:** Board, Western Justice Center; member, ABA: Antitrust and Litigation Sections.

**Career:** Named by Daily Journal as one of "Top 100" lawyers in California. Named as co-lead counsel for the Department of Justice in its lawsuit seeking to block the AT&T/T-Mobile merger.

**Personal:** Harvard University (JD) U.C. Berkeley (AB).

### POON, Julian
Gibson, Dunn & Crutcher LLP, Los Angeles
213 229 7758
jpoon@gibsondunn.com
*Featured in Labor & Employment (California)*

**Practice Areas:** Has handled broad range of cases at the appellate and trial court levels, in federal and state courts across the country, including major wage-and-hour class actions, as well as other complex commercial litigation.

**Career:** Appointed by Chief Justice of California to Judicial Council's Advisory Committee on Civil Jury Instructions, 2012. Law clerk to Justice Antonin Scalia, U.S. Supreme Court, and to Judge J. Michael Luttig, formerly of the U.S. Court of Appeals for the Fourth Circuit.

**Personal:** Harvard Law School, 1999, summa cum laude; recipient of Fay Diploma (first in his class); Note Editor, Harvard Law Review.

### POONJA, Zaitun
Morgan, Lewis & Bockius LLP, Palo Alto
650 843 7540
zpoonja@morganlewis.com
*Featured in Employee Benefits & Executive Compensation (California)*

**Practice Areas:** Zaitun Poonja is a partner in Morgan Lewis's Employee Benefits and Executive Compensation Practice. She specializes in all areas of domestic and foreign equity compensation programs for public and private companies, including U.S. tax, securities, and accounting implications and tax, securities, exchange control, labor law, data privacy, and other legal implications related to use of equity programs in foreign jurisdictions. She advises non-U.S. entities on design and implementation of equity programs for U.S. employees and renders advice on non-qualified deferred compensation arrangements in the U.S. and foreign jurisdictions and compensation matters related to public offerings, acquisitions, and spinoffs.

### POPLAWSKI, Edward G
Sidley Austin LLP, Los Angeles
213 896 6601
epoplawski@sidley.com
*Featured in Intellectual Property (California)*

**Practice Areas:** Partner in Sidley's Los Angeles office, coordinator of the firm's Intellectual Property Litigation practice, and a member of the firm's Executive Committee. Since he began practicing law, he has devoted his practice to intellectual property litigation and predominantly to patent litigation, including jury trials and proceedings before the International Trade Commission (ITC). He has also litigated and tried cases relating to trademark and copyright infringement, trade secret misappropriation and antitrust violations.

**Personal:** Villanova University School of Law, JD, 1983; Drexel University, MS in Electrical Engineering, 1980; Drexel University, BS in Electrical Engineering, 1980, summa cum laude.

### PORTERFIELD, Curtis D
Hunton & Williams LLP, Los Angeles
213 532 2176
cporterfield@hunton.com
*Featured in Insurance (California)*

**Practice Areas:** Curtis Porterfield's practice includes representation of corporate insureds in insurance recovery matters ranging from policy analysis and negotiation to the most complex insurance recovery litigation. His experience includes complex environmental, aerospace, alien tort claims and global warming issues, to name a few. A frequent author and speaker, he has been recognized by Chambers in Insurance Recovery and as a Los Angeles Super Lawyer in every year they have published. In addition to insurance recovery, Curtis has litigated a broad variety of complex business and intellectual property matters, including anticompetitive practices, entertainment, and copyright and trademark issues.

### PRAITIS, Judith
Sidley Austin LLP, Los Angeles
213 896 6637
jpraitis@sidley.com
*Featured in Environment (California)*

**Practice Areas:** Partner in Sidley's Los Angeles office, head of the West Coast Environmental practice and a global co-chair of the firm's Environmental practice. She has broad experience in counseling clients on environmental transactional issues and on air, water and waste management permitting, compliance, release reporting and enforcement issues under California and federal law. She has helped clients develop and implement environmental management systems, audit protocols and confront emerging regulatory environments, such as California's new regulatory regime targeted at greenhouse gas emissions (the California Global Warming Solutions Act of 2006). She routinely advises clients on Proposition 65 matters.

### PRAW, Douglas
Goodwin Procter LLP, Los Angeles
213 426 2664
dpraw@goodwinprocter.com
*Featured in Real Estate (California)*

**Practice Areas:** Mr Praw is a member of the Real Estate, REITs & Real Estate Capital Markets Group and has extensive experience in a wide range of real estate and public finance matters. He has provided counsel to the spectrum of real estate investors, from developers, owners and borrowers to underwriters and municipalities, special districts and other governmental agencies. His acquisition/disposition work includes representation of CommonWealth Partners LLC and its affiliate Fifth Street Properties, in one of the largest real estate transactions in California at the time.

**Personal:** JD, Southwestern University, 2002; BS, Washington University in St. Louis, 1998.

### PRESANT, Sanford C
Greenberg Traurig, LLP, Santa Monica
310 586 7855
PresantS@gtlaw.com
*Featured in Tax (California)*

**Practice Areas:** Chair, Real Estate Fund Practice. Real estate investment trusts (REITs); tax.

**Career:** Selected: California Super Lawyers magazine, 2007-08, 2010-13; Best Lawyers in America, 2008-13; Who's Who in American Law. Rated, AV® Preeminent™ 5.0 out of 5.

**Publications:** Co-Author: 'Carried Interest Proposal Resurfaces, With Changes, in the Job Bill', Pension Real Estate Association Quarterly, Winter 2012; 'Tax Aspects of Real Estate Investments,' two-volume treatise, Thompson West Publishing (2009 Ed.).

**Personal:** LLM, Taxation, Georgetown University Law Center, 1981; JD, cum laude, State University of New York at Buffalo Law School, 1976; BA, Cornell University, 1973.

### PRINGLE, Robert B
Winston & Strawn LLP, San Francisco
415 591 1420
rpringle@winston.com
*Featured in Antitrust (California)*

**Practice Areas:** Mr Pringle's practice focuses on antitrust, trade regulation, and litigation.

**Career:** Mr Pringle represents clients on a range of antitrust matters in state and federal courts and before administrative tribunals. He is particularly experienced handling cases involving unfair competition, securities, and complex business litigation. Mr Pringle also participates in criminal grand jury matters, contested mergers, and many types of civil litigation, including trade secrets and other intellectual property claims, contract disputes, fraud, and RICO claims. In 2010, Mr Pringle was named "Antitrust Lawyer of the Year" by the California State Bar Antitrust & Unfair Competition Section.

### RABINOVITZ, Joel
Irell & Manella, Los Angeles
310 203 7551
jrabinovitz@irell.com
*Featured in Tax (California)*

**Practice Areas:** Joel Rabinovitz is a partner emeritus at Irell & Manella and a member of the firm's tax practice. Mr Rabinovitz has represented numerous foreign investors in connection with their transactions in the United States and both growing technology companies and major U.S. multinationals in connection with their international tax planning. Prior to joining the firm, Mr Rabinovitz was a professor of law at the University of California, Los Angeles, and deputy international tax counsel at the U.S. Department of Treasury.

**Personal:** Harvard University (LLB, magna cum laude); Cornell University (BA).

### RADCLIFFE, Mark F
DLA Piper LLP (US), East Palo Alto
650 833 2266
mark.radcliffe@dlapiper.com
*Featured in Outsourcing (Nationwide), IT & Outsourcing (California)*

**Practice Areas:** IT & Outsourcing.

**Professional Memberships:** Founder, South Bay Trademark Lawyer's Association.

**Career:** His practice focuses on strategic intellectual property advice, private financing, corporate partnering, software licensing, internet licensing, and copyrights and trademark. He is listed in The International Who's Who of Internet, e-Commerce and Data Protection Lawyers and in numerous other guides. In 2009 and 2010, Intellectual Asset magazine named him among the "IAM 250 - The World's Leading IP Strategists."

**Personal:** JD, Harvard University; BS, University of Michigan (magna cum laude).

### RAFATJOO, Hamid
Venable LLP, Los Angeles
310 229 0308
hrrafatjoo@Venable.com
*Featured in Bankruptcy/Restructuring (California)*

**Practice Areas:** Bankruptcy and Creditors' Rights, Corporate, Litigation.

**Career:** Mr Rafatjoo focuses his practice on insolvency and corporate restructurings, corporate transactions, and mergers and acquisitions, either through out-of-court workouts or chapter 11 filings. He represents clients in complex reorganizations throughout the United States. His clients represent a broad spectrum of industries, including entertainment, retail, manufacturing, real estate and hospitality. Prior to joining private practice, he served as a judicial law clerk for the Honorable John E. Ryan, United States

Bankruptcy Court for the Central District of California.
**Personal:** JD, Loyola Law School; BA, cum laude, University of California at Irvine.

## RAINS, Jay
DLA Piper LLP (US), San Diego
858 677 1476
jay.rains@dlapiper.com
*Featured in Corporate/M&A (Southern California)*
**Practice Areas:** Corporate/M&A, Aviation, Communications, Finance, Private Equity, Capital Markets, Life Sciences.
**Career:** He is a member of the firm's Global Board, Executive Committee and Policy Committee and a member of the firm's US Office of the Chair. His practice concentrates on corporate finance, venture capital, strategic partnering, SEC registered public offerings, and mergers and acquisitions.
**Personal:** JD, University of Notre Dame (summa cum laude); BA, College of the Holy Cross (cum laude).

## RANSOM, Rollin A
Sidley Austin LLP, Los Angeles
213 896 6047
rransom@Sidley.com
*Featured in Intellectual Property (California)*
**Practice Areas:** Rollin Ransom is a partner in Sidley's Los Angeles office, where he is co-head of the litigation group. He represents individuals and corporations, including leading media companies, in copyright infringement, trademark infringement, trade secret, software, entertainment, and unfair competition actions, both in prosecuting and defending against such claims. He also maintains an active practice counseling clients on a wide variety of intellectual property, advertising, and Internet-related matters.
**Personal:** University of Michigan Law School, JD, 1993, magna cum laude, Order of the Coif; Northwestern University, BA, 1990, Phi Beta Kappa.

## RAPPEPORT, Ira J
McDermott Will & Emery LLP, Los Angeles
310 551 9314
irappeport@mwe.com
*Featured in Healthcare (California)*
**Practice Areas:** Experience in transaction work for both for-profit and nonprofit healthcare clients. Practice involves numerous issues relating to acquisitions, divestitures, the formation of joint ventures and other affiliations among healthcare providers, including issues related to new corporate structures, organization and operation of partnerships and LLCs. Focuses on mergers and acquisitions of hospitals, medical imaging companies, physician practices, clinics, and other healthcare providers and facilities.
**Professional Memberships:** American Health Lawyers Association; California Society for Healthcare Attorneys; Healthcare Law Section of the Los Angeles County Bar Association.
**Personal:** Villanova University School of Law (JD, cum laude); Washington University (AB, cum laude).

## RASKIN, Jeffrey S
Morgan, Lewis & Bockius LLP, San Francisco
415 442 1219
jraskin@morganlewis.com
*Featured in Insurance (California)*
**Practice Areas:** Head of Insurance Recovery Practice in San Francisco. Advises clients involved in litigation, arbitration, and mediation in matters related to insurance coverage, environmental disputes, intellectual property disputes, and commercial disputes. Handled insurance matters for underlying securities, environmental, asbestos, silica, toxic tort, product liability, intellectual property, directors and officers, errors and omissions claims, and employment practices; also handled first-party claims for loss covered by physical damage and business interruption policies, title policies, and fidelity/crime policies. Advises corporate insureds on matters connected to the procurement of insurance by auditing insurance assets, structuring commercial insurance programs, and identifying potential legal issues.

## RAWLINS, Justin
Winston & Strawn LLP, Los Angeles
213 615 1839
jrawlins@winston.com
*Featured in Bankruptcy/Restructuring (California)*
**Practice Areas:** Justin Rawlins principally represents funds, lending institutions, debtors and creditors' committees in a variety of distressed and commercial transactions, including corporate reorganizations, out of court workouts, and acquisitions.
**Professional Memberships:** Co-Chair of the Legislative Section of the Insolvency Law Committee of the State Bar of California, and as a board member of the American Bankruptcy Institute's Southwest Conference.
**Career:** Mr Rawlins is the head of Winston & Strawn's Los Angeles Restructuring & Insolvency Group. He also currently serves as Hiring Partner in the Los Angeles Office.

## RAZZAK, Amr
Skadden, Arps, Slate, Meagher & Flom LLP & Affiliates, Palo Alto
650 470 4533
amr.razzak@skadden.com
*Featured in Corporate/M&A (Northern California)*
**Practice Areas:** Represents clients in domestic and cross-border M&A, joint ventures, investment and capital markets transactions, as well as board and corporate governance matters. Clients include acquirers, target companies, private equity funds, special committees, financial advisors, and underwriters. Representative transactions: Paradigm Ltd. in its $1 billion acquisition by Apax Partners L.P. and JMI Equity; Advantest in its $1.1 billion unsolicited proposal to acquire Verigy, PMC-Sierra in its acquisition of Wintegra, Yahoo! in $45 billion unsolicited proposal from Microsoft.
**Career:** JD, Georgetown University Law Center, 1998 (cum laude); MSFS, Georgetown University School of Foreign Service, 1998; AB, Brown University, 1986.

## READ, Charles
Jones Day, Los Angeles
213 243 2818
ccread@jonesday.com
*Featured in Energy & Natural Resources (California)*
**Practice Areas:** Charlie Read practices energy and public utilities law in Jones Day's Los Angeles and Washington, D.C. offices. He heads the firm's energy regulatory practice in California, handling matters concerning electric power, telecommunications and pipelines in state and federal court and before the Federal Energy Regulatory Commission, the California Public Utilities Commission and other state commissions. His clients include public utilities, renewable and fossil fuel power producers, energy marketers and traders as well as investors and lenders in these sectors. Charlie has taught a course on energy law at the UCLA Law School.

## REAMER, David C
Skadden, Arps, Slate, Meagher & Flom LLP & Affiliates, Los Angeles
213 687 5052
david.reamer@skadden.com
*Featured in Banking & Finance (California), Banking & Finance (Nationwide)*
**Practice Areas:** A member of the firm's Banking Group. Has participated in numerous financing transactions, representing lenders, investors, borrowers and equity sponsors in a wide range of transactions encompassing a diversity of industries, including media, telecommunications, real estate, gaming, energy and manufacturing. Such transactions have included secured lending transactions, acquisition financings, high-yield offerings, bridge financings, debtor-in-possession financings, workouts, restructurings and project financings.
**Career:** JD, Columbia University School of Law, 1989 (Harlan Fiske Stone Scholar); BA, Emory University, 1985.

## REDCAY, Ronald
Arnold & Porter LLP, Los Angeles
213 243 4002
Ronald.Redcay@aporter.com
*Featured in Antitrust (California)*
**Practice Areas:** Ronald Redcay has won antitrust cases at all levels of both federal and state courts, and has extensive experience in defending antitrust class actions and State Attorney General lawsuits. He currently represents defendants in antitrust and unfair competition cases pending in several federal district courts and in California state courts, and provides counseling to a number of companies on cutting-edge antitrust issues. He also teaches antitrust law and successfully argued an antitrust case before the Supreme Court of the United States.

## REDDICK, C N Franklin
Akin Gump Strauss Hauer & Feld LLP, Los Angeles
310 728 3204
freddick@akingump.com
*Featured in Corporate/M&A (Southern California)*
**Practice Areas:** Co-head, firmwide corporate practice. Has more than 25 years of experience in mergers and acquisitions, corporate finance and public company representations. Represents strategic and financial buyers and sellers in public and private M&A transactions. Represents issuers and institutional investors in public and private debt and equity offerings, restructurings and other financing transactions and advises public companies on securities, corporate governance and other corporate matters.
**Personal:** BA with high honors and great distinction, California State University at San Jose (1977); JD, University of California, Hastings College of the Law, Order of the Coif (1980).

## REINES, Edward R
Weil, Gotshal & Manges LLP, Silicon Valley
650 802 3022
edward.reines@weil.com
*Featured in Intellectual Property (California)*
**Practice Areas:** Edward Reines is a partner in Weil's Patent Litigation Practice, influential both in and out of the courtroom. He chairs the Federal Circuit's Advisory Council and chairs both the Patent Rules Advisory Committee for the Northern District of California and the National Model Jury Instructions Project. He teaches a patent litigation course at Boalt Hall School of Law and Stanford Law School.

## REISNER, Jeffrey M
Irell & Manella, Los Angeles
310 203 7642
jreisner@irell.com
*Featured in Bankruptcy/Restructuring (California)*
**Practice Areas:** Jeffrey Reisner is a partner at Irell & Manella, Chair of the Bankruptcy, Reorganization and Creditors' Rights practice and served on the firm's Executive Committee. Mr Reisner represents companies and high net-worth individuals reorganizing their financial affairs, and as creditors of others in financial distress. He also represents creditors' committees, sellers/acquirers of assets, investors and creditors in bankruptcy and out of court restructurings. Mr Reisner is a Fellow of the American College of Bankruptcy, a member of several professional associations and recipient of various professional recognitions.
**Personal:** New York University (JD/MBA); Cornell University (BS, Industrial and Labor Relations).

## RESSLER, Alison S
Sullivan & Cromwell LLP, Los Angeles
310 712 6630
resslera@sullcrom.com
*Featured in Capital Markets (California), Corporate/M&A (California), Corporate/M&A (Southern California)*
**Professional Memberships:** ABA; CSBA; LACBA.
**Career:** Partner since 1991. Management Committee; Co-head, Global Private Equity Group. Advises corporations, private equity investors, boards and financial advisers on diverse transactions in regulated/unregulated industries. Also advises boards on corporate governance/proxy fights. M&A: Cymer-ASML; Valeant-Medicis; Ares/Teachers-Serta-Simmons Bedding-Advent; Savers-Leonard Green/TPG;

Versa Capital-Central Parking-Standard Parking; Skype/Silver Lake-Microsoft; Valeant-Cephalon; Biovail-Valeant; Central Pacific Financial-Carlyle/Anchorage Capital; Barclays-BGI; Colony Capital-First Republic; Ares/Teachers-Simmons Bedding; Hilton Hotels-Blackstone; Fender-Kaman; Chrysalis-Central Parking; Clear Channel-THL/Bain; HCPI-CNL Retirement; Mattel-Radica; Hilton Hotels Corporation-Hilton Group hotels; Novartis-Chiron. Corporate: acquisition financing, high-yield offerings, debt/equity offerings for REITS, rights offerings, convertible/exchangeable offerings.
**Personal:** Columbia Law (JD, 1983); Brown (BA, 1980).

## RICHLAND, Kent L
Greines, Martin, Stein & Richland LLP, Los Angeles
310 859 7811
krichland@gmsr.com
*Featured in Litigation (California)*
**Practice Areas:** Appellate law.
**Professional Memberships:** California Academy of Appellate Lawyers; American Academy of Appellate Lawyers.
**Career:** Kent Richland, one of the leaders of GMSR's active United States Supreme Court practice, has been lead attorney in hundreds of state and federal appeals involving a wide variety of areas of civil law. His high-profile victories have resulted in his twice being named a California Lawyer of the Year by the State Bar's California Lawyer Magazine. He is frequently asked by the media to comment on appellate matters and often appears as a featured speaker to law student, bar and judges groups.

## RICHMAN, James D
Arnold & Porter LLP, Los Angeles
213 243 4210
James.Richman@aporter.com
*Featured in Real Estate (California)*
**Practice Areas:** James Richman is a Partner in the Real Estate Practice Group. For over 30 years, Mr Richman has negotiated a wide variety of real estate deals, including the purchase and sale of and joint ventures for commercial properties such as office buildings, farms, and medical office and research buildings. He has represented clients in the acquisition of land for the development of subdivisions, shopping centers and office buildings. His clients turn to him for his deep experience with loans; long-term ground leases; commercial, industrial, retail and data center leases; construction and design contracts; workouts; and land use entitlements.

## RIECHERT, Melinda S
Morgan, Lewis & Bockius LLP, Palo Alto
650 843 7530
mriechert@morganlewis.com
*Featured in Labor & Employment (California)*
**Practice Areas:** Melinda Riechert is a partner in Morgan Lewis's Labor and Employment Practice. She specializes in litigation and arbitration of employment disputes for a number of major high-technology and other companies, including defending companies in wage and hour,

wrongful termination, discrimination, and sexual harassment disputes. She also counsels employers on how to avoid litigation.
**Personal:** Attended Stanford Law School, JD, Order of the Coif; University College, London University, LLB, First in Class.

## RINGLER, Michael S
Kirkland & Ellis LLP, San Francisco
415 439 1978
mike.ringler@kirkland.com
*Featured in Corporate/M&A (Northern California)*
**Practice Areas:** Mike Ringler represents business enterprises in a wide range of M&A transactions, including strategic mergers and corporate consolidation transactions, acquisitions and sales of companies, business carveout acquisitions and divestitures, as well as public tender and exchange offers. Mike frequently advises boards of directors, special committees and management teams in connection with public company going private transactions. Mike also advises public companies regarding preparedness for, and responses to, unsolicited acquisition proposals, hostile takeovers, proxy contests and other contests for corporate control.
**Personal:** Georgetown University Law Center, JD, cum laude, 1995; University of Michigan, BS, magna cum laude, 1992.

## RISHWAIN, James
Pillsbury Winthrop Shaw Pittman LLP, Los Angeles
213 488 7111
jrishwain@pillsburylaw.com
*Featured in Real Estate (California)*
**Practice Areas:** Mr Rishwain is Pillsbury's Firm Chair and CEO, and former leader of the firm wide Real Estate Practice, and has extensive transactional experience with emphasis in sophisticated real estate matters including acquisitions, development, finance, capital markets, REITs for high value projects of all types throughout the world. His many honors include the 2005 California Lawyer Attorneys of the Year Award. He has published several market leading articles and serves the community in many ways.
**Personal:** JD, Pepperdine, 1984, cum laude, Moot Court Honor Board, note comment editor Pepperdine Law Review; BA, UCLA, 1981, honors.

## ROBERTS, Gary M
SNR Denton, Los Angeles
213 892 5005
gary.roberts@dentons.com
*Featured in Environment (California)*
**Practice Areas:** Extensive complex litigation, advocacy and counseling experience regarding environmental law, product liability and false advertising matters. Substantial Proposition 65, enforcement response and permitting experience, along with state and federal agency dealings. Class action experience related to chemical exposure issues. Consistently represents Fortune 500 companies and major trade associations.
**Personal:** Stanford Law School, JD, (Articles Editor, Stanford Law Review); Princeton University, cum laude, A.B. Clerk, David R.

Thompson, 9th U.S. Circuit Court of Appeals, 1987-1988.

## ROCCA, Brian C.
Bingham McCutchen LLP, San Francisco
415 393 2394
brian.rocca@bingham.com
*Featured in Antitrust (California)*
**Practice Areas:** Co-chair of Bingham's E-Discovery Practice. Has worked on high-stakes litigation in both civil and criminal contexts in a wide range of industries. Regularly advises clients in connection with governmental antitrust investigations and provides counseling to a prominent trade association relating to alcohol distribution issues. Has litigated numerous complex civil and appellate litigation matters and has significant trial experience. Advises clients on cutting-edge electronic discovery and document retention issues and has litigated several high-profile electronic discovery disputes.
**Personal:** University of Virginia School of Law, Juris Doctor, 2002; University of California, Davis, Bachelor of Arts, 1999.

## ROGERS, Randy
Winston & Strawn LLP, San Francisco
415 591 1406
rrogers@winston.com
*Featured in Bankruptcy/Restructuring (California)*
**Practice Areas:** Representation of financial institutions in commercial transactions, loan workouts and debt restructurings, and chapter 11 cases. Areas of specialized expertise: agriculture; food and beverage; healthcare; real estate.
**Professional Memberships:** Fellow of American College of Bankruptcy. Commercial Finance Committee of ABA. California State Bar Committees on Uniform Commercial Code and Agribusiness.
**Publications:** Books: Collier Farm Bankruptcy Guide (Matthew Bender; 1st ed. 1987; 2nd ed. 1997). Taking Security Interests in Personal Property (Californa CEB 2005). Treatises: Contributor to Collier on Bankruptcy, Collier Bankruptcy Practice Guide, and Collier Bankruptcy Manual. Member, Collier Board of Editors.

## ROHRER, Paul
Loeb & Loeb LLP, Los Angeles
310 282 2270
prohrer@loeb.com
*Featured in Real Estate (California)*
**Practice Areas:** Represents governmental entities, nonprofit educational institutions and developers in land use and entitlement matters in acquisition, sale, optioning and ground leasing of real property and in the making of various agreements, including joint development agreements, owner participation agreements, and construction-related agreements. Works extensively with public/private transactions, air-rights transfers and the creation of special use districts for signage. Rohrer has appeared in front of city councils, planning and architectural commissions, and community redevelopment agency boards in support of his clients' projects.

**Personal:** Yale Law School (JD, 2002); UCLA (BA, summa cum laude, 1999).

## ROLSTON, Chad G.
Latham & Watkins LLP, Silicon Valley
650 463 3079
chad.rolston@lw.com
*Featured in Corporate/M&A (Northern California)*
**Practice Areas:** Associate in Corporate Department. Practice focuses primarily on mergers and acquisitions, where he represents both publicly traded and privately held companies in strategic corporate transactions, as well as private equity funds and their portfolio companies in connection with public and private mergers, leveraged buyouts, acquisitions and dispositions, and general corporate transactional matters.
**Career:** Served in various sales and engineering roles in the enterprise software industry.
**Personal:** BS, American University; JD, Harvard Law School.

## ROMÁN GRIFFITH, Marissa
Akin Gump Strauss Hauer & Feld LLP, Los Angeles
310 552 6408
mroman@akingump.com
*Featured in Media & Entertainment (California)*
**Practice Areas:** Marissa Román Griffith concentrates on media finance and other entertainment transactions, representing domestic and foreign financial institutions, borrowers, distributors and others involved in various aspects of the financing, distribution and production of film and television projects, including multinational tax and co-production arrangements.
**Professional Memberships:** Co-Chair, Entertainment Law Section, Beverly Hills Bar Association (2004-06).
**Career:** Best Lawyer, "Media and Entertainment", 2012 Euromoney Legal Media Group Americas Women in Business Law Awards; "Legal Eagle", Variety magazine's 2012 "Dealmakers Impact Report."
**Personal:** AB, Art History, Princeton University; JD, Stanford Law School.

## ROSE, Stephen
Munger, Tolles & Olson LLP, Los Angeles
213 683 9268
Stephen.Rose@mto.com
*Featured in Tax (California)*
**Practice Areas:** Practice concentrates on the structuring and taxation aspects of complex business transactions. Representations include: Berkshire Hathaway in its acquisitions of H.J. Heinz Company and Oriental Trading Co.; Air Lease Corp. in its IPO on the New York Stock Exchange; The Yucaipa Cos. in the acquisition of a minority interest in Relativity Media.
**Professional Memberships:** Executive Planning Committee, USC Tax Institute (chair); NYU Tax Institute Planning Committee.
**Career:** Partner at the firm.
**Personal:** New York University School of Law (LLM); U.C. Hastings College of the Law (JD); U.C. Berkeley (MBA); U.C. San Diego (BA).

## ROSENBAUM, Gary B
McDermott Will & Emery LLP, Los Angeles
310 284 6133
grosenbaum@mwe.com
*Featured in Banking & Finance (California)*
**Practice Areas:** Concentrates on commercial and corporate finance, private equity and mezzanine investments, workouts and restructurings, and venture lending and leasing. Extensive experience serving as lead counsel for financial institutions on leveraged finance tranactions, including senior and subordinated loans, debtor-in-possession financings, acquisition financings, and troubled loan negotiations and workouts, as well as representing borrowers in secured loan transactions, creditors and debtors in Chapter 11 cases, and buyers and sellers of distressed companies.
**Personal:** JD, UCLA School of Law; BA, Northwestern University.

## ROSS, Jane
Weil, Gotshal & Manges LLP, Silicon Valley
jane.ross@weil.com
*Featured in Corporate/M&A (Northern California)*
**Practice Areas:** Jane Ross is a partner in the Mergers and Acquisitions Practice Group. She has represented acquirers and targets in numerous acquisitions of both public and private companies in the information technology, healthcare and life sciences sectors. She also has extensive experience handling cross-border transactions and complex cross-border joint ventures. Ms Ross' representative clients include Adobe Systems, Dell, eBay, Facebook, Gilead Sciences, Onyx Pharmaceuticals, and salesforce.com.

## ROTHMAN, Rick R
Bingham McCutchen LLP, Los Angeles
213 680 6590
rick.rothman@bingham.com
*Featured in Environment (California)*
**Practice Areas:** Office managing partner of Bingham's Los Angeles office and co-chair of the firm's Environmental and Natural Resources Practice Group. Practice encompasses broad range of environmental and energy laws, including those concerning air quality (stationary and mobile sources), water quality, power plant siting, hazardous substances, impacted properties and Proposition 65. Has experience counseling clients in a number of contexts, including threatened enforcement actions, variance requests, permitting and appeals, due diligence reviews, and meeting state and federal reporting and warning requirements.
**Personal:** Georgetown University Law Center, JD, cum laude, 1989; University of Michigan, BA, 1985.

## ROUX, G Christian
Alston & Bird LLP, Los Angeles
213 576 1103
chris.roux@alston.com
*Featured in Construction (California)*
**Practice Areas:** Represents construction owners, contractors and construction-related service providers with public and private projects involving infrastructure, commercial, industrial and residential works of improvement. Counsels clients with project planning, procurement, drafting and negotiating contracts and claims avoidance. Substantial experience litigating large construction disputes involving claims for extra work, delay, disruption and acceleration.
**Professional Memberships:** California Bar, Washington, D.C. Bar, ABA, Construction Forum; CMAA, Washington, D.C. Chapter (Co-chair Governmental Affairs Committee).
**Career:** Co-chair, Construction and Government Contracts Group.
**Publications:** Co-Author, 'California School Facilities Planning, A Guide to Laws and Procedures for Funding, Siting, Design and Construction'. Author: 'Construction Contract Pass-Through Clauses'.

## RUBALCAVA, Sharon
Alston & Bird LLP, Los Angeles
213 576 1105
sharon.rubalcava@alston.com
*Featured in Environment (California)*
**Practice Areas:** Focuses on air and water quality, toxic emissions, and permitting of major industrial and infrastructure projects, including NEPA/CEQA compliance. Counsels on rulemaking, compliance, permitting, and enforcement actions before a variety of environmental agencies.
**Professional Memberships:** Past Chair, Air Quality Subcommittee, ABA Section on Natural Resources, Energy and Environmental Law. Member, Los Angeles County Bar Association, Environmental Section.
**Career:** Appointed by the Mayor of Los Angeles to the No Net Increase Task Force to reduce emissions from the Port of Los Angeles.
**Personal:** JD, University of California, Los Angeles, 1975; AB, University of California, Los Angeles, 1968.

## RUBIN, Aaron P.
Morrison & Foerster LLP, San Francisco
415 268 6809
arubin@mofo.com
*Featured in IT & Outsourcing (California)*
**Practice Areas:** Aaron Rubin focuses on matters involving intellectual property and technology, including structuring and negotiating license agreements, supply agreements, technology transfers, joint development agreements, IT and business process outsourcing transactions, and other intellectual property and commercial matters relevant to software, hardware, electronic commerce, and other advanced information technology businesses. Mr Rubin regularly advises clients on the intellectual property aspects of their M&A transactions. He also advises clients on legal issues in the areas of social media, e-commerce and other online business models, such as those involving media sharing, user-generated content, social networking, data aggregation and collection, and paid search.

## RUBY, Allen J
Skadden, Arps, Slate, Meagher & Flom LLP & Affiliates, Palo Alto
650 470 4590
allen.ruby@skadden.com
*Featured in Litigation (Nationwide), Litigation (California)*
See under Nationwide for profile.

## RUCK, Charles K
Latham & Watkins LLP, Costa Mesa
714 540 1235
charles.ruck@lw.com
*Featured in Corporate/M&A (Southern California)*
**Practice Areas:** Mergers and acquisitions, capital markets, and general corporate and securities matters. Regularly represents boards of directors in critical transactions, investigations and governance matters. M&A transactions include public company mergers, hostile takeovers, going-private transactions and other strategic acquisitions and divestitures. Corporate finance work includes public and private offerings of both debt and equity securities, representing issuers and underwriters.
**Career:** Latham Executive Committee (2006-10); Clerk – US Court of Appeals; Office of US Trade Representative at World Trade Organization (Geneva).
**Personal:** JD, University of Michigan (Editor Law Review); BA, University of California (Phi Beta Kappa).

## RUHLAND, Christopher
Dechert LLP, Los Angeles
213 808 5714
christopher.ruhland@dechert.com
*Featured in Litigation (California)*
**Practice Areas:** Mr Ruhland represents clients in business disputes and intellectual property matters in a variety of industries including media and entertainment, financial, technology, transportation and healthcare.
**Career:** Former in-house counsel at The Walt Disney Company.
**Personal:** University of California, Irvine (BA, 1991, cum laude); University of California Los Angeles School of Law (JD, 1994, managing editor, UCLA Law Review).

## RUTHERFORD, Jeffrey
Crowell & Moring LLP, Los Angeles
213 622 4750
jrutherford@crowell.com
*Featured in Litigation (California)*
**Practice Areas:** Partner in Crowell & Moring's White Collar & Regulatory Enforcement Group. Focuses practice in white-collar criminal defense. He has defended individuals in a wide array of white-collar criminal matters, including public corruption, tax fraud, health care fraud, procurement fraud, money laundering, bribery, conflict of interest, antitrust, theft of trade secrets, off-label marketing, FCPA, securities fraud and cyber crimes. He has been lead counsel on 12 jury trials and has argued and briefed numerous cases before the Ninth Circuit Court of Appeals.

**Personal:** BA from University of Michigan; JD from University of Minnesota Law School, with honors.

## SACKS, Robert A
Sullivan & Cromwell LLP, Los Angeles
310 712 6640
sacksr@sullcrom.com
*Featured in Securities (Nationwide), Litigation (California)*
**Professional Memberships:** Member, California and New York Bars; ABA; LACBA.
**Career:** Partner since 1990. Extensive experience in wide range of complex business disputes. Represents clients in securities, M&A, antitrust, contracts, corporate governance, investigations and IP matters. Appears in federal/state courts, arbitrations, and before SEC and other agencies. Has handled numerous trials and appeals. Clients: JPMorgan Chase, Cablevision, Goldman Sachs, j2 Global Communications, Collective Brands, Amgen, Bank of Tokyo-Mitsubishi, Philips Electronics, Stifel Niclaus, Solvay, Softbank, Thomas Weisel and VeriFone.
**Personal:** University of Texas Law School (JD, 1982); Harvard University (AB, 1979).

## SAGERMAN, Eric E
Winston & Strawn LLP, Los Angeles
213 615 1829
esagerman@winston.com
*Featured in Bankruptcy/Restructuring (California)*
**Practice Areas:** Mr Sagerman is Chair of the firm's national Restructuring Practice and Managing Partner of its Los Angeles office. He has extensive experience representing debtors, secured creditors, official committees, and a variety of other constituents in complex reorganizations.
**Career:** Mr Sagerman was previously a Partner with the law firm of Murphy Sheneman Julian & Rogers, and received his JD from the University of California at Los Angeles in 1991.
**Publications:** Mr Sagerman is a frequent author and lecturer on topics of insolvency law, and he is co-author with Patrick A. Murphy of the treatise Creditors' Rights in Bankruptcy.

## SALAMONE, Mary
Atkinson, Andelson, Loya, Ruud & Romo, Irvine
949 453 4260
msalamone@aalrr.com
*Featured in Construction (California)*
**Practice Areas:** Mary Salamone has dedicated her entire career exclusively to the area of construction law and has acquired an in-depth knowledge regarding all aspects of construction projects and disputes on behalf of owners and contractors. Her practice encompasses a wide array of construction industry matters such as competitive bidding, contract drafting and negotiations, scheduling and delay issues, defaults/terminations, change order management and statutory payment claims.
**Professional Memberships:** Construction Management Association of America. Western Council of Construction Consumers. Associated Builders and Contractors, Inc. Legal Advisory Subcommittee for the Associated General

Contractors. Neutral on the Large and Complex Case Panel of the American Arbitration Association for construction disputes.
**Publications:** Ms Salamone has authored numerous articles and presented various seminars throughout the US.
**Personal:** University of Rochester - Bachelor of Arts (1984)- Graduated magna cum laude and Phi Beta Kappa. Cornell Law School - Juris Doctor (1987).

### SALTZMAN, Stephen L
Loeb & Loeb LLP, Los Angeles
310 282 2127
ssaltzman@loeb.com
*Featured in Media & Entertainment (California)*
**Practice Areas:** Concentrates on complex international co-production and co-financing transactions including representation of producers, financiers, sales agents and distributors in motion picture and television financing, restructuring and licensing transactions. Utilizes his foreign language capabilities and knowledge of the US and non-US-based film and television industries in representing the interests of international companies and individuals in Hollywood.
**Career:** Partner since 1997.
**Publications:** Speaker and panelist in symposiums in the US and Europe, and his German-speaking practice has been profiled in various German publications.
**Personal:** Columbia University (JD, 1986); Georgetown University (BS, magna cum laude, 1982). Fluent in German and Spanish.

### SAMUELS, Joel G
Sidley Austin LLP, Los Angeles
213 896 6030
jsamuels@sidley.com
*Featured in Bankruptcy/Restructuring (California)*
**Practice Areas:** Bankruptcy partner in Sidley's Los Angeles office. Has represented clients in in-court bankruptcy cases and out-of-court restructurings, including secured and unsecured creditors, creditors' committees and debtors. Representations have included Credit Suisse, AT&T, CIT, Radian Asset Assurance, BlackRock, Exelon Corporation, Federal-Mogul, Dynegy Holdings LLC, Wells Fargo and Fortress Investment Group. Particular experience in real estate insolvencies and restructurings, and litigation of contested matters and adversary proceedings.
**Career:** One-year clerkship with the Honorable James R Browning, Chief Judge of the US Court of Appeals, 9th Circuit.
**Personal:** Stanford Law School, JD, 1984, Order of the Coif; Princeton University, AB, 1981.

### SANCHEZ, Terry
Munger, Tolles & Olson LLP, Los Angeles
213 683 9179
Terry.Sanchez@mto.com
*Featured in Labor & Employment (California)*
**Practice Areas:** Employment litigation defense, including class actions, wrongful discharge, and discrimination actions and other employment-related lawsuits. Recent representations: Warner Bros. in settling its lawsuit with actor Charlie

Sheen; Merrill Lynch in wage-and-hour and forced patronage class actions.
**Professional Memberships:** Los Angeles County Bar Association: Labor and Employment Section; Fellow, College of Labor and Employment Lawyers.
**Career:** Partner at the firm. Named a Top Labor and Employment Lawyer by the Daily Journal in 2012.
**Personal:** Stanford Law School (Order of the Coif); Claremont Men's College (summa cum laude BA).

### SANDERS, Joel S
Gibson, Dunn & Crutcher LLP, San Francisco
415 393 8268
jsanders@gibsondunn.com
*Featured in Antitrust (California)*
**Practice Areas:** Specializes in antitrust litigation and investigations, including class action and private cases, mergers/JVs, counseling, international cartel and other government matters. Matters include federal and state court, Department of Justice, Federal Trade Commission, and international competition authorities. Clients in various industries, including high technology, retail, telecommunications, shipping, consumer services, manufacturing, and professional services.
**Career:** Former law clerk, Honorable Procter Hug Jr of the US Court of Appeals for the Ninth Circuit; former trial attorney in the US Department of Justice's Antitrust Division.
**Personal:** JD, UC Berkeley, Boalt Hall School of Law, 1982, Coif, California Law Review.

### SAVVA, John L
Sullivan & Cromwell LLP, Palo Alto
*Featured in Capital Markets (California)*
**Career:** Managing Partner, Palo Alto office. John has broad public offering, venture capital, M&A and private equity experience involving many clients. He has worked on numerous public and private financings, including initial public offerings, follow-on equity offerings, and convertible and straight debt financings. John represents both underwriters and issuers in a variety of industries, including technology, industrial and consumer products issuers, as well as financial institutions. In addition, he has represented investors and placement agents in numerous venture capital investments.
**Personal:** Partner since 1997. Loyola Law School, JD (summa cum laude)1988. Pitzer College, BA 1985.

### SCHOENHOLZ, William
Buchalter Nemer, Los Angeles
213 891 5004
wschoenholz@buchalter.com
*Featured in Banking & Finance (California)*
**Practice Areas:** Represents banks, commercial finance companies, funds and other institutional investors in complex domestic and international financing transactions ranging from acquisition financing (including leverage buyouts and the financing of tender offers), bridge financing, and working capital financing, typically involving multi-facility secured credit arrangements with

multiple borrowers and cross-border elements. Represents agents in syndicated and club loan transactions, inter-creditor arrangements, and workouts and forbearance arrangements. Represent lenders in private and public foreclosure sales, as well as strict foreclosures, and the exercise of secured creditor remedies under the Uniform Commercial Code.
**Professional Memberships:** Member, Financial Lawyers Conference; Business Law Section, California State Bar; Board of Directors, Inner-City Arts.
**Personal:** USC Law Center, JD; UC Santa Barbara, BA, high honors.

### SCHOPF, Gregory E
Nixon Peabody LLP, San Francisco
415 984 8314
gschopf@nixonpeabody.com
*Featured in Insurance (California)*
**Practice Areas:** Gregory Schopf leads Nixon Peabody's Insurance Industry Team. He regularly represents insurers in insurance coverage and extra-contractual litigation involving most types of policies issued by the industry. He frequently provides coverage advice, claims handling training and policy drafting guidance. Greg also has extensive experience litigating in many jurisdictions and resolving complex business disputes, including theft of trade secrets, breach of contract, complex indemnification issues, bankruptcy, fraud and other tortious conduct. In addition, he is a skilled mediator.
**Personal:** University of California, Hastings College of the Law, JD; University of Portland, BA.

### SCHRADER, David L
Morgan, Lewis & Bockius LLP, Los Angeles
213 612 7370
dschrader@morganlewis.com
*Featured in Litigation (California)*
**Practice Areas:** Managing Partner of the Los Angeles office. Focuses on media sensitive and client critical matters for clients in the energy, manufacturing and life sciences industries, among others. Serves as global litigation strategist to clients in serial litigation. Tried cases in state and federal courts from California to New York. Recently won complete vindication in a civil RICO case described in Corporate Counsel magazine as the company's "worst nightmare." Defeated all claims in their entirety and obtained $2.6 million judgment against the plaintiff.
**Professional Memberships:** Fellow of the American College of Trial Lawyers. Board Member, Center for Civic Mediation.

### SCHROTENBOER, Ronald
Fenwick & West LLP, Mountain View
650 335 7207
rschrotenboer@fenwick.com
*Featured in Tax (California)*
**Practice Areas:** Ronald B Schrotenboer is a partner at Fenwick & West LLP, practicing in the area of taxation. His practice includes both domestic and international federal income tax as well as state income and sales tax. A significant part of his practice includes tax planning for pending transactions. He represents both US-

based companies in domestic and international transactions, as well as foreign-based companies with operations in the US He is also involved with many IRS and state income tax audits, appeals and tax court cases, including § 482 transfer pricing cases.
**Publications:** Mr Schrotenboer has written articles on various tax topics for the Journal of Taxation, Tax Notes, Taxes International, the Journal of State Taxation and other periodicals. He has also spoken for many tax groups including the Alliance for Tax Legal and Accounting Seminars, the Council on International Tax Education and Tax Executive's Institute.

### SCHWARTZ, Tessa
Morrison & Foerster LLP, San Francisco
415 268 7016
tschwartz@mofo.com
*Featured in IT & Outsourcing (California)*
**Practice Areas:** Tessa Schwartz counsels companies on IP issues, and negotiates complex IP and commercial agreements. She advises on a range of strategic transactions, including patent licenses and acquisitions, technology procurement agreements, and complex development, collaboration, strategic alliance, joint venture, and distribution deals. Ms Schwartz also advises companies on the IP aspects of their M&A transactions, and on IP and technology-related disputes. Her clients include telecommunications, wireless, software, hardware, consumer electronics and products, semiconductor, renewable energy, social media, Internet, and other companies. Ms Schwartz is Co-Head of the firm's Technology Transactions Group and Co-Chair of the firm's Cleantech practice.

### SCHWARTZ, William
Morrison & Foerster LLP, San Francisco
415 268 7449
wschwartz@mofo.com
*Featured in IT & Outsourcing (California)*
**Practice Areas:** Represents companies in business transactions/counseling involving IP and technology, including license and development agreements, distribution and commercial activities, and joint ventures. Particularly active in transactional/counseling matters relating to computers, mobile phones and other communications equipment, open source and other software, the Internet, e-commerce and other advanced information technology plus a wide variety of patent licensing matters.
**Career:** Worked in Tokyo and Hong Kong as a reporter and editor for the Asian edition of The Wall Street Journal from 1977 to 1980.
**Personal:** BA, Amherst College, 1976; JD, University of Chicago Law School, 1983.

### SCULL, Nancy
McKenna Long & Aldridge LLP, San Diego
619 699 2457
nscull@mckennalong.com
*Featured in Real Estate (California)*
**Practice Areas:** Nancy Scull represents commercial, industrial, retail and residential developers in all real property transactions. She has a special expertise in mixed use projects, condominium

projects and DRE regulatory matters. She represents publicly held developers, urban high-rise and mixed-use developers, and developers of master planned communities in developing and processing projects and implementing programs to minimize liability. She works with master developers of major communities and urban town centers, advising them on planning, development and long-term governance of their communities and the sale of parcels for merchant builders.

### SELEGUE, Sean
Arnold & Porter LLP, San Francisco
415 471 3169
Sean.SeLegue@aporter.com
*Featured in Litigation (California)*
**Practice Areas:** Sean SeLegue is a business litigation partner and member of the firm's Appellate Practice Group. After clerking at the Ninth Circuit in 1991-92, he has personally argued more than 20 appeals. His notable cases include major construction disputes, partnership disputes in investment management firms, class action litigation, disputes over settlement agreements, unfair competition, real estate, family law and professional liability. He is certified as an appellate specialist by the State Bar of California Board of Legal Specialization.

### SELWYN, Mark D
WilmerHale, Palo Alto
650 858 6031
mark.selwyn@wilmerhale.com
*Featured in Intellectual Property (California)*
**Practice Areas:** Partner in WilmerHale's Litigation/Controversy Department, Co-Chair of the Intellectual Property Litigation Practice Group. Has represented clients in more than thirty patent and other intellectual property cases in federal courts throughout the country and before the International Trade Commission. He has litigated electrical, chemical, mechanical, biotech, software and business method patents.
**Career:** Admitted in California, Massachusetts Bar and New York. Served as law clerk to Hon Naomi Reice Buchwald on the US District Court for the Southern District of New York prior to joining the firm in 1994.
**Personal:** Columbia Law School (JD); Harvard College (AB, magna cum laude).

### SENEKER, Carl (Kim)
Morrison & Foerster LLP, San Francisco
415 268 6619
cseneker@mofo.com
*Featured in Real Estate (California)*
**Practice Areas:** Extensive experience in commercial real estate transactions, secured-debt restructuring and creditors' rights, environmental law, zoning, and land use regulation. Negotiates/documents a variety of substantial real estate debt/equity transactions, with expertise in hotel properties, senior living complexes, property portfolio acquisitions/dispositions, and syndicated financings.
**Professional Memberships:** Member and past President, American College of Real Estate Lawyers; Member, American College of Mortgage

Attorneys, Anglo-American Real Property Institute.
**Career:** Admitted to practice in California.
**Personal:** AB, Stanford University, 1964; JD, Boalt Hall School of Law, 1967. Law clerk, associate Justice William Douglas, US Supreme Court, (1967-68).

### SFREGOLA, Michael F
Gibson, Dunn & Crutcher LLP, Los Angeles
213 229 7558
msfregola@gibsondunn.com
*Featured in Real Estate (California)*
**Practice Areas:** Experience includes structuring of acquisition and financing of hotel, resort, commercial, industrial and residential properties, including multi-jurisdiction and major portfolio acquisitions from private and public sellers in U.S. and Asia. Accomplished tax lawyer, representing domestic and foreign institutional investors, including private equity funds, sovereign wealth funds, and traded and non-traded REITs, in connection with structured finance transactions, mergers, divestitures and workouts, and tax planning with respect to real estate joint ventures.
**Publications:** Lectures on real estate joint ventures and tax and legal issues affecting private equity funds.
**Personal:** JD, University of Southern California, Order of the Coif, 1979.

### SHAPIRO, Jonathan A
WilmerHale, Palo Alto
650 858 6101
jonathan.shapiro@wilmerhale.com
*Featured in Litigation (California)*
**Practice Areas:** Partner, Securities Department; member, Securities Litigation and Enforcement Practice Group. Represents public and financial services companies, officers, directors, investment bankers in matters involving allegations of fraud and breach of fiduciary duty. Defends and conducts internal investigation for subjects of enforcement action by SEC, DOJ, FINRA and other government agencies and self-regulatory organizations.
**Career:** Admitted to California and Massachusetts Bar. Served as law clerk to Hon. Joseph A. DiClerico Jr., US District Court for the District of New Hampshire prior to joining the firm in 1996.
**Personal:** Boston College Law School (JD); Brandeis University (BA, cum laude).

### SHARF, Jesse
Gibson, Dunn & Crutcher LLP, Los Angeles
310 552 8512
JSharf@gibsondunn.com
*Featured in Real Estate (Nationwide), Real Estate (California)*
See under Nationwide for profile.

### SHARRON, Stephanie L
Orrick, Herrington & Sutcliffe LLP, Menlo Park
650 289 7124
ssharron@orrick.com
*Featured in IT & Outsourcing (California)*
**Career:** Ms Sharron is co-chair of the Technology Transactions and Sourcing practice at

Orrick Herrington & Sutcliffe. Ms Sharron advises clients at all stages of maturity on the issues that apply to their business models in light of the rapid changes in business, technology, and law. Ms Sharron counsels companies in connection with technology and intellectual property transactions and related privacy, data security and Internet safety issues. Ms Sharron has represented companies across industries and technologies, including online businesses, software, hardware, mobile, Internet, e-commerce, cloud computing, digital media, retail, automotive, life sciences, cleantech, semiconductor and other technologies.

### SHEMANO, David B
Peitzman Weg LLP, Los Angeles
310 712 0051
dshemano@peitzmanweg.com
*Featured in Bankruptcy/Restructuring (California)*
**Practice Areas:** Represents chapter 11 debtors, creditors' committees, trustees, secured creditors and general unsecured creditors. Leading roles in Halcyon Holding, Club Ventures/David Barton Gym, Pollo West Corp./Mi Pollo. In-depth industry experience in real estate, entertainment, franchising and manufacturing.
**Professional Memberships:** President, Financial Lawyers Conference; Board of Governors, Los Angeles Bankruptcy Forum; Former Member of the Board of Governors, Past Chair of Executive Committee of the Bankruptcy Section, Beverly Hills Bar Association.
**Publications:** Bloomberg Law Reports-Bankruptcy Law, Related bankruptcy program publications for Beverly Hills Bar Association, Los Angeles County Bar Association, American Bankruptcy Institute, Urban Land Institute.

### SHIMADA, Charlene S
Bingham McCutchen LLP, San Francisco
415 393 2369
charlene.shimada@bingham.com
*Featured in Litigation (California)*
**Practice Areas:** Concentrates on securities litigation defense, corporate governance, class actions and complex commercial litigation. Represents a range of clients, including issuing corporations, officers and directors, underwriters, and public accounting firms, not only in private litigation, but also in investigations by the Securities and Exchange Commission, Department of Justice, Internal Revenue Service and Hawaii Department of Commerce and Consumer Affairs.
**Career:** Speaker at securities litigation seminars and seminars on gender and race issues. Has published articles concerning securities litigation.
**Personal:** University of California Berkeley School of Law (Boalt Hall), Juris Doctor, 1979. Stanford University, Bachelor of Arts, With Distinction, 1976.

### SHINDERMAN, Mark
Milbank, Tweed, Hadley & McCloy LLP, Los Angeles
213 892 4411
mshinderman@milbank.com
*Featured in Bankruptcy/Restructuring (California)*
**Practice Areas:** Mr Shinderman is a partner and member of the firm's Financial Restructuring

Group. He has extensive experience in restructurings and corporate reorganizations — restructuring companies inside and outside of bankruptcy, directing bankruptcy-related litigation, and handling the purchase of assets out of bankruptcy. Mr Shinderman often represents creditors' committees, debtors, purchasers of assets from troubled companies, key vendors, and other important constituents in insolvency situations. He also has represented numerous clients involved in litigation and transactions in which the counterparty may be in financial distress, helping the clients mitigate potential bankruptcy risks.

### SHULMAN, Ron
Latham & Watkins LLP, Silicon Valley
650 463 3099
ron.shulman@lw.com
*Featured in Intellectual Property (California)*
**Practice Areas:** Practice focuses on patent litigation, particularly defending companies against claims of infringement. Has broad litigation experience and expertise in information technology, communications, computer software and systems, semiconductors, lasers, and chemical compositions and processes. Also has extensive litigation experience in the life sciences industry, including medical devices and generic pharmaceuticals.
**Career:** Member, Attorney Advisory Committee, US District Court, Northern District of California - drafted local rules for the administration of patent infringement actions; Attorney representative, US District Court, Northern District of California.
**Personal:** JD, Rutgers University School of Law - Newark, 1981; BA, Amherst College, 1977.

### SIEGEL, David
Irell & Manella, Los Angeles
310 203 7129
dsiegel@irell.com
*Featured in Securities (Nationwide), Litigation (California)*
**Practice Areas:** David Siegel is a partner at Irell & Manella, where he leads the securities litigation practice with an emphasis on representing high-profile individual defendants and corporations in civil securities class and investor claims, as well as in SEC and other government enforcement proceedings. Results obtained by Mr Siegel for a number of his clients have received widespread praise from both other members of the Bar practicing in his field and public media.
**Personal:** University of California, Hastings College of Law (JD); University of Florida (BA, Political Science).

### SIEMENS, Reynold M
Pillsbury Winthrop Shaw Pittman LLP, Los Angeles
213 488 7277
reynold.siemens@pillsburylaw.com
*Featured in Insurance (California)*
**Practice Areas:** Represents policyholders in negotiations and disputes with insurers, including major environmental, asbestos, nuclear, and product claims; property and business interruption losses; disputes under D&O, E&O, and cyber liability policies; advertising, aviation, bond, clinical

trial, life, mold, and other coverage matters. Clients include Easton-Bell Sports, PAR Electrical, Clark Realty, Health Net, LG Electronics Mobilecomm USA, Meggitt PLC.

**Publications:** Chapters on product liability insurance and ADR, New Appleman Insurance Law Practice Guide; Chapter on property exclusions, New Appleman on Insurance Law Library Edition.

**Personal:** JD, Harvard Law School (1995); D Phil, Oxford University (1990); B Phil, Oxford University (1985).

## SILVERMAN, Karen E
Latham & Watkins LLP, San Francisco
415 395 8232
karen.silverman@lw.com
*Featured in Antitrust (California)*

**Practice Areas:** Ms Silverman handles antitrust representations of all sorts, including complex transactions, governmental and private enforcement matters and litigation. Her practice encompasses global competition matters arising from transactions, alleged cartels, pricing and distribution issues, and consumer protection and privacy issues. She has particular expertise in the high technology, biotechnology, consumer products, entertainment, media, health care and retail industries.

**Career:** US DOJ, Special Assistant to the Assistant Attorney General (1990-1993); Managing Partner, Latham & Watkins San Francisco office.

**Personal:** JD, University of California, Berkeley, School of Law (Boalt Hall), 1988; BA, Wellesley College, 1985.

## SIMONDS, David
Akin Gump Strauss Hauer & Feld LLP, Los Angeles
310 552 6692
dsimonds@akingump.com
*Featured in Bankruptcy/Restructuring (California)*

**Practice Areas:** David P. Simonds has significant experience representing debtors, official and informal creditors' committees, secured and unsecured creditors, asset acquirors and other parties in interest in chapter 11 cases and out-of-court restructurings.

**Personal:** BS, summa cum laude, 1989, State University of New York at Albany, where he was the president of Signum Laudis, an interdisciplinary honor society; a member of Beta Gamma Sigma, a business honor society; and a recipient of the Deloitte, Haskins & Sells/Harold L. Cannon Memorial Accounting Award. JD, 1992, New York University School of Law, editor, Annual Survey of American Law.

## SINISCALCO, Gary
Orrick, Herrington & Sutcliffe LLP, San Francisco
415 773 5833
grsiniscalco@orrick.com
*Featured in Labor & Employment (California)*

**Practice Areas:** Gary Siniscalco has a nationally recognized EEO practice that involves defense of systemic and class matters before EEOC, OFCCP and in federal courts. He also is a recognized

expert in advising U.S. and foreign companies on EEO compliance and prevention. In addition, Gary has specialized expertise in wrongful termination, trade secrets and whistle-blowing matters. Gary's counseling practice extends beyond the U.S. and includes assisting US multinational companies in dealing with employee issues in foreign jurisdictions. Gary is the co-editor-in-chief of BNA's two-volume international treatise: Restrictive Covenants & Trade Secrets in Employment Law: An International Survey.

## SIOK, Jan
Arnold & Porter LLP, Los Angeles
213 243 4091
Jan.Siok@aporter.com
*Featured in IT & Outsourcing (California)*

**Practice Areas:** Jan Siok concentrates her practice on technology transactions. She advises on a wide variety of transactions involving technology issues, including intellectual property licenses, outsourcing arrangements and mergers and acquisitions, and has represented some of the country's leading companies in the information technology, Internet, media and entertainment, financial services and life sciences fields. Ms Siok has significant transactional experience in the Asia Pacific region. Prior to becoming an attorney, she worked in Bank of Boston's Sydney, Hong Kong and Tokyo offices, where she focused on multinational lending and advised on credit relationships with major companies throughout the region.

## SMITH, Douglas D
Gibson, Dunn & Crutcher LLP, San Francisco
415 393 8390
dsmith@gibsondunn.com
*Featured in Capital Markets (California)*

**Practice Areas:** Capital markets, M&A, securities law compliance. In-depth experience in financial services, real estate, semiconductor, software businesses. Led over 200 public offerings and 50 M&A transactions. Represented underwriters in establishing $100 billion Banknote program for Wells Fargo Bank, $12 billion common stock offering by Wells Fargo to repay TARP funding and $4.5 billion auction of Wells Fargo warrants issued to Treasury Department; Goldman Sachs in Marin Software, Financial Engines and RPX Corporation IPOs; Wells Fargo Securities in $3 billion notes offering for Wells Fargo Bank; Barclays Capital in Xoom Corporation's IPO; and AskJeeves in $2.3 billion sale to IAC/InterActiveCorp.

## SMITH, Wayne
Gibson, Dunn & Crutcher LLP, Irvine
949 451 4108
wsmith@gibsondunn.com
*Featured in Litigation (California)*

**Practice Areas:** Practices commercial and business litigation. Has tried major cases, including class actions, in federal courts and in state courts throughout the country. Has handled securities fraud cases for clients in a range of industries, including financial institutions, for-profit education, home building, computer hardware, software and service, electronics, insurance, defense contracting and entertainment, and health care. Has

also represented accounting firms alleged to have participated with their clients in securities frauds in the savings and loan, insurance, music club, auto parts and real estate industries.

**Personal:** JD, University of California - Los Angeles, 1972, Order of the Coif.

## SNIPES, James C
Covington & Burling LLP, San Francisco
415 591 7071
jsnipes@cov.com
*Featured in Life Sciences (Nationwide), Life Sciences (California)*

**Practice Areas:** Jim Snipes was the founding partner of Covington's life sciences transactional group. He has over 20 years' experience representing pharmaceutical, biotech, and medical device companies in corporate, commercial, and transactional matters, including strategic collaborations; joint ventures; M&A; divestitures; and spin-outs. He has practiced in London and Tokyo and has extensive cross-border experience with Europe and Asia. His clients include early-stage companies, small cap public companies, and Big Pharma.

**Career:** Formerly co-chair of Covington's Life Sciences Group; member of Covington's Management Committee; exchange lawyer at Nagashima & Ohno.

**Personal:** JD, Yale Law School; BA, Oxford University; BA, Swarthmore College.

## SNYDER, David R
Pillsbury Winthrop Shaw Pittman LLP, San Diego
619 544 3369
dave.snyder@pillsburylaw.com
*Featured in Capital Markets (California), Life Sciences (California)*

**Practice Areas:** Chair of firm's Business Department. Mr Snyder specializes in corporate finance and general corporate matters. He has led numerous public offerings of equity and debt securities, represents NASDAQ and NYSE public companies in their on-going SEC reporting obligations and advises on public and private merger and acquisition transactions. Mr Snyder has counseled boards and special committees of directors in contested takeovers and in stockholder litigation in California, Delaware and federal courts.

**Personal:** JD, Cornell Law School (with Distinction; Order of the Coif; Editor, Cornell Law Review), 1974; BA, Michigan State University (high honors, Phi Beta Kappa), 1971.

## SPECTOR, Scott
Fenwick & West LLP, Mountain View
650 335 7251
sspector@fenwick.com
*Featured in Employee Benefits & Executive Compensation (California)*

**Practice Areas:** Scott P Spector chairs the Executive Compensation and Employee Benefits Group at Fenwick & West LLP. He specializes in serving high technology and software clients in designing and implementing executive compensation, equity compensation and other employee benefit arrangements. Mr Spector represents chief executive officers at many technology companies

in contract negotiations. His practice emphasizes the compensation issues that arise in connection with mergers and acquisitions, corporate governance matters involving executive compensation and representation of executives in employment negotiations. Mr Spector is an expert on Section 409A and 162(m) matters.

**Career:** Mr Spector was named to The Best Lawyers in America (2012) in the area of Employee Benefits Law and recognized by Chambers USA as one of the top Employee Benefits and Executive Compensation lawyers in California.

**Publications:** Mr Spector is a frequent speaker at national compensation, governance, and securities law programs, and has written extensively on executive compensation, corporate governance and stock compensation matters.

## SPIEGEL, Bennett
Jones Day, Los Angeles
213 243 2311
blspiegel@jonesday.com
*Featured in Bankruptcy/Restructuring (California)*

**Practice Areas:** Represents debtors, creditors, creditors' committees, trustees, and asset purchasers in corporate restructurings and bankruptcies in a variety of industries.

**Professional Memberships:** ABI, LA Bankruptcy Forum, Financial Lawyers Conference; editorial board of The Bankruptcy Strategist.

**Publications:** Commercial Bankruptcy Litigation, Chapter 3: Jurisdiction and Venue, coauthor, Thomson Reuters (2013); Comparison Shopping Guide for 363 Sales, coauthor, ABI (2009); Clear Channel Muddies the Waters of § 363(m) Mootness Protection, The Bankruptcy Strategist (2008); Bankruptcy Litigation, Chapter 9: Bankruptcy Appeals, coauthor, Thomson Reuters (2007).

**Personal:** Yale University: MBA 1983; JD 1984; Admitted in California, Connecticut, District of Columbia, New Jersey, New York.

## SPIEGEL, John
Munger, Tolles & Olson LLP, Los Angeles
213 683 9152
John.Spiegel@mto.com
*Featured in Securities (Nationwide), Litigation (California)*

**Practice Areas:** Practice focuses on complex business litigation. Recent representations include: Warner Bros. in litigation with actor Charlie Sheen; Transocean in Securities Litigation; Google founders in derivative litigation; Wells Fargo in indenture transfer action.

**Career:** Partner at the firm. Law Clerk for US Supreme Court Justice Byron White; Special Assistant to Deputy Secretary of State Warren Christopher.

**Personal:** Yale Law School (Editor-in-Chief of the Yale Law Journal); Stanford University (AB) (Block S award for varsity athlete (tennis) with highest GPA).

## SPITZER, Mark
Bingham McCutchen LLP, Los Angeles
213 680 6656
mark.spitzer@bingham.com
*Featured in Banking & Finance (California)*
**Practice Areas:** Focuses on commercial law, primarily representing lenders, personal property lessors and other creditors in transactional, workout and litigation matters. Has structured, negotiated and documented a broad variety of finance transactions, including large syndicated credit facilities, middle market loans, letters of credit and other credit enhancement facilities, multistate real estate secured transactions, mezzanine and subordinated credit financings, leveraged leases, asset-based loans, and equipment leases. Experience also includes numerous loan workout transactions and debtor-in-possession financings as well as litigation in California state and US bankruptcy courts.
**Personal:** Duke University School of Law, JD, 1986; Wichita State University, BA, 1982.

## SPRAGUE, Gary D
Baker & McKenzie, Palo Alto
650 856 5510
gary.sprague@bakermckenzie.com
*Featured in Tax (California)*
**Practice Areas:** Tax planning and advice (corporate and international); tax controversies (corporate and international); e-commerce law.
**Professional Memberships:** International Fiscal Association; State Bar of California.
**Career:** Admitted in California (1981). Joined B&M as an associate in 1985. Currently a Partner in Baker & McKenzie LLP, Palo Alto.
**Publications:** "General Report on Main Subject I: Taxation of Income Derived from Electronic Commerce", Cahiers de Droit Fiscal International, Volume 86, IFA 2001 San Francisco Congress.
**Personal:** Stanford University (1977, BA with honors in Political Science, Phi Beta Kappa) and Harvard Law School (1981, cum laude). Also attended Trinity College in Dublin, Ireland.

## SPRATLING, Gary R
Gibson, Dunn & Crutcher LLP, San Francisco
415 393 8222
gspratling@gibsondunn.com
*Featured in Antitrust (California)*
**Practice Areas:** Global expertise regarding anti-cartel enforcement practices of all major competition enforcement authorities. [and development of integrated international defense strategies.] In now over 40 international investigations, has guided numerous successful representations of major organizations and high-ranking individuals facing exposure in multiple jurisdictions.
**Career:** Former United States Department of Justice prosecutor (28 years). Two-time recipient of the Presidential Rank Award, the highest honor conferred on federal government executives. Recipient of the Antitrust Lawyer of the Year Award from State Bar of California. Law360's 10 Most Admired Competition Attorneys (2010). GCR's Cartel Lawyer of the Year (2011).

## STEEL, Michael
Morrison & Foerster LLP, San Francisco
415 268 7350
msteel@mofo.com
*Featured in Environment (California)*
**Practice Areas:** Mr Steel focuses on regulatory compliance, crisis management, dispute resolution, and the defense of enforcement actions under environmental, health, and safety laws. He advises clients on hazardous substance handling, air quality (including greenhouse gas emissions), and employee safety. Mr Steel also represents client in permitting and land use matters for large industrial development projects.
**Professional Memberships:** Board Member, Proposition 65 Clearinghouse and the Air & Waste Management Association (Golden West Chapter); member, California Council for Environmental and Economic Balance.
**Personal:** UC Hastings College of the Law (JD, 1982); UC Davis (BA, 1977).

## STEIN, Stanton 'Larry'
Liner Grode Stein Yankelevitz Sunshine Regenstreif & Taylor LLP, Los Angeles
310 500 3413
lstein@linerlaw.com
*Featured in Media & Entertainment (California)*
**Practice Areas:** Practice includes representation of actors, writers, producers, directors, musicians, entertainment guilds, talent agencies, personal and business management companies, independent production companies, and interactive gaming companies. Renowned for pioneering success in "vertical integration" lawsuits.
**Professional Memberships:** Founder, past President - Public Counsel. Member, Board of Directors, Foundation of the State Bar of California. Member of the Los Angeles County and American Bar Associations.
**Career:** Named top 100 "Power Lawyers" by the Hollywood Reporter, Esq., and "Entertainment Lawyer of the Year" by the Beverly Hills and also the Century City Bar Associations. Named in Daily Journal's 100 Most Influential Lawyers in California. Listed in LawDragon 500 (Top 500 Lawyers in the US). Adjunct Professor of Law at USC and Stanford Law Schools.
**Personal:** University of Southern California (BA with honors; JD).

## STEINBERG, Howard
Greenberg Traurig LLP, Los Angeles
310 586 7702
SteinbergH@gtlaw.com
*Featured in Bankruptcy/Restructuring (California)*
**Professional Memberships:** Member: Los Angeles County Bar Association, Commercial Law and Bankruptcy Section (Bankruptcy Committee); Board, Western Center on Law and Poverty; Century City Bar Association.
**Career:** Member, Winning Team, U.S. News - Best Lawyers 'Law Firm of the Year' in Bankruptcy & Creditor Debtor Rights / Insolvency & Reorganization Law and Litigation – Bankruptcy, 2013. Recipient, 'Deal of the Year Award', International Financial Law Review, 2012. Listed:

Chambers USA Guide, 2007-13. Rated, AV® Preeminent™ 5.0 out of 5.
**Personal:** JD, Boston College Law School; BA, magna cum laude, University of Massachusetts.

## STEINBERG, Michael H
Sullivan & Cromwell LLP, Los Angeles
310 712 6670
STEINBERGM@sullcrom.com
*Featured in Litigation (California)*
**Professional Memberships:** ABA; LACBA; Executive Committee of Board of Directors, Public Counsel.
**Career:** Partner since 1995. Litigation Coordinator, Los Angeles. Focuses practice on commercial trial work. Fellow of American College of Trial Lawyers and has tried a broad range of cases, running the gamut from M&A disputes to false advertising to criminal cases. Represents leading financial, industrial and technology companies including Koninklijke Philips Electronics N.V., NXP N.V., Goldman Sachs & Co., Enbridge, Inc., MPEG LA, L.L.C., VeriFone, Canyon Capital Advisors, and BCE Inc.
**Personal:** Stanford Law School (JD, 1986); UC Berkeley (AB, 1983).

## STEINTHAL, Kenneth
King & Spalding LLP, San Francisco
415 318 1211
ksteinthal@kslaw.com
*Featured in Media & Entertainment (California)*
**Practice Areas:** Kenneth Steinthal has more than 30 years of experience litigating matters in the IP/media sector and several other industries, both in jury and bench trial settings, in the U.S. federal and state court settings (including appellate proceedings), before copyright tribunals in the United States and internationally (where he has earned "rights of audience" to represent his clients), and before other arbitral bodies around the world. Beyond his litigation experience, he also advises on IP rights and licensing matters for clients engaged in wide-scale distribution of audio and audiovisual media content.
**Personal:** BA, Williams College, 1974; JD, Fordham University, 1978.

## STEUBER, David W
Jones Day, Los Angeles
213 243 2457
dsteuber@jonesday.com
*Featured in Insurance (Nationwide), Insurance (California)*
See under Nationwide for profile.

## STEVENS, Mark C
Fenwick & West LLP, Mountain View
650 335 7257
mstevens@fenwick.com
*Featured in Investment Funds (Nationwide), Corporate/M&A (California)*
See under Nationwide for profile.

## STEVENS, Pauline M
Allen Matkins Leck Gamble Mallory & Natsis LLP, Los Angeles
213 622 5555
pstevens@allenmatkins.com
*Featured in Banking & Finance (California)*

**Practice Areas:** Assists clients with structuring and working out complex financial transactions, including syndicated secured transactions, treasury products and derivatives. Clients include commercial banks and other institutional. Has considerable experience working with letters of credit, acceptances, foreign exchange, intellectual property and restricted securities. Recent engagements involved restructuring financing for major homebuilder and structuring private banking products for international bank.
**Career:** 2006 Burton Award; leadership positions in the ABA, State Bar, California State Bar and Los Angeles County Bar Associations, Fellow in American College of Commercial Finance Lawyers.
**Personal:** BA, Vassar College, 1969; JD, University of Pennsylvania Law School, 1972.

## STODDARD, Marshall C
Morgan, Lewis & Bockius LLP, New York
212 309 6350
mstoddard@morganlewis.com
*Featured in Banking & Finance (California), Banking & Finance (Nationwide)*
**Practice Areas:** Marshall C Stoddard, Jr is a partner and Co-Chair of Morgan Lewis & Bockius's Finance and Restructuring Practice. Mr Stoddard represents a wide array of banks and other financial institutions in leveraged finance, asset based lending and intercreditor matters and in workouts and reorganizations. Mr Stoddard has co-authored treatises on lender liability and chapter 11 reorganizations and has been a frequent lecturer and panelist on topics of commercial law. Admitted to practice in several jurisdictions, Mr Stoddard practices primarily in New York City and Los Angeles.

## STONE, Greg
Munger, Tolles & Olson LLP, Los Angeles
213 683 9255
Gregory.Stone@mto.com
*Featured in Intellectual Property (California)*
**Practice Areas:** Specializes in complex civil trials and litigation, including antitrust, intellectual property, and business torts. Recent representations include: Rambus Inc. in antitrust and patent infringement actions; Microsoft Corporation in a patent case against Walker Digital and Philip Morris USA Inc. in various class action cases.
**Professional Memberships:** Boards: Coro Southern California, Constitutional Rights Foundation.
**Career:** Partner at the firm. Former Managing Partner.
**Personal:** Yale Law School; California Institute of Technology (BS,MS in Chemical Engineering).

## STONE, Richard L
Jenner & Block LLP, Los Angeles
213 239 2203
RStone@jenner.com
*Featured in Media & Entertainment (California)*
**Career:** Richard L. Stone is a leading trial lawyer concentrating on antitrust, copyright, anti-piracy, securities and shareholder actions, commercial fraud and related business tort cases, with an emphasis on the media and entertainment indus-

tries. Mr Stone's extensive experience includes representing Fortune 100 and other household-name companies engaged in the entertainment, advertising, communications, Internet, finance, and healthcare industries, among others. In addition to leading numerous jury trials, he represents clients in court-annexed and private arbitrations and other alternative dispute resolution processes. In 2012, The Hollywood Reporter named Mr Stone a "Power Lawyer," one of the top 100 entertainment lawyers in America.

### STORK, Anita F
Covington & Burling LLP, San Francisco
415 591 7050
astork@cov.com
*Featured in Antitrust (California)*

**Practice Areas:** Ms Stork is a Vice-Chair of Covington's Antitrust Practice Group and a former Vice-Chair of the firm's Litigation Practice. She handles cartel and antitrust litigation, as well as internal and governmental investigations. She also advises clients on a variety of competition issues including pricing, exclusive dealing, bundled rebates, and intellectual property licensing. Representative clients include Alps Electric, Philippine Airlines, and Integrated Device Technology.
**Professional Memberships:** Executive Committee of the California State Bar Section on Antitrust and Unfair Competition.
**Personal:** Boalt Hall School of Law, University of California at Berkeley, JD.

### STREISAND, Adam F
Loeb & Loeb LLP, Los Angeles
310 282 2354
astreisand@loeb.com
*Featured in Tax (California)*

**Practice Areas:** Focuses his practice on disputes involving trusts, decedents' estates and conservatorships; obligations of fiduciaries such as trustees, executors, conservators, attorneys and other professionals; accountant and legal malpractice; tax litigation; and copyright and intellectual property disputes.
**Professional Memberships:** Fellow, American College of Trust and Estate Counsel; member of CA State Bar Trusts and Estates Section's Executive Committee; National College of Probate Judges; Advisory Board of the UCLA/CEB Estate Planning Institute; CEB Estate Planning Advisory Committee; Planning Committee of the USC Probate and Trust Conference. Faculty member, National Institute for Trial Advocacy.
**Career:** Became Partner in 1999.

### SULLIVAN, Douglas
Crowell & Moring LLP, San Francisco
415 365 7370
dsullivan@crowell.com
*Featured in Litigation (California)*

**Practice Areas:** Partner with Crowell & Moring's Litigation, Intellectual Property, and Environmental & Toxic Tort Litigation groups. He specializes in complex commercial litigation, including mergers and acquisitions, intellectual property, entertainment, partnership disputes and dissolutions, construction, real estate, environ-

mental, insurance and securities litigation. He has significant trial experience in state and federal courts, having acted as lead counsel in approximately 15 trials.
**Career:** Prior to joining Crowell & Moring, Mr Sullivan was a partner with the San Francisco firm of Folger Levin & Kahn LLP.
**Personal:** Indiana University, BA with distinction, Phi Beta Kappa. University of Virginia School of Law, JD.

### SUN, Brian A
Jones Day, Los Angeles
213 243 2858
basun@jonesday.com
*Featured in Litigation (California)*

**Practice Areas:** Has earned a national reputation as a distinguished trial lawyer specializing in complex business litigation and white-collar criminal defense. He has successfully litigated cases against some of the nation's top trial lawyers. As an assistant US attorney, he distinguished himself by drafting and pioneering the passage of anti-money laundering legislation. Named one of America's 500 leading lawyers in 2005 by Lawdragon magazine. Lectured and written on trial practice and white-collar crime.
**Professional Memberships:** Fellow of the American College of Trial Lawyers. Former President of the Southern California Chinese Lawyers Association and the National Asian Pacific American Bar Association.

### SURPIN, Beni
DLA Piper LLP (US), San Diego
858 638 6950
beni.surpin@dlapiper.com
*Featured in IT & Outsourcing (California)*

**Practice Areas:** IT and Outsourcing.
**Career:** He focuses on counseling international and domestic companies in the wireless, telecom, health care, medical devices, life sciences, food and beverage, fashion and apparel, aviation, automotive and high-tech industries on legal and business issues relating to intellectual property, technology and commercial transactions. He works closely with his clients in creating and setting strategic direction and then structuring and negotiating arrangements to implement these goals. His experience in domestic and international technology and commercial transactions covers a broad spectrum of agreements and structures.

### SWANSON, Daniel G
Gibson, Dunn & Crutcher LLP, Los Angeles
213 229 7430
dswanson@gibsondunn.com
*Featured in Antitrust (California)*

**Practice Areas:** Co-Chair since 1996 of firm's Antitrust Practice. Specializes in domestic/international antitrust and competition law, including civil, criminal and appellate litigation, class actions, mergers/JVs, monopoly/dominance matters, counseling, compliance, amnesty/leniency matters and cartel investigations.
**Professional Memberships:** Officer, IBA Antitrust Committee (2012-); Co-Chair, ABA Antitrust Section's International Committee (2002-06).

### Career:
Has broad trial and appellate experience, M&A and intellectual property expertise, and extensive track record in international matters, including cartel and leniency cases.
**Publications:** Author/editor of numerous antitrust publications.
**Personal:** JD, 1984, magna cum laude, MA, 1984 and PhD (economics), 1985, Harvard University; member, California and Brussels Bars; Solicitor, England and Wales.

### SWANSON, Edward
Swanson & McNamara LLP, San Francisco
415 477 3800
eswanson@swansonmcnamara.com
*Featured in Litigation (California)*

**Practice Areas:** Mr Swanson specializes in white collar and general criminal defense, as well as SEC matters. His case roster includes antitrust, securities fraud, tax fraud, environmental offenses, trade secret theft, and drug offenses. He also serves as a special master and court expert for the federal district court in various civil matters.
**Professional Memberships:** Co-Chair, Northern District of California Federal Criminal Rules and Practice Committee, 2005-present; Lawyer Representative to the Ninth Circuit, 2004-07.
**Career:** Clerk, Chief District Judge Thelton E. Henderson (1992-93); Assistant Federal Public Defender (1993-98).
**Personal:** JD, Stanford Law School, 1991; BA, Stanford University, 1985.

### TABACOPOULOS, Diana
Seyfarth Shaw LLP, Los Angeles
310 201 5255
dtabacopoulos@seyfarth.com
*Featured in Labor & Employment (California)*

**Practice Areas:** Partner at Seyfarth Shaw specializing in complex wage/hour and employment litigation. Lead counsel for global financial institutions, retailers, and media companies in more than 100 California and nationwide putative class and collective actions. Frequently lectures on employment litigation. Quoted in Fortune Magazine, LA Times, and CEO Magazine. Recognized by the Los Angeles Daily Journal as a Top Woman Lawyer in California.
**Professional Memberships:** ABA.
**Career:** Northwestern University School of Law. Joined Seyfarth Shaw in 1992; Partner since 1996. Previously, Associate, Fried Frank Harris Shriver & Jacobson.
**Personal:** Founding Sponsor, Challenger Center (non-profit organization for space science education).

### TANENBAUM, Jeffrey M
Nixon Peabody LLP, San Francisco
415 984 8450
jtanenbaum@nixonpeabody.com
*Featured in Labor & Employment (California)*

**Practice Areas:** Jeff Tanenbaum leads Nixon Peabody's global Labor and Employment practice, overseeing more than 70 attorneys who provide companies with practical, balanced employment solutions and litigation defense. Regarded as one of California's top employment practitioners, Jeff

has garnered national attention for his handling of complex OSHA and Cal/OSHA matters. His practice also includes workplace violence, wrongful termination, employment discrimination, restrictive covenants, collective bargaining and labor arbitrations. His comprehensive understanding of labor and employment law allows him to provide effective, creative, and efficient counsel to many of the world's top businesses.
**Personal:** Georgetown University, JD; Brandeis University, BA.

### TAYLOR, Joseph
Liner Grode Stein Yankelevitz Sunshine Regenstreif & Taylor LLP, Los Angeles
310 500 3547
jtaylor@linerlaw.com
*Featured in Media & Entertainment (California)*

**Practice Areas:** Entertainment, intellectual property, employment matters.
**Professional Memberships:** Mr Taylor is a member of the Beverly Hills Bar Association and the Los Angeles County Bar Association.
**Career:** He represents writers, directors, producers, actors, recording artists, radio and television broadcasters, rights holders, studio and production company executives, talent agents and agencies, managers and management companies, and independent production and distribution companies, among other types of clients, in a wide range of disputes in the motion picture, television, radio and music industries.
**Personal:** Mr Taylor was born in Chicago, and grew up in South Bend, Indiana.

### TAYLOR, Robert P
Arnold & Porter LLP, San Francisco
415 471 3309
Robert.Taylor@aporter.com
*Featured in Antitrust (California)*

**Practice Areas:** Robert Taylor's practice focuses on litigation and counseling with respect to IP and antitrust law as these apply to clients in a diverse group of industries, including electronics, software, chemical, medical devices, pharmaceutical and semiconductor manufacturing. He has tried a number of cases to juries and before the International Trade Commission and has briefed and argued many appeals in such cases.
**Professional Memberships:** He is a Fellow of the American College of Trial Lawyers, former Chair of the Antitrust Section of the American Bar Association and was a member of the 1992 Advisory Commission on Patent Law Reform.

### THAU, Stephen B
Morrison & Foerster LLP, Palo Alto
650 813 5640
sthau@mofo.com
*Featured in Corporate/M&A (California), Life Sciences (California)*

**Practice Areas:** Former co-chair of the firm's global Life Sciences Group and the Emerging Companies & Venture Capital Group. Focuses on the representation of life science, medical device, and other technology companies at all stages of their life cycles, from company formation, equity and debt financings, M&A transactions, strategic alliances, and public offerings. Has represented companies and investors in over 100 venture capital and debt financing transactions, as well as in numerous public offerings, public and private M&A transactions, and collaboration agreements. A frequent speaker on legal and corporate issues in emerging company and venture capital financing matters.

## THAYER, M Patricia
Sidley Austin LLP, San Francisco
415 772 7469
pthayer@sidley.com
*Featured in Intellectual Property (California)*
**Practice Areas:** In a career exceeding three decades, Ms Thayer has represented biotechnology, medical device, software, hardware and consumer retail companies in district court litigation and arbitration. She has tried IP cases in the Northern, Southern and Eastern Districts of California and the Western District of Wisconsin, and before the American Arbitration Association. Ms Thayer is group head for the Northern California IP Litigation Group.
**Personal:** Harvard Law School, JD, 1979, cum laude; Harvard University, BA, 1976, magna cum laude. Admissions: California, U.S. Supreme Court, U.S Court of Appeals 9th Circuit, U.S. Court of Appeals Federal Circuit

## THOMAS, Andrew J
Jenner & Block LLP, Los Angeles
213 239 5155
AJThomas@jenner.com
*Featured in Media & Entertainment (California)*
**Career:** Andrew J. ("A.J.") Thomas is a partner in the Content, Media & Entertainment Practice, with significant experience in copyright and trademark matters. As a leading media and entertainment litigator, Mr Thomas has represented clients at the trial and appellate levels in matters including intellectual property rights, defamation and privacy, right of publicity issues, unfair competition claims, and prior restraints on speech. Clients include motion picture studios, television networks and production companies, book publishers, magazines, newspapers, photo agencies, and advertising companies. Mr Thomas has lectured frequently at universities on media law, defamation and privacy law.

## THOMASES, Andrew N
Skadden, Arps, Slate, Meagher & Flom LLP & Affiliates, Palo Alto
650 470 4580
andrew.thomases@skadden.com
*Featured in Intellectual Property (California)*
**Practice Areas:** Mr Thomases has more than 18 years of experience litigating patent and trade secret cases, including trials before the International Trade Commission (ITC) and appeals to the Federal Circuit. He focuses on handling technically complex matters, including cases involving medical devices, computer technology, semiconductor devices, analog circuits, wireless technology and wafer fabrication tools. Has tried numerous cases before the ITC, representing both patent holders and accused infringers.
**Career:** Amherst College, BA, magna cum laude, 1990; University of Chicago Law School, JD, with

honors, 1994; Former clerk for the US Court of Appeals for the Federal Circuit.

## THOMPSON, Jocelyn
Alston & Bird LLP, Los Angeles
213 576 1104
jocelyn.thompson@alston.com
*Featured in Environment (California)*
**Practice Areas:** Extensive experience in environmental permitting, compliance and auditing, including matters related to air and water quality, CEQA, NEPA, coastal zone permitting, endangered and threatened species, and climate change. Primary clients include companies engaged in renewable and conventional energy generation, mining, oil and gas, goods movement, and general manufacturing.
**Professional Memberships:** American Bar Association; California Bar Association (Environmental Law Section); California Construction and Industrial Materials Association (Environment Committee); American Council on Renewable Energy.
**Personal:** JD, University of California, Los Angeles, 1982; BA, magna cum laude, University of California, Santa Barbara, 1978.

## THUM, Robert B
Pillsbury Winthrop Shaw Pittman LLP, Los Angeles
213 488 7504
robert.thum@pillsburylaw.com
*Featured in Construction (California)*
**Practice Areas:** Mr Thum's practice focuses on major construction contracts and disputes among owners, contractors, designers and sureties. His cases have involved major hospitals, powerplants, rail, dams, refineries, airports, dams, bridges, highways and other infrastructure projects. In addition to contract drafting, Mr Thum litigates construction disputes in federal and state court, and is routinely involved in arbitrations, mediations and ADR.
**Professional Memberships:** Fellow, American College of Construction Lawyers; National Panel of Neutrals, American Arbitration Association; ABA Forum Committee for Construction Industry; AGC of California.
**Career:** Ohio (1970); California (1974).
**Personal:** AB, Princeton University (1967); JD, Cornell Law School (1970).

## TICHY, George
Littler Mendelson, PC, San Francisco
415 433 1940
GTichy@littler.com
*Featured in Labor & Employment (California)*
**Practice Areas:** Wrongful Termination, Wage and Hour Class Actions, Labor Management Relations, Labor Reform Legislation.
**Professional Memberships:** California State Bar; Washington State Bar; Served on behalf of the U.S. Office of Personnel Management as Examiner for the selection of Administrative Law Judges.
**Career:** Mr Tichy has testified before the United States Senate's Subcommittee on Labor and before the House's Subcommittee on Labor Management Relations concerning proposed Labor Reform.

**Publications:** Co-author of a book dealing with labor relation matters and for a number of years has been contributing editor of The Developing Labor Law.
**Personal:** JD, University of Minnesota, 1967; BA, Economics, University of Oregon, with honors.

## TILNER, Mitchell C
Horvitz & Levy LLP, Encino
818 995 0800
mtilner@horvitzlevy.com
*Featured in Litigation (California), Insurance (California)*
**Career:** Mitchell C. Tilner, a partner at Horvitz & Levy, is a California State Bar Certified Appellate Specialist. He has briefed or supervised hundreds of appeals and writ proceedings in state and federal courts. His practice areas include insurance coverage and bad faith, commercial contract and property disputes, entertainment law, and punitive damages. Before joining the firm, he clerked for Hon. Arthur Alarcon of the Ninth Circuit Court of Appeals. Mr Tilner is a member of both the California Academy and American Academy of Appellate Lawyers. He frequently speaks to clients and professional groups on appellate process and brief writing.

## TOBISMAN, Stuart P
Loeb & Loeb LLP, Los Angeles
310 282 2323
stobisman@loeb.com
*Featured in Wealth Management (Nationwide), Tax (California)*
**Practice Areas:** Focuses on estate and tax planning for individuals and in administration of estates and trusts. Clients include prominent individuals in commerce, entertainment industry, banks and trust companies acting as fiduciaries. Also advises owners of closely held businesses on their estate and tax planning.
**Career:** Became Partner at O'Melveny & Myers in 1977. Joined Loeb as Partner in 2006. Trusts and Estates Department Co-Chair.
**Publications:** Lectures at the USC Institute on Federal Taxation, UCLA/CEB Estate Planning Institute and the Practising Law Institute.
**Personal:** UC Berkeley, Boalt Hall School of Law, (JD, 1969); UCLA (AB, 1966).

## TODD, Mary Ann
Munger, Tolles & Olson LLP, Los Angeles
213 683 9520
MaryAnn.Todd@mto.com
*Featured in Corporate/M&A (Southern California)*
**Practice Areas:** Practice focuses on M&A, joint ventures and corporate governance. She represents publicly traded and privately held companies and private equity funds. Recent representations: Berkshire Hathaway in its purchase of Lubrizol Corporation and Burlington Northern; UMG in its acquisition of EMI Recorded Music; 99¢ Only Stores in its going-private transaction.
**Professional Memberships:** Board, California Bar Foundation; Secretary, Fulfillment Fund; Board, Los Angeles Center for Law & Justice.
**Career:** Partner. Her work has been highlighted in The American Lawyer, Law360, the Los Angeles Business Journal and the Daily Journal.

**Personal:** Yale Law School; UC Berkeley (AB).

## TORO, Amy L
Covington & Burling LLP, San Francisco
415 591 7086
atoro@cov.com
*Featured in Life Sciences (California)*
**Practice Areas:** Focus on technology transactions, with particular emphasis on collaboration, joint venture, and license agreements. Represent primarily pharmaceutical companies and biotechnology clients. Clients include AstraZeneca, Gilead Sciences, Sanofi-Aventis, and Amyris Biotechnologies.
**Personal:** University of Virginia, BA, with highest honors; University of California, Berkeley School of Law, JD; University of California at Berkeley, PhD.

## TORPEY, Michael D
Orrick, Herrington & Sutcliffe LLP, San Francisco
415 773 5932
mtorpey@orrick.com
*Featured in Litigation (California)*
**Practice Areas:** Michael Torpey, Managing Partner of the firm and a partner in the San Francisco office, is recognized for his expertise in SEC investigations, securities class actions and breach of fiduciary duty-related matters. Mr Torpey was Orrick's Securities Litigation practice leader from 2004 to 2012. He specializes in litigation involving the Private Securities Litigation Reform Act of 1995, The Securities Act of 1933, the Securities Act of 1934, the Uniform Standards Act and proceedings initiated by the Securities Exchange Commission, the National Association of Securities Dealers and other self-regulatory organizations.

## TOSTA, Timothy
McKenna Long & Aldridge LLP, San Francisco
415 356 4612
ttosta@mckennalong.com
*Featured in Real Estate (California)*
**Practice Areas:** Timothy Tosta procures land use entitlements for some of the California's most complex and controversial development proposals. Honored by the Daily Journal as one of California's Top Real Estate Lawyers, citing his work on Facebook's Headquarters Project in Menlo Park, CA., Tosta's recent work for the Bohannon Development Company on its Menlo Gateway Project, also was heralded by the Daily Journal as one of the State's top five development deals in 2011. Tosta develops innovative strategies and creative solutions for complex projects, delivered with artful diplomacy, yet backed by legal precision and political sophistication.

## TOWNSEND, Robert S
Morrison & Foerster LLP, San Francisco
415 268 7080
rtownsend@mofo.com
*Featured in Corporate/M&A (California), Corporate/M&A (Northern California)*
**Practice Areas:** Mr Townsend is a co-chair of Morrison & Foerster's Global M&A Group and a member of the firm's Executive and

Compensation Committees. He has extensive experience in M&A, private equity, venture capital and corporate governance. He has represented public and private companies in mergers, tender offers, proxy contests, unsolicited transactions, joint ventures, and related financings. He advises CEOs, boards of directors and special committees in strategic/corporate governance issues. Clients include Intel, SoftBank, Visa, Autodesk, VMware, Clorox, Pinnacle Entertainment, and Caesars.
**Personal:** BS, University of California, Berkeley, 1978, with honors; JD, Stanford University Law School, 1984.

## TURNER III, Glenn E
Gibbs Giden Locher Turner Senet & Wittbrodt LLP., Los Angeles
310 552 3400
gturner@ggltsw.com
*Featured in Construction (California)*
**Practice Areas:** Construction Law; Construction Litigation; Real Estate Law.
**Career:** Mr Turner specializes in the representation of prime contractors, owners (public and private), subcontractors, and design professionals. He has over 30 years of experience in trials and arbitrations of major construction disputes involving delay, disruption, extra work claims, lost productivity and abandonment of contract, including a recent $52.1M unanimous jury verdict for client City of Victorville, CA in its fight against Carter & Burgess (now Jacobs Engineering Group) for professional negligence, negligent misrepresentation, breach of fiduciary duty and for breach of contact. Mr Turner has both prosecuted and defended major construction claims.
**Publications:** He has authored numerous articles for construction industry trade publications and is an active speaker on various construction law topics including the false claims act, statutory remedies, and public contracts and procurement regulations.
**Personal:** Pepperdine University (JD),1980; Arizona State University (MBA), 1977; Arizona State University (BS), 1975.

## TYUKODY JR, Daniel
Goodwin Procter LLP, San Francisco
213 612 2450
dtyukody@goodwinprocter.com
*Featured in Litigation (California)*
**Practice Areas:** Mr Tyukody focuses his practice on securities litigation and regulatory enforcement, specializing in defending issuers, officers and directors, and underwriters in securities class actions, derivative cases, M&A cases and SEC proceedings. He counsels audit committees and special committees in conducting internal audit and special investigations and has significant trial and appellate experience in securities and M&A cases, and an exceptional track record in obtaining motions to dismiss.
**Professional Memberships:** He is a member of the Los Angeles, California and American Bar Associations.
**Personal:** JD, The University of Chicago Law School, 1985; BS, Duke University, 1978 (magna cum laude).

## UHLAND, Suzanne
O'Melveny & Myers LLP, San Francisco
415 984 8941
suhland@omm.com
*Featured in Bankruptcy/Restructuring (California)*
**Practice Areas:** Suzanne Uhland is a partner in O'Melveny's San Francisco and Newport Beach offices and Chair of the firm's Restructuring Practice. Suzanne has substantial experience in Chapter 11 cases representing both debtors and creditors as well as buyers in Section 363(b) sales. She also represents financial institutions and public and private companies in connection with out of court restructurings, including exchange offers, financings and distress transactions. Suzanne has expertise in real estate, technology, retail, and healthcare financings and restructurings.

## VAN DONGEN, Troy
Winston & Strawn LLP, San Francisco
415 591 1546
tvandongen@winston.com
*Featured in Tax (California)*
**Practice Areas:** Mr Van Dongen resolves state and local tax controversies. He regularly appears before the California courts and taxing authorities involving a variety of taxes, and has a particularly strong background in property taxation.
**Professional Memberships:** Chair of the State and Local Tax Committee of the California Bar, member of the Tax Section of the San Francisco Bar Association, and the Taxation Committee of the USCIB.
**Publications:** Mr Van Dongen has authored articles in numerous publications, and is the principal author of the Lexis-Nexis Practitioner Insights on California Property Taxation.
**Personal:** Chairman of the Marin County Assessment Appeals Board.

## VANDEVELDE, John
Crowell & Moring LLP, Los Angeles
213 622 4750
jvandevelde@crowell.com
*Featured in Litigation (California)*
**Practice Areas:** Retired partner in Crowell & Moring's White Collar and Regulatory Enforcement Group. He is an experienced trial attorney and a former assistant United States attorney in Los Angeles. Acted as lead prosecutor in a major securities fraud case, United States v Ruth Handler, et al, which resulted in convictions of all charged. Primarily defends clients in criminal matters. He has had approximately thirty additional trials since leaving the government, covering a wide variety of charges in both federal and state courts. Served as former Chairperson of the American Bar Association's West Coast Regional Subcommittee on White-Collar Crime.

## VÁZQUEZ-AZPIRI, A James
Morgan, Lewis & Bockius LLP, San Francisco
415 442 1343
ajvazquez@morganlewis.com
*Featured in Immigration (California), Immigration (Nationwide)*
**Practice Areas:** A James Vázquez-Azpiri is a partner in Morgan Lewis's Labor and Employment Practice. He focuses his practice on business immigration law, assisting corporate clients with hiring and retaining foreign employees with regard to labor certifications, specialty occupation petitions, and intra-company transfers. He is a leading national expert on immigration law compliance in the context of mergers, acquisitions and corporate restructurings. He regularly speaks on business immigration matters and has authored a number of published articles in this area.
**Personal:** Attended Harvard Law School, LLM; New York University School of Law, JD; Princeton University, MA; University of St. Andrews, MA.

## VESELY, Jeffrey M
Pillsbury Winthrop Shaw Pittman LLP, San Francisco
415 983 1075
jeffrey.vesely@pillsburylaw.com
*Featured in Tax (California)*
**Practice Areas:** Leader of the firm's State and Local Tax Practice. Mr Vesely focuses on state and local tax matters, including income, franchise, sales and use, and other taxes. His practice consists of administrative and judicial tax litigation, state and local tax planning and transactional work. Mr Vesely has litigated state and local tax matters throughout the United States, in administrative tribunals, state and federal trial courts, courts of appeal, state supreme courts and the United States Supreme Court.
**Publications:** Judicial Remedies and Administrative Procedures in California Tax Analysis. Distinctions Between Unitary and Nonunitary Businesses: A Practical Guide.

## VETTER, Jeffrey R
Fenwick & West LLP, Mountain View
650 335 7631
jvetter@fenwick.com
*Featured in Capital Markets (California), Corporate/M&A (California)*
**Practice Areas:** Jeffrey R Vetter is a partner in the Corporate Group of Fenwick & West LLP. Mr Vetter's practice concentrates on public and private offerings of securities, mergers and acquisitions, counseling public and late-stage private companies, and other securities law matters. Mr Vetter's recent public offerings include Fusion–io, Inc., Jive Software, Responsys, SuccessFactors and ShoreTel. Mr Vetter also represents underwriters of numerous initial public offerings, including the initial public offerings of Salesforce.com, SiRF Technology Holdings, Omniture, DemandTec and other public and private offerings of debt and equity securities and stock exchange listings. Mr Vetter's mergers and acquisitions transaction experience includes the acquisition of Plateau Systems by SuccessFactors, the sale of Omneon to Harmonic, Postini to Google, VeriSign's acquisition of Network Solutions and Illuminet Holdings, @Home Corporation's acquisition of Excite, and a large number of other transactions involving public and/or private companies. Mr Vetter has also advised companies with respect to corporate governance and SEC matters, activist stockholders and joint ventures.

**Career:** Mr Vetter is listed in Best Lawyers in America for securities and capital markets law, in Chambers USA for capital markets: debt & equity and repeatedly selected as a Northern California "Super Lawyer."

## VISCOUNTY, Perry J
Latham & Watkins LLP, Costa Mesa
714 755 8288
perry.viscounty@lw.com
*Featured in Intellectual Property (California)*
**Practice Areas:** Co-chair of the global Intellectual Property Litigation Practice Group. Focuses on trademark, patent, copyright, trade secrets and licensing disputes, as well as technology and internet litigation.
**Professional Memberships:** INTA, AIPLA, OCPLA.
**Career:** Frequent lecturer for Harvard/USC Business Conference, State Bar of California, UCLA, Board Retailers Association, California Bankers Association and MAGIC. Published articles in TrademarkWORLD, ABA, IP LAW360, Los Angeles Daily Journal and the National Law Journal.
**Personal:** JD, University of Southern California, 1987; BS, University of Southern California, 1984.

## VOGEL, Miriam A.
Morrison & Foerster LLP, Los Angeles
213 892-5929
mvogel@mofo.com
*Featured in Litigation (California)*
**Practice Areas:** Miriam A. Vogel is a member of the firm's Appellate Practice Group. Before joining Morrison & Foerster, Ms Vogel served five years as a Judge of the Los Angeles Superior Court and 18 years as a Justice of the California Court of Appeal, Second Appellate District, Division One, where she authored more than 2,800 opinions and heard more than 8,400 civil and criminal appeals. Ms Vogel (a member of the California Academy of Appellate Lawyers) represents major corporations and individuals primarily on appeal but also in trial court proceedings on case-dispositive motions.

## WALD, Peter A
Latham & Watkins LLP, San Francisco
415 395 8009
peter.wald@lw.com
*Featured in Securities (Nationwide), Litigation (California)*
See under Nationwide for profile.

## WALDMAN, Craig
Jones Day, San Francisco
415 875 5765
cwaldman@jonesday.com
*Featured in Antitrust (California)*
**Practice Areas:** Represents companies in antitrust government investigations and enforcement actions, merger reviews, counseling, and antitrust private litigation. He has extensive experience in mergers, agreements among competitors, vertical distribution issues, price discrimination, criminal antitrust matters, monopolization, and intellectual property licensing and trade regulation. Lectured at Stanford Business School, and Foothill College.

**Professional Memberships:** Executive Committee Member of the Antitrust Section of the State Bar of California.
**Career:** Attorney in the Federal Trade Commission's Mergers I division (1993-96). Adjunct professor at Hastings Law School.

## WALKER, Paul
Sidley Austin LLP, Los Angeles
213 896 6789
pwalker@sidley.com
*Featured in Real Estate (California)*
**Practice Areas:** Mr Walker is a national leader in representing investment banks, domestic and offshore funds, national banks, pension trusts and other sources of capital in (a) the origination of, and investment in, real estate loans, including structured, mezzanine and syndicated real estate-secured financings, (b) real estate loan workouts, restructurings, foreclosure actions, receiverships and bankruptcy actions, (c) loan portfolio purchase and sale transactions, (d) equity investments in real estate assets or investment vehicles, and (e) commercial leasing.
**Personal:** University of Pennsylvania, LLB, 1969; University of Notre Dame, BA, 1966. Admission: California.

## WALL, Daniel
Latham & Watkins LLP, San Francisco
415 395 8240
dan.wall@lw.com
*Featured in Antitrust (California)*
**Practice Areas:** Mr Wall's renowned Antitrust Practice focuses on mergers, single-firm conduct (monopolization), and the application of antitrust to high technology industries. He is a leading antitrust litigator and has represented clients in dozens of private lawsuits and government investigations into proposed mergers, suspected anti-competitive business practices and cartels.
**Professional Memberships:** Counsel Member, ABA Section of Antitrust Law (2005-08); numerous other antitrust section positions.
**Career:** Trial Lawyer, US DOJ, Antitrust Division (1980-82); Chair, Latham & Watkins Global Antitrust and Competition Practice (2002-10).
**Personal:** JD (magna cum laude), Santa Clara University School of Law, 1980; BA, University of California, Davis, 1977.

## WALPER, Thomas
Munger, Tolles & Olson LLP, Los Angeles
213 683 9193
Thomas.walper@mto.com
*Featured in Bankruptcy/Restructuring (California)*
**Practice Areas:** Bankruptcy, insolvency and reorganization matters nationwide.
**Professional Memberships:** Fellow, American College of Bankruptcy.
**Career:** Recognized by 'Turnarounds and Workouts' magazine as one of the country's top 12 bankruptcy lawyers in 1999 and 2002. Participated in many of the country's largest Chapter 11 cases, including Enron, FINOVA, Fruit of the Loom, USG, United Airlines, Refco, Residential Capital, Syms Corporation and Edison Mission Energy. Former head of restructuring at a

Connecticut-based hedge fund specializing in distressed investing.
**Publications:** Co-Author, The Creditors' Committee Manual, published by Warren Gorham & Lamont.
**Personal:** Loyola Law School; University of Southern California (BS, MBA).

## WALSH, Gerard J
Orrick, Herrington & Sutcliffe LLP, Los Angeles
gwalsh@orrick.com
*Featured in Real Estate (California)*
**Career:** Mr Walsh is a partner in the Real Estate group at Orrick. He has deep experience representing public and private entities, developers, corporate users and institutional investors (including pension and opportunity funds, and their advisors) in transactions throughout California and the United States. Mr Walsh focuses his practice on counseling clients in connection with the acquisition, restructuring and disposition of structured debt and equity portfolios across all real estate asset classes including hospitality portfolios, master planned communities, mixed use projects, corporate campuses, residential developments and commercial, industrial and retail centers.

## WAXMAN, Eric S
Skadden, Arps, Slate, Meagher & Flom LLP & Affiliates, Los Angeles
213 687 5251
ewaxman@skadden.com
*Featured in Litigation (California)*
**Practice Areas:** Has a broad commercial litigation practice, with a particular emphasis on securities litigation, director misconduct and related claims. Represents clients, including special committees, in matters involving federal and state securities laws, duties of corporate directors, SEC and stock exchange inquiries and investigations, and contests for corporate control. Has represented Credit Suisse; Leonard Green & Partners, L.P.; TPG Capital, L.P.; Apollo Group, Inc.; Oakley, Inc.; Valeant Pharmaceuticals and Westfield America, Inc. Mr Waxman has tried cases in both state and federal court.
**Career:** JD, University of California at Davis, 1982 (Editor, Law Review); BA, UCLA, 1979 (magna cum laude).

## WEAVER, Elizabeth
Fulbright & Jaworski LLP, Los Angeles
213 892 9290
eweaver@fulbright.com
*Featured in Environment (California)*
**Practice Areas:** Environmental; Toxic Torts; Climate Change; Litigation.
**Career:** Elizabeth Weaver has more than 30 years of experience in environmental law and litigation in a wide range of areas, focusing on Superfund, RCRA, and complex groundwater contamination cases. She has tried Superfund cases to judgment and has experience in all facets of CERCLA practice, including serving as common counsel at complex sites. Elizabeth is currently serving as counsel to a major petroleum company in con-

nection with a range of claims relating to the Portland Harbor Superfund Site.
**Personal:** JD, Duke University School of Law (1980); BA, Duke University (1977).

## WEBSTER, Pamela K
Buchalter Nemer, Los Angeles
213 891 5030
pwebster@buchalter.com
*Featured in Bankruptcy/Restructuring (California)*
**Practice Areas:** Corporate reorganizations, bankruptcy, equity receiverships, workouts and liquidations with a particular emphasis in entertainment, retail, building supply, and technology companies and regulated industries including insurance companies and healthcare providers.
**Professional Memberships:** Fellow, American College of Bankruptcy; Past Chair, California State Bar Committee on Federal Courts; Former Adjunct Professor of Law, Loyola University at Los Angeles, School of Law.
**Career:** Significant Assignments: Blockbuster (counsel to a major studio); MGM Studios (counsel to a significant counter party); EMAK Worldwide, Inc. (counsel to the Special Litigation Committee); Spansion LLC (counsel to the lender); North Pacific Group (counsel to the lender); Mission Insurance Group, Inc., et al. (counsel to the debtor). Represented the prevailing party in In re Grand Chevrolet, Inc., 25 F. 3d 728 (9th Cir. 1994)(cert denied).
**Personal:** U.C. Davis (JD, 1982).

## WEESE, Esther Chang
McDermott Will & Emery LLP, Los Angeles
310 788 1533
echang@mwe.com
*Featured in Healthcare (California)*
**Practice Areas:** Focused on healthcare transactions and regulatory matters. In addition to her transactional experience, handles healthcare regulatory issues, including fraud and abuse/Stark law, and HIPAA privacy for medical schools and academic medical centers. Helps draft contracts and consents, including leases, management agreements and affiliation agreements. Also counsels hospital clients on general counsel-type matters including bylaw and JCAHO reviews.
**Professional Memberships:** A member of the State Bar of California.
**Personal:** University of Southern California - Gould School of Law, JD, 2002; Boston University School of Public Health, MPH, 1999; Dartmouth College, BA, 1997.

## WEG, Howard J
Peitzman Weg LLP, Los Angeles
310 552 3100
hweg@peitzmanweg.com
*Featured in Bankruptcy/Restructuring (California)*
**Practice Areas:** Business restructuring, bankruptcies. Leading roles representing debtors, creditors, investors, buyers, sellers, committees in business workouts and chapter 11 cases, including Applause, Bonaventure Hotel, Petersen Trust, California Power Exchange, Carolco Pictures, Enron, Gateway Metro, Granada Hills Hospital, Halcyon Holding, Namco, PG&E, Shooting Gallery Pictures.

**Professional Memberships:** Regent and Board of Directors, American College of Bankruptcy. Past President, Financial Lawyers Conference. Chair, Education Committee, Executive Committee, California State Bar's Business Law Section.
**Career:** ABA, ABI, Financial Lawyers Conference, L.A. County Bar, State Bar of California.
**Publications:** Commercial Law Journal, California Bankruptcy Court Reporter, Real Estate Law Journal, Business Law News.

## WEHRLI, John
Latham & Watkins LLP, San Diego
858 523 5400
john.wehrli@lw.com
*Featured in Life Sciences (California)*
**Practice Areas:** John Wehrli's practice focuses exclusively on the representation of life science companies in the biotechnology, pharmaceutical, biosimilars and medical device industries, with particular focus on structuring and negotiating complex global "bet-the-company" intellectual property strategic transactions including, corporate partnering, collaborations, strategic alliances, joint ventures, spin-outs, co-marketing, co-promotion and strategic M&A transactions. He also applies his 28 years of industry experience as a research chemist, biologist, software engineer and entrepreneur to provide strategic advice and conduct forensic scientific and intellectual property due diligence to investors, buyers and sellers in public offerings, private placements and financial and strategic M&A transactions.

## WEINBERGER, Jeffrey I
Munger, Tolles & Olson LLP, Los Angeles
213 683 9127
jeffrey.weinberger@mto.com
*Featured in Antitrust (California)*
**Practice Areas:** Practices principally antitrust and patent litigation in trial and appellate courts. Recent cases include: multiple class actions and FTC litigation for AbbVie, Inc.; In Re Androgel Antitrust Litigation.
**Professional Memberships:** Past Chair, State Bar of California: Section of Antitrust and Unfair Competition Law; Past President, Association of Business Trial Lawyers of Southern California.
**Career:** Defense verdict in GlaxoSmithKline v. Abbott, 2011 Top California verdict, arguing antitrust case regarding pharmaceutical patent settlements in U.S. Supreme Court, March 2013.
**Personal:** Columbia Law School (magna cum laude); City College of New York (BA).

## WEIRICK, Bradford P
Gibson, Dunn & Crutcher LLP, Los Angeles
213 229 7765
bweirick@gibsondunn.com
*Featured in Corporate/M&A (California)*
**Practice Areas:** Co-Chair, Emerging Technologies Practice Group; Member, Corporate Department. Focuses on M&A, private equity investment transactions and public and private securities offerings. Substantial experience advising both acquirors/investors and target companies (both public and private) in connection with the negotiation of mergers and acquisitions, strategic

transactions and financings. Advises clients in the technology sector, public companies and private venture-stage companies.

**Professional Memberships:** Member, Advisory Board, U.S.C Technology Commercialization Alliance.

**Publications:** Co-author, Securities in the Electronic Age – A Practical Guide to the Law and Regulation, published in 2000 by Glasser LegalWorks.

**Personal:** JD, University of California (Boalt Hall), 1986.

### WEISS, Shirli Fabbri
DLA Piper LLP (US), San Diego
619 699 3650
shirli.weiss@dlapiper.com
*Featured in Litigation (California)*

**Practice Areas:** Litigation, Class Action, Product Liability.

**Professional Memberships:** Founding Director, Association of Business Trial Lawyers, San Diego Chapter; Founding Member and Master, American Inns of Court, J Clifford Wallace Chapter.

**Career:** She concentrates in civil trial practice in federal and state courts, emphasizing representation of companies and directors and officers in securities litigation and companies in mass product liability/consumer litigation; defense of government proceedings on behalf of corporate directors and officers; and representation of special committees of boards of directors.

**Personal:** JD, University of Miami School of Law (cum laude); BA, University of Massachusetts (cum laude).

### WEISSENBACH, John A
Kirkland & Ellis LLP, Los Angeles
213 680 8130
john.weissenbach@kirkland.com
*Featured in Corporate/M&A (California)*

**Practice Areas:** John A Weissenbach is a partner in the corporate practice of Kirkland's Los Angeles office. John's practice concentrates on business transactions and counseling, with a particular focus on structuring, negotiating, documenting and managing the legal aspects of leveraged buyouts, mezzanine and venture capital investments, public and private mergers and acquisitions, recapitalizations, financial restructurings, private placements, public offerings and risk capital fund formation.

**Personal:** Princeton University (AB, summa cum laude, Phi Beta Kappa, 1977); Harvard Law School (JD, cum laude, 1980).

### WEISSMAN, Barry L
Edwards Wildman Palmer, Los Angeles
310 860 8704
bweissman@edwardswildman.com
*Featured in Insurance (California)*

**Practice Areas:** Represents clients in complex reinsurance, commercial litigation and regulatory matters, including reinsurance arbitrations, litigation in all state and federal courts in California and New York, and international arbitrations. Has represented governments, insurance companies in receivership and reinsurance companies in dis-

pute-related matters, licensing and various legislative and regulatory matters.

**Professional Memberships:** International Association of Insurance Receivers; ARIAS; National Conference of Insurance Legislators.

**Personal:** University of Santa Clara School of Law, JD; University of California, Davis, BA.

### WEISSMANN, Henry
Munger, Tolles & Olson LLP, Los Angeles
213 683 9150
Henry.Weissmann@mto.com
*Featured in Energy & Natural Resources (California)*

**Practice Areas:** Represents regulated industries in administrative proceedings, class actions and challenges to government regulations. Recent matters: representing Southern California Edison Co. at the California PUC regarding extended outages at San Onofre Nuclear Generating Station and defending Verizon in a class action challenging third-party billing.

**Professional Memberships:** American Law Institute; Federalist Society (named Lawyer of the Year by L.A. Chapter in 2011); Conference of California Public Utility Counsel (past President).

**Career:** Partner at firm. Clerked for U.S. Supreme Court Justice Antonin Scalia.

**Personal:** Yale Law School; Claremont McKenna College (BA).

### WELCH, Richard J
Bingham McCutchen LLP, Los Angeles
213 229 8510
rick.welch@bingham.com
*Featured in Private Equity (Nationwide), Corporate/M&A (California)*

**Practice Areas:** Co-chairs Bingham's Corporate Area and is managing partner of the firm's LA office. Engages in general corporate law, focusing on mergers and acquisitions and representation of private equity funds and growth companies. Acted as the lead acquisition counsel in connection with more than 30 management buyouts and portfolio company dispositions, ranging from $250 million to $2 billion, in a wide array of industries. Serves as outside corporate and securities counsel to public and private companies. Has represented issuers and venture capital funds in numerous public and private financings.

**Personal:** Stanford Law School, JD, 1977; Duke University, BA, 1974.

### WHEELER, Raymond
Morrison & Foerster LLP, Palo Alto
650 813 5600
rwheeler@mofo.com
*Featured in Labor & Employment (California)*

**Practice Areas:** Handles employment discrimination and wage/hour class actions, trade secrets/employee-raiding disputes, injunctive actions, and wrongful discharge suits. Represents corporations in collective bargaining, union organizing, and decertification efforts.

**Professional Memberships:** Charter Fellow, College of Labor and Employment Lawyers; Member, and Former Chair, Developing Labor Law Committee, ABA Labor & Employment Law Section; National Advisory Board, Berkeley Journal of Employment and Labor Law.

**Career:** Best Lawyer in America for Labor and Employment Law and one of the top Bay Area Employment Lawyers (The Recorder).

**Personal:** BA, University of Texas; JD, Harvard; Clerk, Honorable Irving Goldberg, US Court of Appeals, Fifth Circuit.

### WILLIAMS, Bart H
Munger, Tolles & Olson LLP, Los Angeles
213 683 9295
Bart.Williams@mto.com
*Featured in Litigation (California)*

**Practice Areas:** High-stakes civil litigation, white-collar criminal defense, internal corporate investigations. Recent representations include: lead counsel for the nation's largest home mortgage lender in a nationwide enforcement action by the Department of Justice; arbitration decision for law firm client in multimillion dollar negligence action; lead counsel for Rambus, Inc. in multi-billion dollar antitrust case against Micron Technology, Inc.

**Professional Memberships:** Fellow, American College of Trial Lawyers.

**Career:** Co-Managing Partner 2005-07.

**Personal:** Starting guard for four years on the Yale Varsity Basketball Team; received the Joe McReynolds Award as the team's Most Valuable Defensive Player his senior year.

### WINTERS, Vernon M
Sidley Austin LLP, San Francisco
415 772 7441
winters@sidley.com
*Featured in Intellectual Property (California)*

**Practice Areas:** Vern Winters is known for leading teams in tough patent cases—and for winning them. Previous Chambers editions noted that he "impresses clients with his 'charismatic and persuasive style in the courtroom'" and that he is "renowned for his sophisticated handling of patent litigation" and his "exceptional knowledge of the law." Regarded as a thought leader in the field, he taught and co-taught Patent Litigation at the University of California, Berkeley School of Law from 2002-2010, and has authored amicus briefs in the Supreme Court and the Federal Circuit. He serves on the N.D. Cal.'s patent litigation Neutrals Panel.

### WITLIN, Scott
Barnes & Thornburg LLP, Los Angeles
310 284 3777
scott.witlin@btlaw.com
*Featured in Labor & Employment (California)*

**Practice Areas:** Scott J Witlin is a partner in the Los Angeles office of Barnes & Thornburg in its Labor and Employment Law Department. Mr Witlin regularly handles employment cases, including wage and hour class actions, before state and federal courts and state administrative agencies. He also handles traditional labor law matters including arbitrations, collective bargaining, union organizing campaigns, and unfair labor practice charges. He represents clients in entertainment and broadcasting, video game, manufacturing, retail, consumer and industrial products, and transportation industries.

**Personal:** Cornell University, School of Industrial and Labor Relations (BS, 1985) Stanford Law School (JD, 1988).

### WITTBRODT, Richard J
Gibbs Giden Locher Turner Senet & Wittbrodt LLP., Los Angeles
310 552 3400
rwittbrodt@ggltsw.com
*Featured in Construction (California)*

**Practice Areas:** Construction Litigation; Construction Law.

**Professional Memberships:** Incoming chair, LEGUS, an International Network of Law Firms; ABA, Forum on the Construction Industry, Division 12 Steering Committee Appointed Member; USGBC LEED AP.

**Career:** Mr Wittbrodt is the Managing Partner of the firm. His primary emphasis is in construction litigation, including prosecuting and defending claims of delay, disruption, defective construction, and contract disputes, for both public and private projects. Richard has represented owners and contractors on complex hospital, hotels, microchip plants, and school construction projects. He is also a frequent lecturer to many construction industry associations.

**Publications:** Published opinion: MW Erectors, Inc. v. Niederhauser Ornamental and Metal Works Company Inc., et al. (2006) 36 Cal.4th 412, 30 Cal.Rptr.3d 755. In addition, he is a prolific author of construction related industry topics.

**Personal:** Pepperdine University School of Law (JD, cum laude),1988; Golden Gate University (MBA, Tax), 1984; University of Michigan (BBA, with distinction, Accounting), 1980; CRA (Michigan, California).

### WOLFE, Scott N
Latham & Watkins LLP, San Diego
858 523 5400
scott.wolfe@lw.com
*Featured in Capital Markets (California), Life Sciences (California)*

**Practice Areas:** Scott Wolfe is the partner-in-charge of the North San Diego office and has practiced with the firm since 1978. He is a seasoned boardroom lawyer who has built up considerable experience advising public and private entities throughout all stages of development, from emerging growth to mature public companies. Clients, particularly in the biotech, telecom, high-technology and REIT industries, as well as investment banking firms, rely on his strategic business advice and legal acumen in the areas of public offerings, private placements, venture capital financings, complex debt offerings and partnering arrangements, as well as mergers and acquisitions.

### WYNNE, Richard
Jones Day, Los Angeles
213 243 2548
rlwynne@jonesday.com
*Featured in Bankruptcy/Restructuring (California), Bankruptcy/Restructuring (Nationwide)*

**Practice Areas:** Richard Wynne's practice focuses upon national debtor and creditor committee representations, significant distressed mergers and acquisition representations as well as counseling companies, board of directors and creditors committees with respect to fiduciary duties, legacy liability issues, and structuring complex commercial transactions. He is a Fellow of the American College of Bankruptcy and is listed in the K&A Restructuring Register as one of the top 72 Restructuring lawyers in the United States. **Personal:** Indiana University (BA, 1979); Columbia Law School (JD, 1982); Parker School of Foreign and Comparative Law, Columbia University (1983).

### YAFFE, Joseph M
Skadden, Arps, Slate, Meagher & Flom LLP & Affiliates, Palo Alto
650 470 4650
joseph.yaffe@skadden.com
*Featured in Employee Benefits & Executive Compensation (Nationwide), Employee Benefits & Executive Compensation (California)*
**Practice Areas:** As head of Skadden's West Coast Executive Compensation and Benefits Group, Mr Yaffe represents individuals and companies in the full range of matters relating to equity compensation and employee benefits plans, including in corporate transactions such as mergers and acquisitions. He regularly counsels senior executives nationwide in executive compensation matters, advises on tax-qualified plan issues, including issues relating to 401(k) and 403(b) plans, and represents clients in negotiations with the Internal Revenue Service and Department of Labor.
**Career:** JD, University of California, Davis School of Law, 1994, Law Review; AB, Columbia University, 1990.

### YANG, Debra Wong
Gibson, Dunn & Crutcher LLP, Los Angeles
213 229 7472
DWongYang@gibsondunn.com
*Featured in Litigation (California)*
**Practice Areas:** Co-Chair of the firm's Crisis Management Practice Group, the White Collar Defense and Investigations Practice Group and the Information Technology and Data Privacy Practice Group. Practice focuses on FCPA, securities, health care, corporate compliance, environmental, cyber intrusions and general litigation.
**Career:** U.S. Attorney for the Central District of California 2002-2007. Served on the Attorney General's Advisory Committee. Served as a DOJ monitor over medical device company and appointed by NY State Court as a monitor over medical distribution company. Former California State judge.
**Personal:** JD, Boston College, 1985; BA, Pitzer College, 1981.

### YEARWOOD, Kahlil
Dechert LLP, San Francisco
415 262 4522
kahlil.yearwood@dechert.com
*Featured in Real Estate (California)*
**Practice Areas:** Mr Yearwood is an associate in the finance and real estate practice and focuses on commercial real estate finance and capital markets. He also represents various CMBS lenders,

loan servicers, private equity firms, and debt fund managers in various transactions.
**Professional Memberships:** Member, California Bar; member, American Bar Association; member, CRE Financial Council.
**Personal:** University of California, Berkeley (BA, 2001); University of California Berkeley School of Law (JD, 2005, American Jurisprudence Award in Corporations).

### YOST, Daniel
Orrick, Herrington & Sutcliffe LLP, Menlo Park
650 614 7385
dyost@orrick.com
*Featured in IT & Outsourcing (California)*
**Career:** Mr Yost is co-chair of the Technology Transactions Group at Orrick. He is deeply experienced in negotiating complex commercial and technology transactions and in intellectual property counseling. He advises companies across various industries, including biotechnology, consumer electronics, energy, entertainment, hardware, Internet, media, semiconductor, services, software, telecommunications and wireless. Representative work includes advising on manufacturing, distribution and sale arrangements for technology companies; privacy, copyright and online pitfalls for Internet companies; domestic and international strategic collaborations; mergers, acquisitions, spin-offs and asset divestitures; service agreements; and venture capital and strategic investments. Clients range from start-ups to established public companies.

### YOST, Nicholas C
SNR Denton, San Francisco
415 882 2440
nicholas.yost@dentons.com
*Featured in Native American Law (Nationwide), Environment (California)*
See under Nationwide for profile.

### YOUNG, Marc D
Morrison & Foerster LLP, Los Angeles
213 892 5659
myoung@mofo.com
*Featured in Real Estate (California)*
**Practice Areas:** Chair of the firm's global Real Estate Group. Concentrates on real estate lending and loan workouts and restructurings. Represents lenders and borrowers in connection with the origination, servicing and restructuring of all types of real estate-related financings, and with respect to workout and restructuring options, intercreditor issues, sales and purchases of distressed debt and remedies. Clients include investment banks, commercial banks, capital companies, mortgage REITs, and opportunity funds.
**Professional Memberships:** California State, Los Angeles County and American Bar Associations.
**Personal:** University of Utah (BA, 1986); University of Utah College of Law (JD, 1991).

### YOUNG, Meryl L
Gibson, Dunn & Crutcher LLP, Irvine
myoung@gibsondunn.com
949 451 4229
*Featured in Litigation (California)*

**Practice Areas:** Co-Chair, Securities Litigation Practice Group. Handles complex business and commercial litigation, with an emphasis on securities and merger and acquisition litigation and related government investigations and proceedings. Represents companies, directors and officers, and accounting firms in class actions, shareholder derivative suits and malpractice actions in both state and federal courts. Has also handled a wide variety of other types of business litigation, including cases involving contract disputes, unfair business practices, misappropriation of trade secrets and other business torts, trademark and patent infringement, antitrust, real estate, employment and insurance issues.
**Personal:** JD, Columbia University, 1980, Harlan Fiske Stone Scholar.

### ZEPPA, Stephanie
SNR Denton, San Francisco
415 882 0319
stephanie.zeppa@dentons.com
*Featured in Corporate/M&A (California)*
**Practice Areas:** Stephanie has extensive experience in corporate finance and securities matters including capital raising transactions, mergers and acquisitions and strategic commercial transactions. Her primary focus is on emerging growth and technology companies, with company-side experience that spans the entire corporate lifecycle, including pre-incorporation planning, general corporate counseling, venture capital financings, strategic commercial transactions, and mergers and acquisitions. Stephanie also regularly works with investors and financial institutions in capital raising transactions for emerging growth companies. She has experience with companies in industries such as mobile, interative entertainment products, new media and digital health.

### ZOVICKIAN, Stephen
Bingham McCutchen LLP, San Francisco
415 393 2382
stephen.zovickian@bingham.com
*Featured in Construction (California)*
**Practice Areas:** Represents owners, public entities, contractors and design-builders in arbitrations, mediations, dispute review boards, and litigation in state and federal court, complemented by a broad base of experience in general commercial litigation. Serves as lead litigation counsel in major real estate, antitrust, intellectual property, partnership, products liability and commercial matters. Outside general counsel to leading California agricultural commodity associations in the wine grape, peach, raisin, prune and dairy industries.
**Personal:** University of California Berkeley School of Law (Boalt Hall), JD, 1977; University of California, Berkeley, BA, summa cum laude, 1974.

### ZUCKERMAN WILLIAMS, Susan
Loeb & Loeb LLP, Los Angeles
310 282 2063
swilliams@loeb.com
*Featured in Media & Entertainment (California)*
**Practice Areas:** Handled more than $2 billion in film financing involving slate deals, overall company capital raises and single picture deals

over past several years. Routinely handles transactions from all sides of the table, acting for financial institutions, major independent production companies, high net worth individuals, completion guarantors and distributors. Assists clients in obtaining soft money benefits — critical for providing financing for independent motion pictures and in negotiating and structuring complex multi picture distribution and co-financing agreements with major studios and international distribution companies.
**Personal:** USC, Gould School of Law (JD, 1986); Tufts University (BA, cum laude, 1983).

### ZUKLIE, Mitchell
Orrick, Herrington & Sutcliffe LLP, Menlo Park
650 614 7649
mzuklie@orrick.com
*Featured in Corporate/M&A (Northern California), Corporate/M&A (California)*
**Career:** Mitchell Zuklie is a nationally recognized emerging companies lawyer in Orrick's Silicon Valley office. He has been named Chair-Elect of Orrick, and assumes the role of Chairman and CEO on March 31, 2013. He focuses on the formation, financing and corporate counseling of technology businesses. He has completed several hundred venture capital financings and numerous public offerings, mergers, acquisitions and technology transactions. Clients include: Fisker Automotive, Nest Labs, Nanosolar, eHarmony, Royal Dutch Shell, Kleiner Perkins Caufield & Byers, Benchmark Capital and Bessemer Venture Partners. Mr Zuklie's leadership includes co-authoring the National Venture Capital Association's model venture capital financing forms.

## ALLEN MATKINS LECK GAMBLE MALLORY & NATSIS LLP

www.allenmatkins.com **tel:** 310 788 2400 **fax:** 310 788 2410

**Managing Partner:** David L Osias
Number of partners: 126
Number of other lawyers: 88

### Firm Overview:

Allen Matkins, founded in 1977, is a California-based law firm with approximately 220 attorneys in four major metropolitian areas of California: Los Angeles, Orange County, San Francisco and San Diego. The firm's core specialities include real estate, real estate and commercial finance, bankruptcy and creditor's rights, construction, land use, natural resources, environmental, corporate and securities, intellecutal property, joint ventures, taxation, employment and labor and dispute resolution and litigation in all these matters.

### Main Areas of Practice:

### Real Estate:

Allen Matkins continues to build upon its long-standing reputation as one of the leading real estate law firms in the United States, having assisted clients in all aspects of law relating to the development, management, financing, acquisition and disposition of real property assets. Because the firm has one of the largest real estate departments in the country, the firm's attorneys bring to every deal their relationships with major players in the real estate industry, including developers, brokers, buyers, sellers, governmental agencies, title companies and consultants.

### Land Use:

The Land Use Practice Group consists of attorneys, government specialists and planners whose mission is to assist the firm's clients in navigating the myriad of federal, state and local legal requirements affecting the environment to develop and maximize the use of real property. The team includes recognized experts on the Subdivision Map Act, planning and zoning law, and structuring public/private partnerships, including redevelopment projects.

### Litigation:

Allen Matkins' comprehensive Litigation Practice is recognized nationwide for its expertise in handling complex business disputes. Expertise ranges from all aspects of real estate litigation (including construction litigation, land use litigation, landlord tenant litigation and condemnation) to business litigation including corporate and partnership disputes, bankruptcy litigation, consumer class action litigation, securities litigation and all aspects of environmental, toxic tort and product litigation.

### Environmental & Natural Resources:

Allen Matkins provides clients with comprehensive administrative, regulatory, transactional and litigation services under all federal, state, and local environmental and land use laws, including laws addressing water and air quality, solid and hazardous waste, sediment contamination, toxic chemicals and pesticides, as well as endangered species and climate change.

### Energy:

The Energy Practice includes representation of owners and operators of domestic energy projects in all phases of financing, permitting, development, and operations, and is among the most comprehensive in California. The firm provides its clients with a deep understanding of the energy industry and practical guidance on virtually every aspect of their businesses.

### Construction:

The Construction Law Group attorneys serve a wide range of national and international clients, including general contractors, developers, owners, construction managers, subcontractors, suppliers, financial institutions, landlords, tenants, architects and engineers in connection with the design and construction of public works projects, publicly financed projects and private development projects.

### Bankruptcy & Creditors' Rights:

Allen Matkins' bankruptcy and creditors' rights attorneys are nationally recognized for their expertise in matters involving debtors and creditors, including out-of-court debt restructurings, state and federal court receiverships, real and personal property foreclosures, asset purchases, and Chapter 11 reorganization cases.

### Corporate & Securities:

The firm's attorneys provide comprehensive corporate representation to domestic and international, public and private companies operating in the biotechnology, finance, technology, banking, retail, manufacturing, natural resources, real estate, and services industries. The practice encompasses mergers and acquisitions, emerging company and venture capital, private equity, public company, and technology and intellectual property.

### Tax:

The Tax Group at Allen Matkins enjoys a national reputation for its sophisticated and innovative approaches to tax issues from taxation with a particular specialty in business organizations to pass-through entities such as partnerships, joint ventures and limited liability companies.

### Labor & Employment:

The firm's attorneys represent both large and small employers, across diverse industries, from *Fortune* 500 companies to start-ups. The practice focuses on litigation, preventive counseling, training, policy preparation and implementation, and alternative dispute resolution.

### Banking & Financial Institutions:

The Banking and Financial Institutions Group provides a broad range of legal services in financing transactions, loan servicing, loan purchase and sale transactions, management of distressed debt and exercise of creditor remedies, bankruptcy, and financial institutions litigation.

### Clients:

The firm's clients include AT&T Corp., Black & Decker, Blackstone Real Estate Advisors, Capmark Finance, Inc., CB Richard Ellis, D.R. Horton, Google, Inc., Hoag Memorial Hospital, Imperial Irrigation District, Kilroy Realty, Legg Mason, Lennar, Metropolitan Life Insurance Co., Mitchell Engineering, Resmark Equity Partners, Sares-Regis Group, Sunstone Hotel Investors, Inc., The Home Depot, Tishman Speyer Properties, Wells Fargo Bank and Westfield America Corp.

### OFFICES

**CALIFORNIA**

**IRVINE:** 1900 Main Street, 5th Floor, CA 92614-7321
Tel: 949 553 1313  Fax: 949 553 8354

**LOS ANGELES:** 1901 Avenue of the Stars, Suite 1800, CA 90067-6019
Tel: 310 788 2400  Fax: 310 788 2410

**LOS ANGELES:** 515 South Figueroa Street, 9th Floor, CA 90071-3398
Tel: 213 622 5555  Fax: 213 620 8816

**SAN DIEGO:** 501 West Broadway, 15th Floor, San Diego, CA 92101-3541
Tel: 619 233 1155  Fax: 619 233 1158

**SAN FRANCISCO:** Three Embarcadero Center, 12th Floor, CA 94111-4074
Tel: 415 837 1515  Fax: 415 837 1516

# Allen Matkins

# BIRD MARELLA BOXER WOLPERT NESSIM DROOKS & LINCENBERG PC

**www.birdmarella.com** **tel:** 310 201 2100 **fax:** 310 201 2110

**Managing Partners:** Paul Chan, Thomas Reichert
Number of shareholders: 18  Number of lawyers: 40
Languages: *English, Chinese, French, Korean, Hebrew, Hindi, Portuguese, Spanish*

### Firm Overview:

Established in 1981 and based in Los Angeles, Bird Marella Boxer Wolpert Nessim Drooks & Lincenberg engages solely in the practice of complex civil and white collar criminal litigation. A litigation boutique by design, the firm is comprised of trial lawyers who defend national and multinational corporations, government agencies, closely held companies, partnerships, and individuals. Bird Marella represents plaintiffs on a selective basis.

### Main Areas of Practice:

**Commercial Litigation:**
Commercial litigation is a defining practice of Bird Marella. The firm has represented clients in federal and state courts and arbitrations in a broad range of disputes that mirror the evolution of global commerce during the past 40 years. The firm is distinctive among litigation boutiques for providing dual civil and white collar criminal counsel, which is of paramount importance for clients facing parallel proceedings.   The growing Pacific Rim practice is also a notable area of firm strength. Several firm attorneys are former Assistant United States Attorneys, many served as judicial clerks, and all are trial-tested.
**Contacts:** Terry Bird, Paul Chan, Mark Drooks, Ronald Nessim, Ekwan Rhow

**Securities Litigation:**
Bird Marella regularly represents parties in disputes involving corporate actions and securities matters, including both public companies as well as closely-held business organizations. The securities litigation practice has involved matters throughout the United States and abroad. In private civil cases, the firm has represented corporations, individuals or corporate committees in individual, derivative, and class action matters in every major commercial center in the country. In SEC investigations, the firm has represented clients in numerous informal and formal investigations, Wells submissions, and post-complaint lawsuits in federal courts across the country. The firm has also represented companies or shareholders in contentious disputes over corporate management and control. Bird Marella also maintains an active practice representing claimants or respondents in broker-dealer FINRA arbitrations and has actively represented various broker-dealers in hundreds of disputes.
**Contacts:** Mark Drooks, Thomas Reichert

**White Collar Criminal Defense & Internal Investigations:**
Bird Marella defends clients in government investigations, trials and appeals in all types of business crimes, with significant specialties in areas of securities,

health care, tax and other fraud cases. The consequences of criminal investigations and prosecutions can run the spectrum, from a hit on stock prices to lifetime debarment and incarceration. The firm mitigates clients' exposure by engaging in discreet and productive negotiations with government agencies where appropriate. Frequently, the firm is able to persuade authorities to forego prosecution and decline charging our clients. Several Bird Marella attorneys have served as former federal prosecutors. Firm attorneys frequently receive ratings as preeminent in white collar criminal defense, and serve as leaders in prominent white collar crime bar associations. When clients' interests are best served by a jury trial, Bird Marella's top-tier trial attorneys are well equipped to go the distance in federal and state courts.
**Contacts:** Terry Bird, Benjamin Gluck, Gary Lincenberg, Vincent Marella, Ronald Nessim

**Entertainment and Intellectual Property Law:**
Bird Marella attorneys have attained industry-altering settlements and verdicts in profit participation cases for producers and creators of iconic television programming and were at the forefront of anti-piracy enforcement actions by Hollywood studios. Firm attorneys represent talent, producers, executives, broadcasters and others in entertainment. In high exposure matters the firm will draw upon its civil, criminal and regulatory practices, a unique combination of resources for an entertainment law firm to offer.
**Contacts:** Paul Chan, Mitch Kamin, Ronald Nessim

**Professional Liability Litigation:**
Since Bird Marella's inception, it has been a "go to" law firm for international, AmLaw100, regional, and boutique law firms and individual lawyers needing advice and representation in matters concerning their legal practice. The firm represents legal professionals, partnerships and firms at trial, in arbitration and mediation, and at the pre-litigation stage of disputes. The firm has represented numerous law firms, from global firms to small boutiques, involving claims

brought by their clients including malpractice claims, breach of fiduciary duty claims, billing disputes and related claims for fraud or other torts, whether such claims arise in a litigation or transactional engagement. Bird Marella also regularly represents law firms or lawyers who are in disputes arising from law firm dissolutions, and partner and partner group departures.
**Contacts:** Joel Boxer, Mark Drooks

**Appellate:**
Bird Marella's appellate attorneys represent clients in complex and important appeals before the United States Supreme Court, the Supreme Court of California, the United States Court of Appeals for the Ninth Circuit, and the California Courts of Appeal.
**Contact:** Thomas Freeman

**Key Clients:**
Bird Marella clients range from Fortune 500 technology leaders, Wall Street executives and health care providers to global retailers, entertainment companies, Internet start-ups, media and sports figures, and international investors and investment advisors. Representative clients include: Charles Schwab, Inc.; Los Angeles Metropolitan Transportation Authority; LG Electronics USA, Inc.; Mattel, Inc.; McDonnell Douglas Corporation; Nokia, Inc.; Samsung Telecommunications America LLC; Toyota Motor Sales U.S.A., Inc.; Western Digital Corporation; The Walt Disney Company.

---

## PRACTICE AREAS

Antitrust Law
Appellate
Business & Commercial Law
Class Action Litigation
Copyright Law
Employment Law
Entertainment Law
Environmental Law
ERISA Litigation
Health Care Fraud & Abuse
Insurance Coverage Disputes
Intellectual Property
Legal Malpractice & Law Firm Disputes
Municipal & Public Utility Law
Products Liability
Real Estate Litigation
RICO (Civil & Criminal)
Securities Law
Tax & Tax Shelter Litigation
White Collar Crimes

## OFFICES

CALIFORNIA

**LOS ANGELES:** 1875 Century Park East, Suite 2300, CA 90067  Email: info@birdmarella.com

# BUCHALTER NEMER

**www.**buchalter.com **tel:** 213 891 0700

**President/CEO/Managing Partner:** Adam Bass
Number of partners: 78   Number of lawyers: 141

## Firm Overview:

Buchalter Nemer is a full-service business law firm representing local, regional and national clients in nine major areas of practice and their subspecialties, among them: banking and finance, corporate, health care, insolvency and financial solutions, litigation, labor and employment, intellectual property, real estate, and tax and estate planning. Buchalter Nemer has offices in Los Angeles, Orange County, San Francisco and Scottsdale. The firm represents an array of industries that include apparel, aircraft, entertainment, financial institutions, solar and renewable energy, technology, transportation and wineries.

## Main Areas of Practice:

### Banking & Finance:

Buchalter Nemer Bank and Finance clients include regional, national and international banks, commercial finance companies, asset-based lenders and specialty lenders, mortgage companies, factors and equipment lessors. The Group's expertise includes secured credit facilities, asset-based lending, financial restructuring, loan workouts, senior/junior secured lending, equipment leasing, asset securitization, acquisition and mezzanine financing, syndicated and club deals, loan portfolio acquisitions and cross-border transactions.
**Contact:** Hamid Namazie **Tel:** 213 891 5544
**Email:** hnamazie@buchalter.com

### Corporate:

Representative transactions handled by Buchalter Nemer's Corporate Practice Group include formation of business entities, contracts, compensation plans, venture capital and private equity financing, IPOs, public company filings and stockholder relations, mergers, acquisitions and joint ventures, fund formation and investment advisor issues, public company regulatory requirements, licensing, strategic partnership or joint venture agreements, family business succession, recapitalizations and securities transactions.
**Contact:** Mark Bonenfant **Tel:** 213 891 5020
**Email:** mbonenfant@buchalter.com

### Health Care:

Buchalter Nemer's Health Care Practice Group clients include health systems, hospitals, academic medical centers, independent practice associations, Federally Qualified Health Centers, medical groups, physicians, provider trade organizations, health care lenders, drug and device companies, specialty hospitals, ambulatory surgery centers, management services organizations, emergency room and hospitalist staffing companies, med-spas and nonprofit research organizations.
**Contact:** Carol Lucas **Tel:** 213 891 5611
**Email:** clucas@buchalter.com

### Insolvency & Financial Solutions:

The firm has a comprehensive national insolvency and restructuring practice active in representing creditor committees in real estate, retail, healthcare and entertainment related bankruptcies, secured and unsecured creditors and debtors in various corporate reorganizations, creditors, purchasers, domestic and foreign commercial banks, investment banks, other lending institutions and distressed debt investors in bankruptcy cases and out of court restructurings.
**Contact:** Bernard D Bollinger **Tel:** 213 891 5009
**Email:** bbollinger@buchalter.com

### Intellectual Property:

The firm's Intellectual Property Group represents an array of industries, from traditional businesses to knowledge-based and alternative energy industries. Buchalter IP attorneys provide intensive strategic counseling, manage the full range of intellectual property transactions, and engage in patent and trademark prosecution and litigation in domestic and international IP markets.
**Contact:** Farah Bhatti **Tel:** 949 224 6291
**Email:** fbhatti@buchalter.com

### Labor & Employment:

Buchalter Nemer Labor and Employment attorneys provide clients with protective counsel that minimizes risk exposure. Risk management solutions include preemptive advice, review of procedures and practices, preparation and implementation of employee handbooks and day-to-day counseling regarding investigations, employee feedback, discipline, leaves-of-absence, return-to-work issues, and terminations. Other key areas of practice include wage and hour class action litigation, sexual harassment training, and litigation defense.
**Contact:** Paul Bressan **Tel:** 213 891 5220
**Email:** pbressan@buchalter.com

### Litigation:

Buchalter Nemer's Litigation Practice Group is known for its financial institutions litigation practice, unfair competition, fraud and misappropriation of trade secrets, RICO claims, product liability, and wage and hour class action litigation. They are also leaders in Receivership Law. Clients include public and privately held companies, insurance companies, startups, nonprofits and governmental agencies in complex multi-issue cases ranging from contract breach to statutory violations.
**Contact:** George Stephan **Tel:** 213 891 5222
**Email:** gstephan@buchalter.com

### Real Estate:

The firm's Real Estate Practice Group has expertise in finance, purchases and sales, leasing, tax credits, land use, water and energy issues, environmental issues and transportation. Clients include institutional lenders, landlords/tenants of commercial properties, airports and investors.
**Contact:** Michael Williamson **Tel:** 213 891 5074
**Email:** mwilliamson@buchalter.com

### Tax & Estate Planning:

Buchalter Nemer's Tax and Estate Planning Practice Group provides tax planning and business structuring for corporations, limited liability companies, partnerships and individuals. Their expertise includes business tax planning, international tax planning, real estate tax credit transactions, real estate tax planning, executive compensation, employee benefits, estate planning and wealth transfer.
**Contact:** Philip J Wolman **Tel:** 213 891 5390
**Email:** pwolman@buchalter.com

## PRACTICE AREAS

Bank & Finance
Corporate
Health Care
Insolvency & Financial Solutions
Intellectual Property
Labor & Employment
Litigation
Real Estate
Tax & Estate Planning

## OFFICES

**CALIFORNIA**
**LOS ANGELES:** 1000 Wilshire Boulevard, Suite 1500, CA 90017-2457
Tel: 213 891 0700   Fax: 213 896 0400

**ORANGE COUNTY:** 18400 Von Karman Avenue, Suite 800, Irvine, CA 92612-0514
Tel: 949 760 1121   Fax: 949 720 0182

**SAN FRANCISCO:** 55 Second Street, Suite 1700, CA 94105-3493
Tel: 415 227 0900   Fax: 415 227 0770

**ARIZONA**
**SCOTTSDALE:** 16435 North Scottsdale Road, Suite 440, AZ 85254-1754
Tel: 480 383 1800   Fax: 480 824 9400

BuchalterNemer
A Professional Law Corporation

# CALDWELL LESLIE & PROCTOR, P.C.

**www.**caldwell-leslie.com **tel:** 213 629 9040 **fax:** 213 629 9022

**Managing Shareholders:** Christopher G Caldwell, Joan Mack, Robyn C Crowther
**Founding Shareholders:** Christopher G Caldwell, Michael R Leslie
Number of shareholders: 13
Number of other attorneys: 17

**OFFICES**

CALIFORNIA

**LOS ANGELES:** 725 South Figueroa Street, 31st Floor,
CA 90017
Tel: 213 629 9040   Fax: 213 629 9022

**Firm Overview:**

Caldwell Leslie & Proctor, PC is a 30-lawyer firm specializing in complex litigation. From its downtown Los Angeles offices, Caldwell Leslie handles matters throughout the United States, combining the superior skills of a large firm with the responsiveness of a small firm. Caldwell Leslie's record of success at trial and in alternative dispute resolution has attracted a loyal roster of blue-chip clients including *Fortune* 500 corporations, closely held businesses, major studios and networks, and foreign companies. Prominent law firms regularly rely on Caldwell Leslie for excellent representation in high-stakes litigation. The firm also has an enviable record in appellate proceedings in California and federal courts, where its vigorous advocacy has resulted in precedent-setting rulings, landmark verdicts and highly satisfied clients. The firm's attorneys reflect the diversity of its clients: over 60 percent are women and minorities, and most have held prestigious federal judicial clerkships. All have top-tier experience and academic credentials.

**Main Areas of Practice:**

**Commercial Litigation:**
Caldwell Leslie handles a wide range of commercial cases, including antitrust, lender liability, licensing, intellectual property, copyright, trademark, insurance coverage, professional liability, real estate and international trade matters. The firm handles both plaintiff and defense work, as well as cases in all different forums, from federal and state court to ADR proceedings (such as FINRA, AAA and UNCITRAL). Many of the cases handled by the firm are class actions, and the firm has a record of success on class certification motions. Caldwell Leslie attorneys are particularly effective in seeking or defending pre-judgment remedies, and have a spectacular record of resolving even the messiest cases on summary judgment. They also have extensive experience litigating issues of constitutional law, civil rights, financial services, insurance and insolvency.
**Contact:** Christopher G Caldwell, Michael R Leslie

**Environmental Law:**
Caldwell Leslie has particular expertise in helping clients deal with federal as well as California environmental laws and regulations, which are among the strictest and most complex in the nation. Caldwell Leslie's lawyers have represented numerous clients in environmental litigation in state and federal trial courts and courts of appeal, as well as before administrative agencies. The firm has successfully handled claims of environmental contamination under the Clean Air Act, Clean Water Act, CERCLA and RCRA and their state court analogs, Proposition 65, Section 17200 unfair business practices claims, nuisance, trespass, contribution, and toxic torts.
**Contact:** Michael R Leslie

**White-Collar Crime & Government Compliance:**
Caldwell Leslie's White-Collar Practice Group has handled matters ranging from major federal tax and securities fraud cases to regulatory matters prosecuted by local authorities, from trials in both the federal and state courts to grand jury investigations that are resolved before

anything becomes public. Clients regularly call on Caldwell Leslie to conduct timely, accurate, confidential internal investigations and assist in development and implementation of corporate compliance programs. Caldwell Leslie has handled numerous matters before the Securities and Exchange Commission; fended off government asset forfeiture actions; and successfully represented clients before the California State Bar, the California Medical Board, the State Insurance Board, the Los Angeles City Ethics Commission, the Federal Election Commission and the Fair Political Practices Commission.
**Contact:** Michael J Proctor, David K Willingham

**Entertainment & Intellectual Property:**
Southern California is home to the world's leading entertainment companies, including Warner Bros., Sony Pictures, Twentieth Century Fox, CBS Broadcasting and Paramount Pictures. These and other studios, networks and production entities have come to rely on Caldwell Leslie's litigation and counseling expertise in matters ranging from intellectual property disputes and trademark infringement to digital piracy and invasion of privacy; from enforcement of licenses to internal investigations of improper conduct. The firm's lawyers have extensive experience resolving contractual and commercial disputes in the industry – expertise which extends to such cutting-edge issues as new media platforms, digitized programming, cybersquatting and de-encryption technology.
**Contact:** Christopher G Caldwell, Linda M Burrow

**Appellate:**
Caldwell Leslie is regularly retained as appellate counsel. The firm has established an enviable record in appeals and extraordinary writ proceedings in the California and federal courts, and has achieved precedent-setting results in environmental, civil rights, constitutional, and other matters. More than a quarter of Caldwell Leslie attorneys are former federal appellate court clerks, whose expertise has helped their clients obtain reversals in many cases that seemed hopeless.
**Contact:** Christopher G Caldwell, Michael R Leslie

**Professional Liability Litigation:**
Caldwell Leslie offers particular expertise in professional liability cases involving claims of malpractice by attorneys and accountants. Several members of the firm lecture regularly on issues involving legal ethics and malpractice prevention, and one shareholder serves on the Los Angeles County Bar Committee on Professional Responsibility and Ethics.
**Contact:** Christopher G Caldwell, Joan Mack

**Labor & Employment:**
Caldwell Leslie works with clients to minimize the risk that personnel actions will result in claims and that claims will become lawsuits. When the sometimes unavoidable lawsuit is filed, the firm helps clients minimize disruption to their business and the expense of defending the claims, while making litigation decisions that are driven by their business goals. Caldwell Leslie attorneys have been remarkably successful in making employment cases go away on summary judgment. In addition, Caldwell Leslie has substantial experience litigating covenants not to compete and misappropriation of trade secrets, as well as advising highly compensated individuals as to their options and obligations upon separating from their former employers.
**Contact:** Robyn C Crowther

**Clients:**
The firm's clientele includes Fortune 500 corporations, closely held businesses, major studios and networks, state and local agencies, foreign companies, community groups, professionals and prominent law firms. Representative clients include: CBS Corporation; Gap Inc.; Morrison & Foerster, LLP; Shell Oil Company; Sony Pictures Entertainment; 20th Century Fox Film Corporation; Universal Music Group; Viacom Inc.; and Warner Bros. Entertainment, Inc.

# Caldwell Leslie

# DICKENSON, PEATMAN & FORARTY

**Managing Directors:** J. Scott Gerien, Gregory J. Walsh
Number of Directors: 10
Number of lawyers: 22
Languages: English, French, Spanish

## Firm Overview:

Based in the Northern California wine country, Dickenson, Peatman & Fogarty serves businesses and individuals throughout the world from its offices in Napa and Sonoma Counties. The firm has been a partner to the wine and hospitality industries since 1964, assisting in a wide range of matters including alcohol beverage law, business and corporate dealings, land use matters, labor and employment, civil litigation, intellectual property, real property transactions, and estate planning and probate. The attorneys and staff of Dickenson, Peatman & Fogarty have a long tradition of community involvement and have served in leadership roles in social, cultural, educational, financial and political institutions.

## Main Areas of Practice:

### Alcohol Beverage:

3 Directors; 10 fee earners based in Napa and Sonoma Counties

- Representation of numerous winery and alcohol beverage producers in acquisition of production and sale licenses from California Alcohol Beverage Control (ABC) and Alcohol and Tobacco Tax and Trade Bureau (TTB), as well as transfers of licenses between entities
- Appearance before California ABC defending clients in administrative proceedings related to license revocation
- Drafting and submission of formal comments responding to Notices of Proposed Rulemaking by the Alcohol, Tobacco, Tax & Trade Bureau on policies governing petitions to establish and modify American Viticultural Areas
- Represented Napa Valley Vintners before California Supreme Court in defending constitutionality of state law protecting Napa Valley appellation of origin

**Key Clients:** Cakebread Cellars, Anchor Brewing Co., Napa Valley Vintners Association, Harlan Estate

**Contact:** Bahaneh Hobel  Tel: 707 252 7122
Email: bhobel@dpf-law.com

### Business:

3 Directors; 8 fee earners based in Napa and Sonoma Counties

- Represented Accolade Wines North America, Inc. in its acquisition of Geyser Peak, Atlas Peak and XYZin brands and inventory from Ascentia Wine Estate, LLC and in its wine production and storage facility lease and vineyard leases with an affiliate of Entertainment Properties Trust
- Represented numerous individuals and wine companies in the purchase and acquisition of premium residential, vineyard and winery properties in Sonoma, Mendocino, Monterey and throughout the state of California
- Represented group of Chinese investors in acquisition of Napa Valley vineyard
- Represented numerous growers and winery owners in connection with complex grape purchase agreements and vineyard leases in a variety of long-term circumstances

**Key Clients:** Accolade Wines, Trefethen Vineyards, Anderson's Conn Valley, Hess Collection, Robert Biale Vineyards

**Contact:** James W Terry  Tel: 707 252 7122
Email: jterry@dpf-law.com

### Intellectual Property:

1 Director; 5 fee earners based in Napa County

- Responsible for maintenance of domestic and international trademark portfolios for two of the five largest U.S. wineries and act as U.S. trademark counsel for wineries from Spain, France, Italy, South Africa, Chile, Brazil, Australia and New Zealand, including two of the largest wineries in Spain and Australia
- Prosecution of over 1,500 trademark applications at USPTO for alcohol beverage products; appearance before Trademark Trial and Appeals Board in over 350 proceedings
- Successfully defended Australian winery in trademark infringement action brought by a U.S. importer in U.S. District Court for the Eastern District of New York
- Successfully obtained preliminary injunction in U.S. District Court for the Northern District of California on behalf of Napa Valley winery enjoining use of trademark by Australian winery
- Obtained judgment for Spanish winery defeating trademark application at USPTO by Tequila producer for mark confusingly similarity to Spanish winery's mark

**Key Clients:** Sutter Home Winery, Ste. Michelle Wine Estates, Antinori California, Miguel Torres, Accolade Wines

**Contact:** J Scott Gerien  Tel: 707 252 7122
Email: sgerien@dpf-law.com

## PRACTICE AREAS

Alcohol Beverage
Business
Intellectual Property
Labor & Employment
Land Use
Litigation
Real Property
Trusts & Estates

## OFFICES:

CALIFORNIA

**NAPA:** 1455 First Street, Suite 301, 94559
Tel: 707 252 7122  Fax: 707 255 6876
Email: dpf@dpf-law.com

**SANTA ROSA:** 50 Old Courthouse Square, Suite 200, 95404
Tel: 707 524 7000  Fax: 707 546 6800
Email: dpf@dpf-law.com

### Labor & Employment:

1 Director; 5 fee earners based in Sonoma County

- Represented purchasing wine company in due diligence and risk analysis of employment issues related to winery purchase
- Prepared all manner of employment documents for wine industry clients including employee handbooks, severance agreements, executive compensation agreements, job descriptions and counseling/termination records
- Obtained dismissals of state and federal administrative actions for winery clients alleging discrimination, harassment, retaliation, whistle blowing and wage and hour claims
- Successfully resolved CalOSHA citations related to seriously injured employees for large and small wineries
- Counseled and represented wine industry clients in the defense and prosecution of state court alleging misappropriation of trade secrets under the Uniform Trade Secrets Act

**Contact:** Gregory J Walsh  Tel: 707 524 7000
Email: gwalsh@dpf-law.com

### Land Use:

4 fee earners based in Napa County

- Advise clients on vineyard and winery establishment and operations, including erosion control plans, use permits, lot line adjustments and compliance with the California Environmental Quality Act (CEQA)
- Advise wine industry trade associations throughout California on local, state and federal regulations affecting vineyards and wineries

# DURIE TANGRI LLP

**www.durietangri.com tel:** 415 362 6666 **fax:** 415 236 6300

**Managing Partner:** Johanna Calabria
**Partners:** Daralyn J Durie, Ragesh K Tangri, Mark A Lemley, Michael H Page, Ryan M Kent, Clement S Roberts, Joshua H Lerner, Joseph C Gratz, Johanna Calabria, David F McGowan
Number of partners: 10   Number of other lawyers: 8

### Firm Overview:

Durie Tangri's attorneys choose to practice law together because they like and respect each other and share a deep commitment to their clients and the firm's underlying values. They are passionate about what they do and this enthusiasm translates into results. Durie Tangri focuses on diverse areas of complex civil litigation, including patent, copyright, privacy litigation, professional liability and class actions.

### Main Areas of Practice:

**Patent:**

Durie Tangri represents companies in patent litigation across the country in cases ranging from biotechnology to e-commerce, solar technology to firewalls.
The firm is trial counsel for Genentech, one of the original and largest biotechnology companies in California, in fending off multiple challenges brought against Genentech's Cabilly patent, which generates hundreds of millions in licensing revenue for Genentech. Durie Tangri successfully defended Guidewire Software in a multi-patent and trade-secret case brought by global consulting giant Accenture. Following years of hard fought litigation in three jurisdictions, the firm successfully brought summary judgment that the key asserted patents were invalid for lack of patentable subject matter, one of the first favorable post-Bilski summary judgment rulings (which is now on appeal). Thereafter the case settled on terms very favorable to Guidewire. This victory paved the way for Guidewire's public offering, the first tech IPO of 2012. The firm also represented Palo Alto Networks, in litigation brought by its larger rival, Fortinet. Fortinet alleged infringement of four patents drawn to firewall technology, trade secret misappropriation and breach of contract. The firm won summary judgment that Palo Alto Networks did not infringe two patents outright and that it did not literally infringe the other two patents, thereby significantly reducing scope of case, which settled shortly thereafter. Durie Tangri represented West Interactive Corporation against patent claims brought by Phoenix Solutions, which claimed to have invented the core speech processing technology underlying automated voice response systems. The firm won summary judgment on all four patents-in-suit—three on summary judgment of invalidity and one on summary judgment of non-infringement—only nine months after the case was filed, which the firm successfully defended on appeal. Durie Tangri also represented seven defendants— Yelp!, Netflix, eHarmony.com, Ticketmaster, LinkedIn, TheStreet.com and Priceline.com—in a lawsuit alleging infringement of a patent related to personalization of Internet content. The firm won summary judgment of

invalidity on behalf of Yelp!, which also effectively resolved the cases against the other six defendants, and then successfully defended the judgment on appeal. Durie Tangri represented Ticketmaster (now Live Nation) in a patent fight against competitor Flash Seats in which the firm secured a summary judgment victory of both noninfringement and invalidity on five claims, and then successfully defended that judgment on appeal.
**Contact:** Daralyn Durie

**Copyright:**

Durie Tangri has extensive experience in groundbreaking copyright cases. The firm's lawyers have litigated copyright cases at every level, including the United States Supreme Court, and have participated in many of the precedent-setting cases in the past decade including Grokster, Napster, LimeWire, Perfect 10, UMG v. Augusto, and Google Book Search. The firm represented the Spanish website RojaDirecta in the Southern District of New York in litigation challenging the United States government's seizure of its domain names on the basis of alleged copyright infringement, the first successful challenge to the government's domain name seizure program. The firm successfully represented Troy Augusto in a precedent-setting Ninth Circuit appeal defending its trial court win establishing the fair use right to resell lawfully obtained promotional CDs. Durie Tangri also secured a decisive victory at the pleadings stage on behalf of Eventbrite in a case alleging copying of a competitor's website content. At present, the firm represents DISH Network in defending its Hopper DVR against copyright challenges brought by each of the major television networks. Along with co-counsel, the firm succeeded in persuading the district court to deny a preliminary injunction, and are defending that win on appeal. The firm represents Google in connection with Google's project of scanning books in major academic library collections and Linden Lab in cases alleging in-world copying of virtual objects in Second Life and challenging Second Life's virtual land ownership rules. Durie Tangri also represents resellers challenging Adobe's restrictive software licensing practices in the Ninth Circuit. The firm filed an amicus brief in Kirtsaeng v. John Wiley & Sons on behalf of independent booksellers that was relied upon by the Supreme Court in

reaffirming copyright's first sale doctrine.
**Contacts:** Mark Lemley, Michael Page, Joseph Gratz

**Privacy:**

Durie Tangri attorneys are at the forefront of virtually all of today's cutting edge Internet privacy cases. The firm was lead counsel in In re Quantcast Advertising Cookie Litigation, a multi-party class action regarding the "respawning" of http cookies used in behavioral advertising. The firm represented Google and its AdMob subsidiary in the multidistrict In re iPhone litigation, which combined a score of suits alleging improper disclosure and use of personally identifiable information and geolocation data. Durie Tangri represented several parties in the Kissmetrics class actions, and were also involved in the pending CarrierIQ privacy class actions. Durie Tangri represents Twitter in privacy litigation. The firm also successfully represented Pandora in the Lalo v. Apple and Freeman v. Apple class actions, and in a Flash Cookie privacy class action litigation, achieving dismissals in all three cases. And the firm represented several parties in the In re Facebook Privacy Litigation and In re Zynga Privacy Litigation class actions, which alleged improper disclosure of Facebook user id's via referrer URLs.
**Contact:** Michael Page

**Professional Liability:**

Durie Tangri attorneys have represented many leading law firms, both Bay Area based and nationwide, in defense of professional liability claims. The firm's breadth of substantive disciplines and commitment to a "generalist" approach to litigation make its lawyers well-suited to step into virtually any professional liability claim, regardless of the underlying field of law.
**Contact:** Ragesh Tangri

**Clients:**

Durie Tangri's clients include Google, Genentech, Netflix, Twitter, THX, Linden Lab, LinkedIn, Yelp!, Shutterfly, Pandora Media, Palo Alto Networks and Guidewire Software.

### PRACTICE AREAS

Intellectual Property
Privacy
Contract & Commercial
Professional Liability
Class Actions

### OFFICES

CALIFORNIA
**SAN FRANCISCO:** 217 Leidesdorff Street, CA 94111
Tel: 415 362 6666   Fax: 415 236 6300
Email: jcalabria@durietangri.com

# Durie Tangri

# FENWICK & WEST LLP

www.fenwick.com

**Chairman:** Gordon K Davidson
**Managing Partner:** Kathryn J Fritz
Number of Partners: 107
Number of other lawyers: 194

## Firm Overview:

Fenwick & West LLP is a national law firm that provides comprehensive legal services to technology and life sciences clients of national and international prominence. The firm has approximately 300 attorneys, with offices in Silicon Valley, San Francisco and Seattle.

## Main Areas of Practice:

### Corporate:

Fenwick & West provides services to technology and life sciences companies at all stages of development, from early start-ups to mature, publicly-traded corporations.

**Mergers & Acquisitions:** Fenwick & West's Mergers and Acquisitions Practice is one of the premier technology M&A practice in the nation. In recent years, the firm has completed more than $250 billion worth of transactions, including significant acquisition programs for leading serial acquirers. Fenwick's Mergers and Acquisitions expertise spans the entire spectrum of technology, including clean technology, life sciences, hardware, internet, software, peripherals and semiconductor companies. Its attorneys are equally adept at small private company transactions and multibillion dollar public transactions. For clients involved in larger deals, the firm's antitrust attorneys are experienced in working with the Department of Justice and Federal Trade Commission in the pre-merger clearance process.

**Public Offerings & Securities Law Compliance:** Fenwick & West's extensive representation of emerging companies has given it substantial depth of experience in public offerings. In recent years, the firm has represented companies or investment banks in more than 150 initial public offerings, which combined, have raised over $10 billion dollars. The firm has helped clients raise billions more in follow-on debt and equity offerings. In addition Fenwick has an active practice counseling publicly-traded technology companies regarding ongoing corporate governance, disclosure and securities law issues.

**Strategic Alliances:** For many technology companies, the path to financing and commercialization begins with their first collaboration or joint venture with an industry partner. Fenwick & West attorneys help clients think through the business, intellectual property, tax and other legal issues that arise in their corporate partnering transactions and joint ventures.

**Executive Compensation:** As an integral part of the Corporate Practice, Fenwick & West attorneys counsel clients on a wide range of complex employee benefits and compensation issues.

**Start-Up Companies:** The firm has represented hundreds of growth-oriented companies from inception through maturity and has over 500 venture capital and private-equity-backed clients. Fenwick & West attorneys understand what it takes to start with only an idea, build a team, found a company, raise venture capital funding and grow a business. They have long-standing ties to more than 275 active venture capital firms, with robust connections to investors at all stages-from angels to late stage rounds-and with all technologies. The group is ranked by Dow Jones as one of the top 5 VC practices in the US.
**Contact:** Richard L Dickson

### Intellectual Property:

Fenwick & West delivers comprehensive, integrated advice regarding all aspects of intellectual property protection and exploitation. In 2012, American Lawyer Media ranked Fenwick as a "Go-To" law firm for *Fortune* 500 companies in the area of intellectual property protection and Intellectual Property Today lists Fenwick as one of the top patent law firms in the US (2011). From providing sophisticated legal defense in precedent-setting lawsuits to crafting unique license arrangements and implementing penetrating intellectual property audits, Fenwick & West's intellectual property attorneys have pioneered and remained at the forefront of legal innovation.
**Contact:** David L Hayes

### Litigation:

The Fenwick & West Litigation Group has the range of experience and critical mass to protect client interests in virtually any dispute, large or small. While the firm's attorneys have extensive litigation experience in a wide range of industries, they have exceptional depth and breadth in the areas of the law critical to their technology clients, including clean technology; life sciences; software and programming; internet and entertainment; computer hardware and peripherals and semiconductors. Fenwick & West is regularly involved in significant cases involving intellectual property (technology transactions, patents, copyrights, trademarks and trade secrets), employment disputes, corporate governance, securities, antitrust and general commercial litigation. In addition to civil litigation, the firm's attorneys are experienced in representing clients in civil and criminal government investigations. The firm is recognized by Corporate Counsel as one of the Top 10 "Go-To" litigation firms in the US for Fortune 100 companies.
**Contact:** Darryl M Woo

### Tax:

Fenwick & West has one of the nation's leading domestic and international tax practices. The Tax Group's dynamic and sophisticated practice stems from a client base that is represented in every geographic region of the United States, as well as a number of foreign countries, and has included over 100 *Fortune* 500 companies and over 40 *Fortune* 100 companies. The group has represented corporate clients in over 70 Tax Court cases and is also nationally recognized for successful tax dispute resolution and litigation—resolving over 100 IRS administrative appeals proceedings. In 2011, the firm was honored by International Tax Review as one of the world's leading tax transactional practices, one of only five law firms in the entire US to earn First Tier status. And, World Tax Review has awarded Fenwick First Tier status every year, most recently in World Tax 2011.
**Contact:** David L Forst

### International Work:

Fenwick & West routinely handles corporate transactions, venture capital financings, licensing transactions and litigation, as well as intellectual property, trademark and tax matters in foreign jurisdictions for its US clients. The firm also represents a growing number of foreign technology companies throughout Asia, Europe and the Middle East on US-related transitions. The firm has particular expertise in the intellectual property issues related to outsourcing.

## OFFICES

### CALIFORNIA

**SILICON VALLEY:** Silicon Valley Center, 801 California Street, Mountain View, CA 94041
Tel: 650 988 8500 Fax: 650 938 5200

**SAN FRANCISCO:** 555 California Street, 12th Floor, CA 94104
Tel: 415 875 2300  Fax: 415 281 1350

### WASHINGTON

**SEATTLE:** 1191 Second Avenue, 10th Floor, WA 98101
Tel: 206 389 4510  Fax: 206 389 4511

# GIBBS GIDEN LOCHER TURNER SENET & WITTBRODT LLP

**www.ggltsw.com** **tel:** 310 552 3400 **fax:** 310 552 0805

**Managing Partner:** Richard J Wittbrodt
**Senior Partner:** William D Locher
Number of partners: 22
Number of other lawyers: 14

**OFFICES**

CALIFORNIA
**LOS ANGELES:** 1880 Century Park East, 12th Floor, CA 90067
Tel: 310 552 3400  Fax: 310 552 0805
Email: marketingdept@ggltsw.com

NEVADA
**LAS VEGAS:** 7450 Arroyo Parkway Crossway, Suite 270, 89113
Tel: 702 836 9800  Fax: 702 836 9802

## Firm Overview:

Gibbs Giden Locher Turner Senet & Wittbrodt LLP, founded in 1978, is a firm with influence and presence in California and Nevada. For three decades, the firm has built a solid reputation for serving the unique interests of clients in the planning, building and closeout of construction projects. The firm is a leader in its core areas of practice: construction law and public contracts; business and commercial law; labor and employment law; real estate law; insurance law and risk management; title insurance; and common interest community law. The firm is committed to working with its clients in 'building for the future'.

## Main Areas of Practice:

### Construction Law & Public Contracts:

The firm provides legal guidance and counseling to clients at every stage of a construction project. The firm's attorneys have extensive experience in virtually every type of construction project, including airports, power plants, hospitals, major sports venues, office buildings, correctional facilities, retail locations, major residential projects, universities, courthouses, petrochemical plants, dams, pipelines, and wastewater and water treatment facilities. The firm represents public and private owners, design professionals, general contractors, subcontractors, and material suppliers with respect to almost every conceivable circumstance that can arise before, during, and after completion of a construction project. The firm's attorneys litigate and counsel clients in the resolution of matters on high profile delay, disruption and cost overrun claims.
**Contacts:** Glenn E Turner, III, Barbara R Gadbois

### Business & Commercial Law:

The firm assists its construction industry clientele in collection matters and the enforcement of statutory mechanics' liens, stop notices, and bond rights, as well as a broad spectrum of publicly and privately held companies in a variety of business transactions and litigation, the secured and unsecured creditors, and real and personal property transactions. The firm handles all aspects of creditor representation in bankruptcy proceedings. For corporate clients, the firm offers services equivalent to those of general counsel, as well as counseling on operational issues.
**Contacts:** William D Locher, Richard J Wittbrodt, Michael I Wayne

### Labor & Employment Law:

The firm offers exceptional and cost-effective representation to employers in all aspects of labor and employment law. The firm's attorneys provide legal counsel to a wide range of private businesses, municipalities and institutions defending against employment claims, including claims of wrongful termination, retaliation, employment discrimination and harassment. The firm's attorneys emphasize preventative counseling and education in order to promote a healthy workplace environment and avoid employment disputes. The firm represents employers in prevailing wage matters before the US Department of Labor and the California Labor Commissioner. The firm also advises public and private entities in negotiating and implementing project labor agreements.
**Contacts:** Gerald A Griffin, Gary E Scalabrini

### Insurance Law & Risk Management:

The firm represents both insureds and insurers in claims and coverage disputes, including first-party property losses, casualty claims, surety claims, reinsurance, excess insurance, and multi-carrier litigation. The firm's attorneys are highly experienced in risk management, as well as the analysis, negotiation and litigation of insurance coverage issues common to the business, real estate, manufacturing, construction, and title insurance industries. The firm advises developers, businesses and public entities regarding risk management and insurance issues on major capital improvement projects, public contracts and specialized insurance programs, including owner and contractor controlled insurance programs, wrap-up insurance, contractor/subcontractor default insurance, surety bonds, and other special risks.
**Contacts:** Theodore L Senet, Steven R Cuneo, Jr

### Real Estate Law:

The firm's attorneys assist clients in all aspects of real property transactions, including acquisitions, financing, development, leasing, management and sales. The firm also assists clients with due diligence investigations and the coordination of environmental assessments and evaluations.
**Contact:** William D Locher

### Healthcare:

The firm focuses on all phases and legal aspects related to the formation, development, syndication, construction and operation of outpatient surgery centers and private medical practices. The firm provides California and Nevada clients with legal services and consulting relating to State and Federal regulatory compliance.
**Contact:** Richard E Haskin

### International Business & Dispute Resolution:

The firm assists clients in international commercial law, private international law and conflicts of law, international arbitration and litigation, and construction law. The firm represents clients involved in international arbitrations arising out of industrial and infrastructure projects, cross-border manufacturing and distribution framework agreements, information and industrial technology licenses and various maritime contracts. The firm's members also serve as arbitrators, in matters conducted under the auspices of the ICC International Court of Arbitration and the Permanent Court of Arbitration in regard to various complex commercial disputes. Particular to the construction industry, the firm assists contractors and specialty subcontractors in connection with various types of agreements including EPC and EPCM contracts for large industrial and infrastructure projects, and provides guidance on claims handling. The firm is experienced with the use and application of the leading conditions and forms of contract used for international projects including the FIDIC suite of contracts.
**Contact:** Nathan D O'Mallley

### Common Interest Community Law:

The firm is recognized as a premier firm in common interest community law and related practice areas of real estate, insurance and construction law. The firm provides a wide variety of legal services to community associations including: interpretation and enforcement of governing documents, assisting with developer to association transition, construction defects and post litigation recovery guidance.
**Contact:** Matthew L Grode

**GIBBS GIDEN** ATTORNEYS AT LAW
LOCHER TURNER SENET & WITTBRODT LLP

# GIBSON, DUNN & CRUTCHER LLP

www.gibsondunn.com

## Firm Overview:

Gibson, Dunn & Crutcher LLP is a leading international law firm. Consistently ranking among the world's top law firms in industry surveys and major publications, Gibson Dunn is distinctively positioned in today's global marketplace with more than 1,100 lawyers and 18 offices. For more information on Gibson Dunn's other practices, visit the firm's website.

## Main Areas of Practice:

### Appellate:

Gibson Dunn has one of the nation's leading appellate practices with broad experience in complex appellate litigation at all levels of the state and federal court systems. The firm has had more than 100 Supreme Court arguments among active lawyers.

### Business Restructuring & Reorganization:

Gibson Dunn has extensive experience in both domestic and multinational insolvencies. The firm's lawyers regularly represent and counsel official creditors' committees, ad hoc creditor groups, secured lenders, investors and companies in out-of-court work-outs and Chapter 11 cases.

### Commercial Litigation & Arbitration:

Gibson Dunn has represented many *Fortune* 500 companies in cases involving securities fraud, antitrust, administrative law, environmental, white-collar crime, business torts, among many others. Many of these cases have included class action claims and involved hundreds of millions of dollars in alleged damages. For an unprecedented second time in a row, Gibson Dunn was named in 2012 as Litigation Department of the Year by *The American Lawyer*, considered the top litigation honor in the United States.

### Corporate & Securities:

Gibson Dunn has deep experience in M&A transactions, including: mergers of public and private companies, stock and asset purchases, tender and exchange offers, restructurings and acquisitions out of bankruptcy, divestitures and spinoffs, leveraged buyouts and private equity investments, strategic investments and joint ventures, special committee representations, and cross-border M&A transactions. The firm has broad experience in capital markets having advised on multiple transactions across a wide spectrum of deal structures.

### Energy & Infrastructure:

Gibson Dunn has extensive and varied experience in the industrial, commercial, financial and political issues that are inherent in the development, financing, construction and operation of major energy and infrastructure facilities. The firm's experience spans from traditional oil and gas production, refining transmission and financing to siting, permitting, construction, operation, divestiture

and acquisition of renewable projects such as wind power, biomass and bio-diesel, hydro, geo-thermal and solar power generation installations, technologies and facilities.

### Finance:

The firm focuses on the representation of lenders, borrowers, underwriters and issuers in a large variety of debt and structured finance transactions, including: leveraged loans, high-yield bond offerings, mezzanine and subordinated debt, project finance, equipment financings, restructurings and securitizations.

### Intellectual Property:

Gibson Dunn assists clients with a wide range of IP issues, including: litigating critical IP disputes, negotiating licenses and joint ventures, navigating regulations governing privacy, trade and the protection of IP, and advocating for change in IP law and policy.

### Labor & Employment:

The firm's recent representations include some of the most prominent labor relations matters in the country, high stakes wage and-hour class actions, high profile ERISA cases, nationally recognized Sarbanes-Oxley 'whistleblower' cases and aggressive advocacy on OSHA issues. The team also has particular depth in a full range of executive compensation and benefits matters. In 2012, *The American Lawyer* named Gibson Dunn the winner in the Labor and Employment category of its biennial 'Litigation Department of the Year' competition.

### Media, Entertainment & Technology:

The firm represents both established and emerging media, entertainment and technology companies and handles clients' most important and complex corporate transactions, litigation, internal investigations and other legal challenges. The group's transactional lawyers are recognized for their expertise in M&A, complex film finance transactions, and joint ventures, while its litigators are well-known for their experience in handling the full array of media and entertainment-related matters, including accounting, contract and profit participation disputes and enforcing film and television distribution agreements.

### Real Estate:

Gibson Dunn handles a variety of matters, including real estate finance, development, sales and acquisitions, land

use and environmental, leasing and workout transactions.

### Securities Litigation, Regulation & Corporate Governance:

The firm is a recognized leader in the defense of securities class actions, derivative litigation and SEC enforcement actions. The firm advises companies on disclosure, accounting and regulatory issues for domestic and foreign regulatory bodies. The partners include nationally recognized securities class action defense counsel, a number of former senior officials with the SEC, NASD and DOJ.

### International Work:

Gibson Dunn's international team consists of US, English, French and German qualified lawyers, many of whom are dual qualified. A long-term European presence and recent office openings in the financial centers of São Paulo, Hong Kong and Beijing give the firm considerable experience in representing clients with international business interests requiring a co-ordinated response within and across national borders. The firm's international offices handle all types of corporate transactions, corporate financing, tax structuring, real estate, litigation, labor and employment and antitrust matters.

---

# GREENBERG GLUSKER FIELDS CLAMAN & MACHTINGER LLP

**www.**GreenbergGlusker.com **tel:** 310 553 3610 **fax:** 310 553 0687

**Managing Partner:** Stephen Smith
Number of partners: 53
Number of lawyers: 85
Languages: *American Sign Language, Arabic, Chinese (Cantonese, Mandarin), English, Farsi, French, German, Hebrew, Korean, Ladino, Russian, Scottish, Spanish, Tagalog, Taiwanese, Vietnamese*

## Firm Overview:

For more than 50 years, Greenberg Glusker has held a unique position in Los Angeles as a full-service litigation and business law firm with particular expertise in entertainment, real estate, corporate, environmental, trusts and estates, litigation, employment and bankruptcy/insolvency.

Committed to providing a wide range of services, Greenberg Glusker combines the personal attention of a boutique firm with the strength and breadth of services customarily found in a multi-office, international firm.

Results-oriented client service is how the firm continues to distinguish itself today. That's what makes Greenberg Gusker *The Counsel You Keep.*®

## Main Areas of Practice:

### Entertainment – Transactional:

5 partners; 10 fee earners based in Los Angeles
**Key Clients:** Tom Cruise, Larry King, Philip Seymour Hoffman, Ubisoft Entertainment, Saban Entertainment
**Contact:** Matt Galsor
**Tel:** 310 201 7437
**Email:** MGalsor@greenbergglusker.com

### Entertainment – Litigation:

9 partners; 14 fee earners based in Los Angeles
**Key Clients:** DreamWorks Animation SKG, Inc., Estate of J.R.R. Tolkien, Classic Media, Fifty-Six Hope Road Music Ltd., Toho-Towa Co., Ltd., Gameloft, Inc., Weinstein Company, Hans Zimmer
**Contact:** Bonnie Eskenazi
**Tel:** 310 785 6857
**Email:** BEskenazi@greenbergglusker.com

### Real Estate:

10 partners; 15 fee earners based in Los Angeles
**Key Clients:** Costco Wholesale Corporation, Majestic Realty Co., Miller Automotive, ValleyCrest, Sequoia/Canongate Golf
**Contact:** Ryan Iwasaka
**Tel:** 310 201 7405
**Email:** Riwasaka@greenbergglusker.com

### Corporate:

7 partners; 12 fee earners based in Los Angeles
**Key Clients:** OPI, Midnite Express, AloXXI, WireTech, Inc., Walton Facilities Management, Pick Up Stix, K2 Network, Promojam, Lime Energy
**Contact:** Joel Weinstein
**Tel:** 310 201 7485
**Email:** JWeinstein@greenbergglusker.com

### Environmental:

2 partners; 3 fee earners based in Los Angeles
**Key Clients:** Union Pacific Railroad Company, Northrop Grumman Corporation, City of Culver City, Dairy Cares, Eni Oil & Gas Co., California Dairies, Inc., Realty Income
**Contact:** David Cranston
**Tel:** 310 785 6897
**Email:** DCranston@greenbergglusker.com

### Trusts & Estates:

4 partners; 7 fee earners based in Los Angeles
**Contact:** Laura Zwicker
**Tel:** 310 785 6819
**Email:** LZwicker@greenbergglusker.com

### Employment:

3 partners; 4 fee earners based in Los Angeles
**Contact:** Olivia Goodkin
**Tel:** 310 201 7446
**Email:** OGoodkin@greenbergglusker.com

### Bankruptcy/Insolvency:

3 partners; 7 fee earners based in Los Angeles
**Key Clients:** Rhythm & Hues Studios, First Citizens Bank, The Home Depot, Cisco Brothers Inc., Cheesecake Factory, Roland Corporation, Avalon Risk Management
**Contact:** Brian Davidoff
**Tel:** 310 201 7520
**Email:** BDavidoff@greenbergglusker.com

### Litigation:

23 partners; 34 fee earners based in Los Angeles
**Key Clients:** Ubisoft Entertainment, Costco Wholesale Corporation, Marvel Entertainment, Starpoint Properties LLC, Transpacific Development Co.
**Contact:** Matthew Falley
**Tel:** 310 201 7442
**Email:** MFalley@greenbergglusker.com

# GREINES, MARTIN, STEIN & RICHLAND LLP

www.gmsr.com **tel:** 310 859 7811 **fax:** 310 276 5261

**Managing Partner:** Timothy T Coates
**Senior Partners:** Irving H Greines, Kent L Richland, Robin Meadow
Number of partners: 12
Number of lawyers: 22
Languages: *English*

**PRACTICE AREAS**
Appellate Law

**OFFICES**
CALIFORNIA
**LOS ANGELES:** 5900 Wilshire Boulevard, 12th Floor
Tel: 310 859 7811   Fax: 310 276 5261

## Firm Overview:

Ever since its founding in 1983, the firm has been one of California's premier civil appellate 'boutiques.' From its base of practice in the California state and federal appellate courts, in recent years the firm has forged a potent United States Supreme Court practice: Since 2006, it has won six of the seven cases it has briefed and argued in the high court. The firm is counsel of record in over 450 published decisions and in many more hundreds of unpublished decisions, and it has acted as amicus counsel in many additional appellate matters. The firm also frequently consults with trial lawyers so as to ensure that their cases are well positioned for a potential appeal. Through its appellate practice, the firm has developed substantive expertise in many areas, including constitutional law, civil rights, governmental torts and immunities, personal injury, insurance coverage and bad faith, complex business disputes, business torts, copyright, unfair competition, antitrust, real estate, entertainment law, environmental law, employment law, maritime law, family law, bankruptcy, professional malpractice, arbitration and probate. The firm's clientele includes national banks and other major national companies; major liability, casualty and title insurance companies; state and local governments; hospitals; public and private universities; entertainment industry companies and individuals; and lawyers.

## Main Areas of Practice:

Appellate Law

## Recent Work:

### California State & Federal Courts

Celador International, Inc. v. ABC (2012) 2012 U.S. App. LEXIS 24820 (9th Cir., unpublished). In a landmark case closely watched by both the entertainment industry and the legal community, the Ninth Circuit upheld a $319 million judgment in favor of the firm's client and rejecting the network's "Hollywood accounting."
**Contact:** Robin Meadow

Howell v. Hamilton Meats, 52 Cal.4th 541 (2011). In a case with multi-billion dollar implications, the California Supreme Court accepted the firm's arguments on behalf of amici curiae and held that a plaintiff's recovery for economic medical damages cannot exceed the lesser of the amount actually accepted by the healthcare provider as payment in full or the reasonable value of services, rather than the face amount of the medical bill.
**Contact:** Robert A Olson

Jules Jordan Video, Inc. v. 144942 Canada Inc., 617 F.3d 1146 (2010). The Ninth Circuit reinstated a multi-million dollar copyright infringement judgment in favor of the firm's client, clarifying the application of the work-for-hire doctrine where a sole proprietorship wholly controls the company that produced and distributed his creative works.
**Contact:** Marc Poster

### United States Supreme Court

L.A. County Flood Control Dist. v. NRDC, Inc., (2013) U.S. Sup. Ct. No. 11-460, 2013 U.S. LEXIS 597. In a closely-watched Clean Water Act case, the Court reversed the Ninth Circuit, holding that the firm's client had not violated the Act simply by moving water through improved portions of a river into other portions of the same river.
**Contact:** Timothy T Coates

Messerschmidt v. Millender, 132 S.Ct. 1235 (2012). In an important decision for law enforcement, the Supreme Court held that sheriffs' deputies were entitled to qualified immunity from civil liability where their search was carried out pursuant to a search warrant, even though the search itself was unlawful.
**Contact:** Timothy T Coates

City of Ontario v. Quon, 130 S.Ct. 2619, (2010). In the first case in which the Supreme Court has considered rights of privacy in electronic communications, the Court ruled unanimously that the Ontario Police Department's review of text messages sent and received by a SWAT team officer on his department-issued pager did not violate the Fourth Amendment's prohibition of unreasonable searches and seizures.
**Contact:** Kent L Richland

Los Angeles County v. Humphries, 131 S.Ct. 447, (2010). In a critical decision for cities and counties, the Supreme Court ruled unanimously that a municipality cannot be subjected to declaratory or injunctive relief in a civil rights action under 42 U.S.C. Section 1983

unless the plaintiff establishes that an injury was inflicted as a result of a policy, custom or practice fairly attributable to the local public entity.
**Contact:** Timothy T Coates

John Van de Kamp, et al. v. Thomas Lee Goldstein, 555 U.S. 335, 129 S.Ct. 855, 172 L.Ed.2d 706 (2009). In a unanimous opinion, the Supreme Court held that the former Los Angeles County District Attorney and Assistant District Attorney were entitled to absolute prosecutorial immunity for decisions concerning the manner in which the District Attorney's office implemented policies and training regarding the use of jail house informants.
**Contact:** Timothy T Coates

Marshall v. Marshall, 547 U.S. 293, 126 S.Ct. 1735,164 L.Ed.2d 480 (2006). The Supreme Court unanimously reversed a judgment against the firm's client, Anna Nicole Smith, clarifying the scope of the so-called "probate exception" to federal jurisdiction.
**Contact:** Kent L Richland

# HORVITZ & LEVY LLP

**www.**horvitzlevy.com **tel:** 818 995 0800 **fax:** 818 995 3157

**Chairman:** Barry R Levy (Chair of Management Committee)
**Managing Partners:** Barry R Levy, Mitchell C Tilner, Frederic D Cohen
Number of partners: 20  Number of lawyers: 30
Languages: *English, Russian*

**PRACTICE AREAS**
Appellate (Civil)

**OFFICES**
CALIFORNIA
**LOS ANGELES:** 15760 Ventura Boulevard, 18th Floor,
Encino, CA 91436-3000
Tel: 818 995 0800   Fax 818 995 3157
Email: http://horvitzlevy.com/contact/email.cfm

## Firm Overview:

Horvitz & Levy LLP is the largest law firm in the United States specializing in civil appellate litigation. Founded in 1957, the firm's services include consulting on trial strategy, assisting trial counsel in preserving and developing issues for appellate review, preparing critical trial court motions in anticipation of appeal, negotiating favorable settlements pending appeal, and full briefing and argument before the appellate courts. The firm appears more often in civil cases in the California appellate courts than any other firm in the state, including appearances in more than 145 cases before the California Supreme Court since 1990 alone. Horvitz & Levy also frequently appears in the US Court of Appeals for the Ninth Circuit and other appellate courts around the country. Since 1990, the firm has prevailed in more than 60 percent of its cases on behalf of appellants - vastly exceeding the average 20 percent success rate. In the last decade, Horvitz & Levy attorneys have reversed more than $1.4 billion in punitive damages awards against the firm's clients.

## Main Areas of Practice:

### Amicus Curiae Support:
Recent work: State Farm General Insurance Co. v. Frake, 197 Cal. App. 4th 568 (2011). In this insurance declaratory relief action, the California Court of Appeal agreed with Horvitz & Levy's amicus briefing and held a deliberate act is not an accident, even if the resulting injuries are unintended. Key Attorneys: Mitchell C Tilner, Lisa Perrochet.

### Class Actions:
Recent work: Bruns v. E-Commerce Exchange, 51 Cal.4th 717 (2011). In a class action case involving application of California's mandatory dismissal statute, Horvitz & Levy successfully obtained a reversal in the California Supreme Court which held that only complete stays toll the operation of the mandatory dismissal statute and that a putative class action stayed during several 'partial stays' of the action should have been dismissed. Key Attorneys: Robert H Wright, Bradley S Pauley.

### Entertainment Law:
Recent work: Don Johnson Productions, Inc. v. Rysher Entertainment, 209 Cal.App.4th 919 (2012). Horvitz & Levy represented the co-producer of the television show Nash Bridges on appeal from an adverse judgment in a dispute over profits with the show's star. The California Court of Appeal reversed in part, agreeing with Horvitz & Levy that the prejudgment interest award of $29.1 million was procedurally defective. The court also agreed that the jury had committed misconduct by adding $8.3 million in prejudgment interest to the damages award. Key Attorneys: Frederic D Cohen, Lisa Perrochet.

### First Amendment & Anti-SLAPP:
Recent work: Cuviello v. City of Oakland, 2011 WL 1979712 (9th Cir. May 23, 2011). In this action by animal rights activists seeking to protest a circus at a sports arena, the Ninth Circuit agreed with Horvitz & Levy's briefing and affirmed a lower court injunction restricting access to certain areas. Key Attorneys: Stephen E Norris, Jeremy B Rosen.

### Healthcare:
Recent work: El-Attar v. Hollywood Presbyterian Medical Center, 198 Cal. App. 4th 664 (2011), review granted, No. S196830 (Cal. Nov. 30, 2011). Horvitz & Levy successfully petitioned the California Supreme Court for review to decide whether a hospital's governing board, rather than its medical staff, can initiate the peer review process in connection with the revocation of a physician's staff privileges. The case is currently pending. Key attorneys: H Thomas Watson, David S Ettinger.

### Insurance Coverage & Bad Faith:
Recent work: Portland General Electric Co. v. Lexington Insurance Co., 248 Or.App. 91, 273 P.3d 165 (2012). Horvitz & Levy secured the reversal of a default judgment entered against its insurance company client in this insurance coverage action. The Oregon Court of Appeals agreed with Horvitz & Levy that the judgment was void in its entirety because the plaintiff's complaint failed to disclose the amount of damages sought. This case has now been accepted for review by the Oregon Supreme Court.
Key Attorneys: Curt C Cutting, Mitchell C Tilner.

### Labor & Employment:
Recent work: Raymond v. Flynt, 2010 WL 3751524 (Sept 28, 2010). Horvitz & Levy successfully represented Larry Flynt and Larry Flynt Productions, Inc. on appeal, obtaining reversal of a sexual harassment judgement awarding plaintiff (a former executive assistant to Mr Flynt) compensatory and punitive damages and attorney fees. Key attorneys: Barry R Levy, Jeremy B Rosen.

### Punitive Damages:
Recent work: Heston v. Taser International, Inc., 2011 WL 1707048 (9th Cir. May 5, 2011). The jury awarded $5.2 million in punitive damages and $1,020,000 in compensatory damages against a global provider of electronic control devices. Horvitz & Levy assisted trial counsel in persuading the district court to vacate all punitive damages, and then persuaded the Ninth Circuit to uphold that result. Key Attorneys: Peder K Batalden, John A Taylor, Peter Abrahams.

### Toxic Tort/Product Liability:
Recent work: O'Neil v. Crane Co., 53 Cal. 4th 335 (2012). Horvitz & Levy obtained a unanimous reversal in the California Supreme Court, which held a product manufacturer cannot be liable for harm caused by another's product unless the defendant's own product contributed substantially to the harm, or the defendant participated in creating a harmful combined use of the products. Key Attorneys: Curt Cutting, Jason Litt.

### Unfair Competition & Other Consumer Law Litigation:
The firm has extensive experience representing clients in disputes involving claims under California's consumer protection statutes, including the Unfair Competition Law (Cal. Business & Professions Code sections 17200 et seq.)

## Clients:
As lead counsel or amicus curiae in appellate matters, Horvitz & Levy LLP regularly represents a wide range of clients and industries, including leading manufacturers, the insurance and entertainment industries, energy and healthcare providers, foreign corporations, public entities, public utilities, and business and professional trade associations. The firm also provides pro bono appellate services to a number of local and national non-profit organizations.

# IRELL & MANELLA LLP

www.irell.com  **tel:** 310 277 1010  **fax:** 310 203 7199

**Managing Partner:** Andrei Iancu
Number of partners: 51
Number of other lawyers: 130

**OFFICES**

LOS ANGELES

**LOS ANGELES:** 1800 Avenue of the Stars, Suite 900,
CA 90067-4276
Tel: 310 277 1010  Fax: 310 203 7199

**NEWPORT BEACH:** 840 Newport Center Drive, Suite 400,
CA 92660-6324
Tel: 949 760 0991  Fax: 949 760 5200

**Firm Overview:**
Irell & Manella LLP is a full-service law firm with offices in Los Angeles and Newport Beach, California. Founded in 1941, Irell is nationally recognized for its intellectual property, litigation, insurance, corporate and tax practices. Irell's clients include *Fortune* 500 corporations, universities, and leading-edge entrepreneurial companies. The firm insists on outstanding academic credentials for their attorneys, while also placing a premium on creativity, experience, and common sense. Irell is big enough to handle the largest and most complex matters, but small enough to maintain excellence at every level.

**Main Areas of Practice:**

**ADR & Arbitration:**
Irell's alternative dispute resolution practice consists of attorneys serving as mediators and arbitrators in complex civil matters. The core of the practice is the ADR Center, established under the leadership of Layn Phillips, a former federal judge and a nationally-prominent mediator and arbitrator.

**Appellate:**
Irell's appellate practice is comprised of litigators who frequently handle appeals and writs in various appellate courts, including the US and state Supreme Courts. The practice includes former US District Court Judge and former Associate Justice of the California Supreme Court Carlos Moreno.

**Bankruptcy, Reorganization & Creditors' Rights:**
Irell's bankruptcy, reorganization and creditors' rights practice handles major corporate reorganizations and creditors' rights matters in various industries. The firm represents troubled companies in developing formal and informal workouts, exchange offers, and other transactions and strategies.

**Corporate/M&A:**
Irell's corporate attorneys represent publicly and privately held acquirers, sellers, targets and financial institutions in a variety of transactions including negotiated mergers and acquisitions, tender and exchange offers, proxy contests, dispositions and spin-offs. The firm has represented companies in numerous industries including technology, communications, entertainment, healthcare, biosciences, retail, manufacturing, energy, gaming, real estate development and finance.

**Finance:**
Irell has advised clients on billions of dollars worth of debt finance transactions, including syndicated credit facilities; second-lien issuances; intercreditor arrangements; LBOs; tender and exchange offers; and asset-based lending, leasing, recapitalization, reorganization and restructuring transactions.

**Entertainment Litigation:**
Irell's expertise in entertainment litigation is diverse and deep, spanning issues involving trademark, copyright, format rights, idea submission, defamation, invasion of privacy, right of publicity, profit participation, royalty payments, vertical integration claims, and the interpretation of recording, film, distribution, and talent contracts.

**Insurance:**
Business entities and individuals named as defendants in complex business litigation consistently retain Irell to assist them in pursuing coverage under policies of professional, commercial, fidelity, crime, directors, officers and umbrella liability insurance.

**Intellectual Property Litigation:**
Irell's nationally recognized IP litigation practice covers IP, including patents, trademarks, copyrights, the protection of trade secrets, and the unfair competition, reexamination and antitrust issues frequently involved in IP matters.

**Intellectual Property Transactions:**
Irell is a leading firm in national and international transactions involving information technology, telecommunications, biotechnology, and the protection of patents, copyrights, trade secrets, trademarks, service marks and trade dress.

**Labor & Employment:**
Irell represents employers in employment relations including wage and hour class action and matters involving employment agreements; arbitration; trade secrets; and unfair competition.

**Litigation:**
Home to one of the nation's premier litigation practices, Irell has represented clients in all manners of complex commercial litigation; intellectual property disputes; securities class actions; entertainment-related litigation; federal and state antitrust problems and unfair competitive practices litigation; environmental matters; labor and employment litigation and arbitration; corporate control contests; federal, state,

and local tax disputes; white-collar criminal defense; defense of SEC enforcement proceedings; and insurance litigation.

**Private Equity:**
Irell frequently represents private equity funds and their portfolio companies, advising initial investments, including financing, tax structure and the satisfaction of regulatory requirements; exit strategies through public offerings or a private sale; and equity offerings, debt financings, and private placements.

**Securities Litigation:**
Irell's securities litigation practice encompasses private litigation, including class action lawsuits arising from federal and state securities laws; shareholder derivative and corporate governance litigation; mergers and acquisitions; representation of parties in connection with inquiries, subpoenas, and investigations commenced by regulatory agencies or prosecuting authorities; internal corporate investigations; and counseling in connection with directors and officers insurance issues.

**Tax:**
With more than 50 years' experience in the tax field, Irell's tax attorneys have expertise in virtually every aspect of federal, state, local, and international taxation of public and privately owned corporations, as well as partnerships, limited liability companies, individuals, trusts, and tax-exempt entities.

**White Collar Defense:**
Irell's white collar defense group represents clients in the defense of criminal, as well as administrative and civil matters, with fraud or criminal overtones. The group, which includes former Enron prosecutor John Hueston, has been actively involved in all stages of the defense of these matters, from preliminary investigation, through grand jury proceedings, to trial. The group also has experience conducting internal investigations and creating corporate compliance programs.

# KLEE, TUCHIN, BOGDANOFF & STERN LLP

**www.ktbslaw.com** **tel:** 310 407 4000 **fax:** 310 407 9090

**Co-Managing Partners:** Lee R Bogdanoff, Michael L Tuchin
Number of partners: 12  Number of other lawyers: 5

**OFFICES**

CALIFORNIA

**LOS ANGELES:** 1999 Avenue of the Stars, 39th Floor,
CA 90067
Tel: 310 407 4000 Fax: 310 407 9090

## Firm Overview:

Klee, Tuchin, Bogdanoff & Stern is a national, boutique law firm that specializes in business reorganizations, corporate insolvency, commercial litigation, bankruptcy-related asset acquisitions, bankruptcy litigation and appellate advocacy, expert witness services in the bankruptcy field and corporate transactions. KTB&S represents debtors, creditors, equity holders, committees, trustees, landlords, potential acquirers of assets, and other parties with interests in financially distressed businesses. The members of KTB&S have decades of experience practicing in the bankruptcy field, and are actively involved in teaching and providing expert witness consultation and testimony. KTB&S's lawyers are headquartered in Los Angeles, California, but regularly handle matters and appear in bankruptcy proceedings throughout the United States. KTB&S is widely recognized as a national leader in its field.

## Main Areas of Practice:

### Debtors:

Gene Douglas and Carlos A Morales: Same sex married debtors whose joint chapter 13 petition was challenged by the US Trustee as a violation of the federal Defense of Marriage Act (DOMA); KTB&S succeeded in obtaining a 20-judge en banc bankruptcy court opinion declaring DOMA unconstitutional which has resulted in a national change in the government's position in opposing same-sex joint filing bankruptcies. Jefferson County, Alabama: KTB&S serves as co-counsel to this chapter 9 municipal debtor with over $4 billion in municipal debt, the largest municipal filing in US history. Metro-Goldwyn-Mayer Studios, Inc. and Affiliates: KTB&S served as co-counsel to Metro-Goldwyn-Mayer and approximately 160 of its affiliates (collectively 'MGM') in connection with their pre-packaged chapter 11 cases. MGM's plan was confirmed by the Bankruptcy Court 29 days following the commencement of the bankruptcy cases. Pacific Sunwear of California (PacSun): KTB&S represented this large, publicly-traded national retailer of action sportswear in connection with its successful out-of-court restructuring. Thorpe Insulation Company: KTB&S is special appellate counsel to Thorpe in connection with over 30 appeals to the District Court and five appeals to the 9th Circuit Court of Appeals stemming from Thorpe's mass asbestos chapter 11 case. The Town of Mammoth Lakes: KTB&S served as co-counsel to Mammoth Lakes in its chapter 9 municipal bankruptcy; successfully negotiated a settlement that greatly reduced a significant pre-filing judgment against the town, permitting Mammoth Lakes to dismiss its chapter 9 bankruptcy in less than 6 months. Washington Mutual, Inc.: chapter 11 debtor holding company for major banking institution seized by the Federal Deposit Insurance Corporation; KTB&S serves as special litigation counsel with respect to potential claims of the debtor against officers, directors and third parties relating to prepetition matters.

### Bondholders & Other Creditors:

Suzuki Motor Corporation: KTB&S serves as counsel to this large publicly-traded Japanese corporation as the largest creditor and debtor in possession lender in connection with the pending chapter 11 case of its United States subsidiary, American Suzuki Motor Corporation. Ableco Finance LLC: KTB&S has represented (and continues to represent) Ableco Finance LLC and its affiliates as a prepetition creditor and debtor in possession lender in a number of cases, including Mahalo Energy (USA), Inc. (major natural gas exploration and development company), Latshaw Drilling Corp. (manufacturer and operator of land based oil and gas drilling rigs) and Deb Shops, Inc. (national retailer of young women's clothing). CBS Television: KTB&S has represented (and continues to represent) CBS in cases across the country. Fremont General Corporation: Counsel to official unsecured creditors committee (comprised of trustee for and holders of senior and junior bond indebtedness) of chapter 11 holding company that owned Fremont Investment & Loan, formerly a bank, now undergoing liquidation; confirmed plan of reorganization pursuant to which creditors have been or will be paid in full. LBI Media, Inc.: Counsel to group of first lien bondholders in connection with the restructuring of this large Spanish language telecommunications company. Nortel Networks, Inc.: Counsel to one of the largest creditors in the chapter 11 cases of one of the world's largest telecommunication companies. Paramount Pictures and Affiliates: KTB&S has represented (and continues to represent) Paramount Pictures, Viacom and several of their affiliates in cases across the country. Real Mex Restaurants, Inc.: KTB&S represented Z Capital Partners as part of a consortium of lenders that acquired substantially all of the assets of this large national Mexican restaurant food chain operator pursuant to a court-approved 363 sale.

### Equity Holders:

203 North LaSalle Street Limited Partnership and Related Entities: Represented investors under chapter 11 reorganization plan on remand from the United States Supreme Court; subsequent plan successfully confirmed. Pittsburgh Penguins: Represented a significant shareholder in the Pittsburgh Penguins hockey team, in connection with the chapter 11 case of that team. President Casinos, Inc.: Represented an official committee of equity holders in the chapter 11 cases of a St. Louis based riverboat casino; successfully negotiated a favorable chapter 11 plan, which was confirmed and resulted in substantial distributions to equity.

### Acquirers & Others:

Suzuki Motor of America, Inc.: KTB&S represents a subsidiary of Suzuki Motor Corporation, as the purchaser of American Suzuki Motor Corporation's (ASMC) motorcycle, ATV and marine divisions in connection with ASMC's pending chapter 11 case. Tribune Company: KTB&S served as co-counsel to partner Kenneth N Klee, court-appointed independent examiner in the chapter 11 cases of Tribune Company et. al. The investigation, and resulting 1400-page report (completed in less than three months), uncovered facts surrounding, and analyzed potential estate causes of action against parties involved in, complex financing transactions and other matters. Enron Creditors Recovery Corp.: KTB&S served as lead counsel for the Enron estate in the so-called "Mega-Claims" litigation against Citigroup, Deutsche Bank and various related parties. This litigation was resolved successfully and resulted in the recovery by the estate of almost $1.7 billion in cash and waivers of in excess of $4.5 billion in claims. IndyMac Bancorp, Inc.: KTB&S is bankruptcy counsel to Alfred H. Siegel, the Chapter 7 Trustee of IndyMac Bancorp, Inc. ('Bancorp'), which is the holding company for IndyMac Bank, F.S.B. Anadarko Petroleum Corporation: KTB&S serves as co-counsel to Anadarko Petroleum Corp. and certain of its subsidiaries, as defendants in actions arising from the Tronox, Inc., et al. bankruptcy cases seeking recovery of up to $25 billion based on alleged pre-bankruptcy fraudulent transfers. Dewey & LeBoeuf: KTB&S serves as counsel to a large group of former partners in connection with bankruptcy case of this former multinational law firm; successfully resolved claims against this group of former partners pursuant to global settlement approved by the bankruptcy court.

Klee, Tuchin, Bogdanoff & Stern LLP

# LITTLER MENDELSON, P.C.

www.littler.com

**Chairman:** Garry Mathiason
**Managing Partners:** Tom Bender and Jeremy Roth

**Firm Overview:**

Littler Mendelson ("Littler") offers a wide range of employment and labor law solutions to assist US-based and multi-national employers with the extraordinary questions and risks that occur in today's litigious environment and constantly shifting regulatory landscape. With more than 950 attorneys and 57 offices, Littler is the world's largest law firm exclusively devoted to representing management in all aspects of employment and labor law. For more than 70 years, the firm has been business' strongest advocate, curbing union abuse when labor was at its height, and now, standing with employers as they face the onslaught of governmental regulation, aggressive plaintiffs' bars and a resurgent labor movement. The firm's attorneys have litigated, mediated and negotiated some of the most influential employment law cases and labor contracts on record.

**Main Areas of Practice:**

Littler is devoted entirely to the practice of employment and labor law. Within this practice, the firm has an array of sub-specialties: affirmative action/OFCCP compliance; alternative dispute resolution; appellate practice; background checks; business restructuring; class actions; competition and trade secret law; complex litigation and jury trials; corporate diversity and inclusion; corporate ethics and compliance; digital workplace; discrimination and harassment; ediscovery; employee benefits; employment taxes; ERISA and benefit plan litigation; executive compensation; employment practices audits; healthcare; higher education; hiring, performance management and termination; immigration; international employment law; labor management relations; leaves of absence and disability accommodation; legislative and regulatory practice; policies, procedures and handbooks; retail; staffing and contingent workers; transportation; wage and hour; whistleblowing and retaliation; workers' compensation; workplace policy institute; workplace privacy and data security; workplace safety and health (OSHA); and training - compliance, ethics, leadership.

**International Work:**

Littler has extensive resources to address the global needs of its clients. The firm's International Practice Group provides counsel on a wide range of matters, from navigating foreign employment laws and international labor relations issues, to applying corporate policies on a global basis. Littler's Global Mobility and Immigration Practice Group is a multicultural, transnational, full-service practice that provides international migration solutions for companies around the world. In October 2010, Littler opened its first office outside of the US in Caracas Venezuela and in 2013 expanded its presence in the region with a second office in Valencia. In February, 2011, it announced its affiliation with TransAsia Lawyers in The People's Republic of China and in December 2011, the firm opened two offices in Mexico City and Monterrey, Mexico.

## PRACTICE AREAS

Affirmative Action/OFCCP Compliance
Alternative Dispute Resolution
Appellate Practice
Background Checks
Business Restructuring
Class Actions
Competition & Trade Secret Law
Complex Litigation & Jury Trials
Corporate Diversity & Inclusion
Corporate Compliance & Ethics
Digital Workplace
Discrimination & Harassment
eDiscovery
Employee Benefits
Employment Taxes
ERISA & Benefit Plan Litigation
Executive Compensation
Employment Practices Audits
Global Mobility & Immigration
Healthcare
Higher Education
Hiring, Performance Management & Termination
Hospitality
International Employment Law
Labor Management Relations
Leaves of Absence & Disability Accommodation
Legislative & Regulatory Practice
Policies, Procedures & Handbooks
Retail
Staffing & Contingent Workers
Transportation
Wage & Hour
Whistleblowing & Retaliation
Workers' Compensation
Workplace Policy Institute
Workplace Privacy & Data Security
Workplace Safety & Health (OSHA)
Training - Compliance, Ethics, Leadership

## USA OFFICES

Albuquerque, Anchorage, Arkansas, Atlanta, Birmingham, Boston, Charlotte, Chicago, Cleveland, Columbia, Columbus, Dallas, Denver, Detroit, Fresno, Gulf Coast, Houston, Indianapolis, Kansas City, L.A. - Century City, City L.A. - Downtown, Las Vegas, Lexington, Long Island, Memphis, Miami, Minneapolis, Milwaukee, Morgantown, Nashville, New Haven, New York, Newark, Northern Virginia, Northwest Arkansas, Orange County, Orlando, Overland Park, Philadelphia, Phoenix, Pittsburgh, Providence, Portland, Reno, Rochester, Sacramento, San Diego, San Francisco, San Jose, Santa Maria, Seattle, St. Louis, Walnut Creek, Washington, DC

## INTERNATIONAL OFFICES

The firm also has offices in Caracas, Valencia, VZ, China, Mexico City and Monterrey.

# LOEB & LOEB LLP

**www.**loeb.com  **tel:** 310 282 2000  **fax:** 310 282 2200

**Chair:** Michael D Beck
Number of partners: 173
Number of other lawyers: 146

## Firm Overview:

Loeb & Loeb LLP is a multi-service law firm with more than 300 attorneys focusing on select core industries and practice areas, rather than endeavoring to be all things to all clients. The firm represents multinational, *Fortune* 100 companies in their mid-market transactions and litigation matters, and serves as primary outside counsel to a multitude of mid-market clients. The firm also represents clients ranging from start-ups to high net worth individuals and families. Loeb & Loeb has offices located in Los Angeles, New York, Chicago, Nashville, Washington DC, Beijing, as well as an affiliate office in Hong Kong. The firm has an established history and nationally-recognized reputation in the entertainment and media industries, and is highly regarded for its depth in financial services and real estate.

Loeb & Loeb prides itself on client matters being conducted and coordinated expertly, efficiently and expeditiously. Its culture is geared towards establishing and strengthening long-term client relationships, with an emphasis on senior attorney involvement in all transactions and matters. Teams are kept to optimal size to provide the highest quality advice, utmost efficiency, and seamless, cost-effective service across practices and offices.

## Main Areas of Practice:

Advertising and promotions; bankruptcy, restructuring and creditors' rights; capital markets, consumer protection defense and unfair competition; corporate; energy; entertainment; environmental; finance; intellectual property; litigation; media; mergers and acquisitions; outsourcing; patent litigation and counseling; privacy; private equity; real estate; securities litigation; sports; talent; tax; technology licensing; trademarks and copyrights; trusts and estates; white-collar criminal defense, corporate compliance and investigations.

## International Work:

Loeb & Loeb assists foreign companies, particularly in Asia and other emerging markets, with cross-border corporate and securities transactions; private equity and venture capital financings; and litigation, arbitration and regulatory proceedings.

Loeb & Loeb also represents companies and individuals in the global entertainment industry in complex co-production, co-financing and cross-border distribution deals.

# MANATT, PHELPS & PHILLIPS, LLP

www.manatt.com **tel:** 310 312 4000 **fax:** 310 312 4224

**CEO & Managing Partner:** William T Quicksilver
**Executive Director:** Edith S Gould
Number of partners: 220  Number of other lawyers: 128

## Firm Overview:

Since its founding in 1965 by two leaders of the banking and finance communities – later joined by a preeminent entertainment lawyer – Manatt has grown into the firm of choice for a sophisticated client base, including *Fortune* 500, middle-market and emerging companies. From its roots in banking and entertainment, the firm has clients in industries as diverse as advertising, energy, financial services, healthcare and real estate.

## Main Areas of Practice:

### Advertising:

The industry-leading Advertising Practice is forged from a group of highly experienced New York-based advertising lawyers, a comprehensive West Coast entertainment and media presence, and an advertising litigation and regulatory base in Washington, DC. The division has its primary focus on the representation of brands in their advertising efforts across media platforms. The combination of IP expertise and prolific experience before the National Advertising Division, FTC and State Attorneys General positions the firm to effectively advise national and international clients.
**Contact:** Linda A Goldstein **Tel:** 212 790 4544
**Email:** lgoldstein@manatt.com

### Entertainment:

Manatt's nationally recognized Entertainment Practice encompasses television, radio, motion pictures, music, digital entertainment, art and advertising. Firm lawyers handle legendary talent, music copyright matters, breach of contract, executive employment agreements, union and guild contracts, entertainment properties leveraging, and innovative brand integration. Manatt has successfully represented entertainment industry clients in bank and equity finance deals, licensing deals, production and distribution restructuring, and acquisition of companies and film and television assets.
**Contact:** Lindsay Conner **Tel:** 310 312 4229
**Email:** lconner@manatt.com
**Contact:** Gary Gilbert **Tel:** 310 312 4232
**Email:** ggilbert@manatt.com

### Financial Services & Banking:

From its beginnings, Manatt has been a leading financial services law firm. Today, the firm counsels more than 300 financial institutions across the nation and abroad. Bringing together lawyers specializing in banking and finance, capital markets, M&A, venture capital, regulatory compliance, tax, and antitrust analysis, the firm is uniquely equipped to serve clients that include commercial banks, domestic and foreign financial holding companies, savings institutions, trust companies, credit unions, and investment banks.
**Contact:** Gordon M Bava **Tel:** 310 312 4205
**Email:** gbava@manatt.com

### Government Relations:

Manatt's top-level government relations attorneys draw upon years of experience gained in elective offices, service on legislative and executive staffs, and senior-appointed positions at every level of government. Together they work to protect the vital interests of the firm's clients in administrative and legislative hearings, rulemakings and regulatory proceedings, government contracts and government assistance agreements, and lobbying.
**Contact:** George D Kieffer **Tel:** 310 312 4146
**Email:** gkieffer@manatt.com

### Healthcare:

Manatt has built one of the nation's most significant healthcare practices, with a dynamic, interdisciplinary team of attorneys and consultants. The firm provides strategic business advice, policy analysis, project implementation and coalition-building services to clients in health IT, healthcare delivery systems and hospitals. The group's combined skill assists clients in antitrust, financing, restructuring, M&A, fraud and abuse, legislative and administrative law, long-term care, and pharmaceuticals and biotechnology.
**Contact:** William S Bernstein **Tel:** 212 830 7282
**Email:** wbernstein@manatt.com

### Litigation:

The firm's litigators are some of the top trial and appellate lawyers in the country. They combine aggressive, creative litigation talent with a deep knowledge of the industries in which clients operate - advertising, healthcare, energy, financial services, entertainment, insurance and real estate. Manatt routinely tries high-stakes, complex cases, including "bet-the-company" litigation, in virtually every substantive area of business law, including antitrust, class actions, corporate investigations and white-collar defense, eminent domain, employment and labor, environmental and toxic torts, intellectual property, securities, technology and patent disputes, and unfair competition.
**Contact:** Matt Kanny **Tel:** 310 312 4225
**Email:** mkanny@manatt.com

### Energy, Environment & Natural Resources:

Manatt lawyers are skilled in dealing with complex environmental and energy regulations, focusing on the global energy industry and, in particular, on companies that develop, produce, market, transport and process energy resources. The firm provides clients with environmental compliance programs and, when compliance becomes environmental controversy, Manatt litigators are trial-experienced counsel and vigorous advocates. Harnessing strength in environmental regulation, energy project development and government relations, the firm applies its sophisticated understanding of the legislative and administrative arenas in turning a complex regulatory system to a client's competitive advantage in areas related to green technology and climate change.
**Contact:** Craig A Moyer **Tel:** 310 312 4353
**Email:** cmoyer@manatt.com

### Real Estate & Land Use:

Manatt has a panoramic knowledge of the real estate landscape, with a diverse practice handling acquisitions and dispositions, development, joint ventures, secured loans, mezzanine financing and preferred equity structures, leasing, management and construction, workouts and foreclosures, reorganization transactions, fund formation, and public/ private offerings of real estate securities. The land use practice is nationally known for strength in complex land use matters and green development. Manatt professionals embrace challenging environmental issues, securing necessary entitlements and approvals by anticipating hurdles and recognizing opportunities.
**Contact:** Tom Muller **Tel:** 310 312 4171
**Email:** tmuller@manatt.com

## OFFICES

### CALIFORNIA
**LOS ANGELES:** 11355 W. Olympic Blvd., CA 90064
Tel: 310 312 4000 Fax: 310 312 4224

**SAN FRANCISCO:** One Embarcadero Center, 30th Floor, CA 94111
Tel: 415 291 7400 Fax: 415 291 7474

**PALO ALTO:** 1841 Page Mill Road, Suite 200, CA 94304
Tel: 650 812 1300 Fax: 650 213 0260

**COSTA MESA:** 695 Town Center Drive, 14th Floor, CA 92626
Tel: 714 371 2500 Fax: 714 371 2550

**SACRAMENTO:** 1215 K Street, Suite 1900, CA 95814
Tel: 916 552 2300 Fax: 916 552 2323

### NEW YORK
**NEW YORK:** 7 Times Square, NY 10036
Tel: 212 790 4500 Fax: 212 790 4545

**ALBANY:** 30 South Pearl Street, 12th Floor, NY 12207
Tel: 518 431 6700 Fax: 518 431 6767

### DISTRICT OF COLUMBIA
**WASHINGTON DC:** One Metro Center, 700 12th Street, NW, Suite 1100, 20005
Tel: 202 585 6500 Fax: 202 585 6600

# MUNGER, TOLLES & OLSON

**www.mto.com tel:** 213 683 9100

**Managing Partners:** Sandra Seville-Jones
Number of partners: 89
Number of lawyers: 184

## Firm Overview:

For more than 50 years, Munger, Tolles & Olson has represented major clients in their most important cases and transactions. The firm is considered among the elite, full-service law firms in the country and has been at or near the top of The American Lawyer's A-List for six straight years. Munger Tolles is known for its selectivity in choosing its lawyers and for its 1:1 partner-to-associate ratio. These qualities mean that all matters receive careful thought and the attention of the partners.

Munger Tolles maintains a national and international practice. The majority of the firm's lawyers clerked for federal judges, and 18 were clerks to US Supreme Court Justices. The firm has built its reputation by offering clients exceptional judgment, creative thinking and a commitment to solving problems. For these reasons, clients have said they call on Munger Tolles in "precedent-setting cases that require a creative mind" and in cases that require "trial lawyers capable of waging war." The firm's clients include such major corporations as Bank of America, Berkshire Hathaway, Edison International, KB Home, LG Display, Oaktree Capital Management, Rambus, Transocean, Verizon and Yucaipa Cos.

The firm's lawyers are committed to serving the community. Munger Tolles consistently devotes more than three percent of collective attorney time to delivering pro bono legal assistance. In particular, the firm has acted as lead counsel in pro bono matters involving gay rights and the right of women to serve in combat.

Commitment to diversity is an integral part of the culture at Munger Tolles. The firm is ranked fourth on The American Lawyer's Diversity Scorecard, and this year, *Chambers Associate* noted that the firm "has one of the highest proportions of ethnic minority partners and associates of any firm we cover in this guide."

## Main Areas of Practice:

Munger Tolles is a full-service law firm. The firm's recent major matters include representing:

- Transocean and certain of its subsidiaries, which owned and operated the Deepwater Horizon drilling rig, in litigation arising from the April 20, 2010 BP oil spill in the Gulf of Mexico. Munger Tolles represents Transocean in multi-district litigation and other civil proceedings and ongoing criminal investigations
- Universal Music Group in the Federal Trade Commission's antitrust review of UMG's acquisition of EMI
- Bank of America, as lead counsel, in multibillion-dollar litigation filed by AIG and many other institutional investors alleging fraud in connection with investments in residential mortgage-backed securities originated or underwritten by BofA and its subsidiaries
- Berkshire Hathaway in its proposed $28 billion acquisition of H.J. Heinz Company
- The Boeing Co. in obtaining a reversal of a $603 million jury verdict from the California Court of Appeal in a fraud and breach of contract case against

ICO Global Communications Limited
- LG Display in the defense of a multistate class action brought on behalf of indirect purchasers stemming from allegations of price-fixing among manufacturers of liquid crystal display panels. The class action was settled in 2012, and Munger Tolles continues to defend LG Display in related suits brought by the direct action plaintiffs, including Best Buy, Target, Radio Shack, Sears and others
- HealthCare Partners in its acquisition by DaVita in a cash and stock transaction valued at $4.42 billion
- Guardian Industries in connection with a significant minority investment by Koch Industries
- HTC in nationwide class action lawsuits seeking hundreds of millions of dollars on behalf of all US residents who had mobile phones containing tracking software in violation of a federal wiretapping statute
- Solvay Pharmaceuticals, a subsidiary of Abbott Laboratories, in a major antitrust case, where the 11th Circuit affirmed a lower court ruling dismissing a complaint by the Federal Trade Commission alleging that so-called "reverse payment" settlements to generic drug manufacturers are anti-competitive

- Bond manager Jeffrey Gundlach and his company DoubleLine Capital LP against TCW. A Los Angeles jury found no damages against Gundlach and awarded him $66.7 million in unpaid wages
- Fox Entertainment Group in dismissing a class action that challenged the "tiering" or bundling of channels in purported violation of the Sherman Act. The 9th Circuit affirmed in a published opinion
- Official Committee of Syms Corp. Equity Securities Holders in the Chapter 11 reorganization of Syms, a discount retailer in the Northeast, and its subsidiaries, including Filene's Basement

## PRACTICE AREAS

Antitrust
Bankruptcy
Corporate
Entertainment
Environmental
Intellectual Property
Labor & Employment
Litigation
Real Estate
Tax
Technology
White Collar

## OFFICES

CALIFORNIA

**LOS ANGELES:** 355 South Grand Avenue, 35th Floor, CA 90071-1560

**SAN FRANCISCO:** 560 Mission Street, 27th Floor, CA 94105

# NOSSAMAN LLP

www.nossaman.com **tel:** 213 612 7800 **fax:** 213 612 7801

**Managing Partner:** E George Joseph (gjoseph@nossaman.com)

**Firm Overview:**

Nossaman LLP, founded in 1942, is a national law firm with 170 professionals working on cutting-edge issues across seven US offices. From building public infrastructure, providing healthcare services, managing natural resources, and successfully handling high-stakes litigation, to entitling private development, closing real estate deals, protecting the workplace, and advocating for legislative changes, Nossaman gets results. Clients of the firm include multinational corporations, public agencies, private businesses, trade associations, non-profits, and individuals.

**Main Areas of Practice:**

**Corporate:**
Nossaman assists corporations, limited liability companies, partnerships, and joint ventures in all stages of their development, whether as start-ups, growth companies or publicly held entities.
**Contact:** Charles S Fiedler **Tel:** 213 612 7800
**Email:** cfiedler@nossaman.com

**Eminent Domain & Valuation:**
Nossaman represents public agencies and other acquiring entities in the acquisition of right of way and other property. The firm also represents landowners and business owners facing both full and partial takings.
**Contact:** Rick E Rayl **Tel:** 949 833 7800
**Email:** rrayl@nossaman.com

**Employment:**
Nossaman provides counseling, advice and litigation services on a broad array of employment related matters, including: harassment, discrimination, wage and hour, trade secrets, wrongful terminations, leave laws, reductions in force/Warn Act, and record retention.
**Contact:** Veronica M Gray **Tel:** 949 833 7800
**Email:** vgray@nossaman.com

**Environment & Land Use:**
Nossaman helps landowners, developers, homebuilders and public agencies to entitle, finance and develop innovative projects. The firm has a national reputation for the successful defense of large infrastructure and land use development projects against environmental challenges.
**Contact:** John J Flynn III **Tel:** 949 833 7800
**Email:** jflynn@nossaman.com
**Contact:** Carollyn B Lobell **Tel:** 949 833 7800
**Email:** clobell@nossaman.com

**Financial Services & Bankruptcy:**
Nossaman represents financial industry clients in virtually every type of litigation, financing transactions, and counseling and advice on regulatory and operational matters. The firm has an extensive bankruptcy practice representing clients affected by the bankruptcies of other entities or engaging in transactions with debtors in Chapter 7, 9 and 11 proceedings.

**Contact:** Allan H Ickowitz **Tel:** 213 612 7800
**Email:** aickowitz@nossaman.com
**Contact:** Robert S McWhorter **Tel:** 916 442 8888
**Email:** rmcwhorter@nossaman.com

**Healthcare:**
Nossaman has served as healthcare law and policy leaders in California for decades. The firm's clients include hospitals and other delivery systems, managed care organizations, research organizations, surgicenters, and discount plans, as well as practice entities and individual professionals.
**Contact:** Richard B Spohn **Tel:** 415 398 3600
**Email:** rspohn@nossaman.com

**Infrastructure:**
Nossaman's internationally recognized Infrastructure Practice Group serves clients from the earliest stages of project and program planning through to procurement, project construction, and beyond. The firm advises on enabling legislation, federal policy and financing issues, procurement methods, and contract negotiations.
**Contact:** Patrick D Harder **Tel:** 213 612 7800
**Email:** pharder@nossaman.com

**Insurance Coverage:**
Nossaman advises policyholders on all aspects of insurance law and has built a strong track record in the trial and appellate courts.
**Contact:** Kurt W Melchior **Tel:** 415 398 3600
**Email:** kmelchior@nossaman.com
**Contact:** Joan M Cotkin **Tel:** 213 612 7800
**Email:** jcotkin@nossaman.com

**Intellectual Property & Media:**
Nossaman provides a broad range of trademark, copyright, trade secret, right of publicity and patent related legal services.
**Contact:** Thomas Dover **Tel:** 213 612 7800
**Email:** tdover@nossaman.com

**Litigation:**
Nossaman's experienced litigators represent clients in all stages of litigation, from pleading and summary judgment through trial and appeal. Nossaman's litigators have strong records of success as both trial and appellate counsel, and as skilled negotiators who

know when and how to advise their clients to achieve the best possible solutions.
**Contact:** Patrick J Richard **Tel:** 415 398 3600
**Email:** prichard@nossaman.com

**Public Pensions & Investments:**
Nossaman provides a full range of legal services and strategic advice to public and private sector clients who manage or advise pension plans on their real estate or alternative investment portfolios.
**Contact:** Yuliya A Oryol **Tel:** 415 398 3600
**Email:** yoryol@nossaman.com

**Public Policy:**
Nossaman helps clients promote their interests and achieve successful results at all levels of government. The firm's success in working with lawmakers, regulators, and the executive branch is the result of the strong relationships the firm maintains, coupled with in-depth, substantive knowledge.
**Contact:** Timothy W Jenkins **Tel:** 202 887 1400
**Email:** tjenkins@nossaman.com

**Real Estate:**
Nossaman represents clients in a variety of real estate transactions – from raw land to fully approved and occupied projects. The firm represents landlords and tenants in the leasing of office, industrial and retail space. It also offers assistance with the formation of limited liability companies, partnerships, and joint ventures created to buy, sell, lease, finance and develop real estate projects.
**Contact:** Karla N MacCary **Tel:** 213 612 7800
**Email:** kmaccary@nossaman.com

**Water:**
Nossaman represents watermasters, water districts, cities, utilities, developers, agricultural growers and processors, design-builders, operators, and local, regional and state agencies on a wide range of environmental, financing, water law and water utility issues, including related litigation.
**Contact:** Alfred E Smith **Tel:** 213 612 7800
**Email:** asmith@nossaman.com

**OFFICES**

CALIFORNIA
**LOS ANGELES:** 777 South Figueroa Street, 34th Floor, CA 90017-5800
Tel: 213 612 7800   Fax: 213 612 7801

The firm also has offices in San Francisco; Orange County; Sacramento; Washington, DC; Austin, TX; Arlington, VA

For additional information, please visit www.nossaman.com.

# O'MELVENY & MYERS LLP

**www.**omm.com **tel:** +1 213 430 6000 **fax:** +1 213 430 6407

**Chair:** Bradley J Butwin
**Managing Partners:** M Randall Oppenheimer (Litigation Department Chair), Warren T Lazarow (Transactions Department Chair), and Mark A Samuels (Vice Chair)
Number of partners: Approximately 200
Number of lawyers: Approximately 800
Languages: *Armenian, Bahasa Indonesia, Bahasa Malaysia, Bengali, Cantonese, Danish, Dutch, English, Farsi, French, German, Greek, Hebrew, Hindi, Italian, Japanese, Korean, Mandarin, Norwegian, Portuguese, Russian, Shanghainese, Spanish, Swedish, Tagalog, Taiwanese*

## Firm Overview:

O'Melveny & Myers LLP, founded in 1885, is an international firm with approximately 800 lawyers in 16 offices across Asia, Europe, and the United States. O'Melveny helps industry leaders across an array of sectors manage the complex challenges of succeeding in the global economy. It is a values-driven firm, guided by the principles of excellence, leadership, and citizenship. The firm's commitment to these values is reflected in its dedication to pro bono work and championing initiatives that increase the diversity of the legal profession.

In the US, O'Melveny is the law firm of choice for local companies as well as large multinationals in virtually every sector. From its birthplace in Los Angeles, the firm has grown to five locations in California, providing clients with critical nexus to one of the world's key economic, technological, and cultural centers. On the Eastern seaboard, the Washington, DC office operates in the heart of political and regulatory power in the US, assisting clients with high-level transactions, litigation, investigations, and public policy issues. In New York, there are approximately 100 lawyers who focus on complex litigation as well as sophisticated mergers and acquisitions, securities offerings, financing, and restructuring, reflecting the city's importance as a financial and business powerhouse.

The US offices work closely with the firm's international network to provide seamless global service.

## Main Areas of Practice:

### Litigation:

Highlights include representing:

- Warner Bros. in litigation over copyrights to the iconic Superman character, securing a series of what press reports called "blockbuster" rulings for the studio—including three important wins in the Ninth Circuit and a summary judgment ruling in the district court
- Bank of America in several complex litigation cases including convincing the Central District of California to dismiss claims seeking to hold BofA liable as successor-in-interest for many billions of dollars of potential liabilities regarding mortgage-backed securities issued by Countrywide Financial Corporation before BofA acquired it
- Allergan, Inc. in a trade secrets trial in California federal court, winning a rare "head start" injunction that significantly restricted the ability of an Allergan competitor to sell a botulinum toxin product in competition with Botox™
- Ford Motor Company in the successful appeal to the Ohio Court of Appeals, Eighth District of a US$2 billion jury verdict—the largest judgment in Ohio's history. The appellate court remanded the case for a new trial
- Jason West and Vince Zampella, creators of the Call of Duty and Modern Warfare video game franchises, in a breach-of-contract and fraud suit against Activision Publishing

### Transactions:

Highlights include representing:

- Several professional sports teams and investors in deals, including the acquisition of the Memphis Grizzlies basketball team, the sale of the San Diego Padres baseball franchise, and the purchase of a controlling interest in Major League Soccer's DC United
- Major investment banks in underwriting billion-dollar-plus offerings for companies such as Wellpoint, Toyota Motor Credit, AvalonBay Communities, Time Warner Cable, and Thermo Fisher Scientific
- Coller Capital on ground-breaking multi-billion dollar transactions resulting in the largest unsyndicated secondaries deal and the second largest secondaries fundraising ever completed
- BGI-Shenzhen in an industry-altering merger with Complete Genomics, Inc. reported as the first time a Chinese company successfully bought a US public company
- International Lease Finance Corp. in two debt offerings including a US$1.5 billion notes offering and a registered public offering of US$750 million

### Regulatory/Government Affairs:

Highlights include advising:

- Clients in Congressional, SEC, DOJ, state attorney general, and self-regulatory investigations
- Financial institutions regarding regulatory and compliance obligations under the Securities Exchange

Act of 1934, the Investment Advisers Act of 1940, the Investment Company Act of 1940, and other federal and state laws and regulations affecting investment companies, advisers, and broker-dealers

- Publicly traded companies on corporate and securities issues, including the public offering process, corporate governance best practices, "option backdating" and restatement issues, and proxy contests
- US and non-US companies on the application of US export controls, economic sanctions, the FCPA, antiboycott, and customs laws to their international activities
- Clients concerning regulatory approvals associated with direct foreign investments in the US, including CFIUS reviews
- US executive branch and judicial appointees, including members of the presidential cabinet, ambassadors, and others who have been selected for high government office, through the nomination and confirmation process

O'MELVENY & MYERS LLP

# PACHULSKI STANG ZIEHL & JONES LLP

**www.**pszjlaw.com **tel:** 310 277 6910 **fax:** 310 201 0760

**Management Committee:** Richard M Pachulski, Dean A Ziehl, Ira D Kharasch, Laura Davis Jones, Henry C Kevane, Robert Feinstein
Number of partners: 35  Number of other lawyers: 30

## Firm Overview:

Pachulski Stang Ziehl & Jones LLP (PSZJ) is the largest corporate restructuring boutique in the US with offices in Los Angeles, San Francisco, Delaware and New York. The firm is chapter 11 debtor's counsel to American Suzuki Motor Corporation and recently represented Solyndra LLC, and Mesa Air Group in their chapter 11 cases. The firm specializes in representing debtors, creditors' committees, trustees, liquidating trusts and private equity funds in complex restructuring and post-confirmation matters. PSZJ also handles sophisticated business litigation and transactional matters in addition to its renowned restructuring practice.

## Main Areas of Practice:

### Business Reorganization & Workouts:

The firm has a nationally recognized bankruptcy practice that is one of the largest in the country. The firm represents all of the major constituencies in bankruptcy proceedings and out of court workouts, including debtors, creditors' committees, equity committees, trustees, secured and major unsecured creditors, bondholders, asset purchasers and third-party plan proponents.

### Litigation:

The firm represents both plaintiffs and defendants in general commercial and business litigation, as well as banking, bankruptcy and insurance litigation. The prosecution and defense of litigation in bankruptcy court is a particular strength and the firm's litigators are well versed in bankruptcy jurisdictional disputes. The firm's national insolvency practice frequently requires client representation in fraudulent conveyance, preference and other bankruptcy-related litigation.

### Corporate & Transactional:

The firm's transactions practice features expertise over a broad spectrum, including real estate purchase and sales, development and commercial leasing; financing and workouts; sales of companies or their assets. The firm's transactional attorneys are uniquely qualified to handle the problems and issues associated with representing clients in complex bankruptcy transactions.

### Technology/Telecommunications:

The firm has considerable experience with the special issues facing high technology/telecommunications debtors and sophisticated acquirers of high technology/telecommunications companies, including Adelphia Communications, At Home, Cable & Wireless USA, Clarent Corporation, Covad Communications Group, Focal Communications, Inacom Communications, Integrated Telecom Express, Key3Media, MagnaChip Semiconductor, Metricom, Northpoint Communications, Pacific Crossing Ltd., Pacific Gateway Exchange, Peregrine Systems, Redback Networks, RFB Cellular, Satelites Mexicanos, Superior TeleCom, trident Microsystems and Yipes Communications

### Retail & Restaurant Chains:

The firm's combination of insolvency, real estate and commercial financial expertise enables members of the firm to represent a wide range of interests arising from the insolvency of large restaurant chains and retail outlets, including Circuit City, Copeland's, G + G Retail, B.U.M. International, Buffets Holdings, Fresh Choice, Real Mex Resturants, Blockbuster, Gas City, Robbins Brothers, Harry & David Holdings and Specialty Restaurant Group.

### Healthcare:

The firm has one of the nation's leading healthcare insolvency practices, with extensive experience in representing various constituencies in the highly regulated and increasingly active healthcare industry, including healthcare providers, trustees and governmental and private creditors in some of the nation's largest bankruptcy cases. Representations include involvement in the bankruptcies of Pacifica Hospital of the Valley, S&B Surgical Centre, San Fernando Mission Community Hospital, Valley Health System, Victor Valley Community Hositoal and Contra Costa Health Care District.

### Transportation:

The firm has represented debtors and creditors' committees in chapter 11 cases of airline carriers and companies engaged in aviation, trucking, logistics and other sectors of the transportation industry, including America West Airlines, Coach America, Fleetwood Enterprises, Flying J, Global Aviation, Jevic Holding Corp., Mesa Air Group, National R.V. and Trans World Airlines.

### Entertainment Insolvency:

The firm has played prominent roles in some of the nation's largest production and distribution company chapter 11 cases, including United Artists, Loews Cinemas, General Cinemas, Mann Theaters, 21st Century Film Group and Quintex Entertainment and has been involved in the cases of high profile entertainers/ athletes, including Toni Braxton, Ronald Isley, Johnny Gill and Mike Tyson as well as record company Deathrow Records and Marion 'Suge' Knight.

## OFFICES

**CALIFORNIA**

**LOS ANGELES:** 10100 Santa Monica Boulevard, 13th Floor, CA 90067
Tel: 310 277 6910   Fax: 310 201 0760
Email: dziehl@pszjlaw.com

**SAN FRANCISCO:** 150 California Street, 15th Floor, CA 94111
Tel: 415 263 7000   Fax: 415 263 7010

**DELAWARE**

**WILMINGTON:** 919 North Market Street, 17th Floor, DE 19801
Tel: 302 652 4100   Fax: 302 652 4400

**NEW YORK**

**NEW YORK:** 780 Third Avenue, 36th Floor, NY 10017-2024
Tel: 212 561 7700   Fax: 212 561 7777

# PEITZMAN WEG LLP

**www.**peitzmanweg.com **tel:** +1 310 552 3100 **fax:** +1 310 552 3101

**Managing Partner:** Howard J Weg
Number of partners: 5
Number of other lawyers: 8

## Firm Overview:

The law firm of Peitzman Weg LLP was founded in 1999 and has since been widely recognized as one of the top bankruptcy, restructuring and business litigation firms in California. The firm combines the sophistication of large global firms with small law firm efficiency to deliver boutique-style personal service to its diverse clientele and other lawyers. The experience of Peitzman Weg LLP attorneys includes representation of chapter 11 debtors, creditors and creditors' committees, institutional lenders, bondholders, buyers of assets and claims, directors and officers, shareholders, partners, members, bankruptcy trustees, and liquidating and litigation trusts. Industry experience includes entertainment, franchisors and franchisees, real estate owners, developers, landlords and tenants, manufacturing and private equity and hedge funds.

## Main Areas of Practice:

The firm's practice focuses on representations of parties involved in out-of-court restructurings, chapter 11 bankruptcies and commercial litigation. Recent major representations include chapter 11 debtor counsel to Sexy Hair Concepts Inc., LLC; Club Ventures Investments LLC/David Barton Gym; Pollo West Corp. and Mi Pollo; Gateway Metro; Ritz Interactive, Inc. (online retailer); Wagstaff Management; and Halcyon Holdings. Some of the firm's non-confidential representations include or have included:

### Debtor Representation:

Applause LLC, plush toy manufacturer of "Dream Pets" and many Disney-based characters; B.I.Commerce Liquidation, Inc.; Chantal Pharmaceutical Corporation; Closet World, Inc.; Club Ventures Investments LLC/David Barton Gym; Gateway Metro, owner of a Class A office building; Halcyon Holdings, Inc., owner of rights to the "Terminator" motion picture franchise; Industrial Parts Depot, Inc.; Laundrymart, Inc., a developer and operator of combined use retail micromalls; New Hotel Associates; Pollo West Corp. and Mi Pollo, Inc., one of the largest franchisees of El Pollo Loco; Ritz Interactive, Inc. (online retailer); Santa Barbara Beach Holding, LLC, owner of undeveloped beachfront property in Santa Barbara, CA; Sexy Hair Concepts LLC; Wagstaff Management, a major KFC restaurant franchisee.

### Committee Representation:

Easyriders, Inc., a magazine publisher; Express.com, an Internet distributor of video products; Illuminations.com, Inc., a national chain selling candles and related accessories; Komag, Incorporated, a leading supplier of thin-film disks; Marine Center, Inc., an international retailer of pleasure craft; Mercury Beauty Company, Inc.; Pacific Baja Light Metals Corporation; Reference Clothing; Steel Horse Automotive Accessories; Video City, Inc; Window Rock Enterprises; Zyan Communications, a broadband

Internet company. Also, as chair of Official Participants Committee in the chapter 11 case of California Power Exchange, the multibillion-dollar electric energy market maker.

### Trustee Representation:

Granada Hills Community Hospital (chapter 7 trustee in liquidating assets); Millennium Pacific Icon Group (chapter 7 trustee in series of complex, inter-related real estate entities); Passport International Entertainment, Inc. (chapter 7 trustee of TV production company); USA Sogo, Inc. (estate with more than $400 million in claims); Yacoubian Enterprises, LP (chapter 11 trustee of limited partnership that held title to three hotel properties in downtown Los Angeles).

### Litigation:

Adventure Parks Group bankruptcy (defend major creditor in lawsuit to recharacterize its claim); Blue Cross (represent in prosecuting fraud claims in bankruptcy court against participants in complex RICO/medical insurance fraud scheme); Coudert Brothers bankruptcy (represented former client in malpractice claim against law firm); Easyriders, Inc. bankruptcy (represented liquidating trust in fraudulent transfer and preference lawsuit against insiders); Essex Properties (represented ground lessor in quiet title action); Enron bankruptcy (represent defendant in action to recover $25 million in alleged fraudulent transfers); Gateway Metro, owner of a Class A office building; Granada Hills Community Hospital (actions on behalf of bankruptcy trustee against former officers and directors for breach of fiduciary duty); Great Transamerican Strand Investments, Inc. (represent defendant in action on guaranty of $160 million in debt); Heller Ehrman LLC bankruptcy (represent Citibank as defendant in $60 million preference action); Illuminations.com bankruptcy (represent trustee in actions against former directors and against insurer on D&O liability policy); MoneyGram

Payment Systems, Inc. (defend contract and tort claims); R.E. & M. Petersen Living Trust (represent philanthropic trust in dispute with Maguire Aviation); Trigem America Corp. bankruptcy (represented liquidating trustee as plaintiff in $55 million preference action and in objections to $200 million claim based on international trade documents).
**Contact:** James Menton, Jr **Tel:** 310 712 0090
**Email:** jmenton@peitzmanweg.com

### Acquisition & Sales:

Columbia Tristar Home Entertainment (purchaser of assets of Destination Films); Granada Hills Community Hospital trustee (seller of real property to Los Angeles Unified School District); Halcyon Holdings, Inc. (seller of rights to "Terminator" franchise and other films); Meridian Health Clubs of California, LLC (purchaser of assets of Bodies In Motion); Ricardo Beverly Hills (purchaser of Skyway Luggage); Santa Barbara Beach Holding, LLC (seller of site of future Ritz Carlton Hotel); The Carolco Liquidating Trust (seller of rights in major film library); Warner Bros. (co-purchaser of assets of Mann Theatres chain); Yacoubian Enterprises, LP trustee (seller of hotel properties).

### Creditor Representation:

The Bank of New York Blue Cross; Cascade Investments, LLC; Citibank; CIGNA; Dreamworks; Equity Office Properties Trust; The Bill and Melinda Gates Foundation Trust; Marubeni Corporation; Natexis; R.E. & M. Petersen Living Trust; Portland General Electric; Powerex Corp.; The Regents of the University of California; Warner Bros.
**Contact:** Howard J Weg **Tel:** 310 712 0088
**Email:** hweg@peitzmanweg.com

695

# ROBBINS GELLER RUDMAN & DOWD LLP

**www.**rgrdlaw.com  **tel:** +1 619 231 1058  **fax:** +1 619 231 7423

**Managing Partners:** 11
Number of partners: 76
Number of lawyers: 200

### Firm Overview:

Robbins Geller Rudman & Dowd LLP ("Robbins Geller" or the "firm") is a limited liability partnership with offices in San Diego, San Francisco, Washington, DC, New York, Chicago, Philadelphia, Atlanta, Boca Raton and London. The firm also has attorneys and advisors in Amsterdam, Netherlands; Paris, France; Rome, Italy; and Melbourne, Australia. With nearly 200 lawyers (many of whom are former federal and state prosecutors or ex-SEC lawyers) and more than 450 total employees, including forensic accountants, economists, damage analysts, investigators, paralegals, database programmers and computer security experts, Robbins Geller has repeatedly been recognized as the world's largest and most successful plaintiffs' securities fraud and antitrust litigation firm. The firm currently advises over 800 institutional investors, including public and multi-employer pension funds, fund managers, banks and insurance companies. The firm's attorneys have achieved the largest recoveries in virtually every type of securities-related litigation. Robbins Geller is responsible for the largest securities class action recovery in history (Enron – over $7.3 billion recovery); the largest-ever options backdating recovery (UnitedHealth – $925 million recovery); the largest opt-out recovery (WorldCom – $657 million recovery); the largest Section 11 credit crisis recovery (Wachovia – $627 million recovery); the largest corporate takeover recovery (Kinder Morgan – $200 million recovery); and secured a historic jury verdict resulting in $2.25 billion in claims for the shareholder class in Household Int'l, Inc.

### Main Areas of Practice:

#### Securities:

Robbins Geller is the leader in the battle against corporate securities fraud, recovering tens of billions of dollars to date for its individual investor and pension fund clients and the classes of investors they represent. Currently, Robbins Geller lawyers are lead or named counsel in approximately 500 securities class action or large institutional investor cases.

Judges across the country praise the firm as "highly skilled attorneys with great experience," "nationally recognized leaders" and the "preeminent" law firm in securities class action litigation. Analysts and publications laud their top-tier status and "expertise in securities matters." The firm's awards and recognition include top rankings in number of and aggregate recoveries on behalf of investor classes year after year.

Robbins Geller's securities team includes dozens of former federal and state prosecutors and trial attorneys, and a top-tier appellate group whose collective work has established numerous legal precedents. Robbins Geller also leverages the expertise of its in-house economic and damage analysts, investigators and forensic accountants (more than any other firm of its kind) in the prosecution of complex securities issues.

#### Antitrust:

Robbins Geller and its senior partners have also been at the forefront of groundbreaking antitrust litigation for the past 20 years. The firm is currently a lead counsel in the "Interchange Fee" antitrust litigation against Visa, Mastercard, and major credit card processing banks that conspired to artificially set and raise the fees merchants are charged when customers use credit, debit cards or ATM cards to make purchases. After years of hard-fought litigation, the case was preliminarily approved on November 9, 2012 for a settlement valued at more than $7.25 billion, the largest antitrust recovery in history.

The previous "largest antitrust recovery" was for the NASDAQ market makers action, where Robbins Geller partners were the lead counsel and recovered over $1 billion for NASDAQ investors who were over-paying for artificially fixed bid-ask spreads. In approving what was then a landmark recovery, the Court commended the lead counsel for its work, saying, "Counsel for the Plaintiffs are preeminent in the field of class action litigation, and the roster of counsel for the Defendants includes some of the largest, most successful and well regarded law firms in the country. It is difficult to conceive of better representation than the parties to this action achieved."

Robbins Geller has a long history and expertise in investigating and prosecuting complex antitrust litigation, and the firm is currently one of the leading firms advising clients on their claims related to the LIBOR-rigging scandal.

## PRACTICE AREAS

Securities
Corporate Mergers & Acquisitions
Shareholder Derivative
Consumer & Insurance Fraud
Antitrust
Human Rights
Public Health & Environment
Intellectual Property
Whistleblower
Appellate

## OFFICES

### GEORGIA
**ATLANTA:** 3424 Peachtree Road, NE, Suite 1650, GA 30326
Tel: 404 504 6500   Fax: 404 504 6501

### FLORIDA
**BOCA RATON:** 120 East Palmetto Park Road, Suite 500, FL 33432
Tel: 561 750 3000   Fax: 561 750 3364

### ILLINOIS
**CHICAGO:** 200 South Wacker Drive, 31st Floor, IL 60606
Tel: 312 674 4674   Fax: 312 674 4676

### NEW YORK
**MANHATTAN:** 52 Duane Street, 7th Floor, NY 10007
Tel: 212 693 1058   Fax: 212 693 7423

**NEW YORK:** 58 South Service Road, Suite 200, Melville, NY 11747
Tel: 631 367 7100   Fax: 631 367 1173

### PENNSYLVANIA
**PHILADELPHIA:** 1845 Walnut Street, 23rd Floor, PA 19103
Tel: 215 988 9546   Fax: 215 988 9885

### CALIFORNIA
**SAN DIEGO:** 655 West Broadway, Suite 1900, CA 92101
Tel: 619 231 1058   Fax: 619 231 7423

**SAN FRANCISCO:** Post Montgomery Center, One Montgomery Street, Suite 1800, CA 94104
Tel: 415 288 4545   Fax: 415 288 4534

### DISTRICT OF COLUMBIA
**WASHINGTON, DC:** 1100 Connecticut Avenue, N.W., Suite 730, 20036
Tel: 202 822 6762   Fax: 202 828 8528

## INTERNATIONAL OFFICES

The firm also has an office in London.

# Robbins Geller Rudman & Dowd LLP

# ROGERS JOSEPH O'DONNELL, PC

**www.**rjo.com **tel:** 415 956 2828 **fax:** 415 956 6457

Number of partners: 21
Number of attorneys: 34

## Firm Overview:

Rogers Joseph O'Donnell represents clients on their most difficult legal problems in six specialized areas of practice. The firm provides effective and nimble representation by focusing its practice on the areas of law it knows well. This all-litigation firm, founded in 1981, has the support structure of a much larger office, including the latest in technological assistance, to handle proceedings of any size in state and federal courts both at trial and on appeal, and to conduct ADR of the most sophisticated disputes.

## Main Areas of Practice:

### Attorney Liability & Conduct:

Rogers Joseph O'Donnell's Attorney Liability and Conduct practice group represents lawyers and law firms in litigation matters including legal malpractice, fee disputes, disqualification, sanctions and State Bar disciplinary matters, and also provides advice and counseling in the areas of ethical compliance and law practice management. The firm has significant experience representing large and small law firms, and regulary is called upon to provide strategic direction and risk management advice.

### Complex Commercial Litigation:

Rogers Joseph O'Donnell represents companies and individuals in complex litigation in a wide variety of industries, including disputes involving complex commercial contracts, federal and state antitrust laws, unfair competition and false advertising statutes, securities and other business fraud claims, consumer class actions against retailers and other business entities, minority squeeze-out claims, and insurance coverage.
**Key Clients:** Constellation Wines, Kapow Technologies, Inc., Via Licensing Corp.

### Construction:

Rogers Joseph O'Donnell has the experience necessary for any clients with a construction problem. Through a unique and comprehensive mix of expertise in both public entity and private construction, the firm represents general contractors, subcontractors, construction, managers, suppliers, owners, sureties, construction lenders, and design professionals. The firm has extensive expertise in legal issues related to construction projects, including contract negotiation, protests of contract award, insurance, extra work and delay claims, liens, false clams, stop notices, surety and employment disputes, terminations, and warranties.
**Key Clients:** Kiewit Corp., ACCO Engineered Systems, Inc., TY Lin International Group.

### Labor & Employment Law:

Rogers Joseph O'Donnell has extensive litigation experience representing employers in individual and class action labor and employment disputes, including jury trials, appeals, administrative hearings, mediations, and arbitrations. The firm has defended wage and hour claims under federal and state law, discrimination and harassment claims based on a variety of different protected categories including age, race, national origin, sex, sexual orientation, religion, and disability, and whistleblower claims including those arising under the State and Federal False Claims Acts.
**Key Clients:** Kmart Corp., Houston Casualty Co., Elk Grove Unified School Dist., Natus Medical, Inc., Workers Compensation Ins. Rating Bureau.

### Environmental Law:

Rogers Joseph O'Donnell represents national and regional manufacturers, developers, property owners, and individuals in disputes and litigation with federal, state, and local environmental regulators, and in private party cost recovery cases arising under state and federal environmental laws. Lawyers in the firm have prosecuted and defended cases under all of the major federal and state environmental statutes. These lawyers have particular expertise in litigation arising under CERCLA (the 'Superfund' law), the Resource Conservation and Recovery Act, and their state law counterparts, California's Proposition 65, and the California Environmental Quality Act.
**Key Clients:** Chevron USA Inc., The Dutra Group, The Regents of the University of California.

### Government Contracts:

Rogers Joseph O'Donnell is nationally recognized as one of the leading government contracts firm in the country and the only such firm headquartered on the West Coast. The firm represents many of the major national government contractors, as well as local and regional companies, in their federal, state, and local contracts. The firm works on all government contract issues, including contract disputes with the Government, disputes between prime and subcontractors, teaming agreements, due diligence in acquisitions and mergers, bid protests, terminations, qui tam and other False Claims Act cases, cost accounting standards, and Multiple Award Schedule Contracts.
**Key Clients:** Nothrop Grumman Corp., SAP America, Inc., Hewlett Packard Corp.

### Retail Industry Trade Regulation:

The Retail Industry Regulation Practice Group represents large retail chains, grocery stores, drug stores, and suppliers to California retailers in a wide variety of regulatory and litigation matters, particularly those involving unfair competition, false advertising, unfair business practices, consumer class actions, California's Proposition 65, hazardous waste handling, weights and measures, and challenges to state statutes, regulations, and municipal ordinances affecting the retail industry. This group regularly advises the firm's clients on compliance with federal, state and local laws in relation to their sales and operations in California and nationwide.
**Key Clients:** Amscan Holdings, Inc., Costco Wholesale Corp., Save Mart Supermarkets, Supervalu, Inc., Walgreen Co.

## PRACTICE AREAS

Attorney Liability & Conduct
Complex Commercial Litigation
Construction
Environmental
Government Contracts
Labor & Employment
Retail Industry Trade Regulation

## OFFICES

CALIFORNIA

**SAN FRANCISCO:** 311 California St, 10th Floor, CA 94104
Tel: 415 956 2828   Fax: 415 956 6457

DISTRICT OF COLUMBIA

**WASHINGTON, DC:** 750 9th Street NW, Suite 710, DC 20001
Tel: 202 777 8950   Fax: 202 347 8429

## Rogers Joseph O'Donnell

# SEDGWICK LLP

www.sedgwicklaw.com **tel:** 415 781 7900 **fax:** 415 781 2635

**Chair of the Firm:** Michael A Tanenbaum
Number of partners: 150
Number of attorneys: 393

## Firm Overview:

Sedgwick LLP has earned a reputation as one of America's best litigation and trial law firms by winning cases and providing clients with sophisticated, result-oriented strategies. Founded in 1933 as a three-person firm in San Francisco, the firm takes pride in its longstanding client relationships and in its well-earned reputation for effective and economical representation of some of the world's largest companies. Today, Sedgwick attorneys have tried cases in 48 out of 50 states and the firm provides multijurisdictional legal services that span the globe.
In recent years, the firm has been retained in mass tort, class action, multidistrict and market share litigation to defend and manage matters as national or regional trial counsel. The firm has served as national, regional and lead liaison counsel for leading international pharmaceutical, automobile, tobacco and medical device manufacturers. The firm's insurance practices comprise one of the largest international insurance industry teams of trial attorneys and policy advisors dedicated to the institutional concerns and successes of insurance carriers.
Sedgwick strives to provide clients with practical strategies that achieve their goals. These strategies may include business counseling for complex transactions, implementing risk prevention protocols, or pursuing alternative dispute resolution options such as commercial arbitration. The firm's attorneys know that effective dispute resolution and dispute avoidance must take into consideration its clients' broader business and legal objectives and not focus exclusively on the details of a specific case.
Along with their substantial legal backgrounds, many Sedgwick attorneys have specialized professional and educational backgrounds in fields such as medicine, engineering, nursing, accounting, aviation and pharmacology, which give them additional insight into their clients' businesses. The firm's practice spans a wide range of specialized areas, enabling its attorneys to draw upon their colleagues' wealth of experience and knowledge to determine the most advantageous strategy for any case.

## Main Areas of Practice:

Sedgwick serves clients throughout the state, nation and world. The firm's clients represent a wide range of industries – automotive, construction, education, electronics, energy, finance, food and beverage, insurance, manufacturing, pharmaceuticals, real estate, retail and transportation, to name a few – and range from privately owned businesses to *Fortune* 100 companies.
Sedgwick areas of practice include: antitrust and unfair competition, appellate, asbestos, bankruptcy and creditors' rights, business litigation, class actions, climate change, complex litigation, corporate, construction, drug and medical devices, e-discovery, employment and labor, environmental and toxic tort, healthcare, intellectual property, land use and natural resources, media, product liability, professional liability defense, real estate and finance, technology, and insurance practices, including admiralty and energy, aerospace, bankruptcy, casualty, climate change, fidelity and surety, international counseling and arbitration, life, health and disability, directors and officers, employment practices liability insurance, environmental, extracontractual/commercial insurance litigation, hydraulic fracturing, managed care, policy drafting/advice, professional liability, property, regulatory matters, reinsurance, and transactional matters.

## OFFICES

### CALIFORNIA

**IRVINE:** 3 Park Plaza, 17th Floor, CA 92614
Tel: 949 852 8200   Fax: 949 852 8282

**LOS ANGELES:** 801 S. Figueroa Street, 19th Floor, CA 90017
Tel: 213 426 6900   Fax: 213 426 6921

**SAN FRANCISCO:** 333 Bush Street, 30th Floor, CA 94104
Tel: 415 781 7900   Fax: 415 781 2635
Email: sedgwick.contact@sedgwicklaw.com

### TEXAS

**AUSTIN:** 919 Congress Avenue, Suite 1250, TX 78701
Tel: 512 481 8400   Fax: 512 481 8444

**DALLAS:** 1717 Main Street, Suite 5400, TX 75201
Tel: 469 227 8200   Fax: 469 227 8004

**HOUSTON:** 1111 Bagby Street, Suite 2300, TX 77002
Tel: 832 426 7000   Fax: 832 426 7009

### ILLINOIS

**CHICAGO:** One North Wacker Drive, Suite 4200, IL 60606
Tel: 312 641 9050   Fax: 312 641 9530

### FLORIDA

**FORT LAUDERDALE:** 2400 E. Commercial Blvd., Suite 1100, FL 33308
Tel: 954 958 2500   Fax: 954 958 2513

**MIAMI:** 9155 South Dadeland Blvd., Dadeland Centre, Suite 1208, FL 33156
Tel: 305 670 4777   Fax: 305 670 7007

### NEW JERSEY

**NEWARK:** Three Gateway Center, 12th Floor, NJ 07102
Tel: 973 242 0002   Fax: 973 242 8099

### NEW YORK

**NEW YORK:** 225 Liberty Street, 28th Floor, NY 10281-1008
Tel: 212 422 0202   Fax: 212 422 0925

### WASHINGTON

**SEATTLE:** 520 Pike Street, Suite 2200, WA 98101
Tel: 206 462 7560   Fax: 206 462 7561

### DISTRICT OF COLUMBIA

**WASHINGTON DC:** 2900 K Street NW Harbourside, Suite 500, DC 20007
Tel: 202 204 1000   Fax: 202 204 1001

## INTERNATIONAL OFFICES

The firm also has offices in Paris, France; Hamilton, Bermuda* and London, England.

* Associated office.

# STRADLING YOCCA CARLSON & RAUTH

**Managing Partner:** Board of Directors
Number of partners: 68  Number of other lawyers: 47

## Firm Overview:

Stradling represents companies and entities, which seek a sophisticated law firm with experienced counsel to guide critical transactions and disputes. Originally founded in 1975 to represent Southern California's most innovative emerging growth companies, Stradling is known today as a leading full-service law firm representing high growth and established organizations across a wide range of industries. The firm has built its practice around its clients' core needs. Stradling's size, structure, and culture allow it to provide big-firm representation with small-firm flexibility and responsiveness. Today Stradling serves established and emerging companies, municipalities, and global organizations using that very premise.

## Main Areas of Practice:

Corporate and securities, venture capital, private equity, mergers and acquisitions, life sciences, securities and complex business litigation, intellectual property litigation, employment litigation, public law, real estate, taxation, bankruptcy, and Article 9 UCC practice.

## Corporate & Securities:

The Corporate Practice focuses on mergers and acquisitions, private equity investments, joint ventures, SEC and SOX compliance and public offerings, venture capital financings and other financings. The firm assists companies in corporate partnering and licensing, technology transactions, corporate governance and taxation. The firm focuses on emerging and established, private and public companies in a variety of sectors including life sciences, healthcare services, technology, software, retail services, clean technology, internet companies, manufacturing, apparel and food services, among others.

## Life Sciences, Medical Devices & Pharmaceuticals:

From cardiac devices to ophthalmic innovation, the lawyers at Stradling assist hundreds of early stage and mature companies through their lifecycle. The firm also assists with company formation, VC and private financing, debt and lease financing, public offerings, securities law, technology transfer, distribution and licensing arrangements, joint ventures and strategic alliances as well as in complex licensing agreements with major international drug companies.

## Complex Business Litigation:

The firm's attorneys regularly prosecute and defend business disputes in state courts, federal courts and arbitration proceedings in California and in multiple jurisdictions across the country. The firm has a proven history of developing and implementing cost-effective litigation strategies. The firm handles alternative dispute resolution, antitrust and unfair competition, appellate advocacy, class action defense, partnership disputes and privacy and information security.

## Securities Litigation:

The firm handles all types of disputes involving the purchase and sale of securities and the fiduciary duties owed to shareholders. It defends companies and individuals sued in securities class actions and derivative cases. The firm prosecutes and defends shareholder disputes, M&A litigation, takeover litigation, proxy contests, broker-dealer disputes, and litigation involving investment fraud. The firm also handles government investigations, including Securities and Exchange Commission ("SEC") inquiries and enforcement proceedings, and Financial Industry Regulatory Authority ("FINRA") inquiries. Stradling also represents audit committees and special committees of boards of directors regarding internal investigations

## Intellectual Property Litigation:

The firm's attorneys are well-seasoned in litigating the full range of intellectual property and business tort cases on behalf of both plaintiffs and defendants. Stradling's IP Team includes attorneys who are licensed before the Patent & Trademark Office with technical backgrounds and expertise in areas such as physics, chemistry, and molecular biology. Areas of expertise include the litigation of complex patent infringement, antitrust, trademark, and other intellectual property cases.

## Employment:

The firm's employment attorneys protect and defend clients by reducing their exposure through effective management of both long-term and immediate employment issues. The firm helps educate clients to try to reduce and prevent claims, and defends them vigorously in state and federal courts when claims occur. The firm assists employers faced with wage and hour issues and class action and with addressing union organizing campaigns.

## Tax:

The firm's tax attorneys structure sophisticated solutions to tax issues arising from virtually every form of business transaction. Their work in this area includes complex corporate reorganizations, acquisitions, mergers, financing (including tax-exempt financing and derivatives), venture capital investments and fund formations, leveraged buy-outs, technology transfers and formation of joint ventures and partnerships, including unique applications of limited liability companies.

## OFFICES

### CALIFORNIA

**NEWPORT BEACH:** 660 Newport Center Drive Suite 1600, CA 92660
Tel: 949 725 400  Fax: 949 725 4100

**SACRAMENTO:** 500 Capitol Mall, Suite 1120, CA 95814
Tel: 916 449 235  Fax 916 441 2034

**SAN DIEGO:** 4365 Executive Drive, Suite 1500, CA 92121
Tel: 858 926 3000  Fax: 858 926 3001

**SAN FRANCISCO:** 44 Montgomery Street Suite 4200, CA 94104-4803
Tel: 415 283 2240  Fax: 415 283 2255

**SANTA BARBARA:** 800 Anacapa Street, Suite A, CA 93101
Tel: 805 730 6800  Fax: 805 730 680

**SANTA MONICA:** 100 Wilshire Boulevard, Suite 440, CA 90401
Tel: 424 214 7000  Fax: 424 214 7010

### NEVADA

**RENO:** 6490 S. McCarran Blvd., Bldg. E, Suite 121, NV 89509
Tel: 775 393 1950  Fax: 775 418 8339

## Public Law:

The firm's Public Law attorneys specialize in the practice of public finance and general public law. Members of the public law department are recognized experts in their practice areas, including federal and state securities laws, federal tax law and state and constitutional law issues. The firm has been involved in nearly every type of financing undertaken by public agencies and over 30 years has helped to develop many innovative financing programs. For over a decade, The firm has consistently ranked among the top bond counsel and disclosure counsel firms in the State of California. Stradling was recently the No. 1 ranked disclosure counsel firm in the country based on the dollar volume for completed transactions.

## Real Estate:

The firm's real estate practice involves the representation of retail, industrial, office and residential developers, landlords and tenants in all aspects of real property acquisition, financing, development, construction, leasing, management, syndication, exchange, and disposition. The firm has developed specialized expertise in matters related to shopping center development, including site acquisition, disposition, regulatory approvals, joint ventures, finance, leasing, operations, reciprocal access and easement agreements, CC&Rs, and tenant disputes. The firm represents both lenders and borrowers in real property secured lending, including construction and permanent financing, loan participations, securitized debt, loan assumptions, workouts, foreclosures, and receiverships.

## Clients:

Ceradyne, Inc., CKE Restaurants, Inc., Kingston Technology Co., Amphastar Pharmaceuticals, Hoag Hospital, County of Orange, City of Newport Beach, Saint John's Health Center, The Irvine Company.

# WILSON SONSINI GOODRICH & ROSATI

**www.**wsgr.com **tel:** 650 493 9300 **fax:** 650 493 6811

**Chairman:** Larry W Sonsini
**Managing Partners:** Douglas Clark, John T Sheridan
Number of partners: 188
Number of attorneys: 600

## Firm Overview:

Wilson Sonsini Goodrich & Rosati is the premier provider of legal services to technology, life sciences, and growth enterprises worldwide, as well as the financial institutions that invest in them. The firm advises and represents clients in a vast array of industries at all stages of development, from venture-backed start-ups to multibillion-dollar global corporations. Wilson Sonsini Goodrich & Rosati is nationally recognized as a leader in the fields of corporate governance and finance, mergers and acquisitions, private equity, securities litigation, employment law, intellectual property and antitrust, among many other areas of law. Over the past five decades, the firm has established its reputation by having a superior knowledge of its clients' industries, as well as deep and long-standing contacts throughout the technology sector.

## Main Areas of Practice:

Wilson Sonsini Goodrich & Rosati's main areas of practice include: corporate law and governance; corporate finance – private equity, public equity and debt finance; mergers and acquisitions; litigation – securities litigation, intellectual property litigation, merger and acquisition litigation, business litigation and counseling, white-collar crime and government investigations, employment law and appeals; intellectual property counseling and transactions – technology transactions, trade secret and employee mobility, intellectual property counseling and patents, global outsourcing transactions, trademarks, consumer regulatory and privacy, copyrights, and advertising; antitrust counseling and litigation; employee benefits and compensation; global generics; export controls and economic sanctions; energy and clean technology; privacy and data security; national security; project development and finance; real estate and environmental; and tax.

## International Work:

With roots in Silicon Valley and offices in technology hubs throughout the US, Wilson Sonsini Goodrich & Rosati long has had a national presence with a global reach. In addition, to better serve its clients overseas, the firm opened its first international office, in Shanghai, China, in 2007, and a second international office, in Hong Kong, in 2010. In October 2011, the firm opened its first European office in Brussels, Belgium, and in December 2012 added an office in Beijing. Over the past five decades, the firm has developed a wide-ranging international practice, with particular strength in Asia, Europe, and North America. Wilson Sonsini Goodrich & Rosati represents both US and foreign clients in a variety of international matters including: cross-border mergers and acquisition transactions, joint ventures, foreign investment, branch operations, intellectual property, and litigation.

## Clients:

Wilson Sonsini Goodrich & Rosati's client base includes: communications and networking, electronics/computer hardware, information services, life sciences and medical devices, media and entertainment, retail and consumer products and services, semiconductors, software, energy technology, and venture capital and financial institutions.

## OFFICES

### CALIFORNIA
**PALO ALTO:** 650 Page Mill Road, CA 94304-1050
Tel: 650 493 9300   Fax: 650 493 6811
Email: wsgr@wsgr.com

**SAN DIEGO:** 12235 El Camino Real, Suite 200, CA 92130-3002
Tel: 858 350 2300   Fax: 858 350 2399

**SAN FRANCISCO:** One Market Plaza, Spear Tower, Suite 3300, CA 94105-1126
Tel: 415 947 2000   Fax: 415 947 2099

### DELAWARE
**GEORGETOWN:** Eight West Laurel Street, DE 19947
Tel: 302 856 4235   Fax: 866 974 7329

### DISTRICT OF COLUMBIA
**WASHINGTON, DC:** 1700 K Street, NW, Fifth Floor, DC 20006-3817
Tel: 202 973 8800   Fax: 202 973 8899

### NEW YORK
**NEW YORK:** 1301 Avenue of the Americas, 40th Floor, NY 10019-6022
Tel: 212 999 5800   Fax: 212 999 5899

### TEXAS
**AUSTIN:** 900 South Capital of Texas Highway, Las Cimas IV, Fifth Floor, TX 78746-5546
Tel: 512 338 5400   Fax: 512 338 5499

### WASHINGTON
**SEATTLE:** 701 Fifth Avenue, Suite 5100, WA 98104-7036
Tel: 206 883 2500   Fax: 206 883 2699

## INTERNATIONAL OFFICES
The firm also has offices in Shanghai, Hong Kong, Beijing and Brussels.

WSGR

Wilson Sonsini Goodrich & Rosati
PROFESSIONAL CORPORATION

# WOLFSDORF IMMIGRATION LAW GROUP

**www.**wolfsdorf.com  **tel:** 310 570 4088  **fax:** 310 570 4080

**Managing Partner:** Bernard P Wolfsdorf
Number of lawyers: 17
Languages: *Afrikaans, Bengali, Chinese (Mandarin and Cantonese), Farsi, French, Georgian, German, Hebrew, Italian, Korean, Portuguese, Russian, Spanish, Turkish*

### Firm Overview:

Established in 1986, Wolfsdorf Immigration Law Group is a full-service immigration law firm that is led by Managing Partner Bernard P Wolfsdorf, who was voted the best immigration lawyer worldwide for three consecutive years from 2010 to 2012 by Who's Who Legal, the International Bar Association (IBA), and the American Bar Association (ABA) official research partner. The firm provides top-quality worldwide immigration and visa services to multinational corporations, small businesses, hospitals, universities, research institutions, and individual clients. The attorneys and legal assistants at Wolfsdorf have expertise in almost every type of immigration case, and they have a track record of achieving success with the most difficult cases. The staff of 17 attorneys and approximately 50 professionals ensures prompt and expert attention to clients' immigration law matters, and the firm maintains offices on both the East and West Coasts (Santa Monica, California and New York City, New York). Mr Wolfsdorf is the past National President of the American Immigration Lawyers Association (AILA).

### Main Areas of Practice:

Wolfsdorf attorneys and legal assistants have expertise in almost every type of US immigration case, and they have a track record of achieving success with even the most difficult cases. The firm serves an extensive and diverse client base, ranging from Fortune 500 corporations to entertainers and leading academic institutions as well as to investors. It also remains committed to handling family immigration, as well as naturalization casework on behalf of individuals.

Wolfsdorf Immigration Law Group's main areas of practice include: US Temporary Visas (for professionals, investors, academics/researchers, artists/athletes/entertainers, individuals of extraordinary ability, visitors, religious workers, students, and trainees); Embassy and Consulate Visa Processing; US Permanent Residency; US Citizenship; Global Business Immigration; Waivers; Immigration Court Proceedings and Deportation Defense; and I-9 Compliance (including audits and worksite enforcement). Wolfsdorf also prepares EB-5 visas and Regional Center Designation applications. EB-5 visas are highly beneficial permanent residence options for immigrant investors. Since there is presently no quota waiting list in this preference category, it enables foreign nationals to obtain permanent residence status more expeditiously than with many other options.

### International Work:

In an increasingly mobile business world and knowledge-based global economy, the success of Wolfsdorf Immigration Law Group's clients depends on the ability to hire and transfer employees across international boundaries seamlessly and efficiently. Through Wolfsdorf's affiliation with a global network of immigration attorneys who have been thoroughly evaluated for credentials, reputation, and quality-service standards, the firm offers effective, single-source solutions for obtaining visitor visas, entry clearance, work authorization, and permanent residence for employees in more than 70 countries around the world. Wolfsdorf's global reach extends to immigration experts in more than 100 countries and is maintained through the collective power of the Alliance of Business Immigration Lawyers (ABIL).

### PRACTICE AREAS

Corporate Immigration Law:
EB-5 & E-Investor Visas
Temporary Work Visas
US Permanent Residency
Embassy/Consulate Visa Processing
US Citizenship
Waivers
Court Proceedings
I-9 Compliance & Audits

### OFFICES

CALIFORNIA
**SANTA MONICA:** 1416 2nd Street, CA 90401
Tel: 310 570 4088   Fax: 310 570 4080
Email: visalaw@wolfsdorf.com

NEW YORK
**NEW YORK:** 641 Lexington Avenue, 15th Floor, NY 10022
Tel: 212 899 5040   Fax: 212 899 5041
Email: visalaw@wolfsdorf.com

WOLFSDORF
Immigration Law Group

## How lawyers are ranked

Every year we carry out thousands of in-depth interviews with clients in order to assess the reputations and expertise of business lawyers worldwide. The qualities we look for (and which determine rankings) include technical legal ability, professional conduct, client service, commercial awareness/astuteness, diligence, commitment, and other qualities most valued by the client. For details of our research team, see p.5.

# CORPORATE/M&A

Commentary about individuals can be found under their firm's paragraph. If the firm has no paragraph (is not ranked) look at Other Notable Practitioners.

**Corporate/M&A**
**Leading Firms**

**Band 1**
Davis Graham & Stubbs LLP *
Hogan Lovells US LLP

**Band 2**
Brownstein Hyatt Farber Schreck, LLP *
Bryan Cave HRO
Cooley LLP
Faegre Baker Daniels
Gibson, Dunn & Crutcher LLP *
Holland & Hart LLP *
Perkins Coie LLP

**Band 3**
Bartlit Beck Herman Palenchar & Scott LLP
Greenberg Traurig, LLP *
Morrison & Foerster LLP *

* Indicates firm with profile.
Alphabetical order within each band. Band 1 is the highest.

## Band 1

### Davis Graham & Stubbs LLP
See profile on p.726

THE FIRM This large, well-established regional group has cemented its position as a leader in the market following a series of strategic lateral hires. The team handles a broad swath of matters, including transactions, securities, asset management and private equity. Clients include Endeavour Capital, Resolute Energy and Golden Minerals.
**Sources say:** "They are very responsive and they have good partner depth."
**KEY INDIVIDUALS Ronald Levine** (see p.720) centers his practice on transactions and corporate finance. He is considered to be "technically very sound" and a "great negotiator" who is "aware of business implications" for his clients. He recently led the team's efforts for Resolute Energy in a debt financing offering of $250 million senior

notes. **Bruce Stocks** (see p.722) handles a wide variety of matters such as reorganizations, recapitalizations and subordinated debt financings, on which he represents the borrowers. He led the team acting for HiRel Systems during its recent $85 million sale. **Christopher Richardson** (see p.721) is managing partner at the firm and is best known for his work in the acquisition and sale of privately held companies. He led the group representing the Gary-Williams Company during the high-value sale of a subsidiary to CVR Energy. **Brian Boonstra** (see p.717) specializes in financial matters, including securities offerings, corporate financings and M&A. He is very experienced in representing domestic clients listed overseas and in other cross-border transactions. He is praised for his "prompt" service, which is "always of the highest quality."

### Hogan Lovells US LLP

THE FIRM This major international firm has a strong presence in Colorado and advises clients on a number of significant deals in three main areas: M&A, capital markets and private equity deals. The firm retains a wide variety of clients, including Regal Entertainment, OptumHealth and UnitedHealth Group.
**Sources say:** "Good international capabilities and a deep bench of specialists."
**KEY INDIVIDUALS Paul Hilton** maintains a broad corporate practice but is best known for his securities work. Clients remark that he is "very practical in his approach," and appreciate his responsiveness and the lengths he will go to in order to learn about his client's company. He was lead partner in the firm's recent work for Royal Gold, overseeing its $200 million acquisition of a stake in a copper-gold project in Canada. The highly respected **George Hagerty** handles a wide range of matters, including M&A, corporate finance and securities offerings. He has had a busy year, with highlights including acting for MarkWest Energy Partners on its $512 million acquisition of Keystone Midstream Services. **Mark Heimlich** focuses on financings and M&A. Clients praise his "keen attention to

detail," his "superior negotiation ability" and his "outstanding written and verbal communication ability."

## Band 2

### Brownstein Hyatt Farber Schreck, LLP
See profile on p.725

THE FIRM This exceptionally busy practice has handled more than 35 transactions in the past year, with a cumulative value of over $10 billion. The team is able to handle the full gamut of matters, including private equity fund formation, securities offerings and corporate restructurings. Clients include KSL Capital Partners, Vail Resorts and Miller Global Properties.
**Sources say:** "The work of the firm is top notch. The research is thorough and the drafting of documentation is exceptional and done quickly."
**KEY INDIVIDUALS** Recent arrival **Gino Maurelli** is an expert in midmarket M&A. He is described as a "phenomenal advocate" who combines "great responsiveness" with a "high degree of technical knowledge and deal management skills." "We put a high degree of trust in him because we know things will always get done, nothing slips down the track," said one client. **Adam Agron** maintains a broad practice covering almost every aspect of corporate transactional law, including LBOs, securities offerings and corporate restructurings. He is "extraordinarily well versed in many diverse aspects of the law," say sources, who also relate that he "goes above and beyond what's needed – not only from a work perspective, but also from a client relationship perspective." **Kevin Cudney** is a highly experienced corporate lawyer who has expertise in a wide array of matters. Clients appreciate that "in addition to providing legal review and applying his legal knowledge, he also has excellent skills and abilities regarding the larger picture."

## Corporate/M&A

### Senior Statesmen

Senior Statesmen: distinguished older practitioners

| | |
|---|---|
| Krendl Cathy S | Krendl Krendl Sachnoff & Way PC (ONP)† |

### Leading Individuals

**Band 1**

| | |
|---|---|
| Hilton Paul | Hogan Lovells US LLP |
| Levine II Ronald R | Davis Graham & Stubbs LLP * |
| Linfield James | Cooley LLP |
| Palenchar James | Bartlit Beck Herman Palenchar & Scott LLP |
| Salter Dean | Bryan Cave HRO |
| Stocks Bruce D | Davis Graham & Stubbs LLP * |
| Wheeler Francis | Cooley LLP |

**Band 2**

| | |
|---|---|
| Agron Adam | Brownstein Hyatt Farber Schreck, LLP |
| Arkell Betty | Holland & Hart LLP * |
| Carroll James H | Faegre Baker Daniels |
| Dietrich Stephen J | Greenberg Traurig, LLP * |
| Hagerty George | Hogan Lovells US LLP |
| Holmes Whitney | Dorsey & Whitney LLP (ONP)† |
| Jensen Garth B. | Bryan Cave HRO |
| Jordaan Hendrik | Morrison & Foerster LLP * |
| Maurelli Gino | Brownstein Hyatt Farber Schreck, LLP |
| Richardson Christopher L | Davis Graham & Stubbs LLP * |
| Stephens Thomas | Bartlit Beck Herman Palenchar & Scott LLP |
| Talley Steven K | Gibson, Dunn & Crutcher LLP * |
| Wright Douglas R | Faegre Baker Daniels |

**Band 3**

| | |
|---|---|
| Allison Sonny | Perkins Coie LLP |
| Attai Robert | Husch Blackwell LLP (ONP)† |
| Boonstra Brian | Davis Graham & Stubbs LLP * |
| Cudney Kevin A | Brownstein Hyatt Farber Schreck, LLP |
| Ford Nathaniel G | Perkins Coie LLP |
| Groll Christina | Holland & Hart LLP * |
| Heimlich Mark L | Hogan Lovells US LLP |
| Lloyd Dominic A | Baker & Hostetler LLP (ONP)† * |
| Platt Michael L | Cooley LLP |
| Ruppert John L | Ballard Spahr LLP (ONP)† * |
| Schlauch Stark Lucy | Holland & Hart LLP * |
| Stark Beau | Gibson, Dunn & Crutcher LLP * |

**Up-and-coming individuals**

| | |
|---|---|
| Fassett Brent | Cooley LLP |

* Indicates individual with profile.
Alphabetical order within each band. Band 1 is the highest.

### Bryan Cave HRO

**THE FIRM** This renowned international firm has a strong presence in the Colorado market. Members of the team assist clients with a wide range of matters, including acquisitions and mergers, offerings of debt and equity securities, and foreign-denominated debt securities. Recent clients include National CineMedia, Dolby Laboratories and Dynamic Materials.

**KEY INDIVIDUALS Dean Salter** is an extremely well-regarded corporate lawyer who is best known for his work on securities and governance issues. He was lead partner in the firm's work for Cimarex Energy on a $750 million issuance of senior notes and a tender offer and consent solicitation for $350 million of its senior notes. **Garth Jensen** represents large public companies across a range of industries in equity and debt offerings, as well as other matters. He is considered to be a thoughtful and responsive attorney who pays attention to the business needs of his clients.

### Cooley LLP

**THE FIRM** This large firm is best known for its close connections with technology companies. This close relationship is reflected by the services offered by the firm, with members of the team frequently called upon to help clients with financings, IPOs and M&A. Recent clients include Allos Therapeutics, Rally Software Development and TechStars.

**KEY INDIVIDUALS James Linfield** is primarily a transactional corporate lawyer, although he also helps clients with other matters such as IPOs. His recent highlights include representing Medivance in its sale to CR Bard for $250 million. **Francis Wheeler** maintains a broad practice helping clients on issues surrounding securities, transactions, governance and compliance, amongst others. He recently represented EffectiveUI in a $70 million cash sale to WPP. **Michael Platt** is well known for his work with emerging companies, particularly in the e-commerce sector. He advises clients on a broad range of work, including venture capital financings and corporate partnering. **Brent Fassett** is noted for his clear focus on representing life sciences healthcare companies. A recent highlight was his work for Miragen Therapeutics on its recent $20 million Series B financing.

### Faegre Baker Daniels

**THE FIRM** The result of a merger between Faegre & Benson and Baker Daniels in early 2012, this well-known Colorado corporate group continues to go from strength to strength. Clients hail from a wide range of industries and include tw telecom, Molson Coors and Double Eagle Petroleum.

**KEY INDIVIDUALS** The highly experienced **James Carroll** has a broad practice that includes securities, M&A and general corporate law. Sources comment favorably on his business aptitude. **Douglas Wright** is an expert in financings and securities transactions for a wide variety of industries. Clients praise his responsiveness and ability to deliver practical, commercial advice.

### Gibson, Dunn & Crutcher LLP
See profile on p.682

**THE FIRM** This small team is regularly engaged in transactions with values ranging from billions of dollars to smaller deals worth several million dollars. It maintains a regional and national practice with clients including Vail Resorts, The Williams Companies and Atmos Energy.

**Sources say:** "*They produce an exceptionally high-quality work product with good customer service.*"

**KEY INDIVIDUALS Steven Talley** (see p.722) concentrates his work on corporate finance transactions and M&A. He is praised for his "*good practical counsel,*" which is "*very solution-oriented.*" **Beau Stark** (see p.722) main-

tains a broad practice advising public and private enterprise clients on issues such as capital markets transactions, securities offerings and private fund formation. Sources attest that he has "*very good financial acumen, which is critical for a deal attorney.*"

### Holland & Hart LLP
See profile on p.727

**THE FIRM** This well-established Colorado firm has a significant corporate team that advises on a wide variety of matters, including LBOs, acquisitions and the divesture of unwanted subsidiaries. Clients include United Launch Alliance, T3Media and SM Energy.

**Sources say:** "*I was very impressed with Holland & Hart's responsiveness, dedication and diligence. I found the firm's approach to solving problems to be quite practical, and always with a view toward prompt resolution of issues in a cost-efficient manner.*"

**KEY INDIVIDUALS Betty Arkell** (see p.716) is well known for her work advising on venture capital investments, LBOs and M&A. Appreciative clients observe that "*she always strives to understand what the customer needs and can pay for.*" **Christina Groll** (see p.718) focuses on M&A, venture capital financings and private debt and equity financings. Sources note that "*although she will ensure that the total picture is considered, she always returns to the key points that are critical to get the best outcome for her client.*" **Lucy Schlauch Stark** (see p.722) maintains a broad practice advising clients on many issues relating to business transactions. She is noted for being "*able to dive down in the details as needed, but she also always kept the big picture in mind.*"

### Perkins Coie LLP
See profile on p.2548

**THE FIRM** This national firm's compact Colorado group is well respected for its work with midmarket clients. The team advises a broad client base drawn from a range of sectors on M&A and securities matters. A typical example of the team's work is its advice to Molson Coors on its $1.9 billion bond offering.

**KEY INDIVIDUALS Sonny Allison** maintains a broad practice that encompasses issues from M&A through to private equity and venture capital. Sources laud his impressive command of technical legal matters. **Nathaniel Ford** has a general focus on corporate law, advising clients on matters including public securities offerings and private equity and venture capital financing. Clients particularly appreciate his ability to communicate effectively with them.

### Band 3

### Bartlit Beck Herman Palenchar & Scott LLP

**THE FIRM** This small but respected team advises midmarket clients on a broad range of corporate issues, such as securities offerings, corporate finance and fund formation. Recent clients include Platte River Equity, Gotham Asset Management and Cheyenne Capital.

**KEY INDIVIDUALS James Palenchar** is highly praised by sources for his ability to work well with all those involved in transactions, and for the detailed expertise he provides. His extensive experience in M&A, SEC and private equity matters is also particularly highlighted by market observers. **Thomas Stephens** is an experienced adviser in matters pertaining to M&A and securities. Commentators are quick to highlight his responsiveness and deep knowledge of the area.

## Greenberg Traurig, LLP
See profile on p.1024

**THE FIRM** This group focuses on private and public financing transactions, governance and regulatory matters, along with M&A. Clients include GenAudio, ANB Bank, Attila Resources and Meyer Burger Technology.

**KEY INDIVIDUALS Stephen Dietrich** (see p.717) is a corporate M&A lawyer with significant experience relating to the automotive industry. Market observers note the regional and national scope of his practice.

## Morrison & Foerster LLP
See profile on p.1990

**THE FIRM** This nationally renowned firm's group in Colorado has been boosted in recent years by a series of partner-level hires. The office has expertise in private equity and represents clients in a number of different industries. Recent highlights include acting for DaVita on its recent $4.4 billion acquisition of Healthcare Partners Holdings.

**KEY INDIVIDUALS Hendrik Jordaan** (see p.719) was one of the lead partners on the $4.4 billion acquisition by Davita. His practice is very much global in breadth and his client list includes KRG Capital Partners, Tronair Holdings and ClearChoice. Sources name him *"a phenomenal lawyer"* who *"thinks very creatively on both transactions and what your business strategies are."*

## Other Notable Practitioners

The *"client-focused"* **Whitney Holmes** recently joined Dorsey & Whitney LLP from Morrison & Foerster. Holmes is praised for being *"very competent in the law"* and for

being able to *"translate that to the end game regarding the client's needs."* Areas of focus include M&A and securities. **John Ruppert** (see p.722) of Ballard Spahr LLP balances a local client list with his work out of state and advises clients on all aspects of corporate law. **Dominic Lloyd** (see p.720) of Baker Hostetler advises clients on corporate finance, M&A and more general corporate work. Clients appreciate his responsiveness and that *"he is the voice of reason,"* which means that *"he gets down to the harder things and resolves them."* **Robert Attai** of Husch Blackwell LLP is noted for his international practice, and has completed deals in the USA, Europe and Asia over the past year. Clients appreciate his ability to form a team and his *"personal attention and acute interest in furthering the interests of his clients."* As one client sums up: *"He gets it: this isn't about legal stuff, it's about getting business done and done right!"* **Cathy Krendl** of Krendl Krendl Sachnoff & Way PC is variously described as *"an institution"* and *"a stalwart of Colorado corporate law."* She primarily acts in mediations and as a special witness, and is noted for her in-depth knowledge of the state's corporate laws.

# INTELLECTUAL PROPERTY

## Intellectual Property
### Leading Firms

**Band 1**
Kilpatrick Townsend & Stockton LLP *

**Band 2**
Cooley LLP
Dorsey & Whitney LLP *
Faegre Baker Daniels
Holland & Hart LLP *
Sheridan Ross PC

**Band 3**
Hogan Lovells US LLP
Merchant & Gould PC
Perkins Coie LLP

\* Indicates firm / individual with profile.
Alphabetical order within each band. Band 1 is the highest.

## Band 1

### Kilpatrick Townsend & Stockton LLP
See profile on p.1109

**THE FIRM** This 32-strong team continues to lead the field in IP matters in Colorado, its formidable capacity in patent litigation, prosecution and trademarks. The global nature of the practice is highlighted by its work for FEXCO, defending allegations of patent infringement in regions including Brazil, Europe and New Zealand.

**Sources say:** *"They are among the best in any national firm. All are solid and, almost without fail, each is of the highest caliber."*

**KEY INDIVIDUALS Darin Gibby** is highly regarded for his counseling, transactions and licensing practice. He is praised for being able to *"provide sound advice with an overview of the big picture."* His clients include First Data,

Western Union, Baxter and Boppy. **Steve Jewett** is a highly rated IP attorney with noted experience in the IT and telecom sectors. Clients appreciate that he is *"very practical in his approach."* **David Sipiora** is the group's senior patent litigator. He is *"outstanding"* and is known as someone who will work exceptionally hard for his clients. He has recently successfully finished a patent infringement case in front of the ITC for key client LSI, brought by Rambus. **Ian Saffer** is praised for his *"broad knowledge in the field"* and for being *"very timely in the work performed."* He continues to represent Broadcast Music in its ongoing copyright enforcement litigation in Colorado.

## Band 2

### Cooley LLP

**THE FIRM** This strong practice is well known for its expertise in patent prosecution and litigation issues. It recently represented Gevo in patent litigation in the District of Delaware in a suit brought by Butamax, successfully fighting off a motion for preliminary injunction. Other clients include Chimei Innolux.

**KEY INDIVIDUALS James Brogan** is held out by sources as a highly experienced courtroom litigator. He recently successfully represented Chimei Innolux against claims of patent infringement brought by Mondis Technology in the Eastern District of Texas. **Wayne Stacy** is a patent litigator who primarily works with the electronics and software sectors. He is retained to handle cases involving security software and microcontrollers as well as thin-film deposition systems and photovoltaics.

## Intellectual Property
### Leading Individuals

**Band 1**

| | |
|---|---|
| Brogan James P | Cooley LLP |
| Gibby Darin J | Kilpatrick Townsend & Stockton LLP |
| Hanlon-Leh Natalie | Faegre Baker Daniels |

**Band 2**

| | |
|---|---|
| Beall Christopher | Levine Sullivan Koch & Schulz (ONP)[†] * |
| Gray Tracy | Holland & Hart LLP * |
| Jewett Steve | Kilpatrick Townsend & Stockton LLP |
| Kinsella Peter J | Perkins Coie LLP |
| London David L | Hogan Lovells US LLP |
| Matava George G | Lathrop & Gage LLP (ONP)[†] |
| Michaels Jane | Holland & Hart LLP * |
| Osman Lee R | Dorsey & Whitney LLP |
| Posthumus John R | Sheridan Ross PC |
| Scull Timothy B | Merchant & Gould PC |
| Sipiora David E | Kilpatrick Townsend & Stockton LLP |
| Stacy Wayne | Cooley LLP |
| Tamkin Greg | Dorsey & Whitney LLP |

**Band 3**

| | |
|---|---|
| Alter Scott M | Faegre Baker Daniels |
| Anderson Andrea | Holland & Hart LLP * |
| Degnan Donald | Holland & Hart LLP * |
| Gergely Peter A | Merchant & Gould PC |
| Havlick Scott | Holland & Hart LLP * |
| Osman Lisa | Dorsey & Whitney LLP |
| Saffer Ian | Kilpatrick Townsend & Stockton LLP |
| Wang Nina | Faegre Baker Daniels |

**Up-and-coming individuals**

| | |
|---|---|
| Sawyer Douglas L. | Perkins Coie LLP |

## Dorsey & Whitney LLP
See profile on p.1583

**THE FIRM** This team is well regarded for its work in the IP sphere, and has noted expertise in IP-related litigation. The firm routinely handles patent and trademark prosecution and clearance, brand management and issues surrounding copyright. Recent work includes acting for EC Sagitar on its defense against allegations of misappropriation of trade secrets.

**Sources say:** *"I can always depend upon these lawyers to represent my interests to the fullest extent."*

**KEY INDIVIDUALS Lee Osman** advises clients across the country on issues such as licensing and portfolio development as well as patent matters. This work includes patent prosecution, examining infringement and disclosure systems. **Greg Tamkin** is a litigator who is an *"excellent writer"* and *"does extremely well at oral arguments."* Clients appreciate the lengths he will go to in order to learn about how a client works in order to better serve their interests. **Lisa Osman** concentrates her practice on matters pertaining to trademarks, including licensing, infringement matters and asset acquisitions.

## Faegre Baker Daniels

**THE FIRM** This team has been in expansion mode and now includes 15 members in its Colorado offices. It is primarily known for its litigation strength but is also well regarded in the trademark prosecution arena. Clients include well-known companies such as Crocs, IBM, Pacific Bioscience Laboratories and Netgear.

**KEY INDIVIDUALS Natalie Hanlon-Leh** is widely regarded as a leader in IP litigation. She recently represented Pacific Bioscience Laboratories against Nutra Luxe MD, in an allegation of patent infringement, trade dress infringement and false advertising. The jury eventually found in favor of the plaintiff and awarded her client $11.6 million in damages. **Scott Alter** maintains a broad practice advising clients on matters ranging from the enforceability of patents to IP due diligence for corporate transactions. **Nina Wang** is an IP litigator who is seen by clients as an outstanding leader in her cases. She was lead partner on the firm's recent work for Netgear, in which her client was accused of six cases of patent infringement by Harris Corporation.

## Holland & Hart LLP
See profile on p.727

**THE FIRM** This respected Colorado firm maintains a broad practice that encompasses trademark and patent prosecution as well as transactional work. Clients are drawn from a wide variety of different industries, and include Photobucket.com, Interval International and Oracle.

**Sources say:** *"Outstanding. The attention to detail is excellent, and I invariably receive analyses that incorporate issues I hadn't previously considered."*

**KEY INDIVIDUALS Tracy Gray** (see p.718) advises clients on a variety of different IP issues, such as portfolio development and management, trademark availability and protection of trade secrets. She is best known for her work for e-business clients and continues to advise Amgen on privacy matters. **Jane Michaels** (see p.720) is an experienced litigator who defends her clients in cases involving patents, trademarks and trade secrets. Sources describe her as *"very practical"* and *"accessible."* **Scott Havlick** (see p.719) is well known for his work in trademarks and domain names. He advises on both foreign and domestic matters, including enforcement, usage and protection strategies. **Donald Degnan** (see p.717) focuses on protecting clients' IP rights through policing and enforcement. He continues to assist Server Technology with various patent strategy and litigation matters. **Andrea Anderson** (see p.716) is noted for her work within trademarks and assists clients with all stages of trademarks, from creation to protection. Clients praise her *"creative strategies"* as well as her ability to *"go after a particular business result."*

## Sheridan Ross PC

**THE FIRM** This large boutique has recently increased its presence in the market with a series of hires at all levels. The firm advises clients on issues relating to both patent and trademark law. The team is best known for its work in patent prosecution, particularly in the field of pharmaceuticals and biotechnology.

**KEY INDIVIDUALS John Posthumus** primarily focuses his practice on litigation work, but also handles matters involving transactions or trademarks.

## Band 3

## Hogan Lovells US LLP

**THE FIRM** This small team is highly regarded for its work on transactional matters and has extensive experience in litigation and patent prosecution matters. Clients include technology giants Apple, movie theater chain Regal Entertainment, and oil and gas consultants Quorum Business Solutions.

**Sources say:** *"I find the men and women at Hogan Lovells to be of the highest legal caliber. This firm is my go-to provider for legal services when I cannot afford to have a mistake or misstep."*

**KEY INDIVIDUALS David London** helps clients with issues dealing with transactional, licensing and outsourcing. Clients say that *"he is among a handful of attorneys across the nation who not only quickly grasp our situation*

*but also deliver high-quality work on time and for an efficient price."*

## Merchant & Gould PC

**THE FIRM** This boutique firm advises clients across the country on IP issues, particularly relating to patents, including prosecution, opinion drafting and portfolio analysis. Clients range from academic institutions to Fortune 500 corporations, and span the full spectrum of industries, such as biotechnology, telecoms and electronics. Key clients include Microsoft, Covidien and Aurora Financial Systems.

**Sources say:** *"Patent law requires lawyers who are not just skilled in the law but who also have a deep understanding of complex technology. Merchant & Gould excels at both of these."*

**KEY INDIVIDUALS Timothy Scull** handles patent procurement, prosecution and portfolio analysis. He is praised for his *"analytical, technical and problem-solving skills,"* and clients appreciate that he *"helps find legally sound and practical solutions to real-world problems."* **Peter Gergely** maintains a broad practice covering trade secret, copyright and patent matters. He recently defended Lippert Components against trade dress infringement allegations brought by Carefree.

## Perkins Coie LLP
See profile on p.2548

**THE FIRM** This team continues to increase in size and has extensive experience in patent litigation and prosecution, licensing transactions and work involving trademarks. The team is noted for its strength in a number of different technologies and its leading clients include Crocs, CenturyLink and Cloudfare.

**KEY INDIVIDUALS Peter Kinsella** is a renowned transactional lawyer with an international practice. He is praised for his pragmatic approach. **Douglas Sawyer** impresses interviewees with his deep technical understanding of sophisticated technology issues. He is know for his litigation and enforcement work.

## Other Notable Practitioners

**Christopher Beall** (see p.716) of Levine Sullivan Koch & Schulz LLP concentrates on litigation matters and also has a noted First Amendment practice. Source describe him as *"highly skilled"* and *"exceptionally knowledgeable."* His clients engage him across the country and include Denver Post, CBS Broadcasting and Viacom. The very experienced **George Matava** of Lathrop & Gage LLP *"is a stalwart of the Colorado IP litigation bar"* and is frequently engaged in defending patent infringement suits, primarily in electronic-based cases.

# LABOR & EMPLOYMENT

Commentary about individuals can be found under their firm's paragraph. If the firm has no paragraph (is not ranked) look at Other Notable Practitioners.

| Labor & Employment |
| --- |
| **Leading Firms** |
| **Band 1** |
| Holland & Hart LLP * |
| Sherman & Howard LLC |
| **Band 2** |
| Davis Graham & Stubbs LLP * |
| Ogletree, Deakins, Nash, Smoak & Stewart PC * |
| **Band 3** |
| Brownstein Hyatt Farber Schreck, LLP * |
| Bryan Cave HRO |
| Faegre Baker Daniels |
| Fisher & Phillips LLP * |
| Jackson Lewis LLP * |
| Littler Mendelson, PC * |

| Labor & Employment | |
| --- | --- |
| **Senior Statesmen** | |
| Senior Statesmen: distinguished older practitioners | |
| Oade K Preston | Bryan Cave HRO |

| **Leading Individuals** | |
| --- | --- |
| **Band 1** | |
| Brown Jessica | Gibson, Dunn & Crutcher LLP (ONP)† * |
| Eurich Gregory | Holland & Hart LLP * |
| Fredrickson Todd | Fisher & Phillips LLP * |
| Husband John | Holland & Hart LLP * |
| Martin Raymond | Wheeler Trigg O'Donnell LLP (ONP)† * |
| Powell Jr David D | Ogletree, Deakins, Nash, Smoak & Stewart * |
| Satriana Daniel | Clisham, Satriana & Biscan LLC (ONP)† |
| **Band 2** | |
| Biggs Jude | Holland & Hart LLP * |
| Deeny Raymond | Sherman & Howard LLC |
| Friesen Daniel | Friesen Lamb LLP (ONP)† |
| Gutierrez Steve | Holland & Hart LLP * |
| Johnson Jeffrey T | Holland & Hart LLP * |
| MacDonald Elizabeth A | Faegre Baker Daniels |
| Newcom Charles W | Sherman & Howard LLC |
| Olsen Theodore | Sherman & Howard LLC |
| Painter Brett | Davis Graham & Stubbs LLP * |
| Savage Janet A | Davis Graham & Stubbs LLP * |
| Siebert W Bernie | Sherman & Howard LLC |
| Webber Erin | Littler Mendelson, PC * |
| Weese Charles W | Lewis, Bess, Williams & Weese P.C. (ONP)† |
| **Band 3** | |
| Berger Bill | Brownstein Hyatt Farber Schreck, LLP |
| Moore Steven W | Ogletree, Deakins, Nash, Smoak & Stewart * |
| Mumaugh Brian | Holland & Hart LLP * |
| Samuels Don | Bryan Cave HRO |
| Silberman Mickey | Jackson Lewis LLP * |
| Will Mary | Faegre Baker Daniels |

| Labor & Employment: Employee Benefits & Compensation | |
| --- | --- |
| **Leading Individuals** | |
| **Band 1** | |
| Odle Kathleen | Sherman & Howard LLC |
| O'Rourke Renée W | Greenberg Traurig, LLP (ONP)† * |
| Strelau Nancy | Brownstein Hyatt Farber Schreck, LLP |
| **Band 2** | |
| Birley Cindy | Davis Graham & Stubbs LLP * |
| Muir Bruce | Sherman & Howard LLC |
| Nadel Darren | Littler Mendelson, PC * |

* Indicates firm/individual with profile.
Alphabetical order within each band. Band 1 is the highest.

## Band 1

### Holland & Hart LLP
See profile on p.727

THE FIRM This substantial, market-leading practice represents employers in a variety of matters such as equal employment issues, class action claims, labor relations work as well as general labor litigation and advisory work. The team is also increasingly handling more ERISA work. Clients include international firms such as Rio Tinto and JPMorgan Chase and more regional companies such as Aspen Skiing Company.

Sources say: "Their work is outstanding. The attorneys provide value added business-oriented legal solutions. I appreciate the sound legal advice they provide and their willingness to take the time to understand my company's business and overall industry."

KEY INDIVIDUALS Gregory Eurich (see p.718) "has an excellent reputation" for his work as a litigation specialist. A "wonderful and great lawyer," he handles cases involving claims of discrimination, collective bargaining agreements and wrongful discharge claims. John Husband (see p.719) is "one of the best around for labor and employment" and helps clients on a broad range of issues including dealing with equal opportunity, occupational safety and affirmative action. The "thoughtful and excellent" Jude Biggs (see p.717) is an experienced attorney who concentrates her practice on counseling work, although she also handles litigation matters. She is regularly retained to help clients anticipate and avoid workplace issues, and resolve them in cases where they have arisen. Jeffrey Johnson (see p.719) is in demand for his labor and employment litigation skills with one source commenting: "I've been uniformly impressed by his legal acumen, he is an excellent oral advocate. He keeps it short and sweet and is witty as well." Another commentator noted: "He does a great job of working with our company as a team and trying to find solutions to challenging issues." Steve Gutierrez (see p.719) is a high-

ly regarded litigator with a great depth of experience in juries trials and appeals. He also assists clients generally with practical advice with regard to compliance with both federal and state laws and best practice training on employment relationships. Brian Mumaugh (see p.720) devotes much of his time to collective actions and is, according to one impressed source, "an outstanding labor and employment attorney who takes the time to not only understand the current matter, but how treatment of an individual matter impacts my company's overall labor and employment strategy."

### Sherman & Howard LLC

THE FIRM This renowned team mixes expertise in traditional labor and employment work with keeping clients fully abreast of new legislation and issues such as employers' rights in the context of social media. The practice handles matters ranging from class actions and union matters

to immigration issues, whistle blowers and employee benefit plans.

Sources say: "There is a good focus on trying to keep costs low while protecting our interests." "The quality was exceptional and this was particularly impressive in light of the volume of work that needed to be accomplished in a short time period."

KEY INDIVIDUALS Kathleen Odle maintains a broad practice encompassing all matters relating to employee benefits with a particular focus on both equity benefits and executive compensation. Charles Newcom has "tremendous experience" in counseling and defending employers. He is linked most closely with work in mine safety and also has long experience assisting clients with Occupational Safety and Health Administration compliance. Theodore Olsen chairs the labor and employment department and offers clients many decades of experience. He helps clients with a broad variety of issues including traditional labor and employment, workplace violence and class actions. Bernie Siebert helps clients with the vast majority of issues arising out of labor and employment. According to one client he is "detail-oriented without sacrificing efficiency, and aware of the needs of our business so he focuses on costs." Raymond Deeny is a noted employer defense litigator who is "very responsive and capable." Bruce Muir concentrates his efforts on employee benefits and is noted by one source as someone who "knows the ERISA laws very well" and "is also a creative thinker."

## Band 2

### Davis Graham & Stubbs LLP
See profile on p.726

THE FIRM This exceptional six-partner group assists clients across all types of claims ranging from discrimination and wrongful dismissal to employee benefits and compensation and noncompetition agreements. It also provides counsel on best practices in respect of employee benefits and the various state and federal laws in this area such as the ERISA. Active clients include the University of

Colorado, Lockhart Geophysical and Adams County Board of Retirement.

**Sources say:** *"Every attorney, every paralegal and every administrator is knowledgeable." "The quality of their work is exceptional. They are very creative and knowledgeable, provide proactive and timely service and ensure that the right resources have been assigned to meet our needs and exceed our expectations."*

**KEY INDIVIDUALS Brett Painter** (see p.721) continues to impress with his blend of counseling and litigation skills. Commentators appreciate that he is *"highly responsive, has a superior ability to identify bottom-line issues and propose solutions and is very personable."* **Janet Savage** (see p.722) is a well-known litigator who is *"very well versed in the law"* and often has *"interesting cases."* In the past year she has handled a number of unfair dismissal and race and other discrimination cases which were all concluded in her clients' favor. **Cindy Birley** (see p.717) is an expert in the field of employee benefits as well as IRS tax compliance issues. An impressed client observes that she is *"highly trustworthy, acts with the utmost integrity and applies innovative approaches to solving problems."*

### Ogletree, Deakins, Nash, Smoak & Stewart PC
See profile on p.1110

**THE FIRM** This sizable Denver practice continues to grow in size and strength year on year. The team is regularly retained to help its regional and national clients on a broad range of matters including class actions, executive terminations and a range of discrimination and health and safety matters. It also handles business immigration matters for multinationals. Active clients include Western Union, Denver International Airport and the Johns Manville Corporation.

**Sources say:** *"They find the very best litigators, and those individuals never disappoint." "They exceed all expectations – and the immigration practice of the firm's Denver office is setting an example of high standards of service at reasonable prices."*

**KEY INDIVIDUALS** The *"fabulous"* **David Powell** (see p.721) is a widely admired litigator. He is regularly consulted by employers for assistance with wrongful discharge claims, discrimination and other contentious matters. **Steven Moore** (see p.720) handles a range of large-scale cases, including class actions and complex discrimination matters for both national and international clients. Appreciative clients say of him: *"He's just got it under control, he's thorough and patient he doesn't get flustered or side-tracked. He is the one you want on a national class action case." "He is very strategic in the way he thinks."*

## Band 3

### Brownstein Hyatt Farber Schreck, LLP
See profile on p.725

**THE FIRM** This group has made a number of strategic hirings over the past year, with new partner Bill Berger epitomizing the increasing strength of its bench. On the lit-igation front the group has had success in cases relating to discrimination and discharge claims, trade secrets and noncompete enforcements. The substantial employee benefits and executive compensation team is also highly regarded.

**Sources say:** *"The firm is responsive, reliable and able to offer practical advice quickly." "Outstanding, very good turn-around and very responsive to our needs."*

**KEY INDIVIDUALS Nancy Strelau,** who heads the practice is considered to be *"the best benefits lawyer in town."* She is also an acknowledged expert on executive compensation and ERISA issues. Clients note that she is *"extremely knowledgeable and practical and totally dedicated to the client's best interests."* New arrival, **Bill Berger** has a broad employment and labor practice which spans wrongful dismissal and discrimination issues, occupational safety and health and collective bargaining matters. He is praised by one client for his *"knowledge and understanding of legal aspects of labor issues and specifically collective bargaining agreements. "*

### Bryan Cave HRO

**THE FIRM** This litigation-focused team defends clients in a broad swathe of matters at state, federal and appellate level. Its expertise encompasses class and collective actions, wrongful termination, discrimination, as well as labor law matters, health and safety and all manner of employee benefits. The group includes Bank of America, Iron Mountain and Westmoreland Coal among its clients.

**KEY INDIVIDUALS Preston Oade** has huge trial experience, including before the Supreme Court, across all facets of employment and labor issues and is also an arbitrator with the American Arbitration Association. **Don Samuels** is an employment litigator who is valued for his experience and for giving practical advice. Armed with an encyclopedic knowledge of labor and employment matters, he has handled a number of high-value employment and labor cases in the past year.

### Faegre Baker Daniels

**THE FIRM** This team assists employers on a wide variety of matters such as compliance with state and federal employment laws and regulations, labor relations and litigation. The group has been boosted by the arrival of Mary Will who brings additional counseling and litigation skill to the team. Highlight work includes acting for Webfilings in a noncompetition and trade secret dispute with Rivet Software. It was successful at the temporary and preliminary injunction stages and the matter was then resolved.

**KEY INDIVIDUALS Elizabeth MacDonald** offers her clients considerable experience with litigation and administrative law matters and has a particular focus on the healthcare industry. Recent notable work includes representing Exempla Healthcare in a federal lawsuit concerning claims involving the Americans with Disabilities Act and the Family And Medical Leave Act. **Mary Will** concentrates her practice on employment compliance and litigation. Her recent cases include acting for IQNavigator when it brought a breach of noncompetition agreement and misappropriation of trade secrets action.

### Fisher & Phillips LLP
See profile on p.1107

**THE FIRM** This compact, Denver-based team offers a wealth of experience in labor and employment counseling and litigation together with employee benefits expertise. It has recently been especially active in employment litigation and collective bargaining.

**KEY INDIVIDUALS Todd Fredrickson** (see p.718) is the firm's managing partner as well as the principal lead on many of the group's cases. He concentrates his practice on representing employers in a range of discrimination and labor law issues. He is highly regarded by market sources, with one commenting: *"He's got a great reputation."*

### Jackson Lewis LLP
See profile on p.1982

**THE FIRM** This popular team focuses entirely on employment and labor law. It handles a range of equal opportunities/discrimination cases and is especially adept at wage and hour matters, including class actions. The team has also developed its own statistical expertise for use in such cases rather than relying on outside consultants. Its client roster includes DaVita, Crocs, Hyatt Hotels and adidas.

**KEY INDIVIDUALS Mickey Silberman** (see p.722) is praised for his *"attentiveness, responsiveness and customer service."* He is head of the Denver group and the firm's national affirmative action group. His recent work includes successfully defending Stryker corporation in a compliance review with regard to pay differentials.

### Littler Mendelson, PC
See profile on p.688

**THE FIRM** This well-established group handles a range of counseling and litigation matters from union negotiations to occupational safety and health, discrimination and wage and hour issues. It is especially well known for its skills in ERISA and privacy matters. Its client base includes large corporates as well as smaller, local businesses in a diverse range of industry sectors and it counts Level 3 Communications, McKesson Corporation and LSI Corporation among its clients.

**Sources say:** *"Absolutely excellent; great people to work with!" "Their professionalism, experience, and their follow through is great. They have a breadth and depth of knowledge."*

**KEY INDIVIDUALS Erin Webber** (see p.723) is reported to be *"a very dynamic and good leader of the office"* as well as *"effective, efficient, thorough and professional."* She is known for her particular focus on discrimination, workplace harassment and disability issues. **Darren Nadel** (see p.721) is a noted employment litigator, best known for his work on ERISA-related issues. Clients reported: *"He is a very experienced lawyer who is looking to provide legal solutions that are tailored to our particular business."* He is also lauded for his *"calm demeanor and ability to counsel us through difficult terminations."*

## Other Notable Practitioners

**Daniel Satriana** of Clisham, Satriana & Biscan LLC is a *"very skilled lawyer"* who *"knows his stuff."* He assists clients with discrimination claims, retaliatory discharge claims and other litigation matters. **Jessica Brown** (see p.717) of Gibson, Dunn & Crutcher LLP concentrates her practice on nationwide class action suits and related counseling. One source noted that she *"effectively advises us on the nature of risks, helps us explore our risk appetite and counsels* on appropriate risk mitigation strategies." Another source commented: *"Jessica's communication skills and work product are uniformly outstanding."* **Raymond Martin** (see p.720) of Wheeler Trigg O'Donnell LLP is a renowned litigator whose *"subject matter expertise in the area is at a very high level."* One grateful client enthused that he *"fought for justice and the truth every step of the way."* **Renée O'Rourke** (see p.721) of Greenberg Traurig, LLP is an *"excellent lawyer"* who *"gives good practical advice."* She is especially experienced within the employee benefits space and is well known for her work on ERISA matters. **Charles Weese** of Ducker, Montgomery, Lewis & Bess PC handles a range of employment and labor litigation and is lauded because *"working with him, it feels like he's an in-house lawyer,"* and *"he doesn't hesitate to make an objective and sober assessment for the benefit of his client."* **Daniel Friesen** of Friesen Lamb LLP is an *"incredibly intelligent attorney"* who can *"find good solutions to resolve litigation."*

# LITIGATION

White-Collar Crime & Government Investigations p.709

Commentary about individuals can be found under their firm's paragraph. If the firm has no paragraph (is not ranked) look at Other Notable Practitioners.

## Litigation: General Commercial
### Leading Firms

**Band 1**
Bartlit Beck Herman Palenchar & Scott LLP
Reilly Pozner LLP
Wheeler Trigg O'Donnell LLP *

**Band 2**
Davis Graham & Stubbs LLP *
Holland & Hart LLP *
Rothgerber Johnson & Lyons LLP

**Band 3**
Arnold & Porter LLP *
Ballard Spahr LLP *
Brownstein Hyatt Farber Schreck, LLP *
Faegre Baker Daniels
Gibson, Dunn & Crutcher LLP *
Greenberg Traurig, LLP *

**Band 4**
Bryan Cave HRO
Dorsey & Whitney LLP *
Haddon, Morgan and Foreman, P.C.
Hill & Robbins PC
Hogan Lovells US LLP
Sherman & Howard LLC
Snell & Wilmer LLP *

*Indicates firm/individual with profile.*
*Alphabetical order within each band. Band 1 is the highest.*

***The editorial is in alphabetical order by firm name.***

## Arnold & Porter LLP
See profile on p.906

**THE FIRM** This team of experienced trial lawyers is regularly retained for matters including contract law, natural resources, product liability, and Indian law issues. A recent highlight has been its representation of Sacramento Municipal Utility District (SMUD) in a claim against the USA concerning the government's failure to dispose of the district's nuclear waste. Other clients include Philip Morris and Harris Corporation.
**Sources say:** *"A very talented group of practitioners."*

## Litigation: General Commercial
### Senior Statesmen

| Senior Statesmen: distinguished older practitioners | |
| --- | --- |
| Bartlit Jr Fred | Bartlit Beck Herman Palenchar & Scott LLP |
| Scarboro James E | Arnold & Porter LLP * |

### Leading Individuals

**Star individuals**

| | |
| --- | --- |
| Reilly Daniel | Reilly Pozner LLP |

**Band 1**

| | |
| --- | --- |
| Baumann Frederick J | Rothgerber Johnson & Lyons LLP |
| Chase Jeffrey | Husch Blackwell LLP (ONP)[†] |
| Fitzpatrick John | Wheeler Trigg O'Donnell LLP * |
| Hill Robert F | Hill & Robbins PC |
| Lyons James M | Rothgerber Johnson & Lyons LLP |
| McCarthy Michael S | Faegre Baker Daniels |
| Palmer David G | Greenberg Traurig, LLP * |
| Thomasch Roger P | Ballard Spahr LLP * |
| Wheeler Malcolm | Wheeler Trigg O'Donnell LLP * |

**Band 2**

| | |
| --- | --- |
| Barker Scott S | Wheeler Trigg O'Donnell LLP * |
| Beyer Timothy R | Bryan Cave HRO |
| Fons Randy | Morrison & Foerster LLP (ONP)[†] * |
| Gallagher Michael J | Davis Graham & Stubbs LLP * |
| Gottschalk Hugh | Wheeler Trigg O'Donnell LLP * |
| Hartley James E | Holland & Hart LLP * |
| Kawanabe Kenzo S | Davis Graham & Stubbs LLP * |
| Kerwin Gregory J | Gibson, Dunn & Crutcher LLP * |
| Koenigs Christopher | Sherman & Howard LLC |
| Macdonald Timothy R | Arnold & Porter LLP * |
| McDermott John V | Brownstein Hyatt Farber Schreck, LLP |
| Michaels Jane | Holland & Hart LLP * |
| O'Donnell Michael | Wheeler Trigg O'Donnell LLP * |
| Scott Donald E | Bartlit Beck Herman Palenchar & Scott LLP |
| Trautman Tucker | Dorsey & Whitney LLP * |

**Band 3**

| | |
| --- | --- |
| Aro Edwin | Arnold & Porter LLP * |
| Duffy Brian L | Greenberg Traurig, LLP * |
| Farbes Jr Hubert A | Brownstein Hyatt Farber Schreck, LLP |
| Goldberg Charles | Rothgerber Johnson & Lyons LLP |
| Groves KC | Ireland Stapleton Pryor & Pascoe PC (ONP)[†] |
| Johnson Tom | Davis Graham & Stubbs LLP * |
| Kanan Gregory B | Rothgerber Johnson & Lyons LLP |
| Low Andy | Davis Graham & Stubbs LLP * |
| Recht Daniel N. | Recht Kornfeld, PC (ONP)[†] |
| Sawtelle James G | Bryan Cave HRO |
| Summers Glen | Bartlit Beck Herman Palenchar & Scott LLP |
| Theis B Lawrence | Bryan Cave HRO |
| Theis Michael | Hogan Lovells US LLP |
| Treece Lawrence W | Brownstein Hyatt Farber Schreck, LLP |

**Band 4**

| | |
| --- | --- |
| Brown Nea | Temkin Wielga & Hardt LLP (ONP)[†] |
| Cohen Jeffrey | Ballard Spahr LLP * |
| Connelly Sean | Reilly Pozner LLP |
| Fairless Carolyn | Wheeler Trigg O'Donnell LLP * |
| Lipinsky Lino | McKenna Long & Aldridge LLP (ONP)[†] * |
| Miller Robert N. | Perkins Coie LLP |
| Musgrave Bobbee J. | Bryan Cave HRO |
| O'Neill Timothy | Snell & Wilmer LLP * |
| Pagliuca Jeffrey S. | Haddon, Morgan and Foreman, P.C. |
| Toll Christopher | Holland & Hart LLP * |

**Up-and-coming individuals**

| | |
| --- | --- |
| Benson Amy | Bryan Cave HRO |
| Olson Eric | Bartlit Beck Herman Palenchar & Scott LLP |
| Rollin Michael | Reilly Pozner LLP |

**KEY INDIVIDUALS Timothy Macdonald** (see p.720) was counsel in the aforementioned matter for SMUD. Areas of excellence include securities law, insurance disputes and breach of contract disputes. **Edwin Aro** (see p.716) has extensive experience in representing companies in civil lawsuits. He is an experienced trial lawyer with a broad litigation practice including breach of duty and insurance coverage disputes. The highly experienced **James Scarboro**

*The editorial is in alphabetical order by firm name.*

(see p.722) is *"one of the deans of the Bar"* and is well known for representing tobacco and diet drug companies.

### Ballard Spahr LLP
See profile on p.2234

THE FIRM This respected firm acts in a broad range of litigation matters. A key strength of the team is its experience in real estate and construction litigation, while it has recently added a financial services litigation capacity with the arrival of Jeffrey Cohen. Clients include Goodyear and DuPont.

Sources say: *"From timeframes to legal clauses, they know all the things we need to take into consideration. They are flexible, responsive whenever we have a problem and are aggressive if needs be."*

KEY INDIVIDUALS Roger Thomasch (see p.723) is *"one of the best litigators in Colorado,"* say sources. He recently represented Goodyear in defense of coordinated product liability class actions. Jeffrey Cohen (see p.717) is a recent arrival from Patton Boggs. He is an expert financial services litigator and advises parties on bond defaults and other issues. Clients say that *"he brings a sense of calmness and detail"* to litigation and note that he is *"very commercially minded."*

### Bartlit Beck Herman Palenchar & Scott LLP
THE FIRM This distinguished litigation group is considered a market leader in Colorado. The team is frequently engaged in some of the most complex high-stakes litigation both within the state and across the country in matters such as commercial litigation, intellectual property and antitrust claims. Recent matters include the trial defense of NL Industries in claims by a number of California municipalities concerning the presence of lead paint in buildings throughout the state.

KEY INDIVIDUALS Donald Scott has a recognized expertise in product liability matters as part of a broader litigation practice. He recently represented investor George Gillett in litigation surrounding the sale of British sporting institution Liverpool Football Club. Glen Summers is recognized for his skilled approach and broad litigation expertise, encompassing intellectual property, securities, employment and commercial disputes. He has recently been defending Frank McCourt, former owner of the Los Angeles Dodgers baseball team, in a high-stakes legal malpractice case. The highly respected and vastly experienced Fred Bartlit is a nationally renowned litigator. His areas of expertise include antitrust and securities litigation. Eric Olson joins the rankings upon the recommendation of sources who are full of praise for his courtroom skills and ability to try cases. He is experienced in representing both defendants and plaintiffs in a wide range of cases.

### Brownstein Hyatt Farber Schreck, LLP
See profile on p.725

THE FIRM This litigation group is recognized for its broad commercial litigation capabilities. The team handles a range of disputes including those stemming from securities, antitrust or corporate governance issues. Clients include Urban Villages and Gunnison Energy Company.

Sources say: *"They are incredibly thorough, better prepared and more knowledgeable than their opponents."*

KEY INDIVIDUALS John McDermott maintains a general civil litigation practice which includes securities litigation. One client reports: *"He is a very good lawyer and litigator, and a strong strategist."* Hubert Farbes has an *"exceptional presence in the courtroom,"* sources say, one of whom also notes: *"He can take complex constitutional questions and reduce them to common sense topics with which no reasonable person could possibly disagree."* He handles disputes arising from areas such as construction, regulatory and natural resource law. Lawrence Treece is an expert on securities, class actions and corporate governance matters and has *"a more than excellent understanding of procedural matters and substantive matters in areas of the law both familiar and arcane,"* says one source.

### Bryan Cave HRO
THE FIRM This group handles a broad range of commercial disputes including antitrust, healthcare and general business litigation. The team recently successfully represented plaintiff Ohio Spine Network in a federal breach of contract trial. Clients include CenturyLink, Xcel Energy and Molson Coors.

KEY INDIVIDUALS Recent arrival Timothy Beyer is highlighted for his tremendous experience and instincts. His broad practice encompasses multiple aspects of commercial litigation ranging from telecommunications to antitrust matters. Cliff Stricklin is noted for his expertise in handling government investigations and inquiries. He recently led a team that defended CH2M Hill in an investigation by the DOJ concerning alleged overtime fraud and false claims of work carried out post-Hurricane Katrina. The experienced Lawrence Theis is noted for his work on antitrust matters. James Sawtelle is highlighted as extremely thorough and very communicative. He is also recommended for his ability to combine legal sense with awareness of business objectives. Bobbee Musgrave is regularly engaged in a broad variety of different cases including class actions, trade regulation and intellectual property litigation. Amy Benson receives warm praise for her skills as a litigator, as well as for her excellent abilities with judges and juries.

### Davis Graham & Stubbs LLP
See profile on p.726

THE FIRM This firm's trial department continues to impress in the Colorado market. Recent highlights include acting for the Farmer's Insurance Exchange and Mid-Century Insurance Company in defense of a class action claiming fraud, breach of contract and bad faith. Other clients include BP and Pfizer.

Sources say: *"The quality of work is uniformly very good. I particularly appreciate the firm's dedication, responsiveness and knowledge of our business and goals."*

KEY INDIVIDUALS Michael Gallagher (see p.718) is *"a first-rate attorney"* who has *"excellent litigation and trial skills."* His practice is often focused on environmental and commercial litigation for oil and gas companies. Kenzo Kawanabe (see p.719) is a *"very effective lawyer"* who is *"one of the top rising stars in the Denver legal community,"* sources say. He is experienced in handling product liability and general commercial litigation. Of counsel David Zisser (see p.723) is noted for his handling of securities litigation and regulatory enforcement matters and is a *"terrific lawyer,"* according to market observers. He represents officers and directors before the Securities and Exchange Commission (SEC) and other bodies. Tom Johnson (see p.719) is a *"thorough, professional and knowledgeable"* advocate noted for his presence in the general commercial litigation space. New entry Andy Low (see p.720) is *"savvy when it comes to what argument will work and when to pick his battles,"* say sources. Clients appreciate his *"profession-*

*The editorial is in alphabetical order by firm name.*

al and pragmatic approach" and his *"disciplined logical analysis of the facts and his eloquent writing skills."*

## Dorsey & Whitney LLP
See profile on p.1583

**THE FIRM** This litigation team is retained to advise on a large swath of commercial litigation matters. It is renowned for its substantial expertise on intellectual property matters and has notable experience in oil and gas and securities litigation.
**KEY INDIVIDUALS** The experienced **Tucker Trautman** has expertise in all aspects of intellectual property litigation. He further assists clients with securities fraud, antitrust and complex commercial litigation.

## Faegre Baker Daniels

**THE FIRM** This firm's litigation team offers a number of areas of expertise including intellectual property litigation, business litigation, product liability and eminent domain matters. Clients include BNP Paribas, USA Hockey and US Bank.
**KEY INDIVIDUALS** **Michael McCarthy** maintains a broad practice encompassing insurance coverage disputes and shareholder derivative actions, among others.

## Gibson, Dunn & Crutcher LLP
See profile on p.682

**THE FIRM** This national firm continues to earn the respect of the Colorado market. Recent highlights for the group include its work for Molycorp and its outside directors for whom the team was retained as lead defense counsel in connection with a shareholders' class action.
**Sources say:** *"The firm is comprised of true legal experts in a wide variety of legal disciplines."*
**KEY INDIVIDUALS** **Robert Blume** (see p.717) uses his background as a former prosecutor to help clients deal with both internal investigations and complex civil litigation. A source observed that *"he was creative in coming up with solutions to help us,"* and that *"he was able to come in and articulate what the strategy was."* **Gregory Kerwin** (see p.719) handles antitrust, insurance, securities and civil litigation. He *"approaches litigation with a winning attitude and manages the client's budget as if it were his own,"* say sources.

## Greenberg Traurig, LLP
See profile on p.1024

**THE FIRM** This well-known firm maintains a solid presence in the Colorado litigation market. The team is recognized for its handling of disputes throughout the region, and is seen to specialize in multidistrict litigation. Clients include Jacob's Engineering and Gray Line Worldwide.
**KEY INDIVIDUALS** Highly experienced trial and appellate advocate **David Palmer** (see p.721) recently acted for a financial institution in a class action by investors following a public offering. Sources say he is *"a very good lawyer"* and note his prominence in antitrust matters. Head of the firm's global litigation practice **Brian Duffy** (see p.718) is *"prominent on the national level,"* say interviewees. He has

extensive experience in handling class actions, employment and product liability cases.

## Haddon, Morgan and Foreman, P.C.

**THE FIRM** This litigation boutique enjoys an outstanding reputation for its white-collar criminal defense work and has a long history of involvement in some of the state's highest profile cases. The group also has a respected practice in general commercial matters. Both areas of expertise have been illustrated by the team's recent handling of cases involving securities law and allegations of insider trading.
**Sources say:** *"They are, and always will be, a band one firm for white-collar investigations."*
**KEY INDIVIDUALS** **Pamela Mackey**'s practice covers a broad range of white-collar matters including criminal proceedings relating to antitrust, tax or environmental law. **Saskia Jordan** is a *"very good criminal defense lawyer"* who is *"good at developing a case theory that is easy to sell and resonates with the jury."* **Jeffrey Pagliuca** is recognized for his strength in commercial litigation and his handling of insurance disputes. He *"should be recognized as a fully-armed litigation samurai,"* said one interviewee. **Harold Haddon** is a venerated figure in the white-collar space. *"There is hardly a major company in this part of the country that doesn't call him when they find themselves in a tangle with the government,"* attests one commentator.

## Hill & Robbins PC

**THE FIRM** This compact team assists clients with complex litigation in a range of areas including antitrust and securities law. The group is also well known for its expertise in representing plaintiffs in class action cases.
**KEY INDIVIDUALS** **Robert Hill** is seen as the expert in this region for plaintiffs' class actions work. He is praised for being both *"intelligent"* and *"the real deal."*

## Hogan Lovells US LLP

**THE FIRM** This team handles a broad range of work including litigation in the healthcare, environmental, white-collar and government investigation spaces. The team recently defended United Health Group with respect to claims of Medicare fraud. Clients include such illustrious names as Apple, Office Depot and Medtronic.
**Sources say:** *"When you look at level of experience and sophistication they rank very highly."*
**KEY INDIVIDUALS** The *"impeccable"* **Daniel Shea** has significant experience in SEC investigations and financial regulatory matters. Clients highlight his ability to spot issues. **Michael Theis** is best known for his extensive experience in healthcare fraud and abuse litigation. He is considered to be *"very knowledgeable about government regulatory issues,"* and is praised for his *"intuition and ability to conduct effective risk assessments."*

## Holland & Hart LLP
See profile on p.727

**THE FIRM** This venerable Colorado firm is well regarded for its handling of general commercial litigation, and is particularly noted for its expertise in finance services litigation. Recent matters include acting for Bacterin

International as plaintiff in a trade secrets and defamation case against a former employee. Clients include JPMorgan Chase, Chevron and United Airlines.
**Sources say:** *"I appreciate that their in-depth knowledge and experience is enhanced by the firm's understanding of local customs and practices."*
**KEY INDIVIDUALS** **Gregory Goldberg** (see p.718) is *"a great courtroom lawyer,"* say sources. He heads the firm's government investigations group. **James Hartley** (see p.719) is *"a very good tactician"* with a *"good strategic mind."* He is recognized for his handling of antitrust and IP litigation pertaining to a wide range of industry sectors. **Jane Michaels** (see p.720) led the team in the aforementioned work for Bacterin International. Sources say she is *"an excellent trial attorney"* and comment favorably on her *"breadth of knowledge"* and *"skill in presenting a case."* **Christopher Toll** (see p.723) maintains a broad practice covering both general commercial and trade secrets work. He assisted in the work for Bacterin International.

## Perkins Coie LLP
See profile on p.2548

**THE FIRM** This firm has a solid reputation in white-collar criminal matters and government investigations. Recent highlights include the team's representation of Westwood Colleges in a class action suit brought against the college. The group subsequently filed a defamation action against the plaintiffs based on their lawyers' conduct in what is the first challenge of its kind to the litigation privilege.
**KEY INDIVIDUALS** **Markus Funk** represents clients in corporate white-collar criminal defense cases. Sources praise his analytical, practical and commercial approach. **Robert Miller** has experience representing all parties in connection with investigations by federal and state prosecutors.

## Reilly Pozner LLP

**THE FIRM** This litigation boutique is widely lauded for its handling of high-stakes civil and criminal litigation. On the commercial side the team recently represented AIG in a complex dispute with Bank of America concerning the terms of its $8.5 billion settlement of claims following the mortgage-backed securities crisis. The firm also handles the full range of white-collar criminal matters, recently acting for RPI Coatings in defense of criminal proceedings following an industrial accident.
**Sources say:** *"The firm does exceptional work and I would consider it to be one of the top firms in Colorado."*
**KEY INDIVIDUALS** Outstanding commercial litigator **Daniel Reilly** is a *"consummate trial lawyer"* with *"tremendous presence in the courtroom,"* sources say. He took the lead in the mortgage-backed securities matters for AIG described above. **Larry Pozner** is recognized for his white-collar criminal work, handling the RPI Coatings matter referred to above. One client enthuses that he is the *"go-to guy for litigation on cases that are significant to us,"* because he is *"responsive, thorough and effective in court."* **Michael Rollin** is *"a skillful and strategic examiner"* who is *"a real team player in every sense of the word,"* say sources. One interviewee notes: *"He has created a very strong reputation*

in the complex litigation and structured financial litigation space." **Sean Connelly** is *"a remarkable appellate advocate,"* say sources. He recently won an appellate reversal on behalf of a whistle-blower in a False Claims Act qui tam action against Kerr-McGee Oil & Gas.

## Richilano Shea LLC

**THE FIRM** This litigation practice enjoys a fine reputation for its expertise in handling white-collar criminal matters. The team assists clients with a broad range of matters including criminal appeals, securities-related issues and criminal antitrust investigations.

**Sources say:** *"If we had a large investigation of a company and we had individuals who needed separate legal representation, we'd go to them."*

**KEY INDIVIDUALS** The highly commended **John Richilano** is a heavily experienced trial lawyer at both state and federal level. He primarily acts on sophisticated white-collar criminal cases. White-collar defense attorney **Kevin Shea** is *"very calm, collected and extremely knowledgeable,"* say sources. Clients add that *"he's not afraid of anything and is willing to fight for what's right, fair and just."*

## Rothgerber Johnson & Lyons LLP

**THE FIRM** This group handles high-stakes commercial and white-collar criminal litigation, and is noted for its activity in the insurance and healthcare sectors. Active clients include Anschultz, US Bank and Health Grades. The team was recently retained as defense counsel for Accord Human resources in a case alleging errors in the payment of unemployment tax.

**Sources say:** *"We got superior service for a very appropriate price."*

**KEY INDIVIDUALS Frederick Baumann** is *"a pleasure to deal with, but you'll always know there is a deep intellect and a strong strategic presence,"* say commentators. He recently acted for Lukoil in connection with a dispute over mining rights in northern Russia. **James Lyons** is a *"thorough legal thinker"* who has an *"absolutely pragmatic view of litigation."* One impressed source reports: *"His advice to clients, whether on tactics or strategy or on the substantive law in a case, is right on target."* The experienced **Charles Goldberg** is noted for his long-standing representation of the Archdiocese of Denver and the Diocese of Fargo in North Dakota as well as educational institutions and other religious bodies. **Gregory Kanan** has an active litigation practice in a number of areas including commercial, antitrust, securities and health law. His antitrust experience includes dealing with monopolies, unlawful dealer termination and price-fixing.

## Sherman & Howard LLC

**THE FIRM** This team has a solid reputation for commercial litigation in areas such as securities fraud, business torts and contract disputes. The team recently acted for Fiserv in defense of class action claims stemming from the Madoff ponzi scheme. Other clients include Nova Leasing and TD Ameritrade.

**Sources say:** *"They're a strong group of attorneys."*

**KEY INDIVIDUALS Christopher Koenigs** offers an *"exquisite work ethic"* with *"top-notch analytical skills and integrity,"* say sources. He maintains a broad practice encompassing areas such as commercial and securities litigation.

## Shoemaker Ghiselli & Schwartz LLC

**THE FIRM** This boutique firm is noted for its provision of defense counsel to officers and directors of companies involved in investigations and appeals, and is recognized for its expertise in cases concerning securities fraud. The team wins plaudits for its successful defense of HEI Resources and its president Charles Cagle in a case alleging violations of the Colorado Securities Act.

**Sources say:** *"Very knowledgeable and experienced with strong business acumen."*

**KEY INDIVIDUALS Andrew Shoemaker** (see p.722) has a firm grasp of securities enforcement stemming from his in-house background at the SEC. He is *"strategic, an excellent writer and is great in court,"* say sources. **Paul Schwartz** (see p.722) is characterized by sources as *"an exceptionally able litigator"* who is *"clearly very smart and practical"* and *"savvy in providing very good strategic advice."*

## Snell & Wilmer LLP
### See profile on p.517

**THE FIRM** This group assists clients with a wide range of matters including real estate and construction disputes, franchise law and securities litigation. The firm's distinguished client roster includes Starbucks, Bank of America and Cimarex Energy.

**KEY INDIVIDUALS Timothy O'Neill** is a product liability lawyer who *"has a national trial reputation."* He recently defended Emerson Electric in a multimillion-dollar indemnity and insurance coverage suit in Texas.

## Wheeler Trigg O'Donnell LLP
### See profile on p.730

**THE FIRM** This firm continues to operate at the forefront of the commercial litigation space in Colorado. The group handles a broad range of matters including medical and legal malpractice, mass torts, appellate work as well as general commercial disputes. Recent matters include representing Ford successfully in the Tenth Circuit Court of Appeals following an $18 million product liability verdict at jury trial. Other clients include BP and AT&T.

**Sources say:** *"The firm provides outstanding quality in both their discovery and their trial work. They are very personable and juries like them. They are highly intelligent and organized, and get great value for their clients."*

**KEY INDIVIDUALS John Fitzpatrick** (see p.718) is a general litigator who is *"very dynamic and very decisive."* He recently defended a Florida hospital in a high-value medical malpractice case. As one source sums up: *"He gets results."* The *"extraordinary"* **Malcolm Wheeler** (see p.425) concentrates his practice on product liability cases and is often sought out to try cases across the country on the

basis of his expertise and experience. **Scott Barker** (see p.716) handles product liability, natural resources and toxic tort issues among others. He recently acted for BP in a class action appeal concerning the alleged underpayment of royalties. **Hugh Gottschalk** (see p.718) is an experienced litigator who has handled cases involving trade secret, trademark infringement and franchise matters. Peers note he is a *"a wonderful lawyer."* **Michael O'Donnell** (see p.721) handles product and professional liability cases. One observer reports that he *"possesses excellent judgment"* and is *"a master at reading the strengths and weaknesses of the other side and in developing a winning strategy."* **Carolyn Fairless**'s (see p.718) practice includes professional liability, product liability and commercial litigation cases. She is *"thorough and well prepared"* and has an *"excellent presence in court,"* say sources.

### Other Notable Practitioners

The experienced **Gary Lozow** of Foster Graham Milstein & Calisher LLP is one of the state's most admired white-collar criminal defense attorneys. His experience encompasses a broad range of matters including securities fraud, tax evasion and Medicaid fraud. **Randy Fons** (see p.718) of Morrison & Foerster LLP has extensive experience handling securities and internal investigations. He has *"credibility with the government, a good manner with clients and good common sense,"* say sources. Commercial litigator **KC Groves** of Ireland Stapleton Pryor & Pascoe PC is a *"first-rate lawyer"* who is *"one of the best trial lawyers in town."* He is *"very smart"* and armed with *"good judgment,"* say sources. Sole practitioner **Patrick Burke** handles all aspects of white-collar criminal litigation. Sources report: *"He cares deeply about his clients, he's really smart and he just has a very insightful mind both for the facts and the law."* **Kevin Evans** of Steese Evans Frankel, PC is noted for his work in complex white-collar criminal investigations throughout the country. He is closely associated with various sports-related cases and also has experience in securities fraud and False Claims Act matters. **Nea Brown** of Temkin Wielga & Hardt LLP concentrates her efforts on natural resources, energy and environmental litigation matters. **Lino Lapinsky** (see p.720) of McKenna Long & Aldridge LLP represents corporate clients in all aspects of commercial litigation. He is *"very thorough,"* *"extraordinarily knowledgeable"* and *"very innovative,"* sources say. His clients include AT&T. **Rick Kornfeld** of Recht Kornfeld, PC is a white-collar criminal defense lawyer who is *"thorough, professional and knowledgeable in the investigation world,"* commentators observe. At the same firm, **Daniel Recht** is *"really savvy about doing what is most effective for clients,"* sources say. He is recognized for his expertise in the commercial litigation space. **Jeffrey Chase** of Husch Blackwell LLP maintains a diverse practice that includes oil and gas, intellectual property and securities litigation. In addition, he is well known for his handling of legal malpractice and breach of fiduciary duty matters.

# NATURAL RESOURCES & ENVIRONMENT

Commentary about individuals can be found under their firm's paragraph. If the firm has no paragraph (is not ranked) look at Other Notable Practitioners.

## Natural Resources & Environment
### Leading Firms

**Band 1**
Davis Graham & Stubbs LLP *
Faegre Baker Daniels
Hogan Lovells US LLP
Holland & Hart LLP *

**Band 2**
Brownstein Hyatt Farber Schreck, LLP *
Bryan Cave HRO
Temkin Wielga & Hardt LLP

**Band 3**
Greenberg Traurig, LLP *
Kaplan Kirsch & Rockwell LLP *
Ryley Carlock & Applewhite *

### Senior Statesmen

Senior Statesmen: distinguished older practitioners

| | |
|---|---|
| Ipsen Henry W. | Bryan Cave HRO |
| Will J Kemper | Burns Figa & Will P.C. (ONP)[†] |

### Leading Individuals

**Band 1**

| | |
|---|---|
| Dunn Daniel | Hogan Lovells US LLP |
| Eddy Ronald M | Sherman & Howard LLC (ONP)[†] |
| Fognani John D | Fognani & Faught, PLLC (ONP)[†] |
| Lawrence Robert W | Davis Graham & Stubbs LLP * |
| Miller Zach C | Davis Graham & Stubbs LLP * |
| Phillips Paul D | Holland & Hart LLP * |
| Rockwood Linda L | Faegre Baker Daniels |
| Spaanstra James R | Faegre Baker Daniels |
| Temkin Elizabeth H | Temkin Wielga & Hardt LLP |

**Band 2**

| | |
|---|---|
| Arfmann Dennis | Hogan Lovells US LLP |
| Forman Wayne F | Brownstein Hyatt Farber Schreck, LLP |
| Jacus John R | Davis Graham & Stubbs LLP * |
| Mathews Mark | Brownstein Hyatt Farber Schreck, LLP |
| Neumann Christopher J | Greenberg Traurig, LLP * |
| Raisch Jerry W | Vranesh and Raisch, LLP (ONP)[†] |
| Reisch Scott H | Hogan Lovells US LLP |
| Sanderson James W | Ryley Carlock & Applewhite |
| Spielman Andrew L | Hogan Lovells US LLP |

**Band 3**

| | |
|---|---|
| Almon Rebecca | Ireland Stapleton Pryor & Pascoe (ONP)[†] |
| Brown Nea | Temkin Wielga & Hardt LLP |
| Clark Scott A | Burns Figa & Will P.C. (ONP)[†] |
| Eid Troy A | Greenberg Traurig, LLP * |
| Hendrix Lynn P | Bryan Cave HRO |
| Jessen Polly | Kaplan Kirsch & Rockwell LLP * |
| King James M | Baker & Hostetler LLP (ONP)[†] * |
| Kornfeld Lynn M | Faegre Baker Daniels |
| McIntosh Carolyn L | Patton Boggs LLP (ONP)[†] |
| Nazarenus Brian | Ryley Carlock & Applewhite |

* Indicates firm/individual with profile.
Alphabetical order within each band. Band 1 is the highest.

## Band 1

### Davis Graham & Stubbs LLP
See profile on p.726

**THE FIRM** Davis Graham & Stubbs has a distinguished track record for natural resources work in Colorado and the Rocky Mountain region. The team's wide-ranging expertise covers major commercial transactions, regulatory compliance, complex litigation and legislative work. In a recent highlight it advised BP America Production Company in relation to air quality control regulatory matters. Other big-name clients include Chevron, Black Hills Energy and Newfield Exploration.

**KEY INDIVIDUALS Robert Lawrence** (see p.720) is an eminent environmental litigator who has a particular focus on water quality, storm water and hazardous waste cases. He also helps clients with compliance, enforcement and administrative proceedings. The *"very highly thought of"* **Zach Miller** (see p.720) is a *"tremendous lawyer"* who is a trusted source of counsel in permitting matters ranging from water rights to mineral processing. **John Jacus** (see p.719) is a nationally recognized air specialist. He is described by commentators as an *"excellent strategic thinker,"* and furthermore is considered to be *"a gentleman and a delight to work with."* He helps clients with litigation and administrative proceedings, and is also experienced on transactional natural resources work.

### Faegre Baker Daniels

**THE FIRM** This highly respected practice counsels clients on matters involving regulatory compliance, environmental due diligence and auditing, with an especially active practice on air quality issues. The group's coverage extends well beyond Colorado, with members of the team handling work as far afield as Canada, New Mexico and Alaska. In one headline-grabbing mandate it advised Energy Fuel Resources on permitting and licensing for the Piñon Ridge Mill project, significant as the first uranium mill in the country to be granted a license in nearly three decades.

**KEY INDIVIDUALS Linda Rockwood** heads the group's environmental practice. She has a strong focus on air quality work, handling a range of permitting, compliance and environmental litigation. **James Spaanstra** maintains a broad counseling practice, helping his commercial, industrial and governmental clients with both compliance and enforcement of federal environmental laws. Sources attest to his knowledgeable and pragmatic counsel. The well regarded **Lynn Kornfeld** has a strong transactional practice in the environmental field that includes issues pertaining to brownfields redevelopments.

### Hogan Lovells US LLP

**THE FIRM** Hogan Lovells's strong practice has expertise that spans environmental permitting and litigation, transactional energy work and regulatory matters. Mining is becoming an increasingly significant part of the firm's practice; for instance it recently advised Twin Metals Minnesota on permitting and environmental compliance for a planned copper, nickel and platinum mine located in northeastern Minnesota. In the last year the firm has also been active on a number of litigations relating to both renewable and traditional energy projects.

**Sources say:** *"They have a lot of insight and knowledge of the EPA and are good working with the EPA as well as the courts. They are also very responsive to any questions or adjustments."*

**KEY INDIVIDUALS Daniel Dunn** is an experienced litigator who is well known for his expertise on defending companies caught up in governmental enforcement actions. He was recently the lead partner defending Antero Resources in a toxic tort lawsuit that alleged that the company had caused injuries through its hydraulic fracturing operations. It was among the first fracturing tort cases, and was dismissed in the District Court. **Dennis Arfmann** is a preeminent air and renewable energy lawyer. He was lead partner for the group's representation of Black Hills in obtaining a greenhouse gas permit for EPA Region 8, the first such permit given in the region. Respected practitioner **Scott Reisch** is the head of the firm's transactional environmental practice, and is also highly regarded for contamination, brownfield and Superfund matters. He recently conducted due diligence for Wabash National's acquisition of Walker Group Holdings, which included facilities throughout the USA and Mexico. **Andrew Spielman** is a specialist public lands attorney who frequently represents ski areas throughout the Rocky Mountains area. He was lead partner counseling Twin Metals Minnesota on its permitting and environmental compliance needs.

### Holland & Hart LLP
See profile on p.727

**THE FIRM** This sizable team does the full range of natural resources work, from oil, gas and mining to brownfields development. On the environmental side of things the group is highly rated for its experience handling air, water and climate change issues.

**Sources say:** *"They have strong ethics, a spirit of collaboration, and a zeal for delivering their clients' aims." "They do a good job and they have excellent lawyers."*

**KEY INDIVIDUALS Paul Phillips** (see p.721) is an environmental litigator who is best known for his prowess on storm water and Superfund proceedings. Sources consider him to be both a *"true gentleman"* and also *"collaborative, kind and wise."*

## Band 2

### Brownstein Hyatt Farber Schreck, LLP
See profile on p.725

**THE FIRM** This group has one of the strongest water practices in the state; in a recent highlight it successfully represented the City of Aurora in the Colorado Supreme Court, where appeals against the Prairie Waters project were rejected by the court. Its broad spread of work also includes notable expertise on environmental issues in the mining and oil and gas sectors.

**Sources say:** *"We are very happy with the quality and completeness of their work. They are appropriate in the way they attack an issue, always keeping in mind the desires of the client." "The work Brownstein Hyatt Farber Schreck has done for us has been of the highest quality, considering work product, timeliness, thoroughness and cost."*

**KEY INDIVIDUALS Wayne Forman** is an expert on water law, environmental and land use litigation and wetlands matters. Recently he achieved a favorable judgment for the group's long-term client Gunnison Energy before the State Engineer, arguing that water produced from oil and gas wells is nontributary and therefore exempt from regulations under Colorado's water rights priority system. Head of practice **Mark Mathews** is a litigator who works on environmental and energy matters. Clients appreciate his *"knowledge of the issues"* and *"his understanding of how to effectuate change to get the desired outcome."*

### Bryan Cave HRO

**THE FIRM** This group is best known for its transactional work in the natural resources space, including project development, M&A and financing. A large part of its client base is drawn from either oil and gas, mining or alternative energy. It also boasts significant expertise in Native American law. Cimarex Energy, Suncor Energy and Laramie Energy have all instructed the firm of late.

**KEY INDIVIDUALS Lynn Hendrix** has a varied practice, but is perhaps best known for his work within the energy space. Clients praise his excellent counsel and professional manner, as well as his superb approach to negotiations and preparation. **Henry Ipsen** is noted for his expertise in litigation and permitting work. A long-standing figure in the Colorado community, recently he has been concentrating on Superfund liability investigations across the Midwest region.

### Temkin Wielga & Hardt LLP

**THE FIRM** This boutique has one of the most respected environmental practices in the state. The experienced team help clients with environmental litigation, compliance and enforcement and risk management.

**Sources say:** *"I have a lot of respect for these guys, they are real environment experts." "They do a lot of complex environmental litigation."*

**KEY INDIVIDUALS Elizabeth Temkin** enjoys a *"tremendous reputation."* As one source put it, *"if you were thinking about the quality practitioners of environmental law in*

*Colorado, hers is one of the first names that would come to mind."* She helps clients on litigation, Superfund and transactional matters. **Nea Brown** is a notable litigator who helps clients on a range of environmental, energy and natural resources cases. Sources note her impressive trial work.

### Band 3

### Greenberg Traurig, LLP
See profile on p.1024

**THE FIRM** This firm combines solid expertise on environmental enforcement actions and litigations with an active transactional practice. The group has an increasing focus on matters pertaining to the uranium industry, including new mining projects and cleanup programs. The firm is also noted for its robust Native American practice, which frequently handles a range of environmental and mining issues.

**KEY INDIVIDUALS Christopher Neumann** (see p.721) has a distinguished track record on matters involving storm water. *"A very aggressive, energetic attorney,"* he takes on cases across the country and his clients include Wildcat Mining, Baker Development and Alpine Waste & Recycling. **Troy Eid** (see p.309) is a former US Attorney who is highly regarded in the Colorado market. He has a special focus on tribal litigation, and in particular the intersection between energy and Native American law.

### Kaplan Kirsch & Rockwell LLP
See profile on p.728

**THE FIRM** This land use, environmental and project development boutique has a strong focus on work for public entities. The team frequently works with local governments in relation to wetlands, storm water and CWA matters. The group is also noted for its sizable client roster in the transport sector.

**Sources say:** *"Both the firm and the individuals are a local powerhouse." "They have a very good reputation."*

**KEY INDIVIDUALS Polly Jessen** (see p.719) is associated with brownfields matters to such a degree that a peer commented: *"I see her on every project in town."* She also counsels clients on issues surrounding contaminated property redevelopment, environmental due diligence and construction contracting.

### Ryley Carlock & Applewhite
See profile on p.515

**THE FIRM** This highly regarded firm helps clients with energy, resources and environmental issues, but is best known for its expertise in water law. The group's bench was

significantly strengthened in 2012 with the arrival of a number of partners from Isaacsons Rosenbaum.

**KEY INDIVIDUALS James Sanderson** is an expert on air quality work, including permitting and rulemaking. He also counsels clients on issues such as land use, waste disposal and underground contamination. **Brian Nazarenus** is a litigator who is highly respected for his work in water law, specifically water rights. His level of expertise is such that he has drafted and testified on proposed legislation in front of the Colorado legislature.

### Other Notable Practitioners

**Ronald Eddy** of Sherman & Howard LLC is a highly regarded environmental litigator. His broad practice encompasses everything from water quality to hazardous waste issues. Peers note that *"he has the right attitude to get the job done promptly."* **John Fognani** of Fognani & Faught, PLLC has *"a great reputation in the natural resources area,"* confirm sources. Past highlights have included defending clients on natural resource damages cases, and prosecuting under a range of environmental statutes and toxic tort actions. Highly experienced partner **Jerry Raisch** of Vranesh and Raisch, LLP helps municipalities and industries to comply with water quality laws and regulation. This includes the establishment of water quality standards and gaining site approvals for municipal facilities. **Scott Clark** of Burns Figa & Will P.C. maintains a broad practice that includes matters dealing with air, regulatory compliance and also brownfields work. **James King** (see p.719) of Baker Hostetler is a traditional hard-rock mining specialist whose practice is largely outside of the country, primarily in Canada. He is an *"outstanding lawyer"* who *"goes above and beyond to give the client alternatives, not just answers."* **Kemper Will** of Burns Figa & Will P.C. is *"just an excellent lawyer"* and is one of the state's best Superfund attorneys. The *"quietly confident"* **Rebecca Almon** of Ireland Stapleton Pryor & Pascoe PC is *"smart, careful and creative"* and *"knows what's important to a client and what isn't."* She specializes in environmental compliance work, including advising on water quality and regulations, wetlands and wastewater. **Carolyn McIntosh** of Patton Boggs LLP is best known for her work in the environmental litigation arena. Armed with a *"very broad-based knowledge,"* she is *"probably one of the best strategic thinkers when it comes to Superfund issues,"* sources said. In addition she is considered to be *"the consummate team player."*

# REAL ESTATE

Commentary about individuals can be found under their firm's paragraph. If the firm has no paragraph (is not ranked) look at Other Notable Practitioners.

## Real Estate
### Leading Firms

**Band 1**
Brownstein Hyatt Farber Schreck, LLP *
Holland & Hart LLP *
Otten Johnson Robinson Neff + Ragonetti PC *

**Band 2**
Ballard Spahr LLP *
Bryan Cave HRO
Faegre Baker Daniels
Sherman & Howard LLC

## Real Estate: Hotels & Leisure
### Leading Individuals

**Band 1**

| | |
|---|---|
| Clowdus W Michael | *Ballard Spahr LLP* * |
| Fischer Rebecca | *Sherman & Howard LLC* |
| James Bruce A | *Brownstein Hyatt Farber Schreck, LLP* |
| Steiner Beat | *Holland & Hart LLP* * |

## Real Estate: Zoning/Land Use
### Senior Statesmen

**Senior Statesmen: distinguished older practitioners**

| | |
|---|---|
| Grimshaw Thomas T | *Spencer Fane Britt & Browne (ONP)[†]* |

### Leading Individuals

**Band 1**

| | |
|---|---|
| Kaplan Stephen H | *Kaplan Kirsch & Rockwell LLP (ONP)[†] * * |
| Ragonetti Thomas J | *Otten Johnson Robinson Neff + Ragonetti* |
| Rockwell Sarah M | *Kaplan Kirsch & Rockwell LLP (ONP)[†] * * |

* Indicates firm/individual with profile.
Alphabetical order within each band. Band 1 is the highest.

*The editorial is in alphabetical order by firm name.*

### Ballard Spahr LLP
See profile on p.2234

**THE FIRM** A stalwart of Colorado real estate, this substantial team is active on a range of matters, from tax credits for affordable housing to commercial financing transactions. The group is also noted for its strong presence in the Colorado ski resorts market, where it has advised on redevelopment work at a number of locations. In 2012, it provided financing advice to owner and developer Breckenridge Grand Vacations, which it helped to gain approval for an Alternative Financial Assurance program. **Sources say:** *"Their work is excellent. I appreciate that their focus is always on getting to the best solution."*

**KEY INDIVIDUALS Michael Clowdus** (see p.717) is *"smart, experienced, fair and balanced in his approach."* He concentrates his efforts on resort developments, where his experience encompasses everything from registration to sales. **Beverly Quail** (see p.721) is best known for her work on behalf of lenders and special servicers. Commentators

## Real Estate
### Senior Statesmen

**Senior Statesmen: distinguished older practitioners**

| | |
|---|---|
| Robinson Frank L | *Otten Johnson Robinson Neff + Ragonetti* |
| Sternberg John D | *Otten Johnson Robinson Neff + Ragonetti* |

### Leading Individuals

**Band 1**

| | |
|---|---|
| Bach Robert H | *Bryan Cave HRO* |
| Barad Edward N | *Brownstein Hyatt Farber Schreck, LLP* |
| Brown Robert | *Sherman & Howard LLC* |
| Donovan Jr Lawrence | *Ryley Carlock & Applewhite (ONP)[†]* |
| Dow Rebecca W | *Holland & Hart LLP* * |
| Holmes Robert A. | *Bryan Cave HRO* |
| Jacobs Paul | *Husch Blackwell LLP (ONP)[†]* |
| Quail Beverly J | *Ballard Spahr LLP* * |
| Ragonetti Thomas J | *Otten Johnson Robinson Neff + Ragonetti* |
| Senn Mark | *Senn Visciano PC (ONP)[†]* |

**Band 2**

| | |
|---|---|
| Calvin Charles D | *Faegre Baker Daniels* |
| Davies Diane B | *Faegre Baker Daniels* |
| Fields Leslie A | *Faegre Baker Daniels* |
| Jones Karen Samuels | *Perkins Coie LLP (ONP)[†]* |
| Kinsman Chris | *Bryan Cave HRO (ONP)[†]* |
| McNeive Lynda A | *Brownstein Hyatt Farber Schreck, LLP* |
| Permut Barry | *Ryley Carlock & Applewhite (ONP)[†]* |
| Sharrer Elizabeth | *Holland & Hart LLP* * |
| Wendel Diana | *Sherman & Howard LLC* |
| Westover Michael | *Otten Johnson Robinson Neff + Ragonetti* |

**Band 3**

| | |
|---|---|
| Cohen Steve | *Husch Blackwell LLP (ONP)[†]* |
| Gale Catherine C | *Brownstein Hyatt Farber Schreck, LLP* |
| Kelley Kevin | *Husch Blackwell LLP (ONP)[†]* |
| Lottner Alan B | *Lottner Rubin Fishman Brown & Saul( ONP)[†]* |

confirm that she *"has an impeccable reputation, and has done a lot of work for sophisticated clients,"* also noting: *"Her level of respect always gets the ball moving."*

### Benjamin, Bain, Howard & Cohen LLC
See profile on p.724

**THE FIRM** Entering the table for the first time, this boutique is highlighted for its prowess on construction work. The team help clients of all sizes on matters such as payment disputes, defect claims and other related issues.

**KEY INDIVIDUALS Alvin Cohen** (see p.717) is a highly regarded trial lawyer, who specializes in construction litigation cases. Sources praise his efficiency and say: *"His understanding of the issues is excellent."* His ability to *"get to the nub of it"* and *"ask clients the important questions right away"* is also highlighted. **Janet Lawler McDaniel** (see p.720) is a first-class construction lawyer who is widely recognized for her strong negotiation skills. Peers note that *"you can tell that she understands what is important for her*

## Real Estate: Construction
### Leading Firms

**Band 1**
Holland & Hart LLP *
Sherman & Howard LLC

**Band 2**
Benjamin, Bain, Howard & Cohen LLC *
Faegre Baker Daniels

### Senior Statesmen

**Senior Statesmen: distinguished older practitioners**

| | |
|---|---|
| Benson Robert E | *Holland & Hart LLP* * |

### Leading Individuals

**Band 1**

| | |
|---|---|
| Arkell J David | *Faegre Baker Daniels* |
| Benjamin James G. | *Benjamin, Bain, Howard & Cohen LLC* * |
| Bridston Kevin | *Holland & Hart LLP* * |
| Cohen Alvin | *Benjamin, Bain, Howard & Cohen LLC* * |
| Cook Michael | *Sherman & Howard LLC* |
| Frost Daniel | *Snell & Wilmer LLP (ONP)[†]* |
| Gunnell Bret | *Sherman & Howard LLC* |
| McDaniel Janet Lawler | *Benjamin, Bain, Howard & Cohen LLC* * |

client and does a good job." The *"very knowledgeable"* **James Benjamin** (see p.716) is best known for his lending expertise, as well as his experience in acting as an expert witness. His oratory skills are highlighted: *"He is a very good speaker who finds an interesting way of putting his point across."*

### Brownstein Hyatt Farber Schreck, LLP
See profile on p.725

**THE FIRM** This sizable team has deep roots in the Colorado real estate market, where it acts for major industry names such as Griffis Residential and Woodward. The group helps clients with a variety of issues including financing, zoning, construction and disputes. Its transactional prowess is underlined by recent mandates; for instance it was instructed by Zocalo Development in relation to the acquisition of a vacant plot of land, and subsequent construction financing, for a large residential complex.

**Sources say:** *"They have a large footprint in the area and have long been recognized as big players."*

**KEY INDIVIDUALS** Highly reputed partner **Edward Barad** concentrates his efforts on advising investors in relation to developments, acquisitions and workouts. He is active both in state and nationally. Managing partner **Bruce James** maintains a broad practice in the hotel and resorts sector, while he is also noted for his expertise on PPP and urban redevelopment projects. In one noted highlight he helped a client to negotiate a lease for a complex multiuse development. **Lynda McNeive** is an experienced commercial real estate lawyer who acts for developers and investors on a wide range of projects. She is singled out by sources for her strong technical capabilities. **Catherine Gale** has had a very busy year, one highlight of which was working for long-term client Zocalo Development on the aforementioned matter. She is especially active on sales and acquisitions, PPP and land use.

## Bryan Cave HRO

**THE FIRM** This full-service firm handles the full gamut of core real estate matters, including acquisitions, financings, commercial leasing, development and land use. The Colorado team is supported by a strong nationwide practice, and has involvement in deals spanning from New York to Los Angeles. In one recent highlight it advised the borrower GD Holdings in relation to refinancing for the Four Seasons Denver Hotel. Clients include Commerce Bank, Citicorp North America and Industrial Income Trust.
**KEY INDIVIDUALS** Head of the department **Robert Holmes** is a highly regarded partner, who frequently acts for lenders in relation to real estate financing transactions. He was recently part of the team that represented BMC Investment in its acquisition from two sellers of five properties in Cherry Creek District in Denver. **Robert Bach** is an outstanding lawyer, praised for his business sense and practicality. He is especially noted for his financing capabilities, acting for a range of lenders, owners and developers. **Chris Kinsman** acts for large developers on construction finance, sales and acquisitions and leasing. One client noted: *"He is an integral part of our team,"* going on to explain that he is *"business-minded and always strives to solve matters without making it a burdensome legal process."*

## Faegre Baker Daniels

**THE FIRM** Faegre Baker Daniels handles transactional real estate work across a broad range of property types; it is especially noted for its work in the affordable housing sector, and is also active on commercial and energy infrastructure deals. Clients include Einstein Noah Restaurant Group, Agrium, Xcel Energy and Lincoln Property. The firm is also praised for its construction law expertise.
**KEY INDIVIDUALS** Construction specialist **David Arkell** is well known for his deep understanding of construction contracts, and also has an active contentious practice. **Charles Calvin** is especially noted for his expertise in commercial real estate and project finance. In a recent highlight he advised Xcel Energy in relation to property issues needed for a bond issuance by Public Service Company of Colorado. **Diane Davies** is the firm's global real estate practice leader and has a broad practice which includes titles, leasing and development and commercial lending. Recent highlights have included leasing and title work for oil and gas and solar facilities. **Leslie Fields** is one of the state's foremost experts on eminent domain law. She has extensive experience on key governmental projects, and has appeared before both the Colorado Court of Appeals and the Supreme Court on novel cases in this field.

## Holland & Hart LLP
See profile on p.727
**THE FIRM** Holland & Hart has one of the most preeminent real estate groups in the region. It handles a wide variety of large-scale projects, ranging from new urban residential and office developments to major ski and golf resorts. The firm's prestigious client roster features well-known names such as Berkeley Homes, Shea Homes and Peak Properties & Development.
**Sources say:** *"Holland & Hart is one of the finest law firms I've ever had the opportunity to work with."* *"Their attention to detail is impeccable."*
**KEY INDIVIDUALS Robert Benson** (see p.716) elicits great respect from sources, who single out his exceptionally deep knowledge in the construction field. Today his focus is upon arbitrations and mediation work. A commentator said: *"Everyone recognizes that he is a very experienced construction lawyer in Colorado and that prestige and respect also makes him more effective as a mediator."* **Kevin Bridston** (see p.717) is a sought after-construction law litigator who represents both plaintiffs and defendants. His expertise ranges from disputes about financial transactions to public works claims. **Rebecca Dow** (see p.717) is an *"extremely bright"* commercial real estate lawyer. Sources appreciate the fact she is *"a deal-maker, not an attorney who finds reasons to break deals up."* She is also *"very hard-working and responsive to client deadlines"* and *"works well under pressure."* **Beat Steiner** (see p.722) helps clients in the resorts industries, and is best known for his work on ski and golf resorts. He handles projects across the USA and internationally, and is praised for being able to *"consistently provide productive solutions to the client."* **Elizabeth Sharrer** (see p.722) helps owners and investors monetize their commercial real estate assets across transactions, leasing, acquisitions and title matters. A source said: *"She is incredibly diligent, reliable and knowledgeable in her field."* She recently advised Shea Properties on the formation of a joint venture and sale of a large office building.

## Otten Johnson Robinson Neff + Ragonetti PC
See profile on p.729
**THE FIRM** This highly regarded group covers transactional work as well as land use, zoning and development matters. In a particular highlight, the team represented the Metropolitan Stadium District in relation to the acquisition of a large portion of its land for the development of a rail link by Regional Transportation District.
**Sources say:** *"They're responsive, they're fast and they deal with a lot of workflow. They know all the nuances and they help me protect my risks."*
**KEY INDIVIDUALS Thomas Ragonetti** is described by a source as *"one of the most brilliant attorneys I know,"* and is also praised as *"very creative, thoughtful and able to get things done."* His broad docket includes matters relating to land use and zoning, public-private transactions and government regulation. *"Super-smart"* attorney **Michael Westover** is *"an excellent real estate lawyer,"* confirm sources. He is well known for his financing expertise in the sector. Last year he advised several multifamily unit devel-

opers in relation to transactional matters. **Frank Robinson** is a founding member of the firm who enjoys a long-standing reputation for transactional real estate work. He was part of the team representing Brookfield Properties Acquisitions in its purchase of an office building in downtown Denver. Sources report that **John Sternberg** is *"one of the brightest real estate lawyers"* in the state, who is *"very detailed-oriented, but can think strategically as well."* He is best known for his work on commercial development, but also has experience representing investors and investment funds.

## Sherman & Howard LLC

**THE FIRM** This Colorado giant houses a top-notch real estate and construction bench. The group maintains a very diversified practice encompassing leasing, acquisitions, developments and sales. On the construction side, the firm is expert in advising owners on contractual issues, and also handles construction-related disputes. Clients include CoBiz Bank, Westpac Investments and East West Partners.
**Sources say:** *"They are responsive, aggressive, good listeners and helpful. They take the time to understand my goals and help our team work toward those goals."*
**KEY INDIVIDUALS** Head of the group **Robert Brown** has a strong focus on transactional work. He is singled out for his excellent commerciality; as one client puts it, *"he is able to practically apply the law to our business needs, and that is what we value the most."* The *"levelheaded"* and *"business-oriented"* **Michael Cook** is considered to be a *"top strategic thinker."* Armed with significant experience, he helps clients with construction litigation and transactional matters. One client notes: *"That broad experience and knowledge base means he can grasp the big picture quickly and dispense advice."* **Rebecca Fischer** is described by a source as *"one of the strongest lawyers you could get anywhere."* She specializes in the hotels and resorts sector, where her practice encompasses construction financing, acquisition and development. *"Knowledgeable and courteous"* **Bret Gunnell** is a trial specialist who takes on cases across the country, but most often in Colorado and Utah. His excellent reputation is endorsed by clients, one of whom explains: *"If we have a major litigation, he is the guy we turn to."* Experienced attorney **Diana Wendel** has a broad-based real estate practice which covers sales and acquisitions, financing and leasing. She is praised for her responsiveness and her technical ability.

## Other Notable Practitioners

The exceptionally well-regarded **Thomas Grimshaw** of Grimshaw & Harring PC has a long-standing reputation for his work on land use, planning and zoning. The *"very well-respected"* **Lawrence Donovan** of Ryley Carlock & Applewhite is noted for his developer side practice, acting for clients in relation to a range of property types including resorts and multifamily units. He is highly experienced on commercial leasing matters, and also handles acquisition and financing. **Daniel Frost** of Snell & Wilmer LLP is a renowned construction specialist, who is singled out for his litigation prowess. As one source put it, *"his experience* *in multimillion-dollar disputes is second to none in the state."* **Paul Jacobs** of Husch Blackwell LLP is widely regarded as a *"very fine lawyer."* He is especially known for his long-standing experience on real estate development for major league sports. Recent highlights include advising the City of Oakland in its bid for a ballpark for its A team. **Steve Cohen** of Husch Blackwell LLP has a broad real estate practice which includes niche expertise in the resort and hotels industry. His commerciality is praised by clients, one of whom notes: *"He is a business lawyer – he doesn't give legal advice for its own sake."* Another confirms: *"He has his eye on the ultimate goal, which is the client"* and is frequently *"instrumental in deals."* **Stephen Kaplan** (see p.719) of Kaplan Kirsch & Rockwell LLP garners excellent feedback from sources, who point to his *"extremely good negotiating skills"* and ability to *"dissect complex problems and quickly drill down to the heart of the issue."* He is a go-to name for many developers and public bodies when it comes to infrastructure developments. **Sarah Rockwell** (see p.721) of Kaplan Kirsch & Rockwell LLP is a highly regarded real estate and land use lawyer who has extensive experience in transit-related development projects. **Mark Senn** of Senn Visciano PC is considered by many to be *"one of the top commercial leasing lawyers in the state."* His *"very good technical knowledge"* and *"very practical"* approach are also singled out. **Barry Permut** of Ryley Carlock & Applewhite attracts respect from peers and clients alike, who characterize him as *"just a fantastic person"* who is *"very straightforward."* His practice covers a range of development, construction and financing work. Director **Alan Lottner** of Lottner Rubin Fishman Brown & Saul, PC is an expert on transactional real estate. His practice extends throughout the Rocky Mountains region, where he works for brokerage companies, financial institutions, developers and home builders. **Kevin Kelley** of Husch Blackwell LLP has an active practice on senior housing, mixed-use developments and hotels. He has a strong reputation among peers, one of whom said: *"He is a very sharp guy, who I have a high opinion of."* He recently acted for Battle One Developer on its development of a resort near Vail. **Karen Samuels Jones** of Perkins Coie LLP is a highly regarded real estate lawyer with a broad practice. Clients laud her uncanny ability to bring opposing sides to a mutual consensus.

# Leaders' Profiles in Colorado

## ANDERSON, Andrea
Holland & Hart LLP, Boulder
303 473 2861
aanderson@hollandhart.com
*Featured in Intellectual Property (Colorado)*
**Practice Areas:** Trademark enforcement, counseling, prosecution, and strategic advice.
**Professional Memberships:** International Trademark Association, American Bar Association – IP Section.
**Career:** Ms Anderson assists companies in the formulation and execution of trademark enforcement and protection strategies designed to maximize the value of their brands. Her practice includes trademark search and clearance, prosecution, and contentious proceedings before the US Patent & Trademark Office, as well as federal court litigation.
**Personal:** BA University of Virginia, MA University of Washington, JD (with highest honors) George Washington University Law School.

## ARKELL, Betty
Holland & Hart LLP, Denver
303 295 8321
barkell@hollandhart.com
*Featured in Corporate/M&A (Colorado)*
**Practice Areas:** Senior partner Emerging Growth, Venture Capital/Private Equity practice; over 35 years experience as corporate/securities lawyer; specializing in venture capital and private equity investments, mergers, acquisitions, and corporate restructurings and counseling. Recently represented Accellos, Inc. in its sale to Accel-KKR, Grotech Ventures in its equity investment in GutCheck, and Coolered Corporation in investment from New World Capital.
**Career:** Best Lawyers 2012 Denver Leveraged Buyouts and Private Equity Lawyer of the Year. Partner, Holland & Hart. Previously Partner, Kirkland & Ellis.

**Personal:** JD (Order of the Coif), MA University of Colorado; BA (with honors) Northwestern University.

## ARO, Edwin
Arnold & Porter LLP, Denver
303 863 2380
Ed.Aro@aporter.com
*Featured in Litigation (Colorado)*
**Practice Areas:** Ed Aro is a trial lawyer who represents companies in civil lawsuits and regulatory matters involving significant financial or reputational exposure. He has served as lead trial counsel in over 30 jury trials, as well as in numerous bench trials and arbitrations. He has tried complex commercial, intellectual property, and employment actions, as well as construction, environmental, real estate, and criminal actions. He regularly counsels businesses concerning corporate governance, internal and government investigations, risk-management, and insurance matters. His clients include major companies in the financial services, software, life sciences, hospitality, real estate development, and telecommunications industries, among others.

## BARKER, Scott S
Wheeler Trigg O'Donnell LLP, Denver
303 244 1824
barker@wtotrial.com
*Featured in Litigation (Colorado)*
**Practice Areas:** 30-year practice focuses on complex civil litigation and class-action lawsuits involving commercial, environmental, natural resources, product liability, toxic tort, and personal injury defense matters. Has tried over 80 cases for international, national, and Western US companies in industries as diverse as energy, pharmaceuticals, consumer products, manufacturing, construction, financial services, recreation, and technology. Clients include BP America Production and Pfizer.

**Professional Memberships:** Fellow, American College of Trial Lawyers.
**Career:** Holland & Hart, 1981-2010.
**Personal:** J.D., Harvard University, 1981; M.Phil., Rhodes Scholar, Oxford University, 1973; BS, US Air Force Academy, 1970).

## BEALL, Christopher
Levine Sullivan Koch & Schulz LLP, Denver
303 376 2406
cbeall@lskslaw.com
*Featured in Intellectual Property (Colorado)*
**Practice Areas:** Represented media and other clients for more than fifteen years on copyright, trademark, false advertising, internet, trade secret and First Amendment issues. Handled numerous preliminary injunction contests over content matters. Defended jury and bench trials of copyright infringement cases in New York and elsewhere. Represented the news media in the Kobe Bryant rape prosecution.
**Career:** Previously a partner in Faegre & Benson, LLP.
**Personal:** Born 11 February 1963. Graduate of Yale University and Duke University School of Law. Former law clerk to Hon. David M. Ebel, US Court of Appeals for Tenth Circuit.

## BENJAMIN, James G.
Benjamin, Bain, Howard & Cohen LLC, Greenwood Village
303 267 6525
jgbenjamin@bbhlegal.com
*Featured in Real Estate (Colorado)*
**Practice Areas:** Commercial Real Estate.
**Professional Memberships:** President of the Denver Bar Association; Executive Council of the Colorado Bar Association; Past President of the Real Estate Section of the Colorado Bar Association; Board of Governors of the Colorado Bar Association; Legislative Policy Committee of the Colorado Bar Association.

**Career:** Jim has over 35 years experience in all aspects of commercial real estate sales, leasing and financing, including shopping centers, office buildings, subdivisions, creation and conversion of condominiums, apartments, and raw land. Former head of the Denver office, real estate department, of the national law firm of McKenna, Connor and Cuneo. Listed in Colorado SuperLawyers Top 100, 2013. Named amongst "Lawyers of the Year" by Law Week Colorado for 2012.
**Publications:** Colorado Real Estate Forms Deskbook, Bradford Publishing.
**Personal:** BA, University of Southern California: JD, Loyola University, Los Angeles.

## BENSON, Robert E
Holland & Hart LLP, Denver
303 295 8234
rbenson@hollandhart.com
*Featured in Real Estate (Colorado)*
**Practice Areas:** Arbitration, mediation and other ADR procedures. Formerly: civil litigation, construction law (contracts, termination, delay, interference, extended performance, changed conditions, change orders, defective design); commercial/business litigation (contracts, business torts, fraud & deceit, anti trust, ethics, legal malpractice).
**Professional Memberships:** Founder, Colorado Bar Association Construction Law Forum; Denver, Colorado, American Bar Associations; American Arbitration Association; College of Commercial Arbitrators.
**Publications:** Author, Arbitration Law in Colorado (2d Ed. 2010); Managing Editor, Colorado Construction Law (5th Ed. 2010); Co-author, 'How to prepare for, take and use a deposition'; CLE/AAA seminars on ADR, construction, malpractice, ethics.
**Personal:** Universities of Pennsylvania and Iowa.

## BIGGS, Jude
Holland & Hart LLP, Boulder
303 473 2707
jbiggs@hollandhart.com
*Featured in Labor & Employment (Colorado)*
**Practice Areas:** Ms Biggs is a trusted adviser to employers and defends employers in litigation. She manages Holland & Hart's MyEmploymentLawAdviser(TM), a national and global employment advice-service.
**Professional Memberships:** American, Colorado and Denver Bar Associations; Employment Law Alliance.
**Publications:** Colorado Wage and Hour Laws, 3rd Edition, 2010; Colorado Employment Law - An Introduction, 3rd Edition, 2010; Contributor, Practitioner's Guide to Colorado Employment Law, CBA 2008; Editor, Colorado Employment Law Letter, 1992 - present.
**Personal:** JD - University of Denver (Order of the Coif) 1988; BS - Regis University 1983.

## BIRLEY, Cindy
Davis Graham & Stubbs LLP, Denver
303 892 7347
cindy.birley@dgslaw.com
*Featured in Labor & Employment (Colorado)*
**Practice Areas:** Employee benefits; executive compensation; pension and profit sharing plans.
**Professional Memberships:** National Association of Public Pension Attorneys; American Society of Pension Professionals & Actuaries; Western Pension & Benefits Conference.
**Career:** Over 25 years of managing all aspects of employee benefits and executive compensation for corporate, public-sector, tax-exempt and church-related organizations across the United States including regularly counseling Boards of Trustees of statewide and local pension plans and VEBA trusts and drafting state legislation.
**Personal:** Admitted, Colorado. LLM in Taxation, University of Denver; JD, University of Michigan; BBA, University of Iowa; Certificate as C.P.A. in Iowa.

## BLUME, Robert
Gibson, Dunn & Crutcher LLP, Denver
303 298 5758
RBlume@gibsondunn.com
*Featured in Litigation (Colorado)*
**Practice Areas:** Focuses on internal investigations, compliance, business crimes and complex civil litigation. Defends clients in enforcement actions and investigations brought by US Department of Justice, SEC and various state law enforcement agencies. Advises on FCPA investigations and compliance initiatives, False Claims Act defense, and US export control and OFAC sanctions issues. Works directly with Boards of Directors and management regarding internal investigations, due diligence practices, compliance programs, disclosure issues, human resource concerns, and the functions of internal audit.
**Career:** Former federal prosecutor, US Department of Justice; Earned four Special Achievement Awards from Attorney General.
**Personal:** JD, Georgetown University, 1992.

## BOONSTRA, Brian
Davis Graham & Stubbs LLP, Denver
303 892 7348
brian.boonstra@dgslaw.com
*Featured in Corporate/M&A (Colorado)*
**Practice Areas:** Mergers & Acquisitions, Private Equity & Venture Capital, and Public Companies & Securities
**Career:** Brian Boonstra's practice focuses on mergers and acquisitions and finance transactions for public and private companies and private equity funds in a broad range of industries, including energy, mining, financial services, healthcare and technology. He also has particular experience representing Canadian companies in connection with mergers and acquisitions, finance transactions and securities compliance in the US
**Personal:** BS, Calvin College; JD, Order of the Coif, University of Colorado

## BRIDSTON, Kevin
Holland & Hart LLP, Denver
303 295 8104
kbridston@hollandhart.com
*Featured in Real Estate (Colorado)*
**Practice Areas:** Construction, real estate, and commercial cases, including trials, appeals, arbitration and mediation. Experience includes disputes regarding basic and complex construction, real estate, commercial property, and complex financial transactions.
**Professional Memberships:** Admitted to practice before the state and federal courts in Colorado and the Tenth Circuit Court of Appeals.
**Career:** Established Holland & Hart's Construction and Real Estate Litigation Practice Group. Partner since 1997.
**Publications:** Co-Editor and Contributor to The Practitioner's Guide to Colorado Construction Law.
**Personal:** University of Colorado School of Law (JD 1988, Order of the Coif); University of Colorado (BA 1985, Phi Beta Kappa).

## BROWN, Jessica
Gibson, Dunn & Crutcher LLP, Denver
303 298 5700
jbrown@gibsondunn.com
*Featured in Labor & Employment (Colorado)*
**Practice Areas:** Represents clients in a wide array of class actions, including employment discrimination and wage and hour class actions, as well as government investigations and individual employment discrimination, harassment, retaliation, trade secret, and noncompete cases, in various state and federal courts and before agencies such as the EEOC and the Civil Rights Division. Has tried employment cases in jury and non-jury settings and argued significant matters in the courts of appeals.
**Career:** Frequent author and speaker on labor and employment issues.
**Personal:** JD, University of Texas, 1993, Executive Editor, Texas Law Review, Order of the Coif.

## CLOWDUS, W Michael
Ballard Spahr LLP, Denver
303 299 7351
clowdus@ballardspahr.com
*Featured in Real Estate (Colorado)*
**Practice Areas:** W. Michael Clowdus is a partner in the Real Estate Department and co-partner-in-charge of the Resort and Hotel Group. He concentrates his practice in resort development. Mr Clowdus has represented developers in the design, documentation, registration, financing (both debt and equity), construction, and marketing and sales, including securities laws issues, of more than 30 high-end fractional projects at major resorts throughout the Rocky Mountain West and in Mexico.
**Professional Memberships:** American Resort Development Association.
**Career:** Admission: Colorado.
**Personal:** University of Denver Sturm College of Law (JD 1975), Member, Order of St. Ives; Duke University (A.B. 1972, cum laude).

## COHEN, Alvin
Benjamin, Bain, Howard & Cohen LLC, Greenwood Village
303 267 6535
acohen@bbhlegal.com
*Featured in Real Estate (Colorado)*
**Practice Areas:** Construction and Real Estate Litigation.
**Professional Memberships:** Panel of Arbitrators, American Arbitration Association; Colorado Bar Association, Construction Law Forum.
**Career:** For 34 years, Al has represented businesses in the construction and real estate industries, including construction contractors and subcontractors, real estate developers, homebuilders and materials suppliers, on both public and private projects. Before starting private practice in 1985, Al was a trial lawyer for the Tennessee Valley Authority handling government construction disputes, with numerous trials in federal court and the Board of Contract Appeals. Al's practice has included disputes involving complex delay and disruption claims, construction defects, bid protests, defective plans and specifications, insurance coverage issues and mechanic's liens. The cases have ranged in size from the largest jury verdict in Colorado history at the time, which Al obtained on behalf of a land developer, to routine mechanic's lien foreclosure actions.
**Personal:** JD, Boston University, cum laude, 1979; BA, magna cum laude, Duke University; 1976.

## COHEN, Jeffrey
Ballard Spahr LLP, Denver
303 299 7308
cohenj@ballardspahr.com
*Featured in Litigation (Colorado)*
**Practice Areas:** Jeffrey Cohen is an accomplished litigator who focuses on commercial and financial disputes. He has experience in complex commercial cases and advises investors, creditors, and municipalities on the litigation aspects of bond defaults and other financial reorganization

issues. He has chaired more than 150 state and federal jury and non-jury trials to verdict. He has experience briefing and arguing appeals and conducting all aspects of discovery and pre-trial motion practice.
**Professional Memberships:** Admissions: Colorado New York.
**Personal:** Brooklyn Law School (JD 1980) Recipient, American Jurisprudence Award in Civil Procedure and Rose Memorial Scholarship Brandeis University (BA 1977, magna cum laude).

## DEGNAN, Donald
Holland & Hart LLP, Boulder
303 473 2724
ddegnan@hollandhart.com
*Featured in Intellectual Property (Colorado)*
**Practice Areas:** Intellectual Property
**Professional Memberships:** INTA; AIPLA; Colorado Bar Association, IP Section. Board Member, Colorado IP Inns of Court.
**Career:** Don works with companies to develop strategies for developing, protecting and enforcing their IP assets. He has substantial experience litigating IP disputes in courts across the country—those involving patents, trademarks, copyrights, domain names, trade secrets, counterfeiting, gray goods and licensing agreements. He is Chair of the firm's IP Department, past Chair of the IP Litigation Practice, and served on the firm's Management Committee.
**Personal:** The University of Iowa: JD (with distinction) and MBA (1991) and BBA (1986)

## DIETRICH, Stephen J
Greenberg Traurig, LLP, Denver
303 572 6502
DietrichS@gtlaw.com
*Featured in Corporate/M&A (Colorado)*
**Practice Areas:** Mergers and acquisitions; corporate finance and securities; corporate restructuring; automobile dealerships; commercial real estate including financing; corporate governance.
**Professional Memberships:** Board of Directors: Big Brothers Big Sisters of Colorado, 2010-present; Families First, Inc. (a Colorado non-profit corporation), 2002-present.
**Career:** Selected: Super Lawyers magazine—Rising Star, 2009-10; Chambers USA Guide, 2010-13. Member: Winning Team, 2010 Chambers and Partners USA Award for Excellence in Real Estate; a Law360 'Real Estate Practice Group of the Year', 2011-12.
**Personal:** JD, Georgetown University Law Center, 1995; BA, summa cum laude, Political Science, University of Minnesota, Twin Cities Campus, 1992.

## DOW, Rebecca W
Holland & Hart LLP, Denver
303 295 8413
rdow@hollandhart.com
*Featured in Real Estate (Colorado)*
**Practice Areas:** Ms Dow's more than 25 years of experience includes all aspects of commercial real estate: large, master-planned developments; representation of home builders; public-private partnerships; multifamily projects; acquisitions; subdivision and entitlement work; retail and com-

mercial leasing; construction contracts; and architect agreements.

**Professional Memberships:** Fellow, American College of Real Estate Attorneys; Colorado Association of Home Builders Executive Committee, Board and Government Affairs Committee Member; CBA Board of Governors; past Chairperson, CBA Real Estate Section Executive Council; Fellow, Colorado Bar Foundation.

**Personal:** JD University of Denver College of Law Order of St. Ives (1983); BS cum laude, University of Colorado (1977).

## DUFFY, Brian L
Greenberg Traurig, LLP, Denver
303 572 6545
DuffyB@gtlaw.com
*Featured in Litigation (Colorado)*

**Practice Areas:** A firm President. Previous Chair, Global Litigation Practice, 2009-13. Class actions; appellate; retail; labor, employment; global energy, infrastructure.

**Career:** Listed: Best Lawyers in America, 2010-13; Super Lawyers, 2006-12; The BTI Client Service All-Star Team for Law Firms, 2010-11. Team Member Law360: 'Product Liability Practice Group of the Year', 2011; 'Employment Practice Group of the Year', 2011; 'Appellate Practice Group of the Year', 2010. AV® Preeminent™ 5.0 out of 5.

**Personal:** JD, University of Colorado Law School, 1991 (Order of the Coif; Notes, Comments Editor, University of Colorado Law Review); BS, summa cum laude, University of South Dakota, 1988.

## EID, Troy A
Greenberg Traurig, LLP, Denver
303 572 6521
EidT@gtlaw.com
*Featured in Native American Law (Nationwide), Natural Resources (Colorado)*

See under Nationwide for profile.

## EURICH, Gregory
Holland & Hart LLP, Denver
303 295 8166
geurich@hollandhart.com
*Featured in Labor & Employment (Colorado)*

**Practice Areas:** Labor and employment law, particularly litigation of labor disputes defending clients against claims of discrimination, wrongful discharge, and collective bargaining agreement actions before state and federal courts in the Western US. Lead Counsel in nearly 100 trials, most of which were jury trials.

**Professional Memberships:** 10th Circuit Credentials Chair and Fellow, College of Labor and Employment Lawyers.

**Career:** Admitted: Colorado and US District Court, District of Colorado (1973); US Court of Appeals, Tenth Circuit (1977); US Supreme Court.

**Personal:** University of Michigan: JD (magna cum laude, Order of the Coif, 1973), BA (cum laude, Phi Beta Kappa, 1970).

## FAIRLESS, Carolyn
Wheeler Trigg O'Donnell LLP, Denver
303 244 1852
fairless@wtotrial.com
*Featured in Litigation (Colorado)*

**Practice Areas:** Managing partner of 80-lawyer Wheeler Trigg O'Donnell. Practices primarily in the areas of professional liability and commercial litigation handling cases extensively in the federal and state courts in Colorado and pro hac vice in several other states. Has successfully defended numerous legal malpractice matters and counts among her clients some of the largest law firms and most respected lawyers in Denver.

**Professional Memberships:** DRI Professional Liability Committee

**Publications:** Writes and presents on ethics issues and how to avoid legal malpractice claims

**Personal:** JD, University of Colorado School of Law, 1998; BS, Computer Science, Tulane University, 1992

## FITZPATRICK, John
Wheeler Trigg O'Donnell LLP, Denver
303 244 1874
fitzpatrick@wtotrial.com
*Featured in Products Liability (Nationwide), Litigation (Colorado)*

**Practice Areas:** Has tried over 200 cases to verdict in 32 states and obtained defense verdicts in the vast majority of them. Considered a "go-to" national trial attorney for high-exposure cases involving birth-trauma claims and other catastrophic medical malpractice matters, allegations of product defects in asbestos, pharmaceuticals, medical devices, and aviation, and chemical releases of toxic substances. Practice includes medical malpractice and personal injury defense, product liability and professional liability defense, commercial and environmental litigation, and toxic tort matters.

**Personal:** JD, University of Notre Dame, 1981; BS, US Military Academy West Point, 1974

## FONS, Randy
Morrison & Foerster LLP, Denver
303 592 2257
rfons@mofo.com
*Featured in Litigation (Colorado)*

**Practice Areas:** Co-chair of the firm's Securities Litigation, Enforcement, and White-Collar Defense Group and co-leads the firm's FCPA and Anti-Corruption Task Force. He represents corporations, their officers, directors, and employees in SEC and other law enforcement investigations. He has assisted numerous boards of directors and their audit committees in conducting internal investigations, often advising clients on remedial measures responsive to the securities issues investigated. He also represents investment advisors, including advisors to hedge funds, in SEC proceedings, and has been appointed as an independent consultant by the FINRA pursuant to an enforcement action brought against a large independent broker-dealer.

## FREDRICKSON, Todd
Fisher & Phillips LLP, Denver
303 218 3650
tfredrickson@laborlawyers.com
*Featured in Labor & Employment (Colorado)*

**Career:** Todd Fredrickson is the Managing Partner of the Denver office and Chair of the firm's Diversity and Inclusiveness Committee. His practice involves representing employers in various matters arising under Title VII of the Civil Rights Act of 1964, the Americans with Disabilities Act, the Family Medical Leave Act, the Age Discrimination in Employment Act, and the Fair Labor Standard Act. Todd has defended employers against claims of discrimination, harassment, and retaliation based on race, religion, sex, national origin, age, and disability. He also represents employers in union campaigns, contract negotiations, grievance arbitrations and unfair labor practice charges.

## GALLAGHER, Michael J
Davis Graham & Stubbs LLP, Denver
303 892 7355
mike.gallagher@dgslaw.com
*Featured in Litigation (Colorado)*

**Practice Areas:** Coal, Oil and Gas, Environmental Law, Commercial Litigation, Mining, Products Liability, White Collar Crime, and Trial.

**Professional Memberships:** American College of Trial Lawyers; American Bar Association, Product Liability Section.

**Career:** Mike Gallagher has a broad range of experience in litigation in state and federal courts throughout the western US and Alaska and before various arbitration forums. He is a trial lawyer who has handled and tried cases in many substantive areas. In recent years, he has focused his practice on litigation involving commercial and environmental issues impacting natural resource companies.

**Personal:** BA, University of Colorado; JD, Duke University

## GOLDBERG, Gregory E
Holland & Hart LLP, Denver
303 295 8099
GGoldberg@hollandhart.com
*Featured in Litigation (Colorado)*

**Practice Areas:** As the Chair of Holland & Hart's Government Investigations practice group, Mr Goldberg defends companies and individuals in litigation and investigations by grand juries, US Attorneys' Offices, the Department of Justice, and federal and state agencies. Mr Goldberg previously served as an Assistant US Attorney, and has tried more than 20 federal civil and criminal trials.

**Career:** Named in The Best Lawyers In America®; Named "Top 50" and "Top 100" by Colorado Super Lawyers; AV Rated, Martindale Hubbell.

**Personal:** JD, Columbia University; AB, Dartmouth College; Graduate Institute of International Studies, Geneva, Switzerland.

## GOTTSCHALK, Hugh
Wheeler Trigg O'Donnell LLP, Denver
303 244 1858
gottschalk@wtotrial.com
*Featured in Litigation (Colorado)*

**Practice Areas:** An excellent legal strategist and trial lawyer. Handles matters involving contract disputes, allegations of fraud and misrepresentation, franchise matters, environmental torts, professional and product liability, and trade secret, copyright, and trademark cases. Employs 30 years of litigation experience and education to effectively present complex and technical information at trial. Has served as national or regional trial counsel in industries as diverse as information technology, energy, manufacturing, and consumer and professional services.

**Professional Memberships:** Fellow, American College of Trial Lawyers; Faculty, National Institute for Trial Advocacy

**Personal:** JD, University of Colorado, 1979; BS, Biochemistry, Northwestern University, 1975.

## GRAY, Tracy
Holland & Hart LLP, Boulder
303 473 2703
TBGray@hollandhart.com
*Featured in Intellectual Property (Colorado)*

**Practice Areas:** IP counseling, transactions, protection, and commercialization; software and technology licensing, development, and distribution; outsourcing; trademarks, copyright, and trade secret protection; internet and e-commerce; domestic and international privacy counseling; consumer protection, promotions and social media.

**Professional Memberships:** IAPP; CIPP; ABA, Information Security, Privacy, and Consumer Protection Sections; Colorado Bar Association, IP and Technology Sections; Boulder County Bar Association.

**Career:** Partner in Intellectual Property Practice. Represents clients ranging from Fortune 100 domestic and international corporations to start-up companies on IP, privacy, information security and regulatory issues.

**Personal:** BA, with honors, Brown University (1988); JD, University of Southern California (1991).

## GROLL, Christina
Holland & Hart LLP, Denver
303 295 8588
CGroll@hollandhart.com
*Featured in Corporate/M&A (Colorado)*

**Practice Areas:** Chris Groll provides strategic and practical transactions advice. She brings nearly 20 years of experience to guide clients in mergers, acquisitions, divestitures, recapitalizations, and asset exchanges. Chris counsels companies and investors alike on private equity and venture capital financings, and she regularly advises clients on corporate governance and day-to-day corporate matters.

**Professional Memberships:** Member, Board of Directors, Association for Corporate Growth, Denver Chapter.

**Career:** Current chair of Holland & Hart's M&A Practice. Recognized in The Best Lawyers in America® and The Legal 500 US Admitted in Colorado and California.
**Personal:** JD, Stanford University, 1994; A.B., Dartmouth College, 1989.

### GUTIERREZ, Steve
Holland & Hart LLP, Greenwood Village
303 295 8531
sgutierrez@hollandhart.com
*Featured in Labor & Employment (Colorado)*
**Practice Areas:** Mr Gutierrez's litigation experience focuses on labor and employment. He regularly consults regarding traditional labor policies and practices that impact the employment relationship.
**Professional Memberships:** American, Colorado, and Colorado Hispanic Bar Associations; Employment Law Steering Committee, Defense Research Institute.
**Career:** Former Chair, Labor and Employment Practice Group; Admitted Colorado (1993); US District Court of Colorado; US Court of Appeals, Tenth Circuit.
**Publications:** Author of diverse articles published in professional journals on Labor and Employment. Respected speaker at conferences nationally on emerging issues in labor and employment.
**Personal:** JD University of Denver 1993; BA University of Northern Colorado 1990.

### HARTLEY, James E
Holland & Hart LLP, Denver
303 295 8237
jhartley@hollandhart.com
*Featured in Litigation (Colorado)*
**Practice Areas:** Partner with primary areas of practice in patent infringement and antitrust litigation. Extensive jury trial experience in complex patent infringement, antitrust, and unfair competition cases. Represents clients before state and federal enforcement agencies. Fellow of the American College of Trial Lawyers and mentioned in leading American publications.
**Professional Memberships:** Former Adjunct Professor at the University of Denver School of Law; former member of the governing Council of the Antitrust Section of the American Bar Association.
**Career:** Admitted to the Colorado Bar (1974).
**Personal:** Received a JD (1974) and a BA (1971) from the University of California at Berkeley.

### HAVLICK, Scott
Holland & Hart LLP, Boulder
303 473 2710
shavlick@hollandhart.com
*Featured in Intellectual Property (Colorado)*
**Practice Areas:** Mr Havlick assists with US and foreign trademark management from the selection, searching, investigation and clearance to registration and proper use. He handles trademark litigation involving counterfeit goods, gray market importation, passing off, reverse passing off, dilution, and fair use. He is the chair of the firm's trademark group.

**Professional Memberships:** INTA; Patent, Trademark and Copyright Sections of ABA and Colorado Bar Association.
**Career:** Admitted: Colorado Bar and US District Court for Colorado (1986); US Court of Appeals, Ninth Circuit (1987) and Tenth Circuit (1991).
**Personal:** JD (1986), University of Utah; BA (1981), University of Colorado.

### HUSBAND, John
Holland & Hart LLP, Denver
303 295 8228
jhusband@hollandhart.com
*Featured in Labor & Employment (Colorado)*
**Practice Areas:** Best of the Bar in labor and employment by 'Denver Business Journal' and Top 50 Colorado Super Lawyer. Colorado Management Lawyer of the Year by Best Lawyers in America® 2013. Tried cases in 20 states and been lead trial counsel in over 500 adversarial proceedings, trials, major arbitrations, or administrative actions, including class and collective actions.
**Professional Memberships:** Fellow, College of Labor and Employment Lawyers; column editor, 'The Colorado Lawyer'; editor, the Colorado Employment Law Letter; Past Management Chair, Officer and Director, Colorado Safety Association; Leadership Denver.
**Personal:** JD University of Toledo (1977), BS Ohio State University (1974).

### JACUS, John R
Davis Graham & Stubbs LLP, Denver
303 892 7305
john.jacus@dgslaw.com
*Featured in Natural Resources (Colorado)*
**Practice Areas:** Energy Industry, Environmental Law, Mining, Oil & Gas Industry, Safety & Health, Brownfields, and Renewable & Alternative Energy, Toxic Torts, Administrative Law.
**Professional Memberships:** Colorado Bar Association, Environmental Law Section (former Chair); American Bar Association, Section of Environment, Energy & Resources (active in leadership); and Rocky Mountain Mineral Law Foundation (Trustee).
**Career:** Practice includes compliance counseling, administrative proceedings and litigation under all major federal and state environmental laws including the Clean Air Act, RCRA, CERCLA, the Clean Water Act, NEPA, and other laws, as well as transactional matters.

### JESSEN, Polly
Kaplan Kirsch & Rockwell LLP, Denver
303 825 7000
pjessen@kaplankirsch.com
*Featured in Natural Resources (Colorado)*
**Personal:** JD, Columbia University; AB, Princeton University

### JOHNSON, Jeffrey T
Holland & Hart LLP, Denver
303 295 8019
jjohnson@hollandhart.com
*Featured in Labor & Employment (Colorado)*
**Practice Areas:** Over 30 years of employer-based employment law litigation and counseling, including employment discrimination, wrongful

discharge, individual employee rights, wage and hour, National Labor Relations Act matters; non-compete and other trade secret matters; and OSHA. Extensive experience in class/collective actions and employment arbitrations.
**Career:** Partner and former Chair of Labor and Employment Practice Group; AAA Arbitrator (Employment Panel); former Chair and Legal Counsel, Colorado Association of Commerce and Industry (CACI); Admitted Colorado (1980); US District Court of Colorado; US Court of Appeals, Ninth and Tenth Circuits.
**Personal:** University of Michigan (JD 1979); (BA 1977).

### JOHNSON, Tom
Davis Graham & Stubbs LLP, Denver
303 892 7487
tom.johnson@dgslaw.com
*Featured in Litigation (Colorado)*
**Practice Areas:** Commercial Litigation, Securities Enforcement, Litigation & Internal Investigations, Toxic Tort Litigation, IP Protection, White Collar Crime, Class & Consolidated Actions, and Defense of Bad Faith Insurance Claims
**Professional Memberships:** American, Colorado, and Denver Bar Associations
**Career:** Tom Johnson's practice focuses on commercial litigation and defense of white collar crime. He has handled natural resources, real estate, healthcare matters, class actions, banking matters, franchise disputes, defense and prosecution of securities fraud claims, pricing disputes, preemptive rights, contract disputes, bankruptcy litigation, employment disputes, distributorship terminations, unfair trade practices cases, and internal investigations.
**Personal:** A.B., Colgate University; JD, University of Illinois.

### JORDAAN, Hendrik
Morrison & Foerster LLP, Denver
303 592 2255
hjordaan@mofo.com
*Featured in Corporate/M&A (Colorado)*
**Practice Areas:** Mr Jordaan advises financial and strategic buyers and sellers in public and private M&A. Structures, negotiates asset acquisitions, stock acquisitions, mergers, LBOs, auctions, tender offers, going-private, and cross-border transactions. Spans varied industries: health care, logistics, natural resources, sports and entertainment, telecommunications, and technology.
**Professional Memberships:** M&A Committee, Distressed M&A Taskforce, and Market Trends Committee, American Bar Association; Colorado Association of Corporate Counsel; and M&A Committee, Colorado Bar Association's Section of Business Law.
**Career:** Licensed: Colorado (1997); HRO (1997).
**Personal:** Southern Methodist University JD (cum laude) (1997); BS (cum laude) (1994).

### KAPLAN, Stephen H
Kaplan Kirsch & Rockwell LLP, Denver
303 825 7000
skaplan@kaplankirsch.com
*Featured in Real Estate (Colorado)*

**Practice Areas:** Mr Kaplan has participated in the negotiation of complicated public-private development and infrastructure partnerships from several different perspectives: as a client, as counsel to a municipality, and as a representative of the United States government. Mr Kaplan has served as the General Counsel of the United States Department of Transportation and served for 7 years as Denver City Attorney. More recently, his practice has focused on redevelopment projects, development of transit oriented development projects, combined transportation and development projects, and structuring project financings.
**Personal:** AB, Harvard College; JD, Harvard Law School.

### KAWANABE, Kenzo S
Davis Graham & Stubbs LLP, Denver
303 892 7541
kenzo.kawanabe@dgslaw.com
*Featured in Litigation (Colorado)*
**Practice Areas:** Commercial Litigation & Trial
**Professional Memberships:** ABA, CBA, National Asian Pacific American Bar Association (first-ever General Counsel), Colorado Legal Services (Board), Center for Legal Inclusiveness (Board), and US-Japan Council.
**Career:** Kenzo Kawanabe is a litigator who represents clients in a variety of matters relating to contract disputes, business torts, products liability, and intellectual property. He has significant litigation and trial experience in high stakes cases. He served on the DGS Executive Committee, and teaches at the National Institute for Trial Advocacy.
**Personal:** BA, University of Colorado (Boettcher Scholar); JD, Georgetown University Law Center; Law Clerk, Colorado Supreme Court

### KERWIN, Gregory J
Gibson, Dunn & Crutcher LLP, Denver
303 298 5700
gkerwin@gibsondunn.com
*Featured in Litigation (Colorado)*
**Practice Areas:** Complex commercial disputes in trial and appellate courts: securities, antitrust, business tort and contract disputes. Lead or second-chair in more than 20 jury trials, bench trials, and arbitrations. Argued and briefed many cases in the Colorado appellate courts, Tenth Circuit and Ninth Circuit.
**Publications:** Chapter on Tenth Circuit practice in The Insiders Guide to State and Federal Appellate Courts (ABA 2012); appellate standards of review and certiorari petitions in: Colorado Appellate Law and Practice (2d ed. West 2007).
**Personal:** JD, Duke Law School, magna cum laude, Editor-in-Chief, Duke Law Journal, Law Clerk, 10th Cir. Judge James Logan.

### KING, James M
Baker & Hostetler LLP, Denver
303 764 4087
jking@bakerlaw.com
*Featured in Natural Resources (Colorado)*
**Career:** James King serves energy and mining exploration and operating companies in transactional and administrative matters concerning acquisitions, leases, sales, joint ventures and limit-

ed liability companies. Jim handles construction contracts, loan documents, title and contract litigation, public land acquisitions, exchanges and use authorizations for natural resources and real estate clients. Jim focuses on all aspects of public land law and energy and mining law, including transactional work involving minerals and litigation before administrative tribunals and state and federal courts in cases concerning mining agreements, mineral properties and rights of mining claimants.

### LAWRENCE, Robert W
Davis Graham & Stubbs LLP, Denver
303 892 7409
robert.lawrence@dgslaw.com
*Featured in Natural Resources (Colorado)*
**Practice Areas:** Environmental Law, Indian Law, Toxic Tort Litigation, Brownfields, Natural Resource Damages, Mining, Uranium Mining, Milling and Reclamation, Energy Industry, and Class Actions
**Professional Memberships:** American College of Environmental Lawyers; Colorado Bar Association, Environmental Law Section; American Bar Association, Natural Resources, Energy and Environmental Law and Litigation Sections; Colorado Legal Aid Foundation
**Career:** Bob Lawrence has practiced environmental law for over 28 years. He has extensive experience in environmental litigation, administrative proceedings, permitting, compliance, and enforcement matters under a wide array of federal and state laws.
**Personal:** BA, Colorado College; JD, University of Colorado Law School

### LEVINE II, Ronald R
Davis Graham & Stubbs LLP, Denver
303 892 7514
ron.levine@dgslaw.com
*Featured in Corporate/M&A (Colorado)*
**Practice Areas:** Asset Management, Mergers & Acquisitions, Private Equity & Venture Capital, and Public Companies & Securities
**Career:** Ron Levine's practice centers on corporate finance and merger and acquisition transactions for public and private companies and private equity firms in a variety of industries including technology, energy, business services, restaurant/retail, investment management, and manufacturing. He has extensive experience in hostile takeover situations and addressing shareholder activist issues, and has served as counsel to both special committees and proponents in going private transactions.
**Personal:** BS, Cornell University; JD, cum laude, Harvard Law School

### LIPINSKY, Lino
McKenna Long & Aldridge LLP, Denver
303 634 4336
llipinsky@mckennalong.com
*Featured in Litigation (Colorado)*
**Practice Areas:** Lino Lipinsky de Orlov represents clients in all aspects of commercial litigation, mediations, arbitrations, and appeals. He has litigated cases in various state and federal courts. Mr Lipinsky has developed expertise in complex busi-

ness cases, particularly those involving trade secrets, intellectual property, creditor's rights, real estate, and employment disputes. He successfully defended a number of the largest trade secrets and discrimination cases litigated in Colorado.
**Professional Memberships:** Faculty of Federal Advocates (President 2013); E Discovery Task Force for the District of Colorado.
**Personal:** JD, New York University School of Law (Law Review); AB, Brown University.

### LLOYD, Dominic A
Baker & Hostetler LLP, Denver
303 764 4101
dlloyd@bakerlaw.com
*Featured in Corporate/M&A (Colorado)*
**Career:** Dominic Lloyd focuses on corporate finance, M&A and general corporate work. Dominic represents issuers and financial investors with senior and mezzanine debt financings and equity capital transactions for companies at all stages of development. He is actively involved in representing investors and companies in connection with venture financings and general corporate matters and has experience representing sellers and financial and strategic buyers in middle market mergers, leveraged buyouts and stock and asset acquisitions and divestitures. Dominic advises clients concerning the formation of, and with respect to investments in, private equity, real estate and oil and gas investment funds.

### LOW, Andy
Davis Graham & Stubbs LLP, Denver
303 892 7327
andrew.low@dgslaw.com
*Featured in Litigation (Colorado)*
**Practice Areas:** Appellate
**Professional Memberships:** Colorado Supreme Court Joint Committee on Appellate Rules, Colorado Civil Jury Instructions Committee, and ABA Reading Group for evaluation of nominations of Justice Sonia Sotomayor and Justice Elena Kagan
**Career:** For more than 20 years, Andy Low has been one of the leading appellate lawyers in Colorado and the Rocky Mountain region. He has briefed and argued appeals in almost every area of civil law. He has written a column on appellate practice since 1991 and lectures frequently.
**Personal:** BA, with high honors, Swarthmore College; JD, magna cum laude, Cornell University

### MACDONALD, Timothy R
Arnold & Porter LLP, Denver
303 863 2334
Timothy.Macdonald@aporter.com
*Featured in Litigation (Colorado)*
**Practice Areas:** Timothy Macdonald is an experienced trial lawyer whose practice focuses on complex civil litigation. He has tried cases and advised clients in various commercial disputes, including breach of contract, environmental, insurance, tort, securities fraud, fiduciary duty, and bankruptcy matters. Mr Macdonald has litigated and resolved disputes on behalf of technology companies, energy companies, airlines, insurance companies, accounting firms, boards of directors, officers, and Indian tribes, among oth-

ers. He has tried cases in federal district court, bankruptcy court, and before arbitration panels. Mr Macdonald also has far-ranging appellate experience, including the First, Second, Ninth, Tenth, D.C., and Federal Circuits.

### MARTIN, Raymond
Wheeler Trigg O'Donnell LLP, Denver
303 244 1863
martin@wtotrial.com
*Featured in Labor & Employment (Colorado)*
**Practice Areas:** Zealous representative of some of Colorado's largest employers in employment and ERISA litigation in federal and state courts for more than 30 years. Has served as regional trial counsel to major corporations in the professional services, consumer products, construction and engineering, energy, health care, publishing, and telecommunications industries. Clients include AT&T, Marriott Hotel Services, Media News Group, FedEx Ground, and MWH Global.
**Publications:** Writes and presents on labor and employment law topics, including workplace violence, wrongful discharge, termination, employee benefits and employment discrimination.
**Personal:** JD, University of Denver, 1977; BA, Morningside College, 1974.

### MCDANIEL, Janet Lawler
Benjamin, Bain, Howard & Cohen LLC, Greenwood Village
303 267 6522
janet.mcdaniel@bbhlegal.com
*Featured in Real Estate (Colorado)*
**Practice Areas:** Construction law, construction litigation, construction contract drafting and negotiation.
**Professional Memberships:** Colorado Bar Association, Construction Law Forum, past Chair; Leadership in Energy and Environmental Design Accredited Professional (LEED AP).
**Career:** Prior to practicing law, Janet worked in commercial construction as a project executive, project manager and project engineer. She has a degree in Construction Management from Colorado State University. She understands complex construction issues. Janet represents general contractors, public and private owners, subcontractors, and material suppliers in drafting and negotiating construction and design contracts, and in various claims and legal disputes, including wrongful termination, delays, defective plans and specifications, defective construction and insurance issues, and mechanic's liens. Janet has been retained as an expert witness on construction issues.
**Personal:** BS, Colorado State University, with high distinction; JD, University of Denver.

### MICHAELS, Jane
Holland & Hart LLP, Denver
303 295 8162
jmichaels@hollandhart.com
*Featured in Intellectual Property (Colorado), Litigation (Colorado)*
**Practice Areas:** Trial lawyer focusing on intellectual property and commercial litigation. Extensive experience in patent, trademark, trade secrets, copyright, business and technology cases.

**Professional Memberships:** Fellow, American College of Trial Lawyers, International Academy of Trial Lawyers, International Society of Barristers; Past President, Denver Bar Association; Named one of Colorado's top ten trial lawyers and Lawdragon's 500 Leading Lawyers.
**Career:** Lead counsel in cases involving a variety of industries, including telecommunications, computers/electronics, Internet, biotech, pharmaceutical, manufacturing, entertainment, sports, real estate, and oil and gas.
**Personal:** JD: Boston University (cum laude), MAT: Harvard University (cum laude), and BA: Wellesley College (with distinction).

### MILLER, Zach C
Davis Graham & Stubbs LLP, Denver
303 892 7391
zach.miller@dgslaw.com
*Featured in Natural Resources (Colorado)*
**Practice Areas:** Environmental, Water, and Natural Resources Law, Public Lands, Mining, Oil & Gas, Coalbed Methane, Energy, and Renewable Energy.
**Professional Memberships:** American College of Environmental Lawyers; Rocky Mountain Mineral Law Foundation.
**Career:** Zach Miller has practiced environmental, water, and natural resources law since 1980. He has broad experience before numerous state and federal courts and agencies in disputes over, and permitting for, oil and gas operations, public land uses, NEPA compliance, water rights, water quality, air quality, hazardous substances, wetlands, pesticides, mining, mineral processing, ski areas, power projects, and related issues.
**Personal:** BA, Colorado College; JD, University of Colorado.

### MOORE, Steven W
Ogletree, Deakins, Nash, Smoak & Stewart PC, Denver
303 764 6801
steven.moore@ogletreedeakins.com
*Featured in Labor & Employment (Colorado)*
**Practice Areas:** Labor and Employment, Employment Litigation, and Class Action Defense. Mr Moore represents employers in employment litigation matters, including class and collective actions.
**Professional Memberships:** American Bar Association, Colorado Bar Association, Denver Bar Association, State Bar of California, and Faculty of Federal Advocates.
**Career:** Admitted to practice in Colorado (1993) and in California (1997).
**Publications:** Mr Moore is a co-editor of the American Bar Association's Labor and Employment Law newsletter. He has also authored numerous labor and employment law articles.
**Personal:** Old Dominion University (BA, 1989), University of Denver College of Law (JD, 1993).

### MUMAUGH, Brian
Holland & Hart LLP, Greenwood Village
303 290 1067
bmumaugh@hollandhart.com
*Featured in Labor & Employment (Colorado)*

**Practice Areas:** Labor and Employment. Represents employers in EEO, FLSA collective actions, wrongful discharge, breach of contract, public policy discharge, non-competes, and trade secrets. Represents management in labor matters, including collective bargaining, complex arbitrations, and Board proceedings under the NLRA and RLA.
**Professional Memberships:** ABA; Colorado and Nebraska Bar Associations; Colorado Defense Lawyers Association; Contributor, 'Colorado Employment Law Letter'.
**Career:** Over 25 years of nation-wide experience representing employers and management in employment disputes/labor and employment issues throughout a broad range of industries. Admitted to courts in a variety of jurisdictions.
**Personal:** JD, Creighton University (1982); BA, University of Nebraska (1979).

### NADEL, Darren
Littler Mendelson, PC, Denver
303 575 5861
dnadel@littler.com
*Featured in Labor & Employment (Colorado)*
**Practice Areas:** Competition and Trade Secret Law, ERISA and Benefit Plan Litigation, Complex Litigation and Jury Trials, Business Restructuring
**Career:** Represents clients in high risk, high value cases involving trade secrets and unfair competition, employee benefits litigation and whistleblower and Sarbanes Oxley matters. Authored materials on employment law topics including agreements employers enter into with their executives and employees, trade secrets and unfair competition litigation, and ERISA litigation.
**Publications:** December, 2012 - Court upholds employee termination 2 days after FMLA request, Employee Benefit News December, 2012 - Tenth Circuit Upholds Employee Termination 2 Days After FMLA Leave Request, Littler ASAP.

### NEUMANN, Christopher J
Greenberg Traurig, LLP, Denver
303 572 6551
NeumannC@gtlaw.com
*Featured in Natural Resources (Colorado)*
**Practice Areas:** Environmental; litigation; governmental affairs; land development; American Indian; global energy and infrastructure.
**Professional Memberships:** Gubernatorial Appointee, Vice Chair, Colorado Solid and Hazardous Waste Commission, 2005-present; Vice Chair, Colorado Air Quality Control Commission, 2004-07; American Society of Civil Engineers; Certified Professional in Erosion and Sediment Control; International Erosion Control Association and more.
**Career:** Selected, Chambers USA Guide, 2007-13; Super Lawyers, Rising Star, 2009, 2011-12; American Marshall Memorial Fellow, 2007. Adjunct Professor, Environmental Litigation and Hazardous Waste Law, University of Colorado School of Law.
**Personal:** JD, Lewis & Clark Law School; BS, Civil Engineering, University of Notre Dame.

### O'DONNELL, Michael
Wheeler Trigg O'Donnell LLP, Denver
303 244 1850
odonnell@wtotrial.com
*Featured in Litigation (Colorado)*
**Practice Areas:** Co-founder and firm chairman. National practice in complex civil litigation involving product liability (particularly for medical devices and pharmaceuticals), professional liability, torts, class actions and mass actions, commercial litigation, and bet-the-company matters. Has appeared as lead counsel in state and federal courts in 25 states. Has served as national and regional counsel for numerous Fortune 500 companies, including General Electric, Advanced Bionics, McKesson, Boston Scientific, Pfizer, and CNA Insurance.
**Professional Memberships:** Fellow, American College of Trial Lawyers; Network of Trial Law Firms.
**Personal:** JD, University of Denver College of Law, 1979; BA, University of Notre Dame, 1976

### O'ROURKE, Renée W
Greenberg Traurig, LLP, Denver
303 572 6544
OrourkeR@gtlaw.com
*Featured in Labor & Employment (Colorado)*
**Practice Areas:** Tax; global benefits and compensation; employee benefits; retirement plans; executive and stock compensation; welfare and fringe benefits.
**Professional Memberships:** Member: American Bar Association Employee Benefits Committee Section of Taxation, Colorado Bar Association, and Denver Bar Association; Member and Past Program Chair, Denver Chapter of the Western Pension and Benefits Conference.
**Career:** Rated, AV® Preeminent™ 5.0 out of 5. Selected, Best Lawyers in America, 2010-13; Chambers USA Guide, 2005-13; Corporate Counsel Black Book, 2007; Super Lawyers magazine, 2006, 2012.
**Personal:** BS, University of Southern Colorado; JD, University of Denver; LLM, University of Denver.

### PAINTER, Brett
Davis Graham & Stubbs LLP, Denver
303 892 7418
brett.painter@dgslaw.com
*Featured in Labor & Employment (Colorado)*
**Practice Areas:** Employment & Labor Law, Commercial Litigation, Trial, and Class & Consolidated Actions.
**Professional Memberships:** Labor & Employment Law Section of the Colorado Bar Association.
**Career:** Brett Painter practices primarily in the field of labor and employment law, including litigating and advising clients in the areas of discrimination, harassment, retaliation, unlawful discharge, layoffs, unfair labor practices, employment agreements, non-competition agreements, union issues, and wage and hour laws. Beyond the employment context, Mr Painter also has a significant commercial litigation practice.

**Personal:** BA with distinction, University of Colorado; JD, Order of St. Ives, University of Denver Sturm College of Law.

### PALMER, David G
Greenberg Traurig, LLP, Denver
303 572 6539
PalmerDG@gtlaw.com
*Featured in Litigation (Colorado)*
**Practice Areas:** Managing Shareholder, Denver Office. Litigation; appellate; global energy and insurance.
**Professional Memberships:** Member: Colorado Bar Association Ethics Committee; Executive Committee, Metro Denver Economic Development Corporation; Trustee, Colorado Legal Aid Foundation; Advisory Council, University of Colorado School of Medicine. Chairman, Board of Directors, Metro Chamber Foundation; Fellow, American Bar Foundation. Director, National Civic League.
**Career:** Selected: Best Lawyers in America, 1982-2013; Super Lawyers, Colorado Super Lawyers, 2006-12. Rated, AV® Preeminent™ 5.0 out of 5.
**Publications:** Articles editor, University of Colorado Law Review.
**Personal:** JD, University of Colorado School of Law, Order of the Coif; AB, History, Johns Hopkins University.

### PHILLIPS, Paul D
Holland & Hart LLP, Denver
303 295 8131
pphillips@hollandhart.com
*Featured in Natural Resources (Colorado)*
**Practice Areas:** Environmental law and litigation. Clean Air Act, Clean Water Act, CERCLA, toxic tort litigation: defense of citizens' suits, EPA enforcement actions. Environmental due diligence. Land use and conservation easements.
**Professional Memberships:** Colorado Bar (1977); US Supreme Court, DC and other Circuit Courts of Appeal.
**Career:** 'Best of the Bar' Environmental Law, 2004, Denver Business Journal. Listed in Best Lawyers, Chambers, Super Lawyers. Fellow, American College of Environmental Lawyers (2010).
**Publications:** Founding editor 'Natural Resources and Environment', ABA's Natural Resources magazine.
**Personal:** JD (1976), Yale; BA magna cum laude (1973), Harvard. Chairman, Holland & Hart Management Committee.

### POWELL JR, David D
Ogletree, Deakins, Nash, Smoak & Stewart PC, Denver
303 764 6800
david.powell@ogletreedeakins.com
*Featured in Labor & Employment (Colorado)*
**Practice Areas:** Employer representation on matters involving restrictive covenants, employment agreements, employee classification and compensation, internal investigations, wrongful discharge, disability accommodation and protected leave, workplace harassment, individual and systemic discrimination, multi-plaintiff litigation.

**Professional Memberships:** American Bar Association (Employment and Litigation Sections), International Society of Barristers, National Employment Law Council, National Bar Association, Academy of Hospitality Industry Attorneys, Colorado Bar Association, Sam Cary Bar Association, Faculty of Federal Advocates.
**Career:** University of Santa Clara (BA, 1980); UCLA Law School (JD, 1983); Law Clerk for the Honorable John L Kane, Jr USDC (1983-84); Deputy District Attorney, Denver, Colorado (1986-90).

### QUAIL, Beverly J
Ballard Spahr LLP, Denver
303 299 7305
quail@ballardspahr.com
*Featured in Real Estate (Colorado)*
**Practice Areas:** Beverly J. Quail is practice leader of the Real Estate Finance Group. She practices in all aspects of real estate, emphasizing financing and development.
**Professional Memberships:** American Bar Association, Delegate for Colorado, Select Committee of House of Delegates, past Chair Real Property, Probate and Trust Law Section; American Bar Foundation, Fellow, Colorado State Chair; Colorado Bar Association; Anglo-American Real Property Institute; American College of Mortgage Attorneys; American College of Real Estate Lawyers; Colorado Bar Foundation, Fellow and Board of Trustees.
**Career:** Admissions: Colorado.
**Personal:** University of Denver Sturm College of Law (JD); University of Southern California (BA).

### RICHARDSON, Christopher L
Davis Graham & Stubbs LLP, Denver
303 892 7420
chris.richardson@dgslaw.com
*Featured in Corporate/M&A (Colorado)*
**Practice Areas:** Banking & Lending, Bankruptcy & Creditors' Rights, Coal Industry, Mergers & Acquisitions, and Oil & Gas Industry.
**Career:** Chris Richardson is the firm's managing partner. His corporate practice focuses on mergers and acquisitions and restructuring work, where he works primarily with private companies in purchase and sale financing transactions. Recently, many of his transactions have been in connection with oil and gas companies as well as advising distressed buyers or sellers of companies.
**Personal:** BA magna cum laude, Duke University; M.A., University of Denver; JD, University of Denver Sturm College of Law

### ROCKWELL, Sarah M
Kaplan Kirsch & Rockwell LLP, Denver
303 825 7000
srockwell@kaplankirsch.com
*Featured in Real Estate (Colorado)*
**Practice Areas:** Ms Rockwell's practice emphasizes land use, real estate and public sector negotiations. Ms Rockwell has represented both public and private sector clients in land use, real estate and municipal law issues associated with complex, small and large-scale development projects, including transit oriented development projects, airports, and residential, industrial and commer-

cial development projects. She has prepared, negotiated and implemented agreements related to a variety of public/private sector development projects, has advised airports on land use compatibility issues and has counseled clients on endangered species issues.

## RUPPERT, John L
Ballard Spahr LLP, Denver
303 299 7304
ruppertj@ballardspahr.com
*Featured in Corporate/M&A (Colorado)*
**Practice Areas:** John L. Ruppert is a partner in the Business and Finance Department and the Mergers and Acquisitions/Private Equity Group. He focuses on mergers and acquisitions, private equity, corporate and commercial finance, business combinations, reorganizations, restructurings, and executive compensation, along with the federal income tax matters relating to these transactions.
**Professional Memberships:** American Bar Association Colorado Bar Association Association for Corporate Growth.
**Career:** Admissions: Colorado Illinois US District Court for the District of Colorado.
**Personal:** New York University School of Law (LLM, Taxation, 1979) University of Denver Sturm College of Law (JD 1978) Northwestern University (BA 1975).

## SAVAGE, Janet A
Davis Graham & Stubbs LLP, Denver
303 892 7341
janet.savage@dgslaw.com
*Featured in Labor & Employment (Colorado)*
**Practice Areas:** Employment & Labor, Commercial Litigation, Arbitration & Dispute Resolution.
**Professional Memberships:** American Board of Trial Advocates; Arbitrator with the American Arbitration Association; American Bar Foundation; American Bar Association, Labor and Litigation Sections; and Colorado Bar Association, Labor Law Committee.
**Career:** Janet Savage has been practicing since 1981 in employment and labor law. She has significant litigation experience, defending claims by employees including all types of discrimination, retaliation, harassment breach of contract, and wrongful discharge claims. A significant portion of her practice involves employment counseling.
**Personal:** BA, with honors, State University of New York; JD, cum laude, Suffolk University.

## SCARBORO, James E
Arnold & Porter LLP, Denver
303 863 2311
James.Scarboro@aporter.com
*Featured in Litigation (Colorado)*
**Practice Areas:** James Scarboro is an experienced litigator who has handled product liability, securities, antitrust, and Indian litigation before Federal and State courts throughout the West. In the area of product liability, Mr Scarboro has been active in the firm's tobacco and diet drug representations.
**Career:** Mr Scarboro served as law clerk to US Supreme Court Justice Byron R. White from 1971

to 1972 and was an associate professor at the University of Colorado School of Law from 1973 to 1978.
**Personal:** JD, University of Colorado School of Law, 1970; BA, Colorado College, 1963.

## SCHLAUCH STARK, Lucy
Holland & Hart LLP, Denver
303 295 8493
mlstark@hollandhart.com
*Featured in Corporate/M&A (Colorado)*
**Practice Areas:** Ms Stark is focused on corporate finance transactions including public and private equity and debt offerings; corporate governance and disclosure issues; and mergers, acquisitions and divestitures. She has represented public and private companies in connection with financings and corporate restructurings; friendly and hostile equity tender offers; debt tender and exchange offers; mergers; and asset carve-outs. In addition, she represents clients in crisis management. Ms Stark chairs the firm's securities and MLP practice groups.
**Professional Memberships:** Colorado and Denver Bar Associations.
**Personal:** JD - University of Colorado (Order of the Coif) 1998; BA - DePauw University 1993.

## SCHWARTZ, Paul
Shoemaker Ghiselli & Schwartz LLC, Boulder
303 530 3452
pschwartz@sgslitigation.com
*Featured in Litigation (Colorado)*
**Practice Areas:** Complex litigation, appeals, and regulatory and internal investigations focusing on securities, corporate governance, and commercial disputes. Heads the firm's appellate practice.
**Professional Memberships:** Colorado Bar Association, Subcommittee on Appellate Practice.
**Career:** Law Clerk to Justice Stephen Breyer and Retired Justice Harry A. Blackmun, US Supreme Court, 1994-95, and Judge Phyllis A. Kravitch, US Court of Appeals for the Eleventh Circuit, 1992-94.
**Personal:** JD with Highest Honors, University of North Carolina School of Law, 1992; Sc.B. Brown University, 1988.

## SHARRER, Elizabeth
Holland & Hart LLP, Denver
303 295 8484
lsharrer@hollandhart.com
*Featured in Real Estate (Colorado)*
**Practice Areas:** As a Partner in the Real Estate Practice Group, Ms Sharrer concentrates on commercial real estate development and financing, land use and annexation issues, all aspects of acquisitions and sales, office park development, leasing, title related issues, loan documentation and opinion letters.
**Professional Memberships:** Denver Bar Association, Colorado Bar Association, US Green Building Council Colorado Chapter Board of Trustees (Immediate Past Chair), Chair, Women in Real Estate (WIRE).
**Personal:** JD University of Michigan (1980), BA University of Michigan (1976).

## SHOEMAKER, Andrew R
Shoemaker Ghiselli & Schwartz LLC, Boulder
303 530 3452
ashoemaker@sgslitigation.com
*Featured in Litigation (Colorado)*
**Practice Areas:** Representation of corporations, board committees, and individual directors and officers in connection with government and internal investigations. Representation of clients in complex disputes involving securities, corporate governance, patent infringement and breach of contract matters.
**Career:** Enforcement attorney, US Securities Exchange Commission (SEC); Special assistant US attorney for the District of Colorado; Judicial clerk, Honorable Charles R Richey (US District Court in Washington, DC). Awarded the Federal Bar Association's Manuel F Cohen Award (Outstanding young SEC attorney) in 1998. JD, University of Virginia School of Law, 1992; BA, summa cum laude, Hampden-Sydney College, 1989. Executive Editor, Virginia Tax Review.

## SILBERMAN, Mickey
Jackson Lewis LLP, Denver
303 225 2400
SilbermM@jacksonlewis.com
*Featured in Labor & Employment (Colorado)*
**Practice Areas:** Affirmative Action Compliance/OFCCP; Diversity; EEO Systemic Discrimination Litigation; Pay Equity Compliance and Litigation; Litigation Statistics.
**Professional Memberships:** National Industry Liaison Group, Legal Counsel to and Executive Committee Member; Center for Corporate Equality, Advisory Board; Colorado Bar Association.
**Career:** Partner, Jackson Lewis LLP, 2004-present; Managing Partner, Denver office, 2007-present; Chair of Affirmative Action-OFCCP Practice Group, 2009-present; Associate, Jackson Lewis, 1996-2003.
**Publications:** Co-author, Affirmative Action Compliance, Association for Corporate Counsel InfoPAK, 2011.
**Personal:** JD, St. John's School of Law, 1994; BA, City University of New York, Queens College, with honors, 1990.

## STARK, Beau
Gibson, Dunn & Crutcher LLP, Denver
303 298 5922
bstark@gibsondunn.com
*Featured in Corporate/M&A (Colorado)*
**Practice Areas:** Advises private equity firms, public companies and private firms in energy and natural resources industries, and technology, recreation, manufacturing, construction and other industries in both international and domestic markets. Has broad experience in all aspects of corporate practice, including public and private mergers and acquisitions, joint ventures, securities and capital markets transactions, executive compensation and private fund formation. Regularly advises boards of directors of public and private companies on strategic decisions and fiduciary duty issues, including takeovers and SEC matters.

**Personal:** JD, University of Colorado, 1995, Order of the Coif, Editor, Law Review; BS, University of Colorado, 1991.

## STEINER, Beat
Holland & Hart LLP, Boulder
303 473 2736
bsteiner@hollandhart.com
*Featured in Real Estate (Colorado)*
**Practice Areas:** Real estate and corporate law. Chairs the firm's Resort, Lodging and Leisure Group. Practice has included ski and golf resorts in Colorado, California, Idaho, Vermont and New Zealand.
**Professional Memberships:** CBA (past Chair, RE Section; Executive Council, Business Section); Secretary of State Advisory Committee; American College of Real Estate Lawyers; American College of Mortgage Attorneys.
**Career:** Partner; Admitted in Colorado (1983), New York (1981).
**Publications:** Frequent lecturer. Published in ABA Real Property, Probate and Trust Journal; Practical Real Estate Lawyer; and Colorado Lawyer.
**Personal:** University of Virginia (JD 1980); (BA 1973, with high honors). Native of Switzerland.

## STOCKS, Bruce D
Davis Graham & Stubbs LLP, Denver
303 892 7424
bruce.stocks@dgslaw.com
*Featured in Corporate/M&A (Colorado)*
**Practice Areas:** Mergers & Acquisitions and Private Equity & Venture Capital
**Career:** Bruce Stocks' practice emphasizes mergers and acquisitions, reorganizations, recapitalizations, joint ventures and other corporate transactions, as well as the representation of borrowers in senior and subordinated debt financings. He has particular experience in private equity transactions, including the representation of investors, private equity funds, and companies in leveraged buyouts and recapitalizations. From an industry perspective, Mr Stocks has significant experience representing clients in the hospitality and gold mining industries.
**Personal:** BA, Brigham Young University; JD cum laude, Brigham Young University, J. Reuben Clark Law School.

## TALLEY, Steven K
Gibson, Dunn & Crutcher LLP, Denver
303 298 5775
stalley@gibsondunn.com
*Featured in Corporate/M&A (Colorado)*
**Practice Areas:** Has extensive experience in mergers and acquisitions of public and private companies, including both auctions and privately negotiated sales. Additionally advises clients on public and private equity issuances and debt offerings. Counsels local, national and international clients from a variety of industries, including telecommunications, technology, manufacturing and energy. Clients include private equity firms, as well as their portfolio companies and other corporate clients.

**Personal:** JD, University of California at Berkeley, 1991, Articles Editor, 'High Technology Law Journal', Order of the Coif.

## THOMASCH, Roger P
Ballard Spahr LLP, Denver
303 299 7301
thomasch@ballardspahr.com
*Featured in Litigation (Colorado)*

**Practice Areas:** For over 40 years, Mr Thomasch has focused on business litigation. He has tried to verdict virtually every type of business/commercial case nationwide, frequently joining cases as lead counsel shortly before trial. He previously chaired the Litigation Department and has been managing partner of the Denver office for over 20 years. He is a former trial attorney with the US Department of Justice.

**Professional Memberships:** American College of Trial Lawyers, American Bar Foundation, Colorado Bar Foundation.

**Career:** Colorado Connecticut.

**Personal:** Duke University School of Law (JD 1967) The College of William & Mary (BA 1964).

## TOLL, Christopher
Holland & Hart LLP, Greenwood Village
303 290 1637
ctoll@hollandhart.com
*Featured in Litigation (Colorado)*

**Practice Areas:** Practice concentrates in complex commercial litigation and trade secrets/covenants not to compete. Procedural specialty in obtaining temporary restraining orders and preliminary injunctions.

**Professional Memberships:** Board of Directors of Faculty of Federal Advocates (2007 - 2009); Board of Directors of Dartmouth Lawyers Association (2006 - present), President (2004-2006).

**Career:** Member, Holland & Hart Management Committee (2010-2012); Chair, Business Litigation practice group (2001 - 2007).

**Personal:** University of Virginia (JD 1985, Editorial Board of Law Review); Dartmouth College (BA 1981, Magna Cum Laude)

## WEBBER, Erin
Littler Mendelson, PC, Denver
303 362 2851
ewebber@littler.com
*Featured in Labor & Employment (Colorado)*

**Practice Areas:** Complex Litigation and Jury Trials; Discrimination and Harassment; Training - Compliance, Ethics, Leadership; Hiring, Performance Management and Termination; Leaves of Absence and Disability Accommodation

**Career:** Defends clients in employment-related disputes before federal and state courts, the Equal Employment Opportunity Commission, the Missouri Human Rights Commission, the Kansas Human Rights Commission and the Colorado Civil Rights Division; Assists with employee and managerial training and provides employment counseling on a daily basis; Office-managing shareholder in Denver; Member of Littler's Board of Directors and the Associates Consideration Committee; Founded the firm's Kansas City, Missouri office in 2006.

## WHEELER, Malcolm
Wheeler Trigg O'Donnell LLP, Denver
303 244 1870
wheeler@wtotrial.com
*Featured in Litigation (Nationwide), Products Liability (Nationwide), Litigation (Colorado)*
See under Nationwide for profile.

## ZISSER, David A
Davis Graham & Stubbs LLP, Denver
303 892 7256
david.zisser@dgslaw.com
*Featured in Litigation (Colorado)*

**Practice Areas:** Securities Enforcement, Litigation & Internal Investigations, White Collar Crime, Commercial Litigation, Trial, and Arbitration & Dispute Resolution.

**Career:** David Zisser practices at the intersection of litigation, corporate and securities law. He focuses on representing individuals and entities in investigations and proceedings involving the United States Securities and Exchange Commission, the Colorado Division of Securities, FINRA, and other regulatory bodies. David has prevailed at trial on behalf of clients charged with financial fraud, false reporting, stock manipulation, and trading on inside information.

**Personal:** BA, The Johns Hopkins University; JD, Georgetown University Law Center.

# BENJAMIN BAIN HOWARD & COHEN, LLC

www.bbhlegal.com **tel:** 303 290 6600 **fax:** 303 290 8323

**Managing Partner:** James G Benjamin
Number of partners: 5
Number of other lawyers: 3

**OFFICES**

COLORADO
**GREENWOOD VILLAGE:** 7315 E. Orchard Road,
Suite E400, CO 80111
Tel: 303 290 6600   Fax: 303 290 8323
Email: acohen@bbhlegal.com

**Firm Overview:**

Benjamin, Bain, Howard & Cohen, LLC occupies a unique position among Colorado law firms. It is a small boutique firm with an emphasis on construction and real estate transactions and dispute resolution. Yet, the accolades bestowed on it are consistent with being one of Colorado's most prestigious firms. This includes the fact that 3 of its 5 partner level attorneys have been recognized by *Chambers*. Also, the firm's managing partner, Jim Benjamin, had the honor of serving as the Denver Bar Association president in 2012-13. All of the firm's partner level attorneys previously worked in large firms. They found, however, that a small firm allows the personal attention and availability of the lead attorney, which is so critical to a successful collaboration between client and attorney. It also allows the firm to deliver results at an effective cost, regardless of the size of the matter.

**Main Areas of Practice:**

**Real Estate:**
The firm represents clients in all aspects of commercial real estate sales, leasing and financing, including shopping centers, office buildings, subdivisions, creation and conversion of condominiums, apartments, industrial projects, hotels, multi-family residential projects, single family subdivisions, golf courses, and raw land development. The firm represented the purchaser in the largest single transaction acquisition of apartment complexes, involving multiple lenders and locations. The firm thereafter provided the legal services converting several of the complexes into condominiums.
**Contact:** James G Benjamin
**Email:** jgbenjamin@bbhlegal.com

**Banking & Finance:**
The firm has a substantial practice representing lenders and borrowers in financing transactions. Currently, the firm represents a major New York real estate investment company in handling all real estate assets obtained from a failed bank. The firm also represented banks and borrowers on various loans for building construction, infrastructure improvements and permanent or bridge loan financing. This included a representation of a Federally insured lender on an $84 million acquisition and development loan and representation of a borrower on a $155 million apartment acquisition loan.
**Contact:** James G Benjamin
**Email:** jgbenjamin@bbhlegal.com

**Construction Law:**
The firm's construction attorneys provide advice to clients before disputes arise. Its attorneys have represented public owners, private developers, and homebuilders in drafting design and construction contracts for commercial and residential projects, including hospitals, a museum, hotels, multi-family and single family homes, and affordable housing projects. They also represent general contractors, subcontractors and material suppliers in reviewing and drafting of construction contracts. A unique aspect of being a small, boutique law firm is that its partners are always available to their clients to personally address problems as they arise, and help resolve problems before they evolve into formal disputes.
**Contact:** Janet Lawler McDaniel
**Email:** janet.mcdaniel@bbhlegal.com

**Construction Litigation:**
A primary focus of the firm's practice is resolving construction disputes. Three of its partner level attorneys, Al Cohen, Janet McDaniel and Jim Bain, devoted most of their work over the last 30 years to construction matters. They represent contractors, subcontractors and suppliers, public owners, private developers, and homebuilders, on public and private projects and in the commercial, industrial and residential sectors. Those disputes include complex delay and disruption claims, construction defects, bid protests, defective plans and specifications, acceleration claims, insurance coverage disputes and mechanic's liens. The firm also has unique resources and experience. Janet McDaniel brings 15 years of experience as a construction manager with a national prime contractor before she embarked on a law career. Al Cohen and Jim Bain both worked for many years as in-house counsel with the government, trying complex construction cases on commercial and industrial projects. They also serve as construction arbitrators.
**Contact:** Alvin M Cohen
**Email:** acohen@bbhlegal.com

**Real Estate Litigation:**
The firm handles numerous disputes arising out of real estate transactions, including disputes between buyers and sellers, property disputes over easements, encroachments and adverse possession, disputes among the developer's partners and disputes between the developer and the lender. Most prominently, one of the firm's partners represented a land developer against a national bank, where the jury awarded the developer a $64 million verdict – the largest in Colorado history at that time. More recently, another partner represented the developer of a golf course community against a claim by the prior developer, in which an arbitration award of $0 was issued on a $40 million claim.
**Contact:** James W Bain
**Email:** jamesbain@bbhlegal.com

**Commercial Litigation:**
The firm's commercial litigators represent business owners and individuals in all types of disputes involving business torts, fraud claims, violations of duties by officers or directors, securities, and insurance bad faith. The firm also represents business owners in claims concerning buy-sell agreements, partner disputes, dissolutions and acquisitions.
**Contact:** Wesley B Howard
**Email:** whoward@bbhlegal.com

**BENJAMIN, BAIN HOWARD & COHEN LLC**

# BROWNSTEIN HYATT FARBER SCHRECK

**www. bhfs.com** **tel:** 303 223 1100 **fax:** 303 223 1111

**Founding Shareholders:** Norman Brownstein, Steve Farber, Frank Schreck, Jack Hyatt (retired)
**Managing Shareholder:** Bruce James
Number of shareholders: 130
Number of other attorneys: 94
Number of policy advisors: 16

## Firm Overview:

Brownstein Hyatt Farber Schreck provides its clients a value that no other western law firm can match – an integrated approach that combines sensible business solutions with a Capitol Hill perspective. The firm's lawyers and policy advisors have built a reputation for providing legal counsel that drives results and connects business leaders to the information they need to make decisions. With 13 offices across the Western US, plus Washington, DC and Atlantic City, Brownstein covers today's important issues.

## Main Areas of Practice:

### Corporate & Business:

Brownstein attorneys regularly handle sophisticated corporate, finance and securities transactions for companies across the US. They focus on matters related to mergers and acquisitions, emerging business and technology, gaming, corporate finance, public and private transactions, municipal and public finance and general corporate representation.

### Gaming:

The Gaming Law Group, based in both Las Vegas and Atlantic City, represents businesses and individuals seeking gaming licenses, liquor licenses and related approvals, from the relevant federal, state and local agencies. The firm renders advice on the structuring of major transactions to minimize gaming issues and assist in obtaining necessary approvals for public offerings, financings, business restructurings and mergers and acquisitions, and additionally, handles gaming issues relating to the acquisitions and new development of hotels, resorts and casinos.

### Government Relations:

The Government Relations Department is a full-service lobbying, public policy and legal representation practice that helps companies, associations, nonprofits and other organizations interpret federal government actions, solve challenges and seize opportunities through interaction with government officials. Their work includes legislative consulting, lobbying, policy development, public relations strategy, and representation in front of Congress, federal agencies and regulatory bodies. With seasoned government relations professionals in every office, Brownstein provides comprehensive service at the federal, state and local levels.

### Litigation:

Representing clients in a wide range of industries, the firm employs an integrated approach to each case. In resolving matters for clients, both inside and outside the courtroom, the firm's litigators draw upon a wealth of trial experience that includes hundreds of jury trials and other major adversarial proceedings, including antitrust, employment and labor, and environmental disputes.

### Natural Resources:

The Natural Resources Department helps clients develop forward-thinking environmental strategies marrying the needs of business and governmental regulatory requirements. Brownstein attorneys frequently partner across practice areas so that when environmental issues arise, they can quickly assemble a team with the specific experience to ensure the transaction is successful.

### Real Estate:

For decades, the firm has been a nationally recognized leader in real estate law. Brownstein is known throughout the United States for the scale and prestige of its work, and its industry relationships are second to none. The Real Estate Department represents sellers, purchasers, landlords, tenants and governments with respect to all facets of real estate law. The firm has significant experience in acquisition and disposition, development, engineering and construction, land use, REITs, taxation, public finance, leasing and nearly every other sub-field in transactional real estate law.

### Water:

The firm's Water Group, regarded as one of the premier water rights practices in the Western US, boasts unparalleled experience in every aspect of water use – acquisition, disposal, development, protection, regulation and permitting, environmental compliance, litigation and legislative advocacy.

### Additional Practice Areas:

Air quality, antitrust, bankruptcy and restructuring, CEQA/NEPA, environmental and remediation, employee benefits, family law, federal funding, hospitality, intellectual property and technology, land use, private equity, public finance, renewable energy, state and local legislation and policy, tax, telecommunications and media, and white-collar.

## Clients:

AIMCO; Alberta Development; Apollo Management, L.P.; Caesars Entertainment; CenturyLink; Dividend Capital; Golden State Water Company; Grupo Cementos de Chihuahua; Gunnison Energy; Hard Rock Hotel Holdings; RockResorts International; San Diego County Water Authority; Southern Nevada Water Authority; UnitedHealth Group; Vail Resorts; Wynn Resorts, Inc.; Westlands Water District.

## OFFICES

### COLORADO
**DENVER:** 410 Seventeenth Street, Suite 2200, 80202-4432
Tel: 303 223 1100  Fax: 303 223 1111

### ARIZONA
**PHOENIX:** One East Washington Street, Suite 2400, 85004
Tel: 602 382 4040  Fax: 602 382 4020

### CALIFORNIA
**LOS ANGELES:** 2029 Century Park East, Suite 2100, 90067-3007
Tel: 310 500 4600  Fax: 310 500 4602

**ORANGE COUNTY:** 300 South El Camino Real, Suite 203, 92672-4070
Tel: 949 498 3879  Fax: 949 498 6197

**SACRAMENTO:** 1415 L Street, Suite 800, 95814-3974
Tel: 916 594 9700  Fax: 916 594 9701

**SAN DIEGO:** 225 Broadway, Suite 1670, 92101-5000
Tel: 619 702 6100  Fax: 619 239 4333

**SANTA BARBARA:** 21 East Carrillo Street, 93101-2706
Tel: 805 963 7000  Fax: 805 965 4333

### DISTRICT OF COLUMBIA
**WASHINGTON, DC:** 1350 I Street, NW, Suite 510, 20005-3305
Tel: 202 296 7353  Fax: 202 296 7009

### NEVADA
**LAS VEGAS:** 100 North City Parkway, Suite 1600, 89106-4614
Tel: 702 382 2101  Fax: 702 382 8135

**RENO:** 50 West Liberty, Suite 1030, 89501
Tel: 775 622 9450  Fax: 775 622 9554

### NEW JERSEY
**ATLANTIC CITY:** 707 White Horse Pike, Suite C-5, 08201
Tel: 609 241 0057  Fax: 609 241 0533

### NEW MEXICO
**ALBUQUERQUE:** 201 Third Street NW, Suite 1700, 87102-4386
Tel: 505 244 0770  Fax: 505 244 9266

**SANTA FE:** 1227 Paseo de Peralta, 87501-2758
Tel: 505 820 3132  Fax: 505 992 1314

# Brownstein Hyatt Farber Schreck

# DAVIS GRAHAM & STUBBS LLP

**tel:** 303 892 9400  **fax:** 303 893 1379

**Managing Partner:** Chris Richardson
Number of equity partners: 69
Number of lawyers: 150

## Firm Overview:

Davis Graham & Stubbs LLP enjoys a strong national reputation for its corporate finance, natural resources, and energy law practices, with a particular focus on securities and M&A transactions, complex commercial litigation, and regulatory guidance. For nearly a century, DGS has ranked among the region's most prominent law firms, consistently offering quality legal services to emerging and established businesses in the Rocky Mountain West.

## Main Areas of Practice:

### Corporate Finance:

DGS has the largest corporate finance and acquisitions practice in the region, with more than 60 lawyers with expertise in complex M&A transactions, securities law, taxation, private equity, asset management, executive compensation, intellectual property and real estate. The size and sophistication of our corporate finance practice gives us deep familiarity with a wide variety of transaction strategies, financing alternatives and regulatory issues. And because the firm works with banks, investment advisers, venture capitalists and private equity firms every day, it is able to stay current on new and evolving deal terms as the transaction marketplace changes.

### Energy & Mining:

DGS provides a seamless array of litigation, transaction, permitting and counseling services in the oil, natural gas, coal, coalbed methane, mining and renewable and alternative energy industries. Combined with the tax, corporate, regulatory, environmental and trial lawyers who are experienced in natural resource matters, DGS offers one of the strongest energy and mining practices in the US.

### Environmental Law:

DGS is staffed with some of the best environmental attorneys in the country who are focused on promoting our clients' businesses, minimizing their costs and ensuring compliance with evolving environmental requirements. The firm handles a broad array of compliance, permitting, transactional and enforcement matters pertaining to air and water quality, solid and hazardous wastes, indoor air/vapor intrusion, underground storage tanks, endangered species, cultural resources, radioactive materials, spills, remediation, cost recovery, contribution and natural resource damages.

### Litigation:

DGS lawyers – including many former prosecutors and public defenders – have substantial records of trying lawsuits in front of juries and judges. Their extensive jury trial experience gives them an advantage in narrowing claims and negotiating favorable settlements. The firm also conducts litigation planning, mediation and other alternative dispute resolution, all forms of pre-trial motion and discovery practice and trials and appeals at all levels.

### Clients:

Anadarko Petroleum, Black Hills Corporation, BP, Brown Shoe Company, Chevron Mining, General Electric, HCA HealthONE, Invidi Technologies, Lovell Minnick Partners, Newmont Mining, NORDAM, Pfizer, Red Robin, Resolute Energy Corporation, Union Pacific Railroad, PDC Energy, and Sage Hospitality.

## PRACTICE AREAS

Antitrust
Appellate
Arbitration & Dispute Resolution
Asset Management
Aviation
Banking & Lending
Bankruptcy & Creditors' Rights
Brownfields
Class & Consolidated Actions
Coal Industry
Coalbed Methane Development
Commercial Litigation
Construction & Real Estate Litigation
Cross-Border Transactions
Employee Benefits
Employment & Labor Law
Energy Industry
Environmental Law
Estate Planning & Administration
Executive Compensation
Health Care
Indian Law
Insurance & Risk Management
Intellectual Property Protection
International
Mergers & Acquisitions
Mining
Oil & Gas Industry
Private Equity & Venture Capital
Products Liability
Public Companies & Securities
Public Lands
Real Estate
Renewable & Alternative Energy
Safety & Health
Securities Enforcement, Litigation & Internal Investigations
Taxation
Toxic Tort Litigation
Trial
Uranium Mining & Development
Water Law
White Collar Crime

## OFFICES

**COLORADO**
**DENVER:** 1550 17th Street, STE 500, CO 80202
Tel: 303 892 9400   Fax: 303 893 1379
Email: info@dgslaw.com

# HOLLAND & HART LLP

www.hollandhart.com  **tel:** 303 295 8000  **fax:** 303 295 8261

**Managing Partner:** Thomas R O'Donnell
**Senior Partner:** John M Husband (Chair, Management Committee)
Number of partners: 222
Number of other lawyers: 230

## Firm Overview:

Holland & Hart LLP delivers integrated legal solutions to regional, national, and international clients of all sizes. Since its inception in 1947, Holland & Hart has grown into a full-service law firm of more than 450 lawyers in 15 offices across the Mountain West and in Washington, DC. The firm stands out in its footprint based on the breadth and depth of experience it offers, and its client-driven culture is personalized, responsive, and innovative.

## Main Areas of Practice:

Holland & Hart is home to nationally recognized practices such as corporate, including emerging growth, mergers and acquisitions and securities; the third-largest environmental practice in the country, according to Law360; energy and natural resources, including mining, for which US News – Best Lawyers recognized Holland & Hart as 2013 "Law Firm of the Year"; intellectual property; litigation; labor and employment; project development and finance; and tax, including employee benefits and private client work.

## International Work:

Holland & Hart's international practice represents clients involved in a broad range of transactions in most Latin American, Pacific Rim and European countries. These representations have included cross-border business transactions, international tax, international dispute resolution, export/import compliance, intellectual property protection overseas, immigration and naturalization, project finance and infrastructure development overseas, international real estate transactions, cross-border natural resources investments, labor and employment issues and avoided deforestation/carbon credits.

## Clients:

Holland & Hart represents businesses and organizations of all sizes, from start-ups to Fortune 50 companies. Holland & Hart's clients include those with headquarters in the firm's footprint, as well as companies doing business in the firm's footprint and seeking the advantages Holland & Hart offers based on top-tier talent, local knowledge, and competitive rate structures.

Clients benefit from the firm's thorough knowledge and deep experience in industries as diverse as aerospace, agriculture, airlines, bioscience, clean technology, construction, energy, finance, healthcare, hospitality, manufacturing, mining, oil and gas, real estate, resorts and recreation, retail, technology, telecommunications and broadband, and water rights and quality, among others.

## PRACTICE AREAS

Banking & Financial Institutions
Business, Corporate, & Finance
Energy, Environment, & Natural Resources
Government
Intellectual Property
International Trade
Labor & Employment
Litigation
Real Estate, Construction, & Development
Tax, Benefits, & Private Client

## OFFICES

### COLORADO

**ASPEN:** 600 East Main Street, Suite 104, CO 81611
Tel: 970 925 3476   Fax: 970 925 9367

**BOULDER:** One Boulder Plaza, 1800 Broadway, Suite 300, CO 80302
Tel: 303 473 2700   Fax: 303 473 2720

**COLORADO SPRINGS:** 90 South Cascade Avenue, Suite 1000, CO 80903
Tel: 719 475 7730   Fax: 719 634 2461

**DENVER:** 555 17th Street, Suite 3200, CO 80202
Tel: 303 295 8000   Fax: 303 295 8261

**GREENWOOD VILLAGE:** 6380 S. Fiddlers Green Circle, Suite 500, CO 80111
Tel: 303 290 1600   Fax: 303 290 1606

### DISTRICT OF COLUMBIA

**WASHINGTON, DC:** 975 F Street NW, Suite 900, DC 20004
Tel: 202 393 6500   Fax: 202 393 6551

### IDAHO

**BOISE:** 101 South Capitol Blvd, Suite 1400, ID 83702
Tel: 208 342 5000   Fax: 208 343 8869

### MONTANA

**BILLINGS:** 401 North 31st Street, Suite 1500, MT 59101
Tel: 406 252 2166   Fax: 406 252 1669

### NEVADA

**CARSON CITY:** 777 East Williams Street, Suite 200, NV 89701
Tel: 775 684 6000   Fax: 775 684 6001

**LAS VEGAS:** 9555 Hillwood Drive, 2nd Floor, NV 89134
Tel: 702 669 4600   Fax: 702 669 4650

**RENO:** 5441 Kietzke Lane, Second Floor, NV 89511
Tel: 775 327 3000   Fax: 775 786 6179

### NEW MEXICO

**SANTA FE:** 110 North Guadalupe, Suite 1, NM 87501
Tel: 505 988 4421   Fax: 505 983 6043

### UTAH

**SALT LAKE CITY:** 222 South Main Street, Suite 2200, UT 84101
Tel: 801 799 5800   Fax: 801 799 5700

### WYOMING

**CHEYENNE:** 2515 Warren Avenue, Suite 450, WY 82001
Tel: 307 778 4200   Fax: 307 778 8175

**JACKSON HOLE:** 25 South Willow Street, Suite 200, WY 83001
Tel: 307 739 9741   Fax: 307 739 9744

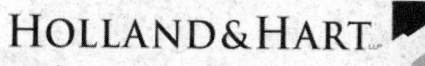

HOLLAND & HART

# KAPLAN KIRSCH & ROCKWELL, LLP

www.kaplankirsch.com **tel:** 303 825 7000 **fax:** 303 825 7005

**Managing Partner:** Stephen H Kaplan
Number of partners: 14
Number of lawyers: 18

**Firm Overview:**

Kaplan Kirsch & Rockwell is a national law firm focused on solving problems that involve environmental, land use, public and private land, infrastructure, energy and transportation law. The firm represents governments, corporations and organizations in complex projects that are subject to intense scrutiny and involve the intersection of private and governmental interests. The firm has a reputation for crafting innovative solutions to high-risk and seemingly intractable problems. The firm's lawyers have been counsel to public agencies and public interest organizations in high-profile environmental litigation, and have served as government counsel at the highest levels of federal and local government. Firm lawyers have a national reputation as handling some of the largest and most sophisticated infrastructure projects, including brownfields redevelopment, airports, highways, energy and water projects and urban transit systems.

**Main Areas of Practice:**

**Environmental, Public Lands & Energy Law:**

17 lawyers

Kaplan Kirsch & Rockwell assists clients in a broad range of environmental compliance and permitting matters. The firm's lawyers have addressed compliance and permitting issues under the CERCLA, RCRA, Endangered Species Act, the Clean Air Act, the Clean Water Act and related state laws. The firm has assisted clients in obtaining environmental permits, in responding to compliance orders and notices of violation, and in negotiating and implementing administrative orders, voluntary cleanup plans and consent orders. The firm's lawyers also have been principal litigation counsel in environmental matters in state and federal courts and agencies throughout the country.

Firm lawyers also engage in litigation and counseling over issues associated with the use of public lands in the United States for transportation, energy and other infrastructure, including land under the jurisdiction of the Bureau of Land Management and Forest Service.
**Contacts:** Lori Potter, Polly Jessen

**Litigation:**

11 lawyers

Firm litigators have successfully represented clients in state and federal courts and administrative forums in dozens of states, most federal appellate courts, many federal district courts, and the US Supreme Court. Many of these matters have been high-profile cases raising complex and precedent-setting issues of environmental, energy, land use, transportation and constitutional law. The firm's dedication to principled, zealous advocacy on behalf of its clients is seen in the diverse range of successful cases, including cases under

the US Constitution, NEPA, the Endangered Species Act, the Clean Water Act, the Federal Aviation Act, other transportation and aviation statutes, the Clean Air Act, CERCLA, RCRA, FLPMA, and state/local land use, energy, and environmental laws.
**Contacts:** John E Putnam, Lori Potter

**Land Use & Project Development:**

6 lawyers

The firm's lawyers understand the structure and requirements of large, complex projects and frequently have taken the leading role as project counsel in convening and supervising a team of attorneys, consultants and professionals with specialized expertise. These projects include complex real estate transactions, brownfields redevelopment, transit-oriented development, energy, water, and transportation infrastructure.
**Contacts:** Stephen H Kaplan, Sarah M Rockwell

**Transportation – Airports:**

16 lawyers

The firm's airports practice is the largest in the nation and it reflects a comprehensive and strategic approach that comes from a deep understanding of the industry. Among the wide range of matters where the firm's lawyers have provided advice are airport expansion; airport fees; regulating on-airport conduct; security; financing; use and access regulations; safety; flight tracks; land use compatibility; leases; and litigation over all of these issues.
**Contacts:** Peter J Kirsch, Daniel S Reimer

**Transportation – Rail & Transit:**

5 lawyers

The firm represents clients in all facets of rail transit and freight rail. The practice reflects a particular focus

on representing state and local governments with issues involving the railroads that serve their communities, including development of plans for commuter rail and transit, and railbanking arrangements. For commuter rail and transit operators, this work includes identifying and securing rights of way, negotiating with and selecting operators of the commuter service, and addressing regulatory, labor, and other issues that arise in the development and operation of urban rail systems.
**Contact:** Charles A Spitulnik

**Conservation Easements:**

3 lawyers

The firm's lawyers have a national reputation gained through more than 30 years of expertise in conservation easements and conservation transactions. Firm lawyers have assisted in the conservation protection of more than 1 million acres.
**Contact:** William M Silberstein

## PRACTICE AREAS

Airports
Alternative Energy & Wind Power, Public Utilities
Brownfields Development
Conservation Easements
Environmental Law
Infrastructure & Highways
Land Use
Litigation
Project Development
Public Lands
Real Estate
Rail & Transit
Transit-Oriented Development

## OFFICES

**COLORADO**
**DENVER:** 1675 Broadway, Suite 2300, CO 80202
Tel: 303 825 7000  Fax: 303 825 7005
Email: info@kaplankirsch.com

**DISTRICT OF COLUMBIA**
**WASHINGTON, DC:** 1001 Connecticut Avenue, NW Suite 800, DC 20036
Tel: 202 955 5600  Fax: 202 955 5616
Email: info@kaplankirsch.com

KAPLAN KIRSCH ROCKWELL

# OTTEN JOHNSON ROBINSON NEFF + RAGONETTI PC

**www.**ottenjohnson.com  **tel:** 303 825 8400  **fax:** 303 825 6525

**Managing Shareholder:** James T Johnson
**Founding Shareholders:** Frank L Robinson, William R Neff, Thomas J Ragonetti, Bruce B Johnson (deceased)
Number of shareholders: 24  Number of other lawyers: 10

## Firm Overview:

Otten Johnson's inception in January 1985 was guided by a single, formative principle: effective partnership between client and counsel. In the years since, a firm recognized for its commitment, inventiveness and practicality has evolved. The result: a synergy between every client's goals and the firm's commitment to realizing them. The firm's desire to serve the full range of their clients' needs has led them to establish practice specialties in land use, real estate, finance, litigation, business transactions and tax, eminent domain and bankruptcy and troubled loans. Due to a rapidly expanding client base, the firm has grown quickly, yet careful attention has guided their growth in a way that empowers each client while preserving the firm structure and values that have been important from the start. Otten Johnson strives to make every client's experience remarkable. For over 28 years, they have done just that. With great optimism and with a continuing commitment to unparalleled client service, they are eager to continue that tradition.

## Main Areas of Practice:

### Real Estate & Real Estate Finance:

Otten Johnson Robinson Neff + Ragonetti PC provides legal services to the real estate industry at the local, national and international levels. Their clients include developers, builders, investors, operators, managers, brokers and title insurers of single and multi-family residential projects, office buildings, retail shopping centers and other commercial projects and resort properties. The firm has represented these clients in all phases of their business from acquisition through development approvals, environmental regulation review and compliance, financing, title insurance matters and construction and development to leasing and disposition. They also have served as lessee's counsel in numerous leasing transactions (including leveraged leases) involving commercial real estate facilities. Additionally, the firm advises its real estate clients on a wide variety of sophisticated federal, state and local tax matters, including entity selection and formation, operational tax matters, partnership taxation, non-profit taxation, property tax assessment protests and appeals and 1031 exchanges.

### Land Use & Eminent Domain:

The firm provides a full range of services to a variety of clients in routine and complex land use and urban development approvals, transaction issues and litigation. The firm handles zoning, subdivision, annexation and related approval matters, both on a standalone basis and as part of their ongoing real estate representation. They frequently provide representation in complex and leading-edge land use and urban development matters, such as large-scale, long-term planned developments, historic preservation projects, development agreements and vested rights arrangements, complex annexation agreements, initiative and referendum elections, public highway and interchange issues, urban renewal projects, special district and other public financing and subsidy arrangements and public-private partnerships and transactions. They also represent clients in complex litigation in the areas of regulatory takings, governmental authority, unauthorized or excessive fees and taxes and the constitutional rights of private property owners. The firm has a well-developed practice in representing property owners facing condemnation as part of a public project.

### Business Transactions & Tax:

The firm represents numerous large and small corporations, partnerships and other business entities in the areas of general corporate, securities, business law and tax. Their services to these clients include providing counsel and representation in debt and equity financings, mergers and acquisitions, venture capital, private placement securities transactions, syndications, formation and restructuring, antitrust, employment contracts, employee benefit plans, product distribution arrangements and franchising, technology issues, including computer law and telecommunications regulation, licensing, trademark and copyright registration and licensing, gaming and tax planning. The firm also provides pro bono counsel to various charitable organizations.

### Bankruptcy & Troubled Loans:

Lender-borrower relationships present many challenges in a troubled economy. The pragmatism and creativity of its lawyers helps Otten Johnson's Bankruptcy & Troubled Loans Practice Group provide efficient, results-oriented counsel to lenders and borrowers with issues related to creditors' rights, loan modifications, workouts, foreclosures, distressed acquisitions and dispositions, financial restructuring and bankruptcies. While the primary focus of the practice has been lender representations, Otten Johnson has also represented numerous borrowers, debtors, receivers, creditors' committees and trustees.

### Litigation:

The firm handles a broad range of complex commercial litigation in the state and federal courts, with particular emphasis on disputes involving the real estate industry and debtor-creditor relations. Otten Johnson litigators have tried cases to judges, juries and arbitrators in matters ranging from construction defect disputes to quiet-title claims to lender liability cases. Sensitive to the danger that litigation costs can often become disproportionate to the amounts at stake in a particular case, the firm's litigators strive to maximize efficiencies and settlement leverage through a process of early case assessment, highly focused discovery and motion practice, and trial presentations designed to highlight the most persuasive evidence while eliminating unnecessary and voluminous details.

### Clients:

The firm represents a diverse clientele of local, national and international entities and individuals operating in a wide array of industries, including: banking; construction; financial services; insurance; investment banking; manufacturing; mortgage; private equity and venture capital; real estate; hotel and resort development and transportation, among others.

# OTTENJOHNSON
## ROBINSON NEFF + RAGONETTI PC

# WHEELER TRIGG O'DONNELL LLP

**www.**wtotrial.com  **tel:** 303 244 1800  **fax:** 303 244 1879

**Chairman:** Michael O'Donnell
**President:** Hugh Gottschalk
**Managing Partner:** Carolyn Fairless
Number of partners: 33
Number of lawyers: 80
Languages: *English*

## Firm Overview:

Trial Tested® civil litigation firm Wheeler Trigg O'Donnell excels at all stages of litigation – pre-trial, trial, post-trial and appellate. The firm also handles arbitrations and related areas of complex civil litigation, including class actions and multidistrict litigation, often as national or regional trial counsel, for professionals and name-brand companies. WTO attorneys have served as lead trial counsel in all 50 states, have tried cases to verdict in 45 states, and have appeared before the US Supreme Court, most of the US circuit courts of appeals, and two-thirds of the US district courts.

Although efficient resolution of disputes is central to WTO's work, the firm and its clients often develop and execute litigation strategies designed not only to resolve cases, but also to shape or change the law in ways beneficial to the clients' larger litigation and business interests.

## Main Areas of Practice:

### Product Liability:

WTO serves as national trial counsel for several manufacturers and distributors of medical devices, such as cochlear implants and stents, and pharmaceuticals, such as antidepressants, HRT, generics and imaging contrast agents. The firm is international, national or regional counsel for manufacturers of automobiles, appliances, industrial equipment and consumer goods.

### Commercial Litigation:

WTO represents companies and individuals from a variety of industries, including insurance, manufacturing, distribution, financial services, natural resources, technology and transportation, in commercial litigation matters involving allegations of breach of contract, breach of warranty, bad faith and fraud and misrepresentation.

### Professional Liability:

WTO defends hospitals, doctors and other health care providers against claims of medical malpractice and negligence. The firm defends law firms and lawyers against claims of legal malpractice. The firm defends accountants, architects, engineers and other professionals against claims of professional malpractice and negligence.

### Personal Injury Defense:

WTO defends personal injury claims involving accidents, engineering and design failure, exposure to toxic substances, unsafe premises, intentional torts and negligent professional representation and care.

### Employment Litigation:

WTO represents management in employment matters involving discrimination and harassment, ERISA, breach of contract, non-compete and trade secret actions, defamation, wrongful discharge, retaliation and related tort claims.

### Environmental Litigation:

WTO represents oil and gas, mining, energy, chemical, engineering and manufacturing companies in environmental lawsuits involving alleged breaches of environmental warranties and insurance issues associated with environmental contamination liabilities, toxic torts, wrongful death, medical monitoring and personal injury.

### Oil & Gas Litigation:

WTO represents companies engaged in the exploration, extraction, refining and distribution of oil and gas and other geological materials.

### Intellectual Property Litigation:

WTO tries copyright, trademark, trade secret and unfair competition matters.

### Investigations/Compliance:

WTO represents corporations, officers, directors and other individuals in federal and state investigations and prosecutions and compliance audits.

### Class Actions:

WTO has a large and experienced defense class action practice that encompasses commercial, insurance, product liability and employment matters. The firm is national trial counsel for all of Whirlpool's class action matters.

## PRACTICE AREAS

Appellate
Class Actions
Commercial Litigation
Employment (Management)
Environmental Litigation
Franchise & Distribution
Insurance
Intellectual Property Litigation
Investigations & Compliance
Legal Malpractice
Medical Malpractice
Oil & Gas Litigation
Personal Injury Defense
Product Liability
Professional Liability
Toxic Torts

## OFFICES

COLORADO
**DENVER:** 370 17th Street, Suite 4500, CO 80202
Tel: 303 244 1800  Fax: 303 244 1879
info@wtotrial.com

### Appellate:

WTO prosecutes appeals and drafts writs in state and federal appellate courts, including the US Supreme Court, in all substantive areas of the law. The firm has particular experience with appeals involving product liability, professional liability, commercial, franchise, employment and insurance matters.

### Clients:

A typical WTO client is a *Fortune* 500 or other large public, private or international company, professional service firm, medical organization, professional, or executive that is highly invested in its brand, products, services, people and customers. Representative clients include General Electric, Pfizer, Whirlpool, Chrysler Group, FedEx Ground, CNA Insurance, Advanced Bionics, Universal Health Services, Allstate, McKesson, Northstar Rx, BP America, Mercedes-Benz, Ford, Toyota, AT&T, Foster Wheeler, Allstate and USAA.

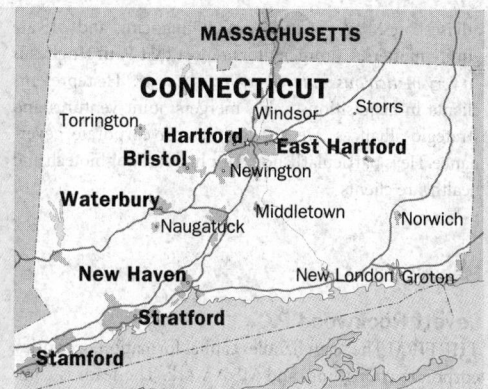

MASSACHUSETTS
CONNECTICUT
Torrington • Windsor • Storrs
**Hartford** • **East Hartford**
**Bristol** • Newington
**Waterbury**
Naugatuck • Middletown • Norwich
**New Haven** • New London • Groton
**Stratford**
**Stamford**

## How lawyers are ranked

Every year we carry out thousands of in-depth interviews with clients in order to assess the reputations and expertise of business lawyers worldwide. The qualities we look for (and which determine rankings) include technical legal ability, professional conduct, client service, commercial awareness/astuteness, diligence, commitment, and other qualities most valued by the client. For details of our research team, see p.5.

# CORPORATE/M&A

Commentary about individuals can be found under their firm's paragraph. If the firm has no paragraph (is not ranked) look at Other Notable Practitioners.

**Corporate/M&A**
**Leading Firms**

**Band 1**
Finn Dixon & Herling LLP

**Band 2**
Day Pitney LLP *
Dickstein Shapiro LLP *
Edwards Wildman Palmer *
Pullman & Comley, LLC *
Robinson & Cole LLP *
Wiggin and Dana LLP *

**Band 3**
Levett Rockwood P.C.
Martin & Chioffi LLP
McCarter & English, LLP *
Murtha Cullina LLP
Shipman & Goodwin LLP

\* *Indicates firm with profile.*
*Alphabetical order within each band. Band 1 is the highest.*

## Band 1

### Finn Dixon & Herling LLP

**THE FIRM** This market-leading team proves popular with both public and private companies. Its expertise includes mergers, spin-offs, joint ventures and general corporate management. The group is also commended for its expertise in buyouts and private equity matters.

**Sources say:** "*They have a very strong reputation for corporate and M&A work. They are doing highly sophisticated work in this area.*" "*The attorneys there are excellent, and it's always a pleasure to work with them.*"

**KEY INDIVIDUALS David Albin** is well known for his M&A and private equity work. His has experience in a range of industries, including e-commerce, government, healthcare, and food and beverages. His client list includes Palm Ventures and Warwick Group. Sources describe him as "*an outstanding lawyer. He is extremely thoughtful and*

detail-oriented.*"* One client states: "*He's always on top of things – he's very responsive with a very quick turnaround time.*" Name partner **Harold Finn** remains a leader in the field. His expertise includes work on behalf of public and private companies in corporate governance matters and M&A. **Michael Herling** is noted for his skill in matters involving private equity and venture capital. His impressive client list includes Capital Partners and Oak Investment Partners. Sources recommend **Charles Downey** for his expertise of M&A, joint ventures, corporate matters and high-level securities issues. He is noted for his skill in matters on behalf of investment funds, including RFE Investment Partners, Florida Capital Partners and Union Capital.

## Band 2

### Day Pitney LLP
See profile on p.1753

**THE FIRM** Day Pitney is a key player in the Connecticut corporate/M&A market. The team advises on the full range of matters, including acquisitions, joint ventures and corporate governance. It is also highly regarded for private equity work.

**Sources say:** "*They're terrific – they're very reliable and extremely responsive.*" "*They have a deep understanding of our business.*"

**KEY INDIVIDUALS David Swerdloff** (see p.748) heads the corporate and M&A practice group throughout Connecticut. He was instrumental in advising Aquarion Water Company on its $38 million bid for a public utility water company. Commentators report: "*He is a very solid attorney – he is very considered and experienced.*" **Scott Beach** (see p.741) is highlighted as an expert in private equity matters. Clients enthuse: "*He is excellent during negotiations. He remains focused on the key objectives,*" adding that "*he's extraordinarily thorough and calm under pressure.*"

### Dickstein Shapiro LLP
See profile on p.911

**THE FIRM** Dickstein Shapiro's Connecticut team is well known for handling the full range of midmarket transactions. The team has a deep knowledge of the energy, education, manufacturing, IT, media and biotechnology industries, among others. The firm's client base includes Harbour Group Industries, Gladstone Investment and the Saint-Gobain Corporation.

**Sources say:** "*The firm has very good knowledge and experience, and the client service is also very strong. They provide excellent support and follow-up on each matter.*" "*The team provides great advice and are very aware of commercial realities when they develop legal strategies.*"

**KEY INDIVIDUALS Thomas Freed** (see p.743) is praised by sources for "*delivering balanced legal advice supported by sound business acumen.*" He advises on mergers, acquisitions, venture capital, private equity, joint ventures and securities matters. **Chris Cerrito** (see p.742) is regarded as "*a very meticulous and thorough attorney. He thinks though our aims when giving advice.*" He proves particularly popular with clients in the technology and life sciences sectors. He recently led the firm in advising Bioformix on the complex conversion of an existing LLC into a Delaware corporation. Commentators describe **Martin Clarke** (see p.742) as "*a very good lawyer with a strong business sense.*" He is commended for his work on behalf of both public and private companies. **John Flaherty** (see p.743) is known in the market for being "*extremely thorough and very committed to his clients.*" He is best known for M&A and capital raising matters, and was a key player in the firm's work for Bioformix.

### Edwards Wildman Palmer
See profile on p.1520

**THE FIRM** Edwards Wildman Palmer is highly regarded for midmarket transactions, and possesses a solid bench of over 15 lawyers. Its expertise includes M&A, joint ventures, spin-offs and divestitures. Its impressive client list includes

HM Life Insurance, Bank of America and United Water Works.

**Sources say:** *"They're very good – responsive, knowledgeable and easy to work with." "The team is extremely impressive – they have the ability to tailor advice to suit our company."*

**KEY INDIVIDUALS James Lotstein** (see p.744) acted for Gerber Scientific on its sale to Vector Capital Corporation for over $280 million. Commentators report: *"He's got a lot of experience, a very calm demeanor, and is very knowledgeable."* Sources describe **Vincent Kiernan** (see p.744) as *"a great advisor – he can see things from the perspective of the client and explain complicated issues succinctly."* His clients include Payflex and Zadspace.

## Pullman & Comley, LLC
See profile on p.750

**THE FIRM** The team is recommended for its work on behalf of private companies in both M&A and private equity matters. Its expertise includes divestitures, acquisitions and corporate governance. Key clients include Stewart EFI.

**Sources say:** *"The availability of their attorneys has been impeccable." "They're very good, and they clearly know this area well."*

**KEY INDIVIDUALS** Clients praise **Andrew Glassman** (see p.743) as *"a highly experienced, knowledgeable, insightful and creative lawyer."* He is noted for his work in the metals industry. He recently advised Greenskies Renewable Energy on the sale of a number of assets for some $30 million. **Nancy Hancock** (see p.744) is chair of the firm's M&A team. She recently advised Connecticut Innovations on its $291 million Jackson Laboratory project. She is also experienced in venture capital matters. Chairman of the firm **Robert Morris** (see p.745) is well known for corporate, partnership and M&A matters. One client states: *"He really understands the viewpoint of our company, and works diligently to ensure our needs are met."*

## Robinson & Cole LLP
See profile on p.751

**THE FIRM** Robinson & Cole is a popular choice with buyers and sellers for M&A and private equity matters. The team is also skilled in handling related asset and stock issues. Its deep industry sector expertise spans aerospace, food and beverage, financial services, healthcare and retail, among others. Key clients include Nielsen, Webster Bank and Preferred Brands International.

**KEY INDIVIDUALS** A highlight for **Eric Dale** (see p.742) was representing Patriot National Bancorp in a $50 million recapitalization transaction. He chairs the firm's emerging companies, private equity and venture capital practice group. His areas of expertise include mergers, acquisitions and organizational matters. **Richard Krantz** (see p.744) acted for FuelCell Energy on its $34.5 million offering of common stock. His expertise includes mergers, acquisitions, securities, spin-offs and restructurings. **John Lynch** (see p.745) acted for Reflexite on its sale to ORAFOL Europe through a triangular merger. This complex matter involved securing US and international antitrust approval.

## Wiggin and Dana LLP
See profile on p.752

**THE FIRM** The firm advises on mergers, acquisitions, structurings, joint ventures, and the purchase and sale of public companies. It has considerable experience in a broad range of industries, including biopharmaceuticals, technology, financial services, manufacturing, media and utilities. Notable clients include AboveNet, Yale-New Haven Hospital and Genpact Limited.

**Sources say:** *"They're really a great asset. I rely on them for practical legal advice." "I've been thoroughly impressed by them."*

**KEY INDIVIDUALS** Sources describe seasoned practitioner **Frank Marco** as *"a good solid lawyer."* He chairs the firm's private equity and emerging companies practice group. He is experienced in capital formation, mergers, acquisitions, public offerings and corporate governance. **William Perrone** (see p.746) is highly regarded for his work on behalf of clients in the technology industry. He advises on M&A, venture capital financing and private equity matters. Commentators report that **Paul Hughes** is *"a very meticulous and well-respected lawyer."* He represents clients in acquisitions, sales, mergers, joint ventures and strategic alliances. He also advises on corporate governance. He is particularly noted for his work for biotech and healthcare clients.

## Band 3

## Levett Rockwood P.C.

**THE FIRM** The team handles capital formation, securities, corporate counseling, and M&A work. The team is commended for its strength in the oil, chemicals, education, advertising and financial services sectors. Its client portfolio includes Bolt Technology, Weld North Holdings and Main Street Resources (MSR).

**Sources say:** *"They always get work done on time, and they're very knowledgeable and experienced." "They cut right to the chase and don't overcomplicate matters."*

**KEY INDIVIDUALS Cheryl Johnson** advised MSR SBIC on the sale of its holding in Disc Graphics for some $70 million. Clients enthuse: *"She is very responsive and knowledgeable."* She is well known for corporate transactions and related tax matters. Sources report that **Barbara Young** is *"exceptionally bright and well informed about the law. Her advice is always well reasoned."* She acts on behalf of both public and private companies. Her expertise includes acquisitions, mergers, divestitures, securities law and the structuring of complex transactions. **Robert Barberi** is singled out for his deep experience in M&A and corporate governance. He recently represented a private individual as an incoming minority shareholder to LTI Boyd in its acquisition by Snow Phipps.

## Martin & Chioffi LLP

**THE FIRM** Martin & Chioffi represents clients in private equity, M&A and corporate matters. The team proves particularly popular with startups, growth companies and private equity firms.

**Sources say:** *"They're very responsive and practical – they know how to get deals done."*

**KEY INDIVIDUALS** Managing partner **Christopher Martin** is highly recommended by clients for his long-standing experience in the market. A recent highlight saw him advise Gallatin Equity Partners on the formation of a private equity fund valued at $150 million. **Gloria Skigen** acted for RiverVest Venture Fund II on the sale of Lutonix to C.R. Bard for some $325 million. One client states: *"She has great technical ability and does things thoroughly. She's also very pragmatic and evenhanded – she deals with things with a cool head."*

## McCarter & English, LLP
See profile on p.1759

**THE FIRM** This firm is best known for its work on behalf of midmarket companies. The team handles M&A, joint ventures, strategic alliances, corporate governance and structuring. Its impressive client list includes Legrand

North America, Nitta Casings, Ortronics and Opera Solutions.

**Sources say:** "*They are good negotiators with a deep knowledge of the area.*"

**KEY INDIVIDUALS Don Borod** (see p.742) is well known for his representation of manufacturing and technology companies. He advises on a range of matters, including joint ventures, establishing foreign entities, M&A and general corporate advice. Observers report: "*He is highly responsive, proactive and dedicated to achieving results.*"

## Murtha Cullina LLP

**THE FIRM** This firm is recommended for M&A, divestitures, structuring, and related securities and tax matters. Its clients include STR Holdings, Connecticut Water Service and Gunther International.

**Sources say:** "*Their attorneys are diligent, experienced and responsive. In transactions they can balance defending their client's position with the need to get the deal done.*"

**KEY INDIVIDUALS** Leading practitioner **Willard Pinney** advised Vector Capital on its $283 million acquisition of Gerber Scientific. He handles corporate and securities matters, as well as cochairing the firm's private equity group. The "*very well thought-of*" **Edward Whittemore** is praised for his experience in corporate governance and regulation, M&A and disposals. He was instrumental in Connecticut Water Services' acquisition of Aqua Maine for over $53 million.

## Shipman & Goodwin LLP

**THE FIRM** The team is praised for its work on behalf of both midmarket companies and larger clients. It is also praised for its work on behalf of emerging companies and quasi-public agencies. The team's industry sector knowledge includes telecom, transport, retail, financial services, agriculture and distribution, among others. The firm's impressive client list includes DISH Network, EchoStar and The Hartford Financial Services Group.

**Sources say:** "*The firm provides excellent client service. They have strong communication and technical skills.*"

**KEY INDIVIDUALS John Lawrence** is commended for his work in corporate, M&A, disposals and private equity transactions. Commentators report: "*I think very highly of him. He's very intelligent and technically proficient.*"

## Other Notable Practitioners

**Mark Farber** of Farber LLC is described as "*an excellent strategic thinker.*" His expertise includes advising public and private companies on general corporate matters and transactional cases. Managing partner of Bingham McCutcheon LLP's Hartford office **Daniel Papermaster** (see p.746) is well known for his transactional work, including M&A and related financing matters. **Henry Beck** of Halloran & Sage LLP is praised for his experience in M&A, equity finance and corporate governance matters. Clients report: "*He is extremely knowledgeable. He always gives us good and well-informed advice.*"

# ENVIRONMENT

Commentary about individuals can be found under their firm's paragraph. If the firm has no paragraph (is not ranked) look at Other Notable Practitioners.

| Environment | |
| --- | --- |
| **Leading Firms** | |
| **Band 1** | |
| Day Pitney LLP * | |
| Murtha Cullina LLP | |
| Robinson & Cole LLP * | |
| **Band 2** | |
| Brown Rudnick LLP * | |
| McCarter & English, LLP * | |
| Pullman & Comley, LLC * | |
| Shipman & Goodwin LLP | |

## Band 1

### Day Pitney LLP

**See profile on p.1753**

**THE FIRM** This large practice group is well known throughout the state for its work in a variety of energy and environmental matters. It is noted for brownfield redevelopment and energy planning as well as in-depth regulatory, transactional and administrative counsel. It is also highlighted for its strong contentious environmental enforcement practice. The team's clients include Dominion Resources, The United Illuminating Company and Yale University.

**KEY INDIVIDUALS** Practice head **Elizabeth Barton** (see p.741) is praised as "*the queen of environmental law in Connecticut,*" and "*a leader in the field.*" She acts on a range of environmental services, including regulatory and administrative advice and litigation. She represented long-term client Dominion Resources in a number of Connecticut Environmental Protection Act lawsuits. **Harold Blinderman** (see p.742) is another key player in

the team. A notable mandate saw him advise the Connecticut Resources Recovery Authority on environmental permitting issues. Environmental litigator **Dean Cordiano** (see p.742) recently acted for Richard Scalise in a $20 million cost recovery action. Observers note: "*He is very well respected by the judges.*"

### Murtha Cullina LLP

**THE FIRM** This market-leading practice has considerable experience in both the energy and environment markets, including traditional and renewable fuels. The team is experienced in environmental permitting, compliance and waste permitting, air, water, and site remediation matters. Key clients include Honeywell, Danaher and ReEnergy Holdings.

**Sources say:** "*The team is very effective in translating legal terminology into lay terms.*" "*A solid environmental department that I have a lot of respect for.*"

**KEY INDIVIDUALS** Commentators praise **Mark Sussman**, noting: "*He is far and away the most well thought-of attorney in Connecticut regarding clean air issues. He conducts himself with dignity and aplomb.*" He is particularly skilled in air and water pollution, waste management and chemical regulation. **Alfred Smith** chairs the firm's regulatory department. Sources report: "*He is a very good lawyer.*" His expertise includes brownfield redevelopment, air quality and environmental issues stemming from corporate, bankruptcy and real estate matters. **Gregory Sharp** is highlighted for his strength in both environmental and regulatory matters. Clients report: "*He's very, very smart and very practical.*" **David Platt** is recommended as "*a highly skilled advocate and a cordial adversary.*" His

| Senior Statesmen | |
| --- | --- |
| **Senior Statesmen: distinguished older partners** | |
| Sharp Gregory A | Murtha Cullina LLP |

| Leading Individuals | |
| --- | --- |
| **Band 1** | |
| Barton Elizabeth C | Day Pitney LLP * |
| Elkow Pamela K | Robinson & Cole LLP * |
| Sussman Mark | Murtha Cullina LLP |
| Trilling Barry J | Wiggin and Dana LLP (ONP)[†] |
| Warren Jane | McCarter & English, LLP * |
| Whitney Diane W | Pullman & Comley, LLC * |
| **Band 2** | |
| Bashaw John R | Brenner, Saltzman & Wallman LLP (ONP)[†] |
| DeRosa Franca L | Brown Rudnick LLP |
| Hoffman Lee D | Pullman & Comley, LLC * |
| Phillips Earl | Robinson & Cole LLP * |
| Ray James | Robinson & Cole LLP * |
| Smith Alfred | Murtha Cullina LLP |
| Wertam John | Shipman & Goodwin LLP |
| **Band 3** | |
| Blinderman Harold M | Day Pitney LLP * |
| Catino Ann M | Halloran & Sage LLP (ONP)[†] |
| Cordiano Dean M | Day Pitney LLP * |
| McCormack Christopher | Pullman & Comley, LLC * |
| Miller Barbara S | Brody, Wilkinson & Ober P C (ONP)[†] |
| O'Connor Gary B | Pullman & Comley, LLC * |
| Platt David | Murtha Cullina LLP |
| Williams Joseph | Shipman & Goodwin LLP |

\* Indicates firm / individual with profile.

[†]ONP = Other Notable Practitioner.

expertise includes environmental remediation and brownfield redevelopment projects.

## Robinson & Cole LLP
See profile on p.751

**THE FIRM** This market-leading firm excels in its compliance work, counsel on land use issues and technical water resources work. The team is particularly well known for its knowledge of the manufacturing, energy and telecom industries. Its impressive client portfolio includes United Technologies, Hamilton Sundstrand and Otis Elevator.
**KEY INDIVIDUALS Pamela Elkow** (see p.743) is highlighted as a "*very good advocate.*" She is well known for her strength in offering comprehensive remediation, negotiation and compliance counsel at a high level. Observers note: "*She is greatly admired in this area.*" **Earl Phillips** (see p.746) is described as "*a really solid, very experienced attorney who deals well with both counterparties and regulatory agencies.*" He recently represented The Durham Manufacturing Company on enforcement actions regarding the effects of on-site solvents. Commentators report that **James Ray** (see p.746) is a highly capable lawyer. He advised New England Container Company on a Superfund cost recovery matter of some $100 million.

## Band 2

## Brown Rudnick LLP
See profile on p.437

**THE FIRM** Brown Rudnick represents a wide range of clients, including property buyers, sellers and tenants in compliance, enforcement and litigation matters. The team is also noted for its skill in advising on environmental strategy. Clients include ACF Industries, PSC Metals and Longroad Asset Management.
**KEY INDIVIDUALS Franca DeRosa** is commended for offering "*a good analysis of the issues – where the law is now*

*and where it will change.*" One client enthused: "*She also has a deep understanding of what buyers and sellers look for.*" A recent highlight for her was advising PSEG on air permitting issues.

## McCarter & English, LLP
See profile on p.1759

**THE FIRM** This firm is noted for its work on environmental issues in real estate transactions. The team has expertise in both remediation and wetlands issues and works on behalf of both public and private organizations. Key clients include Greenfield Partners, Summit Development and the Town of Greenwich.
**KEY INDIVIDUALS Jane Warren** (see p.748) is an experienced litigator who worked on behalf of Summit Development on the $57.5 million sale of a former industrial site. Sources report that "*she's very good and easy to work with.*" One source stated: "*Jane is able to bob and weave through any environmental issues.*"

## Pullman & Comley, LLC
See profile on p.750

**THE FIRM** This environmental team is praised for its strength in energy-related matters, real estate-related environmental issues, compliance and environmental permitting. The firm's impressive client list includes Kleen Energy Systems, UCONN Medical Center and Connecticut Airport Authority.
**KEY INDIVIDUALS Diane Whitney** (see p.748) is known for her work in land use and also in environmental legislative matters. Commentators regard her as "*a very capable and intelligent attorney.*" Hartford-based **Lee Hoffman** (see p.744) is highly regarded for energy-related matters. He recently acted for BNE Energy on the permitting and siting of two commercial-scale wind projects valued at $25 million. **Gary O'Connor** (see p.745) is particularly skilled in brownfield financing and redevelopment. He is well known for his environmental, real estate and regulatory

work on behalf of the Connecticut Airport Authority. Sources say: "*He is always on top of things – we know all our environmental issues are being addressed.*" **Christopher McCormack** (see p.745) advised Iberdrola on the sale of a number of its subsidiaries and subsequent restructuring.

## Shipman & Goodwin LLP

**THE FIRM** This large real estate, land use and environmental group is commended for offering a truly comprehensive service to clients in transactional, permitting and compliance matters. Its clients include Tilcon Connecticut, Guardian Life Insurance Company of America and Getty Realty, among others.
**KEY INDIVIDUALS John Wertam** possesses particular skill in waste and water matters. Clients report: "*He is an excellent attorney – he has a great working knowledge of environmental regulations and how they apply to our business.*" **Joseph Williams** is noted for his work in environmental permitting and litigation. He is also actively involved in climate change and shoreline preservation issues.

## Other Notable Practitioners

Seasoned practitioner **John Bashaw** of Brenner, Saltzman & Wallman LLP is recommended for his skill in defending private individuals in state agency claims. He is also well known for remediation matters. Sources note that **Ann Catino** of Halloran & Sage LLP is "*one of the most knowledgeable environmental lawyers I've ever come across.*" She is highly regarded for federal government and EPA matters. **Barbara Miller** of Brody, Wilkinson & Ober P C advises clients on a wide range of environmental matters, including both transactional and regulatory issues. **Barry Trilling** (see p.748) of Wiggin and Dana LLP is particularly well known for brownfield, contamination and clean air matters. Sources say: "*He's a very knowledgeable and very active lawyer.*"

# HEALTHCARE

Commentary about individuals can be found under their firm's paragraph. If the firm has no paragraph (is not ranked) look at Other Notable Practitioners.

| Healthcare |
| --- |
| **Leading Firms** |

**Band 1**

Pullman & Comley, LLC *
Shipman & Goodwin LLP
Wiggin and Dana LLP *

**Band 2**

Levett Rockwood P.C.
Murtha Cullina LLP
Robinson & Cole LLP *

| **Leading Individuals** |
| --- |

**Band 1**

| Agsten Melinda | Wiggin and Dana LLP |
| --- | --- |
| Baron Collin | Pullman & Comley, LLC * |
| Boyle Lisa | Robinson & Cole LLP * |
| Feldman Joan | Shipman & Goodwin LLP |
| Weaver Maureen | Wiggin and Dana LLP * |

**Band 2**

| DeBarge Michelle Wilcox | Wiggin and Dana LLP * |
| --- | --- |
| Hudner Kennedy | Murtha Cullina LLP |
| Knag Paul | Murtha Cullina LLP |
| Lawrence Jr John H | Shipman & Goodwin LLP |
| Levine David | Cohen and Wolf, PC (ONP)† * |
| Mack David | Shipman & Goodwin LLP |
| Pollack Elliott B | Pullman & Comley, LLC * |
| Tucci Theodore | Robinson & Cole LLP * |
| Volpe Michele | Bershtein Volpe & McKeon, P.C. (ONP)† |
| Weitzman Patricia D | Levett Rockwood P.C. |

*\* Indicates firm / individual with profile.*

*†ONP = Other Notable Practitioner.*

## Band 1

### Pullman & Comley, LLC
See profile on p.750

**THE FIRM** This market-leading team offers a broad range of services including joint ventures, governance, healthcare compliance, investigations and affiliations. The firm's impressive client list includes Yale-New Haven Health Services, Optimus Health Care, Bridgeport Hospital and The Orthopaedic Group.

**Sources say:** "*They really understand the business of healthcare and the realities we face – they offer very practical advice.*"

**KEY INDIVIDUALS** A recent highlight for **Collin Baron** (see p.741) saw him advise Norwalk Health Services on its affiliation with Western Connecticut Health Network. One source enthused: "*He is very strategic and thoughtful – he is a 'bigger picture' person. He has a flair for understanding political interactions and has been very helpful in guiding us through the process.*" **Elliott Pollack** (see p.746) is another key member of the practice group. He recently led the team in representing a physician client in a matter involving revocation of a license to practice.

### Shipman & Goodwin LLP

**THE FIRM** The healthcare arm of this well-respected Hartford firm offers regulatory advice, services relating to patient care, and governance, as well as healthcare litigation and arbitration expertise. The team is also noted for its strength in biotech and bioscience matters.

**Sources say:** "*They are very responsive, which is really crucial for us in our environment – they provide top-notch counsel.*" "*They understand the business side as well as the legal side.*"

**KEY INDIVIDUALS Joan Feldman** is renowned for her understanding of the healthcare industry. She is best known for her work on regulation and privacy issues. Sources note that "*she has worked in a healthcare setting and therefore understands the dynamic in this country. She's creative and willing to think beyond the letter of the law.*" **David Mack** offers healthcare clients expertise in corporate governance and regulatory matters. Commentators say: "*He offers very responsive, sage counsel and is very objective.*" His client base includes bioscience companies, healthcare providers and hospitals. **John Lawrence** is praised as "*very knowledgeable and easy to work with.*" He is particularly highly regarded for corporate and healthcare work, with a deep understanding of practice acquisition.

### Wiggin and Dana LLP
See profile on p.752

**THE FIRM** Wiggin and Dana is highlighted for its integration and M&A work in the healthcare sphere. The team advised Yale-New Haven Hospital on the integration of the Hospital of Saint Raphael, a matter of over $160 million. Other key clients include LeadingAge Connecticut, The William W. Backus Hospital and The Jackson Laboratory.

**Sources say:** "*They have been excellent, really. They are experts in healthcare regulation.*" "*They've just been tremendous.*"

**KEY INDIVIDUALS** Sources say **Melinda Agsten** represented The William W. Backus Hospital in a number of matters including the development of a medical foundation and the reorganization and integration of existing physician employment models. One source enthused: "*She is fantastic – she's a top-notch attorney; no doubt about it.*" **Maureen Weaver** (see p.748) is chair of the firm's healthcare practice. She is commended for being "*an extremely bright, extremely knowledgeable attorney with an excellent reputation with the regulators, who enjoy working with her,*" adding: "*She's responsive, levelheaded, calm, explains things thoroughly and is just fabulous.*" **Michelle Wilcox DeBarge** (see p.742) has advised Western Connecticut Healthcare in developing a regional electronic health information exchange. Sources praise her as "*extremely knowledgeable*" and "*a real problem solver.*"

## Band 2

### Levett Rockwood P.C.

**THE FIRM** This highly acclaimed healthcare team has experience in matters relating to physician alignment, joint ventures and fraud. It also has considerable expertise in M&A and medical malpractice issues. The team's clients include St. Vincent's Medical Center, the Hospital of Saint Raphael and Community Mental Health Affiliates.

**Sources say:** "*The team demonstrates great attention to detail, knowledge of the law and the ability to find creative solutions.*"

**KEY INDIVIDUALS Patricia Weitzman** continues to advise longstanding client St. Vincent's Medical Center on general governance issues. She is commended for being "*extremely accessible – she will always make herself available to take a call, especially if urgent. She is extremely sincere and offers very clear opinions to you as the client.*"

### Murtha Cullina LLP

**THE FIRM** Murtha Cullina offers a full range of services to clients including healthcare acquisitions, reorganizations and restructuring matters. The team is popular with both public and private institutions.

**KEY INDIVIDUALS** Seasoned practitioner **Kennedy Hudner** acts on behalf of both hospitals and physician clients. He possesses particular expertise in healthcare-related contracts. **Paul Knag** is recommended for his skill in regulatory and transactional healthcare cases. Sources say: "*He's very much on the map for healthcare.*"

### Robinson & Cole LLP
See profile on p.751

**THE FIRM** The team at Robinson & Cole remains a popular choice for clients in contract disputes and physician group disputes. Its contentious expertise also includes defending against class actions and government investigations. The team also advises on medical staff law and health policy law.

**Sources say:** "*They are strong in multiple areas, and are always very responsive to our needs.*"

**KEY INDIVIDUALS** The highly acclaimed **Lisa Boyle** (see p.742) is praised by sources for her "*experience, intelligence, clarity and substance – she knows exactly what she's doing.*" Her expertise includes physician recruitment and compensation, management arrangements, clinical integration and healthcare M&A. **Theodore Tucci** (see p.748) brings his background in litigation to bear on healthcare matters, where his expertise includes defending against class actions and prosecuting healthcare fraud claims. He proves popular with pharmaceutical companies, managed care organizations and insurers.

## Other Notable Practitioners

**David Levine** (see p.744) of Cohen and Wolf, PC is well regarded for his transactional and physician-focused prac-tice. Sources recognize him as "*a consummate attorney. Very thorough and precise. His style is professional but relaxed.*" **Michele Volpe** of Bershtein Volpe & McKeon, P.C. remains a prominent player in physician-related work.

# LABOR & EMPLOYMENT

Commentary about individuals can be found under their firm's paragraph. If the firm has no paragraph (is not ranked) look at Other Notable Practitioners.

### Labor & Employment
### Leading Firms

**Band 1**
Day Pitney LLP *
Jackson Lewis LLP *
Shipman & Goodwin LLP
Wiggin and Dana LLP *

**Band 2**
Littler Mendelson, PC *

**Band 3**
Carmody & Torrance LLP
Epstein Becker & Green PC *
McCarter & English, LLP *
Murtha Cullina LLP
Pullman & Comley, LLC *

## Band 1

### Day Pitney LLP
See profile on p.1753
**THE FIRM** Day Pitney offers a full service in labor and employment law, including employee claims involving harassment, whistle-blower matters, noncompetition clauses, and contractual matters. Its clients include Verizon Communications, United Technologies and Aladdin Capital Holdings.
**Sources say:** "*They're very good at getting to know our company and how we operate – it's a very collaborative relationship.*"
**KEY INDIVIDUALS Felix Springer** (see p.747) has vast experience with discrimination cases. He is particularly commended for his calm demeanor at trial. Sources describe him as "*an incredible attorney*" and "*a tremendous trial lawyer – the preparation this man does is just brutal. Truly remarkable.*" **Albert Zakarian** (see p.749) recently defended Sikorsky Aircraft in a reverse discrimination case. Observers describe him as "*a fabulous lawyer and a great manager, everything about him is A+.*" One commentator added: "*He is the consummate professional; a wonderful gentleman and an amazing man.*" A highlight for **Daniel Schwartz** (see p.747) was representing IBG in seeking pro-hibitive action in a noncompetition claim. Sources say: "*He's an excellent practitioner and very hard-working.*"

### Jackson Lewis LLP
See profile on p.1982
**THE FIRM** This market-leading team handles all areas of labor law, including audits relating to wage and hour prac-tices, RICO claims, employment litigation and benefits advice. The team's impressive client base includes UnitedHealth Group, Pfizer and Citizens Financial Group.
**Sources say:** "*They do excellent work and they get excellent results. They're reasonably priced, easy to work with, and their client service is top-notch.*"
**KEY INDIVIDUALS Victoria Chavey** (see p.742) main-tains an excellent reputation in the labor and employment law market. Sources are "*impressed with her approach to discovery; she gives very sound advice and always responds in a timely fashion.*" **Beverly Garofalo** (see p.743) recently defended Energizer Holdings in a pregnancy discrimina-tion case. Commentators report: "*She is just really top-notch at client service and making sure that the client is sat-isfied.*" **Michael Soltis** (see p.747) remains a key player in the Jackson Lewis team. His broad experience includes dis-crimination, family and medical leave, whistle-blower, contract, and public policy claims. He recently acted for Stamford hospital on an asserted age and gender discrimi-nation case. **William Anthony** acted as lead partner on three collective actions relating to the Fair Labor Standards Act (FLSA) on behalf of clients in the pharmaceutical sec-tor. Sources describe him as "*a very practical lawyer, with the ability to connect with businesspeople.*" **Peggy Strange** (see p.748) is well known for her work in employment lit-igation, in both state and federal claims. She has particular expertise in discrimination cases.

### Shipman & Goodwin LLP
**THE FIRM** This labor and employment team works on behalf of private sector employers and in employment matters relating to public entities. The State of Connecticut, the City of Waterbury and Trinity College are just some of the group's clientele.
**Sources say:** "*The team are highly competent, and very knowledgeable of both state and federal law pertaining to labor management issues. They are also very, very skilled at representing us in administrative proceedings.*"
**KEY INDIVIDUALS Brian Clemow** is commended for his depth of knowledge in both federal and state regulations and labor relations matters. One source states: "*He knows this area of law better than anybody else I know, and he is always up to date with changes in the law. He is also someone who is easy to work with – he has a very pleasant personali-ty but is very firm with the people he has to deal with on the other side of the table.*" He represented the City of Waterbury in a matter involving retirees who contested offset pension payments. **Robin Frederick** brings her con-siderable experience to bear on origin and age discrimina-tion cases. Sources comment that she is "*very intelligent, responsive, and offers brilliant advice – my business would not be as successful as it is without her.*" Commentators note that **Saranne Murray** has "*a very good reputation in labor law.*" She is particularly highly regarded for coalition bar-gaining matters.

### Senior Statesmen

**Senior Statesmen: distinguished older partners**

| | |
|---|---|
| Durant E Terry | Durant, Nichols, Houston, Hodgson (ONP)[†] |

### Leading Individuals

**Band 1**

| | |
|---|---|
| Chavey Victoria Woodin | Jackson Lewis LLP * |
| Clemow Brian | Shipman & Goodwin LLP |
| Garofalo Beverly W | Jackson Lewis LLP * |
| Lefeber Peter J | Wiggin and Dana LLP * |
| O'Brien George | Littler Mendelson, PC * |
| Springer Felix J | Day Pitney LLP * |
| Stohler Charles | Carmody & Torrance LLP |
| Zakarian Albert | Day Pitney LLP * |
| Zandy John C | Wiggin and Dana LLP * |

**Band 2**

| | |
|---|---|
| Alexander Lori | Littler Mendelson, PC |
| Frederick Robin G | Shipman & Goodwin LLP |
| Moore Pamela | McCarter & English, LLP * |
| Orleans Jonathan | Pullman & Comley, LLC * |
| Poppick David | Epstein Becker & Green PC |
| Schwartz Daniel L | Day Pitney LLP * |
| Soltis Michael | Jackson Lewis LLP * |
| Stein Peter | Epstein Becker & Green PC * |
| Voigt Richard | McCarter & English, LLP * |
| Waters Barry J | Murtha Cullina LLP |

**Band 3**

| | |
|---|---|
| Anthony William | Jackson Lewis LLP |
| Hawks-Ladds Joshua A | Pullman & Comley, LLC * |
| Katz Stuart M | Cohen and Wolf, PC (ONP)[†] |
| LaVelle Michael N | Pullman & Comley, LLC * |
| Murray Hugh | Murtha Cullina LLP |
| Murray Saranne | Shipman & Goodwin LLP |
| Peikes Lawrence | Wiggin and Dana LLP * |
| Reilly Patricia | Littler Mendelson, PC * |
| Schwartz Daniel | Pullman & Comley, LLC * |
| Strange Margaret 'Peggy' | Jackson Lewis LLP * |
| Vitarelli Richard F | McCarter & English, LLP * |
| Weller Giovanna | Carmody & Torrance LLP |
| Zaino Domenico | Carmody & Torrance LLP |

* Indicates firm / individual with profile.

†ONP = Other Notable Practitioner.

## Wiggin and Dana LLP
See profile on p.752

**THE FIRM** Wiggin and Dana's longstanding employment practice is noted for its high-profile work in discrimination cases, including disability, retaliation and sexual harassment cases. The firm also comprises several specialist benefits lawyers. Its impressive client portfolio includes Fidelco Guide Dog Foundation, Jeffrey Bertolini and NuVasive.

**Sources say:** *"The whole labor group has been tremendous – they can explain things in a way that doesn't go over anybody's head."*

**KEY INDIVIDUALS Peter Lefeber** (see p.744) recently acted on the defense of employers in a matter relating to the termination of a long-term employment contract. A recent highlight for **John Zandy** (see p.749) was acting on a large union campaign matter. He is also recommended for his expertise in labor contracts work. Commentators report: *"He has a very loyal client following."* **Lawrence Peikes** (see p.746) is another key member of the team. He has comprehensive experience in federal court litigation relating to discrimination.

## Band 2

### Littler Mendelson, PC
See profile on p.688

**THE FIRM** The Connecticut branch of Littler Mendelson handles a full range of employment matters, including noncompetition issues, labor issues and employment management. The team's knowledge spans multiple industries, including education, insurance, manufacturing, retail, transport and telecom. Its impressive client list includes Campbell Soup and Pepperidge Farm.

**Sources say:** *"The firm is cost-effective and provides very good legal advice." "They are always timely and efficient."*

**KEY INDIVIDUALS George O'Brien** (see p.745) is a key player in the team. He is recommended for unfair labor practice matters, wrongful dismissal, and breach of contract claims. **Lori Alexander** offers clients a range of employment services. One source stated: *"She's outstanding, I would recommend her for any employment work."* **Patricia Reilly** (see p.747) handles a wide range of employment law issues, including discrimination, trade secrets and unfair trade practices. Observers report: *"She's extremely competent, and offers wise counsel and very well thought-out advice based on solid experience."*

## Band 3

### Carmody & Torrance LLP

**THE FIRM** This noted labor and employment team works on behalf of public and private employers on a range of issues, including employee benefits and labor relations.
**KEY INDIVIDUALS Charles Stohler**'s broad expertise includes whistle-blower claims, discrimination, executive

compensation and noncompete matters. **Giovanna Weller** is recommended for contentious matters. Sources say: *"She does very well – she's an experienced employment litigator."* She is noted for her work in both federal and state courts. **Domenico Zaino** advises clients on a wide range of labor and employment issues, including workplace investigations, antidiscrimination, sexual harassment and trade secret agreements, among others. Interviewees say: *"He has certainly established a very good reputation in this area."*

### Epstein Becker & Green PC
See profile on p.1972

**THE FIRM** This Stamford-based labor and employment practice represents a range of clients, from small private companies to Fortune 500 firms. The team is particularly experienced in working with the healthcare and financial services industries. Clients include the Hispanic Information and Telecommunications Network, Chilton Investment Company and Tata Global Beverages.
**Sources say:** *"They're experts in their fields, easy to work with, and unfailingly pragmatic."*
**KEY INDIVIDUALS David Poppick** brings his impressive litigation skills to bear across the labor law arena. He is particularly skilled in breach of contract claims. Observers note: *"He's terrific, a very strong litigator."* **Peter Stein** (see p.748) remains a popular choice for human resources matters. Sources recommend him for his considerable experience gained in both private practice and in-house.

### McCarter & English, LLP
See profile on p.1759

**THE FIRM** McCarter & English is noted for employment litigation, advising on noncompetition claims, ERISA and immigration issues.
**Sources say:** *"They are tenacious, research matters thoroughly and are able to meet very tight deadlines."*
**KEY INDIVIDUALS Pamela Moore**'s (see p.745) wide-ranging expertise includes discrimination, sexual harassment and affirmative action. She is commended for her ability to *"provide practical advice from a real depth of experience – there is not a topic on which I have questioned her which she's been unable to answer."* This year, the *"absolutely superb"* **Richard Voigt** (see p.748) represented O&G Industries in an OSHA citation case involving fatalities resulting from an explosion. **Richard Vitarelli** (see p.748) is involved in collective bargaining on contracts for major clients, and has experience dealing with employment issues in the energy sector.

### Murtha Cullina LLP

**THE FIRM** This well-respected labor and employment team has experience in contract administration matters, discrimination cases, wage and hour claims and employee benefits. The team acts for both private and public sector clients, including United Parcel Service, 99 Restaurants and the South Central Connecticut Regional Water Authority.

**Sources say:** *"Their advice is always current – they stay abreast of all legislative changes, recent court decisions, and how they may impact us."*
**KEY INDIVIDUALS Barry Waters** is well known for his expertise in the enforcement of restrictive covenants. A recent highlight was advising Wall Street Systems on a complex noncompetition agreement case. Sources say: *"He's a true expert – he's very experienced, and his advice is sound and very practical."* **Hugh Murray** remains a key member of the employment team. Sources say they *"always find him to be impressive."* His experience includes union-related matters, collective bargaining, unfair labour practice, wrongful discharge, discrimination and noncompete clauses.

### Pullman & Comley, LLC
See profile on p.750

**THE FIRM** Pullman & Comley offers employment litigation services as well as counsel on the range of labor law, including advising business clients on liability after termination of contracts. The team's impressive client portfolio includes Cabrera Services, Weeden & Co and the Town of East Windsor.
**Sources say:** *"They are organized, detail-oriented, highly communicative and responsive. They meet our needs and are available to us at all times."*
**KEY INDIVIDUALS Jonathan Orleans** (see p.746) has significant civil rights litigation experience. One source states that *"he's deeply knowledgeable about Connecticut employment law,"* while another adds that *"he was excellent."* **Michael LaVelle** (see p.744) is very highly regarded in this area. He is highlighted for his considerable experience in employment discrimination and wrongful discharge cases. **Joshua Hawk-Ladds** (see p.744) is well known for negotiating labor agreements and other contracts, as well as in labor litigation. Commentators state: *"He has extremely strong verbal and written skills. His expertise and advice often prevent legal issues arising – when they do, he is professional and organized in his approach."* **Daniel Schwartz** (see p.747) is highly regarded for his work on termination claims. He is active at both the federal and state level.

### Other Notable Practitioners

**Stuart Katz** (see p.744) of Cohen and Wolf, PC is recommended for discrimination, harassment and noncompetition matters. **Terry Durant** of Durant, Nichols, Houston, Hodgson & Cortese-Costa, P.C. upholds his well-respected and longstanding labor and employment practice, which is run from the firm's Bridgeport office.

## LITIGATION GENERAL COMMERCIAL

Commentary about individuals can be found under their firm's paragraph. If the firm has no paragraph (is not ranked) look at Other Notable Practitioners.

### Litigation: General Commercial
### Leading Firms

**Band 1**

Day Pitney LLP *

Wiggin and Dana LLP *

**Band 2**

Axinn, Veltrop & Harkrider LLP *

Carmody & Torrance LLP

McCarter & English, LLP *

Robinson & Cole LLP *

Shipman & Goodwin LLP

**Band 3**

Cohen and Wolf, PC

Murtha Cullina LLP

Pullman & Comley, LLC *

## Band 1

### Day Pitney LLP
See profile on p.1753

THE FIRM This outstanding litigation practice has a deep bench of attorneys, advising on a range of complex litigation including mass tort cases, reinsurance disputes, employment issues and breach of contract claims. The firm's impressive client list includes priceline.com, Wells Fargo and Alliance Energy. Notable mandates include representing Saint Francis Hospital in a highly publicized mass tort case, involving over 150 lawsuits alleging past abuse of minors by a now deceased employee.

**Sources say:** "*The attorneys we dealt with there were outstanding. Tremendous counsel with a great track record – they are a cut above the rest.*"

**KEY INDIVIDUALS James Sicilian** (see p.747) has a broad commercial litigation practice, including IP and antitrust matters. One source commented: "*I have a very high regard for Jim. He's an excellent lawyer and a really good guy.*" **Allan Taylor** (see p.748) is well known in the market for his expertise in insurer-side insurance coverage matters. Sources comment that he is "*a very smart guy and a good litigator.*" **Daniel FitzMaurice** (see p.743) represented Travelers Casualty and Surety Company in several claims against its reinsurers, totaling more than $30 million. FitzMaurice is sought for his expertise in contentious insurance, reinsurance and franchising matters. **John Nolan** (see p.745) offers clients more than 40 years of litigation and ADR expertise, having tried over 100 commercial cases in various state and federal courts throughout the USA. Nolan is also sought for his insolvency expertise, having set up the firm's insolvency practice.

### Wiggin and Dana LLP
See profile on p.752

THE FIRM This market-leading 28-partner litigation team is well known for handling complex, high-stakes cases. The practice spans the full spectrum from commercial disputes, to IP litigation, antitrust and white-collar defense. The team acts for clients across a broad range of industries and wins praise for its class actions and appellate work. Recent highlights include defending a former president of Mexico, Ernesto Zedillo Ponce de Leon, against a damages action alleging responsibility for a 1997 massacre of Zapatista insurgents.

**KEY INDIVIDUALS Jack Dunham** (see p.307) recently represented key client Direct Buy in five putative class actions, which were consolidated in the Northern District of Indiana. His areas of expertise range from IP and antitrust claims to employment discrimination matters. The multitalented **Shaun Sullivan** (see p.748) brings more than 30 years' litigation experience to the table, representing clients in all types of dispute ranging from securities litigation to IP disputes. He recently represented GE in claims arising out of a helicopter accident. Litigation specialist, **Jonathan Freiman** (see p.743) chairs the firm's Appellate and Complex Legal Issues Practice Group. Freiman was one of the key lawyers acting on behalf of the former Mexican president, Ernesto Zedillo Ponce de Leon on the damages litigation matter. **James Glasser** is chair of the firm's litigation department, splitting his time between the New Haven and New York offices. He also leads a specialist team of export compliance lawyers advising several global defense manufacturers.

## Band 2

### Axinn, Veltrop & Harkrider LLP
See profile on p.1956

THE FIRM Axinn, Veltrop & Harkrider has a reputation for fielding high-quality lawyers and offers a full range of litigation services, including general commercial, antitrust and IP issues. Major clients include 3M, Unilever and New York Community Bank.

**Sources say:** "*They have a good pool of associates. The quality of the firm's work is excellent.*" "*The complexity of the cases they handle and the sophistication of the practice distinguishes them from competitors.*"

**KEY INDIVIDUALS Thomas Rohback** (see p.747) brings his experience to bear on a range of class action and breach of contract cases. Sources note: "*Tom has old school trial skills and never fails to carefully prepare even the smallest details. He's a consummate gentleman, careful, polite, and makes a great impression on juries.*" **Francis Morrison** (see p.745) is well known for IP litigation, particularly in relation to pharmaceutical patents. Sources say: "*He's terrific and has been around for a long time. A great trial attorney and a dynamite lawyer.*"

### Senior Statesmen

**Senior Statesmen: distinguished older partners**

| | | |
|---|---|---|
| Wade James A | Robinson & Cole LLP * | |

### Leading Individuals

**Band 1**

| | | |
|---|---|---|
| Belt David L | Hurwitz, Sagarin, Slossberg & Knuff (ONP)[†] * | |
| Brady Francis | Murtha Cullina LLP | |
| Dunham Edward Wood | Wiggin and Dana LLP * | |
| Fitzgerald Anthony | Carmody & Torrance LLP | |
| Robertson Jr James K | Carmody & Torrance LLP | |
| Sanson Paul | Shipman & Goodwin LLP | |
| Sicilian James | Day Pitney LLP * | |
| Silvestri Jr Frank J | Levett Rockwood P.C. (ONP)[†] | |
| Sullivan Shaun S | Wiggin and Dana LLP * | |

**Band 2**

| | | |
|---|---|---|
| Ball David A | Cohen and Wolf, PC * | |
| Edelstein Stewart | Cohen and Wolf, PC * | |
| Frank Monte | Cohen and Wolf, PC * | |
| Freiman Jonathan | Wiggin and Dana LLP * | |
| Gold Frederick | Shipman & Goodwin LLP | |
| Morrison III Francis H | Axinn, Veltrop & Harkrider LLP * | |
| Raabe Craig | Robinson & Cole LLP * | |
| Rohback Thomas G | Axinn, Veltrop & Harkrider LLP * | |
| Shearin James T | Pullman & Comley, LLC * | |
| Taylor Allan B | Day Pitney LLP * | |

**Band 3**

| | | |
|---|---|---|
| Babbitt Bradford | Robinson & Cole LLP * | |
| Fisher Timothy S | McCarter & English, LLP * | |
| FitzMaurice Daniel L | Day Pitney LLP * | |
| Fogarty James | Fogarty, Cohen, Selby & Nemiroff (ONP)[†] | |
| Friedman David | Murtha Cullina LLP | |
| Glasser James | Wiggin and Dana LLP | |
| Hamilton Trudie | Carmody & Torrance LLP | |
| Nolan John B | Day Pitney LLP * | |
| Rechen Thomas J | McCarter & English, LLP * | |
| Reif David | McCarter & English, LLP * | |
| Slavin Richard | Cohen and Wolf, PC * | |
| Wyld Robert | Shipman & Goodwin LLP | |

*\* Indicates firm / individual with profile.*

*[†]ONP = Other Notable Practitioner.*

### Carmody & Torrance LLP

THE FIRM This thriving Connecticut outfit runs its litigation practice from offices in Waterbury and New Haven. The team has had great success in advising clients on securities, construction and environmental litigation matters. The team's clients include major corporates, banks and insurers, as well as government entities.

**KEY INDIVIDUALS** "*Top-notch lawyer*" **James Robertson** offers clients valued advice on a wide range of litigation issues. He is described by sources as "*a very good litigator: very pleasant, efficient and he handles cases well.*" **Anthony Fitzgerald** is a seasoned trial lawyer focused on commercial and administrative law. Peers acknowledge him as "*an excellent lawyer,*" who "*absolutely belongs at the top of the table.*" **Trudie Hamilton** is lauded by observers for her trial experience, particularly for personal injury defense cases, medical malpractice and product liability issues.

## McCarter & English, LLP
### See profile on p.1759
**THE FIRM** This 17-partner litigation practice represents clients across a broad range of disciplines. The team is skilled in the areas of business litigation and business tort, intellectual property, construction and professional malpractice. The team is also very active in securities litigation and other finance-related disputes on behalf of clients from the financial services industry. Clients include Wakefern Food, Premier Foods and Thermo Fisher Scientific.
**Sources say:** "*They have a good group with lots of depth. They respond quickly and do a fine job.*"
**KEY INDIVIDUALS Timothy Fisher** (see p.743) has more than 30 years' experience as a litigator, arbitrator and mediator in construction disputes. Other areas of focus include representing clients in trust and probate-related litigation. **Thomas Rechen** (see p.746) recently worked on behalf of Jarrow Formulas, defending an attempt to rescind an employment practices liability insurance policy. **Sources say:** "*He is effective, very committed with strong integrity and ethics – he has been outstanding.*" **David Reif** (see p.747) has a wealth of trial experience across a broad range of matters, encompassing fraud claims, product liability and trade secret cases, among others. Reif cochairs the firm's franchising and distribution law group, earning praise from market sources for his expertise in that field. One peer comments: "*He's a superb litigator; tough, but fair.*"

## Robinson & Cole LLP
### See profile on p.751
**THE FIRM** This firm's 30-partner business litigation group operates from offices in Hartford, New London and Stamford and is supported by other litigation experts at six further offices located in the Northeast and Florida. The team provides a comprehensive litigation service to a diverse client roster of both local and national businesses.
**Sources say:** "*The firm handled our largest law suit in great detail. The team's lawyers are very attentive.*"
**KEY INDIVIDUALS Craig Raabe** (see p.746) is renowned for his commercial litigation skills, frequently representing clients in government contracting, unfair practices and fraud cases. Sources note that "*he put on the best closing argument those present at trial had ever heard. People who saw that were amazed by it.*" Cochair of the firm's litigation section and chair of the business litigation group, **Bradford Babbitt** (see p.741) is praised by sources as a "*really good trial lawyer.*" He is applauded in particular for his contract, business tort, IP and trade secret work. **James**

**Wade** (see p.748) is rated highly by sources who call him "*terrific*" and note that he is "*a huge name at the Bar.*" His practice spans civil and criminal litigation matters and he has a wealth of experience in representing companies across a comprehensive range of commercial disputes.

## Shipman & Goodwin LLP
**THE FIRM** This robust litigation practice takes pride in its fearless approach to litigation. The team maintains a broad litigation practice, with particular expertise in franchising, antitrust and trade regulation matters. Recent highlights include representing Shell Oil and Motiva Enterprises in a series of claims and counterclaims against the owner of a large gasoline terminal.
**Sources say:** "*Outstanding: the senior partners are available to us and they don't just delegate everything. They actually know the ins and outs of the case. We benefit from their experience and their professionalism is never in question.*"
**KEY INDIVIDUALS Paul Sanson** has more than 30 years of experience as a trial lawyer in a broad range of commercial matters and one source commented: "*I'm impressed with his service. He is highly specialized and very knowledgeable.*" Chair of the firm's corporate and financial litigation practice, **Frederick Gold** impresses clients with his litigation prowess. Sources comment that "*his service is outstanding. He could sell tickets to his trials, it's like a TV show, it's remarkable.*" **Robert Wyld** is singled out for his knowledge of complex business and commercial litigation cases, ranging from securities litigation to shareholder disputes. Other areas of expertise include complex trust and estate litigation.

## Band 3

## Cohen and Wolf, PC
**THE FIRM** This 14-partner litigation team regularly deals with complex commercial litigation in the fields of breach of fiduciary duty, breach of contract and fraud. The firm's client roster includes Chicago Title Insurance, William Hale Hubbell and Pursuit Partners.
**Sources say:** "*The work product is consistently excellent. The team is reliable, hard-working and efficient. It is also very reasonable pricewise and an absolute pleasure to deal with in every respect.*"
**KEY INDIVIDUALS David Ball** (see p.741) has been involved in a range of business litigation actions, including partnership disagreements and securities matters. One source noted that he is "*independent minded, has very good judgment on regulatory matters and doesn't just tell me what I want to hear.*" Sources describe litigation chair **Stewart Edelstein** (see p.743) as "*a really terrific lawyer.*" For almost 40 years he has represented clients, ranging from large national companies to local municipalities in all forms of disputes. **Monte Frank** (see p.743) is held in high esteem by sources, one of whom commented: "*His powers of analysis are fantastic. He was able to understand my indus-*

*try quickly, dispensing with the long learning curve we have with most firms.*" **Richard Slavin** (see p.747) is chair of the firm's securities group and the managing partner of its Westport office. He is best known for his extensive experience in banking and securities regulation, as well as related litigation.

## Murtha Cullina LLP
**THE FIRM** This 17-partner litigation department regularly represents local and national companies, as well as municipalities across the full spectrum of litigation matters. The team recently defended United Parcel Service Oasis Supply Corporation against a $13 million damages claim by one of its suppliers.
**Sources say:** "*They're my go-to firm for quick, responsive and thorough work.*"
**KEY INDIVIDUALS Francis Brady** enjoys a strong reputation for all types of insurance coverage litigation, including D&O liability claims and environmental issues. **David Friedman** maintains a very diverse litigation practice, recently defending the law firm Brody Wilkinson PC and one of its attorneys against a professional malpractice claim.

## Pullman & Comley, LLC
### See profile on p.750
**THE FIRM** This well-connected litigation team focus on business litigation, although the team also has expertise in real estate and intellectual property litigation. The successful practice spans Connecticut, with offices in Bridgeport, Hartford, Stamford and White Plains.
**Sources say:** "*Great lawyers: trustworthy, reliable and honest.*"
**KEY INDIVIDUALS** Litigation department chair **James Shearin** (see p.747) offers clients a wealth of trial, appellate, arbitration and mediation experience. Sources describe him as "*a busy and diligent guy, extremely well prepared and very practically minded. He's knowledgeable about what he's doing and he makes very clear and cogent arguments.*"

## Other Notable Practitioners
**David Belt** (see p.741) of Hurwitz, Sagarin, Slossberg & Knuff, LLC is considered an expert in legislation governing antitrust fair trade in Connecticut. Sources say: "*He's number one. Very competent and skilled, low key and unassuming but diligent.*" **Frank Silvestri** of Levett Rockwood P.C. is well known for handling business torts and breach of fiduciary duty cases. Sources note that "*Frank is easy to work with, he's very switched-on and a very experienced guy.*" **James Fogarty** of Fogarty, Cohen, Selby & Nemiroff LLC is praised for his advocacy skills. Sources say: "*He is highly respected throughout the state. He's got a lot of experience and when people need a top-notch lawyer he's the one they go to.*"

# REAL ESTATE

Commentary about individuals can be found under their firm's paragraph. If the firm has no paragraph (is not ranked) look at Other Notable Practitioners.

## Real Estate
### Leading Firms

**Band 1**

Bingham McCutchen LLP *

Robinson & Cole LLP *

**Band 2**

Day Pitney LLP *

Pullman & Comley, LLC *

Shipman & Goodwin LLP

**Band 3**

Cohen and Wolf, PC

McCarter & English, LLP *

Wiggin and Dana LLP *

### Leading Individuals

**Band 1**

| | |
|---|---|
| Appicelli Frank A | Bingham McCutchen LLP * |
| Berkman Jerome | Day Pitney LLP * |
| Berman Garry C | Robinson & Cole LLP * |
| Bryson Susan J | Wiggin and Dana LLP * |
| Hawkins Barry | Shipman & Goodwin LLP |
| Merriam Dwight | Robinson & Cole LLP * |
| Smith R Jeffrey | Bingham McCutchen LLP * |

**Band 2**

| | |
|---|---|
| Byrne Michael P | Day Pitney LLP * |
| Elbaum Steven | Robinson & Cole LLP * |
| Hollister Timothy S | Shipman & Goodwin LLP |
| Lubin Andrew R | Neubert, Pepe & Monteith PC (ONP)† |
| Mallin John | McCarter & English, LLP * |
| Nevins Kent | Shipman & Goodwin LLP |
| Oland Mark | Bingham McCutchen LLP * |
| Proctor Michael | Pullman & Comley, LLC * |

**Band 3**

| | |
|---|---|
| Glickson Andrew A | Pullman & Comley, LCC * |
| Gustafson Donald R | Shipman & Goodwin LLP |
| Kirsch Mark | Cohen and Wolf, PC * |
| O'Hanlan Edward V | Robinson & Cole LLP * |
| Rock William G | Shipman & Goodwin LLP |
| Smith Christopher J | Shipman & Goodwin LLP |

\* Indicates firm / individual with profile.

†ONP = Other Notable Practitioner.

## Band 1

### Bingham McCutchen LLP
See profile on p.1515

**THE FIRM** Bingham McCutchen is able to capitalize on its considerable experience in national real estate matters to handle acquisitions, joint ventures and all financial aspects of property transactions. The firm's impressive client list includes UBS Realty Investors, TIAA Global Private Markets and Pacific Life Insurance.

**Sources say:** "*I've never felt that anybody I've dealt with has been better represented than I have been by Bingham – they're thorough, efficient and very knowledgeable.*"

**KEY INDIVIDUALS** Sources report that **Frank Appicelli** (see p.741) is a "*very highly regarded financing lawyer.*" He recently advised The Hartford on the acquisition of several commercial properties. **Jeffrey Smith** (see p.747) represented UBS Realty Investors in an office acquisition valued at some $610 million. This complex mandate involved the assumption and modification of a $280 million securitized mortgage loan. **Mark Oland** (see p.746) is commended for his work in commercial property. Sources say: "*He's always very well prepared and extremely knowledgeable. He's also an excellent negotiator.*" He advised Platinum Equity on the real estate elements of its acquisition of the image sensors division of Kodak.

### Robinson & Cole LLP
See profile on p.751

**THE FIRM** The firm's leading real estate practice is complemented by its deep construction and environmental expertise. The team is praised for its ability to handle the full range of complex transactional and regulatory real estate and leasing deals. The department counts Amtrak, United Technologies and POKO Partners among its key clients.

**Sources say:** "*They have tremendous resources but still deal with me on a personal level. The attorneys I work with are experts in their field.*"

**KEY INDIVIDUALS** Chair of the Hartford office's real estate group, **Garry Berman** (see p.742) has recently handled a range of work for PepsiCo, including leasing a 540,000 sq ft headquarters in Somers, New York. **Dwight Merriam** (see p.745) is hailed as "*the dean of the land use Bar.*" One source enthused: "*I can't say enough good things about him – he's extremely knowledgeable and attentive to detail.*" He assisted Project Service LLC with negotiating the redevelopment, operation and maintenance of 23 highways across Connecticut, a deal valued at $500 million. **Steven Elbaum** (see p.743) is praised for his "*excellent practice.*" He acted for RiverOak Investment on its purchases of medical, research and office properties with an aggregate value of $75 million. **Edward O'Hanlan** (see p.746) is noted for his considerable experience in land use matters, including real property litigation.

## Band 2

### Day Pitney LLP
See profile on p.1753

**THE FIRM** Day Pitney handles the full range of real estate matters, including land use and environmental issues. It is particularly highly regarded for real estate finance work on behalf of clients in the energy and water industries.

**KEY INDIVIDUALS** **Jerome Berkman** (see p.742) remains a prominent figure in the real estate market. He is highlighted for his excellence in commercial leasing matters, with commentators reporting: "*He is the foremost leasing lawyer in town.*" **Michael Byrne** (see p.742) is commended for his "*very strong and very deep practice – he has a lot of expertise.*" He regularly acts on behalf of banks, investment banks, pension funds and insurance companies.

### Pullman & Comley, LLC
See profile on p.750

**THE FIRM** Pullman & Comley is noted for its work on a variety of property law matters, including the acquisition and sale of commercial property, financing and leasing. The team acts on behalf of both public and private entities, and is highlighted for its deep knowledge of the healthcare industry. Clients include Bridgeport Hospital, People's United Bank and the Connecticut Department of Economic & Community Development.

**Sources say:** "*They are great communicators – you don't need a law degree to understand them.*"

**KEY INDIVIDUALS** Department head **Michael Proctor** (see p.746) advised Consumers Petroleum of Connecticut on the leasing and financing for a number of gas stations/convenience stores. Sources report: "*He's a very good lawyer; very decent and very knowledgeable.*" **Andrew Glickson** (see p.743) recently represented Hattco Management in the sale of a condominium, a deal valued at $18 million. Sources praise him for his problem-solving abilities, saying: "*If there's a roadblock, he'll find a way around it; he's very proactive.*"

### Shipman & Goodwin LLP

**THE FIRM** This established real estate team is well known for transactional works and related environment and land use matters. It is also highlighted for deep expertise in multifamily property work and real estate litigation. Key clients include AvalonBay Communities, LEGO Systems, 1st Alliance Lending and the Connecticut Department of Transportation.

**Sources say:** "*They're extremely responsive, deliver quality work and have a deep knowledge of the marketplace.*"

**KEY INDIVIDUALS** **Barry Hawkins** remains one of the preeminent lawyers in the Connecticut real estate market. He handles both transactional and contentious matters. **Timothy Hollister** is particularly highly regarded for real estate work involving an environmental or land use element. **Donald Gustafson** is noted for real estate acquisitions and joint ventures. Sources describe him as "*very professional and experienced – he has good business sense as well as legal expertise.*" **Kent Nevins** is recommended for his strong transactional practice. One commentator enthused: "*He is the most tenacious problem solver I have ever met.*" **William Rock**'s practice includes project development, conveyancing and finance, in addition to his general commercial real estate work. He is particularly highly regarded for his representation of public sector clients. Observers note: "*He's been tremendous. He's responsive and gives very good advice.*" **Christopher Smith** is described as "*a very knowledgeable and very solid lawyer.*" His expertise includes land use litigation and zoning matters.

## Band 3

### Cohen and Wolf, PC

**THE FIRM** Cohen and Wolf remains a popular choice with a wide range of clients including owners, lenders, developers and government agencies. The team offers a full service, including regulatory and land use matters, permitting and appeals. Its clients include The Somerset Realty Group, Apollo Global Management and the Town of Weston.
**Sources say:** *"Their work is consistently excellent. They are reliable, hard-working and efficient."*
**KEY INDIVIDUALS** Mark Kirsch (see p.744) is highly regarded for transactional real estate work, and is particularly skilled in common interest communities. Sources describe him as *"bright, engaging and thorough."*

### McCarter & English, LLP
See profile on p.1759

**THE FIRM** The Connecticut arm of this national firm offers a full service to clients including leasing, dealing with large and small land parcels, and contaminated property work. The firm is particularly popular with financial institutions and retail and apartment developers. Notable clients include Wal-Mart, The Home Depot, Doral Bank and The Hartford.
**KEY INDIVIDUALS** Clients praise John Mallin (see p.745) as *"a very bright, pragmatic attorney."* He recently advised Evergreen Walk on the negotiation and sale of property valued at $6 million.

### Wiggin and Dana LLP
See profile on p.752

**THE FIRM** This highly recommended real estate group advises on a range of development and redevelopment matters. The team is particularly highly regarded for its expertise in working with educational and healthcare institutions in developing property. Key clients of the firm include The Jackson Laboratory and Mahle Engine Components USA.
**KEY INDIVIDUALS** Susan Bryson (see p.742) proves popular with both public and private institutions. She recently represented Yale-New Haven Hospital on a major merger with St. Raphael's Hospital. Sources are also quick to note that she has *"an excellent reputation for urban redevelopment work."*

### Other Notable Practitioners

Andrew Lubin of Neubert, Pepe & Monteith PC is highlighted for his work in commercial real estate lending. Sources say: *"He's extremely smart and capable."*

# Leaders' Profiles in Connecticut

**APPICELLI, Frank A**
Bingham McCutchen LLP, Hartford
860 240 2984
frank.appicelli@bingham.com
*Featured in Real Estate (Connecticut)*
**Practice Areas:** Deputy co-chair of Bingham's Real Estate Practice Group. Advises insurance companies, commercial banks and other debt providers in mortgage loan transactions involving acquisition and permanent financings, credit tenant loans, construction loans, and revolving credit facilities. Represents real estate developers and owners in acquisitions and dispositions, project development, and commercial leasing involving various property types. Properties in transactions have included retail centers, office complexes, hotels and lodging properties, nursing homes, assisted living projects, multifamily housing projects, condominium projects, industrial and warehouse facilities, and other energy projects.
**Personal:** Georgetown University Law Center, JD, cum laude, 1989; Fairfield University, BA, 1986.

**BABBITT, Bradford**
Robinson & Cole LLP, Hartford
860 275 8209
bbabbitt@rc.com
*Featured in Litigation (Connecticut)*
**Practice Areas:** Brad Babbitt represents a wide variety of businesses in commercial disputes, intellectual property claims and appeals. In addition to contract disputes and business tort claims, Brad's experience includes helping utilities and telecommunications companies defend favorable agency determinations from attack by advocacy groups. He has tried numerous matters to verdict, has substantial experience in arbitration, and handled numerous appeals in Connecticut and at the Second Circuit. Brad is a former clerk to the Honorable William J. Lavery of the Connecticut Appellate Court. Brad co-chairs Robinson & Cole's Litigation Section and is chair of the Business Litigation Group.

**BALL, David A**
Cohen and Wolf, PC, Bridgeport
203 337 4134
dball@cohenandwolf.com
*Featured in Litigation (Connecticut)*
**Practice Areas:** Managing Partner. Practices in state and federal court handling complex commercial litigation cases; shareholder and partnership disputes; business tort claims; securities fraud actions; and administrative appeals. Litigates before the FINRA and has extensive experience handling arbitrations before the American Arbitration Association. Frequently serves as local counsel for national firms on complex litigation matters. Appears before state agencies including the Connecticut Siting Council and the Public Utilities Regulatory Authority on energy-related matters.
**Professional Memberships:** Greater Bridgeport, Connecticut and American Bar Associations, Connecticut Trial Lawyers Association.
**Personal:** Brandeis University (BA cum laude). University of Pennsylvania Law School (JD).

**BARON, Collin**
Pullman & Comley, LLC, Bridgeport
203 330 2219
cbaron@pullcom.com
*Featured in Healthcare (Connecticut)*
**Practice Areas:** Chair, Health Care Department. Over his career has been involved in a wide variety of health care matters encompassing virtually all areas of health care law. Represents hospitals and hospital-affiliated organizations including foundations, physician organizations and parent holding companies; federally qualified health centers; rehabilitation centers; nursing homes; provider groups; and individual and group physicians, dentists and other health care providers.
**Professional Memberships:** Member, American Health Lawyers Association; Former President, Connecticut Health Lawyers Association.
**Personal:** JD, The George Washington University National Law Center; BA, University of Virginia.

**BARTON, Elizabeth C**
Day Pitney LLP, Hartford
860 275 0371
ecbarton@daypitney.com
*Featured in Environment (Connecticut)*
**Career:** Elizabeth Barton has more than 20 years of experience in environmental and land use consultation, permitting, and litigation at the federal, state, and local levels. Her work involves substantial contact with federal agencies, including the United States Environmental Protection Agency and the Army Corps of Engineers, and with state agencies, including the Connecticut Department of Environmental Protection and the Connecticut Department of Health Services. Beth has also worked closely with various federal, state, and local authorities in connection with a number of innovative development projects, including large brownfield restoration projects and smaller urban initiatives.

**BEACH, R Scott**
Day Pitney LLP, Greenwich
203 862 7824
rsbeach@daypitney.com
*Featured in Corporate/M&A (Connecticut)*
**Career:** Scott Beach is chair of the Corporate and Business Law department and chair of the Private Equity and Investment Funds practice group. Mr Beach represents private equity investors and emerging growth companies in formation, debt and equity financing, mergers and acquisitions, strategic joint ventures, technology arrangements, and general corporate matters. He routinely advises clients in structuring and forming private investment funds, partnerships and joint ventures. Scott counsels investment fund principals and managers, and portfolio company executives, in connection with their employment and equity compensation arrangements.

**BELT, David L**
Hurwitz, Sagarin, Slossberg & Knuff, LLC, Milford
203 877 8000
DBelt@hssklaw.com
*Featured in Litigation (Connecticut)*
**Practice Areas:** Practice includes litigation relating to unfair trade practices, antitrust, business torts, employee noncompete agreements, misappropriation of trade secrets, fraud and misrepresentation, interference with contract, breach of contract, and shareholder and partnership disputes.
**Professional Memberships:** Past Chair and current Member of the Executive Committee of the Antitrust and Trade Regulation Section and Member of the Federal Practice Section of the Connecticut Bar Association, the Connecticut Trial Lawyers Association, and Life Fellow of the Connecticut Bar Foundation.
**Career:** Member, Hurwitz, Sagarin, Slossberg & Knuff, LLC (2011-present);Member, Jacobs, Grudberg, Belt, Dow & Katz P.C.(1970-2011); Adjunct Professor of Law, Quinnipiac University School of Law (2004-present); Adjunct Faculty, University of Connecticut School of Law (2002); Senior Topical Editor for Antitrust and Trade Regulation of the Connecticut Bar Journal (2012-present).
**Publications:** Co-author: 12 Connecticut Practice Series: Connecticut Unfair Trade Practices, Business Torts and Antitrust (West

2013). Author: Should the FTC's Current Criteria for Determining 'Unfair Acts or Practices' Be Applied to State 'Little FTC Acts', The Antitrust Source (ABA Section of Antitrust Law, Feb. 2010); Unresolved Issues under the Unfair Trade Practices Act, 82 Conn. B.J. 389 (2008); Unfair Trade Practices, in Connecticut Lawyers Deskbook (Conn. Bar. Assn., 3d ed. 2008); The Standard for Determining "Unfair Acts or Practices" Under State Unfair Trade Practices Acts, 80 Conn. B.J. 247 (2006); Contributing Author: ABA Section of Antitrust Law, Consumer Law Developments (2009).

**Personal:** BA (Economics), magna cum laude, Phi Beta Kappa, 1965, Yale University; LLB, 1970, Yale Law School. Adjunct Professor of Law (Antitrust), Quinnipiac University School of Law.

## BERKMAN, Jerome
Day Pitney LLP, Stamford
203 977 7369
jberkman@daypitney.com
*Featured in Real Estate (Connecticut)*

**Career:** Jerry Berkman has practiced in the area of commercial real estate for over 40 years. He represented the sole urban renewal redeveloper of Stamford, Connecticut, in the construction, financing, and leasing of office buildings, a hotel and a major downtown shopping mall. Jerry has represented the landlord or tenant in commercial leases covering several million square feet of space and has represented the developer of thousands of units of multifamily rental housing. He has also represented borrowers in construction and long-term loans secured by mortgages on unimproved land, office parks, hotels, office buildings, flex buildings, and multifamily residential dwellings.

## BERMAN, Garry C
Robinson & Cole LLP, Hartford
860 275 8204
gberman@rc.com
*Featured in Real Estate (Connecticut)*

**Practice Areas:** Garry Berman chairs the Hartford office's Real Estate Practice Group and the firm's Commercial Real Estate Leasing Practice Group. He is experienced in handling the following sophisticated real estate transactions throughout the United States: office, retail and restaurant leasing and subleasing for landlords and tenants; brokerage matters for landlords, tenants and brokers; the sale, purchase, construction and development of vacant land, improved commercial and industrial properties, and multifamily and student housing complexes for property owners, landlords and tenants; mortgage and construction financing, workouts and loan restructurings for lenders and borrowers; and telecommunications licensing for landlords and tenants.

## BLINDERMAN, Harold M
Day Pitney LLP, West Hartford
860 275 0357
hmblinderman@daypitney.com
*Featured in Environment (Connecticut)*

**Career:** Harold M Blinderman brings over 20 years of experience representing clients in the areas of energy, environmental, land use and public utility law. He regularly represents companies

in siting, permitting, compliance, transactional, and enforcement matters at the federal and state level, and his work involves substantial contact with various federal and state agencies. Harold's experience includes environmental and energy permitting, compliance and litigation matters involving the Clean Water Act, Resource Conservation and Recovery Act, the Clean Air Act, Connecticut's Public Utilities and Environmental Statutes, including the Public Utilities Environmental Standards Act, and other federal and state environmental statutes.

## BOROD, Don
McCarter & English, LLP, Hartford
860 275 6725
dborod@McCarter.com
*Featured in Corporate/M&A (Connecticut)*

**Career:** Mr Borod has experience providing legal representation to manufacturing and technology companies, as well as financial institutions and other businesses, in connection with their domestic business activities in the United States and their international business activities in Europe, Asia and Latin America. He is experienced in numerous areas, including international and domestic mergers and acquisitions; joint ventures and other strategic alliances; general corporate, sales and supply agreements; distributors and sales representatives; technology transfers; and establishing foreign operations. He has also represented several foreign companies in connection with their activities in the United States. For full bio: http://www.mccarter.com/Donald-L-Borod/

## BOYLE, Lisa
Robinson & Cole LLP, Hartford
860 275 8350
lboyle@rc.com
*Featured in Healthcare (Connecticut)*

**Practice Areas:** For more than 24 years, Lisa Boyle has represented health care providers, including hospitals, health systems, physician groups, ambulatory surgery centers, nursing homes, home health agencies and federally qualified health centers on a wide variety of health law matters. Her extensive experience includes advising clients on complex regulatory issues, governance issues, medical staff and peer review issues and complex acquisition, and other transactions. Ms Boyle is co-chair of Robinson & Cole's Health Law Group and lectures frequently on a variety of health care topics.

## BRYSON, Susan J
Wiggin and Dana LLP, New Haven
203 498 4337
sbryson@wiggin.com
*Featured in Real Estate (Connecticut)*

**Practice Areas:** Partner, Real Estate, Environmental and Energy Department. Represents clients on large-scale, mixed use urban development projects involving public and private financing in all aspects of real estate for businesses, hospitals, health care facilities, utility companies, educational institutions, for-profit, nonprofit developers.

**Professional Memberships:** American College of Real Estate Lawyers; Connecticut Bar

Foundation; ABA (Real Estate Section); former State of Connecticut Chair, Forum); Connecticut Bar Association (Real Property Section)**Personal:** BA, Stanford University (1970), JD, with highest honors, from the University of Connecticut School of Law, 1977. Clerked for the Honorable Alva P Loiselle, Connecticut Supreme Court.

## BYRNE, Michael P
Day Pitney LLP, Stamford
203 977 7349
mpbyrne@daypitney.com
*Featured in Real Estate (Connecticut)*

**Career:** Michael Byrne practices in the areas of commercial real estate finance, acquisition, leasing, and development. He regularly represents institutional investors such as insurance companies, banks, pension funds, investment banks, commercial lenders, and corporations. Mike has extensive experience in financing hotels and golf courses, the acquisition and sale of real property, commercial leasing, and the acquisition, sale, and financing of portfolios of performing and non-performing real estate assets.

## CERRITO, Chris
Dickstein Shapiro LLP, Stamford
203 905 4537
cerritoc@dicksteinshapiro.com
*Featured in Corporate/M&A (Connecticut)*

**Practice Areas:** Christopher Cerrito is a partner in Dickstein Shapiro's Mergers and Acquisitions Practice. He focuses on solving the business needs of venture capital investors and startup companies, as well as middle market and Fortune 1000 corporations, particularly in the technology and life sciences sectors. In addition to serving as general outside counsel for many companies across various industries, he handles mergers and acquisitions, securities offerings, corporate governance issues, and intellectual property issues including licensing, collaborations, and joint ventures.

**Personal:** JD, cum laude, from Boston College Law School (1996) and BS, magna cum laude, from Boston College (1993).

## CHAVEY, Victoria Woodin
Jackson Lewis LLP, Hartford
860 522 0404
Victoria.Chavey@jacksonlewis.com
*Featured in Labor & Employment (Connecticut)*

**Practice Areas:** Employment litigation; class actions.

**Career:** Employment litigator for nearly 20 years, including successfully trying cases to verdict in court and arbitration, handling claims of systemic discrimination, arguing appeals.

**Publications:** Bender's Labor & Employment Bulletin, August 2011, "Supreme Court Restricts Class Actions".

**Personal:** Law Clerk, US Court of Appeals for the Second Circuit, The Honorable Thomas J Meskill; Law Clerk, Connecticut Supreme Court, Chief Justice Ellen A Peters; BU School of Law, JD summa cum laude, Editor-in-Chief of BU Law Review.

## CLARKE, Martin A
Dickstein Shapiro LLP, Stamford
203 905 4541
clarkem@dicksteinshapiro.com
*Featured in Corporate/M&A (Connecticut)*

**Practice Areas:** Martin A Clarke is a partner in Dickstein Shapiro's Mergers and Acquisitions Practice. Mr Clarke regularly represents private equity funds as well as public and private companies with mergers, acquisitions, and divestitures. He also counsels corporate clients and emerging companies in connection with numerous business transactions, including joint ventures, restructuring, and debt and equity financing.

**Personal:** Mr Clarke received his JD, cum laude, from Fordham Law School (1994), and earned his BA, with honors in English, from Lehigh University (1987).

## CORDIANO, Dean M
Day Pitney LLP, Hartford
860 275 0179
dmcordiano@daypitney.com
*Featured in Environment (Connecticut)*

**Career:** Dean Cordiano has more than 30 years of experience trying and arbitrating complex securities, commercial and environmental cases. He has tried and arbitrated more than 50 cases to judgment. Dean has experience with cutting-edge environmental cases and has won three verdicts in multimillion-dollar cost-recovery actions, as well as defending complex commercial and business lawsuits. Dean has also conducted numerous arbitrations and other alternative dispute resolution proceedings. His experience as an arbitrator and court-appointed special master allow him to be effective both as an advocate and a problem solver in helping clients find innovative, economical resolutions of their business disputes.

## DALE, Eric
Robinson & Cole LLP, Stamford
203 462 7568
edale@rc.com
*Featured in Corporate/M&A (Connecticut)*

**Practice Areas:** Eric J Dale chairs Robinson & Cole's Business Transactions Practice Group and focuses his work on Mergers & Acquisitions, Emerging Companies, Private Equity and Venture Capital. Eric has extensive experience representing large, multi-national corporations, as well as early stage, public and private companies in negotiating and structuring complex debt and equity transactions, merger and acquisition transactions, partnership relationships, joint venture and strategic alliance agreements, supply chain and outsourcing agreements, and technology licensing agreements. Eric is regarded as a key strategic adviser to his clients, counseling them with respect to the legal implications of their business transactions.

## DEBARGE, Michelle Wilcox
Wiggin and Dana LLP, Hartford
860 297 3702
mdebarge@wiggin.com
*Featured in Healthcare (Connecticut)*

**Practice Areas:** Advises health care providers, systems/trade associations; biotech/pharmaceutical companies; information technology, other

health care-related companies on broad range of regulatory matters, including health care licensure and operations, audits, research compliance, privacy/security (including HIPAA); Medicare/Medicaid; patient care. Chairs HIPAA, health information technology and clinical research practice groups.
**Professional Memberships:** Member, UCONN Health Center IRB. Chair, State Advisory Committee on Patient Privacy and Security. Former member, Legal and Policy Subcommittee of Connecticut Health Information and Technology Exchange. Former Director, Connecticut Health Lawyers Association.
**Personal:** UCONN School of Law, JD, magna cum laude, Editor-in-Chief, UCONN Law Review. Williams College, BA.

### DUNHAM, Edward Wood
Wiggin and Dana LLP, New Haven
203 498 4327
edunham@wiggin.com
*Featured in Franchising (Nationwide), Litigation (Connecticut)*
See under Nationwide for profile.

### EDELSTEIN, Stewart
Cohen and Wolf, PC, Bridgeport
203 368 0211
sedelstein@cohenandwolf.com
*Featured in Litigation (Connecticut)*
**Practice Areas:** Chair of Litigation Group. Forty years' experience representing clients in commercial litigation. His clients include Fortune 500 and other national corporations as well as leading municipalities and notable individuals.
**Professional Memberships:** Certified member of the American Arbitration Association's Commercial Panel.
**Career:** Has taught Civil Litigation courses at Yale Law School for 20 years. Author of ABA book, "How to Succeed as a Trial Lawyer (2013)." He has been a faculty member at National Institute for Trial Advocacy seminars, the Connecticut Trial Advocacy Institute, and bar association seminars, and authored many litigation-related articles.
**Personal:** Oberlin College (BA, magna cum laude) and Cornell University (JD).

### ELBAUM, Steven
Robinson & Cole LLP, Stamford
203 462 7526
selbaum@rc.com
*Featured in Real Estate (Connecticut)*
**Practice Areas:** Steve Elbaum is a member of the firm's Managing Committee and the chair of its Metro New York real estate practice. He represents corporations, developers, municipalities, and international lending institutions in acquisitions and sales of real property, development of mixed-use projects and corporate headquarter campuses, mortgage loan transactions, and office and industrial leases throughout the country. He also counsels public and private clients and municipalities in economic development incentive transactions. He currently represents several Fortune 500 companies in all aspects of their office leasing and rep-

resents several municipalities in urban redevelopment projects.

### ELKOW, Pamela K
Robinson & Cole LLP, Stamford
203 462 7548
pelkow@rc.com
*Featured in Environment (Connecticut)*
**Practice Areas:** Pamela Elkow is a member of the Environmental and Utilities Practice Group, representing clients in remediating or redeveloping brownfields; purchasing or selling businesses or real estate with environmental liabilities or challenges; obtaining permits; providing environmental, health, and safety compliance counseling; and responding to governmental enforcement. Pam represents large companies remediating legacy properties in teams involving in-house counsel and environmental consultants. She represents portfolio companies in the business of acquiring and remediating contaminated properties for investment or resale, municipalities engaged in redevelopment efforts, and also manufacturers or other large institutions with ongoing EH&S issues associated with their business operations.

### FISHER, Timothy S
McCarter & English, LLP, Hartford
860 275 6755
tfisher@mccarter.com
*Featured in Litigation (Connecticut)*
**Career:** Mr Fisher's 30 years of work in the construction industry have equipped him with familiarity with the issues facing owners, contractors and all others involved in bringing projects to successful conclusion. Through claim resolution, counseling during distressed projects, and negotiating and drafting of contracts, Mr Fisher brings to his clients knowledge of the industry and the job-site realities that make or break projects. Public sector projects are a major component of Mr Fisher's practice, including representation of contractors and owners of universities and corrections, marine and major transportation facilities. For full bio: http://www.mccarter.com/Timothy-S-Fisher/

### FITZMAURICE, Daniel L
Day Pitney LLP, Hartford
860 275 0181
dlfitzmaurice@daypitney.com
*Featured in Litigation (Connecticut)*
**Career:** Dan FitzMaurice, a member of the firm's Executive Committee, represents clients in trials, arbitrations, and appeals of complex commercial disputes, with an emphasis on insurance and reinsurance, corporate, banking, franchise, and financial transactions. He is a past Chairman of the Board of Directors of ARIAS-US and currently serves as a co-chair of the ARIAS-US Industry Task Force on improving arbitration. He has handled appeals in the US Courts of Appeals for the Second, Third, Ninth, and District of Columbia Circuits, as well as the Connecticut Supreme Court. Dan has represented parties in proceedings before numerous federal and state agencies.

### FLAHERTY, John
Dickstein Shapiro LLP, Stamford
203 905 4527
flahertyj@dicksteinshapiro.com
*Featured in Corporate/M&A (Connecticut)*
**Practice Areas:** John Flaherty is a partner in Dickstein Shapiro's Mergers and Acquisitions Practice. He focuses primarily on mergers and acquisitions, as well as other strategic investment and capital raising transactions. Mr Flaherty has represented private equity funds, middle market companies whose growth and profitability are based on technology products and services, and large companies undertaking mergers and acquisitions with middle market targets.
**Personal:** Mr Flaherty earned his JD from the University of Chicago School of Law (1991) and his AB from Columbia College (1984).

### FRANK, Monte
Cohen and Wolf, PC, Bridgeport
203 792 2771
mfrank@cohenandwolf.com
*Featured in Litigation (Connecticut)*
**Practice Areas:** Member in Municipal Group. Handles a wide range of commercial litigation matters on behalf of businesses and municipalities, including contract disputes, business torts, real estate, tax appeals, employment, class actions and construction litigation. He has significant experience with arbitration and mediation. Appears before state and federal courts, as well as various state agencies. Mr Frank has served as an attorney trial referee, factfinder and arbitrator for the Judicial District of Danbury since 2000.
**Professional Memberships:** Federal Bar Council, Connecticut Bar Association, Danbury Bar Association.
**Personal:** Cornell University (BA, magna cum laude) and Cornell Law School (JD).

### FREED, Thomas J
Dickstein Shapiro LLP, Stamford
203 905 4529
freedt@dicksteinshapiro.com
*Featured in Corporate/M&A (Connecticut)*
**Practice Areas:** Partner Thomas Freed works with Fortune 1000 companies undertaking middle market mergers and acquisitions and joint ventures, individuals and entities that provide and receive seed and venture capital, and private equity funds and private companies engaged in mergers and acquisitions as well as other strategic lending and capital-raising transactions.
**Professional Memberships:** Member of the American Bar Association and Connecticut Chapter of The Association for Corporate Growth.
**Personal:** State University of New York at Buffalo Law School, JD, 1988; State University of New York at Binghamton, BS, 1985.

### FREIMAN, Jonathan
Wiggin and Dana LLP, New Haven
203 498 4584
jfreiman@wiggin.com
*Featured in Litigation (Connecticut)*
**Practice Areas:** Chairs Appellate and Complex Legal Issues Practice Group; co-chairs Art and

Museum Law Practice Group. Represents clients nationwide in a variety of complex commercial matters, including appeals, transnational disputes, disputes over art and artifacts, and class actions. Patent-related litigation includes appellate victory over Nobel Prize winner. Litigates for and against foreign sovereigns and political parties.
**Personal:** Taught at Yale Law School for six years. Provided Lexis expert commentary on constitutional law. Law Clerk to former Yale Law School dean Judge Louis H Pollak (E.D. Pa.) (1998-99); Yale Law School (Senior Editor, Yale Law Journal) (1998).

### GAROFALO, Beverly W
Jackson Lewis LLP, Hartford
860 331 1535
garofalob@jacksonlewis.com
*Featured in Labor & Employment (Connecticut)*
**Practice Areas:** Employment litigation, advice on behalf of management: discrimination, harassment, retaliation, ADA, FMLA, severance and non-competition agreements.
**Career:** Law Clerk, Hon. Chief Justice Ellen Ash Peters, Connecticut Supreme Court, 1991-92; Day Pitney LLP, 1992-96; Thelen LLP 1996-2008; Jackson Lewis LLP 2008-present. Managing Partner, Hartford. Nominee: Chambers Women in Law Employment Lawyer of the Year 2011.
**Publications:** "Virtual Workplace: Next Frontier of Employer Liability," Connecticut Law Tribune; "Paid Sick Leave: Law of Unintended Consequences," Connecticut Law Tribune; "Striking a Blow Against Identity Theft," Connecticut Law Tribune.
**Personal:** University of Connecticut School of Law, JD, 1991; Colorado College, BA, 1985.

### GLASSMAN, Andrew C
Pullman & Comley, LLC, Hartford
860 541 3316
aglassman@pullcom.com
*Featured in Corporate/M&A (Connecticut)*
**Practice Areas:** Chair, Corporate and Business Department. Represents clients in mergers, acquisitions and financings. Experienced in corporate and commercial law transactions. Advises clients in choice of entity and entity structuring, capital raises, retention of investment banking services, creation of special classes and series of equity, negotiation of shareholders' rights agreements, development of lay employee compensation arrangements and option programs and other structuring issues. Provides general business law advisory services.
**Professional Memberships:** Member, American, Connecticut and New York Bar Associations; Commercial Arbitrators' Panel, American Arbitration Association.
**Personal:** JD, University of Connecticut School of Law; BA, Cornell University; Justice of the Peace.

### GLICKSON, Andrew A
Pullman & Comley, LCC, Stamford
203 674 7935
aglickson@pullcom.com
*Featured in Real Estate (Connecticut)*

**Practice Areas:** Member of the Real Estate Department with a background in architecture and government. Experienced in structuring, public offering and financing of condominiums and property owner associations, including residential, commercial and mixed-use projects. Represents developers and real estate investors in acquisition, sales, leasing and financing transactions, as well as zoning applications and negotiations with redevelopment agencies.
**Professional Memberships:** Connecticut and New York Bar Associations; Fairfield County Bar Association; Fairfield/Westchester Chapter, Real Estate Finance Association; Connecticut House of Representatives 1979-1981; Commissioner, Norwalk Transit District, 1986-present.
**Personal:** JD, with honors, Boston University School of Law; AB Harvard College.

## HANCOCK, Nancy
Pullman & Comley, LLC, Bridgeport
203 330 2118
nhancock@pullcom.com
*Featured in Corporate/M&A (Connecticut)*
**Practice Areas:** Chair, Mergers & Acquisitions, Venture Capital, and Securities sections. Represents business clients throughout life cycle, in capital formation, governance and regulatory matters; manages complex debt and equity capital structures, hybrid securities and shareholders rights documentation; strategic financing; and mergers, acquisitions and divestitures. Diverse business operational experience includes drafting and negotiating sales and procurement documents, intellectual property licenses, e-commerce agreements, joint venture and strategic alliance agreements, and outsourcing agreements. Provides tax-based general business advice.
**Professional Memberships:** American and Connecticut Bar Associations.
**Career:** Admitted, US Tax Court; Executive Committee member.
**Personal:** JD, Cornell University; AB, magna cum laude, Princeton University.

## HAWKS-LADDS, Joshua A
Pullman & Comley, LLC, Hartford
860 541 3306
jhawks-ladds@pullcom.com
*Featured in Labor & Employment (Connecticut)*
**Practice Areas:** Chair, Labor and Employment Section, Litigation Department. Practice includes business, construction, labor and employment, civil rights and municipal law. Experienced in state and federal court trials and before administrative tribunals. Lectures and consults on trial practice, contract, labor and employment law.
**Professional Memberships:** Connecticut Bar Association - mediator, Legal Fee Resolution Board; Executive Committee, Labor and Employment Law Section; Common Law and Statutory Claims Committee. Massachusetts and New York Bar Associations. Connecticut Bar Foundation - James W. Cooper Fellow.
**Personal:** JD, with honors, Western New England University School of Law; BA University of Connecticut.

## HOFFMAN, Lee D
Pullman & Comley, LLC, Hartford
860 424 4315
lhoffman@pullcom.com
*Featured in Environment (Connecticut)*
**Practice Areas:** Counsels clients in environmental law, energy and utility matters, with focus on utility siting, project development and brownfield redevelopment. Additional experience includes litigation in both civil and criminal environmental matters, toxic torts, and representation before administrative agencies.
**Professional Memberships:** Served as chair of Connecticut Governor's Energy Policy Working Group. Steering Committee, Connecticut Business and Industry Association's Environmental Policies Council; Chair, Utility Section, and Treasurer, Environmental Section Connecticut Bar Association; Board, Lawyers Collaborative for Diversity. Former Adjunct Professor, University of Connecticut Law School.
**Personal:** JD, George Washington University; LLM, with highest honors, George Washington University; BA, Tulane University.

## KATZ, Stuart M
Cohen and Wolf, PC, Bridgeport
203 368 0211
SKatz@cohenandwolf.com
*Featured in Labor & Employment (Connecticut)*
**Practice Areas:** Chair of Employment Group. Represents employers in a range of industries in defending discrimination and harassment suits and litigating restrictive covenant, breach of contract, business tort and wage claims. Practices in state and federal courts, often as local counsel for national firms, and appears before the Connecticut Commission on Human Rights and Opportunities, the Department of Labor and other administrative agencies. Counsels employers on personnel-related matters.
**Professional Memberships:** American Bar Association, Connecticut Bar Association, Greater Bridgeport Bar Association, Connecticut Trial Advocacy Institute.
**Personal:** Brandeis University (BA, cum laude). Boston University School of Law (JD).

## KIERNAN, Vincent M
Edwards Wildman Palmer, Stamford
203 353 6801
vkiernan@edwardswildman.com
*Featured in Corporate/M&A (Connecticut)*
**Practice Areas:** Represents early stage and middle market companies seeking to grow by taking advantage of proprietary technology and processes; middle market companies as outside general counsel; private and public companies engaged in mergers and acquisitions; investment banking firms; and individuals and entities seeking or providing seed and venture capital financing.
**Personal:** New York University School of Law, JD; New York University, BA. Vinny provides pro bono legal services for buildOn, a program engaging high school students in their communities while also building over 350 schools around the world. Board of Directors, Stamford Boys and Girls Club.

## KIRSCH, Mark
Cohen and Wolf, PC, Bridgeport
203 337 5554
mkirsch@cohenandwolf.com
*Featured in Real Estate (Connecticut)*
**Practice Areas:** Chair of Real Estate Group. Represents clients in all aspects of commercial real estate, including acquisition, conveyance, financing, leasing and development. Dedicates significant time to commercial lending transactions, both real estate and asset-based. Experienced in the law of common interest communities, including drafting offering statements and other formation documents, community association borrowing, and reviewing and amending common interest community governing instruments.
**Professional Memberships:** American Bar Association, Connecticut Bar Association, Greater Bridgeport Bar Association, Real Estate Finance Association of Connecticut.
**Personal:** State University of New York at Albany (BS, magna cum laude). Boston University School of Law (JD).

## KRANTZ, Richard
Robinson & Cole LLP, Stamford
203 462 7505
rkrantz@rc.com
*Featured in Corporate/M&A (Connecticut)*
**Practice Areas:** Richard A. Krantz chairs Robinson & Cole's Securities Group. Richard's practice covers a broad range of corporate and securities transactions, including representation of issuers and underwriters in public and private securities offerings of debt and equity, acquisitions, mergers, restructurings, and joint ventures. He regularly represents investors and issuers in structuring, negotiating, and documenting various series and classes of debt and equity securities. Additionally, Richard represents public companies with respect to their reporting and disclosure obligations and other requirements under state and federal securities laws. Richard's practice also includes general corporate matters, including distributorships, financings, spin-offs, and rights offerings.

## LAVELLE, Michael N
Pullman & Comley, LLC, Bridgeport
203 330 2112
mlavelle@pullcom.com
*Featured in Labor & Employment (Connecticut)*
**Practice Areas:** Practices in labor and employment law including employment discrimination, labor board and other administrative agency practice and wrongful discharge litigation, and municipal law. Broad trial experience before state and federal civil courts and before administrative agencies that regulate employment. Collective bargaining negotiations in both private and public sector,contract drafting, labor contract administration and trials of grievance arbitration, and preparation of employment guidelines, employee handbooks and manuals.
**Professional Memberships:** Connecticut Association of Municipal Attorneys - officer and director.

**Career:** Serves as a special master for the US District Court.
**Personal:** JD, Boston University; AB, cum laude, Harvard College.

## LEFEBER, Peter J
Wiggin and Dana LLP, New Haven
203 498 4329
plefeber@wiggin.com
*Featured in Labor & Employment (Connecticut)*
**Practice Areas:** Represents management in all aspects of the employment relationship, including union campaigns, unfair labor practices, arbitrations, contract negotiations, strikes, discrimination claims, wage and hour cases, and wrongful discharge suits and related issues. Clients include major health care institutions, manufacturing companies, insurance organizations, utilities, educational institutions, and not-for-profit entities.
**Professional Memberships:** ABA's Labor and Employment Section, and formerly served on the Executive Committee, Connecticut Bar Association Section on Labor and Employment Law.
**Personal:** St. Michael's College (AB, summa cum laude) and University of Connecticut School of Law (JD cum laude); Administrative Editor of the Connecticut Law Review.

## LEVINE, David
Cohen and Wolf, PC, Bridgeport
203 337 4137
DLevine@cohenandwolf.com
*Featured in Healthcare (Connecticut)*
**Practice Areas:** Chair of Business & Corporate and Physicians Practices Groups. Represents business, health care and real estate clients, handling their acquisitions, financing, formation and structural issues. Substantial portion of practice is dedicated to the legal relationships among physicians and the entities with whom physicians contract.
**Professional Memberships:** Co-chairs the LLC Subcommittee of the Business Law Section of the Connecticut Bar Association, serves on the Board of Directors of the Connecticut Health Lawyers Association and is a member of the American Health Lawyers Association.
**Personal:** Brandeis University (AB, magna cum laude). Boston University School of Law (JD).

## LOTSTEIN, James I
Edwards Wildman Palmer, Hartford
860 541 7708
jlotstein@edwardswildman.com
*Featured in Corporate/M&A (Connecticut)*
**Practice Areas:** Jim's practice focuses on corporate and business law. He represents public and private companies in the areas of mergers and acquisitions, corporate governance, joint ventures, private equity investments, financings and general corporate work.
**Professional Memberships:** American Bar Association, Committee on Mergers & Acquisitions; Connecticut Bar Association, Business Law Section Executive Committee; NACD, Steering Committee, CT Chapter.
**Publications:** Jim has authored numerous articles on Connecticut Corporate law. He is the co-author of the Connecticut Business Corporate Act

Sourcebook. Jim teaches a Business Acquisitions course at UConn School of Law.
**Personal:** University of Connecticut, JD, 1968; Northwestern University, BS, 1965.

### LYNCH JR, John B
Robinson & Cole LLP, Hartford
860 275 8242
jlynch@rc.com
*Featured in Corporate/M&A (Connecticut)*
**Practice Areas:** John B Lynch, Jr is Robinson & Cole's managing partner and a practicing member of the Business Transactions and Finance Practice Groups. He regularly represents both buyers and sellers in structuring, negotiating, financing, and documenting sophisticated business acquisition and sale transactions. John works with investment banks, accounting firms, and other professional advisors to provide integrated professional services to clients engaging in merger and acquisition transactions. John also represents both lenders and borrowers in a variety of complex commercial finance transactions, including asset-based financings, secured and unsecured syndicated credit facilities, and leveraged buyout transactions.

### MALLIN, John
McCarter & English, LLP, Hartford
860 275 6728
jrmallin@sbcglobal.net
*Featured in Real Estate (Connecticut)*
**Career:** Mr Mallin has been involved in all aspects of real estate development and financing transactions. His real estate perspective combines with a background in taxation, construction law and litigation, enabling him to format development projects in ways that are more efficient for development while achieving the client's financial and business objectives. He has been able to suggest alternatives that maximize development capacity, ease the permitting/regulatory process and expeditiously achieve financing objectives. He has significant experience in representing lenders and owners in real estate asset workouts and restructurings and in representing owners in tax appeal matters. For full bio:
http://www.mccarter.com/John-R-Mallin/

### MCCORMACK, Christopher
Pullman & Comley, LLC, Bridgeport
203 330 2016
cmccormack@pullcom.com
*Featured in Environment (Connecticut)*
**Practice Areas:** Environmental law and environmental litigation, including enforcement defense, administrative proceedings, insurance coverage and transactional due diligence. Extensive experience in complex remediation liability litigation and complex commercial litigation.
**Professional Memberships:** ABA Section of Environment, Energy and Resources (Vice Chair, Pesticides, Chemical Regulation and Right-to-Know Committee); Environmental Law Section of Connecticut Bar Association (Secretary, Legislative Liaison); ASTM International-Committee E50 on Environmental Assessment Standards (Membership Secretary); Task Group for Revision

of the E1903 Phase II Environmental Site Assessment (Chair).
**Personal:** JD, cum laude, Fordham University School of Law; MA, Eastman School of Music, University of Rochester; BA, cum laude, Yale University.

### MERRIAM, Dwight
Robinson & Cole LLP, Hartford
860 275 8228
dmerriam@rc.com
*Featured in Real Estate (Connecticut)*
**Practice Areas:** Dwight Merriam founded Robinson & Cole's Land Use Group in 1978. Mr Merriam represents land owners, developers, governments, and individuals in land use matters. He is a featured speaker at many land use seminars and has published nine books and over 200 articles. He has been cited in the national press, from The New York Times to People magazine, and has appeared on NBC's Today show, MSNBC, and public television. Mr Merriam served three tours in Vietnam with the Navy, retiring as a captain in 2009 following 31 years of active and reserve service.

### MOORE, Pamela
McCarter & English, LLP, Hartford
860 275 6714
pmoore@mccarter.com
*Featured in Labor & Employment (Connecticut)*
**Career:** Ms Moore is the leader of the Labor and Employment practice group. She concentrates her practice in preventive employment relations, EEO agency proceedings and employment litigation. She has significant experience in the full range of employment law issues, including discrimination, sexual harassment, affirmative action, employment at will, wage and hour, family and medical leave, and workplace violence. Ms Moore has handled numerous cases before federal and state administrative agencies and courts on a wide variety of issues and has tried cases to juries on such issues as age discrimination, employment contract/handbook claims, defamation and whistleblowing. For full bio:
http://www.mccarter.com/Pamela-J-Moore/

### MORRIS, Robert
Pullman & Comley, LLC, Bridgeport
203 330 2109
rmorris@pullcom.com
*Featured in Corporate/M&A (Connecticut)*
**Practice Areas:** Chair, Tax Section. Broad experience in federal and state tax planning and tax litigation matters, mergers and acquisitions, general corporate and partnership law, private securities offerings and estate planning. His practice involves representation of closely held corporations, financial institutions, individuals, trusts and estates.
**Professional Memberships:** American Bar Association - Tax Section; Connecticut Bar Association - Executive Committee, Tax Section; Florida Bar Association - Tax Section; Connecticut Business and Industry Association - Director.
**Career:** Chairman of the Firm; Executive Committee Member.

**Personal:** JD, Cornell Law School; New York University, LLM in Taxation, New York University; BA, Cornell University.

### MORRISON III, Francis H
Axinn, Veltrop & Harkrider LLP, Hartford
860 275 8100
fhm@avhlaw.com
*Featured in Litigation (Connecticut)*
**Practice Areas:** Life sciences; intellectual property and commercial litigation.
**Career:** Francis Morrison's practice focuses on the trial of intellectual property and commercial matters across the United States. He has tried more than 55 cases to verdict or judgment involving technical and other complex matters. He is a Fellow of the American College of Trial Lawyers, a charter Member of the Connecticut Chapter of the American Board of Trial Advocates and is certified in civil trial advocacy by the National Board of Trial Advocacy. Representative matters Include: Lead trial counsel for Actavis/Purepac defendants in a jury trial in In Re Gabapentin Patent Litigation in the US District Court for the District of New Jersey (Hochberg, USDJ) which concluded with a very favorable settlement after two weeks of trial. Co-tried to conclusion (decision pending) for defendant Actavis the case of Pfizer, Inc. v. Teva et al. in the US District Court for the District of Delaware (Sleet, CUSDJ). Nine day trial dealt with claims of infringement and invalidity regarding brand drug Lyrica®. Lead trial counsel for Canadian toy maker Mega Brands Inc. in a lawsuit in the CD California (Selna, USDJ) against Lego Group involving construction toys and related dealings with US Customs and Border Protection. Mega Brands succeeded in reversing Customs' decision restricting imports of certain Mega Brands imports into the US which was based on a mistaken belief that Mega Brands products infringed a trademark registration obtained by Lego. Obtained summary judgment of infringement and validity on behalf of a patentee in California in a bet-the-company case involving electronic temperature monitors. Obtained reversal of District Court's dismissal of contract action (involving commerce valued over a billion dollars) in the Seventh Circuit including reassignment to a new judge on remand. Successfully co-tried to judgment Clearwater v. Evapco, a matter involving claims of trade secret misappropriation in the field of electromagnetic water treatment. Tried to verdict patent infringement claims on behalf of defendant Nidec Corporation involving direct current brushless fans. First chaired TRO hearing on behalf of plaintiff optical fiber manufacturer in Delaware Chancery Court in matter involving technical trade secrets.
**Publications:** Power Attorneys: Business Battlefields, Corporate Connecticut Magazine, 2004. Cross Examination in the Psychology Case. This chapter was prepared in connection with the ABA's publication entitled, Psychological Injuries at Trial.
**Personal:** Duke University School of Law, Durham, North Carolina, JD with distinction. Note and Comment Editor, Duke Law Journal.

College of the Holy Cross, Worcester, Massachusetts; AB Line Officer US Navy 1969-72, USS Grand Canyon (AD-28).

### NOLAN, John B
Day Pitney LLP, Hartford
860 275 0289
jbnolan@daypitney.com
*Featured in Litigation (Connecticut)*
**Career:** Jay Nolan has tried most types of commercial cases in state and federal courts around the country since joining the firm in 1969. In addition to securing verdicts or judgments in almost 100 cases, he has argued appeals in the Connecticut Supreme and Appellate Courts and the First and Second Circuits. He has extensive experience involving disputes between business owners, and has represented institutional clients who have been victimized in sophisticated frauds. Jay started Day Pitney's insolvency practice and has represented institutional creditors, committees, and debtors. Most recently, he has represented electric utilities in the bankruptcies following deregulation.

### O'BRIEN, George
Littler Mendelson, PC, New Haven
203 974 8700
gobrien@littler.com
*Featured in Labor & Employment (Connecticut)*
**Practice Areas:** Labor and employment, labor relations, litigation, arbitration, alternative dispute resolution.
**Professional Memberships:** Connecticut Bar Association; Labor and Employment Section, Executive Committee; Federal Practices Section, Executive Committee; Long Wharf Theatre Board Member; Friends of New Haven Legal Services.
**Career:** Mr O'Brien represents and counsels employers on a wide variety of labor matters. He appears in state and federal courts and represents management before the National Labor Relations Board and other administrative agencies.
**Personal:** JD, University of Connecticut School of Law, with honors; AB, Princeton University, cum laude.

### O'CONNOR, Gary B
Pullman & Comley, LLC, Hartford
860 424 4366
goconnor@pullcom.com
*Featured in Environment (Connecticut)*
**Practice Areas:** Environmental, real estate and development. Experience in regulatory compliance, permitting and litigation, and complex industrial and commercial real estate transactions, particularly those impacted by environmental conditions, including the transfer of state-owned airports to a newly created airport authority. Successfully negotiated federal and state grant and loan agreements on large-scale public and private remediation and redevelopment projects.
**Professional Memberships:** American and Connecticut Bar Associations; Co-chair of the Connecticut General Assembly's Brownfields Working Group; Connecticut DEEP's Comprehensive Evaluation and Transformation of Connecticut's Cleanup Laws Working Group.

**Personal:** JD, with honors, Boston College of Law; BA Boston College.

## O'HANLAN, Edward V
Robinson & Cole LLP, Stamford
203 462 7556
tohanlon@rc.com

*Featured in Real Estate (Connecticut)*

**Practice Areas:** Ted O'Hanlan's practice runs the full gamut of land use matters, from administrative applications and appeals to complex real property litigation, including state and federal wetlands and environmental laws, real property law, title insurance claims and defenses, and constitutional law issues. He serves as attorney trial referee and fact finder/arbitrator for the Connecticut Superior Court and in numerous private arbitrations. Mr O'Hanlan has successfully represented clients before forums such as municipal land use and wetlands agencies, NASD arbitrations, jury and bench trials in state and federal courts, and appeals before the Connecticut Supreme Court.

## OLAND, Mark
Bingham McCutchen LLP, Hartford
860 240 2929
mark.oland@bingham.com

*Featured in Real Estate (Connecticut)*

**Practice Areas:** Concentrates on commercial real estate law and finance, real estate loan workouts, and mortgage law. Represents developers of commercial and residential properties, including privately and publicly owned entities, real estate investment trusts, private equity funds, pension funds, and banking institutions. Represents financial institutions in connection with both their real estate lending and equity investment activities.
**Career:** Speaks on wide range of real estate law topics at seminars and conferences. Served as an adviser to Connecticut Law Revision Commission on a variety of real estate legislation.
**Personal:** Columbia University School of Law, JD, 1972; University of Vermont, BA, 1969.

## ORLEANS, Jonathan
Pullman & Comley, LLC, Bridgeport
203 330 2129
jborleans@pullcom.com

*Featured in Labor & Employment (Connecticut)*

**Practice Areas:** Employment litigation, business litigation. Representation of businesses, non-profits and individuals in trade secrets, non-competition, FLSA, employment discrimination, breach of contract and ERISA cases. Review and preparation of employment policies. Employment counseling. Negotiation and preparation of employment contracts and separation agreements.
**Professional Memberships:** American Bar Association; Connecticut Bar Association- Federal Practice Section Executive Committee; Connecticut Bar Foundation - Fellow; Council on Law in Higher Education.
**Career:** Clerked for Honorable M Joseph Blumenfeld, Senior US District Judge.
**Personal:** JD, New York University School of Law, cum laude; MPA, Princeton University,

Woodrow Wilson School of Public Affairs; BA, Hampshire College.

## PAPERMASTER, Daniel
Bingham McCutchen LLP, Hartford
860 240 2954
daniel.papermaster@bingham.com

*Featured in Corporate/M&A (Connecticut)*

**Practice Areas:** Managing partner of Bingham's Hartford office. Co-chair of Bingham's Transactional Finance Group. Focuses on corporate finance, primarily representing various types of financial institutions, hedge funds and large corporations in financing and restructuring transactions. Practice is concentrated on syndicated bank financings, representing hedge funds in debt and equity investments and cross-border financings as well as institutional investors of privately placed debt. Also represents numerous entities involved in economic development projects in Hartford.
**Personal:** University of Texas School of Law, JD, 1989; University of Michigan, BA, with honors, 1986.

## PEIKES, Lawrence
Wiggin and Dana LLP, Stamford
203 363 7609
lpeikes@wiggin.com

*Featured in Labor & Employment (Connecticut)*

**Practice Areas:** Represents management with respect to employment-related claims, including discrimination, harassment, failure to accommodate, wage and hour violations, breach of non-competition covenants, whistleblower retaliation. Counsels employers regarding compliance with laws and regulations governing the employment relationship, such as Title VII, ADA, ADEA, NLRA, FLSA, FMLA, SOX.
**Professional Memberships:** ABA Labor and Employment Law Section, Federal Labor Standards Legislation subcommittee, FLSA management-side co-chair; Senior Editor, ABA's Fair Labor Standards Act treatise; contributor ABA's Family and Medical Leave Act treatise; named 2013 BTI Client Service All-Star.
**Personal:** BS, University of Maryland, 1984; JD, with honors, George Washington University, 1987.

## PERRONE, William A
Wiggin and Dana LLP, Stamford
203 363 7604
wperrone@wiggin.com

*Featured in Corporate/M&A (Connecticut)*

**Practice Areas:** Bill Perrone is a Partner in Wiggin and Dana's Corporate Department. Bill represents clients on complex, strategic, corporate transactions involving technology-driven companies, including mergers and acquisitions, business process and information technology outsourcing, software development, venture capital financing, and private equity. Bill represents a variety of enterprises at all stages of their development, from emerging technology companies to publicly-traded global entities. Bill has more than twenty-five years of experience counseling investors, buyers and sellers of technology-related assets. This extensive industry experience allows Bill to help clients efficiently achieve practical business out-

comes and structure, finance and implement their corporate strategies.

## PHILLIPS, Earl
Robinson & Cole LLP, Hartford
860 275 8220
ephillips@rc.com

*Featured in Environment (Connecticut)*

**Practice Areas:** Earl Phillips, chair of the Environmental and Utilities Group, has practiced environmental and natural resource law and worked on related utilities projects for over 30 years. Earl's practice includes environmental compliance counseling and risk management, transactional counseling, brownfield development, project and utility permitting, crisis management preparation and response, environmental defense, and liability allocation. He represents various natural resource, heavy manufacturing and recycling clients, and significant pharmaceutical, chemical, and petroleum interests, as well as facility and project developers, municipalities, and utilities. Earl is widely published and lectures to diverse business and legal audiences throughout the United States and abroad.

## POLLACK, Elliott B
Pullman & Comley, LLC, Hartford
860 424 4340
ebpollack@pullcom.com

*Featured in Healthcare (Connecticut)*

**Practice Areas:** Represents physicians in regulatory, licensure, medical staff, transactional, reimbursement, managed care and medical/legal affairs. Serves institutional health care providers including hospitals, nursing homes and substance abuse facilities. Litigates before Department of Public Health, Connecticut Medical Examining Board, Department of Social Services, Office of Health Care Access and in trial and appellate courts.
**Professional Memberships:** Member, Health Law Sections of the American and Connecticut Bar Associations; Hartford County Bar Association; American Health Lawyers Association; Healthcare Financial Management Association. Adjunct Faculty: University of Connecticut Law School.
**Career:** Health Law Editor, ABA Preview.
**Personal:** LLB, Columbia Law School; AB, Columbia College.

## PROCTOR, Michael
Pullman & Comley, LLC, Bridgeport
203 330 2145
mproctor@pullcom.com

*Featured in Real Estate (Connecticut)*

**Practice Areas:** Chair, Real Estate Department; practice includes commercial real estate finance and the acquisition, development, leasing and sale of commercial property; regularly represents banks, hospitals, developers, investors and businesses in all aspects of commercial real estate and real estate finance.
**Professional Memberships:** Member, Real Property Section, American Bar Association; Real Property, Commercial Law and Bankruptcy, and Environmental Law Sections, Connecticut Bar Association; Fairfield County Chapter, Real Estate

Finance Association; Urban Land Institute; Council on Law in Higher Education.
**Personal:** JD magna cum laude, Boston College of Law School; BA cum laude, Connecticut College.

## RAABE, Craig
Robinson & Cole LLP, Hartford
860 275 8304
craabe@rc.com

*Featured in Litigation (Connecticut)*

**Practice Areas:** Craig Raabe has tried many complex civil and criminal cases in state and federal courts. Craig is a Fellow of the American College of Trial Lawyers. His trial experience ranges from representing Fortune 50 companies in complex civil matters, including intellectual property, trade regulation and fraud, to representing public officials in white-collar criminal trials. Craig clerked for the Honorable Arthur H Healey at the Connecticut Supreme Court and has served on numerous court committees at the request of the Chief Judge of the Second Circuit Court of Appeals and the Chief Judge of the District of Connecticut.

## RAY, James
Robinson & Cole LLP, Hartford
860 275 8257
jray@rc.com

*Featured in Environment (Connecticut)*

**Practice Areas:** Jim Ray's practice focuses on counseling clients and litigating environmental, asbestos, and products liability cases. Much of his work involves disputes under the Comprehensive Environmental Response, Compensation, and Liability Act; the Resource Conservation and Recovery Act; underground tank laws; and the public trust doctrine as well as defense of government enforcement actions, third-party claims, and citizen suits. He also defends asbestos, lead-based paint, mold, and products liability cases and counsels clients regarding product recalls with the Consumer Product Safety Commission. Previously, Jim was a senior engineer for the Connecticut Department of Environmental Protection, Hazardous Waste Management Section.

## RECHEN, Thomas J
McCarter & English, LLP, Hartford
860 275 6706
trechen@mccarter.com

*Featured in Litigation (Connecticut)*

**Career:** Mr Rechen is an accomplished trial lawyer and business litigator with over two decades of experience handling commercial disputes on behalf of public and private companies in Connecticut and across the nation. His practice includes the full range of complex civil litigation matters — intellectual property, trade secret, business tort, contract, restrictive covenant, trade regulation and unfair competition claims. His clients include Fortune 50 retailers, product manufacturers, technology companies, professional service firms, financial institutions, construction firms and nonprofit organizations. Mr Rechen also represents property owners and developers in commercial real estate and leasing disputes. For full bio: http://www.mccarter.com/Thomas-J-Rechen/

### REIF, David
McCarter & English, LLP, Hartford
860 275 6703
dreif@mccarter.com
*Featured in Litigation (Connecticut)*
**Career:** Mr Reif has applied his experience and trial skills to a wide range of cases in state and federal courts in Connecticut and other jurisdictions, with more than two dozen jury verdicts and a more extensive number of court trials. A sampling of his cases includes defense and prosecution of fraud and civil RICO claims; representation of lending institutions in significant lender liability litigation; defense of class litigation arising under consumer fraud regulation; and representation of the manufacturers and distributors of consumer and industrial products and chemicals, in both product liability and distribution litigation. For full bio: http://www.mccarter.com/David-A-Reif/

### REILLY, Patricia
Littler Mendelson, PC, New Haven
preilly@littler.com
203 974 8703
*Featured in Labor & Employment (Connecticut)*
**Practice Areas:** Competition and trade secret, wage and hour, complex litigation and jury trials, discrimination and harassment.
**Professional Memberships:** US Supreme Court; US Court of Appeals, 2nd Circuit; US Court of Appeals, 8th Circuit; US District Court, District of Connecticut; Member, Litigation / Labor and Employment sections - American Bar Association; Connecticut Bar Association; New Haven County Bar Association.
**Career:** Patricia E Reilly represents clients in a range of employment law matters, with an emphasis on the litigation of employment discrimination and related torts; wage and hour issues; and trade secrets, restrictive covenants, and unfair trade practices disputes.

### ROHBACK, Thomas G
Axinn, Veltrop & Harkrider LLP, Hartford
860 275 8110
tgr@avhlaw.com
*Featured in Litigation (Connecticut)*
**Practice Areas:** Thomas Rohback is an experienced trial and appellate lawyer.
**Professional Memberships:** Bars of New York, Pennsylvania, Connecticut.
**Career:** Recognized by The National Law Journal as a top litigator, Mr Rohback is often brought in mid-stream to rescue important cases that have gone badly. After discovery had ended, he was brought in and won a jury verdict in state court in West Virginia, American States v. Flippo. After discovery closed, he was brought in to try Pereira v. Cogan (S.D.N.Y.) where he won a $40,000,000 bench verdict in favor of bankruptcy trustee suing directors and officers for breaches of fiduciary duties. He has served as national litigation counsel for Alcoa and other major companies. Among his many jury trials, he tried three cases in three months and obtained directed verdicts in each. Recent representative cases include: Artie's v.

Hartford Fire Insurance Co. (Complex Litigation Docket, Conn.), with class having already been certified and discovery closed, he was brought in and successfully tried to jury verdict this consumer class action where plaintiffs sought over $300 million. Successfully tried significant, confidential ICC commercial arbitration on behalf of Airbus. Combined Energies v. CCI (D. Me.), after defeating jurisdictional challenge based on arbitration clause (1st Cir.), defeated motion for summary judgment in corporate raiding case, and obtained favorable settlement. Asch Webhosting v. Adelphia (D.N.J.), aff'd, rehearing en banc denied (3d Cir.), dismissal of multimillion dollar business tort claims involving Internet service. Barrett v. Toroyan, et al. (Commercial Division N.Y.) (aff'd N.Y. App. Div.) won jury verdict rejecting multimillion dollar claims of breach of fiduciary duties by directors and officers. Kargo Inc. v. Pegaso PCS, S.A. (S.D.N.Y.), dismissal of $112 million tortious interference claim involving a disputed software licensing and hosting agreement. State of Connecticut v. Energy East Corporation defeated State's claims for preliminary injunction, after which State dismissed its multi-million dollar claim without any payment. Removed putative class action against Travelers from New Mexico State Court, then won dismissal of case (D.N.M.).
**Personal:** Columbia University Law School, New York, NY, 1978. Honors: Harlan Fiske Stone Scholar. Columbia University, New York, NY, 1974 MA. Union College, Schenectady, NY, 1973 BA summa cum laude. Honors: Nott Scholar. Phi Beta Kappa.

### SCHWARTZ, Daniel
Pullman & Comley, LLC, Hartford
860 424 4359
dschwartz@pullcom.com
*Featured in Labor & Employment (Connecticut)*
**Practice Areas:** Extensive trial and litigation experience in federal and state courts in commercial litigation and trade secret areas. Represents employers in employment law matters including employment discrimination, restrictive covenants, retaliation, wage/hour and social media/electronic communications.
**Professional Memberships:** Chair of "Social Media" Subcommittee, Labor and Employment Section, Standing Committee on Technology & Information Systems; House of Delegates, American Bar Association; Labor & Employment Section, Connecticut Bar Association.
**Publications:** Author, Connecticut Employment Law Blog.
**Personal:** JD, Washington University School of Law; BA, University of Pennsylvania; "40 Under 40" Award, Hartford Business Journal; "Top 25 Online Voices in Employment Law," HR Examiner.

### SCHWARTZ, Daniel L
Day Pitney LLP, Stamford
203 977 7536
dlschwartz@daypitney.com
*Featured in Labor & Employment (Connecticut)*
**Career:** Daniel L Schwartz is Chair of Day Pitney's Labor and Employment department. Dan

defends employers litigation matters including claims for wrongful termination, discrimination, harassment, invasion of privacy, breach of contract, whistleblower retaliation, violation of wage statutes and infliction of emotional distress. He also represents companies and individuals in injunction hearings arising from and related to non-competition/non-solicitation/non-disclosure obligations. In conjunction with his litigation practice, Dan counsels employers on hiring procedures, employment contracts, employee handbooks, internal investigations, accommodation of disabilities, harassment prevention, termination procedures, and other matters. Dan also represents broker-dealers, investment advisors and registered representatives in litigation and/or FINRA arbitrations.

### SHEARIN, James T
Pullman & Comley, LLC, Bridgeport
203 330 2240
jtshearin@pullcom.com
*Featured in Litigation (Connecticut)*
**Practice Areas:** Chair, Litigation Department. Experience in federal and state courts and before arbitration and mediation panels. Represents clients in business, intellectual property, banking, securities, antitrust and general civil litigation.
**Professional Memberships:** American Bar Association; Connecticut Bar Association - House of Delegates and Executive Committee of Federal Practice and Intellectual Property Sections; Connecticut Bar Foundation, Inc. - treasurer and Fellow; Raymond E. Baldwin Inn of Court; Federal Circuit Bar Association; Magistrate Judge Reappointment Committee.
**Career:** Executive Committee Member.
**Personal:** JD, high honors, University of Connecticut School of Law; BA, summa cum laude, University of Connecticut.

### SICILIAN, James
Day Pitney LLP, Hartford
860 275 0303
jsicilian@daypitney.com
*Featured in Litigation (Connecticut)*
**Career:** Jim Sicilian represents a broad range of business clients in trials and appeals of complex commercial disputes, including intellectual property and antitrust matters, among others. He has represented both plaintiffs and defendants, ranging from multinational Fortune 500 corporations to closely held companies and individuals, in patent, trademark, copyright, trade secret disputes, antitrust, and unfair trade practices cases. Jim served as law clerk for The Honorable Thomas J Meskill, US Court of Appeals for the Second Circuit, 1981-82.

### SLAVIN, Richard
Cohen and Wolf, PC, Bridgeport
203 222 1034
rslavin@cohenandwolf.com
*Featured in Litigation (Connecticut)*
**Practice Areas:** Chair of Securities Group. Practices securities regulation, securities litigation in state and federal courts, and banking regulation. He regularly represents broker-dealers, investment advisors, broker-dealer agents, invest-

ment advisor agents and solicitors, and issuers of securities before federal, state and self-regulatory securities agencies as general counsel, compliance counsel, and in arbitrations before self-regulatory agencies.
**Career:** Previously Director of the Connecticut Banking Department's Securities and Business Investments Division, Chief Enforcement Attorney for the Ohio Division of Securities and Enforcement Staff Attorney for the United States Securities and Exchange Commission.
**Personal:** Case Western Reserve University (BA, MBA) and University of Akron (JD).

### SMITH, R Jeffrey
Bingham McCutchen LLP, Hartford
860 240 2759
jeff.smith@bingham.com
*Featured in Real Estate (Connecticut)*
**Practice Areas:** Focuses on the national representation of institutional investors in all facets of real estate finance, including mortgage and mezzanine financings, syndicated and securitized loans, participation arrangements, joint ventures, workouts, and restructurings. Extensive experience in the purchase and sale of loan portfolios. Clients include life insurance companies, commercial finance companies, pension fund advisers and banks. Represents master and special servicers in connection with the modification, restructuring and enforcement of securitized loans. Strong background in asset-based lending, commercial finance and other forms of secured transactions.
**Personal:** Georgetown University Law Center, JD, 1978; Duke University, BA, cum laude, 1975.

### SOLTIS, Michael
Jackson Lewis LLP, Stamford
203 363 2558
SoltisM@jacksonlewis.com
*Featured in Labor & Employment (Connecticut)*
**Practice Areas:** Employment and labor, with emphasis on disability, health and leave management issues.
**Professional Memberships:** Member of the Connecticut Bar Association; American Bar Association; Defense Research Institute, Employment Law Committee; Connecticut Defense Lawyers Association, Employment Law Subcommittee, Chair.
**Career:** Admitted to practice before various federal courts in New York, Connecticut, Pennsylvania, Texas and Ohio. Author of The Connecticut Employment Law Manual and co-editor of blog on disability, leave and health management issues at www.disabilityleavelaw.com.
**Personal:** Received JD Magna Cum Laude from New York Law School and Master of Laws degree (LLM) in Labor Law from New York University.

### SPRINGER, Felix J
Day Pitney LLP, Hartford
860 275 0184
fjspringer@daypitney.com
*Featured in Labor & Employment (Connecticut)*
**Career:** Felix Springer has more than 30 years of experience handling matters involving employment discrimination, wrongful termination, and civil rights violations. He has tried more than

three dozen jury cases to a conclusion on behalf of management and argued 20 appeals in state and federal appellate courts, almost all as appellee. He also counsels and advises management regarding alternative dispute resolution, training supervisory employees, diversity and inclusion, reductions in force, sexual harassment and other employee investigations, hiring and termination, issues of defamation and privacy, employment agreements, employee handbooks and policies, covenants not to compete, and accommodation of the disabled.

**STEIN, Peter**
Epstein Becker & Green PC, Stamford
203 326 7420
PStein@ebglaw.com
*Featured in Labor & Employment (Connecticut)*
**Practice Areas:** Member of firm, Labor and Employment Practice; Managing Shareholder of the firm's Stamford office. Mr Stein represents both national and regional employers in all aspects of labor and employment law.
**Professional Memberships:** WESFACCA - the Westchester, New York/Southern Connecticut Chapter of the Association of Corporate Counsel.
**Personal:** JD, George Washington University Law School, with honors, 1975; BA, Bucknell University, 1972.

**STRANGE, Margaret 'Peggy'**
Jackson Lewis LLP, Hartford
860 331 1554
StrangeM@jacksonlewis.com
*Featured in Labor & Employment (Connecticut)*
**Practice Areas:** Employment litigation and counseling on behalf of management.
**Professional Memberships:** Connecticut Bar Association; SHRM; Middlesex Chamber of Commerce; admitted to practice: Connecticut, So. Dis. NY and 2nd Cir.
**Career:** Day, Berry & Howard, Hartford, Connecticut 1990-96; Joined Jackson Lewis in 1996; Elevated to Partner 1999.
**Publications:** Recent publications: "Systemic Gender Discrimination Claims on the Rise," and "Using Social Media To Screen Job Candidates."
**Personal:** Named in Connecticut Super Lawyers, Best Lawyers in America, Chambers USA. Curry College (BA Magna Cum Laude 1985); Suffolk University Law School (Cum Laude 1990). Married, one son.

**SULLIVAN, Shaun S**
Wiggin and Dana LLP, New Haven
203 498 4315
ssullivan@wiggin.com
*Featured in Litigation (Connecticut)*
**Practice Areas:** Shaun has represented clients for over thirty years in a variety of complex commercial lawsuits involving Fortune 500 companies. For example, Shaun was lead counsel in a series of private placement class actions that were routinely described in the press as the most complex suits ever filed in Connecticut. His clients have included financial institutions, national accounting firms, public utilities, high tech companies, insurance carriers and aviation manufacturers.

**Professional Memberships:** American College of Trial Lawyers, International Academy of Trial Lawyers, International Bar Association.

**SWERDLOFF, David A**
Day Pitney LLP, Stamford
203 977 7334
daswerdloff@daypitney.com
*Featured in Corporate/M&A (Connecticut)*
**Career:** David Swerdloff advises clients on mergers and acquisitions and general corporate matters. He has negotiated transactions of all sizes, ranging into the hundreds of millions of dollars. Representative industries include defense, medical instruments, food services and technology companies. David's corporate advice addresses a broad range of issues from formation through strategic growth and expansion. He has advised on issues involving the governance of pass-through entities (partnerships and LLCs), the rights of minority owners and management succession planning, and the legal issues faced in managing, exploiting and protecting key business assets.

**TAYLOR, Allan B**
Day Pitney LLP, Hartford
860 275 0225
abtaylor@daypitney.com
*Featured in Litigation (Connecticut)*
**Career:** Allan Taylor, a former law clerk to Justice Thurgood Marshall, represents clients at the trial and appellate level on matters involving complex questions of law, with an emphasis on issues of insurance coverage (for the insurer) and regulated industries. He has briefed and argued appeals in the First, Second, Eleventh and DC Circuits as well as in state appellate courts in Connecticut, Florida, Massachusetts, New Jersey, New York, and Rhode Island. Mr. Taylor is currently chair of the Connecticut State Board of Education and the immediate past-president of the National Association of State Boards of Education.

**TRILLING, Barry J**
Wiggin and Dana LLP, Stamford
203 363 7670
btrilling@wiggin.com
*Featured in Environment (Connecticut)*
**Practice Areas:** Chair, Climate Change and Sustainable Development practice; member of Real Estate, Environmental, and Energy, Clean-Tech, Insurance and Environmental Litigation groups.
**Professional Memberships:** Member, ABA, Connecticut Bar Association. Member, NAIOP (Commercial Real Estate Development Association) national corporate Board, Chair NAIOP Urban Redevelopment National Forum, former Chair and current Member of Environment and Infrastructure Subcommittee of NAIOP national corporate Public Affairs Committee; former President, NAIOP Connecticut and Suburban NY Chapter. Member Connecticut Business and Industry Association Environmental Policy Council.
**Personal:** Admitted in Connecticut, NY, Massachusetts, Pennsylvania, California. JD, 1971, University of California, Berkeley; BA University of California, Los Angeles.

**TUCCI, Theodore**
Robinson & Cole LLP, Hartford
860 275 8210
ttucci@rc.com
*Featured in Healthcare (Connecticut)*
**Practice Areas:** Ted Tucci has litigated significant cases for managed care and health insurers, and health care clients throughout the northeast. His experience includes representation of Fortune 50 health insurers in class actions, consumer litigation, business disputes and regulatory enforcement cases. He also represents multi-hospital healthcare systems in corporate litigation regulatory enforcement matters, and has litigated leading cases regarding medical staff privileges matters. Ted is a board member of business organizations focused on healthcare reform and representation of employers' interests in health insurance and healthcare delivery.

**VITARELLI, Richard F**
McCarter & English, LLP, Hartford
860 275 6755
rvitarelli@mccarter.com
*Featured in Labor & Employment (Connecticut)*
**Career:** Mr Vitarelli advises clients on labor relations and employment law aspects of mergers and acquisitions, union organizing, corporate restructuring, and contract administration. Mr Vitarelli represents only management in labor relations and employment law, including matters involving distressed entities, the National Labor Relations Act, the Railway Labor Act, collective bargaining, union organizing and employee benefits. His clients include employers in the airline, healthcare, construction, paper, manufacturing, trucking and fuel oil industries as well as governmental entities. For full bio: http://www.mccarter.com/Richard-F-Vitarelli/

**VOIGT, Richard**
McCarter & English, LLP, Hartford
860 275 6776
rvoigt@mccarter.com
*Featured in Labor & Employment (Connecticut)*
**Career:** Mr Voigt represents employers in a variety of employment-related matters, including wrongful discharge cases, employment discrimination cases, state and federal court injunction actions, breach of contract cases, trade secret/proprietary information cases, NLRB unfair labor practice proceedings, OSHA citation cases, and wage-hour claims. He has obtained summary judgments in state and federal courts on behalf of employers accused of wrongful discharge, discrimination and breach of contract and in OSHA cases on behalf of employers confronting substantial penalties and/or abatement costs. He has also negotiated collective bargaining agreements and litigated binding interest arbitration on behalf of employers. For full bio: http://www.mccarter.com/Richard-Voigt/

**WADE, James A**
Robinson & Cole LLP, Hartford
860 275 8270
jwade@rc.com
*Featured in Litigation (Connecticut)*

**Practice Areas:** A Fellow of the American College of Trial Lawyers since 1980, Jim Wade has tried numerous criminal and civil cases across the United States. For more than 20 years, Jim served as outside counsel to the Connecticut Democratic Party and has represented three Connecticut Governors in litigation. In the last several years, Jim has tried, on behalf of major corporations and their employees, complex criminal and civil cases involving antitrust, securities fraud, government contracting fraud, mail fraud, and public corruption. He has also represented numerous Fortune 500 companies on various compliance issues.

**WARREN, Jane**
McCarter & English, LLP, Hartford
860 275 6781
jwarren@mccarter.com
*Featured in Environment (Connecticut)*
**Career:** Ms Warren's 27 years of experience as an environmental attorney has made her keenly aware of the need for sophisticated, practical business lawyers who are knowledgeable about issues and opportunities in the highly regulated fields of environmental and land use law. Appreciating the often-varied interests of lending institutions, developers, manufacturers, corporations and regulators, her approach is to be sensitive to how the often conflicting approach of these entities affects her clients' decision-making processes. She brings a multidisciplinary viewpoint to her work and understands the importance of collaboration in this highly specialized area of the law. For full bio: http://www.mccarter.com/Jane-K-Warren/

**WEAVER, Maureen**
Wiggin and Dana LLP, New Haven
203 498 4384
mweaver@wiggin.com
*Featured in Healthcare (Connecticut)*
**Practice Areas:** Advises hospitals, health systems, provider networks, long-term care providers, home health care agencies, hospices, physicians, other health care providers, trade associations on regulatory, patient care, reimbursement, compliance, HIPAA, operational and corporate matters. Health Care Practice Chair, former Chair, firm Executive Committee.
**Professional Memberships:** Legal Committee of LeadingAge, Director Emeritus,Connecticut Business and Industry Association, Director, Association for Long Term Care Financial Managers. Past President, Connecticut Health Lawyers' Association. Former Director of the Connecticut Assisted Living Association. Fellow, American Bar Association and Connecticut Bar Association.
**Personal:** UCLA School of Law, JD (1986); Duke University, AB magna cum laude (1977).

**WHITNEY, Diane W**
Pullman & Comley, LLC, Hartford
860 424 4330
dwhitney@pullcom.com
*Featured in Environment (Connecticut)*
**Practice Areas:** Chair, Environmental Law Department. Represents businesses, individuals and municipalities in all areas of environmental

and land use planning and permitting. Trial and appellate work in both civil and criminal environmental matters, toxic torts, land use, representation before administrative agencies.

**Professional Memberships:** Member, Litigation and Environment, Energy and Resources sections of American Bar Association; Litigation, Environmental, Planning and Zoning sections of Connecticut Bar Association; Hartford County Bar Association; DRI; Board of Directors, Greater Hartford Legal Aid; Editorial Board, Connecticut Law Tribune.

**Personal:** JD, with honors, University of Connecticut School of Law; BA William Smith College; MAT, Colgate University.

---

**ZAKARIAN, Albert**
Day Pitney LLP, Hartford
860 275 0290
azakarian@daypitney.com
*Featured in Labor & Employment (Connecticut)*

**Career:** Al Zakarian is a trial lawyer practicing in the areas of employment and business litigation. He has tried more than 100 cases to verdict in both state and federal courts. In addition, he has substantial experience in alternative dispute resolution, including service as an arbitrator and mediator. Al also advises clients on litigation-avoidance strategies and techniques in both complex and highly sensitive disputes. Al is a fellow of the American College of Trial Lawyers, an advocate of the American Board of Trial Advocates, and a fellow of the College of Labor and Employment Lawyers.

---

**ZANDY, John C**
Wiggin and Dana LLP, New Haven
203 498 4330
jzandy@wiggin.com
*Featured in Labor & Employment (Connecticut)*

**Practice Areas:** Represents employers in labor and employment matters, including NLRB proceedings, collective bargaining, grievances and arbitrations, union campaigns; discrimination, sexual harassment, and wrongful discharge cases; wage and hour matters; OSHA proceedings; affirmative action plans and OFCCP audits; HR matters including discipline/discharge, handbooks, leave/ FMLA policies, employment and non-competition agreements.

**Professional Memberships:** Labor and Employment Law Sections of Connecticut and American Bar Associations.

**Personal:** Attorney - NLRB (Region 29); attorney – Solicitor's Office, US Department of Labor (Region 1); LLM, Labor Law, New York University Graduate School of Law; JD, Valparaiso University School of Law; BA, Miami University (Ohio).

# PULLMAN & COMLEY LLC

**www.pullcom.com** **tel:** 203 330 2000 **fax:** 203 576 8888

**Managing Partner:** D Robert Morris
Number of partners: 60  Number of other lawyers: 23

## Firm Overview:

Established in 1919, Pullman & Comley has earned a reputation as one of the preeminent providers of legal services in New England, serving clients throughout Connecticut, the Northeast and nationally. As a member of the Law Firm Alliance, an international affiliation of law firms, the firm offers its local and regional clients the benefit of global reach. The firm serves major financial institutions, public and private companies of all sizes, health care providers, service businesses, trade associations, manufacturers and emerging growth businesses in the alternative energy and information technology industries, as well as government entities, non-profit organizations and individuals.

## Main Areas of Practice:

### Corporate & Business:

The firm advises clients on a wide range of business issues, including choice of business entity, negotiation of sophisticated commercial agreements and financings, corporate governance, employee benefits, tax, and mergers, acquisitions and divestitures. The firm's attorneys are practical problem-solvers, well-versed in a wide range of transactions involving capital formation, securities law compliance, intellectual property protection, licensing agreements and business franchises, serving clients ranging from start-ups to established businesses.

### Bankruptcy, Creditors' Rights & Financial Restructuring:

The firm's bankruptcy attorneys are experienced in all areas of business bankruptcy including representing debtors, creditors, creditor's committees, trustees, investors and buyers.

### Litigation:

The firm's litigators bring creative and outside-the-box thinking to clients' unique problems, handling all phases of civil and criminal litigation at the state and federal levels. The firm represents clients in business litigation disputes involving contract claims, unfair competition, antitrust litigation and class shareholder derivative actions; defense of consumer protection, privacy and credit reporting claims; commercial foreclosures and lender liability cases; securities litigation and arbitration; construction litigation; intellectual property matters; product liability and product warranty litigation; professional malpractice litigation; insurance coverage litigation; administrative law matters including appellate review; and state and federal white collar crime.

### Energy, Utilities & Telecommunications:

The firm is a leader in the energy field, offering extensive transactional and regulatory experience in electricity and power markets; power plant development and financing; energy procurement, conservation and demand-side management; natural gas markets; emerging alternative energy and biofuels; water utilities and water treatment; and wireless and wireline telecommunications.

### Environmental & Land Use:

The firm counsels clients in all aspects of environmental law, as well as on a full range of planning, zoning, inland wetlands, affordable housing and development matters, including brownfield redevelopment and green development.

### Real Estate:

The firm represents clients on a full range of real estate transactions, including commercial real estate acquisitions and sales; real estate finance transactions; retail and office leasing; residential, commercial and community development projects; creation of condominiums and other common interest ownership structures; real estate loan workouts and restructurings; and urban redevelopment.

### Property Valuation:

The firm provides legal services to commercial property owners, both in tax appeal and eminent domain litigation. Valuation attorneys practice in the areas of real estate, taxation and municipal law, eminent domain, administrative law and litigation.

### Health Care:

The firm has counseled clients in nearly every major sector of the health care industry on regulatory, transactional and business matters. Experienced and innovative attorneys help navigate the complex maze of health care law for a broad range of health care providers, including hospitals, community health centers, nursing homes and other health care institutions, physicians and other health care practitioners.

### Labor & Employment:

The firm advises clients on all aspects of labor and employment law, including preventative counseling and training, employee relations practices, immigration law, and union issues. Its attorneys also litigate employment disputes of every type, including discrimination and retaliation claims, trade secret and noncompete agreements, ERISA claims and other contract and employment-related tort claims.

### Public Finance:

The firm provides bond counsel services to governmental entities and represents underwriters, credit enhancers, businesses, trustees and private individuals. The firm's public finance practice is recognized in Connecticut as well as nationally: over the last ten years, The Bond Buyer has consistently ranked Pullman & Comley within the top five bond counsel firms in the state of Connecticut, a ranking which includes both Connecticut and national firms.

### Trusts & Estates:

The firm advises individual clients on all aspects of estate and gift tax planning, charitable giving and philanthropic planning, business succession planning, estate settlement, trust administration, adoptions, conservatorships, guardianships and probate litigation. In addition, the firm represents many local and out-of-state banks and other trust services institutions as fiduciaries.

## PRACTICE AREAS

Corporate & Business
Environmental
Health Care
Litigation
Property Valuation
Public Finance
Real Estate
Trusts & Estates

## OFFICES

### CONNECTICUT

**BRIDGEPORT:** 850 Main Street, PO Box 7006, CT 06601-7006
Tel: 203 330 2000  Fax: 203 576 8888

**HARTFORD:** 90 State House Square, CT 06103-3702
Tel: 860 424 4300  Fax: 860 424 4370

**STAMFORD:** 107 Elm Street, Four Stamford Plaza, CT 06902-3834
Tel: 203 324 5000  Fax: 203 363 8659

**WATERBURY:** 500 Chase Parkway, Waterbury, CT 06708-3346
Tel: 203 573 9700  Fax: 203 573 9707

### NEW YORK

**WHITE PLAINS:** 777 Westchester Avenue, NY 10604-3520
Tel: 914 705 5355

**PULLMAN & COMLEY** LLC
**ATTORNEYS**

*Pulling Together. Succeeding Together.*

# ROBINSON & COLE LLP

**www.rc.com** **tel:** 860 275 8200 **fax:** 860 275 8299

**Managing Partner:** John B Lynch, Jr
Number of partners: 101 Number of lawyers: 210

## Firm Overview:

Robinson & Cole provides legal solutions to businesses, from start-up ventures to Fortune 100 companies and from nonprofits and educational institutions to state and municipal governmental entities. Since 1845, the firm has expanded to meet the changing needs of clients, representing them in a wide range of matters, including corporate; business and insurance litigation; tax and tax-exempt; finance; public finance; construction, land use, environmental and utilities, and real estate; health law; labor, employment, immigration, and benefits; intellectual property and technology; and government relations. The firm and its lawyers are ranked prominently by many leading legal surveys and rating services* including Chambers USA, U.S. News & World Report Best Law Firms, The Legal 500, Martindale-Hubbell, and Best Lawyers.
*Details about these services and their selection criteria are available on their respective websites.

## Main Areas of Practice:

Services provided by Robinson & Cole fall into four areas through which a broad range of legal solutions are available to regional, national, and international clients.

### Business Services:

The firm provides an array of services to business clients, including corporate and business transactional services such as digital media; distribution and franchise law; e-commerce; emerging company, private equity, and venture capital; intellectual property and technology; life sciences; M&A; securities; and technology and outsourcing transactions. The firm also has sophisticated practice capabilities in the areas of business reorganizations, workouts, and bankruptcy; employment, including counseling and training, employee benefits and compensation, litigation, noncompetition and trade secrets, OSHA compliance, labor relations, and immigration; finance; health care; privacy; public finance; local, state, and federal taxation; tax-exempt organizations; and trade and antitrust law.

### Land Law Services:

For clients who lease, own, manage, develop, or buy and sell real estate assets, the firm has assembled a team of more than 65 professionals with extensive experience in land law matters, including those covering the ownership or leasing of real estate and real property rights; real estate finance; land use and zoning; and real estate development, including affordable housing and community development; construction; crisis management and emergency response; energy, petroleum, telecommunications, and other utilities-related uses; and environmental, sustainability, and climate change matters.

### Litigation Services:

The firm's extensive litigation capabilities are provided by a multi disciplined group of more than 60 lawyers who represent clients in all types of disputes, including antitrust/unfair competition, consumer class action defense, white-collar defense, creditors' rights, trade secrets, securities, breach of contract, employment litigation, and intellectual property litigation. Additionally, the firm has deep experience in admiralty and maritime law, asbestos litigation, construction litigation, e-discovery and information management, health litigation, products liability, real estate litigation and title insurance matters, and matters pertaining to religious organizations. A particular strength of the firm is its insurance and reinsurance capability, which encompasses matters such as fidelity and surety, fire and explosion, large loss property subrogation, liability coverage, marine and inland marine, professional liability insurance, property insurance, and reinsurance and excess insurance. The firm's lawyers are adept at putting clients in the optimal position either to try their cases or to settle them if in their best interest. The firm also offers clients sophisticated capabilities in the areas of alternative dispute resolution and appellate matters.

### Government Relations:

An added benefit that the firm offers to its clients is a "three-state solution" that encompasses all aspects of administrative and legislative lobbying, issue and crisis management, press and public relations, and grass roots organizing in the states of New York, Connecticut, and Rhode Island. The firm's lobbyists help clients achieve their objectives, whether it be the passage, defeat, or modification of legislation or regulations, financial assistance for a development project, or state or local government procurement of client products and services. The firm's team has successfully lobbied on a variety of issues, including insurance, economic development, tax, labor, health care, public utility, environment, banking, finance, transportation, and gaming.

## PRACTICE AREAS

Antitrust & Trade Regulation
Appellate
Banking & Financial Services
Bankruptcy
Business Transactions, Finance & Securities
Construction
Corporate Governance
Employee Benefits, Compensation & ERISA
Employment, Labor & Immigration
Emerging Companies, Private Equity & Venture Capital
Energy & Communications
Environmental
Estate Planning & Probate
Public Finance
Government Relations
Health Law
Insurance
Intellectual Property & Technology
Land Use & Zoning
Litigation
Mergers & Acquisitions
Products Liability
Real Estate Finance, Development & Leasing
Tax-Exempt Organizations
Tax Planning & Representation
White-Collar Defense

## OFFICES

### CALIFORNIA
**LOS ANGELES:** 1600 Rosecrans Avenue, Media Center 4th Floor, Manhattan Beach, CA 90266
Tel: 310 321 7666  Fax: 213 596 0493

### CONNECTICUT
**HARTFORD:** 280 Trumbull Street, CT 06103-3597
Tel: 860 275 8200  Fax: 860 275 8299

**STAMFORD:** 1055 Washington Boulevard, CT 06901-2249
Tel: 203 462 7500  Fax: 203 462 7599

### FLORIDA
**SARASOTA:** 1343 Main Street, Suite 400, FL 34236-5635
Tel: 941 906 6850  Fax: 941 906 6851

### MASSACHUSETTS
**BOSTON:** One Boston Place, 25th Floor, MA 02108-4404
Tel: 617 557 5900  Fax: 617 557 5999

### NEW YORK
**ALBANY:** 111 Washington Avenue, NY 12210-2207
Tel: 518 463 4560  Fax: 518 463 0416

**NEW YORK:** 885 Third Avenue, 28th Floor, NY 10022-4834
Tel: 212 451 2900  Fax: 212 451 2999

### RHODE ISLAND
**PROVIDENCE:** One Financial Plaza, Suite 1430, RI 02903-2485
Tel: 401 709 3300  Fax: 401 709 3399

**RC | ROBINSON & COLE** LLP
ATTORNEYS AT LAW

# WIGGIN AND DANA LLP

www.wiggin.com

**Chair of Executive Committee:** Robert W Benjamin
Number of partners: 76  Number of other lawyers: 68

## Firm Overview:

Wiggin and Dana is a full-service firm, with over 140 attorneys, serving clients domestically and abroad from offices in Connecticut, New York and Philadelphia. Wiggin and Dana provides legal counsel to an international client base of major corporations and institutions, as well as to private businesses, entrepreneurs, individuals and families. Clients turn to Wiggin and Dana for help with specific transactions and complex proceedings such as antitrust and other government investigations, complex commercial litigation, all aspects of franchise, distributor and dealer litigation, real estate, environmental and energy law, the development and financing of healthcare facilities, and the full range of legal services sought by the technology community, including the protection of intellectual property and domestic and international licensing and distribution. The firm also has experience handling sophisticated corporate transactions for international clients and complex administrative proceedings, arbitrations, litigation and enforcement actions across the United States.

## Main Areas of Practice:

### Corporate:

Wiggin and Dana acts as general counsel for a diverse group of businesses. Clients range from large, publicly traded entities with a national or global presence, to established family-owned businesses, and include emerging and entrepreneurial companies. The wide breadth of industries includes biotechnology, pharmaceutical, medical devices, software, internet, healthcare, chemical, utilities and related industries. The firm also handles specific projects, such as mergers and acquisitions, joint venture, strategic alliances and other partnering arrangements and sophisticated forms of debt and equity financing, for an even larger group of clients that includes Fortune 500 companies.

### Healthcare:

Wiggin and Dana has had an extensive Health Law Practice for decades, and remains one of the largest in the region. Attorneys with Wiggin and Dana's Health Law Practice provide general and special legal counsel to a wide spectrum of healthcare organizations. These organizations include academic medical centers, hospitals and hospital systems, long-term care facilities, continuing care retirement communities, assisted living facilities, ambulatory care facilities, home healthcare agencies, hospices, pharmacies, ambulance providers, durable medical equipment suppliers, physicians, and individual practitioners. The Health Law Practice Group also represents state and national trade associations and professional societies active in healthcare policy issues.

### Labor, Employment & Benefits:

Wiggin and Dana's Labor, Employment and Benefits Practice Group provides comprehensive legal counseling to a wide range of employers, carefully guiding management through the maze of increasingly complex labor and employment laws and regulations. The firm's clients come in all sizes, from the large, multi-state corporation to the small start-up business. Its attorneys represent management in a wide array of industries, including manufacturing, biotechnology, healthcare, utilities, banking, construction, financial services, insurance, retail, publishing and education.

### Litigation:

When faced with critical, high-stakes disputes, clients turn to Wiggin and Dana's Litigation Department. The firm's litigators have outstanding strategic and tactical judgment, extensive trial experience with successful results, and the ability to manage costs with sensible rates and staffing. Its Civil, Administrative and White-Collar Litigation Practice has broad experience successfully representing commercial, financial, insurance, manufacturing, utility, healthcare, franchisor, distribution, new technology and professional (medical, legal and accounting) clients. The firm is often asked to appear at advanced stages of litigation that has become particularly risky, complex or difficult. The firm's litigators actually try cases frequently before juries, judges, arbitrators and agencies across the country.

### Real Estate, Environmental & Energy:

Wiggin and Dana provides a full range of focused services to domestic and international owners, developers, professionals, utilities and governmental agencies. Its Real Estate Transactions Group offers experience in all aspects of real estate transactions. The Development and Redevelopment Group focuses on land use and affordable housing issues for institutional, commercial, governmental and individual investors and developers. Its Environmental Group provides clients counsel that helps them comply with environmental regulations, market new technologies and conduct transactions that involve environmental issues. The firm's longstanding Energy and Utilities Practice helps regional energy generators and merchants deal with complex regulatory mandates, build critical infrastructure, complete complex transactions and advance industry issues. Inbound foreign investors throughout the world count on its International Real Estate Group for comprehensive, one-stop real estate transactional and management services for their US properties.

### Private Client Services:

The firm's experienced Private Client Services attorneys help its clients from wide-ranging businesses and professions, deal successfully with complex issues that impact them and their families. From business succession planning to philanthropic arrangements to trusts and estates issues, the firm provides sophisticated counsel that helps families and individuals with substantial assets maximize their wealth for themselves and future generations. It provides a full spectrum of private client services, including business succession planning, charitable planning, estate planning, family and closely-held business planning, family office representation, international private client services, probate litigation and trusts and estate administration services.

### Clients:

The firm serves clients located in the Northeast, as well as throughout the United States, Canada, Europe, Latin America and Asia. The firm acts as general or special counsel for publicly traded corporations, banks, accounting, architectural, engineering and securities firms, public utilities, insurance companies, family-owned businesses, new technology companies and start-ups, hospitals, nursing homes and other healthcare providers, universities, colleges and schools, and individuals. It serves as US counsel for many substantial European companies.

## OFFICES

**CONNECTICUT**

**NEW HAVEN:** One Century Tower, PO Box 1832, 265 Church Street, CT 06508-1832
Tel: 203 498 4400  Fax: 203 782 2889

**HARTFORD:** One CityPlace, 185 Asylum Street, CT 06103-3402
Tel: 860 297 3700  Fax: 860 525 9380

**STAMFORD:** Two Stamford Plaza, 281 Tresser Boulevard, CT 06901
Tel: 203 363 7600  Fax: 203 363 7676

**GREENWICH:** 30 Milbank Avenue, CT 06830
Tel: 203 363 7600  Fax: 203 930 3606

**PENNSYLVANIA**

**PHILADELPHIA:** Two Liberty Place, 50 S 16th Street, Suite 2925, PA 19102
Tel: 215 988 8310  Fax: 215 988 8344

**NEW YORK**

**NEW YORK:** 450 Lexington Avenue, 38th Floor, NY 10017-3913
Tel: 212 490 1700  Fax: 212 490 0536

# WIGGIN AND DANA

## How lawyers are ranked

Every year we carry out thousands of in-depth interviews with clients in order to assess the reputations and expertise of business lawyers worldwide. The qualities we look for (and which determine rankings) include technical legal ability, professional conduct, client service, commercial awareness/astuteness, diligence, commitment, and other qualities most valued by the client. For details of our research team, see p.5.

# DELAWARE: An Introduction

## Contributed by Young Conaway Stargatt & Taylor LLP

For more than a century, Delaware has been the preferred jurisdiction for business. Nearly 1,000,000 business entities are domiciled in Delaware, including over 60% of the Fortune 500 and half of the companies traded on the New York Stock Exchange and NASDAQ. More than 100,000 new corporations, partnerships, and limited-liability companies were formed in Delaware last year. Delaware is a leading jurisdiction for business litigation, and the preferred jurisdiction for businesses seeking to resolve corporate governance disputes and protect their intellectual property rights. Why Delaware?

### Premier Jurisdiction for Business

Businesses consistently choose Delaware as their legal home. The Delaware Secretary of State reports that over the last decade, 63% of the Fortune 500 companies have incorporated in Delaware and the total number of businesses formed in Delaware has grown, on average, 7% [1]. In 2011, 31,472 new corporations and 93,219 new alternative entities formed in Delaware [2]. Delaware's business prestige continues year over year for many reasons, including:

1. The Delaware General Corporation Law – the most dynamic business formation statute in the nation. Delaware's General Corporation Law (DGCL) has been used as a model by many other states, but what sets it apart is the process by which it is regularly updated and revised by the legislature to meet the changing needs of business. The DGCL has benefitted greatly from what has been aptly described as the "unwritten compact between the Bar and the state legislature." [3] In this process, the legislature works closely with members of the Delaware Bar who practice corporate law to continually recommend and draft necessary changes to the DGCL. The result is a statute that is dynamic, yet balanced to meet the needs of all constituencies.

2. The Delaware Limited Liability Company Act and Limited Partnership Act – like the DGCL, these alternative entity statutes are the most advanced and flexible of their kind, and are regularly revised to address current issues and events. Each act is intended "to give maximum effect to the principle of freedom of contract," permitting customized approaches to a wide range of issues, including membership or partner status, managerial control and economic rights.

3. The Delaware Court of Chancery – a unique 220-year-old business court that has written most of the modern US corporation case law. Cases involving corporate and alternative entity issues are concentrated within this court. As a result, the

court generates an adaptive and coherent body of decisional law that builds upon itself daily. Moreover, because of the limited jurisdiction of the court, it has the ability and expertise to resolve business disputes in an expeditious manner. These foundational attributes consistently attract sophisticated litigants and disputes to the Court of Chancery, which, in turn, provides the fodder necessary to help the court continue to build its expertise and prestige in handling such disputes.

### Premier Jurisdiction for Patent Infringement Litigation

Over the past 30 years, the District of Delaware has garnered a reputation as the preferred jurisdiction for patent infringement litigation. In recent years, Delaware has ranked highest among the 94 judicial districts in the USA for the number of patent cases filed per judge, and the number of patent trials conducted. Delaware's district judges enjoy a well-earned reputation for being among the most experienced judges to preside over patent infringement disputes. Along with judicial expertise, litigants enjoy other advantages in this district, including:

1. Procedures favoring efficient resolutions – such as setting case schedules early in the litigation, including a date certain for trial; generally resolving patent cases within 16-24 months; consistent handling of motions to transfer and for summary judgment; and continually fine-tuning case management for efficiency and effectiveness.

2. A collaborative relationship between the federal Bench and Bar – including regular consultation between judges and practitioners about best practices and case management; the Bench's provision of guidance to practitioners for effective advocacy; and the Bench's active participation in and sponsoring of Continuing Legal Education Programs on matters from substantive law to trial practice.

3. An unparalled mediation program handled by magistrate judges with considerable patent law experience – led by magistrate judge Thynge, who has 20 years of experience successfully settling the vast majority of patent cases she mediates. In fact, the district's mediation program has gained national acclaim.

Footnotes:
[1] Delaware Division of Corporations 2011 Annual Report, available at
  http://corp.delaware.gov/2011CorpAR.pdf.
[2] Lewis S. Black, Jr., Why Corporations Choose Delaware, printed and distributed by the Delaware Department of State, Division of Corporations (2007).
[3] Ibid

# BANKRUPTCY/RESTRUCTURING

Commentary about individuals can be found under their firm's paragraph. If the firm has no paragraph (is not ranked) look at Other Notable Practitioners.

## Bankruptcy/Restructuring
### Leading Firms

**Band 1**
Cole, Schotz, Meisel, Forman & Leonard PA *
Morris, Nichols, Arsht & Tunnell LLP *
Richards, Layton & Finger PA *
Young Conaway Stargatt & Taylor LLP

**Band 2**
Blank Rome LLP *
Landis Rath & Cobb LLP *
Pachulski, Stang, Ziehl, Young, Jones & Weintraub PC *
Potter Anderson & Corroon LLP *
Skadden, Arps, Slate, Meagher & Flom LLP & Affiliates *

**Band 3**
Ashby & Geddes *
Bayard, P.A. *
DLA Piper LLP (US) *
Morris James LLP *
Pepper Hamilton LLP *
Reed Smith LLP
Saul Ewing LLP *
Womble Carlyle Sandridge & Rice, LLP *

## Bankruptcy/Restructuring
### Leading Individuals

**Star individuals**

| | |
|---|---|
| Collins Mark D | Richards, Layton & Finger PA * |
| Patton Jr James L | Young Conaway Stargatt & Taylor LLP |
| Silverstein Laurie Selber | Potter Anderson & Corroon LLP * |

**Band 1**

| | |
|---|---|
| Abbott Derek C | Morris, Nichols, Arsht & Tunnell LLP |
| Brady Robert S | Young Conaway Stargatt & Taylor LLP |
| Davis Jones Laura | Pachulski, Stang, Ziehl, Young, Jones |
| Dehney Robert J | Morris, Nichols, Arsht & Tunnell LLP |
| Fatell Bonnie Glantz | Blank Rome LLP * |
| Felger Mark E | Cozen O'Connor (ONP)[†] * |
| Galardi Gregg M | DLA Piper LLP (US) * |
| Gwynne Kurt F | Reed Smith LLP |
| Landis Adam G | Landis Rath & Cobb LLP * |
| Minuti Mark | Saul Ewing LLP |
| Morgan Pauline | Young Conaway Stargatt & Taylor LLP |
| Pernick Norman L | Cole, Schotz, Meisel, Forman & Leonard * |
| Stratton David B | Pepper Hamilton LLP * |

**Band 2**

| | |
|---|---|
| Bowden William P | Ashby & Geddes * |
| Brown Stuart M | DLA Piper LLP (US) * |
| Chehi Mark S | Skadden, Arps, Slate, Meagher & Flom * |
| Daluz Tobey | Ballard Spahr LLP (ONP)[†] * |
| DeFranceschi Daniel J | Richards, Layton & Finger PA * |
| Fournier David M | Pepper Hamilton LLP * |
| Glassman Neil B | Bayard, P.A. * |
| Grohsgal Bruce | Pachulski, Stang, Ziehl, Young, Jones |

**Band 3**

| | |
|---|---|
| Cousins Scott | Cousins, Chipman & Brown, LLP (ONP)[†] |
| Davis Charlene D | Bayard, P.A. * |
| Detweiler Donald J | Pepper Hamilton LLP * |
| Knight John H | Richards, Layton & Finger PA * |
| Kortanek Steven K | Womble Carlyle Sandridge & Rice, LLP |

* Indicates firm / individual with profile.
[†] ONP = Other Notable Practitioner.

| | |
|---|---|
| Kunz III Carl N | Morris James LLP |
| Miller Stephen M | Morris James LLP |
| Monaco Jr Frank A | Womble Carlyle Sandridge & Rice, LLP |
| Nestor Michael R | Young Conaway Stargatt & Taylor LLP |
| Pacitti Domenic E | Klehr Harrison Harvey Branzburg (ONP)[†] |
| Schlerf Jeffrey M | Fox Rothschild LLP (ONP)[†] * |
| Silberglied Russell C | Richards, Layton & Finger PA * |
| Stickles Kate | Cole, Schotz, Meisel, Forman & Leonard * |
| Ward Christopher A | Polsinelli PC (ONP)[†] |

**Band 4**

| | |
|---|---|
| Brown-Edwards Theresa V | Potter Anderson & Corroon LLP * |
| Busenkell Michael | Womble Carlyle Sandridge & Rice, LLP |
| Carickhoff David | Blank Rome LLP * |
| Clark Anthony W | Skadden, Arps, Slate, Meagher & Flom |
| DeBaecke Michael D | Blank Rome LLP * |
| Desgrosseilliers Mark L | Womble Carlyle Sandridge & Rice, LLP |
| Fallon Brett D | Morris James LLP |
| Harron Edwin | Young Conaway Stargatt & Taylor LLP |
| Heath Paul N | Richards, Layton & Finger PA * |
| Kelbon Regina Stango | Blank Rome LLP * |
| Lastowski Michael R | Duane Morris LLP (ONP)[†] |
| Martin Craig | DLA Piper LLP (US) * |
| Morton Edmon L. | Young Conaway Stargatt & Taylor LLP |
| Robinson Richard | Reed Smith LLP |
| Sandler Bradford | Pachulski Stang Ziehl & Jones LLP |
| Stearn Jr Robert J | Richards, Layton & Finger PA * |
| Waite Joel | Young Conaway Stargatt & Taylor LLP |

**Up-and-coming individuals**

| | |
|---|---|
| Chipman William E | Cousins, Chipman & Brown, (ONP)[†] |
| Merchant Michael J | Richards, Layton & Finger PA * |
| Mumford Kerri K | Landis Rath & Cobb LLP * |
| Quirk Marion | Cole, Schotz, Meisel, Forman & Leonard * |

## Band 1

### Cole, Schotz, Meisel, Forman & Leonard PA
See profile on p.1752

THE FIRM This highly regarded team is renowned for its work for debtors in Chapter 11 reorganizations and for its expertise in bankruptcy litigation. The team has earned plaudits for its work as co-counsel on Tribune Company's Chapter 11, a matter involving 111 debtors, including one which holds the majority of assets of the Chicago Cubs. The firm tends not to advise major financial institutions, and so is able to appear on the other side to them.
**Sources say:** "They are terrific and wonderful to work with. They produce work of the highest quality, and are cost-effective and efficient."
**KEY INDIVIDUALS Norman Pernick** (see p.773) cochairs the department and is widely acknowledged for his work on Chapter 11 cases. He is leading the team in the Tribune Company bankruptcy. Sources say he is "a brilliant strategist," and that he is "always available" and "extremely knowledgeable in the bankruptcy arena." **Kate Stickles** (see p.775) is "a strong attorney" who is "able to handle multiple matters under significant time pressure, while maintaining her composure." Noted for her role as a case administrator, she is "remarkable at being able to navigate the shoals." **Marion Quirk** (see p.774) is described as a "deal-oriented, detail-oriented" lawyer, and has played an important role in a number of cases, including the Chapter 11 proceedings for Open Range Communications.

### Morris, Nichols, Arsht & Tunnell LLP
See profile on p.783

THE FIRM This team has a strong reputation for its work in Chapter 11 bankruptcies and restructurings. It appeared as co-counsel representing RG Steel and affiliates in a $1 billion bankruptcy action. Sources praise the team's work as both co-counsel and lead counsel, for which its expertise in litigation is particularly highlighted.
**Sources say:** "The team is coming up with solutions for the client, is very adaptive and good with the business and legal aspects, and is always available to talk. They always return their calls and are very easy to work with, and the level of knowledge within the group is excellent."
**KEY INDIVIDUALS** Group head **Robert Dehney** is highly rated by peers as a key figure within the bankruptcy community. He acted as co-counsel in the RG Steel bankruptcy action and is highly rated as a lawyer who "is very

aware of all the options and what the judges think." "Client-oriented" **Derek Abbott** maintains an exceptionally busy practice and has led the team's efforts in a number of cases, including acting as co-counsel for Delta Petroleum and as debtor's counsel for Related Companies. He is "well rounded, and a very good bankruptcy lawyer in both litigation and case work," and is commended for his practical approach to cases.

### Richards, Layton & Finger PA
See profile on p.785

THE FIRM This large group is noted for the quantity and quality of the cases it tackles. It acts for a broad range of clients involved in every aspect of bankruptcy, including debtors, lenders, investors and all types of creditors. The group is acclaimed for its breadth of talent, and has worked on some of the most significant bankruptcies filed in

Delaware, having recently acted for Washington Mutual, JPMorgan Chase and SP Newsprint.

**Sources say:** *"The lawyers are highly skilled and professional. They deliver creative solutions to difficult problems and are willing to work consensually and, failing that, litigate forcefully."*

**KEY INDIVIDUALS** Practice chair **Mark Collins** (see p.768) is noted for *"looking for business solutions,"* and *"has made a name for getting the biggest cases and then making them run very smoothly."* He recently acted as co-counsel to JPMorgan Chase in the Chapter 11 actions of Coach Am Group. **Daniel DeFranceschi** (see p.769) is *"a terrific litigation strategist"* whose advice and opinion are widely sought by his peers. He is *"not only an effective strategist but he conducts himself with an utterly professional demeanor, and with an open and collegial deportment toward his client."* He recently acted on Blitz USA's Chapter 11. **John Knight** (see p.772) primarily focuses on representing debtors and secured creditors, and is respected for his calm and thoughtful approach to cases. He is currently acting as lead counsel for Chef Solutions and affiliates in its Chapter 11 proceedings. *"Excellent litigator"* **Russell Silberglied** (see p.775) is involved in both bankruptcy litigation and Chapter 11 and Chapter 5 proceedings. He is lead counsel representing a significant unsecured creditor in a Chapter 11 case. **Paul Heath** (see p.771) maintains a broad practice and is praised for his ability to *"bring knowledge and practical guidance to difficult and tense situations."* Often advising on Chapter 11s, he is *"exceptionally well versed in the law"* and is *"very able in court and at the negotiating table."* The *"prompt, practical and efficient"* **Robert Stearn** (see p.775) is lauded for his ability to connect with his clients and really understand their businesses. He was the lead attorney in a recent case in which claims of fraud, civil conspiracy and unjust enrichment against his client were successfully dismissed. **Michael Merchant** (see p.773) has been involved in a number of cases of late, including representing Blitz USA and affiliated debtors in its Chapter 11, and acting for the official committee of unsecured debtors in the Chapter 11 of a retail store operator.

### Young Conaway Stargatt & Taylor LLP

**THE FIRM** Commentators laud this firm's bankruptcy team, which regularly represents debtors, creditors' committees and other significant stakeholders involved in Chapter 11 restructurings and out-of-court negotiations. With offices in both Wilmington and New York, this firm is heavily involved in some of the largest filings in the country. Recent highlights include serving as co-counsel to the debtors in the bankruptcy of Eastman Kodak and affiliates.

**Sources say:** *"They have the client's interests always in mind. They are efficient, and work well individually and together. Young Conaway represents incredible value and I would recommend them to anyone facing bankruptcy."*

**KEY INDIVIDUALS James Patton** remains a pivotal figure at the firm and is regarded by clients as *"the best bankruptcy lawyer in the country."* He is especially rated as a *"thoughtful and respectful"* attorney who has a *"very detailed knowledge of the Bankruptcy Code."* He led the

team's efforts representing the independent manager of Dynegy Holdings in resolving claims of fraudulent conveyances between itself and its parent company, Dynegy. **Robert Brady** impresses clients with his *"hard work and acumen."* His recent highlights include representing Sand Spring and its affiliated debtor entities as restructuring counsel, and acting as lead restructuring counsel to Pemco World Air Services. Chair of the firm's bankruptcy practice, **Pauline Morgan** is *"an excellent leader, very responsive to clients and effective with opposing counsel."* She has *"the best judgment"* and develops a personal relationship with clients, giving *"a degree of trust you can't buy."* She was lead partner for the firm on the Eastman Kodak bankruptcy, and was also involved as restructuring counsel in the PMI Group's Chapter 11 restructuring. **Michael Nestor** is an *"experienced, very practical attorney"* who headed the team representing Solar Trust of America in a series of related Chapter 11 cases. **Joel Waite** is described as *"very smart, technically very good and highly reliable."* He advised on the Chapter 11 restructuring of Bicent Holdings. **Edwin Harron** *"knows his stuff inside and out,"* and has a *"good overall view of the picture"* and *"a wonderful manner of interacting with people."* With a *"disciplined, thoughtful and considerate approach"* to his work, he is seen as a future star. **Edmon Morton** is highly rated by peers, who laud him as both *"practical and smart."* He was involved in the representation of the independent manager in the Dynegy Holdings matter.

## Band 2

### Blank Rome LLP
See profile on p.2235

**THE FIRM** This firm's bankruptcy group represents both creditors and debtors in a wide range of matters, including litigation. The team is especially known for its work representing the committees of unsecured clients, having recently represented the official committees of Solyndra, Bancorp, Centaur and Beacon Power.

**Sources say:** *"The firm was very thorough and professional and achieved my main objective, despite a serious legal battle at the end."*

**KEY INDIVIDUALS Bonnie Glantz Fatell** (see p.770) *"brings a high degree of integrity, rationality and knowledge"* to any case she is involved with, and *"you can expect her to find a resolution and bring a rational, even-minded process to it."* She is highly experienced in bankruptcy reorganizations and related litigation, and recently served as counsel to the creditors' committee for Solyndra. **Michael DeBaecke** (see p.769) *"understands the big picture"* and *"gets things done that are in the best interests of his clients."* He is currently serving as Delaware counsel for a number of creditors. Practice chair **Regina Stango Kelbon** (see p.2220) is renowned as a fierce litigator who fights for her clients. She recently served as counsel to the liquidating trustee in the Mortgage Lenders Network in a case where she successfully reduced the claim pool by more than half. **David Carickhoff** (see p.768) is praised for his patient

approach to clients, his understanding of the law and his ability to deliver results.

### Landis Rath & Cobb LLP
See profile on p.781

**THE FIRM** This boutique bankruptcy firm is well known and respected for its specialty in first chair and conflicts counsel engagements. Recent highlights include serving as bankruptcy counsel to JPMorgan Chase in the Washington Mutual Chapter 11, and serving as first chair to AES Thames in its Chapter 11 bankruptcy.

**Sources say:** *"The work is of consistently high quality, and they have a much-enjoyed ability to keep their eyes on the ball and not allow distractions to come in the way. They have a strong base of knowledge about the Bankruptcy Court and I think that the Court very much respects their work."*

**KEY INDIVIDUALS Adam Landis** (see p.772) has made a name for himself as *"one of the go-to guys for conflict work for bigger representations, because he is such a fantastic lawyer."* He is also noted for his experience in both creditor and debtor cases as both first chair and local counsel, and he is *"very much in demand with out-of-state lawyers."* He was the lead partner serving as bankruptcy counsel to JPMorgan in the Washington Mutual cases. Up-and-comer **Kerri Mumford** (see p.773) is a *"no-nonsense"* lawyer who *"makes a very good presentation to the court"* and is a *"good negotiator."* She *"does a good job for her clients"* because *"she really understands their businesses."*

### Pachulski, Stang, Ziehl, Young, Jones & Weintraub PC
See profile on p.694

**THE FIRM** This is one of the largest boutique bankruptcy firms in Delaware, and is noted not only for the exceptional amount of debtor work that it handles, but also for the increasing number of creditors' committees it represents. Key highlights include representing Point Blank Solutions as lead counsel in its Chapter 11 cases, and representing an ad hoc group comprising a large subset of the holders of Washington Mutual Bank senior notes in Washington Mutual's Chapter 11 cases.

**Sources say:** *"A national firm that has a fantastic bankruptcy group. They've been involved in pretty much every significant case in Delaware for years."*

**KEY INDIVIDUALS** Group head **Laura Davis Jones** is *"one of the top Delaware bankruptcy lawyers"* because of her *"great reservoir of knowledge about transactions."* Her exceptional experience means she has a *"very good working knowledge of the case law,"* so is *"able to recognize patterns and be in a good position to try and gauge the outcome."* She specializes in representing debtors in complex Chapter 11 proceedings and out-of-court dealings. **Bruce Grohsgal** is a *"very bright"* and *"aggressive litigator"* who represents both debtors and creditors' committees. He is particularly noted for his work from the second chair, but also has experience as lead partner, representing a large subset of the holders of Washington Mutual Banking senior notes and their interests in the recent Chapter 11 cases. **Bradford Sandler** has rapidly built a name for himself as co-head of the firm's national creditors' committee practice. He is a "*creative, calm, effective*" lawyer who is also "*quick, smart and aggressive.*"

## Potter Anderson & Corroon LLP
See profile on p.784

THE FIRM This team of seven lawyers is especially renowned for its creditor practice, although recently it has increased its presence in debtor and creditors' committee representation. The group is also active in other creditors' rights areas, including out-of-court restructurings and state law receiverships.

Sources say: "*They exhibit the highest ethics and prompt service, and provide knowledgeable and relevant advice and counsel, excellent legal analysis and presentation, highly polished legal briefs and pleadings, as well as effective and formidable courtroom appearances, at both trial and appellate levels.*"

KEY INDIVIDUALS Laurie Selber Silverstein (see p.775) is "*a first-class bankruptcy and restructuring lawyer with significant experience.*" She "*knows bankruptcy law inside-out,*" "*practices at the most sophisticated level*" and "*exhibits the highest possible integrity in all her dealings.*" She is especially noted for her expertise in representing both creditors' committees and individual creditors. Theresa Brown-Edwards (see p.768) is consistently rated as one to watch, with peers describing her as "*one of the brightest lawyers at the firm.*" She regularly acts as lead partner, including representing special committees, boards of directors and the purchasers of assets in bankruptcies.

## Skadden, Arps, Slate, Meagher & Flom LLP & Affiliates
See profile on p.2008

THE FIRM Specializing in representing debtors, this internationally renowned firm prides itself on minimizing the time its clients spend in Chapter 11, offering prepackaged and pre-negotiated plans. A recent highlight was the firm's work for Travelport and Travelport Holding on its recent restructuring of Travelport Holding's payment-in-kind credit facility.

Sources say: "*I think the firm as a whole is excellent – it's really a very good debtor shop.*" "*Overall, it's a top-notch firm.*"

KEY INDIVIDUALS Mark Chehi (see p.768) is a "*great draftsman*" who writes "*long, complex and detailed bankruptcy plans.*" Specializing exclusively in bankruptcy, he has extensive experience in representing companies in out-of-court restructurings, prepackaged bankruptcies and Chapter 11 cases. Group head Anthony Clark (see p.768) is a "*spectacular litigator*" who routinely represents debtors, creditors and acquirers.

## Band 3

## Ashby & Geddes
See profile on p.778

THE FIRM This 11-strong team maintains a busy practice and is noted for its work representing creditors' committees, in addition to serving as debtors' counsel and in bankruptcy litigation. A highlight for the team was serving as bankruptcy counsel to the equity committee in the Washington Mutual cases.

Sources say: "*This firm is responsive to clients.*"

KEY INDIVIDUALS William Bowden (see p.767) is a "*consummate professional*" who marries being "*extremely practical*" with being "*very capable.*" He led the team representing the equity committee in the Washington Mutual Chapter 11.

## Bayard, P.A.
See profile on p.779

THE FIRM This well-regarded group regularly represents debtors, creditors' committees and equity committees, and is also involved in both prosecuting and defending avoidance actions. A highlight for the team was representing the statutory committee of equity security holders in the Trident Microsystems Chapter 11 cases.

Sources say: "*They are careful, meticulous, knowledgeable and personally very pleasant to work with.*"

KEY INDIVIDUALS Group head Neil Glassman (see p.771) is an experienced bankruptcy lawyer who is routinely called on to represent debtors, official committees of unsecured creditors and others. He is also recognized for his specialization in advising insurance companies through insolvency proceedings, and also in regulatory matters in Delaware. Charlene Davis (see p.769) is a "*marvelous lawyer*" with an "*exceptional track record.*" Especially noted for her litigation skills, she recently served as local counsel for the board of a UK-based pension plan and pension protection fund.

## DLA Piper LLP (US)
See profile on p.1971

THE FIRM This nationally renowned firm's six-member Delaware bankruptcy practice represents companies in financial difficulties, purchasers and investors of distressed companies. The firm operates a national approach to bankruptcy: it is regularly engaged not only in Delaware, but across the whole of the country. Highlights include handling the Northern District of Texas Chapter 11 cases of Reddy Ice and the debt restructuring of PJ Finance Company.

Sources say: "*The quality of their work was excellent – first rate.*"

KEY INDIVIDUALS Head of the firm's nationwide bankruptcy group, Gregg Galardi (see p.770) has "*a very strong track record in large debtor cases.*" He regularly travels the country to represent clients in different states, such as his work on the Reddy Ice Chapter 11 cases. Stuart Brown (see p.768) "*is outstanding,*" according to sources, who praise his expertise and his character. An "*experienced and insightful lawyer,*" he is "*very careful and deliberate*" in his approach. He was part of the team that represented PJ Finance in its debt restructuring. Craig Martin (see p.773) is "*attentive, intelligent, extremely responsive and customer-centric.*" He is also praised for his "*understanding of the story of the case, and getting to the bottom line very quickly.*"

## Morris James LLP
See profile on p.782

THE FIRM This seven-strong team represents both secured and unsecured creditors, interested purchasers of assets, creditors' committees and debtors, and is regularly involved in some of the largest Chapter 11 cases filed in Delaware. Clients include ICM, AFCO Credit and Coltec Industries.

Sources say: "*Their timeliness, attention to detail, and willingness to go the extra mile in terms of client service make a huge difference to us in our approach to Delaware cases.*"

KEY INDIVIDUALS Carl Kunz "*has his head screwed on straight*" and is "*very careful and adept in court,*" where he is noted for his courtroom presence. He is also highlighted for his exceptional paperwork: occasionally, "*his papers are so reliable they end up in judges' opinions.*" Group head Stephen Miller is "*extremely knowledgeable and strategic in his actions,*" and "*pays close attention to detail.*" He regularly represents AFCO Credit in a broad range of matters, including financing issues, fraudulent transfers and adequate protection. Brett Fallon is an experienced litigator who routinely represents both debtors and creditors in bankruptcy proceedings.

## Pepper Hamilton LLP
See profile on p.2248

THE FIRM This well-regarded debtors' shop has also built a solid reputation for its work representing purchasers and creditors' committees, along with other parties. The team is also noted for its expertise in litigation matters such as defense of fraud and avoidance actions. Clients include Washington Mutual creditors' committee, Solar Trust of America creditors' committee, and Ally Financial.

Sources say: "*They prevail in disputes on the merits, even when they are the underdogs. They give excellent, practical and timely advice and counsel. They are user-friendly and helpful to our common clients.*"

KEY INDIVIDUALS David Stratton (see p.775) is a very experienced and respected attorney who is noted for his "*utmost integrity and professionalism.*" In addition to serving as counsel in bankruptcy cases, he is a noted mediator. A recent highlight for him was serving as co-counsel to the Washington Mutual creditors' committee. David Fournier (see p.770) is "*a straight shooter*" who is "*very smooth and smart.*" He has extensive experience representing debtors, creditors' committees, landlords and purchasers. He was involved in the team that represented Capitol Infrastructure as lead counsel in its Chapter 11 cases. Donald Detweiler (see p.769) "*has a strong knowledge of the bankruptcy code*" and represents a large variety of parties both in and outside of court. He also has "*superb judgment and very strong people skills, which makes him an extraordinarily valuable resource to his clients.*"

## Reed Smith LLP

THE FIRM This international firm maintains an office in Delaware that is regularly called on to represent both international and national clients, including lenders, hedge funds and debtors, with a special focus on creditors' committees. Clients include Privet Fund management, CenturyLink and PNC Bank.

**Sources say:** "*Excellent: knowledgeable, thorough, efficient and insightful.*" "*The whole firm is a class-A operation.*"

**KEY INDIVIDUALS Kurt Gwynne** is a noted litigator who "*has tremendous knowledge of the bankruptcy code.*" He has traditionally been seen as a creditors' committee specialist, but has recently been expanding to serve as special counsel in significant cases. **Richard Robinson** is "*fully versed in navigating the bankruptcy code*" and is "*always thinking multiple steps ahead.*" He is regularly engaged to represent both lenders and borrowers.

## Saul Ewing LLP
See profile on p.2249

**THE FIRM** This 15-strong team is well known for its work representing nearly all parties in Chapter 11 cases, with the exception of banks or other financial institutions so as to avoid conflicts of interest. A major highlight for the team was its work as lead debtors' counsel to Hussy Copper and its five related entities.

**Sources say:** "*They demonstrated strong organizational skills and knowledge of bankruptcy proceedings under Chapter 11 rules. We consider them outstanding.*"

**KEY INDIVIDUALS Mark Minuti** is a very experienced litigator who is "*smart and tough*" while also being able to "*explain complex legal issues*" to clients. He was the lead partner involved in the Hussy Copper Chapter 11 case, during which he oversaw the successful bid by Libertas Copper.

## Womble Carlyle Sandridge & Rice, LLP
See profile on p.2049

**THE FIRM** Specializing in Chapter 11 cases, this respected team represents all stakeholders through all proceedings in the bankruptcy courts and frequently takes on first chair work involving substantial amounts of litigation. The busy team has an impressive roster of clients, including Marathon Oil, State of Montana, Royale Linens and Her Majesty the Queen in Right of Canada.

**Sources say:** "*They are getting an increasing role in creditors' committees.*"

**KEY INDIVIDUALS Steven Kortanek** is an experienced bankruptcy lawyer and litigator. He has extensive experience advising a broad range of different industries in the bankruptcy context. He recently served as local counsel to the committee of unsecured creditors in the Chapter 11 of Allen Family Foods. **Frank Monaco** maintains a substantial creditors practice and has been involved in a large number of mediations of late. He recently represented the State of Montana in the Third Circuit Court of Appeals, successfully preventing specific claimants from pursuing state court actions against his client. **Mark Desgrosseilliers** represents debtors, creditors and asset purchasers in bankruptcy and restructuring matters. He represents Carroll Services as plan administrator in the Chapter 11 of Goody's Family Clothing. **Michael Busenkell** is an experienced lawyer who "*you go to when you need a deal done.*" He was recently lead counsel for the official committee of unsecured creditors in the Converting Solutions Chapter 11 case.

## Other Notable Practitioners

**Tobey Daluz** (see p.769) of Ballard Spahr LLP is "*a sharp and experienced lawyer*" who is "*excellent in court.*" She is well known for her work with key clients DuPont and ACE. She has also remained busy with work in real estate cases outside of Delaware. **Mark Felger** (see p.770) of Cozen O'Connor is a noted litigator and mediator with "*superb judgment, particularly concerning the judges and operation of the Delaware bankruptcy court.*" He represents debtors, individual creditors and creditors' committees, among other parties, in major Chapter 11 cases. His burgeoning workload as a mediator has also attracted praise from peers, primarily for his calm approach. **Christopher Ward** of Polsinelli PC has impressed sources with his work in difficult situations. He focuses his practice on debtors and committees of unsecured creditors, and has recently served as lead counsel to the official committee of unsecured creditors in the Open Range Chapter 11, and as special litigation counsel to the Chapter 7 trustee in the same cases. **Scott Cousins** of Cousins, Chipman & Brown, LLP specializes in representing creditors and both official and ad hoc committees of creditors in large Chapter 11 cases as both local and lead counsel. **Domenic Pacitti** of Klehr Harrison Harvey Branzburg LLP is a "*really strong bankruptcy litigator*" who can also turn his hand to creditors' committee work. **Jeffrey Schlerf** (see p.774) of Fox Rothschild LLP is a "*very hard-working*" lawyer who maintains a broad practice, representing most parties involved in Chapter 11 bankruptcy cases. He led the team's efforts as local counsel to Major League Baseball in the recent Chapter 11 case of the Los Angeles Dodgers. **William Chipman** of Cousins, Chipman & Brown, LLP is both a "*really skilled practitioner and a really nice guy,*" who has had "*plenty of court work time*" to hone his skills. **Michael Lastowski** of Duane Morris LLP is an experienced bankruptcy litigator, but is noted for his ability to turn his hand to any kind of matter.

# CHANCERY

Chancery p.758; Mainly Plaintiff p.758

Commentary about individuals can be found under their firm's paragraph. If the firm has no paragraph (is not ranked) look at Other Notable Practitioners.

## Band 1
## Chancery

### Morris, Nichols, Arsht & Tunnell LLP
See profile on p.783

**THE FIRM** This large team frequently represents corporations, partnerships and limited liability companies in some of the largest cases before the Court of Chancery. The group is equally comfortable acting as local counsel or primary counsel, and maintains an exceptionally busy practice, which has recently included successfully having four members of the transaction committee of Barnes & Noble

dismissed from the case arising from the buyout of the booksellers.

**Sources say:** "*Excellent, focused advice based on a deep understanding of our requirements and business drivers, delivered in a very user-friendly manner.*" "*They understand the needs and drivers of the business and strive to achieve the best result for the client and are unafraid to tell you when the matter should not be pursued.*"

**KEY INDIVIDUALS Kenneth Nachbar** is one of the most significant players in the Delaware Court of Chancery. Consistently praised for his creativity, he "*thinks outside the box*" and "*often comes up with inventive solutions and strategies.*" In addition, sources praise his ability to "*master

the material quickly and offer solid advice,*" helped by his "*knack for analyzing a complicated situation and quickly identifying the important issues.*" A "*really tremendously gifted advocate,*" **William Lafferty** is a "*true expert in Delaware law*" and "*a class act,*" who approaches cases "*fairly, professionally and reasonably.*" A "*dogged advocate,*" he was recently involved in the successful defense of Berkshire Hathaway in its shareholder derivative action relating to David Sokol. The "*impressive*" **Jon Abramczyk** maintains a broad practice, including litigation arising from governance and control, and M&A. He recently successfully represented Hallmark and other defendants in the initial trial and subsequent appeal challenging the recapitalization of Crown Media Holdings. **Mark Hurd**'s practice focuses primarily on defending stockholder class and derivative actions. He recently acted as lead partner representing Pfizer against various complaints concerning its acquisition of Icagen. *"A stalwart of the Bar,"* **Gilchrist Sparks** is *"one of the best Delaware chancery lawyers over the past 50 years,"* and continues his exceptional work for the firm in an advisory role.

## Potter Anderson & Corroon LLP

See profile on p.784

**THE FIRM** This large group of more than 30 lawyers handles both transactional and litigation matters. It is able to tackle the largest cases, and is frequently engaged as lead counsel in some of the biggest matters before the Court of Chancery. The large client roster includes Intel, Bank of America, AIG and News Corp.

**Sources say:** *"They have a great sense of the actions and conduct that the judges accept. They can be fierce advocates, are very able counselors and in reacting to arguments made by others they are fully capable of handling litigation on their own." "Highly skilled in the Delaware law."*

**KEY INDIVIDUALS Donald Wolfe** (see p.776) is described as *"the full package,"* due to his *"terrific ability to explain ideas"* and his abilities as a litigator. He is *"very good at cutting through the garbage and can point right to the issues."* He recently led the team defending Robert Rosenkranz, controlling stockholder of Delphi Financial Group, against shareholder litigation arising from Delphi's acquisition of Tokio Marine Holdings. *"A fabulous lawyer,"* **Peter Walsh** (see p.775) *"knows his stuff inside out."* Described as *"very persuasive in oral arguments,"* he is also *"smart, focused and polite – and extremely effective."* He is *"very good at positioning his arguments"* to *"craft a solution to get to that right answer."* He recently represented Hewlett-Packard in several matters relating to the severance of Mark Hurd as CEO. **Kevin Shannon** (see p.775) is *"a good litigator"* who specializes in valuation work and appraisals, in which he is *"certainly one of the best."* He has *"good judgment"* and is *"a good sounding board"* to bounce ideas off. **Stephen Norman** (see p.773) maintains a busy practice working in the Court of Chancery and acting as a counselor to stockholders, officers and directors. He was involved in the team representing Wal-Mart in responding to claims of failure to comply with the FCPA with respect to allegations of bribery in Mexico. **Michael Pittenger** (see p.774) is primarily active on the advisory transactional aspects of chancery work. He was second chair in the defense of David Sokol against allegations of insider trading. The *"extraordinarily energetic"* **Matthew Fischer** (see p.770) is *"undaunted by even Herculean amounts of work that have to be done in a very short time period."* A *"tremendous team player,"* he is *"very much the type of person you want on your side in the heat of battle."* He maintains a broad practice which includes shareholder derivative, class action suits and alternative entities litigation. **Michael Goldman** (see p.771) maintains an *"excellent reputation"* as a senior lawyer whose practice primarily consists of giving advice and formal opinions under Delaware law. **Berton Ashman** (see p.767) is *"a real workhorse"* who is tipped for future success in the Court of Chancery. He was on the team representing Answers Corporation and its directors in litigation arising from the acquisition of Answers.

## Richards, Layton & Finger PA

See profile on p.785

**THE FIRM** The team at Richards, Layton & Finger is one of the biggest in the state, and takes on all types of cases before the Court of Chancery. The practice has been involved in five of the six confidential chancery arbitrations that have been filed to date. It recently represented Goldman Sachs in a derivative case challenging its compensation scheme.

**Sources say:** *"They're very sophisticated when it comes to giving legal advice, but they're also very personable; you feel at ease with them despite their sophistication. The people there are at the top of their game, but they don't come at you like they're better than you." "By reputation, it is the premier firm for corporate transactions in America. Its reputation in the whole country is unparalleled."*

**KEY INDIVIDUALS Gregory Williams** (see p.776) acts as an arbitrator and represents clients in the Court of Chancery. Sources say that *"his knowledge of the Chancery Court is just unsurpassed: as good as you get in terms of knowing the Chancellors and knowing how arguments are likely to play."* In addition, he *"really knows the businesses and wants to find cost-effective solutions for his clients."* **Raymond DiCamillo** (see p.770) is *"a rock star"* because *"his personal demeanor is so accessible, folksy and down-to-earth that you get the benefit of a really sharp analytical lawyer with country lawyer finesse, which is a really rare combination."* **Anne Foster** (see p.770) is a *"very smart lawyer"* who impressed one source because *"she knew the law of the case inside and out. She knew completely what the plaintiff's end-goal was."* **Gregory Varallo** (see p.775) is *"brilliant and charismatic, but he's a thinker as well." "He comes alongside you when you're talking about an issue rather than head on. He thinks with you, which is very rare."* He was the principal lawyer in the Goldman Sachs derivative case challenging its compensation scheme, which is being appealed. **Catherine Dearlove** (see p.769) is *"hard-working, effective and smart."* Sources appreciate that she is *"intellectual and passionate at the same time,"* a *"superb communicator"* and also *"highly responsive."* She can *"navigate the many small details of a litigation matter without losing the big picture"* and is *"very personable and easy to work with."* **Blake Rohrbacher** (see p.774) is an *"extraordinarily smart"* lawyer, and is considered to be *"a walking encyclopedia of Delaware law"* who *"takes an academic approach"* to his work. Sources say that *"he is probably going to be one of the leaders in the Delaware Bar in the future."*

## Skadden, Arps, Slate, Meagher & Flom LLP & Affiliates
### See profile on p.2008

**THE FIRM** This renowned international firm takes on a broad range of litigation at all levels, both within Delaware and around the country. The team is regularly engaged in defense of class and derivative actions, bankruptcy litigation and representation of special committees. It recently represented Express Scripts in the settlement of class action litigation relating to its acquisition of Medco.

**Sources say:** *"They know the law, the players and the strategy, plus they are exceptionally responsive. Skadden is capable of moving from problem to strategy to execution in light speed." "Skadden is exceptionally responsive to client needs. Its lawyers are available at all hours to handle work on an*
expedited basis, as needed. The firm has a very deep bench of talented partners, counsel and associates."*

**KEY INDIVIDUALS Thomas Allingham** (see p.767) is widely lauded as one of the top lawyers in the state and is said to be *"the complete package to litigate a case"* because *"he writes well, he's substantive and he presents well."* He has been involved with the Wilmington Trust case alleging that the company concealed risks in its loan portfolio. Team head **Edward Welch** (see p.776) is an *"excellent advocate"* who is seen as a *"leader in his field."* He is noted for his *"good judgment,"* and often takes the lead role in cases. He was recently involved in defending Novell and its directors in parallel actions in both the Chancery Court and the District Court for Massachusetts relating to Novell's recent acquisition by Attachmate. **Robert Saunders** (see p.774) is a *"well-respected"* and *"exceptional litigator"* who is *"dangerous and extremely good on his feet."* He specializes in defending strike suits and recently took the lead in the firm's representation of BlackRock in a derivative lawsuit brought by common stockholders alleging breach of fiduciary duties by the directors for the fund. **Karen Valihura** (see p.775) is noted as a *"very thorough and good writer"* who is also *"very practical"* and *"very good at advising when to negotiate."* Sources also note her work ethic, saying: *"She's a workhorse – she will really dig deep into a case and devote long hours to figuring out the best way to litigate it."*

## Young Conaway Stargatt & Taylor LLP

**THE FIRM** This compact team specializes in providing advice and litigation skills in hostile takeovers, contesting challengers by stockholders in mergers, transactions within the energy sector and a variety of work in and outside of the bankruptcy court. Its clients include Atlas Energy, Mark Hurd, Gore and Hugh Hefner.

**Sources say:** *"The team is excellent, insightful and prompt."*

**KEY INDIVIDUALS David McBride** is the team's *"superstar"* and is *"very well respected by the court."* According to interviewees, he is *"as solid and honest as you'd ever want to meet,"* and *"a great lawyer and a great guy."* In addition to being *"very good at putting a case together,"* he is noted for his excellent judgment and hailed as *"a lawyer's lawyer."* **Bruce Silverstein** is a *"smart, strategic thinker"* who is *"obviously one of the top choices for the biggest cases."* He recently represented Great Wolf Resorts and its directors in shareholder litigation relating to its acquisition by Apollo Global Management. **Martin Lessner** is a *"top-notch deal lawyer"* who has a *"ready and comprehensive knowledge of Delaware law."* Sources appreciate that he has *"good insight on judges and lawyers,"* and is *"very responsive and commercially practical."*

## Band 2
## Chancery

## Abrams & Bayliss LLP
### See profile on p.777

**THE FIRM** This team is noted for its representation of both plaintiffs and defendants in the Court of Chancery. It is also praised for its work litigating transactional disputes.
**Sources say:** *"A chancery boutique that does sophisticated litigation in the Court of Chancery." "They work very hard and deliver good results with good value."*

**KEY INDIVIDUALS** Described as a *"fighter,"* **Kevin Abrams** is a *"hugely respected figure at the Bar"* and *"a very effective advocate."* He acted on the $7.1 billion merger of Massey Energy and Alpha Natural Resources, representing the Board of Massey. **Thompson Bayliss** is noted for his prowess in written work, and is *"extremely bright, very thoughtful and deliberative."*

## Ashby & Geddes
### See profile on p.778

**THE FIRM** The team at Ashby & Geddes is regularly retained to work as co-counsel by national and international law firms. Its broad remit includes expedited proceedings, both statutory summary and appraisal proceedings, and fiduciary duty litigation. An example of the team's work is its representation of Gould Electric Motor Repair and Jerry Gould, Jr. as lead trial counsel in litigation relating to the dissolution of a Delaware corporation.

**Sources say:** *"They give the highest and most technically accurate advice."*

**KEY INDIVIDUALS Stephen Jenkins** (see p.771) is praised for his *"very good depth of knowledge and experience,"* particularly within the field of proxy contests. Clients appreciate his advice, with one noting: *"I consult him not only on Delaware laws, but federal issues as well; even in New York I will ask for his advice."* The *"hugely respected"* **Lawrence Ashby** (see p.767) enjoys a *"tremendous reputation"* and is much sought for his advice on corporate governance transactions in particular.

## Bouchard Margules & Friedlander PA

**THE FIRM** This boutique firm represents plaintiffs and defendants in litigation matters. It focuses on alternate entity disputes, stockholder class and derivative actions and other matters, and is regularly hired as co-counsel by some of the largest firms in the country.

**Sources say:** *"They have such a good reputation with the courts – you want them to be the face of the case." "Smart aggressive lawyers with a strong track record for success; they win cases for their clients."*

**KEY INDIVIDUALS Andre Bouchard** is a *"highly polished and effective courtroom advocate"* who is *"very good on his feet."* He is noted for the quality of his written work, and is praised for *"thinking through the issues with depth."* He is equally comfortable representing plaintiffs and defendants in derivative actions. **Joel Friedlander** receives praise for his work on corporate governance matters.

## Morris James LLP
### See profile on p.782

**THE FIRM** This distinguished Delaware firm advises and litigates on behalf of clients on disputes ranging from self-dealing transactions for limited partnerships to structuring transactions. Key clients include DuPont, which the team recently represented in a misappropriation of trade secrets case.

Sources say: *"You really cannot overstate the knowledge that they bring – both of the judges and of Delaware law. When you talk to them off the tops of their heads, they've got relevant cases."*

**KEY INDIVIDUALS Clarkson Collins** is a *"very capable lawyer"* who is *"a valuable resource in how to present your ideas."* He is praised for his knowledge of both the judges and their rulings, and *"his knowledge extends beyond Chancery to the District Court as well."* Of late he has represented Rob Ellis in his continuing litigation against Paul Touradji relating to Catequil Management. **Peter Ladig's** *"legal analysis is excellent, his knowledge of Delaware law is brilliant,"* and he is also a *"very personable guy."* He is *"just about everything that you would want with a co-counsel,"* say interviewees. **Lewis Lazarus** is *"highly intelligent and tough but reasonable,"* and is noted for his up-to-date knowledge of all the latest cases in Delaware. He receives particular praise for his perspective: *"He understands beyond the case and sees the bigger picture."* **Edward McNally** *"knows what he's doing,"* and *"has excellent judgment and is well respected,"* according to the market. Sources also appreciate his connections and ability to deal with complex cases. He attained a summary judgment against Bonanza Restaurants in a sizable contract claim.

## Proctor Heyman LLP

**THE FIRM** This boutique firm has earned a strong reputation for its work with LLCs and private companies. One key work highlight saw the group represent BAE Systems Land & Armaments in a matter involving a multidistrict fraudulence conveyance action. The team also represented Isilon Systems in an advancement action. Sources highlight the group's willingness to tackle difficult cases.

Sources say: *"An excellent firm, cost-effective and very efficient. A successful boutique."*

**KEY INDIVIDUALS Kurt Heyman** is a *"real go-to person for advice,"* according to sources. His knowledge of local practice and his ability to think of the big picture when dealing with a case are also well appreciated by clients. He acted as receiver for the liquidation of Buck & Doe Run Valley Farms. Market observers highlight **Vernon Proctor** as a *"well-respected"* and *"very smart and solid"* attorney. He has defended the directors of Suntec Industries in various matters. **Samuel Hirzel** is a *"bright young litigator"* with *"substantive skills"* that sources appreciate. He recently assisted in representing Copart in a fraudulent inducement/breach of contract action.

## Seitz Ross Aronstam & Moritz LLP

**THE FIRM** This firm has quickly established a reputation as a quality practice among clients and peers alike. It is particularly strong in corporate and IP matters, and is well able to deal with large cases. Sources consider it to be a solid alternative to larger firms.

Sources say: *"A cut above." "A smart bunch and reasonable to deal with." "A new, small and excellent firm."*

**KEY INDIVIDUALS CJ Seitz** is appreciated for his good judgment, persuasiveness and intellect. Sources also comment positively on his *"real insight into the judges."* **Brad Aronstam** attracts praise from observers as a *"diligent and smart"* attorney with a strong focus in corporate law.

## Band 1
### Chancery: Mainly Plaintiff

### Grant & Eisenhofer PA
See profile on p.780

**THE FIRM** This longstanding plaintiffs' law firm is renowned for its careful selection of cases, which frequently push and define legal boundaries, and often result in M&A settlements with financial recoveries for the investors. The team recently represented a range of shareholders against El Paso's board of directors, successfully arguing that its merger with Kinder Morgan was disloyal to the shareholders.

Sources say: *"They're much more selective in the cases that they bring: they usually have a much better developed theory in what they're trying to get for the plaintiff, and that thinking shows up with some very good results."*

**KEY INDIVIDUALS** Firm cofounder **Jay Eisenhofer** (see p.770) splits his time between Wilmington and New York. Described as a *"deep thinker"* who is both *"measured and calm,"* he is a *"great strategist"* who recently successfully led the team that secured a $29 million payout from the chairman of Barnes & Noble to settle a shareholder derivative suit. **Stuart Grant** (see p.771) is *"the best in the business"* and *"does a terrific job"* on any case he is involved with. *"Enormously respected by the judges,"* he is *"the reigning king"* of plaintiff lawyers in Delaware. In addition to leading the team's efforts in the El Paso matter, he was involved in the Del Monte Foods shareholders' litigation that resulted in an $89.4 million settlement.

### Prickett, Jones & Elliott PA

**THE FIRM** This chancery group is noted for its work on both plaintiff and defendant cases. Able to effectively maintain separate practices as individuals, its lawyers take on some of the largest cases in front of the Court of Chancery. The team's recent success in the Southern Peru Copper case against Grupo México was one of the most important cases of the year, and resulted in a $1.26 billion award payout to Southern Peru.

Sources say: *"They come up with some really creative theories."*

**KEY INDIVIDUALS Ronald Brown** led the team on the Southern Peru Copper case. He focuses on representing plaintiffs, regularly acting as lead counsel. **Michael Hanrahan** takes on both defense work and plaintiff cases. Sources note that he specializes in advising on cases that are *"interesting, large and need to be brought before the court." "Creative and smart,"* he is a *"very strong advocate"* who *"can see things other people can't see."*

## Band 2
### Chancery: Mainly Plaintiff

### Chimicles & Tikellis

**THE FIRM** This plaintiffs' firm has a long and distinguished history in Delaware, with a string of high-value victories under its belt. The team is equally comfortable as first chair or acting as local counsel in large substantive shareholder suits, especially concerning breach of fiduciary duty by directors.

Sources say: *"A longstanding Delaware firm, and they know their stuff."*

**KEY INDIVIDUALS Pamela Tikellis** is an experienced and well-regarded plaintiff lawyer. She has experience of a wide range of cases, including class actions and derivative litigation.

### Rosenthal, Monhait & Goddess PA

**THE FIRM** This boutique undertakes diverse chancery cases, from LLP work through to banking and insurance. Sources commend the firm for the quality of its work and hold it in high regard, particularly for its high levels of integrity.

Sources say: *"The firm is a preeminent local counsel for chancery cases on the plaintiff side."*

**KEY INDIVIDUALS Norman Monhait** is *"not an easy mark"* for opponents and is well appreciated for his judgment and knowledge. He specializes in class and derivative actions.

## Other Notable Practitioners

**Daniel Rath** (see p.774) of Landis Rath & Cobb is singled out by sources as being *"highly responsive"* and *"well respected by the local Bar and a very capable, experienced courtroom lawyer."* Clients comment that *"his support is deep and well versed."* He acted as lead counsel on the US Education Loan Trust IV. At the same firm, **Rebecca Butcher** (see p.768) *"always provides insightful written work"* and is particularly appreciated by sources for her high-quality work and persuasive arguing ability. She has a broad practice and has advised EMC Mortgage on a number of cases against Bear Stearns Mortgage Funding Trust. Head of the corporate litigation practice at DLA Piper, **John Reed** (see p.774) is a *"hard-nosed litigator"* who is *"well experienced, confident and capable,"* according to sources. **David Jenkins** of Smith, Katzenstein & Jenkins specializes in corporate litigation for all parties from a broad spectrum of industries and professions. **Stephen Brauerman** (see p.768) of Bayard acted for NKS Distributors on a variety of recent litigation. He handles corporate and IP matters, including alternative entity control disputes.

# CORPORATE/M&A

Commentary about individuals can be found under their firm's paragraph. If the firm has no paragraph (is not ranked) look at Other Notable Practitioners.

## Corporate/M&A & Alternative Entities
### Leading Firms

**Band 1**
Morris, Nichols, Arsht & Tunnell LLP *
Potter Anderson & Corroon LLP *
Richards, Layton & Finger PA *

**Band 2**
Delaware Counsel Group LLP
Skadden, Arps, Slate, Meagher & Flom LLP & Affiliates *
Young Conaway Stargatt & Taylor LLP

**Band 3**
Prickett, Jones & Elliott PA

## Corporate/M&A
### Senior Statesmen

**Senior Statesmen: distinguished older practitioners**
Sparks III A Gilchrist    *Morris, Nichols, Arsht & Tunnell LLP*

### Leading Individuals

**Band 1**

| | |
|---|---|
| Alexander Frederick H | *Morris, Nichols, Arsht & Tunnell LLP* |
| Bussard Donald A | *Richards, Layton & Finger PA* * |
| Gentile Mark J | *Richards, Layton & Finger PA* * |
| McBride David | *Young Conaway Stargatt & Taylor LLP* |

**Band 2**

| | |
|---|---|
| Bigler C Stephen | *Richards, Layton & Finger PA* * |
| Haubert William J | *Richards, Layton & Finger PA* * |
| Morton Mark A | *Potter Anderson & Corroon LLP* * |
| Pincus Robert B | *Skadden, Arps, Slate, Meagher & Flom* * |
| Tumas Michael B | *Potter Anderson & Corroon LLP* * |

**Band 3**

| | |
|---|---|
| Daniels Steven | *Skadden, Arps, Slate, Meagher & Flom* * |
| Grossbauer John F | *Potter Anderson & Corroon LLP* * |
| Mullen Thomas A | *Prickett, Jones & Elliott PA* |
| Small John H | *Prickett, Jones & Elliott PA* |

**Up-and-coming individuals**

| | |
|---|---|
| Matthews Scott | *Delaware Counsel Group LLP* |
| Zeberkiewicz John Mark | *Richards, Layton & Finger PA* * |

## Band 1

### Morris, Nichols, Arsht & Tunnell LLP
See profile on p.783

**THE FIRM** This premier Delaware firm is well known for its provision of strong local counsel, although it also acts as lead counsel. It maintains a team large enough to be able to tackle a range of work, from financings to major transactions, as well as day-to-day advice. A recent highlight for the firm was acting as Delaware counsel for Cigna in its recent $3.8 billion acquisition of HealthSpring.
**Sources say:** *"Truly excellent. They are conversant in the law as it is, and would be, interpreted by Delaware courts today. They know the statutory history and case law precedent."*

## Corporate/M&A: Alternative Entities
### Leading Individuals

**Band 1**

| | |
|---|---|
| Altman Paul M | *Richards, Layton & Finger PA* * |
| Habbart Ellisa Opstbaum | *Delaware Counsel Group LLP* |
| Hering Louis G | *Morris, Nichols, Arsht & Tunnell LLP* |
| Kelley Bernard J | *Richards, Layton & Finger PA* * |
| Symonds Jr Robert L | *Stevens & Lee PC (ONP)* [†] |
| Tuthill Walter C | *Morris, Nichols, Arsht & Tunnell LLP* |
| Waxman Scott E | *K&L Gates* * |

**Band 2**

| | |
|---|---|
| Ladner Gregory W | *Richards, Layton & Finger PA* * |
| Leyden Jr James G | *Richards, Layton & Finger PA* * |
| Mazie Eric A | *Richards, Layton & Finger PA* * |
| Mullen Thomas A | *Prickett, Jones & Elliott PA* |
| O'Toole Matthew J | *Stevens & Lee PC (ONP)* [†] |
| Raju Srinivas M | *Richards, Layton & Finger PA* * |

**Band 3**

| | |
|---|---|
| Damon Doneene Keemer | *Richards, Layton & Finger PA* * |
| Feldman Eric N | *K&L Gates* * |
| Froio Nicholas I | *K&L Gates* * |
| Land Allison | *Skadden, Arps, Slate, Meagher & Flom* * |
| Norton Marla | *Bayard, P.A. (ONP)* [†] * |
| Powell Norman | *Young Conaway Stargatt & Taylor LLP* |
| Purpura Mark V | *Richards, Layton & Finger PA* * |
| Small John H | *Prickett, Jones & Elliott PA* |

* Indicates firm / individual with profile.
[†] ONP = Other Notable Practitioner.

*"They are great litigators who provide a great service. They're good to have in your corner."*
**KEY INDIVIDUALS Frederick Alexander** is simply *"the best at corporate work"* because *"he always gives you the right answer."* He is *"brilliant"* and *"has an encyclopedic knowledge of Delaware law."* He took the lead role acting as Delaware counsel on Cigna's acquisition of HealthSpring. **Louis Hering** is *"one of the leading experts on Delaware partnership law"* because he *"really knows the statute and the case law."* He acted as Delaware counsel to EQT Midstream Partners, helping it through both its formation and its IPO of units in an MLP, raising $260 million. **Walter Tuthill** is the recipient of praise for the low-key approach with which he *"effectively resolves negotiating disputes"* in such a manner as to *"make everyone happy, especially his client."* **Gilchrist Sparks** enjoys a *"stellar reputation"* as one of the leading senior figures in Delaware corporate law, and is renowned for his vast experience.

### Potter Anderson & Corroon LLP
See profile on p.784

**THE FIRM** This large group handles both corporate and alternative entity work. The team routinely advises boards of directors and significant stockholders of corporations on a broad range of obligations under Delaware law. It

recently advised key client DuPont on the acquisition of Bunge's stake in Solae a joint venture, and provided counsel to the committee of the board of Quest Software on negotiating its sale for approximately $2.5 billion.
**Sources say:** *"Excellent work delivered timely and professionally."* *"They're very smart and know the Delaware law intricacies, because they deal with it every day."*
**KEY INDIVIDUALS Mark Morton** (see p.773) advises on a range of matters, but is especially noted for his work representing special committees. He was the lead partner advising the special committee in the sale of Quest Software, and was also counsel to the committee of independent directors in the sale of BJ's Wholesale Club. **Michael Tumas** (see p.775) is an *"excellent and practical lawyer"* much admired for his work on structural transactions. *"Extremely responsive,"* he is also *"very practical in terms of giving advice."* Work for key client DuPont remains a significant portion of his practice, and he took the lead role during the acquisition mentioned above. **Nicholas Froio** (see p.770) *"obviously knows the statute and alternative entity law"* and is thought of as a specialist in financial vehicles. Sources note that he is *"extremely honest and creative in his approach to problems."* He was part of the team advising Wells Fargo on several life settlement transactions. **John Grossbauer** (see p.771) is *"smart and reasonable,"* and peers and clients alike state that *"it is always a pleasure working with him."* He took the lead role in assisting LinkedIn to draft its constituent corporate documents, which included a dual-class common stock structure.

### Richards, Layton & Finger PA
See profile on p.785

**THE FIRM** This large and well-regarded group covers the gamut of both corporate and alternative entity work, and is especially noted for its work in cutting-edge transactions. It worked for the special committee of Mediacom on the offer to take the company private in a $3.65 billion deal.
**Sources say:** *"They know their stuff, they're Delaware lawyers, they're steeped in Delaware law... they live and breathe it. They always come up with ways to address problems, because that's all they do. They're just a terrific resource and have all of the information of the case law right at the tips of their fingers."*
**KEY INDIVIDUALS** The *"very commercial"* **Paul Altman** (see p.767) is much admired by outside counsel as *"a great second pair of eyes."* He *"not only spots the Delaware issues, but raises legal and business issues"* as well. The experienced **Donald Bussard** (see p.768) focuses his practice on corporate matters and is highly sought after for advice. He was part of the team that represented BHP Billiton in its purchase of Petrohawk Energy for some $15 billion. **Mark Gentile** (see p.770) is admired for his many qualities, which include an ability to *"inspire confidence"* and the ability to *"establish a rapport and earn clients' confidence*

under difficult circumstances." He is "a very calming experienced hand who can lay out different kinds of views," and is noted for his "mastery and knowledge of the law." **Bernard Kelley** (see p.772) focuses his practice on transactional matters involving alternative entities, which encompasses work on their organization, structuring and operation. **Stephen Bigler** (see p.767) is "just fantastic." "Very calm under pressure," he "is very measured in his advice," which is aided by the fact that "he knows the law backwards and forwards." He recently represented Insight Communications in its $3 billion purchase by Time Warner Cable. **William Haubert** (see p.771) is "terrific" because "he knows the law very well, and he balances the legal requirements with the practicalities." He focuses his practice on general corporate law, encompassing issues such as fiduciary duty, corporate governance and other transactional matters. **Gregory Ladner** (see p.772) is an expert on dissolution of partnerships, regularly helping clients in an area that is light on statutes. He is praised for his "business sense, availability, technical knowledge and the overall quality of his work." Recently he represented the conflicts committee of Global GP in the acquisition of a network of gasoline stations and related assets. **Eric Mazie** (see p.773) focuses on alternative entities and has recently acted as local counsel to a variety of companies, including Honda, Nissan, Toyota and Ally Financial, on matters relating to their securitization programs. **Srinivas Raju** (see p.774) is a "guru of corporate law", with particular expertise in partnership law. He is praised for being "very practical when giving advice" and "quick to respond." One client sums him up by saying: "What he gives you is correct and you get to the right answer quickly." He advised the conflicts committee of Chesapeake Midstream GP during its acquisition of specific assets from an affiliate of its general partner. **James Leyden** (see p.772) continues his work for various Delaware-based alternative entities, including limited partnerships, statutory trusts and limited liability companies. **Doneene Keemer Damon** (see p.769) is an expert in alternative entities. She served as Delaware counsel to BMW for its recent public securitization program, which included advising on the formation of special-purpose entities. **Mark Purpura** (see p.774) is seen as an expert in both limited partnerships and partnership committees. "Very responsive and knowledgeable," he is "always very responsive" and even when "the questions are complex he always gives a clear and decisive answer." **John Mark Zeberkiewicz** (see p.776) is "truly the future of the Delaware Bar," impressing clients and peers alike with "his thoughtful analysis, practical approach, willingness to put himself out there and his ability to take complex, subtle court cases."

## Band 2

### Delaware Counsel Group LLP

**THE FIRM** This small but highly respected boutique focuses exclusively on corporate and alternative entity work. Praised by clients for its warm, inclusive style, the compact team advises clients on a number of both nation-

al and international transactions. Key clients include Accenture, RBS and GE. The international market is of increasing importance to the firm, as it offers advice on Delaware law to foreign companies.

**Sources say:** "Good quality, consistent and efficient. The Delaware counsel group is as good as any of them and is very strong on client care skills." "This firm is interested in its clients, which we really appreciate. It's a much more personal and interested relationship with this law firm."

**KEY INDIVIDUALS** The "extremely intelligent" **Ellisa Opstbaum Habbart** is lauded for "always trying to find the best solution for her client; she doesn't just take a point to take a point, she gets the big picture." Able to provide accurate, timely, relevant and strategic advice, she has an excellent listening capacity and is "attentive to her clients' needs." She was recently retained by Bidz.com relating to an ongoing private acquisition by Glendon Group. **Scott Matthews** is "very knowledgeable" and is "a good mix of being practical and solution-oriented" with a "high-class intellect." He is "very responsive" and is praised for his flexible approach. He was part of the team advising WSP Group on an extension of an existing credit facility, a complex cross-border transaction.

### Skadden, Arps, Slate, Meagher & Flom LLP & Affiliates
See profile on p.2008

**THE FIRM** The team at this internationally renowned firm advises clients on a variety of issues, including joint ventures, acquisitions in bankruptcy and strategic collaborations. Acting almost exclusively as lead counsel, the team has extensive experience, having acted on some of the largest deals seen in Delaware. A key client is Pfizer, for which the team was recently involved with the $11.9 billion sale of Pfizer Nutrition to Nestlé.

**Sources say:** "They are very, very good."

**KEY INDIVIDUALS Robert Pincus** (see p.774) maintains a broad practice advising clients on issues including M&A, restructurings and private equity investments. He recently took the lead in the team's representation of PharmaNet Development in its $600 million sale to inVEntiv Health by JLL Partners. **Steven Daniels**'s (see p.769) practice encompasses nearly all aspects of corporate law, although he is especially noted for his expertise in securities law matters. The "very smart" **Alison Land** (see p.772) advises clients on a wide range of matters including alternative entities, M&A and securities work. She was recently involved in the acquisition of a distributor of medical devices for a multinational conglomerate.

### Young Conaway Stargatt & Taylor LLP

**THE FIRM** This prestigious Delaware firm is best known for its actions as local counsel. Familiar with the law regarding alternative entities, the team is also regularly retained to work on the transactional aspects of either bankruptcy sales or troubled-asset acquisitions. Clients include US Bank, Solar Trust America and Discover Bank. **KEY INDIVIDUALS David McBride** is a "really excellent litigator." Best known for his work on corporate defense

work, he is especially well known for his M&A work. **Norman Powell** is "a lawyer's lawyer." "Smart, quick with ideas, superb in drafting and fast in document turnaround." He is "a dominant intellectual presence in many areas of commercial law, especially at the intersection of the UCC and Delaware-specific law."

## Band 3

### Prickett, Jones & Elliott PA

**THE FIRM** This team is regularly called upon to advise on issues concerning compliance with Delaware general corporation law and fiduciary duty, in addition to structuring transactions. It advises an impressive group of local and national clients.

**Sources say:** "They enjoy a unique reputation among the Delaware firms for handling both plaintiff and defendant work. This unique perspective is much appreciated by clients."

**KEY INDIVIDUALS Thomas Mullen** is an expert on business transactions. Focusing particularly on limited liability companies and partnerships, he "works very hard" and is "easy to spend time with." The experienced **John Small** is particularly noted for his plaintiff-side litigation work, and has experience working with alternative entities.

## Other Notable Practitioners

**Robert Symonds** of Stevens & Lee PC is an experienced corporate and transactional lawyer. He regularly gives third-party legal opinions on various aspects of Delaware law. "Very responsive to clients' needs," he is noted for his keen intellect. At the same firm, **Matthew O'Toole** is a "sharp and well-respected" lawyer who maintains a broad practice, covering all aspects of Delaware corporate law and alternative entities. **Marla Norton** (see p.773) of Bayard, P.A. covers a wide range of corporate law, including third-party opinions and corporate governance, but is especially noted for her expertise on alternative entities. She was recently involved in the terms of financing for NKS Distributors. **Scott Waxman** (see p.775) recently left Potter Anderson & Corroon to found the Wilmington office of K&L Gates. He is considered a "preeminent expert in alternative entities." "An incredible lawyer," he is "very dedicated, really technical and knows his law." Sources note that his "client service is also amazing; he just worked all hours for us." **Eric Feldman** (see p.770) and **Nicholas Froio** also joined K&L Gates from Potter Anderson. Feldman is praised for his "exceedingly broad knowledge of the law" as well as being "consistently practical in his approach." An increasing portion of his practice is advising on potential federal and state legislation relating to anti-money laundering. Froio "obviously knows th statute and alternative entity law" and is thought of as a specialist in financial vehicles. Sources note that he is "extremely honest and creative in his approach to problems."

# INTELLECTUAL PROPERTY

Commentary about individuals can be found under their firm's paragraph. If the firm has no paragraph (is not ranked) look at Other Notable Practitioners.

## Intellectual Property
### Leading Firms

**Band 1**
Fish & Richardson PC
Morris, Nichols, Arsht & Tunnell LLP *
Novak Druce Connolly Bove + Quigg LLP

**Band 2**
Bayard, P.A. *
Potter Anderson & Corroon LLP *
Richards, Layton & Finger PA *

**Band 3**
Ashby & Geddes *
Farnan LLP
Shaw Keller LLP
Young Conaway Stargatt & Taylor LLP

## Band 1

### Fish & Richardson PC

**THE FIRM** A leader not only in Delaware but across the country, this firm is lauded for its specialty in IP matters. The team is especially noted for its deep technical background, with many members of the group holding advanced degrees. Recent highlights for the team include representing Adobe in patent litigation against Tarkus Imaging, winning a jury verdict in the Delaware District Court.

**Sources say:** *"Every effort is made to communicate with the client, and the communications are free of jargon. They understand the difference between pursuing claims just to get a patent issued and pursuing claims of commercial or defensive significance to the patent holder; the lawyers spend their time well."*

**KEY INDIVIDUALS** Experienced head of department **William Marsden** is a highly regarded patent litigation expert. Sources particularly appreciate that he is a *"hard worker who deals well with clients."* **Gwilym Attwell** is an expert in patent prosecution, with his practice covering both local and foreign patents in the fields of biotech and pharmaceuticals. He is noted by clients for his *"subject matter expertise, appreciation of commercial necessity, decisiveness and clear explanations."*

### Morris, Nichols, Arsht & Tunnell LLP
See profile on p.783

**THE FIRM** This venerable Delaware firm represents clients in a broad swathe of IP litigation matters, including patent, unfair competition and antitrust. The team is frequently retained as lead counsel, with a typical example being its defense of Alkermes against allegations of patent infringement in Maryland against Par Pharmaceutical. Key clients for the team include industry giants AstraZeneca, Amazon, Google and GlaxoSmithKline.

**Sources say:** *"It's probably one of the top IP firms in Delaware; it has a mixture of people who do local practice, as well as some first chair lawyers, and remains one of the go-to firms."*

**KEY INDIVIDUALS** The *"phenomenally talented"* **Jack Blumenfeld** remains a *"dean of the Delaware patent Bar"* and is *"still unsurpassed"* thanks to his *"unbelievable capacity for work."* **Mary Graham** concentrates her practice on patents, trade secrets and licensing. Key clients include Merck, and she was recently involved in a patent infringement case representing Aurora, a subsidiary of Agilent. **Karen Jacobs Louden**'s practice is principally focused on patent litigation. She has attracted a lot of attention lately for her work in non-practicing entity cases, taking a lead role in the defense of more than 60 defendants in various patent infringement cases filed by Cyberfone. **Maryellen Noreika** also spends most of her time litigating patent cases, often as first chair. She was involved as lead counsel in the team's representation of Softspikes in a breach of contract action that was filed in the District of Maryland. **Thomas Grimm** typically represents corporate clients in IP litigation. He was the lead attorney in a patent infringement, representing Honeywell in a one-week trial which concluded in favor of his client. Patent litigation expert **Rodger Smith** has recently been involved with the defense of several large technology companies, including Sony, Canon and Zynga, against allegations of patent infringement by Walker Digital.

### Novak Druce Connolly Bove + Quigg LLP

**THE FIRM** This renowned IP boutique firm continues to lead from the front, and having completed its merger with Texan firm Novak Druce + Quigg is now among the largest IP specialist firms in the country. Recent highlights include acting as lead counsel for Glatz, LIPtec and KneX on defending allegations of patent infringement in an ITC investigation. Clients include illustrious names such as Lockheed Martin, Cochlear, Johnson & Johnson and L'Oréal.

**Sources say:** *"The firm has consistently shown the very highest quality of work in its handling of the matter, and we consider ourselves fortunate to have it as our counsel."*

**KEY INDIVIDUALS** **Francis DiGiovanni** maintains a broad practice covering counseling and trademark and copyright litigation, but is best known for his expertise in patent litigation matters. This *"responsive"* lawyer has recently been involved in a false marking case for FMC, successfully obtaining a dismissal of the case. **Patricia Smink Rogowski** is an expert in patent prosecution and counseling. With a background in mechanical engineering, she *"has a deep understanding of patent language nuance and has become a subject matter expert."* Clients especially appreciate that she is able to *"present clear alternatives that allow us to make business decisions with pragmatic confidence."* The highly experienced and *"extraordinarily talent-*

## Intellectual Property
### Senior Statesmen

**Senior Statesmen:** distinguished older practitioners

| | |
|---|---|
| Hutz Rudolf E | Novak Druce Connolly Bove + Quigg LLP |

### Leading Individuals

**Star individuals**

| | |
|---|---|
| Blumenfeld Jack B | Morris, Nichols, Arsht & Tunnell LLP |

**Band 1**

| | |
|---|---|
| Balick Steven J | Ashby & Geddes * |
| Cottrell III Frederick L | Richards, Layton & Finger PA * |
| Horwitz Richard L | Potter Anderson & Corroon LLP * |
| Marsden Jr William | Fish & Richardson PC |
| Shaw John | Shaw Keller LLP |

**Band 2**

| | |
|---|---|
| Graham Mary B | Morris, Nichols, Arsht & Tunnell LLP |
| Louden Karen Jacobs | Morris, Nichols, Arsht & Tunnell LLP |
| Noreika Maryellen | Morris, Nichols, Arsht & Tunnell LLP |
| Rovner Philip A | Potter Anderson & Corroon LLP * |
| Seitz Jr Collins 'CJ' | Seitz Ross Aronstam & Moritz (ONP)[†] |

**Band 3**

| | |
|---|---|
| Day John G | Ashby & Geddes * |
| DiGiovanni Francis | Novak Druce Connolly Bove + Quigg LLP |
| Grimm Thomas C | Morris, Nichols, Arsht & Tunnell LLP |
| Herrmann Richard K | Morris James LLP (ONP)[†] |
| Kirk Richard D | Bayard, P.A. * |
| Smith Rodger | Morris, Nichols, Arsht & Tunnell LLP |

**Band 4**

| | |
|---|---|
| Devlin Tim | Farney Daniels (ONP)[†] |
| Kraft Denise | DLA Piper LLP (US) (ONP)[†] * |
| Matterer Mary B | Morris James LLP (ONP)[†] |
| Moore David E | Potter Anderson & Corroon LLP * |
| Moyer Jeffrey L | Richards, Layton & Finger PA * |
| Poff Adam | Young Conaway Stargatt & Taylor LLP |
| Reed Janet E | Potter Anderson & Corroon LLP * |
| Rogowski Patricia Smink | Novak Druce Connolly Bove + Quigg |

**Up-and-coming individuals**

| | |
|---|---|
| Attwell Gwilym | Fish & Richardson PC |
| Farnan Brian | Farnan LLP |
| Keller Karen E | Shaw Keller LLP |

**Band Star Associate**

| | |
|---|---|
| Brauerman Stephen B. | Bayard, P.A. * |

*\* Indicates firm / individual with profile.*
*[†]ONP = Other Notable Practitioner.*

ed" **Rudolf Hutz** is *"widely recognized as a master trial attorney."* Sources say that *"his gift is in finding and following a strategy from the very beginning of the case that leads the team all the way through discovery and trial to a winning decision."*

## Band 2

### Bayard, P.A.
See profile on p.779

**THE FIRM** This compact team frequently acts as Delaware counsel on complex patent litigation, increasingly focusing on plaintiff actions. The team also includes a transactional IP practice, providing formal opinions on issues such as the enforcement of trademarks. Key clients include Walker Digital, Lupin Pharmaceuticals and Helicos Biosciences.
**Sources say:** *"Very knowledgeable about local practice and federal court litigation in Delaware."*
**KEY INDIVIDUALS Richard Kirk** (see p.772) maintains a broad IP litigation practice and is noted for his *"attention to detail."* Sources add that he is *"dependable, responsive, and knowledgeable of the current law and procedures of the Delaware court."* He has recently been involved in Walker Digital's litigation to monetize several of its patent families. **Stephen Brauerman** (see p.768) has been taking an increasingly prominent role in Bayard's IP practice. He is *"very responsive and courteous,"* and sources are also quick to point out his work ethic, reporting that he handles *"unbelievable amounts of work."*

### Potter Anderson & Corroon LLP
See profile on p.784

**THE FIRM** This IP team takes on cases in areas such as trademarks, patents and copyright litigation. Retained as both lead and local counsel, it represents both plaintiffs and defendants. Key clients include Barnes & Noble, Genentech and GE.
**Sources say:** *"Excellent – absolutely professional, thorough and competent."*
**KEY INDIVIDUALS Richard Horwitz** (see p.771) is a renowned litigation expert and is engaged by both plaintiffs and defendants. Sources praise his *"knowledge of the court and judges, familiarity with Delaware juries and sound judgment."* He *"brings a tremendous amount of knowledge"* to cases and *"knows the ins and out of litigation in Delaware."* He recently acted for key client DuPont on patent procurement and licensing arrangements. **Philip Rovner** (see p.774) is regularly retained in all areas of IP litigation, but is especially noted for his work in trade secrets. Sources praise his *"ability to grasp and articulate IP legal concepts,"* his *"ease of courtroom style"* and his *"willingness to work hard for the success of the team."* He recently acted for Barnes & Noble as lead counsel in a multiparty patent infringement action. **David Moore** (see p.773) is regularly engaged for his litigation skills and recently acted as co-counsel in a patent infringement case which went to trial and subsequently found in favor of his client. **Janet Reed** (see p.774) heads the firm's IP transactional practice and is praised by clients for her expertise in technical matters.

### Richards, Layton & Finger PA
See profile on p.785

**THE FIRM** This compact team is retained as both lead and local counsel to litigate many matters in the Delaware District Court. Key clients include Time Warner Cable, Nokia and Texas Instruments. A recent highlight was the firm's work for IGT in a patent litigation case in the District Court and the Federal Circuit.
**KEY INDIVIDUALS Frederick Cottrell** (see p.769) is an experienced litigator who focuses on IP matters including product liability and patent litigation. Sources appreciate that he *"understands the court exceedingly well"* and that he can act as *"an integral part of the trial team."* **Jeffrey Moyer** (see p.773) is a well-known IP litigator. He recently acted for STMicroelectronics as one of several defendants in a patent infraction case brought by HSM Portfolio.

## Band 3

### Ashby & Geddes
See profile on p.778

**THE FIRM** This renowned litigation firm acts as Delaware counsel in some of the largest cases to reach Delaware, representing both prosecutors and defendants. The team handles cases across the breadth of IP litigation, including patent, trademark and unfair competition. Clients include Amazon, Verizon Wireless and Asahi Glass.
**Sources say:** *"The firm knows the Delaware courts very well, and invariably has helpful insights."* *"They know the Delaware judges better than most people in town."*
**KEY INDIVIDUALS** Chair of the IP group, the *"very thoughtful"* **Steven Balick** (see p.767) *"gives good, solid advice."* He primarily acts as Delaware counsel on various litigation matters, and recently acted for Asahi Glass on a patent infringement case. **John Day** (see p.769) focuses on acting as Delaware counsel on a variety of matters. Sources say that he is *"very knowledgeable about the Delaware courts and local practice,"* and that he is *"very responsive and articulate"* and has a *"strong work ethic."*

### Farnan LLP

**THE FIRM** This recently created family-run firm has made waves with its work as Delaware counsel in cases involving non-practicing entities, acting primarily for the plaintiff. Headed by notable former District Court Judge Joseph Farnan, the firm has impeccable credentials and has enjoyed a rapid build-up in stature since its formation.
**KEY INDIVIDUALS Brian Farnan** is heavily involved with most of the cases that the firm handles. He *"knows what he is doing in the Delaware courts."*

### Shaw Keller LLP

**THE FIRM** This two-partner boutique firm continues its steady trajectory upwards since its formation in late 2011, gaining new clients and making waves in court where the team takes on cases as both local and lead counsel. it recently acted as lead counsel for Oki Data on a patent infringement case of over $50 million. Other clients include Fandango and LivingSocial.
**Sources say:** *"They are not simply a mail drop for local matters. Rather, they become part of the litigation and trial team. When we are squeezed for resources on the outside counsel level, I consider Shaw Keller to be an expanded part of our core group of lawyers working on a case."*
**KEY INDIVIDUALS** Head of the firm and *"exceptional litigator"* **John Shaw** takes on cases including patent infringements, trade secret actions and patent licensing disputes. He offers *"great skills, attention to detail and instincts,"* and *"brings the depth and breadth of skill and experience that clients rely on for creative litigation strategies and sound, thoughtful advice."* New partner **Karen Keller** specializes in patent litigation, particularly in cases involving life sciences. *"Thoughtful, creative and responsive,"* she also *"knows the Delaware judges and local practice inside and out, and has the strong scientific aptitude required to navigate the complex and esoteric technologies at issue."*

### Young Conaway Stargatt & Taylor LLP

**THE FIRM** This distinguished Delaware firm acts as both Delaware and lead counsel on a wide range of matters. Its expertise enables it to handle work involving telecom, biotech and software matters. Clients particularly appreciate the firm's trial room set up in the building, which enables the team to try a dry run case.
**Sources say:** *"I would rate their work as being of the highest standard."*
**KEY INDIVIDUALS** New chair of the IP practice **Adam Poff** handles a wide variety of matters, primarily focusing on patent infringement. Sources praise his work as a local counsel, with one saying: *"He was on top of all procedural requirements, guided us through procedural matters and was a great resource for our out-of-town team."*

### Other Notable Practitioners

**CJ Seitz** of Seitz Ross Aronstam & Moritz LLP primarily focuses his IP practice on patent litigation, both as local and lead counsel. He is extremely well respected by peers for his ability to *"handle multiple disciplines successfully,"* and continues to work as the firm's main representative in this field. **Richard Herrmann** of Morris James LLP focuses his practice on patent litigation. His key clients include DuPont, Whirlpool and Micron. **Denise Kraft** (see p.772) of DLA Piper LLP remains exceptionally busy as a local counsel, advising both other teams within the firm and outside counsel on matters within the Courts of Delaware. She is described as *"thoughtful and wise about how to approach the local judiciary on any given issue."* Founding member of Farney Daniels, **Tim Devlin** is a renowned expert in patent infringement litigation. He is frequently called upon to represent both plaintiffs and claimants in a variety of different fields, principally technology-related. **Mary Matterer** of Morris James LLP maintains a broad litigation practice and has a distinguished track record on patent litigation representing a range of different industries.

# LABOR & EMPLOYMENT

## Band 1

### Young Conaway Stargatt & Taylor LLP

**THE FIRM** This labor group comprises four partners who take on cases ranging from employment discrimination defense to class and collective action defense. Clients include the State of Delaware, DuPont Performance Elastomers and the City of Wilmington. The team recently represented healthcare insurer Blue Cross Blue Shield of Delaware on a class action alleging breach of fiduciary duty under ERISA; the case was eventually dismissed from the District Court before discovery.

**Sources say:** "*They performed with a very good understanding of the issues involved. The preparation is thorough and detailed, and the execution has been very professional.*"

**KEY INDIVIDUALS William Bowser** is "*simply outstanding*" and represents both private and public bodies in a variety of different matters, ranging from union campaigns to wrongful termination lawsuits. Sources praise his "*very calm demeanor,*" noting that "*he brings experience and creativity to every labor dispute*" while appreciating that he is equally prepared to seek resolution as he is litigation. **Scott Holt** advises clients of all sizes on how to com-

ply with state and federal law, and is noted for his "*masterful*" litigation skills. He is able to "*bring tremendous clarity to the issues and is able to provide excellent options and strategies.*" Sources also say that he is "*always accessible and extremely knowledgeable,*" and able to "*think outside of the box.*" **Barry Willoughby** chairs the employment practice and is experienced in a wide variety of cases, including employment discrimination, sexual harassment, due process and equal protection for public clients. "*Client-focused, responsive and cost-effective,*" he "*gives advice that has consistently resulted in positive results.*"

## Band 2

### Potter Anderson & Corroon LLP
See profile on p.784

**THE FIRM** This sizable team takes on work pertaining to general labor and employment, employee benefits and executive compensation matters. Its clients include Delaware State University, Chrysler Group and Wal-Mart. The team recently undertook a case in the Delaware Supreme Court in the state's first examination of the Whistleblower Protection statute.

**Sources say:** "*I find these individuals to be top of their class and always on top of current law and precedents. The research is thorough and they always treat us as a favorite customer, even though we are just another client.*"

**KEY INDIVIDUALS** Head of department **Kathleen Furey McDonough** (see p.773) handles the gamut of labor and employment disputes. She advises a number of higher education institutions, such as Modern Think and the West Virginia Higher Education, on all aspects of employment law. **Wendy Voss** (see p.775) provides counsel to various businesses across the country. She is noted for her "*professional, dedicated service*" and her "*upbeat attitude,*" and clients also appreciate her responsiveness. **Jennifer Brady** (see p.768) is a renowned healthcare and labor and employer lawyer. She advises clients on issues such as unionization, employee supervision and sexual harassment. She is "*one of the best attorneys I have worked with in a local counsel capacity,*" said one client.

### Saul Ewing LLP
See profile on p.2249

**THE FIRM** This small labor and employment team prides itself on defending claims with the aim of reducing litigation. It handles issues including employee benefits, counseling and employee recruitment. The group is particularly noted for its close association with charter schools and other educational bodies, with clients including The Charter School of Wilmington, Newark Charter School and Innovative Schools Development.

**Sources say:** "*It is the preeminent firm in Delaware when it comes to charter school and education law.*" "*Extremely professional and available when needed – always.*"

**KEY INDIVIDUALS James Taylor** devotes a significant amount of his time to counseling higher education institutes. Clients appreciate his long experience of working in the sector and his knowledge of the law, and report that he "*cares about his work and the people he works with – this makes a huge difference.*"

## Band 3

### Morris James LLP
See profile on p.782

**THE FIRM** This three-member team represents employers in a wide range of matters relating to the management of workforces, from litigation to various labor negotiations. The team's client list includes public bodies such as City of Wilmington, Sussex Technical, Indian River School Districts and City of Rehoboth Beach.

**KEY INDIVIDUALS David Williams** takes on a wide variety of work, including litigation-based matters, counseling and arbitration, particularly with respect to collective bargaining agreements. He brings a "*thorough, comprehensive and caring approach, uniformly and without exception*" to his work, and is noted for his close ties with the education sector. **James McMackin** has developed a strong reputation in the field, particularly for his work defending clients in alleged discrimination and retaliation cases.

### Richards, Layton & Finger PA
See profile on p.785

**THE FIRM** This one-partner office dispenses general law advice as well as providing defense in disputes. The team has a strong history in restrictive covenant, contract and wage claims in some of the most prestigious courts in Delaware. Clients range from industry giants to smaller regional companies.

**Sources say:** "*Their advice has been considerate, compliant and accurate.*"

**KEY INDIVIDUALS Jennifer Jauffret** (see p.771) advises clients within the region on a variety of different labor and employment issues. She recently advised a major food company during its recent Chapter 11 reorganization on all ongoing employment issues. Clients particularly appreciate her availability and responsiveness at any time of day. Associate **Lori Brewington** (see p.768) focuses her employment practice on corporate transactions as well as more general issues, including termination situations and compliance.

# REAL ESTATE

Commentary about individuals can be found under their firm's paragraph. If the firm has no paragraph (is not ranked) look at Other Notable Practitioners.

## Real Estate
### Leading Firms

**Band 1**

Richards, Layton & Finger PA [*]

Saul Ewing LLP [*]

Young Conaway Stargatt & Taylor LLP

**Band 2**

Bayard, P.A. [*]

### Leading Individuals

**Band 1**

| | |
|---|---|
| DiPrinzio Eugene A | Young Conaway Stargatt & Taylor LLP |
| Gee William S | Saul Ewing LLP |
| Isken Donald N | Morris, Nichols, Arsht & Tunnell (ONP) [†] |
| Klein Daniel L | Richards, Layton & Finger PA [*] |
| Krapf Robert J | Richards, Layton & Finger PA [*] |

**Band 2**

| | |
|---|---|
| Bloxom IV John M | Morris James LLP (ONP) [†] |
| Hershman Douglas M | Bayard, P.A. [*] |
| Johnson Daniel | Young Conaway Stargatt & Taylor LLP |
| Krapf Daniel H | Saul Ewing LLP |
| Lamb Christopher J | Pepper Hamilton LLP (ONP) [†] [*] |
| Mammarella Thomas | Gordon, Fournaris & Mammarella (ONP) [†] |
| Shaffer Brent | Young Conaway Stargatt & Taylor LLP |

**Associates to watch**

| | |
|---|---|
| Kuffel John C | Young Conaway Stargatt & Taylor LLP |
| Toner Sara | Richards, Layton & Finger PA [*] |

## Real Estate: Zoning/Land Use
### Leading Firms

**Band 1**

Saul Ewing LLP [*]

Young Conaway Stargatt & Taylor LLP

[*] Indicates firm / individual with profile.

[†] ONP = Other Notable Practitioner.

## Bayard, P.A.
See profile on p.779

**THE FIRM** This compact team handles matters across the whole of Delaware and in surrounding states. It undertakes cases involving leasing, litigation and transactions. Clients include lenders, owners of apartment complexes, and various purchasers.

**Sources say:** *"They are excellent; among the leaders in the Delaware market."*

**KEY INDIVIDUALS Douglas Hershman** (see p.771) maintains a diverse practice encompassing lending and transactions, among other matters. He is praised for his *"prompt attention to matters," "clean, concise work"* and *"practical approach."*

## Real Estate: Zoning/Land Use
### Leading Individuals

**Band 1**

| | |
|---|---|
| Forsten Richard | Saul Ewing LLP |
| Goodman Lisa | Young Conaway Stargatt & Taylor LLP |
| Manning William E | Saul Ewing LLP |
| Stabler Wendie C | Saul Ewing LLP |

**Band 2**

| | |
|---|---|
| Dunkle Mark F | Parkowski Guerke & Swayze PA (ONP) [†] |
| Fuqua James A | Fuqua, Yori and Willard, P.A. (ONP) [†] |
| Hoffman A Kimberly | Morris James LLP (ONP) [†] |
| Paradee John W | Prickett, Jones & Elliott PA (ONP) [†] |
| Tarabicos Larry J | Elzufon Austin Reardon Tarlov (ONP) [†] |
| Tracey John | Young Conaway Stargatt & Taylor LLP |

**Up-and-coming individuals**

| | |
|---|---|
| Hansen Stephanie L | Young Conaway Stargatt & Taylor LLP |

## Richards, Layton & Finger PA
See profile on p.785

**THE FIRM** This four-member team covers a wide variety of matters, from land acquisition to financing and construction. Clients range from major lenders to municipalities and home builders. A recent highlight for the team was advising a solar power company on a new energy facility in Delaware.

**KEY INDIVIDUALS Daniel Klein** (see p.772) heads the real estate group and spends much of his time advising on public and private joint ventures. Praised for the *"high quality of work"* and his *"prompt turnaround,"* he was recently involved in the development of a 1 million sq ft warehouse for a retailer. **Robert Krapf** (see p.772) concentrates his practice on real estate transactions, primarily as an adviser. Noted for his national practice, he has a *"great business mind"* and is a *"great technician."* He was recently retained in the development of a large rail-to-ship storage and transfer facility in Delaware. The *"excellent"* and *"very bright"* **Sara Toner** (see p.775) remains a key part of the team and has assisted with a number of matters, including a large community redevelopment project in Delaware.

## Saul Ewing LLP
See profile on p.2249

**THE FIRM** One of the largest real estate practices in the state, this team can handle any issue arising from real estate transactions. It is regularly engaged with development, financing and zoning issues, and can handle projects from formation to completion. The group is also regularly engaged in litigation, including representing commercial and residential entities in title disputes, tax assessment appeals and landlord and tenant issues.

**Sources say:** *"I'd describe the quality of the work as nothing less than excellent, frequently exceeding expectations." "I praise their attention to detail, passion for customers, strate-*gic *thinking, decisiveness, flexibility, cooperation – and they're fun to work with!"*

**KEY INDIVIDUALS Richard Forsten** is an expert in land use matters as well as commercial real estate. His practice covers both transactional and litigation aspects. He continues to act as lead counsel on a 2,000-acre mixed-use project in Middleton, Delaware. **William Gee** is an experienced real estate lawyer well known for his work in multistate acquisitions and financing. **Wendie Stabler** is a *"standout"* at the firm for her work in land use matters. Her diverse range of clients includes golf courses, utilities and educational institutions. She impresses clients with her ability to *"distill complicated matters, speak plainly to nonlawyers and recommend practical ways to achieve goals."* **Daniel Krapf** concentrates his practice on real estate transactions, including workouts, construction finance and acquisitions. He is noted for his attention to detail, his ability to *"think strategically,"* and his decisiveness and flexibility. *"Very active in higher education,"* **William Manning** is a noted litigator who is heavily involved in all the firm's litigious work.

## Young Conaway Stargatt & Taylor LLP

**THE FIRM** This large team is noted for its expertise in nearly all aspects of commercial real estate, encompassing transactional, banking and land use. Highlights for the firm include handling a multimillion-dollar series of major refinancings for a regional developer.

**Sources say:** *"They can do a project from beginning to completion. They have real lawyers doing complex transactions and projects, and they have the support team to do the job."*

**KEY INDIVIDUALS** In addition to handling real estate transactions, banking specialist **Eugene DiPrinzio** represents the lenders in issues surrounding mortgage loans, workouts and restructurings. **Lisa Goodman** is a *"terrific attorney"* who concentrates her practice on land use matters such as acquisitions, code compliance and redevelopment. She is *"knowledgeable"* and praised for her *"nice working style,"* and also works as a mediator. General transaction lawyer **Daniel Johnson** also handles work on the financing side. He has significant experience in dealing with matters involving bond-related financing, negotiating leases and development agreements. **Brent Shaffer** concentrates his practice on finance, advising both lenders and borrowers, including on construction and permanent loans. **John Tracey** focuses exclusively on land use matters and represents clients in all three counties in Delaware. Peers comment that they would recommend Tracey and refer conflicted work to him. Environmental law expert **Stephanie Hansen** is frequently called on to support her colleagues when environmental issues arise in real estate matters. *"Bright and experienced,"* she has significant expertise in the redevelopment of brownfield properties. **John Kuffel** handles a wide variety of different commercial transactional matters, including representing financial institutions in mortgage loans. *"Detail-oriented"* and with an excellent technical background, he is also *"prompt, responsive, knowledgeable, practical and caring."*

## Other Notable Practitioners

**Donald Isken** of Morris, Nichols, Arsht & Tunnell LLP is *"among the top transactional lawyers"* in the state. *"Very detail-oriented,"* he is admired for his strong and dedicated client force. *"Very knowledgeable, very detailed and very active,"* **Thomas Mammarella** of Gordon, Fournaris & Mammarella PA is noted for his client base, which includes many medical practitioners in the state. He helps clients

with land development, land use approval and general transactional matters, among others. **John Bloxom** of Morris James LLP assists commercial and industrial clients with issues including construction, finance and leasing. **Mark Dunkle** of Parkowski Guerke & Swayze PA is an expert in residential real estate planning, land use litigation and eminent domain litigation. **Kimberly Hoffman** of Morris James LLP concentrates her practice on land use matters. She is praised for her fine technical background and her expertise in complex zoning issues. *"Major land use lawyer"* **Larry Tarabicos** of Elzufon Austin Reardon Tarlov & Mondell focuses his practice on residential development, and also advises a number of commercial clients.

He is said to *"know the system and the players."* **Christopher Lamb** (see p.772) of Pepper Hamilton LLP has extensive experience in a wide range of issues, including creditors' rights, real estate and affordable housing. His regional client list includes developers and lenders. **John Paradee** of Prickett, Jones & Elliott PA is particularly active in the counties of Kent and Sussex. He assists residential and commercial clients with transactional matters. **James Fuqua** of Fuqua, Yori and Willard, P.A. is a noted land use lawyer outside of Newcastle County, with one source describing him as *"the go-to lawyer in Sussex County."* He advises residential and commercial clients on closings and refinancings, among other matters.

# Leaders' Profiles in Delaware

### ALLINGHAM II, Thomas J
Skadden, Arps, Slate, Meagher & Flom LLP & Affiliates, Wilmington
302 651 3070
Thomas.Allingham@skadden.com
*Featured in Chancery (Delaware)*
**Practice Areas:** Corporate and securities litigation, including defense of class and derivative actions, with an emphasis on mergers and acquisitions and statutory appraisals.
**Professional Memberships:** Fellow, American College of Trial Lawyers; ABA; DSBA (1978); Admissions to practice: Delaware (1978); US District Court of Delaware (1977); New Jersey (1993); Third Circuit Court of Appeals (1985); US Supreme Court (1986); Second Circuit Court of Appeals (1998).
**Career:** Partner (1986). Adjunct Professor (Mergers & Acquisitions, Directors' Fiduciary Duties), University of Pennsylvania Law School (1997-2002, 2005). Williams College (BA, cum laude, 1974); University of Pennsylvania Law School (JD, 1977).

### ALTMAN, Paul M
Richards, Layton & Finger PA, Wilmington
302 651 7664
altman@rlf.com
*Featured in Corporate/M&A (Delaware)*
**Practice Areas:** Paul Altman chairs the firm's Business Department and heads the Limited Liability Company and Partnership Advisory Group. His practice involves alternative entities, including partnerships and limited liability companies, and focuses primarily on formation of private equity investment funds.
**Professional Memberships:** Mr Altman has held numerous leadership positions in the Delaware State and American Bar Associations, including past chair of both the ABA's Limited Partnership Subcommittee and the Delaware State Bar Association subcommittee that updates

Delaware's limited partnership, general partnership and limited liability company statutes.
**Publications:** Co-authored "Lubaroff & Altman on Delaware Limited Partnerships" and numerous other publications.

### ASHBY, Lawrence C
Ashby & Geddes, Wilmington
302 654 1888
lashby@ashby-geddes.com
*Featured in Chancery (Delaware)*
**Practice Areas:** Larry is of counsel to the Corporate Litigation and Counseling group within the firm where his practice focuses on corporate governance issues, major transactions and the litigation that often accompanies such matters.
**Professional Memberships:** Member, Board of Bar Examiners, 1983-90; Delaware Supreme Court Rules Advisory Committee, 1987-93; Member, Permanent Lawyers Advisory Committee for the United States District Court of Delaware, 1985-88; Member, Delaware State Bar Association and Chairman, Corporate Law Section, 1996-98.
**Personal:** Born Philadelphia, Pennsylvania in 1945; admitted to the Delaware Bar in 1970; Williams College (BA 1967); Vanderbilt University (JD 1970) (Order of the Coif).

### ASHMAN JR, Berton W
Potter Anderson & Corroon LLP, Wilmington
302 984 6180
bashman@potteranderson.com
*Featured in Chancery (Delaware)*
**Practice Areas:** Mr Ashman's practice focuses on corporate and commercial litigation in the Delaware Court of Chancery, including class and derivative actions relating to mergers and acquisition transactions and takeover disputes. He is regularly involved in litigation concerning the internal governance of Delaware corporations, limited partnerships, and other alternative entities and the fiduciary duties of their directors and officers, as

well as statutory proceedings brought pursuant to Delaware's General Corporation Law.
**Personal:** University of Virginia JD 2005; University of Delaware MA 2001; James Madison University BA 1996.

### BALICK, Steven J
Ashby & Geddes, Wilmington
302 654 1888
sbalick@ashby-geddes.com
*Featured in Intellectual Property (Delaware)*
**Practice Areas:** Practice concentrated in the prosecution and defense of patent, trademark, and other intellectual property litigation.
**Professional Memberships:** Member, Permanent Lawyers Advisory Committee, United States District Court for the District of Delaware, 1992-95; Member, Delaware State Bar Association, American Bar Association, and Federal Bar Association.
**Career:** Judicial Clerkship, Delaware Superior Court, 1981-82; Deputy Attorney General, State of Delaware, 1982-86; Joined firm as an associate in 1986; Partner since 1990.
**Personal:** Boston University (JD, 1981); University of Delaware (BA, 1978).

### BIGLER, C Stephen
Richards, Layton & Finger PA, Wilmington
302 651 7724
bigler@rlf.com
*Featured in Corporate/M&A (Delaware)*
**Practice Areas:** Steve Bigler counsels corporations, directors, board committees and investors and provides legal opinions on matters involving Delaware's General Corporation Law and related issues of fiduciary duty arising in various transactional and operational contexts, including entity formation, mergers, acquisitions, divestitures, defensive planning, capital-raising transactions and stockholder meetings.
**Professional Memberships:** Member of the American Bar Association Business Law Section

Mergers and Acquisitions and Corporate Process and Documents Committees, and the Corporate Law Section of the Delaware State Bar Association.
**Career:** Mr Bigler helped draft model financing documents for the National Venture Capital Association.
**Publications:** Numerous articles concerning Delaware corporate law.

### BOWDEN, William P
Ashby & Geddes, Wilmington
302 654 1888 x254
WBowden@ashby-geddes.com
*Featured in Bankruptcy/Restructuring (Delaware)*
**Practice Areas:** Bill's practice concentrates in providing advise to, and appearing in court on behalf of, debtors and other entities experiencing financial distress, official and unofficial committees, significant creditors, lenders, purchasers of assets and other parties in interest in chapter 11 proceedings. Recent engagements include: (i) counsel to the Debtor in the Handy Hardware Wholesale, Inc. case; (ii) Bankruptcy Counsel to the Equity Committee in Washington Mutual; (iii) counsel to the Debtors in the JER Jameson cases; (iv) among other committee engagements, serving as co-counsel and conflicts counsel to the Creditors Committees in the AES Eastern Energy and SP NewsPrint cases; (v) co-counsel to the DIP Lender and Buyer of the assets of Palm Harbor Homes; and (vi) two of the nation's largest inventory liquidators in connection with the store closings and inventory liquidations in the Syms/Filene's Basement cases.
**Professional Memberships:** American Bankruptcy Institute; Bankruptcy Section of the Delaware State Bar Association; Advisory Board to the Views from the Bench Program.
**Personal:** Born Wilmington, Delaware in 1957; admitted to Delaware Bar in 1989; University of

Delaware (BS 1985); Brooklyn Law School (JD 1988).

## BRADY, Jennifer G
Potter Anderson & Corroon LLP, Wilmington
302 984 6042
jbrady@potteranderson.com
*Featured in Labor & Employment (Delaware)*

**Practice Areas:** Ms Brady is the chair of the firm's Litigation Group. She concentrates her practice in the areas of labor and employment law, health law, and commercial litigation. She counsels employers on labor and employment issues, including unionization and collective bargaining, employee supervision, discipline and discharge, sexual harassment, and employment discrimination. Jennifer aslo advises health care providers on a variety of issues, including licensing and certification, fraud and abuse laws, medical privacy and confidentiality, and litigation matters.

## BRAUERMAN, Stephen B.
Bayard, P.A., Wilmington
302 429 4232
sbrauerman@bayardlaw.com
*Featured in Intellectual Property (Delaware), Chancery (Delaware)*

**Practice Areas:** Steve concentrates his practice in the areas of corporate, commercial and intellectual property litigation in Delaware's state and federal Courts. He has litigated a wide array of cases involving mergers and acquisitions, fiduciary duty claims, proxy contests and corporate and alternative entity control disputes, advancement/indemnification, breach of contract, antitrust, securities, patent infringement, copyright infringement, and trademark matters. Steve also counsels clients concerning the General Corporation Law of the State of Delaware and Delaware's alternative entity statutes.

**Professional Memberships:** American Bar Association (Vice-Chair, Limited Liability Companies, Partnerships, and Alternative Entities Subcommittee of the Business and Corporate Litigation Committee; Membership Chair, Intellectual Property Committee); Delaware State Bar Association; Federal Bar Association (Secretary, Delaware Chapter, Co-Coordinator, Federal Trial Practice Seminar); Richard S. Rodney American Inn of Court.

**Career:** In 2012 and 2013, Steve was recognized by Delaware Super Lawyers as a Rising Star in intellectual property litigation. He is a 2010 graduate of the Federal Trial Practice Seminar sponsored by the United States District Court for the District of Delaware and the Federal Bar Association.

**Publications:** "'Judicial Business Judgment' and the Art of Evaluating Derivative Settlements," Delaware Business Court Insider, February 13, 2012; "Court of Chancery Approves Contractual Mechanisms to Protect Self-Interested Transactions," Delaware Business Court Insider, October 17, 2012; "Wasting Away: The Futility of Asserting Waste Claims in the Court of Chancery," Delaware Business Court Insider, August 8, 2012; "Injunction Junction, Not Our Function: Court of

Chancery Grapples with Enjoining Stockholder Votes on Troubled Transactions," Business Law Today, April 2012; "Chancery Court Provides Guidance on Advancement, Indemnification Under Delaware Law," Delaware Business Court Insider, March 28, 2012; see also www.bayardlaw.com/publications

**Personal:** Born August 3, 1981; Johns Hopkins University (BA, with honors, 2003); American University's Washington College of Law (JD, cum laude, 2006) Admitted: DE (2006), NJ (2007), US District Court for the District of DE (2007); US District Court for the District of NJ (2009), Third Circuit Court of Appeals 2009.

## BREWINGTON, Lori
Richards, Layton & Finger PA, Wilmington
302 651 7689
brewington@rlf.com
*Featured in Labor & Employment (Delaware)*

**Practice Areas:** Lori Brewington represents clients in labor and employment issues and commercial disputes. She provides employment advice on corporate transactions, noncompete and separation agreements, and discipline/termination situations. Ms Brewington also assists clients before the EEOC and the Department of Labor in federal courts regarding Title VII, ADA and FMLA claims, and related state law claims.

**Professional Memberships:** Ms Brewington is past chair of the Labor and Employment Section of the Delaware State Bar Association and an associate member of the Delaware Board of Bar Examiners. She is also a member of the American Bar Association and Federal Bar Association.

## BROWN, Stuart M
DLA Piper LLP (US), Wilmington
302 468 5640
stuart.brown@dlapiper.com
*Featured in Bankruptcy/Restructuring (Delaware)*

**Practice Areas:** Bankruptcy, restructuring.
**Career:** He is the managing partner of the firm's Wilmington office. His practice encompasses the representation of institutional lenders, investors and business enterprises in diverse matters, including general business, transactions with bankruptcy estates, anti-bankruptcy transactional consultation, bankruptcy litigation, substantive non-consolidation, securitization and servicing and bankruptcy fraud. He represents traditional and non-traditional funding sources with respect to workouts, claim realization and asset recovery. He is certified by the American Bankruptcy Board of Certification as a business bankruptcy law specialist.
**Personal:** JD, Temple University James E Beasley School of Law (with honors); BS, Boston University (with honors).

## BROWN-EDWARDS, Theresa V
Potter Anderson & Corroon LLP, Wilmington
302 984 6142
tbrown-edwards@potteranderson.com
*Featured in Bankruptcy/Restructuring (Delaware)*

**Practice Areas:** Ms Brown-Edwards concentrates her practice on corporate reorganization and has significant experience representing chapter 11 debtors and debtors-in-possession across

numerous industry lines. She also focuses her attention on purchasers of assets and the protection of creditors' rights, including representations of creditors' committees, ad hoc committees and groups, lenders, landlords, equipment and aircraft lessors, and trade creditors, among others.
**Professional Memberships:** President, Delaware State Bar Association; Delaware Bankruptcy American Inn of Court.
**Career:** Admitted to practice in Delaware, New Jersey and New York.
**Personal:** President's Council of Cornell Women; Board of Governors, St. John's University.

## BUSSARD, Donald A
Richards, Layton & Finger PA, Wilmington
302 651 7716
bussard@rlf.com
*Featured in Corporate/M&A (Delaware)*

**Practice Areas:** Donald Bussard, the senior member of the firm's Corporate Transactional Group, advises corporations, boards of directors and board committees regarding mergers, acquisitions, recapitalizations, stock issuances and corporate governance matters.
**Professional Memberships:** Mr Bussard is a member and former chair of the Council of the Corporation Law Section of the Delaware State Bar Association and a member of the American Bar Association.
**Career:** Recently, Mr Bussard represented Dell Inc. in connection with its proposed acquisition by an investor group including Michael Dell.
**Publications:** Mr Bussard is a contributing author to "The Delaware Law of Corporations and Business Organizations."

## BUTCHER, Rebecca
Landis Rath & Cobb LLP, Wilmington
302 467 4415
butcher@lrclaw.com
*Featured in Chancery (Delaware)*

**Practice Areas:** Corporate, commercial and bankruptcy litigation. Represents entities and individuals within the Court of Chancery. Also represents creditors, lenders and official and unofficial committees in contested matters and adversary proceedings in the federal courts.
**Professional Memberships:** Delaware State Bar Association, former Chair of the Litigation Section; American Bar Association; Phi Delta Phi; International Women's Insolvency & Restructuring Confederation.
**Career:** Partner with Landis Rath & Cobb LLP.
**Personal:** BA with distinction from the University of Virginia, 1996; Vanderbilt University School of Law, 1999, Vanderbilt Journal of Transnational Law, Editorial Board.

## CARICKHOFF, David
Blank Rome LLP, Wilmington
302 425 6434
Carickhoff@BlankRome.com
*Featured in Bankruptcy/Restructuring (Delaware)*

**Practice Areas:** David Carickhoff counsels businesses in bankruptcy proceedings, out-of-court restructurings, and other commercial matters. He has represented clients on all sides of distressed situations, including debtors, creditors'

committees, secured lenders, asset purchasers, plan-of-reorganization proponents, post-confirmation trustees, and individual creditors. Mr Carickhoff also advises current and former directors and officers of distressed companies. For more information:
www.BlankRome.com/Carickhoff

## CHEHI, Mark S
Skadden, Arps, Slate, Meagher & Flom LLP & Affiliates, Wilmington
302 651 3160
Mark.Chehi@skadden.com
*Featured in Bankruptcy/Restructuring (Delaware)*

**Practice Areas:** Focuses on negotiated and contested workouts and out-of-court restructurings, 'prepackaged' and prearranged bankruptcies, and traditional chapter 11. Represents public company debtors, creditors, shareholders, lenders, acquirors, creditors' committees, committee members and board special committees in various matters, including international and cross-border situations and related litigations. Advises officers and directors on governance and fiduciary duty matters, and represents companies confronting mass tort liabilities.
**Professional Memberships:** Member, Turnaround Management Association; Member, INSOL; ABA, Business Bankruptcy Committee Liaison to INSOL; Co-chair, Subcommittee on Business Transactions, ABA Business Bankruptcy Committee.
**Career:** JD, The University of Chicago Law School, 1990; BA, Haverford College, 1980.

## CLARK, Anthony W
Skadden, Arps, Slate, Meagher & Flom LLP & Affiliates, Wilmington
302 651 3080
Anthony.Clark@skadden.com
*Featured in Bankruptcy/Restructuring (Delaware)*

**Practice Areas:** Heads the Wilmington Corporate Restructuring/Bankruptcy Litigation Practice. Handles complex corporate, securities and general litigation matters. Has extensive experience representing debtors, creditors and acquirors in major reorganization cases. Significant Chapter 11 debtor representations include Interstate Bakeries, Refco, Hayes Lemmerz, Spansion, Syms and Filene's.
**Professional Memberships:** President (2001-03) and Bencher, Richard S. Rodney Chapter, American Inns of Court; Member, Board of Visitors, Temple University School of Law.
**Career:** Lecturer, Columbia Law School, 2009; Adjunct Professor, University of Pennsylvania Law School, 2005; JD, Temple University School of Law, 1979; BA, State University of New York at Cortland, 1973.

## COLLINS, Mark D
Richards, Layton & Finger PA, Wilmington
302 651 7531
Collins@rlf.com
*Featured in Bankruptcy/Restructuring (Delaware)*

**Practice Areas:** Mark Collins is chair of the firm's Bankruptcy and Corporate Restructuring Department. He focuses on bankruptcy and creditors' rights, with particular experience representing debtors, lenders, creditors' committees and acquirers.

**Professional Memberships:** Mr Collins is a fellow in the American College of Bankruptcy, co-chair of the Sales Advisory Committee to the American Bankruptcy Institute's Commission to Reform Chapter 11, and chair of the Bankruptcy Section Legislation Committee of the Delaware State Bar Association.

**Career:** Mr Collins has served as lead company counsel and co-counsel in some of the most significant chapter 11 filings in history.

### COTTRELL III, Frederick L
Richards, Layton & Finger PA, Wilmington
302 651 7509
Cottrell@rlf.com
*Featured in Intellectual Property (Delaware)*

**Practice Areas:** Fred Cottrell, a director in the firm's Litigation Department, specializes in intellectual property, antitrust, products liability and commercial law cases. He represents parties in significant patent litigation before the Delaware District Court.

**Professional Memberships:** Mr Cottrell is a member of the American Bar Association and Delaware State Bar Association and is former chair of the DSBA's Intellectual Property Law Section. He chairs the Complex/Business Litigation Committee for the Delaware Superior Court and co-chaired the Delaware District Court's Intellectual Property Law Advisory Committee.

**Career:** Mr Cottrell is a frequent speaker on Delaware District Court and intellectual property litigation practice.

### DALUZ, Tobey
Ballard Spahr LLP, Wilmington
302 252 4440
daluzt@ballardspahr.com
*Featured in Bankruptcy/Restructuring (Delaware)*

**Practice Areas:** Tobey M Daluz is a partner in the Bankruptcy, Reorganization and Capital Recovery Group. Ms Daluz concentrates her practice in the areas of corporate restructuring, workouts, and general bankruptcy litigation. She represents debtors, secured and unsecured creditors, insurers, indenture trustees, and official committees and potential buyers of assets in Chapter 11 bankruptcy cases.

**Professional Memberships:** US Court of Appeals for the Third Circuit, Lawyers Advisory Committee American Bankruptcy Institute (ABI) International Women's Insolvency and Restructuring Confederation (IWIRC).

**Career:** Admissions: Delaware Pennsylvania.

**Personal:** Georgetown University Law Center (JD 1990) University of Pennsylvania (BA 1987).

### DAMON, Doneene Keemer
Richards, Layton & Finger PA, Wilmington
302 651 7526
Damon@rlf.com
*Featured in Corporate/M&A (Delaware)*

**Practice Areas:** Doneene Damon focuses on formation and operational issues relating to Delaware statutory and common law trusts in all types of commercial transactions, including struc-

tured finance, investment funds, real estate financings, liquidation trusts, bond financing and capital securities transactions. She also represents banks and trust companies regarding their trust and agency services.

**Professional Memberships:** Ms Damon is a member of the American Bar Association's Business Law Section Council, past chair of the ABA Committee on Trust Indentures and Indenture Trustees, past co-chair of the ABA Committee on Corporate Director Diversity, and director for the Securitization and Structured Finance Committee.

### DANIELS, Steven
Skadden, Arps, Slate, Meagher & Flom LLP & Affiliates, Wilmington
302 651 3240
steven.daniels@skadden.com
*Featured in Corporate/M&A (Delaware)*

**Practice Areas:** Mr Daniels focuses his practice primarily on mergers and acquisitions and other corporate and securities law matters. Has represented numerous public and private companies concerning acquisitions, dispositions and the purchase and sale of securities, assets and business units in both distressed and traditional settings. Has significant experience representing private equity sponsors and has worked extensively with LLCs and other alternative entities.

**Career:** JD Columbia University School of Law, 1995 (Managing Editor, Columbia Law Review); BA, Queens College, 1992 (magna cum laude, Phi Beta Kappa); clerk to the Honorable E Norman Veasey, Chief Justice, Supreme Court of Delaware, 1995-96.

### DAVIS, Charlene D
Bayard, P.A., Wilmington
302 429 4212
cdavis@bayardlaw.com
*Featured in Bankruptcy/Restructuring (Delaware)*

**Practice Areas:** Charlene practices primarily in the areas are corporate bankruptcy and commercial litigation. She regularly represents debtors, statutory committees, trustees and creditors in many large bankruptcy cases.

**Professional Memberships:** American Bankruptcy Institute; American Bar Association; Delaware State Bar Association (Chair of the Bankruptcy Law Section 2010); Federal Bar Association (President of the Delaware Chapter 1996-97 and 2000-01).

**Career:** Charlene has been recognized as a leading lawyer in bankruptcy and restructuring by both Chambers USA and Lawdragon 3000 (2009-13). She was designated a Delaware Super Lawyer in Philadelphia magazine (2007-10). She is AV® Peer Review Rated by Martindale-Hubbell. Charlene is currently a member of the Special Masters Panel by the United States District Court in Delaware and also serves on Widener University School of Law National Advisory Council. She began her career as an Assistant United States Attorney and joined Bayard in 1988. After entering private practice, she served on the Delaware District Court CJA Blue Ribbon Panel (1989-97); the Delaware District Court Advisory

Committee (1994-2000); Third Circuit Court of Appeals Advisory Committee (1996-98); and the Court of Appeals Bench/Bar Relations Committee (1999). During this period, the judges of Delaware District Court named her as the first recipient of the Caleb R. Layton Service Award.

**Publications:** "The Future Employee Retention Plans and Their Treatment in the Delaware Bankruptcy Court," Financier Worldwide Americas Restructuring & Insolvency Review (2007); "Are You In the Vicinity of Insolvency? Serving More Than One Master," Financier Worldwide Americas Restructuring & Insolvency Review (2004/2005). "Responding to an Appeal and Voluntary Dismissal," Chapter 6, Federal Practice Guide—Federal Appellate Procedure Third Circuit (Lawyers Cooperating Publishing, 1997).

**Personal:** Born Salem, NJ; Ohio Wesleyan University (BA, cum laude, 1968); Widener University's Delaware School of Law (JD, cum laude,1984); Admitted to Supreme Court of Delaware (1984); United States District Court for the District of Delaware (1984); United States Court of Appeals for the Third Circuit (1991); United States Supreme Court (1991).

### DAY, John G
Ashby & Geddes, Wilmington
302 654 1888
jday@ashby-geddes.com
*Featured in Intellectual Property (Delaware)*

**Practice Areas:** Intellectual property litigation; commercial litigation. Church Attorney for the Episcopal Diocese of Delaware.

**Professional Memberships:** Federal Bar Association, Delaware State Bar Association, ABA.

**Career:** Joined Ashby & Geddes as Counsel in 2001, Partner since 2006. Previously at Skadden, Arps, Slate, Meagher & Flom, 1985-95.

**Personal:** Temple University School of Law (JD, cum laude, 1985); Gordon College (BA, 1979).

### DEARLOVE, Catherine
Richards, Layton & Finger PA, Wilmington
302 651 7788
dearlove@rlf.com
*Featured in Chancery (Delaware)*

**Practice Areas:** Catherine Dearlove represents Delaware corporations, limited liability companies and limited partnerships and their directors, officers, investors and other constituencies in litigation in the Delaware Court of Chancery, in other courts and in arbitration. She litigates class and derivative actions, merger disputes, corporate control contests and governance disputes; advises boards of directors on governance and fiduciary duty issues; and represents audit, compensation and special committees concerning internal investigations and transactions. Her clients include public and private companies, venture capital and investment funds, and individuals.

**Professional Memberships:** American Bar Association and Delaware State Bar Association, Business Law and Litigation Sections.

### DEBAECKE, Michael D
Blank Rome LLP, Wilmington
302 425 6412
DeBaecke@BlankRome.com
*Featured in Bankruptcy/Restructuring (Delaware)*

**Practice Areas:** Michael DeBaecke concentrates his practice on bankruptcy reorganizations and related litigation, representing a variety of Chapter 11 debtors, trustees, creditors' committees, secured and unsecured creditors, landlords, asset purchasers, contract parties, and parties in various bankruptcy litigation matters, including preference and fraudulent transfer actions; breach of fiduciary duty actions; breach of contract actions; and lien priority actions. In addition to his national bankruptcy practice, Mr DeBaecke is a former law clerk in the Delaware Court of Chancery and maintains a targeted litigation practice focused primarily on Court of Chancery corporate litigation and District Court commercial litigation. www.BlankRome.com/DeBaecke

### DEFRANCESCHI, Daniel J
Richards, Layton & Finger PA, Wilmington
302 651 7816
DeFranceschi@rlf.com
*Featured in Bankruptcy/Restructuring (Delaware)*

**Practice Areas:** Daniel DeFranceschi, a director in the Bankruptcy and Corporate Restructuring Department, represents debtors and other parties in chapter 11 cases, including secured lenders, purchasers of assets, ad hoc committees of noteholders and other parties.

**Professional Memberships:** Mr DeFranceschi is active in the American Bankruptcy Institute, Turnaround Management Association, American Bar Association, Delaware Bankruptcy Inn of Court and Delaware State Bar Association.

**Career:** Recent clients include Blitz USA; Haight's Cross Communications; Premiere Holdings, a/k/a Six Flags; Hoop Holdings, f/k/a the Disney Stores; Fairfield Residential; Specialty Devices; Mervyns Holdings; Tropicana Entertainment and ResMae Mortgage.

**Publications:** Numerous articles on bankruptcy topics.

### DETWEILER, Donald J
Pepper Hamilton LLP, Wilmington
302 777 6524
detweilerd@pepperlaw.com
*Featured in Bankruptcy/Restructuring (Delaware)*

**Practice Areas:** Partner. Concentrates practice in the areas of corporate restructuring, bankruptcy, liquidating trusts, litigation trusts and complex commercial litigation. Experience representing debtors, creditors' committees, directors and officers, employees, litigants and other parties-in-interest in complex Chapter 11 bankruptcy cases. Has successfully litigated, tried (jury and non-jury), and defended several complex commercial litigation and product liability cases in the state and federal courts of Delaware.

**Professional Memberships:** Member, American Bankruptcy Institute; Bencher, Richard S Rodney Delaware Bankruptcy Inn of Court; Board Member, Supporting KIDDS, Inc.

**Personal:** JD 1992 Widener University School of Law; BA 1986 Villanova University.

## DICAMILLO, Raymond
Richards, Layton & Finger PA, Wilmington
302 651 7786
DiCamillo@RLF.com
*Featured in Chancery (Delaware)*

**Practice Areas:** Raymond DiCamillo is a director in and a vice chair of the firm's Corporate Department. He focuses on advisory and litigation matters relating to Delaware business organizations and their constituents. Mr DiCamillo litigates corporate control, corporate governance, statutory and contractual disputes in the Delaware courts and advises corporate boards and committees with respect to governance, litigation and investigational and transactional issues.
**Professional Memberships:** Mr DiCamillo is a member of the American Bar Association and the Delaware State Bar Association.
**Career:** Mr DiCamillo has lectured at seminars on fiduciary duty and governance issues related to Delaware business organizations.

## EISENHOFER, Jay W
Grant & Eisenhofer PA, Wilmington
302 622 7050
jeisenhofer@gelaw.com
*Featured in Securities (Nationwide), Chancery (Delaware), Litigation (New York)*

**Practice Areas:** Securities litigation; regulatory and corporate governance litigation.
**Professional Memberships:** Member of the Board of the American Constitution Society and the Anti-Defamation League.
**Career:** Co-founder and managing director of G&E. Has served as lead counsel in many of the largest securities class action recoveries in history, including: Tyco, $3.2 billion; United Healthcare, $895 million; Global Crossing, $450 million; Shell, pan-European settlement of $450 million; Marsh & McLennan, $400 million; General Motors, $303 million; and DaimlerChrysler, $300 million. Has served as litigation counsel to many public and private institutional investors, including: California Public Employees Retirement System; Colorado Public Employees Retirement Association; Florida State Board of Administration; Louisiana State Employees Retirement System; Teachers' Retirement System of Louisiana; Ohio Public Employee Retirement Systems; State of Wisconsin Investment Board; American Federation of State; County & Municipal Employees; Service Employees International Union; Amalgamated Bank; Lens Investment Management, Inc.; and Franklin Advisers, Inc.
**Publications:** Has written and lectured widely on securities fraud and insurance coverage litigation, business and employment torts, directors' and officers' liability coverage, and the Delaware law of shareholder rights and directorial responsibilities.
**Personal:** University of Pittsburgh, BA, 1978; Villanova University School of Law, magna cum laude, Order of the Coif, 1986.

## FATELL, Bonnie Glantz
Blank Rome LLP, Wilmington
302 425 6423
Fatell@BlankRome.com
*Featured in Bankruptcy/Restructuring (Delaware)*

**Practice Areas:** Bonnie Fatell has extensive experience in bankruptcy reorganizations, out-of-court restructurings, and other commercial matters. Her practice over 30 years includes representing creditors, creditors' committees, debtors, secured lenders and litigants, as well as serving as chapter 11 trustee and mediator. Representations include: serving as chapter 11 trustee for Woodcrest Country Club; representing creditors' committees in Solyndra, Beacon Power, SemCrude, Uni-Marts, New Century, and American Home Mortgage Holdings; debtors in USGen New England, Alamo and National Car Rental; and significant creditor representations in Overseas Shipping Corp., DBSI, Autobacs Strauss, and Northwest Airlines. She is a frequent writer and speaker. www.BlankRome.com/Fatell

## FELDMAN, Eric N
Potter Anderson & Corroon LLP, Wilmington
302 984 6204
efeldman@potteranderson.com
*Featured in Corporate/M&A (Delaware)*

**Practice Areas:** Mr Feldman practices in the areas of alternative entities and general business, focusing primarily on limited liability companies, general and limited partnerships and statutory trusts, organizational and operational issues relating to such entities, and the utilization of such entities in all types of business, structured finance and securitization transactions. Mr Feldman serves on Delaware's Alternative Entities Subcommittee, responsible for drafting Delaware's preeminent limited liability company and partnership statutes. He is actively involved in both the LLCs, Partnerships and Unincorporated Entities (vice chair) and the Mergers and Acquisitions Committees of the Business Law Section of the American Bar Association.

## FELGER, Mark E
Cozen O'Connor, Wilmington
302 295 2087
mfelger@cozen.com
*Featured in Bankruptcy/Restructuring (Delaware)*

**Practice Areas:** Mark focuses on Chapter 11 business reorganizations, restructurings, and liquidations. Mark's practice includes representing businesses in nonjudicial restructurings and Chapter 11 proceedings, creditors committees, and trustees in complex Chapter 7 cases. Mark is a certified mediator for the Delaware Bankruptcy Court and has an active mediation practice. Mark is certified in business bankruptcy by the American Board of Certification. Mark is licensed to practice in New York, Delaware, New Jersey and Pennsylvania.
**Professional Memberships:** American Bankruptcy Institute, Turnaround Management Association.
**Career:** Co-chair, Bankruptcy, Insolvency, & Restructuring Group; Delaware Office Managing Partner.

**Personal:** Boston University School of Law, JD, 1989.

## FISCHER, Matthew E
Potter Anderson & Corroon LLP, Wilmington
302 984 6153
mfischer@potteranderson.com
*Featured in Chancery (Delaware)*

**Practice Areas:** Mr Fischer practices in the areas of corporate, commercial and alternative entities litigation, and advises directors regarding mergers and acquisitions, tender offers, proxy contests, and shareholder derivative and class action suits. He represented defendants in shareholder class action suits challenging the following mergers/acquisitions: Dell/Silver Lake Partners, Bank of America/Merrill Lynch, Intel/McAfee, Cogent/3M, Dollar-Thrifty/Hertz, Kindred Healthcare/RehabCare, Hughes/EchoStar, Alpha Natural Resources/Massey Energy, Terremark/Verizon, and J.Crew/TPG and also represented Emulex and its directors in response to Broadcom's hostile offer, Australia's BlueScope Steel in appraisal litigation, and PeopleSoft in connection with Oracle's hostile offer.
**Professional Memberships:** Admitted in Delaware (1992), Pennsylvania (1993).

## FOSTER, Anne C
Richards, Layton & Finger PA, Wilmington
302 651 7744
Foster@RLF.com
*Featured in Chancery (Delaware)*

**Practice Areas:** Anne Foster represents clients in corporate and commercial litigation matters, including the representation of corporations, directors and stockholders in corporate governance, indemnification, advancement and fiduciary duty matters.
**Professional Memberships:** Ms Foster is former chair of the Corporate Counseling and Litigation Subcommittee of the Business and Corporate Litigation Committee of the Business Law Section of the American Bar Association, and former chair of the Board on Professional Responsibility of the Supreme Court of Delaware. She is the Chancellor of the Episcopal Diocese of Delaware.
**Career:** Ms Foster has appeared on numerous panels regarding corporate litigation and ethics.

## FOURNIER, David M
Pepper Hamilton LLP, Wilmington
302 777 6565
fournierd@pepperlaw.com
*Featured in Bankruptcy/Restructuring (Delaware)*

**Practice Areas:** Partner. Experienced in secured lending, workout counseling and bankruptcy litigation. Represents secured and unsecured creditors, official creditors' committees and debtors in various industries including retail, food processing, equipment leasing and financing, communications.
**Professional Memberships:** Chair, International Law Section, Delaware Bar Association; Member, Delaware Bankruptcy America Inn of Court; Member, Caesar Rodney Inn of Court.

**Personal:** JD 1989 Villanova University School of Law; BA 1985 Pennsylvania State University.

## FROIO, Nicholas I
Potter Anderson & Corroon LLP, Wilmington
302 984 6156
nfroio@potteranderson.com
*Featured in Corporate/M&A (Delaware)*

**Practice Areas:** Mr Froio concentrates primarily on alternative entities, including statutory trusts, partnerships, limited liability companies and special purpose corporations. He focuses on structural and governance issues relating to alternative entities and their utilization in structured finance, cross-border securitizations and other commercial transactions, including mergers, acquisitions, joint ventures, investment funds, real estate, trust preferred securities, insurance premium financings and life settlements. He regularly provides third-party legal opinions on issues relating to Delaware entities, the Delaware Uniform Commercial Code and other matters of Delaware law. Mr Froio serves on the Delaware committee responsible for drafting the Delaware statutory trust statute.

## GALARDI, Gregg M
DLA Piper LLP (US), New York
212 335 4640
gregg.galardi@dlapiper.com
*Featured in Bankruptcy/Restructuring (Nationwide), Bankruptcy/Restructuring (Delaware)*

**Practice Areas:** Bankruptcy/restructuring.
**Career:** He is co-chair of the firm's Restructuring practice. With extensive US and international restructuring experience, he has represented companies in a wide variety of industries in out-of-court workouts as well as prepackaged, prenegotiated and traditional Chapter 11 cases. He regularly advises clients regarding multijurisdictional filings and change-of-control transactions, as well as the complex regulatory, employment, environmental and other issues that confront public and private companies in financial distress.
**Personal:** JD, University of Pennsylvania Law School (cum laude) University of Pennsylvania Law Review; PhD, Philosophy, MA, Economics, BA, University of Pennsylvania 1979 cum laude.

## GENTILE, Mark J
Richards, Layton & Finger PA, Wilmington
302 651 7722
gentile@rlf.com
*Featured in Corporate/M&A (Delaware)*

**Practice Areas:** Mark Gentile is a director in the firm's Corporate Advisory Group. He advises corporations, officers, directors, board committees and stockholders regarding mergers and acquisitions, divestitures, recapitalizations and corporate governance issues.
**Professional Memberships:** Mr Gentile is an appointed member of the American Bar Association's Committee on Corporate Laws, a member of the ABA Committee on Federal Regulation of Securities, and a member of the Corporate Law Section of the Delaware State Bar Association.
**Publications:** Mr Gentile is a contributing author to "The Delaware Law of Corporations

and Business Organizations" and has authored numerous articles concerning Delaware corporate law.

### GLASSMAN, Neil B
Bayard, P.A., Wilmington
302 429 4224
nglassman@bayardlaw.com
*Featured in Bankruptcy/Restructuring (Delaware)*
**Practice Areas:** Neil focuses his practice on bankruptcy and insolvency law, and insurance and entity law. Neil regularly represents debtors, official committees of unsecured creditors or equity holders, secured lenders, banks and insurance companies, financial institutions and publicly and privately held businesses in large bankruptcy cases and other insolvency proceedings including insurance company insolvencies. An experienced transactional attorney, Neil has also developed a substantial practice representing clients in relation to the law of Delaware business entities including corporations, business trusts, general and limited partnerships, limited liability companies, and conventional and captive insurance companies. Neil has developed a specialty in counseling insurance companies in regulatory matters in Delaware.
**Professional Memberships:** ABI; ABA; DSBA (Member of Bankruptcy and Corporate Law Sections; Member of Statutory Trust Committee; Former President of the Commercial Law Section); Member of Board of Directors of Delaware Captive Insurance Association.
**Career:** Neil joined Bayard in 1986, and serves as Chairman of the Firm. Neil is a published author and frequent speaker on issues and developments in bankruptcy, insolvency and Delaware insurance law. Neil was named by Best Lawyers® as one of the foremost practitioners in his region and has been AV® Peer Review Rated by Martindale-Hubbell for 20 years.
**Publications:** "Racing Against Time in Chapter 11," Financier Worldwide, March 2009 (Threats & Opportunities in the Retail Sector Section); "Equity Committees: A Consequence of the 'Zone of Insolvency,'" American Bankruptcy Institute Journal, December 2005/January 2006; "Equity Committees-Representation of Shareholders in Bankruptcy Cases," Financier Worldwide, 2005 (Restructuring and Insolvency Series); "US Bankruptcy Roundtable," Financier Worldwide, May 2005; "Are You In The Vicinity of Insolvency? Serving More Than One Master," The Americas, 2004/2005 (Restructuring and Insolvency Guide); "Cybergenics: A Corporate Solution to a Bankruptcy Problem," Delaware Law Weekly, November 27, 2002; "Awarding Attorneys' Fees From Class Action Judgments," Case Western Law Review, Vol. 30, 1979.
**Personal:** Born Philadelphia, Pennsylvania, October 14, 1952; Trinity College (BA, 1974); University of Connecticut (MBA, 1978); Case Western Reserve University School of Law (JD, 1981); Admitted: Delaware (1982), US District Court for the District of Delaware (1982), US Court of Appeals for the Third Circuit (1983).

### GOLDMAN, Michael D
Potter Anderson & Corroon LLP, Wilmington
302 984 6007
mgoldman@potteranderson.com
*Featured in Chancery (Delaware)*
**Practice Areas:** Mr Goldman practices in both the corporate counseling and corporate litigation areas. His practice focuses on working directly with in-house counsel and other law firms addressing corporate governance issues or major transactions and the litigation that often accompanies such matters. As a result, he serves as both an advisor and as Delaware litigation counsel for boards of directors, board committees, stockholders, and others involved in corporate governance issues, proxy contests, change of control, going-private, and conflict transactions involving special committee review. He is a past chairman of the Corporation Law Council that drafts the Delaware General Corporation Law.

### GRANT, Stuart M
Grant & Eisenhofer PA, Wilmington
302 622 7070
sgrant@gelaw.com
*Featured in Securities (Nationwide), Chancery (Delaware), Litigation (New York)*
**Practice Areas:** Securities litigation; regulatory and corporate governance litigation.
**Professional Memberships:** Vice-Chairperson, Delaware Judicial Nominating Commission; Board of Trustees for the University of Delaware; Advisory Board for the Weinberg Center for Corporate Governance at the University of Delaware.
**Career:** Co-founder and managing director of G&E. Serves as litigation counsel to many of the largest public and private institutional investors in the world. Has achieved six of the largest settlements in the history of Delaware's Chancery Court, including: In re Digex, Inc. Shareholders Litigation; Teachers' Retirement System of Louisiana v. Greenberg, et al. and American International Group, Inc.; American International Group, Inc., Consolidated Derivative Litigation; and In re ACS Shareholders Litigation. Recent securities litigation representations and settlements include: In re Refco Inc. Securities Litigation, $410 million; In re Delphi Corp Securities Litigation, $325 million; and In re Safety-Kleen Securities Corporation Bondholders Litigation, $200 million plus settlements with the remaining defendants for $84 million.
**Publications:** Has authored a number of articles which have been cited with approval by the US Supreme Court, US Court of Appeals for the 2nd and 5th Circuits and numerous US District Courts.
**Personal:** Brandeis University, BA cum laude, 1982; New York University School of Law, JD,1986.

### GROSSBAUER, John F
Potter Anderson & Corroon LLP, Wilmington
302 984 6131
jgrossbauer@potteranderson.com
*Featured in Corporate/M&A (Delaware)*

**Practice Areas:** Mr Grossbauer practices in the areas of corporation law and corporate governance, advising public and private corporations and their boards of directors with respect to all aspects of Delaware General Corporation Law, including the fiduciary duties of directors and technical compliance with various provisions of the Delaware General Corporation Law. Mr Grossbauer has extensive experience representing both purchasers and sellers in negotiated acquisitions of public and private Delaware corporations, and representing both management and insurgents in proxy contests.
**Professional Memberships:** ABA Business Law Section; Vice-Chair, Council of Delaware Bar Corporation Law Section.
**Personal:** JD, Duke Law School, 1986.

### HAUBERT, William J
Richards, Layton & Finger PA, Wilmington
302 651 7559
Haubert@RLF.com
*Featured in Corporate/M&A (Delaware)*
**Practice Areas:** William Haubert is a director in the firm's Corporate Department. His practice focuses on advisory and transactional matters relating to Delaware corporations. Mr Haubert provides corporate governance, transactional and control dispute advice, and renders legal opinions, with respect to issues of Delaware corporate law.
**Professional Memberships:** Mr Haubert is a member of the Business Law Section of the American Bar Association and the Corporate Law Section of the Delaware State Bar Association.
**Publications:** Mr Haubert is a frequent speaker on Delaware corporate law issues and has authored numerous articles on Delaware corporate law matters.

### HEATH, Paul N
Richards, Layton & Finger PA, Wilmington
302 651 7590
heath@rlf.com
*Featured in Bankruptcy/Restructuring (Delaware)*
**Practice Areas:** Paul Heath, a director in the firm's Bankruptcy and Corporate Restructuring Department, represents debtors, secured creditors, purchasers and other parties in chapter 11 cases.
**Professional Memberships:** Mr Heath is a member of the Delaware State Bar Association, Turnaround Management Association and American Bankruptcy Institute.
**Career:** Mr Heath acted as debtors' counsel in Homer City Funding, MMC Precision Holdings, Reliant Energy Channelview, Advanced Marketing Services, Advanta, Aleris International, Barnes Bay Development, East West Resort Development, Nextmedia Group and PFF Bancorp; lenders' counsel in School Specialty, Building Materials Holding Corporation and PJ Finance Company; and creditors' committee counsel in Filenes.

### HERSHMAN, Douglas M
Bayard, P.A., Wilmington
302 429 4207
dhershman@bayardlaw.com
*Featured in Real Estate (Delaware)*
**Practice Areas:** Real estate law, representing clients throughout Delaware with commercial and

residential transactions, including purchase, sale, refinance and leasing. His representations have included shopping centers, office buildings, apartment complexes and residential subdivisions.
**Professional Memberships:** ABA; DSBA; NYSBA; CIRC; HBADE; DAA; Committee of 100
**Career:** Doug has been recognized as a leading attorney in the field of real estate law by Chambers USA (2006-13), Delaware Super Lawyers (2007-10), and Lawdragon 3000 (2006-12).
**Personal:** University of Delaware (BA, 1983); Syracuse University College of Law (JD, magna cum laude, 1986); Admitted to practice: New York (1987), Delaware (1988), Pennsylvania (1995).

### HORWITZ, Richard L
Potter Anderson & Corroon LLP, Wilmington
302 984 6027
rhorwitz@potteranderson.com
*Featured in Intellectual Property (Delaware)*
**Practice Areas:** Mr Horwitz's practice includes intellectual property, commercial and Delaware corporate litigation, representing corporate clients on patent infringement, antitrust, contract and business tort issues, insurance coverage for D&O, product liability and business tort claims, and Delaware fiduciary duty and related corporate and partnership claims.
**Professional Memberships:** ABA Litigation Section (Co-Chair Corporate Counsel Committee); Intellectual Property Section; Business Law Section; Delaware District Court IP Advisory Committee.
**Career:** Chaired firm's Litigation Group for six years.
**Personal:** Amherst College, 1979; Duke University School of Law, 1982; law clerk to Hon Robert L Clifford, NJ Supreme Court, 1982-83.

### JAUFFRET, Jennifer C
Richards, Layton & Finger PA, Wilmington
302 651 7568
Jauffret@rlf.com
*Featured in Labor & Employment (Delaware)*
**Practice Areas:** Jennifer Jauffret, head of the firm's Labor and Employment Group, represents a wide variety of corporate and business clients concerning Delaware and federal labor and employment law, including advising to prevent litigation and promote compliance, acting as an advocate in litigation at the agency stage or in court, advising on major corporate transactions, and training managers and employees regarding employment laws.
**Professional Memberships:** Past chair and current member of the Delaware State Bar Association's Labor and Employment Section, member of the Delaware State Bar Association's Corporate Counsel Section, member of the American Bar Association's Labor and Employment Section.

### JENKINS, Stephen E
Ashby & Geddes, Wilmington
302 654 1888
sjenkins@ashby-geddes.com
*Featured in Chancery (Delaware)*

**Practice Areas:** Practice concentrated in counseling and litigating on behalf of corporations and other entities and their directors as well as large stockholders, including various activist stockholders; counseling and litigating on behalf of corporate boards and committees, related corporate and commercial litigation, and corporate valuation issues including Delaware statutory appraisals.
**Professional Memberships:** Member, Delaware Court of Chancery Rules Advisory Committee; Member, Delaware State Bar Association, formerly Co-Chair, Committee on Professional Ethics.
**Personal:** Born Wilmington, Delaware 1954; admitted to Delaware Bar 1982; Georgetown University (AB 1976); JD, magna cum laude, (1982), Executive Editor, Georgetown Law Journal; US Army, 1976-79.

## KELBON, Regina Stango
Blank Rome LLP, Philadelphia
215 569 5507
Kelbon@BlankRome.com
*Featured in Bankruptcy/Restructuring (Delaware),*
*Bankruptcy/Restructuring (Pennsylvania)*
See under Pennsylvania for profile.

## KELLEY, Bernard J
Richards, Layton & Finger PA, Wilmington
302 651 7674
Kelley@RLF.com
*Featured in Corporate/M&A (Delaware)*
**Practice Areas:** Bernard Kelley is a director in the firm's Business Department. He focuses on a variety of transactional matters involving alternative entities, including Delaware limited liability companies, limited partnerships, general partnerships and statutory trusts, and is actively involved in the organization, structuring and operation of these types of entities. Mr Kelley also represents banks and trust companies in commercial transactions and regulatory matters.
**Professional Memberships:** Mr Kelley serves on the Statutory Trust Committee and is former chair of the Delaware Banking Law Committee of the Delaware State Bar Association. He is also a member of the American Bar Association.

## KIRK, Richard D
Bayard, P.A., Wilmington
302 429 4208
rkirk@bayardlaw.com
*Featured in Intellectual Property (Delaware)*
**Practice Areas:** Richard D Kirk (Dick) focuses on general business litigation, intellectual property litigation, administrative law, and alternative dispute resolution.
**Professional Memberships:** American Bar Association; Delaware Bar Foundation; Delaware State Bar Association (President, 1993-94); Federal Bar Association; Rules Advisory Committee of the United States District Court for the District of Delaware.
**Career:** Dick clerked for Delaware Supreme Court Justice William Duffy, one of the founding members of what is now Bayard. He joined Bayard in 2005 after 20 years at another Wilmington, Delaware firm. Dick is a director and a shareholder. He was listed in The Best Lawyers

in America® (Woodward/White, Inc., Aiken, SC), under environmental law for more than fifteen years, and is now recognized under administrative law. Dick has been noted as a leading attorney in the field of intellectual property in Delaware by Chambers USA 2006 through 2013. He is also AV® Peer Review Rated by Martindale-Hubbell.
**Personal:** Born Washington, DC, January 23, 1953; Georgetown University (BA, 1975); University of Virginia School of Law (JD, 1978); Admitted to practice in Delaware (1978); United States District Court for the District of Delaware (1980); United States Court of Appeals for the Third Circuit (1982); United States Supreme Court (1984).

## KLEIN, Daniel L
Richards, Layton & Finger PA, Wilmington
302 651 7638
Klein@rlf.com
*Featured in Real Estate (Delaware)*
**Practice Areas:** A senior director in the firm's Real Estate Group, Daniel Klein specializes in complex business transactions, public/private joint ventures and real estate lending work.
**Professional Memberships:** Mr Klein is active in the Real Property Section of the Delaware State Bar Association and in the American Bar Association. He is a member of the Anglo-American Real Property Institute and the American College of Real Estate Lawyers, where he served two terms on its Board of Governors.
**Career:** Mr Klein is listed in "Super Lawyers" and has appeared in "The Best Lawyers in America" every year since its inception.

## KNIGHT, John H
Richards, Layton & Finger PA, Wilmington
302 651 7512
knight@RLF.com
*Featured in Bankruptcy/Restructuring (Delaware)*
**Practice Areas:** John Knight is a director in the firm's Bankruptcy and Corporate Restructuring Department. He represents debtors (including Dallas Stars and Orval Kent Foods), secured creditors and other parties in interest in chapter 11 cases. He has an active secured lender practice, representing the prepetition or DIP lender in many large bankruptcy cases. Mr Knight is also a leader of the firm's substantive non-consolidation opinion team.
**Professional Memberships:** Mr Knight is a member of the state bars of Delaware, Maryland and New Jersey.
**Career:** Mr Knight is a speaker for the American Bankruptcy Institute and the Turnaround Management Association.

## KRAFT, Denise
DLA Piper LLP (US), Washington, DC
302 466 5645
denise.kraft@dlapiper.com
*Featured in Intellectual Property (Delaware)*
**Practice Areas:** Intellectual property.
**Career:** She represents and counsels on business disputes, including intellectual property litigation and complex commercial litigation issues. She has a significant local Delaware counsel practice and is often called upon by corporations and other law

firms from across the country and around the world to serve as counsel for cases pending in the Delaware courts and/or to advise or opine on Delaware law issues.
**Personal:** JD, Catholic University of America, Columbus School of Law; BA, West Virginia Wesleyan College.

## KRAPF, Robert J
Richards, Layton & Finger PA, Wilmington
302 651 7609
krapf@rlf.com
*Featured in Real Estate (Delaware)*
**Practice Areas:** Robert Krapf is president of the firm. A director in the Real Estate Group, he handles a variety of transactional matters involving real estate and land use law.
**Professional Memberships:** Mr Krapf has held many leadership positions in the Delaware State Bar Association and the American Bar Association Real Property, Trust and Estate Law Section, including on their governing boards.
**Career:** Mr Krapf lectures frequently on real estate law. His clients include many of the developers, landlords, banks, conservation organizations, institutions, businesses and industries operating in Delaware.
**Publications:** Mr Krapf has published numerous articles in his field.

## LADNER, Gregory W
Richards, Layton & Finger PA, Wilmington
302 651 7547
Ladner@RLF.com
*Featured in Corporate/M&A (Delaware)*
**Practice Areas:** Gregory Ladner is a director in the firm's Business Department. His practice focuses on rendering advice as to matters of Delaware state law relating to Delaware general, limited and limited liability partnerships and limited liability companies. His work includes rendering advice with respect to mergers, conversions and other structural changes involving partnerships and limited liability companies.
**Professional Memberships:** Mr Ladner is a member of the Delaware State Bar Association and the American Bar Association.
**Career:** Mr Ladner has spoken at continuing legal education programs.
**Publications:** Mr Ladner has published articles concerning Delaware partnerships and limited liability companies.

## LAMB, Christopher J
Pepper Hamilton LLP, Wilmington
302 777 6548
lambc@pepperlaw.com
*Featured in Real Estate (Delaware)*
**Practice Areas:** Partner. Experienced in commercial law in major US corporate venues, including real estate acquisitions, secured financing, leasing and public finance. Litigation experience includes representation of creditors and debtors in workouts, foreclosures, mechanics' lien actions and state court proceedings. Represents financial institutions, developers and investors.
**Professional Memberships:** New Castle County Economic Development Corporation

Business Mentoring Program; Leadership Delaware.
**Personal:** JD, cum laude, 1988 Temple University School of Law; BA, magna cum laude, 1984 La Salle University.

## LAND, Allison
Skadden, Arps, Slate, Meagher & Flom LLP & Affiliates, Wilmington
302 651 3180
allison.land@skadden.com
*Featured in Corporate/M&A (Delaware)*
**Practice Areas:** Ms Land concentrates in the areas of M&A, securities, and Delaware corporate and alternative entity law. She represents clients in mergers, acquisitions, leveraged buyouts, joint ventures, recapitalizations, and spin-offs. Ms Land also advises clients, including equity sponsors and asset management firms, in debt and equity securities offerings, internal governance and Delaware corporate and alternative entity law. She serves on the Corporation Law Council of the Delaware State Bar Association, and its Alternative Entity subcommittee.
**Career:** JD, Ohio State University College of Law, 1992 (summa cum laude); Managing Editor, The Ohio State Law Journal; BS, Lehigh University, 1988.

## LANDIS, Adam G
Landis Rath & Cobb LLP, Wilmington
302 467 4410
landis@lrclaw.com
*Featured in Bankruptcy/Restructuring (Delaware)*
**Practice Areas:** Corporate bankruptcy/restructuring. First-chair and co-counsel representation of debtors and borrowers, official and unofficial committees, secured lenders and other secured creditors, indenture trustees and bondholders, unsecured creditors, asset purchasers, officers and directors, liquidating trusts and plan administrators in workouts, restructurings and Chapter 11 cases.
**Professional Memberships:** American Bankruptcy Institute; Delaware, New York and Massachusetts State Bar Associations; Chair of the Bankruptcy Section of the Delaware State Bar Association (2011). Member of Steering Committee for 2011 ABI/DSBA Delaware Views from the Bench program.
**Career:** Founding Partner Landis Rath & Cobb LLP (2003).
**Personal:** Northeastern University School of Law (JD 1991).

## LEYDEN JR, James G
Richards, Layton & Finger PA, Wilmington
302 651 7620
Leyden@RLF.com
*Featured in Corporate/M&A (Delaware)*
**Practice Areas:** A director in the firm's Limited Liability Company and Partnership Advisory Group, James Leyden focuses on complex transactional matters involving Delaware limited liability companies, limited partnerships, general partnerships, trusts and corporations.
**Professional Memberships:** Mr Leyden is a member of the TriBar Opinion Committee and the American Bar Association's Business Law

Section, and chair of the Delaware State Bar Association committee that drafts Delaware's limited liability company and partnership statutes.
**Publications:** Mr Leyden is co-reporter of the TriBar Opinion Committee report "Third Party Closing Opinions: Limited Liability Companies" and author of numerous articles concerning Delaware LLCs and partnerships.

### MARTIN, Craig
DLA Piper LLP (US), Wilmington
302 468 5655
craig.martin@dlapiper.com
*Featured in Bankruptcy/Restructuring (Delaware)*
**Practice Areas:** Bankruptcy/restructuring.
**Professional Memberships:** Fellow, International Association of Restructuring, Insolvency & Bankruptcy Professionals (INSOL International).
**Career:** He focuses on complex distressed situations and has represented numerous parties in a variety of cases, including equity committees, committees of unsecured creditors, bank groups, indenture trustees and debtors. He has advised purchasers of assets in bankruptcy auctions and court-approved sales and frequently provides bankruptcy-specific advice in complex mergers and acquisition situations involving distressed entities.
**Personal:** JD, University of Houston Law Center (cum laude); MSc, University of Edinburg; BA, Texas Christian University.

### MAZIE, Eric A
Richards, Layton & Finger PA, Wilmington
302 651 7678
Mazie@RLF.com
*Featured in Corporate/M&A (Delaware)*
**Practice Areas:** Eric Mazie heads the firm's Business Trust and Agency Services Group. His practice focuses on a wide range of transactional matters, with emphasis on the use of common law and statutory trusts. He also represents numerous financial institutions that provide trust and agency services in commercial transactions.
**Professional Memberships:** Mr Mazie has chaired the Statutory Trust Committee of the Delaware State Bar Association since 1988.
**Publications:** Mr Mazie co-authored chapters in "The Delaware Law of Corporations & Business Organizations" and "Equipment Leasing - Leveraged Leasing," as well as numerous articles regarding trusts and trustees.

### MCDONOUGH, Kathleen Furey
Potter Anderson & Corroon LLP, Wilmington
302 984 6032
kmcdonough@potteranderson.com
*Featured in Labor & Employment (Delaware)*
**Practice Areas:** Ms McDonough heads the firm's Labor and Employment Practice, exclusively representing management. She represents multinational and local companies before state and federal courts in Delaware and has successfully tried numerous employment-related lawsuits. She represents employers before the EEOC, NLRB and state administrative agencies, and also represents public employers before Delaware's Public Employment Relations Board. She also advises

educational institutions on employment and education law. She chairs the District Court Advisory Committee for the US District Court for the District of Delaware and has held board leadership positions in several non-profit organizations.

### MERCHANT, Michael J
Richards, Layton & Finger PA, Wilmington
302 651 7854
Merchant@RLF.com
*Featured in Bankruptcy/Restructuring (Delaware)*
**Practice Areas:** Michael Merchant, a director in the firm's Bankruptcy and Corporate Restructuring Department, focuses on the areas of bankruptcy and creditors' rights, representing debtors, creditors' committees, purchasers and other parties in chapter 11 cases.
**Professional Memberships:** Mr Merchant is a member of the Delaware State Bar Association, Turnaround Management Association, and Asset Sales and Business Reorganization Committees of the American Bankruptcy Institute.
**Career:** Mr Merchant has served as debtors' counsel in A123 Systems, Blitz USA, Bowe Systec, Urban Brands, Linens 'N Things, New Century, QiMonda, ResMae and Teleglobe; and creditors' committee counsel in Filene's Basement and Ritz Camera.

### MOORE, David E
Potter Anderson & Corroon LLP, Wilmington
302 984 6147
dmoore@potteranderson.com
*Featured in Intellectual Property (Delaware)*
**Practice Areas:** Mr Moore practices commercial litigation in the state and federal courts. He concentrates his practice in intellectual property litigation, and other complex commercial litigation. Mr Moore's experience also includes representing corporate clients in alternative dispute resolution proceedings.
**Career:** Temple University School of Law, LLM in Trial Advocacy, 2004; Temple University School of Law, JD, 1999; Arizona State University, M.Ed., 1996; University of Virginia, BSEd, 1992.

### MORTON, Mark A
Potter Anderson & Corroon LLP, Wilmington
302 984 6078
mmorton@potteranderson.com
*Featured in Corporate/M&A (Delaware)*
**Practice Areas:** Mr Morton concentrates on Delaware corporate law. His clients include public and private corporations, corporate boards and special committees. He provides statutory, structuring and fiduciary duty advice and renders legal opinions on Delaware corporate law matters. Mr Morton chairs the ABA's M&A Committee (more than 4000 members) and serves on the Corporate Council of the Delaware State Bar Association. He is an adjunct law professor at the University of Pennsylvania and the University of Virginia law schools and a frequent author and national speaker on Delaware corporate law.
**Professional Memberships:** Delaware State and American Bar Associations.

### MOYER, Jeffrey L
Richards, Layton & Finger PA, Wilmington
302 651 7525
moyer@RLF.com
*Featured in Intellectual Property (Delaware)*
**Practice Areas:** Jeffrey Moyer is vice chair of the Litigation Department and general counsel of the firm. He has represented some of the world's leading companies in intellectual property and licensing disputes in the Delaware District Court and Delaware Court of Chancery. Mr Moyer also has represented clients in some of the largest civil cases brought in the Delaware Superior Court.
**Professional Memberships:** American Bar Association, Delaware State Bar Association and American Intellectual Property Law Association.
**Career:** Mr Moyer regularly speaks on litigation practice and ethics.
**Publications:** Mr Moyer contributes to the firm's publications concerning litigation practice in Delaware.

### MUMFORD, Kerri K
Landis Rath & Cobb LLP, Wilmington
302 467 4414
mumford@lrclaw.com
*Featured in Bankruptcy/Restructuring (Delaware)*
**Practice Areas:** Corporate bankruptcy/restructuring. Lead and co-counsel representation of debtors, official/unofficial committees, secured lenders and other secured creditors, indenture trustees and bond holders, significant trade and other unsecured creditors and asset purchasers, officers and directors, liquidating trusts and plan administrators.
**Professional Memberships:** Delaware State Bar Association; American Bankruptcy Institute; International Woman's Insolvency & Restructuring Confederation; Delaware Bankruptcy Inns of Court; Bankruptcy section Delaware State Bar Association.
**Career:** Partner Landis Rath & Cobb LLP.
**Personal:** High Point University BA Political Science (1996) Catholic University of America, Magna Cum Laude (JD 2001).

### NORMAN, Stephen C
Potter Anderson & Corroon LLP, Wilmington
302 984 6038
snorman@potteranderson.com
*Featured in Chancery (Delaware)*
**Practice Areas:** Mr Norman practices in the areas of corporate and commercial litigation. He has substantial experience in litigating corporate and commercial disputes in the Court of Chancery and the District Court of Delaware, including class and derivative actions, takeovers, and various proceedings under Delaware corporate and partnership law. Recent representations include Wal-Mart, Google, Nationwide, JP Morgan and HP.
**Professional Memberships:** ABA; Co-Chair of Corporate Governance Subcommittee of Corporate Counsel Committee; Co-Chair of Derivative Subcommittee of Class Action and Derivative Suits Committee.
**Personal:** Law clerk to The Honorable William W Caldwell, Middle District of Pennsylvania.

### NORTON, Marla
Bayard, P.A., Wilmington
302 429 4214
mnorton@bayardlaw.com
*Featured in Corporate/M&A (Delaware)*
**Practice Areas:** Marla concentrates her practice on alternative business entities, corporate governance, and third party legal opinions. Marla has over 25 years of varied experience in corporate and commercial transactions, including securitization transactions, entity formation and governance, mergers and acquisitions, contract negotiation and drafting, and secured lending.
**Professional Memberships:** ABA Business Law Section: -Subcommittee on Business Trusts (Chair); LLC, Partnership and Unincorporated Entities Committee; Legal Opinions Committee; Middle Market/ Small Business Committee; Model Shareholders Agreement Task Force and Forum on Franchising; DSBA, Commercial Law Section: (Partnership and LLC Committee and Statutory Trust Committee) and Corporation Law Section; Legislative Committee of the Delaware Captive Insurance Association; ABA Advisor to the Uniform Law Commission's Series Study Committee (2012) and Series Drafting Committee (current).
**Career:** Marla has been named a leading lawyer in the "Corporate/M&A: Alternative Entities" practice area by Chambers USA from 2008 through 2013. She was also named as a Delaware Super Lawyer for business/corporate law in the June 2007 issue of "Philadelphia" magazine and was named a "Top Lawyer" in 2001 for corporate law based on a survey of the Delaware State Bar Association published by "Delaware Today" magazine. Marla serves on the Board of Directors and as secretary of The Delaware Center for Contemporary Arts and is the past President of her synagogue.
**Publications:** "Lands of Opportunity—Why Cayman and Delaware Entities Rule in Structured Finance," International Securitization & Finance Report, Vol. 9, No. 18, (October 15, 2006).
**Personal:** Born Newark, New Jersey, March 24, 1962; University of Delaware (BA, 1984); George Washington University School of Law (JD, with honors, 1987); Admitted: Delaware (1987), District of Columbia (1990), United States District Court for the District of Delaware (1989).

### PERNICK, Norman L
Cole, Schotz, Meisel, Forman & Leonard PA, Wilmington
302 295 4829
npernick@coleschotz.com
*Featured in Bankruptcy/Restructuring (Delaware)*
**Practice Areas:** Co-Chair of the firm's Bankruptcy & Corporate Restructuring Department and head of Wilmington office. Practices many aspects of bankruptcy and workouts, primarily representing debtors, but also represents creditors' committees, secured and unsecured creditors, and trustees. Served as lead debtor's counsel in numerous high profile Chapter 11 cases, including Leslie Controls, Ritz Camera Centers, Cadence Innovation, J.G. Wentworth, Fedders Corporation, Barzel

Industries, BNA Subsidiaries, and Owens Corning.

**Publications:** Author, Bankruptcy Deadline Checklist.

**Personal:** George Washington University Law School, JD, with honors, 1984.

## PINCUS, Robert B
Skadden, Arps, Slate, Meagher & Flom LLP & Affiliates, Wilmington
302 651 3090
Bob.Pincus@skadden.com
*Featured in Corporate/M&A (Delaware)*

**Practice Areas:** Represents and advises clients in a wide variety of corporate matters, including mergers and acquisitions, private equity investments and unsolicited takeovers. Extensive experience in advising clients and other lawyers in the firm on Delaware law aspects of transactions and fiduciary duty and corporate governance matters. Leads the corporate practice in the firm's Wilmington, Delaware, office.

**Career:** LLM, Securities Regulation, Georgetown University Law Center, 1983; JD, American University, The Washington College of Law, 1980 (magna cum laude); BBA, College of William and Mary, 1977.

## PITTENGER, Michael A
Potter Anderson & Corroon LLP, Wilmington
302 984 6136
mpittenger@potteranderson.com
*Featured in Chancery (Delaware)*

**Practice Areas:** Mr Pittenger practices in the area of corporation law, advising Delaware corporations and their directors, officers, and shareholders about all aspects of Delaware corporate law and governance of Delaware corporations, including fiduciary duties of directors and officers and technical compliance with the Delaware General Corporation Law. He represents corporations, directors, and officers in corporate litigation in the Delaware Court of Chancery, including stockholder class and derivative actions, corporate takeovers, and statutory proceedings.

**Publications:** Co-author, Corporate and Commercial Practice in the Delaware Court of Chancery, a leading treatise on Delaware corporate law and practice in the Court of Chancery.

## PURPURA, Mark V
Richards, Layton & Finger PA, Wilmington
302 651 7588
Purpura@RLF.com
*Featured in Corporate/M&A (Delaware)*

**Practice Areas:** Mark Purpura, a director in the firm's Business Department, focuses on transactional matters relating to Delaware entities, including mergers and acquisitions, initial public offerings, entity formation (including private equity firm and investment fund formation), entity governance, dissolution, joint ventures and financing transactions. He also represents banks, trust companies and other financial institutions in organizational, transactional, regulatory and corporate fiduciary matters.

**Professional Memberships:** Mr Purpura chairs the Banking Law Committee of the Delaware State Bar Association and is a member

of the Business Law Section and the Banking Law Committee of the American Bar Association.

## QUIRK, Marion
Cole, Schotz, Meisel, Forman & Leonard PA, Wilmington
302 651 2007
mquirk@coleschotz.com
*Featured in Bankruptcy/Restructuring (Delaware)*

**Practice Areas:** Represents public and privately held companies in out-of-court restructurings and traditional Chapter 11 cases. Clients include debtors, creditors, lenders and acquirers in all stages of complex restructuring transactions.

**Professional Memberships:** International Women's Insolvency and Restructuring Confederation (IWIRC) American Bankruptcy Institute (ABI), Associate Editor of the ABI Journal Delaware Bankruptcy Chapter of the American Inns of Court, Barrister Combined Campaign for Justice - Communications Co-Chair Fresh Start Scholarship Foundation - Board Member.

**Personal:** Syracuse University, JD, cum laude, 1997 (Executive Editor, Syracuse Law Review, 1996-97).

## RAJU, Srinivas M
Richards, Layton & Finger PA, Wilmington
302 651 7748
Raju@RLF.com
*Featured in Corporate/M&A (Delaware)*

**Practice Areas:** Srini Raju's practice focuses on advisory, transactional and litigation matters relating to Delaware corporations and alternative entities. He litigates corporate control, corporate governance and contractual disputes in Delaware courts, and advises corporate boards, special committees and general partners regarding governance and transactional issues.

**Professional Memberships:** Mr Raju is a member of the American Bar Association and the Delaware State Bar Association.

**Career:** Mr Raju lectures frequently on fiduciary duty and governance issues.

**Publications:** Mr Raju co-authored "Special Committees: Law and Practice," published in 2011 by Oxford University Press, and has written numerous articles.

## RATH, Daniel B
Landis Rath & Cobb LLP, Wilmington
302 467 4420
rath@lrclaw.com
*Featured in Chancery (Delaware)*

**Practice Areas:** Court of Chancery disputes over ownership, control and management of Delaware corporations, partnerships and limited liability companies. First chair and co-counsel representation in cases involving breach of fiduciary duty, partnership agreements and limited liability company agreements and statutory proceedings brought pursuant to the Delaware General Corporation Law, the Delaware Limited Liability Company Act and the Delaware Revised Uniform Limited Partnership Act.

**Professional Memberships:** American Bar Association; Delaware and Pennsylvania State Bar Associations.

**Career:** Founding Partner Landis Rath & Cobb LLP (2003).

**Personal:** Temple University School of Law (JD 1991, cum laude).

## REED, Janet E
Potter Anderson & Corroon LLP, Wilmington
jreed@potteranderson.com
*Featured in Intellectual Property (Delaware)*

**Practice Areas:** Dr Reed leads the firm's intellectual property transactional and counseling practice. With two advanced degrees and ten years of post-graduate training in biochemistry, molecular biology and plant physiology/pathology, Dr Reed focuses her practice on patents for biotechnological inventions in medicine, agriculture and environmental sciences. She represents a diverse array of clients in domestic and foreign patent and trademark prosecution and inter partes proceedings, intellectual property portfolio management and strategic planning, evaluation of new technology, drafting of license and other commercialization agreements, and preparation of opinions on patentability, infringement and freedom to operate.

## REED, John L
DLA Piper LLP (US), Wilmington
302 468 5635
john.reed@dlapiper.com
*Featured in Chancery (Delaware)*

**Practice Areas:** Corporate, litigation.

**Career:** His national practice involves the counseling and representation of corporations, boards of directors, individual officers and directors, special board committees and large investors. He is often called upon by corporations and other law firms from across the country and around the world to serve as counsel for cases pending in the Delaware courts and/or to advise or opine on Delaware law issues for transactions being handled in other jurisdictions but governed by Delaware law.

**Personal:** JD, Widener University School of Law (cum laude); BA, Villanova University (Dean's List).

## ROHRBACHER, Blake
Richards, Layton & Finger PA, Wilmington
302 651 7847
rohrbacher@rlf.com
*Featured in Chancery (Delaware)*

**Practice Areas:** Mr Rohrbacher's practice includes both litigation and transactional matters involving Delaware entities. He litigates corporate governance, M&A, statutory, and contractual disputes in the Delaware courts, and advises directors regarding corporate governance and mergers and acquisitions.

**Career:** Mr Rohrbacher serves on the Court of Chancery Rules Committee and served on the drafting subcommittee responsible for the 2010 nonstock amendments to Delaware's General Corporation Law.

**Publications:** Mr Rohrbacher has published numerous articles on Delaware corporate law, including in "The Business Lawyer," and is a contributing author to "Fundamentals of Corporate

Governance" and "The Delaware Law of Corporations and Business Organizations."

## ROVNER, Philip A
Potter Anderson & Corroon LLP, Wilmington
302 984 6140
provner@potteranderson.com
*Featured in Intellectual Property (Delaware)*

**Practice Areas:** Mr Rovner practices in the areas of complex commercial and corporate litigation, focusing primarily on intellectual property litigation and corporate, commercial and licensing disputes. He has significant trial experience in intellectual property, trade secret and commercial disputes in the United States District Court for the District of Delaware and Delaware's state courts, including the Court of Chancery and the Superior Court. He served on the Complex Business Litigation Committee, the group responsible for providing the framework for the Superior Court's Complex Commercial Litigation Division.

**Personal:** University of Pennsylvania (BA 1981); Fordham University School of Law (JD 1987).

## SAUNDERS, Robert S
Skadden, Arps, Slate, Meagher & Flom LLP & Affiliates, Wilmington
302 651 3170
Rob.Saunders@skadden.com
*Featured in Chancery (Delaware)*

**Practice Areas:** Litigates and tries cases in federal and state courts, concentrating on cases involving the federal securities laws and the governance of business organizations, with emphasis on mergers and acquisitions. Provides transactional advice on the laws governing Delaware business organizations.

**Career:** JD, University of Virginia School of Law, 1991 (Virginia Law Review); AB, Dartmouth College, 1987.

## SCHLERF, Jeffrey M
Fox Rothschild LLP, Wilmington
302 622 4212
jschlerf@foxrothschild.com
*Featured in Bankruptcy/Restructuring (Delaware)*

**Practice Areas:** Commercial bankruptcy, restructurings, workouts. Sports and Entertainment. Certified mediator.

**Professional Memberships:** American Bankruptcy Institute; American Bar Association; Delaware Bankruptcy Inn of Court; Delaware and Pennsylvania State Bar Associations.

**Career:** 25+ years of experience relating to financial industry, as economist at Federal Reserve and commercial bank, and then as attorney.

**Publications:** 'BAPCPA's Impact on Exclusivity Is Hard To Gauge,' The Journal of Corporate Renewal (July 2007); 'Duties of Directors and Managers of Distressed Companies,' Delaware Lawyer (Fall 2010). 'At Bat in Bankruptcy Court,' Delaware Lawyer (Winter 2012/2013).

**Personal:** Trustee, Grand Opera House; Campaign Cabinet, United Way; Executive Committee, MDA.

### SHANNON, Kevin R
Potter Anderson & Corroon LLP, Wilmington
302 984 6112
kshannon@potteranderson.com
*Featured in Chancery (Delaware)*
**Practice Areas:** Mr Shannon practices primarily in the areas of corporate and commercial litigation, including stockholder class and derivative actions in the Delaware Court of Chancery. He litigates and provides advice regarding various proceedings under the Delaware General Corporation Law, including actions for appraisal, indemnification and dissolution. Mr Shannon also has extensive experience litigating disputes involving partnerships, limited partnerships and limited liability companies. With his financial/accounting background, Mr Shannon has been involved in numerous cases involving financial and accounting issues, as well as advising special committees in connection with investigations of alleged wrongdoing, including accounting irregularities.

### SILBERGLIED, Russell C
Richards, Layton & Finger PA, Wilmington
302 651 7545
Silberglied@RLF.com
*Featured in Bankruptcy/Restructuring (Delaware)*
**Practice Areas:** Russell Silberglied practices bankruptcy litigation and chapter 11 law and advises troubled companies' boards of directors concerning fiduciary duties.
**Professional Memberships:** Chair Emeritus: Lex Mundi's Bankruptcy Group.
**Career:** Clients include Velocitel in the Open Range case, Tennenbaum Capital in the Radnor case, debtors' counsel to Charys Holding and Dayton Superior, committee counsel in Spheris and Javo Beverage, and Chapter 15 foreign representative's counsel in WC Wood, Salerno Plastics and John Forsyth Shirt Co. Turnaround and Workouts named Mr Silberglied one of the "Outstanding Young Restructuring Lawyers - 2005."
**Publications:** Numerous articles concerning bankruptcy and fiduciary duty issues.

### SILVERSTEIN, Laurie Selber
Potter Anderson & Corroon LLP, Wilmington
302 984 6033
lsilverstein@potteranderson.com
*Featured in Bankruptcy/Restructuring (Delaware)*
**Practice Areas:** Chair of the firm's Restructuring and Bankruptcy Group. Mrs Silverstein represents corporate entities in national chapter 11 cases in a variety of industries and market sectors, including entities holding secured and unsecured claims, creditors' committees, lenders, agents to lender groups and acquirers. She also represents debtors and trustees. Representative clients include Bank of America, individually and in its capacity as agent to pre and/or post petition lenders under various syndicated facilities and Perot Systems Corporation.
**Professional Memberships:** Fellow, American College of Bankruptcy.
**Personal:** The National Law Center of The George Washington University, JD, with honors, 1985.

### STEARN JR, Robert J
Richards, Layton & Finger PA, Wilmington
302 651 7830
stearn@rlf.com
*Featured in Bankruptcy/Restructuring (Delaware)*
**Practice Areas:** Robert J Stearn Jr is a director in the Bankruptcy and Corporate Restructuring Department. He focuses on bankruptcy litigation, including preference and fraudulent transfer litigation, as well as all types of contested matters.
**Professional Memberships:** Mr Stearn is a member of the Delaware State Bar Association and American Bar Association.
**Career:** Mr Stearn joined the firm in 1990. His clients include large corporate debtors as well as defendants in adversary proceedings and contested matters. He also advises major financial advisors on matters relating to solvency analysis.
**Publications:** Mr Stearn's most recently published articles concern solvency analysis and litigation.

### STICKLES, Kate
Cole, Schotz, Meisel, Forman & Leonard PA, Wilmington
302 651 2001
kstickles@coleschotz.com
*Featured in Bankruptcy/Restructuring (Delaware)*
**Practice Areas:** Concentrates her practice in the areas of bankruptcy, insolvency and creditors' rights, with particular experience representing debtors, official committees, examiners and trustees in chapter 11 cases. Select representative matters include: Barzel Industries Inc., Cambridge Industries Holdings, Inc., DBSI, Inc., Devon Mobile Communications, L.P., Fedders North America, Inc., Fruit of the Loom, Inc., Kaiser Group International, Inc., Noma Company, OMNA Medical Partners, Inc., Owens Corning, Physician Health Corporation, Stuart Entertainment, Inc., Tribune Company, United Companies Financial Corporation, and Washington Mutual, Inc.
**Personal:** Temple University James E. Beasley School of Law, JD, 1989.

### STRATTON, David B
Pepper Hamilton LLP, Wilmington
302 777 6566
strattond@pepperlaw.com
*Featured in Bankruptcy/Restructuring (Delaware)*
**Practice Areas:** Partner; Co-Chairman, Corporate Restructuring and Bankruptcy Practice Group; Partner-in-Charge, Wilmington office. Experienced in representing debtors, creditors' committees, secured creditors, individual creditors. Lead counsel/co-counsel in bankruptcy courts in Delaware, Maryland and New York in Section 304 and Chapter 11 proceedings involving retailers, high-tech companies, entertainment, transportation companies, manufacturing, energy. Handles complex bankruptcy litigation. Advises on bankruptcy and litigation strategy, asset sales, restructurings and dispute resolution.
**Professional Memberships:** Member, American Bankruptcy Institute; Board of Directors, Better Business Bureau of Delaware, Inc.

**Personal:** JD, cum laude, 1978 University of Pittsburgh School of Law; AB, magna cum laude, 1975 Gettysburg College.

### TONER, Sara
Richards, Layton & Finger PA, Wilmington
302 651 7646
toner@rlf.com
*Featured in Real Estate (Delaware)*
**Practice Areas:** Sara Toner handles transactions involving the acquisition, sale, lease, finance and development of commercial real estate properties. She has represented major real estate developers, significant holders of commercial real estate and institutional clients in all types of real estate transactions.
**Professional Memberships:** Ms Toner is vice chair of the Senior Housing Committee of the American Bar Association's Real Property, Trust & Estate Law Section. She is also a member of the Delaware State Bar Association.
**Publications:** Ms Toner is a contributing author of several published articles regarding Delaware real estate law.

### TUMAS, Michael B
Potter Anderson & Corroon LLP, Wilmington
302 984 6029
mtumas@potteranderson.com
*Featured in Corporate/M&A (Delaware)*
**Practice Areas:** Member of the firm's Executive Committee. Mr Tumas concentrates in the area of corporate law, with specific emphasis on mergers and acquisitions, issues of internal governance and commercial transactions involving Delaware corporations, partnerships and limited liability companies. His practice often involves counseling boards of directors, special committees and managers regarding their duties, fiduciary and otherwise. Mr Tumas regularly represents buyers and sellers in negotiated acquisitions. He recently served on the council responsible for drafting Delaware's General Corporation Law.
**Personal:** Mr Tumas is a graduate of the Law School of the University of Pennsylvania.

### VALIHURA, Karen
Skadden, Arps, Slate, Meagher & Flom LLP & Affiliates, Wilmington
302 651 3140
karen.valihura@skadden.com
*Featured in Chancery (Delaware)*
**Practice Areas:** Karen Valihura's practice focuses on corporate, securities and complex commercial litigation matters. Ms Valihura has been the lead trial counsel in various matters in both state and federal court. She has extensive experience in representing clients in high profile corporate and commercial litigation. Ms Valihura has represented various clients in matters involving issues of corporate governance and fiduciary duties of directors, officers and partners.
**Career:** JD, University of Pennsylvania Law School, 1988 (Law Review); BA, Washington & Jefferson College, 1985 (valedictorian; Phi Beta Kappa).

### VARALLO, Gregory V
Richards, Layton & Finger PA, Wilmington
302 651 7772
varallo@rlf.com
*Featured in Chancery (Delaware)*
**Practice Areas:** Gregory Varallo, vice chair of the firm's Corporate Department, focuses on corporate litigation, corporate governance and corporate transactions. He has litigated complex business disputes in courts throughout the US.
**Professional Memberships:** Mr Varallo is a member of the ABA, and past chair of the Subcommittee on Corporate Counseling and Litigation and the Task Force on Litigation Reform and Rules Revision. He served on the editorial board of "The Business Lawyer."
**Publications:** Mr Varallo co-authored "Special Committees: Law and Practice," published in 2011 by Oxford University Press, the first comprehensive guide to this emerging area of practice.

### VOSS, Wendy K
Potter Anderson & Corroon LLP, Wilmington
302 984 6076
wvoss@potteranderson.com
*Featured in Labor & Employment (Delaware)*
**Practice Areas:** Ms Voss practices in the areas of labor and employment and commercial law. She represents management in a variety of industries and locations throughout the United States, providing counsel regarding personnel policies and practices, collective bargaining and related issues, wage and hours practices, reductions in force, employee supervision, discipline and discharge, wrongful harassment, and employment discrimination. She represents employers in federal and state courts and before state and federal administrative agencies, including the EEOC and the NLRB. She also represents public employers in the State of Delaware before the Public Employee Relations Board, in union negotiations and arbitrations.

### WALSH JR, Peter J
Potter Anderson & Corroon LLP, Wilmington
302 984 6037
pwalsh@potteranderson.com
*Featured in Chancery (Delaware)*
**Practice Areas:** Mr Walsh is a corporate and commercial litigator, and routinely handles stockholder class and derivative actions, summary proceedings pursuant to the Delaware General Corporation Law, and alternative entity litigation. He counsels officers and directors of Delaware corporations, primarily as such matters bear upon ongoing or anticipated litigation. Mr Walsh also has significant experience in the representation of corporate and governmental policyholders in insurance coverage litigation in state and federal courts in Delaware. He serves on the Council of the Section of Business Law of the ABA.

### WAXMAN, Scott E
Potter Anderson & Corroon LLP, Wilmington
302 984 6114
swaxman@potteranderson.com
*Featured in Corporate/M&A (Delaware)*
**Practice Areas:** Mr Waxman practices in the areas of tax, alternative entities and general busi-

ness. His practice extends into mergers and acquisitions, joint ventures, business and commercial law, focusing on organizational and operational issues related to statutory trusts, partnerships, limited liability companies and special purpose corporations. Mr Waxman chairs Delaware's Alternative Entities Subcommittee, responsible for drafting Delaware's preeminent partnership and limited liability company statutes. He also serves on Delaware's Statutory Trust Committee, responsible for drafting Delaware's renowned statutory trust statute.

## WELCH, Edward P
Skadden, Arps, Slate, Meagher & Flom LLP & Affiliates, Wilmington
302 651 3060
Edward.Welch@skadden.com
*Featured in Chancery (Delaware)*
**Practice Areas:** Edward Welch is head of the firm's Wilmington office and leader of Wilmington's litigation practice. Concentrates on corporate and securities litigation, including defense of class and derivative actions, with an emphasis on mergers and acquisitions. Frequently represents clients in administrative proceedings, usually in connection with mergers and acquisitions. Provides Delaware General Corporation Law advice with respect to transactional matters.

**Professional Memberships:** Former chairman of the Board of Directors of the Mary Campbell Center, Inc., member of board of directors (1985-2007); former chair, Delaware Corporation Law Council.
**Career:** JD, Villanova University School of Law, 1976; BS, Georgetown University, 1972.

## WILLIAMS, Gregory P
Richards, Layton & Finger PA, Wilmington
302 651 7734
williams@rlf.com
*Featured in Chancery (Delaware)*
**Practice Areas:** Gregory Williams is past president of the firm and chairs the Corporate Department. He advises corporations, their directors and officers, and represents them in courts in Delaware and throughout the US.
**Professional Memberships:** Mr Williams chairs the Chancery Court Rules Committee and is past chair of the Delaware Supreme Court's Litigation Rules Committee. He is a member of the American College of Trial Lawyers and was a member of the Board of Bar Examiners of the State of Delaware.
**Career:** Mr Williams is a neutral with the American Arbitration Association.
**Publications:** Mr Williams co-authored "Meetings of Stockholders."

## WOLFE JR, Donald J
Potter Anderson & Corroon LLP, Wilmington
302 984 6015
dwolfe@potteranderson.com
*Featured in Chancery (Delaware)*
**Practice Areas:** Corporate litigation and advising boards and special committees on transactions, fiduciary responsibilities and corporate governance.
**Professional Memberships:** Fellow, American College of Trial Lawyers; Member, Board of Advisors, University of Pennsylvania Institute for Law and Economics; Co-Chair, Planning Committee Tulane Corporate Law Institute.
**Publications:** Co-author, Wolfe and Pittenger, Corporate and Commercial Practice in the Delaware Court of Chancery (Lexis Law Publishing), annually updated treatise on litigation practice in the nation's premier corporation law tribunal.

## ZEBERKIEWICZ, John Mark
Richards, Layton & Finger PA, Wilmington
302 651 7698
zeber@rlf.com
*Featured in Corporate/M&A (Delaware)*
**Practice Areas:** Mr Zeberkiewicz focuses on transactional matters involving Delaware corporations, including mergers and acquisitions, corporate governance and corporate finance. He is a director in the firm's Corporate Department and a member of the Corporate Advisory Group.
**Career:** Mr Zeberkiewicz has served on drafting subcommittees responsible for amendments to Delaware's General Corporation Law.
**Publications:** Mr Zeberkiewicz is a frequent speaker on Delaware corporate law and governance, and he has published numerous articles in the field of corporate governance and mergers and acquisitions in a variety of professional journals, including "The Business Lawyer," "Insights" and "The M&A Lawyer."

# ABRAMS & BAYLISS LLP

www.abramsbayliss.com **tel:** 302 778 1000 **fax:** 302 778 1001

**OFFICES**

DELAWARE

**WILMINGTON:** 20 Montchanin Road, Suite 200, DE 19807
Tel: 302 778 1000   Fax: 302 778 1001

**Founding partner:** Kevin G Abrams
Number of partners: 3
Number of other lawyers: 9

## Firm Overview:

Abrams & Bayliss LLP is a business litigation and advisory boutique that focuses on high stakes controversies and transactions carrying a high risk of litigation. The firm's practice primarily involves litigation in the Delaware Court of Chancery and the Delaware Supreme Court, proceedings in other Delaware courts, and advice on matters of Delaware corporate, partnership and business law.

## Main Areas of Practice:

### Corporate & Business Litigation:

The firm's Litigation Practice primarily involves actions in the Delaware Court of Chancery, the nation's preeminent corporate and commercial law court, and the Delaware Supreme Court. The firm's partners have been involved in over 200 decisions and many more cases. The firm's litigators have extensive experience representing public and private companies, stockholders, directors and executives in a wide range of business, corporate and alternative entity litigation matters at the trial and appellate level. The firm regularly litigates actions involving corporate control disputes, rights of equity holders, major public and private company controversies, complex transactions, and significant valuation and appraisal proceedings. Unlike many other firms, Abrams & Bayliss represents plaintiffs and defendants, giving their attorneys an added measure of insight on strategic and tactical issues in transactions and litigation. The firm has a proven track record of offensive and defensive litigation, including successfully pursuing and defeating injunction applications, conducting expedited trials, and prosecuting and defending claims for significant monetary, declaratory or equitable relief. In addition to their Delaware practice, Abrams & Bayliss frequently represents clients in other jurisdictions on matters involving Delaware law, corporate or business organization issues, or other commercial disputes.

### Transactional Advice:

The firm's Transactional Practice primarily involves matters where there is a high risk of litigation or which raise complex or novel issues of Delaware law, such as contests for corporate control, private equity and portfolio company matters, going-private transactions, recapitalizations, refinancings, and stockholder or board level disputes. Abrams & Bayliss also advises business entities and their constituents on Delaware issues relating to all phases of their life cycle, ranging from formation questions to ongoing issues involving the payment of dividends and asset sales to end-of-life matters such as dissolution and receiverships. The firm regularly provides advice on the preparation and interpretation of certificates of incorporation and bylaws, whether for newly formed entities, initial public offerings, operating companies with internal disputes, reincorporations, or corporations seeking to amend their existing governance documents. Abrams & Bayliss similarly advises business entities, directors, officers and stockholders on contracts relating to the corporation's governance structure and commercial relationships, including stockholder rights plans, stockholder agreements and indemnification agreements.

### Clients:

Abrams & Bayliss represents a broad array of clients including national and international corporations, limited partnerships, limited liability companies, joint ventures, stockholders, directors, equity investors and executives.

# ASHBY & GEDDES

www.ashby-geddes.com **tel:** 302 654 1888 **fax:** 302 654 2067

**Managing Partner:** Stephen E Jenkins
Number of partners: 18
Number of other lawyers: 11

**Firm Overview:**
Ashby & Geddes is best known for its litigation expertise. The firm represents clients ranging from Fortune 500 corporations to individuals. In addition to its Litigation Practice, Ashby & Geddes has a substantial Corporate Reorganization Practice and regularly provides transactional and opinion services to local, national and international clients in connection with matters involving Delaware law. The firm remains committed to its founding principle of providing the best possible work product at highly competitive rates.

## Main Areas of Practice:

**Bankruptcy:**
Ashby & Geddes represents a wide variety of nationally based enterprises with diverse interests in most of the larger Chapter 11 reorganization proceedings filed in Delaware. These representations include debtors, official and ad hoc committees, significant creditors, lenders, prospective acquirers of assets, and other parties-in-interest. For example, the firm currently represents the Creditors Committee in AES Eastern Energy (among others), the Equity Committee in Tri-Valley Corporation, the Debtors in JER Jameson and Broadstripe LLC, and the Los Angeles Dodgers (Delaware counsel).

**Corporate Litigation & Transactions:**
The firm represents corporate clients, directors, officers and substantial stockholders in stockholder derivative and class actions challenging a wide variety of corporate matters, including business combinations, hostile takeovers, going-private transactions, and proxy contests. In addition, the firm serves as counsel to boards of directors and special committees in connection with proposed transactions, internal investigations, and similar matters requiring Delaware law advice and opinions.

**Intellectual Property Litigation:**
The district of Delaware is one of the most popular jurisdictions in the United States for resolving patent disputes, and the firm's Intellectual Property Group is uniquely structured to serve the needs of both large and small clients on either the plaintiff or defense side of intellectual property litigation. Ashby & Geddes intellectual property lawyers have been asked to serve as Delaware Counsel by many of the preeminent intellectual property firms in the United States, and bring a wealth of experience to litigating patent, trademark, false advertising, and unfair competition cases across a variety of industrial sectors, including pharmaceuticals, telecommunications, electronics, computer hardware and software, internet technologies, biotechnology, medical devices, chemicals, and automotive matters. The breadth of knowledge and experience the firm's lawyers bring to cases in the District of Delaware has resulted in the firm being recognized as one of the top choices in Delaware for intellectual property litigation.

**Commercial Litigation & Transactions:**
Ashby & Geddes attorneys represent corporate and banking clients in the litigation of a wide variety of matters, including contract disputes, secured transactions, product liability claims, environmental matters, business torts, and insurance coverage issues. For instance, the firm has served as counsel to Wyoming and Michigan clients in energy-related litigation and also acted as Delaware counsel to the Association of Tennis Professionals in its successful defense of an action brought by the German Tennis Federation alleging antitrust violations and breaches of fiduciary duties. In addition, the firm advises clients with respect to commercial transactions, including the purchase and sale of businesses and assets, and has considerable experience in providing opinions in connection with such transactions.

**Personal Injury/Medical Malpractice Litigation:**
The firm has extensive experience in litigating personal injury matters, importantly including the successful representation of plaintiffs in medical malpractice cases.

**Clients:**
Ashby & Geddes clients range from large national and multinational businesses (or their directors and officers) in corporate and commercial litigation and insolvency and restructuring, to local businesses in a wide array of commercial matters, and to individual clients in personal injury and medical malpractice cases.

# BAYARD, PA

www.bayardlaw.com  tel: 302 655 5000  fax: 302 658 6395

**Chairman:** Neil B Glassman, Esquire
Number of partners: 10
Number of other attorneys: 8

**OFFICES**

DELAWARE

**WILMINGTON:** 222 Delaware Avenue, Suite 900, PO Box 25130, Wilmington, DE 19899
Tel: 302 655 5000  Fax: 302 658 6395

### Firm Overview:

Established more than 50 years ago, Bayard is one of Delaware's premier law firms. The firm's philosophy is simple—to assure client satisfaction by providing the highest level of legal representation and service for commercial clients in a timely and cost-effective manner. Bayard is known for the sophisticated specialization, found at larger firms, and the attorney accessibility, typically found at smaller firms. Bayard has nationally recognized practices in commercial bankruptcy, corporate and commercial litigation, intellectual property, securitization, and structured finance. Other established practices include entity formation, real estate, insurance, tax, estate planning, estate administration, and domestic relations. Bayard is the sole Delaware member of Meritas, the largest worldwide association of business law firms. The firm's subsidiary, The Delaware Corporation Agency, Inc., a service company affiliate of Bayard, provides document filing services and information and document retrieval services with respect to the records of the Secretary of State of the State of Delaware.

### Main Areas of Practice:

**Bankruptcy & Creditor's Rights:**
Bayard serves as counsel to debtors, statutory committees, trustees, and lenders, as well as other parties in Chapter 11 and Chapter 7 bankruptcy cases. It also represents parties in state court receiverships and insurance company rehabilitations or liquidations and out-of-court workouts. Bayard represents clients in a number of jurisdictions, but it focuses its practice in Delaware; a venue of choice for business reorganizations. It has participated in most of the significant bankruptcy cases in Delaware in the last two decades.

**Corporate & Commercial Litigation:**
Bayard has broad experience in all types of business litigation matters in state and federal courts in Delaware. Bayard has substantial expertise in corporate litigation in the Delaware Court of Chancery, the preeminent state court in the United States for the adjudication of corporate matters. Bayard litigators handle corporate governance cases, including contests for the control of boards of directors; corporate election disputes; stock appraisal cases; stockholder class and derivative actions; proceedings involving the rights of preferred stockholders and debt holders; and, expedited proceedings for the inspection of corporate records. Bayard also litigates commercial disputes in state and federal courts in Delaware and other jurisdictions. Bayard's commercial litigation experience includes business contract, construction, mechanic's lien, and environmental disputes.

**Corporate /Mergers & Acquisitions/Alternative Entities:**
Bayard regularly advises clients in connection with Delaware entity formation and operation, governance advice, third party legal opinions, mergers, acquisitions, conversions and divestitures. Its attorneys are experienced in negotiating and drafting documents, providing advice on the requirements of the Delaware law, and rendering opinions of counsel on Delaware entity law and contract law. Bayard's clients range from small businesses including non-profit agencies to large corporations. Bayard's corporate transactional attorneys focus on transactions involving Delaware business entities, including corporations, partnerships, limited liability companies and statutory trusts. Bayard also handles structured finance and secured transactions.

**Intellectual Property:**
Bayard's Intellectual Property Practice consists of both litigation and transactional components. Bayard's IP litigation practice centers on providing Delaware counsel to firms involved in patent litigation pending in the Delaware federal court, one of the busiest venues for patent litigation in the United States. Bayard's IP litigators have experience in bench and jury trials before each of the Court's judges, and in mediations with the Court's Magistrate Judges. Bayard's transactional IP practice focuses on advising clients on trademark and domain name matters, and preparing, prosecuting, and maintaining state and federal trademark applications. Bayard's transactional IP attorneys also advise clients in connection with merger and acquisition transactions in which intellectual property assets are being acquired, and loan transactions in which intellectual property assets are serving as collateral. Bayard attorneys advise clients regarding software and intellectual property licenses and have experience drafting such licenses.

**Real Estate:**
Bayard has a diverse Real Estate Practice, representing clients engaged in all aspects of the real estate industry in Delaware and surrounding states. Bayard's clients include buyers and sellers of commercial and residential real estate, owners and developers of apartment complexes, office buildings, and residential subdivisions; homebuilders; and banks that lend money secured by real estate. Bayard also handles all aspects of title insurance business in Delaware and acts as an agent for several national title insurance companies.

**Taxation, Estate Planning & Probate:**
Bayard has significant experience in estate and trust planning, estate administration, asset management and disposition, business transactions, tax, and fiduciary litigation. Bayard counsels clients on estate planning involving non-resident spouses, creation of domestic entities by non-resident individuals and businesses, estate and business formation and restructuring, negotiating acquisitions, divisions, and sales. Bayard attorneys routinely assist with the Delaware piece of a client's estate plan, eg, by establishing asset protection, directed, or dynasty trusts, or by re-domiciling existing trusts to Delaware to benefit from its wealth-friendly trust laws. Bayard's estate planning and transactional attorneys work together to advise on the formation and operation of captive insurance companies, and to incorporate the captive as part of a business owner's overall estate plan.

**Family Law:**
Bayard provides a full range of domestic legal services in the areas of divorce and separation, property division, child custody and support, negotiation of prenuptial agreements, and adoption.

# GRANT & EISENHOFER PA

**www.gelaw.com** **tel:** 302 622 7000 **fax:** 302 622 7100

**Managing Partners:** Stuart Grant, Jay Eisenhofer
Number of Attorneys: 75

## Firm Overview:

G&E's continued commitment to excellence is evident through the firm's unparalleled results (including achieving more securities settlements in excess of $100 million than any other law firm). G&E's practice offerings include securities, corporate governance, false claims, antitrust, bankruptcy, and consumer claims litigation. For over 15 years G&E has remained a recognized leader in the area of complex litigation.

## Main Areas of Practice:

### Securities Litigation:

G&E has built a national and international reputation as a leader in securities litigation. In both class action and "opt out" cases, the firm has attracted widespread recognition for protecting investors' rights and recovering damages for investors. The firm has been lead counsel in many of the largest securities class action recoveries in US history, including a $3.2 billion recovery against Tyco International and multi-hundred million dollar recoveries against companies such as General Motors, DaimlerChrysler and Royal Dutch Shell. G&E regularly serves as lead counsel in national securities class actions, and works closely with public and private institutional investors across the globe as lead plaintiffs. G&E was the first law firm in the country to argue the provisions of the Private Securities Litigation Reform Act ("PSLRA") allowing an institutional investor to be appointed as lead plaintiff in a securities class action. The opinion, Gluck, et al. v. Cellstar, which appointed the State of Wisconsin Investment Board as lead plaintiff and G&E as lead counsel, is considered the landmark on the standards applicable to lead plaintiff/lead counsel practice under the PSLRA, resulting in a class recovery of approximately 56% of the class' actual losses, which was, at the time, four times the historical average gross recovery for securities fraud litigation. The firm has recovered over $12.5 billion for institutional shareholders in the last five years alone.

### Corporate Governance:

G&E's experience in advising institutional investors with respect to corporate governance matters is second to none. The firm has successfully used shareholder class and derivative litigation to achieve considerable benefits for shareholders in connection with corporate transactions and breach of fiduciary duty claims, including: a $115 million settlement against former executives of AIG, Delaware Chancery Court's largest derivative shareholder litigation settlement; a $420 million settlement against the directors and majority stockholder of Digex, Inc., the largest reported settlement in Delaware Chancery Court history; and a settlement against the board of Caremark Rx Inc.,

resulting in an additional $3.19 billion in cash consideration. The firm has achieved many landmark decisions and/or settlements in litigation over companies' corporate governance practices, including the seminal case enabling proxy access for shareholders to nominate director candidates and the pioneering case that invalidated "dead hand" shareholder rights plans. The firm has also achieved significant victories in the area of back-dated options. G&E is regularly consulted by some of the world's largest public pension funds and strategic investors, including hedge funds, in connection with general policies and practices that may impact the investor's entire portfolio. As Delaware law practitioners, G&E has particular expertise in corporate governance matters involving Delaware corporations, and is well prepared to advise its clients regarding the current state of the law, but also recent developments and legislative initiatives on the horizon.

### False Claims Litigation:

The impact of corporate wrongdoing is not limited to shareholders and private consumers. When corporate fraud impacts governments, False Claims Acts allow whistleblowers, acting in the name of the government, the right to seek redress against any company, entity or person. G&E counsel work with whistleblowers in all phases of the process, from initial meetings with government officials through the litigation process. Whistleblowers bringing suit under federal and state False Claims Act laws have enabled the government to recover more than $20 billion since 1986. Whistleblowers who initiate false claims cases are entitled to a portion of the money, or a bounty, generally ranging from 15-30% of the government's total recovery. Since 1986, False Claims Act qui tam whistleblowers have been paid more than $2 billion in bounties.

### Antitrust Litigation:

Attorneys in G&E's antitrust practice group have decades of experience prosecuting complex individual and class actions on behalf of individuals and corporations of all sizes that have suffered from wrongdoing. G&E currently serves as lead or co-lead counsel in several class and individual antitrust actions involving claims against manufacturers and producers

of goods and services for monopolization, illegal price fixing, illegal tying arrangements and other violations of antitrust law. In these types of cases, G&E attorneys have obtained settlements on behalf of direct purchasers totaling well over $1 billion. G&E's antitrust attorneys have been recognized by courts and colleagues across the country, regularly speak at major conferences, and contribute materials to academic and other publications.

### Bankruptcy Litigation:

Widely recognized for innovative and aggressive representation of institutional investors, G&E brings that same approach to its bankruptcy litigation practice. With extensive experience in litigation arising out of major US Chapter 11 bankruptcies and other US and offshore insolvency and winding-up proceedings, the firm represents investor clients as creditors in bankruptcy cases, out-of-court workouts and offshore/cross-border insolvency matters. Combining sophisticated complex litigation skills with a practiced understanding of the Bankruptcy Code, G&E's attorneys seek and obtain substantial client recoveries, both in third party litigation on behalf of debtor trustees to recover estate assets and in reorganization plan challenges and actions aimed at increasing distributions to individual and group creditor clients. The firm's attorneys have extensive experience in successfully prosecuting creditor claims in bankruptcy cases of all sizes, defending creditors from debtor "clawback" and other recovery actions.

Grant & Eisenhofer

# LANDIS RATH & COBB LLP

www.lrclaw.com  **tel:** 302 467 4400  **fax:** 302 467 4500

**Managing Partners:** Adam G Landis, Daniel B Rath, Richard S Cobb
Number of Partners: 6
Number of Attorneys: 12

**PRACTICE AREAS**
Corporate Bankruptcy & Restructuring
Corporate & Commercial Litigation

**OFFICES**
DELAWARE
**WILMINGTON:** 919 Market Street Suite 1800, DE 19801
Tel: 302 467 4400   Fax: 302 467 4450

## Firm Overview:

Landis Rath & Cobb LLP was founded in 2003 to provide clients with sophisticated corporate bankruptcy and commercial litigation services outside the formal structure of larger firms where the founding partners previously practiced. Built on a commitment to and respect for clients, the firm's business philosophy has helped shape the firm into the highly-regarded team it is today, as evidenced by their yearly recognition by *Chambers USA* (2004-12).

Landis Rath & Cobb LLP represents sophisticated clients in all aspects of complex commercial restructuring and litigation cases, delivering insightful counsel in a cost effective, efficient manner. Whether working on high profile business restructurings or complex commercial disputes, Landis Rath & Cobb's approach is the same–leveraging professional experience, legal acumen and personal dedication to achieve success for their clients.

## Main Areas of Practice:

### Corporate Bankruptcy & Restructuring:

Landis Rath & Cobb LLP believes that no attorney is better suited to represent a creditor in a bankruptcy case than a lawyer who has represented a debtor, and that no lawyer can give advice in a bankruptcy transaction as well as an attorney who has structured sales for both sellers and buyers.

The diversity of its engagements sets Landis Rath & Cobb's bankruptcy and restructuring practice sets the firm apart. Landis Rath & Cobb provides clients with exceptional insights gained from representing parties with interests across a company's capital structure, including debtors, official committees, officers and directors, secured lenders, asset acquirers, trustees, and unsecured creditors.

Whether advising as lead counsel or partnering with co-counsel, the firm's clients benefit immensely from Landis Rath & Cobb's diverse resume, as they offer unique perspective into all aspects of the bankruptcy process and experienced insight into the likely outcomes that will result from any particular course of action.

**Contact:** Adam G Landis  **Tel:** 302 467 4400
**Email:** landis@lrclaw.com

### Corporate & Commercial Litigation:

Landis Rath & Cobb LLP's corporate and commercial litigation practice handles the full range of business disputes including matters related to corporate governance, breach of fiduciary duties, financing transactions, ownership, control and management of Delaware corporations, partnerships and limited liability companies and the application of the Delaware entity statutes, the General Corporation Law, Limited Liability Company Act, and Revised Uniform Limited Partnership Act. The firm regularly represents significant shareholders, investors, corporations, trustees, directors, partnerships, and limited liability companies in the Delaware Court of Chancery as well as the federal and other state courts of Delaware.

The firm's attorneys are proficient both in negotiating advantageous, practical business solutions for clients and in litigating aggressively when necessary. Most important, they have the experience to advise when either approach, or a combination of them, is required. Achieving success begins with a mutual understanding of the desired result, so Landis Rath & Cobb works closely with each client to establish clear goals and a comprehensive plan of action. Ever mindful that goals and strategies can change, and that time and cost constraints can impact any plan, the firm maintains open and regular communication to ensure that matters continue to move in the agreed upon direction for the most successful results.

**Contact:** Daniel B Rath  **Tel:** 302 467 4400
**Email:** rath@lrclaw.com

LANDIS RATH & COBB LLP

# MORRIS JAMES LLP

www.morrisjames.com **tel:** 302 888 6800 **fax:** 302 571 1750

**Managing Partner:** David H Williams
Number of partners: 43
Number of other lawyers: 18

### Firm Overview:

For over 80 years, Morris James has been serving the needs of its clients such as *Fortune* 500 companies, financial institutions, government agencies, law firms and the community. Morris James' Litigation Group represents a wide variety of domestic and international clients in corporate/fiduciary litigation, bankruptcy business litigation, and employment litigation. Morris James' Transactions Group represents national and international clients, as well as regional clients, engaged in corporate and alternative entity transactions, commercial real estate transactions and business tax and estate planning. The firm's innovative legal work, creative use of technology and responsiveness to client needs have led to many significant client representations. The firm is a member of E. I. du Pont de Nemours and Company's Primary Law Firm Network and ALFA International. Morris James is a leader in alternative fee arrangements and early case assessment procedures as well.

### Main Areas of Practice:

**Litigation:**

**Corporate/Fiduciary Litigation:** The firm devotes a major portion of its litigation practice to corporate disputes and disputes involving limited liability companies, partnerships, trusts and other entities in which fiduciary duty constitutes an integral part of the parties' relationship. Morris James litigators often participate in expedited proceedings before the Delaware Court of Chancery. Members of the Litigation Group have served as counsel for independent board committees to investigate restrictive claims and to negotiate transactions in which certain board members may not be disinterested.
**Contact:** Lewis H Lazarus

**Bankruptcy:** The firm represents creditors, creditors' committees, lenders, debtors, purchasers, investors and other parties-in-interest before bankruptcy and appellate courts throughout the United States. Morris James bankruptcy attorneys also counsel clients in both reorganization and liquidation cases before bankruptcy courts and in out-of-court workouts and debt restructurings.
**Contact:** Stephen M Miller

**Business Litigation:** The firm has a substantial business litigation practice that involves representing clients in complex contract disputes, tort claims and insurance coverage litigation. This practice includes trials before judges and juries in every trial court in Delaware and appeals to the Delaware Supreme Court. Morris James also has a substantial alternative dispute resolution practice, including mediations before the Court of Chancery and arbitrations of business disputes.
**Contact:** Joseph R Slights, III

**Intellectual Property Litigation:** The firm regularly serves as Delaware counsel in intellectual property litigation, including patent, copyright, trademark, trade dress, and associated antitrust disputes. It has also served in a lead role in several trade secret, domain name and IP licensing cases.
**Contact:** Richard K Herrmann

**Employment Litigation:**

The firm represents clients in litigation, claims alleging employment discrimination, wrongful discharge, retaliation, breach of post-employment restrictions, and ERISA violations. This practice includes administrative proceedings, and litigation in Delaware and Federal courts.
**Contact:** David H Williams

**Transactions:**

**Delaware Entities & Structured Finance:** The firm provides strategic advice to clients who are establishing, managing, investing in or financing business ventures that take advantage of Delaware's unique corporate, business and tax laws. A substantial portion of the firm's alternative entity practice involves the use of Delaware special purpose entities in the financing of equipment and facilities and in other structured finance transactions. Morris James transactions attorneys frequently render legal opinions on matters of Delaware and United States federal law, including bankruptcy law, and regularly participate in the drafting of Delaware's corporate and alternative entity legislation.
**Contact:** Michael M Ledyard

**Real Estate & Land Use:** The firm represents many of the major developers, investors and builders doing business in the Delaware real estate industry in a full spectrum of transactions, land use matters and related litigation, including acquisition, construction and permanent financing, work outs, conveyancing, title, condemnation, environmental issues, leasing, rezoning, subdivision, variances and administrative matters.
**Contact:** John H Newcomer

**Business Tax & Related Planning:** The firm represents clients in a variety of business transactions, including entity formation, acquisitions and dispositions, joint ventures, mergers and other reorganizations and business succession planning. Morris James tax attorneys counsel clients in federal, state and local tax matters, and provide tax controversy representation before the I.R.S. and state and local tax authorities, both administratively and in litigation. Attorneys in their estates and trust practice offer guidance concerning dynasty trusts, asset protection trusts and other Delaware-advantaged structures, as well as wealth transfer strategies, sophisticated estate planning techniques and fiduciary litigation.
**Contact:** Mary M Culley

### Clients:

Representative clients include E.I. duPont de Nemours and Company; Apple, Inc.; McMoRan Exploration Co.; Consolidated Rail Corporation; Deutsche Bank Trust Company of Delaware; Wachovia Bank of Delaware; Christiana Care Health Services; City of Wilmington; Blenheim Homes; Woodlawn Trustees; Cadia Rehabilitation; Wilmington Savings Fund Society; Bellvue Realty, Co.; The Onix Group; M&T Bank; Wilmington Parking Authority. Bankruptcy representative clients include: AFCO Credit Corporation; The CIT Group/Business Credit, Inc.; Windsor Frozen Foods Ltd.; HP Hood LLC; DCT Industrial Trust; Quest Diagnostics Incorporated.

### OFFICES

DELAWARE

**WILMINGTON-DOWNTOWN (MAIN OFFICE):** 500 Delaware Avenue, Suite 1500, DE 19801-1494
Tel: 302 888 6800   Fax: 302 571 1750

**WILMINGTON-WEST:** 803 North Broom Street, DE 19806-4624
Tel: 302 655 2599   Fax: 302 655 8831

**NEWARK:** 16 Polly Drummond Hill Road, DE 19711-5703
Tel: 302 368 4200   Fax: 302 368 6259

**DOVER:** 29 North State Street, Suite 100, DE 19901-3832
Tel: 302 678 8815   Fax: 302 678 9063

**GEORGETOWN:** Morris James Wilson Halbrook & Bayard LLP, 107 W Market Street, DE 19947
Tel: 302 856 0015   Fax: 302 856 7116

# MORRIS, NICHOLS, ARSHT & TUNNELL LLP

**www.**morrisnichols.com **tel:** 302 658 9200 **fax:** 302 658 3989

**Managing Partner:** Frederick H Alexander
Number of partners: 39   Number of other lawyers: 47

**OFFICES**

DELAWARE

**WILMINGTON:** 1201 North Market Street, PO Box 1347, DE 19899
Tel: 302 658 9200   Fax: 302 658 3989

### Firm Overview:

Morris, Nichols, Arsht & Tunnell LLP combines a broad national practice of corporate, intellectual property, business reorganization and restructuring, commercial law and litigation with a general business, tax, estate planning and real estate practice within the State of Delaware. The firm acts as lead counsel or co-counsel in matters of national and international significance as well as those affecting its immediate community.

### Main Areas of Practice:

**Banking & Financial Services:**
The firm represents lenders, borrowers, issuers and investors in all forms of financing transactions. It provides bank and insurance regulatory counseling and represents clients before Delaware's Office of the State Bank Commissioner and Department of Insurance.
**Contact:** David A Harris, Walter C Tuthill, Michael Houghton

**Business Reorganization & Restructuring:**
The group has been recognized as one of the premier restructuring and reorganizing practices in the United States. It represents chapter 11 debtors, lenders, creditors, acquirers, ad hoc and official committees, trustees, directors, managers and other parties in restructurings, loan workouts, reorganization proceedings, and in bankruptcy and insolvency related litigation. Attorneys from the group, acting as either lead or local counsel, have had major roles in virtually every significant chapter 11 case to be filed in Delaware over the last three decades.
**Contact:** Robert J Dehney

**Commercial Transactional/Alternative Entities:**
The firm provides a complete range of commercial law services including advice on all types of alternative entity matters. It handles a variety of complex transactions including working with in-house and outside counsel in structuring and documenting such transactions.
**Contact:** Louis G Hering, David A Harris, Walter C Tuthill

**Corporate Counseling:**
The firm advises clients on complex corporate transactions and corporate governance issues. It represents boards of directors or board committees, particularly in transactions that may involve director or stockholder conflicts of interest. It also provides formal legal opinions on matters of Delaware corporate law. Corporate Counseling lawyers have long played an important role in drafting and updating Delaware's corporate statute.
**Contact:** Jeffrey Wolters

**Corporate Litigation:**
The firm's corporate litigation practice focuses on matters related to the law governing corporations and alternative entities. Its proceedings in the Delaware Court of Chancery, Delaware Supreme Court and other courts throughout the US often involve derivative suits or class actions brought in connection with M&A transactions, takeover battles and proxy contests or other claims alleging director negligence or misconduct.
**Contact:** A Gilchrist Sparks III, Kenneth J Nachbar, William M Lafferty, S Mark Hurd

**General Business Litigation:**
The firm provides a full range of general litigation services, appearing before all of the Delaware trial and appellate courts, state and federal, local boards and administrative agencies and before trial and appellate courts nationwide. It represents clients in commercial, contract and business disputes of virtually every kind.
**Contact:** R Judson Scaggs Jr, Megan Ward Cascio

**Intellectual Property:**
The firm is at the forefront of the development of IP law and has the reputation as the premier patent litigation firm in Delaware. It has achieved preeminence in IP litigation in Delaware and nationwide serving as lead counsel in many cases and assisting as co-counsel in other cases brought to Delaware by patent litigators nationwide. In one role or the other, the firm is counsel in nearly half of the intellectual property cases pending in the District of Delaware.
**Contact:** Jack B Blumenfeld, Rodger D Smith II

**Real Estate:**
The firm's real estate practice covers the negotiation and documentation of complex commercial real estate including transactions involving the development, acquisition and sale of commercial property, commercial financing, condominium development, office, retail and industrial leasing and public-private development. It provides advice on zoning and land use matters, real estate tax appeals, eminent domain and condemnation actions and environmental matters.
**Contact:** Donald N Isken

**Regulation/Governmental Affairs:**
The firm represents public entities and agencies, and private sector clients, before legislative bodies and city, county, state and federal regulatory agencies on unclaimed property and other matters. It is actively involved in monitoring, drafting and advocating legislation and regulations that affect clients.
**Contact:** Michael Houghton

**Trust, Estate & Tax:**
The firm acts as trust and fiduciary litigation counsel to Delaware trust companies, national banks conducting trust business in Delaware, individual trustees and beneficiaries of trusts in Delaware and other jurisdictions, and to wealthy families with trusts in Delaware. It also provides federal income, estate, gift and generation skipping transfer tax advice to individuals, trusts, estates, business enterprises and their owners, and charitable organizations nationwide.
**Contact:** Thomas R Pulsifer, Todd A Flubacher

### Clients:

**General Clients:** Abbott Laboratories; Agilent Technologies, Inc.; Alcatel-Lucent; AstraZeneca; AT&T Wireless Services, Inc.; Barclays Financial Corp.; Barnes & Noble Inc.; Cisco Systems, Inc.; Clear Channel Broadcasting, Inc.; Comcast Corp.; Eaton Corporation; eBay Inc.; Echostar Communications Corporation; Edwards Lifesciences; ELAN Corporation plc; Fortistar Capital Inc.; Goodrich Corporation; GlaxoSmithKline; Honeywell International Inc.; INVISTA; Lucite International, Inc.; 3M Company; Merck & Co., Inc.; Motorola, Inc.; Nokia Corporation; Pfizer Inc.; The Dow Chemical Company; TPG Capital; Wal-Mart Stores, Inc.; Wyeth.

**Representative Restructuring/Bankruptcy Engagements:**
Debtors (Overseas Shipholding Group, Inc.; Ormet Corp.; Nortel Networks Corp.; RG Steel; Delta Petroleum; Hancock Fabrics, Inc.; Penn Traffic Company; Trico Marine Services Inc.; Townsends, Inc.; Emivest Aerospace Corp.); Cross-Border Cases (Fraser Papers Inc.; Hollinger Inc.); Official Creditor and Equity Committees (Filenes/Syms; Local Insight Media Holdings Inc.; Sea Containers, Ltd.); Lenders, Bondholders, Agents, Indenture Trustees and Ad Hoc Committees (Fifth Third Bank; Nebraska Book; Harry & David; Orchard Brands; Oriental Trading Co.; Wilmington Trust Company); Acquirers (DISH Network; Luby's Fuddruckers Restaurants; Ritz Camera & Image; Fortistar LLC; Fifth Street Capital); Other Restructuring/Bankruptcy Representations (Sun Capital; T-Mobile; Fox Sports; NBC Universal; Green Plains Renewable Energy; Barclays Bank).

# POTTER ANDERSON & CORROON LLP

www.potteranderson.com

**Chairman:** Donald J Wolfe Jr
Number of partners: 39
Number of other lawyers: 52

**OFFICES**
**WILMINGTON:** 1313 North Market Street, PO Box 951,
DE 19899-0951
Tel: 302 984 6000   Fax: 302 658 1192

**Firm Overview:**

Founded in 1826, Potter Anderson & Corroon LLP has developed a national reputation in the areas of corporate litigation and counseling, structured finance and alternative entities, intellectual property, commercial litigation, business and commercial law, and bankruptcy. Labor and employment, healthcare, trusts and estates, insurance recovery litigation and product liability practice areas round out the firm's primary services.

**Main Areas of Practice:**

**Delaware Corporate Litigation & Counseling:**
The Corporate Litigation Practice centers on litigation seeking injunctive and other equitable and compensatory relief, often on an expedited basis, in connection with disputed questions of internal corporate governance. These suits most frequently focus on the fiduciary obligations of care, loyalty, good faith and disclosure owed by directors and officers in the context of corporate acts and business combinations, including mergers, tender offers, sales of assets and proxy fights. The Counseling Practice also encompasses the many statutory summary proceedings authorized by the Delaware General Corporation Law (DGCL), as well as Delaware's alternative entity statutes, and committed to the subject matter jurisdiction of the Delaware Court of Chancery, viewed by many as the most influential state tribunal in the nation. The practice includes transaction specialists retained to advise corporations and their directors with respect to a multitude of questions and interpretations – ranging from matters of day to day management to the interpretation of the DGCL in matters involving bylaw and charter amendments, annual meetings, indemnification obligations, stock sales and issuances, mergers and acquisitions, and dissolutions. The firm regularly acts as special Delaware counsel in nationally prominent mergers, acquisitions, tender offers, divestitures, spin-offs and other types of business transactions.

**Structured Finance & Alternative Entities:**
The Structured Finance and Alternative Entities Practice focuses primarily on the use of alternative and special purpose business entities (partnerships, limited liability companies, statutory trusts and special purpose corporations) in a wide array of financings, including secured and unsecured financings, acquisition financings, asset-backed and structured financings, project financings, and bankruptcy-remote structures. The attorneys represent lenders, borrowers and other parties in the formation, utilization, termination and dissolution of all forms of alternative entities. The practice's attorneys frequently render third-party legal opinions, which are relied upon by other parties to the transaction, by rating agencies such as Standard & Poor's and Moody's, and by governmental authorities such as the SEC. In the area of bankruptcy-remote transactions, Potter Anderson is one of only two Delaware law firms with a form of legal opinion approved by Standard & Poor's.

**Intellectual Property Litigation & Counseling:**
Potter Anderson's intellectual property practitioners provide services relating to patents, trademarks and copyrights, including preparation and prosecution of patent and trademark applications in the USPTO and preparation of legal opinions regarding intellectual property rights. Potter Anderson has long represented national and local clients in disputes regarding patents, trademarks, copyrights and trade secrets, particularly in the United States District Court for the District of Delaware.

**Commercial Litigation:**
Attorneys represent clients in a wide array of business and commercial litigation matters. For example, in insurance coverage litigation, the firm represents corporate policyholders in actions against their insurers for CGL, D&O, E&O, product hazard and other coverage. The firm also represents clients in litigation involving contract claims, product liability, the Uniform Commercial Code, antitrust, franchise and commercial lending.

**Labor & Employment:**
Labor and employment attorneys represent employers around the country in court and administrative proceedings involving employment discrimination and reverse discrimination claims, non-competition and trade secret controversies, and breach of employment contract claims. Potter Anderson also counsels employers on organized labor issues, workforce restructuring processes, internal investigations, and compliance with the numerous federal and state laws that govern the workplace.

**Business & Commercial Law:**
Potter Anderson provides advice to clients on a full range of legal issues arising from the formation and day-to-day operation of business organizations. Clients include both privately held and public companies with local, regional, national and international operations. The firm provides sophisticated corporate structuring and tax advice in a broad range of transactions, including business formations and choice of entity, mergers and acquisitions and financings.

**Bankruptcy & Restructuring:**
Potter Anderson represents both debtor and nondebtor entities in some of the largest Chapter 11 cases filed across the country. Non-debtor clients include official committees, institutional creditors, debtor-in-possession financiers, acquirers, shareholders, trustees and plan administrators. The firm takes a leading role for its clients in large and middle market bankruptcy cases in Delaware and on the national stage, and also partners as Delaware co-counsel with many preeminent bankruptcy firms. In addition, Potter Anderson assists clients in other restructuring areas, including out-of-court workouts, assignments for the benefit of creditors, state court dissolutions, receiverships and other secured transactions.

**Clients:**
AT&T Inc.; Bank of America; Chrysler LLC; Citigroup Inc.; City of Wilmington; Daimler Trucks North America LLC.; E.I. du Pont de Nemours and Co.; El Paso Corporation; Exxon Corp.; General Motors Corp.; The Goldman Sachs Group, Inc.; Google; Hewlett-Packard Company; Intel Corporation; Kao Corporation; Morgan Stanley; The Nemours Foundation; NRG Energy; Norfolk Southern Corporation; Omnicare, Inc.; Philips Electronics Corporation of North America; Qualcomm Incorporated; State of Delaware; Tyson Foods, Inc.; Wal-Mart Stores, Inc.; The Walt Disney Company; Wells Fargo Bank N.A.; Winterthur Library and Museum.

# RICHARDS, LAYTON & FINGER, P.A.

**www.rlf.com  tel:** 302 651 7700 **fax:** 302 651 7701

**President:** Robert J Krapf
Number of directors: 67
Number of other lawyers: 71

### Firm Overview:

Richards, Layton & Finger, Delaware's largest law firm, has been committed from its founding to helping sophisticated clients navigate complex issues and the intricacies of Delaware law. The firm has participated in many of the groundbreaking cases defining Delaware corporate law, and its lawyers have long played crucial roles in drafting and amending the state's influential business statutes. Clients—including local businesses, global law firms, and Fortune 500 companies—count on the firm's exceptional service and deep, practical understanding of Delaware law.

### Main Areas of Practice:

**Corporate Law & Litigation:**
**Corporate Advisory:** Richards Layton's corporate advisory group is renowned for its skill in counseling Delaware corporations and boards of directors in both ordinary and extraordinary corporate transactions and matters of corporate governance. The lawyers' nuanced understanding of the law makes Richards Layton the firm of choice when national and international institutions need local counsel. In fact, Richards Layton has served as Delaware counsel on the most deals valued at $100 million or more for 10 years running.
**Corporate Litigation:** The firm's corporate litigators have been involved in many of Delaware's ground-breaking cases involving fiduciary duties, corporate governance, mergers and acquisitions, and other aspects of corporate practice. They regularly handle complex litigation involving high stakes and novel issues of law. Serving on the rules committee of the Delaware Court of Chancery and the Delaware Supreme Court and on the committee that reviews Delaware's corporate code, firm attorneys have extraordinary insight into Delaware's laws, judges, and court procedures.

**Alternative Entities & Corporate Trusts:**
**Alternative Entities:** Richards Layton has Delaware's largest and busiest alternative entities practice, and offers authoritative advice on a wide variety of transactional matters involving Delaware limited liability companies, limited partnerships, and general partnerships. Acknowledged leaders in alternative entities law, firm attorneys were actively involved in drafting the Delaware Limited Liability Company Act, the Delaware Revised Uniform Limited Partnership Act, and the Delaware Revised Uniform Partnership Act.
**Trust & Agency Services:** Richards Layton has Delaware's largest and most active corporate trust and

agency practice. The Richards Layton team has played a central role in drafting the Delaware Statutory Trust Act and its amendments, and remains instrumental in assisting clients establish and administer business trusts in Delaware.

**Bankruptcy & Corporate Restructuring:**
With one of the largest and most active bankruptcy practices in Delaware, Richards Layton has been involved in virtually every major chapter 11 case filed in the state. The firm has the depth and experience to serve as lead counsel in all aspects of chapter 11 cases, representing debtors, secured creditors, creditors' committees, acquirers, investors, and other key parties from nearly every business sector. Respected bankruptcy firms throughout the country rely on the firm's expertise, and Richards Layton regularly serves as their co-counsel in many of the largest and most complex bankruptcy cases filed in Delaware.

**General Litigation:**
**Commercial Litigation:** Richards Layton's litigators handle a wide range of business, fiduciary, contract, lender liability, and other commercial disputes in the state and federal courts, including appellate courts. They also have substantial experience with arbitrations and mediations.
**Intellectual Property:** Richards Layton litigates dozens of patent cases in the Delaware District Court, one of the country's most active federal courts for resolving intellectual property disputes. The firm's lawyers are nationally recognized for tackling some of the most difficult IP matters to emerge in that court.
**Labor & Employment:** Developing a deep understanding of clients' employment issues and policies, the firm offers customized solutions to ensure compliance with national and state labor laws, minimize conflicts with employees, and maximize strategic advantages in the defense of employment law disputes.

## PRACTICE AREAS

Alternative Entities
Banking
Bankruptcy & Corporate Restructuring
Business Trust & Agency Services
Commercial Transactions
Corporate
Environmental
Intellectual Property
Labor & Employment
Litigation
Real Estate
Tax/Trusts & Estates

## OFFICES

DELAWARE
**WILMINGTON:** One Rodney Square, 920 North King Street, DE 19801
Tel: 302 651 7700  Fax: 302 651 7701

**Delaware Practice:**
**Commercial Transactions:** Richards Layton lawyers have the skill and knowledge to handle complex, sophisticated business transactions. Practicing across a wide range of transactional and regulatory law disciplines, they provide authoritative guidance regarding Delaware's business statutes and contracts governed by Delaware law.
**Real Estate:** Richards Layton has decades of experience in commercial property transactions throughout Delaware. The firm works with all the key players in real estate transactions, limiting conflicts and expanding opportunities in zoning, land use approvals, and economic development incentives.
**Environmental:** Advising business and industrial clients facing challenging environmental issues, the firm secures permits, addresses compliance matters, and negotiates with state and federal agencies to help clients achieve permitting of sensitive projects. The firm also has successfully negotiated complex development agreements to rehabilitate contaminated "brownfield" properties.
**Tax / Trusts & Estates:** High net worth clients trust Richards Layton to prepare estate plans that reflect the unique advantages of Delaware law – maximizing financial benefits while minimizing taxes, and balancing fiduciary responsibilities with beneficiaries' needs. Delaware trust law provides for specialized, sophisticated trust structures, and the firm's lawyers are skilled at helping clients choose the structures they need.

Rockville · Aspen Hill · Laurel
Potomac · Beltsville
Bethesda · **Silver Spring**
· Chillum
**Virginia** WASHINGTON DC
**Arlington** · Coral Hills
· Annandale · Forestville
· Alexandria
Camp Springs

## How lawyers are ranked

Every year we carry out thousands of in-depth interviews with clients in order to assess the reputations and expertise of business lawyers worldwide. The qualities we look for (and which determine rankings) include technical legal ability, professional conduct, client service, commercial awareness/astuteness, diligence, commitment, and other qualities most valued by the client. For details of our research team, see p.5.

## ANTITRUST

Commentary about individuals can be found under their firm's paragraph. If the firm has no paragraph (is not ranked) look at Other Notable Practitioners.

**Antitrust**
**Leading Firms**

**Band 1**
Arnold & Porter LLP *
Cleary Gottlieb Steen & Hamilton LLP *
Jones Day *

**Band 2**
Covington & Burling LLP *
Skadden, Arps, Slate, Meagher & Flom LLP & Affiliates *
Weil, Gotshal & Manges LLP *

**Band 3**
Crowell & Moring LLP *
Dechert LLP *
Gibson, Dunn & Crutcher LLP *
Hogan Lovells US LLP *
Kirkland & Ellis LLP *
Latham & Watkins LLP *
O'Melveny & Myers LLP *
WilmerHale *
Wilson Sonsini Goodrich & Rosati *

**Band 4**
Baker Botts LLP *
Cadwalader, Wickersham & Taft LLP *
Freshfields Bruckhaus Deringer LLP *
Mayer Brown LLP *
McDermott Will & Emery LLP *
Paul, Weiss, Rifkind, Wharton & Garrison LLP *
White & Case LLP *

**Band 5**
Morrison & Foerster LLP *
Paul Hastings LLP *
Ropes & Gray LLP *
Vinson & Elkins LLP *

*\* Indicates firm with profile.*
*Alphabetical order within each band. Band 1 is the highest.*

## Band 1

### Arnold & Porter LLP
See profile on p.906

**THE FIRM** This group is, without doubt, one of the leading antitrust practices in Washington, DC. Its high-quality attorneys cover the gamut of antitrust issues, from civil litigation to criminal cartel matters and transactional issues. It represents a long list of blue-chip firms, including GE, which it recently represented in the municipal derivatives antitrust litigation.
**Sources say:** *"The quality of the different lawyers we work with there is just outstanding."*
**KEY INDIVIDUALS** The *"exceptional"* **Deborah Feinstein** (see p.861) is highly regarded by both peers and clients as someone who *"demonstrates again and again her ability to work with the agencies and get good results."* She primarily devotes her practice to merger-related work. Recent clients include BP, which she advised on the $2.5 billion sale of a California refinery to Tesoro. **Jonathan Gleklen** (see p.865) is the person to go to *"when you need good, quick advice,"* and is described as a *"very creative, very pragmatic and very accessible"* lawyer. His practice covers a wide range of antitrust areas, with a focus on technology-related matters. He recently represented GE in a joint venture with Microsoft concerning healthcare technology. **Richard Rosen** (see p.888) has a fine reputation among peers, particularly for IT and telecom work. He acted for AT&T on a $1.93 billion acquisition of licenses for wireless spectrum, and was involved in representing Cisco Systems in the review of the $5 billion acquisition of NDS Group. **Douglas Wald** (see p.898) led the firm's representation of GE in the municipal derivatives antitrust litigation. He is both an antitrust litigator and counselor, gaining plaudits for his skills in the courtroom, with one commentator noting his *"ability to take a complex area and distill it for a judge or jury."* **Donna Patterson** (see p.885) has extensive experi-

ence in transactions and litigation involving antitrust issues, with 31 years' experience in the field. She represented Nucor in a series of cases concerning the steel industry.

### Cleary Gottlieb Steen & Hamilton LLP
See profile on p.1963

**THE FIRM** Commentators are unanimous in their praise of Cleary's antitrust practice, pointing in particular to its exceptionally deep bench and the breadth and quality of its work. These attributes are evident from the scope of top-class clients in its portfolio. Highlights include successfully representing Citi, Goldman Sachs and JPMorgan in antitrust litigation related to airline terminal financing.
**Sources say:** *"A fantastic firm that brings its breadth and depth of expertise to bear in the antitrust arena."*
**KEY INDIVIDUALS George Cary** (see p.856) is *"extremely bright,"* according to sources, who praise his *"crisp and clear advice."* He has long been rated by peers as one of the leading lawyers in the area. His high-profile representations include achieving dismissal for GlaxoSmithKline in an antitrust suit concerning alleged price-fixing of drugs in California. **Mark Leddy** (see p.876) is Cleary's managing partner, but remains extremely busy in the antitrust space and is *"a real star,"* according to sources. *"If I could pick one lawyer in the world to be on my team, I would pick him any day. He epitomizes excellence,"* said one interviewee. Leddy recently acted for Whirlpool in antitrust litigation concerning refrigerators. **David Gelfand** (see p.864) is an antitrust lawyer who *"has the full package"* and is highly rated by those in the market for the scope of his practice. His most prominent representations have been for Google, although he has also demonstrated his breadth by acting for Sanofi in alleged monopolization litigation and for Dollar Thrifty on a proposed takeover by auto hire competitor Hertz. The *"terrific"* **Mark Nelson** (see p.883) is seen as one of the rising stars of the DC antitrust Bar, and

## Antitrust
### Senior Statesmen

**Senior Statesmen:** distinguished older practitioners

| | |
|---|---|
| Rill James F | Baker Botts LLP * |
| Sohn Michael N | Davis Polk & Wardwell LLP (ONP)† |

### Leading individuals

#### Band 1

| | |
|---|---|
| Cary George S | Cleary Gottlieb Steen & Hamilton LLP * |
| Feinstein Deborah | Arnold & Porter LLP * |
| Leddy Mark | Cleary Gottlieb Steen & Hamilton LLP * |
| Parker Richard G | O'Melveny & Myers LLP |
| Sims Joe | Jones Day * |

#### Band 2

| | |
|---|---|
| Barnett Thomas O | Covington & Burling LLP * |
| Creighton Susan A | Wilson Sonsini Goodrich & Rosati |
| Denis Paul T | Dechert LLP * |
| Fenton Kathryn M | Jones Day * |
| Garza Deborah A | Covington & Burling LLP * |
| Gelfand David I | Cleary Gottlieb Steen & Hamilton LLP * |
| Gleklen Jonathan | Arnold & Porter LLP * |
| Kattan Joseph | Gibson, Dunn & Crutcher LLP * |
| Kolasky William J | WilmerHale * |
| McDavid Janet L | Hogan Lovells US LLP |
| Muris Timothy J | Kirkland & Ellis LLP * |
| Nannes John M | Skadden, Arps, Slate, Meagher & Flom LLP * |
| Newborn Steven A | Weil, Gotshal & Manges LLP * |
| Proger Phillip A | Jones Day * |
| Rule Charles F | Cadwalader, Wickersham & Taft LLP * |
| Smith Wm. Randolph | Crowell & Moring LLP * |
| Sunshine Steven C | Skadden, Arps, Slate, Meagher & Flom LLP * |
| Yde Paul | Freshfields Bruckhaus Deringer LLP * |
| Zwisler Margaret | Latham & Watkins LLP * |

#### Band 3

| | |
|---|---|
| Antalics Michael | O'Melveny & Myers LLP |
| Arp D Jarrett | Gibson, Dunn & Crutcher LLP * |
| Crisman Jr C Benjamin | Skadden, Arps, Slate, Meagher & Flom LLP * |
| Friedman Paul H | Dechert LLP * |
| Gallo Kenneth A | Paul, Weiss, Rifkind, Wharton & Garrison * |
| Gardiner Kent A | Crowell & Moring LLP * |
| Gidley J Mark | White & Case LLP * |
| Harris Jr H Stephen | Baker & McKenzie (ONP)† |
| Henry Roxann E | Morrison & Foerster LLP |

#### Band 3 (continued)

| | |
|---|---|
| Jacobsen Jr Raymond A | McDermott Will & Emery LLP * |
| Kovner Mark L | Kirkland & Ellis LLP * |
| Malester Ann | Weil, Gotshal & Manges LLP * |
| Mueller Thomas | WilmerHale |
| Nelson Mark W | Cleary Gottlieb Steen & Hamilton LLP * |
| Popofsky Mark | Ropes & Gray LLP |
| Rosen Richard L | Arnold & Porter LLP * |
| Schildkraut Marc | Cooley LLP (ONP)† |
| Schlossberg Bob | Freshfields Bruckhaus Deringer LLP * |
| Sher Scott | Wilson Sonsini Goodrich & Rosati |
| Simons Joseph J | Paul, Weiss, Rifkind, Wharton & Garrison * |
| Smith Stephen | Morrison & Foerster LLP |
| Wiseman Alan | Covington & Burling LLP * |

#### Band 4

| | |
|---|---|
| Bell Robert B | Kaye Scholer LLP (ONP)† * |
| Bernstein Steven K | Weil, Gotshal & Manges LLP * |
| Boland Sean F X | Baker Botts LLP * |
| Brennan Jeffrey W | McDermott Will & Emery LLP * |
| Cohen Michael P A | Paul Hastings LLP |
| Favretto Richard J | Mayer Brown LLP |
| Greenfield Leon B | WilmerHale * |
| Hoffman D Bruce | Hunton & Williams LLP (ONP)† * |
| Klawiter Donald C | Sheppard, Mullin, Richter & Hampton (ONP)† |
| Krauss Joseph G | Hogan Lovells US LLP |
| Lipsky Abbott (Tad) | Latham & Watkins LLP * |
| Moltenbrey MJ | Paul Hastings LLP |
| Nigro Bernard | Fried, Frank, Harris, Shriver & Jacobson (ONP)† |
| Robertson Robert | Hogan Lovells US LLP |
| Roellke Jon R | Bingham McCutchen LLP (ONP)† * |
| Taladay John | Baker Botts LLP * |
| Wald Douglas | Arnold & Porter LLP * |
| Wales David | Jones Day * |
| Winterscheid Joseph F | McDermott Will & Emery LLP * |

#### Band 5

| | |
|---|---|
| Abrams Robert G | Baker & Hostetler LLP (ONP)† * |

#### Band 4 (continued)

| | |
|---|---|
| Bloch Robert E | Mayer Brown LLP |
| Blumenthal William | Clifford Chance US LLP (ONP)† * |
| Brannon Leah | Cleary Gottlieb Steen & Hamilton LLP * |
| Byrne Brian | Cleary Gottlieb Steen & Hamilton LLP * |
| Calsyn Jeremy | Cleary Gottlieb Steen & Hamilton LLP * |
| Calvani Terry | Freshfields Bruckhaus Deringer LLP * |
| Curran Christopher M | White & Case LLP * |
| Egan Jr James C | Weil, Gotshal & Manges LLP * |
| Ewing Kenneth P | Steptoe & Johnson LLP (ONP)† |
| Higgins Claudia R | Kaye Scholer LLP (ONP)† * |
| Imus Neil W | Vinson & Elkins LLP * |
| Kanter Jonathan | Cadwalader, Wickersham & Taft LLP * |
| Libow Daryl A | Sullivan & Cromwell LLP (ONP)† * |
| Lipton Joshua | Gibson, Dunn & Crutcher LLP * |
| MacAvoy Christopher J | Baker Botts LLP * |
| McDonald Bruce | Jones Day * |
| McFalls Michael | Ropes & Gray LLP |
| Meyer David L. | Morrison & Foerster LLP |
| Morse M Howard | Cooley LLP (ONP)† |
| Ondeck Christopher | Crowell & Moring LLP * |
| Patterson Donna | Arnold & Porter LLP * |
| Reznick Robert P | Orrick, Herrington & Sutcliffe LLP (ONP)† |
| Rodriguez Grace | King & Spalding LLP (ONP)† * |
| Scribner John E | Weil, Gotshal & Manges LLP * |
| Seebald Craig | Vinson & Elkins LLP * |
| Sherman William | Latham & Watkins LLP * |
| Sokler Bruce D | Mintz Levin Cohn Ferris Glovsky (ONP)† * |
| Vigdor William R | Vinson & Elkins LLP * |
| Wellford Hill | Bingham McCutchen LLP (ONP)† * |
| Wilson Christine | Kirkland & Ellis LLP * |

#### Up-and-coming individuals

| | |
|---|---|
| Breed Logan M | Hogan Lovells US LLP |
| Hataway C Scott | Paul Hastings LLP |
| Roberti John | Mayer Brown LLP |
| Rosman Mark | Wilson Sonsini Goodrich & Rosati |

* Indicates individual with profile.

†ONP = Other Notable Practitioner.

---

is described as a "*go-to partner for any antitrust question.*" His practice is primarily concerned with M&A antitrust. Along with George Cary, he represented Deutsche Telekom in the attempted sale of T-Mobile to AT&T, in a deal which would have been worth $39 billion. **Jeremy Calsyn** (see p.856) is seen as a "*very fine lawyer*" and an "*extremely responsive, very thorough and hard-working litigator.*" He practices across the antitrust law spectrum, and acted for Bausch & Lomb on its acquisition of Ista Pharmaceuticals. **Brian Byrne** (see p.855) returns to Washington, DC following a three-year secondment in the firm's Brussels office. He is described as an "*incredibly good advocate,*" and is noted for his client management and problem-solving skills. He was part of the team representing 3M in its proposed acquisition of Avery Dennison. **Leah Brannon** (see

p.854) is one of the younger partners coming through at the firm. She is already earning plaudits as a "*really, really good antitrust lawyer*" with a high level of knowledge and intellect. She played a key role in the aforementioned Citi, JP Morgan and Goldman Sachs litigation.

### Jones Day
**See profile on p.919**

**THE FIRM** Jones Day's antitrust practice stands out for its breadth and depth. Boosted by its nationwide and global scope, the firm's hub in Washington, DC has a variety of outstanding antitrust practitioners, with expertise across the board and vast experience of appearing in front of government agencies. It recently acted for Goodrich on its mammoth $18.4 billion merger with United Technologies.

**Sources say:** "*They have a very fine relationship with the agencies. They are well respected and well regarded.*"
**KEY INDIVIDUALS Joe Sims** (see p.892) is described as an "*extraordinary lawyer*" who is a highly prominent figure within the antitrust arena. He has some 42 years' experience across the full spectrum of antitrust practice, and recently led the firm's representation of Texas Instruments in its $6.5 billion acquisition of National Semiconductor. Sources highlight **Kathryn Fenton**'s (see p.862) depth of knowledge and practical approach to advising clients. Described as "*a great lawyer with a phenomenal reputation,*" she epitomizes the strength in depth of the firm's bench. She was part of the team advising Texas Instruments on the National Semiconductor deal. **Phillip Proger** (see p.886) is a "*skilled practitioner*" and a "*top-*

*notch"* antitrust lawyer, according to sources. He practices primarily in cartel and merger work, and heads up Jones Day's antitrust practice group in the USA. He acted for Aetna on its $7.3 billion acquisition of Coventry Health Care. **David Wales** (see p.898) is highly regarded for his skill in interacting with government agencies, having previously worked for both the FTC and the DOJ. He represented ABB in its acquisition of Thomas & Betts. **Bruce McDonald** (see p.2404) splits his time between the firm's Houston and Washington, DC office. Sources praise his experience and his hard-working approach, with one client stating: *"I don't think I've ever encountered a partner who's as prepared as him."* McDonald represented Level 3 Communications in an investigation into its acquisition of Global Crossing.

## Band 2

### Covington & Burling LLP
See profile on p.441

**THE FIRM** This team has quickly cemented itself as a very well-respected player within this space, and is praised for its client-friendly approach. The practice stands out for its litigation expertise, and is also active and strong within merger investigations. Its major recent matters include acting for Citibank in a consolidated class action arising from the LIBOR investigation, and for Expedia in several class actions concerning the hotel booking market.
**Sources say:** *"They are some of the best lawyers we work with – savvy, pragmatic and usually two steps ahead."*
**KEY INDIVIDUALS Thomas Barnett** (see p.851) is a former assistant attorney general for the antitrust division of the DOJ, which, according to sources, means that *"he just knows how things work."* He is described as *"responsive, brilliant and creative,"* and led the firm's representation in the Expedia matter. **Deborah Garza** (see p.864) is another former assistant attorney general. She is described as a *"wonderful lawyer,"* and is praised for her strength in litigation strategy among her broader expertise across the board in antitrust law. She and Barnett cochair the firm's antitrust practice group. Senior counsel **Alan Wiseman** (see p.900) is well respected for his role as an antitrust litigator, with 30 years' experience in class action litigation. His recent highlights include being one of the lawyers heading up the representation of Citibank.

### Skadden, Arps, Slate, Meagher & Flom LLP & Affiliates
See profile on p.2008

**THE FIRM** This team has a tremendous reputation for its work on large transactions, and remains busy and strong in the litigation arena. It has represented clients in some of the largest recent deals in the telecommunications and energy markets, including acting for Sprint Nextel on the $20.1 billion sale of a majority stake of its business to Softbank. In another $20.1 billion transaction, it acted for Anheuser-Busch on the acquisition of Grupo Modelo.
**Sources say:** *"A really phenomenal firm." "They are strong on everything."*

**KEY INDIVIDUALS John Nannes** (see p.883) is a *"sensational"* antitrust lawyer highly respected by peers and clients alike, and has 39 years' experience in the area. His recent highlights include acting for Norfolk Southern, a major railroad company, in class actions relating to anti-competitive conduct concerning fuel surcharges. *"Terrific antitrust lawyer"* **Steven Sunshine** (see p.895) is highly regarded for his work in transactional antitrust and is praised for his *"extremely sharp analytical skills."* He is acting in several major 11-figure deals, including for Anheuser-Busch on the Grupo Modelo transaction. Sources note **Benjamin Crisman**'s (see p.858) ability in commercial problem solving. He is a versatile lawyer who practices antitrust in addition to white-collar work, and has recently represented Marubeni in a $5.3 billion acquisition of Gavilon Holdings.

### Weil, Gotshal & Manges LLP
See profile on p.2015

**THE FIRM** This group is well regarded for its transactional practice, which makes up the majority of its work. Big deals are the norm, with recent major matters including the colossal $38 billion acquisition by Kinder Morgan of gas pipeline company El Paso. The team also acted for Walgreens on the acquisition of a $6.7 billion 45% stake in pharmaceutical retailer Alliance Boots.
**Sources say:** *"They have all the know-how and horsepower, but they also have a pragmatic and reasoned approach."*
**KEY INDIVIDUALS Steven Newborn** (see p.883) is a transactional lawyer who has an *"added layer of insight into how the regulatory system works – he doesn't just quote the rule but can tell you how it works."* He has acted for both Walgreens and Kinder Morgan on major transactions, and represented Johnson & Johnson in the successful completion of the $23.1 billion acquisition of Synthes. **Ann Malester** (see p.879) is highly regarded for her easy-to-work-with approach and experience with the agencies. Her recent work has been largely transaction-focused, including overseeing Medicis Pharmaceutical's sale to Valeant Pharmaceuticals along with Steven Bernstein, in a deal worth $2.6 billion. **Steven Bernstein** (see p.852) is another of Weil's fine crop of transactional antitrust lawyers. He has significant agency expertise, after 12 years working in the FTC, and is praised by sources for his superb intellect. He worked with Ann Malester on the Medicis/Valeant transaction. **James Egan** (see p.860) is a former senior figure in the FTC who focuses on the civil class action side of antitrust. He has been a major part of the team representing Hilton Worldwide in the hotels online booking class action litigation. **John Scribner** (see p.891) is a promising antitrust lawyer who is highly thought of by sources, primarily for his work in transactional antitrust. He recently acted for automotive component manufacturer Nemak on its $215 million acquisition of J.L. French.

## Band 3

### Crowell & Moring LLP
See profile on p.910

**THE FIRM** This firm has a varied and successful antitrust practice, combining high-profile representation in the transactional arena with a successful litigation offering. It has a particular niche in plaintiff litigation for firms opting out of class actions. Notable recent matters include acting as co-counsel for UTC on the finalization of its $18.4 billion deal with Goodrich, following a nine-month review process involving jurisdictions worldwide.
**Sources say:** *"They are very confident and technically skilled in many areas and we get very good, personal representation."*
**KEY INDIVIDUALS Randolph Smith** (see p.893) has an *"outstanding understanding of the law"* and brings *"reasoned analysis"* to his work, according to sources, who also cite him as an *"easy and congenial person to work with."* Smith primarily works on the antitrust aspects of M&A, and led the representation of UTC in the deal with Goodrich. Firm chairman **Kent Gardiner** (see p.864) is described as a *"strategic thinker"* by sources, who are quick to note his ability to convey complex ideas to clients. He is often seen on the plaintiff side in antitrust litigation. He was co-lead counsel for CSX Transportation as defendants in a class action concerning rail freight fuel surcharges. **Christopher Ondeck** (see p.884) is a busy younger partner at the firm who is praised for his *"impressive attention to detail and really deep knowledge,"* as well as his strong advocacy skills. He represented Potandon Produce in the fresh and processed potatoes antitrust litigation.

### Dechert LLP
See profile on p.1969

**THE FIRM** Despite its smaller size, Dechert continues to attract many of the biggest cases, and fields some leading antitrust lawyers. Although its reputation is centered more on litigation, it also has a significant merger practice. The group represented Medco Health Solutions in its gargantuan $29.1 billion merger with Express Script.
**Sources say:** *"They gave practical advice and were great when the litigation came around."*
**KEY INDIVIDUALS Paul Denis** (see p.859) is noted for his impressive knowledge of antitrust law and policy, with one source pointing out that *"he has so much experience with the agencies."* Denis is experienced at dealing with merger filings and antitrust litigation, and recently acted for Inhibitex on its $2.5 billion sale to Bristol-Myers Squibb. **Paul Friedman** (see p.863) handles both transactional and litigation matters. His recent representations include acting as co-lead in a case for Actelion Pharmaceuticals involving the drug Tracleer. He is described as having *"a great deal of insight into industries,"* and as *"a great strategist who is very calm in his demeanor and approach."*

## Gibson, Dunn & Crutcher LLP
See profile on p.682

**THE FIRM** This team builds on its sterling national reputation as one of the leading criminal cartel groups in the USA with a more rounded practice in Washington, DC, including transactional work and noncriminal investigations. Of late it has represented UBS in 17 class actions arising from the LIBOR investigation, and acted for Sony Music in class action cases relating to alleged price-fixing of digital music downloads.

**Sources say:** "*For anything with complexity, I'd turn to them.*" "*They gave advice that was not only good, but practical as well.*"

**KEY INDIVIDUALS Joseph Kattan** (see p.873) has a broad-based antitrust practice with a particular niche in IP-related antitrust matters. Peers are respectful of his experience and abilities in the area. He recently represented Intel in a case brought by the New York Attorney General concerning alleged monopolization. **Jarrett Arp** (see p.850) is a versatile lawyer with a growing profile. He practices primarily in antitrust litigation and counseling. He is antitrust counsel to Microsoft and McDonald's, among others, and was also part of the team representing UBS. **Joshua Lipton** (see p.877) is seen as a "*very talented, very smart guy*" who has quickly established himself as a solid litigator in this area. He is currently representing Aetna in a case brought against Blue Cross Blue Shield of Michigan alleging that a number of contracts with hospitals breached antitrust laws.

## Hogan Lovells US LLP

**THE FIRM** This team has an active and varied antitrust practice handling a great deal of work in front of government agencies as well as civil antitrust litigation. The practice group has ten partners based in Washington, DC, and is noted for its overall bench strength. Recent highlights include representing Verizon in an investigation into a purchase of wireless spectrum.

**Sources say:** "*They were responsive and communicative, and gave good counsel, while helping us find the right avenues and listening to our concerns.*"

**KEY INDIVIDUALS** Sources describe **Janet McDavid** as a "*wonderful*" lawyer and a "*very capable counselor who is savvy with her legal expertise.*" They also note her multifaceted practice, although her recent highlights have been in the government investigation arena. These include being lead counsel in the Verizon investigation mentioned above. Commercial trial lawyer **Robert Robertson** has "*lots of great litigation experience,*" with one peer stating: "*If you were litigating a merger, he'd be one of the people you'd be looking to call.*" Robertson's recent highlights have included advising Illinois Tool Works on potential litigation relating to the sale of part of its business to Graco. **Joseph Krauss** focuses his practice on antitrust, with a particular emphasis on merger-related matters. He was co-lead, along with Janet McDavid, for S1 Corporation on an investigation arising out of its proposed acquisition by ACI Worldwide. According to sources, Krauss "*gives very good antitrust advice in merger control issues.*" **Logan Breed** has won many fans among peers as a "*young leader*" who is

"*very bright and unbelievably good.*" He has particular expertise in antitrust that touches on hi-tech sectors. He led the team representing Research In Motion in its acquisition of part of Nortel's patent portfolio.

## Kirkland & Ellis LLP
See profile on p.1254

**THE FIRM** This solid all-around antitrust practice includes a significant Hart-Scott-Rodino filing presence on the transactional side. It also undertakes a plethora of cases in the pharmaceuticals and energy sectors. Highlights include representing Bristol-Myers Squibb in two acquisitions in the pharmaceuticals arena, worth a combined $9.5 billion.

**Sources say:** "*I always respect Kirkland & Ellis – they have a very good, strong litigation practice, even in regulatory matters.*"

**KEY INDIVIDUALS** "*Outstanding*" of counsel **Timothy Muris** (see p.882) remains a "*very highly regarded*" figure within the antitrust world and is particularly praised for his knowledge and connections at the agencies and his work on Hart-Scott-Rodino second requests. He recently represented Teva in its $6.8 billion acquisition of Cephalon. Clients say they "*can really rely on*" the "*terrific*" **Mark Kovner** (see p.875) for his expertise in merger-related antitrust matters. He recently co-led the team representing NRG Energy in its $1.7 billion acquisition of GenOn Energy. **Christine Wilson** (see p.900) is another younger partner at the firm who is establishing a fine reputation for her "*take-charge attitude*" and "*excellent understanding of the law.*" She co-led on the Bristol-Myers Squibb matter mentioned above.

## Latham & Watkins LLP
See profile on p.446

**THE FIRM** Latham & Watkins has a fine national antitrust practice of which its Washington, DC practice is just a part. The versatile group has strength in litigation and merger clearance and investigation work. It acted for ExxonMobil in an investigation into the sale of the Central American part of its downstream distribution network.

**Sources say:** "*Very bright, dedicated and sophisticated litigation counsel.*"

**KEY INDIVIDUALS** The "*just phenomenal*" **Margaret Zwisler** (see p.902) "*has a number of good attributes,*" including her ability to analyze how the facts fit the law. She is a "*brilliant courtroom lawyer*" and has acted in a number of recent litigation matters, including defending Pharmaceutical Research & Manufacturers of America in a case brought against drug manufacturers alleging price-fixing. Sources praise **Tad Lipsky's** (see p.877) "*encyclopedic knowledge of antitrust cases*" accrued through some 36 years' practice in this area. He recently acted for Neptune Orient Lines in an investigation brought by the European Commission against the liner shipping industry. **William Sherman** (see p.892) receives credit from commentators for his abilities in front of a judge and his straightforward analysis of documents. He was part of the team representing Ford in a major California class action case.

## O'Melveny & Myers LLP
See profile on p.693

**THE FIRM** This group has real presence in the antitrust litigation market, representing blue-chip firms in some of the biggest ongoing cases. This includes representing Apple in both the e-books investigation instigated by the DOJ and the hi-tech employees antitrust litigation. In addition to litigation, the firm also acts for parties in a number of M&A deals.

**Sources say:** "*As solid an antitrust group as you'll find.*"

**KEY INDIVIDUALS Richard Parker** continues to be a worthy and respected member of the leading pack of antitrust lawyers in this area. Commentators are quick to point to his valuable combination of "*great judgment*" and a "*very personable demeanor.*" He has led many of the firm's recent representations, including both of the Apple matters listed above. **Michael Antalics** is an experienced and well-liked practitioner with extensive experience in merger matters, having spent 23 years at the FTC. He was part of the firm's representation of Magma Design Automation in its $523 million acquisition of competitor Synopsys.

## WilmerHale
See profile on p.930

**THE FIRM** WilmerHale demonstrates antitrust capability across the board, with a solid cartel practice in addition to its civil litigation and merger clearance work. The group is consistently rated for its excellent client service, and sources are quick to point out its willingness to go the extra mile. It acted for International Paper on its $4.3 billion acquisition of Temple Inland.

**Sources say:** "*These folks are really, really good lawyers. They're efficient and really customer-focused.*"

**KEY INDIVIDUALS William Kolasky** (see p.875) is a highly regarded antitrust practitioner with 35 years' experience in antitrust litigation and counseling. He is a former chair of WilmerHale's antitrust practice group, and recently acted for Disney in a cable bundling case. **Thomas Mueller** is a "*cartel heavyweight,*" according to sources, who praise his "*very detailed*" approach and legal intellect. He has acted in a number of recent cartel investigations, including for DENSO in a DOJ autoparts investigation. **Leon Greenfield** (see p.867) is described as a "*very, very bright, very effective lawyer,*" with a busy practice covering a broad spectrum of antitrust work, including cartels, merger investigations and counseling. He was part of the team in the DENSO representation.

## Wilson Sonsini Goodrich & Rosati
See profile on p.700

**THE FIRM** This group is building an imposing presence on the East Coast with an impressive Washington, DC office to go alongside its growing New York offering. The team is particularly noted for its expertise in the technology arena, and regularly represents Google in a variety of matters, including the FTC investigation into its search practices.

**Sources say:** "*They have built quite an impressive practice in quite a short amount of time.*"

**KEY INDIVIDUALS Susan Creighton** couples *"deep experience with the agencies"* with her skills as a *"phenomenal thinker and writer and very good oral advocate."* Along with Scott Sher, she regularly represents Google and has recently acted for it in the FTC investigation mentioned above. **Scott Sher** brings an *"active and energetic approach"* to his practice and is described by sources as *"one of the leading younger antitrust lawyers in the country."* In addition to his notable work for Google, he also acted for Seagate Technology on its much-scrutinized $1.375 billion acquisition of the hard drive arm of Samsung Electronics. **Mark Rosman** is noted for his budding criminal cartel practice. He was part of the team representing Universal Surveillance Systems in relation to an alleged monopolization case brought against Checkpoint Solutions.

## Band 4

### Baker Botts LLP
See profile on p.2427

THE FIRM Baker Botts's antitrust team handles merger clearances and investigations, and has an active antitrust litigation practice. It has particular experience in representing clients in the technology and energy sectors. Of note, it recently acted for GKN on its GBP633 million acquisition of Volvo Aero.

**Sources say:** *"It's an excellent antitrust practice. You get the sense you're dealing with people who have a very deep knowledge of the subject."*

**KEY INDIVIDUALS John Taladay** (see p.895) is a *"sensible, straightforward"* antitrust lawyer who produces *"first-class"* results for his clients. An antitrust all-rounder, he represents clients in cartel, civil litigation and merger-related matters. He led the team acting for GKN on the Volvo Aero merger. **Sean Boland** (see p.853) is a *"very fine and very capable"* attorney who has built a fine reputation in the oil and gas industry, with one client describing him as *"one of the best in the country"* in that sector. He was heavily involved in National Oilwell Varco's $2.5 billion acquisition of Robbins & Myers. **Christopher MacAvoy** (see p.879) receives praise as a *"very, very talented"* and *"extremely capable"* practitioner. He is active in the agency space and also handles antitrust litigation, recently representing C&S Wholesale Grocers in a putative class action alleging an anticompetitive conspiracy with another grocery company. **James Rill** (see p.887) is a *"very well-respected"* senior figure at the firm, who *"has an amazing capacity to keep working,"* according to sources. He has over 50 years of experience in antitrust law and has recently deployed this experience for MOSAID Technologies in relation to a complaint filed by Google concerning Nokia patents.

### Cadwalader, Wickersham & Taft LLP
See profile on p.438

THE FIRM This team continues to grow and now numbers 25 attorneys practicing antitrust, led by Rick Rule, former head of the antitrust division at the DOJ. It regularly works with Microsoft, on major matters such as the $8.5

billion acquisition of Skype and as a third party in the investigation into Google's practices.

**KEY INDIVIDUALS Rick Rule** (see p.889) is described by sources as *"quite brilliant"* and *"really strong."* He has been in private practice for 23 years following his departure from the DOJ and is regarded as a leading practitioner, with commentators pointing out his strength in cartel matters. He leads the firm's representation of Microsoft along with Jonathan Kanter. Young partner **Jonathan Kanter** (see p.873) is a *"smart guy"* who is tipped by many to have a *"bright future"* in the antitrust arena. Beyond his extensive work for Microsoft, he has also acted for Fair Search Coalition, another third party in the government's Google investigation.

### Freshfields Bruckhaus Deringer LLP
See profile on p.443

THE FIRM As one of the few European firms to have broken into the Washington, DC market in this area, Freshfields has established a solid antitrust practice. It recently acted for EMI in the investigation of the sale of its music business to Universal, and also advised the company on the disposal of its music publishing arm to a consortium including Sony.

**KEY INDIVIDUALS Paul Yde** (see p.901) is described by one client as *"exceptional and very plugged in as well as being an extremely good technical lawyer,"* and more simply by a peer as a *"really good merger lawyer."* In addition to transactional work he undertakes representations in agency investigations. He led the firm's representation in the aforementioned EMI deals. **Bob Schlossberg** (see p.890) is another of Freshfields' highly respected antitrust practitioners, described as *"outstanding"* by one source. Like Yde, his forte is mergers and joint ventures. He recently represented Rolls-Royce in a proposed joint venture with Pratt & Whitney concerning jet engines. Highly distinguished former FTC head **Terry Calvani** (see p.856) is of counsel at the firm and brings a wealth of experience to the practice group. He recently represented Emirates in private litigation related to the DOJ's air cargo investigation.

### Mayer Brown LLP
See profile on p.1257

THE FIRM This group principally practices antitrust litigation, including cartel and class actions work, and also has a growing reputation for advising on significant M&A. It recently acted for Nestlé on its $11.9 billion acquisition of Pfizer's infant nutrition arm.

**Sources say:** *"They are very knowledgeable advisers, giving practical, immediate and efficient advice."*

**KEY INDIVIDUALS Richard Favretto** is credited by sources as being *"superb at strategy"* and *"able to relate to businesspeople thanks to his very practical approach."* He acted for BNSF Railway on a class action case relating to alleged fixing of fuel surcharge prices. Seasoned practitioner **Robert Bloch** brings 40 years' experience to the table. He is a litigator primarily specializing in work before the DOJ and FTC, while also recently representing Starwood Hotels in the online travel agents civil litigation. Up-and-comer

**John Roberti** has *"really impressed"* peers and clients alike, with one interviewee saying: *"He is not only good with clients but works great with other firms as well."* Roberti's practice encompasses litigation and merger review, and he recently represented United Airlines in two cases concerning alleged violations of antitrust laws.

### McDermott Will & Emery LLP
See profile on p.1258

THE FIRM The McDermott antitrust team practices across antitrust law, with an emphasis on M&A. It has a particular niche in healthcare-related matters, as demonstrated by its representation of Amgen in connection with its $315 million acquisition of KAI Pharmaceuticals.

**Sources say:** *"They are very responsive and very intelligent, give excellent legal analysis and are able to present it in a way that I can easily present to the businesspeople in my firm."*

**KEY INDIVIDUALS Raymond Jacobsen** (see p.871) *"knows antitrust backwards and forwards"* and is *"very well respected at the agencies."* He mainly handles issues relating to M&A, and also undertakes some antitrust litigation. He acted for Amgen on successfully dismissing a case brought by a hospital alleging illegal tying of prices. Commentators call **Jeffrey Brennan** (see p.854) *"one of the best there is in the healthcare space,"* in part due to his previous experience for the FTC working in that area. He has recently been involved in a number of cases involving hospital affiliations. **Joseph Winterscheid** (see p.900) heads up the firm's antitrust group and is a *"really terrific lawyer"* who *"provides exceptional service"* to his clients. He represented HIG Capital in the creation of a joint venture in the logistical sector.

### Paul, Weiss, Rifkind, Wharton & Garrison LLP
See profile on p.1997

THE FIRM Paul Weiss continues to be a substantial contributor to the Washington, DC antitrust market, thanks to its skilled and seasoned litigators. Its expertise covers a range of civil and criminal litigation areas as well as merger clearance matters. It recently acted for MasterCard International on the settlement of a card interchange fee suit.

**Sources say:** *"If I have a really big problem, I go to them. They have great resources and the capability of being tough but also building relationships. Really a terrific law firm."*

**KEY INDIVIDUALS Joseph Simons** (see p.892) is a *"very, very good"* antitrust lawyer with *"great pedigree."* His practice covers the full spectrum of antitrust law, from cartel to class action litigation. He acted for Sharp in the LCD litigation and cartel investigation. **Kenneth Gallo** (see p.864) undertakes IP and general commercial litigation work in addition to antitrust, and has built a reputation as *"an extremely talented guy"* who is praised for his *"absolutely outstanding"* court advocacy, among other things. He and Simons represented MasterCard in the card interchange fee case.

## White & Case LLP
See profile on p.451

**THE FIRM** The team at White & Case is known for its pharmaceutical expertise but is also active more generally in the cartel arena and in M&A. Recent matter of note include representing Par Pharmaceuticals and Paddock Laboratories in a so-called 'pay for delay' case involving the drug AndroGel.

**Sources say:** *"We were impressed by the quality of the work, the availability of their guys and their dedication."*

**KEY INDIVIDUALS Mark Gidley** (see p.865) chairs the firm's global antitrust practice group and is well regarded among peers. He is highly experienced in representing clients in front of the FTC and DOJ, and regularly acts for pharmaceutical companies. He recently represented Shionogi in a sham patent counterclaim case. The *"excellent"* **Christopher Curran** (see p.858) is a commercial litigator who undertakes antitrust cases as part of his wider practice. He is representing Upsher-Smith Laboratories in a petition of certiorari filed in the Supreme Court in relation to a class action concerning drug patents.

## Band 5

### Morrison & Foerster LLP
See profile on p.1990

**THE FIRM** The antitrust practice group at Morrison & Foerster was boosted by the arrival of Roxann Henry from Dewey & LeBoeuf in May 2012. She joins an emerging group that is well regarded by sources for the understanding of economics it can bring to its antitrust work, and for its expertise in the technology sector. Recent cases include representing Elpida Memory in its $2.5 billion sale to Micron.

**Sources say:** *"What differentiates their partners is that they are not only substantively strong, but also very practical and business-oriented problem solvers."*

**KEY INDIVIDUALS** One source calls **Stephen Smith** *"the single smartest lawyer in Washington,"* while others highlight his *"ability to coalesce the issue into actionable, practical advice."* His antitrust practice covers civil litigation and he has a strong reputation in merger-related antitrust work. He recently represented Intel in a $4.1 billion transaction with ASML Holdings. The experienced **Roxann Henry** is an *"excellent lawyer"* with a reputation for being a *"tough, hard-nosed advocate."* She practices across antitrust law and since her arrival at the firm has largely been focusing on cartel and criminal defense matters. **David Meyer** is described as a *"really smart, really strong lawyer"* who *"understands the issues well and is well connected."* He has a wide-ranging antitrust practice with a niche in representing railroads in transportation-related issues. His recent work includes the abovementioned Elpida Memory matter.

### Paul Hastings LLP
See profile on p.1996

**THE FIRM** Paul Hastings bolstered its antitrust team with the addition of MJ Moltenbrey from Dewey & LeBoeuf in

2012. It is a full-service antitrust practice, covering areas such as cartel, transactional and civil class action matters. It acted for SAMSUNG on the recent sale of its hard disk drive business to Seagate Technologies.

**Sources say:** *"They're very creative at an appropriate level and had in-depth knowledge of our industry. They were very practical business lawyers."*

**KEY INDIVIDUALS** Global practice chair **Michael Cohen** was co-lead counsel with Scott Hataway on the SAMSUNG deal mentioned above. He also acts as counsel to the International Seafood Sustainability Foundation. One client says: *"I go to Michael for his global expertise in antitrust."* *"Excellent attorney"* **MJ Moltenbrey** is praised by sources for her *"responsiveness and organizational skills."* Since joining the firm in June 2012 she has represented American Airlines against Sabre Airways and others in an alleged monopolization case concerning booking services. Talented young partner **Scott Hataway** has gained the attention of peers as a *"methodical, fine lawyer."* Primarily a transactional antitrust practitioner, he was co-lead for SAMSUNG, and also acted for Ardea Biosciences on its $1.26 billion acquisition by AstraZeneca.

### Ropes & Gray LLP
See profile on p.1528

**THE FIRM** The Ropes & Gray team splits its practice between litigation and transactional work, with particular expertise in the healthcare sector. Its recent matters include representing Hitachi-LG Data Services in the optical disk drive antitrust litigation, and acting for Becton Dickinson on two large transactions in the healthcare sector.

**Sources say:** *"I have nothing but praise for them."* *"They have some young, bright and dynamic lawyers there."*

**KEY INDIVIDUALS** The *"super-smart"* **Mark Popofsky** garners praise from peers and clients alike, with one interviewee noting that he balances his intellect with *"practical real-world touches."* Popofsky fronts up the litigation work for the firm, and is highlighted for his proficiency in the technology sector, as evidenced by his recent representation of Hitachi-LG Data Services, as mentioned above. **Michael McFalls** concentrates his practice on M&A, acting for clients such as healthcare firm Biomet, which he represented in its acquisition by DePuy. One source calls him *"very diligent and easy to work with."*

### Vinson & Elkins LLP
See profile on p.2459

**THE FIRM** This firm handles litigation and transactional antitrust work, and has expertise in criminal cartel matters. It recently acted for AirTran in a multidistrict class action case in defense of an alleged conspiracy relating to baggage fees.

**KEY INDIVIDUALS** Sources praise **Neil Imus** (see p.870) as a solid antitrust practitioner. He concentrates on M&A issues, and recently acted for Dart Container on the $1 billion acquisition of fellow packaging company Solo Cup. **Craig Seebald** (see p.891) has *"a great cartel practice,"* according to commentators, who also point out that he *"has the personality to work well with different people."* He represented Hitachi in the optical disk drive antitrust liti-

gation. **William Vigdor** (see p.897) is a strong lawyer who focuses on transactional antitrust issues and is recognized by sources for his knowledge of economics and his understanding of the practical aspects of competition law. He was part of the V&E team that acted for IDEXX Laboratories in an FTC investigation concerning diagnostics.

## Other Notable Practitioners

**Stephen Harris** of Baker & McKenzie is known for his expertise on competition issues in Asia and is described by clients as a *"tremendous resource"* and noted for his extraordinary responsiveness. He acted for Prestige Brands on its $600 million acquisition of GlaxoSmithKline's over-the-counter brands business. Former Dewey & LeBoeuf partner **Marc Schildkraut** is a big-name addition to Cooley LLP's antitrust group, joining in May 2012. He is praised by market commentators as being an excellent lawyer in this space. He recently acted for Tesoro on its acquisition of several oil refining assets from BP. **Howard Morse** of Cooley LLP is applauded for his ability to apply his deep antitrust expertise to commercial settings. Sources are quick to point out his strength in hi-tech antitrust, in which field he recently represented Objet in its $1.4 billion merger with Stratasys. **Jon Roellke** (see p.888) of Bingham McCutchen LLP represents clients in the IP, commercial and antitrust arenas. Sources describe him as a *"bright guy"* who is *"very good at building credibility"* with clients. He recently represented Morgan Stanley Capital Group in an investigation into a complex financial transaction. **Bruce Hoffman** (see p.869) of Hunton & Williams LLP is an *"extraordinary analyst"* and *"very insightful"* practitioner who is recognized by sources for his experience in front of the agencies. He is chair of the firm's global antitrust practice.

**Robert Bell** (see p.851) of Kaye Scholer LLP works primarily on M&A-related matters and civil antitrust litigation. He acted for two executives of TRW in the autoparts investigation. Commercial litigator **Claudia Higgins** (see p.869) of Kaye Scholer LLP earns praise for her responsiveness and connections at the FTC. She recently represented space robotics firm MacDonald Dettwiler & Associates in the DOJ investigation into its acquisition of Loral's satellite business. Seasoned antitrust expert **Donald Klawiter** of Sheppard, Mullin, Richter & Hampton LLP is *"really very strong"* and provides *"terrific advice,"* according to sources. He focuses mostly on criminal cartel defense, and has represented clients in several recent cases involving international clients. **Robert Abrams** (see p.849) of Baker Hostetler LLP is a highly seasoned litigator praised for his encyclopedic knowledge and excellent judgment, with one client saying: *"I wouldn't want anyone but him on an antitrust case."* He was lead counsel for a certified class of over 7,000 dairy farmers in the Southeastern milk antitrust litigation. Sources call **Hill Wellford** (see p.899) of Bingham McCutchen LLP a *"really very strong"* younger partner who is *"one to watch."* He has recently represented clients in a number of confidential criminal antitrust investigations. Former general counsel of the FTC,

William Blumenthal (see p.853) of Clifford Chance US LLP is an *"incredibly bright," "deep antitrust thinker"* with a great deal of experience in the area. He practices mainly in merger work and civil antitrust litigation. *"Excellent lawyer"* Bernard Nigro of Fried, Frank, Harris, Shriver & Jacobson LLP practices across the full range of antitrust law with an emphasis on M&A. He has overseen several recent ten-figure deals, including acting for GS Capital Partners and certain equity holders of Suddenlink Communications on Suddenlink's $6.6 billion sale to a consortium of investors. Grace Rodriguez (see p.888) of King & Spalding LLP is a highly regarded litigator who practices across commercial litigation, white-collar crime and antitrust. She recently acted for USPS in a class action

case alleging tying practices. Bruce Sokler (see p.893) of Mintz Levin Cohn Ferris Glovsky and Popeo PC is recognized by sources for his expertise in the healthcare and telecom arenas, with clients pointing out his case strategy skills. He recently acted for Cox Communications in class action litigation concerning the alleged tying of cable services to set-top boxes. Robert Reznick of Orrick, Herrington & Sutcliffe LLP gains plaudits for his *"extraordinarily clear advice"* and legal intellect. He focuses particularly on representing pharmaceutical companies and on IP-related antitrust. He acts as counsel for the Pharmaceutical Security Institute. Kenneth Ewing of Steptoe & Johnson LLP is described as a *"very bright, very thoughtful"* lawyer who mostly represents clients in civil

and criminal antitrust litigation. He recently acted for the National Milk Producers Federation in a series of civil class actions relating to the price of milk. Daryl Libow (see p.877) co-heads Sullivan & Cromwell LLP's practice group and is a *"smart guy,"* according to sources. He has represented JPMorgan Chase in some 40 putative class action suits concerning alleged anticompetitive conduct in the silver futures market. Counsel Michael Sohn (see p.893) of Davis Polk & Wardwell LLP has vast experience in the antitrust arena and continues to play a role at the firm as an elder statesman. Sources describe him as an *"awesome"* presence.

# BANKRUPTCY/RESTRUCTURING

Commentary about individuals can be found under their firm's paragraph. If the firm has no paragraph (is not ranked) look at Other Notable Practitioners.

## Bankruptcy/Restructuring
### Leading Firms

**Band 1**
Arnold & Porter LLP *
Cadwalader, Wickersham & Taft LLP *
Orrick, Herrington & Sutcliffe LLP *

**Band 2**
Akin Gump Strauss Hauer & Feld LLP *
Caplin & Drysdale *
Covington & Burling LLP *
Crowell & Moring LLP *
Dickstein Shapiro LLP *
Wiley Rein LLP *
WilmerHale *

**Band 3**
Arent Fox LLP *
Hogan Lovells US LLP
McKenna Long & Aldridge LLP *
Zuckerman Spaeder LLP

*\* Indicates firm / individual with profile.*
*†ONP = Other Notable Practitioner.*

## Senior Statesmen

| Senior Statesmen: distinguished older practitioners | | |
|---|---|---|
| Inselbuch Elihu | Caplin & Drysdale | |
| Kuney David | Sidley Austin LLP (ONP)† * | |

## Leading Individuals

### Band 1
| | |
|---|---|
| Baxter Michael St Patrick | Covington & Burling LLP * |
| Bernstein Michael | Arnold & Porter LLP * |
| Ellenberg Mark C | Cadwalader, Wickersham & Taft LLP * |
| Frankel Roger | Orrick, Herrington & Sutcliffe LLP * |
| Goldblatt Craig | WilmerHale * |

### Band 2
| | |
|---|---|
| Bran Paul Bennett | Dickstein Shapiro LLP * |
| Dolan Edward | Hogan Lovells US LLP |
| Dowd Mary Joanne | Arent Fox LLP * |
| Friedman Peter M | Cadwalader, Wickersham & Taft LLP * |
| Gold Jason | Wiley Rein LLP * |
| Litt Daniel | Dickstein Shapiro LLP * |
| Orr Kevyn D | Jones Day (ONP)† * |
| Plevin Mark | Crowell & Moring LLP * |
| Savin James R | Akin Gump Strauss Hauer & Feld LLP * |
| Van Norden Lockwood Peter | Caplin & Drysdale |
| Wyron Richard H | Orrick, Herrington & Sutcliffe LLP * |

### Band 3
| | |
|---|---|
| Alberts Sam J | Dentons (ONP)† * |
| Clark Darrell W | Stinson Morrison Hecker LLP (ONP)† |
| Cohen Nelson C | Zuckerman Spaeder LLP |
| Goldstein Bruce | Zuckerman Spaeder LLP |
| Guy Jonathan P | Orrick, Herrington & Sutcliffe LLP * |
| Leblanc Andrew | Milbank, Tweed, Hadley & McCloy (ONP)† * |
| McJunkin John | McKenna Long & Aldridge LLP * |
| Morrison Valerie P | Wiley Rein LLP * |

### Band 4
| | |
|---|---|
| Alberino Scott L | Akin Gump Strauss Hauer & Feld LLP * |
| Auerbach Dennis B | Covington & Burling LLP * |
| Carrigan Daniel | McKenna Long & Aldridge LLP * |
| Laughlin Alexander M | Wiley Rein LLP * |
| Strochak Adam | Weil, Gotshal & Manges LLP (ONP)† * |
| Swett Trevor | Caplin & Drysdale |
| Taylor Mark D | Kilpatrick Townsend & Stockton (ONP)† |

### Up-and-coming individuals
| | |
|---|---|
| Mintz Douglas S | Cadwalader, Wickersham & Taft LLP * |

## Band 1

### Arnold & Porter LLP
See profile on p.906

THE FIRM Arnold & Porter's bankruptcy and corporate restructuring group is acclaimed for bringing New York style and caliber to the local DC market. It maintains a strong national workload and is particularly recognized for its expertise in conducting bankruptcy litigation. Highlights from the past year include representing PMI Mortgage Insurance during its Arizona-based receivership, and acting for the same client on the Chapter 11 bankruptcy of parent PMI Group.
Sources say: *"The level of competency, creativity and responsiveness was exceptional. Enjoyable people to work with and first-rate lawyers." "In addition to being extremely knowl-*

*edgeable on developing legal issues, they really understand our business and business objectives."*
KEY INDIVIDUALS Michael Bernstein (see p.852) *"brings an encyclopedic knowledge of the Bankruptcy Code, an unbelievably tireless energy level and a practical results-oriented approach to bankruptcy issues,"* according to commentators. He heads the firm's bankruptcy practice group and leads many of the team's most high-profile engagements. Clients note that Bernstein is *"a fierce and zealous advocate and skilled negotiator."*

### Cadwalader, Wickersham & Taft LLP
See profile on p.438

THE FIRM This team forms an integral element of Cadwalader's prominent financial restructuring practice.

Members of the team have played significant roles in many nationally prominent restructuring cases. The group acts across the spectrum of bankruptcy matters, with recent highlights including representing the trustee for certain notes and certificates in the large-scale Chapter 11 case of Dynegy Holdings. Cadwalader also currently acts for MBIA Insurance on the Chapter 11 bankruptcy of Residential Capital, in which MBIA is asserting claims in excess of $2 billion.
Sources say: *"I would hire anyone in the team in a second." "They have terrific attorneys in DC."*
KEY INDIVIDUALS Mark Ellenberg (see p.860) is acknowledged by peers as a national heavyweight in the bankruptcy field. Clients are equally impressed, noting that *"he has seen it all; he takes a wise approach and has a steady*

hand to make the best of difficult situations." Ellenberg is praised for his expertise in bankruptcy litigation. He is notably acting for MBIA Insurance on the Residential Capital bankruptcy. **Peter Friedman** (see p.863) is enjoying a key role as counsel to US Bank, as trustee for certain notes and certificates in Dynegy Holdings' Chapter 11 proceedings. In addition to being described as *"very creative,"* he is praised by respondents for being *"energetic and passionate about doing the right thing."* Another notable member of the firm's Washington, DC team is special counsel **Douglas Mintz** (see p.882). He handles the full range of bankruptcy matters for debtors, secured lenders and creditors' committees. Mintz is regularly noted for his intellectual verve and technical prowess.

### Orrick, Herrington & Sutcliffe LLP
See profile on p.1994

**THE FIRM** Orrick's restructuring group is recognized nationally, with many prominent matters being led by lawyers in the Washington, DC office. The team represents a range of clients, including lenders, creditors and debtors. It is best known for its work in mass tort bankruptcies, with examples including acting for the future claims representative on the ongoing WR Grace bankruptcy. The team's diversity is evidenced in other recent highlights, which include a role as debtor's counsel in the Chapter 11 case of Buffalo Thunder Development Authority, and representing Fujifilm in the high-profile bankruptcy of Kodak.

**Sources say:** *"They are good at understanding the big picture and identifying important points, as well as communicating my position to the court."*

**KEY INDIVIDUALS Roger Frankel** (see p.863) has over 40 years of bankruptcy law experience and is cochair of the firm's restructuring group. Interviewees say he is *"very levelheaded in volatile situations,"* and add that *"he is not about ego; it is the way he delivers that garners respect."* Frankel takes a leading role on many of the firm's big-ticket bankruptcy cases, including its recent representation of Buffalo Thunder Development Authority during its Chapter 11 bankruptcy. **Richard Wyron** (see p.901) earns tremendous respect for his accomplished bankruptcy practice. He is particularly recognized for his expertise in mass tort and asbestos-related bankruptcies. Clients say he *"is very trustworthy and will stand up for clients but still remain constructive,"* and note that he is *"good at spotting issues and evaluating them."* **Jonathan Guy** (see p.867) impresses commentators with his *"command of complicated facts and knowledge of the way complex issues play out."* He is a specialist in bankruptcy litigation, where he is noted for his presentation and preparedness.

### Band 2

### Akin Gump Strauss Hauer & Feld LLP
See profile on p.904

**THE FIRM** Akin Gump's bankruptcy and restructuring team in Washington, DC has grown impressively and is considered an important component of the firm's nation-

ally acclaimed financial restructuring practice. It specializes in representing creditors' committees and bondholders. Highlights from the past year include advising the official unsecured creditors' committee on Delta Petroleum's Chapter 11 bankruptcy.

**Sources say:** *"Lots of experience, deep bench, pragmatic, easy to work with." "They have developed a sophisticated and experienced team in DC."*

**KEY INDIVIDUALS James Savin** (see p.889) is credited with having built Akin's formidable reputation in DC, and regularly represents creditors and bondholders in nationally prominent bankruptcies. Clients believe that *"his primary strength is his intelligence and subject matter knowledge,"* with other respondents adding that *"a lot of people don't have the same granular structural knowledge that he does."* Similar to Savin, **Scott Alberino** (see p.849) focuses on creditor and bondholder representations. Peers have been quick to praise him as *"good to work with; he understands what needs to get done and works to get there without a lot of theatrics or time wasting."*

### Caplin & Drysdale
See profile on p.909

**THE FIRM** Caplin & Drysdale retains its reputation as a powerhouse for representing official committees of claimants during asbestos-related bankruptcy cases. The team is acclaimed for its pioneering expertise in the use of Section 524(g) of the Bankruptcy Code and the related tax issues. Away from the realm of asbestos claims, the team is optimally placed to handle any number of mass tort bankruptcy matters.

**Sources say:** *"They have got really strong litigation skills, and are terrific problem solvers and tacticians." "Extraordinarily skilled and disciplined lawyers. They all have different skills and work together as a team."*

**KEY INDIVIDUALS Peter Van Norden Lockwood** is immensely experienced in advising asbestos claimant creditors' committees. Commentators say he is *"brilliant but also completely transparent. In a practice where people are often very heated, nobody ever doubts Peter's integrity."* Clients praise his *"very deep intellectual and analytical ability."* In relation to his bankruptcy litigation skills, sources note that he is *"very quick and alert on his feet in front of a judge."* **Trevor Swett** is *"a very successful litigator and a strong strategic thinker,"* according to respondents. He specializes in bankruptcy litigation, particularly asset recovery. *"He is an exceedingly gifted advocate,"* say clients; *"he has a great manner with judges and knows which arguments to emphasize and which ones to leave out."* **Elihu Inselbuch** is praised as *"the godfather of Caplin's practice."* Sources consider him a *"dominant player nationally in representing committees of asbestos victims."* While his practice is not as active as in the past, Inselbuch is *"still an intellectual force and dynamic personality,"* according to satisfied clients.

### Covington & Burling LLP
See profile on p.441

**THE FIRM** This corporate restructuring and bankruptcy reorganization team handles the full range of bankruptcy matters. It is especially adept at addressing the insurance

asset issues involved in restructuring proceedings. The team has remained busy in the past year, with highlights including representing the official committee of unsecured creditors in the Chapter 11 bankruptcy of large equipment rental company Ahern Rentals.

**KEY INDIVIDUALS Michael St Patrick Baxter** (see p.851) heads up the firm's DC bankruptcy and restructuring team and is widely admired by sources, many of whom note that *"his knowledge and strategic abilities are outstanding."* In addition to more traditional roles, he has recently served as a Chapter 11 bankruptcy trustee, examiner and consumer privacy ombudsman. Of counsel **Dennis Auerbach** (see p.850) is *"well prepared and articulate."* He is the team's resident litigation expert, and commentators state that *"when you're litigating against him, you'd better have done your homework."*

### Crowell & Moring LLP
See profile on p.910

**THE FIRM** Crowell & Moring's financial restructuring and bankruptcy group is acclaimed for its expertise in acting for insurers on mass tort bankruptcies. The team has also developed a significant practice representing lender syndicates, investors and financial institutions. Recent highlights include representing Fireman's Fund and American Automobile Insurance in relation to the bankruptcy of Plant Insulation. Crowell & Moring also represents Alsalam Aircraft in connection with the cross-border bankruptcy of Aveos Fleet Performance.

**Sources say:** *"Some of the best attorneys in the country, with a specialty in asbestos insurance coverage and bankruptcy issues."*

**KEY INDIVIDUALS** The *"knowledgeable, responsive and astute"* **Mark Plevin** (see p.886) is an expert in the bankruptcy litigation and insurance sectors. Interviews note that *"he explains the issues and recommendations in an understandable way."* Plevin splits his time between Washington, DC and San Francisco.

### Dickstein Shapiro LLP
See profile on p.911

**THE FIRM** The well-regarded team in Dickstein Shapiro's Washington, DC office offers expertise in creditor, debtor and committee representations, and is often praised for its strong bench strength. Recent highlights including acting for Florida Pritikin Center on the MSR Resorts bankruptcy and disputes over several iconic hotel properties.

**Sources say:** *"They are very calm, logical and solution-oriented, which is helpful to parties who can get emotional. Their steady hand was invaluable in that process."*

**KEY INDIVIDUALS** The *"very talented"* **Daniel Litt** (see p.877) leads the firm's financial restructuring and bankruptcy practice. He has a diverse practice, and almost three decades of experience in the field. Many interviewees praise his creative approach and foresight during litigation. **Paul Bennett Bran** (see p.853) is highly experienced across a broad range of bankruptcy matters. He played the lead role in acting for Florida Pritikin Center on the MSR Resorts bankruptcy. Respondents are quick to praise his intelligence, with one adding: *"He was terrific, detail-oriented and understood the big picture."*

## Wiley Rein LLP
See profile on p.928

**THE FIRM** This excellent team has the bench strength and experience to handle a wide range of matters. It focuses on acting for distressed companies in bankruptcies and restructurings, representing creditors and lenders, and acting for practice head Jason Gold in his continued role as trustee in various bankruptcy cases. The firm is experienced across a number of industries, with its most recent activities involving the media, real estate, aerospace and retail sectors. It has also developed significant expertise in law firm bankruptcies.

**Sources say:** *"In addition to handling the bankruptcy fully, they were very good at guiding us through the process." "A very nice, collegial and intelligent professional working group."*

**KEY INDIVIDUALS** Practice group leader **Jason Gold** (see p.865) is *"able to handle the technical aspects of a case and also deal with the public relations,"* say satisfied clients. He has particular expertise in acting as a trustee during proceedings, and in acting for bankrupt law firms. Sources praise his effective influence in proceedings, with one noting: *"He had a nice manner and kept everybody very calm throughout the process."* **Alexander Laughlin** (see p.875) has the *"ability to understand the law and mesh it with the client's business,"* according to respondents, many of whom also praise his steady-handed approach during litigation and negotiations. He is experienced within the real estate, retail and automotive industries, among others. **Valerie Morrison** (see p.882) is experienced across a range of bankruptcy matters, including financial reorganizations, Chapter 11 proceedings and receiverships. She is regularly praised for her litigation prowess and practical approach to matters. Healthcare and media are both sectors in which Morrison excels.

## WilmerHale
See profile on p.930

**THE FIRM** WilmerHale's DC-based bankruptcy team focuses primarily on complex bankruptcy litigation and appeals. It regularly advises large financial institutions and other creditors, with a particular emphasis of late on cases involving the treatment of home mortgages. Recent highlights include representing the Loan Syndications Trading Association (LSTA) in the Supreme Court in the RadLAX Gateway Hotel v Amalgamated Bank case.

**Sources say:** *"The way they handled the case was very professional and based on common sense."*

**KEY INDIVIDUALS** The *"truly brilliant"* and *"very talented"* **Craig Goldblatt** (see p.866) has expertise in conducting bankruptcy-related litigation and appeals. He led the firm's representation of LSTA in the RadLAX matter.

## Band 3

### Arent Fox LLP
See profile on p.905

**THE FIRM** This solid bankruptcy and financial restructuring team handles a steady workload of in- and out-of-court restructurings, distressed asset acquisitions and bankruptcy litigation. It is particularly highlighted for its sector-specific expertise in the automotive, real estate, construction, IP and pensions industries. The team is especially active in midmarket, regional debtor cases, an area in which it has experienced notable success.

**Sources say:** *"A highly respected practice involved in a lot of high-profile regional work." "The team provides me with experience, practical business advice and excellent quality work."*

**KEY INDIVIDUALS Mary Joanne Dowd** (see p.860) is the head of Arent Fox's DC bankruptcy team. She is experienced in a number of industries, including the automotive, broadcast, construction and nonprofit sectors. Clients are quick to praise her *"incredible knowledge of bankruptcy in the DC area, and in local and federal courts."*

### Hogan Lovells US LLP

**THE FIRM** This firm's DC restructuring and insolvency practice advises distressed borrowers, debt holders, shareholders and purchasers of distressed assets. Its team is experienced across a range of sectors, including hospitality, aviation and healthcare.

**KEY INDIVIDUALS** The highly regarded **Edward Dolan** is experienced in representing a broad range of clients in bankruptcy and restructuring matters. Sources say he is personable and professional, and praise his ability to translate difficult concepts into layman's terms.

### McKenna Long & Aldridge LLP
See profile on p.922

**THE FIRM** The team at McKenna Long & Aldridge enters the rankings on the back of a successful year. It is recommended as a strong local player and a formidable entity more nationally. It operates across the full range of bankruptcy matters, with particular emphasis of late on advising lenders and vendors on asset dispositions, workouts and restructurings. The team recently advised LPP Mortgage as creditor's counsel on the foreclosure of Underwood Towers, a 450-unit apartment tower in Hartford, Connecticut.

**Sources say:** *"Wise counsel who offer expertise and big case experience."*

**KEY INDIVIDUALS John McJunkin** (see p.881) is a senior partner with a tremendous amount of experience in the bankruptcy industry. He features prominently in many of the team's most high-profile matters, and receives praise for his intelligent approach to issues and his emphasis on bringing cases to a swift solution. **Daniel Carrigan** (see p.856) *"continues to handle a number of sophisticated issues for substantial clients,"* say impressed respondents. He is particularly recognized for his representation of vendors in bankruptcy proceedings. Clients have also been quick to identify his courtroom expertise as a strong point.

## Zuckerman Spaeder LLP

**THE FIRM** This robust practice continues to be highly regarded in the regional restructuring and reorganization market. The team has expertise in acting for trustees on Chapter 7 and Chapter 11 proceedings, and is well placed to handle work in the healthcare, retail, automotive, real estate and hospitality industries. It has extensive experience across the full range of bankruptcy issues, including fraudulent transfer litigation, as well as asbestos and other mass tort issues.

**Sources say:** *"They are very responsive, extremely well organized and practically minded in how they approach cases."*

**KEY INDIVIDUALS Nelson Cohen** is particularly adept at representing clients within the mortgage, real estate and hospitality sectors. Clients praise him as *"smart and very well organized,"* adding that *"he is very disciplined and understands what is required in a case."* **Bruce Goldstein** has more than 30 years' bankruptcy experience across a broad range of areas and industries. He is widely acknowledged for his influence within the local bankruptcy market. *"He can simplify complex situations and is very practical,"* say impressed sources, who also note that he is *"fair minded and reasonable."*

## Other Notable Practitioners

**Sam Alberts** (see p.849) of Dentons is highly regarded for his healthcare and real estate sector expertise. He regularly advises FDIC on bankruptcy issues, and is currently representing the Pension Guaranty Benefit Corporation in connection with the Kodak Chapter 11 cases. **Darrell Clark** of Stinson Morrison Hecker LLP is described as *"a wonderful attorney."* He is well versed in bankruptcies involving the telecommunications, IP, energy and real estate sectors. He has been particularly active of late advising a number of clients on distressed asset purchasing. **Andrew Leblanc** (see p.876) of Milbank, Tweed, Hadley & McCloy LLP frequently plays a leading role in some of his firm's most significant bankruptcy issues. Clients say that *"he understands when things are going as they should, when parties are being reasonable and when they are being unreasonable; he is firm when his clients are being wronged."* **Mark Taylor** of Kilpatrick Townsend & Stockton LLP is recognized for his expertise in bankruptcy issues occurring in the healthcare industry. He is a *"very good, hard-working lawyer"* who *"has done a good job of growing his practice."* He regularly acts as Chapter 11 trustee during bankruptcy proceedings. **Adam Strochak** (see p.894) of Weil, Gotshal & Manges LLP is highlighted as an excellent practitioner when it comes to bankruptcy litigation work. Sources agree that *"he is very good and does top-quality work on some of the biggest, most sophisticated cases."* He is particularly adept within the environmental and insurance industry sectors. **David Kuney** (see p.875) of Sidley Austin LLP is widely regarded as one of the most influential and experienced practitioners in the region. He has built a tremendous reputation for his all-encompassing bankruptcy and restructuring experience, and is also often singled out as an expert in real estate and retail bankruptcies.

# CONSTRUCTION

Commentary about individuals can be found under their firm's paragraph. If the firm has no paragraph (is not ranked) look at Other Notable Practitioners.

## Band 1

### Peckar & Abramson, P.C.
See profile on p.1998

**THE FIRM** This construction powerhouse has a particular focus on government contracts work, and regularly advises major contractors working on federal government projects. The team also acts for contractors in relation to infrastructure projects and condominiums. Highlights include representing a general contractor in a series of disputes with the owner and subcontractor, regarding the construction of a hospital. Power disputes are another key area of focus, and the group advised an engineering, procurement and construction (EPC) contractor on a $240 million claim against the owner of a power project.

**Sources say:** *"Top league." "Very professional, very knowledgeable and very responsive."*

**KEY INDIVIDUALS** A major player in the DC market, **Adrian Bastianelli** (see p.851) impresses sources with his extensive experience across a broad spectrum of construction matters. *"He's one of the most highly respected practitioners in the construction Bar, not only in DC but also nationally,"* say commentators. Clients praise **Michael Branca** (see p.853) as *"super-responsive and very knowledgeable."* He recently acted for the EPC contractor of a nuclear power plant in a series of claims with a value of almost $1 billion.

### Seyfarth Shaw LLP
See profile on p.1262

**THE FIRM** This market-leading construction practice handles a broad range of work, both within the USA and overseas. It is widely recognized for its ability to undertake work arising from large-scale, complex projects such as power plants, wastewater treatment centers and infrastructure developments. Notably, the group advised Capital Project Strategies on the construction and design aspects of the $2 billion Dulles Metrorail extension. The firm also offers strong litigation expertise, and recently acted for Sandy Creek Power Partners on a number of claims arising

from the construction of a $1.5 billion power plant in Texas.

**Sources say:** *"The firm is top-notch and I recommend it without reservation."*

**KEY INDIVIDUALS Bennett Greenberg** (see p.867) has *"a keen understanding of design and build work, as well as the pragmatics of how to address commercial issues."* He has an excellent reputation for his work advising on construction documentation and high-value multiparty disputes. The highly impressive **Richard Preston** (see p.886) is *"the total package: very smart, experienced and unflappable, with the power of intellect and good judgment, and a good people person who deals well with other lawyers and with clients,"* commentators say. He is also an experienced arbitrator both domestically and overseas. **Steven Kmieciak** (see p.874) has extensive expertise in advising on commercial and government construction contracts, and also demonstrates an in-depth understanding of litigation and alternative dispute resolution. He is described by market commentators as *"an exceptional lawyer."* Clients applaud **Sara Beiro Farabow** (see p.861) for her *"prompt and efficient responsiveness and clarity. Whatever the audience, she has the perfect approach, and everyone leaves the meeting with the information they were seeking."* Her practice has considerable international scope, and she regularly acts on international arbitrations in Europe and the Middle East. **David Mancini** (see p.879) is a highly regarded construction lawyer who has handled matters in such jurisdictions as Turkey, India, Russia, Saudi Arabia and Kazakhstan. Clients value his *"very good eye for detail and good strategic command of the facts of a case."*

## Band 2

### Asmar, Schor & McKenna PLLC

**THE FIRM** This well-regarded DC firm advises a range of individuals, small businesses, partnerships and corporations on construction matters. The team undertakes work relating to the drafting and negotiation of construction documentation, project delivery, and any contentious matters that may arise, including defect and insurance claims. The firm's construction clients also benefit from the firm's wider expertise on government contracts, real estate and corporate law.

**Sources say:** *"An excellent firm." "Great customer care."*

**KEY INDIVIDUALS Charles Asmar** heads the construction group at the firm. Commentators praise his *"refreshing no-nonsense approach"* and find him *"efficient and very smart, with a good knowledge of the subject matter."* **Laurence Schor** is an experienced figure with a particular focus on water production facilities. He also undertakes a broad selection of other construction and government contracts matters. **John McKenna** specializes in work relating to construction defects. Clients appreciate his *"excellent attention to detail and analytical skills, prompt responses, reasonable and rational approach in dealing with opposing*

*counsel and fair billing practice."* Up-and-coming construction attorney **Christopher Taggi** is described by clients as *"very knowledgeable, very well prepared and very accurate in his assessment of the outcomes."*

### Bradley Arant Boult Cummings LLP
See profile on p.476

**THE FIRM** This practice is widely recognized for its strong presence in the DC market. It acts for domestic and international contractor clients on construction disputes and award controversies. International disputes is one key area of focus for the group, and work highlights include State

Department operations in regions including the Middle East. The team is also acting for Grunley Construction on a dispute relating to the multimillion-dollar renovation of the Embassy of Brazil in Washington, DC.

**Sources say:** *"They are very helpful with advice, very skilled when proposing strategy and very cost-aware when pursuing a course of action." "It is our go-to firm when there is trouble brewing or trouble to be avoided."*

**KEY INDIVIDUALS Robert Symon** *"quickly identifies the significant issues that need to be addressed and does a terrific job,"* sources say. His clients include Carothers Construction and Forrester Construction. **Douglas Patin** heads the construction group at the firm. He has an excellent reputation for his work on construction disputes, and recently advised Allan A Myers on a series of contract and delay claims relating to a wastewater treatment plant.

## Holland & Knight LLP
### See profile on p.1028

**THE FIRM** This major team combines a strong workload of pure construction matters with significant government contracts expertise. Notably, it advised major contractor Barton Malow on a claim against a municipal government relating to owner abandonment, cardinal changes and default abandonment. Noncontentious highlights for the team include advising on construction law concerning the renovation of the South African Embassy in Washington, DC. The team also acts for such major names as Royal Caribbean Cruises, New York Transportation Authority, Mass Electric Construction and Monument Realty.

**KEY INDIVIDUALS Andrew Stephenson** (see p.894) is a hugely respected construction practitioner and has a top reputation for his work. He acts for owners, contractors and architect-engineers on a range of high-profile matters. *"Outstanding attorney"* and *"seasoned litigator"* **Stephen Brett Shapiro** (see p.891) handles both transactional and contentious construction work. Sources praise *"his speaking and writing abilities, and his astute knowledge of construction law issues."*

## Jones Day
### See profile on p.919

**THE FIRM** An international firm with a strong presence across its home country, Jones Day advises clients on all stages of the construction process, from the preparation of documentation to litigation and alternative dispute resolution. Standout contentious matters for the team include advising a utility owner on a number of claims relating to a landmark power station. Noncontentious highlights include acting for El Paso Electric on the design, construction and operation of a high-profile solar electric generation project in Texas.

**Sources say:** *"A very capable construction group."*

**KEY INDIVIDUALS** Market-leading construction lawyer **Andrew Ness** (see p.883) is hailed as a *"very talented, honorable and smart"* individual, who not only knows the industry in detail, but will also pioneer groundbreaking solutions. **Kevin O'Brien** (see p.884) is well regarded for his contentious construction practice. He acted on a dis-

pute relating to the $800 million expansion of a cement production facility.

## Pillsbury Winthrop Shaw Pittman LLP
### See profile on p.2000

**THE FIRM** This impressive construction team offers broad-based expertise across construction and insurance recovery matters. It covers high-profile transactional work and disputes, and recently defended Weitz Construction against a multimillion-dollar claim brought by CC Aventura, a Hyatt subsidiary. The team also has an increasing presence in renewable energy, both domestically and overseas. Clients in this area include DAMG World Wide and Prenecon.

**KEY INDIVIDUALS David Dekker** wins applause from sources for his recovery practice. He recently acted on a dispute relating to a multibillion-dollar power plant. **Michael Evan Jaffe** has extensive expertise in construction disputes. He is *"a very tenacious litigator – I'd recommend him for that,"* said one interviewee, adding: *"His specialty is tough litigation and he is very talented."* **Michael McNamara** primarily acts on disputes and insurance recovery work. Sources note that he *"has the highest level of professionalism, and does a good job for his clients."* Observers highlight **Jeffrey Gans** as being *"extremely astute in construction law issues, with great insight, great energy and very good ideas when it comes to litigation and disputes."* His practice places a particular focus on troubled project counseling.

## Band 3

## Fox Rothschild LLP
### See profile on p.2242

**THE FIRM** The team at Fox Rothschild handles a range of construction claims, with notable recent highlights including significant fraud investigations. Federal construction law is a major area of focus, and the team has acted for such major players as Alberici Constructors, Hensel Phelps and Burns & McDonnell. It acted for Argo Systems on four cases concerning contracts and the service-disabled veteran status.

**Sources say:** *"A very good practice."*

**KEY INDIVIDUALS** Dispute resolution expert **Larry Harris** (see p.868) acts on domestic and international matters for contractors, subcontractors, owners and design professionals. According to market sources, he is *"as good as it gets. A very competent practitioner and on the shortlist of top DC construction lawyers."* **Dirk Haire** (see p.867) has a well-recognized practice acting for general contractors. He is currently advising Alberici Constructors on a multimillion-dollar fraud investigation.

## McManus Darden & Felsen LLP

**THE FIRM** This solid firm advises clients at all stages of the construction process, from the drafting and negotiating of documentation, through risk assessment and minimization, to the resolution of any disputes that may arise. The team is experienced handling matters that relate to hospitals, schools and power plants, as well as other residential and commercial projects.

**KEY INDIVIDUALS Joseph McManus** has expertise in acting on a range of construction disputes and government contracts work. Notable matters for him include acting for parties in both the public and the private sectors on an arbitration in the Caribbean.

## Seeger Faughnan Mendicino, PC

**THE FIRM** This compact and well-regarded DC firm handles a broad spectrum of construction matters, such as contract preparation, job cost accounting, critical path method (CPM) schedule evaluation and the resolution of any disputes that arise. The firm's client base includes general contractors and subcontractors, design professionals, manufacturers, suppliers and project owners.

**KEY INDIVIDUALS Stephen Seeger** is well regarded for his work as a construction litigator. He also advises clients on all stages of construction, from project conception and contract negotiation to insurance and labor claims.

## Other Notable Practitioners

The outstanding **Joseph West** (see p.899) of Gibson, Dunn & Crutcher LLP is a major player in construction in DC. Sources praise him for being *"extremely good at strategy and understanding the big picture, and able to handle a range of situations – he has done everything and seen everything."* He has a particular focus on work relating to government contracts. **Barbara Werther** of Ober Kaler Grimes & Shriver is a highly experienced construction and government contracts specialist. *"She is creative and comes up with a plan in order to achieve a successful outcome for the client,"* sources say. **Robert Brams** of Patton Boggs LLP wins high praise from clients and peers alike, who say he is *"not only excellent with the law, but also provides the right practical advice and strategic guidance." "He is extremely client-oriented and very effective,"* commentators add. **Herman Braude** of Braude & Margulies, P.C. is a highly experienced practitioner with strong construction and government contracts expertise. He is a market stalwart, with a long-standing presence in this sector. **Geoffrey Keating** (see p.873) of Drinker Biddle & Reath LLP is a well-regarded attorney who has been representing contractors, owners, engineers and sureties for decades. **Joel Rubinstein** of K&L Gates is described by sources as a *"good lawyer with a good reputation."* He is well known for his work acting for subcontractors. **Dan Toomey** of Duane Morris LLP is a respected real estate attorney who represents owners, suppliers, design professionals, contractors and subcontractors in construction litigation. He also has experience of alternative dispute resolution. *"He's got a tremendous amount of litigation experience and is good at presenting facts to judges and juries,"* sources say. **Hal Perloff** of Husch Blackwell LLP wins applause from clients for his *"exceptional knowledge of and practical advice on construction matters."* He is recognized for his government contracts expertise. The well-regarded **Lawrence Prosen** (see p.886) of Thompson Hine LLP is a government contracts expert and regularly acts for contractors and subcontractors in construction litigation.

# CORPORATE/M&A & PRIVATE EQUITY

Commentary about individuals can be found under their firm's paragraph. If the firm has no paragraph (is not ranked) look at Other Notable Practitioners.

## Corporate/M&A & Private Equity — Leading Firms

**Band 1**
Gibson, Dunn & Crutcher LLP *
Hogan Lovells US LLP
Kirkland & Ellis LLP *
Latham & Watkins LLP *
Skadden, Arps, Slate, Meagher & Flom LLP & Affiliates *

**Band 2**
Arnold & Porter LLP *
Covington & Burling LLP *
Fried, Frank, Harris, Shriver & Jacobson LLP *

**Band 3**
Akin Gump Strauss Hauer & Feld LLP *
Baker Botts LLP *
Cleary Gottlieb Steen & Hamilton LLP *
Cooley LLP
Crowell & Moring LLP *
DLA Piper LLP (US) *
Goodwin Procter LLP *
Pillsbury Winthrop Shaw Pittman LLP *
WilmerHale *

**Band 4**
Arent Fox LLP *
Bingham McCutchen LLP *
Morrison & Foerster LLP *
Nixon Peabody LLP *
Proskauer Rose LLP *
Venable LLP *

*\* Indicates firm / individual with profile.*
*† ONP = Other Notable Practitioner.*

## Corporate/M&A & Private Equity — Leading Individuals

**Band 1**

| | |
|---|---|
| Adler Howard B | Gibson, Dunn & Crutcher LLP * |
| Glover Stephen I | Gibson, Dunn & Crutcher LLP * |
| Gorrell Jr J Warren | Hogan Lovells US LLP |
| Kaplan Steven | Arnold & Porter LLP * |
| Lennon Daniel | Latham & Watkins LLP * |
| Rogan Michael P | Skadden, Arps, Slate, Meagher & Flom * |
| Stamas George P | Kirkland & Ellis LLP * |

**Band 2**

| | |
|---|---|
| Director Mark D | Kirkland & Ellis LLP * |
| Evans Stephanie C | WilmerHale * |
| London Jeremy D | Skadden, Arps, Slate, Meagher & Flom * |
| Mazo Mark | Hogan Lovells US LLP |
| Pommerening David | Baker Botts LLP * |
| Sheridan Paul | Latham & Watkins LLP * |
| Varney Andrew | Fried, Frank, Harris, Shriver & Jacobson * |

**Band 3**

| | |
|---|---|
| Burdick Rick L | Akin Gump Strauss Hauer & Feld LLP * |
| Chaplick Trevor J | Proskauer Rose LLP |
| Conner Frank (Rusty) | DLA Piper LLP (US) * |
| Dantzic David S | Latham & Watkins LLP * |
| Gruhin Mark I | Saul Ewing LLP (ONP) † |
| Hutchinson James A | Goodwin Procter LLP * |
| Jack W Andrew | Covington & Burling LLP * |
| Lavin Kevin J | Arnold & Porter LLP * |
| Lincoln Michael | Cooley LLP |
| Mangino Brian | Fried, Frank, Harris, Shriver & Jacobson * |

| | |
|---|---|
| Martin David | Covington & Burling LLP * |
| Mooney Marilyn | Fulbright & Jaworski LLP (ONP) † * |
| Rabinowitz Mitchell L | Crowell & Moring LLP * |
| Robbins Robert B | Pillsbury Winthrop Shaw Pittman LLP * |
| Salvi Lucantonio | Sheppard, Mullin, Richter & Hampton (ONP) † |
| Sherman Andrew J | Jones Day (ONP) † * |
| Sinha Pankaj K | Skadden, Arps, Slate, Meagher & Flom * |
| Welch John | Jones Day (ONP) † * |

**Band 4**

| | |
|---|---|
| Dewis Karen A | Cadwalader, Wickersham & Taft (ONP) † |
| Feigin Samuel E | Nixon Peabody LLP * |
| Fitzgerald Mark | Wilson Sonsini Goodrich & Rosati (ONP) † |
| Gold Michael A | Baker Botts LLP * |
| Herman Andrew M | Kirkland & Ellis LLP * |
| Houle Jeffrey R | DLA Piper LLP (US) * |
| Kahn Sarah E | DLA Piper LLP (US) * |
| Kass Mark | Nixon Peabody LLP * |
| Krus Cynthia M | Sutherland Asbill & Brennan LLP (ONP) † |
| Marks Richard J | DLA Piper LLP (US) * |
| Marquardt Paul | Cleary Gottlieb Steen & Hamilton LLP * |
| Parrino Richard | Hogan Lovells US LLP |
| Reed Michael | DLA Piper LLP (US) * |
| Stuart III James R | Crowell & Moring LLP * |

**Up-and-coming individuals**

| | |
|---|---|
| Sanders David | Foley & Lardner LLP (ONP) † |
| Sheridan Rachel W | Latham & Watkins LLP |
| Ulery Christopher J | Skadden, Arps, Slate, Meagher & Flom * |

## Band 1

### Gibson, Dunn & Crutcher LLP
See profile on p.682

**THE FIRM** Gibson, Dunn & Crutcher is renowned for its high-end DC practice, which is praised for its deep bench of experienced practitioners. The team continues to represent major international companies such as Marriott International, Wolverine Worldwide and Credit Suisse in complex matters that run the gamut of IPOs, acquisitions, mergers and investment transactions. Recent work includes assisting Wolverine Worldwide with the financing of the acquisition of Collective Brands, a transaction that was worth over $1 billion.
**KEY INDIVIDUALS Howard Adler** (see p.849) is held in high regard by market commentators as a leading practitioner in this area. He has worked on numerous sophisticated corporate transactions of late, including TCF Financial's acquisition of more than $800 million in FDIC-insured deposits from Prudential Bank & Trust. He also advised ExactTarget on its $185 million IPO. The *"tremendous"* **Stephen Glover** (see p.865) has *"built up a good practice"* in this market, according to admiring sources. He rep-

resents public and private companies in the full spectrum of corporate requirements, and has been particularly occupied with strategic acquisitions of late. He led the team on the Wolverine Worldwide acquisition financing.

### Hogan Lovells US LLP

**THE FIRM** This group commands a significant share of the market in DC, thanks to its active presence across several major industries in the region. Its expertise in sectors such as aerospace, government services and financial services has established it as a top choice for many key clients, including Bank of America Merrill Lynch, GE Capital and ExxonMobil. Of late, the team has been busy handling numerous mid and large-cap M&A deals, and has been equally active on the private equity side. It recently advised BankAtlantic Bancorp on its recent multibillion-dollar disposal of subsidiary BankAtlantic to BB&T.
**Sources say:** *"They are very strong and deserve recognition."* *"They have sheer bulk, market presence and ability."*
**KEY INDIVIDUALS** According to interviewees, **Warren Gorrell** has a *"preeminent practice"* and is a *"world-class lawyer."* He recently worked alongside colleagues in New York and DC to advise ExxonMobil on the $3.9 billion sale of its Japanese subsidiary. **Mark Mazo** is a well-respected

figure in the M&A world and divides his time between the DC and Paris offices. By virtue of his international practice, he has particular skill in handling cross-border work, including M&A, investments and joint ventures. **Richard Parrino** advises across an impressive range of industry sectors, including healthcare, IT and defense. He has a strong grasp of several key areas of the market, including public offerings and complex securities transactions, and is adept at representing both domestic and international clients.

### Kirkland & Ellis LLP
See profile on p.1254

**THE FIRM** Kirkland & Ellis continues to enjoy a stellar reputation in DC, acting for high-profile clients such as Exelon and MidOcean Partners. The team recently represented Constellation Energy in a highly publicized $7.9 billion merger with Exelon, and now represents the new entity. Kirkland's global capabilities in both mid and large-cap M&A and its private equity prowess are also identified by interviewees as significant strengths offered by the firm.
**Sources say:** *"They do a great volume of transactions and there is very little they haven't seen."*
**KEY INDIVIDUALS** *"Force of nature"* **George Stamas** (see p.894) is credited by market observers as having played a

key role in the success of the firm in DC. He is typically involved in the largest transactions handled by the team, with recent highlights including advising MidOcean Partners on an investment into pet food manufacturer Freshpet, among other matters. **Mark Director** (see p.859) is identified as a talented practitioner with "*a really unusual level of business acumen and legal insight.*" He acts as an "*invaluable resource*" to clients in strategic negotiations, and recently advised Arlington Capital Partners on its sale of Consolidated Precision Products to Warburg Pincus. **Andrew Herman** (see p.869) has developed a respected practice focusing on LBOs and M&A transactions, among other matters. He recently worked alongside Mark Director on the $660 million acquisition of UK-based SHL by The Corporate Executive Board Company.

## Latham & Watkins LLP
See profile on p.446

**THE FIRM** Latham & Watkins is internationally recognized as a leading M&A and private equity firm and has led some of the biggest deals in the DC market. Notably, lawyers recently advised BC Partners and The Carlyle Group on the $3.5 billion acquisition of Hamilton Sundstrand from UTC. The firm continues to receive a healthy volume of work from long-standing client The Carlyle Group, as well as serving numerous other significant names in the private equity industry and other sectors.

**Sources say:** "*The Latham lawyers are very responsive, practical and creative, and share their substantial expertise in a down-to-earth, business-oriented fashion.*"

**KEY INDIVIDUALS** Global corporate department chair **Daniel Lennon** (see p.876) is "*really a go-to guy*" for his clients, who say he "*makes sure that you see the big picture and that the transaction is completed.*" He led the team on the Hamilton Sundstrand acquisition referred to above. Sources are full of praise for **Paul Sheridan** (see p.892), highlighting his "*clear communication skills, responsiveness and practical, business-oriented approach.*" His clients also appreciate his ability to coordinate teams seamlessly across practice areas. He recently advised Tomkins on the $505 million sale of its Schrader business. **David Dantzic** (see p.859) recently advised The Carlyle Group on the purchase of private equity investment manager AlpInvest Partners. Impressed sources highlight his unflappable approach to deals and comment that he is particularly "*adept at complex arguments.*" The "*excellent*" **Rachel Sheridan** comes highly praised as one of the district's most promising young names in corporate finance. Her recent highlights include advising on the debt financing aspects of the Hamilton Sundstrand deal.

## Skadden, Arps, Slate, Meagher & Flom LLP & Affiliates
See profile on p.2008

**THE FIRM** Skadden's DC office houses a leading team of practitioners who are conversant across all aspects of M&A. Lawyers have been involved in some of the largest-scale energy transactions of recent times, including the $6 billion spin-off and subsequent merger of Entergy's trans-

mission business into ITC Holdings. The team here is a key component of the firm's impressive global presence in M&A and, as such, is able to offer clients the benefit of complementary expertise in tax, securities, ERISA and numerous other areas, as well as effective cross-border support.

**Sources say:** "*They have a deep bench of extremely strong lawyers.*" "*Their strengths include taking the lead role in transactions and getting results.*"

**KEY INDIVIDUALS Jeremy London** (see p.878) remains an impressive presence in the market, with particular strength in handling transactions in the energy and healthcare sectors. He recently represented Amerigroup in its acquisition by WellPoint for $4.9 billion. **Pankaj Sinha** (see p.407) heads the DC M&A group and was recently sought out by Corix Utilities to advise on its acquisition of all membership interests in Hydro Star from Highstar Capital Fund II. **Christopher Ulery** (see p.897) has made a positive impression on the market, with observers noting: "*It is very obvious that he is a rising star in this area.*" He was part of the team mandated by HealthSpring to assist with its $3.8 billion purchase by CIGNA. **Michael Rogan** (see p.888) is "*definitely one of the big names in DC,*" according to market observers, and brings the benefit of his experience at the SEC to bear in the matters he handles. He recently represented GenOn Energy in its $6 billion agreement to combine with NRG Energy.

## Band 2

## Arnold & Porter LLP
See profile on p.906

**THE FIRM** Long established as a robust presence in the DC market, Arnold & Porter's corporate team has maintained a busy roster of work in the corporate arena of late, acting for the likes of DC Capital Partners, The Halifax Group and S&T Bancorp. This full-service office is able to support clients through every stage of a transaction, and houses particular strength in regulatory and compliance issues.

**Sources say:** "*They have a very old practice in DC and a long-standing reputation in this area.*"

**KEY INDIVIDUALS Steven Kaplan** (see p.873) is held in extremely high regard by market commentators for his expertise in the field. He has been active on behalf of clients from a range of industry sectors, recently representing Provident New York Bancorp throughout its $40.5 million acquisition of Gotham Bank of New York. **Kevin Lavin** (see p.876) is a respected figure in the market and has been involved in a number of deals in recent times. His clients include The Halifax Group, DC Capital Partners and ManTech International.

## Covington & Burling LLP
See profile on p.441

**THE FIRM** Covington & Burling is lauded by market observers for its sophisticated representation of some of the region's biggest clients, including Pepco Holdings, ExxonMobil and Freddie Mac. The corporate team works

cohesively with lawyers from other practice groups, drawing on a range of industry specialties. Of late, the team has been particularly busy on a number of transactions for key client AstraZeneca, including its $1.26 billion purchase of Ardea Biosciences and an alliance with Bristol-Myers Squibb worth over $3 billion.

**Sources say:** "*They explore all sides of an issue and are highly responsive.*"

**KEY INDIVIDUALS Andrew Jack** (see p.871) recently represented Smith Electric Vehicles in a $75 million joint venture with Chinese auto parts supplier Wanxiang Group. This transaction played to his skills in the industrial manufacturing sector, and to the firm's wider strengths in cross-border transactional work. **David Martin** (see p.362) "*brings substantial experience*" to the table and "*counsels in a levelheaded way.*" He serves as co-head of the firm's securities and capital markets practice.

## Fried, Frank, Harris, Shriver & Jacobson LLP
See profile on p.1975

**THE FIRM** By virtue of its impressive global network, this firm is able to marshal significant resources to serve the needs of its diverse client base. Clients such as Permira, Goldman Sachs and Lee Equity Partners are able to turn to the DC office for the full life-cycle of a transaction, drawing on tax, regulatory and strategic advice. A recent highlight saw the team handling a significant European buyout transaction in which key client Permira acquired enterprise software company Genesys for $1.5 billion.

**Sources say:** "*We find that they have a good market read and they are creative. They are very responsive and make you feel like you're their only client.*"

**KEY INDIVIDUALS Andrew Varney** (see p.897) is "*very creative*" and "*comes up with interesting ideas on structure,*" according to sources. He is skilled across the full spectrum of corporate and securities transactions, including joint ventures, private placements and M&A. The "*excellent*" **Brian Mangino** (see p.879) has deep knowledge of private equity and M&A transactions, regularly assisting major names such as Permira, Deltek and Goldman Sachs in high-value, sophisticated deals.

## Band 3

## Akin Gump Strauss Hauer & Feld LLP
See profile on p.904

**THE FIRM** Akin Gump maintains a strong track record in the DC market, earning praise from a range of market sources for its client-oriented and practical approach. The substantial bench of practitioners represents large and midcap companies on both a domestic and international basis, and cover all aspects of M&A and financing transactions.

**Sources say:** "*They are fantastic – we have been blown away by their service.*"

**KEY INDIVIDUALS Rick Burdick** (see p.855) attracts enthusiastic commentary from clients, with one interviewee noting: "*He is extremely people-smart and his reaction* *time is outstandingly good.*" Burdick has a wealth of experience across domestic and cross-border transactions.

## Baker Botts LLP
See profile on p.2427

**THE FIRM** This team possesses a broad corporate skill set and supports clients in a wide range of transactions in the M&A, joint venture and private equity arenas. Noted for its relationships with a significant share of the region's major clients, Baker Botts operates across a variety of industries, including technology, energy and real estate. Lawyers have recently been engaged by Marriott International to handle the disposal of ExecuStay, and by CameronBlue Capital to assist with its purchase of Aegis Mobile.

**Sources say:** "*Its strongest points are client service levels and attention to detail. Baker Botts lawyers are extremely thorough and always attentive to the client.*"

**KEY INDIVIDUALS David Pommerening** (see p.886) is held in high esteem by market commentators in this space. As well as leading the team on transactions for Marriott International and CameronBlue Capital, he also played a role in GKN's $995 million acquisition of Volvo Aero. **Michael Gold** (see p.865) demonstrates prowess in transactions involving public and private companies, and investment fund investors and issuers, among other clients. He is "*extremely smart, knowledgeable and responsive,*" and recently represented GeoEye subsidiary M. J. Harden Associates in a sale of business to Photo Science.

## Cleary Gottlieb Steen & Hamilton LLP
See profile on p.1963

**THE FIRM** This corporate team stands out for its strong and enduring representation of financial institutions, private equity firms and major international companies. Its recent work includes representing Oriental Financial Group in its purchase of BBVA's Puerto Rico bank for $500 million, and advising market research company GfK on two recent acquisitions. The team includes a considerable number of corporate governance and SEC compliance experts in DC, and offers clients wide-ranging knowledge at every stage of a deal.

**KEY INDIVIDUALS Paul Marquardt** (see p.362) recently counseled OneWest Bank on a joint venture with June Bug Enterprises and on its FDIC-aided deals. He also offers noted regulatory guidance on cross-border matters alongside a robust transactional practice.

## Cooley LLP

**THE FIRM** Cooley has consistently been a visible player in the region and earns particular respect for its vibrant venture capital practice. Maintaining close integration with the North Virginia office, the DC team represents numerous high-profile clients, such as LivingSocial and New Enterprise Associates. On the M&A side, the firm recently represented client mindSHIFT Technologies in its $167 million sale to BestBuy.

**KEY INDIVIDUALS** The impressive **Michael Lincoln's** stellar reputation in this area is much deserved, according to market observers. His recent high-profile work includes advising Webs, Inc on its $117.5 million sale to Vistaprint.

## Crowell & Moring LLP
See profile on p.910

**THE FIRM** Crowell & Moring has a strong offering on the corporate side, handling sophisticated and high-profile transactions for key players such as BAE Systems, Goldman Sachs and UTC. The experienced practitioners recently acted for Saab on its $150 million sale of shares in C3 Technologies.

**Sources say:** "*The quality is excellent and they are always thorough, responsive and proactive.*"

**KEY INDIVIDUALS Mitchell Rabinowitz** (see p.887) is "*very practical, responsive and results-oriented,*" and impresses with his representations of key financial institutions in M&A, joint venture and investment transactions. One satisfied interviewee lauds him as "*one of the best lawyers I have dealt with in my professional career.*" **James Stuart** (see p.895) recently counseled Health Net on the $160 million sale of Medicare PDP, and assisted it in negotiating ongoing commercial agreements. He chairs the firm's corporate group and impresses sources with his experience in the area.

## DLA Piper LLP (US)
See profile on p.1971

**THE FIRM** This strong team of talented individuals is identified as being particularly effective when handling matters for emerging growth and startup companies. It recently acted for BancTrust Financial Group on its recapitalization and subsequently on its sale to Trustmark for approximately $100 million. Lawyers here also possess particular expertise in key regional industries, such as international aerospace and government contracts.

**Sources say:** "*I appreciate the scale and resources behind the lawyers; we get good personal attention there.*"

**KEY INDIVIDUALS Rusty Conner** (see p.858) maintains a vibrant practice, regularly representing financial services companies in M&A and corporate finance transactions. He recently assisted key client Raytheon with its $84 million purchase of Henggeler Computer Consultants. He is described as a "*big-picture guy*" and "*a rockstar.*" Interviewees indicate that **Sarah Kahn**'s (see p.872) experience and ability are a key draw for transactional work. "*She does a marvelous job at mastering the complexities of a deal and converting them into advantages for her client,*" notes one source. The "*excellent*" **Richard Marks** (see p.880) is viewed as a true "*stalwart*" of the DC market and continues to head the department. His practice covers the full spectrum of corporate transactions, including investments, acquisitions and restructurings. **Michael Reed** (see p.887) is "*highly attuned to the details and execution on a transaction,*" according to his clients. He worked alongside Conner on the Raytheon transaction, and also represented Scripps Networks Interactive in its public offering of $500 million. **Jeffrey Houle** (see p.870) has an excellent reputation as cochair of DLA Piper's aerospace, defense and government service transactions practice.

## Goodwin Procter LLP
See profile on p.1522

**THE FIRM** This compact but dynamic bench of corporate attorneys is visible across all areas of the market, acting on the full range of M&A and private equity transactions including LBOs, spin-offs and divestitures. The group is particularly well known in the technology sector, possessing a wealth of knowledge of industry trends and practices. Confidence in the team's skills in the sector was demonstrated with its recent engagement by DST Global to act on an $800 million aggregate investment into Twitter.

**Sources say:** "*A robust fund practice.*" "*We've found them to be excellent.*"

**KEY INDIVIDUALS** "*Strong player*" **James Hutchinson** (see p.870) is a highly skilled private equity transactional lawyer and has an enviable track record in representing investment funds, technology companies and financial services companies. He has recently led on two significant LBO transactions for The Halifax Group and Ridge Capital Partners.

## Pillsbury Winthrop Shaw Pittman LLP
See profile on p.2000

**THE FIRM** This highly active firm receives complex mandates from clients based in DC and further afield. The team has an excellent reputation for client service, and has the ability to coordinate across relevant complementary departments such as tax, employee benefits and IP. Key clients include Williams Capital Group, Asia Alternatives Management and Crescent Real Estate Holdings.

**Sources say:** "*A very good firm – you see them day in, day out doing deals in the region.*" "*Strong points include their customer focus and their thoroughness.*"

**KEY INDIVIDUALS** Head of the firm's corporate and securities practice, **Robert Robbins** (see p.888) is a popular and talented practitioner in this area and has spearheaded some of the team's largest and most high-value transactions.

## WilmerHale
See profile on p.930

**THE FIRM** This firm's DC practice has generated a significant volume of work from its corporate client base over the past year. High-profile names featuring on the roster include BAE Systems, Old Mutual Asset Management and TARGUSinfo, alongside numerous others drawn from a wide variety of industries. The team's recent work includes representing TARGUSinfo during its $650 million sale to Neustar.

**Sources say:** "*They have done an excellent job and exhibited real strength. They have a very good depth of skillful midlevel and junior associates so when they delegate things, they are properly handled.*"

**KEY INDIVIDUALS Stephanie Evans** (see p.861) "*is hard-working and collaborative, and has a good, commonsense approach.*" She recently acted for Old Mutual Asset Management on its sale of Dwight Asset Management to Goldman Sachs.

## Band 4

### Arent Fox LLP
See profile on p.905
THE FIRM The corporate team at Arent Fox has been busy of late, working on varied matters across a wide range of industries. It advises clients from the technology, healthcare and consumer products fields on their corporate deals. The firm houses a full-service practice in DC, and clients benefit from access to all required resources for the full life-cycle of their transactions. Notable clients include Marriott, Stifel, Nicolaus & Company and Toyota Boshoku.
Sources say: "They are extraordinarily competent and very responsive."
KEY INDIVIDUALS The corporate group is headed by Jay Halpern, a key contact at the firm.

### Bingham McCutchen LLP
See profile on p.1515
THE FIRM By virtue of its sophisticated and far-ranging international presence, Bingham McCutchen has the resources to cultivate and maintain highly productive relationships with its clients. The DC office works with such names as Oracle, Honeywell and Citrix Systems, and is highly visible in the midmarket M&A space, as well as the clean technology and telecom sectors.
Sources say: "We have developed a very deep, trusting relationship with them."
KEY INDIVIDUALS Andrew Ray and Carl Valenstein are two of the key contacts at the firm.

### Morrison & Foerster LLP
See profile on p.1990
THE FIRM This international firm serves a range of domestic and international clients from its DC office, utilizing its cross-border experience to provide full coverage of M&A, financing, securities and advisory issues. Regular clients include Deutsche Bank, Citi and Salient Federal Solutions. The team recently advised ManTech Group on its $90 million acquisition of Worldwide Information Network Systems.
Sources say: "It is a strong firm; we regularly see it in the market."
KEY INDIVIDUALS David Lynn and David Slotkin are two key contacts at the firm.

### Nixon Peabody LLP
See profile on p.1526
THE FIRM This team earns respect from market commentators for its commitment to the region and its ability to serve clients in sophisticated cross-border transactions. It is particularly active in representing midmarket and lower midmarket companies in a variety of corporate transactions. The team has cultivated a strong focus on the life sciences, consumer products and energy sectors.
Sources say: "Very timely and responsive." "They're really good at resolving complicated issues and they have an understanding of the business side of things."
KEY INDIVIDUALS Mark Kass (see p.873) is praised for his breadth of experience and client service: "He has the customer's needs in mind and is able to deliver on the variety of things that come up." He demonstrates considerable acumen in international deals and has a particular focus on transactions involving Israeli parties. Samuel Feigin (see p.861) enters the rankings having received glowing feedback from interviewees, one of whom said: "He was able to help figure out solutions, he was creative and he always understood a way to work through issues." Feigin is further commended for his ability to coordinate across departments, drawing in the right specialists to complete a deal.

### Proskauer Rose LLP
See profile on p.2001
THE FIRM This compact but effective group in DC handles numerous complex matters for some of the region's largest players. Bolstered by a close connection with the firm's vibrant New York office, the DC team has recently handled a considerable amount of work for key client New Enterprise Associates, including an investment in excess of $50 million into Nova Medical Centers. Another notable transaction saw the team advising Plateau Systems on its sale to SuccessFactors for over $311 million.
Sources say: "They are top notch – they have a good practice in technology and on an international basis."
KEY INDIVIDUALS Trevor Chaplick has worked on a series of transactions for major client New Enterprise Associates in recent times. These have included private equity investments into Indian companies, playing to Chaplick's particular strength in transactions involving Indian parties.

### Venable LLP
See profile on p.927
THE FIRM The corporate team at Venable has maintained a steady portfolio of work in the area of late, adeptly handling clients' regulatory concerns alongside M&A and financing transactions. The practice sustains ongoing relationships with key clients Zachry Hastings Infrastructure, CWCapital and Manufacturers & Traders Trust.
Sources say: "They are professional and available, provide good strategy and negotiate great deals. They are also able to find experts in relevant fields."
KEY INDIVIDUALS Charles Morton and Sharon Kroupa co-head the corporate department and are key contacts at the firm.

## Other Notable Practitioners

The "extremely knowledgeable" Marilyn Mooney (see p.882) of Fulbright & Jaworski LLP has "massive credibility" in this space, built up through her many years of transactional experience. "She is simply superb," summarizes one enthusiastic source. Karen Dewis of Cadwalader, Wickersham & Taft LLP is able to utilize her considerable skills in the corporate arena to handle domestic and cross-border transactions ranging in value from midmarket to billions of dollars. Foley & Lardner LLP's transactional and securities cochair David Sanders has a "commitment to client service at the very highest level." His practical advice and accessibility are also praised by interviewees. Mark Fitzgerald of Wilson Sonsini Goodrich & Rosati is identified as "friendly, accessible and smart." His expertise spans the technology, defense and life sciences industries. Mark Gruhin is a highly experienced corporate partner at Saul Ewing LLP and "one of the best entrepreneurial attorneys," said one interviewee. "He is creative, sensitive to client needs and persistent in pursuing clients' interests." John Welch (see p.899) of Jones Day earns significant praise from sources, one of whom appreciates that he is "always looking out for the client's best interests." His previous in-house experience and deep expertise further mark him out as a top choice for corporate clients. Andrew Sherman (see p.892), also at Jones Day, is "terrific – a sound practitioner and a savvy lawyer." His recent work includes advising ABM Industries on its acquisition of The Linc Group. Vice chair of the corporate and financial services practice at Sutherland Asbill & Brennan LLP, Cynthia Krus offers assured guidance on corporate matters including public and private securities offerings, M&A and the establishment of business development companies. Lucantonio Salvi of Sheppard, Mullin, Richter & Hampton LLP recently represented Italian private equity firm Clessidra SGR in its acquisition of pharmaceutical company Euticals. He is described as "a good negotiator and team manager, who makes sure the big ideas and small details are addressed in agreements without letting the M&A process get bogged down."

# EMPLOYEE BENEFITS & EXECUTIVE COMPENSATION

Commentary about individuals can be found under their firm's paragraph. If the firm has no paragraph (is not ranked) look at Other Notable Practitioners.

## Employee Benefits & Executive Compensation
### Leading Firms

**Band 1**
Groom Law Group *

**Band 2**
Covington & Burling LLP *
Ivins, Phillips & Barker *
Miller & Chevalier Chartered *
Morgan, Lewis & Bockius LLP *
Steptoe & Johnson LLP

**Band 3**
Davis & Harman LLP
Gibson, Dunn & Crutcher LLP *
Jones Day *

**Band 4**
Alston & Bird LLP *
Arent Fox LLP *
Hogan Lovells US LLP
Kilpatrick Townsend & Stockton LLP *
McDermott Will & Emery LLP *
Proskauer Rose LLP *
Venable LLP *

## Senior Statesmen

**Senior Statesmen: distinguished older practitioners**
Vine John M — *Covington & Burling LLP* *

## Leading Individuals

**Star individuals**
Nussdorf Melanie — *Steptoe & Johnson LLP*

**Band 1**
Ford Gary M — *Groom Law Group* *
Hamburger Paul M — *Proskauer Rose LLP*
Mazawey Louis T — *Groom Law Group* *

**Band 2**
Barker Rosina B — *Ivins, Phillips & Barker* *
Dyson Marianna G — *Miller & Chevalier Chartered* *
Hogans Daniel L — *Morgan, Lewis & Bockius LLP* *
Lawson Kurt — *Hogan Lovells US LLP*
Mason Kent A — *Davis & Harman LLP*
Miller Evan — *Jones Day* *
Moore Amy N — *Covington & Burling LLP* *
Moran Anne — *Steptoe & Johnson LLP*
Oliphant Fred — *Miller & Chevalier Chartered* *
Quintiere Gary G — *Miller & Chevalier Chartered* *
Schmidt William — *K&L Gates (ONP)* †*
Shea Richard C — *Covington & Burling LLP* *
St Martin Andrée M — *Groom Law Group* *

**Band 3**
Charyk William — *Arent Fox LLP* *
Collins Michael — *Gibson, Dunn & Crutcher LLP* *
Cotton Raymond — *Mintz Levin Cohn Ferris Glovsky (ONP)* †*
Hevener Mary — *Morgan, Lewis & Bockius LLP* *
Jew Quana — *Arent Fox LLP* *
Kilberg William J — *Gibson, Dunn & Crutcher LLP* *
Kilgore Scott — *WilmerHale (ONP)* †*
Levine David — *Groom Law Group* *
McGuiness John — *Groom Law Group* *
Myers Donald J — *Morgan, Lewis & Bockius LLP* *
O'Brien Kevin — *Ivins, Phillips & Barker*
Ondrasik Paul — *Steptoe & Johnson LLP*
Schendt Thomas G. — *Alston & Bird LLP* *
Wincek Mark D — *Kilpatrick Townsend & Stockton LLP*

**Up-and-coming individuals**
Keller Eric R — *Paul Hastings LLP (ONP)* †

\* Indicates individual with profile.
† ONP = Other Notable Practitioner.

## Band 1

### Groom Law Group
See profile on p.915
**THE FIRM** This employee benefits and executive compensation boutique has earned a deserved reputation as a powerhouse in the market. The 60 specialized attorneys offer unrivaled depth and breadth across the practice area, with groups dedicated to employee benefit plan design and restructuring, multiemployer pension schemes, fiduciary responsibility, executive compensation and tax issues. The firm is also in a strong position to guide employers through the complexities of healthcare reform, and enjoys close links with the DOL, IRS and Congress which allow it to apprise employers of developing legislation and new policies. Major clients include Prudential Financial, Pfizer and the American Benefits Council.
**Sources say:** *"Almost any one of their partners would have to be considered a major player."*
**KEY INDIVIDUALS Gary Ford** (see p.315) is an authority on plan termination insurance, with one well-placed client observing that *"his experience is pretty much unmatched in this area."* Ford handles the complex resolution of benefit plans issues in cases of bankruptcy for an impressive range of major clients, including American Airlines. **Louis Mazawey** (see p.363) has earned a reputation as a *"real solid lawyer"* in matters touching on ERISA law and executive compensation as well as the design and maintenance of benefits plans to ensure ongoing compliance with government standards. **David Levine** (see p.877) chairs the IRS Advisory Committee on Tax Exempt and

Government Entities and is an acknowledged expert on the redesign of pension plans in the wake of complex M&A. **Andrée St Martin** (see p.893) is described by her peers as *"just extraordinarily good"* and concentrates on complexities arising from Title I of ERISA. She also possesses great expertise in the structuring of products for the welfare and pensions spheres. **John McGuiness** (see p.881) heads the firm's executive compensation group and con-

centrates on executive compensation and retirement plans in both the public and private sectors.

## Band 2

### Covington & Burling LLP
See profile on p.441
**THE FIRM** This group is heavily involved in federal regulation in the employee benefits sphere, exemplified by its ongoing advocacy for the ERISA Industry Committee on proposed new regulations affecting employee benefit plans for large organizations. The team has extensive government experience and is able to draw upon the expertise of the firm's tax, government relations and ERISA litigation groups in order to provide a complete service for clients. The firm also provides ongoing counsel for an impressive array of prestigious clients, including GE, PwC and the NFL.
**Sources say:** *"They provide a very good service, they're responsive and smart and think outside the box."*
**KEY INDIVIDUALS** The *"brilliant"* **Amy Moore** (see p.882) chairs the employee benefits and executive compensation practice and is widely respected for her creative approach to the design and administration of benefits plans. She is currently co-leading the group's work for the ERISA Industry Committee among other matters. **Richard Shea** (see p.892) is described by one client as *"not only an advocate for his clients but for a better retirement system."* He is a veteran of the Treasury Department and specializes in complex benefit plan design as well as providing strategic counsel to PwC, Xerox and other major organizations. **John Vine** (see p.897) serves as senior counsel and is a stalwart of the employee benefits field. His areas of particular focus include incentive compensation, deferred compensation and health and welfare plans.

### Ivins, Phillips & Barker
See profile on p.918
**THE FIRM** This practice offers its clientele an employee benefits service which is closely integrated with the firm's business tax group, allowing the dedicated benefits attorneys to draw on a wide range of knowledge and experience as they advise on health, welfare and pension plans, executive compensation and fringe benefits. The group particularly focuses on Section 409A compliance and the creation of new retirement plan arrangements in the wake of corporate M&A.
**KEY INDIVIDUALS** Armed with years of Congressional experience, **Rosina Barker** (see p.850) is an authority on the implications that tax and ERISA have for employee compensation and has carried out major work in this field for clients. **Kevin O'Brien** specializes in defined benefit plan design, executive compensation and the fiduciary aspects of ERISA, and regularly represents clients in front

of Congress, the IRS, the DOL and the Treasury Department.

## Miller & Chevalier Chartered
See profile on p.923

**THE FIRM** This group's benefits and compensation practice is notable for its depth of expertise in navigating the interface between benefit plans and taxation, as well as displaying great strength in the handling of ERISA litigation and fringe benefits. The firm's elite clientele, many in the Fortune 100, can also draw upon the extensive government experience of the group's attorneys, many of whom have worked at the IRS.

**Sources say:** *"In the benefits world lots of work affects actual people and Miller & Chevalier is sensitive to that. They look beyond the cold legal document and get to what the answer should be."*

**KEY INDIVIDUALS** The *"spectacular"* **Marianna Dyson** (see p.860) focuses on payroll tax and fringe benefits. According to clients, she is *"extremely good and looks at things from a business perspective."* **Fred Oliphant** (see p.884) is lauded by clients for his ability to marry his impressive legal acumen with the practicalities of business. He is a specialist in the federal tax side of benefits, and clients say he *"has been a real asset for us over the years consistently."* **Gary Quintiere** (see p.886) *"brings a lot of thought and judgment to the work that is being done"* and is described as being able to make the complexities of pensions regulations *"crystal-clear"* to a lay audience.

## Morgan, Lewis & Bockius LLP
See profile on p.2246

**THE FIRM** This strong DC practice can also draw upon employee benefits specialists spread across the firm's impressive nationwide network. Attorneys here share close links with the growing tax team and offer a full range of benefits and compensation services including the design, upkeep and compliance of plans and the tax issues arising from M&A, and fringe benefits. The group's client base ranges from multinational corporations to prestigious educational institutions, notable examples of which include Google, Toyota and the George Washington University.

**Sources say:** *"They have a good depth of expertise; they have a lot of people with deep knowledge and great critical faculties."*

**KEY INDIVIDUALS** **Daniel Hogans** (see p.869) is described as *"probably the best nonexecutive compensation litigator in the United States"* by one peer, and spent a number of years in the Office of Benefits Tax Counsel at the Treasury Department. **Mary Hevener** (see p.869) is acknowledged by peers to be *"one of the most knowledgeable fringe benefits lawyers in the country"* and is a particular specialist in the field of stock-based compensation and golden parachutes. **Donald Myers** (see p.883) concentrates his practice on the fiduciary responsibility standards set out in ERISA and regularly advises clients on compliance with these provisions.

## Steptoe & Johnson LLP

**THE FIRM** This team of ERISA experts offers a full service across the gamut of employee benefits issues and is particularly strong in the fiduciary sphere. Lawyers also advise a formidable selection of global banks, asset managers and broker-dealers on complex ERISA issues such as the new regulations on global fee disclosures. Key clients include Goldman Sachs, Deutsche Bank, Morgan Stanley and FINRA.

**KEY INDIVIDUALS** **Melanie Nussdorf** is described by one client as a *"great ERISA attorney. She is excellent at her job and has many great contacts."* She is a leading player in the representation of major financial service providers. **Paul Ondrasik** has many years experience of ERISA class actions and of advisory work to major clients such as the National Electrical Benefit Fund. **Anne Moran** has significant government experience at the ABA and DOL and advises clients on executive compensation and plan compliance issues, especially those arising as a result of recent healthcare reforms.

## Band 3

## Davis & Harman LLP

**THE FIRM** This small but influential firm is well known in DC for its skilled representation of clients' interests before regulatory agencies and Congress. The attorneys possess an impressive degree of government experience and liaise closely with their colleagues in the insurance, tax and legislative groups. Key areas of expertise include the representation of trade associations and the implications of tax and ERISA for employee benefits issues.

**Sources say:** *"When there's a really important employee benefits issue in front of Congress, the IRS or the DOL, Davis & Harman is right in the middle of it."*

**KEY INDIVIDUALS** **Kent Mason** is noted as *"a tremendous advocate from a lobbying perspective"* and represents clients before the IRS, DOL, Treasury and Pension Benefit Guaranty Corporation on a regular basis.

## Gibson, Dunn & Crutcher LLP
See profile on p.682

**THE FIRM** A team of 12 partners forms the DC arm of this respected national practice, with expertise in the drafting of employment agreements and plan compliance. The last year has seen this office assert itself as a significant force in the field of class actions, with a favorable outcome on behalf of client Boeing which resulted in the Seventh Circuit reversing the largest ERISA class action ever certified, in a matter worth $4 billion. The DC group continues to represent Boeing on other ongoing matters in the fields of pension plans and medical benefits. Other key clients include Credit Suisse, Wal-Mart and KV Pharmaceuticals.

**KEY INDIVIDUALS** **William Kilberg** (see p.874) is a former solicitor for the DOL and recently oversaw the successful conclusion of the firm's representation of Boeing in its ERISA class action dispute. **Michael Collins** (see p.857) is cochair of the employee benefits and executive compen-

sation group and has great experience across the benefits field.

## Jones Day
See profile on p.919

**THE FIRM** The nine partners in this office are embedded in the firm's broader international team of over 50 benefits attorneys and also have close links with colleagues in the labor and employment and capital markets groups in DC. While best known for their work in the ERISA litigation sphere, lawyers have recently distinguished themselves in the handling of a major transactional matter for GM. Other notable clients include the New York State Nurses Pension Fund and PNC Financial Services Group.

**KEY INDIVIDUALS** Practice head and ERISA litigation specialist **Evan Miller** (see p.369) is described as *"a very practical and very accomplished lawyer who has a litigator's sense of legal risks."*

## Band 4

## Alston & Bird LLP
See profile on p.1102

**THE FIRM** Alston & Bird offers clients a broad range of services, with particular emphasis on ERISA litigation, executive compensation and health and welfare issues. The group also contains expertise in actuarial issues and related litigation. The team recently advocated for the State of Florida to address the alleged unconstitutionality of its 2011 pension law. The firm's ongoing clientele also include Hilton Worldwide, Coca-Cola and Bank of America.

**Sources say:** *"The breadth and scope of their knowledge and expertise was remarkable."*

**KEY INDIVIDUALS** **Thomas Schendt** (see p.890) is a favorite with clients for both his expertise with qualified plans and his considered counseling. *"Not only is he a good legal tactician and adviser but he is also politically sensitive to the needs of an internal client: he is very considerate of the in-house lawyer and their position in the company and the politics that go with that,"* say clients.

## Arent Fox LLP
See profile on p.905

**THE FIRM** This firm concentrates on the transactional and advisory aspects of employee benefits work and also engages in ERISA litigation. Attorneys are particularly adept at reconciling plans with an individual organization's business model and redesigning dated plans to ensure compliance with changing legislation. Assistance is also provided to real estate companies who require REITs and LLCs to be eligible as ERISA plan investments. The group's clients include CAPTRUST Financial Advisors, the Association of American Medical Colleges and Choice Hotels International.

**Sources say:** *"We completely redesigned our retirement plans and they gave us timely, comprehensive and very practical advice."*

**KEY INDIVIDUALS** **William Charyk** (see p.857) leads the practice and is praised for his *"extensive knowledge"* of the benefits and compensation field. **Quana Jew** (see p.872) is acclaimed by her clients, who say that she provides *"outstanding support in the area of defined benefit plans"* and *"epitomizes what any company would want in a counselor."*

## Hogan Lovells US LLP

**THE FIRM** Hogan Lovells provides a good service for clients seeking counsel on executive and incentive compensation, qualified retirement plans and health and welfare plans. Attorneys can draw upon the expertise of their colleagues for matters touching on the regulation of healthcare, banking and securities, and also benefit from the firm's extensive global presence. Interstate Hotels & Resorts and American National Red Cross are among the organizations represented by the practice.

**KEY INDIVIDUALS Kurt Lawson** concentrates on tax-qualified employment plans, welfare plans and executive compensation and is described as *"a very, very bright guy with lots of experience."*

## Kilpatrick Townsend & Stockton LLP
See profile on p.1109

**THE FIRM** This firm is known for its ability to manage complex matters in the health and welfare benefits area and for its depth of expertise in transactional issues, especially the impact that M&A has on benefits and compensation plans. The firm also provides services in the fields of ERISA litigation, fiduciary counseling and pension fund management.

**KEY INDIVIDUALS** The *"extraordinary"* **Mark Wincek** leads the firm's employee benefits practice group and focuses on qualified plans, executive compensation and fiduciary issues. He is praised by clients as an *"extremely knowledgeable and practical lawyer."*

## McDermott Will & Emery LLP
See profile on p.1258

**THE FIRM** This group concentrates on executive compensation, qualified and nonqualified plans, and issues in the health and welfare sphere. Close relationships with the firm's other offices and government agencies such as the IRS ensure that clients receive targeted and informed counsel. Clients include Publix Super Markets (one of the largest employee-owned companies in the USA), Colgate-Palmolive and the New York Port Authority.

**Sources say:** *"They have a huge breadth of experience and can go to many different sources."*

**KEY INDIVIDUALS** David Rogers heads the firm's global employee benefits practice from DC.

## Proskauer Rose LLP
See profile on p.2001

**THE FIRM** The DC arm of this national powerhouse enjoys a strong relationship with both its counterpart in New York City and the labor and employment group. It offers a full range of employee benefits services, with particular emphasis on tax-qualified retirement plans, ERISA litigation and health and welfare matters. The group maintains close links with the IRS, DOL and Pension Benefit Guaranty Corporation.

**Sources say:** *"Where they have been helpful is letting me know of case decisions as they happen, which makes my job easier."*

**KEY INDIVIDUALS Paul Hamburger** heads the employee benefits practice and is also the leader of its health and welfare subgroup. He is recognized as a *"well-known and very skilled"* attorney.

## Venable LLP
See profile on p.927

**THE FIRM** This team provides clients with advice on retirement, health and welfare plan issues as well as executive compensation matters. Clients benefit from the DC team's close relationship with the firm's Baltimore office.

**Sources say:** *"To me they are effective counsel because they give practical solutions in a timely manner."*

**KEY INDIVIDUALS** Kenneth Hoffman heads the employee benefits and executive compensation practice.

### Other Notable Practitioners

**Eric Keller** of Paul Hastings LLP is praised for being *"very good at identifying risk and then giving very pragmatic advice"* and works within all areas of benefits and compensation, with particular emphasis on the design and maintenance of tax-qualified retirement plans and transactional work. **Raymond Cotton** (see p.858) of Mintz Levin Cohn Ferris Glovsky and Popeo PC has a deserved reputation as *"the foremost expert in the negotiation of college presidential contracts"* and other compensation issues in the higher education sphere. **Scott Kilgore** (see p.874) of WilmerHale provides counsel on ERISA, tax and securities and is an acknowledged authority on executive compensation. He is praised for being *"very helpful on the nitty-gritty."* **William Schmidt** (see p.890) of K&L Gates is a highly respected name in the DC market, with niche expertise in ERISA, particularly related fiduciary counseling.

# ENVIRONMENT

Mainly Transactional p.805

Commentary about individuals can be found under their firm's paragraph. If the firm has no paragraph (is not ranked) look at Other Notable Practitioners.

## Environment
### Leading Firms

**Band 1**
Arnold & Porter LLP *
Hunton & Williams LLP *
Sidley Austin LLP *

**Band 2**
Baker Botts LLP *
Beveridge & Diamond PC *
Crowell & Moring LLP *
Hogan Lovells US LLP
Latham & Watkins LLP *
Van Ness Feldman LLP *
Venable LLP *

**Band 3**
Bingham McCutchen LLP *
Bracewell & Giuliani LLP *
Kirkland & Ellis LLP *
Morgan, Lewis & Bockius LLP *

**Band 4**
Akin Gump Strauss Hauer & Feld LLP *
Covington & Burling LLP *
DLA Piper LLP (US) *
Gibson, Dunn & Crutcher LLP *
Goodwin Procter LLP *
Holland & Knight LLP *
Jones Day *
Katten Muchin Rosenman LLP *
Pillsbury Winthrop Shaw Pittman LLP *
Skadden, Arps, Slate, Meagher & Flom LLP & Affiliates *
Vinson & Elkins LLP *
Weil, Gotshal & Manges LLP *

\* Indicates firm / individual with profile.

†ONP = Other Notable Practitioner.

## Band 1

### Arnold & Porter LLP
See profile on p.906

**THE FIRM** This market-leading firm handles a broad spectrum of environmental matters, including enforcement, climate change, natural resources and air and water quality issues. The team also acts for high-profile clients such as Mosaic and Foster Wheeler on risk mitigation and toxic tort litigation. Standout matters include acting for BP as primary environmental counsel in connection with the Deepwater Horizon oil spill. Other major players on the firm's impressive client list include Monsanto, Exide Technologies and Honeywell.

**Sources say:** *"A very fine firm with very good lawyers."* *"Smart, creative, knowledgeable and very responsive."*

**KEY INDIVIDUALS Joel Gross** (see p.867) is described by sources as *"fabulous – a very highly regarded and very skilled attorney."* He advises high-profile clients on a broad range

## Senior Statesmen

**Senior Statesmen: distinguished older practitioners**

| | | |
|---|---|---|
| Garrett Theodore | Covington & Burling LLP * | |
| Macbeth Angus | Sidley Austin LLP * | |
| Nickel Henry V | Hunton & Williams LLP * | |

## Leading Individuals

**Band 1**

| | |
|---|---|
| Bergeson Lynn L | Bergeson & Campbell PC (ONP)† * |
| Brownell F William | Hunton & Williams LLP * |
| Buente David | Sidley Austin LLP * |
| Bumpers William | Baker Botts LLP |
| Gross Joel M | Arnold & Porter LLP * |
| Knauss Chuck | Katten Muchin Rosenman LLP |
| Milch Thomas | Arnold & Porter LLP * |
| Starr Judson | Venable LLP * |
| Steinberg Michael W | Morgan, Lewis & Bockius LLP * |

**Band 2**

| | |
|---|---|
| Albrecht Virginia S | Hunton & Williams LLP * |
| Biles Blake A | Arnold & Porter LLP * |
| Bourdeau Karl S | Beveridge & Diamond PC * |
| Elliott E Donald | Covington & Burling LLP * |
| Field Andrea Bear | Hunton & Williams LLP * |
| Gaynor Kevin | Vinson & Elkins LLP * |
| Green Douglas H | Venable LLP * |
| Hagen Paul | Beveridge & Diamond PC * |
| Hird David B | Weil, Gotshal & Manges LLP * |
| Holmstead Jeffrey R | Bracewell & Giuliani LLP * |
| Lewis William | Morgan, Lewis & Bockius LLP * |
| Ludwiszewski Raymond B | Gibson, Dunn & Crutcher LLP * |
| Menotti David E | Crowell & Moring LLP * |
| Raher Patrick M | Hogan Lovells US LLP |
| Stoll Richard G | Foley & Lardner LLP (ONP)† |
| Wehrum William L | Hunton & Williams LLP * |
| Weinberg David B | Wiley Rein LLP (ONP)† * |

**Band 3**

| | |
|---|---|
| Banks Jim | Hogan Lovells US LLP |
| Bieke James R | Sidley Austin LLP * |
| Carr Donald A | Pillsbury Winthrop Shaw Pittman LLP |
| Drake Stuart AC | Kirkland & Ellis LLP * |
| Gutter Samuel | Sidley Austin LLP * |
| Kastner Ken | Hogan Lovells US LLP |
| Kirsch Laurence S | Goodwin Procter LLP * |
| Martella Roger | Sidley Austin LLP * |
| Nakayama Granta Y | Kirkland & Ellis LLP * |
| Penna Richard A | Van Ness Feldman LLP * |
| Schwartz Richard | Crowell & Moring LLP * |
| Segal Scott H | Bracewell & Giuliani LLP * |
| Strand Margaret | Venable LLP * |
| Thompson Chet M | Crowell & Moring LLP * |

**Band 4**

| | |
|---|---|
| Broome Shannon | Katten Muchin Rosenman LLP * |
| Edwards Amy L | Holland & Knight LLP * |

| | |
|---|---|
| Giannotto Michael S | Goodwin Procter LLP * |
| Hanson John N | Beveridge & Diamond PC * |
| Harvey Sheila M | Pillsbury Winthrop Shaw Pittman LLP |
| Holewinski Kevin | Jones Day * |
| Jackson Thomas C | Baker Botts LLP * |
| Jennings Deborah E | DLA Piper LLP (US) * |
| Liebesman Lawrence | Holland & Knight LLP * |
| Luxton Jane C | Pepper Hamilton LLP (ONP)† * |
| Martel Jonathan | Arnold & Porter LLP * |
| O'Brien Claudia | Latham & Watkins LLP * |
| Rhyne Katherine L | King & Spalding LLP (ONP)† * |
| Solow Steven P | Katten Muchin Rosenman LLP |
| Sotsky Lester | Arnold & Porter LLP * |
| Tenpas Ronald J | Morgan, Lewis & Bockius LLP * |
| Walsh William J | Pepper Hamilton LLP (ONP)† * |
| Webster Timothy K | Sidley Austin LLP * |
| Wigmore Michael B | Bingham McCutchen LLP * |

**Band 5**

| | |
|---|---|
| Bulleit Kristy | Hunton & Williams LLP * |
| Bumpers Heidi | Jones Day * |
| Coddington Kipp A | Mowrey Meezan Coddington Cloud (ONP)† |
| Daneker Michael D | Arnold & Porter LLP * |
| Danish Kyle W | Van Ness Feldman LLP * |
| Davidson Jeffrey J | Manatt Phelps & Phillips LLP (ONP)† * |
| Friedland David | Beveridge & Diamond PC * |
| Gray Peter | McKenna Long & Aldridge LLP (ONP)† * |
| Hatcher Julia | Latham & Watkins LLP * |
| Israel Brian D | Arnold & Porter LLP * |
| Jaeger Lisa M | Bracewell & Giuliani LLP * |
| Jezouit Debra | Baker Botts LLP * |
| Kaufman Bonni F | Holland & Knight LLP * |
| Meade Kenneth | WilmerHale (ONP)† * |
| Quarles Steven P | Crowell & Moring LLP * |
| Rawson William | Latham & Watkins LLP * |
| Seley Peter | Gibson, Dunn & Crutcher LLP * |
| Stanko Joe | Hunton & Williams LLP * |
| Steinway Daniel M | Baker Botts LLP * |
| Votaw James G | Manatt Phelps & Phillips LLP (ONP)† * |
| Zawatoski Gina M | DLA Piper LLP (US) * |

**Up-and-coming individuals**

| | |
|---|---|
| Franco Sandra | Bingham McCutchen LLP * |
| Nathanson Kirsten L | Crowell & Moring LLP * |
| Traylor Patrick D | Hogan Lovells US LLP |

**Associates to watch**

| | |
|---|---|
| Foley Allison D | Venable LLP * |

of compliance and enforcement matters. The outstanding **Thomas Milch** (see p.882) wins high praise from observers, who describe him as *"top-notch,"* *"a creative* thinker and a really smart lawyer, with a lot of experience negotiating settlements."* He is currently leading the firm's work for BP on the Deepwater Horizon spill. **Blake Biles** (see p.852) is a highly experienced environmental attorney. His practice places particular emphasis on chemical regulatory work. **Lester Sotsky** (see p.893) is known for his expertise in toxic torts. "*He did an absolutely fantastic job. He is practical, smart and focused, and works well as part of a team,*" one source enthused. The well-respected **Jonathan Martel** (see p.362) offers considerable experience advising on CAA matters. He is "*very smart, personable and talented – he is going to be a star,*" sources say. **Brian Israel** (see p.871) is recognized for his in-depth knowledge of natural resources damages litigation, and is singled out for his involvement in the Deepwater Horizon matter. "*He's very smart, with an ability to synthesize a broad array of issues and come up with sound strategies.*" **Michael Daneker**'s (see p.859) toxic tort experience includes matters arising from medical monitoring, personal injury and property damage actions. "*He's a very conscientious lawyer who approaches problems in a practical way,*" sources say.

### Hunton & Williams LLP
**See profile on p.2517**

**THE FIRM** This environmental practice group is best known for its representation of major utilities in air and water matters. The team has extensive expertise in advising on the CAA, the CWA and the Endangered Species Act, and has recently handled groundbreaking cases relating to these statutes. It also regularly undertakes work relating to climate change, mining and chemicals, waste and petroleum. It also has significant capabilities acting on high-profile environmental litigation. Major clients include the Utility Air Regulatory Group, the Waters Advocacy Coalition, Arch Coal and Southern Company.

**Sources say:** "*One of the top firms for environmental law. They are knowledgeable, incredibly client-focused and technically sound.*" "*Top-notch legal help. We need the best to help us and advocate for us, and they really are outstanding.*"

**KEY INDIVIDUALS** Market-leading **William Brownell** (see p.288) is recognized as "*one of the deans of the environmental Bar*" and "*one of the top air lawyers in the country.*" He has particularly strong expertise in advising on the effects of the CAA on utilities. **Virginia Albrecht** (see p.849) is a major player in the field of water and natural resources. She represents a range of development companies, state and local agencies, trade corporations and mining companies. **Andrea Bear Field** (see p.862) wins praise

for her "*fantastic*" CAA expertise. She is highlighted by observers for her extensive experience in the field of environmental law. Clients applaud **William Wehrum** (see p.898) for his "*great technical abilities and understanding of how Washington works – he is a great advocate. He is outstanding on development regulations and understands compliance issues and litigation.*" **Joe Stanko** (see p.894) is known for his strengths as a lobbyist. According to sources, "*he does a very good job of coordinating different trade association issues; he has a good sense of the politics of these issues and also a good sense of judgment.*" **Kristy Bulleit** (see p.855) has an excellent reputation for her work on water-related matters and permitting. Commentators describe her as a "*very effective, intelligent, articulate advocate.*" **Henry Nickel** (see p.884) has decades of experience handling regulatory and enforcement work, including matters relating to the CAA and the NEPA. "*He knows this area of the law in incredible depth, is creative and develops unique theories. Because he has practiced in this area for so long, he has a terrific reputation and receives a great deal of respect from all,*" say clients.

### Sidley Austin LLP
**See profile on p.1264**

**THE FIRM** The environmental team at Sidley Austin is known for its impressive expertise in clean air matters. Notable highlights include acting for diesel engine manufacturer Cummins on CAA compliance issues relating to vehicle emissions, fuels and additives. The large group has an excellent reputation for its prowess in litigation, and regularly defends utilities in clean air matters in the district courts. It also represents federal, state and local governments and national trade associations, regularly undertaking work relating to the energy, transport, telecommunications and banking sectors.

**Sources say:** "*Sidley Austin's senior partners are the best in the business and are always available when you need them.*" "*Very strong competitors on clean air work.*"

**KEY INDIVIDUALS David Buente** (see p.855) is viewed as one of the top environmental practitioners in DC. He recently acted for Coronet Industries on a high-value dispute arising from wrongful death and personal injury claims. **James Bieke** (see p.852) is an experienced Superfund specialist who acted on the Hudson and Housatonic River Superfund sites. "*He is one of the most brilliant and hard-working people I've ever met. He is very good at understanding the science behind environmental law,*" one source said. **Samuel Gutter** (see p.867) is a well-regarded CAA and Superfund expert with extensive experience within the EPA. **Roger Martella** (see p.362) earns high praise from market sources for his environmental work. "*He is one of the next generation. He has a body of government experience and good insight, and is regarded as a credible person to represent industry people.*" **Timothy Webster** (see p.898) has an impressive reputation for his work as an environmental litigator. His capabilities are strengthened by considerable experience in the DOJ. "*One of the preeminent names in environment law,*" **Angus Macbeth** (see p.879) brings invaluable experience to his role at the firm. He has in-depth knowledge of a broad

range of environmental matters, including the CAA and CWA, developed during his four decades of work in the field.

## Band 2

### Baker Botts LLP
**See profile on p.2427**

**THE FIRM** Baker Botts is well known for its prowess in energy and environmental law. In the refining and petrochemicals field, the team advises major clients on product liability lawsuits and toxic torts. In highlights, it recently defended a large agricultural company in a large-scale toxic tort class action. Other areas of expertise include renewable energy, upstream oil and gas, midstream energy and Superfund work. The team has acted for various companies on sediment contamination matters at some of the country's biggest Superfund sites.

**Sources say:** "*Their work is consistently good, and they are able to design practical solutions.*" "*We use them for our high-profile and high-importance issues.*"

**KEY INDIVIDUALS** Leading environmental practitioner **William Bumpers** has recently handled a number of high-profile challenges to EPA rulings, including challenging CAA regulations on behalf of leading cement companies. "*He is absolutely top-notch. He has broad experience, a sharp intellect and a deep roster of contacts in the environmental field. He grasps technical concepts quickly, and is held in very high regard,*" say interviewees. **Thomas Jackson** (see p.871) advises on a broad range of environmental matters, including water quality, natural resources, toxic torts and litigation. **Debra Jezouit** (see p.872) focuses on CAA litigation, compliance and development. Sources say she "*is extremely bright and talented, and knows the regulations backwards.*" **Daniel Steinway** (see p.894) is recognized for his strength in Superfund and cost recovery matters. According to sources, he is "*a go-to lawyer and a tireless rainmaker.*"

### Beveridge & Diamond PC
**See profile on p.907**

**THE FIRM** This environmental law firm earns praise from clients and peers alike for the breadth of its expertise. The team is known for its strength in litigation, and has successfully acted for such leading players as Chevron, Bayer CropScience and Sunoco. It recently represented Statoil in a multimillion-dollar litigation concerning its deepwater oil and gas leases in the Gulf of Mexico. It also advises multinational clients in the retail, pharmaceutical, biotechnology and electronics sectors on environmental matters relating to their products.

**Sources say:** "*An extremely talented group of passionate environmental specialists.*" "*They have an enormous practice and every one of them is knowledgeable.*"

**KEY INDIVIDUALS Karl Bourdeau** (see p.853) is very highly regarded in the DC market. "*He is extraordinarily thoughtful, provides extremely thorough analysis from both a legal and a practical perspective, generates creative legal arguments and has great foresight,*" clients say. **Paul Hagen**

(see p.867) is known for his work on international environmental law and e-waste. Market commentators consider him a *"very talented guy who is smart and cutting a pretty high profile – he is very active in the community."* Representative highlights include advising the Information Technology Industry Council on negotiations relating to Basel Convention regulations for the disposal of electronic equipment. **John Hanson** (see p.868) is an experienced litigator with extensive private and public sector experience. His practice includes representing leading companies and associations before the EPA and the Department of the Interior. **David Friedland** (see p.863) advises a variety of manufacturers, waste management entities and petroleum refineries on a broad spectrum of clean air matters. Observers say he *"is very knowledgeable about engineering issues and their ramifications, pays good attention to detail and is very prompt."*

## Crowell & Moring LLP
See profile on p.910

**THE FIRM** This practice group is widely recognized for its strength in endangered species, mining and renewable energy work. The team is comprised of lawyers with significant government experience, and regularly handles matters involving the Departments of Agriculture, Labor, Interior and Energy, and the EPA. The firm represents an impressive range of major clients, and recently acted for leading coal company Peabody Energy on a dispute relating to accessing private personal records, which was a landmark case in the mining industry.

**Sources say:** *"I was impressed by their strong regulatory analysis and litigation instincts." "They have superb expertise in endangered species work."*

**KEY INDIVIDUALS David Menotti** (see p.881) has a prominent reputation for his work relating to the Federal Insecticide, Fungicide, and Rodenticide Act (FIFRA). He is praised by clients for providing *"excellent legal, regulatory, tactical and technical advice on complicated issues."* Sources say **Richard Schwartz** (see p.891) is *"absolutely exceptional, practical and smart."* His recent work includes acting for a number of agricultural trade associations on a challenge to EPA regulations relating to the CAA. **Chet Thompson** (see p.417) *"deserves a lot of credit – he will be one of the real movers and shakers of the coming years,"* say market commentators. He advises major trade associations on clean air matters. **Steven Quarles** (see p.886) is widely recognized for his expertise in endangered species and natural resources law. One source enthused: *"He is probably one of the country's experts on endangered species activities. He has a great sense of what's possible – he's a good policy lawyer. I'd rate him extremely highly for strategic thinking."* The promising **Kirsten Nathanson** (see p.883) handles complex multiparty Superfund matters for high-profile clients. Sources describe her as *"logical and calm, with a very analytical approach."*

## Hogan Lovells US LLP

**THE FIRM** The highly regarded environment group at Hogan Lovells undertakes a broad variety of work, encompassing commercial transactions, compliance, regulatory and legislative matters and litigation. The team acts for clients in the transport, chemicals, energy, minerals and manufacturing sectors, including Bostik, NV Energy, Lockheed Martin, Edison Mission Energy and SUEZ ENVIRONNEMENT. In highlights, it recently represented Daimler Trucks North America and Detroit Diesel in relation to a successful challenge to nonconformance penalties granted to the benefit of a competitor under the CAA.

**KEY INDIVIDUALS Patrick Raher** handles complex legislative and rulemaking matters. *"It was excellent dealing with him. He's very good at strategizing, is diplomatic and has great people skills,"* said one interviewee. **Jim Banks** is well known for his experience in Superfund and hazardous waste work, as well as CWA litigation. Observers highlight **Ken Kastner** as *"a smart and thoughtful lawyer."* He recently advised Bostik on a number of environmental matters relating to water quality. **Patrick Traylor** is currently advising BHP Billiton's New Mexico operating coal mining company on litigation brought by various nongovernmental organizations under the RCRA, the Surface Mining Control and Reclamation Act, the Endangered Species Act and the NEPA.

## Latham & Watkins LLP
See profile on p.446

**THE FIRM** This firm handles high-value environmental litigation and regulatory work, and has significant experience acting on compliance and consumer product class action defense. Other key areas of focus include climate change, energy and infrastructure work, and pesticide registration. Recent highlights include advising Australia Pacific LNG on environmental issues relating to the $8.5 billion financing for an LNG project in Queensland, Australia. The firm also acts for such high-profile names as The Carlyle Group, ExxonMobil and CropLife America.

**Sources say:** *"Phenomenal expertise in the FIFRA arena."*

**KEY INDIVIDUALS Claudia O'Brien** (see p.884) is praised for her knowledge of water issues and her *"very smart and thoughtful"* approach. She recently advised Edison Mission Energy on regulatory matters affecting power plants. **William Rawson** (see p.887) has an increasingly prominent reputation for his environmental practice. *"He is amazingly approachable, takes the interests of his clients very much to heart and makes sure that they are well represented,"* commentators say. **Julia Hatcher** (see p.868) advises on a broad range of environmental legislation, including the CWA, the Toxic Substances Control Act (TSCA) and the Superfund law.

## Van Ness Feldman LLP
See profile on p.926

**THE FIRM** This team acts for clients across a wide range of industries, including utilities, power and leisure and tourism, offering expertise in climate change, hazardous waste, air pollution, and permitting and compliance for energy projects. It recently advised Alaska Energy Authority on environmental, energy and resource matters relating to the construction of a major dam project. Other highlights include acting for American Electric Power on regulatory matters relating to coal-fired power plants.

**Sources say:** *"I have full confidence in them – they provide superb and professional communications and quality service."*

**KEY INDIVIDUALS Richard Penna** (see p.885) is *"fantastic – very responsive and very knowledgeable."* His clients include Toyota, which he recently advised on air regulatory matters. **Kyle Danish** (see p.301) is recognized for his expertise in climate change, CAA legislation and other environmental policy matters.

## Venable LLP
See profile on p.927

**THE FIRM** Venable is recognized for its work advising on permitting and compliance, as well as policy development and rulemaking under federal environmental legislation. Recent highlights include assisting mining clients in obtaining permits for major projects, and advising on the TSCA and other air, energy and solid waste regulations. The firm's major clients include Perdue Farms, Monumental Sports & Entertainment and the National Oil Recyclers Association.

**Sources say:** *"I am extremely impressed with Venable. They are dedicated to their clients and deliver results in a timely and affordable fashion."*

**KEY INDIVIDUALS Judson Starr** (see p.894) has an excellent reputation for his expertise in environmental law and white-collar crime. His clients have included a major cruise line, a farm equipment manufacturer and a federal district judge. The highly regarded **Douglas Green** (see p.867) heads the firm's environment practice. *"He has an impressive breadth and depth of knowledge of environmental law and strong strategic and political skills, and he is very effective at advising and representing his clients,"* sources say. Observers highlight **Margaret Strand** (see p.894) for her *"tremendous experience in the field, wise and strategic advice and understanding of project development."* She recently advised Romarco Minerals on the permits for a gold mine in South Carolina. Impressive associate **Allison Foley** (see p.862) advises electric and gas utilities clients on matters arising from environmental legislation. She also acts for a number of trade associations.

## Band 3

## Bingham McCutchen LLP
See profile on p.1515

**THE FIRM** The environment practice group at Bingham McCutchen handles a variety of high-value litigation, and continues to be heavily involved in claims arising out of the Deepwater Horizon oil spill as counsel to Anadarko and numerous other clients. The team also has expertise in renewable and conventional energy project development, electricity generation and transmission, and oil and gas work. Key mandates include advising GE on the environmental issues relating to energy project development across the USA.

**KEY INDIVIDUALS Michael Wigmore** (see p.900) heads the team. *"He impresses us with his detailed knowledge of federal and state natural resources law and its impact on* industry. We are proud to have him on our team," said one client. Natural resources specialist **Sandra Franco** (see p.863) is singled out for her knowledge of the CAA and the Renewable Fuel Standard, and advises on enforcement, counseling and litigation. According to sources, *"she has excellent relations with regulators, which is important to facilitate good outcomes. Her ability to understand legal nuances, communicate them clearly and prepare thorough documents with quick turnaround times is impressive."*

## Bracewell & Giuliani LLP
See profile on p.2429

**THE FIRM** This team advises on a broad spectrum of environmental matters, with a focus on oil and gas work. Recent highlights include advising Cabot Oil & Gas on a number of environmental issues, including an internal investigation into allegations of noncompliance with environmental legislation and company policies. Other high-profile clients include Chesapeake Energy, Halliburton and Alaska Industrial Development & Export Authority.
**KEY INDIVIDUALS Jeffrey Holmstead** (see p.335) is rated for his knowledge of the CAA, and highlighted for his *"deep knowledge of the statutes from both sides, in terms of what industries confront in complying and the government in regulating."* Clean air expert **Scott Segal** (see p.891) attracts praise for his strategic thinking. **Lisa Jaeger** (see p.871) recently advised Hovensa and Tesoro Hawaii on CAA regulations relating to refineries in the US Virgin Islands and Hawaii.

## Kirkland & Ellis LLP
See profile on p.1254

**THE FIRM** Kirkland & Ellis is well known for its strength in environmental litigation. The team handles disputes relating to Superfund matters, government enforcement actions, toxic tort suits, class actions and challenges to federal and state rulemaking. The group also has expertise in compliance and regulatory work, including waste management, air and water permitting and environmental site investigation and cleanup. Major clients include BP, Tronox, GM and Berry Plastics.
**Sources say:** *"A very reputable, cost-effective firm that delivers high-quality legal advice and representation."*
**KEY INDIVIDUALS Walter Lohmann** (see p.878) enjoys a market-leading reputation for his environmental transactions practice, and is praised as *"one of the top transaction lawyers in DC."* He advises a number of private equity investment firms on environmental issues arising from acquisitions and divestitures. **Brian Land** (see p.875) earns praise for his knowledge of the field and his skills as a negotiator. Recent work highlights include providing cleanup counseling to CF Industries. **Stuart Drake** (see p.306) is applauded as *"a true expert in the field of US federal and state motor vehicle regulation. He is a tough negotiator with a strong work ethic who delivers quality work and good value for money."* Observer highlight **Granta Nakayama** (see p.883) as *"a top-flight lawyer with especially good insight and experience in matters involving government enforcement."* He brings considerable industry experience to his role at the firm.

## Morgan, Lewis & Bockius LLP
See profile on p.2246

**THE FIRM** This well-established firm handles a variety of environmental matters for a strong client base. Recent highlights include advising the Clean Air Implementation Project on EPA rulemakings and issues relating to climate change. The group also represented the Mellon Foundation in multimillion-dollar Superfund litigation. Other key clients include Minnesota Power, the Campbell Group and Eastman Chemical.
**KEY INDIVIDUALS** The impressive **Michael Steinberg** (see p.894) has a top reputation for his work as a Superfund expert. According to sources, he is *"a superb lawyer and very bright."* One client said: *"He is a first choice with respect to complex environmental matters."* **William Lewis** (see p.877) leads the firm's clean air practice and has extensive experience acting on clean air matters for trade associations and corporate clients. **Ronald Tenpas** (see p.895) recently advised a real estate developer in Hawaii on the proposed designation of a critical habitat for the purposes of recovering endangered species. *"He has tremendous expertise in this area and is very analytical in his approach,"* commentators say.

## Band 4

## Akin Gump Strauss Hauer & Feld LLP
See profile on p.904

**THE FIRM** This team represents a range of clients in litigation, regulatory and transactional matters. It has strong experience acting for clients in the energy sector on CAA and CWA litigation, and in providing comprehensive transactional support. The firm recently represented Metropolitan Edison in a $500 million CAA citizen suit brought by the states of New Jersey and Connecticut. Other clients include FirstEnergy, AES, Pennsylvania Electric and R.T. Vanderbilt.
**Sources say:** *"Good service, quick turnaround, practical advice and fair prices."*
**KEY INDIVIDUALS** Paul Gutermann heads the environment and natural resources group at the firm.

## Covington & Burling LLP
See profile on p.441

**THE FIRM** This firm has a strong track record in environmental litigation. Its key strengths include enforcement and regulatory work relating to air quality and climate change. The team also has experience advising on oil and gas matters and alternative energy sources.
**Sources say:** *"A very solid practice."*
**KEY INDIVIDUALS** The eminent **Theodore Garrett** (see p.864) cochairs the environment practice group. He has decades of experience acting on high-profile environment and natural resources matters nationwide. **Donald Elliott** (see p.861) joined the firm as senior counsel in January 2013. He has long experience advising on environmental issues, including class action suits, product liability, compliance and regulatory work. Sources say: *"He is very able, talented and widely respected."*

## DLA Piper LLP (US)
See profile on p.1971

**THE FIRM** This team regularly handles environmental matters relating to climate change, endangered species, chemicals, pesticides, wetlands and air and water quality. The group advises on state and federal environmental legislation, and has considerable knowledge of such statutes as the CAA and CWA, the RCRA, and the Endangered Species Act. Clients include Tacoma AG, Calvert Cliffs Nuclear Plant, ExxonMobil and Colonial Oil Group.
**Sources say:** *"They have a superior record in data compensation cases and are very cost-effective."*
**KEY INDIVIDUALS Deborah Jennings** (see p.872) heads the firm's national environmental practice. She represents the developers of the Northeast Maglev, a superconducting magnetic levitation train which will connect Washington, DC and Baltimore. According to clients, **Gina Zawitoski** (see p.902) is *"both business-friendly and very technical, which is an important combination for a lawyer."* She is praised for her knowledge of state and federal environmental legislation.

## Gibson, Dunn & Crutcher LLP
See profile on p.682

**THE FIRM** This firm has notable experience in the environmental sphere, and is rated for its strong focus on toxic tort defense work. It acts for a client base from a range of fields, including the aerospace, pulp and paper and semiconductor industries. Standout matters include representing Chevron in a $19 billion environmental damages action relating to oil production in Ecuador. Other major clients include Intel, Global Automakers, International Paper and Lockheed Martin.
**Sources say:** *"They have helped me tremendously in providing proactive and strategic legal advice."*
**KEY INDIVIDUALS Raymond Ludwiszewski** (see p.878) is described as *"a quality lawyer who is very sharp, and who knows the industry and the players."* He recently acted for a number of groups of automakers and dealers in complex and high-profile climate change litigation. **Peter Seley** (see p.891) is applauded for his strategic approach. His broad experience covers mass and toxic tort defense, appellate litigation and challenges to agency action.

## Goodwin Procter LLP
See profile on p.1522

**THE FIRM** This DC practice group represents major financial institutions, trade organizations and chemical, mining and manufacturing multinationals. It recently advised Mitsubishi on a natural resources damages claim relating to a mining site in New Mexico. Other clients include GE, the National Mining Association, Dow Chemical and Umicore.
**KEY INDIVIDUALS** Observers highlight **Laurence Kirsch's** (see p.874) technical engineering background as a strong asset to his environmental practice. *"He is very good – he knows a ton about the EPA and the way it works internally, which is something that comes with years of experience."* **Michael Giannotto** (see p.865) stands out for his impressive mining expertise. *"He is experienced and edu-*

*cated about the issues; he cares about the details and is always prompt to respond,"* say clients.

## Holland & Knight LLP
See profile on p.1028

THE FIRM This firm has a strong local presence and nationwide reach, and advises on a range of environmental matters. The environmental team is integrated with the firm's zoning and land use group, enabling it to provide comprehensive advice on wetlands, endangered species, brownfields redevelopment and hazardous waste. It advised on the environmental issues for the Stonebridge Carras-Constitution Square brownfields redevelopment site, which is being transformed into a 2.6 million sq ft mixed-use development.

Sources say: *"Top-notch staff and very responsive to client needs."*

KEY INDIVIDUALS Amy Edwards (see p.860) has considerable experience acting for clients including developers, local governments, lenders and corporations. She is singled out for her expertise in brownfields redevelopment. Lawrence Liebesman (see p.877) wins praise from clients for his *"focused and well-researched analysis, and articulate and succinctly written reports."* Bonni Kaufman (see p.873) acts as environmental counsel for developer Picerne Military Housing, advising on deals and financing, lead-based paint and mold abatement, asbestos and insurance recovery.

## Jones Day
See profile on p.919

THE FIRM The DC arm of this international firm advises on toxic torts, climate change, vapor intrusion, hydraulic fracturing and rare earths mining. It has extensive experience in litigation, as well as transactions and regulatory matters. Recent highlights include advising Xcel Energy on a series of global warming lawsuits, including a class action brought by individuals whose property was damaged by Hurricane Katrina. Other clients include Midwest Generation and Bridgestone Americas Holding.

Sources say: *"They are strong transactional lawyers, maintain very strong client relationships and are always available."*

KEY INDIVIDUALS Kevin Holewinski (see p.870) heads the firm's global environmental practice. He recently acted for Ethyl Corporation on a multimillion-dollar property damage case. Heidi Bumpers's (see p.855) extensive environmental expertise spans enforcement cases, Superfund and natural resources matters, and private cost recovery settlements.

## Katten Muchin Rosenman LLP
See profile on p.1253

THE FIRM This firm has strengthened its team with some key lateral hires over the past few years, and is increasingly well known for its broad-ranging environmental practice. It advises on compliance and permitting, EPA rulemakings, criminal environmental enforcement defense and incident response. The team recently acted for the Renewable Fuels Association on high-value litigation relating to the California Air Resources Board's Low-Carbon Fuel Standard. Other key clients include GE, Colonial Pipeline, Air Permitting Forum and United Water.

Sources say: *"We have been highly impressed with the firm. All of the attorneys we've dealt with have been attentive, responsive and very knowledgeable."*

KEY INDIVIDUALS CAA expert Chuck Knauss is a *"big name"* in environmental law. *"He has always impressed us with his creative approach to complicated legal issues. He has a unique way of looking at complex matters and his instincts are typically right on the mark,"* sources say. Shannon Broome (see p.854) *"is a veritable Clean Air Act encyclopedia, and her strong technical engineering background has been an invaluable asset to us as well. Her record of success speaks for itself."* Steven Solow *"has a strong depth of knowledge about how the government approaches cases, and is extremely thorough and efficient."*

## Pillsbury Winthrop Shaw Pittman LLP
See profile on p.2000

THE FIRM This team is known for its expertise advising on environmental matters for both domestic and overseas clients. It places particular focus on international, federal and state rulemaking and regulatory issues. Of late, the group has advised on matters relating to CAA and CERCLA legislation.

Sources say: *"A fantastic firm – we were very happy with their work."*

KEY INDIVIDUALS Donald Carr is a CAA expert who also wins recognition for his expertise in endangered species and wildlife law. He is a seasoned litigator who has handled a number of high-profile environmental criminal cases. Sheila Harvey is well known for her in-depth knowledge of the climate change arena. She heads the firm's climate change and sustainability practice.

## Skadden, Arps, Slate, Meagher & Flom LLP & Affiliates
See profile on p.2008

THE FIRM This team advises on transactional and regulatory matters and litigation. It recently performed an environmental, health and safety compliance review of US Airways' operations and advised on a system-wide compliance program. Other highlights include advising First Solar on NEPA legislation and permitting matters in connection with four major projects.

KEY INDIVIDUALS Don Frost (see p.863) operates a wide-ranging practice in the field, with a strong focus on transactions. He recently represented Marubeni in its $5.3 billion acquisition of Gavilon Group.

## Vinson & Elkins LLP
See profile on p.2459

THE FIRM Vinson & Elkins advises on a spectrum of environmental matters, including government enforcement actions and environmental liabilities related to real estate and business transactions. The team also offers in-depth knowledge of climate change, hazardous waste, toxic substances, wildlife and air and water quality work.

KEY INDIVIDUALS Kevin Gaynor (see p.864) is praised as a *"very smart, very creative"* attorney and a *"very good environmental litigator."*

## Weil, Gotshal & Manges LLP
See profile on p.2015

THE FIRM This firm handles a broad variety of environmental work for such clients as GE, Darling International, Seacor Holdings and Leucadia. It advises on regulatory matters relating to greenhouse gas emissions and climate change, and acts on litigation arising from CERCLA legislation, insurance claims, and civil and criminal liability matters. Recent highlights include advising AES Eastern Energy on the environmental aspects of its reorganization, which included the sale of two power plants to the company's creditors.

KEY INDIVIDUALS David Berz (see p.852) heads the firm's environmental practice. Market commentators say he *"is smart and knowledgeable, and gets things done."* Transactional expert Annemargaret Connolly (see p.858) handles compliance and liability matters relating to corporate and real estate deals. David Hird (see p.869) *"is very practical, knows how to cut through complex issues and can deal with opposing counsel in a very productive way,"* sources say. He has extensive experience in environmental litigation.

## Other Notable Practitioners

One of the leading names in the DC environmental law field, Lynn Bergeson (see p.852) of Bergeson & Campbell PC advises corporations and trade associations on hazardous chemicals work. She has particular expertise in conventional and nanoscale chemical regulatory programs and matters relating to emerging transformative technologies. Thomas Mounteer of Paul Hastings LLP wins high praise from clients for being *"fantastic and practical – he can boil things down really well and help us to quantify and mitigate risk. He can also take large amounts of work and process it quickly."* Richard Stoll of Foley & Lardner LLP is known for his ability to handle large, complex litigation. *"He has provided clear guidance on a myriad of issues – his ability to address issues from a political-legal perspective has been greatly appreciated."* William Thomas (see p.417) of Willkie Farr & Gallagher LLP is recognized for his expertise in climate change, and counts major companies, utilities and financiers among his high-profile clients. The impressive David Weinberg (see p.898) of Wiley Rein LLP earns high praise from clients, who say: *"It is hard to imagine a lawyer who knows the issues better. He is highly accessible, with unrivaled expertise in environmental federal law, toxic materials, Superfund work and the transportation of materials."* Katherine Rhyne (see p.887) brings three decades of experience in environmental law to her role at King & Spalding LLP. She focuses on water issues, including water quality, groundwater, wastewater discharge and drinking water. Jane Luxton (see p.879) of Pepper Hamilton LLP is applauded for her industry-specific knowledge, technical expertise and work related to conflict minerals. Sources say: *"She is very strategic – she has a real-*

*ly insightful ability to integrate emerging policy with the underlying law to help us be prepared."* **William Walsh** (see p.898) heads the DC environment and energy group at Pepper Hamilton LLP. *"He is thorough and detailed, and one of the most technically competent attorneys I've ever dealt with,"* one source said. **Jeffrey Davidson** (see p.859) of Manatt Phelps & Phillips LLP *"offers practical solutions with conviction and superior knowledge."* One client said: *"We enjoy working with him on both a professional and a personal level. He is fair and methodical in his thought*

*process."* Also at Manatt Phelps, **James Votaw** (see p.897) is valued by clients as an *"extremely polished and very good counselor who provides consistently sound advice."* His practice covers air and water quality, hazardous waste and pesticides work, and he has significant experience advising clients who work with nanomaterials. **Kipp Coddington** of Mowrey Meezan Coddington Cloud LLP offers considerable expertise in conventional and renewable energy projects, and regularly advises both developers and investors. **Kenneth Meade** (see p.881) of WilmerHale advises

America's Natural Gas Alliance on environmental matters relating to natural gas and EPA regulation. *"He thoroughly analyzes issues and develops the appropriate strategy to execute for maximum results,"* sources say. **Peter Gray** (see p.866) of McKenna Long & Aldridge LLP is recognized for his work in relation to hazardous materials management. *"He provides a unique outside perspective that our department values. He treats us like his only customer, and is thinking many steps ahead to avoid issues we may face,"* sources say.

# HEALTHCARE

Pharmaceutical/Medical Products Regulatory p.810

Commentary about individuals can be found under their firm's paragraph. If the firm has no paragraph (is not ranked) look at Other Notable Practitioners.

## Healthcare
### Leading Firms

**Band 1**
Akin Gump Strauss Hauer & Feld LLP *
Epstein Becker & Green PC *
Hogan Lovells US LLP
King & Spalding LLP *
McDermott Will & Emery LLP *

**Band 2**
Arnold & Porter LLP *
Crowell & Moring LLP *
Dentons *
Fulbright & Jaworski LLP *
Latham & Watkins LLP *
Ober Kaler Grimes & Shriver *
Powers Pyles Sutter & Verville PC
Reed Smith LLP
Sidley Austin LLP *

**Band 3**
Arent Fox LLP *
Drinker Biddle & Reath LLP *
Foley & Lardner LLP *
Mintz Levin Cohn Ferris Glovsky and Popeo PC *
Morgan, Lewis & Bockius LLP *
Ropes & Gray LLP *

\* Indicates firm / individual with profile.
† ONP = Other Notable Practitioner.

*The edit is in alphabetical order by firm name.*

## Akin Gump Strauss Hauer & Feld LLP
### See profile on p.904

**THE FIRM** Akin Gump continues to be considered one of the premier firms for healthcare work in DC. The firm's health industry team routinely handles matters such as reimbursement, fraud, and legislative and regulatory advocacy and compliance. Recent work includes representing LabCorp in obtaining dismissal of a qui tam case related to the False Claims Act and Anti-Kickback Statute. Other clients include Johnson & Johson, Pfizer, Golden Living Centers and Barnabas Health.

## Healthcare
### Senior Statesmen

**Senior Statesmen: distinguished older practitioners**

| | |
|---|---|
| Thornton D McCarty | Dentons * |

### Leading Individuals

**Band 1**

| | |
|---|---|
| Barry Dennis M | King & Spalding LLP * |
| Brennan Jr John T | Crowell & Moring LLP * |
| Bulleit Jr Thomas N | Hogan Lovells US LLP |
| Carder-Thompson Elizabeth | Reed Smith LLP |
| Fitzgerald Mark R | Powers Pyles Sutter & Verville PC |
| Foster Hope S | Mintz Levin Cohn Ferris Glovsky and Popeo * |
| Hastings Douglas A | Epstein Becker & Green PC * |
| Kalb MD Paul E | Sidley Austin LLP * |
| Keough Christopher L | Akin Gump Strauss Hauer & Feld LLP * |
| Leibenluft Robert F | Hogan Lovells US LLP |
| Lerner Arthur N | Crowell & Moring LLP * |
| Luce Gregory M | Skadden, Arps, Slate, Meagher & Flom * |
| Michaels Joel | McDermott Will & Emery LLP * |
| Miles John J | Ober Kaler Grimes & Shriver |
| Robinson Frederick | Fulbright & Jaworski LLP * |
| Salcido Robert S | Akin Gump Strauss Hauer & Feld LLP * |
| Shapiro Snyder Lynn | Epstein Becker & Green PC |
| Singer Toby G | Jones Day (ONP)† * |
| Sullivan T J | Drinker Biddle & Reath LLP * |
| Vickery Ann Morgan | Hogan Lovells US LLP |

**Band 2**

| | |
|---|---|
| Collier H Guy | McDermott Will & Emery LLP * |
| Dowdell Thomas E | Fulbright & Jaworski LLP * |
| Epstein Steven B | Epstein Becker & Green PC |
| Fox Thomas | Reed Smith LLP |
| Fried Bruce Merlin | Dentons * |
| Gage Larry | Alston & Bird LLP (ONP)† * |
| Goldman Roger | Latham & Watkins LLP * |
| Hamme Joel | Powers Pyles Sutter & Verville PC |
| Jacob John | Akin Gump Strauss Hauer & Feld LLP * |

| | |
|---|---|
| Kurlander Stuart | Latham & Watkins LLP * |
| Loepere Carol | Reed Smith LLP |
| Lopez Jr Jorge | Akin Gump Strauss Hauer & Feld LLP * |
| Lundy Seth H | King & Spalding LLP * |
| Lutes Mark | Epstein Becker & Green PC |
| Lutz Holley Thames | Dentons * |
| Main David | Nelson Mullins Riley & Scarborough (ONP)† * |
| Matyas David E | Epstein Becker & Green PC |
| Reider Alan E | Arnold & Porter LLP * |
| Roth Robert | Hooper Lundy & Bookman PC (ONP)† |
| Sarraille William A | Sidley Austin LLP * |
| Thiel Donna Kalani | King & Spalding LLP * |
| Trilling Helen R | Hogan Lovells US LLP |
| Valiant Carrie | Epstein Becker & Green PC * |
| Weinreich Gadi | Dentons * |
| Young Howard J | Morgan, Lewis & Bockius LLP * |
| Zimmerman Eric | McDermott Will & Emery LLP * |

**Band 3**

| | |
|---|---|
| Baumann Linda | Arent Fox LLP * |
| Berson Susan | Mintz Levin Cohn Ferris Glovsky and Popeo * |
| Hyatt Thomas | Dentons * |
| Meron Daniel | Latham & Watkins LLP * |
| Ogrosky Kirk | Arnold & Porter LLP * |
| O'Hare Patrick K | Ober Kaler Grimes & Shriver |
| Philp Mary Susan | Powers Pyles Sutter & Verville PC |
| Saner Robert J | Powers Pyles Sutter & Verville PC |
| Scully Thomas A. | Alston & Bird LLP (ONP)† * |
| Shuren Allison W | Arnold & Porter LLP * |
| Stephens T Reed | McDermott Will & Emery LLP * |
| Webster Stephanie | Akin Gump Strauss Hauer & Feld LLP * |
| Witten Jesse | Drinker Biddle & Reath LLP * |

**Sources say:** *"They are analytically strong, very responsive and have excellent judgment."*

**KEY INDIVIDUALS Christopher Keough** (see p.345) continues to be recognized as a leading practitioner in the field of Medicare and Medicaid reimbursement and com-

pliance. He recently represented the MD Anderson Cancer Center in a reimbursement appeal to the Department of Health & Human Services. Interviewees say he is *"a high-quality attorney."* **Robert Salcido** (see p.398) recently played the lead role in the aforementioned matter for

LabCorp. Sources report that he is *"extremely diligent, very conscious of delivering value for cost"* and is a *"nationally recognized expert on the False Claims Act."* **John Jacob** (see p.871) is a counselor and litigator who is recognized for his representation of healthcare systems, medical research centers and device manufacturers. His areas of expertise include Medicare reimbursement compliance and coverage disputes. **Jorge Lopez** (see p.878) heads the firm's national health industry practice. Sources describe him as *"a really strong attorney"* and a *"phenomenal adviser in the area where healthcare law intersects with FDA regulations."* He is noted for his expertise in Medicare appeals, lobbying and reimbursement work, and has a recognized specialty in cancer care policy and regulation. **Stephanie Webster** (see p.898) is noted for her *"great understanding of healthcare litigation and case law,"* with sources commenting on her ability to *"grasp and understand complex issues so that they may be synthesized and clearly explained to a court."* She recently represented Adventist Health System in a Medicare reimbursement appeal.

## Arent Fox LLP

See profile on p.905

**THE FIRM** Arent Fox's DC healthcare practice is noted for its excellence in regulatory compliance and government enforcement matters, while it continues to handle transactional work. Clients include public hospital district Broward Health, for which it handles compliance and regulatory matters, ranging from Anti-Kickback Statute compliance to False Claims Act investigations.

**Sources say:** *"Healthcare is a highly regulated area and they know it well. They are very highly reputed and well known."*

**KEY INDIVIDUALS Linda Baumann** (see p.851) focuses on fraud and abuse and compliance, and is recognized for her expertise concerning the Anti-Kickback Statute, the Stark Law and the False Claims Act. Sources say she *"is highly knowledgeable about health law, as well as practical in her approach to issues. She is very responsive and understands her client's needs."*

## Arnold & Porter LLP

See profile on p.906

**THE FIRM** The Arnold & Porter FDA and healthcare practice group receives strong reviews from the DC market. The group advises an impressive range of clients, including Alcon Laboratories, Health Management Associates and the Biotechnology Industry Association, in connection with regulatory, transactional and litigation matters. Recent matters include advising the University of North Carolina at Chapel Hill with respect to the structuring and implementation of a joint venture aimed at establishing new models for the financing and delivery of patient care.

**Sources say:** *"Their commitment to quality legal work is reliable firmwide. Moreover, teams are communicative, collegial and integrated, enabling them to provide superior service."*

**KEY INDIVIDUALS Daniel Kracov** (see p.875) heads the firm's FDA and healthcare practice, and is noted for his expertise on the development, approval and marketing of drugs and medical devices. Sources note that he is *"an expert in his area, easily accessible and a pleasure to work with."* Sources report *"very high regard"* for **Alan Reider** (see p.887), noting that *"he has a very good record built upon resolving problems."* Areas of focus include regulatory compliance, reimbursement and fraud and abuse matters. **Allison Shuren** (see p.892) is noted for her handling of regulatory issues, including Medicare coverage, reimbursement and fraud and abuse counseling. Interviewees report that *"she is a terrific source on coverage and reimbursement"* and *"an industry leader in the medical device space."* **Kirk Ogrosky** (see p.884) is commended by sources for his *"great judgment"* in civil and criminal investigations and enforcement pertaining to the healthcare sector. Interviewees also note that *"his work is exceptional."* **Jeffrey Handwerker** (see p.868) is a litigator with a focus on pharmaceutical pricing and investigations and commercial disputes within the pharmaceutical, medical products and biotechnology industries. Sources say: *"He is a wonderful and very prominent lawyer with a lot of experience."*

## Covington & Burling LLP

See profile on p.441

**THE FIRM** The Covington & Burling healthcare industry group has had another impressive year. The firm offers a deep bench of litigators, transactional attorneys and regulatory experts, and counts pharmaceutical companies, healthcare systems and state governments among its impressive client roster. The group recently represented Genentech in an FDA hearing relating to the proposal to withdraw Avastin's breast cancer indication. Other clients include GlaxoSmithKline and PharMerica.

**Sources say:** *"A high-performing firm. They are very responsive and very smart people."*

**KEY INDIVIDUALS** The *"very wise, very pragmatic"* **Richard Kingham** (see p.347) is considered a market-leading attorney in the pharmaceutical regulatory arena. He recently acted as part of a team representing GlaxoSmithKline in connection with criminal and civil investigations into price reporting, product marketing and regulatory submissions concerning the diabetes drug Avandia. **Peter Safir** (see p.889) wins considerable market praise for his *"outstanding support"* in FDA matters. He recently defended Sanofi before the FDA and federal court in connection with inappropriate generic imitations of its Lovenox product. **Michael Labson** (see p.875) receives strong praise from the market, with sources reporting that he is *"very well connected with what is going on with the FDA"* and *"uses his subject matter expertise to advise clients in a very clear and concise way."* He concentrates his practice on pharmaceutical and medical device regulatory matters. **Ellen Flannery** (see p.862) cochairs the firm's food and drug law practice. She recently advised Glaukos in relation to FDA and EU regulation of medical devices. A client source says: *"She identifies the right lines and then works with us to move forward in our business."* The *"fantastic"* **Gerald Masoudi** (see p.880) cochairs the food and drug law practice alongside Flannery. He routinely assists medical product manufacturers in internal investigations relating to misconduct in product development, and advises clients in relation to FDA inspection reports. **Peter Barton Hutt** (see p.870) is *"the dean of the FDA Bar,"* say sources, who also report that he is *"the most prominent FDA lawyer in DC."* He counts national trade associations for the food and drug industries among his clients.

## Crowell & Moring LLP
See profile on p.910

THE FIRM This firm is recognized for its impressive showing in regulatory, transactional and litigation matters pertaining to the healthcare industry. The group has enjoyed a particularly strong year in complex, multijurisdictional litigation, and has handled a number of fraud and abuse and False Claims Act cases for clients of the caliber of Actavis Group. The team also handles regulatory and compliance matters for clients such as Bon Secours Health System and America's Health Insurance Plans.

Sources say: *"The firm is providing excellent service in a very broad range of areas. I'm very impressed."*

KEY INDIVIDUALS John Brennan (see p.287) has an outstanding reputation for fraud and abuse issues and the False Claims Act. Recent work includes representing an attorney and law firm that are under investigation by the DOJ for their role in issuing a legal opinion to a hospital client in an unprecedented False Claims Act violation case. Sources say that *"he is great"* and *"a true healthcare lawyer."* The *"exceptional"* Arthur Lerner (see p.876) cochairs the firm's healthcare group and is considered a market leader for antitrust and managed care issues. He recently advised Coventry Health Care in connection with antitrust issues surrounding its $7.2 billion acquisition by Aetna.

## Dentons
See profile on p.449

THE FIRM Dentons is widely respected for its handling of a broad range of healthcare matters including Medicare and Medicaid reimbursement, healthcare reform policy, regulatory compliance and transactional matters. Recent matters include providing policy and federal government relations counsel to the California Association of Physician Groups. Other clients include AHIMA and the University of Virginia.

Sources say: *"Smart lawyers who are responsive, practical and results-oriented."*

KEY INDIVIDUALS The *"high-quality"* Bruce Merlin Fried (see p.863) took the lead role in the firm's aforementioned work for the California Association of Physician Groups. He handles regulatory and policy matters, and is described by sources as *"responsive, thoughtful, prepared, creative and bright."* Holley Thames Lutz (see p.878) focuses on Medicare and Medicaid regulatory compliance, including investigations and defense work. Clients say she can *"tackle complex problems and make them understandable to nonlawyers."* Gadi Weinreich (see p.898) heads Dentons's global health and life sciences team. He focuses his practice on investigations and enforcement actions, including fraud and abuse cases. Sources report that *"you can count on his good, solid advice."* The *"smart and capable"* Thomas Hyatt (see p.870) is national chair of the firm's healthcare practice. He is an authority in nonprofit and tax-exempt matters in the healthcare sphere, and recently obtained tax exemption for the Michelle Obama 'Let's Move!' campaign aimed at tackling childhood obesity. The highly experienced and *"extremely knowledgeable"* McCarty Thornton (see p.896) is a venerated figure in DC

healthcare circles. He handles health and life sciences litigation, advocacy, regulatory and transactional matters.

## Drinker Biddle & Reath LLP
See profile on p.2238

THE FIRM The Drinker Biddle healthcare practice group offers a broad, holistic service to clients in the health sector. The group has a noted transactional and finance practice, in addition to its regulatory, governmental investigation and litigation expertise. Recent work includes representing the Lahey Clinic and Northeast Health System with respect to the creation of a new common parent entity. Clients include Geisinger Health System Foundation, Atlantic Health System and Bon Secours Health System.

Sources say: *"The lawyers have a depth of understanding in healthcare business operations and serve healthcare clients effectively."*

KEY INDIVIDUALS T J Sullivan (see p.414) handles transactional and tax exemption matters for healthcare clients. Sources say he is *"a leader in the tax exemption field and there is nobody better that you can go to."* Jesse Witten (see p.901) handles white-collar criminal defense and government investigations with respect to the healthcare sector. Sources say he is *"extremely effective, very pragmatic, thorough, and a very good strategist."*

## Epstein Becker & Green PC
See profile on p.1972

THE FIRM Epstein Becker enjoys an outstanding reputation for healthcare law work. The firm is seen as a go-to shop for transactional, regulatory and litigation work in the industry, and is noted for its handling of Medicare reimbursement work. Recent highlights include the representation of American Air Liquide in its bid for Lincare Holdings, a provider of home oxygen. The team's client roster also includes Community Health Network and Riverside Health System.

Sources say: *"They have a huge collection of star healthcare lawyers."*

KEY INDIVIDUALS The *"terrific"* Douglas Hastings (see p.331) offers transactional and regulatory advice to a broad range of entities in the healthcare sector. Sources report that he *"is nationally known for his healthcare and legal expertise. He is also a visionary, extremely informed as to future implications of the health reform."* Lynn Shapiro Snyder recently acted for the Alliance for Quality Nursing Home Care in connection with the drafting of new Medicare payment methodologies. She represents healthcare systems, pharmaceutical companies and other industry bodies. Steven Epstein is commended by sources for being *"fast and efficient in his management of projects."* He recently advised private equity investor Warburg Pincus with respect to a number of acquisitions of healthcare companies. Mark Lutes led the team in the aforementioned work for American Air Liquide. His broad healthcare practice includes advising on Medicare reimbursement and regulatory diligence. Sources remark that he *"consistently provides excellent service."* David Matyas is *"very well regarded"* for a broad healthcare practice that encompasses regulatory compliance, reimbursement strat-

egy and state and federal fraud issues. Recent clients include Frazier Healthcare, which he advised in relation to regulatory aspects surrounding its creation of a new subsidiary. Carrie Valiant (see p.897) is a *"very strong"* attorney with a focus on fraud and compliance matters in the healthcare sector. She cochairs the firm's healthcare fraud group. Bradley Merrill Thompson heads up the firm's medical device regulatory team. He acts for pharmaceutical and medical device companies in connection with FDA regulatory, reimbursement and clinical trial issues.

## Foley & Lardner LLP
See profile on p.2588

THE FIRM The Foley & Lardner healthcare team handles litigation, regulatory compliance, fraud and abuse matters and transactional work. The group recently acted for Valley Baptist Health System in defense of a False Claims Act whistle-blower action. Other clients include Johns Hopkins Health System and Fresenius Medical Care.

Sources say: *"Their attorneys are competent, have a broad range of expertise and a good understanding of our business."*

KEY INDIVIDUALS Lawrence Vernaglia is chair of the firm's healthcare industry team.

## Fulbright & Jaworski LLP
See profile on p.2435

THE FIRM Fulbright & Jaworski's health law team is recognized for its excellence in Medicare and Medicaid reimbursement issues, while it continues to impress observers in the field of healthcare litigation, investigation and enforcement. Recent trial work includes defending Universal Health Services against allegations that it had violated the False Claims Act by submitting false claims for payment to the Virginia Medicaid program. Other clients include Boston Scientific, Duke University and BJC Healthcare.

Sources say: *"Fulbright truly is a full-service firm and the people I've engaged with have been exceptional in going the extra mile to make sure our questions are answered."*

KEY INDIVIDUALS The *"very highly regarded"* Frederick Robinson (see p.393) is the partner-in-charge of the firm's DC health law practice. He defends healthcare clients in government investigations and prosecutions and advises in connection with regulatory compliance programs. He led the team in the aforementioned defense of Universal Health Services. Thomas Dowdell (see p.860) is a *"great lawyer"* and *"very accessible and reliable in his responses,"* say sources. He focuses on Medicare and Medicaid issues, including coverage and reimbursement.

## Hogan Lovells US LLP

THE FIRM Hogan Lovells is unanimously considered to be a market-leading firm for the entire spectrum of healthcare work. The group is able to leverage the firm's considerable global footprint to offer healthcare organizations seamless cross-border regulatory advice, while it also has outstanding capabilities in the FDA space. The team has continued to advise Pharmaceutical Research and Manufacturers of America (PhRMA) in relation to state legislation affecting the pharmaceutical industry, while the

FDA/medical devices team provides FDA regulatory advice to Biomet. Other clients include Abbott Laboratories and GE Healthcare.

**Sources say:** *"They are strategic thinkers who can alert us to what is over the horizon. They are creative and solution-oriented."*

**KEY INDIVIDUALS** The *"intellectual and practical"* **Thomas Bulleit** receives glowing praise from the market for his regulatory and reimbursement-focused healthcare practice. Sources refer to his *"deep understanding of regulatory healthcare structure."* He provides ongoing regulatory and compliance counsel to GE Healthcare and GE Capital, among other blue-chip clients. **Ann Morgan Vickery** is a *"high-quality lawyer"* with a focus on Medicare and Medicaid regulatory issues. Clients include manufacturers, trade associations and other healthcare providers. **Robert Leibenluft** is *"communicative, knowledgeable"* and *"effective in managing litigation,"* say sources. His clients include LabCorp, for which he provides ongoing regulatory and compliance counsel. **Jonathan Kahan** is co-director of the firm's food, drug, medical device and agriculture group. He is a recognized authority on FDA matters, and is described by sources as *"excellent on the regulatory, litigation and investigation fronts."* Recent work includes providing Biomet with healthcare and FDA regulatory counsel. **Helen Trilling** has a broad healthcare regulatory practice with a focus on fraud and abuse matters. Other areas of excellence include coverage and reimbursement of diagnostic and treatment technologies. She continues to play a lead role in the aforementioned work for GE Healthcare and LabCorp. **David Fox** is recognized for his excellence in the FDA space. A source reports: *"We love the tremendous expertise that David Fox brings to our strategic product development initiatives."* **Meredith Manning** is co-director of the firm's pharmaceutical and biotechnology practice and a specialist in FDA compliance, clinical trial issues and drug approvals standards. Sources say she is *"extremely responsive"* and *"provides practical advice in complex areas that can be very gray under the law."* The highly experienced **Robert Brady** is a *"phenomenal lawyer"* who has earned a tremendous level of market respect over the course of an illustrious career. He counsels life sciences clients with respect to product development, new drug applications and civil and criminal enforcement issues.

## Hyman Phelps & McNamara

**THE FIRM** This firm is recognized for its expertise in FDA issues affecting pharmaceutical and medical device companies. The group is adept at handling development and approval matters for new products, while it continues to be seen as a go-to shop for clients in FDA enforcement situations.

**Sources say:** *"An established FDA boutique."*

**KEY INDIVIDUALS Jeffrey Gibbs** is *"an absolutely fantastic attorney,"* with a focus on FDA regulatory matters, say sources. His prior in-house experience at the FDA makes him well placed to advise on the entire spectrum of approvals, marketing and clinical studies issues affecting his clients.

## King & Spalding LLP
See profile on p.445

**THE FIRM** This firm's health practice maintains its position at the forefront of the DC market. The cross-disciplinary team is able to advise clients in the health sector on the full spectrum of matters, including Medicare reimbursement, lobbying, government investigations and corporate transactions. In addition, the firm has a notable FDA and life sciences regulatory offering, enabling it to excel in pharmaceutical and medical products regulatory work. Recent matters include successfully acting for Oakwood Health System in a Medicare reimbursement review relating to a graduate medical education program. Other clients include Christus Health System, Medtronic and Allergan.

**Sources say:** *"Strong technical knowledge, excellent customer service and broad skills."*

**KEY INDIVIDUALS** The *"terrific"* **Dennis Barry** (see p.279) has an excellent reputation in the Medicare and Medicaid sphere, and is often cited for his expertise in reimbursement issues. He led the team in the matter for Oakwood Health System referred to above. **Edward Basile** (see p.851) chairs the firm's FDA and life sciences group. He advises pharmaceutical and medical device companies in relation to FDA approval strategies, compliance issues and investigations. Sources say: *"He's responsive and very knowledgeable."* **Seth Lundy** (see p.878) is recognized for his handling of Medicare and Medicaid reimbursement and billing advice, fraud, and civil and criminal litigation in the healthcare sphere. Sources say: *"He is great and very practical."* The *"high-quality"* **Donna Thiel** (see p.896) is noted for her handling of Medicare coverage, payment and compliance matters. Her clients include healthcare providers, practitioners and suppliers to the industry.

## Kleinfeld, Kaplan & Becker LLP

**THE FIRM** Kleinfeld, Kaplan & Becker is recognized for its strength in the FDA regulatory space. The team handles litigation against the FDA, and is well regarded for its handling of product approval, advertising and promotional issues. Clients include Purdue Pharma, Forest Laboratories, PhRMA and Unilever.

**Sources say:** *"Very responsive, very solid advice and very knowledgeable."*

**KEY INDIVIDUALS** Dan Dwyer is a key contact.

## Latham & Watkins LLP
See profile on p.446

**THE FIRM** The Latham & Watkins healthcare and life sciences practice is particularly noted for its handling of a full range of litigation and regulatory and transactional matters. The group is also highly rated for its work in the FDA space, routinely handling approvals and other matters for pharmaceutical products and medical devices. The team recently advised Medicis Pharmaceutical in connection with its $2.6 billion sale to Valeant Pharmaceuticals International. Other clients include Boston Scientific and United Healthcare.

**Sources say:** *"They are extremely focused on client relations. Whatever day or time, they made sure reviews were timely and their response was extraordinary."*

**KEY INDIVIDUALS Roger Goldman** (see p.866) receives strong praise for his healthcare fraud defense practice. Sources attest that he has *"tremendous experience with complex and sensitive investigations"* and pay tribute to his *"very good judgment."* **Stuart Kurlander**'s (see p.875) broad practice encompasses fraud and abuse cases, litigation and regulatory and reimbursement matters. One client reports: *"I really enjoyed working with him. He is very capable and I was very impressed."* **John Manthei** (see p.879) is global cochair of the firm's healthcare and life sciences practice. He is considered an authority in the FDA regulatory space, and routinely advises pharmaceutical and medical device companies on approval, marketing and delivery strategies. Sources report: *"John is responsive and always provides sound information, strategy and advice."* **Daniel Meron** (see p.881) is global cochair alongside Manthei. He is a noted healthcare litigator with experience of investigatory matters and trial work at state, federal and appellate level. Recent matters include acting for Mariner Healthcare in a high-stakes litigation stemming from an attempted hostile takeover of the company.

## McDermott Will & Emery LLP
See profile on p.1258

**THE FIRM** This firm is recognized for its outstanding health law practice and its coverage of regulatory, litigation, transactional and government relations matters pertaining to the healthcare sector. Recent matters include advising Blue Cross Blue Shield of Michigan in relation to its investment in AmeriHealth. Other clients include Amgen, Centra Health and Inova Health System.

**Sources say:** *"They are timely and effective in supporting negotiations, and provide an excellent and responsive service with solid advice."*

**KEY INDIVIDUALS** The *"terrific"* **Joel Michaels** (see p.368) heads up the firm's health industry advisory practice. He led the team in the aforementioned matter for Blue Cross Blue Shield of Michigan. Areas of expertise include healthcare insurance and regulation. **Guy Collier** (see p.857) is a *"fantastic lawyer"* who offers *"solid advice, and is timely and effective in supporting negotiations,"* say sources. He handles transactional and regulatory matters for health industry clients. **Eric Zimmerman** (see p.902) specializes in legislative work relating to the healthcare sector. He represents a wide range of healthcare organizations before Congress and the Executive Branch. **Reed Stephens** (see p.894) is recognized for his handling of transactional matters, public policy and regulatory enforcement and compliance. His clients include healthcare systems, wholesalers and financial institutions with an interest in the health sector.

## Mintz Levin Cohn Ferris Glovsky and Popeo PC
See profile on p.1523

**THE FIRM** This firm continues to impress in the healthcare space. The team recently provided Catalyst Health

Solutions with corporate and regulatory counsel with respect to matters such as Medicare compliance and fraud and abuse compliance. The firm represents public and private healthcare providers, manufacturers and investors, such as Ampersand Capital Partners, Miraca Life Sciences and CVS Caremark.

**Sources say:** "*The firm understands the healthcare business, has expertise in the associated legal issues and good relationships with regulators.*"

**KEY INDIVIDUALS Hope Foster** (see p.862) is chair of the firm's healthcare enforcement defense group. Sources say she is "*very knowledgeable and thorough,*" as well as "*practical, resourceful and very responsive.*" **Susan Berson** (see p.852) advises healthcare providers in relation to service agreements, transactional matters and network development programs. Sources describe her as "*incredibly smart and well versed in the law.*"

## Morgan, Lewis & Bockius LLP
See profile on p.2246

**THE FIRM** Morgan Lewis is well regarded for its handling of healthcare and FDA regulatory matters, government enforcement and investigations and M&A pertaining to the healthcare arena. It recently defended Chiesi Farmaceutici and Cornerstone Therapeutics in a case alleging false advertising following claims that a peer-reviewed study distributed by the companies was unreliable. A blue-chip client roster also includes Johnson & Johnson and Pfizer.

**Sources say:** "*They are subject matter experts. They have a viewpoint on everything, which is impressive given the complexity of healthcare law in this country.*"

**KEY INDIVIDUALS Kathleen Sanzo** (see p.399) heads up the firm's FDA and healthcare practice, and is an authority on FDA regulatory and compliance matters. Sources report that she is "*prompt, skilled, experienced and client-focused.*" The "*very prominent*" **Howard Young** (see p.901) is recognized for his expertise in healthcare fraud and abuse and transactional matters. He recently advised Perhenon Capital Partners and the Audax Group in connection with their $81.5 million purchase of a membership interest in Injured Workers Pharmacy. The highly experienced **Gary Yingling** (see p.901) is one of the most respected figures in the healthcare Bar. He represents drug industry clients in a full range of FDA-related matters.

## Ober Kaler Grimes & Shriver
See profile on p.1439

**THE FIRM** This firm has a long history in the healthcare arena and is recognized for its handling of Medicare and Medicaid regulatory issues and fraud and abuse matters. The team's clients include health systems, clinical laboratories, community hospitals and physicians groups.

**Sources say:** "*A fantastic firm with great people.*"

**KEY INDIVIDUALS John Miles** is highly regarded for his focus on governmental investigations and antitrust law within the healthcare sector. His clients include health systems, hospitals and physician practices. **Patrick O'Hare** represents healthcare clients on corporate and transaction-

al matters, including M&A, joint ventures and business and tax planning.

## Powers Pyles Sutter & Verville PC

**THE FIRM** Powers Pyles Sutter & Verville is noted for its handling of Medicare and Medicaid reimbursement, fraud and abuse matters, and transactional and litigation work. Clients include hospitals and health systems, academic medical centers and healthcare sector trade associations.

**Sources say:** "*A very good and solid practice.*"

**KEY INDIVIDUALS Mark Fitzgerald** handles Medicare fraud and abuse, healthcare contracting and corporate law relevant to healthcare clients. Observers comment that he is "*a very fine lawyer.*" **Mary Susan Philp** advises clients with respect to federal and state regulatory matters and Medicare and Medicaid reimbursement. Clients include hospitals, health systems and other healthcare providers. **Robert Saner**'s areas of expertise include fraud and abuse and Medicare reimbursement issues. In addition, he regularly advises healthcare clients in connection with legislation and regulation. **Joel Hamme** is an authority on litigation, regulation and reimbursement issues affecting the long-term care sector. Clients include the providers of nursing homes and rehabilitation hospitals.

## Reed Smith LLP

**THE FIRM** The Reed Smith life sciences health industry group has a strong reputation for regulatory and transactional matters and litigation. Recent matters include achieving a successful settlement on behalf of Voyager HospiceCare with respect to a long-running qui tam suit filed by the DOJ. Other clients include HCR ManorCare, HealthSouth, Kindred Healthcare and Omnicare.

**Sources say:** "*The firm was able to provide not only legal advice based on substantive knowledge, but practical advice on how to position arguments and communicate them.*"

**KEY INDIVIDUALS Elizabeth Carder-Thompson** is recognized by clients for her "*excellent service and quality of work.*" She has an outstanding reputation for healthcare regulatory law, and counts hospitals, physicians, hospices and nursing homes among her key clients. **Thomas Fox** took the lead in the aforementioned matter for Voyager HospiceCare. Sources say he is "*very practical and holds strong relationships in the healthcare space.*" **Carol Loepere** chairs the firm's life sciences health industry group. She handles regulatory and legislative issues affecting life sciences and healthcare companies. One interviewee reports: "*She has been spectacularly efficient in coordinating and orchestrating our regulatory issues across multiple jurisdictions.*"

## Ropes & Gray LLP
See profile on p.1528

**THE FIRM** Ropes & Gray covers the full spectrum of regulatory law, litigation and transactional work in the healthcare sphere. Much of the firm's work is slanted toward policy, legislative and regulatory matters, and it has been particularly active for trade associations such as the National Association of Public Hospitals in a range of issues stemming from the implementation of the Affordable Care Act.

The firm also has a highly reputed FDA regulatory and enforcement practice, with clients including Medtronic and Pfizer.

**Sources say:** "*They are delightful to work with. We are thrilled with their performance.*"

**KEY INDIVIDUALS Alan Bennett** focuses on FDA matters, including pharmaceutical approval, marketing and promotion, and is a recognized expert on the Hatch-Waxman Act and life-cycle management. Sources refer to his "*unparalleled knowledge*" and report that he is "*an encyclopedia in this area.*" **Gregory Levine** also focuses on FDA regulation of pharmaceuticals and medical devices. Representative clients include Pfizer, Johnson & Johnson, Stryker and Human Genome Sciences, among others.

## Sidley Austin LLP
See profile on p.1264

**THE FIRM** Sidley Austin continues to impress observers in the DC healthcare arena. The firm handles the full range of matters, including regulatory compliance, litigation, governmental investigations and FDA-related work. Recent matters include representing Celgene in a DOJ investigation concerning the promotion and marketing of products. The firm has also acted for SXC Health Solutions in its $4.4 billion merger with Catalyst Health Solutions. Other clients include Genentech, GlaxoSmithKline, Pfizer and Roche Diagnostics.

**Sources say:** "*Sidley Austin has deep expertise in healthcare matters.*"

**KEY INDIVIDUALS** Investigation and enforcement specialist **Paul Kalb** (see p.872) is a "*client-focused, results-oriented and pragmatic*" attorney, and an "*extremely good strategic thinker,*" say sources. He heads the firm's national healthcare practice and is global coordinator of its life sciences practice. The "*very prompt and responsive*" **Raymond Bonner** (see p.853) heads the firm's food, drug and medical device compliance and enforcement practice. His areas of focus are governmental investigations, enforcement and litigation. **Coleen Klasmeier** (see p.347) heads the firm's food, drug and medical device regulatory practice and is an authority on FDA regulatory matters. Sources attest that she is "*a walking dictionary of FDA law.*" **William Sarraille** (see p.889) handles a broad spectrum of healthcare matters, including Medicare and Medicaid reimbursement, internal investigations, litigation and healthcare contracting. Sources describe him as a "*terrific regulatory healthcare lawyer*" with a "*wide range of experience.*" **Scott Bass** (see p.280) heads the firm's global life sciences team and is recognized for his handling of FDA regulatory and enforcement issues. He is particularly noted by market observers for his representation of dietary supplement manufacturers.

## Skadden, Arps, Slate, Meagher & Flom LLP & Affiliates
See profile on p.2008

**THE FIRM** Skadden enters the rankings this year after receiving warm praise for its work in the pharmaceutical and medical device regulatory space. Recent matters include negotiating an FDA consent decree on behalf of

Terumo Cardiovascular Systems. Other clients include Amylin Pharmaceuticals and Human Genome Sciences.

**Sources say:** *"The team is very diligent, thorough, careful and thoughtful."*

**KEY INDIVIDUALS Gregory Luce** (see p.359) is highly regarded for his handling of civil and criminal litigation and regulatory matters in the healthcare industry. Clients describe him as *"one of the preeminent healthcare litigators in the country,"* with *"a sophisticated national practice."* **John Bentivoglio** (see p.851) represents pharmaceutical, medical device and biotechnology manufacturers in FDA and healthcare regulatory matters. Market observers describe him as *"a compliance expert with fantastic judgment in advising, and very well connected in government and the private sector."*

### Other Notable Practitioners

**Mark Heller** (see p.868) of Goodwin Procter LLP is an expert on FDA regulatory matters, assisting clients with a range of issues including strategy development, pre-market submission and compliance and enforcement matters. Sources attest that he is *"an extraordinary FDA lawyer who has achieved recognition throughout the FDA and regulated industry."* **Michael Gaba** (see p.863) of Holland & Knight LLP represents medical device and biotechnology companies before the FDA, the Centers for Medicare & Medicaid Services (CMS) and Congress. Sources say: *"He is a top CMS attorney."* **Toby Singer** (see p.892) of Jones Day focuses on antitrust matters in the healthcare industry. She recently advised CIGNA on antitrust aspects relating to its $3.8 billion acquisition of HealthSpring. **Thomas Scully** (see p.891) of Alston & Bird LLP focuses his practice on healthcare regulatory and legislative matters. Sources say he is *"a leader in this industry."* At the same firm, **Larry Gage** (see p.863) handles public sector and nonprofit health law and policy. His clients include teaching hospitals, medical schools, and integrated health and hospital systems. **David Main** (see p.879) of Nelson Mullins Riley & Scarborough LLP concentrates on healthcare transactional work, health policy and government relations issues. **Richard Cooper** of Williams & Connolly LLP is a litigator with a focus on the FDA space. Sources describe *"a fantastic litigator"* who is *"very familiar with agencies and the laws."* **Robert Roth** of Hooper Lundy & Bookman PC advises clients on payment, compliance and licensing issues with respect to Medicare and Medicaid. He also handles healthcare litigation at the state and federal trial and appellate court levels. The *"insightful, articulate and creative"* **Bruce Manheim** recently joined WilmerHale from Ropes & Gray. Manheim advises pharmaceutical and biotech companies on legislative and regulatory issues. Sources describe him as *"highly knowledgeable, competent and collegial."*

# IMMIGRATION

Commentary about individuals can be found under their firm's paragraph. If the firm has no paragraph (is not ranked) look at Other Notable Practitioners.

| Immigration |
| --- |
| **Leading Firms** |

| Band 1 |
| --- |
| Duane Morris LLP * |
| Greenberg Traurig, LLP * |
| Morgan, Lewis & Bockius LLP * |

| Band 2 |
| --- |
| Fragomen, Del Rey, Bernsen & Loewy, LLP * |

| Band 3 |
| --- |
| Baker & McKenzie * |
| Hogan Lovells US LLP |
| Maggio & Kattar PC |

*\* Indicates firm / individual with profile.*
*† ONP = Other Notable Practitioner.*

## Band 1

### Duane Morris LLP
See profile on p.2239

**THE FIRM** The Duane Morris immigration practice in Washington, DC has an excellent reputation in the field. The team handles a wide range of immigration matters for companies, including immigrant and nonimmigrant visas, compliance and related training, and the consequences of corporate reorganizations. Individuals are similarly well served, and the firm has expertise in immigration-related criminal matters, asylum and removal, and related litigation.

**Sources say:** *"They are always available, and they know our policies and practices."*

**KEY INDIVIDUALS Denyse Sabagh** is highly regarded for her diverse set of skills. Sources describe her as the *"best of the best,"* noting that *"she is just extraordinary."* She counsels individuals and companies in all areas of immigration and naturalization including EB-5 cases, I-9 compliance, corporate immigration strategy, outbound immigration and removal defense.

### Greenberg Traurig, LLP
See profile on p.1024

**THE FIRM** Greenberg Traurig's business immigration and compliance practice group has earned a stellar reputation among market commentators. Clients come from a large cross-section of industries and the group has notable experience in oil and gas, manufacturing and entertainment. The diverse practice handles a broad spectrum of immigration matters and related litigation. It has seen a significant amount of compliance work, and has lately been managing and working alongside numerous regional centers. Clients include ARAMARK and CVS Caremark.

**Sources say:** *"The business immigration team at Greenberg is extremely knowledgeable and provides wonderful customer service."*

**KEY INDIVIDUALS Laura Foote Reiff**'s (see p.887) *"immigration expertise is unparalleled,"* according to one happy client, and she is considered *"one of the foremost immigration lawyers in the country."* She focuses her practice on business immigration matters and employment compliance. Reiff has recently been involved in creating and managing regional centers, and in challenging the Stop Wage and Program Rules proposed by the DOL. **Martha Schoonover** (see p.890) is described as *"very talented,"* and sources say: *"She makes us feel like we're her only client."* She deals with a broad range of employment-related visa petitions and permanent residency applications. Schoonover also has particular expertise in guiding clients

| Immigration |
| --- |
| **Senior Statesmen** |

| Senior Statesmen: distinguished older practitioners | |
| --- | --- |
| Virtue Paul | Baker & McKenzie |

| **Leading Individuals** | |
| --- | --- |

| Band 1 | |
| --- | --- |
| Hammond Denise | Hammond Immigration Law, P.C. (ONP) † |
| Pelta Eleanor | Morgan, Lewis & Bockius LLP * |
| Sabagh Denyse | Duane Morris LLP |

| Band 2 | |
| --- | --- |
| Benach Andres | Benach Ragland LLP (ONP) † |
| Bord Eric S | Morgan, Lewis & Bockius LLP * |
| Cooper Bo | Fragomen, Del Rey, Bernsen & Loewy, LLP |
| Greenfield Andrew B | Fragomen, Del Rey, Bernsen & Loewy, LLP |
| Reiff Laura Foote | Greenberg Traurig, LLP * |
| Schoonover Martha J | Greenberg Traurig, LLP * |
| Stern Elizabeth Espin | Baker & McKenzie |
| Trow Steve | Trow & Rahal (ONP) † |
| Yanni Palma | Dickstein Shapiro LLP (ONP) † * |

| Band 3 | |
| --- | --- |
| Alexander Jim | Maggio & Kattar PC * |
| Asaad Peter F. | Immigration Solutions Group, PLLC (ONP) † |
| Band Ian P | Hunton & Williams LLP (ONP) † * |
| Dukic Aleksandar | Hogan Lovells US LLP |
| Elliot Thomas | Lichtman & Elliot, PC (ONP) † |
| Freedman Roberta | Clark Hill PLC (ONP) † |
| Lawrence Nancy M | Odin, Feldman & Pittleman, PC (ONP) † |
| Lurie Dawn M | Sheppard, Mullin, Richter & Hampton (ONP) † |
| Melmed Lynden | Berry Appleman & Leiden LLP (ONP) † |
| Pederson Jan | Pederson Immigration Law Group PC (ONP) † |
| Peters M Beth | Hogan Lovells US LLP |
| Rahal Linda | Trow & Rahal (ONP) † |

through government audits and in developing compliance programs.

## Morgan, Lewis & Bockius LLP
See profile on p.2246

**THE FIRM** This integrated immigration and nationality services practice is able to assist clients with their global immigration needs. The Washington, DC team leads the immigration compliance practice and also handles outbound visa petitions and inbound visa and residency applications. The group attracts clients from a variety of industries such as energy, pharmaceuticals, IT and engineering.

**KEY INDIVIDUALS Eleanor Pelta** (see p.885) is *"an insightful, careful thinker,"* according to sources. She has recently been involved in assisting clients in the retail sector with the transfer of high-level executives. She also advises corporate clients on immigration strategy and blanket visa petitions. **Eric Bord** (see p.853) heads the compliance and risk management practice and has extensive experience in employment-based visas. He services clients in a wide range of industries including technology, energy and the media.

## Band 2

## Fragomen, Del Rey, Bernsen & Loewy, LLP
See profile on p.1974

**THE FIRM** This global immigration boutique offers services in a full range of matters including compliance, consular representation, and immigrant and nonimmigrant visa petitions. Clients are also attracted to the firm for its robust outbound visa capabilities.

**KEY INDIVIDUALS Andrew Greenfield** assists a range of companies, organizations and institutions with their visa requirements, and advises them on compliance and the immigration ramifications of corporate restructurings. Sources confirm his aptitude for handling high-volume accounts. **Bo Cooper** is praised by sources for his strong command of developments at the US Citizenship & Immigration Services. Observers comment that he has *"a very effective approach to solving problems at the highest levels."*

## Band 3

## Baker & McKenzie
See profile on p.435

**THE FIRM** Baker & McKenzie's global immigration and mobility practice group continues to work with large corporate clients to help coordinate their immigration needs. The team handles the visa needs of a mobile workforce, and assists in ensuring corporate compliance with immigration regulations, including training HR staff.

**KEY INDIVIDUALS Elizabeth Espin Stern** is highly regarded for her work in business immigration. She repre-

sents multinational companies across a variety of industry sectors and helps them to develop immigration policies and to arrange necessary visas and work permits. **Paul Virtue** has an excellent and long-standing reputation in the immigration law arena. Sources describe him as *"very thoughtful, approachable and downright smart"* and they admire his *"expansive and comprehensive knowledge and hugely effective delivery."* Virtue is knowledgeable in all areas of immigration law, particularly with regards to immigration regulation, policy and legislation.

## Hogan Lovells US LLP

**THE FIRM** Hogan Lovells offers a full service for business immigration and export control matters. The team has particularly sophisticated expertise in dealing with the immigration consequences of M&A. The group counsels a number of universities alongside other clients such as Boxee, Human Rights First and Dr Pepper Snapple Group, in a range of immigration matters.

**Sources say:** *"We have found them to be very thorough and very detail-oriented. They know the process."*

**KEY INDIVIDUALS Beth Peters** assists clients in sponsoring immigrant and nonimmigrant individuals. She also has the expertise to advise clients on the intersection between immigration law and other areas including M&A and export control. Peters recently acted for Kroenke Sports to obtain P-1 status for key players and support staff. **Aleksandar Dukic** is appreciated by clients for being *"very comprehensive in his analysis, and able to explain things to anyone,"* while he is also admired for being *"focused, professional and sharp."* He assists a range of companies, organizations and universities with their immigrant and nonimmigrant visa needs, in addition to providing policy advice.

## Maggio & Kattar PC

**THE FIRM** The team at this boutique immigration firm deals with the whole spectrum of immigration matters including family and employment-based work, naturalization and removal. Lately, the firm has seen an increase in compliance cases as more employer audits are issued. Maggio & Kattar has also been successful in acquiring approval for a number of difficult extraordinary ability cases.

**KEY INDIVIDUALS Jim Alexander** (see p.849) is *"a class act, and a very smart lawyer,"* according to sources. He offers services in a broad range of immigration law matters and has particular expertise in handling immigration issues which arise for same-sex couples and HIV-positive individuals.

## Other Notable Practitioners

**Andres Benach** of Benach Ragland LLP is *"phenomenal"* and *"a very strong advocate"* according to sources. Having just set up his own office, he continues to impress commentators. He is best known for his removal defense work, and the focus for his practice is on litigation. The *"very*

*sharp and very knowledgeable"* **Roberta Freedman** of Clark Hill PLC has strong expertise in J-1 petitions, and she assists many physicians, researchers and academics with their immigration needs. **Palma Yanni** (see p.901) of Dickstein Shapiro LLP is a *"top-notch lawyer,"* according to interviewees. Her skills and expertise cover the full spectrum of immigration, naturalization and removal matters. Yanni is particularly well known for her work representing physicians and researchers. **Thomas Elliot** of Lichtman & Elliot, PC is described as *"very sharp and very well respected"* by sources. He is highly regarded as a strong litigator and is frequently associated with removal and naturalization proceedings. Elliot is an expert in dealing with criminal elements of immigration cases. **Denise Hammond** (see p.868) of Hammond Immigration Law, P.C. focuses her practice on work-related visas and employer compliance. Sources highly recommend her for her personal attention, and she *"wastes no time in telling you straight. Her advice is spot-on and has served us well."* Clients include K12 and BioStat Solutions. **Steve Trow** of Trow & Rahal is unique in being able to advise clients on tax-efficient immigration policies. He also assists many clients in the investor visa categories. Trow is highly regarded as a long-standing practitioner in the field, with an impressive depth of experience. **Peter Asaad** of Immigration Solutions Group, PLLC is considered to be *"very measured and thoughtful,"* according to commentators. Asaad assists US and international corporations with their visa and compliance matters. He also handles immigration matters for investors and entrepreneurs. **Ian Band** (see p.850) of Hunton & Williams LLP is a *"high-caliber and strong practitioner"* according to sources. The focus of his practice is on business and family-related immigration, often with respect to the entertainment industry. **Nancy Lawrence** of Odin, Feldman & Pittleman, PC is praised for her *"extraordinary breadth of experience."* She is consulted on a range of employment and family-based immigration and nationality issues. **Dawn Lurie** of Sheppard, Mullin, Richter & Hampton LLP is recommended for her work on worksite enforcement issues and I-9 compliance. She acts for small and large companies and also for investors and entrepreneurs. **Jan Pederson** of Pederson Immigration Law Group PC is recognized as a very strong advocate for her clients, particularly where difficult consular process issues arise. Pederson also acts in deportation proceedings, for J-1 physicians and for investors. **Linda Rahal** of Trow & Rahal is described as a *"really creative problem solver"* by sources. She is well known for her work assisting many athletes with their visa needs. **Lynden Melmed** of Berry Appleman & Leiden LLP is a former chief counsel of US Citizenship & Immigration Services who is praised for his ability to deal with politically sensitive immigration matters. Sources relate that he is *"very straightforward – he tells it like it is, and is forthcoming especially when dealing with complicated issues."*

## INSURANCE INSURER

Commentary about individuals can be found under their firm's paragraph. If the firm has no paragraph (is not ranked) look at Other Notable Practitioners.

### Insurance: Insurer
### Leading Firms

**Band 1**
Crowell & Moring LLP *
Steptoe & Johnson LLP
Wiley Rein LLP *

**Band 2**
Chadbourne & Parke LLP *
Lewis Baach PLLC
McDermott Will & Emery LLP *
Shipman & Goodwin LLP
Troutman Sanders LLP

**Band 3**
Drinker Biddle & Reath LLP *
Hogan Lovells US LLP
Thompson, Loss & Judge LLP

\* Indicates firm / individual with profile.
†ONP = Other Notable Practitioner.

### Insurance: Insurer
### Leading Individuals

| Band 1 | |
| --- | --- |
| Dixon Gary | Troutman Sanders LLP |
| Raim David | Chadbourne & Parke LLP * |
| Rocap III James | Steptoe & Johnson LLP |
| Standish Daniel J | Wiley Rein LLP * |
| Warin Roger | Steptoe & Johnson LLP |
| Warner Margaret H | McDermott Will & Emery LLP * |

| Band 2 | |
| --- | --- |
| Baach Martin | Lewis Baach PLLC |
| Brunner Thomas W | Wiley Rein LLP * |
| Foggan Laura A | Wiley Rein LLP * |
| Gerstein John R | Troutman Sanders LLP |
| Hendler Clifford B | Crowell & Moring LLP * |
| Hensler David | Hogan Lovells US LLP |
| Ianniello Antonia B | Steptoe & Johnson LLP |
| Judge Thomas J | Thompson, Loss & Judge LLP |
| Kalish Paul W | Crowell & Moring LLP * |
| Lee Harry | Steptoe & Johnson LLP |
| Loss Lewis K | Thompson, Loss & Judge LLP |
| Ruggeri James | Shipman & Goodwin LLP |

| Band 3 | |
| --- | --- |
| Ahari Leslie | Troutman Sanders LLP |
| Andrews Walter J | Hunton & Williams LLP (ONP)† * |
| Christensen Wallace A | Troutman Sanders LLP |
| Constine Jonathan | Troutman Sanders LLP |
| Gische David | Troutman Sanders LLP |
| Hockenbury John C | Drinker Biddle & Reath LLP * |

| Band 4 | |
| --- | --- |
| Cronic Jason P | Wiley Rein LLP * |
| Duchelle John W | Troutman Sanders LLP |
| Gordon Jack B | Lewis Baach PLLC |
| Lopatto Mary | Cozen O'Connor (ONP)† * |
| Ruby Joseph | Lewis Baach PLLC |
| Smethurst Ryan | McDermott Will & Emery UK LLP * |
| Topol David H | Wiley Rein LLP * |

## Band 1

### Crowell & Moring LLP
See profile on p.910

THE FIRM Clients are unanimous in their praise for this firm, which has firmly established itself as a prominent presence on the insurer side of disputes. The team is particularly known for handling mass tort coverage litigation, and also deals with significant reinsurance matters. Recent highlights include representing AmEx Assurance in a high-profile lawsuit concerning accidental death and disability benefits under a travel insurance policy. The group regularly represents major industry players, including United Educators, Transatlantic Reinsurance and Fireman's Fund. **Sources say:** "The firm's overall professionalism, commitment to succeeding, and treatment of clients as equals forges a partnership that delivers hands-on results."
**KEY INDIVIDUALS** Clients highlight **Clifford Hendler's** (see p.868) prowess in developing productive relationships with opposing counsel, which assists in reaching favorable solutions. He has been involved in a number of complex insurance disputes on behalf of Allianz/Fireman's Fund. Client favorite **Paul Kalish** (see p.873) is lauded as being "extremely responsive and prepared for emergency, with an encyclopedic knowledge of insurance coverage." He has recently represented Everest Reinsurance in coverage issues related to the liquidation of Midland Insurance.

### Steptoe & Johnson LLP

THE FIRM Widely recognized as one of the best insurance carrier practices in DC, this group is chosen by clients for its depth of insurance expertise, which extends to a global reach. It regularly represents major insurers in the most sophisticated cases, such as acting for Hartford Accident & Indemnity and New England Reinsurance on torts filed by former NFL players relating to concussions and head trau-

ma. Other major clients include Zurich, The Travelers Companies and Swiss Re.
**Sources say:** "It is a very good group of talented lawyers that we've continued to use on a regular basis. They have great knowledge across the board and are very sensitive to the company's particular outlook on cases."
**KEY INDIVIDUALS** James Rocap is unanimously acknowledged as an "outstanding insurance coverage lawyer" and "one of the smartest guys around." He has recently played a lead role on behalf of Travelers in a coverage dispute involving Tyson Foods. According to peers, **Roger Warin** is a "formidable adversary," while clients report that "there's nothing he hasn't handled." He recently represented two Chartis Insurers in a lawsuit surrounding Secure Conveyancing Insurance Policy (SCIP). **Antonia Ianniello** recently represented two Zurich affiliates in a

complex coverage case. According to one client, she "brings the perfect blend of legal expertise, excellent communication skills and sensitivity to our corporate customers, with a common-sense, practical assessment of how to achieve the best result." **Harry Lee** has a healthy reputation among peers for his courtroom litigation skills. He chairs the firm's global insurance and reinsurance practice group, and focuses on representing major insurers in long-tail claims involving mass tort-related bankruptcies.

### Wiley Rein LLP
See profile on p.928

THE FIRM This high-quality firm offers industry clients impressive depth, with over 50 lawyers offering expertise in insurance coverage matters. The team is particularly singled out for its leading professional liability practice, but also has extensive expertise in reinsurance, healthcare, appellate and regulatory insurance matters. Major clients include XL, CNA and Chubb Group; the team recently represented Chubb subsidiary Federal Insurance in a $56 million D&O dispute against US Bank.
**Sources say:** "We have continued working with them and, in fact, made them our primary outside coverage firm due to the consistently excellent level of representation."
**KEY INDIVIDUALS** "Amazing litigator" **Daniel Standish** (see p.894) has a fine reputation for his expertise in D&O liability claims. He is highly respected by peers, who single him out as a target for referrals. **Thomas Brunner** (see p.854) is a known and respected presence in the coverage litigation space, where he concentrates on asbestos, pharmaceutical, product liability and emerging insurance issues. An "acknowledged expert in the field," **Laura Foggan** (see p.862) has a strong reputation in pollution-related exposure cases and general liability matters. She has recently assisted the Complex Insurance Claims Litigation Association, a trade group of property casualty insurers that often intervenes in insurance appeals. **David Topol** (see p.896) focuses on D&O and professional liability work. He recently represented Ullico Casualty in arbitration relating to surety bonds underwriting. **Jason Cronic** (see p.858) is an "excellent attorney" with a practice devoted to D&O and professional liability coverage work. He has represented several prominent clients, including General Star Indemnity and XL Professional.

## Band 2

### Chadbourne & Parke LLP
See profile on p.1962

THE FIRM This reinsurance-centric practice retains a healthy reputation in the international arbitration space, having vast experience in the London and Bermuda markets. Most notably, the firm won a $275 million arbitration on behalf of Travelers subsidiary St. Paul Reinsurance, which was seeking to recover unpaid losses. Other key clients include Zurich and RenaissanceRe.

**Sources say:** *"You can trust the reinsurance team to do an excellent job for your company and collaborate well with you and your team."*

**KEY INDIVIDUALS David Raim** (see p.389) has *"a very strong reputation"* in the reinsurance arbitration arena. Clients particularly praise his *"ability to manage complex and unusual issues."*

### Lewis Baach PLLC

**THE FIRM** This established practice maintains a strong focus on insurance and reinsurance matters. The team is recognized for its long-standing expertise in dealing with the London market and with toxic tort coverage and casualty claims. For example, the firm has recently been involved with significant asbestos liability disputes on behalf of Lloyd's underwriters.

**Sources say:** *"The firm has a high standard and its attorneys are very willing to explain positions and debate points."*

**KEY INDIVIDUALS Martin Baach** maintains an excellent reputation in the market for his deep experience and expertise in the field. He has played a key role in a number of big-ticket environmental liability coverage matters. **Jack Gordon** appears frequently in reinsurance arbitrations taking place in the London market. **Joseph Ruby**'s practice concentrates on commercial, insurance and reinsurance disputes, both domestically and internationally.

### McDermott Will & Emery LLP

See profile on p.1258

**THE FIRM** This firm has a wealth of experience in various fields of insurance law, from healthcare to reinsurance. The team has had a landmark year, seeing through the long-standing World Trade Center insurance cases to settlement. The firm has also handled a series of matters for Allianz, including coverage disputes, asbestos and environmental cases, and reinsurance claims, the latter arising from brain injury and wrongful death cases involving a series of former NFL players.

**Sources say:** *"The firm has deep knowledge, is very strategic and has excellent collaboration with the client."*

**KEY INDIVIDUALS** Deeply respected practice head **Margaret Warner** (see p.898) is described as a *"no-nonsense lawyer"* and *"a common-sense businessperson, practical in her view of what needs to get done."* She has taken on a lead role in all the firm's most significant representations. New entry **Ryan Smethurst** (see p.893) has been heavily involved in negotiating the main World Trade Center-related settlement. He is praised by clients for his collaborative and strategic approach.

### Shipman & Goodwin LLP

**THE FIRM** Sources are quick to identify this compact team as a fast-growing presence on the insurer side in DC. It handles the full range of insurance disputes. The team continues to serve as institutional counsel to The Hartford, recently representing it in an insurance coverage case concerning complex bankruptcy issues.

**Sources say:** *"A very sophisticated group, willing and able to engage in sophisticated and cutting-edge transactions."*

**KEY INDIVIDUALS** Admired by peers and clients alike, **James Ruggeri** is considered *"an absolute star"* for his *"smart, aggressive, strategic, efficient and productive"* style. His *"vigorous"* approach has earned him the prominent role of regularly representing The Hartford in high-end insurance matters.

### Troutman Sanders LLP

**THE FIRM** This team remains a favorite among clients thanks to its long-standing expertise in representing insurers. The firm covers a diverse range of issues, including D&O, E&O, healthcare and medical malpractice claims. Clients include prominent insurance companies such as CNA and Chubb Group. A recent highlight was the team's win for Federal Insurance in a D&O coverage dispute against Ryerson.

**KEY INDIVIDUALS** Peers and clients are unanimous in their praise of **Gary Dixon**, who is highlighted as a great litigator and strategist. He is renowned for his expertise in D&O and in property and casualty liability matters. **John Gerstein** is praised for his effective courtroom skills. He focuses on D&O and professional liability work. **Leslie Ahari** commands a tremendous amount of respect and recently represented Indian Harbor Insurance in a D&O matter against Quellos Group. Litigator **Wallace Christensen** has a strong reputation for winning difficult cases. He recently acted for Federal Insurance, as mentioned above. **Jonathan Constine** is a respected litigator who recently joined the firm from Hogan Lovells. He focuses on assisting clients with D&O liability matters. **David Gische** is a well-regarded attorney whose client portfolio includes XL Insurance and HCC Insurance Holdings. D&O expert and client favorite **John Duchelle** is praised for his thoughtfulness and ability to achieve results for his clients.

## Band 3

### Drinker Biddle & Reath LLP

See profile on p.2238

**THE FIRM** This established team focuses on insurance coverage matters relating to professional liability and D&O matters. The firm is also known in the market for its expertise in dealing with property and casualty, life insurance, and health and accident insurance cases. The practice has further expertise in the regulatory and transactional insurance space.

**Sources say:** *"Very good coverage lawyers and effective advocates for their clients."*

**KEY INDIVIDUALS** The firm's managing partner **John Hockenbury** (see p.869) is held in high regard by his peers. He is experienced in handling D&O and other professional liability insurance coverage matters.

### Hogan Lovells US LLP

**THE FIRM** This international firm has a healthy insurance presence in Washington, DC. In addition to representing prominent insurers such as Chubb Group and The Travelers Companies, the practice is heavily involved in health insurance on behalf of such companies as United Health and CareFirst. Recent highlights include successfully representing Federal Insurance in a sophisticated class action.

**Sources say:** *"They have been great partners. They are knowledgeable in this area and they have been very effective advocates at both the trial and appellate level."*

**KEY INDIVIDUALS** *"Amazing litigator"* **David Hensler** is highly regarded by peers, who describe him as a *"terrific"* and *"sophisticated"* trial lawyer with deep experience in commercial disputes.

### Thompson, Loss & Judge LLP

**THE FIRM** This firm continues to stand out for its solid insurance practice. The group's remit ranges from D&O and professional liability claims to sophisticated insurance bad faith disputes. Clients applaud the team's collaborative approach and high-quality work product.

**Sources say:** *"They are very attentive and thorough, the quality of their written work is excellent, and they are reasonably priced, too which is amazing."*

**KEY INDIVIDUALS Thomas Judge** is held in high regard by a series of commentators. His insurance practice focuses on D&O and professional liability coverage cases. **Lewis Loss** is singled out as a *"masterful negotiator"* and is praised by clients for achieving good results. While offering the full range of insurance services, he focuses particularly on D&O and professional liability claims.

### Other Notable Practitioners

**Walter Andrews** (see p.850) heads Hunton & Williams LLP's insurance litigation and recovery practice. He handles a range of insurance coverage and bad faith disputes. **Mary Lopatto** (see p.878) recently joined Cozen O'Connor from Chadbourne & Parke. She is held in high regard by peers as an established and highly respected reinsurance practitioner.

## INSURANCE POLICYHOLDER

Commentary about individuals can be found under their firm's paragraph. If the firm has no paragraph (is not ranked) look at Other Notable Practitioners.

| Insurance: Policyholder | |
|---|---|
| **Leading Firms** | |
| **Band 1** | |
| Covington & Burling LLP * | |
| **Band 2** | |
| Dickstein Shapiro LLP * | |
| Jenner & Block LLP * | |
| **Band 3** | |
| Gilbert LLP * | |
| Morgan, Lewis & Bockius LLP * | |
| Orrick, Herrington & Sutcliffe LLP * | |
| Perkins Coie LLP | |
| **Band 4** | |
| Kelley Drye & Warren LLP * | |

| **Leading Individuals** | |
|---|---|
| **Band 1** | |
| Buchanan John | Covington & Burling LLP * |
| Dolin Mitchell F | Covington & Burling LLP * |
| Gilbert Scott D | Gilbert LLP * |
| Greaney William | Covington & Burling LLP * |
| Heintz John | Dickstein Shapiro LLP * |
| Masters Lorelie S | Jenner & Block LLP * |
| Skinner William P. | Covington & Burling LLP * |
| **Band 2** | |
| Goodman Saul | Covington & Burling LLP * |
| Jacobs Matthew L | Jenner & Block LLP * |
| Jacobs Robert P | Perkins Coie LLP |
| Kellner Leon B | Perkins Coie LLP |
| Kolman Mark H | Dickstein Shapiro LLP * |
| Lenhart Benedict M | Covington & Burling LLP * |
| Mayerson Marc S | Orrick, Herrington & Sutcliffe LLP |
| Milone Richard D. | Kelley Drye & Warren LLP * |
| Murray James R | Dickstein Shapiro LLP * |
| Plumer Mark J | Orrick, Herrington & Sutcliffe LLP |
| Reidy Andrew | Dickstein Shapiro LLP * |
| Thompson Gary | Reed Smith LLP (ONP)† |
| Zevnik Paul A | Morgan, Lewis & Bockius LLP * |
| **Band 3** | |
| Buchman Barry I | Gilbert LLP * |
| Chefitz Daniel E | Morgan, Lewis & Bockius LLP * |
| Engh Anna | Covington & Burling LLP * |
| Gallozzi Marialuisa | Covington & Burling LLP * |
| Hecht Philip H | Law Office of Philip H. Hecht PLLC (ONP)† |
| Kazakis Georgia | Covington & Burling LLP * |
| Klein David F | Orrick, Herrington & Sutcliffe LLP |

*\* Indicates firm / individual with profile.*

*†ONP = Other Notable Practitioner.*

## Band 1

### Covington & Burling LLP
See profile on p.441

**THE FIRM** Covington & Burling remains the undisputed leader of DC's insurance policyholder Bar. Its attorneys regularly handle the full range of coverage disputes ranging from sophisticated mass torts to high-stakes professional liability claims. The team has remained involved in some of the most significant long-standing cases over recent years, and has maintained its involvement in market-shaping matters with its representation of the NFL in litigation against over 30 insurers concerning head injuries to several players. Other key clients include BP, ExxonMobil and Northrop Grumman.

**Sources say:** *"An excellent law firm that has got it all: top partners, a deep bench and they get the job done."*

**KEY INDIVIDUALS** The *"very good"* John Buchanan (see p.855) has long-standing experience in insurance coverage litigation, particularly in relation to environmental, pharmaceutical and financial matters. He has recently handled environmental coverage matters for Conrail. *"Terrific"* lawyer Mitchell Dolin (see p.305) remains at the forefront of the industry while continuing to act as practice chair. He has played a lead role in the firm's representation of the NFL in lawsuits against multiple insurers. William Greaney (see p.325) is praised by sources for his *"very strong knowledge of complex legal issues and knowledge of how to present them to both the court and opposing counsel."* He has recently represented Northrop Grumman against The Travelers Companies in a significant environmental insurance coverage matter. William Skinner (see p.407) is considered a *"true expert"* in insurance policyholder disputes and peers are quick to refer work to him. He has taken on a lead role in counseling Chiquita Brands International in long-standing coverage cases. Saul Goodman (see p.866) is lauded as someone who is *"able to successfully juggle numerous matters."* He is renowned in the market for his insurance work pertaining to toxic tort and pollution issues. According to one source, Benedict Lenhart (see p.876) *"maintains an excellent balance between being a zealous advocate for his clients and being a good adversary to deal with."* He has recently represented ExxonMobil and Conrail. Marialuisa Gallozzi (see p.864) is admired by sources for her knowledge and experience in dealing with general liability insurance coverage disputes. Georgia Kazakis (see p.873) earns acclaim from impressed clients for possessing *"a great command of issues and facts."* Anna Engh (see p.861) comes highly recommended as a strong litigator with insurance law expertise. She has recently acted for UnitedHealth in a number of professional liability coverage lawsuits.

## Band 2

### Dickstein Shapiro LLP
See profile on p.911

**THE FIRM** This firm's long-standing expertise in coverage issues earns considerable acknowledgment throughout the market. The group is especially active in the areas of political risk insurance and insurance brokerage, and in the entertainment and sports industries. An impressive client portfolio features Estée Lauder, Beebe Medical Center and Amgen.

**Sources say:** *"They are aggressive and creative – and the carriers know that they are willing to fight to get the coverage for which their insureds bargained."*

**KEY INDIVIDUALS** *"Excellent coverage lawyer"* John Heintz (see p.332) *"brings practicality to the situation and seeks to secure a resolution that is in the best interest of the client,"* according to sources. He has been particularly active in professional liability claims. James Murray (see p.883) enjoys a strong reputation as an *"excellent trial lawyer"* with the ability to earn immediate respect in a courtroom. He recently achieved a victory on behalf of drug manufacturer Immunex in a coverage dispute. Andrew Reidy (see p.887) is appreciated by clients for being *"very levelheaded and very helpful in laying out the pros and cons and various courses of action."* He has represented Caterpillar in its $120 million asbestos insurance coverage action. Peers praise Mark Kolman (see p.875) as *"a very good appellate arguer, with a very good command of facts and extremely smart."*

### Jenner & Block LLP
See profile on p.1252

**THE FIRM** This firm has strength in insurance coverage work across the country on behalf of policyholders. The team has particular expertise in D&O liability claims, as well as handling asbestos-related liability, business interruption, cyber losses and data breach coverage cases. Its DC lawyers have been heavily involved in a series of nationwide matters including the representation of Tyson Foods in Delaware and Olin in Missouri.

**Sources say:** *"In extremely adverse circumstances, they accomplished what would appear to be a miracle. But it was not a miracle, just clever strategy followed by extremely hard work which all bore fruit."*

**KEY INDIVIDUALS** Popular practitioner Lorelie Masters (see p.880) is held in the highest esteem by peers, who *"think the world of her"* and consider her *"an awesome lawyer and person."* She has served as lead counsel for a number of prominent clients, including New Century Liquidating Trust, Tyson Foods and Olin. *"Fabulous"* litigator Matthew Jacobs (see p.871) is applauded by clients, who say he *"commits his soul to your cause."* He recently represented Maximus in an E&O liability insurance coverage lawsuit where damages claimed exceeded $80 million.

## Band 3

### Gilbert LLP
See profile on p.914

THE FIRM This firm continues to be known for the depth of its insurance services, covering mass tort and D&O liability. The group is also regarded for its work in asbestos-related liability cases. The team represents corporate and individual policyholders in a wide range of industries, from pharmaceutical and medical to food.
Sources say: *"They work very hard to deliver terrific results for the client."*
KEY INDIVIDUALS **Scott Gilbert** (see p.865) enjoys a solid reputation in the insurance market as a *"very talented practitioner."* He focuses on bankruptcy, professional liability and product liability insurance matters. Rising star **Barry Buchman** (see p.855) is *"one of the most earnest and dedicated young lawyers seen on that side of the Bar in a long time,"* according to a peer. He has recently been involved in consumer insurance class action disputes.

### Morgan, Lewis & Bockius LLP
See profile on p.2246

THE FIRM This global firm has a well-established DC practice representing policyholders and often plays a lead role in large asbestos coverage disputes. The team has recently acted on behalf of Thorpe Insulation in sophisticated insurance and reorganization issues arising from its asbestos-related bankruptcy. A number of high-profile clients require the group's insurance expertise, including Kimberly-Clark, PepsiCo and Transocean.
Sources say: *"They are very punctual and reliable. Their work product is always very thorough."*
KEY INDIVIDUALS *"Exceptionally good, creative lawyer"* **Paul Zevnik's** (see p.431) practice focuses on captives, financial restructuring and tax bankruptcy insurance cases. Peers note that *"if you are in a case with him, you'd better buckle up as he is really, really tough."* Client favorite **Daniel Chefitz** (see p.857) *"listens to the client's thoughts rather than telling the client what he needs to do."* He regularly acts on behalf of PepsiCo and Zimmer Holdings.

### Orrick, Herrington & Sutcliffe LLP
See profile on p.1994

THE FIRM The 18-strong DC arm of this established nationwide policyholder practice has been involved in a variety of coverage disputes. Recent highlights include the representation of Sony in coverage claims arising from one of the largest data breach cases in history. Other key clients include CITGO, Canadian Pacific Railway and Instagram.
Sources say: *"The firm has quality attorneys and technical staff that are recognized within the insurance industry as very strong professionals who will be well prepared to represent their clients."*
KEY INDIVIDUALS **Marc Mayerson** enjoys a healthy reputation among peers, who know him for his work in D&O and professional liability matters. He has recently represented former directors of Solyndra regarding their D&O insurance in relation to government criminal investigations. Market commentators underline **Mark Plumer's** *"very valuable"* knowledge and experience in insurance coverage, in particular environmental coverage. His practice concentrates on environmental liability, corporate transactional issues and professional liability. The *"outstanding"* **David Klein** is admired by clients for *"his extensive experience."* Recently, he has worked on significant environmental liability and media bankruptcy cases.

### Perkins Coie LLP
See profile on p.2548

THE FIRM This firm is singled out by sources for its growing presence in the DC insurance market. A noteworthy engagement is the group's involvement in a large-scale environmental action in West Virginia on behalf of long-standing client Alpha Natural Resources. The team also handles a range of insurance issues including D&O, cybercrime, data and privacy breach coverage cases.
KEY INDIVIDUALS **Robert Jacobs** is praised by clients for his thoughtful and meticulous approach. He often appears in arbitrations with an international scope. The widely respected **Leon Kellner** earns acclaim for his ability to get to the heart of complex issues and understand the important issues for his clients.

## Band 4

### Kelley Drye & Warren LLP
See profile on p.1985

THE FIRM This firm is identified as a significant player in coverage disputes on behalf of policyholders. The group's core expertise concentrates on D&O liability, environmental issues, construction and media-related matters. Major clients include Warner Bros., The Thermos Company and Hensel Phelps Construction.
Sources say: *"Their lawyers are knowledgeable, professional, and excellent communicators."*
KEY INDIVIDUALS **Richard Milone** is described as *"very precise and persuasive"* by clients. He is acknowledged for his insurance law expertise in connection to IP and false advertising issues.

### Other Notable Practitioners

**Gary Thompson** of Reed Smith LLP is a *"go-to insurance coverage attorney"* for clients. He has recently been involved in coverage matters relating to the hospitality industry, most notably on behalf of the Pyramid Hotel Group. He is also active in the areas of first-party property and business interruption insurance, professional liability and fidelity bonds. **Philip Hecht** recently left K&L Gates to open his own solo practice. He is regarded by commentators as *"a terrific coverage lawyer."*

# INTELLECTUAL PROPERTY

Commentary about individuals can be found under their firm's paragraph. If the firm has no paragraph (is not ranked) look at Other Notable Practitioners.

## Intellectual Property: Patent Prosecution

### Leading Firms

**Band 1**

Finnegan, Henderson, Farabow, Garrett & Dunner LLP *
Foley & Lardner LLP *
Sterne, Kessler, Goldstein & Fox P.L.L.C.
Venable LLP *

**Band 2**

Baker, Donelson, Bearman, Caldwell & Berkowitz, PC *
Banner & Witcoff, Ltd *
Dentons *
Dickstein Shapiro LLP *
WilmerHale *

### Leading Individuals

| Band 1 | |
| --- | --- |
| Sterne Robert G | *Sterne, Kessler, Goldstein & Fox P.L.L.C.* |
| **Band 2** | |
| Becker Stephen | *McDermott Will & Emery LLP* * |
| Cornwell David KS | *Sterne, Kessler, Goldstein & Fox P.L.L.C.* |
| Fox Harold H | *Steptoe & Johnson LLP (ONP)* † |
| Goldstein Jorge A | *Sterne, Kessler, Goldstein & Fox P.L.L.C.* |
| Hill David W | *Finnegan, Henderson, Farabow, Garrett* * |
| Marsh David | *Arnold & Porter LLP* * |
| McBee Susan | *Baker, Donelson, Bearman, Caldwell* * |
| Sartori Michael | *Venable LLP* * |
| Sophir Eric | *Dentons* * |
| **Up-and-coming individuals** | |
| Maebius Steve | *Foley & Lardner LLP* |
| Palan Stephen | *Crowell & Moring LLP* * |

## Arent Fox LLP
See profile on p.905

**THE FIRM** This firm has a comprehensive and well-regarded IP practice, and its copyright and trademarks expertise is particularly renowned. The team's soft IP counseling and transactional practice attract many accolades, and its ability to adroitly manage very large portfolios at a global level is considered one of its fortes. High-profile international brands such as Discovery Communications and Pixar look to Arent Fox to protect and exploit their rights.

**Sources say:** *"They find creative solutions and expedite resolutions."*

**KEY INDIVIDUALS Anthony Lupo** (see p.878) has expertise and experience at the point where advertising, entertainment and digital media converge. He counsels some of the best-known market leaders in these fields on their international branding strategies. **Michael Grow** (see p.867) is hailed as *"an expert in the field"* by peers. He handles copyright and trademark litigation, and counsels leading media and entertainment brands on matters concerning domestic and foreign trademarks, advertising, e-commerce and unfair competition.

## Intellectual Property: Trademark, Copyright & Trade Secrets

### Leading Firms

**Band 1**

Arent Fox LLP *
Arnold & Porter LLP *
Finnegan, Henderson, Farabow, Garrett & Dunner LLP *
Kilpatrick Townsend & Stockton LLP *

**Band 2**

DLA Piper LLP (US) *
McDermott Will & Emery LLP *
Venable LLP *
Wiley Rein LLP *

### Leading Individuals

| Band 1 | |
| --- | --- |
| Ford Ann K | *DLA Piper LLP (US)* * |
| Kilmer Paul | *Holland & Knight LLP (ONP)* † |
| Lupo Anthony V | *Arent Fox LLP* * |
| Mayberry David | *Kilpatrick Townsend & Stockton LLP* |
| **Band 2** | |
| Grow Michael A | *Arent Fox LLP* * |
| Harrison Mark | *Venable LLP* * |
| Joseph Bruce G | *Wiley Rein LLP* * |
| Krugman Gary | *Sughrue Mion PLLC (ONP)* † |

## Arnold & Porter LLP
See profile on p.906

**THE FIRM** Arnold & Porter has long had a good name for its handling of copyright, trademarks and related media and advertising work, and has in recent years established a reputation for IP litigation in these fields. A significant highlight of late saw the firm act as lead counsel for a consortium of major sporting associations, including the NBA, NFL and NHL, in a widely reported action concerning cable television copyright royalties.

**KEY INDIVIDUALS** Head of department **David Marsh** (see p.362) is a noted patent specialist whose practice covers noncontentious and litigious work. He recently led a team acting for Boston Scientific on defending a patent infringement claim brought by OrbusNeich Medical regarding coronary stents. **Matthew Wolf** (see p.901) is highly esteemed for his talents as a patent litigator in the life sciences and biotechnology arena. He has recently scored a string of successes for clients such as Boston Scientific and Hologic.

## Baker, Donelson, Bearman, Caldwell & Berkowitz, PC
See profile on p.2313

**THE FIRM** This esteemed Southern firm's DC office houses one of the city's most impressive patent prosecution practices. The team also prosecutes trademarks and copyrights, and has established an effective global network of IP

## Intellectual Property: Litigation

### Leading Firms

**Band 1**

Covington & Burling LLP *
Finnegan, Henderson, Farabow, Garrett & Dunner LLP *

**Band 2**

Fish & Richardson PC *
WilmerHale *

**Band 3**

Crowell & Moring LLP *
Dickstein Shapiro LLP *
Kirkland & Ellis LLP *
Latham & Watkins LLP *
McDermott Will & Emery LLP *
Sidley Austin LLP *

**Band 4**

Banner & Witcoff, Ltd *
Kilpatrick Townsend & Stockton LLP *
Mayer Brown LLP *
Morrison & Foerster LLP *
Venable LLP *
Weil, Gotshal & Manges LLP *
Williams & Connolly LLP

* Indicates firm / individual with profile.

† ONP = Other Notable Practitioner.

practitioners to help clients register and exploit their IP rights in jurisdictions around the world. The team has excellent competencies in biochemistry, chemistry and electrical and mechanical engineering.

**KEY INDIVIDUALS Susan McBee** (see p.880) is a talented patent attorney with a strong practice in patent and trademark prosecution and portfolio management. Much of her clientele operates in the biotechnology, chemical and life sciences sectors.

## Banner & Witcoff, Ltd
See profile on p.1241

**THE FIRM** This full-service IP law firm represents a diverse client base across a wide variety of engineering and scientific disciplines. The DC office's achievements and standing in litigation – before district and federal courts as well as the ITC – and patent prosecution are particularly well praised by interviewees. Clients include Harley-Davidson, Microsoft, Nokia and Toshiba.

**KEY INDIVIDUALS** Sources describe **Joseph Potenza** (see p.886) as an *"outstanding IP litigator,"* particularly with regard to patent cases. He is a seasoned advocate before the courts and the ITC, and also counsels clients on patent and copyright applications.

## Intellectual Property: Litigation
### Senior Statesmen

**Senior Statesmen:** distinguished older practitioners

| | |
|---|---|
| Farabow, Jr Ford F | Finnegan, Henderson, Farabow, Garrett * |
| Lupo Raphael | McDermott Will & Emery LLP * |

### Leading Individuals

#### Star individuals

| | |
|---|---|
| Dunner Donald R | Finnegan, Henderson, Farabow, Garrett * |

#### Band 1

| | |
|---|---|
| Cordell Ruffin | Fish & Richardson PC |
| Freed Joel | McDermott Will & Emery LLP * |
| Pappas George F | Covington & Burling LLP * |

#### Band 2

| | |
|---|---|
| Davis Mark G | Weil, Gotshal & Manges LLP * |
| Fisch Alan | Fisch Hoffman Sigler LLP (ONP)[†] |
| Gotts Lawrence J | Latham & Watkins LLP * |
| Huntington Danny | Rothwell, Figg, Ernst & Manbeck PC (ONP)[†] |
| Jakes J Michael | Finnegan, Henderson, Farabow, Garrett * |
| Kushan Jeffrey P | Sidley Austin LLP * |
| Potenza Joseph M | Banner & Witcoff, Ltd * |

#### Band 3

| | |
|---|---|
| Donovan Edward C | Kirkland & Ellis LLP * |
| Grant Maximillian | Latham & Watkins LLP * |
| Hadjis Alexander J | Morrison & Foerster LLP * |
| Hoffman Gary M | Dickstein Shapiro LLP * |
| LoCascio Gregg F | Kirkland & Ellis LLP * |
| McKeon Michael J | Fish & Richardson PC |
| Supko Mark | Crowell & Moring LLP * |
| Wallace Jr James H | Wiley Rein LLP * |
| Wolf Matthew M | Arnold & Porter LLP * |

#### Band 4

| | |
|---|---|
| Attridge Daniel F | Kirkland & Ellis LLP * |
| Baskin Stephen E. | Kilpatrick Townsend & Stockton LLP |
| Buroker Brian M | Gibson, Dunn & Crutcher LLP (ONP)[†] * |
| Carrano Cono A | Akin Gump Strauss Hauer & Feld (ONP)[†] * |
| Cavanaugh David L | WilmerHale * |
| Coston William | Venable LLP * |
| Genderson Bruce R | Williams & Connolly LLP |
| Lavelle Joseph | DLA Piper LLP (US) * |
| Lieberman Steven | Rothwell, Figg, Ernst & Manbeck (ONP)[†] |
| McKelvie Roderick R | Covington & Burling LLP * |
| Meyer Richard | Boies, Schiller & Flexner LLP (ONP)[†] |
| Ryan John W | Thompson Hine LLP (ONP)[†] * |
| Sanok Jeffrey D | Crowell & Moring LLP * |
| Soobert Allan | Paul Hastings LLP (ONP)[†] |

#### Up-and-coming individuals

| | |
|---|---|
| Micallef Joseph | Sidley Austin LLP * |
| Moore Matthew | Latham & Watkins LLP * |
| Rosenthal Brian | Mayer Brown LLP |

\* Indicates individual with profile.

[†] ONP = Other Notable Practitioner.

## Covington & Burling LLP
### See profile on p.441

**THE FIRM** Lawyers based at the DC headquarters of this leading IP firm are at the forefront of its nationwide practice. The team is celebrated for trying the most critical cases before federal courts around the country and the ITC. Its work on patent and trademark prosecution, IP transactions and regulatory matters is also renowned in the market. Key clients include Microsoft, Merck and SAMSUNG.

**Sources say:** *"Covington is definitely one of the best firms doing this work in the USA today."*

**KEY INDIVIDUALS George Pappas** (see p.885) has long been one of the preeminent patent and IP litigators in the country. He is described by sources as *"truly exceptional"* and *"at the very top of the game."* He recently led client Warner Chilcott to victory in a patent infringement claim concerning Asacol, a product used for the treatment of ulcerative colitis. The *"very esteemed"* **Roderick McKelvie** (see p.881) is an authority on patent law and litigation, having tried many cases and served as an expert witness on numerous occasions.

## Crowell & Moring LLP
### See profile on p.910

**THE FIRM** Crowell & Moring is held in particularly high regard for the quality of its work in patent infringement claims and trademark and trade secrets litigation. The team has scored a list of notable successes at district and appellate levels, as well as before the ITC. Highlights include securing a $919.9 million jury verdict for DuPont in a trade secrets action regarding its Kevlar-brand aramid fiber following a dispute with Kolon Industries.

**Sources say:** *"The firm is providing excellent service in a very broad range of areas."*

**KEY INDIVIDUALS Mark Supko** (see p.895) is praised by sources, who note that *"his overall knowledge and expertise provide great comfort."* He chairs the firm's IP group and is particularly strong in litigation matters concerning computer, electrical and mechanical engineering patents. **Jeffrey Sanok** (see p.889) specializes in patent procurement and litigation, as well as IP licensing and strategic counseling. He focuses mainly on matters concerning consumer electronics, industrial manufacturing systems, telecommunications and vehicle controls and systems. The *"customer-oriented"* **Stephen Palan** (see p.885) has a comprehensive patent practice covering licensing, procurement, portfolio management and high-stakes litigation. He is also an expert in trade secrets protection. His technical expertise is particularly pronounced with regard to consumer electronics, computer, data networking and wireless technologies.

## Dentons
### See profile on p.449

**THE FIRM** Dentons enters the rankings this year on the back of the IP team's achievements in patent prosecution and reexamination matters. The team offers a full and sophisticated IP service covering litigation, licensing transactions, due diligence, and trademark, copyright, media and internet law.

**Sources say:** *"I was very pleased with all of the services provided. What I like most about their services is their consistently quick responses and direct, comprehensible advice."*

**KEY INDIVIDUALS Eric Sophir**'s (see p.893) practice is concentrated on patent preparation and prosecution, often with an emphasis on business methods, computer hardware and software systems.

## Dickstein Shapiro LLP
### See profile on p.911

**THE FIRM** Dickstein Shapiro fields a 100-strong IP team and is rightly regarded as a litigation powerhouse in this area, with peers at rival firms acknowledging its excellent track record in patent litigation. The DC practice also elicits widespread praise for its patent prosecution and portfolio management work. Chrysler Group and LG Electronics are key clients.

**Sources say:** *"They are people to be taken very seriously – ferocious trial lawyers firing precision-guided missiles throughout the process."*

**KEY INDIVIDUALS Gary Hoffman** (see p.869) chairs the firm's IP group and is regarded as *"a very fine lawyer"* by peers. He is a seasoned patent litigator and has handled cases involving life sciences, chemicals, computer and semiconductor technologies.

## DLA Piper LLP (US)
### See profile on p.1971

**THE FIRM** The US division of this global law firm enters the rankings for DC on the strength of its lauded practice in trademarks, copyright and trade secrets. The team has a pronounced industry focus, with expertise in fashion and design, media, video games and retail. This is a 'cradle to grave' service, taking in portfolio management, prosecution and litigation. Clients include Christie's, Verizon Wireless and ZeniMax Media.

**Sources say:** *"They understand the pressures of a business and how factors other than the law can influence the strategy of the case."*

**KEY INDIVIDUALS Ann Ford** (see p.862) is a branding and trademarks specialist of national renown. She has a loyal following among fashion, media and retail clients, one of whom describes her as *"aggressive but with excellent judgment, very easy to get along with, and keen to minimize legal proceedings."* **Joseph Lavelle** (see p.876) is a highly respected patent litigator who tries and prepares cases centering on automotive technology, computer technology, electronic engineering, financial services and biotechnology. He has significant experience before the ITC, and is praised as *"a fantastic patent lawyer."*

## Finnegan, Henderson, Farabow, Garrett & Dunner LLP
### See profile on p.912

**THE FIRM** This IP powerhouse is headquartered in Washington, DC and is highlighted for its resources in patent, copyright, trademark and trade secrets law. The firm is at the heart of the series of telecommunications hardware patent cases, dubbed the 'smartphone wars', representing Taiwanese manufacturer HTC against Apple in a number of these cases. Other clients include Abbott Laboratories, Boston Scientific, LG Electronics and Sony.

**Sources say:** *"Unquestionably top tier."*

**KEY INDIVIDUALS** Peers praise **Donald Dunner** (see p.860) as a *"great statesman"* in the fields of pharmaceutical, chemical and biological engineering patent litigation. He is particularly well known for his experience of mounting appeals before the court of the Federal Circuit. He recently represented InterDigital Communications in the US Court of Appeals for the Federal Circuit, successfully achieving the reversal of a previous decision in a patent infringement dispute with Nokia. **David Hill** (see p.869) handles a wide variety of work, including patent and trademark prosecution, portfolio management, license agreements and litigation – including Section 337 unfair import investigations before the ITC. **Michael Jakes** (see p.871) is well regarded for his prowess and experience in appeals before the Federal Circuit. He particularly well suited to matters concerning computer hardware, medical device, semiconductor and software patents. **Ford Farabow** (see p.861) is a senior statesman at the patent Bar with a reputation that extends across the country. He focuses on cases regarding contested chemistry, chemical engineering and pharmaceutical rights.

## Fish & Richardson PC

**THE FIRM** Fish & Richardson retains its position as one of the leading patent litigation shops in DC. As well as critical patent cases before the district and federal circuit courts, the team has a stellar reputation for the quality of its Section 337 IP litigation before the ITC. A recent highlight saw the team represent SAMSUNG in a multipatent infringement action concerning videophone technology. **Sources say:** "Hard-working, creative and widely respected." **KEY INDIVIDUALS Ruffin Cordell** is considered to be "exceptional" and one of the best patent litigators in the market. He recently led a team acting for Microsoft on a patent case against St Clair Intellectual Property Consultants regarding the validity of patents regarding PC power management. **Michael McKeon** is one of the firm's top IP trial lawyers and "a very respected practitioner in the DC marketplace." His highlights from the past year include contributing to a team representing multiple defendants – including Gap, Netflix, Orbitz, Amazon.com and eBay – in a patent suit concerning the dynamic generation of applets on web servers.

## Foley & Lardner LLP

See profile on p.2588

**THE FIRM** Foley & Lardner's DC-based IP practice is best known for its strengths in patent prosecution on a national and global level, and for the sophistication of its lawyers' handling of technically complex patent reexaminations, and new inter partes and post-grant reviews. The DC office counts Amgen, Hitachi, Toshiba and United Therapeutics among its clients. **KEY INDIVIDUALS** Patent prosecution expert **Steve Maebius** provides invaluable strategic advice to key clients such as United Therapeutics.

## Kilpatrick Townsend & Stockton LLP

See profile on p.1109

**THE FIRM** This firm has a much-admired trademark and copyright practice, and has recently acted for adidas, Citi, Marriott International and Pearson Education. The group has of late sought to expand further into patent litigation and Section 337 proceedings before the ITC, moves which have successfully brought it wider market recognition. **Sources say:** "One of the best in terms of providing a great mix of substantive expertise and excellent advocacy." **KEY INDIVIDUALS David Mayberry** is universally acknowledged as a highly talented and experienced trademarks law expert. He is primarily a litigator, and specializes in arbitration, mediation or pre-litigation counseling to clients anticipating court proceedings. Sources praise his "deep knowledge of the law." **Stephen Baskin** is "a great client-oriented attorney – he's very quick to respond and doesn't overpromise or provide advice which runs counter to bottom line interests," according to one impressed market observer. Baskin plays a key role in the team's patent litigation practice, and has a subspecialty in nanotechnology.

## Kirkland & Ellis LLP

See profile on p.1254

**THE FIRM** The DC office of this leading national IP player is probably best known for its strengths in litigation at district court, appellate and ITC levels. The team recently acted for Abbott Laboratories on defending challenges to its use of Revigor in its Ensure line of products. Other prestigious clients include GlaxoSmithKline, IBM and Siemens. **Sources say:** "The quality of the work is very, very high." **KEY INDIVIDUALS Gregg LoCascio** (see p.877) recently led the team in the aforementioned matter for Abbott. He is a "superb trial lawyer" with "a good talent for talking to our management and taking on board their concerns," according to one interviewee. **Edward Donovan** (see p.859) is a veteran of numerous complex, high-stakes patent litigations and has tried cases in the country's most demanding jurisdictions for such matters, such as the Eastern District of Texas and the Northern and Southern Districts of California. Interviewees describe him as "a fine lawyer." The "very talented" **Daniel Attridge** (see p.850) has decades of experience in patent infringement, antitrust and unfair competition actions. He has distinguished himself in cases concerning chemical, medical device and pharmaceutical patents.

## Latham & Watkins LLP

See profile on p.446

**THE FIRM** Latham & Watkins is highly regarded for patent litigation in federal and state courts, and has a growing and formidable practice before the ITC headquarters in Washington, DC. The firm's lawyers have been prominent actors in the 'smartphone wars' and have developed a strong niche in Section 101 patentability cases. Clients include Apple, Amazon.com, Honeywell and Jaguar Land Rover. **Sources say:** "Latham made it a point to understand our business objectives, and pursued the litigation with those objectives as paramount." **KEY INDIVIDUALS Lawrence Gotts** (see p.866) is respected throughout the country for his prolific and highly successful work as a patent litigator. He recently led a team acting for Time Warner Cable on a patent infringe-

ment claim brought by Sprint Communications regarding Time Warner's digital home phone service. **Maximillian Grant** (see p.866) thrives in critical, competitive patent trials and ITC Section 337 proceedings, and is global cochair of the firm's IP litigation group. He is lauded by clients for his "practical and confident" approach. **Matthew Moore** (see p.882) is a patent litigator with a number of blue-chip clients in the automotive industry, including Jaguar Land Rover. Sources say he is "extremely responsive, knowledgeable and accessible."

## Mayer Brown LLP

See profile on p.1257

**THE FIRM** Mayer Brown's DC office houses a rich mix of scientifically qualified lawyers with extensive experience in litigating difficult cases. The emphasis there is largely on hi-tech and electronics patent litigation, and the IP team has commendable knowledge of district court, ITC and USPTO procedures. Clients include Cargill, Google and Philips. **KEY INDIVIDUALS** Patent litigator **Brian Rosenthal** is recognized for his talents by a range of clients and peers in the market. He "argues matters extremely well and is excellent at identifying the issues to focus on," according to one source.

## McDermott Will & Emery LLP

See profile on p.1258

**THE FIRM** This firm's DC IP team offers a comprehensive service, deploying experienced and technically adept minds to the registration, management and treatment of patents, trademarks and copyrights and to litigation where these rights are contested. The team's ITC and Section 337 practice is also gaining a respected name in the market. Clients include Hewlett-Packard, HTC, SAMSUNG and Sandoz. **Sources say:** "They are very responsive to our needs, and both aware of and sensitive to the internal workings of our company." **KEY INDIVIDUALS Joel Freed** (see p.863) concentrates primarily on high-stakes, sophisticated IP and related antitrust litigation and is a regular before the ITC. A recent highlight saw him and a team of McDermott attorneys win a substantial settlement from SAMSUNG for client Spansion following a review of the client's patent portfolio. **Stephen Becker** (see p.851) heads up the DC office's patent prosecution service and focuses mainly on engagements involving business methods, computing, semiconductors and telecommunications. One source relates that his "insights into the sensitivities and 'hot buttons' of the USPTO have resulted in favorable outcomes." Senior counsel **Raphael Lupo** (see p.878) remains "unquestionably top-tier" in the eyes of his peers. He recently helped win a favorable judgment from the ITC in defense of a patent infringement claim regarding third-party integrated circuits in flat panel digital televisions.

## Morrison & Foerster LLP
See profile on p.1990

**THE FIRM** MoFo's DC office is a hotbed of IP litigation talent, and continues to impress in this domain, leading high-profile representations in district, federal and ITC court settings. Electrical and chemical engineering are areas of pronounced strength for the team, which includes a number of former federal circuit clerks. It acts for a number of prominent science and technology market leaders, among them Fujitsu, Huawei, Novartis and Toshiba.
**KEY INDIVIDUALS Alexander Hadjis** (see p.328) has extensive experience of high-value patent litigation at district, federal and ITC court proceedings. Sources relate that *"he can provide constructive advice on strategy, and can also communicate with the client very well on either team management or detailed technology issues."*

## Sidley Austin LLP
See profile on p.1264

**THE FIRM** Sidley Austin is considered a go-to firm for sophisticated patent infringement cases by some of the best-known and largest IP-heavy blue-chips in the world today. Aside from patent litigation in district and federal courts, the team is expanding its ITC capability and is developing expertise and experience in the life sciences sector to supplement its already powerful command of consumer electronics technologies. Clients include Apple, Conceptus and Genentech.
**Sources say:** *"They have a lot of very, very skilled attorneys, so they are able to handle very large matters and multiple matters."*
**KEY INDIVIDUALS Jeffrey Kushan** (see p.875) heads the IP practice in Washington, DC. He divides his workload between life sciences litigation and IT and electronics litigation, with a stronger emphasis on the former. He has recently presided over high-value actions for clients Apple and Genentech. **Joseph Micallef's** (see p.881) practice is predominantly geared toward life sciences patent cases, although he has successfully tried cases involving patents arising from all manner of scientific disciplines.

## Sterne, Kessler, Goldstein & Fox P.L.L.C.

**THE FIRM** Sterne Kessler is widely recognized as one of the foremost IP boutiques in the Washington, DC area. The firm is especially highly regarded in the area of patent prosecution and USPTO proceedings. A number of sources highlighted the team's strengths in post-grant patent review, reexaminations and litigation support. Clients include Apple, Google and Reebok.
**Sources say:** *"Professional, diligent, efficient and exceptionally bright."*
**KEY INDIVIDUALS Robert Sterne** is considered to be among the best patent attorneys working in the USA today, and has a particularly strong reputation for handling patent reexamination actions and litigation before the Federal Circuit court and the ITC. Recent matters include successfully representing i4i in a patent infringement case against Microsoft in the US Supreme Court. **Jorge Goldstein**, a founding director of the firm, is a leading authority at the vanguard of patent law concerning

biotechnology, and has a thriving prosecution practice specializing in genomics, cell biology, stem cells and pharmaceuticals. **David Cornwell**'s practice is mainly concerned with patent litigation. He heads the firm's work on clean energy technologies, biotechnology and computer science, and is also much sought after for counsel on post-grant patent reviews. He has recently played a key role in undertaking patent due diligence with respect to potential M&A deals.

## Venable LLP
See profile on p.927

**THE FIRM** Venable is one of the leading firms in DC for IP and is considered a go-to for patent prosecution and trademark, copyright and trade secret-related matters. In addition to prosecution and reexamination work, the team is also strong with regard to the treatment of IP assets in M&A transactions, and in FDA proceedings concerning pharmaceutical patents. Clients include Amneal Pharmaceuticals, Ranbaxy and Sony Mobile.
**Sources say:** *"They are able to recommend courses of action that provide excellent results which lead to the client's full satisfaction."*
**KEY INDIVIDUALS Mark Harrison** (see p.868) chairs the firm's trademarks, copyrights and domain names practice group. He has been a prolific filer of trademark applications during his career, and has represented clients in a number of industries, including pharmaceutical companies. Sources note that he gives *"clean and clear advice."* **William Coston** (see p.858) heads the firm's IP group and commands the utmost respect as a litigator from peers and laypersons for his *"tireless efforts on behalf of his clients."* He tries cases across the spectrum of IP rights and related antitrust matters. **Michael Sartori** (see p.889) heads the firm's patent prosecution practice. He is a registered patent attorney, and also litigates patent cases as well as giving clients advice on their IP strategies. His scientific background is in mechanical engineering and he has very strong links with Japanese firms and official bodies concerned with IP.

## Weil, Gotshal & Manges LLP
See profile on p.2015

**THE FIRM** Weil's IP team in Washington, DC focuses primarily on litigation and counseling related to contentious matters, including Section 337 actions at the ITC. Licensing agreements and other IP-related transactional work is also a strong suit. The lawyers here are particularly well equipped to handle the most complex cases concerning consumer electronics and semiconductor patents. Recent clients include Apple, California Institute of Technology and SAMSUNG.
**KEY INDIVIDUALS Mark Davis** (see p.301) has been busy of late representing Apple in two important matters before the ITC, one against Elan regarding touchscreen patents, and another against Motorola, a major engagement in the 'smartphone wars'.

## Wiley Rein LLP
See profile on p.928

**THE FIRM** This DC firm's IP team is well regarded for its patent litigation work and its track record within copyright and trademark law. The firm has long been celebrated for its expertise in litigation of all kinds, while disputes concerning secondary liability are a forte for the team. Wiley Rein also has a leading practice representing licensees of digital music rights. Clients include Mylan Laboratories, Verizon Wireless and Warren Communication News.
**Sources say:** *"The attorneys display sound commercial sense."*
**KEY INDIVIDUALS Bruce Joseph** (see p.872) chairs the firm's trademark group and is a renowned specialist in trademark protection and litigation matters. He is also much sought after for advice on music recording licensing and protection, and online digital content rights. **James Wallace** (see p.898) is a seasoned patent litigator who has tried cases involving biotechnology, data transmission, pharmaceuticals and satellite communications. Sources relate that he is *"very professional, very well organized and on top of everything."*

## Williams & Connolly LLP

**THE FIRM** Williams & Connolly enters the rankings this year based on its recognized strengths in IP and, in particular, patent litigation, adding luster to its reputation for leading work in the field of pharmaceutical and medical products regulatory law. Although patent litigation relating to technologies in this field is a forte for the team, it also has considerable resources at its disposal for work regarding consumer electronics and telecommunications.
**KEY INDIVIDUALS Bruce Genderson** is singled out for his *"very impressive"* patent litigation practice. He leads the firm's efforts in this domain, and has represented companies operating in the principal areas of patent litigation, namely consumer electronics, pharmaceuticals and medical devices.

## WilmerHale
See profile on p.930

**THE FIRM** WilmerHale is a national player in IP, and its DC team handles the full range of related matters. The team's expertise in patent prosecution, reexamination and portfolio management, as well as patent litigation, is rightly recognized as being among the district's best, and the firm has an excellent name in Section 337 actions before the ITC. Clients include Pfizer and Smith & Nephew.
**KEY INDIVIDUALS David Cavanaugh** (see p.857) handles patent litigation and noncontentious IP counseling and strategy matters for a diverse range of clients, including many from the biotechnology, diagnostics and medical device sectors.

## Other Notable Practitioners

**Richard Meyer** of Boies, Schiller & Flexner LLP is a seasoned patent and trademark litigator who has tried Bench and jury trials, and also ITC and USPTO proceedings concerning IP assets in a vast range of technical disciplines.

According to one source, the *"stellar"* **Alan Fisch** of Fisch Hoffman Sigler LLP is a *"true business partner in every sense of the word – not just a great legal technician but also able to meld business concerns into an overall legal strategy."* He is a prolific trial lawyer whose work largely falls in the computer and electrical engineering spaces. As a former Administrative Trademark Judge with the Trademark Trial & Appeal Board, **Gary Krugman** of Sughrue Mion PLLC is much sought after for his counsel on branding matters, be they noncontentious engagements or hard-fought litigation. **Brian Buroker** (see p.855) of Gibson, Dunn & Crutcher LLP is best known in IP circles as a patent litigator and appellate specialist with an emphasis on cases concerning consumer electronics, computer and telecommunications technologies. **Harold Fox** heads Steptoe & Johnson LLP's DC-based patent prosecution team. He is

much admired for his command of matters involving a truly impressive range of technical and scientific disciplines, from biotechnology through nanotechnology to materials science. **Danny Huntington** of Rothwell, Figg, Ernst & Manbeck PC handles the full spectrum of patent law work, taking in prosecution, portfolio counseling, transactional matters and litigation. He is also well known for his extensive experience in patent interferences. **Paul Kilmer** (see p.874) of Holland & Knight LLP is a *"very well-regarded"* specialist in copyright, trademark and unfair competition matters. His practice is international in nature, and he advises clients on brand protection strategies in jurisdictions the world over. **Steven Lieberman** of Rothwell, Figg, Ernst & Manbeck PC is a much-admired patent litigator with several recent victories under his belt from cases concerning contested rights in biotechnology,

medical devices and pharmaceuticals at district court, appellate and ITC level. **John Ryan** (see p.889) of Thompson Hine LLP handles litigious and noncontentious patent work in all its guises, including prosecution and portfolio management. One client reports that *"he understands my issues and provides practical and sound legal advice, at great value."* **Allan Soobert** of Paul Hastings LLP is praised by clients for his understanding and experience of patent litigation, particularly cases with an electrical engineering bent. Recent clients include AT&T, Research In Motion and The Washington Post. **Cono Carrano** (see p.856) of Akin Gump Strauss Hauer & Feld LLP is aclaimed for his *"deep technical knowledge paired with unequaled litigation experience."* His main areas of focus are electronics, optics, semiconductors, software and wireless technologies.

# LABOR & EMPLOYMENT

Commentary about individuals can be found under their firm's paragraph. If the firm has no paragraph (is not ranked) look at Other Notable Practitioners.

## Labor & Employment
### Leading Firms

**Band 1**
Gibson, Dunn & Crutcher LLP *
Jones Day *
Morgan, Lewis & Bockius LLP *
Paul Hastings LLP *

**Band 2**
Seyfarth Shaw LLP *

**Band 3**
Akin Gump Strauss Hauer & Feld LLP *
Littler Mendelson, PC *
Ogletree, Deakins, Nash, Smoak & Stewart, PC *

**Band 4**
Proskauer Rose LLP *

## Band 1

### Gibson, Dunn & Crutcher LLP
#### See profile on p.682

**THE FIRM** Gibson, Dunn & Crutcher is widely acknowledged as a preeminent firm for labor and employment law. The team was established as an extraordinary force in the class actions sphere with its precedent-setting victory in Spano v Boeing, which saw the Seventh Circuit reverse the largest ERISA class action ever certified, on grounds of typicality. Health law remains a cornerstone of the practice, which deploys OSHA expertise to good effect in defense of multiple prominent employers. The firm also advises on a wide range of employment matters, including discrimination, equal opportunities and trade secrets. The practice's elite clientele includes Wal-Mart, Boeing, Merrill Lynch and Ford.

**Sources say:** *"They have the ability to look at things with strategic vision and help us plan an end-game strategy that works with our business model."*

**KEY INDIVIDUALS William Kilberg** (see p.874) is the practice group's senior partner and is a veteran of the DOL. He was lead partner on the much-publicized case brought against Boeing by the NLRB, and continues to be a leading light in the firm's class action practice. **Eugene Scalia** (see p.890) has a wide practice in the employment sphere, with a focus on DOL statutes and matters pertaining to the NLRA. Peers praise his as being *"very strategically focused – he can communicate with clients and is very business-minded."* *"The dean of the OSHA Bar,"* **Baruch Fellner** (see p.862) is the acknowledged expert on occupational health law and has represented the US Chamber of Commerce. He is also a frequent industry spokesperson in the media.

### Jones Day
#### See profile on p.919

**THE FIRM** This team consists of 16 attorneys with particular expertise in the fields of wage and hour class actions, trade secrets and ADA cases, as well as traditional labor law. The team has demonstrated its skill in class action and collective bargaining with its representation of Bloomberg against the EEOC, and with its role in the negotiation of new collective bargaining agreements for some 45,000 employees on behalf of Verizon. The firm's Railway Labor Act group is consistently engaged by railroads and airlines on a variety of high-stakes issues, including the representation of the National Railway Labor Conference in a matter involving national multiemployer collective bargaining on behalf of over 30 major railroads.

**KEY INDIVIDUALS Eric Dreiband** (see p.860) has served as general counsel to the EEOC and is active in wage and hour issues, discrimination, whistle-blowing and litigation. One peer describes him as *"one of the best employment litigators in this town, hands down."* **Alison Marshall** (see p.880) *"has a particular capability in class action and certain statistical, analytical approaches to defense,"* complement-

### Senior Statesmen

**Senior Statesmen: distinguished older practitioners**

| | |
|---|---|
| Cohen Charles | Morgan, Lewis & Bockius LLP * |

### Leading Individuals

**Star individuals**

| | |
|---|---|
| Brown Barbara B | Paul Hastings LLP |

**Band 1**

| | |
|---|---|
| Kilberg William J | Gibson, Dunn & Crutcher LLP * |
| Scalia Eugene * | Gibson, Dunn & Crutcher LLP * |

**Band 2**

| | |
|---|---|
| Chatilovicz Peter | Seyfarth Shaw LLP * |
| Dreiband Eric S | Jones Day * |
| Fellner Baruch A | Gibson, Dunn & Crutcher LLP * |
| Livingston Donald R | Akin Gump Strauss Hauer & Feld LLP * |
| Marshall Alison | Jones Day * |
| Mollen Neal D | Paul Hastings LLP |
| Nager Glen | Jones Day * |
| Willner Ken | Paul Hastings LLP |

**Band 3**

| | |
|---|---|
| Branciforte Jason | Littler Mendelson, PC * |
| Cohn Joel M | Akin Gump Strauss Hauer & Feld LLP * |
| Fortney David | Fortney & Scott, LLC (ONP)† |
| Kelly Deborah | Dickstein Shapiro LLP (ONP)† * |
| Lorber Lawrence Z | Proskauer Rose LLP |
| McCutchen Tammy D | Littler Mendelson, PC * |
| Nash Daniel L | Akin Gump Strauss Hauer & Feld LLP * |
| Skelly Paul | Hogan Lovells US LLP |
| Smith Robert J | Morgan, Lewis & Bockius LLP * |
| Speights Grace E | Morgan, Lewis & Bockius LLP * |
| Stevens Michael L | Arent Fox LLP (ONP)† * |
| Topolski Douglas | Ogletree, Deakins, Nash, Smoak & Stewart * |

*Indicates individual with profile.
†ONP = Other Notable Practitioner.

ing her focus on complex employment litigation. **Glen Nager** (see p.374) is chair of the firm's issues and appeals practice, and is praised by clients as being *"great at getting the picture as quickly as possible and strategizing how to get a good result from where you are."* He is currently assisting in the firm's representation of GE, among other matters.

## Morgan, Lewis & Bockius LLP
See profile on p.2246

**THE FIRM** Morgan, Lewis & Bockius has justifiably earned a reputation in DC for top-quality labor and employment work. Partners in this group have a great depth of government experience, and are often consulted by policymakers and legislators. The firm is recognized as a powerful force in collective bargaining, class action and discrimination cases. Recent work highlights include counseling the US Postal Service on labor relations, and representing Maxim Healthcare Services, the largest privately held healthcare organization in the USA, in multiple class actions. Other key clients include American Airlines, Lockheed Martin and Hewlett-Packard.

**Sources say:** *"Their bench of lawyers is probably second to none as far as covering all aspects of the HR practice."*

**KEY INDIVIDUALS** A former member of the NLRB, **Charles Cohen** (see p.857) is lauded as a *"senior statesman of the trade labor Bar,"* and specializes in representing senior management in complex labor and employment matters. **Grace Speights** (see p.893) focuses on class claims and is currently representing Amtrak in connection with a purported nationwide race discrimination class action. **Robert Smith** (see p.893) is a widely respected practitioner in the labor and employment field, and has years of experience in class and collection actions. He is currently engaged in the representation of Maxim Healthcare Services in relation to four nationwide class actions.

## Paul Hastings LLP
See profile on p.1996

**THE FIRM** Paul Hastings is widely known for its high-quality nationwide labor and employment practice, in which the DC office plays an important part. The accomplished attorneys are particularly strong in wage and hour class action and discrimination cases, as well as in the field of appellate and traditional labor law. The representation of airlines in connection to labor issues has long been a mainstay of the practice, as exemplified by the ongoing representation of American Airlines in its Chapter 11 proceedings and attendant renegotiation of labor contracts. Other clients include GlaxoSmithKline, Goldman Sachs and the Federal Reserve Board of Governors.

**Sources say:** *"Excellent employment lawyers."*

**KEY INDIVIDUALS Barbara Brown** is singled out by peers as *"a natural go-to"* for sex discrimination cases, an area in which she has recently been active for Dollar Tree Stores. She has also achieved a victory in front of the Supreme Court for GlaxoSmithKline with her colleague **Neal Mollen**, who is the firmwide lead on the American Airlines matter. **Ken Willner** is described by one peer as *"bright, thorough, measured and good in court,"* and is cur-

rently engaged with the representation of the FAA in multiple ongoing class action proceedings.

**Band 2**

## Seyfarth Shaw LLP
See profile on p.1262

**THE FIRM** Seyfarth Shaw undertakes work across the labor and employment field, and the DC practice has particular strength in labor relations in the hotels and retail industries. The group recently oversaw collective bargaining agreements for more than 6,000 union employees on behalf of the Hotel Association of Washington, DC, and has also carried out work for the American Hotel & Lodging Association. The firm has also recently undertaken work for the American Bar Association, the Washington Service Contractors Association and the City of Baltimore.

**Sources say:** *"They give sound, practical advice that in-house counsel can actually use."*

**KEY INDIVIDUALS** The *"terrific"* **Peter Chatilovicz** (see p.857) handles NLRA matters and is chief labor counsel for the Hotel Association of Washington, DC.

**Band 3**

## Akin Gump Strauss Hauer & Feld LLP
See profile on p.904

**THE FIRM** Akin Gump Strauss Hauer & Feld routinely handles the full range of labor and employment matters, with a particular focus on wage and hour collective and class actions. It recently defended Starbucks against the NLRB, and has an ongoing advisory relationship with the NFL. Other clients include Ernst & Young, The Home Depot and Family Dollar.

**Sources say:** *"A combination of strategy and execution is responsible for their doing a great job. It really is an excellent firm."*

**KEY INDIVIDUALS Donald Livingston** (see p.877) is a respected labor and employment practitioner. His recent engagements include defending Freeman Co. against a discrimination lawsuit brought by the EEOC. **Joel Cohn** (see p.857) is noted for his expertise in wage and hour and discrimination collective and class actions. **Daniel Nash** (see p.374) is a seasoned trial lawyer of whom one client says: *"He's a counselor's counselor; he provides the sort of sage advice that you look for in a senior lawyer, and is the person you call when a lawyer needs advice."*

## Littler Mendelson, PC
See profile on p.688

**THE FIRM** The DC branch of this nationwide labor and employment firm is ideal for ongoing counseling and class actions in the wage and hour and discrimination fields. The attorneys offer a variety of educational training initiatives and are appreciated by clients for their efficiency, practicality and responsiveness.

**Sources say:** *"Their national footprint makes them nimble with respect to employment matters in a way other large firms can't be."*

**KEY INDIVIDUALS Tammy McCutchen** (see p.881) is a veteran of the DOL and is widely regarded as an expert on wage and hour law and audits. The *"phenomenal"* **Jason Branciforte** (see p.853) deals with the full range of labor and employment law, and is admired by clients for his strategic approach.

## Ogletree, Deakins, Nash, Smoak & Stewart, PC
See profile on p.1110

**THE FIRM** This nationwide firm offers a broad range of labor and employment services, and the DC office has particular strength in OSHA, labor relations, discrimination and wage and hour cases. Current clients include Lockheed Martin, Glencore and the National Federation of Independent Business.

**KEY INDIVIDUALS Douglas Topolski** (see p.896) recently joined Ogletree's DC office from McGuireWoods in Baltimore. He is well versed across all areas of labor and employment law, and is frequently called upon to provide advice and training on union avoidance techniques and positive employee relations.

**Band 4**

## Proskauer Rose LLP
See profile on p.2001

**THE FIRM** The DC wing of this giant of the labor and employment world benefits from close links to the firm's New York office and its DC employee benefits and executive compensation group. The team is well equipped to handle most labor issues, and is particularly expert in dealing with regulatory issues and matters arising from the ADA. Clients include the US Chamber of Commerce, Amgen and Ford.

**KEY INDIVIDUALS Lawrence Lorber** is head of the DC labor and employment practice group, and has frequently testified before Congress in an advisory capacity. He offers counsel on equal opportunities and wage and hour matters, among other areas.

## Other Notable Practitioners

At Hogan Lovells US LLP, **Paul Skelly**'s practice spans the full spectrum of labor and employment work. He continues to be regularly called upon to provide counsel on the preparation of executive employment agreements, reductions in force and matters concerning federal and state law compliance, and represents a fine choice of counsel for employment litigation. **Michael Stevens** (see p.894) of Arent Fox LLP maintains an active traditional labor law practice and is also routinely sought after for his expertise in employment disputes and executive employment matters. As one satisfied client asserts, Stevens is *"very smart, practical, and always available when I call him."* **Deborah Kelly** (see p.873) is head of the labor and employment practice at Dickstein Shapiro LLP. She elicits much praise from the market, with clients describing her as *"thorough, quick and responsive,"* and peers highlighting her excellent abilities as a trial lawyer. In a recent highlight, Kelly acted for Under Armour in a dispute regarding an alleged breach

of a nonsolicit/noncompete agreement against a former employee. Fortney & Scott, LLC's **David Fortney** maintains a broad labor and employment practice, but is particularly recommended as a go-to attorney for advice on general labor issues and affirmative action programs. Sources

reserve particular praise for his overall technical skill and strategic approach to matters.

# LITIGATION

Commentary about individuals can be found under their firm's paragraph. If the firm has no paragraph (is not ranked) look at Other Notable Practitioners.

## Litigation
### Leading Firms

**Band 1**
Williams & Connolly LLP

**Band 2**
Baker Botts LLP *
Gibson, Dunn & Crutcher LLP *
Hogan Lovells US LLP *
Kirkland & Ellis LLP *
WilmerHale *

**Band 3**
Arnold & Porter LLP *
Covington & Burling LLP *
Jones Day *
O'Melveny & Myers LLP *
Sidley Austin LLP *
Skadden, Arps, Slate, Meagher & Flom LLP & Affiliates *
Steptoe & Johnson LLP
Zuckerman Spaeder LLP

**Band 4**
Crowell & Moring LLP *
Dickstein Shapiro LLP *
Goodwin Procter LLP *
Latham & Watkins LLP *
Mayer Brown LLP *
Miller & Chevalier Chartered *

## Litigation: General Commercial
### Senior Statesmen

**Senior Statesmen: distinguished older practitioners**

| | | |
|---|---|---|
| Vardaman John W | | Williams & Connolly LLP |

### Leading Individuals

**Band 1**

| | |
|---|---|
| Jeffress Jr William H | Baker Botts LLP |
| Roberts Michele A | Skadden, Arps, Slate, Meagher & Flom * |
| Sullivan Jr Brendan V | Williams & Connolly LLP |
| Villa John K | Williams & Connolly LLP |

**Band 2**

| | |
|---|---|
| Aldock John D | Goodwin Procter LLP * |
| Assaf Eugene F | Kirkland & Ellis LLP * |
| Hensler David | Hogan Lovells US LLP |
| Hoover Craig A | Hogan Lovells US LLP |
| Kendall David | Williams & Connolly LLP |
| McDaniels William E | Williams & Connolly LLP |
| Nields John W | Covington & Burling LLP * |
| Wilkinson Beth A. | Paul, Weiss, Rifkind, Wharton (ONP)[†] * |
| Yannucci Thomas D | Kirkland & Ellis LLP * |

**Band 3**

| | |
|---|---|
| Bray John | King & Spalding LLP (ONP)[†] * |
| Burchfield Bobby R | McDermott Will & Emery LLP (ONP)[†] * |
| Burgoyne Robert | Fulbright & Jaworski LLP (ONP)[†] *. |
| Butswinkas Dane | Williams & Connolly LLP |
| Caldwell Joe R | Baker Botts LLP * |
| Cullen Thomas | Jones Day * |
| Esposito Joseph P. | Hunton & Williams LLP (ONP)[†] * |
| Gersch David | Arnold & Porter LLP * |
| Lyle Michael J | Weil, Gotshal & Manges LLP (ONP)[†] * |
| Ogden David W | WilmerHale * |
| Raffman Mark S | Goodwin Procter LLP * |
| Schreiber Scott | Arnold & Porter LLP * |
| Sooy Kathleen Taylor | Crowell & Moring LLP * |
| Wahl Barbara S | Arent Fox LLP (ONP)[†] * |

**Up-and-coming individuals**

| | |
|---|---|
| Hogan E. Desmond | Hogan Lovells US LLP |

## Litigation: Securities
### Leading Individuals

**Band 1**

| | |
|---|---|
| Bruch Gregory S | Willkie Farr & Gallagher LLP (ONP)[†] * |
| Downey Kevin | Williams & Connolly LLP |
| Eggleston W Neil | Kirkland & Ellis LLP * |
| Romatowski Peter J | Jones Day * |
| Villa John K | Williams & Connolly LLP |
| Warin Joseph | Gibson, Dunn & Crutcher LLP * |

**Band 2**

| | |
|---|---|
| Kilduff Jeffrey | O'Melveny & Myers LLP * |
| Mann Michael D | Richards Kibbe & Orbe LLP (ONP)[†] |
| Meyers Jim | Orrick, Herrington & Sutcliffe (ONP)[†] * |
| Schreiber Scott | Arnold & Porter LLP * |

**Up-and-coming individuals**

| | |
|---|---|
| Bartholomew Christian | Weil, Gotshal & Manges LLP (ONP)[†] * |

*Indicates firm / individual with profile.*
[†]*ONP = Other Notable Practitioner.*

## Band 1

### Williams & Connolly LLP

**THE FIRM** This remarkable litigation powerhouse handles an impressive range of cases, offering expertise in everything from breach of contract actions to the defense of major consumer class actions. The team represents both individuals and institutions in the most complex of cases, as illustrated by its role in the $1 billion litigation between the joint liquidators of Carlyle Capital and several entities affiliated with The Carlyle Group. Other notable clients include Bank of America, Bayer and UBS.
**Sources say:** *"They possess a combination of intellect, work ethic and client focus."*
**KEY INDIVIDUALS Brendan Sullivan** is a preeminently experienced practitioner who has litigated in federal and state courts throughout the country. He divides his respected practice between complex commercial litigation and white-collar criminal defense, and represents numerous Fortune 500 companies. **John Villa** is highly respected

as a leading individual in the litigation arena. He concentrates his practice on corporate, securities and financial litigation, with particular expertise in legal malpractice defense. The *"outstanding"* **David Kendall** can draw on his tremendous amount of experience as a litigator in multiple civil and criminal cases at the trial and appellate level. He is highly regarded by commentators for his widespread expertise and remains a key member of the team. **William**

**McDaniels** is an enormous asset to the team as a senior litigator who specializes in civil litigation and white-collar criminal defense work. He offers extensive experience across a broad spectrum of sectors, and is a noted trial lawyer. **Kevin Downey** impresses sources with his experience in commercial and securities litigation, with one peer commenting: *"He has a great reputation and deservedly so – he has all the qualities of a very good litigator and counselor."* As well as representing government officials, CEOs and corporate executives, Downey also works on behalf of law firms and large corporations. **Dane Butswinkas** garners a significant amount of praise for his commercial litigation and arbitration practice. Commentators enthuse: *"He has great judgment and a very good manner with juries and clients."* **John Vardaman** continues to be a force to be reckoned with in complex civil and criminal litigation matters. Sources characterize him as being *"outstanding in every respect,"* with the ability to give *"superb judgment and advice."* **David Zinn** proves to be a very popular choice for white-collar criminal defense cases and complex civil litigation. Market sources commend his *"great approach and good bedside manner,"* and identify him as a *"real rising star"* in the white-collar space. The *"extraordinary"* **Robert Cary** has shifted his practice focus in recent years to criminal defense litigation, while maintaining his noted ability to handle civil matters. His recent work includes advising clients on government investigations and issues arising from securities fraud.

## Litigation: White-Collar Crime & Government Investigations

### Senior Statesmen

**Senior Statesmen: distinguished older practitioners**

| | | | | |
|---|---|---|---|---|
| Cacheris Plato | Trout Cacheris PLLC (ONP)[†] | | Miller Laura Ariane | Nixon Peabody LLP (ONP)[†] * |
| Hibey Richard | Miller & Chevalier Chartered * | | Silbert Earl J | DLA Piper LLP (US) (ONP)[†] * |

### Leading Individuals

**Star individuals**

| | | | | |
|---|---|---|---|---|
| Sullivan Jr Brendan V | Williams & Connolly LLP | | | |
| Weingarten Reid | Steptoe & Johnson LLP | | | |
| **Band 1** | | | Bunnell Stevan E | O'Melveny & Myers LLP |
| Bennett Robert S | Hogan Lovells US LLP | | Downey Kevin | Williams & Connolly LLP |
| Eggleston W Neil | Kirkland & Ellis LLP * | | Ettinger Mitchell S | Skadden, Arps, Slate, Meagher & Flom * |
| Green Thomas C | Sidley Austin LLP * | | Ifrah A Jeff | Ifrah PLLC (ONP)[†] * |
| Jeffress Jr William H | Baker Botts LLP | | Levine Barry Wm | Dickstein Shapiro LLP * |
| Taylor III William W | Zuckerman Spaeder LLP | | Nassikas John | Arnold & Porter LLP * |
| Warin Joseph | Gibson, Dunn & Crutcher LLP * | | Nields John W | Covington & Burling LLP * |
| **Band 2** | | | Pollack Barry J | Miller & Chevalier Chartered * |
| Burton Preston | Poe & Burton PLLC (ONP)[†] | | Rauh Carl S | Hogan Lovells US LLP |
| Cobb Ty | Hogan Lovells US LLP | | Rochon Mark J | Miller & Chevalier Chartered * |
| Hoffinger Adam S | Morrison & Foerster LLP (ONP)[†] * | | Rowley John | Baker & McKenzie (ONP)[†] |
| Hopson Mark D | Sidley Austin LLP * | | **Band 4** | |
| Inglima Philip | Crowell & Moring LLP * | | Banoun Raymond | Cadwalader, Wickersham & Taft (ONP)[†] * |
| Krakoff David S. | BuckleySandler LLP (ONP)[†] * | | Best Stephen A | Brownstein Hyatt Farber Schreck (ONP)[†] |
| Levy Michael N | Bingham McCutchen LLP * | | Braga Stephen | Law Office of Stephen L. Braga (ONP)[†] |
| Lowell Abbe David | Chadbourne & Parke LLP (ONP)[†] * | | Brown Blair G | Zuckerman Spaeder LLP |
| Poe Gregory L | Poe & Burton PLLC (ONP)[†] | | Bruce Carol | K&L Gates (ONP)[†] * |
| Robbins Lawrence | Robbins, Russell, Englert, Orseck (ONP)[†] | | Bruce Eric B | Kobre & Kim LLP (ONP)[†] * |
| Romatowski Peter J | Jones Day * | | Cary Robert | Williams & Connolly LLP |
| Salky Steven M | Zuckerman Spaeder LLP | | Connolly Thomas | Wiltshire & Grannis LLP (ONP)[†] * |
| Schertler David | Schertler & Onorato LLP (ONP)[†] | | Cooper James W | Arnold & Porter LLP * |
| Schuelke III Henry F | Blank Rome LLP (ONP)[†] * | | Fisher Alice S | Latham & Watkins LLP * |
| Shapiro, Esq. Howard | WilmerHale * | | Grimm Bernie | Law Office of Bernard Grimm (ONP)[†] |
| Spivack Peter S | Hogan Lovells US LLP | | Leeper Charles S | Drinker Biddle & Reath LLP (ONP)[†] * |
| Trout Robert P | Trout Cacheris PLLC (ONP)[†] | | MacDougall Mark J | Akin Gump Strauss Hauer & Feld (ONP)[†] * |
| Wilkinson Beth A. | Paul, Weiss, Rifkind, Wharton & Garrison * | | Madigan Michael J | Orrick, Herrington & Sutcliffe LLP (ONP)[†] |
| Zinn David | Williams & Connolly LLP | | McCool Steven | Mallon & McCool, LLC (ONP)[†] |
| Zuckerman Roger E | Zuckerman Spaeder LLP | | Tuohey Mark H | Brown Rudnick LLP (ONP)[†] |
| **Band 3** | | | Van Gelder Barbara | Dickstein Shapiro LLP * |
| Anthony Stephen | Covington & Burling LLP * | | **Up-and-coming individuals** | |
| Asbill Henry W | Jones Day * | | Carpenter-Holmes Amy K | Bingham McCutchen LLP (ONP)[†] * |
| Barta Michael J | Baker Botts LLP | | Chen Shawn J. | Cleary Gottlieb Steen & Hamilton (ONP)[†] * |
| Behre Kirby D | Paul Hastings LLP (ONP)[†] | | Heberlig Brian M | Steptoe & Johnson LLP |
| Boss Barry | Cozen O'Connor (ONP)[†] * | | Koehler Kristin Graham | Sidley Austin LLP * |
| | | | Wise Andy | Miller & Chevalier Chartered * |
| | | | **Associates to watch** | |
| | | | Curry Lauren E | Brown Rudnick LLP (ONP)[†] |

*\* Indicates individual with profile.*
*[†]ONP = Other Notable Practitioner.*

### Band 2

#### Baker Botts LLP
**See profile on p.2427**

**THE FIRM** This firm's DC office is staffed with a significant bench of respected lawyers who frequently handle a combination of white-collar, securities and complex commercial litigation. The team recently obtained a significant victory for Liberty Media following years of litigation against Vivendi Universal, with the jury awarding Liberty EUR765 million in damages. It was also successful in its representation of Marathon Oil Company and Marathon GTF Technology in the Delaware Court of Chancery. Other notable clients included Drummond Company and Samsung Electronics.
**Sources say:** *"Baker Botts has a solid team of very strong lawyers."*
**KEY INDIVIDUALS** The *"phenomenal"* **William Jeffress** has a stellar track record in successfully handling general commercial litigation, and is also considered to be one of the *"deans of the white-collar defense Bar."* His recent work includes defending the former CFO of Bank of America in litigation related to the bank's acquisition of Merrill Lynch. **Joe Caldwell** (see p.856) remains a respected member of the team whose practice encompasses both commercial litigation and white-collar criminal defense. He has represented clients from a wide range of sectors, illustrating the breadth of his trial expertise. **Michael Barta** attracts a huge amount of praise from clients for his criminal defense practice, as well as his growing general commercial litigation portfolio. His recent work includes representing Samsung Electronics and several of its US affiliates in nine pending patent litigation matters across the country. Sources comment: *"He is a great litigator who performs well in the courtroom."*

#### Gibson, Dunn & Crutcher LLP
**See profile on p.682**

**THE FIRM** This preeminent DC firm is fully integrated within a wide-reaching national network as impressively broad as its litigation practice. The large team handles a staggering number of cases, focusing on securities, white-collar and general commercial litigation. Its recent work includes representing Facebook and its founder, Mark Zuckerberg, in a highly publicized breach of contract action and a separate patent infringement case. Its client base also includes Janus Capital, the Investment Company Institute and the Business Roundtable.
**Sources say:** *"They are extremely responsive, very knowledgeable, and very helpful to us."*
**KEY INDIVIDUALS** **Joseph Warin** (see p.423) is singled out by sources as *"a very practical person"* who offers particular expertise in securities and white-collar litigation. Described as *"a tireless worker who is effective in resolving massive, complicated cases,"* Warin also has a tremendous reputation for his expertise in government investigations and litigation related to the Foreign Corrupt Practices Act (FCPA).

#### Hogan Lovells US LLP

**THE FIRM** This litigation behemoth fields an impressive team of lawyers with a wide range of expertise spanning commercial and white-collar criminal matters. Clients also benefit from its closely linked regulatory practice, which is largely housed in the DC office. The team recently secured an important win for Millennium Laboratories in a false advertising case brought against its competitor Ameritox. The jury unanimously found Ameritox's advertisements to contain false information.
**Sources say:** *"They are great litigation strategists and are simply terrific when it comes to client relations; they are extremely responsive and go out of their way to provide the highest level of service."*
**KEY INDIVIDUALS** The *"outstanding"* **Robert Bennett** maintains an active practice representing corporations and individuals in white-collar criminal litigation and investigations. He is held in high regard by commentators for his extensive experience in the arena. Practice cochair **Craig Hoover** is a popular choice for clients facing class actions and other complex litigation. His recent work includes defending numerous Blue Cross Blue Shield companies against a host of antitrust challenges brought against the Blue Cross system as a whole. Sources report: *"We are enormously impressed with him."* Former federal prosecutor **Ty**

**Cobb** has a *"superb"* securities and white-collar criminal litigation practice, built upon years of experience across the country. He chairs the firm's securities enforcement and compliance practice. **David Hensler** is held in high esteem for his experience representing defendants and plaintiffs in a wide range of complex commercial disputes. His practice also includes a particular focus on insurance litigation. **Peter Spivack** elicits significant praise in his capacity as leader of the firm's investigations, white-collar and fraud practice. He has particular expertise in representing clients from within the life sciences arena, exemplified by his recent work for medical device manufacturer Orthofix. Sources highlight his *"ability to analyze and provide solutions to our practical problems."* Former chief federal prosecutor **Carl Rauh** brings a wealth of experience to his current role of criminal defense lawyer. Sources highlight his *"excellent client service,"* and praise him as a practitioner who *"doesn't hesitate in getting into the weeds of a case."* Rising star **Desmond Hogan** is highly recommended by market commentators as *"a very fine lawyer and a good writer"* who has *"the whole package."* He focuses predominantly on commercial litigation and has particular expertise in high-value class actions.

## Kirkland & Ellis LLP
See profile on p.1254

**THE FIRM** This renowned firm houses a sizable team of talented attorneys singularly dedicated to litigating complex and high-value disputes. The team demonstrates its broad legal knowledge and versatility by handling cases across a huge array of areas, and is highly regarded for its trial experience. Its recent work includes representing Constellation Energy Group in the defense of multiple shareholder class action suits filed after its announced merger with Exelon. Other notable clients include Hershey, ConocoPhillips and Boeing.
**Sources say:** *"They are very practical lawyers who know the law very well and write brilliant appellate briefs and motions, but also tie advice to what the client wants to do from a business perspective."*
**KEY INDIVIDUALS Thomas Yannucci** (see p.901) has a celebrated commercial litigation practice and offers particular expertise in class actions. He is praised as being *"very articulate and business-minded,"* and continues to defend Hershey in a raft of antitrust actions brought against it. **Neil Eggleston** (see p.860) has a glowing reputation in the litigation arena for his specialist skills in white-collar criminal defense, with clients enthusing: *"Neil is a person you definitely want to have fighting your corner."* He also renowned for his expertise in securities litigation. **Eugene Assaf** (see p.850) is characterized as *"an extraordinarily bright, analytical and responsive"* commercial litigator who is also *"articulate in explaining the law in a way that the layperson can understand."* He is able to handle a wide range of cases, with recent highlights including acting for Honeywell in a much-publicized False Claims Act case brought by the DOJ.

## WilmerHale
See profile on p.930

**THE FIRM** This highly experienced litigation practice is extremely well versed in a wide range of civil disputes, and also frequently defends individuals and companies in criminal investigations. It is further commended for its strong securities litigation capabilities. It recently acted for Freshfields Bruckhaus Deringer on dismissing a complaint filed by RSM, alleging that Freshfields had engaged in corrupt activities while representing Grenada in an international arbitration.
**Sources say:** *"They blend sheer brainpower and legal knowledge with a lot of practical know-how."*
**KEY INDIVIDUALS Howard Shapiro** (see p.891) is the highly respected chair of the firm's litigation and controversy department, and is particularly noted for his white-collar criminal defense practice. Sources comment that he is *"a phenomenal lawyer who is incredibly responsive to client requests."* **David Ogden** (see p.884) enters the rankings backed by significant praise for his broad-based civil and regulatory litigation practice. He is characterized as an *"extremely talented, hands-on lawyer"* by one source, and is *"hugely approachable and very responsive."* Clients also appreciate his previous experience as Deputy Attorney General of the United States.

## Band 3

## Arnold & Porter LLP
See profile on p.906

**THE FIRM** This full-service firm prides itself on providing exceptional client service and top-quality trial skills. It tackles a plethora of matters involving securities litigation and white-collar investigations, and works on a national and international scale. It is also recognized for its commercial litigation expertise. The team recently represented Titan America in a number of class actions alleging price-fixing in the cement and concrete production industry in Florida.
**Sources say:** *"The lawyers really understand our business, enabling them to come up with the most practical and strategic ways of handling our litigation matters."*
**KEY INDIVIDUALS** Senior counsel **David Gersch** (see p.864) is hailed as a *"very strong litigator"* who garners praise for the diversity of his practice. His recent work includes representing Honeywell in two large class actions. **Scott Schreiber** (see p.891) maintains an active general commercial litigation practice and is increasingly recognized for his focus on securities litigation. Clients praise his *"methodical and thorough"* approach to cases and highlight his strong understanding of regulatory matters. **John Nassikas** (see p.883) is described as a *"phenomenal litigator"* by market sources, who also commend his experience of working with regulators across the country. He specializes in white-collar criminal defense and related civil litigation. **James Cooper** (see p.858) elicits substantial praise for his experience in a range of white-collar criminal matters, with sources stating: *"He's a very good trial lawyer."* He is

also described as *"extremely intelligent and strategic,"* and *"has good working relationships with everyone."*

## Covington & Burling LLP
See profile on p.441

**THE FIRM** This firm is renowned for dealing with complex and novel litigation issues involving white-collar criminal defense and commercial disputes. The team's caseload illustrates the broad array of industries the litigators engage with, such as life sciences and aerospace. It recently represented Samsung Electronics in a multibillion-dollar class action emerging from alleged price-fixing of liquid crystal displays found in a variety of electronics. Sources particularly highlight the depth of regulatory expertise offered by the firm alongside its litigation practice.
**Sources say:** *"They've always had an enormous amount of depth in white-collar and commercial litigation, and in arbitration."*
**KEY INDIVIDUALS John Nields** (see p.884) has a solid background in white-collar litigation and also focuses on commercial disputes. Sources regard him as *"a client's dream who thinks, breathes and lives your case,"* while also praising his trial skills. The *"terrific"* **Stephen Anthony** (see p.850) can draw on his previous experience as a federal prosecutor when acting for clients in white-collar criminal defense matters and internal investigations. His recent work includes representing Johnson & Johnson in a range of investigations and civil lawsuits.

## Jones Day
See profile on p.919

**THE FIRM** This impressive DC team is supported by the firm's extensive international network and significant bench of experienced trial lawyers. The office handles a broad range of litigation matters, including white-collar criminal defense and securities litigation, and is considered to be particularly adept in the commercial disputes arena. Alongside representing IBM and Bayer, its recent work includes successfully defending a patent held by Myriad Genetics.
**Sources say:** *"They are very good from top to bottom."*
**KEY INDIVIDUALS Peter Romatowski** (see p.888) is highlighted as *"the go-to lawyer for investigation and securities cases for many companies,"* and additionally maintains an active white-collar criminal defense practice. Sources characterize him as a *"tremendous lawyer"* who is particularly praised for his analytical skills. **Thomas Cullen** (see p.858) is heralded as a *"very strong commercial litigator,"* and recently obtained a dismissal for GM after former employees claimed that the company unlawfully reduced retirement benefits. Commentators also draw attention to his expertise as a trial lawyer. **Henry Asbill** (see p.850) is held in high esteem by commentators for his expertise in white-collar criminal defense. Sources praise him as *"a uniquely creative trial strategist who finds ways to win very hard cases."*

## O'Melveny & Myers LLP
See profile on p.693

THE FIRM This firm has a thriving securities litigation practice and also impresses with its expertise in white-collar criminal and commercial matters. Its broad-based expertise attracts clients from a wide range of sectors. The talented team recently acted for Bank of America on defending actions brought by the Attorneys General of Nevada and Arizona. It also recently represented Ford before the Ohio Court of Appeals and was successful in having a $2 billion judgment overturned.

KEY INDIVIDUALS **Stevan Bunnell** brings a wealth of experience to his white-collar criminal and civil litigation practice, having served as a prosecutor for many years. He is praised by market commentators for his *"thoughtful and thorough"* approach. **Jeffrey Kilduff** chairs O'Melveny's securities litigation practice and is held in high regard for his breadth of expertise in this arena. He remains closely involved in the defense of Fannie Mae against a number of securities class actions.

## Sidley Austin LLP
See profile on p.1264

THE FIRM Sidley Austin's DC litigation practice handles an impressive range of commercial, securities and white-collar criminal defense matters. It houses more than 200 litigators and is an integral part of the firm's wider global network, allowing for a truly multijurisdictional service. The team's recent work includes representing Bank of America in a number of investigations into mortgage securitization. Other clients include Tyson Foods, KPMG and Johnson & Johnson.

Sources say: *"They have a deep, talented bench of former prosecutors and regulators from across the US and the globe."*
KEY INDIVIDUALS Senior counsel **Thomas Green** (see p.326) is highly respected for his leading white-collar criminal defense practice and extensive trial experience. His recent work includes representing the former CEO of Freddie Mac in several securities disputes and an SEC enforcement action. **Mark Hopson** (see p.870) is the managing partner of the firm's DC office and is highly regarded for his expertise in white-collar criminal defense matters. His notable experience as a trial lawyer is particularly highlighted by market commentators. His recent work includes representing several pharmaceutical companies in a number of extensive FCPA investigations. **Kristin Koehler** (see p.874) enters the rankings having earned significant praise for her white-collar criminal defense practice. She is also noted for her experience in civil litigation. Clients particularly commend her responsiveness and practical approach to handling matters.

## Skadden, Arps, Slate, Meagher & Flom LLP & Affiliates
See profile on p.2008

THE FIRM Skadden's respected DC office is noted for its expertise in a wide range of commercial litigation and white-collar criminal proceedings. Commentators highlight its deep bench of litigators and extensive global network, and its ability to handle multifaceted disputes. The group recently represented Community Health Systems and its subsidiary Quorum Health Resources in a range of contentious matters. Its client base also includes Pfizer, UBS and Medtronic.

Sources say: *"They have top lawyers from around the world and have the resources to do anything."*
KEY INDIVIDUALS **Michele Roberts** (see p.393) is lauded by peers and clients alike as *"an extremely talented trial lawyer"* who concentrates on both commercial and criminal litigation. Her recent work includes representing Host Hotels & Resorts in a civil fraud action against the company's real estate brokers. **Mitchell Ettinger** (see p.861) cochairs the firm's government enforcement and litigation group, and focuses on civil and criminal litigation. He recently represented Rosetta Stone in a highly significant case that confirmed its right to bring trademark infringement claims against Google.

## Steptoe & Johnson LLP

THE FIRM This DC office has a significant bench of attorneys dedicated to litigation and renowned for their impeccable trial skills. The team is adept at handling sophisticated, multijurisdictional cases within the areas of white-collar criminal defense and complex commercial litigation. Its recent work includes representing UK-based IMI and its US subsidiary CCI in an extensive FCPA investigation.

Sources say: *"They have a well-oiled team that worked relentlessly on my behalf, and they were masters at what they were doing."*
KEY INDIVIDUALS **Reid Weingarten** is a star of the criminal defense Bar. He receives extensive praise from peers and clients, with one source stating: *"I have never seen or heard a more eloquent and articulate advocate in the courtroom."* Weingarten tackles cases *"with courage and great skill,"* and provides clients with the *"extremely important feeling that you're in good hands."* **Brian Heberlig** is highly regarded for his experience in FCPA matters and is characterized as someone who *"deals with matters clearly and efficiently."* He recently successfully defended DOJ trial attorney Edward Sullivan in a long-running investigation into the prosecution of Alaskan senator Ted Stevens.

## Zuckerman Spaeder LLP

THE FIRM This compact yet highly effective DC office fields a highly regarded litigation team, which tackles complex civil and commercial litigation, as well as white-collar criminal defense. Its recent work includes representing Dominique Strauss-Kahn in criminal and civil matters relating to allegations brought against him. The team also acted for the official committee of unsecured creditors in the Tribune bankruptcy.

Sources say: *"Their work is of the highest quality and they have a very innovative approach to their litigation practice."*
KEY INDIVIDUALS **William Taylor** is lauded by peers as *"an incredibly experienced criminal defense lawyer"* who has tallied up numerous successes before the federal and state courts nationwide. He is characterized by one source as a *"consummate trial lawyer."* The *"excellent"* **Steven Salky** has amassed a huge amount of experience in the litigation field and is held in high regard by market commentators. He is

particularly adept at representing financial services executives in civil and criminal litigation. Firm founder **Roger Zuckerman** is adept at handling a wide array of civil and criminal defense litigation. Sources acknowledge his *"knack of simplifying complicated situations,"* and applaud his attention to client service. **Blair Brown** is a new addition to the rankings and is commended for his civil and criminal litigation practice. He represents corporations and individuals in a wide range of disputes, and offers significant experience in successfully trying cases.

## Band 4

## Crowell & Moring LLP
See profile on p.910

THE FIRM Crowell & Moring's DC office offers significant litigation capabilities across a range of sectors. It acts for an impressive range of national clients, including DuPont, for which the team managed to obtain almost $920 million damages in the biggest ever US contested trade secrets verdict. DuPont alleged that Kolon, a competitor, had stolen over 150 trade secrets relating to DuPont's Kevlar product.

Sources say: *"The team is very confident and technically skilled in many areas, and definitely values us as a client – we know that whatever the issue is, it will be addressed promptly and efficiently."*
KEY INDIVIDUALS Department head **Kathleen Taylor Sooy** (see p.893) is widely regarded as *"very experienced and strategic."* She concentrates on commercial and product liability litigation, and is also commended for her approach to client service. **Philip Inglima** (see p.871) has notable expertise within the white-collar crime field and is praised for his ability to *"handle individual and corporate representation with equal aplomb."* Market sources further praise his ability to *"nimbly adapt to a number of different areas."*

## Dickstein Shapiro LLP
See profile on p.911

THE FIRM This expanding DC branch prides itself on maintaining a thriving litigation team, with many lawyers possessing expertise across a wide range of practice areas. Its focus extends to antitrust, insurance and IP litigation, and it frequently handles multijurisdictional disputes. The team is comfortable representing both individuals and companies, and its client base includes Carson Helicopter, Novell and Meritor.

Sources say: *"They provide first-rate counsel based on decades of experience, and help navigate extremely tricky matters safely."*
KEY INDIVIDUALS The respected **Barry Levine** (see p.877) cochairs the white-collar practice and also maintains a focus on commercial litigation. His recent work includes representing the former executive of Berkshire Hathaway subsidiaries, David Sokol, in a range of matters associated with his Lubrizol stock transactions. **Biz Van Gelder** (see p.897) leads the Congressional investigations practice and is noted for her experience in white-collar defense matters. She is praised for her ability to be *"really*

*creative on behalf of her clients,"* and one source enthused: *"Her representation is worth its weight in gold."*

## Goodwin Procter LLP
See profile on p.1522

THE FIRM This notable DC group specializes in complex commercial litigation and is a popular choice among a wide range of clients. The team offers a number of services, including class action litigation, product liability, criminal defense and insurance litigation. Recent highlights include successfully representing Quicken Loans before the Supreme Court in a case concerning the Real Estate Settlement Procedures Act.

Sources say: *"The firm is particularly adept at analyzing complex issues and drafting briefs and motions."*

KEY INDIVIDUALS John Aldock (see p.849) is characterized by sources as a *"fantastically talented litigator."* He focuses his national practice on complex commercial litigation, and is described as *"very strategic and experienced."* His recent work includes representing Arrowood Indemnity in long-running litigation relating to alleged fraud and involving over 10,000 plaintiffs. Mark Raffman (see p.887) is highlighted for his complex commercial litigation practice and offers expertise in a range of other areas, including product liability and mass tort litigation. He represented Lafarge North America against claims alleging the client promoted defective drywall from China.

## Latham & Watkins LLP
See profile on p.446

THE FIRM This litigation group enters the rankings having earned praise for its complex civil and criminal litigation practice. Its broad base of clients benefit from the firm's significant network of US-based and international offices. The team recently achieved a significant win for HCA after five years of litigation against the Foundation for Seacoast Health, which sought over $1 billion in damages; the court rejected the plaintiff's claims in their entirety.

Sources say: *"The team has a diversity of strengths and a capacity to look at a contentious issue from all the standpoints necessary for outstanding representation."*

KEY INDIVIDUALS Alice Fisher (see p.862) is the managing partner of the firm's DC office and a new entry to the rankings. She focuses on white-collar criminal investigations and is particularly praised for her ability to draw on her experience as former DOJ Assistant Attorney General. She currently works on behalf of HCA in a range of matters.

## Mayer Brown LLP
See profile on p.1257

THE FIRM Mayer Brown's DC office is recognized for its ability to handle a wide range of disputes, and has access to an impressive global bench of litigators. The team recently secured a victory for Foster Poultry Farms, having been hired only a month before the trial. Another recent highlight involved representing Lockheed Martin in defending a challenge brought against its 401(k) plans.

Sources say: *"The team consistently delivers insightful counsel, superior advocacy and results."*

KEY INDIVIDUALS Dan Himmelfarb cochairs the firm's DC litigation practice, and is a key contact at the firm.

## Miller & Chevalier Chartered
See profile on p.923

THE FIRM This firm's respected team of litigators has expertise in trying cases, enhanced by extensive experience serving in government roles. The group works closely with the firm's criminal tax and FCPA and international anti-corruption teams. It is particularly commended by sources for its dedicated approach to client service.

Sources say: *"Their approach is proactive, very balanced and practical – they do not jump to the most expensive solutions."*

KEY INDIVIDUALS Barry Pollack (see p.886) can draw on his previous accountancy experience when litigating sophisticated financial matters. Sources praise his *"professional demeanor and candid approach,"* and highlight his ability to *"communicate effectively and efficiently."* Mark Rochon (see p.888) chairs the litigation practice and is praised for his extensive white-collar criminal defense experience. Sources also commend his *"extraordinarily good ability to relate to people."* Richard Hibey (see p.869) is hailed as *"one of the real veterans of the DC trial Bar,"* having represented clients in an impressive range of white-collar criminal defense matters. Sources consider him *"a trusted and excellent"* choice of litigator. Andy Wise (see p.900) is a new addition to the rankings and has a growing litigation practice representing both individuals and corporations in investigations and white-collar criminal defense. Market sources highlight him as someone who *"will soon be a star if he isn't already."*

## Other Notable Practitioners

Raymond Banoun (see p.850) cochairs the business fraud group at Cadwalader, Wickersham & Taft LLP. He deals with a myriad of cases across the spectrum of criminal and civil enforcement litigation, and is considered *"wonderful and experienced"* by market sources. Christian Bartholomew (see p.851) of Weil, Gotshal & Manges LLP maintains a solid practice in securities enforcement and litigation, and is particularly adept at handling FCC investigations. Clients highlight his experience and ability to handle a broad spread of matters. Kirby Behre of Paul Hastings LLP has a growing reputation for his *"absolute ferociousness toward defense litigation."* He is currently representing two former executives of IndyMac Bank in a $300 million suit brought by the Federal Deposit Insurance Corporation. Stephen Best heads the white-collar criminal defense and investigations group at Brownstein Hyatt Farber Schreck, LLP and maintains an active practice within this area. Clients commend him as an *"extremely knowledgeable and practical adviser."* Barry Boss (see p.853) of Cozen O'Connor has a tremendous reputation as *"a very fierce advocate in the white-collar area"* and is particularly praised for his proactive approach. Sources further note that he is *"dedicated to achieving the*

*best results for his clients."* Stephen Braga of the Law Office of Stephen L. Braga, PLLC is an experienced white-collar criminal defense practitioner, and is respected by commentators for his broad range of expertise in the field. John Bray (see p.854) is a senior partner at King & Spalding LLP and an experienced trial lawyer. He has dealt with a range of matters across the civil and criminal litigation spectrum. Carol Bruce (see p.854) of K&L Gates has significant experience in representing individuals and corporations in criminal and civil litigation. Sources applaud her dedication to client service, as well as her ability to *"clearly explain complex legal issues."* Eric Bruce (see p.854) of Kobre & Kim LLP is a respected white-collar criminal defense litigator, and is particularly noted for his FCPA expertise. Sources also highly commend his trial experience. His recent work includes defending Pankesh Patel in a high-profile trial involving allegations of FCPA violations. Gregory Bruch (see p.854) of Willkie Farr & Gallagher LLP draws from a wealth of governmental experience gained serving as a senior enforcement official at the SEC. He has a thriving securities litigation practice and is seen as being *"at the top of his game."*

Bobby Burchfield (see p.289) of McDermott Will & Emery LLP is a popular choice of commercial litigator, with a highly impressive trial record. His recent work includes representing manufacturing companies CNH Global and BorgWarner in separate health benefit class actions brought by separate retiree groups. Robert Burgoyne (see p.855) of Fulbright & Jaworski LLP has amassed a substantial amount of experience in commercial litigation. Sources commend his devotion to client service, stating that *"he gives you his full attention in any matter."* His recent clients include the Law School Admission Council and Shell. Preston Burton of Poe & Burton PLLC is a highly regarded white-collar criminal defense practitioner, and is highlighted as *"a phenomenal trial lawyer and a great strategist."* Sources additionally comment that *"he is an incredibly effective advocate for his clients."* Plato Cacheris of Trout Cacheris PLLC is an *"outstanding"* member of the DC criminal defense Bar. He is a highly experienced practitioner, whose expertise spans a wide range of investigatory matters. His practice also includes a focus on civil litigation.

Amy Carpenter-Holmes (see p.856) of Bingham McCutchen LLP is a new addition to the rankings, and is rapidly building a solid reputation for representing clients from a range of industry sectors in various government investigations. Market sources are impressed with her ability to *"go toe-to-toe with senior lawyers."* Shawn Chen (see p.857) of Cleary Gottlieb Steen & Hamilton LLP primarily concentrates on white-collar criminal defense but is also recommended for his experience in commercial and securities-related matters. Thomas Connolly (see p.858) of Wiltshire & Grannis LLP is recognized for his white-collar criminal defense expertise. Commentators agree that he is *"very analytical and thorough,"* and *"is someone who knows how to get to the finish line in the best possible way."* Lauren Curry is an associate at Brown Rudnick LLP and enters the rankings having earned numerous recommendations. Market sources highlight her *"very positive attitude and* enthusiasm," and praise her as someone who *"provides tireless support."* One client noted that she *"distilled millions of pages of material into readable and very useful briefing notes."* **Joseph Esposito** (see p.861) of Hunton & Williams LLP has a respected commercial litigation practice and is praised by clients for his ability to *"take the time to understand our business and our interests."* Sources also confirm that *"he is hard-working, insightful, organized and very good at executing a strategy."* **Bernie Grimm** has recently set up his own litigation practice and is hailed as *"an excellent trial lawyer"* who is *"always willing to take on a challenging case."* He is reputed to have *"a terrific demeanor in the courtroom."* **Adam Hoffinger** (see p.869) of Morrison & Foerster LLP is a former Assistant US Attorney and brings this substantial experience to the table when representing individuals and corporations in high-stakes criminal and civil litigations. Commentators regard him as a *"very talented"* litigator whose trial expertise is particularly highlighted.

**Jeff Ifrah** (see p.870) of Ifrah PLLC is highly regarded for his white-collar defense practice and is praised for his *"very entrepreneurial"* approach. He is characterized as an attorney who is *"very well prepared and cares a lot about his clients."* **David Krakoff** (see p.875) of BuckleySandler LLP is described as *"an outstanding attorney"* and is respected for his criminal and civil litigation practice. He is experienced in representing both individuals and corporations in a range of often high-profile matters. **Charles Leeper** (see p.876) heads the white-collar litigation practice at Drinker Biddle & Reath LLP and is also a managing partner of the firm. Commentators highlight his trial expertise and his *"comprehensive knowledge of the facts."* Bingham McCutchen LLP white-collar litigation practice head **Michael Levy** (see p.877) is heralded as *"a master at representing individuals and groups in complex white-collar cases."* His recent highlights include representing former Fannie Mae executive Thomas Lund in an SEC investigation and related charges. **Abbe David Lowell** (see p.878) of Chadbourne & Parke LLP is highly praised by sources for his white-collar criminal defense expertise. Commentators are quick to applaud his recent success on behalf of John Edwards, the former presidential candidate, who faced charges related to his election campaign. **Michael Lyle** (see

p.879) of Weil, Gotshal & Manges LLP is recommended for his expertise in commercial litigation. His recent work includes successfully representing SEACOR Holdings in its defense of claims brought against it following on from the Deepwater Horizon explosion. **Mark MacDougall** (see p.879) of Akin Gump Strauss Hauer & Feld LLP brings his prior experience as a federal prosecutor to his criminal defense practice. He represents a range of US-based and international companies and individuals. **Michael Madigan** of Orrick, Herrington & Sutcliffe LLP is characterized as a *"highly skilled defense lawyer"* who is particularly noted for his trial expertise. He recently achieved an acquittal on all counts for his client in a significant FCPA enforcement action. Market sources commend *"how he strategically deals with issues before trial"* and consider him to be a *"great negotiator."* **Michael Mann** of Richards Kibbe & Orbe LLP is highly recommended for his securities litigation and enforcement practice, with sources commenting that his understanding of international regulatory concerns puts him *"in a league of his own."* He is further characterized as *"smart, thoughtful and creative."*

**Steven McCool** of Mallon & McCool, LLC enters the rankings having earned praise for his criminal defense practice, with commentators noting that he is *"quick on his feet, absolutely tenacious and will fight for his client."* Sources further praise his *"strong courtroom presence."* **Jim Meyers** (see p.881) of Orrick, Herrington & Sutcliffe LLP is a highly respected securities litigator. Recent highlights include representing former StarMedia executive Adriana Kampfner in an SEC enforcement action, negotiating a favorable settlement that included no monetary payment. **Laura Ariane Miller** (see p.882) of Nixon Peabody LLP maintains a *"sterling reputation in DC"* for defending clients against civil and criminal allegations. She has amassed an enormous amount of experience within this area, and market sources highlight her ability to bring a *"practical, real-world approach to issues."* **Gregory Poe** of Poe & Burton PLLC is highly esteemed for his experience in the white-collar criminal defense arena. He is considered to be *"incredibly diligent and thoroughly prepared,"* and his experience in trial advocacy is also particularly commended. **Lawrence Robbins** of Robbins, Russell, Englert, Orseck, Untereiner & Sauber LLP brings his time serving

as a former Assistant US Attorney to his civil and criminal litigation practice. Sources consider him *"a skilled trial lawyer"* and highlight his appellate litigation practice as a significant strength. **John Rowley** (see p.889) of Baker & McKenzie is a former Assistant US Attorney, and his practice includes a focus on False Claims Act litigation and FCPA investigations. Market sources characterize him as *"very knowledgeable, practical and a focused strategist."* **David Schertler** of Schertler & Onorato LLP has conducted a wide range of civil and criminal litigation, and *"has had a series of really interesting and topical cases with very good results throughout the years."* In the courtroom, he is *"very good on his feet"* and possesses *"the ability to simplify complex issues into common language."* **Henry Schuelke** (see p.891) of Blank Rome LLP is renowned for representing individuals and corporations in a wide range of white-collar criminal matters. Market sources enthuse that *"he's an absolute joy to work with"* and consider him *"a really well-respected white-collar litigator."* **Earl Silbert** (see p.892) of DLA Piper LLP (US) is considered one of the *"most revered lawyers in Washington"* for his well-established criminal and civil defense litigation practice. Before entering private practice, he served as the US Attorney for the District of Columbia.

**Robert Trout** of Trout Cacheris PLLC has amassed over 35 years of experience conducting civil and criminal litigation, and is applauded as *"an exceptional lawyer"* who is *"very effective in the courtroom."* **Mark Tuohey** is an *"extremely experienced and supportive"* white-collar litigator at Brown Rudnick LLP. His recent work includes representing a senior BP official, Gregory Walz, in civil and criminal matters arising from the Deepwater Horizon explosion. **Barbara Wahl** (see p.897) heads the commercial litigation practice at Arent Fox LLP, and is praised for her *"tremendous commitment, energy and passion."* Sources also commend her significant trial experience. **Beth Wilkinson** (see p.900) of Paul, Weiss, Rifkind, Wharton & Garrison LLP is lauded by peers as *"a highly regarded trial lawyer."* She has a broad practice covering white-collar criminal defense, product liability, internal investigations and commercial litigation. She is described as *"super smart and very energetic."*

# MEDIA & ENTERTAINMENT

Commentary about individuals can be found under their firm's paragraph. If the firm has no paragraph (is not ranked) look at Other Notable Practitioners.

## Media & Entertainment

### Leading Firms

**Band 1**
Covington & Burling LLP *
Davis Wright Tremaine LLP *
Jenner & Block LLP *
Levine Sullivan Koch & Schulz LLP *

**Band 2**
Arnold & Porter LLP *
Holland & Knight LLP *
Kirkland & Ellis LLP *
Latham & Watkins LLP *
Williams & Connolly LLP

**Band 3**
Mitchell Silberberg & Knupp LLP
Skadden, Arps, Slate, Meagher & Flom LLP & Affiliates *
WilmerHale *

### Leading Individuals

**Band 1**

| | |
|---|---|
| Baine Kevin T | Williams & Connolly LLP |
| Corn-Revere Robert | Davis Wright Tremaine LLP |
| Handman Laura R | Davis Wright Tremaine LLP |
| Levine Lee | Levine Sullivan Koch & Schulz LLP * |
| Smith Paul M | Jenner & Block LLP * |
| Yannucci Thomas D | Kirkland & Ellis LLP * |

**Band 2**

| | |
|---|---|
| Barnett Robert B | Williams & Connolly LLP |
| Berlin Seth D | Levine Sullivan Koch & Schulz LLP * |
| Carome Patrick J | WilmerHale * |
| Fabrizio Steven B | Jenner & Block LLP * |
| Garrett Robert A | Arnold & Porter LLP * |
| Hentoff Thomas G | Williams & Connolly LLP |
| Kendall David | Williams & Connolly LLP |
| Sanford Bruce W | Baker & Hostetler LLP (ONP) † * |
| Siegel Nathan E | Levine Sullivan Koch & Schulz LLP * |
| Sullivan Michael D | Levine Sullivan Koch & Schulz LLP * |
| Tobin Charles D | Holland & Knight LLP * |
| Weiswasser Stephen A | Covington & Burling LLP * |
| Wimmer Kurt A | Covington & Burling LLP * |

**Band 3**

| | |
|---|---|
| Bernthal Eric L | Latham & Watkins LLP * |
| Kaufman Kenneth M | Manatt Phelps & Phillips LLP (ONP) † |
| Metalitz Steven | Mitchell Silberberg & Knupp LLP |
| Schwartz Eric J. | Mitchell Silberberg & Knupp LLP |
| Sloan Cliff | Skadden, Arps, Slate, Meagher & Flom * |
| Ward Brown Jay | Levine Sullivan Koch & Schulz LLP * |

* Indicates firm / individual with profile.
† ONP = Other Notable Practitioner.

## Media & Entertainment: Mainly Regulatory

### Leading Firms

**Band 1**
Covington & Burling LLP *
Wiley Rein LLP *

**Band 2**
Latham & Watkins LLP *

**Band 3**
Dow Lohnes PLLC
Skadden, Arps, Slate, Meagher & Flom LLP & Affiliates *

### Leading Individuals

**Band 1**

| | |
|---|---|
| Corn-Revere Robert | Davis Wright Tremaine LLP |
| Rosenstein Mace J | Covington & Burling LLP * |
| Wiley Richard E | Wiley Rein LLP * |

**Band 2**

| | |
|---|---|
| Bernthal Eric L | Latham & Watkins LLP * |
| Weiswasser Stephen A | Covington & Burling LLP * |

**Band 3**

| | |
|---|---|
| Cook Bush Antoinette | Skadden, Arps, Slate, Meagher & Flom * |
| Feore John R | Dow Lohnes PLLC * |
| Goodman Jack N | Law Offices of Jack N Goodman (ONP) † |
| Kirby Kathleen A | Wiley Rein LLP * |

**Up-and-coming individuals**

| | |
|---|---|
| DelNero Matthew | Covington & Burling LLP * |

*The edit is in alphabetical order by firm name.*

### Arnold & Porter LLP
See profile on p.906

**THE FIRM** Arnold & Porter is acknowledged by sources as a leading media and entertainment firm and it has particularly established itself at the forefront of internet copyright and content litigation. In a recent highlight it acted on behalf of a consortium of major sports leagues, including MLB, the NFL, the NBA and the NHL, in a high-profile copyright royalties dispute.
**Sources say:** *"Client service is very important for them: they always get back promptly and I know when I call them their number-one priority is us."*
**KEY INDIVIDUALS Robert Garrett** (see p.864) is *"an excellent lawyer, who is hard-working, knowledgeable and articulate,"* and receives much praise for his work on copyright matters. He is the lead partner representing the consortium of major sports league in the copyrights royalties litigation mentioned above.

### Covington & Burling LLP
See profile on p.441

**THE FIRM** This premier practice continues to excel across the media and entertainment space, handling high-profile litigation and regulatory work for top clients including the NFL, Amazon.com and a host of major television networks. This robust and experienced team champions a holistic approach to the provision of its legal services and offers clients a 360-degree view of any media issue. A recent success was representing The Tennis Channel in a discriminatory carriage lawsuit against Comcast.
**Sources say:** *"A first-class law firm." "Terrific at everything – we never fail to get the very best from them."*
**KEY INDIVIDUALS Mace Rosenstein** (see p.888) is a *"standout"* lawyer *"who everybody looks to,"* and with regard to regulatory issues, in particular, he is regarded by sources as having *"experience second to none."* He continues to advise an array of top clients on FCC matters. The excellent **Kurt Wimmer** (see p.427) deals with the whole gamut of media and entertainment issues from privacy and IP to technology and advertising. He is described as *"a very practical business lawyer, who is very good at boiling down what something means and applying it in an intelligent business way."* **Stephen Weiswasser** (see p.899) has established a solid reputation in both transactional and regulatory work. He continues to represent clients in FCC litigation. Recent highlights include high-profile work for the Tennis Channel and the NFL. **Matthew DelNero** (see p.859) is lauded by peers and clients as *"a real star"* who is *"responsive and offers great counsel and good advice."* DelNero focuses on media, policy, communication and technology, and in a recent highlight represented the American Council on Education before the Copyright Royalties Board.

### Davis Wright Tremaine LLP
See profile on p.2544

**THE FIRM** This firm has established an impeccable reputation as one of the region's strongest media and First Amendment litigation firms and its lawyers are heralded as among the best in the district. The team maintains a fine track record acting on behalf of clients before the US Supreme Court and appellate courts nationwide. Among its key clients are Random House, The Wall Street Journal and CBS, which it recently successfully represented before the US Supreme Court in a landmark case against the FCC.
**Sources say:** *"First-rate!"*
**KEY INDIVIDUALS Robert Corn-Revere** is regarded as an expert First Amendment and regulatory attorney and enjoys a superb reputation acting for high-profile clients, such as CBS, before the US Court of Appeals and Supreme Court. *"He is simply first-rate in all regards, on top of his game and has a razor-sharp mind,"* reports one highly impressed source. Appellate practice cochair **Laura Handman** focuses on media and IP law and represents an excellent choice of counsel for newspapers, magazine and internet publishers, broadcasters and film studios. She has considerable experience in libel, First Amendment and privacy matters, and is regarded by peers as an outstanding litigator who is *"poised, self-confident and knowledgeable."*

## Dow Lohnes PLLC

**THE FIRM** Dow Lohnes is well versed across the spectrum of media, entertainment and IP work, and maintains a fine track record in litigation and regulatory matters. It is a particularly good choice of counsel for television clients and is also noted for its expertise in the new media arena.

**Sources say:** "*The firm is able to leverage its knowledge of the industry to guide us and help make business decisions.*"

**KEY INDIVIDUALS John Feore** (see p.862) is noted for his regulatory work and represents broadcast networks, television stations and radio clients before the FCC as well as other regulatory bodies. "*He has an uncanny ability to deliver great legal advice in a business-savvy way,*" reports one impressed interviewee.

## Holland & Knight LLP

See profile on p.1028

**THE FIRM** This well-rounded media team continues to demonstrate particular strengths in defamation and 'access to information' cases. A recent highlight includes successfully intervening and opening up court files regarding a murder trial, acting on behalf of a consortium of leading television stations, networks and newspapers. It counts Fox Television, Associated Press and The New York Times among its distinguished client roster.

**Sources say:** "*The lawyers are incredibly responsive, provide both perspective and practical advice, and are efficient and proactive.*"

**KEY INDIVIDUALS** National media team head **Charles Tobin** (see p.418) has extensive experience in freedom of information and libel disputes and elicits particular praise from commentators for his "*very effective courtroom manner.*"

## Jenner & Block LLP

See profile on p.1252

**THE FIRM** This formidable team dominates both the traditional and new media arenas and continues to be acknowledged as one of the best in the business on copyright issues. Of particular note is its groundbreaking work with Disney and other major motion picture studios against Hotfile.com, a 'cyberlocker' site. It also maintains a fine reputation representing the interests of recording artists and other clients before the US Copyright Royalty Judges.

**Sources say:** "*They have a deep bench of talent and really understand our business.*"

**KEY INDIVIDUALS** Commentators describe **Paul Smith** (see p.409) as an "*extremely good and able appellate litigator*" and applaud his "*superb ability to come up with a solution and walk the line on an argument.*" His enviable client list includes Viacom, PBS and WNET. Sources single out **Steven Fabrizio** (see p.861) as a "*good, hard-nosed litigator,*" adding that "*he is very hard-working, smart and proactive.*" He is currently representing Disney in the aforementioned matters against Hotfile.com, concerning internet copyright infringement.

## Kirkland & Ellis LLP

See profile on p.1254

**THE FIRM** This excellent practice continues to demonstrate strength in the areas of First Amendment, libel and general media issues. It deals predominantly with traditional media entities but continues to expand its work advising online and other new media clients.

**KEY INDIVIDUALS** Peers describe **Thomas Yannucci** (see p.901) as a "*first-class litigator*" who is "*smart, experienced and thorough.*" He maintains a fine track record for class action work in IP, defamation and First Amendment matters.

## Latham & Watkins LLP

See profile on p.446

**THE FIRM** This experienced team covers a broad range of regulatory, litigation and transactional work across media, IP and privacy. The group is also well equipped to handle both national and international media finance and investment matters. In a recent highlight, it lead the NFL Players Association to an important victory over the NFL in litigation concerning revenue distribution.

**Sources say:** "*Great firm – very responsive.*" "*They know their field and have information and responses at their fingertips.*"

**KEY INDIVIDUALS Eric Bernthal** (see p.852) is adept at advising investors, radio and television stations on the whole spectrum of media and entertainment issues, including transactional work, regulatory matters and disputes. A highlight from this year includes handling a TV rights renewal for Eurosport regarding the US Open tennis tournament.

## Levine Sullivan Koch & Schulz LLP

See profile on p.921

**THE FIRM** This boutique firm has continued to enhance its position as a leader in the media, IP and First Amendment space. The strong and experienced team continues to enjoy a good reputation for complex First Amendment Litigation, and retains a distinguished client base including The New York Times, Viacom and NBCUniversal.

**Sources say:** "*They are the epitome of a boutique firm: smart, nimble and responsive.*"

**KEY INDIVIDUALS** "*Superb lawyer*" **Lee Levine** (see p.355) "*has excellent instincts, is a terrific writer and understands businesses well.*" He is currently defending CBS Interactive against a defamation action filed by a former NBA player. **Jay Ward Brown** (see p.898) is noted by market sources for his "*detail-oriented, practical and responsive*" approach to matters. This year he has defended various eminent media establishments against defamation actions brought against them. **Seth Berlin** (see p.852) practice covers a broad array of media and entertainment matters, including libel, First Amendment, copyright and trademark litigation, and represents an excellent choice of counsel for clients in radio, television, newspapers and magazines. The esteemed **Michael Sullivan** (see p.414) has over three decades' worth of experience representing a raft of high-profile media clients in libel, privacy and copyright

disputes. **Nathan Siegel** (see p.892) is well versed in a variety of contentious media matters, including First Amendment, libel and IP. In a recent highlight he is defending ESPN against a defamation suit brought by a leading sports personality.

## Mitchell Silberberg & Knupp LLP

**THE FIRM** This group handles litigation and transactional work across the board, from new media and technology, to IP and international trade enforcements. The team regularly represents top clients including PBS, Universal and National Geographic, and in a recent highlight it acted for American Society of Composers, Authors & Publishers (ASCAP) in connection with the establishment of fair license rates with YouTube to stream public performances over the internet.

**Sources say:** "*Very high quality.*" "*A unique set of lawyers – very skilled.*"

**KEY INDIVIDUALS Steven Metalitz** wins much praise for his abilities as an advocate and is lauded by clients for his "*encyclopedic knowledge of copyright.*" He is currently representing the ASCAP in the aforementioned case regarding licensing rates with YouTube. **Eric Schwartz** is "*extremely knowledgeable about international copyright issues as well as domestic copyright law.*" He counsels clients on a range of IP matters, but is particular renowned for his work with clients in film and music.

## Skadden, Arps, Slate, Meagher & Flom LLP & Affiliates

See profile on p.2008

**THE FIRM** The DC office of this international firm offers clients a multidisciplinary approach to media and entertainment issues and handles litigation, regulatory and transactional matters for some of the biggest media and communications entities in the country. This includes representing clients in litigation matters in front of the courts of appeal and US Supreme Court. It counts Boston Red Sox, Warner Bros. and Disney among its impressive client base.

**Sources say:** "*They are excellent!*"

**KEY INDIVIDUALS Antoinette Cook Bush** (see p.858) is in charge of the firm's communications group and deals primarily with regulatory matters. "*She has an excellent mix of intellectual legal ability and people skills. She is extremely thorough in her preparation and a true expert in dealing with governmental officials,*" sources report. **Cliff Sloan** (see p.892) is an "*excellent all-around lawyer*" with a primary focus on litigation, and comes recommended for his broad array of expertise, not least with regard to trademark and copyright infringement. In a recent highlight, he successfully acted for Rosetta Stone in a landmark trademark infringement case against a major search engine.

## Wiley Rein LLP

See profile on p.928

**THE FIRM** Wiley Rein has retained its position as a leading light for regulatory work. However, this undisputed area of strength is further complemented by the team's broad interdisciplinary approach to media law, which also covers expertise in licensing, privacy, advertising and IP, among other areas. The firm is currently representing a group of radio and television broadcasters, including CBS and Gray Television, in a variety of matters, ranging from regulatory compliance and issues concerning online privacy restrictions to negotiating retransmission consent agreements.

**Sources say:** *"We are very impressed and very pleased. The work has been wonderful. I can't imagine doing our work without their counsel."*

**KEY INDIVIDUALS** Communications practice head **Richard Wiley** (see p.900) is noted for his wealth of experience concerning regulatory issues, having previously served as chairman of the FCC. He represents a host of top clients and took a leading role in the aforementioned matters for CBS and Gray Television. **Kathleen Kirby** (see p.874) comes recommended for her work on First Amendment and FCC matters. Clients appreciate her responsiveness and proactive approach as well as her *"ability to stay on top"* of a situation.

## Williams & Connolly LLP

**THE FIRM** This firm is renowned in the market for its excellent litigation capabilities and maintains a superb track record on First Amendment and media disputes.

Matters covered range from defamation and invasion of privacy to reporters' privilege and copyright.

**KEY INDIVIDUALS Kevin Baine** receives much praise for his effectiveness in court and is regarded by interviewees as a *"person you turn to when there is a lot on the line."* He is predominantly plaintiff-focused, representing major organizations in libel and First Amendment cases. **Robert Barnett** is noted for his work with clients throughout the publishing world, including a huge assortment of authors from the worlds of fiction and business writing, and is routinely called upon for his strengths in contract and contentious matters. The superb **Thomas Hentoff** *"knows what he's talking about,"* comment impressed sources. His practice is primarily focused on First Amendment, media and IP disputes. **David Kendall** has extensive litigation experience across a variety of practice areas, but within the media sphere he is particularly recognized for his representation of high-profile clients in First Amendment and copyright trials.

## WilmerHale
See profile on p.930

**THE FIRM** This team primarily focuses on litigation, but is also noted for its transactional strength. It remains an excellent choice of counsel for matters concerning digital copyright and trademark infringement, as well as First

Amendment litigation. The group recently filed an amicus brief in the US Supreme Court on behalf of media entities including Facebook and Yahoo!.

**Sources say:** *"Bright, creative lawyers."*

**KEY INDIVIDUALS Patrick Carome** (see p.856) is an accomplished and experienced media litigator, with over 25 years of experience. He has a fine track record in matters relating to privacy, defamation and press access, and is especially recognized for his mastery in defending internet companies from liability for unlawful third-party content.

## Other Notable Practitioners

Sole practitioner **Jack Goodman** advises clients on licensing, public policy, IP and various other media matters, and is particularly noted by peers for his work in the regulatory space. Baker & Hostetler LLP's **Bruce Sanford** (see p.399) comes highly recommended for his representation of high-profile newspaper and magazine publishers and enjoys a fine reputation for his work in libel and First Amendment litigation. At Manatt Phelps & Phillips LLP, **Kenneth Kaufman** continues to work with clients from the entire spectrum of the media and entertainment world, and is noted for his strengths across copyright, music licensing, internet law and new technologies.

# REAL ESTATE

Zoning/Land Use p.835

Commentary about individuals can be found under their firm's paragraph. If the firm has no paragraph (is not ranked) look at Other Notable Practitioners.

| Real Estate |
|---|
| **Leading Firms** |
| **Band 1** |
| Arent Fox LLP * |
| Arnold & Porter LLP * |
| DLA Piper LLP (US) * |
| Goulston & Storrs |
| Holland & Knight LLP * |
| Venable LLP * |
| **Band 2** |
| Bingham McCutchen LLP * |
| Hogan Lovells US LLP |
| Mayer Brown LLP * |
| Pillsbury Winthrop Shaw Pittman LLP * |
| Womble Carlyle Sandridge & Rice, LLP * |
| **Band 3** |
| Greenstein Delorme & Luchs |
| Grossberg Yochelson Fox & Beyda |

## Band 1

### Arent Fox LLP
See profile on p.905

**THE FIRM** This top-quality practice handles a broad range of real estate work, covering sports arenas, hospitality and leisure, senior living facilities and real estate bonds. The team acts for major developers and investors on a local, national and international scale, and clients benefit from the strong support of the firm's tax, environmental and corporate groups. The team has represented the Association of American Medical Colleges in the development, financing and sale of several properties. Other clients include Quadrangle Development and Marriott International.

**Sources say:** *"An elite, full-service real estate firm. It is very cost-effective, not just with billing rates but through its more focused and efficient efforts."*

**KEY INDIVIDUALS Richard Newman** (see p.884) is widely recognized as a specialist in bond financing. He represented the Association of American Medical Colleges in the $216 million financing for the development of an office building in downtown Washington, DC. **Mark Katz** (see p.873) is a highly regarded real estate practitioner. He undertakes a range of transactional work and financing for clients including US Real Estate Partners, Goldman Sachs and Marathon Asset Management. **Michael Leahy** (see

p.876) advises clients on a broad spectrum of transactional matters. Sources are *"very impressed with the way he runs a deal. He's a straight shooter and when he said he'd do something he did it. He has a no-nonsense approach."* Hospitality expert **Kimberly Wachen** (see p.897) is well known for her work representing Marriott. She also offers expertise in senior living facilities and senior living companies work.

### Arnold & Porter LLP
See profile on p.906

**THE FIRM** Arnold & Porter's real estate group is highly regarded for its commercial real estate work, and regularly acts on complex and high-value developments, hospitality transactions, debt and equity financing and PPP. Recent work highlights include acting for Vornado Realty Trust on the leasing of a major office building following the bankruptcy of the anchor tenant. Real estate clients benefit from expertise drawn from the firm's government contracts, tax and environmental groups. The team represents a number of leading names, such as JBG, Penzance Properties, McCaffery Interests and StonebridgeCarras.

**Sources say:** *"I have been very impressed by Arnold & Porter's real estate group. They are very responsive and think ahead to ensure smooth closings, and they are among the brightest and most professional attorneys I have worked with."*

## Real Estate
### Senior Statesmen

**Senior Statesmen: distinguished older practitioners**

| | | | |
|---|---|---|---|
| Beyda Richard | Grossberg Yochelson Fox & Beyda | Tucker Stefan | Venable LLP * |

### Leading Individuals

**Star individuals**

| | |
|---|---|
| Goodwin Michael | Arnold & Porter LLP * |

**Band 1**

| | |
|---|---|
| Epstien Jay | DLA Piper LLP (US) * |
| Hagner John D | Womble Carlyle Sandridge & Rice, LLP |
| Klein Frederick L | DLA Piper LLP (US) * |
| Parmley Bruce E | Hogan Lovells US LLP |
| Rosenthal Barry P | Bingham McCutchen LLP * |
| Weisel Sheldon J | Goulston & Storrs |
| Willner Keith J | Mayer Brown LLP |

**Band 2**

| | |
|---|---|
| Engel John | Pillsbury Winthrop Shaw Pittman LLP |
| Fields Wendy | Katten Muchin Rosenman LLP (ONP)† |
| Gage Robert J | Covington & Burling LLP (ONP)† * |
| Gart Ron | Seyfarth Shaw LLP (ONP)† * |
| Gottlieb Robert G | Venable LLP * |
| Greenstein Abraham | Greenstein Delorme & Luchs |
| Henneburg Frank H | Mayer Brown LLP |
| Horowitz Philip | Venable LLP * |
| Humes Gary | Arnold & Porter LLP * |
| Kahn David S | Holland & Knight LLP * |
| Keitelman Jeffrey R | DLA Piper LLP (US) * |
| Moyer Dennis K | Buchanan Ingersoll & Rooney (ONP)† * |
| Newman Richard | Arent Fox LLP * |
| Rogers Ed | Reed Smith LLP (ONP)† |
| Schiff Janis Boyarsky | Holland & Knight LLP * |
| Silver David C | Holland & Knight LLP * |
| Weld King Carol | Hogan Lovells US LLP |

| | |
|---|---|
| White Wendelin A | Pillsbury Winthrop Shaw Pittman LLP * |

**Band 3**

| | |
|---|---|
| Fox Allen H | WilmerHale (ONP)† * |
| Katz Mark M | Arent Fox LLP * |
| Kaufman Thomas F | Goulston & Storrs |
| Leahy Michael H | Arent Fox LLP * |
| Migdal Nelson F | Greenberg Traurig, LLP (ONP)† * |
| Perkins Jennifer | Arnold & Porter LLP * |
| Pickett J Michael | Bingham McCutchen LLP * |
| Rassman Franz R | Fried, Frank, Harris, Shriver (ONP)† * |
| Rothenberg Pamela V | Womble Carlyle Sandridge & Rice, LLP |
| Tiedemann Charles Welch (Chad) | Holland & Knight LLP * |
| Wachen Kimberly | Arent Fox LLP * |
| Wilcox Justine E | Nixon Peabody LLP (ONP)† * |
| Yogodzinski Debra D | Reed Smith LLP (ONP)† |

**Band 4**

| | |
|---|---|
| Bodansky Robert | Seyfarth Shaw LLP (ONP)† * |
| David Richard G | Womble Carlyle Sandridge & Rice, LLP |
| Gelman Jeffrey H | Saul Ewing LLP (ONP)† |
| Haberl Heather | Covington & Burling LLP (ONP)† * |
| Luchs Richard W | Greenstein Delorme & Luchs |
| Millspaugh Thomas E D | Venable LLP * |
| Ratino John M | Goulston & Storrs |
| Rifkind Amy B | Arnold & Porter LLP * |
| Scanlon Tara A | Holland & Knight LLP * |

**Associates to watch**

| | |
|---|---|
| Dafoe Colette A | Nixon Peabody LLP (ONP)† * |

### Real Estate: Zoning/Land Use
### Leading Individuals

**Band 1**

| | |
|---|---|
| Dwyer Maureen | Goulston & Storrs |
| Glasgow Jr Norman | Holland & Knight LLP * |
| Quin Whayne S | Holland & Knight LLP * |

**Band 2**

| | |
|---|---|
| Briggs David W | Holland & Knight LLP * |
| Feola Phil | Goulston & Storrs |
| Prince Allison | Goulston & Storrs |

**Band 3**

| | |
|---|---|
| Collins Christopher H | Holland & Knight LLP * |
| Giordano Cynthia | Saul Ewing LLP (ONP)† |
| Tummonds Paul | Goulston & Storrs |

*  Indicates firm / individual with profile.

† ONP = Other Notable Practitioner.

**KEY INDIVIDUALS Michael Goodwin** (see p.866) heads the real estate department at Arnold & Porter. Recent highlights for him include advising Host Hotels & Resorts on the $400 million acquisition of the Grand Hyatt Hotel in Washington, DC. **Gary Humes** (see p.870) regularly acts on large-scale complex transactions. He and Goodwin advised Louis Dreyfus Property on the $1 billion acquisition of 2.2 million sq ft in air rights. **Jennifer Perkins** (see p.885) regularly handles commercial real estate sales and acquisitions, leasing and financing, on both a local and a national scale. **Amy Rifkind**'s (see p.887) broad practice includes development, build-to-suit transactions, financing and PPP.

### DLA Piper LLP (US)
See profile on p.1971

**THE FIRM** This outstanding real estate group acts on a broad range of complex and significant transactions for its high-profile clients. Recent standout matters include acting for major developer Penzance on a 173,000 sq ft build-to-suit lease. The firm also advises Pfizer on various real estate transactions, including the negotiation of a lease and the sale of a number of properties. Other key clients include Citizens Bank, The Blackstone Group, Wells Real Estate Funds and Tishman Speyer.

**Sources say:** *"They continue to be preeminent lawyers in the field." "We had a very good experience – I was very happy with their work."*

**KEY INDIVIDUALS** Market-leading practitioner **Jay Epstien** (see p.310) heads the US real estate team at DLA Piper. He is *"the cream of the crop,"* according to market commentators, and is described as *"extremely bright,* extremely experienced and really good at working out a compromise. He's good at figuring out how to protect the client."* **Frederick Klein** (see p.347) leads the firm's real estate group in DC, and has a top reputation for his work on sales and partnerships. He earns high praise from sources, who consider him *"outstanding – he understands the legal aspects and is easy to work with from a business perspective, and he's very responsive."* **Jeffrey Keitelman** (see p.873) is a well-respected attorney who has acted on a number of very high-profile matters of late. One example was acting on the $118 million purchase of a Bluemont Way building as Verisign's headquarters.

### Goulston & Storrs

**THE FIRM** This highly impressive real estate practice has extensive expertise in zoning and land use matters, in addition to considerable capabilities acting on development, financings, joint ventures and military housing privatization. The team acted for MRP Realty on applying for approvals from the Zoning Commission for the first stage of the Florida Rock Planned Unit Development. It has also secured approvals from the Zoning Commission for Georgetown University's plans for a new campus. Other high-profile clients include Clark Enterprises, Boston Properties, Archstone and the Pebblebrook Hotel Trust.

**Sources say:** *"A great real estate practice."*

**KEY INDIVIDUALS Maureen Dwyer** is well known for giving high-quality zoning advice to a strong university client base. Sources say: *"She has knowledge of the area, is easy to work with and thoughtful,"* and *"good at identifying the issues and developing a strategy to overcome them."* Clients applaud **Sheldon Weisel** for being *"exceptionally knowledgeable about the market options and creative strategies."* One added: *"He has clearly brought added value to our engagement and we have the highest regard for him."* **Allison Prince** is a very highly regarded zoning lawyer. *"She's extremely knowledgeable, and is really good at pushing the ball forward and getting issues resolved,"* sources say. **Paul Tummonds** is singled out by commentators as one of the rising stars of land use law. He advised Skyland Holdings on zoning issues for the Skyland Town Center. **Thomas Kaufman** is a financing specialist recognized for his ability to handle large, complex transactions. *"He has a vibrant practice and is one of those guys who's so smart that he can figure out new difficult issues – he can tear them apart and put them back together as a solved puzzle,"* observers say. Sources praise **John Ratino** for being *"very incisive and good at hitting the issues that are going to save his client money."* Recent highlights include acting for Carr Properties on a number of transactions and financings. **Phil Feola** has an excellent reputation for his top-level land use work. *"He is brilliant, talented, smart and creative,"* market commentators say. He recently assisted Forest City Enterprises with land use approvals for a large-scale mixed-use development.

### Holland & Knight LLP
See profile on p.1028

**THE FIRM** The substantial team at Holland & Knight covers the full spectrum of real estate and zoning work, and has particular strength in large-scale mixed-use developments and work in the hospitality and retail sectors. The team is acting for Roadside Development on the landmark $300 million redevelopment of the O Street Market, which involves retail space, condominiums, apartments and a hotel. Standout matters for the firm's land use group include acting for the Chinese Embassy in Washington, DC on the construction of a new embassy building.

**KEY INDIVIDUALS** *"One of the preeminent land use lawyers,"* **Norman Glasgow** (see p.865) wins high praise from clients and peers alike for being *"very good and very practical."* He is currently advising on zoning issues for the high-profile redevelopment of the Watergate Hotel. Sources hail **Whayne Quin** (see p.886) as the *"dean of land use law."* He brings decades of experience to his role at the firm, and notably advised McMillan on a mixed-use planned development on a reservoir site in Washington, DC. Experienced land use attorney **David Briggs** (see p.854) *"knows the ins and outs of DC in a way that very few people do,"* say interviewees. *"The level of detail to which he explores issues and manages outcomes is quite exceptional,"* sources add. **David Kahn** (see p.872) is a highly regarded real estate practitioner applauded for his skills as a litigator. He recently acted for a life insurance company on the drafting and negotiation of a 450,000 sq ft lease. **Janis Boyarsky Schiff** (see p.890) has a broad commercial real estate practice, acting for owners, investors and property managers. *"She's very savvy and knows how to do a good job for her client,"* say sources. **David Silver** (see p.892) advises owners, developers, large corporations and pension funds on a variety of real estate matters. According to peers, he *"is very smart and extremely experienced, knows the issues and knows what's important."* Well-regarded real estate expert **Christopher Collins** (see p.857) recently advised on a major shopping center development. Observers highlight him as *"excellent, knowledgeable, reasonable and thorough – a lawyer who does a fine job."* *"The most important thing about* **Chad Tiedemann** (see p.896) *is the way he looks out for our business. He's thinking ahead about the risks that we're facing and is almost like a part of our business,"* said one client. Tiedemann regularly acts for major DC developers and investors, including investment advisers, insurance companies, pension funds and high net worth individuals. **Tara Scanlon** (see p.890) is a well-respected real estate practitioner. She recently advised on the high-profile O Street Market development, as well as a $192 million apartment purchase.

## Venable LLP
See profile on p.927

**THE FIRM** A leader in the DC market, Venable handles the full spectrum of real estate matters for its clients. The team works on a local, regional and national scale, on commercial, industrial and residential developments, including transactions relating to office buildings and hotels. It also excels on work involving specialized property classes. Notably, the group acted for Baker & McKenzie on the negotiation and extension of the lease for its Washington, DC office. The firm's impressive client base also includes

Safeway, The World Bank, the Canadian Embassy in Washington, DC and Fannie Mae.

**Sources say:** *"They're all very knowledgeable and have a deep team."*

**KEY INDIVIDUALS Robert Gottlieb** (see p.866) earns great praise for his work for major local developers. He also has plenty of experience representing other parties, including acting for Kiplinger Washington Editors on the sale of its 116,000 sq ft office building. **Philip Horowitz** (see p.870) is known for his broad practice, which ranges from sales and leasing matters to zoning work. Clients praise him for being *"knowledgeable, articulate, reasonable and responsive."* According to sources, he excels on tough transactions. **Thomas Millspaugh** (see p.882) heads the real estate group at Venable. Clients consider him to be *"very personable, very knowledgeable and easy to work with. He understands the motivations on each side of the table."* The eminent **Stefan Tucker** (see p.897) brings decades of invaluable real estate experience to his role at the firm.

## Band 2

### Bingham McCutchen LLP
See profile on p.1515

**THE FIRM** This team's excellent real estate offering sees it act for major developers, owners and investors, as well as a range of private equity and distressed opportunity funds, pension funds, PPPs and educational institutions. Major names represented by the team include Wells Fargo, TD Bank, Global Retail Investors and Perseus Realty. Highlights include acting for Paradigm Development Company on the acquisition of a $145 million multifamily development.

**Sources say:** *"They are detail-oriented and have the depth of knowledge to cover complex deals."*

**KEY INDIVIDUALS Barry Rosenthal** (see p.888) is a very highly regarded real estate and real estate finance specialist. He impresses clients with his *"years of experience and his standing in the real estate community."* One added: *"He protects our interests while moving things forward."* The *"terrific"* **Michael Pickett** (see p.886) is earning increasingly impressive praise. In the words of one commentator, *"his legal prowess is top-notch, his organizational skills have been nothing short of perfect, and he is pleasant interacting with the other side."* Pickett is a highly promising practitioner and recently acted for the JBG Companies on a purchase and joint venture relating to a large-scale development in Virginia.

### Hogan Lovells US LLP

**THE FIRM** A major player in the DC real estate market, this firm undertakes a broad range of work that includes leasing, financing, acquisitions, joint ventures and land use. Clients include Kingdom Hotel Investments, Qatari Diar and the Schwan Foundation. The firm benefits from its global network of offices, which enables the team to handle matters on an international scale. The team recently advised Bright Start Holdings, an investment arm of the family of His Highness Sheikh Mohammed bin Rashid Al

Maktoum, on the proposed Four Seasons Resort Dubai, to be located on an 11-acre natural waterfront site in the Arabian Gulf.

**Sources say:** *"Top quality, very smart and very knowledgeable."*

**KEY INDIVIDUALS** Clients value **Bruce Parmley** for his *"precision, excellence and reliability."* He recently acted for Gaylord Entertainment on the $210 million sale of its management business to Marriott International. **Carol Weld King** has particular expertise in acting on real estate transactions for clients in the hospitality sector. According to sources, she *"is able to blend incredible legal and business judgment, and is a truly excellent practitioner."*

## Mayer Brown LLP
See profile on p.1257

**THE FIRM** This firm acts for a strong client base of institutional providers, including pension funds, insurance companies, opportunity funds and hedge funds, as well as various banks and developers. Major names represented by the team include Starwood Capital and Archstone. Work highlights include acting for a leading life insurance company on a variety of matters, including the $158 million financing of an office building in Washington, DC, and the origination of a mortgage loan for another office building in DC.

**Sources say:** *"Very professional, conscientious and client-focused."*

**KEY INDIVIDUALS Keith Willner** is a major name in the DC real estate market. He acted for Starwood Capital on a series of transactions with a combined value of $700 million. *"I think he's the best real estate lawyer I know. He has all the tools – he's fabulous and he knows how to get the right result,"* said one interviewee. The *"brilliant"* **Frank Henneburg** has an excellent reputation for his work in the hospitality sector. He was described by one source as *"an excellent, organized and efficient practitioner who really impressed me."*

## Pillsbury Winthrop Shaw Pittman LLP
See profile on p.2000

**THE FIRM** This strong real estate group is well respected for its commercial approach and financing expertise. The team acts for such key names as Boston Properties, DAG Petroleum, Clark Realty Capital and Grosvenor Americas. Highlights for the group include advising the shopping center REIT Saul Centers on a number of acquisitions and financings, to the value of $800 million. The firm has also acted for Walton International on the acquisition of a commercial, residential and hotel development with a developed value of $1.5 billion.

**Sources say:** *"I would give the real estate group very high marks. They're very smart and sensitive to the issues that are important to you, and they make sure they're paying attention to them all the time. Top-notch and on top of their game."*

**KEY INDIVIDUALS John Engel** advises major clients including investors, developers and nonprofit institutions on high-value real estate transactions. Observers say that he is *"solution-oriented and business-oriented, and doesn't*

*lose sight of the business aspects when doing a deal."* **Wendelin White** (see p.899) has an excellent reputation for her transactional real estate expertise. According to sources, she is *"tremendous, very incisive, capable and creative. She can handle all kinds of negotiations, has good judgment and solves problems."*

## Womble Carlyle Sandridge & Rice, LLP
**See profile on p.2049**
**THE FIRM** This real estate group is known for its strong work relating to residential and commercial properties, including office buildings, shopping centers, multifamily housing and luxury hotels. The team handles leasing, financing, development, sales and acquisitions, for such clients as Wells Fargo, Kettler, Realty Management Services and the Abbey Road Property Group.
**Sources say:** *"Very well regarded."*
**KEY INDIVIDUALS** The outstanding **John Hagner** is widely recognized as one of the deans of the DC real estate market. According to market commentators, he is *"an eminence, an anchor and a really strong real estate attorney."* **Pamela Rothenberg** is *"very well regarded, and a very high-profile person for the firm,"* sources say. Her recent work includes acting for a leading developer on a ground lease transaction for a multifamily apartment community. Commercial real estate expert **Richard David** is described by market observers as *"an excellent, strong and experienced lawyer who is a pleasure to work with."*

## Band 3

### Greenstein Delorme & Luchs
**THE FIRM** The group at Greenstein Delorme & Luchs is praised for its strong real estate work. It acts on a broad range of matters, including drafting and negotiating for sales and acquisitions, and preparing financing commitments. Leasing is another key area of focus, and the group has negotiated leases with international entities and governmental entities at federal, state and local level. The firm also has a strong record in real estate litigation, regularly handling disputes relating to contracts, title matters and mechanics' liens.

**Sources say:** *"Well-known and well-respected practitioners."*
**KEY INDIVIDUALS Abraham Greenstein** has an excellent reputation in the DC market. Commentators say that he is *"such an expert in leasing and a joy to work with."* **Richard Luchs** has in-depth transactional real estate experience, as well as considerable expertise in handling various methods of alternative dispute resolution. In the words of one commentator, he is *"clearly the best-known lawyer in the tenants' rights and landlord-tenant arena."*

### Grossberg Yochelson Fox & Beyda
**THE FIRM** This well-established DC firm handles mainly transactional real estate work. The team regularly acts for borrowers and lenders on financing for commercial and residential properties, including hotel transactions and property development. Leasing is another area of focus, and the group acts for a number of landlords and tenants on complex office, industrial, retail and ground leases.
**KEY INDIVIDUALS Richard Beyda** acts for some of DC's major developer families, and regularly handles sales and acquisitions, leasing and real estate finance.

### Other Notable Practitioners
**Wendy Fields** of Katten Muchin Rosenman LLP is noted for her ability to handle large-scale, complex transactions. According to sources, she is *"a master practitioner. She has the wisdom, knowledge and experience that few lawyers possess, and is also a creative thinker."* Clients praise **Robert Gage** (see p.864) of Covington & Burling LLP as being *"very effective and very responsive, and available 24/7."* He heads the department at the firm and advised Intercell on the sublease of its headquarters and pharmaceutical manufacturing facility. **Ron Gart** (see p.864) of Seyfarth Shaw LLP is a highly experienced attorney with a broad real estate practice. *"He works on very complex, very significant transactions and is very capable,"* peers say. Commercial real estate expert **Dennis Moyer** (see p.882) of Buchanan Ingersoll & Rooney PC handles acquisitions, sales and leasing. He regularly acts for institutional investors on joint ventures and mortgage financings. **Ed Rogers** of Reed Smith LLP acts for a range of clients, including major joint ventures, and is developing his expertise in zoning matters

relating to biofuels. *"I've been very impressed with him,"* said one peer, adding: *"He's the kind of attorney who is always thinking two moves down the path."* **Allen Fox** (see p.863) of WilmerHale is a well-regarded lawyer who regularly handles sales and acquisitions, leasing and financing and has decades of experience acting on real estate matters. **Cynthia Giordano** of Saul Ewing LLP has accumulated decades of experience in zoning and land use. She acts for developers, homeowners and institutional and commercial clients. **Nelson Migdal** (see p.368) heads the real estate group at Greenberg Traurig, LLP. His practice covers real estate and hospitality work, and his recent highlights include advising the owners of a high-profile luxury hotel. **Franz Rassman** (see p.887) of Fried, Frank, Harris, Shriver & Jacobson LLP is recognized for his leasing expertise. *"When we have a big assignment we go to him,"* said one interviewee. *"He brings knowledge and skill and is a deal-maker who is practical and knows the law. He is good at finding a different way to look at things."* **Justine Wilcox** (see p.900) leads the practice at Nixon Peabody LLP, and handles large-scale complex real estate transactions for a range of high-profile clients. *"She's a true professional in every way. She knows her stuff and never loses her cool,"* sources say. **Debra Yogodzinski** of Reed Smith LLP has a strong local development practice, and acts for many joint ventures. *"She's so impressive, a very good lawyer who is smart and a delight to work with,"* according to observers. **Robert Bodansky** (see p.853) of Seyfarth Shaw LLP is applauded by market commentators for the breadth of his practice and his ability to act on highly complex matters. His client base includes private developers and owners, and public sector pension funds. **Jeffrey Gelman** of Saul Ewing LLP is highlighted for his experience working on multifamily residential developments, and commercial and industrial properties. **Heather Haberl** (see p.867) of Covington & Burling LLP has recently advised Joy Global on various real estate matters, including the sale of a drilling products business. **Colette Dafoe** (see p.859) of Nixon Peabody LLP is a highly regarded associate with expertise in commercial real estate transactions.

# TAX

Commentary about individuals can be found under their firm's paragraph. If the firm has no paragraph (is not ranked) look at Other Notable Practitioners.

## Tax
### Leading Firms

**Band 1**
Bingham McCutchen LLP *
Skadden, Arps, Slate, Meagher & Flom LLP & Affiliates *

**Band 2**
Baker & McKenzie *
Caplin & Drysdale *
Ivins, Phillips & Barker *
Latham & Watkins LLP *
McDermott Will & Emery LLP *
Miller & Chevalier Chartered *

**Band 3**
Baker & Hostetler LLP *
Covington & Burling LLP *
Fried, Frank, Harris, Shriver & Jacobson LLP *
Morgan, Lewis & Bockius LLP *
Steptoe & Johnson LLP *
Sutherland Asbill & Brennan LLP *

**Band 4**
Freshfields Bruckhaus Deringer LLP *
Jones Day *

\* Indicates firm / individual with profile.
†ONP = Other Notable Practitioner.

## Tax
### Leading Individuals

**Band 1**

| | | |
|---|---|---|
| Gideon Kenneth W | Skadden, Arps, Slate, Meagher & Flom * | |
| Goldberg Jr Fred T | Skadden, Arps, Slate, Meagher & Flom * | |
| Kafka Gerald A | Latham & Watkins LLP * | |
| McKee Bill | Bingham McCutchen LLP * | |
| Oosterhuis Paul W | Skadden, Arps, Slate, Meagher & Flom * | |
| Rosenbloom H David | Caplin & Drysdale | |
| Rubin Blake D | McDermott Will & Emery LLP * | |
| Schneider Leslie | Ivins, Phillips & Barker * | |
| Silverman Mark | Steptoe & Johnson LLP | |

**Band 2**

| | |
|---|---|
| Culbertson Robert E | Covington & Burling LLP * |
| Farmer F Scott | Bingham McCutchen LLP * |
| Fisher Miriam L | Latham & Watkins LLP * |
| Gertzman Stephen | Miller & Chevalier Chartered * |
| Gibbs Lawrence B | Miller & Chevalier Chartered * |
| Hicks Hal | Skadden, Arps, Slate, Meagher & Flom * |
| Magee John B | Bingham McCutchen LLP * |
| May Gregory | Freshfields Bruckhaus Deringer LLP * |
| Nelson William F | Bingham McCutchen LLP * |
| Pari Joseph | Linklaters (ONP)† |
| Paul William M | Covington & Burling LLP * |
| Roady Celia | Morgan, Lewis & Bockius LLP * |
| Rudnick Robert | Shearman & Sterling LLP (ONP)† |
| Terr Leonard | Baker & McKenzie * |
| Wellen Robert H | Ivins, Phillips & Barker * |
| Wells Stephen E | McDermott Will & Emery LLP * |
| West Philip | Steptoe & Johnson LLP |
| Wiacek Raymond | Jones Day * |
| Williams Jr B John | Skadden, Arps, Slate, Meagher & Flom * |

**Band 3**

| | |
|---|---|
| Brockway David H | Bingham McCutchen LLP * |
| Cavanagh Rita A | Latham & Watkins LLP * |
| Feagles Prentiss | Hogan Lovells US LLP (ONP)† |
| Heltzer Harold J | Crowell & Moring LLP (ONP)† * |
| Howe Joseph | Arnold & Porter LLP (ONP)† * |
| Kaden Alan S | Fried, Frank, Harris, Shriver & Jacobson * |
| Keyes Kevin M | Fried, Frank, Harris, Shriver & Jacobson * |
| Lewis Patricia G | Caplin & Drysdale |
| Libin Jerome B | Sutherland Asbill & Brennan LLP |
| Madan Raj | Bingham McCutchen LLP * |

| | |
|---|---|
| Mann Phillip L | Miller & Chevalier Chartered * |
| McCarty Philip A | McDermott Will & Emery LLP * |
| Michel Scott D | Caplin & Drysdale |
| Paravano Jeffrey H | Baker & Hostetler LLP * |
| Riedy James | McDermott Will & Emery LLP * |
| Schmidt Paul | Baker & Hostetler LLP * |
| Shashy Abraham N M | King & Spalding LLP (ONP)† * |
| Skillman Richard W | Caplin & Drysdale |
| Sparagna Giovanna T | Sutherland Asbill & Brennan LLP |
| Stack Robert | Ivins, Phillips & Barker |
| Westbrook Reeves C | Covington & Burling LLP * |

**Band 4**

| | |
|---|---|
| Alter Michael J | Fried, Frank, Harris, Shriver & Jacobson * |
| Bailey Arthur L | Steptoe & Johnson LLP |
| Beller Herbert N | Sutherland Asbill & Brennan LLP |
| Bennett Mary | Baker & McKenzie * |
| Birnkrant Henry | Alston & Bird LLP (ONP)† |
| Bowers Chris | Bingham McCutchen LLP * |
| Bucholtz Harold | Holland & Knight LLP (ONP)† * |
| Carlisle Linda E | White & Case LLP (ONP)† * |
| Chip William W | Covington & Burling LLP * |
| DeNovio Nicholas J | Latham & Watkins LLP * |
| Dunahoo Carol A | Baker & McKenzie * |
| Femia Rocco V | Miller & Chevalier Chartered * |
| Friedman Jeffrey A | Sutherland Asbill & Brennan LLP |
| Goldman Joseph | Jones Day * |
| Gomez Armando | Skadden, Arps, Slate, Meagher & Flom * |
| Granwell Alan Winston | DLA Piper LLP (US) (ONP)† * |
| Joseph James P | Arnold & Porter LLP (ONP)† * |
| Korb Donald L | Sullivan & Cromwell LLP (ONP)† * |
| LeDuc André | Skadden, Arps, Slate, Meagher & Flom LLP * |
| Luchsinger Dan | Covington & Burling LLP * |
| Nilles Kathleen M | Holland & Knight LLP (ONP)† * |
| Sadler Alex E | Ivins, Phillips & Barker * |
| Stansbury Claude B | Freshfields Bruckhaus Deringer LLP * |
| Suringa Dirk | Covington & Burling LLP * |
| Toro Emin | Covington & Burling LLP * |
| Warren James | Miller & Chevalier Chartered * |
| Whiteway Andrea | McDermott Will & Emery LLP * |
| Zakupowsky Alexander | Miller & Chevalier Chartered * |

## Band 1

### Bingham McCutchen LLP
**See profile on p.1515**

**THE FIRM** This leading firm is able to offer service of the highest level across a range of tax matters. It demonstrates particular proficiency in the handling of controversies, and in undertaking high-value cases in the area of international and domestic tax planning. It is distinguished from other firms in the region for its expertise in the sphere of transfer pricing, and attracts further recognition for its ability to handle complex matters arising from tax partnership issues. These considerable strengths are reflected in the stature of its clients, who include Lehman Brothers, GE Capital and Dow Chemical.

**Sources say:** *"A go-to firm. They have a number of very high-quality tax partners, and good depth and breadth."*

**KEY INDIVIDUALS** Co-head of department **Bill McKee's** (see p.881) practice incorporates the entire range of matters relating to federal taxation. He has a particular interest in partnership taxation, and recently offered counsel to Energy Transfer Partners concerning a multibillion-dollar acquisition. Clients praise *"a clear thinker and an excellent communicator"* who is client-focused and has *"extraordinary technical tax expertise."* **Scott Farmer** (see p.861) handles disputes with the IRS, and advises on all areas of international tax planning. He undertakes work for foreign organizations conducting business in the USA, and for domestic organizations operating abroad. Clients speak highly of an individual who *"brings creative and thoughtful solutions to issues."* **John Magee** (see p.360) co-leads the firm's transfer pricing practice and is among its leading tax controversy partners. He has earned a reputation among clients as *"a world-class tax litigator,"* and is celebrated by peers for bringing to his work *"a very high-quality manner of presentation."* He has acted for clients such as Dow Chemical and Santander in matters arising from disputes with the IRS. **William Nelson** (see p.375) co-heads the department and enjoys a reputation among clients as *"an excellent advocate with super technical expertise who goes the extra mile."* Peers recognize an individual who *"would be at the very top of anyone's list in the areas of litigation and controversy."* **David Brockway** (see p.854) has established a practice that incorporates most aspects of tax planning. He has a particular emphasis on corporate dispositions and acquisitions and international tax matters. **Raj Madan** (see p.360) lends further strength to his firm's controversy and litigation practice. He is particularly well known for advocating on behalf of financial organizations. He is renowned in the market for *"bringing an entrepreneurial, engaged spirit to his representation."* **Chris Bowers's** (see p.853) practice covers all areas of domestic and international tax planning and controversy, focusing on cross-border M&A, cross-border financing and foreign tax credit planning.

## Skadden, Arps, Slate, Meagher & Flom LLP & Affiliates
See profile on p.2008

THE FIRM For its depth of experience, the caliber of its practitioners and the range of its expertise, the tax group at this firm is almost unrivaled. It operates across all areas of tax law, including joint ventures, transfer pricing, bankruptcy, restructurings, financings, acquisitions, dispositions, spinoffs and partnerships. In each of these cases it is able to act in matters domestic, international and interjurisdictional. Additional strength is found in its ability to handle controversies and litigation, and the firm is renowned for the talent it is able to bring to matters involving the IRS. Its many distinguished clients include CIGNA, Merrill Lynch and Yahoo!.

Sources say: *"A very thoughtful team with very strong domestic, international and government contacts. They can handle very high-end controversy, and very high-end deals. They have the full package."*

KEY INDIVIDUALS Kenneth Gideon (see p.320), one of the leaders of his firm's tax litigation team, has established a practice that includes issues pertaining to tax planning and controversy, transaction advice and representing clients before the IRS and the US Treasury. He also offers advice on restructurings and M&A. Co-head of department Fred Goldberg (see p.322) represents clients in matters arising from a broad array of compliance and transactional matters. He acts on behalf of private individuals, businesses and the tax-exempt in all stages and forms of administrative appeal, civil audit and litigation. Paul Oosterhuis's (see p.885) practice incorporates a variety of matters in international and domestic tax. He has particular strength in joint venture transactions and internal restructurings, M&A, spinoff transactions and transactions concerning post-acquisition integration. Additional areas of activity include representing companies in IRS controversies, audits and appeals. *"Top-notch international practitioner"* Hal Hicks (see p.869) has built a practice comprising international tax planning, controversy, M&A, transfer pricing and foreign tax credits. He represents partnerships and multinational corporations, and has attracted such distinguished clients as IBM, Coca-Cola and GE. John Williams (see p.426) handles federal tax litigation and controversy matters, representing clients in administrative appeals, IRS examinations and the federal courts. He has forged a reputation in the market as *"a terrific litigator, with just about every credential you could want."* Armando Gomez (see p.866) is recognized by clients as an *"expert in certain federal tax specialties, who takes a leadership role in transactions and works well with counterparties."* He also handles international partnerships and joint ventures, offers advice concerning the structuring of investments in renewable energy projects and private equity funds, and represents clients in a range of matters before the US Treasury and the IRS. André LeDuc's (see p.876) diverse federal tax practice is characterized by a preponderance of advisory work connected to the income taxation of tax-advantaged financial products, bankruptcy and financial restructurings.

## Band 2

### Baker & McKenzie
See profile on p.435

THE FIRM This impressive firm offers a wide range of tax services across a variety of industry sectors. It is able to act in the fields of post-merger integrations, tax dispute resolution, restructuring, and treaty and tax policy, and is especially well regarded for its handling of matters relating to transfer pricing and tax controversy. The firm has developed a formidable reputation for the expertise and authority it brings to matters with an international focus. Key clients include JPMorgan Chase, General Dynamics and Boeing.

Sources say: *"The Washington office is certainly very strong, with a very good group of people." "The firm has long been known in the tax area for its international reach."*

KEY INDIVIDUALS Leonard Terr (see p.895) offers advice on M&A, planning and securing rulings on restructurings involving multiple jurisdictions. He also has experience in multijurisdiction tax controversy, international tax regulations, and tax case settlements. Peers praise a *"thoughtful and bright"* individual who *"knows the area and is a very good guy."* Carol Dunahoo (see p.860) handles international tax controversies, policy, and planning and compliance. She has represented clients before the US Treasury and the IRS, and is known for having *"good connections around the world."* Mary Bennett (see p.851) brings a wealth of experience in the field of international tax planning, policy matters and controversy. She has represented clients before the IRS in tax controversy matters, and is particularly adept at international dispute resolution and transfer pricing.

### Caplin & Drysdale
See profile on p.909

THE FIRM This organization specializes in controversy and international tax planning. It is particularly adept in the field of regulatory and legislative advocacy, M&A and financings relating to financial products and institutions. It has recently undertaken a range of high-value matters on behalf of significant clients, and is renowned for its strength in matters featuring cross-border elements, such as those generated by the holding of offshore accounts.

Sources say: *"The firm has some very good people, and does good work."*

KEY INDIVIDUALS David Rosenbloom is regarded in the market as *"his firm's outstanding, leading light."* His practice encompasses most aspects of tax controversy and international tax planning, including competent authority proceedings and tax treaty issues, transfer pricing and the taxation of inbound investments. Patricia Lewis also practices in the area of international tax. She has particular expertise in competent authority matters and transfer pricing, offering guidance in the field of tax audits and tax planning advice in relation to compliance with foreign transfer and US pricing rules. Scott Michel brings considerable strength to his firm in the field of domestic tax. He represents corporations and individuals in civil tax examinations and corporate internal tax investigations, and

offers domestic compliance advice to foreign organizations operating in the USA, and to US citizens who are resident abroad. Richard Skillman brings his knowledge of international and domestic tax law to a range of work in the areas of corporate tax planning and controversy. His broad practice incorporates employee benefits, executive compensation and tax accounting.

### Ivins, Phillips & Barker
See profile on p.918

THE FIRM This highly specialized firm offers counsel in a number of areas, including domestic corporate matters, tax accounting and estate planning. Its clients include a number of Fortune 100 companies, and it is recognized in the market for its expertise in international work, controversy and M&A. Further praise is generated by the technical proficiency, experience and authority of the firm's attorneys.

Sources say: *"They are extremely competent in corporate tax matters, and extremely accommodating, responsive and flexible."*

KEY INDIVIDUALS Leslie Schneider's (see p.890) practice incorporates tax controversy, tax planning and accounting methods. He handles IRS examinations and appeals, the valuation and taxation of inventories and the structuring of transactions. He has represented numerous companies in the Fortune 500. *"Superb corporate lawyer"* Robert Wellen (see p.899) represents clients pursuing tax policy determinations and private letter rulings from the IRS, and handles a range of matters involving the planning, structuring and negotiating of business transactions. He also arbitrates in commercial disputes inflected by tax issues. Robert Stack heads the firm's international tax practice. He structures inbound and outbound ventures for business clients, and handles international tax concerns arising from the area of e-commerce. Fellow practitioners regard him as *"a strong international practitioner and somebody to have a lot of confidence in."* Alex Sadler (see p.889) has particular expertise in representing clients engaged in tax litigation and administrative controversies with state tax authorities, the IRS and the DOJ.

### Latham & Watkins LLP
See profile on p.446

THE FIRM The tax group at this firm handles a broad array of tax matters, including those pertaining to tax exemption, international and transactional tax, and benefits and compensation. Recent clients include organizations such as Riverstone Holdings, Wells Fargo and Shea Homes, for whom it offered representation before the US Tax Court in a matter arising from the accounting methods adopted by home builders.

Sources say: *"A very well-managed firm that takes client service very seriously. They do what it takes to get the deal done."*

KEY INDIVIDUALS Gerald Kafka (see p.342) chairs his firm's tax controversy practice. He has represented a range of distinguished clients before the US Tax Court and US Court of Federal Claims, and is regarded by fellow practitioners as *"a very fine tax litigator."* Miriam Fisher (see p.313) practices in the area of federal tax controversy and litigation. Much of her work is characterized by an emphasis on criminal and civil tax matters, and she has appeared before state tax authorities, the IRS and the DOJ. She is *"bright, has good judgment, is great with clients, and very effective,"* according to sources. **Rita Cavanagh** (see p.857) adds further strength to her firm's controversy and litigation practice. She has represented a number of distinguished clients before the US Tax Court, the US Court of Federal Claims and the IRS. Cross-border specialist **Nicholas DeNovio** (see p.859) handles work in jurisdictions around the Americas, Europe and Asia. He represents non-US and domestic multinationals in a range of matters concerning financings and group structuring, M&A and spinoffs.

## McDermott Will & Emery LLP
See profile on p.1258

**THE FIRM** The standalone tax practice at this well-established firm covers all aspects of corporate tax, with an emphasis on transactional, advisory and controversy work. It is well known for handling significant M&A deals and corporate restructurings, and for being particularly active in matters containing a cross-border dimension. Its clients include Tyco International and Johnson & Johnson, for which it has offered counsel in a multibillion-dollar transaction regarding the acquisition of medical device manufacturer Synthes.

**Sources say:** *"We have had a long relationship with McDermott's Washington office, and we are very happy with their service." "The people at this firm are true leaders."*

**KEY INDIVIDUALS Blake Rubin** (see p.889) has developed a fine reputation for his structuring of real estate and partnership transactions, and for handling matters in the field of policy, planning and controversy. Fellow practitioners regard him as *"an absolutely sterling individual,"* and *"one of the standout people for real estate."* Head of practice **Stephen Wells** (see p.899) handles a variety of transactional work involving domestic and foreign corporations. He has played a key role in the structuring of a host of significant corporate joint ventures, spinoffs and M&A, and has additional expertise in the formulation of tax strategies for the use of clients engaged in large transactions. **Philip McCarty** (see p.880) offers advice to prominent public companies on a variety of international and domestic issues, including consolidated returns, tax accounting, global joint ventures and financial products. He recently handled a multibillion-dollar matter involving Johnson & Johnson's acquisition of Synthes. **James Riedy** (see p.887) draws on his considerable international expertise to handle cross-border planning issues for multinationals, and to advise on foreign tax credits, sourcing and foreign currency. Interviewees say he is *"extremely smart, knows his stuff, and is easy for people to work with."* **Andrea Whiteway** (see p.899) has considerable experience in the structuring of complex partnership transactions, and handles corporate M&A and the acquisitions and dispositions of operating businesses and real estate.

## Miller & Chevalier Chartered
See profile on p.923

**THE FIRM** All aspects of federal income tax are covered by this well-regarded firm, which is recognized for its creative and client-focused approach. A number of its attorneys have strong ties with government, facilitating the formulation of informed and effective strategies when engaged in controversy. Additional areas of expertise include transactional work, reorganizations and restructurings, and work relating to tax enforcement. Key clients include ExxonMobil, Citi and Sempra Energy.

**KEY INDIVIDUALS Stephen Gertzman**'s (see p.865) practice is characterized by an emphasis on tax accounting. He is praised by peers as *"a very highly regarded, standout figure."* **Lawrence Gibbs** (see p.865) has established a diverse and impressive practice addressing an array of tax issues in the field of business transactions, tax planning and legislation. He has assisted clients involved in IRS rulings, audits and appeals. **Phillip Mann** (see p.879) specializes in offering legislative and policy advice in matters involving the US Treasury and the IRS. He is also available for consultation over transfer pricing, and has acquired a roster of prominent domestic and international clients. **Rocco Femia**'s (see p.862) practice covers tax controversy, planning and policy matters. Clients have sought his expertise in order to resolve international and domestic tax disputes, and in order to minimize tax costs when making international investments. **James Warren** (see p.898) handles controversy, accounting, and planning and consulting. He assists clients in making applications to the IRS for private letter rulings, and offers representation to those involved in audit and appeals controversies. **Alexander Zakupowsky**'s (see p.901) tax controversy practice is distinguished by a particular interest in transfer pricing and tax accounting. He is especially well known for competent authority proceedings, advance pricing agreements and advising clients making a variety of appeals to the IRS.

## Band 3

### Baker & Hostetler LLP
See profile on p.2119

**THE FIRM** This practice is characterized by a focus on corporate and government tax. Within this area it has forged a dynamic rulings practice, and a capacity for handling international restructuring, structuring and planning issues on both an inbound and outbound basis. It shows a particular strength in the handling of complex tax controversy matters, as exemplified by its representation of a Securities Investor Protection Act trustee in a multibillion-dollar matter concerning the liquidation of Bernard L. Madoff Investment Securities.

**KEY INDIVIDUALS Jeffrey Paravano** (see p.885) handles a range of tax matters, including cross-border and domestic tax planning, venture capital, corporate and partnership transactions and litigation. He has represented clients on Capitol Hill, and before an array of enforcement officials and policy makers. Head of department **Paul Schmidt** (see p.890) works on a variety of matters in the field of international and corporate tax. His clients include a number of Fortune 500 companies, and he attracts praise for offering a level of analysis that *"has been really helpful as we look at issues that have come up about tax in our industry."*

## Covington & Burling LLP
See profile on p.441

**THE FIRM** This firm's areas of expertise cover all facets of international tax, including acquisitions, regulatory and legislative advice, structural tax planning for multinationals, transfer pricing and cross-border transactions. It has developed a strong reputation for its handling of IRS-related controversy, and is admired by clients for its innovative and creative approach. Beneficiaries of these attributes include such distinguished organizations as Microsoft, United Technologies and GE Energy Financial Services.

**Sources say:** *"The main thing we use them for is IRS controversy work. They are excellent. The associates are very skilled, knowledgeable and polished."*

**KEY INDIVIDUALS Robert Culbertson** (see p.858) specializes in the handling of controversy resolution and international planning for domestic and non-US multinationals. Clients praise a practitioner who *"has excellent international tax expertise, is a very careful analyst of the statute, and very well respected by Washington policy makers."* The *"extremely learned"* **William Paul** (see p.885) represents clients before the IRS, the US Treasury and Congress. He also handles the taxation of investment funds, financial products and financial transactions. **Sources say:** *"He can take a very complex thing and make it understandable, and is able to isolate the salient points."* **Reeves Westbrook** (see p.899) cochairs Covington & Burling's tax group. He counsels large corporate taxpayers on cross-border financings and transfer pricing, acquisitions and dispositions and non-US and domestic joint ventures and partnerships. **Dirk Suringa**'s (see p.895) practice is comprised of a variety of international tax planning and controversy matters. Sources say he is *"an extremely capable person: extremely bright, remarkably smooth and personable."* **Emin Toro** (see p.896) brings to large multinational companies a practice that incorporates counseling and controversy. He attracts praise for offering a service in which *"the client gets first-rate knowledge in the tax area, along with responsiveness and innovative ideas."* **William Chip** (see p.857) also advises and represents a number of large multinationals. He is particularly well regarded for handling high-stakes tax examinations and strategic joint ventures and acquisitions, and for applying sophisticated financial instruments to corporate finance and risk management. Practice cochair **Dan Luchsinger** (see p.878) handles most aspects of corporate tax, though he is perhaps best known for the expertise he brings to the structuring of joint ventures and partnerships. He is regularly involved in cross-border acquisitions and dispositions, and inbound and outbound cross-border investments and financings.

## Fried, Frank, Harris, Shriver & Jacobson LLP
See profile on p.1975

**THE FIRM** The tax group at this firm's Washington, DC office is able to handle the majority of matters arising from asset management and corporate transactions. It has particular strength in dispositions, M&A, joint ventures and spinoffs, and in complex domestic and cross-border transactions. The team also handles tax controversies, including its successful representation of Shamrock Holdings in a multimillion-dollar dispute with the IRS.

**Sources say:** *"Extremely knowledgeable, and practical in the advice they give."*

**KEY INDIVIDUALS Alan Kaden**'s (see p.872) practice is characterized by a particular emphasis on the structuring and negotiation of spinoff transactions and dispositions, and taxable and tax-free corporate acquisitions. He is also a renowned litigator, and is regarded by clients as an *"incredibly smart and very practical"* individual. **Kevin Keyes** (see p.874) is regarded by peers as an *"extremely impressive and very capable"* practitioner. He specializes in corporate acquisitions and dispositions, cross-border financing and investments, the taxation of financial products and capital formation. **Michael Alter**'s (see p.850) federal income tax practice is also focused on the negotiation and structuring of tax-free and taxable acquisitions and dispositions. Clients find him *"very helpful, and good at what he does."*

## Morgan, Lewis & Bockius LLP
See profile on p.2246

**THE FIRM** This practice covers tax exemption, general consultation and controversy, and payroll and fringe benefits. It is particularly strong in the fields of tax compliance, dispute resolution, transaction advice and establishing the provision of guidance from the US Treasury and the IRS. It recently offered complex transactional tax advice to Appleton Papers, ConocoPhillips and Total.

**KEY INDIVIDUALS Celia Roady** (see p.888) handles a variety of work for tax-exempt organizations, many of which are large charities. She advises on the structuring of investments, represents clients looking to establish limited liability companies and is regarded by peers as a practitioner who is *"excellent in the nonprofit area, and very hardworking."*

## Steptoe & Johnson LLP

**THE FIRM** This firm's 13-partner tax group incorporates the entire range of federal and international taxation. It has expertise in international and domestic transactional planning, tax exemption and employee benefits, international tax compliance, and state and local tax. Additional strength resides in the firm's considerable experience in litigation, and in its record of advocating before the IRS and the US Treasury.

**Sources say:** *"They really put the client first. They have great depth of expertise, and this enables them to handle with ease all the work we send them."*

**KEY INDIVIDUALS Mark Silverman** is best known for his distinguished planning and transactional practice, in which area he assists large public corporations in the structuring of spinoff transactions and M&A. Head of department **Philip West** handles international tax issues for a range of clients, both foreign and domestic. According to sources, he *"brings a very unique and valuable perspective to issues that other advisers do not offer."* **Arthur Bailey** specializes in controversy and litigation, with particular expertise in the defense of tax-advantaged and cross-border investments. He recently represented John Hancock Life Insurance in a matter concerning the treatment of leveraged leases.

## Sutherland Asbill & Brennan LLP

**THE FIRM** The large tax group at this well-regarded firm is able to handle matters arising from almost every aspect of this practice area, at both federal and international levels. It has established particular strength in cross-border activity and outbound acquisitions, and regularly undertakes work that involves drawing on its special knowledge of tax law in Europe and Asia. Recent clients include FedEx, Coca-Cola and the Altria Group.

**KEY INDIVIDUALS** Practice chair **Jerome Libin** works across the entire range of international and corporate tax matters, focusing particularly on those in the fields of tax planning and transfer pricing, corporate acquisitions, international and domestic financial transactions, and controversy and litigation. **Giovanna Sparagna**'s practice covers controversy matters arising from cross-border financing, M&A and cross-border service and supply agreements. She also advises multinationals on international tax planning. **Herbert Beller** handles IRS representations, transactional tax planning and controversies. He has particular expertise in the planning of restructurings – including tax-free and taxable acquisitions – for domestic and non-US organizations. **Jeffrey Friedman** handles the full range of state and local tax planning and controversy matters, including those pertaining to sales and use, unclaimed property and property tax, franchise and income.

## Band 4

### Freshfields Bruckhaus Deringer LLP
See profile on p.443

**THE FIRM** This firm's dynamic tax group uses its impressive global connections to handle a range of cross-border, international and domestic matters. It is particularly proficient in the field of investment funds, financings, cross-border taxable and tax-free M&A, spinoffs and restructurings. It also represents organizations engaged in controversies arising from both international and domestic tax disputes.

**Sources say:** *"We have used them for about six years to advise on the handling of public money. They are very good."*

**KEY INDIVIDUALS Gregory May** (see p.880) is best known for the work he undertakes for sovereign wealth funds, companies and financial institutions in global tax transactions. Recent highlights include handling a matter for EMI Group regarding its transfer from Terra Firma to Citibank. **Claude Stansbury** (see p.894) also works in a multinational and cross-border capacity, handling disposals, financings, acquisitions and restructurings. He also handles tax controversy matters arising from international arbitration disputes, and the structuring of operating arrangements and joint ventures in nascent economies.

## Jones Day
See profile on p.919

**THE FIRM** This firm handles a substantial range of tax matters in the areas of audits and appeals, transfer pricing and international planning, acquisitions, competent authority and controversy. Clients admire the breadth and depth of its attorneys, who have undertaken work for a number of significant organizations. These include Bank of America, to whom it offered advice concerning the structuring of cross-border financings with international banks.

**Sources say:** *"What distinguishes them for me is the investment they make in their clients: they really make an effort to know comprehensively the companies with which they are working. They believe in high-quality client service without compromise."*

**KEY INDIVIDUALS Raymond Wiacek**'s (see p.899) international transactional practice incorporates matters in the field of transfer pricing, M&A, international pricing and IP planning, cross-border financings, and transaction-related disputes with the IRS and foreign governments. **Joseph Goldman**'s (see p.866) practice is composed of an array of domestic and international tax matters. He recently counseled Lehman Brothers in a matter regarding the deposition of an offshore investment, and is regarded as an individual who *"has fabulous knowledge of the business, a great work ethic and honesty."*

## Other Notable Practitioners

**Joseph Pari** of Linklaters has established a strong reputation for his federal income tax practice, which is characterized by an emphasis on spinoffs, M&A, acquisition financing and restructurings. **Robert Rudnick** of Shearman & Sterling LLP specializes in a range of matters in the field of federal income tax, including tax controversy, partnership tax, corporate tax and the taxation of financial products. He was recently involved in a multibillion-dollar dispute with the IRS concerning the tax treatment of derivatives implemented to hedge financial risk. **Joseph Howe** (see p.337) of Arnold & Porter LLP heads his firm's tax practice. He specializes in partnerships, structuring funds, REITs, complex real estate and business transactions in Europe, Asia and the USA. Interviewees describe an individual who is *"sharp, very focused, and always offers helpful analysis."* **Abraham Shashy** (see p.891) leads the tax group at King & Spalding LLP, and is admired for his creative approach to a practice that focuses on controversy, planning and regulatory matters. He handles this work for tax-exempt organizations, individual clients and foreign and domestic businesses. **Prentiss Feagles** of Hogan Lovells US LLP attracts considerable approbation for the sophistication of his approach to matters in the domain of corporate tax and partnerships. His practice concentrates on dispositions,

M&A, debt restructurings, joint ventures, investment fund structuring and private and public real estate partnerships. **Henry Birnkrant** (see p.852) of Alston & Bird LLP specializes in the taxation of cross-border and domestic business transactions and transfer pricing matters. He recently secured a substantial sum for Autoliv in a matter concerning the relief of transfer pricing adjustments. **Harold Bucholtz** (see p.855) of Holland & Knight LLP has established a practice serving as counsel in the sphere of tax-exempt financings for organizations engaged in cross-border and domestic activities. **Linda Carlisle** (see p.856) of White & Case LLP practices in the field of international and domestic tax. She handles a range of work including the taxation of corporate reorganizations and corporations, the divestments and acquisitions of US businesses

and companies, infrastructure transactions and PPP. **Alan Granwell** (see p.866) of DLA Piper LLP (US) commands respect for the depth of knowledge he brings to cross-border planning for multinational corporations, in which area he handles IP migrations, cross-border leasings, dispositions, acquisitions, business restructurings, and international insurance and transportation. **James Joseph** (see p.872) of Arnold & Porter LLP represents clients engaged in planning matters, litigation and controversy. He has handled litigations in the appellate and federal district courts, the US Court of Federal Claims and the US Tax Court, and has represented tax-exempt organizations, individuals and corporations before the IRS appeals office. **Donald Korb** (see p.349) of Sullivan & Cromwell LLP has established a practice that concentrates on transaction

planning and IRS examinations and appeals. He is particularly active in financings, acquisitions, dispositions and mergers, and is experienced in transfer pricing and matters concerning transferee liability in intermediary transactions. **Kathleen Nilles** (see p.884) of Holland & Knight LLP undertakes a variety of work for tax-exempt and governmental organizations, focusing on the resolution of critical tax and business organizational issues. **Harold Heltzer** (see p.868) of Crowell & Moring LLP focuses on tax planning for partnership formation, acquisitions and divestitures. He is known among sources to be *"very knowledgeable and thorough: a go-to person when you are dealing with the audit and appeals process."*

# TECHNOLOGY & OUTSOURCING

Commentary about individuals can be found under their firm's paragraph. If the firm has no paragraph (is not ranked) look at Other Notable Practitioners.

## Technology & Outsourcing
### Leading Firms

**Band 1**

| | |
|---|---|
| Mayer Brown LLP * | |
| Pillsbury Winthrop Shaw Pittman LLP * | |

**Band 2**

| | |
|---|---|
| Latham & Watkins LLP * | |
| Morrison & Foerster LLP * | |
| Venable LLP * | |
| White & Case LLP * | |

### Leading Individuals

**Star individuals**

| | |
|---|---|
| Zahler Robert | Pillsbury Winthrop Shaw Pittman LLP |

**Band 1**

| | |
|---|---|
| Klein Allen | Latham & Watkins LLP * |
| Masur Daniel A | Mayer Brown LLP |
| Nagel Trevor | White & Case LLP * |
| Oser Aaron M | Pillsbury Winthrop Shaw Pittman LLP |

**Band 2**

| | |
|---|---|
| Alberg James L | Pillsbury Winthrop Shaw Pittman LLP * |
| Ford Christopher D | Morrison & Foerster LLP * |
| Hutchings Jeffrey D | Pillsbury Winthrop Shaw Pittman LLP * |
| Kendall Joseph E | Pillsbury Winthrop Shaw Pittman LLP |

**Band 3**

| | |
|---|---|
| Bodor Brian R | Pillsbury Winthrop Shaw Pittman LLP * |
| Dottori Mario F | Pillsbury Winthrop Shaw Pittman LLP * |
| Garrote Nora | Venable LLP * |
| Hasty Robert | White & Case LLP * |
| Rhodes Linda | Mayer Brown LLP |
| Wolsk Jeremiah M | Latham & Watkins LLP * |
| Zottola A.J. | Venable LLP * |

**Associates to watch**

| | |
|---|---|
| Schaffner Derek | Mayer Brown LLP |

*\* Indicates firm / individual with profile.*
*Alphabetical order within each band. Band 1 is the highest.*

## Band 1

### Mayer Brown LLP
See profile on p.1257

**THE FIRM** Several sources single out Mayer Brown as one of the leading outsourcing teams in the country, and it continues its long run at the very top of the US market. The firm acts for some of the world's mostly widely known names in finance, retail and consumer goods on all their outsourcing needs. The firm's breadth of expertise is shown in its relationships with clients such as LightSquared, which it has recently represented in a variety of matters, including the negotiation of master servicing, supply and spectrum licensing agreements.

**Sources say:** *"I would strongly recommend Mayer Brown for similar projects that require a seasoned negotiator who has relevant business, industry and legal subject matter expertise. They were able to quickly understand the nature and scope of the project, understand our objectives and concerns, get up to speed with where we were in the timeline and propose an effective negotiation strategy that aligned accordingly."*

**KEY INDIVIDUALS** *"Phenomenal lawyer"* **Daniel Masur** is exceptionally highly regarded for his outsourcing work on behalf of numerous high-profile clients. His recent work includes leading on the abovementioned matters for LightSquared. **Linda Rhodes** advises an impressive national and international client base on the full range of outsourcing contracts. She also played a significant role on the work for LightSquared. Clients are enthusiastic about **Derek Schaffner**, who *"has clear and deep subject matter expertise and was able to leverage his industry knowledge to provide alternative approaches and anticipate and interpret the supplier's concerns."*

### Pillsbury Winthrop Shaw Pittman LLP
See profile on p.2000

**THE FIRM** This firm his highlighted as being among the best in the country for outsourcing work, and its bench

strength is especially impressive. Its clients include global financial services giants, governments, large retailers and manufacturers. The group recently handled call center and desktop support outsourcing agreements for one of the country's biggest names in finance.

**Sources say:** *"The firm receives the highest marks in this practice area. It has an advanced, sophisticated and commercially informed practice with a deep bench."*

**KEY INDIVIDUALS** Sources praise the *"brilliant"* **Robert Zahler** for his astute marshaling skills and exemplary industry knowledge and experience. Clients of all stripes go to him for advice on all manner of outsourcing contracts. **Aaron Oser** is a *"tremendous"* attorney whose recent work has included numerous outsourcing deals on behalf of household-name clients. Clients are enthusiastic about Oser's level of skill and service, and *"cannot recommend him highly enough."* **James Alberg** (see p.272) offers clients outstanding insight into their needs, having spent many years working in-house. He is another of the firm's highly rated outsourcing partners, and has *"a high level of customer service and an understanding of how large organizations operate."* Clients appreciate **Joseph Kendall's** flexibility and creativity in structuring and negotiating complex, sizable outsourcing agreements. He advises across all industries and has an especially strong following among healthcare clients. **Jeffrey Hutchings** (see p.870) has advised on numerous impressive mandates in his years of work in the outsourcing space. **Brian Bodor** (see p.853) is *"very experienced and knowledgeable, creative, and a good sparring partner, with a good understanding of the business environment."* Both are particularly rated for their BPO and ITO work, and represent major retailers and financial services organizations, among many others. **Mario Dottori** is also a leading choice for IT outsourcing and is a strong negotiator with an impressive domestic and global client base.

## Band 2

### Latham & Watkins LLP
See profile on p.446

**THE FIRM** This established firm maintains a strong presence in the technology and outsourcing space, and is highly regarded for its prowess in the fields of complex BPO and ITO transactions. Its lawyers are recognized as key players in the technology sector, complementing the firm's specialist outsourcing capabilities. The team works with clients from a wide variety of industries, such as financial services, pharmaceutical and travel. Members of the practice offer expertise on both the vendor and customer sides of transactions. The team recently advised Old Mutual Life Assurance, Nedbank and Mutual & Federal on a multiyear managed network services transaction that involved multiple parties.
**KEY INDIVIDUALS** *"Thought leader"* **Allen Klein** (see p.874) is singled out for his breadth of expertise across a range of complex transactions. Klein is vastly experienced in handling both domestic and international matters, and recently represented a leading international entity in a complex mobile payment partnership. One market commentator noted: *"The representation we obtained from Allen Klein exceeded our expectations."* **Jeremiah Wolsk** (see p.901) is a notable figure in the ITO and BPO field. He is best known for his work with telecommunications, life sciences and energy clients, where he practices on an international scale. His practice focuses on global technology development, distribution and licensing transactions.

### Morrison & Foerster LLP
See profile on p.1990

**THE FIRM** Morrison & Foerster's outsourcing group continues to handle a diverse range of business-critical work. The team draws on the firm's wider expertise in a wealth of practice areas to provide comprehensive support to an international clientele. Its lawyers are experienced in the

specific concerns that affect transactions from a variety of industries, including life sciences, financial services and clean technology. The practice attracts market-leading clients such as Ingersoll-Rand, Novartis and the Howard Hughes Medical Institute, the latter of which it recently represented in a sizable facilities management outsourcing. **Sources say:** *"First-class; working with them is a pleasure."*
**KEY INDIVIDUALS** Global sourcing group chair **Christopher Ford** (see p.314) is recommended for his *"expertise in the IT field, diligence and sound guidance."* He is experienced in the full spectrum of ITO and BPO outsourcing transactions, joint ventures and licensing matters on an international scale. He recently advised Bank of America on an $850 million card processing services outsourcing transaction.

### Venable LLP
See profile on p.927

**THE FIRM** This highly regarded firm is singled out for the quality of its client service. Sources are effusive in their praise of the team's understanding of their business needs, noting its excellent responsiveness and impressive depth of knowledge. Venable's technology group offers a significant breadth of practice, representing companies of all sizes on both the customer and vendor sides. The team is recognized for its expertise across a variety of matters involving technology, e-commerce, privacy and data security. Its attorneys are regularly retained by industry leaders from the hospitality, automotive, entertainment and financial services sectors to act on both domestic and cross-border issues. Clients include Software AG USA and CAPS.
**Sources say:** *"They offer a proven, national presence in the complicated world of online information technology."*
**KEY INDIVIDUALS Nora Garrote** (see p.864) earns praise for her *"in-depth understanding of the key issues involved in technology transactions."* Sources value her commercial acumen, with one noting: *"In addition to offering pure legal advice, we have often asked for her assistance in*

*developing business and tactical strategies."* Garrote also offers substantial transactional experience in Latin America. Market commentators are impressed by **A.J. Zottola**'s (see p.902) responsiveness, attention to detail and deep subject matter knowledge. Interviewees praise his *"thoughtful and practical"* advice and regard him as a *"prime resource."* He recently assisted COLA with the completion of a sizable cloud computing and data storage arrangement.

### White & Case LLP
See profile on p.451

**THE FIRM** White & Case is distinguished by its focus on strategic sourcing transactions. Members of the team are retained to act on complex global matters by a host of prominent clients, such as Coca-Cola and the Commonwealth Bank of Australia. Its lawyers work alongside the firm's overseas offices to provide expert advice on long-term projects. Coca-Cola Enterprises and The Coca-Cola Company recently sought the group's advice on a considerable transatlantic BPO agreement relating to accounting and finance services.
**KEY INDIVIDUALS** *"Extraordinarily good lawyer"* **Trevor Nagel** (see p.374) chairs the firm's global sourcing and technology transactions practice. He maintains an excellent reputation in the field of strategic sourcing, regularly advising international market leaders. Nagel continues to represent Commonwealth Bank of Australia in long-term transactions. **Robert Hasty**'s (see p.868) practice is characterized by an international focus that has seen him advise on a range of multinational agreements. He has amassed a wealth of expertise in technology-related transactions and complex sourcing arrangements. Recent work highlights include representing Best Buy in a series of sourcing transactions.

## TELECOM, BROADCAST & SATELLITE

Commentary about individuals can be found under their firm's paragraph. If the firm has no paragraph (is not ranked) look at Other Notable Practitioners.

### Telecom, Broadcast & Satellite — Leading Firms

**Band 1**
Covington & Burling LLP *
Kellogg, Huber, Hansen, Todd, Evans & Figel, PLLC
Wiley Rein LLP *
Wilkinson Barker Knauer LLP *
Willkie Farr & Gallagher LLP *
Wiltshire & Grannis LLP *

**Band 2**
Bingham McCutchen LLP *
Dow Lohnes PLLC
Hogan Lovells US LLP
Latham & Watkins LLP *
Lawler, Metzger, Keeney & Logan LLC
Skadden, Arps, Slate, Meagher & Flom LLP & Affiliates *
WilmerHale *

**Band 3**
Davis Wright Tremaine LLP *
Jenner & Block LLP *
Milbank, Tweed, Hadley & McCloy LLP *
Mintz Levin Cohn Ferris Glovsky and Popeo PC *
Sidley Austin LLP *

**Band 4**
Akin Gump Strauss Hauer & Feld LLP *
Cahill Gordon & Reindel LLP *
Drinker Biddle & Reath LLP *
Goldberg Godles Wiener & Wright
Kelley Drye & Warren LLP *
Lerman Senter PLLC
Levine, Blaszak, Block & Boothby LLP
Pillsbury Winthrop Shaw Pittman LLP *
Squire Sanders (US) LLP *
Steptoe & Johnson LLP
TLP: Telecommunications Law Professionals PLLC

\* Indicates firm / individual with profile.
†ONP = Other Notable Practitioner.

### Telecom, Broadcast & Satellite — Leading Individuals

| Star individuals | |
|---|---|
| Wiley Richard E | Wiley Rein LLP * |

**Band 1**

| | |
|---|---|
| Casserly James L | Willkie Farr & Gallagher LLP * |
| Kellogg Michael | Kellogg, Huber, Hansen, Todd, Evans |
| Metzger Jr A Richard | Lawler, Metzger, Keeney & Logan LLC |
| Nakahata John T | Wiltshire & Grannis LLP * |
| Nuechterlein Jonathan | WilmerHale * |
| Rosenstein Mace J | Covington & Burling LLP * |
| Tramont Bryan N | Wilkinson Barker Knauer LLP * |
| Tritt Cheryl | Wilkinson Barker Knauer LLP * |

**Band 2**

| | |
|---|---|
| Barker James H | Latham & Watkins LLP * |
| Brill Matthew | Latham & Watkins LLP * |
| Cook Bush Antoinette | Skadden, Arps, Slate, Meagher & Flom * |
| Farquhar Michele C | Hogan Lovells US LLP |
| Feore John R | Dow Lohnes PLLC * |
| Gerstell Glenn S | Milbank, Tweed, Hadley & McCloy LLP * |
| Goldberg Henry | Goldberg Godles Wiener & Wright |
| Janka John P | Latham & Watkins LLP * |
| Kaufman Steven M | Hogan Lovells US LLP |
| Keeney Regina | Lawler, Metzger, Keeney & Logan LLC |
| Kiser Chérie Renee | Cahill Gordon & Reindel LLP * |
| Lawson David L | Sidley Austin LLP * |
| Levine Henry D | Levine, Blaszak, Block & Boothby LLP |
| Lipman Andrew D | Bingham McCutchen LLP * |
| Michalopoulos Pantelis | Steptoe & Johnson LLP |
| Panahy Dara A | Milbank, Tweed, Hadley & McCloy LLP * |
| Schneider Mark | Sidley Austin LLP * |
| Senkowski R Michael | Wiley Rein LLP * |
| Swanson M Anne | Dow Lohnes PLLC * |
| Symons Howard | Mintz Levin Cohn Ferris Glovsky and Popeo * |
| Voltmer Ralph C | Covington & Burling LLP * |
| Walker Helgi C | Wiley Rein LLP * |
| Wright Christopher | Wiltshire & Grannis LLP * |

**Band 3**

| | |
|---|---|
| Aamoth Robert J | Kelley Drye & Warren LLP |
| Angstreich Scott H | Kellogg, Huber, Hansen, Todd, Evans |
| Blaszak James S | Levine, Blaszak, Block & Boothby LLP |
| Davidson Tom W | Akin Gump Strauss Hauer & Feld LLP * |
| Dori Yaron | Covington & Burling LLP * |
| Feder Samuel L | Jenner & Block LLP * |
| Fitzgerald Ari Q | Hogan Lovells US LLP |

| | |
|---|---|
| Glist Paul | Davis Wright Tremaine LLP |
| Greenberg Eric Dodson | Paul Hastings LLP (ONP)† |
| Hammer Michael H | Willkie Farr & Gallagher LLP * |
| Jacobs Bruce D | Pillsbury Winthrop Shaw Pittman LLP * |
| Jain Samir | WilmerHale * |
| Johnson Jennifer A | Covington & Burling LLP * |
| Jones Thomas | Willkie Farr & Gallagher LLP * |
| Lerman Steven A | Lerman Senter PLLC |
| Margie Paul | Wiltshire & Grannis LLP * |
| Martin Marc S | K&L Gates (ONP)† * |
| McBride Andrew G | Wiley Rein LLP * |
| Mechanick Maury J | White & Case LLP (ONP)† * |
| Phillips Carter G | Sidley Austin LLP * |
| Solomon David H | Wilkinson Barker Knauer LLP * |
| Zaragoza Richard R | Pillsbury Winthrop Shaw Pittman LLP |

**Band 4**

| | |
|---|---|
| Buono Francis | Willkie Farr & Gallagher LLP * |
| Campbell Patrick S | Paul, Weiss, Rifkind, Wharton (ONP)† * |
| Daubert Todd D | Dentons (ONP)† * |
| Giunta Tara K | Paul Hastings LLP (ONP)† |
| Gray Todd | Dow Lohnes PLLC * |
| Hane John | Pillsbury Winthrop Shaw Pittman LLP |
| Heitmann John | Kelley Drye & Warren LLP |
| Kelly Robert | Squire Sanders (US) LLP * |
| Leventhal Norman P | Holland & Knight LLP (ONP)† * |
| Nalda Carlos M | Squire Sanders (US) LLP * |
| Northrop Carl | TLP: Telecommunications Law Professionals |
| Olcott Bruce | Squire Sanders (US) LLP * |
| Phillips Laura | Drinker Biddle & Reath LLP * |
| Richter Jennifer | Patton Boggs LLP (ONP)† |
| Schlager Ivan A | Skadden, Arps, Slate, Meagher & Flom * |
| Stankey Robert | Davis Wright Tremaine LLP |
| Stockdale Don | Mayer Brown LLP (ONP)† |
| Victory Nancy J | Wiley Rein LLP * |
| Wilhelm William | Bingham McCutchen LLP * |
| Wiltshire William M | Wiltshire & Grannis LLP * |

| Up-and-coming individuals | |
|---|---|
| DelNero Matthew | Covington & Burling LLP * |
| Roisman Natalie | Wilkinson Barker Knauer LLP * |
| Zachary Heather | WilmerHale * |

| Associates to watch | |
|---|---|
| Milne Karen | Akin Gump Strauss Hauer & Feld LLP * |

## Band 1

### Covington & Burling LLP
See profile on p.441

**THE FIRM** This team continues to attract big-ticket work across the communications arena, advising top clients on disputes, corporate transactions and regulatory developments. Its specialists are prized for their high-level strategic advice and superb service skills. The group represents telecom giant CenturyLink in a variety of regulatory issues, and acted for the company on an appeal of an FCC order reforming the intercarrier compensation and universal service regimes. Other standout matters include assisting Saban Brands with the development and launch of a national children's television programming network. **Sources say:** *"An excellent firm with substantial resources and a broad array of expertise." "They provide excellent client service, and are aware of the cutting-edge issues across the telecom space."* **KEY INDIVIDUALS** *"Terrific lawyer"* **Mace Rosenstein** (see p.888) attracts plaudits from across the market. Highlights include advising Microsoft on its regulatory strategy in light of the release of the Windows 8 Mobile Operating System. **Ralph Voltmer** (see p.897) is noted for his work advising various telecom and broadcasting clients on corporate transactions. In a recent highlight, he acted for Infotel Broadband Services on the establishment of a number of development and licensing agreements. Clients commend **Yaron Dori** (see p.860) as being *"deeply knowledgeable on telecom issues, and highly practical."* He also garners particular praise for his expertise in cutting-edge issues. Peers are impressed by **Jennifer Johnson**'s (see p.872) communications expertise, which is called on by major industry names for litigation proceedings, policy issues and corporate activities. **Matthew DelNero** (see p.859) is a *"fabulous lawyer,"* whose clients value his commercial nous: *"He is a very practical business lawyer, who has found a way to straddle legal analysis and business deals."*

## Kellogg, Huber, Hansen, Todd, Evans & Figel, PLLC

**THE FIRM** This established team maintains its reputation as a litigation specialist. Peers draw attention to the team's prowess at trial and appellate level, which is enhanced by experience representing both plaintiffs and defendants. Its lawyers are singled out as high-quality practitioners and respected for the extent of their telecommunications expertise. The group continues to work with industry leaders such as Verizon and AT&T.

**Sources say:** *"Excellent litigators on telecommunications matters."*

**KEY INDIVIDUALS** *"Terrific lawyer"* **Michael Kellogg** impresses market commentators, who single him out for his expertise in the regulatory and litigation fields. **Scott Angstreich** continues to be highly regarded for his expertise in telecom disputes.

## Wiley Rein LLP
See profile on p.928

**THE FIRM** This market leader fields a deep bench of experts with a cumulative wealth of communications experience. Its talents in the field attract a range of major international and domestic clients, including AT&T, Deutsche Telekom and the United States Telecom Association. In global highlights, the firm chaired and led the multinational committee of leading industry names that participated in the ITU/UN treaty negotiations for the World Conference on International Telecommunications. Demonstrating its renowned capabilities in the FCC regulatory sphere, the team also represented CTIA in connection with the development of new legislation granting the FCC authority to conduct incentive auctions.

**Sources say:** *"A strong communications practice which employs some of the finest lawyers in the country."* *"Excellent substantive knowledge."*

**KEY INDIVIDUALS** The *"peerless"* **Richard Wiley** (see p.900) is a former chairman of the FCC and acts for a range of market luminaries, including Deutsche Telekom. He is widely respected for his contributions to the field of DC communications law, and is described by one market source as *"a great leader in our space."* **Michael Senkowski**'s (see p.891) notable mandates include assisting Iridium Satellite with the replacement of its global mobile satellite system. Impressed peers regard him as *"excellent – a really good lawyer."* **Andrew McBride** (see p.880) is an *"excellent attorney"* whose valuable litigation expertise includes deep knowledge of appellate law. He continues to act for Verizon Wireless, including on a set of class actions regarding the leasing and use of common short codes for marketing purposes. **Helgi Walker** (see p.898) is a *"terrific lawyer – very knowledgeable."* She receives high praise for her work in the appellate arena, where she is known as a *"star talent – very smart and diligent."* **Nancy Victory** (see p.897) is a *"very experienced lawyer"* who is highly respected for her knowledge of the telecommunications industry. She acted for

Verizon Wireless on its acquisition of a swath of spectrum, valued at $3.9 billion.

## Wilkinson Barker Knauer LLP
See profile on p.929

**THE FIRM** Clients call on this well-established practice for issues spanning the communications spectrum. The firm has a sterling reputation for regulatory matters, and assists leading names with enforcement proceedings, accessibility compliance and FCC transactional approval. The firm successfully defended Comcast in an FCC investigation regarding compliance with the order approving the client's acquisition of a controlling stake in NBCUniversal. M&A highlights include representing satellite company DBSD North America and TerreStar Networks in obtaining approval for their separate sales to DISH Network, for a total of approximately $3 billion.

**Sources say:** *"Not only do they have great legal depth, but they are able to marry it with strategic execution."* *"The firm is one of the strongest and most highly regarded in the communications policy arena."*

**KEY INDIVIDUALS** **Bryan Tramont** (see p.896) maintains his reputation as a true leading light of the DC communications arena, and enthusiastic market sources laud his *"keen insight, understanding of the FCC regulatory landscape, and legendary approach to client care."* He is further singled out by one client as *"an incredible asset to our work, and one of the most strategic, effective attorneys practicing in communications today."* The *"excellent"* **Cheryl Tritt**'s (see p.896) recent successes include securing spectrum allocation for wideband medical implant devices on behalf of a medical research foundation. **David Solomon** (see p.893) is *"a go-to lawyer for enforcement work and appellate litigation."* His high-profile client roster includes industry behemoths Comcast and CenturyLink. **Natalie Roisman** (see p.888) was formerly a policy adviser at the FCC's Media Bureau, and continues to build on her reputation as a private practitioner. She is *"a skilled lawyer and a master at client relations."*

## Willkie Farr & Gallagher LLP
See profile on p.2016

**THE FIRM** This superb team has an extensive background in communications work, and can offer expert guidance in transactions, litigation and the development of compliance strategies. Its high-caliber client roster features satellite service providers, competitive carriers and cable television operators. Recent clients include NBCUniversal, which the team advised on content licensing requests from distributors of multichannel video programming or online video. As counsel for competitive carrier COMPTEL, the firm led a coalition of carriers and trade associations in its mandamus petition to compel action by the FCC on the regulator's special access rulemaking. The FCC subsequently committed to complete the rulemaking in 2013.

**Sources say:** *"A fine firm, which attracts big clients."* *"Very strong in cable work."*

**KEY INDIVIDUALS** **James Casserly** (see p.856) is *"an extremely good lawyer,"* whose broad-based experience includes advising major national names on policy develop-

ments and corporate transactions. **Thomas Jones** (see p.872) is highly praised for his work in the competitive carriers arena, and advised COMPTEL on the abovementioned dispute. **Michael Hammer** (see p.867) is chair of the firm's communications, media and privacy group, and counts Comcast among his big-ticket clients. Clients can call on **Francis Buono**'s (see p.855) extensive expertise in data privacy and security issues, including the establishment of global compliance strategies, the use of customer data and dealing with transactional risks.

## Wiltshire & Grannis LLP
See profile on p.931

**THE FIRM** This practice receives widespread praise for its technical understanding and acts for some of the world's biggest technology brands, including Google, which the team advises on a variety of FCC and international regulatory issues. Other clients include local and international telecom names such as Sorenson Communications, Level 3 Communications and Sprint Nextel. Of late, the team advised General Communications on the overhaul of two FCC subsidy programs, negotiating a more favorable treatment for its client and its fellow Alaska-based carriers.

**Sources say:** *"Top-flight service – I rate the firm very highly."* *"A very strong knowledge of the telecommunication rules and laws in the US."* *"One of the best firms – they are thoughtful and strategic, and produce high-quality work product."*

**KEY INDIVIDUALS** Clients are highly impressed by **John Nakahata** (see p.883), lauding his understanding not only of telecom regulation but also of the systems and technologies used by telecom clients. **Christopher Wright** (see p.901) achieved a major victory in a dispute over the FCC's Phoenix Forbearance Order, which established a more stringent test for dominance in the telecom sector. When the order was challenged by Qwest, AT&T and Verizon, Wiltshire & Grannis acted for the 16 entities who intervened on behalf of the FCC, and the FCC's decision was ultimately upheld by a Tenth Circuit ruling. Clients value **Paul Margie**'s (see p.880) dedication to their interests, commending him as *"a very intelligent attorney with good political instincts, who works hard to press his client's case."* Further praise alludes to his combination of the *"practical and scholarly,"* and to his ability to pick up and master complex technical concepts. **William Wiltshire**'s (see p.900) long experience in this field includes roles at the FCC, as well as private practice work as an adviser and as an advocate. He advised DIRECTV on the FCC's sunset review of legislation prohibiting cable operators from being granted exclusive carriage rights.

## Band 2

## Bingham McCutchen LLP
See profile on p.1515

**THE FIRM** Bingham McCutchen receives widespread praise for its attention to the commercial realities facing clients. The telecommunications practice offers an enviable depth of expertise, spanning a broad range of regulatory, transactional and litigious matters. The practice attracts a diverse range of industry leaders, including Deere & Company and Level 3 Communications, the latter of which it represented before the FCC with regard to the terms offered for leases of high-capacity circuits by Qwest, Verizon and AT&T.

**Sources say:** *"The team is really supportive and diligent."*

**KEY INDIVIDUALS William Wilhelm** (see p.900) is widely praised for providing *"terrific, highly responsive client service."* He handles a variety of regulatory and transactional work, with a particular focus on digital media, new communications applications, wireless and wireline technology. Wilhelm advises a number of domestic and international market leaders, including Vonage Holdings. *"Fine lawyer"* **Andrew Lipman** (see p.877) continues to be held in high regard and is singled out for his extensive industry knowledge. He led on the Level 3 Communications matter mentioned above.

### Dow Lohnes PLLC

**THE FIRM** This firm's diverse client base includes a range of broadcasters, telecom companies and communication device manufacturers. Matters concerning the allocation and use of spectrum have been increasingly dominant in its workload, which also includes asset sales and advising on changes in FCC regulations. In transactional issues, the team represented Cox Communications in obtaining approval for a $3.6 billion sale of 20 MHz of Advanced Wireless Spectrum. It also acted for Garmin International on a successful challenge by GPS manufacturers to a new broadband service from LightSquared that would interfere with GPS services.

**Sources say:** *"Excellent – they are extremely knowledgeable and very responsive."*

**KEY INDIVIDUALS** Highly regarded **John Feore** (see p.862) is well known for his strength in broadcasting issues. His highlights include representing Granite Broadcasting in a federal antitrust lawsuit brought by Nexstar Broadcasting. **Anne Swanson** (see p.895) is valued by clients as a *"truly outstanding lawyer – very tenacious, always responsive and a really hard worker."* Her regulatory experience is a further asset, with sources highlighting that *"she knows the FCC and its workings inside out."* Clients prize **Todd Gray's** (see p.866) commitment to service, and that he is *"very client-centric and extraordinarily responsive."* He is also a well-respected figure in the public broadcasting industry.

### Hogan Lovells US LLP

**THE FIRM** This team is renowned for its high-quality guidance to major domestic and international players. Its practitioners are particularly well regarded for the commercial perspective they bring to client service. Work for top mobile telecom clients includes advising T-Mobile USA on a variety of regulatory matters before the FCC and US Congress, and assisting Vodafone with national security matters relating to its acquisition of Cable & Wireless. In international mandates, the team acted for the government of Mexico on its acquisition of a three-satellite system and related procurement and deployment issues.

**Sources say:** *"Good at deploying people in a seamless and integrated manner." "Absolutely great – very pragmatic, clever people."*

**KEY INDIVIDUALS Michele Farquhar** has an extensive background in communications work. In a standout mandate, she assisted Gogo with obtaining FCC approval for its provision of internet access to customers on commercial flights. **Steven Kaufman** is *"extremely good at thinking through transactions."* In a recent highlight, he acted for GE on its sale of the GE-23 satellite for more than $200 million. **Ari Fitzgerald** has a strong reputation for his skills across the telecom and wireless arena. His impressive client roster includes T-Mobile and Vodafone.

### Latham & Watkins LLP
See profile on p.446

**THE FIRM** Latham & Watkins's communications practice is best known for its regulatory strength, representing numerous market leaders before the FCC, federal courts and state public utility commissions. The group additionally offers broad capabilities in transactional work, and its lawyers are also recognized for their expertise in communications-related financing matters. It recently represented a number of clients from the wireless industry in a successful opposition to the AT&T/T-Mobile merger.

**KEY INDIVIDUALS** The *"incredibly talented"* **Matthew Brill** (see p.854) is well versed in transactional, regulatory and litigious matters, and regularly appears before the FCC on behalf of clients. He played a leading role in the aforementioned AT&T/T-Mobile matter, alongside **James Barker** (see p.850). Barker earns praise for his broad transactional expertise, and also has considerable communications-related litigation experience and knowledge of the regulatory requirements facing companies. Firmwide communications practice chair **John Janka** (see p.871) is held in high regard for his *"excellent legal drafting skills and great judgment on how to handle difficult challenges."* Over the course of his distinguished career he has advised clients on a wide range of regulatory and transactional issues.

### Lawler, Metzger, Keeney & Logan LLC

**THE FIRM** This boutique retains its status as a highly respected player and fields a team of talented attorneys. It advises clients on the full spectrum of regulatory issues, representing leaders from the wireless, cable, wireline and satellite arenas. Clients also benefit from the team's considerable regulatory expertise.

**Sources say:** *"Talented people."*

**KEY INDIVIDUALS** The *"brilliant"* **Richard Metzger** remains a standout figure in the field of communications law and commands much respect within the industry. He elicits particular praise for his expertise in regulatory matters. **Regina Keeney** is extremely well regarded by the legal community and is noted for her deep understanding of telecommunications policy and the regulatory landscape.

### Skadden, Arps, Slate, Meagher & Flom LLP & Affiliates
See profile on p.2008

**THE FIRM** This practice is widely respected for its strength in policy-related matters. The practice offers expertise on a broad range of regulatory issues, most notably in the cable, wireless, wireline and broadcasting fields. Its attorneys continue to advise industry leaders, acting for Sprint Nextel before the FCC on numerous occasions, and for DISH Network in a recent substantial acquisition.

**Sources say:** *"Very capable and customer-oriented."*

**KEY INDIVIDUALS** *"Superb lawyer"* **Antoinette Cook Bush** (see p.858) is recommended for her strengths in the legislative field. She leads the communication group and also provides expert assistance on communications-related transactions, drawing clients from the telephone, satellite, broadcast, cable and mobile communications arenas. Her recent clients include Sprint Nextel and DigitalGlobe. Market commentators describe **Ivan Schlager** (see p.401) as *"knowledgeable, insightful and well connected."* He works with a variety of clients, such as private equity companies, telecommunications providers and media companies. Recent work highlights include representing Hughes Telematics in its acquisition by Verizon.

### WilmerHale
See profile on p.930

**THE FIRM** This well-regarded team continues to act for several of the market's top names, and of late has represented a number of clients in FCC proceedings. AT&T in particular has contributed substantially to the firm's caseload, calling on the team in matters relating to intercarrier compensation and universal service reform, as well as new FCC powers to undertake 'incentive auctions' designed to free up spectrum for broadband users. The group also acted for Verizon as the main industry petitioner in the appeal of the FCC's net neutrality rules. Further big names in the client base include Comcast, the National Cable & Telecommunications Association (NCTA) and CenturyLink.

**KEY INDIVIDUALS Jonathan Nuechterlein** (see p.884) is a *"top-league guy,"* who advises clients on some of the firm's biggest mandates. He acted for Comcast and the NCTA on their opposition to the electric power industry's attempt to overturn an FCC decision regarding the pricing of infrastructure access. Clients value **Samir Jain** (see p.871) as an adviser who offers *"the whole package – he's very responsive and a good writer, and he understands the industry."* He is assisting Globalstar with its evolution from a first-generation to a second-generation satellite constellation, advising on a variety of concomitant regulatory issues. **Heather Zachary** (see p.901) continues to develop her communications practice, representing clients in high-profile regulatory issues and disputes. Her work for AT&T includes representing it as both petitioner and intervener-respondent in connection with various aspects of the FCC's intercarrier compensation and universal service reform.

## Band 3

### Davis Wright Tremaine LLP
See profile on p.2544

**THE FIRM** Davis Wright Tremaine represents both established industry figures and emerging entities in a wide range of regulatory, transactional and litigious matters. Recent work highlights include advising FanVision on European broadcaster licensing issues concerning an interactive sports television service at 2012 Formula 1 Grand Prix races.

**Sources say:** "*They are business-oriented lawyers – they understand that we are trying to do business and help to analyze business risk very well.*"

**KEY INDIVIDUALS Paul Glist** has a wealth of expertise in regulatory and compliance matters, frequently acting on behalf of leading figures in the technology, software and communications industries. Sources reserve particular praise for his strategic approach to matters. **Robert Stankey** is "*knowledgeable, thoughtful and reasonable,*" commentators note. Clients particularly benefit from his experience in handling complex compliance and regulatory issues.

### Jenner & Block LLP
See profile on p.1252

**THE FIRM** Jenner & Block is recognized as a key player in the communications field and has notable expertise in the media, telecom, cable and wireless areas. Its attorneys offer wide-ranging knowledge and experience in regulatory matters, transactions and disputes at both trial and appellate level.

**KEY INDIVIDUALS** Practice chair **Samuel Feder** (see p.861) is notable for his regulatory expertise, drawing on his experience as former general counsel to the FCC and as adviser to FCC commissioners. He acts on behalf of a range of clients from the media, telecom, cable and technology industries. Feder also offers highly regarded insight into the key transactional and regulatory litigation issues faced by companies.

### Milbank, Tweed, Hadley & McCloy LLP
See profile on p.448

**THE FIRM** The telecommunications team at Milbank is closely integrated with the firm's space and satellite practice, providing clients with enviable market intelligence and strategic business-focused advice. The lawyers have experience in a wide range of matters, including satellite procurement, transponder lease agreements and international regulations. The group is notable for its cross-border expertise, drawing on the capabilities of the firm's overseas offices, and its members are regularly retained by high-profile clients such as Goldman Sachs and Morgan Stanley. Recent highlights include representing Seaborn Networks in the planning and development of a direct submarine cable between the USA and Brazil.

**Sources say:** "*Very effective, responsive and easily accessible to both ourselves and our clients.*"

**KEY INDIVIDUALS** Established industry presence **Glenn Gerstell** (see p.865) is noted for his expertise on global acquisitions and financings for industry leaders in the communications space. "*I have always relied on his deep knowledge and understanding of the law and how it pertains to the telecom industry,*" reports one enthusiastic interviewee. Gerstell led on the aforementioned matter for Seaborn Networks. Clients rely on **Dara Panahy**'s (see p.885) mastery of business strategy and ability to guide them through complex aerospace and communications-related transactions. He provides expert advice on financings, financial restructuring, and acquisitions and their regulatory implications.

### Mintz Levin Cohn Ferris Glovsky and Popeo PC
See profile on p.1523

**THE FIRM** This communications team is praised for its breadth of experience within the satellite, wireless, cable and telecommunications fields. Its attorneys represent clients in litigious matters and offer expert regulatory counsel on a range of issues, including spectrum legislation and net neutrality. The team has been retained by Discovery Communications and T-Mobile USA over the past year.

**Sources say:** "*They have become a valued and trusted resource. They do not hesitate to bring in other resources, even from other offices in other cities, when required, and these lawyers work seamlessly together.*"

**KEY INDIVIDUALS** Interviewees are impressed with the extent of **Howard Symons**'s (see p.895) legislative expertise. Much esteemed by peers and clients, his practice focuses on wireless, satellite, cable and telecommunications work. He regularly appears before the FCC on behalf of clients, and is particularly experienced in spectrum, cybersecurity, net neutrality and program carriage.

### Sidley Austin LLP
See profile on p.1264

**THE FIRM** The team is well known for its stellar appearances before the FCC and federal district and appellate courts, and also offers full regulatory counsel and transactional advice. AT&T continues to retain the firm on regulatory matters, and the team has recently worked with News Corporation and Fox Television Stations on media ownership appeals and indecency litigation.

**KEY INDIVIDUALS David Lawson** (see p.876) "*quickly gets to the heart of the matter and is willing to do the work necessary to provide the legal product I need in a timely manner – and sometimes with absurd deadlines placed on him,*" reports one satisfied client. Lawson is well known for the caliber of his work for AT&T, which he has advised on a range of regulatory proceedings related to competition matters. **Mark Schneider** (see p.890) continues to be highly regarded for his regulatory expertise. He has recently represented U.S. Cellular in matters involving compliance with regulations pertaining to the provision of 911 service. **Carter Phillips** (see p.384) maintains an excellent reputation among peers and clients, particularly for his appellate work. He has recently acted for News Corporation and Fox Television on challenges to the FCC's rules governing the cross-ownership of newspapers, broadcast properties and multiple television station ownership.

## Band 4

### Akin Gump Strauss Hauer & Feld LLP
See profile on p.904

**THE FIRM** This group represents clients from a variety of communications industries, and has significant transactional and regulatory experience. The team is noted for its FCC capabilities and ability to understand the needs of both domestic and international businesses. The practice has also handled a wide range of financing, M&A and services agreement matters. Clients include GE and Laser Light Communications.

**KEY INDIVIDUALS Tom Davidson** (see p.859) is valued for his impressive industry experience and is also described as "*thorough, responsive and knowledgeable.*" He heads the practice and serves as outside counsel to Laser Light Communications. The "*knowledgeable and efficient*" **Karen Milne** (see p.882) specializes in communications and regulatory work. Her recent clients include Oaktree Capital Management.

### Cahill Gordon & Reindel LLP
See profile on p.1960

**THE FIRM** The practice is equally well versed in FCC representation and transactional matters, frequently advising clients on regulatory proceedings, divestitures and financings, and litigation. Both established and emerging clients look to the team for advice throughout the corporate lifecycle. In the past year the team has represented Cable One before the FCC, in a number of VoIP, video and internet access issues.

**Sources say:** "*They are extremely knowledgeable and their advice has always been timely and accurate.*" "*Very strong, extremely client-focused, and accessible.*"

**KEY INDIVIDUALS** "*Phenomenal lawyer*" **Chérie Kiser** (see p.874) impresses market commentators, with one highly satisfied client stating: "*Chérie is very aware of the realities of business and always takes that into account, often answering the questions that we should have asked.*" Kiser is currently advising Polycom on a number of transactional and regulatory matters.

### Drinker Biddle & Reath LLP
See profile on p.2238

**THE FIRM** The team at Drinker Biddle & Reath is held in high regard for the deep industry knowledge in the communications practice and the government and regulatory affairs practice. Its lawyers regularly appear before the FCC and are well known for their expertise in the broadcasting space. The team also represents clients in the sale and acquisition of communications assets, and is sought after to assist with licensing and antitrust issues. Highlights from the past year include representing Sprint Nextel in its 800 MHz mediations, and advising the Puerto Rico Telephone Company on video service franchise proceedings.

**Sources say:** *"They have a very profound knowledge of the local telecom market."*

**KEY INDIVIDUALS Laura Phillips** (see p.885) is president of the Federal Communications Bar and continues to offer expertise in regulatory counseling and strategic policy development to a range of technology, wireless and wireline clients. She is singled out for *"her knowledge of the FCC, interpretation of the rules and ability to explain them."* Phillips acts as national counsel to Sprint Nextel, advising on federal telecommunications regulatory and business issues.

## Goldberg Godles Wiener & Wright

**THE FIRM** This boutique has a strong reputation in the satellite space and continues to be a highly regarded player in the communications market. It advises both established and emerging companies on regulatory issues and key transactional concerns. Regular clients include satellite companies, telecommunications carriers and broadcasters. **KEY INDIVIDUALS** The highly respected **Henry Goldberg** remains a well-known figure in the market and is recommended for his strengths in the satellite field.

## Kelley Drye & Warren LLP
See profile on p.1985

**THE FIRM** This firm maintains a notable presence in the telecom market, with a commendable awareness of industry trends and developments. It is well known for its competitive carrier and cable industry expertise, and for its understanding of investigations and enforcement issues. Lawyers also offer experienced counsel to overseas clients that need to navigate the US regulatory system. Of late, it has advised Mediacom Communications on all telephony service offerings.

**Sources say:** *"Their knowledge of the industry is strong, and we increasingly rely on them to spot industry developments and how they can be advantageous."*

**KEY INDIVIDUALS Robert Aamoth** is commended for his work in the field of international telecommunications law. His practice focuses on common carrier regulation and telecommunications-related antitrust matters. He also handles complex appellate litigation. Practice co-head **John Heitmann** has amassed a wealth of experience in compliance, regulatory, enforcement and transactional matters. He regularly appears before the FCC and various state public utilities commissions, and is particularly notable for his representation of competitive carriers and cable companies – the latter with regard to telephony issues. Clients include Mediacom Communications.

## Lerman Senter PLLC

**THE FIRM** Lerman Senter is respected as an established player in the communications field. Members of the practice are noted for their extensive experience of FCC procedures and the regulatory landscape that businesses need to navigate. They also have broad transactional capabilities, and have notably advised on a number of substantial sales and acquisitions. Interviewees are quick to praise the team's understanding of the key issues faced by the industry.

**KEY INDIVIDUALS** Managing partner **Steven Lerman** is well regarded for the caliber of his work in the broadcasting sector. He has advised clients from the television and radio industry on numerous regulatory issues and transactions.

## Levine, Blaszak, Block & Boothby LLP

**THE FIRM** Levine, Blaszak, Block & Boothby maintains its reputation as a strong telecommunications boutique. It offers specialist advice on transactional, regulatory, compliance and litigious matters. The team is particularly well regarded for its efforts to assist clients in the use of new and cutting-edge technologies.

**KEY INDIVIDUALS Henry Levine** is known for his work with industry leaders such as IBM and Goldman Sachs. He has negotiated numerous telecommunications contracts, and is a skilled litigator in the field of carrier disputes. **James Blaszak** represents clients in a range of regulatory and public policy issues, drawing on his experience at the FCC and the Common Carrier Bureau. Clients also benefit from his familiarity with a wealth of telecommunications-related agreements.

## Pillsbury Winthrop Shaw Pittman LLP
See profile on p.2000

**THE FIRM** This well-known firm retains its reputation for expertise in the regulatory field, and is particularly recognized for its work in the satellite industry. The communications practice also continues to expand in the fields of new technology, wireless and broadcasting. The team recently acted for NewSat on the acquisition of satellite spectrum licenses and the negotiation of complex related documents. Other clients include Mercury Capital Partners.

**KEY INDIVIDUALS Richard Zaragoza** is singled out as a highly effective practitioner who has the respect of peers and clients. This former president of the Federal Communications Bar Association is noted for his work for leaders from the broadcasting, financial and private equity sectors. He represents the National Alliance of State Broadcasters Associations. **Bruce Jacobs** (see p.871) is best known for his work with new technology companies, bringing to bear his extensive FCC experience. He is currently advising LightSquared on the deployment of its 4G wireless network. Sources emphasize the importance of **John Hane**'s vast industry knowledge. He focuses on communications law and policy work, and regularly handles cutting-edge matters such as the reallocation of spectrum for mobile broadband. He played a significant role in the NewSat matter mentioned above.

## Squire Sanders (US) LLP
See profile on p.2129

**THE FIRM** Squire Sanders is commended for its depth of experience in the telecom regulatory arena and is well known as a player in the wireless communications and spectrum policy space. The group is also notable for its strengths in both the public and private sector, acting for clients such as Panasonic Avionics and the government of Bermuda. In addition, the practice draws on the firm's

global reach to offer highly regarded cross-border expertise to market leaders.

**Sources say:** *"They have a solid commercial awareness of other activities in the telecom space that impact our business, or that may impact the regulatory environment affecting our business."*

**KEY INDIVIDUALS Bruce Olcott** (see p.884) is described as *"conscientious, detailed and thorough,"* and highlighted for his experience and good judgment. Recent work highlights include acting for Horizon Wi-Com on the sale of its WCS spectrum to AT&T. *"Exceptionally knowledgeable and thoughtful,"* **Robert Kelly** (see p.873) is noted for his remarkable *"ability to break down complicated matters into simple concepts."* He heads the department and recently led the team acting as general counsel to the 800 MHz Transition Administrator. Peers recognize **Carlos Nalda** (see p.883) as being *"superb in the satellite field."* His practice has gone from strength to strength in the past year, acting for clients on a wide range of domestic and international issues. His practice focuses on wireless telecommunication and satellite-related matters that involve transactional, regulatory and policy issues. He advises Panasonic Avionics on the implementation of its global aeronautical broadband communications system.

## Steptoe & Johnson LLP

**THE FIRM** Steptoe & Johnson's internet and media practice is well known for its expertise in telecommunications matters, advising both national and international clients. The team is known for its breadth of expertise in the satellite and wireless fields, acting for clients such as DISH and Inmarsat; it has recently acted for DISH in numerous FCC proceedings, including defending a plan to roll out a hybrid satellite/terrestrial service to set up a US mobile broadband network.

**KEY INDIVIDUALS** *"Consummate professional"* **Pantelis Michalopoulos** is held in high regard for his wide-ranging industry knowledge. Clients praise his mastery of complex issues, with one noting: *"He has unparalleled institutional knowledge of our company, coupled with a keen sense of strategy for how to navigate regulatory requirements at the FCC."*

## TLP: Telecommunications Law Professionals PLLC

**THE FIRM** This telecommunications boutique focuses on wireless communications, regularly advising clients on regulatory, transactional and litigious matters. Recent work has included acting as chief outside regulatory counsel to MetroPCS on a wide range of matters.

**Sources say:** *"They are excellent all around: they take very good care of our interests, have a deep understanding of our business, and do a great job of balancing legal issues against business practicality."*

**KEY INDIVIDUALS** Communications expert **Carl Northrop** is a well-established figure in the market. Interviewees remark: *"He has an outstanding grasp of FCC regulatory policy combined with an excellent ability to understand the business consequences of regulatory actions."*

## Other Notable Practitioners

**Eric Greenberg** of Paul Hastings LLP *"has a very practical mind with a commercial bent,"* market sources report. He has been acting for LIN Media on the acquisition of 13 network affiliates of New Vision Television, which at the time of writing was pending FCC approval. At the same firm, **Tara Giunta** is highly regarded for her compliance expertise, advising international market leaders on business-critical issues. She recently represented Ridgemont Equity Partners in a range of FCC and national security regulatory matters. White & Case LLP's **Maury Mechanick** (see p.881) is an established practitioner with specialist knowledge of the satellite industry. He offers a breadth of expertise in finance-related, transactional and regulatory matters.

**Patrick Campbell** (see p.856) of Paul, Weiss, Rifkind, Wharton & Garrison LLP is recognized as an expert in the field of satellite law. Sources value his ability to understand their business needs and guide them through the regulatory system. **Todd Daubert** (see p.859) chairs the communications and technology group at Dentons and has an impressive breadth and depth of experience on a range of communications-related issues. He represents investors, broadcasters, software developers and communications providers in a variety of regulatory and transactional and litigious matters. **Jennifer Richter** cochairs Patton Boggs LLP's technology and communications practice. She offers a wealth of expertise in transactional, regulatory and policy matters within the communications space. Market commentators describe **Marc Martin** (see p.880) of K&L Gates

as *"practical, creative and understanding of commercial realities,"* and recommend him *"without hesitation."* He consistently works with industry leaders, advising on issues such as spectrum licenses, joint ventures and distribution agreements. Holland & Knight LLP's **Norman Leventhal** (see p.876) is an established figure in the market, and brings more than four decades of experience to bear on matters. He is best known for his work with leading members of the satellite, broadcast and telecom industries. **Don Stockdale** of Mayer Brown LLP *"brings intelligence and good judgment to bear for us,"* report satisfied clients. He handles FCC-related matters for clients such as AT&T.

# Leaders' Profiles in District of Columbia

## ABRAMS, Robert G
Baker & Hostetler LLP, Washington, DC
202 861 1699
rabrams@bakerlaw.com
*Featured in Antitrust (District of Columbia)*
**Career:** Profiled by The American Lawyer as having made one of "the most important lateral moves in 2011" and one of the "biggest stars" from the former Howrey law firm to hit "the open market," Bob Abrams chairs BakerHostetler's nationwide Antitrust group, which has more than doubled in size in the past two years. A Fellow in the American College of Trial Lawyers with more than 30 years of trial experience, Bob has tried cases on behalf of both plaintiffs and defendants, including class actions, antitrust and other complex commercial cases. Prior to joining BakerHostetler, Bob co-chaired Howrey's Global Litigation Group.

## ADLER, Howard B
Gibson, Dunn & Crutcher LLP, Washington, DC
202 955 8589
hadler@gibsondunn.com
*Featured in Corporate/M&A (District of Columbia), Capital Markets (Nationwide)*
**Practice Areas:** Represents corporations, investment banks, REITs and private equity firms in M&A and securities offerings. M&A: Represented Saxon Capital in its sale to Morgan Stanley (2006); Ameriquest Capital in the sale of Long Beach Acceptance Corporation to AmeriCredit and the sale of its mortgage business to CitiGroup (2007); Arlington Capital (Cambridge Major Laboratories; NLX, LLC; Secor); Capital One Finance Corp. (various acquisitions). Finance: IPOs—Friedman, Billings Ramsey; American Capital Strategies; Corporate Executive Board; American Home Mortgage; Saxon Capital; Franklin Bank; numerous follow-on offerings and major 144A transactions.

**Personal:** JD, New York University; Note and Comment Editor, Law Review.

## ALBERG, James L
Pillsbury Winthrop Shaw Pittman LLP, Washington, DC
202 663 9123
james.alberg@pillsburylaw.com
*Featured in Outsourcing (Nationwide), Technology (District of Columbia)*
See under Nationwide for profile.

## ALBERINO, Scott L
Akin Gump Strauss Hauer & Feld LLP, Washington, DC
202 887 4027
salberino@akingump.com
*Featured in Bankruptcy/Restructuring (District of Columbia)*
**Practice Areas:** Focuses on corporate restructurings, with an emphasis on official and unofficial creditors' committees, bondholder groups, and bank steering groups in large, complex cases both out of court and in Chapter 11. Represents bondholders, noteholders, bank lenders, institutional investors, private equity firms, hedge funds and other interested parties. Has also represented debtors in possession, bank agents, post-petition lenders and acquirers of distressed assets.
**Career:** Judicial extern, Honorable James E. Massey; Clerk, Honorable C. Ray Mullins.
**Personal:** BA, cum laude, Boston College (1997); JD, with honors, Emory University School of Law, managing editor, Emory International Law Review (2000).

## ALBERTS, Sam J
Dentons, Washington, DC
202 408 7004
sam.alberts@dentons.com
*Featured in Bankruptcy/Restructuring (District of Columbia)*
**Practice Areas:** Restructuring and insolvency, commercial litigation and distressed healthcare.

Experience in complex domestic and cross-border business and government-related restructurings, bankruptcies and litigations. Representing the FDIC on several failed banks, including Corus, K Bank, First Regional, Capitol Bancorp and previously WAMU. Representing the PBGC in Kodak. Representing customers and claimholders in broker-dealer insolvencies, including Lehman Brothers and Refco. Represented interests in distressed healthcare cases, including official committees in The Clare at Water Tower, Middlebrook Pharmaceuticals, Greater Southeast Community Hospital, Pennsylvania in the AHERF cases and debtor in Response Oncology.
**Personal:** The George Washington University Law School, 1992, JD; New York University, 1987, BA.

## ALBRECHT, Virginia S
Hunton & Williams LLP, Washington, DC
202 955 1943
valbrecht@hunton.com
*Featured in Environment (District of Columbia)*
**Practice Areas:** Virginia Albrecht's practice focuses exclusively on environmental law and administrative law - in particular, the Clean Water Act (CWA) wetlands and storm water programs, the Endangered Species Act (ESA), the National Environmental Policy Act (NEPA) and other federal regulatory programs that affect the use of land and water. Experience in permit negotiation, litigation of policy issues, lobbying Congress and the Administration, enforcement defense, and compliance counseling. Representative clients include development companies, agricultural and mining companies, state and local agencies, and trade associations. Extensive experience with federal environmental agencies both in Washington and in district and regional offices.

## ALDOCK, John D
Goodwin Procter LLP, Washington, DC
202 346 4240
jaldock@goodwinprocter.com
*Featured in Litigation (District of Columbia)*
**Practice Areas:** Mr Aldock serves as the firm's General Counsel. His nationwide practice focuses on commercial litigation, including class actions, mass torts, insurance, securities, international, RICO, ERISA, commercial arbitration and business litigation. He has represented law firms in state and federal court litigation alleging professional malpractice and represented lawyers before state grievance committees, as well as accounting firms in strategic advice and litigation matters. He served as Special Counsel to the 20 US and international corporate members of the Center for Claims Resolution.
**Personal:** JD, University of Pennsylvania Law School (cum laude); BS, Northwestern University.

## ALEXANDER, Jim
Maggio & Kattar PC, Washington, DC
202 483 0053
jalexander@maggio-kattar.com
*Featured in Immigration (District of Columbia)*
**Practice Areas:** Managing Shareholder, Immigration law. Jim is a nationally recognized expert in the immigration law field with a focus on employment-based immigration, immigration issues arising from corporate mergers and acquisitions, employer compliance, and complex naturalization matters. Jim is routinely engaged by clients from a wide range of industries including finance, aviation, defense and technology. Jim is a frequent lecturer at international and national events on various immigration topics including for the American Immigration Lawyers Association, the Federal Bar Association and the District of Columbia Bar Association.
**Publications:** Jim has authored a variety of publications for the American Immigration Lawyers

Association, the American Bar Association and Thomson Reuters Aspatore Books. He has also been quoted in national publications including Workforce Management, InfoTech and Telecom News, and The Legal Times and NPR.

## ALTER, Michael J
Fried, Frank, Harris, Shriver & Jacobson LLP, New York
202 639 7094
Michael.Alter@friedfrank.com
*Featured in Tax (District of Columbia)*
**Practice Areas:** Tax partner. Practice focuses on federal income taxation, with particular emphasis on the structuring and negotiation of taxable and tax-free acquisitions and dispositions, reorganizations and spin-off transactions, as well as tax planning for debt and equity securities offerings and financings.
**Career:** Joined in 2000; became partner in 2006.
**Personal:** JD, with honors, George Washington University Law School (1997); BA, magna cum laude, Union College (1993).

## ANDREWS, Walter J
Hunton & Williams LLP, McLean
703 714 7642
wandrews@hunton.com
*Featured in Insurance (District of Columbia)*
**Practice Areas:** Insurance coverage litigation and counseling, and reinsurance. Represent clients in coverage and bad faith disputes involving professional liability, D&O, business interruption, product liability, mass tort, construction defect, reinsurance, e-commerce issues, and other emerging claims. Matters involve a variety of insurance contracts, including professional liability, first party property, reinsurance and general liability insurance policies. Extensive experience in trial and appellate courts nationwide as well as reinsurance arbitrations.
**Professional Memberships:** Admitted to practice in Virginia, Florida and the District of Columbia.
**Personal:** BA, Swarthmore College, 1979. JD, University of Chicago Law School, 1982.

## ANTHONY, Stephen
Covington & Burling LLP, Washington, DC
202 662 5105
santhony@cov.com
*Featured in Litigation (District of Columbia)*
**Practice Areas:** Stephen Anthony is Deputy Chair of Covington's global litigation practice. His practice focuses on white collar criminal defense and corporate internal investigations. He has represented corporations and individuals in government investigations of allegations such as accounting fraud, consumer fraud, international trade control violations, violations of laws governing the manufacture and marketing of pharmaceutical products, and violations of the Foreign Corrupt Practices Act. He has tried 32 cases before juries. He also advises companies regarding the design, implementation, and review of compliance programs and regarding the conduct of corporate internal investigations.
**Personal:** Columbia University, JD, Dartmouth College, AB.

## ARP, D Jarrett
Gibson, Dunn & Crutcher LLP, Washington, DC
202 955 8678
jarp@gibsondunn.com
*Featured in Antitrust (District of Columbia)*
**Practice Areas:** Specializes in antitrust counseling and complex litigation defending domestic and international clients before US courts. Significant experience with respect to civil and criminal government antitrust investigations and a wide range of industries.
**Professional Memberships:** Co-chair, 2014 ABA/IBA International Cartel Workshop; former Editor-In-Chief, Antitrust Report.
**Career:** Partner since 2002; Adjunct Professor of Law, Washington & Lee Law School, 2002-2005; Captain, US Army's 101st Airborne Division, 1992-94.
**Publications:** Author/editor of numerous books, chapters, articles and papers on domestic and international antitrust law.
**Personal:** JD, College of William & Mary, 1991; BA, Wheaton College, 1988.

## ASBILL, Henry W
Jones Day, Washington, DC
202 879 5414
hasbill@jonesday.com
*Featured in Litigation (District of Columbia)*
**Practice Areas:** Extensive national first-chair, winning jury trial experience. Over 35 years of defending clients in more than 100 major trials against a broad spectrum of criminal and civil charges. Profiled in The National Law Journal's special "Winning" report highlighting successful strategies from the nation's top litigators. Former adjunct professor of trial practice at Georgetown University Law Center.
**Professional Memberships:** Fellow- American College of Trial Lawyers. Past president and Fellow of the American Board of Criminal Lawyers. Former director of the National Association of Criminal Defense Lawyers. Board member of NACDL's White Collar Criminal Defense College.

## ASSAF, Eugene F
Kirkland & Ellis LLP, Washington, DC
202 879 5196
eugene.assaf@kirkland.com
*Featured in Litigation (District of Columbia)*
**Practice Areas:** Gene Assaf has represented corporate clients, as defense and as plaintiff's Counsel, on a variety of commercial, financial and technological disputes before judges, juries and arbitration panels across the country. He has represented a diverse group of clients, including BASF, Siemens, Honeywell, Raytheon, AOL and SIPC on matters including contract disputes, fraud claims, environmental matters, statutory claims, intellectual property claims and class actions. An accomplished trial lawyer, Mr Assaf takes significant cases to trial.

## ATTRIDGE, Daniel F
Kirkland & Ellis LLP, Washington, DC
202 879 5012
daniel.attridge@kirkland.com
*Featured in Intellectual Property (District of Columbia)*
**Practice Areas:** Mr Attridge has practiced in Kirkland's Washington office since 1980 and was the office's managing partner from 1998 to 2013. He is now the Dean of the Columbus School of Law at The Catholic University of America. He has litigated cases before federal and state courts, administrative agencies, and arbitration panels throughout the United States. His cases have involved a wide range of industries and practice areas, including intellectual property (patents, trade secrets, trademarks, false advertising), antitrust, contracts, insurance, and corporate/securities.
**Personal:** University of Pennsylvania (BA, 1976); Georgetown University Law Center (JD, 1979).

## AUERBACH, Dennis B
Covington & Burling LLP, Washington, DC
202 662 5226
dauerbach@cov.com
*Featured in Bankruptcy/Restructuring (District of Columbia)*
**Practice Areas:** Specializes in financial, bankruptcy, and white-collar litigation — especially litigation with a fraud or breach of fiduciary duty dimension. Matters handled in recent years include representation of clients on breach of fiduciary duty claims arising out of bankruptcies and corporate acquisitions; and concerning allegations of securities or other financial fraud. Mr Auerbach also represents clients on a variety of bankruptcy matters, and maintains an active pro bono practice.
**Personal:** BA (1984) from Princeton University, and JD (1989) from Harvard Law School.

## BAND, Ian P
Hunton & Williams LLP, Washington, DC
202 955 1913
iband@hunton.com
*Featured in Immigration (District of Columbia)*
**Practice Areas:** Mr Band's practice focuses exclusively on business immigration law. He has in-depth experience providing legal services and counseling in all aspects of business immigration law to corporate and individual clients. Mr Band represents businesses and individuals before the US Citizenship and Immigration Services, the Department of Labor, the State Department, Department of Homeland Security and US consular offices. He also counsels businesses on I-9 compliance and related investigations.
**Professional Memberships:** DC and Maryland Bar, American Immigration Lawyers Association.

## BANOUN, Raymond
Cadwalader, Wickersham & Taft LLP, Washington, DC
202 862 2426
ray.banoun@cwt.com
*Featured in Litigation (District of Columbia)*
**Practice Areas:** Co-Chair, Business Fraud Group. Represents corporations and financial institutions, their audit committees, and executives in all aspects of criminal and securities enforcement matters before federal and state agencies, and in litigation before all courts. Conducts internal investigations and compliance audits, formulates compliance programs, and advises with respect to their implementation and related governance issues. Specializes in matters involving the Foreign Corrupt Practices Act, money laundering and asset forfeiture, the anti-fraud provisions of the securities and commodities statutes, economic sanctions, export control and anti-boycott laws and regulations, criminal tax and antitrust violations, banking, healthcare, government procurement and bankruptcy fraud, and the False Claims Act. Regularly interacts with DOJ, SEC, federal and state prosecutors, Inspectors General and regulatory agencies. Co-author of "Money Laundering, Terrorism and Financial Institutions".
**Professional Memberships:** Fellow, American College of Trial Lawyers.
**Personal:** JD, George Washington University Law School; BA, City College of New York.

## BARKER, James H
Latham & Watkins LLP, Washington, DC
202 637 2231
jim.barker@lw.com
*Featured in Telecommunications (District of Columbia)*
**Practice Areas:** Represents a wide range of telecommunications, media and technology industry clients on transactional, controversy, appellate and compliance matters. He has particular expertise advising clients on spectrum auction and multichannel video programming distributor issues.
**Professional Memberships:** Member, Florida and District of Columbia bars.
**Career:** Deputy Office Managing Partner, Washington, D.C.
**Personal:** JD, University of Virginia School of Law, 1990, Notes Editor, Virginia Law Review; BA Washington & Lee University, summa cum laude, 1987; Clerkship, Hon. Peter T. Fay, United States Court of Appeals for the Eleventh Circuit.

## BARKER, Rosina B
Ivins, Phillips & Barker, Washington, DC
202 393 7600
rbarker@ipbtax.com
*Featured in Employee Benefits & Executive Compensation (District of Columbia)*
**Practice Areas:** Rosina Barker's practice focuses on tax and ERISA issues raised by employee benefit plans and executive compensation. She drafts, interprets and negotiates stock-based plans, non-qualified deferred compensation plans, change-in-control agreements, severance agreements and employment agreements, and advises on issues raised by Code sections 83, 409A, 162(m), 457A, 280(g), 402(b) and other tax rules. She advises and represents clients before the IRS, Labor Department and Pension Benefit Guaranty Corporation, with respect to the tax and ERISA issues raised by qualified retirement plans including cash balance plans, 401(k) plans, and ESOPs.

In addition, Rosina counsels clients on deduction, accrual and other tax issues arising from contributions to and distributions from pension and welfare benefit plans, as well as the tax, ERISA and other laws governing their medical, severance, insurance, and other employee benefit plans.
**Professional Memberships:** Fellow, American College of Employee Benefits Counsel; Bloomberg BNA Pension & Benefits Advisory Board; Advisory Board, Center for Tax Law and Employee Benefits, the John Marshall Law School; Chair, D.C. Bar, Employee Benefits Committee, (Tax Section) (2003-06); Co-Editor-in-Chief (1997-2001) and Editorial Board, Benefits Law Journal; DC Bar (Tax Section); ABA (Tax Section); ERISA Roundtable.
**Career:** Majority Tax Staff, US House Ways and Means Committee, 1983–91; Partner, Ivins, Phillips & Barker since 1997
**Publications:** Numerous publications, including treatise chapters in The 409A Handbook (BNA 2010) and Cash Balance Plans (Aspen 2003), numerous articles in Tax Notes, BNA Pension and Benefits Reporter, and Benefits Law Journal. Frequent speaker at professional educational institutions including DC Bar, ABA Tax Section, ACI, America Law Institute/ABA, and NYU Institute on Federal Taxation.
**Personal:** Harvard University, AB 1979 (cum laude); Harvard Kennedy School of Government, MPP 1983; Georgetown University Law Center, JD 1990 (magna cum laude, Order of the Coif, Nelson T. Hartson Memorial Award)

### BARNETT, Thomas O
Covington & Burling LLP, Washington, DC
202 662 5407
tbarnett@cov.com
*Featured in Antitrust (District of Columbia)*
**Practice Areas:** Co-chair of the firm's global antitrust practice. In private practice and government, has been involved in large mergers (Merck/Schering-Plough; Facebook/Instagram), online competition matters, private antitrust litigation, criminal matters (auto parts and air cargo), and the Supreme Court.
**Career:** Assistant Attorney General for Antitrust, heading Division (2005-2008), DAAG for Civil Enforcement (2004-2005). Chair of OECD Competition subcommittee (2006-2008), Steering Committee of the ICN (2005-2008). Before 2004, a leader in Covington's antitrust practice. Taught multiple classes at Georgetown and Virginia law schools.
**Personal:** Personal: Harvard Law School, magna cum laude (1989); LSE, M. Sc., Fulbright Scholar (1986).

### BARRY, Dennis M
King & Spalding LLP, Washington, DC
202 626 2959
dbarry@kslaw.com
*Featured in Healthcare (Nationwide), Healthcare (District of Columbia)*
See under Nationwide for profile.

### BARTHOLOMEW, Christian
Weil, Gotshal & Manges LLP, Washington, DC
202 682 7070
christian.bartholomew@weil.com
*Featured in Litigation (District of Columbia)*
**Practice Areas:** Christian Bartholomew leads Weil's securities enforcement and litigation efforts in Washington, DC and Miami. He represents financial institutions and public companies, and their officers and directors, in enforcement matters brought by the DOJ, SEC, FINRA, and other regulatory agencies, as well as in private securities litigation. He earlier served as the Senior Trial Counsel for the SEC's Southeast Regional Office – where he was undefeated during his tenure and prosecuted numerous precedent-setting cases – and is widely considered a recognized leader in the area of the SEC's Dodd-Frank whistleblower rules.
**Personal:** McGill University (BA, 1982); University of Virginia (JD, 1987).

### BASILE, Edward
King & Spalding LLP, Washington, DC
202 626 2903
EBasile@kslaw.com
*Featured in Life Sciences (Nationwide), Healthcare (District of Columbia)*
**Practice Areas:** FDA/ healthcare with over 25 years of experience interpreting the laws and regulations of the food and drug administration.
**Professional Memberships:** The District of Columbia Bar.
**Career:** Prior to joining King & Spalding, Mr Basile served as Deputy General Counsel for the Advanced Medical Technology Association, the primary trade association for the medical device industry.
**Personal:** Mr Basile received a BS in mechanical engineering from Lafayette College in 1969 and his law degree in 1972 from the National Law Center, George Washington University where he graduated Order of the Coif.

### BASS, Scott
Sidley Austin LLP, Washington, DC
202 736 8684
sbass@sidley.com
*Featured in Life Sciences (Nationwide), Healthcare (District of Columbia)*
See under Nationwide for profile.

### BASTIANELLI III, Adrian L
Peckar & Abramson, P.C., Washington, DC
202 293 8815
abastianelli@pecklaw.com
*Featured in Construction (District of Columbia)*
**Practice Areas:** Mr Bastianelli's practice focuses on construction law, government contract law, and mediaton/arbitration.
**Professional Memberships:** Past Chair, ABA Forum on the Construction Industry; Past-Member Board of Governors, American College of Construction Lawyers; Past President, Washington Building Congress.
**Career:** Co-Managing Partner in Washington, DC office; Construction lawyer; Law Clerk US Court of Claims; Civil Engineer (Professional

Engineer - Inactive). Admitted to practice in the District of Columbia.
**Publications:** Editor: The Construction Lawyer, Journal of the American College of Construction Lawyers, Federal Government Construction Contracts; Chapter Author for numerous construction law books.
**Personal:** For more information, visit our website at www.pecklaw.com

### BAUMANN, Linda
Arent Fox LLP, Washington, DC
202 857 6239
linda.baumann@arentfox.com
*Featured in Healthcare (District of Columbia)*
**Practice Areas:** Linda Baumann's practice focuses on health care fraud and abuse, compliance, internal investigations, and Medicare/Medicaid reimbursement. She counsels clients on matters involving the Stark Law, Anti-Kickback Statute, and the False Claims Act. Linda represents a wide range of companies from Fortune 50 corporations and national chains to community providers and professional associations. She advises clients on all aspects of False Claims Act cases, from subpoena response through successful negotiation and settlement. She has worked with clients under corporate integrity agreements, served as outside regulatory counsel, and conducted due diligence in connection with acquisitions and financing.

### BAXTER, Michael St Patrick
Covington & Burling LLP, Washington, DC
202 662 5164
mbaxter@cov.com
*Featured in Bankruptcy/Restructuring (District of Columbia)*
**Practice Areas:** Advising creditors, debtors and committees in corporate restructurings and bankruptcy reorganization. He has been involved in many notable bankruptcy cases, including Borders, Ahern Rentals, Trump Entertainment, Chrysler, General Motors, and Congoleum.
**Professional Memberships:** American Law Institute; American College of Bankruptcy; National Bankruptcy Conference; International Insolvency Institute.
**Career:** Covington, 1983 to present. Adjunct Professor, George Washington University Law School.
**Publications:** Contributing editor, 'Norton Bankruptcy Law and Practice 3d'. He has published extensively in the insolvency area and is a frequent speaker at professional programs.
**Personal:** LLM, Harvard Law School, 1983; LLB, University of Western Ontario, 1979.

### BECKER, Stephen
McDermott Will & Emery LLP, Washington, DC
202 756 8608
sbecker@mwe.com
*Featured in Intellectual Property (District of Columbia)*
**Practice Areas:** Member of intellectual property, media and technology department, and leads firm's patent procurement group. Concentrates on patent matters with special emphasis on semicon-

ductor electronics, circuits, telecommunications, business methods and computer-related inventions.
**Professional Memberships:** Admitted in District of Columbia, Maryland and Virginia; US Court of Appeals for Federal Circuit; US Patent and Trademark Office; American Bar Association.
**Publications:** Author of 'Patent Applications Handbook', published annually since 1992, and 'Patents Throughout the World'.
**Personal:** George Washington University Law School, JD (with honors), 1975; University of Wisconsin - Madison, MSEE, 1967; Illinois Institute of Technology, BSEE, 1966.

### BELL, Robert B
Kaye Scholer LLP, Washington, DC
202 682 3570
robert.bell@kayescholer.com
*Featured in Antitrust (District of Columbia)*
**Practice Areas:** Robert Bell, Co-Head of Kaye Scholer's Antitrust practice, has extensive experience in securing antitrust clearance for mergers and acquisitions from both the Department of Justice and the Federal Trade Commission. He also represents companies and individuals in criminal antitrust investigations. Robert regularly provides antitrust counseling on issues ranging from competitor collaborations to vertical distribution arrangements. He has represented clients from a wide variety of sectors, including imaging, communications, defense, entertainment, manufacturing, mining, chemicals and transportation. Robert frequently writes articles on antitrust topics, which have been published in Global Competition Review, Legal Times and National Law Journal.

### BENNETT, Mary
Baker & McKenzie, Washington, DC
202 452 7045
mary.bennett@bakermckenzie.com
*Featured in Tax (District of Columbia)*
**Practice Areas:** Mary Bennett advises on international tax planning, controversy, and policy matters. She has particularly deep experience in tax treaty, transfer pricing, and international dispute resolution issues.
**Professional Memberships:** American Bar Association; Business and Industry Advisory Committee; International Fiscal Association; National Foreign Trade Council; The Tax Coalition; US Council for International Business.
**Career:** Ms Bennett has more than 30 years of international tax experience, including senior positions with the US Treasury (US Treasury's Deputy International Tax Counsel) and the OECD (Head of the Tax Treaty & Transfer Pricing Division).
**Personal:** LLM, Boston University; JD, Columbia University; AB, Harvard University.

### BENTIVOGLIO, John T
Skadden, Arps, Slate, Meagher & Flom LLP & Affiliates, Washington, DC
202 371 7560
John.Bentivoglio@skadden.com
*Featured in Healthcare (District of Columbia)*

**Practice Areas:** Focuses on assisting pharmaceutical, medical device, and biotechnology manufacturers in FDA and healthcare regulatory counseling, compliance program development and implementation, and representation of companies in civil and criminal investigations by federal and state agencies. Has conducted dozens of internal investigations and compliance assessments for manufacturers.

**Career:** US Department of Justice: Associate Deputy Attorney General (1998-2000); Counsel to the Deputy Attorney General & Special Counsel for Health Care Fraud (1997-98); Trial Attorney, Criminal Division (1996-97). Committee on the Judiciary, US Senate: Professional Staff Member (1988-92); Legislative Assistant (1986-88). JD, Georgetown University Law Center; BA, University of California, Berkeley.

### BERGESON, Lynn L
Bergeson & Campbell PC, Washington, DC
202 557 3801
lbergeson@lawbc.com
*Featured in Environment (District of Columbia)*

**Practice Areas:** Regulatory, litigation, and science policy issues associated with TSCA, FIFRA, CPSA, and other chemical product approval and defense, nanotechnology, biobased chemicals, and other emerging transformative technologies.

**Professional Memberships:** Past Chair, ABA Section of Environment, Energy, and Resources (SEER)(2005-06); Member, Board of Directors, Earth Day Network; ANSI Nanotechnology Standards Panel Steering Committee; Editorial Board, 'Nanotechnology Law and Business', 'The Environmental Forum', 'Pesticide & Toxic Chemical News', 'Environmental Quality Management', 'Chemical Processing', and 'Pollution Prevention Review', among others. Member of the District of Columbia Bar; Bar Association of the District of Columbia; American Bar Association; Women's Bar Association of the District of Columbia; The Cosmos Club.

**Publications:** Selected publications include 'TSCA and the Regulation of Renewable Chemicals', Industrial Biotechnology (2012); 'Pesticide Data Compensation in the EU and Canada', Bloomberg BNA Daily Environment Report (2012); 'Nanotechnology: Environmental Law, Policy, and Business Considerations', ABA (2010); 'Genomics and Environmental Regulation: Science, Ethics, and Law' (2008); 'Nanotechnology Deskbook', ELI (2008); 'Nanotechnology and the Environment' (2008); TSCA and Engineered Nanoscale Substances' (2007); 'The TSCA Basic Practice Book', ABA (2000); 'The FIFRA Basic Practice Book', ABA (2000).

**Personal:** Columbus School of Law, Catholic University of America (Member, Law Review); Michigan State University (BA, magna cum laude).

### BERLIN, Seth D
Levine Sullivan Koch & Schulz LLP, Washington, DC
202 508 1122
sberlin@lskslaw.com
*Featured in Media & Entertainment (District of Columbia)*

**Practice Areas:** Over twenty years experience representing media clients in libel, invasion of privacy, copyright, trademark, and related First Amendment cases. Served as Adjunct Professor in media law at University of Maryland College of Journalism. Testified before the US Senate Judiciary Committee on 'Cameras in the Courtroom'.

**Professional Memberships:** Past Governing Board, ABA Forum on Communications Law; Founder, Media Advocacy Workshop.

**Publications:** Co-author, "Newsgathering and the Law"; Author, "Planned Parenthood v. ACLA: Are the Nuremberg Files and 'Wanted' Posters Protected Advocacy or Unprotected Threat?"

**Personal:** Born 17 July 1966. Graduate of Brown University and Harvard Law School.

### BERNSTEIN, Michael
Arnold & Porter LLP, Washington, DC
202 942 5577
Michael.Bernstein@aporter.com
*Featured in Bankruptcy/Restructuring (District of Columbia)*

**Practice Areas:** Bankruptcy, corporate restructuring, and related litigation.

**Professional Memberships:** Fellow, American College of Bankruptcy; Board of Directors, American Bankruptcy Institute

**Career:** For more than 20 years, Mr Bernstein has been involved in complex bankruptcy and restructuring matters, and related litigation, in courts throughout the United States.

**Publications:** Mr Bernstein has co-authored two books and has published many articles on bankruptcy-related topics. He has also testified before Congress concerning bankruptcy issues. He is a frequent lecturer, has been interviewed by major newspapers and on television and radio, and has been recognized as a leading bankruptcy lawyer by numerous publications.

### BERNSTEIN, Steven K
Weil, Gotshal & Manges LLP, Washington, DC
202 682 7502
steven.bernstein@weil.com
*Featured in Antitrust (District of Columbia)*

**Practice Areas:** Steven Bernstein, partner in Washington DC, focuses on antitrust counseling and litigation, emphasizing M&A. He has represented numerous clients before the FTC and DOJ and successfully obtained antitrust clearance for major transactions in various industries. He has also successfully represented clients in non-merger matters before the antitrust enforcement agencies and in private litigation. Prior to joining Weil, he served as Assistant Director of the FTC's Bureau of Competition, where he led the Mergers I Division in carrying out the FTC's merger enforcement program.

**Personal:** University of Miami (BBA in Accounting, 1988); Northwestern University School of Law (JD, 1991).

### BERNTHAL, Eric L
Latham & Watkins LLP, Washington, DC
202 637 2236
eric.bernthal@lw.com
*Featured in Media & Entertainment (District of Columbia)*

**Practice Areas:** Represents both public and privately-held clients in all facets of their transactional, corporate, controversy, litigation and regulatory needs. Particular expertise in advising corporate clients on mergers and acquisitions and the full range of governance, litigation, regulatory and financial matters.

**Professional Memberships:** Member, District of Columbia bar.

**Personal:** JD, George Washington University Law School, 1970; BA, Columbia University, 1967.

### BERSON, Susan
Mintz Levin Cohn Ferris Glovsky and Popeo PC, Boston
202 661 8715
SBerson@mintz.com
*Featured in Healthcare (District of Columbia)*

**Practice Areas:** Susan is Managing Member of the firm's Washington, DC office. She advises healthcare companies, including managed care organizations, pharmacy benefit managers, behavioral health companies, specialty care companies, and integrated delivery systems, often in the context of strategic affiliations and complex service agreements. Susan has advised some of the nation's largest government programs in connection with strategic regulatory matters including participation in Medicare Parts C and D, Medicaid and innovative programs integrating state and federal health benefits. She has negotiated some of the nation's largest pharmacy service agreements, and also advises on complex mergers, acquisitions, and joint ventures.

**Personal:** BA, University of Rochester; JD, Columbia University.

### BERZ, David
Weil, Gotshal & Manges LLP, Washington, DC
202 682 7190
david.berz@weil.com
*Featured in Environment (District of Columbia)*

**Practice Areas:** David Berz heads Weil's Environmental Practice. He serves as lead counsel in civil and criminal environmental matters involving federal and state water, air, and hazardous waste and substance statutes. He routinely counsels clients regarding environmental issues that arise in mergers, acquisitions and bankruptcies. Mr Berz also has experience handling declaratory judgment cases brought to resolve insurance coverage disputes in a variety of contexts. He regularly advises multinational corporations, their senior management and boards of directors in developing environmental compliance programs, and serves as environmental counsel to several financial institutions.

**Personal:** George Washington University (BA, 1970); (JD, 1973).

### BIEKE, James R
Sidley Austin LLP, Washington, DC
202 736 8848
jbieke@sidley.com
*Featured in Environment (District of Columbia)*

**Practice Areas:** Partner in Sidley's Washington, DC office. Practice focuses on environmental and natural resources law and policy, with an emphasis on complex scientific, technical, economic and legal issues. Provides advice to clients under the Comprehensive Environmental Response, Compensation and Liability Act (CERCLA), the Resource Conservation and Recovery Act (RCRA), the Toxic Substances Control Act (TSCA), the Clean Air Act, and the Clean Water Act.

**Personal:** New York University Law School, LLM, 1971; University of Michigan Law School, JD, 1970, Order of the Coif; University of Michigan, MA, 1970; Sacred Heart Seminary, BA, 1967. Supreme Court law clerk.

### BILES, Blake A
Arnold & Porter LLP, Washington, DC
202 942 5836
Blake.Biles@aporter.com
*Featured in Environment (District of Columbia)*

**Practice Areas:** Blake Biles provides services to businesses on a range of environmental requirements, encompassing counseling, transactions, rulemakings, compliance audits, and enforcement and appellate litigation. He has particular expertise concerning hazard and risk assessments, potential liabilities associated with chemicals and other commercial products, hazard communication and right-to-know, biotechnology, nanotechnology, consumer product safety, and related product liability matters.

**Career:** Served the US EPA in the Agency's Office of Water Enforcement and the Office of the General Counsel; thereafter first Director of the new-chemicals review program in the EPA's Office of Toxic Substances.

**Personal:** University of Kansas, JD 1975, BA 1968.

### BIRNKRANT, Henry
Alston & Bird LLP, Washington, DC
202 239 3319
henry.birnkrant@alston.com
*Featured in Tax (District of Columbia)*

**Practice Areas:** Focuses on transfer pricing, including planning, APAs and controversy, and federal income taxation of domestic and cross-border transactions.

**Professional Memberships:** Chair, Tax Treaty Subcommittee of the Taxation Committee of the US Council for International Business; Board of advisors of the Journal of International Taxation; Thomson West Tax Advisory Board; invited participant, OECD Transfer Pricing Experts consultations; fellow, American College of Tax Counsel; Washington International Tax Study Group; American Bar Association Tax Section; International Fiscal Association.

**Career:** Leads firm's Tax Section.

**Personal:** New York University (LLM, 1983); Columbia University (JD, 1979); University of Rochester (BA, magna cum laude, 1976).

### BLUMENTHAL, William
Clifford Chance US LLP, Washington, DC
william.blumenthal@cliffordchance.com
*Featured in Antitrust (District of Columbia)*
**Practice Areas:** Advises clients on all aspects of antitrust law, including mergers and acquisitions, joint ventures, horizontal and vertical restraints, monopolization, predatory pricing, distribution agreements and consumer protection issues. Prior to joining Clifford Chance, was General Counsel of the Federal Trade Commission, where he served as the agency's chief law officer. Responsibilities included advising the Commission, its members, and its staff on law and policy; representing the agency in federal and state courts; supervising agency reports to the President and to Congress; and advising on proposed legislation.
**Career:** Brown University, AB and MA in economics. Harvard University, JD.

### BODANSKY, Robert
Seyfarth Shaw LLP, Washington, DC
202 828 3577
rbodansky@seyfarth.com
*Featured in Real Estate (District of Columbia)*
**Practice Areas:** Real estate, M&A, institutional investments
**Professional Memberships:** PREA, NAPPA, ABA
**Career:** Practice emphasizes real estate, alternative investments and business transactions. Real estate practice focuses on sale, acquisition, development, financing and leasing of commercial properties for government pension funds, institutional owners and developers, as well as structuring joint ventures and other real estate related transactions. Also serves as investment counsel for government and private pension funds with respect to alternative investments. Significant expertise in mergers and acquisitions, cross-border transactions and co-location of foreign companies into the US.
**Personal:** JD, with honors, George Washington University; BA, with honors, Syracuse University.

### BODOR, Brian R
Pillsbury Winthrop Shaw Pittman LLP, Washington, DC
202 663 9145
brian.bodor@pillsburylaw.com
*Featured in Technology (District of Columbia)*
**Practice Areas:** Advises clients on numerous types of sourcing and technology-related initiatives. He represents both large, global and mid-market clients in the areas of information technology outsourcing (ITO), business process outsourcing (BPO), procurement, strategic joint ventures, systems development and integration, software licensing, intellectual property transfers and telecommunications initiatives. Advises clients during the early stages of structuring complex delivery arrangements, leads negotiations on behalf of clients, and subsequently advises clients on operating and managing supplier relation-

ships. Serves both government and private entities.
**Career:** Admitted: District of Columbia, Arizona, Colorado.
**Personal:** JD, University of Michigan Law School, 1996; BA, Cornell University, 1993.

### BOLAND, Sean F X
Baker Botts LLP, Washington, DC
202 639 7799
sean.boland@bakerbotts.com
*Featured in Antitrust (District of Columbia)*
**Practice Areas:** Antitrust and Competition Law, Litigation Practice.
**Professional Memberships:** District of Columbia Bar; United States Court for the District of Columbia; United States Court of Appeals for the District of Columbia Circuit.
**Career:** Mr Boland's practice consists of representing companies before the US and international antitrust enforcement agencies. His areas of experience include mergers and acquisitions, joint ventures, intellectual property and transactional antitrust. He has also represented large and small companies in criminal antitrust proceedings and in complex civil antitrust litigation.
**Personal:** JD, Georgetown University Law Center, 1978; AB (magna cum laude), Georgetown University, 1975.

### BONNER, Raymond A
Sidley Austin LLP, Washington, DC
202 736 8679
rbonner@sidley.com
*Featured in Healthcare (District of Columbia)*
**Practice Areas:** Partner and member of Sidley's Executive Committee. He concentrates his practice on representing life science companies in connection with government investigations, enforcement proceedings and litigation. These investigations and related enforcement matters involve clinical studies, marketing practices, pricing and reimbursement, product safety and reporting, good manufacturing practices ("GMP"), quality system regulation ("QSR"), and HAACP. He has counseled FDA and its Special Prosecution Staff investigating the healthcare industry and developed extensive FFDCA experience.
**Personal:** New York University School of Law, JD, 1985; University of Maryland, BA, 1980, summa cum laude. Admissions: District of Columbia, Maryland, Pennsylvania.

### BORD, Eric S
Morgan, Lewis & Bockius LLP, Washington, DC
202 739 6040
ebord@morganlewis.com
*Featured in Immigration (District of Columbia)*
**Practice Areas:** Eric S. Bord is an immigration and nationality law partner in Morgan Lewis's Labor and Employment Practice. His practice focuses on the US and global visa needs of companies ranging from promising start-ups to industry leaders. He oversees the firm's immigration risk management practice, including I-9 and E-Verify counseling, immigration audits and investigations, and immigration due diligence. A frequent speaker on visa and compliance issues in

the recruitment, hiring, transfer, and retention of international personnel, Eric partners with in-house teams to obtain temporary and permanent visas for business, scientific, and executive personnel.
**Personal:** Emory University JD and BA.

### BOSS, Barry
Cozen O'Connor, Washington, DC
202 912 4818
bboss@cozen.com
*Featured in Litigation (District of Columbia)*
**Practice Areas:** Barry focuses his practice on complex criminal matters, particularly involving allegations of white-collar crime. He has extensive jury trial experience, and has successfully defended individuals and corporations under investigation for a range of alleged criminal activity, including: price-fixing, money laundering, fraud/false statements, environmental offenses, gambling, corruption, and racketeering.
**Professional Memberships:** ABA; American Board of Criminal Lawyers; National Association of Criminal Defense Lawyers.
**Career:** Office Managing Partner, Washington, D.C.
**Publications:** Co-authored, Federal Criminal Practice, 800-page treatise for criminal defense attorneys.
**Personal:** George Washington University Law School, JD, with High Honors, Order of the Coif, 1985; Bates College, BA, 1982

### BOURDEAU, Karl S
Beveridge & Diamond PC, Washington, DC
202 7896019
kbourdeau@bdlaw.com
*Featured in Environment (District of Columbia)*
**Practice Areas:** Practices principally in a wide range of litigation, regulatory, transactional and legislative matters involving hazardous substance and hazardous waste issues under the federal Resource Conservation and Recovery Act, the Comprehensive Environmental Response, Compensation and Liability Act, and analogous state laws. Mr Bourdeau also represents clients on a variety of international environmental, chemical risk assessment, and federal Information Quality Act issues. Clients include companies in the chemical, iron and steel, oil and gas, consumer product, communications, high technology, pharmaceutical, pulp and paper, and waste management technology industries. He also represents trade associations on environmental policy, regulatory, and litigation matters.

### BOWERS, Chris
Bingham McCutchen LLP, Washington, DC
202 373 6134
chris.bowers@bingham.com
*Featured in Tax (District of Columbia)*
**Practice Areas:** Advises clients on all aspects of international tax planning and controversy. Clients include many of the largest US and foreign financial institutions as well as large, multinational companies. Focuses on cross-border financing, cross-border mergers and acquisitions, and foreign tax credit planning.

**Career:** Has co-authored articles in leading tax journals on a wide range of international topics, including managing cross-border service structures and Subpart F and PFIC issues.
**Personal:** University of Chicago Law School, JD, high honors, 1997; Fordham University, BA, summa cum laude, 1994.

### BRAN, Paul Bennett
Dickstein Shapiro LLP, Washington, DC
202 420 3144
branp@dicksteinshapiro.com
*Featured in Bankruptcy/Restructuring (District of Columbia)*
**Practice Areas:** Paul Bran has represented national and regional banks and other financial institutions, the FDIC, and RTC in their capacity as conservator and receiver of failed financial institutions, mezzanine lenders, hedge funds, unsecured creditors' committees, trustees, creditors' trusts, debtors, and bankruptcy asset purchasers. His practice includes out-of-court workouts and restructurings, as well as bankruptcies, state court receiverships, related proceedings, and commercial litigation in various jurisdictions across the United States. He also has a solid knowledge of post-judgment collection practices.
**Personal:** Georgetown University Law Center (JD, 1985); University of Maryland (BA, 1982).

### BRANCA, Michael A
Peckar & Abramson, P.C., Washington, DC
202 293 8815
mbranca@pecklaw.com
*Featured in Construction (District of Columbia)*
**Practice Areas:** Mr Branca concentrates in construction and public contract law, including the representation of general contractors and construction managers. His practice involves bid protests, contract administration advice, litigation of disputes, and counseling and litigation on compliance and false claims matters.
**Professional Memberships:** Member of Board of Governors of the Construction and Public Contract Law Section of the Virginia State Bar. Admitted to practice law in Virginia and the District of Columbia.
**Career:** Partner in the Washington, DC office.
**Publications:** Co-Author: Virginia Construction Law; Lead Editor: Federal Government Construction Contracts; Associate Editor: Construction Lawyer.
**Personal:** For more information, please visit: www.pecklaw.com

### BRANCIFORTE, Jason
Littler Mendelson, PC, Washington, DC
202 414 6867
jbranciforte@littler.com
*Featured in Labor & Employment (District of Columbia)*
**Practice Areas:** Discrimination and Harassment; Labor Management Relations; Training; Policies, Procedures and Handbooks; Legislative and Regulatory
**Professional Memberships:** U.S. Court of Appeals, 1st, 3rd, 10th Circuit U.S. Court of Appeals, D.C. Circuit U.S. District Court, District of Columbia U.S. District Court, Eastern District

of New York U.S. District Court, District of Maryland U.S. District Court, District of Colorado

**Career:** Title VII The Americans with Disabilities Act The Age Discrimination in Employment Act The Family and Medical Leave Act The National Labor Relations Act The Fair Labor Standards Act The McNamara-O'Hara Service Contract Act The Walsh-Healey Public Contracts Act The Worker Adjustment and Retraining Notification Act

## BRANNON, Leah
Cleary Gottlieb Steen & Hamilton LLP, Washington, DC
202 974 1508
lbrannon@cgsh.com
*Featured in Antitrust (District of Columbia)*

**Practice Areas:** Focuses on antitrust matters, including counseling, mergers, antitrust litigation, appellate litigation. Has represented clients in various industries including high technology, advertising, consumer products, manufacturing, pharmaceuticals. Work has involved litigation in federal and state courts; has advised clients in merger and non-merger investigations by the DOJ, the FTC, state agencies, and the European Commission.

**Career:** Joined firm, 2003; became partner, 2008; Clerkships: Chief Justice William H Rehnquist, US Supreme Court (2002-03); Chief Judge Douglas H. Ginsburg, US Court of Appeals, DC Circuit (2000-01); JD, magna cum laude, Harvard Law School (1999); BA, with highest distinction, University of Virginia (1995).

## BRAY, John
King & Spalding LLP, Washington, DC
202 626 5618
jbray@kslaw.com
*Featured in Litigation (District of Columbia)*

**Practice Areas:** Over 40 years experience in civil and criminal litigation in federal district courts including: asbestos liability, federal tax, environmental, defense procurement, insurance coverage, antitrust cases, and cases presenting a host of business, financial and government regulatory issues. Has also been involved in numerous historic criminal conspiracy cases and trials throughout the US dealing with complex issues in: tax, antitrust claims, international investigations, fraudulent conveyances, environmental issues and insurance coverage.

**Professional Memberships:** Fellow of the American College of Trial Lawyers.

**Personal:** Undergraduate degree from St Louis University and JD degree from St Louis University School of Law.

## BRENNAN, Jeffrey W
McDermott Will & Emery LLP, Washington, DC
202 756 8127
jbrennan@mwe.com
*Featured in Antitrust (District of Columbia)*

**Practice Areas:** Partner in the antitrust practice and has extensive experience within the pharmaceutical and healthcare industries. Focuses his practice on mergers, litigation, government investigations, and counseling.

**Professional Memberships:** Member, District of Columbia and New York Bars; American Bar Association Section of Antitrust Law.

**Career:** Formerly Associate Director of the Federal Trade Commission's Bureau of Competition.

**Personal:** College of the Holy Cross, AB, 1981; Georgetown University Law Center, JD, 1985, Editor of the American Criminal Law Review.

## BRENNAN JR, John T
Crowell & Moring LLP, Washington, DC
202 624 2760
jbrennan@crowell.com
*Featured in Healthcare (Nationwide), Healthcare (District of Columbia)*
See under Nationwide for profile.

## BRIGGS, David W
Holland & Knight LLP, Washington, DC
202 828 5001
david.briggs@hklaw.com
*Featured in Real Estate (District of Columbia)*

**Practice Areas:** David Briggs is a member of the Real Estate Section at Holland & Knight, where he focuses on the practice of commercial real estate development and land use. Mr Briggs has broad experience with commercial office and retail leasing, acquisition and sale of commercial real property, private development agreements, lending transactions, condominium development and state and local regulations and controls of real property, with special emphasis in the areas of land use, zoning, construct permitting and compliance, and business licensure in the District of Columbia and Virginia.

## BRILL, Matthew
Latham & Watkins LLP, Washington, DC
202 637 1095
matthew.brill@lw.com
*Featured in Telecommunications (District of Columbia)*

**Practice Areas:** Mr Brill's practice includes a broad range of regulatory, litigation, and transactional matters involving telecommunications and media issues as well as emerging technologies. He represents clients including cable operators, Internet service providers, wireless carriers, and e-commerce companies in proceedings before the FCC and federal courts, and also advises investors and lenders in connection with mergers and acquisitions and financing transactions.

**Professional Memberships:** FCBA, DC Bar

**Career:** Former Senior Legal Advisor at the Federal Communications Commission

**Personal:** JD, Harvard Law School, magna cum laude, 1996; BA, Dartmouth College, summa cum laude, 1991

## BROCKWAY, David H
Bingham McCutchen LLP, Washington, DC
202 373 6021
david.brockway@bingham.com
*Featured in Tax (District of Columbia)*

**Practice Areas:** Practice focuses on tax planning, with a particular emphasis on international tax matters. Has been engaged in an active general business tax practice for more than 30 years, concentrating on corporate acquisitions and disposi-

tions, cross-border structured finance and asset-based finance transactions, and international tax planning.

**Career:** Former chief of staff, Joint Committee on Taxation of the US Congress.

**Personal:** Harvard Law School, JD, 1971; Cornell University, BA, 1968.

## BROOME, Shannon
Katten Muchin Rosenman LLP, Oakland
shannon.broome@kattenlaw.com
*Featured in Environment (District of Columbia)*

**Practice Areas:** Chair of Katten's Air Quality and Climate Change Practice and Executive Director of the Air Permitting Forum, a trade group of Fortune 100 companies advocating on Clean Air Act issues. Counsels clients and represents them in litigation on environmental matters before federal courts and administrative agencies. Represents a range of clients in automotive, oil and gas, renewable fuels, energy, and manufacturing industries. Former head of General Electric's Clean Air programs.

**Personal:** Boalt Hall School of Law, JD, 1990, Order of the Coif; UCLA, BSChE, 1985.

## BROWNELL, F William
Hunton & Williams LLP, Washington, DC
202 955 1555
bbrownell@hunton.com
*Featured in Climate Change (Nationwide), Environment (District of Columbia)*
See under Nationwide for profile.

## BRUCE, Carol
K&L Gates, Washington, DC
202 778 9426
carol.bruce@klgates.com
*Featured in Litigation (District of Columbia)*

**Practice Areas:** Carol Elder Bruce is a white collar criminal defense and complex civil litigation attorney. Mrs. Bruce represents clients in grand jury investigations, Civil Investigative Demands, and in criminal and civil trials and appeals. She also represents clients in matters before both houses of Congress and in internal corporate investigations. A Fellow in the American College of Trial Lawyers, she was Independent Counsel in the investigation of a Cabinet Secretary, Deputy Independent Counsel in the investigation of a sitting Attorney General, and a Special Counsel in the investigation in the Senate of a US Senator.

## BRUCE, Eric B
Kobre & Kim LLP, Washington, DC
202 664 1903
eric.bruce@kobrekim.com
*Featured in Litigation (District of Columbia)*

**Practice Areas:** Eric B. Bruce is an experienced trial lawyer who has served as lead counsel in numerous high-profile white-collar crime and government enforcement trials. Mr Bruce focuses his practice on the representation of companies and individuals in the US, Europe, and Asia who are the subject of US government investigations concerning a wide range of allegations, including public corruption, bribery, securities law violations, antitrust violations, money laundering, tax evasion and other regulatory issues.

**Career:** Prior to joining Kobre & Kim, Mr Bruce served in the U.S. Department of Justice for more than a decade: as Counselor to the Attorney General of the U.S., as Senior Counsel to the Assistant Attorney General for the Criminal Division at the U.S. Department of Justice, and as an Assistant U.S. Attorney at the U.S. Attorney's Office for the Southern District of New York. Before his time at the U.S Department of Justice, Mr Bruce practiced at a large law firm in Washington DC.

**Personal:** Mr Bruce received a B.A from Lafayette College and a JD from the University of Maryland School of Law where he served as an Articles Editor for the Maryland Law Review and was awarded membership in the Order of the Coif.

## BRUCH, Gregory S
Willkie Farr & Gallagher LLP, Washington, DC
202 303 1205
gbruch@willkie.com
*Featured in Securities (Nationwide), Litigation (District of Columbia)*

**Practice Areas:** Represents public companies, audit committees and special committees, broker-dealers, hedge funds and asset managers, accountants and lawyers, and other institutions and individuals in connection with civil and criminal securities law enforcement, compliance and litigation. Has been lead counsel for securities enforcement and related matters of number of leading companies and financial services firms, including Time Warner Inc., Adelphia Communications Corp., Cablevision Systems Corp., Hain-Celestial Corp., E*Trade Capital Markets, and Van Wagoner Capital Management.

**Personal:** JD, with high distinction, University of Iowa College of Law, 1985; Editor-in-Chief, Iowa Law Review. AB, Stanford University, 1982. See http://www.willkie.com/GregoryBruch

## BRUNNER, Thomas W
Wiley Rein LLP, Washington, DC
202 719 7225
tbrunner@wileyrein.com
*Featured in Insurance (District of Columbia)*

**Practice Areas:** Chairman Emeritus, Insurance Practice. Counsels insurers in major trial/appellate cases; 30+ years' experience in coverage litigation for insurers. One of Legal Times' "Leading Insurance Lawyers" and Corporate Counsel's "Best Lawyers in America" for excellence in business litigation.

**Professional Memberships:** 2012 recipient, Wiley A. Branton Award, Washington Lawyers' Committee for Civil Rights and Urban Affairs.

**Career:** Adviser, American Law Institute, Project to Develop Principles of the Law of Liability Insurance; Leapfrog Investments, a social private equity firm with assets over $135 million investing in microinsurance in Africa and Asia.

**Personal:** Yale Law School (JD); Columbia University (AB, cum laude).

## BUCHANAN, John
Covington & Burling LLP, Washington, DC
202 662 5366
JBuchanan@cov.com
*Featured in Insurance (Nationwide), Insurance (District of Columbia)*
**Practice Areas:** Complex insurance disputes and transactions, including coverage for data breach, environmental, media/IP, D&O/E&O/fidelity, cyber, railroad and satellite claims.
**Professional Memberships:** Advisor, American Law Institute Principles of Liability Insurance Law Project; ABA Insurance Coverage Litigation Committee; ABA Mediation Quality Task Force.
**Career:** Has represented policyholders exclusively since 1982; teaches graduate-level Insurance Litigation course, Connecticut Law School's Insurance Law Center; party arbitrator.
**Publications:** Recent presentations and articles include 'Settlement Landmines in Recent Caselaw,' 'Protecting Privilege While Preserving Coverage,' 'Comerica Conundrum: Settlement vs. Forfeiture,' 'Top 10 Insurance Traps,' 'Ancillary Arbitration Clauses.'
**Personal:** JD, Harvard; Honours BA (1st Class), Oxford; AB, Princeton.

## BUCHMAN, Barry I
Gilbert LLP, Washington, DC
202 772 2305
buchmanb@gotofirm.com
*Featured in Insurance (District of Columbia)*
**Practice Areas:** Partner specializing in complex civil litigation and dispute resolution, focusing on representation of policyholders in insurance recovery disputes. Handles complex civil matters including disputes over insurance coverage for asbestos, lead paint, benzene and other toxic tort claims; disputes over D&O and E&O coverage, and disputes over coverage for "first party" losses. Also represents companies in complex commercial disputes inlcuding allegations of unfair competetition and other business torts. Significant experience representing companies in the automotive industry.
**Professional Memberships:** Bar Admissions: District of Columbia, Virginia, Maryland.
**Career:** Active pro bono practice. Member, Board of Directors of the Washington Lawyers' Committee for Civil Rights and Urban Affairs.
**Publications:** Speaks and writes extensively on insurance coverage issues and has been quoted in leading business and legal publications.
**Personal:** JD, American University, Washington College of Law, summa cum laude (1997); BA, Inidana University, with distinction, Phi Beta Kappa (1994).

## BUCHOLTZ, Harold
Holland & Knight LLP, Washington, DC
202 457 5930
harold.bucholtz@hklaw.com
*Featured in Tax (District of Columbia)*
**Career:** Harold R. Bucholtz's practice is divided between the representation of tax-exempt organizations and tax-exempt finance. A particular focus is on counseling US tax-exempt organizations operating outside of the US and non-US tax exempt organizations engaging in activities within the US He also has considerable experience with the tax-exempt financing of airport and other transportation facilities, healthcare facilities, housing, and downtown redevelopment. He has extensive experience in obtaining rulings, technical advice and other types of IRS determinations and in monitoring and influencing federal tax legislation and regulations.
**Personal:** University of Virginia School of Law, JD; Georgetown University, LLM, Taxation

## BUENTE, David
Sidley Austin LLP, Washington, DC
202 736 8111
dbuente@sidley.com
*Featured in Products Liability (Nationwide), Environment (District of Columbia)*
**Practice Areas:** Partner in Sidley's Washington, DC office and global co-chair of Environmental practice. Represents clients in complex litigation and rulemaking matters, with an emphasis on Clean Air/Water Acts, Superfund, environmental criminal and toxic tort matters. Represented many corporations in complex federal environmental enforcement matters with Justice and EPA, and advised trade associations on diverse environmental issues and in environmental toxic tort cases.
**Professional Memberships:** American Bar Association, Sections on Environment, Energy and Resources and Litigation, American College of Environmental Lawyers; Defense Research Institute.
**Personal:** University of Pennsylvania Law School, JD, 1975; Lehigh University, BS, 1968. Admission: District of Columbia.

## BULLEIT, Kristy
Hunton & Williams LLP, Washington, DC
202 955 1547
kbulleit@hunton.com
*Featured in Environment (District of Columbia)*
**Practice Areas:** Practice focuses on national and state level environmental law issues, with particular emphasis on administrative, legislative, enforcement defense and counseling matters under the Clean Water Act (CWA). She is admitted to the United States Supreme Court and the Unites States Court of Appeals for the Second, Fourth, Sixth and Ninth Circuits, and District of Columbia.
**Professional Memberships:** Member, District of Columbia and Virginia State Bars.
**Personal:** JD, Boston University, cum laude, 1982; BA, University of Detroit, summa cum laude, 1979.

## BUMPERS, Heidi
Jones Day, Washington, DC
202 879 7616
hhbumpers@jonesday.com
*Featured in Environment (District of Columbia)*
**Practice Areas:** Superfund and natural resource damage, EPCRA, OSHA, and asbestos enforcement litigation; negotiated voluntary cleanup agreements and private cost recovery settlements. Client counseling matters include establishing a comprehensive environmental management system for a high-tech client, coordinating environmental matters and legislative strategy for a multinational tire manufacturer, and advising on international regulations, compliance audits, records retention, multimedia inspections, and release reporting. Regularly lectures and has published numerous articles on environmental law issues.
**Professional Memberships:** Oregon and Washington, DC Bar associations.
**Career:** Section Chief, EPA Office of Enforcement.

## BUONO, Francis
Willkie Farr & Gallagher LLP, Washington, DC
202 303 1104
fbuono@willkie.com
*Featured in Telecommunications (District of Columbia)*
**Practice Areas:** Advises financial institutions, information service providers, retailers, software and hardware providers, communications companies, insurance companies, and cloud computing providers on various US and international data privacy and data security laws/issues including: development of globally effective privacy policies and data security compliance programs; use of customer "big data" in connection with new business initiatives both online/offline; privacy risks raised by M&A and by disclosure of data to government regulators; and negotiation of complex privacy and data security agreements. Has represented companies facing enforcement proceedings by federal regulators for possible privacy and data security violations, and counseled companies that have experienced data security breaches.
**Personal:** JD(summa cum laude), Georgetown University, 1992. BA(magna cum laude), Georgetown University, 1987. See: http://www.willkie.com/FrancisBuono

## BURCHFIELD, Bobby R
McDermott Will & Emery LLP, Washington, DC
202 756 8003
bburchfield@mwe.com
*Featured in Government (Nationwide), Litigation (District of Columbia)*
See under Nationwide for profile.

## BURDICK, Rick L
Akin Gump Strauss Hauer & Feld LLP, Washington, DC
202 887 4110
rburdick@akingump.com
*Featured in Corporate/M&A (District of Columbia)*
**Practice Areas:** Chairs firm's International Corporate Transactions Practice. Represents both strategic acquirers and targets in a wide variety of public and private merger and acquisition transactions with emphasis on cross-border transactions and the energy sector. Represents both issuers and underwriters in connection with securities offerings of a variety of debt and equity securities. Provides advice to boards of directors and special committees on corporate governance matters.
**Professional Memberships:** District of Columbia Bar Association.
**Career:** Member, Board of Directors, AutoNation, Inc. (NYSE) and CBIZ, Inc. (NYSE).
**Personal:** BSC, University of Santa Clara (1973); JD, College of William & Mary (1976).

## BURGOYNE, Robert
Fulbright & Jaworski LLP, Washington, DC
202 662 4513
rburgoyne@fulbright.com
*Featured in Litigation (District of Columbia)*
**Practice Areas:** Complex civil litigation.
**Career:** A lawyer in the Washington, DC office of Fulbright & Jaworski since 1982, Bob Burgoyne has handled a broad range of complex litigation in trial and appellate courts across the country, including cases involving antitrust claims; copyright infringement; long-term fuel contracts; sovereign liability; loans; project finance contracts; distressed debt; government contracts; individual and class-action civil rights claims; constitutional challenges to state statutes; challenges to federal regulations; and disputes with federal agencies.
**Personal:** JD, cum laude, University of North Carolina (1982); BA, summa cum laude, Philosophy, Ohio Wesleyan University (1978).

## BUROKER, Brian M
Gibson, Dunn & Crutcher LLP, Washington, DC
202 955 8541
bburoker@gibsondunn.com
*Featured in Intellectual Property (District of Columbia)*
**Practice Areas:** Extensive trial and lead counsel experience in high-stakes patent litigation. Argued and won numerous patent appeals at the Federal Circuit. Led litigation teams in wide range of technologies including mobile devices, electronics, financial services, e-commerce, and software on complex array of issues including reexamination, transfer and MDL.
**Professional Memberships:** Admitted in Virginia, DC, U.S. Supreme Court, Federal Circuit and District Courts in DC, EDVA and ED Texas.
**Career:** Clerk, William Bryson, Federal Circuit, 1996-97.
**Personal:** JD, Georgetown University, 1996, magna cum laude, Editor, Georgetown Law Journal. BS, North Carolina State University, 1992, cum laude, electrical engineering, computer engineering.

## BYRNE, Brian
Cleary Gottlieb Steen & Hamilton LLP, Washington, DC
202 974 1850
bbyrne@cgsh.com
*Featured in Antitrust (District of Columbia)*
**Practice Areas:** Global antitrust and competition law matters, including merger reviews by the U.S. DOJ and FTC, the European Commission, and other authorities; antitrust litigation; and US criminal investigations, EU cartel proceedings, and other antitrust enforcement matters. Spent over 3 years in Brussels (2008-2011) representing clients before the European Commission. Representative clients include ConocoPhillips, Dow Chemical, Air Liquide, Molson Coors, Valeo and Whirlpool.

**Professional Memberships:** California and DC Bars; ABA Antitrust Section.
**Career:** Joined firm, 1995; became partner, 2004. JD, magna cum laude, University of Michigan Law School (1995); BA, magna cum laude, Brown University (1992).

### CALDWELL, Joe R
Baker Botts LLP, Washington, DC
202 639 7788
joe.caldwell@bakerbotts.com
*Featured in Litigation (District of Columbia)*
**Practice Areas:** Complex Business Litigation, Corporate Investigations, Labor and Employment, White Collar Criminal Defense, Professional Liability, Litigation Practice
**Professional Memberships:** District of Columbia Bar; New Jersey State Bar; United States Courts of Appeals for the Second, Fourth, Sixth and District of Columbia Circuits; United States Supreme Court; American College of Trial Lawyers, Fellow; Council for Court Excellence, Board Member
**Career:** Complex civil litigation and white collar criminal defense and investigations
**Personal:** LLM, Georgetown University Law Center; JD, Rutgers University School of Law; M.P.A., Harvard University; AB (with distinction), political science, Syracuse University

### CALSYN, Jeremy
Cleary Gottlieb Steen & Hamilton LLP, Washington, DC
202 974 1522
jcalsyn@cgsh.com
*Featured in Antitrust (District of Columbia)*
**Practice Areas:** Focuses on transactional antitrust matters, criminal and civil investigations, and antitrust litigation. Representative clients include Alpha Natural Resources, ArcelorMittal, Asahi Glass, Bimbo Bakeries, Deutsche Post/DHL, Dollar Thrifty, The Dow Chemical Company, Google, NSK, Stanley Black & Decker, Warburg Pincus and Western Digital.
**Professional Memberships:** California and DC Bars; ABA Antitrust Section.
**Career:** Joined firm, 1999; became partner, 2008. JD, magna cum laude, Georgetown University Law Center (1999); BS, summa cum laude, Southwest Missouri State University (1995); Law clerk, Judge Louis F. Oberdorfer of the U.S. District Court for the District of Columbia (2000-2001).

### CALVANI, Terry
Freshfields Bruckhaus Deringer LLP, Washington, DC
202 777 4505
terry.calvani@freshfields.com
*Featured in Antitrust (District of Columbia)*
**Practice Areas:** Terry practices antitrust law in Freshfields' Washington, DC office focusing on acquisitions/joint ventures and their review by competition agencies. He also advises clients in civil and criminal investigations by both federal and state authorities. Terry served as commissioner of the US FTC where he was acting chairman, and later as a member of the Irish Competition Authority and director of the Criminal Cartels

Division. During that period, he was an active member of advisory committees for the EU Competition Directorate.

### CAMPBELL, Patrick S
Paul, Weiss, Rifkind, Wharton & Garrison LLP, Washington, DC
202 223 7323
pscampbell@paulweiss.com
*Featured in Telecommunications (District of Columbia)*
**Practice Areas:** Partner in Communications and Technology Group. Concentrates on transactional, corporate and regulatory matters. Has worked extensively on behalf of numerous domestic and foreign telecommunications, satellite, media and Internet companies. Experience has included representing satellite operators and customers in negotiations of agreements for obtaining satellite systems, and telecommunications clients in proceedings before FCC. Has provided regulatory and corporate advice to companies, financial institutions and investors in public and private equity and high-yield offerings involving communications entities. Has advised clients on dispute resolution and litigation matters. Member of Federal Communications Bar Association and Practicing Law Institute's Telecommunications Convergence Advisory Committee.

### CARLISLE, Linda E
White & Case LLP, Washington, DC
202 626 3666
lcarlisle@whitecase.com
*Featured in Tax (District of Columbia)*
**Career:** Linda E. Carlisle practices international and domestic tax law and concentrates within the areas of taxation of corporations and corporate reorganizations, flow-through entities, such as partnerships, limited liability companies, as well as Subchapter S corporations. She also focuses on Public-Private Partnerships (or PPPs) and infrastructure transactions, and is one of the foremost practitioners in this area. In addition, Ms. Carlisle assists clients with employee stock ownership plans (ESOPs), intercompany pricing issues, financial derivative product issues and legislative, regulatory and administrative tax matters. To view a comprehensive biography, please visit www.whitecase.com/lcarlisle.

### CAROME, Patrick J
WilmerHale, Washington, DC
202 663 6610
patrick.carome@wilmerhale.com
*Featured in Media & Entertainment (District of Columbia)*
**Practice Areas:** Partner, Litigation/Controversy, Regulatory/Government Affairs Departments. Focus: Internet law, defamation, privacy, copyright, trademark, Freedom of Information Act, press access, reporters' privilege and other First Amendment matters. Has represented a broad range of media clients, including: Time Warner, craigslist, eBay, Google, Yahoo!, The Washington Post, New York Times, Los Angeles Times and ABC.

**Career:** In-house counsel for Washington Post; counsel to US House of Representatives Select Committee to Investigate Covert Arms Transactions with Iran; Law Clerk, Hon. Milton Polack (US District Court, SDNY).
**Personal:** Harvard Law School (JD, 1983, magna cum laude); Boston College (BA, summa cum laude, 1980).

### CARPENTER-HOLMES, Amy K
Bingham McCutchen LLP, Washington, DC
202 373 6085
amy.carpenter-holmes@bingham.com
*Featured in Litigation (District of Columbia)*
**Practice Areas:** Represents financial institutions, Fortune 500 companies and senior executives in connection with government investigations and related enforcement proceedings. Has conducted internal investigations on behalf of boards of directors and audit committees of major public corporations. Represents clients in matters involving the Department of Justice, the Securities and Exchange Commission, congressional committees and other regulators in cases alleging violations of securities fraud, accounting fraud, criminal tax, Foreign Corrupt Practices Act, public corruption, criminal antitrust and other criminal statutes.
**Personal:** American University, Washington College of Law, Juris Doctor, Summa Cum Laude, 1997. Cornell University, Bachelor of Science, With Honors, 1994.

### CARRANO, Cono A
Akin Gump Strauss Hauer & Feld LLP, Washington, DC
202 887 4136
Ccarrano@akingump.com
*Featured in Intellectual Property (District of Columbia)*
**Practice Areas:** Mr Carrano is a registered patent attorney, specializing in complex patent litigation. His litigation experience primarily involves semiconductors, electronics, software, wireless and optics technology. He has represented clients before the US District Courts, the International Trade Commission (ITC) and the US Court of Appeals for the Federal Circuit. He has also worked extensively with patent trial counsel in various European and Asian countries.
**Personal:** Hofstra University School of Law (JD, 1994); Polytechnic University (MS, Electrical Engineering, 1988); Stony Brook University, State University of New York (BE, Electrical Engineering, 1984)

### CARRIGAN, Daniel
McKenna Long & Aldridge LLP, Washington, DC
202 496 7436
dcarrigan@mckennalong.com
*Featured in Bankruptcy/Restructuring (District of Columbia)*
**Practice Areas:** Since 1981, Daniel Carrigan has pursued a diversified bankruptcy/insolvency and insurance company insolvency related practice throughout the United States.
**Professional Memberships:** Congressman Walter Chandler American Inn of Court (Master),

Former Co-Chairman, ABA Chapter 11 Subcommittee Task Force on State and Regulatory Insolvency Proceedings.
**Career:** Law clerk to the Honorable Henry D. Evans, U.S. Bankruptcy Court for the District of Maryland (1980-1981); U.S. Army, Judge Advocate General Corps in Fort Devens, Massachusetts (1976-1980).
**Personal:** JD, Georgetown University Law Center; BA, Georgetown University, cum laude, Phi Beta Kappa.

### CARY, George S
Cleary Gottlieb Steen & Hamilton LLP, Washington, DC
202 974 1920
gcary@cgsh.com
*Featured in Antitrust (District of Columbia)*
**Practice Areas:** Antitrust and litigation, including M&A, government investigations, antitrust in high-tech and intellectual property. Representative clients/matters: Google (AdMob), Western Digital (Hitachi HDD), Sabre Holdings (U.S. Airways, American Airlines), Abbott (Solvay), Dow Chemical (Rohm & Haas), ConocoPhillips, AspenTech (Hyprotech), Broadcom (Qualcomm), Equitable Resources (Dominion).
**Professional Memberships:** California and DC Bars. ABA Antitrust Section, (former Chair, Government Antitrust Litigation Committee).
**Career:** Deputy Director, Bureau of Competition, FTC (1995-98). Irell & Manella (1984-95). Trial Attorney, FTC Bureau of Competition (1976-84). JD, University of California, Berkeley (1976). BA, University of California, Santa Cruz, Economics (1973).
**Publications:** "Antitrust Implications of Abuse of Standard-Setting"

### CASSERLY, James L
Willkie Farr & Gallagher LLP, Washington, DC
202 303 1119
jcasserly@willkie.com
*Featured in Telecommunications (District of Columbia)*
**Practice Areas:** Specializes in communications policymaking and transactions involving video programming and distribution, broadband Internet, and new technologies. Produced outcome-changing advocacy in Federal Communications Commission, judicial and legislative proceedings. Former Senior Legal Advisor to FCC Commissioner Susan Ness, active in implementing Telecommunications Act of 1996 and deliberations regarding competitive safeguards, universal service, intercarrier compensation, spectrum auctions, children's television programming, etc. Recent highlight: FCC regulatory counsel to Comcast in purchase of majority stake in NBC Universal from GE.
**Personal:** JD, Harlan Fiske Stone Scholar, Columbia University School of Law, 1976. AB, magna cum laude, Tufts University, 1973. See: http://www.willkie.com/JamesCasserly

## CAVANAGH, Rita A
Latham & Watkins LLP, Washington, DC
202 637 2140
rita.cavanagh@lw.com
*Featured in Tax (District of Columbia)*
**Practice Areas:** Tax controversy and litigation matters. Audits, appeals, and before trial and appellate courts.
**Professional Memberships:** Member, District of Columbia bar and ABA Section of Taxation.
**Career:** Adjunct Professor, Georgetown University Law Center, George Washington University National Law Center; Associate Tax Legislative Counsel at the Department of Treasury.
**Publications:** Co-author, Litigation of Federal Tax Controversies (Warren, Gorham & Lamont); Co-author, "Navigating on OPR Disciplinary Proceeding," 127 Tax Notes 789 (2010); Co-author, "Do IRS Appeals' Office Ex Parte Prohibitions Need Strengthening?", 122 Tax Notes 1591 (2009).
**Personal:** JD, Yale Law School; MA, University of California, Berkeley; BA, SUNY Albany, NY.

## CAVANAUGH, David L
WilmerHale, Washington, DC
202 663 6025
david.cavanaugh@wilmerhale.com
*Featured in Intellectual Property (District of Columbia)*
**Practice Areas:** Partner in the Intellectual Property Department, and member of the Intellectual Property Litigation Practice Group and Life Sciences/Medical Devices Interdisciplinary Group.
**Career:** Has broad legal experience in industry and private practice. Provides clients with strategic, business-focused counseling in procurement, management and exploitation of their intellectual property. Extensive experience in all aspects of IP practice, including IP litigation, patent procurement, technology transfer and licensing, and due diligence for corporate transactions. Prior to joining WilmerHale in 2001, was senior patent counsel at Boston Scientific Corporation.
**Personal:** JD, George Washington University Law School; MA, Washington Theological Union; BME, Villanova University.

## CHARYK, William
Arent Fox LLP, Washington, DC
202 857 6162
william.charyk@arentfox.com
*Featured in Employee Benefits & Executive Compensation (District of Columbia)*
**Practice Areas:** Bill Charyk served for twelve years as the firm's Managing Partner and continues to serve on the executive committee. His practice focuses on employee benefit/executive compensation tax planning, and the taxation of partnerships, where he has served as tax counsel to a wide variety of syndicated and closely held limited partnerships, particularly entities developing products that are marketed to retirement plan and other tax-exempt investors. Additionally, he has served as outside counsel to a number of other law firms in internal dispute resolution and retire-

ment plan structuring. George Washington University, JD, 1973; The Johns Hopkins University, BA, 1970.

## CHATILOVICZ, Peter
Seyfarth Shaw LLP, Washington, DC
202 828 5330
pchatilovicz@seyfarth.com
*Featured in Labor & Employment (District of Columbia)*
**Practice Areas:** Labor and employment.
**Career:** Mr Chatilovicz specializes in handling labor and employment law matters on behalf of management. He handles collective bargaining negotiations, union avoidance, representation, unfair labor practice, and other National Labor Relations Act matters for clients throughout the country. He also advises clients on discrimination, ADA, family and medical leave, wage and hour and affirmative action matters. Recognized in 'Washington Business Journal' as top Washington, DC Lawyer - Employment.
**Publications:** Lectured to industry and professional groups throughout the country and has written numerous articles in his field.
**Personal:** JD, University of Miami School of Law.

## CHEFITZ, Daniel E
Morgan, Lewis & Bockius LLP, Washington, DC
202 739 5760
dchefitz@morganlewis.com
*Featured in Insurance (District of Columbia)*
**Practice Areas:** Focused on policyholder insurance recovery counseling and litigation. Advises and represents businesses in connection with insurance coverage and legacy liability issues arising from environmental, asbestos, toxic tort, business interruption, and product liability claims. Also represents medical device and pharmaceutical clients in pursuing coverage under the Bermuda Form. In addition to traditional insurance recovery actions, advises business on the use of captive insurance and qualified settlement funds to ring-fence long tail liabilities from discontinued operations.

## CHEN, Shawn J.
Cleary Gottlieb Steen & Hamilton LLP, Washington, DC
202 974 1552
schen@cgsh.com
*Featured in Litigation (District of Columbia)*
**Practice Areas:** White-collar criminal defense, securities enforcement, and complex civil litigation. Represents public corporations, financial institutions, and individuals in a wide range of government investigations involving alleged insider trading, securities fraud, money laundering, and foreign corrupt payments.
**Professional Memberships:** Co-chair of the ABA Subcommittee on Corporate Prosecutions.
**Career:** Joined firm, 2004; became partner, 2008. Assistant U.S. Attorney, District of Connecticut (1999-2004). Clerkships: Chief Judge Jon O. Newman, U.S. Court of Appeals, Second Circuit (1995-96); Judge Louis F. Oberdorfer, U.S. District Court, District of Columbia (1996-97). JD, Yale

Law School (1995); BA, summa cum laude, University of Michigan (1992).

## CHIP, William W
Covington & Burling LLP, Washington, DC
202 662 5229
wchip@cov.com
*Featured in Tax (District of Columbia)*
**Practice Areas:** Advising multinational enterprises based in Asia, the Americas, Europe, and the Middle East on global tax planning. Formulating IP transfer pricing strategies (including APAs). Resolving cross-border tax controversies (including Competent Authority).
**Professional Memberships:** US Council for International Business (Co-Chair, Transfer Pricing Subcommittee); ABA Tax Section (Chair, OECD Subcommittee).
**Career:** Law firm Partner (19 years). Global audit firm Partner (10 years). Marine Corps (3 years).
**Publications:** Over 45 articles and treatise chapters.
**Personal:** Yale University, BA 1971 (magna cum laude, Phi Beta Kappa); Cambridge University, MA 1973 (first class honours); Yale Law School, JD 1979 (editor, Yale Law Journal).

## COHEN, Charles
Morgan, Lewis & Bockius LLP, Washington, DC
202 739 5710
ccohen@morganlewis.com
*Featured in Labor & Employment (District of Columbia)*
**Practice Areas:** Charles Cohen is senior counsel in Morgan Lewis's Labor and Employment Practice. His practice focuses on representing senior management in complex labor and employment law matters in the private sector. From 1994 to 1996, Charles served as a member of the National Labor Relations Board (NLRB). Prior to that presidential appointment, he held executive and staff labor law positions with the NLRB, as well as in private practice. His experience includes representing clients in collective bargaining issues in all facets of labor and employee relations, including litigation.
**Personal:** University of Pittsburgh School of Law, JD, Tulane University, BA.

## COHN, Joel M
Akin Gump Strauss Hauer & Feld LLP, Washington, DC
202 887 4065
jcohn@akingump.com
*Featured in Labor & Employment (District of Columbia)*
**Practice Areas:** Has a national employment practice that focuses primarily on defending against wage and hour and employment discrimination class actions in federal and state courts. Has successfully tried both Fair Labor Standards Act collective actions and Title VII class actions. Has argued appeals in most of the United States Courts of Appeals.
**Professional Memberships:** Ohio and District of Columbia Bars; American Bar Association and its Section of Labor and Employment Law.

**Career:** Appellate Litigation Division, Equal Employment Opportunity Commission; Office of Representation Appeals, National Labor Relations Board
**Personal:** BA, University of Wisconsin (1971); JD, Catholic University of America (1976).

## COLLIER, H Guy
McDermott Will & Emery LLP, Washington, DC
202 756 8009
gcollier@mwe.com
*Featured in Healthcare (District of Columbia)*
**Practice Areas:** Member of health law department, focusing on transactional and related regulatory issues for health industry clients, including hospitals and health systems, public companies, private equity firms, academic medical centers, post-acute providers, medical group practices, and pharmaceutical suppliers and distributors.
**Professional Memberships:** American Health Lawyers Association; Health Law Section of District of Columbia Bar and Virginia State Bar.
**Career:** Previously served in Office of General Counsel for Department of Health and Human Services.
**Personal:** University of Richmond School of Law, JD, 1976; Johns Hopkins University, MPH, 1978; University of Virginia, BA, 1972.

## COLLINS, Christopher H
Holland & Knight LLP, Washington, DC
202 457 7841
chris.collins@hklaw.com
*Featured in Real Estate (District of Columbia)*
**Practice Areas:** Christopher H. Collins focuses his practice on zoning and land use law, historic preservation, municipal law, building code and foreign mission and international organization matters. He has considerable experience representing a broad range of local, national and international clients, including residential, commercial, retail and industrial developers, financial institutions, asset managers, hotels and hospitality providers, schools and universities, foreign governments, nonprofit organizations, religious institutions, and property owners and commercial tenants in all areas of land use law and real estate development. He represents clients before all of the federal and local land use regulatory agencies in District of Columbia.

## COLLINS, Michael
Gibson, Dunn & Crutcher LLP, Washington, DC
202 887 3551
mcollins@gibsondunn.com
*Featured in Employee Benefits & Executive Compensation (District of Columbia)*
**Practice Areas:** Focuses on all aspects employee benefits and executive compensation. Practice runs the gamut of tax, ERISA, corporate, and securities law aspects of stock option, restricted stock, and employee stock purchase plans; tax-qualified retirement plans, nonqualified deferred compensation; SERPs; executive employment agreements, golden parachutes and change in control arrangements; and performance bonus and incentive plans.

**Personal:** JD, Notre Dame Law School, 1995; received six American Jurisprudence awards for best performance in a class; editor of the Notre Dame Law Review; received Elijah Watt Sells Award for May 1991 CPA Exam; received the Dean O'Meara Award for distinctive academic performance.

### CONNER, Frank (Rusty)
DLA Piper LLP (US), Washington, DC
202 799 4221
frank.conner@dlapiper.com
*Featured in Corporate/M&A (District of Columbia)*
**Practice Areas:** Corporate/M&A, Private Equity
**Career:** He is managing partner of the DC office and focuses on mergers and acquisitions, corporate finance and related strategic matters, with a particular emphasis on financial services companies. He has extensive experience in mergers and acquisitions of both public and privately held entities, including joint ventures and strategic alliances. He represents both underwriters and issuers in a variety of securities offerings and private placements.
**Personal:** JD, University of Virginia School of Law; BA, University of Virginia (with high distinction)

### CONNOLLY, Annemargaret
Weil, Gotshal & Manges LLP, Washington, DC
202 682 7037
annemargaret.connolly@weil.com
*Featured in Environment (District of Columbia)*
**Practice Areas:** Annemargaret Connolly practices environmental law, advising clients on a wide range of concerns in all types of business transactions working with clients to quantify and contractually allocate potential liabilities in a manner that facilitates clients' business objectives. She works with consultants and engineers to quantify potential liabilities, drafts and negotiates contract language allocating environmental liability risks between the parties, and counsels clients on compliance generally as well as a variety of environmental topics, including climate change, renewable energy, sustainability, occupational safety, and shareholder, successor and lender liability.

### CONNOLLY, Thomas
Wiltshire & Grannis LLP, Washington, DC
202 730 1339
tconnolly@wiltshiregrannis.com
*Featured in Litigation (District of Columbia)*
**Practice Areas:** Mr Connolly is the head of Wiltshire & Grannis's litigation practice. Routinely recognized as one of the leading practitioners in his area, Mr Connolly focuses on trial practice and matters of complex criminal and civil litigation, as well as internal and governmental investigations.
**Professional Memberships:** Fellow of the American College of Trial Lawyers.
**Career:** Clerk for the Hon. James H. Michael, Jr., 1987-88. Assistant United States Attorney in the Eastern District of Virginia and the District of Columbia, 1990-2000.
**Personal:** College of William & Mary, JD, 1987. Northwestern University, BA, 1984.

### COOK BUSH, Antoinette
Skadden, Arps, Slate, Meagher & Flom LLP & Affiliates, Washington, DC
202 371 7230
Antoinette.Bush@skadden.com
*Featured in Telecommunications (District of Columbia), Media & Entertainment (District of Columbia)*
**Practice Areas:** Heads Skadden's Communications Group. Represents companies in transactional, regulatory, and legislative matters involving communications issues. A significant portion of her practice is devoted to representing clients before the Federal Communications Commission. Clients include entities involved in the programming, broadcast, mobile communications, cable, satellite, and telephone businesses. Also represents a number of not-for-profit companies.
**Career:** Executive Vice President, Northpoint Technology, Ltd./BroadwaveUSA, Inc. (2000-03); Senior Counsel, U.S. Senate Committee on Commerce, Science and Transportation (1987-93). JD, Northwestern University School of Law, 1981; BA, Wellesley College, 1978.

### COOPER, James W
Arnold & Porter LLP, Washington, DC
202 942 6603
James.W.Cooper@aporter.com
*Featured in Litigation (District of Columbia)*
**Practice Areas:** James W. Cooper is a partner in Arnold & Porter LLP's white collar criminal defense and litigation practice groups. His experience includes internal investigation and crisis management in response to federal grand jury investigations, administrative subpoenas and inquiries, congressional interest and whistleblower allegations. He advises clients in matters involving antitrust cartel prohibitions, the Foreign Corrupt Practices Act, Bank Secrecy Act/ Anti-Money Laundering laws, health care fraud allegations, export control, and the federal False Claims Act.
**Career:** Former Deputy Chief, Criminal Division, US Attorney's Office for the District of Columbia; Former Trial Attorney, DOJ Public Integrity Section

### COSTON, William
Venable LLP, Washington, DC
202 344 4813
wdcoston@Venable.com
*Featured in Intellectual Property (District of Columbia)*
**Practice Areas:** IP litigation (patent and trademark), antitrust litigation, commercial litigation, antitrust counseling, and advertising and marketing
**Professional Memberships:** American College of Trial Lawyers
**Career:** Chair of Venable's Intellectual Property Division. Concentrates on litigation and counseling in antitrust and intellectual property matters. Experienced with consumer products, technology, pharmaceutical, transportation, and retail industries. Three years in the U.S. Department of Justice's Antitrust Division (Attorney General's Distinguished Achievement Awards), including a stint as Special Assistant United States Attorney.

**Personal:** JD, cum laude, Harvard Law School, 1975; BA, highest honors and high distinction, University of Michigan, 1972

### COTTON, Raymond
Mintz Levin Cohn Ferris Glovsky and Popeo PC, Boston
202 434 7322
RDCotton@mintz.com
*Featured in Employee Benefits & Executive Compensation (District of Columbia)*
**Practice Areas:** Ray is a partner at Mintz Levin and also Vice President of Higher Education for ML Strategies, LLC. He primarily represents higher education and other non-profit executives and boards of trustees. His clients include colleges, universities, associations, and other non-profits. He has represented over 350 university boards of trustees, college presidents, and other non-profit executives during his more than 25 years in practice.
**Career:** Ray is a frequent speaker on the programs of the American Council on Education, the Association of Governing Boards, and other Higher Education Associations.
**Personal:** BA, Monmouth University; MS, Harvard University; JD, Harvard University.

### CRISMAN JR, C Benjamin
Skadden, Arps, Slate, Meagher & Flom LLP & Affiliates, Washington, DC
202 371 7330
Benjamin.Crisman@skadden.com
*Featured in Antitrust (District of Columbia)*
**Practice Areas:** Focuses on antitrust, trade regulation and white collar crime matters. Has obtained U.S. Department of Justice and Federal Trade Commission approval for a number of high-profile and complex U.S. and international mergers and acquisitions. Specializes in technology, defense sector and natural resources. Regularly counsels clients on sophisticated, cross-border joint ventures and compliance programs. Represents clients in international cartel and antitrust grand jury investigations.
**Career:** JD, Creighton University, 1975 (Senior Editor, Creighton Law Review); BA, Syracuse University, 1970.

### CRONIC, Jason P
Wiley Rein LLP, Washington, DC
202 719 7175
jcronic@wileyrein.com
*Featured in Insurance (District of Columbia)*
**Practice Areas:** Represents directors and officers liability insurers and other professional liability insurers in a range of coverage and liability matters in federal and state courts across the country. Counsels insurers with respect to coverage issues arising from policyholder bankruptcy; regularly represents insurers' interests in connection with resolution of complex securities claims through litigation and alternative dispute resolution procedures. Has significant experience with respect to rescission actions and other litigation in defense of insurers' rights.
**Professional Memberships:** Professional Liability Underwriting Society.

**Personal:** University of Chicago Law School (JD); Tulane University (BA, cum laude).

### CULBERTSON, Robert E
Covington & Burling LLP, Washington, DC
202 662 5004
rculbertson@cov.com
*Featured in Tax (District of Columbia)*
**Practice Areas:** International tax planning and controversy resolution, focusing on foreign tax credit and deferral issues. Advises on structural and transactional tax planning; handles IRS audits, appeals, and rulings; represents clients in regulatory and legislative processes.
**Career:** 30 plus years international tax experience. Served as IRS Associate Chief Counsel International, where significant projects included regulations on foreign tax credits, subpart F, outbound transfers, and conduits, as well as rewrite of transfer pricing regulations and OECD guidelines. Congressional tax staffer during 1986 Tax Reform Act.
**Personal:** Graduate of Yale University and Harvard Law School.

### CULLEN, Thomas
Jones Day, Washington, DC
202 879 3924
tfcullen@jonesday.com
*Featured in Litigation (District of Columbia)*
**Practice Areas:** Tim Cullen is head of the worldwide Global Disputes Practice at Jones Day. He regularly leads multinational teams in the most complicated commercial matters. He has tried federal and state jury cases, argued federal appeals, and been lead counsel in US and international arbitrations. Tim has led cases involving antitrust claims, trade secret disputes, shareholder disputes, cross-border mergers and international trade disputes, just to name a few, and has done so in cases arising out of Europe, the Middle East, Latin America, Russia, and Asia. For more than 15 years, Tim has been an active member of the CPR, a leading group of lawyers focused on alternative dispute resolution. Tim is also a Member of the American College of Trial Lawyers, an honor given to fewer than one percent of active trial lawyers.

### CURRAN, Christopher M
White & Case LLP, Washington, DC
202 626 3643
ccurran@whitecase.com
*Featured in Antitrust (District of Columbia)*
**Career:** Mr Curran, a trial lawyer, is a partner in White & Case's Washington, DC office, where he heads the litigation practice. Mr Curran represents domestic, foreign and sovereign clients in complex civil litigation at all levels in federal and state courts. A significant part of his practice focuses on issues of international law and federal-government regulation, especially antitrust. He has won high-stakes verdicts and judgments in trial courts across the country, and has successfully argued appeals in the District of Columbia, Second, Fourth, Eleventh and Federal Circuits. To view a comprehensive biography, please visit www.whitecase.com/ccurran.

## DAFOE, Colette A
Nixon Peabody LLP, Washington, DC
202 585 8393
cdafoe@nixonpeabody.com
*Featured in Real Estate (District of Columbia)*
**Practice Areas:** Represents clients on various aspects of real estate including real property acquisition and disposition; leasing; financing; and development. Also works on multifamily housing matters involving seniors housing and care, such as apartments, active adult communities, congregate care facilities, assisted living facilities, nursing homes, and CCRCs. Handles commercial, portfolio, and securitized loan workouts and restructurings, as well as distressed property sales.
**Personal:** Northeastern University School of Law, JD; Tufts University School of Medicine, M.P.H.; St. Lawrence University, BS.

## DANEKER, Michael D
Arnold & Porter LLP, Washington, DC
202 942 5177
Michael.Daneker@aporter.com
*Featured in Environment (District of Columbia)*
**Practice Areas:** Michael Daneker concentrates his practice on environmental law and toxic tort litigation. Mr Daneker has defended citizen action suits, Superfund litigation, Clean Water Act litigation, state law actions, natural resource damage claims, and regulatory enforcement matters related to complex contaminated sites. He has also served as primary defense counsel in numerous class action lawsuits around the United States, mass joinder, and other large toxic tort actions, including personal injury, medical monitoring, and property damage actions.

## DANISH, Kyle W
Van Ness Feldman LLP, Washington, DC
202 298 1876
kwd@vnf.com
*Featured in Climate Change (Nationwide), Environment (District of Columbia)*
See under Nationwide for profile.

## DANTZIC, David S
Latham & Watkins LLP, Washington, DC
202 637 2112
david.dantzic@lw.com
*Featured in Corporate/M&A (District of Columbia)*
**Practice Areas:** Experience in mergers and acquisitions, general company representation, and structuring and negotiating cross-border transactions on behalf of both financial sponsors and strategic clients. Work has included public and private M&A, going private transactions, carve-out acquisitions, consortium arrangements and joint ventures in a wide range of business sectors, involving aerospace and defense, automotive and transportation, industrial and technology companies.
**Career:** Local Chair, Corporate Department.
**Personal:** JD, Harvard Law School, 1994; BA, Cornell University, 1989.

## DAUBERT, Todd D
Dentons, Washington, DC
202 408 6458
todd.daubert@dentons.com
*Featured in Telecommunications (District of Columbia)*
**Practice Areas:** Mr Daubert, Chair of legacy Dentons's Telecommunications Regulatory practice, advises companies with respect to a broad range of technology, communications and privacy issues involving transactional, regulatory, litigation and appellate matters. Ranging in size from national wireless and wireline carriers to startup technology companies, his client base includes service providers, developers, investors, and companies that rely on technology. Leveraging his dual backgrounds in engineering and the law, Todd delivers innovative solutions that help clients achieve strategic objectives while minimizing risk.
**Personal:** Duke University School of Law, 1993, JD, with honors; Oklahoma State University, 1990, Bachelor of Architectural Engineering

## DAVIDSON, Jeffrey J
Manatt Phelps & Phillips LLP, Washington, DC
202 585 6678
jdavidson@manatt.com
*Featured in Environment (District of Columbia)*
**Practice Areas:** Davidson focuses his practice on environmental litigation and enforcement, the practical resolution of environmental issues in corporate and real estate transactions, and environmental compliance counseling with respect to existing and emerging regulatory programs. His clients have included Fortune 10 companies, mid-size companies, family businesses, individuals, trade associations and public interest groups. His litigation experience includes appellate representation in state and federal courts, including the Supreme Court of the United States. Additionally, he is a formally trained mediator and has resolved numerous environmental disputes through mediation.
**Career:** Duke University, JD, MA, 1977. AB, 1973.

## DAVIDSON, Tom W
Akin Gump Strauss Hauer & Feld LLP, Washington, DC
202 887 4011
tdavidson@akingump.com
*Featured in Telecommunications (District of Columbia)*
**Practice Areas:** Represents clients in regulatory matters and commercial transactions in the domestic and international telecommunications, media, entertainment, wireless, and high-technology industries, including video program suppliers and distributors, competitive local exchange, interexchange carriers, satellite systems, wireless operators, radio, television, broadband providers, cable television systems, equipment manufacturers, private radio operators and providers of new technologies and services. Represents private equity funds, banks, issuers of debt and equity, financial institutions, unsecured and secured creditors in communications regulatory and transactional matters.

**Career:** Trial attorney, Federal Communications Commission's Broadcast Bureau (now Media Bureau).
**Personal:** BA (with distinction); JD (cum laude), University of Wisconsin.

## DAVIS, Mark G
Weil, Gotshal & Manges LLP, Washington, DC
202 682 7258
mark.davis@weil.com
*Featured in International Trade (Nationwide), Intellectual Property (District of Columbia)*
See under Nationwide for profile.

## DELNERO, Matthew
Covington & Burling LLP, Washington, DC
202 662 5543
mdelnero@cov.com
*Featured in Telecommunications (District of Columbia), Media & Entertainment (District of Columbia)*
**Practice Areas:** Partner representing leading information technology, telecommunications, and media companies in policy development, regulatory compliance, and commercial transactions, among other settings. Routinely counsels clients in legal and regulatory matters that bring to bear his expertise in spectrum policy, privacy and data protection, program and network distribution, content licensing, and regulations governing the ownership of telecommunications and media properties.
**Professional Memberships:** FCBA (Co-Chair, Wireless Committee), IAPP
**Personal:** Harvard Law School (JD, magna cum laude, 2003); Tufts University (BA, summa cum laude, 1998)

## DENIS, Paul T
Dechert LLP, Washington, DC
202 261 3430
paul.denis@dechert.com
*Featured in Antitrust (District of Columbia)*
**Practice Areas:** Mr Denis, deputy chair of the firm's global litigation practice, advises clients on the antitrust implications of business practices, structures transactions to obviate competition law issues, resolves investigations, and litigates matters.
**Professional Memberships:** Member, New York and District of Columbia Bars; member, International Bar Association and American Bar Association, Antitrust Section.
**Career:** Counselor to the Assistant Attorney General; Acting Deputy Assistant Attorney General for Regulation of the Antitrust Division, U.S. Department of Justice
**Personal:** Villanova University (BA, 1980, summa cum laude); University of Michigan (M.A., 1983); University of Michigan Law School (JD, 1984, cum laude)

## DENOVIO, Nicholas J
Latham & Watkins LLP, Washington, DC
202 637 1034
nicholas.denovio@lw.com
*Featured in Tax (District of Columbia)*
**Practice Areas:** Represents large multinational corporations on complex cross-border transac-

tions involving mergers and acquisitions, spin-offs, financings and group structuring. Has represented many world leading corporations on multibillion dollar transactions covering jurisdictions around the world. Also has represented a number of these companies in Tax Controversies with the IRS.
**Professional Memberships:** Member, DC, Florida and New York State bars.
**Career:** Chair, International Tax Practice; Chair, University of Chicago Federal Tax Conference Planning Committee; Member GWU/IRS International Tax Conference Planning Board; IRS Deputy Chief Counsel, 2003-05
**Personal:** LLM, New York University, 1987; JD, University of Miami, 1986; BBA, University of Miami, 1983.

## DIRECTOR, Mark D
Kirkland & Ellis LLP, Washington, DC
202 879 5151
mark.director@kirkland.com
*Featured in Corporate/M&A (District of Columbia)*
**Practice Areas:** Represents public companies and private equity firms on mergers and acquisitions, securities, corporate finance and other commercial matters. Regularly counsels boards and management teams on corporate governance, public reporting, compliance and crisis response. Recent representative clients include Arlington Capital Partners, CEB, Constellation Energy, Crestview Partners, Exelon, FTI Consulting, MidOcean Partners, New Mountain Capital, Quad-C Management, Sagent Pharmaceuticals and Tutor Perini.
**Career:** Prior experience as public company and private equity portfolio company senior executive and general counsel.
**Personal:** Admitted, NY and DC Harvard College, BA, magna cum laude, 1980; Harvard Law School, JD, cum laude, 1984.

## DOLIN, Mitchell F
Covington & Burling LLP, Washington, DC
202 662 5219
mdolin@cov.vom
*Featured in Insurance (Nationwide), Insurance (District of Columbia)*
See under Nationwide for profile.

## DONOVAN, Edward C
Kirkland & Ellis LLP, Washington, DC
202 879 5289
edward.donovan@kirkland.com
*Featured in Intellectual Property (District of Columbia)*
**Practice Areas:** Practice focused on intellectual property litigation including patents, trade secrets, trademarks, and related contract, antitrust, and unfair competition claims. Has represented clients in trials, preliminary injunction hearings, claim construction hearings, arbitrations and before the ITC in technology areas including data networking, wireless communications, semiconductor processing, pharmaceuticals and medical devices. Patent infringement trial experience in state and federal courts as well as the ITC and Federal Circuit Court of Appeals. Experience counseling clients on appeals regarding patent-related issues

involving industry standards, and FDA-implementation of the Hatch-Waxman Act.
**Personal:** George Washington University Law School, JD, 1993.

### DORI, Yaron
Covington & Burling LLP, Washington, DC
202 662 5444
ydori@cov.com
*Featured in Telecommunications (District of Columbia)*
**Practice Areas:** Co-chair of Covington & Burling's Communications & Media Practice Group; focuses on telecommunications, privacy and consumer protection law, with an emphasis on strategic planning, policy development, commercial transactions, investigations and enforcement, and regulatory compliance.
**Professional Memberships:** Past-President, Federal Communications Bar Association.
**Career:** Represents clients before federal and state regulatory agencies and the U.S. Congress on various policy issues. His unique experience in telecommunications, privacy and consumer protection matters enables him to advise clients on a range of issues in which these disciplines intersect.
**Personal:** Brandeis University, BA, 1992; Boston College Law School, JD, 1996.

### DOWD, Mary Joanne
Arent Fox LLP, Washington, DC
202 857 6059
mary.dowd@arentfox.com
*Featured in Bankruptcy/Restructuring (District of Columbia)*
**Practice Areas:** Mary Jo Dowd is a partner in the bankruptcy and financial restructuring practice. She represents debtors and creditors in bankruptcy court and out-of-court debt restructures, particularly in the automotive, broadcast, construction, intellectual property, real estate and nonprofit areas. She represents entities purchasing assets from bankruptcy estates and entities with contracts, leases, IP licenses, supply agreements, and other business relationships with debtors or potential debtors, and litigates lift stays, plan confirmations, claim objections, contract and lease assumptions and rejections, preferences and fraudulent transfers. State University of New York at Buffalo, JD, 1980.

### DOWDELL, Thomas E
Fulbright & Jaworski LLP, Washington, DC
202 662 4503
tdowdell@fulbright.com
*Featured in Healthcare (District of Columbia)*
**Practice Areas:** Health.
**Professional Memberships:** American Bar Association, Health Law Section
**Career:** Tom Dowdell is a partner in Fulbright's Washington, D.C. office and a member of the firm's health law group and government relations practice. His practice emphasizes Medicare/Medicaid program certification, coverage, and payment issues; graduate medical education; subacute care provider issues; physician and hospital ventures; fraud and abuse; compliance matters; physician and nonphysician practitioner coding and billing; federal health care legislation;

and federal, state and administrative litigation against government agencies.
**Personal:** JD, The George Washington University Law School (1987); BA, cum laude, Public Policy, University of Pennsylvania (1982)

### DRAKE, Stuart AC
Kirkland & Ellis LLP, Washington, DC
202 879 5094
stuart.drake@kirkland.com
*Featured in Climate Change (Nationwide), Environment (District of Columbia)*
See under Nationwide for profile.

### DREIBAND, Eric S
Jones Day, Washington, DC
202 879 3720
esdreiband@jonesday.com
*Featured in Labor & Employment (District of Columbia)*
**Practice Areas:** Represents companies in all aspects of civil rights, employment discrimination, whistleblower, and wage and hour investigations, litigation and counseling.
**Career:** General Counsel, United States Equal Employment Opportunity Commission; Deputy Administrator, US Department of Labor; Wage and Hour Division; Associate Independent Counsel, Office of Independent Counsel Kenneth W Starr; Clerk, Chambers of the Honorable William J Bauer, US Court of Appeals for the 7th Circuit.
**Personal:** AB, Princeton University; MTS, Harvard University; JD, with honors, Northwestern University School of Law; articles editor, Northwestern University Law Review.

### DUNAHOO, Carol A
Baker & McKenzie, Washington, DC
202 452 7049
carol.dunahoo@bakermckenzie.com
*Featured in Tax (District of Columbia)*
**Practice Areas:** International tax dispute resolution, transfer pricing, treaty matters, compliance, policy.
**Professional Memberships:** International Fiscal Association.
**Career:** Previously U.S. Competent Authority and Director, International; U.S. Treasury Associate International Tax Counsel; principal, PricewaterhouseCoopers.
**Publications:** Anti-Avoidance Rules and Tax Treaties (Taxmann, International Taxation, 2012); Contract Conclusion and Agency Permanent Establishments: Here, There, and Everywhere? ( IBFD, 2010); Source Country Taxation of Foreign Corporations: Evolving Permanent Establishment Concepts (Taxes, 2008); Towards a U.S. Tax Treaty Policy for the Future (NFTC 2005) (coauthor); Income Tax Treaties of the United States (WG&L, 1999 ed.) (coauthor).
**Personal:** JD, Harvard Law School; BA, summa cum laude, Yale College; DAAD Fellow, Bonn University.

### DUNNER, Donald R
Finnegan, Henderson, Farabow, Garrett & Dunner LLP, Washington, DC
202 408 4062
don.dunner@finnegan.com
*Featured in Appellate Law (Nationwide), Intellectual Property (District of Columbia)*
**Practice Areas:** Has litigated numerous cases in the federal district courts, but is best known for his appellate practice before the U.S. Court of Appeals for the Federal Circuit, where he has argued more cases than any other litigator. He was instrumental in the court's establishment, chairing its advisory committee for its first ten years and helping draft the court rules. He has technical experience in the areas of chemical engineering, chemistry, biotechnology, and pharmaceuticals.
**Personal:** Purdue University (BS, Chemical Engineering, 1953); Georgetown University Law Center (JD, 1958).

### DYSON, Marianna G
Miller & Chevalier Chartered, Washington, DC
202 626 5867
mdyson@milchev.com
*Featured in Employee Benefits & Executive Compensation (District of Columbia)*
**Practice Areas:** Fringe benefits and payroll taxes, including consulting, compliance reviews, and federal and state tax controversies; tip reporting; accountable plans; mobile workforce issues; FICA taxation of deferred compensation; cross-border compensation; worker classification; penalty abatement; and information reporting.
**Career:** Former Chair of Miller & Chevalier's Executive Committee. Served as a Senior Attorney in the Office of IRS Associate Chief Counsel (Employee Benefits and Exempt Organizations). Member of Commissioner's Information Reporting Program Advisory Committee.
**Personal:** LLM (Taxation), Georgetown University Law Center, 1990; JD, University of Louisville School of Law, 1979; BA, University of Louisville, 1975.

### EDWARDS, Amy L
Holland & Knight LLP, Washington, DC
202 955 3000
amy.edwards@hklaw.com
*Featured in Environment (District of Columbia)*
**Practice Areas:** Partner and Co-Chair of the National Environment Team and Military Installation Redevelopment Team, Edwards has assisted developers, lenders and corporations negotiate environmental issues, including due diligence, environmental insurance, indemnification, cost recovery, and cleanup issues in complex real estate transfers, base closure and corporate M&A transactions, and represented companies in enforcement proceedings. She was the editor/contributing author of the ABA's book entitled Implementing Institutional Controls at Brownfields and Other Contaminated Sites and an advisor to NCCUSL during its development of the Uniform Environmental Covenants Act. She frequently writes and lectures on brownfields, sustainable development, climate change and related topics.

### EGAN JR, James C
Weil, Gotshal & Manges LLP, Washington, DC
202 682 7036
jim.egan@weil.com
*Featured in Antitrust (District of Columbia)*
**Practice Areas:** James Egan's practice focuses on antitrust counseling and litigation. He represents corporate clients in a range of industrial sectors, and has acted as lead counsel in federal, state and administrative litigation involving price fixing, mergers, joint ventures, boycotts, and other horizontal and vertical restraints. He served as Director of Litigation for the FTC's Bureau of Competition. Prior to being named Director of Litigation, Mr Egan held various FTC positions including Assistant Director for mergers and joint ventures and Assistant Director for general litigation.
**Personal:** University of South Florida (BA, 1966); St John's University (JD, 1971).

### EGGLESTON, W Neil
Kirkland & Ellis LLP, Washington, DC
202 879 5016
neil.eggleston@kirkland.com
*Featured in Securities (Nationwide), Litigation (District of Columbia)*
**Practice Areas:** Neil Eggleston focuses his practice in the area of defense of corporations and individuals accused of a civil and criminal fraud-related offenses. He has extensive experience in internal investigations, both as part of defending against allegations of fraudulent conduct and in response to internal corporate concerns about possible wrongdoing. He also has substantial experience in defending against allegations of government procurement fraud, including allegations of violations of the Foreign Corrupt Practices Act, antitrust violations, and health care fraud.
**Professional Memberships:** American College of Trial Lawyers.
**Personal:** Duke University, BA, 1975; Northwestern University School of Law, JD, 1978.

### ELLENBERG, Mark C
Cadwalader, Wickersham & Taft LLP, Washington, DC
202 862 2238
mark.ellenberg@cwt.com
*Featured in Bankruptcy/Restructuring (Nationwide), Bankruptcy/Restructuring (District of Columbia)*
**Practice Areas:** Advises debtors and creditors in complex financial restructuring, workout and bankruptcy matters. Leading role in some of the most significant and innovative recent restructuring matters including the Lehman bankruptcy cases, LyondellBasell, U.S. Treasury in CIT Group, Northwest Airlines, Geneva Steel, Zenith Laboratories, Grove Worldwide, Winstar, Jitney Jungle, XL Insurance in restructuring SCA, New Jersey Insurance Superintendent as Rehabilitator of Mutual Benefit Life, and Michigan Insurance Commissioner as Rehabilitator of Confederation Life. Advises major investment banks and hedge funds on swap, forward, repo and derivatives issues, monoline insurance issues, and structured finance transactions. Advises secured creditors concerning a wide variety of real estate matters,

including casinos, shopping centers, office buildings, and apartment buildings.
**Career:** Adjunct professor, Georgetown University Law Center.
**Publications:** Contributing author, Cadwalader Restructuring Review (www.restructuringreview.com).
**Personal:** JD, Georgetown University Law Center; BS, Cornell University.

### ELLIOTT, E Donald
Covington & Burling LLP, Washington, DC
202 662 5631
delliott@cov.com
*Featured in Environment (District of Columbia)*
**Practice Areas:** Environment, Public Policy, Energy, and Litigation. Served as Assistant Administrator and General Counsel of Environmental Protection Agency (1989-91). Advises on regulatory and compliance issues including Clean Air, wetlands and site clean-ups and exposure claims involving lead, asbestos and chemicals. Advises hedge funds and event-driven investors on environmental and related litigation and public policy matters including fracking and renewable energy. Recent representations: Smelter site clean-ups in Kansas for Mueller Industries.
**Personal:** JD, Yale Law School, 1974. BA, summa cum laude, Phi Beta Kappa, Yale College, 1970. See: http://www.cov.com/delliott/ Also Professor (Adjunct) of Law, Yale Law School http://www.law.yale.edu/faculty/EElliott.htm

### ENGH, Anna
Covington & Burling LLP, Washington, DC
202 662 5221
aengh@cov.com
*Featured in Insurance (District of Columbia)*
**Practice Areas:** Represents policyholders in insurance coverage litigation and in insurance settlement contexts for a variety of claims, including asbestos, breast implants, lead, and other mass torts; environmental liability; aviation losses; political risks; first party property damage including hurricane claims; directors and officers; and errors and omissions claims. Significant experience in trial and appellate courts and in arbitration forums.
**Career:** Clerked for Hon. John Butzner, Jr., U.S. Court of Appeals, Fourth Circuit, 1989-1990.
**Personal:** William and Mary Law School (JD, 1989), Order of the Coif, managing editor, William and Mary Law Review; Davidson College (BA, 1981); Phi Beta Kappa.

### EPSTIEN, Jay
DLA Piper LLP (US), Washington, DC
202 799 4100
jay.epstien@dlapiper.com
*Featured in Real Estate (Nationwide), Real Estate (District of Columbia)*
See under Nationwide for profile.

### ESPOSITO, Joseph P.
Hunton & Williams LLP, Washington, DC
202 419 2155
jesposito@hunton.com
*Featured in Litigation (District of Columbia)*
**Practice Areas:** Mr Esposito's trial experience includes: a jury trial in the Eastern District of

Virginia "Rocket Docket" between competitors in the student loan industry; a patent infringement jury trial in New Jersey concerning memory chips, which was named to the National Law Journal's 2007 Defense Hot List; a customs fraud jury trial in the Court of International Trade; a major antitrust suit in Iowa involving high fructose corn syrup; and a complex corporate tax case in the U.S. Tax Court regarding depreciation of equipment in the steel industry. He has been elected to membership in the American Law Institute.

### ETTINGER, Mitchell S
Skadden, Arps, Slate, Meagher & Flom LLP & Affiliates, Washington, DC
202 371 7444
Mitchell.Ettinger@skadden.com
*Featured in Litigation (District of Columbia)*
**Practice Areas:** Co-Chair of the Government Enforcement Litigation Group. For more than 20 years, has represented corporations and individuals in federal and state grand jury investigations, complex civil litigation and matters before administrative agencies. Experience in internal investigations, False Claims Act, Foreign Corrupt Practices Act, health care fraud, procurement fraud and alleged violations of federal and state conflict of interest provisions, in matters involving simultaneous criminal, civil, administrative, and congressional proceedings.
**Professional Memberships:** Fellow, American College of Trial Lawyers.
**Career:** U.S. Air Force, Judge Advocate. LLB, Columbus School of Law, Catholic University of America; BS, Chemistry, Northern Arizona University.

### EVANS, Stephanie C
WilmerHale, Washington, DC
202 663 6355
stephanie.evans@wilmerhale.com
*Featured in Corporate/M&A (District of Columbia)*
**Practice Areas:** Ms Evan's is Vice Chair of WilmerHale's Corporate Practice. Her practice concentrates on advising domestic and international clients on a wide range of transactions including mergers and acquisitions, joint ventures and strategic alliances, venture and private equity financings, public and private offerings and debt financings; practice involves transactions in a variety of industries including financial services, defense, and technology; previously worked as an associate at Deutsche Bank Securities.
**Career:** Admitted to DC Bar. Joined firm in 1997.
**Personal:** George Washington University Law School (JD, 1996); Baylor University (BBA, summa cum laude, 1993).

### FABRIZIO, Steven B
Jenner & Block LLP, Washington, DC
202 639 6040
sfabrizio@jenner.com
*Featured in Media & Entertainment (District of Columbia)*
**Career:** Steven Fabrizio founded and Co-Chairs the Firm's nationally recognized Content, Media & Entertainment Practice and is regarded as one of the preeminent copyright and content protec-

tion litigators in the country. Mr Fabrizio litigates cases involving new technologies and advanced media, as well as "offline" and traditional media cases. Mr Fabrizio regularly advises clients on content protection and enforcement strategies, and on sophisticated copyright issues involving the application of copyright to new technologies and business models. Clients also seek Mr Fabrizio's representation on issues including computer security and privacy, trade secret and trademark.

### FARABOW, Sara Beiro
Seyfarth Shaw LLP, Washington, DC
202 828 3591
sfarabow@seyfarth.com
*Featured in Construction (District of Columbia)*
**Practice Areas:** International and US Construction; Government Contracts
**Career:** Leads Seyfarth's International Dispute Resolution Group. Counsels clients on domestic and international construction projects, including industrial, hotel development, timeshare, airports, mass transit, bridges, military barracks, wastewater treatment and power plants. Negotiates contracts for public and private projects throughout Europe, the Middle East, South America and Asia-Pacific. Experienced in federal trials and international arbitration. Contributor to the ConsensusDOCS Guidebook.
**Publications:** Co-Author, Strategies for International Arbitration: Leading Lawyers on Navigating Arbitrations in a Global Climate, Thomson Reuters Westlaw (2012)
**Personal:** LLM, International & Comparative Law, Georgetown University; JD, College of William & Mary

### FARABOW, JR, Ford F
Finnegan, Henderson, Farabow, Garrett & Dunner LLP, Washington, DC
202 408 4044
ford.farabow@finnegan.com
*Featured in Intellectual Property (District of Columbia)*
**Practice Areas:** Practice includes trials in federal district and state courts throughout the United States, domestic and foreign arbitrations, and mini-trials and other alternative dispute resolution processes. Has served as lead counsel in numerous patent, trade secret, and licensing disputes. Technical experience include chemistry, pharmaceuticals, chemical engineering, and materials science. At the appellate level, he has handled and won numerous cases in the U.S. Court of Appeals for the Federal Circuit.
**Personal:** Clemson University (BS, Chemical Engineering, 1959); George Washington University National Law Center (JD, 1963).

### FARMER, F Scott
Bingham McCutchen LLP, Washington, DC
202 373 6772
scott.farmer@bingham.com
*Featured in Tax (District of Columbia)*
**Practice Areas:** Advises clients on all aspects of international tax planning and controversy with the Internal Revenue Service. Clients include US firms engaged in non-US business activities as well as non-US-based firms operating within the

United States. Frequent lecturer at the World Trade Institute and the Tax Executives Institute. Has written frequently on international tax topics.
**Career:** Member of the ABA Tax Section's Committee on Foreign Activities of US Taxpayers.
**Personal:** George Washington University, LLM, 1983; University of North Carolina School of Law, JD, 1982; North Carolina State University, BA, magna cum laude, 1979.

### FEDER, Samuel L
Jenner & Block LLP, Washington, DC
202 639 6092
sfeder@jenner.com
*Featured in Telecommunications (District of Columbia)*
**Career:** Samuel L. Feder is Chair of Jenner & Block's Communications Practice. Mr Feder, who was formerly the General Counsel of the Federal Communications Commission (FCC), represents cable, telecom, wireless, satellite, media and technology companies in a wide variety of matters including litigation, proceedings before regulatory agencies and transactions. Mr Feder has represented clients on numerous significant matters before the FCC, including net neutrality, video competition, intercarrier compensation and major transactions. Mr Feder has also appeared before courts across the country in both trial-level and appellate matters.

### FEIGIN, Samuel E
Nixon Peabody LLP, Washington, DC
202 585 8250
sfeigin@nixonpeabody.com
*Featured in Corporate/M&A (District of Columbia)*
**Practice Areas:** Sam Feigin is Vice Chairman of the Business and Finance Department. He handles both corporate transactions and employment matters, primarily in high tech, life sciences, footwear/clothing, consumer products, and new media. He serves as general counsel to funds, as well as public and private companies, guiding them through financings, M&A, right-sizing, employment, non-compete, and governance matters. He is widely recognized in the executive employment arena, representing both boards and executives. Sam chairs Israel Business, and has long represented European and Israeli companies doing business in the US.
**Personal:** Yale University, BA, George Washington University, JD.

### FEINSTEIN, Deborah
Arnold & Porter LLP, Washington, DC
202 942 5015
Deborah.Feinstein@aporter.com
*Featured in Antitrust (District of Columbia)*
**Practice Areas:** Deborah Feinstein is a leading antitrust lawyer, principally focusing on merger and acquisition matters, and conduct investigations, before the US Federal Trade Commission (FTC) and US Department of Justice (DOJ). She is named by National Law Journal as one of the "50 Most Influential Women Lawyers in America" and Global Competition Review named her global "Lawyer of the Year" in 2010. Ms. Feinstein has advised clients on hundreds of transactions, involving virtually all sectors of the economy. She

has particular experience with clients whose businesses involve retail, food, consumer products, healthcare, chemicals, automotive parts, and government contractors.

### FELLNER, Baruch A
Gibson, Dunn & Crutcher LLP, Washington, DC
202 955 591
bfellner@gibsondunn.com
*Featured in Labor & Employment (District of Columbia)*
**Practice Areas:** Practice focuses on employment law with special emphasis on occupational safety, health and consumer product safety. Extensive experience in litigation, including cases in all courts of appeals and two major constitutional cases in the U.S. Supreme Court, and recent seminal decision in Company Doe v. CPSC.
**Career:** Served as NLRB Supervisory Appellate Counsel, Department of Labor OSHA Counsel for appellate and regional litigation, and Pension Benefit Guaranty Corporation Associate General Counsel for Litigation.
**Publications:** Frequent speaker and author on OSHA; including first hornbook on OSHA, and numerous articles on current OSHA developments.
**Personal:** JD, Harvard Law School, 1968.

### FEMIA, Rocco V
Miller & Chevalier Chartered, Washington, DC
202 626 5823
rfemia@milchev.com
*Featured in Tax (District of Columbia)*
**Practice Areas:** International tax consulting and advocacy for domestic and foreign clients. Helps businesses avoid or resolve controversies with US and foreign tax authorities involving US international tax rules, transfer pricing, and US tax treaties. Advances client interests before the IRS, the US Treasury Department, and Congress.
**Career:** Former Associate International Tax Counsel at the US Treasury Department; involved in the negotiation of the 2003 US-Japan tax treaty; advised senior officials on significant tax legislation in 2003 and 2004.
**Personal:** JD, Georgetown University Law Center, magna cum laude, 1995; BA, Duke University, 1991.

### FENTON, Kathryn M
Jones Day, Washington, DC
202 879 3746
kmfenton@jonesday.com
*Featured in Antitrust (District of Columbia)*
**Practice Areas:** Represents clients in mergers and acquisitions and on competitive issues before the Department of Justice, the Federal Trade Commission, the Department of Transportation, and the Federal Communications Commission. Advises on antitrust issues of joint ventures, distribution, information exchanges, and dealings with competitors. She has written and lectured on competition issues, professional responsibility, conflicts of interest, and legal ethics. Listed in Lawdragon 500 Leading Lawyers in America, The

Best Lawyers in America, D.C. Super Lawyers, and Who's Who in American Law.
**Professional Memberships:** 2007-08 Chair of the ABA Section of Antitrust Law.

### FEORE, John R
Dow Lohnes PLLC, Washington, DC
202 776 2786
jfeore@dowlohnes.com
*Featured in Telecommunications (District of Columbia), Media & Entertainment (District of Columbia)*
**Practice Areas:** For over 35 years, John Feore has represented media, entertainment, and telecommunications companies, as well as lenders and investors, before the Federal Communications Commission, Congress and other agencies in Washington, DC. As head of the Dow Lohnes Communications Group, he has been involved in scores of major transactions providing buyers, sellers, and financiers with expert counsel in structuring their transactions to ensure compliance with federal regulatory requirements. He counsels some of the largest media companies, wireless providers, programmers, emerging broadcast networks, and investors on sophisticated communications law strategies.
**Personal:** Georgetown University (JD, 1974); University of Wisconsin (MA, 1969); Boston College (BA, 1968).

### FIELD, Andrea Bear
Hunton & Williams LLP, Washington, DC
202 955 1558
afield@hunton.com
*Featured in Environment (District of Columbia)*
**Practice Areas:** Andrea Bear Field focuses on environmental and administrative law, representing clients in federal rulemakings and litigation arising under the Clean Air Act and other environmental statutes, with an emphasis on representing companies in Clean Air Act enforcement matters and on environmental permitting issues. Representative clients: electricity generating, paper, coal, oil, and chemical companies. Recognitions: named among The Best Lawyers in America for Environmental Law each year since 1989, among Washingtonian magazine's 'Top Lawyers' for environmental law since 2004, and as a Washington, DC 'Super Lawyer' since 2007. She is a member of the American College of Environmental Lawyers.

### FISHER, Alice S
Latham & Watkins LLP, Washington, DC
202 637 2263
alice.fisher@lw.com
*Featured in Litigation (District of Columbia)*
**Practice Areas:** Ms. Fisher specializes in government investigations and other white collar & criminal enforcement, advising multi-national corporations and financial institutions on matters including: international criminal matters relating to alleged bribery under the FCPA; economic sanction and export control issues; healthcare fraud, securities fraud and procurement fraud. Handles complex civil litigation, often parallel to criminal investigations.

**Professional Memberships:** Member, DC and Virginia bars.
**Career:** Office Managing Partner. Prior: Co-Chair, Global White Collar Practice Group; Assistant Attorney General in charge of the Criminal Division, US Department of Justice
**Personal:** JD, Catholic University, Columbus School of Law, 1992; BA, Vanderbilt University, 1989.

### FISHER, Miriam L
Latham & Watkins LLP, Washington, DC
202 637 2178
Miriam.Fisher@lw.com
*Featured in Tax (District of Columbia), Tax (Nationwide)*
See under Nationwide for profile.

### FLANNERY, Ellen J
Covington & Burling LLP, Washington, DC
202 662 5484
eflannery@cov.com
*Featured in Healthcare (District of Columbia)*
**Practice Areas:** Ellen Flannery co-chairs the firm's Food and Drug Law Practice Group. She advises clients on regulation of medical devices, pharmaceuticals, and biological products. Ms. Flannery's experience includes: helping clients develop strategic plans with respect to the appropriate premarket pathway and development plan for obtaining FDA marketing clearance or approval, including personalized medicine pathways; advising on dispute resolution with FDA, including representing clients in Medical Devices Dispute Resolution Panel proceedings; advising companies undertaking product recalls or responding to FDA quality system inspections; advising on advertising and promotion; conducting regulatory due diligence.
**Personal:** Boston University School of Law, JD, 1978.

### FOGGAN, Laura A
Wiley Rein LLP, Washington, DC
202 719 3382
lfoggan@wileyrein.com
*Featured in Insurance (District of Columbia)*
**Practice Areas:** Chair, Insurance Appellate Practice. 25 years complex trial/appellate insurance litigation experience involving allocation, coverage, products/completed operations, policy conditions, pollution, and business risk. Counsels on emerging risks, global warming, nanotechnology, Section 111 and bad faith exposures. Represents insurers in arbitration/ADR proceedings.
**Professional Memberships:** Former Chair, ABA Insurance Coverage Litigation Committee; Member, American College of Coverage and Extracontractual Counsel, Federation of Defense/Coverage Counsel, Defense Research Institute.
**Career:** Law360's "10 Most Admired Insurance Attorneys"; DC's "Top 50 Women Lawyers"; Business Insurance's "Women to Watch".
**Personal:** George Washington University (JD, with high honors); University of Pennsylvania (MS Ed; BA, magna cum laude).

### FOLEY, Allison D
Venable LLP, Washington, DC
202 344 4416
adfoley@Venable.com
*Featured in Environment (District of Columbia)*
**Practice Areas:** Environmental law, regulatory
**Professional Memberships:** ASTM Committee E-50 on Environmental Assessment, Risk Management, and Corrective Action
**Career:** Practice focuses on environmental compliance and administrative issues critical to the utility industry and related regulatory and legislative advocacy in connection with a range of environmental and chemical laws including TSCA, RCRA, CERCLA and FIFRA. Ms. Foley also counsels public and private entities on regulatory and compliance issues associated with infrastructure and land development projects, often subject to the National Environmental Policy Act.
**Personal:** JD, University of Pennsylvania Law School, 2007; BA, cum laude, Georgetown University, 2003

### FORD, Ann K
DLA Piper LLP (US), Washington, DC
202 799 4140
ann.ford@dlapiper.com
*Featured in Intellectual Property (District of Columbia)*
**Practice Areas:** Intellectual Property, Trademark, Copyright.
**Career:** She is chair of the firm's Trademark, Copyright and Media Group. She practices in US and international trademark and copyright law, including the emerging law governing use and protection of IP on the internet. She advises clients in business and transactional aspects of IP, as well as litigation and pre-litigation protective measures, and works with clients to acquire, develop, and exploit IP assets, restructure IP assets for tax planning, and develop joint venture arrangements to support co-branding.
**Personal:** JD, Duke University School of Law; BA, Georgetown University.

### FORD, Christopher D
Morrison & Foerster LLP, Washington, DC
202 887 1512
cford@mofo.com
*Featured in Outsourcing (Nationwide), Technology (District of Columbia)*
See under Nationwide for profile.

### FORD, Gary M
Groom Law Group, Washington, DC
202 857 0620
gford@groom.com
*Featured in Employee Benefits & Executive Compensation (Nationwide), Employee Benefits & Executive Compensation (District of Columbia)*
See under Nationwide for profile.

### FOSTER, Hope S
Mintz Levin Cohn Ferris Glovsky and Popeo PC, Washington, DC
202 661 8758
HSFoster@mintz.com
*Featured in Healthcare (Nationwide), Healthcare (District of Columbia)*

**Practice Areas:** Hope represents healthcare providers, manufacturers, payors and investors on legal, transactional, regulatory and strategic matters. She represents clients facing federal and state government investigations and enforcement under federal and state False Claims Acts and qui tam provisions, the Food, Drug, and Cosmetic Act, Medicare/Medicaid billing and pricing laws, kickback and self-referral prohibitions; negotiates Corporate Integrity Agreements with the HHS Office of Inspector General ("OIG"); assists with voluntary and government-mandated compliance programs; advises on voluntary disclosures to the government.
**Professional Memberships:** D.C. Bar, ABA, ABF; AHLA.
**Personal:** BA, Wellesley College. JD, with honors, George Washington University National Law Center.

### FOX, Allen H
WilmerHale, Washington, DC
202 663 6087
allen.fox@wilmerhale.com
*Featured in Real Estate (District of Columbia)*
**Practice Areas:** Complex real estate investment, development, financing, leasing and sales transactions, including joint ventures and forward commitments, as well as purchase and sale of distressed loans, workouts and restructuring transactions and foreclosures. Served as counsel to insurance companies and other institutional investors, pension fund advisers, national and local developers, and real estate service providers on office, multi-family residential, retail, hotel, industrial and mixed-use transactions, and as counsel for major corporations nationwide on lease and build-to-suit transactions.
**Personal:** JD, with Honors, George Washington University Law School; BA, cum laude, Washington University in St. Louis/Phi Beta Kappa.

### FRANCO, Sandra
Bingham McCutchen LLP, Washington, DC
202 373 6019
s.franco@bingham.com
*Featured in Environment (District of Columbia)*
**Practice Areas:** Represents clients in litigation matters involving environmental and natural resources compliance, rulemaking, and enforcement. Experience litigating matters before the US Court of Appeals for the D.C. Circuit, and has worked on numerous suits involving government and private party claims at the district and appellate levels. Advises on matters concerning environmental and natural resource laws.
**Career:** Co-author of two articles for the American Bar Association on transmission line siting.
**Personal:** Georgetown University Law Center, Juris Doctor, Magna Cum Laude, 1999; University of Florida, Master of Arts, 1996; The University of Chicago, Bachelor of Science, 1993.

### FRANKEL, Roger
Orrick, Herrington & Sutcliffe LLP, Washington, DC
202 339 8513
rfrankel@orrick.com
*Featured in Bankruptcy/Restructuring (Nationwide), Bankruptcy/Restructuring (District of Columbia)*
**Career:** Roger Frankel, co-chair of the Global Restructuring Group, has practiced in the areas of business reorganization and creditors' rights since 1972, with an emphasis on bringing business and common sense to complex legal transactions. Mr Frankel represents major institutions, court-appointed fiduciaries and ad hoc committees in debt restructuring and reorganization matters ranging from out-of-court workouts to proceedings under state insolvency statutes and the Federal Bankruptcy Code. He also has substantial experience in the area of municipal and tribal distressed debt.

### FREED, Joel
McDermott Will & Emery LLP, Washington, DC
202 756 8080
jfreed@mwe.com
*Featured in Intellectual Property (District of Columbia)*
**Practice Areas:** Practice covers nearly every aspect of intellectual property law and its interface with antitrust, including jury and bench trials, appellate advocacy, licensing, proceedings before the United States Patent and Trademark Office, and International Trade Commission actions. Has served as lead counsel in a wide range of high technology cases.
**Professional Memberships:** Admitted in District of Columbia and Virginia; registered before U.S. Patent and Trademark office.
**Career:** Former patent examiner; served as outside instructor at U.S. Patent and Trademark Office; adjunct professor at Georgetown University Law Center.
**Personal:** Georgetown University Law Center (JD); Lehigh University (BA, BS).

### FRIED, Bruce Merlin
Dentons, Washington, DC
202 408 9159
bruce.fried@dentons.com
*Featured in Healthcare (District of Columbia)*
**Practice Areas:** Healthcare law and policy expert who counsels and represents health plans, physician organizations, hospital groups, health benefit exchanges, healthcare information technology and data companies, pharmaceutical and biotech companies and other healthcare organizations with regard to Medicare, Medicaid, the Affordable Care Act, HIPAA and other federal healthcare programs and policies.
**Professional Memberships:** American Health Lawyers Association; District of Columbia and Florida Bar Associations.
**Career:** Director, Centers for Medicare & Medicaid Services (then: Health Care Financing Administration); member, board of directors of health plans, hospital companies, health IT firms, and non-profit organizations; frequent speaker

and columnist. Managing partner, Dentons' Washington DC office.

### FRIEDLAND, David
Beveridge & Diamond PC, Washington, DC
202 289 6047
dfriedland@bdlaw.com
*Featured in Environment (District of Columbia)*
**Practice Areas:** Mr Friedland's practice touches every aspect of the regulation of air pollution under the Clean Air Act and state and local air pollution statutes and regulations. He has assisted scores of clients in commenting on proposed rules, including PSD/NSR regulations, numerous MACT standards, the "credible evidence" rule, federal and state Title V rules, greenhouse gas regulations, and state and local rules. He has litigated many of these rules in the D.C. Circuit and elsewhere. He has defended companies in Clean Air Act suits brought by federal and state regulators and citizen groups.

### FRIEDMAN, Paul H
Dechert LLP, Washington, DC
202 261 3398
paul.friedman@dechert.com
*Featured in Antitrust (District of Columbia)*
**Practice Areas:** Mr Friedman is the managing partner of the Washington, D.C. office. He represents parties in merger and non-merger investigations and has served as lead counsel in multi-defendant class and non-class actions throughout the country.
**Professional Memberships:** Member, District of Columbia Bar; admitted to practice before the U.S. Supreme Court and numerous federal courts; member, American Bar Association Antitrust Section, co-chair, Communications and Digital Technology Industries Committee
**Personal:** The University of Chicago (BA, 1975); Boston University School of Law (JD, 1978)

### FRIEDMAN, Peter M
Cadwalader, Wickersham & Taft LLP, Washington, DC
202 862 2347
peter.friedman@cwt.com
*Featured in Bankruptcy/Restructuring (District of Columbia)*
**Practice Areas:** Focuses on bankruptcy counseling and litigation on behalf of major parties in high stakes, complex financial restructurings. Senior member of Cadwalader's team in its highly successful representation of the United States of America and the Presidential Task Force on the Auto Industry as secured lender and acquirer in Chrysler and General Motors bankruptcies. Advised LyondellBasell in all aspects of its chapter 11 cases. Represented debtors including Caribbean Petroleum, Xerium Technologies, Northwest Airlines, Enron, WorldCom, and Armstrong World Industries. Represented secured and unsecured lenders and committees in cases including Dynegy, Blockbuster, Inner City Media, Owens Corning, Lehman Brothers, UTGR, and USG.
**Career:** Adjunct professor, Georgetown University Law Center; former adjunct professor, Howard University Law School.

**Publications:** Contributing author, Cadwalader Restructuring Review (www.restructuringreview.com).
**Personal:** JD, Northwestern University School of Law (Order of the Coif; cum laude; Editor, Journal of Criminal Law and Criminology); BA, Trinity College (with honors).

### FROST JR, Don J
Skadden, Arps, Slate, Meagher & Flom LLP & Affiliates, Washington, DC
202 371 7422
Don.Frost@skadden.com
*Featured in Environment (District of Columbia)*
**Practice Areas:** Heads Skadden's Environmental and Climate Change practices. Has a diverse environmental corporate-based practice (including transactional, project development, and bankruptcy matters) and a complex and broad-based environmental litigation (including enforcement matters, cost recovery and contribution actions, administrative cleanup and permitting proceedings, administrative rule and record challenges, toxic tort actions, and alternative dispute resolution proceedings) and environmental/climate change regulatory counseling practice. For over 20 years, has helped clients forge strategic, practical problem-solving approaches to environmental matters.
**Career:** JD, Duke University School of Law, 1988 (with honors); M.A., Resource Economics and Policy, Duke University, 1988; BA, Carleton College, 1983 (cum laude).

### GABA, Michael M
Holland & Knight LLP, Washington, DC
202 955 3000
michael.gaba@hklaw.com
*Featured in Healthcare (District of Columbia)*
**Career:** Federal policy leader of the firm's national Healthcare & Life Sciences Team, Gaba practices federal regulatory and legislative life sciences law. He represents medical device and biotech companies before the FDA, CMS and other agencies of the Public Health Service on a range of business strategy and policy issues focused on pre-market entry strategies and post-market compliance. These include product approvals, labeling claims, advertising, enforcement matters, as well as Medicare coverage, coding and reimbursement determinations. Gaba writes extensively and lectures on policy issues, including: the intersection of FDA product approval and CMS reimbursement strategies; and defending FDA enforcement actions.

### GAGE, Larry
Alston & Bird LLP, Washington, DC
202 239 3614
Larry.Gage@alston.com
*Featured in Healthcare (District of Columbia)*
**Practice Areas:** Focuses primarily on public sector and nonprofit health law and policy.
**Career:** In 1981, Larry founded the National Association of Public Hospitals and Health Systems (NAPH). Served as president of NAPH for over 30 years, developing and achieving enactment of Medicare and Medicaid reimbursement reforms that are the economic lifeblood of hospi-

tals serving a disproportionate number of elderly and low-income patients.

**Publications:** 'Transformational Governance: Best Practices for Public and Nonprofit Hospitals and Health Systems', published by The American Hospital Association's Center for Healthcare Governance, November 2012.

**Personal:** AB (1968) Harvard College; JD (1972) Columbia Law School.

### GAGE, Robert J
Covington & Burling LLP, Washington, DC
202 662 5636
rgage@cov.com
*Featured in Real Estate (District of Columbia)*

**Practice Areas:** Chair of Real Estate Group, his practice focuses on commercial real estate, including acquisitions, joint ventures, financings, development, construction, leasing and sales. He also has a significant practice representing not-for-profit organizations, including quasi-governmental entities. Representative clients include: Union Station Redevelopment Corporation, PEPCO Holdings, Inc., RREEF, Ourisman Automotive Group, IBM Corporation, and National Academies of Sciences.

**Professional Memberships:** Member, DC Bar Association and DC Building Industry Association.

**Personal:** JD (cum laude), Harvard Law School, 1977; MPP, Harvard University John F Kennedy School of Government, 1977; BA (summa cum laude), Kent State University, 1973.

### GALLO, Kenneth A
Paul, Weiss, Rifkind, Wharton & Garrison LLP, Washington, DC
202 223 7356
kgallo@paulweiss.com
*Featured in Antitrust (District of Columbia)*

**Practice Areas:** Partner in the Litigation Department and Managing Partner of the firm's Washington, DC office. Has substantial trial experience in antitrust, patent and major commercial disputes. Has tried cases involving banking and payments industries, computer hardware and software products, medical and telecommunications equipment, and biotechnology products. Represents clients in civil criminal government antitrust investigations and lawsuits involving claims related to alleged monopolization, tying, mergers and acquisitions, price-fixing and the interplay between antitrust and intellectual property laws. Also has substantial experience in patent and other intellectual property litigation. Clients include MasterCard, BASF, Sharp and Genentech, among others.

### GALLOZZI, Marialuisa
Covington & Burling LLP, Washington, DC
202 662 5344
mgallozzi@cov.com
*Featured in Insurance (District of Columbia)*

**Practice Areas:** Marialuisa has 25 years of experience in providing settlement and strategic advice on insurance coverage issues and is one of the leads for Covington's Strategic Risk and Crisis Management initiative. She has recovered over $400 million from insurers for her clients for

product recall, medical device, food contamination, crime, catastrophe/business interruption, asbestos, environmental, D&O and other losses. She has particular expertise in insurer insolvencies.

**Personal:** New York University School of Law (JD, 1986), Harvard University (AB, 1982, cum laude).

### GARDINER, Kent A
Crowell & Moring LLP, Washington, DC
202 624 2578
kgardiner@crowell.com
*Featured in Antitrust (District of Columbia)*

**Practice Areas:** Chairman of Crowell & Moring LLP and partner in Antitrust Group specializing in antitrust and other complex litigation, including class actions, antitrust/intellectual property cases, and multi-district litigation. Litigates antitrust cases and other complex cases for both plaintiffs and defendants, represents clients in grand jury investigations and other proceedings before the Department of Justice. Counsels and trains companies/trade associations.

**Career:** Previously a trial attorney with the Antitrust Division of the US Department of Justice.

**Personal:** State University of New York at Binghamton, BA; Georgetown University Law Center, JD, 1984 - cum laude.

### GARRETT, Robert A
Arnold & Porter LLP, Washington, DC
202 942 5444
Robert.Garrett@aporter.com
*Featured in Sports Law (Nationwide), Media & Entertainment (District of Columbia)*

**Practice Areas:** Robert Garrett's practice focuses on copyright and telecommunications law, particularly as it affects the sports and entertainment industries and the distribution of copyrighted works over new and traditional media. His clients have included the major sports leagues, motion picture studios, recording companies, municipal and foreign governments, and broadcast and cable television networks. He has practiced extensively before the federal courts, Copyright Office, Copyright Royalty Board and Federal Communications Commission. He also has handled various copyright related matters before the PTO, USTR, State Department, WIPO and Congress.

### GARRETT, Theodore
Covington & Burling LLP, Washington, DC
202 662 5398
tgarrett@cov.com
*Featured in Environment (District of Columbia)*

**Practice Areas:** Extensive experience in environmental compliance, permits, transactions, regulatory policy and enforcement issues, including air, water, climate, and site remediation matters.

**Career:** Law clerk to Chief Justice Warren Burger, US Supreme Court. Special assistant to Assistant Attorney General William Rehnquist, USDOJ.

**Publications:** Editor, principal author, 'Environmental Guide for Corporate Counsel'; editor, 'RCRA Compliance Manual'; co-author, 'Clean Air Deskbook'; 'Environmental Litigation',

'The Clean Water Act Handbook'; 'Environmental Liability and Insurance Recovery'; numerous articles concerning environmental law.

**Personal:** Past Chair, ABA Section of Environment, Energy and Resources. Member, American College of Environmental Lawyers. Columbia Law School, JD; Yale University, BA.

### GARROTE, Nora
Venable LLP, Washington, DC
202 344 8543
negarrote@Venable.com
*Featured in Technology (District of Columbia)*

**Practice Areas:** Nora focuses her practice on intellectual property and technology transactions and counseling, and computer and Internet/new media law. This includes licensing, systems implementation, transfers/acquisitions, cloud computing, hosting, website, manufacturing, OEM, development, joint venture and services agreements. Her in-depth IP and commercial transactions experience leads to practical and creative solutions regarding her clients' use, exploitation and disposition of intangibles and technology assets in a variety of industries and subject matters, including in the IT, healthcare, insurance, Internet, hospitality financial services and energy fields.

**Personal:** JD, Columbia University Law, 1983 (Stone Scholar); AB, Bryn Mawr College, magna cum laude, 1980.

### GART, Ron
Seyfarth Shaw LLP, Washington, DC
202 828 5320
rgart@seyfarth.com
*Featured in Real Estate (District of Columbia)*

**Practice Areas:** Commercial real estate investment, development, management, leasing and finance.

**Professional Memberships:** Advisory Board of ULI-Washington District Council; Urban Land Institute; District of Columbia, Maryland and Virginia State Bars; District of Columbia Building Industry Association, National Multi-Housing Council

**Career:** Mr Gart has over 30 years experience in counseling clients on commercial real estate development, finance (including mezzanine debt), asset management, asset purchase and sales, commercial leasing, and mixed-use development and planned communities. He counsels institutions in their direct investment and investors in joint ventures.

**Personal:** JD, The George Washington University, The National Law Center; BA, The George Washington University

### GARZA, Deborah A
Covington & Burling LLP, Washington, DC
202 662 5146
dgarza@cov.com
*Featured in Antitrust (District of Columbia)*

**Career:** With more than 30 years of experience in the private and public sectors, Ms. Garza has been involved in many major antitrust matters, including the merger of Exxon and Mobil, the U.S. Government's suit against Microsoft, and other civil and criminal matters involving Fortune 500 companies. She practices in all areas of

antitrust law, counseling clients on transactions, complex litigation, and government investigations. Ms. Garza previously served as Deputy Assistant Attorney General and then as Acting Assistant Attorney General for Antitrust at the U.S. Justice Department. From 2004 to 2007, she chaired the Congressionally-created Blue Ribbon Antitrust Modernization Commission.

### GAYNOR, Kevin
Vinson & Elkins LLP, Washington, DC
202 639 6688
kgaynor@velaw.com
*Featured in Environment (District of Columbia)*

**Practice Areas:** Heads the firm's DC office's Environmental Practice.

**Professional Memberships:** Member: Environment, Energy, and Natural Resources Steering Committee, DC Bar; Environment and Litigation Sections, American Bar Association.

**Career:** Admitted to Connecticut Bar in 1973, District of Columbia Bar in 1978, and Maryland Bar in 1991. Joined the firm as a Partner in 1993.

**Publications:** Challenges Plaintiffs Face in Litigating Federal Common-Law Climate Change Claims, 40 The Environmental Law Reporter 10845, September 2010 and Unresolved CERCLA issues after Atlantic Research and Burlington Northern, 40 The Environmental Law Reporter 11198, December 2010

### GELFAND, David I
Cleary Gottlieb Steen & Hamilton LLP, Washington, DC
202 974 1690
dgelfand@cgsh.com
*Featured in Antitrust (District of Columbia)*

**Practice Areas:** Antitrust and litigation. Represents clients in M&A before DOJ and FTC; litigates cases in state and federal courts; counsels clients on antitrust aspects of proposed transactions. Spent three years (2001-2004) in Brussels representing clients before European Commission. Recent transactions: Dollar Thrifty's acquisition by Hertz; Google's acquisitions of Motorola Mobility, Admeld, AdMob; GlaxoSmithKline's acquisition of Stiefel; DSM's acquisition of Ocean Nutrition Canada; IMS Health's acquisition of SDI; Current antitrust litigation representations: ArcelorMittal, Sanofi, and Whirlpool.

**Career:** Joined firm, 1991; became partner, 1997. JD, summa cum laude, Georgetown University Law Center (1987); BS, magna cum laude, University of Pennsylvania (1981).

### GERSCH, David
Arnold & Porter LLP, Washington, DC
202 942 5125
David.Gersch@aporter.com
*Featured in Litigation (District of Columbia)*

**Practice Areas:** Experienced trial and appellate lawyer who has appeared as Lead Counsel in numerous complex antitrust, commercial and tort actions.

**Career:** Mr Gersch has a broad litigation practice representing clients in significant antitrust, insurance and products liability matters. He has successfully tried cases involving diet drugs and

transfusion-AIDS and high stakes commercial disputes. He has argued appeals in the United States Courts of Appeal and the state appellate courts. Other actions handled by him include defense of class action, intellectual property, pension, and toxic tort suits.
**Personal:** JD, New York University School of Law, 1982; AB, Oberlin College, 1978.

### GERSTELL, Glenn S
Milbank, Tweed, Hadley & McCloy LLP, Washington, DC
202 835 7585
gerstell@milbank.com
*Featured in Telecommunications (District of Columbia)*
**Practice Areas:** Mr Gerstell serves as the managing partner of the Washington, DC office and heads the firm's Global Communications practice and its Milbank TAARS® (Tax Account Analysis and Recovery Services) practice. Mr Gerstell focuses on the global communications industry, overseeing a wide range of financings, acquisitions and commercial transactions around the globe for telecom operators, equipment vendors and debt and equity investors in the industry. He has led some of the most innovative and complex transactions in the telecom industry, many of which were recognized as "deals of the year" by leading industry publications.

### GERTZMAN, Stephen
Miller & Chevalier Chartered, Washington, DC
202 626 6080
sgertzman@milchev.com
*Featured in Tax (District of Columbia)*
**Practice Areas:** Represents clients on full range of tax accounting issues; in planning, administratively, and in litigation. His industry experience covers virtually every sector of the economy.
**Career:** Recognized as one of nation's preeminent tax accounting lawyers. His treatise, Federal Tax Accounting, is considered leading authority on the topic. Chaired ABA Tax Section's Tax Accounting Committee, various subcommittees and task forces. His writings have been cited by IRS and the courts.
**Personal:** JD, University of Florida School of Law, high honors, Order of the Coif, 1972; MA (Accounting), University of Florida, 1970; BSBA, University of Florida, high honors, 1968.

### GIANNOTTO, Michael S
Goodwin Procter LLP, Washington, DC
202 346 4124
mgiannotto@goodwinprocter.com
*Featured in Environment (District of Columbia)*
**Practice Areas:** For over 20 years, Mr Giannotto has advised and litigated on behalf of numerous corporations and trade associations involved in mining, manufacturing, and defense contracting in connection with all of the major federal environmental laws and their state analogues. These include the Resource Conservation and Recovery Act, Clean Water Act, Comprehensive Environmental Response, Compensation and Liability Act, Toxic Substances Control Act, National Environmental Policy Act,

Emergency Planning and Community Right To Know Act, and Federal Land Policy and Management Act.
**Personal:** JD, Harvard Law School, 1978 (magna cum laude); BA, University of Pennsylvania, 1975 (summa cum laude).

### GIBBS, Lawrence B
Miller & Chevalier Chartered, Washington, DC
202 626 6005
lgibbs@milchev.com
*Featured in Tax (District of Columbia)*
**Practice Areas:** Deals with the IRS at all levels including tax planning; tax audits and administrative appeals; tax litigation and judicial appeals; exempt organizations; research and experimentation credit; tax legislation; and tax regulation.
**Career:** Former IRS Commissioner. Recipient of the Tax Council Policy Institute's Pillar of Excellence Award, FBA's Distinguished Service Award, Department of the Treasury's Alexander Hamilton Award, and TEI's Distinguished Service Award.
**Publications:** Erwin N. Griswold Lecture before the American College of Tax Counsel: Constancy and Change in Our Federal Tax System, The Tax Lawyer.
**Personal:** LLB, University of Texas School of Law, 1963; BA, Yale University, 1960.

### GIDEON, Kenneth W
Skadden, Arps, Slate, Meagher & Flom LLP & Affiliates, Washington, DC
202 371 7540
Kenneth.Gideon@skadden.com
*Featured in Tax (District of Columbia), Tax (Nationwide)*
See under Nationwide for profile.

### GIDLEY, J Mark
White & Case LLP, Washington, DC
202 626 3609
mgidley@whitecase.com
*Featured in Antitrust (District of Columbia)*
**Career:** Mark Gidley chairs White & Case's Global Antitrust/Competition practice. He focuses on mergers, acquisitions, and cartel cases, often with a transnational focus. He has significant experience in trying criminal and civil antitrust price-fixing cases and merger cases. His work often features investigations of transnational firms in grand jury investigations, parallel class action suits, and civil investigations of pricing and other competitive practices. His cases often involve investigations by competition agencies outside the United States such as the European Commission, national European authorities and competition agencies in Canada, Korea, Australia, New Zealand and Japan. To view his biography, visit www.whitecase.com/mgidley.

### GILBERT, Scott D
Gilbert LLP, Washington, DC
202 772 2277
gilberts@gotofirm.com
*Featured in Insurance (District of Columbia)*
**Practice Areas:** Founder and Chairman of the firm. Practice focus is on complex multiparty dispute resolution. Internationally recognized inno-

vator in strategic ADR. Primary policyholder negotiator and drafter of the Wellington Agreement, one of the largest insurance settlements in US history. Founder of and Counsel to the Center for Claims Resolution. Primary insurance negotiator and strategist for mass tort defendants, as well as bankruptcy trusts, bankruptcy claimant committees, and groups of individual tort claimants. Adjunct professor at University of Chicago Law School and Duke University Law School.
**Professional Memberships:** Bar Admissions: District of Columbia; US Supreme Court; US Court of Appeals for the District of Columbia; US District Court for the District of Columbia; US Court of International Trade.
**Career:** Recipient of the Center for Public Resources Award for Innovation in Alternative Dispute Resolution; served on the Board of Directors of the Asbestos Claims Facility; Member, Board of Directors of the Washington Legal Clinic for the Homeless and the Legal Aid Society of the District of Columbia; Founder and Editor, Chicago Forum, 1978-79.
**Personal:** JD, University of Chicago (1979); BA, Northwestern University (1975).

### GLASGOW JR, Norman
Holland & Knight LLP, Washington, DC
202 419 2460
norman.glasgowjr@hklaw.com
*Featured in Real Estate (District of Columbia)*
**Practice Areas:** Partner is the practice group leader of Holland & Knight's Washington, D.C. Land Use Group and represents real estate developers in zoning, building code and historic preservation law matters before the Board of Zoning Adjustment, Zoning Commission, State Historic Review Board, Commission of Fine Arts and development issues before the D.C. City Council. He has handled numerous cases before the Board of Zoning Adjustment and Zoning Commission and represents clients in street and alley closings. He is active in civic affairs, addressing the area's affordable housing crisis by working extensively with nonprofit housing providers and community development corporations.

### GLEKLEN, Jonathan
Arnold & Porter LLP, Washington, DC
202 942 5454
Jonathan.Gleklen@aporter.com
*Featured in Antitrust (District of Columbia)*
**Practice Areas:** Jonathan Gleklen's antitrust practice focuses on antitrust issues affecting clients in high technology and network industries, including government merger review and investigations of alleged anticompetitive conduct, civil litigation, and counseling. He regularly represents clients before the Antitrust Division of the Department of Justice, the Federal Trade Commission, and state attorneys general.
**Publications:** He served as the Editorial Chair of Antitrust Law Developments (Seventh Edition, 2012), the leading two volume antitrust treatise, and for more than a decade on the editorial board of Antitrust Law Journal, serving as Editorial Chair in 2008 and 2009.

### GLOVER, Stephen I
Gibson, Dunn & Crutcher LLP, Washington, DC
202 955 8593
siglover@gibsondunn.com
*Featured in Corporate/M&A (District of Columbia)*
**Practice Areas:** Co-Chair, firm's M&A practice. Represents public and private companies in M&A, joint ventures, equity and debt offerings and corporate governance matters.
**Professional Memberships:** Advisory board, BNA's 'M&A Law Report'; editorial board, 'The M&A Lawyer'. Member, Securities Regulation, Negotiated Acquisitions and Venture Capital Committees, ABA's Business Law Section. Member, DC Bar Board of Governors. Former Chair, DC Bar Community Economic Development Project. Former Co-Chair, DC Bar Corporations, Securities, Finance Committee.
**Career:** Former Adjunct Professor, Georgetown University Law Center.
**Publications:** Author/co-author of corporate and securities law books/articles.
**Personal:** JD, Harvard Law School, 1980. Law clerk, US Supreme Court Justice Marshall.

### GOLD, Jason
Wiley Rein LLP, Washington, DC
202 719 4136
jgold@wileyrein.com
*Featured in Bankruptcy/Restructuring (District of Columbia)*
**Practice Areas:** Chair, Bankruptcy & Financial Restructuring Practice. 30+ years experience in restructuring and insolvency matters. As a bankruptcy trustee for 20+ years, has liquidated/restructured dozens of businesses. Board Certified in Business Bankruptcy Law (American Board of Certification) and is a member of its Board of Directors.
**Professional Memberships:** Board of Directors, National Association of Bankruptcy Trustees; Chair, American Bankruptcy Institute, Telecommunications/Technology Committee (2006-10); Standing Panel of Bankruptcy Trustees, U.S. Bankruptcy Court EDVA.
**Career:** DC's "Top 100 Lawyers" (2011-2012);Virginia's "Top 50 Lawyers" (2011); Super Lawyers
**Personal:** Columbus School of Law, The Catholic University of America (JD); American University (BA).

### GOLD, Michael A
Baker Botts LLP, Washington, DC
202 639 7724
michael.gold@bakerbotts.com
*Featured in Corporate/M&A (District of Columbia)*
**Practice Areas:** Capital Markets and Securities Offerings, Corporate Investigations, Corporate Practice, Corporate Governance and Compliance Counseling, Cross-Border Transactions, Joint Ventures, Mergers and Acquisitions, Private Equity Funds, Securities Law Enforcement and Regulation, Venture Capital and Emerging Companies
**Professional Memberships:** District of Columbia Bar; New York State Bar; American Bar Association, Mergers & Acquisitions Committee;

District of Columbia Bar Association; New York Bar Association

**Personal:** JD (with honors), University of Chicago Law School, 1993; BS of Economics (cum laude), Finance, The Wharton School of the University of Pennsylvania, 1988; BA (cum laude), European History, University of Pennsylvania, 1988

### GOLDBERG JR, Fred T
Skadden, Arps, Slate, Meagher & Flom LLP & Affiliates, Washington, DC
202 371 7110
Fred.Goldberg@skadden.com
*Featured in Tax (District of Columbia), Tax (Nationwide)*
See under Nationwide for profile.

### GOLDBLATT, Craig
WilmerHale, Washington, DC
202 663 6483
craig.goldblatt@wilmerhale.com
*Featured in Bankruptcy/Restructuring (District of Columbia)*
**Practice Areas:** Practice focuses on bankruptcy-related litigation and appeals. Has argued two bankruptcy cases in the Supreme Court, prevailing in both. Has represented parties in many of the most complex bankruptcy disputes, including the Lehman bankruptcy, matters arising out of Enron's collapse, asbestos and mass tort bankruptcies, and the foreclosure crisis.
**Professional Memberships:** Chair, ABA Business Bankruptcy Committee's Subcommittee on Bankruptcy Appeals.
**Personal:** University of Chicago Law School (JD 1993); Georgetown University (BA 1990). Law clerk, Hon. Richard D. Cudahy, US Court of Appeals for the Seventh Circuit, (1993-94); Hon. David H. Souter, US Supreme Court, (1995-96).

### GOLDMAN, Joseph
Jones Day, Washington, DC
202 879 5437
jagoldman@jonesday.com
*Featured in Tax (District of Columbia)*
**Practice Areas:** Joe Goldman has been a tax partner at Jones Day since 2000. His practice involves structuring and documenting international transactions, including mergers and acquisitions, post-acquisition integration of global businesses, supply chain restructurings, and intellectual property licensing; transfer pricing; and defending disputes with the IRS. He works extensively with clients in the pharmaceutical, chemical, spirits, services, energy, electronics, and automotive industries. He is a member of the ABA (Taxation Section), DC Bar, and NY State Bar.
**Personal:** NYU, LLM (Taxation); Columbia Law School, JD (Articles Editor, Journal of Transnational Law); Yeshiva University (BS, Accounting, magna cum laude).

### GOLDMAN, Roger
Latham & Watkins LLP, Washington, DC
202 637 2253
roger.goldman@lw.com
*Featured in Healthcare (District of Columbia)*
**Practice Areas:** Represents companies in False Claims Act and white collar criminal litigation

---

with an emphasis on healthcare and government contract fraud defense. Particular expertise in representing major healthcare and government contractor corporations in qui tam proceedings.
**Professional Memberships:** Member, District of Columbia and Utah bars.
**Publications:** Co-author, You Cannot Be Serious: DOJ's Efforts to Create an Ex Post Facto Application for Changes to the Anti-Kickback Statute Intent Standard, ABA Healthcare Fraud Conference, May 2012.

### GOMEZ, Armando
Skadden, Arps, Slate, Meagher & Flom LLP & Affiliates, Washington, DC
202 371 7868
Armando.Gomez@skadden.com
*Featured in Tax (District of Columbia)*
**Practice Areas:** Advises on a broad range of tax issues, including structuring and financing of US and cross-border partnerships and joint ventures, with a particular emphasis on renewable energy projects. Represents clients in federal and state tax controversy matters, including in connection with audits, appeals, mediation and litigation. Regularly appears before the U.S. Department of the Treasury and the Internal Revenue Service in administrative and policy matters.
**Career:** Internal Revenue Service, Attorney-Advisor (1994-96); National Commission on Restructuring the Internal Revenue Service, Chief Counsel (1996-97). LLM, Georgetown University Law Center, 1997; JD, Georgetown University Law Center, 1994; AB, Duke University, 1991.

### GOODMAN, Saul
Covington & Burling LLP, Washington, DC
202 662 5472
sgoodman@cov.com
*Featured in Insurance (District of Columbia)*
**Practice Areas:** Represents policyholders in complex insurance coverage disputes, transactions and advice. Experience includes coverage for wide range of losses, including asbestos, pharmaceutical and other mass torts, environmental, D&O, ERISA, IP and first party property losses. Chair of Covington's 100-member policyholder practice group from 1997 to 2009, during which time the group twice received the Chambers Awards for Excellence in Insurance (2007, 2009).
**Career:** Partner at Covington since 1989. Law Clerk to Justice Potter Stewart, US Supreme Court (1979-80).
**Publications:** "Settling Insurance Coverage Disputes," New Appleman Insurance Law Practice Guide (2007).
**Personal:** BA, cum laude, Yale, 1975; JD, Virginia, 1978.

### GOODWIN, Michael
Arnold & Porter LLP, Washington, DC
202 942 5558
Michael.Goodwin@aporter.com
*Featured in Leisure & Hospitality (Nationwide), Real Estate (District of Columbia)*
**Practice Areas:** Michael Goodwin focuses on real estate development, hospitality, public/private partnerships, and debt and equity financing transactions. He represents developers, institutions and

---

governmental organizations in all aspects of commercial development projects, including land acquisition, ground leases, debt and equity financing, and is heavily involved in structuring and negotiating public incentives for development such as TIFs, PILOTs and tax abatement. He also represents hotel owners and operators in the acquisition, development and operation of hospitality properties nationwide, including full service, convention center and resort hotels.
**Professional Memberships:** He is a Fellow of the American College of Real Estate Lawyers.

### GOTTLIEB, Robert G
Venable LLP, Washington, DC
202 344 8526
rggottlieb@Venable.com
*Featured in Real Estate (District of Columbia)*
**Practice Areas:** Structuring and negotiating complex real estate, partnership and business transactions; tax planning
**Professional Memberships:** Member of American College of Real Estate Lawyers
**Career:** Mr Gottlieb advises real estate developers, tenants, management and leasing companies, and investors, on tax planning and real estate, capital formation, financing and business transactions. From 1984 to 2007, Mr Gottlieb taught law school, most recently as an adjunct professor at Georgetown University Law Center teaching a graduate-level course.
**Publications:** Speeches – Frequent lecturer at continuing professional education programs
**Personal:** JD, with honors, George Washington University, 1976; BA, cum laude, Pennsylvania State University, 1973

### GOTTS, Lawrence J
Latham & Watkins LLP, Washington, DC
202 637 2384
lawrence.gotts@lw.com
*Featured in Intellectual Property (District of Columbia)*
**Practice Areas:** Litigation and trial of patent and other intellectual property disputes in a broad array of technologies. Practices before federal district courts, the Court of Federal Claims, the ITC and US Court of Appeals for the Federal Circuit. Provides strategic business counseling on intellectual property issues including patent and other intellectual property portfolio management, defensive intellectual property procedures, design-around initiatives, and intellectual property due diligence and assessment.
**Professional Memberships:** Member, DC and Virginia state bars, admitted USPTO.
**Personal:** JD, George Washington University Law School, 1985; BS, University of Maryland, 1980.

### GRANT, Maximillian
Latham & Watkins LLP, Washington, DC
202 637 2267
max.grant@lw.com
*Featured in Intellectual Property (District of Columbia)*
**Practice Areas:** Experienced first chair trial lawyer. Represents patentees and defendants in the litigation and trial of patent infringement matters

---

before federal district courts and the ITC. Provides strategic business counseling on intellectual property issues. Clients range from Fortune 100 to emerging companies/inventors. Former US Navy SEAL team leader, co-inventor of two US patents.
**Professional Memberships:** Member, DC and Illinois state bars.
**Career:** Co-Chair, Global Intellectual Property Litigation Group recognized with Chambers "Excellence Award" in 2012
**Personal:** JD, University of Chicago Law School, 1996; MA, Georgetown University, 1989; BS, US Naval Academy, 1988.

### GRANWELL, Alan Winston
DLA Piper LLP (US), Washington, DC
202 799 4190
alan.granwell@dlapiper.com
*Featured in Tax (District of Columbia)*
**Practice Areas:** International Tax.
**Career:** His practice encompasses representing multinational corporations on cross-border planning, to include acquisitions, dispositions and business restructurings, IP migrations, services arrangements, repatriation planning, international insurance, international transportation, cross-border leasing, transfer pricing and the use of bilateral tax treaties. He advises high net-worth individuals on cross-border tax planning and structuring.
**Personal:** LLM, New York University School of Law; LLM, Taxation, Boston University School of Law; JD, Boston University School of Law; AB, Middlebury College.

### GRAY, Peter
McKenna Long & Aldridge LLP, Washington, DC
202 496 7707
pgray@mckennalong.com
*Featured in Environment (District of Columbia)*
**Practice Areas:** Peter L. Gray serves as Chair of the Environment, Energy and Product Regulation Department. Peter has worked on a broad range of environmental matters, including disputes over responsibility for cleanup of contaminated property, challenges to state and federal environmental regulations, enforcement cases involving hazardous materials, arbitration of data compensation claims under FIFRA involving use of pesticide data, and climate change planning and advocacy. Peter was a founder of the Association of Climate Change Officers and serves as a board member.
**Personal:** JD, The George Washington University Law School, 1985; MS, The George Washington University, 1982; BS, University of Maryland, 1979;

### GRAY, Todd
Dow Lohnes PLLC, Washington, DC
202 776 2571
tgray@dowlohnes.com
*Featured in Telecommunications (District of Columbia)*
**Practice Areas:** Todd Gray founded and leads the Public Broadcasting and Educational Telecommunications Practice at Dow Lohnes that specializes in telecommunications matters for

educational institutions, state and local governmental agencies and nonprofit organizations. He represents more than 300 public broadcasting stations, including 11 state public broadcasting networks, and numerous other public and private non-profit licensees. He also works with many of the country's major universities and university systems. A noted expert in the FCC's Educational Broadband Service (EBS), Mr Gray represents over 600 EBS stations, including some of the country's largest EBS users, and is also counsel to the National EBS Association.

### GREANEY, William
Covington & Burling LLP, Washington, DC
202 662 5486
wgreaney@cov.com
*Featured in Insurance (Nationwide), Insurance (District of Columbia)*
See under Nationwide for profile.

### GREEN, Douglas H
Venable LLP, Washington, DC
202 344 4483
dhgreen@Venable.com
*Featured in Environment (District of Columbia)*
**Practice Areas:** Environmental law, regulatory
**Career:** Chairs Venable's Environmental Practice Group with a practice focusing on complex litigation, enforcement defense, and counseling under national environmental statutes, including RCRA, TSCA, CERCLA and CAA, as well as state environmental laws. Lead counsel for the Utility Solid Waste Activities Group, an association of over 110 energy industry operating companies and associations on solid and hazardous waste and chemical regulatory, compliance, and enforcement issues. Also assists a wide range of clients with day-to-day environmental-related compliance assistance and enforcement defense matters.
**Personal:** JD, with honors, George Washington University, 1983; BA, cum laude, Connecticut College, 1979.

### GREEN, Thomas C
Sidley Austin LLP, Washington, DC
202 736 8069
tcgreen@sidley.com
*Featured in Litigation (Nationwide), Litigation (District of Columbia)*
See under Nationwide for profile.

### GREENBERG, Bennett D
Seyfarth Shaw LLP, Washington, DC
202 828 5336
bgreenberg@seyfarth.com
*Featured in Construction (District of Columbia)*
**Practice Areas:** Construction; Government Contracts
**Professional Memberships:** Design-Build Institute of America
**Career:** Co-chair of Seyfarth's national Construction Practice. Negotiates and drafts contracts for various parties to the construction process involved in complex construction projects. Counsels clients on procurement-related issues, contract administration, risk management and dispute avoidance, and has extensive experience preparing claim documentation in support of equitable adjustments to contracts. Has suc-

cessfully mediated, litigated, and arbitrated large complex, multi-party construction disputes.
**Publications:** Authored numerous chapters for construction law textbooks and construction law articles, and lectures nationally on a variety of construction law topics.
**Personal:** JD, Georgetown University School of Law

### GREENFIELD, Leon B
WilmerHale, Washington, DC
202 663 6972
leon.greenfield@wilmerhale.com
*Featured in Antitrust (District of Columbia)*
**Practice Areas:** Partner, Antitrust and Competition Group. Represents clients in complex antitrust-related matters. Practice focuses on cutting edge Section 2 litigation and agency matters, has secured antitrust clearance for major acquisitions, litigated cases in federal and state court and counseled clients on many types of antitrust issues. Broad experience in matters outside the antitrust area, including securities regulatory matters and litigation and complex business litigation.
**Publications:** Associate Editor of the Antitrust Law Journal.
**Personal:** JD, with honors, University of Chicago Law School, BS, with honors, Pennsylvania State University, 1986.

### GROSS, Joel M
Arnold & Porter LLP, Washington, DC
202 942 5705
Joel.Gross@aporter.com
*Featured in Environment (District of Columbia)*
**Practice Areas:** Represents and advises clients in litigation and non-litigation matters under federal and state environmental laws, with a special emphasis on compliance, enforcement and bankruptcy issues. Advises clients on compliance strategies to minimize the risk of enforcement actions, and has represented a wide range of clients in connection with ongoing civil and or criminal enforcement actions under the Clean Air Act, the Clean Water Act, and the Resource Conservation and Recovery Act.
**Career:** Served as chief of the Environmental Enforcement Section at the Department of Justice.
**Personal:** JD, NYU School of Law, 1977; MA and BA, Yeshiva University, 1975.

### GROW, Michael A
Arent Fox LLP, Washington, DC
202 857 6389
michael.grow@arentfox.com
*Featured in Intellectual Property (District of Columbia)*
**Practice Areas:** Michael Grow is co-chair of the intellectual property group at Arent Fox. His practice focuses on foreign and domestic litigation and transactional work in the fields of trademark, copyright, unfair competition, right of publicity, advertising, technology transfer and licensing. Michael has represented clients in civil actions and appeals in state and federal courts throughout the US. He also counsels clients on trademark selection and registration; copyright protection; computer law; franchise law; and licensing.

Michael also has assisted in securing legislation directed at enhancing intellectual property rights and he has testified before committees in both house of Congress on bills affecting intellectual property rights.
**Personal:** George Washington University, JD, 1975; Weber State College, BA, 1972; Fluent in Italian and Spanish.

### GUTTER, Samuel
Sidley Austin LLP, Washington, DC
202 736 8167
sgutter@sidley.com
*Featured in Environment (District of Columbia)*
**Practice Areas:** Partner in Sidley's Washington, DC office, practicing in the Environmental group. He developed his environmental experience at the US Environmental Protection Agency, where he served for eight years with the Offices of General Counsel, Enforcement and Federal Activities. His positions included lead staff attorney for Superfund, vehicle emissions, fuel economy and noise matters. His practice includes enforcement and regulatory litigation under RCRA, CERCLA, TSCA, the Clean Water Act and the Clean Air Act.
**Personal:** The George Washington University Law School, JD, 1977, Order of the Coif; Tufts University, BA, 1974, magna cum laude.
**Admission:** District of Columbia.

### GUY, Jonathan P
Orrick, Herrington & Sutcliffe LLP, Washington, DC
202 339 8516
jguy@orrick.com
*Featured in Bankruptcy/Restructuring (District of Columbia)*
**Career:** Jonathan Guy, a litigation partner at Orrick, represents clients in complex, high-profile commercial litigation matters in state and federal trial and appellate courts throughout the United States. He has 20 years of experience in a wide variety of litigation matters. In recent years, his practice has focused on bankruptcy litigation, particularly for energy and commodity companies. He is active in pro bono and community responsibility, running those programs for Orrick's DC office. Before practicing as a lawyer, he was in charge of operations for Commerzbank and Swiss Bank's global derivatives groups.

### HABERL, Heather
Covington & Burling LLP, Washington, DC
202 662 5817
hhaberl@cov.com
*Featured in Real Estate (District of Columbia)*
**Practice Areas:** Represents local regional, and national owners, property managers, tax-exempt organizations, and other users in all aspects of real estate transactions involving the acquisition, disposition, financing, leasing and construction of office buildings, industrial parks, manufacturing facilities and power projects. Representative clients include RREEF, ACLI and Ourisman Automotive Group.
**Professional Memberships:** DC, NY and NJ Bars; CREW DC.
**Career:** Of Counsel of the Real Estate Group at Covington & Burling LLP.

**Personal:** The George Washington University Law School, JD with highest honors, 2001; George Washington University Law Review. Bryn Mawr College, MA, 1996. Hamilton College, BA, 1994, cum laude.

### HADJIS, Alexander J
Morrison & Foerster LLP, Washington, DC
202 887 1560
ahadjis@mofo.com
*Featured in International Trade (Nationwide), Intellectual Property (District of Columbia)*
See under Nationwide for profile.

### HAGEN, Paul
Beveridge & Diamond PC, Washington, DC
202 789 6022
phagen@bdlaw.com
*Featured in Environment (District of Columbia)*
**Practice Areas:** Mr Hagen advises US and multinational corporate and public interest clients on environmental compliance, product stewardship and corporate governance matters. He helps clients identify and comply with market access, material restriction, energy efficiency, conflict minerals disclosure, and resource protection measures. Works extensively with companies in the electronics, chemicals and pharmaceuticals sectors on supply chain, compliance, and sustainability matters. Has assisted clients with development of product take-back and recycling programs. His international work includes representing clients on issues arising under international agreements, including the Basel Convention, the Cartagena Protocol on Biosafety, the Montreal Protocol, and the Stockholm POPs Convention.

### HAIRE, Dirk D
Fox Rothschild LLP, Washington, DC
202 461 3114
DHaire@foxrothschild.com
*Featured in Construction (District of Columbia)*
**Practice Areas:** Government contracts; construction law. Procurement matters, including bid protests, debriefings, teaming and subcontracting arrangements, contract negotiation, claims litigation, FAR ethics/compliance, audits/cost allowability, government investigations, False Claims Act.
**Professional Memberships:** Associated General Contractors (AGC) of America Board of Directors, FAR Committee Chair, Service & Supply Council Executive Committee; AGC of Metropolitan DC; Design-Build Institute of America; Construction Financial Management Association.
**Career:** AGC of America, Senior Director; Holland and Knight LLP, Partner; Smith, Currie & Hancock LLP, Partner; Fox Rothschild LLP, Partner
**Personal:** George Washington University Law School, JD; Ball State University, BS.

### HAMMER, Michael H
Willkie Farr & Gallagher LLP, Washington, DC
202 303 1110
mhammer@willkie.com
*Featured in Telecommunications (District of Columbia)*
**Practice Areas:** Chair, Communications, Media & Privacy Department. Counsels/participates in

legislative/administrative agency representation of cable television operators/video programmers. Provides government relations services/advice on regulatory approval and related issues to large media mergers and new technology, Internet, and satellite business transactions. Recent highlights: securing approval for Comcast Corp. to buy majority stake in NBC Universal from GE; securing approval for Time Warner Inc. to spin off Time Warner Cable, securing approval for Comcast Corp. and Time Warner Inc. to acquire assets of Adelphia.
**Personal:** JD, George Washington University Law School, 1979. BA, Rutgers, The State University of New Jersey, 1976. See:http://www.willkie.com/MichaelHammer

### HAMMOND, Denise
Hammond Immigration Law, P.C., Rockville
301 917 6901
Denise@HammondImmigration.com
*Featured in Immigration (Nationwide), Immigration (District of Columbia)*
**Practice Areas:** Voted as one of the Washington D.C. Area's Best Lawyers in The Washington Post and Washingtonian and one of the Top 10 Immigration Attorneys in Washington, D.C. by Legal Times, Ms. Hammond specializes in corporate immigration law, including work visas and I-9 and E-Verify matters. She regularly receives referrals from major multinational law firms and guest lectures at the George Washington University Law School and the American University College of Law.
**Professional Memberships:** Ms. Hammond is Co-Chair of the ABA Immigration Committee (International Section). She has served as Chair of the Annual Conference of the American Immigration Lawyers Association ("AILA") and held other AILA appointments. She chaired the Immigration Section of the Bar Association of Montgomery County, Maryland and was a Delegate to the White House Conference on Small Business, and Special Counsel to the National Association of Women Business Owners Capital Area Chapter.
**Career:** Ms. Hammond joined the U.S. Department of Justice as a trial attorney in 1980 and received a Special Commendation from the Assistant Attorney General. She joined Pierson, Ball & Dowd (now Reed Smith) in 1983 and established her practice in 1985.
**Publications:** Ms. Hammond has written many articles on various business immigration topics.

### HANDWERKER, Jeffrey L
Arnold & Porter LLP, Washington, DC
202 942 6103
Jeffrey.Handwerker@aporter.com
*Featured in Healthcare (District of Columbia)*
**Practice Areas:** Jeffrey Handwerker focuses his practice on pharmaceutical pricing and investigations, government contracts, and commercial litigation involving the pharmaceutical, medical products, and biotechnology industries. He advises pharmaceutical and medical technology companies on pricing and contracting matters arising under the Veterans Health Care Act, the Medicaid

Rebate Act, the Deficit Reduction Act of 2005, the Medicare Modernization Act, and the Patient Protection and Affordable Care Act. He also advises pharmaceutical companies on important issues confronting the industry, including healthcare reform implementation, First Amendment issues in pharmaceutical promotional activities, and novel issues under the federal and state Anti-Kickback laws.

### HANSON, John N
Beveridge & Diamond PC, Washington, DC
202 789 6015
jhanson@bdlaw.com
*Featured in Environment (District of Columbia)*
**Practice Areas:** Federal and State trial, appellate court and agency work covering environmental, natural resource, antitrust, unfair trade and advertising, product liability, securities, shareholder derivative, energy, personal injury, and general economic matters. Served as an arbitrator and mediator and represents clients in alternative dispute resolution proceedings. Before Beveridge & Diamond, from 1972-79 was an attorney in the Civil Division of the United States Department of Justice in Washington, where he received an assistant attorney general's Special Commendation Award and the attorney general's Meritorious Service Award.

### HARRIS, Larry D
Fox Rothschild LLP, Washington, DC
202 461 3117
ldharris@foxrothschild.com
*Featured in Construction (District of Columbia)*
**Practice Areas:** Construction Litigation; Arbitration/Mediation; Government Contracts.
**Professional Memberships:** Member, American Arbitration Association National Roster of Neutrals; President, American College of Construction Lawyers; American Bar Association Forum on the Construction Industry: Member; Governing Committee; Chair; Founding Co-Chair, Diversity Committee; Member, Diversity Committee; Fellow, College of Commercial Arbitrators; Founding Officer, George Washington University Law School, Black Law Alumni Association; Construction Committee Member, International Institute for Conflict Prevention and Resolution
**Career:** Best Lawyers in America; International Who's Who of Business Lawyers-Construction; Washington DC Super Lawyers Construction Litigation.
**Personal:** George Washington University Law School, JD (with honors); University of Dayton, BS.

### HARRISON, Mark
Venable LLP, Washington, DC
202 344 4019
mbharrison@Venable.com
*Featured in Intellectual Property (District of Columbia)*
**Practice Areas:** Trademarks, Copyrights and Domain Names, Intellectual Property, Trademark Litigation
**Professional Memberships:** International Trademark Association

**Career:** Mark Harrison chairs Venable's Trademark, Copyright & Licensing group. He focuses on trademark, unfair competition and copyright issues. He is a former Examining Attorney of the U.S. Patent and Trademark Office. He has successfully argued cases before the Court of Appeals for the Federal Circuit and the Trademark Trial and Appeal Board of the U.S. Patent and Trademark Office, several of which are citable as precedent.
**Personal:** JD, Rutgers University School of Law, BA, State University of New York at New Paltz

### HASTINGS, Douglas A
Epstein Becker & Green PC, Washington, DC
202 861 1807
dhastings@ebglaw.com
*Featured in Healthcare (Nationwide), Healthcare (District of Columbia)*
See under Nationwide for profile.

### HASTY, Robert
White & Case LLP, Washington, DC
202 626 3600
rhasty@whitecase.com
*Featured in Technology (District of Columbia)*
**Career:** Robert Hasty is in the Sourcing and Technology Transactions Group at White & Case. He advises clients on legal and business issues in sourcing, other complex technology-centric arrangements, and the IT/IP aspects of M&A transactions. He has negotiated transactions across North America, Europe, the Middle East, South Africa and Asia-Pac. With twenty years experience, he has advised clients in an array of industries on virtually all aspects of IT and business process outsourcing. His practice also focuses on strategic alliances and joint ventures, IP development and telecommunications services and systems integration agreements. To view his biography, visit www.whitecase.com/rhasty.

### HATCHER, Julia
Latham & Watkins LLP, Washington, DC
202 637 2238
julia.hatcher@lw.com
*Featured in Environment (District of Columbia)*
**Practice Areas:** Represents clients on full range of matters, from compliance advice to rulemaking to enforcement to litigation. Possesses deep expertise in federal and state laws that control chemicals at every life cycle stage as well as the intersection of these laws with toxic tort liability. Has worked extensively in Clean Air Act and climate change arenas. Possesses specialized technical and business knowledge of the chemicals, semiconductor and automotive industries.
**Professional Memberships:** Member, District of Columbia bar.
**Career:** Vice-chairs Latham's new Chemical Regulatory, Product Strategy & Defense Practice Group.
**Personal:** JD, Georgetown University Law Center; BA, Mount Holyoke College.

### HEINTZ, John
Dickstein Shapiro LLP, Washington, DC
202 420 5373
heintzj@dicksteinshapiro.com
*Featured in Insurance (Nationwide), Insurance (District of Columbia)*
See under Nationwide for profile.

### HELLER, Mark A
Goodwin Procter LLP, Washington, DC
202 346 4107
mheller@goodwinprocter.com
*Featured in Healthcare (District of Columbia)*
**Practice Areas:** Mr Heller serves as chair of the firm's FDA Group and is a member of the Life Sciences Practice. He focuses on the Food and Drug Administration's and Federal Trade Commission's laws and regulations, and in the FDA context, assists clients with strategy development, the premarket submission process, compliance issues, enforcement matters, development of legislation, and administrative and judicial appeals. Mr Heller has lectured widely on medical device law and participated in teaching courses on device regulation.
**Personal:** JD, University of Wisconsin-Madison Law School, 1973; BA, University of Wisconsin-Madison, 1970 (with honors).

### HELTZER, Harold J
Crowell & Moring LLP, Washington, DC
202 624 2565
hheltzer@crowell.com
*Featured in Tax (District of Columbia), Tax (Nationwide)*
**Practice Areas:** Partner and chair of Crowell & Moring's Tax Group. Represents corporate, partnership, and individual clients in tax matters. Specializes in tax planning for acquisitions/partnership formation/divestitures, and other transactions. Represents clients in tax litigation and administrative practice before the IRS and state tax agencies.
**Career:** Served in the Office of Tax Legislative Counsel for the US DOT; trial attorney in Tax Division of the US DOJ.
**Personal:** JD from New York University; Master of Laws Degree from Georgetown University. Adjunct Professor in the LLM Tax Program at the Georgetown University Law Center. Author of 'Coping with IRS Audits'.

### HENDLER, Clifford B
Crowell & Moring LLP, Washington, DC
202 624 2928
chendler@crowell.com
*Featured in Insurance (District of Columbia), Insurance (Nationwide)*
**Practice Areas:** Co-Chair of Crowell & Moring LLP's Insurance/Reinsurance Group. Serves as national counsel for ACE USA Insurance Companies (formerly CIGNA Property & Casualty Companies). Has orchestrated the successful negotiation of global resolutions of disputes involving dozens of insurance companies and underlying case policyholder liabilities.
**Career:** Appointed by the US District Court for the District of Columbia to mediate to resolution

a 20-year dispute regarding taped conversations recorded by former President Richard Nixon. **Personal:** Undergraduate degree from Yale University with honors, 1975; JD from Stanford Law School, 1978, Order of the Coif Member.

### HERMAN, Andrew M

Kirkland & Ellis LLP, Washington, DC
202 879 5224
andrew.herman@kirkland.com
*Featured in Corporate/M&A (District of Columbia)*
**Practice Areas:** Predominately advises private equity funds and their portfolio companies, and public companies with mergers, acquisitions, leveraged buy-outs and growth equity investments. Provides general corporate, securities and corporate governance advice to companies; represented clients in acquisitions of professional sports franchises. Clients include MidOcean Partners, Arlington Capital, Quad-C Management, Revolution Growth, Fortress, Tutor Perini, Monumental Sports and Entertainment (holding company of the Washington Wizards and Washington Capitals), Carolina Hurricanes, Bushnell, totes Isotoner, South Beach Diet, FTI Consulting, and Corporate Executive Board. **Personal:** Columbia Law School, JD, 1995. University of North Carolina, MS with Honors, Accounting, 1992; BA, Business Administration, 1991.

### HEVENER, Mary

Morgan, Lewis & Bockius LLP, Washington, DC
202 739 5982
mhevener@morganlewis.com
*Featured in Employee Benefits & Executive Compensation (District of Columbia)*
**Practice Areas:** Mary B. "Handy" Hevener is a partner in Morgan Lewis's Employee Benefits and Executive Compensation Practice. Her practice focuses on income and payroll taxability and deduction of benefits provided to employees and independent contractors, including stock options and other stock-based compensation; executive income deferrals; golden parachutes; and a wide range of fringe benefits, from health and life insurance and educational assistance to cars, planes, cafeterias and prizes. **Personal:** Graduated from University of Virginia School of Law (1978, JD, with honors) and Wellesley College (1974, BA, cum laude). Admitted to practice in the District of Columbia and Virginia.

### HIBEY, Richard

Miller & Chevalier Chartered, Washington, DC
202 626 5888
rhibey@milchev.com
*Featured in Litigation (District of Columbia)*
**Practice Areas:** White-collar criminal and antitrust matters; corporate and federal securities law; and complex commercial transactions. **Career:** Represented high-profile clients in cases involving espionage, human rights violations, and RICO; published articles on the Foreign Corrupt Practices Act, jury selection, grand jury defense practice, health care fraud, and civil liberties in the

aftermath of 9/11; and for 13 years Adjunct Professor of Criminal Law at American University, WDC. **Personal:** LLM (Trial Advocacy), Georgetown University Law Center, 1966; JD, Georgetown University Law Center, 1965; AB, LeMoyne College, cum laude, 1962. Doctor of Laws (Honorary) Barry University, 2002.

### HICKS, Hal

Skadden, Arps, Slate, Meagher & Flom LLP & Affiliates, Washington, DC
202 371 7290
Hal.Hicks@skadden.com
*Featured in Tax (District of Columbia)*
**Practice Areas:** Global head of Skadden's International Tax practice. Advises on a broad range of international tax issues for multinational corporations, partnerships and other entities involving tax planning and controversy. Has broad-based experience, particularly in international M&A, foreign tax credit, transfer pricing and subpart F. Represents clients in acquisitions, dispositions, internal restructurings and post-acquisition integration efforts, and in audits and appeals before the IRS. **Career:** International Tax Counsel, U.S. Department of the Treasury (2005-07); Associate Chief Counsel (International), IRS (2003-05). LLM, New York University School of Law; JD, University of Virginia School of Law; BA, College of William and Mary.

### HIGGINS, Claudia R

Kaye Scholer LLP, Washington, DC
202 682 3653
claudia.higgins@kayescholer.com
*Featured in Antitrust (District of Columbia)*
**Practice Areas:** Claudia Higgins focuses her practice on antitrust counseling and litigation involving mergers and acquisitions. She represents Fortune 500 companies in antitrust matters before the Department of Justice, the Federal Trade Commission (FTC) and in federal court litigation. Formerly Assistant Director for Regional Litigation for the FTC, Claudia achieved numerous litigation successes and was recognized by the FTC for her contributions over two decades with notable citations, including the FTC's Distinguished Service and Paul Rand Dixon Awards. Her expertise spans many industries, including transportation, defense, high technology, pharmaceuticals, medical devices, mining, chemicals, energy and many types of consumer products.

### HILL, David W

Finnegan, Henderson, Farabow, Garrett & Dunner LLP, Washington, DC
202 408 4013
david.hill@finnegan.com
*Featured in Intellectual Property (District of Columbia)*
**Practice Areas:** Practice includes patent and trademark litigation, prosecution, licensing negotiations, dispute resolution, and portfolio management. He has particular technical experience in the mechanical and electrical arts. His litigation background includes numerous patent infringe-

ment trials and appeals, and trademark and unfair competition matters in state and federal courts. He has also served as an arbitrator or mediator in numerous cases. **Personal:** U.S. Military Academy (BS, 1969); Boston University (MS, Business Administration, with honors, 1974); George Washington University National Law Center (JD, 1977; LLM, with highest honors, 1981).

### HIRD, David B

Weil, Gotshal & Manges LLP, Washington, DC
202 682 7175
david.hird@weil.com
*Featured in Environment (District of Columbia)*
**Practice Areas:** Mr Hird is a partner in Weil's Environmental Group. A former senior trial attorney in the Department of Justice's Environmental Enforcement Section, his practice focuses on environmental litigation, transactions and counseling. He has litigated cases under CERCLA, RCRA, the Clean Water Act, and the Clean Air Act, and has defended clients in environmental criminal prosecutions. He also works on bankruptcy cases involving environmental liabilities. His practice also involves insurance coverage disputes under various forms of coverage, including products liability, directors and officers liability, political risk, property and fiduciary liability. **Personal:** Cornell (AB); Michigan (AM); NYU (JD).

### HOCKENBURY, John C

Drinker Biddle & Reath LLP, Washington, DC
202 842 8857
john.hockenbury@dbr.com
*Featured in Insurance (District of Columbia)*
**Practice Areas:** Focuses on directors' and officers' liability insurance and other professional liability insurance areas. More than 20 years of experience in claims monitoring, mediation and arbitration of coverage disputes and product development in the professional liability area. **Professional Memberships:** American Bar Association; District of Columbia Bar Association; Maryland Bar Association; Professional Liability Underwriting Society. **Personal:** The George Washington University Law School, JD, cum laude 1986; Moravian College, BA, 1973.

### HOFFINGER, Adam S

Morrison & Foerster LLP, Washington, DC
202 887 6924
ahoffinger@mofo.com
*Featured in Litigation (District of Columbia)*
**Practice Areas:** Complex civil and white-collar criminal litigation and trial practice, including securities, healthcare, FCPA, money laundering, antitrust, and export controls. Counsels corporations and individuals in internal investigations, Congressional inquiries, and compliance matters. **Career:** Admitted in D.C. and NY. Fellow, American College of Trial Lawyers. Assistant United States Attorney for the Southern District of New York (1985-1990). U.S. Department of Justice Director's Award for Superior

Performance. Adjunct Professor, George Washington University Law School, 2008-present. **Personal:** BA, Trinity College, 1978; JD, Fordham University School of Law, 1982.

### HOFFMAN, D Bruce

Hunton & Williams LLP, Washington, DC
202 955 1500
bhoffman@hunton.com
*Featured in Antitrust (District of Columbia)*
**Practice Areas:** D. Bruce Hoffman, former Deputy Director of the Federal Trade Commission's Bureau of Competition, is the head of Hunton & Williams' competition practice. Hoffman practices extensively in merger clearance, including representing Universal Music in its acquisition of EMI, and Delta in its acquisition of Northwest. He also handles antitrust litigation across the US, and represents clients in antitrust and consumer protection government investigations before the FTC, DOJ, E.U., and State Attorneys General. During Hoffman's tenure at the FTC (2001-2004), he oversaw the Bureau's antitrust enforcement activities, including merger reviews, litigation, and policy development.

### HOFFMAN, Gary M

Dickstein Shapiro LLP, Washington, DC
202 420 2228
hoffmang@dicksteinshapiro.com
*Featured in Intellectual Property (District of Columbia)*
**Practice Areas:** Focuses on intellectual property law, unfair competition, and computer law, including litigation, licensing, and creation of asset management programs. Has participated in more than 140 intellectual property lawsuits and prepared more than 175 licensing agreements. **Professional Memberships:** American Intellectual Property Law Association, Intellectual Property Owners Association. **Personal:** University of Pennsylvania (BSEE); The George Washington University Law School (JD).

### HOGANS, Daniel L

Morgan, Lewis & Bockius LLP, Washington, DC
202 739 5510
dhogans@morganlewis.com
*Featured in Employee Benefits & Executive Compensation (District of Columbia)*
**Practice Areas:** Daniel L. Hogans is a partner in Morgan Lewis's Employee Benefits and Executive Compensation Practice. He focuses his practice on handling a variety of benefits and compensation matters, including equity and incentive compensation plans, employment arrangements, nonqualified deferred compensation plans, ERISA, qualified retirement plans, pension and profit-sharing plans, ESOPs and related S corporation issues. **Personal:** He is a graduate of College of William & Mary, Marshall-Wythe School of Law (1993, JD); University of Virginia (1990, MS); and George Mason University (1989, BS). Mr Hogans is admitted to practice in the District of Columbia.

## HOLEWINSKI, Kevin
Jones Day, Washington, DC
202 879 3797
kpholewinski@jonesday.com
*Featured in Environment (District of Columbia)*
**Practice Areas:** Oversees the firm's Environmental, Health and Safety Practice. Substantial complex civil, environmental, toxic tort, class action, and criminal litigation experience. Represents clients in civil enforcement actions, criminal investigations, insurance coverage litigation, toxic tort litigation, and cost recovery litigation. Has developed extensive litigation experience in air and groundwater contamination matters, human and ecological risk assessment issues, climate change, and the pursuit of claims against the federal government. Has extensive catastrophic event experience.
**Career:** At the DOJ, he was lead trial counsel in several of the most significant enforcement matters and received a number of awards for his trial work.

## HOLMSTEAD, Jeffrey R
Bracewell & Giuliani LLP, Washington, DC
202 828 5852
jeff.holmstead@bgllp.com
*Featured in Climate Change (Nationwide), Environment (District of Columbia)*
See under Nationwide for profile.

## HOPSON, Mark D
Sidley Austin LLP, Washington, DC
202 736 8188
mhopson@sidley.com
*Featured in Litigation (District of Columbia)*
**Practice Areas:** Managing partner of Sidley's Washington, DC office, and a global coordinator of the firm's White Collar: Government Enforcement and Litigation practice. Mark has represented clients in many headline-making cases as well as those deliberately kept out of the spotlight. In addition to criminal and civil trial litigation matters, he regularly represents clients in connection with congressional investigations, internal investigations and other enforcement matters.
**Professional Memberships:** Fellow of the American College of Trial Lawyers and a Fellow of the American Bar Foundation. He served as a trial practice instructor and an adjunct professor at the Georgetown University Law Center.

## HOROWITZ, Philip
Venable LLP, Washington, DC
202 344 4746
phorowitz@Venable.com
*Featured in Real Estate (District of Columbia)*
**Practice Areas:** Phil Horowitz focuses on complex private sector and public/private real estate transactions, including purchase and sale, office, retail and government leasing, financings and related entity and development matters, representing owners, developers and institutional users of real estate.
**Professional Memberships:** Past President of the American College of Real Estate Lawyers, the country's most prestigious honorary organization for practicing real estate lawyers. A member of the Anglo-American Real Property Institute. Adjunct faculty member teaching Real Estate Planning at Washington College of Law, The American University.
**Personal:** JD, Georgetown University Law Center, 1973; AB, magna cum laude, Upsala College, 1970.

## HOULE, Jeffrey R
DLA Piper LLP (US), Washington, DC
202 799 4208
jeffrey.houle@dlapiper.com
*Featured in Corporate/M&A (District of Columbia)*
**Practice Areas:** Corporate, M&A.
**Career:** He is chair of the firm's Defense and Government Services Transactional practice. His experience is global in scope. He has represented clients on six continents and in more than 30 countries. He focuses on companies in the government services industry, representing middle market and Fortune 500 companies in M&A matters. He has represented Fortune 500 companies and members of the Forbes 400 and has closed more than $5 billion in transactions.
**Personal:** OPM, Harvard Business School; LLM, Georgetown University Law Center; JD, Western New England College; AB, Boston College.

## HOWE, Joseph
Arnold & Porter LLP, Washington, DC
202 942 5230
Joseph.Howe@aporter.com
*Featured in Tax (District of Columbia), Capital Markets (Nationwide)*
See under Nationwide for profile.

## HUMES, Gary
Arnold & Porter LLP, Washington, DC
202 942 5001
Gary.Humes@aporter.com
*Featured in Real Estate (District of Columbia)*
**Practice Areas:** Gary Humes is primarily involved in build-to-suit transactions and large-scale office leases, securitized lease financings, public private partnerships and other complex transactions involving the Federal Government, and real estate development and financing. Clients include FORTUNE 500 companies, non-profit organizations, large law firms, and real estate developers. He structures and negotiates tax-exempt and taxable financings, ground and space leases, purchase agreements, design and construction contracts, and brokerage and development management agreements.
**Personal:** JD from Cornell Law School (1981), SM from University of Chicago (1974), PhD candidate in Theoretical Physics from University of Chicago (1974-76), BA from Wesleyan University (1972).

## HUTCHINGS, Jeffrey D
Pillsbury Winthrop Shaw Pittman LLP, Washington, DC
202 663 8163
jeffrey.hutchings@pillsburylaw.com
*Featured in Technology (District of Columbia)*
**Practice Areas:** Partner, Global Sourcing Practice. Represents clients in complex sourcing transactions with emphasis on information technology and business process outsourcing contracts. Assists major corporations and government agencies - domestically and abroad - structure and negotiate long-term, multimillion-dollar contracts for data processing, telecommunications, systems development and integration, desktop/local access network (LAN) support, claims processing, trade processing, contact center, human resources and other services.
**Professional Memberships:** ABA; Bar Association of the District of Columbia; Virginia Bar Association.
**Career:** Admitted: District of Columbia, Commonwealth of Virginia, and State of Washington.
**Personal:** JD, Duke University School of Law, 1983; AB, Duke University, 1979.

## HUTCHINSON, James A
Goodwin Procter LLP, Washington, DC
202 346 4293
JHutchinson@goodwinprocter.com
*Featured in Corporate/M&A (District of Columbia)*
**Practice Areas:** Mr Hutchinson, a partner in the firm's Business Law Department and a member of the Private Equity Group, practices in the areas of corporate, securities and private equity transactional law, primarily on behalf of private investment funds and their portfolio companies. His practice involves a full range of corporate and commercial transactions, including leveraged buyouts, mergers and acquisitions, venture capital transactions, joint ventures and general corporate matters for public and private companies and private equity investment groups.
**Personal:** JD, Georgetown University, 1993 (cum laude); BA, University of Pennsylvania, 1988.

## HUTT, Peter Barton
Covington & Burling LLP, Washington, DC
202 662 5522
phutt@cov.com
*Featured in Food & Beverages (Nationwide), Healthcare (District of Columbia)*
**Practice Areas:** Food and drug regulation; biotechnology.
**Professional Memberships:** Institute of Medicine of National Academy of Sciences; FDA Science Board Working Group on agency science needs.
**Career:** Chief Counsel FDA (1971-75). Teaches Food and Drug Law at Harvard Law School (1994-present). Noted by Washingtonian magazine as one of Washington's 50 best lawyers and 100 most influential people; by European Counsel as best FDA regulatory specialist; Business Week and Legal Times as unofficial dean of Food and Drug lawyers.
**Publications:** Co-author 'Food and Drug Law: Cases and Materials' 3rd edition 2007.
**Personal:** Harvard (LLB); NYU (LL.M, in Food/Drug Law); Yale (BA).

## HYATT, Thomas
Dentons, Washington, DC
202 408 3947
tom.hyatt@dentons.com
*Featured in Healthcare (District of Columbia)*
**Practice Areas:** Chair of legacy Dentons's Health Care practice. Focuses on corporate, tax exemption, and governance issues for nonprofit health care providers. Represents hospitals, integrated delivery systems, academic medical centers, health maintenance organizations, provider associations, physician clinics, and health related organizations. Also represents college and university organizations and institutions on governance and public policy matters.
**Professional Memberships:** American Health Lawyers Association: Board of Directors, 1992-1998; Chair Emeritus, Faculty Member, Tax Issues in Healthcare Organizations Seminar; Charter Fellow.
**Publications:** Co-author, The Law of Tax-Exempt Healthcare Organizations (3rd Ed.).
**Personal:** University of Pittsburgh, 1982, JD; Boston College, 1979, BA

## IFRAH, A Jeff
Ifrah PLLC, Washington, DC
202 524 4140
jeff@ifrahlaw.com
*Featured in Litigation (District of Columbia)*
**Practice Areas:** Defense of federal investigations for clients in the internet advertising, igaming, government contracting, healthcare and financial services industries.
**Professional Memberships:** Bar Admissions: DC, MD, NY, NJ. ABA Criminal Justice Section; American Health Lawyers Association; ABA Business Law Section; ABA Procurement Law Section; International Masters of Gaming Law
**Career:** Prior to founding Ifrah Law, Jeff was of counsel at Paul Hastings and then shareholder at Greenberg Traurig. Prior to entering private practice, Jeff served as a Special Assistant US Attorney in the District of New Jersey and he served his country as a JAG Officer in the Judge Advocate General's Corps of the US Army.
**Publications:** Jeff is co-author of Federal Sentencing for Business Crimes, the only comprehensive treatise on federal sentencing in the context of business and white-collar crimes. He and the attorneys of Ifrah Law author the blogs CrimeInTheSuites.com and FTCBeat.com.
**Personal:** JD, Benjamin N. Cardozo School of Law, Yeshiva University, 1992; MA, Yeshiva University, 1992; BA, Yeshiva University, 1989.

## IMUS, Neil W
Vinson & Elkins LLP, Washington, DC
202 639 6675
nimus@velaw.com
*Featured in Antitrust (District of Columbia)*
**Practice Areas:** US antitrust including litigation and practice before the DOJ, FTC and State Attorneys General in HSR, merger and acquisitions and other agency antitrust investigations and in antitrust litigation.
**Professional Memberships:** ABA Antitrust Section - Long Range Planning Committee.
**Career:** Partner.
**Publications:** Co-editor: Premerger Notification Practice Manual, Fourth Ed.
**Personal:** Georgetown University Law Center (JD, magna cum laude, 1985); George Washington University (MBA, Beta Gamma Sigma, 1981); Davidson College (BS, cum laude, 1975).

## INGLIMA, Philip
Crowell & Moring LLP, Washington, DC
202 624 2795
pinglima@crowell.com
*Featured in Litigation (District of Columbia)*
**Practice Areas:** Partner in Crowell & Moring's White Collar and Regulatory Enforcement Group. Devoted his career to both government and private practice in a broad range of public corruption and business fraud investigations and prosecutions. Represents clients in several of the most prominent pending federal white-collar criminal proceedings. Has represented business clients in both internal investigations and grand jury probes.
**Career:** While serving as Senior Associate Independent Counsel in the investigation of then-secretary of the Interior Bruce Babbitt, Inglima led a team examining allegations of perjury/bribery/improper influence peddling and campaign finance fraud.
**Personal:** JD from Georgetown University Law Center.

## ISRAEL, Brian D
Arnold & Porter LLP, Washington, DC
202 942 6546
Brian.Israel@aporter.com
*Featured in Environment (District of Columbia)*
**Practice Areas:** Brian Israel, a partner in Arnold & Porter LLP's Washington, DC office, concentrates his practice in environmental litigation and counseling. Mr Israel represents corporations in matters involving contaminated properties, including toxic tort lawsuits and Natural Resource Damages (NRD) claims. Prior to joining Arnold & Porter, Mr Israel was an Honors Trial Attorney in the Environmental Enforcement Section at the U.S. Department of Justice. Mr Israel is currently lead counsel on several of the largest NRD cases in the country. His counseling practice focuses on regulatory compliance and environmental issues in corporate transactions.

## JACK, W Andrew
Covington & Burling LLP, Washington, DC
202 662 5232
ajack@cov.com
*Featured in Corporate/M&A (District of Columbia)*
**Practice Areas:** Corporate and Securities. Chair - Clean Energy Industry Group.
**Career:** Broad corporate transactional and governance advisory experience. Representative clients: Joy Global, Smith Electric Vehicles, Energy Conversion Devices, JLG Industries, DC Sports Commission, NFL, multiple board committees. Transactions: Joy Global acquisition of LeTourneau Technologies (2011), NYFIX merger into NYSE (2009), Joy Global acquisition of Continental Global (2008), Securities offerings for Smith Electric (2011), Joy Global (2011), ECD (2008) and JLG (2002/03/05), JLG merger into Oshkosh (2006), Washington Nationals relocation to Washington (2002-06), Cleveland Browns relocation and expansion (1996-99).
**Personal:** George Washington University, (JD, 1986, with highest honors; BA, 1983).

## JACKSON, Thomas C
Baker Botts LLP, Washington, DC
202 639 7710
thomas.jackson@bakerbotts.com
*Featured in Environment (District of Columbia)*
**Practice Areas:** Tom Jackson handles all aspects of environmental law, including client counseling, permitting, trial court and appellate litigation, administrative hearings and arbitrations, and legislative matters. He also helps clients assess proposed rules and other public documents such as Environmental Impact Statements.
**Professional Memberships:** District of Columbia Bar, US Court of Federal Claims, US Courts of Appeals (for the Third, Fifth, Ninth, Eleventh, Federal, and District of Columbia Circuits), US District Court for the District of Columbia, US Supreme Court.
**Personal:** JD (with honors), Harvard Law School (1984), BA (summa cum laude), Political Science, Amherst College (1981).

## JACOB, John
Akin Gump Strauss Hauer & Feld LLP, Washington, DC
202 887 4582
jjacob@akingump.com
*Featured in Healthcare (District of Columbia)*
**Practice Areas:** Represents healthcare systems, major academic medical centers and community hospitals and has extensive experience in counseling and litigation regarding Medicare and Medicaid regulatory matters. Advises hospitals and other health industry entities on regulatory and policy issues including reimbursement and compliance counseling; legislative and regulatory policy analysis, drafting and advocacy; potential fraud and abuse and overpayment matters; voluntary disclosures; federal investigations; due diligence associated with business arrangements, public debt offerings, private placements.
**Professional Memberships:** American Health Lawyers Association.
**Personal:** AB, Colgate University, 1988; JD, cum laude, American University Washington College of Law, 1993; Executive Editor, American University Law Review.

## JACOBS, Bruce D
Pillsbury Winthrop Shaw Pittman LLP, Washington, DC
202 663 8077
bruce.jacobs@pillsburylaw.com
*Featured in Telecommunications (District of Columbia)*
**Practice Areas:** Mr Jacobs specializes in representing innovative companies regulated by the FCC. These include or have included LightSquared, which launched the first North American Mobile Satellite Service system and received the first FCC license for an Ancillary Terrestrial Component, permitting it to reuse its satellite spectrum to operate a nationwide terrestrial system; XM, which launched the first domestic satellite radio system; and the Voice on the Net Coalition, a trade association of leading technology companies that helped keep VOIP technology largely unregulated.
**Career:** Admitted: DC and Maryland.

**Personal:** JD, Harvard Law School, 1980; BA, New College, 1976.

## JACOBS, Matthew L
Jenner & Block LLP, Washington, DC
202 639 6096
mjacobs@jenner.com
*Featured in Insurance (District of Columbia)*
**Career:** Matthew L. Jacobs is a member of the Insurance Litigation and Counseling and Reinsurance Practices. Mr Jacobs handles complex, multi-party insurance coverage litigation matters in state and federal courts, as well as in mediations and arbitrations. He advises corporations on the availability of coverage for claims such as directors' and officers' liability, errors and omissions, Chinese drywall, business interruption, property loss arising from climate catastrophes, product liability, regulatory investigations and environmental matters. Mr Jacobs is a widely sought after lecturer, media resource and author on insurance coverage topics and serves on the Editorial Board of The Environmental Claims Journal.

## JACOBSEN JR, Raymond A
McDermott Will & Emery LLP, Washington, DC
202 756 8028
rayjacobsen@mwe.com
*Featured in Antitrust (District of Columbia)*
**Practice Areas:** Head of regulation and government affairs department. Focuses on mergers, acquisitions and other antitrust work, with significant experience in defense, high-tech, consumer product, energy and health care industries. Successfully defended over 200 complex mergers, acquisitions and joint ventures in US, Europe and Far East. One of the first to obtain amnesty for client under Justice Department's expanded amnesty program.
**Professional Memberships:** Former chairman of two American Bar Association Committees.
**Personal:** Georgetown University Law Center (JD); University of Delaware (BA, cum laude).

## JAEGER, Lisa M
Bracewell & Giuliani LLP, Washington, DC
202 828 5844
lisa.jaeger@bgllp.com
*Featured in Environment (District of Columbia)*
**Practice Areas:** Focuses her practice on environmental and natural resources law and policy. Advises industrial sector clients on clean air, climate change and energy efficiency issues, representing them before regulatory agencies, in judicial rulemaking challenges and before Congress. Works with clients in a variety of industrial sectors to resolve regulatory and legislative problems relating to water, waste disposal and other environmental areas.
**Career:** Served at the US Environmental Protection Agency as acting general counsel and deputy general counsel.
**Personal:** JD, Widener University Law School, 1990; BA, Catholic University of America, 1984.

## JAIN, Samir
WilmerHale, Washington, DC
202 663 6083
samir.jain@wilmerhale.com
*Featured in Telecommunications (District of Columbia)*
**Practice Areas:** Accomplished litigator and regulatory lawyer who regularly appears before appellate and trial courts and administrative agencies for telecommunications carriers, Internet and e-commerce companies, and other technology-related clients. Extensive experience litigating cases of first impression and advising in areas such as online content liability, privacy and data security, electronic surveillance, national security and public safety, targeted advertising, online child safety, regulation of broadband access, wireless, satellite, broadcast, and information services, and regulatory issues arising from investments in communications industry.
**Personal:** JD, Harvard Law School (magna cum laude); BS, Stanford University.

## JAKES, J Michael
Finnegan, Henderson, Farabow, Garrett & Dunner LLP, Washington, DC
202 408 4045
mike.jakes@finnegan.com
*Featured in Intellectual Property (District of Columbia)*
**Practice Areas:** Focuses on patent litigation and related counseling in the areas of computers, electronics, semiconductors, software, and medical devices. He has been lead counsel on numerous patent cases, including trials in federal district courts, the U.S. International Trade Commission, and before arbitration panels. He has argued over 25 appeals at the U.S. Court of Appeals for the Federal Circuit. Also argued for the petitioners in landmark U.S. Supreme Court case, Bilski v. Kappos.
**Personal:** Duke University (BS, Electrical Engineering, summa cum laude, 1979); Johns Hopkins University (MS, Computer Science, 1983); Georgetown University Law Center (JD, magna cum laude, 1986).

## JANKA, John P
Latham & Watkins LLP, Washington, DC
202 637 2289
john.janka@lw.com
*Featured in Telecommunications (District of Columbia)*
**Practice Areas:** Focuses on telecommunications, media and technology sectors. Counsels on regulatory, transactional and controversy matters, including acquiring and protecting spectrum rights; developing, purchasing and financing new businesses; procuring and deploying communications facilities; developing strategic alliances; selling and leasing communications capacity; strategic planning; and effectuating changes in legal frameworks.
**Professional Memberships:** DC and California bars.
**Career:** Global Chair, Communications Practice.
**Publications:** Editor, Technology, Media and Telecommunications Review. "Changing Federal

Policies in Response to the Broadband Revolution," New Jersey Lawyer (Oct. 2012).
**Personal:** JD, UCLA School of Law, 1987; BA, Duke University, 1984; Judicial Clerk, Hon. Cynthia Hall, 9th Circuit.

## JENNINGS, Deborah E
DLA Piper LLP (US), Washington, DC
202 799 5357
deborah.jennings@dlapiper.com
*Featured in Environment (District of Columbia)*
**Practice Areas:** Environmental, litigation, energy sector.
**Career:** She chairs the firm's Environmental Group and practices in environmental and energy law. She has extensive experience with litigation and negotiations relating to air, water, and hazardous waste permit issues, as well as transportation, cleanup and disposal of hazardous substances. In recent years, a primary focus of her practice has been on Clean Air Act issues. She represents electric power generating companies in state energy administrative proceedings, particularly in obtaining Certificates of Public Convenience and Necessity, and in energy related litigation.
**Personal:** JD, Georgetown University Law Center; BA, University of Maryland (with honors).

## JEW, Quana
Arent Fox LLP, Washington, DC
202 857 8947
quana.jew@arentfox.com
*Featured in Employee Benefits & Executive Compensation (District of Columbia)*
**Practice Areas:** Quana Jew is the tax/ERISA/wealth planning practice leader. Quana is skilled in tax, regulatory and design issues applicable to profit-sharing/401(k) plans, 403(b) plans, and 457 plans. She designs and advises clients on executive incentive and deferred compensation arrangements (409A arrangements). Quana's practice also includes counseling clients on health/welfare plans, including COBRA, HIPAA and the Affordable Care Act. A significant part of Quana's practice involves benefit plan related issues in the context of business acquisitions and reorganizations and voluntary compliance programs and audits. University of Wisconsin, JD, 1990; University of Wisconsin, MA, 1987; University of Wisconsin, BA, 1984.

## JEZOUIT, Debra
Baker Botts LLP, Washington, DC
202 639 7728
debra.jezouit@bakerbotts.com
*Featured in Environment (District of Columbia)*
**Practice Areas:** All aspects of the Clean Air Act, including compliance, litigation, rule development.
**Professional Memberships:** District of Columbia Bar; Virginia State Bar; American Bar Association, Environment, Energy and Resources Section; Women's Bar Association.
**Career:** She is widely recognized for her experience in Clean Air Act issues, representing such clients as electric generating companies, cement manufacturers, pharmaceutical companies, and

chemical companies. She handles a wide variety of matters, including New Source Review, New Source Performance Standards, MACT compliance, EPA investigations, audits and air permitting.
**Personal:** JD, University of Virginia School of Law, 1990; BA, international affairs, George Washington University, 1986.

## JOHNSON, Jennifer A
Covington & Burling LLP, Washington, DC
202 662 5552
jjohnson@cov.com
*Featured in Telecommunications (District of Columbia)*
**Practice Areas:** Counsels clients in developing and pursuing strategic business and policy objectives before the FCC and Congress, and through transactions and other business arrangements. Broadcast clients, including major trade associations and station group owners, benefit from her particular expertise with respect to network/affiliate issues, spectrum issues, retransmission consent arrangements, and other policy and business issues facing the industry. Ms. Johnson also assists investment clients in structuring, evaluating and pursuing potential media investments.
**Career:** Partner and Co-Chair of Covington's Communications and Media Practice; former Co-Chair of Covington's Technology and Media Group
**Personal:** Harvard Law School, JD, 1994 (cum laude)

## JONES, Thomas
Willkie Farr & Gallagher LLP, Washington, DC
202 303 1111
tjones@willkie.com
*Featured in Telecommunications (District of Columbia)*
**Practice Areas:** Partner, Telecommunications Department. Specializes in wireline and wireless common carrier regulation. Represented leading competitive providers of telecommunications service in virtually every major FCC competition proceeding. Successfully opposed Qwest Phoenix forbearance petition, establishing important FCC precedent, and promoted major reforms to FCC pole attachment rules. Testified on common carrier regulation of broadband before Subcommittee on Telecommunications and Internet of the House Energy and Commerce Committee. Experienced in FCC complaint and investigation proceedings and in regulatory issues associated with corporate transactions, business plan development and new product offerings.
**Personal:** JD, Georgetown University Law Center, 1992. BA, Georgetown University, 1988. See:http://www.willkie.com/ThomasJones

## JOSEPH, Bruce G
Wiley Rein LLP, Washington, DC
202 719 7258
bjoseph@wileyrein.com
*Featured in Intellectual Property (District of Columbia)*
**Practice Areas:** Chairs Copyright Practice, handling copyright infringement and license fee litigation, copyright and digital content protection

legislation, regulation, inter-industry standards activities, and licensing. Named by Legal Times as one of the DC region's "Leading Intellectual Property Lawyers" and by Washingtonian magazine as one of "Washington's Top Lawyers." Extensive experience in issues relating to the Internet, music and sound recording license fee proceedings, and digital content protection measures (DRMs).
**Career:** Advisory Board, Bloomberg BNA Patent, Trademark & Copyright Journal.
**Personal:** Harvard Law School (JD, magna cum laude); Editor, Harvard Law Review; University of Pennsylvania (BA, BS, summa cum laude).

## JOSEPH, James P
Arnold & Porter LLP, Washington, DC
202 942 5355
James.Joseph@aporter.com
*Featured in Tax (District of Columbia)*
**Practice Areas:** Mr Joseph advises tax-exempt clients on tax and other operational issues, as well as corporations in structuring their charitable giving programs. His clients include charities, foundations, universities, advocacy groups, and international organizations. He represents corporations, partnerships, tax-exempt organizations, and individuals in Internal Revenue Service (IRS) audits, proceedings before the IRS Appeals Office, and in litigation in the US Tax Court, the US Court of Federal Claims, and federal district and appellate courts. He also works with corporate and tax-exempt clients on governance, compensation, and other tax matters.
**Personal:** JD, 1989, Georgetown University Law Center; BA, 1984, Georgetown University.

## KADEN, Alan S
Fried, Frank, Harris, Shriver & Jacobson LLP, Washington, DC
202 639 7073
Alan.Kaden@FriedFrank.com
*Featured in Tax (District of Columbia)*
**Practice Areas:** Partner. Chair of Washington, DC tax department and co-managing partner of the Washington office. Practices in all the principal areas of tax law, with particular emphasis on the structuring and negotiation of taxable and tax-free corporate acquisitions, reorganizations and spin-off transactions, structuring of investment funds, development of partnership and other joint-venture arrangements for various business ventures and tax planning for financings and other capital formation transactions. Adjunct Professor of Law, Georgetown University.
**Career:** Joined in 1981; became partner in 1987.
**Personal:** JD, Columbia Law School (1981), member, Columbia Law Review; BS, magna cum laude, University of Pennsylvania (1978).

## KAFKA, Gerald A
Latham & Watkins LLP, Washington, DC
202 637 2198
gerald.kafka@lw.com
*Featured in Tax (District of Columbia), Tax (Nationwide)*
See under Nationwide for profile.

## KAHN, David S
Holland & Knight LLP, Washington, DC
202 457 7199
david.kahn@hklaw.com
*Featured in Real Estate (District of Columbia)*
**Practice Areas:** Head of the firm's Real Estate Transactions Practice for the Mid-Atlantic Region, practices in the areas of commercial real estate development and finance, and commercial leasing. He represents numerous real estate developers, as well as institutional owners, investors and lenders, including domestic and foreign insurance companies, pension funds and national banks in connection with their real estate development/investment activities nationwide. This representation includes the negotiation and documentation of purchase and sale agreements, development agreements, construction and permanent loan agreements, deeds of trust, ground leases, loan and equity participations, joint venture agreements, construction contracts, and office and retail leases.

## KAHN, Sarah E
DLA Piper LLP (US), Washington, DC
202 799 4210
sarah.kahn@dlapiper.com
*Featured in Corporate/M&A (District of Columbia)*
**Practice Areas:** Corporate/M&A & Private Equity
**Career:** She is co-chair of the firm's Aerospace, Defense and Government Services Transactional practice and focus on mergers and acquisitions and private equity transactions. She represents clients in connection with acquisitions of both private and public companies, with special experience in acquisitions for clients in international aerospace, defense and government services. She assists private equity clients with portfolio company acquisitions, follow-on investments and portfolio company sales.
**Personal:** JD, Georgetown University Law Center; BA University of North Carolina at Chapel Hill.

## KALB MD, Paul E
Sidley Austin LLP, Washington, DC
202 736 8050
pkalb@sidley.com
*Featured in Healthcare (District of Columbia)*
**Practice Areas:** Head of Sidley's national Healthcare practice and serves as a global coordinator of its Life Sciences practice. He brings an uncommon clinical perspective, grounded in his experience as an attending physician at the Memorial Sloan-Kettering Cancer Center, to bear in his work for a wide range of healthcare clients. He has successfully represented many of the world's leading drug, biotech and device manufacturers and hospitals in criminal, civil, and administrative enforcement actions involving healthcare fraud and abuse and off-label promotion. He has led teams that defended numerous matters and negotiated ground-breaking settlement agreements and Corporate Integrity Agreements.

### KALISH, Paul W
Crowell & Moring LLP, Washington, DC
202 624 2644
pkalish@crowell.com
*Featured in Insurance (District of Columbia),
Insurance (Nationwide)*
**Practice Areas:** Co-chair of Crowell &
Moring's Insurance/Reinsurance Group. Serves as
national counsel for property and casualty companies regarding toxic tort, environmental and
other types of coverage issues. Serves as counsel
for the Coalition for Litigation Justice, a group
formed by property and casualty insurers to
address abuses in the mass tort litigation environment.
**Professional Memberships:** Served as co-chair
for the American Bar Association Section of
Litigation's 2002 Annual Meeting, a member of
ABA's Task Force on the State of the Civil Justice
System, and a co-chair of the Section of
Litigation's Pretrial Practice and Discovery
Committee.

### KANTER, Jonathan
Cadwalader, Wickersham & Taft LLP,
Washington, DC
202 862 2436
jonathan.kanter@cwt.com
*Featured in Antitrust (District of Columbia)*
**Practice Areas:** Represents major corporations
in connection with merger, joint venture, and civil
non-merger investigations before the U.S. DOJ,
the FTC, and state antitrust authorities. Highly-
regarded for work in internet/technology industry.
Represents numerous companies in the area,
including Microsoft in the landmark US v.
Microsoft and N.Y. v. Microsoft settlements.
Recent representations of Microsoft include its
acquisition of Skype and Yahoo!'s search business,
as a third party in the FTC's ongoing investigation
of Google, the DOJ's review of Google/ITA, and
Google's proposed partnership with Yahoo!.
Representations in other industries include
Bacardi in a joint venture with Brown Forman
and its recent victory in Johnson Brothers Liquor
Company v. Bacardi U.S.A. Represents and advises
energy companies, including in non-public mat-
ters currently pending before the FTC.
**Personal:** JD, Washington University; BA, State
University of New York at Albany.

### KAPLAN, Steven
Arnold & Porter LLP, Washington, DC
202 942 5998
Steven.Kaplan@aporter.com
*Featured in Corporate/M&A (District of Columbia)*
**Practice Areas:** Counsel to corporations in
financial services, life sciences, transportation, and
other industries, with emphasis on mergers and
acquisitions, capital markets, corporate gover-
nance and SEC compliance. Former Responsible
Partner for Corporate and Securities Practice
Group.
**Career:** Lead attorney in business combination
and divestiture transactions valued in the tens of
billions of dollars. Representative clients include:
CSX, Barnes & Noble, CML Healthcare, Provident
New York Bancorp, Asahi Kasei and Cain
Brothers.

**Publications:** Articles in Legal Times, National
Law Journal, and Banking Expansion Reporter.
**Personal:** JD, magna cum laude, Georgetown
Law Center, 1978; BA, New College, 1975.

### KASS, Mark
Nixon Peabody LLP, Washington, DC
202 585 8181
mkass@nixonpeabody.com
*Featured in Corporate/M&A (District of Columbia)*
**Practice Areas:** Mark Kass focuses his practice
on corporate finance, mergers and acquisitions
and commercial transactions. His industry expertise encompasses information technology, life sciences, new media, and telecommunications. He
has extensive experience in international transactions including Europe, Israel and the Far East. Mr
Kass represents clients in a wide array of business
transactions, including technology transfers, intellectual property rights, distribution and marketing arrangements. A significant portion of his
practice involves representation of leading Israeli
and Israeli-related hi-tech and life science companies doing business in the United States.
**Personal:** Columbia University, JD, Harlan Fiske
Stone Scholar Yale University, BA, cum laude

### KATTAN, Joseph
Gibson, Dunn & Crutcher LLP, Washington,
DC
202 955 8239
jkattan@gibsondunn.com
*Featured in Antitrust (District of Columbia)*
**Practice Areas:** Competition practice focused
on M&A, enforcement agency representations, litigation, and counseling. Mr Kattan has shepherded numerous transactions through the merger
review process. Major transactions include
Applied Materials/Varian, Intel/McAfee,
Intel/STMicroelectronics, Applied
Materials/Brooks, Seagate/Maxtor, and
Sony/BMG. Client roster includes companies in a
wide range of industries, including many of the
world's leading technology companies. Broad
experience in monopolization/dominance investigations and litigations, including IP anti-trust litigations.
**Publications:** Mr Kattan has published numerous articles on competition law. He has presented
by invitation at many government hearings and
has advised competition authorities throughout
the world.

### KATZ, Mark M
Arent Fox LLP, Washington, DC
202 857 6260
mark.katz@arentfox.com
*Featured in Real Estate (District of Columbia)*
**Practice Areas:** Mark Katz, chairman of Arent
Fox, is sought after for commercial real estate,
joint venture, transactional and finance work
including distressed real estate investing and senior and mezzanine financings. He represents private equity funds and investment banks with
extensive experience in acquisition, development
and disposition of real estate assets throughout
the US and Caribbean. He also represents
investors in acquisitions of performing and non-
performing real estate asset portfolios. National

and international clients include The Goldman
Sachs Group, Inc., AllianceBernstein, Union
Investment Group, JBG Companies and the
Tampa Bay Rays. University of Virginia, JD, 1983;
Oberlin College, BA, 1979.

### KAUFMAN, Bonni F
Holland & Knight LLP, Washington, DC
202 419 2547
bonni.kaufman@hklaw.com
*Featured in Environment (District of Columbia)*
**Practice Areas:** Partner in the Public Policy and
Regulation Group of Holland & Knight, where
she focuses on environmental law. Kaufman represents real estate, industrial, transportation, and
manufacturing clients in a wide variety of matters,
including regulatory enforcement and compliance, corporate and real estate transactions and
litigation. Kaufman has successfully defended
clients in environmental enforcement actions,
particularly those involving contaminated property, natural resources, pesticide product labeling
and distribution, RCRA, Superfund, asbestos,
lead-based paint, SPCC requirements and refrig-
erants. She also advises military housing and commercial developers on environmental issues and
counsels clients on climate change and sustainability issues.

### KAZAKIS, Georgia
Covington & Burling LLP, Washington, DC
202 662 5423
gkazakis@cov.com
*Featured in Insurance (District of Columbia)*
**Practice Areas:** Represents policyholders in
negotiating and litigating complex insurance coverage disputes involving a wide array of underlying liabilities, including construction defect, environmental, asbestos, intellectual property, defamation, cyberspace, securities, bankers professional
liability, crime/fraud fidelity, employment, errors
and omissions, political risks, as well as first-party
property and business interruption losses.
Industries represented include the hospitality
industry, manufacturers, pharmaceutical companies, financial institutions, private equity companies, non-profits, and utilities. In addition to significant trial and litigation experience, has an
active non-litigation and counseling practice.
**Publications:** Managing editor of Coverage,
ABA Insurance Coverage Litigation Committee.
**Personal:** Harvard Law School, JD, University of
Virginia, BA.

### KEATING, Geoffrey T
Drinker Biddle & Reath LLP, Washington, DC
202 230 5673
Geoffrey.Keating@dbr.com
*Featured in Construction (District of Columbia)*
**Practice Areas:** Of Counsel, Construction,
Government Contracts. Practice emphasizes pub-
lic works construction, international infrastruc-
ture and government contracts, including Iraq
and Afghanistan reconstruction and power in
Tanzania. Counsel to contractors, engineers, pub-
lic/private owners and sureties. Also serves as arbi-
trator.
**Professional Memberships:** American Bar
Association, Public Contract Law Section; former

chair Construction Claims Committee; American
College of Construction Lawyers; West Group
Construction Advisory Board; International Law
Institute; Center for International ADR.
**Career:** Recently served as consultant on public
contract law and policy for new Iraqi Government
and Government of Vietnam.
**Personal:** JD, The George Washington University
Law School; BA, Ohio Wesleyan University.

### KEITELMAN, Jeffrey R
DLA Piper LLP (US), Washington, DC
202 799 4102
jeffrey.keitelman@dlapiper.com
*Featured in Real Estate (District of Columbia)*
**Practice Areas:** Real estate.
**Career:** He practices in commercial real estate
law representing local, national, and international
owners, users, lenders, managers, and brokers in
acquisition/disposition, leasing, development,
financing, property management, and related
matters involving office buildings, office and
industrial parks, shopping centers, headquarters
facilities, and mixed-use developments. He counsels in real estate related litigation and bankruptcy
matters, as well as public/private partnership and
government-related transactions. He is a member
of the firm's Policy Committee.
**Personal:** JD, Columbia University School of
Law; BA, Brown University (magna cum laude).

### KELLY, Deborah
Dickstein Shapiro LLP, Washington, DC
202 420 4772
kellyd@dicksteinshapiro.com
*Featured in Labor & Employment (District of
Columbia)*
**Practice Areas:** Deborah Kelly is head of the
firm's Employment Practice as well as Deputy
General Counsel. She focuses her practice on civil
litigation with emphasis on employment law. She
defends employers against class action suits; counsels companies in all areas of employment including advice and litigation concerning non-competes, anti-solicits, and other restrictive covenants;
conducts training on EEO compliance and
human resources issues, including social media;
drafts employee policy manuals; and represents
companies in employment claims up to and
including jury trial litigation.
**Personal:** Washington College of Law (American
University, JD); Johns Hopkins University (MA,
PhD); University of Vermont (BS).

### KELLY, Robert
Squire Sanders (US) LLP, Washington, DC
202 626 6216
robert.kelly@squiresanders.com
*Featured in Telecommunications (District of
Columbia)*
**Practice Areas:** Lead Partner Squire Sanders'
Communications Practice Group, has practiced
telecommunications and technology law since
1981. Extensive experience in wireless communications and spectrum policy. General Counsel to
the 800 MHz Transition Administrator charged
with administering spectrum reconfiguration of
over 2,000 public safety, private and commercial
systems. Negotiates transactions involving acquisi-

tions in telecommunications industry; advises regarding transactional, legislative and regulatory matters, appearing before US regulatory authorities; coauthor of the Spectrum Regulation Handbook. Counsel to principal trade association for Intelligent Transportation Systems in the US since 1992, advising ITS industry on a wide array of issues involving deployment of emerging technologies.

**KEOUGH, Christopher L**
Akin Gump Strauss Hauer & Feld LLP, Washington, DC
202 887 4038
ckeough@akingump.com
*Featured in Healthcare (Nationwide), Healthcare (District of Columbia)*
See under Nationwide for profile.

**KEYES, Kevin M**
Fried, Frank, Harris, Shriver & Jacobson LLP, Washington, DC
202 639 7022
Kevin.Keyes@FriedFrank.com
*Featured in Tax (District of Columbia)*
**Practice Areas:** Tax partner. Concentrates in all areas of federal income taxation, including the taxation of financial products, capital formation, private equity and other investment activity, cross-border financing and investment, and acquisition and disposition transactions. Adjunct Professor of Law, Georgetown University. Author, The Federal Taxation of Financial Instruments and Transactions; contributing author, Collier's on Bankruptcy Taxation. Chairmanship, Financial Transactions Committee, American Bar Association; founding chair, Financial Instruments and Products Committee, Tax Section, DC Bar Association.
**Career:** Joined as partner in 1998.
**Personal:** JD, Case Western Reserve University (1983), Order of the Coif; BS, Bowling Green State University (1979).

**KILBERG, William J**
Gibson, Dunn & Crutcher LLP, Washington, DC
202 955 8573
wkilberg@gibsondunn.com
*Featured in ERISA Litigation (Nationwide), Employee Benefits & Executive Compensation (District of Columbia), Labor & Employment (District of Columbia)*
**Practice Areas:** Employment, benefits, labor. Significant ERISA, FLSA, age, EEO, ADA, NLRA matters before US Supreme Court, US Courts of Appeals. Lead counsel for Boeing in NLRB challenge to opening of South Carolina plant; won ERISA challenge to Maryland "Fair Share" law, 4th Circuit; established NLRA contract coverage doctrine, 1st Circuit, and FLSA joint employer test, 3rd cir; numerous ERISA stock drop and fee cases.
**Career:** Solicitor, US Department of Labor; Associate Solicitor; General Counsel, Federal Mediation Service; White House Fellow, Labor Secretary George Shultz.
**Publications:** "NLRB v. Boeing: Analysis of a Failed Prosecution", NYU Labor Conference; "ERISA Litigation", PLI Securities Litigation.

**KILGORE, Scott**
WilmerHale, Washington, DC
202 663 6116
scott.kilgore@wilmerhale.com
*Featured in Employee Benefits & Executive Compensation (District of Columbia)*
**Practice Areas:** Mr Kilgore represents companies and executives on a range of matters involving executive employment, executive and equity compensation, and employee benefits, and related transactional advice. He drafts and negotiates employment, retention, severance and parachute agreements, both in and outside of transactions. He chaired Wilmer Cutler's pre-merger employment and compensation counseling practice.
**Professional Memberships:** Participates in the labor, tax (compensation and benefits), and business sections of the American Bar Association and the National Association of Stock Plan Professionals.
**Personal:** University of Virginia School of Law (JD; Virginia Law Review; Order of the Coif); Virginia Tech (BA, summa cum laude).

**KILMER, Paul**
Holland & Knight LLP, Washington, DC
202 663 7269
paul.kilmer@hklaw.com
*Featured in Intellectual Property (District of Columbia)*
**Practice Areas:** Paul Kilmer practices in the areas of trademark and copyright law, including international aspects of those fields, along with negotiating intellectual property (IP) agreements, IP litigation, IP aspects of mergers and acquisitions, Internet domain name matters and counseling regarding the right of publicity and false advertising. He has chaired committees for the International Trademark Association, the American Bar Association and the D.C. Bar and has served on U. S. Department of State Intellectual Property Rights Missions to Paraguay, Serbia and Turkey. He has spoken around the world on trademark and copyright topics before business and legal groups.

**KINGHAM, Richard F**
Covington & Burling LLP, Washington, DC
202 662 5268
rkingham@cov.com
*Featured in Life Sciences (Nationwide), Healthcare (District of Columbia)*
See under Nationwide for profile.

**KIRBY, Kathleen A**
Wiley Rein LLP, Washington, DC
202 719 3360
kkirby@wileyrein.com
*Featured in Media & Entertainment (District of Columbia)*
**Practice Areas:** Co-Chair Media Group. Represents radio/television broadcasters and digital/online platforms on transactional, content licensing, regulatory/policy matters, including matters before the FCC and Congress. Inductee in the National Freedom of Information Hall of Fame. Author of Keeping It Legal, A Media Law Handbook for the Newsroom. Expertise in news-

gathering and First Amendment issues. Counsel for the RTDNA (1994-Present).
**Professional Memberships:** Co-Chair, FCBA Video Programming/Distribution Committee; Past Chair, Mass Media Practice Committee; Member, ABA Communications Law Forum; Past National Chair, Women in Communications Law.
**Career:** Radio-broadcaster (1978-88).
**Personal:** Columbus School of Law, Catholic University of America (JD); University of Virginia (BS).

**KIRSCH, Laurence S**
Goodwin Procter LLP, Washington, DC
202 346 4440
lkirsch@goodwinprocter.com
*Featured in Environment (District of Columbia)*
**Practice Areas:** Mr Kirsch, chair of the firm's Environmental Practice, is an litigator, counselor and transactional attorney, with matters involving air, groundwater, hazardous waste, sediments, toxic substances regulation and indoor air quality. He has counseled clients on matters involving the Comprehensive Environmental Response, CERCLA or Superfund, Resource Conservation and Recovery Act, Clean Air Act, Clean Water Act, Safe Drinking Water Act, Toxic Substances Control Act, and the Occupational Safety and Health Act.
**Personal:** JD, Harvard Law School, 1982; MS, University of Pennsylvania, 1979; BAS, University of Pennsylvania (College of Engineering and Applied Science), 1979 (summa cum laude, Phi Beta Kappa).

**KISER, Chérie Renee**
Cahill Gordon & Reindel LLP, Washington, DC
202 862 8950
ckiser@cgrdc.com
*Featured in Telecommunications (District of Columbia)*
**Practice Areas:** Leads communications practice. Advises wireline, wireless, cable, broadband, Internet, broadcast and satellite communications providers, communications-related systems and equipment companies. Represents clients before the FCC, state regulatory agencies, and in federal and state litigation. Advises on legislative actions concerning the communications industry. Obtains international regulatory approval for communications companies doing business in other countries. Regulatory counsel in transactions including negotiation of network, equipment, services, interconnection, peering, marketing, and revenue sharing agreements.
**Career:** Earlier, Chérie was a Senior Regulatory Attorney for Sprint Communications Company.
**Personal:** JD, Catholic University of America Columbus School of Law; BA, University of Minnesota

**KLASMEIER, Coleen**
Sidley Austin LLP, Washington, DC
202 736 8132
cklasmeier@sidley.com
*Featured in Life Sciences (Nationwide), Healthcare (District of Columbia)*
See under Nationwide for profile.

**KLEIN, Allen**
Latham & Watkins LLP, Washington, DC
202 637 1029
allen.klein@lw.com
*Featured in Outsourcing (Nationwide), Technology (District of Columbia)*
**Practice Areas:** Domestic and international commercial and technology transactions, information technology and business process outsourcings, and mergers and acquisitions. Has worked on groundbreaking transactions, including an innovative joint venture between a coffee retailer and a mobile payments company, an outsourcing by a chemical company of logistics functions supporting a multi-billion dollar plant, an outsourcing by a Revenue Service of the processing of electronically filed returns, and an implementation of large enterprise VoIP networks by a consortium of financial institutions.
**Professional Memberships:** Member, D.C. and New York bars.
**Personal:** JD, State University of New York, Buffalo, 1978; BA, Cornell University, 1975.

**KLEIN, Frederick L**
DLA Piper LLP (US), Washington, DC
202 799 4101
frederick.klein@dlapiper.com
*Featured in Real Estate (Nationwide), Real Estate (District of Columbia)*
See under Nationwide for profile.

**KMIECIAK, Steven J.**
Seyfarth Shaw LLP, Washington, DC
202 828 5381
skmieciak@seyfarth.com
*Featured in Construction (District of Columbia)*
**Practice Areas:** Construction; Government Contracts
**Professional Memberships:** American Bar Association (Forum Committee of the Construction Industry); Associated General Contractors of America (Contract Documents Committee; International Construction Committee); National Construction Dispute Resolution Committee.
**Career:** Mr Kmieciak counsels on commercial and government construction contract matters and specializes in the litigation, arbitration, avoidance and resolution of disputes. His experience includes projects involving industrial facilities, dredging, above- and below-ground heavy rail mass transit systems, bridges, buildings, airport facilities, container seaports and wharves, and civil works. He also has extensive international construction and international arbitration experience. He is an arbitrator on the AAA Construction Panel.

**KOEHLER, Kristin Graham**
Sidley Austin LLP, Washington, DC
202 736 8359
kkoehler@sidley.com
*Featured in Litigation (District of Columbia)*
**Practice Areas:** Partner in Sidley's Washington, DC office. Her practice involves representing corporations and individuals in all phases of white collar criminal and complex civil litigation matters, including internal investigations, grand jury

proceedings, trial proceedings, and appeals. Handles numerous United States Department of Justice investigations involving healthcare fraud, criminal antitrust and FCPA violations. Experience representing clients in qui tam actions brought by the Civil Fraud Division of the Department of Justice and State AG investigations. Negotiated numerous Corporate Integrity Agreements with the Office of Inspector General, and participated in jury trials in a number of federal courts.

**KOLASKY, William J**
WilmerHale, Washington, DC
202 663 6357
william.kolasky@wilmerhale.com
*Featured in Antitrust (District of Columbia)*
**Practice Areas:** Partner, Antitrust and Competition Group. Practice includes full range of antitrust representation and counseling. Secured antitrust clearance from Federal Trade Commission and Department of Justice for several hundred mergers and acquisitions, including Second Request investigations; coordinates merger reviews in multiple other jurisdictions worldwide, including European Commission. Represents companies and individuals in criminal and civil antitrust investigations; represents clients in broad range of private litigation.
**Career:** Deputy Assistant Attorney General for International Enforcement, Antitrust Division, US Department of Justice. Taught antitrust law at the Washington College of Law of American University.
**Personal:** AB, Dartmouth College; JD, Harvard University.

**KOLMAN, Mark H**
Dickstein Shapiro LLP, Washington, DC
202 420 2280
kolmanm@dicksteinshapiro.com
*Featured in Insurance (District of Columbia)*
**Practice Areas:** Lead trial counsel in the litigation and trial of complex insurance coverage cases for major policyholders. Has first-chaired more than a dozen coverage trials, 150 civil and criminal jury trials, and 1,000 other contested cases.
**Professional Memberships:** American, Federal, DC, and Maryland Bar Associations.
**Career:** Assistant State's Attorney, Baltimore City (1971-75); Chief, Circuit Court Division, Baltimore County State's Attorney's office (1975-80); assistant federal public defender, District of Maryland (1980); chief, Criminal Division, US Attorney's Office, District of Maryland (1980-84); private practice (1984 to present).
**Personal:** Bucknell University (BA); University of Maryland School of Law (JD).

**KORB, Donald L**
Sullivan & Cromwell LLP, Washington, DC
202 956 7675
korbd@sullcrom.com
*Featured in Tax (District of Columbia), Tax (Nationwide)*
See under Nationwide for profile.

**KOVNER, Mark L**
Kirkland & Ellis LLP, Washington, DC
202 879 5129
mark.kovner@kirkland.com
*Featured in Antitrust (District of Columbia)*
**Practice Areas:** Resident in the Washington, DC, office, Mr Kovner is a senior member of Kirkland & Ellis LLP's Antitrust and Competition Group with more than 23 years' experience in US and international M&A clearances, complex antitrust litigation in federal and state courts, and real-world counseling. Mr Kovner's practice focuses in particular on consumer products, high technology, energy, life sciences, defense and pharmaceutical industries. He is also an Adjunct Professor of Antitrust Law at Georgetown University Law School (2001-present).
**Personal:** Brandeis University (BA, honors in economics, 1986); Georgetown University Law Center (JD, cum laude, 1989).

**KRACOV, Daniel**
Arnold & Porter LLP, Washington, DC
202 942 5120
Daniel.Kracov@aporter.com
*Featured in Healthcare (District of Columbia)*
**Practice Areas:** Mr Kracov is a partner and heads the firm's FDA and Healthcare Practice. He assists clients in negotiating the broad range of regulatory challenges relating to the development, approval, manufacture, and marketing of drugs, biologics and medical devices. He handles complex investigations and enforcement matters, the development of regulatory corporate compliance programs, and due diligence in financings, mergers and acquisitions. He has a widely-recognized expertise in biomedical product-related public policy matters, including Congressional investigations.
**Personal:** JD, University of Virginia, 1988; BA, University of Maryland, 1985.

**KRAKOFF, David S.**
BuckleySandler LLP, Washington, DC
202 349 7950
dkrakoff@buckleysandler.com
*Featured in Litigation (District of Columbia)*
**Practice Areas:** Mr Krakoff represents corporations and individuals in high-stakes white collar and complex civil litigation. Mr Krakoff's experience includes a variety of government enforcement, internal investigation, audit committee and trial matters involving financial services, securities, accounting, FCPA, antitrust, healthcare and environmental matters. He currently represents a former BP executive in ongoing civil and criminal investigation related to the Deepwater Horizon incident in the Gulf of Mexico, the former CEO of an oil drilling company in an SEC complaint alleging FCPA violations, a senior bank executive in the Libor investigation, and executives in the international auto parts cartel investigations. In 2011-12, he represented an individual in the FCPA Sting Case criminal trial in the District of Columbia that ended in a hung jury mistrial and the subsequent dismissal of all charges by the Department of Justice. In 2012, he obtained summary judgment after discovery was completed, on

behalf of the former Controller of Fannie Mae in the largest securities class action when it was filed eight years before.
**Publications:** FCPA: Were the Sting Trials Doomed From the Start? (Business Crimes Bulletin 2012). FCPA: Recent Enforcement Activity Sounds Warning for Financial Services Industry (Business Crimes Bulletin 2011).

**KUNEY, David**
Sidley Austin LLP, Washington, DC
202 736 8650
dkuney@sidley.com
*Featured in Bankruptcy/Restructuring (District of Columbia)*
**Practice Areas:** Senior counsel in Sidley's Washington, DC office. Mr Kuney's concentration is in representing both debtors and creditors in complex Chapter 11 cases, including complex partnership cases, retail bankruptcies, real estate bankruptcies and corporate cases. He has extensive litigation and appellate experience and has served as lead counsel in both jury and non-jury civil matters throughout the United States.
**Personal:** Adjunct Professor, Georgetown University Law Center, "Bankruptcy and Creditors' Rights" (2000-present); Adjunct Professor at American University, Washington College of Law, "Business Reorganizations and Bankruptcy" (1984-1998). New York Law School (2013).

**KURLANDER, Stuart**
Latham & Watkins LLP, Washington, DC
202 637 2169
stuart.kurlander@lw.com
*Featured in Healthcare (District of Columbia)*
**Practice Areas:** 25 years of experience providing regulatory, reimbursement, fraud and abuse compliance, corporate and litigation counsel to healthcare industry. Extensive experience advising clients on federal, state and global healthcare regulatory issues, including Medicare and Medicaid, compliance, and HIPAA. Diverse client base includes academic medical centers, managed care companies and medical technology manufacturers. Routinely advises leading private equity, investment banking, and venture capital firms on health care M&A transactions and financings.
**Professional Memberships:** Member, DC bar.
**Personal:** JD, Saint Louis University School of Law, 1988; MHA, Saint Louis University, 1988; BA, Indiana University, 1984.

**KUSHAN, Jeffrey P**
Sidley Austin LLP, Washington, DC
202 736 8914
jkushan@sidley.com
*Featured in Intellectual Property (District of Columbia)*
**Practice Areas:** Partner in Sidley's Washington, DC office where he serves as practice group chair for the Patent group. His practice focuses on Hatch-Waxman patent litigation, patent appeals, and complex patent administrative proceedings, including patent reexamination and reissue proceedings. He performs patent portfolio reviews for clients, both for pre-litigation purposes and incidental to licensing or acquisitions. He represents

clients, including trade associations, on domestic and international patent policy matters.
**Personal:** The George Washington University Law School, JD, 1992, with honors; University of North Carolina - Chapel Hill, MA in Chemistry, 1987; College of William and Mary, BS in Chemistry, 1985.

**LABSON, Michael S**
Covington & Burling LLP, Washington, DC
202 662 5220
mlabson@cov.com
*Featured in Healthcare (District of Columbia)*
**Practice Areas:** Mike Labson's practice spans the range of pharmaceutical, biologics, and medical device regulation. He provides strategic advice in dealing with the FDA, DEA, and other agencies. He has litigated a variety of cases in the life sciences area. He works actively on legislative matters and provides regulatory support on M&A, securities, and commercial transactions.
**Career:** Judicial Clerk, Hon. David M. Ebel, U.S. Court of Appeals for the Tenth Circuit (1994-95); Staff Consultant, Price Waterhouse Strategic Consulting Group (1989-91).
**Personal:** Harvard Law School, JD 1994, magna cum laude, Officer Harvard Law Review; Harvard University, AB 1989, magna cum laude.

**LAND, Brian R**
Kirkland & Ellis LLP, Washington, DC
202 879 5956
brian.land@kirkland.com
*Featured in Environment (District of Columbia)*
**Practice Areas:** Partner with 23 years of experience in the environmental aspects of corporate transactions, including environmental due diligence, environmental liability and risk allocation, financings, restructurings, public offerings, and SEC environmental disclosure. Negotiates indemnities and insurance coverage for complex environmental risks. Enforces environmental indemnification rights and manages the post-sale resolution of environmental issues. Advises and counsels on remediation and cleanup matters, including under CERCLA, RCRA, and state cleanup programs. Counsels clients regarding environmental regulatory compliance matters.
**Personal:** The George Washington University Law School, JD, 1989 with Honors; University of Michigan; Washington University, BS, 1983.

**LAUGHLIN, Alexander M**
Wiley Rein LLP, McLean
703 905 2827
alaughlin@wileyrein.com
*Featured in Bankruptcy/Restructuring (District of Columbia)*
**Practice Areas:** Represents clients on all aspects of commercial litigation and distressed asset sales in bankruptcy, complex financial restructure planning, creditors' rights litigation, representation of trustees in bankruptcy, and loan restructure and workout agreements. Has extensive commercial litigation and courtroom experience in U.S. Bankruptcy Courts. Board Certified in Business Bankruptcy Law by the American Board of Certification.

**Professional Memberships:** ABA; American Bankruptcy Institute; Board of Directors, Vice President, Secretary and former President, Northern Virginia Bankruptcy Bar Association.
**Career:** Attorney-Advisor to Special Trial Judge Daniel J. Dinan, U.S. Tax Court.
**Personal:** Gonzaga University School of Law (JD); James Madison University (BS).

## LAVELLE, Joseph
DLA Piper LLP (US), Washington, DC
202 799 4780
joe.lavelle@dlapiper.com
*Featured in Intellectual Property (District of Columbia)*
**Practice Areas:** Intellectual Property: Litigation
**Career:** He focuses primarily on the preparation and trial of patent infringement cases, and has handled a number of successful appeals to the Court of Appeals for the Federal Circuit. He has tried a number of Section 337 proceedings before the US International Trade Commission (ITC), as well as handled cases before the US Court of Federal Claims and appeals to the Court of Appeals for the Federal Circuit. He also is licensed to practice before the USPTO.
**Personal:** JD, University of Pittsburgh School of Law, summa cum laude; BS, Physics, Wilkes University

## LAVIN, Kevin J
Arnold & Porter LLP, Washington, DC
202 942 5461
Kevin.Lavin@aporter.com
*Featured in Corporate/M&A (District of Columbia)*
**Practice Areas:** Kevin Lavin's practice focuses on mergers and acquisitions, private equity, public securities offerings and venture capital. Mr Lavin has represented companies, private equity sponsors and venture capital funds in numerous public and private mergers and acquisitions and securities offerings. His clients operate in many different industries, although he has special expertise in the government services, information technology and communications sectors. Mr Lavin regularly counsels boards of directors concerning fiduciary duties and Securities Act and Exchange Act compliance matters, including Sarbanes-Oxley compliance.
**Personal:** JD, Georgetown University Law Center, 1988; AB, Georgetown University, 1985.

## LAWSON, David L
Sidley Austin LLP, Washington, DC
202 736 8088
dlawson@sidley.com
*Featured in Telecommunications (District of Columbia)*
**Practice Areas:** Partner in Sidley's Washington, D.C. office and co-chair of its Communications Regulatory practice. Represents AT&T Inc. and other communications clients on wide range of competition-related matters involving state and federal regulation, mergers and acquisitions, constitutional and appellate litigation and complex federal district court litigation. He has represented AT&T in merger proceedings at the Department of Justice, Federal Trade Commission, Federal Communications Commission, European

Commission, and numerous state and foreign competition authorities for more than a decade. He has been a lead advocate for AT&T in a broad range of rulemaking and complaint proceedings at the Federal Communications Commission.

## LEAHY, Michael H
Arent Fox LLP, Washington, DC
202 857 6222
michael.leahy@arentfox.com
*Featured in Real Estate (District of Columbia)*
**Practice Areas:** Michael Leahy is a partner in the real estate practice representing private equity funds, real estate developers, and publicly held REITs in a wide variety of real estate matters, including purchases and sales, development projects, and financings and exchanges. His experience includes structuring sophisticated joint ventures for the ownership of improved real properties and their development, advising on the federal income tax aspects of real estate transactions, and assisting in the formation of entities to own and operate real estate projects. Duke University School of Law, JD (with distinction), 1970; Yale University, BA (cum laude), 1967.

## LEBLANC, Andrew
Milbank, Tweed, Hadley & McCloy LLP, Washington, DC
202 835 7574
aleblanc@milbank.com
*Featured in Bankruptcy/Restructuring (District of Columbia)*
**Practice Areas:** Mr Leblanc is a partner and a member of the firm's Financial Restructuring and Litigation & Arbitration Groups. He focuses on complex commercial litigation, financial restructuring and international arbitration, with a particular focus on contested issues arising in bankruptcy cases. He regularly represents official committees, secured and unsecured creditors, debtors, and bidders in bankruptcy cases, as well as financial institutions as defendants in adversary proceedings brought as part of bankruptcy cases. Mr Leblanc's practice is trial-focused, and he regularly appears before bankruptcy, district and appellate courts throughout the country.

## LEDDY, Mark
Cleary Gottlieb Steen & Hamilton LLP, Washington, DC
202 974 1570
mleddy@cgsh.com
*Featured in Antitrust (District of Columbia)*
**Practice Areas:** U.S. and European antitrust law, including civil and criminal litigation, analysis of competitive issues in mergers and acquisitions, and appearances before antitrust regulatory agencies and the U.S. federal courts. Representative clients: 3M; Alcoa; ArcelorMittal; Asahi Glass; Bank of America; Coca-Cola; ENI S.p.A.; Goldman Sachs; Google; Molson Coors; Whirlpool.
**Professional Memberships:** Massachusetts and DC Bars; U.S. Supreme Court and various circuit courts of appeal.
**Career:** Joined firm as partner, 1986. Resident in firm's Brussels office (1991-94). US Department of Justice (1972-86); Deputy Assistant Attorney

General (1984-1986). JD, Boston College Law School (1971); BA, Boston College (1968).

## LEDUC, André
Skadden, Arps, Slate, Meagher & Flom LLP & Affiliates, Washington, DC
202 371 7320
Andre.LeDuc@skadden.com
*Featured in Tax (District of Columbia)*
**Practice Areas:** Has a broad-based federal tax practice. Advises with respect to the federal income taxation of bankruptcy and financial restructurings, asset-based financings and infrastructure and tax-advantaged financial products, particularly cross-border transactions. Practice includes both planning and controversy work.
**Professional Memberships:** American Law Institute Federal Income Tax Advisory Group (1987-95).
**Career:** Adjunct Professor of Law, Graduate Tax Program, Chicago-Kent College of Law (1985-90 and 1993-present); Adjunct Professor of Law, University of Miami (1993-95); Counsel, U.S. Senate Committee on Finance (1981-83). JD, Harvard University, 1978 (cum laude); AB, Princeton University, 1975 (summa cum laude).

## LEEPER, Charles S
Drinker Biddle & Reath LLP, Washington, DC
202 842 8877
charles.leeper@dbr.com
*Featured in Litigation (District of Columbia)*
**Practice Areas:** Charles S Leeper is Co-Head of Drinker Biddle & Reath's White Collar Criminal Defense and Corporate Investigations Team. His practice focuses on the defense of white collar criminal investigations and prosecutions, congressional inquiries and related civil proceedings.
**Career:** Recently, Mr Leeper successfully defended his client, an attorney, in the four-month long trial of FCPA conspiracy and substantive charges in US v. Goncalves, et al. Mr Leeper previously served as an Assistant US Attorney for the District of Columbia, where he investigated and prosecuted an array of complex cases and served as Deputy Chief of the Special Prosecutions Unit.

## LENHART, Benedict M
Covington & Burling LLP, Washington, DC
202 662 5114
blenhart@cov.com
*Featured in Insurance (District of Columbia)*
**Practice Areas:** Partner practicing in insurance and litigation. Serves as Vice Chair for Covington's Insurance Practice Group. Lead role on scores of major insurance claims for policyholder clients. Assists clients in developing "big picture" strategy for resolving insurance claims, including how best to use litigation and settlement together for best and most efficient result. Helped clients to achieve more than 350 insurance settlements. Particular experience with the London Market, solvent schemes of arrangement, and complex multi-party claims.
**Professional Memberships:** ABA; NARTC.
**Personal:** Harvard Law School (JD, 1989, cum laude); University of Michigan (BA, 1985, high honors).

## LENNON, Daniel
Latham & Watkins LLP, Washington, DC
202 637 2347
dan.lennon@lw.com
*Featured in Private Equity (Nationwide), Corporate/M&A (District of Columbia)*
**Practice Areas:** Represents private equity firms and companies in major, complex transactions. Particular expertise in representing private equity firms in connection with leveraged buy-outs and has been involved in some of the largest LBO transactions in history.
**Professional Memberships:** Member, District of Columbia and Maryland State bars.
**Career:** Global Chair, Corporate Department.
**Personal:** JD, Catholic University of America, 1990; BA, University of Notre Dame, 1987.

## LERNER, Arthur N
Crowell & Moring LLP, Washington, DC
202 624 2820
alerner@crowell.com
*Featured in Healthcare (Nationwide), Healthcare (District of Columbia)*
**Practice Areas:** Co-Chair of Crowell & Moring's HealthCare Group. Focuses on antitrust/transactions/fraud and abuse issues for managed care organizations/healthcare providers/other healthcare entities. Advises/represents HMOs, other managed-care organizations/hospitals/pharmaceutical/medical device/supply companies/professional and trade associations/prescription benefit management firms/medical group practices/group purchasing organizations/charitable groups/other. Handles mergers and acquisitions/joint ventures/Federal Employees Health Benefit Program compliance/disputes, Medicare Advantage and ERISA matters/DOJ, FTC antitrust proceedings.
**Professional Memberships:** Member: Board of Directors, American Health Lawyers Association; Former Chair: AHLA Antitrust Practice Group; Former Chair: ABA Antitrust Section's Federal Civil Enforcement Committee.
**Career:** Directed FTC's healthcare antitrust program/attorney advisor to FTC Chairman/assistant to director of the Bureau of Competition.

## LEVENTHAL, Norman P
Holland & Knight LLP, Washington, DC
202 828 1860
norm.leventhal@hklaw.com
*Featured in Telecommunications (District of Columbia)*
**Practice Areas:** Partner in the firm's Public Policy and Regulation Practice Group, with more than 45 years of experience in communications, media and intellectual property law, representing a multitude of industry leaders and new entrants in the broadcast, telecom/common carrier, wireless, domestic and international satellite, radio equipment manufacturing, and media production and distribution industries. He has also advised many media companies on issues relating to copyright, trademark and the Internet, as well as other new technology matters. During his career, Leventhal has appeared before numerous federal agencies, Congress and both state and federal courts.

**LEVINE, Barry Wm**
Dickstein Shapiro LLP, Washington, DC
202 420 2237
levineb@dicksteinshapiro.com
*Featured in Litigation (District of Columbia)*
**Practice Areas:** Barry Wm Levine is the co-leader of Dickstein Shapiro's Business Litigation Practice and White Collar Criminal Defense & Investigations Practices. Has represented dozens of defendants in major white-collar crime cases, including numerous high-ranking elected and appointed public officials, lawyers, bankers, and business people. He has defended class action lawsuits on behalf of corporate defendants, and has litigated as both plaintiff's and defendant's counsel regarding antitrust, healthcare, insurance, law firm partnership disputes, and energy.
**Personal:** New York University (BS); University of California at Berkeley (Boalt Hall) (JD); Institut Universitaire de Hautes Etudes Internationale, Geneva, Switzerland.

**LEVINE, David**
Groom Law Group, Washington, DC
202 861 5436
dlevine@groom.com
*Featured in Employee Benefits & Executive Compensation (District of Columbia)*
**Practice Areas:** Provides counsel on the tax and fiduciary aspects of retirement and welfare employee benefit plans and on tax-exempt organization corporate and tax issues. Clients include large multinational corporations, large state and local public pension and welfare retirement arrangements, financial institutions, and trade associations.
**Professional Memberships:** Admitted in New York and the District of Columbia. Chair, Legislative Subcommittee, Employee Benefits Committee, Tax Section, American Bar Association. Chair, Internal Revenue Service Advisory Committee on Tax Exempt and Governmental Entities (ACT), 2011-2013.
**Personal:** JD, University of Pennsylvania, 1997. BA, Johns Hopkins University,1994 (General and Departmental Honors).

**LEVINE, Lee**
Levine Sullivan Koch & Schulz LLP, Washington, DC
202 508 1110
llevine@lskslaw.com
*Featured in First Amendment Litigation (Nationwide), Media & Entertainment (District of Columbia)*
See under Nationwide for profile.

**LEVY, Michael N**
Bingham McCutchen LLP, Washington, DC
202 373 6680
michael.levy@bingham.com
*Featured in Litigation (District of Columbia)*
**Practice Areas:** Co-chair of Bingham's White Collar Investigations and Enforcement Group. Practice focuses on white collar defense, investigations, and representation of corporations and individuals in connection with government enforcement initiatives. Has represented numerous Fortune 500 companies, high-ranking public officials, civic leaders and prominent corporate executives throughout the US in major criminal cases and congressional, SEC and other governmental investigations involving alleged violations of fraud, securities, tax, antitrust, Foreign Corrupt Practices Act (FCPA), environmental, obstruction of justice, bribery, wiretapping and other criminal statutes.
**Personal:** Harvard Law School, JD, magna cum laude, 1988; Yale University, BA, summa cum laude, 1985.

**LEWIS, William**
Morgan, Lewis & Bockius LLP, Washington, DC
202 739 5145
wlewis@morganlewis.com
*Featured in Environment (District of Columbia)*
**Practice Areas:** Senior counsel in the Environmental Practice and Leader of the Clean Air Practice; has more than 30 years experience in dealing with federal and state clean air issues. Serves as counsel to the Clean Air Implementation Project, an organization of major corporations that addresses those EPA rulemakings and guidance that will affect a broad cross-section of American industry. Represented a broad range of corporate and trade association clients on clean air issues in appellate litigation, rulemaking proceedings, enforcement actions, new source review and Title V permitting matters, and compliance counseling.

**LIBOW, Daryl A**
Sullivan & Cromwell LLP, Washington, DC
202 956 7650
libowd@sullcrom.com
*Featured in Antitrust (District of Columbia)*
**Professional Memberships:** ABA; ASIL; BADC; CBA; ABCNY; NYSBA.
**Career:** Partner since 1994. Managing Partner, Washington, D.C. office. Co head, Antitrust Group. Has been Lead counsel in broad range of criminal and civil antitrust litigation, government investigations and merger clearance activity. Has counseled clients on joint ventures, vertical distribution and pricing arrangements and antitrust compliance. Practice also includes securities litigation, complex commercial litigation and representing clients in connection with agency enforcement actions, grand jury proceedings and congressional investigations and hearings.
**Personal:** Cornell Law School (JD, 1986); London School of Economics and Political Science (LLM, 1982); Harvard University (AB, 1981).

**LIEBESMAN, Lawrence**
Holland & Knight LLP, Washington, DC
202 955 3000
lawrence.liebesman@hklaw.com
*Featured in Environment (District of Columbia)*
**Practice Areas:** Partner in the Government Section, he is a nationally recognized environmental lawyer and formerly a Senior Trial Attorney at the Department of Justice. His practice emphasizes wetlands, water pollution, environmental impact assessment and endangered species law. Liebesman has participated in landmark Supreme Court Clean Water Act and Endangered Species Act cases. He has negotiated permits for numerous commercial, residential, public works and mining projects and has successfully defended challenges to those permits. He is the co author of the Endangered Species Deskbook for the Environmental Law Institute (2d Ed. 2010) and teaches wildlife law at GW Law School.

**LIPMAN, Andrew D**
Bingham McCutchen LLP, Washington, DC
202 373 6033
andrew.lipman@bingham.com
*Featured in Telecommunications (District of Columbia)*
**Practice Areas:** Has spent more than 30 years developing Bingham's Telecommunications, Media and Technology Group. Practices in virtually every aspect of communications law and related fields, including regulatory, transactional, litigation, legislative and land use. Represents clients in both the private and public sectors, including those in the areas of local, long distance and international telephone common carriage; Internet services and technologies; conventional and emerging wireless services; satellite services; broadcasting; competitive video services; telecommunications equipment manufacturing; and other high-technology applications.
**Personal:** Stanford Law School, JD, 1977; University of Rochester, BA, summa cum laude, 1974.

**LIPSKY, Abbott (Tad)**
Latham & Watkins LLP, Washington, DC
202 637 2283
tad.lipsky@lw.com
*Featured in Antitrust (District of Columbia)*
**Practice Areas:** Internationally recognized competition law, economics and policy expert; extensive worldwide experience.
**Professional Memberships:** Co-Chair, US Chamber of Commerce, International Competition Policy Working Group; ABA Antitrust Section, International Task Force; BNA Antitrust and Trade Regulation Report, Advisory Board; Journal of Competition Law & Economics, Advisory Board.
**Career:** Chief Competition Counsel, Coca-Cola Co.; Deputy Assistant Attorney General, US Department of Justice.
**Publications:** Managing Antitrust Compliance Through the Continuing Surge in Global Enforcement, 75 ANTITRUST L. J. 965 (2009); Improving Competitive Analysis, 16 GEO. MASON L. REV. 805 (2009).
**Personal:** JD, Stanford Law School; MA, Stanford University; BA, Amherst College.

**LIPTON, Joshua**
Gibson, Dunn & Crutcher LLP, Washington, DC
202 955 8226
JLipton@gibsondunn.com
*Featured in Antitrust (District of Columbia)*
**Practice Areas:** Specializes in antitrust litigation, merger investigations, and counseling. Represents clients in a broad range of industries in trial and appellate litigation (including class actions) involving issues such as price-fixing, mergers, group boycotts, vertical restraints, monopolization, and unfair competition. Mr Lipton has significant experience in government investigations of mergers and acquisitions, as well as US and international government investigations concerning cartels, exclusionary conduct, and other types of vertical and horizontal arrangements.
**Personal:** JD, magna cum laude, University of Michigan Law School, 1998; BA, Amherst College, 1994.

**LITT, Daniel**
Dickstein Shapiro LLP, Washington, DC
202 420 4747
littd@dicksteinshapiro.com
*Featured in Bankruptcy/Restructuring (District of Columbia)*
**Practice Areas:** Daniel Litt leads the firm's Financial Restructuring & Bankruptcy Practice. He has been a bankruptcy practitioner since 1979. In addition, he has represented numerous clients in complex commercial litigation for more than 29 years. He represents clients (creditors, debtors, trustees, creditors' committees, and equity holders) in bankruptcy courts throughout the United States. He has participated in hundreds of bankruptcy cases involving retail and manufacturing businesses, commercial real estate, airlines, government contracting, technology-related businesses, radio, television, telecommunications businesses, satellite companies, financial institutions, real estate contractors, and many other commercial businesses.
**Personal:** Syracuse University (BS, 1974); Georgetown University (JD, 1978).

**LIVINGSTON, Donald R**
Akin Gump Strauss Hauer & Feld LLP, Washington, DC
202 887 4242
dlivingston@akingump.com
*Featured in Labor & Employment (District of Columbia)*
**Practice Areas:** Represents large employers in all aspects of civil rights and employment discrimination law, with emphasis on employment litigation. Has served as defense litigation counsel in numerous fair employment class actions.
**Professional Memberships:** Elected Member, College of Labor and Employment Lawyers; Member, American Bar Association, Labor and Employment Law Section and Equal Employment Opportunity Committee; Member, Georgia and District of Columbia Bars.
**Career:** Former General Counsel, US Equal Employment Opportunity Commission.
**Publications:** 'EEOC Litigation and Charge Resolution' (BNA 2005), the only comprehensive book on EEOC litigation.
**Personal:** AB and JD, University of Georgia.

**LOCASCIO, Gregg F**
Kirkland & Ellis LLP, Washington, DC
202 879 5290
gregg.locascio@kirkland.com
*Featured in Intellectual Property (District of Columbia)*

**Practice Areas:** Gregg LoCascio is an Intellectual Property Partner with experience in patent, trademark, false advertising, and trade secret matters. He routinely serves as first chair in litigation matters before juries, judges, and arbitration panels. An engineer by training, he has expertise in many fields and excels at making complex technologies understandable by all. In addition to a string of recent jury trial wins, he is also a successful advocate on patent appeals before the U.S. Court of Appeals for the Federal Circuit.
**Personal:** Virginia Polytechnic Institute and State University, BS, 1992. University of Notre Dame Law School, JD, 1995.

### LOHMANN, Walter H
Kirkland & Ellis LLP, Washington, DC
202 879 5923
walter.lohmann@kirkland.com
*Featured in Environment (District of Columbia)*
**Practice Areas:** Walter Lohmann leads the firm's Environmental Transactional and Restructuring Practice Group. His practice focuses on managing environmental compliance and liability issues as they arise in the context of corporate transactions, restructurings and bankruptcies, both in the US and around the world, including conducting or coordinating environmental assessments, retaining and supervising technical experts, counseling clients on deal and bankruptcy related environmental liability issues, drafting and negotiating contracts and court filings, and pursuing resolution of environmental liability issues through interaction with governmental authorities and coordination of remedial actions.
**Personal:** Cornell University, AB, 1980; George Washington University Law School, JD, 1983.

### LONDON, Jeremy D
Skadden, Arps, Slate, Meagher & Flom LLP & Affiliates, Washington, DC
202 371 7535
Jeremy.London@skadden.com
*Featured in Corporate/M&A (District of Columbia)*
**Practice Areas:** Concentrates his practice in the areas of mergers and acquisitions, corporate finance, securities law and general corporate matters. Has represented acquirors, targets and financial advisors in a number of significant transactions, including public and private acquisitions and divestitures, negotiated and contested public acquisitions, and other corporate matters. Counsels sellers, private equity firms and management in leveraged buyout transactions and firm clients in joint ventures and other strategic alliances.
**Career:** JD, The George Washington University School of Law, 1997 (with highest honors; Order of the Coif); BA, University of Michigan, 1993.

### LOPATTO, Mary
Cozen O'Connor, Washington, DC
202 463 2502
mlopatto@cozen.com
*Featured in Insurance (District of Columbia)*
**Practice Areas:** Newly-joined Cozen O'Connor with more than 25 years of experience in insurance and reinsurance dispute resolution. Handled more than 100 arbitrations on both ceding and

assuming sides. Areas of expertise include asbestos, product liability, catastrophe reinsurance, reinsurance allocation, boiler and machinery, workers compensation, life and health, financial reinsurance, and contract wording. Specializes in complex and large-scale international arbitration disputes under the Bermuda form and subject to the Bermuda International Conciliation and Arbitration Act 1993.
**Professional Memberships:** Former Chairman, AIDA Reinsurance and Insurance Arbitration Society (ARIAS-U.S.).
**Personal:** Catholic University of America (JD 1986); Princeton University (AB 1976).

### LOPEZ JR, Jorge
Akin Gump Strauss Hauer & Feld LLP, Washington, DC
202 887 4385
jlopez@akingump.com
*Featured in Healthcare (Nationwide), Healthcare (District of Columbia)*
**Practice Areas:** Chair, national health industry practice.Clients include academic medical centers, specialty hospitals, pharmaceutical companies, medical device companies, and retail pharmacies. Special focus on: health policy issues (has advised clients on virtually every major Congressional health initiative considered in last 20 years, including recently enacted health care reform legislation); regulatory and policy issues related to cancer care; application of the federal fraud and abuse laws to the hospital, pharmaceutical and pharmacy industries; HIPAA and other privacy issues.
**Personal:** BA, summa cum laude, and MA, Catholic University of America; JD, cum laude, Harvard Law School, 1984.

### LOWELL, Abbe David
Chadbourne & Parke LLP, Washington, DC
202 756 8001
adlowell@chadbourne.com
*Featured in Litigation (District of Columbia)*
**Practice Areas:** Abbe David Lowell is the head of Chadbourne's Litigation Department and chair of the Firm's White Collar Defense, Regulatory Investigations and Litigation Group. His practice focuses on litigation, special investigations and regulatory enforcement. Mr Lowell has represented numerous high-profile clients and provided counsel in matters of national and international importance. He has successfully tried numerous complex civil and criminal cases throughout the United States, and has briefed and argued dozens of appeals before federal and state appeals
**Personal:** Columbia Law School, JD, 1977; Columbia College, BA,1974.

### LUCE, Gregory M
Skadden, Arps, Slate, Meagher & Flom LLP & Affiliates, Washington, DC
202 371 7310
Greg.Luce@skadden.com
*Featured in Healthcare (Nationwide), Healthcare (District of Columbia)*
See under Nationwide for profile.

### LUCHSINGER, Dan
Covington & Burling LLP, Washington, DC
202 662 5175
dluchsinger@cov.com
*Featured in Tax (District of Columbia)*
**Practice Areas:** Practices in a broad range of federal income tax issues, including the structuring of partnerships and joint ventures; corporate acquisitions and corporate dispositions; planning international and cross border financings; restructurings involving foreign withholding, subpart F minimization, and foreign tax credit utilization; inbound and outbound property transfers, including United States real property.
**Career:** Mr Luchsinger has taught Taxation of Partnerships at the Georgetown University Law Center for the last decade.
**Personal:** JD, magna cum laude, Order of the Coif, Georgetown Law Journal, Georgetown University Law Center, JD (1992); BS, summa cum laude, Phi Beta Kappa, University of Minnesota (1988).

### LUDWISZEWSKI, Raymond B
Gibson, Dunn & Crutcher LLP, Washington, DC
202 955 8665
rludwiszewski@gibsondunn.com
*Featured in Climate Change (Nationwide), Environment (District of Columbia)*
**Practice Areas:** Has handled numerous significant environmental and natural resources litigation matters, including constitutional issues before the Supreme Court.
**Career:** Served as General Counsel and Assistant Administrator for Enforcement at United States Environmental Protection Agency; was Special Counsel to Assistant Attorney General for Environment and Natural Resources Division and Associate Deputy Attorney General at the United States Justice Department. Environmental enforcement cases: US v Westvaco, US v Lockheed Martin, US v Tyco, US v Bethlehem Steel, US v General Motors and US v Raymark.
**Publications:** Author/speaker on environmental issues.
**Personal:** JD, Harvard Law School, 1984, Articles Editor, Harvard Law Review. Law Clerk, Judge Henry Friendly.

### LUNDY, Seth H
King & Spalding LLP, Washington, DC
202 626 2924
slundy@kslaw.com
*Featured in Healthcare (District of Columbia)*
**Career:** Lundy focuses on health care matters, concentrating on federal and state regulation of health care providers and manufacturers, including corporate compliance, the Anti-Kickback Statute, the Stark Law, false claims, and medicare and medicaid reimbursement. His experience includes: corporate compliance; government investigations; developing business strategies to meet changing regulatory schemes; effecting mergers and the creation of new health care entities; working with federal regulators and legislators to initiate, revise and interpret new regulations; and billing and reimbursement advice.

**Personal:** 1996 - JD, with honors, George Washington University National Law Center; 1991 - BA, cum laude, Amherst College.

### LUPO, Anthony V
Arent Fox LLP, Washington, DC
202 857 6000
anthony.lupo@arentfox.com
*Featured in Intellectual Property (District of Columbia)*
**Practice Areas:** Anthony Lupo co-chairs the entertainment/intellectual property group of the firm. He is one of the "go to" intellectual property lawyers on the East Coast for television and movie studios, including representing Pixar, Discovery Channel, Travel Channel, WB, Turner, and Disney. He also represents a number of European fashion companies such as Diesel, Lacoste, Escada, Hugo Boss, Geox, and Benetton in all aspects of their US distribution, licensing, and/or intellectual property. He also specializes in post mortem publicity rights and represents the estates of Albert Einstein, Steve McQueen, Maria Callas, and The Marx Brothers. Anthony's intellectual property and e-commerce experience includes representing computer and technology companies in offering online marketplaces including assisting Apple in setting up the first viable online music store. Finally, Anthony has a great deal of experience in assisting clients in protecting and enforcing their portfolios on a global basis. In this regard, he has assisted a number of foreign governments in revising their intellectual property laws to comply with international IP treaties, including assisting the governments of Indonesia, Vietnam, Egypt, and Saudi Arabia.

### LUPO, Raphael
McDermott Will & Emery LLP, Washington, DC
202 756 8366
rlupo@mwe.com
*Featured in Intellectual Property (District of Columbia)*
**Practice Areas:** Focuses primarily on patent litigation and counseling. Extensive patent trial experience as lead counsel in federal district courts and before International Trade Commission. Presented and argued over 100 appeals before Court of Appeals for Federal Circuit and its predecessor. Has represented clients in complex technology including semiconductor and computer-related technologies and medical devices.
**Professional Memberships:** Has been accepted by eleven federal district courts as a recognized patent law expert and expert on Patent Office matters.
**Personal:** George Washington University (BSEE, JD); Associate Professor, George Washington University Law School.

### LUTZ, Holley Thames
Dentons, Washington, DC
202 408 6836
holley.lutz@dentons.com
*Featured in Healthcare (District of Columbia)*
**Practice Areas:** Concentrates her practice on Medicare/Medicaid compliance actives related to

coverage and reimbursement issues, as well as clinical research compliance. Counsels on Medicare coverage and reimbursement issues, including graduate medical education, disproportionate share payment adjustments and Medicaid financing arrangements including provider-tax and supplemental payment models. Advises on formation and operational structure issues, provider enrollment and successor liability in the merger and acquisition context. With regard to research, she focuses on NIH grant fund compliance, scientific misconduct defense and human subjects protections. She also defends providers against CMS allegations of non-compliance, negotiates settlement agreements with HHS OIG.

**LUXTON, Jane C**
Pepper Hamilton LLP, Washington, DC
202 220 1437
luxtonj@pepperlaw.com
*Featured in Environment (District of Columbia)*
**Practice Areas:** Partner. Environmental practice with focus on regulation of toxic substances, particularly metals, under the full range of federal and state environmental laws, as well as international environmental regulation. Expertise includes climate change-related issues, Endangered Species Act, natural resource damage actions, energy, fisheries and coastal zone management issues. Extensive experience in international trade matters and litigation.
**Professional Memberships:** Vice Chair at Large and past Chair, International Environmental Law Committee, American Bar Association's Section on Environment, Energy and Resources.
**Career:** Former General Counsel, National Oceanic and Atmospheric Administration.
**Personal:** JD 1976 Cornell University; AB, cum laude, 1973 Harvard University.

**LYLE, Michael J**
Weil, Gotshal & Manges LLP, Washington, DC
202 682 7157
michael.lyle@weil.com
*Featured in Litigation (District of Columbia)*
**Practice Areas:** Michael Lyle is the Managing Partner of Weil's Washington, DC office, a member of the firm's Management Committee, and Co-head of its Product Liability Practice. He is an accomplished trial lawyer with numerous successes at trial and on appeal in a range of complex cases in US federal and state courts. He also represents clients in sensitive congressional and governmental investigations relating to the FCA, product recalls, and other civil matters.
**Professional Memberships:** Faculty Member, National Institute for Trial Advocacy.
**Personal:** University of Rochester (BA, 1985); Case Western Reserve University School of Law (JD, 1988).

**MACAVOY, Christopher J**
Baker Botts LLP, Washington, DC
202 639 7709
christopher.macavoy@bakerbotts.com
*Featured in Antitrust (District of Columbia)*

**Practice Areas:** Antitrust and Competition Law, Litigation Practice
**Professional Memberships:** District of Columbia Bar; Supreme Court of the United States; United States Court of Appeals for the Third, Fourth, Fifth, Sixth, Ninth and District of Columbia Circuits; United States District Court for the District of Columbia
**Career:** Chris MacAvoy's practice focuses on mergers, antitrust counseling and litigation and government investigations. Mr MacAvoy's experience includes mergers and joint ventures, distribution practices, price discrimination and trade association activities.
**Personal:** JD, Georgetown University Law Center, 1982; BA, Harvard University, 1979

**MACBETH, Angus**
Sidley Austin LLP, Washington, DC
202 736 8271
amacbeth@sidley.com
*Featured in Environment (District of Columbia)*
**Practice Areas:** Senior counsel in Sidley's Washington, D.C. office, with more than 40 years experience in the practice of environmental law. He has extensive experience handling multi-facility enforcement cases under the Clean Air Act and Clean Water Act and has dealt repeatedly with state-federal issues under RCRA and the hazardous waste management statutes. He has briefed and argued major issues in both federal district and appellate courts, including numerous challenges to agency rules in the Courts of Appeals and has negotiated numerous settlements with federal and state regulators.
**Professional Memberships:** President of the American College of Environmental Lawyers (ACOEL).

**MACDOUGALL, Mark J**
Akin Gump Strauss Hauer & Feld LLP, Washington, DC
202 887 4510
mmacdougall@akingump.com
*Featured in Litigation (District of Columbia)*
**Practice Areas:** Practice focuses on white collar criminal defense with extensive experience in cases involving financial fraud, civil claims and criminal investigations that cross international borders. A recognized authority in the emerging legal specialty of reputation recovery, represents clients in combating obstacles that arise when individuals and organizations are the targets of false public accusations by the media, government officials or commercial competitors.
**Professional Memberships:** Fellow, American College of Trial Lawyers.
**Career:** Federal Prosecutor, Criminal Division (Fraud Section), U.S. Department of Justice.
**Personal:** BA, University of Notre Dame (1978); MBA, Boston University (1979); JD, George Washington University Law School (1985).

**MADAN, Raj**
Bingham McCutchen LLP, Washington, DC
202 373 6681
raj.madan@bingham.com
*Featured in Tax (District of Columbia), Tax (Nationwide)*

**MAGEE, John B**
Bingham McCutchen LLP, Washington, DC
202 373 6229
john.magee@bingham.com
*Featured in Tax (District of Columbia), Tax (Nationwide)*
See under Nationwide for profile.

**MAIN, David**
Nelson Mullins Riley & Scarborough LLP, Washington, DC
*Featured in Healthcare (District of Columbia)*
**Practice Areas:** Experience handling health care transactional work, fraud and abuse and other regulatory compliance issues with focus on the formation and development of health technology companies. Frequent advocate for clients' interests before Congress and state and federal regulatory bodies, including various issues relating to health care reform and health information technology incentive programs.
**Professional Memberships:** American Health Lawyers Association; Health Care Technology Network of Greater Washington, Founder; Health Management Academy.
**Career:** District of Columbia; Commonwealth of Virginia; U.S. Supreme Court.
**Publications:** Frequent author/presenter on heath care issues.

**MALESTER, Ann**
Weil, Gotshal & Manges LLP, Washington, DC
202 682 7500
ann.malester@weil.com
*Featured in Antitrust (District of Columbia)*
**Practice Areas:** Ann Malester focuses her practice on antitrust counseling and litigation. Prior to joining Weil, she was Deputy Director of the FTC's Bureau of Competition, where she supervised antitrust enforcement activities throughout the agency. During her 12 previous years as an Assistant Director, she headed FTC merger enforcement in several market sectors, including the defense, pharmaceutical, biotech and medical device and equipment industries, and led the Mergers I Division in investigating, litigating or obtaining consent agreements in hundreds of significant mergers, acquisitions and joint ventures.
**Personal:** Bryn Mawr College (BA); George Washington University Law School (JD).

**MANCINI, David C**
Seyfarth Shaw LLP, Washington, DC
202 828 5360
dmancini@seyfarth.com
*Featured in Construction (District of Columbia)*
**Practice Areas:** Construction; government contracts; commercial litigation
**Professional Memberships:** ABA; Fourth, Fifth, D.C. and Federal Circuits; Virginia, D.C., Maryland and Texas bars
**Career:** US and international construction, government contracts, insurance coverage and commercial transactions. Market sectors include power, industrial, infrastructure, commercial, multi-family housing, education, spacecraft, military and government services.

**Publications:** "Boiler and Machinery Insurance," Appleman on Insurance; Construction Briefing Papers: "Preserving Claim Rights;" "Performance Bonds: Expectation vs. Reality," "Mini-Trials [and ADR]." Conference/seminar publications include: "Proving Construction Damages;" "Concentrated Course, Government Contracting;" "Fundamentals, Construction Law;" "Managing Design Responsibility and Liability."
**Personal:** JD, Georgetown University; BS, Finance, cum laude, University of Maryland.

**MANGINO, Brian**
Fried, Frank, Harris, Shriver & Jacobson LLP, Washington, DC
202 639 7258
Brian.Mangino@FriedFrank.com
*Featured in Private Equity (Nationwide), Corporate/M&A (District of Columbia)*
**Practice Areas:** Corporate partner. Focuses his practice on private equity transactions, mergers and acquisitions, minority investments, strategic partnerships, spin-offs and joint ventures, representing private equity firms and public and private companies. Also advises on corporate governance issues, defensive strategy, securities law compliance and other general corporate matters. Clients include private investment funds managed by Goldman, Sachs & Co.; Permira Advisors LLC; and Citadel Investment Group and their portfolio companies.
**Career:** Joined in 2000; became partner in 2006.
**Personal:** JD, University of Virginia (1998); BA, University of Virginia (1995).

**MANN, Phillip L**
Miller & Chevalier Chartered, Washington, DC
202 626 5890
pmann@milchev.com
*Featured in Tax (District of Columbia)*
**Practice Areas:** Tax counseling, tax controversies, and legislative and policy work with IRS and US Department of Treasury for domestic and foreign-based clients.
**Career:** Received ABA Section of Taxation Distinguished Service Award, 2012; received 2009 Parker C. Fielder Award for Outstanding Service and Achievement in Oil and Gas Taxation; former President, American Tax Policy Institute; former Chair, Section of Taxation, American Bar Association; former Chair, IRS Commissioner's Advisory Group; Tax Legislative Counsel and Deputy Tax Legislative Counsel for US Department of Treasury.
**Personal:** LLB, University of Texas School of Law, 1962; BBA, University of Texas at Austin, 1962.

**MANTHEI, John**
Latham & Watkins LLP, Washington, DC
202 637 2211
john.manthei@lw.com
*Featured in Healthcare (District of Columbia)*
**Practice Areas:** Focuses on regulatory matters involving the Food and Drug Administration (FDA) for the medical device, pharmaceutical, biotechnology, food and dietary supplement industries. His practice also includes assisting

clients with all aspects of FDA-regulated product life cycle, including civil and criminal compliance and enforcement. Since 2000, Mr Manthei has represented the pharmaceutical, biotechnology and medical device industries as counsel in nearly every major FDA legislative initiative.
**Career:** Global Co-chair of the Health Care and Life Sciences Practice; served as Majority Counsel for the US House of Representatives' Committee on Energy and Commerce (1998-2000).

## MARGIE, Paul
Wiltshire & Grannis LLP, Washington, DC
202 730 1352
pmargie@wiltshiregrannis.com
*Featured in Telecommunications (District of Columbia)*
**Practice Areas:** Mr Margie focuses on telecommunications and technology law. He advises wireless and wireline service providers, ISPs, manufacturers, investors, satellite companies, and software companies, on telecommunications regulation, mergers, spectrum, roaming, pricing, licensing, and equipment certification. He represents clients before the FCC, courts, Executive Branch, and international forums.
**Career:** Vodafone/UN Foundation partnership lead (2005-08); Legal Advisor, FCC Commissioner Copps (2001-05); Senior Commerce Counsel and Commerce Counsel, Senator Rockefeller (1999-2001); Wiley, Rein & Fielding (1996-99).
**Personal:** University of Chicago Law School, JD, with honors. Editor-in-Chief, The University of Chicago Legal Forum. Haverford College, BA, with honors. US Representative, Telecoms Sans Frontieres.

## MARKS, Richard J
DLA Piper LLP (US), Washington, DC
202 799 4202
richard.marks@dlapiper.com
*Featured in Corporate/M&A (District of Columbia)*
**Practice Areas:** Corporate/M&A and Private Equity
**Career:** He assists companies, banks and other institutional lenders and investors with secured and unsecured commercial finance transactions, leveraged and strategic acquisitions and restructurings and private equity investments. He has broad experience representing borrowers and lenders in senior and mezzanine corporate loans, syndicated and unitranche loan facilities, asset-based and cash flow lines of credit, structured finance and acquisition financings and works with lenders, private equity and mezzanine funds and institutional investors in the purchase, sale and financing of their portfolio companies.
**Personal:** JD, University of Maryland School of Law; BSEE, Northwestern University

## MARQUARDT, Paul
Cleary Gottlieb Steen & Hamilton LLP, Washington, DC
202 974 1648
pmarquardt@cgsh.com
*Featured in Corporate/M&A (District of Columbia), International Trade (Nationwide)*
See under Nationwide for profile.

## MARSH, David
Arnold & Porter LLP, Washington, DC
202 9425068
David.Marsh@aporter.com
*Featured in Life Sciences (Nationwide), Intellectual Property (District of Columbia)*
See under Nationwide for profile.

## MARSHALL, Alison
Jones Day, Washington, DC
202 879 7611
abmarshall@jonesday.com
*Featured in Labor & Employment (District of Columbia)*
**Practice Areas:** An active litigator with extensive experience handling complex employment litigation matters including employment discrimination class actions, FLSA collective and state wage and hour class actions, and whistleblower claims. Routinely counsels employers on ADA compliance, OFCCP enforcement and compliance, pay equity issues, wage and hour law developments, and reductions in force. She also represents companies on ADA Title III accessibility matters.
**Professional Memberships:** ABA (Equal Employment Opportunity and the Employee Rights and Responsibilities Committees of the Labor and Employment Law Section). National Association of College and University Attorneys.

## MARTEL, Jonathan
Arnold & Porter LLP, Washington, DC
202 942 5470
Jonathan.Martel@aporter.com
*Featured in Climate Change (Nationwide), Environment (District of Columbia)*
See under Nationwide for profile.

## MARTELLA, Roger
Sidley Austin LLP, Washington, DC
202 736 8097
rmartella@sidley.com
*Featured in Climate Change (Nationwide), Environment (District of Columbia)*
See under Nationwide for profile.

## MARTIN, David
Covington & Burling LLP, Washington, DC
202 662 5128
dmartin@cov.com
*Featured in Corporate/M&A (District of Columbia), Securities (Nationwide)*
See under Nationwide for profile.

## MARTIN, Marc S
K&L Gates, Washington, DC
202 778 9859
marc.martin@klgates.com
*Featured in Telecommunications (District of Columbia)*
**Practice Areas:** Marc Martin structures, negotiates, and provides strategic counseling for telecom, media, and technology transactions, including licensing agreements, distribution agreements, joint ventures, technology procurement agreements and other transactions involving information technology assets, telecommunications facilities and spectrum licenses, and programming and digital media. Mr Martin writes and negotiates content and application distribution agreements

for over the mobile wireless, broadcast, cable, satellite and online network platforms. He represents companies, entrepreneurs and investors before the Federal Communications Commission, Executive Branch, Congress and the courts in matters involving telecom, media, and technology transactions, policy matters, regulatory proceedings and commercial disputes.

## MASOUDI, Gerald F.
Covington & Burling LLP, Washington, DC
202 662 5063
gmasoudi@cov.com
*Featured in Healthcare (District of Columbia)*
**Practice Areas:** Mr Masoudi is co-chair of Covington's food and drug practice. He advises drug, device and biologic sponsors and manufacturers on regulatory and enforcement matters, with particular focus on manufacturing, promotion and postmarketing surveillance.
**Career:** He previously served as Chief Counsel (2007-09) and Deputy Chief Counsel (2004-05) of FDA. He also served as a Deputy Assistant Attorney General in the Antitrust Division at the Department of Justice (2005-07). Before joining FDA in 2004, Mr Masoudi was a trial and appellate litigator in private practice.
**Personal:** The University of Chicago Law School, JD, with high honors; Amherst College, BA.

## MASTERS, Lorelie S
Jenner & Block LLP, Washington, DC
202 639 6076
lmasters@jenner.com
*Featured in Insurance (Nationwide), Insurance (District of Columbia)*
**Career:** A partner in the Insurance Litigation and Counseling Practice, Lorelie S. Masters has won significant decisions, trials, and arbitrations enforcing insurance coverage for clients including Tyson Foods, New Century Liquidating Trust, and Dow Corning Corp. A sought-after writer and speaker, Ms. Masters helped organize forums addressing insurance implications of Super-storm Sandy in late 2012. She has been named one of the Top 50 Women Attorneys in DC, and is a former member of the ABA Commission on Women in the Profession. Her Liability Insurance in International Arbitration: The Bermuda Form won the British Insurance Law Association's 2012 Book Prize.

## MAY, Gregory
Freshfields Bruckhaus Deringer LLP, Washington, DC
202 777 4500
gregory.may@freshfields.com
*Featured in Tax (District of Columbia)*
**Practice Areas:** Greg is a partner based in Freshfields Bruckhaus Deringer's Washington, DC office. Greg's international tax practice focuses on cross-border transactions, including mergers and acquisitions, work-outs, structured finance and international joint ventures. He advises many financial institutions on derivatives and other complex financial transactions. Greg is a member of the Permanent Scientific Committee of the International Fiscal Association and president-elect of its USA branch. Before entering private

practice, he clerked for Justice Powell of the Supreme Court of the United States.

## MAZAWEY, Louis T
Groom Law Group, Washington, DC
202 861 6608
LMazawey@groom.com
*Featured in Employee Benefits & Executive Compensation (Nationwide), Employee Benefits & Executive Compensation (District of Columbia)*
See under Nationwide for profile.

## MCBEE, Susan
Baker, Donelson, Bearman, Caldwell & Berkowitz, PC, Washington, DC
202 508 3450
smcbee@bakerdonelson.com
*Featured in Intellectual Property (District of Columbia)*
**Practice Areas:** Shareholder and chair of the Life Sciences Intellectual Property Team. Registered patent attorney with practice focused in the fields of biotechnology, chemistry, material science and engineering. Experienced in patent and trademark portfolio management for large companies and in IP due diligence during acquisitions and licensing negotiations. Represents clients in chemical, biotechnology and engineering fields.
**Professional Memberships:** American and Frederick County, Maryland Bar Association. American Intellectual Property Lawyers Association.
**Career:** D.C., 1998. U.S. Court of Appeals Federal Circuit, 1997; MD, 1996 and USPTO, 1994.
**Personal:** George Mason University School of Law (JD-1996), highest honors; Alderson Broaddus (BS Chem-1987), Cumlaude

## MCBRIDE, Andrew G
Wiley Rein LLP, Washington, DC
202 719 7135
amcbride@wileyrein.com
*Featured in Telecommunications (District of Columbia)*
**Practice Areas:** Chair, Communication Litigation; Co-chair, Appellate Practice. 25+ years of trial, appellate and Supreme Court experience in telecommunications, Internet services, administrative law, constitutional law and general commercial litigation involving copyright, commercial speech, utility deregulation and privacy law. DC Communications Law "Lawyer of the Year" 2013.
**Professional Memberships:** Federal Communications Bar Association; ABA.
**Career:** Special Assistant, DOJ, Office of Legal Counsel; Associate Deputy Attorney General, Office of the Deputy Attorney General; Assistant U.S. Attorney, U.S. Attorney's Office for the Eastern District of Virginia/Chief of Appeals for the District.
**Personal:** Stanford Law School (JD); College of the Holy Cross (BA).

## MCCARTY, Philip A
McDermott Will & Emery LLP, Washington, DC
202 756 8145
pmccarty@mwe.com
*Featured in Tax (District of Columbia)*

**Practice Areas:** Advises clients, predominantly large publicly held companies, on a wide range of domestic and international tax issues, including issues relating to global joint ventures, financial products, tax accounting and lease financing.
**Career:** Former partner in the Washington National Tax Services Department at a global accounting firm, associate tax legislative counsel in Office of Tax Policy, U.S. Department of Treasury and law clerk for Judge William M. Fay of the United States Tax Court. Currently an adjunct faculty member, Georgetown University Law Center.
**Personal:** University of Denver (JD); New York University School of Law (LLM); University of Colorado (BS).

### MCCUTCHEN, Tammy D
Littler Mendelson, PC, Washington, DC
202 842 3400
tmccutchen@littler.com
*Featured in Labor & Employment (District of Columbia)*
**Practice Areas:** Wage and Hour; Legislative and Regulatory Practice; Staffing and Contingent Workers; Policies, Procedures and Handbooks; Class Actions
**Professional Memberships:** District of Columbia, Illinois
**Career:** Former Administrator of the U.S. Department of Labor's Wage and Hour Division, Ms. McCutchen is a leading authority on federal and state wage and hour laws. Before her work at the Department of Labor, Ms. McCutchen was Senior Counsel at The Hershey Company in Hershey, Pennsylvania.
**Personal:** JD, Northwestern University, cum laude, 1990; BA, Western Illinois University, summa cum laude, 1987

### MCDONALD, Bruce
Jones Day, Washington, DC
832 239 3822
bmcdonald@jonesday.com
*Featured in Antitrust (District of Columbia), Antitrust (Texas)*
See under Texas for profile.

### MCGUINESS, John
Groom Law Group, Washington, DC
202 861 6625
jmcguiness@groom.com
*Featured in Employee Benefits & Executive Compensation (District of Columbia)*
**Practice Areas:** Executive Principal and head of firm's Executive Compensation Practice Group. Concentrates practice on executive compensation arrangements for large public companies. Has particular expertise in the tax, securities law, and ERISA issues for executive deferred compensation and equity compensation arrangements.
**Career:** Admitted in the District of Columbia. Worked as a C.P.A. before attending law school.
**Publications:** Has written articles and spoken on topics such as deferred compensation rules under Code section 409A, performance-based compensation, SEC's executive compensation disclosure rules, rabbi trusts, and Sarbanes-Oxley Act.

**Personal:** University of Virginia (BS, with distinction, 1987); William and Mary (JD, 1993).

### MCJUNKIN, John
McKenna Long & Aldridge LLP, Washington, DC
202 496 7312
jmcjunkin@mckennalong.com
*Featured in Bankruptcy/Restructuring (District of Columbia)*
**Practice Areas:** For over 25 years, John McJunkin's practice has been focused on loan restructuring and workouts, business insolvencies and commercial litigation. Mr McJunkin works extensively with creditors and debtors in protecting their rights during workouts, litigation, foreclosures, and bankruptcy. As part of his work for his creditor clients, Mr McJunkin regularly negotiates and documents restructurings and workout arrangements of complex commercial lending relationships. Mr McJunkin also assists commercial borrowers in workout negotiations and bankruptcy planning. As part of his bankruptcy practice, Mr McJunkin routinely helps clients acquire assets in the context of insolvency.

### MCKEE, Bill
Bingham McCutchen LLP, Washington, DC
202 373 6580
william.mckee@bingham.com
*Featured in Tax (District of Columbia)*
**Practice Areas:** Co-leader of Bingham's Tax Group. Practice encompasses all areas of federal taxation, with a special emphasis on partnership taxation. One of the founding partners of McKee Nelson, which joined Bingham in 2009. Frequent speaker at seminars around the US on the subject of partnership taxation and author of numerous articles.
**Career:** Former tax legislative counsel, US Treasury Department.
**Publications:** Co-author, 'Federal Taxation of Partnerships and Partners'; Co-author, 'Structuring and Drafting Partnership Agreements: Including LLC Agreements.'
**Personal:** Harvard Law School, JD, magna cum laude, 1969; Yale University, BA, cum laude, 1966.

### MCKELVIE, Roderick R
Covington & Burling LLP, Washington, DC
202 662 5195
rmckelvie@cov.com
*Featured in Intellectual Property (District of Columbia)*
**Practice Areas:** Handles IP and commercial matters at the trial and appellate level.
**Professional Memberships:** Member and former President of Giles Rich American Inn of Court; Member, Board of Directors of the International Judicial Academy and National Model Patent Jury Instruction Committee.
**Career:** United States District Judge for the District of Delaware 1992-2002. Presided over more than 200 patent infringement cases, including over 30 patent infringement trials. Teaches Patent Enforcement at George Washington University Law School.
**Publications:** Communicating with Judges in IP Cases; Forum Selection in Patent Cases

**Personal:** Harvard University, BA, 1968; University of Pennsylvania Law School, JD, 1973

### MEADE, Kenneth
WilmerHale, Washington, DC
202 663 6196
kenneth.meade@wilmerhale.com
*Featured in Environment (District of Columbia)*
**Practice Areas:** Partner, Regulatory and Government Affairs Department; member Environmental, Public Policy and Strategy and Government Regulatory Litigation Practice Groups. Practice focuses on counseling, enforcement and transactional issues with particular emphasis on Clean Air Act and climate change, development of natural resources, federal and state environmental laws, and transactions.
**Professional Memberships:** ABA Section of Environment, Energy and Resources, Air and Waste Management Association, Environmental Law Institute and ASTM.
**Publications:** Co-author of The Clean Air Act Amendments: Strategies for the 1990s and The Clean Air Act Amendments: Updated Strategies.
**Personal:** JD, George Washington University Law School; BA, University of Michigan.

### MECHANICK, Maury J
White & Case LLP, Washington, DC
202 626 3635
mmechanick@whitecase.com
*Featured in Telecommunications (District of Columbia)*
**Career:** To view a comprehensive biography, please visit www.whitecase.com/mmechanick.

### MENOTTI, David E
Crowell & Moring LLP, Washington, DC
202 624 2984
dmenotti@crowell.com
*Featured in Environment (District of Columbia)*
**Practice Areas:** Practice emphasizes the regulation of air pollution under the Clean Air Act, and the regulation of hazardous substances under laws such as the Federal Insecticide, Fungicide, and Rodenticide Act; the Toxic Substances Control Act; the Federal Food, Drug, and Cosmetic Act; and the Clean Air Act. Menotti also represents clients with matters arising under related state laws and regulations.
**Professional Memberships:** Environmental sections of the American and District of Columbia Bar Associations.
**Personal:** JD, University of Pennsylvania Law School, 1967 (magna cum laude; Editor, 'University of Pennsylvania Law Review,' 1966-67; Order of the Coif); AB, Syracuse University, 1964.

### MERON, Daniel
Latham & Watkins LLP, Washington, DC
202 637 2218
daniel.meron@lw.com
*Featured in Healthcare (District of Columbia)*
**Practice Areas:** Regulatory, investigatory and litigation expertise across broad range of healthcare and life sciences matters. Represents hospitals and other providers, health plans, medical device companies and pharmaceutical manufacturers in investigations and litigation. Provides regulatory and compliance counseling and advocates before

CMS and FDA on sensitive and high-stakes matters.
**Career:** Co-Chair, Healthcare & Life Sciences Practice Group; Co-Chair, Healthcare Services and Providers Industry Group; General Counsel, HHS (2006-07); Principal Deputy Assistant Attorney General (Civil), DOJ, 2003-06.
**Personal:** JD, Harvard Law School; AB Harvard College. Law Clerk to Justice Anthony M. Kennedy (Supreme Court) and Laurence H. Silberman (DC Circuit).

### MEYERS, Jim
Orrick, Herrington & Sutcliffe LLP, Washington, DC
202 339 8487
jmeyers@orrick.com
*Featured in Litigation (District of Columbia)*
**Practice Areas:** Jim Meyers has consistently achieved successful results for clients in the full range of SEC, PCAOB and FINRA enforcement investigation and litigation matters, including alleged accounting and financial fraud, auditor liability and broker-dealer issues, insider trading, and alleged false statements or omissions in SEC filings and elsewhere. Mr Meyers has also successfully represented clients in private securities litigation. Prior to joining Orrick, Mr Meyers served as Assistant Chief Litigation Counsel in the Securities and Exchange Commission's Division of Enforcement. During his tenure, he received the Chairman's Award for Excellence and the Capital Markets Award.

### MICALLEF, Joseph
Sidley Austin LLP, Washington, DC
202 736 8492
jmicallef@sidley.com
*Featured in Intellectual Property (District of Columbia)*
**Practice Areas:** Partner in Sidley's Intellectual Property practice. He represents clients with all types of intellectual property needs in many different circumstances. His litigation experience includes all phases of litigation, from commencement of suit, through fact and expert discovery, motion practice and trial, and he has appeared before federal district and appellate courts, federal agencies, and private arbitration panels. His case work has involved innovations in such cutting edge technologies as computer microarchitecture, multiprocessor computer systems, synchronous dynamic random access memory, search engines, digital rights management, semiconductor fabrication techniques, cellular communications technology, satellite television, computer graphics and voice messaging systems.

### MICHAELS, Joel
McDermott Will & Emery LLP, Washington, DC
202 756 8375
jmichaels@mwe.com
*Featured in Healthcare (Nationwide), Healthcare (District of Columbia)*
See under Nationwide for profile.

**MIGDAL, Nelson F**
Greenberg Traurig, LLP, Washington, DC
202 331 3180
MigdalN@gtlaw.com
*Featured in Leisure & Hospitality (Nationwide), Real Estate (District of Columbia)*
See under Nationwide for profile.

**MILCH, Thomas**
Arnold & Porter LLP, Washington, DC
202 942 5030
Thomas.Milch@aporter.com
*Featured in Environment (District of Columbia)*
**Practice Areas:** Thomas Milch is Chair of Arnold & Porter and former head of the firm's national Environmental Group. His practice covers environmental enforcement, litigation, and counseling. He has served as lead counsel on complex Superfund cleanups, highly visible regulatory investigations, allocation disputes, and toxic tort lawsuits. Over the last several years, he has represented BP on key environmental aspects of the Deepwater Horizon oil spill.He is also a former adjunct environmental law professor at Georgetown Law Center.
**Personal:** JD, Yale Law School, 1976; BA, Yale University, 1973, summa cum laude.

**MILLER, Evan**
Jones Day, Washington, DC
202 879 3840
emiller@jonesday.com
*Featured in ERISA Litigation (Nationwide), Employee Benefits & Executive Compensation (District of Columbia)*
See under Nationwide for profile.

**MILLER, Laura Ariane**
Nixon Peabody LLP, Washington, DC
202 585 8313
lmiller@nixonpeabody.com
*Featured in Litigation (District of Columbia)*
**Practice Areas:** Represents corporations and individuals in criminal, civil, and Congressional investigations and enforcement actions, including Foreign Corrupt Practices Act, False Claims Act, and securities, tax, health care and antitrust laws. Conducts internal investigations on behalf of Audit Committees and corporations in the US and overseas.
**Professional Memberships:** Admitted in Virginia and DC, the United States Supreme Court, and numerous federal courts. Former Chair, ABA Criminal Litigation Committee.
**Career:** Clerked at the United States Supreme Court for Justice Byron R. White.
**Personal:** Yale Law School, JD; Harvard University, Kennedy School of Government, MPP; University of Michigan, BA.

**MILLSPAUGH, Thomas E D**
Venable LLP, Washington, DC
202 344 4596
temillspaugh@Venable.com
*Featured in Real Estate (District of Columbia)*
**Practice Areas:** Real estate investment, development and finance. All major property types. Transactions include joint ventures, purchases/sales, leases and financings (including workouts).

**Professional Memberships:** Pension Real Estate Association; Urban Land Institute; Advisory Board, CTIC.
**Career:** Multi-faceted career in real estate. Practice is divided between local work in the Mid-Atlantic region and national work across the US Clients include real estate funds, investment managers, developers, banks and individual investors. Advanced real estate knowledge includes corporate, tax, bankruptcy, environmental and other areas affecting real estate.
**Personal:** JD, University of Virginia; BA, Highest Honors, UNC - Chapel Hill (Phi Beta Kappa, Morehead Scholar).

**MILNE, Karen**
Akin Gump Strauss Hauer & Feld LLP, Washington, DC
202 416 5024
kmilne@akingump.com
*Featured in Telecommunications (District of Columbia)*
**Practice Areas:** Concentrates on domestic and international communications matters related to broadcast, satellite, telecommunications, wireless and advanced technology companies, including issues related to licensing, rulemakings, regulatory compliance, acquisitions and commercial transactions.
**Career:** Worked in international and domestic business development for ZDNet and CNET Networks, Inc.
**Personal:** BA magna cum laude in English in 1996 from Manhattanville College. JD summa cum laude in 2004 from American University's Washington College of Law, Order of the Coif, American University Law Review.

**MINTZ, Douglas S**
Cadwalader, Wickersham & Taft LLP, Washington, DC
202 862 2475
douglas.mintz@cwt.com
*Featured in Bankruptcy/Restructuring (District of Columbia)*
**Practice Areas:** Experience in all aspects of bankruptcy and restructuring. Primarily represents secured lenders and bondholders. Best known for his work representing United States Treasury in the General Motors and Chrysler bankruptcies. Recently represented Barclays (Contec, LandSource), J.P. Morgan (Station Casinos, Extended Stay) and Whippoorwill (Trailer Bridge) as secured lenders. Deep knowledge of municipal bankruptcies such as Stockton and Jefferson County, representing bondholders. Extensive experience with asset sales in and out of bankruptcy (Auto companies, DDMG, private pre-bankruptcy shipping company). A leader in close out of safe harbored derivatives and structuring bankruptcy remote entities.
**Publications:** Frequent author and Managing Editor, Cadwalader Restructuring Review (www.restructuringreview.com).
**Personal:** JD, University of Virginia School of Law; BA, University of Maryland (magna cum laude).

**MOONEY, Marilyn**
Fulbright & Jaworski LLP, Washington, DC
202 662 4678
mmooney@fulbright.com
*Featured in Corporate/M&A (District of Columbia)*
**Practice Areas:** Mergers & Acquisitions; Corporate Securities; Corporate Governance; International.
**Professional Memberships:** Society of Corporate Secretaries and Governance Professionals, Securities Law Committee; American Bar Association, Federal Regulation of Securities Committee.
**Career:** Chair of Fulbright's M&A practice group; Heads the Corporate and Securities practice in the Washington, DC office. Named "Best Lawyers in America," "Leading Lawyers in America" by Lawdragon and "Legal Elite" by SmartCEO magazine. For more than 25 years, she has handled corporate and securities matters for major multinational companies.
**Personal:** JD, University of Pennsylvania Law School (1976); BA, summa cum laude, University of Pennsylvania (1973).

**MOORE, Amy N**
Covington & Burling LLP, Washington, DC
202 662 5390
anmoore@cov.com
*Featured in Employee Benefits & Executive Compensation (District of Columbia)*
**Practice Areas:** Amy Moore advises some of the world's largest multinational companies on a wide range of tax, ERISA, health care, and employment law issues concerning all types of compensation arrangements and benefit programs. She represents companies in audits and contested agency proceedings; she counsels plan fiduciaries and asset managers on pension investments; and she advises on executive compensation and employee benefits issues in corporate transactions and litigation.
**Personal:** University of Virginia School of Law, JD, 1983; Virginia Law Review, Articles Editor; University of Virginia, MA, 1978; Mount Holyoke College, AB, 1976, summa cum laude and Phi Beta Kappa.

**MOORE, Matthew**
Latham & Watkins LLP, Washington, DC
202 637 2278
matthew.moore@lw.com
*Featured in Intellectual Property (District of Columbia)*
**Practice Areas:** Extensive trial and appellate experience representing patentees and defendants and provides strategic IP business counseling. Represented numerous Fortune 100 companies. Appointed liaison counsel on behalf of 270 defendants in the largest Multi-District Litigation patent case in history, and obtained summary judgment of invalidity on 46 asserted claims. Served as lead counsel to obtain judgment of invalidity on 62 claims for client Amazon and 616 claims for client Freddie Mac.
**Personal:** LLM, George Washington University Law School, 2000, JD, Syracuse University College of Law, 1995; MS, Systems Engineering, University

of Pennsylvania, 1993; BS, Electrical Engineering, Syracuse University, 1991.

**MORRISON, Valerie P**
Wiley Rein LLP, McLean
703 905 2826
vmorrison@wileyrein.com
*Featured in Bankruptcy/Restructuring (District of Columbia)*
**Practice Areas:** More than 25 years experience representing diverse clients in a wide range of restructurings, Chapter 11 reorganization cases, liquidations, receivership proceedings and litigation matters. Clients include reorganizing businesses, creditors, committees, bankruptcy trustees, and purchasers of distressed assets. Named a "Top Bankruptcy Lawyer" by Washingtonian magazine. Recognized as one of the "Best Lawyers in America" and as a Washington, DC and Virginia "Super Lawyer" in the areas of bankruptcy and creditor-debtor rights. Board Certified in Business Bankruptcy Law by the American Board of Certification.
**Personal:** George Washington University Law School (JD); George Washington University (BA, with distinction).

**MOYER, Dennis K**
Buchanan Ingersoll & Rooney PC, Washington, DC
202 452 7988
dennis.moyer@bipc.com
*Featured in Real Estate (District of Columbia)*
**Career:** Dennis is a Shareholder in the firm's Financial Services and Real Estate Sections. His practice focuses on commercial real estate and commercial financing, including acquisition, financing and leasing matters. His experience encompasses all aspects of the acquisition, development, financing, management and leasing of commercial real estate, including the structuring of joint ventures and mortgage financings between real estate operators and institutional investors. He also counsels corporate tenants, governmental agencies, institutional lenders and real estate brokers in many aspects of real estate law. He earned his JD from Georgetown University Law Center and is actively involved in his community.

**MURIS, Timothy J**
Kirkland & Ellis LLP, Washington, DC
202 879 5105
tim.muris@kirkland.com
*Featured in Antitrust (District of Columbia)*
**Practice Areas:** Timothy Muris is Of Counsel to the Antitrust and Competition group in Kirkland's Washington, D.C., office. Tim represents clients on a variety of antitrust matters, including merger and non-merger investigations. He also advises clients on an array of consumer protection issues, and has testified before numerous US Congressional Committees on antitrust, consumer protection and regulatory and budget issues. Tim served as FTC Chairman from 2001-04, Director of the FTC's Bureau of Consumer Protection from 1981-83, and Director of the FTC's Bureau of Competition from 1983-85.

**MURRAY, James R**
Dickstein Shapiro LLP, Washington, DC
202 420 3409
murrayj@dicksteinshapiro.com
*Featured in Insurance (District of Columbia)*
**Practice Areas:** Professional Development
Leader of Dickstein Shapiro's Insurance Coverage
Group. Represents corporate policyholders on
professional indemnity, directors and officers,
securities fraud, and mortgage insurance.
**Professional Memberships:** He is admitted to
practice in the District of Columbia, New York,
and Washington. He also is admitted to practice
before the U.S. Supreme Court and various
Courts of Appeals.
**Personal:** Mr Murray received a BA from the
University of Montana and a BA in law from
Oxford University. He received a B.C.L. (graduate
law degree) from Oxford University and a JD
from Harvard Law School. He is a Rhodes
Scholar.

**MYERS, Donald J**
Morgan, Lewis & Bockius LLP, Washington,
DC
202 739 5666
dmyers@morganlewis.com
*Featured in Employee Benefits & Executive
Compensation (District of Columbia)*
**Practice Areas:** Donald J. Myers is a senior
counsel in Morgan Lewis's Employee Benefits and
Executive Compensation Practice. He focuses his
practice on the fiduciary responsibility provisions
of ERISA, and has experience counseling clients
on related securities, banking, and insurance
issues.
**Professional Memberships:** Mr Myers is a
charter fellow of the American College of
Employee Benefits Counsel and a board member
of BNA Pension & Benefits Advisory Board.
**Personal:** Graduated from Georgetown
University Law Center (LLM), Cornell Law School
(JD), and College of the City of New York (BA).
Admitted to practice in the District of Columbia.

**NAGEL, Trevor**
White & Case LLP, Washington, DC
202 626 3616
tnagel@whitecase.com
*Featured in Outsourcing (Nationwide), Technology
(District of Columbia)*
See under Nationwide for profile.

**NAGER, Glen**
Jones Day, Washington, DC
202 879 5464
gdnager@jonesday.com
*Featured in Labor & Employment (District of
Columbia), Appellate Law (Nationwide)*
See under Nationwide for profile.

**NAKAHATA, John T**
Wiltshire & Grannis LLP, Washington, DC
202 730 1320
jnakahata@wiltshiregrannis.com
*Featured in Telecommunications (District of
Columbia)*
**Practice Areas:** Mr Nakahata leads the
telecommunications practice at Wiltshire &
Grannis, focusing on telecommunications, cable,

and Internet regulation before the FCC, courts
and Congress.
**Career:** Chief of Staff, the FCC, 1997-98 (other
positions 1995-97); U.S. Senate counsel, Sen.
Lieberman. Major transactions include: D.T. –
VoiceStream; Frontier – Verizon; Level 3 – Global
Crossing.
**Publications:** Authored articles including the
2012 and 2013 US chapter in 'Getting the Deal
Through, Telecoms and Media';"Regulating
Information Platforms: the Challenge of
Rewriting Communications Regulation from the
Bottom Up' (Journal on Telecommunications &
High Technology Law).
**Personal:** Harvard Law School, JD. Wesleyan
University, BA.

**NAKAYAMA, Granta Y**
Kirkland & Ellis LLP, Washington, DC
202 879 5074
granta.nakayama@kirkland.com
*Featured in Environment (District of Columbia)*
**Practice Areas:** Mr Nakayama represents companies whose products or services are regulated by
the U.S. Environmental Protection Agency, the
Consumer Product Safety Commission, the
Department of Energy, and state government
agencies. His work includes the defense of civil
and criminal enforcement actions, litigation
involving regulations, permits, and rate proceed-
ings, and agency rulemakings and Congressional
matters.
**Career:** U.S. Environmental Protection Agency,
Assistant Administrator for the Office of
Enforcement and Compliance Assurance, 2005-
09. US Navy, LT, 1981-86.
**Personal:** Massachusetts Institute of Technology,
SB, SM, (Nuclear Engineering) 1981. George
Mason University School of Law, JD, 1994.

**NALDA, Carlos M**
Squire Sanders (US) LLP, Washington, DC
202 626 6659
carlos.nalda@squiresanders.com
*Featured in Telecommunications (District of
Columbia)*
**Practice Areas:** Specialization: Partner advises
private and public sector clients on broad range of
domestic and international policy, regulatory and
transactional issues in the communications sector
with particular focus on satellite and wireless matters. Practices before the FCC and has represented
clients in licensing, spectrum allocation, transaction review and other proceedings. Also advises
clients internationally on commercial issues, foreign market access and telecommunications regulation. Has participated in international telecommunications conferences, satellite coordinations
and joint venture development. Has advised companies providing a wide range of communications
services, including advanced Internet, wireless,
and satellite services, in the US and around the
world.

**NANNES, John M**
Skadden, Arps, Slate, Meagher & Flom LLP
& Affiliates, Washington, DC
202 371 7500
John.Nannes@skadden.com
*Featured in Antitrust (District of Columbia)*
**Practice Areas:** Broad antitrust practice
includes cartel investigations in the US and
Europe, multidistrict treble-damage litigation, and
domestic and international mergers and acquisi-
tions. Substantial experience in network industries
such as airlines, railroads, trucking, securities,
energy.
**Professional Memberships:** Board of Trustees
of the Legal Aid Society of Washington, D.C., and
Board of Directors of the District of Columbia
Bar Foundation.
**Career:** Acting Assistant Attorney General (2001)
and Deputy Assistant Attorney General, Antitrust
Division, U.S. Department of Justice (1998-2001);
Law Clerk to Justice William Rehnquist (1974-75).
JD (1973) and B.BA (1970), University of
Michigan.
**Personal:** Recipient of the Learned Hand Award
(2009).

**NASH, Daniel L**
Akin Gump Strauss Hauer & Feld LLP,
Washington, DC
202 887 4067
dnash@akingump.com
*Featured in Labor & Employment (District of
Columbia), Sports Law (Nationwide)*
See under Nationwide for profile.

**NASSIKAS, John**
Arnold & Porter LLP, Washington, DC
202 942 6820
John.Nassikas@aporter.com
*Featured in Litigation (District of Columbia)*
**Practice Areas:** Responsible partner for the
firm's national and international white collar
practice, advises and defends companies and indi-
viduals in criminal investigations and prosecu-
tions, particularly in the areas of healthcare fraud,
financial fraud, antitrust, government contracts,
SEC enforcement, and global anti-corruption.
Concentrates on complex parallel criminal and
civil litigations and internal corporate investigations.
**Professional Memberships:**
**Career:** Assistant US Attorney for the Eastern
District of Virginia, 1991 to 1995.
**Personal:** JD, University of Virginia, 1984; BA,
magna cum laude, Yale University, 1981.

**NATHANSON, Kirsten L**
Crowell & Moring LLP, Washington, DC
202 624 2887
knathanson@crowell.com
*Featured in Environment (District of Columbia)*
**Practice Areas:** Partner in the firm's
Environment, Energy & Resources Group, focusing on environmental litigation, enforcement
defense, risk assessment, and regulatory counseling under the major federal environmental and
public lands statutes. Her litigation experience
covers the Clean Water Act, Clean Air Act,
Endangered Species Act, FIFRA, NEPA, SMCRA,

RCRA, and CERCLA, encompassing citizen suit
defense, regulatory challenges, remediation cost
recovery and defense, Administrative Procedure
Act actions, and EPA enforcement.
**Career:** Serves as Past President of the
Washington, D.C. Chapter of the Women's Energy
Network. Past President and member of the Board
of Trustees of the Energy & Mineral Law
Foundation.

**NELSON, Mark W**
Cleary Gottlieb Steen & Hamilton LLP,
Washington, DC
202 974 1622
mnelson@cgsh.com
*Featured in Antitrust (District of Columbia)*
**Practice Areas:** US practice includes extensive
merger work and antitrust counseling, as well as
civil litigation and FTC administrative proceed-
ings. European practice involves merger cases at
both EU and Member State levels, and defending
actions involving alleged restraints of trade and
abuses of dominant position. Represents clients in
a wide range of industries.
**Professional Memberships:** Member of the
DC and New York Bars. ABA Antitrust Section
Leadership.
**Career:** Became partner, 2002. Harvard Law
School (JD, magna cum laude), 1992; Cornell
University (BS), 1989. Law clerk, Judge Andrew
Kleinfeld, U.S. Court of Appeals, Ninth Circuit
(1992-93).

**NELSON, William F**
Bingham McCutchen LLP, Washington, DC
202 373 6782
william.nelson@bingham.com
*Featured in Tax (District of Columbia), Tax
(Nationwide)*
See under Nationwide for profile.

**NESS, Andrew D**
Jones Day, Washington, DC
202 879 7675
adness@jonesday.com
*Featured in Construction (District of Columbia)*
**Practice Areas:** Assists owners and contractors
with troubled projects, solving complex construction and design-related problems without need
for formal dispute resolution whenever practicable. In litigated matters, he has served as lead
counsel on large construction disputes that were
resolved in federal and state courts and via
domestic and international arbitrations. The
projects that Andy has assisted encompass a broad
range of energy, industrial and process, government, institutional, commercial, and building
projects across the United States and internationally.
**Professional Memberships:** Fellow of the
American College of Construction Lawyers. Chair
of the ABA Forum on the Construction Indsutry.

**NEWBORN, Steven A**
Weil, Gotshal & Manges LLP, Washington,
DC
202 682 7000
steven.newborn@weil.com
*Featured in Antitrust (District of Columbia)*

**Practice Areas:** Steve Newborn, global Head of Weil's Antitrust Practice, specializes in high stakes antitrust litigation and 'bet the company' mergers for Fortune 100 companies encompassing a wide array of industries and international venues. He has successfully obtained approvals for several hundred transactions, many of which had run into regulatory problems before he was retained. He is ranked by every publication as one of the best in the profession and has been called the "best antitrust lawyer of his generation." Prior to joining Weil, he led Clifford Chance's global Antitrust Group. Before that he ran the FTC's merger enforcement program.

### NEWMAN, Richard
Arent Fox LLP, Washington, DC
202 857 6170
richard.newman@arentfox.com
*Featured in Real Estate (District of Columbia)*
**Practice Areas:** Richard Newman represents clients in all phases of real estate acquisition, development, financing, leasing and disposition, as well as nonprofit and for-profit organizations in federal and local tax matters. He also provides services as borrower's counsel, underwriter's counsel, credit enhancement counsel, trustee's counsel, servicer/originator counsel and bond counsel to clients nationally in the municipal and public finance area. His clients include credit enhancers, numerous cultural institutions, public policy groups, quasi-governmental entities, and nonprofit organizations. Case Western Reserve University, JD, 1980; New York University, BA, 1977.

### NICKEL, Henry V
Hunton & Williams LLP, Washington, DC
202 955 1561
hnickel@hunton.com
*Featured in Environment (District of Columbia)*
**Practice Areas:** Henry Nickel's practice focuses on complex administrative and judicial proceedings arising under the Clean Air Act, Clean Water Act, and National Environmental Policy Act. He has represented companies in virtually every major Clean Air Act rulemaking and related judicial review proceeding. He has briefed and argued numerous cases in federal Circuit Courts and District Courts throughout the country and defended major Clean Air Act enforcement actions and citizen suits. He has counseled a broad spectrum of clients on environmental permitting strategies and corporate compliance programs.

### NIELDS, John W
Covington & Burling LLP, Washington, DC
202 236 5530
jnields@cov.com
*Featured in Litigation (District of Columbia)*
**Practice Areas:** John Nields specializes in antitrust and other civil litigation, arbitration, and white collar criminal defense. He has particular expertise in criminal appeals and matters involving the U.S. Congress. As special counsel for the Justice Department, Mr Nields successfully prosecuted top FBI officials for authorizing secret searches into the homes of innocent American cit-

izens. In private practice, he defended Webster Hubbell against a series of indictments filed by the independent counsel investigating former President Clinton. He also served as chief counsel of the House panel investigating the Iran-Contra scandal.
**Personal:** University of Pennsylvania Law School; Yale University

### NILLES, Kathleen M
Holland & Knight LLP, Washington, DC
202 457 1815
Kathleen.Nilles@hklaw.com
*Featured in Tax (District of Columbia)*
**Practice Areas:** Taxation; Exempt Organizations; Native American Indian Law.
**Professional Memberships:** Intertribal Tax Alliance, Board of Directors.
**Career:** Kathleen M. Nilles focuses her practice on resolving critical tax and business organizational issues for tax-exempt and governmental entities. She regularly handles IRS audits and other tax controversies for Indian tribal governments and tax-exempt organizations. She also spearheads federal tax policy and legislative issues for a wide spectrum of organizations, governmental units and companies.
**Publications:** Tribal Business Structure Handbook (2009: Native American Financial Officers Association); Tax Exempt Status of Health Care Organizations (BNA Health Law and Business Portfolio).

### NUECHTERLEIN, Jonathan
WilmerHale, Washington, DC
202 663 6850
jon.nuechterlein@wilmerhale.com
*Featured in Telecommunications (District of Columbia)*
**Practice Areas:** Chair, Communications, Privacy, and Internet Law Practice Group. Practice focuses on appellate litigation and telecommunications law. Has represented major telecommunications clients before the federal courts and the FCC in connection with broadband services, Internet policy and antitrust issues.
**Career:** Previously served as FCC Deputy General Counsel and Assistant to the Solicitor General.
**Publications:** Author (with Phil Weiser) of Digital Crossroads: American Telecommunications Policy in the Internet Age (MIT Press 2005, 2007).
**Personal:** Yale University (JD 1990, BA 1986 (summa cum laude)). Law clerk to Justice David Souter (Supreme Court, 1991-92) and Judge Stephen Williams (DC Circuit, 1990-91).

### O'BRIEN, Claudia
Latham & Watkins LLP, Washington, DC
202 637 2181
claudia.o'brien@lw.com
*Featured in Environment (District of Columbia)*
**Practice Areas:** Represents clients in agency petitions, rulemaking proceedings and litigation, as well as on compliance and enforcement, in a full range federal environmental statutes. Has particular expertise in all aspects of the Clean Air Act and FIFRA, as well as the Clean Water Act, RCRA,

and the ESA, and regulations impacting genetically engineered plants. Possesses specialized technical and business knowledge of power plants (both fossil-fueled and biomass-fueled) and the pesticide industry, as well as particular expertise in toxicology and risk assessment.
**Career:** Air Quality and Climate Change Practice Group Chair.
**Personal:** JD, Georgetown University Law Center; BA, Yale University.

### O'BRIEN, Kevin
Jones Day, Washington, DC
202 879 7678
kobrien@jonesday.com
*Featured in Construction (District of Columbia)*
**Practice Areas:** For 25 years Kevin has represented owners, contractors and design professionals on public/private construction projects in the areas of dispute resolution, project counseling and contract negotiation. His practice has focused on the energy industry (nuclear, fossil, renewable) and other infrastructure projects such as chemical, refinery, aerospace, water treatment, subway, tunnel, highway and telecommunication facilities. He is an experienced trial lawyer in federal and state courts, international and domestic arbitrations. He has served as counsel on some of the largest infrastructure projects in the world.
**Publications:** Author of numerous works and speaks regularly on construction issues.

### OGDEN, David W
WilmerHale, Washington, DC
202 663 6440
david.ogden@wilmerhale.com
*Featured in Litigation (District of Columbia)*
**Practice Areas:** Chair, Government and Regulatory Litigation Practice Group. Complex civil litigation and government enforcement actions. Commercial and public international litigation and arbitration, including contract disputes, expropriation, enforcement of judgments; antitrust and competition; False Claims Act and fraud; anti-discrimination; environmental; Constitutional, and administrative law. Strategic advice and crisis management.
**Career:** U.S. Deputy Attorney General 2009-2010; Assistant Attorney General, Civil Division, USDOJ 1999-2001; Chief of Staff and Counselor to U.S. Attorney General 1997-1999; Associate Deputy Attorney General 1995-1997; Deputy General Counsel, U.S. Department of Defense (1994-1995); Public Member, Administrative Conference of United States (2010—present).

### OGROSKY, Kirk
Arnold & Porter LLP, Washington, DC
202 942 5330
Kirk.Ogrosky@aporter.com
*Featured in Healthcare (District of Columbia)*
**Practice Areas:** Mr Ogrosky is a trial attorney who defends companies and executives in False Claims Act; Anti-Kickback Statute; Food, Drug, and Cosmetic Act; and FCPA matters. Since 2000, he has taken 37 defendants through trial to verdict. In his last 15 federal trials, juries have reached verdicts in his favor. He has been

described by his peers as "one of the premier health care experts in the United States."
**Career:** Former head of criminal healthcare fraud at DOJ from 2006 to 2010. Former AUSA in Miami from 1999-2004. He teaches health care fraud as an Adjunct Professor at Georgetown.

### OLCOTT, Bruce
Squire Sanders (US) LLP, Washington, DC
202 626 6615
bruce.olcott@squiresanders.com
*Featured in Telecommunications (District of Columbia)*
**Practice Areas:** Focuses on regulatory and transactional issues involving wireless and wireline communications services using satellite, cellular, Internet, fiber and other broadband networks. Assists in securing domestic and international authorizations for acquisition, construction and operation of commercial and private communications networks; and in licensing, leasing, coordination and transfer of spectrum rights. Represents clients in rulemakings and consultations before regulatory authorities, often seeking removal of legal barriers to new communications services. Negotiates agreements for communications equipment and services including purchase, distribution, carriage and transmission capacity on satellite, wireless and wireline communications systems and indefeasible rights of use on fiber networks.

### OLIPHANT, Fred
Miller & Chevalier Chartered, Washington, DC
202 626 5834
foliphant@milchev.com
*Featured in Employee Benefits & Executive Compensation (District of Columbia)*
**Practice Areas:** Employee benefits and executive compensation offered by Fortune 500 companies, with an emphasis on federal tax.
**Career:** Over 30 years experience representing clients before the IRS, Department of Treasury, and Department of Labor. Has extensive experience with executive compensation and unfunded deferred compensation programs, and also tax-qualified defined benefit plans, 401(k) savings plans and ESOPs; also advises clients regarding health plans, cafeteria plans, VEBAs, other welfare and fringe benefit programs, and IRS nonbank custodian rules.
**Personal:** JD, University of Michigan Law School, cum laude, 1975; AB, University of North Carolina at Chapel Hill, Phi Beta Kappa, 1971.

### ONDECK, Christopher
Crowell & Moring LLP, Washington, DC
202 624 2855
condeck@crowell.com
*Featured in Antitrust (District of Columbia)*
**Practice Areas:** Partner in Crowell & Moring LLP's Antitrust Group. He focuses his practice on all aspects of antitrust law, including defending mergers, acquisitions and joint ventures, antitrust litigation and government investigations, and antitrust compliance issues. Ondeck has handled antitrust matters in a number of industries, including aerospace, agriculture, alcoholic bever-

ages, appliances, associations, building materials, defense, directory publishing, educational publishing, energy, forestry products, medical devices, metals, mining, oil and gas, packaging, pharmaceuticals, software, and telecommunications.
**Personal:** University of Virginia, BA, 1992; University of Virginia School of Law, JD

### OOSTERHUIS, Paul W
Skadden, Arps, Slate, Meagher & Flom LLP & Affiliates, Washington, DC
202 371 7130
Paul.Oosterhuis@skadden.com
*Featured in Tax (District of Columbia)*
**Practice Areas:** Global head of Skadden's Regulatory practices and represents clients on a wide range of international and domestic tax matters with experience in international M&A, post-acquisition integration transactions, spin-offs, internal restructurings and joint ventures. Represents US and non-US multinational companies in nontransactional international tax planning, including transfer pricing matters. Also counsels clients on IRS controversy matters, including audits and appeals, and has negotiated various advance pricing agreements, prefiling agreements and competent authority agreements.
**Career:** Legislation Counsel (1977-78) and Legislation Attorney (1973-76), Joint Committee On Taxation. JD, Harvard University (1973); BA, Brown University (1969).

### ORR, Kevyn D
Jones Day, Washington, DC
202 879 5560
korr@jonesday.com
*Featured in Bankruptcy/Restructuring (District of Columbia)*
**Practice Areas:** Has practiced in the areas of business restructuring, financial institution regulation, and commercial litigation since 1983. Served in federal government in leadership positions in DOJ, RTC and FDIC. Has assisted clients with government RFPs, inspector general audits and special prosecutor investigations. He is a frequent lecturer at professional conferences and law schools and has testified before the U.S. Congress regarding bankruptcy and financial institution regulation.
**Professional Memberships:** Member of the bars of Florida and the District of Columbia, the ABA, and the American Bankruptcy Institute. Recently recognized by Washingtonian Magazine as a Top Lawyer.

### PALAN, Stephen
Crowell & Moring LLP, Washington, DC
202 624 2710
spalan@crowell.com
*Featured in Intellectual Property (District of Columbia)*
**Practice Areas:** Partner in Crowell & Moring's Intellectual Property Group. His practice focuses on intellectual property litigation and counseling, including world-wide strategic patent procurement and licensing, and trade secret protection. He has extensive experience in wireless, wireline, and data networking technologies, including access technologies, protocols, modulation, encod-

ing schemes and terminal design. He has worked extensively with international communication standards. Experienced in technologies such as digital and analog circuits, computer-software applications, consumer electronics, automotive fuel cells, and automotive emission control systems - and all aspects of US patent practice.
**Career:** Former Patent Examiner in the USPTO.

### PANAHY, Dara A
Milbank, Tweed, Hadley & McCloy LLP, Washington, DC
202 835 7521
DPanahy@milbank.com
*Featured in Telecommunications (District of Columbia)*
**Practice Areas:** Mr Panahy is a partner and a member of the Transportation and Space Finance Group. He represents satellite operators, aerospace manufacturers, launch services providers, communications companies, banks, private equity firms and hedge funds in numerous financings involving public offerings, high yield debt, investment grade bonds, project and vendor financings, mergers & acquisitions, financial restructuring and reorganizations and in negotiating project contracts. He counsels clients on regulatory and trade matters, including licensing of satellite, wireless and wireline communications systems, economic sanctions, foreign direct investment, anti-bribery and corrupt practices, national security and export control laws and regulations and risk management.

### PAPPAS, George F
Covington & Burling LLP, Washington, DC
202 662 5594
gpappas@cov.com
*Featured in Intellectual Property (District of Columbia)*
**Practice Areas:** Lead Counsel in more than 350 cases, including over 150 patent cases.
**Professional Memberships:** US District Court of Delaware Judges' IP Advisory Committee; Committee Member, New Jersey and Maryland District Court Local Patent Rules.
**Career:** Fellow and Chairman of the Complex Litigation Committee, American College of Trial Lawyers. Lectured on patent law at 32 Federal Judicial Center workshops. Chairman of Editorial Committee and co-author of "Anatomy of a Patent Case" (2009), prepared by the American College of Trial Lawyers and published with Federal Judicial Center. The book has been distributed to all judges of the federal judicial branch.

### PARAVANO, Jeffrey H
Baker & Hostetler LLP, Washington, DC
202 861 1770
jparavano@bakerlaw.com
*Featured in Tax (District of Columbia)*
**Career:** Managing Partner of BakerHostetler's Washington, D.C., office, Jeff Paravano previously served as Chair of the firm's Tax Group. He has a broad-based practice involving tax litigation; corporate, partnership and venture capital transactions; and domestic and cross-border tax planning. He also represents clients' interests before

federal policy makers, enforcement officials and on Capitol Hill. He previously served as Senior Advisor to the Assistant Secretary, Tax Policy, United States Department of Treasury, where he was responsible for providing advice on a range of tax policy and technical issues, including tax legislation and corporate, partnership, REIT and financial sector tax guidance.

### PATTERSON, Donna
Arnold & Porter LLP, Washington, DC
202 942 5006
Donna.Patterson@aporter.com
*Featured in Antitrust (District of Columbia)*
**Practice Areas:** Donna Patterson has represented numerous clients in Federal Trade Commission (FTC) and Department of Justice (DOJ) Antitrust Division investigations of proposed mergers and acquisitions, in state and federal court antitrust and complex commercial litigation, and as an antitrust counselor.
**Career:** She was Deputy Assistant Attorney General in the Antitrust Division of the United States Department of Justice (1997-2000) with responsibility for supervising the investigations and litigation of dozens of proposed transactions including US v Lockheed, US v Primestar, and US v Aetna; and for supervising the division's Health Care Task Force.

### PAUL, William M
Covington & Burling LLP, Washington, DC
202 662 5300
wpaul@cov.com
*Featured in Tax (District of Columbia)*
**Practice Areas:** Advises clients on federal income tax matters, with a focus on the taxation of financial products, financial transactions and investment funds. Advises in both the domestic and cross-border contexts. Specialties also include representing industry groups and other clients before the Treasury Department, the Internal Revenue Service and Congress.
**Professional Memberships:** Immediate Past Chair, ABA Tax Section (2012-13); Fellow, American College of Tax Counsel; Member, American Law Institute, Board of Trustees, American Tax Policy Institute.
**Career:** Deputy Tax Legislative Counsel, US Treasury Dept. (1988-89).
**Personal:** Johns Hopkins University, BA, (1973); University of Michigan, JD, magna cum laude, (1977).

### PELTA, Eleanor
Morgan, Lewis & Bockius LLP, Washington, DC
202 739 5050
epelta@morganlewis.com
*Featured in Immigration (Nationwide), Immigration (District of Columbia)*
**Practice Areas:** Eleanor Pelta is a partner in Morgan Lewis's Labor and Employment Practice. With her practice focused on immigration and nationality law, Eleanor assists corporate clients with the international transfer of key personnel from executives to specialized professionals. She is particularly knowledgeable about managing high-volume employee transfers, managing an interna-

tionally mobile workforce, and all aspects of immigration compliance. Eleanor is the immediate past President of the American Immigration Lawyers Association.
**Personal:** Attended Harvard Law School, JD; Princeton University, AB

### PENNA, Richard A
Van Ness Feldman LLP, Washington, DC
202 298 1870
rap@vnf.com
*Featured in Environment (District of Columbia)*
**Practice Areas:** Advises clients on motor vehicle emissions standards, fuel economy regulations, alternative fuels, plant sitings and operations, control of emissions of hazardous air pollutants from surface coating and other manufacturing processes, hazardous waste control, permitting, compliance, and enforcement matters. Played a leading role in the Clean Air Act considerations resulting in the 1990 amendments. Frequent speaker on Clean Air Act issues, mobile source emissions, and fuel economy programs.
**Career:** Assistant Director, National Commission on Air Quality, 1979-81; Attorney, Office of Enforcement and General Counsel, US Environmental Protection Agency, 1971-77.

### PERKINS, Jennifer
Arnold & Porter LLP, Washington, DC
202 942 5350
Jennifer.Perkins@aporter.com
*Featured in Real Estate (District of Columbia)*
**Practice Areas:** Ms. Perkins provides legal services related to acquisitions, dispositions, development, financings, and leasing of commercial real estate projects. For more than 25 years, a significant part of her practice has focused on leasing from the perspective of both owners and users regionally and nationally. Her projects encompass millions of square feet, including anchor office leases, retail occupancy agreements, government leases and work outs of leases in distress.
**Professional Memberships:** American Bar Association, District of Columbia Bar Association, Maryland Bar Association, Greater Washington Commercial Association of REALTORS and Commercial Real Estate Women.

### PHILLIPS, Carter G
Sidley Austin LLP, Washington, DC
202 736 8270
cphillips@sidley.com
*Featured in Telecommunications (District of Columbia), Appellate Law (Nationwide)*
See under Nationwide for profile.

### PHILLIPS, Laura
Drinker Biddle & Reath LLP, Washington, DC
202 842 8891
Laura.Phillips@dbr.com
*Featured in Telecommunications (District of Columbia)*
**Practice Areas:** Over 25 years' experience working on a wide variety of telecommunications projects. Counsels wireless and wired entrepreneurs on issues related to the development of technologies, net neutrality, spectrum policy, network interconnection and compensation. Outside counsel to a national wireless carrier, handling

mediations with hundreds of FCC licensees. Counsels clients on government policies, mandates, enforcement and compliance matters. Experienced in regulatory billing, acquisitions, contract disputes and business issues.

**Professional Memberships:** President, Federal Communications Bar Association.

**Personal:** American University, Washington College of Law, JD 1986; Trinity College, BA 1980, departmental honors, economics.

### PICKETT, J Michael
Bingham McCutchen LLP, Washington, DC
202 373 6071
michael.pickett@bingham.com
*Featured in Real Estate (District of Columbia)*

**Practice Areas:** Focuses on commercial real estate law. Involved in all aspects of real estate transactions, including single-asset and portfolio sales and acquisitions, equity investments and joint ventures, financings for borrowers and lenders as well as real estate debt restructurings. Clients include banks and other financial institutions, pension fund advisers, developers and investors.

**Career:** Former asset manager with a District of Columbia bank holding company, concentrating in real estate loan workouts, restructures, foreclosures and bankruptcies.

**Personal:** Washington University School of Law in St. Louis, JD, 1989; DePauw University, BA, 1986.

### PLEVIN, Mark
Crowell & Moring LLP, Washington, DC
415 365 7446
mplevin@crowell.com
*Featured in Bankruptcy/Restructuring (District of Columbia), Insurance (California)*

**Practice Areas:** Chair of Crowell & Moring's Bankruptcy Group. Focuses his practice on litigating in the bankruptcy and insurance coverage areas. Assumed lead counsel role on behalf of insurers in key asbestos bankruptcy cases including Mid-Valley (the Halliburton subsidiaries), Quigley, Combustion Engineering, Federal-Mogul, Harbison-Walker, and JT Thorpe. Serves as bankruptcy counsel to both the American Insurance Association and the Coalition for Litigation Justice, a group formed by property and casualty insurers to advance awareness about asbestos issues. In insurance coverage, served as lead counsel representing insurers in cases involving environmental, asbestos, and products liability underlying claims.

### POLLACK, Barry J
Miller & Chevalier Chartered, Washington, DC
202 626 5830
bpollack@milchev.com
*Featured in Litigation (District of Columbia)*

**Practice Areas:** Represents individuals and corporations in criminal matters (including internal investigations, grand jury proceedings, trials, sentencings, appeals, and post-conviction proceedings) and in other government enforcement and oversight matters, such as SEC proceedings and congressional investigations.

**Career:** Fellow, American College of Trial Lawyers; Secretary, National Association of Criminal Defense Lawyers; President of the Board of the Mid-Atlantic Innocence Project; Adjunct Faculty, Georgetown University Law Center. Former Certified Public Accountant.

**Personal:** JD, Georgetown University Law Center, magna cum laude, Order of the Coif, 1991; BS, Indiana University, with high honors, 1986.

### POMMERENING, David
Baker Botts LLP, Washington, DC
202 639 1147
david.pommerening@bakerbotts.com
*Featured in Corporate/M&A (District of Columbia)*

**Practice Areas:** David is the Head of the Corporate Practice in the DC office and a Member of the firm's Corporate Department. Dave's practice includes substantial experience in mergers, acquisitions, joint ventures and financial transactions, including corporate restructurings. He also advises clients on corporate governance matters, compliance with federal securities laws and protections against hostile takeovers. He represents buyers and sellers in acquisitions and dispositions of public and private companies, including transactions in regulated industries such as the energy, defense, healthcare and communications industries.

**Personal:** JD, University of Virginia School of Law, 1985; AB, summa cum laude, Duke University, 1982.

### POTENZA, Joseph M
Banner & Witcoff, Ltd, Washington, DC
202 824 3000
jpotenza@bannerwitcoff.com
*Featured in Intellectual Property (District of Columbia)*

**Practice Areas:** Litigation, ITC investigations, licensing, counseling.

**Professional Memberships:** Chair, ABA-IPL; former publications officer, ABA-IPL; former member, ABA Standing Committee Federal Judiciary; former chair, ABA Science and Technology Section; past member, ABA Standing Committee Publishing Oversight; founding member, past president, Giles S. Rich American Inn of Court; and member, AIPLA, BADC, DC Bar and FCBA.

**Career:** Principal shareholder, Banner & Witcoff. Joined firm in 1976. Former law clerk, Chief Judge Phillips; engineering technician, Xerox; patent examiner, USPTO.

**Publications:** 'Patent Trial Advocacy Casebook', 'Patent Litigation Strategies Handbook'.

**Personal:** BSEE, Rochester Institute of Technology; JD, Georgetown. Adjunct Professor at Georgetown and Northwestern.

### PRESTON, Richard
Seyfarth Shaw LLP, Washington, DC
202 828 5370
rpreston@seyfarth.com
*Featured in Construction (District of Columbia)*

**Practice Areas:** Founding Partner, Construction Practice Group

**Professional Memberships:** American Bar Association; ABC; AGC

**Career:** Focuses practice on all aspects of US and international construction. Represents private and public clients in drafting and negotiating contracts, administering complex projects, resolving disputes before US courts and in domestic and international arbitration proceedings.

**Publications:** Author of 'Alternatives to the Courthouse,' published by Construction Law Advisor, and co-author of the 'Contractor's Handbook of Business, Finance, and Law,' and ASCE's 'Manual #73, Quality in the Constructed Project.' Has served as editor of the Public Contract Law Journal.

**Personal:** JD, cum laude, Washington and Lee University

### PROGER, Phillip A
Jones Day, Washington, DC
202 879 4668
paproger@jonesday.com
*Featured in Antitrust (District of Columbia)*

**Practice Areas:** Phil Proger practices antitrust law with an emphasis on matters before US and international enforcement agencies, including mergers and cartel investigations, as well as antitrust litigation. Testified before Congress (House and Senate), the Federal Trade Commission, the Antitrust Modernization Commission, and the International Competition Policy Advisory Committee. Chaired Firm's global competition practice from 1994-2012.

**Professional Memberships:** Chair, ABA Section Of Antitrust Law (1998-99). ABA Board of Governors (2003-06). The American Law Institute. Fellow American Bar Foundation. Advisory Board BNA Antitrust & Trade Regulation Report and The M&A Lawyer. US Chamber of Commerce Antitrust Council.

### PROSEN, Lawrence
Thompson Hine LLP, Washington, DC
202 263 4141
Lawrence.Prosen@ThompsonHine.com
*Featured in Construction (District of Columbia)*

**Career:** Larry, who holds a degree in architecture, is a partner in the firm's Construction practice group, focusing his practice on government contracts and all aspects of both public and private/commercial construction litigation. His experience includes representing construction contractors and subcontractors in bid protests, litigation matters and contract disputes, including delay, impact, loss of productivity, changes and geotechnical/differing site condition claims. He has handled domestic and international projects, and has represented clients before many federal agencies. His project work includes assisting clients in a variety of industries, including infrastructure, environmental, office, commercial, process and manufacturing, energy production/transmission and real estate.

### QUARLES, Steven P
Crowell & Moring LLP, Washington, DC
202 624 2665
squarles@crowell.com
*Featured in Environment (District of Columbia)*

**Practice Areas:** Partner in Crowell & Moring's Environment, Energy & Resources Group. His practice includes counseling, litigation and legislative representation for a wide range of renewable and other energy, forest products, mining, agricultural and land development associations and companies; policy coalitions; state and local governments; and land conservation trusts. He addresses issues concerning federal wildlife laws, ESA, MBTA, and Bald and Golden Eagle Protection Act (BGEPA), federal lands (including mineral, forestry, land exchange, siting and access law), and water pollution (including matters involving nonpoint source controls, point source permitting, impaired waters and Total Maximum Daily Loads, and wetlands regulation).

### QUIN, Whayne S
Holland & Knight LLP, Washington, DC
202 663 7274
whayne.quin@hklaw.com
*Featured in Real Estate (District of Columbia)*

**Practice Areas:** Whayne S. Quin practices in the area of municipal law, land use, zoning, urban planning, building codes, historic preservation, and environmental matters. Clients include builders, developers, property owners, educational and financial institutions, nonprofit organizations, chanceries, international and national agencies. As an urban strategist, he consults nationally with private sector in land use, planning, historic preservation, housing and building-related matters. Community involvement has included: Chairman, National Building Museum (currently); Chairman, Children's National Medical Center; President, Friends of National Zoo; Governor, Urban Land Institute; Trustee, Federal City Council; Greater Washington Board of Trade, and Safe Kids Worldwide.

### QUINTIERE, Gary G
Miller & Chevalier Chartered, Washington, DC
202 626 1491
gquintiere@milchev.com
*Featured in Employee Benefits & Executive Compensation (District of Columbia)*

**Practice Areas:** Employee benefits and executive compensation.

**Career:** Over 40 years experience helping clients develop workable, common-sense solutions to difficult and sensitive matters, including compliance and audit issues involving tax-qualified plans of all varieties (including floor-offset arrangements); employment, severance and change-of-control agreements; stock-based plans and cash bonus awards; deduction and plan funding issues; Medicare secondary payor matters; fiduciary standards and prohibited transaction rules; welfare plan matters involving health reform legislation, VEBAs, 401(h) accounts and 105(h) issues; and plan restructuring, freezes, terminations and anticutback rules.

**Personal:** JD, The George Washington University National Law Center, with honors, 1969; AB, Lafayette College, 1966.

**RABINOWITZ, Mitchell L**
Crowell & Moring LLP, Washington, DC
202 624 2785
mrabinowitz@crowell.com
*Featured in Corporate/M&A (District of Columbia)*
**Practice Areas:** Partner in Crowell & Moring's Corporate Group. Practice focuses on US and international corporate matters, including M&A, private equity investments, joint ventures and corporate finance transactions. His unique understanding of the financial services industry and its regulatory environment provides clients with comprehensive legal counsel that safeguards their long-term business objectives.
**Personal:** The Wharton School, BS, 1989 - summa cum laude; University of Pennsylvania, BA, 1989 - summa cum laude; Harvard Law School, JD, 1993 - cum laude; Harvard's Kennedy School of Government, 1993.

**RAFFMAN, Mark S**
Goodwin Procter LLP, Washington, DC
202 346 4259
mraffman@goodwinprocter.com
*Featured in Litigation (District of Columbia)*
**Practice Areas:** Mr Raffman's practice includes complex litigation (particularly class actions), product liability (including silica litigation), insurance litigation (including coverage and consumer litigation), professional ethics and liability litigation, domestic and international commercial litigation/arbitration, and toxic tort and mass casualty litigation. He has represented clients before state and federal trial and appellate courts, administrative agencies and arbitration panels.
**Career:** BTI Consulting Group recognized Mr Raffman as a Client Service All-Star based on interviews with more than 300 general counsel and Fortune 1000 organizations.
**Personal:** JD, Harvard Law School, 1986 (magna cum laude); BA, Williams College, 1982 (summa cum laude; co-valedictorian).

**RAIM, David**
Chadbourne & Parke LLP, Washington, DC
202 974 5625
draim@chadbourne.com
*Featured in Insurance (District of Columbia), Insurance (Nationwide)*
See under Nationwide for profile.

**RASSMAN, Franz R**
Fried, Frank, Harris, Shriver & Jacobson LLP, Washington, DC
202 639 7101
Franz.Rassman@FriedFrank.com
*Featured in Real Estate (District of Columbia)*
**Practice Areas:** Real estate partner. Practice focuses primarily on acquisitions and dispositions of office buildings, shopping centers and hotels, commercial leasing, joint ventures, real estate lending, workouts and creditors' rights. Represents private and public commercial real estate investors and developers, supermarket operators, retail tenants, investment funds, pension funds, banks and other financial institutions. Authors and lectures extensively on a variety of topics, including construction lending, title insurance, loan restructur-

ings, commercial leasing, and landlord and tenant bankruptcies.
**Career:** Joined as partner in 2008.
**Personal:** JD, American University, Washington College of Law (1982); BS, Pi Sigma Alpha, University of Delaware (1979).

**RAWSON, William**
Latham & Watkins LLP, Washington, DC
202 637 2230
William.Rawson@lw.com
*Featured in Environment (District of Columbia)*
**Practice Areas:** 25 years of experience and deep expertise across diverse practice areas pertaining to the manufacture and use of chemicals, including petitions, agency rulemakings, challenging and defending agency final rules, consumer product class actions, Congressional investigations, high stakes investigative reporting, and client counseling. Testified twice before the Senate Committee on the Environment and Public Works on TSCA reauthorization.
**Professional Memberships:** Board of Directors, Environmental Law Institute
**Career:** Chair, Environment, Land & Resources Department (DC); Chair, global Chemical Regulation, Product Strategy & Defense Practice Group
**Publications:** TSCA Deskbook, Environmental Law Institute (1999, 2012)
**Personal:** Stanford University Law School, Amherst College

**REED, Michael**
DLA Piper LLP (US), Washington, DC
202 799 4229
michael.p.reed@dlapiper.com
*Featured in Corporate/M&A (District of Columbia)*
**Practice Areas:** Corporate, M&A, private equity.
**Career:** He concentrates his practice on public and private mergers and acquisitions, corporate finance, complex structured finance and private investment fund transactions, joint venture and strategic alliance transactions, corporate governance and securities regulation. He represents publicly and privately held companies and private equity firms, with an emphasis on financing institutions and diversified companies and advises and represents boards of directors on a variety of matters.
**Personal:** LLM Boston University; LLB, University of Western Ontario Law School; BA, Wilfrid Laurier University (with honors).

**REIDER, Alan E**
Arnold & Porter LLP, Washington, DC
202 942 6496
Alan.Reider@aporter.com
*Featured in Healthcare (District of Columbia)*
**Practice Areas:** Alan Reider has more than 30 years experience representing national pharmaceutical, medical device and healthcare corporations, as well as institutional providers and individual practitioners and suppliers. His representation focuses on regulatory, compliance, and enforcement issues involving Federal programs, including fraud and abuse, reimbursement, and coverage. Alan has been Lead Counsel on several

major enforcement cases and appears before federal agencies, including CMS, the OIG, the Department of Justice, and US Attorneys Offices throughout the country.
**Personal:** JD, Boston University School of Law, 1975; MPH, University of Texas School of Public Health, 1972; AB, Brown University, 1971.

**REIDY, Andrew**
Dickstein Shapiro LLP, Washington, DC
202 420 2535
reidya@dicksteinshapiro.com
*Featured in Insurance (Nationwide), Insurance (District of Columbia)*
**Practice Areas:** Andrew Reidy is a partner in Dickstein Shapiro's Insurance Coverage Practice. For more than 24 years, he has represented policyholders in disputes against insurance companies for a wide variety of policies, including commercial liability, directors and officers (D&O), property, errors and omissions, crime, and fidelity policies. He offers clients a full range of insurance-related services, from counseling companies on how to maximize an insurance recovery to representing policyholders in mediation, arbitration, litigation, and trial in state and federal courts.
**Personal:** JD from The George Washington University Law School (1987) and BA, cum laude, from Boston College (1984).

**REIFF, Laura Foote**
Greenberg Traurig, LLP, McLean
703 749 1372
ReiffL@gtlaw.com
*Featured in Immigration (Nationwide), Immigration (District of Columbia)*
**Practice Areas:** Co-Managing Shareholder, Tysons Corner Office. Co-Chair, Business Immigration Group. Co-Chair, Global Human Capital Solutions.
**Professional Memberships:** Founder and Legal Counsel, Essential Workers Immigration Coalition; Member, US Chamber of Commerce, Labor and Employment Subcommittee on Immigration; HRLA, Co-chair of organization honoring HR professionals in the DC metropolitan area.
**Career:** Listed: Chambers Global Guide, 2008-13; Chambers USA Guide, 2006-13; Best Lawyers in America, 2008-13; Human Resource Executive magazine, 'Top 20 Immigration Attorneys in America', 2011-12.Team Member, Law360 'Employment Practice Group of the Year', 2011.
**Personal:** JD, with honors, George Washington University Law School; BA, magna cum laude, American University.

**RHYNE, Katherine L**
King & Spalding LLP, Washington, DC
202 626 3743
krhyne@kslaw.com
*Featured in Environment (District of Columbia)*
**Practice Areas:** Focuses on chemical risk assessment issues in the context of environmental regulation or tort litigation. Experience includes environmental tort litigation, environmental litigation, scientific programs, environmental regulation, and site-specific risk assessment.

**Professional Memberships:** Advisory Board, Virginia Environmental Law Journal, University of Virginia Law School, Dean's Council, Indiana University School of Public and Environmental Affairs. Served as Member of the Executive Council of the Harvard Center for Risk Analysis at the Harvard School of Public Health.
**Personal:** University of Virginia, Phi Beta Kappa; University of Virginia Law School, 1980.

**RIEDY, James**
McDermott Will & Emery LLP, Washington, DC
202 756 8314
jriedy@mwe.com
*Featured in Tax (District of Columbia)*
**Practice Areas:** Partner in tax department. Main area of work includes US federal income tax law applicable to cross-border transactions and investments. Practice encompasses both US multinational investments outside the US and non-US, multinational investments in the US. Practice includes consulting on technical tax matters, advising on major corporate acquisitions, corporate internal restructuring and transfer pricing.
**Professional Memberships:** Past Co-Chair of International Tax Committee of District of Columbia Bar.
**Personal:** University of Kansas College of Law (JD); Georgetown University Law Center (LLM); Kansas State University (BS).

**RIFKIND, Amy B**
Arnold & Porter LLP, Washington, DC
202 942 6137
Amy.Rifkind@aporter.com
*Featured in Real Estate (District of Columbia)*
**Practice Areas:** Amy Rifkind has a broad practice with a focus on real estate development, public-private partnerships and corporate real estate matters. She has significant experience in the area of government real estate, representing owners in the procurement, administration, and financing of federal leases. She also regularly handles purchases, dispositions, leases, and build-to-suits for real estate developers and other users and owners of real estate, and represents borrowers and lenders in all aspects of real estate financings including construction loans and securitized debt financings.
**Personal:** Ms Rifkind was named the 2009 Top Washington Lawyer-Real Estate by the Washington Business Journal.

**RILL, James F**
Baker Botts LLP, Washington, DC
202 639 7883
james.rill@bakerbotts.com
*Featured in Antitrust (District of Columbia)*
**Practice Areas:** Antitrust, Competition Law, Litigation
**Professional Memberships:** District of Columbia Bar; United States Supreme Court; United States Court of Appeals - District of Columbia
**Career:** One of America's foremost antitrust attorneys. Assistant Attorney General - U.S. Department of Justice's Antitrust Division; Chairman - ABA Antitrust Section; Co-Chair, U.S.

Department of Justice's International Competition Policy Advisory Committee, whose report was a building block for creation of the International Competition Network. Recipient of Global Competition Review and ABA Section of Antitrust Law Lifetime Achievement Awards, and the U.S. Department of Justice's Sherman Award. **Personal:** LLB., Harvard Law School; AB, Dartmouth College

### ROADY, Celia
Morgan, Lewis & Bockius LLP, Washington, DC
202 739 5279
croady@morganlewis.com
*Featured in Tax (District of Columbia)*
**Practice Areas:** Celia Roady is a partner in Morgan Lewis's Tax Practice. Ms Roady's practice focuses on tax and governance issues affecting tax-exempt organizations, including charities, foundations, colleges and universities, museums, and other nonprofit organizations. She was appointed by the Internal Revenue Service to be a member of its Advisory Committee on Tax-Exempt and Government Entities for 2010–13. She also chairs the annual conference on "Representing and Managing Tax-Exempt Organizations," sponsored by Georgetown Law Center, and was named by Legal Times as one of Washington, D.C.'s "leading lawyers" in the tax field.

### ROBBINS, Robert B
Pillsbury Winthrop Shaw Pittman LLP, Washington, DC
202 663 8136
robert.robbins@pillsburylaw.com
*Featured in Corporate/M&A (District of Columbia)*
**Practice Areas:** Leader of Pillsbury's Corporate and Securities Section. Expertise in securities offerings, mergers, acquisitions and restructurings, private equity, and representation of committees of independent directors of public corporations.
**Career:** Annual ALI-ABA seminars: Co-Chair, 'Private Placements and Regulation D', faculty, 'Fundamentals of Securities Regulation'.
**Personal:** JD, Harvard Law School (cum laude); AB, Cornell University (magna cum laude).

### ROBERTS, Michele A
Skadden, Arps, Slate, Meagher & Flom LLP & Affiliates, Washington, DC
202 371 7250
Michele.Roberts@skadden.com
*Featured in Litigation (Nationwide), Litigation (District of Columbia)*
See under Nationwide for profile.

### ROBINSON, Frederick
Fulbright & Jaworski LLP, Washington, DC
202 662 4534
frobinson@fulbright.com
*Featured in Healthcare (Nationwide), Healthcare (District of Columbia)*
See under Nationwide for profile.

### ROCHON, Mark J
Miller & Chevalier Chartered, Washington, DC
202 626 5819
mrochon@milchev.com
*Featured in Litigation (District of Columbia)*
**Practice Areas:** White-collar defense in criminal and civil matters/Internal Investigations.
**Career:** He has tried over 160 cases to a jury; argued before appellate courts across the United States; and represented individuals against allegations of government contracting fraud, export controls violations, insider trading allegations, shareholder suits, and accounting and bank fraud allegations. He has conducted FCPA investigations around the world on behalf of multinational corporations; is a former trial chief for the Public Defender Service for the District of Columbia; and frequently lectures on trial practice, internal investigations, and compliance issues.
**Personal:** JD, Stanford University, 1983; BS, Western Michigan University, 1980.

### RODRIGUEZ, Grace
King & Spalding LLP, Washington, DC
202 626 5508
gmrodriguez@kslaw.com
*Featured in Antitrust (District of Columbia)*
**Practice Areas:** Complex civil litigation, antitrust matters, internal investigations, and white-collar criminal defense. Represents clients in civil and criminal matters involving antitrust and securities issues.
**Professional Memberships:** Member of the National Board of Directors of Appleseed. Member of the New York and District of Columbia Bars.
**Personal:** JD, Columbia University BA, cum laude, Harvard University

### ROELLKE, Jon R
Bingham McCutchen LLP, Washington, DC
202 373 6119
jon.roellke@bingham.com
*Featured in Antitrust (District of Columbia)*
**Practice Areas:** Focuses on antitrust, intellectual property, corporate governance and other commercial litigation, primarily representing clients in the financial services, healthcare and high technology industries. Handles class action and other complex litigation matters in state and federal courts and regularly represents clients on antitrust issues before state and federal agencies. Counsels domestic and multinational companies on competition issues, including refusals to deal, distribution and franchising restraints, tying arrangements, group purchasing, price discrimination, exclusive dealing, leveraging, joint ventures, and trade association activities.
**Personal:** Boston College Law School, JD, cum laude, 1987; San Francisco State University, BA, magna cum laude, 1983.

### ROGAN, Michael P
Skadden, Arps, Slate, Meagher & Flom LLP & Affiliates, Washington, DC
202 371 7550
Michael.Rogan@skadden.com
*Featured in Corporate/M&A (District of Columbia)*

**Practice Areas:** Global co-head of Skadden's Transactions practices. Focuses on mergers and acquisitions, securities regulation, corporate finance and corporate governance. Experienced in SEC matters and provides corporate and securities law advice to a number of public companies. Clients include electric and gas utilities, diversified energy companies and private investment funds, as well as US industrial and financial service companies. Has an active corporate governance practice and regularly advises boards and board committees on the Sarbanes-Oxley Act, compliance and internal investigation matters.
**Career:** JD, University of Connecticut, 1974; BA, Oberlin College, 1970.

### ROISMAN, Natalie
Wilkinson Barker Knauer LLP, Washington, DC
*Featured in Telecommunications (District of Columbia)*
**Practice Areas:** Ms. Roisman advises clients on policy and regulatory issues related to media and telecommunications, including consumer privacy. She works with equipment manufacturers, wireless carriers, broadcasters, cable operators, online video distributors and content owners to develop and execute advocacy strategies for industry-wide rulemakings, adjudicatory and enforcement proceedings, regulatory compliance, and transactions. In addition, she advises investors and the financial community regarding acquisitions and the impact of Congressional, Executive Branch, FCC and FTC policy actions on relevant industries.
**Professional Memberships:** Federal Communications Bar Association Executive Committee, ABA Forum on Communications Law and Women in Communications Law, Women's Bar Association of D.C. Working Group on Advancement and Retention of Women.
**Career:** Worked in private practice and served as attorney-advisor in the FCC's Media Bureau.
**Personal:** Adjunct faculty at George Washington University Law School and advisor to the Federal Communications Law Journal.

### ROMATOWSKI, Peter J
Jones Day, Washington, DC
202 879 7625
pjromatowski@jonesday.com
*Featured in Securities (Nationwide), Litigation (District of Columbia)*
**Practice Areas:** Oversees the firm's SEC Enforcement Practice and also practices white-collar criminal defense. Represents US public companies and foreign issuers, their directors, board committees, and executives, as well as broker/dealers, private investment firms, and law firms, in internal, SEC, CFTC, SRO, and state regulatory investigations. His criminal practice includes corporate and individual clients from four continents in US grand jury and congressional investigations and trials involving the full range of federal law issues.
**Professional Memberships:** American College of Trial Lawyers.

**Career:** Assistant US attorney (1979-86), Chief of the Securities and Commodities Fraud Unit (1984-86), Southern District of New York.

### ROSEN, Richard L
Arnold & Porter LLP, Washington, DC
202 942 5499
Richard.Rosen@aporter.com
*Featured in Antitrust (District of Columbia)*
**Practice Areas:** Richard Rosen represents clients in mergers and acquisitions and in civil and criminal enforcement matters before the federal antitrust agencies, as well as antitrust counseling and litigation. His practice focuses on clients in the telecommunications, information technology and media industries, and includes representation of clients before the Federal Communications Commission.
**Career:** Prior to joining Arnold & Porter LLP, he served as Chief of the Communications and Finance Section of the US Department of Justice Antitrust Division, Assistant Director of the Federal Trade Commission's Bureau of Competition, and as Attorney Advisor to the Chairman of the Federal Trade Commission.

### ROSENSTEIN, Mace J
Covington & Burling LLP, Washington, DC
202 662 5460
mrosenstein@cov.com
*Featured in Telecommunications (District of Columbia), Media & Entertainment (District of Columbia)*
**Practice Areas:** Mr Rosenstein's practice focuses on communications law and policy and media and telecommunications transactions. He has particular expertise in foreign investment in media and telecommunications, and works with both strategics and investors to develop creative business concepts that address structural media ownership limitations. He also is involved in spectrum policy and in complex rulemaking and waiver proceedings before the FCC and in the federal courts.
**Professional Memberships:** FCBA
**Career:** Partner and Co-Chair, Industries, Regulatory and Legislative Umbrella Group; Media, Internet & Telecommunications Industry Group
**Personal:** University of Chicago Law School, JD, 1984; Harvard College, AB (cum laude) 1975.

### ROSENTHAL, Barry P
Bingham McCutchen LLP, Washington, DC
202 373 6078
barry.rosenthal@bingham.com
*Featured in Real Estate (Nationwide), Real Estate (District of Columbia)*
**Practice Areas:** Co-chair of Bingham's Real Estate Practice Group. More than 25 years of experience representing clients in sophisticated real estate and finance-related matters. Involved in all aspects of transactional real estate, including acquisitions, sales, financing, joint ventures, partnerships, debt and equity restructurings, leasing, and real estate development. Clients include banks, insurance companies and other financial institutions; pension fund advisers; institutional

investors; and owners, operators and developers of real estate.

**Career:** Fellow, American College of Real Estate Lawyers.

**Personal:** University of Pennsylvania Law School, JD, 1974; University of Rochester, BA, cum laude, 1970.

### ROWLEY, John
Baker & McKenzie, Washington, DC
202 835 6151
john.rowley@bakermckenzie.com
*Featured in Litigation (District of Columbia)*

**Practice Areas:** Partner, Baker & McKenzie's North American Litigation, Corporate Compliance & Risk Management, and Investigations & Business Crimes Practice Groups. Leads the Firm's national False Claims Act team and specializes in Foreign Corrupt Practices Act, procurement fraud and financial investigations. Over 25 years experience handling complex civil disputes and white-collar criminal cases.

**Career:** Assistant US Attorney and Section Chief for Eastern District of Virginia; Staff Director, U.S. Department of Defense Panel for Review of Misconduct Allegations at the U.S. Air Force Academy.

**Personal:** University of Notre Dame, MBA; University of Richmond, JD; State University of New York, BA

### RUBIN, Blake D
McDermott Will & Emery LLP, Washington, DC
202 756 8424
brubin@mwe.com
*Featured in Tax (District of Columbia)*

**Practice Areas:** Member of tax department; practices in area of federal taxation, with particular emphasis on partnership and real estate taxation. Practice includes planning, policy and controversy matters. Extensive experience structuring large partnership and real estate transactions.

**Professional Memberships:** Admitted in DC and Pennsylvania; former chair of District of Columbia Bar Section of Taxation; served as chair of Real Estate Taxation Committee of American Bar Association; founder and president of Washington, DC, Center for Public Interest Tax Law.

**Personal:** University of Pennsylvania Law School, JD, 1980; Wharton School, University of Pennsylvania, MBA, 1980; Haverford College, BA, 1976.

### RULE, Charles F
Cadwalader, Wickersham & Taft LLP, Washington, DC
202 862 2420
rick.rule@cwt.com
*Featured in Antitrust (District of Columbia)*

**Practice Areas:** Managing Partner, Washington, DC Office and Head, Antitrust Group. Focuses on all aspects of US and international antitrust, including mergers, joint ventures, IP licensing, civil and criminal investigations by national antitrust authorities, and trial and appellate antitrust litigation. Represents major international corporations including: Microsoft Corporation;

ExxonMobil; US Airways Inc.; Celanese Corporation; Northrop Grumman Corporation; Goldman, Sachs & Co.; Morgan Stanley; Financial Security Assurance; the National Basketball Association; Bacardi & Company Ltd.; Eli Lilly & Company; and Goodyear Tire and Rubber Co.

**Career:** Assistant Attorney General in charge of the Antitrust Division, US Justice Department (1986-89); Deputy Assistant Attorney General (1984-86).

**Personal:** JD, University of Chicago Law School; BA, Vanderbilt University.

### RYAN, John W
Thompson Hine LLP, Washington, DC
202 263 4114
John.Ryan@ThompsonHine.com
*Featured in Intellectual Property (District of Columbia)*

**Career:** John has been involved in patent matters for the last 25 years, initially working on the erythropoietin litigation against Amgen, then working in-house as Vice President and Chief Patent Counsel for a diagnostic company, IGEN International, Inc., run by Amgen's founder. Over his last 15 years of law firm practice, he co-chaired a couple of IP practice groups and handled a variety of patent matters such as patent litigation, due diligence & risk analysis, freedom to operate opinions on multi-million dollar products, and portfolio management. He also taught Licensing of Intellectual Property as an adjunct professor at Albany Law School.

### SADLER, Alex E
Ivins, Phillips & Barker, Washington, DC
202 662 3456
asadler@ipbtax.com
*Featured in Tax (District of Columbia)*

**Practice Areas:** Represents businesses and individuals in litigation and administrative controversies with the IRS and state revenue authorities. Specialties include tax litigation, tax controversy, tax compliance, IRS Appeals, research credit, tax credits and incentives, economic substance, tax shelters, structured transactions, insurance, valuation, charitable contributions, and tax practice and procedure.

**Professional Memberships:** Vice Chair, D.C. Bar, Tax Audits and Litigation Committee; American Bar Association, Tax Section, Court Practice and Procedure and Administrative Practice Subcommittees; Federal Bar Association, Tax Section.

**Career:** Partner, Ivins, Phillips & Barker (2011 to present); Partner, Crowell & Moring LLP (2002 to 2011); Trial Attorney, U.S. Department of Justice, Tax Division, Civil Trial Section (1997 to 2002).

**Publications:** February-March 2012 - Requests for Admission in Federal Tax Litigation: Uses, Limitations, Rules, and Strategic Consideraions, Journal of Tax Practice & Procedure; September 2011- Navigating the Research Credit, Tax Notes; January 2012- Federal Circuit Clarifies Third-Party Return Information Disclosure Exception, Tax Analysts; September 2011- Overcoming Appeals' Bad Rap (quotations in article by J. Coder), Tax Notes; April-May 2009- Scope of

Pretrial Discovery: A Key Difference in Litigating Tax Cases in the Tax Court and Refund Tribunals, Journal of Tax Practice & Procedure

**Personal:** Recipient, Attorney General's Distinguished Service Award Recipient, Tax Division's Outstanding Attorney Award.

### SAFIR, Peter O
Covington & Burling LLP, Washington, DC
202 662 5162
psafir@cov.com
*Featured in Life Sciences (Nationwide), Healthcare (District of Columbia)*

**Career:** Peter Safir represents pharmaceutical and biotechnology companies on all aspects of regulation, including drug/biologic development and approval, marketing, manufacturing, and compliance issues. He has litigated many cases protecting data exclusivity for pioneer products and structured numerous patent settlements between research based companies and ANDA applicants. He has advised companies on promotional practices; GMP compliance and with respect to Anti-Kickback statutes; and defended companies and individuals in FDA and DOJ criminal and civil enforcement proceedings. Professorial Lecturer in Food and Drug Law at George Washington University Law School 1991-2013.

**Personal:** BA Princeton University 1967; JD Yale Law School 1972.

### SALCIDO, Robert S
Akin Gump Strauss Hauer & Feld LLP, Washington, DC
202 887 4095
rsalcido@akingump.com
*Featured in Healthcare (Nationwide), Healthcare (District of Columbia)*
See under Nationwide for profile.

### SANFORD, Bruce W
Baker & Hostetler LLP, Washington, DC
202 861 1626
bsanford@bakerlaw.com
*Featured in First Amendment Litigation (Nationwide), Media & Entertainment (District of Columbia)*
See under Nationwide for profile.

### SANOK, Jeffrey D
Crowell & Moring LLP, Washington, DC
202 624 2995
jsanok@crowell.com
*Featured in Intellectual Property (District of Columbia)*

**Practice Areas:** Partner in Crowell & Moring's Intellectual Property Group. Specializes in IP law, including patent infringement litigation and licensing, patent interferences and strategic patent and trademark acquisition and counseling. Practice encompasses a range of electrical, mechanical, electro-mechanical and aeronautical technologies, including telecommunications, computer architectures and software, consumer electronics, vehicle control systems, navigation systems and automotive and jet engine systems. Litigates throughout the US in areas of patent infringement, trademark infringement and product liability. Lead counsel for the plaintiff in the

landmark en banc decision in Knorr-Bremse Systeme fuer Nutzfahrzeuge GmbH v Dana Corp et al, 383 F.3d 1337.

### SANZO, Kathleen M
Morgan, Lewis & Bockius LLP, Washington, DC
202 739 5209
ksanzo@morganlewis.com
*Featured in Life Sciences (Nationwide), Healthcare (District of Columbia)*
See under Nationwide for profile.

### SARRAILLE, William A
Sidley Austin LLP, Washington, DC
202 736 8195
wsarraille@sidley.com
*Featured in Healthcare (Nationwide), Healthcare (District of Columbia)*

**Practice Areas:** Partner and senior member of Sidley's Healthcare practice group. Concentrates on a variety of healthcare matters, including Medicare and Medicaid reimbursement, coverage and coding, pharmaceutical price reporting, issues related to the marketing and promotion of pharmaceuticals and medical devices, internal investigations, clinical research issues, Stark and Anti-Kickback Law analyses, healthcare acquisitions and due diligence, healthcare contracts, administrative litigation, legislative matters, audits, privacy and security, representation of witnesses and companies before Congressional Committees, and the defense of healthcare criminal and False Claims Act matters.

**Personal:** Harvard Law School, JD, 1989; Yale University, BA, 1985, cum laude.

### SARTORI, Michael
Venable LLP, Washington, DC
202 344 4004
masartori@Venable.com
*Featured in Intellectual Property (District of Columbia)*

**Practice Areas:** Patent Prosecution, Intellectual Property Litigation, Intellectual Property.

**Career:** Dr. Sartori chairs Venable's Patent Prosecution & Counseling practice. A registered patent attorney, he focuses on patent prosecution, litigation, opinions and portfolio counseling. He works in areas of electrical, computer, software, communications, electro-mechanical and mechanical inventions. He is experienced with successfully appealing patent applications and post-issuance proceedings at the USPTO. He received several patents for inventions from his research. He was a Patent Examiner with the USPTO.

**Personal:** JD, cum laude, Georgetown University Law Center; PhD, University of Notre Dame; MSEE, University of Notre Dame; BSEE, University of Notre Dame.

### SAVIN, James R
Akin Gump Strauss Hauer & Feld LLP, Washington, DC
202 887 4417
jsavin@akingump.com
*Featured in Bankruptcy/Restructuring (District of Columbia)*

**Practice Areas:** Practice focuses on corporate restructurings and bankruptcy law, with an emphasis on creditors' committees and informal and formal bondholder and secured creditor committees in large, complex Chapter 11 cases and out-of-court restructurings. Represents bondholders, noteholders, secured creditors, institutional investors, hedge funds, post-petition lenders and acquirers of distressed assets. Representations encompass a variety of industries and involve multijurisdictional and cross-border matters.
**Professional Memberships:** Member, District of Columbia and New York Bars.
**Personal:** BS, Wharton School at the University of Pennsylvania (1994); JD, Emory University School of Law, Member, Emory Law Journal (1997).

## SCALIA, Eugene
Gibson, Dunn & Crutcher LLP, Washington, DC
202 955 8500
escalia@gibsondunn.com
*Featured in Labor & Employment (District of Columbia)*
**Practice Areas:** Co-Chair of firm's Labor and Employment Practice Group, and Chair of Administrative Law and Regulatory Practice Group. Experienced in a broad range of labor and employment matters (including discrimination law, wage-hour, traditional labor, and ERISA) and regulatory matters involving SEC, FCC, CFTC, Department of Transportation, and other agencies. Public Member, Administrative Conference of the United States.
**Career:** 2002-03, Solicitor of Labor: principal legal officer, Department of Labor, responsible for government litigation involving ERISA, OSHA, Family/Medical Leave Act, wage-hour, and Sarbanes-Oxley. 1992-93, Special Assistant to Attorney General of US.
**Publications:** More than 30 articles and papers.
**Personal:** JD, University of Chicago: Editor-in-Chief, 'Law Review'.

## SCANLON, Tara A
Holland & Knight LLP, Washington, DC
202 457 7150
tara.scanlon@hklaw.com
*Featured in Real Estate (District of Columbia)*
**Practice Areas:** Co-Chair of the firm's National Retail Development and Leasing Team in the Real Estate Section, Tara concentrates her practice on commercial real estate transactions which include development matters, sales and acquisitions, and retail and office leasing. She has extensive experience in retail real estate transactions representing institutional and entrepreneurial owners of regional malls, shopping centers and high end street retail projects in connection with various leasing, finance, operational and transactional matters. Other areas of experience include commercial finance involving construction and permanent real estate loans, asset-based lending and equity investments, and the restructure of debt and security instruments.

## SCHENDT, Thomas G.
Alston & Bird LLP, Washington, DC
202 239 3330
thomas.schendt@alston.com
*Featured in Employee Benefits & Executive Compensation (District of Columbia)*
**Practice Areas:** Focuses on qualified/nonqualified plan matters before US Federal agencies, including the IRS, Department of Labor, PBGC and others. Tom handles audits, civil and criminal investigations, voluntary compliance initiatives and a variety of other matters before the agencies.
**Professional Memberships:** Co-Chair, IRS Liaison Group for the Mid-Atlantic Region; Co-Chair Bloomberg/BNA Pension & Benefits Advisory Board; senior Reviewer of Pension and Benefits Advisory Board.
**Career:** Previously employed by the IRS as technical assistant to the Associate Chief Counsel, Employee Benefits and Exempt Organizations (EBEO) for the Office of Chief Counsel.
**Personal:** BS (1980), MBA (1981), JD (1985) Marquette University.

## SCHIFF, Janis Boyarsky
Holland & Knight LLP, Washington, DC
202 862 5994
janis.schiff@hklaw.com
*Featured in Real Estate (District of Columbia)*
**Practice Areas:** Janis focuses her practice in retail, office and mixed-use development, financing and leasing. Her clients include national and regional retailers, owners, investors, managers, brokers and developers. She recently served as the firm's Client Service Partner and founded the firm's Rising Stars program, which provides leadership, marketing, and management training for women attorneys in the firm. She serves on the Board of Directors of Easter Seals, Junior Achievement and the Washington DC Board of Trade and is a member of Commercial Real Estate Women (CREW), Women in Retail Real Estate (WIRRE), and the International Council of Shopping Centers (ICSC).

## SCHLAGER, Ivan A
Skadden, Arps, Slate, Meagher & Flom LLP & Affiliates, Washington, DC
202 371 7810
Ivan.Schlager@skadden.com
*Featured in Telecommunications (District of Columbia), International Trade (Nationwide)*
See under Nationwide for profile.

## SCHLOSSBERG, Bob
Freshfields Bruckhaus Deringer LLP, Washington, DC
202 777 4500
robert.schlossberg@freshfields.com
*Featured in Antitrust (District of Columbia)*
**Practice Areas:** For over 25 years, clients have been calling on Bob to represent them on antitrust matters. He is well-known for practicing before the FTC and the DOJ's Antitrust Division. Bob's strength lies in successfully guiding national and international transactions through antitrust review. He has worked with chemicals, consumer goods, energy, industrial machinery, medical devices, pharmaceuticals, publishing, software and

transportation industries. Bob is past chair of the M&A Committee of the ABA Antitrust Section and editor of the Antitrust Section treatise on M&A. He is a non-governmental advisor to the US agencies in connection with the International Competition Network.

## SCHMIDT, Paul
Baker & Hostetler LLP, Washington, DC
202 861 1760
pschmidt@bakerlaw.com
*Featured in Tax (District of Columbia)*
**Career:** Paul Schmidt has a wide range of experience in corporate and international tax matters, particularly in US trade or business issues, permanent establishment and taxable presence issues, cross-border financing, transfer pricing, cross-border business expansion/restructuring, subpart F income, treaty interpretation, foreign tax credit planning, hedging transactions, the tax treatment of foreign sales corporations and extraterritorial income exclusion, and FATCA. Paul regularly handles issues related to examination by the IRS, including representing clients before IRS Appeals, and he assists clients in obtaining private letter rulings. He also frequently advises clients in connection with issues raised by foreign tax authorities.

## SCHMIDT, William
K&L Gates, Washington, DC
202 778 9373
william.schmidt@klgates.com
*Featured in Employee Benefits & Executive Compensation (District of Columbia)*
**Practice Areas:** William Schmidt, a partner in the investment management, hedge funds, and alternative investments practice group, works in the areas of institutional investing and employee benefits, with particular emphasis on fiduciary responsibility matters under the Employee Retirement Income Security Act of 1974. He advises major financial institutions, including banks, insurance companies, registered investment advisers and large employee benefit plans about ERISA restrictions relating to plan investments and to fee arrangements for investment management and plan administrative services.

## SCHNEIDER, Leslie
Ivins, Phillips & Barker, Washington, DC
202 393 7600
lschneider@ipbtax.com
*Featured in Tax (District of Columbia)*
**Practice Areas:** Practiced Federal tax law for more than 30 years with emphasis on planning and controversies in the areas of income tax accounting, accounting methods, depreciation and inventories. Work includes advising clients on the filing of accounting method change requests with the Internal Revenue Service, obtaining advance rulings on accounting method issues from the Internal Revenue Service, advocating tax policy positions before Internal Revenue Service and Treasury Department; commenting on proposed regulations, and handling controversies at the Appeals Division within the Internal Revenue Service, as well as litigating tax cases in the U.S. Tax Court and U.S. Claims Court. One particular

specialty is advising on the implementation and operation of the LIFO inventory method. Also served as an expert witness on accounting method issues in several court cases.
**Professional Memberships:** American Bar Association (Tax Section), District of Columbia Bar (Tax Section), American Institute of Certified Public Accountants (Tax Accounting Technical Resource Panel).
**Career:** Office of Tax Legislative Counsel, U.S. Treasury Dept. 1971-73; Special Assistant to Assistant Secretary (Tax Policy), U.S. Treasury Dept. 1973; Partner, Ivins, Phillips & Barker since 1978.
**Publications:** FEDERAL INCOME TAXATION OF INVENTORIES (3 Vols. Thompsen Reuters); BNA Portfolio 75-3, Tax Accounting Problems of Contractors; numerous articles in Journal of Taxation, The Tax Adviser, and other publications. Frequent speaker at professional education institutes on tax law matters, including institutes sponsored by American Bar Association, Tax Executives Institute, Federal Bar Association, District of Columbia Bar, New York University Institute on Taxation, University of Southern California Tax Institute, Southern Federal Tax Institute, Mid-America Tax Conference and Virginia Tax Institute; Adjunct Professor of Law, Georgetown University Law Center, 1980-85.
**Personal:** Born in Bronx, NY; BS, University of Maryland 1967 (Magna Cum Laude, Phi Kappa Phi, Beta Alpha Psi); JD Georgetown University Law Center, 1971, (member, Board of Editors, Georgetown Law Journal); Member of bars of District of Columbia and Maryland, CPA, Maryland, 1971 (awarded Gold Medal for highest score on CPA exam).

## SCHNEIDER, Mark
Sidley Austin LLP, Washington, DC
202 736 8058
mschneider@sidley.com
*Featured in Telecommunications (District of Columbia)*
**Practice Areas:** Practiced with Sidley's Communications group since 1984, except for several years of service at the Federal Communications Commission. Practices before the FCC and Federal and state courts in the broadcast, media, common carrier, international and wireless fields. Represents television and radio stations, wireless operators, telephone companies, equipment manufacturers, private radio operators and lending institutions regarding FCC regulations and other communications law issues.
**Personal:** Georgetown University Law Center JD, 1984, magna cum laude, Georgetown Law Journal, Executive Editor, Editorial Board, 1983-84; Haverford College, BA, 1981.

## SCHOONOVER, Martha J
Greenberg Traurig, LLP, McLean
703 749 1374
SchoonoverM@gtlaw.com
*Featured in Immigration (Nationwide), Immigration (District of Columbia)*
**Practice Areas:** Co-Chair, Business Immigration and Compliance Group.

**Career:** Listed: Chambers Global Guide, 2012-13; Chambers USA Guide, 2009-13; The Best Lawyers in America, 2010-12; The Washingtonian Magazine, Washington's Top Lawyers, 2009, 2011; Legal 500 US, 2009-12. Rated, AV® Preeminent™ 5.0 out of 5.
**Personal:** JD, University of Virginia School of Law, 1980 (Attended Harvard Law School 1975-76); BA, summa cum laude, History and French, University of Richmond, 1975 (Phi Beta Kappa).

**SCHREIBER, Scott**
Arnold & Porter LLP, Washington, DC
202 942 5672
Scott.Schreiber@aporter.com
*Featured in Litigation (District of Columbia)*
**Practice Areas:** Co-Chair of the Securities Enforcement and Litigation Practice, Chair of the Class and Derivative Actions Practice and global litigation coordinator. Serves as Lead Counsel to corporations, directors, special litigation committees and accountants in securities, derivative, and accounting fraud actions and related internal, Justice Department, SEC, and PCAOB investigations, and in defending officers and directors in failed bank and other litigation.
**Career:** Served as Special Counsel to US Congress, Committee on the Judiciary; and the US Senate Select Committee on Intelligence.
**Personal:** JD, Columbia Law School; law clerk to Hon. William H. Timbers, (USCA, 2nd Cir.).

**SCHUELKE III, Henry F**
Blank Rome LLP, Washington, DC
202 772 5815
HSchuelke@BlankRome.com
*Featured in Litigation (District of Columbia)*
**Practice Areas:** Since Henry Schuelke's departure from the US Attorney's Office of the District of Columbia as Executive Assistant US Attorney, Mr Schuelke has represented scores of clients—corporations and their directors, officers and employees, members of Congress, Committees of Congress, Executive Branch officials, and law firms—as a founding partner of the Washington, DC firm, Janis, Schuelke & Wechsler. Mr Schuelke's practice has included representation of senior corporate executives in diverse criminal matters, including accounting fraud, securities fraud, FCPA violations, criminal tax, environmental crimes, criminal antitrust, and healthcare fraud. Many of these matters involved parallel SEC enforcement actions.
www.BlankRome.com/HSchuelke

**SCHWARTZ, Richard**
Crowell & Moring LLP, Washington, DC
202 624 2905
rschwartz@crowell.com
*Featured in Environment (District of Columbia)*
**Practice Areas:** Partner in Crowell & Moring's Environment, Energy & Resources Group. Advises clients on the Clean Water Act, Clean Air Act, Resource Conservation and Recovery Act (RCRA), and the Superfund Act. Focuses on environmental litigation, has worked extensively with scientific/technical expert witnesses in environmental and toxic tort cases. Defends companies against "citizen suits" by environmental groups.

Routinely advises industrial clients on the federal and state hazardous waste laws. Has also advised clients regarding the Superfund Act, and defended them in Superfund litigation.
**Personal:** Yale College, BA, 1970; University of Michigan Law School, JD, 1973 - cum laude.

**SCRIBNER, John E**
Weil, Gotshal & Manges LLP, Washington, DC
202 682 7096
john.scribner@weil.com
*Featured in Antitrust (District of Columbia)*
**Practice Areas:** John Scribner's practice focuses on complex antitrust matters, emphasizing mergers. He successfully represented Apple in the purchase of various patents from Novell and Nortel. He recently represented Nemak, a subsidiary of Alfa SAB de CV, the largest industrial conglomerate in Mexico, in its acquisition of J.L. French. He regularly counsels clients including Sanofi-Aventis, Applied Materials, Dell, and Abbott Laboratories on potential transactions. Previously, he spent five years as a litigation attorney with the FTC where he was actively involved in merger and non-merger investigations in a wide range of industries, including defense, pharmaceuticals, medical devices and high technology.

**SCULLY, Thomas A.**
Alston & Bird LLP, Washington, DC
202 239 3459
thomas.scully@alston.com
*Featured in Healthcare (District of Columbia)*
**Practice Areas:** Focuses on health care regulatory and legislative matters. Advises clients on health policy and strategies for health care delivery.
**Professional Memberships:** Serves on Advisory Board of George Bush Presidential Library; Executive Council of the Harvard School of Public Health; Dartmouth Medical School; and is General Partner with Welsh, Carson, Anderson & Stowe (NYC).
**Career:** Administrator, Centers for Medicare & Medicaid Services (CMS), (2001 to 2004), President and CEO, Federation of American Hospitals (1994-2001); Deputy Assistant for Domestic Policy, President George H.W. Bush, Associate Director OMB (1989-1993).
**Personal:** JD (1986) – Catholic University; BA (1979) – University of Virginia.

**SEEBALD, Craig**
Vinson & Elkins LLP, Washington, DC
cseebald@velaw.com
*Featured in Antitrust (District of Columbia)*
**Practice Areas:** Co-chair of V&E's Antitrust Group; focuses on defending companies involved in criminal and civil government investigations and follow-on litigation, defending mergers and joint ventures before the antitrust agencies, providing antitrust counseling and representing companies in civil litigation.
**Personal:** George Washington University Law School, JD (cum laude), 1992; Franklin & Marshall College, BA, 1989.

**SEGAL, Scott H**
Bracewell & Giuliani LLP, Washington, DC
202 828 5845
scott.segal@bgllp.com
*Featured in Environment (District of Columbia)*
**Practice Areas:** Head of the firm's government practice and founding partner in the Policy Resolution Group. Assists clients with effective participation in the legislative and regulatory processes in the areas of environment, energy, trade, and consumer issues. Has led campaigns for clients in financial services, health care and other fields. Assists clients with strategic planning and communications in changed circumstances through public-affairs initiatives, monitoring, advocacy and negotiations with the US Congress and federal government agencies.
**Personal:** JD, The University of Texas School of Law, 1989; BA, Emory University, 1986.

**SELEY, Peter**
Gibson, Dunn & Crutcher LLP, Washington, DC
202 887 3689
pseley@gibsondunn.com
*Featured in Environment (District of Columbia)*
**Practice Areas:** Co-chair of the Environmental Litigation & Mass Torts Practice Group. Over the past 20 years, he has handled cases under most federal and a number of state environmental statutes, and has extensive experience in mass and toxic tort defense, as well as international environmental tort and enforcement defense. He also has written several articles and book chapters concerning a wide range of domestic and international environmental issues.
**Career:** Co-chair of the Environmental Litigation & Mass Torts Practice Group.
**Personal:** JD, Cornell Law School, 1993, cum laude, associate editor of the Cornell Law Review.

**SENKOWSKI, R Michael**
Wiley Rein LLP, Washington, DC
202 719 7249
msenkowski@wileyrein.com
*Featured in Telecommunications (District of Columbia)*
**Practice Areas:** Chairs the Telecommunications Practice, specializing in telephony, wireless, international and Internet issues. Named one of Washingtonian magazine's "Best Lawyers." Included in the "International Who's Who of Business Lawyers," and Euromoney's "Guide to the World's Leading Telecommunications Lawyers."
**Professional Memberships:** Federal Communications Bar Association; Past Chairman, Federal Bar Association.
**Career:** Former Chief of Staff for the Chairman of the FCC; Legal Advisor to the Chairman of the FCC; Acting Deputy Chief, Office of General Counsel, FCC; US Representative, International Telecommunications Satellite Organization Panel of Legal Experts (2002).
**Personal:** George Washington University Law School (JD, with honors); Yale University (BA).

**SHAPIRO, Stephen Brett**
Holland & Knight LLP, Washington, DC
202 955 3000
stephen.shapiro@hklaw.com
*Featured in Construction (District of Columbia)*
**Practice Areas:** Construction Industry Practice Group Leader and Partner in the Litigation Section, focuses his practice on construction law, public contracts and commercial litigation. Building on his experience representing contractors, public and private owners, architects, engineers and construction managers, he has developed extensive knowledge in all aspects of construction procurement, contract administration, claims, government contract and construction litigation, bid protests, regulatory compliance and subcontractor, supplier and surety relations. Mr Shapiro is a frequent speaker on topics relevant to the construction industry.

**SHAPIRO, ESQ., Howard**
WilmerHale, Washington, DC
202 663 6606
howard.shapiro@wilmerhale.com
*Featured in Litigation (District of Columbia)*
**Practice Areas:** Chair, Litigation/Controversy Department. Focus: white-collar criminal defense, complex civil trials, internal investigations. Represents companies and individuals in criminal and regulatory enforcement investigations and in trials throughout the United States and conducts internal investigations for banking and corporate clients in connection with regulatory and criminal probes in the United States, Europe and Asia.
**Career:** General Counsel, Federal Bureau of Investigation; Assistant United States Attorney, Southern District of New York; Associate Professor of Law, Cornell Law School. Awarded the National Intelligence Distinguished Service Medal and recipient of numerous Department of Justice awards.
**Personal:** JD, Yale Law School; BA, Williams College.

**SHASHY, Abraham N M**
King & Spalding LLP, Washington, DC
202 626 5614
hshashy@kslaw.com
*Featured in Tax (District of Columbia)*
**Practice Areas:** Practice includes transactional tax planning for, and tax controversy representation of, multinational corporations in a variety of domestic and international contexts. Those contexts include partnerships and joint ventures, capital market and finance transactions, business combinations and reorganizations, mergers and acquisitions. Mr Shashy's clients comprise companies from the energy, finance, technology, telecommunications, media, real estate and industrial sectors.
**Personal:** New York University School of Law, 1975, LLM, Managing Editor, Tax Law Review University of Florida Levin College of Law, 1973, JD, University of Florida Law Review; Order of the Coif.

## SHEA, Richard C
Covington & Burling LLP, Washington, DC
202 662 5599
rshea@cov.com
*Featured in Employee Benefits & Executive Compensation (District of Columbia)*
**Practice Areas:** Richard Shea chairs Covington's Employee Benefits and Executive Compensation practice and is regarded as one of the nation's leading thinkers on employee benefits law and policy. He specializes in guiding clients successfully through high-stakes legislative, rule-making, litigation, audit, benefit design, and transactional challenges, typically involving hundreds of millions or billions of dollars.
**Career:** Associate Benefits Tax Counsel, Treasury Department, 1989-91; Judicial Clerk, Hon. Carl McGowan, US Court of Appeals, 1983-84.
**Personal:** University of Virginia School of Law, JD, 1983 (Executive Editor, Virginia Law Review); Fulbright Fellow, Universidad Católica del Perú, 1976-77; Amherst College, AB, magna cum laude, 1976.

## SHERIDAN, Paul
Latham & Watkins LLP, Washington, DC
202 637 2287
paul.sheridan@lw.com
*Featured in Corporate/M&A (District of Columbia)*
**Practice Areas:** Represents private equity firms, their portfolio companies and other clients in acquisitions, divestitures and other significant transactions. Practice includes counseling companies on governance matters.
**Career:** Recipient of Law360's 2012 Private Equity MVP award which honors "attorneys whose achievements in major litigation or transactions have set a new standard for accomplishment in corporate law." In 2009, The National Law Journal included him as one of the 40 "rising stars" under age 40 in the Washington legal community.
**Personal:** Harvard College (BA, 1993), University of Virginia School of Law (JD, 1996).

## SHERMAN, Andrew J
Jones Day, Washington, DC
202 879 3686
ajsherman@jonesday.com
*Featured in Corporate/M&A (District of Columbia)*
**Practice Areas:** Focuses on legal and strategic aspects of business growth, including developing strategies to leverage intellectual property and technology assets, as well as international corporate transactional, M&A, and franchising matters.
**Career:** Partner; serves as an Adjunct Professor in the University of Maryland's MBA Program and at Georgetown University's Law School.
**Publications:** Author of 23 books on the legal and strategic aspects of business growth, franchising, capital formation, M&A, and leveraging of intellectual property. He also has authored similar articles for trade and business publications.
**Personal:** American University Washington College of Law (JD, 1986); University of Maryland (BA, 1983).

## SHERMAN, William
Latham & Watkins LLP, Washington, DC
202 637 1094
william.sherman@lw.com
*Featured in Antitrust (District of Columbia)*
**Practice Areas:** Specializes in complex multi-party antitrust class action litigation in federal and state courts. Has represented numerous Fortune 100 companies and multinational corporations and financial institutions in connection with nationwide and worldwide cartel claims. Recently achieved dismissal of conspiracy claims regarding $5.3 billion LBO, successfully argued for dismissal of foreign claims against numerous airlines based upon the FTAIA, and defeated allegations of conspiracy in the automotive industry to restrict Canadian exports to the US.
**Professional Memberships:** DC and New York bars; numerous federal courts.
**Personal:** JD, Magna Cum Laude, Washington College of Law, 1987; BA, Cornell University, 1982.

## SHUREN, Allison W
Arnold & Porter LLP, Washington, DC
202 942 6525
Allison.Shuren@aporter.com
*Featured in Healthcare (District of Columbia)*
**Practice Areas:** Allison Shuren focuses her practice on a variety of health care regulatory and fraud and abuse in the context of government enforcement and compliance issues. She advises a broad group of clients, including pharmaceutical, medical device, and biotechnology companies, physician practice management companies and physician practices, hospital and academic medical centers, ambulatory surgery centers, diagnostic imaging centers, and health care professional societies.
**Career:** Formerly a practicing critical care pediatric nurse practitioner concentrating in cardiovascular and neonatal pediatric surgery.
**Personal:** JD, University of Michigan Law School, 1998; MSN, University of Florida, 1994; BSN in Nursing, Salem State College, 1987.

## SIEGEL, Nathan E
Levine Sullivan Koch & Schulz LLP, Washington, DC
202 508 1184
nsiegel@lskslaw.com
*Featured in Media & Entertainment (District of Columbia)*
**Practice Areas:** Represented media in First Amendment and intellectual property cases for 20 years. Cases include Food Lion v ABC, Knievel v ESPN, Wen Ho Lee v US Taught First Amendment law at University of Maryland Law School.
**Professional Memberships:** Former President, Media Law Resource Center Defense Counsel Section; former Chair of Reporter's Privilege Task Force and New Legal Developments committees.
**Career:** Previously in-house litigation counsel at ABC,Inc.
**Publications:** Co-editor, Journal of International Media and Entertainment Law; Co- Author, "Handcuffing the Press" (New York Law Journal); "Newsgathering and Privacy Rights."

**Personal:** Born 24 December 1963; JD, Yale Law School.

## SILBERT, Earl J
DLA Piper LLP (US), Washington, DC
202 799 4517
earl.silbert@dlapiper.com
*Featured in Litigation (District of Columbia)*
**Practice Areas:** Litigation, white-collar.
**Career:** He focuses on white-collar crime investigations and trials, civil and criminal tax, securities, defense procurement, environment, healthcare, and representation of lawyers and law firms on ethical, malpractice, and partnership issues. He had a distinguished career in public service before entering private practice, including serving as the first Watergate prosecutor and US attorney for the District of Columbia. He has written extensively in the area of white-collar crime, the attorney-client privilege, work product doctrine, RICO, and other litigation issues.
**Personal:** LLB, Harvard Law School; BA, Harvard University.

## SILVER, David C
Holland & Knight LLP, Washington, DC
202 457 7097
david.silver@hklaw.com
*Featured in Real Estate (District of Columbia)*
**Practice Areas:** David Silver is a Partner in the firm's Real Estate Section and practices in the areas of real estate acquisition, development, financing, and commercial leasing. His practice includes the representation of large developers, pension funds and institutional owners, as well as large corporations in connection with their real estate activities in the Washington, DC metropolitan area and nationally. This representation includes buying, selling, developing, financing and/or leasing office buildings, shopping centers, residential buildings, hotels and mixed-use sites. He also represents Holland & Knight in all of its real estate activities nationally. He is also a Certified Public Accountant.

## SIMONS, Joseph J
Paul, Weiss, Rifkind, Wharton & Garrison LLP, Washington, DC
202 223 7370
jsimons@paulweiss.com
*Featured in Antitrust (District of Columbia)*
**Practice Areas:** Partner and Co-Chair, Antitrust Group. Formerly Director of Bureau of Competition at Federal Trade Commission (FTC). Extensive experience representing clients before FTC, Department of Justice (DOJ) and Congress in a wide range of antitrust and regulatory matters, from the largest mergers and acquisitions to price fixing and novel predation and vertical restraints cases. Nominated by DOJ and approved by Federal Communications Commission as trustee for Cingular/AT&T Wireless and Bell Atlantic/GTE/Vodafone transactions. Co-developed Critical Loss Analysis' technique for market definition and competitive effects analysis, which is widely-used by courts, FTC, DOJ, and recently incorporated into revised US Merger Guidelines.

## SIMS, Joe
Jones Day, Washington, DC
202 879 3863
jsims@jonesday.com
*Featured in Antitrust (District of Columbia)*
**Practice Areas:** Due to pioneering efforts in antitrust was recognised in March 2010 by The National Law Journal as one of "The Decade's Most Influential Lawyers." The only antitrust lawyer to be recognised (twice, in 2001 and 2009) as "Dealmaker of the Year" by The American Lawyer. 2006 US antitrust Chambers "Awards for Excellence" winner. Represents clients in antitrust and related regulatory areas, including litigation, counseling, and agency practice, and has broad experience with mergers and acquisitions. Has acted as lead antitrust counsel on some of the most significant transactions of recent years, many in technology, telecommunications, and electronic media.

## SINGER, Toby G
Jones Day, Washington, DC
202 879 4654
tgsinger@jonesday.com
*Featured in Healthcare (Nationwide), Healthcare (District of Columbia)*
**Practice Areas:** Antitrust counseling and litigation practice, with an emphasis in the healthcare industry, especially with respect to health care transactions. She has been named a Chambers USA leading lawyer annually from 2007 to 2013 and was selected to be included in the 2007 through 2013 editions of The Best Lawyers in America for the Washington, DC area.
**Professional Memberships:** ABA; American Health Lawyers Association (Past Chair, Antitrust Practice Group); District of Columbia Bar.
**Publications:** She has spoken and published on antitrust subjects on numerous occasions and is on the Advisory Board of BNA's Health Law Reporter.

## SINHA, Pankaj K
Skadden, Arps, Slate, Meagher & Flom LLP & Affiliates, Washington, DC
202 371 7307
Pankaj.Sinha@skadden.com
*Featured in Corporate/M&A (District of Columbia), Energy & Natural Resources (Nationwide)*
See under Nationwide for profile.

## SKINNER, William P
Covington & Burling LLP, Washington, DC
202 662 5470
wskinner@cov.com
*Featured in Insurance (Nationwide), Insurance (District of Columbia)*
See under Nationwide for profile.

## SLOAN, Cliff
Skadden, Arps, Slate, Meagher & Flom LLP & Affiliates, Washington, DC
202 371 7040
Cliff.Sloan@skadden.com
*Featured in Media & Entertainment (District of Columbia)*
**Practice Areas:** Has litigated at all levels of federal and state courts, including six US Supreme Court arguments, numerous arguments in the

U.S. Courts of Appeals, and matters in trial and district courts across the US. Focuses on cases involving intellectual property, administrative law, commercial disputes, securities law, tax controversies and constitutional issues. Advises on new media, copyright, trademark and First Amendment matters.
**Career:** General Counsel, Washingtonpost.Newsweek Interactive (2000-08); Associate Counsel, President of the United States (1993-95); Assistant, Solicitor General, U.S. Department of Justice (1989-91); JD Harvard Law School (magna cum laude) (1984); BA, Harvard College (magna cum laude) (1979).

### SMETHURST, Ryan
McDermott Will & Emery UK LLP, London
202 756 8036
rsmethurst@mwe.com
*Featured in Insurance (District of Columbia)*
**Practice Areas:** Based in the firm's Washington, DC office. Focuses on litigation and counsels clients regarding insurance and reinsurance disputes nationwide. Represents the WTC Captive Insurance Company with respect to its defense of approximately 10,000 bodily injury suits by Fire Department of New York, New York Police Department, and construction personnel relating to their rescue, recovery, and debris removal work at the World Trade Center site on and after September 11, 2001.
**Personal:** George Mason University School of Law, JD, (cum laude), 1999, Cornell University, BA, 1993.

### SMITH, Paul M
Jenner & Block LLP, Washington, DC
202 639 6060
psmith@jenner.com
*Featured in First Amendment Litigation (Nationwide), Appellate Law (Nationwide), Media & Entertainment (District of Columbia)*
See under Nationwide for profile.

### SMITH, Robert J
Morgan, Lewis & Bockius LLP, Washington, DC
202 739 5065
rsmith@morganlewis.com
*Featured in Labor & Employment (District of Columbia)*
**Practice Areas:** Robert J. Smith is a partner in Morgan Lewis's Labor and Employment Practice. His practice involves the defense of complex individual, collective and class actions alleging violations under Federal and State wage hour laws, employment discrimination statutes and ERISA. He consults with public, private and international organizations in connection with confidential ethics and other sensitive investigations and in the private sector on organizational restructuring and development of effective intellectual property, confidentiality, non-competition and executive employment agreements.
**Personal:** Attended Georgetown University Law Center, JD; Cornell University School of Industrial and Labor Relations, MS, Mount St. Mary's University (Maryland), BS.

### SMITH, Wm. Randolph
Crowell & Moring LLP, Washington, DC
202 624 2700
wrsmith@crowell.com
*Featured in Antitrust (District of Columbia)*
**Practice Areas:** Co-chair of Crowell & Moring's Antitrust Group, and member of the firm's Executive Committee and Management Board. Practice involves mergers/acquisitions/joint ventures/trade association law/cartel enforcement and the intersection of antitrust laws and intellectual property. Recent matters include acting as lead antitrust counsel for SBC Communications Inc. in connection with its acquisition of AT&T, to defending clients in multi-jurisdictional cartel investigations. Other clients: Alcoa, AT&T Inc., Cingular Wireless, CropLife America, CSX Transportation, DuPont, Hillenbrand Industries, Rio Tinto Energy, and United Technologies Corporation.
**Career:** Completed six years of service with the FTC, positions included serving as executive assistant to the chairman.

### SOHN, Michael N
Davis Polk & Wardwell LLP, Washington, DC
202 962 7000
michael.sohn@davispolk.com
*Featured in Antitrust (District of Columbia)*
**Practice Areas:** Michael Sohn, a former General Counsel of the Federal Trade Commission, is known for his involvement in sensitive and complex international antitrust matters where he has been especially recognised for his ability to facilitate innovative agreements between his clients and reviewing government authorities. Mr Sohn's practice encompasses a broad range of antitrust and consumer protection matters, with particular focus on the antitrust aspects of mergers and acquisitions and government investigations of allegedly anticompetitive conduct. Mr Sohn served for many years as the head of the antitrust practice group at a major Washington law firm.

### SOKLER, Bruce D
Mintz Levin Cohn Ferris Glovsky and Popeo PC, Washington, DC
202 434 7303
BDSokler@mintz.com
*Featured in Antitrust (District of Columbia)*
**Practice Areas:** Bruce serves as head of Mintz Levin's Antitrust & Federal Regulation Section. In over 30 years in private practice, he has extensive experience in both antitrust and communications regulation and litigation, including associated First Amendment and copyright law matters. In the antitrust area, he represents Fortune 100 companies, not-for-profits, start-up entities, and domestic and international joint ventures, with a particular expertise in the communications, health care and retail industries. His experience spans government investigations, including merger reviews, and antitrust litigation, including antitrust class actions.
**Professional Memberships:** ABA Antitrust Section, Litigation Section.

**Personal:** BA, Princeton University; JD, Georgetown University.

### SOLOMON, David H
Wilkinson Barker Knauer LLP, Washington, DC
202 783 4141
dsolomon@wbklaw.com
*Featured in Telecommunications (District of Columbia)*
**Practice Areas:** Mr Solomon's practice areas include mass media, telecommunications and administrative law, with a particular emphasis on enforcement and administrative litigation. During the past year, Mr Solomon represented many major US communications companies in FCC enforcement and complaint proceedings, including Comcast and T-Mobile, USA.
**Professional Memberships:** Member, Federal Communications Bar Association
**Career:** First Enforcement Bureau Chief, Federal Communications Commission (1999-2005). FCC Deputy General Counsel (1994-1999) and FCC Assistant General Counsel for Administrative Law (1987-94).
**Personal:** JD, cum laude, Harvard Law School, 1981; AB, magna cum laude, Harvard College, 1976. Selected as one of the Best Lawyers in America in the Communications Law category (2011-2013 editions); Super Lawyers (2012-2013 editions).

### SOOY, Kathleen Taylor
Crowell & Moring LLP, Washington, DC
202 624 2608
ksooy@crowell.com
*Featured in Litigation (District of Columbia)*
**Practice Areas:** Partner and head of Crowell & Moring's national litigation class action group. Focuses practice on national litigation, acting as national counsel to companies in commercial and product liability litigation. Experience also includes coordination of strategies in the litigation, government relations and public relations arenas. Handles significant RICO litigation, including federal appellate practice. Acts as an account manager for the firm's work as a DuPont primary law firm and became the fourth lawyer inducted into DuPont Legal's Leaders Circle.
**Personal:** College of William and Mary, BA, University of Virginia, M.A., George Washington University Law School, JD, 1984

### SOPHIR, Eric
Dentons, Washington, DC
202 408 6470
eric.sophir@dentons.com
*Featured in Intellectual Property (District of Columbia)*
**Practice Areas:** Eric Sophir counsels clients on protecting innovations, gaining market share, resolving patent disputes, and monetizing patents. His practice includes various aspects of patent law, including patent preparation and prosecution, infringement and validity analysis in patent litigation, and post-grant proceedings. His clients range from Fortune 50 companies to startup companies. His global patent procurement efforts and patent analysis involves technologies including semicon-

ductors, telecommunications, internet technology, cloud computing, financial systems, software, and business methods. He also advises on post-grant proceedings, due diligence, clearance and landscape analysis, non-infringement opinions, licensing, infringement defenses, and enforcement efforts.
**Personal:** Franklin Pierce Law Center, JD; Cornell University, BS

### SOTSKY, Lester
Arnold & Porter LLP, Washington, DC
202 942 5170
Lester.Sotsky@aporter.com
*Featured in Environment (District of Columbia)*
**Practice Areas:** Heads the firm's Environmental Practice, experienced in toxic tort and environmental litigation (civil, criminal and appellate) and regulatory counseling. Lead counsel in toxic tort cases involving chemicals, radioactive materials, health and wrongful death claims, and class actions. Advises clients on risk liability mitigation strategies and crisis management. Named top Washington Environmental Lawyer 2009 by Washington Business Journal. Experienced in Clean Water Act, hazardous waste, contaminated sites, and compliance and audit programs.
**Publications:** 'Protecting Against Environmental Litigation'; 'Compartmentalizing Environmental Liabilities'; 'A Q&A Guide to Environmental Law in The U.S.'
**Personal:** JD, Yale Law School, 1979; BA, Brandeis University, 1976.

### SPEIGHTS, Grace E
Morgan, Lewis & Bockius LLP, Washington, DC
202 739 5189
gspeights@morganlewis.com
*Featured in Labor & Employment (District of Columbia)*
**Practice Areas:** Grace E. Speights is a partner in Morgan Lewis's Labor and Employment Practice, Managing Partner of the Washington, D.C. office, Deputy Practice Group Leader of the Labor and Employment Practice, chair of the Systemic Litigation Practice, and co-chair of the firm's Diversity Committee. She focuses her practice on counseling and defending clients in connection with employment discrimination claims, primarily class claims, and on counseling clients regarding best practices for corporate diversity initiatives. Grace has handled many employment discrimination class action cases.
**Personal:** Attended George Washington University National Law Center, JD; University of Pennsylvania, BA

### ST MARTIN, Andrée M
Groom Law Group, Washington, DC
202 861 6642
ams@groom.com
*Featured in Employee Benefits & Executive Compensation (District of Columbia)*
**Practice Areas:** Andrée represents corporate plans, multiple employer plans, Taft-Hartley plans, mutual funds, insurers, banks, investment managers, plan administrators, and other

providers to employee benefit plans. She focuses primarily on issues related to Title I of ERISA and code section 4975, including fiduciary responsibility and prohibited transaction matters, and the structuring of new investment funds and other products and services for the pension and welfare plan market.

**Career:** Litigation Attorney, U.S. Department of Labor, Solicitor's Office, (PBSD); Associate General Counsel, UMWA Health & Retirement Funds.

**Personal:** JD, cum laude, Harvard Law School. BA, summa cum laude, Spring Hill College.

## STAMAS, George P
Kirkland & Ellis LLP, Washington, DC
202 879 5090
george.stamas@kirkland.com
*Featured in Corporate/M&A (District of Columbia)*

**Practice Areas:** A senior partner in the Washington and New York offices advising leading corporations and investors on complex business transactions, including M&A, buy-outs, private equity investing, IPOs, and restructurings, in numerous industries including energy, finance, construction, healthcare, and professional sports and counseling corporations and boards on corporate governance matters. Representative clients: Constellation Energy, MidOcean Partners, FTI Consulting, New Enterprise Associates, SRA International, Tutor-Perini, Monumental Sports, Sagent Pharmaceutical.

**Career:** Special Counsel, SEC Enforcement. Vice Chairman, Deutsche Bank Alex Brown.

**Personal:** Wharton, University of Pennsylvania, 1973; University of Maryland School of Law, JD, 1976.

## STANDISH, Daniel J
Wiley Rein LLP, Washington, DC
202 719 7130
dstandish@wileyrein.com
*Featured in Insurance (District of Columbia)*

**Practice Areas:** Chairs the Insurance Practice. Nationally recognized as a leading attorney in professional liability insurance coverage matters and disputes, has 20+ years of experience counseling insurance clients on issues relating to professional liability lines of coverage and representing professional liability insurers in coverage litigation before federal and state courts across the country. Best Lawyers, Insurance Law (2013).

**Professional Memberships:** Board of Directors, PLUS Foundation; Past President and Trustee, Professional Liability Underwriting Society.

**Career:** Assistant U.S. Attorney for the District of Columbia.

**Personal:** The University of Chicago Law School (JD); Bowdoin College (AB, magna cum laude).

## STANKO, Joe
Hunton & Williams LLP, Washington, DC
202 955 1529
jstanko@hunton.com
*Featured in Environment (District of Columbia)*

**Practice Areas:** Mr Stanko's practice focuses on issue advocacy before congressional, White House and other executive branch officials. He serves as

head of the federal government relations team, with particular experience in policy issues related to global climate change, renewables and biofuels, energy production, Homeland Security, the Clean Air Act and other environmental laws. Mr Stanko also provides strategic planning for corporations developing long-term business planning.

**Professional Memberships:** DC Bar Association; American Bar Association; U.S. Chamber of Commerce Energy, Clean Air and Natural Resources Committee.

**Personal:** JD, Boston University School of Law, 1989; BA, Economics, Boston University, 1984.

## STANSBURY, Claude B
Freshfields Bruckhaus Deringer LLP, Washington, DC
202 777 4500
claude.stansbury@freshfields.com
*Featured in Tax (District of Columbia)*

**Practice Areas:** Claude is a partner based in Freshfields Bruckhaus Deringer's Washington, DC office and has a wide ranging tax practice advising large corporations on domestic and international restructurings, mergers, acquisitions and disposals. Claude also has extensive experience advising private equity funds on fund and portfolio company investment structures, take-privates, financing of portfolio companies and leveraged recapitalizations, workouts, PIPES and convertible securities and tax-advantaged exits.

## STARR, Judson
Venable LLP, Washington, DC
202 344 4886
jwstarr@venable.com
*Featured in Environment (District of Columbia)*

**Practice Areas:** Mr Starr focuses on corporate governance and compliance initiatives for clients facing serious and complex environmental contingencies. He represents corporations and individuals under investigation for environmental and white-collar offenses. He chaired Venable's Environmental Group for two decades – the only group in the nation that focuses exclusively on representing clients facing environmental crimes issues.

**Career:** He was the first Director and Chief of the Environmental Crimes Section, U.S. Department of Justice. He has authored numerous publications on environmental crimes issues, and testifies before state and federal legislative bodies. He co-chairs the annual ALI-ABA Conference on Environmental Crimes.

## STEINBERG, Michael W
Morgan, Lewis & Bockius LLP, Washington, DC
202 739 5141
msteinberg@morganlewis.com
*Featured in Environment (District of Columbia)*

**Practice Areas:** For more than 30 years has focused exclusively on environmental law matters, with special emphasis on litigation and counseling involving (1) hazardous waste issues under the Resource Conservation and Recovery Act, (2) Superfund cleanup and liability issues under federal and state laws, and (3) environmental justice issues under federal and state civil rights laws.

Represents multi-industry coalitions that conduct advocacy on policy issues affecting these programs. Has testified before Congress and administrative agencies.

**Career:** Served as the Assistant Chief of the Environmental Defense Section at the U.S. Department of Justice.

## STEINWAY, Daniel M
Baker Botts LLP, Houston
202 639 7902
daniel.steinway@bakerbotts.com
*Featured in Environment (District of Columbia)*

**Practice Areas:** Air Quality, Compliance and Enforcement, Environmental Practice, Government Relations, International Environmental Law, Mining and Metals, Natural Resources, Toxic Tort and Environmental Litigation, Waste and Remediation, Water Quality.

**Professional Memberships:** District of Columbia Bar; State Bar of Michigan; United States Court of Appeals, District of Columbia Circuit; United States District Court, Southern District of Texas; American Bar Association, Tort Trial and Insurance Practice Section; Committee on Energy Resources, former Chairman; Federal Bar Association, Environment, Energy, and Natural Resources Section, former Chairman.

**Personal:** JD (with honors), The George Washington University Law School, 1976; BSE. (cum laude), University of Michigan, 1972.

## STEPHENS, T Reed
McDermott Will & Emery LLP, Washington, DC
202 756 8129
trstephens@mwe.com
*Featured in Healthcare (District of Columbia)*

**Practice Areas:** Member of firm's health law department and trial department; represents clients primarily in health care industry, including large drug manufacturers, wholesalers, and health care systems. Defends clients in government investigations, and advises clients on mergers & acquisitions, public policy and health care fraud and abuse compliance matters.

**Professional Memberships:** American Bar Association; DC Bar Association; American Health Lawyers Association.

**Career:** Former attorney with the Department of Justice, Civil Frauds (1995-2003); DOJ Special Commendation for Outstanding Service; Judicial Clerkship, United States District Court for the Eastern District of Pennsylvania.

**Personal:** Stanford Law School (JD); Princeton University (BA).

## STEPHENSON, Andrew W
Holland & Knight LLP, Washington, DC
202 955 3000
andrew.stephenson@hklaw.com
*Featured in Construction (District of Columbia)*

**Practice Areas:** Construction Industry Practice Group partner practicing in construction and labor law, representing owners, architect-engineers, general contractors, and construction managers in virtually all phases of the private and public sectors of the domestic and international construction industry. Stephenson's construction

experience covers the drafting and negotiation of construction contract documents, counsel during project administration, and dispute resolution on a wide-range of both medium size and large, complex building and infrastructure projects, including billion dollar design-build projects. He also has been involved in the construction of numerous power generation facilities, including nuclear, fossil fuel and alternative energy power plants.

## STEVENS, Michael L
Arent Fox LLP, Washington, DC
202 857 6382
michael.stevens@arentfox.com
*Featured in Labor & Employment (District of Columbia)*

**Practice Areas:** Mike Stevens represents management clients in diverse and complex labor and employment law matters, both across the country and internationally. He regularly advises clients on compliance and transaction issues and assists them in various types of employment litigation, including discrimination, harassment, retaliation, wrongful discharge, wage and hour, restrictive covenant and trade secret litigation. He also has an active labor relations practice involving union organizing, negotiations, arbitrations and NLRB proceedings.

## STRAND, Margaret
Venable LLP, Washington, DC
202 344 4699
mnstrand@Venable.com
*Featured in Environment (District of Columbia)*

**Practice Areas:** Peggy Strand concentrates on counseling, government relations and litigation in environmental programs. She is known for her work with wetlands, endangered species, environmental review and environmental compliance for infrastructure projects. She has substantial experience advising on regulatory requirements of federal and state natural resources and pollution control law.

**Career:** Ms. Strand was Chief of the Environmental Defense Section US Justice Department Environmental and Natural Resources Division from 1984-91.

**Publications:** The Wetlands Deskbook (Island Press).

**Personal:** JD, College of William and Mary, Marshall-Wythe School of Law, 1976; MA, University of Rhode Island, 1971; BA, University of Rochester, 1968.

## STROCHAK, Adam
Weil, Gotshal & Manges LLP, Washington, DC
202 682 7001
adam.strochak@weil.com
*Featured in Bankruptcy/Restructuring (District of Columbia)*

**Practice Areas:** Adam Strochak concentrates his practice in corporate restructuring, representing both debtors and creditors in restructuring matters in and out of court. Mr Strochak's practice focuses on litigation of high-stakes disputes involving financial reorganization, bankruptcy and insolvency. In chapter 11 cases, Mr Strochak

has represented debtors from diverse industries, including power generation, real estate, banking, manufacturing, energy, telecommunications, computers, steel, healthcare, building products and retail sales. Major debtor representations include General Growth Properties, Washington Mutual, AES Eastern Energy, WorldCom, Global Crossing, Enron, Silicon Graphics, Eagle-Picher Industries and Metallurg.
**Personal:** University of Vermont (BA), George Washington University Law (JD).

### STUART III, James R
Crowell & Moring LLP, Washington, DC
202 624 2865
jstuart@crowell.com
*Featured in Corporate/M&A (District of Columbia)*
**Practice Areas:** Chair of Crowell & Moring's Corporate Group and member of the Executive Committee. Concentrates practice on mergers, stock and asset acquisitions, joint ventures, and debt and equity financing transactions, including private placements, venture capital investments and secured credit facilities. Has extensive experience negotiating and drafting a wide range of commercial and corporate contracts, including technology licensing, development and collaboration agreements, large scale IT hardware and software procurement agreements, management agreements, supply, distribution and manufacturing agreements, shareholder and LLC operating agreements, teaming, partnership and alliance agreements, and system integration and outsourcing arrangements.
**Personal:** JD from Harvard Law School.

### SULLIVAN, Michael D
Levine Sullivan Koch & Schulz LLP, Washington, DC
202 508 1116
msullivan@lskslaw.com
*Featured in First Amendment Litigation (Nationwide), Media & Entertainment (District of Columbia)*
See under Nationwide for profile.

### SULLIVAN, T J
Drinker Biddle & Reath LLP, Washington, DC
202 230 5157
TJ.Sullivan@dbr.com
*Featured in Healthcare (Nationwide), Healthcare (District of Columbia)*
See under Nationwide for profile.

### SUNSHINE, Steven C
Skadden, Arps, Slate, Meagher & Flom LLP & Affiliates, Washington, DC
202 371 7860
Steve.Sunshine@skadden.com
*Featured in Antitrust (District of Columbia)*
**Practice Areas:** North American group leader of the firm's Antitrust and Competition practice. Represents clients in connection with antitrust aspects of litigation, mergers and acquisitions, counseling and grand jury investigations into allegations of price fixing or other cartel conduct. Grand jury representations include investigations into electrodes, industrial diamonds, electronic components and chemicals.

**Career:** Deputy Assistant Attorney General in charge of Merger Enforcement, Antitrust Division, U.S. Department of Justice (1993-95). JD, Boston College Law School (Law Review, magna cum laude, Order of the Coif); AB, Brown University.

### SUPKO, Mark
Crowell & Moring LLP, Washington, DC
202 624 2734
msupko@crowell.com
*Featured in Intellectual Property (District of Columbia)*
**Practice Areas:** Partner and chair of Crowell & Moring LLP's Intellectual Property Group. Practice devoted to IP litigation for 15 plus years, heavy emphasis on patent litigation in the computer, electrical and mechanical arts for corporate clients in many industries - aerospace, automotive, consumer electronics, digital imaging, oil refining, and telecommunications. Experienced in all aspects of patent litigation, from pre-suit investigations and opinions through trial and appeal. Successfully litigated patent infringement cases involving a variety of technologies: computer network infrastructures, wireless information systems, digital image-enhancement, digital printers, Internet applications, business methodologies, cable-television signal processing, medical devices, tobacco curing, paperless couponing.

### SURINGA, Dirk
Covington & Burling LLP, Washington, DC
202 662 5436
dsuringa@cov.com
*Featured in Tax (District of Columbia)*
**Practice Areas:** Mr Suringa advises clients regarding the Federal income tax aspects of domestic and international transactions and represents clients before the IRS, the Treasury Department, and in the Federal courts.
**Professional Memberships:** DC and Florida Bars; International Fiscal Association, USA Branch, Vice President and Secretary; American Bar Association, Foreign Lawyers Forum, Vice-Chair.
**Career:** Partner in the Tax Practice Group. Treasury Department, Office of International Tax Counsel, Attorney-Advisor, 2000 to 2003.
**Publications:** BNA Tax Management Portfolio on the Foreign Tax Credit Limitation.
**Personal:** Harvard Law School, JD, 1996, magna cum laude. Princeton University, BA, Phi Beta Kappa, 1992.

### SWANSON, M Anne
Dow Lohnes PLLC, Washington, DC
202 776 2534
aswanson@dowlohnes.com
*Featured in Telecommunications (District of Columbia)*
**Practice Areas:** Represents spectrum licensees in adjudication, rulemaking, and enforcement proceedings before the FCC, other agencies, federal courts. Advises communications, navigation, and transportation companies on FCC policy, equipment authorization, and certification matters. Counsels institutional investors with expertise in intersection of communications and bank-

ruptcy laws. Broadcast experience encompasses shared services and affiliation agreements and relationships with subscription media.
**Professional Memberships:** ABA (Communications Forum, former Governing Committee Member); Federal Communications Bar Association (former President, Treasurer, ABA Delegate); DC Bar; Cosmos Club, Washington, DC.
**Career:** Editor, President's Daily News Summary, White House, Washington, DC, 1974-75; law clerk to Hon CB Renfrew, ND Calif., 1979-80, and Hon RD Cudahy, Seventh Circuit, 1980. Joined firm as Partner, 1997.
**Personal:** Georgetown University (LLM, 1997); Yale Law School (JD, 1979); Princeton University (MPA, 1979); WV University (BS, 1974), magna cum laude.

### SYMONS, Howard
Mintz Levin Cohn Ferris Glovsky and Popeo PC, Washington, DC
202 434 7305
HJSymons@mintz.com
*Featured in Telecommunications (District of Columbia)*
**Practice Areas:** Howard chairs Mintz Levin's Communications Practice. A communications industry veteran with more than 30 years experience, including several years as a Congressional adviser on landmark policy issues, Howard represents cable, wireless and telecommunications companies and trade associations before regulatory agencies, Congress, and courts.
**Professional Memberships:** Federal Communications Bar Association.
**Career:** Senior Counsel, House Subcommittee on Telecommunications; Adjunct Professor National Law Center, George Washington University; staff attorney, Public Citizen's Congress Watch.
**Publications:** Frequent moderator and speaker at continuing legal education seminars; witness at Congressional and state legislative hearings.
**Personal:** BA, Yale University; JD, Harvard Law School.

### TALADAY, John
Baker Botts LLP, Washington, DC
202 639 7909
john.taladay@bakerbotts.com
*Featured in Antitrust (District of Columbia)*
**Practice Areas:** Antitrust and Competition Law, Litigation Practice
**Professional Memberships:** District of Columbia Bar; United State Supreme Court; United States District Court for the District of Columbia
**Career:** Mr Taladay has extensive experience in complex merger reviews, cartel investigations, and anticompetitive practice cases before the FTC, DOJ European Commission and other international agencies. He is recognized for his international competition policy leadership and his expertise in the technology, media, telecommunications, software and pharmaceuticals sectors, and traditional industries including automotive, mining, metals, agriculture, chemicals and electronics.

**Personal:** LLM Georgetown, 1999; JD, University of North Carolina, 1989; BS, Pennsylvania State University, 1986

### TENPAS, Ronald J
Morgan, Lewis & Bockius LLP, Washington, DC
202 739 5435
rtenpas@morganlewis.com
*Featured in Environment (District of Columbia)*
**Practice Areas:** Co-chairs Environmental and Climate Change Practices; active in White Collar, Appellate, and Congressional Investigations Practices. Environmental practice involves litigation and counseling under pollution and natural resources statutes. Practice includes compliance counseling, internal investigations, responding to government civil and criminal enforcement actions and investigations, defending against government natural resource damage claims, administrative challenges to agency regulations, and providing project and transactional due diligence.
**Career:** Former Assistant Attorney General, Environment and Natural Resources Division, U.S. Department of Justice; Associate Deputy Attorney General (USDoJ); U.S. Attorney, Southern District of Illinois; Assistant U.S. Attorney (MD, MDFL); Law clerk to Chief Justice Rehnquist

### TERR, Leonard
Baker & McKenzie, Washington, DC
202 452 7087
Leonard.Terr@bakermckenzie.com
*Featured in Tax (District of Columbia)*
**Practice Areas:** Leonard B Terr is a Partner in the Washington, DC office of Baker & McKenzie. He has over 30 years' experience representing US and foreign-based multinationals, foreign governments, international organisations and trade associations in all phases of international tax practice, including international tax planning and transactions, transfer pricing and tax controversies involving a wide variety of industries and jurisdictions.
**Professional Memberships:** Mr Terr serves as Chairman of the firm's North American Tax Practice. He also serves on the Editorial Board, Tax Management International Journal; the Council, International Fiscal Association-USA Branch; the Advisory Board, George Washington University - IRS International Tax Conference; the Steering Committee, Organization of Multinational Insurance Taxation, chair, Practice Council, NYU Law School International Tax Program; and as chair, Washington International Tax Study Group.
**Career:** Mr Terr served as International Tax Counsel of the US Treasury Department. He previously served as law clerk to Chief Judge Wilson Cowen of the US Court of Appeals for the Federal Circuit. He is adjunct professor of international tax law at the Georgetown University Law Center. Mr Terr is listed in the top tiers of Chambers Global, The World's Leading Lawyers and Chambers USA, America's Leading Lawyers; in the 'Best of the Best' in the field of International Tax - Transfer Pricing, Euromoney Legal Group's Guide

to the Worlds Leading Attorneys; in Euromoney's World's Leading Tax Advisers; in the Leading Corporate Tax Lawyers and Who's Who of Corporate Tax Lawyers, Law Business Research; and in the Top U.S. Corporate Tax Advisers, The International Tax Review.

**Personal:** Mr Terr holds an AB from LaSalle University, an AM and PhD from Brown University and a JD from Cornell University.

## THIEL, Donna Kalani
King & Spalding LLP, Washington, DC
202 626 2393
dthiel@kslaw.com
*Featured in Healthcare (District of Columbia)*

**Practice Areas:** Represents health care providers, and practitioners in their operations and compliance efforts with particular focus on Medicare and Medicaid Reimbursement and Fraud and Abuse. She concentrates her practice on regulatory issues, including Stark law and anti-kickback counseling, and administrative litigation challenging claims denials and RAC, ZPIC and OIG audits

**Professional Memberships:** DC and American Bar Associations. American Health Lawyers Association.

**Career:** Licensed in District of Columbia. Named an Outstanding Healthcare Fraud and Compliance Lawyer, Nightingale's Healthcare News (2008).

**Personal:** Boston University School of Law, JD, 1982; Drew University, BA, 1979, cum laude.

## THOMAS, William L
Willkie Farr & Gallagher LLP, Washington, DC
202 303 1210
wthomas@willkie.com
*Featured in Climate Change (Nationwide), Environment (District of Columbia)*
See under Nationwide for profile.

## THOMPSON, Chet M
Crowell & Moring LLP, Washington, DC
202 624 2655
cthompson@crowell.com
*Featured in Climate Change (Nationwide), Environment (District of Columbia)*
See under Nationwide for profile.

## THORNTON, D McCarty
Dentons, Washington, DC
202 408 6432
d.mccarty.thornton@dentons.com
*Featured in Healthcare (District of Columbia)*

**Practice Areas:** Healthcare fraud and abuse counseling and defense, including anti-kickback, False Claims Act, civil monetary penalty and exclusion actions. Health Care compliance, including structuring compliance programs, corporate integrity agreements, Board of Directors counseling. Also: Office of Inspector General (OIG) advisory opinions and voluntary disclosures.

**Professional Memberships:** Member, American Health Lawyers Association.

**Career:** Former Chief Counsel to the Inspector General, US Department of Health & Human Services (HHS) for 12 years. Former white-collar crime prosecutor, US Department of Justice.

**Personal:** Stanford Law School, JD, high honors; Stanford University, BA.

## TIEDEMANN, Charles Welch (Chad)
Holland & Knight LLP, Washington, DC
202 457 7156
chad.tiedemann@hklaw.com
*Featured in Real Estate (District of Columbia)*

**Practice Areas:** Partner in the firm's Real Estate Section, he has practiced in the areas of venture formation, finance, development and leasing for over 30 years. He represents developers and owners as well as opportunity funds, investment banking firms, insurance companies, foreign investors, high net worth individuals, pension funds and banks in connection with their real estate investments throughout the United States. Engagements have included every property type and size, from a national portfolio of regional shopping malls and programmatic investment relationships for office portfolios to "one-off" hotel transactions. He also has extensive experience with workouts and foreclosures.

## TOBIN, Charles D
Holland & Knight LLP, Washington, DC
202 955 3000
charles.tobin@hklaw.com
*Featured in First Amendment Litigation (Nationwide), Media & Entertainment (District of Columbia)*
See under Nationwide for profile.

## TOPOL, David H
Wiley Rein LLP, Washington, DC
202 719 7214
dtopol@wileyrein.com
*Featured in Insurance (District of Columbia)*

**Practice Areas:** Represents professional liability insurers in coverage matters before state and federal courts across the country, serving as coverage and monitoring counsel in connection with claims under financial institution, mutual fund, investment advisor and D&O policies. Regularly represents insurers' interests in connection with resolution of complex securities claims through litigation and alternative dispute resolution procedures.

**Professional Memberships:** Professional Liability Underwriting Society.

**Career:** Management Consultant, McKinsey & Company (2001-2002); Trial Attorney, U.S. Department of Justice, Environmental Enforcement Section (1997-2001).

**Personal:** Yale Law School (JD); Cornell University (BA).

## TOPOLSKI, Douglas
Ogletree, Deakins, Nash, Smoak & Stewart, PC, Washington, DC
202 263 0242
Douglas.Topolski@odnss.com
*Featured in Labor & Employment (District of Columbia)*

**Practice Areas:** Represents employers in all aspects of relationships concerning unions and matters arising under the National Labor Relations Act and related laws and regulations with an emphasis on creating and maintaining positive employee relations. Represents employers

in matters within the full spectrum of employment laws and regulations.

**Professional Memberships:** American and Maryland Bar Associations.

**Career:** Shareholder. Admitted in Maryland as well as the bars of the Supreme Court and several Federal District and Circuit Courts.

**Publications:** Frequent presenter to employer and attorney groups.

**Personal:** University of Baltimore School of Law (JD, 1984; University of Maryland Baltimore County (BA 1981).

## TORO, Emin
Covington & Burling LLP, Washington, DC
202 662 5481
etoro@cov.com
*Featured in Tax (District of Columbia)*

**Practice Areas:** Represents clients in tax controversies, including audits, administrative appeals, competent authority proceedings, and litigation. Co-author of "Examination and Appeals," Practical Guide to US Transfer Pricing, Third Edition (2012). Advises on tax-optimal cross-border and domestic structures, transfer pricing, treaty issues, and audit preparation.

**Career:** Clerk to the Honorable Clarence Thomas, U.S. Supreme Court, 2002-2003, and the Honorable Karen LeCraft Henderson, U.S. Court of Appeals, District of Columbia Circuit, 2000-2001.

**Personal:** JD, with highest honors, Order of the Coif, North Carolina Law Review, University of North Carolina at Chapel Hill (2000); BA, summa cum laude, Palm Beach Atlantic University (1997).

## TRAMONT, Bryan N
Wilkinson Barker Knauer LLP, Washington, DC
202 783 4141
btramont@wbklaw.com
*Featured in Telecommunications (District of Columbia)*

**Practice Areas:** Mr Tramont's practice areas include telecommunications, mass media and administrative law and policy. During the past year, Mr Tramont has provided strategic FCC counsel to many high-profile clients, including Verizon Communications and Comcast Corporation, two of the largest communications companies in the USA. The Managing Partner of the firm, he led the firm's unprecedented expansion over the past four years.

**Professional Memberships:** President, Federal Communications Bar Association (2010-11); Member, FCBA Executive Committee (2011-12). Governing Committee Member, American Bar Association Forum on Communications Law (2008-11). Co-Chair, Department of Commerce Spectrum Management Advisory Committee (2008-11); Member (2011-present). Adjunct Professor of Law, Catholic University of America School of Law, Communications Law Institute (2000-present). Visiting Professor, University of Colorado Interdisciplinary Telecommunications Program (2005-present). Chair, Telecommunications Executive Committee, Federalist Society (2012-present); Member (2001-

present). Practitioner in Residence, Syracuse University College of Law (2007). Member, The American Law Institute (2013-present).

**Career:** Chief of Staff, Federal Communications Commission (2003-05). Senior Legal Advisor to FCC Chairman Michael Powell (2002-03). Senior Legal Advisor to FCC Commissioner Kathleen Abernathy (2001-02). Senior Legal Advisor to FCC Commissioner Harold Furchtgott-Roth (2000-01). Law Clerk, Hon. Duane Benton, Missouri Supreme Court (1993-94).

**Personal:** JD, Yale Law School, 1993; BA, summa cum laude, George Washington University, 1989. Selected as one of the Best Lawyers in America in the Media and Communications Law categories (2011-2013 editions). Chosen as one of eleven Leading Lawyers in the country by Legal 500 US 2010-2012 (Telecoms and Broadcast: Regulatory category). Named one of Washingtonian's Top Communications Lawyers (2009-2010, 2011-2012). Named by Super Lawyers as one of Washington, D.C.'s Super Lawyers (2011-2012). Guided WBK to US News-Best Lawyers "Law Firm of the Year" in the Communications Law category (2011-2012).

## TRITT, Cheryl
Wilkinson Barker Knauer LLP, Washington, DC
202 783 4141
ctritt@wbklaw.com
*Featured in Telecommunications (District of Columbia)*

**Practice Areas:** Ms Tritt offers counsel to a wide range of communications companies, focusing specifically on wireless, satellite, broadband, and Internet and VoiP technology. During the past year, Ms Tritt has represented T? Mobile USA, a subsidiary of Deutsche Telekom, in the Federal Communications Commission's latest look at Universal Service Fund issues- the roughly $8 billion (USD) fund set aside for companies serving high-cost areas, low income consumers, rural health care providers, and schools and libraries, and intercarrier compensation, also a multi-billion regime. Ms Tritt also assisted the Alfred Mann Foundation's successful effort to reallocate certain radio spectrum that will allow it to develop a groundbreaking wireless medical device that can reanimate paralyzed limbs and attack other neuromuscular disorders.

**Professional Memberships:** Federal Communications Bar Association.

**Career:** Common Carrier Bureau Chief, Federal Communications Commission.

**Personal:** JD, cum laude, Northwestern University School of Law, 1976; MS, Northwestern University, 1970; BS, cum laude, University of Nebraska, 1969. Washington, DC Super Lawyers, 2007-2011. Named one of 2010's "Washington's Most Influential Women Lawyers" in The National Law Journal. Selected as one of the Best Lawyers in America in the Communications Law category (2006-2012 editions).

## TUCKER, Stefan
Venable LLP, Washington, DC
202 344 8570
sftucker@Venable.com
*Featured in Real Estate (District of Columbia)*
**Practice Areas:** Stef Tucker represents clients ranging from entrepreneurs and professionals to publicly traded enterprises, such as real estate investment trusts. His practice encompasses the entire range of subjects from mergers and acquisitions, to entity planning, structuring and formation, to asset protection and preservation, to business transactions, to family business planning and wealth preservation. He is experienced in federal and state income, estate and gift taxation, including planning and audits.
**Publications:** Wrote a major treatise and about 50 articles on income and estate taxation and business planning
**Personal:** JD, University of Michigan, 1963; B.BA, University of Michigan, 1960

## ULERY, Christopher J
Skadden, Arps, Slate, Meagher & Flom LLP & Affiliates, Washington, DC
202 371 7327
Chris.Ulery@skadden.com
*Featured in Corporate/M&A (District of Columbia)*
**Practice Areas:** Focuses on mergers and acquisitions and general corporate and securities matters. Has represented purchasers, sellers and financial advisors in a wide variety of transactions, including international and domestic acquisitions and divestitures, private and public acquisitions and divestitures, and auctions. Also has represented clients in connection with joint ventures and other strategic alliances and the formation of private investment funds. These transactions have involved companies operating in a variety of industries, including financial services, energy and technology.
**Career:** JD, Ohio State University College of Law, 1997; BA, Kent State University, 1993.

## VALIANT, Carrie
Epstein Becker & Green PC, Washington, DC
202 861 1857
cvaliant@ebglaw.com
*Featured in Healthcare (District of Columbia)*
**Practice Areas:** Member of Firm, Health Care and Life Sciences Practice; Co-Chairs the firm's Health Care Fraud group; Member of the firm's Board of Directors. Ms. Valiant focuses on fraud and abuse, including anti-kickback and false claims matters, representation in government and internal investigations, corporate compliance programs, voluntary disclosures, and Stark Law.
**Professional Memberships:** American Health Lawyers Association, Women Business Leaders of the U.S. (Board of Directors), Health Care Industry Foundation (Board of Directors)
**Personal:** JD, George Washington University Law School, with honors, 1983; BA, State University of New York at Buffalo, magna cum laude, 1977.

## VAN GELDER, Barbara
Dickstein Shapiro LLP, Washington, DC
202 420 4845
vangelderb@dicksteinshapiro.com
*Featured in Litigation (District of Columbia)*
**Practice Areas:** Biz Van Gelder is the leader of Dickstein Shapiro's Congressional Investigations Practice and co-leader of its White Collar Criminal Defense & Investigations Practice, where she focuses on white-collar defense and healthcare cases. She represents clients in congressional and criminal fraud investigations as well as qui tam, Foreign Corrupt Practices Act, False Claims Act, civil RICO, and employment litigation. She has counseled clients—including boards, audit committees, and management—on internal compliance and ethics programs, the conduct of internal investigations, and Sarbanes-Oxley issues.
**Personal:** JD from Emory University School of Law (1976) and BA from Boston University (1972).

## VARNEY, Andrew
Fried, Frank, Harris, Shriver & Jacobson LLP, Washington, DC
202 639 7032
Andrew.Varney@FriedFrank.com
*Featured in Corporate/M&A (District of Columbia)*
**Practice Areas:** Corporate partner and head of the Washington, DC transactions group. Represents clients in a broad range of transactions with a focus on representing private equity fund investors in secondary transactions. Also has extensive experience in mergers and acquisitions, joint ventures and corporate governance counseling.
**Career:** Joined in 1989; became partner in 1995.
**Personal:** JD, cum laude, Harvard Law School (1987); BA, summa cum laude, Middlebury College (1984).

## VICTORY, Nancy J
Wiley Rein LLP, Washington, DC
202 719 7344
nvictory@wileyrein.com
*Featured in Telecommunications (District of Columbia)*
**Practice Areas:** Chair, Wireless Group. Extensive experience in communications policy including securing approvals for communications transactions. Advises broad cross-section of the industry on business implications of regulatory policy; represents clients before the FCC, Congress and the Administration. Minority Media & Telecommunications Council Hall of Fame Inductee. Legal 500 "Rising Star".
**Professional Memberships:**
**Career:** Assistant Secretary of Commerce for Communications and Information and Administrator of NTIA (2001-2003); Chair, FCC Advisory Committee for WRC-07; Chair, FCC Independent Panel Reviewing the Impact of Hurricane Katrina on Communications Networks (2006).
**Personal:** Georgetown University Law Center (JD, cum laude); Princeton University (BA, with honors).

## VIGDOR, William R
Vinson & Elkins LLP, Washington, DC
202 639 6737
wvigdor@velaw.com
*Featured in Antitrust (District of Columbia)*
**Practice Areas:** Practices antitrust before the Federal Trade Commission, the Department of Justice, state attorneys general and federal courts; assists clients with foreign merger control.
**Professional Memberships:** ABA Section of Antitrust Law; American Economics Association.
**Career:** Former FTC Deputy Assistant Director.
**Publications:** "The Irrelevant Market: 'Direct Proof' of Merger Anticompetitive Effects," 2011 ABA Section of Antitrust Law Spring Meeting; "U.S. Merger Control: A Discussion with V&E About Process and Current Trends," Acquisition International, October 2012.
**Personal:** Economics PhD, University of Iowa (1994); JD, The George Washington University (1990); BA Emory University (1981).

## VINE, John M
Covington & Burling LLP, Washington, DC
202 662 5392
jvine@cov.com
*Featured in Employee Benefits & Executive Compensation (District of Columbia)*
**Practice Areas:** Concentrating on employee benefits for over 35 years. His practice covers deferred compensation, stock option, and fringe benefit programs, as well as pension, § 401(k), employer stock, and welfare plans. Counsel to The ERISA Industry Committee and Fiduciary Counselors Inc.
**Career:** Senior member, and the former head, of the Employee Benefits Group at Covington & Burling LLP.
**Publications:** "Prudent Investing," "ERISA Rights and Responsibilities," and "The Fiduciary Exception," Tax Management Compensation Planning Journal (2010 and 2012).
**Personal:** Harvard Law School, JD, 1969; Harvard Law Review. Amherst College, AB, 1966, magna cum laude, Phi Beta Kappa.

## VOLTMER, Ralph C
Covington & Burling LLP, Washington, DC
202 662 5479
rvoltmer@cov.com
*Featured in Telecommunications (District of Columbia)*
**Practice Areas:** Corporate law focusing on telecommunications, media, and technology. Advises US and foreign multinational companies, start-up ventures, and investors in cross-border transactions and US-based transactions, including M&A, joint ventures, strategic alliances, financings, and transfer of intellectual property, with a particular focus on India. Clients include Qualcomm, Reliance Industries, Balkrishna Industries, National Geographic, Interglobe, OmniActive Health Technologies, Infotel Broadband Services.
**Professional Memberships:** NY, DC Bar Associations.

**Career:** Serves as Chair of Covington's India Practice; judicial clerk US District Court, the District of Delaware (1987-88).
**Personal:** Georgetown (JD, mcl, Order of the Coif, 1987); UC (MA, 1984), Wheaton College (BA, 1982).

## VOTAW, James G
Manatt Phelps & Phillips LLP, Washington, DC
202 585 6610
jvotaw@manatt.com
*Featured in Environment (District of Columbia)*
**Practice Areas:** Votaw's practice encompasses environmental matters under the Clean Air and Clean Water Acts, the federal hazardous waste statute, Resource Conservation and Recovery Act, the Toxic Substances Control Act, the Comprehensive Environmental Response, Compensation, and Liability Act and other principal environmental laws. He represents clients in a wide range of environmental defense, counseling, permitting and transactional matters. Votaw helps clients recognize and manage their environmental risks and liabilities intelligently and cost-effectively. He has particular experience assisting companies involved in manufacturing or using engineered nanomaterials and is a frequent speaker on this topic.

## WACHEN, Kimberly
Arent Fox LLP, Washington, DC
202 775 5749
kimberly.wachen@arentfox.com
*Featured in Leisure & Hospitality (Nationwide), Real Estate (District of Columbia)*
**Practice Areas:** Kimberly Wachen chairs the Hospitality Industry Group and is a partner in the real estate group. She represents clients in a wide variety of commercial real estate, financing and corporate transactions involving hotels, senior living facilities, office buildings, shopping centers and multi-family residential projects. Ms Wachen has overseen some of the largest hotel and senior living transactions nationally. Ms Wachen is consistently recognized as one of the leading real estate lawyers in Washington, DC.
**Personal:** University of Pennsylvania, JD, 1992; Duke University, AB, 1988.

## WAHL, Barbara S
Arent Fox LLP, Washington, DC
202 857 6415
barbara.wahl@arentfox.com
*Featured in Litigation (District of Columbia)*
**Practice Areas:** Barbara Wahl is a partner and former Chair of the Complex Commercial Litigation Group at Arent Fox. She has extensive experience in litigating disputes involving commercial contracts, business torts, intellectual property including the areas of trademark, trade dress, trade secrets and copyright, trusts and estates, and eminent domain. Her practice involves all phases of litigation, from counseling, preparation and filing of a lawsuit, discovery, pre- and post-trial motions, trial and appellate review. She also represents clients in mediation and other forms of alternative dispute resolution. She has been exten-

sively involved in creative settlement arrangements to resolve business disputes.

### WALD, Douglas
Arnold & Porter LLP, Washington, DC
202 942 5112
Douglas.Wald@aporter.com
*Featured in Antitrust (District of Columbia)*
**Practice Areas:** Douglas Wald's practice focuses on a broad range of antitrust matters, including counseling, private litigation (such as federal class actions), representation before governmental agencies, and appellate proceedings. He advises clients on matters involving marketing, pricing, and distribution restrictions (Sherman Act 1), price discrimination (Robinson-Patman Act), monopolization (Sherman Act 2), and joint ventures and acquisitions (Clayton Act 7).
**Career:** Mr Wald clerked for Judge William H. Timbers on the US Court of Appeals for the Second Circuit.

### WALES, David
Jones Day, Washington, DC
202 879 5451
dpwales@jonesday.com
*Featured in Antitrust (District of Columbia)*
**Practice Areas:** Dave is the Practice Leader for Jones Day's global Antitrust Group and represents clients in a variety of industries on all aspects of antitrust, including mergers and acquisitions, criminal grand jury investigations, dominant firm conduct, distribution arrangements, licensing, and competitor collaborations.
**Career:** Dave served as a senior official in both US antitrust agencies. From 2008 to 2009, he oversaw all of the FTC's antitrust enforcement as acting director of the Bureau of Competition. From 2001 to 2003, Dave was counsel to the assistant attorney general in the Department of Justice's Antitrust Division.

### WALKER, Helgi C
Wiley Rein LLP, Washington, DC
202 719 7349
hwalker@wileyrein.com
*Featured in Telecommunications (District of Columbia), Appellate Law (Nationwide)*
**Practice Areas:** Co-chairs the Appellate Practice. Represents clients in appellate, litigation and regulatory matters. Named to The American Lawyer's nationwide list of "45 Under 45" (2011).
**Career:** Associate Counsel to the President of the United States (2001-2003); Law Clerk, Honorable Clarence Thomas, U.S. Supreme Court (1995-1996) and Honorable J. Harvie Wilkinson III, U.S. Court of Appeals for the Fourth Circuit (1994-1995).
**Personal:** University of Virginia School of Law (JD) (Executive Editor, Virginia Law Review; Order of the Coif); University of Virginia (BA).

### WALLACE JR, James H
Wiley Rein LLP, Washington, DC
202 719 7240
jwallace@wileyrein.com
*Featured in Intellectual Property (District of Columbia)*
**Practice Areas:** Chair, Patent Practice. 30+ years experience litigating patents in the fields of

communications satellites, data transmission, network interface devices, Internet business methods, pharmaceuticals, biotechnology and semiconductors. Successfully represented NTP, Inc. in $612.5 million settlement with Research In Motion. Recognized as a "Leading Intellectual Property Attorney" by Legal Times, one of the "Best Lawyers in America" in intellectual property law and "Life Sciences Star" by Euromoney's LMG Life Science (2012).
**Career:** Trial Attorney, U.S. Department of Justice, Antitrust Division; Patent Examiner, U.S. Patent and Trademark Office.
**Personal:** Georgetown University Law Center (JD); University of South Carolina (BSEE).

### WALSH, William J
Pepper Hamilton LLP, Washington, DC
202 220 1424
walshw@pepperlaw.com
*Featured in Environment (District of Columbia)*
**Practice Areas:** Of Counsel; Head, Washington office Environmental Practice Group. Defends liability and negotiates technical solutions in lawsuits pursuant to a variety of environmental statutes and in personal injury litigation. Advocates changes to environmental regulations and policy and provides counsel on a broad range of environmental issues involving innovative scientific, regulatory, legal and policy questions.
**Professional Memberships:** Member, Committee on Review and Evaluation of Army Non-Stockpile Chemical Material Disposal Program, National Academy of Science.
**Career:** Former Section Chief, US Environmental Protection Agency Office of Enforcement.
**Personal:** JD 1978 George Washington University National Law Center; BS, cum laude, 1968 Manhattan College.

### WARD BROWN, Jay
Levine Sullivan Koch & Schulz LLP, Washington, DC
202 508 1136
jbrown@lskslaw.com
*Featured in Media & Entertainment (District of Columbia)*
**Practice Areas:** Twenty years representing news/entertainment companies in content and newsgathering litigation, including Gilman v Eliot Spitzer & Slate.com, Rodriguez v HBO, Dan Snyder v Washington City Paper, Hatfill v N.Y. Times, and Bartnicki v Vopper in U.S. Supreme Court.
**Professional Memberships:** Chair, Media Law Resource Center Institute Board of Trustees; past Governing Committee ABA Forum on Communications Law.
**Career:** Journalist who produced or otherwise was associated with 75 of Fred W. Friendly's award-winning programs on the Constitution, law and ethics.
**Personal:** BA University of Minnesota; MS Columbia University Graduate School of Journalism; JD New York University School of Law.

### WARIN, Joseph
Gibson, Dunn & Crutcher LLP, Washington, DC
202 887 3609
fwarin@gibsondunn.com
*Featured in International Trade (Nationwide), Securities (Nationwide), Litigation (District of Columbia)*
See under Nationwide for profile.

### WARNER, Margaret H
McDermott Will & Emery LLP, Washington, DC
202 756 8228
mwarner@mwe.com
*Featured in Insurance (District of Columbia), Insurance (Nationwide)*
**Practice Areas:** Partner-in-charge of controversies business unit. Complex litigation, arbitration and strategic counseling practice specializing in the international insurance/reinsurance markets. Experience covers a wide range of issues and disputes encompassing virtually all lines of insurance. Clients include most participants in the insurance markets including major domestic and foreign insurers, specialty carriers, captive insurers, brokers and policyholders.
**Personal:** University of Notre Dame (JD); St. Lawrence University (BA).

### WARREN, James
Miller & Chevalier Chartered, Washington, DC
202 626 5959
jwarren@milchev.com
*Featured in Tax (District of Columbia)*
**Practice Areas:** Specializes in legal, accounting and regulatory aspects of utility taxation. Represents clients in tax controversies and a broad spectrum of operational and transactional tax matters. Has testified before several Congressional committees and at Treasury hearings regarding utility-related legislative and administrative issues, and in numerous rate proceedings as an expert tax witness.
**Professional Memberships:** ABA, Tax Section.
**Career:** Former tax partner in several national law and international accounting firms.
**Personal:** BA-Stanford University, JD and LLM(Taxation)-NYU School of Law, MS(Accounting)-NYU Graduate School of Business. New York, New Jersey and DC Bars and CPA in New York and New Jersey.

### WEBSTER, Stephanie
Akin Gump Strauss Hauer & Feld LLP, Washington, DC
202 887 4049
swebster@akingump.com
*Featured in Healthcare (District of Columbia)*
**Practice Areas:** Practices in the areas of Medicare and Medicaid reimbursement. Counsels hospitals regarding payment and compliance, and represents them in administrative and federal court litigation.
**Professional Memberships:** American Bar Association; Advisory Board, Bureau of National Affairs Medicare Report; American Health Lawyers Association; Co-Chair, Children's Hospital Affinity Group, American Health

Lawyers Association; Health Care Financial Management Association; Women's Bar Association of the District of Columbia.
**Personal:** University of Virginia (JD, 1994); Yale University (BA, cum laude, 1990).

### WEBSTER, Timothy K
Sidley Austin LLP, Washington, DC
202 736 8138
twebster@sidley.com
*Featured in Environment (District of Columbia)*
**Practice Areas:** Partner in Sidley's Washington, DC office. His practice includes both civil and criminal environmental matters, as well as regulatory advocacy and related compliance counseling. He has been involved in a variety of cases under the Clean Air Act, the National Environmental Policy Act, the Clean Water Act, and CERCLA, as well as 'toxic tort' litigation. He also advises clients on food and drug-related matters where environmental issues are implicated, for example, under the Federal Insecticide, Fungicide, and Rodenticide Act.
**Personal:** University of Virginia School of Law, JD, 1991; Carleton College, BA, 1986. Admissons: District of Columbia, Virginia.

### WEHRUM, William L
Hunton & Williams LLP, Washington, DC
202 955 1637
wwehrum@hunton.com
*Featured in Environment (District of Columbia)*
**Practice Areas:** Mr Wehrum's practice focuses on air quality issues, including compliance counseling, permit negotiations, enforcement, and regulatory and legislative advice. He served for two years as acting assistant administrator for air and radiation at the US Environmental Protection Agency. As EPA's senior official on air issues, he was responsible for all aspects of the agency's air program - from stationary sources, to motor vehicles and fuels, to climate change.

### WEINBERG, David B
Wiley Rein LLP, Washington, DC
202 719 7102
dweinberg@wileyrein.com
*Featured in Environment (District of Columbia)*
**Practice Areas:** Chairs the firm's Environment & Safety Practice Group with more than 35 years of experience in administrative and environmental law, specializing in environmental, occupational health and safety, transportation, product safety and pesticide matters. He has been listed for over a dozen years in "The Best Lawyers in America," rated by Euromoney as one of the "World's Leading Environmental Lawyers," and named one of "America's Top 20 Environmental Lawyers" by the Guide to the World's Leading Environment Lawyers.
**Personal:** Georgetown University Law Center (LL.M); University of Pennsylvania Law School (JD); Yale University (AB).

### WEINREICH, Gadi
Dentons, Washington, DC
202 408 9166
gadi.weinreich@dentons.com
*Featured in Healthcare (District of Columbia)*

**Practice Areas:** One of the Global Chairs of legacy Dentons's Healthcare and Life Sciences Sector, Mr Weinreich represents drug and medical device manufacturers, academic medical centers, hospitals and other healthcare organizations in connection with False Claims Act/qui tam whistleblower actions, DOJ, HHS-OIG and Congressional investigations. Routinely counsels with respect to product pricing, promotion, sales, and support, physician alignments and relationships, clinical integration and co-management initiatives, corporate integrity matters, and voluntary disclosures.
**Personal:** Cambridge University, LLM, 1992; Harvard Law School, JD, 1987; Brown University, Honors BA, 1983, Phi Beta Kappa.

### WEISWASSER, Stephen A
Covington & Burling LLP, Washington, DC
202 662 5508
SWeiswasser@cov.com
*Featured in Media & Entertainment (District of Columbia)*
**Practice Areas:** Media, new media, content, telecommunications, and technology industries. Work includes strategic consulting, M&A, joint ventures and other transactions, international, litigation and corporate governance.
**Professional Memberships:** ABA, FCBA, International Radio & Television Society Foundation (past President).
**Career:** EVP and GC Gemstar - TV Guide International 1999-2000; President & CEO Americast 1995-98; SVP Capital Cities/ABC, Inc. 1986-95 (President Capital Cities/ABC Multimedia Group 1993-95; EVP ABC News 1991-93; EVP ABC Television Network Group 1991; GC 1986-91).
**Personal:** Harvard (JD, mcl, 1966); Johns Hopkins 1962-63 (Woodrow Wilson Fellowship); Wayne State (BA, distinction, 1962).

### WELCH, John
Jones Day, Washington, DC
202 879 3483
jwelch@jonesday.com
*Featured in Corporate/M&A (District of Columbia)*
**Practice Areas:** Concentration on complex cross-border mergers and acquisitions, joint ventures, corporate governance, and general corporate counseling. John has advised clients on M&A and joint venture activities in the aerospace and defense, telecommunications, media, real estate, IT, and energy industries.
**Career:** Diverse experience includes executive vice president and general counsel of a telecommunications company. As an international corporate lawyer, John has practiced law in London, Los Angeles, and Washington, D.C. Graduated magna cum laude from Harvard Law School, 1982.

### WELLEN, Robert H
Ivins, Phillips & Barker, Washington, DC
202 393 7600
rwellen@ipbtax.com
*Featured in Tax (District of Columbia)*
**Practice Areas:** Bob Wellen has practiced Federal tax law for more than 35 years with an emphasis on planning corporate transactions. His

work includes planning and negotiating corporate mergers and acquisitions, joint ventures, financings, equity offerings, spin-offs and other transactions, as wel as optimizing corporate structures from a tax standpoint; representing clients before the IRS and in litigation; obtaining advance rulings from the IRS on business transactions; advocating tax policy positions before the IRS and Treasury Department; arbitrating commercial controversies involving tax issues (e.g., issues in tax sharing agreements); and serving as expert witness in commercial litigation involving tax issues.
**Professional Memberships:** American Bar Association (Tax Section), American College of Tax Counsel, District of Columbia Bar (Tax Section), Federal Bar Association.
**Career:** Judge Advocate General's Corps, U.S. Naval Reserve, active duty 1971-75; Fulbright & Jaworski, 1975-93 (Partner, 1979-93); Adjunct Professor of Law, Georgetown University Law Center, 1979, 1983-85; Partner, Ivins, Phillips & Barker since 1993.
**Publications:** Numerous outlines, articles and book reviews in Practising Law Institute proceedings, TAXES, Tax Notes and Journal of Taxation. Frequent speaker at professional education institutes on tax law matters, including institutes sponsored by American Law Institute/American Bar Association, Practising Law Institute, Tax Executives Institute, Federal Bar Association, District of Columbia Bar, New York University, University of Chicago, Penn State University/Dickinson College of Law, University of California at Los Angeles, University of Miami and Southern Federal Tax Institute.
**Personal:** Born in Jersey City NJ; BA, Yale College 1968 (magna cum laude, Phi Beta Kappa); JD Yale Law School, 1971; LLM (Taxation) Georgetown University Law Center, 1975.

### WELLFORD, Hill
Bingham McCutchen LLP, Washington, DC
202 373 6268
hill.wellford@bingham.com
*Featured in Antitrust (District of Columbia)*
**Practice Areas:** Advises clients in antitrust matters, especially those relating to government enforcement or the intersection between technology, intellectual property and competition. Practice is international in scope, with active cases and government investigations in the Americas, Asia and Europe. Counseling practice covers all aspects of antitrust law and many issues of related consumer protection law. Has taught and lectured widely on antitrust and technology issues.
**Career:** Former chief of staff, Antitrust Division, US Department of Justice, Washington, DC. Co-chair of ABA Federal Civil Enforcement Committee.
**Personal:** University of Virginia School of Law, JD, 1995; Dartmouth College, BA, 1992.

### WELLS, Stephen E
McDermott Will & Emery LLP, Washington, DC
202 756 8316
swells@mwe.com
*Featured in Tax (District of Columbia)*
**Practice Areas:** Partner-in-charge of Washington DC tax practice. Focuses on taxation of transactions involving US and foreign corporations, including formation of corporate ventures, reorganizations and restructurings, corporate distributions and liquidations, and corporate acquisitions and dispositions, including spinoffs. Highly instrumental in structuring and implementing many of the largest corporate M&As, joint ventures and spinoffs undertaken by various prominent publicly held multinational corporations as well as privately owned companies.
**Professional Memberships:** Former Vice Chairman of the Institute For Research on the Economics of Taxation.
**Personal:** Georgetown University Law Center (JD, LLM); University of Maryland (BS).

### WEST, Joseph D
Gibson, Dunn & Crutcher LLP, Washington, DC
202 955 8658
jwest@gibsondunn.com
*Featured in Construction (District of Columbia), Government (Nationwide)*
**Practice Areas:** Extensive experience with government and construction contracts. Represents contractors, subcontractors and government agencies. Areas of expertise include contract counseling, dispute avoidance/resolution, internal investigations, False Claims Act matters, and suspension/debarment issues. Has engaged in cases before various United States Courts of Appeals and District Courts, United States Court of Federal Claims, and Boards of Contract Appeals.
**Professional Memberships:** Fellow, American College of Construction Lawyers.
**Career:** Registered Professional Engineer and former officer of the United States Navy Civil Engineer Corps.
**Personal:** JD, George Washington University, 1977, with high honors, editor of 'The George Washington Law Review,' Order of the Coif.

### WESTBROOK, Reeves C
Covington & Burling LLP, Washington, DC
202 662 5150
rwestbrook@cov.com
*Featured in Tax (District of Columbia)*
**Practice Areas:** Advising multinational corporate taxpayers on tax audits, controversies and litigation, transfer pricing planning and controversies, cross-border planning and restructurings, valuation methods and standards, and regulatory and legislative matters.
**Professional Memberships:** D.C. Bar; IBA Tax Committee, Conference Coordinator, ABA Tax Section.
**Career:** Mr Westbrook is a co-chair of the tax practice group at Covington & Burling.
**Publications:** Co-author, Chapter 21: Examination and Appeals, Practical Guide to US Transfer Pricing.

**Personal:** Yale Law School, JD, 1974; Yale Law Journal, editor. Vanderbilt University, BA, 1971, magna cum laude, Phi Beta Kappa.

### WHITE, Wendelin A
Pillsbury Winthrop Shaw Pittman LLP, Washington, DC
202 663 8360
wendelin.white@pillsburylaw.com
*Featured in Real Estate (District of Columbia)*
**Practice Areas:** Head of Washington, DC, Real Estate Group. Practice concentration: in development, acquisitions, and financings of office, hotel, retail, multifamily and mixed use properties, and in joint ventures, including public-private ventures. Represents both public and private companies, including public and private REITs.
**Professional Memberships:** DC Bar, Florida Bar, ABA, Economic Club of Washington, Commercial Real Estate Women, DC Building Industry Association.
**Career:** Trustee, Washington Real Estate Investment Trust; Director, Chevy Chase Trust Company; Director, Georgetown University Hospital; General Counsel, Economic Club of Washington.
**Personal:** BA, Sweet Briar College; MFA, University of California at Irvine; JD, University of Miami.

### WHITEWAY, Andrea
McDermott Will & Emery LLP, Washington, DC
202 756 8425
awhiteway@mwe.com
*Featured in Tax (District of Columbia)*
**Practice Areas:** Head of the firm's pass-throughs practice. Substantial experience in sophisticated tax planning involving the use of partnerships, including in the dispositions and acquisitions of real estate and operating businesses, complex partnership transactions, and real estate investment trusts.
**Professional Memberships:** First woman to serve as chair of the Real Estate Committee of the American Bar Association Section of Taxation.
**Personal:** University of Maryland School of Law, JD (with honors), 1992; Georgetown University Law Center, LLM (with distinction), 1995; Cornell University, BA, 1989.

### WIACEK, Raymond
Jones Day, Washington, DC
202 879 3908
rjwiacek@jonesday.com
*Featured in Tax (District of Columbia)*
**Practice Areas:** Oversees the firm's Tax Practice. His practice involves the tax and business aspects of corporate and international transactions, including structured and cross-border financings, mergers and acquisitions, restructurings, transfer pricing, and international licensing for intellectual property, as well as disputes with the IRS and foreign governments related to such transactions. Testified on international tax matters before the House Ways and Means Committee, Senate Finance Committee, Senate Foreign Relations Committee, and IRS. Named a top lawyer in The World's Leading Lawyers, America's

Leading Lawyers for Business, International Tax Review, and other publications. Former adjunct Professor, advanced corporate taxation, Georgetown law.

## WIGMORE, Michael B
Bingham McCutchen LLP, Washington, DC
202 373 6792
michael.wigmore@bingham.com
*Featured in Environment (District of Columbia)*
**Practice Areas:** Co-chair of Bingham's Environmental and Natural Resources Group. Represents clients with respect to public lands and natural resources matters in court, before Congress, and before federal and state administrative agencies. Has successfully represented clients in obtaining and defending permits for projects such as high-voltage electric transmission lines, oil and gas development, undersea fiber optic cables, and waterfront commercial real estate developments.
**Career:** Formerly a nuclear engineer with the General Electric Company/Knolls Atomic Power Laboratory.
**Personal:** George Washington University Law School, JD, with high honors, 1990; United States Merchant Marine Academy, BS, with highest honors, 1984.

## WILCOX, Justine E
Nixon Peabody LLP, Washington, DC
202 585 8745
jwilcox@nixonpeabody.com
*Featured in Real Estate (District of Columbia)*
**Practice Areas:** Represents clients on various aspects of real estate including purchase and sale of real property (all asset classes) and mortgage loans and servicing, financing of real property, ground lease financings, and leasing.
**Professional Memberships:** Member, Federal City Council; Board Member, Girl Scout Council of the Nation's Capital; Member, The Economic Club of Washington, DC; Board Member, Rachael's Women's Center.
**Career:** Formerly Managing Partner of the firm's Washington, DC, office; previously an attorney at US Department of Housing and Urban Development and analyst at Ginnie Mae.
**Personal:** Suffolk University Law School, JD; Goucher College, BA.

## WILEY, Richard E
Wiley Rein LLP, Washington, DC
202 719 7010
rwiley@wileyrein.com
*Featured in Telecommunications (District of Columbia), Media & Entertainment (District of Columbia)*
**Practice Areas:** Firm Chairman. Chair of the United States' preeminent Communications Practice. A former FCC Chairman and widely recognized as the leading communications attorney in the country. Dubbed the "Father of High-Definition" television, he has received 2 Emmy Awards from the Academy of Television Arts and Sciences. Received American Lawyer's Lifetime Achiever Award 2012, named by Bloomberg Businessweek as one of Washington, DC's "Power Brokers," by Best Lawyers as its 2011 Washington,

DC Administrative/Regulatory "Lawyer of the Year," one of "The Decade's Most Influential Lawyers" by the National Law Journal and one of Washington's 30 "Superstar" lawyers by Washingtonian magazine. He has been called "Telecommunications' Ubiquitous Man of Influence" (The New York Times), "The Sixth Commissioner" (Los Angeles Times), and the "Brand Name of Communications Bar" (The American Lawyer).
**Professional Memberships:** Past Chair, American Bar Association Section on Administrative Law and Regulatory Practice; Past President, Federal Bar Association and Federal Communications Bar Association; FCC's Advisory Committee on Digital Television (1987-1996).
**Career:** FCC Chairman, Commissioner and General Counsel.
**Personal:** Georgetown University (LLM); Northwestern University (JD; BS, with distinction).

## WILHELM, William
Bingham McCutchen LLP, Washington, DC
202 373 6027
william.wilhelm@bingham.com
*Featured in Telecommunications (District of Columbia)*
**Practice Areas:** Advises technology companies on policy, state and federal regulation, and commercial transactions and disputes related to the development and deployment of new communications applications, voice and video services, digital media, and broadband wireless and wireline networks. Clients include leading technology innovators, venture-backed startups and established Fortune 500 companies. Often advises on new or novel legal issues related to technology.
**Career:** Frequent speaker at industry events. Has written hundreds of articles on telecommunications policy.
**Personal:** Catholic University of America, Columbus School of Law, Juris Doctor, 1993; College of the Holy Cross, Artis Baccalaureate, 1989.

## WILKINSON, Beth A.
Paul, Weiss, Rifkind, Wharton & Garrison LLP, Washington, DC
202 223 7340
bwilkinson@paulweiss.com
*Featured in Litigation (District of Columbia)*
**Practice Areas:** Beth Wilkinson, a Partner in the Litigation Department, is widely acknowledged as one of the nation's leading trial lawyers. Last year, the Federal Trade Commission retained Beth to conduct its antitrust investigation of Google, which was recently concluded. Beth currently represents Pfizer in a securities class action case and the NFL in connection with the concussion lawsuits. She is lead counsel for Pfizer, having achieved four consecutive jury trial victories in product liability litigation. Beth also has successfully prosecuted criminals in high-profile federal trials, including Oklahoma City bomber Timothy McVeigh and his accomplice Terry Nichols.
**Career:** Former assistant US Attorney, played a leading role in prosecution and conviction of

Oklahoma City bombers Timothy McVeigh and Terry Nichols.
**Personal:** JD, University of Virginia School of Law, 1987. BA, Princeton University, 1984.

## WILLIAMS JR, B John
Skadden, Arps, Slate, Meagher & Flom LLP & Affiliates, Washington, DC
202 371 7080
BJohn.Williams@skadden.com
*Featured in Tax (District of Columbia), Tax (Nationwide)*
See under Nationwide for profile.

## WILSON, Christine
Kirkland & Ellis LLP, Washington, DC
202 879 5011
christine.wilson@kirkland.com
*Featured in Antitrust (District of Columbia)*
**Practice Areas:** Christine Wilson is a partner in Kirkland's Washington, DC, office. She is an antitrust and consumer protection practitioner who represents clients before the Antitrust Division of the US Department of Justice, the Federal Trade Commission, state attorneys general, the European Commission and other global authorities on an array of antitrust and consumer protection issues. She served as chief of staff to Timothy Muris during his tenure as FTC chairman. She holds a leadership position in the American Bar Association's Antitrust Section and co-founded The Grapevine, a women's network for DC professionals in the antitrust and consumer protection arenas.

## WILTSHIRE, William M
Wiltshire & Grannis LLP, Washington, DC
202 730 1350
wwiltshire@wiltshiregrannis.com
*Featured in Telecommunications (District of Columbia)*
**Practice Areas:** Mr Wiltshire is a founding partner of Wiltshire & Grannis LLP. He advises communications, media, satellite, and other high-tech companies on strategic, regulatory, licensing, spectrum, merger, and other transactional issues. He represents clients before the FCC, Congress and the administration.
**Career:** Founding member of the Communications Practice group, Gibson, Dunn, & Crutcher LLP (1996-98); Senior Legal Advisor to Chief, FCC International Bureau, and Special Counsel to Chief, FCC Mass Media Bureau (1994-96); Associate, Williams and Connolly LLP (1988-94).
**Personal:** University of Virginia School of Law, JD, 1988, Order of the Coif. Princeton University, BA, 1984, summa cum laude.

## WIMMER, Kurt A
Covington & Burling LLP, Washington, DC
202 662 5278
kwimmer@cov.com
*Featured in First Amendment Litigation (Nationwide), Media & Entertainment (District of Columbia)*
See under Nationwide for profile.

## WINTERSCHEID, Joseph F
McDermott Will & Emery LLP, Washington, DC
202 756 8061
jwinterscheid@mwe.com
*Featured in Antitrust (District of Columbia)*
**Practice Areas:** Head of the firm's global antitrust & competition practice. Practice focuses on US and international antitrust law. Advises clients on competition issues in mergers, acquisitions and joint ventures, including US and international premerger notification requirements.
**Career:** Joined McDermott after 24 years of practice with another leading international law firm, where he headed their Brussels Office (1989-94); former chair of ABA Antitrust Section International Antitrust Committee and Vice-Chair of Corporate Counseling Committee; private sector advisor to DOJ/FTC International Competition Network delegation.
**Personal:** University of Notre Dame (JD, magna cum laude and BA, summa cum laude).

## WISE, Andy
Miller & Chevalier Chartered, Washington, DC
awise@milchev.com
202 626 5818
*Featured in Litigation (District of Columbia)*
**Practice Areas:** Defends clients in criminal, regulatory, and administrative investigations and represents individuals and business organizations in complex criminal trials in federal and state courts. Has tried more than 50 cases to resolution before juries and judges in Federal and state courts.
**Career:** Conducted internal investigations into potential violations of US laws and regulations, including the FCPA, Internal Revenue Code, and False Claims Act. Worked at the Public Defender Service, where he defended indigent clients charged with serious criminal offenses in DC Superior Court.
**Personal:** JD, The University of Michigan Law School, cum laude, 1997; BA, Swarthmore College, 1992.

## WISEMAN, Alan
Covington & Burling LLP, Washington, DC
202 662 5069
awiseman@cov.com
*Featured in Antitrust (District of Columbia)*
**Career:** Alan Wiseman is recognized as one of the world's leading competition lawyers and has concentrated his practice on antitrust class actions for the past 35 years. He has extensive litigation experience, usually representing defendants, but also has obtained extraordinary settlements on behalf of plaintiffs. He represents clients in mergers and acquisitions, as well as global cartel investigations. He has tried antitrust cases before juries and the bench, as well as argued in many appellate courts, including the U.S. Supreme Court. Prior to joining Covington, Alan was Co-Chair of Howrey's Antitrust Practice Group.
**Personal:** Georgetown University Law Center, JD.

**WITTEN, Jesse**
Drinker Biddle & Reath LLP, Washington, DC
202 230 5146
Jesse.Witten@dbr.com
*Featured in Healthcare (District of Columbia)*
**Practice Areas:** Partner, Commercial Litigation Group; member White Collar Criminal Defense and Corporate Investigations Team. Counseling and defense of clients in government investigations and enforcement actions alleging Medicare/Medicaid fraud, Anti-Kickback Statute and Stark Laws violations; defense of False Claims Act litigation; assistance with voluntary disclosure of regulatory violations.
**Professional Memberships:** Admitted, District of Columbia and Illinois. American Health Lawyers Association.
**Career:** Before joining Drinker Biddle, served as a Deputy Associate Attorney General and Deputy Assistant Attorney General in the United States Department of Justice.
**Personal:** JD, magna cum laude, Harvard Law School, 1991. AB, Phi Beta Kappa, Princeton University, 1988.

**WOLF, Matthew M**
Arnold & Porter LLP, Washington, DC
202 942 5462
Matthew.Wolf@aporter.com
*Featured in Intellectual Property (District of Columbia)*
**Practice Areas:** Matthew Wolf is a partner in Arnold & Porter LLP's Intellectual Property and Litigation Practice Groups. He has secured victories as lead trial and appellate counsel in some of the most significant cases brought by and against major technology companies. His professional activities focus on patent, trade secret, licensing and business tort issues, particularly in matters involving medical and biomedical technologies and computer hardware and software. He has litigated in federal district and appellate courts throughout the US.
**Personal:** JD, University of Virginia School of Law, 1994; BA, Political Science, Yale University, 1990.

**WOLSK, Jeremiah M**
Latham & Watkins LLP, Washington, DC
202 637 2200
jeremiah.wolsk@lw.com
*Featured in Technology (District of Columbia)*
**Practice Areas:** Represents a wide range of clients, both domestic and international, in licensing, development, supply, distribution, telecommunications services, joint venture, technology transfer, and outsourcing agreements. Particular expertise in licensing, development, supply and distribution agreements in the life sciences, energy, chemical and industrial manufacturing industries; procurement and service agreements in the wireline, wireless and satellite industries; and ITO and BPO agreements in the retail, financial services, manufacturing, telecommunications, chemical, pharmaceutical and automotive industries.
**Professional Memberships:** Member, District of Columbia and Maryland state bars.

**Personal:** JD, Washington University, 1996; BA, Johns Hopkins University, 1992.

**WRIGHT, Christopher**
Wiltshire & Grannis LLP, Washington, DC
202 730 1325
cwright@wiltshiregrannis.com
*Featured in Telecommunications (District of Columbia)*
**Practice Areas:** Mr Wright has been the head of the appellate practice at Wiltshire & Grannis since 2001. He represents clients before the Supreme Court and federal courts of appeals on diverse matters. He also counsels a wide variety of communications companies before the FCC.
**Professional Memberships:** Former President, Edward Coke Appellate Inn of Court. Current Officer, Federal Communications Bar Association.
**Career:** Clerked for Chief Justice Burger, 1981-82. Office of the Solicitor General, 1984-94. General Counsel, FCC, 1997-2001.
**Personal:** Stanford Law School, JD, 1980, Order of the Coif. Harvard College, AB, 1974, Phi Beta Kappa.

**WYRON, Richard H**
Orrick, Herrington & Sutcliffe LLP, Washington, DC
202 339 8514
rwyron@orrick.com
*Featured in Bankruptcy/Restructuring (District of Columbia)*
**Career:** Rick Wyron represents creditors, debtors, committees, equity holders, asset purchasers and other parties-in-interest in bankruptcy proceedings and non-judicial restructurings. He has represented, among other clients, a multi-state retailer in its successful reorganization, a national manufacturer in confirming its pre-packaged reorganization plan, and the purchaser of assets of an aircraft manufacturer in a 363 sale. He has significant asbestos-related bankruptcy expertise, representing companies facing asbestos liabilities and court-appointed fiduciaries and others in pending cases and before trusts created under confirmed plans. He also represents Indian tribal entities and lenders in out-of-court workouts and debt restructurings for tribal gaming enterprises.

**YANNI, Palma**
Dickstein Shapiro LLP, Washington, DC
202 420 2275
yannip@dicksteinshapiro.com
*Featured in Immigration (Nationwide), Immigration (District of Columbia)*
**Practice Areas:** Leader of Dickstein Shapiro's Immigration Practice. Represents businesses and individuals on employment-based immigration matters. Works with corporations in employment verification and work site enforcement matters, as well as with individuals on family-based applications and naturalization. Represents clients before the U.S. Citizenship and Immigration Service, the Department of Labor, consular offices of the Department of State, and in federal court.
**Career:** A former president of the American Immigration Lawyers Association, she's a frequent author and has been called on to testify before Congress on immigration matters.

**Personal:** Mount Holyoke College (BA, 1976), Northwestern University School of Law (JD, 1979).

**YANNUCCI, Thomas D**
Kirkland & Ellis LLP, Washington, DC
202 879 5056
thomas.yannucci@kirkland.com
*Featured in First Amendment Litigation (Nationwide), Litigation (District of Columbia), Media & Entertainment (District of Columbia)*
**Practice Areas:** Chair of Kirkland's Firmwide Management Committee (2001-10), Chair Emeritus (2010- ). Trial and Appellate Counsel in individual and class action suits involving defamation, antitrust, IP, securities, government enforcement and regulatory matters (DOJ, FDA, EPA, FTC, SEC), and commercial fraud and RICO. Served as an arbitrator for complex commercial cases for the American Arbitration Association.
**Personal:** University of Notre Dame, AB, 1972. University of Notre Dame Law School, JD, 1976; Editor-in-Chief, Notre Dame Law Review; Law Clerk to Honorable John Danaher, U.S. Court of Appeals for the D.C. Circuit, 1976-77; Deptartment of Justice, 1977-80.

**YDE, Paul**
Freshfields Bruckhaus Deringer LLP, Washington, DC
202 777 4500
paul.yde@freshfields.com
*Featured in Antitrust (District of Columbia)*
**Practice Areas:** Paul's practice involves representing parties before the DOJ, FTC, and State Attorneys General on the antitrust aspects of M&A, joint ventures, distribution and intellectual property arrangements, and other competitive conduct. He acts as lead counsel on complex matters in a variety of industries, including a continuous docket of merger and conduct investigations at the DOJ and FTC. He litigates antitrust cases before federal and state courts and in federal administrative proceedings. Paul previously held positions in government antitrust enforcement, serving as counsel to two Federal Trade Commissioners and as a litigation attorney in the FTC's Bureau of Competition.

**YINGLING, Gary L**
Morgan, Lewis & Bockius LLP, Washington, DC
202 739 5610
gyingling@morganlewis.com
*Featured in Healthcare (District of Columbia)*
**Practice Areas:** Partner Gary Yingling is a leader in the firm's FDA practice. His clients, including those in the pharmaceutical, medical device and food industries, as well as IRBs and trade associations, benefit from his professional experience, first with the Food & Drug Administration, where he served in the office of the general counsel, and later as president of the Food & Drug Law Institute. He also was director of the Over-the-Counter Drug Review in the FDA's Bureau of Drugs.

**YOUNG, Howard J**
Morgan, Lewis & Bockius LLP, Washington, DC
202 739 5461
hyoung@morganlewis.com
*Featured in Healthcare (District of Columbia)*
**Practice Areas:** Advises a broad range of healthcare organizations—including hospitals, hospices, home health agencies, retail and specialty pharmacies, skilled nursing facilities, physicians, vision care providers, medical suppliers, GPOs, and distributors as well as pharmaceutical and device manufacturers—on fraud and abuse, regulatory, and compliance program and transactional matters, and represents clients on federal and state investigations and self-disclosures involving False Claims Act, Anti-Kickback, Stark Law, quality of care, coding, and billing matters.
**Professional Memberships:** American Health Lawyers Association; Health Law Section, American Bar Association; Health Care Compliance Association
**Career:** Former Deputy Branch Chief with Office of Counsel to the Inspector General

**ZACHARY, Heather**
WilmerHale, Washington, DC
202 663 6794
heather.zachary@wilmerhale.com
*Featured in Telecommunications (District of Columbia)*
**Practice Areas:** Partner, Regulatory and Government Affairs Department; member, Communications, Privacy and Internet Law Practice. Practice focuses on communications regulation, civil litigation (appellate and trial), and counseling on privacy and information security.
**Professional Memberships:** Member, District of Columbia Bar, Oregon State Bar, US Supreme Court Bar, Federal Communications Bar Association, American Bar Association.
**Publications:** Navigating Communications Regulation in the Wake of 9/11, 57 Federal Communications Law Journal 351 (2005) (co-authored with Jamie S. Gorelick and John H. Harwood II).
**Personal:** Yale Law School (JD); University of Southern California (BA, Phi Beta Kappa; Valedictorian).

**ZAKUPOWSKY, Alexander**
Miller & Chevalier Chartered, Washington, DC
202 626 5950
azakupowsky@milchev.com
*Featured in Tax (District of Columbia)*
**Practice Areas:** Federal income tax, controversies, international transfer pricing, tax accounting, and Federal tax issues of special interest to investor owned public utilities.
**Professional Memberships:** American Bar Association, Section of Taxation, Chair Committee on Tax Accounting Problems (1978-80), Section of Public Utility, Communications and Transportation Law, Vice Chair Taxation and Accounting Committee (current); Federal Bar Association; American Institute of Certified Public Accountants.

**Career:** Treasury, Office of Tax Policy 1976-78; Washington DC tax practice for over 35 years.

## ZAWITOSKI, Gina M
DLA Piper LLP (US), Baltimore
410 580 4291
gina.zawitoski@dlapiper.com
*Featured in Environment (District of Columbia)*

**Practice Areas:** Environment.
**Career:** She has a diverse environmental law practice which focuses principally on environmental matters relating to corporate and real property transactions and a broad range of regulatory compliance and permitting matters, including wastewater management, hazardous waste and natural resource matters. She acts as environmental counsel to manufacturers, mining and aggregates companies, private equity firms, real estate investment managers, developers and others. In 2008, the Maryland Daily Record named her among Maryland's Top 100 Women.
**Personal:** JD, University of Maryland School of Law, with honor; BA, University of Maryland Baltimore County, magna cum laude

## ZEVNIK, Paul A
Morgan, Lewis & Bockius LLP, Washington, DC
202 739 5755
pzevnik@morganlewis.com
*Featured in Insurance (Nationwide), Insurance (District of Columbia)*

See under Nationwide for profile.

## ZIMMERMAN, Eric
McDermott Will & Emery LLP, Washington, DC
202 756 8148
ezimmerman@mwe.com
*Featured in Healthcare (District of Columbia)*

**Practice Areas:** Member of firm's health law department and government strategies practice group. Recognized Medicare law and policy authority. Helps clients navigate federal legislative and regulatory processes related to Medicare coverage, coding, reimbursement and compliance. Represents hospitals and health systems, ambulatory surgery centers, clinical laboratories, pharmaceutical, biotechnology and device manufacturers and suppliers, and medical trade associations.
**Professional Memberships:** Admitted in Maryland and District of Columbia; American Health Lawyers Association, Board of Directors (2008-2010); Chair, American Health Lawyers Association's Regulation, Accreditation and Payment Practice Group (2004-07).
**Personal:** George Mason University School of Law (JD); George Washington University (MBA); Emory University, (BA).

## ZOTTOLA, A.J.
Venable LLP, Washington, DC
202 344 8546
ajzottola@Venable.com
*Featured in Technology (District of Columbia)*

**Practice Areas:** Technology Transactions and Outsourcing, Intellectual Property, Privacy and Data Security, Franchise and Distribution, Advertising and Marketing, Corporate
**Career:** A.J. Zottola works at the intersection of commerce and technology, focusing his practice on the sale, use, or exploitation of intellectual property and other intangible and technology assets in dispositions, acquisitions, licensing, sourcing, service, marketing, distribution, and other strategic relationships on behalf of US and foreign clients in a variety of industries.
**Publications:** A.J. Zottola is a frequent presenter and author
**Personal:** JD, cum laude, Catholic University of America, Columbus School of Law; BA, Bucknell University

## ZWISLER, Margaret
Latham & Watkins LLP, Washington, DC
202 637 1092
margaret.zwisler@lw.com
*Featured in Antitrust (District of Columbia)*

**Practice Areas:** Ms. Zwisler is an antitrust litigator with over 35 years of experience. She has successfully represented antitrust defendants in numerous trials and achieved significant victories for them through both procedural and substantive dispositive motions. She is widely recognized as one of the leading class action defense lawyers in the country.
**Professional Memberships:** Member, District of Columbia bar. Member, Section of Antitrust Law, ABA.
**Career:** Immediate past Global Co-Chair, Antitrust and Competition Practice
**Personal:** JD (high honors), George Washington University Law School, 1976; BA (cum laude), Saint Mary's College, Notre Dame IN 1971

# ADDUCI, MASTRIANI & SCHAUMBERG, L.L.P.

www.**adduci.com  tel:** 202 467 6300  **fax:** 202 466 2006

**Managing Partner:** V James Adduci, II
Number of partners: 12
Number of other lawyers: 17

**OFFICES**

DISTRICT OF COLUMBIA
**WASHINGTON:** 1133 Connecticut Avenue, NW, DC 20036
Tel: 202 467 6300 Fax: 202 466 2006

## Firm Overview:

For over 30 years, Adduci, Mastriani & Schaumberg, LLP has provided thorough, expert counsel to meet clients' unique legal needs in the fields of international trade, intellectual property litigation and customs transactions. The firm specializes in pursuing clients' legal actions effectively and efficiently before federal regulatory agencies and tribunals, including the US International Trade Commission ("ITC"), US Department of Commerce ('DOC'), Federal Courts, and US Customs and Border Protection ('Customs'). Many of the firm's attorneys have worked as legal counsel or advisors to one or more of these government agencies facilitating the maintenance of good working relations with these offices. Extensive experience in litigating importrelated intellectual property, anti-dumping, countervailing duty and customs cases enables the firm to handle its clients' international trade concerns rapidly and at a reasonable cost.

## Main Areas of Practice:

### Section 337 Investigations:

The firm's most recognized expertise is in litigating Section 337 cases. In fact, it has been involved in nearly a quarter of the 850+ Section 337 investigations that have been filed before the ITC. The firm's attorneys have both served as legal counsel to the ITC and helped revise its statutes, rules and procedures adding to their familiarity with the process. The firm has represented complainants as well as respondents, thus providing its clients the benefit of highly effective legal strategies and guidance regardless of their role in a particular case. In addition, the firm has been involved with a wide range of products, including semiconductors, computer peripheral equipment, mobile telephone handsets, cartridges, animal feed products, industrial machinery, pharmaceutical compositions, ceramic capacitors, printing devices,machine vision software and automotive parts. The second edition of the firm's book entitled, 'A Lawyer's Guide to Section 337 Investigations Before the U.S. International Trade Commission' was published by the American Bar Association.

### Anti-Dumping & Countervailing Duty Investigations:

The firm has been active in anti-dumping cases since the early 1980s. It has represented domestic and foreign clients in various anti-dumping and countervailing duty investigations before the DOC, the ITC and in appeals before the US Court of International Trade in cases involving such varied products as outboard motors, anti-friction bearings, flat panel displays,

agricultural products and aramid fiber. Certain attorneys are NAFTA binational panelists and have been involved in reviews of high profile anti-dumping and countervailing duty cases.

### Customs Transactions:

Effectively guiding importers through the maze of Customs regulations is an integral part of the firm's International Trade Practice. The firm's Washington, DC location allows attorneys to act quickly and effectively at the headquarters level to resolve the varied difficulties clients may face. The attorneys at the firm offer more than 100 years of combined experience in working for Customs.

### Related International Trade Investigations:

US and foreign companies seek the firm's broad expertise in investigations designed to control access by foreign competitors to the US market. On the other hand, the firm has also successfully obtained export licenses for its clients for goods, such as computer hardware and software, telecommunications equipment and various electronic products and components.

### Intellectual Property Litigation:

The firm has extensive experience in Federal Court litigation, appellate practice and arbitration. Its cases have involved disputes regarding patents, trademarks, trade secrets and copyrights. In addition to litigating intellectual property and unfair competition cases, the firm also represents clients in general commercial and business regulation disputes.

## Clients:

The firmrepresents both domestic and international clients, including companies in the industrial, semiconductor, computer, telecommunications, pharmaceutical and automotive industries. The firm has also represented foreign governments in countervailing duty cases and advises those clients regarding anti-dumping and Section 337 law and practices.Adduci,Mastriani & Schaumberg, LLP is committed to providing excellence by listening to clients, offering realistic legal evaluations, developing strategies and implementing those strategies cost effectively. The firm's practice continues to grow through referrals from existing clients.

## International Work:

International trade law is one of the core areas of the firm's practice and one for which Adduci, Mastriani & Schaumberg, LLP has become best known.

# AKIN GUMP STRAUSS HAUER & FELD LLP

www.akingump.com **tel:** 202 887 4000 **fax:** 202 887 4288

**Chairperson:** Kim Koopersmith
Number of lawyers: 850

**Firm Overview:**
Recognized for its sophisticated clients and capabilities as well as its outstanding team of professionals, Akin Gump Strauss Hauer & Feld is one of the world's largest law firms, with 18 offices and over 850 lawyers in more than 50 practice disciplines. Akin Gump's steadfast dedication to providing exemplary client service and its visionary leadership are key factors in this first-generation law firm's swift rise to the top of the profession.

**Main Areas of Practice:**

**Corporate & Securities:**
Akin Gump advises on mergers and acquisitions, corporate finance and securities, international transactions, investment fund management, private equity and corporate restructuring, providing counsel on US and international tax and governance issues.

**Energy:**
The firm is a leading advisor to energy companies and provides a full range of legal services, including corporate transactions, project finance and development, and advocacy. Energy clients include public and private companies, financial institutions, private equity firms and sovereign states working across the energy value chain from independent exploration and production activity to renewable energy investment. Key practice strengths include knowledge of global and domestic energy markets, broad and deep transactional experience, as well as attention to strategic considerations.

**Financial Restructuring:**
Akin Gump has represented committees of bondholders, noteholders, institutional investors and trade creditors in more than 250 major restructurings since 1999. Among its most significant recent engagements are the representations of the official creditors' committees in the Delta Air Lines, Calpine Corporation, World Com, Inc. and Washington Mutual, Inc. bankruptcies.

**Global Project Finance:**
Recognized for its project finance and implementation work, the firm has significant experience representing lenders, developers, suppliers, underwriters and sovereign states in project finance and implementation projects to meet some of the world's most complex infrastructure needs in the areas of construction, including airports and highways, energy, mining, shipping and maritime, as well as water and sanitation.

**Intellectual Property:**
The firm provides counsel on patent litigation, trademark, copyright, trade secret and unfair competition matters to *Fortune* 500 companies, multinational corporations and entertainment conglomerates, as well as small businesses, universities, research foundations, government agencies and individual inventors.

**Investment Funds Private Equity:**
Akin Gump provides comprehensive representation - from initial organization and funding, through managing extraordinary growth – for many of the largest and most prominent funds in the world, including both hedge funds and private equity funds. Helping to build leading private equity franchises from the ground up is a hallmark of the practice. The group advises on all aspects and phases of private equity business – from structuring and organizing a private equity firm and all of the funds it sponsors, to assisting in the evaluation of investment opportunities, to structuring and completing investments and structuring and implementing exit strategies.

**International Trade:**
The firm's lawyers, economists, and other professionals provide representation in the areas of anti-dumping and countervailing duty litigation, customs laws, export controls and economic sanctions, antiboycott laws, WTO dispute resolution proceedings, and other trade proceedings and trade policy.

**Labor & Employment:**
The firm provides advice and representation to employers regarding all aspects of employment law and labor relations, handling major class action wage-hour and EEO litigation, as well as traditional matters such as collective bargaining and discrimination suits. The group's lawyers advise on the labor aspects of major corporate reorganizations and acquisitions, help restructure labor contracts in bankruptcy, design and implement employee health and welfare benefit plans, and for those employers with facilities in Europe, assist with complying with the social legislation of the European Union.

**Litigation:**
With more than 300 lawyers, Akin Gump's Litigation Group includes attorneys who have served as clerks at every level of the federal and state court systems; members of the American Academy of Appellate Lawyers; former prosecutors; and former officials at the SEC, FTC, DOJ and many other federal agencies. Akin Gump's litigators are accustomed to handling matters of exceptional complexity, such as nationwide class actions, parallel civil and administrative proceedings, and nationwide and multidistrict litigation.

**Public Law & Policy:**
Akin Gump has one of the world's most sophisticated and diverse US and international public law and policy practices, representing corporations, individuals, non-profits, foreign governments, and coalitions and trade associations.

## OFFICES

### CALIFORNIA

**LOS ANGELES:** 2029 Century Park East, Suite 2400, CA 90067
Tel: 310 229 1000  Fax: 310 229 1001

**LOS ANGELES (DOWNTOWN):** 633 West Fifth Street, Suite 5000, CA 90071-2081
Tel: 213 254 1200  Fax: 213 254 1201

**SAN FRANCISCO:** 580 California Street, Suite 1500, CA 94104
Tel: 415 765 9500  Fax: 415 765 9501

### DISTRICT OF COLUMBIA

**WASHINGTON DC:** Robert S Strauss Building, 1333 New Hampshire Avenue, NW, DC 20036
Tel: 202 887 4000  Fax: 202 887 4288

### NEW YORK

**NEW YORK:** One Bryant Park, NY 10036
Tel: 212 872 1000  Fax: 212 872 1002

### PENNSYLVANIA

**PHILADELPHIA:** Two Commerce Square, 2001 Market Street, Suite 4100, PA 19103
Tel: 215 965 1200  Fax: 215 965 1210

### TEXAS

**AUSTIN:** 300 West 6th Street, Suite 2100, TX 78701
Tel: 512 499 6200  Fax: 512 499 6290

**DALLAS:** 1700 Pacific Avenue, Suite 4100, TX 75201
Tel: 214 969 2800  Fax: 214 969 4343

**HOUSTON:** 1111 Louisiana Street, 44th Floor, , TX 77002
Tel: 713 220 5800  Fax: 713 236 0822

**LONGVIEW:** Austin Bank Building, 911 West Loop 281, Suite 211-40, TX 75604
Tel: 903 297 7400  Fax: 903 297 7402

**SAN ANTONIO:** 300 Convent Street, Suite 1500, TX 78205
Tel: 210 281 7000  Fax: 210 224 2035

## INTERNATIONAL OFFICES

The firm has offices in Beijing, Hong Kong, London, Moscow, Abu Dhabi, Geneva and Singapore.

# Akin Gump
## STRAUSS HAUER & FELD LLP

# ARENT FOX LLP

**www.**arentfox.com **tel:** 202 857 6000 **fax:** 202 857 6395

**Chairman:** Mark Katz
**Managing Partner:** Matthew Clark

## Firm Overview:

Arent Fox LLP, founded in 1942, is internationally recognized in core practice areas where business and government intersect. With more than 350 lawyers, the firm provides strategic legal counsel and multidisciplinary solutions to clients that range from Fortune 500 corporations to trade associations. The firm has offices in Washington, DC, New York City and Los Angeles.

## Main Areas of Practice:

### Advertising, Sweepstakes & Promotions:

Focuses on media, television, and consumer products companies in all aspects of advertising and promotions including: clearing promotions and advertising globally, advertising and trade regulation law, and federal and state investigations.

### Automotive:

Focuses on business, franchise and consumer litigation, corporate and real estate transactions, vehicle safety law, regulatory, distribution and franchise, intellectual property, antitrust, environmental and emissions, consumer lending, customs and international trade, restructuring and bankruptcy.

### Bankruptcy & Financial Restructuring:

Represents creditors' committees, bondholders, note holders, secured creditors, lender syndicates, debtors, Chapter 11 trustees, and financing providers in bankruptcy proceedings.

### Corporate:

Broad-based corporate experience includes mergers and acquisitions, corporate finance, joint ventures and strategic alliances, corporate governance, and public and private offerings of equity and debt. Handles transactions for private equity funds, public companies, and midmarket private companies. Active in brand licensing and franchise transactions.

### Government Relations:

Assists companies, trade associations, universities, governmental organizations, and other nonprofits to attain their objectives by advocating at the federal, state, and local levels. Counsels on elections and political activity law.

### Health Care:

Provides coordinated representation in all aspects of healthcare law, including reimbursement/coverage issues, Stark regulations, anti-kickback matters, fraud and abuse counseling, regulatory issues, false claims defense, HIPAA/health privacy advice, RACs, telemedicine, and e-health.

### Insurance & Reinsurance:

Advises US and European insurers, reinsurers, and brokers on multistate licensing projects, tax issues, regulatory compliance matters, and state investigations. Counsels clients on cross-border acquisitions including public company employment. Advises US and international insurers and producers on compliance, licensing, and surplus lines eligibility issues.

### Intellectual Property (IP):

Offers a range of services related to the acquisition, enforcement, and commercial exploitation of IP rights and assets. Has extensive experience prosecuting and defending against infringement claims in state and federal courts throughout the United States.

### International Trade:

Represents and advises clients in a range of cross-border matters, such as customs/import compliance; global trade policy; international trade litigation, including litigation before US Court of International Trade and US Court of Appeals for the Federal Circuit. Represents clients before the US Trade Representative office; export controls and sanctions, including compliance with the Arms Export Control Act and ITAR; and international anti-corruption and the FCPA.

### Labor & Employment:

Counsels on employment litigation, labor management relations, occupational safety and health, employee benefits, immigration, federal contractors, and public accommodations.

### Litigation:

Represents plaintiffs and defendants in federal and state courts across the country and in dispute resolution worldwide. The practice encompasses bankruptcy and financial reorganization, commercial, construction, employment and labor, ERISA, government contracts, insurance, intellectual property, international trade, life sciences, sports/media/entertainment, real estate, white collar crime, FCPA, False Claims Act, and health care.

### Non-Profit:

Represents tax-exempt organizations on matters relating to tax, government relations, finance, real estate, labor, intellectual property, antitrust, and litigation. Serves as general counsel to associations and nonprofit organizations and provides counsel to educational institutions, hospitals, trade and professional organizations, religious institutions, museums, foundations, and public charities.

### Real Estate:

Handles projects nationally and internationally for institutional and private investors in joint venture formation and structuring, portfolio acquisition and sale, land acquisition and development, construction, financing, leasing, management, brokerage and sale. Advises on such projects as office buildings, shopping centers, hotels, factories, warehouses, research and development parks, and residential developments.

### Sports:

Counsels clients in the sports industry on all types of transactions, such as acquisitions and sales of franchises, arena stadium development and financing, naming rights agreements, sponsorship agreements, media rights agreements, issues with labor and employment, venue arrangements, and representation agreements with marketing agencies.

### Tax & Estate Planning:

Focus on all areas of federal and state tax law, representing taxpayers before the Internal Revenue Service, state tax authorities and courts that have jurisdiction over federal tax disputes. Provides comprehensive estate planning, tax planning, business succession planning, charitable planning, and wealth management services.

### Telecommunications:

Handles services in all aspects of the telecommunications industry, including transactions, licensing, regulatory compliance and advocacy, and litigation. Serves clients ranging from well-established international telecommunications corporations to emerging entrepreneurs.

### White-Collar:

Handles all stages of a government investigation, including parallel civil and criminal proceedings involving multiple agencies and across multiple jurisdictions. Conducts sensitive internal investigations, provides compliance and ethics training, guides clients through complex governmental audits and investigations.

# ARNOLD & PORTER LLP

www.arnoldporter.com  **tel:** 202 942 5000  **fax:** 202 942 5999

**Chairman:** Thomas H Milch
**Managing Partner:** Richard M Alexander
Number of partners: 248  Number of other lawyers: 580

**Firm Overview:**
Arnold & Porter LLP is an international firm with a deep understanding of the changing business environment as it intersects with law, public policy and business. The firm brings a valuable perspective and proven track record of experience in cross-border regulation, litigation and transactional law.

**Main Areas of Practice:**

**Antitrust/Competition & Consumer Protection:**
Strong tradition in antitrust/competition policy. Works with clients from various industries on matters under federal, state and European laws governing competition, pricing, distribution, advertising, intellectual property.

**Appellate & Supreme Court:**
Broad experience under federal and state law including administrative, antitrust, banking, bankruptcy, constitutional law, criminal law, employment, environmental, ERISA, healthcare, IP, national security, preemption, product liability and telecommunications.

**Attorney Liability:**
Long history of defending attorneys in civil lawsuits and disciplinary proceedings.

**Bankruptcy:**
Represents secured and unsecured creditors, parties dealing with distressed businesses, investors and asset purchasers, committees, debtors and equity holders.

**Corporate & Securities:**
Experience in M&A, private equity and corporate control matters. Represents issuers, underwriters, and security holders in a full range of public and private offerings of debt and equity securities.

**Employment:**
Works on a national scale to assist clients with high-stakes litigation, counseling and corporate/transactional employment matters.

**Environmental:**
Represents corporations, developers, utilities and public agencies in a wide range of environmental regulatory matters including litigation.

**FDA & Healthcare:**
Advises pharmaceutical, biotechnology, medical device, and other healthcare entities on regulation matters including fraud and abuse, pricing and contracting, coverage and reimbursement.

**Financial Services:**
Handles legal, business, and regulatory issues encountered by financial institutions, including growth and expansion, regulatory, financial products and services, capital markets, corporate governance.

**Government Contracts:**
Advises companies conducting business with government agencies on white-collar crime, compliance programs, litigation, corporate transactions, privatization, outsourcing, policy and legislation.

**Intellectual Property:**
Handles acquisition, protection, exploitation, and enforcement of IP rights relating to computer and information technology, internet, pharmaceuticals, biotechnology.

**International Arbitration:**
Highly regarded practice with long-standing ties to Latin America. Has advised on international arbitration projects for the US and international clients. Serve as advisers, advocates and arbitrators in economic disputes between sovereign governments and private investors.

**International Trade:**
Represents domestic and foreign corporations, institutions and individuals in virtually all aspects of international trade activity.

**Life Sciences/Biotech:**
Attuned to the current state of play and future of genomics, proteomics, bioinformatics, biochips, pharmacogenetics and other current technological developments.

**Litigation:**
Major firm practice with more than half of its US lawyers involved. Product liability, antitrust and securities are traditional areas of strength. Diverse work includes civil, criminal, regulatory, commercial, national, international matters.

**National Security Law & Policy:**
Offers sophisticated guidance on national homeland security decision-making process and in dealings with the US Dept of State, the US Dept of Defense, other national security agencies, the US Congress.

**Private Client Services:**
Counsels clients on complex estate planning, tax, real estate, family disputes, business organization and succession planning.

**Product Liability:**
Defends large and complex mass tort matters, acting both as national and trial counsel in cases asserting personal injury and property damage claims.

**Real Estate:**
Structures real estate deals for owners and developers in connection with acquisition, development, construction, financing, leasing, management and sale of office buildings, shopping centers, industrial sites, multifamily projects, hotels, resorts, recreational developments.

**Securities Enforcement & Litigation:**
Represents clients in SEC investigations, class action securities litigation, shareholder derivative litigation, accounting irregularities, breach of fiduciary duty and criminal investigations by federal and state prosecutors.

**Tax:**
Advises on all major areas of corporate, partnership, employment, individual, trusts and estates, gift tax law.

**Telecommunications:**
Provides international regulatory, administrative, litigation and legislative advice to corporations, government entities, individuals.

**White-Collar Criminal Defense:**
Represents individuals and corporations in grand jury and administrative enforcement proceedings, criminal trials, internal investigations.

## OFFICES

**DISTRICT OF COLUMBIA**
**WASHINGTON DC:** 555 Twelfth Street, NW, DC 20004-1206
Tel: 202 942 5000  Fax: 202 942 5999

**CALIFORNIA**
**LOS ANGELES:** 777 South Figueroa Street, 44th Floor, CA 90017-5844
Tel: 213 243 4000  Fax: 213 243 4199

**PALO ALTO:** 1801 Page Mill Road, Suite 110, CA 94304-1216
Tel: 650 798 2920  Fax: 650 798 2999

**SAN FRANCISCO:** Three Embarcadero Center, 7th Floor, CA 94111-4024
Tel: 415 471 3100  Fax: 415 471 3400

**COLORADO**
**DENVER:** 370 Seventeenth Street, Suite 4500, CO 80202-1370
Tel: 303 863 1000  Fax: 303 832 0428

**NEW YORK**
**NEW YORK:** 399 Park Avenue, NY 10022-4690
Tel: 212 715 1000  Fax: 212 715 1399

**VIRGINIA**
**MCLEAN:** 1600 Tysons Boulevard, Suite 900, VA 22102-4865
Tel: 703 720 7000  Fax: 703 720 7399

## INTERNATIONAL OFFICES
The firm also has offices in London and Brussels.

ARNOLD & PORTER LLP

# BEVERIDGE & DIAMOND, P.C.

www.bdlaw.com **tel:** 202 789 6000 **fax:** 202 789 6190

Number of principals: 53   Number of other attorneys: 47

## Firm Overview:

Beveridge & Diamond, P.C. focuses on environmental and natural resource law, land use, and litigation. The firm handles complex compliance, product stewardship and litigation matters nationwide. The litigation practice includes alternative dispute resolution capabilities and extends beyond traditional environmental law, to include a wider range of issues involving the chemical, petroleum, consumer products and real estate industries, including environmental toxic torts and oil and gas litigation. The firm also offers a robust white collar litigation group.

## Main Areas of Practice:

### Environmental:

Beveridge & Diamond's practice encompasses all areas of environmental law, and the firm's long history and experience allow it to successfully handle the most significant and complicated domestic and international environmental matters. The firm represents clients on environmental issues related to air, surface water and groundwater, solid and hazardous wastes, environmental reporting and disclosure, and compliance with the wide array of federal and state environmental laws and regulations. It also represents clients across the country with regard to environmentally contaminated properties, including brownfields projects, and in negotiations with buyers, sellers, developers, and insurers of these properties. The firm advises on a broad range of market access, product design, use, take-back and recycling in the US and in key markets worldwide. In addition, it provides strategic advice to clients with regard to their environmental management systems, and assists clients with their environmental due diligence efforts in the US and across the world. On climate change-related issues, the firm advises and represents major industry associations and corporations in the chemical, municipal waste incineration, transportation, energy, consumer product, and other sectors on the new federal greenhouse gas (GHG) reporting rule, emissions inventories, control measures, and credit and trading issues arising under domestic and international regulatory regimes. On these and other issues, the firm advocates before federal and state environmental agencies to advance clients' interests.

### Environmental Litigation/Enforcement Defense:

The firm represents clients challenging agency actions and defending against government enforcement actions and citizen suits. It represents clients in cases brought under the federal 'Superfund' law, other federal and state statutes, and common law regarding the extent and timing of remediation, who should pay for the remediation, and related contract and damages claims. The firm also represents clients in NEPA, takings and related land use matters.

### Toxic Tort, Chemical, General Civil Litigation & ADR:

The Litigation Practice focuses on technical matters involving expert testimony, often involving chemicals and petroleum. It represents clients in toxic tort, product liability, and mass tort litigation, and is national counsel for two clients with respect to methyl tertiary butyl ether and perchloroethylene. The firm also has extensive experience in other types of litigation involving expert testimony, including pesticide data compensation and commercial litigation that may involve environmental or chemical issues, as well as oil and gas matters.

### White-Collar Defense & Compliance:

The firm represents companies and individuals in white collar criminal litigation, from the initial grand jury investigation through trial. In the area of environmental defense, it combines extensive Criminal Defense Practice with environmental law expertise to provide comprehensive and effective defenses. It also provides corporate compliance audits to anticipate the risk of criminal exposure and facilitate its avoidance.

### Project Development / Natural Resources:

The firm represents industrial, commercial, residential, and non-profit, clients in efficiently and effectively securing local, state and federal land use and environmental permits and approvals. Representative projects include multi-family housing, residential subdivisions, shopping malls, banks, restaurants, industrial campuses, power plants and other mining and energy developments. When necessary, the firm defends project approvals in state and federal trial and appellate courts. The firm provides sophisticated land-use counsel on projects big or small, greenfield or brownfield, and local or national in nature. It possesses the ability to assemble and manage high-quality teams of engineers and consultants and develop good working relationships with permit-granting authorities and associated staff and legal counsel.

### International Work:

As clients pursue international trade and investment opportunities, the firm has expanded its International Environmental Practice to help companies identify, understand, and comply with the expanding body of international, national and sub-national environmental law governing products and activities in countries and regions throughout the world.

Work includes advising on chemical registration requirements, including REACH, market-access requirements for electronics, consumer products and GMOs, and product take-back and recycling requirements in key markets. The firm advises on the growing web of supply chain management, due diligence and disclosure requirements that global companies face from regulators and customers, including emerging due diligence and disclosure and requirements relating to sourcing timber products and conflict minerals. The firm also advises on expanding corporate social responsibility requirements and issues related to forced labor in the supply chain. The firm has deep expertise advising clients on the negotiation and implementation of key multilateral environmental agreements, including the Basel Convention, Cartagena Protocol, Stockholm POPs Convention, FCCC and the Montreal Protocol.

## Clients:

The firm represents domestic and international resource and energy companies, electronics manufacturers, manufacturers of pharmaceuticals, glass, steel, paper, and other products, petroleum refiners, chemical companies, makers of pesticides, biotechnology companies, producers of raw materials, public transportation agencies, major retailers, telecommunications companies, municipal water and sewer authorities, state and local government, food and consumer products companies, financial institutions, trade associations, real estate developers and property managers.

**Contact:** Benjamin F Wilson, Managing Principal
**Email:** bwilson@bdlaw.com

## OFFICES

**DISTRICT OF COLUMBIA**
**WASHINGTON DC:** Suite 700, 1350 I Street, NW,
DC 20005-3311
Tel: 202 789 6000 Fax: 202 789 6190
Email: contact.bd@bdlaw.com

**CALIFORNIA**
**SAN FRANCISCO:** Suite 1800, 456 Montgomery Street,
CA 94104-1251
Tel: 415 262 4000 Fax: 415 262 4040

**MARYLAND**
**BALTIMORE:** Suite 2210, 201 North Charles Street,
MD 21201-4150
Tel: 410 230 1300 Fax: 410 230 1389

**MASSACHUSETTS**
**WELLESLEY:** 15 Walnut Street, Suite 400, Wellesley,
MA 02481-2133
Tel: 781 416 5700 Fax: 781 416 5799

**NEW JERSEY (BY APPOINTMENT ONLY)**
**ENGLEWOOD:** 50 East Palisade Avenue, Suite 208,
NJ 07631-2931
Tel: 201 568 2797 Fax: 201 568 2792

**NEW YORK**
**NEW YORK:** 15th Floor, 477 Madison Avenue, NY 10022-5802
Tel: 212 702 5400 Fax: 212 702 5450

**TEXAS**
**AUSTIN:** 98 San Jacinto Boulevard, Suite 1420, TX 78701-4039
Tel: 512 391 8000 Fax: 512 391 8099

# BUCKLEYSANDLER LLP

www.buckleysandler.com  **tel:** 202 349 8000  **fax:** 202 349 8080

**Chairman & Executive Partner:** Andrew L Sandler
**Managing Partners:** Benjamin B Klubes, John P Kromer
Number of partners: 30   Number of other lawyers: 121

### Firm Overview:

With more than 150 lawyers in Washington, DC, New York, Los Angeles, and Orange County, BuckleySandler provides best-in-class legal counsel to meet the challenges of its financial services industry and other corporate and individual clients across the full range of government enforcement actions, complex and class action litigation, and transactional, regulatory, and public policy issues.

Currently, BuckleySandler represents the 10 largest banks in the United States, nine of the top 10 mortgage lenders, the top 10 mortgage servicers, the top 10 credit card issuers, and numerous community banks and non-bank financial services companies. Over the past two decades, firm attorneys have served as lead defense counsel in more than 100 high-stakes class actions, represented clients in a multitude of state and federal enforcement proceedings, and had a hand in drafting many of the significant laws that impact the financial services industry.

### Main Areas of Practice:

#### Litigation:

This practice includes the defense of leading banks, financial services firms, and other companies and their executives in class actions, complex civil litigation, and arbitration proceedings. The firm defends clients in cases involving allegations of discrimination, predatory lending, unfair competition and deceptive trade acts and practices, fraud, false statements, false claims, and breach of contract, as well as other claimed violations of regulations and laws governing their business activities.

#### Enforcement:

The firm represents financial services companies before the US Department of Justice, the Consumer Financial Protection Bureau, the Federal Trade Commission, the Securities and Exchange Commission, the Office of Inspector General, the Federal Housing Finance Agency, the Department of Housing and Urban Development, federal bank regulators, state attorneys general, and other federal and state regulatory agencies. The firm's experience, gained over decades, is invaluable in helping to defend the interests of companies and executives in examinations and investigations relating to financial services matters.

#### Regulatory:

BuckleySandler advises financial institutions in connection with regulatory examinations and supervision matters initiated by state and federal agencies. The firm's attorneys, some of whom have served as senior bank regulators, help guide clients through the examination process, provide day-to-day advice on compliance matters, and design effective risk management strategies. They counsel clients on pre-examination preparation, assist them with responding to regulators' inquiries, and engage with regulators throughout examinations to ensure favorable outcomes, in both legal and business objectives.

#### White Collar Defense:

Corporations and their officers and directors turn to the firm's leading white collar defense attorneys when faced with grand jury investigations and other white collar criminal matters. With decades of experience handling complex parallel proceedings involving concurrent government enforcement and civil litigation, congressional investigations, and/or multiple class actions, BuckleySandler attorneys have the depth of experience needed to help clients navigate and emerge from sensitive investigations and litigation with their reputations and businesses intact.

#### Licensing & Chartering:

BuckleySandler assists clients with obtaining new lending, servicing, collection, insurance or money transmitter licenses, or obtaining "change of control" approvals for existing licensees, and assists banks and investment groups in analyzing charter alternatives and obtaining new charters. The firm assists new entrants, such as private equity investors, as well as ongoing businesses in structuring operations and transactions to minimize regulatory burden and facilitate the closing of transactions.

#### Counseling & Compliance:

Clients rely on the firm to provide sophisticated day-to-day compliance and risk management advice to ensure that their existing operations and new programs comply with ever-changing state and federal requirements. It assists clients with developing and implementing comprehensive compliance management programs, including written policies, training, and ongoing monitoring needed to ensure compliance with fair lending laws, federal and state consumer protection statutes, consumer financial privacy and information security regulations, and anti-money laundering requirements.

#### Transactional:

BuckleySandler represents community banks, bank holding companies, and other financial services companies in mergers, acquisitions, and related transactional matters. The firm represents clients in negotiating joint ventures and outsourcing arrangements, as well as licensing and e-commerce agreements. As part of this service, the firm conducts regulatory and legal due diligence or other risk assessments for clients considering acquisitions or strategic alliances.

#### Public Policy:

BuckleySandler assists clients in analyzing and responding to the full range of bank legislative and regulatory initiatives, including the Dodd-Frank Act and its implementation by the CFPB and other federal agencies. It is also at the forefront of establishing the legal infrastructure for the electronic delivery of financial services.

### PRACTICE AREAS

Banking
Commercial Lending
Consumer Finance
Corporate & Transactional
Counseling & Compliance
E-Commerce
Fair & Responsible Banking
Government Enforcement
Licensing & Chartering
Litigation
Mortgages
Unfair, Deceptive & Abusive Acts and Practices

### OFFICES

**CALIFORNIA**

**IRVINE:** 3121 Michelson Drive, Suite 210, CA 92612
Tel: 949 398 1360  Fax: 949 398 1390

**SANTA MONICA:** 100 Wilshire Blvd, Suite 1000, CA 90401
Tel: 310 424 3900  Fax: 310 424 3960

**DISTRICT OF COLUMBIA**

**WASHINGTON, DC:** 1250 24th Street, NW, Suite 700, DC 20037
Tel: 202 349 8000  Fax: 202 349 8080

**NEW YORK**

**NEW YORK:** 1133 Avenue of the Americas, Suite 3100, NY 10036
Tel: 212 600 2400 Fax: 212 600 2405

# CAPLIN & DRYSDALE

**www.**caplindrysdale.com **tel:** 202 862 5000 **fax:** 202 429 3301

**President:** Scott D Michel
**Hiring Partner:** Niles A Elber
Number of partners: 35   Number of lawyers: 68
Languages: *English, Korean, Spanish, French, German, Albanian, Dutch, Flemish, Hebrew, Italian, Mandarin*

**Firm Overview:**

Founded by former IRS commissioner Mortimer Caplin, Caplin & Drysdale is a boutique tax law firm with offices in Washington, DC and New York. The firm provides a full range of tax and legal services to companies, organizations, and individuals throughout the United States and around the world. It also provides counseling on matters relating to bankruptcy, creditors' rights, exempt organizations, political activity, complex litigation, employee benefits, private clients, corporate law, and white-collar defense. For more information, visit www.caplindrysdale.com.

## Main Areas of Practice:

**Corporate, Business & Transactional Tax:**
Caplin & Drysdale has broad experience advising and representing public companies, other business entities, and their principals in tax planning and controversy matters. Such business entities include domestic and foreign financial institutions, manufacturing companies, insurance companies, and hedge fund managers. The firm's areas of substantive tax experience relevant to these entities include corporate tax, partnership tax, subchapter S, the taxation of regulated investment companies and real estate investment trusts, the taxation of insurance companies and products, tax accounting, financial products, and payroll and other withholding taxes.
**Contact:** Richard W Skillman **Tel:** 202 862 5034
**Email:** rskillman@capdale.com

**Complex Litigation:**
Caplin & Drysdale litigators are regularly asked to handle complex business, financial, and commercial disputes that have put a business in peril. The firm also represents plaintiffs around the world seeking to have their rights vindicated through the court system.
**Contact:** Trevor W Swett **Tel:** 202 862 5081
**Email:** tswett@capdale.com

**Corporate Law:**
Caplin & Drysdale counsels a range of clients in corporate law matters, including M&A, joint ventures, and choice of business entities and alternative organizational structures. The firm also has extensive experience with corporate governance and transactions for non-profit organizations.
**Contact:** William M Klimon **Tel:** 202 862 5022
**Email:** wklimon@capdale.com

**Bankruptcy & Creditors' Rights:**
For over 30 years, Caplin & Drysdale's bankruptcy litigation practice has protected the rights of creditors in courts throughout the United States. The firm is regularly retained in Chapter 11 bankruptcy cases to analyze and resolve high profile, complex and cutting-edge disputes. From the unique to the routine, the practice encompasses the full range of issues potentially affecting creditors in bankruptcy proceedings.
**Contact:** Peter Van Noyden Lockwood **Tel:** 202 862 5065
**Email:** plockwood@capdale.com

**Employee Benefits:**
The firm provides legal advice to employers and plan service providers in the following areas: design and administration of qualified plans, legislative and regulatory changes, representation before the Internal Revenue Service, compliance with Title I of ERISA, executive compensation, health and welfare benefits, tax-exempt and governmental employer representation, financial institution and service provider counseling, and employee benefits dispute resolution.
**Contact:** Richard W Skillman **Tel:** 202 862 5034
**Email:** rskillman@capdale.com

**Exempt Organizations:**
Serving some of the nation's most prominent private foundations, public charities and other non-profit organizations, the firm has handled a wide range of operational and governance issues for exempt organizations. The group counsels clients on political and lobbying issues, assists clients in raising revenue through a variety of business structures, advises regarding unrelated business tax issues, and monitors relevant legislative and regulatory activities. The firm also represents clients in high profile, complex IRS examinations.
**Contact:** Marcus S Owens **Tel:** 202 862 5020
**Email:** mowens@capdale.com

**International Tax:**
Caplin & Drysdale advises clients on matters relating to the taxation of international transactions, operations, and investments and transfer pricing, including tax-efficient structuring of cross-border investments and transactions, as well as optimum use of tax treaties, foreign tax credits, tax deferral, and entity classification.
**Contact:** H David Rosenbloom **Tel:** 202 862 5037
**Email:** drosenbloom@capdale.com

**Political Law:**
The firm regularly counsels clients on the laws pertaining to government ethics, lobbying, and campaign finance. The group's attorneys have represented clients on both sides of the political aisle, including corporations, trade associations, connected and non-connected political action committees, political parties, private individuals, presidential campaigns and high profile federal, state, and local candidates.
**Contact:** Trevor Potter **Tel:** 202 862 5092
**Email:** tpotter@capdale.com

**Private Client:**
Caplin & Drysdale counsels individuals and families on domestic and cross-border income and estate planning issues, including the use of trusts, foundations and wills and the application of tax treaties. The firm represents domestic and international clients in disputes with the IRS regarding their income, estate, gift and generation skipping transfer tax liabilities.
**Contact:** Beth Shapiro Kaufman **Tel:** 202 862 5062
**Email:** bkaufman@capdale.com

**Tax Controversies, Tax Litigation, Tax Crimes:**
Caplin & Drysdale has been engaged in this practice area for over 45 years, with significant experience in all phases of tax controversy, fraud and tax litigation. The firm also has a robust practice in the area of voluntary disclosures, particularly involving undeclared offshore accounts, which has been an increasing focus of IRS enforcement efforts.
**Contact:** Scott D Michel **Tel:** 202 862 5030
**Email:** smichel@capdale.com

**White-Collar Defense:**
With significant experience and Washington 'know-how,' Caplin & Drysdale's federal white-collar prosecution has represented clients in numerous types of white-collar criminal inquiries, including allegations of government procurement and program fraud, antitrust and securities offenses, mail fraud, wire fraud, customs violations, money laundering and campaign finance and public corruption investigations. Companies have also engaged the firm to conduct internal investigations of potential wrongdoing and report its results and recommendations to the appropriate corporate officials.
**Contact:** Mark E Matthews **Tel:** 202 862 5082
**Email:** mmatthews@capdale.com

**OFFICES**

DISTRICT OF COLUMBIA
**WASHINGTON DC:** One Thomas Circle, NW, Suite 1100, DC 20005
Tel: 202 862 5000   Fax: 202 429 3301

NEW YORK
**NEW YORK:** 600 Lexington Avenue, 21st Floor, NY 10022
Tel: 212 379 6000   Fax: 212 379 6001

# CROWELL & MORING LLP

www.crowell.com **tel:** 202 624 2500 **fax:** 202 628 5116

**Chairman:** Kent A Gardiner
**Managing Partner:** Ellen M Dwyer
Number of Partners: 195 Number of Lawyers: 520

**Firm Overview:**

Crowell & Moring LLP is an international law firm representing clients in litigation and arbitration, regulatory, and transactional matters. The firm is internationally recognized for its representation of Fortune 500 companies in high-stakes litigation, as well as its ongoing commitment to pro bono service and diversity. Fueled by the firm's leadership in alternative fee arrangements, Crowell & Moring recently instituted a legal project management initiative to enhance the firm's ability to manage legal projects in a way that meets client goals, and also helps to ensure that the firm's profitability is highly aligned with the results and value delivered to clients.

**Main Areas of Practice:**

**Antitrust:**
The group remains at the forefront of the most recent sophisticated transactions: successful clearance of United Technologies' $18.4 billion acquisition of Goodrich; representation of Coventry Health in its $5.7 billion sale to Aetna; and DuPont's $4.9 billion sale of its coatings business. Major results include multi-million dollar recoveries for clients like Oracle and Motorola who were victims of the DRAM and LCD price-fixing conspiracies and dismissal of antitrust claims against clients Kaiser Health, Yamaha, DuPont, and Motorola.

**Transactions & Corporate/Securities:**
The group is transaction-oriented, focusing predominately on mergers/acquisitions, joint ventures, corporate securities and finance, investment funds, commercial finance, commercial contracts, and outsourcing arrangements, IP arrangements, and financial institutions regulatory advice.

**Environment, Energy & Resources:**
The group has a national reputation with corporations, trade associations and others due to its successful efforts to shape regulatory policies and litigate disputes for clients in the mining, oil/gas, agriculture, alternative energy, defense and related sectors such as water/air quality, public land use, endangered species, site cleanup, pesticides, health and safety, and consumer products regulation.

**Government Contracts:**
The group has a 40-year history of unrivaled excellence, depth and success. The world's largest and most prominent contractors, and small to mid-size companies, turn to the group who are industry leaders. The group offers a full range of advice, including bid protests, claims, counseling, and litigation.

**Healthcare:**
The group provides a range of litigation, transactional and counseling services to clients nationwide. From hospitals and hospital systems, to payors, managed care companies, pharmaceutical companies, academic medical centers, government contractors, and established and start-up medical device/biotech companies.

**Insurance/ Reinsurance:**
The group represents clients in a variety of coverage and reinsurance matters and has experience in property and casualty, life, healthcare, accident health, management liability, and financial lines insurance matters. The group handles complex insurance litigation, negotiations, mediations, ADR, and insurance bankruptcy matters.

**Intellectual Property:**
The group represents many leading technology companies in both defending and asserting infringement claims in federal courts, as well as before the US ITC. The group is one of the leading players in the patent procurement arena and also serves as counsel for companies with an interest in ICANN's new gTLD program.

**International Trade & Dispute Resolution:**
The group provides a complete suite of services to assist the challenges of international businesses. The experienced group guides governments, businesses, and individuals as they structure investments and work across borders to trade goods and services, open new markets and settle disputes. The group works closely with the firm's subsidiary C&M International to craft government policies for countries.

**Litigation & Trial:**
A core strength of the firm is the Litigation Group, which brings and defends lawsuits for clients in nationwide and global courts, on matters spanning all practice and industry competencies. The firm has represented clients in over 1,400 trials and approximately 700 appeals. In 2011, the firm represented DuPont in a trade secret theft case against Kolon that resulted in a $919.9 million jury verdict for DuPont.

**White Collar & Regulatory Enforcement:**
The group has substantial trial experience, along with pragmatic counseling and negotiating capabilities, defending clients under FCPA, qui tam action brought under the False Claim Act, securities and commodities fraud, and more. In 2011, the firm led a successful defense in the landmark Lindsey Manufacturing Company FCPA case.

**PRACTICE AREAS**

Advertising & Product Risk Management
Antitrust
Aviation
Bankruptcy & Creditors' Rights
C&M International
Corporate/Securities
E-Discovery & Information Management
Environment, Energy & Resources
Financial Services
Government Affairs
Government Contracts
Healthcare
Insurance/Reinsurance
Intellectual Property
International Dispute Resolution
International Trade
Labor & Employment
Litigation & Trial
Plaintiff's Recovery
Tax
Torts
Trade Associations
Trade Secrets
White Collar & Regulatory Enforcement

**OFFICES**

DISTRICT OF COLUMBIA
**WASHINGTON DC:** 1001 Pennsylvania Avenue NW, DC 20004
Tel: 202 624 2500  Fax: 202 628 5116

NEW YORK
**NEW YORK:** 590 Madison Avenue, 20th Floor, NY 10022
Tel: 212 223 4000  Fax: 212 223 4134

CALIFORNIA
**LOS ANGELES:** 515 South Flower St., 40th Floor, CA 90071
Tel: 213 622 4750  Fax: 213 622 2690
**ORANGE COUNTY:** 3 Park Plaza, 20th Floor, CA 92614
Tel: 949 263 8400  Fax: 949 263 8414
**SAN FRANCISCO:** 275 Battery Street, 23rd Floor, CA 94111
Tel: 415 986 2800  Fax: 415 986 2827

ALASKA
**ANCHORAGE:** 1029 W. 3rd Avenue Suite 402, AK 99501
Tel: 907 865 2600  Fax: 907 865 2680

WYOMING
**CHEYENNE:** 205 Storey Boulevard, Suite 120, WY 82009
Tel: 307 996 1400  Fax: 307 996 1419

**INTERNATIONAL OFFICES:**

Belgium, United Kingdom and Egypt (Affiliate), and Saudi Arabia (Strategic Alliance with Al-Enizy & Associates).

# DICKSTEIN SHAPIRO LLP

www.dicksteinshapiro.com **tel:** 202 420 2200 **fax:** 202 420 2201

**Chairman:** Michael E Nannes
**Managing Partner, Washington, DC:** Richard J Leveridge
**Managing Partner, New York:** Howard Graff
**Managing Partner, California Offices:** James H Turken
Number of Partners: 120
Number of Attorneys: 310

**Firm Overview:**
Dickstein Shapiro LLP, founded in 1953, is internationally recognized for its work with clients, from start-ups to Fortune 500 corporations. Dickstein Shapiro provides strategic counsel and develops multidisciplinary legal solutions by leveraging its core strengths—litigation, regulatory, transactions, and advocacy—to successfully advance clients' business interests. The firm has offices in Los Angeles, New York, Orange County, Silicon Valley, Stamford, and Washington, DC.

**Main Areas of Practice:**

**Complex Dispute Resolution:**
Dickstein Shapiro's Complex Dispute Resolution (CDR) Practice provides comprehensive solutions to avoid, limit, and resolve complex litigation and liability problems. The firm's CDR attorneys succeed at helping clients maximize recoveries and minimize exposure through creative, cost-effective dispute resolution alternatives and strategies.

**Corporate & Finance:**
The Corporate and Finance Practice is international in scope and involves representation of some of the world's largest corporations, commercial banks, investment banks, and venture capital firms. This practice ranges from small, traditional transactions to large, highly complex transactions, and provides a full range of corporate, financial, and transactional legal services to its clients.

**Energy:**
Dickstein Shapiro's multiservice Energy Practice offers a complete range of services to companies that develop, finance, operate, acquire, sell, restructure, or manage large energy infrastructure projects, including renewable and conventional power plants, transmission lines, pipelines, and water desalination plants. The practice has second-to-none capabilities and experience, particularly with respect to federal and state electric and gas regulation, domestic and international energy transactions, litigation, compliance, and enforcement matters.

**Government Law & Strategy:**
Dickstein Shapiro seeks to advance clients' interests before the legislative and executive branches of government – a practice unique to Washington, DC. Attorneys and advisors provide support in a number of areas, including public policy, government contracts, State Attorneys General, global security, political law, and congressional investigations.

**Insurance Coverage:**
Dickstein Shapiro's premier Insurance Coverage Group – one of the nation's largest – represents policyholders around the country in disputes with their insurers. Many of the firm's insurance coverage attorneys are nationally recognized as leaders in insurance recovery, and attorneys have briefed and argued many of the most important and best-known decisions favorable to policyholders in federal and state appellate courts. The firm has helped clients recover $5 billion in the last five years alone from insurers and insurance brokers under a wide range of policies.

**Intellectual Property:**
Combining decades of litigation experience with a robust procurement and asset management practice, Dickstein Shapiro's Intellectual Property attorneys devise strategies to help clients protect IP assets while maximizing their value. The firm has handled litigations on both the plaintiff side and defense side involving claims from a few million to hundreds of millions of dollars. The practice also develops comprehensive IP programs and strategies encompassing all aspects of clients' intellectual property needs, including asset management, patent and trademark procurement, licensing, and counseling.

**Litigation:**
With more than 200 litigators in offices nationwide, Dickstein Shapiro's attorneys provide the highest level of integrated representation in numerous inter-related areas, and excel in litigating and settling complex, high-stakes business disputes. Whether through trial verdicts, arbitrations, settlements, or other litigation alternatives, Dickstein Shapiro's litigators seek the best outcome possible for their clients' goals and their bottom line.

**DICKSTEIN**SHAPIRO LLP

## FINNEGAN, HENDERSON, FARABOW, GARRETT & DUNNER, LLP

**www.**finnegan.com **tel:** 202 408 4000 **fax:** 202 408 4400

**Chairman:** Richard B Racine
**Managing Partner:** Barbara Clarke McCurdy
Number of partners: 143  Number of lawyers: 391
Languages: *Chinese, French, German, Guajarati, Hebrew, Hindi, Japanese, Korean, Portuguese, Russian, Spanish, Urdu*

### Firm Overview:

Finnegan, Henderson, Farabow, Garrett & Dunner, LLP is one of the largest law firms in the world focusing solely on intellectual property law. With over 375 lawyers and offices in the United States, Europe, and Asia, Finnegan practices all aspects of patent, trademark, copyright, and trade secret law, including counseling, prosecution, licensing, and litigation. Finnegan also represents clients on IP issues related to international trade, portfolio management, the Internet, e-commerce, government contracts, antitrust, and unfair competition. The firm offers full-service IP legal and technical experience in virtually every industry including electronics, computers and software, industrial manufacturing, consumer products, medical devices, biotechnology, pharmaceuticals, chemicals, and alternative energy. Nearly 400 of Finnegan's legal professionals hold degrees in scientific disciplines (90 hold PhDs); 290 are registered to practice before the US Patent and Trademark Office (USPTO); and 65 are former USPTO patent examiners. Surveys conducted by legal and business publications consistently rank Finnegan as one of the leading intellectual property law practices in the world. In Managing Intellectual Property's 2005-12 World IP surveys, the firm was ranked as #1 or #2 Tier US law firm for contentious and non-contentious patent and trademark work; Chambers USA also ranked Finnegan as a top intellectual property law firm from 2008-12; and in 2012, the American Lawyer honored Finnegan with its IP Litigation Department of the Year Award. The publications cited the firm's winning record, technical expertise, and deep bench of talent in all aspects of IP litigation, including trials, appeals, interferences at the USPTO, and US International Trade Commission proceedings.

### Main Areas of Practice:

Finnegan's attorneys practice solely intellectual property law, including: patent prosecution; patent opinions and counseling; advanced patent office procedures, including oppositions, reexaminations, and reissues; patent transactions, including due diligence and licensing; patent litigation; trademark prosecution and counseling; trademark litigation; trade secrets; and copyrights.

### Recent Work:

- Representation of Akamai Technologies, Inc. in a Federal Circuit en banc appeal. The Federal Circuit reversed a panel decision that Limelight did not infringe Akamai's patented technology because it had not performed all of the steps of a method claim. The en banc court determined that a party can still show induced infringement under circumstances where both the inducer and the induced party each perform some of the steps of a method claim. The court found that Limelight could be held liable for induced infringement and reversed and remanded the case for further proceedings.
- Representation of Research in Motion (RIM) at the US International Trade Commission (ITC) regarding electronic cameras. The ITC issued a final determination in favor of RIM that the only asserted claim of Kodak's US Patent No. 6,292,218 for electronic cameras was invalid. Kodak was seeking to exclude all RIM BlackBerry devices from the US.
- Representation of Interdigital in Federal Circuit appeal. The Federal Circuit reversed decision by the ITC against InterDigital that found Nokia did not infringe two InterDigital patents relating to 3G cellular telephone technology. The Federal Circuit also affirmed the ITC's decision that InterDigital's substantial patent licensing program satisfied the ITC's domestic industry requirement.
- Argued before the US Supreme Court in Bilski v Kappos, a landmark case on the patentability of business methods. The court rejected the limiting 'machine-or-transformation' test and confirmed that business methods are not excluded from patenting.
- Representation of AOL in negotiating an agreement with Microsoft to receive $1.056 billion for selling more than 800 patents and granting Microsoft a license on its remaining 300 patents and patent applications. The effective price of approximately $1.2 million per acquired patent set a new record.
- Representation of AstraZeneca and Shionogi Pharmaceuticals in a Federal Circuit appeal. The Federal Circuit upheld the lower court decision of the District of Delaware and affirmed the validity of the patent covering AstraZeneca PLC's cholesterol-reducing drug Crestor®, rejecting arguments by generics makers that it is invalid and unenforceable.
- Representation of United Technologies Corp. in the Eastern District of Virginia, which granted summary judgment for UTC, ruling that it did not infringe Rolls-Royce's patent related to jet engine fans. All claims and counterclaims were dismissed with prejudice, terminating Rolls-Royce's quest for an injunction and almost $4 billion in damages plus increased damages for alleged willful infringement.
- Represents Toyota Motor Corporation in numerous prosecution matters involving filing and prosecution of US utility and design patent applications as well as transactional work ranging from patent licensing agreements, complex Cooperative Research and Development Agreements, to research and development projects with US government agencies.
- Prepares and prosecutes hundreds of patent applications in the US and globally for Caterpillar, and assists with other patent issues involving issues of validity, infringement, government contracts, and licensing. Finnegan also plays a significant role protecting Caterpillar's trademarks around the world.

### Clients:

Abbott Labs, BlackBerry, Caterpillar, Eli Lilly and Company, FedEx, HTC Corp., LG Electronics, Mitsubishi Heavy Industries, Otsuka Pharmaceuticals, Philips Electronics, Pronova BioPharma Norge AS, and Rambus.

## FINNEGAN

# FOSTER, MURPHY, ALTMAN & NICKEL, PC

**www.**fostermurphy.com **tel:** 202 822 4100 **fax:** 202 822 4199

Number of partners: 4
Number of lawyers: 6

## Firm Overview:

The firm was established in May 2011, when David Foster, Barbara Murphy, James Altman and David Nickel left the law firm of Miller & Chevalier Chartered to form the Washington, DC law firm of Foster, Murphy, Altman & Nickel, PC. Relying on 30 years of prior experience, the new firm concentrates its practice on Section 337 investigations before the US International Trade Commission (ITC), as well as judicial review and Customs' enforcement of orders issued thereunder. Such litigation involves primarily patent, trademark, and copyright infringement and misappropriation of trade secrets. The firm represents both domestic and foreign companies as complainants and respondents in these fast-paced, often bet-the-company investigations. In their new smaller, boutique firm setting, Foster Murphy lawyers are able to continue to provide the high-level of experience, judgment and litigation skills for which they are known in Section 337 matters. This boutique Section 337 firm is at the forefront of those who practice at the ITC's intersection of intellectual property and international trade law. The group's lawyers have deep experience in a variety of related bodies of law and litigation forums, as well as that gained from serving in senior government positions. The firm continues to partner with other law firms (typically larger IP or litigation firms) on Section 337 matters, creating litigation teams that are both successful and efficient for clients.

## Main Areas of Practice:

### Section 337 Investigations:

The Foster Murphy firm has one of the strongest and most experienced Section 337 practices in the country, having litigated approximately 160 Section 337 cases in private practice, which represents close to 20 percent of the cases filed since 1974, when Section 337 took its current form. The firm is considered a go-to firm for Section 337 experience and guidance. Because of the breadth and depth of the lawyers' experience, the firm is able to provide clients and co-counsel with real value in the form of strategic advice and counseling on their matters.

For 30 years, the firm's attorneys have been engaged in all aspects of Section 337 investigations, including preparing complaints; engaging in extensive and concentrated discovery; handling expedited motions; working with ITC staff; appearing in hearings before numerous administrative law judges; briefing issues of violation and remedy to the ITC; and engaging in appellate review. The firm has represented domestic and foreign companies pursuing and defending against Section 337 relief in cases involving all types of unfair acts, including patent, trademark, copyright and/or trade dress infringement, as well as claims of false advertising, trade secret misappropriation, and gray market goods. These cases have covered the gamut of industries and technologies, including semiconductor chips, consumer goods, chemicals, industrial machinery, communication devices, and computer software. As most Section 337 investigations involve patent infringement, the firm often collaborates and works effectively as co-counsel with its clients' existing patent counsel in these rapid investigations, providing much needed expertise in assisting these firms and clients through the rigorous demands of a Section 337 investigation.

The firm's lawyers are experienced in IP litigation in the United States and internationally, including litigation in the federal district courts. The benefits of that collective experience and continuous involvement in the field are numerous. In most ITC cases, disputes are high-stakes and time is of the essence. Knowing what strategies will be successful and how to comply with the ITC's unique rules – as opposed to learning it on the job – can make an enormous difference in both the outcome and the cost of litigation.

## PRACTICE AREAS

ITC Section 337 Litigation
Intellectual Property Litigation
International Trade Regulation
US Customs Border Enforcement

## OFFICES

DISTRICT OF COLUMBIA
**WASHINGTON:** 1899 L St, NW, Suite 1150, DC 20036
Tel: 202 822 4100 Fax: 202 822 4199
Email: bmurphy@fostermurphy.com

### US Customs Border Enforcement:

In addition to its Section 337 practice before the ITC, the firm has a leading practice involving enforcement issues related to Section 337 cases before US Customs and Border Protection. US Customs and Border Protection is charged with assisting in the border enforcement of US intellectual property rights in a variety of contexts, including enforcement of Section 337 orders, trademark and copyright recordation, counterfeiting, and gray market imports. In order to maximize the potential benefit from these resources, the firm works with US IPR owners to ensure the most effective implementation of Customs enforcement capabilities. The firm's lawyers also interact with Customs to avoid or mitigate the adverse effects of such enforcement activities.

**Contact:** Barbara A Murphy
**Tel:** 202 822 4102
**Email:** bmurphy@fostermurphy.com

# GILBERT LLP

www.gotofirm.com **tel:** +1 202 772 2200 **fax:** +1 202 772 3333

**Chairman:** Scott D Gilbert
Number of partners: 10
Number of lawyers: 29
Languages: *English*

## Firm Overview:

Gilbert LLP is a Washington, DC-based law firm focused on insurance recovery and litigation and on strategic consulting. Whether it's strategic advice, negotiation or litigation, the firm approaches all matters with the goal of creating a tailored, cost-effective solution to the problems at hand. The firm brings creativity, strategic thinking and substantial experience to every matter it handles.

## Main Areas of Practice:

### Insurance Recovery & Litigation:

Gilbert LLP lawyers have helped clients recover more than $30 billion in insurance assets. The firm's focus is insurance and it only represents clients seeking coverage, never insurers. The firm provides high-level sophisticated advice to corporate and individual policyholders, crafting cost-effective and creative strategies to pursue fast and robust insurance recoveries for their significant claims. Gilbert LLP lawyers have decades of experience negotiating with, and if necessary, litigating against, insurers. Firm lawyers understand that more disputes are settled in the conference room than in the courtroom, so the firm specializes in settlement. Often, the firm can resolve clients' insurance claims on a favorable basis without litigation. In the event negotiations do not yield the desired results, Gilbert LLP's skilled litigators are prepared to go to court with a strategy that aims to win the maximum settlement in the minimum time. The firm's goal always is to craft the strategy and resolution that meets each client's specific needs.

### Strategic Consulting:

Gilbert LLP realizes that insurance recovery is often part of a broader solution. That is why the firm's lawyers are also liability strategists. They design and implement comprehensive solutions where insurance alone will not achieve a client's business goals. To accomplish this, the firm takes a multidisciplinary approach to solving clients' liability problems. The firm employs a broad range of mechanisms, some of which its lawyers invented, to deal with otherwise intractable liability problems, including alternative dispute resolution techniques such as mediation and arbitration, corporate reorganizations, joint claim-processing facilities, bankruptcy mechanisms including "pre-packaged" plans of reorganization, risk-transfer mechanisms such as excess of risk insurance policies, and assignments of insurance proceeds to tort claimants. Firm Chairman Scott Gilbert was a pioneer in the use of ADR to resolve insurance coverage disputes and was the principal drafter of the Wellington Agreement, an insurance treaty that remains one of the largest insurance settlements in US history. The firm's attorneys can guide clients through the full array of risk management and insurance options to mitigate exposure and protect the client's business.

## Clients:

The firm's clients include business entities, debtors and creditors in bankruptcy matters, trusts and committees formed in such cases, law firms, accounting firms and other professional organizations, non-profits and individuals. Gilbert LLP also has a very robust public service practice representing individuals and public interest organizations.

**PRACTICE AREAS**

Insurance Recovery & Litigation (policyholder)
Strategic Consulting

**OFFICES**

DISTRICT OF COLUMBIA:
**WASHINGTON, DC:** 1100 New York Avenue, NW,
Suite 700, DC 20005
Tel: 202 772 2200 Fax: 202 772 3333
Email: info@gotofirm.com

# GROOM LAW GROUP

www.groom.com **tel:** 202 857 0620 **fax:** 202 659 4503

**Managing Partner:** John F McGuiness
**Firm Chair:** Stephen M Saxon
Number of principals: 32  Number of other lawyers: 31

### Firm Overview:

Groom Law Group, Chartered has been at the forefront of developments in the nation's employee benefits laws since Congress passed ERISA in 1974, drawing many of its attorneys from the federal agencies that regulate employee benefits and forging strong ties with key players in all three branches of government.
With over sixty attorneys dedicated to the employee benefits practice, Groom offers clients unparalleled coverage of issues and disputes arising from ERISA, the Tax Code, securities laws, HIPAA, COBRA, ADEA, and the many other laws that govern employee benefits. Working in nine different practice groups, Groom's attorneys build upon their diverse backgrounds to share a common understanding of employee benefits law that enables them to integrate their efforts across areas of specialization to produce the best results for their clients. The firm prides itself on offering state-of-the-art advice on best practices and emerging trends in employee benefits to a diverse group of clients across the country. The firm recently expanded to serve the employee benefits needs of clients maintaining plans covering workers in Puerto Rico. Groom emphasizes a team approach to clients that assures responsive and efficient service.

### Main Areas of Practice:

#### Executive Compensation:

Executive compensation practices have recently received unprecedented attention from the media, corporate shareholders, Congress, the IRS, and the SEC. The attorneys in Groom's Executive Compensation Group navigate this highly charged climate for clients, helping them to design and implement executive compensation arrangements that satisfy corporate objectives while holding up under the scrutiny of federal regulatory agencies.

#### Fiduciary Responsibility:

From the first regulations and exemptions issued by the Department of Labor to issues seen in today's news, the attorneys in the Fiduciary Responsibility Group have helped to shape every major administrative initiative related to ERISA's fiduciary responsibility provisions. Their long-standing relationships with senior policy-makers at the Department of Labor enable them to provide state-of-the-art advice and effective advocacy for *Fortune* 100 plan sponsors and major players throughout the community of plan service providers.

#### Governmental Plans:

Governmental plans are some of the largest plans in the nation, and while exempt from ERISA and significant parts of the Internal Revenue Code, they are subject to state or local law and special rules under the Internal Revenue Code. The firm represents many state and local plans of all types, including Code 401(a), Code 403(b) and Code 457 plans.

#### Health & Welfare:

The attorneys in Groom's Health and Welfare Group are regularly called upon to advise and provide planning assistance to employers, trustees, administrators, boards of directors and other plan fiduciaries and professionals on a wide variety of ERISA and tax issues. The group is playing a major role helping clients meet the challenges posed by the massive new federal healthcare reform legislation. The firm provides an array of services to managed care organizations, insurance companies, benefit funds, trade associations, benefits consulting firms, and others on a broad range of health and welfare matters.

#### Litigation:

Combining across-the-board expertise in employee benefits law with a recognition that some disputes can and must be won in the courts, Groom takes on cases throughout the country for plan sponsors, financial institutions, managed care organizations, service providers, trade associations, and other clients who are seeking practical, tough-minded representation in employee benefits disputes.

#### Multiemployer/Taft-Hartley Plans:

Groom's attorneys have been working on multiemployer plan issues since before the Multiemployer Pension Plan Amendments Act of 1980 was passed. Since then, the firm has continued to focus on multiemployer plan issues, representing both multiemployer pension and welfare plans, as well as contributing employers, with respect to issues such as plan funding, fiduciary compliance, mass withdrawal, insolvency, and compliance with 'endangered' and 'critical' status requirements.

#### Plan Design & Taxation:

Groom's Plan Design and Taxation Group has earned a national reputation for its expertise in the creation and operation of all forms of employee benefit programs. Drawing on decades of experience, the attorneys on this team work with *Fortune* 100 companies, associations, government entities, churches, and financial institutions to design and maintain plans that adhere to regulatory standards and evolve to meet the needs of their sponsors.

#### Plan Funding & Restructuring:

Drawing on their unparalleled experience and longstanding relationships with key federal agencies, Groom's Plan Funding and Restructuring Group negotiates and litigates benefits issues and provides creative, forward-looking advice on pension and health liabilities to clients involved in corporate transactions, bankruptcies, and restructurings outside bankruptcy.

#### Policy & Legislation:

Drawing on their substantive expertise and hands-on experience – one member of the firm's group was the tax and pension counsel to the House Ways and Means Committee and another was the chief legislative liaison for the Department of Labor – Groom works on benefits-related policies and legislation with members of Congress and the Executive Branch on behalf of trade associations, plan sponsors, financial institutions, healthcare organizations, and other clients from the benefits community.

#### Clients:

Representative Clients: American Benefits Council, Blue Cross Blue Shield Association, California State Teachers Retirement System, Eli Lilly, Hess Corporation, Ohio Public Employees Retirement System, Pfizer, Prudential Financial, Toshiba America.

# HOLLINGSWORTH LLP

www.hollingsworthllp.com  **tel:** 202 898 5800  **fax:** 202 682 1639

**Managing Partner:** Donald W Fowler
Number of partners: 29  Number of other lawyers: 34

### Firm Overview:

As the *National Law Journal* said in naming Hollingsworth LLP to its Midsize Hot List, "Big cases don't necessarily demand big law firms". The firm specializes in complex civil litigation and associated regulatory counseling, providing its clients with experienced attorneys capable of handling all aspects of large litigation challenges, while effectively managing litigation spend in ways big firms cannot match. Hollingsworth LLP works with clients to achieve not only jury and bench trial verdicts, but also pretrial summary judgments, post-trial appellate decisions, third-party allocations of responsibility, and negotiated settlements. The firm's expertise extends beyond traditional litigation and counseling into innovative alternative dispute resolution in domestic and international forums. Representing some of the largest and most respected companies in a number of major industries, the firm's success is reflected in the favorable results obtained for its clients over the past thirty years.

### Main Areas of Practice:

**Complex Litigation:**
Clients turn to Hollingsworth LLP as a 'go to' firm for high-stakes litigation. The firm's attorneys have successfully tried cases in courts across the country and handled appellate proceedings before many federal and state appellate courts, including before the US Supreme Court. The firm's reported federal and state victories stand as testament to the scope of the firm's practice and record of success.

**Pharmaceuticals & Medical Devices:**
The firm represents pharmaceutical and medical device manufacturers, often appearing as national trial or coordinating counsel. The firm handles these matters through all phases of the litigation, from the earliest pre-trial proceedings through *Daubert* hearings, trials, and appeals. Clients rely on the firm's expertise in registration, clinical research, and labeling issues to advance their interests in regulatory matters involving the Food & Drug Administration and related litigation.

**Toxic Torts & Products Liability:**
The firm defends class actions, mass torts, and single-site suits arising from alleged chemical exposures and defective products, defends federal agency proceedings, and provides associated regulatory representation and counseling.

**Environmental:**
Hollingsworth LLP's environmental practice encompasses the full spectrum of business, regulatory, and litigation issues regularly confronted by companies. The firm advises clients on the impact of state and federal regulatory requirements, evaluates, designs, and audits compliance programs, and assists clients in managing environmental aspects of business transactions. The firm also defends against federal and state enforcement actions, as well as private actions involving environmental law violations.

**Insurance:**
The firm has pursued insurance recoveries for environmental liabilities, product liabilities, construction, and other claims involving amounts upwards of a billion dollars on behalf of its corporate client base.

**Government Investigations:**
The firm represents US and foreign companies in complex federal, state, and congressional investigations, corporate internal investigations and compliance reviews, and collateral civil litigation and federal and state regulatory proceedings. This aspect of the firm's practice includes civil and criminal investigations and litigation under federal and state fraud regulatory statutes.

**Financial Institutions:**
Hollingsworth LLP's attorneys represent officers, directors, and shareholders of financial institutions in connection with litigation and investigations. The firm works closely with financial institutions and their regulatory counsel to defend the conduct of the institutions and their officials and to pursue damages claims as warranted.

**Federal Claims & Government Contracts:**
The firm prosecutes federal contract and Fifth Amendment taking and due process cases, and related regulatory litigation against federal, state, and local governments. The firm handles all aspects of government procurement, from bid preparation, contract negotiation, and bid protests to claim preparation, negotiation, and dispute resolution arising from government procurement.

### Recent Work:

- Ending longstanding property damage and personal injury claims brought by thousands of Ecuadorian citizens against a US corporation under the Alien Tort Statute with a *Daubert* ruling that excluded the plaintiffs' expert testimony, see Arias v. DynCorp, _F. Supp. 2d_, 2013 WL 821168 (DDC 2013), a victory that earned two Hollingsworth LLP partners recognition as AmLaw "Litigators of the Week." Wolfe, J. (2013, March 7). Litigators of the Week: Eric Lasker and Rosemary Stewart of Hollingsworth LLP. The American Lawyer. Retrieved March 8, 2013 from http://americanlawyer.com

- Securing a defense verdict in the first bellwether trial conducted in statewide consolidated products liability litigation, see Bessemer v. Novartis Pharm. Corp., No. MID-L-1835-08-MT (N.J. Super. Ct. 2010) – followed by two consecutive defense verdicts in related cases remanded from federal multidistrict litigation proceedings, see Hogan v. Novartis Pharm. Corp., No. 1:06-CV-260 (E.D.N.Y. 2011), and see Brodie v. Novartis Pharm. Corp., 4:10-CV-138-HEA (E.D. Mo. 2012)

- Obtaining summary judgment on failure-to-warn claims absent proof that the allegedly inadequate warning caused the plaintiff's injuries. See Eberhart v. Novartis Pharm. Corp., No. 1:08-CV-2542-WSD, 2011 WL 5289372 (N.D. Ga. Oct. 31, 2011)

- Successfully defending summary judgment on appeal to the Second Circuit in a wrongful death case seeking $30 million in damages that questioned the enforceability of a choice-of-law provision in an employment agreement. See McPhee v. General Elec. Int'l, 426 Fed. App'x 33 (2d Cir. 2011)

- Convincing the Mississippi Supreme Court to reaffirm its adherence to *Daubert*'s gatekeeping requirements. See Sherwin-Williams Co. v. Gaines, 75 So.3d 41 (Miss. 2011)

- Being named for the second time in three years to the *National Law Journal*'s Midsize Hot List, an annual list that recognizes the accomplishments of twenty midsize firms in the US

**OFFICES**

DISTRICT OF COLUMBIA

**WASHINGTON DC:** 1350 I Street, NW, DC 20005
Tel: 202 898 5800  Fax: 202 682 1639
Email: info@hollingsworthllp.com

THE NATIONAL
LAW JOURNAL
2012 MIDSIZE
HOT LIST

thirtyyears
Hollingsworth LLP
Litigation Matters.®

# IFRAH PLLC

**www.**ifrahlaw.com    **tel:** 202 524 4140    **Fax:** 202 524 4141

**Chairman:** A Jeff Ifrah
**Managing Partner:** A Jeff Ifrah
Number of partners: 4
Number of lawyers: 12
Languages: *English, Farsi, French, Hebrew*

### Firm Overview:

Ifrah Law was formed in October of 2009 for the express purpose of bringing the sophistication of a large firm and the personalized service of a smaller firm to clients who have critical litigation matters.

Ifrah Law's attorneys include a former special assistant US attorney, a former attorney in the Counterterrorism Section of the National Security Division of the US Department of Justice and in the Manhattan District Attorney's Office, a former FTC attorney, and a number of highly trained veterans from some of the nation's largest and most respected law firms. Founder Jeff Ifrah is a frequent speaker, author and commentator on white-collar crime issues and the co-author of the book Federal Sentencing for Business Crimes, the only complete treatise on the topic. As a result, the firm has established relationships and credibility with federal prosecutors and investigators in such agencies as the Justice Department, the FTC, SEC and DOD, among others. The firm also publishes two blogs, www.crimeinthesuites.com and www.ftcbeat.com.

### Main Areas of Practice:

**Financial Services:**

- Representation of a former dotcom executive who was indicted for securities fraud. Ifrah Law was responsible for a 70 percent reduction in the client's sentence
- Representation of a Russian corporation that was charged with violating the Commodity Futures Trading Commission (CFTC) Act. The case was settled for a small fine and the company's website, which the government sought to shut down, remains operable outside of the US.

**Government Contracting:**

- Representation of a government contractor faced with potential suspension and debarment from a federal agency. Ifrah Law obtained a decision of no debarment period for its client.
- Representation of a government contractor who was excluded from a procurement competition. Ifrah Law filed a bid protest and held negotiations with the Department of Justice, which resulted in the client being permitted to rejoin the bidding and to submit a revised bid.

**Healthcare:**

- Negotiated a favourable plea agreement for the owner of a pharmaceutical supply company who was indicted for conspiracy to defraud the US government.
- Representation of a global healthcare leader in a False Claims Act qui tam suit that Ifrah Law got dismissed within a year of its client being served the suit.

**iGaming:**

- Representation of a leading online poker company in a case claiming breach of contract, breach of fiduciary duty, breach of the covenant of good faith and fair dealing, unjust enrichment and fraud. Ifrah Law won a dismissal of the trial and won three more moves to dismiss orders in subsequent actions.
- Representation of an online poker company and individual poker professionals in the first class action suit brought by former US poker players. In an argument in the US District Court for the Southern District of New York, Ifrah Law won a dismissal of all claims against the poker pro defendants, as well as all Racketeer Influenced and Corrupt Organizations Act (RICO) claims against the corporate defendants.

**Internet Advertising & Marketing:**

- Representation of an e-commerce merchant in a case against an interactive advertising agency. Ifrah Law won the case against the client in addition to securing judgement for $250,000 in legal fees prior to the start of the case.
- Representation of a payment processing company from whom federal authorities in Maryland seized over $2 million in alleged illegal proceeds in connection with illegal sports betting. Ifrah Law obtained the first settlement on record where the Department of Justice agreed to refund over $1 million of proceeds that were initially represented to the Court as illegal proceeds.

## PRACTICE AREAS

Financial Services
Government Contracting
Healthcare
iGaming
Internet Advertising & Marketing
Data Privacy
Online Piracy

## OFFICES

**DISTRICT OF COLUMBIA**
**WASHINGTON:** 1717 Pennsylvania Ave, N.W., Suite 650, DC 20006
Tel: 202 524 4140   Fax: 202 524 4141
Email: info@ifrahlaw.com

**MARYLAND**
**BALTIMORE:** 111 S. Calvert Street, Suite 2700, MD 21202
Tel: 443 570 6622

**VIRGINIA**
**NORTHERN VIRGINIA:** 1818 Library Street, Suite 500, Reston, VA 20190
Tel: 703 801 8472

**Data Privacy:**

- Representation of businesses and individuals with counsel on information storage and rights of retrieval, including criminal background websites and children's privacy protections online through COPPA.
- Representation of a Middle Eastern leader in a case in which private information from a hacker computer was posted by a blogger. This information posed a national security risk to the politician's country and the US. Ifrah Law successfully utilized takedown notices to get the blogger's Internet Service Providers, as well as Facebook, to remove the information.

**Online Piracy:**

- Ifrah Law has handled legal disputes for and against Internet marketers, Internet service providers, companies operating websites, 'app' developers and Internet advertisers. Clients include many of the largest interactive gaming companies and industry associations in the world.
- Representation of a client whose computer was hacked, using the Digital Millennium Copyright Act (DMCA) to have content removed on the basis of copyright infringement.

# IVINS, PHILLIPS & BARKER

www.ipbtax.com **tel:** 202 393 7600 **Fax:** 202 393 7601

**Managing Partner:** Eric R Fox
Number of partners: 23  Number of other lawyers: 10

## Firm Overview:

Founded in 1936 by two of the original members of the United States Board of Tax Appeals (now the Tax Court), Ivins, Phillips & Barker operates as a tax and employee benefits specialty law firm for domestic corporations, US and foreign-based multinationals, and individuals with significant wealth. The firm represents approximately one-third of the *Fortune* 100 on federal tax (including employee benefits) matters. Because tax work is the firm's sole occupation, the firm's relationships with clients depend completely on continuing satisfaction with the firm's tax work.

## Main Areas of Practice:

### Corporate Tax Planning & Advice:

Ivins, Phillips & Barker handles all types of corporate transactions, including internal restructurings, acquisitions, dispositions, spinoffs and joint ventures, for both public and closely held companies. The firm has extensive experience in obtaining advance rulings from the IRS and consulting with IRS and Treasury officials regarding tax policy matters. The firm also advises corporate clients on issues that arise daily in corporate tax departments. These matters may require only a few hours of work or even only one telephone call.

### Employee Benefits:

Few firms of any size can match the resources Ivins, Phillips & Barker has dedicated to ERISA, executive compensation and other employee benefits. Nine partners devote their full time to this area, with a practice covering the spectrum of employee benefits matters, including: design, implementation and compliance work for tax-qualified pension, savings and welfare benefit plans (including 401(k) and cash balance plans, VEBAs, and cafeteria plans), non-qualified deferred compensation plans, golden parachutes, stock options programs, rabbi trusts, and executive welfare benefit programs. The firm's work also involves negotiating and drafting employee benefits aspects of acquisitions, spinoffs and other divestitures, as well as practice before the IRS, Department of Labor and PBGC and ERISA litigation. The firm also has considerable experience managing the special problems facing multinationals that must deal with conflicting foreign regulatory schemes.

### Income Tax Accounting:

Unlike most law firms, Ivins, Phillips & Barker has developed nationally-recognized expertise in tax accounting issues, including: issues pertaining to inventories (particularly dollar-value LIFO and the uniform capitalization method), income and expense accruals, accounting for long-term contracts (government and non-government), accounting for R&D costs, capitalization versus deduction issues, timing of deductions for employee benefit programs, and financial transactions. The firm's work ranges from planning and consulting on design and establishment of cost accounting systems as they affect tax compliance, to handling accounting method changes, to controversies with the IRS.

### International Tax:

Ivins, Phillips & Barker is involved in all issues concerning United States taxation of international business, including issues pertaining to foreign tax credits, subpart F income, treaties, tax-favorable foreign corporate structures and financing techniques, foreign acquisitions and restructurings, FSCs, sourcing, section 936 corporations, and transfer pricing and other section 482 issues. The firm's lawyers analyze these issues in connection with international business operations, proposed transactions, foreign corporate restructuring activities and controversies with the IRS.

### Trusts, Estates & Closely Held Business Planning:

For seven decades, Ivins, Phillips & Barker has represented individuals and families, often for multiple generations, and designed arrangements to help implement their financial and family goals. In particular, the firm helps clients address complex issues involving closely held businesses and other assets in light of estate, gift and income tax considerations. Each client has unique priorities, family situations, and business and philanthropic interests, and the firm's lawyers work closely with clients to understand fully their thoughts on long-term planning and on the legacies—both financial and non-financial—they seek to provide. The firm makes estate planning recommendations tailored to achieve each client's goals, prepares the documents necessary to implement such plans and reviews the plans periodically for appropriate revisions.

### Tax Controversies, Litigation & Arbitration:

Ivins, Phillips & Barker regularly represents taxpayers undergoing IRS audits and the IRS Appeals process and litigates tax cases at both the trial and appellate levels.

As an example, in 2001, the firm successfully represented United Dominion Industries in the United States Supreme Court in a rare case involving corporate consolidated returns. The firm has been successful with the IRS and in court in the overwhelming majority of these cases, often settling such cases favorably without a trial. The firm's lawyers also serve as expert witnesses and as arbitrators in commercial disputes involving tax issues (including disputes involving tax sharing agreements).

## Clients:

Acxiom, Alex Brown Realty, Allegheny Technologies, Inc., Amazon, American International Group (AIG), Alex Brown Realty, Bayer Corporation, BKD, LLP, The Boeing Company, Boston Properties, Capital Group Companies, Cheesecake Factory, Chrysler Group LLC, Cone Mills Corporation, Crowe, Horwath LLP, Delphi Corporation, Dole Food Company, Inc., Dominion Resources, Inc., Dresser, Inc., Eaton Corporation, Federal Express, Fidelity Investments, First American Corporation, Fisher Scientific International, Ford Motor Company, General Electric Company, General Motors Corporation, Grant Thornton, H. J. Heinz Company, Henkel of America, Inc., Hitachi High Technologies America, Inc., Husqvarna, IBM Corporation, Intermet Corporation, International Cemetery, Cremation & Funeral Association, Jacobs Engineering Group, Inc., Lockheed Martin Corporation, Milliken & Company, National Fuel Gas Company, Nissan North America, Inc., Owens & Minor, Rent for Rain, RSM McGladrey, SABIC Innovative Plastics, Saudi Aramco, Sodexo, Textron, Inc., Unisys Corporation, United Technologies Corporation, Valero Energy Corporation, Vulcan Materials Company, William M. Mercer, Incorporated, Wilmington Trust Company, Xerox Corporation.

**OFFICES**

CALIFORNIA

**LOS ANGELES:** 1875 Century Park East, Suite 600, CA 90067
Tel: 310 551 6633   Fax: 310 551 1188

DISTRICT OF COLUMBIA

**WASHINTON, DC:** 1700 Pennsylvania Avenue, NW, Suite 600, DC 20006
Tel: 202 393 7600   Fax: 202 393 7601

# JONES DAY

www.jonesday.com

**Managing Partner:** Steven J Brogan
Number of partners: 858  Number of total lawyers: 2452

## Firm Overview:

Jones Day has evolved and grown throughout its history, staying in step with rapidly changing business and legal environments. Today, it is one of the largest firms in the US, and clients benefit from the strength of its multidisciplinary teams and the seamless transfer of resources across multiple jurisdictions and borders.

## Main Areas of Practice:

**Hertz acquires Dollar Thrifty Automotive Group:**
Advised Hertz on the antitrust aspects of its US$2.3 billion acquisition of Dollar Thrifty Automotive Group, including the negotiation of a consent order required to obtain FTC approval.
**Client:** Hertz Global Holdings, Inc.
**Contacts:** Joe Sims, Michael H Knight, Ryan C Thomas
**Email:** jsims@jonesday.com; mhknight@jonesday.com; rcthomas@jonesday.com

**Myriad Genetics maintains victory in reconsidered Federal Circuit appeal concerning patent eligibility for isolated DNA molecules:**
The Federal Circuit, for a second time, determined that Myriad's patent claims directed to isolated DNA molecules are patent-eligible, and "are obtained in the laboratory and are man-made, the product of human ingenuity."
**Client:** Myriad Genetics, Inc.
**Contacts:** Brian M Poissant, Gregory A Castanias, Laura A Coruzzi PhD
**Email:** bmpoissant@jonesday.com; gcastanias@jonesday.com; lacoruzzi@jonesday.com

**SAP acquires Ariba for $4.3 billion:**
Advised SAP in its US$4.3 billion acquisition of Ariba, Inc., a leading cloud-based collaborative business commerce network. The transaction adds business-to-business collaboration in the cloud to SAP's existing solutions.
**Client:** SAP AG
**Contacts:** Daniel R Mitz, Jonn R Beeson
**Email:** drmitz@jonesday.com; jbeeson@jonesday.com

**Xcel Energy obtains Ninth Circuit affirmation of dismissal of global warming claims:**
Defended Xcel Energy before the U.S. Court of Appeals for the Ninth Circuit and lower courts against federal common law public nuisance litigation claiming that global warming is destroying the Native Village of Kivalina, Alaska.
**Client:** Xcel Energy Inc.
**Contacts:** Thomas E Fennell, Michael L Rice, Kevin P Holewinski
**Email:** tefennell@jonesday.com; mlrice@jonesday.com; kpholewinski@jonesday.com

**Goodrich merges with United Technologies:**
Advised Goodrich in its US$18.4 billion merger with United Technologies Corporation, considered one of ten mega deals (more than US$10 billion) of 2011.
**Client:** Goodrich Corporation
**Contact:** Lyle G Ganske, James P Dougherty
**Email:** lganske@jonesday.com; jpdougherty@jonesday.com

**R.J. Reynolds successfully challenges constitutionality of graphic cigarette warning labels:**
Secured a ruling in the U.S. Court of Appeals for the D.C. Circuit affirming a District Court finding that the U.S. Food and Drug Administration's proposed graphic warning labels on cigarette packs are unconstitutional. The court agreed with Reynolds' arguments that the FDA requirement was compelled speech that violates the companies' First Amendment rights.
**Client:** R.J. Reynolds Tobacco Company
**Contact:** Noel J Francisco
**Email:** njfrancisco@jonesday.com

**GM pension plan to transfer US$29 billion of assets in ground-breaking de-risking transaction:**
Continuing a tradition of advising GM on ground-breaking employee benefits matters, Jones Day advised the company in a transaction that will result at closing in the largest single-employer plan termination and pension risk transfer in US history.
**Client:** General Motors Company
**Contact:** Evan Miller, Jere R Thomson, Peter E Izanec
**Email:** emiller@jonesday.com; jrthomson@jonesday.com; peizanec@jonesday.com

**National Federation of Independent Business challenges constitutionality of individual health-insurance mandate:**
Represented NFIB in closely followed constitutional litigation challenging the Patient Protection and Affordable Care Act, arguing that Congress exceeded its enumerated powers in enacting the Act's so-called "individual mandate" requiring individuals to purchase health insurance or pay a monetary penalty.
**Client:** National Federation of Independent Business
**Contacts:** Michael A Carvin
**Email:** macarvin@jonesday.com

## PRACTICE AREAS

Antitrust & Competition Law
Banking & Finance
Business Restructuring & Reorganization
Business & Tort Litigation (USA)
Business Restructuring & Reorganization
Capital Markets
Corporate Criminal Investigations
Employee Benefits & Executive Compensation
Energy
Environmental, Health & Safety
Financial Institutions Litigation & Regulation
Global Disputes
Government Regulation
Healthcare
Insurance Recovery
Intellectual Property
Issues & Appeals
Labor & Employment
Mergers & Acquisitions
Private Equity
Projects & Infrastructure
Real Estate
Securities Litigation & SEC Enforcement
Tax

## OFFICES

Irvine, CA; Los Angeles, CA; San Diego, CA; San Francisco, CA; Silicon Valley, CA; Washington, DC; Miami, FL; Atlanta, GA; Chicago, IL; Boston, MA; New York, NY; Cleveland, OH; Columbus, OH; Pittsburgh, PA; Dallas, TX; Houston, TX

**Abbott Laboratories wins FLSA overtime exemption case concerning pharmaceutical sales representatives:**
The U.S. Court of Appeals for the Seventh Circuit decided a significant case under the Fair Labor Standards Act, ruling in favor of Abbott in a collective action lawsuit. The Court held that the pharmaceutical sales representatives before it fell within the administrative exemption to the FLSA's overtime requirements as a matter of law, reversing a contrary holding of the district court and a US$3.5 million judgment.
**Client:** Abbott Laboratories
**Contact:** Daniel E Reidy, Michael J Gray, Brent D Knight
**Email:** dereidy@jonesday.com; mjgray@jonesday.com; bdknight@jonesday.com

**Procter & Gamble divests Pringles snacks business to Kellogg:**
Advised P&G in the divestiture of its Pringles snacks business to The Kellogg Company in a US$2.7 billion all-cash transaction.
**Client:** The Procter & Gamble Company
**Contact:** Robert A Profusek, Randi C Lesnick
**Email:** raprofusek@jonesday.com; rclesnick@jonesday.com

# KELLER AND HECKMAN LLP

**www.khlaw.com** **tel:** 202 434 4100 **fax:** 202 434 4646

**Chairman:** John B Dubeck, Partner and Chair, Management Committee
Number of partners: 40  Number of lawyers: 76

## Firm Overview:

Keller and Heckman, founded in 1962, has a broad practice in the areas of regulatory law, litigation and business transactions, serving both domestic and international clients. The firm is a pioneer in the use of interdisciplinary approaches to problem-solving. Since 1971, the firm has had an in-house scientific staff that works closely with the attorneys on matters of technical complexity. Many of Keller and Heckman's attorneys have government experience and expertise in multiple areas of the law.

## Main Areas of Practice:

### FOOD & DRUG:

Keller and Heckman has a comprehensive and extensive food and drug practice. The firm promotes, protects and defends products made by the spectrum of industries regulated by the U.S. Food and Drug Administration (FDA), and similar authorities throughout the world.
**Email:** fooddrug@khlaw.com

### Food & Beverages:

The firm represents companies and trade associations in all areas of the food and beverage industry, including pet foods, dietary supplements and infant formula. The firm counsels clients on compliance issues, including GMP requirements and product recalls; assists clients with food additive petitions; and advises clients on labeling.

### Packaging:

Keller and Heckman has a comprehensive practice in the regulation of packaging materials for food, drugs, cosmetics and other FDA-regulated products. The firm counsels clients in all matters relating to these products, including the suitability of packaging components, inspection of manufacturing facilities, and quality assurance programs. The firm's website, www.packaginglaw.com, is the premier source of information on laws and regulations that affect packages and packaging materials.

### Drugs:

The firm counsels clients on all aspect of human and animal drug requirements, including the preparation and submission of NDAs and ANDAs, and labeling requirements. The firm also assists clients with import and export regulations for drugs.

### Medical Devices:

The firm has extensive experience counseling clients on medical device regulations. The firm assists clients with the proper classification of devices, liability issues, preparation and submission of premarket notifications and Device Master Files, product recalls, preparation for FDA inspections, responding to FDA enforcement actions, and quality system requirements.

### Cosmetics:

The firm advises clients on the full range of cosmetic regulatory compliance issues, including labeling and advertising requirements, the classification of a product as a cosmetic or a drug, potential product liability issues, safety testing of ingredients, GMP requirements, and responding to enforcement actions.

### Tobacco:

The firm provides legal and scientific support to tobacco product companies and their suppliers with respect to the statutory and regulatory requirements imposed by the Tobacco Act.

### LITIGATION:

Keller and Heckman's nationally-recognized litigation attorneys aggressively represent its clients' interests before federal and state courts, and regulatory and industry sanctioned bodies. The firm's attorneys also participate as advocates in arbitrations, mediations and other alternative dispute regulation forums. They often work within multi-disciplinary teams consisting of in-house scientific staff and regulatory attorneys with specialized knowledge. **Email:** lit@khlaw.com

### Administrative:

The firm's litigators represent clients from a wide range of industries—including food, pharmaceutical, medical device, consumer products, chemical and pesticide, and telecommunication—before federal regulatory bodies.

### Advertising & Unfair Competition:

The firm has represented clients in competitor, consumer and regulatory agency enforcement actions—at the federal, state and local levels. On the state level, the firm has successfully defended companies in the food, dietary supplement, pharmaceutical and other industries against claims brought under unfair trade practices acts.

### Commercial Litigation:

The firm represents companies—from multi-national corporations to small businesses—in a full range of commercial litigation, including breach of contract, consumer actions, insurance claims and franchise disputes. The firm also represent clients in trade secret disputes, including ones involving computer software and confidentiality clause enforcement.

### Product Liability/ Personal Injury Defense:

The firm represents manufacturers, distributors and trade associations in product liability litigation in both state and federal courts. The firm's clients benefit from an expert technical staff, especially in complex cases, where toxicity and other scientific issues are involved.

### Environmental & Toxic Tort Litigation:

The firm's litigators represent companies and trade associations in a broad range of environmental and toxic tort litigation matters involving issues such as environmental contamination, alleged toxic exposures, enforcement actions by federal and state agencies, and insurance coverage.

### Employment Litigation:

The firm represents employers against charges of employment contract breaches, discrimination, improper termination and workplace injury.

## PRACTICE AREAS

Advertising & Promotion
Antitrust
Biotechnology
Business Counseling & Transactional
Chemical Control
Employment & Labor
Environmental
Environmental Toxic Tort
Food & Drug
Fuels
Government Relations
Green Chemistry
Health & Safety Compliance Audit
Insurance Coverage
Intellectual Property
International Regulatory Affairs
International Trade
Litigation
Pesticides
Privacy, Data Security & Digital Media
Product Safety
REACH
Telecommunications
Tobacco
Trade & Professional Associations
Transportation
Workplace Safety & Health

## OFFICES

DISTRICT OF COLUMBIA
**WASHINGTON:** 1001 G Street NW, Suite 500 West, DC 20001
Tel: 202 434 4100  Fax: 202 434 4646

CALIFORNIA
**SAN FRANCISCO:** One Embarcadero Center, Suite 2110, CA 94111
Tel: 415 948 2800  Fax: 415 948 2808

## INTERNATIONAL OFFICES

The firm also has offices in Belgium (Brussels) and China (Shanghai).

# LEVINE SULLIVAN KOCH & SCHULZ, LLP

www.lskslaw.com

Total number of lawyers: 32

## Firm Overview:

LSKS is a national law firm with a distinct mission – serving the legal needs of media organizations, journalists and other creative professionals in matters involving the content of news and entertainment, advocacy, newsgathering activities, and intellectual property rights.

The firm is privileged to serve as regular litigation counsel to a variety of news organizations, book and magazine publishers, entertainment companies, and digital and interactive media, handling their defamation, privacy, newsgathering, access, copyright, trademark, and related matters around the country. Given its depth of expertise in these fields, LSKS is often sought out for matters that raise particularly challenging legal issues or require an expedited response, such as preliminary injunction proceedings and emergency petitions. As a result, LSKS has been involved in some of the most significant litigated First Amendment, intellectual property and newsgathering disputes of recent years.

## Main Areas of Practice:

### Defamation, Privacy & Publicity:

LSKS regularly defends its clients against allegations of defamation, invasion of privacy, product disparagement, misappropriation of name, likeness or right of publicity, and other causes of action asserting reputational or emotional damage caused by publication, broadcast or content distribution. The firm has been called upon to represent virtually every major media company and has litigated many of the leading cases through trial and appellate decisions.

### Copyright, Trademark & Other IP:

LSKS has handled precedent-setting litigation involving the application of the Digital Millennium Copyright Act and the range of issues surrounding the protection of rights in the digital age. The firm serves a diverse group of individual and corporate IP clients, providing a broad spectrum of IP services – from counseling on copyright and trademark issues, to licensing content and publicity rights, to large-scale litigation of IP cases on behalf of both plaintiffs and defendants.

### Content Regulation & Censorship:

LSKS has a wealth of experience litigating in this challenging area of First Amendment law, including combating both traditional prior restraints and less conventional efforts at censorship. The firm has protected civic organizations' right to demonstrate publicly, vindicated the rights of newspaper publishers to be free from government retaliation, and advocated against government policies that seek to punish the broadcast of purportedly "indecent" content.

### Access & Freedom of Information:

Since its founding, LSKS has been at the forefront of efforts to define and defend constitutional, common law and statutory rights of access to information of importance to the public. The firm regularly secures access to court proceedings and records, represents media organizations in efforts to videotape and photograph judicial proceedings, and obtains government documents under open records laws. It has litigated the boundaries of access law in seeking to secure the public's right to information about Guantanamo detainees and to the proceedings of military commissions created since 9/11.

### Subpoena Matters:

LSKS has been on the forefront of recent battles to protect the reporter's privilege, regularly representing journalists and news organizations who have been subpoenaed to provide documents and testimony. The firm's attorneys have authored the leading treatise and scholarly articles on the subject of a reporter's right to refuse to testify about confidential sources and newsgathering work product, and have testified in support of "shield law" legislation before state and federal lawmaking bodies. LSKS attorneys also have established themselves as leaders in the emerging area of law governing subpoenas seeking the identity of anonymous Internet posters.

### Newsgathering Liability:

LSKS counsels publishers, broadcasters and journalists in connection with their newsgathering activities, and regularly defends against claims arising from efforts to gather the news, whether those efforts entail the use of investigative tools such as hidden cameras, "ride-alongs" with police, or more basic reporting techniques. LSKS has successfully defended some of the most significant cases in this area, including the most recent Supreme Court case, *Bartnicki v. Vopper*.

### Marketing & Corporate Expression:

LSKS advises corporate clients on compliance issues and liability exposure associated with promotional activities, including by providing counseling, negotiation, and litigation services relating to electronic, telephonic, and direct-mail solicitations, sweepstakes and contests, and sponsorship and licensing agreements.

### Risk Management & Counseling:

The firm's attorneys provide advice concerning print, broadcast, cable, film and Internet communications prior to their public dissemination, and advise clients concerning potential liability that could arise from the use of particular investigative techniques. LSKS also has substantial experience in addressing insurance coverage and related risk management issues for media organizations and others involved in disseminating information to the public.

### International Media Law:

LSKS is regularly asked to provide counsel to clients in international contexts. The firm has been involved in some of the most significant Internet jurisdiction cases worldwide, and its lawyers have supervised the litigation of trademark disputes around the world. The firm's attorneys are regularly asked to speak at conferences, write, teach, and provide other services to advance the cause of free expression around the globe.

## OFFICES

**DISTRICT OF COLUMBIA**
**WASHINGTON DC:** 1899 L Street, NW, Suite 200, DC 20036
Tel: 202 508 1100   Fax: 202 861 9888

**NEW YORK**
**NEW YORK:** 321 W 44th Street, Suite 1000, NY 10036
Tel: 212 850 6100   Fax: 212 850 6299

**PENNSYLVANIA**
**PHILADELPHIA:** 1760 Market Street, Suite 1001, PA 19103
Tel: 215 988 9778   Fax: 215 988 9750

**COLORADO**
**DENVER:** 1888 Sherman Street, Suite 370, CO 80203
Tel: 303 376 2400   Fax: 303 376 2401

LSKS **LEVINE SULLIVAN KOCH & SCHULZ, LLP**

# MCKENNA LONG & ALDRIDGE LLP

www.mckennalong.com **tel:** +1 202 496 7500 **fax:** +1 202 496 7756

**Chairman:** Jeffrey K Haidet
**Managing Partner:** T Mark Flanagan, Jr
**California Executive Partner:** Kurt L Kicklighter
Number of lawyers: 575

**Firm Overview:**

McKenna Long & Aldridge LLP (MLA) is an international law firm with more than 575 attorneys and public policy advisors in 13 offices and 11 markets. The firm is uniquely positioned at the intersection of law, business and government, representing clients in the areas of complex litigation, corporate law, energy, environment, finance, government contracts, health care, infrastructure, insurance, intellectual property, private client services, public policy, real estate, and technology.

**Main Areas of Practice:**

**Corporate:**

The Corporate department at MLA offers sophisticated guidance to clients seeking advice on a wide variety of corporate and transactional matters, ranging from the financing and structuring of public and private deals, including related tax consideration and planning, to general corporate counseling and governance.
**Contact:** Wayne N Bradley **Tel:** 404 527 4044
**Email:** wbradley@mckennalong.com

**Environment, Energy & Product Regulation:**

MLA established its environmental practice group more than 50 years ago to counsel chemical companies, oil and gas producers, and defense contractors on the first environmental enforcement actions.
**Contact:** Peter L Gray **Tel:** 202 496 7707
**Email:** pgray@mckennalong.com

**Intellectual Property & Technology:**

The highly-regarded IP attorneys at MLA skillfully apply their legal knowledge, technical savvy and business acumen to help clients address today's unique challenges and strategically create, manage and benefit from their IP assets. Realizing that the protection of intellectual property is now a global matter, MLA has developed a deep knowledge and understanding of domestic and international issues.
**Contact:** Song K Jung **Tel:** 202 496 7413
**Email:** sjung@mckennalong.com

**Government Contracts:**

MLA's Government Contracts team consists of more than 70 attorneys and professional advisors throughout five offices – including former members of key government procuring agencies, the Justice Department, Congress and its committees. The firm's experience covers every aspect of Government Contracts, all government agencies and all key industry sectors – aerospace and defense, electronics, communications, IT, technical services, financial, stability operations, construction, transportation, health care, biodefense, and the life science fields.

**Contact:** Michael R Rizzo **Tel:** 213 243 6193
**Email:** mrizzo@mckennalong.com

**Health Care:**

The cross-practice health care team focuses on protecting existing client interests and anticipating strategic opportunities. Bringing together attorneys and public policy advisors from the health care regulatory, public policy, government contracts, litigation, employee benefits, tax and corporate practices, MLA's health care team uses their diverse experience to deliver comprehensive legal and public policy services to our clients who range from providers and managed care organizations to pharmaceutical manufacturers and technology vendors.
**Contact:** Cindy Gillespie **Tel:** 202 496 7684
**Email:** cdgillespie@mckennalong.com
**Contact:** Summer Martin **Tel:** 404 527 4910
**Email:** shmartin@mckennalong.com

**Litigation:**

MLA litigators handle a wide-range of matters, from sophisticated business and commercial cases, class actions, and multi-district litigation, to professional liability and dispute matters. The Litigation practice includes many attorneys with particular experience in specialty courts such as bankruptcy, the Court of Federal Claims, and the Federal Circuit Court of Appeals, as well as attorneys who have the experience, skills and knowledge to represent clients before the Supreme Court, and federal and state courts across the country.
**Contact:** Tami Lyn Azorsky **Tel:** 202 496 7573
**Email:** tazorsky@mckennalong.com

**Public Policy & Regulatory Affairs:**

MLA is a nationally recognized leader in the complex field of government affairs, as it provides clients with a broad range of legal, governmental and political experience. MLA houses a highly acclaimed Public Policy and Regulatory Affairs practice with more than 60 attorneys and professionals, in seven offices in the US, and Brussels. The bipartisan team is composed of professionals who have held public office and served as

diplomats, as well as those who have previously served as staff and advisors to US presidents, governors, Members of Congress, and mayors.
**Contact:** Gordon D Giffin **Tel:** 404 527 4020
**Email:** ggiffin@mckennalong.com

**Real Estate:**

MLA's Real Estate team offers clients a multi-disciplinary experience that spans the spectrum of real estate development, investment and finance. Well aware that conducting business today requires a critical evaluation of potential risks, responsibilities and rewards, the firm's real estate attorneys focus on practical and innovative solutions to complex problems that arise in real estate transactions.
**Contact:** William F Timmons **Tel:** 404 527 8380
**Email:** btimmons@mckennalong.com

McKenna Long & Aldridge LLP

# MILLER & CHEVALIER CHARTERED

www.millerchevalier.com **tel:** 202 626 5800 **fax:** 202 626 5801

**Chair:** Anthony F Shelley
**Number of lawyers:** 90
**Languages:** *Arabic, Armenian, Azerbaijani, Danish, French, German, Hebrew, Italian, Japanese, Mandarin, Russian, Spanish, and Turkish*

**Firm Overview:**
Founded in 1920, Miller & Chevalier is a Washington, DC law firm with a global perspective and leading practices in tax, employee benefits (including ERISA), international law and business, white collar and internal investigations, complex litigation, and government affairs. Over the past three years, Miller & Chevalier has represented nearly 50% of the Global 25 and more than 40% of the U.S. Fortune 50. A trusted partner to clients throughout the United States and around the world, Miller & Chevalier assists them with their most complex problems and strategic opportunities.

**Main Areas of Practice:**

**Tax:**
Miller & Chevalier was founded as the first federal tax practice in the United States. The firm's administrative and tax controversy practice solves clients' most difficult problems administratively and in the courts. The firm has successfully litigated several of the largest tax cases in U.S. history. In the area of tax planning and consulting, the firm regularly handles all of the U.S. federal tax aspects of complex, multi-billion dollar, multinational transactions. In addition, the firm represents clients in complex tax policy matters. Miller & Chevalier lawyers have a broad range of technical experience and industry background, spanning financial products and structured finance, international tax, tax accounting, corporate tax, partnership tax, transfer pricing, S corporations, criminal tax, tax policy, tax credits and incentives, taxation of natural resources, and withholding tax issues.
**Contact:** Patricia J Sweeney **Tel:** 202 626 5926

**International:**
Miller & Chevalier's international practice offers clients experience with a wide variety of trade and investment policy issues, as well as many aspects of the increasingly interrelated areas of international legal and regulatory compliance. The firm's experience includes the Foreign Corrupt Practices Act (FCPA) and international anti-corruption laws; U.S. anti-boycott regimes; civilian and military export controls; economic sanctions; customs; antidumping, countervailing duty, safeguards, and market disruption proceedings; and trade policy and legislation. The firm has proven experience handling complex and diverse projects throughout the world; and in the past three years alone, Miller & Chevalier lawyers have been on the ground in more than 40 countries.
**Contact:** Kathryn Cameron Atkinson **Tel:** 202 626 5957

**Litigation:**
Litigation comprises two-thirds of the firm's practice, with Miller & Chevalier lawyers combining extensive civil and criminal trial experience, both jury and non-jury, with deep technical capabilities in the substantive areas of tax; white collar crime and internal investigations; ERISA and fiduciary issues; False Claims Act and *qui tam* matters; and government contracts. In addition to the firm's focused litigation experience, it has depth in disputes involving complex commercial transactions. Miller & Chevalier's lawyers have appeared before more than 25 different federal agencies, many state courts, the vast majority of the federal trial courts in the country, every federal court of appeals, and the United States Supreme Court.
**Contact:** Mark Rochon **Tel:** 202 626 5819

**Employee Benefits:**
Miller & Chevalier's employee benefits practice offers a full range of consulting, planning, and controversy services to clients facing the challenges of increased audit and regulatory scrutiny in the benefits area. In addition, the practice features significant ERISA litigation capabilities, as well as policy experience, which is critical in a business environment characterized by tremendous regulatory and legislative change. The employee benefits group advises clients in a variety of areas, including qualified plans; non-qualified deferred compensation; non-ERISA fringe benefits; health and welfare benefits, including health reform implementation; payroll taxes; worker classification; information reporting; and penalty abatement.
**Contact:** C Frederick Oliphant, III **Tel:** 202 626 5834

**Government Affairs:**
Miller & Chevalier focuses on helping domestic and foreign clients design and shape policy and comply with both U.S. and international legislation and regulation. The firm offers more than just critical access to key decision makers; it provides substantive representation to clients on tax, employee benefits, healthcare, international trade, and energy policy issues. The firm also provides the knowledge, background in government, and substantive experience clients need to frame their issues credibly and successfully.
**Contact:** Marc J Gerson **Tel:** 202 626 1475

Miller & Chevalier Chartered

# OLSSON FRANK WEEDA TERMAN MATZ PC

**www.ofwlaw.com** **blog:** www.agfdablog.com **tel:** 202 789 1212 **fax:** 202 234 3550

**Chairman:** Richard L Frank
**Managing Principal:** Dennis R Johnson
Number of lawyers: 28
Number of senior policy advisors: 10

## Firm Overview:

Since its founding in 1979 as a two lawyer boutique specializing in representing clients regulated by the US Department of Agriculture (USDA) and the US Food and Drug Administration (FDA), OFW Law has grown to become one of the nation's premiere law firms in the USDA, FDA, and related areas with 38 lawyers and Senior Policy Advisors. The firm represents its clients before federal agencies, the courts, and Congress.

## Main Areas of Practice:

### Food & Beverage:

The firm represents clients manufacturing, marketing, and distributing the entire range of FDA-regulated food products, including conventional foods, dietary supplements, medical foods, and infant formula, as well as cosmetics. The firm counsels clients regarding compliance with all applicable federal requirements, guidance documents, and informal policies, including those governing food safety; product claims; labeling and advertising; product formulation, manufacturing, and packaging; registration and recordkeeping; and compliance matters such as inspections and recalls. The firm has been actively involved with every law enacted in the last 30 years that affects the regulation of food, including the FDA Food Safety Modernization Act (2011). The firm also counsels its beverage alcohol clients on the interface between the requirements of the Alcohol and Tobacco Tax and Trade Bureau and the FDA.

### Agriculture:

The firm represents clients before a wide range of USDA agencies, including the Food Safety and Inspection Service; the Farm Service Agency; the Food and Nutrition Service; the Agricultural Marketing Service; the Animal and Plant Health Inspection Service; the Grain Inspection, Packers and Stockyards Administration; the Risk Management Agency; and USDA Rural Development, as well as with the Commodity Futures Trading Commission. The firm's lawyers and Senior Policy Advisors have worked with officials in, and have themselves served at, the highest levels of USDA. The firm's personnel have real world experience as agricultural producers and processors. They provide guidance on food safety matters, regulatory compliance, and crisis management to most of the nation's largest USDA-regulated plants. The firm's professionals work within not only agriculture law, but also the business of innovative 21st century agriculture, including energy development, production, and use.

### Medical Device:

The firm provides comprehensive counseling and advocacy on medical device matters. These services include the development of strategies to bring medical devices to market; compliance with all applicable requirements; classification and reclassification of medical devices; pre- and post-distribution issues related to labeling, advertising, and promotion; responding to FDA enforcement actions; preparing for and managing FDA inspections; conducting product recalls; import and export issues; "due diligence" reviews; assisting with FDA issues related to SEC filings and business transactions; and representation in litigation. The firm's lawyers, including several who worked at FDA, have an in-depth understanding of the regulatory process related to the development, manufacturing, and marketing of medical devices; they also have the ability to interact effectively with FDA personnel.

### Pharmaceuticals, Biologics, & Controlled Substances:

The firm advises its clients on every aspect of the regulatory process related to bringing an innovator or generic drug or biologic product to market, including strategic planning and submission of pre-approval applications. The firm represents clients on the entire range of issues related to marketed products, including labeling, advertising, recordkeeping and reporting obligations, and inspection and compliance issues. The firm advises clients on evaluating and marketing products under over-the-counter drug monographs or other exceptions to premarket approval requirements. The firm's lawyers are especially knowledgeable about the pharmaceutical distribution chain and pharmaceutical company-sponsored communications programs that are targeted at individuals based on their personal information. The firm serves clients involved with the manufacture and distribution of drugs that are designated as controlled substances or listed chemicals by the Drug Enforcement Administration (DEA).

### Public Policy:

The firm's bi-partisan, public policy practice includes a former Secretary of Agriculture and a former Member of Congress who, for eight years, served as the Ranking Member of the US House Committee on Agriculture, as well as senior Senate and House Committee staff, agency heads, and other experienced legislative professionals. The firm's professionals are among the most effective in Washington, working with Congress, federal agencies, and the White House. The firm regularly represents, and advocates on behalf of, food, drug, healthcare information technology, and medical device companies; agricultural coalitions and cooperatives; energy developers and producers; trade and professional associations; and Native American tribes.

### Environmental:

The firm provides a full range of representation in connection with environmental laws administered by the Environmental Protection Agency (EPA), as well as in connection with lawsuits under common law based on allegations of trespass, nuisance, and the like related to modern agricultural practices.

### Animal Feeds & Drugs:

The firm represents clients in matters involving FDA's regulation of animal feed (including pet food), as well as animal drugs intended for use in animal feed. The firm has extensive experience with issues related to the manufacture, distribution, and marketing of animal feed.

### Civil Litigation & Criminal Defense:

The firm represents businesses and individuals in all aspects of FDA, USDA, DEA, and EPA regulatory, civil, and criminal litigation before the courts or the agencies' administrative law judges.

### Clients:

The firm has clients ranging from well known, multinational, publicly traded companies and major national trade associations to start-up enterprises and individuals.

OFW LAW

OLSSON FRANK WEEDA TERMAN MATZ PC

# SLOVER & LOFTUS LLP

www.sloverandloftus.com **tel:** 202 347 7170 **fax:** 202 347 3619

Number of lawyers: 12
Languages: *English, Spanish*

### Firm Overview:

Slover & Loftus LLP is a national law firm founded in 1967 and specializes in commercial transactions, litigation, and arbitration in transportation, energy, and administrative law. Clients include investor-owned, municipal, and cooperative utilities, bulk commodity rail shippers, port authorities, state and local entities, regional railroads, and trade associations. The firm engages in trial and appellate advocacy in federal and state courts, federal and state administrative agencies, and before arbitral tribunals. Slover & Loftus LLP's attorney biographies and additional information on the firm, including its practice areas and representative engagements, is available on the firm's website: www.sloverandloftus.com.

### Main Areas of Practice:

**Rail Transportation:**

Slover & Loftus LLP has effectively represented shippers in major Surface Transportation Board proceedings, including rulemakings, declaratory order proceedings, unreasonable practice proceedings, mergers, railroad construction, railroad abandonments, and rate cases. The firm has also represented clients in commercial disputes with all of the major US railroads in federal courts, state courts, and arbitrations. In addition, Slover & Loftus LLP regularly counsels shippers in the negotiation and administration of rail transportation contracts and railcar purchases and leases, and it has extensive experience in rail service matters, accessorial fee disputes, railroad and customer liability issues, federal preemption, and corporate transactional work involving railroad and rail asset acquisitions.

**Energy & Fuel Supply:**

Slover & Loftus LLP has extensive experience representing clients in the coal supply arena, including the representation of coal purchasers in the negotiation of new contracts, renegotiation of existing contracts, price adjustment audits, and contract buy-outs or buy-downs. The firm has also represented clients in litigation and arbitration over coal supply arrangements.

**Electric & Natural Gas:**

Slover & Loftus LLP represents utilities in electric regulatory matters, including most of the major rulemakings of the past decade and individual utility proceedings involving requirements and proposals for open access tariffs, management of transmission systems by independent system operators, and compliance with FERC reporting and filing requirements for public utilities. The firm has also counseled clients on power purchase and sale agreements. In addition, Slover & Loftus LLP has represented gas clients through FERC's restructuring of the nation's natural gas pipelines, from its early rulemaking stage, through the promulgation of FERC's Order 636, to federal court review by the D.C. Circuit.

**Port Authorities, Public Entities & General Commodities:**

Slover & Loftus LLP has represented major US port authorities in connection with port terminal and dock rail switching services. The firm has also represented and counseled various state and local entities in connection with rail acquisition, environmental mitigation, and service preservation issues. In addition, Slover & Loftus LLP has represented and counseled chemical, iron ore, taconite, wood and building products, steel, agriculture and many other bulk commodity, recyclable materials, and intermodal/exempt traffic shippers in connection with

commercial agreements and common carrier rail transportation arrangements.

**Regional Railroads, Motor Carriers & Water Carriers:**

Slover & Loftus LLP has assisted numerous entrepreneurs and diversified companies in establishing new rail carriers through line purchases and leases from larger railroads. The firm has also structured and negotiated rail line acquisition transactions, trackage rights arrangements, labor protection issues, and financing. In addition, Slover & Loftus LLP has extensive experience in railroad and rail asset acquisition due diligence, in railroad construction, acquisition, and abandonment proceedings before the Surface Transportation Board, and in Federal Railroad Administration safety and Railroad Retirement Board compliance matters. The firm has also represented a variety of barge lines and ocean carriers.

---

## SLOVER & LOFTUS LLP

# VAN NESS FELDMAN LLP

**www.vnf.com** **tel:** 202 298 1800 **fax:** 202 338 2361

**Chairman:** Richard Agnew
Number of partners: 59 Number of lawyers: 97
Languages: *Dutch, English, French, Italian, Spanish*

**Firm Overview:**

Van Ness Feldman has one of the largest and most highly regarded energy regulatory practices in the United States. The firm offers a comprehensive suite of business strategy, project development, transactional, litigation and regulatory law and policy services in the interrelated areas of energy, environment, natural resources, real estate and land use.

**Main Areas of Practice:**

**Energy Project Development & Transactions:**

- Advising the Alaska Energy Authority on energy and environmental regulatory matters involved in the development of the proposed Susitna Watana Hydroelectric project, the largest new dam project undertaken in the United States in more the 40 years
- Representing Transmission Developers Inc. on development of an innovative and market changing high-voltage, direct current (HVDC) transmission project
- Advising Blackstone Energy Partners, L.P. on US federal regulatory issues associated with its $1.5 billion equity investment in Cheniere Energy Partners, L.P. to fund Cheniere's development and construction of the Sabine Pass liquefaction project
- Advising Columbia Gas Transmission, LLC on implementing a 10-15 year modernization program to enhance, repair and rebuild its pipeline system as necessary

**Strategic Advice on US Regulation & Policy:**

- Advocacy work for BrightSource Energy including work on Capitol Hill and the Executive Branch
- Managing the Coal Utilization Research Council which has secured nearly $15 billion in federal incentives
- Monitoring CFTC developments with regard to recent regulatory changes introduced by the Dodd-Frank Act
- Representing McKesson Corporation on public policy issues before both Congress and federal agencies

**Energy Regulation & Policy:**

- Providing strategic and policy guidance, and regulatory counsel to Boardwalk Pipeline Partners, Kinder Morgan, NiSource, EQT Corporation, Dominion Cove Point LNG, and others on pipeline safety and FERC issues
- Providing energy regulatory counsel to Newfoundland and Labrador Hydro and its parent company, Nalcor Energy, related to the financing and development of a new $2.9 billion hydroelectric facility and construction of a 1,100 kilometer transmission line
- Counselling electric utilities and renewable energy

developers on FERC, NERC, and ISO/RTO compliance matters, interconnection and transmission service issues, and transactions

**Clean Air Act Regulation, Climate Change & Emissions Trading:**

- Providing counsel on numerous greenhouse gas emissions trading transactions
- Representing Toyota in the landmark rulemaking that resulted in standards for Model Year 2017-25 vehicles
- Founder and chief counsel of a coalition of companies called the Coalition for Emission Reduction Policy (CERP), which includes electric power companies, financials, and project developers
- Serving as general counsel to the FutureGen Industrial Alliance, a multi-company consortium that is the private side of a public-private partnership to construct a near-zero emissions coal-fired power plant utilizing carbon capture and sequestration

**Land, Water & Natural Resources Permitting, Regulation, Litigation & Policy**

- Working on behalf of Augusta Resources to secure a permit from the US Forest Service and other agencies for the development of a copper mine
- Serving as counsel to electric utilities on electric transmission and power station siting/permitting matters
- Representing Sealaska Corporation in selecting Native lands to enable the preservation of 40,000 acres of forestland and Native sacred and cultural sites while permitting Sealaska to pursue economic development activities
- Advising North Slope Borough on federal policy issues related to oil and gas development and federal management of land and ocean resources
- Successfully representing PacifiCorp in a challenge to FERC orders denying interim conditions at the Klamath hydroelectric project

**Transportation:**

- Assisting major utility trade associations in preventing immediate enforcement of a BNSF Railway tariff pertaining to "coal dust" from loaded coal trains in the Powder River Basin

- Counselling Consumers United for Rail Equity in advocating for modifications to federal railroad laws and policy to address railroad abuse of market power and anticompetitive practices

**Real Estate, Land Use & Zoning:**

- Representing a Fortune 100 company in one of 2011's largest Seattle property acquisitions, including associated land purchase, negotiation and documentation, and related real estate, tax, and environmental due diligence
- Representing a large e-commerce company in the lease and development of new corporate headquarters
- Representing the University of Washington in various land use, real estate transactions and administrative law matters related to the construction of a campus transportation network
- Advising Investco Financial Corp on land use/zoning matters related to the development of an urban "conservation community" and compliance with flood plain regulations for several industrial land holdings

VanNess
Feldman
ATTORNEYS AT LAW

WASHINGTON, DC • SEATTLE, WA

# VENABLE LLP

www.venable.com **tel:** 202 344 4000 **fax:** 202 344 8300

**Chairman:** James L Shea
**Vice Chairman:** Brian L. Schwalb
**Managing Partners:** Lindsay B. Meyer and Robert L. Waldman
Number of partners: 285
Number of other lawyers: 260

**Firm Overview:**
Founded more than a century ago, Venable LLP provides first-in-class legal services as primary counsel to a worldwide clientele of large corporations, mid-sized organizations, and high net worth entrepreneurs and individuals. One of The American Lawyer's top 100 law firms, Venable has a long history of investing the time to understand the needs of its clients and delivering exceptional client service. Venable advises clients on a broad range of business law, regulatory, legislative, complex litigation, and the full range of intellectual property disciplines. The firm has built its practice around leading attorneys who have served in senior corporate, regulatory, prosecutorial, legislative, and Executive Branch positions.

**Main Areas of Practice:**

**Corporate Law & Business Transactions:**
Venable represents and advises individual and corporate clients on banking and financial services matters, bankruptcy and creditors' rights, banking regulatory issues, corporate finance and securities, employee benefits and executive compensation, franchise and distribution, mergers and acquisitions, mezzanine finance, real estate and real estate finance, strategic alliances and joint ventures, taxation, technology transactions and outsourcing, and trusts and estates. Venable represents and advises state and local governments and nonprofit organisations on municipal and tax-exempt finance and tax compliance. Clients include Fortune 100 corporations, entrepreneurs, family businesses, venture capitalists, underwriters, investors of all descriptions, state and local governments, and nonprofit corporations and associations, including healthcare and educational institutions.

**Government & Regulatory Affairs:**
Venable advises clients on a wide array of legislative, government contract, regulatory, civil, and criminal matters before state and federal authorities. The Venable team has extensive experience working with officials in the Executive Branch including agencies such as the Departments of Agriculture, Energy, Defense, Health and Human Services, Homeland Security, Justice, Treasury, and Transportation. Venable attorneys also work closely with the Environmental Protection Agency, Federal Trade Commission, Federal Communications Commission, Postal Regulatory Commission, U.S. Postal Service, Food and Drug Administration, Consumer Product Safety Commission, OSHA, U.S. Patent and Trademark Office, the Federal Reserve Board and other financial services regulatory agencies. Venable provides its clients with a full complement of government affairs and legislative support, including political analysis, issue management, and direct advocacy, as well as preparation of draft legislation, Congressional testimony, and committee report language.

**Litigation:**
Venable's Litigation Practice is broad enough to handle virtually all areas of civil and criminal law, and deep enough to handle bet-the-company litigation. General counsel at Fortune 500 companies look to the firm's trial lawyers on matters ranging from defense of class actions to internal investigations. Venable handles all major areas of litigation including appellate, products liability and toxic torts, commercial disputes, labor and employment, antitrust, construction, intellectual property, class action, and SEC and white-collar defense. Venable's many former federal prosecutors have considerable experience conducting internal investigations and representing clients in administrative and grand jury investigations.

**Technology & Intellectual Property:**
Venable's IP attorneys practice in every aspect of intellectual property law, including patent, trademark, copyright, trade secret, antitrust, and unfair competition. With technical backgrounds extending across a host of industries and technologies, the firm's attorneys advise clients on all issues pertaining to domestic and foreign patents, trademarks, and copyrights. Venable also negotiates and drafts domestic and international licenses, joint venture and technology transfer agreements, and research contracts. Venable's IP litigators represent clients before the International Trade Commission and aggressively enforce and defend intellectual property claims in venues across the country.

# WILEY REIN LLP

www.wileyrein.com

## OFFICES

**DISTRICT OF COLUMBIA**
**WASHINGTON:** 1776 K Street NW, DC 20006
Tel: 202 719 7000  Fax: 202 719 7049

**VIRGINIA**
**MCLEAN:** 7925 Jones Branch Drive, VA 22102
Tel: 703 905 2800  Fax: 703 905 2820

## Firm Overview:

Wiley Rein is a Washington, DC firm with a global reputation. The firm is comprised of more than 275 attorneys who practice where business and governments intersect, providing clients with high-end counsel in regulatory, litigation, public policy and corporate law. Clients–ranging from multinational corporations to trade associations to high-profile individuals–receive coordinated legal counsel on complex and critically-important matters in industries that include communications, defense, financial services, insurance, intellectual property, manufacturing, pharmaceuticals and health care.

## Main Areas of Practice:

### Appellate:

The group, which includes six former Supreme Court clerks, partners with expertise in areas including communications, patent and copyright, environmental, international trade, government contracts and election law to provide expertise in the federal and state appellate systems. The firm's lawyers are continually involved in litigation across the legal spectrum in cases of national importance. For more information: www.wileyrein.com/appellate.

### Communications:

The firm's pre-eminent communications group, one of the nation's largest, represents clients in virtually all aspects of the law governing the media and telecommunications industry, including international and satellite, litigation, media, telephony and wireless services. The practice also handles the full scope of media transactions – from headline-making, billion dollar mergers to the sale of a single radio station – and business disputes and regulatory initiatives. For more information: www.wileyrein.com/communications.

### Bankruptcy & Financial Restructuring:

The group, comprised of business bankruptcy lawyers board-certified by the American Board of Certification, former judicial clerks and bankruptcy trustees, handles bankruptcy transactions and restructuring matters in a wide range of areas, including: construction and real estate; financial restructuring and creditors' rights; litigation/appeals; aviation/airports; media and telecommunications; representation of franchisors in franchisee insolvencies/bankruptcies; government contracts; and healthcare. For more information: www.wileyrein.com/bankruptcy.

### Election Law & Government Ethics:

The firm represents many of the country's largest corporations, trade associations, non-profit organizations, public officials, political parties, individual campaign committees and candidates. Its attorneys regularly advise clients on the laws and rules pertaining to lobbying, political contributions, political action committees, ethics and the use of corporate facilities for political purposes. The group also litigates First Amendment and equal-protection challenges to election laws; voting rights cases; redistricting and ballot access disputes; and defends clients in Federal Election Commission litigation and criminal proceedings. For more information: www.wileyrein.com/electionlaw.

### Environment & Safety:

The firm represents clients in traditional pollution control compliance and litigation and has a unique ability to handle pesticide and chemical competition and regulatory matters. In addition, the group specializes in battery and electronics industry issues, the regulation of the transportation of hazardous products and the laws applicable to environmental advertising and marketing. The attorneys also assist clients on a variety of occupational health and product stewardship issues. For more information: www.wileyrein.com/environment_safety.

### Food & Drug:

Wiley Rein provides comprehensive legal counsel to clients in the pharmaceutical, biotechnology, medical device and food industries. While known for creative solutions, the Food & Drug Law Practice works with clients on day-to-day compliance strategies that advance their business interests and bottom line. Wiley Rein lawyers regularly advise clients on compliance involving the promotion and marketing of drugs, devices, foods and dietary supplements. For more information: www.wileyrein.com/food&drug.

### Government Contracts:

The group handles every aspect of government contracting, including bid protests, disputes, commercial litigation, terminations, mergers and acquisitions and regulatory issues. Clients rely on the firm for advice and representation on local and international procurement related matters and the firm's attorneys regularly appear in every legal forum that addresses government contract issues, including the U.S. Government Accountability Office, U.S. district courts and courts of appeals, the U.S. Court of Federal Claims, U.S. Court of Appeals for the Federal Circuit and the numerous agencies falling under the umbrella of the Board of Contract Appeals. For more information: www.wileyrein.com/govcontracts.

### Insurance:

The group counsels and litigates in state and federal trial and appellate courts across the country on matters concerning general liability coverage, professional liability coverage, property insurance (including first and third party coverage), reinsurance disputes, construction, health insurance, fraud, privacy and regulatory disputes. The group often represents the insurer's interests in resolving complex underlying claims such as securities and derivative litigation, mass tort actions and bankruptcy matters. For more information: www.wileyrein.com/insurance.

### Intellectual Property:

Wiley Rein handles the full range of issues faced by owners and users of patents, copyrights, trademarks and trade secrets. The group – widely known for securing a $612 million settlement for the firm's client in the Blackberry patent dispute – often assists clients with emerging issues, including privacy and information security, digital rights and protections and international IP issues. For more information: www.wileyrein.com/ip.

### International Trade:

The group advises and represents clients in: antidumping and countervailing duty related issues; export-import control, sanctions, and customs matters; actions brought under Section 201 of the Trade Act and Section 337 of the Tariff Act; and proceedings before international tribunals. Additionally, the firm represents foreign and domestic clients in corporate structuring, international financial transactions, Treasury Department sanctions and embargoes, licensing and distributorship arrangements, government export financing, export trade certificates of review and the Foreign Corrupt Practices Act. For more information: www.wileyrein.com/trade.

# WILKINSON BARKER KNAUER, LLP

**www.**wbklaw.com **tel:** 202 783 4141 **fax:** 202 783 5851

**Managing Partner:** Bryan N Tramont
Number of partners: 40 Number of lawyers: 49

## Firm Overview:

Wilkinson Barker Knauer combines the capabilities, standards, and expertise of a large-firm practice with the value, flexibility, and client-oriented personal style that only a smaller firm can deliver. With one of the largest communications practices in the country, the firm maintains a 50+-year tradition of excellence in providing counsel on regulatory, corporate, transactional, and litigation matters. The firm also is at the cutting edge in the rapidly evolving areas of privacy and cybersecurity, as well as in legal issues facing the energy industry. The firm's clients range from the largest communications and technology companies in the world to small start-ups.
The firm attracts top talent from both the government and the private sector. In 2012, the Justice Department's Chief Privacy Officer (Nancy Libin) became a partner in the firm, along with one of the communications bar's leading broadcast lawyers (David Oxenford) and two leading energy lawyers (Jim Albright and Greg Sopkin). Many of the firm's attorneys are former senior government officials and former in-house counsel. The firm emphasizes collaboration, which enables clients to fully access its diverse pool of talent to ensure that their interests are protected and advanced as legal and policy frameworks evolve rapidly.
Wilkinson Barker Knauer is ranked as one of the country's top tier communications law firms by Chambers USA, Legal 500, and U.S. News-Best Lawyers, and was named the "Law Firm of the Year" for 2011-2012 in the communications law category by U.S. News-Best Lawyers.

## Main Areas of Practice:

### Wireless Communications:

- Represented Verizon Wireless in its $3.6 billion acquisition of spectrum licenses from cable companies
- Providing ongoing regulatory compliance counsel to T-Mobile and other wireless carriers
- Advising multiple clients, including CTIA–The Wireless Association® and T-Mobile, in FCC proceedings adopting sweeping reforms to the universal service fund and intercarrier compensation mechanisms
- Represented DISH Network in gaining FCC authority to provide terrestrial wireless service nationwide
- Assisted Alfred Mann Foundation in gaining approval of a new technology to help victims recover from strokes and traumatic brain or spinal cord injury

### Media Content & Distribution:

- Was lead counsel for NBCUniversal and project counsel for Comcast Corporation in Comcast's $30 billion acquisition of control of NBCU; providing continuing counsel to NBCUniversal on a full range of strategic and regulatory matters
- Represented Comcast in successful administrative litigation defending claims of program carriage rule violations, and in an FCC investigation regarding compliance with an Internet-related condition of the order approving its NBCUniversal purchase
- Advising content owners, network providers, equipment manufacturers, and online distributors on the regulatory implications of new mobile and Internet-based video distribution business models

- Providing on-going strategic advice on regulatory matters to major media companies, including Viacom, Cox Enterprises, and Educational Media Foundation
- Representing Bonneville International and Hubbard Broadcasting in multiple transactions, including Hubbard's recent $505 million purchase of 17 radio stations
- Providing on-going regulatory counsel to the National Association of Broadcasters on a broad range of issues

### Wired Communications:

- Providing ongoing strategic FCC counsel to Verizon Communications on key regulatory and policy issues
- Won positive rulings from the FCC and the D.C. Circuit for CenturyLink (formerly Qwest) in litigation to stop "traffic pumping" schemes that have been estimated to cost industry and consumers $330-$440 million per year
- Represented Windstream Communications in obtaining regulatory approvals for its $2.3 billion acquisition of PAETEC

### Energy Regulation:

- Representing Nebraska electric rural distribution cooperatives in federal litigation regarding wholesale electricity rates
- Providing on-going strategic advice to telecom companies on federal/state regulatory issues in the smart grid, home energy management and demand response aggregation marketplaces
- Representing major gas and electric utility companies in state and federal regulatory matters, as well as in contractual matters involving gas transportation,

## PRACTICE AREAS

Administrative and Court Litigation
Broadband & IP-Enabled Services
Communications & Video Accessibility
Corporate & Commercial Transactions
Energy Regulation
FCC Enforcement
FTC & Consumer Protection
International & Satellite Communications
Media Content & Distribution
Network & Consumer Equipment
Privacy, Data Protection & Cybersecurity
Smart Grid
State Regulation
Tower Siting & Infrastructure
Wired Communications
Wireless Communications

## OFFICES

DISTRICT OF COLUMBIA
**WASHINGTON:** 2300 N Street NW, Suite 700, DC 20037
Tel: 202 783 4141 Fax: 202 783 5851
COLORADO
**DENVER:** 1755 Blake Street, Suite 470, CO 80202
Tel: 303 626 2350 Fax 303 626 2351

electric interconnections, distributed generation, and resource planning and rate issues

### Consumer Equipment & Technology:

- Representing Consumer Electronics Association and others in FCC implementation of new law increasing accessibility of consumer devices to individuals with disabilities
- Providing strategic counsel to industry associations and major manufacturers of consumer equipment on key regulatory and policy issues

### Network Infrastructure:

- Representing telecom trade associations on tower siting environmental policy issues in connection with broadband build-out
- Assisting tower companies and wireless operators in historic preservation and environmental compliance
- Providing strategic counsel to industry associations and major manufacturers of network infrastructure on key regulatory and policy issues

### Privacy, Data Protection & Cybersecurity

Providing strategic counsel and advice in the communications, technology, and financial services industries regarding evolving privacy laws and policies.

WILKINSON ) BARKER ) KNAUER ) LLP

# WILMERHALE

www.wilmerhale.com **tel:** 202 663 6000 **fax:** 202 663 6363

**Managing Partners:** Susan W Murley, Robert T Novick
Number of partners: 309
Number of lawyers: 1,258

## Firm Overview:

WilmerHale's 1,000+ lawyers work in five firm-wide practice departments addressing those matters of the most importance to its clients' business needs across the globe. The firm fields interdisciplinary teams of experienced and sophisticated lawyers and utilizes the most current technology to help its clients anticipate obstacles, seize opportunities and get the case successfully resolved, regulatory approval obtained, or the deal done as promptly and cost-effectively as possible.

## Main Areas of Practice:

### Litigation/Controversy:

The firm demonstrated the breadth and depth of its litigation capabilities in 2012 as the firm's busy teams took 14 cases to trial, securing high-profile wins across the United States and internationally. The firm made more than 35 oral arguments in 11 different state and federal appellate courts, clinching many victories. The appellate team filed 40 US Supreme Court briefs throughout the year and argued four cases before the Court in the last completed term, while the firm's international arbitration lawyers managed an international commercial and investment arbitration portfolio of more than 80 active cases with more than $84 billion in dispute.
**Contact:** Howard M Shapiro **Tel:** 202 663 6606
**Email:** howard.shapiro@wilmerhale.com

### Intellectual Property:

The Intellectual Property Department had a busy year as the technical, scientific and IP law hub of the firm. In addition to playing a critical role in some of the most high-profile patent litigation matters to unfold in the United States and internationally—including cases for Facebook, GE and Intel—intellectual property lawyers helped clients navigate the far-reaching changes ushered in by the passage of the America Invents Act. The patent prosecution practice continued to grow, as attorneys filed 13% more patent applications and obtained 34% more patents than in 2011, and represented multiple clients in inter partes review proceedings before the newly constituted Patent Trial and Appeal Board. The firm's US and EU trademark practices handled a high volume of applications, opposition and cancellation proceedings, infringement litigation, and other contested matters.
**Contact:** Donald R Steinberg **Tel:** 617 526 6453
**Email:** don.steinberg@wilmerhale.com

### Regulatory & Government Affairs:

The firm's regulatory and policy expertise was at the core of many of the year's most significant matters. The firm continued its work for BP in the aftermath of the Deepwater Horizon accident, while addressing congressional and other inquiries for HSBC and a number of the largest domestic financial institutions. The firm handled significant antitrust litigation; helped clients in the United States and Europe respond to civil and criminal antitrust probes in the automotive, shipping, financial, rail and natural gas industries, among others; and assisted with merger clearance filings for major acquisitions. Clients like AT&T and Verizon turned to WilmerHale for spectrum auction, network transition and net neutrality work. The firm represented a growing number of clients in matters before the new Consumer Financial Protection Bureau and the Committee on Foreign Investment in the United States. The firm helped cleantech companies navigate the regulatory approval process for alternative energy projects; handled government contract matters across a range of industries and government agencies; and assisted many clients with compliance and enforcement issues related to US economic sanctions, export controls and trade policy.
**Contact:** Randolph D Moss **Tel:** 202 663 6640
**Email:** randolph.moss@wilmerhale.com

### Securities:

The Securities Department continued to work with clients to respond to some of the most sensitive and high-stakes government investigations across a range of industries, including banking and financial services, oil and gas, high technology, and health care and pharmaceuticals. The firm's representations, which are often confidential and invariably involve matters of great sensitivity, involved sophisticated cross-disciplinary teams spanning multiple continents. The firm regularly represent clients in parallel proceedings, involving multiple government agencies, venues, and US and non-US jurisdictions. A number of matters ended in 2012 with no charges filed; at the same time, the firm is also currently litigating against the SEC on behalf of clients in a number of judicial and administrative proceedings. In addition to

WilmerHale's robust investigatory practice, the firm has represented clients in many private suits in courts around the US—and over the past year have prevailed in securities class actions, derivative actions, and merger-related suits. The firm has also successfully concluded a pro bono representation of a Washington DC-based children's charity that lost half of its endowment to a Ponzi scheme. WilmerHale invites you to view a list of Securities highlights.
**Contact:** William R McLucas **Tel:** 202 663 6622
**Email:** william.mclucas@wilmerhale.com

### Transactional:

It was an active and successful year for the firm's transactional lawyers, who served as issuers' counsel or underwriters' counsel in more than 30 public offerings and Rule 144A placements raising approximately $10 billion in 2012; advised on more than 100 M&A transactions in the United States, Asia and Europe with an aggregate value of approximately $15 billion; completed more than 200 venture capital financings with an aggregate value of approximately $1.5 billion; and negotiated more than 100 significant technology transactions and licensing deals in the life sciences and high-tech industries. Among many other matters, the firm closed numerous funds for fund sponsors and investors; represented an array of leading financial institutions in precedent-setting, multi-billion-dollar bankruptcy litigation; and handled major real estate transactions.
**Contact:** Steven D Singer **Tel:** 212 295 6307
**Email:** steven.singer@wilmerhale.com

## OFFICES

### CALIFORNIA

**LOS ANGELES:** 350 South Grand Avenue, Suite 2100, CA 90071
Tel: 213 443 5300  Fax: 213 443 5400

**PALO ALTO:** 950 Page Mill Road, CA 94304
Tel: 650 858 6000  Fax: 650 858 6100

### DISTRICT OF COLUMBIA

**WASHINGTON, DC:** 1875 Pennsylvania Avenue, NW, DC 20006
Tel: 202 663 6000  Fax: 202 663 6363

### MASSACHUSETTS

**BOSTON:** 60 State Street, MA 02109
Tel: 617 526 6000  Fax: 617 526 5000

**WALTHAM:** 850 Winter Street, MA 02451
Tel: 781 966 2000  Fax: 781 966 2100

### NEW YORK

**NEW YORK:** 7 World Trade Center, 250 Greenwich Street, NY 10007
Tel: 212 230 8800  Fax: 212 230 8888

## INTERNATIONAL OFFICES

The firm also has offices in Beijing, Berlin, Brussels, Frankfurt, London and Oxford.

# WILTSHIRE & GRANNIS LLP

**www.**wiltshiregrannis.com **tel:** 202 730 1300 **fax:** 202 730 1301

**Managing Partner:** Mark A Grannis
Number of partners: 20
Number of lawyers: 29
Languages: *English, French, Italian, Spanish*

### Firm Overview:

Wiltshire & Grannis LLP ("W&G") is one of the premier communications, information technology, and litigation law firms in North America. The firm's clients include Fortune 500 companies, entrepreneurs, investors, individuals, and other organizations. As former senior government officials, federal prosecutors, Congressional staff, and experienced litigators, W&G lawyers advise their clients on how decision makers think, how legal and political institutions work in the real world, and how those institutions can affect a transaction or business plan.

### Main Areas of Practice:

**Communications & Internet: Regulation & Licensing:**
W&G's communications, Internet, and technology practice—ranked in Band One by *Chambers USA*—is home to legal, policy, and engineering experts in virtually every area of communications and technology law, and has played a major role in shaping US regulation in these areas. W&G represents carriers, equipment providers, software companies, ISPs, telecommunications users, undersea cable operators, satellite providers, media companies, and investors. The firm assists its clients in regulatory, licensing, and enforcement proceedings before the Federal Communications Commission (FCC), Federal Trade Commission (FTC), the National Telecommunications and Information Administration (NTIA), State Department, the International Telecommunication Union, and other US and foreign government agencies on the full range of communications and technology regulatory issues, including wireline, wireless, roaming, satellite, and spectrum regulation; media (including satellite and cable); Internet and VoIP regulation; and accessibility rules.

**Communications & Internet: Mergers, Acquisitions & Financing:**
Transactions are central to W&G's communications practice. The firm assists large and small entities seeking FCC approval of transactions, such as mergers and acquisitions; transfers of wireline, wireless, broadcast, or satellite licenses; and spectrum leasing. It also supports client financing activities. Recent representations include: General Communication Inc. in establishment of its wireless joint venture with Alaska Communications Systems Group; DIRECTV in its offering of senior notes and establishment of a revolving credit facility; Tyco International in its spin-off of ADT Corporation and reorganization of its security business; NEATT Wireless in its sale of spectrum to AT&T; and ABRY Partners in its sale of Atlantic Broadband.

**International Trade, Investment, & National Security:**
W&G's renowned international trade and investment practice assists clients in obtaining investment and national security-related approvals from the Committee on Foreign Investment in the United States (CFIUS), the "Team Telecom" agencies, the Defence Security Service, and in complying with US wiretapping and surveillance laws. Recent representations include: TE Connectivity in its acquisition of Deutsch Group, and Level 3 in its acquisition of Global Crossing. W&G counsels clients and assists them in obtaining transaction approvals under US and multilateral economic sanctions and export controls, and has recently assisted clients in obtaining licenses for transactions with Cuba, Iran, Sudan, and Syria. W&G represents companies before the US Trade Representative and foreign governments in WTO matters, market access disputes, and bilateral and regional trade negotiations, with a particular focus on China, India, Indonesia, Latin America, and the Middle East.

**Litigation: Supreme Court & Appellate:**
W&G attorneys brief and argue a wide variety of cases in the Supreme Court, including cases involving antitrust, communications law, employee benefits, torts, and criminal law. In the federal courts of appeals, W&G attorneys are involved in many of the most consequential cases in communications law each year, as well as a broad array of appeals in other substantive areas. This breadth of experience permits W&G to preserve victories at administrative agencies and trial courts, and to challenge adverse decisions. Recent matters include representing webcasters in a constitutional challenge to the Copyright Royalty Board in the DC Circuit and the Supreme Court; a foreign government in a Foreign Sovereign Immunities Act case in the DC Circuit and Supreme Court; and major telecommunications companies in the Supreme Court and various courts of appeals. W&G also filed amicus briefs on behalf of the leaders of the Democratic Party in health care cases decided by the Supreme Court in 2012, and more recently has filed amicus briefs in the courts of appeals and the Supreme Court in bankruptcy cases.

**Litigation: White Collar, Civil, Criminal, & Government Investigations:**
W&G represents large companies and individuals in civil litigation and government investigations before federal courts, state courts, arbitrators, and administrative tribunals. Led by Thomas Connolly, a former federal prosecutor, and widely recognized as one of the leading trial lawyers in Washington, DC, the firm's trial litigation practice handles all stages of litigation, administrative investigations, and internal investigations—from formal discovery, to administrative investigations, through trial. Recent matters include representing Freddie Mac in relation to Justice Department investigations, defending foreign executives accused of tax, antitrust, and bribery crimes by the United States, defending a sovereign government sued in federal court, asserting, defending, and protecting privacy rights, and representing a wide range of communications companies in FCC enforcement actions and in investigations related to procurement, the Federal Universal Service Fund, E-Rate, and consumer billing practices.

**PRACTICE AREAS**
Communications & Internet: Mergers, Acquisitions & Financing
Communications & Internet: Regulation & Licensing
International Trade, Investment, & National Security
Litigation: Supreme Court & Appellate
Litigation: White Collar, Civil, Criminal, & Government Investigations

**OFFICES**
DISTRICT OF COLUMBIA
**WASHINGTON:** 1200 Eighteenth Street NW, Suite 1200, DC 20036
Tel: 202 730 1300  Fax: 202 730 1301
Email: info@wiltshiregrannis.com

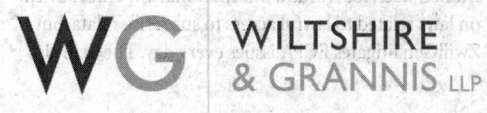

# ZWILLGEN PLLC

**www**.zwillgen.com  **tel:** 202 296 3585  **fax:** 202 706 5298  **blog:** blog.zwillgen.com

**Founding Partner:** Marc Zwillinger
Number of Attorneys: 10

### Firm Overview:

ZwillGen has built a strong practice counseling the nation's leading internet companies and handling their highest profile online legal issues. Through this work, ZwillGen attorneys have been leaders and significant contributors shaping the ongoing evolution and future landscape of the field of internet law.

Following years of running practice groups at the nation's largest law firms, ZwillGen was created with the intention of delivering thoughtful and practical solutions more efficiently. Today, ZwillGen offers unique services from a team of highly specialized attorneys, some of whom have spent the last 15 years developing their knowledge and experience with leading clients, firms and issues. In addition, ZwillGen makes legal advice more accessible to its clients by replacing the traditional hourly law firm model with innovative approaches that directly align firm incentives with client success.

Since its inception, ZwillGen lawyers have investigated, litigated and counseled on a wide range of internet issues, including:

- Cybercrime
- Information Security
- Privacy
- Surveillance
- Subpoena Compliance
- Online Marketing
- Behavioral Advertising
- Internet Gambling
- Satellite and Video Game Privacy
- Intellectual Property Theft
- And more

### Main Areas of Practice:

**Information Privacy & Security:**
ZwillGen attorneys advise clients on the forefront of privacy and security issues and have a deep base of experience in providing sound, common sense judgment in unchartered areas of the law and in advising clients on best practices. They not only provide counseling and draft privacy policies and terms of service, but they regularly represent clients in privacy and security investigations before the FTC. Many of ZwillGen's attorneys are also Certified Information Systems Security Professionals (CISSPs) and know how to converse with and translate the answers from clients' IS staff or IS contractors when a security breach occurs.

**Law Enforcement & Subscriber Data:**
The firm's attorneys advise the world's most prominent internet providers on their rights and responsibilities in responding to requests for subscriber information by law enforcement, criminal defendants and civil litigants. Not only does ZwillGen have experts who have published articles, taught law school courses, and trained state, federal and international law enforcement on laws related to lawful access to subscriber data, but ZwillGen litigates ECPA issues every day. The firm also

has in-house and outside counsel expertise in developing subpoena compliance programs. Whether it is CALEA, ECPA, FISA, RIPA or any other grounds for the government to seek data from providers, ZwillGen can assist.

**Litigation:**
Although ZwillGen prides itself on helping its clients to achieve their objectives while mitigating litigation risk without incurring liability, litigation is inevitable in some cases. Accordingly, ZwillGen attorneys have defended clients in a variety of consumer class action litigation suits, criminal investigations, civil forfeiture cases and other actions in state superior and federal district courts, and they have also pursued copyright, DMCA and computer fraud claims against infringers and hackers of clients' content and systems. ZwillGen regularly defends clients in regulatory inquiries and investigations by Congress, the Dept. of Justice and State Attorney Generals.

**Gaming, Social Gaming and Gambling:**
ZwillGen has been engaged to advise a number of the most prominent names in the game industry in their most critical legal matters. ZwillGen works with both industry-leading game publishers and a number of

smaller developers on issues related to apps, traditional videogames and MMORPGs. No matter the game, ZwillGen can assist you in compliance with laws related to games of skill, games of chance and fantasy sports.

### Clients:

In 2012, ZwillGen provided legal services to over 100 clients – from Fortune 500 companies to start ups. The firm represents prominent internet portals, internet service providers, video game publishers, social application developers and social networking websites, cable and satellite television providers, media entities, wireless carriers, online poker and fantasy sports providers, internet and computer security firms, investment banks, and a variety of traditional brick and mortar businesses in connection with their online practices. Among others, the firm and its lawyers have represented Yahoo!, Airbnb, Zynga, Cablevision, Quora, Pandora, Blizzard, Carpathia and The New York Times.

## OFFICES

### DISTRICT OF COLUMBIA

**WASHINGTON, DC:**
ZwillGen PLLC
1705 N St NW, DC 20036
Tel: 202 296 3585  Fax: 202 706 5298
Email: staff@zwillgen.com

### CALIFORNIA

**SAN FRANCISCO:**
ZwillGen Law LLP
915 Battery Street, Second Floor
Tel: 415 590 2342  Fax: 415 590 2339
Email: staff@zwillgen.com

## How lawyers are ranked

Every year we carry out thousands of in-depth interviews with clients in order to assess the reputations and expertise of business lawyers worldwide. The qualities we look for (and which determine rankings) include technical legal ability, professional conduct, client service, commercial awareness/astuteness, diligence, commitment, and other qualities most valued by the client. For details of our research team, see p.5.

## Contents:

# FLORIDA: An Introduction

## Contributed by Bilzin Sumberg Baena Price & Axelrod LLP

Florida has a dynamic, diverse community and an increasingly pro-business environment. Internationally renowned for its tourism industry, the state's political leadership is focused on creating and maintaining a competitive business climate by streamlining regulations, expanding global access through its ports, and developing a multilingual, educated workforce.

As a global hub, Florida is considered the strategic and economic center of the Americas, with increasing business investment within Florida from Central and South America, the Caribbean, Europe – particularly Russia – and Asia. Virtually every major global logistics integrator has a presence in Florida. In particular, South Florida's infrastructure is growing, with major expansion projects at Miami International Airport and PortMiami, improving the region's links to the world by air and sea. PortMiami and Florida East Coast Railway have partnered to restore and improve rail access to the port; once complete, goods imported through the port will be able to reach 70% of the US consumer market in less than four days.

The state has a significant and growing presence in industry sectors such as life sciences, cleantech, infotech, aviation, logistics, financial and professional services, and manufacturing[1]. Florida's well-established industries are tourism, agriculture, and construction.

### Business and Tax Environment

In 2012, Chief Executive Magazine ranked Florida as the second best state in which to do business, moving up from the previous year's third place ranking. Florida's improvement is attributed to business tax and regulatory reforms that contributed to the creation of more than 140,000 private sector jobs, one of the biggest unemployment decreases in the nation, and a high net migration of people into the state[2].

Florida has no corporate franchise tax on capital stock, no state-level property tax assessment, no property tax on business inventories, and no sales and use tax on goods manufactured or produced in Florida for export outside the state[3].

### Infrastructure

Florida is the nexus of the western hemisphere's transportation links. The state is focused on expanding its cargo and passenger transportation infrastructure, key components of Florida's significance as an international business center. Miami International Airport, the world's largest gateway to Latin America and the Caribbean, handles 82% of all air imports and 81% of all exports between the US and the Latin American and Caribbean region. To connect passengers, All Aboard Florida will provide a rail service between Miami and Orlando.

### Environmental Permitting & Enforcement

Environmental permitting and enforcement is generally coordinated either by the Florida Department of Environmental Protection or one of several water management districts.

Land use and growth management continue to be important issues in Florida. However, in 2011 state planning functions were transferred to the Department of Economic Opportunity, and much of the state's growth management activities now take place within the context of economic development.

### Real Estate

Real estate is a vital part of Florida's economy. Over the past several years, interest by foreign investors in Florida's real estate market has grown significantly. In 2012, foreign buyers, purchasing primary and secondary homes, and often paying cash, spent $10.7 billion on residential real estate in Florida. Latin American and Caribbean buyers accounted for 35% of all foreign purchases in Florida[4].

### Import/Export

Florida has significant natural advantages for international trade, including a central location in the Americas, a long coastline with functional ports, and a globally connected population. With the expansion of the Panama Canal and the dredging of PortMiami, it is anticipated that Florida's share of US exports to Latin and South America, currently at 40%, will grow exponentially in the coming decade[5]. Florida is home to more than 55,000 exporters – the second highest number in the United States[6].

## Hospitality and Tourism

With more than 405,000 hotel rooms statewide spread over 4,443 properties, the tourism industry has a $67 billion impact on Florida's economy[7]. The Miami hotel market is undergoing increasing expansion while the rest of the US is still recovering. Miami Beach, the highest performing submarket, is almost fully absorbed and is experiencing one of the strongest growth rates of any major submarket in the country, outperforming national averages.

In parts of South Florida where prime hotel sites have already been built up, investors are choosing to buy from existing stock then renovating to increase property value and room rates[8].

## Life Sciences

After years of aggressive, coordinated efforts, Florida has established itself as a hub for the life sciences industry, which includes biotech, medical devices, pharmaceuticals and health care. Today, Florida is home to some of the nation's most highly regarded research centers, nearly 1,000 biotech, pharmaceutical and medical device companies, and more than 44,000 healthcare establishments[9]. Leading medical facilities like the world-renowned Bascom Palmer Eye Institute at the University of Miami, Cleveland Clinic, University of Florida Shands Hospital, Miami Children's Hospital, and Mayo Clinic all reside in Florida. In 2008, the University of Miami opened The Launch Pad, a center to strengthen entrepreneurial culture by providing entrepreneurs, innovators and inventors with the resources and guidance they need to develop and grow companies.

## Technology

The 23-county region known as Florida's High Tech Corridor ranks as the fourth largest technology hub in the U.S[10]. Florida's research universities, research institutes and federal and private research organizations spend more than $7 billion annually on R&D in the state[11]. Successful partnerships between public organizations and private industry are key drivers of this growth.

Footnotes:

[1] www.invest-in-usa.org
[2] http://chiefexecutive.net
[3] www.eflorida.com
[4] http://realtormag.realtor.org
[5] www.avisonyoung.com
[6] www.floridaexportdirectory.com
[7] www.visitflorida.org
[8] www.nytimes.com
[9] www.eflorida.com
[10] www.floridahightech.com
[11] www.eflorida.com

# ANTITRUST

Commentary about individuals can be found under their firm's paragraph. If the firm has no paragraph (is not ranked) look at Other Notable Practitioners.

### Antitrust
### Leading Firms

**Band 1**
Kenny Nachwalter PA *

**Band 2**
Boies, Schiller & Flexner LLP *
Carlton Fields, P.A. *

**Band 3**
Akerman Senterfitt
Baker, Donelson, Bearman, Caldwell & Berkowitz *
Bilzin Sumberg Baena Price & Axelrod LLP *
Holland & Knight LLP *

## Band 1

### Kenny Nachwalter PA
See profile on p.1029

**THE FIRM** This group once again leads the pack in the Florida antitrust market, earning widespread acclaim for the national scope of its workload, which covers opt-out and direct action suits as well as international cartel cases. The firm is most prominent for its plaintiff-side practice, and also undertakes defense work, acting for large public and private companies and individual entrepreneurs. It is noted for its strength in matters involving the pharmaceutical sector, and additional expertise in the transportation, insurance and real estate industries, among others.

**Sources say:** *"It's been the top firm for antitrust in Florida for some time."*

**KEY INDIVIDUALS** The *"very creative and talented"* **Richard Arnold** is an *"outstanding"* and *"preeminent"* antitrust lawyer. He has extensive experience prosecuting antitrust claims in a plethora of industries, including automotive, telecommunications, banking and healthcare. **William Blechman** is a *"go-to guy"* for antitrust law, described by sources as a *"smart, aggressive and passionate"* lawyer. His impressive resume includes significant experience in cases involving alleged international cartels, particularly in relation to food and industrial manufacturing processes. **Scott Perwin** is also a notable part of the exceptional antitrust bench at the firm, and is called *"one of the top guys"* for antitrust by commentators. The distinguished **Michael Nachwalter** has long been one of the big names in this arena. In addition to his antitrust practice, he is also active in alternative dispute resolution and general commercial litigation.

### Antitrust
### Senior Statesmen

**Senior Statesmen:** distinguished older practitioners
Nachwalter Michael — Kenny Nachwalter PA

### Leading Individuals

**Band 1**

| | | |
|---|---|---|
| Arnold Richard | Kenny Nachwalter PA | |
| Blechman William | Kenny Nachwalter PA | |
| Coutroulis Chris S | Carlton Fields, P.A. * | |
| Hoffman Jerome | Holland & Knight LLP * | |
| Litchford Hal | Baker, Donelson, Bearman, Caldwell * | |
| Perwin Scott | Kenny Nachwalter PA | |
| Silverman Lawrence D | Akerman Senterfitt | |
| Singer Stuart | Boies, Schiller & Flexner LLP | |

**Band 2**

| | |
|---|---|
| Nagin Stephen | Peretz Chesal and Herrmann, PL (ONP)† |
| Ross David L | Greenberg Traurig, LLP (ONP)† * |
| Steinberg Marty | Bilzin Sumberg Baena Price & Axelrod LLP * |
| Turken Robert W | Bilzin Sumberg Baena Price & Axelrod LLP * |

**Up-and-coming individuals**

| | |
|---|---|
| Dominguez Manuel J | Cohen, Milstein, Sellers & Toll, LLP (ONP)† |

*\* Indicates firm / individual with profile.*
*† ONP = Other Notable Practitioner.*

## Band 2

### Boies, Schiller & Flexner LLP
See profile on p.1958

**THE FIRM** This antitrust team focuses largely on the litigation aspects of antitrust law, and is recognized for its representation of clients in both plaintiff and defense-side work. Notable recent mandates include representing Fresh Del Monte Produce in antitrust litigation involving allegations of anticompetitive behavior in the pineapple market. The team also acted for Office Depot alongside a number of other corporate plaintiffs who have opted out of class actions in respect of the California LCD antitrust litigation.

**Sources say:** *"A consistent player in a lot of the big cases."*

**KEY INDIVIDUALS Stuart Singer** is a *"very bright antitrust lawyer, both analytically and on the litigation side."* In addition to his antitrust practice, he is also active in intellectual property and energy-related litigation. One source enthused: *"He is a superb lawyer who not only obtains results but is at the forefront of some very interesting legal issues. I give him an unqualified recommendation."*

### Carlton Fields, P.A.
See profile on p.1020

**THE FIRM** Carlton Fields is recognized for its specialization in class action defense and trade regulation within the antitrust sphere, and for its expertise in matters relating to class certification. The practice encompasses both litigation and counseling, and its work of late has included cases in such diverse areas as the pharmaceutical, technology and healthcare industries.

**Sources say:** *"They are very strong in this area."*

**KEY INDIVIDUALS** The *"effective and well-versed"* **Chris Coutroulis** (see p.989) is held in high regard by sources for the *"breadth of his experience"* in antitrust. He focuses on antitrust and trade regulation across a variety of sectors, including food and telecommunications. *"He's extremely solid,"* said one interviewee.

## Band 3

### Akerman Senterfitt
See profile on p.1014

**THE FIRM** Akerman Senterfitt remains an active presence in this area, despite the retirement of Ronald Ravikoff in 2012. The team represents both plaintiffs and defendants in antitrust litigation, and also handles merger clearance work. In recent highlights, it advised SAMSUNG on its implementation of a national unilateral pricing policy, one of the largest such policies ever implemented in the USA.

**Sources say:** *"A highly respected, class-act firm."*

**KEY INDIVIDUALS Lawrence Silverman** is a *"superb antitrust lawyer"* who is *"as good as there is."* Sources praise his courtroom presence and articulate style, as well as his knowledge of legal trends. He has notable expertise in computing and related technology areas.

### Baker, Donelson, Bearman, Caldwell & Berkowitz
See profile on p.2313

**THE FIRM** Baker Donelson made its first foray into Florida by way of its merger with Orlando firm Litchford & Christopher in November 2011. The office now benefits from the national scope of the Baker firm, coupled with the Florida antitrust experience of the existing office. The practice encompasses litigation and counseling on antitrust matters, including cases resulting from government investigations and vertical integration.

**Sources say:** *"A very strong group."*

**KEY INDIVIDUALS Hal Litchford** (see p.998) anchors the firm's Florida antitrust practice and is recommended by one peer as *"someone I would send work to in a conflict situation."* He has substantial experience in a wide variety of areas in addition to antitrust, including trade secrets and IP.

### Bilzin Sumberg Baena Price & Axelrod LLP
See profile on p.1018

**THE FIRM** New to the rankings this year, the antitrust component of this firm was boosted by the addition of Marty Steinberg and four other lawyers from Hunton & Williams in April 2012. The team's experience cuts across all areas of antitrust law, with an emphasis on litigation. Notably, it represented Tech Data and the bankruptcy estate of All American Semiconductor as opt-out plaintiffs in the LCD antitrust action.

**Sources say:** *"They just take the ball and run with it – they've been fantastic."*

**KEY INDIVIDUALS Marty Steinberg** (see p.1009) cochairs the firm's litigation group and has a broad practice covering white-collar crime, IP and product liability in addition to antitrust law. He recently represented Vulcan Materials in its defense of a putative class action relating to the concrete industry. Sources describe him as a *"first-rate, hard-working lawyer,"* and note his communication skills and *"high degree of intellect."* One commentator calls **Robert Turken** (see p.1011) *"the best lawyer I've seen on his feet,"* while others are quick to praise his *"photographic memory"* and his skill at giving *"very clear"* advice. He undertakes a substantial amount of antitrust work as part of his complex commercial practice, and co-led the firm in its abovementioned representation of Tech Data and All American Semiconductor.

### Holland & Knight LLP
See profile on p.1028

**THE FIRM** This group is highlighted for its expertise in healthcare-related antitrust work, which includes a major long-running hospital case. The firm is also proficient across a broad spectrum of industries and has a substantial presence in Florida, with seven offices statewide.

**KEY INDIVIDUALS Jerome Hoffman** (see p.995) is a lawyer who *"has all the skills,"* according to commentators. Peers recommend him for his abilities in this field, and highlight his previous experience as lead counsel to the state of Florida in a variety of antitrust cases as a strong asset for the practice.

### Other Notable Practitioners

**David Ross** (see p.1005) of Greenberg Traurig, LLP is praised as *"a wonderful all-round lawyer."* An experienced trial lawyer, he tries matters across a variety of areas in addition to antitrust, including securities and complex commercial litigation. **Stephen Nagin** of Peretz Chesal and Herrmann, PL is best known for his expertise in antitrust and intellectual property law, and is described as *"a go-to guy for antitrust."* He is a trial lawyer with extensive experience, and his ability as an adviser is also highlighted by sources. *"Rising star"* **Manuel Dominguez** of Cohen, Milstein, Sellers & Toll, LLP is *"a natural who is on top of his game,"* say sources. He is recognized for his impressive work on plaintiff-side antitrust and consumer protection litigation.

# BANKING & FINANCE

Commentary about individuals can be found under their firm's paragraph. If the firm has no paragraph (is not ranked) look at Other Notable Practitioners.

## Banking & Finance
### Leading Firms

**Band 1**
Greenberg Traurig, LLP *
Shutts & Bowen LLP
White & Case LLP *

**Band 2**
Akerman Senterfitt
Avila Rodriguez Hernandez Mena & Ferri LLP
Hunton & Williams LLP *
Stearns Weaver Miller Weissler Alhadeff & Sitterson, P.A.

**Band 3**
Gunster *
Holland & Knight LLP *
Squire Sanders (US) LLP *

**Band 4**
Broad and Cassel
Foley & Lardner LLP *

## Banking & Finance: Public Finance
### Leading Individuals

**Band 1**
| | | |
|---|---|---|
| Bloom Warren S | Greenberg Traurig, LLP * |
| del Castillo Albert A | Greenberg Traurig, LLP * |
| Reiter Luis | Squire Sanders (US) LLP * |
| Vogel III Edward W | Holland & Knight LLP * |

**Band 2**
| | |
|---|---|
| MacLennan Alexandra M | Squire Sanders (US) LLP * |
| Stanton Joseph | Broad and Cassel |

**Band 3**
| | |
|---|---|
| Fleischer Frank N | GrayRobinson, PA (ONP)[†] * |
| Gang Robert C | Greenberg Traurig, LLP * |
| Lever Chauncey | Foley & Lardner LLP |
| Smith-Lalla Lori | Greenberg Traurig, LLP * |
| Wilson Jéan E | Greenberg Traurig, LLP * |

**Up-and-coming individuals**
| | |
|---|---|
| Magee Emily | Foley & Lardner LLP |

* Indicates firm / individual with profile.
[†] ONP = Other Notable Practitioner.

## Band 1

### Greenberg Traurig, LLP
See profile on p.1024

**THE FIRM** This 48-strong banking and finance team has a longstanding presence in the market, providing a wide scope of services across the public finance, regulatory and transactional fields. Notable strengths include commercial lending, structured finance and bond counsel work. The firm's recent clients include leading banks such as Goldman Sachs and Deutsche Bank, as well as companies such as Western Union and Van Kampen Asset Management.

## Banking & Finance: Regulatory
### Leading Individuals

**Star individuals**
| | |
|---|---|
| Brown Bowman | Shutts & Bowen LLP |

**Band 1**
| | |
|---|---|
| Avila Alcides | Avila Rodriguez Hernandez Mena & Ferri |
| Vázquez-Bello Clemente L. | Gunster |

**Band 2**
| | |
|---|---|
| Basile Michael | Stroock & Stroock & Lavan LLP (ONP)[†] |
| Fornaris Carl A | Greenberg Traurig, LLP * |
| Greeley Jack | Smith Mackinnon PA (ONP)[†] |

**Band 3**
| | |
|---|---|
| Bader Gregory K. | Gunster |
| Hale Russell | Akerman Senterfitt |
| Hernandez Patricia M | Avila Rodriguez Hernandez Mena & Ferri |
| Jones Rod | Shutts & Bowen LLP |
| Stutts Charles | Holland & Knight LLP * |
| Townes Virginia B | Akerman Senterfitt |

**Up-and-coming individuals**
| | |
|---|---|
| Fernandez Andres A. | Gunster |

## Banking & Finance: Transactional
### Leading Individuals

**Band 1**
| | |
|---|---|
| Alonso Fernando C | Hunton & Williams LLP * |
| Alvarez Victor M | White & Case LLP * |
| Alvarez-Farré Emilio J | White & Case LLP * |
| Ames Stuart | Stearns Weaver Miller Weissler Alhadeff |
| Sirven José E | Holland & Knight LLP * |

**Band 2**
| | |
|---|---|
| Avila Alcides | Avila Rodriguez Hernandez Mena & Ferri |
| Dulin Amy G | Hughes Hubbard & Reed LLP (ONP)[†] * |
| Fornaris Carl A | Greenberg Traurig, LLP * |
| Greeley Jack | Smith Mackinnon PA |
| Houser Bradley D | Akerman Senterfitt |
| Jaffe Arvin J | Broad and Cassel |
| Loumiet Carlos | DLA Piper LLP (US) (ONP)[†] * |
| Siegel Robert M | Bilzin Sumberg Baena Price (ONP)[†] * |
| Viana Carlos | White & Case LLP * |

**Band 3**
| | |
|---|---|
| Arnhols William C | Akerman Senterfitt |
| Dewey Joe | Holland & Knight LLP * |
| Mitrione Michael V | Gunster |
| Yadley Barbara | Holland & Knight LLP * |

**Sources say:** "I find the firm to offer a very client-focused approach with an absolutely seamless execution." **KEY INDIVIDUALS Warren Bloom** (see p.986) continues to attract strong praise for his outstanding public finance work. He frequently works with US Bank, advising it on a wide range of bond and restructuring matters. Public finance specialist **Albert del Castillo** (see p.989) recently joined the firm from Squire Sanders. Clients praise him for "taking a very candid approach – he is solu-

tion-oriented but always protects us in reaching goals. I have absolute faith in him and his decisions." Fellow public finance attorney **Jéan Wilson** (see p.1012) works with many of the state's cities and counties. He recently represented the City of Atlanta in a finance plan for the expansion of the international airport, totaling nearly $475 million. **Robert Gang** (see p.992) is also recognized for his work in this field. He frequently represents public school districts across the state. Respected for both his regulatory and transactional knowledge, **Carl Fornaris** (see p.992) earns praise for his "strong command of the practice area – the breadth of his experience is incredible." He continues to work with both national and international financial service firms, advising them on state and countrywide regulation issues and transactional matters. **Lori Smith-Lalla** (see p.1008) is highlighted as being "fantastic. She is professional, responsive and awesome on the details."

### Shutts & Bowen LLP

**THE FIRM** Longstanding local firm Shutts & Bowen maintains an exemplary reputation for its work in banking and finance. With a multitude of finance-related services available, this large group offers a full range of expertise in areas such as acquisition, trade, consumer and real estate finance. The practice is particularly recognized for its outstanding regulatory experience and frequently works with national and foreign institutions to successfully navigate them through the myriad of regulations in the state.
**Sources say:** "Terrific – they are the gold standard for traditional regulatory work in Florida."
**KEY INDIVIDUALS** Highly respected practitioner **Bowman Brown** is acknowledged for his leading work in the regulatory field. He is "without a doubt the top lawyer for banking regulation issues," say interviewees, with one adding: "I always go direct to him – he is just fantastic." Brown continues to advise global banks on a range of regulatory needs, as well as transactions. Former banking regulator **Rod Jones** is praised for his "encyclopedic regulatory knowledge." His practice focuses on advising community banks on regulatory issues.

### White & Case LLP
See profile on p.451

**THE FIRM** White & Case's banking and finance team retains its leading position in the transactional sphere. Clients emphasize the firm's Miami location as a particular plus, as it serves as an ideal platform to focus on Latin American work – an area in which the firm's presence continues to grow. The group excels at advising multinational corporations, financial institutions and governmental entities on both domestic and cross-border transactions.
**Sources say:** "They have the incredible ability to combine their impressive local market knowledge with New York-quality and resources."

**KEY INDIVIDUALS Carlos Viana** (see p.1011) is highly valued by clients, who recommend him as an attorney with "*outstanding capabilities; he is a great negotiator and strategist with stellar knowledge.*" He is adept at handling a range of financings and is frequently involved in cross-border deals, thanks to his experience in the Latin American markets. **Victor Alvarez** (see p.983) is also respected for his Latin America transactional presence. Sources say he is an "*efficient and thorough attorney – he is always able to put forth an alternative solution based on his vast market experience.*" **Emilio Alvarez-Farré** (see p.983) is recognized for his "*valuable knowledge in structured and traditional corporate finance.*" He is a formidable presence in cross-border M&A transactions and their associated financings.

## Band 2

### Akerman Senterfitt
See profile on p.1014

**THE FIRM** This group represents borrowers and issuers in the full range of transactional matters. The firm is adept at handling a variety of complex transactions, offering services in areas such as acquisition finance, syndicated loans and revolving credit facilities. Peers also acknowledge the group's presence in the regulatory and public finance markets, where it regularly works with financial institutions on operational matters and acts as bond counsel to various entities.

**Sources say:** "*A firm with incredible talent and capabilities.*"

**KEY INDIVIDUALS** Respected practitioner **Bradley Houser** is particularly valued for his expertise in REITs. Standout recent matters include acting as issuer's counsel for ARMOUR Residential REIT on a $2.1 billion offering. In the regulatory sphere, **Virginia Townes**'s litigation experience is utilized by various financial institutions in a range of disputes involving regulators, customers and other parties. Sources describe practice chair **William Arnhols** as "*a very sophisticated lawyer who is technically proficient and understands all the complexities of each deal.*" He recently acted as lead counsel to The GEO Group in connection with its senior credit facilities. **Russell Hale** continues to focus on a broad range of tax and banking matters. In the past year he has been responsible for writing legislation, which was later enacted, to grant taxpayers relief from harsh transferee liability.

### Avila Rodriguez Hernandez Mena & Ferri LLP
**THE FIRM** This boutique firm continues to make a big impression on the banking and finance scene. It offers an array of services, and is particularly respected for its standout regulatory experience. It frequently works with domestic and international banks, as well as multinational companies, offering them a complete advisory package on an impressive range of regulatory matters.

**Sources say:** "*Their lawyers are knowledgeable problem solvers and creative in targeting different solutions.*"

**KEY INDIVIDUALS** Peers cite **Alcides Avila** as "*undoubtedly one of the leaders in banking regulatory work.*" His experience across the gamut of regulation matters makes him a popular choice with clients for representation in this field. Alongside this, he continues to advise financial institutions on establishing and expanding US-based operations. Fellow co-founder **Patricia Hernandez** is also recommended for her regulatory experience. She often represents clients before the various regulatory agencies and advises them on compliance and enforcement actions.

### Hunton & Williams LLP
See profile on p.2517

**THE FIRM** Hunton & Williams's team has great strength in transactional work. The group maintains a particular focus on cross-border deals, and regularly represents both domestic and foreign financial institutions and companies in a range of transactions. Its US-based client list includes leading names such as Bank of America Merrill Lynch and Citibank, while foreign institutions such as Banco Santander and Banco Internacional de Costa Rica are among its international following.

**Sources say:** "*I have great peace of mind when they are on our side – they are reliable and accountable, and have a lot of initiative.*"

**KEY INDIVIDUALS** Sources describe **Fernando Alonso** (see p.983) as a "*business-oriented, pragmatic and creative individual who offers solutions to complex matters.*" He continues to gain significant recognition for his work with several leading Spanish banks, including Banco Santander and Sabadell United Bank.

### Stearns Weaver Miller Weissler Alhadeff & Sitterson, P.A.
**THE FIRM** This practice offers a full range of advice on secured and unsecured credit transactions. With impressive strength as lenders' counsel, it regularly works with financial institutions such as Bank of America, Citibank and Wells Fargo. A key strength of the practice is its ability to represent lenders in their dealings with private equity and hedge fund borrowers.

**KEY INDIVIDUALS** Practice head **Stuart Ames**'s expertise in commercial lending, acquisition finance and asset-based lending earns him a strong reputation among peers, who describe him as a "*top-notch transactional lawyer.*" He regularly represents leading market lenders in a wide variety of financial transactions.

## Band 3

### Gunster
See profile on p.1025

**THE FIRM** Homegrown firm Gunster's banking and finance group continues to make a strong impression on the Florida market. Particularly noted for its exceptional work in the regulatory field, the team frequently advises both local and foreign financial institutions on all manner of compliance matters. Major strengths include work in relation to anti-money laundering laws and the Bank Secrecy Act (BSA). It is also acknowledged for its successful representation of several banks in regulatory enforcement actions.

**Sources say:** "*They are attentive, and have a strong turnaround time and great follow-up to their work.*"

**KEY INDIVIDUALS Clemente Vázquez-Bello**'s practice focuses on anti-money laundering work, which "*he does so well.*" His specialist knowledge in this niche area regularly attracts both domestic and foreign banks, who continue to seek his counsel on regulation matters. Described as a "*professional and accommodating attorney,*" **Gregory Bader** is acknowledged for his financial regulation work as well as his experience in M&A transactions. On the transactional side, **Michael Mitrione** is recognized for his broad experience. He has represented several domestic banks in acquisitions through mergers of other financial institutions of late. **Andres Fernandez** is praised by peers for his experience in money laundering matters and continues to work with clients on a range of regulation compliance issues.

### Holland & Knight LLP
See profile on p.1028

**THE FIRM** This dedicated banking and finance group covers a broad range of services in the Florida market across the regulatory, public finance and transactional spectrum. Clients recommend the practice for its depth and wide footprint in the state. Notable strengths include acquisition and real estate finance, bank regulation issues and various other advisory work. It has recently been busy representing banks in Federal Deposit Insurance Corporation (FDIC) investigations.

**Sources say:** "*A firm with all kinds of talent and expertise to call on – impressive depth.*"

**KEY INDIVIDUALS José Sirven** (see p.1008) maintains an impressive reputation in the transactional sphere. He is widely experienced and routinely represents both borrowers and lenders in complex transactional matters. He is also noted for his knowledge of the Latin American market. Peers describe **Edward Vogel** (see p.1011) as "*an absolutely exceptional attorney and a leader in public finance.*" He continues to be acknowledged for his bond work. With a focus on regulatory matters, **Charles Stutts** (see p.1009) has played a lead role in the firm's handling of FDIC investigations, and has represented former directors and officers in such matters. Sources describe **Joe Dewey** (see p.990) as "*responsive, knowledgeable and reliable.*" He is particularly valued for his prowess in real estate finance. One client describes him as "*a very diplomatic communicator who always manages to deliver the right message in the best way. I never have to question whether he has anything other than our best interests at heart.*" Tampa-based **Barbara Yadley** (see p.1012) is well versed in the field of commercial lending. She frequently represents loyal client Jabil Circuit in numerous banking and finance matters, and recently advised it in connection with a credit facility transaction.

### Squire Sanders (US) LLP
See profile on p.2129

**THE FIRM** A firm favorite for all aspects of public finance, Squire Sanders offers a complete array of services within this exclusive sphere. The group continues to stand out for its exemplary bond counsel work, representing the state and many cities, counties and special districts in matters including airport bond financings and various bond refundings. The team is also recommended for its work as disclosure and underwriters counsel.

**Sources say:** "As bond counsel they are top without doubt, due to the depth of their practice and their experience. They are who we look to whenever we have challenging work."

**KEY INDIVIDUALS** Managing partner **Luis Reiter** (see p.1004) is described by one client as "one of the finest attorneys I have ever worked with." He earns praise for his debt work, where his wealth of local knowledge is highly valued by those he advises. Sources also highlight **Alexandra MacLennan** (see p.999), who frequently works as counsel in healthcare, higher education and project financings.

## Band 4

### Broad and Cassel

**THE FIRM** This firm is acknowledged for its proficiency in lender-side representation. Offering a wide range of advice, the team also works hand in hand with other practices at the firm to provide seamless representation in matters such as foreclosure and restructuring. The attorneys are also valued for their public finance work and the team frequently acts as counsel to a large number of government authorities.

**Sources say:** "A highly effective firm that focuses on its strengths and excels at them."

**KEY INDIVIDUALS Joseph Stanton** is a respected practitioner in the public finance arena. Hailed as a "very unique

and capable bond lawyer whose work is always of the highest quality," he has recently acted as bond counsel for the Orlando-Orange County Expressway Authority and as disclosure counsel for the Florida Governmental Utility Authority. Department Chair **Arvin Jaffe** continues to earn praise for his broad financial services practice, consistently representing a wide variety of institutional lenders.

### Foley & Lardner LLP
See profile on p.2588

**THE FIRM** With a focus on public finance work, this group is valued in its role as counsel to both government and private entities. The team continues to increase its presence in Latin America. Recent highlights include representing the Puerto Rico Public Buildings Authority in several complex bond sales and subsequent financial projects. Other strengths include a broad transactional practice working with both borrowers and lenders on a range of matters.

**Sources say:** "They are thorough and responsive, and have a collaborative method of working with others that gets the deal done."

**KEY INDIVIDUALS** Sources describe **Chauncey Lever** as an "oracle of municipal finance in Florida, whose years of experience are reflected in his encyclopedic knowledge." He is singled out for his excellent municipal bond work. Acknowledged for her work in both public and healthcare finance, **Emily Magee** is described as a "smart, articulate and confident attorney." She recently acted as bank counsel to Banc of America Public Capital.

### Other Notable Practitioners

Sources describe **Robert Siegel** (see p.1007) of Bilzin Sumberg Baena Price & Axelrod LLP as "an analytical, thoughtful and practical attorney." His practice focuses on commercial lending, securitizations and restructuring matters. **Frank Fleischer** (see p.991) of GrayRobinson, PA is strongly recommended for his disclosure counsel work. Alongside this, he frequently acts as underwriters' counsel in municipal finance matters. Of counsel **Michael Basile** of Stroock & Stroock & Lavan LLP stands out for his regulatory practice. He frequently advises a number of regional and national banks on compliance issues. Peers acknowledge **Jack Greeley** of Smith Mackinnon PA for his presence in the transactional market. He is also adept at handling regulatory matters. Renowned for his cross-border work, **Carlos Loumiet** (see p.998) of DLA Piper LLP (US) is praised for his experience in Latin America. Sources value "his strong contacts in the international market that have developed from his frequent activity with the Latin American community." He continues to focus on international project finance work across the world. With a particular emphasis on Latin America, **Amy Dulin** (see p.990) of Hughes Hubbard & Reed LLP works with clients on a range of corporate and structured finance transactions. Recent highlights include work with Banco Santander (Brasil) on a $1 billion financing deal for Gerdau and its subsidiaries.

---

# BANKRUPTCY/RESTRUCTURING

Bankruptcy/Restructuring p.939

Commentary about individuals can be found under their firm's paragraph. If the firm has no paragraph (is not ranked) look at Other Notable Practitioners.

## Band 1

### Berger Singerman
See profile on p.1017

**THE FIRM** This exceptional firm has a superb track record for conducting the largest, most high-profile bankruptcy and restructuring assignments throughout the region, especially on the debtor side. The firm has continued its high-profile representation of the Chapter 11 trustee for the bankruptcy estate of Rothstein Rosenfeldt & Adler, an immensely high-profile assignment involving the largest Ponzi scheme fraud in the history of Southern Florida.

**Sources say:** "The team is easy to trust and respect, and enjoyable to have on the other side." "They have the bench strength and the expertise. They are knowledgeable, hardworking, prepared and principled."

**KEY INDIVIDUALS** Firm cofounder **Paul Steven Singerman** (see p.1007) is praised as being "amazing" and

simply "the best" for his bankruptcy practice. Sources are extraordinarily impressed by his in-depth expertise in the field, and by his handling of some of the most significant bankruptcies in the region. In addition to his lead in the Rothstein Rosenfeldt & Adler matter, he and **Jordi Guso** (see p.994) recently led the team representing high-end furniture retailer Robb & Stucky in its Chapter 11 proceedings. Guso is hailed as "a gentleman attorney" who is "articulate, smart and one of the best lawyers in the area." He has a sterling practice with superb expertise in both creditor and debtor representations. **Brian Gart** (see p.992) is defined as a "very hard-working lawyer" who is "able to resolve a number of issues very quickly" and "communicates comprehensively while in court." He recently led the team acting for HearUSA as debtor-in-possession in its Chapter 11 proceedings and 363 sale to Siemens Hearing. **Howard Berlin** (see p.985) is currently assisting Singerman in acting for the plan trustee in the Taylor, Bean & Whitaker

Chapter 11 case. One particularly impressed interviewee praised him as "one of the strongest bankruptcy attorneys I've ever met," while another added: "His ability to relate to real situations is very good – he is a tremendously smart person who performs sophisticated work." Heralded as a "very authoritative and well-respected" lawyer, **Brian Rich** (see p.1004) has a strong and wide-ranging bankruptcy practice. He and **Douglas Bates** (see p.984) recently led the team acting for radio station operator Black Crow Media on its large-scale and high-profile Chapter 11 proceedings. Bates is rated by peers as being "among the finest young bankruptcy lawyers in the state," and is "very well respected by judges." **Leslie Cloyd** (see p.988) has a varied and exceptional bankruptcy practice. She is currently representing the liquidating trustee in the Lancer Partners Chapter 11, and also worked alongside Singerman on the nationwide restructuring of HNI HoldCo, formerly known as Medical Staffing Network.

## Bankruptcy/Restructuring
### Leading Firms

**Band 1**

Berger Singerman *

Bilzin Sumberg Baena Price & Axelrod LLP *

Genovese Joblove & Battista, PA

Greenberg Traurig, LLP *

Kozyak Tropin & Throckmorton

Stichter, Riedel, Blain & Prosser PA *

**Band 2**

Akerman Senterfitt

Fowler White Boggs

Smith Hulsey & Busey

Stearns Weaver Miller Weissler Alhadeff & Sitterson, P.A.

Trenam Kemker, Attorneys

**Band 3**

DLA Piper LLP (US) *

Glenn Rasmussen, P.A. *

GrayRobinson, PA

Holland & Knight LLP *

Meland Russin & Budwick PA

Rice Pugatch Robinson & Schiller, PA

White & Case LLP *

**Band 4**

Baker & Hostetler LLP *

Broad and Cassel

Burr & Forman LLP *

Carlton Fields, P.A. *

Foley & Lardner LLP *

Latham, Shuker, Barker, Eden & Beaudine LLP

Markowitz Ringel Trusty + Hartog P.A.

### Bilzin Sumberg Baena Price & Axelrod LLP
**See profile on p.1018**

**THE FIRM** This full-service firm has a terrific reputation for representing a broad range of parties in bankruptcy and restructuring matters, including debtors, trustees, creditors, lenders and committees. The team recently represented secured lender LNR Partners in the bankruptcy proceedings of Sagamore, and has also recently represented Cordia Communications as debtor.

**Sources say:** *"I have found them to be extremely skilled, capable and collegial." "The team is very professional; everything runs smoothly."*

**KEY INDIVIDUALS Scott Baena** (see p.984) is chair of the firm's restructuring and bankruptcy group. He is *"nationally renowned"* for his practice, which covers creditors' rights, workouts, bankruptcy and financing matters. Sources laud him as an *"all-around superb attorney ."* He recently served as counsel to a number of prestigious universities in a $24 million fraudulent transfer lawsuit brought against them by a Chapter 7 trustee. **Mindy Mora** (see p.1001) is chair of the Business Law Section of the Florida Bar, and has a *"good reputation"* for counseling high visibility clients. She recently represented Cabi SMA as debtor and debtor-in-possession in its Chapter 11 proceedings. Sources report that *"she is very smart"* and *"a great litigator,"* and she is especially *"effective in court when the client is in a difficult circumstance."* **Jay Sakalo** (see

## Bankruptcy/Restructuring
### Senior Statesmen

**Senior Statesmen: distinguished older practitioners**

| | |
|---|---|
| Carter Francis L | Katz, Barron, Squitero, Faust, Friedberg, Grady, English & Allen PA (ONP)[†] |
| Cohen Jules | Akerman Senterfitt |
| Gilbert Leonard H | Holland & Knight LLP * |
| Stichter Don M | Stichter, Riedel, Blain & Prosser PA * |
| Zusmann Samuel J | Holland & Knight LLP * |

### Leading Individuals

**Star individuals**

| | |
|---|---|
| Singerman Paul Steven | Berger Singerman * |

**Band 1**

| | |
|---|---|
| Baena Scott L | Bilzin Sumberg Baena Price & Axelrod LLP * |
| Battista Paul J | Genovese Joblove & Battista, PA |
| Bloom Mark D | Greenberg Traurig, LLP * |
| Busey Stephen D | Smith Hulsey & Busey |
| Colton Roberta | Trenam Kemker, Attorneys |
| Genovese John H | Genovese Joblove & Battista, PA |
| Glenn Robert B | Glenn Rasmussen, P.A. |
| Goldberg Michael I | Akerman Senterfitt |
| Guso Jordi | Berger Singerman * |
| Kozyak John W | Kozyak Tropin & Throckmorton * |
| Mora Mindy A | Bilzin Sumberg Baena Price & Axelrod LLP * |
| Rasile Craig | DLA Piper LLP (US) * |
| Redmond Patricia | Stearns Weaver Miller Weissler Alhadeff |
| Riedel Harley E | Stichter, Riedel, Blain & Prosser PA |
| Throckmorton Charles W | Kozyak Tropin & Throckmorton * |

**Band 2**

| | |
|---|---|
| Blain Russell | Stichter, Riedel, Blain & Prosser PA * |
| Blanco Leyza | GrayRobinson, PA * |
| Cimo David C | Genovese Joblove & Battista, PA |
| Gart Brian | Berger Singerman * |
| Green Elizabeth A | Baker & Hostetler LLP * |
| Kirk Donald R | Fowler White Boggs |
| Lauria Thomas E | White & Case LLP * |
| Leshaw James P S | Leshaw Law, P.A. (ONP)[†] |
| Lopez-Castro Corali | Kozyak Tropin & Throckmorton * |
| Markowitz Jerry M | Markowitz Ringel Trusty + Hartog P.A. * |
| Moorefield Jr Harold | Stearns Weaver Miller Weissler Alhadeff |
| Salazar Luis | Salazar Jackson LLP (ONP)[†] * |
| Shuker R Scott | Latham, Shuker, Barker, Eden & Beaudine |
| Soriano Robert A | Greenberg Traurig, LLP * |
| Warren Jeffrey W | Bush Ross, PA (ONP)[†] |
| Wolfson Mark J | Foley & Lardner LLP |

**Band 3**

| | |
|---|---|
| Bast Jeffrey P | Bast Amron LLP (ONP)[†] |
| Berlin Howard J | Berger Singerman * |
| Budwick Michael | Meland Russin & Budwick PA |
| Charbonneau Robert | Ehrenstein Charbonneau Calderin (ONP)[†] |
| Dell-Powell Denise | Burr & Forman LLP |
| Dillworth Drew M | Stearns Weaver Miller Weissler Alhadeff |
| Emmanuel John | Fowler White Boggs |
| Gilbert Robert N | Carlton Fields, P.A. * |
| Hutton III John B | Greenberg Traurig, LLP * |

| | |
|---|---|
| Jackson Cynthia | Smith Hulsey & Busey |
| Kobert Roy | Broad and Cassel |
| Prosser Richard | Stichter, Riedel, Blain & Prosser PA |
| Pugatch Chad P | Rice Pugatch Robinson & Schiller, PA |
| Rice Arthur Halsey | Rice Pugatch Robinson & Schiller, PA |
| Rice Edwin G | Glenn Rasmussen, P.A. |
| Russin Peter | Meland Russin & Budwick PA |
| Sakalo Jay M | Bilzin Sumberg Baena Price & Axelrod LLP * |

**Band 4**

| | |
|---|---|
| Amron Brett | Bast Amron LLP (ONP)[†] |
| Anderson Rod | Holland & Knight LLP * |
| Bates Douglas | Berger Singerman * |
| Boeke Noel | Holland & Knight LLP * |
| Cloyd Leslie | Berger Singerman * |
| Fendrick Keith | Holland & Knight LLP * |
| Golden Eric | Burr & Forman LLP |
| Hartley Andrea | Akerman Senterfitt |
| Hartog Ross | Markowitz Ringel Trusty + Hartog P.A. * |
| Jennis David | Jennis & Bowen |
| Kane Jon | Burr & Forman LLP |
| Lehman Thomas | Levine Kellogg Lehman Schneider (ONP)[†] |
| Leslie Stephen R | Stichter, Riedel, Blain & Prosser PA |
| Levine David M | Levine Kellogg Lehman Schneider (ONP)[†] |
| Postler Charles | Stichter, Riedel, Blain & Prosser PA * |
| Rich Brian G | Berger Singerman * |
| Rosendorf David L | Kozyak Tropin & Throckmorton |
| Schatzman Robert | GrayRobinson, PA * |
| Schiller Lisa | Rice Pugatch Robinson & Schiller, PA |
| Shraiberg Bradley | Shraiberg, Ferrara & Landau P.A. (ONP)[†] |
| Solomon Steven J | GrayRobinson, PA * |
| Stichter Scott | Stichter, Riedel, Blain & Prosser PA * |
| Terzo Frank | GrayRobinson, PA * |
| Zaron Andrew | DLA Piper LLP (US) * |

**Up-and-coming individuals**

| | |
|---|---|
| Calderin Jacqueline | Ehrenstein Charbonneau Calderin (ONP)[†] |
| Grossman Scott M | Greenberg Traurig, LLP * |
| Harris Amy | Stichter, Riedel, Blain & Prosser PA * |
| Ketchum Elena | Stichter, Riedel, Blain & Prosser PA * |
| Parrish Jimmy D | Baker & Hostetler LLP * |
| Peterson Edward | Stichter, Riedel, Blain & Prosser PA |
| Samole David | Kozyak Tropin & Throckmorton * |
| Underwood Scott | Fowler White Boggs |

**Associates to watch**

| | |
|---|---|
| Appleby Keith | Hill Ward Henderson (ONP)[†] |
| Suarez Jesus | Genovese Joblove & Battista, PA |

* Indicates firm / individual with profile.
[†] ONP = Other Notable Practitioner.

p.1005) has a broad-ranging practice, handling all manner of bankruptcy representation and litigation. Sources say he is "very experienced, thoughtful and capable," and his working style is "very impressive – he possesses great command of the law." He and Baena recently represented a number of investment funds in connection with the Rothstein Rosenfeldt Adler Ponzi scheme case.

## Genovese Joblove & Battista, PA

**THE FIRM** This large bankruptcy boutique firm has an impeccable reputation across a diverse range of restructuring and bankruptcy matters, including representing debtors, committees, trustees, creditors, equity holders and distressed asset purchasers. It also represents receivers in state and federal courts. However, the group comes most recommended by peers as a first choice for referrals and debtor representations.

**Sources say:** "I have a very high regard for them. The team is dedicated and bright, and performs well." "A powerhouse of great lawyers."

**KEY INDIVIDUALS** Practice head **John Genovese** is a hugely experienced, "smart, honorable, solid lawyer," say sources. He is renowned for his litigation expertise, with sources describing his style as "aggressive yet reasonable," and noting that he "tries to reach a business decision first to negate the need for unnecessary litigation." Equipped with a "strong investment banking background," **Paul Battista** "continues to do outstanding work" and is well respected by peers, who acknowledge that "he's very smart, pragmatic and a worthy adversary." **David Cimo** maintains a strong reputation for his bankruptcy litigation practice, with sources noting that he is "very thorough and aggressive, yet not overly so – he doesn't let himself get wrapped up in it and is very professional." The up-and-coming **Jesus Suarez** enters the rankings this year on the back of strong praise from peers. Sources are "very impressed with the way he handles himself."

## Greenberg Traurig, LLP
### See profile on p.1024

**THE FIRM** This international powerhouse is consistently involved in a major proportion of the region's most complex, high-profile bankruptcy and restructuring matters. In recent highlights, the team represented the official equity committee in the Chapter 11 of HearUSA. It also continues to represent BankUnited Financial in its Chapter 11 proceedings.

**Sources say:** "The depth and breadth of expertise in the firm has been an important aid in exploring the financial, Chapter 11 restructuring, tax and real estate matters involved in the case." "They have very smart lawyers who understand that service and responsiveness are critical."

**KEY INDIVIDUALS Mark Bloom** (see p.986) cochairs the national practice group and is praised as being "extremely intelligent, capable, articulate, knowledgeable, cordial and professional." Sources also applaud "his ability to take complicated issues and translate them clearly, along with providing practical advice which allows us to progress quickly." **John Hutton** (see p.995) has a deep "understanding of the law and the dynamics of the process," say sources. He is cur-

rently representing Goldman Sachs as lender in a $119 million mortgage loan, with respect to the Chapter 11 bankruptcy of Swiss Chalet and GP West. **Scott Grossman** (see p.993) is described as a "very diligent person" who has "outstanding knowledge, skill, integrity and responsiveness." Clients report that he "ensures that not only is the big picture in place, but all the details are included too; he really rolls up his sleeves and works hard." The "strong" **Robert Soriano** (see p.1008) is widely respected among interviewees. He recently represented Sovereign Bank as a lender of $37 million to National Gold Exchange in its initial Chapter 11 bankruptcy, which subsequently changed to a Chapter 7 liquidation.

## Kozyak Tropin & Throckmorton

**THE FIRM** This talented Florida boutique has a stellar reputation for undertaking a wide variety of restructuring and bankruptcy litigation issues. The team is involved in many significant bankruptcy matters, including the recent Rothstein Rosenfeldt Adler Ponzi case, in which it represented the Razorback Group, the largest group of creditor victims.

**Sources say:** "Smart, honorable, solid lawyers. They strive to reach a business decision first before exploring litigation."

**KEY INDIVIDUALS John Kozyak** (see p.997) cochairs the firm's bankruptcy practice. He has "a great reputation" in the marketplace, with many sources reporting that he is "aggressive and assertive," and "the consummate gentleman" in proceedings. Described as a "solid, honest and effective lawyer," **Charles Throckmorton** (see p.1010) handles bankruptcy, as well as related litigation and creditors' rights matters. Sources report that his "strategy, intellect and writing abilities enable him to present a succinct and clear argument on the most complex of arguments to the court." **Corali Lopez-Castro** (see p.998) is held in exceptionally high regard for her "professional" practice and is "exceedingly practical and results-driven." She is currently serving as co-counsel for the Official Committee of Unsecured Creditors in BankUnited's Chapter 11 bankruptcy cases. **David Rosendorf** is lauded for his superb experience across a range of debtor and creditor representations, as well as bankruptcy litigation. Clients report that he is accustomed to dealing with "very complex issues," and has "great analytical skills." **David Samole** (see p.1005) is characterized as "smart, insightful, efficient and practical" by sources. His recent highlights include acting for the bankruptcy trustee for MetroBank Financial Services.

## Stichter, Riedel, Blain & Prosser PA
### See profile on p.1036

**THE FIRM** This Florida-based bankruptcy group has immense expertise in providing debtor-side representation to companies large and small. It continues to earn praise for its roles in major real estate-related bankruptcies, including representing Taylor, Bean & Whitaker, the largest independent mortgage lender in the USA, as debtor-in-possession.

**Sources say:** "The team is skilled and straightforward. They conduct the highest level of work around." "They're really excellent and wonderful to work with."

**KEY INDIVIDUALS** With an impressive statewide practice, **Russell Blain** (see p.985) is "the ultimate ambassador and diplomat," and "handles a lot of large matters." He is particularly praised for leading the team acting for Taylor, Bean & Whitaker. Sources note that he is "very thorough and good on his feet," with "a huge amount of experience." **Harley Riedel** has an eminent reputation as "one of the best debtor lawyers in the state." Sources describe him as a "very effective advocate" with "good negotiating skills and great courtroom presentation." **Edward Peterson** is highly regarded, with sources commending his working style: "In this business, you have to know when to put the pressure on and when to ease it back – Edward can do that." Clients also describe him as "very easy to work with; he's always responsive and professional." He recently acted alongside Blain on behalf of Taylor, Bean & Whitaker. Described as a "market leader" in the Fort Myers area, **Stephen Leslie** has been "developing rapidly" in the bankruptcy and restructuring sector. He recently represented Rick Johnson Auto & Tire in its Chapter 11 bankruptcy cases. Firm founder **Don Stichter** (see p.1009) is considered one of the most experienced bankruptcy experts in the state, particularly in relation to his knowledge of and exposure to some of the most complex debtor matters to have occurred in the region. The "very talented" **Elena Ketchum** (see p.996) "handles herself well, and her working style and knowledge fit well within the firm." She is commended for her superb expertise on both the creditor and debtor sides. The up-and-coming **Amy Harris** (see p.994) is "extremely detail-oriented" as well as "bright and nice to deal with." She recently aided in the representation of Taylor, Bean & Whitaker in its Chapter 11 case. Another of the firm's new entries in this year's rankings, **Charles Postler** (see p.1003) is highlighted by peers for his excellent transactional bankruptcy practice. Sources praise him as "very knowledgeable and thorough, and a terrific draftsperson." **Scott Stichter** (see p.1009) is "coming along rapidly as a major player in the local market," and recently acted as the lead lawyer representing Cordoba Ranch Development in its Chapter 11 case. Sources "think highly of him" and report that "he is good in court." Highlighted as an "excellent lawyer," **Richard Prosser** handles all types of bankruptcy matters, and is especially renowned for his bankruptcy litigation prowess.

## Band 2

## Akerman Senterfitt
### See profile on p.1014

**THE FIRM** This impressive national firm is primarily known for its superb representation of creditors, as demonstrated by its continued representation of the unsecured creditors committee in the Rothstein Rosenfeldt Adler bankruptcy case. It also continues to provide outstanding representation to the 50 clawback defendants in the Madoff case.

**Sources say:** "I strongly respect and trust the team at Akerman." "A very responsive team – we're very glad to have them fighting our corner."

**KEY INDIVIDUALS** The team is headed by **Michael Goldberg**, *"a market leader"* with renowned expertise in international Ponzi schemes. He is described by clients as *"very customer-oriented; he's always available, his work is very thorough and he's hugely particular about his choice of words."* **Andrea Hartley** is particularly appreciated for being *"delightful and smart."* She is an immensely respected figure in the sector, and has a broad-ranging bankruptcy and reorganization practice. **Jules Cohen** chairs the firm's bankruptcy practice and is regarded as an *"expert in his field"* who *"knows how to respond to a wrench in the works."*

## Fowler White Boggs

**THE FIRM** This team's recent expansion has increased its capabilities across all manner of creditor and debtor representation, and has further allowed it to undertake matters on behalf of an international client base. However, the group remains especially lauded for its expertise in representing creditors. It continues to act for an enviable number of financial institutions, including Wells Fargo, EverBank and Monarch Alternative Funds.

**Sources say:** *"Strengths include their responsiveness, their broad creditors' rights knowledge, and their communication between different practice groups to provide efficient, fast knowledge on various areas of expertise."*

**KEY INDIVIDUALS** With a wealth of bankruptcy litigation experience, **John Emmanuel** is a highly respected and sought-after lawyer. He was recently appointed to serve as a Consumer Privacy Ombudsman in the Robb & Stucky Chapter 11 bankruptcy . **Donald Kirk** is described as an *"experienced lawyer in commercial finance and creditors' rights, who is responsive and strives to manage the case in an efficient manner while providing excellent service."* The up-and-coming **Scott Underwood** *"has the ability to swiftly learn and understand issues of a matter which has a constantly changing landscape,"* say sources.

## Smith Hulsey & Busey

**THE FIRM** This full-service Jacksonville-based firm maintains a sterling reputation for its professional bankruptcy litigation and restructuring practice across a wide range of issues. The group recently represented 356 investors in a hedge fund, which owned 80 percent of two resort developments which filed for bankruptcy.

**Sources say:** *"The team is very talented at providing creative business solutions, with the close attention to detail required to wrap up transactional work. Their client service is also top-notch – you are able to build personal relationships with the team."*

**KEY INDIVIDUALS** Firm chairman and litigation practice group leader **Stephen Busey** is *"tremendous and focused,"* with commendable experience in complex commercial litigation and insolvency matters. Sources say: *"He uses litigation as a tool rather than a strategy, while his out-of-court people skills and financial acumen are essential to being an effective restructuring lawyer."* **Cynthia Jackson** is an experienced litigator in bankruptcy and general commercial litigation. She represents both creditors and debtors in Chapter 11 and Chapter 7 proceedings. Peers

report that she is *"a pleasure to deal with – she's smart and forever calm, and achieves good results."*

## Stearns Weaver Miller Weissler Alhadeff & Sitterson, P.A.

**THE FIRM** This statewide full-service firm is highlighted primarily for its litigation expertise and its expertise in representing creditors and trustees. The firm's litigation practice is held in particularly high regard, and recently provided trial counsel to Isaac Jimmy Mayer, who is being sued by the trustee in the Madoff Ponzi scheme. It is also acting as lead counsel to the plaintiff trustee, the firm's very own Drew Dillworth, in the highlight Ginn v Dillworth matter.

**KEY INDIVIDUALS Patricia Redmond** is *"always on top of her game,"* say sources. She has a leading practice covering creditors' rights issues and restructurings. Not only is she *"extremely effective as a lawyer,"* say interviewees, but *"she also teaches you; she is smart and motivates you to learn."* **Harold Moorefield** chairs the firm's business restructuring department and is commended for having a diverse practice. He has a strong line in representing major institutional creditors and trustees in bankruptcy and insolvency cases. Sources regard him as *"a great and intelligent lawyer."* **Drew Dillworth** is praised for his *"great breadth of experience,"* which he utilizes when dealing with all aspects of bankruptcy and restructuring matters. He also serves as a court-appointed fiduciary in bankruptcy proceedings.

## Trenam Kemker, Attorneys

**THE FIRM** This regional full-service firm has an incredible reputation for representing creditors across the financial, real estate and healthcare sectors, among others. The team also has an excellent practice representing debtors, as well as Chapter 7 and Chapter 11 trustees. In recent highlights, it acted as debtor's counsel to Custom Cable in its Chapter 11 bankruptcy.

**KEY INDIVIDUALS** According to one particularly impressed interviewee, **Roberta Colton** *"is a great lawyer and stateswoman; she can be an advocate and a teacher – I trust her completely."* Others go on to say: *"She possesses great confidence and knowledge; it's an absolute pleasure to work with her."*

## Band 3

### DLA Piper LLP (US)
See profile on p.1971

**THE FIRM** Since opening its Miami branch in 2011, DLA has developed an excellent and recognized bankruptcy and restructuring offering in the region, backed up by the firm's strong national resource network. Its docket of high-profile cases has recently included representing Bank of America as administrative agent in relation to the Fontainebleau Las Vegas Hotel and Casino Chapter 11 proceedings.

**Sources say:** *"As a new firm to the Miami market, it has made an impressive investment to its office as well as the community. They really utilize their resources."*

**KEY INDIVIDUALS** Managing partner of the Miami office, **Craig Rasile** (see p.1004) is described as *"the kind of lawyer who takes all the stress away from the experience."* He is best known for his representation of major financial institutions and creditors, and for his excellent litigation capabilities. One especially impressed client said: *"His responsiveness was like nothing I'd ever seen; his attentiveness and expertise were second to none."* **Andrew Zaron** (see p.1013) is appreciated for his *"dogged and very smart"* approach. He and Rasile represented US Bank as indenture trustee in connection with $120 million debt issuance to BankUnited.

## Glenn Rasmussen, P.A.
See profile on p.1023

**THE FIRM** Glenn Rasmussen's Tampa-based practice is recommended for its excellent quality insolvency work involving the representation of debtors, creditors, lenders, trustees and parties involved in distressed M&A matters. The firm has particular strength in creditor-side assignments, as shown by its continued representation of clients such as Bank of America, Fifth Third Bank and US Bank.

**KEY INDIVIDUALS Robert Glenn** is *"thoroughly knowledgeable while grounded in good common sense,"* say sources; *"he's got a feel for the law that you can't duplicate anywhere."* Interviewees are particularly impressed by his experience and expertise in creditors' rights issues. Equipped with a varied skill set, **Edwin Rice** is defined as a *"very sharp and capable lawyer"* who is *"good at sorting through information and analyzing how pieces fit together."*

## GrayRobinson, PA

**THE FIRM** This team continues to develop a sterling reputation across a range of bankruptcy and restructuring work, especially in the representation of major creditors. It recently represented Brickell Central in connection with the bankruptcy proceedings of Cabi SMA Tower. Other key clients have recently included the Official Committee of Unsecured Creditors of E-Brands.

**Sources say:** *"The team is adept and its negotiating skills are impressive and effective."* *"They work well as a team and aggressively defend their clients."*

**KEY INDIVIDUALS** Renowned for her cross-border expertise, **Leyza Blanco** (see p.986) has quickly built a superb reputation for undertaking Chapter 15 issues. Commentators hail her as *"one of the rising stars in the bankruptcy community"* and describe her working style as *"creative; she approaches problems in a thoughtful and practical way."* With a *"very strong financial understanding,"* **Steven Solomon** (see p.1008) is described as *"very practical, results-oriented"* and *"super smart."* He recently assisted **Robert Schatzman** (see p.1006) in representing the unsecured creditors committee, and subsequently acting as co-counsel to the liquidating trustee, of Gulfstream International. Schatzman is known as a *"wonderful lawyer"* who is *"always working hard."* **Frank Terzo** (see p.1010) is highlighted in particular for his strength in creditor and committee representations. He is described as a *"very good negotiator; he is very practical and knows that litigation isn't the only option."*

## Holland & Knight LLP
See profile on p.1028

**THE FIRM** This large national firm has a glowing reputation for handling major financial institution and creditor-side matters. The group recently represented Wells Fargo Bank in a number of significant restructuring matters, and also counts the likes of RAIT Financial Trust and Jabil Circuit as key clients.

**Sources say:** *"I am extremely impressed with the firm – not only with the partners, but with their paralegals and assistants as well. Everyone is very helpful and willing to go the extra mile."*

**KEY INDIVIDUALS** *"Talented and strong litigator"* **Rod Anderson** (see p.983) represents an array of financial institutions and creditors. He continues to represent Jabil Circuit as one of the largest unsecured creditors in the Nortel Networks bankruptcy cases pending in Canada, Delaware and the UK. **Noel Boeke** (see p.986) is *"extremely responsive and attentive to detail,"* say sources; *"he is also very smart, diplomatic and adept in dealing with the opposition."* He is currently representing Bill Maloney as Chapter 11 trustee to Earthfirst Technologies and Electric Machinery Enterprises. The *"outstanding"* **Keith Fendrick** (see p.991) has a broad-ranging practice and is heralded for his ability to *"ensure that the client has a good understanding of the legal process."* Seasoned authority **Leonard Gilbert** (see p.993) has been undertaking *"exceedingly strong work as a mediator."* He was recently appointed as a mediator in adversary proceedings relating to the bankruptcy proceedings of Taylor, Bean & Whitaker. Sources note that *"people trust and respect him."* **Samuel Zusmann** (see p.1013) has tremendous levels of experience, and all-encompassing knowledge of the bankruptcy and restructuring sector. One peer said: *"He's forgotten more law than I'll ever know!"*

## Meland Russin & Budwick PA

**THE FIRM** This Miami-based boutique maintains a stellar reputation for conducting corporate reorganizations at a level that belies its compact but efficient size. Its litigation practice comes in for high praise, as does its expertise in real estate-related bankruptcy issues. The team recently represented the trustee in the Palm Beach Finance Partners bankruptcy.

**Sources say:** *"They're doing a great job."*

**KEY INDIVIDUALS** **Peter Russin** is one of the cofounders of the firm, and is known for his insolvency work on behalf of debtors, lenders, creditors' committees and trustees. **Michael Budwick** has a wide-ranging practice acting for creditors, debtors and trustees, among other parties, across various industries.

## Rice Pugatch Robinson & Schiller, PA

**THE FIRM** This bankruptcy boutique has strength across all manner of creditor, debtor and trustee representation, and is also highlighted for its excellent bankruptcy litigation capabilities.

**Sources say:** *"They have a very good reputation in the marketplace."*

**KEY INDIVIDUALS Chad Pugatch** undertakes bankruptcy work across a wide spectrum of arenas, including bankruptcy and commercial litigation, and corporate restructurings. **Arthur Halsey Rice** is *"very well regarded by judges,"* according to sources, and has accumulated a significant amount of experience in litigation and bankruptcy law. With a hugely varied practice dealing with both creditor and debtor matters, **Lisa Schiller** is *"well regarded by lawyers, judges and clients."*

## White & Case LLP
See profile on p.451

**THE FIRM** White & Case's Florida practice group benefits from the international law firm's extensive network of resources and talent. The group is renowned for advising multinational corporations and large financial institutions on complicated domestic and cross-border transactions and dispute resolution proceedings.

**KEY INDIVIDUALS Thomas Lauria** (see p.352) is global practice head of the financial restructuring and insolvency group. He is known nationally for his track record in some of the country's most significant bankruptcy assignments.

## Band 4

## Baker & Hostetler LLP
See profile on p.2119

**THE FIRM** Baker Hostetler's Orlando-based office has a developing and increasingly recognized bankruptcy and restructuring practice. The group is highlighted for its prominent debtor-side practice, and for its coverage of bankruptcy issues occurring in the real estate, hospitality, healthcare, construction and technology sectors. The firm currently serves as debtor's counsel to Richard and Audrey Haisfield in a Chapter 11 reorganization of a number of real estate and equine companies.

**Sources say:** *"They are excellent from a strategic standpoint – real outside-the-box thinkers who create non-traditional ways to get to the end result."*

**KEY INDIVIDUALS Elizabeth Green** (see p.993) is one of the group's most renowned practitioners. Commentators are supremely impressed, with one saying: *"She is articulate and tremendously professional."* Green has a wide-ranging bankruptcy practice, and is most recommended for her work on the debtor-side. The up-and-coming **Jimmy Parrish** (see p.1003) has a *"great knowledge of the law, the ability to negotiate positive outcomes and a perfect litigating style."* Sources also describe him as *"very practical; someone who wants to explore resolutions."* He and Green recently represented Tempus Resorts in its restructuring of $250 million in debt.

## Broad and Cassel

**THE FIRM** While renowned for its committee and creditor representations, this well-respected firm handles a wide variety of bankruptcies, workouts and reorganizations. The group recently represented shipping company Trailer Bridge in its reorganization and in related antitrust claims, involving jurisdictions across Florida, the Dominican

Republic and Puerto Rico. The team is also noted for its recent activity on Chapter 7 matters.

**KEY INDIVIDUALS Roy Kobert** is chair of the firm's bankruptcy and creditors' rights practice group. He is described as *"a very good lawyer"* who is *"very bright"* and proves his worth by *"the high quality of his practice."*

## Burr & Forman LLP
See profile on p.1019

**THE FIRM** This full-service firm is highlighted for its excellent up-and-coming bankruptcy team. The group is best known for its creditor-side practice, acting for major financial institutions, secured lenders, committees and 363 bidders, among other parties. Its enviable client list includes BankFIRST, Regions Bank and Lloyds of London.

**Sources say:** *"Very, very bright lawyers."*

**KEY INDIVIDUALS** Sources praise **Denise Dell-Powell** as an attorney who *"understands the business part of the equation."* She is best known for her sterling work on behalf of lenders, having recently acted for the likes of Canyon Capital Realty Advisors and SunTrust Bank. **Eric Golden** is an expert in representing creditors and lenders in major bankruptcy litigation-related issues as well as restructurings and workouts. He is described as a *"knowledgeable and experienced"* attorney who provides *"excellent service; he is attentive and will actually call to ask you if the team is meeting expectations."* **Jon Kane** is praised for his *"total understanding of the law, and he does a good job of explaining the issues and works hard to keep clients informed."* His recent highlights include representing the Official Committee of Unsecured Creditors for the estate of Lydia Cladek.

## Carlton Fields, P.A.
See profile on p.1020

**THE FIRM** This group's small but highly effective team has excellent capabilities in sophisticated bankruptcy proceedings, and is highlighted in particular for its secured creditor-side expertise and its work for major financial institutions and trustees.

**KEY INDIVIDUALS Robert Gilbert** (see p.993) is experienced in a wide range of representations, acting for creditors, committees, trustees, debtors, and others. He is recommended particularly for his ability to manage egos in proceedings, with interviewees lauding his capacity to pull complex situations together and marshal fellow parties.

## Foley & Lardner LLP
See profile on p.2588

**THE FIRM** Foley's solid bankruptcy and restructuring offering in Florida is supported by the firm's extensive national capabilities. The group handles a wide range of issues, and is highlighted in particular for its expertise in representing secured creditors. Recent highlights include representing Fifth Third Bank as secured lender on a $15 million loan secured by home units and vacant land, in the Chapter 11 proceedings of Fiddler's Creek.

**Sources say:** *"They are very knowledgeable about the client's needs."*

**KEY INDIVIDUALS** With nearly 30 years' experience in the field, **Mark Wolfson** has knowledge of bankruptcy and restructuring matters of all types and size. Sources report that *"he can think like a client and anticipate what your needs will be."*

### Latham, Shuker, Barker, Eden & Beaudine LLP

**THE FIRM** This Orlando-based group acts for a broad range of creditors and companies, but is perhaps best known for its excellent work on behalf of debtors.
**Sources say:** *"One of the go-to debtor groups in Florida."*
**KEY INDIVIDUALS Scott Shuker** is held in high esteem by his peers. He is described as *"phenomenal and really smart; he truly knows the law well,"* and is *"able to produce solutions easily."*

### Markowitz Ringel Trusty + Hartog P.A.

**THE FIRM** This well-established and respected boutique firm offers a full range of services across the bankruptcy and restructuring field. It is currently representing the trustee – the firm's own Ross Hartog – in the bankruptcy proceedings of Harris Food Group. Clients enthusiastically note the firm's great value for money.
**KEY INDIVIDUALS Jerry Markowitz**'s (see p.999) *"expertise runs so deep across the spectrum of the reorganization and insolvency world that he can find a solution very quickly,"* say sources. He also has a *"great demeanor; he can either get out in court and fight or sit at a desk, performing both tasks with dogged commitment."* **Ross Hartog** (see

p.994) has a solid practice handling a wide range of bankruptcy and restructuring matters. He was recently assigned as trustee to Harris Food Group.

### Other Notable Practitioners

**Luis Salazar** (see p.1005) recently formed his own firm in Miami, Salazar Jackson LLP. His practice covers a broad range of bankruptcy and related litigation. **Jeffrey Warren** of Bush Ross, PA is renowned for his experience in Chapter 11 reorganizations, and in- and out-of-court proceedings. Clients commend the *"knowledge and confidence he brings to the table."* **Jeffrey Bast** of Bast Amron LLP is quickly developing a sterling reputation for bankruptcy and insolvency work, with a particular emphasis on creditors' rights issues. Sources regard him as *"high quality, high in integrity and straightforward."* At the same firm, **Brett Amron** *"continues to impress."* Sources note that he is *"smart, young and aggressive – neither Brett nor Jeffrey will back down from the big guys."* **Robert Charbonneau** of Ehrenstein Charbonneau Calderin is lauded in particular for his representation of creditors and committees, and for his bankruptcy litigation expertise. A *"very bright and capable"* attorney, he undertakes *"solid, quality work."* **Jacqueline Calderin**, also of Ehrenstein Charbonneau Calderin, is regarded as a superb up-and-coming expert doing impressive creditors' committee and Chapter 7 trustee work. **Thomas Lehman** is one of the founding partners of Levine

Kellogg Lehman Schneider + Grossman LLP, and cochair of the firm's bankruptcy practice. He handles a broad range of bankruptcy and distressed business assignments. Fellow practice group cochair **David Levine** of Levine Kellogg Lehman Schneider + Grossman LLP represents parties across the spectrum of the bankruptcy field. **Bradley Shraiberg** of Shraiberg, Ferrara & Landau P.A. is described as a *"real energetic go-getter"* with a *"growing presence"* in the bankruptcy and restructuring sector. Sources say he is *"young, smart and creative."* Of counsel **Francis Carter** heads the bankruptcy and creditors' rights practice group at Katz, Barron, Squitero, Faust, Friedberg, Grady, English & Allen PA. He is best known for his superb expertise as a mediator. **David Jennis** of Jennis & Bowen is held in high regard for his experience of bankruptcy, workout, restructuring and related litigation issues. Sources claim that they *"can't say nice enough things about him – he's amazing!"* **James Leshaw** recently left Greenberg Traurig to form Leshaw Law, P.A. He is a *"seasoned bankruptcy attorney and a very quick thinker"* who is able to *"break down complex problems and efficiently work through collaborative solutions."* The up-and-coming **Keith Appleby** recently joined Tampa-based Hill Ward Henderson from Fowler White Boggs. He is known for his *"great rapport with judges"* and his *"collegial personality."*

# CONSTRUCTION

Construction p.944

Commentary about individuals can be found under their firm's paragraph. If the firm has no paragraph (is not ranked) look at Other Notable Practitioners.

## Band 1

### Carlton Fields, P.A.
See profile on p.1020

**THE FIRM** This standout construction group handles matters in all areas of construction law, including contracts, administration and insurance. The team offers litigation services in relation to a vast array of projects, including those involving schools, airports and hotels. Its enviable client roster includes KB Home, CB Richard Ellis and CH2M Hill.
**Sources say:** *"I was very impressed with their legal proficiency and the firm's capability. All were highly responsive and worked very well with me as outside counsel, as well as working very well with our clients."*
**KEY INDIVIDUALS** Sources note that **George Meyer** (see p.1001) is *"the best construction transactional lawyer in the state"* and that *"he's touched pretty much every major transaction in the state."* Recently he has been working on behalf of Hunt Construction Group on the expansion of the San Diego Convention Center. The impressive **Luis Prats** (see p.1004) has been kept busy with litigation involving condominium construction issues. According to interviewees, *"he's incredibly driven with a great work ethic and is highly*

*knowledgeable in the field."* The eminent **Cary Wright** (see p.1012) is known for his impressive expertise in construction contracts and insurance matters. One interviewee reports: *"I can't say enough good things about him. He's a great lawyer."* **Charles Cacciabeve** (see p.987) offers particular expertise in construction contracts. Observers note that he is *"a top-drawer guy. He's a very good construction lawyer and the kind of guy you want to deal with."* **Patricia Thompson** (see p.1010) centers her highly acclaimed practice around litigation, with a focus on the construction industry. Sources reveal that she is *"a gifted surety lawyer. She is very smart and is willing to get into the detail of a case."* Surety law authority **Bruce King** (see p.996) is *"very smart and very highly regarded."* Sources add that *"his knowledge of bonding and insurance is second to none."* Construction regulation and litigation attorney **Hardy Roberts** (see p.1005) maintains his highly regarded practice from the firm's Tampa office. Sources say: *"He's a very well-rounded lawyer. He does everything well."* One commentator added: *"What I valued most about Hardy was that he knew his way around the Florida courts and has deep familiarity with construction law in the Florida field."* The preeminent **Michael Nuechterlein** (see p.1002) is extremely highly regarded for his mediation work in the construction field.

### Moye, O'Brien, O'Rourke, Pickert & Dillon, LLP
See profile on p.1032

**THE FIRM** This luminary construction boutique has an impressive national and international reach. The team prides itself on forging long-term relationships and is famed for undertaking very high-profile matters, exemplified by its work for the PCL/Archer Weston joint venture on the I-4/Lee Roy Selmon Expressway Connector Interchange. Other clients include Odebrecht Construction and Peter Kiewit & Sons.
**Sources say:** *"The best of the best – a fantastic firm."*
**KEY INDIVIDUALS** According to sources, **James Moye** (see p.1001) is *"so incredibly good, extremely logical and academic. He understands both the industry and the legal side."* He has been working on the aforementioned matter for PCL and Archer Western. The esteemed **Sean Dillon** (see p.990) has recently been acting for Odebrecht Construction on a project at Miami International Airport relating to the construction of a $350 million elevated light rail system. **Stephen Pickert** (see p.1003) is a highly regarded Florida construction lawyer who has made his mark over the past year representing TD Thompson

## Construction
### Leading Firms

**Band 1**
Carlton Fields, P.A. *
Moye, O'Brien, O'Rourke, Pickert & Dillon, LLP *
Peckar & Abramson, P.C. *

**Band 2**
Akerman Senterfitt
Becker & Poliakoff PA *
Ciklin Lubitz Martens & O'Connell
Ferencik, Libanoff, Brandt, Bustamante & Williams
Greenberg Traurig, LLP *
Holland & Knight LLP *
Vezina Lawrence & Piscitelli

**Band 3**
Broad and Cassel
Daniels Kashtan
Kirwin Norris PA
Shutts & Bowen LLP
Siegfried, Rivera, Lerner, De La Torre & Sobel, PA
Wright, Fulford, Moorhead and Brown P.A.

**Band 4**
Bilzin Sumberg Baena Price & Axelrod LLP *
Foley & Lardner LLP *
GrayRobinson, PA
Mills Paskert Divers PA
Phelps Dunbar LLP *

## Construction
### Senior Statesmen

**Senior Statesmen: distinguished older practitioners**

| | |
|---|---|
| Leiby Larry R | Malka & Kravitz, P.A. (ONP)[†] |
| Nuechterlein Michael F | Carlton Fields, P.A. * |
| Siegfried Steven | Siegfried, Rivera, Lerner, De La Torre & Sobel, PA |
| Welbaum R Earl | Welbaum, Guernsey, Hingston, Greenleaf & Gregory LLP |

### Leading Individuals

**Star individuals**

| | |
|---|---|
| Alexander Bruce | Ciklin Lubitz Martens & O'Connell |

**Band 1**

| | |
|---|---|
| Ashby Kimberly | Akerman Senterfitt |
| Cacciabeve Charles J | Carlton Fields, P.A. * |
| Downs III Joseph W | Daniels Kashtan |
| Ferencik Robert E | Ferencik, Libanoff, Brandt, Bustamante |
| Gentile Melinda S | Peckar & Abramson, P.C. * |
| Hornreich Michael | Greenberg Traurig, LLP * |
| Kirwin Brian P | Kirwin Norris PA |
| Lesser Steven | Becker & Poliakoff PA * |
| Meyer George J | Carlton Fields, P.A. * |
| Moye James E | Moye, O'Brien, O'Rourke, Pickert & Dillon * |
| Prats Luis | Carlton Fields, P.A. * |
| Reisman Stephen H | Peckar & Abramson, P.C. * |
| Subin Ben | Holland & Knight LLP * |
| Weiss Christopher | Christopher Weiss Attorney at Law (ONP)[†] |
| Wilson Michael | Broad and Cassel |
| Wright Wm Cary | Carlton Fields, P.A. * |

**Band 2**

| | |
|---|---|
| Alfert, Jr Robert | Broad and Cassel |
| Brandt A Peter | Ferencik, Libanoff, Brandt, Bustamante |
| Carey Michael R | Carey, O'Malley, Whitaker & Manson (ONP)[†] |
| Dannecker John H | Shutts & Bowen LLP |
| Dillon Sean M | Moye, O'Brien, O'Rourke, Pickert & Dillon * |
| Dudley Frederick | Holland & Knight LLP * |
| Durkin Denis L | Baker & Hostetler LLP (ONP)[†] * |
| Kashtan Michael F | Daniels Kashtan |
| Keiner Jeffrey | GrayRobinson, PA * |
| King Bruce C | Carlton Fields, P.A. * |

| | |
|---|---|
| Lawrence II Joseph W | Vezina Lawrence & Piscitelli |
| Libanoff Ira L | Ferencik, Libanoff, Brandt, Bustamante & |
| Martin Gregory S | Gregory S. Martin & Associates (ONP)[†] |
| Pickert Stephen W | Moye, O'Brien, O'Rourke, Pickert & Dillon * |
| Piscitelli Michael A | Vezina Lawrence & Piscitelli |
| Sobel Stuart | Siegfried, Rivera, Lerner, De La Torre |
| Thompson Patricia H | Carlton Fields, P.A. * |
| Vezina, III W Robert | Vezina Lawrence & Piscitelli PA |
| Weintraub Lee | Becker & Poliakoff PA (ONP)[†] |

**Band 3**

| | |
|---|---|
| Bell Brent C | Shutts & Bowen LLP |
| Bercun Bohm Stacy | Akerman Senterfitt |
| Brown Curtis L | Wright, Fulford, Moorhead and Brown P.A. |
| Capps Bryan | Kirwin Norris PA |
| Chaves Richard R | Ciklin Lubitz Martens & O'Connell |
| Cotney Trenton | Trent Cotney, P.A. (ONP)[†] |
| Dogali Andy | Forizs and Dogali P.A. (ONP)[†] |
| Haimo Adam | Bilzin Sumberg Baena Price & Axelrod LLP * |
| Lane Joe | Lowndes Drosdick Doster Kantor (ONP)[†] |
| Miller James C | Greenberg Traurig, LLP * |
| Murphy PE Michael G | Greenberg Traurig, LLP * |
| Norris Bruce | Kirwin Norris PA |
| Roberts III Hardy L | Carlton Fields, P.A. * |
| Schimmel Seth M | Phelps Dunbar LLP |
| Stein Gary M | Peckar & Abramson, P.C. * |
| Trip Warren | Bedell, Dittmar, DeVault, Pillans (ONP)[†] |
| Vento John | Trenam Kemker, Attorneys (ONP)[†] |

**Up-and-coming individuals**

| | |
|---|---|
| Feldman Bret | Phelps Dunbar LLP |

* Indicates firm / individual with profile.
[†]ONP = Other Notable Practitioner.

Construction in relation to a significant third party action brought against it.

## Peckar & Abramson, P.C.
### See profile on p.1998

**THE FIRM** This leading construction practice maintains a focus on handling complex commercial issues for building and civil contractor clients, often in an international capacity. The team has the ability to manage all aspects of a construction project, including contract review and litigation of a wide range of issues. The group prides itself on its dedicated approach to client service, while still maintaining an impressive depth and breadth of expertise.

**Sources say:** "*Very impressed with the firm. They're extremely well thought of and I find them to be very professional and are always seen to be providing great counsel.*" "*Their service is wonderful – they're very responsive and very client sensitive.*"

**KEY INDIVIDUALS Melinda Gentile** (see p.993) is known by peers as "*a very good construction lawyer.*" She is currently involved in a complex case involving a residential condominium project on Miami Beach and is considered an expert in a range of construction matters, including delay issues, securities and insurance claims. **Stephen Reisman** (see p.1004) is an "*excellent lawyer*" who has recently been involved in negotiating construction contracts for one of the past year's largest private works projects in Florida. Sources "*value his counsel tremendously*" and consider him an expert in construction defects. **Gary Stein** (see p.1009) maintains an excellent reputation for construction law. Sources say: "*He's quiet and strong. He*

knows his business." He also offers expertise in compliance issues relating to minority contractors in public-private projects.

## Band 2

### Akerman Senterfitt
#### See profile on p.1014

**THE FIRM** The multidisciplinary team at this impressive firm is able to offer a full range of services for construction projects, from land use issues to dispute resolution. It exhibits particular expertise in public infrastructure and transport projects. Recent trends have seen the firm expand its cross-border reach and increase its representation of South American clients. Clients include Resorts

World Miami, Dacra Development and Palace Management Group.

**Sources say:** "*A terrific firm.*"

**KEY INDIVIDUALS** The superb **Kimberly Ashby** has notably been working on behalf of the City of Orlando on the high-value 'Venues' project, which will see the building of a new Performing Arts Center and a new Sports Arena, and the renovation of the Citrus Bowl Stadium in Orlando. **Stacy Bercun Bohm** has been acting for Resorts World Miami on a $3 billion construction project involving the building of a hotel and convention centre. Sources praise her as "*a marvelous attorney – very bright, very aggressive and always informed.*"

## Becker & Poliakoff PA
See profile on p.1016

**THE FIRM** This prominent construction team maintains a broad-based practice despite its smaller size. The group continues to represent owners, developers and condominium associations, and is increasingly prominent in contractor defense matters and in representing contractors. The firm has launched a public-private partnership team, a multidisciplinary arm of the practice aimed at developing public/private projects. Clients include Carnival Corporation, Swire Properties and Zurich Surety.
**Sources say:** "*They're eminently qualified in this area of specialization and are very responsive.*"
**KEY INDIVIDUALS** One source praises **Steven Lesser** as "*a very gifted construction lawyer – my first choice nationally.*" Commentators are in awe of the knowledge Lesser has at his fingertips, and relate that "*he is extremely fair and knowledgeable in construction law.*" He recently acted for Carnival Corporation in a design dispute worth in excess of $7.5 million. Peers note that **Lee Weintraub** has "*become quite a force in Florida*" and say that "*he's right at the cutting edge of what's going on. An extremely good construction lawyer.*" He has been representing Meisner Electric in a complex construction arrangement concerning the New Marlins Baseball Park.

## Ciklin Lubitz Martens & O'Connell
**THE FIRM** This distinguished team offers counsel on the full range of construction-related matters. The firm is renowned in the market for its construction defect litigation work, which it undertakes on behalf of both contractors and developers.
**Sources say:** "*Dedicated, experienced attorneys who communicate well with the client.*"
**KEY INDIVIDUALS** **Bruce Alexander**'s reputable practice is now more heavily weighted towards arbitration and mediation cases, although he maintains his excellent reputation as a "*top-drawer*" construction attorney. Interviewees single him out as "*the go-to construction mediator.*" **Richard Chaves** is renowned as "*an expert in Florida construction law.*" He has expertise in an array of construction matters, including insurance, lien law and contracts review.

## Ferencik, Libanoff, Brandt, Bustamante & Williams
**THE FIRM** Sources praise this impressive boutique construction firm. The team advises a variety of parties involved in construction projects, including owners, developers and contractors. The group prides itself on its drive to find creative and innovative solutions to problems.
**Sources say:** "*A very good firm with top-drawer guys. They're well thought of.*"
**KEY INDIVIDUALS** **Robert Ferencik** is praised by sources as "*a very competent, sharp guy.*" He deals with construction litigation cases, product liability litigation and related professional liability claims. **Peter Brandt** has cultivated a great reputation in the Florida construction law market. Sources note that "*he's a gentleman; he's brilliant and very capable in construction. He's also a great mediator.*"

**Ira Libanoff** focuses his practice on large construction projects. Sources speak highly of his abilities in construction claims and construction liens law.

## Greenberg Traurig, LLP
See profile on p.1024

**THE FIRM** This construction practice retains lawyers with diverse backgrounds in engineering and the wider construction industry, meaning it is able to deal with even the most complex technical issues. The group has worked with a variety of parties involved in large construction projects and is moving into the green building sector, while maintaining its reputation in defects litigation matters. Clients include National Public Finance Guarantee, Glimcher Development and Kayne Anderson Real Estate Advisors.
**Sources say:** "*A fantastic law firm.*"
**KEY INDIVIDUALS** The eminent **Michael Hornreich** (see p.995) maintains a top-flight reputation in a range of construction matters. One source labeled him "*a fantastic construction lawyer. I have a lot of respect for him.*" **James Miller**'s (see p.1001) strength in construction law is supported by his engineering background. One source comments that "*he's unique; he's not only a good lawyer but knows the specifics of construction.*" **Michael Murphy** (see p.1002) centers his construction practice around providing counsel for contractors and developers in the event of a breach of contract, delay or disruption in construction and in lien foreclosure matters.

## Holland & Knight LLP
See profile on p.1028

**THE FIRM** This thriving practice handles a broad range of construction matters, including litigation, dispute resolution and financial issues for contractors, developers and investors alike. The team has a strong reputation for producing extremely high-quality work.
**Sources say:** "*They did an excellent job for us. My advice would be to go nowhere but Holland & Knight in Florida. You need someone who knows substantive law, which they did, and you also need people who have a relationship with the licensing department. I have no hesitation in recommending them. You frankly couldn't find anybody better.*"
**KEY INDIVIDUALS** **Ben Subin** (see p.1009) receives high praise across the board. One source enthuses: "*I would unqualifiedly recommend him. He's a good sounding board – he's very calm, organized and methodical in his approach to problems. He's very good at calming situations to allow a resolution.*" "*Standout lawyer*" **Frederick Dudley** (see p.990) offers particular expertise in construction lien law. One impressed client reveals that "*he did an excellent job. He is very cordial, easy to work with, responsive and friendly.*"

## Vezina Lawrence & Piscitelli
**THE FIRM** This boutique construction team runs a successful practice from its Fort Lauderdale and Tallahassee offices. The group is famed for its horizontal infrastructure and conflict work, but also advises clients on the full range of construction law issues, from environmental matters to litigation.

**Sources say:** "*For horizontal infrastructure work there is no law firm that touches them. They're outstanding.*"
**KEY INDIVIDUALS** **Rob Vezina** is known to peers as "*a solid attorney across the board.*" He receives praise for his ability and drive to get deals done, and sources are impressed by his excellent connections in the Florida transportation department. Sources call the impressive **Joseph Lawrence** a "*top-drawer*" attorney. He maintains an enviable reputation in construction law and also has expertise in surety matters. **Michael Piscitelli** is highly regarded for his expertise in both construction and contracts law, including disputes, defective design claims and breach of contract claims.

### Band 3

## Broad and Cassel
**THE FIRM** This group advises on a range of construction matters, including contractual negotiations, design defect claims and termination disputes. The team has recently seen a shift from construction defect work to a more transactional-focused practice, particularly in the aviation industry and in large road improvement projects. Clients include Greater Orlando Aviation Authority, Lions Gable Realty and John Knox Village.
**Sources say:** "*Broad and Cassel has excellent construction attorneys with backgrounds or degrees in engineering or architecture. This provides the firm with firsthand knowledge of typical construction practices and issues faced by owners, contractors and subcontractors. I would highly recommend Broad and Cassel for its construction expertise.*"
**KEY INDIVIDUALS** **Michael Wilson** mainly works with private clients and has particular expertise in distressed condominium projects. Sources applaud his client service and say he is "*a top drawer guy.*" **Robert Alfert** brings his background in architecture and an enviable level of trial experience to bear on a variety of construction matters. He is also renowned for his public sector work, claims avoidance and contracts counsel. "*He's the most knowledgeable attorney on the construction side that I've ever worked with,*" said one client.

## Daniels Kashtan
**THE FIRM** This respected construction practice is well regarded in the fields of dispute resolution, contract negotiation and construction litigation. The team acts on behalf of architects and engineers, among other professionals. It is also noted by sources for its exemplary insurance defense work.
**Sources say:** "*Very fine construction lawyers.*"
**KEY INDIVIDUALS** **Joseph Downs** remains a very prominent presence in insurance defense work. Sources are quick to confirm his position as a leading lawyer in this space. **Michael Kashtan** is widely recognized in the market for his work in construction litigation, mediation and arbitration. He represents professional clients in the full range of contractual construction disputes.

## Kirwin Norris PA

**THE FIRM** This team's depth and experience are applauded by sources. The firm's construction group puts creative resolution of disputes at the heart of its practice, which spans a full range of services, from drafting and negotiation of construction contracts to litigation. The firm has experience in acting on behalf of a range of parties to a construction project.

**KEY INDIVIDUALS Brian Kirwin** has a robust construction practice. He focuses on advising public and private clients on construction and design contracts, and also has experience in construction litigation. **Bryan Capps** is known as a quality trial attorney with a strong construction focus. He has a particular talent for construction defect cases. **Bruce Norris** is a *"great lawyer"* whose background lies in the construction engineering sector. He brings this experience to bear in drafting contracts, construction litigation and alternative dispute resolution.

## Shutts & Bowen LLP

**THE FIRM** This high-quality firm has six offices spanning Florida and offers a full range of construction services, including litigation, construction administration, liens and product liability claims. The team also possesses particular expertise in hotel development, and acts for a diverse client base.

**Sources say:** *"The lawyers are outstanding – a good solid group."*

**KEY INDIVIDUALS John Dannecker** is recognized by peers for his masterful skill in complex construction litigation. Sources note that *"he's a superstar and has developed a reputation in multiparty litigation. He's really a great lawyer."* **Brent Bell** is renowned for being *"very creative. You go to him and he gets it done."* He is highly regarded for his proactive approach to problem solving, and focuses his practice on litigation in the construction field.

## Siegfried, Rivera, Lerner, De La Torre & Sobel, PA

**THE FIRM** This noteworthy construction practice represents general contractors. The team is experienced in representing all parties to a construction project and maintains an impressive specialty in the condominium warranty area. The group has managed both public and private projects, including theme parks and airports, with great success.

**Sources say:** *"A major player in the Miami market in condominium matters."*

**KEY INDIVIDUALS Stuart Sobel** is a solid trial lawyer with a focus on construction issues. He has much experience in this field and is applauded for his ability to invent innovative ways of improving his service to clients using technology. **Steven Siegfried** is praised by commentators as an *"excellent construction lawyer."* He has dealt with all stages of a construction project, from negotiation of contracts to providing counsel on design defect claims.

## Wright, Fulford, Moorhead and Brown P.A.

**THE FIRM** This construction-focused boutique runs its successful Florida practice from its Altamonte Springs office. The group acts on behalf of a range of clients in reviewing contracts and claims preparation work, as well as litigation and appellate work.

**KEY INDIVIDUALS Curtis Brown** maintains a well-regarded construction practice with a focus on delay claims. He is also notably involved in construction industry educational programs.

## Band 4

### Bilzin Sumberg Baena Price & Axelrod LLP
See profile on p.1018

**THE FIRM** This skilled construction team is kept busy with several ongoing high-profile commercial matters on both the transactional and litigation sides. The team has implemented innovative ways to improve client service and address new trends by creating a construction industry blog.

**Sources say:** *"Top-notch – the best firm I've ever dealt with. They are unique in the fact that they have a high level of business acumen."*

**KEY INDIVIDUALS Adam Haimo** (see p.994) is recognized by peers for his contracts negotiation work. Sources say he is *"excellent to work with, bright and responsive."* He also has experience in breach of contract claims and construction litigation.

### Foley & Lardner LLP
See profile on p.2588

**THE FIRM** This prominent nationwide firm is known for advising and litigating on behalf of clients in matters concerning construction claims. The team also has expertise in insurance coverage issues and construction liens law. Clients include The Alliant Company and Lennar Homes.

**Sources say:** *"An outstanding job – professional and responsive."*

**KEY INDIVIDUALS David Harper** is a key contact in the Tampa office.

### GrayRobinson, PA

**THE FIRM** This much-admired construction practice has experience in handling a whole range of construction issues, from contract negotiations to litigation and advising on complex dispute resolution for both public and private sector clients. The team has worked on matters involving sewage treatment plants, jails and schools. Clients include Jacobs Engineering Group, Siemens and Lexington Insurance.

**Sources say:** *"Their work has been consistently outstanding. No firm in Florida has exceeded the service we get from GrayRobinson."*

**KEY INDIVIDUALS Jeffrey Keiner** (see p.996) is credited with having a *"very strong work ethic,"* and sources also note that *"he is intelligent and responsive."* He is skilled in the area of horizontal infrastructure projects.

### Mills Paskert Divers PA

**THE FIRM** The Tampa office of this boutique litigation firm has experience in representing both public and private clients in construction disputes statewide. It handles all aspects of the construction process with great expertise and skill.

**Sources say:** *"They do great work – I really respect them. They're a top rate law firm."*

**KEY INDIVIDUALS Seth Mills** is a key contact.

### Phelps Dunbar LLP
See profile on p.1383

**THE FIRM** This construction group maintains a regionally focused practice and is proud of its strong client relationships both in and outside of Florida. The team has skill in drafting contracts, trial experience and appellate expertise in the construction area, and has worked on both public and private construction projects. URS Corporation Southern, AMEC Earth & Environmental and Instar Services Group are among its key clients.

**KEY INDIVIDUALS Seth Schimmel** focuses on construction matters for developer clients, and also has experience in working on defect claims for owner clients. He led the team in work for AMEC Earth & Environmental relating to a dam failure claim. **Bret Feldman** recently represented InStar Services Group in a breach of contract claim worth approximately $400,000. He provides a full range of construction services, including negotiating contracts and mediation, arbitration and litigation of construction disputes.

## Other Notable Practitioners

**Denis Durkin** (see p.990) of Baker & Hostetler LLP is acclaimed by sources as *"smart and talented."* He maintains a particular focus on Louisiana clients and deals with a broad range of construction industry cases. He also has experience in claims arising out of the renewable energy market. **Gregory Martin** of Gregory S. Martin & Associates, P.A. is lauded for his mediation work and his experience with managing construction projects and litigation. Sources remark: *"He'll get to the bottom line faster than others and get the case solved."* **Trenton Cotney** of Trent Cotney, P.A. is highly recommended by sources, who say his *"attentiveness, expertise and customer service are his strengths."* He works in all areas of construction litigation and arbitration. **Joe Lane** of Lowndes Drosdick Doster Kantor & Reed, PA handles extremely large construction litigation cases and insurance work. Market opinion is that he is a *"well-regarded lawyer."* **John Vento** of Trenam Kemker, Attorneys focuses in the main on handling construction litigation for contractor clients. **Larry Leiby** of Malka & Kravitz, P.A. has a wealth of experience in contractual issues. Commentators note that he is *"very well regarded and a very fine lawyer."* **Earl Welbaum** of Welbaum, Guernsey, Hingston, Greenleaf & Gregory LLP is much admired for his vast experience and superior knowledge of a full range of construction services. Sole practitioner **Christopher Weiss** has built up a strong reputation in the field of construction law in Florida. He runs his practice from his Orlando offices and is particularly highly regarded in construction litigation. **Michael Carey** of Carey, O'Malley, Whitaker & Manson PA is a litigation specialist and works on behalf of all parties in the construction industry. **Warren Trip** of Bedell, Dittmar, DeVault, Pillans & Coxe is praised for his polished service and well-rounded experience. Observers suggest that he is

"*very smart, very good and very professional.*" **Andy Dogali** of Forizs and Dogali P.A. has been successful in handling civil litigation claims with a particular focus on the con-

struction industry. He represents a variety of clients from the construction sector.

# CORPORATE/M&A & PRIVATE EQUITY

Commentary about individuals can be found under their firm's paragraph. If the firm has no paragraph (is not ranked) look at Other Notable Practitioners.

## Corporate/M&A & Private Equity
### Leading Firms

**Band 1**
Akerman Senterfitt
Greenberg Traurig, LLP *
Holland & Knight LLP *

**Band 2**
Shumaker Loop & Kendrick LLP
White & Case LLP *

**Band 3**
Berger Singerman *
Bilzin Sumberg Baena Price & Axelrod LLP *
Broad and Cassel
Carlton Fields, P.A. *
Foley & Lardner LLP *
Gunster *
Hill Ward Henderson *
Hogan Lovells US LLP
McDermott Will & Emery LLP *
Shutts & Bowen LLP

**Band 4**
Baker & Hostetler LLP *
Glenn Rasmussen, P.A. *
Hunton & Williams LLP *
Smith Hulsey & Busey
Stearns Weaver Miller Weissler Alhadeff & Sitterson, P.A.
Trenam Kemker, Attorneys

## Band 1

### Akerman Senterfitt
**See profile on p.1014**
**THE FIRM** This Florida heavyweight is a preeminent name in middle-market transactional work, serving clients drawn from a wide array of industries. The team is regularly sought out by public and private companies, including high-profile private equity funds, for advice on investments, public offerings and M&A. Akerman Senterfitt's lawyers are consistently praised for their ability to translate the legal requirements of their clients into practical business solutions, as well as their nationwide and international reach. Highlights include advising Carrols Restaurant Group on its acquisition of 278 Burger King restaurants across the country, and representing the Comvest Group in its $780 million purchase of Tekelec.

## Corporate/M&A & Private Equity
### Senior Statesmen

**Senior Statesmen: distinguished older practitioners**

| | | |
|---|---|---|
| McGuigan Thomas R | Squire Sanders (US) LLP (ONP) [†] * | |

### Leading Individuals

**Star individuals**

| | | |
|---|---|---|
| Epstein Gary M | Greenberg Traurig, LLP * | |
| Grammig Robert J | Holland & Knight LLP * | |

**Band 1**

| | |
|---|---|
| Aronson Daniel H | Berger Singerman * |
| Awner Jonathan L | Akerman Senterfitt |
| Beloff Donn A | Greenberg Traurig, LLP * |
| de Armas Luis A | Shutts & Bowen LLP |
| Doliner Nathaniel L | Carlton Fields, P.A. * |
| Felman David S | Hill Ward Henderson * |
| Freeland Jorge | White & Case LLP * |
| Klinghoffer Teddy D | Akerman Senterfitt |
| Rasmussen Robert C | Glenn Rasmussen, P.A. |
| Roddenberry Stephen | Akerman Senterfitt |
| Yadley Gregory | Shumaker Loop & Kendrick LLP |

**Band 2**

| | |
|---|---|
| Axelrod Alan D | Bilzin Sumberg Baena Price & Axelrod LLP * |
| Barkus David A | Greenberg Traurig, LLP * |
| Bates David G. | Gunster |
| Bell Rodney H | Holland & Knight LLP * |
| Danco Sharon Docherty | Glenn Rasmussen, P.A. |
| Danzi Mark A | Hill Ward Henderson * |
| Davis Gardner F | Foley & Lardner LLP |
| MacCullough Kara L | Greenberg Traurig, LLP * |
| March Bruce I | Greenberg Traurig, LLP * |
| Mitrione Michael V | Gunster |
| Perez Luis J | Hogan Lovells US LLP |
| Rosner Ira N | Greenberg Traurig, LLP * |
| Roston Carl D | Akerman Senterfitt |

| | |
|---|---|
| Siskind Harris C | McDermott Will & Emery LLP * |
| Teblum Gary | Trenam Kemker, Attorneys |

**Band 3**

| | |
|---|---|
| Alvarez-Farré Emilio J | White & Case LLP * |
| Bacheller Chester E | Holland & Knight LLP * |
| Higbee Robert Alan | Shutts & Bowen LLP |
| McAleavey Tom | Holland & Knight LLP * |
| Pasternack Marshall | Bilzin Sumberg Baena Price & Axelrod LLP * |
| Seifer David | Stearns Weaver Miller Weissler Alhadeff |
| Smith Darrell C | Shumaker Loop & Kendrick LLP |
| Starcher Doug | Broad and Cassel |
| Traber Martin A | Foley & Lardner LLP |
| Vazquez Steven W | Foley & Lardner LLP |
| Watts-FitzGerald Abigail | Weiss Serota Helfman Pastoriza (ONP) [†] |

**Band 4**

| | |
|---|---|
| Decker Jeffrey E | Baker & Hostetler LLP * |
| Denmon Richard A | Carlton Fields, P.A. * |
| Houser Bradley D | Akerman Senterfitt |
| Lear Steven D | Bilzin Sumberg Baena Price & Axelrod LLP * |
| Levenson Fred | McDermott Will & Emery LLP * |
| Lewis Jr M Richard | Smith Hulsey & Busey |
| Miller Alison W | Stearns Weaver Miller Weissler Alhadeff |
| Parker Clayton | K&L Gates (ONP) [†] * |
| Reinert Peter | Lowndes Drosdick Doster Kantor (ONP) [†] |
| Wells David E | Greenberg Traurig, LLP * |
| Wright Kenneth C | Baker & Hostetler LLP * |

**Associates to watch**

| | |
|---|---|
| Arrieta Alejandro M | Alvarez Arrieta & Diaz-Silveira (ONP) [†] |
| Black David | Berger Singerman * |

\* Indicates firm / individual with profile.
[†] ONP = Other Notable Practitioner.

**Sources say:** "*They provide excellent service and attention to detail.*" "*This is a technical, knowledgeable team that works together.*"
**KEY INDIVIDUALS** The "*top-notch*" **Jonathan Awner** is "*a great lead partner and a good provider of practical business and legal advice.*" He recently acted on behalf of Shandong Heavy Industry Group-Weichai Group in its

EUR374 million acquisition of a controlling interest in Ferretti Group. **Teddy Klinghoffer** is "*extremely knowledgeable and an asset to his clients,*" according to feedback from market sources. He is highly regarded for his expertise in healthcare issues. **Stephen Roddenberry** is praised for his broad practice, and represents sellers, buyers and investors in a range of corporate transactions. The "*very* bright" **Carl Roston** acted on the abovementioned Comvest Group transaction, and also advised Ideal Image Development and its parent company H.I.G. Capital on the sale of Ideal Image Development. **Bradley Houser** offers valuable knowledge of REITs and special-purpose acquisition companies, and has broad experience in corporate and banking matters.

## Greenberg Traurig, LLP
See profile on p.1024

THE FIRM Sources are quick to highlight the caliber and depth of this team, which continues to successfully represent a variety of high-profile names in Florida. Berggruen Holdings, Pine Tree Equity and SBA Communications are among the clients calling on its expertise for securities and M&A matters. The firm's cross-border capacity, particularly in Latin America, has proven to be a further attractive feature. In one highly publicized transaction, Greenberg Traurig attorneys guided Justice Holdings through its multibillion-dollar acquisition of Burger King Worldwide Holdings.
Sources say: *"An excellent corporate practice."*
KEY INDIVIDUALS **Gary Epstein** (see p.991) is *"one of the deans"* of corporate practice in Florida, and enjoys a tremendous reputation in the state. *"Everyone loves him – he's down to earth and great at mentoring,"* enthused one interviewee. Fort Lauderdale-based **Donn Beloff** (see p.984) is regarded as a *"terrific lawyer,"* whose experience covers a wide range of industries. Standout work includes leading the team that advised Justice Holdings on its Burger King acquisition. **Ira Rosner** (see p.1005) is highly regarded by peers for the strength of his practice. He represented client Equity One on a series of transactions including a $76.9 million secondary public offering. The *"very practical and no-nonsense"* **David Barkus** (see p.984) is renowned as a *"great resource"* for clients and *"a tremendous corporate and M&A attorney."* He was recently engaged by client MasTec North America in the sale of DirectStar TV for $105.6 million. **Kara MacCullough** (see p.999) *"is an excellent lawyer, and people think very highly of her."* She represented longstanding client SBA Communications in a series of transactions with a total worth of over $1 billion. **Bruce March** (see p.999) maintains a broad practice advising clients on private equity, M&A and public and private securities offerings. He is *"very business-oriented and understands the legal aspects of an issue as well as a businessperson's point of view."* Operating out of the firm's Miami office, **David Wells** (see p.1012) is a talented corporate finance expert with a wealth of experience. He guides clients through a range of transactions as well as offering advice on corporate governance and compliance.

## Holland & Knight LLP
See profile on p.1028

THE FIRM This firm's strength in corporate and private equity matters is evidenced by its enviable client roster and a collection of high-quality mandates. The team enjoys a substantial volume of business from the healthcare and pharmaceutical industries, and assisted PharMerica with

its successful defense of a $700 million hostile takeover bid by Omnicare. The corporate specialists at Holland & Knight are commended for their ability to coordinate with other departments in order to provide a holistic service to clients. Further key names in the team's client roster include Auxilium Pharmaceuticals and Highpoint Tower Technology.
Sources say: *"They have both the knowledge of the law and the practical counsel to get the deal done." "A significant presence across the state."*
KEY INDIVIDUALS The *"extremely talented and well-regarded"* **Robert Grammig** (see p.993) is lauded as a major player in the Florida market, and an *"incredibly business-oriented and pragmatic lawyer."* A high-volume workload includes defending PharMerica against a threatened hostile takeover, as well as advising a number of the team's other key clients on acquisitions and dispositions. Among various highlights, **Rodney Bell** (see p.984) represented sunscreen manufacturer Sun & Skin Care Research in its sale to a private equity firm. He is a well-known figure in the region, with extensive knowledge of corporate governance issues. **Chester Bacheller** (see p.983) is *"a highly intelligent and very practical"* lawyer, noted for his excellent reputation. Interviewees laud **Tom McAleavey** (see p.999) for his attention to detail. Standout matters include advising Jabil Circuit on its $132.2 million acquisition of Telmar Network Technology.

## Band 2

### Shumaker Loop & Kendrick LLP

THE FIRM Shumaker Loop & Kendrick is highly regarded for its prolific corporate practice, which operates out of its offices in Tampa and Sarasota. The team advises a wide variety of middle-market companies, as well as Fortune 500 players with international operations. The firm is able to guide clients through the full spectrum of corporate activity, including M&A and dispositions.
Sources say: *"Very active and well respected."*
KEY INDIVIDUALS Co-administrator of the corporate group **Gregory Yadley** is skilled in a range of corporate matters and has a strong track record in securities work. **Darrell Smith** is *"well respected in the area"* and maintains his dynamic practice in the Tampa office. His broad experience includes handling national and cross-border work.

### White & Case LLP
See profile on p.451

THE FIRM This international heavyweight attracts high-quality mandates by virtue of its stellar reputation both on the M&A and the private equity side. The firm is well established as a popular choice for clients in Florida, and mandates from Boyne Capital Partners, H.I.G. Capital and Codina Partners confirm the firm's reputation in this arena. Its lawyers also acted for Steiner Leisure, a Bahamas-based company, on the $177 million acquisition of Ideal Image Development.
Sources say: *"Offers an international scope of expertise."*

KEY INDIVIDUALS **Jorge Freeland** (see p.992) is characterized as a *"terrific lawyer"* by market observers. He acts as lead partner on many of the team's major deals, including the Steiner Leisure acquisition and the purchase of numerous KFC and Yum! Brands franchises by Boyne Capital. **Emilio Alvarez-Farré** (see p.983) continues to represent long-standing client SphereInvest Americas, advising the company on several transactions. He is well known for his expertise in cross-border M&A deals.

## Band 3

### Berger Singerman
See profile on p.1017

THE FIRM This firm has a long-established reputation as an impressive force in the Florida market, and receives resounding praise from market sources. The team is well equipped to advise clients such as HearUSA, Seitlin Insurance and International Bedding across the full spectrum of corporate, securities and M&A matters. High-stakes mandates include assisting HearUSA with the sale of its assets in bankruptcy, achieving a total price at bankruptcy auction of $129.3 million.
Sources say: *"Impressed with their performance – both their level of diligence and their ability to discover creative solutions to hard business problems."*
KEY INDIVIDUALS Group leader and *"very smart lawyer"* **Daniel Aronson** (see p.983) is a prominent figure in the Florida market and offers clients the benefit of many years of experience. He is noted for his *"intense attention to detail."* Seitlin Insurance engaged him to act on its sale to Marsh & McLennan Agency this year. **David Black** (see p.985) is an *"extremely knowledgeable"* associate based in the firm's Fort Lauderdale office, praised by clients for being *"always available, and leaving no stone unturned."* Sources also attest to impressive business acumen.

### Bilzin Sumberg Baena Price & Axelrod LLP
See profile on p.1018

THE FIRM Bilzin Sumberg's corporate and securities attorneys offer a comprehensive service to clients, adeptly handling a sector-spanning workload including energy, healthcare and technology matters. Of late, the team's commercial capabilities have been proven in several high-profile transactions, one of which saw the firm guiding China Fire & Security Group through an intricate merger and restructure valued at $265.5 million.
Sources say: *"A wonderful firm." "They do an excellent job with relationship building and have a wide breadth of knowledge."*
KEY INDIVIDUALS **Alan Axelrod** (see p.983) stands out as a *"very talented"* practitioner who *"always finds the right conclusion, and gets the deal done."* He continues in his role as chair of the group and has a long-standing reputation in the state. **Marshall Pasternack's** (see p.1003) highly active practice includes representing Swerdlow Development in the establishment of several joint venture agreements relating to a proposed mixed-use development in Miami. **Steven Lear** (see p.997) is lauded by market com-

mentators as *"extremely thorough, responsive and commercial,"* and one interviewee notes: *"He knows the right points to emphasize and how to negotiate them into an agreement."*

## Broad and Cassel

**THE FIRM** Broad and Cassel maintains its strong reputation in Florida, and its eight offices provide the firm with excellent coverage across the state. The team has valuable expertise in guiding clients through complex transactions, representing a number of emerging growth clients as well as more established names. In one standout matter, the lawyers assisted FFP, doing business as Matrix Health, with its $5 million acquisition of Medex Health and Medex Biocare Pharmacy.

**KEY INDIVIDUALS Doug Starcher** has been involved in some of the team's most significant transactions of late, and is regarded by clients as a trusted adviser through M&A and structuring issues.

## Carlton Fields, P.A.
See profile on p.1020

**THE FIRM** Carlton Fields advises a diverse roster of clients, which features major names from the manufacturing, healthcare and banking industries. The expertise of its corporate specialists covers the gamut of transactional activity, and they are recognized by observers as significant players in the Florida market.

**KEY INDIVIDUALS** Tampa-based **Nathaniel Doliner** (see p.990) is an eminent figure in the Florida corporate community, with a wealth of experience in transactional mandates. **Richard Denmon** (see p.989) advises a range of public and private clients on securities, private equity and M&A issues.

## Foley & Lardner LLP
See profile on p.2588

**THE FIRM** This thriving international firm is identified by peers as a strong competitor in the Florida market. The team offers corporate advice from four offices across the state, aiding its representation of a wide range of local clients. In one highlight, the group assisted Tortuga Imports with a complex cross-border transaction involving the consolidation of several domestic and international companies into a holding company. Attorneys also handled the sale of a controlling interest in this holding company to a major Jamaican food company.

**Sources say:** *"From a Florida standpoint they are very active and well respected."*

**KEY INDIVIDUALS** Admired by peers for his skills in this area, **Gardner Davis** is described as a *"terrific lawyer."* He has considerable experience in high-value M&A transactions. Tampa-based **Martin Traber** has particular expertise in both private and public securities offerings as well as M&A activity. He is a well-respected figure in Florida. **Steven Vazquez** has cultivated a highly successful practice serving clients across the full spectrum of corporate finance and securities transactions.

## Gunster
See profile on p.1025

**THE FIRM** Gunster operates a vibrant corporate practice across its ten Florida offices, attracting high-value mandates from clients based locally and across the country. Its workload spans a range of industries, including banking, agriculture and technology. One standout matter saw lawyers acting on behalf of HCBF Holding during its acquisition of four branches of Grand Bank. Other major clients include AT&T, US Sugar and Bankrate.

**Sources say:** *"Extremely responsive and seamless service."*

**KEY INDIVIDUALS David Bates** is lauded by sources, who note that he is *"very practical, with great common sense."* He is also valued for his impressive commitment to client service. **Michael Mitrione** is a *"highly reputable"* specialist who is singled out as a *"very knowledgeable"* adviser.

## Hill Ward Henderson
See profile on p.1027

**THE FIRM** Clients of this practice benefit from the team's collective wealth of experience, which covers a wide range of private equity and strategic corporate transactions. The group is also praised for its consistently high-quality client service. KLH Capital, Mangrove Equity Partners and Asbury Automotive are among those calling on the firm, which lately acted for Ballast Point Ventures on a $30 million purchase of preferred equity from Tower Cloud.

**Sources say:** *"They're very pragmatic, and very good at not just providing us with the legal answer to something but the practical answer as well."*

**KEY INDIVIDUALS David Felman** (see p.991) is highlighted by peers as a strong presence in the arena. He advised Lifestyle Family Fitness on the proposed sale of $70 million worth of assets to LA Fitness. **Mark Danzi** (see p.989) is commended by clients for his commercial nous, and has a *"very good feel for the market."* He is also *"very hard-working, and always available."*

## Hogan Lovells US LLP

**THE FIRM** This team continues to enjoy highly productive relationships with key local clients, and interviewees also speak highly of the firm's impressive international reach. Attorneys are regularly sought out for their expertise in M&A and private equity matters and are strongly supported by Hogan Lovells's enviable global network.

**KEY INDIVIDUALS Luis Perez** is a talented specialist who is commended for his transactional experience. He regularly works on cross-border deals, particularly those with a Latin American element.

## McDermott Will & Emery LLP
See profile on p.1258

**THE FIRM** This team supports its clients in various high-value transactions, handling a broad spectrum of M&A mandates and private equity deals. Standout matters include assisting private equity giant H.I.G. Capital with a series of acquisitions across the food and healthcare industries. Further key clients include the ComVest Group and Banyan Equity Management. Operating out of its Miami

base, the practice is commended as a highly active group across the state.

**Sources say:** *"Excellent work – very organized and efficient, they understood the issues and how to deal with them."*

**KEY INDIVIDUALS Harris Siskind** (see p.1008) leads the practice and receives high praise from market sources, who describe him as *"very smart, responsive and efficient."* **Fred Levenson** (see p.997) is a valuable member of the team and recently advised client TeamHealth on its purchase of The Exigence Group, a major provider of healthcare across the country.

## Shutts & Bowen LLP

**THE FIRM** This team of attorneys offers experience spanning all aspects of corporate activity, including a variety of M&A transactions and joint ventures. The firm also offers valuable compliance advice, acting for clients across a spectrum of sectors including energy, aviation and manufacturing. In one highlight, the practice represented Kirkhill Aircraft Parts in its acquisition of Aaxico Sales.

**Sources say:** *"They give sound advice with a quick turnaround – they're very attentive to my needs."*

**KEY INDIVIDUALS** Commentators *"can't speak more highly"* of **Luis de Armas**, who is an *"excellent lawyer."* He is a well-known figure in international transactions and has a long-standing reputation in Miami. **Robert Alan Higbee** recently advised Yara International on a CAD40 million strategic investment. He has considerable experience in corporate and securities transactions.

## Band 4

## Baker & Hostetler LLP
See profile on p.2119

**THE FIRM** This firm has a strong track record for its work in the state, guiding clients such as Adventist Health System and LightPath Technologies through corporate and securities transactions. Its corporate specialists seamlessly coordinate with other departments such as the tax, litigation and IP teams in order to provide a full service to clients. Mandates include advising Adventist Health System on a series of joint ventures with medical research facilities.

**Sources say:** *"They're great business lawyers and negotiators – I have tremendous confidence in them and in their legal and business acumen."*

**KEY INDIVIDUALS Jeffrey Decker** (see p.989) has spearheaded a range of significant transactions, and is regarded by sources as an *"extremely bright transactional lawyer."* Orlando-based **Kenneth Wright** (see p.1012) has a long-standing practice, and advises clients from a wide range of industries.

## Glenn Rasmussen, P.A.
See profile on p.1023

**THE FIRM** This dynamic team maintains a prolific practice in mid-market M&A and corporate finance. The firm has been at the forefront of a number of substantial transactions, including the $13.8 million sale of E Solutions to

Knology, in which the practice represented the vendor. A close integration with the bankruptcy and insolvency group also generates significant amounts of work for the corporate team.

KEY INDIVIDUALS Robert Rasmussen is valued for his "*in-depth knowledge and negotiation skill.*" He acted for Vertical IT Solutions on the sale of substantially all of its assets to Konica Minolta Business Solutions for $3.2 million. Sharon Docherty Danco earns glowing endorsements from clients, who appreciate her guidance through high-value deals.

## Hunton & Williams LLP
See profile on p.2517

THE FIRM Hunton & Williams enjoys an impressive reputation for its work in this arena, and is particularly noted for its representation of leading financial institutions. The firm's international footprint attracts clients from a variety of jurisdictions, including Santander and MercadoLibre. A busy workload includes advising Sabadell United Bank on its acquisition of Lydian Private Bank's $1.6 billion net assets.

KEY INDIVIDUALS Fernando Alonso is the head of the corporate department in Miami.

## Smith Hulsey & Busey

THE FIRM This firm has consolidated its position as a strong presence in the Florida market. The team regularly represents clients across a broad range of industries and is commended for its experience in the healthcare sector, act-ing on behalf of clients such as Baptist Health System, OnCure Medical and Shands Healthcare.

Sources say: "*The team brought an in-depth understanding both of the law and of the things that were important in getting this transaction done.*"

KEY INDIVIDUALS Richard Lewis is valued by his clients as a "*very practical, business-savvy lawyer.*" He spearheads the department and enjoys an excellent reputation in the region.

## Stearns Weaver Miller Weissler Alhadeff & Sitterson, P.A.

THE FIRM Stearns Weaver's corporate team offers wide-ranging expertise which covers the full spectrum of corporate and private equity transactions. The firm advised Bank of America on the formation of a number of joint ventures, and represented BFC Financial in its acquisition of Bluegreen. Its client roster also features names such as Addison Capital Partners, Telefónica and FabSouth.

Sources say: "*Very responsive and knowledgeable with a good command of the practice.*"

KEY INDIVIDUALS Clients enthuse that David Seifer is "*just excellent, and very responsive.*" Practice highlights include representing Wadley Crushed Stone in the creation of a high-value joint venture with CSX Transportation. Alison Miller is a "*very good lawyer,*" who led the team advising BankAtlantic Bancorp on the disposal of its subsidiary BankAtlantic for over $300 million.

## Trenam Kemker, Attorneys

THE FIRM Florida stalwart Trenam Kemker maintains its excellent standing in the state, and peers commend the firm as a significant force in the market. Operating out of offices in Tampa and St. Petersburg, this team assists clients with various corporate transactions, and offers the benefits of strong complementary teams specializing in tax and compliance issues.

KEY INDIVIDUALS Gary Teblum is a highly regarded figure, who has a wealth of experience advising clients ranging from entrepreneurial companies to nationally recognized names.

## Other Notable Practitioners

Abigail Watts-FitzGerald of Weiss Serota Helfman Pastoriza Cole & Boniske PA is renowned for her experience in the field. She practices out of the firm's Miami-Dade office. Clayton Parker (see p.1003) of K&L Gates is identified by sources as a "*smart lawyer.*" He advises clients based in multiple jurisdictions on a range of corporate transactions. Peter Reinert leads the corporate and securities practice at Lowndes Drosdick Doster Kantor & Reed, PA. He offers wide-ranging knowledge in public and private securities transactions as well as M&A and investment activities. Thomas McGuigan (see p.1000) is a "*well-respected and very distinguished*" member of the corporate team at Squire Sanders (US) LLP. Alejandro Arrieta of Alvarez Arrieta & Diaz-Silveira, LLP attracts excellent feedback from clients, who describe him as "*responsive and knowledgeable, with good overall command of the topics.*"

# ENVIRONMENT

Commentary about individuals can be found under their firm's paragraph. If the firm has no paragraph (is not ranked) look at Other Notable Practitioners.

| Environment |
| --- |
| **Leading Firms** |
| **Band 1** |
| Greenberg Traurig, LLP * |
| Hopping Green & Sams, PA |
| Lewis, Longman & Walker PA |
| **Band 2** |
| Akerman Senterfitt |
| Carlton Fields, P.A. * |
| Gunster * |
| Holland & Knight LLP * |
| Oertel, Fernandez, Bryant & Atkinson, P.A |
| White & Case LLP * |
| **Band 3** |
| Berger Singerman * |
| Broad and Cassel |
| Shook, Hardy & Bacon LLP * |
| * Indicates firm with profile. |

## Band 1

## Greenberg Traurig, LLP
See profile on p.1024

THE FIRM This outstanding environment team works closely with the firm's real estate practice to provide smooth and comprehensive support to clients. The group advises on matters ranging from due diligence in environmental issues to criminal enforcement, and is noted for its work in air, water and soil pollution matters. The firm's impressive client roster includes Mosaic Fertilizer, Coronet Industries and CEMEX.

Sources say: "*Really high-caliber lawyers.*"

KEY INDIVIDUALS The highly respected Kerri Barsh (see p.984) has recently been working on a groundbreaking case in the US Supreme Court regarding coastal permitting issues within a maritime admiralty case. Sources praise her "*knowledge and ability to get things done.*" David Weinstein (see p.1012) is a leading environmental lawyer who provides high-level service in sophisticated environmental litigation matters. Sources note that "*he is the big name in environmental litigation.*" He has continued to represent Coronet Industries in a large multiparty environmental litigation case. Christopher Torres (see p.1010) has been representing Mosaic Fertilizer against a class action claiming damage caused by process water discharge during Hurricane Frances. Sources comment that "*he's very good, very thorough and knowledgeable, as well as being clear-thinking.*"

## Hopping Green & Sams, PA

THE FIRM This high-quality and diverse environmental team prides itself on the depth of its practice. The team assists with land development and due diligence matters, and has experience in advising on the regulatory side of nuclear projects for Progress Energy, and Florida Power and Light. The firm also has a very successful infrastructure and financing arm, which interacts directly with the environmental team and is renowned for its lobbying capabilities.

Sources say: "*Definitely a standout firm, based on the areas it covers and the expertise it offers.*"

## Environment
### Senior Statesmen

**Senior Statesmen: distinguished older practitioners**

| | | |
|---|---|---|
| Thomson Parker | Hogan Lovells US LLP (ONP)[†] | |
| Varn Jacob D | Fowler White Boggs (ONP)[†] | |

### Leading Individuals

#### Band 1

| | | |
|---|---|---|
| Alderman Silvia M | Akerman Senterfitt | |
| Barkett John | Shook, Hardy & Bacon LLP | |
| Barsh Kerri | Greenberg Traurig, LLP [*] | |
| Burgess Rick J. | Gunster | |
| Cole Terry | Gunster | |
| Halsey Douglas | White & Case LLP.[*] | |
| Lockett Laurel E | Carlton Fields, P.A. [*] | |
| Malefatto Alfred J | Lewis, Longman & Walker PA | |
| Matthews Frank E | Hopping Green & Sams, PA | |
| McAliley Neal | White & Case LLP (ONP)[†] [*] | |
| Parsons Philip S | Philip S. Parsons, Attorney at Law (ONP)[†] | |
| Schulman Clifford | Weiss Serota Helfman Pastoriza (ONP)[†] | |
| Schwenke Roger D | Carlton Fields, P.A. [*] | |
| Sellers Lawrence | Holland & Knight LLP [*] | |
| Sims Roger | Holland & Knight LLP [*] | |
| Smallwood Mary F | GrayRobinson, PA (ONP)[†] [*] | |
| Weinstein David B | Greenberg Traurig, LLP [*] | |

#### Band 2

| | | |
|---|---|---|
| Curtin Lawrence | Holland & Knight LLP [*] | |
| Dee David S | Gardner, Bist, Wiener, Wadsworth (ONP)[†] | |
| DeMeo Ralph A | Hopping Green & Sams, PA | |
| Goldstein Michael R | The Goldstein Environmental Law Firm (ONP)[†] | |
| Lewis Steve | Lewis, Longman & Walker PA | |
| Lewis Terry | Lewis, Longman & Walker PA | |
| Neely Robyn | Akerman Senterfitt | |
| Nelson Howard E | Bilzin Sumberg Baena Price (ONP)[†] [*] | |

| | | |
|---|---|---|
| Noble Ron | Fowler White Boggs (ONP)[†] | |
| Pence William L | Baker & Hostetler LLP (ONP)[†] [*] | |
| Preston William D | William D Preston PA (ONP)[†] | |
| Rillstone Douglas | Broad and Cassel | |
| Walker Steve | Lewis, Longman & Walker PA | |

#### Band 3

| | | |
|---|---|---|
| Alves James S | Hopping Green & Sams, PA | |
| Coglianese Matthew P | Rasco Klock Reininger Perez (ONP)[†] | |
| Diffenderfer Robert P | Lewis, Longman & Walker PA | |
| Fernandez Segundo J | Oertel, Fernandez, Bryant & Atkinson, P.A [*] | |
| Hearne Frank L | Mechanik Nuccio Hearne & Wester, (ONP)[†] | |
| Lichtstein Jason | Akerman Senterfitt | |
| Maurer Thomas K. | Foley & Lardner LLP (ONP)[†] | |
| McNally John | John J McNally P.A. | |
| Oertel Ken | Oertel, Fernandez, Bryant & Atkinson, P.A [*] | |
| Olsen Eric T | Hopping Green & Sams, PA | |
| Petrovich Michael P | Hopping Green & Sams, PA | |
| Phillips Luna E. | Gunster | |
| Poole Samuel E. | Berger Singerman [*] | |
| Thompson Daniel | Berger Singerman [*] | |
| Torres Christopher | Greenberg Traurig, LLP [*] | |

#### Up-and-coming individuals

| | | |
|---|---|---|
| Cole Edward | Akerman Senterfitt | |

#### Associates to watch

| | | |
|---|---|---|
| Lewis Brooke E. | Hopping Green & Sams, PA | |
| Lumpkin Cristina | Bilzin Sumberg Baena Price & Axelrod (ONP)[†] [*] | |

[*] Indicates individual with profile.
[†] ONP = Other Notable Practitioner.

**KEY INDIVIDUALS Frank Matthews** has a highly regarded practice focusing on wetlands and water resources, and also has expertise in phosphate mining projects, including taking those cases through to litigation. He maintains a legislative practice and is involved in lobbying. Sources say: "*Frank is the best wetland attorney in the state.*" **Ralph DeMeo**'s environmental clients benefit from his impressive experience in representing municipal interests in the areas of solid waste and solid waste disposal, both as an opponent and as a proponent of waste facilities. Observers note that "*Ralph is an excellent attorney. He practices at an exceptional level.*" The highly respected **Eric Olsen** is renowned for his work in mitigation banking, and for his role in the creation of statutes in that arena. Sources agree that he is "*a very smart young attorney.*" **James Alves**'s solid environmental practice has seen him represent a number of waste water utilities and mining interests in a variety of environmental issues. **Michael Petrovich** maintains a highly regarded environmental practice, focusing on resource recovery and hazardous waste disposal. He also has experience in dealing with issues arising out of contaminated sites at the federal level. Rising star **Brooke Lewis**'s environmental practice impresses across the board. One source remarks: "*I can't say enough about her. What impressed me is her command and her intelligence.*" Lewis works in all areas of environmental law and has experience working with the Electrical Power Plant Siting Act.

### Lewis, Longman & Walker PA

**THE FIRM** This star quality firm has offices across Florida and is applauded for the depth and level of specialization in its top-drawer environmental practice. The team has a wealth of experience in this area, including dealing with brownfields redevelopment, environmental permitting and issues arising from real estate transactions.

**Sources say:** "*They're high-quality lawyers who work very collaboratively to make sure they take all the information within the firm and apply it to the client, so they end up with some tremendous work. Very high-caliber lawyers.*"

**KEY INDIVIDUALS** The outstanding **Alfred Malefatto** brings a tremendous amount of experience in environmental litigation to his cases. Sources are impressed with his service and relate that "*he's a great lawyer and really takes care of his clients,*" with one interviewee noting that

"*he's a tenacious litigator.*" **Steve Lewis** is deemed an authority in submerged land issues. He also has experience in permitting issues relating to large-scale development and has represented clients before a range of public bodies in environmental matters. **Terry Lewis** continues to represent a number of public clients, including regional and local governing bodies, in a range of issues, including environmental permitting and compliance. "*Terry is a first-rate lawyer*" in these arenas, according to interviewees. **Steve Walker** is praised as "*a phenomenal attorney,*" with sources noting that "*there is a substantial benefit to a calm and steady demeanor in resolving problems and you can't get calmer and steadier than Steve Walker.*" He deals with a range of environmental issues, with a particular focus on water-related matters. **Robert Diffenderfer** is a "*top-notch lawyer*" who is well respected for his broad environmental and public infrastructure practice. He advises public and private clients on a range of environmental matters.

### Band 2

#### Akerman Senterfitt
#### See profile on p.1014

**THE FIRM** This highly regarded environmental practice includes lawyers who have backgrounds within governmental bodies in the environmental field, giving them niche insight into the workings of the regulatory system. The team is well known for its wetlands practice and its highly specialized forestry practice. Its impressive client list includes Verizon Wireless, Landstone Communities and The City of Miami.

**Sources say:** "*Excellent – a really superb firm.*"

**KEY INDIVIDUALS Silvia Alderman** is highly regarded for her land use and wetlands work, and is also involved in the Central Florida Water Initiative. Sources praise her excellent reputation with regulators, and label her "*a bright, capable lawyer.*" Sources have nothing but praise for **Robyn Neely**, saying that "*she has a very good practice. She is a very bright person and is liked by clients.*" She maintains a successful environmental practice, and is kept busy on matters involving soil and groundwater contamination. **Jason Lichtstein** has recently been representing Hialeah Plaza in a matter regarding the redevelopment of contaminated land in Miami-Dade County. **Edward Cole** obtained a degree in forestry before becoming an attorney, and brings this niche knowledge to bear in a range of administrative and litigation matters. Sources note that "*he's a very persistent person and very efficient,*" and "*he's also a very practical lawyer who understands the client's perspective. He has a good business mind.*"

#### Carlton Fields, P.A.
#### See profile on p.1020

**THE FIRM** This proficient environmental practice has experience in handling matters for clients in the onshore oil and gas sector. The firm's innovative environmental insurance practice complements its environmental transactional capabilities, and sources also enthuse about its expertise in advising on brownfield matters.

**KEY INDIVIDUALS Laurel Lockett** (see p.998) is considered an expert in brownfields work and petroleum programs. In relation to brownfield programs, sources agree that "*Laurel is extremely knowledgeable in the statutes, rules and guidelines, and maintains a great relationship with the government.*" **Roger Schwenke** (see p.1006) maintains a strong environmental practice and a superb reputation in Florida. One source says: "*He's a founding father in the subject area and maintains that high-level position.*"

## Gunster
See profile on p.1025

**THE FIRM** This high-quality environmental group has been involved in litigation relative to the Numeric Nutrient Criteria Development program. The firm's highly integrated team works in partnership with lobbyists to challenge permits and tackle administrative rule challenges and litigation matters.

**Sources say:** "*Excellent delivery of what the client is looking for. A really excellent firm to work with – we have constant communication and fulfillment of commitments to do work. It's great working with a full-service firm; they really work as a team.*"

**KEY INDIVIDUALS Rick Burgess** handles environmental regulation and litigation. He is valued highly by sources, one of whom notes that "*he excels at the strategic thinking and the development of the overall legal strategy.*" **Terry Cole** brings in-depth experience to his broad environmental practice, and is especially rated in land issues and permitting matters. Interviewees praise him as "*a very fine lawyer.*" **Luna Phillips** is applauded by sources for her work in administrative law litigation at the state level. Feedback suggests that "*she is phenomenal at bridging the gulf between the regulators and clients in order to resolve issues. As she continues to grow and widen her practice, she will be unstoppable.*"

## Holland & Knight LLP
See profile on p.1028

**THE FIRM** This talented environmental team offers a broad range of environmental services, including work relating to permitting issues, administrative litigation and rule challenging. The group offers expertise on climate change and brownfield redevelopment, and has experience in working on behalf of major waste management firms as well as industrial land owners.

**KEY INDIVIDUALS Roger Sims** (see p.1007) has impressive experience in environmental law. Sources highlight his expertise on the subject of water management districts, noting that "*he's a particularly important person in that subject area.*" **Lawrence Sellers** (see p.1006) balances his successful environmental practice with involvement in lobbying in this area. Observers say that "*he's a practitioner as well as a lobbyist, which keeps him current and knowledgeable about public policy.*" **Lawrence Curtin** (see p.989) is renowned for his expertise in the powerplant sector. Sources say his strengths lie in "*his vast knowledge of the environmental field and his ability to make quick decisions.*"

## Oertel, Fernandez, Bryant & Atkinson, P.A

**THE FIRM** This Tallahassee-based environmental boutique represents both public and private clients, and advises on regulatory issues and enforcement cases. The talented group deals with matters in air, water and waste, and prides itself on cultivating longstanding relationships with clients.

**KEY INDIVIDUALS Segundo Fernandez** (see p.991) was a former assistant general counsel in Florida Department of Environmental Regulation, and brings his insight and experience to bear on a wide range of environmental issues. **Ken Oertel** (see p.1002) maintains a broad-based environmental practice. Sources highlight his notable expertise in coastal regulation.

## White & Case LLP
See profile on p.451

**THE FIRM** This international firm retains a diverse environmental practice from its Miami office. The team has a specific focus on environmental litigation and has represented clients in areas ranging from wetlands and endangered species to contaminated sites. In addition, the group manages regulatory matters, land use disputes and environmental litigation. Clients include R.E. Jacobs Group, Sierra Properties and New Hope Power Company.

**Sources say:** "*An extremely high-quality firm. They're thoroughly knowledgeable about very arcane regulations regarding environmental issues and all of the legal research and discovery that go with them.*"

**KEY INDIVIDUALS Neal McAliley** (see p.1000) focuses on environmental litigation and is renowned for his extensive knowledge of federal agencies in relation to compliance issues. Sources praise his service, commenting that "*his knowledge of the process, people and the law is excellent. He's great at guiding us through the process. A super communicator.*" **Douglas Halsey** (see p.994) has a fantastic reputation in environmental law. Sources praise "*his overall knowledge of environmental law and his relationships with the agencies involved,*" and comment on his "*tremendous amount of experience.*"

## Band 3

## Berger Singerman
See profile on p.1017

**THE FIRM** This much-admired environmental team deals with transactions involving environmental issues and maintains a particular focus on water management matters. The group also has experience in assisting with matters relating to air, coastal and endangered species. Clients include Corrections Corporation Of America, Colgate-Palmolive and Lake Environmental Resources.

**Sources say:** "*We would highly recommend them to anyone. We are very satisfied.*"

**KEY INDIVIDUALS Samuel Poole** (see p.1003) is an authority on matters regarding water management districts. Sources comment that "*he knows the regulations and understands the issues from both a regulatory standpoint and a practical standpoint. He understands the business aspect

*and I would absolutely recommend him.*" **Daniel Thompson** (see p.1010) is kept busy consulting with clients on environmental protection issues. He recently represented Colgate-Palmolive in a groundwater cleanup case regarding contamination problems at a PET chemical site.

## Broad and Cassel

**THE FIRM** This environmental practice scores highly in permitting and litigation matters. The team is familiar with working on behalf of aviation, manufacturing and transport sector clients, and is also experienced in the agricultural industry, dealing with animal protection matters. The firm's client list includes Florida Farm Bureau, Florida Home Builders Association and Florida Land Council.

**Sources say:** "*Their work has been outstanding. They're on point, they understand the background and they've got the proper connections with government agencies. They're timely and available to the client.*"

**KEY INDIVIDUALS Douglas Rillstone** handles work across environmental law and land use but is particularly respected in the areas of wetland mitigation and mitigation banks. Consensus opinion is that "*he's very, very aware of the subject matter and he is very well connected with the environmental community.*"

## Shook, Hardy & Bacon LLP
See profile on p.1644

**THE FIRM** This environmental practice is highly regarded for its high-quality lawyers. The team handles a plethora of environmental issues, including litigation and compliance work, and has managed complex multiparty and private party environmental claims. Clients include Motorola Solutions and Freescale Semiconductor.

**KEY INDIVIDUALS** The "*exceptional*" **John Barkett** is renowned for his work in Superfund allocation cases, and is also recognized in mediation and litigation in the environmental field. Sources state that "*he has a well-respected practice and national reputation.*" He currently serves as special master with respect to the Florida Everglades restoration.

## Other Notable Practitioners

**Mary Smallwood** (see p.1008) of GrayRobinson, PA is a highly reputable administrative lawyer with a focus on environmental litigation. Sources commend her and say that she is "*a really well-regarded lawyer who does great work.*" **David Dee** of Gardner, Bist, Wiener, Wadsworth Bowden, Bush, Dee, LaVia & Wright P.A. has an impressive breadth of experience in environmental matters. He offers particular expertise in environmental permitting issues. **Howard Nelson** (see p.1002) of Bilzin Sumberg Baena Price & Axelrod LLP is known for his judgment and ability in environmental matters, particularly in relation to permitting. Sources highlight that "*he knows the regulatory arena and brings an analytical approach to it. He has an ability to hone in on the key issues.*" **Ron Noble** of Fowler White Boggs focuses on site remediation matters and brownfields issues. "*We have a great relationship with him,*" said one client, adding: *"He's really learned our business and has done a great job for us. The biggest thing is that he's always available."* **William Pence** (see p.1003) of Baker & Hostetler LLP works with property owners on contamination matters, with a particular focus on compliance in that area. Sources also rate his knowledge of water management issues. **Frank Hearne** of Mechanik Nuccio Hearne & Wester, P.A. brings his impressive experience to bear on a variety of environmental matters. Sources name him *"a leading practitioner in the Tampa area,"* and add that *"he's well respected."* **Thomas Maurer** of Foley & Lardner LLP brings a wealth of experience to environmental regulatory cases. He has experience working in matters involving water, waste and air contamination. **Parker Thomson** of Hogan Lovells US LLP is a commercial litigator with a wealth of experience in environmental matters, and is highly regarded in Florida in this area. **Jacob Varn** of

Fowler White Boggs has an incredible reputation in the Florida environmental arena and maintains an active environmental practice. He recently acted for Patriot Transportation Holdings on securing approvals for a large sustainable community project. **Cristina Lumpkin** (see p.999) of Bilzin Sumberg Baena Price & Axelrod LLP is renowned in the market for her *"good strong work ethic."* Sources also note: *"She writes well, has good rational thinking and is an all-around first-rate environmental lawyer."* **Clifford Schulman** of Weiss Serota Helfman Pastoriza Cole & Boniske PA has a great reputation in environmental mediation and real estate and land use matters. Sources suggest that he is *"a master of just about everything,"* and praise him as *"a great, great strategic thinker."* **Michael Goldstein** of The Goldstein Environmental Law Firm P.A. is renowned in the environmental market for his superior expertise in brownfields-related work. Sources enthuse

that *"he's a phenomenal practitioner and marketer of brownfields."* **Philip Parsons** of Philip S. Parsons, Attorney at Law focuses on the legislative side of environmental law and has an excellent reputation in water law. Sources agree that *"he's clearly one of the leading water lawyers in the state."* Sole practitioner **William Preston** is *"well respected"* in Florida environmental law. He runs his practice from Tallahassee, and advises clients on a range of compliance, regulation and enforcement matters. **Matthew Coglianese** of Rasco Klock Reininger Perez Esquenazi Vigil & Nieto, P.L. provides support in a wide range of environmental permitting and litigation issues. He has vast experience in dealing with regulators and is praised by peers as a solid lawyer in this area. **John McNally** focuses his solo practice on environmental litigation. He guides clients through the intricacies of environmental compliance in large real estate transactions.

# HEALTHCARE

Commentary about individuals can be found under their firm's paragraph. If the firm has no paragraph (is not ranked) look at Other Notable Practitioners.

### Healthcare
### Leading Firms

**Band 1**
Broad and Cassel
McDermott Will & Emery LLP *

**Band 2**
Akerman Senterfitt
Duane Morris LLP *
Hogan Lovells US LLP
Holland & Knight LLP *

**Band 3**
Carlton Fields, P.A. *
K&L Gates *
Smith Hulsey & Busey

**Band 4**
Foley & Lardner LLP *
Fowler White Boggs
GrayRobinson, PA
Shutts & Bowen LLP

*Indicates firm with profile.*
*Alphabetical order within each band. Band 1 is the highest.*

## Band 1

### Broad and Cassel

**THE FIRM** Broad and Cassel's health law practice group represents major national healthcare organizations doing business in Florida. It advises on a comprehensive range of regulatory matters, transactions and disputes. Recent highlights include working with the Florida Health Care Association as lead legislative counsel, and advising several

hospitals and health systems on a DOJ investigation into certain cardiac implants.

**Sources say:** *"Responsive, thorough and very experienced."*
**KEY INDIVIDUALS Gabriel Imperato** cochairs the firm's white-collar criminal and civil fraud defense group. He often advises on matters concerning healthcare fraud and internal investigations. Peers say *"he is a great lawyer,"* while clients praise his *"very good quality work,"* especially when appearing before government agencies. **Lester Perling** has extensive experience in the healthcare industry and is a board-certified practitioner in that space. He represents clients in Health Insurance Portability and Accountability Act (HIPAA), reimbursement and fraud matters, and is singled out for his transactional expertise and work with physician groups. **Mike Segal** heads the firm's health law practice and has tremendous expertise in advising an array of healthcare providers. He is noted for his work with physician groups, in particular, and has carved out an impressive niche in the state as a thought leader in accountable care organization issues. Tallahassee-based **Douglas Mannheimer** cochairs the governmental relations practice and the health law practice group. He is well known for representing leading healthcare organizations before the state's regulatory boards. According to clients, he is *"extremely detailed, making sure all points that need to be brought up are covered."* **Stephanie Russo** advises numerous providers across the state and the country. Her areas of expertise cover HIPAA, Stark Law and the False Claims Act. She is a leading choice for clients seeking advice on government investigations and relation litigation. **Stephen Siegel** is well known for his advisory work and is also a *"top-notch transactional lawyer,"* according to

sources. He recently worked with Imperato on representing big-name providers in the aforementioned DOJ investigation. **Michael Bittman** recently joined the team from GrayRobinson. He is a market favorite, thanks to his intelligent, collaborative and proactive representation of clients in deals and before state regulatory boards. Sources describe him as *"very accessible, efficient"* and a *"consummate negotiator."*

### McDermott Will & Emery LLP
See profile on p.1258

**THE FIRM** McDermott Will & Emery has one of the country's largest health industry groups. Its Florida team covers the full spectrum of needs and advises leading clients on transactions, disputes and compliance. The group is extremely strong on M&A and has advised TeamHealth on several deals of late, including its purchase of The Exigence Group.

**Sources say:** *"Specialized resources, quick response to needs and friendly, competent staff."*
**KEY INDIVIDUALS Gary Scott Davis** (see p.301) is the go-to lawyer in Florida for *"complex matters related to large health systems or managed care companies."* Clients say he *"supports his client's position, is a great adviser and is completely candid."* He is currently advising Nemours Children's Hospital on all issues related to its establishment in Orlando. **Ira Coleman** (see p.297) has one of the state's top M&A practices and is also called upon by his loyal clients to provide comprehensive day-to-day advice. Sources describe him as *"very talented,"* *"client service-oriented and confident."* Coleman *"understands the key issues and solves problems rather than just identifying them."* **Jerry**

**Sokol** (see p.1008) is widely recognized as one of the leading deal lawyers in the Florida healthcare market. One impressed client described him as the *"best transactional attorney in the country,"* with exemplary *"breadth of knowledge, timeliness and professionalism."* **Amanda Jester** is noted for her strong work on behalf of physician groups, particularly on M&A, joint ventures and advisory issues. According to clients, she *"has excellent communication skills, is very patient with questions, and responds in detail."*

## Band 2

### Akerman Senterfitt
See profile on p.1014

**THE FIRM** This Florida stalwart has a large team of board-certified healthcare attorneys. It advises physician groups, hospitals, managed care organizations and other clients on disputes, transactions and regulatory work. Highlights include successfully representing Compass Health Systems, Florida's largest psychiatric group practice, in its Medicare prepayment review repeal.

**Sources say:** *"It has a long history with state matters and many experienced attorneys who used to work for the state."*

**KEY INDIVIDUALS Marshall Burack** is able to handle all manner of healthcare work and is widely acknowledged for his transactional expertise. He has advised on numerous multimillion-dollar M&A transactions in the past several years. Practice chair **Kirk Davis** is noted for his litigation expertise and is a top choice for healthcare providers seeking advice on sensitive disputes. He also provides his clients with ongoing regulatory compliance counsel. Peers describe him as a *"very fine lawyer."* **Joseph Rugg**'s in-house experience has given him tremendous insight into clients' needs and has brought him a loyal following among medical practices for joint ventures and mergers. Sources say he is *"very good in the representation of physician groups."*

### Duane Morris LLP
See profile on p.2239

**THE FIRM** This team combines the benefits of a large national footprint with specialized local knowledge of the healthcare market. The firm has an impressive team of Medicare and Medicaid specialists who are highly qualified to advise on reimbursement and other issues. Other areas of expertise include Stark Law, contracts and M&A.

**Sources say:** *"A specialist in reimbursement in the Miami area."*

**KEY INDIVIDUALS Nanette O'Donnell** is described as a *"terrific attorney"* and an *"excellent healthcare lawyer."* She is noted for her extensive experience working with HMOs on transactions and ongoing advisory matters. **Joanne Erde** is nothing short of prolific in the Medicaid space, recently advising dozens of clients on reimbursement and billing and Medicaid rules. Sources describe her as *"very bright"* and acknowledge her *"tremendous reputation."*

### Hogan Lovells US LLP

**THE FIRM** It is no surprise that this national regulated industry powerhouse has an impressive Florida healthcare offering. Recent work includes representing research institute Jackson Laboratory in the development of it $1.2 billion genomics research lab. Clients note the team's effective incorporation of in-depth industry knowledge into deals, compliance and day-to-day advisory matters

**Sources say:** *"The firm's strengths are its intellectual depth, subject matter expertise and practical advice."*

**KEY INDIVIDUALS** With both an MD and a JD, **Michael Levinson** brings a unique perspective to his practice. Clients say he offers *"great ideas and insight,"* and is *"level-headed, thoughtful, responsive and helpful."* His recent undertakings include several large-scale transactions. Clients are especially enthusiastic about the *"exceptional"* **Craig Smith**, who *"helps business leaders see opportunities to expand market share and to avoid potential pitfalls."* He is highly recommended for his regulatory expertise and clients are quick to praise his impressive presence before state and federal bodies. **Mark Sterling** led on the aforementioned Jackson Laboratory matter, and is a widely respected transactional lawyer. Clients say: *"He really joins your team, which is remarkable. He's on the sidelines with you, he's so knowledgeable."*

### Holland & Knight LLP
See profile on p.1028

**THE FIRM** This team is called upon to provide its tremendous industry expertise on some of the nation's leading M&A deals. It recently acted as healthcare and insurance counsel to the buyer on Express Scripts' purchase of Medco Health Solutions for $29.1 billion. In addition to its strong advisory and transactional work, the team is well equipped to handle a broad range of healthcare disputes.

**KEY INDIVIDUALS Maria Currier**'s (see p.989) clients go to her for transactions, contract and regulatory work, and praise her for being *"very knowledgeable, always providing good results and being very cost-effective."* Currier was one of the key partners advising Express Scripts on its Medco acquisition. **Morris Miller** (see p.1001) is one of the leading lights in the Tallahassee market. He is well known and widely respected for his focus on the long-term care industry and represents many leading operators in that space **Shannon Hartsfield Salimone** (see p.1005) is recommended by peers and clients for her *"excellent regulatory advice,"* which she has honed from her base in the state capital. She is especially well versed in the ins and outs of HIPAA.

## Band 3

### Carlton Fields, P.A.
See profile on p.1020

**THE FIRM** This firm advises clients on compliance, disputes and transactions, and has a great reputation for its work with hospitals and other local healthcare providers. With several offices around the state, the firm is able to provide its local clientele with comprehensive geographic coverage.

**Sources say:** *"They are always accessible to us and have the resources needed to provide the research we need ASAP."*

**KEY INDIVIDUALS James Kennedy** (see p.996) is one of the most active and respected hospital lawyers in the state. He advises many of the state's leading medical centers on the full spectrum of its legal needs. Sources call him *"talented"* and *"a very fine lawyer."* **Donald Schmidt** (see p.1006) is one of the country's most respected healthcare antitrust lawyers. He is a seasoned litigator and advises major healthcare providers on civil and criminal matters.

## K&L Gates
See profile on p.2245

**THE FIRM** The healthcare team at K&L Gates deals with a wide range of matters. It advises all types of national healthcare providers and businesses on state and federal compliance, expansions and reorganizations. When clients find themselves subject to government or payor audits or investigations, the team offers counsel and defends against enforcement actions.
**Sources say:** *"It has a transactional focus and great lawyers."*
**KEY INDIVIDUALS William Spratt** (see p.1009) has significant experience in acquisitions, sales, mergers and reorganizations of healthcare businesses, as well as fraud and abuse counseling, and federal and state regulatory compliance. Sources say he is *"very special and bright"* and *"an excellent lawyer."* **Marc Auerbach** (see p.983) is noted for his broad healthcare practice. He is adept at a range of transactional matters in the healthcare sector, and additionally represents clients in fraud and abuse matters. *"He impressed me on the other side of a case,"* said one interviewee.

## Smith Hulsey & Busey

**THE FIRM** Smith Hulsey & Busey is a leading name in North Florida and represents a diverse array of healthcare providers from its Jacksonville base. The team advises on reimbursement, licensing, compliance and M&A. It acts for numerous clients and has cultivated relationships with some of the region's most active players over several decades.
**Sources say:** *"Their strengths are their knowledge, proficiency, and experience in healthcare and M&A." "We consider them part of our team."*
**KEY INDIVIDUALS Jeanne Helton** is a leading choice for hospitals, HMOs and physician groups, who turn to her for her breadth of experience, particularly on federal regulatory issues. Sources say she is *"very responsive and creative in solving legal problems."* **Richard Lewis** is a talented transactional lawyer, who is widely respected by peers and clients. His loyal client base is especially impressed with his hands-on attention, saying: *"He responds quickly and gets his hands dirty with the complicated documents required for transactions."*

## Band 4

### Foley & Lardner LLP
See profile on p.2588

**THE FIRM** Foley has an excellent presence in Florida and is a strong national player as well. The team is popular with leading hospital clients, and also represents names like Florida's Blood Centers and Community Blood Centers of Florida. The team recently advised Florida Blood Services on its $300 million merger to form OneBlood, which is now the USA's second largest blood bank after the American Red Cross.
**Sources say:** *"Very good healthcare knowledge broadly, as well as in niche areas."*
**KEY INDIVIDUALS Gary Koch** is highly rated by clients for his Stark and antikickback expertise. He *"is very thorough and wants to ensure you get the right answer and all the info required to reach your goals,"* said one interviewee. **Nathaniel Lacktman** has expertise in an array of federal healthcare issues, including fraud and abuse, Stark, Medicare and antikickback laws. Clients are effusive in their praise, with one saying: *"I would describe Nate as the regulatory guidance expert. I look to him to provide interpretation of the regulations and he has been invaluable in getting to the right person."*

## Fowler White Boggs

**THE FIRM** This team offers full-service advice to its healthcare clients, handling disputes, transactions and regulatory matters for key names such as Humana and Family Health Center. The group is singled out for its crossover expertise in healthcare employment issues, and is also widely respected for its medical malpractice litigation work.
**KEY INDIVIDUALS Edward Waller** is a litigation expert and acts as lead counsel on some of the firm's most sensitive cases. He has extensive experience in class action defense. Peers say he is an *"excellent lawyer"* who is *"very well respected"* in healthcare law. **Kathy Tayon** has an excellent transactional practice and impresses clients with her soup-to-nuts expertise. One impressed client describes her as *"reliable, timely and a pleasant person to deal with."*

## GrayRobinson, PA

**THE FIRM** GrayRobinson's healthcare group advises leading healthcare providers across the state on transactions, antitrust matters and labor and employment issues. It has developed an enthusiastic following and its clients are full of praise for its in-depth knowledge of Florida's regulatory requirements.

**Sources say:** *"Strong governance support, including Sunshine Law knowledge, legislative affairs and medical staff affairs."*
**KEY INDIVIDUALS William Boyles** (see p.986) is praised for his expert handling of a wide range of healthcare transactions, including M&A and joint ventures. He is lauded as *"meticulous and timely,"* and commentators say he has a *"great broad practice with a growing reputation in Florida."*

## Shutts & Bowen LLP

**THE FIRM** This team's client base includes many large healthcare providers, as well as pharmaceutical and medical device manufacturers. Clients single out the firm's expertise in M&A and employment work as particular highlights of the practice. Recent highlights include acting for Trident Medical Center on establishing its plan to house The Medical University of South Carolina's outpatient medical residency program.
**Sources say:** *"Their timing and comprehension are outstanding." "Senior leadership, vast experience and excellent relationships with regulators."*
**KEY INDIVIDUALS Linda Robison** is the group's chair and a leading name in the firm for expert transactional work. She advised shareholders of Intensive Care Consortium on the sale of their controlling interest to another entity. She provides *"superb service,"* according to clients, and can *"share her wealth of knowledge, having done so many deals."*

## Other Notable Practitioners

**Michael Cherniga** (see p.988) of Greenberg Traurig, LLP is highly regarded for his litigation, regulatory and transactional work. He is the firm's health and FDA group chair and is able to capitalize on the firm's tremendous presence in Florida and around the nation to advise top-shelf healthcare clients on a wide range of services. M&A expert **Joshua Kaye** (see p.995) of DLA Piper LLP (US) earns *"ten out of ten"* from his enthusiastic clients, with one describing him as *"stellar – really at the top of his game."* Kaye's recent work includes acting as lead counsel advising Synergy Health on its merger with SRI/Surgical Express. **Bruce Lamb** of Gunster is recognized for his impressive regulatory and litigation expertise. He advises many of Florida's top hospitals, including St. Athony's Hospital and St. Joseph's Hospital. Clients say he is *"extremely responsive"* and *"very collaborative, consultative and measured, but lets you know when you are not on the right track."*

# IMMIGRATION

Commentary about individuals can be found under their firm's paragraph. If the firm has no paragraph (is not ranked) look at Other Notable Practitioners.

## Immigration
### Leading Firms

**Band 1**
Greenberg Traurig, LLP *
Kurzban, Kurzban, Weinger, Tetzeli & Pratt

**Band 2**
Fowler White Boggs
Fragomen, Del Rey, Bernsen & Loewy, LLP *
Gunster *
Rifkin and Fox-Isicoff PA

**Band 3**
Montiel Davis & Fonte, P.L.

### Leading Individuals

**Star individuals**

| | |
|---|---|
| Kurzban Ira J | Kurzban, Kurzban, Weinger, Tetzeli & Pratt |

**Band 1**

| | |
|---|---|
| Flynn III William J | Fowler White Boggs |
| Fox-Isicoff Tammy | Rifkin and Fox-Isicoff PA |
| Gonzalez Enrique | Fragomen, Del Rey, Bernsen & Loewy, LLP |
| Levin Oscar | Greenberg Traurig, LLP * |
| Saleh Anis N | Saleh & Associates (ONP) [†] |
| Tobocman Sarah Lea | Gunster |

**Band 2**

| | |
|---|---|
| Cordero Luis A | Cordero & Associates PA (ONP) [†] |
| Hernandez Eugenio | Avila Rodriguez Hernandez Mena (ONP) [†] |
| Montiel Davis Magda | Montiel Davis & Fonte, P.L. |
| Pratt John Patrick | Kurzban, Kurzban, Weinger, Tetzeli & Pratt |
| Rifkin Larry S | Rifkin and Fox-Isicoff PA |
| Shane Michael | Shane & Shane, P.A. (ONP) [†] |
| Tetzeli Helena | Kurzban, Kurzban, Weinger, Tetzeli & Pratt |

**Band 3**

| | |
|---|---|
| Berger David | Bernstein & Berger PA (ONP) [†] |
| Brauwerman Jeffrey N | Brauwerman, Sibirsky & Miranda (ONP) [†] |
| Carmichael Jay | Gunster |
| Casablanca Maria Isabel | Casablanca Legal Group (ONP) [†] |
| Chichoni Hector A | Duane Morris LLP (ONP) [†] |
| Hoyos Maite | Maite Hoyos PA (ONP) [†] |
| Kramer Mary E | Law Office of Mary E Kramer, P.A (ONP) [†] |
| Raleigh Thomas L | Akerman Senterfitt (ONP) [†] |

**Up-and-coming individuals**

| | |
|---|---|
| Cooper Glenn M. | GrayRobinson, PA (ONP) [†] * |
| Roeper Jennifer G | Fowler White Boggs |

**Associates to watch**

| | |
|---|---|
| Ribeiro Mariana R. | Gunster |

\* Indicates firm / individual with profile.
[†] ONP = Other Notable Practitioner.

## Band 1

### Greenberg Traurig, LLP
See profile on p.1024

**THE FIRM** Greenberg Traurig is renowned in Florida for its strong business immigration practice. The team repre-

sents individuals and companies in a variety of employment-based immigration matters. It has particular expertise in developing immigration strategies for corporate clients, and in assisting clients with I-9 compliance issues. **KEY INDIVIDUALS Oscar Levin** (see p.998) is well regarded for his work in business immigration. According to sources, "*he can figure out what is right for each individual person and situation and provide a tailormade approach.*" He has recently represented a range of high-profile clients in complicated immigration matters involving political sensitivities and international law.

### Kurzban, Kurzban, Weinger, Tetzeli & Pratt

**THE FIRM** This widely recognized immigration team advises small and large businesses on their employment-based immigrant and non-immigrant visa needs. It also assists with worksite compliance and is lauded for its immigration-related litigation work. Lately, the firm has taken on an increasing amount of litigation relating to the EB-5 investor visa category.
**KEY INDIVIDUALS Ira Kurzban** is a well-known figure in the immigration field, and recently acted as lead counsel on an EB-5 litigation matter. Sources have "*tremendous respect*" for his abilities. **John Pratt** is experienced in all areas of immigration law, including immigrant and non-immigrant visas, deportation and removal, and federal court litigation. Lately he has acted for a number of entertainment industry clients from Latin America. **Helena Tetzeli** is a respected member of the legal community with expertise in both immigration law and commercial litigation. Her clients include high net worth individuals, investors, and organizations.

## Band 2

### Fowler White Boggs

**THE FIRM** Fowler White Boggs has a strong presence in Florida and is recognized as one of the leading immigration practices. Areas of expertise include I-9 compliance, immigrant and non-immigrant investor visas, and labor certifications. The team has recently successfully represented Tampa General Hospital, Moffitt Cancer Center and Tampa Bay Rays in various visa matters.
**Sources say:** "*They are very client-focused and extremely responsive. They make it as easy as possible to get the answers that I need quickly.*"
**KEY INDIVIDUALS William Flynn** is described as "*a superstar*" and praised by sources for the breadth of his knowledge and experience. He assists individuals and corporations with their visa, residency and audit requirements, and regularly represents them before the relevant authorities. **Jennifer Roeper**'s broad range of experience within immigration law enables her to assist corporate clients with compliance issues and individuals subject to

deportation proceedings. She "*provides solid advice that I trust,*" said one commentator.

### Fragomen, Del Rey, Bernsen & Loewy, LLP
See profile on p.1974

**THE FIRM** This renowned boutique immigration firm continues to enjoy a solid reputation in Florida. It provides solutions for large corporate clients in various immigration matters, including investor visas, business travelers, and corporate immigration strategy.
**KEY INDIVIDUALS Enrique Gonzalez** manages the firm's Coral Gables office. He is an expert in managing immigration strategies for clients, and in handling EB-5 investor visas.

### Gunster
See profile on p.1025

**THE FIRM** Gunster's integrated immigration practice remains a strong contender in Florida. The team has handled a large number of investor visa matters of late, and has a wealth of experience in training human resources professionals on immigration matters. The firm's clients hail from a variety of industries, including banking, healthcare, technology, hospitality and pharmaceuticals.
**Sources say:** "*I have worked with a number of immigration law firms and it is one of the best.*"
**KEY INDIVIDUALS Sarah Lea Tobocman** is widely recognized for her work assisting healthcare facilities and professionals in their immigration needs. She is described by one impressed source as "*probably the most knowledgeable immigration attorney that I've worked with.*" **Jay Carmichael** "*is very practical, and knows the immigration services inside out,*" say sources. Clients benefit from his background in and knowledge of federal government matters. Carmichael advises individuals, corporations and organizations in a variety of industries, on a range of immigration needs. **Mariana Ribeiro** is noted by sources for her "*very good judgment and intuition.*" She mainly advises clients on employment-based immigration matters, and is fluent in Spanish and Portuguese.

### Rifkin and Fox-Isicoff PA

**THE FIRM** With the addition of an office in Peru, this long-established firm is even better placed to service its clients with Latin American links. The team maintains an outstanding reputation in all areas of immigration law, including employment-based and family-based matters, labor certification and deportation.
**KEY INDIVIDUALS Tammy Fox-Isicoff** is praised for her "*cutting-edge knowledge*" of immigration matters. She is an expert in EB-5 investor visas and is also highly regarded for her work in deportation. **Larry Rifkin** is well known and respected in the immigration law community as a long-standing practitioner. He has a wealth of experience in all matters relating to immigration and naturalization.

## Band 3

### Montiel Davis & Fonte, P.L.

**THE FIRM** This boutique practice offers services in all areas of immigration law, including employment and family-based visa work and removal defense. The firm has two offices in Florida and is known for its ability to assist a variety people in their wide-ranging immigration needs.

**KEY INDIVIDUALS** Founding partner **Magda Montiel Davis** is described as *"superb"* by impressed sources. She has a notable longstanding presence in the immigration law arena.

### Other Notable Practitioners

**Eugenio Hernandez** of Avila Rodriguez Hernandez Mena & Ferri LLP specializes in business immigration, assisting corporations with their immigration needs for international employees. He has been busy of late advising clients on investor visa categories. **Jeffrey Brauwerman** of

Brauwerman, Sibirsky and Miranda, P.A. is a former immigration judge and is well known in the field for his deportation and removal work, as well as complex citizenship cases. **Maria Isabel Casablanca** of Casablanca Legal Group acts for individuals and corporations on the full gamut of immigration matters. She is highly regarded for her work in deportation and related litigation. **Luis Cordero** of Cordero & Associates PA has a broad practice in immigration and nationality law. He has recently acted for large corporate clients, high net worth individuals, and those involved in complex deportation matters. **Hector Chichoni** of Duane Morris LLP offers an extensive array of immigration services to his corporate and individual clients. He has recently advised a portfolio of investors and business clients on outbound visa requirements. **Michael Shane** of Shane & Shane, P.A. is well regarded in the immigration law arena for having a well-rounded practice and particular expertise in family-based immigration work. Sources describe him as *"a very good attorney."* **Mary Kramer** of Law Office of Mary E Kramer, P.A maintains a

solid reputation in the field of deportation proceedings, and immigration-related criminal matters. **Anis Saleh** of Saleh & Associates practices in all areas of immigration and nationality law, and is particularly admired for his work representing individuals in family-based cases. **Maite Hoyos** is a sole practitioner in the field of corporate immigration. She is particularly well known for her work with the entertainment industry. **David Berger** of Bernstein & Berger PA is a new entrant to the table. He is well respected in the immigration law field and is praised by sources for his wealth of experience. Clients recommend **Thomas Raleigh** of Akerman Senterfitt for his *"client-focused approach and pragmatic advice."* He has experience in corporate transactional work, and specializes in corporate immigration law. Recent clients include Somfy Systems, Coulisse and Pelliconi. **Glenn Cooper** (see p.988) of GrayRobinson, PA is a fluent French speaker and specializes in business immigration. He has recently been involved in assisting professional athletes, investors and multinational companies, among others.

# INSURANCE

Commentary about individuals can be found under their firm's paragraph. If the firm has no paragraph (is not ranked) look at Other Notable Practitioners.

**Insurance**
**Leading Firms**

**Band 1**
Akerman Senterfitt
Carlton Fields, P.A. *
Radey, Thomas, Yon & Clark

**Band 2**
Colodny, Fass, Talenfeld, Karlinsky, Abate & Webb PA *
Foley & Lardner LLP *
Pennington, P.A.

**Band 3**
Butler Pappas Weihmuller Katz Craig LLP
Fowler White Boggs

## Band 1

### Akerman Senterfitt
See profile on p.1014

**THE FIRM** This prominent firm is prized for its extensive experience in managing complex coverage disputes, class actions and insurer bad faith claims. The group also handles sophisticated regulatory issues from its well-connected Tallahassee office. The practice possesses notable healthcare industry expertise, and represents a number of major insurance companies, including Liberty Mutual, Allstate and American International.

**KEY INDIVIDUALS Marcy Levine Aldrich** is highly respected for her wealth of experience defending insurers against class actions. Market sources describe her as *"affable and professional."*

**Insurance**
**Senior Statesmen**

**Senior Statesmen:** distinguished older practitioners
| Cox W Donald | Fowler White Boggs |

**Leading Individuals**

**Band 1**
| Aldrich Marcy Levine | Akerman Senterfitt |
| Brown Daniel C | Carlton Fields, P.A. * |
| Delegal Mark | Pennington, P.A. |
| Yon David A | Radey, Thomas, Yon & Clark |

**Band 2**
| Cruz-Brown Kelly A | Carlton Fields, P.A. * |
| Karlinsky Fred | Colodny, Fass, Talenfeld, Karlinsky, Abate * |
| Maida Thomas J | Foley & Lardner LLP |
| Meenan Timothy J | Blank & Meenan, PA (ONP)[†] |
| Thomas Harry O | Radey, Thomas, Yon & Clark |

**Band 3**
| Colodny Mike | Colodny, Fass, Talenfeld, Karlinsky, Abate * |
| Levine A Kenneth | Cozen O'Connor (ONP)[†] * |
| Miller Travis L | Radey, Thomas, Yon & Clark |
| Neal Austin | Foley & Lardner LLP |
| Pelle Anthony | Carlton Fields, P.A. * |

**Up-and-coming individuals**
| Strickland Nate Wesley | Foley & Lardner LLP |
| Webb Katherine | Colodny, Fass, Talenfeld, Karlinsky, Abate * |

* Indicates firm / individual with profile.
Alphabetical order within each band. Band 1 is the highest.

### Carlton Fields, P.A.
See profile on p.1020

**THE FIRM** Carlton Fields has built its broad insurance practice on a strong foundation of insurance litigation experience. Clients are hugely satisfied with the group's knowledge and results in complex coverage disputes, bad faith claims, class actions, regulatory matters and various other issues, such as D&O liability claims. The group also concentrates on regulatory issues in the health and life insurance sectors.

**Sources say:** *"Carlton Fields is a traditional insurer practice and is quite good in this field."*

**KEY INDIVIDUALS Daniel Brown** (see p.987) is held in high regard for his experience representing insurers in the life, health, property and casualty sectors. Market sources laud him as *"very confident and professional,"* and describe his working style as *"very direct and to the point – he tells you like it is."* **Kelly Cruz-Brown** (see p.989) concentrates her practice on administrative law and regulation matters, and is regarded as *"knowledgeable, connected and a pleasant person to boot"* by commentators. **Anthony Pelle** (see p.1003) enters the rankings amid a flurry of praise from commentators, who describe him as *"attentive and extremely knowledgeable."* He focuses on insurance coverage and bad faith litigation, but also deals with class actions.

### Radey, Thomas, Yon & Clark

**THE FIRM** This preeminent firm's highly respected regulatory practice prides itself on having a team of experienced practitioners, two of whom are former regulators. Clients appreciate the team's depth of knowledge in handling issues regarding the formation, acquisition and merging of regulated companies. It handles the full range of regulatory issues, from rate and form filings to appealing decisions made in administrative hearings and commercial arbitrations.

**KEY INDIVIDUALS David Yon** can draw on his extensive experience in the Insurance Commissioner's Office when handling regulatory matters concerning life and health issues as well as property and casualty issues. **Harry Thomas** has amassed over 30 years of experience litigating and arbitrating insurance coverage and regulatory disputes. He is recognized for his particular expertise in the construction sector. **Travis Miller** continues to impress clients and peers alike with his diverse practice, featuring insurance regulatory law, administrative law, and business and transactional law.

## Band 2

### Colodny, Fass, Talenfeld, Karlinsky, Abate & Webb PA
See profile on p.1021

**THE FIRM** This major insurance regulatory presence has enduring connections to the most prominent regulators across the country and a great depth of industry knowledge. Its practitioners stand out for their responsiveness to client needs and ability to tackle challenging cases. The team has recently provided a rewrite of Florida's automobile insurance law for Property Casualty Insurers Association of America.

**Sources say:** *"I'm hard-pressed to find anything they don't excel in – at every turn they've been a great resource to us."*
**KEY INDIVIDUALS Fred Karlinsky** (see p.995) is singled out as a major player in the regulatory field. Sources say: *"No-one does more than him in terms of quality and quantity."* Department head **Mike Colodny** (see p.988) is hailed as a *"fountain of knowledge"* in regulatory matters. Sources appreciate his attentiveness, with one saying: *"He's very good at devising strategy and moving resources. I don't think our company would be around without him."* **Katherine Webb** (see p.1011) handles a range of regulatory issues. Market commentators describe her as *"nothing short of*

spectacular: she's a hard worker, constantly doing the work I need and giving the counsel I need."*

### Foley & Lardner LLP
See profile on p.2588

**THE FIRM** This Tallahassee-based practice has a healthy reputation for handling regulatory matters, as well as sophisticated insurance transactions. The firm can draw on the varied expertise of its lawyers, encompassing the corporate, litigation and tax arenas. Current clients include Lloyd's America, Geico and FFVA Mutual Insurance Company.

**Sources say:** *"The team helps with corporate governance, compliance with records laws, and advice and compliance with the Florida government. We are absolutely satisfied."*
**KEY INDIVIDUALS Thomas Maida** is managing partner of the Tallahassee office and enjoys a reputation as *"an incredible attorney."* Clients regard him as *"politically sensitive"* and *"smart and very articulate – he's very good at picking the right words."* **Austin Neal** represents domestic and international insurers and reinsurers in transactional, regulatory, administrative and legislative matters. He recently acted for Lloyd's underwriters in connection with a reinsurer application. New entry **Wes Strickland** is held in high regard for his transactional and regulatory insurance expertise. Clients praise his ability to litigate in the complex political environment of Florida's highly regulated insurance industry.

### Pennington, P.A.

**THE FIRM** This full-service firm is exclusive to Florida and is celebrated for its ability to handle regulatory issues and defend insurance companies across a broad spectrum of areas, including medical malpractice, automobile negligence and workers' compensation. The regulatory team works closely with the governmental and legislative affairs team to ensure clients receive an expert, up-to-date service.
**Sources say:** *"They are very politically savvy and have strong relationships with legislators and regulators in the Insurance Department."*
**KEY INDIVIDUALS Mark Delegal** is principally known as an exceptional lobbyist, and is regarded as being among

the elite with regard to his legislative insurance practice. Commentators describe him as *"extremely responsive and very creative,"* with *"strong analytical and interpretive skills."* He also *"has an uncanny ability to get people to listen to him."*

## Band 3

### Butler Pappas Weihmuller Katz Craig LLP

**THE FIRM** This established firm is widely regarded as having one of Florida's leading insurance defense practices, having amassed an impressive amount of experience within this area. It is acting in a broad range of insurance practice areas on behalf of insurers, including insurance fraud, bankruptcy and reinsurance. The Florida team operates out of offices in Miami, Tampa and Tallahassee.
**KEY INDIVIDUALS** Managing partner **Douglas Berry** is a key contact for the firm's coverage defense practice.

### Fowler White Boggs

**THE FIRM** Fowler White Boggs has a broad insurance practice featuring expert defense against a number of class actions, covering property, casualty and health issues, insurance fraud and regulatory matters. The team represents a series of major insurance companies, including Nationwide, Geico and Metlife.
**Sources say:** *"A very good defense firm."*
**KEY INDIVIDUALS** Highly respected department head **Donald Cox** specializes in insurance regulatory litigation.

## Other Notable Practitioners

**Timothy Meenan** of Blank & Meenan, PA earns praise from market sources for his strong insurance regulatory practice, aided by his previous experience working for the government. **Kenneth Levine** (see p.998) recently joined the new West Palm Beach office of Cozen O'Connor from Edwards Wildman Palmer. Levine is recommended for his regulatory practice, and also handles transactional matters. Market sources regard him as *"a very hard worker who we are able to reach out to night or day."*

# LABOR & EMPLOYMENT

Commentary about individuals can be found under their firm's paragraph. If the firm has no paragraph (is not ranked) look at Other Notable Practitioners.

| Labor & Employment | |
| --- | --- |
| **Leading Firms** | |
| **Band 1** | |
| FordHarrison LLP * | |
| Greenberg Traurig, LLP * | |
| Stearns Weaver Miller Weissler Alhadeff & Sitterson, P.A. | |
| **Band 2** | |
| Akerman Senterfitt | |
| Fisher & Phillips LLP * | |
| **Band 3** | |
| Baker & Hostetler LLP * | |
| Constangy, Brooks & Smith, LLP | |
| Fowler White Boggs | |
| Jackson Lewis LLP * | |
| Morgan, Lewis & Bockius LLP * | |
| Thompson, Sizemore, Gonzalez & Hearing, PA | |
| **Band 4** | |
| Duane Morris LLP * | |
| GrayRobinson, PA | |
| Hogan Lovells US LLP | |
| Hunton & Williams LLP * | |
| Ogletree, Deakins, Nash, Smoak & Stewart, PC * | |
| Phelps Dunbar LLP * | |

| Labor & Employment | |
| --- | --- |
| **Senior Statesmen** | |
| Senior Statesmen: distinguished older practitioners | |
| Coleman Patrick D | GrayRobinson, PA * |
| Fleming Joseph Z | Greenberg Traurig, LLP * |

| **Leading Individuals** | | |
| --- | --- | --- |
| **Star individuals** | | |
| Casey Michael W | Duane Morris LLP | |
| McCrea Jr Richard C | Greenberg Traurig, LLP * | |
| Zinober Peter W | Greenberg Traurig, LLP * | |
| **Band 1** | | |
| Caulkins Charles | Fisher & Phillips LLP * | |
| Connor Terence G | Hunton & Williams LLP * | |
| Dickinson John | Constangy, Brooks & Smith, LLP | |
| Eisenberg Susan Nadler | Akerman Senterfitt | |
| Garwood Thomas | FordHarrison LLP * | |
| Gonzalez Thomas M | Thompson, Sizemore, Gonzalez & Hearing | |
| Kofman Robert | Stearns Weaver Miller Weissler Alhadeff | |
| McKenna Susan | Jackson Lewis LLP * | |
| Turk Robert | Stearns Weaver Miller Weissler Alhadeff | |
| Weitzman Allan H | Proskauer Rose LLP (ONP)[†] | |
| **Band 2** | | |
| Andrews William H | GrayRobinson, PA | |
| Beveridge Cathy | Fowler White Boggs | |
| Bramnick James | Akerman Senterfitt | |
| Brown James | FordHarrison LLP * | |
| Buesing Karen Meyer | Akerman Senterfitt | |
| Cheskin Mark R | Hogan Lovells US LLP | |
| deMeza Jr William B | Holland & Knight LLP (ONP)[†] * | |
| Estevez Anne Marie | Morgan, Lewis & Bockius LLP * | |
| Gallion Theresa M | Fisher & Phillips LLP * | |
| Grogan Michael K | Allen, Norton & Blue (ONP)[†] | |
| Hament Andrew | FordHarrison LLP * | |
| Hanley Mark A | Glenn Rasmussen, P.A. (ONP)[†] | |
| Hearing Gregory A | Thompson, Sizemore, Gonzalez & Hearing | |
| Holshouser Eric J | Fowler White Boggs | |
| Hyde Kevin E | Foley & Lardner LLP | |

| | |
| --- | --- |
| Kitchen F Damon | Constangy, Brooks & Smith, LLP |
| Malfitano Michael | Constangy, Brooks & Smith, LLP |
| Peterson Ralph | Beggs & Lane |
| Phillips John | Phelps Dunbar LLP |
| Shaughnessy Kevin W | Baker & Hostetler LLP * |
| Stage Jon | Stearns Weaver Miller Weissler Alhadeff |
| **Band 3** | |
| Ackerbaum Cox Joyce | Baker & Hostetler LLP * |
| Block David | Jackson Lewis LLP * |
| Farmer II Guy O | GrayRobinson, PA * |
| Kornreich David | Fisher & Phillips LLP * |
| Kunkel Daniel H | Kunkel Miller & Hament |
| Mandel Jeffrey E | Fisher & Phillips LLP * |
| Radford William R | Ogletree, Deakins, Nash, Smoak & Stewart * |
| Riegel Jr Robert G | Fowler White Boggs |
| Tuschman Richard D | Akerman Senterfitt |
| Zelek Mark E | Morgan, Lewis & Bockius LLP * |
| **Band 4** | |
| Bernstein Steve | Fisher & Phillips LLP * |
| Corbin Peter | FordHarrison LLP * |
| Lerner Brian L | Kim Vaughan Lerner LLP |
| Muldowney Patrick M | Baker & Hostetler LLP * |
| Silverman Scott T | Akerman Senterfitt |
| Sniffen Robert J. | Sniffen & Spellman P.A. (ONP)[†] |
| Spector David I | Akerman Senterfitt |
| Symons Robin | Gordon & Rees, LLP (ONP)[†] |
| Ward Alysa | Glenn Rasmussen, P.A. |
| Williams Jennifer T | Akerman Senterfitt |
| Zandy Aaron L | FordHarrison LLP * |
| **Associates to watch** | |
| Schwartz Jurate | Proskauer Rose LLP (ONP)[†] |

* Indicates firm / Individual with profile.
[†]ONP = Other Notable Practitioner.

## Band 1

### FordHarrison LLP
See profile on p.1108

**THE FIRM** Working out of offices in Tampa, Miami, Orlando and Jacksonville, this impressive labor and employment boutique offers comprehensive coverage of the Florida market. It handles all elements of labor and employment law for a stellar client list, and recently defended Publix Super Markets against a claim from a former employee alleging an FMLA violation following the termination of his position. The team is also engaged in substantial multijurisdictional union negotiations.

**Sources say:** *"They are our go-to firm for labor work. We are very happy with them and wouldn't even want to consider anyone else."*

**KEY INDIVIDUALS Thomas Garwood** (see p.992) is one of the preeminent figures at the Florida labor Bar and is known as a vastly experienced attorney with grounding in negotiation and advocacy as well as litigation. He has played a key role in multijurisdictional union negotiations. **James Brown** (see p.987) has recently represented IAP World Services in an NLRB unfair labor practice case. He is a veteran mediator, and has experience in over 800 labor and employment mediations. **Andrew Hament** (see p.994) offers a flexible service, encompassing both counsel and litigation. He has represented clients in both state and federal courts. Among the cases he handles are drug abuse, trade secrets, union grievances and sexual harassment investigations. **Aaron Zandy** (see p.1013) has impressed clients, who believe that *"he is a brilliant advocate, very good at put-*

*ting people at ease"* and that *"he provides a huge benefit to our company."* **Peter Corbin** (see p.988) brings over three decades of experience to his practice, which is centered on defending employers in a wide range of industries from complaints or suits relating to discrimination, harassment and wrongful termination.

### Greenberg Traurig, LLP
See profile on p.1024

**THE FIRM** Greenberg Traurig fields a large employment team in Florida, consisting of 26 partners, counsel and associates. The group's cumulative experience forms a solid foundation for its standing as a regular choice for big-name clients. The practice offers regular support to

Goodyear in all of its employment and labor matters, including a nationwide misclassification and unpaid overtime case. It also represented Benson's in a theft of trade secrets, unfair competition and Computer Fraud Act violation case against two former property managers.

**KEY INDIVIDUALS Richard McCrea** (see p.1000) is one of the stellar names in the Florida labor market. He is widely acknowledged as one of the most able employment litigators in the state, and has undertaken some of the most prominent cases involving general employment matters, trade secrets and civil rights. **Peter Zinober** (see p.1013) is *"a very experienced lawyer with excellent analytical capabilities."* Recognized by peers as being among the team's most formidable practitioners, he is the cochair of the firm's global labor and employment practice. He was lead partner in representing Ryan, LLC in a theft of trade secrets case. **Joseph Fleming** (see p.991) has considerable experience as an employment litigator, and has represented a diverse range of clients in the full variety of cases. He is particularly well renowned for his abilities in cases involving opposition to union organization efforts and collective bargaining negotiations.

## Stearns Weaver Miller Weissler Alhadeff & Sitterson, P.A.

**THE FIRM** The Stearns Weaver team covers the greater part of the state from its impressive spread of offices in Fort Lauderdale, Tallahassee, Miami and Tampa. It has established itself as one of the prime practices for employment work on behalf of large companies, and frequently serves prominent financial institutions among its varied client list. It has recently been particularly active in whistleblower retaliation claims, matters relating to the FMLA and discrimination claims: areas for which it is highly acclaimed by the wider market.

**Sources say:** *"Stearns has a really strong operation and a good, broad practice."*

**KEY INDIVIDUALS Robert Kofman** is described by impressed clients as *"the godfather of employment law in south Florida."* He is among the leading figures in the state for employment law, and cochairs the Stearns team. Sources note that *"he lends a level of gravitas which is hard to get."* Group cochair **Robert Turk** is a highly visible and well-regarded figure in this market. A client describes him as *"one of the people that I most respect in the legal sphere."* He earns particular praise for his compassionate and industrious approach. Clients are enthusiastic in their praise of **Jon Stage**, who is a well-acclaimed litigator at the firm. He has particular expertise in contentious matters relating to the FMLA, the FLSA and the Florida Civil Rights Act.

## Band 2

### Akerman Senterfitt
See profile on p.1014

**THE FIRM** This team handles a full range of employment issues and has recently been involved in a series of sophisticated discrimination cases. For example, the firm was engaged by cruise line Carnival Corporation in a race discrimination and retaliation case in which it successfully obtained a summary judgment in favor of the client. The group has also acted for Travelpro in a high-value case in defense of allegations by two former executives claiming wrongful dismissal and sex discrimination.

**KEY INDIVIDUALS** Leading practitioner **Susan Nadler Eisenberg** regularly represents employers in contentious matters, and has done so in both federal and state courts. Her profile is aided by an exemplary reputation for cases involving working hours and wages. **James Bramnick** is the chair of the firm's national labor and employment practice. Having practiced for over three decades in representing management in labor matters, he has accrued both

experience and distinction in the Florida market. **Karen Meyer Buesing** also specializes in representing management in contentious matters, though she also offers day-to-day counsel to her clients, as well as training services. **Richard Tuschman** operates a broad practice and offers both counsel and litigation services to his clients. He is especially prominent for his work in contentious matters involving the FLSA and the FMLA. **David Spector** recently served as lead partner in the representation of Sysco Foods in national origin discrimination litigation. He frequently handles sophisticated disputes for high-profile clients. **Scott Silverman** has handled employment matters of virtually every type throughout his career. He is particularly well versed in representing employers before the NLRB, and is also lauded for his drafting ability when assembling contracts and employee manuals for clients. The versatile **Jennifer Williams** has undertaken a wide range of work for clients, including conducting training sessions with employees. She also has extensive experience of drafting documentation and in handling discrimination cases and wage and hour issues.

## Fisher & Phillips LLP
See profile on p.1107

**THE FIRM** From its offices in Fort Lauderdale, Orlando and Tampa, this team is well positioned to offer its services to clients across the state, as well as on a national level. As part of a firm dedicated entirely to labor and employment matters, the Florida practice is part of a strong tradition of handling the full spectrum of relevant issues. It recently successfully defended an employer in a complicated race discrimination worth $300,000. Other prominent clients include The Auto Club Group, Ryder System and General Dynamics.

**KEY INDIVIDUALS** Fort Lauderdale managing partner **Charles Caulkins** (see p.988) has cultivated an exceptional reputation across the state for his work in labor and employment. Clients offer praise for his thorough approach in developing and implementing programs to prevent contentious issues arising. **Theresa Gallion** (see p.992) is known for using her deep experience to good effect in the courtroom, and is among the group's most prominent litigators. Although she has been engaged by clients from a large range of industries, she has a particular focus on representing educational and healthcare institutions, as well as telecommunications and retail companies. **David Kornreich** (see p.997) has extensive experience in all manner of labor and employment matters. Peers respect him as a highly knowledgeable practitioner in the Florida labor sphere. **Jeffrey Mandel** (see p.999) manages the firm's Orlando office. He is especially practiced in handling public sector issues, an area for which he is regularly applauded by his peers. **Steve Bernstein** (see p.985) is *"really really terrific"* in the eyes of impressed clients. They reserve special praise for his *"very instructive and calm demeanor on cases that can be very emotional."*

## Band 3

### Baker & Hostetler LLP
See profile on p.2119

**THE FIRM** This five-partner Orlando practice has a multijurisdictional presence that enhances its offering in collective actions. It also represents significant players in the leisure and hospitality and healthcare sectors, where it is traditionally strong, but is equally adept at getting favorable results and providing preventive advice to the likes of Siemens Energy and Piper Aircraft. The team covers a diverse set of matters, ranging from trade secret misappropriation and antidiscriminatory advice to nationwide FLSA suits.

**Sources say:** *"They are very flexible and receptive."*

**KEY INDIVIDUALS Kevin Shaughnessy** (see p.1007) has substantial experience in multijurisdictional class action suits. He coordinates the employment group and features in several high-stakes matters. **Joyce Ackerbaum Cox** (see p.983) is sought after for her ability to resolve complex disputes for employers. She is experienced in handling FLSA cases and successfully represented Adventist Health Systems in a series of lawsuits alleging violation. **Patrick Muldowney** (see p.1001) is admitted to both New York and Florida courts and advises large employers in various sectors on FLSA compliance. He has recently been managing high-profile personnel transitions for major clients.

### Constangy, Brooks & Smith, LLP

**THE FIRM** This team focuses exclusively on management employment matters and its client list includes major national and regional names. Four of the firm's 23 offices are in Florida, with the latest one at Port St. Lucie added in 2010. This concentration of resources, combined with leading labor practices in other states, helps this boutique to stand out as a choice for employers.

**KEY INDIVIDUALS John Dickinson** is a trusted name among peers and is known for his well-established expertise in wage and hour compliance. **Damon Kitchen** is known for his able litigation practice, defending employers against a range of claims arising from antidiscrimination and breach of contract issues as part of his varied practice. **Michael Malfitano** *"really impresses with his ability to bring everything to a down-to-earth level when it comes to employment law,"* according to clients.

### Fowler White Boggs

**THE FIRM** This established Florida firm has nearly 70 years of local experience and provides ongoing employment advice to key regional names from its five offices. Clients prize the team's deep experience in public sector collective bargaining, and its matters are spread over litigation, union negotiations and compliance advice. It counts Blue Cross Blue Shields of Florida and the Adecco Group among its distinguished clientele.

**Sources say:** *"Fowler White Boggs consistently exceeds our expectations on work involving public sector contract negotiations and employee grievances."*

**KEY INDIVIDUALS Cathy Beveridge** is *"a font of knowledge and practicality"* to clients, who add that *"she's been* *around and she knows a lot."* She has recently been involved in complex discrimination cases. **Eric Holshouser** serves several high-profile public sector employers, whom he advises on contract negotiations, employee grievances and items relating to breaches of contract. He also has a distinguished record in achieving workable solutions in sensitive, senior executive terminations. **Robert Riegel** is *"a great litigator, negotiator and public speaker"* in the eyes of clients, and counts industrial, aviation and financial employers among those for whom he has achieved outstanding results. He heads the firm's labor and employment department.

## Jackson Lewis LLP
### See profile on p.1982

**THE FIRM** This team is part of an extensive, national network devoted entirely to advising and representing management in labor and employment issues. The Florida arm of this boutique workplace law firm benefits from three well-placed offices in Miami, Orlando and Jacksonville. It represents household names in high-stakes litigation and counts Pfizer and IBM among its clients. The team has secured favorable judgments for employers involving significant applications of the Florida Civil Rights Act.

**KEY INDIVIDUALS Susan McKenna** (see p.1000) is described enthusiastically by clients as *"the first person we call on in employment issues"* and *"delightful"* to work with whether she is giving preventive advice and training or handling difficult disputes. Her practice encompasses litigation and proactive management training. **David Block** (see p.986) is an accomplished litigator working from the firm's Miami office. His multiple Bar admissions include various courts in Florida, Maryland, New York and the US Supreme Court.

## Morgan, Lewis & Bockius LLP
### See profile on p.2246

**THE FIRM** This group benefits from a powerful national network which attracts matters of significant complexity to its Florida team. Recent eye-catching client wins show that the team builds actively on the impressive results achieved for existing blue-chip clients and is growing its statewide reputation. It advises Office Depot and Morgan Stanley on employment matters.

**KEY INDIVIDUALS Anne Marie Estevez** (see p.991) leads in employment cases ranging from discrimination and disability matters to FLSA class actions for large, institutional clients in finance and education. She has achieved some impressive judgments in defending employers against potentially costly class certification. **Mark Zelek** (see p.1013) creates an *"excellent"* experience for clients, according to sources. In addition to his work with clients, he leads the firm's international labor and employment practice and is managing partner for the Miami office.

## Thompson, Sizemore, Gonzalez & Hearing, PA

**THE FIRM** This management-side boutique has a strong following in Tampa and is known for both private and public sector work. The practice earns extensive praise

from clients and draws on the deep experience of practitioners versed in both preventive compliance advice and employment litigation.

**Sources say:** *"Just a phenomenal firm in terms of experience, knowledge and unbelievable rates. You really feel like you're a part of them."*

**KEY INDIVIDUALS Thomas Gonzalez** *"embodies all the characteristics that any lawyer would like to have,"* according to commentators, who also laud his *"tremendous work ethic."* Managing partner **Gregory Hearing** is an experienced litigator who inspires confidence in peers due to his involvement in sophisticated employment cases and his active role in the Florida Bar.

## Duane Morris LLP
### See profile on p.2239

**THE FIRM** Duane Morris's Florida team is a trusted resource for national employers in the transport, healthcare and engineering sectors. Its successful representations before the NLRB and experience with union negotiations, FLSA and Florida Medical Leave Act matters earn it resounding client praise.

**Sources say:** *"They had full dedication and very proactive, client-oriented service."*

**KEY INDIVIDUALS Michael Casey** is *"a fantastic lawyer"* according to peers and *"gets some very good results for clients."* Clients enthuse that he is *"fabulous,"* while others add that he *"stands out"* and is relentless in fighting their corner.

## GrayRobinson, PA

**THE FIRM** This group has enviable statewide coverage through its ten offices and has increased the size of its employment team. It has significant public sector clients, including Orange County, but also represents several private sector employers in the energy and healthcare industries. The team recently represented Star One Staffing in defending against claims pertaining to the FLSA, RICO and various state law torts.

**KEY INDIVIDUALS William Andrews** has an established reputation for his public sector work, but has recently also been involved in defending logistics and business services companies in contentious cases. Interviewees describe **Guy Farmer** (see p.991) as *"a very smart guy who gets the job done for clients."* He has secured favorable outcomes for energy sector employers in Title VII and FCRA matters as well as union claims. **Patrick Coleman** (see p.988) is regarded a *"very valued resource"* and clients are *"absolutely impressed"* by his employment work.

## Hogan Lovells US LLP

**THE FIRM** Clients appreciate the national and international reach of this firm, which has a dedicated employment partner in Miami supported by several associates. It is a favored firm in complex litigation, particularly for class action suits or delicate matters of tortious interference and trade secrets. It works with some prestigious higher educa-

tion employers on sensitive employment discrimination disputes.

**Sources say:** *"For labor and employment advice, or something of a grave matter, Hogan Lovells would be my number-one choice."*

**KEY INDIVIDUALS Mark Cheskin** is a leading trial lawyer who earns accolades for being *"very astute"* and able to find *"creative, effective solutions to problems,"* according to clients.

## Hunton & Williams LLP
### See profile on p.2517

**THE FIRM** The Miami office at this national firm has a reputation for high-quality work that is well suited to its complementary strength in litigation. Its labor practice is integrated with the firm's full-service, multijurisdictional offering yet offers considerable specialist experience from its senior partners.

**Sources say:** *"They are all smart, efficient, well prepared and diligent. I highly recommend them."*

**KEY INDIVIDUALS** According to sources, **Terence Connor** (see p.988) *"is one of the smartest lawyers in the employment area."* A peer adds that he is the go-to person if clients have a highly sophisticated case that could go to jury trial.

## Ogletree, Deakins, Nash, Smoak & Stewart, PC
### See profile on p.1110

**THE FIRM** Ogletree Deakins has offered its national employment services in Florida since 2004, when it opened branches in Miami and Tampa. The team has served household names in leisure and retail such as Royal Caribbean Cruises and Kmart. It has recently achieved a summary judgment for a major restaurant chain against a former employee alleging sexual harassment and retaliatory termination in violation of the Florida Civil Rights Act.

**Sources say:** *"I just want to be aware of the practicalities of the law; in every instance, I feel they've been spot-on with their advice."*

**KEY INDIVIDUALS William Radford** (see p.1004) is a distinguished practitioner with extensive experience in labor and employment matters.

## Phelps Dunbar LLP
### See profile on p.1383

**THE FIRM** This group handles an impressive variety of class action cases arising from FLSA legislation as well as discrimination claims by individuals. The market sees this as an energetic team with lawyers whose reputations are on the rise.

**Sources say:** *"They are truly experts in their field, and are professional, fair and efficient."*

**KEY INDIVIDUALS John Phillips** is a respected employment lawyer with recognized expertise in discrimination cases. He has recently defended employers in Title VII and multimillion-dollar retaliation claims.

## Other Notable Practitioners

Clients describe **Allan Weitzman** of Proskauer Rose LLP as *"extremely responsive and focused"* as well as resourceful in pinpointing the right support in other jurisdictions and practice areas. He heads the Boca Raton labor and employment group. **William deMeza** (see p.989) of Holland & Knight LLP has an established reputation in workplace health and safety litigation and also provides preventive counsel and effective litigation for employers across the full range of labor and employment issues. He has recently been involved in significant age and disability discrimination cases as well as FLSA claims. **Michael Grogan** of Allen, Norton & Blue is a seasoned labor and employment partner who covers a full range of management-side issues from this Florida boutique's Jacksonville office. **Mark Hanley** of Glenn Rasmussen, P.A. earns market praise for his deep understanding of employment law. He provides

advice and litigation defense for several notable public sector and nonprofit organizations. **Alysa Ward**, also of Glenn Rasmussen, P.A., is praised by clients for bringing a valuable understanding and application of the law to their employment issues. **Kevin Hyde** of Foley & Lardner LLP is active both in strategic, preventive advice to employers and in defending litigation relating to wages and discrimination. He is admitted to both the Florida and Virginia Bars and is managing partner for the firm's Jacksonville office. **Ralph Peterson** of Beggs & Lane has considerable experience in labor and employment matters and heads the firm's employment defense team. He is known as a go-to lawyer in Pensacola for labor negotiations and employment litigation. **Daniel Kunkel** of Kunkel Miller & Hament is a longstanding practitioner whose work spans public sector labor relations and proactive employment advice, seminars and representation of management in litigation. **Brian Lerner** of Kim Vaughan & Lerner LLP is

*"extremely responsive to clients' needs"* according to sources, who add that *"he also gives very good, practical advice."* He has successfully defended employers against a diverse range of claims, while having also achieved significant results for employees. Tallahassee practitioner **Robert Sniffen** of Sniffen & Spellman P.A. is a respected labor and employment authority who is active in several associations pertinent to management and HR law. **Robin Symons** of Gordon & Rees, LLP successfully integrates her employment work with commercial litigation and insurance matters. Employment practices liability is a special focus and she is known for her work in bad faith disputes resolution. **Jurate Schwartz** of Proskauer Rose LLP *"is a perfectionist who always seeks to provide the highest level of service,"* enthuses a client. Sources praise her levels of responsiveness and communication as evidence that she *"is always thinking about client issues."*

# LATIN AMERICAN INVESTMENT

Commentary about individuals can be found under their firm's paragraph. If the firm has no paragraph (is not ranked) look at Other Notable Practitioners.

| Latin American Investment |
| --- |
| **Leading Firms** |
| **Band 1** |
| Greenberg Traurig, LLP * |
| White & Case LLP * |
| **Band 2** |
| Avila Rodriguez Hernandez Mena & Ferri LLP |
| Hogan Lovells US LLP |
| Hughes Hubbard & Reed LLP * |
| Hunton & Williams LLP * |
| **Band 3** |
| DLA Piper LLP (US) * |
| Foley & Lardner LLP * |
| Harper Meyer Perez Hagen O'Connor Albert & Dribin LLP * |
| Holland & Knight LLP * |
| K&L Gates * |
| *Indicates firm with profile.* |

## Band 1

### Greenberg Traurig, LLP

See profile on p.1024

**THE FIRM** This firm is regarded as one of the strongest players in the Florida market, and its strengths extend to its Latin America practice. It regularly counsels US companies expanding into Latin America, and is equally active on behalf of Latin American entities in the USA. Highlights include assisting Venezuela's Delcop Group with its acquisition of Xerox Colombia, and acting for the lead arranger on two senior secured credit facilities to major Mexican corporations. The Miami-based team is ably supported by an office in Mexico City.

Sources say: *"Very creative in identifying working solutions to transactional challenges."* *"Effective deal-makers who close transactions and don't caught up in any nonsense."* *"Extremely strong advisory capabilities in key functional areas."*

**KEY INDIVIDUALS Patricia Menéndez-Cambó** (see p.1001) chairs the firm's global practice group. A fluent Spanish speaker, sources applaud *"her outstanding commercial and client relationship skills, her ability to identify solutions to complex transactional challenges, and the way she carries negotiations."* **Juan Pablo Cappello** (see p.988) also earns significant praise. *"He's extremely practical and solution-oriented,"* remarked one source, adding: *"He's a deal-maker who never loses the forest for the trees."* **Randy Bullard** (see p.987) advised Satelites Mexicanos on a high-yield issuance valued at $435 million, and on a $35 million follow-on offer. **Enrique Martin** (see p.999) was the lead partner advising Brazilian social network developer Mentez on the spin-off of its online payment platform Paymentez. Sources praise him as a *"truly bilingual and bicultural"* practitioner. **Yosbel Ibarra** (see p.995) focuses on cross-border M&A, in addition to debt and project finance. He has assisted with a number of the firm's highlight deals, including the Delcop Group matter mentioned above.

### White & Case LLP

See profile on p.451

**THE FIRM** White & Case's São Paulo and Mexico City offices play an increasingly important role in its Latin America practice, but Miami remains an important hub for the region. This is particularly the case with respect to finance matters. The team acted for Telefónica Móviles Colombia on its receipt of a $400 million bridge loan from

a syndicate comprising HSBC USA and JPMorgan Chase, among others. Project finance is a particular strong suit, demonstrated by the group's advice to Colombian power company ISAGEN on the financing of an 820 MW hydro-electric project.

Sources say: *"Very committed and dedicated, providing very detailed and valuable advice."* *"Responsive and highly qualified practitioners."*

**KEY INDIVIDUALS** Project finance is one of **Carlos Viana**'s (see p.1011) primary areas of focus. He is also much sought after for his advice on corporate, acquisition and trade finance, and is commended as a *"good negotiator and strategist"* by Latin American clients. Sources hold **Victor Alvarez**'s (see p.983) project finance expertise in high regard. His highlights include advising Bank of Tokyo-Mitsubishi and Sumitomo Mitsui Banking as lead arrangers on a receivables purchase facility valued at up to $500 million. **Emilio Alvarez-Farré** (see p.983) specializes in M&A and is described as *"dynamic, knowledgeable and accommodating."* **Christian Hansen** (see p.330) acted for Grupo Bimbo's technology holding company and its affiliates on a multimillion-dollar IT outsourcing deal with Hewlett-Packard.

## Band 2

### Avila Rodriguez Hernandez Mena & Ferri LLP

**THE FIRM** This boutique practice is highly reputed for its work in the financial space, and continues to make impressive inroads in M&A and related corporate issues. It also acts as regional general counsel to G4S, recently advising on its acquisition of Brazilian security specialist Vanguarda Segurança e Vigilância. Other major clients include

Ferragamo Latin America, Banco de Credito Del Peru and Amadeus North America.
**Sources say:** *"They have a strong team and we've always encountered full availability and quick responses from them."* **KEY INDIVIDUALS** Founding partner **Alcides Avila** is held in high esteem for his three decades of experience in finance matters. He frequently counsels Latin American banks on their US operations. According to sources, **Marco Ferri** *"stands out for his understanding of business law and for his close attention to clients' needs and interests."* He leads on many of the firm's M&A highlights. **Patricia Hernandez** focuses on M&A and finance, with notable expertise in banking regulatory matters.

## Hogan Lovells US LLP

**THE FIRM** This practice is well known as a strong contender in the project finance sphere, and also offers impressive capabilities in banking and corporate work. Its Latin American practice has a strong focus on Venezuela and Brazil, and clients can draw on the expertise of its

Caracas-based team. The group continues to act for Petróleos de Venezuela (PDVSA), and advised the state-owned oil giant on a $3 billion series of infrastructure contracts with the Hyundai group of companies and Wilson Engineering.
**Sources say:** *"Its knowledge of the region is one of its strengths." "It pays a lot of attention to getting things right."* **KEY INDIVIDUALS Miguel Zaldivar** co-heads the firm's infrastructure, project and public finance practice. Sources highlight his particular niche acting as the intermediary on Sino-Latin American matters. His highlights include advising Refineria del Pacífico Eloy Alfaro on the development and financing aspects of a major project in Ecuador. **José Valdivia** *"is an absolute pleasure to work with, and knows deal-making in Latin America very well,"* say sources. **Luis Perez** has extensive experience across the board in corporate matters, and was one of the lead partners on the PDVSA matter described above.

## Hughes Hubbard & Reed LLP
### See profile on p.1981

**THE FIRM** The departure of New York-based attorney Ed Vidal saw this firm refocus its Latin American resources firmly in its Miami office. Finance remains a clear strength of the team, which is also increasingly active in high-value M&A throughout the region. Highlights include advising Brazilian mining corporation Vale on obtaining a $3 billion loan from 27 international banks, and acting for the lead arrangers on a $500 million dual-currency line of credit to BRF-Brasil Foods.
**Sources say:** *"Client service is phenomenal." "Sound advice with the right level of business knowledge."* **KEY INDIVIDUALS Amy Dulin**'s (see p.990) expertise in the banking and finance space extends to handling M&A on behalf of financial institutions. In standout matters, she advised Banco Davivienda on its $801 million acquisition of HSBC's Costa Rican, Honduran and Salvadoran assets. **Federico Goudie** (see p.993) cochairs the Latin America group. He represented the Central Bank of Paraguay in its recent currency swap program with IFC – the first time IFC had reached such an agreement with any Latin American central bank. Senior counsel **Timothy McCarthy** (see p.1000) is lauded for his decades of experience in M&A and securities law. He has particular insight into Brazil-related issues, and is a member of the Brazilian-American Chamber of Commerce of Florida.

## Hunton & Williams LLP
### See profile on p.2517

**THE FIRM** This group receives excellent feedback for its high-quality services, and is a popular choice for transactional matters involving a Latin American component. The group counts ExxonMobil, Banco Santander, IFC and Banco Internacional de Costa Rica among its clients, and offers guidance on matters of finance, M&A and project development. It continues to advise WASACE on all aspects of its ongoing trans-Atlantic submarine cable project, and also acted for Citibank on a $30 million loan to Dominican Republic-based telecom operator Tricom.

**Sources say:** *"It's reliable and accountable, and takes a lot of ownership of clients' matters." "I have a lot of confidence in them."* **KEY INDIVIDUALS** Practice head **Fernando Alonso** (see p.983) is regarded as *"an outstanding attorney"* by peers. He recently acted for Promerica Financial on its acquisition of a majority stake in Ecuadorian financial institution Banco de la Producción. His expertise also encompasses finance and securities transactions. Sources recommend **Fradyn Suárez** (see p.1009) for her hard-working attitude and understanding of financial issues. She has advised IFC on high-value loans advanced to entities across the region.

## Band 3

### DLA Piper LLP (US)
### See profile on p.1971

**THE FIRM** This global powerhouse continues to cement its position in Latin American work. The practice has attracted a number of new clients of late, including the region's largest independent investment bank, BTG Pactual. Other luminaries in its client roster include Pfizer, AT&T and Banco Santander Brasil. The Miami office continues to be an integral part of the firm's regional offering, supported by teams based in Chicago, New York, Mexico City and São Paulo.
**KEY INDIVIDUALS Carlos Loumiet** (see p.998) has more than 30 years of experience in transactions relating to Latin America. Recent highlights include continued work in connection with the Boulevard Turistico del Atlantico toll road project.

### Foley & Lardner LLP
### See profile on p.2588

**THE FIRM** Since opening its Miami office in 2007, Foley has developed a solid Latin America practice focused on corporate and finance work. It is particularly active in Puerto Rico, where it represents a number of state-owned entities, including the Government Development Bank, the Municipal Finance Agency and the Public Buildings Authority. Among its mandates for the latter, it advised on the issuance of a series of bonds intended to fund the renovation and construction of more than 100 public schools.
**Sources say:** *"Client service is impeccable."*
**KEY INDIVIDUALS** Practice chair **Francisco Cerezo** continues to impress sources. *"He demonstrates an extraordinary level of dedication to client service and customer satisfaction,"* remarked one interviewee. Of counsel **John Murphy** acted for development bank Corporación Andina de Fomento on a $30 million credit facility to a financial institution.

### Harper Meyer Perez Hagen O'Connor Albert & Dribin LLP
### See profile on p.1026

**THE FIRM** This boutique practice advises on corporate, real estate, tax and immigration matters, in addition to litigation. It is increasingly engaged by Latin American clients to advise on investment in the USA, particularly in the South Florida region. Sources cite the firm's compact size as a particular asset, enabling fast turnaround times and highly personalized service. Standout matters include major acquisitions within the restaurant industry.

**Sources say:** *"The firm's strength is its identification with, and strenuous advancement of, its clients' interests."*

**KEY INDIVIDUALS** Founding partner **George Harper** is fluent in Spanish, and is well known as a leading aviation finance attorney. Sources describe him as *"a diligent and vigilant commercial counsel."*

## Holland & Knight LLP
See profile on p.1028

**THE FIRM** This team's corporate and commercial expertise attracts a broad swath of clients, including major names from the medical, banking and hospitality industries. Recent highlights include advising a noted private equity firm on its investment in Virgin Mobile Latin America, and representing Drummond Company in its negotiations for the development of a coal-loading port facility in

Colombia. Miami remains the headquarters of the Latin America practice, but clients can also draw on the talents of Bogotá-based experts since the firm's Colombian office opened in June 2012.

**Sources say:** *"Service is excellent and very commercially oriented."*

**KEY INDIVIDUALS** Practice founder **George Mencio** (see p.1000) advised InterContinental Hotels on its franchise agreements for the development of two new Holiday Inn hotels in northern Colombia. He is fluent in Spanish and Portuguese.

## K&L Gates
See profile on p.2245

**THE FIRM** K&L Gates continues to expand its Latin American capabilities, following lateral hires and the recent opening of its São Paulo office. In Miami, a core part of its practice remains advising clients on tax structuring for their activities in Latin America. In one highlight, it represented online educator Open English in connection

with its operations in seven Latin American jurisdictions, including Venezuela, Colombia and Peru.

**Sources say:** *"I have been extremely pleased with the partners' level of knowledge."*

**KEY INDIVIDUALS Richard Winston** (see p.1012) is rated highly for his cross-border tax expertise. Clients remark on his ability *"to handle a variety of difficult matters with thought and creativity."* He is an ongoing adviser to BlackBerry (formerly Research In Motion) and Plastipak Holdings on Latin American tax issues.

### Other Notable Practitioners

**Pedro Antonio Alvarez** left White & Case in mid-2012 to cofound transactional boutique Alvarez Arrieta & Diaz-Silveira, LLP. A number of clients have followed him to his new firm, and one source describes his work product, creativity and availability as being *"at the highest level."*

# LITIGATION

General Commercial p.965; White-Collar Crime & Government Investigations p.967

Commentary about individuals can be found under their firm's paragraph. If the firm has no paragraph (is not ranked) look at Other Notable Practitioners.

*The edit is in alphabetical order by firm name.*

## Akerman Senterfitt
See profile on p.1014

**THE FIRM** This firm fields a large team skilled in complex commercial litigation. It is particularly well known for its capabilities in bankruptcy and real estate disputes, handling such matters efficiently and with ease, according to clients. The team handles a number of high-profile cases at both state and federal level, and nationwide clients benefit from its impressive network of offices throughout the country.

**Sources say:** *"The team is prompt in its response to our questions and has a good awareness of our business needs."*

**KEY INDIVIDUALS Joseph Foster** is renowned for his litigation work in the banking sector and comes highly recommended by clients. One says: *"I have a great deal of respect for him. He always keeps me posted about any changes or nuances in the law."* According to one interviewee, **William Heller** is *"really top drawer. He knows what he is talking about and has always impressed me."* Heller is much respected as a litigator, having acted on various high-value cases. Multiple sources recognize **David Spector** as a rising star in the field. His practice centers around professional liability and sophisticated fraud cases. *"He works with us in the spirit of partnership and is one of the best lawyers I've dealt with,"* observes one client.

## Bedell, Dittmar, DeVault, Pillans & Coxe
**THE FIRM** From its Jacksonville base, this firm makes a strong showing on the litigation front, with a broad practice offering expertise in several types of litigation. It handles commercial and criminal cases at both state and federal level, and is active in numerous sectors including environment, construction and personal injury. The team may be smaller in size than some of its competitors, but it certainly lives up to its reputation as a litigation heavyweight.

**Sources say:** *"They're tremendous."*

**KEY INDIVIDUALS John DeVault** attracts praise as a *"phenomenal"* lawyer and is regarded as *"one of the best attorneys in North Florida."* His practice centers around commercial litigation. With prior experience in the State Attorney's Office, **Henry Coxe** is well known in Florida for his handling of white-collar criminal trials and investigations. Interviewees describe him as *"excellent"* and say that he *"works very hard and is well respected."*

## Berger Singerman
See profile on p.1017

**THE FIRM** This firm is noted for its admirable strength in Fort Lauderdale and Miami, where it handles a broad range of litigation matters. Several clients highlight its exceptional capability in bankruptcy litigation in addition to its proficiency in commercial disputes. Another attractive feature of the practice is its competitive pricing, which is said to compare favorably with other firms of a similar size. Commentators agree the group consists of thoughtful, intelligent and creative attorneys.

**Sources say:** *"The firm is excellent; it has a deep bench and a lot of talented lawyers at all levels."* *"Working with the group is a pleasure."*

**KEY INDIVIDUALS James Gassenheimer** (see p.992) is described as *"tenacious, smart and hard-working."* He *"gets great results and has an excellent courtroom presence,"* according to one satisfied client. As cochair of the firm, **Mitchell Berger** (see p.985) makes a valued contribution to many of the litigation team's most notable cases. He receives a good deal of positive feedback singling him out as *"a talented trial lawyer with a strong skill set and strategic approach."* **Etan Mark** (see p.999) earns impressive feedback from a range of market sources: *"He's exceptional and capable of handling a lot of cases at the same time by himself without referring to other colleagues."* Commentators agree that he is experienced beyond his years.

## Bilzin Sumberg Baena Price & Axelrod LLP
See profile on p.1018

**THE FIRM** This 12-partner team remains a popular choice among clients, who value its responsiveness combined with a deep bench and considerable deal experience. It is active in litigation of all kinds, including bankruptcy, environment, product liability and real estate disputes. Sources agree that the firm is increasing its visibility in this space, and it continues to win significant mandates.

**Sources say:** *"An exceptionally well-qualified law firm."* *"I could sing its praises all day."*

**KEY INDIVIDUALS Marty Steinberg** (see p.1009) receives numerous upbeat client reviews for both his com-

*The editorial is in alphabetical order by firm name.*

## Litigation: General Commercial
## Leading Firms

**Band 1**
Colson Hicks Eidson *
Greenberg Traurig, LLP *
Kenny Nachwalter PA *
Podhurst Orseck P.A. *

**Band 2**
Bedell, Dittmar, DeVault, Pillans & Coxe
Bilzin Sumberg Baena Price & Axelrod LLP *
Boies, Schiller & Flexner LLP *
Carlton Fields, P.A. *
Hill Ward Henderson *
Hogan Lovells US LLP
Holland & Knight LLP *
Kozyak Tropin & Throckmorton
Richman Greer PA *
Stearns Weaver Miller Weissler Alhadeff & Sitterson, P.A.

**Band 3**
Akerman Senterfitt
Berger Singerman *
Hunton & Williams LLP *
King, Blackwell, Zehnder & Wermuth, PA
Shook, Hardy & Bacon LLP *
Tew Cardenas LLP
Weil, Gotshal & Manges LLP *
White & Case LLP *

**Band 4**
Broad and Cassel
Coffey Burlington
Gunster *
Jones, Foster, Johnston & Stubbs, P.A.
Kluger, Kaplan, Silverman, Katzen & Levine, P.L. *
McDermott Will & Emery LLP *
Page, Mrachek, Fitzgerald & Rose PA
Rumberger, Kirk & Caldwell
Squire Sanders (US) LLP *

\* *Indicates firml with profile.*
*Alphabetical order within each band. Band 1 is the highest.*

mercial and white-collar crime litigation practice. *"He's just top-notch and enjoys a wonderful reputation,"* says a source. As cochair of the firm's litigation group, **Michael Kreitzer** (see p.997) leads on several of the team's most prominent cases. He is *"an excellent court advocate, quick on his feet and well prepared,"* according to observers. His broad practice covers complex commercial disputes, lender liability and related financial institution litigation. **Mitchell Widom** (see p.1012) is widely regarded as a go-to lawyer for complex litigation matters. One client states: *"At trial he was clearly the most prepared, quickest thinker and the most articulate."* Widom makes his debut in the rankings this year on the back of such laudatory feedback.

### Black, Srebnick, Kornspan & Stumpf, P.A.
**THE FIRM** This Miami-based litigation boutique continues to earn high praise from market commentators for its high-profile white-collar litigation practice. It is skilled in a variety of areas, including civil litigation and criminal defense work. Sources agree the firm is capable of handling the most complex cases thanks to its admirable depth of experience in a broad range of sectors.
**Sources say:** *"The group is absolutely first rate, with very creative outside-the-box thinking and a really sophisticated approach to its cases."*
**KEY INDIVIDUALS** With decades of trial experience, **Roy Black** is universally praised by market observers as *"one of the best lawyers down here, hands down."* The *"excellent"* **Howard Srebnick** handles high-profile and complex white-collar criminal and civil litigation, and has a particular focus on financial matters. He is known to be *"very good in trial,"* with one lawyer saying he is *"as thoughtful as you can get."* **Larry Stumpf** leads the firm's civil litigation practice and is particularly renowned for his expertise in commercial contract and unfair competition claims.

### Boies, Schiller & Flexner LLP
See profile on p.1958
**THE FIRM** This firm wins praise for its consistently high-quality performance in the litigation sphere. Sources affirm that the team is well versed in resolving disputes, be it by litigation, arbitration or mediation. Furthermore, the group has the capacity to handle disputes in a broad range of sectors, from intellectual property to healthcare. It acts in both state and federal courts as it has an extensive country-wide footprint.
**Sources say:** *"We go back to the firm due to its quality and success rate. The lawyers I use work very well with us."*
**KEY INDIVIDUALS Stuart Singer** is widely viewed as *"an outstanding advocate who is very smart with a strong academic background."* He is credited with a profound knowledge of legal ethics matters in addition to an admirable courtroom presence. **Carlos Sires** is praised for his skill as a trial lawyer, and acts on several of the firm's most significant litigation cases.

### Broad and Cassel
**THE FIRM** This Florida stalwart has an established market presence with a total of eight offices throughout the state. The practice is broad and covers a wide range of commercial litigation matters. White-collar criminal defense is also an area of expertise for the group. It recently advised Staffing Concepts International on a $25 million contract dispute.
**Sources say:** *"The team is extremely responsive and effective. The level of professionalism and talent it offers sets it apart from other law firms."*
**KEY INDIVIDUALS Mark Raymond** comes highly recommended as an *"excellent"* lawyer, esteemed for his admirable litigation skills. As managing partner of the Miami office, he leads on a number of the firm's most prominent cases. **Patricia Lebow** manages the West Palm Beach office and is credited with a can-do approach. One client enthuses: *"I trust her experience and judgment – when she talks, I listen. She's my go-to attorney."* *"Fantastic"* recent arrival and former federal prosecutor **Jon Sale** is extremely well respected for his expertise in complex white-collar matters. Commentators highlight that he is *"very plugged into what's happening in the case"* and *"very good at figuring out a strategy."*

### Carlton Fields, P.A.
See profile on p.1020
**THE FIRM** This litigation team wins praise from all quarters for its responsiveness and sound judgment, combined with first-class client-handling skills. An impressive number of its attorneys are singled out for praise, illustrating a deep bench and broad skill set. The group receives recognition for its capabilities in both general commercial litigation and white-collar crime cases. With offices in Miami, Orlando, St Petersburg, Tallahassee, Tampa and West Palm Beach, the firm provides excellent coverage across the state and is therefore able to provide clients with a comprehensive service.
**Sources say:** *"Just a pleasure to work with."*
**KEY INDIVIDUALS Michael Pasano** (see p.1003) is described as *"an excellent all-rounder"* and *"a world-class lawyer"* by clients and attorneys universally impressed by his handling of complex white-collar litigation. He is also well known for his formidable work ethic and creative approach to cases. One commentator states: *"I've seen him win things no-one else could."* **Stephen Bronis** (see p.987) is well respected around the state for his active white-collar practice. Fellow lawyers say that *"he presents himself in the courtroom in a low key but persuasive manner,"* and that *"his intellect makes him stand out."* Experienced white-collar litigator **Adam Schwartz** (see p.1006) maintains his reputation as a specialist in healthcare and False Claims Act litigation. He is valued for the experience he gained working at the US Attorney's Office in New York. Based in the firm's Tampa office, **Edward Page** (see p.1002) has strong litigation experience across a variety of criminal and civil matters, and has argued numerous jury and bench trials during his career. As a qualified pilot and flight instructor, he also remains in demand as an aviation law specialist. New entry **Paul Calli** (see p.987) specializes in both white-collar and complex commercial litigation, and receives high praise for his well-rounded trial skills. One impressed practitioner described him as being both an *"outstanding writer"* and *"absolutely terrific on his feet in the courtroom."* **Benjamine Reid** (see p.1004) acts as lead counsel in a number of high-profile class actions. According to sources, he is *"superb in front of a jury"* and has had *"some great results."* Interviewees regard **Thomas Meeks** (see p.1000) as a successful litigator with a good deal of trial experience. One remarks: *"He does a wonderful job and is always accessible."* **Gary Sasso** (see p.1006) is described as a *"fantastic lawyer and a great person."* His practice focuses on securities fraud and business litigation. **Bruce Berman** (see p.985) is *"very astute and attuned to nuances in civil procedure and case strategy,"* according to sources. He represents both domestic and international clients in a variety of complex commercial disputes. **Chris Coutroulis** (see p.989) is lauded for his antitrust expertise and his extensive experience in class actions. He operates across a broad range of sectors, including insurance, automotive and energy. **Edward Gerecke** (see p.993) is well regarded for his detailed knowledge of product liability

*The editorial is in alphabetical order by firm name.*

## Litigation: General Commercial

### Senior Statesmen

**Senior Statesmen:** distinguished older practitioners

| | |
|---|---|
| Colson Dean | Colson Hicks Eidson |
| Liles Rutledge R | Liles, Gavin, Costantino & George (ONP)[†] |
| Nachwalter Michael | Kenny Nachwalter PA |
| Thomson Parker | Hogan Lovells US LLP |

### Leading Individuals

**Star individuals**

| | |
|---|---|
| Stearns Eugene | Stearns Weaver Miller Weissler Alhadeff |

**Band 1**

| | |
|---|---|
| Bass Hilarie | Greenberg Traurig, LLP[*] |
| Coffey Kendall B | Coffey Burlington |
| Critchlow Richard H | Kenny Nachwalter PA |
| Davis Alvin B | Squire Sanders (US) LLP[*] |
| DeVault John | Bedell, Dittmar, DeVault, Pillans & Coxe |
| Diaz Victor M | V M Diaz & Partners (ONP)[†] |
| Gonzalez Ervin A. | Colson Hicks Eidson |
| Greer Alan | Richman Greer PA[*] |
| Hill III Benjamin H | Hill Ward Henderson[*] |
| Josefsberg Robert C | Podhurst Orseck P.A.[*] |
| King David B | King, Blackwell, Zehnder & Wermuth, PA |
| Martinez Roberto | Colson Hicks Eidson |
| Matthews Joseph M | Colson Hicks Eidson |
| Podhurst Aaron S | Podhurst Orseck P.A.[*] |
| Reilly Kenneth J | Shook, Hardy & Bacon LLP |
| Ross David L | Greenberg Traurig, LLP[*] |
| Singer Stuart | Boies, Schiller & Flexner LLP |
| Soto Edward | Weil, Gotshal & Manges LLP[*] |
| Steinberg Marty | Bilzin Sumberg Baena Price & Axelrod LLP[*] |
| Stubbs Sidney A | Jones, Foster, Johnston & Stubbs, P.A. |
| Tropin Harley S | Kozyak Tropin & Throckmorton[*] |
| Wakshlag Stanley | Kenny Nachwalter PA |

**Band 2**

| | |
|---|---|
| Aragon Rudolph F. | White & Case LLP[*] |
| Bohrer Sanford | Holland & Knight LLP[*] |
| Davidson Barry | Hunton & Williams LLP[*] |
| Eidson Mike | Colson Hicks Eidson |
| Foster Joseph E | Akerman Senterfitt |
| Kluger Alan J | Kluger, Kaplan, Silverman, Katzen & Levine[*] |
| Licko Carol A | Hogan Lovells US LLP |
| Moss Edward A | Shook, Hardy & Bacon LLP |
| Mrachek L Louis | Page, Mrachek, Fitzgerald & Rose PA |

| | |
|---|---|
| Nichols Tracy A | Holland & Knight LLP[*] |
| Raymond Mark F | Broad and Cassel |
| Reid Benjamine | Carlton Fields, P.A.[*] |
| Richard Barry | Greenberg Traurig, LLP[*] |
| Richman Gerald F | Richman Greer, P.A.[*] |
| Sires Carlos | Boies, Schiller & Flexner LLP |
| Stumpf Larry | Black, Srebnick, Kornspan & Stumpf, P.A. |
| Tew Thomas | Tew Cardenas LLP |

**Band 3**

| | |
|---|---|
| Berger Mitchell W | Berger Singerman[*] |
| Bloodworth Darryl | Dean, Mead, Egerton, Bloodworth (ONP)[†] |
| Brochin Robert M | Morgan, Lewis & Bockius LLP (ONP)[†] |
| Busey Stephen D | Smith Hulsey & Busey (ONP)[†] |
| Gassenheimer James D | Berger Singerman[*] |
| Geraghty William P | Shook, Hardy & Bacon LLP |
| González Daniel E | Hogan Lovells US LLP |
| Hayden Donald J | Baker & McKenzie (ONP)[†] |
| Heller William P | Akerman Senterfitt |
| Jiménez Marcos Daniel | McDermott Will & Emery LLP[*] |
| Kirk WL | Rumberger, Kirk & Caldwell |
| Kreitzer Michael N | Bilzin Sumberg Baena Price & Axelrod LLP[*] |
| Lebow Patricia | Broad and Cassel |
| Lowry Patricia E | Squire Sanders (US) LLP[*] |
| Meeks Thomas J | Carlton Fields, P.A.[*] |
| Miner Curtis B | Colson Hicks Eidson |
| Murphy Lewis F | Squire Sanders (US) LLP[*] |
| Sasso Gary L | Carlton Fields, P.A.[*] |
| Silverman Steve I | Kluger, Kaplan, Silverman, Katzen & Levine[*] |
| Swerdloff Nicolas | Hughes Hubbard & Reed LLP (ONP)[†] |
| Waggoner Dennis P | Hill Ward Henderson[*] |
| Wells David M. | Gunster |
| Wilson William | Holland & Knight LLP[*] |
| Young Terry C | Lowndes Drosdick Doster Kantor ( ONP)[†] |

**Band 4**

| | |
|---|---|
| Atkinson Jr. David R | Gunster |

| | |
|---|---|
| Barlow Mahlon | Sivyer Barlow & Watson, P.A. (ONP)[†] |
| Becerra Jacqueline | Greenberg Traurig, LLP[*] |
| Berman Bruce J | Carlton Fields, P.A.[*] |
| Betensky Gary | Richman Greer, P.A. |
| Blackwell Bruce B | King, Blackwell, Zehnder & Wermuth, PA |
| Brodsky Richard E | The Brodsky Law Firm (ONP)[†] |
| Clarke Mercer K | Clarke Silvergate, PA (ONP)[†] |
| Coulson David A | Greenberg Traurig, LLP[*] |
| Coutroulis Chris S | Carlton Fields, P.A.[*] |
| Garcia Linares Manuel A | Richman Greer PA[*] |
| Gerecke Edward W | Carlton Fields, P.A.[*] |
| Hill William K | Gunster |
| Ianno Jr Joseph | Carlton Fields, P.A.[*] |
| Kim Jay | Kim Vaughan Lerner LLP (ONP)[†] |
| Knight David T | Hill Ward Henderson[*] |
| Lieberman Philippe | Kluger, Kaplan, Silverman, Katzen & Levine |
| McClure Frederick | DLA Piper LLP (US) (ONP)[†] [*] |
| Moskowitz Adam M | Kozyak Tropin & Throckmorton[*] |
| Pace Christopher | Weil, Gotshal & Manges LLP[*] |
| Pollack David | Stearns Weaver Miller Weissler Alhadeff |
| Prieto Peter | Podhurst Orseck P.A.[*] |
| Rodriguez Raquel | McDonald Hopkins LLC (ONP)[†] |
| Rose Alan | Page, Mrachek, Fitzgerald & Rose PA |
| Schultz Thomas | Tew Cardenas LLP |
| Shapiro Jay B | Stearns Weaver Miller Weissler Alhadeff |
| Spector David I | Akerman Senterfitt |
| Thielhelm Jr Robert W | Baker & Hostetler LLP (ONP)[†] [*] |
| Varner III Joseph H. | Holland & Knight LLP[*] |
| Widom Mitchell E | Bilzin Sumberg Baena Price & Axelrod LLP |

**Up-and-coming individuals**

| | |
|---|---|
| Mark Etan | Berger Singerman[*] |
| Sastre Hildy | Shook, Hardy & Bacon LLP |

**Associates to watch**

| | |
|---|---|
| Wall Ethan | Richman Greer PA[*] |

---

law. Observers describe him as *"extremely knowledgeable and thorough."* **Joseph Ianno** (see p.995) is recognized as *"a well-connected and effective lawyer."* He runs a broad practice encompassing fraud and corporate misconduct claims. **Kevin Napper**'s (see p.1002) wide-ranging white-collar workload includes a focus on FCPA matters, antitrust and healthcare litigation. He is recommended by clients for his *"common sense"* approach to litigation.

### Coffey Burlington

**THE FIRM** This Miami-based team joins the rankings this year thanks to positive recommendations from a variety of market sources. It focuses on business litigation and white-collar criminal defense work, having earned an enviable reputation in both areas. The group is active across a wide array of sectors, including construction, healthcare and media. Class action litigation is a further area of expertise for the team.

**Sources say:** *"The team has built up an exceptional practice and has some great talent coming through."*

**KEY INDIVIDUALS Kendall Coffey** receives a raft of praise from clients and competitors alike. One source states: *"He is well thought of by the courts and a brilliant lawyer. He is very pleasant to deal with and has great litigation skills."* As a former US attorney for the Southern District of Florida, Coffey has a top-flight reputation in the state and is highly regarded by his peers.

### Colson Hicks Eidson

See profile on p.1022

**THE FIRM** This well-established firm maintains its reputation as a first port of call for litigation matters in Florida. It offers expertise in product liability, medical malpractice and white-collar crime cases. It also has a particular specialty in aviation disputes. The group's presence extends beyond the state border as it handles contentious matters across the USA and in Central and South America.

**Sources say:** *"A top-notch, thoughtful firm."*

**KEY INDIVIDUALS Ervin Gonzalez** is a leading market figure with a top-flight reputation. One interviewee states: *"He is a fantastic lawyer, just terrific. He works incredibly hard and is very dedicated to his work and craft."* **Roberto**

*The editorial is in alphabetical order by firm name.*

## Litigation: White-Collar Crime & Government Investigations
### Leading Firms

**Band 1**
Black, Srebnick, Kornspan & Stumpf, P.A.
Carlton Fields, P.A. *
Greenberg Traurig, LLP *
Moscowitz & Moscowitz, PA
Podhurst Orseck P.A. *

**Band 2**
Holland & Knight LLP *
Kobre & Kim LLP *
Raskin & Raskin PA
Zuckerman Spaeder LLP

**Band 3**
Leventhal & Slaughter PA
Lewis Tein PL
Markus & Markus, PLLC

## Litigation: White-Collar Crime & Government Investigations
### Senior Statesmen

**Senior Statesmen: distinguished older practitioners**

| | |
|---|---|
| Sonnett Neal R | Neal R Sonnett PA (ONP)[†] |

### Leading Individuals

**Star individuals**

| | |
|---|---|
| Black Roy | Black, Srebnick, Kornspan & Stumpf, P.A. |
| Josefsberg Robert C | Podhurst Orseck P.A. * |
| Pasano Michael S | Carlton Fields, P.A. * |

**Band 1**

| | |
|---|---|
| Bronis Stephen J | Carlton Fields, P.A. * |
| Coxe Henry M | Bedell, Dittmar, DeVault, Pillans & Coxe |
| Hogan John M | Holland & Knight LLP * |
| Jung William F | Jung & Sisco (ONP)[†] |
| Markus David | Markus & Markus, PLLC |
| Moscowitz Jane W | Moscowitz & Moscowitz, PA |
| Moscowitz Norman A | Moscowitz & Moscowitz, PA |
| Quiñon Jose M | Jose M Quinon PA (ONP)[†] |
| Raskin Jane | Raskin & Raskin PA |
| Raskin Martin R | Raskin & Raskin PA |
| Sale Jon A | Broad and Cassel |
| Schnapp Mark P | Greenberg Traurig, LLP * |
| Shohat Edward R | Shohat, Loewy and Shohat (ONP)[†] |
| Skolnick Holly R | Greenberg Traurig, LLP * |
| Srebnick Howard M | Black, Srebnick, Kornspan & Stumpf, P.A. |
| Srebnick Scott A | Scott A Srebnick, PA (ONP)[†] |
| Weinberg Jr Morris "Sandy" | Zuckerman Spaeder LLP |
| Zimet Bruce A | Bruce A Zimet PA (ONP)[†] |

**Band 2**

| | |
|---|---|
| Denaro Jack M | Jack M Denaro (ONP)[†] |
| George Peter E | George & Titus PA (ONP)[†] |
| Lafferty Latour | Fowler White Boggs (ONP)[†] |
| Lauro John | Lauro Law Firm (ONP)[† *] |
| Leventhal Robert A | Leventhal & Slaughter PA |

| | |
|---|---|
| Lewis Guy A | Lewis Tein PL |
| Mandel David S | Mandel & Mandel LLP (ONP)[†] |
| Martinez Roberto | Colson Hicks Eidson |
| Menchel Matthew I | Kobre & Kim LLP * |
| Prieto Peter | Podhurst Orseck P.A. * |
| Schwartz Adam P | Carlton Fields, P.A. * |
| Trombley Gary | Trombley & Hanes |

**Band 3**

| | |
|---|---|
| Aaron William | Sole Practitioner (ONP)[†] |
| Binhak Stephen J | The Law Office of Stephen James (ONP)[†] |
| Calli Paul | Carlton Fields, P.A. * |
| Fernandez Jr Jack E | Zuckerman Spaeder LLP |
| Fugate Lee | Zuckerman Spaeder LLP |
| Harris Ivan P | Morgan, Lewis & Bockius LLP (ONP)[†] |
| Kehoe Greg W | Greenberg Traurig, LLP * |
| Lourie Andrew | Kobre & Kim LLP * |
| Napper Kevin J | Carlton Fields, P.A. * |
| Page Edward J | Carlton Fields, P.A. * |
| Sanchez Lilly Ann | The LS Law Firm (ONP)[†] |
| Shapiro Hy | Hogan, Greer & Shapiro (ONP)[†] |
| Shepherd Bill | Holland & Knight LLP * |
| Slaughter Jr Harrison T | Leventhal & Slaughter PA |
| Steinberg Marty | Bilzin Sumberg Baena Price & Axelrod LLP * |
| Tein Michael | Lewis Tein PL |

**Up-and-coming individuals**

| | |
|---|---|
| Marcus Jeffrey | Kenny Nachwalter PA |

**Associates to watch**

| | |
|---|---|
| Rashbaum Daniel L. | Kobre & Kim LLP * |

* Indicates firm / individual with profile.
[†]ONP = Other Notable Practitioner.

**Martinez** is *"a fine trial lawyer – one of the best there is. He is a role model for all young lawyers in Florida,"* according to one source. His long-standing experience is regarded as a great asset to the team. **Joseph Matthews** is widely regarded is a leader in the field of dispute resolution in Florida. His practice centers around insurance, construction and professional liability litigation. **Mike Eidson** is lauded by market commentators as a *"well-known and experienced lawyer at the top of his game."* He acts on a number of high-value cases for a varied client base. **Curtis Miner** is described as *"a tremendous lawyer, smart and capable of handling intellectually complex work."* His areas of expertise include product liability, personal injury and white-collar criminal defense. **Dean Colson** remains a greatly experienced figure in the litigation sphere and draws praise across the board as an *"absolutely excellent lawyer."* He is active largely in aviation and product liability cases.

### Greenberg Traurig, LLP
See profile on p.1024

**THE FIRM** Clients and peers heap praise on this respected firm, which makes a strong showing in both commercial and white-collar criminal disputes. Its widespread network is cited as a key factor in the team's success as it is able to serve clients with multijurisdictional requirements. The group operates across numerous sectors, including healthcare, insurance and finance. In a recent highlight, the team successfully represented Merrill Lynch in a class action brought by around 100 public pension plans in Florida. **Sources say:** *"Cordial and professional yet tenacious and brilliant all at the same time."*

**KEY INDIVIDUALS** As cochair of the firm's white-collar criminal practice, **Mark Schnapp** (see p.1006) maintains his reputation as being *"very creative and very smart."* His practice includes FCPA cases, healthcare fraud and complex civil litigation, and he is particularly praised for his effective handling of corporate investigations. New entry and former Assistant US Attorney **Greg Kehoe** (see p.995) is considered to be *"a very effective trial lawyer."* He handles a broad spectrum of white-collar matters. Sources describe

**Hilarie Bass** (see p.984) as *"very good on her feet, smart, bright and eloquent."* She maintains her reputation as a renowned litigator, and is esteemed for her insight and detailed court preparation. **David Ross** (see p.1005) is a standout figure at the practice, with peers regarding him as *"a top-notch attorney."* As chair of the litigation department, he leads on several of the team's most significant mandates. *"Outstanding trial lawyer"* **Barry Richard** (see p.1005) is lauded for his extensive experience in financial services and securities litigation. He also has a notable specialism in government and election law. **David Coulson** (see p.989) *"has the ability to see through irrelevant facts and focus on what's important,"* according to one observer. He also receives praise for his excellent courtroom manner. Market commentators regard **Jacqueline Becerra** (see p.984) as *"a real powerhouse in the courtroom."* She has a wide-ranging practice, covering mandates ranging from employment to patent litigation. **Holly Skolnick** (see p.1008) works from the firm's Miami office and offers a wealth of experience in white-collar matters, particularly securities litigation. She has a strong reputation among fellow lawyers, who describe her as *"a very fine lawyer, smart and hard-working."*

### Gunster
See profile on p.1025

**THE FIRM** This firm offers unrivaled coverage throughout Florida, with a total of ten offices within the state. It handles all kinds of business litigation, from product liability to securities matters. Another strong suit for the team is its intellectual property litigation practice. Observers note that the group is particularly prevalent in the construction and real estate sectors. It recently represented Bank of America in a $45 million dispute relating to the enforcement of indemnity obligations. **Sources say:** *"The firm houses some outstanding lawyers."*
**KEY INDIVIDUALS David Wells** is a widely respected practitioner with a wealth of experience. One source describes him as *"a thorough and meticulous hard worker."* **William Hill** is a well-regarded attorney who leads on a number of the team's most significant cases. He is noted for his shareholder litigation work. **David Atkinson** is

*The editorial is in alphabetical order by firm name.*

regarded as an asset to the team, skilled in complex commercial litigation and class action disputes.

### Hill Ward Henderson
See profile on p.1027

THE FIRM This firm houses a talented team of litigators much admired for their calm and thorough outlook. The team remains busy handling disputes in a whole host of sectors such as construction and real estate, to name but a few. It acts out of Tampa but has extensive reach throughout Florida and beyond. Clients include both national companies and private individuals.

Sources say: *"A knowledgeable team with a good understanding of the law, capable of grasping complex construction issues."*

KEY INDIVIDUALS **Benjamin Hill** (see p.994) is described as *"a lion of the Florida Bar. He is universally respected across the state."* He is greatly esteemed for his longstanding experience and his detail-oriented approach and jury handling skills. **Dennis Waggoner** (see p.1011) has a wide-ranging practice handling everything from professional liability to securities and shareholder litigation. Interviewees are effusive in their praise, with one stating: *"He is one of the most effective trial lawyers I have met in Florida. He's a very strategic thinker; juries love him."* **David Knight** (see p.996) is credited with a great ability to explain complex legal matters clearly to nonlawyers. He offers expertise on a broad spectrum of topics, including intellectual property and technology litigation.

### Hogan Lovells US LLP

THE FIRM This international powerhouse has a considerable presence in Florida, representing clients in a wide variety of disputes. Commercial litigation is the group's principal focus and, as part of a global firm, it is also able to offer counsel on complex cross-border disputes. The team operates at state and federal level but also represents clients in international arbitration proceedings. Clients include big-ticket international companies in addition to more domestic players.

KEY INDIVIDUALS **Carol Licko** has an *"excellent reputation"* for her extensive litigation work. She specializes in commercial and environmental disputes, and is also credited with particular knowledge of the life sciences and healthcare sectors. **Daniel Gonzalez** is a fluent Spanish speaker and has noteworthy experience with Latin American arbitrations that have moved to Florida. **Parker Thomson** earns deep respect as a seasoned practitioner who brings a wealth of litigation experience to the table. Sources confirm that he remains an active presence in the market.

### Holland & Knight LLP
See profile on p.1028

THE FIRM This full-service firm handles both commercial and white-collar criminal litigation. It is active in a variety of industries, including healthcare, transport and financial services. Sources appreciate the group's excellent coverage thanks to its eight offices across Florida. Government investigations are a further area of strength

for the team thanks to its noteworthy experience in this field. Holland & Knight also excels in securities litigation and is regarded as a go-to firm for such disputes.

Sources say: *"The team is very quick at responding. If we need something for the following day, or even the same day, it reacts very quickly."* *"Helpful and practical. I would recommend the firm for any kind of action."*

KEY INDIVIDUALS Litigation section leader and *"terrific lawyer"* **John Hogan** (see p.995) is hailed by fellow practitioners as an *"acknowledged leader in white-collar criminal litigation."* With years of prior work in government positions, he is particularly valued for his *"wealth of practical experience"* and thoughtful approach to litigation. He represents corporate clients in a broad spectrum of white-collar litigation, internal investigations and compliance issues. **Bill Shepherd** (see p.1007) draws praise from clients and peers alike for his even-handed approach. One interviewee observes: *"First and foremost he has great judgment and a far greater sense of the bigger picture. He is not drawn in to unnecessary conflicts or fights if they do not serve the client."* **Sanford Bohrer** (see p.986) is *"a gifted lawyer with a highly visible practice."* Sources acknowledge that he is establishing an international reputation after acting on several high-profile disputes. One interviewee claims that he *"gets cases resolved quickly"* and is a *"brilliant"* practitioner. **Tracy Nichols** (see p.1002) is described as *"extremely talented and very bright. She's a strategic thinker and clients love her."* She has a healthy reputation for clearly grasping issues and advising her clients accordingly. **William Wilson** (see p.1012) *"is bright and gifted and does a great job,"* according to market commentators. His practice focuses largely on commercial litigation. As *"one of the most respected lawyers in Tampa,"* **Joseph Varner** (see p.1011) continues to impress with his effective courtroom manner. He is particularly noted for his expertise in personal injury and professional negligence matters.

### Hunton & Williams LLP
See profile on p.2517

THE FIRM This firm maintains its market visibility thanks to its deep expertise in commercial disputes across a broad range of sectors. As the firm has a well-established global footprint, the Miami-based group is able to collaborate with other offices where necessary in order to assist clients with multijurisdictional requirements.

Sources say: *"They are very focused on making the client happy."* *"All the partners are bright and knowledgeable of the subject matter."*

KEY INDIVIDUALS **Barry Davidson** (see p.989) is a well-known and respected market figure with decades of litigation experience to his name. He represents a range of heavyweight clients in commercial litigation before the state and federal courts.

### Jones, Foster, Johnston & Stubbs, P.A.

THE FIRM This well-regarded firm handles a broad range of litigation matters, serving clients in the environment, construction and real estate sectors, among others. With offices in West Palm Beach and Jupiter, the litigation team is able to provide statewide coverage. Observers agree that

the group is highly client-focused and offers an excellent all-around service.

Sources say: *"The lawyers all know their craft well; they're very bright."*

KEY INDIVIDUALS **Sidney Stubbs** (see p.1009) is an esteemed practitioner who brings a wealth of experience to the table. Peers admire his outstanding litigation skills and say he is *"very wise, with impeccable judgment."*

### Kenny Nachwalter PA
See profile on p.1029

THE FIRM This team of highly regarded litigation specialists continues to make its presence felt in the market. Sources agree it is one of the best litigation outfits in Florida, covering everything from professional liability to intellectual property disputes. It offers a strong white-collar criminal defense practice in addition to notable expertise in government investigations. The group also excels in antitrust matters and complex business litigation.

Sources say: *"The team had a good understanding of our goals, strategy and budget. The billing was transparent."*

KEY INDIVIDUALS **Richard Critchlow** is regarded as a *"trusted and hands-on adviser,"* and credited with a broad knowledge of professional liability issues. **Stanley Wakshlag** wins high praise from numerous sources, with one describing him as *"a prince of a gentleman and a great, smart lawyer."* He is particularly renowned for his expertise in securities matters. The *"superb"* **Michael Nachwalter** remains an active market figure, esteemed for his longstanding experience and in-depth knowledge of alternative dispute resolution. **Jeffrey Marcus** enters the rankings this year following a raft of effusive feedback. *"He is very smart and has a keen eye for understanding the dynamics and strategy of a case,"* say interviewees. He is also praised for his *"thorough and conscientious"* approach.

### King, Blackwell, Zehnder & Wermuth, PA

THE FIRM This Orlando-based independent handles business and civil litigation, and is esteemed for its wide-ranging experience and depth of practice. It is particularly active in personal injury and professional malpractice disputes, but also covers more general commercial litigation. Sources agree that the firm is able to offer a personalized service due to its compact size but has the sector-specific knowledge of a larger firm.

KEY INDIVIDUALS **David King** is greatly admired for his extensive trial experience. He is a high-profile litigator who has tried dozens of cases throughout his distinguished career. One interviewee describes him as *"a detail-oriented lawyer's lawyer."* **Bruce Blackwell** is a well-regarded attorney running a strong commercial litigation practice.

### Kluger, Kaplan, Silverman, Katzen & Levine, P.L.
See profile on p.1030

THE FIRM This eight-partner team maintains a significant market presence, handling complex commercial litigation in addition to real estate, probate and matrimonial disputes. It also covers intellectual property and professional liability litigation. With offices in Miami and Boca

*The editorial is in alphabetical order by firm name.*

Raton, the firm is able to offer a full service to local and national clients alike. Work highlights include representing Dollar Tree Stores in a $25 million damages dispute.
**KEY INDIVIDUALS Alan Kluger** (see p.996) focuses on business litigation. He receives positive recognition from several sources, with one noting: *"He's a commercial litigator who always does a good job. He always has a solid grasp of the case."* **Steve Silverman** (see p.1007) attracts much praise from clients, who commend his broad skill set. *"His organization skills and leadership of the team allowed us to defend our case successfully,"* said one client, while another remarked: *"He does a good job at thinking one step ahead."* **Philippe Lieberman** (see p.998) is lauded for his business-focused approach and detailed knowledge of the financial services industry. He is also recognized for his expertise in real estate litigation.

### Kobre & Kim LLP
See profile on p.1031
**THE FIRM** This compact team continues to attract positive reviews from both clients and competitors. It is steadily increasing its market visibility throughout Florida, in addition to handling cross-border disputes. White-collar crime work is a key feature of the practice, with several lawyers having a specialty in this area. The group is particularly lauded for providing practical and useful advice within a quick timeframe. Sources also highlight the firm's transparent billing practice and competitive rates.
**Sources say:** *"Very well known and well respected among those who do sophisticated, complex white-collar work."* *"Small but their imprint is huge already."*
**KEY INDIVIDUALS Matthew Menchel** (see p.1000) has years of white-collar criminal experience from time spent in the US Attorney's Office and as a former Assistant District Attorney. He has a reputation for being *"a great tactician in the courtroom."* New entry **Andrew Lourie** (see p.998) is described as *"a very good strategic thinker who is very in tune with clients' needs."* He continues to make a name for himself in the Florida litigation scene, acting on a series of high-profile cases. His practice focuses on civil litigation relating to offshore trusts and asset recovery. **Daniel Rashbaum** (see p.1004) receives much praise from a variety of sources, hence his debut appearance in the rankings. He is *"excellent on his feet"* and also wins plaudits for his *"unrelenting energy and problem-solving abilities."* He is renowned for his expertise in joint venture and partnership disputes.

### Kozyak Tropin & Throckmorton
**THE FIRM** This well-regarded boutique earns respect for its wide-ranging practice, which encompasses commercial, securities and professional malpractice litigation. It has an established presence in the state and attracts numerous high-profile mandates. Sources note that the group is particularly experienced in representing plaintiffs in Ponzi scheme cases. The team is also particularly strong in bankruptcy litigation.
**Sources say:** *"A great reputation for class actions."*
**KEY INDIVIDUALS** The *"excellent"* **Harley Tropin** (see p.1011) maintains an impressive presence in the Florida

litigation market. Peers acknowledge his skill in the courtroom while also crediting him with the ability to put together strong teams of lawyers who *"do a great job."* **Adam Moskowitz** (see p.1001) is renowned for his class action litigation work. He recently acted as co-lead counsel in a nationwide consumer class action case against Wells Fargo and QBE Insurance. He is described as *"extremely tenacious"* and is popular with juries.

### Leventhal & Slaughter PA
**THE FIRM** This compact firm acts out of Orlando and remains well regarded for its white-collar crime practice. Areas of expertise include tax and government contact fraud in addition to theft of trade secrets disputes. The group is widely thought of as a first port of call in the Orlando area for such matters.
**KEY INDIVIDUALS Robert Leventhal** is admired for his considerable caseload and ability to handle multiple matters at once. He wins praise from a variety of sources, one of whom states: *"He's terrific – the best white-collar crime lawyer in the Orlando area by far."* **Harrison Slaughter** remains a greatly experienced litigation expert specializing in white-collar criminal defense.

### Lewis Tein PL
**THE FIRM** This successful practice handles a mixture of white-collar criminal defense and commercial litigation work. It also deals with regulatory matters and securities and tax disputes. Operating out of Coconut Grove, the firm is a popular choice for local clients.
**KEY INDIVIDUALS Guy Lewis** is a highly experienced practitioner, having served as US attorney for the Southern District of Florida. He attracts positive recognition for his extensive trial work, which covers public corruption, white-collar crime and money laundering cases. **Michael Tein** is described as *"smart and tenacious."* His practice focuses on high-profile commercial and white-collar crime cases. He represents corporates and individuals in a variety of civil and criminal matters.

### Markus & Markus, PLLC
**THE FIRM** This small but dynamic firm continues to impress clients and fellow practitioners alike with its high-profile white-collar criminal defense work. Recent highlights include successfully defending Dr Ali Shaygan against multiple counts of illegally prescribing pain medications, and representing film director Billy Corben in a case of alleged contempt.
**Sources say:**
*"They're young people with sharp minds, so I feel like I'm in very good hands."* *"They got us the most wonderful results."*
**KEY INDIVIDUALS** Impressed lawyers describe **David Markus** as *"wickedly smart and a terrific trial lawyer."* His practice encompasses a range of criminal defense proceedings and he has particular expertise in federal matters. Clients say that he is *"thrilling"* to watch in court and that *"his passion, appreciation and enjoyment for his work are contagious."*

### McDermott Will & Emery LLP
See profile on p.1258
**THE FIRM** The litigation team at this global firm is recognized for its prowess in both commercial and healthcare disputes, with the latter being a particular specialty for the group. It continues to represent Blue Cross Blue Shield of Florida in a number of class actions. Furthermore, the firm's worldwide network enables the Miami-based litigation team to act for international clients with complex multijurisdictional needs.
**KEY INDIVIDUALS Marcos Daniel Jiménez** (see p.995) continues to make his market presence felt by leading on a number of the team's most significant matters. He recently won title to property valued at $65 million on behalf of CDR Créances.

### Moscowitz & Moscowitz, PA
**THE FIRM** This esteemed boutique attracts widespread praise for its white-collar criminal defense practice. Civil litigation is another strong suit for the firm, as is business litigation. Sources agree that this highly capable team handles a good deal of complex mandates and has an impeccable reputation throughout Florida.
**Sources say:** *"A bright, tough and smart firm."*
**KEY INDIVIDUALS Jane Moscowitz** is hailed as *"a terrific all-round lawyer."* *"Her written product is first-rate. If I were in trouble, I'd hire her,"* stated one interviewee. Moscowitz's practice focuses on federal and state criminal defense and business litigation. Market commentators describe **Norman Moscowitz** as *"a very smart guy."* He is active in white-collar criminal defense trials and represents a varied clientele, including large companies and private individuals.

### Page, Mrachek, Fitzgerald & Rose PA
**THE FIRM** This group specializes in commercial litigation and operates across a broad range of sectors, including healthcare, construction and real estate. It offers expertise in corporate and partnership disputes, shareholder derivative actions and professional negligence cases. A recent highlight saw the group successfully represent property developer Old Marsh Partners in an action relating to a failed real estate purchase.
**Sources say:** *"The team responded wonderfully, listened very well and conducted thorough research."*
**KEY INDIVIDUALS Louis Mrachek** remains a popular choice among both peers and clients, who commend his diligent approach and in-depth knowledge of the litigation process. One source enthuses: *"His preparation prior to the arbitration was outstanding."* **Alan Rose** also receives considerable praise from market observers. He is described by one as *"the brightest lawyer I've ever known. It's an absolute pleasure to work with him."*

### Podhurst Orseck P.A.
See profile on p.1033
**THE FIRM** This litigation boutique has established a formidable reputation as one of the best in the Florida market. It is exclusively dedicated to trial and appellate litigation, and as such has extensive experience in this area. It

*The editorial is in alphabetical order by firm name.*

has a notable specialty in aviation disputes but is equally renowned for its product liability and securities work. The team's expertise extends to white-collar crime litigation, in which it defends a mixture of companies and individuals. Clients agree that the firm is of the highest caliber, praising its hard-working and driven staff lawyers who turn out a strong product.

**Sources say:** *"An exceptional firm in South Florida. From top to bottom, the people are fantastic."*
**KEY INDIVIDUALS Robert Josefsberg** (see p.995) remains a popular choice among his fellow practitioners, who call him *"the dean of the profession"* and say that *"he is the best."* **Aaron Podhurst** (see p.1003) *"has a great court-room persona and does very well,"* according to clients. He also wins plaudits for his persuasive abilities and communication skills. **Peter Prieto** (see p.1004) splits his practice between white-collar criminal and complex commercial litigation. Interviewees regard him as *"an outstanding lawyer – smart, responsive and thorough."*

## Raskin & Raskin PA

**THE FIRM** This two-partner team remains a Florida stalwart covering a broad range of administrative and commercial litigation. It also runs a successful white-collar criminal defense practice. The group's activity extends to numerous sectors, such as banking and finance, healthcare and aviation. Sources agree that the group offers a high level of client service while being pragmatic and commercially aware.

**Sources say:** *"The team can handle truly complex, sophisticated criminal matters, and gets better results than larger firms."*
**KEY INDIVIDUALS Jane Raskin** is highly regarded for her securities fraud experience, and noted for her expertise in healthcare litigation. One client enthuses: *"She's great to deal with and has incredible strategic vision."* **Martin Raskin** enjoys a reputation as a superb lawyer who is well versed in commercial and criminal litigation. *"He was appropriately sympathetic but also very realistic. He displayed a good combination of empathy and honesty,"* said one source.

## Richman Greer PA
See profile on p.1034

**THE FIRM** This firm fields a strong litigation team with admirable experience in a host of sectors, from real estate to intellectual property. The group covers complex commercial litigation in addition to professional malpractice and product liability disputes. Market commentators highlight the team's detail-oriented approach and commercially aware outlook.

**Sources say:** *"Lean, mean consummate trial lawyers. They know how to try cases and do it efficiently."*
**KEY INDIVIDUALS Alan Greer** (see p.993) maintains a stellar reputation as a formidable litigator. Clients greatly appreciate his level of experience in the field. **Gerald Richman** (see p.1005) is admired for his courtroom manner and ability to process large amounts of information quickly and effectively. He has a broad practice that includes antitrust, securities and contract litigation. **Gary**

Betensky (see p.985) is renowned for his expertise in business litigation law, and is also highly proficient in personal injury claims. He is credited with a meticulous approach and staunch dedication to his clients. **Manuel Garcia Linares** (see p.992) makes his ranking debut following effusive feedback from market commentators praising him as *"an excellent all-arounder. A top-of-the-line defense attorney."* He is active in a variety of areas, including probate and trust and class action litigation. Talented associate **Ethan Wall** (see p.1011) continues to make a name for himself in the Florida litigation market. Interviewees acknowledge that he makes a valuable contribution to several of the team's most significant cases.

## Rumberger, Kirk & Caldwell

**THE FIRM** This dedicated litigation firm is a strong player in the Florida market, with offices in Orlando, Miami, Tallahassee and Tampa. It represents a mixture of local and national clients before state and federal courts, concentrating largely on commercial and business litigation. It is active in a range of sectors, including retail, healthcare, insurance and transport.

**Sources say:** *"A highly client-focused and responsive team."*
**KEY INDIVIDUALS** Interviewees commend **WL Kirk** for his extensive commercial litigation expertise. He is an experienced trial lawyer with a *"brilliant legal mind,"* and is *"phenomenal in front of a jury."*

## Shook, Hardy & Bacon LLP
See profile on p.1644

**THE FIRM** This 24-partner team enjoys a superb reputation in Florida and beyond for its wide-ranging litigation work. It handles a varied caseload, including environment and employment disputes and product liability matters. With a solid network of offices in the USA and abroad, the firm is well placed to serve clients with multijurisdictional needs. In a recent highlight, the group represented Bausch & Lomb in product liability litigation involving 1,800 plaintiffs.

**Sources say:** *"The group has really broad expertise and did a brilliant job."*
**KEY INDIVIDUALS** Market observers hail **Kenneth Reilly** as *"a magnificent lawyer with a keen ability to think quickly on his feet and execute a plan flawlessly."* He is renowned for his work in tobacco cases. **Edward Moss** is *"a senior trial attorney and litigator with gravitas who is very well respected,"* according to sources. He is lauded as *"honest, smart and strategically capable."* **William Geraghty** *"offers excellent quality and is a remarkable trial strategist,"* say interviewees. He represents a number of high-profile clients, such as Philip Morris USA. **Hildy Sastre** is widely regarded as *"top trial counsel for mass torts."* Her practice centers around product liability issues.

## Squire Sanders (US) LLP
See profile on p.2129

**THE FIRM** This international firm remains a respected player in Florida, with a presence in Miami, Tampa and West Palm Beach. The group is greatly experienced in a broad spectrum of contentious matters, from securities

and shareholder litigation to product liability disputes. The team is also particularly renowned for its class action work and multidistrict litigation capabilities.

**Sources say:** *"A solid firm with an admirable statewide presence."*
**KEY INDIVIDUALS Alvin Davis** (see p.989) receives high praise from clients, who claim that *"his experience and knowledge are incomparable."* His strategic approach is a further asset, according to sources. **Patricia Lowry** (see p.998) is particularly renowned for her expertise relating to litigation in the pharmaceutical and medical device industries. **Lewis Murphy** (see p.1001) is a seasoned practitioner who focuses on shareholder and insurance litigation. He is lauded for his communication skills and high levels of client service.

## Stearns Weaver Miller Weissler Alhadeff & Sitterson, P.A.

**THE FIRM** Market observers heap praise on this firm's exemplary litigation practice, which encompasses commercial disputes, product liability matters and securities fraud. The sizable team includes 29 partners across four offices, and handles some of the most complex litigation in the state and beyond. Antitrust litigation is a further area of expertise for the group.

**Sources say:** *"The firm produces impeccable work."*
**KEY INDIVIDUALS Eugene Stearns** draws positive reviews from clients. One states: *"He is without doubt one of the toughest, most tenacious lawyers I have ever encountered."* Another adds: *"He is accomplished and smart, and gets great results."* **Jay Shapiro** is hailed as a responsive and thorough attorney with a keen ability to make complex legal matters comprehensible to nonlawyers. His practice focuses on high-value commercial litigation. **David Pollack** is described as *"a very bright attorney who cuts right to the key issues and is highly skilled at articulating his position."* He makes a first appearance in the rankings due to much laudatory feedback and a considerable market presence.

## Tew Cardenas LLP

**THE FIRM** This full-service firm offers expertise in a variety of sectors, including aviation, construction, energy and financial services. It covers commercial litigation for a diverse clientele, from domestic to international players. It acts before both state and federal courts, handling complex class actions. Securities litigation is a further area of expertise for the group.

**Sources say:** *"A talented firm."*
**KEY INDIVIDUALS Thomas Tew** continues to impress, with observers calling his work *"outstanding."* He has a sterling reputation for his expertise in securities disputes. **Thomas Schultz** is credited with wide-ranging experience as a litigator in unfair competition and professional liability matters. He also has considerable expertise in joint venture and partnership litigation.

*The editorial is in alphabetical order by firm name.*

### Weil, Gotshal & Manges LLP
See profile on p.2015

**THE FIRM** This internationally renowned firm maintains its considerable foothold in the Florida market, handling a broad range of litigation matters. The group operates across numerous sectors but is particularly experienced in disputes in the healthcare industry. It benefits from the firm's strong global network, which enables it to ably serve clients with complex, cross-border needs. A recent highlight saw the team successfully representing Procter & Gamble in significant product liability litigation.
**Sources say:** *"A major firm with a significant presence in South Florida."*
**KEY INDIVIDUALS Edward Soto** (see p.1008) is lauded for his *"creative approach to legal issues."* Observers claim he has *"a focused style in the courtroom that achieves great results."* He serves as lead partner in the firm's representation of Procter & Gamble. **Christopher Pace** (see p.1002) *"stands out from the crowd,"* according to one interviewee. Another source adds: *"He can think outside the box while maintaining a practical perspective."* Pace is particularly renowned for his work in antitrust disputes.

### White & Case LLP
See profile on p.451

**THE FIRM** This international heavyweight has a well-established practice in Florida. It handles a broad range of litigation matters and also offers notable expertise in arbitration and mediation. The group is active in a number of sectors but is particularly experienced in the financial services industry. Prominent clients include Arvida, Bryant Miller and Deloitte & Touche.
**Sources say:** *"The team developed a keen awareness of our business needs."*
**KEY INDIVIDUALS Rudolph Aragon** (see p.983) is regarded as *"an excellent lawyer who is responsive and easy to work with."* He is esteemed as a skilled litigator with considerable experience of acting before both state and federal courts.

### Zuckerman Spaeder LLP

**THE FIRM** Sources are most complimentary about this firm's white-collar crime practice, describing it as uniformly effective and helpful. The lawyers are admired for their capacity to think strategically and deploy their resources efficiently. Areas of expertise include healthcare fraud and False Claims Act litigation. While the firm is renowned for its strong offering in Florida, it also has distinguished practices in several other states.
**Sources say:** *"The team gets excellent results."* *"Top-notch. The white-collar practice at Zuckerman Spaeder is terrific."*
**KEY INDIVIDUALS** Former federal prosecutor and *"terrific trial lawyer"* **Morris Weinberg** has over 30 years' experience in white-collar criminal litigation and remains a popular choice among clients. One source calls him *"an incredible strategic thinker with a Herculean work ethic,"* adding that he is *"excellent at deconstructing the facts of a complex case and repackaging them into a very coherent strategy."* **Jack Fernandez** focuses largely on criminal cases in the healthcare sector. He receives recognition for his

diverse skill set and substantial trial experience. *"He is able to get on with people from different walks of life. Judges obviously respect him and he easily relates to juries,"* say interviewees. **Lee Fugate** has *"an incredible reputation as a trial lawyer"* and *"is an absolutely solid contributor to the firm."* Peers acknowledge his longstanding experience and are impressed with his down-to-earth, measured approach.

### Other Notable Practitioners

Peers recognize seasoned white-collar litigator **William Aaron** as a *"smart lawyer"* who *"is very industrious and gets things done."* He has a broad-based white-collar criminal defense practice, which also incorporates environmental and drug prosecutions and administrative matters. **Mahlon Barlow** of Sivyer Barlow & Watson, P.A. represents a wide variety of clients before state and federal courts. He focuses on securities and intellectual property litigation. Sole practitioner **Stephen Binhak** is popular with both peers and clients, who describe him as *"a smart, creative thinker."* His practice covers a range of white-collar crime issues, including tax and securities fraud. In Orlando, **Darryl Bloodworth** of Dean, Mead, Egerton, Bloodworth, Capouano & Bozarth PA is recognized as a seasoned attorney who focuses on business and commercial disputes. An impressed market source reports that *"his years of experience make him such a good lawyer."* **Robert Brochin** of Morgan, Lewis & Bockius LLP is known as a strong commercial lawyer. He co-leads the firm's litigation practice and is highly rated for his performance in the courtroom. One source describes him as a *"terrific trial lawyer who you'd fear as opposition."* **Richard Brodsky** of The Brodsky Law Firm receives positive recognition as a *"tenacious opponent."* From its Miami base, the practice centers around complex commercial litigation. **Stephen Busey** of Smith Hulsey & Busey is widely known for his expertise in bankruptcy litigation. He attracts praise for his analytical mind and calm approach.

**Mercer Clarke** of Clarke Silverglate, PA runs a broad practice encompassing construction litigation, medical malpractice and product liability. He also covers aspects of employment law. Sole practitioner **Jack Denaro** is based in Miami and has a solid reputation among fellow lawyers for his handling of white-collar criminal litigation and criminal defense matters. **Victor Diaz** is the founding partner of litigation boutique V M Diaz & Partners in Miami Beach, and focuses on sophisticated commercial and business litigation. He continues to be praised by sources as an *"excellent advocate"* who is *"very good with complicated cases."* **Peter George** of George & Titus PA in Tampa is a highly accomplished criminal trial litigator who is praised by interviewees for his strategic approach to cases and his *"first-rate"* written product. With prior experience working at the SEC, **Ivan Harris** of Morgan, Lewis & Bockius LLP is known for his practical and technical knowledge of securities compliance and regulation. One client highlighted his ability to *"resolve things in the most efficient way possible."* The *"very smart"* **Donald Hayden** chairs Baker & McKenzie's dispute resolution practice in the Miami office, and handles a range of complex commercial litigation and

international arbitrations. He is praised for his personable manner and is *"excellent with clients and opposing counsel alike."* *"Terrific"* white-collar litigator **William Jung** of Jung & Sisco has *"impeccable pedigree and a very low key style,"* according to impressed market sources. His wide-ranging workload also includes healthcare fraud, professional malpractice, personal injury and appellate litigation. Interviewees describe **Jay Kim** of Kim Vaughan & Lerner LLP as *"an impressive practitioner."* He is also credited with admirable litigation and communication skills. Former federal prosecutor **Latour Lafferty** is head of the white-collar crime practice at Fowler White Boggs, and advises a range of clients on investigations, compliance and enforcement matters. Impressed interviewees report that he is *"very bright,"* and *"vigorously and fairly represents his clients."* Recent work highlights include representing Country Super Buffet in an immigration and human trafficking prosecution. **John Lauro** (see p.997) is the founder and managing partner of Lauro Law Firm and is regarded as *"a very skilful trial lawyer."* As a former federal prosecutor, he has a wealth of experience in sophisticated criminal and commercial litigation and investigations. **Rutledge Liles** of Liles, Gavin, Costantino & George is highly regarded as a seasoned attorney with a great deal of experience to his name. As managing partner, he leads on a number of the firm's key cases. **David Mandel** of Miami-based firm Mandel & Mandel LLP enjoys a healthy reputation as someone who *"works very hard and dedicates himself to his cases."* He splits his time between white-collar criminal litigation and complex commercial disputes.

**Frederick McClure** (see p.1000) of DLA Piper LLP (US) heads the litigation group for the firm's Florida offices. He focuses on complex commercial disputes and is described as *"absolutely terrific."* Miami-based sole practitioner **Jose Quiñon** has decades of experience handling general criminal and white-collar defense work. He continues to impress interviewees, who describe him as *"outstanding."* **Raquel Rodriguez** of McDonald Hopkins LLC in Miami is singled out by peers as a high-quality litigator. She handles a broad range of commercial disputes for both local and national clients. **Lilly Ann Sanchez** of The LS Law Firm is described as a *"talented lawyer"* with a focus on white-collar crime matters. Sources report that her Miami-based firm is increasing its market visibility. **Hy Shapiro** of Hogan, Greer & Shapiro is a greatly experienced white-collar criminal defense attorney. Peers say: *"He is definitely a lawyer's lawyer. He's not flashy, but gets great results."* **Edward Shohat** of Shohat, Loewy and Shohat is well known as a seasoned criminal defense attorney. He appears regularly in state and federal courts around the country. **Neal Sonnett** of Neal R Sonnett PA is well respected across the state for his extensive knowledge of white-collar litigation and criminal justice policy. He specializes in defending individuals and corporations facing prosecution. Peers admire his level of activity and extensive experience. *"Great lawyer"* **Scott Srebnick** of Scott A Srebnick, PA is based in Miami and known for his familiarity with criminal trial and appellate litigation. He represents numerous professionals facing allegations of white-collar crime and business fraud. **Nicolas Swerdloff** (see p.1010) is managing partner of Hughes Hubbard & Reed LLP's Miami office and is well respected by his peers in Florida. He regularly advises clients on financial services, securities and professional liability disputes. His clients include Lorillard Tobacco Company, BNP Paribas and ALSTOM. **Robert Thielhelm** (see p.1010) heads the litigation team at Baker & Hostetler LLP. He handles commercial litigation across a variety of sectors, including pharmaceuticals, construction

and transport. He is also renowned for his strength in appellate law. **Gary Trombley** is the founding partner of Trombley & Hanes in Tampa, and gains recognition for his handling of a wide range of white-collar criminal and civil cases. Fellow lawyers describe him as *"a fighter"* in the courtroom, and say that *"he shows up on every case because he deserves to."* **Terry Young** of Lowndes Drosdick Doster Kantor & Reed, PA handles a number of high-profile com-

mercial, divorce and personal injury disputes. **Bruce Zimet** is based in Fort Lauderdale and maintains a busy practice incorporating white-collar, securities and appellate litigation. Market sources describe him as *"exceptional"* and agree that he remains *"one of the best Florida lawyers and one of the go-to guys."*

## LITIGATION APPELLATE

| Litigation: Appellate | |
|---|---|
| **Senior Statesmen** | |
| Senior Statesmen: distinguished older practitioners | |
| Harding Major B | Ausley & McMullen, PA (ONP)[†] |

| **Leading Individuals** | |
|---|---|
| **Band 1** | |
| Cantero Raoul | White & Case LLP (ONP)[†] * |
| Eaton Joel D | Podhurst Orseck P.A. (ONP)[†] * |
| Kreusler-Walsh Jane | Kreusler-Walsh, Compiani & Vargas (ONP)[†] |
| Perwin Joel | Joel S. Perwin, P.A. (ONP)[†] |
| Richard Barry | Greenberg Traurig, LLP (ONP)[†] * |
| Rogow Bruce S | Alters Law Firm (ONP)[†] |
| Ross Lauri Waldman | Ross & Girten (ONP)[†] |
| Scherker Elliot H | Greenberg Traurig, LLP (ONP)[†] * |
| Sorondo Jr Rodolfo | Holland & Knight LLP (ONP)[†] * |
| Strafer Richard | G Richard Strafer PA (ONP)[†] |
| Walbolt Sylvia H | Carlton Fields, P.A. (ONP)[†] * |

| **Band 2** | |
|---|---|
| Brannock Steven L | Brannock & Humphries (ONP)[†] |
| Conigliaro Matthew J | Carlton Fields, P.A. (ONP)[†] * |
| Giddings Katherine E | Akerman Senterfitt (ONP)[†] |
| Glazier Robert | Sole Practitioner (ONP)[†] |
| Klein Larry | Holland & Knight LLP (ONP)[†] * |
| Lumish Wendy F | Carlton Fields, P.A. (ONP)[†] * |
| Mills John S | The Mills Firm (ONP)[†] |
| Pohl Beverly | Broad and Cassel (ONP)[†] |
| Rosenthal Stephen F | Podhurst Orseck P.A. (ONP)[†] * |
| Sandridge Hala A | Fowler White Boggs (ONP)[†] |

| **Band 3** | |
|---|---|
| Cope Gerald | Akerman Senterfitt (ONP)[†] |
| Elligett Raymond | Buell & Elligett (ONP)[†] |
| Levy Jay M | Jay M Levy PA (ONP)[†] |
| Little Hoffman Nancy | Nancy Little Hoffman PA (ONP)[†] |
| Mercier Vargas Rebecca | Kreusler-Walsh, Compiani (ONP)[†] |
| Srebnick Scott A | Scott A Srebnick, PA (ONP)[†] |

| **Up-and-coming individuals** | |
|---|---|
| Culpepper Berman Ceci | Fowler White Boggs (ONP)[†] |

\* *Indicates individual with profile.*
[†] *ONP = Other Notable Practitioner.*

### Notable Practitioners

Miami-based criminal law specialist **Richard Strafer** is known as *"a warrior,"* and impresses with *"his courage and commitment."* The sole practitioner is held in high regard by his peers, who say that he is *"incredibly knowledgeable about issues of criminal procedure and law."* **Jane Kreusler-Walsh** of Kreusler-Walsh, Compiani & Vargas, PA has a fine reputation for her wide-ranging appellate practice, based in West Palm Beach. She has *"quiet confidence and impeccable integrity,"* and is especially praised for *"knowing her way around complex legal issues and making it look easy."* Experienced appellate litigator **Lauri Waldman Ross** of Ross & Girten is *"incredibly well respected"* among interviewees, who say that she is *"both fierce in her advocacy and fair in her work."* Sole practitioner **Joel Perwin** is noted as *"one of the premier appellate lawyers in Miami."* He specializes in commercial disputes and personal injury trial support, and receives especially high praise for his oral advocacy skills. **Barry Richard** (see p.1005) is based in Greenberg Traurig, LLP's Tallahassee office and is noted by market commentators as being *"very good and very professional."* He has extensive experience of arguing high-profile appellate cases nationwide, in both federal and state courts. Also at Greenberg Traurig, **Elliot Scherker** (see p.1006) is known for his *"commanding presence in the courtroom,"* with one source saying that *"he can just knock you away with his skills."* Scherker is currently engaged by BDO USA in a high-value accounting malpractice appeal, and has also represented Lorillard Tobacco. Former Florida Supreme Court Justice **Raoul Cantero** (see p.987) of White & Case LLP is known as the *"cream of the crop."* Commentators laud his ability to be *"both an aggressive advocate and a gentleman."* Deeply experienced sole practitioner **Bruce Rogow** continues to impress as *"a leading and very experienced advocate"* who *"can zero in to the heart of a dispute."* He wins plaudits for his performance in the courtroom, with one source saying: *"When he starts speaking you are immediately entranced by what he's saying."* Seasoned litigator **Joel Eaton** (see p.990) of Podhurst Orseck P.A. maintains an excellent reputation for appellate matters, having recently appeared in the Florida Supreme Court in a matter concerning the interpretation of the Federal Aviation Act's immunity provision. He is particularly praised for his *"tremendous instinct about how to run a case"* and his *"superb"* written skills. Fellow Podhurst

Orseck practitioner **Stephen Rosenthal** (see p.1005) impresses clients with his *"extremely creative legal analysis skills,"* and is described as being *"very smart and passionate about his work."* He also focuses on complex torts and commercial litigation, and recently argued a product liability appeal against Traxxas, concerning the allegedly negligent design of a can of car fuel. **Sylvia Walbolt** (see p.1011) of Carlton Fields, P.A. is *"incredibly well respected"* among peers, who consider her to be *"the grand dame of appellate practice in the state."* She has extensive experience arguing a broad range of appellate matters, both within Florida and out of state. Former Deputy Solicitor General of Florida **Matthew Conigliaro** (see p.988) is based at Carlton Fields's office in St Petersburg. He is commended as *"a very solid, hard-working lawyer who is a great researcher and writer."* His colleague **Wendy Lumish** (see p.998) is based in the firm's Miami office, and maintains a healthy reputation in high-value product liability and catastrophic injury appeals. With extensive experience in this field, she is also sought after as trial support on such cases.

The deeply experienced **Rodolfo Sorondo** (see p.1008)of Holland & Knight LLP is *"clearly one of the best."* He is highly praised for his client-focused approach to appellate litigation, and for being *"easy to work with and very responsive."* His most recent work includes representing Del Monte Fresh Produce Company in an appeal relating to an award of damages resulting from a business dispute. **Larry Klein** (see p.996) practices from Holland & Knight's West Palm Beach office and is highlighted for his *"ability to distill the core legal issues on an appeal and put aside the irrelevant."* Interviewees are impressed by his comprehensive knowledge of appellate procedure, gained through years spent as a District Court of Appeal judge. **Steven Brannock** of Brannock & Humphries handles a broad range of appellate litigation. He is particularly well known for his tobacco-related practice. Fellow lawyers say that *"his written product is very good and effective,"* and *"he represents his clients well."* Sole practitioner **Robert Glazier** works out of Miami and is described as *"very smart and analytically very strong."* His presentation skills are also praised, with one lawyer describing him as *"very candid but never overstated."* **Beverly Pohl** of Broad and Cassel *"has a terrific reputation"* for arguing both civil and criminal appeals in state and federal courts. Clients commend her *"phenomenal"* knowledge of appellate procedure. **Hala Sandridge** of Fowler White Boggs is respected for being "*good at translating the legal principles at play into a practical result.*" Clients appreciate that "*she really puts in the hours to understand the issues within the case.*" Sandridge recently represented Odyssey Marine Exploration in a high-profile appeal concerning the decision to return salvaged antique coins to the Spanish government. **Katherine Giddings** of Akerman Senterfitt is hailed by one client as "*very intelligent and very accessible. Every time I've had a problem in the past she's answered or called me right back.*" She recently acted for Florida Home Builders Association in an appeal before the Fourth District Court of Appeal relating to condominium unit sales contracts. **John Mills** of The Mills Firm has a presence in both Tallahassee and Jacksonville, and continues to handle a wide range of appellate matters. He is described by one market commentator as being "*brilliant on his feet.*" **Rebecca Mercier Vargas** practices from Kreusler-Walsh, Compiani &

Vargas, PA's office in West Palm Beach and is praised by interviewees as a "*good and sharp*" lawyer. Miami-based sole practitioner **Scott Srebnick** has a strong reputation throughout the state of Florida, and is commended for his handling of both criminal appeals and trial litigation. Sole practitioner **Jay Levy** is known for handling a broad range of civil, family and administrative appeals. One lawyer described him as "*a charming person who comes across well in the courtroom,*" also noting that there is "*practically no type of case he couldn't take on.*" From her office in Fort Lauderdale, **Nancy Little Hoffman** maintains her broad-based civil appellate practice and continues to impress peers in Florida. They say: "*She handles herself well and is very pleasant to deal with as an adversary.*" As a former District Court of Appeal judge, **Gerald Cope** of Akerman Senterfitt is very well respected among fellow practitioners for his experience in appellate litigation. He is cochair of

the firm's appellate practice and is praised for having a "*brilliant mind*" and for being "*amazing in the court.*" **Major Harding** of Ausley & McMullen, PA has a "*great reputation*" for appellate litigation within the state of Florida and beyond. A former Chief Justice of the Florida Supreme Court, he is a seasoned appellate litigator and also has experience within the field of alternative dispute resolution. Up-and-comer **Ceci Culpepper Berman** of Fowler White Boggs focuses on complex commercial and bankruptcy appeals. She is highly rated by clients, who praise her understanding of appellate procedure and say that "*she knows exactly how to present and argue a case persuasively on paper.*" Tampa-based **Raymond Elligett** of Buell & Elligett stands out to market commentators as an "*extremely fine lawyer*" who is "*very effective in oral argument.*"

# REAL ESTATE

Commentary about individuals can be found under their firm's paragraph. If the firm has no paragraph (is not ranked) look at Other Notable Practitioners.

*The edit is in alphabetical order by firm name.*

## Akerman Senterfitt
See profile on p.1014

**THE FIRM** This group continues to guide clients through all stages of a real estate transaction, from land use and zoning issues to the acquisition and disposition of real property. It recently advised The Genting Group on the $230 million acquisition of the Miami Herald Property. The enviable client list also includes Flagler Development Group, Prologis and Swire Properties.
**Sources say:** "*Their performance has been excellent. Highly competent, highly efficient and highly responsive.*"
**KEY INDIVIDUALS Cecelia Bonifay** manages land use and zoning for sophisticated property clients. She is noted by peers for her wealth of experience in mixed-use projects and has handled large-scale developments for industrial clients. **Manuel Fernandez** handles real estate financing and transactions, regularly representing secured lenders. Sources report that "*he is excellent*" and note that he is "*so strong and a real player in the market.*" **Andrew Smulian** is a highly competent real estate transactional lawyer in Florida. Sources say: "*He's top of the line. He's a good, smart lawyer who is ethical and talented.*" **Richard Bezold** played a key role in the aforementioned matter for The Genting Group. "*He's excellent, very responsive, succinct and economically efficient,*" say sources. **Neisen Kasdin** led the team in the Genting Group matter and is recognized for his skill in land use and zoning matters. He has also taken a leading role in representing Swire Properties in zoning issues pertaining to the Brickell CitiCentre project. **Theresa McLaughlin** is recognized for her work handling the acquisition and leasing of large retail projects. Sources

report that "*she's very easy to work with, she is very good at communicating with the client and is super smart. She's also very detail-oriented and thorough in her work.*" **Janice Russell** handles the acquisition, development and financing of property, often with respect to the hospitality industry. She recently represented Emigrant Bank in a complex $15 million mortgage loan and equity investment. **Eric Rapkin** handles the leasing, acquisition and disposal of commercial property. He recently advised Parmenter Realty Partners on the acquisition of three office buildings. **Susanne Zabloudil** is an up-and-coming real estate transactional lawyer who works closely with the firm's corporate group. She recently represented Carrols Restaurant Group in its acquisition of 278 Burger King franchise restaurants.

## Baker & Hostetler LLP
See profile on p.2119

**THE FIRM** This firm is noted for its expertise in land use and zoning matters, regularly advising clients on planning issues, permitting and development orders. The group recently represented Disney in a negotiation for the transfer of land; other clients include Acacia Capital, Orlando Magic and City of Orlando.
**Sources say:** "*The firm's performance was excellent. What they're really good at is listening to the client and figuring out what the client is asking for.*"
**KEY INDIVIDUALS Ted Brown** (see p.987) has a great reputation in land use and zoning matters. According to one interviewee, he "*is business savvy and knows what is doable and what is not doable.*" **Alberto Bustamante** (see p.987) is also recognized for his land use expertise. Sources highlight his business-friendly temperament, noting that

"*he's not combative or intense – he's even-keeled, which is always good in negotiations.*"

## Bercow Radell & Fernandez P.A.

**THE FIRM** This respected real estate boutique handles land use issues including comprehensive plans, due diligence reviews and zoning approvals. The group acts for a range of public and private sector clients, including Barry University, BP and City of Miami Community Redevelopment Agency.
**Sources say:** "*No one can go wrong in using that firm for land use and zoning work.*"
**KEY INDIVIDUALS Jeffrey Bercow** has a comprehensive land use and zoning practice, and regularly advises clients on real estate regulation and permitting programs. Clients include developers, property owners and institutional clients.

## Berger Singerman
See profile on p.1017

**THE FIRM** This sophisticated real estate practice covers all areas of real property work. The team works closely with the firm's bankruptcy team in order to offer clients financial advice on distressed real estate matters. Clients include Stiles, Lubert-Adler and Royal Caribbean Cruise Lines.
**Sources say:** "*They are very reputable. I have found them to be responsive, diligent, creative and professional.*"
**KEY INDIVIDUALS James Berger** (see p.985) is an expert on real estate restructuring and loan financing issues. One impressed market source reports: "*If we're structuring a very complex transaction we use James. He's a big-picture guy.*" **Marc Shuster** (see p.1007) is noted for his strength in commercial real estate work. Observers name him "*a deal-*

*The editorial is in alphabetical order by firm name.*

## Real Estate
### Leading Firms

**Band 1**
Bilzin Sumberg Baena Price & Axelrod LLP *
Greenberg Traurig, LLP *

**Band 2**
Akerman Senterfitt
Broad and Cassel
Carlton Fields, P.A. *
Hill Ward Henderson *
Holland & Knight LLP *
Lowndes Drosdick Doster Kantor & Reed, PA
Shutts & Bowen LLP
Stearns Weaver Miller Weissler Alhadeff & Sitterson, P.A.
White & Case LLP *

**Band 3**
DLA Piper LLP (US) *
Foley & Lardner LLP *
GrayRobinson, PA
Greenspoon Marder
Squire Sanders (US) LLP *
Trenam Kemker, Attorneys

**Band 4**
Berger Singerman *
Dean, Mead, Egerton, Bloodworth, Capouano & Bozarth PA
Gunster *
Rogers Towers PA
Smith Hulsey & Busey

## Real Estate
### Senior Statesmen

**Senior Statesmen: distinguished older practitioners**
Walker Jr H William    *White & Case LLP* *

### Leading Individuals

**Band 1**

| | | |
|---|---|---|
| Bilzin Brian L | *Bilzin Sumberg Baena Price & Axelrod LLP* * |
| Brown II C David | *Broad and Cassel* |
| Bruton Burt | *Greenberg Traurig, LLP* * |
| Gorson Matthew B | *Greenberg Traurig, LLP* * |
| Halula John F | *Holland & Knight LLP* * |
| Henderson III Thomas N | *Hill Ward Henderson* * |
| Saul Gary | *Greenberg Traurig, LLP* * |
| Somerstein Barry | *Greenspoon Marder* |
| Sullivan Michael J | *Greenberg Traurig, LLP* * |
| Sumberg John C | *Bilzin Sumberg Baena Price & Axelrod LLP* * |
| Tague Brian | *Tew Cardenas LLP (ONP)* † |

**Band 2**

| | |
|---|---|
| Brittain David R | *Trenam Kemker, Attorneys* |
| Eckhard Richard D | *Holland & Knight LLP* * |
| Fernandez Manuel A | *Akerman Senterfitt* |
| Lash Nancy B | *Greenberg Traurig, LLP* * |
| Mitchell Stephen J | *Squire Sanders (US) LLP* * |
| Pope Nicholas A | *Lowndes Drosdick Doster Kantor & Reed* |
| Ryan Michael | *Lowndes Drosdick Doster Kantor & Reed* |
| Shindell James W | *Bilzin Sumberg Baena Price & Axelrod LLP* * |
| Slater James | *Broad and Cassel* |
| Smulian Andrew | *Akerman Senterfitt* |

**Band 3**

| | |
|---|---|
| Amaducci-Adams Suzanne | *Bilzin Sumberg Baena Price* * |
| Berger James L | *Berger Singerman* * |
| Cowan Kevin | *Shutts & Bowen LLP* |
| Lester Jr Edgel C | *Carlton Fields, P.A.* * |
| McLaughlin Theresa M | *Akerman Senterfitt* |
| Ridley Fred S | *Foley & Lardner LLP* |
| Rolando Margaret A. | *Shutts & Bowen LLP* |

| | |
|---|---|
| Rollnick Neil S | *Hinshaw & Culbertson (ONP)* † |
| Russell Janice L | *Akerman Senterfitt* |
| Seay James E L | *Holland & Knight LLP* * |
| Sollner Richard | *Trenam Kemker, Attorneys* |
| Stiss Carey A | *Bilzin Sumberg Baena Price & Axelrod LLP* * |
| Weber William | *Hughes Hubbard & Reed LLP (ONP)* † * |
| Wilson III Harry M | *Smith Hulsey & Busey* |

**Band 4**

| | |
|---|---|
| Bedke Michael | *DLA Piper LLP (US)* * |
| Bezold Richard | *Akerman Senterfitt* |
| Brockman Christopher C | *Holland & Knight LLP* * |
| Deutch Jeffrey A | *Broad and Cassel* |
| Drobner David S | *Carlton Fields, P.A.* * |
| Evora Orlando L | *Greenberg Traurig, LLP* * |
| Fildes Richard J | *Lowndes Drosdick Doster Kantor & Reed* |
| Freedman Robert S | *Carlton Fields, P.A.* * |
| Kriss Ronald A. | *Stroock & Stroock & Lavan LLP (ONP)* † |
| MacFarland Richard | *Broad and Cassel* |
| Mehta Eileen B | *Bilzin Sumberg Baena Price & Axelrod LLP* * |
| Rapkin Eric D. | *Akerman Senterfitt* |
| Scheu William | *Rogers Towers PA* |
| Seymour Brian | *Gunster* |
| Shuster Marc S. | *Berger Singerman* * |
| Vainder Steven | *White & Case LLP* * |
| Wasil J Donald | *Shutts & Bowen LLP* |
| Weaver Ronald | *Stearns Weaver Miller Weissler Alhadeff* |
| Zelkowitz Steven | *GrayRobinson, PA* * |

**Up-and-coming individuals**

| | |
|---|---|
| Ferrer Barbara | *Holland & Knight LLP* * |
| Zabloudil Susanne | *Akerman Senterfitt* |

\* *Indicates firm / individual with profile.*
† *ONP = Other Notable Practitioner*

---

*maker,"* with one interviewee noting that *"he understands our end game and he understands how to protect us from a legal perspective."*

## Bilzin Sumberg Baena Price & Axelrod LLP
See profile on p.1018

**THE FIRM** This outstanding real estate practice covers all areas of property law, land use and zoning, including complex commercial transactions, leasing, joint ventures and condominiums. The team has been managing the resurgence in real estate transactional work with gusto, and has been involved in major projects and financings. Clients include Lennar, Wexford Capital and Fortune International.

**Sources say:** *"They are extremely highly regarded in this area. They don't seek to make things more complicated. That is why when we look at our most meaningful loan closings, they're top of our list."*

**KEY INDIVIDUALS** The esteemed **Brian Bilzin** (see p.985) receives outstanding feedback from the market. Sources note that he is *"sharp and practical,"* and has *"a Solomon-touch that helps parties see eye to eye and get things done."* He recently advised Lennar on the acquisition and disposal of distressed real estate asset investments. **Stanley Price** (see p.1004) is a leading authority on land use and zoning matters. He continues to use his expertise to analyze land use policy for owner, investor and developer clients. Sources note: *"He always delivers. He offers a wealth of experience in a very political process."* Commentators highlight **John Sumberg's** (see p.1010) legal and commercial acumen. He has handled some of the largest hotel, retail and condominium projects in Florida, and one interviewee reveals that *"he's a think tank and is able to think through complex structuring."* **Carter McDowell** (see p.1000) is also renowned for his land use and zoning capability. Commentators rate him as *"a force,"* and comment that *"he knows the code forwards and backwards, which is critical in terms of getting things done."* **James Shindell** (see p.1007) impresses interviewees, one of whom reports that *"he knows how to focus on the important issues, disregard the less important ones and explain it all. He gets the deals done."* Shindell has a wealth of experience in handling leasing matters relating to complex commercial transactions. Sources praise zoning expert **Albert Dotson's** (see p.990) *"unique skill set,"* and note that *"he is able to navigate the political landscape for the client."* He handles high-value mixed-use projects, and has particular expertise in land use and zoning in hotel work. **Carey Stiss** (see p.1009) is a highly rated transactional real estate attorney. Sources rate his high levels of experience and label him a *"top-notch"* lawyer. **Eileen Mehta** (see p.1000) handles approvals and appeals in the land use and zoning arena. She notably represented Palmer Trinity Private School in an appellate matter regarding land use. **Suzanne Amaducci-Adams** (see p.983) is very familiar with hospitality and hotel projects. Sources say that she *"provides wonderful service and brings particular expertise"* to projects. She advised TotalBank on the origination of a loan secured by Grand Beach Hotel in Miami Beach.

## Broad and Cassel

**THE FIRM** This firm is noted for its expertise in all aspects of residential, commercial and mixed-use real estate work. It regularly guides clients through the maze of land use and environmental laws and regulations, and is also recognized for its work in leasing, acquisitions and real estate financings. Clients include Altman Development, BankUnited, GL Homes and Florida Crystals.

*The editorial is in alphabetical order by firm name.*

## Real Estate: Zoning/Land Use
### Leading Firms

**Band 1**

Bilzin Sumberg Baena Price & Axelrod LLP *

Fowler White Boggs

Greenberg Traurig, LLP *

Gunster *

Hopping Green & Sams, PA

Lowndes Drosdick Doster Kantor & Reed, PA

Shubin & Bass *

**Band 2**

Akerman Senterfitt

Baker & Hostetler LLP *

Bercow Radell & Fernandez P.A.

Carlton Fields, P.A. *

GrayRobinson, PA

Greenspoon Marder

Holland & Knight LLP *

Shutts & Bowen LLP

Stearns Weaver Miller Weissler Alhadeff & Sitterson, P.A.

**Band 3**

Broad and Cassel

Foley & Lardner LLP *

Rogers Towers PA

**Sources say:** *"They've been excellent. They have very good skills and technical knowledge."*

**KEY INDIVIDUALS** Firm chairman **David Brown** receives outstanding feedback for his transactional practice. Interviewees praise his business acumen and commitment to client service, with one observer attesting that he is *"a top-notch real estate lawyer: one of the most impressive real estate attorneys I've ever seen."* **Clifford Hertz** represents clients in complex land use and zoning matters. He is noted for his strong knowledge of local government matters, with one observer commenting: *"I've been very impressed with Cliff's ability to provide expertise relevant to the politics of the approval process."* The *"outstanding"* **James Slater** is recognized for his transactional work in the real estate arena. He recently assisted Enclave at Northwood with the purchase of a 188-unit apartment project in Clearwater, Florida. **Jeffrey Deutch** is managing partner of the firm's Boca Raton office and an expert in real estate finance. Sources note that he is *"really outstanding,"* with one interviewee commenting that he has *"a very creative mind oriented towards solutions and making deals."* Commentators agree that **Richard MacFarland** *"has wonderful technical skills"* and *"probably understands land purchase and title better than any attorney in the state."* He chairs the firm's real estate practice group and focuses his practice on high-value commercial real estate transactions.

## Carlton Fields, P.A.
### See profile on p.1020

**THE FIRM** This robust firm offers a broad range of services, including land use, transactional, financial and litigation matters. The group represents creditors, developers and property owners in all stages of real estate work, from

## Real Estate: Zoning/Land Use
### Senior Statesmen

**Senior Statesmen:** distinguished older practitioners

| Kantor Hal | Lowndes Drosdick Doster Kantor & Reed |
| Siemon Charles L | Siemon & Larsen, PA (ONP)[†] |

### Leading Individuals

**Band 1**

| Bercow Jeffrey | Bercow Radell & Fernandez P.A. |
| Bonifay Cecelia | Akerman Senterfitt |
| Fitzgerald Miranda | Lowndes Drosdick Doster Kantor & Reed |
| Goldstein Joseph | Holland & Knight LLP * |
| Linnan Nancy G | Carlton Fields, P.A. * |
| Mayol Juan J | Holland & Knight LLP * |
| Mele Dennis | Greenspoon Marder |
| Pappas M Lynn | Gunster |
| Powell David L | Hopping Green & Sams, PA |
| Price Stanley B | Bilzin Sumberg Baena Price & Axelrod LLP * |
| Schulman Clifford | Weiss Serota Helfman Pastoriza (ONP)[†] |
| Shelley Linda Loomis | Fowler White Boggs |
| Shubin John K | Shubin & Bass |
| Weaver Ronald | Stearns Weaver Miller Weissler Alhadeff |

**Band 2**

| Bass Jeffrey S | Shubin & Bass |
| Brindell James R. | Gunster |
| Brown Ted R | Baker & Hostetler LLP * |
| Grindstaff Michael J | Shutts & Bowen LLP |
| Hall Donald R | Gunster |
| Hertz Clifford | Broad and Cassel |
| Law Rhea | Fowler White Boggs |
| McDowell Carter N | Bilzin Sumberg Baena Price & Axelrod LLP * |
| Orshefsky Debbie M | Greenberg Traurig, LLP * |
| Woodson R Duke | Foley & Lardner LLP |

**Band 3**

| Bricklemyer Keith | Bricklemyer Smolker & Bolves PA (ONP)[†] |
| Delegal Susan F | Billing, Cochran, Lyles, Mauro (ONP)[†] |
| Dotson Jr Albert E | Bilzin Sumberg Baena Price & Axelrod LLP * |
| Dougherty Lucia A | Greenberg Traurig, LLP * |
| Hainlin Jr Theodore | Rogers Towers PA |
| Kendig-Schrader Julie | Greenberg Traurig, LLP * |
| Leonhardt Frederick | GrayRobinson, PA * |

**Band 4**

| Bouthillier Reggie L | Greenberg Traurig, LLP * |
| Brodeen Karen A. | Fowler White Boggs |
| Bustamante III Alberto S | Baker & Hostetler LLP * |
| Hunter Jr Gary K | Hopping Green & Sams, PA |
| Kasdin Neisen | Akerman Senterfitt |

**Up-and-coming individuals**

| Garcia-Serra Mario | Greenberg Traurig, LLP * |
| Kibert Nicole C | Carlton Fields, P.A. * |

\* *Indicates firm / individual with profile.*

[†] *ONP = Other Notable Practitioner*

land use and permitting disputes to development and acquisition.

**Sources say:** *"Highly competent, efficient, accessible and responsive."*

**KEY INDIVIDUALS Nancy Linnan** (see p.998) is a *"standout lawyer"* who has earned a fantastic reputation

among peers and clients for her thorough and tenacious approach to land use and administrative law matters. The highly experienced **Edgel Lester** (see p.997) centers his practice on transactional real estate work, and is praised as *"a great all-around real estate attorney."* **David Drobner** (see p.990) is deemed to be *"highly competent, efficient, responsive and affable"* by sources. He maintains a successful transactional real estate practice with a focus on commercial leasing. **Robert Freedman** (see p.992) is known in the market for his condominium work and management of issues relating to timeshare property. Sources label him *"very knowledgeable,"* and *"a good attorney."* **Nicole Kibert** (see p.996) is a rising star of the Florida real estate community. She works on condominium projects, including mixed-use, commercial and residential projects.

## Dean, Mead, Egerton, Bloodworth, Capouano & Bozarth PA

**THE FIRM** This firm offers expertise in the full spectrum of real estate matters. The team services developers, investors, lenders and other parties in all aspects of commercial property law.

**KEY INDIVIDUALS** Stephen Bozarth is a key contact.

## DLA Piper LLP (US)
### See profile on p.1971

**THE FIRM** This multidisciplinary practice is noted for handling leasing disputes, major acquisitions and complex litigation. It recently acted for The Goodman Company on litigation stemming from a dispute over development rights. The firm's impressive client list also includes Leucadia National and St Andrews Bay Land Company.

**Sources say:** *"They're doing a really good job. I haven't found anyone comparable to DLA."*

**KEY INDIVIDUALS Michael Bedke** (see p.984) led the team in the aforementioned matter for The Goodman Company. Sources note that *"he is professional, knowledgeable and courteous, prompt and extremely helpful."*

## Foley & Lardner LLP
### See profile on p.2588

**THE FIRM** This solid real estate practice works with business clients on a variety of real estate matters, including financing, acquisitions, sales and leasing disputes with respect to residential, commercial or mixed-use properties. It is also noted for its strength in land use and zoning matters.

**KEY INDIVIDUALS Duke Woodson** acts for both private commercial clients and public bodies on matters relating to land use and zoning. Sources highlight his prior experience in a government regulatory agency, and suggest that *"he is particularly well qualified to deal with government agencies."* **Fred Ridley** is a highly rated real estate transactions lawyer with particular expertise in hotel, resorts and golfing projects. He also has experience in multifamily condominium projects.

## Fowler White Boggs

**THE FIRM** This leading real estate practice offers a strong bench with diverse expertise. The team is highly rated in

*The editorial is in alphabetical order by firm name.*

land use and zoning law, and sources value its political insight and outstanding customer service. Its impressive client list includes Convergent Capital, Patriot Transportation Holdings and Plum Creek Land Company. **Sources say:** *"A high-grade firm with first-class lawyers."*
**KEY INDIVIDUALS Linda Loomis Shelley** is an *"A+ attorney"* whose diverse skill set encompasses land use, environmental permitting and litigation. She recently represented Convergent Capital in a matter involving land use approvals for a 500-acre development project. **Rhea Law** is praised by commentators as being *"extremely competent, responsive and credible."* She has represented Newland Real Estate Group in a range of entitlement and permitting matters of late. **Karen Brodeen** worked closely with Shelley for Patriot Transportation Holdings on matters relating to the amendment of the City of Tampa Comprehensive Plan. Her broad practice includes expertise in administrative, land use and environmental law.

## GrayRobinson, PA

**THE FIRM** This firm handles land use matters and transactional real estate work. The land use and zoning team is adept at administrative litigation, lobbying and counsel on permitting issues, while the transactional team handles leasing, acquisitions and dispositions for a range of commercial and residential clients.
**KEY INDIVIDUALS Frederick Leonhardt** (see p.997) represents public and private sector clients in land use and zoning issues. He is highly experienced in dealing with state and local government, and is ideally placed to lead his clients through the maze of land use laws and regulations. **Steven Zelkowitz** (see p.1013) is recognized for his expertise in the sale, purchase and leasing of commercial property. One source comments that he is *"the best transaction attorney I have run into in 30 years."*

## Greenberg Traurig, LLP
See profile on p.1024

**THE FIRM** This impressive real estate group has benefited from the influx in foreign financial investment and is handling a number of large retail and condominium projects in Florida. It offers high quality across the board in both transactional and land use and zoning matters. The team recently represented Swire Properties in acquiring, developing and subsequently leasing the properties involved in the Brickell CitiCentre project. Other clients include Industrial Income Trust and CMC Group.
**Sources say:** *"The firm was excellent. It offers complete expertise, and has a very quick response rate and a high level of service."*
**KEY INDIVIDUALS Michael Sullivan** (see p.1010) earns excellent praise for his real estate practice, and is noted for his focus on the hospitality industry. Sources suggest that *"he is extremely knowledgeable and practical, adds a great deal of value and is very efficient."* **Burt Bruton** (see p.987) has a tremendous reputation for his abilities in real estate financing transactions. He has been assisting on the $1 billion Brickell CitiCentre project over the past year. **Matthew Gorson** (see p.993) is admired by sources, who attest that *"he has a preeminent reputation."* He maintains an active

real estate practice in Florida, with a specific focus on transactional matters. **Gary Saul** (see p.1006) is primarily known for his work on condominium development, and has experience of working on a number of hotel projects. Consensus opinion suggests that he is *"the top condominium lawyer in the state."* **Nancy Lash** (see p.997) has also been involved in the Brickell CitiCentre acquisition and leasing matters, and has handled a number of real estate transactions in the industrial sector. Sources praise her client service and reveal that *"she is very responsive and smart, knows the market and is very practical."* The *"highly competent"* **Debbie Orshefsky** (see p.1002) maintains a fine reputation in land use and zoning. She is cochair of the firm's national land development practice and is adept at multijurisdictional development permitting. **Lucia Dougherty** (see p.990) is further proof of the firm's impressive depth of land use talent. She has been working with CMC Group on an ongoing matter relating to the proposed renovation of the Miami Beach Convention Center. **Julie Kendig-Schrader** (see p.996) is lauded for her knowledge of land use law. She is rated for guiding clients through intricate land use regulatory schemes. **Reggie Bouthillier** (see p.986) has been working with Tallahassee Memorial Hospital on all aspects of the acquisition and development of a freestanding emergency room. One *"very, very impressed"* interviewee praised his *"exemplary"* level of service. **Orlando Evora** (see p.991) has an excellent reputation in the real estate market in Florida. He offers expertise in all stages of the acquisition and development process, including financing, permitting and leasing of property. **Mario Garcia-Serra** (see p.992) has recently been advising Astor Development on the highly complicated land use and zoning processes required in the Merrick Manor development.

## Greenspoon Marder

**THE FIRM** This quality real estate group has extensive real estate experience in a full range of matters, from small residential transactions to large, complex commercial matters, and remains highly regarded for its expertise in land use and zoning matters. The team is particularly noted for its handling of timeshare and resort work.
**KEY INDIVIDUALS Dennis Mele** maintains a strong reputation in land use and zoning work. He is able to draw on previous experience in land planning and local government to advise owner and developer clients on a range of complex matters. **Barry Somerstein** is widely considered to be one of the leading attorneys in the Florida real estate sphere. He handles transactional, leasing and financing matters.

## Gunster
See profile on p.1025

**THE FIRM** This firm has a stellar reputation for land use work, representing public and private clients in the full range of zoning and land use matters. The team serves as head land use counsel to New England Development for the redevelopment of the Palm Beach Fashion Outlets mall. The firm is also noted for its strength in all aspects of transactional real estate work and real estate financing,

recently representing US Sugar in the acquisition of 28,000 acres of sugar cane land. Other clients include Huizenga Holdings and The Related Group.
**Sources say:** *"Outstanding. On a scale of one to ten I would give them ten."*
**KEY INDIVIDUALS Lynn Pappas** continues to stand out as a *"go-to person"* for her abilities in complex commercial real estate land use matters. **James Brindell** has cultivated a very successful environmental and land use practice, and is praised as *"a very capable senior lawyer."* **Donald Hall** has a highly regarded land use practice and offers particular expertise in urban development. He has also worked on mixed-use, condominium and commercial developments. **Brian Seymour** is noted for his land use litigation skill. Sources have the utmost confidence in him and report that *"he thinks well on his feet, is always right and offers the correct advice every time."*

## Hill Ward Henderson
See profile on p.1027

**THE FIRM** This Tampa-based real estate practice works with automotive dealerships, sports clients and major financial institutions on the financing, acquisition and sale of real property. Clients include Asbury Automotive Group, USAmeriBank and PulteGroup.
**Sources say:** *"A well-respected Tampa firm."* *"I like their style."*
**KEY INDIVIDUALS Thomas Henderson** (see p.994) maintains his strong transactional real estate practice. One market source reveals that *"he has an excellent reputation and my dealings with him have been very professional and very well done."*

## Holland & Knight LLP
See profile on p.1028

**THE FIRM** This reputable firm's high-quality real estate practice covers financings, transactional work and land use and zoning. The group recently advised Morris Publishing on the Florida real estate aspects of its Chapter 11 reorganization plan. Other clients include Beazer Homes, Liberty Property Trust and IKEA.
**Sources say:** *"The service is absolutely excellent. I am a very satisfied customer."*
**KEY INDIVIDUALS** Commentators describe land use and zoning expert **Juan Mayol** (see p.999) as *"clearly one of the most respects lawyers in this arena."* He recently represented Blue Lake in the purchase of land for a retail center development. **Joseph Goldstein** (see p.993) is *"entrepreneurial, focused, and a problem solver,"* say sources. He recently represented Simon Property Group in land use issues affecting shopping centers in Miami-Dade County. **John Halula** (see p.994) excels in real estate transactions and financing. Clients rate his *"excellent style and work ethic."* He recently advised HSBC Realty Credit Corporation on a $226 million loan workout matter. **Richard Eckhard** (see p.990) is renowned as a quality transactional real estate lawyer. Notably, he has been working with DeBartolo Development on a major retail development project in Hawaii. **James Seay** (see p.1006) has cultivated a highly reputable transactional real estate prac-

*The editorial is in alphabetical order by firm name.*

tice. Sources relate that he is *"a very skilled lawyer both on the technical side and practical business side."* **Barbara Ferrer** (see p.991) is an up-and-coming real estate lawyer whom sources describe as *"a good person and a good professional."* She handles a variety of real estate and banking transactions, with a focus on multifamily housing and complex commercial work. **Christopher Brockman** (see p.987) is noted for his talent in leasing agreements. Sources opine that *"he has a lot of experience in the industry and is always helpful. He's a skilled attorney and has the right approach."*

## Hopping Green & Sams, PA

**THE FIRM** This top-rated firm offers the full range of land use and zoning services, assisting clients with challenges to regulatory decisions and policy, due diligence and the overall development of a project. The group has a wealth of experience and takes pride in its ability to preempt issues in a development project before they arise.

**KEY INDIVIDUALS David Powell** has acquired expertise in a broad range of land use and zoning issues relating to the planning and entitlement of complex real estate developments. **Gary Hunter** has experience in all aspects of the real estate land use and zoning process, including representing clients before local and state government in relation to entitlement claims.

## Lowndes Drosdick Doster Kantor & Reed, PA

**THE FIRM** This sophisticated real estate practice assists clients with a variety of land use and transactional real estate matters. It represented a landowner group in South Lake County in an appeal to the local government decision to adopt policies that would have limited the scope for residential development. Other clients include The Klein Company and Rollins College.

**Sources say:** *"They can pull in experts on everything. They have that diversity."*

**KEY INDIVIDUALS Miranda Fitzgerald** is highly respected by peers and regulators in the industry. She led the team on the aforementioned matter for the South Lake County landowners. Sources attest: *"She is probably the best land use lawyer in Orlando these days. She's a very hard worker, diligent and does an excellent job."* **Nicholas Pope** is rated by sources as an attorney who is *"good to work with."* He is recognized for his transactional work and has particular expertise in hotel and hospitality developments. **Michael Ryan**'s real estate practice focuses on transactions, financing and distressed assets. One impressed client notes: *"He's been just spectacular."* **Richard Fildes** advises clients on a range of real estate matters, including transactions, commercial leasing and hotel and resort development. Commentators report that **Hal Kantor** is *"head and shoulders above anyone else in the market,"* with one interviewee suggesting that *"if you have an argument to make, I don't think you'd ever find someone better to make it for you."* Kantor has a huge amount of experience in land use, zoning and property rights litigation.

## Rogers Towers PA

**THE FIRM** This robust real estate team handles matters relating to commercial offices, retail and leisure projects on behalf of its owner and developer clients. It also handles real estate financing and taxation issues on behalf of financial institutions and developers.

**Sources say:** *"An excellent firm."*

**KEY INDIVIDUALS Theodore Hainline** works in land use and government relations, and is a recognized regulatory expert. He is also deemed an expert in zoning, permitting and comprehensive planning matters. Sources praise **William Scheu**'s demeanor and say that *"he's a real gentleman. He's smart and a real professional."* He manages real estate transactions and specializes in retail and commercial property acquisition.

## Shubin & Bass

See profile on p.1035

**THE FIRM** This boutique firm maintains an enviable land use practice. The group works on behalf of both public and private clients, and prides itself on offering a service that balances creativity and common sense.

**KEY INDIVIDUALS** The preeminent **John Shubin** is known to be *"very effective"* in all zoning and land use matters, and specializes in land use litigation and government relations. **Jeffrey Bass** focuses on litigation relating to entitlement disputes, development, zoning disagreements and regulatory conflicts.

## Shutts & Bowen LLP

**THE FIRM** This flourishing practice advises clients on all aspects of real estate law, including financing, title insurance, litigation, leasing and the buying and selling of property. The firm counts homebuilders, commercial developers and financial institutions among its clients.

**KEY INDIVIDUALS Kevin Cowan** focuses on development and transactional work in the property space. Sources attest that *"he's very practical and very smart – he's got a nice way about him that is very effective."* **Michael Grindstaff** advises clients on land use issues. Sources name him *"a very qualified, solid attorney."* **Margaret Rolando** works on condominiums, resorts and mixed-use projects, often with respect to the purchase, sale and financing of property. Interviewees attest that *"she's got a great reputation and she's very, very smart."* Miami-based **Donald Wasil** is recognized for his handling of commercial real estate transactions. His clients include financial institutions, developers and investors.

## Smith Hulsey & Busey

**THE FIRM** This respected real estate team handles acquisitions, sales and leasing, often with respect to condominium and timeshare properties. It has particular expertise in commercial loan closing and workouts relating to distressed property. Clients include Wells Fargo Bank, Baptist Medical Center and St. Vincent's Medical Center.

**Sources say:** *"They're responsive and they're the total package for us. They can do it all."*

**KEY INDIVIDUALS** Sources praise **Harry Wilson**'s real estate practice, reporting that he is *"extremely intelligent*

and well versed in the law."* He has recently handled high-value real estate and foreclosure matters for a group of six senior lenders.

## Squire Sanders (US) LLP

See profile on p.2129

**THE FIRM** This impressive Tampa-based firm has cultivated a talented real estate group that works closely alongside the firm's specialist hospitality practice to provide a seamless and holistic service to hotel and leisure clients. The group is also familiar with the ins and outs of affordable housing transactions, and represents lenders and borrowers in loan foreclosures and workouts relating to real property. Clients include Marriott International and KeyBank.

**Sources say:** *"I'd strongly recommend them."*

**KEY INDIVIDUALS Stephen Mitchell** (see p.1001) has an excellent reputation in the Florida market for negotiating leasing agreements. Sources report: *"Steve is like a legend in Florida. He's a very prominent attorney."*

## Stearns Weaver Miller Weissler Alhadeff & Sitterson, P.A.

**THE FIRM** Stearns Weaver is noted for its broad property expertise, and advises clients on all stages of the development, financing and acquisition or disposal of real estate. The firm's municipal law and land use department regularly guides clients through a labyrinth of state regulatory requirements, while the real estate team continues to handle loan workouts, foreclosures and distressed property. Clients include the City of Doral, the Trump Organization and Carlisle Development Group.

**Sources say:** *"It has very good knowledge of the real estate field. It has great depth."*

**KEY INDIVIDUALS Ronald Weaver** is recognized for his expertise in land use and zoning law. Sources say that he is *"extremely knowledgeable about the zoning process and has a close business relationship with all of the important local and state government employees."*

## Trenam Kemker, Attorneys

**THE FIRM** This high-quality real estate practice works on behalf of a number of property clients, including lenders, buyers, sellers and developers. The team is rated by clients for its talent and reliability.

**Sources say:** *"The service is very good. It's a well-diversified firm."*

**KEY INDIVIDUALS** Sources report that **David Brittain** *"is extremely efficient, and he doesn't mince his words."* In addition, he is *"extremely knowledgeable about real estate and taxation aspects."* He is highly rated for his condominium work as well as his work on easements and leases. **Richard Sollner** has a robust real estate finance practice, and represents financial institutions, developers and other borrowers in a range of complex real estate financing transactions.

*The editorial is in alphabetical order by firm name.*

## White & Case LLP
See profile on p.451

THE FIRM This skilled real estate team focuses on complex, high-profile transactions involving pre-sale components and complex leasing arrangements. It also offers expertise in foreclosure litigation, high-rise condominiums, hospitality and gaming projects. Clients include Crocker Partners, Standard Pacific of Florida and Codina Partners.

Sources say: *"Absolutely excellent – it's the best firm I deal with. When I want something taken care of expediently and professionally, I send it to them."*

KEY INDIVIDUALS The venerated **William Walker** (see p.1011) handles high-profile real estate transactions, and recently represented the McClatchy Company in its relocation of the Miami Herald Newspaper. Sources comment that *"he is very calming in negotiations – he handles them very well and very professionally."* **Steven Vainder** (see p.1011) worked closely alongside Walker in the Miami Herald relocation, and is also noted for his transactional expertise. Sources note that he is *"very easy to work with and obviously very knowledgeable."*

## Other Notable Practitioners

**Keith Bricklemyer** of Bricklemyer Smolker & Bolves PA is a land use expert who handles Developments of Regional Impact, zoning issues and planning disputes for his owner and developer clients. **Susan Delegal** of Billing, Cochran, Lyles, Mauro & Ramsey, P.A. is noted for her expertise in zoning and land use matters. Her knowledge of telecom law means she is well placed to handle land use issues affecting telecom companies. The *"brilliant and creative"* **Neil Rollnick** of Hinshaw & Culbertson brings an extensive amount of experience to bear on a range of real estate financing work. He offers expertise in asset-secured institutional loans and commercial leasing disputes. **William Weber** (see p.1012) of Hughes Hubbard & Reed LLP is described by sources as *"a very good lawyer, and very knowledgeable."* He has worked with many high-profile clients and focuses his real estate practice on transactional work. **Charles Siemon** of Siemon & Larsen, PA is an expert planning lawyer with vast experience in land use and zoning matters. The highly respected **Clifford Schulman** of Weiss Serota Helfman Pastoriza Cole & Boniske PA has a sterling reputation in environmental law and zoning matters related to major real estate transactions. **Brian Tague** of Tew Cardenas LLP handles a range of transactional matters, including sales and acquisitions relating to condominium and mixed-use developments. Sources label him *"an excellent attorney."* **Ronald Kriss** of Stroock & Stroock & Lavan LLP enters the rankings for the first time after receiving warm praise from the market. Sources describe him as *"meticulous, thorough and very professional."*

# TAX

Commentary about individuals can be found under their firm's paragraph. If the firm has no paragraph (is not ranked) look at Other Notable Practitioners.

## Tax
### Leading Firms

**Band 1**
Baker & McKenzie *
Greenberg Traurig, LLP *

**Band 2**
Akerman Senterfitt
Carlton Fields, P.A. *
Dean, Mead, Egerton, Bloodworth, Capouano & Bozarth PA
Fowler White Boggs
Gutter Chaves Josepher Rubin Forman Fleisher PA
Holland & Knight LLP *
White & Case LLP *

**Band 3**
Barnett, Bolt, Kirkwood, Long & McBride
Bilzin Sumberg Baena Price & Axelrod LLP *
Comiter Singer Baseman & Braun LLP
Gunster *
Hill Ward Henderson *
Madsen Goldman & Holcomb, LLP
Packman, Neuwahl & Rosenberg
Proskauer Rose LLP *

*\* Indicates firm / individual with profile.*
*Alphabetical order within each band. Band 1 is the highest*

## Band 1

### Baker & McKenzie
See profile on p.435

**THE FIRM** This leading Florida practice is able to draw on considerable local bench strength and bring the firm's formidable global resources to bear on complex international tax work. The team handles M&A and financial transactions, transfer pricing, and federal and state tax controversy work. Clients include large multinational corporate clients, foreign governments and high net worth individuals with considerable cross-border assets.

**Sources say:** *"It's a terrific law firm with terrific people."*

**KEY INDIVIDUALS** Miami managing partner **Robert Hudson** is praised by sources for his expertise in international tax matters, and particularly for his work on behalf of Latin American clients investing in the USA. He is valued by sources as *"a gentleman and a terrific lawyer."* **James Barrett** (see p.984) heads the firm's Miami tax practice and is *"an excellent attorney,"* according to sources. He specializes in federal income tax planning on behalf of international clients. He also has a significant Florida State advisory practice and extensive experience in international restructuring work.

Associate **Steven Hadjilogiou** (see p.994) is recognized by peers as a rising star in the Florida tax market. Acting alongside more senior members of his team, he advises clients on a variety of federal and local tax issues, as well as partnerships and international tax matters.

## Tax
### Senior Statesmen

**Senior Statesmen:** distinguished older practitioners

| | |
|---|---|
| Boggs Jack | Fowler White Boggs |
| Ullman Samuel C | Bilzin Sumberg Baena Price & Axelrod LLP * |
| Weinstein Andrew | Holland & Knight LLP * |

### Leading Individuals

**Band 1**

| | |
|---|---|
| August Jerald David | Fox Rothschild LLP (ONP)[†] * |
| Barrett James | Baker & McKenzie * |
| Burke David P | Carlton Fields, P.A. * |
| Comiter Richard | Comiter Singer Baseman & Braun LLP |
| Duffy Don | Akerman Senterfitt |
| Egerton Charles | Dean, Mead, Egerton, Bloodworth |
| Hudson Jr Robert F | Baker & McKenzie |
| Lederman Alan S. | Gunster |
| Maser Joel D | Greenberg Traurig, LLP * |
| Panoff Robert | Robert E Panoff PA (ONP)[†] |
| Raattama Henry | Akerman Senterfitt |
| Rosenberg Michael | Packman, Neuwahl & Rosenberg |
| Schindler Ozzie A | Greenberg Traurig, LLP * |

**Band 2**

| | |
|---|---|
| Barnett Leslie | Barnett, Bolt, Kirkwood, Long & McBride |
| Bokor Bruce | Johnson Pope Bokor Ruppel & Burns, LLP |
| Conley Keane Cristin A | Carlton Fields, P.A. * |
| Entin Seth J | Greenberg Traurig, LLP * |
| Ginsburg Dennis | Packman, Neuwahl & Rosenberg |
| Goldstein Richard M | Bilzin Sumberg Baena Price & Axelrod LLP * |
| Horowitz Mitchell | Fowler White Boggs |
| Josepher Richard | Gutter Chaves Josepher Rubin Forman |
| Kosnitzky Michael | Boies, Schiller & Flexner LLP (ONP)[†] |
| Minton Michael D | Dean, Mead, Minton & Zwemer |
| Pierce Robert | Ausley & McMullen, PA (ONP)[†] |
| Press Martin R | Gunster |
| Rubin Charles | Gutter Chaves Josepher Rubin Forman |
| Sawyer Ed | White & Case LLP * |
| Sherman William | Holland & Knight LLP * |
| Townsend William D | Fowler White Boggs |

**Band 3**

| | |
|---|---|
| Chaves Robert | Gutter Chaves Josepher Rubin Forman |
| Cordero Frank | Akerman Senterfitt |
| Hale Russell | Akerman Senterfitt |
| Looney Stephen | Dean, Mead, Egerton, Bloodworth |
| Rohrer William D | Carlton Fields, P.A. * |
| Silva Michael | DLA Piper LLP (US) (ONP)[†] * |
| Tingle Philip | McDermott Will & Emery LLP (ONP)[†] * |
| Warner Jonathan | Jonathan H. (Jason) Warner (ONP)[†] |

**Associates to watch**

| | |
|---|---|
| Hadjilogiou Steven | Baker & McKenzie * |

[†]ONP = Other Notable Practitioner

## Tax: Employee Benefits
### Leading Individuals

**Band 1**

| | |
|---|---|
| Davis James B | Gunster |
| Dixon Sharon Quinn | Stearns Weaver Miller Weissler (ONP)[†] |
| Ward Alton C | Hill Ward Henderson * |

**Band 2**

| | |
|---|---|
| Barber Steven K | Shutts & Bowen LLP (ONP)[†] |
| Canan Michael J | GrayRobinson, PA (ONP)[†] |
| Friedman Robert J | Holland & Knight LLP * |
| Hurt Richard T | Akerman Senterfitt |
| Salomon Peter | Akerman Senterfitt |
| Watson Roberta | Trenam Kemker, Attorneys (ONP)[†] |

## Tax: Estate Planning
### Leading Individuals

**Band 1**

| | |
|---|---|
| Benford Norman J | Greenberg Traurig, LLP * |
| Detzel Lauren | Dean, Mead, Egerton, Bloodworth |
| Koren Edward | Holland & Knight LLP * |
| Nelson Barry | Nelson & Nelson PA (ONP)[†] * |
| Pratt David | Proskauer Rose LLP |
| Stone Bruce M | Goldman Felcoski & Stone PA (ONP)[†] |
| Tescher Donald | Tescher & Spallina PA (ONP)[†] |
| Zeydel Diana S.C. | Greenberg Traurig, LLP * |

**Band 2**

| | |
|---|---|
| Bokor Bruce | Johnson Pope Bokor Ruppel & Burns (ONP)[†] |
| Boyett Christopher W | Holland & Knight LLP * |
| Bronstein Joel | Bronstein, Carlson, Gleim & Smith (ONP)[†] |
| Bucher Elaine M | Gunster |
| Comiter Richard | Comiter Singer Baseman & Braun LLP |
| Kavoukjian Michael E | White & Case LLP * |
| Sparks Brian | Hill Ward Henderson * |

**Band 3**

| | |
|---|---|
| Gortz Albert W | Proskauer Rose LLP |
| Kirkwood Peter | Barnett, Bolt, Kirkwood, Long & McBride |
| Packman Kevin | Holland & Knight LLP * |
| Spivey Barry | Law Offices of Barry F. Spivey (ONP)[†] |

## Tax: State & Local
### Leading Individuals

**Band 1**

| | |
|---|---|
| Barton Bernard | Holland & Knight LLP * |
| Ervin James M | Holland & Knight LLP * |
| Goldman Robert S | Madsen Goldman & Holcomb, LLP |
| Holcomb Mark E | Madsen Goldman & Holcomb, LLP |
| Larsen Peter O | Akerman Senterfitt |
| Townsend William D | Fowler White Boggs |
| Ware Rex D | Fowler White Boggs |
| Weber Victoria | Hopping Green & Sams, PA (ONP)[†] |

**Band 2**

| | |
|---|---|
| Hale Russell | Akerman Senterfitt |

## Greenberg Traurig, LLP
See profile on p.1024

**THE FIRM** Market sources single out this Florida stalwart for the sophistication of its tax practice and its ability to marshal tax expertise from five locations across the state, on both a nationwide and global level. The firm handles tax planning, tax dispute and estate planning work on behalf of a broad range of illustrious clients, often acting on matters with a substantial international element. It recently acted for Justice Holdings on its acquisition of Burger King Worldwide.

**Sources say:** *"They are highly ethical, timely and good on responses, and they certainly know their material."*

**KEY INDIVIDUALS Joel Maser** (see p.999) is a highly regarded tax lawyer with expertise in complex real estate deals as part of a broader corporate transactional practice. **Norman Benford** (see p.985) is known for his sophisticated estate planning work, which covers trust and estate administration, as well as business succession for high net worth individuals and families. Sources say he is *"great to work with, a true professional. He is pragmatic, practical and commercial."* **Ozzie Schindler** (see p.1006) handles a broad spectrum of international tax work out of the firm's Miami office, with a particular focus on acting for clients based in Latin America. He advises clients on both private and corporate tax planning. **Diana Zeydel** (see p.1013) is a highly respected estate planning lawyer who handles complex multijurisdictional planning and disputes work. Recent highlights have included work on overseas trust disputes, estate administration, marital disputes and probate work. **Seth Entin** (see p.990) is noted by sources for his international tax work and his ability to *"pinpoint the crux of the issue at hand"* when it comes to complex tax matters.

## Band 2

### Akerman Senterfitt
See profile on p.1014

**THE FIRM** This national firm covers a broad range of tax work, including transactional tax matters, tax planning and employee benefits, tax controversy and litigation. The firm's well-regarded team of Florida tax attorneys is spread across a number of offices throughout the state, and handles both local and national tax work. It frequently acts on behalf of high-profile clients, including Citigroup, Daimler Financial and Ford.

**KEY INDIVIDUALS Don Duffy** is an *"extremely well-known and highly respected"* tax attorney, according to sources, who also praise his extensive technical skill. His broad expertise encompasses tax planning and advising clients under investigation by the IRS. Displaying a strong transactional focus, he advises domestic and international clients on debt finance, private equity, joint venture, M&A and international transfer pricing agreement work. **Peter Larsen** chairs the firm's national tax group and specializes in tax controversy work. He acts on behalf of a variety of the firm's high-profile clients, both at the advice and litigation stage, including his recent representation of Tyson

Foods in state tax disputes. **Henry Raattama** is a well-regarded tax practitioner based in the firm's Miami office and specializes in advising nonprofit organizations. As well as advising clients on tax planning, he has extensive expertise in the area of estate planning. **Richard Hurt** is an *"excellent tax lawyer,"* according to impressed market sources. He is known for his expertise in employee benefits, profit sharing and welfare benefit work. **Peter Salomon** is found by sources to be an *"extraordinarily, intuitively bright person."* His practice covers advising clients on the full range of executive compensation matters. The *"excellent"* **Frank Cordero** chairs the firm's federal tax practice, and is noted for his M&A work, as well as his international transactional practice and knowledge of complex debt restructuring. **Russell Hale**'s tax practice covers a broad swathe of Florida banking and corporate tax work, complemented by his work on national state and local tax matters. Sources note his recent joint venture tax work.

### Carlton Fields, P.A.
See profile on p.1020

**THE FIRM** Carlton Fields handles tax litigation, inbound and outbound international tax planning, partnership, joint venture and voluntary disclosure work for a broad range of clients. The firm is also noted by sources for its formidable transactional tax practice.

**KEY INDIVIDUALS** Tampa-based **David Burke** (see p.987) is *"excellent on the transactional side,"* according to his peers. This forms a key part of his broad tax expertise, which encompasses tax planning at the federal, state and international level, as well as controversy work. **William Rohrer** (see p.1005) is an experienced tax attorney and certified accountant who focuses on international and domestic tax planning work. He acts for a range of public and private corporate clients out of the firm's Miami office, and is *"fantastic to work with,"* according to sources. **Cristin Conley Keane** (see p.988) is a shareholder in the firm's Tampa office, and specializes in acting for closely held and nonprofit clients.

### Dean, Mead, Egerton, Bloodworth, Capouano & Bozarth PA

**THE FIRM** This consummate full-service Florida firm is noted for its highly regarded statewide tax practice. The firm is best known for its estate planning work, but also shows considerable prowess in corporate tax, M&A and state and local tax issues.

**Sources say:** *"Its lawyers are among the top tax people in the state."*

**KEY INDIVIDUALS Lauren Detzel** is *"a class act,"* according to sources, and is noted for her expertise in estate planning. She chairs the firm's estate and succession department, and specializes in acting on behalf of closely held businesses and high net worth families. **Charles Egerton** is *"a fantastic lawyer"* with an excellent reputation for tax planning and tax controversy work, especially when acting on behalf of clients from the real estate industry. He is regarded by sources as one of the leading lawyers in the state. **Michael Minton** acts as the firm's president, as well as chairing the firm's agribusiness team. His tax expertise

covers business succession, estate and gift tax planning as well as federal income tax work. Well-respected tax lawyer **Stephen Looney** chairs the firm's tax department. His practice is primarily transaction and M&A-based, with more work of late coming in the tax controversy area.

### Fowler White Boggs

**THE FIRM** This well-regarded tax team has four offices across Florida and handles the full range of tax work on behalf of high-profile clients, including Tropicana and Time Warner. Clients benefit from the firm's full-service tax offering, prevalent regional presence and strong connections with governmental tax collection agencies such as the IRS and the Florida Department of Revenue.

**KEY INDIVIDUALS Mitchell Horowitz** heads the firm's tax department from Tampa and is *"extremely bright and knowledgeable,"* according to commentators. Recent work highlights include advising high net worth individuals on various tax controversy matters. **William Townsend** is known for his state and local tax work, and has recently been handling tax planning work for several prominent national corporate clients, taking on matters relating to state tax in Florida and elsewhere. **Rex Ware** has a wealth of experience when it comes to acting on complex state and local tax matters. He has handled local tax controversy and audit work for several prestigious clients of late. Veteran tax lawyer **Jack Boggs** is the *"éminence grise of estate planning,"* according to peers. He maintains an active tax practice and is able to deploy over 40 years of experience in the service of the firm's clients.

### Gutter Chaves Josepher Rubin Forman Fleisher PA

**THE FIRM** This well-known tax boutique continues to win approbation from sources for its expertise and bench strength, especially when it comes to blooding talented younger lawyers. The eight-strong team is based in Boca Raton, and handles estate planning, tax controversy, transactional matters and international tax work.

**KEY INDIVIDUALS Charles Rubin** is an *"excellent international tax lawyer,"* according to sources. He has considerable expertise in tax planning work and in matters relating to tax-exempt and charitable organizations. **Richard Josepher** is noted for his partnership and S-Corp taxation expertise, and is known among sources as a tax practitioner of considerably high quality. **Robert Chaves** displays expertise in probate, asset protection and international and domestic estate planning. Sources view him as a key player in the Florida tax market.

### Holland & Knight LLP
See profile on p.1028

**THE FIRM** The Florida offices of this well-regarded, full-service national firm undertake a large amount of international tax work, focusing on both inbound and outbound investments, and restructuring matters. The firm also handles a substantial number of domestic tax issues, encompassing a strong transactional practice, as well as estate planning and employee benefits advice.

**KEY INDIVIDUALS James Ervin** (see p.991) is a stalwart of the state and local tax Bar in Florida. His recent work includes advising clients on corporate income tax matters matters concerning the Florida Department of Revenue. His practice covers the full range of tax advice, from audits to assessment protest, litigation and legislative lobbying. Tampa-based **Bernard Barton** (see p.984) is *"excellent and super practical,"* according to sources, who also value his ability to manage high-risk cases. Though best known for advising clients on state and local taxation, he also has a formidable federal tax advice practice. **Edward Koren** (see p.997) chairs the firm's private wealth service group, and is praised by sources for his expertise and ferocious work ethic. Aside from estate planning, he shows expertise in contentious transfer tax work and matters involving the IRS. Sources say: *"He is the succession planning maven."* **Christopher Boyett** (see p.986) is another member of Holland & Knight's estate planning practice. He focuses on succession and tax planning for closely held businesses and high net worth individuals, as part of a broader estate and trust administration offering. **William Sherman** (see p.1007) is lauded by sources for his international tax practice, including a particular specialism in foreign taxation. He has recently advised a number of international clients on complex cross-border tax structuring matters. **Andrew Weinstein** (see p.1012) brings over 40 years of Florida tax expertise to bear on tax controversy matters, and is praised by sources for his deep expertise and the quality of his tax advice. **Kevin Packman** (see p.1002) is an up-and-coming lawyer who has expertise in estate planning, tax controversy and creditor protection planning. He has recently acted on behalf of clients engaged in voluntary disclosure to the IRS. Miami-based **Robert Friedman** (see p.992) is noted by sources for his employee benefit work. As well as advising clients on executive compensation, he is singled out by peers for his ERISA expertise.

## White & Case LLP
See profile on p.451

**THE FIRM** This compact team wins praise for the quality of its tax work and its ability to punch above its weight. The Florida office of this global firm undertakes federal, state and international matters, including private client, transactional, tax controversy and tax-exempt organization work. The firm's client list speaks for itself, including household names like Deutsche Bank Trust Company and JPMorgan Chase.

**KEY INDIVIDUALS Michael Kavoukjian** (see p.995) is the global head of the firm's private client practice. Recent highlights include international estate planning work involving assets worth billions of dollars. **Ed Sawyer** (see p.1006) is *"a very, very bright guy,"* according to sources, who go on to praise his impressive work ethic. He chairs the firm's Florida practice, and has recently been advising Latin American clients on US sales, acquisitions and restructurings.

## Band 3

### Barnett, Bolt, Kirkwood, Long & McBride
**THE FIRM** This Tampa-based business boutique has recently expanded the size of its tax team to include nine full-time attorneys. The firm advises private individuals and closely held businesses on corporate and transaction tax matters, estate planning and employee benefits, with a particular specialism in aviation tax work.

**KEY INDIVIDUALS Leslie Barnett** is well known for his statewide estate and succession planning practice. His illustrious client base includes high net worth individuals, the owners of closely held businesses and executives. **Peter Kirkwood** is an expert in estate planning, and a recognized leader in the field. Alongside experience in the transactional end of tax work, he also has substantial expertise in acting on behalf of charities and tax-exempt organizations.

### Bilzin Sumberg Baena Price & Axelrod LLP
See profile on p.1018

**THE FIRM** This three-partner tax, trusts and estates team acts on behalf of US and overseas clients, both private and corporate, in inbound and outbound tax work. The tax planning advice provided by the firm covers income tax, estate and business succession planning and cross-border planning work. The firm also undertakes a significant amount of transactional work.

**KEY INDIVIDUALS Richard Goldstein** (see p.993) chairs the firm's tax group and is praised by sources as an attorney who *"gets the deal done."* Clients laud him for his *"first-rate combination of knowledge of the law and acute business sense."* **Samuel Ullman** (see p.1011) is *"a dean of the Florida tax Bar,"* according to impressed market sources. He specializes in acting for clients on transactional tax matters, as well as those pertaining to tax-exempt organizations, and state and federal tax controversies.

### Comiter Singer Baseman & Braun LLP
**THE FIRM** This venerable firm offers the full range of tax services, including asset protection, partnership and corporate work, transactional tax advice and controversy work. It is also noted by sources for its strength in estate planning. Recent highlights for the eight-member team include large-scale real estate restructuring matters.

**KEY INDIVIDUALS Richard Comiter** is a *"brilliant lawyer,"* according to sources, who note that he is *"excellent with private companies."* His expertise extends to federal income and estate tax planning, complex business transactions, succession and wealth preservation planning and asset protection.

### Gunster
See profile on p.1025

**THE FIRM** This West Palm Beach tax team offers clients deep expertise in corporate, partnership and international tax work, tax controversy advice, and trust and estate planning. Key clients include DR Beachfront Real Estate and Capital City Banking Group.

**Sources say:** *"I have always been impressed with their abilities."*

**KEY INDIVIDUALS James Davis** specializes in employee benefits work and is *"one of the most brilliant, intuitive tax attorneys I've ever met,"* said one interviewee. Davis is head of the firm's tax department and handles all aspects of employee benefits on behalf of the firm's clients. **Alan Lederman** is noted by peers for his international and federal tax prowess. Enthusiastic sources say *"he has a photographic memory, he knows statute off by heart and he is very bright,"* while also praising his ability to educate clients in complex tax issues. **Martin Press** specializes in tax controversy work and is *"excellent,"* according to sources. He is an expert in matters involving the IRS, and is well known for acting in this sphere. Peers hail **Elaine Bucher** as an *"exceptional attorney in the area of estate and tax planning. She is extremely knowledgeable and competent, and works well with her clientele."* Her practice tends to focus on wills, trusts and estates.

### Hill Ward Henderson
See profile on p.1027

**THE FIRM** This Tampa firm wins praise for its broad tax practice, with market sources hailing its strength when acting on S-Corp, FACTA, transactional and 401k compliance matters. The firm's eight-partner tax team handles a large amount of venture capital, private equity and joint venture transactional tax work, and regularly acts for the likes of Asbury Automotive Group and Lincare.

**Sources say:** *"They are very professional, with a strong focus on their clients."*

**KEY INDIVIDUALS Alton Ward** (see p.1011) is co-head of the firm's tax practice and is noted for his strong employee benefits portfolio. His areas of expertise include profit sharing plans, retirement plans, ESPOs and 401k plans. **Brian Sparks** (see p.1009) is a noted trusts and estates expert. His impressive client base includes high net worth individuals, high ranking executives and the owners of closely held businesses.

### Madsen Goldman & Holcomb, LLP
**THE FIRM** This three-partner boutique focuses on advising clients on state and local taxation, and is regarded as a go-to source for state and local tax advice by many other Florida firms. The firm's attorneys handle property, transactional and income tax work, in addition to advising on tax controversy matters.

**KEY INDIVIDUALS Robert Goldman** is *"very well thought of in the state,"* according to impressed sources, and is noted for his mastery of state and local tax work. **Mark Holcomb** is a trusted state and local tax practitioner. Peers reveal they feel comfortable referring work to this Florida tax stalwart.

### Packman, Neuwahl & Rosenberg
**THE FIRM** This compact Florida tax boutique is praised by market sources for its international tax work for a range of high-profile clients. On the domestic front the firm handles tax controversy work, estate planning and gift tax work, while also advising on tax issues relating to charitable and tax-exempt organizations.

Sources say: *"A great tax boutique that has always done a good job."*

**KEY INDIVIDUALS** **Michael Rosenberg** is a highly regarded international tax lawyer, who combines all the benefits of an experienced tax attorney with those of a qualified CPA. His practice focuses on acting for foreign clients investing in the USA, as well as estate planning for high net worth individuals. **Dennis Ginsburg** is *"a great international tax lawyer,"* according to impressed sources. His further areas of expertise include wealth preservation advice and estate planning.

## Proskauer Rose LLP
### See profile on p.2001
**THE FIRM** The Boca Raton office of this well-respected international firm displays particular strength in its adroit handling of wealth management matters for a swath of high net worth individuals. In addition, charitable organizations, business owners, families and estates are also well catered for in this sphere. Enthusiastic clients are especially keen to highlight its advisory capabilities and sector knowledge.

Sources say: *"The service has been, in a word, excellent: thorough, knowledgeable, personal and of the highest professional caliber."*

**KEY INDIVIDUALS** According to impressed sources, **David Pratt** is *"one of the most advanced estate planning attorneys when it comes to high-end, wealthy clients."* He is a specialist in the areas of estates and trusts, and is highly regarded and well respected by peers and clients alike, who call him *"fantastic, very hands-on,"* and *"extremely knowledgeable."* The *"exceptionally bright and diligent"* **Albert Gortz** has a wealth of experience and a wide-ranging practice that counsels families and high net worth individuals on issues relating to financial, charitable, estate and personal planning work.

## Other Notable Practitioners

The highly experienced **Robert Pierce** of Ausley & McMullen, PA takes on a wide range of taxation matters, with probate, estate and business law all falling under his remit. He is also known for his extensive knowledge of Florida state tax law. **Jerald David August** (see p.983) of Fox Rothschild LLP is hailed as a *"Subchapter S corporations guru"* and is known as one of the top tax lawyers in the state. His practice covers international taxation, corporate and partnership taxation, tax litigation and controversy and federal tax matters. Federal tax practitioner **Sharon Quinn Dixon** of Stearns Weaver Miller Weissler Alhadeff & Sitterson, P.A. is *"extremely knowledgeable, practical"* and an *"outstanding attorney,"* according to her peers. She is well versed in advising business clients on executive compensation and employee benefit plans, and her practice also caters for individual clients in relation to estate plans, including federal estate and gift tax issues. **Barry Nelson** (see p.1002) of Nelson & Nelson PA is *"the number-one asset protection guy in the state of Florida,"* according to one enthusiastic peer. Of late he has handled a number of high-value estate planning matters for families and individuals, including gift tax and asset protection issues. Sole practitioner **Robert Panoff** *"has a great reputation for his tax work,"* and brings his considerable experience to bear on a broad range of tax issues, including international controversies, fraud, appeals, litigation and audits. **Victoria Weber** of Hopping Green & Sams, PA is at the top of her game, according to peers. For over three decades she has handled a multitude of Florida state tax matters, including planning and controversies. She also represents statewide trade associations before the Department of Revenue and Legislature. The *"fabulous"* **Michael Kosnitzky** of Boies, Schiller & Flexner LLP has *"deep knowledge that is second to none,"* say impressed clients. The S Corp tax expert has handled a range of high-value cases for clients such as Leftfield Pictures of New York and Wynn Resorts. **Steven Barber** of Shutts & Bowen LLP is highly thought of by peers, who recognize his extensive experience in employment benefits law, in addition to his vast knowledge of ERISA transactional and compliance issues. The design and implementation of employee benefit plans is an area

in which his expertise is particularly noted. Trust and estate specialist **Donald Tescher** of Tescher & Spallina PA is a leading name for high net worth individuals, families and businesses seeking counsel and advice in this sphere. His experience is exemplified by his previous role as chairman of the Tax Section of the Florida Bar. **Joel Bronstein** of Bronstein, Carlson, Gleim & Smith, PA handles all manner of tax issues for a broad range of corporate clients. He is also adept at taking on matters in state taxation, probate and trust law, federal income taxation and estate and gift taxation, and he has considerable experience in the healthcare sector. **Michael Canan** of GrayRobinson, PA handles a number of IRS audits, covering retirement plans and employee benefits. His practice also takes in the establishment and maintenance of ESOPs. **Roberta Watson** of Trenam Kemker, Attorneys has a strong reputation in employee benefits work. Her broad practice takes in a range of ERISA, benefits and compensation issues. International tax law specialist **Michael Silva** (see p.1007) of DLA Piper LLP (US) *"is extremely attentive and responsive to clients. He understands that clients need and want clear-cut answers, which is what he gives, in a reassuring manner."* His recent highlights include advising Fortune 200 company MasTec on its $1.3 billion expansion into India, Libya and Brazil. Now a sole practitioner, **Barry Spivey** wins plaudits for his high levels of activity on matters concerning probate and wills. He also handles significant estate planning and trusts matters. McDermott Will & Emery LLP Miami partner **Philip Tingle** (see p.1010) has a unique practice that covers tax aspects relating to renewable energy. His clients include Exelon, ArcLight Capital Partners and Olympus Power. **Jonathan Warner** of Law Offices of Jonathan H. (Jason) Warner, PA is *"a very strong, solid all-around tax lawyer,"* according to his peers. From his Miami base, his practice focuses on international taxation and international estate planning. Estate planning expert **Bruce Stone** of Goldman Felcoski & Stone PA is known to be *"very good analytically, with very good drafting ability. He is also very knowledgeable on all areas of wills and trusts."* **Bruce Bokor** of Johnson Pope Bokor Ruppel & Burns, LLP is highly regarded by peers. He is adept at handling both tax and estate planning.

# Leaders' Profiles in Florida

**ACKERBAUM COX, Joyce**
Baker & Hostetler LLP, Orlando
407 649 4077
jacox@bakerlaw.com
*Featured in Labor & Employment (Florida)*
**Career:** Martindale-Hubbell AV-rated, Joyce Ackerbaum Cox focuses on advising and representing employers in a wide variety of employment issues. She litigates matters involving discrimination, harassment, wage and hour claims, and disputes arising out of employment and noncompete agreements and trade secret issues. Joyce handles cases and provides consultation on accessibility compliance under the Americans with Disabilities Act (ADA). Finally, she counsels and trains employers on issues including employment policies and procedures, proper hiring, disciplining and termination methods, sexual harassment, the ADA, the Family and Medical Leave Act and the Fair Labor Standards Act, and prepares and advises employers on executive contracts.

**ALONSO, Fernando C**
Hunton & Williams LLP, Miami
305 810 2570
falonso@hunton.com
*Featured in Latin American Investment (Florida), Banking & Finance (Florida)*
**Practice Areas:** Fernando C Alonso has practiced in the corporate and securities, banking and international fields for more than 20 years. Mr Alonso's clients include a broad range of publicly owned and privately held US and foreign companies and financial institutions. Mr Alonso has led numerous significant acquisitions, mergers, joint ventures and other business transactions, including those involving cross-border complexities. He represents companies in connection with their equity and debt financings. Mr Alonso regularly represents foreign clients in connection with US acquisitions, as well as domestic companies with their international expansion. Most recently, Mr Alonso has been involved in renewable energy projects and in assisting European consortia with infrastructure projects in the U.S. and Latin America.
**Career:** Chairman of the Latin American Practice Group. The firm was selected by Chambers and Partners USA as the recipient of the 2009 Award for Excellence for Latin American Investment.
**Personal:** Received his BA with distinction in history in 1980 from Yale College, graduated summa cum laude and as a member of phi beta kappa, and JD 1983 Yale Law School.

**ALVAREZ, Victor M**
White & Case LLP, Miami
305 995 5223
valvarez@whitecase.com
*Featured in Latin American Investment (Florida), Banking & Finance (Florida)*
**Career:** Mr Alvarez is engaged primarily in the representation of financial institutions and sponsors/borrowers in corporate, project and structured finance transactions, particularly in Latin America. To view a comprehensive biography, please visit www.whitecase.com/valvarez.

**ALVAREZ-FARRÉ, Emilio J**
White & Case LLP, Miami
305 995 5219
ealvarez@whitecase.com
*Featured in Corporate/M&A (Florida), Latin American Investment (Florida), Banking & Finance (Florida)*
**Career:** Emilio J Alvarez-Farré is a partner in White & Case's Miami office. He concentrates on mergers and acquisitions, including privatizations, and financing transactions with a particular focus on Latin America. To view a comprehensive biography, please visit www.whitecase.com/ealvarez.

**AMADUCCI-ADAMS, Suzanne**
Bilzin Sumberg Baena Price & Axelrod LLP, Miami
305 350 2370
samaducci@bilzin.com
*Featured in Real Estate (Florida)*
**Practice Areas:** Real estate development and finance; commercial leasing; construction and development; acquisition and disposition of assets; CMBS; hotels; marinas.
**Professional Memberships:** Commercial Real Estate Women (CREW)-Miami, Past President, 2014 National Convention Co-Chair, Board Member 2009-present; The Orange Bowl Committee.
**Career:** Daily Business Review, Top Dealmakers of the Year Award – Hotel, 2012; CREW-Miami, Networking Deal of the Year Award, 2010-12; National Real Estate Investor, Outstanding Women in Real Estate Award, 2010; South Florida Business Journal, Heavy Hitters in Commercial Real Estate, 2011.
**Personal:** JD (cum laude), University of Miami School of Law, 1993; BA (cum laude), Vanderbilt University, 1990.

**ANDERSON, Rod**
Holland & Knight LLP, Tampa
813 227 8500
rod.anderson@hklaw.com
*Featured in Bankruptcy/Restructuring (Florida)*
**Practice Areas:** Rod Anderson represents public and private companies, banks, insurance companies, financial institutions, investors, debtors, and other parties in litigation and financial matters. Mr Anderson's practice involves representing these types of clients in workouts, litigation, and bankruptcy cases. His extensive chapter 11 bankruptcy experience includes representing debtors, secured creditors, creditors' committees, equity interests, purchasers of assets, landlords, and licensors. He also represents parties in litigation in Federal District Courts, Bankruptcy Courts, and State Courts involving issues such as credit litigation, lien enforcement and priority contests, mortgage foreclosures, lender liability actions, fraudulent transfer actions and other types of litigation.

**ARAGON, Rudolph F**
White & Case LLP, Miami
305 371 2700
raragon@whitecase.com
*Featured in Litigation (Florida)*
**Career:** Rudy Aragon is a Commercial Litigation Partner in the firm's Miami office. Mr Aragon represents regional and national clients, as well as clients from Latin America, Europe and Asia. Throughout his career, he has tried over 80 cases, including more than 35 jury trials. He has argued numerous appeals in state and federal courts. Some of his most significant matters include the representation of corporate and individual defendants in litigation arising from the failures of Premium Sales, Amerifirst Savings & Loan, Sunrise Savings & Loan and Southeast Bank. To view a comprehensive biography, please visit www.whitecase.com/raragon.

**ARONSON, Daniel H**
Berger Singerman, Miami
305 714 4377
daronson@bergersingerman.com
*Featured in Corporate/M&A (Florida)*
**Career:** With over 25 years of experience in complex corporate, securities and transactional matters, Mr Aronson focuses his practice on domestic and cross-border mergers and acquisitions, public and private securities offerings, other sophisticated finance and capital markets transactions and counseling public, private and non-profit entities on strategic business, finance, governance, restructuring and transactional matters. He has represented clients in a variety of industries and markets, including biotechnology, computer hardware and software, consumer products, employee outsourcing, traditional and specialty financial services, gaming, health care products and services, information technology, media and entertainment, pharmaceuticals, restaurants, telecommunications, transportation and travel services. In addition, he has counseled private equity, venture capital, investment and real estate opportunity funds in fund formation, acquisition, investment, governance and "exit" activities. Frequent lecturer and author; Adjunct Professor of Law at the University of Florida Levin College of Law; Member of the Executive Advisory Board of the Center for Entrepreneurship & Innovation at the University of Florida; and sits on the Boards of numerous organizations.

**AUERBACH, Marc H**
K&L Gates, Miami
305 539 3304
marc.auerbach@klgates.com
*Featured in Healthcare (Florida)*
**Practice Areas:** Marc H Auerbach represents a wide range of healthcare entities in structuring and negotiating transactions, particularly on the financing and structural issues related to business development. He advises physician groups, HMOs, hospitals, diagnostic facilities and equipment manufacturers on fraud and abuse, developing compensation structures, and assisting in the purchase or sale of entities and physician groups. Mr Auerbach is also particularly experienced in e-health issues, including telemedicine, online health services, online content, HIPAA and HITECH Act issues, Web site development, online health advertising, and general review of applications of traditional health law issues in the digital environment.

**AUGUST, Jerald David**
Fox Rothschild LLP, West Palm Beach
561 804 4401
jaugust@foxrothschild.com
*Featured in Tax (Florida)*
**Practice Areas:** Federal corporate, partnership and international taxation(in-bound and out-bound) estate planning, tax controversy/litigation.
**Professional Memberships:** ABA Section of Taxation, American Law Institute, American College of Tax Counsel, American College of Trusts and Estates Counsel, American Tax Policy Institute.
**Career:** Co-Chair, Taxation & Wealth Planning; Pennsylvania's 'Top Rated Lawyers,' Taxation and Wealth Planning, The Wall Street Journal, Philadelphia Inquirer (2012); 'West Palm Beach Tax Lawyer of the Year'.
**Personal:** BS, BA – Wharton School, University of Pennsylvania (1974); JD University of Pittsburgh School of Law (1977); LLM, Taxation, New York University School of Law (1980).

**AXELROD, Alan D**
Bilzin Sumberg Baena Price & Axelrod LLP, Miami
305 350 2369
aaxelrod@bilzin.com
*Featured in Corporate/M&A (Florida)*
**Practice Areas:** Corporate and securities, including mergers and acquisitions, public securities transactions, equity and debt private placements, venture capital financings, secured and unsecured credit facilities, corporate recapitalizations and restructurings, corporate governance and compliance, joint venture, strategic alliance, employment and consulting agreements.
**Professional Memberships:** Admitted to Florida, New York. The Florida Bar; Dade County Bar Association; American Bar Association, Mergers and Acquisitions Committee; New York State Bar Association, Business Law Section Securities Regulation Committee.
**Career:** Chair, Bilzin Sumberg's Corporate & Securities Practice.
**Personal:** JD, Stanford University, Board of Editors, Stanford Law Review; BA (Phi Beta Kappa, Magna Cum Laude), Bucknell University.

**BACHELLER, Chester E**
Holland & Knight LLP, Tampa
813 227 8500
chet.bacheller@hklaw.com
*Featured in Corporate/M&A (Florida)*
**Career:** Mr Bacheller focuses on M&A, securities and international transactions. For over 25 years he has focused on mergers, acquisitions and dis-

positions; public offerings of securities; SEC reporting and compliance matters; and international business transactions. Mr Bacheller's mergers and acquisitions practice focuses on representing significant US and Foreign companies in domestic and cross-border transactions. He has been the lead lawyer on dozens of major multinational M&A transactions and public securities offerings, including IPOs, high yield bonds and investment grade debt, including "Overnight" public offerings.

## BAENA, Scott L
Bilzin Sumberg Baena Price & Axelrod LLP, Miami
305 350 2403
sbaena@bilzin.com
*Featured in Bankruptcy/Restructuring (Florida)*
**Practice Areas:** Chair, Bilzin Sumberg's Restructuring & Bankruptcy Practice.
**Professional Memberships:** Admitted to Florida, US District Court (Southern and Northern Districts of Florida), US Bankruptcy Court (Middle District of Florida), US Court of Appeals (First, Third, Fourth and Eleventh Circuits), US Supreme Court.
**Career:** Served as a Commissioner on Uniform Law Commission. Active in development of Florida's commercial laws for over 30 years, beginning with co-sponsor of the 1980 revisions to Article 9, Uniform Commercial Code (Chapter 679, Florida Statutes). Counsel in major bankruptcy proceedings including Fontainebleau Las Vegas, W. R. Grace, Tousa, US Gypsum, Heilig-Meyers, ContiFinancial, Crown Vantage, NAL Finance Group, Southeast Banking Corp., Cenvill Development, National Merchandise, Empire Toy, Hillsborough Holdings, Atlas Air, TradeWinds Airlines, Eastern Airlines, Pan Am, and Air Florida. Has received Chambers USA's highest ranking in Restructuring & Bankruptcy since the publication's inaugural year in Florida; Recognized by The Best Lawyers in America for over 25 years; Named The Best Lawyers in America's 2012 "Miami Litigation & Bankruptcy Lawyer of the Year." Only Florida lawyer included in K&A Restructuring Register as one of "America's Top 100 Restructuring Professionals" for seven consecutive years.
**Personal:** JD (with honors), George Washington University, 1974; BBA, George Washington University, 1970.

## BARKUS, David A
Greenberg Traurig, LLP, Miami
305 579 0724
BarkusD@gtlaw.com
*Featured in Corporate/M&A (Florida)*
**Practice Areas:** David Barkus concentrates his practice on mergers and acquisitions and private equity. David represents private equity funds and public and private companies in domestic and cross border transactions. His industry experience includes aviation and aerospace, computer software and information technology, construction, consumer products, education, energy, food and beverage, franchising, gaming, health care and restaurants.

**Professional Memberships:** Adjunct Professor, University of Miami School of Law Spring 2012, Fall 2012, Spring 2013 Transactional Externship Program.
**Career:** Best Lawyers in America, 2011-13; Chambers USA, 2009-13.
**Personal:** JD, with High Honors, University of Florida Levin College of Law; BBA, University of Miami.

## BARRETT, James
Baker & McKenzie, Miami
305 789 8957
james.barrett@bakermckenzie.com
*Featured in Tax (Florida)*
**Practice Areas:** US federal income tax planning focusing on inbound and outbound international tax issues with a specific emphasis on IP transfers and international joint ventures.
**Professional Memberships:** American Bar Association (ABA); Florida Bar Tax Section;International Fiscal Association (IFA).
**Career:** Principal, Baker & McKenzie, Miami.
**Publications:** Numerous articles including "The Tax Benefits and Obstacles to US Businesses in Transferring Foreign Intellectual Property to Foreign Affiliates," Florida Bar Journal, May, 2012.
**Personal:** Born December 10, 1959, Brooklyn, NY; LLM, New York University, 1985; JD, University of Chicago, 1984; AB (magna cum laude), Duke University, 1981.

## BARSH, Kerri
Greenberg Traurig, LLP, Miami
305 579 0772
BarshK@gtlaw.com
*Featured in Environment (Florida)*
**Practice Areas:** Co-Chair, National Environmental Practice. Land Development. Global Energy/Infrastructure. Natural Resources.
**Professional Memberships:** NSSGA Council of Counsel; Miami-Dade Limestone Products Association; ABA Environment, Energy & Resources Section; Trustee, FABA; Builders Assoc. of South Florida.
**Career:** Listed: Best Lawyers in America, 2007-13; Super Lawyers magazine, 2007-12; Chambers USA Guide, 2007-13; one of 25 'Influential Business Women of 2011', South Florida Business Journal. Rated, AV® Preeminent™ 5.0 out of 5; Top Impact Law Leaders, Business Leader magazine 2010.
**Personal:** JD, magna cum laude, University of Miami School of Law; BA, magna cum laude, University of Missouri.

## BARTON, Bernard
Holland & Knight LLP, Tampa
813 227 8500
bernie.barton@hklaw.com
*Featured in Tax (Florida)*
**Career:** Bernie Barton represents entrepreneurs, public companies and regulated industries in business transactions focusing on federal, state and local taxation issues from advance planning to tax controversy matters. He negotiates and manages acquisitions and dispositions for numerous clients. He has expertise in the federal and state tax effects of purchasing and owning aircraft,

counseling on tax-efficient structures to reduce the state tax cost of acquisition yet maintaining and maximizing federal income tax benefits all in compliance with Federal Aviation Administration Regulations. He also represents key management executives in employment engagement and severance agreements.

## BASS, Hilarie
Greenberg Traurig, LLP, Miami
305 579 0745
BassH@gtlaw.com
*Featured in Litigation (Florida)*
**Practice Areas:** GT President. Litigation.
**Professional Memberships:** American Bar Association: Chair, Litigation Section (2010-11). Chair, Rules and Calendar, 2012-14; State Delegate for Florida, 2010-; House of Delegates. The Florida Bar Foundation, President.
**Career:** Listed, Best Lawyers in America, Chambers USA Guide; Fellow, American College of Trial Lawyers; recipient, Silver Medallion, Miami Coalition of Christians and Jews, February 2011; recipient, Most Effective Lawyer Award, Appellate category, Daily Business Review, 2010. Lawdragon Leading 500 Lawyers in America. Lawyer of the Year: Bonding and Finance Law - 2013; Mergers and Acquisitions - 2012. Rated, AV® Preeminent™ 5.0 out of 5.
**Personal:** JD, summa cum laude, University of Miami School of Law; BA, magna cum laude, George Washington University.

## BATES, Douglas
Berger Singerman, Miami
305 714 4361
dbates@bergersingerman.com
*Featured in Bankruptcy/Restructuring (Florida)*
**Practice Areas:** Douglas Bates is often involved in complex, multi-faceted business reorganizations throughout Florida. In addition to representing chapter 11 debtors, Doug also represents creditors' committees, trustees, purchasers of assets in § 363 sales, telecommunications companies, and various real estate companies in out-of-court workouts. He has been involved in numerous bankruptcy litigation matters as well, including prosecution and settlement of multiple avoidance actions arising in the TOUSA, Supra Telecommunications and Main Street USA bankruptcy cases.
**Professional Memberships:** Mr Bates is an active member of the Business Law Section of The Florida Bar; Chairman, Business Law Section of The Florida Bar Membership/Law School Relations Committee; Member, Pro-Bono Committee of The Bankruptcy Bar Association Southern District of Florida.

## BECERRA, Jacqueline
Greenberg Traurig, LLP, Miami
305 579 0534
BecerraJ@gtlaw.com
*Featured in Litigation (Florida)*
**Practice Areas:** Litigation.
**Professional Memberships:** Managing Director, American Bar Association Section of Litigation; Member, Miami-Dade County School Board Ethics Advisory Council; Member and

Former President, Federal Bar Association, South Florida Chapter; Cuban American Bar Association.
**Career:** Listed: Chambers USA Guide, 2005-13; Best Lawyers of America, 2010-13; Florida Trend magazine 'Legal Elite', Litigation, 2009-10; Federal Bar Association's Young Federal Lawyers Award, 2000; Director's Award for Superior Performance, Executive Office for the United States Attorneys, 2001; Tim Evans Memorial Award for Outstanding Performance as an Assistant United States Attorney, 2001.
**Personal:** JD, Yale Law School; BA, cum laude, University of Miami.

## BEDKE, Michael
DLA Piper LLP (US), Tampa
813 222 5924
michael.bedke@dlapiper.com
*Featured in Real Estate (Florida)*
**Practice Areas:** Real estate.
**Career:** He heads the Real Estate group in Florida, where he represents clients in all aspects of real estate and commercial financing work. He is also National Co-Chair of the firm's Rail Sector. He has been at the forefront of this area through his advocacy of high-speed rail, light rail, commuter rail, transportation-oriented development, his work on inland port projects, his lecturing on green leases and in his role as president of Connect Us and general counsel to Earth Charter US.
**Personal:** JD, University of Florida, with honors; BA, University of Florida, with high honors.

## BELL, Rodney H
Holland & Knight LLP, Miami
305 374 8500
rodney.bell@hklaw.com
*Featured in Corporate/M&A (Florida)*
**Career:** Rod Bell is a Partner in the Business Law Section, and leads the South Florida Securities Practice. Mr Bell practices in the areas of securities, mergers and acquisitions, venture capital and corporate governance. He regularly represents public and private companies in financing and acquisition transactions. Mr Bell assists pharmaceutical, software and other technology companies with licensing, development, product acquisition and other arrangements. In addition, he advises public companies, boards of directors and their audit committees on disclosure and compliance matters arising out of Securities and Exchange Commission rules.

## BELOFF, Donn A
Greenberg Traurig, LLP, Fort Lauderdale
954 768 8283
BeloffD@gtlaw.com
*Featured in Corporate/M&A (Florida)*
**Practice Areas:** Corporate and securities; mergers and acquisitions; public and private securities offerings (as both issuer's and underwriter's counsel); private equity and venture capital transactions; corporate governance, financial, and transactional matters.
**Professional Memberships:** Member, Florida Bar; Member, District of Columbia Bar Association.

**Career:** Selected: Best Lawyers in America, 2006-12; Chambers USA Guide, 2007-13; Florida Super Lawyers, 2007-13; 'Legal Elite', Florida Trend magazine, 2004, 2009. Rated, AV® Preeminent™ 5.0 out of 5.

**Personal:** JD, Georgetown University Law Center; BS, Rensselaer Polytechnic Institute.

### BENFORD, Norman J
Greenberg Traurig, LLP, Miami
305 579 0660
BenfordN@gtlaw.com
*Featured in Wealth Management (Nationwide), Tax (Florida)*

**Practice Areas:** Chair Emeritus, Trusts & Estates/Wealth Management.

**Professional Memberships:** Adjunct professor, University of Miami School of Law in the Estate Planning LLM and JD programs; Member, Advisory Committee, Philip E. Heckerling Institute on Estate Planning; Fellow, Past Regent (and Executive Committee member), American College of Trust and Estate Counsel; Past President, American College of Trust and Estate Counsel Foundation; Academician, International Academy of Estate and Trust Law.

**Career:** Listed: Chambers USA Guide, 2008-13; Super Lawyers, 2006-12; Best Lawyers in America, every edition. Rated, AV® Preeminent™ 5.0 out of 5.

**Personal:** LLB, Yale Law School; BA, Yale University.

### BERGER, James L
Berger Singerman, Fort Lauderdale
954 712 5141
JBerger@bergersingerman.com
*Featured in Real Estate (Florida)*

**Career:** James L Berger is Managing Partner of Berger Singerman. James represents both lenders and developers in real estate restructuring matters and lenders, buyers and sellers in multimillion-dollar complex loan transactions and refinancing. Mr Berger has represented several developers, investors, buyers and sellers with respect to distressed real estate. Such representations have involved over $1,000,000,000 of troubled real estate assets. Additionally, he has represented significant real estate transactions, including the acquisition and financing of a $72 million high rise office tower and separate parking structure (constructed in part on two separate ground leased parcels) in downtown Miami, the sale of a $130 million office complex in downtown Ft. Lauderdale, the acquisition of an $80 million office park and an adjacent $15 million dollar development tract, the acquisition of air rights above the Florida East Coast Railway, and related construction and maintenance easements, for the development of a high rise condominium project in downtown Miami.

### BERGER, Mitchell W
Berger Singerman, Fort Lauderdale
954 714 5140
mberger@bergersingerman.com
*Featured in Litigation (Florida)*

**Practice Areas:** Mitchell W Berger is Co-Chair of Berger Singerman. He concentrates his practice in business law and business litigation.

**Career:** Entrepreneur Hall of Fame, Nova Southeastern University (2010). Co-Lawyer of the Year, National Law Journal (2000). Excellence Award, South Florida Water Management District (2001). Distinguished Lecturer at Nova Southeastern School of Business and Entrepreneurship (2000). While he served on the Board of the South Florida Water Management District, the Board and the Agency received the Environmental Merit Award 2000 from the US Environmental Protection Agency Region 4, for appreciation and recognition of outstanding environmental stewardship. Best Lawyers of America.He has represented Par Pharmaceuticals, In Re: Microcrystalline Cellulose Antitrust Litigation, and In Re: Buspirone Antitrust Litigation. Valley Drug Company, In Re: Terazosin Hydrochloride Antitrust Litigation. Waste Management, City of Pembroke Pines vs Waste Management, Inc. Rinker Materials, Florida East Coast Railway, LLC vs City of West Palm Beach Mastec in Church & Tower, Inc. vs Broward County. Al Gore and Joseph Lieberman, before the Florida Supreme Court in the matter entitled Bush vs Gore.

### BERLIN, Howard J
Berger Singerman, Miami
305 714 4365
hberlin@bergersingerman.com
*Featured in Bankruptcy/Restructuring (Florida)*

**Practice Areas:** Experience representing corporate debtors, secured lenders, creditors' committees, and individual creditors in federal, bankruptcy and state court insolvency proceedings, out of court workouts, debt restructuring negotiations, and business reorganization proceedings and serves as the trustee for Piper Aircraft Corporation Irrevocable Trust, a large, lengthy and complex trusteeship which has generated payment of 100% of eligible claims. Howard is a former Chairperson of Florida Bar Business Law Section Bankruptcy UCC Committee.

### BERMAN, Bruce J
Carlton Fields, P.A., Miami
305 539 7415
bberman@carltonfields.com
*Featured in Litigation (Florida)*

**Practice Areas:** Commercial disputes in federal and state trial and appellate courts and in domestic and international arbitration tribunals, involving corporate, securities, aviation/product liability, intellectual property, health law, real estate and commercial lending.

**Professional Memberships:** Admitted to practice in Florida. Past Chair, Civil Procedure Rules Committee and Rules of Judicial Administration Committee, The Florida Bar.

**Publications:** "Berman's Florida Civil Procedure," (Florida Practice Series, West Group Publishing 2011-12); Speaker, "Civil Procedure, Civil Trial Certification Review Course," (The Florida Bar, 2011).

**Personal:** JD, Boston University School of Law 1972; MBA, Columbia University, 1972; BA, Williams College, 1968.

### BERNSTEIN, Steve
Fisher & Phillips LLP, Tampa
813 769 7513
sbernstein@laborlawyers.com
*Featured in Labor & Employment (Florida)*

**Career:** Steve Bernstein is a Partner in the Tampa office. He maintains a traditional labor practice in which he represents employers throughout the United States in both state and federal courts, as well as before the National Labor Relations Board, the US Department of Labor, the Equal Employment Opportunity Commission, and other state and federal agencies. Steve has played a primary role in advising clients in response to union organizing campaigns, unfair labor practice charges, corporate campaigns, collective bargaining, and economic work stoppages. He also advises clients on compliance with the WARN Act, USERRA, the FMLA, and the ADA.

### BETENSKY, Gary
Richman Greer, P.A., West Palm Beach
561 803 3517
gbetensky@richmangreer.com
*Featured in Litigation (Florida)*

**Practice Areas:** Gary Betensky is Board Certified by the Florida Bar in Business Litigation Law. He specializes in complex business litigation in state and federal courts with extensive experience in matters relating to non-competition/non-solicitation agreements, misappropriation of trade secrets, business torts, contracts, partnership disputes, employment law, trademark disputes, class actions, and internet/telephone marketing law.

**Professional Memberships:** Mr Betensky is admitted to practice in the United States District Court for the Southern, Middle and Northern Districts of Florida, the United States Court of Appeals for the Eleventh Circuit, as well as the state courts of Florida. He has been admitted pro hac vice in other federal district courts in the United States.

**Career:** Mr Betensky is a former Chair of the Professional Ethics Committee of The Florida Bar and is currently a Circuit Correspondent Supervisor of the Business Torts Litigation Committee of the ABA Section of Litigation.

**Publications:** "Water Transfer: Shall We Sink or Swim Together", 7 Nova Law Journal 523, Nova Law Review, Spring, 1983.

**Personal:** Boston University, BS in Public Communication, 1975; Nova University Law Center, JD, 1984 (Notes/Comments Editor of The Law Review). President, Palm Beach County Regional Office of American Jewish Committee.

### BILZIN, Brian L
Bilzin Sumberg Baena Price & Axelrod LLP, Miami
305 350 2363
bbilzin@bilzin.com
*Featured in Real Estate (Florida)*

**Practice Areas:** Founding Partner of Bilzin Sumberg. At the forefront of Real Estate law in South Florida for more than 30 years, Brian han-

dles all major commercial real estate matters, from sales, purchases and leases to financing, workouts and reorganizations. In the area of general corporate law, his practice also includes mergers and acquisitions, joint ventures and lending matters, including structured financings.

**Professional Memberships:** Greater Miami Jewish Federation, Chair of the Board, 2013, General Campaign Chair, 2012-13, Board Member, 2000-present; Jackson Memorial Foundation, Board and Executive Committee; United Way of Miami-Dade, Trustee; Mt. Sinai Hospital, Founder.

**Career:** Has received Chambers USA's highest ranking in Real Estate since the publication's inaugural year in Florida and has been recognized by The Best Lawyers in America for over a decade. In 2012, Brian was one of seven "Distinguished Attorneys" featured by the South Florida Legal Guide. In 2011, he was named The Best Lawyers in America's "Miami Real Estate Lawyer of the Year."

**Personal:** JD, Boston University, Editor of the Boston University Law Review, 1970; BA, University of Michigan, 1967.

### BLACK, David
Berger Singerman, Fort Lauderdale
954 712 5167
dblack@bergersingerman.com
*Featured in Corporate/M&A (Florida)*

**Career:** David Black assists clients with corporate transactions and commercial real estate. David counsels closely-held companies, including entrepreneurial organizations and individuals. Some of David's significant representations include: representation of Seitlin Insurance (Seitlin & Company and Seitlin Benefits Corporation) in its sale to Marsh & McLennan Agency; representation of the successful plan proponent in a series of reorganization transactions for the largest hotel in Pittsburgh that included the client's acquisition of all the equity in the debtor; representation of a private equity fund in successful acquisition and restructuring of $24 million of senior and subordinated debt obligations of major supplier of car wash systems with international operations; and representation of Gulfstream International Group and its affiliates in connection with its bankruptcy reorganization, including pre-petition negotiations and agreements for aircraft and engine lease arrangements, debtor-in-possession financing, and ultimately, the sale of the going concern pursuant to a contested auction under Section 363.

### BLAIN, Russell
Stichter, Riedel, Blain & Prosser PA, Tampa
813 229 0144
rblain@srbp.com
*Featured in Bankruptcy/Restructuring (Florida)*

**Practice Areas:** Chapter 11 business reorganizations; workouts and out-of-court loan and debt restructurings; asset acquisitions and sales in bankruptcy cases.

**Professional Memberships:** Fellow, American College of Bankruptcy. The Florida Bar, Business Law Section (Chair, 2008-09; Secretary/Treasurer, 2006-07; Legislation Chair, 2005-06;

Bankruptcy/Uniform Commercial Code Chair, 2002-03; Executive Council Member, 1997-present). The Tampa Bay Bankruptcy Bar Association (President, 1999-2000). Hillsborough County Bar Foundation Board of Trustees (President, 2010-12); Ferguson-White American Inn of Court (President, 2011-12; Treasurer, 1995-2009). Member, American Bar Association, Hillsborough County Bar Association, Commercial Law League of America, American Bankruptcy Institute. Listed in The Best Lawyers in America. Listed in Florida Trend's Legal Elite, Hall of Fame. Listed in Law & Politics' Top 100 Florida Super Lawyers.
**Career:** Stichter, Riedel, Blain & Prosser, P.A. (1985-present); Jacobs, Robbins & Gaynor, P.A. (1981-85); Blain & Cone, P.A. (1978-81); Gibbons, Tucker, McEwen, Smith, Cofer & Taub (1977-78).
**Publications:** "Hands Across the Border: Court-to-Court Communications in International Insolvency Cases"(co-authored with Stephen R. Leslie and Amy Denton Harris) and Member of Faculty and Steering Committee; Stetson University College of Law Fifth International Symposium on Bankruptcy," (Freiburg, Germany, 2005). "The Personal Injury Defendant as Debtor in Bankruptcy" Hillsborough County Bar Association Lawyer (co-authored with C. Timothy Corcoran, III, 2000). "When Legal Worlds Collide: The Personal Injury Plaintiff Files Bankruptcy," Hillsborough County Bar Association Lawyer (co-authored with C. Timothy Corcoran, III, 1999). "Lien Rights and Construction Lending Responsibilities and Liabilities in Florida," 29 University of Florida Law Review 411 (1977) (awarded Gertrude Brick Law Apprentice Prize). Guest Lecturer, Advanced Bankruptcy, University of Florida College of Law and Stetson University College of Law.
**Personal:** BA, Vanderbilt University, 1974 (magna cum laude), JD, University of Florida College of Law, 1977. Senior Executive Editor, University of Florida Law Review.

### BLANCO, Leyza
GrayRobinson, PA, Miami
305 416 6880
leyza.blanco@gray-robinson.com
*Featured in Bankruptcy/Restructuring (Florida)*
**Practice Areas:** Director of South Florida Creditors' Rights Group. Insolvency and business litigation matters, including bankruptcy, assignments for the benefit of creditors, workouts, cross-border proceedings, and receiverships. Represents creditors, committees, receivers, assignees, trustees and debtors. Serves as receiver, examiner and special master.
**Professional Memberships:** Florida Bar; US Court of Appeals, Eleventh Circuit; US District Courts of Florida, Northern, Middle, Southern Districts. Business Law Section Bankruptcy/UCC Committee, Chair; Bankruptcy Bar Association, Southern District of Florida, Past President; International Women's Insolvency; Restructuring Confederation, Florida Network Past Co-Chair and Director; Florida International University College of Law Pro Bono Bankruptcy Clinical Program, Adjunct Professor; American Bankruptcy Institute, Caribbean Insolvency

Symposium, Steering Committee; Dade County Bar Association; American Bar Association; Hispanic National Bar Association; Cuban American Bar Association.
**Career:** Notable recent cases include In re: British American Insurance Co. Ltd., 425 B.R. 883 (Bankr. S.D. Fla 2010); In re: British American Isle of Venice (BVI) Ltd., 2010 WL 5209232 (Bankr. S.D. Fla 2010), where she set precedent in cross-border insolvency proceedings. She speaks on insolvency and diversity issues at the international and national level.
**Personal:** University of Miami, JD (magna cum laude, 1996); University of Miami, BA (1992); Fluent in Spanish; Presents financial literacy program at high schools and universities.

### BLOCK, David
Jackson Lewis LLP, Miami
305 577 7600
BlockD@jacksonlewis.com
*Featured in Labor & Employment (Florida)*
**Practice Areas:** Specializes in the practice of labor and employment law, including expertise in the areas of multi-plaintiff and class action employment litigation, FLSA, and alternative dispute resolution programs.
**Professional Memberships:** Executive Council of Labor & Employment Section of The Florida Bar, Member of the New York Bar, and Member of the Academy of Florida Management Attorneys.
**Career:** Attorney at Jackson Lewis for the past 25 years.
**Publications:** Former Editor of FMLA-Business and Legal Reports.
**Personal:** University of Pennsylvania, JD; Cornell University School of Industrial and Labor Relations, BS. DOB 8 January 1960. Married with two children.

### BLOOM, Mark D
Greenberg Traurig, LLP, Miami
305 579 0537
BloomM@gtlaw.com
*Featured in Bankruptcy/Restructuring (Nationwide),*
*Bankruptcy/Restructuring (Florida)*
**Practice Areas:** Co-Chair, National Business Reorganisation, Financial Restructuring Practice.
**Professional Memberships:** Co-Chair, INSOL International Annual Regional Conference on International Insolvency, May 2012. American College of Bankruptcy: Vice President, 2010-present, Fellow, 1998-present, Board of Regents, 2003-07, Board of Directors, 2007-09.
**Career:** Listed: Chambers USA Guide, 2003-13; Best Lawyers in America, 1993-2013; The K&A Restructuring Register, America's Top 100; 'Hall of Fame Legal Elite', Florida Trend, 2009-12; 'Legal Elite', Florida Trend, 2004-08, 2011; 'South Florida's Top Lawyers', South Florida Legal Guide. Rated, AV® Preeminent™ 5.0 out of 5.
**Personal:** JD, with honors, University of Maryland School of Law; BA, Yale University.

### BLOOM, Warren S
Greenberg Traurig, LLP, Orlando
407 999 2520
BloomW@gtlaw.com
*Featured in Banking & Finance (Florida)*

**Practice Areas:** Co-Chair, National Public Finance Practice. Municipal securities and finance; leveraged lending transactions; workout transactions.
**Professional Memberships:** Member, National Association of Bond Lawyers; Florida Bar Association; New York State Bar Association.
**Career:** Selected: Orlando Public Finance Lawyer of the Year, Best Lawyers, 2011; Best Lawyers in Orlando, Orlando magazine, 2010; Best Lawyers in America, 2007-13; 'Legal Elite', Florida Trend magazine, 2007, 2009, 2011-12; Super Lawyers magazine, 2006-12; Chambers USA Guide, 2006-13. Rated, AV® Preeminent™ 5.0 out of 5.
**Personal:** JD, with honors, University of Miami School of Law; BA, with honors, Duke University.

### BOEKE, Noel
Holland & Knight LLP, Tampa
813 227 6525
noel.boeke@hklaw.com
*Featured in Bankruptcy/Restructuring (Florida)*
**Practice Areas:** Partner in the firm's Bankruptcy Group, Noel Boeke's practice specializes in bankruptcy, creditors' rights litigation, commercial litigation, asset sales and acquisitions, business contract negotiations, consumer finance defense litigation and Uniform Commercial Code issues. He has represented various types of business clients, financial institutions and other creditors, including commercial banks, finance subsidiaries of manufacturers, corporations, receivers, bankruptcy trustees, and individuals, as well as chapter 11 debtors, and creditor committees. Mr Boeke is on the Board of Trustees for the Turnaround Management Association and past president of the Florida Chapter. Mr Boeke served over seven years in the US Navy.

### BOHRER, Sanford
Holland & Knight LLP, Miami
305 789 7678
sandy.bohrer@hklaw.com
*Featured in Litigation (Florida)*
**Practice Areas:** Partner in the firm's Litigation Section and head of the firm's class action team, Sandy Bohrer focuses his practice on civil litigation, emphasizing business litigation, class actions, media and communication law, appeals, business torts, and intellectual property disputes. His class action defense practice includes litigation all over the country. He has participated in many major media cases arising in South Florida or reaching the Florida Supreme Court, representing the press in oral arguments before the Court. He has represented publishers and broadcasters in approximately 100 defamation, privacy and intellectual property cases. Additionally, he founded Florida's First Amendment Hotline.

### BOUTHILLIER, Reggie L
Greenberg Traurig, LLP, Tallahassee
850 425 8517
BouthillierR@gtlaw.com
*Featured in Real Estate (Florida)*
**Practice Areas:** Governmental affairs; land use; growth management; environmental; land development; real estate; administrative law.

**Professional Memberships:** Board Member, Tallahassee Area Chamber of Commerce Board of Directors, 2012-Present; Associate Sustaining Member, North Florida Urban Land Institute (ULI), 2012-Present.
**Career:** Listed: The Best Lawyers in America, Environmental Law and Environmental Litigation, 2006-13; Legal 500 US, 2008-09, 2012; Florida Super Lawyers, 2006-09. Team Member, a Law360 'Real Estate Practice Group of the Year', 2011-12. Rated, AV® Preeminent™ 5.0 out of 5.
**Personal:** JD, cum laude, University of Miami School of Law, 1992; BA, Political Science, Florida International University, 1989.

### BOYETT, Christopher W
Holland & Knight LLP, Miami
305 789 7790
christopher.boyett@hklaw.com
*Featured in Tax (Florida)*
**Professional Memberships:** Fellow, American College of Trust and Estate Counsel; Florida Bar Real Property, Probate and Trust Law Section.
**Career:** Mr Boyett chairs the Private Wealth practice in South Florida. He advises wealthy families on sophisticated estate planning strategies and counsels family businesses on tax and succession planning. He advises both institutional and individual clients on estate and trust administration and litigation issues. He is an Adjunct Professor at the University of Miami School of Law, Graduate Program in Taxation.
**Publications:** "Portability," Dade County Bar Association, February 2013; "2010 and Beyond - The Transfer Tax Odyssey," Practical Tax Strategies, April 2010.

### BOYLES, William
GrayRobinson, PA, Orlando
407 843 8880
william.boyles@gray-robinson.com
*Featured in Healthcare (Florida)*
**Practice Areas:** Shareholder specializing in health and corporate law with emphasis on transactions including mergers and acquisitions, federal and state taxation; formation of for profit and not for profit corporations, joint ventures and other business entities, and tax exempt entities.
**Professional Memberships:** The Florida Bar, Board Certified in Tax Law; American Bar Association; American Association of Certified Public Accountants; Orange County Bar Association; American Association of Attorney/CPA's; Florida Institute of Certified Public Accountants; "AV" Rated by Martindale-Hubbell; Florida's Leading Attorneys; Florida Trend "Legal Elite," 2007-09, 2012 (listing of Florida's top attorneys as determined by a vote of Florida lawyers); Florida Super Lawyers, 2006-12.
**Career:** Represented a number of hospitals, physician groups and other organizations in all aspects of health law related issues, including tax and business issues. Has assisted in the formation of physician hospital joint ventures in Florida, and in the structuring and formation of health care networks, and the purchase and sale of physician practices. Extensive experience in working with tax exempt organizations including governmental

and community hospital systems. Has served as lead counsel in the sale of a hospital and its ancillary providers. Was instrumental in the formation and development of, and obtaining the tax exempt status of numerous tax exempt organizations (including healthcare organizations and private foundations).

**Personal:** University Of Florida, BSBA (1973); University of Florida, JD (1977); University of Florida, LLM (Taxation, 1978).

### BROCKMAN, Christopher C
Holland & Knight LLP, Orlando
407 244 1123
chris.brockman@hklaw.com
*Featured in Real Estate (Florida)*

**Practice Areas:** Christopher C Brockman is the practice group leader for Holland & Knight's Central Florida Real Estate Practice and the former head of Holland & Knight's National Retail Team. He focuses his practice in the area of real estate law, with special emphasis on commercial real estate transactions, including commercial leasing matters. Mr Brockman frequently speaks and writes on issues affecting the retail industry and is recognized as a top real estate attorney in Florida.

### BRONIS, Stephen J
Carlton Fields, P.A., Miami
305 530 4066
sbronis@carltonfields.com
*Featured in Litigation (Florida)*

**Practice Areas:** Complex litigation, including financial fraud, business fraud, federal program fraud, health care fraud, securities fraud and regulatory fraud, FCPA, and abuse cases.
**Professional Memberships:** Admitted to practice in Florida, Colorado, District of Columbia, US Supreme Court, and US Tax Court. Former Executive Director, White-Collar Division and Former Chair, White Collar Crime Committee, American Bar Association; Past President, Florida Association of Criminal Defense Lawyers.
**Career:** Martindale-Hubbell AV Rating.
**Publications:** Featured in "Fed's Tough Stance on Bribes Suffers Setback," Daily Business Journal Justice Watch (January 9, 2012).
**Personal:** JD, Duke University Law School, 1972; BA, University of Florida, 1969.

### BROWN, Daniel C
Carlton Fields, P.A., Tallahassee
850 513 3617
dbrown@carltonfields.com
*Featured in Insurance (Florida)*

**Practice Areas:** Insurance litigation, insurance regulation, class action defense, regulatory and administrative law, commercial litigation, state and local tax, and constitutional litigation.
**Professional Memberships:** Admitted in Florida and the US Supreme Court. Litigation Section and Tort and Insurance Section, American Bar Association.
**Career:** Martindale-Hubbell AV Rating. Assistant Attorney General, Florida (1977-78) (1986-88).
**Publications:** "Protecting Trade Secrets: Problems at the Intersection of Florida's Public Records Laws and Regulatory Demands Under the

Florida Insurance Code," Federation of Regulatory Counsel Journal (Fall 2010).
**Personal:** JD (with high honors), Florida State University College of Law, 1974; BA (with honors), University of South Florida, 1971.

### BROWN, James
FordHarrison LLP, Orlando
407 418 4342
jbrown@fordharrison.com
*Featured in Labor & Employment (Florida)*

**Practice Areas:** Labor and employment.
**Career:** Jim Brown concentrates his practice on labor relations law, employment discrimination law, defense of wage and hour matters and mediation. He regularly represents employers before the NLRB, the State of Florida Public Employees Relations Commission and the US DOL. Jim is a certified mediator who has mediated over 800 labor and employment cases. He represents companies and employers in a variety of industries including healthcare, transportation, government contracting, and the public sector such as cities, towns and school boards. He earned his JD from the University of North Carolina at Chapel Hill in 1970.

### BROWN, Ted R
Baker & Hostetler LLP, Orlando
407 540 7915
trbrown@bakerlaw.com
*Featured in Real Estate (Florida)*

**Career:** Ted Brown represents owners and developers in land acquisition and development. He designs and implements the strategic plans to obtain land use entitlements, including environmental permits. He previously worked for Arvida Company, which developed master-planned communities around the US. Ted is a full member of the Urban Land Institute, where he has served on the National Policy Council, the Environmental Council, Community Development Council and Senior Housing Council. He is also a member of the Environmental Law Institute and the Congress of New Urbanism. He is frequently sought out to speak on issues of land use, development and the environment.

### BRUTON, Burt
Greenberg Traurig, LLP, Miami
305 579 0593
BrutonB@gtlaw.com
*Featured in Real Estate (Florida)*

**Practice Areas:** Real estate; American Indian law; commercial real estate; financing; secured transactions; Florida mortgage and transfer taxes.
**Professional Memberships:** Fellow, American College of Real Estate Lawyers; Member, Real Property, Probate and Trust Law Section of The Florida Bar, Committees on Legislative Review, Mortgage Law, Title Insurance, Legal Opinions, Land Trusts and Other Business Entities.
**Career:** Selected: Best Lawyers in America, 2005-13; Best Lawyers 'Lawyer of the Year', Litigation-Real Estate-Miami, 2013; Super Lawyers magazine, 2006-12; Chambers USA Guide, 2006-13; Florida Trend magazine, 2004-12.

**Personal:** JD, University of Miami School of Law; BA, University of North Carolina at Chapel Hill.

### BULLARD, Randy A
Greenberg Traurig, LLP, Miami
305 579 0532
BullardR@gtlaw.com
*Featured in Latin American Investment (Florida)*

**Practice Areas:** Corporate and securities; financial institutions; cross-border financing transactions; international banking and finance; mergers and acquisitions; joint ventures and strategic alliances; domestic company and foreign private issuers securities offerings.
**Professional Memberships:** Member: Council of the Americas, International Bar Association, American Bar Association.
**Career:** Listed, Chambers Global, Banking & Finance and Corporate/M&A, 2008-12; Chambers Latin America, Banking & Finance, 2009-13; Chambers USA, Latin American Investment, 2008-13; Latin Business Chronicle, Latin America's Top 50 Legal Stars, 2012.
**Personal:** JD, cum laude, Harvard Law School, 1992; AB, Politics and American Studies, Princeton University, 1989.

### BURKE, David P
Carlton Fields, P.A., Tampa
813 229 4207
dburke@carltonfields.com
*Featured in Tax (Florida)*

**Practice Areas:** Federal, state and international taxation planning, and business planning, state and federal tax controversies, including tax audits and appeals before the IRS.
**Professional Memberships:** Admitted in Florida, Ohio, US Tax Court, US Court of Federal Claims. Section of Taxation and Committee on State and Local Taxes, American Bar Association; Chair, Florida Bar Tax Certification Committee, The Florida Bar.
**Career:** Board Certified in Taxation by The Florida Bar. Martindale-Hubbell AV Rating.
**Personal:** LLM, New York University School of Law, 1982; JD (with honors), Cleveland-Marshall College of Law, 1980; BA (with honors), Cleveland State University, 1977.

### BUSTAMANTE III, Alberto S
Baker & Hostetler LLP, Orlando
407 540 7900
abustamante@bakerlaw.com
*Featured in Real Estate (Florida)*

**Career:** Alberto Bustamante's practice encompasses a range of real estate transactions, including commercial, industrial, office and retail development, leasing and sales. Alberto offers counsel with entity structuring, environmental law, land use and zoning. His experience in government affairs, corporate law, mergers and acquisitions, and not-for-profit corporations provides a balanced understanding of clients' business needs and a practical application to facilitate success in achieving their goals. Alberto counsels companies, developers, property managers, landlords and tenants on sophisticated transactions throughout the US and abroad. A significant portion of his expe-

rience has been focused on the restaurant and services industry, sales, leasing and franchising.

### CACCIABEVE, Charles J
Carlton Fields, P.A., Orlando
407 244 8224
ccacciabeve@carltonfields.com
*Featured in Construction (Florida)*

**Practice Areas:** Construction litigation, intellectual property litigation, and general commercial litigation. Represents owners, general contractors, subcontractors, suppliers, architects, and engineers. Extensive experience in drafting and negotiating construction contract documents.
**Professional Memberships:** Admitted to practice in Florida. Forum on the Construction Industry, American Bar Association; former Chair, Construction Law Committee, Orange County Bar Association; instrumental in setting up Orange County Bar Arbitration Services; AAA Panel Arbitrator.
**Career:** Martindale-Hubbell AV Rating.
**Publications:** Co-Author, "Florida Construction Law: What Do You Do When...?" (National Business Institute 1996).
**Personal:** JD (with honors); University of Florida College of Law, 1981; BA, Rollins College, 1978.

### CALLI, Paul
Carlton Fields, P.A., Miami
305 530 4065
pcalli@carltonfields.com
*Featured in Litigation (Florida)*

**Practice Areas:** Complex commercial litigation and white collar matters, sensitive civil and regulatory matters.
**Professional Memberships:** Admitted to practice in Florida, The Florida Bar's Grievance Committee 11-I (2012-15); Criminal Justice Section, American Bar Association, National Association of Criminal Defense Lawyers.
**Career:** Martindale-Hubbell AV Rating.
**Publications:** Co-Author, "Corporate Internal Investigations: A Modern Cost of Doing Buisness (2012); "White Collar Criminal Practice in Florida - Perspectives from the Prosecution and Defense: Foreign Corrupt Practices Act Developments and Trends," American Bar Association White Collar Crime Section (September 2011).
**Personal:** JD, University of Miami School of Law, 1993; BA, University of Connecticut, 1989.

### CANTERO, Raoul
White & Case LLP, Miami
305 371 2700
rcantero@whitecase.com
*Featured in Litigation (Florida), Appellate Law (Nationwide)*

**Career:** Raoul Cantero, Partner and Former Justice, leads White & Case's Miami Appellate Practice and handles cross-border disputes involving Latin America. Appointed to the Florida Supreme Court in 2002, Mr Cantero was the first justice of Latino descent to sit on the Court. Throughout the course of his career, he has handled more than 300 appeals, including several multimillion dollar appeals for various high-profile organizations. In 2007, he was honored by the

Cuban American Bar Association with the creation of the Justice Raoul G Cantero, III Diversity Enhancement Scholarship at Florida State University. To view a comprehensive biography, please visit www.whitecase.com/rcantero.

## CAPPELLO, Juan Pablo
Greenberg Traurig, LLP, Miami
305 579 0655
JPC@gtlaw.com
*Featured in Latin American Investment (Florida)*
**Practice Areas:** Cross-border corporate finance, mergers and acquisitions, private equity, venture capital, and joint ventures.
**Professional Memberships:** Global Advisory Board Member, Knight Foundation, Endeavor Global; Legal Advisory Board Latin American. Venture Capital Association; Advisory Board of the Institute of Global International Effectiveness at the Kelly School of Management, Indiana University.
**Career:** Recipient, 'Top 50 Entrepreneur Award', Business Leader Magazine, 2012; Listed: Chambers Latin America, Corporate M&A, 2009-13; Chambers Global, Corporate/M&A, 2005-09 and 2011-13; Chambers USA Guide, 2007-13.
**Personal:** JD, New York University School of Law, 1992; BA, with honors, Duke University, 1989.

## CAULKINS, Charles
Fisher & Phillips LLP, Fort Lauderdale
954 847 4700
ccaulkins@laborlawyers.com
*Featured in Labor & Employment (Florida)*
**Career:** Charles Caulkins is the Managing Partner of the Fort Lauderdale office and a member of the firm's Management Committee. He advises employers on the development and implementation of preventive labor relations programs, including management education and training, to avoid charges and lawsuits, protect trade secrets, and resolve disputes. He regularly counsels employers on union related matters. He also handles employment related litigation and arbitrations before state and federal courts and administrative agencies involving claims of discrimination, wrongful discharge, breach of contract, OSHA and other statutory claims.

## CHERNIGA, Michael J
Greenberg Traurig, LLP, Tallahassee
850 425 8505
ChernigaM@gtlaw.com
*Featured in Healthcare (Florida)*
**Practice Areas:** Co-Chair, National Health & FDA Business Group.
**Professional Memberships:** Member: Florida Bar (Administrative and Health Law Sections); American Bar Association; American Health Lawyers Association. Formerly Member: Special Florida Bar and Florida legislative task forces.
**Career:** Selected: Super Lawyers magazine, 2008-09, 2011-12; Chambers USA Guide, 2009-13; Best Lawyers in America, 2006-13; 'Legal Elite', Florida Trend Magazine, 2004. Rated, AV® Preeminent™ 5.0 out of 5.
**Personal:** JD, Florida State University College of Law, 1981; BS, Florida State University, 1978.

## CLOYD, Leslie
Berger Singerman, Fort Lauderdale
954 712 5125
lcloyd@bergersingerman.com
*Featured in Bankruptcy/Restructuring (Florida)*
**Practice Areas:** Leslie Cloyd is a long time practitioner in the bankruptcy courts of South Florida, and is proficient in handling all aspects of complex Chapter 11 cases. Although she is best known for her representation of debtors in complex restructuring cases, she also has experience representing creditors committees, lenders, unsecured creditors, taxing authorities, asset purchasers in Section 363 sales, litigants and trustees. Ms Cloyd is also known for representing distressed businesses and individuals with significant debt in out of court workouts or assignments for benefit of creditors.
**Professional Memberships:** Vice Chair for International Women's Insolvency Confederation, Florida Network.

## COLEMAN, Ira
McDermott Will & Emery LLP, Miami
305 347 6556
icoleman@mwe.com
*Featured in Healthcare (Florida), Healthcare (Nationwide)*
See under Nationwide for profile.

## COLEMAN, Patrick D
GrayRobinson, PA, Jacksonville
904 632 8484
Patrick.Coleman@gray-robinson.com
*Featured in Labor & Employment (Florida)*
**Practice Areas:** Board Certified labor and employment law attorney. Practices in the areas of labor and employment law, litigation, and mediation. Significant experience in handling appeals to both state and federal courts. Certified by the United States District Court for the Middle District of Florida to serve as a mediator in civil cases. Mediates cases in a variety of areas, primarily in the area of labor and employment law. Experienced in wage-hour litigation, noncompete and trade secret litigation, union avoidance and collective bargaining.
**Professional Memberships:** The Florida Bar, Labor and Employment Law Section (1973-present), Past Member of Executive Committee, Past Editor of Labor Section of the Florida Bar Journal; Jacksonville Bar Association, Professional Ethics Committee, Chairman (1987-88 and 1992-93); Christian Legal Society.
**Personal:** Vanderbilt University, JD (1971); Duke University, BA (1968).

## COLODNY, Mike
Colodny, Fass, Talenfeld, Karlinsky, Abate & Webb PA, Fort Lauderdale
954 492 4010
mcolodny@cftlaw.com
*Featured in Insurance (Florida)*
**Practice Areas:** Mr Colodny focuses on insurance regulatory law, governmental consulting and the representation of insurance companies, national corporations and banking institutions before government regulatory agencies and in business transactional matters.

**Career:** As former General Counsel for the Florida Residential Property and Casualty Joint Underwriting Association and its successor, Citizens Property Insurance Corporation, Mr Colodny was instrumental in negotiating several billion dollars in related catastrophe claims funding. He also represented the State of Louisiana in drafting its residual market legislation and obtaining its windstorm association's tax-exempt status. He served as a member of Florida Underwriter Magazine's Editorial Advisory Board.

## CONIGLIARO, Matthew J
Carlton Fields, P.A., Tampa
813 229 4254
mconigliaro@carltonfields.com
*Featured in Litigation (Florida)*
**Practice Areas:** Appellate and complex commercial litigation involving tort litigation, health care, products liability, coverage, intellectual property, constitutional issues, dissolution matters, and pro bono criminal defense representation.
**Professional Memberships:** Admitted to practice in Florida and US Supreme Court. Former Chair, Appellate Practice Section, The Florida Bar; Defense Research Institute.
**Career:** Board Certified in Appellate Practice by The Florida Bar. Martindale-Hubbell AV Rating. Deputy Solicitor General of Florida (2001-02), Law Clerk, Fifth DCA (1995-97).
**Publications:** "Highlights From Appellate Practice Decisions, 2009-10," (18 The Record 12 Fall 2010).
**Personal:** JD (cum laude), Tulane Law School, 1995; BA, University of North Carolina, 1992.

## CONLEY KEANE, Cristin A
Carlton Fields, P.A., Tampa
813 229 4211
ckeane@carltonfields.com
*Featured in Tax (Florida)*
**Practice Areas:** Federal and state tax matters with respect to individual, corporate, and tax exempt organizations, and pass-through entity tax matters, includability of income items, characterization of gain or loss, tax-advantaged transaction planning, closely-held businesses and not-for-profit organizations.
**Professional Memberships:** Admitted in Florida and US Tax Court. Co-Chair, LLCs, Partnerships, and Unincorporated Entities and Membership Committees, Business Law Section of the American Bar Association.
**Career:** Board Certified in Tax Law by The Florida Bar. Martindale-Hubbell AV Rating.
**Personal:** LLM, University of Florida College of Law, 1998; JD, University of Florida College of Law, 1997; BA, Duke University, 1994.

## CONNOR, Terence G
Hunton & Williams LLP, Miami
305 810 2517
tconnor@hunton.com
*Featured in Labor & Employment (Florida)*
**Practice Areas:** Senior Counsel practicing employment litigation, including complex cases; handles cases in employment litigation, arbitration, and matters under the Railway Labor Act.

Tries cases to bench, jury and arbitration panels. Certified civil mediator.
**Professional Memberships:** American, Florida and Dade County Bar Associations; Fellow of the College of Labor & Employment Lawyers; member of the Academy of Florida Management Attorneys.
**Career:** Air Force Judge Advocate 1968-73; Department of Justice, Civil Rights Division 1973-76; Labor Counsel, National Airlines 1976-79.
**Publications:** Chapter editor on Employment: The Privacy and Data Security Law Desk Book, 2010; Author, Anomalous Decisions On Private Arbitration, Law360, February 5, 2009. The Consideration Of Arrest And Conviction Records In Employment Decisions: A Critique Of The EEOC Guidance co-author with Kevin J. White, to be published Seton Hall University Law Rev. June 2013.

## COOPER, Glenn M.
GrayRobinson, PA, Miami
305 913 0529
glenn.cooper@gray-robinson.com
*Featured in Immigration (Florida)*
**Practice Areas:** Shareholder in Employment and Labor, Immigration and International practice groups. Focuses on assisting US companies, foreign companies, investors and professionals regarding US immigration laws. Assists clients regarding US nonimmigrant visa, immigrant visa permanent residence and naturalization applications. Advises US employers regarding immigration compliance and advises clients on corporate, business and contract law matters.
**Professional Memberships:** The Florida Bar; US District Court, Southern District of Florida; Greater Miami Chamber of Commerce; Florida Chamber of Commerce; Beacon Council Miami-Dade Economic Development Agency; Greater Fort Lauderdale Alliance Economic Development Agency; French-American Chamber of Commerce of Florida; Quebec Florida Chamber of Commerce; American Immigration Lawyers Association.
**Personal:** University of Florida, BS (International Business, 1995); Nova Southeastern University, JD (1998); Fluent in French and Spanish.

## CORBIN, Peter
FordHarrison LLP, Jacksonville
904 357 2002
pcorbin@fordharrison.com
*Featured in Labor & Employment (Florida)*
**Practice Areas:** Labor and employment.
**Career:** Peter Corbin focuses his practice on defending employers in discrimination, harassment and wrongful termination litigation in many industries, including trucking, construction, and retail. He has been in private practice in the labor and employment area for more than 35 years. He has handled numerous trials in state and federal courts throughout the US, and before various administrative agencies. He has also handled numerous traditional labor matters, including administrative proceedings before the NLRB, union elections, collective bargaining, arbitration

proceedings, injunctions, and wage-hour matters. He earned his JD, cum laude, from Mercer University School of Law.

### COULSON, David A
Greenberg Traurig, LLP, Miami
305 579 0754
CoulsonD@gtlaw.com
*Featured in Litigation (Florida)*

**Practice Areas:** Chair, Miami Litigation Department. Jury trials and arbitrations; class action defense; product liability; shareholder securities fraud defense; breach of contract and business torts.
**Professional Memberships:** Board of Directors: GableStage Theater; Jackson Memorial Hospital Foundation; Spellman-Hoeveler American Inns of Court. Member, American Bar Association.
**Career:** Selected: The Best Lawyers of America, 2010-13; one of 'South Florida's Top Lawyers', South Florida Legal Guide, 2011-13; Super Lawyers magazine, 2006-12; 'Florida Legal Elite', Florida Trend magazine, 2007. Rated, AV® Preeminent™ 5.0 out of 5.
**Personal:** JD, cum laude, Harvard Law School, 1988; BA, magna cum laude, University of Miami, 1985.

### COUTROULIS, Chris S
Carlton Fields, P.A., Tampa
813 229 4301
ccoutroulis@carltonfields.com
*Featured in Antitrust (Florida), Litigation (Florida)*

**Practice Areas:** Business litigation including antitrust, class actions, mass torts, environmental litigation, professional and accounting malpractice, securities fraud.
**Professional Memberships:** Admitted to practice in Florida and the US Supreme Court. Past Chair, Vertical Restraints Antitrust Section, American Bar Association; Antitrust and Trade Regulation Certification Committee, The Florida Bar.
**Career:** Board Certified in Antitrust and Trade Regulation Law by The Florida Bar. Martindale-Hubbell AV Rating.
**Publications:** Co-Author, "Carlton Fields Class Action Survey: Best Practices in Reducing Cost and Managing Risk in Class Action Litigation" (April 2012).
**Personal:** JD, Columbia University School of Law, 1979; BA (magna cum laude), Wesleyan University, 1975.

### CRUZ-BROWN, Kelly A
Carlton Fields, P.A., Tallahassee
850 513 3610
kcruz-brown@carltonfields.com
*Featured in Insurance (Florida)*

**Practice Areas:** Insurance regulation and administrative law, representing individuals, insurers, and other entities regulated by the Florida Department of Financial Services and Office of Insurance Regulation, Department of Health, and other state agencies.
**Professional Memberships:** Admitted to practice in Florida. Chair, Tort Trial and Insurance

Practice Section, Insurance Regulation Committee, American Bar Association.
**Career:** Martindale-Hubbell AV Rating.
**Publications:** Co-Author, "Protecting Trade Secrets: Problems at the Intersection of Florida's Public Records Laws and Regulatory Document Demands Under the Florida Insurance Code," (FORC Journal Fall 2010).
**Personal:** JD, Florida State University College of Law, 1992; BS (with honors), Florida State University, 1989.

### CURRIER, Maria
Holland & Knight LLP, Miami
305 374 8500
maria.currier@hklaw.com
*Featured in Healthcare (Florida), Healthcare (Nationwide)*

**Career:** Maria Currier chairs the firm's national Healthcare & Life Sciences Team. With over 25 years of experience serving the healthcare industry, her practice focuses on healthcare reform, accountable care organizations, mergers and acquisitions, joint ventures, healthcare regulatory matters, Stark, fraud and abuse, managed care and international business ventures for healthcare clients. She is Board Certified in Health Law as recognized by The Florida Bar Board. She has served as counsel to hospitals, large physician groups, nursing homes, home health companies, complex integrated health systems, physician-hospital organizations, physician management companies, provider networks, prepaid health plans and Medicare Advantage Plans.

### CURTIN, Lawrence
Holland & Knight LLP, Tallahassee
850 224 7000
larry.curtin@hklaw.com
*Featured in Environment (Florida)*

**Practice Areas:** Partner in the Public Policy and Regulation Practice Group in the Government Law Section, practicing administrative and governmental law, focusing on environmental matters. Curtin regularly provides advice on permitting and enforcement matters involving federal, state, and local administrative agencies. He has substantial experience in administrative law, including adjudicatory hearings and rulemaking activities. Curtin has extensive experience in permitting major industrial facilities in Florida, including siting of electrical power plants, transmission lines, and natural gas pipelines. He has represented clients before the Florida Legislature for more than 25 years, primarily involving environmental, land use, and administrative law matters.

### DANZI, Mark A
Hill Ward Henderson, Tampa
813 227 8484
mdanzi@hwhlaw.com
*Featured in Corporate/M&A (Florida)*

**Practice Areas:** Securities and corporate law, public and private securities offerings, mergers, acquisitions, securities compliance, corporate governance, general corporate matters.
**Professional Memberships:** AV rated by Martindale-Hubbell, Best Lawyers in America,

Florida Trend's Legal Elite, Florida Super Lawyers. National Chair of American Bar Association's Private Equity and Venture Capital Committee.
**Career:** Previously with the US Securities & Exchange Commission. Corporate transactions and securities matters including multi-million to multi-billion dollar acquisitions of public and private companies, IPOs, traditional preferred stock financings and other securities matters.
**Personal:** JD, American University, Washington College of Law, summa cum laude, 1996; BA, Bucknell University, 1994.

### DAVIDSON, Barry
Hunton & Williams LLP, Miami
305 810 2539
bdavidson@hunton.com
*Featured in Litigation (Florida)*

**Practice Areas:** Barry Davidson's practice focuses in the area of civil litigation throughout the State of Florida, with an emphasis on complex and class action business litigation, intellectual property, antitrust and products litigation. He also represents airlines and hotel companies and does eminent domain work. Mr Davidson has represented every major US air carrier and several foreign carriers, either separately or in industry litigation, and his firm represents the International Air Transport Association.
**Professional Memberships:** Member, Florida Bar; ABA, Antitrust Section; American Bar Foundation (Life Fellow).
**Personal:** University of Florida Levin College of Law (JD, 1967); Vanderbilt University (BA, 1964).

### DAVIS, Alvin B
Squire Sanders (US) LLP, Miami
305 577 2835
alvin.davis@squiresanders.com
*Featured in Litigation (Florida)*

**Practice Areas:** Partner whose practice focuses on litigation and arbitration in products liability, securities class actions, environmental claims, regulatory proceedings, contractual issues and a host of utilities-related disputes. Litigates at trial and appellate levels for major national and international companies including utilities, manufacturers, insurers, law firms and airlines. Listed in The Best Lawyers in America for more than fifteen years. Recognized among South Florida's Legal Elite by Florida Trend magazine since 2004; top lawyer by South Florida Legal Guide 2003-10 and designated as one of Florida's top 100 Super Lawyers since 2006. Lectures regularly to The Florida Bar.

### DAVIS, Gary Scott
McDermott Will & Emery LLP, Miami
305 347 6520
gsdavis@mwe.com
*Featured in Healthcare (Florida), Healthcare (Nationwide)*

See under Nationwide for profile.

### DECKER, Jeffrey E
Baker & Hostetler LLP, Orlando
407 649 4017
jdecker@bakerlaw.com
*Featured in Corporate/M&A (Florida)*

**Career:** Jeff Decker focuses on domestic and international M&A, joint venture, strategic alliance, securities and finance transactions for public and private companies across a broad range of sectors, including technology, energy, manufacturing, financial and business services and hospitality. Mr Decker represents issuers in public and private debt and equity securities offerings, including private equity and venture capital transactions and other financing transactions. He represents public companies in reporting and compliance matters, proxy solicitations, corporate governance and other matters, and advises Boards of Directors and committees with respect to corporate transactions and fiduciary matters.

### DEL CASTILLO, Albert A
Greenberg Traurig, LLP, Miami
305 579 0545
delCastilloA@gtlaw.com
*Featured in Banking & Finance (Florida)*

**Practice Areas:** Public finance; global energy and infrastructure.
**Professional Memberships:** Fellow, American College of Bond Counsel. Member: National Association of Bond Lawyers; Georgetown University Board of Regents. Emeritus Member, Georgetown University Law Center Law Alumni Board.
**Career:** Listed: The Best Lawyers In America, 2006-13; Chambers USA Guide, 2006–13; Super Lawyers magazine, Florida Super Lawyers, 2007-12; Florida Trend magazine, 'Legal Elite', Public Finance and Bonds, 2006, 2007, 2011. Rated, AV® Preeminent™ 5.0 out of 5.
**Personal:** JD, cum laude, Georgetown University Law Center, 1982 (Editor, Law and Policy in International Business); BA, magna cum laude, Georgetown University, 1979.

### DEMEZA JR, William B
Holland & Knight LLP, Tampa
813 227 8500
bill.demeza@hklaw.com
*Featured in Labor & Employment (Florida)*

**Practice Areas:** Partner in the Litigation Section, Bill deMeza's practice consists of counseling employers about employment issues and defending them in charges and lawsuits brought by employees or governments. A significant segment of his practice focuses on overtime litigation and employee safety and health issues. Clients include media networks, restaurants, manufacturers, financial institutions, pharmaceutical companies, government contractors, and mining companies. He has served as employers' counsel in race, sex, sexual harassment, age, religion, national origin, handicap (disability) employment discrimination and retaliation charges and litigation, minimum wage/overtime lawsuits, union avoidance and disputes, whistleblower actions and OSHA citations and enforcement proceedings.

### DENMON, Richard A
Carlton Fields, P.A., Tampa
813 229 4219
rdenmon@carltonfields.com
*Featured in Corporate/M&A (Florida)*

**Practice Areas:** Securities regulation, corporation finance, mergers and acquisitions, and general corporate law, including complex securities law and corporate matters.

**Professional Memberships:** Admitted in Florida and New York. Committee on the Federal Regulation of Securities, Business Law Section, American Bar Association; Florida Venture Forum Board of Directors.

**Career:** Martindale-Hubbell AV Rating. Special Counsel to Assistant Director of the Office of Tender Offers (1986-89), and Attorney Advisor and Senior Counsel (1984-86), Division of Corporation Finance, Securities and Exchange Commission, Washington DC.

**Personal:** JD, State University of New York at Buffalo, 1982; BS, State University of New York at Binghamton, 1979.

## DEWEY, Joe
Holland & Knight LLP, Miami
305 789 7746
joe.dewey@hklaw.com
*Featured in Banking & Finance (Florida)*

**Career:** Joe Dewey practices in the area of finance and real estate. Mr Dewey regularly represents commercial banks, life insurance companies and other financial institutions in commercial lending transactions, including construction and permanent real estate financing, healthcare real estate finance and asset based lending, such as receivable, inventory, equipment and working capital facilities. He has substantial experience in syndicated and other co-lending arrangements, representing both lead lenders and participant lenders. He is an adjunct professor of law at the University of Miami School of Law, teaching real estate transactions.

## DILLON, Sean M
Moye, O'Brien, O'Rourke, Pickert & Dillon, LLP, Maitland
407 622 5250
SDillon@moopd.com
*Featured in Construction (Florida)*

**Practice Areas:** Construction law and litigation, commercial litigation, management labor and employment law. Has extensive experience representing US and international contractors and engineering firms in the USA in multi-million dollar contracts and claims.

**Professional Memberships:** The Florida Bar; The State Bar of Georgia; American Bar Association (Member, Forum Committee on the Construction Industry and Public Contract Law and Litigation Sections).

**Career:** Board certified in construction law by The Florida Bar; Senior Partner of Moye, O'Brien, O'Rourke, Pickert & Dillon, LLP (with affiliate office in Chicago, Illinois); admitted to Florida Bar and Georgia Bar; US District Court, Southern, Middle and Northern Districts of Florida; US Court of Appeals, Federal and Eleventh Circuits.

**Personal:** Received Bachelor of Science in Building Construction Technologies (with high honors) from the University of Florida and Juris

Doctor (with honors) from the University of Florida. Member of Florida Blue Key.

## DOLINER, Nathaniel L
Carlton Fields, P.A., Tampa
813 229 4208
ndoliner@carltonfields.com
*Featured in Corporate/M&A (Florida)*

**Practice Areas:** Mergers and acquisitions and corporate law, including joint ventures and strategic alliances, public-private transactions. Extensive experience in mergers and acqusitions involving manufacturing, technology, health care companies. Advises boards of directors of public companies and board committees as to Sarbanes-Oxley and corporate governance issues.

**Professional Memberships:** Admitted in Florida. Former Vice Chair, ABA International M&A Subcommittee; Former Chair, ABA Section of Business Law; American Law Institute; Fellow, American Bar Foundation; American College of Tax Counsel.

**Career:** Martindale-Hubbell AV Rating.

**Personal:** LLM, University of Florida College of Law, 1977; JD, Vanderbilt University Law School, 1973; BA, George Washington University, 1970.

## DOTSON JR, Albert E
Bilzin Sumberg Baena Price & Axelrod LLP, Miami
305 350 2411
adotson@bilzin.com
*Featured in Real Estate (Florida)*

**Practice Areas:** Government procurement contracts; land development; administrative law; government relations; public-private partnerships.

**Professional Memberships:** 100 Black Men of America, Chairman Emeritus; The Orange Bowl Committee, Past President; Blue Ribbon Commission on Judicial Campaigns; Wilkie D. Ferguson, Jr. Bar Association.

**Career:** In 2009, chosen as a member of the Federal Judicial Nominating Commission, a statewide panel charged with selecting finalists for presidential appointments to district judgeships, US attorneys and US marshals; Reappointed in 2011 to a second, two-year term.

**Personal:** JD, Vanderbilt University, Bennett Douglas Bell Memorial Prize for academic achievement and high ethical standards, 1987; AB, Dartmouth College, 1982.

## DOUGHERTY, Lucia A
Greenberg Traurig, LLP, Miami
305 579 0603
DoughertyL@gtlaw.com
*Featured in Real Estate (Florida)*

**Practice Areas:** Co-Chair, Miami Land Development & Zoning Practice. Government procurement. Counsel, Greater Miami Convention and Visitors Bureau.

**Professional Memberships:** Myeloma Institute Advisory Board Member, University of Arkansas. Former Chair, Archbishop's Charities and Development Drive, Miami-Dade County. Chair, Miami Beach Chamber of Commerce.

**Career:** Selected: Super Lawyers, 2006-12; Best Lawyers in America, 2006-13. Rated, AV® Preeminent™ 5.0 out of 5.

**Publications:** Featured, 'Lucia A Dougherty & Adrienne F Pardo: Empresses of the Skyline', South Florida CEO, 2006.

**Personal:** LLM, University of Miami School of Law; JD, Oklahoma City University School of Law; MLS, University of Oklahoma; BS, Syracuse University.

## DROBNER, David S
Carlton Fields, P.A., Miami
305 539 7354
ddrobner@carltonfields.com
*Featured in Real Estate (Florida)*

**Practice Areas:** Commercial leasing and real estate, representing interest of both landlords and tenants in office lease negotiations, commercial and residential real estate-collateralized loans and title insurance, commercial real estate-related litigation and collections, including foreclosures and title clearing actions.

**Professional Memberships:** Admitted to practice in Florida. Real Property, Probate and Trust Law Section Landlord/Tenant Committee, The Florida Bar; American Bar Association; International Council of Shopping Centers.

**Career:** Martindale-Hubbell AV Rating.

**Publications:** Co-Author "Tenant Leasing Strategies: Improving Your Position" Counsel to Counsel Magazine.

**Personal:** JD (with honors), University of Florida College of Law, 1985; BS (highest honors), University of Florida, 1982.

## DUDLEY, Frederick
Holland & Knight LLP, Tallahassee
850 224 7000
fred.dudley@hklaw.com
*Featured in Construction (Florida)*

**Practice Areas:** Senior Counsel in the firm's Government Section, he is a Florida Bar Board Certified Construction Lawyer with over 40 years of experience in real estate practice, emphasizing construction liens, licensing and disciplinary cases. He served 16 years in the Florida Legislature, retiring from the Florida Senate in 1998, where he chaired the Senate Judiciary Committee. His construction law practice includes lien litigation, administrative proceedings for rule challenges, as well as licensure applications and disciplinary proceedings, lobbying the Florida Legislature on behalf of numerous clients, and serving as a litigation consultant and expert witness.

## DULIN, Amy G
Hughes Hubbard & Reed LLP, Miami
305 373 5664
dulin@hugheshubbard.com
*Featured in Latin American Investment (Florida), Banking & Finance (Florida)*

**Practice Areas:** Concentrates on cross-border financial transactions, including structured trade and commodity financings, acquisition financings, project finance and restructurings.

**Career:** Partner, Hughes Hubbard & Reed. Co-Chair, Financial Services Group. Admitted NY and Florida.

**Personal:** Yale University BA, 1988, cum laude ; NYU School of Law JD, 1992.

## DURKIN, Denis L
Baker & Hostetler LLP, Orlando
407 649 4053
ddurkin@bakerlaw.com
*Featured in Construction (Florida)*

**Career:** A civil trial lawyer, Denis Durkin has acted as trial counsel in diverse civil litigation matters, including: a $53 million junk bond securities fraud class action; multimillion-dollar construction contract disputes in various state and federal courts and before administrative appeals boards; federal bid protests, copyright, trademark and patent disputes; ad valorem tax assessment appeals; defamation claims; eminent domain claims; federal and state employment discrimination claims and product liability defense. Denis advises clients on federal procurement and construction contract matters and lectures on litigation-related topics.

## EATON, Joel D
Podhurst Orseck P.A., Miami
305 358 2800
JEaton@Podhurst.com
*Featured in Litigation (Florida)*

**Practice Areas:** Appellate.

**Career:** Has handled civil appeals in state and federal courts for 37 years, and is a former Chairman of the Florida Supreme Court's Appellate Rules Committee. He also served two terms as a Member of the Supreme Court's Committee on Standard Jury Instructions in Civil Cases. He is a co-founder of the American Academy of Appellate Lawyers, is listed in Best Lawyers of America, and served as an Adviser to the American Law Institute's Restatement of the Law (Third) Torts: Liability for Physical Harm.

**Personal:** Harvard University (JD cum laude, 1975); Yale University (BA 1965).

## ECKHARD, Richard D
Holland & Knight LLP, Tampa
813 227 6417
rick.eckhard@hklaw.com
*Featured in Real Estate (Florida)*

**Practice Areas:** The head of the firm's Tampa Real Estate Practice, he specializes in the acquisition, development and sale of real estate with emphasis on acquisition, development and leasing (including build to suit and leveraged leases) of office, retail, and industrial properties. He represents national and regional developers, landlords and tenants. He is Board Certified in Real Estate Law and lectures on real estate transaction topics, and currently serves as the Vice-Chairman of The Florida Bar Real Property, Probate and Trust Law Section's committee on real estate leasing.

## ENTIN, Seth J
Greenberg Traurig, LLP, Miami
305 579 0615
EntinS@gtlaw.com
*Featured in Tax (Florida)*

**Practice Areas:** Tax-efficient structures for foreign operations and investments by US companies and individuals, Tax-efficient structures for US operations and investments by foreign companies and individuals, Cross-border mergers, acquisitions, dispositions, restructurings, asset transfers and joint ventures.

**Career:** Listed in Best Lawyers in America, Chambers Global, Chambers USA: America's Leading Lawyers for Business, Chambers and Partners Latin America, The Legal 500 US and Super Lawyers, and is an Adjunct Professor of International Taxation at the University of Miami School of Law.

**Personal:** JD, summa cum laude, University of Miami School of Law; MPA, Barry University; MBA, Barry University; BTL, Talmudic University.

### EPSTEIN, Gary M
Greenberg Traurig, LLP, Miami
305 579 0894
EpsteinG@gtlaw.com
*Featured in Corporate/M&A (Florida)*

**Practice Areas:** Managing Shareholder, Tel Aviv office. Chair, Global Corporate and Securities Practice. Co-Chair, Israel Practice. M&A; securities; globalisation, commercialisation; gaming.

**Career:** Chairman, team ranked as the No.1 corporate law firm in Miami, selected by corporate directors, in annual Legal Industry Research Study by Corporate Board Member magazine (tenth consecutive year), 2002-09, 2011-12 (2010 study did not include rankings by city). Listed: Legal 500 US, 2008-12; Chambers Global, 2008-09, 2011-13; Chambers USA Guide, 2003-13; 'Star performer', 2008-10; Best Lawyers in America, 1985-2013.

**Personal:** JD, Harvard Law School, 1980; MA, English and American Literature, New York University, 1970; BA, Yeshiva University, 1969.

### ERVIN, James M
Holland & Knight LLP, Tallahassee
850 224 7000
jim.ervin@hklaw.com
*Featured in Tax (Florida)*

**Professional Memberships:** The Florida Bar, Tax Section, Executive Council.

**Career:** Mr Ervin has a multi-forum state tax practice that covers the legislative, administrative and judicial areas. Through a proactive his approach, tax issues can be avoided before they become problems; or, problems solved through legislative action or litigation. Mr Ervin also handles assessment negotiations with auditors and the preparing, filing and resolving of protests against assessments. Through his longstanding relationships with the Department of Revenue, Mr Ervin assists clients in tax inquiries to facilitate tax planning and to resolve any questions concerning potential tax liability.

### ESTEVEZ, Anne Marie
Morgan, Lewis & Bockius LLP, Miami
305 415 3330
aestevez@morganlewis.com
*Featured in Labor & Employment (Florida)*

**Practice Areas:** Anne Marie Estevez is a partner in Morgan Lewis's Labor and Employment Practice. She represents state, national, and international clients in the full spectrum of employment and discrimination matters, primarily focusing on defending and trying complex class, mass and collective action employment and accessibility (ADA) cases. She also advises companies on

employment, wage/hour, and accessibility laws, reclassifications and restructures, executive contracts, high level terminations, reductions in force, agency investigations, and business models involving various employment and independent contractor arrangements.

**Personal:** Attended University of Miami School of Law, JD, With Honors; University of Miami, BA, With Honors.

### EVORA, Orlando L
Greenberg Traurig, LLP, Orlando
407 418 2380
EvoraO@gtlaw.com
*Featured in Real Estate (Florida)*

**Practice Areas:** Co-Managing Shareholder, Orlando Office. Real Estate.

**Professional Memberships:** The Catholic Foundation of Central Florida, Inc., The Florida Bar, Metro Orlando Economic Development Commission and Boy Scouts of America.

**Career:** Listed: Chambers USA Guide; Florida, Transactions & Finance/ Florida, Land Use & Zoning, The Legal 500 US: Volume IV; Best Lawyers in America; Super Lawyers magazine; 'Legal Elite', Florida Trend Magazine. Rated, AV® Preeminent™ 5.0 out of 5.

**Personal:** JD, Florida State University College of Law; BA, Business Administration, Rollins College.

### FARMER II, Guy O
GrayRobinson, PA, Jacksonville
904 598 9929
Guy.Farmer@gray-robinson.com
*Featured in Labor & Employment (Florida)*

**Practice Areas:** Partner in the Labor and Employment Group, represents employers locally, regionally and nationally in the full range of employment-related issues. Has defended employers in more than 1,000 cases nationwide involving allegations of employment discrimination and other employment and labor-related matters. His litigation and appellate practice has included the defense of employers in cases involving individual claims, claims by federal and state governments and significant class actions. He also counsels and represents employers in connection with labor union issues, including resisting union organizing efforts, defending against unfair labor practice charges, appearing in labor arbitrations and negotiating collective bargaining agreements.

### FELMAN, David S
Hill Ward Henderson, Tampa
813 227 8483
dfelman@hwhlaw.com
*Featured in Corporate/M&A (Florida)*

**Practice Areas:** Securities offerings, corporate governance, venture capital, private equity, mergers, acquisitions, joint ventures, partnerships, general corporate advice.

**Professional Memberships:** AV rated by Martindale-Hubbell, Best Lawyers in America, Florida Trend's Legal Elite, Florida Super Lawyers. Founder, Florida Directors Institute; Board of Directors, Florida Venture Forum. Former Chair, The Florida Bar Business Law Section, current member, Executive Council.

**Career:** Practice Leader, Corporate & Tax Group. Serves public companies in securities and governance matters, and institutional venture capital investors in mergers and acquisitions.

**Personal:** JD, with distinction, Duke University School of Law, 1982; BA, magna cum laude, Wake Forest University, 1979.

### FENDRICK, Keith
Holland & Knight LLP, Tampa
813 227 6707
keith.fendrick@hklaw.com
*Featured in Bankruptcy/Restructuring (Florida)*

**Practice Areas:** Partner in the firm's Bankruptcy Practice Group Mr Fendrick focuses his practice on bankruptcy and creditors' rights, corporate reorganizations and restructurings, and commercial litigation. He has represented financial institutions, corporations, insurance companies, and creditor groups in numerous large Chapter 11 cases around the country. He has also worked with secured and unsecured creditors in workouts, non-bankruptcy corporate reorganizations, and acquisitions of troubled businesses. He recently was appointed Receiver by the Securities and Exchange Commission. Mr Fendrick is a former director of the Tampa Bay Bankruptcy Bar Association and panelist at the National Conference of Bankruptcy Judges.

### FERNANDEZ, Segundo J
Oertel, Fernandez, Bryant & Atkinson, P.A., Tallahassee
850 521 0700
sfernandez@ohfc.com
*Featured in Environment (Florida)*

**Practice Areas:** Mr Fernandez served as Assistant General Counsel, and Deputy General Counsel of the Florida Department of Environmental Regulation (later FDEP) from 1977 to 1983. He holds a BS in Biology from the University of Miami, a JD from Samford University, Cumberland School of Law and an LLM in Ocean and Coastal Law (area of concentration: environmental and land use law) from the University of Miami. He represents public and private clients throughout Florida in water and air permitting, infrastructure permitting, mining, water use and utility regulation, environmental enforcement and compliance matters, and solid and hazardous waste disposal issues.

### FERRER, Barbara
Holland & Knight LLP, Miami
305 789 7453
barbara.ferrer@hklaw.com
*Featured in Real Estate (Florida)*

**Practice Areas:** Partner in the firm's Real Estate Section, Barbara focuses her practice on representing clients in real estate and banking transactions, including acquisitions, disposition, development and financing of multifamily housing projects, hotels, retail, charter schools, office, warehouse and mixed-use projects. Her practice is dedicated to working with national and community banks on sophisticated commercial and real estate financing projects. She also represents banks and other financial institutions on public/private financing transactions.

### FLEISCHER, Frank N
GrayRobinson, PA, Tampa
813 273 5000
frank.fleischer@gray-robinson.com
*Featured in Banking & Finance (Florida)*

**Practice Areas:** Shareholder and Chair of the GrayRobinson Public Finance practice group. Has been disclosure counsel to many issuers and represented numerous underwriters in municipal finance matters. Has been involved in innovative and unique bond financings for water and wastewater systems, reclaimed water, water desalination, electric systems, resource recovery facilities, hospitals, schools, museums, performing arts centers, convention centers, and dry docks. Also an experienced securities attorney who has handled numerous initial public offerings and private placements.

**Professional Memberships:** American Bar Association; The Florida Bar; Hillsborough County Bar Association; National Association of Bond Lawyers; Maine Bar Association.

**Career:** Currently serves as disclosure counsel for the Cities of Marco Island, Port St. Lucie, Sarasota, St. Petersburg and Tampa, Tampa Bay Water, Pasco County, the Hillsborough County Aviation Authority, the Tampa Port Authority, the First Florida Governmental Financing Commission, The University of South Florida, Reedy Creek Improvement District (Disney), Tampa General Hospital, Lakeland Regional Hospital and H. Lee Moffitt Cancer Center. Has been involved in more than $25 billion in public finance offerings. Florida Trend "Legal Elite," 2005-09; Best Lawyers in America, 2003-13; Florida Super Lawyers, 2006-12.

**Personal:** The Wharton School of the University of Pennsylvania, BS, Economics (1960); Boston University School of Law, JD (1965); Georgetown University Law Center, LLM in Taxation (1968)

### FLEMING, Joseph Z
Greenberg Traurig, LLP, Miami
305 579 0517
FlemingJ@gtlaw.com
*Featured in Labor & Employment (Florida)*

**Practice Areas:** Litigation, labor and employment; environmental, land use and natural resources; entertainment; arts and sports law; intellectual property; defamation law; media law; constitutional law; ADA, accessibility, building, life safety codes.

**Professional Memberships:** Member, The American Law Institute. Fellow, College of Labor & Employment Lawyers.

**Career:** Listed: Best Lawyers in America; International Who's Who of Management Labor and Employment Lawyers; Florida Super Lawyers Magazine, 'Top Lawyers in South Florida'; South Florida Legal Guide; Chambers USA Guide. Rated, AV® Preeminent™ 5.0 out of 5.

**Personal:** LLM (Labor Law) NYU Law and JD University of Virginia.

## FORNARIS, Carl A
Greenberg Traurig, LLP, Miami
305 579 0500
FornarisC@gtlaw.com
*Featured in Banking & Finance (Florida)*

**Practice Areas:** Co-Chair, National Financial Institutions Group. Global; corporate and securities; mergers, acquisitions.
**Professional Memberships:** General Counsel, Florida International Bankers Association.
**Career:** Member: team selected, Chambers and Partners for 'Corporate & Finance - Law Firm of the Year (Florida-Based)' Award, Chambers Latin America Awards, 2010-11; team ranked as the No.1 corporate law firm in Miami as selected, corporate directors, in the annual 'Legal Industry Research Study,' Corporate Board Member magazine (10th consecutive year), 2002-09, 2011-12. Listed, Best Lawyers, 2008-13; Super Lawyers magazine, 2007-12.
**Personal:** JD, The Catholic University of America, Columbus School of Law, 1993; BS, University of Miami, 1990.

## FREEDMAN, Robert S
Carlton Fields, P.A., Tampa
813 229 4149
rfreedman@carltonfields.com
*Featured in Real Estate (Florida)*

**Practice Areas:** Condominium, subdivision and timeshare development, master planned and mixed-use communities and commercial development.
**Professional Memberships:** Admitted in Florida. Chair, Hospitality, Timesharing and Common Interest Development Group, American Bar Association; Fellow/Chair of Programs Committee, American College of Real Estate Lawyers; Vice Chair, Legislative Review Committee, Real Property, Probate and Trust Law Section, The Florida Bar.
**Career:** Martindale-Hubbell AV Rating.
**Publications:** Co-Author, "Summary of the 2011 Florida Laws Impacting Condominiums, Homeowners Associations and Cooperatives," eReport, ABA Section of Real Property, Trust and Estate Law (October 2011).
**Personal:** JD, Stetson University College of Law, 1990; AB, Duke University, 1987.

## FREELAND, Jorge
White & Case LLP, Miami
305 995 5247
jfreeland@whitecase.com
*Featured in Corporate/M&A (Florida)*

**Career:** Jorge L Freeland is head of White & Case's domestic Corporate & Securities Department in the Miami office. He has extensive experience in mergers and acquisitions, having represented a number of buyers, sellers and intermediaries in transactions involving assorted industries. He has also advised management groups, special committees and senior and subordinated lenders in sophisticated, highly leveraged acquisitions, tender offers, divestitures and going-private transactions. His experience has enabled him to assist US and offshore clients in designing innovative acquisition structures to address various financing and tax considerations. To view a comprehensive biography, please visit www.whitecase.com/jfreeland.

## FRIEDMAN, Robert J
Holland & Knight LLP, Miami
305 374 8500
robert.friedman@hklaw.com
*Featured in Tax (Florida)*

**Career:** Robert Friedman leads Holland & Knight's benefits and ERISA practice with more than 25 years' experience in all aspects of benefits work, including drafting, qualification and compliance of defined benefit and defined contribution plans; ESOPs; corporate acquisitions and mergers; plan transfers, mergers and terminations; governmental plans; fiduciary matters; investment and hedge funds; executive compensation, non-qualified deferred compensation; and ERISA litigation.
**Publications:** "Target Date Fund: Don't Set Them and Forget Them," ERISA Alert, March 28, 2011; "Federal Taxation of Healthcare Benefits for Same Sex Couples," ERISA Alert, November 3, 2011.

## GALLION, Theresa M
Fisher & Phillips LLP, Tampa
813 769 7500
tgallion@laborlawyers.com
*Featured in Labor & Employment (Florida)*

**Career:** Theresa Gallion is a Partner in the Tampa office. She represents clients in a wide variety of industries, with particular emphasis on hospitality, health care, telecommunications, and retail. She has extensive bench and jury trial experience, having successfully tried approximately 40 cases. Her expertise is defending matters arising under Title VII of the Civil Rights Act of 1964, Age Discrimination in Employment Act, Americans with Disabilities Act, Family and Medical Leave Act, and the Equal Pay Act.

## GANG, Robert C
Greenberg Traurig, LLP, Miami
305 579 0886
GangR@gtlaw.com
*Featured in Banking & Finance (Florida)*

**Practice Areas:** Public finance; education; special taxing districts; general municipal; utilities.
**Professional Memberships:** Member, National Association of Bond Lawyers; Member, Local Government Law Section of The Florida Bar; Director, Florida Grand Opera.
**Career:** Best Lawyers in America. Super Lawyers magazine. AV® Preeminent™ 5.0 out of 5. Lectured and panelist for: Florida School Finance Officers Association, Florida Government Finance Officers Association, the Council of Great City Schools; Florida School Board Attorneys Association, Florida Association of District School Superintendents, American Governmental Leasing Association, Bond Buyer Public Finance Conference, Urban Land Institute.
**Personal:** JD, University of Virginia School of Law; BA, Princeton University.

## GARCIA LINARES, Manuel A
Richman Greer PA, Miami
305 373 4021
mlinares@richmangreer.com
*Featured in Litigation (Florida)*

**Practice Areas:** Manuel Garcia-Linares is a member of the Florida Bar and is admitted to practice before the United States District Courts for the Southern and Middle Districts of Florida, and the United States Court of Appeals for the Eleventh Circuit. He specializes in complex commercial and business litigation, officer and director liability, real estate litigation, probate and trust litigation, professional malpractice (legal and accounting) and class action litigation.
**Professional Memberships:** Mr Garcia-Linares is a Past President of the Cuban American Bar Association (Board of Directors, 2002, 2005 to present, Treasurer 2002, Immediate Past Vice President 2007-08, President-Elect 2009, President 2010), Past President of the Cuban American Bar Foundation (President 2011), and a member of the American Bar Association (House of Delegates 2012), and Dade County Bar Association.
**Career:** Manuel Garcia-Linares was a judicial intern to United States District Court Judge George Arceneaux, Jr., E. D. Louisiana and a law clerk to the Honorable Juan Ramirez, Jr., 11th Judicial Circuit. He serves as the Firm's Managing Shareholder and has been a member of the firm since 1993. He also holds a Certified Public Accountant license from the State of Florida.
**Personal:** Mr Garcia-Linares graduated with a Bachelor of Business Administration in Accounting from the University of Miami and received his Juris Doctor, magna cum laude, from Tulane Law School. While at the University of Miami, he served as the vice president of administration of Alpha Kappa Psi and was a member of the varsity crew team. While at Tulane, he was an associate editor of The Tulane Law Review, a member of La Alianza Del Derecho, and a volunteer for the Internal Revenue Services' Volunteer Income Tax Assistance Program.

## GARCIA-SERRA, Mario
Greenberg Traurig, LLP, Miami
305 579 0837
Garcia-SerraM@gtlaw.com
*Featured in Real Estate (Florida)*

**Practice Areas:** Co-Chair, Miami Land Development & Zoning Practice. Governmental affairs; Environmental.
**Professional Memberships:** Board of Directors: Latin Builders Association; Harvard Club of Miami; Salvadoran American Humanitarian Foundation. Member: American Bar Association; Cuban American Bar Association.
**Career:** Listed: Super Lawyers magazine — Rising Star, 2009-12; Chambers USA Guide, 2012-13.
**Personal:** JD, magna cum laude, University of Miami School of Law, 2002; BA, cum laude, Government/Political Science, Harvard University, 1998.

## GART, Brian
Berger Singerman, Fort Lauderdale
954 712 5130
bgart@bergersingerman.com
*Featured in Bankruptcy/Restructuring (Florida)*

**Practice Areas:** Mr Gart has over 25 years of experience in complex business bankruptcy cases, bankruptcy litigation matters, out-of-court restructurings, and other types of insolvency proceedings. He represents public and private business debtors, secured creditors, official creditors' committees, trustees, DIP lenders, plan funders, landlords, liquidators, banks and other financial institutions, indenture trustees and equity security holders. Mr Gart also focuses a significant portion of his practice representing purchasers of assets and distressed businesses under Section 363 of the Bankruptcy Code and structuring DIP financing in connection with such transactions. He has been specially admitted in Bankruptcy Courts throughout the United States.
**Career:** Listed, Best Lawyers in America, 2004, 2007, 2008; Listed, Chambers & Partners USA Guide, 2003-07; listed as one of 'South Florida's Top Lawyers', South Florida Legal Guide, 2002-06. Prior to joining Berger Singerman, Mr Gart was a shareholder at Greenberg Traurig, where he helped build its Reorganization and Bankruptcy Practice and worked on many large and complex restructuring matters locally, regionally and nationally.

## GARWOOD, Thomas
FordHarrison LLP, Orlando
407 418 2315
tgarwood@fordharrison.com
*Featured in Labor & Employment (Florida)*

**Practice Areas:** Labor and employment.
**Career:** Tom Garwood is certified by the Florida Bar as a Specialist in Labor and Employment Law. He excels in the counseling of business and management for successful strategies and effective solutions to deal with the legal challenges encountered in the workplace. He also has extensive experience as a negotiator and advocate in labor law proceedings and as a trial attorney in employment litigation. Tom was inducted as a Fellow in the National College of Labor and Employment Lawyers in 1997. He is also admitted as an Associate in the American Board of Trial Advocates.

## GASSENHEIMER, James D
Berger Singerman, Miami
305 714 4383
jgassenheimer@bergersingerman.com
*Featured in Litigation (Florida)*

**Practice Areas:** James Gassenheimer has extensive jury and non-jury trial experience in State, Federal and Bankruptcy court, having tried over 100 cases to jury verdict or judgment. His practice includes real estate related litigation, complex commercial litigation, bankruptcy litigation, employment litigation, aviation litigation, franchise litigation and admiralty and maritime litigation and the defense of corporations in a variety of tort and product liability litigation.

**Professional Memberships:** James is Board Certified as a Civil Trial Lawyer by The Florida Bar Board of Legal Specialization. Additionally, he is Board Certified in Civil Trial Advocacy by the National Board of Trial Advocacy.

### GENTILE, Melinda S
Peckar & Abramson, P.C., Miami
305 358 2600
mgentile@pecklaw.com
*Featured in Construction (Florida)*

**Practice Areas:** Ms Gentile is a Florida Bar Board Certified Specialist in Construction law. She focuses the application of her expertise in construction law on project administration assistance and resolution of attendant disputes. She is a Florida Circuit Civil Mediator and also serves as an Arbitrator.
**Professional Memberships:** NAWIC, CASF and AGC. Admitted to practice law in Florida.
**Career:** Partner in the Miami office. She has also served as a Broward County Magistrate.
**Publications:** Ms Gentile authors articles and lectures on construction law topics.
**Personal:** For more information, please visit: www.pecklaw.com

### GERECKE, Edward W
Carlton Fields, P.A., Tampa
813 229 4306
egerecke@carltonfields.com
*Featured in Litigation (Florida)*

**Practice Areas:** Product liability and personal injury defense including extensive experience in prescription drug, medical device and OTC product defense.
**Professional Memberships:** Admitted to practice Florida, US Supreme Court. President, Tampa Bay Chapter, American Board of Trial Advocates; Defense Research Institute; International Association of Defense Counsel; Product Liability Committee, Litigation Section, American Bar Association.
**Career:** National Board of Trial Advocates, Certified Civil Trial Attorney. Martindale-Hubbell AV Rating.
**Publications:** Co-Author, "Mensing: Effects and Opportunities," For the Defense (October 2012).
**Personal:** JD (with honors), Indiana University School of Law, 1981; BS (with distinction), Purdue University, 1978.

### GILBERT, Leonard H
Holland & Knight LLP, Tampa
813 227 8500
leonard.gilbert@hklaw.com
*Featured in Bankruptcy/Restructuring (Florida)*

**Practice Areas:** Leonard Gilbert represents financial institutions and other institutional lenders in commercial finance, creditors' rights, and commercial litigation. Regarding insolvency and restructuring, he has represented national and international banks, other financial institutions, and creditors' committees. He serves as court appointed mediator in numerous insolvency matters. He is past president of The Florida Bar and past co-chair of the Insolvency Section of the IBA. He presently is a Member of the ABA Standing Committee on the Federal Judiciary and active in

ABA's Business Law Section and International Insolvency Institute. He received the American College of Bankruptcy's 2011 Distinguished Service Award.

### GILBERT, Robert N
Carlton Fields, P.A., West Palm Beach
561 650 8007
rgilbert@carltonfields.com
*Featured in Bankruptcy/Restructuring (Florida)*

**Practice Areas:** Bankruptcy law representation of creditors, landlords, franchisers, creditors committees, trustees, and debtors. Out of court workouts, compositions, and assignments for the benefit of creditors. General commercial litigation involving commercial paper, secured lending and letters of credit.
**Professional Memberships:** Admitted in Florida. American Bankruptcy Institute; Past President, Bankruptcy Bar Association, Southern District of Florida; Advisor to the Caribbean Law Institute.
**Career:** Martindale-Hubbell AV Rating.
**Personal:** JD (cum laude), University of Miami School of Law, 1980; BA (magna cum laude), Alma College, 1977.

### GOLDSTEIN, Joseph
Holland & Knight LLP, Miami
305 789 7782
joseph.goldstein@hklaw.com
*Featured in Real Estate (Florida)*

**Practice Areas:** Partner in Holland & Knight's Real Estate Section, he practices land use and environmental law. Mr Goldstein generally represents the interests of developers, major corporations, professional sports franchises, hospitals and universities in efforts to protect their property rights and seek governmental approvals, permits, incentives and other entitlements in complex matters. He has represented dozens of the most significant development projects in South Florida from conception to completion during his more than 25 years of practice.

### GOLDSTEIN, Richard M
Bilzin Sumberg Baena Price & Axelrod LLP, Miami
305 350 2371
rgoldstein@bilzin.com
*Featured in Tax (Florida)*

**Practice Areas:** Federal income tax planning; inbound and outbound international tax issues; mergers and acquisitions; tax controversies; estate planning.
**Professional Memberships:** The Florida Bar, Sections on Taxation; State Bar of Texas; Real Property, Probate and Trust Law.
**Publications:** "Proper Planning for Debt Workouts" (GlobeSt.com, September 2009); "Estate Planning in a Low Interest Rate Environment" (Journal of Practical Estate Planning, December 2003-January 2004).
**Personal:** LLM (Taxation), New York University, 1984; JD, University of Miami School of Law, 1983; BS, State University of New York at Albany, 1980.

### GORSON, Matthew B
Greenberg Traurig, LLP, Miami
305 579 0777
GorsonM@gtlaw.com
*Featured in Real Estate (Florida)*

**Practice Areas:** Greenberg Traurig Co-Chairman. Real estate.
**Professional Memberships:** Chairman, Downtown Miami Charter School; Founder, Mt Sinai Hospital and Baptist Hospital; Former Board of Governors, Greater Miami Chamber of Commerce; Executive Committee/Board Member: United Way of Miami-Dade, Tulane University. Board Member: American Diabetes Association.
**Career:** Listed: SunPost 50, 'The most influential South Floridians', SunPost, 2008; Florida Super Lawyers Magazine; The Best Lawyers in America, every edition; ranked 1, Real Estate, Chambers USA Guide, every edition; Legal Elite, Florida Trend Magazine. Rated, AV® Preeminent™ 5.0 out of 5.
**Personal:** JD, University of Chicago; BS, cum laude, Tulane University.

### GOUDIE, Federico
Hughes Hubbard & Reed LLP, Miami
305 379 7229
goudie@hugheshubbard.com
*Featured in Latin American Investment (Florida)*

**Practice Areas:** Latin America; International Finance and Corporate Practice including advising international financial institutions in structured and trade financings, project financings, and derivative transactions and advising multi-national corporations and international financial institutions in mergers and acquisitions, private equity transactions, capital market transactions, and general corporate and commercial matters.
**Career:** Partner, Hughes Hubbard & Reed; admitted in New York and Florida. Chair of Latin American Practice Group.
**Personal:** Florida State University, B.A. 1994; NYU School of Law JD 1997. Fluent in Portuguese and Spanish. Proficient in Italian.

### GRAMMIG, Robert J
Holland & Knight LLP, Tampa
813 227 8500
robert.grammig@hklaw.com
*Featured in Corporate/M&A (Florida)*

**Career:** Mr Grammig leads Holland & Knight's Public Companies and Securities Practice. For over 30 years, he has focused on corporate, securities and commercial law matters, including M&A; public offerings, private placements; periodic reporting and compliance matters under the Securities Exchange Act of 1934; corporate governance matters; contests for corporate control; executive compensation and other business law matters. He has significant experience in international business transactions in Latin America, Europe, the Middle East and Asia, representing both United States and foreign entities. Mr Grammig regularly advises boards of directors, audit committees, compensation committees and special committees regarding corporate governance matters.

### GREEN, Elizabeth A
Baker & Hostetler LLP, Orlando
407 649 4036
egreen@bakerlaw.com
*Featured in Bankruptcy/Restructuring (Florida)*

**Career:** Elizabeth Green practices in the areas of bankruptcy and creditors' rights and represents corporate debtors and secured creditors, unsecured creditors, committees, bondholders and trustees in bankruptcy cases of corporate and individual debtors. Liz also has experience with out-of-court workouts, assignments for the benefit of creditors and in the representation of receivers. Liz has been recognized in Best Lawyers in America, Orlando Magazine's Top Lawyers, Florida Trend's Legal Elite and Florida "Super Lawyers" since 2006 and in Chambers USA: America's Leading Top Lawyers for Business since 2012. She is rated AV Preeminent by Martindale-Hubbell. Liz lectures extensively on Chapter 11 issues.

### GREER, Alan
Richman Greer PA, Miami
305 373 4010
agreer@richmangreer.com
*Featured in Litigation (Florida)*

**Practice Areas:** Alan G Greer, who concentrates in civil commercial litigation, is certified by The Florida Bar in both business litigation and in civil trial practice. His other areas of emphasis are: civil appeals, civil litigation, commercial and complex litigation, intellectual property litigation, officer and director representation, and professional malpractice.
**Professional Memberships:** A Fellow of the American College of Trial Lawyers (and a Trustee of its Foundation as well as past Chair of its Professionalism Committee), the International Society of Barristers, and the American Bar Foundation, Mr Greer serves as a faculty member and lecturer for the National Institute of Trial Advocacy, teaching continuing legal education courses. Mr Greer is admitted to The Florida Bar, the New York Bar, the Bar of the District of Columbia, the Federal Bars for several District Courts and Circuit Courts of Appeal, the US Tax Court, the US Court of Claims and the US Supreme Court.
**Career:** After serving six years of active duty in the US Navy Mr Greer began his legal career with his current law firm in 1969 becoming a shareholder in 1971.
**Publications:** Mr Greer has authored a number of articles on issues relating to professionalism which have appeared in over 25 bar journals and other publications as well as the author of the book Choices and Challenges, Lessons on Faith, Hope and Love, (Morgan James Publishing 2009).
**Personal:** US Naval Academy (BS 1961); University of Florida College of Law (JD 1969).

### GROSSMAN, Scott M
Greenberg Traurig, LLP, Fort Lauderdale
954 768 5212
GrossmanSM@gtlaw.com
*Featured in Bankruptcy/Restructuring (Florida)*

**Practice Areas:** Business reorganization and financial restructuring; bankruptcy litigation; bankruptcy tax matters; creditors' and debtors' rights; commercial litigation.
**Professional Memberships:** Bankruptcy Bar Association of the Southern District of Florida, (Second Vice President, 2012-present; Secretary, 2011-12; Treasurer, 2010-11). Member: Local Rules Advisory Committee for the United States Bankruptcy Court for the Southern District of Florida; American Bankruptcy Institute; American Bar Association.
**Career:** Selected: Best Lawyers in America, 2011-13; Super Lawyers — Rising Star, 2009, 2012; Legal 500 US, 2009.
**Personal:** JD, with honors, The George Washington University Law School, 1999; MAcc, University of Florida, 1996; BS, with honors, Accounting, University of Florida, 1996.

### GUSO, Jordi
Berger Singerman, Miami
305 755 9500
jguso@bergersingerman.com
*Featured in Bankruptcy/Restructuring (Florida)*
**Practice Areas:** Jordi Guso represents debtors, official committees and secured creditors in the areas of bankruptcy, insolvency and debtor-creditor relations. He frequently represents purchasers of assets in §363 sales. Mr Guso's experience includes debtor's counsel in a number of aviation related cases, including Aloha Airlines, Atlas Air and Gemini Air Cargo; counsel to various single and multi-family residential developers in court supervised and out of court restructurings; counsel to senior lender in distressed residential/golf course planned development in southwest Florida; counsel to aircraft lessor to international cargo carrier; counsel to regional developers of second and vacation home communities in connection with sale of substantially all their assets; and counsel to anti-ballistic product manufacturer in connection with the sale of its business to $8 billion private equity firm.

### HADJILOGIOU, Steven
Baker & McKenzie, Miami
305 789 8909
steven.hadjilogiou@bakermckenzie.com
*Featured in Tax (Florida)*
**Practice Areas:** Tax planning focusing on inbound and outbound international tax issues, with emphasis on transfer pricing, the taxation of partners and partnerships, corporations and high-net worth clients; state and local tax.
**Professional Memberships:** ABA Section of Taxation & Young Lawyers Division (2009-10 Chair, Tax Law Committee); Florida Bar Tax Section (2010-12 Director, Section Administration)(2008-10 Chair, New Tax Lawyer Committee).
**Career:** Adjunct Professor, University of Miami Tax LLM Program.
**Publications:** Primary drafter of the US Supreme Court amicus curae brief in Knight v. Commissioner, on behalf of the Florida Bar Tax Section. Numerous articles and presentations on international tax issues.

### HAIMO, Adam
Bilzin Sumberg Baena Price & Axelrod LLP, Miami
305 350 7226
ahaimo@bilzin.com
*Featured in Construction (Florida)*
**Practice Areas:** Complex commercial litigation, real estate, construction litigation, banking litigation, construction defect and delay cases, commercial foreclosures, litigation of business torts, breach of contract and tortious interference; construction transactional practice includes preparation and review of contractor, architect, and engineer agreements; involved in providing legal counsel throughout the construction process.
**Professional Memberships:** Admitted to Florida, US District Court, Southern and Middle Districts of Florida; The Florida Bar; American Bar Association; Lawyers for Children America, National Board of Directors.
**Personal:** JD, Washington University School of Law, 2001; Brandeis University, BA, magna cum laude, with high honors in American Studies, 1998.

### HALSEY, Douglas
White & Case LLP, Miami
305 995 5268
dhalsey@whitecase.com
*Featured in Environment (Florida)*
**Career:** Mr Halsey's practice covers all aspects of environmental and land use law, including litigation, transactional advice and regulatory matters. Mr Halsey has tried numerous cases in state and federal court with a special emphasis on cost recovery claims and land use disputes involving wetlands and endangered species. He has represented manufacturers, developers, and property owners in complex civil litigation and defended enforcement actions brought by the EPA and other federal, state, and local government agencies under the Clean Water Act, CERCLA, RCRA, CAA, NEPA, and parallel state and local government regulatory schemes. To view his biography, please visit www.whitecase.com/dhalsey.

### HALULA, John F
Holland & Knight LLP, Miami
305 789 7796
john.halula@hklaw.com
*Featured in Real Estate (Florida)*
**Practice Areas:** John Halula maintains practices in the areas of real estate with a concentration on institutional finance. He represents various domestic and international lenders providing construction and permanent financing for multi-family residential, retail, office and industrial projects. He has substantial experience analyzing land use, zoning, building and water law issues, and development agreements and construction contracts. Halula assists conduit lenders in the origination of mortgage loans to be pooled in connection with the issuance of mortgage pass-through certificates. He also represents clients in real estate transactions involving sales, acquisitions, sale-leasebacks, ground leases, building and space leases and like-kind exchanges.

### HAMENT, Andrew
FordHarrison LLP, Melbourne
321 724 5633
ahament@fordharrison.com
*Featured in Labor & Employment (Florida)*
**Practice Areas:** Labor and employment.
**Career:** Andy Hament represents management in all areas of employment and labor law. He is certified by the Florida Bar as a specialist in Labor and Employment Law. He regularly advises private and public sector employers in discipline and discharge, reductions-in-force, collective bargaining, union grievance/ arbitrations, discrimination issues, sexual harassment investigations, executive employment and severance agreements, trade secret and non-compete issues, drug abuse and drug testing, the Family and Medical Leave Act and violence in the workplace. He received his JD from University of Baltimore School of Law in 1981.

### HANSEN, Christian W
White & Case LLP, Miami
305 995 5272
chansen@whitecase.com
*Featured in Transportation (Nationwide), Latin American Investment (Florida)*
See under Nationwide for profile.

### HARRIS, Amy
Stichter, Riedel, Blain & Prosser PA, Tampa
813 229 0144
aharris@srbp.com
*Featured in Bankruptcy/Restructuring (Florida)*
**Practice Areas:** Chapter 11 business reorganizations; workouts and out-of-court loan and debt restructurings; asset acquisitions and sales in bankruptcy cases.
**Career:** Amy Denton Harris joined Stichter, Riedel, Blain & Prosser P.A. in March of 2003 and became a shareholder in 2010. Mrs Harris received her JD with honors in 2002 from the University of Florida. While in law school, Ms Harris interned for The Honorable Paul M Glenn, Chief Bankruptcy Judge, Middle District of Florida, and The Honorable Michael G Williamson, Bankruptcy Judge, Middle District of Florida. She also is licensed as a certified public accountant, having passed all four parts of the examination on her first attempt (something accomplished by a small percentage of applicants). She is past chair of the Accounting Circle at the University of South Florida. She regularly represents debtors, committees, creditors, trustees, purchasers, and other parties in bankruptcy cases, assignments for the benefit of creditors, and out-of-court workouts. She is also active in the firm's representation of borrowers and guarantors in state court litigation initiated by lenders. She has been particularly active in the representation of independent and franchised restaurant chains in Chapter 11 cases.

### HARTOG, Ross
Markowitz Ringel Trusty + Hartog P.A., Miami
305 670 5000
rhartog@mrthlaw.com
*Featured in Bankruptcy/Restructuring (Florida)*
**Practice Areas:** Ross Hartog is a shareholder in the firm's Bankruptcy and Creditors' Rights practice group. He concentrates his practice on the representation of debtors, creditors, committees, trustees, assignees, and receivers in insolvency matters including chapter 7 and chapter 11 bankruptcy cases, assignments for the benefit of creditors, and receiverships.
**Professional Memberships:** American Bankruptcy Institute, National Association of Bankruptcy Trustees, Past-President of the Bankruptcy Bar Association for the Southern District of Florida, Best Lawyers in America.
**Career:** Ross Hartog is a member of the panel of chapter 7 bankruptcy trustees for the Southern District of Florida and in addition to serving as a chapter 7 trustee, serves as a chapter 11 trustee and an assignee for the benefit of creditors.
**Personal:** For more information, please visit the firm's website at www.mrthlaw.com.

### HENDERSON III, Thomas N
Hill Ward Henderson, Tampa
813 227 8406
thenderson@hwhlaw.com
*Featured in Real Estate (Florida)*
**Practice Areas:** All facets of real property law. Special emphasis in real estate acquisition and development, real estate finance.
**Professional Memberships:** Top Ten Attorneys in the State by Florida Super Lawyers, Inaugural member, Florida Trend's Legal Elite Hall of Fame, AV rated by Martindale-Hubbell, Best Lawyers in America, America's Leading Lawyers, American College of Mortgage Attorneys, American College of Real Estate Lawyers.
**Career:** Founding shareholder and Vice Chairman. Land acquisition, development, commercial property sales transactions, finance and title insurance matters. Loan originations, renewals and workouts.
**Personal:** JD, University of Virginia, 1968; BA, cum laude, Vanderbilt University, 1965.

### HILL III, Benjamin H
Hill Ward Henderson, Tampa
813 227 8420
bhill@hwhlaw.com
*Featured in Litigation (Florida)*
**Practice Areas:** Commercial litigation, professional liability, consumer products.
**Professional Memberships:** Past President, The Florida Bar; Top Ten Attorneys in State by Florida Super Lawyers, Inaugural member, Florida Trend's Legal Elite Hall of Fame; AV rated by Martindale-Hubbell, Best Lawyers in America, Florida Lawyer of the Year, George Carr Award for Excellence in Federal Practice, Stetson University's College of Law Ben Watkins Award; Chair, American Bar Association Lawyers' Professional Liability Committee.
**Career:** Complex litigation including professional liability, products liability and general commercial matters.
**Personal:** JD, University of Florida College of Law, 1967; BS, BA, The Citadel, with honors, 1963.

**HOFFMAN, Jerome**
Holland & Knight LLP, Tallahassee
850 224 7000
jerome.hoffman@hklaw.com
*Featured in Antitrust (Florida)*
**Practice Areas:** Partner in Litigation Section, practicing primarily in antitrust, consumer fraud, RICO, and Medicaid and Medicare fraud, qui tam and other health care regulatory matters. Served as Chief of the Antitrust Section of the Florida Attorney General's Office, handling cases involving bid rigging, price fixing, monopolization and other restraints of trade; and as General Counsel for the Florida Agency for Health Care Administration, where he supervised 40 attorneys responsible for prosecuting Medicaid overpayments, regulating hospitals, nursing homes, assisted living facilities and prosecuting disciplinary cases before the Board of Medicine. Board Certified in Antitrust Law by the Florida Bar.

**HOGAN, John M**
Holland & Knight LLP, Miami
305 374 8500
john.hogan@hklaw.com
*Featured in Litigation (Florida)*
**Practice Areas:** John Hogan serves as the firmwide Chair of Holland & Knight's Litigation Section. He is a White Collar litigator and has tried over 75 jury trials. His experience includes civil and criminal litigation in the areas of Internal Investigations, securities fraud and Foreign Corrupt Practices Act issues. Hogan is the former chief of staff to the Attorney General of the United States and served as Acting United States Attorney for the Northern District of Georgia in Atlanta. He also served as chief assistant state attorney for Miami-Dade County, Florida, where he successfully tried several nationally significant cases.

**HORNREICH, Michael**
Greenberg Traurig, LLP, Orlando
407 418 2397
HornreichM@gtlaw.com
*Featured in Construction (Florida)*
**Practice Areas:** Co-Chair, Construction Litigation Practice. Engaged exclusively in Construction law -; Formulating project delivery systems. Contract negotiations. Development of claims and damage models, defense of claims, and dispute resolution during construction projects. Tried major construction disputes in jury and bench trials, and arbitration.
**Professional Memberships:** Member: Associated General Contractors of America (AGC).
**Career:** Selected: Florida Super Lawyers magazine, 2006-12; 'Legal Elite', Florida Trend Magazine, 2004-12; Best Lawyers in America, 2003-13; Chambers USA Guide, 2003-13. Rated, AV® Preeminent™ 5.0 out of 5.
**Personal:** JD, University of Florida Levin College of Law; BS, Environmental Engineering, University of Florida.

**HUTTON III, John B**
Greenberg Traurig, LLP, Miami
305 579 0788
HuttonJ@gtlaw.com
*Featured in Bankruptcy/Restructuring (Florida)*
**Practice Areas:** Business reorganization, financial restructuring; bankruptcy litigation; purchase, sale of assets of financially distressed companies; indenture trustee representations; hospitality industry restructurings; financial institution liquidation.
**Professional Memberships:** Member, Bankruptcy Bar Association for the Southern District of Florida; Immediate Past Board Chairman, Family Resource Center of Dade County; Member: American Bankruptcy Institute; Dade County Bar Association; Co-Chair of the American Bankruptcy Institute, Asset Sale Committee.
**Career:** Best Lawyers in America, 2009-13; Super Lawyers, 2006-12; 'Legal Elite', Florida Trend, 2005-07; Chambers USA, 2005-13; AV® Preeminent™ 5.0 out of 5.
**Personal:** JD, Columbia University School of Law; BA, with honors, Johns Hopkins University.

**IANNO JR, Joseph**
Carlton Fields, P.A., West Palm Beach
561 650 8008
jianno@carltonfields.com
*Featured in Litigation (Florida)*
**Practice Areas:** Trial counsel in claims involving fraud, conspiracy, theft of trade secrets, breach of fiduciary duty, and other corporate misconduct claims.
**Professional Memberships:** Admitted in Florida and US Court of Appeals, Eleventh Circuit. Co-Chair, Class and Derivative Actions Subcommittee, Section of Business Law, American Bar Association.
**Career:** Martindale-Hubbell AV Rating.
**Publications:** Co-Author, "Annual Review of Developments in Business and Corporate Litigation," Ch. 7, Class Action Law, ABA Section of Business Law, Committee on Business and Corporate Litigation (2012 ed. Vol. 1).
**Personal:** JD (cum laude), Stetson University College of Law, 1986; BS (President's Honor Roll), University of Florida, 1984.

**IBARRA, Yosbel A**
Greenberg Traurig, LLP, Miami
305 579 0706
IbarraY@gtlaw.com
*Featured in Latin American Investment (Florida)*
**Practice Areas:** Corporate and securities; global; global energy and infrastructure; mergers and acquisitions. Assists Latin American and European businesses doing business in the US and Latin America.
**Career:** Listed: Chambers Global, Corporate & Finance Latin America, and USA Guide; member, team ranked as the No.1 corporate law firm in Miami, as selected by corporate directors, in the annual 'Legal Industry Research Study' by Corporate Board Member magazine; Latin Lawyer Magazine, M&A Deal of the Year Award, 2008; The Times, 'Future Stars of America', 2008.

**Personal:** JD, New York University School of Law; BS, with honors, University of Florida.

**JIMÉNEZ, Marcos Daniel**
McDermott Will & Emery LLP, Miami
305 329 4458
mjimenez@mwe.com
*Featured in Litigation (Florida)*
**Practice Areas:** Mr Jiménez handles complex business and white-collar criminal litigation. In 2011, Marc was featured in The National Law Journal's "Winning" issue and the Daily Business Review as South Florida's "Most Effective Lawyer" in Complex Business Litigation.
**Career:** Mr Jiménez served as the US Attorney for the Southern District of Florida from 2002-05, leading approximately 230 prosecutors in nationally significant cases. He served as an Assistant US Attorney from 1988-92, successfully first-chairing numerous criminal trials and appeals.
**Personal:** Born in Havana, Cuba, he speaks Spanish and graduated third in his class from the University of Miami School of Law.

**JOSEFSBERG, Robert C**
Podhurst Orseck P.A., Miami
305 358 2800
RJosefsberg@Podhurst.com
*Featured in Litigation (Florida)*
**Practice Areas:** A broad range of civil and criminal litigation in all federal and state courts.
**Career:** One of Miami-Dade County's premiere trial lawyers, listed annually since 1987 in the Best Lawyers in America in two categories-Business Litigation and Criminal Law. Past President and Dean of the International Academy of Trial Lawyers, a Fellow of the American College of Trial Lawyers and a member of the American Board of Trial Advocates. He has served on the American Bar Association Standing Committee on the Judiciary, as Chairman of the Southern District of Florida Judicial Evaluation Committee, and the Florida State University Law School Board of Visitors. In addition to commercial practice, he also handles the firm's white-collar criminal defense work - an outgrowth of his background as an assistant US attorney for the Southern District of Florida, as Special Counsel to the Dade County Grand Jury, and member of numerous commissions and task forces in the area of criminal law, including the US Supreme Court Advisory Committee on Criminal Rules and Chairmanship of the Florida Bar's Criminal Law Certification Committee.
**Personal:** BA Dartmouth College, 1959; JD Yale Law School, 1962.

**KARLINSKY, Fred**
Colodny, Fass, Talenfeld, Karlinsky, Abate & Webb PA, Fort Lauderdale
954 332 1749
fkarlinsky@cftlaw.com
*Featured in Insurance (Florida)*
**Practice Areas:** Mr Karlinsky, Shareholder, leads the firm's Insurance Regulatory and Government Affairs Divisions. He represents insurers and reinsurers throughout the United States and internationally in a wide variety of

business, operational, regulatory, transactional and governmental matters.
**Professional Memberships:** Among others, he is a member of the Insurance Regulatory Examiners Society Foundation Board of Directors and Federation of Regulatory Counsel.
**Career:** He lectures in London and Bermuda on insurance and reinsurance issues. He is admitted to the Roll of Solicitors of the Senior Courts of England and Wales. He is an Adjunct Professor at Florida State University College of Law.

**KAVOUKJIAN, Michael E**
White & Case LLP, Miami
212 819 8403
mkavoukjian@whitecase.com
*Featured in Wealth Management (Nationwide), Tax (Florida)*
**Career:** Mr Kavoukjian is chairman of the Firm's Private Clients Group. He advises high-net-worth individuals and families worldwide in all aspects of estate planning, including tax-advantaged transfers of assets, multigenerational planning, the taxation of trusts and estates, charitable giving, pre-nuptial and post-nuptial planning, and issues relating to change of residence. Working closely with investment advisors, insurance planners and accountants, he ensures a coordinated approach to clients' needs. Michael also has broad experience in the administration of trusts and estates and complex estate-related litigation, both international and domestic, including high-stakes will contests and construction proceedings. To view his biography, please visit www.whitecase.com/mkavoukjian.

**KAYE, Joshua**
DLA Piper LLP (US), Miami
305 423 8521
joshua.kaye@dlapiper.com
*Featured in Healthcare (Florida)*
**Practice Areas:** Health Care.
**Career:** He is co-chair of the firm's Health Care sector and concentrates his practice in health care mergers and acquisitions and the development of innovative business models within the health care industry. He advises clients in all aspects of federal and state health care regulatory matters, including anti-kickback, self referral laws, state licensure, Certificate of Need, insurance laws and HIPAA.
**Personal:** JD, University of Miami School of Law (magna cum laude); BA, University of Florida (with honors).

**KEHOE, Greg W**
Greenberg Traurig, LLP, Tampa
813 601 4253
KehoeG@gtlaw.com
*Featured in Litigation (Florida)*
**Practice Areas:** Litigation; global - Africa.
**Professional Memberships:** Member, Herbert G. Goldburg Inn of Court (Criminal Law); Hillsborough County Bar Association; International Bar Association; National Association of Criminal Defense Lawyers; New York State Bar Association; The Florida Bar. Membership Officer, IBA Criminal Law Committee, January 2011-Present.

**Career:** Listed, Best Lawyers in America, 2009-13; Super Lawyers magazine, 2007-12; Florida Trend, 'Legal Elite', 2004, 2008-09, 2011-12. Rated, AV® Preeminent™ 5.0 out of 5.

**Personal:** JD, St. John's University School of Law, 1979 (Dean's List; Law Review, June 1979); AB, summa cum laude, Political Science-English, Boston College, 1976.

## KEINER, Jeffrey
GrayRobinson, PA, Orlando
407 244 5644
jeffrey.keiner@gray-robinson.com
*Featured in Construction (Florida)*

**Practice Areas:** Trial lawyer since 1974 in personal injury, wrongful death, complex commercial litigation, construction, Endangered Species, RCRA, CERCLA, power plants, permitting, administrative proceedings; architect, engineer, land use and real estate litigation, water, wastewater and storm water, legal, medical and accounting malpractice, intellectual property; ADA/Fair Housing Act litigation, sports, entertainment, intellectual property litigation. Florida Supreme Court certified mediator since 1989 and a member of the American Arbitration Association Complex and Commercial Arbitration Panel. A neutral and advocate in several hundred arbitrations and mediations including matters exceeding $100 million. Serves as mediator, arbitrator, special master. Energy and industrial process facilities, contracts, intellectual property, construction.

**Professional Memberships:** Supreme Court; State and Federal Courts; Florida Bar, Trial Lawyers, IP, Environmental Land Use, Sports Entertainment Sections; American Bar Association, Forum Committee on Construction; American Arbitration Association; American Institute Architects; American College Barristers; Million Dollar Advocates Forum; Federal Bar Association; College of Master Advocates and Barristers.

**Personal:** University of Michigan, JD (1974); Miami University, Ohio, AB 1968; Lt. USS AULT, DD-698, 1968-71.

## KENDIG-SCHRADER, Julie
Greenberg Traurig, LLP, Orlando
407 418 2417
Kendig@gtlaw.com
*Featured in Real Estate (Florida)*

**Practice Areas:** Environmental; land development; transportation; carbon credits; climate change; green building and sustainable development; global energy and infrastructure.

**Professional Memberships:** Member: Board of Directors, Osceola/Kissimmee Chamber of Commerce; Land Use and Environmental Law Section, Florida Bar; Administrative Law Section, Florida Bar.

**Career:** Listed: Florida: Land Use & Zoning, The Legal 500 US: Volume IV; Best Lawyers in America; Super Lawyers magazine.

**Personal:** JD, University of Florida Levin College of Law; MA, University of Florida; BA, University of Florida.

## KENNEDY III, James J
Carlton Fields, P.A., Tampa
813 229 4379
jjkennedy@carltonfields.com
*Featured in Healthcare (Florida)*

**Practice Areas:** Representation of hospitals, physicians, multi-specialty clinics, and other health care providers. Extensive experience in health care business transactions, hospital-physician joint ventures, managed care contracting, risk management issues, and fraud and abuse prevention.

**Professional Memberships:** Admitted in Florida and Illinois. American Health Lawyers Association; Florida Academy of Hospital Lawyers; The Florida Bar.

**Career:** Board Certified as Health Law Specialist by The Florida Bar. Martindale-Hubbell AV Rating. Panelist, "Impact of Health Reform on Medical Professionals," AM Best Co., webinar (February 3, 2011).

**Personal:** JD, DePaul University, 1982; BS, Florida State University, 1979.

## KETCHUM, Elena
Stichter, Riedel, Blain & Prosser PA, Tampa
813 229 0144
eketchum@srbp.com
*Featured in Bankruptcy/Restructuring (Florida)*

**Practice Areas:** Chapter 11 business reorganizations; workouts and out-of-court loan and debt restructurings; assignments for the benefit of creditors; asset acquisitions and sales in bankruptcy cases.

**Professional Memberships:** The Tampa Bay Bankruptcy Bar Association (Chair 2011-12, President 2010-11, member of Board of Directors, 2006-12); active member of Business Law Section of The Florida Bar; The Hillsborough County Bar Association (Receipient of James M "Red" McEwen Award for Outstanding Service to the Bar and the Community, 2006); American Bankruptcy Institute; International Women's Insolvency & Restructuring Confederation.

**Career:** Joined Stichter, Riedel, Blain & Prosser, P.A. in 2001. Prior to joining the firm, Ms Ketchum was an Assistant State Attorney with the State Attorney's Office for the Thirteenth Judicial Circuit, Hillsborough County, Florida, assigned to the Felony Division. Rated "AV Preeminent" by Martindale-Hubbell. She has been invited to speak on insolvency related matters, including workouts, assignments for the benefit of creditors and other bankruptcy related topics.

**Personal:** JD, University of Florida College of Law (with honors); BA, Agnes Scott College (with high honors); Phi Beta Kappa.

## KIBERT, Nicole C
Carlton Fields, P.A., Tampa
813 229 4205
nkibert@carltonfields.com
*Featured in Real Estate (Florida)*

**Practice Areas:** Represents developers in the creation of planned communities, condominiums, and subdivisions with special emphasis on projects involving sustainable development.

**Professional Memberships:** Admitted in Florida. Executive Council, Chair-Elect of Environmental and Land Use Law Section, The Florida Bar.

**Career:** Certified mediator; LEED® Accredited Professional.

**Publications:** Co-Author, "Summary of the 2011 Florida Laws Impacting Condominiums, Homeowners Associations and Cooperatives," eReport, ABA Section of Real Property, Trust and Estate Law (October 2011).

**Personal:** JD (high honors), University of Florida (2003); MS, University of Florida (2000); BS, George Washington University (1997); Humboldt University of Berlin (2002); University of Costa Rica (2001)

## KING, Bruce C
Carlton Fields, P.A., Miami
305 539 7244
bking@carltonfields.com
*Featured in Construction (Florida)*

**Practice Areas:** Commercial litigation and appeals specializing in construction and surety cases.

**Professional Memberships:** Admitted in Florida, Pennsylvania, US Court of Federal Claims. Vice-Chair, Fidelity and Surety Law Committee, American Bar Association; American Arbitration Association.

**Career:** Board Certified in Construction Law by The Florida Bar. Martindale-Hubbell AV rating.

**Publications:** "The Surety's Exposure to Delay Damages," Fidelity & Surety Law Committee, Tort and Insurance Practice Section, ABA (January 2011); "Liability of the Performance Bond Surety for Delay, Consequential and Liquidated Damages," Surety Claims Institute (2009).

**Personal:** JD, University of Pittsburgh, 1978; BA (cum laude), Allegheny College, 1975.

## KLEIN, Larry
Holland & Knight LLP, West Palm Beach
561 650 8304
larry.klein@hklaw.com
*Featured in Litigation (Florida)*

**Practice Areas:** Partner in the Litigation Section with a practice concentrating on appeals and trial support and also serves as an arbitrator, mediator and special master. Mr Klein was appointed to Florida's 4th District Court of Appeal in 1993, where he served until 2009. He has argued more than 50 cases in the Florida Supreme Court and hundreds of cases in the Florida and Federal appellate courts. Mr Klein's significant Florida Supreme Court representations include: Great Southern Bank v. First Southern Bank, Hermanson v. State of Florida, and International Bankers Insurance Company v. Arnone.

## KLUGER, Alan J
Kluger, Kaplan, Silverman, Katzen & Levine, P.L., Miami
305 379 9000
akluger@klugerkaplan.com
*Featured in Litigation (Florida)*

**Practice Areas:** Recently described as a "power-house trial attorney" by a major Manhattan newspaper, Alan is a veteran courtroom lawyer who represents some of the nation's largest financial institutions, Fortune 500 corporations, emerging entrepreneurs, major commercial real estate developers and national private equity groups in their most challenging litigation matters. He is also a trusted legal advisor to a number of celebrities and other high-profile individuals on matrimonial and family law issues. Many of his current clients have come to him after first facing him as an adversary. His success in litigation, he will tell you, is won well before he ever sets foot in a court-room.

**Professional Memberships:** American Bar Association; The New York State Bar; The Florida Bar; Dade County Bar Association; Florida Supreme Court Society.

**Career:** Admitted to the Florida Bar (1975); District of Columbia Bar (1978); U.S. Supreme Court, 1979; New York State Bar (1981); US District Court, Southern and Middle Districts of Florida (1981, 1982); Eastern and Southern Districts of New York (2009); US Court of Appeals, First Circuit (2004), Second Circuit (1985), Third Circuit (1991), Fifth Circuit (1975), Ninth Circuit, (1982), Tenth Circuit (1996), Eleventh Circuit, (1981). Founding Member of Kluger Kaplan Silverman Katzen & Levine, P.L.

**Personal:** University of Miami School of Law, JD, cum laude (1975); Bryant University, BS, magna cum laude (1972); thirty years of notable contributions to the South Florida legal, business and charitable communities. President of personally funded Private Charitable Foundation dedicated to funding the needs in the Jewish, Medical and Educational spheres. Possesses a world class collection of Latin American Art dating from 1945 to the present. Founder of University of Miami School of Medicine Sylvester Comprehensive Cancer Center.

## KNIGHT, David T
Hill Ward Henderson, Tampa
813 227 8478
dknight@hwhlaw.com
*Featured in Litigation (Florida)*

**Practice Areas:** Commercial litigation, antitrust and trade regulation, construction and design litigation.

**Professional Memberships:** Board Certified in Civil Trial Law, Business Litigation, and Antitrust and Trade Regulation Law by The Florida Bar, Board Certified by National Board of Trial Advocacy, Best Lawyers in America, AV Rated by Martindale-Hubbell, Florida Trend's Legal Elite, Florida Super Lawyers Top 100, American Bar Foundation Fellow, American College of Trial Lawyers Fellow.

**Career:** Complex business litigation including extensive work in business torts.

**Personal:** JD, University of Florida College of Law, 1974; BA, Emory University, 1971.

## KOREN, Edward
Holland & Knight LLP, Tampa
813 227 8500
ed.koren@hklaw.com
*Featured in Wealth Management (Nationwide), Tax (Florida)*
**Professional Memberships:** ABA's Real Property, Probate and Trust Law Section, Past Chair; ACTEC, Estate and Gift Tax Committee, Past Chair and Regent.
**Career:** Edward F Koren chairs Holland Knight's Private Wealth Practice. He assists high net worth clients, entrepreneurs and multi-generational businesses to attain and maintain their financial and estate planning goals. He also handles IRS transfer tax controversies involving succession and income taxes, and is involved in probate and trust litigation.
**Publications:** "Estate and Personal Financial Planning," a five-volume treatise by West that covers planning for asset accumulation and transfer throughout life and through inheritance.

## KORNREICH, David
Fisher & Phillips LLP, Orlando
407 541 0852
dkornreich@laborlawyers.com
*Featured in Labor & Employment (Florida)*
**Career:** David Kornreich is a Partner in the Orlando office. He represents private and public employers in all types of labor and employment matters, including collective bargaining, labor arbitration, non-jury and jury trials in state and federal courts, arguments before state and federal appellate courts, and administrative proceedings before the NLRB, the US Department of Labor, the EEOC, and other federal, state, and local agencies. Kornreich served with both the US Department of Labor in Washington, DC and the National Labor Relations Boards of Tampa and Miami prior to entering private practice.

## KOZYAK, John W
Kozyak Tropin & Throckmorton, Miami
305 372 1800
jk@kttlaw.com
*Featured in Bankruptcy/Restructuring (Florida)*
**Practice Areas:** Commercial bankruptcy, receivership and commercial litigation.
**Professional Memberships:** Fellow, American College of Bankruptcy (1992-); Fellow, American Academy of Trial Lawyers (2005-), ABA Business Bankruptcy (1980-).
**Career:** Former Managing Partner, Chair, Litigation Department of major firm. Co-founder, Kozyak Tropin & Throckmorton (1982-present). Represents corporate debtors, secured/unsecured creditors, equity, management, committees, trustees in major bankruptcies, including all aspects of real estate financing-related litigation. Has been appointed Trustee and Receiver.
**Personal:** University of Illinois (BS Marketing, cum laude, 1970); Washington University School of Law (JD, 1975).

## KREITZER, Michael N
Bilzin Sumberg Baena Price & Axelrod LLP, Miami
305 350 2384
mkreitzer@bilzin.com
*Featured in Litigation (Florida)*
**Practice Areas:** Co-Chair of Litigation Practice Group; one of Miami's premier trial lawyers representing entrepreneurs, major financial institutions, real estate developers, and private equity groups in complex and challenging business litigation matters.
**Professional Memberships:** Board Certified in Business Litigation, The Florida Bar. Consistently recognized by Chambers, Benchmark Litigation, Best Lawyers in America, Local Litigation Stars, Florida Trend's Legal Elite; AV® Preeminent™ 5.0 out of 5, Litigation Counsel of America.
**Personal:** JD, with honors, National Law Center at George Washington University, 1987; BS, magna cum laude, University of Florida, 1984. Chair Emeritus, The Wolfsonian-FIU Museum; Chair, Friends of WLRN Radio/TV.

## LASH, Nancy B
Greenberg Traurig, LLP, Miami
305 579 0884
LashN@gtlaw.com
*Featured in Real Estate (Florida)*
**Practice Areas:** Co-Chair, Miami Real Estate. Real estate operations; complex commercial real estate transactions; commercial leasing/lending, including ground leases.
**Professional Memberships:** Member: Florida Bar Association, Real Property, Probate and Trust Law Section; CREW Member. Trustee, United Way.
**Career:** Honored: 'Women Extraordinaire', Business Leader Magazine, 2011. Listed: Best Lawyers in America, 2008-13; Super Lawyers, 2006-07, 2009-12. Selected, Daily Business Review 'Top Dealmaker of the Year - Industrial (Real Estate) Category', 2012. Shortlisted, Chambers USA 'Women in Law' Awards, 2012. Rated, AV® Preeminent™ 5.0 out of 5.
**Personal:** JD, Boston University School of Law, 1987; BA, cum laude, Duke University, 1984.

## LAURIA, Thomas E
White & Case LLP, Miami
305 995 5282
tlauria@whitecase.com
*Featured in Bankruptcy/Restructuring (Nationwide), Bankruptcy/Restructuring (Florida), Bankruptcy/Restructuring (New York)*
See under Nationwide for profile.

## LAURO, John
Lauro Law Firm, Tampa
813 222 8990
JLauro@laurolawfirm.com
*Featured in Litigation (Florida)*
**Practice Areas:** White-collar criminal defense, commercial litigation.
**Professional Memberships:** American Bar Association, Association of the Bar of the City of New York, Federal Bar Association, Hillsborough County Bar Association, The Florida Bar, The New York Bar, The District of Columbia Bar, Federal Court Bars in Florida, New York, and District of Columbia.
**Career:** John F Lauro is a former federal prosecutor in New York City with a national white collar criminal defense and commercial litigation practice. Mr Lauro has offices in Florida and New York City and handles a broad array of complex commercial and criminal matters involving allegations of securities fraud, foreign corrupt practices, computer crimes, contract disputes, healthcare fraud, tax fraud, money laundering, anti-trust, and other matters. He represents businesspeople and professionals in connection with complex securities, healthcare, and other matters around the country.

## LEAR, Steven D
Bilzin Sumberg Baena Price & Axelrod LLP, Miami
305 350 2390
slear@bilzin.com
*Featured in Corporate/M&A (Florida)*
**Practice Areas:** Mergers and acquisitions; joint ventures; corporate and securities; partnerships and strategic alliances; private equity and corporate finance; taxation.
**Professional Memberships:** The Florida Bar, Member of Executive Council of Business Law Section and Recording Secretary of the Chapter 608 Redrafting Committee of Business Law Section; American Bar Association; American Institute of Certified Public Accountants; Florida Institute of Certified Public Accountants; American Association of Attorneys-Certified Public Accountants.
**Career:** JD, LLM, CPA; partner in the Bilzin Sumberg Corporate and Securities Department; practicing more than 25 years, including heading the legal departments of two large Florida companies; Listed: Chambers, 2010-Present; Best Lawyers in America 2011-Present; Lawdragon 500, Finalist, 2007 and 2008; Daily Business Review, South Florida Top Dealmakers of the Year, Finalist, 2010; Double Finalist, 2007; Daily Business Review, South Florida Most Effective Lawyers, 2005.
**Personal:** LLM (Taxation), University of Florida, 2002; JD, summa cum laude, University of Florida Levin College of Law, Senior Managing Editor, University of Florida Law Review, 1986; BS (Accounting), cum laude, University of Vermont, 1978.

## LEONHARDT, Frederick
GrayRobinson, PA, Orlando
407 843 8880
fred.leonhardt@gray-robinson.com
*Featured in Real Estate (Florida)*
**Practice Areas:** Shareholder in the Banking and Finance, Education, Environmental, Government, Land Use, Real Estate, and Utilities practice areas. Experience includes dealing with federal, state and local governments on behalf of private and government clients. Background in state and local government law matters including permitting and procurement.
**Professional Memberships:** American Bar Association; The Florida Bar; Orange County and Volusia County Bar Associations; Member of Florida, North Carolina and Washington, D.C. Bar; Designated Professional Lobbyist, Florida Association of Professional Lobbyists.
**Career:** AV Rated by Martindale-Hubbell. Listed in Leading Florida Attorneys in the areas of Real Estate/Land Use and Local Government Law. Florida Trend "Legal Elite," continuously since 2004. Most Influential Businessman, Orlando Business Journal, 2004-05; Nominee for Most Influential Man, 2011. 50 Most Powerful People, Orlando Magazine, 2010-12. Top Central Florida Lawyers, Orlando Magazine. Top 25 Power Players, Orlando Sentinel. Selected for Best Lawyers in America continuously since 2006. Florida Super Lawyers, continuously since 2006. Who's Who in American Law, Who's Who in Florida, Who's Who in the USA, and Who's Who in the World.
**Personal:** University of Florida, BA (Psychology, 1971); University of Florida, JD (1974).

## LESTER JR, Edgel C
Carlton Fields, P.A., Tampa
813 229 4231
elester@carltonfields.com
*Featured in Real Estate (Florida)*
**Practice Areas:** Commercial and real estate transactions including secured, unsecured and asset-based loans, real estate and equipment sales, leases and acquisitions, loan workouts. Serves as title agent for mutliple title insurance companies.
**Professional Memberships:** Admitted to practice in Florida, US Court of Appeals. Chair, Finance Subcommittee, Business Law Section, American Bar Association; American College of Commercial Finance Lawyers; Association of Commercial Finance Attorneys; Real Estate Investment Council.
**Career:** Martindale-Hubbell AV Rating.
**Publications:** "Tenant Leasing Strategies: Improving Your Position" (Counsel to Counsel Magazine, 2006).
**Personal:** JD, University of Kentucky, 1982; MA, Middle Tennessee State University, 1975; BA, Vanderbilt University, 1972.

## LEVENSON, Fred
McDermott Will & Emery LLP, Miami
305 347 6552
flevenson@mwe.com
*Featured in Corporate/M&A (Florida)*
**Practice Areas:** Focuses on a broad range of corporate counseling and sophisticated domestic and international transactions – primarily private equity (leveraged buyouts), domestic and international mergers, acquisitions and divestitures, venture capital investments and financings, private and public offerings of equity and debt securities, restructurings, joint ventures, strategic alliances, and real estate acquisitions and financings.
**Professional Memberships:** Admitted to practice in Florida.
**Personal:** University of Miami School of Law, JD, 1993; University of Miami School of Business, MBA, 1990; Tulane University, BSM, 1988.

## LEVIN, Oscar
Greenberg Traurig, LLP, Miami
305 579 0880
Levin0@gtlaw.com
*Featured in Immigration (Florida)*
**Practice Areas:** Board Certified in Immigration and Nationality Law. Founder, Immigration Department.
**Professional Memberships:** Member, The Florida Bar; American Immigration Lawyers Association (AILA); Dade County Bar Association; Member, The Florida Bar Association, Immigration and Nationality Law Certification Committee.
**Career:** Listed: Florida Super Lawyers, 2006-12; Chambers USA Guide, 2006-13; Chambers Global, 2011-13; as a leading practitioner in field, The International Who's Who of Corporate Immigration Lawyers, 2005-08.
**Publications:** Publishes and lectures in the US, Europe and Asia on immigration and nationality matters.
**Personal:** JD, University of Florida Levin College of Law; BA, University of Florida.

## LEVINE, A Kenneth
Cozen O'Connor, West Palm Beach
*Featured in Insurance (Florida)*
**Practice Areas:** For almost two decades, has provided substantive counsel to industry and government clients concerning all aspects of insurance and warranty regulation, including licensing, mergers/acquisitions, market conduct/financial examinations, rate/form filings, reinsurance, accounting issues, coverage litigation, holding company formation, and administrative litigation.
**Professional Memberships:** Federation of Regulatory Counsel; American Bar Association; International Association of Insurance Receivers, INSOL International, Half-Axe International, Certified Insurance Mediator, Florida Department of Financial Services.
**Publications:** Has published numerous articles and given speeches on various topics in all lines.
**Personal:** Tulane University Law School, JD; Tulane Freeman School of Business, BSM; Tulane, AB.

## LIEBERMAN, Philippe
Kluger, Kaplan, Silverman, Katzen & Levine, P.L., Miami
305 379 9000
plieberman@klugerkaplan.com
*Featured in Litigation (Florida)*
**Practice Areas:** Philippe has nearly twenty years of experience representing and advising domestic and international entities and individuals, including Fortune 500 companies, entrepreneurs and developers, in complex business disputes involving real estate, commercial foreclosures, lender liability, financial fraud, partnership and shareholder agreements, fiduciary obligations, corporate governance, shareholder derivative issues, property insurance and breach of contract. He handles cases in courts throughout the United States, and in arbitrations before the American Arbitration Association (AAA) and National Association of Securities Dealers (NASD).

Philippe uses his knowledge and understanding of finance and business to grasp the broader issues and develop creative strategies to exceed his clients' expectations and goals.
**Professional Memberships:** Dade County Bar Association; The American Bar Association; The Florida Bar; Grievance Committee 11 N (1999 - 2004), Committee Chair (2002-04).
**Career:** Admitted to The Florida Bar (1994); US District Court, Southern District of Florida (1995); US District Court, Middle District of Florida (2006). Founding Member of Kluger Kaplan Silverman Katzen & Levine, P.L.
**Publications:** "Expropriation, Torture and Jus Cogens under the Foreign Sovereign Immunities Act: Siderman de Blake v Republic of Argentina," 24 University of Miami Inter-American Review 5033 (1993).
**Personal:** University of Miami School of Law, JD, cum laude (1994); New York University, BS (Finance and International Business), cum laude (1991); Greater Miami Jewish Federation, Olam leadership; born in Europe and fluent in French.

## LINNAN, Nancy G
Carlton Fields, P.A., Tallahassee
850 513 3611
nlinnan@carltonfields.com
*Featured in Real Estate (Florida)*
**Practice Areas:** Environmental/land use, administrative law, and government consulting.
**Professional Memberships:** Admitted in Florida and US Supreme Court. Chair, Florida Chamber Growth Management Leadership Task Force. Chair, Tallahassee Leon County Civic Center Authority.
**Career:** Martindale-Hubbell AV Rating. Assistant Secretary, Florida Department of Community Affairs (1983-85); Assistant Deputy Attorney General and Chief, Division of Cabinet Affairs for the Florida Attorney General (1979-83); Assistant General Counsel for Governor (1977-78).
**Publications:** Panelist, "A New Era for Land Use Management," FSU College of Law Environmental Law Forum (November 2011).
**Personal:** JD (with honors), Florida State University College of Law, 1974; BA, Dickinson College, 1970.

## LITCHFORD, Hal
Baker, Donelson, Bearman, Caldwell & Berkowitz, Orlando
407 367 5401
hlitchford@bakerdonelson.com
*Featured in Antitrust (Florida)*
**Practice Areas:** Shareholder with practice devoted to the litigation, trial and appeal of significant business-related disputes. Experience includes antitrust and trade regulation matters, non-compete and trade secret law and intellectual property law.
**Professional Memberships:** DC, Orange County, Florida and American Bar Associations. Board Certified by the Florida Bar in Antitrust and Trade Regulation.
**Career:** Florida, 1979. DC (1978) US District Court, Middle, Southern and Northern Districts of Florida (1980, 1981). US Court of Appeals,

Fifth and Eleventh Circuits (1981). US Supreme Court and US Court of Appeals, Federal Circuit (1988).
**Personal:** University of Virginia School of Law, JD, 1978.

## LOCKETT, Laurel E
Carlton Fields, P.A., Tampa
813 229 4139
llockett@carltonfields.com
*Featured in Environment (Florida)*
**Practice Areas:** Environmental and commercial real estate law, including industrial and domestic wastewater, storage tank regulation, landfill, used oil and hazardous waste permitting and regulation, Florida Brownfields designation and redevelopment, asbestos and indoor air quality issues.
**Professional Memberships:** Admitted in Florida. Group Vice-Chair, Environmental and Land Use Subcommittees, Real Property, Probate and Trust Law Section, American Bar Association.
**Career:** Martindale-Hubbell AV Rating.
**Publications:** "DEP Streamlines Process for Implementing Restrictive Covenants Required for Cleanup Closure With Conditions," Florida Specifier (September 2012).
**Personal:** JD, Boston University College of Law, 1984; BA (with honors), Smith College, 1977.

## LOPEZ-CASTRO, Corali
Kozyak Tropin & Throckmorton, Miami
305 372 1800
clc@kttlaw.com
*Featured in Bankruptcy/Restructuring (Florida)*
**Practice Areas:** Bankruptcy, receiverships, creditors' rights and commercial litigation.
**Professional Memberships:** President, Cuban American Bar Association (2006); Panel of Federal Bankruptcy Trustees, Southern District of Florida (1998-2002); Chair, Executory Contracts Subcommittee (ABA Business Law Section) (2009-11); Chair, Bankruptcy Litigation Subcommittee (ABA Business Law Section)(2011-present).
**Career:** Specializes in representing creditors and debtors in Chapter 11 bankruptcy cases, receivers, and Trustees in Chapter 7. Kozyak Tropin & Throckmorton (1990-95 and 1997-present); Hahn Loeser & Parks (Cleveland, Ohio, 1995-97).
**Personal:** Brown University (AB, 1987); University of Miami School of Law (JD, 1990, cum laude).

## LOUMIET, Carlos
DLA Piper LLP (US), Miami
305 423 8543
carlos.loumiet@dlapiper.com
*Featured in Latin American Investment (Florida), Banking & Finance (Florida)*
**Practice Areas:** Latin American investment.
**Career:** For more than 30 years he has advised clients in the business and financial services fields. He has been involved in numerous mergers and acquisitions, securities offerings, venture capital deals, financings, infrastructure projects and other commercial transactions, often across borders. He has dealt with regulators and other governmental

authorities in different countries and in a variety of contexts.
**Personal:** JD, Yale Law School; MA and BA, Oxford University (with First Class Honors (Marshall Scholarship); BA, Yale University (summa cum laude) Phi Beta Kappa.

## LOURIE, Andrew
Kobre & Kim LLP, Miami
305 967 6107
andrew.lourie@kobrekim.com
*Featured in Litigation (Florida)*
**Practice Areas:** Andrew C Lourie is an experienced trial attorney who practices in the areas of government enforcement defense, international judgment enforcement and asset recovery, investigations and monitorships, and financial products and services litigation. Mr Lourie has represented numerous corporate officers in matters involving bribery/FCPA, IEEPA, securities and commodities futures, insider trading, and various other laws with international applications. He is engaged by major international corporations to conduct internal investigations in connection to the FCPA.
**Career:** Prior to joining Kobre & Kim, Mr Lourie served in various high-level positions with the US Department of Justice, including as Principal Deputy Assistant Attorney General and Chief of Staff for the Criminal Division and as Chief of the Public Integrity Section. Mr Lourie also served as an Assistant US Attorney in the Southern District of Florida, where he investigated and prosecuted securities fraud and healthcare fraud cases and headed the West Palm Beach office. He also served as an Assistant US attorney in the District of New Jersey, focusing on public corruption matters. Prior to working as an Assistant US Attorney, Mr Lourie practiced at Gibson, Dunn & Crutcher LLP in New York.

## LOWRY, Patricia E
Squire Sanders (US) LLP, West Palm Beach
561 650 7214
patricia.lowry@squiresanders.com
*Featured in Litigation (Florida)*
**Practice Areas:** Partner with more than 25 years' experience defending products including prescription and over-the-counter medications and medical devices, and representing employers in whistleblower and other employment claims. Listed as national products liability star in Benchmark Litigation in 2009; Who's Who Legal: Florida for product liability; The Best Lawyers in America; Florida Super Lawyers – Top 50 Females; Florida Trend's Legal Elite; and previously listed in Lawdragon 500 Leading Lawyers in America.
**Professional Memberships:** American College of Trial Lawyers, Fellow; FBA, Palm Beach County, president 2004-05; Supreme Court of Florida's Judicial Ethics Advisory Committee, chair; International Association of Defense Counsel.

## LUMISH, Wendy F
Carlton Fields, P.A., Miami
305 539 7266
wlumish@carltonfields.com
*Featured in Litigation (Florida), Products Liability (Nationwide)*

**Practice Areas:** Appellate practice with focus on products liability, personal injury, and medical malpractice defense, and legal issues of national significance.

**Professional Memberships:** Admitted in Florida and Minnesota. Fellow, American Academy of Appellate Lawyers; Product Liability Advisory Council.

**Career:** Board Certified in Appellate Practice by The Florida Bar. Martindale-Hubbell AV Rating. Distinguished Service Award, presented by the Products Liability Advisory Council (2006).

**Publications:** Co-Author, "Time For A Legislative Overhaul of the Sunshine in Litigation Act," The Florida Bar Journal (May 2011).

**Personal:** JD (cum laude), University of Miami School of Law, 1981; BA (suma cum laude), Lehigh University, 1978.

### LUMPKIN, Cristina
Bilzin Sumberg Baena Price & Axelrod LLP, Miami
305 350 7241
clumpkin@bilzin.com
*Featured in Environment (Florida)*

**Practice Areas:** Environmental and land use law, including regulatory, litigation, and transactional matters; environmental due diligence; site investigation and remediation; and environmental permitting, including wetlands, waste management, and limestone mining.

**Professional Memberships:** Admitted to Northern District of Florida, Southern District of Florida, and US Court of Appeals for the Eleventh Circuit. American Bar Association; Florida Association of Environmental Professionals; South Florida Association of Environmental Professionals; Commercial Real Estate Women (CREW)-Miami.

**Personal:** JD, summa cum laude, University of Miami School of Law, 2006; BA, MA, Geography, University of Hawaii at Manoa; Board Member, Centro Campesino Farmworker Center, Inc.

### MACCULLOUGH, Kara L
Greenberg Traurig, LLP, Fort Lauderdale
954 768 8255
MacCulloughK@gtlaw.com
*Featured in Corporate/M&A (Florida)*

**Practice Areas:** Corporate and securities; mergers and acquisitions.

**Professional Memberships:** Member: The Florida Bar, Business Law Section; International Section; American Bar Association.

**Career:** Selected: Best Lawyers in America, 2012-13; Chambers USA Guide, 2006-13; 'Top Dealmakers of the Year', Daily Business Review, 2011 winner and finalist 2007-10; Florida Super Lawyers magazine, 2010.

**Personal:** JD, magna cum laude, Order of the Coif, University of Miami School of Law; BA, cum laude, Wellesley College.

### MACLENNAN, Alexandra M
Squire Sanders (US) LLP, Tampa
813 202 1353
alexandra.maclennan@squiresanders.com
*Featured in Banking & Finance (Florida)*

**Practice Areas:** Partner with 25+ years' experience as bond, disclosure and underwriters counsel in transactions financing facilities for health care, higher education, airports, electric utilities and traditional municipal projects, among others. Represents public hospital districts and non-profit hospital organizations, as well as serves as bond counsel on state level public education and environmental projects bond programs. Listed in The Best Lawyers in America each year since 2006. Leads Squire Sanders disclosure group and frequent panelist on municipal securities and disclosure matters.

**Professional Memberships:** Fellow, American College of Bond Counsel; Member, Board of Directors of the National Association of Bond Lawyers.

### MANDEL, Jeffrey E
Fisher & Phillips LLP, Orlando
407 541 0850
jmandel@laborlawyers.com
*Featured in Labor & Employment (Florida)*

**Career:** Jeffrey Mandel is the Managing Partner of the Orlando office. He represents private and public-sector employers in all aspects of employment and labor law. He counsels clients on employment issues, including: employment discrimination and retaliation, civil rights, ADA accommodations, FMLA compliance, wage and hour, military leave, employment policies, employment agreements, and non-competition and trade secret agreements. He litigates employment discrimination and retaliation cases before state and federal courts and administrative agencies. His practice also includes representation of employers before the National Labor Relations Board and the Florida Public Employees Relations Commission, as well as representing management in labor arbitrations.

### MARCH, Bruce I
Greenberg Traurig, LLP, Fort Lauderdale
954 768 8227
MarchB@gtlaw.com
*Featured in Corporate/M&A (Florida)*

**Practice Areas:** Corporate and securities; mergers and acquisitions; buyouts, recapitalizations.

**Career:** Selected: Winning Deal Team - Distressed M&A Deal of the Year (Over $100mm), 2011 Turnaround Awards, The M&A Advisor, 2011; Chambers USA Guide, 2007-13; Best Lawyers in America, 2011-13; one of the Top Lawyers in Florida, South Florida Legal Guide, 2004-05, 2009-12; Top Dealmakers of the Year 2010 - International Corporate (M&A) Category, Daily Business Review, 2010; Top Dealmakers of the Year Finalist - International Corporate (M&A) Category, Daily Business Review, 2011.

**Personal:** JD, New York University School of Law; BA, cum laude, Economics, Brandeis University.

### MARK, Etan
Berger Singerman, Miami
305 714 4360
emark@bergersingerman.com
*Featured in Litigation (Florida)*

**Career:** Etan Mark focuses his practice on business litigation and, as a Certified Fraud Examiner, has a particular passion for the analysis and dissection of claims of fraud. Etan is a former federal law clerk and splits his practice in state and federal court. He has litigated and resolved cases brought under the Racketeering Influenced and Corrupt Organizations Act (RICO), has extensive experience in disputes concerning the purchase and sale of commercial real estate, shareholder derivative actions, alleged insurance fraud and alleged government contract fraud. Etan regularly advises clients on corporate governance and fiduciary duty matters. Some of Etan's significant representations include: defense counsel to international bank accused of assisting former South American head-of-state launder millions of dollars and commit fraud under RICO; counsel to engineering company accused of violations under the False Claims Act, RICO, the Florida Deceptive and Unfair Trade Practices Act and common law fraud; and counsel to real estate developers in connection with all aspects of their business, including foreclosure litigation, contract disputes with purchasers, warranty issues, partnership disputes and regulatory compliance.

### MARKOWITZ, Jerry M
Markowitz Ringel Trusty + Hartog P.A., Miami
305 670 5000
jmarkowitz@mrthlaw.com
*Featured in Bankruptcy/Restructuring (Florida)*

**Practice Areas:** Jerry Markowitz's practice focuses on all aspects of debtor and creditor rights including workouts, bankruptcy, bankruptcy litigation, asset recovery, insolvency, receiverships, reorganization, restructuring, and mediation.

**Professional Memberships:** Past-President of the Bankruptcy Bar Association for the Southern District of Florida, Co-Chair of the American Bankruptcy Institute Southeast Bankruptcy Workshop Advisory Board, Southeast Regional Co-Chair of the American Bankruptcy Institute Endowment Fund, Past-President of the University of Miami School of Law Alumni Association, and Best Lawyers in America.

**Career:** Managing Shareholder and founder of Markowitz, Ringel, Trusty + Hartog, P.A., a civil law practice founded in 1980.

**Personal:** For more information, please visit the firm's website at www.mrthlaw.com.

### MARTIN, Enrique J
Greenberg Traurig, LLP, Miami
305 579 0857
EJM@gtlaw.com
*Featured in Latin American Investment (Florida)*

**Practice Areas:** Corporate and securities; mergers and acquisitions; private equity.

**Professional Memberships:** Member: Council of the Americas; The Florida Bar; American Bar Association; Director, US - Mexico Bar Association.

**Career:** Rated, AV® Preeminent™ 5.0 out of 5. Listed: Chambers USA Guide, 2007-13; Best Lawyers in America, 2008-13; 'Florida Legal Elite', Florida Trend magazine, 2007-09; Florida Super Lawyers magazine, 2007, 2009-12; member, team selected by Chambers and Partners for 'Corporate & Finance - Law Firm of the Year (Florida-Based)' Award, Chambers Latin America Awards, 2010-11.

**Personal:** JD, University of Pennsylvania Law School; BS, cum laude, Finance, Florida State University.

### MASER, Joel D
Greenberg Traurig, LLP, Orlando
407 418 2389
MaserJ@gtlaw.com
*Featured in Tax (Florida)*

**Practice Areas:** Tax; real estate; real estate funds; hospitality.

**Professional Memberships:** Active Member, Executive Council, The Florida Bar Tax Section and is the Chair-Elect of the Tax Section.

**Career:** Selected: Best Lawyers in America, 2005-13; Super Lawyers magazine, 2007-12; Chambers USA Guide, 2003-13. Team Member, a Law360 'Real Estate Practice Group of the Year', 2011-12.

**Personal:** JD, magna cum laude, University of Miami School of Law; BS, with honors, University of Florida.

### MAYOL, Juan J
Holland & Knight LLP, Miami
305 789 7787
juan.mayol@hklaw.com
*Featured in Real Estate (Florida)*

**Practice Areas:** Partner in Holland & Knight's Real Estate Section and practices in the areas of land use, zoning and governmental. He represents builders, retailers, financial institutions, educational facilities, developers and institutional owners in all aspects of land use law through the entire entitlement process, from comprehensive planning to zoning and subdivision approvals. Mayol also represents vendors in connection with procurement matters. Mayol has developed extensive experience in the representation of charter schools and in the re-entitlement process of failed real estate assets. In addition, Mayol assists clients in connection with environmental matters as those may impact their development projects.

### MCALEAVEY, Tom
Holland & Knight LLP, Orlando
407 425 8500
tom.mcaleavey@hklaw.com
*Featured in Corporate/M&A (Florida)*

**Career:** Tom McAleavey practices in the area of mergers and acquisitions, securities and corporate governance. His experience has included domestic and cross-border private company acquisitions and dispositions, public company mergers and acquisitions, tender offers and proxy contests. He has represented both issuers and underwriters in public offerings and private placements of debt and equity securities. He has advised public companies on disclosure, compliance and governance matters arising out of SEC regulations, stock exchange rules and listing standards, and other regulatory and corporate requirements.

## MCALILEY, Neal
White & Case LLP, Miami
305 995 5255
nmcaliley@whitecase.com
*Featured in Environment (Florida)*

**Career:** Mr McAliley's areas of practice include environmental litigation, regulatory matters before governmental agencies, and general civil and criminal litigation. He also leads the firm's Climate Change group. Mr McAliley advises clients on a wide range of environmental issues, including federal agency permitting, wetland jurisdiction, airport environmental issues and the criminal enforcement of federal environmental laws. Mr McAliley is highly experienced regarding litigation with federal agencies under NEPA, the Endangered Species Act and related federal environmental statutes. To view a comprehensive biography, please visit www.whitecase.com/nmcaliley.

## MCCARTHY, Timothy J
Hughes Hubbard & Reed LLP, Miami
305 379 5575
mccarthy@hugheshubbard.com
*Featured in Latin American Investment (Florida)*

**Practice Areas:** Securities and capital markets; corporate; corporate governance; equipment finance; banking and financial services; international joint ventures and other strategic alliances; Latin America; mergers and acquisitions; project finance.

**Career:** Coudert Brothers (resident in Rio de Janeiro, Brazil office 1977-86); Hughes Hubbard & Reed LLP Partner 1995-2011(Chair/Co-chair of Latin American practice), Senior Counsel 2012
**Personal:** Harvard University, AB, 1967 (cum laude); University of Michigan Law School, JD, 1972; Fluent in Portuguese.

## MCCLURE, Frederick
DLA Piper LLP (US), Tampa
813 222 5908
fredrick.mcclure@dlapiper.com
*Featured in Litigation (Florida)*

**Practice Areas:** Litigation: general commercial.
**Career:** He is an experienced litigator who concentrates in conflict resolution. He holds a number of leadership positions within the firm, including managing partner of the Tampa office and practice group leader of the Litigation practice in Tampa, National Diversity and Inclusion Partner and a member of the firm's Executive and Policy Committees.
**Personal:** JD, University of Cincinnati; BA, Earlham College.

## MCCREA JR, Richard C
Greenberg Traurig, LLP, Tampa
813 318 5723
McCreaR@gtlaw.com
*Featured in Labor & Employment (Florida)*

**Practice Areas:** Board Certified: Labor and Employment and Civil Trial Lawyer, Florida Bar Board of Legal Specialization and Education.
**Professional Memberships:** Vice-Chair, Miles for Moffitt Board of Directors; Past Chair: The Florida Bar, Labor & Employment Section; The

Florida Bar, Board of Legal Specialization and Education.
**Career:** Listed: Best Lawyers in America; Super Lawyers magazine, 'Top 100 Super Lawyers', Florida. Fellow, College of Labor and Employment Lawyers; The International Who's Who of Management Labour & Employment Lawyers, 2009-12. Rated, AV® Preeminent™ 5.0 out of 5.
**Personal:** JD, Rutgers School of Law - Newark; BA, Rutgers College - New Brunswick.

## MCDOWELL, Carter N
Bilzin Sumberg Baena Price & Axelrod LLP, Miami
305 350 2355
cmcdowell@bilzin.com
*Featured in Real Estate (Florida)*

**Practice Areas:** Land use and zoning; administrative law; appellate law; hospitality and marinas; government relations.
**Professional Memberships:** American Institute of Certified Planners; Urban Land Institute; International Council of Shopping Centers; Florida Atlantic Builders Association (FABA); Builders Association of South Florida, President's Award, 2005.
**Career:** Counsel for: The Fontainbleau, The Ritz Carltons South Beach and Key Biscayne, St Regis Bal Harbour; Dolphin, Miami International and Pembroke Lakes Malls; Miami Beach, Conch Harbor and River Cove Marinas; Ocean Club, Consultatio Bal Harbour and Fontainbleau II Condominiums; and Dolphin Commerce Center. Consistently recognized by Chambers USA, The Best Lawyers in America, and Florida Super Lawyers; AV® Peer Review Rated, Martindale-Hubbell, 25+ years.
**Personal:** JD (cum laude), University of Miami School of Law, University of Miami Law Review member; MAURP (Phi Beta Kappa), University of Florida; BA (cum laude), Harvard College.

## MCGUIGAN, Thomas R
Squire Sanders (US) LLP, West Palm Beach
561 650 7278
thomas.mcguigan@squiresanders.com
*Featured in Corporate/M&A (Florida)*

**Practice Areas:** Specialized in corporate, securities, public/private financings and M&A for public and privately held entities for 35+ years. Represents clients in public and private debt, equity and hybrid financings and in investments in private and public entities. Advises clients on SEC reporting and corporate governance requirements. Represents purchasers, sellers and investors in M&A transactions involving privately and publicly held companies, individuals in US and international transactions and regulated entities including healthcare and financial institutions. Consistently recognized as a top leader within the legal community and nationally ranked in corporate/M&A law by Chambers USA and The Best Lawyers in America.

## MCKENNA, Susan
Jackson Lewis LLP, Orlando
407 246 8429
McKennaS@jacksonlewis.com
*Featured in Labor & Employment (Florida)*

**Practice Areas:** Litigation experience includes Title VII, Age Discrimination in Employment Act, Equal Pay Act, ADA, FMLA and FLSA. Counsels employers and conducts management training on workplace law issues.
**Professional Memberships:** Federal Bar Association, The Florida Bar, Orange County Bar, Central Florida Association for Women Lawyers, Hotel Human Resources Association, Central Florida Hotel and Lodging Association.
**Career:** Jackson Lewis, 2000 to present; Garwood McKenna, 1984-2000; Akerman Senterfitt, 1982-84.
**Publications:** Published several articles on employment law issues.
**Personal:** Indiana University, BA, summa cum laude, 1978; Duke University School of Law, JD, 1982. Recognized by peers in national, state and local publications.

## MEEKS, Thomas J
Carlton Fields, P.A., Miami
305 530 4063
tmeeks@carltonfields.com
*Featured in Litigation (Florida)*

**Practice Areas:** Complex business cases, including commercial fraud, contract disputes, trade secrets and intellectual property matters, and the defense of corporate officers and directors, including securities litigation.
**Professional Memberships:** Admitted in Florida and Georgia. Former Co-Chair, Civil Procedure Rules Committee, The Florida Bar; Past Vice Chair, Ad Hoc Committee on Attorney Admissions, Peer Review & Attorney Grievance, US District Court, Southern District of Florida; Past Chair, Ad Hoc Committee on Rules and Procedures, US District Court, Southern District of Florida.
**Career:** Martindale-Hubbell AV Rating.
**Personal:** JD, University of Florida College of Law, 1979; BA (high honors), University of Florida, 1975.

## MEHTA, Eileen B
Bilzin Sumberg Baena Price & Axelrod LLP, Miami
305 350 2380
emehta@bilzin.com
*Featured in Real Estate (Florida)*

**Practice Areas:** Land use, local government law, appeals. Partner in Bilzin Sumberg's Government Relations & Land Development Group.
**Professional Memberships:** Admitted to Florida, US District Court (Southern District of Florida), US Court of Appeals (Eleventh Circuit); Coral Gables Chamber of Commerce.
**Career:** Benchmark Appellate, Eleventh Circuit Litigation Star, 2013; The Best Lawyers in America, 1995 - Present; Daily Business Review's Most Effective Lawyers, Winner, Real Estate Law

2012, Finalist, Public Interest 2011; Rated, Martindale-Hubbell® AV Preeminent®.
**Personal:** JD (cum laude), University of Miami School of Law, 1977; BA (with high distinction), Florida International University, 1977.

## MENCHEL, Matthew I
Kobre & Kim LLP, Miami
305 967 6108
matthew.menchel@kobrekim.com
*Featured in Litigation (Florida)*

**Practice Areas:** Matthew I Menchel is a highly-regarded and experienced trial lawyer who has served as lead counsel in numerous high-profile white-collar criminal and complex civil trials. Mr Menchel focuses his practice on the representation of companies and individuals who are a subject of wide range of allegations, including securities law violations, antitrust violations, Foreign Corrupt Practices Act ("FCPA") enforcement, money laundering, and tax evasion, among other regulatory issues. He regularly represents domestic and international clients in connection with investigations brought by the US Government, including the US Department of Justice, the US Securities and Exchange Commission, and the Federal Energy Regulatory Commission ("FERC"), to name a few.
**Career:** Prior to joining Kobre & Kim LLP, Mr Menchel served in the US Attorney's Office for the Southern District of Florida where he worked in Economic Crimes and Public Corruption units handling large complex white-collar cases. As Chief of the Criminal Division, Mr Menchel supervised over 150 federal prosecutors. Mr Menchel also served for eleven years as an Assistant District Attorney in the New York County District Attorney's Office during which time he trained numerous Assistant District Attorneys in trial advocacy as a Director of Legal Training.
**Personal:** Among many experienced trial attorneys at the firm, Mr Menchel stands out for his skill in the courtroom. He regularly serves as the principal trial lawyer in the firm's most important trials and is Director of the firm's Center for Trial Advocacy.

## MENCIO JR, George
Holland & Knight LLP, Miami
305 374 8500
george.mencio@hklaw.com
*Featured in Latin American Investment (Florida)*

**Career:** Mr Mencio is co-leader of the firm's International and Cross Border Transactions Practice Group, Chair of International Initiatives, and member of the Directors' Committee. He focuses on cross-border M&A and joint venture transactions, dispute resolution, administrative matters relating to international trade and commerce and transportation industry. He's experienced in analysis of foreign countries' competition, licensing and franchise laws; foreign investment restrictions affecting mergers and acquisitions; currency restrictions; and joint ventures. His clients include multinational concerns in transportation, tourism, mining and agricultural sectors, major airlines, software and technology companies, and providers of goods and services in the international arena.

### MENÉNDEZ-CAMBÓ, Patricia
Greenberg Traurig, LLP, Miami
305 579 0766
PMC@gtlaw.com
*Featured in Latin American Investment (Florida)*

**Practice Areas:** Mergers and acquisitions; joint ventures and strategic alliances; capital markets; cross-border financing transactions; project finance; international regulatory and antitrust matters.
**Professional Memberships:** Board Member: Council of the Americas; University of Pennsylvania Law School; Institute for International and Comparative Law.
**Career:** At Greenberg Traurig, Patricia serves as Chair of the Global Practice, Co-Chair of the Global Energy and Infrastructure Practice and as Vice President of GT. Patricia has been lead counsel on numerous first-time cross-border transactions throughout the United States, Latin America and Europe. Listed: Chambers USA; Chambers Latin America; Chambers Global; International Financial Law Review; Best Lawyers in America; Legal 500 Latin America; Super Lawyers; Winning Team, Latin Lawyer Deal of the Year - Restructuring Award, 2012; Winning Team, Distressed M&A Deal of the Year (Over $100mm), 2011 Turnaround Awards, The M&A Advisor. Selected by National Law Journal: 50 Most Influential Minority Lawyers in America, 2008; 50 Most Influential Women Lawyers in America, 2007; 100 Most Influential Lawyers in America, 2006; 40 Under 40, 2005. Also selected Young Global Leader, World Economic Forum.
**Personal:** JD, University of Pennsylvania Law School, 1989; BBA, Economics, University of Miami, 1986.

### MEYER, George J
Carlton Fields, P.A., Tampa
813 229 4140
gmeyer@carltonfields.com
*Featured in Construction (Florida)*

**Practice Areas:** Real property transactions, construction law, commercial loan transactions, condominium law, preparation, negotiation, and administration of design and construction contracts.
**Professional Memberships:** Admitted to practice in Florida and US Supreme Court. Fellow, American College of Real Estate Lawyers; Past Chair, Forum on Construction Industry, American Bar Association; Past Chair and Executive Committee Member, Real Property, Probate and Trust Law Section, The Florida Bar.
**Career:** Board Certified in Construction Law by The Florida Bar. Martindale-Hubbell AV Rating.
**Personal:** JD (with honors), University of Tulsa College of Law, 1985; BA, BS, State University of New York, Stony Brook, 1974, 1978.

### MILLER, James C
Greenberg Traurig, LLP, Orlando
407 317 8554
MillerJC@gtlaw.com
*Featured in Construction (Florida)*

**Practice Areas:** Construction law; contracts, litigation; global; power; transportation; green building and sustainable development; catastrophe planning and response; defense and homeland security.
**Career:** Board certified Construction Lawyer, past licensed Professional Engineer in the fields of civil, mechanical and control systems engineering. Held PE licenses in several states, including New Mexico, South Carolina, Florida, Georgia and California. Listed: Legal 500 US, 2011-12; Chambers USA Guide, 2008-09, 2012-13.
**Personal:** JD, Georgia State University College of Law; MBA, International Management, California State University Los Angeles; MS, Civil Environmental Engineering, University of California at Irvine; BA, Mechanical Engineering, California State University Fullerton. LEED AP.

### MILLER, Morris H
Holland & Knight LLP, Tallahassee
850 224 7000
morris.miller@hklaw.com
*Featured in Healthcare (Florida)*

**Career:** Mr Miller, a Partner on Holland & Knight's Healthcare & Life Sciences Team, focuses on transactional and regulatory matters within the healthcare and senior living industries. Mr Miller represents owners and operators of healthcare and senior living facilities and businesses and has structured, negotiated, and documented numerous acquisitions, dispositions, leases, financings, and other transactions. He represents healthcare entities in matters involving federal and state 'anti-kickback' and patient self-referral laws; Medicare and Medicaid reimbursement issues; health facility licensure and other healthcare regulatory issues; and various kinds of contracts for health care facilities, senior living facilities, and medical practices.

### MITCHELL, Stephen J
Squire Sanders (US) LLP, Tampa
813 202 1302
stephen.mitchell@squiresanders.com
*Featured in Real Estate (Florida)*

**Practice Areas:** Partner focusing on real estate development, commercial real estate, banking/finance, hotel/conference center development, international law and administrative law. Listed in The Best Lawyers in America. Designated a Florida Super Lawyer in Florida Trend.
**Professional Memberships:** Hillsborough County Aviation Authority, past chair, board of directors; ACI-NA, past board member; Florida 2020 Energy Study Commission; Central Florida Technology Transit Corridor Consortium, past chair; The Florida Bar, International and Real Property Law Sections; US delegation to the Union International des Avocats, board of governors; International Committee, Tampa Chamber of Commerce, past chair; member, Board of Trustees, University of South Florida.

### MORA, Mindy A
Bilzin Sumberg Baena Price & Axelrod LLP, Miami
305 350 2414
mmora@bilzin.com
*Featured in Bankruptcy/Restructuring (Florida)*

**Practice Areas:** Corporate restructuring, creditor's rights, workouts and bankruptcy; asset protection; commercial finance; commercial real estate litigation.
**Professional Memberships:** The Florida Bar, Business Law Section, Chair 2011-12; Association of Commercial Finance Attorneys, Executive Board; Bankruptcy Bar Association of South Florida; American Bar Association, Business Law Section, Business Bankruptcy Committee; International Women's Insolvency and Restructuring Confederation.
**Career:** Admitted to Florida, California, New York, US District Court (Eastern and Southern Districts of New York, Central District of California, Southern and Northern Districts of Florida), US Bankruptcy Court (Middle District of Florida).
**Personal:** JD, NYU School of Law, 1982; BBA, GW University, 1979.

### MOSKOWITZ, Adam M
Kozyak Tropin & Throckmorton, Miami
305 377 0652
amm@kttlaw.com
*Featured in Litigation (Florida)*

**Practice Areas:** Class action litigation.
**Professional Memberships:** American Trial Lawyers Association, Florida Trial Lawyers, American Bar.
**Career:** Experienced in all forms of class action claims, including RICO, antitrust, deceptive and unfair trade practices, and breach of contracts. He frequently leads Kozyak Tropin & Throckmorton's participation in multi-state class action litigation that involves teams of class action firms from around the nation.
**Personal:** Syracuse University (BA); University of Miami School of Law (JD, cum laude).

### MOYE, James E
Moye, O'Brien, O'Rourke, Pickert & Dillon, LLP, Maitland
407 622 5250
jmoye@moopd.com
*Featured in Construction (Florida)*

**Practice Areas:** Practice Areas: Construction. Has extensive experience representing US and international contractors, construction managers and engineering firms in the USA, the Caribbean basin, Central America and Canada in multi-million dollar contract reviews, contract negotiations, bid reviews and protests, claim preparation and disputes in all types of proceedings (dispute resolution boards, arbitrations and court).
**Professional Memberships:** State Bar of Georgia; The Florida Bar; Texas Bar; American Bar Association (Member, Sections on Labor and Employment Law, Forum on the Construction Industry); Fellow, Litigation Counsel of America, Diversity Law Institute; Certified Arbitrator, Florida Supreme Court; Court of Federal Claims Bar Association.
**Career:** Board certified in construction law by The Florida Bar; admitted to Georgia Bar (1982), Florida (1989); Texas (2012); Senior Partner of Moye, O'Brien, O'Rourke, Pickert & Dillon, LLP, Florida (24 years); admitted to US District Court, Middle and Southern Districts of Florida; US District Court of Northern Georgia; US Court of Appeals, Fifth, Eleventh and DC Circuits; US Supreme Court; Adjunct Professor, University of Central Florida, Dept. of Civil, Environmental & Construction Engineering.
**Publications:** Co-Author, "Construction Law," USA Chapter, The European Lawyer Reference Series, 2012.
**Personal:** Received a BSE (cum laude) from University of Central Florida in 1978 and a JD from University of Florida in 1981 as a member of the Law Review; inducted into Eta Kappa Nu (Electrical Engineering National Honor Society), Tau Beta Pi (Engineering National Honor Society) and Omicron Delta Kappa; and a member of the President's Leadership Council.

### MULDOWNEY, Patrick M
Baker & Hostetler LLP, Orlando
407 649 4002
pmuldowney@bakerlaw.com
*Featured in Labor & Employment (Florida)*

**Career:** Patrick Muldowney represents private- and public-sector management clients in traditional labor and employment law issues with respect to issues such as discrimination, sexual harassment, labor-management relations, family and medical leave, public employee rights, minimum wage/overtime compensation and covenants not to compete. Pat handles matters in federal and state courts and before agencies such as the National Labor Relations Board, US Equal Employment Opportunity Commission, Florida Commission on Human Relations, and Florida Division of Administrative Hearings. He is an adjunct professor at Rollins College, teaching a course on labor and employment law in the Master of Human Resources program.

### MURPHY, Lewis F
Squire Sanders (US) LLP, Miami
305 577 2957
lewis.murphy@squiresanders.com
*Featured in Litigation (Florida)*

**Practice Areas:** Led Squire Sanders' advocacy group in Florida for ten years. Has more than 30 years' experience with complex litigation especially "bet-the-company," corporate control, securities fraud, fiduciary duty class actions, derivative litigation, special litigation committees and internal board investigations in many industry sectors. Represents insurance carriers in matters including take-over battles, class actions for insurance retail sales improprieties and investigations by the Florida insurance regulators and Florida Attorney General into systemic insurance sale practices. Has extensive experience with domestic and international commercial litigation including discovery in Western Europe and Latin America, and arguing many appellate cases.

## MURPHY PE, Michael G
Greenberg Traurig, LLP, Orlando
407 999 2509
MurphyMG@gtlaw.com
*Featured in Construction (Florida)*

**Practice Areas:** Litigation; product liability and mass torts litigation; global energy and infrastructure; construction litigation; OSHA; creditor's rights and commercial litigation.
**Professional Memberships:** Member: The American Society of Civil Engineers; The National Society of Professional Engineers; Construction Specifications Institute.
**Career:** Selected, Chambers USA Guide, 2009-13. Team Member: Law360 'Product Liability Practice Group of the Year', 2011; Law360 'Employment Practice Group of the Year', 2011.
**Publications:** Frequent speaker on issues related to construction litigation and OSHA compliance.
**Personal:** JD, Rutgers School of Law-Camden; MS, University of Central Florida; BS, Civil / Structural Engineering, Drexel University; LTJG, US Naval Reserve, 1986-89.

## NAPPER, Kevin J
Carlton Fields, P.A., Tampa
813 229 4312
knapper@carltonfields.com
*Featured in Litigation (Florida)*

**Practice Areas:** White collar criminal defense, governmental investigations, internal investigations, complex civil trial law.
**Professional Memberships:** Admitted in Florida, North Dakota, and US Supreme Court. Fellow, American Bar Foundation; Past Co-Chair, Corporate Criminal Liability Subcommittee, Past Co-Chair, Criminal Justice Section White Collar Crime Committee, American Bar Association; Chair, 13A Grievance Committee, The Florida Bar; National Association of Criminal Defense Lawyers.
**Career:** Martindale-Hubbell AV Rating. Assistant State Attorney, Deputy Chief, Hillsborough County State Attorney's Office (1987-93). Special Assistant US Attorney (1989-90).
**Personal:** JD, University of North Dakota School of Law, 1984; BA (with honors), Moorhead State University, 1981.

## NELSON, Barry
Nelson & Nelson PA, North Miami Beach
305 932 2000
barry@estatetaxlawyers.com
*Featured in Tax (Florida)*

**Practice Areas:** Estate planning, asset protection, probate administration, tax law, corporate/partnership/LLC/business law, special needs trusts.
**Professional Memberships:** Past Chairman, Asset Protection Committee, member of the Business Planning Committee of the American College of Trust and Estate Counsel (ACTEC); Adjunct Professor 1998-2009, University of Miami School of Law LLM, Taxation; Founding Chairman Asset Protection Committee of the Real Property, Probate and Trust Law Section The Florida Bar; Past President, Greater Miami Tax Institute; Member Florida Institute of Certified

Public Accountants (FICPA); Co-Founder The Victory Center for Autism and Behayioral Challenges; Founding Chairman, National Ambassadors, American Committee for the Weizmann Institute of Science; Mayor Town of Golden Beach, 1993-95.
**Career:** Florida Bar Board Certified Tax and Wills and Trusts and Estates Attorney; listed consecutively, Best Lawyers in America since 1995; recognized as top lawyer by South Florida Legal Guide, Florida Super Lawyers and Florida Trend's Legal Elite.
**Publications:** Presented for the University of Miami Heckerling Institute on Estate Planning, the Notre Dame Tax and Estate Planning Institute, the Southern Federal Tax Institute, ACTEC, FICPA and the Florida Bar. Published articles in numerous professional journals. Introduced, coordinated and co-authored with Florida Bar committee members Asset Protection in Florida (Florida Bar CLE).
**Personal:** State University of New York at Binghamton, BS, Magna Cum Laude, 1974 and MS, Accounting, 1975. University of Miami, JD, Cum Laude, 1981 and LLM, Taxation, 1987. Lives in Golden Beach, Florida with his wife, Judith, and four children.

## NELSON, Howard E
Bilzin Sumberg Baena Price & Axelrod LLP, Miami
305 350 2386
hnelson@bilzin.com
*Featured in Environment (Florida)*

**Practice Areas:** Environmental counseling and litigation; inverse condemnation; regulatory matters including platting, permitting, groundwater contamination, hazardous waste, wetlands, and DRIs.
**Professional Memberships:** Chair, Fort Lauderdale Code Enforcement Board; Co-Chair, Environmental Sub-Committee, Builders Association of South Florida; Board Member, South Florida Association of Environmental Professionals; National Association of Industrial and Office Properties of South Florida.
**Career:** Chair of Bilzin Sumberg's Environmental Practice. Consistently recognized by Chambers USA, The Best Lawyers in America, and Florida Super Lawyers; Martindale-Hubbell™ Top Rated Lawyer, Land Use & Zoning, 2013.
**Personal:** JD, Nova Southeastern University, 1991; MAURP, University of Florida, 1985; BA, University of Florida, 1980.

## NICHOLS, Tracy A
Holland & Knight LLP, Miami
305 374 8500
tracy.nichols@hklaw.com
*Featured in Litigation (Florida)*

**Practice Areas:** Practice Group Leader of the firm's National Securities Litigation Group. She served as the lead lawyer representing issuers, directors, officers and underwriters in over three dozen securities class actions. She obtained one of the largest Rule 11 sanctions against plaintiffs and their counsel for filing a frivolous securities fraud case. She was a founding member of the Volunteer

Lawyers' Project for the Southern District of Florida, providing pro bono assistance to indigent clients. She's currently the co-Chair for the fundraising campaign for Miami Legal Services and a frequent lecturer at the state and national level on securities topics.

## NUECHTERLEIN, Michael F
Carlton Fields, P.A., Tampa
813 229 4109
mnuechterlein@carltonfields.com
*Featured in Construction (Florida)*

**Practice Areas:** Construction law, including litigation, arbitration, mediation, consulting and advising on construction related matters including contracts, claims, mechanic liens, design professional malpractice.
**Professional Memberships:** Admitted to practice in Florida. Fellow, American College of Construction Lawyers; Chair, Governing Committee, Forum on Construction Industry, American Bar Association; International Bar Association.
**Career:** Construction Master Arbitrator, American Arbitration Association; Certified Mediator, International Mediation Institute. Martindale-Hubbell AV Rating.
**Publications:** ABA Forum on Construction Industry: Lessons Learned: Agreements Outside the Contract Documents That Facilitate A Successful Project (2007).
**Personal:** JD (cum laude), University of Michigan Law School, 1973; BA, University of Michigan, 1965.

## OERTEL, Ken
Oertel, Fernandez, Bryant & Atkinson, P.A., Tallahassee
850 521 0700
koertel@ohfc.com
*Featured in Environment (Florida)*

**Practice Areas:** The founder of the firm, Mr Oertel has degrees in Biology and Law from New York University. He represents public and private clients in the areas of administrative, environmental, land use, agriculture, water use, wetlands and takings law, including permitting and litigation. His experience includes: Assistant US Attorney, Southern District of Florida; General Counsel, Florida Board of Trustees of the Internal Improvement Trust Fund; General Counsel, Department of Professional Regulation; and first Director of the Division of Administrative Hearings. He is the author of a book on Administrative Law.

## ORSHEFSKY, Debbie M
Greenberg Traurig, LLP, Fort Lauderdale
954 768 8234
OrshefskyD@gtlaw.com
*Featured in Real Estate (Florida)*

**Practice Areas:** Co-Chair, National Land Development Practice.
**Professional Memberships:** Member: Urban Land Institute; National Transit Oriented Development Product Council; Urban Land Institute Southeast Florida/Caribbean District Council, Executive Committee (member); Curtis Program Statewide Transportation Initiative;

'Connecting Florida' (founder). Member, Real Estate Development Advisory Board, Master of Science, Nova Southeastern University, 2010-Present.
**Career:** Selected: '100 Heavy Hitters in Commercial Real Estate', South Florida Business Journal, May 2011; Chambers USA Guide, 2004-13; Best Lawyers in America, 2006-13; Super Lawyers magazine, 2006-10, 2012; 'Top Lawyers', South Florida Legal Guide, 2005-12.
**Personal:** JD, George Washington University Law School; BA, summa cum laude, Washington University.

## PACE, Christopher
Weil, Gotshal & Manges LLP, Miami
305 416 3700
christopher.pace@weil.com
*Featured in Litigation (Florida)*

**Practice Areas:** Christopher R J Pace, a partner in Weil's Complex Commercial Litigation and Appellate practice groups, has extensive experience as lead counsel in numerous successful trials and appeals. He represents clients in US federal and state courts and focuses on large class actions and multi-district litigation, intellectual property disputes, and commercial cases. He is a former law clerk to Supreme Court Justice Anthony Kennedy and a former Assistant United States Attorney for the Southern District of Florida.
**Personal:** Southern Methodist University (BBA); University of Pennsylvania Law School (JD, first in class).

## PACKMAN, Kevin
Holland & Knight LLP, Miami
305 349 2261
kevin.packman@hklaw.com
*Featured in Tax (Florida)*

**Practice Areas:** Controversy; offshore tax compliance; international private wealth; preimmigration tax planning.
**Professional Memberships:** AICPA Foreign Trust Task Force, 2011-Present; AICPA FBAR Task Force, 2009-Present; ABA RPTE, Tax Litigation and Controversy Section, Co-Vice Chair, 2010-12, Chair 2012-13; Florida Bar - Tax Law Section, 2002-Present, Civil Tax Procedure, Chair, 2008-09, International Trusts & Estates, Vice Chair, 2011-12.
**Career:** Kevin Chair's the firm's Offshore Compliance Team; advises clients on Foreign Bank Account Reporting compliance; and guides clients through IRS examinations and audits. Additionally, Kevin assists taxpayers, whether coming into, remaining inside or leaving the United States, with wealth preservation, and tax planning.

## PAGE, Edward J
Carlton Fields, P.A., Tampa
813 229 4308
epage@carltonfields.com
*Featured in Litigation (Florida)*

**Practice Areas:** White collar criminal, aviation, product liability, wrongful death, and general commercial matters; regulatory enforcement including FBI, IRS, ATF, SEC, FDA, and Customs and Border Patrol Investigations.

**Professional Memberships:** Admitted in Florida, District of Columbia. Fellow, American Bar Foundation.

**Career:** Board Certified Criminal Trial Lawyer, The Florida Bar; Board Certified Criminal Trial Advocate, The National Board of Trial Advocacy; Martindale-Hubbell AV Rating; Former Deputy Independent Counsel, Office of Independent Counsel Kenneth Starr, Washington, DC (1998-99).

**Personal:** JD, University of Tulsa College of Law, 1981; BA, University of South Florida, 1978. Instrument-rated commercial pilot and flight instructor.

### PARKER, Clayton

K&L Gates, Miami
305 539 3306
clayton.parker@klgates.com
*Featured in Corporate/M&A (Florida)*

**Practice Areas:** Partner Clayton Parker has broad experience in representing public and private companies, including those in the telecommunications, manufacturing, shipping, alternative energy, software, and biotech sectors, in North America, Latin America, the European Union, Asia (with particular experience in The People's Republic of China) and Australia. He also represents private equity firms and their portfolio clients, hedge funds, venture capital funds, and entrepreneurs in diverse legal matters with an emphasis on IPOs, secondary offerings, SEC filings, Sarbanes-Oxley compliance, mergers and acquisitions, reverse merger transactions, secured lending, antitrust, employment issues, licensing and leasing agreements, distribution agreements, and joint ventures.

### PARRISH, Jimmy D

Baker & Hostetler LLP, Orlando
407 649 4048
jparrish@bakerlaw.com
*Featured in Bankruptcy/Restructuring (Florida)*

**Career:** Jimmy Parrish practices in the Bankruptcy, Restructuring and Creditors' Rights group and has extensive experience in a broad range of insolvency and business bankruptcy matters. Jimmy is Board Certified in Business Bankruptcy by the American Board of Certification and has represented corporate debtors, committees, trustees, secured lenders and other creditors in virtually every industry, including agriculture, airline, healthcare, manufacturing, communications, real estate and hospitality. Jimmy has been honored in current and past editions of the Florida Trend's Legal Elite and Florida Super Lawyers and is a member of the American Bankruptcy Institute and the Central Florida Bankruptcy Law Association.

### PASANO, Michael S

Carlton Fields, P.A., Miami
305 530 4064
mpasano@carltonfields.com
*Featured in Litigation (Florida)*

**Practice Areas:** Complex criminal, civil, antitrust and trade regulation, and securities litigation, including fraud and money-laundering,

forfeitures, tax issues, FDA, FTC and SEC cases, antitrust and environmental issues.

**Professional Memberships:** Admitted to practice in Florida, District of Columbia, Missouri, and US Supreme Court; Florida Association of Criminal Defense Lawyers.

**Career:** Martindale-Hubbell AV Rating. Formerly with the US Attorney's Office, Washington, DC and Southern District of Florida.

**Publications:** Co-author: "Internal Investigations: Why Two Are Better Than One," ABA White Collar Crime Newsletter (Spring 2009).

**Personal:** JD, Yale Law School, 1976; BA (summa cum laude), Georgetown University, 1973.

### PASTERNACK, Marshall

Bilzin Sumberg Baena Price & Axelrod LLP, Miami
305 350 2356
mpasternack@bilzin.com
*Featured in Corporate/M&A (Florida)*

**Practice Areas:** Corporate practice with primary emphasis on joint ventures and strategic alliances; mergers and acquisitions.

**Professional Memberships:** The Florida Bar; Florida Institute of Certified Public Accountants; United Way of Miami-Dade, Trustee; Coral Gables Cinematheque, Board of Directors; Adjunct Professor, University of Miami School of Law, Real Property Development LLM Program.

**Career:** Consistently recognized by Chambers USA, The Best Lawyers in America, and Florida Super Lawyers. Daily Business Review's Top Dealmakers of the Year Award, Real Estate - Hotel, 2010.

**Personal:** LLM, New York University, 1983; JD, University of Florida Levin College of Law, 1980; BS/BA, University of Florida, 1977.

### PELLE, Anthony

Carlton Fields, P.A., Miami
305 539 7274
apelle@carltonfields.com
*Featured in Insurance (Florida)*

**Practice Areas:** Insurance coverage, bad faith litigation, life, health, disability, including ERISA claims, property and casualty, liability insurance, complex commercial litigation and personal injury.

**Professional Memberships:** Admitted in Florida, California. Chair, Defense Research Institute Insurance Regulatory Committee; Former Chair, ABA TIPS Health and Disability Committee; Former member of the Board of Governors of the Association of Life Insurance Counsel.

**Career:** Martindale-Hubbell AV Rating.

**Publications:** Co-Author, "The World of Evolving Annuity Products," For the Defense Magazine published by the Defense Research Institute (2008).

**Personal:** JD (with honors), University of Florida College of Law, 1980; BA (high honors), University of Florida, 1978.

### PENCE, William L

Baker & Hostetler LLP, Orlando
407 649 4095
wpence@bakerlaw.com
*Featured in Environment (Florida)*

**Career:** Bill Pence represents utilities, municipalities, manufacturing facilities, bulk fuel pipeline and terminal facilities, developers and property owners in connection with the management of liabilities associated with contaminated properties. He also provides counsel on compliance with a broad range of environmental regulatory programs, including regulation of pipelines by PHMSA. Bill has significant experience managing the investigation and remediation of former manufactured gas plant, petroleum and chlorinated solvent contaminated sites; prosecution and defense of private party cost recovery actions; and defense of enforcement actions under CERCLA, RCRA, CWA, Pipeline Safety Act, and similar state regulatory programs, including regulation of landfills.

### PICKERT, Stephen W

Moye, O'Brien, O'Rourke, Pickert & Dillon, LLP, Maitland
407 622 5250
swpickert@moopd.com
*Featured in Construction (Florida)*

**Practice Areas:** Construction litigation involving contracts, construction defects, bonds, liens, delay claims, business torts and statutory claims for public, private, commercial and residential projects and representing owners, developers, general contractors, subcontractors, material suppliers and design professionals.

**Professional Memberships:** The Florida Bar, The ABA, AGC, ABC, Associated Owners & Developers, Construction Law Committee of The Florida Bar.

**Career:** Board certified in construction law by The Florida Bar; admitted to The Florida Bar in 1981; Senior Partner, Moye, O'Brien, O'Rourke, Pickert & Dillon, LLP; admitted in the US District Court for the Southern and Middle Districts of Florida and the United States Court of Appeals for the Fifth, Ninth and Eleventh Circuits, and the US Supreme Court.

**Publications:** Author: Civil Theft A Reemerging Weapon in Everyday Commercial Disputes, The Florida Bar Journal; lectured with The Associated General Contractors of America.

**Personal:** Bachelor of Science in Banking and Finance in 1978 from The University of Florida with high honors and graduated in 1981 from The University of Florida Law School with honors and as a member of The Law Review; AV (highest) rating by Martindale-Hubbell; Best Lawyers in America; Orlando's Best Lawyers; Florida Super Lawyers; Who's Who Legal (Florida Construction).

### PODHURST, Aaron S

Podhurst Orseck P.A., Miami
305 358 2800
APodhurst@Podhurst.com
*Featured in Litigation (Florida)*

**Practice Areas:** A broad range of civil litigation, including complex commercial litigation, aviation and mass tort litigation in all federal and state courts.

**Career:** His distinguished career has brought him honors and offices from virtually every major legal organization, including the presidencies of the International Academy of Trial Lawyers and The Florida Justice Association, fellowship in the American College of Trial Lawyers, Member of Board of Governors of Association of Trial Lawyers of America, membership in the International Society of Barristers and the Inner Circle of Advocates, and chairmanship of important aviation committees of the American Bar Association, American Association For Justice and The Florida Justice Association. Although he made his reputation as one of the nation's premiere plaintiff's aviation lawyers, and continues to hold that status, he has guided the firm in recent years to its status as one of the major commercial litigation firms in South Florida.

**Personal:** BA from the University of Michigan in 1957, and Harland Fiske Stone Scholar and Juris Doctorate Degree from Columbia University.

### POOLE, Samuel E.

Berger Singerman, Fort Lauderdale
954 712 5153
spoole@bergersingerman.com
*Featured in Environment (Florida)*

**Career:** Sam Poole has extensive experience in planning and zoning in the development and redevelopment of Florida's cities. He has two decades of experience addressing both conventional and new urbanism land development issues in Florida. Working for both private and public sector clients, Sam has prepared comprehensive plans, plan amendments, and land use codes enabling development of mixed use new urbanism projects from towns to neighborhoods to individual buildings. Sam has particular skills dealing with environmental constraints impacting the use of land and water, recognized by his service as Executive Director of the South Florida Water Management District from 1994 to 1999, where he directed a staff of 1700 with annual budgets of $500 million to restore the Everglades and protect South Florida's water supply and flood mitigation system.

### POSTLER, Charles

Stichter, Riedel, Blain & Prosser PA, Tampa
813 229 0144
cpostler@srbp.com
*Featured in Bankruptcy/Restructuring (Florida)*

**Practice Areas:** Mr Postler specializes in negotiating and drafting complex documents, including asset purchase agreements, stock purchase agreements, real estate documentation, debtor in possession loan documents, plans of reorganization and disclosure statements. Mr Postler also heads up the Firm's transactional practice while also making regular bankruptcy court appearances.

**Professional Memberships:** Hillsborough County Bar Association Tampa Bay Bankruptcy Bar Association American Bar Association,

Corporation, Banking and Business Law Member, American Bankruptcy Institute Turnaround Management Association.

**Career:** Charles A Postler joined the firm as a partner in 1991 after working eight years with the law firm of Fowler, White, Gillen, Boggs, Villareal and Banker, P.A. in Tampa, Florida, where he was a partner at the time of his departure. During his tenure with the Fowler, White law firm, he specialized in securities law, mergers and acquisitions, and corporation and banking law. Also while at Fowler, White, he served as co-counsel with the Stichter, Riedel law firm in the Trust America Chapter 11 bankruptcy case. Mr Postler specializes in negotiating and drafting complex documents, including asset purchase agreements, stock purchase agreements, real estate documentation, debtor in possession loan documents, plans of reorganization and disclosure statements. Mr Postler also heads up the Firm's transactional practice while also making regular bankruptcy court appearances. He recently headed up the firm's successful representation of two publicly traded companies, Accentia Biopharmaceuticals, Inc. and Biovest International, Inc. together with multiple related companies and he closed the restructuring of a $107 million loan on a British Virgin Island resort.

## PRATS, Luis
Carlton Fields, P.A., Tampa
813 229 4102
lprats@carltonfields.com
*Featured in Construction (Florida)*

**Practice Areas:** Complex commercial disputes, including all types of construction law and litigation involving defective construction, breach of contract, business torts fraud.
**Professional Memberships:** Admitted in Florida and US Court of Appeals. Chair Division 1 Steering Committee, The Forum on the Construction Industry, Litigation Section, American Bar Association; Chair of Judicial Relations Committee and member of Construction Law Certification Committee, The Florida Bar.
**Career:** Board Certified in Construction Law by The Florida Bar. Martindale-Hubbell AV Rated.
**Publications:** "International Mediation," (International Construction Law, ABA Forum on Construction Industry, 2009).
**Personal:** JD, Stetson University College of Law, 1981; BA, Stetson University, 1978.

## PRICE, Stanley B
Bilzin Sumberg Baena Price & Axelrod LLP, Miami
305 350 2374
sprice@bilzin.com
*Featured in Real Estate (Florida)*

**Practice Areas:** Represents developers, owners and institutional clients in land use/zoning matters; growth management; DRIs; entitlements; represents religious and private educational facilities.
**Professional Memberships:** Admitted to practice in Florida and New York. The Florida Bar; Dade County Bar Association; Chair, Local Policy

Council, Floridians for Smarter Growth; Counsel, Builders Association of South Florida; Latin Builders Association; Former Chair, Building and Zoning Committee, Miami Chamber of Commerce.
**Career:** Chair of Bilzin Sumberg's Government Relations & Land Development Group; Principal draftsman of important land use legislation in Florida.
**Personal:** JD, Syracuse University, 1969; BS (with honors), New York University, 1966.

## PRIETO, Peter
Podhurst Orseck P.A., Miami
PPrieto@podhurst.com
*Featured in Litigation (Florida)*

**Practice Areas:** A former federal prosecutor with significant trial experience. Prieto practices in the areas of complex civil litigation and white-collar criminal defense, representing individual and corporate clients in civil litigation, including commercial, business torts, securities fraud and class action litigation. He defends individual and corporate clients in criminal investigations and prosecutions involving public corruption, banking and healthcare fraud, and aviation and environmental violations. Prieto has represented clients in litigation in a variety of industries, including the healthcare, telecommunications, petroleum, aviation, entertainment and banking industries. Prieto has extensive experience prosecuting and defending RICO claims. He has also been involved at leadership level in several multi-district litigation ("MDL"), proceedings.

## RADFORD, William R
Ogletree, Deakins, Nash, Smoak & Stewart, PC, Miami
305 374 0506
william.radford@ogletreedeakins.com
*Featured in Labor & Employment (Florida)*

**Practice Areas:** Labor and Employment Law on behalf of management, including all phases of traditional public and private sector labor law. Develops best employment practices and defends through trial, complaints of federal and state employment law violations.
**Professional Memberships:** American Bar Association (Labor and Employment Section, and Litigation Section), The Florida Bar, Dade County Bar Association, Litigation Counsel of America.
**Career:** Admitted to practice in Florida.
**Publications:** Past contributor to the Developing Labor Law, a publication of the American Bar Association's Labor and Employment Law Section.
**Personal:** Wittenberg University (BA, 1963), University of Michigan Law School (JD, 1965).

## RASHBAUM, Daniel L.
Kobre & Kim LLP, Miami
305 967 6138
daniel.rashbaum@kobrekim.com
*Featured in Litigation (Florida)*

**Practice Areas:** Daniel L Rashbaum is an experienced trial lawyer who focuses his practice on cross-border white-collar criminal defense matters and regulatory investigations. Mr Rashbaum has extensive experience advising multinational companies and executives in investigations involving accounting fraud, money laundering, corruption, Foreign Corrupt Practice Act ("FCPA") enforcement, Office of Foreign Asset Control ("OFAC") violations, bid-rigging and anti-competitive conduct, among other issues. Mr Rashbaum also regularly represents clients in connection with investigations brought by the US Department of Justice and US Securities and Exchange Commission.
**Career:** Prior to joining Kobre & Kim LLP, Mr Rashbaum served as an Assistant US Attorney at the US Attorney's Office for the Southern District of Florida. While serving as an Assistant US Attorney, Mr Rashbaum served in the US Attorney's Office's Special Prosecutions Section where he conducted more than 30 jury trials and handled several oral arguments before the US Court of Appeals for the Eleventh Circuit. Before his time at the US Attorney's Office, Mr Rashbaum practiced at Skadden, Arps, Slate, Meagher & Flom, LLP and Morvillo, Abramowitz, Grand, Iason, & Anello, P.C. in New York.

## RASILE, Craig
DLA Piper LLP (US), Miami
305 423 8539
craig.rasile@dlapiper.com
*Featured in Bankruptcy/Restructuring (Florida)*

**Practice Areas:** Restructuring, bankruptcy.
**Career:** He focuses in the insolvency area, emphasizing bankruptcy, corporate restructuring, creditors' rights, workouts and commercial litigation in several industries, including retail, healthcare, energy, telecommunications, gaming, transportation, franchise operations, manufacturing, REITs and financial institutions. Recent engagements involve the representation of corporate and partnership debtors, trustees, indenture trustees and creditor and equity committees as well as financial institutions and other secured creditors in complex chapter 11 reorganization cases and chapter 7 cases and in out-of-court workouts.
**Personal:** JD, University of Miami School of Law; AB, Grinnell College (with honors).

## REID, Benjamine
Carlton Fields, P.A., Miami
305 539 7222
breid@carltonfields.com
*Featured in Litigation (Florida)*

**Practice Areas:** Antitrust, appellate, class action, commercial, environmental, and product liability ligitation.
**Professional Memberships:** Admitted in Florida, Georgia and the US Supreme Court. Fellow, American Bar Foundation; Co-Managing Director, Chair, Products Liability Committee, Chair Task Force on the Judiciary, Co-Chair Civil Justice Institute, American Bar Association; Director, Product Liability Advisory Council.
**Career:** Martindale-Hubbell AV Rating; Chair, Carlton Fields Board of Directors.
**Publications:** "Decisions on the Fly" (Litigation Magazine 2004); "The Trial Lawyer as Story Teller: Reviving a Lost Art" (Litigation Magazine 2002).
**Personal:** JD (cum laude), University of Georgia School of Law; BA, University of North Carolina at Chapel Hill.

## REISMAN, Stephen H
Peckar & Abramson, P.C., Miami
305 358 2600
sreisman@pecklaw.com
*Featured in Construction (Florida)*

**Practice Areas:** Mr Reisman is a Florida Bar Board Certified Specialist in Construction law. He represents contractors and construction professionals in the negotiation and preparation of contracts and the resolution of contract disputes, defects claims, delay claims and related matters. His construction law practice includes project administration assistance for the early identification and resolution of potential conflicts.
**Professional Memberships:** Admitted to practice law in Florida and before the United States Supreme Court.
**Career:** Mr Reisman is the Vice Chairman of Peckar & Abramson and is based out of the Miami office.
**Personal:** For more information, please visit: www.pecklaw.com

## REITER, Luis
Squire Sanders (US) LLP, Miami
305 577 7710
luis.reiter@squiresanders.com
*Featured in Banking & Finance (Florida)*

**Practice Areas:** Managing partner of Squire Sanders' Miami office with extensive experience in all aspects of governmental and governmental/private finance, having served as bond counsel and represented underwriters and banks since 1980. Experience includes a wide variety of transactions, both new money and refinancing, including project finance, revenue obligations, general obligations and other tax-based financings, which have financed airports, seaports, water and sewer facilities, electric facilities, healthcare facilities, sports facilities, housing projects and economic development undertakings. Listed in The Best Lawyers in America since 2006; 2012 Miami Public Finance Law Lawyer of the Year by The Best Lawyers in America.

## RICH, Brian G
Berger Singerman, Tallahassee
850 561 3010
brich@bergersingerman.com
*Featured in Bankruptcy/Restructuring (Florida)*

**Career:** Brian Rich's practice includes representation of debtors, creditors' committees, bankruptcy Trustees and secured creditors. Mr Rich has been the firm's primary bankruptcy counsel in numerous complex Chapter 11 cases. He has overseen the wind-down process of several large cases wherein the claims reconciliation process involved claims ranging from $100 million to over $1.5 billion. He services clients throughout the State of Florida and nationally. Mr Rich has prosecuted and defended numerous of adversary proceedings seeking the recovery of avoidable transfers in Bankruptcy Courts throughout the country. Additionally, he has represented numerous real estate developers in real estate "work-outs" and out-of-court restructurings. Mr Rich has also represented bankruptcy trustees in numerous fraud related cases seeking recovery for victims of "ponzi schemes" and real estate fraud. He received his JD from University of Miami School of Law and BS from Temple University.

## RICHARD, Barry
Greenberg Traurig, LLP, Tallahassee
850 425 8503
RichardB@gtlaw.com
*Featured in Litigation (Florida)*

**Practice Areas:** Litigation: Class actions, financial services, securities and shareholder, appellate; American Indian Law.
**Professional Memberships:** Charter Member, American Academy of Appellate Lawyers; Fellow, American College of Trial Lawyers.
**Career:** Selected: Best Lawyers in America, 2006-13; 'Lawdragon 3000 Leading Lawyers in America', Lawdragon.com, 2006, 2010; Super Lawyers magazine, 2006-12; Among the '100 Most Influential Lawyers', The National Law Journal, 2006; 'Leading Litigators in America', Lawdragon 500, 2006; Recipient, Florida Bar, 'Traditions of Excellence Award', 2005. Rated, AV® Preeminent™ 5.0 out of 5.
**Personal:** JD, University of Miami School of Law; BA, University of Miami.

## RICHMAN, Gerald F
Richman Greer, P.A., West Palm Beach
561 803 3500
grichman@richmangreer.com
*Featured in Litigation (Florida)*

**Practice Areas:** Gerald F Richman is Board Certified by the Florida Bar in Civil Trial since 1983 and Business Litigation emphasizing antitrust, securities, contract, construction, corporate, banking, civil RICO, professional liability, consumer, civil rights, probate, real estate, mortgage foreclosure, land use, brokerage and class action litigation, representing both plaintiffs and defendants.
**Professional Memberships:** Fellow of the American College of Trial Lawyers and International Society of Barristers; National Board Member of the American Board of Trial Advocates. He is former President of the Florida Bar and Dade County Bar Association; past Chair, Florida Commission on Human Relations; Palm Beach County Economic Council Board Member; Member Criminal Justice Commission; Past Chair, 4th DCA Judicial Nominating Commission.
**Career:** Law clerk US District Judge, Middle District of Florida, awarded the Presidential Service Badge for Honorable service at the White House while serving in the Army's Judge Advocate General Corps. Joined the firm in 1969 and has been President since 1987. Lead Counsel in 2000 in Presidential election contest case, Jacobs vs. Seminole County, Palm Beach County Lead Counsel for Obama 2008; National Lead Litigation Counsel, Palm Beach County 2012.
**Personal:** Degrees in Building Construction, with honors, and Juris Doctor at the University of Florida.

## ROBERTS III, Hardy L
Carlton Fields, P.A., Tampa
813 229 4105
hroberts@carltonfields.com
*Featured in Construction (Florida)*

**Practice Areas:** Complex commercial disputes, including construction litigation and regulation.
**Professional Memberships:** Admitted in Florida. Co-Vice Chair of Construction Law Committee and member of Civil Procedure Rules Committee, The Florida Bar; ABA Forum on the Construction Industry.
**Career:** Board Certified in Construction Law by The Florida Bar. General Counsel and Interim Secretary, Florida Department of Business and Professional Regulation (2000-03).
**Publications:** "The Design/Build Process: A Guide to Licensing and Procurement Requirements in the Fifty States and Canada," Florida Chapter, ABA Forum on the Construction Industry(2010).
**Personal:** JD (with honors), University of Florida, 1995; BS (high honors), University of Florida, 1992.

## ROHRER, William D
Carlton Fields, P.A., Miami
305 539 7294
wrohrer@carltonfields.com
*Featured in Tax (Florida)*

**Practice Areas:** International tax, business transactional planning, inbound tax-advantaged structures, real estate investing within the US, outbound foreign tax credit optimization structures.
**Professional Memberships:** Admitted to practice in Florida, District of Columbia, Ohio, New York. Co-Chair, International Law Section, International Tax Committee, Tax Section, American Bar Association; Board of Directors, Globalaw.
**Career:** Martindale-Hubbell AV Rating. Certified public accountant.
**Publications:** Technical Editor, "Foreign Income and Foreign Taxpayers," (Federal Income Taxation, 3d Edition, Hornbook Series, Ch. 12).
**Personal:** LLM, New York University School of Law, 1987; JD, Ohio State University Moritz College of Law, 1981; BSBA (cum laude), Ohio State University, 1978.

## ROSENTHAL, Stephen F
Podhurst Orseck P.A., Miami
305 358 2800
srosenthal@podhurst.com
*Featured in Litigation (Florida)*

**Practice Areas:** Partner focusing on appeals and complex civil trial litigation, including mass tort, class actions, commercial disputes and constitutional law.
**Professional Memberships:** US Supreme Court; US Courts of Appeals for the Second, Fifth, Seventh, Ninth and Eleventh Circuits; US District Court, SD Florida and MD Florida; Florida Bar; District of Columbia Bar; American Association for Justice; Florida Justice Association.
**Career:** US Department of Justice, Civil Division, Federal Programs Branch; Law clerk to US Circuit

Judge Rosemary Barkett (11th Cir.) and to US District Judge Mark Wolf (DMass).
**Personal:** Harvard Law School (JD, cum laude, 1996), Harvard College (BA, magna cum laude, 1992).

## ROSNER, Ira N
Greenberg Traurig, LLP, Miami
305 579 0844
Rosnerl@gtlaw.com
*Featured in Corporate/M&A (Florida)*

**Practice Areas:** Corporate and securities, mergers and acquisitions, healthcare, infrastructure, retail industry, REITS, energy.
**Professional Memberships:** Member: American Bar Association; Florida Bar Corporations and Securities Law and Business Law Committees. Board Member, Florida Chapter of the National Association of Corporate Directors.
**Career:** Listed: Best Lawyers in America, 2007-13; Chambers USA, 2008, 2010-13; Super Lawyers magazine, 2006-12. Member, team ranked as the No.1 corporate law firm in Miami, 'Corporate Board Member' magazine. Rated, AV® Preeminent™ 5.0 out of 5.
**Personal:** JD, New York University School of Law, Member, Law Review; BA, Political Science, Binghamton University State University of New York.

## ROSS, David L
Greenberg Traurig, LLP, Miami
305 579 0523
RossD@gtlaw.com
*Featured in Antitrust (Florida), Litigation (Florida)*

**Practice Areas:** Co-Chair, National Products Liability & Mass Torts Practice. Litigation; antitrust and trade regulation; life sciences; professional malpractice liability.
**Professional Memberships:** Past Chairman: Business Law Section and Business Litigation Committee, The Florida Bar. Member, American Bar Association Litigation Section.
**Career:** Listed: PLC Dispute Resolution Handbook, 2008; Best Lawyers in America, 1989-13; 'The law and leading lawyers worldwide', Dispute Resolution, Vol. 1, 2007/08; Chambers USA Guide, 2003-13; Super Lawyers, 2006-12; 'Top Ten Lawyers of the Year', The Lawyers Weekly, 2003. Rated, AV® Preeminent™ 5.0 out of 5.
**Personal:** JD, University of Chicago Law School; BS, Northwestern University.

## SAKALO, Jay M
Bilzin Sumberg Baena Price & Axelrod LLP, Miami
305 375 6156
jsakalo@bilzin.com
*Featured in Bankruptcy/Restructuring (Florida)*

**Practice Areas:** Chapter 11 reorganizations; workouts, out-of-court debt restructuring; bankruptcy and commercial loan transactions; bankruptcy litigation; commercial finance.
**Professional Memberships:** Admitted in Florida; US Courts of Appeal (Third and Fourth Circuits); US District Court (Southern District of Florida, District of Maryland). American

Bankruptcy Institute; The Florida Bar, Business Law Section; Bankruptcy Bar Association of the Southern District of Florida.
**Career:** Consistently recognized by Chambers USA, The Best Lawyers in America, and Florida Trend's Legal Elite. Law360, "Rising Legal Stars," 2010.
**Personal:** JD (with honors), University of Florida Levin College of Law, 1998; BS/BA (with honors), University of Florida, 1995.

## SALAZAR, Luis
Salazar Jackson LLP, Miami
305 374 4802
Salazar@salazarjackson.com
*Featured in Bankruptcy/Restructuring (Florida)*

**Practice Areas:** Business bankruptcy and reorganizations, workouts, distressed acquisitions and commercial litigation.
**Professional Memberships:** Founding member, Florida Fiduciary Forum; Board member, Turnaround Management Association, Florida; Co-Chair, International Committee, American Bankruptcy Institute.
**Career:** Listed, Best Lawyers in America, 2007-12; Listed, 'Super Lawyer', Florida Super Lawyers Magazine, 2006-12; Listed, Legal 500 US, 2009-11 editions; Recommended, PLC Which Lawyer Guide, Restructuring and Insolvency, 2008 and 2009.
**Personal:** MBA, University of Miami; JD, Columbia University School of Law; BA, magna cum laude, Drew University; Founder, South Florida End-of-the-World-as-We-Know-It Film Festival.

## SALIMONE, Shannon Hartsfield
Holland & Knight LLP, Tallahassee
850 224 7000
shannon.salimone@hklaw.com
*Featured in Healthcare (Florida)*

**Career:** Ms Salimone is the Regulatory and Litigation Leader of the firm's national Healthcare & Life Sciences Team. She practices in the area of health law, advising clients on state and federal healthcare regulatory matters including corporate and regulatory compliance, HIPAA and data privacy, Medicare conditions of participation, licensure, prescription drug distribution and pharmaceutical pedigree requirements and responding to data breaches. Her clients include hospitals, assisted living facilities, health plans, medical technology companies, home health agencies, nursing homes, pharmaceutical manufacturers and distributors, benefit managers, durable medical equipment companies, tissue banks, clinical laboratories, medical management companies, and other healthcare industry members.

## SAMOLE, David
Kozyak Tropin & Throckmorton, Miami
305 728 2926
das@kttlaw.com
*Featured in Bankruptcy/Restructuring (Florida)*

**Practice Areas:** Bankruptcy, creditor rights, corporate reorganizations, liquidations, workouts and financially distressed transactions representing debtors, creditors, committees, trustees, guarantors and asset purchasers.

**Career:** Represents commercial landlords, creditor committees, lenders and other types of creditors in contested Chapter 11 proceedings. Handles complex trustee matters, in addition to clients facing potential exposure for avoidable transfers under the Bankruptcy Code. Shareholder at Kozyak Tropin & Throckmorton (2012-).
**Publications:** Managing the Minefield of Post-Confirmation Suits and Jurisdiction, American Bankruptcy Institute Journal, Feb. 2008. New Law, New Tools for Creditors, Business Law Today, Nov./Dec. 2006. Homestead Exemption No Longer "Debtors' Paradise", American Bankruptcy Institute Journal, Jan. 2006.

### SASSO, Gary L
Carlton Fields, P.A., Tampa
813 229 4256
gsasso@carltonfields.com
*Featured in Litigation (Florida)*
**Practice Areas:** Securities and consumer fraud class actions, complex litigation at trial and appellate levels.
**Professional Memberships:** Admitted in Florida, District of Columbia, and Pennsylvania. Past member, ABA Death Penalty Steering Committee. Fellow: International Academy of Trial Lawyers, American Academy of Appellate Lawyers, American Law Institute.
**Career:** Martindale-Hubbell AV Rating. Law Clerk, US Supreme Court; Law Clerk, US Court of Appeals, District of Columbia Circuit.
**Publications:** Co-Author, "Class Actions," (Strategic Partnering Between Inside and Outside Counsel, Treatise, 2011 edition).
**Personal:** JD (magna cum laude), University of Pennsylvania Law School, 1977; BS (magna cum laude), Wharton School, University of Pennsylvania, 1974.

### SAUL, Gary
Greenberg Traurig, LLP, Miami
305 579 0846
SaulG@gtlaw.com
*Featured in Real Estate (Florida)*
**Practice Areas:** Real estate; condominiums; financing.
**Professional Memberships:** Member, The Florida Bar, Condominium and Planned Development Committee.
**Career:** Listed: Best Lawyers in America, 2006-13; 'Hall of Fame Legal Elite', Florida Trend magazine, 2009-12; Florida: Transactions & Finance, The Legal 500 US: Volume IV; Real Estate, Who's Who Legal: Florida, 2008; Super Lawyers magazine, 2006-11; 'Top Lawyer', South Florida Legal Guide, 2005, 2010-12; Chambers USA Guide, 2003-13. Team Member, a Law360 'Real Estate Practice Group of the Year', 2011-12. Rated, AV® Preeminent™ 5.0 out of 5.
**Personal:** JD, University of Pennsylvania Law School; BS, Pennsylvania State University.

### SAWYER, Ed
White & Case LLP, Miami
305 995 5213
esawyer@whitecase.com
*Featured in Tax (Florida)*

**Career:** Mr Sawyer represents a range of clients, including institutional health care providers, real estate development companies, sales and marketing companies, health insurance providers and managed care companies in M&A, financing, regulatory, general corporate and tax matters. Mr Sawyer has substantial experience with both the tax and non-tax aspects of joint ventures, limited partnerships, limited liability partnerships, limited liability companies, corporations, and trusts and estates. Mr Sawyer is also a certified public accountant and, prior to entering private practice, he was an assistant professor of law at the University of Florida College of Law. To view his biography, please visit www.whitecase.com/esawyer.

### SCHATZMAN, Robert
GrayRobinson, PA, Miami
305 416 6880
robert.schatzman@gray-robinson.com
*Featured in Bankruptcy/Restructuring (Florida)*
**Practice Areas:** Has practiced Business Bankruptcy Chapter 11, out-of-court workout and restructuring law for more than 35 years. Represents debtors, court appointed committees, secured creditors, asset acquisitions in 363 sales, Chapter 11 plan proponents and Liquidating Trustees in complex Chapter 11 cases in Florida, Delaware and Bankruptcy Courts in other Jurisdictions. Litigated bankruptcy Chapter 5 causes of action. Represents both assignees and assignors in Assignments for the Benefit of Creditors in state court assignments. Serves as Mediator, mediating main case disputes as well as adversary suits in the Bankruptcy Courts in Delaware and Southern District of Florida.

### SCHERKER, Elliot H
Greenberg Traurig, LLP, Miami
305 579 0579
ScherkerE@gtlaw.com
*Featured in Litigation (Florida)*
**Practice Areas:** Co-Chair, National Appellate Practice. Chair, Miami Appellate Practice. Appeals: civil, bankruptcy, criminal, environmental, land use, securities. Litigation: government, constitutional; white-collar criminal; trial support.
**Professional Memberships:** Member, American Law Institute; appointed by Chief Justice to Judicial Evaluations Committee, Florida Supreme Court, 2006-07; Member, Board of Legal Specialization & Education, The Florida Bar, 2006-12.
**Career:** Listed: Best Lawyers in America, 2001-13; Chambers USA Guide, 2003-13; 'Legal Elite', Florida Trend Magazine, 2004-12; among 'Top Lawyers', South Florida Legal Guide, 2004-12. Rated, AV® Preeminent™ 5.0 out of 5.
**Personal:** JD, University of Miami School of Law; BA, University of Miami.

### SCHINDLER, Ozzie A
Greenberg Traurig, LLP, Miami
305 579 0762
SchindlerO@gtlaw.com
*Featured in Tax (Florida)*
**Practice Areas:** Tax planning, particularly for high-net worth clients, structuring investments

into the United States, pre-immigration tax planning and other aspects of cross-border planning.
**Professional Memberships:** Florida Bar, New York Bar.
**Career:** Selected: Best Lawyers in America, 2006-13; Chambers USA Guide, 2004-13; Chambers Global', 2008-09, 2011-12. Recipient, American Jurisprudence Awards for International Business Transactions and Family Law.
**Personal:** LLM, New York University School of Law; JD, University of Florida Levin College of Law; BS, University of Florida.

### SCHMIDT, Donald R
Carlton Fields, P.A., Tampa
813 229 4319
dschmidt@carltonfields.com
*Featured in Healthcare (Florida), Healthcare (Nationwide)*
**Practice Areas:** Health care law, including physician peer review proceedings and litigation related to medical staff matters; major business litigation; antitrust litigation and counseling for national and regional companies; civil and criminal investigations by state and national enforcement agencies.
**Professional Memberships:** Admitted in Florida and US Supreme Court. Past Vice-Chair, Health Care Industry Committee, American Bar Association; Federal Bar Association.
**Career:** Martindale-Hubbell AV Rating; former Lieutenant, United States Navy.
**Personal:** JD (with honors), University of Notre Dame Law School, 1979; BA (with honors), University of Notre Dame, 1970.

### SCHNAPP, Mark P
Greenberg Traurig, LLP, Miami
305 579 0541
SchnappM@gtlaw.com
*Featured in Litigation (Florida)*
**Practice Areas:** Co-Chair, White Collar Criminal Practice. Litigation; global; government litigation.
**Professional Memberships:** Member, Judicial Nominating Commission, S.D. Fla., 2006-08; former President, Assistant United States Attorneys Association; Appointed by Chief Judge Zloch to Ad Hoc Committee on Attorney Admissions, Peer Review and Attorney Grievance, S.D. Fla.
**Career:** Listed: Best Lawyers in America, 2006-13; Super Lawyers, 2006-12; 'Florida's Legal Elite', 2006-07, 2010; Chambers USA Guide, 2004-13; 'Top Lawyers in South Florida', South Florida Legal Guide, 2004-05, 2010-12. Rated, AV® Preeminent™ 5.0 out of 5; among others.
**Personal:** JD, Hofstra University School of Law; BS, Electrical Engineering, New York University.

### SCHWARTZ, Adam P
Carlton Fields, P.A., Tampa
813 229 4336
aschwartz@carltonfields.com
*Featured in Litigation (Florida)*
**Practice Areas:** White collar criminal defense, False Claims Act (qui tam/whistleblower) and health care matters, FCPA, FDIC litigation, corporate compliance, grand jury practice and proce-

dure, internal investigations, securities and accounting fraud.
**Professional Memberships:** Admitted in Florida, New York, Pennsylvania, New Jersey. Co-Chair, Florida Region, Criminal Justice Section, American Bar Association; Supreme Court Bar Admissions Committee, The Florida Bar.
**Career:** Martindale-Hubbell AV Rating.
**Publications:** Co-Author, "United States v. Santos: Deciphering the Majority and Taking Lessons from the Plurality," (DRI: The Voice of the Defense Bar, October 2008).
**Personal:** JD (cum laude), Temple University School of Law, 1995; BA, Saint Joseph's University, 1991.

### SCHWENKE, Roger D
Carlton Fields, P.A., Tampa
813 229 4152
rschwenke@carltonfields.com
*Featured in Environment (Florida)*
**Practice Areas:** Environmental, land use, real estate, and secured financing law.
**Professional Memberships:** Admitted in Florida and US Court of Appeals, DC Circuit. ABA Advisor, Drafting Committee on Uniform Environmental Covenants Act, American Bar Association; Fellow, American Bar Foundation; Fellow, American College of Real Estate Lawyers; Fellow, American College of Environmental Lawyers.
**Career:** Martindale-Hubbell AV Rating.
**Publications:** Speaker, "Recent Developments in Institutional Controls," (Hillsborough County Bar Association, Environmental Land Use, February 2011).
**Personal:** JD (with honors), University of Florida College of Law, 1969; BA, The Ohio State University, 1966. Order of the Coif.

### SEAY, James E L
Holland & Knight LLP, Orlando
407 244 1117
james.seay@hklaw.com
*Featured in Real Estate (Florida)*
**Practice Areas:** Partner in the firm's Real Estate Section, practices in the area of commercial real estate law, with an emphasis on the representation of developers of commercial, mixed-use and residential projects, and acquisition and disposition of income-producing properties. He is experienced in representation of developers of and investors in real estate projects, including tax deferred exchanges, and sale and purchase of agricultural property; and acquisition, financing, and sale of office and industrial properties, residential subdivisions, apartment complexes, and shopping centers. He is a graduate of Leadership Orlando and a Member of the National Association of Office and Industrial Parks.

### SELLERS, Lawrence
Holland & Knight LLP, Tallahassee
850 224 7000
larry.sellers@hklaw.com
*Featured in Environment (Florida)*
**Practice Areas:** Partner in the firm's Government Section, practicing administrative and governmental law focusing on environmental

matters. He regularly provides advice on permitting and enforcement before a variety of federal, state and local agencies. He has substantial experience in administrative law, including adjudicatory hearings and rulemaking. For more than 25 years, he has represented clients before the Florida Legislature, primarily on environmental, land use and administrative law. He is a member of the Florida Bar's Board of Governors, a past-chair of the Environmental and Land Use Law Section, and is a Board Certified State and Federal Government Administrative Practice Lawyer.

### SHAUGHNESSY, Kevin W
Baker & Hostetler LLP, Orlando
407 649 4014
kshaughnessy@bakerlaw.com
*Featured in Labor & Employment (Florida)*
**Career:** Board certified in labor and employment law, Kevin Shaughnessy represents local and national companies in all facets of labor and employment law, including harassment, discrimination, civil rights and section 1981 claims. Focuses on class action and multiplaintiff cases and helps clients manage the impact of high profile discrimination cases. He has handled numerous jury trials and appeals in state and federal court and provides counsel on a variety of complicated and sensitive employment and corporate compliance issues. His union experience includes election campaigns, collective bargaining, arbitrations, unfair labor practice charges and proceedings before state and federal agencies.

### SHEPHERD, Bill
Holland & Knight LLP, West Palm Beach
561 650 8338
william.shepherd@hklaw.com
*Featured in Litigation (Florida)*
**Practice Areas:** Mr Shepherd is a trial lawyer who defends individuals and corporations in state and federal government investigations and grand jury investigations. He also assists the general counsel of public and private companies in conducting sensitive internal inquiries. Mr Shepherd's extensive trial practice background also serves to support his practice in complex civil litigation involving fraud and the False Claims Act. Mr Shepherd is the chair of the American Bar Association's 20,000-member Criminal Justice Section, a member of its Global Anti-Corruption Task Force, and former division director of its White Collar Crime Division.

### SHERMAN, William
Holland & Knight LLP, Fort Lauderdale
954 468 7902
bill.sherman@hklaw.com
*Featured in Tax (Florida)*
**Practice Areas:** Tax; international transactions; offshore tax compliance.
**Professional Memberships:** American Bar Association Section of Taxation-US Activities of Foreigners and Tax Treaties Committee Chair; American College of Tax Counsel, Fellow.
**Career:** William B Sherman, Holland & Knight's Tax Team Chair, practices in the areas of domestic and international taxation. He has provided sophisticated tax planning for mergers and acqui-

sitions, restructurings, joint ventures and investments for clients in the hospitality, petrochemicals, aluminum, tobacco, real estate, transportation, telecommunications, retailing, investment management and pharmaceuticals industries.
**Publications:** Post-Fiscal Cliff: What the New American Taxpayer Relief Act Does and Does Not Do, January 2, 2013.

### SHINDELL, James W
Bilzin Sumberg Baena Price & Axelrod LLP, Miami
305 375 6141
jshindell@bilzin.com
*Featured in Real Estate (Florida)*
**Practice Areas:** Real estate development and finance; workouts, restructuring and finance, joint ventures and strategic alliances; sales, purchases and leases of real property and transfers of equity interests.
**Career:** Bilzin Sumberg's Real Estate Practice Group Leader.
**Publications:** Author, "Foreign Investors Buoy South FL," (Real Estate Forum, July 2011); Co-author, "Investment Analysis Buying into Distress: Don't Discount Due Diligence When Purchasing Troubled Loans," (Commercial Investment Real Estate, July-August 2010).
**Personal:** JD, University of North Carolina at Chapel Hill, 1979; BS (summa cum laude), University of South Florida, 1976.

### SHUSTER, Marc S.
Berger Singerman, Fort Lauderdale
954 712 5106
mshuster@bergersingerman.com
*Featured in Real Estate (Florida)*
**Career:** Marc Shuster focuses his practice in commercial real estate transactions, both healthy and distressed, and corporate M&A deal work. He has extensive experience in cross-border deals, including representing clients in acquiring land or other rights in the Caribbean for the construction of hotels and joint ventures involving hotel, port, retail, restaurant and marina development. Marc regularly assists borrowers and lenders in distressed business transactions and troubled loan work-outs. Additionally, Marc represents entrepreneurs and businesses in restructurings and as a business advisor on best practices across their internal operations.

### SIEGEL, Robert M
Bilzin Sumberg Baena Price & Axelrod LLP, Miami
305 350 2421
rsiegel@bilzin.com
*Featured in Banking & Finance (Florida)*
**Practice Areas:** Commercial finance, including representation of lenders and borrowers in asset based, real estate/construction lending; bulk loan purchases/sales and other mortgage banking transactions; workouts; acquisition/financing distressed assets in and out of bankruptcy; UCC; representation of mortgage originators defending against investor "buy back" claims.
**Professional Memberships:** Admitted to practice in Florida and US District Court; Steering Committee for Florida Bar Legal Opinions

Report; Miami Finance Forum; American Bar Association; National Law Firm Advisory Board on Legal Opinions.
**Personal:** JD (with honors) University of Miami School of Law, 1985.

### SILVA, Michael
DLA Piper LLP (US), Miami
305 423 8530
michael.silva@dlapiper.com
*Featured in Tax (Florida)*
**Practice Areas:** Tax.
**Career:** His practice focuses on international tax law with emphasis on US investment structures, cross-border tax issues, tax treaty planning, withholding obligations of US real property investments and US activities of foreign banks. He advises foreign clients on US income, estate and gift tax consequences of alternative inbound investment structures while utilizing income, estate and gift tax treaties to minimize tax and regulatory burdens.
**Personal:** JD, University of Florida Levin College of Law; MA, University of Florida; BA, University of Florida.

### SILVERMAN, Steve I
Kluger, Kaplan, Silverman, Katzen & Levine, P.L., Miami
305 379 9000
SSILVERMAN@klugerkaplan.com
*Featured in Litigation (Florida)*
**Practice Areas:** Steve has over twenty-five years of experience representing individuals and businesses in state and federal courts in complex business disputes and litigation, including issues relating to corporate and other commercial torts, breach of fiduciary duty and corporate governance issues, and officer and director liability; all aspects of real estate transactions, including purchase, development and financing, disposition and acquisition of distressed assets, restrictive covenants, and foreclosure; adversary litigation in bankruptcy courts; professional liability; and class actions. Steve has distinguished himself as a trial lawyer and advocate by realizing that the first step in any case is to understand the client's business and business goals, rather than approach each case as a routine series of legal and procedural battles. Prior to co-founding Kluger, Kaplan, Silverman, Katzen & Levine, Steve was a Managing Director, the Chair of the Litigation and Dispute Resolution Department, and a co-founder of the Distressed Asset Group at Kluger, Peretz, Kaplan & Berlin. Steve's leadership roles and depth of experience enable him to handle a wide range of business disputes in any forum.
**Professional Memberships:** American Bar Association; The Florida Bar; Dade County Bar Association.
**Career:** Admitted to the Florida Bar (1985); US District Court, Southern District of Florida (1986); US Bankruptcy Court, Southern District of Florida (1986); US Court of Appeals, Third, Ninth and Eleventh Circuits (1986). Founding Member of Kluger Kaplan Silverman Katzen & Levine, P.L.

**Publications:** American Bar Association, Tort, Trial & Insurance Practice Section, Panel Participant: "Recent Developments & Ethical Issues in Class Actions", Phoenix, AZ (April 9-10, 2010). Commercial Real Estate Workouts, Turnarounds & REO, Event Chair; Panel Participant: Intercreditor Issues in Commercial Real Estate Workouts, Lecturer: Special Issues For Acquirers of Distressed Condo Projects, and Panel Moderator: Working Through a Distressed Commercial Real Estate Loan, Irvine, California (July 2008). Commercial Real Estate Workouts, Turnarounds & REO, Event Chair; Panel Participant: Intercreditor Issues in Commercial Real Estate Workouts, Lecturer: Special Issues With Condo Projects, and Panel Moderator: Working Through a Distressed Commercial Real Estate Loan, Miami, Florida (October 2008). Distressed Real Estate Symposium, Panel Participant: Distressed Condo Hotels, Miami, Florida, (March 2008).
**Personal:** University of Miami School of Law, JD (1985); State University of New York at Albany, BA, cum laude (1982); IMPACT, Diabetes Research Institute Foundation, former President; Friends of Sylvester, University of Miami School of Medicine Sylvester Comprehensive Cancer Center.

### SIMS, Roger
Holland & Knight LLP, Orlando
407 425 8500
roger.sims@hklaw.com
*Featured in Environment (Florida)*
**Practice Areas:** Partner in the firm's Government Section and Chair of the Water Resources Team, he practices in the areas of water law and environmental and land use law. He is experienced in groundwater, surface water, wetlands, solid waste and hazardous waste issues. He deals with many agencies on a regular basis, including Florida's Water Management Districts and the Florida Department of Environmental Protection. He served as chair of the Florida Bar Environmental and Land use Law Section (1988) and on the American Bar Association Standing Committee on Environmental Law from 2000-03.

### SINGERMAN, Paul Steven
Berger Singerman, Miami
305 714 4343
psingerman@bergersingerman.com
*Featured in Bankruptcy/Restructuring (Nationwide), Bankruptcy/Restructuring (Florida)*
**Practice Areas:** Paul Steven Singerman concentrates his practice in troubled loan workouts, real estate restructurings, insolvency matters and commercial transactions. In addition, he is regularly involved in distressed business M&A work, both on the buy and sell sides. Significant representations include representation of the Official Committee of Unsecured Creditors Taylor, Bean & Whitaker Mortgage Corp. (TBW). Prior to its bankruptcy, TBW was the largest independent mortgage originator in the United States. Headquartered in Ocala, Florida, TBW employed approximately 2,500 people across the United States in its main business and employed another

1,500 people in various subsidiaries. This case involves approximately $5 billion in claims; counsel to Judge Herbert Stettin as Chapter 11 Trustee for the law firm of Rothstein, Rosenfeldt & Adler, P.A. This case is reported to be the largest Ponzi scheme in Florida history and involves approximately $1.2 billion in claims; served as debtor's counsel in Aloha Airlines, Adva-Lite, Inc., Puig Development, and Levitt and Sons; and as co-counsel to the debtors in the chapter 11 cases of AT&T Latin America, Atlas Air/Polar Air Cargo, and the TOUSA, Inc. et al cases.

**Professional Memberships:** The Florida Bar; US District Court for the Southern, Middle, and Northern Districts of Florida; Eleventh Circuit Court of Appeals; Supreme Court of the United States; Dade County and American Bar Associations; the Florida Bar (Business Law Section: Chair, 1995-96 Chair Elect, 1994-95, secretary/treasurer, 1993-94; Chairman, Legislation Committee, 1992-93; Chairman, Bankruptcy/UCC Committee, 1990-91 Continuing Legal Education, Special Programs and Meetings Committee, 1987-90); Member, Executive Council of the Business Law Section, 1986 to present; Special Committee on Opinion Standards (the Special Committee authored the Report on Standards for Opinions of Counsel in Business Transactions); Southern District of Florida Bankruptcy Bar Association (Director, 1997-2000; Chairman of Pro Bono Committee, 1999-2000); President, The Bankruptcy Bar Foundation of the Southern District of Florida (A 501(c)(3) entity dedicated to pro bono endeavors) (2000 to present); ellow, The American College of Bankruptcy; The American Law Institute; American Bankruptcy Institute; Commercial Law League of America; The Spellman-Hoeveler American Inn of Court.

### SIRVEN, José E
Holland & Knight LLP, Miami
305 374 8500
jose.sirven@hklaw.com
*Featured in Banking & Finance (Florida)*
**Career:** Jose E Sirven leads Holland & Knight's Financial Institutions practice. He has practiced in the corporate, mergers and acquisitions, banking and international fields for 30 years. Mr Sirven has represented international and domestic financial services clients in complex regulatory issues, acquisitions, divestitures, and credit transactions involving myriad collateral types as well as unsecured facilities. On cross-border transactions he has a particular emphasis on Latin America. He also has a national practice acting for lenders that lend against fine art collateral.
**Personal:** 2006 finalist Daily Business Review's Most Effective Lawyer Award-International; 2007 finalist Daily Business Review's Top Dealmaker-International Corporate deals.

### SISKIND, Harris C
McDermott Will & Emery LLP, Miami
305 347 6555
hsiskind@mwe.com
*Featured in Corporate/M&A (Florida)*

**Practice Areas:** Practice focuses on mergers and acquisitions, private equity transactions, private fund formation and securities. Has handled many complex transactions, including private equity acquisitions and divestitures, public and private company financings, Securities Exchange Act reporting for public companies, public securities offerings, and private equity fund formation and hedge fund formation.
**Professional Memberships:** Admitted to practice in Florida.
**Personal:** University of Florida College of Law, JD (with honors), 1993; Dartmouth College, BA, 1990.

### SKOLNICK, Holly R
Greenberg Traurig, LLP, Miami
305 579 0860
SkolnickH@gtlaw.com
*Featured in Litigation (Florida)*
**Practice Areas:** Litigation.
**Professional Memberships:** Chair, Greenberg Traurig Pro Bono Program; President/Founder, Greenberg Traurig Fellowship Foundation. President of the Board of Directors of Americans for Immigrant Justice. Member: Board of Advisors, University of Miami Law School, Center for Ethics and Public Service.
**Career:** Listed: Best Lawyers in America, 2005-13; Lawdragon 3000 Leading Lawyers in America, Lawdragon.com, 2006, 2010; Women Extraordinaire, South Florida Business Leader magazine, 2009; Chambers USA Guide, 2004-13; Super Lawyers magazine, 2006-12; 'Top Lawyers in South Florida', South Florida Legal Guide, 2004-05, 2010-12.
**Personal:** JD, Harvard Law School; BA, University of Wisconsin-Madison.

### SMALLWOOD, Mary F
GrayRobinson, PA, Tallahassee
850 412 2004
mary.smallwood@gray-robinson.com
*Featured in Environment (Florida)*
**Practice Areas:** Shareholder in the Administrative and Environmental practice groups. Has concentrated her practice in the area of environmental law for more than 33 years. Has represented a variety of private and public sector clients in matters including groundwater remediation for petroleum contamination, federal Superfund cleanups, dredge and fill permitting, air pollution, and surface water management. Has handled such diverse matters as air pollution permitting and enforcement, major marina permitting and medical waste incinerators.
**Professional Memberships:** The Florida Bar; Board Certified in State and Federal Government and Administrative Practice, State and Federal Government and Administrative Practice Certification Committee, Administrative Law Section, Executive Council, Environmental and Land Use Section, Executive Council.
**Career:** From 1981 to 1986 served as General Counsel to the Florida Department of Environmental Regulation, now the Department of Environmental Protection (DEP). During 1986 and 1987, Ms Smallwood served as Director of the

Division of Environmental Permitting for DEP. Has served as an adjunct professor at Florida State University College of Law teaching Florida Environmental Law and Florida Administrative Practice. Recognized in Best Lawyers in America for more than 10 years and is named in Florida Super Lawyers from 2006 to 2012. "AV" rated by Martindale-Hubbell.
**Personal:** University of Florida, BA (1969); Florida State University College of Law, JD (magna cum laude, 1977)

### SMITH-LALLA, Lori
Greenberg Traurig, LLP, Fort Lauderdale
954 765 0500
smithlallal@gtlaw.com
*Featured in Banking & Finance (Florida)*
**Practice Areas:** Public Finance.
**Professional Memberships:** Member, National Association of Bond Lawyers; Member, Florida Bar City, County and Local Government Law Section.
**Career:** Finalist, Daily Business Review, "Top Dealmaker of the Year – Public Finance," 2012; Listed, Daily Business Review, "Top Dealmaker of the Year – Public Finance," 2008.
**Personal:** JD, cum laude, University of Bridgeport School of Law; BA, Political Science, University of Connecticut.

### SOKOL, Jerry J
McDermott Will & Emery LLP, Miami
305 347 6514
jsokol@mwe.com
*Featured in Healthcare (Florida)*
**Practice Areas:** National practice concentrated on transactional aspects of healthcare law with an emphasis on mergers and acquisitions, joint ventures and various contractual arrangements in health care industry. Developed a niche in healthcare private equity transactions. Experience includes numerous sales, acquisitions and mergers of a variety of healthcare entities with a practice focus on ambulatory surgery centers, medical imaging, national and regional large physician practice companies, and other for-profit outpatient service providers.
**Personal:** University of Florida College of Law (JD); University of Texas at Austin (MPA); University of Texas at Austin (BBA, with honors).

### SOLOMON, Steven J
GrayRobinson, PA, Miami
305 416 6880
steven.solomon@gray-robinson.com
*Featured in Bankruptcy/Restructuring (Florida)*
**Practice Areas:** Shareholder and a member of the firm's Bankruptcy and Creditors' Rights Group. With 20 years of experience in business bankruptcy Chapter 11, receiverships, assignments for the benefit of creditors and out-of-court workouts, Steven practices in courts throughout the State of Florida and nationally. Regularly represents debtors, creditors' committees, lenders, trustees and buyers of assets out of bankruptcy or other insolvency proceedings. Represents a number of institutional clients on a national basis.
**Career:** Certified Insolvency and Restructuring Advisor. Listed in Best Lawyers in America, 2010-

12; Chambers USA, 2012, 2013; Florida Super Lawyers, 2006-13; Florida Trend "Legal Elite," 2008-09, 2011.

### SORIANO, Robert A
Greenberg Traurig, LLP, Tampa
813 318 5700
SorianoR@gtlaw.com
*Featured in Bankruptcy/Restructuring (Florida)*
**Practice Areas:** Business reorganization and financial restructuring; litigation; creditor rights representation.
**Professional Memberships:** Member: The Florida Bar; New York Bar; American Bar Association; American Law Institute; Hillsborough County Bar Association; American Bankruptcy Institute. Fellow, American College of Bankruptcy. Founding Director, Tampa Bay Bankruptcy Bar Association.
**Career:** Listed: Chambers USA Guide; Best Lawyers in America 1993-2013; Florida Super Lawyers, 2006-12; 'Legal Elite', Florida Trend magazine, 2009-10, 2012. Rated, AV® Preeminent™ 5.0 out of 5.
**Publications:** Contributing editor, Collier Bankruptcy Practice Guide; Chapter 11 Theory and Practice.
**Personal:** JD, cum laude, Syracuse Law School; AB, Rutgers College.

### SORONDO JR, Rodolfo
Holland & Knight LLP, Miami
305 374 8500
rodolfo.sorondo@hklaw.com
*Featured in Litigation (Florida)*
**Practice Areas:** Mr Sorondo leads the firm's South Florida's Appellate practice. He was a trial lawyer from 1979-92. He served with distinction as both a trial judge (1992-97) on Florida's Circuit Court (Miami-Dade County), and as an appellate judge (1997-2002) on Florida's Third District Court of Appeal. He was awarded the Justice Gerald Kogan Judicial Distinction Award (1998) and the Justice Award (2004). He lectures extensively on jury selection, the imposition of sanctions for fraud on the courts, and appellate advocacy. In 2012, he was named one of three "Most Effective Lawyers" in appellate law by the Daily Business Review.

### SOTO, Edward
Weil, Gotshal & Manges LLP, Miami
305 577 3177
edward.soto@weil.com
*Featured in Litigation (Florida)*
**Practice Areas:** Edward Soto is a senior trial partner and Head of the Litigation Department for Weil's Miami office. His practice focuses on trial and supervision of high-value complex commercial civil litigation, and he has an extensive, 30-year track record of winning these cases at every phase of litigation, whether in state or federal courts or before arbitration panels. He has substantial experience with antitrust, business torts, employment, fraud, insurance, products liability, and securities cases, among others, and also handles internal investigations. Notable clients include Procter & Gamble, United Healthcare, Fiserv, Inc.,

American Airlines, ESPN, Inc., Exxon Mobil and General Electric.
**Personal:** Florida State University (BA); Columbia University School of Law (JD).

### SPARKS, Brian
Hill Ward Henderson, Tampa
813 222 8515
bsparks@hwhlaw.com
*Featured in Tax (Florida)*
**Practice Areas:** Taxation, estate and asset planning, business succession, trust and probate administration.
**Professional Memberships:** Fellow, American College of Trust and Estate Counsel; Board Certified Wills, Trusts & Estates Law; AV rated by Martindale-Hubbell; Best Lawyers in America; Florida Trend's Legal Elite; Florida Super Lawyers.
**Career:** Tax, estate, asset protection and privacy protection planning for wealthy individuals, business executives, professionals and closely held businesses and tax controversy matters. Held active leadership positions with The Florida Bar.
**Personal:** LLM Taxation, New York University, 1986; JD, St. Louis University, 1985; BS, Southeast Missouri State University, 1978.

### SPRATT, JR, William J
K&L Gates, Miami
305 539 3320
william.spratt@klgates.com
*Featured in Healthcare (Florida)*
**Practice Areas:** A former health care administrator, William J Spratt, Jr represents health care providers and companies servicing the health care industry. He structures acquisitions, sales, mergers, and reorganizations of health care businesses. He counsels clients on fraud and abuse matters, federal and state regulatory compliance, antitrust issues, managed care arrangements, Medicare and Medicaid reimbursement issues, and aspects of interstate and international health care transactions. He is former Chair of the Florida Bar Health Law Certification Committee and has taught Health Law as an adjunct faculty member in the Master of Health Administration program at Florida Atlantic University.

### STEIN, Gary M
Peckar & Abramson, P.C., Miami
305 358 2600
gstein@pecklaw.com
*Featured in Construction (Florida)*
**Practice Areas:** Mr Stein is certified by the Florida Bar as a Construction Law Specialist. His practice involves the representation of construction professionals in the litigation, arbitration and mediation of construction contract claims, delay claims, construction defect claims and related matters. His practice includes the negotiation and preparation of construction documents, project administration during construction and risk management.
**Professional Memberships:** Mr Stein is currently general counsel for the South Florida Chapter of the Associated General Contractors of America ("AGC").
**Career:** Mr Stein is co-managing partner of the Miami office of Peckar & Abramson.

**Personal:** For more information, please visit: www.pecklaw.com

### STEINBERG, Marty
Bilzin Sumberg Baena Price & Axelrod LLP, Miami
305 350 7310
msteinberg@bilzin.com
*Featured in Antitrust (Florida), Litigation (Florida)*
**Practice Areas:** Co-Chair of Bilzin Sumberg's Litigation Practice. Class actions, complex commercial litigation, contract disputes, business torts, securities litigation, IP, antitrust, product liability, internal investigations, health care fraud and abuse. Former US Senate Chief Counsel and federal prosecutor; selected as receiver and monitor by the federal government.
**Professional Memberships:** Admitted to Florida, Ohio, District of Columbia; Fellow, American College of Trial Lawyers and International Academy of Trial Lawyers; American Bar Foundation; American Pharmaceutical Association; American Inns of Court; American Association of Corporate Counsel.
**Publications:** Lectures at conferences and General Counsel Roundtables on litigation matters. Adjunct professor, American University, Canisius College.

### STICHTER, Don M
Stichter, Riedel, Blain & Prosser PA, Tampa
813 229 0144
dstichter@srbp.com
*Featured in Bankruptcy/Restructuring (Florida)*
**Practice Areas:** Chapter 11 business reorganizations; workouts and out-of-court loan and debt restructurings; asset acquisitions and sales in bankruptcy cases.
**Professional Memberships:** Founder and past-President, the Tampa Bay Bankruptcy Bar Association. Past President, Hillsborough County Bar Association; honored by the Florida Bar as outstanding local bar President. One of first three Florida Lawyers selected as a Fellow of the American College of Bankruptcy. Named in 2001 by Hillsborough County Bar as Most Outstanding Lawyer. First recipient of the highest award of the Tampa Bay Bankruptcy Bar Association (the Douglas P McClurg Award) for outstanding lifetime contribution to the bankruptcy bar; Member, the Florida Bar, American Bar Association, Hillsborough County Bar Association, American Bankruptcy Institute, Tampa Bay Bankruptcy Bar Association.
**Career:** Attorney, Antitrust Division, US Department of Justice, Washington, DC, Assistant United States Attorney, Tampa. Private practice since 1962. Co-founded Stichter, Riedel, Blain & Prosser, P.A. in 1974.
**Publications:** Co-authored publications on bankruptcy law for The Florida Bar, Speaker on bankruptcy law topics at seminars sponsored by The Florida Bar and other groups.
**Personal:** BA, Colgate University, 1951. LLB, University of Wisconsin, 1957 (Order of the Coif). Member, Editorial Board, University of Wisconsin Law Review.

### STICHTER, Scott
Stichter, Riedel, Blain & Prosser PA, Tampa
sstichter@srbp.com
*Featured in Bankruptcy/Restructuring (Florida)*
**Practice Areas:** Chapter 11 business reorganizations; workouts and out-of-court loan and debt restructurings; asset acquisitions and sales in bankruptcy cases.
**Professional Memberships:** Tampa Bay Bankruptcy Bar Association (past director) Hillsborough County Bar Association American Bar Association Member, American Bankruptcy Institute Member, Alumni Council, Wake Forest University College of Law, 1994-2003 Member Turnaround Management Association American Bar Foundation (Fellow) Florida Bar Foundation (Fellow).
**Career:** Scott A Stichter is a 1984 graduate of Vanderbilt University with a Bachelor of Arts, majoring in Economics. Mr Stichter received a Juris Doctor from Wake Forest University in 1987, where he served as a member of the Moot Court Board, 1985-87 and the American Bar Association National Appellate Advocacy Team. Mr Stichter joined Stichter, Riedel, Blain & Prosser, P.A. in 1987. Mr Stichter regularly represents debtors, committees, creditors, buyers and other parties in bankruptcy cases and out-of-court workouts. He is the recipient of pro bono awards from the Florida Bar Association and Hillsborough County Bar Association. He serves as the director of the Tampa Bay Bankruptcy Bar Association and the Bay Area Legal Services, Inc and previously served on the Alumni Council for Wake Forest University College of Law (1994-2005).

### STISS, Carey A
Bilzin Sumberg Baena Price & Axelrod LLP, Miami
305 350 2419
cstiss@bilzin.com
*Featured in Real Estate (Florida)*
**Practice Areas:** Real estate; distressed property; condominiums; construction law; leasing; purchase and sales; real estate development; real estate finance; restructuring.
**Professional Memberships:** Admitted to practice in Florida and US District Court (Southern District of Florida).
**Career:** Represented lenders, property owners and developers in several complicated loan, leasing, distressed asset and other transactions. Frequent lecturer on distressed asset and other real estate topics.
**Personal:** JD (cum laude), University of Florida Levin College of Law, 1982; BA (magna cum laude), Tulane University, 1979; London School of Economics, 1978.

### STUBBS, Sidney A
Jones, Foster, Johnston & Stubbs, P.A., West Palm Beach
561 659 3000
sstubbs@jonesfoster.com
*Featured in Litigation (Florida)*
**Practice Areas:** Commercial litigation with focus on law firms, ranging from firm dissolutions

to charges of malpractice; business tort litigation; corporate merger and acquisition disputes.
**Professional Memberships:** Fellow, American College of Trial Lawyers (Florida Chair 2006-07); Life Fellow, American Bar Foundation; served on The Florida Bar Board of Governors; and as President of the Palm Beach County Bar Association.
**Career:** Awarded Palm Beach County Bar Association's Individual Professionalism Award, 2005; Past-President, firm's Board of Directors; Special Counsel to The Honorable Bob Graham, Governor, State of Florida, 1983.
**Personal:** JD, University of Florida (1965), Executive Editor of the 'University of Florida Law Review;' BS, Florida State University.

### STUTTS, Charles
Holland & Knight LLP, Tampa
813 227 8500
charles.stutts@hklaw.com
*Featured in Banking & Finance (Florida)*
**Career:** Charles Stutts represents banks, trust companies, securities broker-dealers and investment advisers in FDIC, OCC, Federal Reserve Board and FINRA matters. He also represents boards of directors and executive management of these institutions in breach of fiduciary duty and other civil and administrative enforcement matters. A substantial portion of Mr Stutts' practice also involves the representation of money services businesses on consumer compliance matters. He is a former general counsel to the Florida Department of Banking and Finance (now the Office of Financial Regulation) where he developed the agency's banking, mortgage lending and securities regulation policies and was a lobbyist.

### SUÁREZ, Fradyn
Hunton & Williams LLP, Miami
305 810 2595
fsuarez@hunton.com
*Featured in Latin American Investment (Florida)*
**Practice Areas:** Fradyn Suarez is a partner in the Corporate and Project Finance and Latin America practice groups. She regularly advises commercial, bilateral and multilateral financial institutions and borrowers in connection with cross-border financing transactions involving Latin America and the Caribbean and other emerging markets, including project finance transactions, acquisition financings, syndicated loans, restructurings and bond offerings. Fradyn also advises private equity funds and other investor clients in connection with the structuring and documentation of joint ventures and equity and debt investments in Latin America.
**Personal:** JD, University of Florida Levin College of Law, 2002; BA, Smith College, 1998.

### SUBIN, Ben
Holland & Knight LLP, Orlando
407 425 8500
ben.subin@hklaw.com
*Featured in Construction (Florida)*
**Practice Areas:** As a partner and Practice Group Leader of Holland & Knight's Florida Construction Industry Group, Ben Subin focuses on domestic and international construction con-

tracting and federal government contracts, including the pursuit and defense of bid protests at the federal, state and local government level. He represents contractors, owners and manufacturers on a range of industrial, commercial, energy and infrastructure projects, including power plants, seawater desalination facilities, water/wastewater treatment facilities, reservoirs, citrus processing facilities, wind turbine projects, commercial buildings, hospitals and retail centers. He has extensively represented EPC contractors and turbine manufacturers on power plant projects domestically and abroad.

### SULLIVAN, Michael J
Greenberg Traurig, LLP, Orlando
407 418 2376
SullivanM@gtlaw.com
*Featured in Leisure & Hospitality (Nationwide), Real Estate (Florida)*
**Practice Areas:** Co-Chair, Hospitality Group. Real estate; gaming; financial institutions.
**Professional Memberships:** Board of Directors: Central Florida Yale Club; Orlando Metropolitan YMCA. Member, Yale Alumni Real Estate Association.
**Career:** Listed: Best Lawyers in Orlando, Orlando Magazine, 2010; Best Lawyers in America, 2005-13; Legal 500 US, 2007-10, 2012; Super Lawyers, 2006-12; Chambers USA Guide, 2004-13. Rated, AV® Preeminent™ 5.0 out of 5. Member, Winning Team, 2010 Chambers and Partners USA Award for Excellence in Real Estate. Team Member, a Law360 'Real Estate Practice Group of the Year', 2011-12.
**Personal:** JD, with honors, University of Connecticut School of Law; BA, Yale University.

### SUMBERG, John C
Bilzin Sumberg Baena Price & Axelrod LLP, Miami
305 374 7580
jsumberg@bilzin.com
*Featured in Real Estate (Florida)*
**Practice Areas:** Managing Partner of Bilzin Sumberg. One of the most highly regarded commercial real estate attorneys in South Florida, with over 35 years of experience representing foreign and domestic real estate developers, investors and owners in major real estate matters across the country. Represents businesses and investors from Latin America, Europe and Asia looking to invest in the South Florida market.
**Professional Memberships:** United Way of Miami-Dade, Board of Directors, Trustee, Finance Committee; Greater Miami Jewish Federation, Board of Directors, Audit Committee Chair, Financial Management Committee; Sundari Foundation Lotus House Women's Shelter, Board of Directors, Finance and Governance Committee; Miami-Dade County Mayor's Business Leaders Roundtable.
**Career:** John has received Chambers USA's highest ranking in Real Estate since the publication's inaugural year in Florida and has been recognized by The Best Lawyers in America for over a decade. In 2013, John was named The Best Lawyers in America's "Miami Real Estate Lawyer of the Year."

He has also been consistently ranked by Florida Super Lawyers and the South Florida Legal Guide, and has received numerous accolades from the South Florida Business Journal, including the Book of Law's Top Managing Partner 2012, Leading Lawyer 2011, and One of 10 Ultimate CEOs in 2010. Rated, Martindale-Hubbell AV® Preeminent™ 5.0 out of 5.0.
**Personal:** JD, Yale University, editor and published author, Yale Law Journal, and editor, Yale Review of Law and Social Action, 1974; BA, Yale University, magna cum laude, 1971.

### SWERDLOFF, Nicolas
Hughes Hubbard & Reed LLP, Miami
305 379 5571
swerdloff@hugheshubbard.com
*Featured in Litigation (Florida)*
**Practice Areas:** Complex international and domestic commercial litigation and arbitration, with an emphasis on financial services, securities, professional liability and foreign sovereign litigation, as well as product liability litigation.
**Professional Memberships:** Member, American Arbitration Association Panel of Neutrals. Member, American Bar Association, International Law and Litigation Sections. Past Chair & Member, Executive Council, Florida Bar International Law Section.
**Career:** Partner, Hughes Hubbard & Reed LLP. Member, firm Executive Committee. Managing Partner, Miami office.
**Personal:** SUNY at Stony Brook, BA, Anthropology and Economics, 1980 (cum laude). Fordham University School of Law, JD, 1983 (cum laude, Fordham Law Review, Dean's List).

### TERZO, Frank
GrayRobinson, PA, Miami
813 273 5000
frank.terzo@gray-robinson.com
*Featured in Bankruptcy/Restructuring (Florida)*
**Practice Areas:** Chair of GrayRobinson's Bankruptcy and Creditors' Rights Group. Concentrates on Insolvency matters, including representation of corporate and consumer clients in complex workouts, bankruptcies, assignment for the benefit of creditors, and receiverships. Also represents creditor's committees and Chapter 11 and 7 trustees. Practice also encompasses both the prosecution and defense of all forms of complex bankruptcy litigation, including preference, fraudulent transfers and complex contested matters.
**Professional Memberships:** The Florida Bar; American Bankruptcy Institute, Committee on Health Care Insolvency; American Bar Association, Business Bankruptcy Committee; St. John's University School of Law LLM, Bankruptcy Faculty Advisory Board; Nova Southeastern University, Former Adjunct Professor of Bankruptcy Law; Florida International University, Adjunct Professor of Bankruptcy Law; Bankruptcy Bar Association of the Southern District of Florida, Past Director; US Bankruptcy Court Committee, Past Co-Chairman; US Trustee Liaison Committee, Past Co-Chairman.
**Personal:** Nova Southeastern University Shepard Broad Law Center, JD (with Honors, Order of the

Coif 1991); University of Cincinnati, BS (Economics, 1970).

### THIELHELM JR, Robert W
Baker & Hostetler LLP, Orlando
407 649 4072
rthielhelm@bakerlaw.com
*Featured in Litigation (Florida)*
**Career:** Robert Thielhelm is a civil trial lawyer who represents clients in a variety of industries, including real estate, construction and development, pharmaceutical supply, vacation ownership, power generation, transportation, commercial leasing, security, lending, cruise line and theme park. His practice involves representing clients in all manner of business tort litigation, contract actions, commercial fraud, mechanic's lien and mortgage foreclosures, unfair competition, misappropriation of trade secrets, tortious interference and deceptive and unfair trade practices claims. Rob has represented clients in partnership disputes, shareholder derivative actions, patent and trademark infringement actions and constitutional/local government cases in both state and federal court.

### THOMPSON, Daniel
Berger Singerman, Tallahassee
850 561 3010
dthompson@bergersingerman.com
*Featured in Environment (Florida)*
**Practice Areas:** Daniel Thompson concentrates his practice in governmental and administrative law, specializing in environmental law. Includes licensing, permitting, enforcement, policy development, bid disputes, rulemaking, administrative and civil litigation, and appearances before legislative and administrative bodies.
**Career:** Representative cases include federal court litigation over applicability of Clean Water Act permitting requirements to South Florida Water Management District, and administrative litigation over whether to permit the widening of 20 miles of US 1 through wetlands in the Everglades and Florida Keys. Previously, Deputy Secretary of the Florida Department of Environmental Protection, and before then General Counsel. Former adjunct Professor, Florida State University College of Law. While at DEP, chief litigation and legislative strategist for the State of Florida's response to the "Everglades Lawsuit," negotiating 1991 Settlement Agreement, 1993 Statement of Principles and implementing legislation.

### THOMPSON, Patricia H
Carlton Fields, P.A., Miami
305 539 7239
pthompson@carltonfields.com
*Featured in Construction (Florida)*
**Practice Areas:** Construction, surety, fidelity and other commercial insurance coverage, employment, and commercial litigation.
**Professional Memberships:** Admitted to practice in Florida. Board of Governors, American College of Construction Lawyers; Fellow, American Bar Foundation; Florida Bar Grievance Committee 11(B).
**Career:** Martindale-Hubbell AV Rating.

**Publications:** Co-Author: "Claims Considerations for the Insurer Under a Financial Institution Bond When the FDIC is Claimant," ABA TIPS Fidelity and Surety Law Committee (October 27, 2011); "Can Direct Mean Direct? Untangling The Web of Causation in Fidelity Coverage," (XVI Fidelity Law Journal 125, 2010).
**Personal:** JD, Vanderbilt University, 1976; BA (magna cum laude), Saint Olaf College, 1973.

### THROCKMORTON, Charles W
Kozyak Tropin & Throckmorton, Miami
305 377 0655
cwt@kttlaw.com
*Featured in Bankruptcy/Restructuring (Florida)*
**Practice Areas:** Bankruptcy, debtors' and creditors' rights, workouts, commercial litigation: appeals.
**Professional Memberships:** Fellow, American College of Bankruptcy; American Bar Association; American Bankruptcy Institute; Bankruptcy Bar Association for Southern District of Florida.
**Career:** Represents high net worth individuals, debtors, secured/unsecured creditors, equity, management, committees, trustees in major Florida bankruptcies. Also specializes in bankruptcy appeals and commercial/business litigation trial and appellate practice. Co-founder and shareholder, Kozyak Tropin & Throckmorton, P.A., 1983-present. Associate, Mahoney Hadlow & Adams, 1979-83.
**Personal:** University of Virginia School of Law (JD, 1979); Duke University (BA, magna cum laude, 1976).

### TINGLE, Philip
McDermott Will & Emery LLP, Miami
305 347 6536
ptingle@mwe.com
*Featured in Tax (Florida)*
**Practice Areas:** Member of tax department. Concentrates practice on the electric generation and gas industries. Experience includes working with major utilities and independent power producers on partnership and corporate tax issues, restructurings and reorganizations, mergers and acquisitions and other tax planning issues, including contract restructurings. Regularly provides tax advice on contribution in aid of construction, normalization, renewable energy credits and other power industry topics.
**Personal:** University of Florida College of Law (LLM); University of Florida College of Law (JD, with honors); Tulane University (BSM).

### TORRES, Christopher
Greenberg Traurig, LLP, Tampa
813 318 5721
TorresCh@gtlaw.com
*Featured in Environment (Florida)*
**Practice Areas:** Litigation – Toxic tort, mass tort, class action, land use, complex commercial, white collar. Member, GT's Environmental & Toxic Tort Practice.
**Professional Memberships:** Vice-Chair, ABA Environmental Enforcement and Crimes. Board Member, Glazer Children's Museum.
**Career:** Chambers USA, 2011-13; Florida 'Legal Elite', Litigation, 2011-13.

**Publications:** Environmental Enforcement and Crimes Annual Reports, The Year in Review 2011-13, ABA Section of Environment, Energy, and Resources. 'An Art of War Lesson Applied to Mass Torts: The Lone Pine Strategy', ABA Environmental Enforcement and Crimes Committee Newsletter, March 2011.
**Personal:** JD, Harvard Law School, 1997; BA, magna cum laude, New York University, 1993.

**TROPIN, Harley S**
Kozyak Tropin & Throckmorton, Miami
305 372 1800
hst@kttlaw.com
*Featured in Litigation (Florida)*
**Practice Areas:** Commercial litigation.
**Career:** Co-founder, Kozyak Tropin & Throckmorton. Regularly represents and defends companies in their most significant litigation. Co-lead trial counsel for plaintiffs: In Re: Managed Care. Chairman of Litigation Steering Committee in Premium Sales. Lead trial counsel for defendants in Aguiar v. Leor (suit dismissed - billion dollar partnership dispute). Recognized in "Best Lawyers in America" since 1989, named in top-tier litigation category, "Bet-The-Company Litigation" (2006 - present). Voted "Most Effective Lawyer" by Daily Business Review (2005, 2012).
**Personal:** George Washington University (BA, 1974); University of Miami School of Law (JD, 1977, cum laude).

**TURKEN, Robert W**
Bilzin Sumberg Baena Price & Axelrod LLP, Miami
305 350 2381
rturken@bilzin.com
*Featured in Antitrust (Florida)*
**Practice Areas:** Litigation: antitrust (civil and regulatory), securities, financial services, class actions.
**Professional Memberships:** Florida Bar, US District Court (Northern, Southern, Middle Districts of Florida), US Court of Appeals (First, Second, Third, Fifth, Eleventh Circuits).
**Career:** Head of firm's Antitrust and Securities Litigation Groups. Recognized by The Best Lawyers in America, Benchmark Litigation, Florida Super Lawyers, Florida Trend's Legal Elite, AV® Preeminent™ 5 out of 5. Counsel in major MDL antitrust cases, including LCD, CRT, DRAM and SRAM. Group named Benchmark Litigation's 2013 "Antitrust Firm of the Year—South."
**Personal:** JD, Duke University School of Law, 1980; BA, Duke University, 1977.

**ULLMAN, Samuel C**
Bilzin Sumberg Baena Price & Axelrod LLP, Miami
305 350 7300
sullman@bilzin.com
*Featured in Tax (Florida)*
**Practice Areas:** Tax, including business tax; tax controversy; tax-exempt organizations; bankruptcy and insolvency tax; state and local tax; mergers, acquisitions and joint ventures.
**Professional Memberships:** Admitted to practice in Florida and in the US Tax Court. Board Certified by The Florida Bar in Taxation;

American Law Institute (Fellow); American College of Tax Counsel (Fellow).
**Career:** Adjunct Professor, University of Florida Levin College of Law, Graduate Tax Program.
**Personal:** LLM in Taxation, University of Miami School of Law, 1975; JD, University of Florida Levin College of Law, 1967; BA (with honors), University of Florida, 1965.

**VAINDER, Steven**
White & Case LLP, Miami
305 995 5226
svainder@whitecase.com
*Featured in Real Estate (Florida)*
**Career:** Mr Vainder leads the Americas Real Estate Group. He advises clients on acquisitions, dispositions, operations, leasing, management, development and financing. Representing investors, owners and other stakeholders, Steven has participated in numerous complex real estate projects, including retail, mixed-use, hotels, office and industrial parks. He has extensive experience representing lenders and private equity funds with the restructuring, repositioning, disposition and acquisition of distressed real estate loans and assets. Steven was one of the first attorneys in Florida to gain LEED accreditation by the US Green Building Council to advise clients on green/sustainable building practices. To view his biography, please visit www.whitecase.com/svainder.

**VARNER III, Joseph H.**
Holland & Knight LLP, Tampa
813 227 6703
joe.varner@hklaw.com
*Featured in Litigation (Florida)*
**Practice Areas:** Joseph H Varner, III, is experienced in complex commercial litigation, business torts and unfair competition, securities litigation, professional negligence, and personal injury and wrongful death litigation. He has litigated complex cases ranging from corporate shareholder disputes to intellectual property battles to wrongful death arising from medical malpractice. He has obtained significant jury verdicts and settlements in commercial and personal injury litigation and has conducted numerous jury trials in state and federal court. Mr Varner is Board Certified in Civil Trial Law, a certified mediator in state and federal court, and Fellow in the American College of Trial Lawyers.

**VIANA, Carlos**
White & Case LLP, Miami
305 995 5251
cviana@whitecase.com
*Featured in Latin American Investment (Florida), Banking & Finance (Florida)*
**Career:** To view a comprehensive biography, please visit www.whitecase.com/cviana.

**VOGEL III, Edward W**
Holland & Knight LLP, Lakeland
863 499 5356
ed.vogel@hklaw.com
*Featured in Banking & Finance (Florida)*
**Practice Areas:** Banking and finance; public finance.

**Professional Memberships:** National Association of Bond Lawyers.
**Career:** Edward W Vogel, III has been the primary Holland & Knight partner responsible for numerous industrial development, city, county, and special district bond issues and has played a key role as bond counsel for the first tax increment bonds issued in Florida. His areas of practice include tax-exempt bond financing, corporate financing and corporate leveraged leasing.
**Publications:** "Florida Supreme Court Reverses Decision Regarding Referendum Approval for Tax Increment Financing," Public Finance, Alert - September 19, 2008.

**WAGGONER, Dennis P**
Hill Ward Henderson, Tampa
813 227 8426
dwaggoner@hwhlaw.com
*Featured in Litigation (Florida)*
**Practice Areas:** Commercial litigation, professional liability, securities and shareholder litigation, appellate, class action and complex mass tort.
**Professional Memberships:** AV rated by Martindale-Hubbell, Best Lawyers in America, Florida Trend's Legal Elite, Florida Super Lawyers.
**Career:** Practice Leader in Litigation Group. Complex commercial litigation in state and federal trial courts. Defense of professional malpractice actions. Has handled appeals before the US Supreme Court, the US Court of Appeals, the Florida Supreme Court and Florida's District Courts of Appeal.
**Personal:** JD, cum laude, Harvard University, 1985; BA, summa cum laude, Boston College, 1982.

**WALBOLT, Sylvia H**
Carlton Fields, P.A., Tampa
813 229 4255
swalbolt@carltonfields.com
*Featured in Litigation (Florida)*
**Practice Areas:** Appellate law in federal and state court, in all areas including tort, products liability.
**Professional Memberships:** Admitted in Florida and US Supreme Court. Fellow and Former President, American Academy of Appellate Lawyers; Fellow, American College of Trial Lawyers; Life Member, American Law Institute.
**Career:** Board Certified in Appellate Law and Antitrust and Trade Regulation Law by The Florida Bar. Martindale-Hubbell AV Rating.
**Publications:** "Twenty Tips from a Battered and Bruised Oral-Advocate Veteran," The Appellate Advocate, ABA Journal of the Section of Litigation, (Winter 2011).
**Personal:** JD, University of Florida College of Law, 1963; BA, University of Florida, 1961.

**WALKER JR, H William**
White & Case LLP, Miami
305 995 5205
wwalker@whitecase.com
*Featured in Real Estate (Florida)*
**Career:** Mr Walker's areas of practice include all aspects of real estate acquisition and disposition,

ownership, use, development and finance, and general corporate matters. He has participated in and represented owners of, investors in and lenders to numerous complex real estate projects, including those of major domestic and international developers. Mr Walker has also participated in the planning, development, financing and sale of major commercial properties, commercial/retail/hotel mixed use projects, planned residential communities, including primary housing, resort housing and hospitality properties, and planned office/commercial/industrial projects. To view a comprehensive biography, please visit www.whitecase.com/wwalker.

**WALL, Ethan**
Richman Greer PA, Miami
305 373 4000
ewall@richmangreer.com
*Featured in Litigation (Florida)*
**Practice Areas:** Ethan Wall concentrates in complex internet, intellectual property, and social media law. Ethan litigates trademark infringement, trade secrets, internet related cases, and advises clients on social media legal and business issues.
**Professional Memberships:** President-Elect of the Dade County Bar Young Lawyers Section and Founder of its Law and Technology Committee.
**Publications:** Ethan frequently presents and publishes articles on the effect of social media and the internet on the law (http://ethanwall.com), authors the Social Media Law and Order blog (http://SocialMediaLawandOrder.com), and co-authored The Social Media Guide for Lawyers (http://SocialMediaGuideforLawyers.com).
**Personal:** Nova Southeastern University (JD 2007)(cum laude).

**WARD, Alton C**
Hill Ward Henderson, Tampa
813 222 8703
award@hwhlaw.com
*Featured in Tax (Florida)*
**Practice Areas:** Taxation, executive compensation, employee benefits, qualified retirement plans.
**Professional Memberships:** "Employee Benefits Lawyer of the Year 2010," Best Lawyers in America, AV rated by Martindale-Hubbell, Florida Trend's Legal Elite, Florida Super Lawyers; Past President, Florida West Coast Employee Benefits Council; Chairman and Founding Member, Tampa Bay Pension Council.
**Career:** Practice Leader for Executive Compensation and Employee Benefits Group, which is the largest in the Southeast. Serves as employee benefits counsel for The Florida Bar.
**Personal:** JD, Law Review, Stetson University College of Law, 1982; BA, University of Georgia, 1970.

**WEBB, Katherine**
Colodny, Fass, Talenfeld, Karlinsky, Abate & Webb, Tallahassee
850 577 0398
kwebb@cftlaw.com
*Featured in Insurance (Florida)*

**Practice Areas:** Ms Webb, Shareholder, focuses on government relations and insurance regulatory law.
**Professional Memberships:** Ms Webb is a member of the Florida Bar Association, United States District Court for the Middle District of Florida, the Association of Insurance Compliance Professionals and the Florida Association of Professional Lobbyists.
**Career:** Ms Webb was named as the 2011 "Most Outstanding Lobbyist" by a major trade organization. She is an Adjunct Professor at Florida State University College of Law, and has had significant involvement in crafting and passage of insurance regulation regarding property and casualty, workers' compensation and health related issues.

## WEBER, William
Hughes Hubbard & Reed LLP, Miami
305 379 5568
weber@hugheshubbard.com
*Featured in Real Estate (Florida)*
**Practice Areas:** Real estate workouts and recapitalizations; development and finance; joint ventures; public/private partnerships; hotel and resort development and management agreements; direct investment in US real estate through offshore fund structures.
**Professional Memberships:** Member and Past Co-chair of Hotel, Resorts and Hospitality Committee of the American College of Real Estate Lawyers; Fellow of the American Bar Association.
**Career:** Senior Counsel. Co-Chair of Real Estate Department.
**Personal:** BA, Stetson University; JD, University of Florida School of Law where he was editor-in-chief of the University of Florida Law Review.

## WEINSTEIN, Andrew
Holland & Knight LLP, Miami
305 374 8500
andrew.weinstein@hklaw.com
*Featured in Tax (Florida)*
**Career:** 'Andy' Weinstein, with 45 years' experience handling complex domestic and international tax planning and compliance matters for ultra high-net-worth individuals, currently focuses on multi-jurisdictional tax compliance. He has represented clients in civil and criminal tax matters before the IRS and DOJ, from early stages of examinations and investigations through termination. He structured and implemented the largest expatriate matter in US history; reorganized ownership and control of two major international oil tanker fleets; structured domestic and foreign trusts involving cross-border investments and business activities; coordinated large-scale global trust projects; and handled tax planning for transactions involving several billions of dollars.

## WEINSTEIN, David B
Greenberg Traurig, LLP, Tampa
813 318 5701
WeinsteinD@gtlaw.com
*Featured in Environment (Florida)*
**Practice Areas:** Litigation - Environmental, Land Use, Real Estate, Mass Torts, Class Actions, Business, White-Collar Criminal Defense; Chair, GT's Environmental & Toxic Tort practice.

**Professional Memberships:** Member: NY, DC, Florida Bars; Chair, ABA Environmental Enforcement & Crimes Committee; NACDL; Goldburg-Cacciatore Criminal Law American Inn of Court; WEDU (PBS) Board.
**Career:** Listed: Best Lawyers in America; Legal 500 (Toxic Tort Defense); Who's Who Legal (both Environmental & Business Lawyers); Chambers and Partners USA Guide; Super Lawyers (Florida Top 100); Florida 'Legal Elite' Hall of Fame; Tampa Bay Business Journal 'Who's Who in Business'.
**Publications:** Over 30 articles, papers, and chapters.
**Personal:** University of Florida - JD, BSBA.

## WELLS, David E
Greenberg Traurig, LLP, Miami
305 579 0713
WellsD@gtlaw.com
*Featured in Corporate/M&A (Florida)*
**Practice Areas:** Corporate and securities; mergers and acquisitions; corporate governance; private equity.
**Professional Memberships:** Florida Bar; Business Law Section of Florida Bar; President, Board of Directors, North Grove Neighborhood Association.
**Career:** Selected: The Best Lawyers in America, 2008-13; Chambers USA Guide, 2007-13; South Florida Legal Guide 'Top Attorney for Corporate and Business', 2013; Finalist, Daily Business Review, 'Top Dealmaker of the Year - Corporate (Domestic) Category', 2012; Florida Super Lawyers Magazine, 2007, 2010-12; Finalist, Upper Middle Market Deal of the Year, The M&A Advisor, 2011.
**Personal:** JD/MBA, University of Michigan, 1991; BA, Colgate University, 1987.

## WIDOM, Mitchell E
Bilzin Sumberg Baena Price & Axelrod LLP, Miami
305 375 6127
mwidom@bilzin.com
*Featured in Litigation (Florida)*
**Practice Areas:** Commercial litigation, class actions, lender liability, construction, partnership disputes, land use litigation.
**Professional Memberships:** Admitted to Florida, US District Court Florida (Southern, Middle and Northern), US Court of Appeals (Eleventh Circuit); American Bar Association; The Association of Trial Lawyers in America; Crohn's & Colitis Foundation of America, Executive Board Member.
**Career:** Bilzin Sumberg's Litigation Practice Group Leader. Super Lawyers, Top 100 Lawyers in Florida, 2008-present; Benchmark Litigation, Local Litigation Stars, 2009-present; The Best Lawyers in America, 2009-present; Florida Super Lawyers, 2007-present; Florida Trend's Legal Elite, 2005-present; South Florida Legal Guide, Top Lawyers, 2009-present; Martindale-Hubbell™, 2012 Top Rated Lawyers® in Construction; South Florida Business Journal, Heavy Hitters in the Non-Profit Industry, 2005; Crohn's & Colitis Foundation of America, Fundraiser of the Year

award, 2008, Modell Business Leadership Award, 2011; Dorothy Shula Award for Outstanding Volunteerism, United Way of Miami-Dade, Finalist, 2008.
**Personal:** JD, with honors, University of Florida, Levin College of Law, 1984; BS (Accounting), with honors, University of Florida, 1981.

## WILSON, Jéan E
Greenberg Traurig, LLP, Orlando
407 999 2521
WilsonJ@gtlaw.com
*Featured in Banking & Finance (Florida)*
**Practice Areas:** Co-Managing Shareholder, Orlando office. Chair, Orlando and Atlanta Public Finance Departments. Public finance, public-private partnerships, economic development, infrastructure; and transportation.
**Professional Memberships:** Board of Visitors, Florida A&M University School of Law; Board of Directors, YMCA Black Achievers Program; Board Member, Valencia Community College Foundation; Past President, Florida Chapter of the National Bar Association.
**Career:** Listed, Best Lawyers in America; Chambers USA Guide; Super Lawyers magazine; rated, AV® Preeminent™ 5.0 out of 5; 'One of six most respected and admired lawyers', Orlando Magazine, 1997.
**Personal:** JD, with honors, University of Florida Levin College of Law; BS, with honors, Finance, DePaul University.

## WILSON, William
Holland & Knight LLP, Orlando
407 425 8500
bwilson@hklaw.com
*Featured in Litigation (Florida)*
**Practice Areas:** Mr Wilson is a partner and Board Certified Civil Trial Lawyer, concentrating on significant commercial litigation. He was selected as Trial Lawyer of the Year 2008 by the Central Florida Chapter of ABOTA and was named 2011 Orlando Lawyer of the Year for Bet the Company Litigation by Best Lawyers in America. He serves as a member of the Florida Federal Judicial Nominating Commission, SunTrust Bank Central Florida Board of Directors, and Junior Achievement Board of Directors. He is Former Chairman of the Florida Bar Trial Lawyers Section and the Florida Bar Code and Rules of Evidence Committee.

## WINSTON, Richard L
K&L Gates, Miami
305 539 3350
richard.winston@klgates.com
*Featured in Latin American Investment (Florida)*
**Practice Areas:** Richard Winston focuses on structuring and analyzing cross-border transactions for US and non-US multinationals doing business in Latin America and Europe. He has a primary concentration on cross-border taxation.
**Professional Memberships:** Regional Vice-President, International Fiscal Association, USA Branch; Brazilian-American Chamber of Commerce.
**Career:** Ranked in Chambers Global among the top 20 US international tax lawyers.

**Personal:** JD and BA from the University of Virginia (Editor, Virginia Law Review and Executive Editor, Virginia Tax Review). LLM (Taxation) from New York University.

## WRIGHT, Kenneth C
Baker & Hostetler LLP, Orlando
407 649 4001
kwright@bakerlaw.com
*Featured in Corporate/M&A (Florida)*
**Career:** A seasoned securities, finance and transactional advisor, Kenneth Wright's practice encompasses transaction structuring, acquisitions, dispositions, public and private offerings of securities, structured finance and international financings and transactions. Ken has served as lead counsel in many complex and substantial acquisitions, dispositions, mergers and financings. Ken's practice includes public and private entities in the US and foreign jurisdictions (including China). He represents clients in the areas of financial services, investment fund formation and management, communications, technology, power and energy (including renewable energy), real estate, vehicle dealerships, agriculture, insurance, manufacturing, healthcare (including large medical practices), tax-exempt organizations and resort and timeshare development.

## WRIGHT, Wm Cary
Carlton Fields, P.A., Tampa
813 229 4135
cwright@carltonfields.com
*Featured in Construction (Florida)*
**Practice Areas:** Construction disputes including construction claims, defective products, mold and other sick building syndrome issues, and insurance coverage litigation.
**Professional Memberships:** Admitted in Florida and US Supreme Court. American Bar Association Governing Committee; Chair, Construction Law Committee, RPPTL Section, The Florida Bar.
**Career:** Board Certified in Construction Law by The Florida Bar. Martindale-Hubbell AV Rating.
**Publications:** Chapter Author, "Construction Insurance: a Guide for Attorneys and Other Professionals," American Bar Association Forum on the Construction Industry (2011).
**Personal:** JD (cum laude), Stetson University College of Law, 1990; BS (with honors) University of Florida, 1985.

## YADLEY, Barbara
Holland & Knight LLP, Tampa
813 227 6434
barbara.yadley@hklaw.com
*Featured in Banking & Finance (Florida)*
**Career:** Barbara M Yadley represents companies, banks and other financial institutions in all aspects of commercial lending transactions, including the areas of commercial asset based lending, cash flow lending, and commercial real estate finance. She represents clients in matters involving the UCC, mortgage law, title insurance, Florida loan transaction taxes, loan syndications and participations, intercreditor and subordination arrangements, synthetic leases and project finance, healthcare facilities, mortgage warehous-

ing, letters of credit and banker's acceptances, complex interest rate structures, inventory and accounts financing, vehicle floor plans, workout agreements, usury, commercial lending forms review, and borrower's opinions.

### ZANDY, Aaron L
FordHarrison LLP, Orlando
407 418 2304
azandy@fordharrison.com
*Featured in Labor & Employment (Florida)*
**Practice Areas:** Labor and employment.
**Career:** Aaron Zandy is a Board Certified Specialist in Labor and Employment Law who represents employers and management. He is an experienced trial lawyer, having tried a variety of discrimination, harassment, and retaliation claims under federal and state law. He also has extensive traditional labor law experience, including collective bargaining, union campaigns, and labor arbitrations. He is a highly acclaimed speaker, and trainer, and regularly provides high-intensity, high-content seminars and classes for HR professionals and managers. Aaron received his JD, with honors, from Ohio Northern University College of Law in 1997.

### ZARON, Andrew
DLA Piper LLP (US), Miami
305 423 8523
andrew.zaron@dlapiper.com
*Featured in Bankruptcy/Restructuring (Florida)*
**Practice Areas:** Finance, bankruptcy, restructuring.
**Career:** He represents a broad range of clients including corporations, financial institutions, individual and corporate debtors, secured and unsecured creditors, landlords, creditors committees, bondholder committees, indenture trustees, bankruptcy trustees, state-court assignees and buyers and investors considering investment in distressed situations. He has extensive experience in securitized loan transactions, secured and unsecured bond transactions and the establishment of bankruptcy remote special-purpose entities, and

he has rendered legal opinions in connection with such transactions.
**Personal:** JD, University of Florida Levin College of Law; BS, University of Pennsylvania, The Wharton School (magna cum laude), Economics

### ZELEK, Mark E
Morgan, Lewis & Bockius LLP, Miami
305 415 3303
mzelek@morganlewis.com
*Featured in Labor & Employment (Florida)*
**Practice Areas:** Mark E Zelek is a partner in Morgan Lewis's Labor and Employment Practice. He currently serves as the Miami office's managing partner and team leader of Morgan Lewis's International Employment Practice Group. Mark's practice focuses on counseling and representing employers in the full spectrum of employment and employee benefits law matters, including FLSA, noncompete and trade secrets, and discrimination litigation and arbitration.
**Personal:** Attended Columbia University Law School, JD; Yale University, BA.

### ZELKOWITZ, Steven
GrayRobinson, PA, Miami
305 416 6880
steven.zelkowitz@gray-robinson.com
*Featured in Real Estate (Florida)*
**Practice Areas:** Managing Shareholder in GrayRobinson's Miami office. Concentrates in complex real estate, financing, land use and zoning matters for domestic and foreign private clients as well as governmental entities. Experience in the sale and purchase of all types of real estate, securitized lending, leasing, construction, title insurance, developer representation with a concentration in condominium and hotel development projects, as well as representation of county, municipal and community redevelopment agencies. Experience in public/private transactions, including large scale transportation and public works projects as well as obtaining state and local tax incentives for businesses relocating to the State of Florida. Significant governmental law experience. Serves as general and special counsel to a

number of Community Redevelopment Agencies in South Florida including the North Miami CRA, North Miami Beach CRA, Hallandale Beach CRA and Naranja Lakes CRA.
**Professional Memberships:** Biscayne Corridor Community Redevelopment Agency, Commissioner; Miami Shores Village Historic Preservation Board, Chairman; Greater Miami Chamber of Commerce, Trustee Member; North Miami Beach Chamber of Commerce, Member; North Miami Chamber of Commerce, Trustee Member; Fort Lauderdale Chamber of Commerce, Trustee Member; Florida Redevelopment Association; Association of Florida Developers, Inc.
**Personal:** Rutgers University School of Law, JD (1989); Rutgers University, MCRP (1989); University of Massachusetts, BS (1983).

### ZEYDEL, Diana S.C.
Greenberg Traurig, LLP, Miami
305 579 0575
ZeydelD@gtlaw.com
*Featured in Wealth Management (Nationwide), Tax (Florida)*
**Practice Areas:** Chair, Trusts & Estates/Wealth Management.
**Professional Memberships:** Regent: American College of Trust and Estate Counsel. Chair: Estate and Gift Tax Committee. Academician to The International Academy of Estate and Trust Law, February 2013. Bar Admissions: Florida; New York.
**Career:** Listed: Best Lawyers in America, 2008-13; Chambers USA, 2007-13; Super Lawyers, 2006-12. AV® Preeminent™ 5.0 out of 5.
**Publications:** Author, 'Developing Law on Changing Irrevocable Trusts: Staying Out of the Danger Zone', Real Property, Trust and Estate Law Journal, Spring 2012.
**Personal:** LLM, New York University School of Law; JD, Yale Law School; BA, summa cum laude, Yale University.

### ZINOBER, Peter W
Greenberg Traurig, LLP, Tampa
813 318 5725
ZinoberP@gtlaw.com
*Featured in Labor & Employment (Florida)*
**Practice Areas:** Co-Chair, Global Labor & Employment Practice. Co-Chair, Global Human Capital Solutions Practice.
**Professional Memberships:** Member: American Board of Trial Advocates; Board of Trustees, University of Florida Levin College of Law. Past Chairman, The Florida Bar Labor Law Section; Chairman, Designation Coordinating Committee, Florida Bar; Fellow, American Bar Foundation.
**Career:** Listed: 'Florida's Elite Lawyers', Labor and Employment, Florida Trend magazine; One of the 100 Top Employment Lawyers in the US Human Resource Executive Magazine, 2009-12.
**Personal:** LLM, Labor Law, George Washington University, 1971; JD, University of Florida Levin College of Law, 1969; BA, English Literature, University of Florida, 1965.

### ZUSMANN, Samuel J
Holland & Knight LLP, Orlando
407 244 1102
szusmann@hklaw.com
*Featured in Bankruptcy/Restructuring (Florida)*
**Practice Areas:** Partner in the firm's Litigation Section, Sam Zusmann concentrates his practice in bankruptcy and workout law, representing creditors, debtors, examiners, trustees, and creditors' committees. He is experienced in cases involving manufacturing organizations; wholesale and retail businesses; service businesses, including truck lines, laundries, and restaurants; crop and livestock farming; and hotel, commercial, residential, and resort developments. He has represented appellants and appellees in district and circuit courts. He is a Fellow of the American College of Bankruptcy and an active leader and frequent lecturer at the national level in the fields of bankruptcy and debtors' and creditors' rights.

# AKERMAN SENTERFITT

**www.**akerman.com  **tel:** 305 374 5600  **fax:** 305 374 5095

**Chairman & CEO:** Andrew Smulian

### Firm Overview:

Akerman is a leading transactions and trial law firm known for its core strengths in middle market M&A, within the financial services and real estate industries, and for a diverse Latin America practice. With more than 550 lawyers and government affairs professionals and a network of 19 offices, the firm is ranked among the top 100 law firms in the US by The National Law Journal NLJ 250 (2012).

### Main Areas of Practice:

**Corporate, M&A & Securities:**

Leading corporate, M&A, private equity, securities/capital markets, and securities regulation team. Advise public and private companies, including private equity funds, on M&A, securities offerings, financings and other transactional matters, with a strong focus on the middle market.

**Litigation:**

Trial lawyers in offices throughout the US with vast experience in commercial litigation and international arbitration.

**Real Estate:**

Substantial experience in complex transactions, development and construction projects, economic development incentives, environmental matters, public-private initiatives, and litigation.

**Taxation:**

Represents financial services companies, national retailers, and technology and software companies in state and local tax planning, controversy, legislation, audit defense, and litigation.

**Bankruptcy & Reorganization:**

Team of bankruptcy, creditors' rights, and reorganization lawyers with particular strength in representing financial institutions as well as experience in SEC matters, including Ponzi scheme cases.

**Intellectual Property:**

Deep industry experience with intellectual property matters involving biomedical devices, electrical engineering, information technology, telecommunications, healthcare, entertainment, and sports.

**Healthcare:**

Providing counsel on complex regulatory, risk management, and corporate matters to hospitals and health systems, pharmacy-related organizations, health insurers and managed care organizations, and other industry stakeholders.

**Government Affairs & Public Policy:**

Bi-partisan team located in Washington, DC, New York, and Florida. Experience in appropriations, education, healthcare, insurance, transportation and infrastructure, Native American affairs, and international trade.

**Labor & Employment:**

Represents employers in virtually every major industry with all aspects of labor and employment law compliance and litigation, workplace safety, immigration, and non-compete/trade secret issues.

**Trusts, Estates & Family Services:**

Counsel to high-net worth individuals and families, providing personalized strategies for estate planning, wealth and business preservation, probate, trust and guardianship administration and litigation, family and marital law, and employee and retirement benefits.

### OFFICES

**CALIFORNIA**

**LOS ANGELES:** 725 South Figueroa Street, 38th Floor, CA 90017
Tel: 213 688 9500  Fax: 213 627 6342

**COLORADO**

**DENVER:** 1400 Wewatta Street, Suite 500, CO 80202
Tel: 303 260 7712  Fax: 303 260 7714

**FLORIDA**

**BOCA RATON:** 2424 North Federal Highway, Suite 410, FL 33431
Tel: 561 862 4000  Fax: 561 368 4668

**FORT LAUDERDALE:** 350 East Las Olas Boulevard, Suite 1600, FL 33301
Tel: 954 463 2700  Fax: 954 463 2224

**JACKSONVILLE:** 50 North Laura Street, Suite 3100, FL 32202
Tel: 904 798 3700  Fax: 904 798 3730

**MIAMI:** One Southeast Third Avenue, 25th Floor, FL 33131
Tel: 305 374 5600  Fax: 305 374 5095

**NAPLES:** 9128 Strada Place, Suite 10205, FL 34108
Tel: 239 449 5600  Fax: 239 449 5658

**ORLANDO:** 420 South Orange Avenue, Suite 1200, FL 32801
Tel: 407 423 4000  Fax: 407 843 6610

**PALM BEACH:** 125 Worth Avenue, Suite 330, FL 33480
Tel: 561 659 8660  Fax: 561 659 8679

**TALLAHASSEE:** 106 East College Avenue, 12th Floor, FL 32301
Tel: 850 224 9634  Fax: 850 222 0103

**TAMPA:** 401 East Jackson Street, Suite 1700, FL 33602
Tel: 813 223 7333  Fax: 813 223 2837

**WEST PALM BEACH:** 222 Lakeview Avenue, Suite 400, FL 33401
Tel: 561 653 5000  Fax: 561 659 6313

**NEVADA**

**LAS VEGAS:** 1160 Town Center Drive, Suite 330, NV 89144
Tel: 702 634 5000  Fax: 702 380 8572

**NEW YORK**

**NEW YORK:** 335 Madison Avenue, 26th Floor, NY 10017
Tel: 212 880 3800  Fax: 212 880 8965

**TEXAS**

**DALLAS:** 2001 Ross Avenue, Suite 2550, TX 75201
Tel: 214 720 4300  Fax: 214 981 9339

**UTAH**

**SALT LAKE CITY:** 170 South Main Street, Suite 950, UT 84101
Tel: 801 907 6900  Fax: 801 355 0294

**VIRGINIA**

**TYSONS CORNER:** 8100 Boone Boulevard, Suite 630, VA 22182
Tel: 703 790 8750  Fax: 703 448 1801

**DISTRICT OF COLUMBIA**

**WASHINGTON, DC:** 750 9th Street, NW, Suite 750, DC 20001
Tel: 202 393 6222  Fax: 202 393 5959

**WISCONSIN**

**MADISON:** One South Pinckney Street, Suite 700, WI 53703
Tel: 608 257 5335  Fax: 608 257 2029

# ASTIGARRAGA DAVIS

**www.**astidavis.com **tel:** 305 372 8282 **fax:** 305 372 8202

**Contact:** José I Astigarraga
Number of partners: 9
Number of lawyers: 19
Languages: *English, Italian, Portuguese and Spanish*

## Firm Overview:

Astigarraga Davis is a boutique law firm focused on international and other business disputes. Latin Lawyer describes the firm as a 'small but prestigious boutique' with a reputation for 'high-value, multi-jurisdictional arbitration and litigation in Latin America.' The firm has an extensive cross-border practice, its lawyers having handled business disputes emanating from virtually every country in the Western Hemisphere as well as elsewhere in the world. The firm's strengths focus on international arbitration, international litigation and financial services litigation including creditors' rights, bankruptcy and class actions. Its international arbitration practice handles cases before the major international arbitral institutions, including the International Chamber of Commerce and the International Centre for Dispute Resolution. As a testament to its dedication to its clients, the firm was presented with the Outstanding Client Service award by *Chambers* for the Latin America region. With its international network of lawyers worldwide, the firm manages complex disputes in foreign jurisdictions for its clients, including in developing and executing strategies for multi-jurisdictional cases and high-profile controversies, particularly in Latin America and the Caribbean. The firm's asset recovery team has pursued fraudsters and corrupt officials around the world to recover misappropriated assets, particularly from fraudulent transactions originating in Latin America and the Caribbean.

## Main Areas of Practice:

### International Litigation:

Astigarraga Davis litigates in US federal and state courts, prosecutes and defends arbitrations in the US and abroad and supervises litigation in courts outside the United States. It often represents foreign litigants in obtaining discovery assistance from US federal courts pursuant to 28 U.S.C. Section 1782, which authorizes discovery in the U.S. for use in foreign proceedings. The firm presently is involved in multiple Section 1782 proceedings in federal courts for the purpose of obtaining evidence and testimony in connection with pending proceedings in Brazil, Ecuador, Mexico, Canada and elsewhere. The firm's lawyers know the foreign systems, their rules and the right questions to ask in connection with disputes pending in Latin America. Using its extensive international experience, multi-lingual capabilities, multi-cultural background and broad network of contacts in the region, the firm also manages substantial disputes in Latin America and supervises business litigation pending in courts there.

### International Arbitration:

The firm has a leading international arbitration practice handling cases before the major international arbitral institutions. The firm's work was recognized when it was awarded the worldwide prize for regional and niche firm of the year by the Global Arbitration Review. The firm's lawyers are active in arbitration initiatives. José Astigarraga, for example, was one of ten delegates first appointed by the United States Government to advise the NAFTA Commission on the development and use of international arbitration and dispute resolution. He serves as Vice President of the London Court of International Arbitration, is a member of the American Arbitration Association's International Rules Advisory Committee and has lectured extensively on international litigation and arbitration.

### Fraud Prosecution & Asset Recovery:

Working with its international network of lawyers and contacts developed over the years, the firm has pursued fraudsters and other corrupt actors in a variety of jurisdictions to recover fraudulently obtained assets. Practice head Edward H Davis, Jr is a certified fraud examiner and has lectured extensively on fraud prosecution and international asset recovery. Currently, Astigarraga Davis acts as co-general counsel to the Joint Liquidators of Stanford International Bank Limited, in connection with the liquidation of the Antigua-based bank at the centre of a multi-billion fraud affecting more than twenty-thousand victims. The firm has been involved in liquidation-related activities and litigation throughout the world leading to important recoveries for the benefit of the estate and victims. The firm has also represented a number of governments in pursuing stolen assets in high-profile grand corruption cases.

### Financial Services Litigation:

Astigarraga Davis has extensive litigation experience representing lenders, creditors, banks and other financial institutions in disputes in the United States and abroad. As well, the firm represents investors in disputes arising out of investments and other financial transactions. The firm represents lenders and creditors domestically in bankruptcy courts in Florida and other states, and internationally in Latin America, including in multi-jurisdictional insolvencies. Practice head Gregory Grossman has broad bankruptcy experience, having handled a diverse array of cases in a number of domestic bankruptcy courts and has lectured on a variety of insolvency-related topics. The firm filed the first Chapter 15 Bankruptcy in the State of Florida when it successfully obtained 'foreign main case' recognition of insolvency proceedings for a failed financial institution overseas.

The firm has litigated with, and on behalf of, foreign trustees seeking to enlist the aid of US bankruptcy courts to bar creditors from seizing collateral or other assets in the US. The recognized experience in this area led the World Bank to engage José Astigarraga as a consultant to assess the region's insolvency systems.

### Other Litigation:

The firm also has extensive experience in intellectual property litigation, with capabilities including trademark, trade secret, internet, e-commerce and media law disputes both domestically and abroad. Edward Mullins, a former chair of the Florida Bar Media and Communications Law Committee, has represented newspapers, magazines, radio and television stations, and television networks in numerous lawsuits involving libel, slander, invasion of privacy, intentional infliction of emotional distress, tortious interference with advantageous relationships, trademark infringement, copyright infringement and other publication disputes. The firm's deep knowledge allows it to represent its corporate clients in domain name disputes, intellectual property infringement claims based on the internet and similar publication claims.

### Clients:

Astigarraga Davis' clients include multinational companies, global banks, *Fortune* 500 corporations, other public and private companies, and states and their instrumentalities.

## ASTIGARRAGA DAVIS
### THE POWER OF FOCUS®

# BECKER & POLIAKOFF, P.A.

www.becker-poliakoff.com **tel:** 954 987 7550 **fax:** 954 985 4176

**Managing Shareholder:** Gary Rosen
**Management Committee:** Yolanda Cash Jackson, Rosa de la Camara, Steve Lesser, Joe Adams, Allen Levine, Ken Direktor, Gary Rosen
Number of Shareholders: 45
Number of Lawyers, Lobbyists and other Professionals: 155

**Firm Overview:**
Becker & Poliakoff gained a reputation early in its history for being nimble, aggressive advocates for its clients. Forty years later, the firm is well-established with eight primary practice groups in offices throughout Florida and in New York, New Jersey, Washington, DC, Northern Virginia, and Prague. "Legal and Business Strategists" defines who they are and how they approach their work. Board Certification of attorneys and other high level credentialing is expected, and encouraged through firm training programs. Each of the two largest practice groups sponsor an annual, three day intensive, hands-on, experiential learning program. The Client CARE Center is a dedicated client service team that handles client inquiries in a timely, efficient manner to ensure client service is the highest priority.

## Communication
The firm's blogs provide analysis, insight and dialogue on several topics:

**Koz on Gaming:**
www.kozongaming.blogspot.com

**Eminent Domain Law in Florida:**
www.eminentdomainlawflorida.com/blog.html

**The Customs & International Trade Law Blog:**
www.customsandinternationaltradelaw.com

**Public Private Partnership Exchange:**
www.p3exchange.blogspot.com

**The Florida Construction Law Authority:**
www.floridaconstructionlawauthority.com

**Business Litigation Perspectives:**
www.businesslitigationperspectives.com

**The Corporate & Capital Law Blog:**
www.corporatecapitalblog.com

**IP and Information Law Monitor:**
www.informationlawmonitor.com

**Condos Y Asociaciones Residenciales en la Florida:**
www.condoyasociacionesflorida.com

**Condominium & HOA Law Blog:**
www.floridacondohoalawblog.com

## Main Areas of Practice:

**Construction Law & Litigation:**
- Seventeen (17) Board Certified Construction Attorneys considered experts by the Florida Bar; one of the largest dedicated teams of experts in Florida
**Representative Clients:** Carnival Corporation; Swire Properties; Zurich Surety; W.G. Yates & Company; School Board of Broward County; AECOM; Meisner Electric; Turnberry Associates
**Contact:** Steven Lesser
**Email:** slesser@becker-poliakoff.com

**Business Litigation:**
- Sixty-plus litigators throughout Florida, New York, New Jersey and Northern Virginia
- Board Certified Experts by the Florida Bar
- Lender Liability Practice led by Helen Davis Chaitman
**Representative Clients:** Ultimate Software Group; Isle of Capri Casino; Town of Southwest Ranches; Federal Deposit Insurance Corporation (FDIC); Region's Bank.
**Contact:** Allen Levine **Email:** alevine@becker-poliakoff.com

**Government Law & Lobbying:**
- Lawyers and Lobbyists at the Local, State and Federal Levels of Government
- Tallahassee and Washington, DC lobbying offices
**Representative Clients:** AT&T; Isle of Capri Casino; Oracle; Florida Gulf Coast University; Dade Medical College; Miami Dade County, Miami Dade County School Board; Miami Dade Expressway Authority; Palm Beach Solid Waste Authority.Municipalities: Cape Coral, Hollywood, Southwest Ranches, Davie, Opa Locka.
**Contact:** Bernie Friedman
**Email:** bfriedman@becker-poliakoff.com

**Real Estate:**
- Transactions, Land Use, Entitlements, Finance, Leasing, Planned Development
- REO and Special Assets
**Representative Clients:** TD Bank, Lender Processing Services (LPS), CMC Development, Stiles, JGB Bank, Region's Bank, Fort Capital Management LLC.
**Contact:** Jennifer Bales Drake
**Email:** jdrake@becker-poliakoff.com

**Corporate:**
- New York office in Wall Street area
- Securities, Corporate, Capital Markets and Corporate Finance, Broker-Dealer and Investment Advisers, Hedge Funds, In House Legal Services, Private Equity, Regulatory, SEC Disclosure and Securities Regulation
**Representative Clients:** DLH Holdings Corp; Spencer Savings Bank, S.L.A. Authentidate Holding Corp.; Capital Guardian Wealth Management, LLC; Cairn Capital North America, Inc.; Reva Capital Markets, LLC; WBI Investments, Inc.; Garden State Securities, Inc.; Aegis Capital Corp.; Flintlock Construction Services, L.L.C.; National Securities Corporation.
**Contact:** Victor DiGioia
**Email:** vdigioia@becker-poliakoff.com

**Customs & International Trade:**
- Assist importers, brokers, transporters, exporters, warehouses and others with Federal importation laws and regulations
**Representative Clients:** multi national importers and exporters across multiple industries (aerospace, electronics, food, drug, cosmetic, apparel; customs brokers and freight forwarders.
**Contact:** Jennifer Diaz **Email:** jdiaz@becker-poliakoff.com

**Intellectual Property & Emerging Technologies:**
- Based in Northern Virginia strategically located near the US Patent & Trade Office
- Global patent protection and American patent services
- Academic Innovation
- Commercialization
- Copyright
- Trademarks and Service Marks
**Representative Clients:** Universities, research and innovation centers, inventors, entrepreneurs.
**Contact:** Richard Litman
**Email:** rlitman@becker-poliakoff.com

**Community Association Law:**
- General Counsel to 4,000+ Boards of Condominium and Homeowner Associations
- Legislative Advocacy
**Representative Clients:** Seven Lakes Association, Frenchmen's Creek, Inc., Continuum on South Beach.
**Contact:** Ken Direktor
**Email:** kdirektor@becker-poliakoff.com

**OFFICES**

**FLORIDA**

**FORT LAUDERDALE:** Emerald Lake Corporate Park, 3111 Stirling Road, FL 33312-6525
Tel: 954 987 7550   Fax: 954 985 4176
Email: care@becker-poliakoff.com
The firm also has offices in New York, New Jersey, Northern Virginia and Washington, DC

**INTERNATIONAL OFFICES**
Prague (Czech Republic)

# BECKER & POLIAKOFF
## Legal and Business Strategists

# BERGER SINGERMAN

www.bergersingerman.com **tel:** 305 755 9500 **fax:** 305 714 4340

**Co-Chair:** Mitchell W Berger
**Co-Chair:** Paul Steven Singerman
**Managing Partner:** James L Berger
Number of partners: 41  Number of other lawyers: 28

**Firm Overview:**

From the firm's offices in Miami, Fort Lauderdale, Boca Raton and in the state capital of Tallahassee, Berger Singerman serves an international client base with respect to matters involving Florida issues. The firm's attorneys are widely recognized as among the best in their field by independent third party sources, and many have held prestigious positions in industry, in the legal community and in public service. The firm distinguishes itself not by the size of its firm, but by its passion for client service.

The firm also recognizes the need to create value for its clients, by resolving a dispute that is impacting a business, by finding a way to get a 'stuck' transaction done, by resolving an issue with an agency, etc. The firm understands that its ultimate responsibility is to assist clients to enhance their income, or reduce their expenses.

The firm serves three primary markets: leading companies, successful individuals, and other law firms.

**Leading Companies:** The firm assists its clients in creating competitive advantage. The firm's clients undoubtedly face significant, if not severe, competition. The challenge of owners, senior managers and even directors is to position its clients' company so as to create and maintain competitive advantage. Berger Singerman lawyers are experienced at working with owners, senior managers and directors.

**Successful Individuals:** Berger Singerman services relationships with business executives, entrepreneurs, professionals, and other wealthy individuals. Whereas most law firms make serving big businesses their priority, Berger Singerman also focuses on the individuals who manage the large corporations or are building tomorrow's successful businesses. Working with leading independent investment and business advisors, the firm assists individuals in building and protecting their wealth through every stage of their life. Recognizing that the needs of individuals change as they mature, the firm has lawyers focused on the challenges at each stage of one's life.

**Other Law Firms:** The foundation of the firm is the referral work that it does for law firms from around the world. Law firms of all size honor the firm by their referral of their most important clients when special counsel, conflict counsel, or Florida counsel is needed. Referring law firms tell Berger Singerman that they refer matters to them because: its attorneys are recognized as among the very best in the market as evidenced by the percentage honored by independent sources; most of its attorneys practiced at large national firms or leading regional firms before making the personal decision to join it to enjoy the firm's unique collaborative culture; other attorneys respect the firm's commitment to strategically limit its practice to areas where it is among the very best in the market area; and referring attorneys appreciate its commitment to enhancing their client relationship through the substantive quality of the firm's legal work and its commitment to providing excellent service for their clients.

**OFFICES**

FLORIDA

**MIAMI:** 1450 Brickell Avenue, Suite 1900, FL 33131
Tel: 305 755 9500   Fax: 305 714 4340

**FORT LAUDERDALE:** 350 East Las Olas Boulevard,
Suite 1000, FL 33301
Tel: 954 525 9900   Fax: 954 523 2872
Email: info@bergersingerman.com

**TALLAHASSEE:** 125 South Gadsden Street, Suite 300,
FL 32301
Tel: 850 561 3010   Fax: 850 561 3013

**BOCA RATON:** 2650 North Military Trail, Suite 240,
FL 33431
Tel: 561 241 9500   Fax: 561 998 0028

## Main Areas of Practice:

### Business Reorganization:

The size, depth and international reputation of its Business Reorganization Team distinguish Berger Singerman. Berger Singerman has one of the largest business reorganization practice groups in the region and its members are consistently involved in the most significant business bankruptcy cases and out of court workouts in the region. The team represents business debtors, creditors' committees, trade creditors, institutional and non-institutional secured creditors and lessors, court appointed trustees, receivers and assignees for the benefit of creditors. The team also represents strategic and financial investors in a variety of insolvency-related merger and acquisition engagements, including acquisition of distressed businesses, divisions, assets and intellectual property of such businesses.

### Dispute Resolution:

The Dispute Resolution Team handles a wide variety of complex commercial disputes in federal and state courts and alternative dispute resolution engagements throughout Florida and across the United States. The team has handled multi-million dollar class action disputes and lender liability cases. The team represents regional, national and international clients ranging from Fortune 500 companies to entrepreneurs. Team members bring specialized expertise in business torts such as fraud, breach of fiduciary duty, theft of trade secrets, and tortious interference with business relationships and contracts, to support more aggressive theories and recoveries in this area. The team also features specialized expertise in employment law and non-compete cases and regularly handles employment termination cases, non-compete and other covenant enforcement actions, and various other claims employees assert.

### Government & Regulatory:

Berger Singerman's Government and Regulatory Team represents a variety of private and public sector clients in regulatory matters before federal, state, regional and local agencies. The members of the team have had meaningful involvement in shaping the landscape of environmental and land use law in Florida during their long and distinguished careers. In addition, the members are recognized as leaders in the fields of healthcare regulation, waste management, governmental procurement, bid protests and white-collar crime prevention.

### Business, Finance & Tax:

Berger Singerman's Business, Finance and Tax Team represents corporate and individual clients in sophisticated international, domestic and foreign transactions. The firm's Business, Finance and Tax Team possesses expertise in corporate, securities, real estate, financing, technology, intellectual property, aviation and tax matters. The Business, Finance and Tax Team attorneys bring multi-disciplinary legal expertise to structure, negotiate, document and close complex business transactions. Most of the Business, Finance and Tax Team's attorneys practice across the traditional legal boundaries of corporate, securities, mergers and acquisitions, commercial real estate, financing and tax. The team utilizes a cross-disciplinary approach – tax partners often structure, negotiate, and handle an entire business deal, rather than merely the 'tax portion' of a transaction – the real estate attorneys have significant experience with complex corporate structuring and transactions, employment agreements and other business agreements – and most of the Business, Finance and Tax Team's lawyers are experienced in transactions which are implemented within a bankruptcy case. By using all the expertise of attorneys familiar with many legal disciplines, the Business, Finance and Tax Team delivers more effective legal representation in a cost-effective manner.

# BILZIN SUMBERG BAENA PRICE & AXELROD LLP

www.bilzin.com **tel:** 305 374 7580 **fax:** 305 374 7593

**Managing Partner:** John C. Sumberg
Number of Partners: 59 Number of other lawyers: 110

**OFFICES**

FLORIDA

**MIAMI:** 1450 Brickell Avenue, 23rd Floor, FL 33131-3456
Tel: 305 374 7580  Fax: 305 374 7593
Email: info@bilzin.com

## Firm Overview:

Bilzin Sumberg is a commercial law firm serving domestic and international clients with timely and efficient service, and unmatched depth and breadth of experience in a variety of industries. The firm views each of its clients and the matters in which it represents them as unique and of paramount importance. Whether in the courtroom or in the boardroom, the firm shoulders every client issue as its own.

## Main Areas of Practice:

### Corporate & Tax:

Bilzin Sumberg's Corporate and Tax Group assists clients in matters of local, national and global scope, in industries such as manufacturing and distribution, healthcare products and services, energy, banking and financial services, hotels and restaurants, pharmaceuticals, real estate, technology and telecommunications. The group regularly represents clients in M&A transactions, including sales, going private transactions, recapitalizations, joint ventures and strategic alliances and corporate finance and capital markets transactions, such as private equity, venture capital, public and private offerings of equity and debt securities. The group handles Securities Exchange Act reporting, corporate governance and general corporate matters such as non-competition arrangements, executive compensation and licensing. It also provides tax analysis and advice in the structuring of corporate, real estate and other commercial transactions, as well as advising clients on planning to minimize individual and corporate income taxes, and taxes related to inbound and outbound investments. Clients are represented in tax controversy, estate planning, probate and trust administration, advanced strategies to minimize estate, gift and generation-skipping taxes, multi-generational tax planning and the establishment of charitable giving plans and organizations.

### International:

Bilzin Sumberg's multidisciplinary International Group represents domestic and international clients ranging in size from individual investors to large, privately held and publicly traded companies. The team's attorneys routinely handle complex cross-border corporate transactions, including mergers and acquisitions, joint ventures and restructurings; tax and wealth preservation planning; franchise, distribution, technology and intellectual property licensing and other commercial arrangements; environmental permitting and other regulatory activities; as well as cross-border litigation matters and international disputes before US courts and international arbitration panels.

### Litigation:

Bilzin Sumberg's Litigation Group maintains a national practice in complex commercial litigation, with broad civil trial and litigation experience in litigation planning and analysis, ADR - including arbitration and mediation, trial and appeal. The litigation lawyers handle cases involving antitrust matters, partnership disputes, business torts, breach of contract, construction defects, bankruptcy, intellectual property, eminent domain, securities and products liability litigation. In addition, the group has significant experience in representing clients in regulatory disputes before various federal and state agencies, as well as in international arbitration panels.

### Real Estate:

Bilzin Sumberg's Real Estate Group provides legal counsel statewide and nationally across a broad range of commercial real estate practice areas, including financing, capital markets, purchase and sale of property, leasing and restructuring of distressed property and loans. The group provides counsel in every facet of commercial real estate transactions for all types of property, including hotel, hotel/condos, mixed-use properties, marinas, retail, office, industrial, entertainment facilities, distressed property and undeveloped land. In addition, Bilzin Sumberg represents the largest special servicer of CMBS loans in the country, which has serviced in excess of 145 pools of CMBS loans totaling more than $240 billion in principal - and relating to real property interests in all 50 states.

### Government Relations & Land Development:

Bilzin Sumberg's Government Relations and Land Development Group represents both public and private clients on matters securing government contracts, permitting, zoning and regulatory relief from government agencies. The group is experienced in land use and growth management, platting and replatting, zoning, government contracts and procurement. In addition, the group's attorneys have extensive experience representing clients in all types of regulatory and enforcement actions throughout Florida involving local, state and federal agencies. The team handles all aspects of natural resource permitting, including permit applications, appeals, compliance issues and enforcement defense. This includes marina permitting and operation, wetland and stormwater permitting, land development and property rights protection, landfill permitting and regulation, hazardous waste compliance and regulation, and the redevelopment of brownfield sites. Bilzin Sumberg has represented clients in administrative proceedings, trial and appellate litigation, and its attorneys have served as special counsel to several Florida local governments and governmental authorities.

### Restructuring & Bankruptcy:

Bilzin Sumberg's Restructuring and Bankruptcy Group is a regional and national player in complex in-court and out-of-court reorganizations, restructurings, workouts and assignments for the benefit of creditors. The attorneys have backgrounds in accounting, finance and banking, and have represented virtually every type of restructuring and bankruptcy constituency - including debtors, pre- and post-bankruptcy lenders, trade creditors, landlords, bondholders, trustees, official committees, liquidating trustees, assignees for the benefit of creditors and asset purchasers. In addition, they have served as trial counsel in many high profile bankruptcy-related litigations.

### Clients:

Bilzin Sumberg's clients span a multitude of industries including automotive dealerships, construction, environmental, financial services, energy, healthcare, hotels, resorts and restaurants, manufacturing and distribution, marinas, non-profits, public-private partnerships, real estate, real estate funds, retail, software, technology and telecom, sports and entertainment, transportation and more.

Bilzin Sumberg
ATTORNEYS AT LAW

Be judged by the company you keep.

# BURR AND FORMAN LLP

www.burr.com   **tel:** 800 GET BURR

**Chairman:** Lee Thuston
Managing Partners: 9   Number of partners: 178   Number of lawyers: 288

**Firm Overview:**
Burr & Forman is a full service law firm with a long history of serving clients in Alabama, Florida, Georgia, Mississippi and Tennessee. The firm's forward-thinking approach allows it to provide legal solutions appropriate to the needs of its clients. With nearly 300 attorneys, Burr & Forman offers a wide range of business and litigation services to diverse clients with local, national and international interests.

**Main Areas of Practice:**

**Automotive:**
Represents automotive dealerships in claims associated with franchise agreements, breach of contract, sales and acquisitions, non-competes and wrongful termination.

**Banking & Finance:**
Represents lenders of all types in lending and financial transactions for working capital needs, refinancings, specific personal and real property asset acquisitions and development and company acquisitions in the middle and large corporate markets.

**Commercial Litigation:**
Represents financial institutions, businesses and officers and directors in complex commercial disputes and securities litigation.

**Corporate & Tax:**
Represents businesses and not-for-profits of all sizes and in all stages of development in complex business matters, mergers and acquisitions, capital raises and regulatory compliance issues.

**Creditors' Rights & Bankruptcy:**
Represents financial services institutions, asset-based lenders and local, regional and national banks in significant and complex bankruptcy proceedings.

**Construction:**
Represents owners, contractors, suppliers and design professionals in all construction-related transactional matters and in the litigation or dispute resolution of all construction claims.

**Economic Development:**
Leading economic development firm in the Southeast. Projects reflect a diversity of industries and represent over $16 billion of capital investment and over 25,000 new jobs created.

**Environmental:**
Represents industries, developers, financial institutions and individuals in environmental matters related to business strategy, permitting and regulatory compliance, litigation, sustainability, and administrative proceedings.

**Financial Services Litigation:**
Represents banks, mortgage, finance and credit card companies in all types of litigation involving deceptive loan origination, predatory lending, wrongful foreclosure, mortgage fraud and statutory violation claims.

**Health Care:**
Represents all types of health care organizations in a variety of litigation, regulatory, compliance, licensure and corporate law matters.

**Insurance Regulatory:**
Represents all types of businesses and insurance entities in connection with structuring solutions to their business insurance needs and maintaining regulatory compliance.

**Labor & Employment:**
Represents employers of all sizes in matters ranging from drafting policies and handbooks to defending against the entire gamut of employment-related claims.

**Maritime & Transportation:**
Represents clients whose businesses are in, around or near navigable waters with all types of litigation claims, financing activities, contract negotiations, employment matters and other regulatory issues.

**Products Liability:**
Represents clients in all industries with products and premises liability, personal injury, industrial and construction site accidents, pharmaceuticals, medical devices, mass torts and toxic tort cases.

**Real Estate:**
Represents commercial real estate development companies in land planning, entitlement and development, governmental incentives, title matters, acquisition and disposition and performing and distressed assets.

**Securities Litigation:**
Represents broker-dealers and investment bankers in disputes, such as mutual-fund class-actions, derivative contracts trials, government enforcement actions and constitutional challenges to municipal securities rules.

**Technology:**
Represents businesses in protection of, and licensing strategies for, intellectual property, contract negotiation, growth, investment and acquisition strategies.

**Clients:**
American Cast Iron Pipe Company; ADTRAN; American Suzuki Motor Corporation; Assuranceforeningen Gard-gjensidig; Bank of America; Bank of Tampa; Brasfield and Gorrie General Contractors; Brice Building Company; Budgetext; Capital One; Charles Schwab & Co., Inc.; Circle K; Citibank; City of Tampa; Coastal Forest Products; Coca-Cola Enterprises; CVS Caremark; Daniel Realty Company; Dillard's; East Alabama Medical Center; First American; Founders Insurance Company; Gray Construction; HealthSouth Corporation; Laboratory Corporation of America; Mercedes-Benz U.S. International, Inc.; M/I Homes; Millard Maritime; Morgan Keegan & Co.; National Steel Car; Nissan Motors of America, Inc.; Nutech Medical Inc.; Nu Tech Spine, Inc.; ProAssurance; RockTenn Company; Rinnai; Standard Insurance; Southpace Properties; SunTrust Mortgage; Synovus Bank; Tacala; Tenet Healthcare Corporation; Guardian Life; ThyssenKrupp; Time Insurance Company; TriNovus Capital, LLC; UAB Health Services Foundation; United States Steel; Wells Fargo Bank; Wells Fargo Advisors; Whirlpool

## OFFICES

### FLORIDA
**FT. LAUDERDALE:** Las Olas Centre I, 450 East Las Olas Boulevard, Suite 700, FL 33301
Tel: 954 414 6200   Fax: 954 414 6201

**ORLANDO:** 200 South Orange Avenue, Suite 800, FL 32801
Tel: 407 540 6600   Fax: 407 540 6601

**TAMPA:** One Tampa City Center, Suite 3200, FL 33602
Tel: 813 221 2626   Fax: 813 221 7335

### ALABAMA
**BIRMINGHAM:** 420 North 20th Street, Suite 3400, AL 35203
Tel: 205 251 3000   Fax: 205 458 5100

**MOBILE:** RSA Tower, 11 North Water Street, Suite 22200, AL 36602
Tel: 251 344 5151   Fax: 251 344 9696

**MONTGOMERY:** RSA Tower, 201 Monroe Street, Suite 1950, AL 36104
Tel: 334 241 7000   Fax: 334 262 0020

### GEORGIA
**ATLANTA:** 171 17th Street, NW Suite 1100, GA 30363
Tel: 404 815 3000   Fax: 404 817 3244

### MISSISSIPPI
**JACKSON:** The Heritage Building, 401 E Capitol Street, Suite 100, MS 39201
Tel: 601 355 3434   Fax: 601 355 5150

### TENNESSEE
**NASHVILLE:** 700 Two American Center, 3102 West End Avenue, TN 37203
Tel: 615 724 3200   Fax: 615 724 3290

BURR ••• FORMAN LLP
*results matter*

# CARLTON FIELDS, P.A.

www.carltonfields.com **tel:** 813 223 7000 **fax:** 813 229 4133

**President & CEO:** Gary L Sasso
**Managing Partners:** Steven J Brodie, Luis Prats, Gary L Sasso
Number of shareholders: 194  Number of other attorneys: 104
Languages: *English, Chinese, French, German, Greek, Macedonian, Mandarin, Portuguese, Russian, Spanish, Thai*

## Firm Overview:

Founded in 1901, Carlton Fields provides legal services across practice areas to clients that include Fortune 500 companies, national and local corporations, state and local public entities and individuals.

## Main Areas of Practice:

### Appellate Practice & Trial Support:

Carlton Fields has Florida's largest group of lawyers devoted exclusively to an appellate and trial support practice, and the state's largest number of board certified appellate lawyers. They have handled appeals and trial support in 21 US states and territories, and addressed a broad range of issues including commercial, products liability, health care, and constitutional and statutory claims.

### Bankruptcy & Creditors' Rights:

Carlton Fields has extensive creditors' rights, insolvency, reorganization and workout experience. The firm represents commercial lenders, creditors' committees, Chapter 11 and Chapter 7 trustees, equity holders, indenture trustees, corporate debtors and others.

### Business Litigation & Trade Regulation:

Carlton Fields represents corporations in state and national litigation, including class actions involving consumer fraud, antitrust, securities and environmental claims, and litigates business disputes. It appears for clients on antitrust issues, including advertising, prospective mergers and acquisitions, government filings, pricing and marketing practices, and franchising and licensing agreements.

### Construction:

Carlton Fields provides legal services concerning all aspects of construction law, including pre-bid considerations; contract drafting and letting; construction administration, liens, bonds, insurance, and mediation; and arbitration and trial. Firm projects include office buildings, condominiums, power plants, airports, highways, stadiums and convention centers.

### Corporate, Securities & Tax:

Carlton Fields handles a wide array of corporate transactions including initial and secondary public offerings, corporate governance and compliance advice, mergers and acquisitions and asset based financing. The firm's attorneys provide tax planning advice at the federal, state and local level, and handle tax controversy cases before the IRS and state and local governments.

### Government Law & Consulting:

Carlton Fields provides strategic planning and counseling in all regulated areas, including business and professional; land use and zoning; health and insurance; environmental law; education law; bid processes and public procurement; governmental affairs and lobbying; and rulemaking, challenges and other administrative proceedings.

### Healthcare:

Carlton Fields assists clients, including hospitals, DME and pharmaceutical companies, nursing homes, physician practice groups, medical associations, health insurance companies and universities with their compliance, regulatory, transactional and litigation matters.

### Insurance:

Carlton Fields' insurance representation includes insurance coverage matters, property damage claims, bad faith, class action defense, representation before the insurance regulator, regulatory litigation and business litigation.

### Intellectual Property:

Carlton Fields represents clients in acquiring, perfecting, and transferring rights to intellectual property, and in claims involving infringement and unfair competition. The firm's attorneys are experienced with technology-related e-commerce issues, computer law, licensing, software publishing and copyright protection.

### Labor & Employment:

Carlton Fields represents employers in litigation and agency matters, including discrimination and harassment claims, wage-hour lawsuits, discharge decisions and other job actions, OSHA, WARN, IRCA, executive contracts and union issues.

### Products & Toxic Tort Liability:

Carlton Fields has defended matters involving pharmaceuticals and medical devices, chemical products, tobacco, automobiles and auto parts, sporting goods and recreational products, electrical equipment, power equipment and security systems.

### Real Estate & Finance:

Carlton Fields represents clients in all aspects of real property acquisition, development, investment, regulation, title insurance, financing, leasing, ownership, and use and transfer.

### Real Property Litigation:

Carlton Fields represents title companies, developers, lenders, buyers, sellers, property management companies, receivers, surveyors, real estate brokers and agents, appraisers and owners in all forms of real estate litigation.

### Securities:

Carlton Fields has a full-service securities practice, including representation in mergers and acquisitions, business organizations, corporate finance matters, compliance with federal and state regulatory bodies, and securities litigation.

### White-Collar:

Carlton Fields handles all areas of white collar representation and civil cases involving allegations of criminal conduct. Secured acquittal of executive in largest prosecution of individuals under the FCPA since the US Department of Justice began enforcing the act.

## International Work:

Carlton Fields represents US and non-US clients that are establishing subsidiaries, acquiring companies, participating in joint ventures and contracting abroad. The firm also helps foreign companies establish a US presence, and supports foreign and domestic clients in transactional business matters and strategic tax planning.

**OFFICES**

**FLORIDA**

**TAMPA:** 4221 West Boy Scout Boulevard, Suite 1000, FL 33607-5780
Tel: 813 223 7000  Fax: 813 229 4133
Email: info@carltonfields.com

**MIAMI:** Miami Tower, 100 SE Second Street, Suite 4200 FL 33131-2113
Tel: 305 530 0050  Fax: 305 530 0055

**ORLANDO:** CNL Center at City Commons, 450 S Orange Avenue, Suite 500, FL 32801-3370
Tel: 407 849 0300  Fax: 407 648 9099

**ST PETERSBURG:** First Central Tower, 300 Central Avenue, Suite 1500, FL 33701-3832
Tel: 727 821 7000  Fax: 727 822 3768

**TALLAHASSEE:** 215 S Monroe Street, Suite 500, FL 32301-1866
Tel: 850 224 1585  Fax: 850 222 0398

**WEST PALM BEACH:** CityPlace Tower, 525 Okeechobee Boulevard, Suite 1200, FL 33401-6350
Tel: 561 659 7070  Fax: 561 659 7368

**GEORGIA**

**ATLANTA:** One Atlantic Center, 1201 W Peachtree Street, NW, Suite 3000, GA 30309-3455
Tel: 404 815 3400  Fax: 404 815 3415

**NEW YORK**

**NEW YORK:** Standard Oil Building, 26 Broadway, 22nd floor, NY 10004-1808
Tel: 212 785 2577  Fax: 212 785 5203

CARLTON FIELDS

# COLODNY, FASS, TALENFELD, KARLINSKY, ABATE & WEBB, PA

**www.**cftlaw.com  **tel:** 954 492 4010  **fax:** 954 492 1144

**Managing Shareholder:** Mike Colodny
**Shareholders:** Mike Colodny, Joel S Fass, Howard M Talenfeld, Fred E Karlinsky, Maria Elena Abate, Katherine Scott Webb, Richard J Fidei
Number of partners: 7
Number of other lawyers: 21 (excluding partners)

**OFFICES**

FLORIDA

**FORT LAUDERDALE:** One Financial Plaza, 23rd Floor, 100 Southeast Third Avenue, FL 33394
Tel: 954 492 4010  Fax: 954 492 1144

**TALLAHASSEE:** 215 S. Monroe Street, Suite 701, FL 32301
Tel: 850 577 0398  Fax: 850 577 0385

## Firm Overview

For nearly four decades, Colodny, Fass, Talenfeld, Karlinsky, Abate & Webb has represented US and international clients in insurance regulatory, transactional and administrative law, insurance defense, complex commercial litigation and governmental affairs.

## Main Areas of Practice

### Insurance Regulatory & Transactional Law:
Colodny, Fass, Talenfeld, Karlinsky, Abate & Webb represents property and casualty insurers, surplus lines insurers, life and health insurers, reinsurers, captives, risk retention groups, risk purchasing groups, brokers, associations, managing general agencies, agents, reinsurance intermediaries, premium finance companies and other related insurance entities. With a former insurance commissioner and former insurance regulators on staff, the firm affords clients significant regulatory experience involving a wide range of licensing and compliance issues, and handles corporate formation and financing; mergers and acquisitions; adding lines of business; state expansion applications; market conduct and financial examinations; financial and solvency issues; statutory accounting procedures; risk-based capital levels; capital infusion issues; rate, form and rule filings; as well as agent and agency matters. Firm attorneys participate in speaking engagements, author articles, host regular webinars on insurance and related topics, and regularly attend meetings of the National Association of Insurance Commissioners (NAIC), National Conference of Insurance Legislators, and International Association of Insurance Supervisors. The firm hosts an annual Florida Insurance Summit attended by state and national insurance industry policymakers, regulators, elected officials and international insurance executives.
**Contact:** Fred E Karlinsky **Tel:** 954 332 1749
**Email:** fkarlinsky@cftlaw.com
**Contact:** Mike Colodny **Tel:** 954 332 1740
**Email:** mcolodny@cftlaw.com
**Contact:** Richard J Fidei **Tel:** 954 332 1758
**Email:** rfidei@cftlaw.com

### Administrative & Appellate Law:
The firm represents clients before state and federal appellate courts and regularly handles Florida Ch. 120 administrative and regulatory proceedings, bid protests, challenges and license proceedings before state agencies and the Division of Administrative Hearings.
**Contact:** Maria Elena Abate **Tel:** 954 332 1752
**Email:** mabate@cftlaw.com

### Commercial Litigation:
Experienced in litigating complex and sophisticated commercial matters, the firm represents a wide variety of business interests, including insurers and related companies, banks and real estate developers. The firm focuses on the defense of class action insurance litigation, bad faith claims, constitutional challenges, declaratory judgments and other high-risk matters.
**Contact:** Maria Elena Abate **Tel:** 954 332 1752
**Email:** mabate@cftlaw.com

### Governmental Consulting:
The firm provides lobbying and governmental consultation to insurance and other private and public sector clients before the Executive and Legislative branches of Florida government and insurance regulatory bodies on a nationwide basis. The firm has represented Citizens Property Insurance, the Florida Insurance Commissioner, the Florida Governor, the Florida Department of Business and Professional Regulation and the Florida Division of Rehabilitation and Liquidation.
**Contact:** Katherine Scott Webb **Tel:** 850 701 3103
**Email:** kwebb@cftlaw.com
**Contact:** Fred E Karlinsky **Tel:** 954 332 1749
**Email:** fkarlinsky@cftlaw.com

### Employment Law:
Colodny, Fass, Talenfeld, Karlinsky, Abate & Webb has represented private and public employers in wage and hour claims, and Title VII, ADA and ADEA claims encompassing age, national origin, race, sex and disability discrimination claims. Representation is also provided before governmental agencies such as the Equal Employment Opportunity Commission and the Florida Human Relations Commission, as well as in state and federal courts and administrative tribunals. Services include recommending policies and practices that comply with regulatory principles, and advising clients regarding the regulatory implications of business decisions.
**Contact:** Maria Elena Abate **Tel:** 954 332 1752
**Email:** mabate@cftlaw.com

### International Work:
The firm has represented multiple international reinsurance companies in a variety of reinsurance issues, such as obtaining status as an eligible reinsurer in Florida and "certified" reinsurer in New York, which allows the posting of reduced collateral for certain reinsurance contract obligations, and a variety of contract and ceding carrier insolvency and liquidation issues.

For a number of years, Shareholder Fred Karlinsky has served as an instructor for the London, England-based Insurance Market Conferences, which provide extensive training for the London and Lloyd's insurance market. He has lectured in London and Bermuda on insurance and reinsurance issues, as well as on the state of the Florida and US regulatory and political markets. He has also presented at the US Property and Casualty Insurance School in Sidney Sussex College in Cambridge, London. Mr Karlinsky was admitted to the Roll of Solicitors of the Senior Courts of England and Wales in 2011.
**Contact:** Fred E Karlinsky **Tel:** 954 332 1749
**Email:** fkarlinsky@cftlaw.com

### Clients:
American Bankers Insurance Company of Florida; Arch Insurance Group; Assurant, Inc.; Broward County League of Cities; Broward County School Board; Canopius Underwriting Bermuda Limited; Fairfax Financial Holdings Limited; FCCI Insurance Group; Florida Peninsula Insurance Company; Florida Property & Casualty Association; Florida Police Chiefs Association; Guarantee Insurance Company; Guy Carpenter & Company, LLC; Marsh & McLennan Companies, Inc.; Mercer, LLC; Property Casualty Insurers Association of America; Risk Management Solutions, Inc.; Security First Insurance Company; Southern Oak Insurance Company; United Automobile Insurance Company; Universal Insurance Holdings of North America; XL Reinsurance America, Inc.

# COLSON HICKS EIDSON

www.colson.com  **tel:** 305 476 7400  **fax:** 305 476 7444

**Managing Director:** Dean Colson
Number of partners: 12

## Firm Overview:

Colson Hicks Eidson, one of Miami's oldest and most accomplished law firms, is considered among the top trial firms in the United States, having won hundreds of multi-million dollar verdicts and settlements for its clients. With decades of experience in personal injury, commercial, securities, business torts, insurance, professional liability litigation and white-collar criminal defense, as well as domestic and international arbitration, the firm enjoys a long history of landmark decisions that have resulted in national and international recognition.

## Main Areas of Practice:

### Personal Injury & Wrongful Death:

Colson Hicks Eidson has decades of experience in prosecuting personal injury actions on behalf of its clients. The firm has handled hundreds of multi-million dollar cases arising from wrongful death, traumatic brain injuries, spinal cord injuries and burn cases. In 2009, Ervin Gonzalez was appointed by a Federal Judge to serve on the Plaintiff's Steering Committee for Chinese Drywall Litigation. And in 2010 Gonzalez was appointed by a Federal Judge to serve on the Plaintiff's Steering Committee for the BP Oil Spill Litigation.

### Commercial & Business Litigation:

Colson Hicks Eidson handles cases involving complex insurance, construction, intellectual property, and other commercial matters as well as fraud and other business torts. Firm members litigate business lawsuits to judges, juries and arbitration panels. The firm has prosecuted and defended bad faith claims involving major insurance companies. Members of the firm have served as receivers appointed by the United States District Court and the firm's partners have served on plaintiffs' committees in some of the most complex, multi-party class action securities fraud and RICO cases in South Florida. Members of the firm have represented owners, contractors, developers, design professional, lenders, and insurers in construction disputes. The firm has obtained numerous multi-million dollar verdicts, judgments, arbitration awards and settlements on behalf of small and large business enterprises, individual entrepreneurs, and in class action cases involving real estate, lender liability, professional malpractice and other business disputes. The firm is currently representing 17 counties in the State of Florida suing the major online travel companies for failure to collect hotel occupancy taxes.

### Domestic & International Arbitration:

Unlike most trial law firms, Colson Hicks Eidson is equally comfortable representing business clients as advocates in arbitration, both domestic and international. One of the firm's members serves as a member of the board of directors of the American Arbitration Association and members serve regularly as arbitrators as well as advocates in arbitration proceedings.

### White-Collar Criminal Defense:

With the former United States Attorney for the Southern District of Florida, Roberto Martínez and former Assistant United States Attorney Curtis Miner, the firm offers extensive experience and expertise in federal criminal investigation and SEC enforcement actions. These experienced federal litigators have represented businesses and their officers in connection with investigations and trials in matters including securities, insider trading, money laundering, Foreign Corrupt Practices Act, asset foreiture, tax, healthcare, bank fraud, environmental, antitrust, obstruction of justice, export, RICO and extortion in laws.

### Product Liability:

Colson Hicks Eidson has litigated cases involving the design and manufacture of airplanes, motor vehicles, boats, tires, medical devices, and children's toys. Long considered one of the innovators in the field of product liability law, Mike Eidson, a founding partner of the firm, served as the national co-lead counsel in the multi-district Ford/Firestone litigation for all personal injury claims.

### Professional Negligence:

Colson Hicks Eidson has handled dozens of medical malpractice cases that have resulted in verdicts and settlements in excess of one million dollars since the firm won the first million-dollar medical malpractice verdict in the United States. The firm has also handled significant legal malpractice cases for both plaintiffs and defendants. Colson Hicks Eidson has been selected to defend several national and regional law firms when they have been accused of professional negligence.

### Aviation:

Colson Hicks Eidson has represented many clients in litigation arising out of the crashes of commercial and private aircraft over the past two decades. The firm often works in conjunction with local counsel in other states and countries. In several mass death cases, the firm has represented a majority of the passengers in the plane. The firm also has handled individual claims in private aviation crashes relating to failed component parts, faulty design and manufacture and inadequate warnings.

### Recent Cases of Note:

In 2005, the firm obtained a $60.9 million award, the largest amount ever awarded in a Federal Tort Claims Act case in the country. In 2005, a Miami jury awarded a $65.1 million verdict on behalf of a client against Eller Media Company for the electrocution death of a client's 12-year-old son. In 2003, the firm negotiated a settlement of $100 million in a grave desecration case against Service Corporation International, the world's largest cemetery and funeral company, to settle the individual and class action claims of victims with loved ones buried at Menorah Gardens funeral homes in Florida. In 2002 the firm obtained a $19 million judgment in federal court in Miami against the Government of Aruba on behalf of racecar promoter Ralph Sanchez in connection with the failed efforts to build a racetrack in Aruba. In 2001 the firm obtained a federal court judgment in the amount of $16 million confirming an arbitration award against the Miccosukee Tribe of Indians arising out of a breach of contract regarding the management of the Indian's gambling operations. Two of the firm's partners served as co-lead trial counsel on behalf of the Plaintiff class in The Premium Sales case, the largest mass fraud case in South Florida history. The case was settled after the start of trial for $170,000,000. The firm represented a Canadian telecommunications company in a complex commercial litigation case involving breach of contract, fraud and intentional interference of a business relationship. Firm members won a jury verdict of $31.2 million for their client, SIRIT Technologies Inc., against Able Telcom-whose largest shareholder is MCI WorldCom, Inc.

## OFFICES

**FLORIDA**

**CORAL GABLES:** 255 Alhambra Circle, Penthouse, FL 33134-7414
Tel: 305 476 7400  Fax: 305 476 7444

**DISTRICT OF COLUMBIA**

**WASHINGTON, DC:** 2101 L Street NW, 10th Floor, DC 20037
Tel: 202 386 6706  Fax: 202 386 6706

**LOUISIANA**

**NEW ORLEANS:** 600 Carondelet Street, Rooms 810 & 812, LA 70130
Tel: 305 476 7400  Fax: 305 476 7444

# GLENN RASMUSSEN, P.A.

www.glennrasmussen.com **tel:** 813 229 3333 **fax:** 813 229 5946

**OFFICES**

FLORIDA

**TAMPA:** 100 South Ashley Drive, Suite 1300,
FL 33602-3333
Tel: 813 229 3333  Fax: 813 229 5946

## Firm Overview:

Founded in 1983, Glenn Rasmussen, P.A. is a commercial law firm designed to provide clients with shareholder-level skills and service, as well as small-firm economy and attention. The firm is committed to practicing in core areas that are essential to its clients, rather than trying to be all things to all people. By limiting the practice to what the firm does best, the goal is to deliver services at a higher level of skill and sophistication.

The firm is proud that its reputation is bolstered by peer recognition. Peer review and evaluation have led to the inclusion of 100% of its shareholders in peer-reviewed directories of top lawyers, including *The Best Lawyers in America®*, *Chambers USA*, *Florida Super Lawyers®*, *Florida Trend Magazine's Florida Legal Elite™*, and *Who's Who Legal in American Law*. All shareholders are AV® Peer Review Rated in the *Martindale-Hubbell Law Directory*. In addition, the firm has a shareholder who is Board Certified by The Florida Bar Board of Legal Specialization and Education in each of its practice areas for which board certification is possible. The firm has also won *Tampa Bay Business Journal's* "Best Places to Work" designation for five years in a row.

The firm serves clients in Tampa, St. Petersburg, Orlando, Sarasota, Ft. Myers, and surrounding areas. Through its membership in Meritas, an "invitation only" worldwide organization of 175 independent business law firms with over 6,900 lawyers, Glenn Rasmussen, P.A. affords clients the global reach and breadth of an international firm with the convenience of a trusted local advisor.

## Main Areas of Practice:

### Banking & Insolvency:
The firm represents financial institutions and commercial lenders in both credit transactions and debt-enforcement proceedings. Capabilities in credit transactions extend to commercial loans, acquisition loans, asset-based loans, agricultural loans, mortgage warehousing, syndication financing, intercreditor agreements, motor vehicle floor plan financing, loan participations, construction and permanent real estate loans, and letter of credit and bankers' acceptance facilities.
Insolvency is an important aspect of credit transactions, and the firm enjoys a reputation for its work in complex bankruptcy, foreclosure, receivership, and credit workout matters. The bankruptcy group has experience representing debtors, receivers, and secured and unsecured creditors in all aspects of bankruptcy and insolvency matters. The firm's lawyers are well versed in creditors' rights litigation, including particularly replevin, garnishment, attachment, execution of judgments, and fraudulent conveyance.

### Commercial Litigation:
The firm has experience in virtually every area of commercial litigation and represents clients in a variety of forums, including state and federal courts and administrative agencies in Florida, as well as in other jurisdictions throughout the United States.
The commercial litigation group frequently litigates significant commercial disputes involving the substantive laws of banking, taxation, antitrust, franchising, real estate, corporations, construction, non-competes, securities regulation, and municipal governments. The group also has substantial experience with mediation, arbitration, and other alternative dispute resolution procedures.

### Construction:
The firm represents contractors, subcontractors, owners (public and private), sureties, architects, and engineers in a variety of matters, including contract drafting and negotiation, construction claims, contract disputes, bid protests, failures, mold litigation, OSHA citations, and architect/engineer malpractice.

### Corporate Finance:
The corporate finance group is particularly noted for skills in corporate governance, securities law, and mergers and acquisitions, and also has substantial experience with respect to spin-offs, tender offers, redemptions, recapitalizations, securities offerings, corporate governance, real estate syndication, family-owned businesses, venture capital investments, SEC reporting and compliance, proxy and consent solicitations, shareholder control arrangements, director and officer liability issues, partnerships and limited liability companies, stock option and other executive benefit plans, and mergers and acquisitions (friendly and hostile). With respect to financial institutions, the corporate finance practice includes corporate lending and bank mergers, acquisitions, and securities offerings.

### Labor & Employment:
The labor and employment group has substantial experience in defending employers in a variety of employment law proceedings, including retaliation, wage and hour, discrimination, whistleblowers, EEOC proceedings/charges, negligent hiring and retention, Americans with Disabilities Act, and other employment torts.
The firm also provides clients with effective counseling and implementation of personnel policies and procedures, including employee handbooks and supervisory training, to assist in the prevention of legal problems.

### Real Estate:
The firm has a comprehensive real estate practice involving all aspects of the acquisition, development, financing, leasing, and disposition of commercial and residential properties.

# GREENBERG TRAURIG LLP

www.gtlaw.com **tel:** 212 801 9200 **fax:** 212 801 6400

**Chief Executive Officer:** Richard A Rosenbaum
**Co-chairs:** Cesar L Alvarez, Matthew B Gorson
Number of partners: 840   Number of other lawyers: 1000

## Firm Overview:

Greenberg Traurig, LLP is an international business law firm with approximately 1800 attorneys and governmental professionals working in 36 offices across the United States, Europe, Latin America, the Middle East, and Asia. Greenberg Traurig works with clients to address their multi-disciplinary cross border needs.

## Main Areas of Practice:

### Corporate & Securities:

Clients are helped with the legal aspects of organizing, operating, financing and expanding businesses, including: complex M&A and business combinations, divestitures, restructurings and bankruptcy reorganizations; private equity and venture capital financings; leveraged buyouts, IPOs and underwritten securities offerings; project financings; securitizations; going-private, credit enhancement, derivatives, and syndicated lending transactions; and broker-dealer and investment company advisory matters.

### Litigation:

The team comprises more than 600 litigators across a global platform. They assist clients with antitrust; appellate; commercial litigation; class actions; construction; eDiscovery and eRetention; environmental; fiduciary litigation; financial services; IP litigation; international dispute resolution; labor and employment; media and entertainment; products liability, including pharmaceutical, medical device and healthcare; real estate, securities and shareholder, and technology-related litigation; trial practice; and white collar criminal defense.

### Real Estate:

The firm's representation and counsel includes local, national and international real estate transactions affecting commercial, residential, retail and industrial properties, including: acquisitions; traditional and securitized financing; planning and development; hotels; condominium and co-operative offerings; leasing; sale/leaseback transactions; tax free exchanges; and foreclosures, litigation and restructurings.

### Tax, Trusts & Estates:

The tax attorneys help clients develop and implement tax strategies to maximize returns and minimize taxes. Wealth preservation attorneys advise high net worth individuals, families and closely held businesses grow family assets through planning. The firm has developed tax saving techniques and designed innovative wealth preservation programs to facilitate the transfer of family wealth.

### Intellectual Property:

The team offers strategies for the protection of intellectual property of clients in all technologies, from biotechnology, pharmaceuticals, medical devices and chemistry to mechanical, electronics and computer software and e-commerce.

### Government:

The team includes former elected officials, top aides and policy makers from the federal, state and local government bodies. They represent corporations, municipalities and organizations before the legislative and executive branches in state and local government to provide clients with representation in virtually any form.

### Global Trade:

The team advises clients on trade agreements, trade legislation and lobbying, antitrust and Foreign Corrupt Practices Act counseling, US Foreign Military Sales Program, US anti-boycott and embargo regulations, identification of complex export control for hi-tech, defense and aerospace companies, defense of corporations in export-related criminal investigations and unfair trade cases.

### Business Reorganization & Financial Restructuring:

As part of an integrated national network of professionals who focus their practice on reorganizations, bankruptcies, restructurings, workouts and buyouts, the firm's team is responds quickly to complex troubled situations arising anywhere and in any industry.

### Employment:

Team members work with clients the full employment relationship; handle matters involving union avoidance and organizational work; formulate strategies to anticipate problems; keep them informed of new developments in the law; assist in drafting policies and procedures; and defend the company against discrimination charges at the agency level and in court.

### Entertainment:

With offices in the centers of the entertainment industry, Greenberg Traurig has a pre-eminent, multi-disciplinary Entertainment Practice. The team focuses on the music, motion picture, television, live stage and cable industries, including the convergence of new technologies, digital delivery systems and the role of advertising and sponsor-driven financing models.

### International Practice Group:

This multi-disciplinary team includes senior lawyers who have been the chief legal officers at major multinational companies and have been involved in some of the largest transactions in recent times in markets as diverse as Latin America and Israel, and in industries that include telecommunications, media, technology, real estate, aviation, entertainment, life sciences and financial services.

### Business Immigration:

Members are experienced in corporate immigration law, particularly multinational non-immigrant visa and permanent residency work. They represent clients in such industries as finance, tourism, insurance, electronics, healthcare, shipping and pharmaceuticals with their immigration needs.

### Public Finance:

Team members serve the needs of state and local issuers and underwriters in all areas of public finance. The firm has broad experience in tax-exempt financing. For the past several years, the firm has been among the top bond counsel firms in the US, according to the ranking criteria developed by Securities Data Co. and The Bond Buyer.

### Environment:

The integrated international team assists clients with permitting, compliance, and other regulatory matters; transactions; administrative proceedings; civil and criminal enforcement; and environmental and toxic tort litigation.

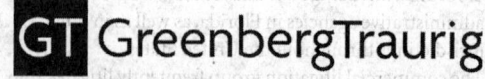

# GUNSTER

www.gunster.com **tel:** 800 749 1980 **fax:** 561 655 5677

**Managing Partner:** H William Perry
Number of shareholders: 108  Number of other lawyers: 62

## Firm Overview:

Established in 1925, Gunster is a full-service Florida law firm with 11 offices around the state providing counsel to leading businesses and individuals. The firm's statewide presence and culture reflect its status as Florida's law firm for business. Gunster serves clients from its offices in Fort Lauderdale, Jacksonville, Miami, Orlando, Palm Beach, Stuart, Tallahassee, Tampa, The Florida Keys, Vero Beach and its headquarters in West Palm Beach, with more than 160 attorneys and 200 committed support staff. Gunster is ranked among the National Law Journal's list of the 250 largest law firms.

## Main Areas of Practice:

### Banking & Financial Services:
Gunster's Banking & Financial Services practice handles a broad range of matters, including new bank formations, mergers and acquisitions, anti-money laundering, Bank Secrecy Act, lending, licensing, foreclosures, lender liability, bankruptcy, technology, employment, SEC compliance, and tax, among others. The practice has established an excellent reputation in Florida and in Latin America.

### Business Litigation:
Gunster Business Litigation attorneys specialize in various matters including product liability defense, construction litigation, professional liability defense, toxic tort litigation, securities litigation, intellectual property litigation, real estate litigation, class action appeals, and financial services litigation.

### Construction:
Gunster's Construction practice advises industry leaders on issues such as contract drafting and analysis, commercial/residential design defects, liens and bonds, Miller Act claims, class actions, and delay/inefficiency/scheduling claims.

### Corporate:
Gunster Corporate practice attorneys provide proactive counsel on a comprehensive range of services including business transactions, mergers and acquisitions, business entity selection and structuring, joint ventures and strategic alliances, executive compensation, corporate finance, private equity, intellectual property, securities offerings and compliance, and corporate governance.

### Environmental & Land Use:
Gunster attorneys guide and defend clients across Florida through regulatory issues for land use, development and environmental matters, including government development approvals, developments of regional impact, comprehensive plan amendments, property rights defense and eminent domain issues.

### Government Affairs:
Gunster's Government Affairs practice, led by a former chair of the Florida Public Service Commission, represents clients before the executive, administrative, legislative and regulatory levels of state government. The firm understands how decisions made in Tallahassee affect businesses statewide.

### Health Law:
Gunster attorneys have direct experience working with state and federal health care regulators and represent a range of health care entities in matters such as practice acquisitions, managed care litigation, professional licensure defense, facility construction, and peer review and credentialing issues.

### Immigration:
Gunster's Immigration practice handles employment-based visas (temporary and permanent), representation of foreign investors and counseling companies with respect to policies, procedures and compliance issues.

### International:
Gunster International practice attorneys have experience in European, Latin American, Middle Eastern and Asian countries, and work on both inbound and outbound business matters and cross-border disputes. Key areas include international arbitration, mediation and litigation; international banking transactions and regulatory matters; international business transactions; tax and business structuring; and franchising, distribution and licensing.

### Labor & Employment:
Gunster's Labor & Employment practice regularly represents clients in state and federal courts and administrative proceedings for matters that include disability and discrimination claims, employment contracts and benefit disputes, among other matters.

### Private Wealth Services:
Gunster's Private Wealth Services attorneys provide a single point of service for a full-spectrum of client needs including trust and estate planning; probate, trust and guardianship litigation; fiduciary representation; asset protection and business succession planning.

### Real Estate:
Gunster's Real Estate practice provides comprehensive representation for all types of real estate assets including commercial, residential, industrial, multifamily and mixed-use. Key services include acquisitions and dispositions; construction; financing, including debt restructuring and distressed assets; and leasing and management.

### Tax:
As one of Florida's largest law-based tax departments, Gunster's Tax attorneys counsel for-profit and exempt entities on international, federal and Florida tax matters, advising on compliance and planning. Key areas include formation of business entities, special purpose entities, nonprofits and joint ventures, as well as structuring employee benefit plans and executive compensation.

### Technology & Entrepreneurial Companies:
Gunster's practice focuses on legal issues facing technology and entrepreneurial companies, such as venture capital and private equity financing, Internet services, software and hardware acquisitions, privacy and security matters and marketing issues.

GUNSTER
FLORIDA'S LAW FIRM FOR BUSINESS

# HARPER MEYER PEREZ HAGEN O'CONNOR & DRIBIN LLP

www.harpermeyer.com **tel:** +1 305 577 3443 **fax:** +1 305 577 9921

**OFFICES**

FLORIDA

**MIAMI:** 201 South Biscayne Boulevard, Suite 800
FL 33131
Tel: 305 577 3443    Fax: 305 577 9921

## Firm overview:

Harper Meyer Perez Hagen O'Connor Albert & Dribin LLP is a full-service international corporate and transactional law firm with offices in Miami, Florida and legal networks around the world. The firm's professional contacts and track record are particularly strong throughout the region, permitting a prolific practice in domestic and cross-border transactions throughout the region.

The firm represents clients in a wide variety of matters and transactions, both complex and routine, across a broad spectrum of industries. For example, Harper Meyer attorneys structure projects in finance, aviation, real estate and hospitality, and other complex cross-border transactions involving banking and securitization of lenders' rights, communications and technology law, intellectual property law and licensing. They also assist clients with international and domestic tax and estate planning matters, as well as immigration and naturalization.

Recognized as a leading attorney in the Latin American region with respect to cross border and US business transactions, the firm's chairman, George R Harper, recently completed his tenure as president of the Inter-American Bar Association. He has also served as chairman of the International Law Section of the Florida Bar, and as a member of the Advisory Council of the American Bar Association (ABA)'s Latin American Law Initiative. A recipient of the Inter-American Law Review's Lawyer of the Americas Award, Mr. Harper was also recently named one of the Top 30 Lawyers for Latin America by the Latin Business Chronicle.

James M Meyer concentrates his practice on the representation of US and Latin-American based multinational corporations, financial institutions, manufacturers, franchisors, restaurateurs and family offices in general corporate matters, commercial transactions, cross-border leasing, sales and acquisitions of capital equipment. His experience in such matters also extends throughout the Caribbean. He serves as the L2B Group's Vice Chairman for the US and Latin America.

Managing partner Steven H Hagen practices in the international, tax and corporate transactions arenas, structuring international businesses with a focus on international tax planning and estate planning. He represents high net worth individuals and major Latin American corporations who are inbound to the US or who have business interests in the US. In that capacity, Mr Hagen assists in the formation of domestic and international corporate entities and limited liability companies, as well as in such business transactions as sales and acquisitions. He serves as a Director of and has now been appointed Chairman-Elect of the Transnational Taxation Network and Co-Chair for International Law Section of the Florida Bar.

Patrick J O'Connor represents domestic and international clients in trademark registration proceedings, patent and trademark licensing negotiations, and review and commercialization of intellectual property assets. He also litigates breach of contract claims, franchise disputes, antitrust claims and intellectual property matters, among others. He litigated one of the digital copyright disputes of the decade up to the US Supreme Court.

Founding Partner Manuel A Perez's practice focuses on international transactional matters, cross-border purchases and financing, general corporate law and real estate. Aside from international business practice, Mr Perez is the founder of The X Family Foundation, dedicated to providing support to families affected by the fragile X syndrome.

Ronald Albert has experience in a broad array of corporate transactions, including mergers, acquisitions and divestitures, partnerships, joint ventures and LLC's; closely-held corporations, shareholders' agreements, employment agreements and restrictive covenants; corporate finance, institutional finance and public finance and contracts. He has represented many different types of clients, including professional sports franchises and facilities, as well as technology companies.

Practicing since 1975, Michael Dribin is a Board Certified Wills, Trusts and Estates Lawyer since 1986; is a Fellow of the American College of Trusts and Estates Counsel since 1990 (member, Fiduciary Litigation Committee); and is Probate and Trust Law Division Director of the Real Property Probate and Trust Section of the Florida Bar. Mr Dribin is an Estate Planning Advisor in the University of Miami Masters in Estate Planning program, an active member of the Probate and Guardianship Court Committee of the Dade County Bar Association and Past President of the Estate Planning Council of Miami.

## Main Areas of Practice:

Harper Meyer's Corporate Business Transaction Practice supports the full range of transactions key to business formation, finance and operations for a broad range of domestic and international clients, ranging from incorporation and general corporate advice to corporate financing and mergers and acquisitions. Additionally, the firm's corporate experience includes work in such specialized fields as the representation of Latin American airlines and cross-border aircraft and capital equipment leasing, as well as other transportation arenas, the hospitality industry, agriculture, technology and intellectual property law, with clients in a variety of structures and sizes. While much of the firm's practice consists of corporate and commercial transactions, Harper Meyer also does a substantial amount of work for high net worth individuals and families in connection with real estate, immigration and tax planning. In addition, Harper Meyer offers its clients a full scope of trust and estate services. Estate planning services include the development of plans for the management and disposition of wealth in the event of incapacity or death. The firm offers advice to their clients as to the implications of Federal estate, gift and generation-skipping taxes and as to the means of reducing the impact of those taxes. They help clients work through the often confusing aspects of the administration of estates, trusts and guardianships. In the administration of estate and trusts, we advise fiduciaries as to Federal estate tax issues and assist in the preparation of estate tax returns.

**Key Clients:** Harper Meyer's client portfolio includes large Latin American companies as well as high net worth individuals doing business in the US. For example, James Meyer serves as General Counsel to Campero USA Corp, national restaurant chain (a well known Central American brand). The firm also serves as the outside general counsel for several large family owned businesses based in Latin America. Harper Meyer handles a variety of outbound work as well, including the representation of several large US-based manufacturers and several US and Latin America-based banks.

# HILL WARD HENDERSON

**www.hwhlaw.com** **tel:** 813 221 3900 **fax:** 813 221 2900

**Managing Shareholder:** R James Robbins, Jr
Number of shareholders: 58
Number of other lawyers: 33

**OFFICES**

FLORIDA
**TAMPA:** 101 East Kennedy Boulevard, Suite 3700
FL 33602
Tel: 813 221 3900   Fax: 813 221 2900

## Firm Overview:

Since its inception in 1986, Hill Ward Henderson has grown steadily based on a client-focused philosophy. This philosophy combines the talent, resources, capabilities and technologies of a large firm with the flexibility, responsiveness and personal attention of a smaller firm. At its cornerstone, the firm has an obligation and a commitment to their valued clients of integrity, professionalism and timely, efficient delivery of quality legal services. Based in Tampa, Florida, Hill Ward Henderson is a full-service law firm that caters to the varied needs of local, statewide and national clients that span a broad range of industries and professions. The firm represents public and private companies, providing legal representation in a variety of practice concentrations.

## Main Areas of Practice:

### Litigation:

The Litigation Group at Hill Ward Henderson represents corporations in state and national litigation matters including: antitrust and trade regulation, appellate, class action and complex mass tort, commercial, consumer products, criminal defense, eminent domain, employment, industrial/commercial products, insurance, intellectual property and trade secrets, international disputes and resolution, mediation, non-compete, personal injury defense, products liability, professional liability and securities litigation.
**Contact:** Dennis P Waggoner

### Real Estate:

Hill Ward Henderson's Real Estate Group is widely regarded as one of the elite practices in Florida for its depth of personnel, experience and knowledge applied to all aspects of commercial real estate. The firm represents clients in a vast range of complex issues and transactions in a number of areas, including: acquisition and development, commercial leasing, entity formation and tax structuring, finance, property tax litigation, real property litigation and zoning and land use.
**Contact:** Jonathan P Jennewein

### Corporate & Tax:

The Corporate and Tax Group at Hill Ward Henderson represents public and private companies of all sizes in corporate matters and business transactions. Hill Ward Henderson attorneys serve in the following areas of practice: general corporate advice, mergers and acquisitions, securities and corporate governance matters, joint ventures and partnerships, tax planning, venture capital and private equity.
**Contact:** David S Felman

### Bankruptcy & Creditors' Rights:

At Hill Ward Henderson, the Bankruptcy and Creditors' Rights Group regularly handles a broad variety of sophisticated bankruptcy reorganization and liquidation matters, creditors' rights litigation, foreclosure proceedings, problem loan workouts, lender liability litigation and other related complex commercial litigation cases. The firm represents and advises many of the state's leading financial institutions, private lenders, investment groups, leasing companies, public and private corporations, commercial landlords and real estate investment entities in all aspects of the debtor/creditor relationship.
**Contact:** Keith T Appleby

### Construction & Design:

Hill Ward Henderson represents private developers, government agencies, architects, engineers, design-build firms, homebuilders, construction managers, general contractors, subcontractors and suppliers. Attorneys in the Construction and Design Group serve in the following areas of practice: claim avoidance, construction claims, contractor documents and project management, design claims, insurance and surety issues, as well as mediation, arbitration and litigation.
**Contact:** Timothy A Hunt

### Executive Compensation & Employee Benefits:

Hill Ward Henderson has one of the largest employee benefits practices in the Southeast. The Executive Compensation and Employee Benefits Group provides a full range of services in connection with the establishment and maintenance of all types of employee benefit and executive compensation plans. Attorneys serve in the following areas of practice: executive compensation, fiduciary and prohibited transactions, health and welfare plans, professional employer organizations, qualified retirement plans, representation before federal agencies and tax-exempt organizations.
**Contact:** Alton C Ward

### Automotive:

Hill Ward Henderson serves as counsel to publicly and privately held companies that conduct business within the automotive industry. Many of the firm's clients own or operate multiple automotive dealerships, and among these, almost all of the franchise brands sold in the United States are represented. As part of the transactional practice, the firm assists clients in acquisitions and divestitures, real estate matters, land use and zoning issues, joint ventures, securities law compliance, tax strategies, preferred lending and vendor relationships, and general corporate governance items. The firm's litigation and regulatory attorneys assist clients with sales, finance, insurance compliance, consumer and products liability litigation, regulatory investigations and equity ownership disputes.
**Contact:** R James Robbins, Jr

### Healthcare:

The Healthcare Group at Hill Ward Henderson offers a wide range of services to a variety of clients within the healthcare industry. Attorneys at the firm provide advice and assistance across a broad spectrum of state and federal regulatory issues, as well as transactional and operational matters. A wide range of litigation services and administrative representation are also provided.
**Contact:** R Reid Haney

### Trusts & Estates:

Hill Ward Henderson represents a wide range of clients in the area of Trusts and Estates including wealthy individuals, multigenerational families, business owners, professionals, charities and other nonprofit organizations and professional fiduciaries. The Trusts and Estates Group provides a wide range of services including estate planning, asset protection planning, estate, trust and probate administration, family business succession planning, charitable gift planning, fiduciary controversies and litigation representation.
**Contact:** Linda D Hartley

### Clients:

Some of the firm's representative clients include: Asbury Automotive Group, Inc.; Bay Care Health System Inc.; Chrysler, LLC; Gerdau Ameristeel Corporation; Global Imaging Systems, Inc.; Honeywell International, Inc.; Latt Maxcy Corporation; Lifestyle Family Fitness, Inc.; OSI Restaurant Partners, LLC; Progress Energy; Pulte Home Corporation; R.J.Reynolds Tobacco Company; Raymond James & Associate, Inc.; SRI Surgical Express, Inc.; SunTrust Banks, Inc.; Tampa Bay Buccaneers; Tropicana Products, Inc.; Verizon Florida; Walter Energy, Inc.

# HOLLAND & KNIGHT LLP

**www.**hklaw.com **tel:** 305 374 8500 **fax:** 305 789 7799

**Managing Partner:** Steven Sonberg

## Firm Overview:

Founded in 1889, Holland & Knight has grown into one of the largest law firms in the United States. With more than 1,000 lawyers and legal colleagues in 40 countries, the firm has a reputation for understanding clients' business issues and staying abreast of the knowledge and trends that shape their industries. Interdisciplinary practice groups and industry-based teams provide clients with access to attorneys throughout the firm, regardless of location.

**Diversity:** Holland & Knight believes that clients receive the highest quality service when their legal teams reflect the marketplace in which they do business. This fundamental belief remains a core part of the firm's identity. Holland & Knight is consistently ranked as one of the top law firms nationally for the total number of minority partners as well as Hispanic attorneys.

## Main Areas of Practice:

### Banking & Financial Services:

Almost 140 lawyers comprise Holland & Knight's Banking and Finance Practice, which is as diverse as the needs of the industry it serves. From asset finance for clients operating in the global transportation industry to sophisticated real estate financings, and from multi-billion-dollar tribal financings for Native Americans to the defense of financial institutions in fiduciary disputes, the firm operates at the forefront of the banking and financing industry. The banking and finance group regularly counsels domestic and foreign banks, financial institutions and institutional investors as well.

### Construction:

Holland & Knight has extensive experience in all matters related to construction industry claims and litigation, and practices in state and federal courts as well as boards of contract appeals throughout the United States. The firm also counsels clients on construction operations, corporate compliance, structuring and negotiating industry agreements, public-private partnerships, project administration, risk management, government contracts and procurement law, and international construction.

### Corporate, M&A & Securities:

More than 150 lawyers regularly advise public and private companies in a broad range of domestic and international corporate transactions, corporate financings and securities law matters.

### Intellectual Property:

Attorneys in the IP Practice have significant experience handling the issues surrounding complex patent, trademark, copyright, trade secret and unfair competition issues. The team is experienced in a wide array of technical disciplines, and many of Holland & Knight's attorneys and professionals hold degrees in areas such as computer and software engineering, electrical engineering and mechanical engineering.

### Labor, Employment & Benefits:

Holland & Knight exclusively represents management in matters involving current and former employees. The firm advises clients in all areas of labor and employment, including civil rights, discrimination and retaliation; labor and employment class actions; labor relations for management; non-competition, trade secrets and defecting employees; OSHA, workplace safety and whistleblower claims; ERISA/employee benefits and executive compensation; and immigration, nationality and consular law.

### Leisure & Hospitality:

Holland & Knight represents owners, operators, lenders, investors and brands in development, structuring, governance, acquisition, financing, restructuring, management and dispute resolution throughout the world, for projects ranging from hotels, resorts and mixed-use projects to timeshare, fractional, branded residential, golf and marina properties.

### Litigation:

With almost 450 lawyers, Holland & Knight has one of the largest litigation practices in the country. Former federal prosecutors and regulatory officials form a key part of the group, which handles multi-million-dollar class actions, securities litigation, product liability, mass tort cases and white-collar criminal defense.

### Public Policy & Regulation:

Holland & Knight's Public Policy and Regulation Practice Group consists of more than 100 lawyers and other professionals engaged in federal, state and local government affairs, regulatory counseling and related disciplines.

### Real Estate & Land Use:

With more than 200 lawyers, Holland & Knight's Real Estate Practice is among the largest of any US law firm. Nearly all of the firm's offices are staffed to provide clients with superior local, national and international service when handling the wide variety of issues related to real estate transactions, regulations and litigation.

### Tax:

Holland & Knight has almost 100 lawyers directly involved in all types of taxation matters – international, federal, state and local, employee benefits and executive compensation. The firm's services are both preventive and remedial. Clients range from Fortune 100 companies to individuals protecting their personal and business assets.

### Transportation:

Holland & Knight lawyers serve public and private sector clients operating in the many facets of the transportation industry. The firm's Transportation Team is a recognized international leader and has extensive experience in the areas of aviation, freight rail, infrastructure, maritime and shipping, mass transit and public transportation, and trucking and logistics.

### Wealth Management:

Holland & Knight's estate planning group is the largest and most sophisticated of any law firm in the United States. Holland & Knight's approach and platform is different from all other law firms because its lawyers focus almost exclusively on the needs of high-net-worth estates. They are nationally recognized in fields as diverse as estate and generation-skipping transfer tax planning, sophisticated charitable giving, probate litigation, IRS litigation, life insurance planning, business succession planning, asset protection, international taxation, charitable organizations and private foundations.

### Clients:

Holland & Knight represents a diverse client base. Public and privately held businesses involved in transactions and complex dispute resolution proceedings consider Holland & Knight their strongest legal advocate. The firm partners with clients who have interests spread throughout the United States and abroad, including start-up entrepreneurial enterprises, middle market companies, Fortune 100 corporations and major, internationally headquartered businesses.

**OFFICES**

FLORIDA

**MIAMI:** 701 Brickell Avenue, Suite 3000, FL 33131
Tel: 305 374 8500   Fax: 305 789 7799

The firm also has offices in: Atlanta, GA; Boston, MA; Chicago, IL; Fort Lauderdale, FL; Jacksonville, FL; Lakeland, FL; Los Angeles, CA; New York, NY; Orlando, FL; Portland, OR; San Francisco, CA; Tallahassee, FL; Tampa, FL; Tysons Corner, VA; Washington, DC; West Palm Beach, FL

**INTERNATIONAL OFFICES**

Abu Dhabi, Beijing, Bogotá and Mexico City

Holland & Knight

# KENNY NACHWALTER, P.A.

www.kennynachwalter.com **tel:** 305 373 1000 **fax:** 305 372 1861

**Chief Executive Officer:** Richard H Critchlow
**Chief Operating Officer:** Thomas H Seymour
Number of Shareholders nationwide: 17  Number of lawyers nationwide: 25

## Firm Overview:

Since its founding in 1978, Kenny Nachwalter, P.A., has devoted its practice to complex business litigation, including antitrust, securities, professional liability, intellectual property, common law business torts, and white-collar criminal defense. Kenny Nachwalter is frequently retained in cases involving complicated economic and factual issues, multiple counsel, parties, and interrelated cases, competing claims, intense and problematic discovery, and substantive issues requiring superior legal scholarship, analytic ability, and forensic skills. Kenny Nachwalter regularly litigates in federal and state courts as well as various arbitration tribunals. The firm also represents clients before federal administrative bodies and in white-collar criminal investigations.

## Main Areas of Practice:

### Antitrust:

The line separating competitive from anti-competitive conduct by people in the same business is a line that the firm has litigated in scores of cases. The firm's Antitrust Practice involves cases in federal and state courts nationwide, representing large public and private corporations, individual entrepreneurs, and government entities, including clients in the airline, automobile, dairy, grocery, insurance, real estate, rental car, pharmaceutical, publishing, telecommunications, transportation and shipping industries.

The firm often represents individual claimants and groups of claimants who opt out of nationwide class actions to pursue their antitrust claims independently – these have included conspiracy cases involving domestic and international cartels and monopolization cases. The firm also provides antitrust counseling on issues ranging from the formation of joint ventures to the structuring of distribution networks. The firm's attorneys have also taught antitrust law and have served as special assistant attorneys general in several states.

### Complex Business Litigation:

The firm regularly represents plaintiffs and defendants in "bet the company" litigation, where dollar amounts, consequences and complexity demand skilled analysis. These disputes, litigated in state and federal courts and argued before administrative bodies and arbitration tribunals, cover the gamut of business and legal matters, including trade secrets, tax and accounting issues, securities violations, fraudulent conveyances and Ponzi schemes, RICO, class and derivative actions, director and officer liability, corporate and partnership disputes, lender liability, False Claims Act and qui tam matters, construction and commercial lease disputes, as well as other real estate-related matters, trade libel, tortious interference, franchise and business opportunities, noncompetition clauses, contracts, fraud, and other common law and statutory business torts.

### Intellectual Property Litigation:

The firm's Intellectual Property Practice offers full-service litigation protection to clients' rights. The firm has represented makers of computer software, clothing, automobiles, handbags, jewelry and accessories, and the satellite broadcaster of network television signals. Often the firm investigates and prosecutes civil injunctive and damage actions against individuals and companies infringing upon, counterfeiting, or diluting the trademarks and copyrights of the legitimate owners.

### Professional Liability:

The firm regularly defends attorneys, auditors, accountants, securities brokers, engineers, architects, and consultants against claims by clients, third parties, and regulatory agencies against claims that can severely disrupt professionals' businesses and threaten their reputations and futures.

The firm defends national and local law and accounting firms in proceedings in state and federal court and before arbitration panels and has defended claims including malpractice, breach of fiduciary duty, RICO, securities law violations, aiding and abetting Ponzi schemes or breaches of duty, breach of contract, fraud, misrepresentation, and fraudulent conveyances. These claims arise out of professional services in an array of substantive areas, such as estates and trusts, tax, litigation and discovery, real estate, corporate planning and advice, corporate mergers and acquisitions, internal investigations, and Ponzi schemes allegedly perpetrated by those firm's clients.

The firm also represents attorneys accused of misconduct before the Florida Bar and assists firms in conducting internal investigations. Attorneys and other professionals also regularly seek the firm's advice in preventative and risk management capacities, where the firm works closely with clients to provide thorough advice and help establish appropriate safeguards and protective procedures.

### Securities:

The firm's Securities Practice involves class action defense of Securities and Exchange Acts claims, derivative actions and complex D&O litigation. It also includes representation in regulatory actions commenced by the SEC and other enforcement agencies. The firm also handles arbitrations for and defends brokerage firms and registered representatives before the New York Stock Exchange and the National Association of Securities Dealers. The firm also represents brokerage firms and their employees, securities issuers and their managements and directors, and accountants in SEC, NYSE and NASD investigations, as well as securities brokers in federal and state criminal prosecutions.

### White-Collar Criminal Practice:

The firm represents clients in the United States and internationally who are involved in grand jury and government investigations, civil enforcement matters, and parallel litigation. Firm attorneys have represented public and privately held corporations, business executives, accountants, lawyers, judges, bankers, physicians, securities brokers and others who are targets or subjects of criminal investigation or prosecution in investigations in Florida and throughout the United States by the Department of Justice, State Attorneys General, the SEC and the IRS. Firm attorneys have also investigated and handled sensitive internal investigations and criminal matters in areas including antitrust, foreign corrupt practices, securities, environmental, healthcare, government contracting, real estate, financial services, insurance and accounting issues.

# KLUGER, KAPLAN, SILVERMAN, KATZEN & LEVINE, P.L.

**www.**klugerkaplan.com **tel:** 305 379 9000 **fax:** 305 379 3428

**Founding Partners:** Alan J Kluger, Abbey L Kaplan, Steve I Silverman, Bruce A Katzen, Todd A Levine, Philippe Lieberman, Jason S Marks, Michael S Perse

Number of partners: 8
Number of lawyers: 28
Languages: *English, French, Spanish*

## Firm Overview:

Kluger, Kaplan, Silverman, Katzen & Levine, P.L. is a boutique litigation firm with offices in Miami and Boca Raton, Florida. The firm focuses on the resolution of complex, high-stakes disputes involving all aspects of business and corporate litigation including real estate, probate, securities and financial fraud, corporate governance, bankruptcy, complex matrimonial matters, professional liability, intellectual property disputes, and class actions, in state and federal courts, and in AAA, FINRA and ICC Arbitration. The firm's veteran litigators are often retained to appear in federal and state courts throughout the country in 'bet the company' type cases as a result of their aggressive, results oriented, creative, and focused approach to problem solving.

## Main Areas of Practice:

**Commercial Litigation & Alternative Dispute Resolution:**
The firm handles all facets of business and commercial disputes, including contract, tort, shareholder, joint venture and partnership conflicts; lender liability; disputes involving trade secrets, covenants not to compete, and unfair and deceptive trade and business practices; merger and acquisition and post-closing disputes related to purchase-price adjustments; director and officer liability; disputes involving creditor's rights and adversary proceedings in bankruptcy court; fraudulent transfers, and other piercing-the-corporate-veil issues; accounting malpractice; franchise disputes; investor fraud and stockbroker liability disputes; and class actions, including those relating to securities fraud and consumer claims.

**Real Estate & Construction Litigation:**
The firm represents developers, mezzanine lenders, property owners, design professionals, general contractors, construction managers, specialty trade contractors, material suppliers, and governmental entities in all aspects of real estate and construction litigation, including workouts and litigation related to distressed assets and restructuring of existing relationships; lender liability issues and commercial foreclosures; restrictive covenants and title issues; brokerage fee disputes on large real estate projects; land trust, joint venture and partnership disputes; property insurance claims; analysis and defense of construction contracts and bonds; claim recognition and issues

related to defect, delay, and equitable adjustments; construction lien and bond perfection, enforcement and defense; and the identification of, and strategic advice regarding, the avoidance, early resolution and litigation of actual or potential construction delay damages.

**Intellectual Property Litigation:**
The firm's attorneys handle all aspects of intellectual property litigation, including litigation involving license agreements; trademarks; infringement claims involving architectural plans and building designs; intellectual property ownership disputes; trade secret litigation; litigation under Florida's Deceptive and Unfair Trade Practices Act; and claims involving non-compete and non-disclosure agreements.

**Matrimonial Litigation:**
The firm's matrimonial practice works with high net worth and high profile clients who are either entering into a marriage, or ending one, to help protect their financial and personal interests. The firm has particular expertise representing high profile sports and entertainment professionals with their matrimonial issues.

**Probate, Trust, Guardianship & Fiduciary Litigation:**
The firm handles a wide range of probate issues, including trust disputes; family partnerships; will contests; fraud, undue influence and incapacity claims; creditor disputes; fiduciary and trustee misconduct; interference with inheritance rights; and interpretations of wills and trusts. On numerous

occasions the firm has represented highly public and well known individuals and families, and their related business interests, on trust and probate issues.

## Clients:

The firm represents national and international businesses spanning diverse industries, as well as high net worth individuals. Representative clients include: Lennar Corporation; Dollar Tree Stores, Inc.; Turnberry, Ltd.; Winthrop Realty Trust; United Homes International, Inc.; Hard Rock Café International (USA), Inc.; CEVA Logistics; Seminole Tribe of Florida, Inc.; Smart For Life Weight Loss; Adelphia Communications; Sandata Technology, Inc.; Aztec Group, Inc.; R.K. Associates; Laquer Corporate Realty Group; International Sales Group LLC; Yoo Ltd. d/b/a Philippe Starck by Yoo; Prodigy International; Turnberry Aviation Management; Brendan Airways LLC/USA 3000 Airlines; Jet Trading and Leasing, LLC; Sargent Avborne; Pacific Scientific Aviation Services Company; and Alex Rodriguez and his related entities.

## PRACTICE AREAS

Litigation in State, Federal & Appellate Courts, and Arbitration before AAA, FINRA & ICC.

## OFFICES

**FLORIDA**

**MIAMI:** 201 S. Biscayne Blvd., Miami Center – 17th Floor, 33131
Tel: 305 379 9000   Fax: 305 379 3428
Email: SSilverman@klugerkaplan.com

**BOCA RATON:** 2000 Glades Road, Suite 300, 33431
Tel: 561 962 3135   Fax: 561 613 4100
Email: SSilverman@klugerkaplan.com

KLUGER KAPLAN
KLUGER, KAPLAN, SILVERMAN,
KATZEN & LEVINE, P.L.

# KOBRE & KIM LLP

**www.kobrekim.com** **tel:** 305 967 6100 **fax:** 305 967 6120

**Founding Partners:** Steven G Kobre, Michael S Kim
Number of partners: 17
Number of lawyers: 57
Languages: *Afrikaans, Cantonese, Dutch, French, German, Hebrew, Hindi, Italian, Japanese, Korean, Mandarin, Russian, Spanish, Telugu*

**Firm Overview:**
Kobre & Kim LLP devotes 100% of its practice to litigation and arbitration, conducting much of its work as special conflicts counsel in international financial and commercial cases. The firm has a unique business model in that it does not seek ongoing client relationships and instead focuses on discrete special litigation counsel engagements. As such, the firm offers clients a conflict-free team of advocates able to act against virtually any institutional entity. Kobre & Kim LLP is also unusual in that it is one of few litigation boutiques that focus on cross-border disputes, offering US-qualified attorneys working alongside English barristers and solicitors. Many of the firm's cases involve simultaneous proceedings in various US and non-US courts, as well as the offshore jurisdictions (e.g., BVI, Cayman Islands, etc.), and various major international dispute resolution centers in Asia, Europe and the Americas.

**Main Areas of Practice:**

**Financial Products & Services Litigation:**
The firm regularly handles high-stakes litigation and arbitration for major participants in the financial services industry, as both claimants and defendants, involving some of the most complex financial instruments in today's market, including interest rate swaps, credit default swaps, mortgage-backed securities, auction-rate securities and collateralized debt obligations. Several of the firm's lawyers are former federal prosecutors from the SEC-CFTC-DOJ Securities & Commodities Fraud Task Force and former enforcement attorneys from the US Securities and Exchange Commission.
In addition, Kobre & Kim LLP attorneys are able to draw on the firm's analysts, who have detailed knowledge in specific financial product areas such as commodities, securities, derivatives and insurance products.

**Bankruptcy & Debtor-Creditor Disputes:**
Kobre & Kim LLP offers US-qualified attorneys practicing alongside UK-qualified barristers and solicitors experienced in handling insolvency and debt disputes. The firm regularly represents secured and unsecured creditors, debtors, bondholders, and distressed debt investors, in disputes that often require navigating significant competing interests. Operating in multiple jurisdictions in the US, UK, Hong Kong, and offshore jurisdictions, the firm's lawyers are particularly experienced in multi-jurisdictional insolvency disputes.

**International Judgment Enforcement & Offshore Asset Recovery:**
Kobre & Kim LLP is the only firm able to deliver in one package the full spectrum of expertise in global asset recovery matters. The firm's lawyers include several former US Department of Justice and US Securities

and Exchange Commission lawyers with deep experience in international asset investigations and forfeiture, who are co-authors of several books on international asset recovery. The team also includes English solicitors and barristers with a significant track record in litigating in various offshore jurisdictions; in particular, the firm's two English Queen's Counsel have significant experience both attacking and defending offshore structures, including in the context of cross-border insolvency.

**Government Enforcement Defense / Parallel Class & Derivative Actions:**
Kobre & Kim LLP is the only litigation boutique with former US federal prosecutors stationed permanently in Europe and Asia. Led by more than a dozen former government attorneys, the firm's trial attorneys routinely represent institutional and individual clients in some of the highest-profile government investigations into businesses operating in the Americas, Europe and Asia. The firm's government enforcement defense experience, also gives it an edge in handling class or derivative actions brought in the context of criminal or regulatory investigations, with an eye towards avoiding the pitfalls and exploiting the opportunities created by parallel proceedings.

**Investigations & Monitorships:**
The firm has conducted numerous high-profile investigations on behalf of boards or audit committees of some of the largest public and private companies in the world in a variety of industries. The firm is one of the few law firms to have teams of former US prosecutors practicing out of offices in Europe and Asia, as well as the Americas. As a result, the firm has especially valuable experience dealing with varying attorney-client privilege laws, country-specific data protection laws, non-US employment laws, and other special issues that arise in international investigations.

Courts and government agencies also regularly invite the firm to serve as a monitor for institutions facing significant regulatory compliance issues.

**Joint Venture & Partnership Disputes:**
Kobre & Kim LLP's Joint Venture & Partnership Disputes team is retained to handle prominent joint venture and partnership disputes, providing aggressive and independent advocacy even in cases of numerous, overlapping institutional stakeholders' interests. Recent engagements include the real estate, hospitality and gaming, utilities, telecommunications and energy sectors.

**International Arbitrations:**
The firm has experience in a wide range of international and industry forums, including the ICC, HKIAC, SIAC, UNCITRAL, AAA/ICDR, LCIA, DIFC, ICSID, FINRA, ICE, LIFFE, and NFA, among others. Kobre & Kim LLP's team includes practiced arbitrators consisting of Fellows of the Chartered Institute of Arbitrators, the Hong Kong and Singapore Institutes of Arbitrators, a member of the London Court of International Arbitration, and many other arbitration panels.

**Trusts & Estates Litigation:**
Kobre & Kim LLP has advocated in some of the most high-profile trusts disputes acting on behalf of trustees, beneficiaries, and protectors in respect of alleged breaches of trust and fiduciary duty, as well as misappropriate of assets. The firm has handled cross-border trusts and estates litigation in the Americas, Europe, Asia and offshore jurisdictions.

# MOYE, O'BRIEN, O'ROURKE, PICKERT & DILLON LLP

**www.moopd.com** **tel:** 407 622 5250 **fax:** 407 622 5440

**Managing Partner:** James E Moye
**Senior Partners:** James E Moye, John C O'Rourke, Jr, Stephen W Pickert, Sean M Dillon
Number of other lawyers: 10
Languages: *English, Spanish*

## Firm Overview:

Established in 1989, Moye, O'Brien, O'Rourke, Pickert & Dillon, LLP dedicates the entirety of its practice to the representation of national and multinational clients in all aspects of the construction industry throughout the United States of America (from California to Maine to Florida), the Caribbean basin, Central America, Europe, Middle East and Canada. In the last 23 years, the firm has developed and maintained long-standing 20-year relationships with clients in the construction industry, including national and multinational general contractors, owners, design professionals, and other construction-related entities.

The firm's philosophy is to provide high quality legal services at a fair rate, while always striving to extricate their clients from unavoidable controversies at the earliest practicable, most economical, and beneficial juncture. By doing so, the firm seeks to establish long-term, ongoing client relationships. The engineering and building construction backgrounds of a number of the firm's attorneys allow the firm to employ a creative problem-solving approach, which is custom-tailored to the specific needs of each and every client. Each case, large or small, is just as important as any other and commands the firm's complete attention.

## Main Areas of Practice:

### Construction:

The representation of individuals and companies in the construction industry is a highly complex field of law. The firm's practice is distinct in that it provides construction-related legal services to clients on a nationwide and international basis from its single office in Florida. In the firm's view, it is one situation for a law firm to have multiple offices and serve clients in proximity of each of its offices and quite a different situation entirely for clients to request that Moye, O'Brien, O'Rourke, Pickert & Dillon, LLP handle legal matters throughout the United States and internationally from a single office in Florida. Nationwide, the firm has decades of experience with literally scores of projects involving various state department of transportation agencies as well as local government entities coast-to-coast. The firm's legal work involves projects as diverse as seismic retrofit work on the Golden Gate Bridge on the West Coast to multi-billion dollar airport projects on the East Coast, and from bridge demolition projects as far south as the Middle East to high-speed rail projects (Acela) in the Northeast. Transactional work and problem solving and litigation activities related to water treatment plants, reservoirs, high schools, airport expansions, high-speed rail, highways, bridges, dams, residential and commercial high-rises, parking structures, and smaller residential disputes make up a typical work day. The practice also includes dispute resolution and lawsuits concerning threshold inspections, soil stability studies, environmental assessments, design negligence, and construction defects.

The firm's practice includes dispute resolution proceedings and/or litigation with owners, developers, general contractors, and others in the construction arena, including architects, engineers, sureties, insurance companies and subcontractors.

The attorneys also provide legal consultation on transactional-related work (e.g. reviewing RFPs, negotiation and consummation of contracts, concession agreements, design-build agreements, design sub-consultant agreements, subcontracts, purchase orders, and public-private partnership contracts).

### Commercial Litigation:

The firm represents clients in a variety of contract and tort disputes.

### Clients:

Moye, O'Brien, O'Rourke, Pickert & Dillon, LLP is also unique in that it has developed and maintained 15 to 20-year relationships with many clients in the construction industry, including national and multinational construction managers, general contractors, design professionals and other construction-related entities.

Clients include a number of household names in the US construction industry such as:
ARCADIS U.S., Inc.; Baker Concrete Construction; Balfour Beatty Infrastructure, Inc.; HDR Engineering, Inc.; J. Raymond Construction Company; Jennings Construction Services, LLC; Kiewit Infrastructure West Co.; MACTEC Engineering & Consulting, Inc./AMEC; Mitsubishi Heavy Industries America, Inc; Odebrecht Construction, Inc.; Parsons-Odebrecht, Joint Venture; PCL Civil Constructors, Inc.; PCL Construction Services, Inc.; Peter Kiewit Sons', Inc.; Sauer, Inc.; Shimmick Construction Company, Inc.; Shimmick-Obayashi, Joint Venture; Walsh Construction (Archer-Western); ZOM Companies.

### International Work:

The firm advises international companies operating within the US. The firm also advises US companies on their foreign activities.

## PRACTICE AREAS

Dispute Resolution in Construction
Contract Review & Negotiation
Construction Litigation
Commercial Litigation

## OFFICES

FLORIDA
**MAITLAND:** 800 S. Orlando Avenue, FL 32751
Tel: 407 622 5250   Fax: 407 622 5440

# PODHURST ORSECK, P.A.

**www.**podhurst.com

**Founding & Managing Partner:** Aaron S Podhurst
Number of partners: 9
Number of other lawyers: 3
Number of other lawyers (Of Counsel): 1

**OFFICES**

FLORIDA
MIAMI: City National Bank Building, 25 West Flagler
Street, Suite 800, FL 33130-1780
Tel: 305 358 2800  Fax: 305 358 2382
Email: info@podhurst.com

## Firm Overview:

Podhurst Orseck continues a legal practice, established over four decades ago, concentrating exclusively in trial and appellate litigation. The firm is dedicated to offering the highest caliber legal representation in both federal and state trial and appellate courts. The firm's commercial practice focuses on complex civil litigation of all types, including class actions. The firm serves as litigation counsel to several major corporations and represents companies and individuals in complex and significant commercial litigation. The firm's general tort practice places a major emphasis upon representing claimants in aviation, mass torts and products liability litigation. From its inception, the firm has also developed an appellate practice that handles appeals of not only the firm's trial lawyers, but of other lawyers throughout the nation, in the various state and federal appellate courts, including the United States Supreme Court. The firm's practice serves clients residing or based throughout the United States, and in several foreign countries.

## Main Areas of Practice:

### General Tort Practice Concentrating in Mass Torts & Product Liability Litigation:

Since its inception, a significant portion of the firm's trial practice has been general tort law. The firm's experience runs the gamut of such cases from mass tort cases to complex products liability, to business-related torts. Literally thousands of general negligence and product liability cases of all sorts have been prepared, negotiated or tried by the members of the firm. An abbreviated listing of the type of cases handled would include all types of general negligence cases (from premises liability to boating accidents), product liability cases (involving cranes, automobiles, rollover and tire tread separation, food processing equipment, marine engines, pharmaceuticals, hand tools and ladders, to name a few) and complex legal, accounting, architectural and engineering malpractice claims.

### Aviation Litigation:

A major emphasis within the firm's general tort practice is aviation litigation. The firm is recognized worldwide for its work as a plaintiffs' aviation law firm. Podhurst Orseck believes that it has handled more plaintiffs' aviation cases than any other firm in the southeastern United States and more foreign air crashes than almost any other firm in the country. The firm has represented multiple victims of major air disasters over the past four decades, most of them as lead counsel or in another leading role. In addition, the firm has handled in excess of 100 small or light plane and helicopter crashes involving private, non-commercial aircraft.

### Commercial Litigation:

Nearly fifty percent of the firm's trial and appellate litigation involves the resolution of corporate and commercial disputes. Its practice varies from the most complex commercial cases to simple contract litigation. The firm's commercial clientele includes Fortune 500 companies, small and middle-sized companies and private individuals.

### Class Actions:

The firm has a very active class action and multi-district litigation practice. Members of the firm have been court appointed lead or liaison counsel in numerous major class actions, ranging from securities litigation, investor fraud cases, pharmaceutical, consumer, healthcare and insurance litigation. In addition, firm lawyers have chaired and served on the steering committee of many national multi-district litigation proceedings in federal courts involving products defects, consumer fraud, major commercial aviation crashes and other mass torts. Significant firm resources have been invested, and a sizeable support staff trained and developed to service this practice area.

### Probate & Matrimonial Litigation:

For many years, the firm has represented clients in the field of probate and matrimonial litigation. It has been engaged in litigation involving marital dissolution, child custody and property settlement agreements. The firm has also represented clients in claims challenging pre-nuptial agreements. Further, the firm has had substantial experience in litigation involving post-dissolution of marriage proceedings pertaining to modifications, as well as will contests and complex probate litigation.

### Criminal Litigation:

Because some of its partners are former federal prosecutors, the firm has a special interest and concentration in the areas of white-collar crime and commercial fraud. The focus of this practice is the representation of individuals, corporate executives and corporations in both state and federal proceedings, ranging from grand jury investigations to criminal prosecutions and appeals. The firm has handled litigation involving environmental matters, bank fraud, tax fraud, mail and wire fraud, RICO violations, securities fraud, antitrust price fixing, bar grievances, official corruption, Foreign Corrupt Practices Act and various other economic crimes. The firm has also handled quasi-criminal forfeitures and seizures of assets.

### Appellate Practice:

Two of the firm's attorneys devote their practice exclusively to appellate litigation and complex trial level motions, handling all in-house matters as well as referrals from attorneys and clients all over the United States. They practice primarily in the United States Court of Appeals for the Eleventh Circuit, the Florida Supreme Court and the intermediate Florida District Courts of Appeal. The firm's appellate practice mirrors the substantive diversity of the firm's trial practice, and includes plaintiff's personal injury, and wrongful death cases, including aviation related matters, and commercial cases of all types, including class actions.

### Recognition:

Many of the firm's members are recognized annually by their peers for their work as trial and appellate lawyers, regionally, nationally and internationally. The firm has also been recognized by numerous publications, including the National Law Journal, which in 2012 named Podhurst Orseck to the 'Litigation Boutiques Hot List.' Also, in 2013, seven of the firm's nine partners were selected by their peers for inclusion in the 'Best Lawyers in America Guide;' seven of the firm's partners were named 'Top Lawyers in South Florida' and one 'Up and Comer' by the 'South Florida Legal Guide'; eight of the firm's partners were named 'Florida Super Lawyers' and two others 'Rising Stars' by 'Super Lawyers Magazine' and five of the firm's partners were named as being among 'Florida's Legal Elite' by 'Florida Trend Magazine'.

# RICHMAN GREER, P.A.

www.richmangreer.com **tel:** 305 373 4000 **fax:** 305 373 4099

**Managing Shareholder:** Manuel A Garcia-Linares
Number of partners: 15 Number of other lawyers: 10

### Firm Overview:

Richman Greer P.A., has developed an international reputation for successfully handling complex business litigation in State and Federal courts. The firm, founded in 1961, is best known for its tenacious and effective courtroom presence. This trial capability allows the firm to negotiate favorable results for clients not involved in litigation. The firm also handles corporate transactions, real estate, estate planning, family law and employment matters. The firm's industry expertise reflects the New Economy (i.e. telecommunications, media and entertainment), highly regulated businesses (i.e. financial services, energy and manufacturing) and the traditional economy of South Florida (real estate and construction, agriculture, tourism and transportation). The firm also represents high net worth individuals, units of state and local government and non-profits. Recognition: Shareholders are regularly recognized by their peers in the top ranks of Florida's lawyers. 11 shareholders have been selected by "Best Lawyers in America". Richman Greer P.A. was named top medium sized law firm in Florida for 2012 by "Super Lawyers" magazine.

### Main Areas of Practice:

**Complex Commercial Litigation:**
The firm has a long history in all types of business litigation, including commercial class action lawsuits, First Amendment cases and securities fraud matters. Richman Greer acts as counsel to Fortune 500 corporations facing litigation in Florida and is regularly retained on litigation steering committees by the world's largest law firms. Richman Greer lawyers have served on American Arbitration Association panels and have been appointed to serve as mediators for federal and state litigation. Many firm attorneys are board certified by the Florida Bar in civil trial law, and/or business litigation. In addition, members of the firm have been named as fellows of the American College of Trial Lawyers, the International Society of Barristers, and the American Board of Trial Advocacy. The firm's alumni include a senior United States Court of Appeals judge, a United States District judge and several state court trial judges.

**Condominium Litigation:**
The firm had a major role in the first Florida Supreme Court decision regarding condominium law and has successfully defended a critical case brought by the Federal Trade Commission in its investigation of condominium sales practices. The firm remains a leader in condominium law development, representing both developers and condominium associations.

**Corporate/Business Services:**
Richman Greer provides general business representation and counseling, such as assisting in corporate formations or other transactions, and representing parties in business sales acquisitions and other negotiations.

**Employment Litigation:**
Richman Greer represents employers in matters of racial, ethnic, sexual, age and disability discrimination, as well as sexual harassment and fair employment practices. The firm also represents employers in Equal Employment Opportunity Commission proceedings at the administrative level.

**Environmental Law:**
The firm handles disputes regarding land use, environmental compliance, water quality, contamination and has litigated environmental contamination cases.

**Estate Planning, Probate & Trusts:**
Richman Greer represents clients in probate court litigation, including will contests and estate administration disputes, and provides estate planning services and trust administration. The partner heading this area of practice is board certified by the Florida Bar in wills, trusts and estates.

**Family Law:**
Richman Greer has a substantial practice in family law including dissolution of marriage and child custody matters, with particular expertise in representing business executives, sports and entertainments figures and spouses of such individuals. The partner heading this area of practice is board certified by the Florida Bar in marital and family law.

**Insurance Defense:**
The firm represents insurance carriers, claims administrators and self-insured entities in the defense of legal and accounting malpractice tort claims.

**Intellectual Property, Communications & Technology:**
The firm has litigated major trademark, copyright and patent litigation cases in federal court, successfully defending the rights of international corporate clients.

**Manufacturer/Product Liability:**
The firm represents numerous manufacturers, distributors and self-insured entities in the defense of product liability claims.

**Officer/Director Representation:**

The firm has defended officers and directors of several public companies, including failed financial institutions.

**Real Estate/Construction:**
The firm represents major institutional lenders, developers, buyers, sellers and managers of commercial and residential property in real estate development, financing and litigation. This includes significant construction litigation matters, such as failure to fulfill contractual obligations, allegations of defects, and disagreements over financial responsibility. One of the firm's attorneys is board certified by the Florida Bar in real estate.

**Securities Litigation:**
The firm has been actively involved in significant antitrust and securities litigation, including shareholder's lawsuits and alleged violations of securities law.

### Clients:

Representative clients of the firm include: EmCare, Inc., Magic City Casino, 3M Company f/k/a Minnesota Mining and Manufacturing Co., Merrill Lynch, Procter & Gamble, the Lockton Companies, Simon Property Group, Greenberg Traurig, P.A., Price Waterhouse Coopers, LLP, International Textile Group Inc., TotalBank, AXA Assurance, Inc., Logisticare Solutions, LLC, Borden Dairy Company, Florida Conference of Seventh Day Adventists, Union Bank, Saveology.com, LLC and Blue Nectar Spirits Co., LLC.

### International Work:

With language capabilities in English, Spanish and Polish membership in Meritas, a leading worldwide association of business law firms, Richman Greer regularly serves overseas clients, having represented foreign governments, banks, airlines, television stations, investment and insurance interests and individuals.

### OFFICES

**FLORIDA**

**MIAMI:** 396 Alhambra Circle, North Tower, 14th Floor, Miami, FL 33134
Tel: 305 373 4000 Fax: 305 373 4099

**WEST PALM BEACH:** One Clearlake Centre, Suite 1504, 250 Australian Avenue South, West Palm Beach, FL 33401-5016
Tel: 561 803 3500 Fax: 561 820 1608

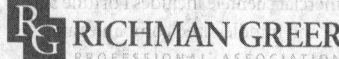

# SHUBIN & BASS, P.A.

**Contact:** John K Shubin

## Firm Overview:

Established in 1992, Shubin & Bass continues to define itself as a small law firm which handles mission critical matters for a select number of public and private institutional clients, local governments, and large law firms who place a premium on their ability to handle the most complex litigation and administrative matters. They are not a large law firm, and do not aspire to be a large law firm, and they do not measure their success by the number of lawyers they employ or the number of new files opened. The firm instead measures its success purely by the results obtained for its clients and the level of trust they place in their abilities.

## Main Areas of Practice:

**Land Use, Administrative, & Municipal Litigation:**
Throughout the State of Florida, the firm has represented the interests of property owners, governmental bodies, and affected individuals and advocacy groups in all types of litigation and administrative proceedings addressing the proposed development of land and government's regulation of land. This representation includes matters relating to eminent domain and the prosecution and defense of claims for inverse condemnation.

**Business Litigation & Dispute Resolution:**
The firm has extensive experience in the litigation of complex business and real estate disputes throughout the State of Florida. The firm is highly selective with respect to the litigation it undertakes on behalf of clients, and limits its caseload to those cases which present unique issues of law or which would benefit from the firm's experience in having litigated and tried many complex cases involving its core practice areas. The firm is also regularly called upon to serve as local counsel to numerous national law firms with respect to litigation in the state and federal courts in Florida, and prides itself in its ability to identify, negotiate, and consummate the settlement of extremely contentious matters.

**Strategic Regulatory Analysis & Governmental Affairs:**
The firm possesses lawyers with an academic background in economics and public policy analysis, particularly in the context of regulated industries, and combines this academic perspective with years of litigation and public advocacy experience at all levels of municipal, state, and federal government. This balance of theoretical and practical experience enables the firm to offer counsel to clients whose businesses or investments are directly affected by governmental regulation policies. Although most of this representation involves analysis of the regulation of land, it has also offered counsel with respect to water rights, timber rights, and the regulation of various extractive industries, particularly limerock mining.

**Appellate Practice:**
The firm has considerable experience in representing its clients before state and federal appellate courts, particularly with respect to complex or novel legal issues presented in the land use, municipal law, and commercial litigation contexts. Many of the published opinions arising out of the firm's representation of its clients before these appellate tribunals are well recognized as definitive caselaw in these respective practice areas.

## Clients:

The firm's clients include or have included: AIMCO Properties, L.P.; American Financial Realty Trust; Atlantic Civil Engineering; Bahia Mar Development, LLC; Bal Harbour Shops; Bath Club Entertainment, LLC; BCOM, Inc.; Bouygues Civil Works Florida, Inc.; Brickell Equities Corporation; Chartis, Inc.; Citadel Investment Group; City of Aventura; City of Coral Gables; City of North Miami; City of Palm Bay; City of Vero Beach; Codina Group, Inc.; The Congress Group, Inc.; Core Communities; Crescent Real Estate Equities, L.L.C.; Delaware North Companies; Flagler Development Company; Flagstone Property Group; Florida Association for Women Lawyers, Miami-Dade Chapter; Florida Power & Light; Florida Rock & Sand Company; Garrison Investment Group; Gator Investments; GB/JT Hotel; Partners; GFS Corporation; Grovenor House; Hellman Worldwide Logistics; Home Depot; Indian River County; Intervest Properties; JHMB, LLC; Maefield Development; MBF Healthcare Partners; Miami Marlins; Midtown Partners, LLC; The Mills Corporation; Montenay Power Corporation; 9000 Centre Associates; The Peebles Corporation; Performing Arts Center Foundation; Premier Developers; Properties of Hamilton; Related Group of Florida; Residential Funding Corporation; Rock Spring Properties, Ltd.; Rouse Companies; St. Lucie County; Stranahan House; Sunny Development, LLC; Swerdlow Development Group; State of Florida, Florida Department of State; Town of Golden Beach, Union Labor Life Insurance Company; University of Miami; Village of Key Biscayne; White Rock Quarries; and Woolbright Development Corporation.

**PRACTICE AREAS**

Land Use, Administrative & Municipal Litigation
Business Litigation & Dispute Resolution
Strategic Regulatory Analysis & Governmental Affairs
Appellate Practice

**OFFICES**

FLORIDA

MIAMI: 46 SW 1 Street, Third Floor, Fl 33130
Tel: 305 381 6060  Fax: 305 381 945

# STICHTER, RIEDEL, BLAIN & PROSSER, PA

www.srbp.com **tel:** 813 229 0144 **fax:** 813 229 1811

**Founding Partners:** Don M Stichter, Harley E Riedel
Number of partners: 11
Number of other lawyers: 6

**OFFICES**

FLORIDA

**TAMPA:** 110 E. Madison Street, Suite 200, FL 33602
Tel: 813 229 0144  Fax: 813 229 1811

## Firm Overview:

Stichter, Riedel, Blain & Prosser, PA specializes in the representation of parties in bankruptcy cases, insolvency matters, out-of-court workout arrangements, negotiations related to the restructuring of commercial loans, assignments for the benefit of creditors, and related civil litigation. The firm's shareholders have more than 250 years of cumulative experience in the insolvency practice and can bring this experience and expertise to bear in all types of insolvency and loan work-out situations. The firm is rated AV by Martindale-Hubbell. Eighty-two percent of the firm's lawyers are also individually rated as 'AV Preeminent Lawyers' by Martindale-Hubbell. All four of the name shareholders and Elena P Ketchum have served as presidents and chairs of the Tampa Bay Bankruptcy Bar Association, and Edward J Peterson and Scott A Stichter currently serve on the Board of Directors. Don M Stichter, Harley E Riedel and Russell M Blain are Fellows of the American College of Bankruptcy. Mr Stichter was named the Outstanding Lawyer in Hillsborough County, Florida in 2003 and was the first recipient of the Douglas P McClurg Lifetime Achievement Award presented by the TBBBA in 2004. Mr Riedel became the third recipient of the McClurg Award in 2007. Mr Blain was the Chair of the Business Law Section of the Florida Bar in 2008-09 and remains a member of its executive council. He is also the immediate past president of the Hillsborough County Bar Foundation and the immediate past president of the Ferguson-White American Inn of Court. Scott A Stichter currently serves on the Board of Directors for Bay Area Legal Services, Inc.

## Main Areas of Practice:

Stichter, Riedel, Blain & Prosser, PA advises clients faced with insolvency or bankruptcy issues or faced with potential loan defaults. It regularly represents parties in cases pending in all of the bankruptcy courts in Florida, as well as in other states. It represents parties to Assignment cases under Chapter 727 of the Florida Statutes. It also regularly represents borrowers and guarantors in foreclosure and deficiency actions pending in the state courts of Florida. The firm has offices in Tampa and Fort Myers. As a 'boutique' insolvency firm, Stichter Riedel begins many of its engagements as a result of referrals from other professionals who have a long-standing attorney-client or accountant-client relationship with the client.

## Clients:

The firm has represented numerous debtors in Chapter 11 cases as well as substantial creditors, purchasers, defendants, committees, trustees, or other parties in interest in many significant Chapter 11 and Chapter 7 cases. The largest segment of its practice consists of the representation of corporate debtors in Chapter 11 cases. Clients range from small companies to large publicly-owned corporations. Most cases involve companies with assets, liabilities, or annual revenues in excess of $5 million, ranging in size to companies with assets and liabilities of more than $3 billion. Among the more significant debtor representations are: Hillsborough Holdings Corp., formerly known as The Jim Walter Corporation, and its 32 subsidiaries, with assets and liabilities of more than $3 billion; Koger Properties, Inc., a New York Stock Exchange company at the time of filing with assets and liabilities of more than $500 million; The Koger Partnership, Ltd., a publicly traded limited partnership with assets and liabilities of more than $200 million; Bicoastal Corporation, formerly known as The Singer Company, with assets in excess of $500 million and over $2 billion in asserted claims; Lykes Bros. Steamship Co., Inc., the third largest US Flag international shipping company with assets and liabilities in excess of $300 million; Jumbosports Inc., a major national retailer of sporting goods with 59 stores in more than 20 states and assets and liabilities of more than $300 million; Moltech Power Systems, Inc., a Gainesville-based manufacturer of rechargeable batteries with annual revenues of $140 million and assets and liabilities of approximately $80 million; Taylor Bean & Whitaker Mortgage Corp.,which was in mid-2009 the largest privately owned mortgage company in the country with assets and liabilities in excess of $1 billion; Ocala Funding LLC, a wholly-owned subsidiary of Taylor Bean which originated and sold loans to Taylor Bean and had assets and liabilities in excess of $1 billion; and more than 15 real estate entities in the Odyssey Family of Companies, including more than $200 million in debt.

Among numerous substantial creditor and purchaser representations are: the Official Creditors' Committee in Anchor Glass, the third largest US glass manufacturer with liabilities of more than $600 million; Outback Steakhouse, Inc., the successful purchaser of the designation rights to 76 restaurants in the Delaware Chapter 11 case of Chi-Chi's, Inc.; and a class of consumer creditors in the New Jersey case of American Family Publishers (a Time, Inc. subsidiary). Following the economic recession of 2008, which resulted in significant financial pressure on real estate businesses in Florida, a large part of the firm's work has been devoted to the resolution of billions of dollars in real estate loans, often in out-of-court negotiations. An extensive list of other public representations is set forth on the firm's website. Lawyers with Stichter, Riedel, Blain & Prosser, PA have been involved in more than 400 reported decisions including matters in the Circuit Courts of Appeals, the US District Courts, and the US Bankruptcy Courts.

## How lawyers are ranked

Every year we carry out thousands of in-depth interviews with clients in order to assess the reputations and expertise of business lawyers worldwide. The qualities we look for (and which determine rankings) include technical legal ability, professional conduct, client service, commercial awareness/astuteness, diligence, commitment, and other qualities most valued by the client. For details of our research team, see p.5.

## Contents:

# ANTITRUST

Commentary about individuals can be found under their firm's paragraph. If the firm has no paragraph (is not ranked) look at Other Notable Practitioners.

### Antitrust
### Leading Firms

**Band 1**
Alston & Bird LLP *
King & Spalding LLP *

**Band 2**
Bondurant, Mixson & Elmore, LLP

**Band 3**
Bryan Cave LLP
Jones Day *
Rogers & Hardin LLP *
Vaughan & Murphy

## Band 1

### Alston & Bird LLP
See profile on p.1102

THE FIRM One of the undoubted leaders in both civil and criminal antitrust litigation in the Georgia market, this group receives rave reviews from commentators for the capability of its attorneys and the overall strength of the practice. It continues to represent an impressive roster of blue-chip clients, including Dell and Nokia, the latter of whom it has acted for in the LCD antitrust class action litigation alleging price-fixing. In addition, it recently represented auto safety parts manufacturer Autoliv in a government investigation.
Sources say: *"They were outstanding. We were able to draw on their knowledge, experience and global network and they delivered a result that was far beyond our expectations."*
KEY INDIVIDUALS Sources are quick to flag up the excellent **Randall Allen** (see p.1074) as a *"very talented and skilled"* antitrust litigator. In addition to his antitrust work, he also undertakes general commercial litigation, practic-

### Senior Statesmen

**Senior Statesmen:** distinguished older practitioners
Bondurant Emmet J  Bondurant, Mixson & Elmore, LLP

### Leading Individuals

**Band 1**

| | | |
|---|---|---|
| Allen Randall L | Alston & Bird LLP * | |
| Cashdan Jeffrey | King & Spalding LLP * | |
| Murphy Jr Charles C | Vaughan & Murphy * | |
| Watson G Patrick | Bryan Cave LLP | |

**Band 2**

| | |
|---|---|
| Biegel Adam J | Alston & Bird LLP * |
| Bonder Teresa T | Alston & Bird LLP * |
| Lowrey IV Frank M | Bondurant, Mixson & Elmore, LLP |
| Myers Kimberly L | Rogers & Hardin LLP * |
| Powers Tony G | Rogers & Hardin LLP * |
| Wofford Jr M Russell | King & Spalding LLP * |

**Band 3**

| | |
|---|---|
| Berhold Jeffrey L | Jeffrey L. Berhold, P.C. (ONP)[†] |
| Kenny Michael | Alston & Bird LLP * |
| Kontio Peter | Alston & Bird LLP * |
| Krugman Edward B | Bondurant, Mixson & Elmore, LLP |
| McGibbon James R. | Sutherland Asbill & Brennan LLP (ONP)[†] |
| Newton Trammell | Jones Day * |
| Rhodes Thomas | Smith Gambrell & Russell LLP (ONP)[†] * |

**Associates to watch**
Hopkinson Christine A  King & Spalding LLP *

\* Indicates firm / individual with profile.

[†]ONP = Other Notable Practitioner

Biegel (see p.1076) has built an excellent profile in antitrust law which belies his years. He is described as *"well plugged in and very knowledgeable"* by commentators, particularly in relation to his familiarity with the workings of the DOJ. Head of the practice **Teresa Bonder** (see p.1076) is highly regarded both as a *"tremendous case manager"* and also for her *"top-notch"* litigation skills. Lately she has represented First Multiple Listing Service in defense of a class action alleging that real estate commissions were fixed by various firms. *"Very, very good"* trial lawyer **Michael Kenny** (see p.1087) undertakes antitrust work as part of a general commercial practice, which also includes financial services and trade secrets litigation. He has recently acted for SunTrust Banks in defense of a class action alleging that the setting of interchange and merchant discount fees by the Visa and MasterCard credit card networks was in violation of Sections 1 and 2 of the Sherman Act. **Peter Kontio** (see p.1087) has worked on many of the group's biggest cases lately, including acting for Nokia and Equifax, the latter of whom he represented in a purported conspiracy against one of its customers. He is highly regarded among sources, particularly for his *"understated and focused"* approach to matters.

### King & Spalding LLP
See profile on p.445

THE FIRM With a high-quality broad antitrust practice, which includes cartel defense and criminal investigations in addition to more general civil antitrust litigation and counseling, this firm is able to cover all of the bases. It has recently represented UCB in relation to an alleged vitamins cartel matter and has counseled MillerCoors on pricing and distribution issues, as well as continuing to act for a host of other major corporations including Coca-Cola and The Home Depot.

ing out of both Atlanta and Silicon Valley. Among his recent highlights is acting for Mohawk Industries in two cases concerning alleged anticompetitive conduct. **Adam**

Sources say: *"For sure they're a top firm."*

**KEY INDIVIDUALS** The much-admired **Jeffrey Cashdan** (see p.1078) enjoys a reputation in the Georgia market that very few practitioners can match. He has recently been involved in a number of class action cartel matters, including acting for Kemira in a case concerning the sale of hydrogen peroxide. Sources regard **Russell Wofford** (see p.1100) as *"a really great resource"* and reserve particular praise for the practicality of his knowledge base. Among his recent highlights is acting for Palmyra Medical Center in litigation relating to alleged anticompetitive tying practices. Senior associate **Christine Hopkinson** (see p.1085) is developing an excellent name in the field and wins much praise from the market, with one source describing her as a *"smart lawyer who writes well,"* while another is quick to comment: *"I have great confidence in the advice she gives."*

## Band 2

### Bondurant, Mixson & Elmore, LLP

**THE FIRM** This team thrives on its status as a pure litigation boutique, utilizing small, streamlined teams to take on big-ticket litigation as well as smaller cases. Sources especially praise the practice's efficiency and the litigation skills of its attorneys. Recent case highlights include successfully defending the Albany-Dougherty County Hospital Authority in proceedings brought by the FTC and the Georgia Attorney General.

**Sources say:** *"They provide quality representation on the litigation side."* *"They can do major litigation efficiently and smartly."*

**KEY INDIVIDUALS Frank Lowrey** is frequently seen in major Georgia antitrust work and impresses sources with his knowledge and writing ability. Of late he has headed up the plaintiffs' class counsel team in a case against several large manufacturers of insulation. **Edward Krugman** is a practitioner who commands respect from his peers for his litigation skill and experience, which includes antitrust work as part of a broader portfolio that also takes in IP and employment disputes, among others. **Emmet Bondurant** is variously lauded as *"a dean of antitrust"* and *"one of the*

*great lawyers in this field."* He remains an active presence for the firm and has recently worked on cases involving CompuCredit as well as the hospital authority case referred to above.

## Band 3

### Bryan Cave LLP

**THE FIRM** A firm with a heavy litigation focus, Bryan Cave specializes particularly in representing clients who have opted out of class actions. Lately it has acted for The Home Depot as a plaintiff in an action alleging price-fixing of shipping costs to Puerto Rico.

**KEY INDIVIDUALS Patrick Watson** comes highly recommended by peers and clients alike and is described as an experienced and practical lawyer. His plaintiff opt-out practice is particularly well regarded, although he undertakes a wide variety of antitrust cases.

### Jones Day
**See profile on p.919**

**THE FIRM** As in many other areas, this firm's strength is its exceptional global reach. More counseling-focused than many of the other groups in Georgia, it receives praise for its risk management, distribution and Robinson-Patman work.

**Sources say:** *"I wouldn't consider using anyone else. They have excellent resources and connections throughout the globe and coordinate seamlessly."*

**KEY INDIVIDUALS Trammell Newton** (see p.1091) is a highly experienced practitioner who has a breadth of antitrust expertise including criminal and class action work. He is described by commentators as *"giving really good, practical advice"* and also praised for his ability to tailor his counseling to make it as relevant as possible.

### Rogers & Hardin LLP
**See profile on p.1111**

**THE FIRM** This compact, litigation-oriented department has strength in complex private actions as well as in criminal work, and is particularly noted by peers for the quali-

ty of its litigators. Recently the team represented Key Property Solutions in a government investigation into foreclosure bidding within Georgia, and also acted for Johns Manville in a case concerning the alleged price-fixing of fiberglass insulation.

**KEY INDIVIDUALS** The highly regarded **Kimberly Myers** (see p.1091) is one of the key members of the team. Her litigation practice also takes in IP, securities and general commercial disputes, as well as contentious litigation matters. Commentators describe **Tony Powers** (see p.1094) *"an agile adversary and strategist"* who has *"great judgment."* He led on the aforementioned matters for Key Property Solutions and Johns Manville.

### Vaughan & Murphy

**THE FIRM** Vaughan & Murphy has something of a niche in criminal defense work, with over half of its work coming from that side and commentators viewing it as a go-to firm in that arena. In spite of this, the group also remains well versed in all areas of contentious antitrust work.

**KEY INDIVIDUALS** *"Experienced litigator"* **Charles Murphy** (see p.1091) continues to be regarded as *"one of the best criminal defense lawyers"* in the region and unsurprisingly remains a first choice among peers to refer criminal antitrust defense work to. Alongside his much-lauded criminal work, Murphy also remains highly sought after for his expertise in civil antitrust matters, including complex class actions.

### Other Notable Practitioners

**Thomas Rhodes** (see p.1094) heads up Smith Gambrell & Russell LLP's antitrust offering and has over 35 years' experience in antitrust work across a wide variety of areas, including in M&A. Sole practitioner **Jeffrey Berhold** is noted for his expertise in antitrust and white-collar criminal defense work. He wins much praise from peers, not least for the commitment he shows to his clients. **James McGibbon** of Sutherland Asbill & Brennan LLP is held in high esteem by market commentators for his experience in the antitrust arena. He maintains a practice in both litigation and counseling across a broad array of antitrust areas.

# BANKING & FINANCE

Commentary about individuals can be found under their firm's paragraph. If the firm has no paragraph (is not ranked) look at Other Notable Practitioners.

## Banking & Finance
### Leading Firms

**Band 1**
King & Spalding LLP *
Parker, Hudson, Rainer & Dobbs LLP

**Band 2**
Alston & Bird LLP *
Jones Day *
Paul Hastings LLP *

**Band 3**
Greenberg Traurig, LLP *
Hunton & Williams LLP *
Troutman Sanders LLP

**Band 4**
Burr & Forman LLP *
Sutherland Asbill & Brennan LLP
Womble Carlyle Sandridge & Rice, LLP *

### Leading Individuals

**Band 1**

| | | |
|---|---|---|
| Acord Noland Bobbi | Parker, Hudson, Rainer & Dobbs LLP |
| Alford Carolyn Zander | King & Spalding LLP * |
| Blumen Rick D | Alston & Bird LLP * |
| Conrad Albert H | King & Spalding LLP * |
| Cushing Paul M | Alston & Bird LLP * |
| Dobbs C Edward | Parker, Hudson, Rainer & Dobbs LLP |
| Molen Chris D | Paul Hastings LLP |

**Band 2**

| | | |
|---|---|---|
| Davis Cindy JK | Greenberg Traurig, LLP * |
| Dempster Hazen H | Troutman Sanders LLP |
| Grice Richard | Alston & Bird LLP * |
| Jordan Hilary P | McGuireWoods LLP (ONP)[†] |
| LaFiandra Aldo L | Jones Day * |
| Schneider John | Hunton & Williams LLP * |
| Snow Edgar | Burr & Forman LLP |

**Band 3**

| | | |
|---|---|---|
| Brazell Cindy | Jones Day * |
| Leveille Michael | Greenberg Traurig, LLP * |
| Llorens Jr Hector E | King & Spalding LLP * |

**Band 4**

| | | |
|---|---|---|
| Bratcher Timothy | Jones Day * |
| Currey Kathleen O | Parker, Hudson, Rainer & Dobbs LLP |
| Palmer Stephen D | Greenberg Traurig, LLP * |

**Up-and-coming individuals**

| | | |
|---|---|---|
| Roberts Harrison | Parker, Hudson, Rainer & Dobbs LLP |

[†]ONP = Other Notable Practitioner

*The edit is in alphabetical order by firm name.*

## Alston & Bird LLP
See profile on p.1102

**THE FIRM** Alston & Bird has a reputation for fielding high-quality lawyers and working on many of the state's

## Banking & Finance: Mainly Regulatory
### Leading Firms

**Band 1**
Bryan Cave LLP

**Band 2**
Troutman Sanders LLP
Womble Carlyle Sandridge & Rice, LLP *

**Band 3**
Alston & Bird LLP *
Paul Hastings LLP *
Smith Gambrell & Russell LLP *

### Senior Statesmen

**Senior Statesmen:** distinguished older practitioners
Cheatham Richard R    *Troutman Sanders LLP*

### Leading Individuals

**Star individuals**
Moeling Walter G        *Bryan Cave LLP*

**Band 1**

| | | |
|---|---|---|
| Kanaly Mark C | Alston & Bird LLP * |
| Knudson Kathryn L | Bryan Cave LLP |
| MacDonald III Ralph F | Jones Day * |
| Powell Thomas O | Troutman Sanders LLP |

**Band 2**

| | | |
|---|---|---|
| Blanchard Gerald L | Bryan Cave LLP |
| Daniel Chris | Paul Hastings LLP |
| Dunlevie Steven S | Womble Carlyle Sandridge & Rice, LLP |

**Up-and-coming individuals**

| | | |
|---|---|---|
| Ghegan David W | Troutman Sanders LLP |
| Klingler Robb | Bryan Cave LLP |
| Stevens James W | Troutman Sanders LLP |

* Indicates firm / individual with profile.
Alphabetical order within each band. Band 1 is the highest.

most prominent cases. In addition to maintaining its traditional strength in lender and borrower representation, the firm has earned additional commendations for its burgeoning regulatory practice, which now services several of the region's leading banks. In terms of lender representation, Wells Fargo and SunTrust remain marquee clients, with both seeking the firm's counsel in connection with various complex matters over the past year.
**Sources say:** *"The attorneys were extremely pragmatic and real problem solvers. They didn't get bogged down in details that were irrelevant to what the clients were trying to accomplish. They're very user-friendly."*
**KEY INDIVIDUALS Rick Blumen** (see p.1076) is cochair of the firm's international finance and debt products group. He is considered to be *"the best leveraged finance lawyer in Atlanta"* by many sources. He garners strong feedback, eliciting praise for his work ethic and the ease with which he is able to connect with clients. He recently assisted SunTrust with its underwriting of EW Scripps's

$212 million purchase of nine television stations. **Paul Cushing** (see p.1079) is held in high esteem by many peers who praise his proficiency in acting on behalf of financial institutions. He has particular strength in overseeing loans made to REITs, exemplified by his representation of Wells Fargo in extending a $483.5 million loan to Rouse Properties. Market opinion of **Richard Grice** (see p.1083) is one of unanimous acclaim, with interviewees hailing his *"subject matter knowledge"* and *"superb attention to detail."* He handles a wide range of borrower representations and recently assisted Graphic Packaging with the negotiation and execution of a $2 billion senior credit facility. **Mark Kanaly** (see p.1086) is very *"highly regarded"* and is singled out for praise on account of his ability to *"get great results for clients."* He has been invaluable as the firm has gained traction within the regulatory arena.

## Bryan Cave LLP

**THE FIRM** This Atlanta-based practice forms part of Bryan Cave's impressive global bank regulatory network. It maintains its status as the market leader for the region, with its team of experienced attorneys displaying particular aptitude in the area of community bank representation. The firm has additionally been sought for its strategic expertise, as both troubled and stable banks attempt to restructure their organizations in order to comply with a multitude of regulatory changes. The team's clients include Reliance Trust, Synovus Bank and SouthCrest Financial Group.
**KEY INDIVIDUALS Walter Moeling** is considered one of the most respected banking lawyers in the American south-east. He is said to be very knowledgeable in the area of community banks, drawing on over four decades of experience. He recently represented Reliance Trust, advising it on the acquisition of a trust servicing business. **Kathryn Knudson** offers clients an excellent advisory service and is increasingly commended for her ability to provide actual, practical advice. Furthermore, she is noted as being very well respected with regulators. Sources praise **Gerald Blanchard** for his excellent technical command, and for his admirable ability to anticipate imminent alterations to regulatory frameworks and advise clients accordingly. **Robb Klingler** is a new entrant to the rankings. Peers are especially impressed, many of whom commend his focus and knowledge in the area.

## Burr & Forman LLP
See profile on p.1105

**THE FIRM** Burr & Forman has great strength in the representation of lenders, and undertook a variety of commercial assignments during the past year. The firm is particularly active in the syndicated loan market, in which it services a range of financial institutions. Its client-base includes a number of Georgia's more prominent banks, with Wells Fargo, Regions and Flagstar serving as three such examples.

Sources say: *"The firm combines a high level of legal and transactional knowledge with common sense and good business acumen."*

KEY INDIVIDUALS Sources highlight **Edgar Snow**'s superb *"work ethic, timeliness and creativity."* He acts on behalf of a number of the state's largest financial institutions.

## Greenberg Traurig, LLP
See profile on p.1024

THE FIRM Greenberg Traurig is able to handle a variety of cases, ranging from syndicated credit transactions to asset-based financings, and has the advantage of the firm's breadth of global resources. The firm also possesses significant expertise in the PPP domain, and recently undertook a significant assignment for the City of Atlanta. The firm also represents the likes of Rabobank Nederland, which the team recently acted for on the bank extending a $1 billion credit facility to AGCO.

Sources say: *"They performed exceptionally well."*

KEY INDIVIDUALS **Cindy Davis** (see p.1079) is an expert in deals with Latin American components and is particularly adept at dealing with Mexican borrowers. Market sources hail her negotiation skills and capacity to handle cross-border assignments. **Michael Leveille** (see p.1088) is able to strike a *"great balance between the legal issues and the business issues,"* say sources. He is particularly noted for his strength in the representation of lenders and was recently called upon to represent Wells Fargo Capital Finance in a $101 million loan. **Stephen Palmer** (see p.1092) has an excellent reputation for undertaking asset-based lending transactions, for which he has earned substantial acclaim from market sources. *"I'm 100% sure he can handle anything we throw at him,"* remarked one source.

## Hunton & Williams LLP
See profile on p.2517

THE FIRM Hunton & Williams is capable of undertaking a wide array of work within the commercial lending field, and operates primarily in the middle market. The group is renowned for adopting a longer-term approach to its clients, many of which have been with the firm for several years. The team is highly active in cross-border assignments, and frequently demonstrates great expertise in foreign jurisdictions.

Sources say: *"What we've always appreciated is that they have a deep bench of attorneys that we can pull in when required."*

KEY INDIVIDUALS The *"excellent"* **John Schneider** (see p.1095) receives extremely positive feedback from a number of sources. He has *"great business acumen,"* say several commentators, who add that he provides *"forward-thinking advice"* and an *"excellent level of service."* His advice is most frequently sought in commercial lending matters.

## Jones Day
See profile on p.919

THE FIRM This global powerhouse maintains its strong presence in the Georgia marketplace. Its partners are active on a substantial number of diverse matters and are lauded for their capacity to handle both borrower and lender representations. Notable clients on the borrower side include Asbury Automotive Group, Cumulus Media and GE, while on the lender side the firm is frequently called upon to assist several leading financial services companies.

KEY INDIVIDUALS A market source singles out **Aldo LaFiandra** (see p.1088) for particular praise: *"He is able to size up any situation and provide us with the probabilities of various events happening."* He has been engaged on a number of assignments across a broad range of industries. **Cindy Brazell** (see p.1077) is an exceptionally talented attorney, acting on behalf of various financial services companies. She possesses particular expertise in commercial real estate financing. **Timothy Bratcher** (see p.1077) is an expert in lender representations, and has represented several leading financial institutions throughout the past year. **Ralph MacDonald** (see p.1089) concentrates primarily on transactional and regulatory work. He is highly active in the failed bank acquisition market and, in the opinion of sources, is *"one of the technically strongest lawyers"* in the state.

## King & Spalding LLP
See profile on p.445

THE FIRM Renowned for its strength in acquisition financing arrangements, King & Spalding's distinguished finance practice maintains its status as one of the most illustrious in Georgia. The firm caters primarily to the middle market and has earned national recognition for the combined value of deals it has helped to broker. The firm recently provided counsel to ING Capital in a $100 million project finance transaction.

Sources say: *"They are very good at negotiating in a commercial and constructive manner."*

KEY INDIVIDUALS Lauded for her ability to *"conceptualize issues and implement that into complex transactions,"* **Carolyn Alford** (see p.1074) is frequently engaged on the firm's most substantial matters. She recently represented SunTrust Bank in the formation of a $1.25 billion revolving credit facility for a large petroleum distributor. Interviewees were keen to highlight **Albert Conrad** (see p.1079) as a *"fantastic lawyer"* whom clients can rely on to consistently dispense *"sagacious advice."* His name is prominent in the area of lender representation, and he counts JPMorgan Chase as one of his notable clients. **Hector Llorens** (see p.1088) has recently undertaken a great deal of project finance work, notably serving as lead partner in the ING Capital matter. He is a *"very bright and very skilled lawyer,"* in addition to being *"very personable and able to work with other lawyers in an efficient manner."*

## Parker, Hudson, Rainer & Dobbs LLP

THE FIRM The 17 attorneys in this dominant commercial finance group are adept at handling the entire spectrum of financial matters, possessing particular strength in the field of asset-based lending. The firm retains a core group of key practitioners, with several of its longer serving partners earning universal acclaim for both their interpersonal skills and general technical ability. Bank of America remains a significant client and continues to engage the firm on a number of matters.

Sources say: *"Their knowledge of the law is second to none. They really make sure that we're aware of any potential pitfalls."*

KEY INDIVIDUALS Clients are keen to praise the *"unflappable"* **Bobbi Acord Noland**, citing her motivational skills and calm demeanor as invaluable to their assignments. She garners specific praise for her aptitude in facilitating large transactions, and JPMorgan Chase and Bank of America figure among her impressive list of clients. The market perception of the tremendously experienced **Edward Dobbs** remains extremely positive. He is lauded for his ability to *"provide strategic input"* rather than simply *"providing recommendations based on the current situation."* **Kathleen Currey** deals extensively with financial institutions and is identified by clients as being *"incredibly detail-oriented."* Praised for his ability to *"understand legal issues"* without *"getting bogged down in the business issues,"* **Harrison Roberts** continues to cement his status as one of the firm's rising stars. He acts for a number of high-profile financial institutions and is integral in the negotiation and documentation of loans.

## Paul Hastings LLP
See profile on p.1996

THE FIRM Underpinned by a preeminent national practice, Paul Hastings has an Atlanta-based financial group with the capabilities to undertake a variety of high-profile assignments. The firm has a long-standing presence in the local market and works closely with its New York leveraged finance team to provide clients with an integrated service. It has several high-profile clients, including Facebook.

Sources say: *"They're terrific and good value. They're very business-focused, willing to provide business advice in addition to stellar legal advice."*

KEY INDIVIDUALS Sources note that **Chris Molen** *"brings a high value of service"* to every engagement. He is recognized as being one of the preeminent practitioners in Georgia. His highlights include representing GE Capital Markets in a $280 million loan. **Chris Daniel** is a *"thoroughly excellent lawyer who looks after his client's interests and puts them first,"* say clients. He has particular expertise in the intricacies of payment processing systems.

## Smith Gambrell & Russell LLP
See profile on p.1113

THE FIRM This firm is recognized for its strength in the regulatory compliance domain. The practice is well integrated within the firm and, in conjunction with the commercial litigation group, is able to act for banks on matters involving regulatory agencies.

KEY INDIVIDUALS Robert Schwartz is the firm's main point of contact for bank regulatory matters.

## Sutherland Asbill & Brennan LLP

THE FIRM Sutherland Asbill & Brennan is highly regarded for its representation of financial institutions and lenders. The firm is proficient in handling a broad spec-

trum of banking and finance matters, including commercial lending and regulatory issues.
**KEY INDIVIDUALS** Knox Dobbins is a key contact in the firm's Atlanta office.

### Troutman Sanders LLP

**THE FIRM** This prosperous and growing practice group combines a thriving regulatory practice with a solid borrower and lender team, and this collaborative potential enables the firm to provide banks with a broad range of services. The group's knowledge of the Southeast marketplace has been invaluable in helping several banks increase their local footprint. The firm also recently acquired two specialists from Kilpatrick Townsend, bolstering the group's already superb regulatory prowess in particular.
**KEY INDIVIDUALS** The experienced **Hazen Dempster** garners accolades from several market sources and is particularly highly rated for his work with borrowers. **Thomas Powell** is increasingly recognized as one of the state's most talented regulatory attorneys. He is active in the transac-

tional sphere and is an expert on the regulatory component of transactions. **David Ghegan** is held in high regard by a number of his peers. He is proficient in both the regulatory and transactional arenas and is regarded as one the most talented younger attorneys in his area. Senior counsel **Richard Cheatham** recently arrived from Kilpatrick Townsend & Stockton. He is a seasoned authority in the regulatory space in particular, and several sources praise his superb intellect. He continues to act on behalf of several financial institutions. Also arriving from Kilpatrick, regulatory expert **James Stevens** is identified by market sources as one of the state's best up-and-coming attorneys.

### Womble Carlyle Sandridge & Rice, LLP
See profile on p.2049

**THE FIRM** This firm has a heavy emphasis on lender representations and is frequently called upon to advise the region's premier banks; for example, BNC Bancorp often engages the firm in this capacity. Additionally, the firm's financial institution department is adept at assisting banks

with their efforts to comply with the intricacies of both state and federal regulations.
**Sources say:** "My overall impression of the firm is excellent."
**KEY INDIVIDUALS** The vastly experienced **Steven Dunlevie** is touted as the "heart of the practice" by observers. He leads in many of the firm's more significant engagements. Recognized for his ability to "think outside the box," Dunlevie is famed for his energetic and effusive personality, and "garners tremendous respect" from both clients and peers.

### Other Notable Practitioners

**Hilary Jordan** of McGuireWoods LLP is one of the region's most experienced practitioners. He is managing partner of the firm's Atlanta office and is an expert in leveraged finance transactions.

# BANKRUPTCY/RESTRUCTURING

Commentary about individuals can be found under their firm's paragraph. If the firm has no paragraph (is not ranked) look at Other Notable Practitioners.

## Band 1

### Alston & Bird LLP
See profile on p.1102

**THE FIRM** Alston & Bird's bankruptcy practice continues to justify its strong position in the Georgia marketplace. Its attorneys are credited with being particularly proficient litigators, adept at representing a gamut of different clients in the courtroom. Renowned for its aptitude at dealing with either domestic or national matters, the Atlanta-based team is comfortable undertaking both creditor and debtor

representations across a wide range of industries. Its recent work highlights include representing Sea Launch Company in its Chapter 11 proceedings.
**Sources say:** "I am impressed with both the depth and experience at Alston & Bird generally, and by their ability to bring the right person and experience level to any given issue."
**KEY INDIVIDUALS** The preeminent **Dennis Connolly** (see p.1079) draws effusive praise from one peer, who remarks: "If I could choose anyone to hire, it would be him." He was lead partner in the Sea Launch Company case. **Grant Stein** (see p.1098) is identified as being "elegant in his presentation." "I like the way he thinks ahead and anticipates issues," said one source, "rather than merely responding to initiatives from our adversaries." Recently, he was involved in the representation of Dell, Bank of America and US Bank in relation to the ongoing Lehman Brothers bankruptcy case. Acknowledged by sources as an "excellent bankruptcy attorney," **John Weitnauer** (see p.1100) remains one of the firm's leading bankruptcy practitioners. He recently led the team that served as debtors' counsel to Scovill Fasteners in its recent Chapter 11 bankruptcy filing. **Jason Watson** (see p.1099) is "great to work with," say sources, and commended for his almost instinctive ability to forge a "good relationship with clients and opposing counsel." He is currently providing representation to Synovus Bank as it seeks to recoup over $100 million of outstanding loans.

### King & Spalding LLP
See profile on p.445

**THE FIRM** The 13 lawyers that comprise King & Spalding's Georgia bankruptcy practice consistently provide clients with a level of service commensurate with the firm's historical strength. In addition to being able to han-

dle all aspects of traditional bankruptcy representation, the firm has particular expertise in tackling distressed M&A transactions and is frequently tasked with providing counsel to a number of parties involved in these complex issues. Matters involving Cagle's, Imperial Tobacco and AIG Baker have ensured the firm's talented bench has remained active in recent months.
**Sources say:** "If anyone told me that they needed a good law firm for bankruptcy, I'd point them in the direction of King & Spalding. They have consistently exceeded my expectations."
**KEY INDIVIDUALS** "Excellent bankruptcy attorney" **Sarah Borders** (see p.1076) is adept at providing counsel to both creditors and debtors, and is perhaps best known in the legal community for her continued representation of GE Capital. Distressed M&A expert **Paul Ferdinands** (see p.1081) is particularly well respected by sources, many of whom identify him as one of the premier attorneys in the Georgia marketplace. His recent highlights include representing Cagle's in its Chapter 11 case. The experienced **James Pardo** is universally identified as a "leading lawyer" in the area. He recently represented Imperial Tobacco in the ongoing Flintkote bankruptcy matter. **Harris Winsberg** (see p.1100) is "incredibly deep and knowledgeable," noted one source, while another claimed that "he does not just wait for questions to arise and instead keeps us informed of exactly what is happening." **Jesse Austin** (see p.1075) is frequently engaged in both domestic and national matters. Sources maintain that he "very much deserves his reputation" as one of the leading bankruptcy attorneys in the state, on account of his being "immediately available to clients and very practical with his advice." He recently joined the team from Paul Hastings.

## Bankruptcy/Restructuring
### Senior Statesmen

**Senior Statesmen:** distinguished older practitioners

| | |
|---|---|
| Cohen Ezra H | Troutman Sanders LLP |
| Meir Dennis | Kilpatrick Townsend & Stockton LLP |

### Leading Individuals

**Star individuals**

| | |
|---|---|
| Dobbs C Edward | Parker, Hudson, Rainer & Dobbs LLP |

**Band 1**

| | |
|---|---|
| Austin Jesse | King & Spalding LLP * |
| Borders Sarah | King & Spalding LLP * |
| Connolly Dennis J | Alston & Bird LLP * |
| Ferdinands Paul K | King & Spalding LLP * |
| Kurzweil David | Greenberg Traurig, LLP * |
| Lurey Alfred | Kilpatrick Townsend & Stockton LLP |
| Meyers Todd | Kilpatrick Townsend & Stockton LLP |
| Pardo Jr James | King & Spalding LLP |
| Stein Grant T | Alston & Bird LLP * |
| Weitnauer John C | Alston & Bird LLP * |

**Band 2**

| | |
|---|---|
| Anderson Eric W | Parker, Hudson, Rainer & Dobbs LLP |
| Cifelli James | Lamberth, Cifelli, Stokes & Stout, P.A. |
| Cranshaw David W | Morris, Manning & Martin, LLP |
| DeBorde Frank W | Morris, Manning & Martin, LLP |
| Dorsey Rufus Thomas | Parker, Hudson, Rainer & Dobbs LLP |
| Durlacher Erich N | Burr & Forman LLP |
| Kaufman Mark S | McKenna Long & Aldridge LLP * |
| Kelley Jeffrey W | Troutman Sanders LLP |
| Levengood J Michael | McKenna Long & Aldridge LLP * |
| Marsh Gary W | McKenna Long & Aldridge LLP * |
| Williamson Robert | Scroggins & Williamson |
| Winsberg Harris Bryan | King & Spalding LLP * |

**Band 3**

| | |
|---|---|
| Duedall Mark | Bryan Cave LLP |
| Herzog Jr Richard B | Nelson Mullins Riley & Scarborough (ONP) † |
| Isbell John F | Thompson Hine LLP (ONP) † |
| Levin Matthew W | Kilpatrick Townsend & Stockton LLP |
| Mills John W | Barnes & Thornburg LLP (ONP) †,* |
| O'Hearn Paul Burke | Burr & Forman LLP |
| Rankin Jr James S | Parker, Hudson, Rainer & Dobbs LLP |
| Rosenblatt Paul M | Kilpatrick Townsend & Stockton LLP |
| Sewell Jr. Henry F | McKenna Long & Aldridge LLP * |
| Stieglitz Graham H | Burr & Forman LLP |
| Thomson, Jr. John A | Womble Carlyle Sandridge & Rice (ONP) † |
| Watson Jason H | Alston & Bird LLP * |

**Up-and-coming individuals**

| | |
|---|---|
| Elrod John | Greenberg Traurig, LLP * |
| Mercer Robert M. D. | Bryan Cave LLP |

\* Indicates individual with profile.

† ONP = Other Notable Practitioner

## Band 2

### Kilpatrick Townsend & Stockton LLP
See profile on p.1109

**THE FIRM** This team is renowned for the ability of its attorneys to combine a dynamic, aggressive courtroom presence with a reasoned and thorough approach to negotiation. Much of the firm's recent work has involved the representation of creditors' committees.

**Sources say:** "When you hire a firm like Kilpatrick, you're saying: 'I'm serious, I've hired the best, I'm not going to back down to you'."

**KEY INDIVIDUALS Alfred Lurey** is renowned as a "great person to deal with." Backed by more than 40 years of experience, "he knows exactly what he's doing and has the experience and knowledge" to deal with any situation. He recently represented the official committee of unsecured creditors for NetBank. **Todd Meyers** is identified as "one of the lead practitioners in the industry." He is noted as being "very aggressive in pursuit of fiduciary duties" and a dynamic litigator. He recently advised the official creditors committee for BankUnited Financial Corporation, in which the debtor had in excess of $500 million of unsecured debt. **Matthew Levin** is a skilled bankruptcy practitioner whom sources praise for a consistently strong standard of work. **Paul Rosenblatt** is able to "produce some tremendous results in a number of difficult cases," according to sources. He was prominent in the firm's representation of the official equity committee for Sage Crest Holdings, a failed hedge fund. The seasoned **Dennis Meir** is lauded for displaying a tremendous "depth of knowledge in his field," excellent responsiveness, and for his ability to provide a "high-quality work product."

### McKenna Long & Aldridge LLP
See profile on p.922

**THE FIRM** As a result of its 2012 merger with Luce Forward, this firm was able to strengthen its already substantial Atlanta footprint, gaining both the expertise and the attorneys of the former California-based firm. While McKenna Long is proficient in all areas of bankruptcy law, it has recently been engaged in a number of Chapter 9 restructuring cases. For example, the group recently represented Suffolk Regional Off-Track Betting Corporation in significant Chapter 9 proceedings.

**Sources say:** "It wasn't only that they did really good technical work -- it was actually pleasant to work with them." "They're superb at explaining things to normal people."

**KEY INDIVIDUALS Mark Kaufman** (see p.1086) "is fantastic," mentioned one source: "He is a very bright guy, as analytically sound as anyone I have ever worked with, and, moreover, a very conscientious and fine lawyer." He recently represented International Management Associates as the court-appointed investors committee in relation to a major Ponzi scheme fraud case. **Gary Marsh's** (see p.1089) recent highlights include acting for The Cliffs Club & Hospitality Group in its Chapter 11 proceedings. Sources are immensely "impressed with his ability to home in on the most important issues, prioritize, and deliver." **Michael Levengood** (see p.1088) immediately "garners the respect of the other parties' professionals," say sources, thus "allowing him to take a leadership role in negotiations." He recently provided counsel to Suffolk Regional Off-Track Betting in its recent Chapter 9 proceedings. According to one client, **Henry Sewell** (see p.1096) exhibits all of the qualities of a "great lawyer." He recently worked on behalf of the official committee of unsecured creditors for Cagle's, involving claims of over $80 million.

### Parker, Hudson, Rainer & Dobbs LLP

**THE FIRM** This strong East Coast firm has excellent expertise in the representation of secured creditors, often working in close proximity with the related asset-based lending team and providing clients with a comprehensive and collaborative approach. The team has a strong client list consisting of major financial institutions, such as Regions Bank, Wells Fargo Bank and Zions First National Bank.

**Sources say:** "They're tactically very strong and they're great at crafting creative solutions to any problems that one inevitably faces – including bringing parties in contention with each other to common ground."

**KEY INDIVIDUALS** The "unparalleled" **Edward Dobbs** continues to justify his reputation as the state's leading bankruptcy attorney. His courtroom presence draws particular praise: "It's like watching an artist," said one source, with another saying that Dobbs was "absolutely unbelievable in front of a judge." He is currently acting on behalf of The Colonial BancGroup as post-confirmation debtor in its Chapter 11 case. **Eric Anderson** recently acted as counsel to Jeffrey Kerr, the Chapter 7 trustee for Silverton Financial Services, in connection with a significant bank failure. "Talk about a guy who can get stuff done," said one source: "He gets it done in a timely manner, professionally and within the budget." The "particularly impressive" **Rufus Dorsey** recently acted as lead partner in the firm's representation of former Sea Island Company CEO Dennie McCrary as he sought roughly $27 million from his former employers. **James Rankin** is commended for his "excellent negotiation techniques," which clients believe make the "implementation of a defined strategy more achievable." He was part of the team acting on behalf of Evolution CDC SPV in the $70 million CDC Corporation bankruptcy proceedings.

## Band 3

### Greenberg Traurig, LLP
See profile on p.1024

**THE FIRM** Greenberg Traurig's financial restructuring department is renowned for the quality of its out-of-court work, offering expertise across a broad range of industries. The firm benefits from its significant global presence, enabling the Atlanta-based attorneys to draw upon a wealth of international resources. On the creditor side, the group's highlights include advising the unsecured creditors of Money Tree and Money Tree of Georgia.

**Sources say:** "They struck exactly the right tone of aggression and professionalism in front of the judge."

**KEY INDIVIDUALS David Kurzweil** (see p.1088) chairs the Atlanta-based bankruptcy practice and is one of the state's best-known practitioners. Clients commend him for being "zealous in the courtroom," with one source speaking of having "tremendous confidence in him." His recent highlights include providing counsel to Agricultural Funding

Solutions, the lender to the bankrupt Dairy Production Systems and its affiliates. **John Elrod** (see p.1081) is lauded as a *"very capable practitioner"* who is comfortable in both debtor and creditor representations. He is regularly engaged by Wells Fargo Bank on a variety of different matters.

## Morris, Manning & Martin, LLP

**THE FIRM** This firm's solid bankruptcy and restructuring practice maintains a strong regional presence. Its attorneys are lauded for their familiarity with the intricacies of creditor's rights practice and, as such, have enabled the firm to gain substantial traction within this area. The 11-strong group has additional expertise in lender representations, capabilities recently showcased in its representation of First Citizens Bank and Trust Company as lender in the workout of a $27 million development loan secured by Hampton Island.

**Sources say:** *"They do an excellent job of understanding what our goals are and they make an effort to do things exactly as we want."*

**KEY INDIVIDUALS David Cranshaw** is *"extremely organized"* and *"strategic in looking for practical solutions to issues."* In recent highlights, he represented a number of secured creditors, including SunTrust Bank, AloStar Bank of Commerce, Cornerstone Bank, Multibank and Colony Capital, in a range of workout, bankruptcy litigation and restructuring matters. The *"business-minded"* **Frank DeBorde** recently advised the unsecured creditors of GLC in relation to an alleged Ponzi scheme. According to sources: *"Everybody is very impressed by his outcomes and tangible, considered presence in dealing with other attorneys and problematic situations."*

## Troutman Sanders LLP

**THE FIRM** This full-service firm maintains a significant presence in Georgia. Its practitioners benefit from both the global reach of the firm and from their close proximity to the firm's commercial litigation attorneys. The firm has recently been engaged in a number of Chapter 11 filings, acting on behalf of committees, creditors and debtors. Its recent highlights include acting as co-counsel to Allied Holdings in the company's bankruptcy proceedings.

**KEY INDIVIDUALS Jeffrey Kelley** is well equipped to handle the entire spectrum of bankruptcy work. His recent workload has included a variety of out-of-court restructurings and Chapter 11 matters, earning him plaudits for the quality of his representations. Seasoned authority **Ezra Cohen** combines an active practice with an extensive knowledge of legal developments, and is especially strong in debtor-side representations.

## Band 4

## Bryan Cave LLP

**THE FIRM** Bryan Cave is traditionally renowned for its strength in bankruptcy litigation, but has recently developed a strong line in distressed transactions. The bankruptcy practitioners work closely with the firm's market-leading bank regulatory practice and, as such, possess detailed knowledge of the application of the Bankruptcy Code to financial institutions. Premier Bank Holding and MidFirst Bank are key clients.

**KEY INDIVIDUALS** Since joining the firm in 2011, **Mark Duedall** has garnered significant acclaim for the consistency of his legal representation. He recently represented Premier Bank Holding in the divestiture of an operating bank. A newcomer to the rankings, **Robert Mercer** led the team acting for the liquidation trustee in the Sea Island Company bankruptcy cases. Sources commend his exceptional communication skills.

## Burr & Forman LLP
### See profile on p.1105

**THE FIRM** This firm, headquartered in Alabama, remains competitive in the Georgia market, maintaining a sizable team of Atlanta-based bankruptcy attorneys as part of its strong South Eastern footprint. The firm operates predominantly in the middle market, dedicating much of its time towards lender representation. Recent clients include Georgia Gulf Corporation and Wells Fargo Bank.

**Sources say:** *"They really understand business as well as the legal side of transactions. They're very conscious about how much work goes into deals based on the economics."*

**KEY INDIVIDUALS** *"Out-of-the-box-thinker"* **Erich Durlacher** brings a creative approach to advocacy. He recently represented Global SFI Holdings as the 363 stalking-horse bidder and purchaser in the distressed acquisition of assets of fastener and tack button-manufacturer Scovill. The *"very well-seasoned"* **Paul O'Hearn** is a go-to adviser to Wells Fargo Bank, frequently aiding in the facilitation of a number of commercial lot loans to high net worth individuals. **Graham Stieglitz** is adept at both bankruptcy and commercial litigation. He continues to provide ongoing representation to Georgia Gulf Corporation in relation to a number of bankruptcy-related issues.

## Lamberth, Cifelli, Stokes & Stout, P.A.

**THE FIRM** This Atlanta-based boutique has both experience and expertise in all aspects of bankruptcy law. Renowned for the quality of its debtor representations, the firm remains an attractive and effective alternative to the state's larger full-service firms, offering favorable billing rates and a comparable level of representation.

**Sources say:** *"An excellent law firm."* *"What I like about them is that I don't ever have to follow up and call."*

**KEY INDIVIDUALS** Both peers and clients are effusive in their praise of **James Cifelli**. He is recognized as being one of the state's leading practitioners. Sources describe him as a *"very good litigator,"* who is both *"tenacious and conciliatory."*

## Paul Hastings LLP
### See profile on p.1996

**THE FIRM** This firm's bankruptcy practice is truly national in scope, and the clients of its Atlanta-based group benefit greatly from the collaborative potential that the firm's extensive national footprint provides. The team has a strong line in representing senior secured lenders, including in relation to syndicated credit facilities. GE Capital is an example of one such client which the firm continues to service in connection to a number of complex restructuring and insolvency issues.

**Sources say:** *"They're in the market every day in leading mid-market cases; they really have a great understanding of market-based solutions."*

**KEY INDIVIDUALS** Ted Smith is a key contact.

## Scroggins & Williamson

**THE FIRM** Scroggins & Williamson is one of the state's leading bankruptcy boutiques, and has created a highly successful niche for itself in the field of debtor representations. The firm is considered a first choice among peers for referrals and conflicts, exemplifying the strength of its reputation in the legal community.

**Sources say:** *"They're very effective and efficient."*

**KEY INDIVIDUALS** Managing partner **Robert Williamson** is universally regarded as *"an excellent lawyer,"* garnering acclaim from a variety of sources. *"He's a very bright guy,"* claimed one such individual, *"he's a very bright lawyer and he has great connections."*

## Other Notable Practitioners

**John Isbell** (see p.1085) of Thompson Hine LLP has enjoyed an active year, and recently represented CDC Software in relation to a potential $287 million distressed takeover. *"His responsiveness is terrific,"* noted one client, while another lauded his familiarity with the nuances of the law. **John Thomson** of Womble Carlyle Sandridge & Rice, LLP is particularly strong in the area of creditor representations, and lists Rialto Capital Partners and Branch Banking & Trust among his key clients. Sources are especially impressed with his ability to *"keep a creditor out of trouble."* The *"very knowledgeable"* **Richard Herzog** (see p.1084) of Nelson Mullins Riley & Scarborough LLP earns the approval of clients for his all-encompassing bankruptcy expertise. **John Mills** (see p.1090) of Barnes & Thornburg LLP is a new addition to the rankings. He splits his time between the firm's Atlanta and Los Angeles offices, and is universally regarded as a *"fine lawyer"* whom peers single out on account of his extensive knowledge.

# CONSTRUCTION

Commentary about individuals can be found under their firm's paragraph. If the firm has no paragraph (is not ranked) look at Other Notable Practitioners.

| Construction Leading Firms |
|---|
| **Band 1** |
| Kilpatrick Townsend & Stockton LLP * |
| Smith, Currie & Hancock LLP * |
| Sutherland Asbill & Brennan LLP |
| **Band 2** |
| Alston & Bird LLP * |
| Troutman Sanders LLP |
| Weinberg, Wheeler, Hudgins, Gunn & Dial, LLC |
| **Band 3** |
| Hendrick, Phillips, Salzman & Flatt P.C. |
| Seyfarth Shaw LLP * |

## Band 1

### Kilpatrick Townsend & Stockton LLP
See profile on p.1109

**THE FIRM** The Kilpatrick Townsend team has long been recognized as one of the market-leading construction groups in the state. Its strong team routinely handles some of the most valuable and high-profile matters in the market. For example, it has continued to advise the City of Atlanta regarding all aspects of its $6 billion airport expansion. It also recently represented Alstom Transportation, successfully defending it in a multimillion-dollar claim. The team serves clients from diverse industries in any matter related to construction, and has expertise in both transactional matters and litigation.

**Sources say:** *"We have found the services and depth at the firm to be outstanding. I have gotten to know many of the other attorneys in the construction department over the years and come away with a strong positive impression of their skill and commitment to their clients."*

**KEY INDIVIDUALS** Practice head **Brian Corgan** is one of the most highly regarded figures in the market. Clients are effusive in their endorsement of his work. One observes: *"I have never worked with anybody who commands all aspects of a case like Brian does."* **William Dorris** has been a key player in the group's work for the City of Atlanta. He is known to be *"extremely competent, easygoing and very, very professional."* Clients add that he is *"extremely well prepared and understands our business completely."* Litigation department chair **Randall Hafer** is able to bring his considerable courtroom experience to bear on construction-related disputes. He has recently been acting for the Massachusetts Department of Transportation in issues surrounding the largest highways project undertaken in the USA. **Neal Sweeney** has extensive experience in the real estate market. He is primarily engaged in large-scale public works projects, and also has considerable expertise with public contracts. **Chad Theriot** enjoys a growing reputation for his work, which is centered predominantly around construction litigation and claims avoidance. Clients have been par-

| Senior Statesmen | | |
|---|---|---|
| **Senior Statesmen: distinguished older practitioners** | | |
| Abernathy Thomas E | Smith, Currie & Hancock LLP * | |
| Asselin Thomas H | Smith Gambrell & Russell LLP (ONP) † | |
| Kelleher, Jr Thomas J | Smith, Currie & Hancock LLP * | |
| Shapiro J Ben | Baker, Donelson, Bearman (ONP) † | |

| Leading Individuals | |
|---|---|
| **Star individuals** | |
| Fletcher Jennifer W | Sutherland Asbill & Brennan LLP |
| **Band 1** | |
| Beck Philip E | Smith, Currie & Hancock LLP * |
| Coleman, Jr Aubrey L | Smith, Currie & Hancock LLP * |
| Corgan Brian | Kilpatrick Townsend & Stockton LLP |
| Davis Lee C | Sutherland Asbill & Brennan LLP |
| Dial David | Weinberg, Wheeler, Hudgins, Gunn & Dial * |
| Dorris William | Kilpatrick Townsend & Stockton LLP |
| Genberg Ira | Troutman Sanders LLP |
| Hafer Randall F | Kilpatrick Townsend & Stockton LLP |
| Riggs Jr Frank E | Troutman Sanders LLP |
| Robey Ronald G | Smith, Currie & Hancock LLP * |
| Spangler III John I | Alston & Bird LLP * |
| Sweeney Neal | Kilpatrick Townsend & Stockton LLP |
| **Band 2** | |
| Butler, III James F | Smith, Currie & Hancock LLP * |
| Chambers Robert C | Smith, Currie & Hancock LLP * |
| Crewdson Robert L | DLA Piper LLP (US) (ONP) † |
| Flynn John T | Weinberg, Wheeler, Hudgins, Gunn & Dial * |
| Hendrick David R | Hendrick, Phillips, Salzman & Flatt P.C. |
| Hughes Jr William H | Alston & Bird LLP * |
| Klein Linda A | Baker, Donelson, Bearman, Caldwell (ONP) † |
| McCabe F Barry | Sutherland Asbill & Brennan LLP |
| Nelson Eric L | Smith, Currie & Hancock LLP * |
| Smith George Anthony | Weinberg, Wheeler, Hudgins, Gunn & Dial * |
| Wenick George D | Smith, Currie & Hancock LLP * |
| **Band 3** | |
| Cahalan Scott D | Smith Gambrell & Russell LLP (ONP) † |
| Fussell Herman L | Foltz Martin LLC (ONP) † |
| Gary T Bart | Freeman Mathis & Gary, LLP (ONP) † |
| Ginsberg Ross D | Weinberg, Wheeler, Hudgins, Gunn & Dial * |
| Ingraham C Walker | Seyfarth Shaw LLP * |
| Kowalski Jack | Burr & Forman LLP (ONP) † |
| Stair Kent | Carlock, Copeland & Stair, LLP (ONP) † |
| Wildman William R | Sutherland Asbill & Brennan LLP |
| **Up-and-coming individuals** | |
| Cole Danielle J | Peckar & Abramson, P.C. (ONP) † * |
| Theriot Chad V | Kilpatrick Townsend & Stockton LLP |

\* Indicates individual with profile.
† ONP = Other Notable Practitioner

### Smith, Currie & Hancock LLP
See profile on p.1112

**THE FIRM** This team is one of the best-established construction groups in the area, and has a rich history of impressive performance in this sector. It offers comprehensive coverage of all areas of construction law to clients from a wide spread of industries. The group is often involved in some of the most sophisticated matters within the construction sphere. Recent clients include SCANA, Georgia-Pacific, Molson Coors and Caddell Construction. It can draw upon its national network of offices for additional resources when managing large, multistate projects.

**Sources say:** *"They have a wonderful reputation and the longest history of any team, and there are a number of good lawyers there."*

**KEY INDIVIDUALS Philip Beck** (see p.1076) is a widely recognized and acclaimed fixture of the Georgia construction market. He splits his practice between dispute resolution and dispute avoidance. As well as representing a large number of contractors, he also serves owners, subcontractors and designers. The deeply experienced **Aubrey Coleman** (see p.1079) has become renowned as one of the leading authorities on construction matters in the Atlanta market and beyond. **Ronald Robey** (see p.1094) is particularly noted for his skill at drafting construction contracts. These include contracts in the public and private sector for a diverse range of projects, including hospitals, casinos and airports. He also has vast experience working with numerous government bodies. **James Butler** (see p.1077) is also a specialist in the negotiation of construction contracts. Alongside this, he maintains an active practice covering design-build projects and EPC. **Robert Chambers** (see p.1078) has been involved with clients from both the public and private sphere, and is an experienced figure in construction disputes. Clients believe that he is especially *"very good in cases involving underground construction."* **Eric Nelson** (see p.1091) *"has a very commanding presence and a good way about him. I would give him very high marks,"* says an impressed client. He is recognized by the market as a growing name in the dispute resolution field. **George Wenick** (see p.1100) is admired as a highly capable litigator with an international focus to a large part of his work. He has experience in litigation involving Chinese, European and Latin American jurisdictions and clients. **Thomas Abernathy** (see p.1074) brings a wealth of experience to the team. He frequently represents contractors, subcontractors and owners of complex projects. **Thomas Kelleher** (see p.1087) is highly respected by market commentators for his deep expertise and experience in handling government contracts.

### Sutherland Asbill & Brennan LLP

**THE FIRM** The Georgia arm of this established national practice regularly handles big-ticket construction engagements on behalf of its clients. For example, the team

ticularly impressed by his steadfast attention to detail in preparing their cases.

recently acted for Lend Lease in relation to disputes worth $200 million relating to the deconstruction of the last building to be removed at Ground Zero. Other notable clients include Black & Veatch and Wright Brothers Construction.

**KEY INDIVIDUALS** When speaking of **Jennifer Fletcher**, sources are consistently enthusiastic and effusive about her ability and stature in the field. She brings extensive experience in litigation to her construction practice, and is praised as being an excellent force at the heart of the team. **Lee Davis** is praised by clients for his charismatic approach to handling matters. He is an accomplished litigator, arbitrator and negotiator whose dispute resolution skills are highly regarded. He recently represented Black & Veatch in a high-profile and complex matter regarding multiple power plants nationwide. **Barry McCabe** focuses his practice on the dispute resolution side of construction matters. He recently led the team representing EMCOR Group in high-value claims arising from disruption and labor inefficiency during the construction of a new hospital. **William Wildman** has over 25 years of construction litigation and contract negotiation experience. He has recently assisted the DeKalb County School System in the review of all contracts in the $500 million Special Purpose Local Option Sales Tax (SPLOST) construction program.

## Band 2

### Alston & Bird LLP
See profile on p.1102

**THE FIRM** This group is widely recognized as a significant player in the Georgia market and throughout the Southeast. It offers assistance in all areas of construction law, typically to owners and contractors, and is regularly engaged by significant clients including GenOn Energy, Skanska USA Building and AIG Global Real Estate. It has recently been acting on behalf of Superior Rigging in a complicated dispute regarding the Miami Marlins baseball stadium.

**KEY INDIVIDUALS** **John Spangler** (see p.1098) is seen as a *"top-notch lawyer"* by impressed clients. He was lead partner in representing DACA in a $3.5 million case against the general contractor in the construction of Mayport Naval Air Station. **William Hughes** (see p.1085) offers full coverage of any construction-related issue. He has significant experience in the Chinese and South American markets, but is also active domestically. He recently represented ReEnergy Holdings in its project to convert a coal-fired power station to use sustainable fuel.

### Troutman Sanders LLP

**THE FIRM** This firm is active in all forms of dispute resolution relating to the construction sector. The team is also heavily involved in drafting construction contracts, and has recently undertaken such work for Southern Company Services, drafting seven contract templates. Other key clients include Georgia-Pacific, Foster Wheeler AG and Watts Water Technologies.

**KEY INDIVIDUALS** Clients believe that group leader **Ira Genberg** consistently offers excellent service. He can draw upon deep experience and an esteemed reputation in the field, something appreciated by clients. **Frank Riggs** has over 30 years of dedicated construction law experience. The highly esteemed Riggs was the lead partner in drafting contracts for Southern Company Services.

### Weinberg, Wheeler, Hudgins, Gunn & Dial, LLC

**THE FIRM** This team specializes in construction litigation and disputes, areas in which it is well received by clients. It recently represented Wood Group in a $9 million subrogation claim brought against it by Factory Mutual. It also defended Sheffer Engineering in a $2 million suit concerning damages and project delays following the collapse of a temporary cofferdam. Other notable clients include Veolia Water, Siemens Energy and the American Bridge Company.

**Sources say:** *"Outstanding construction lawyers who have a national reputation of achieving great results for their clients."*

**KEY INDIVIDUALS** Department head **David Dial** (see p.1080) has a broad base of experience, having represented clients across the country and abroad. Clients are delighted with his courtroom presence, and say that *"his cross-examinations, in very clear terms, were devastating."* **John Flynn** (see p.1081) *"is a real pleasure to work with. He is very professional and knowledgeable,"* according to sources. His practice has a particular focus on government contract disputes, and he has noteworthy experience in overseas work. **Tony Smith** (see p.1097) has garnered the respect of the wider market in his many years of experience. Interviewees observe that *"he has an excellent reputation and he is a very good, very knowledgeable lawyer."* He has expertise in contract negotiation, arbitration and litigation. **Ross Ginsberg** (see p.1082) is especially adept at defending clients who approach projects from the design perspective. While holding a prominent local reputation, he is also present in a number of national matters.

## Band 3

### Hendrick, Phillips, Salzman & Flatt P.C.
**THE FIRM** This construction law boutique offers its services in all potential issues relating to projects. Its ten-lawyer team has carved out a competitive niche for itself in the market, and is regularly engaged by a range of clients, though it is particularly known for its work in representing subcontractors.

**KEY INDIVIDUALS** Deeply experienced senior partner **David Hendrick** is *"an excellent lawyer,"* according to sources. His practice is centered around contracting and claim matters, as well as dispute resolution.

### Seyfarth Shaw LLP
See profile on p.1262

**THE FIRM** Seyfarth Shaw is a regular choice for contractors, and offers a wide range of services from its dedicated

team, though it is particularly adroit in dispute resolution and litigation. It is part of the firm's excellent and wide-reaching national construction offering. It has recently represented The Winter Construction Company in claims of over $50 million against the owner of a mixed-use project.

**KEY INDIVIDUALS** **Walker Ingraham** (see p.1085) is chair of the Atlanta office's litigation department and has a strong focus on construction disputes. He was co-lead partner on the Winter Construction Company case, and has recently assisted Gay Construction in a variety of matters.

### Other Notable Practitioners

**Ben Shapiro** (see p.1096) of Baker, Donelson, Bearman, Caldwell & Berkowitz, PC is among the best-known names in the market. His immense experience has contributed to him being acclaimed as a recognized expert for all manner of construction-related disputes. **Linda Klein** (see p.1087) is department head at Baker, Donelson, Bearman, Caldwell & Berkowitz, PC's Atlanta office. She is particularly involved in disputes related to construction projects. **Robert Crewdson** (see p.1079) of DLA Piper LLP (US) earns the praise of clients who observe that *"he is very professional with great efficiency, and is also great at watching our budget."* He handles both dispute resolution and contract drafting. **Jack Kowalski** is chair of Burr & Forman LLP's construction law practice. An *"aggressive and honest"* attorney, he chiefly represents contractors, though he also has experience in engagements for clients in the automotive industry. **Herman Fussell** of Foltz Martin LLC is a veteran litigator who also undertakes alternative dispute resolution. He is an active and highly regarded figure in the Atlanta market. **Scott Cahalan** (see p.1077) of Smith Gambrell & Russell LLP is predominantly engaged in drafting construction contracts, though he is also active in litigation and dispute resolution. He represents a broad spread of clients, including contractors, owners, designers and subcontractors. **Thomas Asselin** (see p.1075) of Smith Gambrell & Russell LLP is principally known for his abilities as an arbitrator, and has been involved in numerous large and complex projects. **Bart Gary** is a founding partner of Freeman Mathis & Gary, LLP and head of both the litigation and construction law departments. He earns praise from the market for his work in representing subcontractors. **Kent Stair** of Carlock Copeland & Stair, LLP has deep experience in this sphere. He specifically represents design individuals in all possible issues arising during a construction project, and draws admiration from the wider market. **Danielle Cole** (see p.1078) of Peckar & Abramson, P.C. has a fast-growing reputation in this field. She has handled projects in all phases, from conception to completion, and provides assistance on all construction issues.

# CORPORATE/M&A

Commentary about individuals can be found under their firm's paragraph. If the firm has no paragraph (is not ranked) look at Other Notable Practitioners.

## Corporate/M&A
### Leading Firms

**Band 1**
Alston & Bird LLP *
Jones Day *
King & Spalding LLP *

**Band 2**
Paul Hastings LLP *
Rogers & Hardin LLP *
Sutherland Asbill & Brennan LLP

**Band 3**
Kilpatrick Townsend & Stockton LLP *
McKenna Long & Aldridge LLP *
Troutman Sanders LLP

**Band 4**
Bryan Cave LLP
DLA Piper LLP (US) *
Morris, Manning & Martin, LLP
Nelson Mullins Riley & Scarborough LLP *
Womble Carlyle Sandridge & Rice, LLP *

### Leading Individuals

**Star individuals**

| | |
|---|---|
| Baxley C William | King & Spalding LLP * |

**Band 1**

| | |
|---|---|
| Egan Michael | King & Spalding LLP * |
| Fox Steven E | Rogers & Hardin LLP * |
| Hardin Edward J | Rogers & Hardin LLP * |
| Stockton David | Kilpatrick Townsend & Stockton LLP |

**Band 2**

| | |
|---|---|
| Blackburn W Stanley | Kilpatrick Townsend & Stockton LLP |
| Capers John | King & Spalding LLP * |
| Jeffries M Hill | Alston & Bird LLP * |
| Jospin Walter | Paul Hastings LLP |
| Kelley John J | King & Spalding LLP |
| Layson Frank | Jones Day * |
| McMahon Teri Lynn | Alston & Bird LLP * |
| Noe Elizabeth H | Paul Hastings LLP |
| Richards Russell | King & Spalding LLP * |
| Thomas Lizanne | Jones Day * |
| Zamer John E | Jones Day * |

**Band 3**

| | |
|---|---|
| Baltz Raymond E | King & Spalding LLP * |
| Belenky Erik | Jones Day * |
| Bradley Wayne N | McKenna Long & Aldridge LLP * |
| Dickerson Jr W Brinkley | Troutman Sanders LLP |
| Golden Jonathan | Arnall Golden Gregory LLP (ONP) [†] * |
| Hussle Robert C | Rogers & Hardin LLP * |
| Kaufman Mark D | Sutherland Asbill & Brennan LLP |
| McNeill Thomas R | Bryan Cave LLP |
| Ortwein William Scott | Alston & Bird LLP * |
| Pascual Rey | Paul Hastings LLP |
| Rowland William B | Jones Day * |
| Smith John F Sandy | Womble Carlyle Sandridge & Rice, LLP |

| | |
|---|---|
| Smith William Calvin | King & Spalding LLP * |
| Stein Jeffrey | King & Spalding LLP * |
| Townsend Keith M | King & Spalding LLP * |

**Band 4**

| | |
|---|---|
| Barkley W Benjamin | Kilpatrick Townsend & Stockton LLP |
| Blum Theodore I | Greenberg Traurig, LLP (ONP) [†] * |
| Brown David | McKenna Long & Aldridge LLP * |
| Carlson Mark A B | Baker, Donelson, Bearman (ONP) [†] * |
| Cicchillo Jr Richard | Kilpatrick Townsend & Stockton LLP |
| Davis Bryan E | Jones Day * |
| DeLisle Joe | Miller & Martin PLLC (ONP) [†] * |
| Hollingsworth II Michael E | Nelson Mullins Riley & Scarborough * |
| Koontz Eric A | Troutman Sanders LLP |
| Leet Alan C | Rogers & Hardin LLP * |
| Miller Rick | Bryan Cave LLP |
| Moore III Randolph A | Alston & Bird LLP * |
| Opler Stephen | Ballard Spahr LLP (ONP) [†] * |
| Patel Rahul | King & Spalding LLP * |
| Pile Robert J | Sutherland Asbill & Brennan LLP |
| Rafter Michael | Baker, Donelson, Bearman, Caldwell * |
| Schwartz Arthur Jay | Smith Gambrell & Russell LLP (ONP) [†] * |
| Silverman Jeremy C | McKenna Long & Aldridge LLP * |
| Spelios Louis C. | Bryan Cave LLP |
| Thunhorst David G | Rogers & Hardin LLP * |
| Yates David R | Hunton & Williams LLP (ONP) [†] * |
| Yates John C | Morris, Manning & Martin, LLP |

**Up-and-coming individuals**

| | |
|---|---|
| Alexander Joseph | DLA Piper LLP (US) * |
| McGaughey Ann-Marie | McKenna Long & Aldridge LLP * |
| Silver Joseph | DLA Piper LLP (US) * |

**Associates to watch**

| | |
|---|---|
| White Darcy | Paul Hastings LLP |

* Indicates firm / individual with profile.
[†]ONP = Other Notable Practitioner

## Band 1

### Alston & Bird LLP
**See profile on p.1102**

**THE FIRM** Firmly established as one of Georgia's preeminent corporate and M&A practices, Alston & Bird retains its premier billing. The group has enhanced its reputation through its involvement in a number of sophisticated and high-profile transactions. Indicative highlights include its representation of AuthenTec in its $365 million sale to corporate giant Apple, a role which also serves to exemplify the firm's impressive standing in the technology sector. Other key clients include Graphic Packaging International and Home Depot.

**Sources say:** "Alston & Bird is world-class." "They really focus on the relationship with the client and not solely on the next big deal."

**KEY INDIVIDUALS** Sources identify **Hill Jeffries** (see p.1085) as an "excellent securities and M&A attorney," in particular. He played an integral part in providing counsel to Genuine Parts in relation to its investment in Exego Group. **Teri McMahon** (see p.1090) is frequently called upon to represent private equity firms, such as MSouth Equity Partners, in a variety of transactional matters. She is lauded as a "great lawyer." **William Scott Ortwein** (see p.1092) combines an active Georgia practice with a strong presence in both the New York and Chicago legal markets. He is commended for demonstrating familiarity with a number of different industries, and has garnered a solid reputation as an "excellent lawyer." He continues to serve as lead partner in the firm's representation of AuthenTec.

**Randolph Moore** (see p.1090) recently led the team acting on behalf of Whitney Holding Company as it negotiated the sale of a banking subsidiary to Mississippi-based Hanock Holding Company. He is noted for the quality of his work on behalf of financial institutions, and is praised as "hard-working, loyal and dedicated."

### Jones Day
**See profile on p.919**

**THE FIRM** Jones Day is recognized as having one of the strongest practices in the state, with its extensive global footprint enabling the Atlanta-based group to draw upon a wealth of legal resources worldwide. While it is prepared to operate within the mid-market, the firm is most frequently engaged in relation to the market's largest transactions. The team recently acted on behalf of Eastman

Chemical as it acquired specialty chemical producer Solutia in a $4.8 billion deal.

**Sources say:** "I have a towering level of professional respect for the practice"

**KEY INDIVIDUALS Frank Layson** (see p.1088) recently joined the firm from Paul Hastings, bringing with him a diverse and well-established practice. Clients respect his ability to dispense "thoughtful advice in a timely and efficient manner." The "extremely well-respected" **Lizanne Thomas** (see p.1099) is partner-in-charge of the firm's Atlanta office. "She does a truly great job," say sources, many of whom also praise her as "one of the best M&A lawyers in the Southeast." She recently played a key role in advising Georgia Gulf throughout its $2.1 billion merger with PPG Industries. **John Zamer** (see p.1101) is a "very impressive and professional" practitioner. He is seen as a go-to attorney on a variety of corporate governance issues, in addition to serving as lead partner on a number of the firm's most sophisticated and high-profile transactions. **William Rowland** (see p.1095) wins tremendous acclaim this year for his lead in representing Eastman Chemicals in its headline-grabbing $4.8 billion purchase of Solutia, one of the largest deals in the Southeast in 2012. Recent lateral hire **Erik Belenky** (see p.1076) earns praise for his impressive business acumen, with one interviewee reporting that his recommendations *"make sense both commercially and practically."* He has a broad practice and is proficient at representing clients from a number of industries. **Bryan Davis** (see p.1079) is described as *"smart, experienced, and client-focused."* He earns plaudits for being able to bring the full experience and capabilities of his firm to bear on any assignment. He recently played an integral part in the team's advice to Cumulus Media as it purchased Citadel Broadcasting in a $2.4 billion deal.

### King & Spalding LLP
See profile on p.445

THE FIRM This 16-partner team is prominent in several high-profile deals and retains its status as one of the leading practices in the state. The firm boasts an unparalleled bench strength, and, as such, is able to undertake a broad range of engagements across diverse industries. Additionally, the corporate practice has a strong leveraged finance component which enables the firm to be particularly active in the private equity buy-out arena. The group's client roster includes General Electric, Home Depot and Georgia Pacific.

Sources say: *"They have extraordinary depth in the corporate area." "They're always looking for better ways to service their clients; they're always attentive to what clients are doing."*

KEY INDIVIDUALS **William Baxley** (see p.1075) remains a towering figure in the market, perceived by sources to be both a *"fantastic lawyer"* and a *"very sharp guy."* He recently served as lead partner on behalf of Immucor throughout its $1.97 billion sale to TPG Capital. Hailed as a *"fantastic transactional lawyer"* by market sources, **Michael Egan** (see p.1081) is a dominant force in the field. *"I'd use him anywhere in the world,"* remarked one interviewee; *"he truly is unique."* His recent clients include Winn-Dixie Stores and HD Supply. **John Capers** (see p.1078) led the team advising GlaxoSmithKline in its acquisition of the product rights to Toctino. He earns unanimous approval from peers for his transactional capabilities, with one interviewee stating that *"he gets the job done in a way that people really respect."* Renowned for his strength in capital markets, **John Kelley** is one of the firm's most respected corporate practitioners. He was part of the team that acted on behalf of Beazer Homes in a sizable note offering. Senior partner **Russell Richards** (see p.1094) is identified by interviewees as a *"consummate M&A professional."* He has a diverse practice and offers robust representation across a wide range of industries. He recently represented electrical products manufacturer Cooper Industries in its acquisition of Azonix. **Raymond Baltz** (see p.1075) leads the firm's corporate department and is vastly experienced

in a variety of transactional matters. Sources describe him as a *"very organized and detailed lawyer,"* citing his adroitness in the representation of private equity funds as one of his primary strengths. Noted for his representation of Beazer Homes in its recent notes offering, **Cal Smith** (see p.1097) garners praise for his level of client service. Described by sources as being both *"hard-working"* and *"smart,"* he is further acclaimed for the quality of his written work and is generally regarded as one of the firm's most promising young partners. The *"extremely talented"* **Jeffrey Stein** (see p.1098) is hailed as an *"outstanding securities lawyer,"* and is said to possess both *"excellent legal skills"* and *"strong business judgment."* **Keith Townsend** (see p.1099) is, according to one source, *"a superb young lawyer"* who *"knows everything there is to know about securities law."* He was recently involved in the IPO of Ignite Restaurant Group, advising lead underwriter Credit Suisse Securities. **Rahul Patel** (see p.1092) is a newcomer to the ranks, earning inclusion on the strength of an active year in which, among other assignments, he represented LexisNexis Risk Solutions. Commentators consider him to be technically exceptional, with one interviewee describing him as an *"absolute star when it comes to M&A."*

## Band 2

### Paul Hastings LLP
See profile on p.1996

THE FIRM This mainstay of the Georgia market is recommended for the standard of its corporate representations, with clients commending the intellectual depth of the firm's attorneys, in addition to their ability to both envision and implement creative solutions. The group is especially noted for its recent work in the healthcare space, having handled multiple IPOs of companies in the domain, such as Greenway Medical Technologies. Other key clients include ExamWorks Group, Monitise and Home Depot.

Sources say: *"They've performed exceptionally well. I think they have intellectual depth; they have excellent multilayered continuity and they come up with creative solutions."*

KEY INDIVIDUALS **Walter Jospin** is a vastly experienced transactional attorney who garners specific praise for his representation of mid-market companies. He has substantial experience in M&A and governance work. Department chair **Elizabeth Noe** is renowned for her expertise in high-yield debt offerings. She recently played a key role in advising ExamWorks Groups in a $250 million offering of unsecured notes. Highly regarded transactional attorney **Rey Pascual** is *"a pleasure to deal with,"* say sources. He served as lead partner in the firm's representation of Greenway Medical Technologies, aiding the company in preparation for its IPO. **Darcy White** continues to be perceived as one of the state's most distinguished associates. She advises a broad range of clients in connection with a range of corporate issues.

### Rogers & Hardin LLP
See profile on p.1111

THE FIRM This Atlanta-based firm has an array of highly skilled attorneys, each possessing considerable strength within the corporate sphere. While the group undertakes a wide range of transactional and corporate work, several sources remark on the standard of its special committee representations, an area in which the firm has particular expertise. The firm recently advised Ned Davis Research and Davis, Mendel & Regenstein in connection with a $112 million sale to Euromoney.

Sources say: *"They are professional and always responsive to my questions and needs. I've never felt I'm down the list in priority even when I'm asking something that is not a priority."*

KEY INDIVIDUALS **Edward Hardin** (see p.1083) garners unanimous approval from interviewees; he is identified as being both *"supremely competent"* and *"very responsive,"* in addition to being commended for his level of professionalism and his communication skills. He is regularly engaged on a variety of corporate matters. Founding partner **Steven Fox** (see p.1081) is a talented practitioner who is able to draw on over 35 years of transactional experience. *"What I like most about him,"* says one client, *"is that, in addition to being a very good technical lawyer, he understands the practicalities of the business world."* He recently represented Primerica in relation to both a $375 million debt offering and a $180 million public offering of shares. **Robert Hussle** (see p.1085) brings considerable expertise to his assignments. He is regarded as a solid young attorney, and is much sought after for his work in the corporate arena. He recently acted on behalf of Rock-Tenn in its acquisition of Mid South Packaging. Sources note that **David Thunhorst** (see p.1099) is *"always willing to explain things, and to listen and change his mind based on the client's input and information."* He recently oversaw the firm's representation of SouthStar Energy Services. **Alan Leet** (see p.1088) is a renowned corporate practitioner, highly regarded for his competency in the transactional field. He undertakes a range of engagements across a number of different industries.

### Sutherland Asbill & Brennan LLP

THE FIRM Traditionally renowned for its market-leading tax practice, this firm's corporate group has recently enjoyed a considerable degree of success within the transactional arena. The firm has acted on a number of significant matters and can list First Data and Spectrum Brands among its most illustrious clients. The team is also highlighted for its in-depth expertise in advising clients undertaking joint ventures.

KEY INDIVIDUALS **Mark Kaufman** has continued to advise multinational mining group Rio Tinto in relation to the sale of its Alcan Cable division. One of the firm's most prominent transactional practitioners, he is identified by clients as a trusted adviser. **Robert Pile** is applauded for his impressive experience and business sense. He recently supervised the team representing Honeywell in its $500 million acquisition of EMS Technologies.

## Band 3

### Kilpatrick Townsend & Stockton LLP
See profile on p.1109

**THE FIRM** Kilpatrick's superb corporate practice undertakes a broad spectrum of matters, ranging from international M&As and complex governance issues to advising companies on the specific rules and regulations associated with securities law. Notable recent clients include Royal Ten Cate, Delta Air Lines and Interface.

**Sources say:** *"Kilpatrick provides an appropriate level of staffing that can handle fast-paced transactions without extraordinary expense."*

**KEY INDIVIDUALS David Stockton** is recognized as a true luminary in the corporate sphere. He is praised for his ability to *"understand the rules and the parameters of what is needed in a transaction,"* with one source asserting that he is an *"absolutely tremendous lawyer."* He recently advised Servidyne in its merger with Scientific Conservation. The *"very meticulous"* **Stanley Blackburn** recently represented Royal Ten Cate throughout its acquisition of Performance Materials. He is familiar with the intricacies of a number of corporate disciplines and remains a strong presence within the legal marketplace. **Benjamin Barkley** is an experienced transactional attorney, capable of providing *"practical and seasoned advice,"* in addition to displaying a *"thorough understanding of a client's needs."* He recently worked extensively with Delta Air Lines in connection with several public debt offerings. Characterized by his *"rare ability to balance true legal expertise with solid business acumen,"* **Richard Cicchillo** remains an integral part of the firm's corporate practice. He continues to represent Zodiac Aerospace, a French aeronautics company, as it seeks to strengthen through strategic acquisitions.

### McKenna Long & Aldridge LLP
See profile on p.922

**THE FIRM** McKenna Long is acclaimed for its capabilities in undertaking international transactions and for its expertise in representing mid-market companies. The firm works closely with a number of government contractors and is thus a popular choice for clients with engagements containing municipal elements. Key clients include Home Depot, HD Supply and Coca-Cola.

**Sources say:** *"I've been very pleased with the quality of their work and the intensity of their approach."*

**KEY INDIVIDUALS** Department chair **Wayne Bradley** (see p.1077) is commended for his ability to tackle big-picture issues and offer clients practical advice. He recently supported Home Depot in relation to a number of recent acquisitions. Seasoned expert **Jeremy Silverman** (see p.1097) has *"a good business sense, and knows when to let a point go."* Clients also go on to praise his vast intelligence and personable approach. He recently led in the representation of PhaseOne Communications throughout its sale to The SI Organization. Sources praise **David Brown** 's (see p.1077) *"extraordinarily efficient"* approach which enables him to *"eliminate needless complexity."* He represents Gentiva Health Services in a range of corporate issues and currently heads the firm's corporate finance group.

**Ann-Marie McGaughey** (see p.1090) has, according to one source, *"distinguished herself"* over the course of the past year, with interviewees keen to highlight their *"complete faith in her advice."* She recently advised leading US sales and lease ownership and specialty retailer Aaron's as it purchased a stake in Perfect Home Holdings for $15.4 million.

### Troutman Sanders LLP

**THE FIRM** This Southeastern powerhouse is able to draw upon its expertise in securities and transactional matters to assist in advising an enviable roster of clients. Interviewees highlight the pragmatism of the corporate group, lauding its ability to combine legal knowledge with business acumen. The firm recently handled a $4.3 billion securities offering for Southern Company, in addition to providing advice on a range of mid-market acquisitions.

**KEY INDIVIDUALS Brinkley Dickerson** is praised for being a steadfast representative on behalf of his clients. He played an integral part in the firm's representation of AGCO in its $928 million acquisition of GSI Holdings. **Eric Koontz** continues to work closely with Southern Company, utilizing his substantial expertise in securities law to provide advice in connection with a number of public offering issues.

## Band 4

### Bryan Cave LLP

**THE FIRM** Bryan Cave's M&A group is vastly experienced in handling both corporate and transactional matters. The firm's extensive footprint enables the Atlanta-based practitioners to draw upon a wealth of international resources, providing clients with industry-specific expertise where necessary. One of the team's more impressive recent mandates saw it represent Shaw Industries as it undertook a joint venture with Closure Turf.

**KEY INDIVIDUALS** Lauded for his analytical approach, managing partner **Thomas McNeill** handles matters across a diverse range of industries. He recently acted on behalf of Beverage House in its sale to German company Martin Bauer. Recognized for his familiarity with REITs in particular, **Rick Miller** is perceived to be a particularly good businessman who understands his clients' businesses. **Louis Spelios** recently assisted Document Technologies in several substantial acquisitions. Clients highlight his superb handling of complex transactions.

### DLA Piper LLP (US)
See profile on p.1971

**THE FIRM** DLA's highly effective Atlanta practice receives recognition for its high-quality venture capital work. While the firm represents a diverse range of clients, it retains core expertise in the technology field. Indicative highlights include the team's representation of iContact in its $180 million sale to Vocus. Clients are quick to highlight the speed and efficiency for which the group is renowned, in addition to praising the firm's aptitude for handling time-sensitive engagements.

**Sources say:** *"They're deal guys. They do a lot of them and they know exactly what to do."*

**KEY INDIVIDUALS Joseph Alexander** (see p.1074) is considered one of the strongest young lawyers within the state. He has repeatedly demonstrated his proficiency in providing advice to private equity funds and, through his representation of Navigation Capital, recently illustrated his strength in the transactional field. One source noted that he is *"very good at managing both projects and clients, and at keeping things pointing in the right direction."* **Joseph Silver** (see p.1097) earns unanimous approval from clients, particularly for his work in the venture capital sphere. His recent clients include iContact, Teavana and Connecture.

### Morris, Manning & Martin, LLP

**THE FIRM** Morris Manning & Martin remains a force within both the corporate and transactional marketplaces, and is lauded for its proficiency in representing emerging companies and undertaking venture capital issues. Its key clients include Ericsson Television, Liaison Technologies and PowerPlan.

**Sources say:** *"They contextually understand our business and the challenges we face."*

**KEY INDIVIDUALS John Yates** is, according to one client, *"the hardest-working man in the startup world."* He has an active presence in the technology sphere, and recently represented SmartSynch as it was acquired by Itron.

### Nelson Mullins Riley & Scarborough LLP
See profile on p.2276

**THE FIRM** A variety of market sources extol the corporate capabilities of this Southeastern firm. The attorneys in its Atlanta office are able to undertake various complex transactional matters, and clients regularly praise the level of service offered which they feel is commensurate with the firm's strong standing within the legal community.

**KEY INDIVIDUALS** Acknowledged as being a *"really good lawyer"* with a *"dynamic personality,"* **Michael Hollingsworth** (see p.1084) is recommended for his aptitude in a range of transactional matters.

### Womble Carlyle Sandridge & Rice, LLP
See profile on p.2049

**THE FIRM** This firm's corporate team works closely with its banking attorneys. The subsequent level of collaboration enables the firm to offer clients a fully-integrated service, and also serves to differentiate the group from many of its competitors. Its key clients include HD Supply, NCR and Intellinet.

**Sources say:** *"They've been very responsive and knowledgeable."*

**KEY INDIVIDUALS Sandy Smith** is well versed in both transactional and corporate governance issues. One effusive client labeled him *"extraordinary,"* applauding his *"very insightful, very intelligent and very balanced approach."* He is regularly engaged by clients such as Transcend Services to handle its prominent M&A deals.

## Other Notable Practitioners

The vastly experienced **Jonathan Golden** (see p.1082) of Arnall Golden Gregory LLP is active on a range of transactional and corporate matters. He wins tremendous praise from his peers: "*He has terrific name recognition and is a fine lawyer.*" **Michael Rafter** (see p.1094) of Baker, Donelson, Bearman, Caldwell & Berkowitz, PC is particularly valued for his expertise in REITs. His recent highlights include representing Strategic Storage Trust, a public non-traded REIT, in relation to the registration of a $1 billion follow-on public offering. Identified as being both "*sharp and attentive,*" **Stephen Opler** (see p.1092) of Ballard Spahr LLP is widely recognized for his transactional capa-

bilities. He is able to draw upon his experience in the banking sector to inform his representation of both companies and financial institutions. **Theodore Blum** (see p.1076) of Greenberg Traurig, LLP is an experienced transactional attorney, recognized by peers for his ability to both formulate and close complex deals. Much of his work is multi-jurisdictional, highlighting his capacity for conducting international transactions. **Joe DeLisle** (see p.1080) of Miller & Martin PLLC earns praise for his ability to "*ask the right questions*" in order to "*narrow down risks.*" He is further lauded for his capacity to "*figure out alternatives that are best for his clients, while providing solutions that the other side can live with.*" **Arthur Jay Schwartz** (see p.1096) of Smith Gambrell & Russell LLP recently advised

Brightwell Payments in connection with its acquisition of Directo. He is vastly experienced within the corporate sphere and continues to offer an impressive level of legal representation. **David Yates** (see p.1101) of Hunton & Williams LLP advises companies in relation to both national and global transactions. He is recommended for his ability to combine "*business acumen*" with a "*superb legal skill set,*" with sources keen to highlight his stellar client service. **Mark Carlson** (see p.1078) of Baker, Donelson, Bearman, Caldwell & Berkowitz, PC "*always offers thoughtful options where there are multiple solutions to a given problem,*" say sources. Interviewees further commend his expediency, his organizational skills and his professional demeanor.

# ENERGY

Commentary about individuals can be found under their firm's paragraph. If the firm has no paragraph (is not ranked) look at Other Notable Practitioners.

| Energy | |
|---|---|
| **Leading Firms** | |
| **Band 1** | |
| Troutman Sanders LLP | |
| **Band 2** | |
| Alston & Bird LLP * | |
| Balch & Bingham LLP * | |
| McKenna Long & Aldridge LLP * | |
| Mercer Thompson LLC | |
| Sutherland Asbill & Brennan LLP | |

| **Leading Individuals** | |
|---|---|
| **Star individuals** | |
| Greene Kevin C | *Troutman Sanders LLP* |
| **Band 1** | |
| Dowdy L Craig | *McKenna Long & Aldridge LLP* * |
| Edwards Jr Robert | *Troutman Sanders LLP* |
| Mercer John T W | *Mercer Thompson LLC* |
| Short Jr Herbert J | *Sutherland Asbill & Brennan LLP* |
| **Band 2** | |
| Black Franzoni Dorothy | *Sutherland Asbill & Brennan LLP* |
| Degnan Peter | *Alston & Bird LLP* * |
| Fozzard Peter | *Sutherland Asbill & Brennan LLP* |
| Marzo Brandon F | *Troutman Sanders LLP* |
| McCrary Dan H | *Balch & Bingham LLP* |
| Thompson Richard E | *Mercer Thompson LLC* |
| Wells Della Wager | *Alston & Bird LLP* * |

*\* Indicates firm / individual with profile.*
*Alphabetical order within each band. Band 1 is the highest.*

## Band 1

### Troutman Sanders LLP

**THE FIRM** The nine-attorney team at Troutman Sanders is regarded as a leader in this expanding area. It regularly handles rate cases, fuel cost recovery proceedings and integrated resource planning matters, and is known for the renewable energy limb of its practice. A major highlight of

late was assisting Georgia Power in relation to the construction of two new nuclear units at Plant Vogtle.
**KEY INDIVIDUALS Kevin Greene** receives plaudits for his experience, levelheadedness and the thoroughness of his preparation. He is well known for representing utilities before state regulatory commissions. **Robert Edwards** is held in high regard by commentators for his foresight and extensive knowledge of the area. **Brandon Marzo** has recently been involved in a number of high-profile matters. A noteworthy example is assisting Georgia Power with regard to the construction of three combined cycle units at Plant McDonough.

## Band 2

### Alston & Bird LLP
See profile on p.1102
**THE FIRM** Alston & Bird's energy team is renowned for its public power work. In this area, it regularly handles acquisition, operation, hedging and management matters for some of the sector's largest entities. A significant highlight of late is its assistance of Public Gas Partners in the establishment of additional natural gas suppliers.
**KEY INDIVIDUALS Peter Degnan** (see p.1080) is labeled "*excellent*" by market sources. He recently represented Municipal Electric Authority of Georgia on its involvement in the state's high-profile nuclear power project. **Della Wager Wells** (see p.1100) is highly regarded for her experience as bond counsel. She counts Municipal Electric Authority, Municipal Gas Authority of Georgia and Public Gas Partners as clients.

### Balch & Bingham LLP
See profile on p.475
**THE FIRM** Balch & Bingham has developed from an energy boutique into a full-service firm, though the energy sector remains crucial to its vision and constitutes a significant proportion of its workload. It recently helped

Mackinaw Power prepare an application to renew the market-based rate authority for its four power plants in Georgia. Other key clients include Southern Company Service and GreyStone Power.
**Sources say:** "*They are a true all-around energy firm.*"
**KEY INDIVIDUALS** Described as a "*lawyer's lawyer,*" **Dan McCrary** receives praise for his conscientiousness, writing skills and willingness to address complex issues head-on.

### McKenna Long & Aldridge LLP
See profile on p.922
**THE FIRM** McKenna Long & Aldridge's energy team has an impressively diverse client list including independent power producers, municipalities and national retail chains. Notable names include AGL Resources, Commerce Energy and Tenaska. The team recently represented Atlanta Gas Light in a regulatory dispute concerning the encroachment of a municipal natural gas system in the company's certificate area.
**Sources say:** "*Dependable, with a lot of knowledge.*"
**KEY INDIVIDUALS Craig Dowdy** (see p.1080) is considered to be an "*outstanding regulatory lawyer.*" He acted as lead partner on the Atlanta Gas Light matter.

### Mercer Thompson LLC
**THE FIRM** This boutique is known for its activity in the transactional area of energy work. Recently it has been involved in major finance, project development and M&A work on power and high-voltage transmission projects. It recently acted as lead counsel to Georgia Power in establishing a DOE loan guarantee for the Plant Vogtle nuclear power plant expansion. It also assisted Mississippi Power in relation to a DOE loan guarantee for the Kemper County IGCC Project.
**Sources say:** "*They are a very good boutique energy firm.*"
**KEY INDIVIDUALS John Mercer** earns plaudits for his adeptness at transactional matters. His client roster includes Wisconsin Electric Power. **Richard Thompson** has a diverse practice. He has worked on coal, gas, wind,

solar and biomass projects, and has a wealth of international experience.

## Sutherland Asbill & Brennan LLP

**THE FIRM** Sutherland Asbill & Brennan represents clients on a diverse range of issues, including acquisitions, project development and bond offerings. Recent highlights include representing Oglethorpe Power on the offering and issuance of first mortgage bonds for the construction

of a nuclear generating facility. Other significant clients include Associated Electric Cooperative and Wolverine Power Supply Cooperative.

**KEY INDIVIDUALS Herbert Short** is a distinguished transactional and securities lawyer. He was the lead partner on the Oglethorpe Power matter. Other clients include Hoosier Energy Rural Electric Cooperative. **Dorothy Black Franzoni** recently represented Southern Maryland Electric Cooperative on the development of a solar generating

facility. **Peter Fozzard** is singled out by satisfied sources for his extensive subject knowledge and attentiveness to client needs.

# ENVIRONMENT

Commentary about individuals can be found under their firm's paragraph. If the firm has no paragraph (is not ranked) look at Other Notable Practitioners.

## Environment
## Leading Firms

**Band 1**
King & Spalding LLP *
Troutman Sanders LLP

**Band 2**
Alston & Bird LLP *
Hunton & Williams LLP *
Jones Day *
Kazmarek Geiger & Laseter LLP

**Band 3**
HunterMaclean
Kilpatrick Townsend & Stockton LLP *
McKenna Long & Aldridge LLP *
Morris, Manning & Martin, LLP
Mowrey Meezan Coddington Cloud LLP

*Indicates firm with profile.*
*Alphabetical order within each band. Band 1 is the highest.*

## Band 1

### King & Spalding LLP
See profile on p.445

**THE FIRM** King & Spalding's team remains preeminent in environmental litigation. Its lawyers regularly appear in federal and state courts, and have a wealth of experience before the Georgia Office of State Administrative Hearings. It has particular prowess in water rights and issues arising under the Clean Air Act (CAA). Of late, it has been representing Power4Georgians in its high-profile coal-fired power plant construction project in Washington County, Georgia. Other key clients include GE, Atlanta Regional Commission and Acuity Brands.
**Sources say:** *"Excellent service, highly professional. I would recommend them without hesitation."*
**KEY INDIVIDUALS** Practice head **Patricia Barmeyer** (see p.1075) enjoys a fine reputation as *"the dean of the Georgia environmental Bar."* Sources particularly laud her extensive knowledge of federal and state regulations. She acted as lead partner on the high-value Power4Georgians matter. **Charles Tisdale** is well known for his expertise in Superfund matters. Clients benefit from his deep experience in the field. **Lewis Jones** (see p.1086) has played an instrumental role in the widely publicised Tri-State Water Wars litigation. The case centers around clients' access to

federal reservoir Lake Sidney Lanier being challenged by the states of Alabama and Florida. **Leslie Oakes**'s (see p.1092) client roster includes Power4Georgians and Roark Capital Group. He has extensive experience in matters involving air, water and hazardous waste. The remediation side of **Amelia Magee**'s (see p.1089) practice is highly regarded. She has helped clients with the preparation of notifications and investigative reports, and the implementation of remedies. **Adam Sowatzka** (see p.1097) recently rejoined the firm from Baker, Donelson, Bearman, Caldwell & Berkowitz, PC. He is lauded by sources as *"very thorough and very fair in his practice."*

### Troutman Sanders LLP

**THE FIRM** The 17-strong team at Troutman Sanders offers assistance in relation to a range of matters including regulatory compliance, environmental due diligence and related litigation. It has a diverse client roster, which includes energy companies, chemical manufacturers and financial institutions. Notable highlights include representing Dominion Resource Services in Superfund enforcement actions, and assisting Oxbow Carbon with its proposed acquisition of a sulfur manufacturing facility.
**KEY INDIVIDUALS Margaret Campbell** has a wealth of experience in issues pertaining to air quality statutes. She represented Southern Company Services and Mississippi Power in a Clean Air Act Section 114 information request from the EPA. **Douglas Henderson** is held in high regard by commentators, with one singling out his performance on tricky issues. His client roster includes Cisco and PNM Resources. **John Johnson** has advised Delta Air Lines on regulatory compliance matters, enforcement actions, transactions and environmental remediation liability. He is particularly strong in RCRA permit negotiations. **Gregory Blount** has represented trade associations and local governments in relation to rules governing water quality, coastal development and hazardous waste management. **Hollister Anne Hill** stands out for her expertise in RCRA corrective action issues. She counts Delta Air Lines as a client. **Randy Brogdon** played a key role in the Oxbow matter. Other clients include PNM Resources and Southern Power. **Andrea Rimer** has been representing Dominion Resources in Superfund enforcement actions in Virginia and North Carolina.

## Band 2

### Alston & Bird LLP
See profile on p.1102

**THE FIRM** Alston & Bird offers a far-ranging environmental practice. The team is well equipped to service clients in environmental compliance, enforcement and litigation matters. It is also highly regarded for its work in land use and development. Significant clients include Cabot, AMAVC Chemical and Electrolux. The team has recently been representing the Municipal Electric Authority of Georgia in the development of two additional nuclear reactors at Plant Vogtle.
**KEY INDIVIDUALS Douglas Arnold** (see p.1074) is an *"incredible resource,"* according to commentators. He recently represented logistics giant UPS in regulatory and compliance matters regarding air and water emissions. The *"excellent"* **Lee DeHihns** (see p.1080) is considered to be *"a real statesman of environmental law."* He recently assisted King America Finishing with enforcement proceedings arising under the Georgia Water Quality Control Act (GWQCA).

### Hunton & Williams LLP
See profile on p.2517

**THE FIRM** The environmental team at Hunton & Williams is known for its representation of interstate oil and gas pipeline companies. It has formidable experience in design, construction, testing and maintenance issues. The group also provides compliance and incident-response advice, and regularly engages with federal regulators, such as the EPA, PHMSA and FWS.
**Sources say:** *"They are absolutely first-rate and have a national reputation on pipeline matters."*
**KEY INDIVIDUALS Robert Hogfoss** (see p.1084) is an expert in issues arising from the National Gas Pipeline Safety Act (NGPSA), the Clean Water Act (CWA) and the Oil Pollution Act (OPA). The *"very responsive"* **Catherine Little** (see p.1088) offers notable expertise in hazardous waste issues and matters arising under the Toxic Substances Control Act (TSCA).

### Jones Day
See profile on p.919

**THE FIRM** The Atlanta arm of this established global presence is heavily involved in a range of cutting-edge environmental matters including climate change, rare earth mining and hydraulic fracturing. Key clients include Eastman, Georgia Gulf and J.F. Lehman & Company. The team recently represented 3D Systems in the environmental aspects of its acquisition of Z Corporation.

**Sources say:** *"They helped us get through what could have been a crisis. They were very sensitive to the importance of the matter, and very responsive."*

**KEY INDIVIDUALS** The highly experienced **Christine Morgan** (see p.1091) is *"a delight to work with,"* according to impressed sources. She has recently been providing environmental advice to PCS Nitrogen. Interviewees highlight **Graham Holden's** (see p.1084) excellence in air quality matters. He has been advising Oglethorpe Power on the acquisition of existing power plant facilities. The *"extremely helpful"* **Jack Grady** (see p.1082) is applauded for his *"complete understanding of the regulatory process from both sides,"* and his effectiveness in dealing with authorities.

## Kazmarek Geiger & Laseter LLP

**THE FIRM** This boutique firm offers an environmental practice that spans transactional, regulatory and contentious matters. The team is known for its handling of environmental issues in significant financing transactions. It has served as national environmental counsel to LNR Partners, and represented Balfour Beatty Communities in the purchase and lease of a number of military housing projects across the country. Other clients include Energen and Selig Enterprises.

**Sources say:** *"I think they are all excellent attorneys."*

**KEY INDIVIDUALS Richard Horder** is *"absolutely first-rate,"* according to sources. He has over 35 years' experience in the field and a particular area of focus is the Clean Water Act (CWA) and the legal issues relating to compliance with it. **Skip Kazmarek** was a lead partner on the Balfour Beatty Communities matter. He has also handled environmental litigation, Superfund and transactional issues for AGL Resources. **Scott Laseter** focuses on all elements of environmental law, including regulatory compliance and dispute resolution. He counts significant financial institutions, REITs and real estate companies among his clients. Managing partner **Carol Geiger** acted as a lead partner on the Balfour Beatty Communities matter. She is highly regarded for her regulatory compliance counseling.

## Band 3

### HunterMaclean

**THE FIRM** HunterMaclean's environmental practice encompasses an array of areas, including hazard communication, insurance coverage, remediation, waste management and wetland assessment. The team is well known for performing environmental due diligence investigations and continues to handle significant liability litigation.

**KEY INDIVIDUALS Andrew Ernst** is noted for his in-depth knowledge of the state's Coastal Marshlands Protection Act (CMPA) and Shore Protection Act.

### Kilpatrick Townsend & Stockton LLP
See profile on p.1109

**THE FIRM** The team at Kilpatrick Townsend & Stockton is adept on the full range of environmental issues, including transactional planning, compliance counseling and litigation. It has represented Georgia Ports Authority in issues arising from its Savannah Harbor Deepening Project. It has also been assisting Glynn County with the purchase of a brownfield property on the federal Superfund list. Other clients include Knoxville Utilities Board, Nestlé USA and Allied Systems Holding.

**KEY INDIVIDUALS Susan Richardson** is one of the attorneys involved in the Georgia Ports Authority matter. She has significant experience in wastewater permitting and enforcement issues. The *"very responsive"* **Gary Sheehan** has been representing the City of Atlanta in matters surrounding the development of a water reservoir in a former rock quarry. He is well known for his expertise in issues arising under the Clean Air Act (CAA).

## McKenna Long & Aldridge LLP
See profile on p.922

**THE FIRM** McKenna Long & Aldridge is renowned for its handling of matters pertaining to the CWA. It also has considerable experience in regulatory issues arising under the ESA, the CAA and the CMPA. The team has recently been representing the State of Georgia in the Tri-State Water Wars litigation.

**Sources say:** *"They are very knowledgeable."*

**KEY INDIVIDUALS Todd Silliman's** (see p.1097) practice is focused on environmental litigation. Recent activity includes acting as lead counsel for High Point on a prominent case against the National Park Service in relation to convenient water access.

## Morris, Manning & Martin, LLP

**THE FIRM** Morris, Manning & Martin's environmental team regularly advises clients on the impact of environmental considerations on corporate real estate. A particular area of focus is the redevelopment of contaminated properties. Key clients include Equity One and Metlife Financial.

**KEY INDIVIDUALS Gerald Pouncey** has recently been assisting Branch Capital Partners with an expansive redevelopment project. According to commentators: *"He has developed a very good practice and is very solid."* **Heather Friedman** has represented clients in the regulatory and transactional aspects of hazardous site cleanups. Sources say: *"She understands her business. She speaks sense and really adds value with her practical advice."*

## Mowrey Meezan Coddington Cloud LLP

**THE FIRM** This firm houses lawyers experienced in litigation, regulatory, transactional and public policy matters. It has a strong reputation in the redevelopment of brownfield sites, and regularly advises clients on risk-allocation issues. It recently represented Georgia Industry Environmental Coalition in Voluntary Remediation Program Act (VRPA) compliance issues.

**KEY INDIVIDUALS Douglas Cloud** was the lead partner on the Georgia Industry Environmental Coalition matter. Interviewees applaud his handling of regulatory matters. **Robert Mowrey** was recently involved in the firm's representation of Walter Energy in a high-value class action dispute involving air emissions and water discharges. **David Meezan** continues to command respect from sources. His forte is the transportation of hazardous materials. He has also undertaken prominent climate change work. **Max Zygmont**'s profile continues to grow, with sources quick to speak of his activity. He counts Walter Energy and Municipal Electric Authority of Georgia as clients.

## Other Notable Practitioners

**David Moore** of Balch & Bingham LLP is said to be *"an excellent lawyer and expert in water law."* He has 20 years'

experience in environmental litigation, permitting and counseling. **Gordon Alphonso** of McGuireWoods LLP focuses on air, and solid and hazardous waste issues. He is *"a very responsive lawyer, who was very interested in getting to know our business,"* according to sources. **Barbara Gallo** (see p.1082) of Krevolin & Horst, LLC is singled out as a leading environmental lawyer by sources. She has acted for a range of clients including manufacturers, developers and local governments. **Stephen O'Day** (see p.1092) of Smith Gambrell & Russell LLP is deeply experienced in the sector. He recently represented Belectric in the sale of a 30 MW solar generation project in California to Constellation

Energy. **Joan Sasine** of Bryan Cave LLP is highly regarded for her work on water pollution and hazardous waste matters. She also advises clients on complex real estate and M&A issues. Clients consider **Leah Knowlton** (see p.1087) of Miller & Martin PLLC to be *"professional, straightforward and creative."* She has been serving as lead defense counsel for Coca-Cola in a lawsuit investigating contamination at a Superfund site. **John Spinrad** (see p.1098) of Arnall Golden Gregory LLP concentrates on environmental due diligence. He has particular expertise in the structuring of real estate transactions.

# HEALTHCARE

Commentary about individuals can be found under their firm's paragraph. If the firm has no paragraph (is not ranked) look at Other Notable Practitioners.

## Healthcare
### Leading Firms

**Band 1**

Alston & Bird LLP *

King & Spalding LLP *

Parker, Hudson, Rainer & Dobbs LLP

**Band 2**

Arnall Golden Gregory LLP *

McKenna Long & Aldridge LLP *

Nelson Mullins Riley & Scarborough LLP *

**Band 3**

Baker, Donelson, Bearman, Caldwell & Berkowitz, PC *

Morris, Manning & Martin, LLP

Smith Moore Leatherwood LLP *

## Band 1

### Alston & Bird LLP
See profile on p.1102

**THE FIRM** This nationally recognized healthcare practice continues to offer clients a very high level of service which is commensurate with its stellar reputation within the legal industry. Both the transactional and regulatory elements of healthcare law are capably undertaken by this Atlanta-based group, enabling representation of a diverse and substantial client base. The firm recently represented global medical technology giant Getinge in a number of substantial acquisitions, the largest of which was the purchase of Atrium Medical in a $680 million deal.

**Sources say:** *"Their attorneys have an excellent grasp of the industry and are superb at what they do."*

**KEY INDIVIDUALS Mitch Mitchelson** (see p.1090) has been singled out by his peers as one of the state's leading healthcare fraud attorneys. He frequently adopts an adversarial position to the government, defending companies against which accusations of fraud have been made. According to one source, **Michelle Williams** (see p.1100) is *"not only substantively strong, she is also very knowledgeable and consistent."* She is particularly well versed in regulatory matters and is perceived to be both *"analytically strong"*

and *"a good advocate for her clients."* **Donna Bergeson** (see p.1076) is known for her proficiency in both litigation and regulatory compliance matters. She works closely with Emory Healthcare in connection with a number of pre-existing and proposed joint ventures. **Steven Pottle** (see p.1093) is a respected transactional attorney with an in-depth knowledge of the healthcare industry. He is described as a *"deal facilitator"* by sources and was integral in the firm's recent representation of Getinge, assisting the Swedish-based firm in a series of strategic acquisitions.

### King & Spalding LLP
See profile on p.445

**THE FIRM** King & Spalding's healthcare team retains its status as one of the finest within Georgia. It has both the breadth and depth of expertise to ably advise clients across the entire spectrum of healthcare-related matters, boasting notable strength in the transactional, regulatory and litigation spheres. Clients have remarked favorably upon the firm's robust national presence, citing its extensive legal footprint as one of its key differentiators. The team represents a selection of healthcare systems and pharmaceutical companies and can list Piedmont Healthcare and Purdue Pharma among its most substantial clients.

**Sources say:** *"They provide high-quality legal work coupled with highly developed business understanding."*

**KEY INDIVIDUALS** Practice leader **Glen Reed** (see p.1094) is one of the most distinguished healthcare attorneys within the state. In the words of one particularly effusive commentator, he is *"as good a healthcare attorney as there is."* He works extensively with healthcare systems and recently acted on behalf of Piedmont Healthcare as it finalized the $150 million acquisition of Henry Medical Center. **Richard Shackelford** (see p.1096) is a hugely experienced practitioner and remains central to much of the firm's more complicated work. *"He's not afraid to roll up his sleeves and be creative,"* reported one source. *"Whereas a lot of people will take the safe route, he's more forward-looking and can delve into complex areas that some people shy away from."* He is a respected litigator, with his successful defense of Omnicare against allegations of improper submission of

### Leading Individuals

**Band 1**

| | |
|---|---|
| Parker John | Parker, Hudson, Rainer & Dobbs LLP |
| Reed Glen | King & Spalding LLP * |
| Shackelford Richard L | King & Spalding LLP * |

**Band 2**

| | |
|---|---|
| Basarrate Armando L | Parker, Hudson, Rainer & Dobbs LLP |
| Berg Robert N | Epstein Becker & Green PC (ONP) [†] |
| Hendrix Glenn P | Arnall Golden Gregory LLP * |
| Hudson Paul | Parker, Hudson, Rainer & Dobbs LLP |
| Keenan Robert M | King & Spalding LLP * |
| Kelly James P | Kelly Law Firm PC (ONP) [†] |
| Mitchelson Jr William (Mitch) R | Alston & Bird LLP * |
| Polvino Kathlynn Butler | McKenna Long & Aldridge LLP * |
| Roeder Kim H | King & Spalding LLP * |
| Rubinger Hedy S | Arnall Golden Gregory LLP * |
| Wheeler Sara Kay | King & Spalding LLP * |
| Williams Michelle A | Alston & Bird LLP * |

**Band 3**

| | |
|---|---|
| Baker Thomas William | Baker, Donelson, Bearman, Caldwell * |
| Bergeson Donna P | Alston & Bird LLP * |
| Herrin Barry S | Smith Moore Leatherwood LLP * |
| Jones Jr Stanley S | Nelson Mullins Riley & Scarborough LLP * |
| Madison Michele P | Morris, Manning & Martin, LLP |
| McGinty Charlene L | McKenna Long & Aldridge LLP * |
| Mohan Daniel J | Morris, Manning & Martin, LLP |
| Myers Lawrence J | Smith Moore Leatherwood LLP * |
| Plowman Rebekah N | Jones Day * |
| Pottle Steven L | Alston & Bird LLP * |
| Rawls James C | McKenna Long & Aldridge LLP * |
| Saul H Carol | Arnall Golden Gregory LLP * |
| Street Phillip | Paul Hastings LLP (ONP) [†] |
| Threlkeld Robert C | Morris, Manning & Martin, LLP |
| Watt Tobin N | Smith Moore Leatherwood LLP * |
| Welch Sidney Summers | Arnall Golden Gregory LLP * |

**Up-and-coming individuals**

| | |
|---|---|
| Barry Michael | Arnall Golden Gregory LLP * |

* Indicates firm / individual with profile.

[†] ONP = Other Notable Practitioner

prescriptions serving as a prominent example of his courtroom competency. Renowned for his dexterous representation of home healthcare providers, **Robert Keenan** (see p.1087) enjoys a strong reputation within the healthcare industry. He is acknowledged as an *"expert within his area of specialty."* **Kim Roeder** (see p.1094) is reportedly *"very well versed in the boardroom environment,"* and adopts an *"organized and focused"* approach toward engagements. She is noted for both her strength in transactional matters and her grasp of issues pertaining to regulatory compliance. **Sara Kay Wheeler** (see p.1100), known for her *"strong investigatory practice,"* has enjoyed a particularly active year, having been tasked with representing a number of health systems into which government investigations had been conducted. Her *"excellence in the compliance area"* has also been remarked upon by enthusiastic sources and serves to illustrate her versatility.

### Parker, Hudson, Rainer & Dobbs LLP

**THE FIRM** Renowned for its proficiency in complex certificate of need and licensure matters, Parker, Hudson, Rainer & Dobbs's healthcare group has established a strong presence within the Georgia market and continues to service an impressive range of clients. The firm has earned unanimous approbation from clients, many of whom have spoken at length about its masterful grasp of regulatory work and extensive network of relevant contacts. The group is frequently engaged by healthcare providers and can list Phoebe Putney Health System and DaVita among its solid client roster.

**Sources say:** *"This firm is very detailed-oriented. They are knowledgeable and have useful contacts throughout the industry."*

**KEY INDIVIDUALS** Founding partner **John Parker** brings over three decades' worth of experience to his healthcare practice. He is noted for his proficiency in *"dealing with regulatory issues"* and elicits praise for his in-depth *"knowledge of accounting treatment pertaining to healthcare economics."* He was recently chosen by the governor of Georgia to challenge the widespread health reform legislation enacted by President Obama in 2010. **Armando Basarrate** is acknowledged as an expert in certificate of need and regulatory matters. He is perceived to be *"very acute in his analysis"* and *"presents very well."* One enthusiastic commentator was keen to highlight **Paul Hudson**'s impressive standard of work, noting that he approaches each engagement with an impressive *"level of sophistication."* He is recommended for his transactional expertise within the healthcare sector.

### Band 2

### Arnall Golden Gregory LLP
See profile on p.1103

**THE FIRM** This full-service firm is recommended for the breadth of its healthcare practice, with its team of well-regarded attorneys proficient in handling a wide array of matters. It is also acknowledged for its more specific expertise, with several market commentators keen to high-

light the firm's strength in the regulatory compliance and long-term care arenas. Over the past year, the team has advised a number of healthcare providers in a range of transactional, regulatory and litigation engagements.

**Sources say:** *"They are diligent and exhaustive in their research."* *"They provide economic rates for high-quality work."*

**KEY INDIVIDUALS Glenn Hendrix** (see p.1084) is heralded for his ability to *"operate across the regulatory sphere very adeptly."* He is renowned for his expertise in the long-term care market and continues to work closely with Kindred Healthcare on an appellate issue. **Hedy Rubinger** (see p.1095) serves as the practice group leader and possesses a core expertise in the regulatory sphere. She recently advised Genesis Healthcare on the regulatory ramifications of a multistate restructuring and a $2.4 billion divestiture. One enthusiastic client referred to her as *"phenomenal,"* naming her the *"best regulatory attorney around."* Commended for her *"strong base of experience and broad subject grasp,"* **Carol Saul** (see p.1095) remains at the forefront of the firm's healthcare practice. *"She's as good a HIPAA lawyer as there is,"* remarked one source, while another asserted that she was *"terrific within her sphere."* **Sidney Welch** (see p.1100) is recommended for her *"strong physician practice"* and represents clients on a wide range of regulatory matters. **Michael Barry** (see p.1075) has been integral in the firm's representation of Southeast Georgia Health System, assisting with both transactional and licensure issues. He has been acknowledged favorably by a number of market sources, one of whom cites his *"extreme competence"* and *"can-do"* attitude as particular strengths.

### McKenna Long & Aldridge LLP
See profile on p.922

**THE FIRM** Practitioners at this firm are typified by their adept representation of nonprofit hospital systems; Northside Hospital is perhaps the most notable example of such a client and it continues to engage the firm on a variety of complex and varied matters. Clients appreciate the thorough approach exhibited by the talented team of attorneys, with the firm's ability to navigate the political landscape also singled out for praise.

**Sources say:** *"The firm is very organized, quick in responding and very detailed in its research and work product."*

**KEY INDIVIDUALS Kathlynn Butler Polvino** (see p.1093) regularly undertakes work for Northside Hospital and has handled both licensure and regulatory issues over the past year. She is singled out for praise by several market commentators: *"She is a superb attorney,"* says one source, *"with critical thinking and analytical skills that complement her legal acumen."* The *"incredibly responsive"* **Charlene McGinty** (see p.1090) is lauded for her grasp of regulatory compliance matters. She is described as being particularly *"knowledgeable about both healthcare and regulatory issues"* and is further commended for her familiarity with the intricacies of the wider healthcare industry. Experienced litigator **James Rawls** (see p.1094) has enjoyed a particularly active year in which he distinguished himself by assisting DeKalb Medical Center throughout its ultimately successful attempt to overturn an injunction.

He is said to *"understand the business needs of clients and balance that very well with the law."*

### Nelson Mullins Riley & Scarborough LLP
See profile on p.2276

**THE FIRM** This firm's expanding healthcare practice provides counsel upon a wide range of issues, including litigation, whistle-blower actions and certificate of need matters. The Georgia team works primarily with healthcare providers and healthcare service companies and is renowned for its ability to draw upon an extensive array of industry-specific national resources to provide pertinent and practical advice.

**KEY INDIVIDUALS Stanley Jones** (see p.1086) is regarded by sources as an *"effective advocate in the lobbying space, particularly in behavioral health issues."* He is vastly experienced and is habitually engaged in connection to many of the more complex matters undertaken by the firm.

### Band 3

### Baker, Donelson, Bearman, Caldwell & Berkowitz, PC
See profile on p.2313

**THE FIRM** This firm is lauded for its competency in a number of niche regulatory areas, with expertise in HIPAA compliance constituting one such specialty. Its talented and hard-working attorneys are sought out by a number of healthcare providers and typically adopt a creative approach to both the regulatory and transactional matters upon which they are engaged.

**KEY INDIVIDUALS Thomas Baker** (see p.1075) garners plaudits for his prominence within the transactional sphere and is active in connection to a variety of healthcare-related acquisitions and divestitures. Baker is regarded as *"a very smart, capable attorney"* and is understood to be *"very knowledgeable."*

### Morris, Manning & Martin, LLP

**THE FIRM** This group maintains an impressive reputation within the healthcare industry, with its impressive breadth of clients demonstrative of its regional strength. Its core expertise is in the representation of healthcare systems, with Piedmont Healthcare and Emory Healthcare serving as two particularly noteworthy examples.

**Sources say:** *"The firm has competitive rates, it's efficient and it has a strong knowledge of the certificate of need process in Georgia."*

**KEY INDIVIDUALS Michele Madison** has enjoyed a particularly active year, in which she has led many of the firm's headline matters. Sources hail both the breadth of her knowledge base and her prowess within the regulatory sphere. **Daniel Mohan** has an excellent knowledge of both the regulatory and transactional environments in Georgia. One source said: *"He's a great guy, a great lawyer and he has a strong practice."* He led the team that advised Ty Cobb Healthcare System as it sought regulatory approval for its newly opened hospital. **Robert Threlkeld**'s practice focuses heavily upon licensure and certificate of need issues. He is identified by sources as being an *"excellent litigator,"* and is lauded for his creative, client-oriented approach. He recently represented HealthSouth as it successfully overturned a decision not to award a certificate of need for its new inpatient rehabilitation hospital.

## Smith Moore Leatherwood LLP
See profile on p.2048

**THE FIRM** This experienced team of five attorneys is widely known for its representation of healthcare providers and typically provides high-caliber advice upon a range of transactional, licensure and regulatory issues. Of particular note is the firm's recent representation of Blue Ridge Healthcare System, in which the team provided counsel throughout the merger of two hospitals and the subsequent corporate reorganization.
**Sources say:** *"I have been very impressed with them." "Their work is excellent and thorough."*
**KEY INDIVIDUALS Barry Herrin** (see p.1084) enjoys a strong reputation for both his transactional capabilities and his awareness of regulatory frameworks. He is said to

*"provide excellent service"* and can count SunCrest Healthcare amongst his robust stable of clients. The *"extremely talented"* **Tobin Watt** (see p.1099) receives praise for his detailed knowledge of the healthcare market. He is central to the firm's ongoing representation of Emory University Health System. According to one client, **Lawrence Myers** (see p.1091) adopts a *"very responsive, thorough and practical"* approach to representation, providing clients with *"accurate and well thought-out"* responses. He is recommended for his skillful handling of certificate of need matters.

## Other Notable Practitioners

The vastly experienced **James Kelly** of Kelly Law Firm PC is noted for his strength in relation to regulatory and reimbursement issues. One peer perceives him to be *"one of the nationwide experts in his field,"* while another refers to him as *"one of the most respected practitioners in his niche of the market."* **Robert Berg** of Epstein Becker & Green PC is recommended for his proficient representation of physician groups and his competency in transactional matters. He is noted for his ability to provide *"practical solutions to complex problems."* **Phillip Street** of Paul Hastings LLP has impressed sources with his *"level of service and responsiveness, his creativity and his focus upon finding solutions that enable clients to achieve their goals."* He is best known for his transactional expertise and enjoys an active practice within this area. **Rebekah Plowman** (see p.1093) has attracted praise for her personable and client-oriented approach, having been described as *"well spoken and intelligent"* by one individual. She is particularly active in both regulatory matters and government investigations.

# IMMIGRATION

Commentary about individuals can be found under their firm's paragraph. If the firm has no paragraph (is not ranked) look at Other Notable Practitioners.

| Immigration |
| --- |
| **Leading Firms** |
| **Band 1** |
| Fragomen, Del Rey, Bernsen and Loewy, LLP * |
| **Band 2** |
| Alston & Bird LLP * |
| Arnall Golden Gregory LLP * |
| Kuck Immigration Partners LLC |
| Ogletree, Deakins, Nash, Smoak & Stewart, PC * |
| Troutman Sanders LLP |
| **Band 3** |
| Fisher & Phillips LLP * |
| FordHarrison LLP * |
| McKenna Long & Aldridge LLP * |
| Kramer & Alfano PC |
| Seyfarth Shaw LLP * |
| *  Indicates firm with profile. |
| Alphabetical order within each band. Band 1 is the highest. |

## Band 1

### Fragomen, Del Rey, Bernsen and Loewy, LLP
See profile on p.1974

**THE FIRM** Renowned for its impressive international reach, this specialist firm retains its status as Georgia's premier immigration practice. Its breadth of expertise is unparalleled within the state, with the highly skilled team advising upon a range of corporate immigration issues. Recent work includes advice to foreign-headquartered clients on issues stemming from their US expansion and M&A-related immigration issues. The firm is also heavily involved in legislative negotiations with the government.

**Sources say:** *"They're terrific in terms of their global reach, their knowledge and their timeliness."*
**KEY INDIVIDUALS** Heralded as the *"grandmaster of the Atlanta immigration world,"* the *"internationally known"* **Daryl Buffenstein** continues to justify his outstanding reputation. He undertakes a great deal of *"higher-end advocacy"* and is justifiably viewed as one of the *"deans of the Atlanta immigration Bar."* **Deborah Marlowe** handles a variety of corporate immigration matters and is frequently engaged by companies within the food and nutrition sector. Peers are effusive in their assessment of her aptitude, citing her comprehensive grasp of complex immigration issues as one of her greatest strengths. Sources have identified the talented **Karen Winarsky** as an *"excellent lawyer."* She is particularly active in the broadcast media arena. **Kyle Sherman** is commended for his exemplary client-oriented approach. His practice focuses upon the immigration aspects of M&A, an area in which he gains substantial market recognition.

## Band 2

### Alston & Bird LLP
See profile on p.1102

**THE FIRM** Recommended for its corporate immigration capabilities, Alston & Bird is engaged by a diverse range of clients to undertake matters pertaining to regulatory compliance. The firm also has strong international links and is proficient in assisting corporations with the nuances of L-1 visa applications. The Georgia team continues to work closely with UPS, advising the logistics behemoth on the

specifics of both its immigration policy and employment verification compliance, among other things.
**KEY INDIVIDUALS Eileen Scofield** (see p.1096) *"does a great job on the I-9 side and on workforce authorization,"* say sources, and is *"nationally known within compliance."* Her recent clients include UPS, Rose Acre Farms and Sidel.

### Arnall Golden Gregory LLP
See profile on p.1103

**THE FIRM** This prominent Atlanta-based firm attains praise for its familiarity with the German legal landscape. Its team of multilingual attorneys is proficient in handling both complex immigration compliance matters and EB-5 visa applications. In a recent highlight, it represented NIIT Technologies in relation to visa processing for a large group of foreign nationals.
**Sources say:** *"They have a very good reputation among the German business community within the USA."*
**KEY INDIVIDUALS Teri Simmons** (see p.1097) has a well-established presence in both Georgia and Germany and is heralded by clients as a *"terrific lawyer"* who is reliable and timely. She was integral in the firm's recent visa work for NIIT Technologies.

### Kuck Immigration Partners LLC

**THE FIRM** This immigration boutique is accomplished in its representation of both corporations and individuals. In the past year, it has been active in helping corporate clients comply with new state legislation. Additionally, it continues to be highly regarded across a wide spectrum of immigration litigation cases.
**Sources say:** *"Its reputation, aggressive stance and willingness to defend clients in court are excellent."*

**KEY INDIVIDUALS Charles Kuck** is widely acknowledged as one of the state's standout immigration attorneys. According to one source, he has an *"outstanding reputation,"* with another noting that his local renown enables him to be a *"voice for the profession."* He is perceived to be *"at the forefront of immigration litigation work"* and is highly recommended for his courtroom prowess.

## Ogletree, Deakins, Nash, Smoak & Stewart, PC

See profile on p.1110

**THE FIRM** This firm's corporate immigration practice is one of the largest in the state and is regularly called upon to tackle both regional and national immigration matters. As a dedicated labor and employment boutique, the firm is particularly qualified to deal with matters that require familiarity with both employment and immigration law. For example, it has recently successfully represented employers in FLSA cases brought by H-2B foreign workers.

**Sources say:** *"I think they're very effective and thorough. They've always been very successful for us."*

**KEY INDIVIDUALS** Lauded by peers for being both *"careful and thoughtful,"* **Jay Ruby** (see p.1095) remains a key player in the corporate immigration scene and is frequently engaged in the firm's most substantial matters. He has great familiarity with H-2B visas and is said to *"convey a lot of confidence"* in his expert dealings. Highly skilled attorney **Rebecca Sigmund** (see p.1096) is noted for the quality of the advice she provides in relation to I-9 compliance matters. One source commended the *"sense of empathy"* that she displays with visa applicants, while another identified her as being *"responsive and knowledgeable."* Well known for the strength of the work she handles for higher education institutions, **Sarah Hawk** (see p.1084) is perceived by peers to be *"approachable and very good at explaining things."* Her recent activity includes advising a university client in relation to immigration compliance and training, and visas.

## Troutman Sanders LLP

**THE FIRM** This compact yet highly skilled practice continues to advise a number of the state's leading corporations on the implications of immigration legislation. Georgia-Pacific and Southern Company are two such examples, with both companies recently engaging the firm in a variety of matters. The group is noted for its I-9 audit work and for the expertise it exhibits in the procurement of L-1 visas for foreign nationals.

**KEY INDIVIDUALS** Effusive market commentator single out **Aimee Todd**'s tremendous intelligence. Her grasp of the implications of immigration legislation attracts particular praise. Practice leader **Mark Newman** is a sophisticated lawyer, praised for his work in and out of court. He has recently been integral in assisting clients in obtaining blanket L approval.

## Band 3

### Fisher & Phillips LLP

See profile on p.1107

**THE FIRM** This well-regarded labor and employment boutique impresses clients with the breadth of immigration services it offers. The team is specifically noted for its familiarity with the O-1 visa application process and has assisted several outstanding athletes and researchers in obtaining permanent residence via this method. It is further noted for its competency within the technology industry.

**KEY INDIVIDUALS** The *"excellent"* **Kim Thompson** (see p.1099) heads the firm's immigration practice; she is perceived to be *"very intelligent"* and is adept at handling a broad range of immigration matters.

### FordHarrison LLP

See profile on p.1108

**THE FIRM** FordHarrison's Georgia immigration practice commands a strong reputation within the legal community, drawing specific praise for its aptitude in handling complex I-9 compliance matters. In a recent highlight, the group helped an IT staffing company to find a solution to its compliance with US Citizenship & Immigration Services and DOL H-1B regulations.

**Sources say:** *"The knowledge base of the team is fantastic."* *"I feel very confident in the quality of advice I'm receiving."*

**KEY INDIVIDUALS Geetha Adinata** (see p.1074), known for her expertise in immigration compliance issues, is praised for her *"very collaborative"* approach. *"She's my go-to immigration attorney,"* noted one effusive source, while another praised her *"conscientious"* attitude.

## McKenna Long & Aldridge LLP

See profile on p.922

**THE FIRM** This firm is well-equipped to handle a range of corporate immigration issues, from procuring visas for foreign nationals to providing clients with advice on the specifics of legislative compliance. The practice is recommended for its timely completion of engagements. Recent clients include Blue Cube Software, Jacada and Cbeyond.

**Sources say:** *"I have confidence in working with the whole team; they're very thorough and very detail-oriented."*

**KEY INDIVIDUALS** Practice leader **James Levine** (see p.1088) is acknowledged by commentators as being both resourceful and knowledgeable. *"If I have a particularly tricky question,"* remarked one source, *"I'll pick up the phone and give him a call."* He is currently assisting a major motorcycle manufacturer in its attempts to procure a P-1 visa for an athlete.

## Kramer & Alfano PC

**THE FIRM** This dedicated immigration practice is identified by market commentators as one of the strongest boutiques in the state, noted for its representation of both companies and individuals. The commendably versatile team is equally well-versed in family immigration matters and the specifics of visa applications.

**KEY INDIVIDUALS** Former American Immigration Lawyers Association president **Myron Kramer** is one of the most respected attorneys at the Georgia immigration Bar, able to draw upon over 30 years of experience and advise clients on virtually all aspects of immigration legislation. Several market commentators acknowledge the consistency of his work product. **Lea Alfano**, lauded for her expertise in family immigration, retains her status as one of the most promising attorneys within the state.

## Seyfarth Shaw LLP

See profile on p.1262

**THE FIRM** The immigration practice of this nationally renowned firm enjoys a growing reputation within the Georgia market. The team is frequently sought out for its prowess within the regulatory sphere, tasked with ensuring that clients are in compliance with both federal and state legislative frameworks.

**Sources say:** *"They are outstanding. I can find counsel on everything I need with Seyfarth."*

**KEY INDIVIDUALS Sharon Poorak** (see p.1093) gains unanimous approval from a variety of market commentators. Multiple sources identify her as an *"excellent lawyer,"* with a *"thoughtful and creative"* approach. She is a recent addition to the firm's roster, having joined from Frazier, Soloway and Poorak in 2012. **James King** (see p.1087) cochairs the firm's national immigration practice and is renowned for his expertise in I-9 compliance matters. He works closely with a number of Fortune 500 companies, in addition to assisting a diverse range of companies throughout the visa application process.

## Other Notable Practitioners

**Romy Kapoor** of Kapoor Law Group, LLC is considered to be an *"expert in labor certification issues."* *"He's a terrific guy,"* said one peer; *"I think he really knows his stuff and approaches the practice in a good way."* **Jay Solomon** of The Law Offices of Jay I. Solomon has a superb reputation in the Georgia legal landscape, and is especially well known for his expertise in labor certification. One source praised

his propensity to act as a *"mentor toward newer practitioners,"* while another commended his impressive client roster. **Socheat Chea** of The Law Offices of Socheat Chea PC is heralded as an *"expert in deportation and asylum"* matters. He is perceived to be *"creative at coming up with solutions"* and has *"strong advocacy skills."* Identified as an *"excellent deportation lawyer"* by his peers, **Glenn Fogle** of The Fogle Law Firm LLC is particularly noted for his representation of individuals and his immigration appellate work. Sources highlight his impressive track record, with one individual describing him as *"the most successful litigator in the Eleventh Circuit."* **David Whitlock** (see p.1100) of Miller & Martin PLLC earns the admiration of numerous sources for his expert handling of immigration compliance issues. *"He's very analytical,"* remarked one impressed individual, in addition to being *"very zealous in his representation of clients."* **Robert Banta** of Banta Immigration Law Ltd is a vastly experienced immigration attorney, recom-

mended for both his consistency and his broad knowledge base. He is well-versed in all aspects of immigration law and regularly assists corporations in both visa procurement and I-9 compliance matters. Known in particular for his familiarity with the nuances of Japanese immigration legislation, **Robert Johnson** (see p.1086) of Baker, Donelson, Bearman, Caldwell & Berkowitz, PC continues to offer clients robust representation across the entire immigration spectrum. **Anton Mertens** of Burr & Forman LLP handles a variety of complex immigration matters and has established a solid reputation for representing foreign investors. **Carolina Colin-Antonini** of The Antonini Law Firm is regarded as one of the leading immigration litigators in Georgia. One source labeled her a *"top-notch deportation lawyer,"* while another extolled her *"extraordinary"* grasp of immigration legislation.

# INTELLECTUAL PROPERTY

Commentary about individuals can be found under their firm's paragraph. If the firm has no paragraph (is not ranked) look at Other Notable Practitioners.

## Intellectual Property
### Leading Firms

**Band 1**
Kilpatrick Townsend & Stockton LLP *

**Band 2**
Alston & Bird LLP *
Finnegan, Henderson, Farabow, Garrett & Dunner LLP *
Sutherland Asbill & Brennan LLP

**Band 3**
Ballard Spahr LLP *
Greenberg Traurig, LLP *
King & Spalding LLP *
Meunier Carlin & Curfman, LLC
Womble Carlyle Sandridge & Rice, LLP *

**Band 4**
Duane Morris LLP *
Fish & Richardson PC
Morris, Manning & Martin, LLP
Troutman Sanders LLP

## Band 1

### Kilpatrick Townsend & Stockton LLP
See profile on p.1109

THE FIRM The Atlanta office of this full-service law firm fields an excellent IP team with trademark, copyright, advertising and licensing capabilities, along with a strong patent prosecution and litigation practice. Electronic and software technologies are areas of particular strength. The team recently represented Dr Jan Voda in an action against Medtronic, achieving a $9.9 million verdict.
**Sources say:** *"They really are fantastic in the IP arena."*
**KEY INDIVIDUALS** *"Great attorney"* **Mitchell Stockwell** focuses on dispute resolution, licensing transactions and patent infringement litigation. He represented Dr Voda in the aforementioned Medtronic case. **Miles Alexander** is

### Leading Individuals

**Band 1**

| | |
|---|---|
| Alexander Miles | Kilpatrick Townsend & Stockton LLP |
| Askew Anthony B | Meunier Carlin & Curfman, LLC |
| Beck Joseph M | Kilpatrick Townsend & Stockton LLP |
| Ewing Jim | Kilpatrick Townsend & Stockton LLP |
| Flinn Patrick J | Alston & Bird LLP * |
| Hawkins Holmes | King & Spalding LLP * |
| Needle Bill | Ballard Spahr LLP * |
| Nodine Larry | Ballard Spahr LLP * |
| Pratt John | Kilpatrick Townsend & Stockton LLP |
| Swann Jerre | Kilpatrick Townsend & Stockton LLP |
| Taylor Roger D | Finnegan, Henderson, Farabow, Garrett * |

**Band 2**

| | |
|---|---|
| Baber Bruce | King & Spalding LLP * |
| Boice William | Kilpatrick Townsend & Stockton LLP |
| Brewster William H | Kilpatrick Townsend & Stockton LLP |
| Carron Virginia L | Finnegan, Henderson, Farabow, Garrett * |
| Jameson Louis Norwood | Duane Morris LLP * |
| Kadaba Wab P | Kilpatrick Townsend & Stockton LLP |
| Katz Joel A | Greenberg Traurig, LLP * |
| Lunsford III Rodgers | Smith Gambrell & Russell LLP (ONP)† * |
| North John L | Kasowitz, Benson, Torres (ONP)† * |
| Rosenberg Sumner | Ballard Spahr LLP * |
| Smith III Frank G | Alston & Bird LLP * |
| Stockwell Mitchell G | Kilpatrick Townsend & Stockton LLP |

**Band 3**

| | |
|---|---|
| Bower R Bruce | Finnegan, Henderson, Farabow, Garrett * |
| Griffin III Malvern U | Sutherland Asbill & Brennan LLP |
| Henn Jr R Charles | Kilpatrick Townsend & Stockton LLP |
| Hobbs Jr Michael D | Troutman Sanders LLP |
| Kirsch Gregory J | Smith Gambrell & Russell LLP (ONP)† |

| | |
|---|---|
| Kuester Jeffrey R | Taylor English Duma LLP (ONP)† |
| McGrath Robin L | Paul Hastings LLP (ONP)† |
| McKeon Tina Williams | Kilpatrick Townsend & Stockton LLP |
| Pappas Peter G | Sutherland Asbill & Brennan LLP |
| Ragland Jr William M | Womble Carlyle Sandridge & Rice, LLP |
| Rosenbloom Robert | Greenberg Traurig, LLP * |
| Salyers Douglas D | Troutman Sanders LLP |
| Schaetzel Stephen M | Meunier Carlin & Curfman, LLC |
| Vaughan James F | Womble Carlyle Sandridge & Rice, LLP |

**Band 4**

| | |
|---|---|
| Davis Jr Theodore H | Kilpatrick Townsend & Stockton LLP |
| Dyer III William B | Finnegan, Henderson, Farabow, Garrett * |
| Fry John | Morris, Manning & Martin, LLP |
| Gaudet Matthew | Duane Morris LLP |
| Harrison Bryan G | Morris, Manning & Martin, LLP |
| Johnson, Jr. James H. | Sutherland Asbill & Brennan LLP |
| Katz Mitch A | Ballard Spahr LLP * |
| Kodish Thad C | Fish & Richardson PC |
| Lischer Dale | Smith Gambrell & Russell LLP (ONP)† * |
| Long William F | McKenna Long & Aldridge LLP (ONP)† * |
| Petty W Scott | King & Spalding LLP * |
| Powell Michael J | Baker, Donelson, Bearman, Caldwell (ONP)† * |
| Xia Tim Tingkang | Morris, Manning & Martin, LLP |

**Up-and-coming individuals**

| | |
|---|---|
| Fritts Laura | Kasowitz, Benson, Torres (ONP)† * |
| Green Christopher O. | Fish & Richardson PC |
| Park Steven | Paul Hastings LLP (ONP)† |
| Quicker Katrina M | Ballard Spahr LLP * |

**Associates to watch**

| | |
|---|---|
| Brown Charley | Ballard Spahr LLP * |

* Indicates firm / individual with profile.
†ONP = Other Notable Practitioner

well known and well regarded in the Georgia market. He works with the MLK Jr Estate on a range of matters relating to the intellectual property of Dr Martin Luther King, Jr. Sources say he is *"an excellent lawyer and a persuasive advocate – an excellent example of the way lawyers ought to be."* Interviewees describe **Joseph Beck** as *"one of the leading copyright lawyers in Atlanta."* He recently represented HathiTrust and a number of universities in defending a copyright infringement claim relating to the digitization and accessibility of library books. *"Outstanding attorney"* **Jim Ewing** focuses on strategy and patent matters, specializing in the medical device, telecom technology, e-commerce and software fields, among others. The *"very bright"* **John Pratt** specializes in patent prosecution and maintains a fine track record for patent work concerning woodwork tools and furniture. He is chair of the firm's IP department. Experienced practitioner **Jerre Swann** maintains a fine reputation in the market, where he focuses on trademark, copyright and advertising matters. Key clients include GlaxoSmithKline. **William Boice** is a litigator with experience in complex patent and trade secret litigation. His areas of expertise include electronic technology and software. **William Brewster** is recognized as *"a leading trademark litigator"* in the Georgia market. He recently represented adidas in an action brought against Herbalife, relating to the TREFOIL (three-leaf) logo. Sources also describe him as *"a very tenacious lawyer – a very hard-working and skilled practitioner in the field."* The *"very personable"* **Charles Henn** elicits particular praise for his expertise in mediation. He has a broad IP practice and has developed a niche in representing university clients. He recently acted for the Tournament of the Roses Association on a domain name and e-commerce dispute surrounding the Rose Bowl. **Wab Kadaba** is managing partner of the Atlanta office and is particular sought after for his strengths in IP disputes, including patent, trademark and trade secret litigation. Commentators single him out as being *"very easy to work with."* **Theodore Davis** concentrates on trademark, copyright, false advertising and unfair competition matters. He is particularly experienced in trade dress and trademark, with clients highlighting his extensive knowledge of past cases before the trademark trial and appeal board of the USPTO. He recently represented Coty in a trade dress infringement case relating to a pedicure product. **Tina Williams McKeon** recently joined the firm from Meunier Carlin & Curfman, LLC. She is a *"truly outstanding lawyer,"* held in high regard by peers. She focuses on the life sciences sector, with expertise in pharmaceutical, biotechnology and medical technology patents.

## Band 2

### Alston & Bird LLP
See profile on p.1102

**THE FIRM** The Atlanta office of this well-regarded national firm offers a range of IP services, including patent and trademark portfolio management, as well as transactional, licensing and advertising work. It has particular strength in patent litigation, and has recently represented

such clients as The Home Depot, Merial and Kids II. It also acted for Georgia-Pacific on 11 patent infringement actions against competitors, gaining a general exclusion order at the ITC.
**Sources say:** *"The IP team there is a powerhouse."*
**KEY INDIVIDUALS Patrick Flinn** (see p.1081) is recognized by sources as *"an IP litigation leader in Atlanta."* He has a particular focus on patent litigation in fluid mechanics and hi-tech sectors, including software, optics and telecommunications. **Frank Smith** (see p.1097) has a *"stellar reputation"* for his disputes-focused practice, which covers patent, copyright and antitrust matters. He was lead counsel on the 11 actions for Georgia-Pacific.

### Finnegan, Henderson, Farabow, Garrett & Dunner LLP
See profile on p.912

**THE FIRM** This national IP firm maintains a strong Atlanta presence with practitioners from technology-specific practice groups, including life sciences, electronic and computer, mechanical, metallurgical and chemical. The team is also noted for its dedicated trademark practice. In addition, sources are quick to recommend the group's adroit handling of appellate work and patent prosecution. Key clients include AOL, Research In Motion and Toshiba.
**KEY INDIVIDUALS Virginia Carron** (see p.1078) is a well-regarded practitioner, described by peers as *"a super counselor to her clients."* She advises Fuente Cigar on worldwide IP strategy, including patent and trademark procurement, as well as various types of litigation. Her practice covers hardware, software, telecom and chemical technologies, among others. **Bruce Bower**'s (see p.1076) practice includes litigation, strategy, prosecution and licensing in patent matters. Sources highlight his *"very analytical"* approach to matters and applaud his *"good interpersonal skill set."* **William Dyer** (see p.1081) has a strong patent litigation practice, with particular expertise in hi-tech matters including electronics and software. He also covers portfolio development, due diligence issues and opinion work. The *"very well-respected"* **Roger Taylor** (see p.1098) is noted for his experience in advising Japanese and Pacific Rim clients on US IP matters. He was lead partner in the defense of Mitsubishi Heavy Industries and Mitsubishi Power Systems at the ITC and in two district court actions.

### Sutherland Asbill & Brennan LLP
**THE FIRM** The Atlanta office of this full-service firm offers a range of IP services, including counseling, prosecution, licensing, litigation and transactional due diligence. The client roster includes such well-known names as Coca-Cola, GE Energy and Georgia-Pacific.
**KEY INDIVIDUALS Malvern Griffin** has a particular focus on patent work, covering technologies such as computer hardware and software, telecommunications and wireless, and optics. He is described as being an outstanding attorney by market attorneys. The highly regarded **James Johnson** concentrates on trademark, copyright, unfair competition and domain name issues. He has experience in strategy and counseling, including international portfolio management. **Peter Pappas** has particular

expertise in prosecution, covering chemical and mechanical patents, trademark prosecution and transactional work. Sources reserve particular praise for his approach to client service.

## Band 3

### Ballard Spahr LLP
See profile on p.2234

**THE FIRM** The Atlanta office of this full-service firm has litigation capability across the full range of IP matters, including patent, trademark, copyright and trade secret. The group also offers patent prosecution services in the pharmaceutical, biotechnology, electrical and nanotechnology fields, among others. Clients appreciate the firm's competitive and responsive service, reserving particular praise for the team's strengths in the courtroom.
**Sources say:** *"There are some really, really strong lawyers at Ballard Spahr."*
**KEY INDIVIDUALS** *"Excellent IP practitioner"* **Bill Needle** (see p.1091) is a well-rounded practitioner with experience in patent, trademark, copyright and trade secret matters. **Larry Nodine** (see p.1092) leads the IP litigation group and is described as *"very knowledgeable and very client-oriented."* His trial experience covers patent, trademark and copyright cases across a number of technologies, including pharmaceuticals, avionics and programming. **Sumner Rosenberg** (see p.1095) is managing partner of the Atlanta office. In addition to litigation expertise, he has experience in trademark, copyright and patent prosecution matters, with a particular focus on electronic, communication and computer technology. The *"outstanding"* **Mitch Katz** (see p.1086) is practice leader of the patents group and specializes in patent prosecution for pharmaceutical, nano and chemical technology clients. **Katrina Quicker** (see p.1094) principally concentrates on the biotechnology and pharmaceutical fields. As well as patent prosecution and counseling, she has experience in trademark, trade dress, trade secret and copyright litigation. IP associate **Charley Brown** (see p.1077) has a diverse practice encompassing patent prosecution, copyright, trademark and trade secret work across a variety of technologies. Clients especially appreciate his *"accessible and direct"* approach to matters.

### Greenberg Traurig, LLP
See profile on p.1024

**THE FIRM** This firm has an excellent national reputation and fields a broad IP offering from its Atlanta office, with a strong focus on media, entertainment and technology. The team has a fine track record in handling IP-related matters in the television, music, internet and publishing industries, acting for a prestigious client base that includes Microsoft, The Recording Academy, AOL and the estate of Michael Jackson.
**Sources say:** *"I have found Greenberg Traurig to be incredibly protective of our interests but without rushing to litigation."*

**KEY INDIVIDUALS** Peers regard **Joel Katz** (see p.1086) as *"the household name for entertainment law in Atlanta."* He principally concentrates on trademark, copyright, licensing and branding issues. The excellent **Robert Rosenbloum** (see p.1095) has particular experience in music IP, including licensing agreements. *"The level of consistency and quality of his work product is always at the highest,"* note enthusiastic sources.

## King & Spalding LLP
See profile on p.445

**THE FIRM** King & Spalding's Atlanta office provides a range of IP services, with a particular focus on high-stakes patent litigation. Life sciences and electronic communications technology are particular key areas for the group, with clients including Nokia, IBM and Daiichi Sankyo. In a recent highlight, the team acted as co-counsel for Google in its successful litigation with Oracle.

**KEY INDIVIDUALS** *"Very strong lawyer"* **Holmes Hawkins** (see p.1084) is head of the IP practice group. Alongside patent infringement litigation and re-examination proceedings, his practice includes general IP counseling. **Bruce Baber** (see p.1075) has a *"stellar reputation"* in the market, according to peers, and focuses largely on contentious IP matters. His expertise covers trademark, copyright, counterfeiting and false advertising disputes, as well as the prosecution and protection of IP assets. He splits his time between the Atlanta and New York offices. Market sources recognize **Scott Petty** (see p.1093) for his *"reputation in patent prosecution."* In addition to this, his experience extends to trademark and copyright matters, ranging from licensing to litigation.

## Meunier Carlin & Curfman, LLC

**THE FIRM** One of the newer players in the Atlanta IP community, this agile boutique continues to expand its bench and increase its profile in the market. The team offers a range of IP services, including patent prosecution, transactional due diligence, portfolio management and trademark work. The group also has litigation capabilities.

**KEY INDIVIDUALS** *"Outstanding practitioner"* **Anthony Askew** is much noted for his patent and trademark work, in addition to his copyright litigation expertise. The highly regarded **Stephen Schaetzel** is recommended for his district and Federal Circuit experience. His practice covers trademark, copyright and false advertising matters, as well as patent disputes.

## Womble Carlyle Sandridge & Rice, LLP
See profile on p.2049

**THE FIRM** A full-service business firm with offices across the USA, Womble Carlyle maintains a solid presence in the Atlanta market. Servicing both litigation and prosecution needs, the team has worked with clients including Graphic Packaging, Remington Arms and Sonoco Developments.

**KEY INDIVIDUALS** **William Ragland** is a well-regarded litigator whose practice covers a range of IP disputes, including patent infringement, false advertising and unfair competition claims, as well as trademark infringement. He recently represented Kingspan Insulation in defending a trademark infringement action relating to the pink color of insulation. **James Vaughan** co-leads the IP practice and maintains a fine reputation in the Atlanta market. He has handled a number of cases for Graphic Packaging International, including eight inter partes re-examinations – proceedings in which he has particular expertise.

## Band 4

### Duane Morris LLP
See profile on p.2239

**THE FIRM** The Atlanta office of this full-service firm maintains a strong patent litigation practice, in addition to its strengths in trademark, copyright and brand protection work. The team recently represented Aeroflex in defending a trade secrets and breach of contract suit brought by BAE Systems, obtaining summary judgment. Other notable clients include Affinity Labs of Texas and Laser Dynamics.

**KEY INDIVIDUALS** **Louis Norwood Jameson** is chair of the IP practice group and managing partner of the Atlanta office. He is *"a very good litigator,"* according to sources, and his practice covers trademark, patent, copyright, and false advertising disputes, among others. Recent work includes trials at both district and Federal Circuit level. **Matthew Gaudet** is a well-known litigator, focusing on patent and technology disputes. He has trial experience in various district courts as well as before the US Court of Appeals.

### Fish & Richardson PC

**THE FIRM** The Atlanta office of this excellent national IP firm specializes in patent prosecution and litigation. The team works across electrical, computer, chemical and mechanical technologies. Key clients include Google and SAMSUNG.

**KEY INDIVIDUALS** **Christopher Green** works across IP counseling and disputes, and is particularly known for his patent litigation expertise. Market sources describe **Thad Kodish** as *"a super practitioner and a super manager,"* and single out his diligent approach: *"He doesn't leave any stone unturned."* Kodish recently represented SAMSUNG in a dispute relating to optical disk drive and interface patents.

### Morris, Manning & Martin, LLP

**THE FIRM** This full-service firm practices across patent, trademark, trade secret and copyright matters, with transactional, counseling, prosecution and litigation capabilities. The Atlanta office has particular expertise in representing Asian clients entering the US market, and maintains a fine track record for its work in the nanotech, computer and internet technology arenas.

**KEY INDIVIDUALS** **John Fry** is a well-regarded attorney with a broad IP practice, covering counseling, licensing, transactional and litigation matters. He recently acted for Ingenico on a patent infringement case, resulting in a damages award of $15 million. **Bryan Harrison** focuses on IP infringement matters. He also has expertise in antitrust and unfair competition issues, having previously worked as a trial attorney for the US Department of Justice Antitrust Division. He recently represented Optimum Power Solutions in a patent infringement action against Apple and other well-known electronics companies. IP practice head **Tim Tingkang Xia** focuses on patent prosecution and litigation in hi-tech fields such as nanotechnology, supercomputing and bioinformatics. Clients appreciate his *"efficient and proactive"* approach.

### Troutman Sanders LLP

**THE FIRM** The Atlanta office of Troutman Sanders handles a variety of IP matters, from copyright infringement litigation to portfolio transfers. The team has real strength in prosecution and counseling work, acting as primary counsel and prosecution provider to Google, The Southern Company, Georgia Institute of Technology and Reed Elsevier/LexisNexis. Other recent work includes representing Polygroup in multiple simultaneous IP actions domestically and abroad.

**KEY INDIVIDUALS** **Michael Hobbs**'s practice covers prosecution, licensing and litigation across a range of IP areas, including trademark, trade secret and copyright. He recently represented composer Malek Jandali as plaintiff in a copyright infringement action against the American-Arab Anti-Discrimination Committee. The highly regarded **Douglas Salyers** focuses on patent litigation, alongside counseling and alternative dispute resolution.

## Other Notable Practitioners

**John North** (see p.1092) of Kasowitz, Benson, Torres & Friedman LLP focuses on pharmaceuticals, electronics and chemical technologies. Clients appreciate his *"ability to convey highly technical language in clear and understandable terms."* At Kasowitz, Benson, Torres & Friedman LLP, **Laura Fritts** (see p.1081) concentrates on patent litigation, with a particular emphasis on pharmaceuticals and chemical patents. She has recently acted on a number of 'Hatch-Waxman' patent cases for clients including Covidien and Watson Laboratories. Much admired, **William Long** (see p.1089) of McKenna Long & Aldridge LLP is an experienced litigator, particularly in patent cases. His patent practice covers pharmaceutical, computer, chemical, mechanical and medical device technologies. **Jeffrey Kuester** heads the patent practice at Taylor English Duma LLP. He has extensive experience in patent prosecution and litigation, as well as licensing and counseling across a range of IP matters. Paul Hastings LLP's **Robin McGrath** is *"an outstanding lawyer,"* according to market sources. She recently acted for real estate website operator Move as defendant in patent infringement claims, obtaining summary judgment in favor of the client. At the same firm, **Steven Park** is noted for his *"amazing electronics prosecution practice,"* and is also singled out for his energetic approach to matters. He is working with Research In Motion in a number patent litigations, relating to voicemail, video streaming and wireless chip technologies. Toshiba is another key client. **Rodgers Lunsford** (see p.1089) of Smith Gambrell & Russell LLP specializes in IP disputes and litigation, with trademark and copyright being particular areas of strength. He also has prosecution, technology transfer, trade mark enforcement and IP counseling capabilities. At the same firm, **Dale Lischer** (see p.1088) works primarily in patent prosecution and litigation, alongside trademark and copyright matters. His work ranges across a wide variety of technologies and products, including nuclear fuel cells, soft drink packaging, sewing machines and firearms. He has particular expertise in

mechanical, electrical and computer-related patent prosecution. **Michael Powell** (see p.1093) of Baker, Donelson, Bearman, Caldwell & Berkowitz, PC is experienced in litigation and transactional matters across the range of IP, from patent and trademark to false advertising and antitrust-related matters. His areas of expertise include software, telecommunications, online marketing, apparel

and other consumer goods. **Gregory Kirsch** recently joined Smith Gambrell & Russell LLP from Ballard Spahr. Kirsch maintains an excellent reputation in the market. Recent highlights include handling the procurement, analysis and portfolio management of Digital Envoy's US and international patents relating to internet protocol technology.

# LABOR & EMPLOYMENT

Commentary about individuals can be found under their firm's paragraph. If the firm has no paragraph (is not ranked) look at Other Notable Practitioners.

| Labor & Employment |
| --- |
| **Leading Firms** |
| **Band 1** |
| Alston & Bird LLP * |
| Ogletree, Deakins, Nash, Smoak & Stewart, PC * |
| Paul Hastings LLP * |
| **Band 2** |
| Elarbee, Thompson, Sapp & Wilson, LLP |
| Fisher & Phillips LLP * |
| FordHarrison LLP * |
| Kilpatrick Townsend & Stockton LLP * |
| RaFuse, Hill & Hodge LLP |
| Seyfarth Shaw LLP * |
| Troutman Sanders LLP |
| **Band 3** |
| Constangy, Brooks & Smith, LLP |
| Greenberg Traurig, LLP * |
| Jackson Lewis LLP * |
| Jones Day * |
| King & Spalding LLP * |
| Littler Mendelson, PC * |
| McKenna Long & Aldridge LLP * |
| Munger & Stone |
| Rogers & Hardin LLP * |
| **Band 4** |
| Freeman Mathis & Gary, LLP |
| HunterMaclean |
| Hunton & Williams LLP * |
| McGuireWoods LLP * |
| Miller & Martin PLLC * |
| Morris, Manning & Martin, LLP |
| Sutherland Asbill & Brennan LLP |
| Taylor English Duma LLP |

*Indicates firm with profile.*
*Alphabetical order within each band. Band 1 is the highest.*

## Band 1

### Alston & Bird LLP
**See profile on p.1102**

**THE FIRM** This Atlanta-based behemoth continues to act on behalf of a range of illustrious clients across the full spectrum of employment issues. The team is especially noted for its work on large collective action lawsuits; in one highlight it advised Prudential Insurance in relation to an

alleged breach of the FLSA. OSHA work is another area of acknowledged strength.

**Sources say:** *"They're excellent." "Really good problem solvers – they handled any problems that arose masterfully."*
**KEY INDIVIDUALS Steve Ensor** (see p.1081) is skilled in the intricacies of ADA and is *"highly regarded within the legal community."* He works extensively with UPS, ensuring that the logistics giant continues to comply with the ever-changing ADA landscape. **Lisa Cassilly** (see p.1078) is singled out by sources as being *"one of the top performers in her field."* She is noted for her proficiency in the representation of executive interests and is regularly sought out to conduct internal investigations. According to one commentator, **Clare Draper** (see p.1080) is *"outstanding; he's one of the best labor and employment practitioners I've ever known."* Another source hails his ability to *"pick and choose the right battles, weighing the business interests of a case against the legal aspects."* He continues to act on behalf of Global Payments in an ongoing discrimination case. The vastly experienced **Thomas Kilpatrick** (see p.1087) retains a core expertise in labor negotiations. He counsels clients in a variety of related areas, ranging from union avoidance to negotiating collective bargaining agreements. *"Go-to attorney"* **Charles Morgan** (see p.1091) is heralded for his *"excellent judgment."* As one source noted, *"he adopts a business-oriented approach to each matter."* He is known for his expertise on OSHA. Clients are unanimous in their positive appraisal of **Robert Riordan** (see p.1094). He's perceived to be *"delightful to work with,"* as well as *"extremely communicative and a good strategic thinker."* He attains further praise for his familiarity with the FLSA; recently acting for Prudential Insurance on the aforementioned matter. **Glenn Patton** (see p.1093) was recently engaged by UPS as it sought to implement a centralized FMLA protocol. He has a notably diverse practice and he is called upon to dispense advice in relation to both traditional labor and employment matters.

### Ogletree, Deakins, Nash, Smoak & Stewart, PC
**See profile on p.1110**

**THE FIRM** This national labor and employment boutique provides clients with cutting-edge representation across a wide spectrum of related work. The firm's OSHA practice continues to grow, with a number of clients seeking out its considerable expertise on OSHA compliance issues in the past year. It boasts an enviable stable of clients, with Coca-

Cola Refreshments USA, Georgia-Pacific and Nissan serving as three particularly significant examples.

**Sources say:** *"The work has been very strong. They've been very prompt in getting back to us. If there were region-specific issues, they were good at pulling in lawyers from those areas."*
**KEY INDIVIDUALS Homer Deakins** (see p.1080) is widely regarded as a doyen of the employment area. Market commentators identify him as a *"fine lawyer"* and note that he continues to *"serve as a senior statesman to the firm and the community." "Very fine lawyer"* **Margaret Campbell** (see p.1078) chairs the firm's whistle-blower response team and is regularly called upon to act as defense counsel in investigations. She is also extremely well versed in class and collective action litigation. **Craig Cleland** (see p.1078) recently advised Flowers Foods in a class action suit brought under the FLSA. *"He's a great lawyer and instills great confidence in his clients,"* according to one client. He is also applauded for his strength in the labor arena: *"When we have some traditional labor work, he's certainly one of the top people on my list."* **Tracey Barbaree** (see p.1075) specializes in defending employers against FLSA class action cases. Of late, she has been involved in several race and discrimination cases. The highly regarded **Gregory Hare** (see p.1084) stands out for the breadth of his practice. He is particularly well versed in wrongful termination claims and restrictive covenants. **Dara DeHaven** (see p.1080) is acclaimed for the quality and the scope of her preventive practice, advising clients as to how they can best comply with regulatory mandates. In the words of one peer: *"She has a very good reputation and she's a good lawyer."* According to one client, **Daniel Turner** (see p.1099) *"has shown exceptional knowledge and expertise in class action cases." "He's so good,"* the client continued, *"that we import him to other markets. We're willing to fly him around because he's so good."* **Jon Gumbel** (see p.1083) has a commendably diverse employment practice. He is sought out in connection to ERISA matters and claims brought under the FMLA and ADA.

### Paul Hastings LLP
**See profile on p.1996**

**THE FIRM** This impressive group is noted for the sophistication of the work that it habitually undertakes. Its Atlanta-based practitioners are well versed across the full gamut of employment law, and possess especially strong expertise in discrimination and wage and hour matters.

## Labor & Employment

### Senior Statesmen

**Senior Statesmen: distinguished older practitioners**

| | |
|---|---|
| Boisseau Richard | Kilpatrick Townsend & Stockton LLP |
| Deakins Jr Homer L | Ogletree, Deakins, Nash, Smoak & Stewart * |
| Johnson Weyman | Paul Hastings LLP |

### Leading Individuals

**Band 1**

| | |
|---|---|
| Ashe Jr R Lawrence | Parker, Hudson, Rainer & Dobbs LLP* |
| Coil James | Kilpatrick Townsend & Stockton LLP |
| Griffith Patricia | FordHarrison LLP *, |
| Hughes III Hunter R | Rogers & Hardin LLP * |
| Johnston Michael | King & Spalding LLP * |
| Rafuse Nancy E | Ashe Rafuse & Hill LLP * |
| Weirich Geoff | Paul Hastings LLP |
| Wilson Stanford | Elarbee, Thompson, Sapp & Wilson, LLP |
| Wymer John F | Sherman & Howard LLC (ONP)† |

**Band 2**

| | |
|---|---|
| Campbell Margaret H | Ogletree, Deakins, Nash, Smoak & Stewart * |
| Cleland A Craig | Ogletree, Deakins, Nash, Smoak & Stewart * |
| D'Cruz Jason | Morris, Manning & Martin, LLP |
| Dent Leslie | Paul Hastings LLP |
| Ensor R Steve | Alston & Bird LLP * |
| Gerakitis Richard | Troutman Sanders LLP |
| Hankins Richard B | McKenna Long & Aldridge LLP * |
| Mathis Ben | Freeman Mathis & Gary, LLP |
| McIver Tex | Fisher & Phillips LLP *, |
| Munger Tom | Munger & Stone |
| Perlowski Henry M | Arnall Golden Gregory LLP (ONP)† * |
| Schreter Lee | Littler Mendelson, PC * |
| Stone Benjamin | Munger & Stone |
| Sudbury Deborah A | Jones Day * |
| Tyson Patrick R | Constangy, Brooks & Smith, LLP |
| Wasser Neil H | Constangy, Brooks & Smith, LLP |
| Wilson Brent | Elarbee, Thompson, Sapp & Wilson, LLP |
| Wozniak Todd | Greenberg Traurig, LLP * |

**Band 3**

| | |
|---|---|
| Arbery W Christopher | Hall, Arbery & Gilligan, LLP (ONP)† * |
| Beale R Daniel | McKenna Long & Aldridge LLP * |
| Buckler Robert H | Troutman Sanders LLP |
| Cassilly Lisa H | Alston & Bird LLP * |
| Draper IV Clare H | Alston & Bird LLP * |
| Duffie L Traywick | Littler Mendelson, PC * |
| Gignilliat R Read | Elarbee, Thompson, Sapp & Wilson, LLP |
| Gordon David L | Jackson Lewis LLP * |
| Haas III W Melvin | Constangy, Brooks & Smith, LLP |
| Hager Ashley Z | Troutman Sanders LLP |
| Herring II Wade W | HunterMaclean |
| Hill Jr William B | Ashe Rafuse & Hill LLP * |
| Kassin Thomas | FordHarrison LLP * |
| Kelly Ashley | Arnall Golden Gregory LLP (ONP)† * |
| Kilpatrick J Thomas | Alston & Bird LLP * |
| Lawrence-Hardy Allegra J | Sutherland Asbill & Brennan LLP |
| Long-Daniels David | Greenberg Traurig, LLP * |
| Mack Curtis L | McGuireWoods LLP |
| Matchett Sam | King & Spalding LLP * |

| | |
|---|---|
| McDonald Timothy | Thompson Hine LLP (ONP)† * |
| Newman Stuart | Seyfarth Shaw LLP * |
| Powell Kurt | Hunton & Williams LLP * |
| Prucino Diane L | Kilpatrick Townsend & Stockton LLP |
| Riddell Stephen | Troutman Sanders LLP |
| Sullenberger Douglas R | Fisher & Phillips LLP * |
| Thompson John E | Fisher & Phillips LLP * |

**Band 4**

| | |
|---|---|
| Ackourey Mary Anne | Freeman Mathis & Gary, LLP |
| Alden John W | Kilpatrick Townsend & Stockton LLP |
| Barbaree Tracey T | Ogletree, Deakins, Nash, Smoak & Stewart * |
| Bartlett Brett C | Seyfarth Shaw LLP * |
| Christopher Thomas H | Kilpatrick Townsend & Stockton LLP |
| Ciucci Joseph A | Duane Morris LLP (ONP)† |
| DeHaven Dara L | Ogletree, Deakins, Nash, Smoak & Stewart * |
| Gevertz David | Baker, Donelson, Bearman (ONP)† * |
| Gumbel Jon M | Ogletree, Deakins, Nash, Smoak & Stewart * |
| Hagaman David C | FordHarrison LLP * |
| Hall Jr Warren R | Hall, Arbery & Gilligan, LLP (ONP)† * |
| Hare Gregory J | Ogletree, Deakins, Nash, Smoak & Stewart * |
| Kachmar Shawn A | HunterMaclean |
| Keenan Mark L | McKenna Long & Aldridge LLP * |
| Mintz Jeffrey M | Jackson Lewis LLP * |
| Monroe Jr John L | FordHarrison LLP * |
| Morgan Charles H | Alston & Bird LLP * |
| Munger Stephen X | Jackson Lewis LLP * |
| Newsome Jerry | Littler Mendelson, PC * |
| Pangborn Susan W | Kilpatrick Townsend & Stockton LLP |
| Patton Glenn G | Alston & Bird LLP * |
| Pittman Cleek Alisa | Elarbee, Thompson, Sapp & Wilson, LLP |
| Pointer Ann Margaret | Fisher & Phillips LLP * |
| Polly Jr Ronald G | Hawkins Parnell Thackston & Young (ONP)† |
| Principe William K | Constangy, Brooks & Smith, LLP |
| Rebel Thomas P | Fisher & Phillips LLP * |
| Riordan Robert P | Alston & Bird LLP * |
| Sapp J Lewis | Elarbee, Thompson, Sapp & Wilson, LLP |
| Spanos Peter R | Burr & Forman LLP (ONP)† |
| Stevens Robert C. | Seyfarth Shaw LLP * |
| Taylor Mark | Taylor English Duma LLP |
| Tetrick Jr David | King & Spalding LLP * |
| Turner Daniel E | Ogletree, Deakins, Nash, Smoak & Stewart * |
| Warren Frederick L | FordHarrison LLP * |

**Up-and-coming individuals**

| | |
|---|---|
| Briggs Benjamin | Seyfarth Shaw LLP * |
| Harris Brian M. | Morris, Manning & Martin, LLP |
| Johnson Louisa | Seyfarth Shaw LLP * |

**Associates to watch**

| | |
|---|---|
| Neely Yendelela | Kilpatrick Townsend & Stockton LLP |

\* Indicates individual with profile.

†ONP = Other Notable Practitioner

The group's strength in highly significant class action lawsuits is identified by multiple sources, with the successful defense of CSX Transportation against claims of racial discrimination serving as a particularly noteworthy recent example.

**Sources say:** *"I found the team that I worked with to be really top-notch when it came to litigation."*

**KEY INDIVIDUALS** Senior statesman **Weyman Johnson** is singled out for his *"brilliance in employment law issues."* He is particularly proficient in handling both OSHA and FLSA matters and garners tremendous respect within the legal community. **Geoff Weirich**, known for his expertise in discrimination and wage and hour cases, is *"very well respected in the class action world."* *"He does an incredible job,"* attests one client; *"for the big cases, I would go to him."* Known to be both *"practical and effective,"* **Leslie Dent** has enjoyed an impressive year in which she has been victorious in a number of high-profile cases. She undertakes a great deal of class action defense work and earns market approbation for her work in this area. As one source put it, *"in terms of understanding the issues and strategy, she did a great job."*

## Band 2

### Elarbee, Thompson, Sapp & Wilson, LLP

**THE FIRM** This firm's compact size belies the scope and complexity of much of the work it undertakes. The group specializes in the representation of senior management and top-level executives, providing counsel pertaining to the intricacies of both labor and employment law.

**Sources say:** *"For a smaller boutique firm, they have done an incredible job of attracting a client base that would be anyone's envy."*

**KEY INDIVIDUALS** The *"very accessible"* **Stanford Wilson** is acclaimed for both his litigation skills and the efficacy of the counsel he provides to employers seeking to anticipate and avoid litigation. *"I've seen him doing training sessions and he does a wonderful job,"* noted one client. **Brent Wilson** is said to possess a *"good reputation as a trial lawyer"* and to be *"involved in high-profile matters."* He handles a wide range of matters and his practice spans both employment law and traditional labor matters. **Read Gignilliat** works exclusively with employers, providing counsel in relation to a variety of claims brought by employees. *"He's a star,"* exclaimed one enthusiastic source, *"he's the hardest-working lawyer I've ever met. If I had an employment issue, he'd be my number-one guy."* **Alisa Pittman Cleek** is known to have a *"good trial practice"* and to be *"very good at client service."* She specializes in the representation of restaurant chains and chemical and mining operators. **Lewis Sapp** has a diverse practice and is experienced in multiplaintiff discrimination defense suits and in a variety of labor relations matters.

### Fisher & Phillips LLP

See profile on p.1107

**THE FIRM** This large boutique remains a key player within the Georgia labor and employment sphere. The robust team has a commendable breadth of knowledge and can offer specific expertise in both EEOC and OSHA matters. A notable highlight was the firm's defense of Hamilton Growers against an EEOC class action lawsuit.

**Sources say:** "*The quality control and the emphasis on customer service are the most consistent that I've ever seen.*" **KEY INDIVIDUALS** Hailed for his intelligent and practical approach to engagements, **Tex McIver** (see p.1090) continues to dispense "*great advice*" and to provide clients with "*continual follow-up.*" Over the past twelve months, he worked with The Sauers Group as it sought to defend itself against the potential legal ramifications of departing employees. **Douglas Sullenberger** (see p.1098) is a widely respected traditional labor attorney, recommended for the thorough advice he imparts to employers upon a range of union matters. "*His practice is broad and his experience is deep,*" noted one commentator. **John Thompson** (see p.1099) is highly rated in the wage and hour field. As one client put it, "*he is the quintessential labor and employment lawyer – really one of the best in his field.*" The source went on to add: "*He's one of the smartest lawyers I've ever worked with.*" The "*extremely responsive*" **Thomas Rebel** (see p.1094) is noted for the exemplary level of service he provides to clients. He is particularly well versed in the legislative impact of the FLSA. **Ann Margaret Pointer** (see p.1093) is an experienced practitioner who focuses predominantly upon the representation of senior executives. She is recommended for her ability to vigorously defend employers who are facing class action lawsuits.

## FordHarrison LLP
See profile on p.1108

**THE FIRM** Known for its representation of several prominent airline carriers, FordHarrison enjoys a strong presence within the state. It provides counsel to employers on a wide range of specialist areas, including government agency investigations and collective bargaining. An engagement of particular note saw the firm represent PETA in a significant breach of contract case. Other substantial clients include Piedmont Airlines, ING and Randstad.

**Sources say:** "*I've found them to be very reliable and very balanced. Not only do they provide you with insight into what the issue is, but they also map out the options for business decisions.*"

**KEY INDIVIDUALS Patricia Griffith** (see p.1083) ascends to the top band after having received unanimous market approbation for her prowess as a litigator. "*She's probably one of the premier litigators in the country — not just in Georgia,*" noted one source, while others were keen to commend her outstanding grasp of legal concepts. **Thomas Kassin** (see p.1086) is nationally recognized for his work with airline carriers. He is also well versed in the legislative impact of the Railway Labor Act and represents a plethora of clients in this regard. **David Hagaman** (see p.1083) is an active litigator who frequently tries cases before the NLRB. He is also highly regarded for his skills as a mediator. **John Monroe** (see p.1090) elicits consistent praise from his peers and is identified as an "*extremely capable attorney.*" He handles a range of litigation and arbi-

tration work in the field; his assignments range from breach of contract and wage and hour disputes to discrimination and harassment claims. **Frederick Warren** (see p.1099) is a respected authority in both the labor and employment arenas. "*He's amazingly accessible. Whenever I need him, he's always there and he is very thoughtful in his analysis of different situations,*" said one client.

## Kilpatrick Townsend & Stockton LLP
See profile on p.1109

**THE FIRM** Kilpatrick Townsend & Stockton is highly distinguished for both its proactive and reactive capabilities. While its core expertise is in providing advice to employers embroiled in litigation, it also counsels employers as to how they can best prevent potential lawsuits being filed against them. One of its more notable successes was obtained in the representation of a national steel fabricating company against claims of racial discrimination brought by an employee.

**Sources say:** "*I work with them on a general labor law perspective. I've had a positive experience with them; they've offered reliable advice and guidance.*"

**KEY INDIVIDUALS Richard Boisseau** is "*one of the greatest lawyers I've ever met,*" enthused one market commentator. He has long been regarded as one the state's strongest lawyers in the labor relations field. **James Coil** remains an "*outstanding lawyer*" and is one of the driving forces behind the firm's regional prominence in employment matters. He provides particularly strong representation in large discrimination lawsuits and wage and hour matters. Key partner **Diane Prucino**'s wide-ranging practice encompasses employee terminations, discrimination allegations and wage and hour cases. Clients applaud her practical approach to casework and her ability to "*look at things from all angles.*" "*Outstanding trial lawyer*" **John Alden** is, according to one source, "*a very practical, solution-oriented practitioner.*" He assists management in a broad range of areas, including claims brought under the FLSA, and OSHA compliance matters. **Thomas Christopher** recently represented a contractor as it attempted to withdraw from a multiemployer pension plan. He is highlighted for his familiarity with restrictive covenant matters. **Susan Pangborn** is noted for the dexterity and vigor of her defense against both multiplaintiff and single-plaintiff lawsuits. She is further singled out for skill at conducting internal investigations. Leading associate **Yendelela Neely** concentrates her practice on OSHA compliance, wage and hour matters and discrimination cases. "*I'm amazed at just how much she's picked up,*" commented one source.

## RaFuse, Hill & Hodge LLP
See profile on p.1104

**THE FIRM** This highly distinguished boutique retains its status among Georgia's elite. The accomplished team attains widespread acclaim for its ability to defend employers against lawsuits filed in connection with a variety of employment-related statutes. Abbott Laboratories, Waffle House and Cox Enterprises are among its prestigious client list.

**Sources say:** "*If I knew that a case were going to go to trial, I'd certainly use Ashe Rafuse & Hill.*" "*They are a phenomenal firm.*"

**KEY INDIVIDUALS Nancy Rafuse** (see p.1094) is head of the firm's employment law and litigation department. In a recent highlight she successfully defended Procter & Gamble against allegations of racial discrimination. Sources value her exceptional work ethic and formidable intelligence; she is further considered to be both an "*excellent defense attorney*" and a "*tough negotiator.*" Market commentators identify **William Hill** (see p.1084) as a "*tremendous trial attorney*" and highlight the former judge's prowess as a litigator.

## Seyfarth Shaw LLP
See profile on p.1262

**THE FIRM** This national labor and employment boutique has an enviable reputation within the state. The robust team of 28 attorneys is known for its success in litigation and possesses strength in both traditional labor matters and complex wage and hour cases. Recent clients include Wells Fargo, Caesars Entertainment and Cox Media Group.

**Sources say:** "*I would rate their performance as exceptional.*" "*They're very good at looking at cases from a strategic level.*"

**KEY INDIVIDUALS Stuart Newman** (see p.1091) has an excellent track record in the negotiation of collective bargaining agreements, as evinced in the recent representation of Cox Media Group. He receives favorable feedback from interviewees, with his "*ability to look at a situation and craft an argument*" the source of particular praise. Department chair **Brett Bartlett** (see p.1075) is identified as a leader in wage and hour matters. "*He knows the ins and outs of the FLSA better than anybody I've ever worked with,*" noted one client. "*Creative thinker*" **Robert Stevens** (see p.1098) comes highly recommended for his expertise in employment discrimination and trade secret matters. Clients appreciate the commerciality of his advice. Labeled as an "*up-and-coming lawyer*" by interviewees, **Benjamin Briggs** (see p.1077) is acclaimed for his burgeoning OSHA compliance practice. He is also sought out for his class action defense work, and was recently retained in such a capacity by Steak 'N Shake. Newly promoted partner **Louisa Johnson** (see p.1086) is noted for her wage and hour defense work. "*She understands our business and is realistic about aims and is a pleasure to work with,*" said one client.

## Troutman Sanders LLP

**THE FIRM** This firm has an excellent reputation for handling complex class and collective action defense work. It further stands out for its strong labor law practice, which ranges from the negotiation and administration of labor agreements to advising management in union elections. The Atlanta team recently defended Chick-fil-A against allegations of racial discrimination.

**KEY INDIVIDUALS Richard Gerakitis** is praised by clients for his outstanding connections around the state. He leads the firm's labor and employment practice and is particularly well versed in the intricacies of the FLSA.

Robert Buckler is highly rated for his tremendous client service. He was successful in his recent defense of Gray Television in a single-plaintiff age discrimination case. Stephen Riddell continues to work extensively with restaurant chain Chick-fil-A and recently oversaw a large racial discrimination class action lawsuit. He is business savvy and appreciated for the great rapport he develops with clients. Ashley Hager retains a core expertise in both ADA and FLSA matters. Interviewees speak highly of her legal acumen, and also single out her ability to understand business considerations.

## Band 3

### Constangy, Brooks & Smith, LLP

THE FIRM Constangy, Brooks & Smith attains strong market approval for the strength of its OSHA practice group and also has expertise on labor relations matters. In one headline-grabbing engagement the firm counseled Kindred Nursing Centers East in the Specialty Healthcare case.

Sources say: *"We are highly impressed with their labor team." "They make you feel very valued as a customer."*

KEY INDIVIDUALS The *"nationally known"* Neil Wasser is praised for his impressive OSHA practice. *"He is a very innovative lawyer,"* noted one interviewee, *"and he's done an excellent job of moving the firm into a contemporary and competitive mode."* Patrick Tyson is hailed for his ability to *"shape a message for the senior leaders of the company."* Interviewees were keen to acclaim his grasp of occupational safety matters, with one interviewee stating: *"I would not hesitate to recommend him to a client for OSHA-related work."* Melvin Haas is a recognized expert on traditional labor matters, drawing upon over three decades' worth of experience. Sources are quick to praise his abilities: *"I have worked with him extensively over the years and he has always done an outstanding job for me,"* a client confirmed. Renowned for his *"encyclopedic"* knowledge of OSHA issues, William Principe remains a key member of the firm's Atlanta office. He is recommended by clients for his dexterity in preparing companies for citation.

### Greenberg Traurig, LLP
See profile on p.1024

THE FIRM This firm continues to advise clients on an array of employment services, including class and collective actions, employment litigation and restrictive covenants. It is also considered a go-to firm for clients seeking advice in connection to ERISA matters. The team recently attained a favorable verdict for TowerSite Services, who it defended against a racial discrimination lawsuit brought by the EEOC.

Sources say: *"They're an aggressive, optimistic, can-do firm."*

KEY INDIVIDUALS Todd Wozniak (see p.1100) is an accomplished trial lawyer and is regularly called upon to provide counsel in large class action lawsuits. David Long-Daniels (see p.1089) is the cochair of the firm's national labor and employment practice. His courtroom demeanor

has been described as both *"charming and disarming,"* with clients also praising his ability to unpick the depositions of opposing witnesses.

### Jackson Lewis LLP
See profile on p.1982

THE FIRM This firm is a respected presence in Atlanta and acts on behalf of a number of large employers from a range of industries. The group is noted for its work on employment discrimination cases, class actions and traditional labor law work. Clients include Aaron's, Waffle House and WorldPay.

Sources say: *"They are practical and provide solutions that go beyond merely identifying issues."*

KEY INDIVIDUALS In the words of one interviewee, David Gordon (see p.1082) is *"very practical, very level-headed and always an asset to any team."* He serves as the managing partner of the firm's Georgia office. Stephen Munger (see p.1091) is considered by sources to be *"at the forefront of a great many wage and hour issues."* He is also praised for his pragmatic approach. Jeffrey Mintz (see p.1090) is noted within the Georgia legal market for his strength in traditional labor law. He has advised many employers on preventive labor relations and union elections.

### Jones Day
See profile on p.919

THE FIRM This established practice specializes in class action defense work and is frequently called upon for both regional and national matters. The team was recently hired as defense counsel by R.J. Reynolds in connection to an age discrimination nationwide class action lawsuit.

Sources say: *"They did a nice job in a particularly challenging case."*

KEY INDIVIDUALS Sources agree that Deborah Sudbury (see p.1098) is an excellent attorney, capable of handling sensitive matters with *"delicacy and respect."* She recently represented IBM in a wage and hour matter brought by two plaintiffs.

### King & Spalding LLP
See profile on p.445

THE FIRM This firm retains a strong labor and employment practice, servicing an impressive stable of clients from its Atlanta office. The team is acclaimed for its vigorous defense of clients and is often hired to handle complex class action lawsuits. Of particular note is the firm's ongoing representation of The Progressive Corporation in a substantial multiplaintiff discrimination case.

KEY INDIVIDUALS Michael Johnston (see p.1086) is a well-known figure in the Georgia legal community with a broad range of experience both in and out of the courtroom. He is currently representing Bass Pro Outdoor World against a racial discrimination lawsuit brought by the EEOC. The highly acclaimed Sam Matchett (see p.1089) specializes in employment litigation. *"People absolutely rave about Sam; his clients regard him as highly effective,"* enthused one peer. David Tetrick (see p.1098) is particularly active in the ERISA litigation sphere. He

recently represented SunTrust Banks in a large ERISA class action matter.

### Littler Mendelson, PC
See profile on p.688

THE FIRM This national labor and employment boutique is dedicated to assisting employers facing large-scale collective and class action lawsuits. Clients praise the depth of resources available to the Georgia team, citing the firm's national strength as one if its key differentiators. The group habitually handles a substantial amount of FLSA work and its bench includes several attorneys that specialize in wage and hour matters.

Sources say: *"I've found them to be competitive on price. What makes them appealing is that they have a footprint everywhere."*

KEY INDIVIDUALS Lee Schreter (see p.1096) attains a wealth of positive feedback for her work in the wage and hour arena. According to one source, *"she does a wonderful job dealing with clients"* and provides a superb work product. Traywick Duffie (see p.1080) is a vastly experienced practitioner, who is identified by sources as a respected authority on employment litigation matters. The *"very impressive"* Jerry Newsome (see p.1091) garners praise for his growing practice. He has a core expertise in restrictive covenant matters.

### McKenna Long & Aldridge LLP
See profile on p.922

THE FIRM McKenna Long & Aldridge's employer services group specializes in assisting government contractors. The group also boasts an additional expertise in traditional labor matters and routinely appears before the NLRB on behalf of employers. The firm continues to work closely with Foxwoods Resort Casino and also lists Rosetta Stone and WebMD among a robust roster of clients.

Sources say: *"They're always available to us and they get back to me very quickly."*

KEY INDIVIDUALS Richard Hankins's (see p.1083) practice concentrates primarily upon traditional labor matters. He led the firm's recent representation of Boeing in a case that was brought before the NLRB. Daniel Beale (see p.1076), recommended as an *"outstanding practitioner in this area,"* is applauded for his ability to dispense practical advice and avoid getting *"mired down in theoretical minutiae." "If I had the opportunity to work with him in the future, I'd jump at it,"* said one source. In the words of one client, Mark Keenan (see p.1087) *"is an outstanding, no-nonsense attorney who gives us our money's worth and is a greatly valued resource for everyone on my staff."* He is further identified as possessing *"highly refined expertise in organized labor and collective bargaining engagements."* He recently advised The Home Depot in a matter before the NLRB.

### Munger & Stone

THE FIRM This compact boutique has carved a highly successful niche for itself within the Georgia labor and employment market. Its willingness to represent both employers and employees has afforded the team a unique perspective on the two sides of the litigation process.

**Sources say:** *"They've done some remarkable things for a firm their size." "They're really strong in noncompete matters."*

**KEY INDIVIDUALS Benjamin Stone** is revered by peers as a *"straightforward, no-nonsense type of litigator,"* capable of combining his strong analytical skills with an extensive knowledge of employment laws. Founding partner **Tom Munger** continues to command the respect of both peers and clients. He is singled out for his ability to produce *"complex and fantastic briefs."*

## Rogers & Hardin LLP
See profile on p.1111

**THE FIRM** While it is primarily known for its litigation capabilities, Rogers & Hardin retains a dynamic and multifaceted labor and employment practice, offering a range of services to clients such as Dataliant, Ameris Bancorp and Sharp Business Systems. The firm has recently been called upon to provide representation in restrictive covenant disputes, having acted in such a capacity for Athens Paper.

**Sources say:** *"They're an outstanding firm." "They're very selective and are generally very high-performing lawyers."*

**KEY INDIVIDUALS Hunter Hughes** (see p.1085) is, according to one source, an *"excellent litigator with a great manner in front of both judge and jury,"* renowned for his *"phenomenal work product."* He combines an active practice with his duties as a mediator and is perceived to be a leading authority within the Atlanta legal market.

## Band 4

## Freeman Mathis & Gary, LLP

**THE FIRM** This growing regional boutique operates primarily within the middle market and offers special expertise in the restaurant and hospitality industries. The group receives particular recognition for its work with governmental entities and is further acclaimed for its cost-effective attitude toward engagements. The firm recently obtained a favorable resolution for AGCO in a series of class action claims filed under the ADEA.

**Sources say:** *"We get prompt, good service and they're reasonably priced."*

**KEY INDIVIDUALS** The *"very practical"* **Ben Mathis** recently distinguished himself by serving as lead partner in his firm's representation of Sapheon in a trade secrets dispute. He possesses a *"very knowledgeable business mind"* and is commendably *"unafraid of litigation."* **Mary Anne Ackourey** has proven herself to be a very strong practitioner, having recently achieved favorable outcomes in several employment cases. One of her work highlights entailed representing Express Premium Finance in a complex, multiparty lawsuit.

## HunterMaclean

**THE FIRM** Market sources recommend this group on account of its prominence in Savannah. The group is fur-

ther acknowledged for its ability to assist clients that are the target of governmental investigations, combining a familiarity with the local legal landscape with an in-depth knowledge of the relevant legislation. Notable clients include Waffle House, JCB and Coby Electronics.

**Sources say:** *"My belief is that they are a top-flight law firm." "They're very strong and are the marquee firm for south Georgia."*

**KEY INDIVIDUALS Wade Herring** is a highly respected Savannah-based practitioner, commended for his courtroom proficiency and his *"common-sense"* approach. Of particular note was his successful defense of The Landings Club against an allegation of discrimination. **Shawn Kachmar** earns the approbation of several sources, one of whom notes that he *"does an exceptional job and brings a really proactive approach to litigation."* He has enjoyed an active year, a highlight of which was the representation of Gulfstream Aerospace on an age discrimination case.

## Hunton & Williams LLP
See profile on p.2517

**THE FIRM** The employment team at Hunton & Williams continues to provide its clients with an extensive range of services in this practice area. The group represents clients from a diverse cross-section of industries and is perhaps best known for its defense of large class action lawsuits.

**KEY INDIVIDUALS Kurt Powell** (see p.1093) has a strong regional reputation and is widely regarded for both his mastery of legal minutiae and his drafting skills.

## McGuireWoods LLP
See profile on p.2519

**THE FIRM** This firm continues to represent a number of large employers in the state; its illustrious client roster includes McDonald's and Kellogg. Its attorneys have recently obtained a number of favorable verdicts while defending clients against EEOC charges.

**Sources say:** *"They know us well enough to partner the right attorneys with us and they understand our business."*

**KEY INDIVIDUALS** Clients are keen to praise **Curtis Mack**'s knowledge of the legal landscape in Atlanta. *"He's one of the greatest attorneys I've ever known,"* reported one client; he *"does an absolutely brilliant job at being able to switch gears as appropriate."*

## Miller & Martin PLLC
See profile on p.2317

**THE FIRM** Best known for its capacity to handle large multiplaintiff lawsuits, Miller & Martin continues to enjoy a solid reputation in Georgia. The team serves a diverse range of employers, numbering Atlanta Regional Commission and Coca-Cola Refreshments USA among its more prominent clients.

**Sources say:** *"They've been a really great asset for us, both in terms of giving great counsel and helping us to think outside the box."*

**KEY INDIVIDUALS** Christopher Parker heads the firm's Atlanta practice.

## Morris, Manning & Martin, LLP

**THE FIRM** The five attorneys that make up this broad-based labor and employment practice are able to couple an in-depth understanding of executive employment issues with a comprehensive grasp of restrictive covenant matters. Noted clients include Ericsson Television, Georgia Gulf and TitleMax Holdings.

**Sources say:** *"Their service is excellent and I'm very grateful to have the chance to work with them."*

**KEY INDIVIDUALS Jason D'Cruz** has, according to one client, *"always been incredibly thorough and does a great job."* He is also described as an *"amazing resource"* and has a high degree of familiarity with claims filed under the EEOC statute. The *"stellar"* **Brian Harris** recently distinguished himself in the firm's successful representation of Becham and CrossLink Orthopaedics in a restrictive covenants case. He is said to provide clients with an *"excellent service"* and is further commended for his in-depth knowledge of his practice area.

## Sutherland Asbill & Brennan LLP

**THE FIRM** This firm has a long history in the Atlanta market and continues to adroitly represent its diverse stable of clients. Wage and hour matters constitute a core component of the team's growing labor and employment practice. The group is also well equipped to handle alternative dispute resolution, offering both mediation and arbitration services to clients.

**KEY INDIVIDUALS Allegra Lawrence-Hardy** is widely regarded as one of the most talented younger practitioners in the state. She is recommended by several of her peers and attains praise for her ability to handle multijurisdictional matters.

## Taylor English Duma LLP

**THE FIRM** Taylor English Duma enters the rankings after having substantially bolstered its Atlanta-based labor and employment practice with a number of key additions. The firm continues to offer strong expertise on individual and class action discrimination law suits.

**Sources say:** *"They've grown fantastically over the last few years."*

**KEY INDIVIDUALS Mark Taylor** is, according to one interviewee, *"one of the strongest attorneys in Atlanta."* Sources identify him as one of the linchpins of the firm, citing his tenacity and intelligence as two of his strongest characteristics.

## Other Notable Practitioners

**Henry Perlowski** (see p.1093) of Arnall Golden Gregory LLP is perceived to be a *"phenomenal employment lawyer." "He understands my business better than some of my own employees,"* claimed one interviewee, while others highlighted his intelligent approach to engagements. He recently represented BFG Supply in connection to a competition dispute. Lauded by sources as being both *"practical"* and *"reliable,"* **Ashley Kelly** (see p.1087) of Arnall Golden Gregory LLP continues to dispense high-quality advice across the entire spectrum of employment issues. She is thought of as being *"extremely knowledgeable on a national basis"* and as *"somebody that both in-house lawyers and HR professionals can rely upon."* Sources confirm that **Joseph Ciucci** of Duane Morris LLP *"is a tremendously good litigator."* They also highlight that he has a *"great memory"* and is *"very methodical throughout the entire deposition process."* He is noted for his expertise in connection to EEOC matters. The vastly experienced **Peter Spanos** of Burr & Forman LLP has an incredibly varied practice. He is well versed in both EEOC and FLSA matters and is justifiably referred to as a *"well-rounded practitioner"* by interviewees. **David Gevertz** (see p.1082) of Baker, Donelson, Bearman, Caldwell & Berkowitz, PC is particularly noted for his adroit handling of restrictive covenant disputes. He

is currently advising Waffle House in connection to an ongoing discrimination case. **Timothy McDonald** (see p.1090) of Thompson Hine LLP is recommended for his strength in the employee benefits area. Sources value his ability to wrestle with the more esoteric aspects of a case, while one particular commentator praises his *"knowledge of the ins and outs of litigation."* **Christopher Arbery** (see p.1074) of Hall, Arbery & Gilligan, LLP specializes in the representation of employers and enjoys a reputation as a *"very strong"* practitioner. Renowned for his client service skills, **Warren Hall** (see p.1083) is the founding partner of Hall, Arbery & Gilligan, LLP and is recommended for his broad and comprehensive knowledge of employment law. He is further acknowledged for his prowess as a litigator.

**Ronald Polly** of Hawkins Parnell Thackston & Young LLP is noted for his competency in the employment litigation arena; he is particularly experienced in assisting corporations that face multiplaintiff actions. **John Wymer** recently joined Sherman & Howard LLC from Paul Hastings. He is described by market commentators as being *"excellent with clients."* His practice encompasses the entire spectrum of labor and employment disputes and his courtroom demeanor is the source of particular critical acclaim. Lawrence Ashe recently joined Parker, Hudson, Rainer & Dobbs LLP from RaFuse Hill & Hodges. Perceived as being *"one of the deans of class action defense work,"* he is lauded for his ability to combine an exceptional group of legal intricies with a broader *"practical awareness."*

# LITIGATION

White-Collar Crime & Government Investigations p.1065

Commentary about individuals can be found under their firm's paragraph. If the firm has no paragraph (is not ranked) look at Other Notable Practitioners.

| Litigation: General Commercial Leading Firms |
| --- |
| **Band 1** |
| Alston & Bird LLP * |
| Bondurant, Mixson & Elmore, LLP |
| King & Spalding LLP * |
| **Band 2** |
| Kilpatrick Townsend & Stockton LLP * |
| Rogers & Hardin LLP * |
| Sutherland Asbill & Brennan LLP |
| Troutman Sanders LLP |
| **Band 3** |
| Doffermyre Shields Canfield & Knowles, LLC * |
| Jones Day * |
| McKenna Long & Aldridge LLP * |
| Parker, Hudson, Rainer & Dobbs LLP |
| **Band 4** |
| Arnall Golden Gregory LLP * |
| Bryan Cave LLP |
| Chilivis, Cochran, Larkins & Bever LLP |
| Fellows LaBriola LLP |
| Greenberg Traurig, LLP * |
| Holland & Knight LLP * |
| HunterMaclean |
| Hunton & Williams LLP * |
| Morris, Manning & Martin, LLP |
| Paul Hastings LLP * |
| Womble Carlyle Sandridge & Rice, LLP * |

*\* Indicates firm with profile.*
*Alphabetical order within each band. Band 1 is the highest.*

## Band 1

### Alston & Bird LLP
See profile on p.1102

**THE FIRM** This leading litigation practice continues to set the standard for excellence within the state. The team is acclaimed for its ability to serve high-end clients; its continued representation of Dell, McDonald's and Nokia both establishes the validity of this assertion and demonstrates the firm's prominence within the higher echelons of the corporate world. While commercial litigation remains the team's core focus, it does possess additional strength in the white-collar crime arena, thus boasting a diversity that few other regional practices can rival.

**Sources say:** *"There's no question that they're an excellent litigation practice."*

**KEY INDIVIDUALS** According to sources, white-collar crime specialist **Michael Brown** (see p.1077) is a *"sharp, bright and effective attorney."* He formed part of the team that provided counsel to Autoliv throughout a recent government investigation. **William Mitchelson** (see p.1090) is a highly competent white-collar criminal lawyer with a practice geared toward companies in investigation. He garners particular praise for his work in the healthcare sector. *"First-class"* litigator **Judson Graves** (see p.1083) is singled out by one interviewee as being a *"superb lawyer in all respects."* His is a broad practice, with a strong focus in medical malpractice defense. Cochair of the firm's general commercial litigation practice, **Todd David** (see p.1079) recently distinguished himself by obtaining a favorable verdict in a $37 million arbitration proceeding. *"For securities fraud and class action cases, he is the gold standard in town,"* enthused one client. **Cari Dawson** (see p.1079) elicits praise for her *"outstanding command of case law"* and impresses clients with her intelligent approach toward liti-

gation. She continues to act on behalf of Toyota Motor Sales in a complex consumer class action case. The *"outstanding"* **James Grant** (see p.1082) is held in high regard for his ability to expediently *"bring people to a consensus."* He is further commended for his ability to *"acknowledge the weaknesses of cases"* and formulate his arguments accordingly. **Michael Kenny** (see p.1087) is recommended for his ability to handle complex commercial litigation matters. In the words of one peer, it is his *"combination of energy, intellect and creativity that sets him apart."* **Peter Kontio** (see p.1087) commands an admirable reputation for both his civil and criminal litigation capabilities, servicing what one source terms an *"impressive portfolio of clients."* He is currently representing Syniverse Technologies in its attempts to dismiss a series of class action lawsuits. **John Latham** (see p.1088) is a skilled and talented attorney who focuses his practice on securities litigation. Market commentators are unanimous in their favorable assessment of his courtroom capabilities, with his impressive track record drawing particular praise. **Bernard Taylor** (see p.1098) is *"well respected for his legal acumen and is a familiar player in the civic activities of the community."* According to one peer, *"he's reached an experience and comfort level in the courtroom that is magical and fun to watch."*

### Bondurant, Mixson & Elmore, LLP

**THE FIRM** The name Bondurant, Mixson & Elmore remains synonymous with excellence within the Georgia litigation domain. The firm is differentiated by its representation of both plaintiffs and defendants. Its experience with both sides of the litigation process allows it to formulate arguments with likely adversarial stances in mind. It recently acted on behalf of a number of law firms in a series of appellate matters.

## Litigation: General Commercial
### Senior Statesmen

**Senior Statesmen:** distinguished older practitioners

| | |
|---|---|
| Bondurant Emmet J | Bondurant, Mixson & Elmore, LLP |
| Clay A Stephens | Kilpatrick Townsend & Stockton LLP |
| Dalton John | Troutman Sanders LLP |
| Rogers CB | Rogers & Hardin LLP * |

### Leading Individuals

**Band 1**

| | |
|---|---|
| Chandler John A | King & Spalding LLP * |
| Cohen Lori G | Greenberg Traurig, LLP * |
| Davis Varner Chilton | King & Spalding LLP * |
| Fellows Henry | Fellows LaBriola LLP * |
| Graves Judson | Alston & Bird LLP * |
| Persons Ray | King & Spalding LLP * |
| Sinkfield Richard H | Rogers & Hardin LLP * |
| Tanis Elizabeth Vranicar | King & Spalding LLP * |

**Band 2**

| | |
|---|---|
| Balser David L | King & Spalding LLP * |
| Boice William | Kilpatrick Townsend & Stockton LLP |
| Bowers Michael J | Balch & Bingham LLP (ONP)[†] |
| Bramlett Jeffrey | Bondurant, Mixson & Elmore, LLP |
| Cahoon Susan | Kilpatrick Townsend & Stockton LLP |
| Canfield Kenneth | Doffermyre Shields Canfield & Knowles |
| David Todd R | Alston & Bird LLP * |
| Doffermyre Everette L | Doffermyre Shields Canfield & Knowles |
| Fleming John H | Sutherland Asbill & Brennan LLP |
| Hill Jr William B | Rafuse Hill & Hodges LLP (ONP)[†] * |
| Holley II William J | Parker, Hudson, Rainer & Dobbs LLP |
| Loveland Joseph | King & Spalding LLP * |
| Mixson H Lamar | Bondurant, Mixson & Elmore, LLP |
| Parker Stephanie | Jones Day * |
| Pryor Jill A | Bondurant, Mixson & Elmore, LLP |
| Reinhardt Daniel S | Troutman Sanders LLP |
| Remar Robert B | Rogers & Hardin LLP * |

**Band 3**

| | |
|---|---|
| Anderson Peter J | Sutherland Asbill & Brennan LLP |
| Bracken II Lawrence J | Hunton & Williams LLP * |
| Calvert Matthew J | Hunton & Williams LLP * |
| Custer William V | Bryan Cave LLP |
| Daniel Laurie Webb | Holland & Knight LLP * |
| Daniel Jr Harold T | Holland & Knight LLP * |
| Dawson Cari K | Alston & Bird LLP * |
| Deming N Karen | Troutman Sanders LLP |
| Floyd John | Bondurant, Mixson & Elmore, LLP |
| Garrett G Lee | Jones Day * |
| Grant James C | Alston & Bird LLP * |

| | |
|---|---|
| Kenny Michael | Alston & Bird LLP * |
| Kontio Peter | Alston & Bird LLP * |
| Latham John L | Alston & Bird LLP * |
| Maines J Allen | Holland & Knight LLP * |
| Martin R Matthew | McKenna Long & Aldridge LLP * |
| Powers Tony G | Rogers & Hardin LLP * |
| Rothman Robert L | Arnall Golden Gregory LLP * |
| Taylor Bernard | Alston & Bird LLP * |
| Thornton M Robert | King & Spalding LLP * |
| Withrow Jr William N | Troutman Sanders LLP |
| Zacks David M | Kilpatrick Townsend & Stockton LLP |

**Band 4**

| | |
|---|---|
| Almond John J | Rogers & Hardin LLP * |
| Bogan III James F | Kilpatrick Townsend & Stockton LLP |
| Coleman Jr Ronald T | Parker, Hudson, Rainer & Dobbs LLP |
| Curvin Thomas W | Sutherland Asbill & Brennan LLP |
| Grantham Mark E | DLA Piper LLP (US) (ONP)[†] * |
| Horst Jeffrey D | Krevolin & Horst, LLC (ONP)[†] * |
| Klein Linda A | Baker, Donelson, Bearman, Caldwell (ONP)[†] * |
| Knapp Jr Halsey G | Foltz Martin LLC (ONP)[†] |
| Knowles Ralph | Doffermyre Shields Canfield & Knowles |
| Krugman Edward B | Bondurant, Mixson & Elmore, LLP |
| LaBriola Stephen T | Fellows LaBriola LLP * |
| Lowrey IV Frank M | Bondurant, Mixson & Elmore, LLP |
| MacNaughton John P | Morris, Manning & Martin, LLP |
| McConnell Michael J | Jones Day * |
| Menendez Kenneth G | Epstein Becker & Green PC (ONP)[†] * |
| Murphy Jr George L | Kilpatrick Townsend & Stockton LLP |
| Ragland Jr William M | Womble Carlyle Sandridge & Rice, LLP |
| Rainer Marbury | Parker, Hudson, Rainer & Dobbs LLP |
| Schneider Richard A | King & Spalding LLP * |
| Sharp Joseph | Rafuse Hill & Hodges LLP (ONP)[†] * |
| Sherrill John A | Seyfarth Shaw LLP (ONP)[†] * |
| Shields Robert | Doffermyre Shields Canfield & Knowles |
| Smith E Kendrick | Jones Day * |
| Tatum John | HunterMaclean |
| Terry Michael B | Bondurant, Mixson & Elmore, LLP |
| Trigg Mark G | Greenberg Traurig, LLP * |
| Weiss Terry R | Greenberg Traurig, LLP * |

## Litigation: White-Collar Crime & Government Investigations
### Leading Individuals

**Band 1**

| | |
|---|---|
| Cochran Anthony L | Chilivis, Cochran, Larkins & Bever LLP |
| Cowen Stephen | King & Spalding LLP * |
| Deane Jr Richard H | Jones Day * |
| Maloy Bruce | Maloy Jenkins Parker (ONP)[†] |
| Samuel Donald F | Garland, Samuel & Loeb P.C. (ONP)[†] |
| Wray Christopher A | King & Spalding LLP * |

**Band 2**

| | |
|---|---|
| Bever Thomas Dean | Chilivis, Cochran, Larkins & Bever LLP |
| Brown Michael L | Alston & Bird LLP * |
| Froelich Jr Jerome J | McKenney & Froelich (ONP)[†] |
| Gillen Craig A | Gillen, Withers & Lake, LLC (ONP)[†] |
| Mitchelson Jr William (Mitch) R | Alston & Bird LLP * |
| Morris Bruce H | Finestone & Morris LLP (ONP)[†] |
| Murphy Paul B | King & Spalding LLP * |
| O'Neil Catherine | King & Spalding LLP * |

**Band 3**

| | |
|---|---|
| Griffin Daniel P | Miller & Martin PLLC (ONP)[†] * |
| Monnin Paul N | DLA Piper LLP (US) (ONP)[†] * * |
| Whitley Joe D | Greenberg Traurig, LLP * |

**Up-and-coming individuals**

| | |
|---|---|
| Pak Byung | Ballard Spahr LLP (ONP)[†] * |

*Indicates firm / individual with profile.*
[†] *ONP = Other Notable Practitioner*

---

**Sources say:** "*The level of sophistication of their work certainly warrants their position at the top of this legal community.*"

**KEY INDIVIDUALS** Both peers and clients are vociferous in their praise of seasoned litigator **Emmet Bondurant**. He continues to be regarded as "*a very fine trial lawyer,*" drawing especial praise for his skillful navigation of the political landscape that often surrounds the legislative process. The "*highly regarded*" **Jill Pryor** is an experienced trial and appellate attorney. Interviewees particularly appreciate her intellectual grasp of many of the more nuanced aspects of litigation. **Jeffrey Bramlett** is revered by sources for his strong legal malpractice defense practice. "*He knows how to get to the point and represents his clients well,*" commented one source, while another said: "*He's a serious lawyer to whom I'd entrust the most serious of matters.*" **Lamar Mixson** is an active commercial litigator who commands an enviable reputation in the Atlanta area. He is particularly skilled in the representation of plaintiffs and is widely regarded as a tenacious and aggressive courtroom advocate. **John Floyd**'s practice focuses primarily on RICO litigation. "*He has to be one of the most articulate lawyers I've ever come across,*" noted one source. "*He has impressed me immensely.*" Interviewees were effusive in their assessment of **Frank Lowrey**'s litigation ability. Sources commend him for his confident and pragmatic approach to engagements. He is regarded as an "*extraordinary lawyer who is superb at dealing with appellate cases.*" **Edward Krugman** is, in the words of one peer, an "*excellent lawyer whom I wouldn't hesitate to involve in a case.*" He routinely represents both plaintiffs and defendants and retains a core expertise in the representation of manufacturing and direct selling companies. Peers single out **Michael Terry** as a strong commercial litigator with a specific expertise in appellate matters. He is further praised for the controlled aggression he exhibits within the courtroom.

### King & Spalding LLP
**See profile on p.445**

**THE FIRM** This litigation powerhouse retains its stellar reputation with the sector, with both its virtually unparalleled depth of resources and its prominent product liability group pinpointed as particular strengths. Its large and impressive bench houses considerable expertise in both civil and criminal litigation matters, with its commercial team routinely prevailing in high-profile class action suits and its white-collar defense group numbering among the most visible in the state.

**Sources say:** "*Excellent in all regards.*" "*They have an extraordinary reputation.*"

**KEY INDIVIDUALS Stephen Cowen** (see p.1079) is recommended for his strength in the white-collar crime arena. Sources agree that *"he is one of the best lawyers to ever practice in this area."* **Christopher Wray** (see p.1101) has enjoyed a particularly active year, in which he has represented a diverse array of clients from the pharmaceutical and energy sectors. Peers remark favorably upon his national presence, in addition to highlighting his superb skill set and *"amazing credentials."* **Catherine O'Neil** (see p.1092) is *"a brilliant attorney"* and is esteemed by market commentators for her experience with criminal litigation. She is said to be *"encyclopedic in her preparation and grasp of the facts"* and commands a strong regional reputation. **Paul Murphy** (see p.1091) is a *"highly professional"* attorney, capable of providing clients with a *"smooth and polished"* work product. He regularly conducts internal investigations on behalf of healthcare corporations. **Elizabeth Vranicar Tanis** (see p.1098) continues to enhance her reputation as a prodigiously talented litigator. She is identified as being *"erudite and accomplished"* and is frequently sought out for her expertise in accounting firm liability matters. **Chilton Davis Varner** (see p.302) is, according to interviewees, *"one of the finest trial lawyers in the country."* *"She's one of those attorneys who can try a case anywhere in the country and be embraced by both jury and judge for her scholarship and her ability to use the courtroom as a classroom to teach onlookers,"* reports one impressed source. The *"pragmatic"* **David Balser** (see p.1075) is identified by sources as a *"fine litigator"* who *"neither incurs legal expenses needlessly, nor litigates for the sake of litigation."* *"A lawyer of exceptional professionalism,"* **Joseph Loveland** (see p.1089) receives positive feedback from a variety of sources. He is said to be an *"excellent strategist"* and an excellent trial attorney. Capable of drawing upon over three decades' worth of experience, **John Chandler** (see p.1078) commands an outstanding reputation within the Atlanta legal community. He is said to exercise *"superb legal judgment"* and often acts on behalf of both law and accounting firms. **Ray Persons** (see p.1093) is revered by myriad sources for his courtroom demeanor. *"He's the consummate gentleman and clients love him,"* noted one source, while another added: *"Jurors love him because they like his approach."* **Robert Thornton** (see p.1099) is widely acclaimed for his competency in a range of litigation matters. His practice centers primarily upon shareholder claims and securities litigation. **Richard Schneider** (see p.1096) specializes in product liability cases. He is respected for the considerable depth of experience that he brings to matters.

## Band 2

### Kilpatrick Townsend & Stockton LLP
See profile on p.1109

**THE FIRM** The robust litigation team is commended for its strength across numerous industry sectors. It ably litigates on behalf of many large and medium-sized defendants and is unfazed by complex or esoteric legislation. The firm's prominence in trade secret litigation has been

noted by several commentators, as has its capacity to adroitly handle both IP and construction litigation assignments. One recent success was obtained on behalf of local firm Alston & Bird in connection to a long-standing dispute between partners. **Sources say:** *"They've done a spectacular job for us in litigation matters."* *"They are very comprehensive, clear and consistent."*

**KEY INDIVIDUALS Stephens Clay** continues to *"command tremendous respect among his peers"* and maintains an active practice. He recently provided counsel to Alston & Bird as it sought to resolve a substantial partner dispute. **William Boice** has a rich and varied practice, combining expertise in litigation with a comprehensive knowledge of issues pertaining to both the employment and IP sectors. He is hailed as a *"superb lawyer"* by those who have had the opportunity to closely observe his courtroom performance. He is currently advising Google in relation to several patent litigation cases. Senior market sources consider **Susan Cahoon** to be *"a very effective practitioner,"* characterized by the *"first-rate"* service she provides to clients. She oversees a variety of high-profile cases, with her ongoing representation of manufacturing giant Andritz serving as one such example. Identified as a *"very fine lawyer"* by market commentators, **David Zacks** is a noted healthcare litigator. He recently provided counsel to a quadriplegic plaintiff in a lawsuit brought against a lawn mower manufacturer. **George Murphy** undertakes all aspects of commercial litigation and is regularly hired by large companies seeking representation. Georgia-Pacific recently engaged him to handle the appellate aspects of a distributorship dispute. **James Bogan** is singled out for his competency in appellate litigation. He continues to be engaged by AT&T Advertising & Publishing in relation to an ongoing class action matter that recently reached the appellate stage.

### Rogers & Hardin LLP
See profile on p.1111

**THE FIRM** This thriving litigation boutique elicits praise for the diversity and breadth of its Atlanta-based practice. Its compact team of core practitioners offers a stellar service while maintaining a cost-effective pricing model. The firm is routinely hired to handle large class actions, with its defense of SouthStar Energy in a consumer class action matter serving as one of its more notable recent successes. **Sources say:** *"I think that they do an excellent job in commercial litigation and that they're very effective."*

**KEY INDIVIDUALS** The *"very distinguished"* **CB Rogers** (see p.1095) remains a *"preeminent Atlanta litigator."* He is perceived to be a *"legend"* within the legal community and a leading figure of the firm's litigation practice. **Richard Sinkfield** (see p.1097) is singled out for commendation by several senior market sources. *"He has such an amazing presence that he makes everyone else feel inferior,"* reported one interviewee, while another noted that *"jurors find it very easily to listen to him and judges appreciate having him in their courtroom."* **Robert Remar** (see p.1094) is, according to one source, blessed with a *"gift for explaining things clearly."* His expertise spans the spectrum of commercial litigation matters and he continues to work closely with

Georgia-Pacific. Sources appreciate **Tony Powers**'s (see p.1094) *"sophisticated practice."* He is perceived as being *"on the shortlist one would go to for referrals in the state"* and is deeply experienced in all manner of commercial litigation engagements. **John Almond** (see p.1074) recently acted as part of a team representing the current and former directors of Wells REIT in a series of class actions totaling $140 million in damages. Almond has a solid reputation within the Georgia market and remains an integral member of the firm's regional platform.

### Sutherland Asbill & Brennan LLP

**THE FIRM** This stalwart of the Southeastern legal landscape offers a high degree of expertise in a number of litigation specialties, including professional liability and work in the financial services and education sectors. The group is further acclaimed for the strength of its securities litigation practice, which remains among Georgia's most prominent. Among its key clients, the firm can count City of Atlanta, DeKalb County School District and Immucor. **KEY INDIVIDUALS John Fleming** is lauded for his admirable commitment to client service and analytical approach. He was successful in obtaining a summary dismissal for Transocean in a recent class action lawsuit. Highly experienced litigator **Peter Anderson** is held in high esteem for his expertise in securities litigation defense. He has acted for clients in numerous trials at both state and federal level. **Thomas Curvin** has carved out a reputation for himself in the commercial litigation arena and is singled out as a particularly adept insurance litigator.

### Troutman Sanders LLP

**THE FIRM** This well-regarded Atlanta-based firm routinely dispenses sage advice on a multitude of litigation issues. Energy litigation remains an integral facet of this group's practice; it recently assisted Alabama Power as it obtained summary judgment in connection with a clean air enforcement lawsuit. Other clients include SunTrust Banks and Reed Construction Data.

**KEY INDIVIDUALS John Dalton** is a senior member of the firm's commercial litigation team. Peers are effusive in their appraisal of his skills, with peers praising his excellent trial skills and impressive breadth of experience. **Daniel Reinhardt** is a very well-respected commercial litigator skilled in the intricacies of both employment and environmental litigation. He led the firm's successful defense of Alabama Power in a recent engagement. Practice leader **William Withrow** concentrates primarily on advising telecommunication companies throughout the litigation process. Sources laud his ability to handle large class action defense assignments. **Karen Deming** possesses a particularly strong reputation in the product liability sphere. She is further recognized for her management of mass tort claims.

## Band 3

### Doffermyre Shields Canfield & Knowles, LLC
See profile on p.1106

THE FIRM This boutique specializes in acting on behalf of plaintiffs, typically in large class action lawsuits. Its practice is defined by its diversity and houses a number of highly talented attorneys, each of whom is adept in advising across a range of different industries. Market commentators hail the firm's ability to exercise controlled aggression within the courtroom.

Sources say: *"I've always admired their ability to take the appropriate plaintiff cases. They've been very successful in their own niche."*

KEY INDIVIDUALS *"Top-notch plaintiffs lawyer"* **Kenneth Canfield** is held in high regard by sources. He is labeled a *"brilliant litigator,"* and is further highlighted for his *"extremely strategic"* approach to engagements. **Everette Doffermyre** wins praise for his strong plaintiff-oriented practice. He is active in connection with many of the firm's more complex engagements. According to one interviewee, **Ralph Knowles** is *"regarded as one of the best mass tort plaintiff lawyers in the Southeastern region."* He continues to have a robust practice spanning a plethora of industries. **Robert Shields** is recognized as a *"really good appellate lawyer,"* who is said to possess *"great legal skills."* He has an enviable track record and a well-established regional reputation.

### Jones Day
See profile on p.919

THE FIRM This group's expansive litigation practice has the capacity to handle both regional controversies and, by drawing upon its global resources, multistate class action cases. Acclaimed by clients for the complexity of the cases it routinely undertakes, Jones Day continues to service a vast array of recognizable clients, including Expedia, Southern Company and Atlantic Southeast Airlines.

Sources say: *"The Atlanta litigation team is very knowledgeable of the law, responsive and sensitive to client needs."*

KEY INDIVIDUALS **Richard Deane** (see p.1080) is widely regarded as one of the strongest white-collar crime practitioners in the state. He is said to combine his prodigious intelligence with a *"style and wit"* that lends him a certain gravitas in the courtroom. He recently represented a multinational firm as it sought to defend itself against allegations of fraud. **Stephanie Parker** (see p.1092) is *"generally recognized as one of the best attorneys in the region"* and is *"recognized worldwide for her strength in the defense of tobacco companies."* She recently obtained a favorable verdict in a matter handled on behalf of R.J. Reynolds. **Lee Garrett** (see p.1082) is a highly experienced trial lawyer who possesses expertise in both personal injury and product liability matters. He continues to work with Yamaha, handling the appellate aspects of a substantial lawsuit. **Michael McConnell** (see p.1090) is revered as a *"strong corporate litigator"* and his counsel is sought by a selection of both regional and global corporations. He has lately handled a number of shareholder class action defense suits. **Kendrick Smith** (see p.1097) has devoted much of

his time to the representation of Educational Testing Services, and played a vital role in the ultimately favorable resolution that the company was able to procure.

### McKenna Long & Aldridge LLP
See profile on p.922

THE FIRM This national firm's Georgia litigation practice maintains a solid market presence and continues to service a healthy selection of clients. The team possesses particular strength in a number of niche areas, and its stable of litigators generates specific praise for its expertise in healthcare, bankruptcy and insurance litigation. Recent clients include SunTrust Bank, Dow Chemical and Pike Nurseries.

Sources say: *"They excel in the role of being problem solvers."*

KEY INDIVIDUALS The *"excellent"* **Matthew Martin** (see p.1089) is described as being *"a fantastic lawyer in every way"* and an *"aggressive litigator."* He is currently representing CIBC World Markets as it seeks to defend itself against accusations of fraud, gross negligence and breach of fiduciary duty.

### Parker, Hudson, Rainer & Dobbs LLP

THE FIRM This compact yet effective Atlanta group remains a competitive alternative to larger national firms. The team is active in connection with financial services disputes and its clients include Regions Bank, Goldman Sachs and Barclays Capital.

Sources say: *"I have a lot of respect for the firm. Their briefs have been outstanding. They do outstanding work."*

KEY INDIVIDUALS The *"exceptionally smart"* **William Holley** is identified as an astute and incisive attorney by a variety of market sources. He is further acclaimed as an *"outstanding tactician"* and, in recent months, has furnished advice for BB&T on multiple occasions. Departmental chair **Ronald Coleman** has a thriving practice, focused entirely upon litigation. He recently acted on behalf of Quest Diagnostics, handling the post-trial elements of a medical malpractice action. **Marbury Rainer** is a securities expert, specializing in related litigation matters. He is lauded for his ability to ensure that *"clients don't end up fighting about things they don't need to fight about."*

## Band 4

### Arnall Golden Gregory LLP
See profile on p.1103

THE FIRM This group is recommended for its creative approach to commercial litigation, with many clients seeking out its expertise for their most complex matters. It has a particularly strong track record in healthcare litigation, drawing upon the firm's historical expertise in this sector. It recently represented SavaSeniorCare in a matter pertaining to disputed contractual provisions.

Sources say: *"The quality of their work is excellent."*

KEY INDIVIDUALS Sources find **Robert Rothman** (see p.1095) to be an *"excellent advocate"* who *"doesn't argue about irrelevancies."* He represented Emory University in a recent dispute.

### Bryan Cave LLP

THE FIRM This Atlanta-based firm continues to warrant recognition for its prowess in litigation. It has disputes experience in areas such as transportation, healthcare and financial services. One recent engagement entailed the representation of corporate juggernaut Google in connection to a negligence action.

KEY INDIVIDUALS The outstanding **William Custer** is perceived to approach matters in a very thorough and clear manner.

### Chilivis, Cochran, Larkins & Bever LLP

THE FIRM Specialist firm Chilivis Cochran has the expertise to handle both commercial litigation and white-collar crime cases in an expedient and proficient manner. Its team of dedicated litigators continues to offer comprehensive guidance to clients seeking counsel in a broad range of matters.

Sources say: *"A prestigious boutique with very well thought-of litigators"*

KEY INDIVIDUALS **Anthony Cochran** is identified as being an *"excellent advocate on both white-collar and commercial litigation matters."* *"If I needed counsel myself,"* said one peer, *"he'd be the attorney that I'd contact."* White-collar crime specialist **Tom Bever** is described by sources as an *"excellent trial lawyer"* and enjoys a strong reputation within the legal community.

### Fellows LaBriola LLP

THE FIRM This Atlanta-based litigation boutique is equipped to handle all varieties of dispute resolution. Market opinion widely hails the firm's ability to act on large-scale cases. Another attractive feature of the practice is its willingness to offer clients a range of alternative billing arrangements.

Sources say: *"They really punch above their weight."*

KEY INDIVIDUALS **Henry Fellows** (see p.1081) elicits a superb critical response from a variety of market sources. *"When he walks into court, he has instant credibility,"* said one source, while another pinpointed the *"calming ability that he exudes in court."* His practice encompasses the entire commercial litigation spectrum. The *"terrific"* **Stephen LaBriola** (see p.1088) attracts recognition for the breadth of his practice and the strength of the representation he offers.

### Greenberg Traurig, LLP
See profile on p.1024

THE FIRM Greenberg Traurig continues to distinguish itself for both the quality and consistency of its work in the product liability sphere. The firm has a vibrant trial practice and is commended for its willingness to provide vigorous representation in court when more moderate attempts at resolution have been exhausted.

Sources say: *"I think that they do outstanding work; they work very hard but they are also very mindful of the business aspects of litigation."*

KEY INDIVIDUALS *"If I had a matter of sufficient magnitude, I wouldn't hesitate to use him again,"* reported one impressed client of **Joe Whitley** (see p.1100). He has a number of *"excellent relationships and contacts"* and is recommended for his white-collar work. **Lori Cohen** (see p.1078), known nationally for her superb product liability practice, retains her status as one of Atlanta's premier litigators. *"She is fantastic: a top-notch individual,"* said one interviewee. Another labeled her a *"great trial attorney with a superb record."* She continues to act on behalf of Medtronic in a vast array of engagements. According to one market commentator, **Mark Trigg** (see p.1099) is *"among the top civil litigators in the region"* and is further identified as a *"very solid practitioner whom one would trust with complex matters."* **Terry Weiss**'s (see p.1099) practice focuses upon the representation of broker houses sued for mismanagement. He is recommended for his ability to *"formulate strategies and take steps designed to limit a company's litigation risk."*

## Holland & Knight LLP
### See profile on p.1028

**THE FIRM** This compact team punches above its weight when it comes to litigation matters. The group handles a broad range of cases, inclusive of appellate, RICO and product liability matters. In a recent work highlight, the team defended Atlanta Independent School System in a class action suit that challenged its school's use of taxes for economic development. The team acts as counsel to a diverse client list that includes Bondurant, Embraco and Toyota Financial Savings Bank.

**Sources say:** *"I've worked with a number of individuals at the firm; I've seen how they operate and I've been impressed."*

**KEY INDIVIDUALS Harold Daniel** (see p.1079) focuses his established practice on litigation involving antitrust, business torts and general commercial matters. Sources commend him as a trial lawyer who has *"vast experience with juries and complex business disputes."* **Laurie Webb Daniel** (see p.1079) is described by observers as someone who has *"both the respect and the ear of the appellate courts."* Recently, she formed part of the team acting for Terrabrook Vista Lakes, defending a putative class action brought against it regarding a real estate development in the vicinity of a bomb range dating from the Second World War. **Allen Maines** (see p.1089) recently joined the firm from Paul Hastings. He is noted for his *"ability to make deals happen."* *"I would say that he's the brightest and best attorney that I've worked with,"* one source reported.

## HunterMaclean

**THE FIRM** HunterMaclean is the largest firm in Savannah and the team continues to set the litigation standard in that market. The group has experience of handling the entire gamut of commercial litigation matters and frequently handles cases for clients of national import as well as non-profit entities.

**KEY INDIVIDUALS John Tatum** undertakes litigation matters relating to business torts, ERISA and fraud. He commands the respect of the legal market, with sources enthusing about his technical ability and trial prowess.

## Hunton & Williams LLP
### See profile on p.2517

**THE FIRM** This firm has a broad-based practice that encompasses areas such as e-discovery, commercial litigation and bankruptcy. The group advises market-leading national clients from many different industries and is well supported by other departments within the firm. Sources are particularly appreciative of the team's professional approach toward matters.

**Sources say:** *"They're conscientious, responsive and attentive to details."*

**KEY INDIVIDUALS** Head of the e-discovery group **Lawrence Bracken** (see p.1076) contributes over 25 years of experience to his practice. Observers hail him as a knowledgeable attorney who is business-savvy and always available. His practice is varied, with specific expertise in the defense of class actions. **Matthew Calvert** (see p.1077) is described as an *"anchor for the practice"* and is well regarded by clients for his intellect, attention to detail and high levels of responsiveness. His practice has an enviable scope and covers commercial disputes, real estate and pharmaceutical litigation.

## Morris, Manning & Martin, LLP

**THE FIRM** Morris, Manning & Martin's Atlanta-based team frequently handles multistate litigation in a variety of industries. The team has a specialty in class action lawsuits, which has seen it defend The Home Depot in a series of multiplaintiff product liability and consumer fraud cases that spanned multiple states. In a further work highlight the team has acted as lead counsel to Ingenico in a patent infringement case. The firm's portfolio includes clients such as SunTrust Bank, Georgia Gulf and Direct General.

**Sources say:** *"The firm has an excellent litigation department."* *"I'm impressed with the level of support that they gave us."*

**KEY INDIVIDUALS John MacNaughton** has a solid reputation among sources for the quality of the legal advice he dispenses. He has deep experience in multiparty, multistate litigation.

## Paul Hastings LLP
### See profile on p.1996

**THE FIRM** This nationally renowned team demonstrates impressive abilities in the litigation field. Sources remark favorably upon the firm's legal footprint, citing its practice in other states as one of its primary strengths. Of particular note is the group's defense of Regions Bank in relation to allegations of fraud and conspiracy.

**Sources say:** *"Their resources are second to none."*

**KEY INDIVIDUALS William Whitner** is a key contact.

## Womble Carlyle Sandridge & Rice, LLP
### See profile on p.2049

**THE FIRM** The team at Womble Carlyle has a deep range of experience in areas such as mass torts, trade secrets and antitrust. The group is well placed to draw upon the firm's expertise in other offices, making it particularly suited to advise a range of clients involved in commercial disputes. In a recent work highlight, the team represented Transcend

Services in an action by shareholders to enjoin the company's merger with Nuance Communications. The group's clients include Jack Cooper Transport, Pennington Seed and Reynolds American.

**Sources say:** *"The quality of the firm's work is excellent."*

**KEY INDIVIDUALS William Ragland** focuses his practice on disputes stemming from areas such as copyrights, IP, technology and patents. Sources hail him as an *"efficient, knowledgeable and proficient"* attorney, who is well connected within the local community.

## Other Notable Practitioners

**Bruce Maloy** of Maloy Jenkins Parker impresses sources by the ease with which he provides consistently high-quality advice in all situations. His white-collar practice encompasses defending individuals accused of SEC violations, fraud and tax evasion. **Donald Samuel** of Garland, Samuel & Loeb P.C. is, according to sources, one of the deans of the white-collar Bar. He undertakes a wide range of criminal defense at both state and federal level. **Jerome Froelich** of McKenney & Froelich tries a wide variety of criminal cases and is praised by sources as an *"accomplished and unafraid"* attorney. His practice focuses on criminal trials, including RICO and drug conspiracy. **Craig Gillen** of Gillen, Withers & Lake, LLC contributes 30 years of experience to his litigation practice. He focuses on criminal defense matters, in which he represents government agents and professionals. **Bruce Morris** of Finestone & Morris LLP is singled out by sources for his ability to be aggressive when the situation demands. Observers enthuse that he is *"really effective and extremely sharp."* He handles sophisticated criminal defense and civil litigation matters. **Byung Pak** (see p.1092) of Ballard Spahr LLP is *"thorough, diligent and creative"* and has impressed sources through the professionalism he exhibits throughout engagements. He has a broad-based practice that encompasses internal investigations, regulatory compliance and civil litigation. **Michael Bowers** of Balch & Bingham LLP is hailed for his hands-on litigation style, with sources commending his consistently meticulous approach toward a case. He focuses on representing private entities in conflict with governmental bodies. **Mark Grantham** (see p.1083) of DLA Piper LLP (US) has a practice with a strong international focus that saw him represent GDF SUEZ Energy Central America in a recent matter concerning the disputed redevelopment of a coal-fired power plant in Panama. At the same firm, white-collar practitioner **Paul Monnin** (see p.1090) is *"a great adviser and a strategic thinker"* who wins praise from clients for his familiarity with relevant legal concepts. In a recent work highlight, he represented GE Capital in a $4 million federal litigation suit brought with the intention of recovering funds converted by a joint venture partner. **Kenneth Menendez** (see p.1090) of Epstein Becker & Green PC recently represented personnel staffing company Johnson Service Group in a sexual harassment case. Sources commend him as a *"wise and experienced"* lawyer who is accessible at all hours. **Halsey Knapp** of Foltz Martin LLC represents clients involved in sophisticated business litigation and is also experienced in civil litigation. His corporate litigation practice includes trade secrets and restrictive covenants. **John Sherrill** (see p.1096) of Seyfarth Shaw LLP brings deep experience and knowledge to his dispute resolution practice. He recently represented an architectural joint venture in a contract dispute regarding the design of Hartsfield-Jackson airport's new terminal. He is also well versed in general commercial litigation matters. **Jeffrey Horst** (see p.1085) of Krevolin & Horst, LLC is well received by interviewees, who single out his technical ability for praise. He concentrates his practice on commercial litigation including business torts, professional liability and IP. **Daniel Griffin** (see p.1083) of Miller &

Martin PLLC advises clients on a diverse range of white-collar matters, including income tax offenses, money laundering and mortgage fraud. He is also well experienced in grand jury and internal investigations. Observers comment favorably on his work ethic. **William Hill** (see p.1084) of Rafuse Hill & Hodges LLP has the respect of clients and peers alike, who enthuse that he is not only a very fine lawyer but also a stellar adversary. Of late, he represented Atkins North America and a former employee in a civil action regarding a single-vehicle rollover. **Linda Klein** (see p.1087) heads up the Baker, Donelson, Bearman, Caldwell & Berkowitz, PC litigation department

and is an "*unbelievably energetic, positive, intelligent and creative lawyer,*" according to sources. She centers her practice around commercial dispute resolution, inclusive of contract law and professional liability. **Joseph Sharp** (see p.1096) of Rafuse Hill & Hodges LLP focuses his practice on commercial litigation across a range of industries and is experienced in multidistrict cases and class action. In a recent key mandate, he defended Leon Jones Feed & Grain in a case brought against it regarding insufficient workers' compensation coverage.

# REAL ESTATE

Commentary about individuals can be found under their firm's paragraph. If the firm has no paragraph (is not ranked) look at Other Notable Practitioners.

| Real Estate |
|---|
| **Leading Firms** |
| **Band 1** |
| Alston & Bird LLP * |
| King & Spalding LLP * |
| Sutherland Asbill & Brennan LLP |
| **Band 2** |
| Arnall Golden Gregory LLP * |
| Morris, Manning & Martin, LLP |
| Troutman Sanders LLP |
| **Band 3** |
| Bryan Cave LLP |
| Greenberg Traurig, LLP * |
| Kilpatrick Townsend & Stockton LLP * |
| McKenna Long & Aldridge LLP * |
| Seyfarth Shaw LLP * |
| Smith Gambrell & Russell LLP * |

*\* Indicates firm with profile.*
*Alphabetical order within each band. Band 1 is the highest.*

## Band 1

### Alston & Bird LLP
See profile on p.1102
**THE FIRM** This outstanding team continues to be involved in a number of Georgia's most valuable and prominent commercial real estate matters. The group recently advised Paramount Group on its $158 million acquisition of 2099 Pennsylvania Avenue. It has also represented Bank of America in the enforcement of a mortgage loan. It serves a number of other illustrious clients, including KPMG and Industrial Developments International.
**Sources say:** "*An excellent firm with excellent lawyers.*"
**KEY INDIVIDUALS Timothy Pakenham** (see p.1092) is an experienced practitioner who covers a broad range of real estate issues. Impressed clients believe him to be

"*incredibly knowledgeable on issues surrounding real estate.*" He recently represented Metropolitan Life Insurance in its acquisition of Reynolds Plantation. **Mark Rusche** (see p.1095) is acclaimed by the wider market as "*an excellent lawyer*" and is valued for his expertise in leasing. He led the firm's representation of SHP IV in the $100 million acquisition of three senior housing projects in Florida. **James Farris** (see p.1081) is particularly renowned for his skills in joint ventures in the real estate sphere. He recently assisted Industrial Developments International with a complicated $200 million joint venture with a state pension fund. As co-leader of the firm's real estate finance and investment group, **Allison Ryan** (see p.1095) is involved in some of its most valuable work. She was the lead partner in both the Paramount Group acquisition and the Bank of America matter.

### King & Spalding LLP
See profile on p.445
**THE FIRM** This market-leading team has been active in a range of high-value matters for its stellar client base. Included in these is its representation of Morgan Stanley in over $2.5 billion of investments both overseas and domestically. Its ten-partner team offers coverage of the spectrum of real estate issues, reflected in its work for Jamestown which entails fund formation, various acquisitions and many complex financings. Other highlights include representing Prologis in formation and fundraising for various investment funds and joint ventures.
**Sources say:** "*A wonderful, well-regarded firm.*"
**KEY INDIVIDUALS Mason Stephenson** (see p.1098) is said to be "*a legend in Georgia real estate,*" a title earned during over 40 years of activity in the field. He took the lead for GE Capital in its mortgage loans, one of over $1 billion and another of $575 million, to investment funds managed by The Blackstone Group. **Joshua Kamin** (see

p.1086) is a fast-rising team member, applauded as "*an extremely polished young attorney*" who sources believe is "*very articulate and thoughtful.*" He has been especially active recently, acting for both Jamestown and GE Capital. "*High-quality lawyer*" **Timothy Goodwin** (see p.1082) has a particular emphasis in his practice on the formation of investment funds, financing, construction and leasing. He has been one of the key partners in representing Morgan Stanley and has also worked on behalf of Brookdale Investors Six in acquiring and financing $500 million of assets. **Dan Heller** (see p.1084) is said to be "*one heck of a lawyer who is very solid in terms of drafting and his knowledge of the law.*" He has been involved in the representation of IVG Institutional Funds in the sales of an Illinois office building and a retail development in Boston for a total of $163 million. **Clayton Howell** (see p.1085) is building a reputation as an able lawyer with a growing profile in the market. He took a lead role in acting for Post Apartment Homes on a variety of matters, including acquisitions, development and financing. He frequently represents equity investors and developers.

### Sutherland Asbill & Brennan LLP
**THE FIRM** This group is widely acknowledged as one of the traditional big hitters in the Georgia real estate market, with clients quick to acclaim the high standard of service on offer. The team has recently been engaged by Oglethorpe Power in its $529 million acquisition of two combined cycle facilities. It has also represented Worthing Southeast Builders in developing and financing multiple residential projects in Georgia and North Carolina with a total value of over $200 million.
**KEY INDIVIDUALS** Enthusiastic clients are quick to praise **Alfred Adams** for his business-focused and pragmatic approach to finding solutions. He was lead partner in representing Worthing Southeast Builders. **James**

## Real Estate
### Leading Individuals

**Band 1**

| | |
|---|---|
| Adams Jr Alfred G | Sutherland Asbill & Brennan LLP |
| Jordan James B | Sutherland Asbill & Brennan LLP |
| Pakenham Timothy J | Alston & Bird LLP * |
| Rusche Mark C | Alston & Bird LLP * |

**Band 2**

| | |
|---|---|
| Block Mark A | Seyfarth Shaw LLP * |
| Dent Miriam | Rogers & Hardin LLP (ONP)† * |
| Farris Jr James G | Alston & Bird LLP (ONP)† * |
| Fisher Scott A | Arnall Golden Gregory LLP * |
| Foltz Joseph B | Foltz Martin LLC (ONP)† |
| Goodwin Timothy J | King & Spalding LLP * |
| Haley Victor P | Sutherland Asbill & Brennan LLP |
| Hicks M Maxine | DLA Piper LLP (US) (ONP)† * |
| Kamin Joshua M | King & Spalding LLP * |
| Kauss Andrew | Kilpatrick Townsend & Stockton LLP |
| Orr III A Summey | Hartman Simons & Wood LLP (ONP)† |
| Parks John R | Bryan Cave LLP |
| Sharbaugh Charles | Carlton Fields, P.A. (ONP)† * |
| Sheley Raymond | Sheley & Hall (ONP)† |
| Specht Scott A | Jones Day (ONP)† * |
| Stephenson Mason W | King & Spalding LLP * |
| Westmoreland Jr Carl | Morris, Manning & Martin, LLP |

**Band 3**

| | |
|---|---|
| Dobbins Carolyn B | Rogers & Hardin LLP (ONP)† * |
| Farris Gary W | Burr & Forman LLP |
| Fowler Candace L | Kilpatrick Townsend & Stockton LLP |
| Gryboski Thomas | Morris, Manning & Martin, LLP |
| Hales Jr H Edward | Sutherland Asbill & Brennan LLP |
| Heller Dan | King & Spalding LLP * |
| Howell D Clayton | King & Spalding LLP * |
| Kerman Michael G | Sutherland Asbill & Brennan LLP |
| Kraft Kenneth H | Parker, Hudson, Rainer & Dobbs (ONP)† |
| Krevolin Douglas P | Krevolin & Horst, LLC (ONP)† * |
| Levin Jay J | Bryan Cave LLP |
| Morris John G | Morris, Manning & Martin, LLP |
| Ryan Allison M | Alston & Bird LLP * |
| Simons Robert D | Hartman Simons & Wood LLP (ONP)† |
| Skinner Philip G | Arnall Golden Gregory LLP * |
| Stevens William | McKenna Long & Aldridge LLP |
| Walker Homer Lee | Morris, Manning & Martin, LLP |
| Williams Andrew C | Morris, Manning & Martin, LLP |
| Willis A Michelle (Shelli) | Troutman Sanders LLP |
| Young Malcolm D | Smith Gambrell & Russell LLP * |

**Up-and-coming individuals**

| | |
|---|---|
| Kennedy Steven L. | Seyfarth Shaw LLP * |

\* Indicates individual with profile.
†ONP = Other Notable Practitioner

**Jordan** is seen by peers as an intellectual leader in the field, and is applauded for his detail-oriented approach to matters. He is also lauded for his expertise in leasing and development work. **Victor Haley** has vast experience in this field, and has represented a number of hotel operators and resort developers. He earns particular acclaim for his expertise in timberland issues. **Edward Hales** can draw upon many years of experience in the sector to support his

practice. He is greatly respected by his peers. **Michael Kerman** remains a popular choice with clients, who praise his dedication and deep understanding of their business needs. He is admitted to practice in both Florida and Georgia.

## Band 2

### Arnall Golden Gregory LLP
See profile on p.1103

**THE FIRM** This Atlanta-based team has established itself as a leading authority on local real estate matters, and can be considered among the foremost groups for transactions in the region. A large team of 22 partners and 31 other professionals offers particular strength in subsidised financing. It has recently advised Smashburger on its acquisition of new properties and plans to expand into further sites. **KEY INDIVIDUALS Scott Fisher** (see p.1081) places the representation of developers, owners and investors at the heart of his practice, and specialises in the structuring and closing of commercial real estate transactions and joint ventures. The head of the leasing practise, as well as the cross-border practice, **Philip Skinner** (see p.1097) is seen as *"very good on the leasing area, very practical, easy to work with and very knowledgeable."* He has a broad practice incorporating the representation of owners, investors and developers on a variety of transactions.

### Morris, Manning & Martin, LLP
**THE FIRM** This firm covers all aspects of real estate finance and development, offering clients a comprehensive service through its experienced team. The group is well-embedded in the local market and recently represented Regent Partners in the development of a mixed-use hotel, office and retail project at a value of approximately $100 million. It has also been engaged by OliverMcMillan in the development of a nine-acre mixed-use project in Atlanta's former nightclub district, valued at over $1 billion. Other clients include Noble Investment Group and Peachtree Hotel Group.
**KEY INDIVIDUALS Carl Westmoreland** has a particular focus on land use and zoning issues, areas for which he is greatly esteemed. He is applauded as *"one of the top zoning attorneys in the city"* and can draw on extensive experience to support his practice. As head of the hospitality practice, **Thomas Gryboski** has established an impressive reputation for work of this kind, although he is also active in real estate acquisitions, joint ventures and numerous other transactions. Founding partner **John Morris** brings over 40 years' experience in the real estate field to the team, and is consistently involved in the group's nationwide transactions. He is recognized as being particularly adept in representing sponsors of real estate investment trusts. One source lauds **Homer Walker** as *"one of the best leasing lawyers I know."* He has considerable expertise dealing with real estate investment trusts and joint ventures, and was lead partner in the firm's representation of Regent Partners. **Andrew Williams** is praised by clients for his *"brilliant, practical and prompt"* advice. He deals with most

aspects of commercial real estate, including financing, development and acquisitions of projects.

### Troutman Sanders LLP
**THE FIRM** Interviewees single out the Troutman Sanders team for its capabilities in both the leasing and development practices. While it is able to draw upon the firm's extensive national network to coordinate complex projects across a number of jurisdictions, it also maintains a considerable presence in the local market. This large group can call upon experts in the fields of real estate funding, leasing, development and acquisition to round off a full-service offering.
**KEY INDIVIDUALS Shelli Willis** has strong legal skills and does very well for her clients, according to interviewees. She predominantly represents major banking and financial institutions in the financing of real estate projects.

## Band 3

### Bryan Cave LLP
**THE FIRM** The team has recently represented the Metropolitan Atlanta Rapid Transit Authority (MARTA) in the ongoing development of Lindbergh City Center, as well as its development of a new Medical Center Station. It is also particularly adroit in representing lenders in major commercial projects and developments, and is noted for the strength of its national presence alongside its offering from Atlanta.
**KEY INDIVIDUALS Jay Levin** is a well-regarded figure in the market with extensive expertise in a range of real estate matters. He has been involved in the financing of hotels, office buildings and industrial sites, and alongside impressive commercial clients has also represented a number of government agencies. **John Parks** is a well-known figure in the Atlanta market and has built a strong local reputation for his work in complicated transactions and major projects. His practice covers the greater part of real estate matters, encompassing acquisition, financing, leasing and development.

### Greenberg Traurig, LLP
See profile on p.1024

**THE FIRM** This team continues to expand its share of the Atlanta market, and is able to draw upon the firm's imposing national network and resources to supplement its presence. It draws particular acclaim for its expertise in hospitality projects. It handles the entire range of real estate matters, including funding and representation of institutional lenders for projects.
**KEY INDIVIDUALS** Of counsel Michael Ward is a key contact at the group's Atlanta office.

### Kilpatrick Townsend & Stockton LLP
See profile on p.1109

**THE FIRM** The Kilpatrick Townsend team remains an active and visible feature of the Atlanta market and is appreciated by clients for its high standard of service.

Among other valuable engagements, it was recently instructed by Gables Metropolitan to represent it in sales of over $100 million of assets. It was also involved in the sale of a multifamily, $150 million portfolio in Texas.

Sources say: *"The service has always been superb."*

KEY INDIVIDUALS Andrew Kauss is *"an excellent lawyer"* according to respectful peers. Clients believe that *"he has superior business judgment, gives practical advice, is a fierce advocate and understands the critical legal issues that impact our business."* Candace Fowler was the lead partner in both the Gables Metropolitan transaction and the multifamily portfolio sale. Said to be *"very, very smart"* by impressed sources, she specializes in portfolio disposals and acquisitions.

### McKenna Long & Aldridge LLP
See profile on p.922

THE FIRM This team has recently been expanded by the firm's merger with Luce, Forward, Hamilton & Scripps. Well known for its ability to handle especially complex issues, it has recently represented Tenaska in the sophisticated financing and development of its Imperial Solar Energy Center South project. It was also engaged by PNC Bank on a $61 million construction loan for development of an urban mixed-use project.

Sources say: *"They have a very high level of expertise and are very knowledgeable. My go-to firm for complicated situations."*

KEY INDIVIDUALS William Stevens is said to be *"very much an acknowledged expert"* in the field. An experienced and established name in the market, his practice leans towards the representation of lenders and purchasers in large-scale projects.

### Seyfarth Shaw LLP
See profile on p.1262

THE FIRM Seyfarth Shaw's national real estate practice is led from its Atlanta office, and is commended by clients for its excellent service and sharp responsiveness in dealing with their needs. In addition to its national outlook, it upholds an impressive profile in the Georgia market. Its large team handles a diverse client base, including clients in the banking and retail industries.

KEY INDIVIDUALS Clients say that Mark Block (see p.1076) *"has the ability to focus on the legal points that matter most to our business."* He frequently represents equity investors and developers on a range of complex issues. Steven Kennedy (see p.1087) offers a practice with a particular emphasis on lenders, developers and investors in commercial, retail and industrial leasing and development matters. He also represents a significant number of investment portfolios.

### Smith Gambrell & Russell LLP
See profile on p.1113

THE FIRM In addition to covering all major areas of real estate law, this group offers experience and specialist knowledge in several niche areas. These include military and student housing projects, as well as timberland matters. It coordinates with its offices in New York and Jacksonville to orchestrate large-scale projects, but maintains a firm presence in the Atlanta market. It is often engaged by lenders in relation to industrial projects.

KEY INDIVIDUALS Malcolm Young (see p.1101) has become a recognized expert in dealing with the acquisition, leasing and sale of commercial office buildings. He also has great experience in transactions involving hotels and motels, and in other matters relating to the hospitality industry.

### Other Notable Practitioners

Maxine Hicks (see p.1084) of DLA Piper LLP (US) has had an active year, recently representing the Project Master Development team in the high-value Georgia Multi-Modal Passenger Terminal. Clients appreciate her expertise in PPP, and believe that *"she is a real community treasure and represents the firm really well."* Managing partner Summey Orr of Hartman Simons & Wood LLP brings more than 25 years' experience to the team. Said to be *"a terrific attorney and deal-maker who is very practical,"* he is greatly regarded in the field as a highly able practitioner. He specializes in joint ventures advising foreign investors on real estate acquisitions within the USA. Also of Hartman Simons & Wood LLP, department head Robert Simons is applauded by interviewees for his expertise in handling retail-related real estate matters. Miriam Dent

(see p.1080) of Rogers & Hardin LLP covers all areas of real estate, but has lately undertaken a great deal of work in related matters concerning senior living and healthcare. Known to be *"very knowledgeable and a very aggressive negotiator,"* clients say that *"she is in tune with what judges want to see and what juries want."* Carolyn Dobbins (see p.1080) of Rogers & Hardin LLP specializes in real estate funding from the perspectives of both borrowers and lenders. She maintains a particular focus on funding for senior housing developments, and is praised by clients for her extensive preparation when dealing with their issues. Charles Sharbaugh (see p.1096) of Carlton Fields, P.A. *"has been a superlative real estate lawyer in Atlanta forever,"* according to market sources. He represents private equity funds and other entities in a range of real estate transactional and financing work. Raymond Sheley, founding partner of Sheley & Hall, consistently impresses interviewees who believe him to be *"an exceptional lawyer who is very clear-sighted, very practical and very, very honest."* He has particular expertise in data center leasing transactions. Scott Specht (see p.1098) of Jones Day has over 30 years' experience in the Georgia real estate market which he brings to bear in his all-purpose practice. He recently represented GA-MET in a $112 million loan secured by an office building in Atlanta. Clients note that he is *"able to present a complex structure in a document in a way that people can understand."* Gary Farris of Burr & Forman LLP is a founding partner of the firm's Atlanta office. He is known in the market for his representation of commercial lenders. Krevolin & Horst, LLC founding partner Douglas Krevolin (see p.1087) is a prominent player in the market. He has focused his practice on representing lenders and developers, as well as emerging companies and entrepreneurs. He is particularly expert in loans and funding. Kenneth Kraft of Parker, Hudson, Rainer & Dobbs LLP is the founder of the firm's real estate arm. He has experience working directly in the hotel industry which informs his practice. Sources observe: *"He has been around a long time and is an excellent lawyer. He has a really good practice and knows his stuff."* Joseph Foltz of Foltz Martin LLC serves a broad variety of clients from numerous industries, including lenders, developers and owners. He represents owners of hotels and office buildings, and can also draw upon his previous work in the corporate sector.

# TAX

Commentary about individuals can be found under their firm's paragraph. If the firm has no paragraph (is not ranked) look at Other Notable Practitioners.

## Tax
### Leading Firms

**Band 1**
Alston & Bird LLP *
Chamberlain, Hrdlicka, White, Williams & Aughtry *
King & Spalding LLP *
Sutherland Asbill & Brennan LLP

**Band 2**
Kilpatrick Townsend & Stockton LLP *
McKenna Long & Aldridge LLP *
Paul Hastings LLP *

**Band 3**
Jones Day *
Morris, Manning & Martin, LLP

### Leading Individuals

**Star individuals**

| | |
|---|---|
| Aughtry David D | Chamberlain, Hrdlicka, White, Williams * |
| Cohen N Jerold | Sutherland Asbill & Brennan LLP |

**Band 1**

| | |
|---|---|
| Clark Reginald J | Sutherland Asbill & Brennan LLP |
| Coalson Jr John L | Alston & Bird LLP * |
| Genz Peter | King & Spalding LLP * |
| Hishon Robert H | The Hishon Firm, LLC (ONP)† |
| Kaywood Sam K | Alston & Bird LLP * |
| Lange Mark S | McKenna Long & Aldridge LLP * |
| Marzetti Phil | Paul Hastings LLP |
| Petrik Michael T | Alston & Bird LLP * |
| White Benjamin T | Alston & Bird LLP * |

**Band 2**

| | |
|---|---|
| Allan John M | Jones Day * |
| Ashraf Saba | McKenna Long & Aldridge LLP * |
| Cullinan Thomas A | Sutherland Asbill & Brennan LLP |
| Fowler Lynn E | Kilpatrick Townsend & Stockton LLP |
| Gregory Cleburne E | Arnall Golden Gregory LLP (ONP)† * |
| Harris Morton A | Hatcher, Stubbs, Land, Hollis (ONP)† |
| Hasson Jr James K | Sutherland Asbill & Brennan LLP |
| Hodges Charles | Kilpatrick Townsend & Stockton LLP |
| Immerman Leon Andrew | Alston & Bird LLP * |
| Lokey Jr James | King & Spalding LLP * |
| Wasserman Michael G | Holt Ney Zatcoff & Wasserman (ONP)† |
| Willoughby David | Rogers & Hardin LLP (ONP)† * |

**Band 3**

| | |
|---|---|
| Altman Allen D | Greenberg Traurig, LLP (ONP)† * |
| Benton Mary T | Alston & Bird LLP * |
| Brewer Cassady V | Morris, Manning & Martin, LLP |
| Crisafi Frank A | Bryan Cave LLP (ONP)† |
| Haley Nedom A | Baker, Donelson, Bearman (ONP)† * |
| Sheppard Hale E | Chamberlain, Hrdlicka, White, Williams * |
| Tresh Eric S | Sutherland Asbill & Brennan LLP |
| Wright W. Scott | Sutherland Asbill & Brennan LLP |

**Up-and-coming individuals**

| | |
|---|---|
| Gries Matthew J | Sutherland Asbill & Brennan LLP |

**Associates to watch**

| | |
|---|---|
| Calhoun Clark | Alston & Bird LLP * |

* Indicates firm / individual with profile.
†ONP = Other Notable Practitioner

## Band 1

### Alston & Bird LLP
See profile on p.1102

**THE FIRM** Underpinned by an extensive bench of talented attorneys, this firm's preeminent taxation practice justifiably retains its position among the market leaders. The team has an almost unparalleled depth and has the requisite expertise to handle international tax, federal income tax, and state and local tax matters. The group represents a selection of Fortune 100 companies, with corporate behemoths Walmart, Delta Air Lines and UPS regularly seeking out the firm in connection with a variety of complex issues.

**Sources say:** "They have a very solid federal and state tax practice within Georgia."

**KEY INDIVIDUALS** "Renowned as a dean of the state and local tax Bar in Georgia," **John Coalson** (see p.1078) continues to earn unanimous approval from interviewees. One source claimed that he has one of the strongest practices within the state, while another highlighted his proficiency in unclaimed property matters. **Sam Kaywood** (see p.1086) enjoys a strong relationship within the legal market and is regularly engaged by several of the state's largest corporations. "I'd use him for any international tax matter," noted one commentator. **Michael Petrik** (see p.1093), known for his dexterous handling of state and local taxation matters, commands an "impressive standing within the community" and is perceived as "very technically proficient." He is further recommended for his ability to undertake complex multistate work. According to one client, **Benjamin White** (see p.1100) is a noted "problem solver." He is said to exhibit a "high degree of expertise" and to be "highly responsive to a client's needs." He is particularly well versed in the area of tax exemption and continues to work closely with Georgia Aquarium. Lauded for both his "great technical skills" and his transactional capabilities, **Andy Immerman** (see p.1085) remains active in connection to a number of federal tax matters. He is said to be an "extremely bright and talented" practitioner. **Mary Benton** (see p.1076) primarily handles tax controversy and litigation matters and is hailed as a "super lawyer" by her peers. She recently represented Health Management Associates in a number of tax assessments. Leading associate **Clark Calhoun** (see p.1077) is said to "provide a lot of technical guidance" and is widely regarded as a "good technical writer." He is primarily engaged in connection to state and local tax controversy matters.

### Chamberlain, Hrdlicka, White, Williams & Aughtry
See profile on p.2432

**THE FIRM** This group maintains an exemplary reputation for its substantive expertise within the tax controversy and litigation spheres. Sources are effusive in their appraisal of the level of representation offered by the team. Its handling of middle-market matters is singled out for particular praise, as is the standard of the attorneys retained by the firm.

**Sources say:** "They are clearly a premier tax litigation firm and are very good in all areas of taxation."

**KEY INDIVIDUALS David Aughtry** (see p.1075) commands a superb reputation and is considered to be the "leading practitioner within the tax controversy area." "When it comes to federal tax litigation," said one commentator, "he has more courtroom experience than anyone in Atlanta." **Hale Sheppard** (see p.1096) is recommended for his tax controversy capabilities. He elicits praise for the quality of representation he provides in connection to trial, appellate and audit matters and is identified by sources as being a "very strong tax lawyer."

### King & Spalding LLP
See profile on p.445

**THE FIRM** Peers are unanimous in their approbation of this firm's transactional tax capabilities. The tax practice draws heavily upon the firm's substantial expertise within the corporate sphere, providing clients with a comprehensive and integrated service. The firm is further renowned for its familiarity with the specific taxation elements involved in the formation of REITs.

**Sources say:** "They have strong legal expertise and they understand our goals as a client."

**KEY INDIVIDUALS** "Top-notch lawyer" **Peter Genz** (see p.1082) is renowned for his expertise in the field of REIT formation. "I'm not sure he has an equal in the country," asserted one peer, while another highlighted his intelligent and energetic approach to engagements. The vastly experienced **James Lokey** (see p.1089) is at the forefront of many of the more complex matters undertaken by the firm and focuses his practice primarily upon transactional tax matters.

### Sutherland Asbill & Brennan LLP

**THE FIRM** This thriving US outfit continues to service a vast array of premium clients; it is frequently appointed to serve as national state tax counsel by several of the Fortune 100, an area in which the group retains a core expertise. The team is also noted for its strength in tax controversy litigation, as was evidenced by its recent representation of Comcast, in which the firm successfully procured a $15 million tax refund for the telecommunications giant. Clients applaud the group's grasp of technical minutiae and its ability to combine business considerations with the more esoteric aspects of legislation when crafting resolutions.

**KEY INDIVIDUALS Jerold Cohen** has an almost unparalleled reputation within the state and is widely considered to be a leading example of a tax lawyer on all levels. Sources were quick to highlight his expertise in the field, and particularly note his aptitude for handling complex tax controversy matters. **Reginald Clark** is held out as being one of the most eminent corporate tax attorneys in the state, and is applauded for his transactional expertise. He also garners particular praise for his representation of academic institutions. **James Hasson** is highly regarded by peers as a leading tax exemption attorney in the state. He often acts in an adversarial role to the government, vigorously representing a range of tax-exempt organizations. **Thomas Cullinan** is particularly well versed in tax controversy issues and routinely handles related matters for several of the firm's largest clients. **Eric Tresh** enters the rankings following widespread market endorsement. He led the firm's successful representation of Comcast and is commended for his industry and technical expertise. **Scott Wright** earns accolades for his strength in connection to state and local tax matters. He is particularly adept in handling matters that require an in-depth knowledge of the energy industry. The promising **Matthew Gries** is gradually establishing himself as a leading authority on federal tax matters. He is praised for his client-oriented approach and ability to maintain impressive thoroughness and responsiveness throughout the course of any engagement.

## Band 2

### Kilpatrick Townsend & Stockton LLP
See profile on p.1109

**THE FIRM** This full-service firm is particularly skilled in federal tax controversy matters, providing adroit representation throughout the litigation process. The group's courtroom proficiency attracts praise from clients, as does its competence when adopting an adversarial position to the IRS. The firm is engaged by organizations from a multitude of different industries and can count Equifax, Goldsboro and Avanti as three of its more substantial recent clients.

**Sources say:** *"The firm has always been professional and provides high-quality work. They provide timely responses and excellent follow-up."*

**KEY INDIVIDUALS** According to one client, **Lynn Fowler** *"does an exceptional job. If we get into any complicated tax issues, he has the answer very quickly."* Another source emphasized the quality of Fowler's work product, claiming that *"he really understands my business and has helped me to navigate many issues."* He concentrates primarily on the intricacies of transactional taxation. **Charles Hodges's** *"expertise in dealing with the IRS and his attention to details are incredible,"* enthused one client. *"His experience and passion for dealing with IRS-related matters is very apparent and he has been a great source of comfort to our company."* He is an experienced, well-regarded litigator and is recommended accordingly.

### McKenna Long & Aldridge LLP
See profile on p.922

**THE FIRM** This impressive tax group is recognized primarily for its strength in transactional tax matters. The team's work is frequently conducive to collaboration, and tax practitioners often work closely with members of the firm's standalone corporate group, bringing both technical expertise and awareness of practical business concerns to engagements. A recent highlight is the firm's representation of The Home Depot, in which it oversaw the taxation elements of a $48 million acquisition.

**Sources say:** *"They are excellent; they are technically proficient, practical and very responsive."*

**KEY INDIVIDUALS Mark Lange** (see p.1088) *"is the best tax attorney I've ever worked with,"* reported one client. He is renowned for his proficiency in transactional taxation matters and is regarded as being *"excellent from a technical standpoint."* He handled the tax structuring for HD Supply in its recent $195 million acquisition of Peachtree Business Products. **Saba Ashraf** (see p.1074) is recommended for her ability to *"understand business constraints and to propose very practical and helpful solutions."* She was integral in the firm's recent representation of The Home Depot.

### Paul Hastings LLP
See profile on p.1996

**THE FIRM** This two-partner tax team is particularly adept at structuring large and sophisticated transactions in a tax-efficient manner. The firm's impressive national platform contributes to an impressive client roster – one that includes GE and Bank of America – while its regional prowess is exemplified by its recent representation of Georgia-based Greenway Medical Technologies.

**Sources say:** *"They are exceptional, very efficient and business-oriented."*

**KEY INDIVIDUALS Phil Marzetti** is acknowledged as a leading tax attorney. *"His efforts and expertise have been used to develop us from both a tax and strategic standpoint and saved us million of dollars,"* reported one satisfied client.

## Band 3

### Jones Day
See profile on p.919

**THE FIRM** This firm's three-partner tax group attains recognition for its aptitude in handling complex multistate income matters. The team is also well versed in the tax issues that arise from corporate reorganizations and is frequently engaged in such a capacity.

**KEY INDIVIDUALS** According to sources, **John Allan** (see p.1074) is *"very well known for his state and local tax work."* He is widely praised for his ability to address a variety of multistate income issues.

### Morris, Manning & Martin, LLP

**THE FIRM** Morris, Manning & Martin maintains its strong regional reputation. The firm works extensively with developing companies and has an impressive track record in assisting organizations to overcome the manifold taxation hurdles they face in their nascency.

**Sources say:** *"The attorneys on our team provide top-notch service and are very responsive." "They are excellent, timely and on point."*

**KEY INDIVIDUALS Cassady Brewer** is recommended for his experience in wealth planning matters. He continues to work closely with a number of exempt organizations.

## Other Notable Practitioners

The vastly experienced **Morton Harris** of Hatcher, Stubbs, Land, Hollis & Rothschild, LLP has been practicing for over five decades. Regarded by peers as highly cerebral and a *"legend,"* he continues to command an excellent reputation at both a domestic and a national level. Much of his work is focused upon estate and retirement planning, for which he is highly recommended. **Michael Wasserman** of Holt Ney Zatcoff & Wasserman, LLP has a broad practice and is proficient in handling both federal and state and local tax matters. He maintains an excellent reputation. **David Willoughby** (see p.1100) of Rogers & Hardin LLP is particularly well versed in the intricacies of international taxation law. One effusive source said: *"I got to see firsthand his thorough practice, his analytical skills and his ability to communicate to us his client's position on various matters. I think he's top-notch."* **Allen Altman** (see p.1074) of Greenberg Traurig, LLP is renowned for his ability to dispense pertinent and practical advice to high net worth individuals. Within his particular niche, he is perceived as *"top-drawer."* **Frank Crisafi** of Bryan Cave LLP earns unanimous approbation from interviewees. He is commended for his excellent responsiveness and reliable advice, as well as for his superb international tax expertise. **Nedom Haley** (see p.1083) of Baker, Donelson, Bearman, Caldwell & Berkowitz, PC is, according to one commentator, *"an excellent and practical lawyer."* He is skilled in handling a broad range of tax and corporate matters, getting plaudits for both his efficiency and his affable disposition. Identified as one of the leading tax controversy experts within the state, **Robert Hishon** of The Hishon Firm, LLC is particularly sought after for the tenacity and dexterity he exhibits inside the courtroom. Sources say: *"He is right at the top and among the best."* **Cleburne Gregory** (see p.1083) of Arnall Golden Gregory LLP has a *"great reputation"* within the state and is frequently engaged in matters of transactional taxation.

# Leaders' Profiles in Georgia

**ABERNATHY, Thomas E**
Smith, Currie & Hancock LLP, Atlanta
404 582 8013
teabernathy@smithcurrie.com
*Featured in Construction (Georgia)*
**Practice Areas:** Tom Abernathy has represented owners and contractors regarding the award, performance and resolution of disputes on various types of construction projects. His experience involves high-rise commercial, industrial, power, heavy and highway, bridges and government contract projects. He has represented clients in federal and state courts, arbitration and mediation. He also has extensive experience in federal government construction and has represented clients before federal agency boards of contract appeals.
**Professional Memberships:** He is a Fellow in the American College of Construction Lawyers and was Chair of the American Bar Association, Section of Public Contract Law.

**ADINATA, Geetha**
FordHarrison LLP, Atlanta
404 888 3940
gadinata@fordharrison.com
*Featured in Immigration (Georgia)*
**Practice Areas:** Business Immigration
**Career:** Geetha Adinata concentrates her practice on all facets of business immigration and I-9 and E-Verify compliance. She works with local, national, and multinational companies to develop strategies to meet their short-term and long-term needs for foreign workers. She works closely with management to evaluate temporary and permanent work options for foreign workers, develops streamlined processes for companies to bring in foreign workers, and develops proactive strategies for overcoming potential issues and risks before they arise. Geetha received her JD from the University of Florida College of Law in 2005.

**ALEXANDER, Joseph**
DLA Piper LLP (US), Atlanta
404 736 7890
joe.alexander@dlapiper.com
*Featured in Corporate/M&A (Georgia)*
**Practice Areas:** Corporate M&A/private equity.
**Career:** He is Chair of the firm's Corporate and Private Equity practices in the Southeast and a member of the Leadership Committee for the US Corporate and Private Equity practices. He is a member of the firm's Executive and Policy Committees. Diversity & The Bar magazine has named him one of ten Leading Law Firm Rainmakers nationwide. He has been recognized as a Georgia Super Lawyer Rising Star and among Georgia's Legal Elite.
**Personal:** JD, Duke University School of Law; BBA, University of Georgia, with honors.

**ALFORD, Carolyn Zander**
King & Spalding LLP, Atlanta
404 572 3551
czalford@kslaw.com
*Featured in Banking & Finance (Georgia)*

**Practice Areas:** Represents lenders and borrowers in debt financings, including syndicated and single lender senior credit facilities (for both leveraged and investment grade credits), asset based loans, mezzanine financing and third-party sponsored loan programs.
**Professional Memberships:** Atlanta Bar Association; Women's Finance Exchange; State Bar of Georgia, Chair of the Legal Opinion Committee of the Business Law Section; fellow of the American College of Investment Counsel.
**Personal:** BA, Duke University, magna cum laude, 1989, Phi Beta Kappa; JD Harvard Law School, cum laude, editor of 'Harvard Journal on Legislation'.

**ALLAN, John M**
Jones Day, Atlanta
404 581 8012
jmallan@jonesday.com
*Featured in Tax (Georgia)*
**Practice Areas:** Has assisted clients in addressing multistate income, net worth, capital stock, sales and use, property, and local excise taxes. He has handled tax matters in almost all of the 50 states. Regularly represents clients before state tax agencies and in proceedings before the Multistate Tax Commission. Speaks frequently on state and local tax matters before such groups as the Council on State Taxation, the Institute for Professionals in Taxation, the Tax Executives Institute, and the Federation of Tax Administrators.
**Professional Memberships:** Chair of Georgia Bar's Tax Section. Member, ABA Tax Section's State and Local Tax Committee.

**ALLEN, Randall L**
Alston & Bird LLP, Atlanta
404 881 7196
randall.allen@alston.com
*Featured in Antitrust (Georgia)*
**Practice Areas:** Concentrates on complex commercial litigation, class actions and arbitration, with emphasis on antitrust litigation and counseling. Argued in front of United States Supreme Court and numerous US Court of Appeals. Litigated many cases in federal and state trial courts throughout the United States, including civil and criminal jury trials. Frequently appears before the Department of Justice and Federal Trade Commission on behalf of large public clients.
**Career:** Former chair, firm's Antitrust and Litigation Groups. Former Partner in Charge, firm's Silicon Valley office. Former Chair, Antitrust Committee of Georgia Bar.
**Personal:** BA (1982), JD (1986) – Georgia State University.

**ALMOND, John J**
Rogers & Hardin LLP, Atlanta
404 420 4610
jalmond@rh-law.com
*Featured in Litigation (Georgia)*

**Practice Areas:** Complex business litigation, trial practice, commercial disputes. Areas of expertise include corporate and business organizations law, securities, defense of officers and directors, and business ownership disputes.
**Professional Memberships:** Master and Past President, Bleckley Inn of Court, Georgia State University College of Law; Business Litigation Committee of the Business Law Section, State Bar of Georgia.
**Personal:** JD, University of Chicago, with honors (1978); Editor-in-Chief, The University of Chicago Law Review (1977-78); BA, University of Cincinnati, magna cum laude (1974); Clerk to The Hon John Minor Wisdom (1978-79); Super Lawyers and Best Lawyers in America (Commercial Litigation).

**ALTMAN, Allen D**
Greenberg Traurig, LLP, Atlanta
678 553 2640
AltmanA@gtlaw.com
*Featured in Tax (Georgia)*
**Practice Areas:** Tax; trusts and estates; corporate and securities; global benefits and compensation; estate planning; mergers, acquisitions and divestitures.
**Career:** Selected: Best Lawyers in America, 2007-13; 'Georgia's Legal Elite', Georgia Trend, 2008-12; Super Lawyers magazine and Georgia Super Lawyers magazine, 2006-12; Chambers USA Guide, 2009-13. Rated, AV® Preeminent™ 5.0 out of 5.
**Personal:** LLM, Taxation, New York University School of Law; JD, cum laude, University of Miami School of Law; BSBA, University of Florida.

**ARBERY, W Christopher**
Hall, Arbery & Gilligan, LLP, Atlanta
404 442 8778
carbery@hagllp.com
*Featured in Labor & Employment (Georgia)*
**Practice Areas:** Mr Arbery defends and advises management on employment discrimination, workplace harassment, wage and hour, disabilities, family and medical leave, employment agreements, covenants not to compete, and whistleblower claims. He regularly defends clients in single- and multi-plaintiff claims and has handled class and collective actions involving a variety of industries.
**Professional Memberships:** State Bar of Georgia; American Bar Association; Atlanta Bar Association.
**Career:** Hall, Arbery & Gilligan LLP (2010-current); Hunton & Williams LLP (1996-2010); Kilpatrick & Cody (1994-96); JD, University of Georgia School of Law, 1994; BA, Harvard University, 1988.
**Publications:** Employment Class Actions, National Law Journal, 2003; 'Reasonable Woman' Standard In Sexual Harassment Claims, Georgia Law Review, 1993.

**ARNOLD, Douglas S**
Alston & Bird LLP, Atlanta
404 881 7637
doug.arnold@alston.com
*Featured in Environment (Georgia)*
**Practice Areas:** Mr Arnold represents clients in all stages of environmental and toxic tort litigation. Has successfully defended clients in more than 75 lawsuits and enforcement actions in EPA Region 4, involving Superfund, Clean Water Act, RCRA, TSCA, and EPCRA. Also represented clients in similar matters in Arizona, California, Colorado, Illinois, Iowa, Louisiana, Massachusetts, Michigan, New York, Ohio, Puerto Rico, Texas, Virginia and Washington.
**Professional Memberships:** Prior chair, ABA Environmental Litigation Committee; ABA Environmental Enforcement Committee; and State Bar of Georgia Environmental Section.
**Career:** Current chair, firm's Environmental Practice.
**Personal:** University of Georgia (JD, 1991); University of Virginia (BA, 1988).

**ASHE JR, R Lawrence**
Ashe Rafuse & Hill LLP, Atlanta
404 253 6001
lawrenceashe@AsheRafuse.com
*Featured in Labor & Employment (Georgia)*
**Practice Areas:** Employment law, civil rights, related litigation matters. Nationally recognized for class-action and employee selection expertise; the National Law Journal noted as 'dean of the management class action bar'; Atlanta Magazine: Top Ten Georgia Attorneys (2010-2012). Atlanta Employment, Litigation Lawyer of Year 2012, Best Lawyers.
**Professional Memberships:** Fellow, American College of Trial Lawyers, and Fellow, College of Labor and Employment Lawyers; Northern District of Georgia Representative, Eleventh Circuit Court of Appeals' Committee on Lawyer Qualifications and Conduct; Honorary Consul for Poland to the State of Georgia.
**Personal:** AB, High Honors – Princeton University; LLB, Honors – Harvard Law School.

**ASHRAF, Saba**
McKenna Long & Aldridge LLP, Atlanta
sashraf@mckennalong.com
*Featured in Tax (Georgia)*
**Practice Areas:** Saba Ashraf is the leader of MLA's tax practice group and concentrates on the structuring and effecting of complex business transactions. Her practice focuses on corporate and partnership taxation with particular emphasis on domestic and international mergers, acquisitions and spin-offs; recapitalizations; leveraged buyouts; going private transactions; partnerships and joint ventures; fund formations; private equity investments; debt restructurings and loan workouts; securitizations; tax aspects of investment in real estate; and inbound and outbound investment transactions.

**Career:** New York University (LLM, 1997) Hofstra University (J.D., 1993) New York University (BS, 1990)

## ASSELIN, Thomas H
Smith Gambrell & Russell LLP, Atlanta
404 815 3772
tasselin@sgrlaw.com
*Featured in Construction (Georgia)*
**Practice Areas:** Partner, Construction Section. Handled legal matters in 29 states, the District of Columbia, Puerto Rico, US Virgin Islands, Canada, Europe, including projects involving office buildings, hotels, conference centers, bank buildings, apartments, condominiums, sewage treatment plants, power plants, prisons, airports, highway and bridge work, governmental and military facilities. Mediator and arbitrator.
**Professional Memberships:** Civil Engineering Honor Society Chi Epsilon; Sigma Xi Honorary Society.
**Personal:** BS, Civil Engineering, Northeastern University, 1964; MS, Construction Management, Massachusetts Institute of Technology, 1966; JD, Northwestern University, 1969. Georgia Super Lawyer, Construction and Surety, 2004-2012; Best Lawyers in America, Construction Law.

## AUGHTRY, David D
Chamberlain, Hrdlicka, White, Williams & Aughtry, Atlanta
404 658 5486
david.aughtry@chamberlainlaw.com
*Featured in Tax (Georgia), Tax (Nationwide)*
**Practice Areas:** Tax, tax controversy and litigation.
**Professional Memberships:** Southern Federal Tax Institute (Past President and Chairman of Board); fellow, American College of Tax Counsel; fellow, International Society of Barristers; Board; State Bar of Georgia, Chairperson, Budget Committee and Investment Committee (1989-94).
**Career:** Shareholder – Chamberlain, Hrdlicka, White, Williams & Aughtry (1982 – present); Internal Revenue Service as a Trial Attorney, Office of the Chief Counsel; Emory University, Tax Controversy, Adjunct Professor, Masters of Taxation Program (LLM) (1988-94) and JD Program (1996-98) (2003).
**Personal:** The Citadel, BA, English, 1975; University of South Carolina, JD; M Acctcy, 1978; Emory University, LLM Taxation, 1982.

## AUSTIN, Jesse
King & Spalding LLP, Atlanta
404 572 2882
jaustin@kslaw.com
*Featured in Bankruptcy/Restructuring (Georgia)*
**Practice Areas:** Concentrates practice in bankruptcy law, particularly Chapter 11 reorganization cases and large commercial workouts. A principal focus of his workout and insolvency practice is the representation of institutional senior secured lenders in syndicated credit facilities, with particular experience in debtor-in-possession lending in the healthcare, communications, automotive, energy and retail areas.

**Personal:** BS, Business Administration, Phi Beta Kappa, University of North Carolina (1976). JD, with distinction and MBA from Emory University (1980). Fellow, American College of Bankruptcy.

## BABER, Bruce
King & Spalding LLP, Atlanta
404 572 4826
bbaber@kslaw.com
*Featured in Intellectual Property (Georgia)*
**Practice Areas:** Intellectual property and technology law with focus in patent, trademark, trademark counterfeiting, false advertising and copyright infringement cases before the International Trade Commission and the United States Patent and Trademark Office. Substantial experience in the protection of trademarks, copyrights and other forms of intellectual property, including registration applications prosecution and implementation of worldwide protection strategies.
**Professional Memberships:** American Bar Association; Atlanta Bar Association; State Bar of Georgia.
**Personal:** BA, with distinction, Princeton University, 1976; JD, cum laude, Duke University, Order of the Coif, 1979.

## BAKER, Thomas William
Baker, Donelson, Bearman, Caldwell & Berkowitz, PC, Atlanta
404 221 6510
tbaker@bakerdonelson.com
*Featured in Healthcare (Georgia)*
**Practice Areas:** Represents healthcare providers and suppliers of goods and services to the health industry in variety of healthcare business transactions, including mergers, acquisitions, joint ventures, and financing. Also skilled in matters involving Medicare reimbursement and fraud and abuse.
**Professional Memberships:** State Bar of Georgia, American Health Lawyers Association and Georgia Academy of Healthcare Lawyers.
**Career:** Licensed in Georgia. Named an Outstanding Physician Practice Lawyer by Nightingale's Healthcare News (2009). Adjunct Faculty, Auburn Physicians Executive MBA Program, teaching The Legal Aspects of Health Care Business Transactions.
**Personal:** Vanderbilt University, J.D., 1981; Georgia State University, M.B.A., 1978; Syracuse University, A.B., 1972

## BALSER, David L
King & Spalding LLP, Atlanta
404 572 2782
dbalser@kslaw.com
*Featured in Litigation (Georgia)*
**Practice Areas:** David Balser represents publicly traded corporations, privately held businesses, and corporate executives in trials, arbitrations and appeals in complex business litigation matters throughout the US. Mr Balser represents both plaintiffs and defendants, and many of the cases he handles involve matters of significant strategic importance to his clients. Mr Balser handles cases involving: contract disputes and business torts; corporate governance, shareholder and partnership disputes; consumer class actions; securities

class actions; governmental disputes; and professional liability matters.
**Personal:** JD, University of Michigan Law School, cum laude, 1987; BA, University of Pennsylvania, magna cum laude, 1984.

## BALTZ, Raymond E
King & Spalding LLP, Atlanta
404 572 4715
rbaltz@kslaw.com
*Featured in Corporate/M&A (Georgia)*
**Practice Areas:** Represents private equity funds in leveraged buyout transactions and corporations in strategic M&A transactions. Also has experience with joint ventures and strategic alliances, and general corporate and securities matters.
**Professional Memberships:** State Bar of Georgia.
**Career:** Mr Baltz served as editor of the Boston University Law Review.
**Personal:** BS, Eastern Nazarene College, 1986; JD summa cum laude, Boston University 1995.

## BARBAREE, Tracey T
Ogletree, Deakins, Nash, Smoak & Stewart, PC, Atlanta
404 881 1300
tracey.barbaree@ogletreedeakins.com
*Featured in Labor & Employment (Georgia)*
**Practice Areas:** Concentrates practice in employment litigation. Extensive experience defending employers in individual and class-based discrimination claims, as well as class and collective action litigation regarding misclassification and off-the-clock claims under wage and hour laws. Recognized as one of Georgia's top employment lawyers by 'Atlanta Magazine.'
**Career:** Shareholder; adjunct professor, Georgia State University College of Law.
**Personal:** BA, magna cum laude, Vanderbilt University (1986); JD, with honors, The Ohio State University College of Law (1990), Order of the Coif, 'Ohio State Law Review' Managing Editor. Judicial clerk for the Hon. Richard C Freeman, US District Court, Northern District of Georgia.

## BARMEYER, Patricia
King & Spalding LLP, Atlanta
404 572 3563
pbarmeyer@kslaw.com
*Featured in Environment (Georgia)*
**Practice Areas:** Regulatory compliance and environmental litigation in the areas of water, waste, air and environmental tort issues. Former assistant attorney general for the State of Georgia. Expertise combines detailed knowledge of environmental law with courtroom experience in environmental cases.
**Professional Memberships:** American Bar Association (Member, Section on natural resources, energy and environmental law); American Bar Foundation; Atlanta Bar Association; fellow, Atlanta Volunteer Lawyers Foundation (past President); State Bar of Georgia.
**Personal:** BA, Hollins College, 1968; JD, cum laude, Harvard University, 1971.

## BARRY, Michael
Arnall Golden Gregory LLP, Atlanta
404 873 8698
michael.barry@agg.com
*Featured in Healthcare (Georgia)*
**Practice Areas:** Partner in the Corporate Practice and the Healthcare and Life Sciences Practice. Health care transactional and regulatory law; fraud and abuse analysis and advice; strategic alliances, joint ventures, acquisitions, divestitures, general business and operational matters.
**Professional Memberships:** American Bar Association; American Health Lawyers Association.
**Publications:** See, www.agg.com
**Personal:** University of Georgia, Master of Business Administration, 2005; University of Georgia School of Law, Juris Doctorate, 1996; University of Georgia, Bachelor of Business Administration, 1993, Cum Laude; "Outstanding Young Alumni," University of Georgia Terry College of Business; Nightingale's Outstanding Physician Lawyer Recipient; Georgia Super Lawyers, Georgia Trend Legal Elite ratings.

## BARTLETT, Brett C
Seyfarth Shaw LLP, Atlanta
404 888 1875
bbartlett@seyfarth.com
*Featured in Labor & Employment (Georgia)*
**Practice Areas:** Partner and Chairperson of Seyfarth's Atlanta, Georgia Labor & Employment Department; Leader in National Wage & Hour Litigation Practice Group. Preventative pay practices counselor who also defends Fortune 500 employers against complex class and collective actions in which employees allege unpaid minimum wage, overtime, and other compensation.
**Professional Memberships:** ABA; New York Bar Association; Georgia Bar
**Career:** Practicing since 1999. Defending complex class and collective action wage and hour cases since 2001.
**Publications:** Co-authored the definitive treatise, Wage & Hour Collective and Class Litigation.
**Personal:** Attended Oberlin College and Mercer University School of Law. NCAA All American Swimmer.

## BAXLEY, C William
King & Spalding LLP, Atlanta
404 572 3580
bbaxley@kslaw.com
*Featured in Corporate/M&A (Georgia)*
**Practice Areas:** Domestic and international mergers and acquisitions and joint ventures in the consumer products, telecom, banking, insurance, transportation, retail and restaurants industries, involving public company mergers, private company acquisitions and dispositions, joint ventures, strategic investments, going private transactions, special committee representations, tender offers and proxy contests.
**Professional Memberships:** American Bar Association; State Bar of Georgia.
**Personal:** BS, summa cum laude, University of Alabama, 1986; JD, magna cum laude, Harvard University, 1989. Named one of the top 15 young

Atlanta lawyers by 'The Fulton County Daily Report' in 2002.

## BEALE, R Daniel
McKenna Long & Aldridge LLP, Atlanta
404 527 8489
dbeale@mckennalong.com
*Featured in Labor & Employment (Georgia)*

**Practice Areas:** – Dan Beale focuses his practice in employment law, representing employers in litigation and administrative charges and investigations in a broad range of employment disputes. In addition to formal litigation and administrative claims, Mr Beale regularly provides guidance to employers regarding compliance with federal, state and local employment laws. Mr Beale has a particular focus in handling noncompete and other restrictive covenant matters. Mr Beale also has an active practice in representing executives of public and private companies in negotiating employment agreements and separation arrangements.
**Personal:** J.D., Harvard Law School, cum laude; BA, Emory University, Phi Beta Kappa.

## BECK, Philip E
Smith, Currie & Hancock LLP, Atlanta
404 582 8028
pebeck@smithcurrie.com
*Featured in Construction (Georgia)*

**Practice Areas:** Construction law; government contracts; commercial litigation. Practice includes both drafting and negotiating design and construction contracts, and claims/dispute resolution (litigation, arbitration, and mediation).
**Professional Memberships:** Vice Chair, ConsensusDocs Content Advisory Council. Associated General Contractors of America: Board of Directors; Chair, Contract Documents Forum; Past Chair, Service and Supply Council.
**Career:** Consistently recognized by Chambers USA, Best Lawyers in America, and Georgia Super Lawyers.
**Personal:** University of Tennessee College of Law (JD, Order of the Coif, Moot Court Board); University of Tennessee (MBA, Finance; BS, High Honors; Phi Kappa Phi; Omicron Delta Kappa; Beta Gamma Sigma).

## BELENKY, Erik
Jones Day, Atlanta
404 581 8349
ebelenky@jonesday.com
*Featured in Corporate/M&A (Georgia)*

**Practice Areas:** Erik Belenky's practice is focused on mergers and acquisitions, where he represents public and private companies, special committees, and financial advisors in the full range of domestic and cross-border acquisitions, divestitures, strategic alliances, and corporate restructurings.
**Career:** Represents public and private companies, special committees of independent directors and financial advisors in the full range of domestic and cross-border acquisitions, divestitures, strategic alliances, and corporate restructurings; also regularly advises boards of directors on corporate governance matters.

**Personal:** BA, Colby College; JD, Duke University.

## BENTON, Mary T
Alston & Bird LLP, Atlanta
404 881 7255
mary.benton@alston.com
*Featured in Tax (Georgia)*

**Practice Areas:** Multistate tax controversy and litigation involving all tax types. Handles all aspects of state and local tax disputes—audits, administrative conferences and hearings, jury and bench trials and appellate work. Also maintains a multistate transactional practice, helping clients navigate through complexities in acquisitions, dispositions and reorganizations, and an economic incentive practice working with clients in the process of expanding a physical plant or adding headcount, relocating or opening a new facility to identify, claim and maintain state tax credits that directly benefit a company's bottom line.
**Personal:** The University of Texas (J.D., 1996); Southern Methodist University (BA, 1993).

## BERGESON, Donna P
Alston & Bird LLP, Atlanta
404 881 7278
donna.bergeson@alston.com
*Featured in Healthcare (Georgia)*

**Practice Areas:** Academic medical center legal issues, healthcare contracting, regulatory compliance.
**Professional Memberships:** Member, State Bar of Georgia; Georgia Academy of Health Care Attorneys (past president); American Health Lawyers.
**Career:** Former chair, Alston & Bird Health Care Group. Former chair, firm's governing board. Chair, firm's Investment Committee. Past General Counsel of the Emory Clinic, Inc. Frequent author and speaker on compliance and life sciences-related legal issues. Certified as a professional coder by the American Academy of Professional Coders.
**Personal:** BA, University of South Carolina (1981), magna cum laude; JD, University of South Carolina (1984).

## BIEGEL, Adam J
Alston & Bird LLP, Atlanta
404 881 4692
adam.biegel@alston.com
*Featured in Antitrust (Georgia)*

**Practice Areas:** Antitrust counseling and complex litigation, including commercial and antitrust litigation, with substantial experience representing clients in matters involving pricing, mergers, joint ventures, trade associations, distribution, government investigations and antitrust compliance.
**Professional Memberships:** Council, American Bar Association Antitrust Section; Board, Georgia Bar Antitrust Section; VP, Federalist Society Atlanta Chapter; Member, Federal and Atlanta bars, American Counsel Association and American Health Lawyers Association.
**Publications:** Contributor, ABA Antitrust Section's 'Antitrust Law Developments', West's 'Antitrust Adviser', ABA Business Law Section's

'In-House Counsel's Essential Toolkit' and GLG's 'International Comparative Guide to Competition Litigation'.
**Personal:** BA (1993) Emory University, JD (1998) University of Chicago.

## BLOCK, Mark A
Seyfarth Shaw LLP, Atlanta
404 885 6718
mblock@seyfarth.com
*Featured in Real Estate (Georgia)*

**Practice Areas:** Real estate.
**Professional Memberships:** ICSC; NAIOP; Real Estate Group of Atlanta
**Career:** Mr Block specializes in commercial real estate development and finance. He represents developers and investors in the construction, leasing, and acquisition of mixed use projects, office buildings, shopping centers, apartments, and other commercial facilities. He has extensive experience in negotiating joint venture arrangements. Mr Block also represents financial institutions in connection with all phases of financing and loan workouts.
**Personal:** JD, University of North Carolina, with honors (1983); BBA., Emory University, summa cum laude (1980).

## BLUM, Theodore I
Greenberg Traurig, LLP, Atlanta
678 553 2620
BlumT@gtlaw.com
*Featured in Corporate/M&A (Georgia)*

**Practice Areas:** Chair, Atlanta Corporate and Securities Practice. Mergers and acquisitions; venture capital corporate finance.
**Career:** Selected, Best Lawyers in America, 2007-13; Super Lawyers and Georgia Super Lawyers magazines, 2008-12; 'Georgia's Legal Elite', Georgia Trend, 2008-12; 'Georgia 2006 Rising Star,' Atlanta Magazine and Georgia Super Lawyers. Rated, AV® Preeminent™ 5.0 out of 5.
**Publications:** Quoted, 'M&A in the Technology Sector', Financier Worldwide, June 2009; Co-Author, 'Israel on our mind, Israeli businesses have reasons to thrive in entrepreneurial Georgia', Atlanta Jewish Life Magazine, 2006.
**Personal:** JD, Northwestern University School of Law; AB, University of Michigan.

## BLUMEN, Rick D
Alston & Bird LLP, Atlanta
404 881 7895
rick.blumen@alston.com
*Featured in Banking & Finance (Georgia)*

**Practice Areas:** Debt finance, secured and unsecured syndicated credit facilities, structured finance, private placements, high-yield debt offerings, mezzanine finance, acquisition finance.
**Professional Memberships:** Member, State Bar of Georgia.
**Career:** Co-Chair, firm's Global Finance & Debt Products Group; Chairman of firm's Partners' Committee. Served as counsel to several of the largest US commercial banks and their investment bank affiliates, private equity firms and large and mid-sized debt issuers. Former judicial intern with the Honorable Lawrence S Margolis, US Court of

Federal Claims. Former intern with President Jimmy Carter.
**Personal:** BA, Emory University (1986); JD, George Washington University (1990).

## BONDER, Teresa T
Alston & Bird LLP, Atlanta
404 881 7369
teresa.bonder@alston.com
*Featured in Antitrust (Georgia)*

**Practice Areas:** Antitrust and other commercial litigation, including in the class action context; antitrust counseling with respect to mergers, acquisitions, and sales and marketing activities; and appearances before antitrust regulatory agencies and the US federal courts. Representative clients: Delta Air Lines; Equifax, Inc; First Multiple Listing Service, Inc.; Mohawk Industries, Inc.; Prairie Farms Dairy, Inc.; SunTrust Banks, Inc.
**Career:** Chair of the firm's Antitrust Group.
**Personal:** JD (1991) – University of California, Berkeley; BA, summa cum laude, (1987) – Amherst College.

## BORDERS, Sarah
King & Spalding LLP, Atlanta
404 572 3596
sborders@kslaw.com
*Featured in Bankruptcy/Restructuring (Georgia)*

**Practice Areas:** Extensive experience representing both creditors and debtors in some of the nation's largest workouts, restructurings and bankruptcy cases. Insolvency practice spans a number of industries, with a particular focus on complex issues in financing insolvent entities.
**Career:** Fellow in The American College of Bankruptcy. Past President of the Bankruptcy Section of the State Bar of Georgia.
**Personal:** J.D., University of Virginia BS, Louisiana State University

## BOWER, R Bruce
Finnegan, Henderson, Farabow, Garrett & Dunner LLP, Atlanta
404 653 6465
bruce.bower@finnegan.com
*Featured in Intellectual Property (Georgia)*

**Practice Areas:** Managing partner of Finnegan's Atlanta office. He counsels companies with complex patent issues, including litigation, strategic counseling, prosecution, and licensing. He has litigated patent disputes in various district courts, the US International Trade Commission, and the US Court of Appeals for the Federal Circuit. His practice includes ex parte and inter partes matters before the US Patent and Trademark Office. His technical and industry experience includes electrical and computer technology, semiconductors, and medical devices.
**Personal:** Bucknell University (BS, Electrical Engineering, cum laude, 1987); American University, Washington College of Law (J.D., cum laude, 1992).

## BRACKEN II, Lawrence J
Hunton & Williams LLP, Atlanta
404 888 4035
lbracken@hunton.com
*Featured in Litigation (Georgia)*

**Practice Areas:** Larry has represented clients in federal and state courts throughout the United States in a broad range of cases, particularly the litigation of class actions and other cases involving allegations of unfair and deceptive trade practices, alleged violations of business statutes and regulations, related business torts, and complex contract disputes. Larry also has extensive experience representing clients in internal investigations and litigation involving cyber security and privacy issues in the US and other countries; alleged misappropriation of trade secrets; and technology service agreement disputes. His clients include providers and purchasers of technology products and services, major banks and commercial lenders, consumer finance companies and other businesses in the financial services industry, retailers, electric utilities, and municipalities. In addition, Larry has negotiated, arbitrated and litigated more than 350 insurance coverage matters involving general and excess liability, D&O liability, E&O, technology E&O, property, business interruption and time element, pollution liability, inland marine, and other types of insurance coverage.

### BRADLEY, Wayne N
McKenna Long & Aldridge LLP, Atlanta
404 527 4044
wbradley@mckennalong.com
*Featured in Corporate/M&A (Georgia)*
**Practice Areas:** Wayne N. Bradley serves as Chair of MLA's Corporate Department and on the Board of Directors of the Firm. Mr Bradley has deep experience in advising public and private companies in connection with a variety of strategic matters, including mergers, acquisitions, divestitures, joint ventures and strategic alliances. He also works with clients on corporate finance, distress, commercial contracts, commercial lending and internal investigation matters. He has particularly extensive experience representing non-US companies in connection with their US operations and transactions. In addition, Mr Bradley advises clients in the private equity and venture capital industry.
**Personal:** JD, Emory University School of Law, with distinction, 1990; BA, Rutgers College, 1983

### BRATCHER, Timothy
Jones Day, Atlanta
404 581 8606
tbratcher@JonesDay.com
*Featured in Banking & Finance (Georgia)*
**Practice Areas:** Experienced in representing lenders and borrowers in most types of domestic and cross-border, secured and unsecured financing transactions, including asset-based financing, recourse and non-recourse factoring and invoice discounting, insured or letter of credit backed receivables transactions, and other forms of account receivables financing, acquisition financing, multicurrency transactions, equipment leasing and financing, and loan syndications and participations.
**Professional Memberships:** Member of the faculty of the National Business Institute's commercial lending seminars. Member of the State Bar of Georgia.

### BRAZELL, Cindy
Jones Day, Atlanta
404 581 8294
cbrazell@jonesday.com
*Featured in Banking & Finance (Georgia)*
**Practice Areas:** More than 20 years experience representing lenders and borrowers in a wide range of debt financings, including syndicated, club and single lender; secured and unsecured; cash flow, asset based and real estate loans; mezzanine loans and work outs. Many of these transactions include complex intercreditor arrangements and multiple debt tranches.
**Professional Memberships:** Atlanta Bar Association (Past Chair, Business & Finance Section); State Bar of Georgia; Women's Finance Exchange; 2011 Women of Excellence; Leadership Atlanta, Class of 2011.

### BRIGGS, Benjamin
Seyfarth Shaw LLP, Atlanta
404 885 6713
bbriggs@seyfarth.com
*Featured in Labor & Employment (Georgia)*
**Practice Areas:** Partner in Seyfarth Shaw's Atlanta, Georgia Labor and Employment Department; national practice focusing on complex wage & hour class and collective action litigation; OSHA litigation and counseling; discrimination, retaliation and harassment litigation; non-compete and trade secrets litigation and counseling; and workplace compliance counseling.
**Professional Memberships:** Georgia Bar; Atlanta Bar Association.
**Career:** Practicing since 1999.
**Publications:** Chapter author, Wage & Hour Collective and Class Litigation; Defending the Mixed-Motive Retaliation Case, ALI ABA Practical Litigator; chapter author, Georgia Human Resources Manual, A Guide to Georgia and Federal Employment Laws and Regulations.
**Personal:** JD, Georgia State University; BA, University of Miami.

### BROWN, Charley
Ballard Spahr LLP, Atlanta
678 420 9410
browncf@ballardspahr.com
*Featured in Intellectual Property (Georgia)*
**Practice Areas:** Charley F Brown is a member of the Trademark and Copyright Group and Intellectual Property Litigation Group, as well as the electrical and communications technology, software and business methods, biotechnology, pharmaceutical, and medical technology practice teams in the Patents Group. His practice includes patent, copyright, trademark, and trade secret litigation; patent prosecution; client counseling; and opinion work.
**Professional Memberships:** State Bar of Georgia.
**Career:** Admissions: Georgia.
**Personal:** Education: Mercer University (BBA, computer information systems, 1999; JD 2002) and Georgia Institute of Technology (MS, bioinformatics, 2004).

### BROWN, David
McKenna Long & Aldridge LLP, Atlanta
404 527 4927
dbrown@mckennalong.com
*Featured in Corporate/M&A (Georgia)*
**Practice Areas:** David Brown is the head of the MLA's Corporate Finance Group and has experience in a broad range of corporate finance, merger and acquisition, and private equity transactions. Mr Brown represents issuers in connection with initial and secondary public offerings, "shelf" offerings, and Rule 144A, PIPE and private placement transactions. He advises public company clients and institutional shareholders on SEC reporting and disclosure requirements, corporate governance, proxy contests, and other corporate and securities matters. He is a member of the firm's private equity fund formation practice, and frequently represents fund sponsors in the formation of private equity funds.

### BROWN, Michael L
Alston & Bird LLP, Atlanta
404 881 7589
mike.brown@alston.com
*Featured in Litigation (Georgia)*
**Practice Areas:** Concentrates practice on defending individuals and corporations in criminal matters, representing corporations and individuals in government investigations, and conducting internal corporate investigations.
**Career:** 1999-2005, served as an Assistant United States Attorney in Georgia and Florida, and tried more than 30 criminal jury trials. Received several awards from the DOJ as a result of his investigative and trial skills. Has argued appeals before the Eleventh and Sixth Circuit Courts of Appeals.
**Personal:** JD (1994) University of Georgia; BA (1991) Georgetown University.

### BUTLER, III, James F
Smith, Currie & Hancock LLP, Atlanta
404 582 8025
jfbutler@smithcurrie.com
*Featured in Construction (Georgia)*
**Practice Areas:** Construction dispute resolution; international construction projects: contentious and non-contentious; international arbitration; substantial experience with EPC projects; government contracts; environmental law.
**Professional Memberships:** Co-Chair, ABA Construction Litigation Section, Construction Defects Subcommittee; ABA Forum on the Construction Industry International Construction Contracts Steering Committee; IBA, International Construction Projects Subcommittee; Dispute Review Board Foundation. Admitted: New York, Florida, Texas, Washington, North Carolina, Kentucky, Arkansas and Georgia.
**Career:** Consistently recognized as leading construction lawyer by Chambers USA, International Who's Who of Business Lawyers-Construction, and Georgia Super Lawyers.
**Personal:** University of Kentucky College of Law, JD; Duke University, AB; Harvard University, Advanced Mediation Program.

### CAHALAN, Scott D
Smith Gambrell & Russell LLP, Atlanta
404 815 3711
scahalan@sgrlaw.com
*Featured in Construction (Georgia)*
**Practice Areas:** Partner representing owners, contractors, others in construction and commercial matters. Drafts construction contracts, advises during construction, construction litigation, arbitration, mediation. Adjunct Professor, author, speaker on construction contracts, green building, insurance, lien law, claims. Drafted form contracts for Associated Owners and Developers.
**Professional Memberships:** American Bar Association – Construction Forum; Associated Builders and Contractors; American Institute of Architects; American Council of Engineering Companies.
**Personal:** BS, Construction Engineering, Iowa State University, 1984; JD, cum laude, University of Georgia, 1994. Admitted in Georgia, US District Court, NDGA, US Court of Appeals, 11th Circuit. Super Lawyer, Georgia-Construction, 2009-10, Business Edition, 2011.

### CALHOUN, Clark
Alston & Bird LLP, Atlanta
404 881 7553
clark.calhoun@alston.com
*Featured in Tax (Georgia)*
**Practice Areas:** State and local tax controversy and litigation matters. Represents clients on a wide range of state income, property, and sales/use tax matters. Appeared before state administrative agencies and numerous state trial and appellate courts.
**Professional Memberships:** Serves as an officer for the Taxation Section of the State Bar of Georgia and served on a task force responsible for the creation of the Georgia Tax Tribunal. Frequent contributor to 'State Tax Notes' and speaks regularly before state tax audiences for COST and TEI.
**Personal:** BA (2002) Vanderbilt University; JD (2005) University of Georgia.

### CALVERT, Matthew J
Hunton & Williams LLP, Atlanta
404 888 4117
mcalvert@hunton.com
*Featured in Litigation (Georgia)*
**Practice Areas:** Mr Calvert's litigation practice includes complex commercial disputes, consumer class actions, product liability, including medical device and pharmaceutical litigation, toxic torts, public finance, real estate and eminent domain. He was named Business Litigation Super Lawyer, Atlanta Magazine and Georgia Super Lawyers, 2005-12, Georgia Trend, as a Member of Georgia's 'Legal Elite' in the Personal Injury category, 2005-08, and Who's Who Legal in the Product Liability category, 2007. Mr Calvert served as Editor-in-Chief of the Washington & Lee University Law Review and as a Law Clerk to the Honorable John Minor Wisdom, US Court of Appeals, Fifth Circuit, 1979-80.

## CAMPBELL, Margaret H
Ogletree, Deakins, Nash, Smoak & Stewart, PC, Atlanta
404 881 1300
meg.campbell@ogletreedeakins.com
*Featured in Labor & Employment (Georgia)*
**Practice Areas:** Employment, Class and Collective Action, Whistleblower, and Employment Contract Litigation, Appellate Practice, Corporate Investigations, Employment and Labor.
**Professional Memberships:** American, Georgia, and Atlanta Bar Associations, Virginia State Bar, National Association of Women Lawyers, Georgia Association of Women Lawyers.
**Career:** Admitted: Georgia, Virginia, US Supreme Court, US Courts of Appeals (Fourth, Sixth, and Eleventh Circuits). Fellow, College of Labor and Employment Lawyers.
**Publications:** 17 Georgia Jurisprudence, "Liability for Intentional Acts Committed in the Employment Setting," Lawyers Cooperative Publishing 1995.
**Personal:** Goucher College (AB, with Honors in Economics, 1978), Washington & Lee University School of Law (JD, 1981).

## CAPERS, John
King & Spalding LLP, Atlanta
404 572 4658
jcapers@kslaw.com
*Featured in Corporate/M&A (Georgia)*
**Practice Areas:** Corporate transactions, including domestic and international mergers, acquisitions, securities offerings, joint ventures and governmental and quasi-governmental borrowings. Extensive experience in public offerings of corporate finance and merger, acquisition and joint venture transactions involving different industry groups, including telecommunications, technology, and retail companies. M&A experience includes representing public and private companies, boards of directors and special committees, and financial advisors to companies involved in M&A transactions.
**Professional Memberships:** American Bar Association; Atlanta Bar Association; State Bar of Georgia.
**Personal:** Vanderbilt University, high honors, 1975; JD, high honors, University of Georgia School of Law, Order of Coif, 1978.

## CARLSON, Mark A B
Baker, Donelson, Bearman, Caldwell & Berkowitz, PC, Atlanta
404 589 3400
mcarlson@bakerdonelson.com
*Featured in Corporate/M&A (Georgia)*
**Practice Areas:** Mark helps his clients to structure, negotiate and execute middle market M&A deals, joint ventures and other business combinations as well as general business transactions. His industry experience includes transactions and strategic initiatives in wireless technology, manufacturing, private equity, financial services, medical devices and international transactions.
**Professional Memberships:** Listed: Best Lawyers in America; Georgia Super Lawyers

Rising Star. Member: Georgia State Bar, American Bar Association, Atlanta Bar Association
**Career:** Licensed: Georgia; Tennessee; California; Massachusetts
**Personal:** Harvard Law School, J.D; Dartmouth College, BA

## CARRON, Virginia L
Finnegan, Henderson, Farabow, Garrett & Dunner LLP, Atlanta
404 653 6452
virginia.carron@finnegan.com
*Featured in Intellectual Property (Georgia)*
**Practice Areas:** Practices patent and trademark litigation, counseling, and prosecution. Her litigation experience includes numerous trials before US district courts and at the US International Trade Commission, and appeals to the US Court of Appeals for the Federal Circuit. She also provides counseling on licensing and transactional matters. Her client base includes computer software and hardware companies, members of the telecommunications industry, the world's largest manufacturer of hand-made cigars, and a large international chemical and minerals corporation.
**Personal:** Mississippi State University (BS, Biomedical Engineering, cum laude, 1989); Emory University (J.D., with distinction, 1992).

## CASHDAN, Jeffrey
King & Spalding LLP, Atlanta
404 572 4818
jcashdan@kslaw.com
*Featured in Antitrust (Georgia)*
**Practice Areas:** Antitrust, merger and acquisition and complex business litigation counseling, including securities, purported class actions and appellate matters.
**Professional Memberships:** American Bar Association (Vice-Chair, Sherman Act Section 2, Antitrust and Litigation Sections); Editorial Board for the 2000 Annual Review of Antitrust Law Developments; 'Antitrust Law Journal' (former editor); Atlanta Bar Association; Illinois State Bar; State Bar of Georgia (Chair, Antitrust Section).
**Personal:** BA, cum laude, Claremont McKenna College, 1987; London School of Economics and Political Science; JD, University of Chicago, 1990.

## CASSILLY, Lisa H
Alston & Bird LLP, Atlanta
404 881 7945
lisa.cassilly@alston.com
*Featured in Labor & Employment (Georgia)*
**Practice Areas:** Concentrates on the representation of management interests with a special emphasis on litigated matters involving all types of employment claims in administrative proceedings, arbitrations and in trial and appellate courts throughout the country. Extensive experience conducting internal investigations, handling SOX and other whistleblower claims and prosecuting and defending actions involving claims for breach of restrictive covenants, employee piracy, breach of fiduciary duties and trade secret misappropriation.
**Career:** Leader, firm's Labor and Employment Group.

**Personal:** BA (1981), MA (1983) University of Florida; JD (1987) Emory University.

## CHAMBERS, Robert C
Smith, Currie & Hancock LLP, Atlanta
404 582 8035
rcchambers@smithcurrie.com
*Featured in Construction (Georgia)*
**Career:** Bob Chambers is Managing Partner of the firm and has practiced construction law for almost 30 years. Bob represents owners, general contractors, subcontractors, architects, surety companies and other entities on a wide range of construction projects, including high rises, highways, bridges, and industrial complexes. He has worked on both public and private projects including projects administered by the US Army Corps of Engineers, the US Navy, the US EPA, and numerous state and local public entities. Bob serves as General Counsel for the Georgia Highway Contractors Association, as well as the Georgia Asphalt Pavement Association.

## CHANDLER, John A
King & Spalding LLP, Atlanta
404 572 4646
jchandler@kslaw.com
*Featured in Litigation (Georgia)*
**Practice Areas:** Tries business cases. Numerous complex professional liability, securities, insurance and RICO cases. Has represented all of the Big Four accounting firms, and several major law firms.
**Professional Memberships:** Past President of the Atlanta Bar Association, the Atlanta Council of Younger Lawyers, the Atlanta Legal Aid Society, the Atlanta Volunteer Lawyers Foundation. Chair of the Fulton County Ethics Board and of the City of Atlanta Board of Ethics. Member of the International Association of Defense Counsel.
**Personal:** Vanderbilt, (JD, 1972, Order of Coif, Managing Editor, "Vanderbilt Law Review"); University of Tennessee (BS, 1966).

## CLELAND, A Craig
Ogletree, Deakins, Nash, Smoak & Stewart, PC, Atlanta
404 870 1718
craig.cleland@ogletreedeakins.com
*Featured in Labor & Employment (Georgia)*
**Practice Areas:** Defends and counsels employers.
**Professional Memberships:** American, Atlanta, & Georgia Bar Ass'ns.
**Career:** Partner since 2003.
**Publications:** Contributor, Employment Discrimination Law (4th, & forthcoming 5th eds.), Black's Law Dictionary (9th ed.), Garner's Modern American Usage (3d ed.).
**Personal:** BTI Client Service All-Star. Law Clerk, Hon. Marvin Shoob, US District Court, Atlanta. Georgia State University (JD 1992). Editor, Georgia State University Law Review. Best Oralist, McKenzie-McPhail Moot Court Competition. Yale University (STM 1983). Vanderbilt University (M Div 1981). Valdosta State College (BA 1978). Adjunct Professor, Employment Discrimination Law, Georgia State University College of Law. Harvard Mediation Program.

## COALSON JR, John L
Alston & Bird LLP, Atlanta
404 881 7482
john.coalson@alston.com
*Featured in Tax (Georgia)*
**Practice Areas:** Focuses on counseling/planning as well as dispute and litigation work in the state and local tax area, and unclaimed property.
**Professional Memberships:** Fellow, American College of Tax Counsel; Advisory Board, NYU Inst. On State and Local Taxation and Paul Hartman Memorial Inst. on State and Local Taxation; Editorial Board of the 'Journal of Multistate Taxation and Incentives'; Unclaimed Property Professionals Organization.
**Publications:** Authored over 100 professional papers and a dozen law review articles, as well as the 'BNA Portfolio on Unclaimed Property'.
**Personal:** BBA with highest distinction, Emory University (1974); JD summa cum laude, University of Georgia (1977).

## COHEN, Lori G
Greenberg Traurig, LLP, Atlanta
678 553 2385
CohenL@gtlaw.com
*Featured in Products Liability (Nationwide), Litigation (Georgia)*
**Practice Areas:** Chair, Pharmaceutical, Medical Device and Health Care Litigation Group. Co-Chair, Atlanta Litigation Practice.
**Professional Memberships:** Co-Chair, Pharmaceutical and Health Law Subcommittee, Class Action Committee, ABA, 2008-10; Member, International Association of Defense Counsel and Product Liability Advisory Council. Editor for three national publications.
**Career:** Listed: 'Litigator of the Week', The AmLaw Litigation Daily (8 March 2012); Products Liability and Mass Torts – Pharmaceutical and Medical Devices, The Legal 500: United States, 2010-12; Best Lawyers in America; Super Lawyers. Rated, AV® Preeminent™ 5.0 out of 5. (Among others.)
**Personal:** JD, Emory University School of Law; BA, Duke University.

## COLE, Danielle J
Peckar & Abramson, P.C., Atlanta
404 872 4343
dcole@pecklaw.com
*Featured in Construction (Georgia)*
**Practice Areas:** Ms Cole's construction law practice focuses on the representation of construction managers, general contractors, and other project participants, with whom she collaborates to pursue successful procurement, performance, and completion of construction projects. She provides counsel, assistance, and advocacy to clients through both transactional and dispute-related services, including the performance of corporate-counsel functions, negotiating/drafting contracts, project administration, dispute avoidance/resolution, and representation in litigation/arbitration proceeding.
**Professional Memberships:** Chair: International Construction Division, ABA Forum on the Construction Industry; Past-Chair:

Construction Section, Atlanta Bar Association; NAWIC; AGC; Admitted to practice in Georgia and Missouri.
**Career:** Partner
**Personal:** For more information visit: www.pecklaw.com

### COLEMAN, JR, Aubrey L
Smith, Currie & Hancock LLP, Atlanta
404 582 8011
alcoleman@smithcurrie.com
*Featured in Construction (Georgia)*
**Practice Areas:** Construction Law, Government Contracts, and Suretyship.
**Career:** Aubrey Coleman is a Senior Partner at Smith, Currie & Hancock LLP and has practiced construction law for over 40 years representing general contractors, subcontractors, owners, designers, and sureties. His background ranges from negotiating and drafting contracts to trying disputes before juries, judges, and boards in numerous states. He has lectured at several law schools and colleges. He is admitted to practice before many District Courts, Courts of Appeal, and the United States Supreme Court.
**Personal:** Mr Coleman graduated Phi Beta Kappa from Tulane University and from Vanderbilt Law School where he was Managing Editor of the law review. He was a Captain in the US Army after law school.

### CONNOLLY, Dennis J
Alston & Bird LLP, Atlanta
404 881 7269
dennis.connolly@alston.com
*Featured in Bankruptcy/Restructuring (Georgia)*
**Practice Areas:** Representation of debtors and creditors' committees in large Chapter 11 bankruptcy cases. Engagements include representing parties in interest in major Chapter 11 cases such as Delta Air Lines, Refco, Inc., Delphi, Chrysler, General Motors, Enron Corp., Zale Corporation, Einstein-Noah Bagel, Inc., AmeriServe, Winn-Dixie, Sea Launch and SONICblue. Represented Enron Corp. Examiner in Enron Corp. bankruptcy.
**Professional Memberships:** Fellow, American College of Bankruptcy; President-Elect, Southeastern Bankruptcy Law Institute.
**Publications:** Published widely in 'Legal Times' and the 'Bankruptcy Strategist'.
**Personal:** BA, University of Michigan (1982); JD, cum laude, University of South Carolina (1986).

### CONRAD, Albert H
King & Spalding LLP, Atlanta
404 572 4807
cconrad@kslaw.com
*Featured in Banking & Finance (Georgia)*
**Practice Areas:** Representing banks and lending institutions in private debt financings and major financing transactions. Serves as the principal outside lawyer for a number of the firm's corporate and REIT clients.
**Professional Memberships:** American Bar Association (Banking Law Section); American College of Commercial Finance Lawyers (former Chair, Uniform Commercial Code Committee);

Atlanta Bar Association; State Bar of Georgia (Chair, Corporate and Banking Law Section).
**Personal:** BS, with highest honors, University of Tennessee, 1972; JD, University of Virginia, Omicron Delta Kappa; Phi Kappa Phi; Order of the Coif, 1975. Frequent speaker on lending-related topics.

### COWEN, Stephen
King & Spalding LLP, Atlanta
404 572 4688
scowen@kslaw.com
*Featured in Litigation (Georgia)*
**Practice Areas:** Special matters focusing on white-collar criminal defense of corporations, individuals, and civil fraud matters, including healthcare, government procurement, securities, tax, antitrust, foreign payments and campaign finance investigations. Representations have included defense of government and congressional inquiries and litigation of civil fraud and misrepresentation actions. Extensive government experience as a prosecutor and civil litigator. Frequent lecturer on corporate investigations.
**Professional Memberships:** State Bar of Georgia, Florida and the District of Columbia.
**Personal:** Emory University, 1969; JD, Harvard Law School, 1972.

### CREWDSON, Robert L
DLA Piper LLP (US), Atlanta
404 736 7827
robert.crewdson@dlapiper.com
*Featured in Construction (Georgia)*
**Practice Areas:** Construction, real estate, litigation and arbitration, projects and infrastructure.
**Career:** His national practice focuses on the legal needs of national owners, developers, and contractors in the construction industry, emphasizing risk management and claims avoidance. He advises national development firms and owners in the preparation of form contract documents, internal contracting procedures, claims avoidance practices and in-house staff training. He handles major disputes and litigation involving construction projects.
**Personal:** JD, University of Virginia; MA, College of William and Mary; BA, University of the South.

### CUSHING, Paul M
Alston & Bird LLP, Atlanta
404 881 7578
paul.cushing@alston.com
*Featured in Banking & Finance (Georgia)*
**Practice Areas:** Representing financial institutions and companies in corporate finance transactions, including syndicated financings, secured financings, acquisition financings, asset-based loans, structured financings, public and private debt issuances and restructurings and workouts. Extensive representation of financial institutions in the financing of REITs and other real estate companies.
**Professional Memberships:** Member, National Association of Real Estate Investment Trusts; former Chairman, Business Law Section, Georgia State Bar and the UCC Subcommittee of the Business Law Section of the Georgia State Bar. Admitted in Georgia and North Carolina.

**Personal:** BA, magna cum laude (1984) and JD (1987) – Vanderbilt University.

### DANIEL, Laurie Webb
Holland & Knight LLP, Atlanta
404 817 8500
laurie.daniel@hklaw.com
*Featured in Litigation (Georgia)*
**Practice Areas:** Partner in the firm's Litigation Section, she chairs the Appellate Practice Team at Holland & Knight. Her appellate practice addresses a wide range of substantive issues. Daniel's active motions practice includes class action and other types of complex litigation. She has substantial experience in the trial courts and has argued before the United States Supreme Court. Daniel has served as a commentator for CNN on Supreme Court arguments and on the faculty of many continuing legal education programs.

### DANIEL JR, Harold T
Holland & Knight LLP, Atlanta
404 817 8500
harold.daniel@hklaw.com
*Featured in Litigation (Georgia)*
**Practice Areas:** Partner in the firm's Litigation Section, maintains a firm wide commercial litigation practice. He has handled many lengthy jury trials and routinely deals with complex factual and legal issues involving antitrust, securities, business torts and commercial law. Daniel represented the Eleventh Circuit on the Standing Committee of the Federal Judiciary of the American Bar Association from 2000-03. He is a fellow of the American College of Trial Lawyers, a former President of the State Bar of Georgia, and received the Distinguished Service Award of the State Bar of Georgia in 2001.

### DAVID, Todd R
Alston & Bird LLP, Atlanta
404 881 7357
todd.david@alston.com
*Featured in Litigation (Georgia)*
**Practice Areas:** Complex commercial litigation, including, class actions, securities, D&O, E&O, purchase price adjustments, professional liability. Lead counsel in numerous class actions, trials, arbitrations and mediations.
**Professional Memberships:** State Bar of New York; State Bar of Georgia.
**Career:** Co-chair, Litigation Group; former Chair, firm's Management Committee; Law clerk for US District Judge Marvin H Shoob.
**Publications:** Published by 'University of Tennessee Business Law Journal', 'Securities Regulation Law Journal', 'The National Law Journal', 'The Journal of Investment Compliance', 'Directors Monthly', 'The Trial Lawyer', National Association of Corporate Directors', and 'Legal Times'.
**Personal:** BA, Queens College (1982); JD, Northeastern University (1985).

### DAVIS, Bryan E
Jones Day, Atlanta
404 581 8631
bedavis@jonesday.com
*Featured in Corporate/M&A (Georgia)*

**Practice Areas:** Bryan Davis advises public and private companies, private equity firms, and investment banking firms, focusing primarily on mergers and acquisitions, buyouts, joint ventures, strategic alliances, and corporate governance matters. Bryan's extensive transactional and advisory experience spans a range of industries, including software, business services, manufacturing, consumer products, restaurants, and telecommunications.
**Professional Memberships:** Member of the American Bar Association's Public Company Acquisitions Task Force. Bryan also serves on the Georgia Corporate Code Revision Committee.

### DAVIS, Cindy JK
Greenberg Traurig, LLP, Atlanta
678 553 7350
DavisCindy@gtlaw.com
*Featured in Banking & Finance (Georgia)*
**Practice Areas:** Financial institutions; business reorganization and financial restructuring; asset-based and cash flow lending and financial services; acquisition financings; cross-border lending; debtor-in-possession financings; workouts and restructuring.
**Professional Memberships:** Zoo Atlanta, Leadership Council; Governing Board, Commercial Finance Association Education Foundation; Member, State Bar of Georgia and State Bar of Florida; Past President, The Women's Finance Exchange, Atlanta chapter.
**Career:** Selected, Chambers USA Guide, 2007-13; 'Georgia's Legal Elite', Georgia Trend, 2010, 2012; 'Legal Dealmaker', Atlanta Business Chronicle. Rated, AV® Preeminent™ 5.0 out of 5.
**Personal:** BBA, Accounting, cum laude, University of Massachusetts Amherst; JD, with honors, University of Florida.

### DAVIS VARNER, Chilton
King & Spalding LLP, Atlanta
404 572 4789
cvarner@kslaw.com
*Featured in Litigation (Nationwide), Products Liability (Nationwide), Litigation (Georgia)*
See under Nationwide for profile.

### DAWSON, Cari K
Alston & Bird LLP, Atlanta
404 881 7766
cari.dawson@alston.com
*Featured in Litigation (Georgia)*
**Practice Areas:** Complex business litigation matters with particular focus on the defense of class actions, including consumer, insurance, toxic tort, product liability, and environmental class actions in both state and federal courts nationwide and MDL's.
**Career:** Chair, firm's Class Action Team, Litigation and Trial Practice Group. Lead class action counsel defending Toyota Motor Corporation in approximately 200 economic loss class actions in the Unintended Acceleration, Marketing, Sales Practices, and Products Liability Multi-District Litigation.
**Publications:** Frequent lecturer and author on the defense of class actions and commercial litigation.

**Personal:** Harvard University (JD, 1993); Princeton University (AB, 1990)

## DEAKINS JR, Homer L

Ogletree, Deakins, Nash, Smoak & Stewart, PC, Atlanta
404 881 1300
homer.deakins@ogletreedeakins.com
*Featured in Labor & Employment (Georgia)*
**Practice Areas:** Labor and Employment Law, Employment Litigation.
**Professional Memberships:** Lawyers Club of Atlanta.
**Career:** Admitted Georgia, South Carolina, Tennessee, Texas, D.C., New York, US Supreme Court, US Court of Appeals (Second, Fourth, Fifth, Sixth, Eleventh Circuits, D.C.); ABA; Listed in The Best Lawyers in America (Labor/Employment 'Lawyer of the Year' in Atlanta); Fellow, College of Labor and Employment Lawyers (Georgia Representative, Eleventh Circuit Board of Directors).
**Publications:** Authored "Cross-Examining the Plaintiff in an Employment Tort Case" Litigating the Employment Tort Case (ABA).
**Personal:** Southern Methodist University (1957), University of Texas School of Law (cum laude, 1960).

## DEANE JR, Richard H

Jones Day, Atlanta
404 581 8502
rhdeane@jonesday.com
*Featured in Litigation (Georgia)*
**Practice Areas:** Corporate criminal investigations and general litigation practice. Served as Chief of the Criminal Division of the US Attorney's Office and as a US magistrate judge. Experienced in all aspects of grand jury operations and investigations. Appointed by President Clinton as US attorney for the Northern District of Georgia. Led office in prosecuting a wide range of criminal matters and defended the government in civil suits. Served on the Attorney General's Advisory Committee to offer advice on policy matters and substantive issues.
**Publications:** Lectured extensively on grand jury practice and procedures. Adjunct Professor, Georgia State University College of Law.

## DEGNAN, Peter

Alston & Bird LLP, Atlanta
404 881 7743
pete.degnan@alston.com
*Featured in Energy & Natural Resources (Georgia)*
**Practice Areas:** Energy law, with an emphasis on public power project financing. Recent matters include extensive involvement in the creation and financing of new nuclear units and several transactions involving the sale of nuclear power on an assumption of the construction risk basis.
**Professional Memberships:** Member of the State Bar of Georgia, Atlanta Bar Association.
**Personal:** BS, US Naval Academy (1968); USMC (1968-1973); JD, Syracuse University (1976).

## DEHAVEN, Dara L

Ogletree, Deakins, Nash, Smoak & Stewart, PC, Atlanta
404 881 1300
dara.dehaven@ogletreedeakins.com
*Featured in Labor & Employment (Georgia)*
**Practice Areas:** Labor and Employment, Litigation.
**Professional Memberships:** American Bar Association, Georgia State Bar, Atlanta Bar Association, Bleckley Inn of Court, Lawyers Club Atlanta.
**Career:** Admitted to practice in Georgia, various US Courts of Appeal, US District Courts, and US Supreme Court. She is a frequent speaker to national business, professional, and civic organizations. She is an Atlanta and Corporate Counsel Super Lawyer, Georgia Trend Legal Elite, Best Lawyers in America, Chambers Leading Lawyer and a Member, Board of Visitors, Duke University School of Law.
**Personal:** Duke University (BA, 1973; M.A., 1974), Duke University School of Law (J.D., 1980).

## DEHIHNS III, Lee A

Alston & Bird LLP, Atlanta
404 881 7151
lee.dehihns@alston.com
*Featured in Environment (Georgia)*
**Practice Areas:** Environmental regulatory and litigation matters, including air quality, climate change, toxic chemicals, water quality and quantity, wetlands, corporate audits, debarment, white-collar criminal, and hazardous waste.
**Professional Memberships:** Past Chair, American Bar Association's Section of Environment, Energy and Resources 2007-2008, ABA House of Delegates 2009-2015. Chair, ABA Delegation to the UN Rio+20 Sustainable Development Conference, Rio de Janeiro.
**Career:** Frequent speaker and author on water quality and quantity, sustainability, corporate environmental responsibility, citizen suits and climate change. Listed in leading US legal publications.
**Personal:** BS, University of Scranton (1967); JD, Catholic University of America (1974). US Navy Officer 1967-69.

## DELISLE, Joe

Miller & Martin PLLC, Atlanta
404 962 6438
jdelisle@millermartin.com
*Featured in Corporate/M&A (Georgia)*
**Practice Areas:** Joe DeLisle concentrates his practice on mergers, acquisitions and divestitures, private debt and equity and venture capital transactions, securities laws, corporate formation and governance, shareholders, partnership and joint venture agreements, and other general business and commercial matters. Prior to joining Miller & Martin PLLC, Mr DeLisle led the corporate and tax group at a mid-sized Atlanta law firm and before that practiced in the corporate group of an Atlanta-based, national law firm. Before becoming a lawyer, Mr DeLisle was an environmental engineer for four years with Law Engineering &

Environmental Services, Inc. and earned his Professional Engineer License.

## DENT, Miriam

Rogers & Hardin LLP, Atlanta
404 420 4608
mdent@rh-law.com
*Featured in Real Estate (Georgia)*
**Practice Areas:** Commercial real estate and finance with extensive experience in all aspects of real estate business transactions on a nationwide basis. Specializes in complex, multi-state multi-property commercial real estate acquisitions and dispositions. Additional expertise in asset based finance, with emphasis on sale-leaseback transactions with REITs, and representation of both landlords and tenants in all areas of commercial leasing, including office, retail and multi-use developments.
**Professional Memberships:** Atlanta Bar Association; State Bar of Georgia; American Bar Assocation.
**Personal:** BA, summa cum laude, Miami University, 1984; JD, Vanderbilt University, Order of the Coif, Associate Editor, Vanderbilt Law Review, 1987.

## DIAL, David

Weinberg, Wheeler, Hudgins, Gunn & Dial, LLC, Atlanta
404 832 9513
ddial@wwhgd.com
*Featured in Construction (Georgia)*
**Practice Areas:** Complex trial practice involves the representation of corporations and individuals involved in almost every aspect of business in the United States. Has significant experience in construction law, representing all entities involved in the construction industry. Has handled matters in 40 states, Washington, DC, Puerto Rico, The Bahamas, Canada and Australia. Also represents clients nationally in products liability, transportation and premises liability matters.
**Career:** Martindale-Hubbell AV-rated; Selected as Georgia 'Super Lawyer' in Construction Litigation from 2004-13; Listed in 'Best Lawyers in America' in Construction Law for 2006-13; Named among 'America's Leading Business Lawyers' for 2004-13; Names one of Chartis, Inc.'s Top Ten Attorneys for 2010; Named Best Lawyers' 2012 and 2013 Atlanta Litigation – Construction Lawyer of the Year.
**Personal:** BA, summa cum laude, University of Georgia, 1980, Phi Beta Kappa; JD, Baylor University School of Law, First Graduate, 1983.

## DOBBINS, Carolyn B

Rogers & Hardin LLP, Atlanta
404 420 4644
cdobbins@rh-law.com
*Featured in Real Estate (Georgia)*
**Practice Areas:** Representation of borrowers and lenders in private debt financing transactions, including secured and unsecured senior credit facilities, asset-based financings; acquisition financing; real estate loans; structured finance transactions and securitizations. Significant expertise in financing for the seniors housing industry.

**Professional Memberships:** Atlanta Bar Association; American Bar Association; State Bar of Georgia; Women's Finance Exchange.
**Personal:** JD, with distinction, Emory University School of Law; Order of the Coif; Executive Articles Editor, Emory Law Journal; MBA (Finance), Georgia State University; AB (Chemistry), Duke University.

## DOWDY, L Craig

McKenna Long & Aldridge LLP, Atlanta
404 527 4180
cdowdy@mckennalong.com
*Featured in Energy & Natural Resources (Georgia)*
**Practice Areas:** Mr Dowdy' s work includes strategic counseling and commercial and regulatory litigation. He represents utilities, large end-use customers, long distance companies, competitive local exchange carriers, and resellers in matters before state regulatory agencies, FERC, and the courts. He has represented clients in matters involving electric energy supply agreements; natural gas supply contracts; electric, natural gas, and telecommunications certificates, tariffs, and rule-makings; electric generation and natural gas capacity supply proceedings; electric and natural gas integrated resource planning; pipeline replacement programs; and rate case litigation.
**Personal:** JD, Georgia State University College of Law, 1988 BS, Electrical Engineering Auburn University, 1979

## DRAPER IV, Clare H

Alston & Bird LLP, Atlanta
404 881 7191
clare.draper@alston.com
*Featured in Labor & Employment (Georgia)*
**Practice Areas:** Litigates class actions and individual lawsuits, including wage/ hour, employment discrimination and WARN cases, restrictive covenant matters, and employment agreement disputes. Advises clients regarding full range of workplace issues. Handles union campaigns, negotiations and avoidance training. Drafts affirmative action plans and defends OFCCP audits.
**Career:** Over 25 years advising clients and litigating employment disputes throughout the country. Frequent speaker on employment law and human resources topics.
**Publications:** Author of several publications, the latest of which is 'Workplace Privacy: A Guide for Attorneys and HR Professionals' from Pike & Fisher/BNA.
**Personal:** BA (1982) Yale University; JD (1985) Vanderbilt University.

## DUFFIE, L Traywick

Littler Mendelson, PC, Atlanta
404 233 0330
TDuffie@littler.com
*Featured in Labor & Employment (Georgia)*
**Practice Areas:** Complex litigation and jury trials, labor management relations, and wage and hour
**Career:** Traywick represents corporate clients in a broad range of employment and labor law, including employment litigation, union organizing, wage and hour and Employee Retirement Income Security Act matters. He has successfully

defended numerous class and collective matters and countered union organizing campaigns in more than 40 states. He has successfully defended single plaintiff, multiple plaintiff and class action litigation involving: race, age, sex, pregnancy, disability, retaliation, and other employee claims. Traywick has designed and implemented programs on compliance with the avoidance of employment litigation and union organizing.

### DYER III, William B
Finnegan, Henderson, Farabow, Garrett & Dunner LLP, Atlanta
404 653-6470
bill.dyer@finnegan.com
*Featured in Intellectual Property (Georgia)*
**Practice Areas:** Focuses on patent litigation in US district courts and before the US International Trade Commission. With experience in more than 50 lawsuits, he manages all aspects of litigation, including development of case strategy, discovery, motions practice, and trial litigation. He is also involved in IP counseling, including opinion writing, due diligence studies, and patent portfolio development. His practice focuses on electrical, electronics, and information technology, including related software systems.
**Personal:** Virginia Military Institute (BS, Electrical Engineering, 1985); Cumberland School of Law at Samford University (J.D., 1992).

### EGAN, Michael
King & Spalding LLP, Atlanta
404 572 4753
megan@kslaw.com
*Featured in Corporate/M&A (Georgia)*
**Practice Areas:** Mr Egan's practice covers mergers and acquisitions, joint ventures and strategic alliances, and corporate governance. He also has substantial experience in cross-border transactions and represents several non-US companies in their US investment activities.
**Professional Memberships:** American Bar Association; International Bar Association; State Bar of Georgia.
**Career:** He serves as Counsel for the Atlanta Falcons NFL franchise and has previously served as European Transactions Counsel to The Coca-Cola Company.
**Personal:** BA, University of North Carolina, 1978; JD, cum laude, Harvard University, Phi Beta Kappa, 1982; Morehead Scholar, University of North Carolina.

### ELROD, John
Greenberg Traurig, LLP, Atlanta
678 553 2259
ElrodJ@gtlaw.com
*Featured in Bankruptcy/Restructuring (Georgia)*
**Practice Areas:** Practice includes representation of secured and unsecured creditors, creditors' committees, corporate debtors, indenture trustees and fiduciaries in chapter 11 cases, insolvency related litigation, and out-of-court workouts.
**Career:** Member, Alabama, Florida, and Georgia bars; American Bankruptcy Institute; Georgia Trend magazine 'Legal Elite', 2012; Georgia Super Lawyers, 'Rising Star', 2010-13; Recognized, 'Dealmakers', Atlanta Business Chronicle, April 16,

2009; Former law clerk, Hon. Tamara O. Mitchell, US Bankruptcy Court, N.D. Ala.
**Personal:** JD, Samford University, Cumberland School of Law, 2001; BA, University of the South (Sewanee), 1997.

### ENSOR, R Steve
Alston & Bird LLP, Atlanta
404 881 7448
steve.ensor@alston.com
*Featured in Labor & Employment (Georgia)*
**Practice Areas:** Representing management for over 19 years in all areas of labor and employment law, including employment litigation, traditional labor union relations and affirmative action planning.
**Professional Memberships:** Member of the State Bar of Georgia, the Georgia Bar Association and the American Bar Association.
**Publications:** Lectures and writes extensively in all areas of labor and employment law. Frequent speaker and panelist for the American Management Association and the Institute for Applied Management and Law.
**Personal:** BA, Duke University (1982); JD, Wake Forest University (1985).

### FARRIS JR, James G
Alston & Bird LLP, Atlanta
404 881 7896
jay.farris@alston.com
*Featured in Real Estate (Georgia)*
**Practice Areas:** Concentrates on commercial real estate investment, joint ventures, borrower financing, development, and leasing involving all major property types. Represents institutional investors (including REITs and pension funds), well-capitalized developers and corporate owners. Extensive experience in representing developers and owners of industrial distribution facilities.
**Professional Memberships:** Pension Real Estate Association (PREA); Association of Foreign Investors in US Real Estate (AFIRE); State Bar of Georgia (Real Property Law Section); Atlanta Bar Association.
**Personal:** BA with High Honors, Wesleyan University (1984); JD, Order of the Coif and Law Review, University of North Carolina (1989).

### FELLOWS, Henry
Fellows LaBriola LLP, Atlanta
404 586 2050
hfellows@fellab.com
*Featured in Litigation (Georgia)*
**Practice Areas:** Representation of businesses, corporations, partnerships and individuals in business and commercial litigation, including breach of fiduciary duty, fraud, employment, breach of contract, computer theft, trade secrets, restrictive covenant, securities, real property, and RICO cases, for past 33 years.
**Professional Memberships:** Fellow of the American College of Trial Lawyers since 2007; Best Lawyers in America listing; Member of American Bar Association, Georgia State Bar, and Atlanta Bar Association ("ABA"); past Chair of Courts Committee of the ABA; past Chair of Litigation Section of the ABA.

**Career:** Law Clerk to Chief Judge Charles A. Moye, Jr., US District Court for the Northern District of Georgia, 1978-80; private practice for 33 years from 1980 through the current year.
**Personal:** BS, Bucknell University, 1975; JD, Georgetown Law, 1978.

### FERDINANDS, Paul K
King & Spalding LLP, Atlanta
404 572 3450
pferdinands@kslaw.com
*Featured in Bankruptcy/Restructuring (Georgia)*
**Practice Areas:** Bankruptcy and commercial matters, focusing on representing parties in connection with transactions occurring in Chapter 11 cases, debtors in connection with business bankruptcy cases and with the bankruptcy aspects of structured finance transactions. Represents Chapter 11 debtors in a variety of industries, creditors' committees, parties in connection with the purchase and sale of secured and unsecured claims, institutional lenders extending debtor-in-possession financings, and companies in out-of-court debt restructurings.
**Professional Memberships:** American Bar Association; Atlanta Bar Association (Member, Section on Banking and Bankruptcy); State Bar of Georgia.
**Personal:** BA, magna cum laude, University of Virginia, 1983; JD, Stanford University, 1986.

### FISHER, Scott A
Arnall Golden Gregory LLP, Atlanta
404 873 8618
scott.fisher@agg.com
*Featured in Real Estate (Georgia)*
**Practice Areas:** Commercial Real Estate: Primarily represents developers, owners and investors in structuring and closing commercial real estate transactions. Extensive experience in the structuring of joint ventures and real estate funds for the acquisition, development and financing of real estate projects.
**Professional Memberships:** International Council of Shopping Centers; American Bar Association.
**Career:** JD, Boston University Law School, 1979; BA, MA, University of Pennsylvania, 1976.
**Publications:** "A Primer on RE Private Equity Fund Formation" June, 2010, Multi-Housing News; "Mixing Legal Issues with Mixed Use" June, 2008 Shopping Center Business Magazine; "What's a Developer to Do?" March, 2008 Shopping Center Business.

### FLINN, Patrick J
Alston & Bird LLP, Atlanta
404 881 7920
patrick.flinn@alston.com
*Featured in Intellectual Property (Georgia)*
**Practice Areas:** Resolution of technology-based disputes, particularly patent and trade secret litigation.
**Professional Memberships:** Member of the Bars of California and Georgia.
**Career:** Partner in IP Litigation, Alston & Bird, 1995-present; Partner, Morrison & Foerster, 1989-1995.

**Publications:** Writer and lecturer on subjects of law and technology. Author of the 'Handbook of Intellectual Property Claims and Remedies'. Speaks regularly at national CLE presentations on patent law, computer law and other technology subjects.
**Personal:** AB, Stanford University (1978); JD, Georgetown University (1982). Member of the Board of Directors, Georgia Legal Services Program.

### FLYNN, John T
Weinberg, Wheeler, Hudgins, Gunn & Dial, LLC, Atlanta
404 832 9516
jflynn@wwhgd.com
*Featured in Construction (Georgia)*
**Practice Areas:** Practice focuses primarily on construction contract and government contract disputes. Has represented owners, architects, engineers, prime contractors and subcontractors in various state and federal courts and before the various Boards of Contract Appeals, the US Court of Federal Claims, General Accounting Office and Small Business Administration. Has represented clients throughout the continental United States, Alaska, Hawaii, Puerto Rico, Italy and Honduras.
**Professional Memberships:** American Bar Association, Public Contract Law Section, Atlanta Bar Association.
**Career:** Martindale-Hubbell AV-rated; Selected Georgia "Super Lawyer" in Construction Litigation; listed in "Best Lawyers in America" in Construction Law for 2008-12; Named top Business Lawyer by Chambers USA for 2008-12.
**Personal:** BA, Texas Tech University, 1968; JD, University of Texas, 1970; LLM, Government Contract Law, George Washington University, 1977.

### FOX, Steven E
Rogers & Hardin LLP, Atlanta
404 420 4603
sef@rh-law.com
*Featured in Corporate/M&A (Georgia)*
**Practice Areas:** Corporate finance, corporate governance, mergers and acquisitions and securities work for public and privately-held companies in the US and abroad, including representation of issuers, underwriters, bidders, target companies, financial advisors, boards of directors and board committees.
**Professional Memberships:** Atlanta Bar Association; State Bar of Georgia (former Chairman, Business Law Section); American Bar Association (Member of Federal Regulation of Securities Committee and Corporate Governance Committee).
**Personal:** BA, University of North Carolina, 1968; JD, University of Michigan, 1973.

### FRITTS, Laura
Kasowitz, Benson, Torres & Friedman LLP, New York
404 260 6132
lfritts@kasowitz.com
*Featured in Intellectual Property (Georgia)*
**Practice Areas:** Laura Fahey Fritts focuses her practice on pharmaceutical and chemical patent

litigation. She has extensive experience litigating patent cases arising from the filing of Abbreviated New Drug Applications. She has represented both branded and generic pharmaceutical companies in litigation involving drugs used to treat ulcers, depression, osteoporosis, erectile dysfunction, parathyroid disorders, hyperphosphatemia, attention deficit disorder, arthritis and chronic pain. Laura's practice also covers a broad spectrum of technology patent litigation. She is registered to practice before the US Patent and Trademark Office.

**Career:** Listed in Georgia Super Lawyers® 2012 and 2013 as a Rising Star.

## GALLO, Barbara
Krevolin & Horst, LLC, Atlanta
404 888 0169
gallo@khlawfirm.com

*Featured in Environment (Georgia)*

**Practice Areas:** Barbara H. Gallo is a Partner at Krevolin & Horst. She handles permitting, compliance, and enforcement issues in all areas of environmental law; handles civil and administrative litigation before federal and state courts and agencies; advises on legislative and rulemaking issues; assists with corporate and real estate transactions, including brownfield transactions, conservation easements, and mitigation banking; advises on the development and implementation of sustainable practices; and advises on climate change issues and how they impact business decisions. Her clients have included manufacturers, energy and alternative energy companies, recyclers, waste hauling and waste disposal companies, wastewater treatment facilities, healthcare providers, developers, lenders, governmental entities, and individuals.

**Professional Memberships:** American Bar Association, Environment, Energy and Resources Section; State Bar of Georgia, Environmental Law Section (Chair 1995); Atlanta Bar Association, Environmental and Toxic Tort Section (Member of Board of Directors, 1998-2011, Chair 2002); Association of Women Environmental Professionals (Steering Committee, 2000-present) Georgia Chapter of the Air & Waste Management Association; Georgia Association of Women Lawyers; National Association of Environmental Professionals.

**Career:** Ms Gallo has over 25 years of experience as an environmental attorney and has been recognized by her peers as one of the preeminent environmental attorneys in Georgia. In 2013, she was recognized by her peers as one of the Top Ten Attorneys in Georgia. From 1985 to 1996, she was a Senior Assistant Attorney General in the Georgia Department of Law's Environmental Division.

**Personal:** Barbara enjoys golf, fine dining and fine wine.

## GARRETT, G Lee
Jones Day, Atlanta
404 581 8013
ggarrett@jonesday.com

*Featured in Litigation (Georgia)*

**Practice Areas:** His practice emphasizes complex litigation and has involved First Amendment,

product liability, construction, contract, and environmental related issues. Has significant experience in bankruptcy related litigation and has argued cases before US District Courts, US Courts of Appeal, the US Supreme Court, the Georgia Supreme Court, the Georgia Court of Appeals, the US Government Board of Contract Appeals, the EPA, and other state and local courts.

**Professional Memberships:** American Board of Trial Advocates.

**Publications:** Written and lectured extensively, including seminars sponsored by The National Law Journal and the Practising Law Institute.

## GENZ, Peter
King & Spalding LLP, Atlanta
404 572 4935
pgenz@kslaw.com

*Featured in Tax (Georgia), Capital Markets (Nationwide)*

**Practice Areas:** Corporate, partnership, and real estate tax matters, as well as tax controversies. Particularly qualified in matters relating to structuring inbound foreign investment, real estate investment trusts and troubled company workouts.

**Professional Memberships:** American Bar Association; State Bar of Georgia; The Florida Bar.

**Career:** served as an attorney-advisor to Chief Judge Howard A Dawson, Jr of the United States Tax Court (1980-82).

**Publications:** NAREIT Annual Law and Accounting Conference, ABA Tax Section Real Estate Committee panels, Southern Federal Tax Institute, Georgia Federal Tax Conference.

**Personal:** MLT, Georgetown University, 1982; JD, University of Florida, 1980; BSBA, University of Florida, 1975.

## GEVERTZ, David
Baker, Donelson, Bearman, Caldwell & Berkowitz, PC, Atlanta
404 221 6512
dgevertz@bakerdonelson.com

*Featured in Labor & Employment (Georgia)*

**Practice Areas:** Vice Chairperson of Baker Donelson's Labor & Employment Department with over seventeen years' experience representing public and privately-held companies throughout the country in complex employment litigation. His practice also involves litigating accommodations claims brought against places of public accommodation and counseling clients on employment law compliance and litigation avoidance.

**Professional Memberships:** Atlanta, Georgia and American Bar Associations.

**Career:** Licensed in Georgia. Named "One of Top Ten Employment Lawyers Under 40" (Employment Law360, March 2010); Georgia Super Lawyers (2009-2012); Georgia Legal Elite (2007-2012).

**Personal:** Harvard Law School, JD, cum laude, 1995. Emory University, BA, 1992, Phi Beta Kappa.

## GINSBERG, Ross D
Weinberg, Wheeler, Hudgins, Gunn & Dial, LLC, Atlanta
404 832 9543
rginsberg@wwhgd.com

*Featured in Construction (Georgia)*

**Practice Areas:** Complex trial practice in a variety of commercial settings. Practice emphasis has been in construction litigation with a particular focus on the defense of design professionals in potentially high exposure litigation. Licensed to practice in Massachusetts, Connecticut and Georgia and involved as counsel all over the US. Also, represents clients in employment and civil rights related matters.

**Career:** Selected as a 'Rising Star' by Super Lawyers Massachusetts magazine and as a Super Lawyer by Georgia Super Lawyers magazine.

**Personal:** BA, Tufts University, 1990; JD, Emory University School of Law, 1993; Most Outstanding Third Year Law Student.

## GOLDEN, Jonathan
Arnall Golden Gregory LLP, Atlanta
404 873 8700
jonathan.golden@agg.com

*Featured in Corporate/M&A (Georgia)*

**Practice Areas:** Corporate law; mergers and acquisitions.

**Professional Memberships:** American Bar Association; State Bar of Georgia.

**Career:** Admitted to practice 1961. Chairman of the firm. Business activities: Director, Sysco Corporation (NYSE), 1983-present; Director, Rich Products Corporation, 1984-present; Director, Profit Recovery Group International, Inc. (NASDAQ), 1996-2005; Director, Intermedics, Inc. (NYSE), 1983-88; Director, Automatic Service Company (AMEX), 1970-76; Director, Butler Shoe Corporation (NYSE), 1965-68; Chairman, Livingston Foundation, 1989-present; Trustee, Southern Center for International Studies; Trustee, Woodruff Arts Center.

**Personal:** Born 1937. Princeton University, 1959; Harvard Law School, 1962. Adjunct Professor, Emory Law: Securities and Corporate Finance 1974-79; Mergers and Acquisitions 1988-89, 2009-10.

## GOODWIN, Timothy J
King & Spalding LLP, Atlanta
404 572 3588
tgoodwin@kslaw.com

*Featured in Real Estate (Georgia)*

**Practice Areas:** Real estate lawyer experienced in structuring and formation of investment funds, sales and acquisitions, financing, development, construction and leasing. Also experienced in dealing with REITs and tax-exempt pension fund investors, often requiring complex tax and ERISA structuring.

**Professional Memberships:** American Bar Association; Atlanta Bar Association; New York State Bar Association; State Bar of Georgia (Real Property Law Section).

**Personal:** Mr Goodwin received his BA, summa cum laude, in history from Boston College in 1987 where he graduated Phi Beta Kappa and

scholar of the College. He received his JD with distinction from Emory Law School in 1990.

## GORDON, David L
Jackson Lewis LLP, Atlanta
404 586 1845
gordond@jacksonlewis.com

*Featured in Labor & Employment (Georgia)*

**Practice Areas:** Employment counseling and litigation.

**Professional Memberships:** American Bar Association.

**Career:** Joined Jackson Lewis 1983, elevated to Partner 1990. Managing Partner, Atlanta, Member, Firm Management Committee, Counsel to the Firm

**Publications:** 'Sexual Harassment Claims After Vinson: Will the Floodgates Swing Open?' and 'The Americans with Disabilities Act of 1990: Questions, Answers and Compliance Strategies', both published in The Atlanta Lawyer, the publication of the Atlanta Bar Association.

**Personal:** University of North Carolina at Chapel Hill, JD, 1983 and BS, 1978; George Washington University, MA, Legislative Affairs, 1980.

## GRADY, Jack
Jones Day, Atlanta
404 581 8316
jhgrady@jonesday.com

*Featured in Environment (Georgia)*

**Practice Areas:** Jack Grady represents clients in litigation, transactions, investigations, and regulatory matters involving all environmental media. Jack's practice has included general litigation matters, including defense claims under the federal False Claims Act.

**Career:** Jack has successfully defended CERCLA parent-operator liability cases and has served as common counsel to a PRP group. He has assisted clients in the creation, sale, and purchase of emission reduction credits and negotiated a carbon sequestration agreement for the creation of greenhouse gas emission credits. While at the DOJ, Jack was trial counsel in several significant environmental enforcement matters and received a number of awards.

## GRANT, James C
Alston & Bird LLP, Atlanta
404 881 7859
jim.grant@alston.com

*Featured in Litigation (Georgia)*

**Practice Areas:** Complex commercial litigation with extensive experience in trial and appellate matters. Litigated matters in more than 15 states. Has tried more than 15 cases to jury verdict or final arbitration award.

**Professional Memberships:** Litigation and Appellate sections of the Atlanta Bar Association. Serve on advisory board of the local chapter of the Make-A-Wish Foundation and Jack and Jill late stage cancer Foundation.

**Career:** Member of firm's Partners' Committee and Financial Partner; Former Co-leader of firm's 150-member Litigation and Trial Practice Group.

**Personal:** AB (1986) University of Michigan; JD (1989) Vanderbilt University.

## GRANTHAM, Mark E
DLA Piper LLP (US), Atlanta
404 736 7801
mark.grantham@dlapiper.com
*Featured in Litigation (Georgia)*
**Practice Areas:** Litigation and arbitration, international arbitration.
**Professional Memberships:** International Bar Association; American and Federal Bar Associations; Fellow, American Bar Foundation.
**Career:** He focuses his practice on trial and appellate work in both state and federal courts and complex arbitration matters in domestic and international arbitration forums. He has substantial experience in domestic and international arbitration matters involving the design engineering profession, trade disputes, and general commercial disputes.
**Personal:** JD, University of Georgia; BA, University of Virginia.

## GRAVES, Judson
Alston & Bird LLP, Atlanta
404 881 7279
jud.graves@alston.com
*Featured in Litigation (Georgia)*
**Practice Areas:** Concentrates practice in jury trial work with emphasis on products liability, medical malpractice, defamation and intellectual property.
**Professional Memberships:** Member of State Bar of Georgia, Florida Bar, Atlanta Bar Association, American Bar Association, and Lawyers Club of Atlanta.
**Career:** Fellow of the American College of Trial Lawyers. Named by 'Best Lawyers' as one of three Lawyers of the Year in Litigation in 2009.
**Publications:** Published in 'Journal of the Medical Association of Georgia', 'Journal of College and University Law' and 'Georgia State Bar Journal'.
**Personal:** BA, Dartmouth College (1969); JD, with distinction, Emory University School of Law (1975).

## GREGORY, Cleburne E
Arnall Golden Gregory LLP, Atlanta
404 873 8634
greg.gregory@agg.com
*Featured in Tax (Georgia)*
**Practice Areas:** Tax aspects of mergers and acquisitions; corporate, partnership, S corporation, REIT income taxation; advising on nonqualified executive compensation for both public and private companies; US tax issues concerning inbound and outbound foreign investment.
**Professional Memberships:** Georgia Bar Association; American Bar Association Tax Section; Past President, Trustee Atlanta Tax Forum; Past President, Trustee Georgia Federal Tax Conference.
**Career:** Admitted to practice, State of Georgia, 1973; Law Clerk to the Honorable Charles Clark, Justice US Court of Appeals for the Fifth Circuit, 1973-74; BA Washington & Lee University, 1969; JD University of Georgia, 1973; LLM, Taxation, Emory University, 1978.

## GRICE, Richard
Alston & Bird LLP, Atlanta
404 881 7576
richard.grice@alston.com
*Featured in Banking & Finance (Georgia)*
**Practice Areas:** Emphasizes representation of domestic and foreign commercial banks, underwriters and debt issuers in financings including recapitalizations, leveraged buyouts and other acquisition financings, public debt issues, private placements, cross-border financings and various asset-based financings. He also represents creditors and debtors in pre-bankruptcy restructurings and Chapter 11 proceedings.
**Career:** Former leader of firm's Global Finance and Debt Products Group. Serves on firm's Financial Advisory Committee. Listed in a leading US legal publication for the years 1995-2012.
**Publications:** Written and lectured on numerous topics of interest to commercial lenders and borrowers.
**Personal:** BA, University of Wisconsin (1981); JD, Cornell University (1984).

## GRIFFIN, Daniel P
Miller & Martin PLLC, Atlanta
404 962 6154
dgriffin@millermartin.com
*Featured in Litigation (Georgia)*
**Practice Areas:** Danny Griffin has more than 24 years of experience in white collar criminal cases, grand jury and internal investigations, defending False Claims Act cases, and civil litigation. He clerked for United States District Court Judge Harold L Murphy and served five years (1997-2002) as an Assistant United States Attorney for the Northern District of Georgia where he had responsibility for prosecuting fraud, tax and public corruption cases. He is consistently recognized as one of Georgia's most effective criminal defense attorneys, and over the course of the last eight years has convinced federal prosecutors to dismiss seven indictments.

## GRIFFITH, Patricia
FordHarrison LLP, Atlanta
404 888 3831
pgriffith@fordharrison.com
*Featured in Labor & Employment (Georgia)*
**Practice Areas:** Labor and Employment
**Career:** Patricia Griffith concentrates her practice on employment litigation, including individual and class action discrimination and harassment cases, employment contracts, wage/hour claims, and other employment-related actions. She tries cases in federal and state courts and before administrative agencies. Patricia has had substantial jury and class certification experience. She is adept at mediating disputes, reducing the likelihood of protracted litigation, and has served as an arbitrator for the State Bar of Georgia. She received her JD, with honors, from the University of Georgia School of Law in 1982.

## GUMBEL, Jon M
Ogletree, Deakins, Nash, Smoak & Stewart, PC, Atlanta
404 881 1300
jon.gumbel@ogletreedeakins.com
*Featured in Labor & Employment (Georgia)*
**Practice Areas:** Discrimination Litigation; Noncompete and Unfair Competition Litigation; Employee Benefits Litigation; Executive Compensation Litigation; Advice and Counsel Regarding Human Resources Issues; Collective Bargaining Negotiations; Unfair Labor Practices; Arbitrations; and Drafting of Noncompete, Executive and Collective Bargaining Agreements.
**Professional Memberships:** American Bar Association, State Bar of Georgia, Gwinnett County Division of Human Resources Management Association.
**Career:** Admitted to practice in Georgia.
**Publications:** Mr Gumbel is a frequent speaker before groups such as HRMA and SHRM and has authored numerous articles regarding labor law, employment laws and noncompete litigation.
**Personal:** Western Illinois University (BBA, 1982), University of Florida (J.D., 1986).

## HAGAMAN, David C
FordHarrison LLP, Atlanta
404 888 3838
dhagaman@fordharrison.com
*Featured in Labor & Employment (Georgia)*
**Practice Areas:** Labor and Employment
**Career:** Dave Hagaman represents management in labor and employment law matters with a focus on employer-employee relations, union organizing campaigns, NLRB cases, arbitrations, labor negotiations, wage and hour matters, employer/supervisor training and employment discrimination litigation. He has tried numerous cases before the NLRB and in federal and state court and represented employers before the Equal Employment Opportunity Commission. Dave frequently lectures on labor and equal employment opportunity law and state related subjects for employer groups, and state and local chambers of commerce. He received his JD from the University of Georgia School of Law.

## HALEY, Nedom A
Baker, Donelson, Bearman, Caldwell & Berkowitz, PC, Atlanta
404 221 6505
nhaley@bakerdonelson.com
*Featured in Tax (Georgia)*
**Practice Areas:** Nedom Haley concentrates his practice in the areas of tax and municipal finance. He has experience in tax controversy work, ERISA, estate planning and general tax practice.
**Professional Memberships:** Atlanta, Georgia, Montana, District of Columbia and American Bar Associations. National Association of Bond Lawyers.
**Career:** Licensed in Georgia, Montana and the District of Columbia. Trial attorney, Office of the Chief Counsel for the Internal Revenue Service, Washington, DC, 1971-74. Navy officer with highest grade of Lieutenant, discharged 1983.

**Personal:** Georgetown University Law Center, LLM, 1973. Emory University, JD, 1970. Georgia Institute of Technology, BSIM, 1965.

## HALL JR, Warren R
Hall, Arbery & Gilligan, LLP, Atlanta
404 442 8777
whall@hagllp.com
*Featured in Labor & Employment (Georgia)*
**Practice Areas:** Employment covenant litigation, employment discrimination defense, federal contractor compliance, and employment-related contract drafting, review, and revision for companies and individuals.
**Career:** Hall, Arbery & Gilligan LLP (2008-Present); Alston & Bird, LLP (partner 2000-08; associate 1994-2000); law clerk for Honorable Ernest Tidwell, USDC, Northern District of Georgia (1992-94).
**Publications:** "Keeping Your Genies in the Bottle: 10 Steps to Protect Your Most Sensitive Secrets", Ga. Bar Journal, December 2008. "Proving Disability in the Performance of Manual Tasks: the Supreme Court's Latest ADA Decision", Ga. Bar Journal, August 2002.
**Personal:** AB (1988) Princeton University; JD (1992) University of Georgia, Managing and Editorial Board of the Georgia Law Review (1990-92).

## HANKINS, Richard B
McKenna Long & Aldridge LLP, Atlanta
404 527 8372
rhankins@mckennalong.com
*Featured in Labor & Employment (Georgia)*
**Practice Areas:** Richard Hankins leads the firm's labor and employment law division. For more than 25 years, Mr Hankins has advised US corporations with regard to a wide variety of complex labor relations matters, such as large-scale union organizing and decertification campaigns, unfair labor practice charges, strikes and secondary boycotts, union jurisdictional disputes, and successor employer claims. He works closely with management on labor relations strategies related to new facilities, plant closings and consolidations, as well as during acquisitions and divestitures. He co-edits the blog www.laborrelationstoday.com.
**Personal:** JD, University of Mississippi School of Law, BA, Freed-Hardeman College.

## HARDIN, Edward J
Rogers & Hardin LLP, Atlanta
404 420 4601
jhardin@rh-law.com
*Featured in Corporate/M&A (Georgia)*
**Practice Areas:** Independent director representations, corporate governance, internal investigations, domestic and international corporate transactions, M&A, recapitalizations, and reorganizations.
**Professional Memberships:** Atlanta, Georgia, American & International Bar Associations; American Law Institute; Georgia Corporate Code Revision Commission; Past Chairman: Business and Banking Law Section; Securities Committee of the Georgia Bar.

**Personal:** BA (with honors), Wesleyan University, 1965; JD, Founders Medal, Order of Coif, Editor in Chief of Law Review, Vanderbilt University (1968). Chairman of Gateway LLC, a homeless services center; President, Georgia Legal Services Foundation; Co-Chair, Regional Commission on Homelessness; Member, Council on Foreign Relations; Chairman Grady Hospital Board of Visitors.

## HARE, Gregory J
Ogletree, Deakins, Nash, Smoak & Stewart, PC, Atlanta
404 881 1300
greg.hare@ogletreedeakins.com
*Featured in Labor & Employment (Georgia)*
**Practice Areas:** Employment litigation, HR advice, discrimination/harassment, restrictive covenants, business divorce disputes, union avoidance, labor arbitrations, franchise/distribution disputes.
**Professional Memberships:** Board of Directors – Society for Human Resource Management (SHRM) -Atlanta; American, Georgia & Atlanta Bar Associations; Lawyers Club & Commerce Club – Atlanta.
**Career:** US Supreme Court, 11th, 8th & 6th Circuits, Georgia courts & NLRB. Super Lawyer – Georgia Law & Politics. Martindale Hubbell AV Rated.
**Publications:** Frequent publisher/speaker on HR/employment law issues, including SHRM National Conference.
**Personal:** UNC Law School (JD With Honors 1991); LeMoyne College, Industrial & Labor Relations (BS Cum Laude, Top Graduate 1988).

## HAWK, Sarah J
Ogletree, Deakins, Nash, Smoak & Stewart, PC, Atlanta
404 881 1300
sarah.hawk@ogletreedeakins.com
*Featured in Immigration (Georgia)*
**Practice Areas:** Immigration. Advise clients on current immigration legislation, and has comprehensive knowledge and extensive experience in a broad range of immigration petitions, nonimmigrant and immigrant visa applications, consular processing, waiver cases and outbound placement. She conducts I-9 compliance training, performs I-9 audits and advises on immigration policy for companies.
**Professional Memberships:** Philippine-American Chamber of Commerce of Georgia, Japan-America Society of Georgia, Georgia Asian-Pacific Bar Association, National Association of Asian-American Professionals, National Asian-Pacific Bar Association
**Career:** Admitted to practice in Georgia, Georgia Supreme Court
**Personal:** Agnes Scott College (BA 1992), Agnes Scott College (M.A.T. 1993), Georgia State University (J.D., 2000).

## HAWKINS, Holmes
King & Spalding LLP, Atlanta
404 572 2443
hhawkins@kslaw.com
*Featured in Intellectual Property (Georgia)*

**Practice Areas:** Intellectual property law, focusing on patent litigation, including patent infringement lawsuits involving computer systems and software, internet-related technologies, telecommunications and electronics systems, financial service models, consumer products, medical devices, patents, trademarks, copyrights and licensing matters.
**Professional Memberships:** American Bar Association; Atlanta Bar Association; American Intellectual Property Law Association; Georgia Institute of Technology, Atlanta (visiting Professor); State Bar of Georgia (Intellectual Property Section).
**Personal:** BEE, high honors, Georgia Institute of Technology, 1990; JD, cum laude, University of Georgia, 1993. National Institute of Trial Advocacy, National Trial Skills program, Colorado.

## HELLER, Dan
King & Spalding LLP, Atlanta
404 572 4919
dheller@kslaw.com
*Featured in Real Estate (Georgia)*
**Practice Areas:** Active since 1980 in the full range of commercial real estate transactions. Practice includes acquisitions, dispositions, development, leasing, financing, joint ventures and portfolio transactions for both public and private companies.
**Personal:** J.D., cum laude, Harvard University BA, magna cum laude, Yale University

## HENDRIX, Glenn P
Arnall Golden Gregory LLP, Atlanta
404 873 8692
glenn.hendrix@agg.com
*Featured in Healthcare (Georgia)*
**Practice Areas:** False Claims Act defense; commercial litigation and arbitration, including international arbitration; complex Medicare/Medicaid reimbursement litigation.
**Professional Memberships:** US Department of State Advisory Committee on International Law; Delegate, ABA House of Delegates; Past Chair, ABA Section of International Law; American Health Lawyers Association; International Bar Association; President, Atlanta International Arbitration Society.
**Publications:** Extensive writing and speaking engagements.
**Personal:** JD, with distinction, Emory Law School (1985); BA, New College of Florida (1982).

## HERRIN, Barry S
Smith Moore Leatherwood LLP, Atlanta
404 962 1027
barry.herrin@smithmoorelaw.com
*Featured in Healthcare (Georgia)*
**Practice Areas:** Barry Herrin is a Partner in the Atlanta office. His practice is devoted to healthcare and hospital law and policy, with emphasis in operational and governance issues, transactional matters, mergers and acquisitions, health information management issues, privacy law, and compliance matters. Mr Herrin counsels clients regularly on HIPAA compliance and has particularized knowledge in several unusual healthcare legal

matters, such as involuntary sterilization, court-ordered medical procedures, 'right to die''issues, and physician-assisted suicide, among others. He is a Fellow of the American College of Healthcare Executives and a Life Member of the National Eagle Scout Association.

## HERZOG JR, Richard B
Nelson Mullins Riley & Scarborough LLP, Atlanta
404 322 6152
richard.herzog@nelsonmullins.com
*Featured in Bankruptcy/Restructuring (Georgia)*
**Practice Areas:** Business Bankruptcy Partner; Leader, Debt Finance and Restructuring Practice.
**Professional Memberships:** Past President, Atlanta Bar Association; Director, John Marshall Law School; Fellow, American Bar Foundation; Trustee, Georgia Legal History Foundation; Trustee, Fellow, Atlanta Bar Foundation; Fellow, Georgia Lawyers Foundation; Georgia Trend Magazine's Legal Elite; Atlanta Magazine's 100 Best Georgia Lawyers.
**Career:** Represented over $100 million debt in bankruptcies of multi-location retailers, nursing homes, textiles and trucking.
**Publications:** Author, 'Bankruptcy: A Concise Guide for Creditors and Debtors', Fortune Business Book Club Selection.
**Personal:** JD cum laude, BA University of Georgia; Law Clerk, W H Drake, USB Ct NDGA; USNR.

## HICKS, M Maxine
DLA Piper LLP (US), Atlanta
404 736 7809
maxine.hicks@dlapiper.com
*Featured in Real Estate (Georgia)*
**Practice Areas:** Real estate.
**Career:** She has extensive experience in the acquisition, development, leasing, distressed assets, clubs and recreational amenities, state and federal regulation of real property, mixed-use community goverance and municipal matters. She is a noted author and lecturer on issues relating to master-planned communities and has been invited to speak before several highly esteemed professional organizations. She is the chair of the firm's Atlanta office Real Estate team and is a certified public accountant in the State of Georgia.
**Personal:** JD, Georgia State University College of Law; BBA, West Georgia College.

## HILL JR, William B
Ashe Rafuse & Hill LLP, Atlanta
404 253 6025
williamhill@AsheRafuse.com
*Featured in Labor & Employment (Georgia), Litigation (Georgia)*
**Practice Areas:** Concentrates practice in complex commercial litigation, products liability, Lanham Act, and employment defense. Recognized as one of Georgia's top litigators, and as one of the "Top 100" attorneys by Law and Politics Magazine and Atlanta Magazine.
**Professional Memberships:** Committee on Standards of the Profession – State Bar of Georgia; Legal Education Study Committee –

State Bar of Georgia; Georgia Defense Lawyers Association; Defense Research Institute.
**Career:** Former Deputy Attorney General; former State and Superior Court Judge, Fulton County, Georgia.
**Personal:** Washington & Lee University, BA (1974); JD (1977).

## HOGFOSS, Robert
Hunton & Williams LLP, Atlanta
404 888 4042
rhogfoss@hunton.com
*Featured in Environment (Georgia)*
**Practice Areas:** Robert Hogfoss' practice focuses exclusively on energy, environmental and administrative law, with emphasis on Pipeline Safety Act, Clean Water Act, Oil Pollution Act, RCRA, CERCLA and TSCA issues. Experience in compliance advice, enforcement defense, administrative adjudication and environmental litigation. Representative clients: oil and natural gas pipelines, manufacturers, and the pulp and paper industry. Recognized by Chambers 'Clients' Guide to Leading US Business Lawyers' as a leading lawyer in the Environmental Practice, and as one of the top Georgia Environmental/Land Use lawyers, selected by Georgia attorneys and published in Atlanta magazine and Georgia Super Lawyers magazine, 2004-2013.

## HOLDEN, G Graham
Jones Day, Atlanta
404 581 8220
ggholden@jonesday.com
*Featured in Environment (Georgia)*
**Practice Areas:** Advises electric utilities, petrochemical companies, cement manufacturers and other heavy industries in the interpretation, administration, and enforcement of environmental regulatory laws. His practice concentrates on the Clean Air Act and related state and local air quality laws, where he assists clients in the application, negotiation, and adjudication of air operating permits. He also advises clients on the creation and application of new air quality laws and related regulations.
**Professional Memberships:** State Bar of Georgia, The Florida Bar, ABA, Air and Waste Management Association, Environmental Law Institute.

## HOLLINGSWORTH II, Michael E
Nelson Mullins Riley & Scarborough LLP, Atlanta
404 322 6080
michael.hollingsworth@nelsonmullins.com
*Featured in Corporate/M&A (Georgia)*
**Practice Areas:** Corporate/M&A; private equity; joint ventures.
**Professional Memberships:** Southern Capital Forum; American Bar Association, Section of Business Law; Association for Corporate Growth; Thomson Reuters Advisory Board; Business and Finance Section of Atlanta Bar Association.
**Career:** Managing Partner, Atlanta office; Co-Chairs M&A Group; Founded Southeastern M&A Forum; Named Georgia Super Lawyer; one of Georgia Trend's Most Effective Lawyers publication.

**Personal:** Born July 21, 1970. Attended Tulane University of Louisiana, Cumberland School of Law at Samford University and University of Alabama School of Law. Serves on Membership Committee of Ansley Golf Club. Member of the Cathedral of St. Philip.

### HOPKINSON, Christine A
King & Spalding LLP, Atlanta
404 572 3560
chopkinson@kslaw.com
*Featured in Antitrust (Georgia)*

**Practice Areas:** Hopkinson focuses on antitrust and other complex commercial litigation and has extensive experience representing clients in federal courts around the country. Litigated many types of antitrust claims on behalf of plaintiffs and defendants, including price-fixing, tying, monopolization, and price discrimination claims among others, in both class- and non-class actions. Also litigated many types of complex commercial disputes, including consumer class actions, a variety of breach of contract actions, and government contracting disputes.

**Personal:** J.D., Columbia University BA, the University of Wisconsin

### HORST, Jeffrey D
Krevolin & Horst, LLC, Atlanta
404 888 9594
horst@khlawfirm.com
*Featured in Litigation (Georgia)*

**Practice Areas:** Jeff handles a broad spectrum of complex business litigation matters including appeals, business torts, contracts, corporate governance, entertainment, franchise, insurance coverage, intellectual property, officer and director liability, professional liability, RICO, securities, shareholder disputes, and trade secrets litigation.

**Professional Memberships:** Fellow, American Academy of Trial Counsel; Atlanta Bar Association, Member Chair; Judicial Poll Committee, 2002-2003; Litigation Section Chair; Courts Committee, 2001 – 2002; Sole Practitioners/Small Firm Section; Lawyers Club of Atlanta; Executive Committee Chair, Rules, Practice and Judiciary Committee; Bond Community Federal Credit Union Board of Directors.

**Career:** Jeff leads one of the top litigation and trial practices in Atlanta. The breadth, depth, and extraordinary credentials of Krevolin & Horst's litigation team are unusual for a small firm. All of the firm's litigators previously worked for large firms, and most clerked for federal judges. Jeff has been recognized by his peers and selected multiple times by Georgia Trend and Atlanta magazines as one of the most effective business litigators in Georgia. Many attorneys refer clients to Jeff because of his creative approach, trial experience, professionalism, and successful track record in handling cutting edge legal issues. He has tried cases in five states and has handled a number of high profile matters covered in the media including The New York Times, Wall Street Journal, and Los Angeles Times. Jeff was one of the principal counsel in a 5 month jury trial selected by the National Law Journal as a top ten jury defense

verdict. Jeff works with a range of clients from individuals to large corporations. Recently Jeff was hired 2 months before trial to defend the CEO and EVP of a $1 billion Georgia financial institution in a shareholder derivative suit. After a 7-day trial, the jury rendered a defense verdict. Jeff's practice is divided equally between representing plaintiffs and defendants. While representing plaintiffs, Jeff has verdicts or settlements aggregating millions of dollars over the last five years. His success on appeals exceeds 80 percent. Jeff was previously a partner at Bondurant, Mixson & Elmore.

**Personal:** Jeff is married and has eight year old twin daughters who keep him very busy and entertained outside the office.

### HOWELL, D Clayton
King & Spalding LLP, Atlanta
404 572 2741
chowell@kslaw.com
*Featured in Real Estate (Georgia)*

**Practice Areas:** Focuses on the representation of developers in complex, urban development transactions, the representation of institutional investors in structuring real estate equity investments and the representation of developers, investors and owners in connection with the acquisition, financing and sale of real estate assets. Mr Howell has represented these clients in the office, apartment, condominium, retail, industrial and senior-living sectors throughout the United States.

**Personal:** Mr Howell received his BA in psychology from Davidson College in 1993 and his JD from the University of Georgia in 1998.

### HUGHES III, Hunter R
Rogers & Hardin LLP, Atlanta
404 420 4622
hhughes@rh-law.com
*Featured in Labor & Employment (Georgia)*

**Practice Areas:** Employment law; concentration on collective and class actions. Mediator in complex cases including Wal-Mart, Publix, Coca Cola, Home Depot, Sears, FedEx and Boeing.

**Professional Memberships:** Atlanta, Georgia and American Bar Associations, Georgia Arbitrators Forum, American Employment Law Council; AAA Commercial Panel; Past Chairman of EEO Committee of Administrative Section of ABA; Past President, Program Chair, EEO Committee of Labor & Employment Section of ABA.

**Personal:** BA and JD (with honors), University of Virginia, 1965-70. Fellow, American College of Employment Lawyers; Board of Directors, Atlanta International Arbitration Society; Board of Directors, American College of Civil Trial Mediators.

### HUGHES JR, William H
Alston & Bird LLP, Atlanta
404 881 7273
bill.hughes@alston.com
*Featured in Construction (Georgia)*

**Practice Areas:** Mr Hughes' "birth to earth" construction practice includes drafting and negotiating design, construction, design/build, engi-

neer/procure/construct, construction management and joint venture contracts; counseling project participants during construction; and mediating, arbitrating and litigating disputes after project completion.

**Career:** Mr Hughes provides services for energy, infrastructure, healthcare, hospitality, multi-family and multi-use projects throughout the U.S and in Mexico, the Caribbean, South America and Asia. Over the course of his career he negotiated contracts for over $11 billion in construction work and litigated or arbitrated over $1.4 billion in claims.

**Personal:** BA, University of North Carolina (1980); JD, University of Virginia (1983).

### HUSSLE, Robert C
Rogers & Hardin LLP, Atlanta
404 420 4633
rhussle@rh-law.com
*Featured in Corporate/M&A (Georgia)*

**Practice Areas:** Advises private and public companies in capital raising and merger and acquisition activities. Represents issuers in public and private offerings of debt and equity securities, advises public companies regarding disclosure and other reporting obligations, forms investment funds and advises buyers and sellers in acquisitions and dispositions of companies, divisions or assets.

**Professional Memberships:** Atlanta Bar Association (Director and Past Chairman, Business & Finance Section); State Bar of Georgia (Chairman, Business Law Section; Chairman, Securities Committee); New York State Bar Association; American Bar Association.

**Personal:** AB, cum laude, Wabash College, 1987; JD, magna cum laude, Indiana University, 1990.

### IMMERMAN, Leon Andrew
Alston & Bird LLP, Atlanta
404 881 7532
andy.immerman@alston.com
*Featured in Tax (Georgia)*

**Practice Areas:** Partner in firm's Federal Income Tax and International Tax Groups. Concentrates on tax planning and transactional work, including mergers and acquisitions, joint ventures, partnerships, limited liability companies and corporations.

**Professional Memberships:** Past Chair of Committee on Taxation (American Bar Association, Business Law Section) and Partnership and LLC Committee (State Bar of Georgia, Business Law Section); President, Southeast Business Tax Forum; Life Fellow, American Bar Foundation; former Editorial Board Member, 'Business Law Today'.

**Personal:** JD (1982) Yale University; PhD (1978), MA (1976) Princeton University; MA (1976) University of Minnesota; BA (1973) Carleton College.

### INGRAHAM, C Walker
Seyfarth Shaw LLP, Atlanta
404 885 6717
cingraham@seyfarth.com
*Featured in Construction (Georgia)*

**Practice Areas:** Construction; Commercial Litigation.

**Professional Memberships:** American Arbitration Association; American Bar Association.

**Career:** Co-chair of the firm's national Construction Practice group and Chair of the Atlanta Litigation Department. Mr Ingraham represents US-based and international owners, contractors, design professionals and others in a variety of construction-related matters. He has served as lead Counsel in construction, design and environmental remediation disputes throughout the US, trying more than one hundred cases to verdict or arbitration award. His work also includes drafting and negotiating contracts, and advising clients on contracting and claims avoidance issues.

**Personal:** JD, Emory University; BSES, Vanderbilt University School of Engineering.

### ISBELL, John F
Thompson Hine LLP, Atlanta
404 541 2913
John.Isbell@ThompsonHine.com
*Featured in Bankruptcy/Restructuring (Georgia)*

**Career:** John is a partner in the Business Restructuring, Creditors' Rights & Bankruptcy practice group and is based in the firm's Atlanta office. He concentrates his practice in the areas of bankruptcy and insolvency law, including insolvency-related commercial litigation in both state and federal courts. John represents secured lenders, debtors/borrowers, official committees of unsecured creditors, landlords, and other parties in interest in relation to, among other things, bankruptcy cases, receivership litigation, workouts, restructurings and state court foreclosures and confirmation proceedings. John frequently lectures on bankruptcy and commercial litigation topics before bar and trade groups, as well as continuing legal education programs.

### JEFFRIES, M Hill
Alston & Bird LLP, Atlanta
404 881 7823
hill.jeffries@alston.com
*Featured in Corporate/M&A (Georgia)*

**Practice Areas:** Securities and corporate finance, mergers, acquisitions and dispositions, corporate governance, and the general representation of public and private companies.

**Professional Memberships:** A founding director of the Business and Finance Law Section of the Atlanta Bar Association; member of the Georgia Business Corporation Code Revision Committee.

**Career:** Past co-leader of firm's corporate and transactional practice. Listed in two leading US legal publications. Best Lawyers' 2011 and 2013 Atlanta Lawyer of the Year for securities law.

**Publications:** Authored numerous articles on securities, corporate governance and M&A topics.

**Personal:** BA, with high distinction (1977), JD (1980) – University of Virginia.

## JOHNSON, Louisa
Seyfarth Shaw LLP, Atlanta
404 888 1023
lojohnson@seyfarth.com
*Featured in Labor & Employment (Georgia)*
**Practice Areas:** Partner in Seyfarth Shaw's Atlanta, Georgia office. Defends management in collective, class, and hybrid lawsuits in which employees allege unpaid minimum wage, overtime, and other compensation.
**Professional Memberships:** ABA, Employment Rights & Responsibilities; Georgia Bar
**Publications:** Chapter Author, "Chapter 19 – Enforcement Actions Filed by US Secretary of Labor," Wage & Hour Collective and Class Litigation, ALM Law Journal Press (2012); Contributing Author, Fair Labor Standards Act, Cummulative Supplement, ABA Section of Labor and Employment Law (2009-2010); Contributor to Seyfarth Shaw's Wage Hour Litigation Blog (www.wagehourlitigation.com).
**Personal:** JD, University of Virginia School of Law; BA, University of Virginia

## JOHNSON, Robert N
Baker, Donelson, Bearman, Caldwell & Berkowitz, PC, Atlanta
404 443 6718
RJohnson@bakerdonelson.com
*Featured in Immigration (Georgia)*
**Practice Areas:** US and Global Business Immigration. Represents US and foreign-owned multinational corporations in connection with employment and international transfer of executives, managers and specialists.
**Professional Memberships:** American Immigration Lawyers Association; Georgia Bar; Japan-America Society.
**Career:** Global employment/immigration and general corporate counseling services. Conversational Japanese.
**Publications:** Authored numerous articles on variety of business immigration topics. Author, Note, Board of Directors of Rotary International v. Rotary Club of Duarte: Redefining Associational Rights, 1988 BYU L Rev 141 (1988).
**Personal:** Brigham Young University (BA), BYU's J. Reuben Clark Law School (JD). Editor, BYU Law Review (1987-88); Editor, BYU International Law Annual (1986-87).

## JOHNSTON, Michael
King & Spalding LLP, Atlanta
404 572 3581
mjohnston@kslaw.com
*Featured in Labor & Employment (Georgia)*
**Practice Areas:** Labor, ERISA and employment law matters, representing clients in pharmaceutical, grocery, food service and distribution, soft drinks, manufacturing, technology, entertainment and healthcare industries.
**Professional Memberships:** American Bar Association, Litigation, Labor and Employment Law Sections. (Disability Subcommittees, EEO Liaison Committee). Atlanta Bar Association, Labor and Employment Law Sections. State Bar of Georgia, Labor and Employment Law Sections.

The Florida Bar, Labor and Employment Law Sections.
**Personal:** BS, with academic distinction, US Air Force Academy, 1975; LLM, Georgetown University, 1986; JD, with high honors, University of Florida, Order of the Coif, 1980.

## JONES, Lewis B
King & Spalding LLP, Atlanta
404 572 2742
lbjones@kslaw.com
*Featured in Environment (Georgia)*
**Practice Areas:** Tort and environmental litigation focusing on general environmental litigation and environmental aspects of project development, with a particular emphasis on water rights and water resources.
**Professional Memberships:** Georgia State Bar-Environmental Section. Atlanta Bar. American Bar Association – Natural Resources & Environment Section (Co-chair of 2010 Eastern Water Law Conference, Planning Committee for Eastern Water Law Conference 2008).
**Publications:** Southeast regional editor for Eastern Water law and policy reporter (from Nov 2007).
**Personal:** BS, summa cum laude, University of the South, 1989; MS, University of Wisconsin, 1995; JD, cum laude, Harvard, 1998.

## JONES JR, Stanley S
Nelson Mullins Riley & Scarborough LLP, Atlanta
404 322 6133
stan.jones@nelsonmullins.com
*Featured in Healthcare (Georgia)*
**Practice Areas:** Government relations and administrative law, healthcare public policy.
**Professional Memberships:** State Bar of Georgia, American Bar Association, American Health Lawyers Association.
**Career:** Extensively involved in the mental health movement and law in Georgia since working on gubernatorial and presidential commissions for the Carter family and Governor Sonny Perdue.
**Personal:** Juris Doctor, cum laude, University of Georgia School of Law; Masters and Bachelors of Arts in Modern History and Economics, Oxford University; Rhodes Scholar; Bachelor of Arts, History, magna cum laude, Harvard College.

## KAMIN, Joshua M
King & Spalding LLP, Atlanta
404 572 4849
jkamin@kslaw.com
*Featured in Real Estate (Georgia)*
**Practice Areas:** Includes mergers, acquisitions, and project developments, with emphasis on structuring real estate equity investments and representing real estate developers in all aspects of their business.
**Personal:** BA in political science from Emory University in 1992, and his JD from the University of Pennsylvania Law School in 1995. Mr Kamin was a senior editor of the University of Pennsylvania Journal of International Business Law, a Member of Penn Law's National Moot Court Team, and a Member of the Sharswood Law Club.

## KANALY, Mark C
Alston & Bird LLP, Atlanta
404 881 7975
mark.kanaly@alston.com
*Featured in Banking & Finance (Georgia)*
**Practice Areas:** Focuses on the representation of banks and other financial institutions, as well as the consultants, accountants and investment bankers who work with those companies. Assists companies with private and public securities offerings, mergers and acquisitions, underwritings, corporate formations and restructurings, recapitalizations, corporate governance and a host of related complex regulatory issues.
**Professional Memberships:** Georgia Bankers Association, Community Bankers Association of Georgia, the National Association of Corporate Directors and the Society of Corporate Secretaries and Governance Professionals.
**Career:** Chair, firm's Financial Services & Products Group.
**Personal:** JD (1996) – University of Oklahoma; BSE (1993) – University of Pennsylvania.

## KASSIN, Thomas
FordHarrison LLP, Atlanta
404 888 3839
tkassin@fordharrison.com
*Featured in Labor & Employment (Georgia)*
**Practice Areas:** Labor and Employment
**Career:** Tom Kassin focuses his practice on airline labor and employment. He counsels clients on all types of personnel and labor relations matters that arise under the Railway Labor Act. Tom has extensive experience in handling a wide range of airline arbitration cases, having successfully represented clients in more than 300 cases. Tom received his JD from University of Virginia School of Law in 1976.

## KATZ, Joel A
Greenberg Traurig, LLP, Atlanta
678 553 2222
KatzJ@gtlaw.com
*Featured in Intellectual Property (Georgia)*
**Practice Areas:** Founding Shareholder; Co-Managing Shareholder Emeritus – Atlanta Office. Chair, Global Entertainment and Media Practice.
**Professional Memberships:** Board Director, Luxure Media Group, 2012-present; Board of Directors, MultiplyLive, 2012-present; Chairman, USO Entertainment Advisory Council, 2010-Present; Member, Music Advisory Board, Hunter College 2011-Present, Board of Directors, Kiz Toys, Inc., 2010-Present; Board Member, Charity Partners, LLC, 2009-Present; Initial Board of Directors, GRAMMY Museum; General Counsel, Former Chairman, The Recording Academy.
**Career:** 'The Power 100', Billboard Magazine; Law360 MVP; 'Most Powerful List Music Edition", Major Label News; 'Power Lawyers: Top 100 Outside Counsel', Hollywood Reporter; 'Service Award', ELI, GRAMMY Foundation; 'Spirit of Excellence Award', T.J. Martell Foundation; Georgia Music Hall of Fame Inductee.
**Personal:** JD, University of Tennessee College of Law; BA, economics and PhD, honorary, CUNY Hunter College.

## KATZ, Mitch A
Ballard Spahr LLP, Atlanta
678 420 9392
katzma@ballardspahr.com
*Featured in Intellectual Property (Georgia)*
**Practice Areas:** Mr Katz is Chair of the Intellectual Property Department. He is also partner-in-charge of the Patents Group. He is also a member of the Chemical Patent Practice Team. Mr Katz's practice is focused on domestic and international patent procurement, client counseling, and opinion writing, and, reexaminations and international opposition proceedings.
**Professional Memberships:** American Chemical Society, Division of Chemistry and Law.
**Career:** Adjunct Professor, Emory University School of Law Admissions: Georgia Virginia USPTO.
**Personal:** Education: Georgetown University Law Center, JD Virginia Polytechnic Institute and State University, BS.

## KAUFMAN, Mark S
McKenna Long & Aldridge LLP, Atlanta
404 527 4120
mkaufman@mckennalong.com
*Featured in Bankruptcy/Restructuring (Georgia)*
**Practice Areas:** Concentrating in the representations of financially troubled municipalities or state appointed receivers or emergency managers for distressed cities, Mark Kaufman is currently serving as counsel to the Governor-appointed Receiver for Harrisburg, PA. He is co-chair of the firm's Municipal Reform and Innovation practice, an author of recent articles addressing evolving municipal distress legal principles and a frequent speaker nationally at conferences focused on Chapter 9 and out-of-court municipality work outs. Mark has spent most of his 40 year career representing secured creditors, lenders, investors, and committees, not infrequently litigating contentious issues.
**Personal:** J.D., Harvard University; BA, Cornell University

## KAYWOOD, Sam K
Alston & Bird LLP, Atlanta
404 881 7481
sam.kaywood@alston.com
*Featured in Tax (Georgia)*
**Practice Areas:** Federal income tax, international tax, cross border M&A, joint ventures. Experience with most forms of cross-border investment, particularly in Canada, Europe and Latin America.
**Professional Memberships:** Former Chair, ABA Tax Section Committee on US Affairs of Foreigners and Tax Treaties; Council Director, International Fiscal Association; Secretary, International Bar Association, Tax Committee; Member, State Bar of Georgia.
**Career:** Chair, firm's Federal Income Tax Group. Adjunct Professor of Tax, Emory University School of Law.
**Publications:** Frequent author and lecturer on international tax topics.
**Personal:** BS, Babson College (1979); JD, Emory University (1986).

**KEENAN, Mark L**
McKenna Long & Aldridge LLP, Atlanta
404 527 4647
mkeenan@mckennalong.com
*Featured in Labor & Employment (Georgia)*
**Practice Areas:** Mark Keenan advises employers on labor and employment issues with expertise before the National Labor Relations Board. He has a national practice assisting employers with employee relations strategies, including lawfully responding to union organizing and managing existing union relationships. He represents diverse industries, including healthcare, manufacturing, and distribution, as well as employers with multiple union and union free locations. He also has extensive employment litigation experience with a particular focus on "switching sides" cases (such as non-compete/non-solicit and trade secret matters).
**Personal:** J.D., University of Illinois College of Law, magna cum laude; BBA, University of Iowa

**KEENAN, Robert M**
King & Spalding LLP, Atlanta
404 572 3591
RKeenan@kslaw.com
*Featured in Healthcare (Georgia)*
**Practice Areas:** Mergers and acquisitions focusing on health systems, hospitals, pharmaceutical and medical device companies, pharmacy benefit management companies, physicians and physician organizations, and managed care organizations on a wide variety of federal and state regulatory matters, including health information privacy, fraud and abuse, certificate of need, reimbursement, licensure and managed care/ insurance issues.
**Professional Memberships:** Georgia Academy of Healthcare Attorneys; American Health Lawyers Association; Health Law Section of the American Bar Association; State Bar of Georgia.
**Personal:** BS, University of Illinois, 1985; JD, University of Georgia, 1988.

**KELLEHER, JR, Thomas J**
Smith, Currie & Hancock LLP, Atlanta
404 582 8016
tjkelleher@smithcurrie.com
*Featured in Construction (Georgia)*
**Practice Areas:** Tom Kelleher has extensive government and construction contract experience on the spectrum of issues involving bidding, changes, differing site conditions, delays, and terminations. He has represented clients on hospital projects, airport facilities, research laboratories, convention facilities, prisons, federal and state courthouse and office complexes, and resort hotels and has practiced before the various federal government boards of contract appeals, as well as federal and state courts. In addition, he has represented clients in mediations, as well as arbitration proceedings. Tom is a frequent lecturer and author of several publications.

**KELLY, Ashley**
Arnall Golden Gregory LLP, Atlanta
404 873 7020
ashley.kelly@agg.com
*Featured in Labor & Employment (Georgia)*

**Practice Areas:** Co-chair of the Litigation Group and Deputy General Counsel for the Firm; employment law; business litigation. Practice focuses on representing employers in discrimination, competition, wage and hour, employment contract and other litigation.
**Professional Memberships:** State Bar of Georgia; numerous federal district and appellate courts.
**Career:** Clerked for the Honorable Jacques Wiener, Jr., Fifth Circuit Court of Appeals.
**Publications:** Numerous speaking and writing engagements detailed at www.agg.com. Publications include "Inside the Minds: Mediation and Arbitration Best Practices," Aspatore Books, 2007.
**Personal:** JD, with distinction, Order of the Coif, Emory Law School (1997); BA, summa cum laude, Vanderbilt University (1993).

**KENNEDY, Steven L.**
Seyfarth Shaw LLP, Atlanta
404 885 6735
skennedy@seyfarth.com
*Featured in Real Estate (Georgia)*
**Practice Areas:** Real Estate.
**Career:** Mr Kennedy focuses his practice on lender, landlord, tenant, developer and investor representation in office, retail, industrial and multi-family development and leasing matters. He represents developers in all aspects of the acquisition, development, construction, financing, joint venture formation, leasing and sale of multi-family, office and retail developments. He represents institutional lenders in connection with secured financing, acquisition line of credit, letter of credit refinancing, and construction loan transactions, and represents investor portfolios with respect to the acquisition, structuring and financing of multifamily portfolios.
**Personal:** JD, University of North Carolina School of Law; BA, Duke University.

**KENNY, Michael**
Alston & Bird LLP, Atlanta
404 881 7179
mike.kenny@alston.com
*Featured in Antitrust (Georgia), Litigation (Georgia)*
**Practice Areas:** Trial and complex commercial litigation, including antitrust, IP, finance, business and class action lawsuits. Lead trial counsel in defense of major corporations in jury trials throughout the US, and successful defense of more than 100 class actions. Significant results for corporate plaintiffs, securing more than $1 billion in jury results and settlements. Lead counsel in 12 cases with more than $1 billion in dispute. Lead appellate counsel in more than 35 commercial cases as well as constitutional and election law cases.
**Personal:** BA, Oakland University (1978); MA, Northwestern University (1980); JD, Emory University (1984).

**KILPATRICK, J Thomas**
Alston & Bird LLP, Atlanta
404 881 7819
tom.kilpatrick@alston.com
*Featured in Labor & Employment (Georgia)*

**Practice Areas:** Complex and class action employment litigation and traditional labor law.
**Professional Memberships:** Member of the Board of Directors of the Georgia Chamber of Commerce and serves as Counsel to the Chamber for labor and employment matters. General Counsel for Boy Scouts of America, Atlanta Area Council.
**Career:** Senior member of the firm's Labor and Employment Law Group. Member of the Bars of Georgia and Tennessee, the United States Supreme Court and various federal trial and appellate courts nationwide.
**Publications:** Lectures frequently throughout the country on labor management matters.
**Personal:** BS (1965), JD (1968) – University of Tennessee.

**KING, James W**
Seyfarth Shaw LLP, Atlanta
404 885 6720
jking@seyfarth.com
*Featured in Immigration (Georgia)*
**Practice Areas:** Business immigration and workforce compliance.
**Professional Memberships:** Georgia State Bar; American Immigration Lawyers Association.
**Career:** Mr King co-chairs Seyfarth Shaw's nationwide Business Immigration Practice Group, assisting clients with global immigration needs and leading the group's immigration process and systems strategy. He works closely with the Immigration Compliance Center and its Seyfarth Workforce Authorization Team (SWATeam) to counsel clients about I-9 compliance, E-Verify, social security mismatch letters, and related issues. He is also conversationally fluent in the French and German languages.
**Personal:** JD, University of Georgia Law School; BS, Georgetown University.

**KLEIN, Linda A**
Baker, Donelson, Bearman, Caldwell & Berkowitz, PC, Atlanta
404 221 6530
lklein@bakerdonelson.com
*Featured in Construction (Georgia), Litigation (Georgia)*
**Practice Areas:** Managing shareholder, firm's Georgia offices. Practice includes business dispute resolution, including contract law, construction law, fidelity and surety law, professional liability.
**Professional Memberships:** Georgia (first woman President, 1997), American (Chair, House of Delegates, second ranking Association officer 2010-2012; Chair, ABA Day, Congressional Lobbying, 2013; Chair, Tort Trial Insurance Practice Section 2003-2004; Chair, Coalition for Justice, 2006-2009) Bar Associations. American Law Institute. Southface Energy Institute, President.
**Career:** Licensed, Georgia. Recipient, ABA Margaret Brent Women Lawyers of Achievement Award; Randolph Thrower Commitment to Equality Award.
**Personal:** Washington & Lee University, JD, 1983, Order of Coif, Hon.; Union College, BA, 1980.

**KNOWLTON, Leah**
Miller & Martin PLLC, Atlanta
404 962 6455
lknowlton@millermartin.com
*Featured in Environment (Georgia)*
**Practice Areas:** Ms Knowlton has represented clients in civil and criminal environmental litigation and counseled clients on environmental regulatory compliance and permitting matters for more than 25 years. She has defended clients in state and federal enforcement matters and private-party litigation arising from chemical releases, wastewater discharges, soil contamination, wetlands filling, air permit violations and vapor intrusion. She develops and implements environmental, health and safety programs in compliance with ISO standards, and negotiates environmental contracts and remediation plans in connection with corporate, real estate and financing transactions for clients. She is a LEED Accredited Professional.

**KONTIO, Peter**
Alston & Bird LLP, Atlanta
404 881 7172
peter.kontio@alston.com
*Featured in Antitrust (Georgia), Litigation (Georgia)*
**Practice Areas:** Represents domestic and international corporations in the telecom, technology, automotive and information services industries in complex litigation, arbitrations and government and internal investigations in the US and abroad. Counsels clients on antitrust and intellectual property matters.
**Career:** Co-Chair of Alston & Bird's 300+ attorneys Litigation Area. Twice appointed by the US District Court to serve on the Board of Directors of the Federal Defenders Program for the Northern District of Georgia and served as President of the organization.
**Personal:** AB 1970 (Phi Beta Kappa) Clark University; JD 1973 (Law Review) University of Chicago Law School.

**KREVOLIN, Douglas P**
Krevolin & Horst, LLC, Atlanta
404 888 9575
krevolin@khlawfirm.com
*Featured in Real Estate (Georgia)*
**Practice Areas:** Business transactions, corporate law, commercial real estate, financing transactions, technology.
**Professional Memberships:** Atlanta Bar Association, Member, Banking and Business Law Section, Corporate Law Section, Real Property Section, State Bar of Georgia, Member, Real Property Section.
**Career:** Doug Krevolin has focused his practice for more than 30 years on representing entrepreneurs, emerging-growth companies, owner-managed businesses, real estate developers and lenders. Doug has represented clients in acquiring all types of real property, from raw land to shopping centers, apartment projects, office buildings, and hotels, and in the development, financing, and leasing of numerous properties. He is outside general counsel to a number of businesses and regularly advises clients on formation, financing,

acquisitions and sales, contracts, and corporate governance matters. Doug is a graduate of the Wharton School of the University of Pennsylvania and Emory University School of Law and has been recognized by his peers and named to the Georgia Super Lawyers list since 2005 and has been recognized for several years as one of the top lawyers in Georgia by Georgia Trend magazine.
**Personal:** Doug is an avid golfer when not working or spending time with his wife and son.

## KURZWEIL, David
Greenberg Traurig, LLP, Atlanta
678 553 2680
KurzweilD@gtlaw.com
*Featured in Bankruptcy/Restructuring (Georgia)*
**Practice Areas:** Chair, Atlanta Business Reorganization and Financial Restructuring. Co-Chair, National Financial Institutions. Asset-based lending; creditors' rights; commercial litigation.
**Career:** Member, Winning Team, US News – Best Lawyers "Law Firm of the Year" in Bankruptcy & Creditor Debtor Rights / Insolvency & Reorganization Law and Litigation – Bankruptcy, 2013. Ranked: No. 6, top bankruptcy lender lawyers by active cases, The Deal magazine, February 2011. Selected, 'Georgia's Legal Elite', Georgia Trend, 2008, 2011-12; Super Lawyers magazine, 2006-12; Chambers USA Guide, 2004-13. Rated, AV® Preeminent™ 5.0 out of 5.
**Personal:** JD, Emory University School of Law; BS, Cornell University.

## LABRIOLA, Stephen T
Fellows LaBriola LLP, Atlanta
404 586 2020
slabriola@fjl-law.com
*Featured in Litigation (Georgia)*
**Practice Areas:** Stephen T. LaBriola, rated AV by Martindale Hubble, is a partner with Fellows LaBriola LLP, a litigation-based law firm. He is a former prosecutor with extensive jury trial experience. His peers have identified him as a "Super Lawyer" and among "Georgia's Legal Elite." Mr LaBriola received his JD from NYU School of Law in 1985.
**Professional Memberships:** Immediate Past Chair of the Litigation Section of the Atlanta Bar Association; Past President of the Lamar Inn of Court affiliated with Emory School of Law; Chair of the Advertising Subsection of the Ethics and Professionalism Section of the American Bar Association; Member of the Federal Bar Association; Member of the State Bar of Georgia.
**Career:** Fellows LaBriola LLP: Partner since 1992; Hurt Richardson: 1989-92; Denver District Attorneys Office: 1986-89; Law Clerk Justices Neighbors and Vollack of the Colorado Supreme Court: 1985-86.

## LAFIANDRA, Aldo L
Jones Day, Atlanta
404 581 8312
alafiandra@jonesday.com
*Featured in Banking & Finance (Georgia)*
**Practice Areas:** More than 20 years of experience in the areas of lending and business reorganizations. He represents borrowers (including portfolio companies of private equity funds) and

lenders in various types of credit arrangements, including cash flow, secured, asset-based, and mezzanine loans. Many of these transactions include complex intercreditor arrangements and multiple tranches of debt. A significant portion of Al's practice focuses on workouts and restructurings of troubled credits, where he represents lenders (including secured creditors and bondholders) and debtors in complex out-of-court workouts, debt restructurings, and chapter 11 bankruptcy cases. Leads the Atlanta Office Banking & Finance Practice.

## LANGE, Mark S
McKenna Long & Aldridge LLP, Atlanta
404 527 8386
mlange@mckennalong.com
*Featured in Tax (Georgia)*
**Practice Areas:** Mark S. Lange has deep experience in transactional tax matters and counsels clients on domestic and international corporate mergers and acquisitions, partnerships, joint ventures, alliances, limited liability companies, and other pass-through venture capital and hedge fund transactions. Mr Lange also has substantial experience in advising on a wide variety of tax-exempt entity matters, including tax-exempt health care providers. He regularly represents clients before the Internal Revenue Service and state Departments of Revenue and has also litigated tax controversies in state court and in the United States Tax Court.

## LATHAM, John L
Alston & Bird LLP, Atlanta
404 881 7915
john.latham@alston.com
*Featured in Litigation (Georgia)*
**Practice Areas:** Partner in firm's Securities Litigation and Corporate Transactions & Securities Groups. Counsels numerous public companies on corporate governance and disclosure matters and represents issuers, officers and directors in securities disputes and internal investigations.
**Career:** Chairman of the Georgia Corporate Code Revision Subcommittee on Officer And Director Liability and Indemnification (2003 – present). Appointed Special Assistant Attorney General, State of Georgia Teachers and Employees Retirement Fund and Office of Treasury and Fiscal Services (1998 – present) (securities matters).
**Personal:** JD (1979) Emory University; BA (1976) University of Toledo.

## LAYSON, Frank
Jones Day, Atlanta
404 581 8541
flayson@jonesday.com
*Featured in Corporate/M&A (Georgia)*
**Practice Areas:** Practice focuses on mergers, acquisitions, joint ventures and strategic alliances. Extensive experience in representing leading companies in a wide variety of cross border transactions.
**Personal:** Emory University (BA 1988), University of Georgia (JD 1991). Pro bono coun-

sel to the National Center for Civil & Human Rights.

## LEET, Alan C
Rogers & Hardin LLP, Atlanta
404 420 4616
aleet@rh-law.com
*Featured in Corporate/M&A (Georgia)*
**Practice Areas:** Mergers, asset and stock acquisitions, joint ventures, strategic alliances, leveraged buy-outs and public and private equity and debt offerings. Advises boards of directors and board committees relating to corporate governance issues, M&A transactions and takeover defenses.
**Professional Memberships:** American Bar Association; State Bar of Georgia (Member of Corporate Code Revision Committee).
**Career:** Previously served as Counsel to the Central Law Department of Commerzbank AG in Frankfurt, Germany (1993-94); prior to law school, was a CPA with "Big Eight" accounting firm.
**Personal:** BS in Accountancy (high honors), University of Illinois, 1978; JD (with honors), Emory University, 1982.

## LEVEILLE, Michael
Greenberg Traurig, LLP, Atlanta
678 553 7314
LeveilleM@gtlaw.com
*Featured in Banking & Finance (Georgia)*
**Practice Areas:** Business reorganization and financial restructuring; financial institutions; asset-based lending; second-lien transactions; Workouts and restructurings; factoring.
**Professional Memberships:** Member, Georgia Bar Association.
**Career:** Listed: The Best Lawyers in America, Banking and Finance Law, 2013; Chambers USA Guide, 2005-06, 2012-13; Super Lawyers magazine, 2004-05. Member, Winning Team, US News – Best Lawyers 'Law Firm of the Year' in Bankruptcy & Creditor Debtor Rights / Insolvency & Reorganization Law and Litigation – Bankruptcy, 2013.
**Personal:** JD, Washington University in St. Louis School of Law, 1989 (Member, Order of the Coif; Member, Washington University Law Quarterly); BA, Economics, Clemson University, 1986.

## LEVENGOOD, J Michael
McKenna Long & Aldridge LLP, Atlanta
404 527 4830
mlevengood@mckennalong.com
*Featured in Bankruptcy/Restructuring (Georgia)*
**Practice Areas:** Bankruptcy court representation of debtors in possession, trustees, creditors, and other interested parties in corporate reorganizations and prosecuting and defending bankruptcy litigation matters including avoidance actions and injunctive relief.
**Professional Memberships:** American Bankruptcy Institute, American Bar Association 1980 – 2012, Atlanta Bar Association, Adjunct Faculty teaching business bankruptcy law course at the University of Georgia School of Law.
**Personal:** JD (1980), University of Georgia School of Law; BA (1977), University of Georgia.

## LEVINE, James D
McKenna Long & Aldridge LLP, Atlanta
404 527 4090
jlevine@mckennalong.com
*Featured in Immigration (Georgia)*
**Practice Areas:** James (Jim) Levine has an active immigration practice. Mr Levine represents domestic and multinational corporations in planning for temporary and long-term employment of foreign nationals in the United States. As a critical component of his practice, Mr Levine provides his clients with strategic advice concerning their short and long-term immigration law alternatives so that the clients can make informed decisions about issues having significant business and personal consequences.
**Personal:** JD, Yale Law School, 1982 BA, University of North Carolina, 1979

## LISCHER, Dale
Smith Gambrell & Russell LLP, Atlanta
404 815 3741
dlischer@sgrlaw.com
*Featured in Intellectual Property (Georgia)*
**Practice Areas:** Partner practicing in all areas of patent law with a focus on patent litigation. Also works in trademark and copyright matters. Served as an expert in patent cases and prepared and prosecuted patents in a wide range of electrical and mechanical technologies. Renders clearance opinions, including design alternatives. Regularly involved in trademark matters for clients.
**Professional Memberships:** State Bar of Georgia; Illinois Bar.
**Personal:** BS, Electrical Engineering, Iowa State University; JD, University of Michigan. Admitted to US Patent and Trademark Office. Georgia Super Lawyer, Intellectual Property Litigation, 2009.

## LITTLE, Catherine
Hunton & Williams LLP, Atlanta
404 888 4047
clittle@hunton.com
*Featured in Environment (Georgia)*
**Practice Areas:** Practice focuses on energy, environmental and administrative law at federal, state and local levels. Emphasis on regulatory compliance, enforcement defense and administrative adjudication under the Pipeline Safety Act, Clean Water Act, including wetlands, Oil Pollution Act and CERCLA. Experience includes natural resource damage assessment claims, endangered species and hazardous waste issues, as well as matters arising under TSCA. Clients include oil and natural gas pipelines, other utility and manufacturing concerns. Recognized by Chambers as a leading lawyer in the Environmental Practice, and among Georgia's top Energy and Natural Resources lawyers, Atlanta magazine and Georgia Super Lawyers magazine, 2008-2013.

## LLORENS JR, Hector E
King & Spalding LLP, Atlanta
404 572 3523
hllorens@kslaw.com
*Featured in Banking & Finance (Georgia)*

**Practice Areas:** Financial transactions focusing on debt financings, including secured and unsecured credit facilities, inventory and receivables financing, leveraged buyouts, recapitalizations and acquisition financings, mezzanine financing, structured finance, securitizations and debtor-in-possession financing. His practice includes the representation of foreign and domestic lenders, as well as borrowers.
**Professional Memberships:** American Bar Association; Atlanta Bar Association (Member, section on banking and bankruptcy); State Bar of Georgia.
**Career:** From 1986-87, he served as law clerk to the Honorable Robert S Vance, US Court of Appeals, Eleventh Circuit.
**Personal:** B Arch, Auburn University,1983; JD, Columbia University, 1986.

### LOKEY JR, James
King & Spalding LLP, Atlanta
404 572 4927
jlokey@kslaw.com
*Featured in Tax (Georgia)*
**Practice Areas:** Real estate and private equity investment fund formation, private equity investment structures, real estate transactions (representing both developers and financial institutions in connection with new investments as well as 'workouts'), corporate joint ventures, acquisitions and reorganizations, investments by non-US persons (including foreign governments) in the United States, and tax problems of tax-exempt organizations.
**Professional Memberships:** American Bar Association (Member, Taxation Section); Atlanta Bar Association; State Bar of Georgia.
**Personal:** BS, David Lipscomb University, magna cum laude, 1974; JD, Vanderbilt University, Founder's Medal for First Honors, Order of the Coif.

### LONG, William F
McKenna Long & Aldridge LLP, Atlanta
404 527 4170
wlong@mckennalong.com
*Featured in Intellectual Property (Georgia)*
**Practice Areas:** Bill Long is an experienced litigator in the Intellectual Property Practice at McKenna Long & Aldridge focusing on patent and other intellectual property and technology-related disputes. Bill has tried and arbitrated cases involving a wide range of technology and intellectual property issues. Bill has served as lead counsel in patent litigation involving a wide range of intellectual property and technology issues, including patent disputes involving computer software and hardware, pharmaceutical products (including Hatch-Waxman cases), chemicals, medical devices, industrial machines, and consumer products. Mr Long is registered to practice before the US Patent and Trademark Office.

### LONG-DANIELS, David
Greenberg Traurig, LLP, Atlanta
678 553 4744
Long-DanielsD@gtlaw.com
*Featured in Labor & Employment (Georgia)*

**Practice Areas:** Co-Chair, Global Labor and Employment Practice. Commercial Litigation.
**Career:** Recipient, Air Force Meritorious Service Medal. Selected: Super Lawyers magazine, 2009-13; 'Top 100 Lawyers in Georgia', Super Lawyers magazine, 2013; 'Georgia's Legal Elite', Georgia Trend, 2006, 2008-12. Rated, AV® Preeminent™ 5.0 out of 5.
**Publications:** Co-Author: 'Hybrid' State Class and Federal Collective Actions: Procedural Frameworks and Discovery Issues and Approaches', ACI's 14th National Forum on Wage & Hour Claims and Class Actions, January 30-31, 2012; 'Recent Trends in Wage-and-Hour Litigation: When a Wage Claim is No Longer Just a Wage Claim', MCCA 10th Annual CLE Expo, March 2011; 'A Primer on the Class Action Fairness Act of 2005: Jurisdiction, Removal and Settlement Requirements', ACI 11th National Forum on Wage-and-Hour Claims and Class Actions, January 2011.
**Personal:** JD Mercer University, Walter F. George School of Law , cum laude; Law Review.

### LOVELAND, Joseph
King & Spalding LLP, Atlanta
404 572 4783
jloveland@kslaw.com
*Featured in Litigation (Georgia)*
**Practice Areas:** Senior partner with over 30 years of trial experience; regularly lead counsel in cases at the trial and appellate level involving breach of contract, fraud, misappropriation of trade secrets, corporate alter ego, fraudulent conveyance, antitrust and RICO matters.
**Professional Memberships:** Fellow – American College of Trial Lawyers; Chair – ACTL Federal Rules of Civil Procedure Committee; American Bar Association; Georgia and Texas state Bars; Bar of US Supreme Court, 4th, 5th, 6th and 11th Circuit Courts; Boardmember – National Institute of Trial Advocacy; Board Chair of Georgia Appleseed.
**Personal:** BA, University of North Carolina, 1973; JD, Harvard, 1976.

### LUNSFORD III, Rodgers
Smith Gambrell & Russell LLP, Atlanta
404 815 3628
rlunsford@sgrlaw.com
*Featured in Intellectual Property (Georgia)*
**Practice Areas:** Partner who primarily litigates intellectual property disputes and who serves effectively as ADR neutral. He also supervises litigation abroad, directs trademark enforcement programs, counsels clients on intellectual property matters, prosecutes applications to register intellectual property and transfers intellectual property rights and technology.
**Professional Memberships:** American Intellectual Property Law Association; International Trademark Association (firm membership).
**Personal:** BS, Mechanical Engineering, Vanderbilt University; JD, cum laude, University of Georgia. Admitted to practice in Georgia, District of Columbia, USPTO. World's Leading Trademark Professionals; Best Lawyers in

America, Intellectual Property Law; Georgia Super Lawyer, Intellectual Property Litigation; Georgia Trend magazine Legal Elite.

### MACDONALD III, Ralph F
Jones Day, Atlanta
404 581 8622
cmacdonald@jonesday.com
*Featured in Banking & Finance (Georgia)*
**Practice Areas:** Practice emphasizes securities, mergers and acquisitions and corporate governance, especially for financial institutions (including REITs, investment managers and broker-dealers), and financial products. Featured in The Best Lawyers in America, Best Lawyers in Atlanta, Georgia Super Lawyers, and in Who's Who Legal (2007). He is a frequent speaker and author on matters related to financial and investment services and products.
**Professional Memberships:** ABA (Business Law Section), Alabama State Bar, and Atlanta and Georgia Bar Associations, and the National Association of Corporate Directors.
**Personal:** University of Virginia (JD 1979; MBA 1979), Washington and Lee University (BS 1975).

### MAGEE, Amelia S
King & Spalding LLP, Atlanta
404 572 3357
amagee@kslaw.com
*Featured in Environment (Georgia)*
**Practice Areas:** Her experience in the manufacturing sector is valuable in addressing both the technical and legal aspects of regulatory environmental issues.
**Career:** Amy Magee joined King & Spalding in 1989 after serving as an environmental coordinator for a manufacturing company, where she focused primarily on EPCRA reporting and general environmental compliance issues for the company's two main manufacturing facilities and several satellite blending operations located throughout the United States.
**Personal:** JD, cum laude, Georgia State University. BS, Carnegie Mellon University.

### MAINES, J Allen
Holland & Knight LLP, Atlanta
404 815 2500
allen.maines@hklaw.com
*Featured in Litigation (Georgia)*
**Practice Areas:** J. Allen Maines is partner in the firm's Atlanta office and member of the Litigation Section. He focuses on major commercial litigation and arbitration, including class actions, and corporate investigations. Maines has served as lead trial counsel to some of the world's largest entities in controversies of major significance, including securities and shareholder disputes, competitive disputes, information technology and intellectual property claims, breaches of contract, product liability and toxic tort, consumer claims, employment and insurance coverage disputes, and alleged RICO, fraud, breach of fiduciary duty and negligence actions.

### MARSH, Gary W
McKenna Long & Aldridge LLP, Atlanta
404 527 4150
gmarsh@mckennalong.com
*Featured in Bankruptcy/Restructuring (Georgia)*
**Practice Areas:** Gary Marsh focuses on general commercial litigation and bankruptcy, workouts and debtor/creditor law. He represents creditors and debtors in Chapter 11 reorganization proceedings, out of court restructurings and debtor/creditor litigation. He also represents court appointed receivers, examiners and trustees. Mr Marsh is Board Certified in Business Bankruptcy and Creditor's Rights by the American Board of Certification.
**Professional Memberships:** Fellow, American College of Bankruptcy, Director, American Bankruptcy Institute, Director, Southeastern Bankruptcy Law Institute, Director, Emory Bankruptcy Developments Journal
**Career:** Adjunct Bankruptcy Professor at Emory University School of Law.
**Personal:** J.D., Emory University; BA, American University, cum laude.

### MARTIN, R Matthew
McKenna Long & Aldridge LLP, Atlanta
404 527 8478
rmmartin@mckennalong.com
*Featured in Litigation (Georgia)*
**Practice Areas:** Matt Martin has over 30 years of experience in complex commercial litigation including product liability and toxic tort, securities, corporate governance, contractual disputes, bankruptcy, creditors' rights, lender liability, trade secrets, and real estate. He has appeared as lead counsel in state and federal courts throughout the United States and has tried over 50 jury trials.
**Professional Memberships:** American Bar Association, Ethics and Professionalism Committee, Litigation Section
**Personal:** JD, University of Georgia Law School, magna cum laude, (Law Review, Order of the Coif); BS, Duke University, summa cum laude.

### MATCHETT, Sam
King & Spalding LLP, Atlanta
404 572 2414
smatchett@kslaw.com
*Featured in Labor & Employment (Georgia)*
**Practice Areas:** Employment relationship matters, emphasis in labor and employment litigation in state and federal courts, governmental agencies and arbitration tribunals, including employment discrimination matters. Advice on avoidance of employee-related problems, presenting seminars concerning all aspects of employment law. Litigation involving Civil Rights Acts of 1866 and 1964, Age Discrimination in Employment Act and Americans with Disabilities Act.
**Professional Memberships:** Appeals Court of Georgia; Georgia State Bar; Institute of Applied Management and Law (IAML) (faculty Member).
**Personal:** BA, magna cum laude, Morehouse College, 1981; JD, University of Georgia, 1984.

## MCCONNELL, Michael J
Jones Day, Atlanta
404 581 8526
mmcconnell@jonesday.com
*Featured in Litigation (Georgia)*
**Practice Areas:** Mike heads up the Securities Litigation and SEC Enforcement Section in Jones Day's Atlanta office and has extensive experience handling complex commercial litigation with a special focus on securities litigation and corporate governance disputes. The matters litigated frequently involve accounting and valuation issues and have included securities fraud claims, investigations and inquiries by the Securities and Exchange Commission, class and derivative claims alleging breach of fiduciary duty, merger and acquisition disputes, and other matters ancillary to shareholder litigation such as inspection actions, and internal investigations. Mike has been recognized in Georgia Super Lawyers (2007-2013) and Best Lawyers (2013).

## MCDONALD, Timothy
Thompson Hine LLP, Atlanta
404 407 3623
Tim.McDonald@ThompsonHine.com
*Featured in Labor & Employment (Georgia)*
**Career:** Tim is a partner in the Labor & Employment practice group. He focuses his practice on litigation and counseling related to employment and employee benefits issues. He defends employers against class action and individual employment claims nationally, and advises them on employment practices and benefits issues. In addition, Tim represents fiduciaries, benefit plans and employers in employee benefits litigation encompassing individual and class action cases throughout the country. Tim is admitted to practice in federal courts across the country as well as the states of Georgia, Pennsylvania and New Jersey and the District of Columbia.

## MCGAUGHEY, Ann-Marie
McKenna Long & Aldridge LLP, Atlanta
404 527 8354
amcgaughey@mckennalong.com
*Featured in Corporate/M&A (Georgia)*
**Practice Areas:** Ann-Marie McGaughey is co-head of the MLA's Mergers & Acquisitions Group. She focuses on the general corporate representation of both publicly and privately-held companies in a wide array of industries. She has particular skill in representing non-US based companies in connection with US transactions and operations, specifically with North American trans-border transactions. Ms McGaughey has significant experience in mergers, acquisitions, divestitures, joint ventures and strategic alliances, commercial lending transactions, and general contract negotiations. She often serves as lead outside counsel, managing the provision of all legal services required to meet a client's needs.

## MCGINTY, Charlene L
McKenna Long & Aldridge LLP, Atlanta
404 527 4660
cmcginty@mckennalong.com
*Featured in Healthcare (Georgia)*

**Practice Areas:** Charlene McGinty concentrates her practice in the areas of health law and regulatory compliance. She represents a broad range of healthcare providers and companies, including hospitals and health systems, physicians and physician organizations, academic medical centers, ancillary service providers and other related entities on a variety of matters, including transactional, operational and regulatory work. She has represented clients in the areas of federal and state regulation, mergers and acquisitions, restructurings and divestitures, and corporate governance, and internal investigations and compliance matters.
**Personal:** J.D., University of Kentucky College of Law; BA, University of Kentucky

## MCIVER, Tex
Fisher & Phillips LLP, Atlanta
404 240 4234
tmciver@laborlawyers.com
*Featured in Labor & Employment (Georgia)*
**Career:** Tex McIver is a partner in the Atlanta office. In his 40 year career, Tex has assisted clients nationally and internationally in their compliance efforts involving federal and state employment laws. He advises employers concerning mergers and acquisitions, consolidation and streamlining of organizations. Tex has also successfully defended employers in more than 200 union organizing campaigns, and he regularly handles contract negotiations, arbitrations, defense of corporate campaigns and the full range of strikes, lockouts and other interruptions of work. Tex has also presented seminars to businesses and client groups concerning a broad range of employment law and legislative issues.

## MCMAHON, Teri Lynn
Alston & Bird LLP, Atlanta
404 881 7266
teri.mcmahon@alston.com
*Featured in Corporate/M&A (Georgia)*
**Practice Areas:** Practice focuses on mergers, acquisitions and divestitures, private-equity fund and portfolio representations, corporate finance, leveraged buyouts, general corporate law, corporate governance, and in-bound international transactions. Negotiates and drafts purchase agreements, shareholders and employment agreements, and documents typical in management-led or private-equity buyouts. Currently serves on Partners' Committee of Alston & Bird.
**Professional Memberships:** American Bar Association; State Bar of Georgia; Atlanta Bar Association (Past Chair, Business and Finance Section).
**Publications:** Authored numerous articles and lectures frequently on mergers and acquisitions, private-equity and securities topics.
**Personal:** BA, Duke University (1984); JD, University of Michigan (1987).

## MENENDEZ, Kenneth G
Epstein Becker & Green PC, Atlanta
404 923 9076
kmenendez@ebglaw.com
*Featured in Litigation (Georgia)*

**Practice Areas:** Member of Firm, Litigation Practice; Managing Shareholder of the firm's Atlanta office. Mr Menendez's experience is in complex business litigation, with concentrations in employment, financial transactions, defamation, construction, and general corporate litigation. He also has extensive experience with mediation, arbitration, and other forms of alternative dispute resolution.
**Professional Memberships:** American Bar Association, Litigation Section and Forum Committee on the Construction industry; Atlanta Bar Association; Lawyers Club of Atlanta; Leadership Atlanta; State Bar of Georgia
**Personal:** J.D., Northwestern University School of Law, 1980; BA, Vanderbilt University, magna cum laude, 1977.

## MILLS, John W
Barnes & Thornburg LLP, Atlanta
*Featured in Bankruptcy/Restructuring (Georgia)*
**Practice Areas:** Bankruptcy; Creditor Rights; Real Estate; Lending; Commercial Litigation.
**Professional Memberships:** California, Georgia and New York State Bars; Atlanta Bar (Treasurer – Bankruptcy Law Section); Beverly Hills Bar (Executive Committee – Bankruptcy Law Section); Financial Lawyers Conference.
**Career:** Associate, Wyman Bautzer Kuchel & Silbert, Los Angeles (1990-1991); Associate, Katten Muchin Rosenman, Los Angeles (1991-1992); Partner, Feder & Mills, Los Angeles (1992-2002); Partner, Kilpatrick Townsend (2002-2009); US Supreme Court; Ninth and Eleventh Circuit Courts of Appeals; all State and Federal Court in California, Georgia and New York.
**Personal:** Wofford College (BA, 1982); Emory University School of Law (JD, 1990).

## MINTZ, Jeffrey M
Jackson Lewis LLP, Atlanta
404 586 1830
MintzJ@jacksonlewis.com
*Featured in Labor & Employment (Georgia)*
**Practice Areas:** Labor law on behalf of management, including preventive counsel and training; union organizing/elections; unfair labor practice proceedings before the NLRB; collective bargaining; matters before EEOC and state administrative agencies
**Professional Memberships:** State Bar of Georgia; American Bar Association, Labor/Employment Section
**Career:** Jackson Lewis since 1980; Managing Partner, Atlanta office, 2006-2010
**Publications:** Contributing author, Winning NLRB Elections and Employer's Guide to Union Organizing Campaigns, 2007
**Personal:** Emory University School of Law, JD 1980; University of Virginia, BA with distinction, 1977. AV rated by Martindale-Hubbell; Georgia Super Lawyers/Labor. Board Member, The Hambidge Center

## MITCHELSON JR, William (Mitch) R
Alston & Bird LLP, Atlanta
404 881 7661
mitch.mitchelson@alston.com
*Featured in Healthcare (Georgia), Litigation (Georgia)*
**Practice Areas:** Concentrates on defense of government investigations, internal corporate investigations, False Claims Act litigation and corporate legal compliance.
**Career:** Co-Chair of the Firm's Health Care Litigation Team and Chair of False Claims Act Working Group. Former Assistant US Attorney for the Middle District of Florida, Criminal Division.
**Publications:** Authored articles on voluntary disclosures to the government, conducting plea negotiations with government prosecutors, development of corporate compliance plans, and incorporating sentencing guidelines considerations into criminal trial strategies.
**Personal:** AB, Duke University (1982); JD, University of Chicago (1985).

## MONNIN, Paul N
DLA Piper LLP (US), Atlanta
404 736 7804
paul.monnin@dlapiper.com
*Featured in Litigation (Georgia)*
**Practice Areas:** Litigation, Regulatory.
**Career:** An active trial lawyer who focuses on white-collar criminal matters and complex civil litigation. From 2002 to 2008, he served as an Assistant United States Attorney with the United States Attorney's Office for the Northern District of Georgia in Atlanta. He served as deputy chief of the Economic Crime Section from 2006 to 2008.
**Personal:** JD, Vanderbilt University Law School (Articles & Symposium Editor, Vanderbilt Law Review; AB, Harvard University (magna cum laude).

## MONROE JR, John L
FordHarrison LLP, Atlanta
404 888 3881
jmonroe@fordharrison.com
*Featured in Labor & Employment (Georgia)*
**Practice Areas:** Labor and Employment
**Career:** John Monroe has represented employers in the litigation and arbitration of virtually every type of claim that may arise out of the employment relationship including claims of employment discrimination/harassment, breach of contract, unfair competition, misappropriation of trade secrets, claims arising under state and federal wage/hour laws and FMLA laws, employment/business torts, claims involving minority shareholder rights and business "divorces". John has extensive experience prosecuting and defending claims for injunctive relief, and has tried numerous jury cases to verdict. He received his JD, with honors, from the University of North Carolina School of Law.

## MOORE III, Randolph A
Alston & Bird LLP, Atlanta
404 881 7794
randy.moore@alston.com
*Featured in Corporate/M&A (Georgia)*

**Practice Areas:** Focuses his practice on the areas of mergers and acquisitions, corporate finance and related strategic matters, with emphasis on financial services companies. Regularly provides advice to board members and management teams in connection with structuring and negotiating complex business transactions, and represents companies and investment banks in public and private offerings of debt and equity securities. Also counsels clients on the application and implementation of the Dodd-Frank Wall Street Reform and Consumer Protection Act.
**Professional Memberships:** American Bankers Association; Community Bankers Association of Georgia; Georgia Bankers Association.
**Personal:** BA, BA, (1988) American University; JD (1994) University of Virginia.

### MORGAN, Charles H
Alston & Bird LLP, Atlanta
404 881 7187
charlie.morgan@alston.com
*Featured in Labor & Employment (Georgia)*
**Practice Areas:** Represents employers in connection with all matters relating to labor, employment, occupational safety and compliance, including jury trials and class and collective actions; litigating occupational safety and health matters before administrative bodies and appellate courts; assisting employers in multi-agency investigations; defending employers in traditional labor matters; conducting internal investigations; and developing corporate compliance programs.
**Professional Memberships:** Member of the State Bar of Georgia and the Atlanta Bar Association.
**Personal:** JD (1988) – Vanderbilt University School of Law; BA (1985) – Emory University.

### MORGAN, Christine M
Jones Day, Atlanta
404 581 8215
cmmorgan@jonesday.com
*Featured in Environment (Georgia)*
**Practice Areas:** Emphasis in the areas of environmental counseling on compliance, enforcement, risk management and transactional issues and in environmental litigation. She has represented clients on issues arising under the Clean Water Act, RCRA, EPCRA, Superfund, and the Clean Air Act, and State equivalents. Her extensive transactional experience includes analyzing risks associated with environmental liabilities in corporate and real estate transactions, and in developing innovative options for management of identified environmental risks.
**Professional Memberships:** Georgia Bar Association (Environmental Law Section), Metro Atlanta Chamber of Commerce (Environmental Policy Committee), Atlanta Bar Association, and the Georgia Association of Women Lawyers.

### MUNGER, Stephen X
Jackson Lewis LLP, Atlanta
404 525 8200
mungers@jacksonlewis.com
*Featured in Labor & Employment (Georgia)*
**Practice Areas:** Employment counseling and litigation with extensive experience in trials and employment and wage and hour class and collective actions on behalf of management. Member of firm's Class Action Committee.
**Professional Memberships:** State Bars of Michigan and Georgia and the American Bar Association
**Career:** Jackson Lewis 1985 to present, partner 1990. The Fishman Group 1983–1985.
**Publications:** "Plant Closures and Relocations under the national labor relations Act" Georgia State University Law Review, Fall 1988.
**Personal:** University of Florida, BA 1977, Wayne State University, J.D. 1983. Married with three sons. Enjoys traveling overseas with family,running and triathlons.

### MURPHY, Paul B
King & Spalding LLP, Atlanta
404 572 4730
pbmurphy@kslaw.com
*Featured in Litigation (Georgia)*
**Practice Areas:** Practice focuses on white collar criminal defense, internal corporate investigations, complex civil litigation, and corporate compliance and governance matters.
**Career:** Served as the United States Attorney for the Southern District of Georgia, under appointments by the Attorney General and later by the United States District Court. From October 2001 – January 2004, he served as Associate Deputy Attorney General and as Chief of Staff to the Deputy Attorney General. From July 1997 – October 2001, he worked as an Assistant United States Attorney in the Southern District of Georgia.

### MURPHY JR, Charles C
Vaughan & Murphy, Atlanta
404 577 6550
cmurphy@vaughanandmurphy.com
*Featured in Antitrust (Georgia)*
**Practice Areas:** Antitrust (criminal, civil and counseling); white-collar criminal defense; complex civil litigation; business litigation; arbitration and mediation.
**Professional Memberships:** American Bar Association, Sections of Antitrust and Litigation; State Bars of Georgia and Tennessee; Federal Bar Association.
**Career:** Staff Attorney, Federal Trade Commission, 1973-75; Trial Attorney, US Department of Justice, Antitrust Division, 1975-80; Vaughan & Murphy, 1980-present.
**Personal:** Born, May 22, 1946; BA, Rutgers University, 1969; JD, University of Tennessee, College of Law, 1973.

### MYERS, Kimberly L
Rogers & Hardin LLP, Atlanta
404 420 4637
kmyers@rh-law.com
*Featured in Antitrust (Georgia)*
**Practice Areas:** Complex private litigation, including antitrust, securities fraud and trademark matters; governmental investigations and legal proceedings brought by the US Department of Justice and SEC; internal corporate investigations as special counsel.

**Professional Memberships:** American Bar Association, Antitrust Section; Georgia Bar Association, Intellectual Property Section & Antitrust Section, Chair (2009-10) and Board Member (2004-11); Atlanta Bar Association.
**Personal:** BM (summa cum laude), Millsaps College, 1983; MSW, Southern Baptist Theological Seminary, 1986; JD (with distinction), Emory University School of Law, Order of the Coif, Emory Law Journal, Managing Editor, 1992. Member, Board of Advocates for School of Social Work, Baylor University.

### MYERS, Lawrence J
Smith Moore Leatherwood LLP, Atlanta
404 962 1040
larry.myers@smithmoorelaw.com
*Featured in Healthcare (Georgia)*
**Practice Areas:** Larry Myers' practice concentrates on civil and administrative litigation, with an emphasis on health care, pharmaceuticals and medical devices, toxic torts, and professional negligence and licensing. His practice includes the representation of hospitals, physicians, specialty practice groups and other providers in certificate of need and related issues, and litigation in the courts and before the Georgia Department of Community Health. He is a trained mediator and is registered as a neutral in general mediation by the Georgia Commission on Dispute Resolution. Larry is a member of the Firm's Management Committee, and is partner-in-charge of the Atlanta office.

### NEEDLE, Bill
Ballard Spahr LLP, Atlanta
678 420 9320
needlew@ballardspahr.com
*Featured in Intellectual Property (Georgia)*
**Practice Areas:** Mr Needle is former chair of the firm's Intellectual Property Department and has represented clients in a wide range of IP matters for more than 40 years.
**Career:** Court-appointed Special Master in numerous patent cases ADR panelist with JAMS Special Assistant Attorney General for the State of Georgia on IP law issues Fellow, Lawyers Foundation of the State Bar of Georgia Adjunct Professor, Georgia State University College of Law Admissions: Georgia.
**Publications:** "Trademark Law," chapter in Association of Technology Managers Technology Transfer Practice Manual, 3rd edition.
**Personal:** Education: Emory University School of Law, JD Georgia Institute of Technology, BS.

### NELSON, Eric L
Smith, Currie & Hancock LLP, Atlanta
404 582 8061
elnelson@smithcurrie.com
*Featured in Construction (Georgia)*
**Practice Areas:** Eric Nelson is a Partner with the firm and practices in the areas of engineering and construction and government contracts. He represents owners, engineers, general contractors, EPC and design-build contractors, construction managers, and subcontractors. Most recently his practice has focused on the energy (including alternative energy) and healthcare markets, infra-

structure, and federal construction. Mr Nelson has tried cases in federal and state courts throughout the country and before the various federal boards of contract appeals. He also represents clients in alternative dispute resolution and has arbitrated claims from $1 million to over $100 million, domestically and abroad. In addition to dispute resolution, Mr Nelson frequently advises clients on front-end project transactions and on federal construction issues, such as the False Claims Act, Miller Act, small business programs, costs and pricing, compliance, and claims.

### NEWMAN, Stuart
Seyfarth Shaw LLP, Atlanta
404 885 7993
snewman@seyfarth.com
*Featured in Labor & Employment (Georgia)*
**Practice Areas:** Labor and employment.
**Professional Memberships:** American, Georgia, Atlanta Bar Associations; Lawyers Club of Atlanta.
**Career:** Mr Newman focuses on complex labor-management relations, including negotiation of national and local collective bargaining agreements, trying cases before the NLRB and courts, advising on overcoming union "corporate campaigns," and strategically participating in employment litigation.
**Publications:** Publishes articles on labor law subjects. Serves as an editor on the ABA's "The Developing Labor Law."
**Personal:** JD, Albany Law School, cum laude; BA, State University of New York with honors; member, Board of Trustees, N.Y. Military Academy. Leisure activities include three-day eventing and fox hunting.

### NEWSOME, Jerry
Littler Mendelson, PC, Atlanta
404 760 3907
jnewsome@littler.com
*Featured in Labor & Employment (Georgia)*
**Practice Areas:** Competition and Trade Secrets Discrimination and Harassment Hiring, Performance Management and Termination Training – Compliance, Ethics, Leadership
**Career:** For the past twenty-two years, Jerry has represented companies in lawsuits and agency proceedings involving all aspects of employment law. He primarily devotes his practice to litigating non-competition and trade secret matters, drafting non-competition agreements, and assisting clients with proactive measures to protect their trade secrets and proprietary business information. Jerry also handles matters involving: non-solicitation agreements and minority shareholder rights disputes, employment tort and contract claims, whistleblower and retaliation claims, discrimination and harassment litigation, employee benefits litigation, and wage and hour issues.

### NEWTON, Trammell
Jones Day, Atlanta
404 581 8308
tnewton@jonesday.com
*Featured in Antitrust (Georgia)*
**Practice Areas:** Over 40 years antitrust and trade regulation experience, including representa-

tion of clients before federal and state agencies on merger and other regulatory issues, and in class actions and other civil and criminal antitrust litigation.

**Professional Memberships:** ABA, the State Bar of Georgia, and the Bars of the US District Court for the Northern District of Georgia, the US Court of Appeals for the Eleventh Circuit, and the US Supreme Court.

**Personal:** University of North Carolina (AB, 1970; Morehead Scholar); Columbia University (JD 1973).

### NODINE, Larry
Ballard Spahr LLP, Atlanta
678 420 9422
nodinel@ballardspahr.com

*Featured in Intellectual Property (Georgia)*

**Practice Areas:** Mr Nodine is a partner in the Intellectual Property Department and partner leader of the Intellectual Property Litigation practice group. He is also a member of the Trademarks, Copyrights, and Higher Education practice groups.

**Professional Memberships:** American Bar Association State Bar of Georgia Master of the Bench, Atlanta Intellectual Property American Inn of Court International Trademark Association WIPO Domain Name Dispute Panelist.

**Career:** Adjunct Professor, Emory University School of Law Admissions: Georgia US Court of Appeals for the Fourth, Fifth, Ninth, Eleventh, and Federal Circuits.

**Personal:** Education: Emory University School of Law, JD Emory University, BA.

### NORTH, John L
Kasowitz, Benson, Torres & Friedman LLP, Atlanta
404 260 6103
jnorth@kasowitz.com

*Featured in Intellectual Property (Georgia)*

**Practice Areas:** John North's practice focuses on patent litigation and related antitrust controversies, as well as, a number of trade secret and trademark disputes. Many international corporations have relied on John as lead counsel in major patent litigations, including some of the world's largest pharmaceutical corporations, a cutting edge minerals technologies company and a major entertainment company. John has substantial trial experience, and has handled cases involving a range of technologies including interactive program guides, internet, electronic coupons and other electronics issues, pharmaceuticals, various chemical products, medical products and a variety of minerals.

**Career:** Named among Best Lawyers in America.

### OAKES, Leslie
King & Spalding LLP, Atlanta
404 572 3314
loakes@kslaw.com

*Featured in Environment (Georgia)*

**Practice Areas:** Experienced in permitting and enforcement actions, air and water pollution and hazardous waste. Environmental due diligence in a number of complex transactions involving industrial facilities and properties. Over 11 years

as environmental engineer with the Environmental Protection Division, Georgia Department of Natural Resources. At EPD, Mr Oakes conducted compliance inspections, wrote permits and participated in agency enforcement proceedings. He worked in the air, hazardous waste and water branches.

**Professional Memberships:** American Bar Association; State Bar of Georgia.

**Personal:** BME, Georgia Institute of Technology, 1974; MS, Georgia State University, 1981; JD, Georgia State University, 1986.

### O'DAY, Stephen E
Smith Gambrell & Russell LLP, Atlanta
404 815 3527
soday@sgrlaw.com

*Featured in Environment (Georgia)*

**Practice Areas:** Partner in charge environmental, sustainability. Toxic tort litigation, hazardous waste cleanups, compliance with and litigation under all environmental laws (Clean Water Act, Clean Air Act, Resource Conservation and Recovery Act, Superfund, others), mold litigation, waste management and landfill issues, renewable energy transactions. Frequent speaker sustainability, environmental liability, compliance, risk management.

**Professional Memberships:** American Bar Association, Litigation, Environment, Energy and Resources, and Torts, Trial and Insurance Practice Sections; Metropolitan Atlanta Chamber of Commerce.

**Personal:** BA, Furman University, 1976; JD, Harvard Law School, 1979. Georgia Institute of Technology, environmental law instructor. Georgia Super Lawyer, Best Lawyers in America, Environmental Law.

### O'NEIL, Catherine
King & Spalding LLP, Atlanta
404 572 2704
coneil@kslaw.com

*Featured in Litigation (Georgia)*

**Practice Areas:** Ms O'Neil represents companies and individuals in a variety of civil and criminal regulatory enforcement matters, parallel civil litigation and internal corporate investigations. She also has significant experience handling complex commercial litigation matters and conducting corporate compliance reviews.

**Career:** Prior to joining the firm, Ms O'Neil served from 2003 to 2005 as an Associate Deputy Attorney General in the US Department of Justice. Ms. O'Neil also served as the national director of the Organized Crime Drug Enforcement Task Force (OCDETF) Program.

**Personal:** J.D., cum laude, Harvard University M.P.P., Harvard University BA, with highest distinction, University of Virginia

### OPLER, Stephen
Ballard Spahr LLP, Atlanta
678 420 9390
oplers@ballardspahr.com

*Featured in Corporate/M&A (Georgia)*

**Practice Areas:** Stephen A Opler is a partner in the Business and Finance Department whose background in accounting, investment banking,

and private equity gives him a uniquely valuable deal perspective. He serves as senior advisor to public and private companies and private equity firms nationwide in mergers and acquisitions. Mr Opler has represented clients in the broadcast, manufacturing, financial, and professional services industries in matters involving investments, mergers and acquisitions, and general corporate issues.

**Career:** Admissions: Georgia.

**Personal:** University of Alabama School of Law (JD 1985) University of Virginia (BS 1981).

### ORTWEIN, William Scott
Alston & Bird LLP, Atlanta
404 881 7936
scott.ortwein@alston.com

*Featured in Corporate/M&A (Georgia)*

**Practice Areas:** Represents companies in a variety of industries in the areas of corporate governance, securities offerings and mergers and acquisitions. Regularly advises Boards of Directors and Special Committees in complex corporate transactions. Has represented public companies and investment banks in public equity and debt securities offerings with proceeds of over $30 billion and has been involved in more than 75 public and private company mergers, acquisitions and dispositions with consideration of over $15 billion.

**Career:** Co-leader, Alston's Corporate Transactions Department.

**Personal:** The University of North Carolina at Chapel Hill (JD, MBA, 1994); University of the South (BA, 1991).

### PAK, Byung
Ballard Spahr LLP, Atlanta
678 420 9344
pakb@ballardspahr.com

*Featured in Litigation (Georgia)*

**Practice Areas:** Byung J Pak is a partner in the Litigation Department and Practice Leader of the Korea Initiative. His practice focuses on representing individuals and corporate entities in government investigations and prosecutions and conducting internal corporate investigations.

**Professional Memberships:** National Asian Pacific American Bar Association, American Bas Association, State Bar of Georgia, Atlanta Bar Association.

**Career:** Admissions: Georgia, US Court of Appeals for the Seventh, Eighth, and 11th Circuit, US District Court for the Northern District of Georgia, US District Court for the Central District of Illinois.

**Personal:** University of Illinois College of Law (JD 1998) Stetson University (BBA 1995).

### PAKENHAM, Timothy J
Alston & Bird LLP, Atlanta
404 881 7755
tim.pakenham@alston.com

*Featured in Real Estate (Georgia)*

**Practice Areas:** Development and financing of commercial real estate. Extensive experience in acquisition, development, management and financing of hotel and destination properties as well as real estate finance, including lease-related financings for lender and borrower clients.

**Professional Memberships:** American College of Real Estate Lawyers; Urban Land Institute; Pension Real Estate Association; Real Property Section of the State Bar of Georgia; Atlanta Bar Association.

**Career:** Former two term member and chairman of firm's Partners' Committee.

**Publications:** Written or spoken on real estate matters, particularly real estate finance.

**Personal:** BA, University of Notre Dame (1978); JD (1983), MBA (1983) – Duke University.

### PALMER, Stephen D
Greenberg Traurig, LLP, Atlanta
678 553 2260
PalmerS@gtlaw.com

*Featured in Banking & Finance (Georgia)*

**Practice Areas:** Financial institutions; business reorganization and financial restructuring; asset-based lending; workouts and restructurings.

**Professional Memberships:** Member, Georgia Bar Association.

**Career:** Awarded, Order of the Coif; inducted, Phi Kappa Phi. Selected, Super Lawyers magazine, Georgia Rising Star, 2007, 2009-12; 'Georgia's Legal Elite', Georgia Trend, 2008, 2011-12; Chambers USA Guide, 2008-13.

**Personal:** JD, with distinction, Emory University School of Law, Graduated second in a class of 260, Member, Emory Law Journal; BBA, summa cum laude, banking and finance, Mississippi State University.

### PARKER, Stephanie
Jones Day, Atlanta
404 581 8552
separker@jonesday.com

*Featured in Litigation (Georgia)*

**Practice Areas:** A trial attorney who specializes in the defense of product liability cases. She has represented clients in the tobacco, chemical, pharmaceutical, gasoline, medical device, and automotive industries. Extensive experience in managing nationwide discovery in multiple plaintiff, multiple court cases. Featured in Georgia Trend magazine as one of its "Women in Business" and on its list of the best lawyers in Georgia, and The Wall Street Journal has written about several of her cases. Named one of the "Top 50 Women Attorneys" in Georgia.

**Professional Memberships:** Master of the American Inns of Court (Bleckley Inn). The American Law Institute.

### PATEL, Rahul
King & Spalding LLP, Atlanta
404 572 4754
rpatel@kslaw.com

*Featured in Corporate/M&A (Georgia)*

**Practice Areas:** Practice focuses on mergers and acquisitions, joint ventures, strategic corporate transactions, and general corporate work and cross-border transactions, particularly transactions involving Indian companies. Represented both underwriters and issuers in corporate finance transactions and general corporate and securities matters.

**Professional Memberships:** Past President of the University of Florida College of Law Alumni

Council, and currently serves as a member of the Board of Trustees for the University of Florida Law School and President-Elect of the University of Florida Alumni Association.
**Personal:** J.D., with honors, University of Florida BA, with honors, University of Florida

**PATTON, Glenn G**
Alston & Bird LLP, Atlanta
404 881 7785
glenn.patton@alston.com
*Featured in Labor & Employment (Georgia)*
**Practice Areas:** Represents management in employment-related litigation, including complex discrimination class actions, wage/hour collective actions and restrictive covenant/trade secret litigation. Advises clients on ADA and FMLA compliance, wage and hour audits, employee handbooks, employment agreements, and employee discipline. Also represents management in traditional labor matters, including contract negotiations, labor arbitrations and unfair labor practice proceedings.
**Professional Memberships:** State Bar of Georgia; Atlanta Bar Association.
**Personal:** AB, Duke University (1991) (Phi Beta Kappa); JD, University of Virginia (1996), Editorial Board Member, 'Virginia Journal of Social Policy and the Law'.

**PERLOWSKI, Henry M**
Arnall Golden Gregory LLP, Atlanta
404 873 8684
henry.perlowski@agg.com
*Featured in Labor & Employment (Georgia)*
**Practice Areas:** Chair, Employment Law Practice Team. National practice litigating executive contract and compensation, discrimination, wage and hour, employee benefits, competition and other employee-related disputes on behalf of employers.
**Professional Memberships:** State Bar of Georgia; Numerous Federal District and Appellate Courts; Georgia Representative, Employment Law Alliance; American Bar Association.
**Career:** Admitted to the Bar in 1993. Joined Arnall Golden Gregory in 1995 and was elected to partnership in 2002.
**Publications:** Frequently published and quoted on employment matters.
**Personal:** Born 30 August 1967. JD, University of North Carolina (high honors; Order of the Coif); BA, Duke University.

**PERSONS, Ray**
King & Spalding LLP, Atlanta
404 572 2494
rpersons@kslaw.com
*Featured in Litigation (Georgia)*
**Practice Areas:** Focuses on complex litigation, including class actions and mass torts. Regularly appears before the state and federal courts and has been Lead Counsel in more than 70 jury trials. Has written numerous articles and conducted lectures across the country on strategies for defending complex cases.
**Professional Memberships:** American Board of Trial Advocates; American College of Trial Lawyers; Atlanta Bar Association; Federation of

Insurance and Corporate Counsel; International Society of Barristers; State Bar of Georgia.
**Personal:** BS, Armstrong State University, 1975; JD, Ohio State University, 1978.

**PETRIK, Michael T**
Alston & Bird LLP, Atlanta
404 881 7479
mike.petrik@alston.com
*Featured in Tax (Georgia)*
**Practice Areas:** Concentrates his practice on multistate tax representation for businesses, including income tax, franchise tax, sales/use tax, and other state and local taxes.
**Professional Memberships:** Serves on numerous boards including Georgia Chamber of Commerce and the Vasser Woolley Foundation.
**Career:** Chair of the firm's State and Local Tax Group.
**Publications:** Frequent lecturer before professional groups and has authored or contributed articles appearing in various national tax journals, including constitutional questions involving the due process and commerce clauses.
**Personal:** BS (1979), BA (1979) – Eastern Illinois University; JD, Duke University (1983).

**PETTY, W Scott**
King & Spalding LLP, Atlanta
404 572 2888
spetty@kslaw.com
*Featured in Intellectual Property (Georgia)*
**Practice Areas:** Obtained or assisted in the procurement and management of hundreds of US and foreign patents, the majority of which are in the computer software, Internet and communication technologies fields and the financial services industry.
**Publications:** He served as the author of the monthly "InternetInfo.Column," published in Intellectual Property Today, a national magazine for the legal community, over an eight-year span.
**Personal:** JD, cum laude, Georgia State University. MBA, Georgia Institute of Technology. MSEE, Georgia Institute of Technology. BEE, Georgia Institute of Technology.

**PLOWMAN, Rebekah N**
Nelson Mullins Riley & Scarborough LLP, Atlanta
404 322 6111
Rebekah.Plowman@nelsonmullins.com
*Featured in Healthcare (Georgia)*
**Practice Areas:** Partner, Healthcare and Life Sciences Practice, Atlanta; Chair, Fraud and Abuse Practice. Practice focuses on defending Medicare fraud and abuse claims, including government investigations and qui tam actions. Extensive experience handling allegations of regulatory fraud and abuse, overpayments, kickbacks, and reimbursement appeals; and providing advice regarding compliance development and implementation, internal investigations and self-disclosure, corporate integrity and IRO requirements, and due diligence for provider acquisitions.
**Professional Memberships:** American Health Lawyers Association, Healthcare Liability and Litigation Practice Group, Vice Chair; American Bar Association.

**Personal:** JD, Indiana University, cum laude, Indiana Law Review, 1991; BSN, Indiana University, cum laude, 1987.

**POINTER, Ann Margaret**
Fisher & Phillips LLP, Atlanta
404 240 4223
apointer@laborlawyers.com
*Featured in Labor & Employment (Georgia)*
**Career:** Ann Margaret Pointer is a partner in the Atlanta office. She has represented management in labor and employment matters for more than 30 years. As counsel to many US companies and US subsidiaries of global companies in a variety of businesses, her areas of practice include advising on compliance issues and defending employers against class, collective and individual discrimination, pay, retaliation, and harassment complaints and lawsuits under many federal and state employment and discrimination laws. She is also experienced in collective bargaining negotiations, and she works with clients under threat of expensive class and collective action lawsuits.

**POLVINO, Kathlynn Butler**
McKenna Long & Aldridge LLP, Atlanta
404 527 8140
kpolvino@mckennalong.com
*Featured in Healthcare (Georgia)*
**Practice Areas:** Kathlynn Butler Polvino practices exclusively in the area of health care law, with a focus on strategic planning initiatives. She has extensive experience representing health care providers in complex transactions involving acquisitions, dispositions, joint ventures, and other affiliations. She advises health care providers concerning certificate of need (CON) and other health care regulatory matters, and handles health care related litigation.
**Professional Memberships:** American Health Lawyers Association, Georgia Academy of Healthcare Attorneys, Former Chair of the Health Law Section of the State Bar of Georgia.
**Personal:** J.D., Emory University School of Law, with distinction; BA, Boston University, cum laude.

**POORAK, Sharon**
Seyfarth Shaw LLP, Atlanta
404 885 6754
spoorak@seyfarth.com
*Featured in Immigration (Georgia)*
**Practice Areas:** Senior counsel in the Business Immigration group of Seyfarth Shaw LLP representing corporate clients in a variety of industries. Develops comprehensive immigration plans for corporations to ensure consistency and compliance with all regulations. Named as a "Leading Immigration Attorney" by International Who's Who of Corporate Immigration Lawyers; International Who's Who of Business Lawyers.
**Professional Memberships:** American Immigration Lawyers Association (AILA).
**Career:** Practicing since 1986; Previous AILA Board Member; Previous AILA National Director.
**Personal:** Georgia State University College of Law, Atlanta, GA

**POTTLE, Steven L**
Alston & Bird LLP, Atlanta
404 881 7554
steve.pottle@alston.com
*Featured in Healthcare (Georgia)*
**Practice Areas:** Health care transactions, such as mergers and acquisitions, public and private securities offerings, joint ventures, formation transactions and advising boards of directors. Clients include public and private companies, not-for-profit organizations and financial sponsors and advisors.
**Professional Memberships:** American Health Lawyers Association; Georgia and Atlanta Bar Associations.
**Career:** Firm leadership positions have included Chair of Health Care Group (compliance, policy, FDA and corporate), Chair of Life Sciences Task Force and Co-Chair of Technology Group.
**Personal:** BA (1983) University of Washington; JD (1987) Vanderbilt University (Law Review).

**POWELL, Kurt**
Hunton & Williams LLP, Atlanta
404 888 4015
kpowell@hunton.com
*Featured in Labor & Employment (Georgia)*
**Practice Areas:** Mr Powell's practice focuses on representing management in labor and employment law matters, including employment litigation, trade secret and non-compete litigation, union avoidance, collective bargaining, and preventive employee relations counseling. He has extensive experience in defending class actions and collective actions involving wage and hour issues. He is a member of Leadership Atlanta and has received recognition in 'Who's Who in Law and Accounting', as published in Atlanta Business Chronicle, as an Employment Litigation Super Lawyer, as published in Atlanta Magazine and as a Georgia Legal Elite.
**Professional Memberships:** State Bar of Georgia and American Bar Association.

**POWELL, Michael J**
Baker, Donelson, Bearman, Caldwell & Berkowitz, PC, Atlanta
678 406 8707
mpowell@bakerdonelson.com
*Featured in Intellectual Property (Georgia)*
**Practice Areas:** Mr Powell represents businesses in transactional and litigation matters involving patent, trademark, trade dress, copyright, trade secret and related issues. With 22 years' experience, Mr Powell also mediates cases involving intellectual property rights.
**Professional Memberships:** Atlanta, Georgia and American Bar Associations. INTA, AIPLA and Intellectual Property Owners Association.
**Career:** Licensed in Georgia. Registered by US Patent & Trademark Office. Selected to Top 100 Georgia Super Lawyers 2010-2012, to Georgia's Legal Elite 2007, 2009-2012, and to Best Lawyers in America: Copyright Law, 2013.
**Personal:** Georgia State University College of Law, JD, 1991. Loyola University, New Orleans, BS Physics, 1988.

**POWERS, Tony G**
Rogers & Hardin LLP, Atlanta
404 420 4632
tpowers@rh-law.com
*Featured in Antitrust (Georgia), Litigation (Georgia)*
**Practice Areas:** Complex business litigation representing companies, officers and directors in private actions and governmental investigations alleging violations of antitrust laws; represents corporations, corporate officers, directors and special committees in securities matters, class actions, internal investigations and investigations and proceeding by the DOJ and SEC.
**Professional Memberships:** Master, Lamar Inn of Court (Emory Law School) affiliated with the American Inns of Court; Antitrust Section, State Bar of Georgia; Atlanta and American Bar Associations.
**Personal:** JD, Yale Law School, 1979; MA, 1975, BA (highest honors), 1974, University of Tennessee; Phi Kappa Phi. Former University of Miami School of Law Faculty Member.

**QUICKER, Katrina M**
Ballard Spahr LLP, Atlanta
678 420 9330
quickerk@ballardspahr.com
*Featured in Intellectual Property (Georgia)*
**Practice Areas:** Katrina M Quicker is a partner in the Intellectual Property Department and member of the Patents, Intellectual Property Litigation, and Higher Education Groups. Her practice focuses on IP litigation in federal courts and before the US International Trade Commission.
**Professional Memberships:** State of Georgia, Special Assistant Attorney General, intellectual property matters Barrister, Atlanta Intellectual Property American Inn of Court.
**Career:** Admissions: Georgia US District Court for the Northern District of Georgia US Court of Appeals for the Eleventh Circuit US Supreme Court USPTO.

**RAFTER, Michael**
Baker, Donelson, Bearman, Caldwell & Berkowitz, PC, Atlanta
404 443 6702
mrafter@bakerdonelson.com
*Featured in Corporate/M&A (Georgia)*
**Practice Areas:** Shareholder who represents real estate investment trusts, real estate funds and other companies in public and private offerings of securities, mergers and acquisitions, Sarbanes-Oxley Act compliance and general corporate law. Represents domestic and foreign clients in structuring, negotiating, and documenting mergers and acquisitions. Frequent speaker at non-traded REIT industry conferences and other related events.
**Professional Memberships:** Atlanta Bar Association, State Bar of Georgia, Investment Program Association, Real Estate Investment Securities Association, National Association of Real Estate Investment Trusts.
**Career:** Licensed in Georgia.

Personal: John Marshall Law School, Chicago (JD–1996, cum laude). University of Tennessee (BS–1990).

**RAFUSE, Nancy E**
Ashe Rafuse & Hill LLP, Atlanta
404 253 6002
nancyrafuse@AsheRafuse.com
*Featured in Labor & Employment (Georgia)*
**Practice Areas:** Concentrates practice in employment law, litigation, civil rights, and collective and class actions. An experienced trial lawyer, Nancy has successfully tried multiple cases to jury verdicts in Title VII and § 1981 actions. Named by The National Law Journal to the "40 under 40," and a top employment lawyer in Georgia by Georgia Trend Magazine; Atlanta Magazine: Top 100 Georgia Attorneys (2012).
**Professional Memberships:** Board Member, Children's Healthcare of Atlanta Foundation; Fellow, Wage & Hour Defense Institute.
**Personal:** BBA, cum laude (1988) and JD, magna cum laude (1991) University of Georgia; Order of the Coif; Georgia Law Review.

**RAWLS, James C**
McKenna Long & Aldridge LLP, Atlanta
404 527 4060
jrawls@mckennalong.com
*Featured in Healthcare (Georgia)*
**Practice Areas:** James C. Rawls concentrates in health care and media law and commercial litigation. His particular areas of concentration include litigation involving hospitals and litigation involving the news media. His clients include major hospitals, a major national newspaper chain, television and radio stations and the Georgia Association of Broadcasters.
**Professional Memberships:** American Bar Association, Litigation Section; Lamar Inn of Court Master; State Bar of Georgia.
**Personal:** J.D., Yale Law School; BA, Mississippi State University, with highest distinction.

**REBEL, Thomas P**
Fisher & Phillips LLP, Atlanta
404 240 4255
trebel@laborlawyers.com
*Featured in Labor & Employment (Georgia)*
**Career:** Tom Rebel is the Managing Partner in the Atlanta office. He practices extensively in the areas of wage and hour, affirmative action, education and disability law. He has also handled many NLRA matters, including representation and unfair labor practice cases, and matters arising under the Occupational Safety and Health Act. He is a member of the National Association of College and University Attorneys, he has authored articles on preemption under ERISA, and he was co-editor of a compendium of labor and employment articles for the National Association of College and University Attorneys.

**REED, Glen**
King & Spalding LLP, Atlanta
404 572 3393
gareed@kslaw.com
*Featured in Healthcare (Georgia), Healthcare (Nationwide)*

**Practice Areas:** Focuses on general representation of healthcare systems; specialized regulatory support to healthcare technology, pharmaceutical and device companies; and specialized projects involving compliance planning, healthcare industry restructuring, reimbursement, fraud and abuse, antitrust, managed care, healthcare policy and new service development.
**Professional Memberships:** American Bar Association; American Health Lawyers Association Fellow; Georgia Academy of Hospital Attorneys; State Bar of Georgia.
**Personal:** BA, University of Tennessee, 1972; JD, Yale, 1976.

**REMAR, Robert B**
Rogers & Hardin LLP, Atlanta
404 420 4631
rremar@rh-law.com
*Featured in Litigation (Georgia)*
**Practice Areas:** Complex commercial and business disputes, employment, administrative law, class actions, civil rights/constitutional law, arbitrator and mediator.
**Professional Memberships:** Fellow, American College of Trial Lawyers; Federal, American, Atlanta Bar Associations; Master, Lamar Inn of Court.
**Career:** Adjunct Professor, Georgia State University College of Law. Bar Council, USDC, NDGa. Board of Directors (President), Federal Defender Program. Hearing Officer, Georgia Public Service Commission. ACLU Board of Directors (Vice-President and Treasurer). City of Atlanta Board of Ethics.
**Personal:** JD, Boston College, 1974. 'Best Lawyers in America'; 'Who's Who in America'; 'Who's Who in American Law'; Top 100 Georgia 'Super Lawyers'.

**RHODES, Thomas**
Smith Gambrell & Russell LLP, Atlanta
404 815 3551
trhodes@sgrlaw.com
*Featured in Antitrust (Georgia)*
**Practice Areas:** Partner, head of Firm's Antitrust and Trade Regulation Practice. Industry experience includes airlines, copper wire, buses, sporting goods, software industrial machinery, medical devices, aluminum products, motor homes, construction products, automotive parts, agricultural products, paper, steel, ceramics, food products, chemicals, hospitals, healthcare, trade and professional associations. Lead counsel in large antitrust cases. Handles antitrust side of mergers and acquisitions.
**Professional Memberships:** American Bar Association; American Law Institute Life Member.
**Personal:** Davidson College, 1968; University of Virginia Law School, 1971. Best Lawyers in America, Antitrust Law; Georgia Super Lawyer; Legal 500 US 2009 Southeast Mergers, Acquisitions and Buyouts: Antitrust Lawyers.

**RICHARDS, Russell**
King & Spalding LLP, Atlanta
404 572 4695
rrichards@kslaw.com
*Featured in Corporate/M&A (Georgia)*

**Practice Areas:** Focuses his practice on the representation of publicly-held and privately-owned companies in mergers and acquisitions, joint ventures and other corporate transactions and in corporate governance matters.
**Professional Memberships:** American Bar Association; Atlanta Bar Association; BTI Consulting Group, Inc's 2002 Client Service All-Star Team; State Bar of Georgia.
**Personal:** Graduated, with high honors, from the University of Tennessee (BS in accounting) in 1971 and with high honors from Duke University Law School in 1974 where he served as executive editor of The Duke Law Journal and was a Member of the Order of the Coif.

**RIORDAN, Robert P**
Alston & Bird LLP, Atlanta
404 881 7682
bob.riordan@alston.com
*Featured in Labor & Employment (Georgia)*
**Practice Areas:** Employment counseling and litigation on class and individual basis, with emphasis on wage/hour disputes, whistleblower claims, business torts, and unfair competition claims including breach of restrictive covenants.
**Professional Memberships:** American Bar Association Employment Section–Committee on Equal Employment Opportunity; Georgia Bar Association–Litigation and Employment Law Sections; Atlanta Bar Association–Litigation and Employment Law Sections.
**Career:** Former department chair; over 20 years trial experience. Listed in 'Best Lawyers in America'.
**Publications:** 'The Whistleblowing Provisions of Sarbanes-Oxley: Discerning the Scope of 'Protected Activity', Hofstra Labor & Employment Law Journal (2006).
**Personal:** AB (1980), JD (1984) – Duke University.

**ROBEY, Ronald G**
Smith, Currie & Hancock LLP, Atlanta
404 582 8018
rgrobey@smithcurrie.com
*Featured in Construction (Georgia)*
**Practice Areas:** Ron has practiced construction and government contracts law exclusively for 35 years. He is admitted in Georgia, Florida, Kentucky, Michigan, Nevada and New York. Ron has negotiated and drafted hundreds of construction and design contracts. He has handled construction and insurance disputes, from small lien claims to disputes over $100 million. The projects have included hospitals, wastewater treatment plants, prisons, casinos (domestically and in Macau), highways, airports, manufacturing facilities, locks and dams, steel plants, superfund sites, power plants, office buildings, and federal government facilities. His federal government experience includes claims against the COE, DOD, VA, and the FAA.

**ROEDER, Kim H**
King & Spalding LLP, Atlanta
404 572 4675
kroeder@kslaw.com
*Featured in Healthcare (Georgia)*

**Practice Areas:** Focuses on representation of public and private healthcare providers, including hospital systems, academic medical centers, physician practice groups and suppliers. Ms Roeder advises public and private healthcare providers in complex transactions involving acquisitions, dispositions, affiliations and joint ventures. She assists healthcare facilities, physicians and government contractors in implementing compliance programs, as well as conducting compliance assessments and internal investigations. Ms Roeder also represents healthcare providers in responding to Department of Justice and Office of Inspector General investigations and qui tam actions.
**Personal:** AB, with distinction, Cornell University, JD, Case Western Reserve University.

**ROGERS, CB**
Rogers & Hardin LLP, Atlanta
404 420 4606
CBR@rh-law.com
*Featured in Litigation (Georgia)*
**Practice Areas:** Complex litigation and trial practice, including malpractice defense, disciplinary matters, commercial and business disputes, class actions and employment law.
**Professional Memberships:** Member of American College of Trial Lawyers and a former State Chairman; Member of the American Law Institute.
**Personal:** BA, Emory University, 1951; LLB, Emory University School of Law, 1953. Served as adjunct professor of law at Emory University. Was a founder of the Lumpkin, Bleckley and Lamar American Inns of Court.

**ROSENBERG, Sumner**
Ballard Spahr LLP, Atlanta
678 420 9440
rosenbergs@ballardspahr.com
*Featured in Intellectual Property (Georgia)*
**Practice Areas:** Mr Rosenberg is a partner in the Intellectual Property Department. He is a member of the Trademarks, Copyrights, and Intellectual Property Litigation Groups, and a member of the Electrical/Communications Technology and Mechanical patent practice teams. Mr Rosenberg's patent practice focuses on computer software and hardware.
**Professional Memberships:** Master of the Bench, Atlanta Intellectual Property American Inn of Court Patent and Trademark Section and Environmental Law Section State Bar of Georgia.
**Career:** Admissions: Georgia.
**Personal:** Education: University of Michigan Law School, JD Massachusetts Institute of Technology, BS; MS.

**ROSENBLOUM, Robert**
Greenberg Traurig, LLP, Atlanta
678 553 2250
RosenbloumB@gtlaw.com
*Featured in Intellectual Property (Georgia)*
**Practice Areas:** Co-Chair, Entertainment Practice – Atlanta. Technology, media and telecommunications.
**Professional Memberships:** Governing Committee Member, ABA Forum on

Entertainment & Sports Industries; Deputy General Counsel, Recording Academy; Executive Committee Member, GRAMMY Foundation Entertainment Law Initiative, 2012-13.
**Career:** Listed, Best Lawyers in America, 2005-13; Variety's Dealmakers Impact Report, 2012; Super Lawyers magazine, 2004-13; 'Power Lawyers: Top 100 Most Influential Entertainment Lawyers in America', The Hollywood Reporter, 2011. Nominated, 'Leading Lawyer in Media' by in-house counsel and peers.
**Publications:** Guide to the World's Leading Technology, Media & Telecommunications Lawyers, 3rd edition.
**Personal:** JD, magna cum laude, Harvard Law School; BA, summa cum laude, Duke University.

**ROTHMAN, Robert L**
Arnall Golden Gregory LLP, Atlanta
404 873 8668
robert.rothman@agg.com
*Featured in Litigation (Georgia)*
**Practice Areas:** Co-Chair of the firm's Litigation Department; trial and appellate practice in state and federal courts; alternative dispute resolution; complex business and partnership disputes, fiduciary duty and media law issues.
**Professional Memberships:** Member, ABA Board of Governors, 2011-14; Past Chair, ABA Section of Litigation, 2008-09; Member, American Law Institute; Member, ABA Forum on Communications Law.
**Publications:** Author, "Drafting Complaints in the Post-Iqbal World," Litigation, Volume 36, Number 4, American Bar Association, Spring 2010.
**Personal:** JD, with highest honors, Florida State University (1982); Editor-in-chief, Florida State University Law Review, 1981-1982; BS, with high honors, University of Florida (1974).

**ROWLAND, William B**
Jones Day, Atlanta
404 581 8961
wbrowland@jonesday.com
*Featured in Corporate/M&A (Georgia)*
**Practice Areas:** Oversees the Transactional Practice in Jones Day's Atlanta Office. His practice focuses on representing clients based in North America, Europe, and Asia in complex corporate transactions. He has extensive experience in public and private mergers and acquisitions, divestitures, joint ventures, strategic alliances, and other commercial matters. He is actively involved in advising on corporate governance and strategic planning issues.
**Professional Memberships:** State Bar of Georgia, Vice Chairman of Business Law Section. Member of the board of directors of the Alliance Theatre and Chinese Children Charities.

**RUBINGER, Hedy S**
Arnall Golden Gregory LLP, Atlanta
404 873 8724
hedy.rubinger@agg.com
*Featured in Healthcare (Georgia)*
**Practice Areas:** Represents healthcare providers including nursing homes, assisted living facilities, hospitals, ambulatory surgery centers and physi-

cians in matters of operations, regulatory compliance, change of ownership, reimbursement, certificate of need and employment.
**Professional Memberships:** American Health Lawyers Association; American College of Healthcare Executives; and Georgia Women Healthcare Executives, Past President.
**Career:** Admitted to Bar in 1989. Chair of the Advisory Council of the Health Law Partnership, which provides pro bono legal services to families of ill children.
**Personal:** Law degree from Columbia Law School. Recently named one of the "Top 50 Female Georgia Super Lawyers." Enjoys running, cycling and travel.

**RUBY, Jay C**
Ogletree, Deakins, Nash, Smoak & Stewart, PC, Atlanta
404 881 1300
jay.ruby@ogletreedeakins.com
*Featured in Immigration (Georgia)*
**Practice Areas:** Immigration, including advice to foreign and US corporations regarding temporary and permanent employment-based visa options (US and global), Form I-9 compliance, H-1B/H-2B Wage/Hour compliance and INA 274B compliance.
**Professional Memberships:** American Immigration Lawyers Association; International Who's Who of Corporate Immigration Attorneys
**Career:** Admitted to practice in Georgia, Louisiana, US Supreme Court
**Publications:** Successful Partnering Between Inside and Outside Counsel chapter on "Immigration", Thomson Reuters/Association of Corporate Counsel. "Employment and Immigration Law Compliance in Heightened Enforcement Environment", Inside the Minds Aspatore Books. "A New Immigration Enforcement Regime", Executive Counsel.
**Personal:** Indiana University (BA, 1989), Louisiana State University (J.D., 1992).

**RUSCHE, Mark C**
Alston & Bird LLP, Atlanta
404 881 7281
mark.rusche@alston.com
*Featured in Real Estate (Georgia)*
**Practice Areas:** Acquisitions, dispositions, commercial office leasing, joint venture work and senior housing transactions on a nationwide basis. Handled over $4 billion in senior housing transactions. Represented Virgin Galactic in the development agreement and lease at Spaceport America. Currently handling a sale/leaseback program of office properties nationwide for a national bank.
**Career:** Former co-leader of the firm's Real Estate Group. Frequent writer and speaker on commercial leasing and other topics. Board of editors, 'Commercial Leasing Law & Strategy', a nationally circulated monthly newsletter.
**Personal:** BA, Furman University (1981); JD, cum laude, Order of the Coif, University of South Carolina (1985).

**RYAN, Allison M**
Alston & Bird LLP, Atlanta
404 881 7439
allison.ryan@alston.com
*Featured in Real Estate (Georgia)*
**Practice Areas:** Specializes in major development, leasing and equity deals, as well as complex real estate financing. In addition, she focuses on urban, mixed-use developments and joint venture transactions.
**Professional Memberships:** State Bar of Georgia; Atlanta Bar Association; Commercial Real Estate Women; National Association of Women Lawyers.
**Career:** Co-leader, firm's Real Estate Finance & Investment Group.
**Personal:** BBA (1993), JD (1996) – University of Michigan.

**SAUL, H Carol**
Arnall Golden Gregory LLP, Atlanta
404 873 8694
carol.saul@agg.com
*Featured in Healthcare (Georgia)*
**Practice Areas:** Member, Healthcare and Life Sciences Practice. Fraud and Abuse; Compliance Counseling and Defense; Regulatory Counseling for Mergers and Acquisitions; HIPAA Compliance; Hospital-Physician Alignment; home health and hospice.
**Professional Memberships:** American Health Lawyers Association; ABA Health Law Section (member, ABA Task Force on HITECH Act Compliance); Health Care Compliance Association (certified in healthcare compliance); Community Health Accreditation Program, past member of Board of Directors; Women Business Leaders of the US Healthcare Industry; board member, Georgia Campaign for Power and Potential.
**Personal:** JD, University of Virginia, 1982; MA, University of South Carolina, 1977; BA, University of Georgia, Phi Beta Kappa, 1975; Georgia Super Lawyer 2008, 2009, 2011, 2012.

**SCHNEIDER, John**
Hunton & Williams LLP, Atlanta
404 888 4148
jschneider@hunton.com
*Featured in Banking & Finance (Georgia)*
**Practice Areas:** John Schneider leads Hunton & Williams' Lending Services Group and serves on the firm's Financial Institutions Steering Committee. Mr Schneider's practice focuses on representing banks, financial institutions, alternative investment funds and collateral managers, including extensive experience representing such parties in financing transactions, work-outs, restructurings and bankruptcies.
**Professional Memberships:** Member, State Bars of Georgia and New York; Member, Legal Advisory Committee, The Loan Syndication and Trading Association; Member, Turnaround Management Association; Member, Commercial Finance Association, Atlanta Chapter.
**Personal:** JD, University of Georgia School of Law, Editor-in-Chief, Georgia Journal of

International and Comparative Law, 1988; BA, St. John's University, 1984.

## SCHNEIDER, Richard A
King & Spalding LLP, Atlanta
404 572 4889
dschneider@kslaw.com
*Featured in Products Liability (Nationwide), Litigation (Georgia)*

**Practice Areas:** Representing clients on a diverse array of fronts for more than 30 years, including Georgia-Pacific Corporation, Honeywell International Inc, Brown & Williamson Tobacco Corporation, RJ Reynolds Tobacco Company, Square D Company, Brown-Forman Corporation and Bank of America. In addition to an active litigation practice, Mr Schneider is one of the leaders of the firm's E-discovery Practice Group, devoted to counseling with clients on emerging e-discovery issues.
**Personal:** BA, high honors, Auburn University Main Campus, JD, summa cum laude, Mercer University.

## SCHRETER, Lee
Littler Mendelson, PC, Atlanta
404 760 3938
lschreter@littler.com
*Featured in Labor & Employment (Georgia)*

**Practice Areas:** Class Actions; Wage and Hour
**Professional Memberships:** American Bar Association; Atlanta Bar Association
**Career:** Lee represents employers in complex class and collective actions involving overtime and other wage-related claims and specializes in helping employers develop forward-thinking compliance measures that reduce wage and hour disputes and other employment-related issues. She also represents clients in connection with all other types of labor and employment matters arising under federal and state laws such as the: FLSA, Equal Pay Act, and Service Contract Act.
**Publications:** Editor and contributing author to the "Fair Labor Standards Act" published by the American Bar Association

## SCHWARTZ, Arthur Jay
Smith Gambrell & Russell LLP, Atlanta
404 815 3632
jschwartz@sgrlaw.com
*Featured in Corporate/M&A (Georgia)*

**Practice Areas:** Partner in mergers and acquisitions, finance, securities, commercial leasing, technology. Represents buyers, sellers, financing parties in mergers and acquisition transactions and practices in business acquisition and divestiture transactions involving complex financing structure issues. Represents borrowers, secured, unsecured lenders in financing transactions and public companies and underwriters in public equity and debt offerings.
**Professional Memberships:** Lawyers Club of Atlanta; State Bar of Georgia; American Jewish Committee, Atlanta Board of Trustees; Jewish Federation of Greater Atlanta, Life Trustee; UNC Board of Visitors
**Personal:** AB, History and Political Science, University of North Carolina at Chapel Hill, 1969; JD, Emory University, 1972.

## SCOFIELD, Eileen MG
Alston & Bird LLP, Atlanta
404 881 7375
eileen.scofield@alston.com
*Featured in Immigration (Georgia)*

**Practice Areas:** Directs National Employment Verification and Global Visa Practice. Advises on compliance policies/practices to ensure proper work authorization for US workers, pursuant to merger & acquisition activity, general compliance practices, internal audits, contractor-subcontractor issues, and multi-agency government audits, investigations and litigation. Manages corporate/individual global relocation, investment, employment and family visa matters. Liaises with senior executives at DHS, E-Verify, USCIS, ICE, CBP and SSA. Manages immigration related labor law matters, and represents clients before US DOJ OSC.
**Publications:** US News and World Report, Law360, SHRM, American Corporate Counsel, TAPPI, American Immigration Lawyers Association, West Law Publishing, National Constitution Center.

## SEWELL JR., Henry F
McKenna Long & Aldridge LLP, Atlanta
404 527 4830
hsewell@mckennalong.com
*Featured in Bankruptcy/Restructuring (Georgia)*

**Practice Areas:** Henry Sewell focuses his practice in the areas of bankruptcy and restructuring while also maintaining a commercial litigation practice. He has represented numerous examiners, creditors' committees, trustees and creditors in complex Chapter 11 cases. He also has extensive experience litigating corporate governance and real estate disputes as well as state court enforcement actions on behalf of lenders.
**Professional Memberships:** Director, Southeastern Bankruptcy Law Institute; Past Chairman, Bankruptcy Section of the Atlanta Bar Association; State Bar of Georgia; Association of Insolvency and Restructuring Advisors.
**Personal:** JD, University of Richmond; BA, Washington & Lee University, cum laude.

## SHACKELFORD, Richard L
King & Spalding LLP, Atlanta
404 572 4995
rshackelford@kslaw.com
*Featured in Healthcare (Georgia), Healthcare (Nationwide)*

**Practice Areas:** Mr Shackelford represents health systems, academic medical centers, pharmacy providers, health plans, long term care facilities, physician organizations, pharmacy benefits managers, pharmaceutical and medical device companies, and managed care organizations in a wide variety of litigation and regulatory matters. He has litigated numerous complex matters for healthcare clients in federal and state courts around the country, including numerous class actions.
**Professional Memberships:** Immediate Past President of the American Health Lawyers Association ("AHLA"). Past President of the

Georgia Academy of Healthcare Attorneys (2001-02).
**Personal:** BA, University of Georgia, 1976; JD, University of Georgia, 1979.

## SHAPIRO, J Ben
Baker, Donelson, Bearman, Caldwell & Berkowitz, PC, Atlanta
678 406 8709
bshapiro@bakerdonelson.com
*Featured in Construction (Georgia)*

**Practice Areas:** Senior counsel in the Construction group, where he represents owners, general contractors, subcontractors, suppliers and design professionals in construction disputes in state and federal courts, arbitration and mediation.
**Professional Memberships:** A co-founder of Georgia Legal Services Program. Fellow: American College of Construction Lawyers. Past chair: Construction Law Section of the Atlanta Bar Association. Member: Atlanta, Georgia, and American Bar Associations, and US Court of Federal Claims. Past President: Associated Builders and Contractors of Georgia, Inc.; Georgia Super Lawyer.
**Career:** Georgia, 1966.
**Personal:** Emory University School of Law, JD, 1967 (law review). Former Trustee of Emory University.

## SHARBAUGH, Charles
Carlton Fields, P.A., Atlanta
404 815 3388
csharbaugh@carltonfields.com
*Featured in Real Estate (Georgia)*

**Practice Areas:** Asset-based financing, lending arrangements, joint ventures, partnership syndications, debt restructuring, acquisition of distressed assets and loans, foreign capital sources partnerships, construction companies, representing lenders in secured transactions, disposition of large assets, sale leaseback transactions and Section 42 tax credit transactions.
**Professional Memberships:** Atlanta Opera, Midtown Alliance, President of Druid Hills Golf Club, Urban Land Institute, Zoo Atlanta, Woodruff Arts Center.
**Career:** Martindale-Hubbell AV rating.
**Personal:** JD (with honors) Duke University School of law, 1974; BA (with honors), The Pennsylvania State University, 1971

## SHARP, Joseph
Ashe Rafuse & Hill LLP, Atlanta
404 253 6028
joesharp@AsheRafuse.com
*Featured in Litigation (Georgia)*

**Practice Areas:** Concentrates practice in commercial litigation, and has significant experience litigating cases in a variety of areas including intellectual property, financial services, real estate, entertainment, restrictive covenants, and employment. Has been involved in numerous complex matters, including securities class actions, consumer class actions, and actions consolidated before the Judicial Panel on Multi-District Litigation.

**Professional Memberships:** Member, Defense Research Institute; Member, American Bar Association; Member, Georgia Defense Lawyers Association.
**Personal:** BBA, Accounting, University of Georgia (1989); JD, cum laude, University of Georgia School of Law (1993); Managing Editor of the Georgia Law Review; Marion Smith Scholar.

## SHEPPARD, Hale E
Chamberlain, Hrdlicka, White, Williams & Aughtry, Atlanta
404 658 5441
hale.sheppard@chamberlainlaw.com
*Featured in Tax (Georgia)*

**Practice Areas:** Tax audits, tax appeals, tax litigation, tax collection defense, and international tax disputes and compliance.
**Professional Memberships:** Georgia, Texas, Florida, and Washington, DC Bars.
**Publications:** Articles published in Practical Tax Lawyer, Journal of Tax Practice & Procedure, Taxes Magazine, Tax Management International Journal, Journal of International Tax, Journal of Multi-State Tax & Incentives, Tax Notes International, Practical Tax Strategies, Journal of Taxation, Corporate Business Taxation, International Tax Journal, Tax Adviser, and many other journals.
**Personal:** University of Kansas (BS, distinction, MA, honors, JD); Universidad de Chile (LLM, highest distinction); University of Florida (LLMT, graduate tax scholar).

## SHERRILL, John A
Seyfarth Shaw LLP, Atlanta
404 885 6703
jsherrill@seyfarth.com
*Featured in Litigation (Georgia)*

**Practice Areas:** Commercial litigation; ADR.
**Professional Memberships:** ABA (DR Section Governing Council); Georgia Bar Association; CPR and American Arbitration Association Commercial, Construction and USOC Olympic Panels; Fellow, College of Commercial Arbitrators, American College of Civil Trial Mediators.
**Career:** Represents clients in all types of civil disputes at the trial and appellate levels in federal and state courts. Focuses on general commercial litigation, construction, zoning and land use, and ADR. Has acted as an arbitrator in over 200 arbitrations and a mediator in over 500 commercial cases of all types.
**Personal:** JD, Duke University Law School; AB, University of North Carolina.

## SIGMUND, Rebecca L
Ogletree, Deakins, Nash, Smoak & Stewart, PC, Atlanta
404 881 1300
rebecca.sigmund@ogletreedeakins.com
*Featured in Immigration (Georgia)*

**Practice Areas:** Advises companies on immigration alternatives for prospective employees and matters relating to employment eligibility of workers.
**Professional Memberships:** Georgia State Bar (Chair, International Law Section 2008-10; Exec.

Comm. Member, 2004-2012), American Immigration Lawyers Association (Board of Governors; President, Atlanta Chapter, 1995-1996).
**Career:** Admitted to practice in Georgia, US District Ct. (N.D. of Georgia). 2006 S. Phillip Heiner Award by Atlanta Volunteer Lawyers Foundation for Pro Bono work. Georgia Super Lawyers, 2006-13; Best Lawyers in America, 2009-12.
**Publications:** Speaks and writes extensively on business immigration law.
**Personal:** Furman University (BA, 1980), Georgia State University (J.D., 1988).

## SILLIMAN, Todd
McKenna Long & Aldridge LLP, Atlanta
404 527 4914
tsilliman@mckennalong.com
*Featured in Environment (Georgia)*
**Practice Areas:** Mr Silliman represents clients in environmental litigation, regulatory enforcement matters, and transactions involving natural resources. For more than a decade, he has represented the State of Georgia in litigation and administrative proceedings concerning reservoirs that provide water supply to the majority of Georgia's population. Though he has a particular emphasis on water supply, water quality, wetlands, and coastal marshlands, he has extensive experience in federal and state environmental laws that regulate air emissions, hazardous substances, pesticides, and brownfields redevelopment.
**Personal:** J.D., University of Virginia School of Law, 1993; BA, University of North Carolina, 1990, with honors and highest distinction.

## SILVER, Joseph
DLA Piper LLP (US), Atlanta
305 423 8530
michael.silva@dlapiper.com
*Featured in Corporate/M&A (Georgia)*
**Practice Areas:** Corporate/M&A.
**Professional Memberships:** The Florida Bar, Certified Expert in Tax Law and International Law since 2008; Florida Bar Board Certification Committee for International Law; Florida Bar Tax Section, Vice-Chair of International Tax Committee; Free Trade of the Americas (FTAA), Administrative Secretarial, Inc.
**Career:** He focuses on international tax law, with emphasis on US investment structures, cross-border tax issues, tax treaty planning, withholding obligations of US real property investments and US activities of foreign banks.
**Personal:** JD, University of Florida College of Law; MA, Accounting and Financial Reporting, University of Florida, BS, University of Florida

## SILVERMAN, Jeremy C
McKenna Long & Aldridge LLP, Atlanta
404 527 4901
jsilverman@mckennalong.com
*Featured in Corporate/M&A (Georgia)*
**Practice Areas:** Jeremy C. Silverman is co-head of MLA's Mergers & Acquisitions Group. He has extensive M&A experience, especially in connection with the acquisition or sale of privately-held targets. Complementing MLA's long-standing top-

tier government contracts practice, he has particular skill leading transactions involving federal government contractors and advising clients in the federal sector on corporate matters. In addition, Mr Silverman frequently assists clients in the health care industry with M&A and other strategic transactions. He also has deep non-M&A transactional experience, including assisting clients to structure and effectuate joint venture, strategic alliance and other complex commercial relationships.

## SIMMONS, Teri A
Arnall Golden Gregory LLP, Atlanta
404 873 8612
teri.simmons@agg.com
*Featured in Immigration (Georgia)*
**Practice Areas:** Partner and leader, international and immigration. Represents US and foreign clients on US investment planning, immigration issues; strategic counseling for M&As, cross-border personnel movement, expatriate contracting.
**Professional Memberships:** AILA; Chair, Atlanta Sister Cities Commission; Board member, German American Chamber, Atlanta Council on International Relations.
**Career:** Qualified, 1989. Joined AGG, 1991.
**Publications:** Co-authored "US Immigration Law: Employer Compliance," Law Firm Partnership & Benefits Report, May 2010; "H-1Bs and Third Party Worksites: I've a Feeling We're not in Kansas Anymore," June 2010.
**Personal:** JD, University of Georgia; University of Tübingen; MA, University of Virginia; BA, Furman University. Fluent in German.

## SINKFIELD, Richard H
Rogers & Hardin LLP, Atlanta
404 420 4605
rsinkfield@rh-law.com
*Featured in Litigation (Georgia)*
**Practice Areas:** Trial and appellate advocacy in complex business litigation, including class actions, securities, business torts, and director, officer and professional liability litigation. Commercial and business dispute resolution, mediation and arbitration. Conducts seminars on diversity and business development.
**Professional Memberships:** Fellow, American College of Trial Lawyers; Fellow, International Academy of Trial Lawyers; Member, International Association of Defense Counsel.
**Personal:** BS, Tennessee State University, 1968; JD, Vanderbilt University, 1971. Served on ABA Special Commission on Evaluation of Professional Standards. Director, Weyerhaeuser Company & Chairman, Governance & Corporate Responsibility Committee; Trustee, Vanderbilt University; Advisory Board, Georgia Appleseed Center for Law & Justice.

## SKINNER, Philip G
Arnall Golden Gregory LLP, Atlanta
404 873 8798
philip.skinner@agg.com
*Featured in Real Estate (Georgia)*
**Practice Areas:** Commercial Real Estate, Partner; Co-Chair, Leasing Practice and Cross-border Team. Represents US and international

parties in the acquisition, joint venture, development, financing and leasing of commercial properties.
**Professional Memberships:** Georgia Bar Association; NAIOP; ICSC; International Bar Association; American Bar Association (International Section).
**Career:** Joined Arnall Golden Gregory LLP 1979; became Partner 1986.
**Publications:** "New, Burgeoning Wave of Foreign Real Estate in American CRE: Fact or Fiction?"; "'Marrying For Money' – Structuring Joint Ventures Between Developers and Equity Investors"; "Mixed-Use: A Practical Perspective on Legal Issues".
**Personal:** Michigan State University, 1975; Emory University School of Law, 1978.

## SMITH, E Kendrick
Jones Day, Atlanta
404 581 8343
eksmith@jonesday.com
*Featured in Litigation (Georgia)*
**Practice Areas:** Multi-state tax controversies, complex commercial litigation, constitutional challenges, shareholder disputes, adversary proceedings in bankruptcy court and appeals. He has tried cases before administrative agencies and in State and Federal courts throughout the country. He is widely published and lectures extensively before professional groups nationwide, including the Tax Executive Institute, the Institute for Professionals in Taxation, Council for State Taxation, National Business Institute, National Trust Real Estate Association and Georgia Institute for Continuing Legal Education. Ken is a fifth generation Atlantan.
**Professional Memberships:** Council on State Taxation; Institute for Professionals in Taxation, Lumpkin Inn of Court (Master)

## SMITH, George Anthony
Weinberg, Wheeler, Hudgins, Gunn & Dial, LLC, Atlanta
404 832 9576
tsmith@wwhgd.com
*Featured in Construction (Georgia)*
**Practice Areas:** Serves as advocate and arbitrator on cases related to domestic and international dispute resolution, focusing on power, water and wastewater, transportation and other major infrastructure projects.
**Professional Memberships:** International, American, Georgia, and Kentucky Bar Associations; American College of Construction Lawyers; Centre for International Legal Studies; London Court of International Arbitration; Construction Panel Advisory Committee of the CPR Institute for Dispute Resolution (former Chair).
**Publications:** Has lectured and written extensively on many topics of interest to the construction industry and the international arbitration community.
**Personal:** BA, with Distinction, University of Kentucky, 1970; JD, with High Distinction, University of Kentucky College of Law, 1973.

## SMITH, William Calvin
King & Spalding LLP, Atlanta
404 572 4875
wcsmith@kslaw.com
*Featured in Corporate/M&A (Georgia)*
**Practice Areas:** Mr Smith's practice focuses on mergers and acquisitions and other strategic corporate transactions for public companies. His practice also consists of a broad range of corporate matters, including securities matters and corporate finance transactions. He also regularly advises clients regarding corporate governance and SEC reporting and disclosure matters.
**Personal:** Emory University (J.D., 1996) Wake Forest University ( 1991)

## SMITH III, Frank G
Alston & Bird LLP, Atlanta
404 881 7240
frank.smith@alston.com
*Featured in Intellectual Property (Georgia)*
**Practice Areas:** Intellectual property litigation, including patents and copyrights; antitrust; white-collar crime. Litigated complex matters in federal courts in Alabama, California, Delaware, Florida, Georgia, Illinois, Iowa, Louisiana, Michigan, Mississippi, New York, North Carolina, South Carolina, Massachusetts, Michigan, Tennessee, Texas, Virginia, Washington, D.C. and Wisconsin.
**Professional Memberships:** State Bar of Georgia.
**Career:** Former chair of firm's IP-Litigation Group. Former member of firm's Partners' Committee. Named 'Best Lawyers' 2012 Atlanta Lawyer of the Year in the litigation-patent area.
**Publications:** Numerous articles on intellectual property and litigation.
**Personal:** BA, Davidson College (1974) (Phi Beta Kappa); JD, Stanford University (1977) (order of the coif).

## SOWATZKA, Adam G
King & Spalding LLP, Atlanta
404 572 3508
asowatzka@kslaw.com
*Featured in Environment (Georgia)*
**Practice Areas:** Advises clients regarding the environmental aspects of regulatory compliance, corporate transactions, and sustainable development. He has significant experience in assisting clients in the defense of administrative, civil, and criminal proceedings involving permitting and environmental enforcement matters at the federal and state levels.
**Professional Memberships:** Georgia State Bar–Environmental Law Section American Health Lawyers Association American Bar Association–Environment, Energy, and Resources Section Atlanta Bar Association Georgia Asylum and Immigration Network, Volunteer
**Personal:** J.D., cum laude, Vermont Law School M.S.E.L., magna cum laude, Vermont Law School BS, cum laude, University of Wisconsin-Green Bay

## SPANGLER III, John I
Alston & Bird LLP, Atlanta
404 881 7146
john.spangler@alston.com
*Featured in Construction (Georgia)*
**Practice Areas:** Construction litigation and arbitration of schedule, delay, interference, acceleration, changed conditions, water intrusion, and reimbursable cost disputes. Project experience includes government contracting, industrial/EPC, high rise commercial, health care, and professional and college sports arenas.
**Professional Memberships:** Atlanta Bar Association, Construction Law Section (Chair 1994-95); American Bar Association (Construction Industry Forum and Litigation Sections); Forum Governing Committee (2004-07); State Bar of Georgia (Litigation Section).
**Publications:** Authored numerous articles on construction law issues; co-editor of 'The Construction Contracts Book' (ABA 2004).
**Personal:** AB, University of Illinois (1977); JD, Washington University (1980).

## SPECHT, Scott A
Jones Day, Atlanta
404 581 8580
saspecht@jonesday.com
*Featured in Real Estate (Georgia)*
**Practice Areas:** Heads up the Real Estate Practice in Jones Day's Atlanta Office and has more than 30 years of experience in the real property area, with emphases on real estate secured lending (including workouts/restructures), real property development, acquisition and disposition, and corporate real estate services. He is listed in Georgia Super Lawyers and in Georgia Trend magazine's 'Legal Elite'.
**Professional Memberships:** State Bar of Georgia (Real Property Law and Corporate and Banking Law Sections), The Florida Bar (Real Property, Probate and Trust Law Sections), and the Atlanta Bar Association (Real Estate Law and Business and Finance Law Sections).

## SPINRAD, John
Arnall Golden Gregory LLP, Atlanta
404 873 8666
john.spinrad@agg.com
*Featured in Environment (Georgia)*
**Practice Areas:** Mr Spinrad chairs AGG's Environmental Practice Team and is a partner in the firm's Business Litigation and Real Estate Departments. He has practiced exclusively in the area of environmental law for 25 years. Mr Spinrad advises clients with regard to Brownfields, environmental remediation and due diligence issues, and structuring transactions to minimize or apportion environmental liabilities. He also counsels clients regarding environmental permitting and defends them in environmental enforcement actions.
**Professional Memberships:** Georgia Brownfield Association board member/Government Affairs committee chair.
**Personal:** JD, with honors, Duke School of Law (1983); BA, with high distinction, University of Virginia (1980).

## STEIN, Grant T
Alston & Bird LLP, Atlanta
404 881 7285
grant.stein@alston.com
*Featured in Bankruptcy/Restructuring (Georgia)*
**Practice Areas:** Practice includes representation of debtors, secured and unsecured creditors, creditors' committees, and fiduciaries in complex out-of-court workouts, debt restructurings, bankruptcy cases, financial transactions and all parties in bankruptcy related litigation.
**Professional Memberships:** Fellow, American College of Bankruptcy, member, Board of Directors and former member, Board of Regents; Former Chair and President, Association of Insolvency and Restructuring Advisors (AIRA); Former Chair and President, Southeastern Bankruptcy Law Institute.
**Career:** Listed in leading legal publications.
**Publications:** Written numerous articles on bankruptcy, workout, and related litigation topics. Regularly lectures around the country.
**Personal:** BBA, Emory University (1978); JD, University of Georgia (1981).

## STEIN, Jeffrey
King & Spalding LLP, Atlanta
404 572 4729
jstein@kslaw.com
*Featured in Corporate/M&A (Georgia)*
**Practice Areas:** Corporate finance transactions and securities matters, focusing on public offerings, representing corporate issuers and underwriters in shelf registrations of investment-grade debt securities, medium-term note programs, high-yield securities offerings and initial public offerings of common stock. Advice regarding SEC reporting and disclosure requirements, securities transactions and corporate governance and compliance matters.
**Professional Memberships:** American Bar Association (Legal Opinions Committees); New York State Bar Association; New York City, County and State Bar Associations (Tri-Bar Legal Opinion Committee); State Bar of Georgia.
**Personal:** BA, summa cum laude, Yeshiva University, 1977; JD, Harvard University, 1980.

## STEPHENSON, Mason W
King & Spalding LLP, Atlanta
404 572 4945
mstephenson@kslaw.com
*Featured in Real Estate (Georgia)*
**Practice Areas:** Commercial real estate law, representing banks, credit companies, life insurance companies, pension funds and institutional investors in secured financings and equity investments in income properties, including office buildings, hotels, apartments and industrial properties. Extensive experience in workout, restructure and foreclosure of real estate investments.
**Professional Memberships:** American College of Real Estate Lawyers; Atlanta Bar Association (former Chairman, Real Estate Section); State Bar of Georgia (former Member, Executive Committee, Real Estate Section).
**Personal:** AB, cum laude, Phi Beta Kappa, Davidson College, 1968; JD, University of

Chicago, 1971. Frequent lecturer on commercial real estate and ethics topics.

## STEVENS, Robert C.
Seyfarth Shaw LLP, Atlanta
404 885 6727
bstevens@seyfarth.com
*Featured in Labor & Employment (Georgia)*
**Practice Areas:** Labor and Employment/Trade Secrets and Non-competes.
**Professional Memberships:** ABA
**Career:** Mr Stevens' practice focuses on representing companies and executives in restrictive covenant and trade secret disputes in federal and state court nationally and in defending companies in employment discrimination cases and wage-hour collective actions nationally. He is a hands-on litigator and strategist who has confronted the spectrum of legal and procedural issues in both restrictive covenant/trade secret disputes and employment litigation.
**Personal:** JD, University of Alabama, Magna Cum Laude and Order of the Coif.

## SUDBURY, Deborah A
Jones Day, Atlanta
404 581 8443
dsudbury@jonesday.com
*Featured in Labor & Employment (Georgia)*
**Practice Areas:** Leads the Labor and Employment Practice in the Atlanta Office, specializing in defense of class and collective actions, having successfully represented many large companies in defeating class certification. Represented employers before state and federal trial and appellate courts and in a variety of state law wrongful discharge, contract, and tort claims. Her extensive trial experience includes successfully defending clients in bench and jury trials.
**Professional Memberships:** ABA and the state bar associations of California, Illinois, and Georgia.
**Publications:** Frequent national speaker on employment law and class action defense topics and author of a book on plant closing laws.

## SULLENBERGER, Douglas R
Fisher & Phillips LLP, Atlanta
404 240 4252
dsullenberger@laborlawyers.com
*Featured in Labor & Employment (Georgia)*
**Career:** Doug Sullenberger is a Partner in the Atlanta office. His practice focuses on traditional labor law, including representing and advising employers on union related matters. Sullenberger has also developed a series of interactive training program experiences for managers and supervisors on union avoidance and other labor relations issues. He has been recognized as one of the 'Top 100 Labor Lawyers' in the US since 2005, based on cases before the NLRB.

## TANIS, Elizabeth Vranicar
King & Spalding LLP, Atlanta
404 572 4660
etanis@kslaw.com
*Featured in Litigation (Georgia)*
**Practice Areas:** Co-leader of the Professional Liability Practice; Extensive trial and arbitration experience, and focuses her practice on general lit-

igation matters, with an emphasis on class actions; securities litigation; litigation involving public accounting firms, law firms and other professional services providers.
**Career:** Fellow of the American College of Trial Lawyers; Chair – Business Litigation Committee of the Business Section of the State Bar of Georgia; Chair – Board of Directors of Georgia Appleseed.
**Personal:** J.D., highest honors, Loyola University Chicago BA, University of Illinois

## TAYLOR, Bernard
Alston & Bird LLP, Atlanta
404 881 7288
bernard.taylor@alston.com
*Featured in Litigation (Georgia)*
**Practice Areas:** Over 30 years of experience representing Fortune 100 companies as lead trial attorney in complex litigation involving commercial litigation, class actions, mass torts, products liability, and toxic tort lawsuits filed in various jurisdictions throughout the US.
**Professional Memberships:** Fellow of the American College of Trial Lawyers; American Bar Association; Atlanta Bar Association, Gate City Bar Association; General Counsel, DeKalb County, Georgia Chapter of 100 Black Men of America.
**Career:** Co-chair of the firm's Products Liability Group; former chair of firm's management committee; and, former Detroit, Michigan, police investigator.
**Personal:** BA (1979) Wayne State University; JD (1982) Vanderbilt University.

## TAYLOR, Roger D
Finnegan, Henderson, Farabow, Garrett & Dunner LLP, Atlanta
404 653 6480
roger.taylor@finnegan.com
*Featured in Intellectual Property (Georgia)*
**Practice Areas:** Assists domestic and foreign corporations in obtaining patent protection for their inventions; protecting their intellectual property rights; and defending them against charges of infringement in state and federal courts. He has represented computer, electronic, and manufacturing companies in patent infringement litigation in US district courts. He has served as managing partner of the firm's Atlanta office and as the resident partner and manager of Finnegan's Tokyo, Japan, office.
**Personal:** University of Arkansas (BS, Electrical Engineering, 1973); George Washington University Law Center (J.D., with honors, 1980).

## TETRICK JR, David
King & Spalding LLP, Atlanta
404 572 3526
dtetrick@kslaw.com
*Featured in Labor & Employment (Georgia)*
**Practice Areas:** Focusing on the defense of sponsors and fiduciaries of employee benefit plans in ERISA litigation matters. He defends clients in a variety of ERISA class actions involving employer stock in 401(k) plans, calculation of benefits from long term disability plans, breach of fiduciary duty claims, as well as individual ERISA

claims and other employee benefits litigation. Representative clients include The Coca-Cola Company, United Parcel Service, The Home Depot, Inc. SunTrust Banks, Inc., and Bank of America.

**Personal:** JD, with honors, University of Florida. BA, University of Central Florida.

---

### THOMAS, Lizanne
Jones Day, Atlanta
404 581 8411
lthomas@jonesday.com
*Featured in Corporate/M&A (Georgia)*

**Practice Areas:** Partner-in-Charge of the 150 lawyer Atlanta Office and Global Chair of the firm's Corporate Governance Team. Experienced in public and private mergers and acquisitions and defensive planning. She advises boards of directors on corporate governance, shareholder activism, and director liability issues. Frequently advises special committees on transactional, investigative and litigation matters. With real-world experience as a public company Director (for Krispy Kreme) and as a director and audit committee chair for other organizations, she lectures on governance at seminars sponsored by the Practising Law Institute, the ABA, NYSE's Corporate Board Member and throughout the world.

---

### THOMPSON, John E
Fisher & Phillips LLP, Atlanta
404 240 4257
jthompson@laborlawyers.com
*Featured in Labor & Employment (Georgia)*

**Career:** John Thompson is a partner in the Atlanta office. His practice focuses on wage and hour law, emphasizing issues relating to minimum wage, overtime, timekeeping, and wage-payment requirements. He assists employers in preventive efforts designed to ensure compliance, and he handles both investigations conducted by government agencies and litigation in the wage and hour area. John has served as a Special Assistant Attorney General for wage-hour matters for the State of Georgia. He has also addressed wage-hour topics in presentations to numerous employer groups and in articles appearing in both human resources publications and industry journals.

---

### THOMPSON, Kim Kiel
Fisher & Phillips LLP, Atlanta
404 231 1400
kthompson@laborlawyers.com
*Featured in Immigration (Georgia)*

**Career:** Kim Thompson is a partner in the Atlanta office. She serves as chair of the firm's Global Immigration Practice Group and co-chair of the International Employment Practice Group. Kim's practice focuses on immigration and nationality law. Her practice includes extensive visa work, handling both temporary and permanent visa cases, as well as advice regarding compliance with the Form I-9, including government audits of I-9 forms and discrimination and document abuse provisions of the Immigration Reform and Control Act of 1986. She is a frequent lecturer on immigration topics and she advises

employers regarding best practices in immigration-related employment issues.

---

### THORNTON, M Robert
King & Spalding LLP, Atlanta
404 572 4778
bthornton@kslaw.com
*Featured in Litigation (Georgia)*

**Practice Areas:** Litigation focusing primarily on the areas of shareholder claims, director and officer liability and insurance, securities, SEC and NASD investigations, audit committee and other internal investigations, consumer fraud class actions, professional liability and legal ethics.
**Professional Memberships:** American Bar Association; Atlanta Bar Association; State Bar of Georgia.
**Career:** Represented acquiring companies, acquired companies, controlling shareholders, minority shareholders, directors and officers, and special committees of directors in connection with shareholder class and derivative claims involving mergers and acquisitions.
**Personal:** BA, cum laude, Princeton University, 1973; JD, cum laude, Harvard, 1976.

---

### THUNHORST, David G
Rogers & Hardin LLP, Atlanta
404 420 4615
dthunhorst@rh-law.com
*Featured in Corporate/M&A (Georgia)*

**Practice Areas:** Focuses primarily on mergers and acquisitions, corporate governance, securities matters, business transactions and commercial law. Advises boards of directors and special committees on matters relating to corporate governance issues. Experience counseling financially troubled companies and their Boards of Directors and assisting clients in workouts and restructuring transactions.
**Professional Memberships:** State Bar of Georgia (Member, Corporate Code Committee of the Business Law Section; Member, Securities Committee of the Business Law Section).
**Personal:** BA, Emory University, Phi Beta Kappa, 1987. JD, magna cum laude, University of Pennsylvania Law School, Member, University of Pennsylvania Law Review; Order of the Coif, 1990.

---

### TOWNSEND, Keith M
King & Spalding LLP, Atlanta
404 572 3517
ktownsend@kslaw.com
*Featured in Corporate/M&A (Georgia)*

**Practice Areas:** Significant experience in advising public company clients on SEC reporting and disclosure requirements, corporate governance issues and other corporate/ securities matters.
**Personal:** Bachelor of Arts degree, summa cum laude, from the University of Tennessee in 1996 where he was a member of Phi Beta Kappa. Mr Townsend received his JD from the University of Virginia School of Law in 1999 where he graduated Order of the Coif. He is a Member of the State Bar of Georgia, the Atlanta Bar Association and the American Bar Association.

---

### TRIGG, Mark G
Greenberg Traurig, LLP, Atlanta
678 553 2415
TriggM@gtlaw.com
*Featured in Litigation (Georgia)*

**Practice Areas:** Co-Chair, Atlanta Business Litigation Group.
**Career:** Listed, The Best Lawyers in America, 2010-13; Super Lawyers magazine, 2004-08, 2010-13; 'Top 100 Lawyers in Georgia', 2012-13; 'Litigation Stars' in Georgia, Benchmark Litigation Guide, 2009 and 2011-13; 'Guide to Leading US Litigation Lawyers', 2005-06, 2008, 2010-12; Georgia Trend magazine 'Legal Elite', 2006 and 2010-12. Rated, AV® Preeminent™ 5.0 out of 5.
**Personal:** JD, Emory University School of Law, 1986 (National Moot Court Team; The Order of Barristers; Outstanding Member of Emory Moot Court Society); MDiv Candidate, Candler School of Theology, Emory University, 1982-83; BA, Philosophy, Millsaps College, 1982.

---

### TURNER, Daniel E
Ogletree, Deakins, Nash, Smoak & Stewart, PC, Atlanta
404 881 1300
daniel.turner@ogletreedeakins.com
*Featured in Labor & Employment (Georgia)*

**Practice Areas:** Represents employers in all aspects of employment law litigation and counseling. Extensive experience representing employers in discrimination and wage and hour class and collective actions, having served as lead counsel in more than 40 such cases.
**Professional Memberships:** ABA, American Employment Law Counsel
**Publications:** Co-author, Chapter 4 of Employment Discrimination Law, "Application of Adverse Impact to Employment Decisions" (ABA 2007), and updates thereto.
**Personal:** Adjunct Professor of Litigation, Georgia State University College of Law (2009 and 2011); BA, cum laude, University of West Georgia (1992); JD, cum laude, Georgia State University College of Law (1995), Assistant Managing Editor, Georgia State University College of Law Review.

---

### WARREN, Frederick L
FordHarrison LLP, Atlanta
404 888 3828
rwarren@fordharrison.com
*Featured in Labor & Employment (Georgia)*

**Practice Areas:** Labor and Employment
**Career:** Rick Warren handles all aspects of labor and employment law, including traditional labor law, employment litigation and wage and hour matters. He litigates cases before federal and state courts and administrative agencies throughout the country. He defends individual and class action cases and has substantial jury trial experience. Rick also handles numerous mediations and arbitrations. He devotes a significant part of his practice to preventive law and advising clients how to avoid/resolve labor and employment disputes and litigation. He received his JD, cum laude, from the University of Georgia School of Law in 1981.

---

### WATSON, Jason H
Alston & Bird LLP, Atlanta
404 881 4796
jason.watson@alston.com
*Featured in Bankruptcy/Restructuring (Georgia)*

**Practice Areas:** Represents secured lenders and special servicers in significant Chapter 11 cases. In addition, routinely assists clients in acquiring assets from bankruptcy estates and has represented several franchisors in bankruptcy cases throughout the country.
**Professional Memberships:** Member of the board of directors of the Southeastern Bankruptcy Law Institute, and a member of the State Bar of Georgia, the New York State Bar Association and the American Bankruptcy Institute.
**Career:** Chair, firm's Bankruptcy, Reorganization & Workouts Group.
**Personal:** J.D. (1996) Mercer University; BA (1993) University of Georgia.

---

### WATT, Tobin N
Smith Moore Leatherwood LLP, Atlanta
404 962 1026
tobin.watt@smithmoorelaw.com
*Featured in Healthcare (Georgia)*

**Practice Areas:** Toby Watt has been practicing healthcare law for more than 25 years, representing hospitals, physician groups and various ancillary providers on a variety of health care matters. He has been significantly involved in managed care contracting and hospital and physician relationships (involving joint ventures, compensation arrangements, gainsharing, and other matters), compliance programs, and mergers and acquisitions. Mr Watt has a long-standing background in helping devise innovative relationships between hospitals and physicians, and between hospitals and employed staff to address quality of care and clinical integration. Mr Watt is currently involved in accountable care organization issues and formation.

---

### WEISS, Terry R
Greenberg Traurig, LLP, Atlanta
678 553 2603
WeissTR@gtlaw.com
*Featured in Litigation (Georgia)*

**Practice Areas:** Securities litigation; securities enforcement, regulatory; broker-dealer litigation and arbitration; appellate.
**Career:** Listed: Super Lawyers, 2006, 2010-13; 'Top 100 Lawyers in Georgia', 2012-13; Georgia Trend, 'Legal Elite', Securities Litigation, 2009-12; Legal 500 US, 2012. Team Member: Law360 'Employment Practice Group of the Year', 2011; Law360 'Appellate Practice Group of the Year', 2010. Rated, AV® Preeminent™ 5.0 out of 5.
**Publications:** Editor: 'Broker-Dealer Litigation: 2011 Annual Survey', ABA Journal, March 1, 2012; Broker-Dealer Litigation: 2010 Annual Survey', ABA Journal, June 1, 2011.
**Personal:** JD, Emory University School of Law, 1986 (Recipient, Book Award); BA, with high honors, Emory University, 1983.

## WEITNAUER, John C
Alston & Bird LLP, Atlanta
404 881 7780
kit.weitnauer@alston.com
*Featured in Bankruptcy/Restructuring (Georgia)*
**Practice Areas:** Bankruptcy, debtor or creditor counsel in large Chapter 11 cases, and bankruptcy related litigation (e.g., fraudulent transfer claims).
**Professional Memberships:** Fellow, American College of Bankruptcy, Georgia and American Bar Associations, American Bankruptcy Institute, Turnaround Management Association.
**Publications:** Author, 'The Bankruptcy Court's Watchdog: The Appointment, Role and Power of Examiners Today'; Co-author, 'Business Valuation and Bankruptcy'; Contributing editor, 'Norton Bankruptcy Law and Practice' and 'Bankruptcy Litigation Manual'; Editorial Board, American Bankruptcy Institute's 'ABI Journal'; co-author, 'Problem Loan Strategies'.
**Personal:** BA (1974) Washington and Lee University; JD (1977) University of Georgia.

## WELCH, Sidney Summers
Arnall Golden Gregory LLP, Atlanta
404 873 8182
sidney.welch@agg.com
*Featured in Healthcare (Georgia)*
**Practice Areas:** Partner in healthcare practice representing physicians and physician practices nationally in all aspects of their practice.
**Professional Memberships:** Chair, American Bar Association, Physician Issues; Vice Chair, American Health Lawyers Association, Physicians' Organizations.
**Career:** Joined AGG in 2007.
**Publications:** Publications and speeches detailed at www.agg.com.
**Personal:** Masters in Public Health from George Washington University School of Medicine. Undergraduate education at Davidson and Amherst Colleges. Nightingale's Outstanding Physician Lawyer Recipient. Georgia Super Lawyers and Martindale-Hubbell AV ratings. Co-Chair of AGG's Diversity Committee and Women's Initiative.

## WELLS, Della Wager
Alston & Bird LLP, Atlanta
404 881 7891
della.wells@alston.com
*Featured in Energy & Natural Resources (Georgia)*
**Practice Areas:** Municipal bond law and authority representation and related corporate, tax and securities matters involving taxable and tax-exempt financings for electric and gas facilities and commodities, water and sewerage facilities and other public projects on behalf of governmental entities.
**Professional Memberships:** Member of the National Association of Bond Lawyers and has served two terms on the Executive Committee of the Atlanta Contemporary Art Center.
**Personal:** BA, magna cum laude, University of Georgia (1980); MA, University of Virginia (1983); JD, with distinction, Emory University (1986).

## WENICK, George D
Smith, Currie & Hancock LLP, Atlanta
404 582 8037
gdwenick@smithcurrie.com
*Featured in Construction (Georgia)*
**Practice Areas:** Construction law; government contracts. Primarily focused on trials and arbitrations involving large, complex projects, especially power, heavy/highway, and manufacturing projects; international litigation/arbitration in China, Latin America, and Europe; and litigation of False Claims Act and bid protest matters.
**Professional Memberships:** American Bar Association Forum on the Construction Industry and Public Contract Law Section.
**Career:** Pennsylvania Department of Transportation, Office of Chief Counsel; Smith & Fleming, Partner; Smith, Currie & Hancock LLP, Partner. Consistently recognized by Chambers USA, Legal 500, and Georgia Super Lawyers.
**Personal:** JD, University of Pittsburgh School of Law; BS, University of Pittsburgh. Languages: French, Spanish, and Italian.

## WHEELER, Sara Kay
King & Spalding LLP, Atlanta
404 572 4685
skwheeler@kslaw.com
*Featured in Healthcare (Georgia)*
**Practice Areas:** Experience in the creation and implementation of corporate compliance programs, including the negotiation of corporate integrity agreements (CIAs) with the United States Department of Health and Human Services, Office of Inspector General. Other areas of expertise include experience in Medicare and Medicaid reimbursement arrangements, fraud and abuse concerns, internal investigations and other compliance issues, clinical research compliance, privacy matters, managed care arrangements and healthcare litigation.
**Personal:** BA University of Pennsylvania, BSN, magna cum laude, University of Pennsylvania, JD, cum laude, Wake Forest University.

## WHITE, Benjamin T
Alston & Bird LLP, Atlanta
404 881 7488
ben.white@alston.com
*Featured in Tax (Georgia)*
**Practice Areas:** Exempt organizations, estate and tax planning.
**Professional Memberships:** Fellow, American College of Trust and Estate Counsel; founding faculty member, American Institute for Philanthropic Studies; former President, Harvard Law School Association of Georgia; Member, American Bar Association Section of Real Property, Probate and Trust Law and Exempt Organizations Committee, Tax Section.
**Career:** Co-chair, firm's Exempt Organizations and Wealth Planning Group.
**Publications:** Co-author, 'Georgia Estate Planning, Will Drafting and Estate Administration Forms-Practice' and author, 'Foundation Desk Reference: A Compendium of Private Foundation Rules'.

**Personal:** AB, University of North Carolina (1969); JD, Harvard University (1973).

## WHITLEY, Joe D
Greenberg Traurig, LLP, Atlanta
678 553 7339
WhitleyJ@gtlaw.com
*Featured in Litigation (Georgia)*
**Practice Areas:** Chair, Atlanta White Collar Practice and Shareholder/Member, Washington DC White Collar Practice.
**Professional Memberships:** Chair-Elect and Member, ABA Section of Administrative Law and Regulatory Practice; Member, ABA Section of Litigation and ABA Criminal Justice Section; Member, National Association of Former US Attorneys.
**Career:** First General Counsel at DHS; DOJ Acting Associate Attorney General, Principal Deputy Associate Attorney General, Deputy Assistant Attorney General Criminal Division, US Attorney for the Northern and Middle Districts of Georgia, Assistant District Attorney for State of Georgia.
**Personal:** JD, University of Georgia School of Law; BA, University of Georgia.

## WHITLOCK, David C
Miller & Martin PLLC, Atlanta
404 962 6102
dwhitlock@millermartin.com
*Featured in Immigration (Georgia)*
**Practice Areas:** Dave Whitlock has over 25 years experience in business immigration, compliance, employment counseling, and training. In addition, Dave has extensive experience handling employment-related visa work, including both temporary and permanent visa cases, as well as advice regarding compliance with the I-9, discrimination, and document abuse provisions of the Immigration Reform and Control Act of 1986 and litigation arising under that statute. He is a frequent lecturer and presenter on immigration and compliance topics and best practices in employment-related topics.

## WILLIAMS, Michelle A
Alston & Bird LLP, Atlanta
404 881 7594
michelle.williams@alston.com
*Featured in Healthcare (Georgia)*
**Practice Areas:** Life sciences/health care transactions, Medicare/Medicaid surveys, enforcement actions and regulatory compliance, including whistleblower actions. Experience in mergers and acquisitions of hospitals, blood banks, and laboratories, including transactions requiring Attorney General approval and/or non-profit to for-profit conversion; Commissioner, DHHS Advisory Commission on Childhood Vaccines.
**Professional Memberships:** Member, American Health Lawyers Association, former vice chair of Hospitals and Healthcare Systems Practice Group; President, Georgia Academy of Hospital Attorneys; former Chairman, American Red Cross Southern Region Blood Services Board.
**Personal:** BS/BS, Michigan State University; MT, Butterworth Hospital; JD (1986) Case Western Reserve University.

## WILLOUGHBY, David
Rogers & Hardin LLP, Atlanta
404 420 4634
dwilloughby@rh-law.com
*Featured in Tax (Georgia)*
**Practice Areas:** US federal, state, local and international taxation, including corporate, partnership, executive, and real estate taxation, and federal and state tax controversies. Particularly qualified in structuring corporate mergers and acquisitions, joint venture alliances, and real estate and financing transactions, as well as limited liability companies and partnerships.
**Professional Memberships:** American Bar Association, Tax Section; State Bar of Georgia, Taxation Law Section; Atlanta Tax Forum.
**Personal:** JD, Vanderbilt University, 1985; Order of the Coif; Articles Editor, Vanderbilt Law Review, 1984-85; BS in Accountancy, Murray State University (summa cum laude), 1982.

## WINSBERG, Harris Bryan
King & Spalding LLP, Atlanta
404 572 4605
hwinsberg@kslaw.com
*Featured in Bankruptcy/Restructuring (Georgia)*
**Practice Areas:** Focuses in the areas of bankruptcy law and corporate restructuring matters. Also has significant experience on a wide variety of litigation matters, such as litigation related to fraudulent conveyances and preference actions.
**Professional Memberships:** State Bar of Georgia (Past-Chair, Bankruptcy Section); Atlanta Bar Association (Bankruptcy Section); The Florida Bar (Business Law Section); American Bankruptcy Institute; Board Member, Southeastern Bankruptcy Law Institute.
**Personal:** University of Florida (JD, with honors, 1997); University of Florida (BA, with honors, 1994).

## WOFFORD JR, M Russell
King & Spalding LLP, Atlanta
404 572 4711
rwofford@kslaw.com
*Featured in Antitrust (Georgia)*
**Practice Areas:** Practice focuses on antitrust and complex commercial litigation, specializing in antitrust matters related to intellectual property in the pharmaceutical, biotechnology and medical devices industries.
**Professional Memberships:** Antitrust Section of the American Bar Association and Antitrust Law Section of the State Bar of Georgia.
**Personal:** After graduating with high honors from Princeton University in 1983, he served in the US Army as an infantry officer, earning ranger, airborne, air assault and expert Infantryman qualifications. Following a year's graduate study in political philosophy at the University of Glasgow, Russ graduated in 1991 from the University of Chicago Law School.

## WOZNIAK, Todd
Greenberg Traurig, LLP, Atlanta
678 553 7326
WozniakT@gtlaw.com
*Featured in Labor & Employment (Georgia)*

**Practice Areas:** Labor and employment; litigation.

**Professional Memberships:** Member, Advisory Board for Employment & ERISA, Strafford Publications; American Bar Association (Litigation, Labor & Employment, and Employee Benefit Sections); State Bar of Georgia, Litigation and Labor & Employment Sections; Atlanta Bar Association; American Health Lawyers Association.

**Career:** Rated, AV® Preeminent™ 5.0 out of 5. Listed, Chambers USA Guide, 2007-13.

**Publications:** Contributing Author, Employment Discrimination Law 5th ed., 2012. Author/speaker, 'Top Ten Labor & Employment Issues for 2009', The Human Resource Management Association, 2009.

**Personal:** JD, cum laude, University of Michigan Law School; AB, summa cum laude, Duke University.

**WRAY, Christopher A**
King & Spalding LLP, Atlanta
404 572 3544
cwray@kslaw.com
*Featured in Litigation (Georgia)*

**Practice Areas:** Chair of the special matters and government investigations practice, providing counsel on a variety of corporate, securities and fraud matters, including white-collar criminal and regulatory enforcement matters, whistleblower complaints, and corporate internal investigations.

**Career:** Prior to joining the firm, Mr Wray served from 2003-05 as the 33rd assistant attorney general in charge of the US Department of Justice's (DOJ) Criminal Division, having been nominated by President George W Bush and confirmed by the US Senate for that position.

**Personal:** BA, cum laude, Yale University, 1989; JD, cum laude, Yale Law School, 1992.

**YATES, David R**
Hunton & Williams LLP, Atlanta
404 888 4238
dyates@hunton.com
*Featured in Corporate/M&A (Georgia)*

**Practice Areas:** Mr Yates's practice focuses on international and domestic public and private mergers and acquisitions, divestitures, investments, joint ventures and strategic transactions. He also advises private equity funds and their portfolio companies in all types of complex business transactions, and he represents clients seeking to engage in infrastructure and concession projects through public-private partnerships. His clients include a broad range of publicly owned and privately held US and foreign companies. He has been involved in numerous significant acquisitions, mergers, joint ventures, concessions and other business transactions, including those involving cross-border complexities.

**YOUNG, Malcolm D**
Smith Gambrell & Russell LLP, Atlanta
404 815 3774
myoung@sgrlaw.com
*Featured in Real Estate (Georgia)*

**Practice Areas:** Partner and head of Commercial Real Estate Practice representing developers, owners and managers of commercial real estate in complex transactions involving development, leasing and sale of major industrial projects; purchase, operation, management and sale of fresh and salt water marinas; acquisition, sales, leasing and management of major office complexes and hospitality transactions involving sales, financing, development and operation of hotels and motels. Structuring real estate investments and investment vehicles for all types of commercial properties.

**Personal:** BA, Political Science, Trinity University, 1965; JD, Vanderbilt University, 1968.

**ZAMER, John E**
Jones Day, Atlanta
404 581 8266
jzamer@jonesday.com
*Featured in Corporate/M&A (Georgia)*

**Practice Areas:** A broad range of corporate and securities work. He directs the mergers and acquisitions representation for clients with active acquisition programs. He advises as to corporate governance, takeover preparedness, joint ventures and strategic alliances. He advises boards and board committees. He represents investment funds relative to their formation and as to their investments. Regularly lectures on merger and acquisition topics. He has been listed in The Best Lawyers in America, Georgia Super Lawyers, 'Top 100 Georgia Super Lawyers', and Who's Who Legal.

**Personal:** Duke University (Editorial Board, Law Journal; JD with distinction 1977).

# ALSTON & BIRD LLP

www.alston.com **tel:** 404 881 7000 **fax:** 404 881 7777

**Managing Partner:** Richard R Hays
Number of partners: 347 Number of other lawyers: 471

## Firm Overview:

Alston & Bird is a major US law firm with more than 800 attorneys offering services in virtually every practice area, from antitrust to wealth planning. For 14 consecutive years, Alston & Bird has been ranked on the 'Fortune 100 Best Companies To Work For' list.

## Main Areas of Practice:

### Capital Markets/Mergers & Acquisitions:

The firm's attorneys have extensive experience with complex mergers and acquisitions, spin-offs, going-private transactions, joint ventures and similar transactions for clients in a broad range of industries, representing bidders, target companies, stockholders, boards of directors and financial advisors. Alston & Bird lawyers have been involved in all aspects of leveraged buyouts and distressed sales and can handle the acquisition and financing of public and nonpublic companies of any size. Global outsourcing is a strength of the firm as well.

### Energy & Sustainability:

Alston & Bird provides energy industry clients with nationally recognized expertise in virtually every aspect of the law affecting the energy industry, from electric and natural gas regulation and project development and financing to carbon management, energy supply transactions and public policy.

### Financial Services:

The firm's banking, insurance, investment management, broker-dealer, mutual fund, payment systems and alternative investment vehicle clients are provided a wide range of corporate governance, merger and acquisition, regulatory, litigation, securities and structured finance services. The Payments Group has global experience in all sectors of the industry, including merchant acquiring, card issuing, mobile payments, ecommerce, card schemes and payment networks, gift cards, healthcare payments and B2B payments.

### Global Finance:

The firm's finance attorneys represent domestic and foreign financial institutions, underwriters, alternative investment funds and other providers and servicers of debt capital. The firm represents the most active issuers, originators, servicers, trustees, master servicers, fund managers, investors, rating agencies and insurers. The firm has extensive experience in structuring and closing transactions with complex structures in a wide variety of asset classes.

### Healthcare:

Alston & Bird is home to one of the most extensive, full-service healthcare practices in the United States, comprised of over 100 lawyers with demonstrated corporate, securities, merger and acquisition and regulatory compliance expertise, including former health policy and enforcement experts from the Centers for Medicare and Medicaid Services, the US House of Representatives, the US Senate and the White House.

### Intellectual Property:

Numbering more than 160 lawyers, Alston & Bird's IP practice is one of the largest and most highly regarded in any general practice firm in the United States. The group provides a full range of intellectual property services, including patentability and prosecution, litigation, patent maintenance, counseling regarding infringement avoidance, and validity and infringement studies and opinions.

### Legislative & Public Policy:

Alston & Bird's legislative team is uniquely positioned to advise clients in a bipartisan, bicameral manner on public policy issues. The firm represents clients before Congress, the executive branch and regulatory agencies.

### Litigation:

Alston & Bird's 330 litigators have litigated in virtually every major industrialized jurisdiction, including those in Latin America, Europe and Asia. The firm's litigation experience includes antitrust, bankruptcy, construction, environmental and land development, ERISA, international trade and regulatory, labor and employment, securities, products liability and class actions.

### Real Estate Finance:

Alston & Bird's more than 60-attorney, industry-focused real estate investment and finance practice provides the full range of capabilities needed to serve sophisticated clients. It handles massive multiproperty and multijurisdictional transactions, while maintaining specialized expertise focused on specific property types. In addition, with a leading real estate capital markets practice, the group is poised at the intersection of the industry, where assets meet capital.

### Tax:

With more than 80 tax lawyers, Alston & Bird has one of the largest and most acclaimed law firm tax practices in the United States, providing coverage in international, federal, state and local taxation; employee benefits; executive compensation; wealth planning; exempt organizations; and transfer pricing.

### International Work:

Alston & Bird's multidisciplinary team has structured deals and handled disputes around the globe. The firm's international practice has extensive experience in planning, structuring and implementing business deals in virtually every major commercial jurisdiction in the world. The firm can find and help select the best local counsel, as well as help determine the optimal structure, for business transactions abroad, whether it involves an acquisition, joint venture, licensing arrangement, technology transfer, manufacturing contract, distribution agreement or other arrangement.

### Clients:

Aflac, Assurant Inc., Bank of America, The Boeing Company, Dell Inc., Delta Air Lines, Inc., The Dow Chemical Company, Genuine Parts Company, IMERYS, McKesson Corporation, Mohawk Industries, Inc., Nokia, The Prudential Insurance Company of America, Sabre, Tenet Healthcare Corporation, Toyota, UnitedHealth Group, UPS and Wells Fargo.

## OFFICES

### GEORGIA

**ATLANTA:** One Atlantic Center, 1201 West Peachtree Street, GA 30309-3424
Tel: 404 881 7000  Fax: 404 881 7777
Email: info@alston.com

### CALIFORNIA

**LOS ANGELES:** 333 South Hope Street, 16th Floor, CA 90071
Tel: 213 576 1000  Fax: 213 576 1100

**SILICON VALLEY:** 275 Middlefield Road, Suite 150, CA 94025-4004
Tel: 650 838 2000  Fax: 650 838 2001

**VENTURA COUNTY:** 2801 Townsgate Road, Suite 215, CA 91361
Tel: 805 497 9474  Fax: 805 497 8804

### DISTRICT OF COLUMBIA

**WASHINGTON DC:** The Atlantic Building, 950 F Street, NW, DC 20004-1404
Tel: 202 239 3300  Fax: 202 239 3333

### NEW YORK

**NEW YORK:** 90 Park Avenue, NY 10016-1387
Tel: 212 210 9400  Fax: 212 210 9444

### NORTH CAROLINA

**CHARLOTTE:** Bank of America Plaza, 101 South Tryon Street, Suite 4000, NC 28280-4000
Tel: 704 444 1000  Fax: 704 444 1111

**RESEARCH TRIANGLE:** 4721 Emperor Blvd, Suite 400, NC 27703-8580
Tel: 919 862 2200  Fax: 919 862 2260

### TEXAS

**DALLAS:** 2828 N. Harwood Street, Suite 1800, TX 75201
Tel: 214 922 3400  Fax: 214 922 3899

## INTERNATIONAL OFFICES

The firm also has an office in Brussels.

# ARNALL GOLDEN GREGORY LLP

**www.**agg.com **tel:** 404 873 8500 **fax:** 404 873 8501

**Chairman:** Jonathan Golden
**Managing Partner:** Glenn P Hendrix
Number of partners: 96   Number of lawyers: 157
Languages: *French, German, Gujarati, Hebrew, Hindi, Korean, Malayalam, Mandarin, Russian, Spanish, Ukrainian*

**Firm Overview:**
Arnall Golden Gregory LLP, founded in 1949, has offices in Atlanta, Washington and Miami. AGG advises growing public and private companies on mergers and acquisitions, capital markets financing, strategic alliances, joint ventures, regulatory compliance, litigation and other business-related matters.

**Main Areas of Practice:**

**Corporate & Securities:**
23 Partners; 37 fee earners
- Represented the biological medical device company CryoLife in its acquisition of Cardiogenesis for approximately $24 million.
- Represented Indian client NIIT in the complex sale of US subsidiary Element K Corporation to SkillSoft Corporation for $110 million.

**Key Clients:** SunTrust, Sysco Corp., Rich Products, Verizon Communications, Rollins Inc., NIIT USA
**Contact:** Sherman A Cohen **Tel:** 404 873 8630
**Email:** sherman.cohen@agg.com

**Healthcare:**
14 Partners; 27 fee earners
- Represented Genesis HealthCare LLC, in a multistate corporate restructuring and $2.4 billion sale of its real estate assets.
- Defending several national long-term care chains in a series of ongoing federal investigations.

**Key Clients:** Pruitt Corp., Formation Capital LLC, Kindred Healthcare, Gwinnett Health System Inc., SavaSeniorCare Administrative Services
**Contact:** Hedy Silver Rubinger **Tel:** 404 873 8724
**Email:** hedy.rubinger@agg.com

**Litigation:**
30 Partners; 47 fee earners
- AGG is representing SavaSeniorCare in a fight for control of the $1.4 billion long-term care chain initiated by a billionaire real estate investor who is the lessor of most of SavaSeniorCare's facilities.
- In a case with enormous e-discovery and logistics challenges, AGG represented the medical products company CryoLife in a lawsuit arising out of the breach of an exclusive distribution agreement that made CryoLife the sole distributor of the defendant's product in most of the world.

**Key Clients:** CryoLife Inc., SSC Equity Holdings (SavaSeniorCare), Emory University/Emory Healthcare, Rad Source Technologies
**Contact:** Robert L Rothman **Tel:** 404 873 8668
**Email:** robert.rothman@agg.com

**Global Logistics & Transportation:**
21 Partners; 25 fee earners
- Represented Lufthansa Cargo involving claims arising from alleged damage to temperature-sensitive pharmaceutical products.
- Represented Rich Products in the sale of subsidiary KangXin Logistics (KXL).

**Key Clients:** JAS Worldwide, Kuehne & Nagel, Inc., Avalon Risk Management, Agility Logistics, UTi Worldwide, DHL Global Forwarding, Lufthansa German Airlines, Chartis, RSA Insurance, Hellmann Worldwide Logistics
**Contact:** Andrew R Spector **Tel:** 305 537 2002
**Email:** andrew.spector@agg.com

**Bankruptcy, Creditors' Rights & Financial Restructuring:**
6 Partners; 13 fee earners
- Represent one of the world's largest financial companies in bankruptcy litigation matters.
- Longtime representative of Fortune 100 company Verizon Communications in its bankruptcy matters.

**Key Clients:** Debtors, secured and unsecured creditors, equity share holders, indenture trustees, crditors' committees, purchasers of insolvent companies, bankruptcy trustees
**Contact:** Darryl Scott Laddin **Tel:** 404 873 8120
**Email:** darryl.laddin@agg.com

**Privacy:**
5 Partners; 9 fee earners
- Represented a major Georgia company in a consumer regulatory matter before the Georgia Office of Consumer Protection.
- Advised a publicly traded corporation regarding the potential jurisdiction of the Consumer Financial Protection Bureau over the operations of multiple subsidiaries.

**Key Clients:** Companies, associations and government entities seeking the best approach to utilizing consumer information, safeguarding consumer privacy and responding to data breaches.
**Contact:** Robert R Belair **Tel:** 202 677 4040
**Email:** robert.belair@agg.com

**International Business:**
11 Partners; 17 fee earners

- Over a 10 year period represented a major international real estate company in the purchase, sale and financing of real estate with a total transaction value exceeding $8 billion.
- Representing Sysco Corporation in its domestic and international mergers and acquisitions.

**Key Clients:** Sysco Corporation, NIIT (USA) Inc., CryoLife Inc., JAS Worldwide, Porsche Car North America, Helsinn Healthcare S.A., Kuehne + Nagel
**Contact:** Abe J Schear **Tel:** 404 873 8752
**Email:** abe.schear@agg.com

**Government Investigations & White Collar Crime:**
10 Partners; 14 fee earners
- Representing a large public company in a False Claims Act investigation.
- Successfully represented former CEO and treasurer of publicly traded nursing home chain in parallel civil and criminal investigations.

**Key Clients:** Public corporations, closely-held businesses involved in government investigations, internal investigations, criminal investigations and trials.
**Contact:** Aaron M Danzig **Tel:** 404 873 8504
**Email:** aaron.danzig@agg.com

Arnall Golden Gregory LLP
Attorneys at Law

# ASHE RAFUSE & HILL LLP

**www.**AsheRafuse.com **tel:** 404 253 6000  **fax:** 404 253 6060

**Chair:** R Lawrence Ashe, Jr
**Managing Partner:** Nancy E Rafuse
Number of partners: 6  Number of other lawyers: 10
Languages: *English, Spanish*

## Firm Overview:

Based in Atlanta, Georgia, Ashe Rafuse & Hill LLP maintains a national trial and litigation practice focusing on employment, civil rights, products liability, intellectual property, and commercial disputes. Dedicated to delivering the highest quality legal services and advice, the firm has established a reputation for recruiting and developing outstanding courtroom attorneys with significant jury trial experience.

## Main Areas of Practice:

### Employment Law & Civil Rights:

4 Partners; 10 fee earners

Ashe Rafuse & Hill LLP represents and advises clients on virtually every aspect of employment law, including representation of employers in response to claims asserted under non-discrimination statutes (e.g. Title VII, ADEA, ADA, Executive Order 11246) and traditional labor laws, as well as other employment-related statutes (e.g. FLSA, FMLA). The firm's employment practice also includes civil rights matters under Titles II, VI, and IX and Section 1981, as well as customer accommodation claims. Representative successes include:

- Nancy Rafuse and William Hill, a former trial court judge, successfully tried multiple public accommodation cases throughout the Southeast to complete defense verdicts on behalf of a major restaurant chain
- William Hill and Jim Swartz concluded a trial on behalf of a multinational manufacturer with judgment as a matter of law at the close of plaintiff's evidence, thereby defeating plaintiff's Section 1981 race discrimination and retaliation claims

**Key Clients:** CVS Caremark Corporation, Abbott Laboratories, The Home Depot, Inc., The Procter & Gamble Company, United Parcel Service, Waffle House, Inc., Cox Enterprises, Kronos, Inc.
**Contact:** Nancy E Rafuse **Tel:** 404 253 6002
**Email:** nancyrafuse@AsheRafuse.com

### Collective & Class Actions:

4 Partners; 10 fee earners

Ashe Rafuse & Hill LLP is a "go-to" firm for the defense of Rule 23 employment class actions and collective actions under the Fair Labor Standards Act. The firm's partners have tried to conclusion and won more Rule 23 employment discrimination class actions than any other management employment firm in the country and have defeated class certification in dozens of cases.

- Nancy Rafuse and Jim Swartz represent national employers in collective and class actions defending claims for off-the-clock work, meal and rest break pay, unpaid travel time and unpaid security checks
- Nancy Rafuse and Jim Swartz successfully negotiated

a $34 million settlement of eleven nationwide wage-and-hour class actions filed in six venues against a national retail pharmacy chain

**Key Clients:** CVS Caremark Corporation, The Home Depot, Inc., Sysco Corporation.
**Contact:** Jim Swartz **Tel:** 404 253 6046
**Email:** jimswartz@AsheRafuse.com

### Commercial Litigation:

3 Partners, 9 fee earners

Ashe Rafuse & Hill LLP's Commercial Litigation Division is composed of trial lawyers who prosecute and defend multifaceted, sophisticated commercial matters and who have substantial trial and appellate experience in federal and state courts in Georgia and throughout the country, as well as multi-district litigation experience. Representative successes include:

- The Superior Court of Fulton County appointed William Hill as Special Master to identify and take custody of the personal papers of Coretta Scott King, the late widow of Dr Martin Luther King, Jr; Hill's Report to the Court regarding numerous complex legal issues enabled conclusion of the litigation
- William Hill and Joe Sharp successfully represented a former General Motors franchisee in the only arbitration against GM arising from the Memorandum of Understanding executed by GM and the National Association of Minority Automobile Dealers, which MOU was occasioned by the termination of numerous dealerships preceding GM's bankruptcy
- The Superior Court of Laurens County appointed Ken Hodges, a former District Attorney, to serve as a Receiver to oversee the seizure of 11 business establishments, marshal their assets and those of 13 individual defendants, put some of the businesses back into lawful operation and ensure compliance with the law and the Court's orders

**Key Clients:** American Suzuki Motor Corporation, The Procter & Gamble Company, Abbott Laboratories.
**Contact:** William B Hill, Jr **Tel:** 404 253 6025
**Email:** williamhill@AsheRafuse.com

### Products Liability Litigation:

3 Partners, 5 fee earners

## PRACTICE AREAS

Alternative Dispute Resolution
Employment Law & Litigation
Civil Rights
Class & Collective Actions
Commercial Litigation
Intellectual Property Litigation
Investigations (Government & Corporate)
Products Liability Litigation
Receiverships
White-Collar Criminal Defense

## OFFICES

GEORGIA

**ATLANTA:** 1355 Peachtree Street NE, Suite 500, GA 30309-3232
Tel: 404 253 6000  Fax: 404 253 6060

Ashe Rafuse & Hill LLP regularly represents manufacturers, distributors, suppliers, and service providers in the automotive, aviation, pharmaceutical, and commercial and consumer product industries nationwide. Representative successes include:

- William Hill successfully represented an automotive manufacturer in two mesothelioma cases tried simultaneously to the same jury in 2007
- William Hill recently earned summary judgment for an international pharmaceutical manufacturer in wrongful death litigation
- William Hill achieved voluntary dismissal of all claims against a fixed-base operator in a wrongful death action arising out of an aircraft accident

**Key Clients:** Abbott Laboratories, American Suzuki Motor Corporation, Chrysler, Inc.
**Contact:** William B Hill, Jr **Tel:** 404 253 6025
**Email:** williamhill@AsheRafuse.com

### Intellectual Property Litigation:

2 Partners, 6 fee earners

Ashe Rafuse & Hill LLP represents companies prosecuting and defending against false advertising, unfair competition, trademark infringement, and patent license claims in federal courts throughout the country. Representative successes include:

- On behalf of an Atlanta homebuilder, William Hill and Joe Sharp earned a favorable resolution in a multiple-count copyright infringement case
- William Hill and Joe Sharp represented various pharmaceutical companies asserting Lanham Act claims against competitors falsely advertising allegedly substitutable products
- Joe Sharp successfully and aggressively represented an electronic payments company in a number of trademark infringement matters

**Key Clients:** Rovi Corporation, Shionogi Pharma, Inc.
**Contact:** Joseph C Sharp **Tel:** 404 253 6028
**Email:** joesharp@AsheRafuse.com

A|R|H
Ashe Rafuse & Hill LLP

# BURR AND FORMAN LLP

www.burr.com **tel:** 800 GET BURR

**Chairman:** Lee Thuston
Managing Partners: 9  Number of partners: 178  Number of lawyers: 288

## Firm Overview:

Burr & Forman is a full service law firm with a long history of serving clients in Alabama, Florida, Georgia, Mississippi and Tennessee. The firm's forward-thinking approach allows it to provide legal solutions appropriate to the needs of its clients. With nearly 300 attorneys, Burr & Forman offers a wide range of business and litigation services to diverse clients with local, national and international interests.

## Main Areas of Practice:

**Automotive:**
Represents automotive dealerships in claims associated with franchise agreements, breach of contract, sales and acquisitions, non-competes and wrongful termination.

**Banking & Finance:**
Represents lenders of all types in lending and financial transactions for working capital needs, refinancings, specific personal and real property asset acquisitions and development and company acquisitions in the middle and large corporate markets.

**Commercial Litigation:**
Represents financial institutions, businesses and officers and directors in complex commercial disputes and securities litigation.

**Corporate & Tax:**
Represents businesses and not-for-profits of all sizes and in all stages of development in complex business matters, mergers and acquisitions, capital raises and regulatory compliance issues.

**Creditors' Rights & Bankruptcy:**
Represents financial services institutions, asset-based lenders and local, regional and national banks in significant and complex bankruptcy proceedings.

**Construction:**
Represents owners, contractors, suppliers and design professionals in all construction-related transactional matters and in the litigation or dispute resolution of all construction claims.

**Economic Development:**
Leading economic development firm in the Southeast. Projects reflect a diversity of industries and represent over $16 billion of capital investment and over 25,000 new jobs created.

**Environmental:**
Represents industries, developers, financial institutions and individuals in environmental matters related to business strategy, permitting and regulatory compliance, litigation, sustainability, and administrative proceedings.

**Financial Services Litigation:**
Represents banks, mortgage, finance and credit card companies in all types of litigation involving deceptive loan origination, predatory lending, wrongful foreclosure, mortgage fraud and statutory violation claims.

**Health Care:**
Represents all types of health care organizations in a variety of litigation, regulatory, compliance, licensure and corporate law matters.

**Insurance Regulatory:**
Represents all types of businesses and insurance entities in connection with structuring solutions to their business insurance needs and maintaining regulatory compliance.

**Labor & Employment:**
Represents employers of all sizes in matters ranging from drafting policies and handbooks to defending against the entire gamut of employment-related claims.

**Maritime & Transportation:**
Represents clients whose businesses are in, around or near navigable waters with all types of litigation claims, financing activities, contract negotiations, employment matters and other regulatory issues.

**Products Liability:**
Represents clients in all industries with products and premises liability, personal injury, industrial and construction site accidents, pharmaceuticals, medical devices, mass torts and toxic tort cases.

**Real Estate:**
Represents commercial real estate development companies in land planning, entitlement and development, governmental incentives, title matters, acquisition and disposition and performing and distressed assets.

**Securities Litigation:**
Represents broker-dealers and investment bankers in disputes, such as mutual-fund class-actions, derivative contracts trials, government enforcement actions and constitutional challenges to municipal securities rules.

**Technology:**
Represents businesses in protection of, and licensing strategies for, intellectual property, contract negotiation,

## OFFICES

**GEORGIA**
**ATLANTA:** 171 17th Street, NW Suite 1100, GA 30363
Tel: 404 815 3000  Fax: 404 817 3244

**ALABAMA**
**BIRMINGHAM:** 420 North 20th Street, Suite 3400, AL 35203
Tel: 205 251 3000  Fax: 205 458 5100

**MOBILE:** RSA Tower, 11 North Water Street, Suite 22200, AL 36602
Tel: 251 344 5151  Fax: 251 344 9696

**MONTGOMERY:** RSA Tower, 201 Monroe Street, Suite 1950, AL 36104
Tel: 334 241 7000  Fax: 334 262 0020

**FLORIDA**
**FT. LAUDERDALE:** Las Olas Centre I, 450 East Las Olas Boulevard, Suite 700, FL 33301
Tel: 954 414 6200  Fax: 954 414 6201

**ORLANDO:** 200 South Orange Avenue, Suite 800, FL 32801
Tel: 407 540 6600  Fax: 407 540 6601

**TAMPA:** One Tampa City Center, Suite 3200, FL 33602
Tel: 813 221 2626  Fax: 813 221 7335

**MISSISSIPPI**
**JACKSON:** The Heritage Building, 401 E Capitol Street, Suite 100, MS 39201
Tel: 601 355 3434  Fax: 601 355 5150

**TENNESSEE**
**NASHVILLE:** 700 Two American Center, 3102 West End Avenue, TN 37203
Tel: 615 724 3200  Fax: 615 724 3290

growth, investment and acquisition strategies.

## Clients:

American Cast Iron Pipe Company; ADTRAN; American Suzuki Motor Corporation; Assuranceforeningen Gard-gjensidig; Bank of America; Bank of Tampa; Brasfield and Gorrie General Contractors; Brice Building Company; Budgetext; Capital One; Charles Schwab & Co., Inc.; Circle K; Citibank; City of Tampa; Coastal Forest Products; Coca-Cola Enterprises; CVS Caremark; Daniel Realty Company; Dillard's; East Alabama Medical Center; First American; Founders Insurance Company; Gray Construction; HealthSouth Corporation; Laboratory Corporation of America; Mercedes-Benz U.S. International, Inc.; M/I Homes; Millard Maritime; Morgan Keegan & Co.; National Steel Car; Nissan Motors of America, Inc.; Nutech Medical Inc.; Nu Tech Spine, Inc.; ProAssurance; RockTenn Company; Rinnai; Standard Insurance; Southpace Properties; SunTrust Mortgage; Synovus Bank; Tacala; Tenet Healthcare Corporation; Guardian Life; ThyssenKrupp; Time Insurance Company; TriNovus Capital, LLC; UAB Health Services Foundation; United States Steel; Wells Fargo Bank; Wells Fargo Advisors; Whirlpool

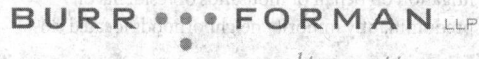

BURR ••• FORMAN LLP
*results matter*

# DOFFERMYRE SHIELDS CANFIELD & KNOWLES, LLC

www.dsckd.com **tel:** 404 881 8900 **fax:** 404 881 3007

**OFFICES**

GEORGIA

**ATLANTA:** 1355 Peachtree Street, Suite 1600, GA 30309-3269
Tel: 404 881 8900   Fax: 404 881 3007

## Firm Overview:

Doffermyre Shields Canfield & Knowles, LLC, represents businesses and individuals who have been harmed by the wrongful conduct of others in a wide variety of civil litigation, including complex business disputes, class actions, multi-district proceedings, environmental matters, and personal injury cases. Most of the firm's work is done on the basis of contingent fees rather than hourly rate billing.

## Main Areas of Practice:

### Bankruptcy:

The firm oftentimes is hired by receivers and bankruptcy trustees to pursue claims on behalf of estates that lack funds to pay lawyers on an hourly basis or prefer to reduce their financial risk. Without the firm's willingness to handle these claims on a contingent fee, many would never be brought. The firm has handled claims for trustees and receivers in such industries as aviation, finance, hedge funds, environmental concerns, insurance, and others.

### Business Litigation:

The firm represents businesses in courts, mediation and private arbitration. While experienced in defending business cases, the firm now almost exclusively represents companies that have been wronged. The firm's clients include all types of businesses from family enterprises to large corporations in cases involving breach of contract, fraud, RICO, lender liability and banking matters, intellectual property, business divorces, anti-trust, real estate, insurance coverage issues, and business torts.

### Class Actions:

The firm has long been known for its work on behalf of consumers and small businesses in major class actions around the country. Firm lawyers routinely serve as lead Counsel or on court-appointed steering committees in class actions, such as the Masonite hard board siding litigation involving allegedly defective building products, the Managed Care multi-district litigation in which the nation's doctors challenged the business practices of the country's largest HMOs, and the national breast implant products liability litigation. These and other cases have resulted in the recovery of billions of dollars in compensation and damages.

### Environmental Litigation:

For decades, the firm's lawyers have been at the forefront of environmental litigation and have successfully handled individual lawsuits, class actions, and mass tort cases seeking relief for both personal injuries and property damage. Much of the firm's recent work has involved "environmental justice" litigation on behalf of thousands of residents of predominantly minority neighborhoods located close to major pollutant sources. Firm lawyers are accustomed to collaborating with some of the world's leading scientists on environmental matters and have experience with the major federal regulatory statutes.

### Intellectual Property Litigation:

The firm has handled intellectual property litigation, including patent, trademark and copyright disputes. Ordinarily, though not exclusively, the firm is associated by intellectual property specialists who seek to take advantage of the trial experience of the firm's lawyers and the firm's willingness to work on a contingent fee.

### Insurance Litigation:

The firm has extensive experience litigating with insurance companies in a wide variety of matters, including claims on behalf of doctors whose disability insurers denied their claims, consumers who were overcharged for health insurance, beneficiaries who were denied payment on life insurance policies, and policyholders whose insurers refused to pay judgments against them. In addition, the firm routinely deals with issues relating to insurance coverage in connection with its work on other cases.

### Personal Injury Litigation:

Over the years, the firm has settled and tried countless personal injury claims arising from automobile wrecks, trucking collisions, airplane crashes, explosions, fires, electrical disasters, and numerous other types of incidents. The firm also has significant experience in medical malpractice and toxic tort cases.

### Products Liability Litigation:

The firm has won many individual, mass tort, and class action cases involving defective products, including faulty medical devices, poorly designed automobiles, hazardous consumer products, shoddy building materials, and unduly dangerous drugs. Several of the firm's cases are milestones, including Banks v ICI Americas, Inc., which dramatically changed Georgia law and remains the leading case in the field.

### Professional Negligence:

The firm is often asked to handle claims against those who may not have met the appropriate standard of care governing their professional responsibilities. The firm, for example, has represented investors and businesses who have been injured by the negligence of lawyers and accountants.

### Toxic Torts:

The firm has a long history of successfully prosecuting cases involving personal injuries from exposure to hazardous substances. Illustrative clients include the family of a railroad engineer who died of cancer from his on-the-job exposure to diesel exhaust; a severely brain-damaged child who was harmed by organic solvents during her mother's pregnancy; participants in a clinical drug trial that went awry; and people who were injured from exposure to such substances as lead, DDT, and PCBs.

### Uncommon & Other Litigation:

The firm prides itself on its work in cases involving unusual facts, novel legal issues, unanswered constitutional questions, or matters of significance from a public policy standpoint. For instance, in 1990, several years before the highly publicized trials involving O J Simpson, the firm won what the media called the country's first civil murder case on behalf of the family of a woman who believed she had been killed by her husband. Other matters that demonstrate the breadth of the firm's practice in this area include major political litigation, representation of indigent criminal defendants in death penalty cases, constitutional lawsuits involving voting rights and First Amendment issues, and defense of a leading civil rights organization facing legal action by the Ku Klux Klan.

# FISHER & PHILLIPS LLP

www.laborlawyers.com **tel:** 404 231 1400 **fax:** 404 240 4249

**Chairman:** Roger K Quillen
Number of partners: 151
Number of senior counsel: 7
Number of counsel: 28
Number of associates: 95

## Firm Overview:

Fisher & Phillips LLP does only one thing: represent employers in labor and employment matters. The firm's commitment to value dates to its founding in 1943. Clients benefit from the attorneys' deep and broad expertise in labor and employment law. The firm's focus provides clients with reduced start-up times, greater cost efficiencies, and better outcomes. The firm's business-like approach brings a practical perspective to today's labor and employment law problems.

## Main Areas of Practice:

### Affirmative Action Plans:

Fisher & Phillips drafts affirmative action plans and policies and represents clients in enforcement proceedings before the OFCCP.

### Employee Benefits:

The firm handles pension and benefit matters under ERISA, continuation of insurance coverage issues under COBRA, and compliance issues under HIPAA. Attorneys prepare qualified employee benefit plans, executive compensation programs and health and welfare benefit plans.

### Employee Defection & Trade Secrets Practice Group:

This group concentrates on issues surrounding employee defection, employee recruitment and trade secrets protection. This includes litigating and advising clients on covenants not to compete; non-solicitation, non-recruitment, non-disclosure agreements; trade secrets and protection of confidential business information; and related matters.

### Employment Discrimination & Harassment:

Fisher & Phillips lawyers regularly defend employers against claims of discrimination, harassment and retaliation brought under Title VII of the Civil Rights Act of 1964, the Americans with Disabilities Act, the Age Discrimination in Employment Act, and similar federal and state laws.

### Global Immigration Practice:

The firm provides a single solution for global immigration needs, managing immigration services for clients to allow their employees to work legally in any country. Their end-to-end case management, utilizing cutting-edge software, ensures that global expatriate and non-local staff maintain proper immigration status throughout employment.

### International Employment Practice:

The International Employment Practice Group consists of attorneys experienced in providing legal advice to international employers on human resources and immigration matters (inbound and outbound) on a global basis, as well as on matters pertaining to employees working in the United States who are governed by international laws. The firm contributes to clients' business success by helping them navigate through complex global human resources issues.

### Labor Relations:

The firm assists its non-union clients in remaining union free and represents its unionized clients in collective bargaining, arbitration and unfair labor practice cases.

### Mergers, Acquisitions & Divestitures:

Fisher & Phillips advises clients on the labor, employment and benefits aspects of buying or selling a business, including union representation issues, benefit plan mergers and terminations, severance plans, executive employment agreements, and withdrawal liability issues.

### Workplace Safety & Catastrophe Management:

The firm provides practical guidance to develop and maintain effective workplace safety and health management programs. Attorneys assist employers in responding to inspections, defending litigation, and managing workplace catastrophes.

### Wage & Hour Laws:

Fisher & Phillips performs audits of compliance status, preparation for and representation of clients during government wage-hour investigations, defense of wage-hour lawsuits, review and design of pay plans, and advice on exempt/non-exempt classifications.

### Clients:

The firm has a broad and diverse client base, representing a wide range of public and private employers. Some clients are large multinational corporations with thousands of employees; others are smaller entrepreneurial businesses. Clients include employers in a wide variety of industries.

## OFFICES

**GEORGIA**
**ATLANTA:** 1075 Peachtree Street, NE, Suite 3500, GA 30309
Tel: 404 231 1400  Fax: 404 240 4249
Email: fp@laborlawyers.com

**NORTH CAROLINA**
**CHARLOTTE:** Tel: 704 334 4565  Fax: 704 334 9774

**ILLINOIS**
**CHICAGO:** Tel: 312 346 8061  Fax: 312 346 3179

**SOUTH CAROLINA**
**COLUMBIA:** Tel: 803 255 0000  Fax 803 255 0202

**TEXAS**
**DALLAS:** Tel: 214 220 9100  Fax: 214 220 9122
**HOUSTON:** Tel: 713 292 0150  Fax: 713 292 0151
**SAN ANTONIO:** Tel: 210 227 5434  Fax: 210 227 5421

**COLORADO**
**DENVER:** Tel: 303 218 3650  Fax: 303 218 3651

**FLORIDA**
**FORT LAUDERDALE:** Tel: 954 525 4800  Fax: 954 525 8739
**ORLANDO:** Tel: 407 541 0888  Fax: 407 541 0887
**TAMPA:** Tel: 813 769 7500  Fax: 813 769 7501

**CALIFORNIA**
**IRVINE:** Tel: 949 851 2424  Fax: 949 851 0152
**LOS ANGELES:** Tel: 213 330 4500  Fax: 213 330 4501
**SAN DIEGO:** Tel: 858 597 9600  Fax: 858 597 9601
**SAN FRANCISCO:** Tel: 415 490 9000  Fax: 415 490 9001

**MISSOURI**
**KANSAS CITY:** Tel: 816 842 8770  Fax: 816 842 8767

**NEVADA**
**LAS VEGAS:** Tel: 702 252 8131  Fax: 702 252 7411

**KENTUCKY**
**LOUISVILLE:** Tel: 502 561 3990  Fax: 502 561 3991

**MAINE**
**PORTLAND:** Tel: 207 774 6001  Fax: 207 775 6407

**NEW JERSEY**
**MURRAY HILL:** Tel: 908 516 1050  Fax: 908 516 1051

**LOUISIANA**
**NEW ORLEANS:** Tel: 504 522 3303  Fax: 504 529 3850

**OHIO**
**CLEVELAND:** Tel: 440 838 8800  Fax: 440 838 8805
**COLUMBUS:** Tel: 614 221 1425  Fax: 614 221 1409

**PENNSYLVANIA**
**PHILADELPHIA:** Tel: 610 230 2150  Fax: 610 230 2151

**ARIZONA**
**PHOENIX:** Tel: 602 281 3400  Fax: 602 281 3401

**OREGON**
**PORTLAND:** Tel: 503 242 4262  Fax: 503 242 4263

**DISTRICT OF COLUMBIA**
**WASHINGTON DC:** Tel: 202 429 3707  Fax: 202 429 3709

**TENNESSEE**
**MEMPHIS:** Tel: 901 526 0431  Fax: 901 526 8183

**MASSACHUSETTS**
**BOSTON:** 617 722 0044  Fax: 617 371 2950

# FORDHARRISON LLP

www.fordharrison.com **tel:** 404 888 3800 **fax:** 404 888 3863

**Firm Managing Partner:** C Lash Harrison
**Co-Firm Managing Partner:** Herbert E Gerson
Number of partners: 84
Number of other lawyers: 83

## Firm Overview:

Founded in 1978, FordHarrison has evolved into one of the premier national labor and employment law firms with 20 offices, including three of counsel affiliate offices, in key US markets. The firm provides labor and employment legal services to employers in areas including employment litigation, discrimination, harassment, class action litigation, affirmative action, wrongful termination, wage and hour law, ADA/FMLA, government contracts, airline labor law, labor union organizing, collective bargaining, arbitration, reductions in force, mergers and acquisitions, employment contracts, antitrust and unfair competition, alternative dispute resolution, business immigration, international law, employee benefits and workplace safety.

## Main Areas of Practice:

### Employment:

FordHarrison advises clients on all matters affecting the employment relationship. The firm's attorneys design policies and practices that minimize the risk of successful claims of discrimination, equal pay violations, breaches of employment contract and wrongful or retaliatory discharges. FordHarrison attorneys counsel clients on the changes in federal and state wage and hour laws, Family and Medical Leave Act (FMLA), the Americans With Disabilities Act (ADA) and Health Insurance Portability and Accountability Act (HIPAA). The firm's attorneys and consultants evaluate employment vulnerabilities through personnel audits, reviews of personnel policies or handbooks, and management training; develop and assist in implementing affirmative action plans; and advise clients on health and safety issues, including the establishment of workable safety programs, compliance with the Occupational Safety and Health Act (OSHA) and compliance with employee 'right to know' statutes.

### Labor Law:

Collective bargaining and union organizing drives can be handled successfully if management teams are given the knowledge and insight necessary to deal with these issues. FordHarrison attorneys represent and advise employers in all phases of labor relations matters as they arise under the NLRA and RLA.

### Litigation:

The proliferation of state and federal laws creating employee rights has prompted an increasing number of lawsuits that make their way into court. In addition to representation of management in employment disputes, the firm also represent clients in all types of business litigation. FordHarrison attorneys litigate such matters as employment contracts, trade secrets, unfair competition and covenants not to compete and also have significant experience in class action litigation. The

firm has successfully opposed class certification in most cases where it has been lead counsel. This experience has given the firm special knowledge about the process in defending class action lawsuits that translates into cost savings for employer clients. Preventing protracted litigation is always a key goal and FordHarrison attorneys are leaders in achieving results through preventative strategies.

### Employee Benefits:

FordHarrison's employee benefits group has experience in assisting numerous public and private employers with their compensation and benefit plans. Some of the issues that the firm advises employers on are related to pension plans, profit sharing plans, trusts, welfare benefit plans, leave policies and Department of Labor investigations.

### Immigration:

The firm's attorneys provide immigration advice to clients who hire or transfer foreign employees. In compliance with the Immigration Reform and Control Act, FordHarrison assists clients in obtaining temporary visas and permanent resident status ('Green Cards') in the United States, obtains necessary labor certification and temporary work permits, and counsels employers on hiring and transferring foreign employees.

### Government Contracts:

FordHarrison advises current and potential government contractors and subcontractors about their labor and employment obligations, assists contractors in their compliance efforts, and defends contractors in enforcement proceedings.

### International Law:

FordHarrison actively manages labor and business matters on behalf of its clients in multiple jurisdictions around the world. FordHarrison attorneys collaborate with highly regarded practice groups in leading general practice and labor and employment law firms located around the world to provide a complete range of core business and labor and employment law services.

## OFFICES

### GEORGIA
**ATLANTA (HEAD OFFICE):** 271 17th Street, NW, Suite 1900, GA 30363
Tel: 404 888 3800 Fax: 404 888 3863
Website: www.fordharrison.com

### ALABAMA
**BIRMINGHAM:** Tel: 205 244 5900 Fax: 205 244 5901

### CALIFORNIA
**LOS ANGELES:** Tel: 213 237 2400 Fax: 213 237 2401
**SAN FRANCISCO:** Tel: 415 277 5430

### DISTRICT OF COLUMBIA
**WASHINGTON DC:** Tel: 202 719 2000 Fax: 202 719 2077

### FLORIDA
**JACKSONVILLE:** Tel: 904 357 2000 Fax: 904 357 2001
**MELBOURNE:** Tel: 321 724 5970 Fax: 321 724 5979
**MIAMI:** Tel: 305 808 2100 Fax: 305 808 2101
**ORLANDO:** Tel: 407 418 2300 Fax: 407 418 2327
**TAMPA:** Tel: 813 261 7800 Fax: 813 261 7899
**WEST PALM BEACH:** Tel: 561 659 5646 Fax: 561 659 1260

### ILLINOIS
**CHICAGO:** Tel: 312 332 0777 Fax: 312 332 6130

### MINNESOTA
**MINNEAPOLIS:** Tel: 612 486 1700 Fax: 612 486 1701

### NEW JERSEY
**BERKELEY HEIGHTS:** Tel: 973 646 7300 Fax: 973 646 7310

### NEW YORK
**NEW YORK:** Tel: 212 453 5900 Fax: 212 453 5959

### NORTH CAROLINA
**ASHEVILLE:** Tel: 828 687 4029 Fax: 828 687 4471

### SOUTH CAROLINA
**SPARTANBURG:** Tel: 864 699 1100 Fax: 864 699 1101

### TENNESSEE
**MEMPHIS:** Tel: 901 291 1500 Fax: 901 291 1501
**NASHVILLE:** Tel: 615 574 6700 Fax: 615 574 6701

### TEXAS
**DALLAS:** Tel: 214 256 4700 Fax: 214 256 4701

## OF COUNSEL AFFILIATE OFFICES

The firm also has Of Counsel Affiliate offices in Boston, MA; Akron/Cleveland, OH; and Houston, TX

## Clients:

The firm's clients, located throughout the US, include airlines, hospitals and other healthcare organizations, manufacturers, financial services firms, colleges and universities, print and broadcast media, government contractors, hotels and resorts, restaurants, local and state governments, automobile dealerships, retailers, transportation companies, and many other small, medium and large employers.

**FORDHARRISON** LLP
THE RIGHT RESPONSE AT THE RIGHT TIME

# KILPATRICK TOWNSEND & STOCKTON LLP

www.KilpatrickTownsend.com **tel:** 404 815 6500 **fax:** 404 815 6555

**Chair:** Paul M Aguggia
**Co-Managing Partners:** Maureen A Sheehy, J Henry Walker IV
Total number of lawyers: more than 620

## Firm Overview:

Kilpatrick Townsend & Stockton LLP is a multipractice, international law firm. Kilpatrick Townsend lawyers are experienced in a wide range of corporate, intellectual property and litigation services. For more information, please visit: www.kilpatricktownsend.com.

## Main Areas of Practice:

### Business & Finance:

The business and finance lawyers offer valuable counsel through a wide range of corporate business and financial services to clients at every end of the business spectrum, from Fortune 500 companies to promising start-ups. The firm's Financial Institutions Practice covers the legal, business and regulatory issues for financial institutions, including mergers and acquisitions, corporate, securities and regulatory matters, enforcement, financial products and services, capital markets, executive compensation and corporate governance. The firm's real estate lawyers represent large commercial developers, leading lenders, Fortune 500 corporations and the federal government in equity investment and capital formation vehicles, as well as acquisitions, development, financing (debt and equity), ownership, management, leasing, and dispositions of all types of commercial real estate. The firm's business and finance services include the following: bankruptcy and financial restructuring; contracts and commercial agreements; corporate governance, cross-border transactions; economic development; employee benefits, executive compensation and fiduciary counseling; franchising; green economy; investment management; joint ventures and strategic alliances; licensing and procurement; mergers and acquisitions; outsourcing; private equity; real estate finance and capital markets, including distressed debt and workouts, real estate capital markets, and real estate finance; real estate investment and development; securities; and tax.

### Construction & Infrastructure:

The Construction and Infrastructure Practice is an internationally recognized team of more than 35 professionals exclusively focused on construction law. The practice has assisted clients with construction matters in all US states and more than 25 countries, and regularly handles a variety of high profile, complex matters on global projects with scopes as substantial as $15 billion. Through the team's exclusive focus on construction-related issues, the lawyers have a vast amount of experience in virtually every type of construction project, including wastewater treatment plants, airports, tunnels, prisons, hospitals, office buildings, sports arenas, schools, hotels and resorts, power plants and industrial facilities.

### Government & Regulatory:

The Government and Regulatory Practice is a valuable resource for clients in need of lawyers experienced in legislative matters, lobbying and monitoring pending legislation and regulatory developments. Built around a core of accomplished lawyers as well as former lobbyists and government executives, this team represents clients before US federal agencies and Congress on a broad range of issues. The firm's government and regulatory services include the following: environmental and land use; financial institutions regulation; government contracting; government relations; and Native American affairs.

### Intellectual Property:

The Intellectual Property Practice is diverse with an outstanding record of helping clients grow and protect innovative businesses, products and brands. More than 135 of its patent lawyers and staff have advanced degrees in various scientific or engineering disciplines. The firm's Intellectual Property services include the following: advertising; appellate litigation; copyright; patent litigation; patent prosecution and counseling; patent reexamination and reissue; trademark, including anti-counterfeiting and gray market, international strategy, internet, portfolio strategy and management, and trademark and trade dress litigation; trade secret; and transactional intellectual property, including due diligence and licensing.

### Litigation:

The Litigation Practice includes more than 230 lawyers with the depth of knowledge and experience to effectively handle the most complex commercial case, and the flexibility to represent clients in the routine business disputes that require efficient resolution. The firm appears on behalf of clients in state and federal trial and appellate courts throughout the US, and before arbitration tribunals and mediators around the world. The firm's litigation services include the following: advertising litigation; alternative dispute resolution; antitrust and trade regulation; appellate and supreme court; catastrophic injury; class actions; complex business litigation; construction litigation; consumer product safety; directors and officers litigation; employment litigation; environmental litigation; insurance recovery; intellectual property litigation; Native American litigation; privacy and data security; product liability; securities litigation; subprime and credit markets litigation; tax controversy; and white-collar crime and special investigations.

### Labor & Employment:

The firm's labor and employment lawyers' mission is not only focused on defining and implementing global employment litigation strategies and employment counsel, but also to serve as a strategic partner to provide business direction on its clients' overall approach to human capital. The firm's lawyers have extensive experience in all aspects of the employer-employee relationship. The firm's labor and employment services include the following: employment counseling; employment litigation and class actions; international employment issues; labor relations and union avoidance; OSHA litigation; RIFS and severance plans; and wage and hour issues.

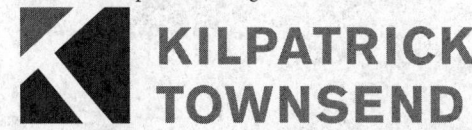

KILPATRICK TOWNSEND

# OGLETREE, DEAKINS, NASH, SMOAK & STEWART, P.C.

**www.**ogletreedeakins.com **tel:** 800 603 1252 **fax:** 404 870 1732

**Chairman:** Mr Kim F Ebert
Number of partners: 360
Number of lawyers: 675
Languages: *Creole, English, Filipino, French, German, Japanese, Mandarin Chinese, Romanian, Spanish*

## Firm Overview:

Ogletree Deakins is one of the largest labor and employment law firms representing management. The firm has a deep bench of more than 650 labor and employment lawyers located in 43 offices across the United States and in Europe. Ogletree Deakins has a well-developed footprint and is dedicated to providing professional, cost-effective services across the full spectrum of labor and employment law. The firm represents a diverse range of clients, from start-up companies to Fortune 50 corporations. Ogletree Deakins' primary focus is client service – a message that is emphasized in the firm's tagline: "Employers and Lawyers, Working Together." As this suggests, the firm is dedicated to partnering with in-house legal and human resources colleagues to deliver timely, client centered counsel and representation.

Ogletree Deakins prides itself on an outstanding staff of experienced legal professionals. The firm and attorneys consistently receive recognition from select organizations and publications. For example, Ogletree Deakins was named "Law Firm of the Year" in both the Litigation – Labor & Employment and the Employment Law – Management categories in the 2013 edition of U.S. News – Best Lawyers "Best Law Firms" rankings. The firm also has more than 160 attorneys who are listed in the 2013 edition of Best Lawyers in America and more than 70 attorneys are named "Leaders in their Field" in the 2012 edition of Chambers USA.

Ogletree Deakins has a long tradition of diversity among its lawyers and staff. The firm's commitment to diversity has been recognized by such organizations as the Minority Law Journal and MultiCultural Law magazine.

## Main Areas of Practice:

Ogletree Deakins works daily with employers in connection with their workplace needs. From traditional labor issues to employment litigation, from workplace safety to employee benefits, from wage and hour advice to class action defense, Ogletree Deakins has experienced professionals in all areas of labor and employment law who provide efficient, client-focused service.

## PRACTICE AREAS

Employment Law
Traditional Labor Relations
Employee Benefits
Class Action
Workplace Safety & Health
Unfair Competition & Trade Secrets
Affirmative Action Programs & OFCCP Compliance
Wage & Hour
Immigration
International
Litigation
Governmental Affairs
Ethics Compliance, Investigations & Whistleblower Response
Sports & Entertainment
Appellate
E-Discovery & Records Retention
Construction Law
Environmental Law

## OFFICES

Birmingham, AL; Phoenix, Tucson, AZ; Los Angeles, Orange County, San Diego, San Francisco, Torrance, CA; Denver, CO; Stamford, CT; Washington, DC; Miami, Tampa FL; Atlanta, GA; Berlin, Germany; Chicago, IL; Indianapolis, IN; New Orleans, LA; Boston MA; Detroit Metro, MI; Minneapolis, MN; Kansas City, St. Louis, MO; Jackson, MS; Charlotte, Raleigh, NC; Morristown, NJ; Las Vegas, NV; New York City, NY; Cleveland, OH; Portland, OR; Philadelphia, Pittsburgh, PA; Charleston, Columbia, Greenville, SC; Memphis, Nashville, TN; Austin, Dallas, Houston, San Antonio, TX; St. Thomas, USVI.

Email: clientservices@ogletreedeakins.com

# Ogletree Deakins

Employers & Lawyers, Working Together

# ROGERS & HARDIN LLP

www.rh-law.com  tel: 404 522 4700  fax: 404 525 2224

**Executive Committee:** Edward J Hardin, Dan F Laney, Phillip S McKinney, Brett A Rogers, David G Thunhorst
Number of partners: 24  Number of other lawyers: 19

**Firm Overview:**

Though smaller than many of its peers, Rogers & Hardin believes that it is generally considered one of Atlanta's 'major' law firms. An unwavering commitment to professional excellence has enabled the firm to maintain a level and quality of practice equal to that of much larger firms. Unlike the leveraged, team-staffing approach utilized by many large, institutional firms, Rogers & Hardin, with its more than one-to-one partner to associate ratio, emphasizes low-leverage, partner-centric staffing and the significant involvement of one or more senior lawyers having technical expertise and practical experience in the relevant subject matter, as well as overall responsibility for each representation. The firm believes that this service-delivery model improves the overall work product, ensures continuity of service and is highly cost-effective.

**Main Areas of Practice:**

**Antitrust:**
Extensive experience in antitrust matters, including general antitrust litigation, defense of class actions and representation in government investigations.
**Contact:** Kimberly L Myers  **Tel:** 404 420 4637
**Email:** kmyers@@rh-law.com

**Commercial Real Estate:**
Regularly represents financial institutions, developers, investors, owners and operators in transactions involving the acquisition, disposition, development, financing and leasing of, and investments in, real estate projects throughout the United States.
**Contact:** Miriam J Dent  **Tel:** 404 420 4608
**Email:** mdent@rh-law.com

**Complex Litigation:**
Vast experience in a variety of complex business litigation matters, resulting in a national reputation for effectively representing clients in high-stakes cases with complex factual and logistical problems, class actions, and matters involving injunctive or other extraordinary relief.
**Contact:** John J Almond  **Tel:** 404 420 4610
**Email:** jalmond@rh-law.com

**Corporate Governance:**
Actively engaged in counseling management and boards of directors and board committees with respect to fiduciary duty issues, day-to-day internal governance issues, best practices, shareholder relations, risk management, internal and external investigations, compliance with the full range of laws, rules and regulations related thereto.
**Contact:** Edward J Hardin  **Tel:** 404 420 4601
**Email:** jhardin@rh-law.com

**Employment Law:**
Nationally recognized practice involving a broad spectrum of claims, including discrimination, wrongful discharge, wage and hour, ERISA, noncompete/restrictive covenant, whistleblower claims and fraud, including class actions.
**Contact:** Hunter R Hughes  **Tel:** 404 420 4622
**Email:** hhughes@rh-law.com

**Finance:**
Advises clients in a wide variety of financing transactions, including revolving credit and term loan facilities, acquisition financing, highly leveraged and mezzanine financing, senior and subordinated debt instruments, real estate loans, asset-based financings, securitizations, lease financing and DIP and restructuring financing.
**Contact:** Carolyn B Dobbins  **Tel:** 404 420 4644
**Email:** cdobbins@rh-law.com

**Financial Services Litigation & Regulation:**
Exceptional depth and experience in defending broker-dealers, investment advisors, banks, hedge funds, managers, brokers and other securities professionals before FINRA and AAA and in connection with enforcement proceedings and investigations brought by the SEC, FDIC, the SROs and state securities commissions.
**Contact:** Jeffrey W Willis  **Tel:** 404 420 4619
**Email:** jwillis@rh-law.com

**Intellectual Property:**
Advises clients on the development, management and protection of IP portfolios both in business transactions and in litigation.
**Contact:** Phillip S McKinney  **Tel:** 404 420 4618
**Email:** pmckinney@rh-law.com

**Mergers & Acquisitions:**
Highly-regarded in the representation of acquirors and target companies, as well as special committees, financial advisors, investors and competing bidders, in many different industries in both negotiated and hostile transactions.
**Contact:** Steven E Fox  **Tel:** 404 420 4603
**Email:** sfox@rh-law.com

**Products Liability:**
Wide ranging expertise, including class action and mass tort experience with building materials and pharmaceuticals.
**Contact:** S Gardner Culpepper  **Tel:** 404 420 4623
**Email:** gculpepper@rh-law.com

**Securities Transactions:**
Routinely represents issuers and other market participants in private placements and public offerings of equity, investment and non-investment grade debt and "hybrid" securities, including both primary and secondary offerings, Rule 144A transactions and structured financings.
**Contact:** Robert C Hussle  **Tel:** 404 420 4633
**Email:** rhussle@rh-law.com

**Taxation:**
Integral to the firm's complex transactional practice, providing effective tax planning in support of all practice areas. The Tax Group has extensive experience in the structuring of LLC and corporate mergers and acquisitions, joint ventures, strategic alliances, real estate and workout transactions, and executive compensation packages, as well as tax controversies and international taxation.
**Contact:** David D Willoughby  Tel: 404 420 4634
**Email:** dwilloughby@rh-law.com

**International Work:**
Through its extensive network of worldwide affiliates, the firm has access to the expertise and market knowledge of lawyers around the globe.

**PRACTICE AREAS**

Antitrust
Corporate
Employment
Finance
Intellectual Property
Litigation
Products Liability
Real Estate
Taxation

**OFFICES**

GEORGIA
**ATLANTA:** 2700 International Tower, 229 Peachtree Street NE, GA 30303
Tel: 404 522 4700 Fax: 404 525 2224

ROGERS & HARDIN

# SMITH, CURRIE & HANCOCK LLP

www.smithcurrie.com  **tel:** 404 521 3800  **fax:** 404 688 0671

**Managing Partner:** Robert C Chambers
Number of attorneys: 53
Languages: *Croatian, English, French, Italian, Japanese, Korean, Serbian, Spanish*

**OFFICES**

GEORGIA

**ATLANTA:** 2700 Marquis One Tower, 245 Peachtree Center Avenue NE, GA 30303-1227
Tel: 404 521 3800  Fax: 404 688 0671

## Firm Overview:

Since the firm's founding in 1965, Smith, Currie & Hancock LLP has focused on delivering practical, business-oriented counsel to the construction industry. One of the first law firms to recognize the need for legal services for the construction industry, the firm provides comprehensive legal services in all aspects of construction law. The firm also has an extensive practice in government contracting, environmental law, and commercial litigation. As part of its government contracting practice, the firm handles matters relating to timber, concessionaire contracting, federal contracts for natural resources, access to federal lands, and compliance with federal environmental rules. The firm serves a growing base throughout the United States and internationally. In 2011 and 2012, prominent firms (Ernest C. Brown & Company and Saltman & Stevens, P.C.) merged with Smith, Currie & Hancock, expanding the firm's practice in California and Washington, DC. As leaders of construction industry organizations and frequent speakers at industry conferences and workshops, many of the firm's attorneys bring successful careers as government or private engineering and construction professionals to their law practice. The firm's books, Common Sense Construction Law (4th Edition) and Federal Government Construction Contracts (2nd Edition), are both widely used as textbooks in construction law courses and as practical, everyday reference materials by construction professionals. The firm has significant experience in resolving clients' disputes in all forms of Alternative Dispute Resolution (ADR) proceedings and decades of demonstrated litigation success.

## Main Areas of Practice:

### Construction:

The firm represents clients in litigation and other forms of dispute resolution and serves as counsel on front-end work and as advisors during the course of construction. Attorneys have extensive experience assisting clients at every stage and facet of a project, including: contract preparation and negotiation, labor and human resources issues, safety and health matters, project finance, insurance and bonding, contract administration, claims avoidance, and claims preparation, prosecution, and defense. Both domestically and internationally, the firm advises on a wide array of public and private projects such as energy, transportation and infrastructure, commercial, process and industrial, healthcare, and governmental works.

### Government Contracts:

Smith, Currie & Hancock has decades of experience navigating the complex regulations governing federal contracting. Attorneys regularly assist clients entering the federal market and advise experienced federal contractors. Attorneys advise clients on complex federal construction and compliance matters, including bid protests, ethics compliance, cost and pricing data, fraud and false claims, Buy American Act, Davis-Bacon Act, Miller Act bonds, subcontracting, and small business teaming arrangements. The firm has extensive experience handling disputes before the various boards and courts and defending clients against government investigations and claims. The firm's

attorneys have advised on projects ranging from civil works such as dams and levees to federal office buildings and courthouses, hospital projects, international projects, major research facilities, and military training, housing, and headquarters facilities.

### Environmental:

The firm's services range from assistance during the pre-acquisition phase of property transactions, to the prosecution or defense of environmental indemnification or cost recovery actions, to structuring effective responses to Superfund and other environmental enforcement actions. The firm regularly provides advice and assistance on environmental matters to public and private owners, manufacturers, transporters, and many other consulting, construction, and industrial concerns. Many environmental clients are actively involved in the environmental construction and environmental consulting fields and working on Superfund clean-ups, asbestos abatement projects, and numerous other remediation projects.

### Commercial Litigation:

In addition to its nationally recognized construction-related practices, the firm regularly represents clients in state and federal courts, as well as in arbitration and other forms of ADR throughout the country concerning commercial transactions and contract disputes. Issues such as non-compete agreements, resolution of disputes arising out of joint venture agreements, and defense of personal injury or wrongful death actions arising out of construction projects are examples of this litigation.

### International Work:

The firm represents clients on a regular basis on projects in Central and South America, the Caribbean, Europe, Asia, Australia, Africa and the Middle East. The firm has served as counsel in multiple arbitrations before various international arbitration tribunals. The firm is also called on frequently to advise on construction related matters globally.

### Clients:

Clients range from leading Engineering News Record's Top 400 Contractors, to small family-held general contractors, to large public and private owners. The firm also represents other clients involved in the construction industry including subcontractors, construction managers, architects, engineers, sureties, insurance companies, suppliers, construction trade associations, lending institutions, and real estate developers.

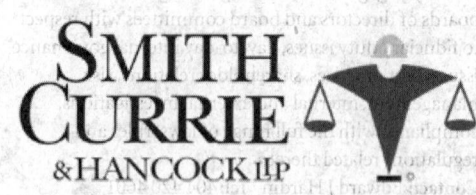

# SMITH, GAMBRELL & RUSSELL LLP

www.sgrlaw.com **tel:** 404 815 3500 **fax:** 404 815 3509

**Managing Partner:** Stephen M Forte

## Firm Overview:

Since its inception in 1893, the lawyers at Smith, Gambrell & Russell have pursued a vision of building one of the premier full-service business firms in the US. Today, the firm serves corporate counsel and executives across the globe with offices in Atlanta, GA, Jacksonville, FL, New York, NY, Washington, DC, and Frankfurt, Germany. SGR's attorneys offer clients guidance in specific areas of law and deliver specialized levels of legal service within those areas. A dedicated group of more than 180 attorneys and 150 support personnel serves the needs of clients with expert legal counsel, responsiveness, value, skill and professionalism.

## Main Areas of Practice:

General corporate, securities and taxation; general commercial and civil litigation; construction, public contracts, and suretyship law; commercial real estate; environmental; intellectual property; international.

### Aviation:

SGR has one of the longest standing aviation practices in the US and has been widely known for its aviation law expertise since the 1920s. The firm represented Eastern Airlines from its inception in 1927 to its merger with Texas Air Corporation in 1986. SGR now represents lessors, financiers, aircraft owners and other airlines in their domestic and international aircraft transactions, including direct purchases, sales and sale and leasebacks with various kinds of debt financing and leveraged and operating leases.
**Contact:** Howard E Turner

### Bankruptcy:

SGR's Bankruptcy Practice is one of the leading bankruptcy practices in the Southeastern US, having extensive experience in non-judicial financial reorganization and bankruptcy representation of creditor and equity committees, secured and unsecured creditors, equity security holders, indenture trustees, debtors and purchasers of insolvent companies.
**Contact:** Ronald E Barab

### Corporate:

The Corporate Practice of SGR assists clients in a variety of industries in all aspects of their business operations and commercial transactions, including mergers and acquisitions. Clients range from large publicly-held corporations to small closely held companies and include public companies, general and limited partnerships, joint ventures, limited liability companies and sole proprietorships.
**Contact:** Jonathan M Minnen

### Intellectual Property:

The firm's Intellectual Property Practice counsels clients on how to protect their intellectual property and on strategies to develop complete intellectual property portfolios. They advise on the patentability of inventions and the availability of trademarks and service marks, and prosecute applications for patent and applications to register trademarks, service marks and copyrights. The team also litigates intellectual property and unfair competition disputes and assists in the transfer, taxation and licensing of intellectual property and technology, including transfers in mergers and acquisitions.
**Contact:** Gregory J Kirsch

### International:

The firm has a large International Practice that assists foreign-based companies in establishing and maintaining operations in the US. The firm also provides counsel to domestic entities seeking to expand operations internationally.
**Contact:** Hans-Michael Kraus

### Litigation:

SGR's Litigation Practice is quite varied, and litigators handle cases ranging from bet-the-company matters in antitrust, securities and complex business disputes, including class action and major product liability cases, to litigation in specialized areas involving construction, real estate and disputes involving financial institutions and public companies. A significant number of cases are international in scope.
**Contact:** David C Newman

### Real Estate:

Serving clients in the real estate industry and also those engaged in real estate transactions incidental to other businesses, SGR's Real Estate Practice has a broad base of experience relating to acquisitions, development, financing, ownership, management, leasing and dispositions of various types of commercial real estate. Clients include commercial banks and other institutional lenders, investment banks and conduits, institutional investors, public and private companies, landlords and tenants and commercial developers.
**Contact:** Malcolm D Young, Jr

### Environmental:

Lawyers in SGR's Environmental Practice represent clients in connection with toxic tort litigation, environmental clean up litigation, enforcement actions, hazardous waste cleanups and landfill issues and regularly advise clients on environmental aspects of business and financial transactions, such as mergers and acquisitions and real estate transactions. This group also counsels clients on legal issues in a sustainability context offering an innovative, interdisciplinary approach to addressing a wide range of 'green' issues. Clients include manufacturers, oil companies, hazardous materials transporters, real estate developers, lenders, chemical companies, insurance companies, municipalities and numerous other types of businesses, individuals and institutions.
**Contact:** Stephen E O'Day

### Tax:

The firm's Tax Practice provides sophisticated federal, state and local tax planning and advice that minimizes taxes relating to increasingly complex tax laws and business transactions. SGR represents taxable corporations (both public and privately held) and pass-through entities such as S corporations, general and limited partnerships, limited liability companies and joint ventures.
**Contact:** Scott A Harty

### Clients:

Aircastle Limited; Blue Bird Body Co.; CIBA Vision Corporation; Gerdau Ameristeel, Inc.; Given Imaging; Hardin Construction Company; Innospec Inc.; KIA Motors Corporation; The Morgan Crucible Company; Novartis Corporation; The Quikrete Companies, Inc.; Republic National Distributing Company; The Roman Catholic Archdiocese of Atlanta; Southwest Airlines Co.; SunTrust Banks Inc.; Tokyo Electron Limited; Wells Fargo Bank, N.A.

## OFFICES

### ATLANTA

**GEORGIA:** Promenade, 1230 Peachtree Street, NE, Suite 3100, GA 30309
Tel: 404 815 3500   Fax: 404 815 3509

### DISTRICT OF COLUMBIA

**WASHINGTON DC:** 1055 Thomas Jefferson Street, NW, Suite 400, DC 20007
Tel: 202 403 2100   Fax: 202 263 4348

### FLORIDA

**JACKSONVILLE:** Bank of America Tower, 50 N Laura Street, Suite 2600, FL 32202
Tel: 904 598 6100   Fax: 904 597 6300

### NEW YORK

**NEW YORK:** 250 Park Avenue, Suite 1900, NY 10177
Tel: 212 907 9700   Fax: 212 907 9800

## INTERNATIONAL OFFICES

The firm has an office in Frankfurt, Germany.

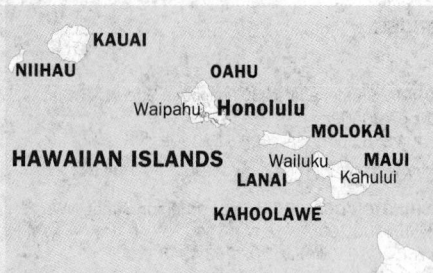

KAUAI

NIIHAU                    OAHU

Waipahu  **Honolulu**

MOLOKAI

**HAWAIIAN ISLANDS**    Wailuku   **MAUI**

LANAI   Kahului

KAHOOLAWE

*Pacific Ocean*    Hilo

HAWAII

## How lawyers are ranked

Every year we carry out thousands of in-depth interviews with clients in order to assess the reputations and expertise of business lawyers worldwide. The qualities we look for (and which determine rankings) include technical legal ability, professional conduct, client service, commercial awareness/astuteness, diligence, commitment, and other qualities most valued by the client. For details of our research team, see p.5.

# BANKRUPTCY/RESTRUCTURING

Commentary about individuals can be found under their firm's paragraph. If the firm has no paragraph (is not ranked) look at Other Notable Practitioners.

| Bankruptcy/Restructuring |
| --- |
| **Leading Firms** |

**Band 1**
Cades Schutte LLP
Case Lombardi & Pettit *
Klevansky Piper, LLP
Wagner Choi & Verbrugge

**Band 2**
Ashford & Wriston
Carlsmith Ball LLP *
Gelber, Gelber & Ingersoll, A Law Corporation
Goodsill Anderson Quinn & Stifel
Moseley Biehl Tsugawa Lau & Muzzi
O'Connor Playdon & Guben
Rush Moore LLP

| Leading Individuals |  |
| --- | --- |
| **Band 1** | |
| Choi Chuck C | *Wagner Choi & Verbrugge* |
| Dreher Nicholas C | *Cades Schutte LLP* |
| Gelber Don | *Gelber, Gelber & Ingersoll* |
| Guben Jerrold K | *O'Connor Playdon & Guben* |
| Klevansky Simon | *Klevansky Piper, LLP* * |
| Pettit Ted N | *Case Lombardi & Pettit* * |
| Roesser Tom E | *Carlsmith Ball LLP* * |
| Tius Susan | *Rush Moore LLP* |
| Wagner James A | *Wagner Choi & Verbrugge* |
| **Band 2** | |
| Davison Walter C | *Goodsill Anderson Quinn & Stifel* |
| Duca James N | *Lyons, Brandt, Cook & Hiramatsu (ONP)* † |
| Muzzi Christopher J | *Moseley Biehl Tsugawa Lau & Muzzi* |
| Piper Alika L | *Klevansky Piper, LLP* * |
| Shaw Cuyler | *Ashford & Wriston* |
| Young Theodore D C | *Cades Schutte LLP* |

*\* Indicates individual with profile.*
*† ONP = Other Notable Practitioner.*

## Band 1

### Cades Schutte LLP

**THE FIRM** The stellar team at Cades Schutte continues its highly impressive record in offering a wealth of services in all aspects of the bankruptcy and restructuring sector, ranging from foreclosure and enforcement of security interests, to the defense of lender liability claims.
**KEY INDIVIDUALS** An impressed peer said of **Nicholas Dreher**: *"I think the world of him. He's a super nice guy and very, very smart."* He specializes in bankruptcy and creditors' rights, workouts, and corporate finance. **Theodore Young** is *"very good at litigating and does a great job,"* say sources. He is best known for his expertise in representing banks and creditors.

### Case Lombardi & Pettit
See profile on p.1128

**THE FIRM** This impressive bankruptcy group is highlighted for its superb handling of creditor-side engagements in all manner of reorganization and liquidation matters. Recent highlights include representing Kahala Senior Living Community in a major bond refunding.
**KEY INDIVIDUALS Ted Pettit** (see p.1124) is praised for being *"practical, a hard worker and super smart."* He is a founding member of the Hawaii Bankruptcy Bar Association, and as such is regarded as one of the sector's foremost authorities.

### Klevansky Piper, LLP

**THE FIRM** This leading firm provides a wide range of services, and undertakes all aspects of workouts, corporate restructurings and creditor claims. Clients of the group include both Hawaii-based and international individuals and companies.
**KEY INDIVIDUALS Simon Klevansky** (see p.1123) is renowned as a *"very professional and excellent litigator,"* and is especially recommended for his work on large Chapter 7 cases. **Alika Piper** (see p.1124) has an excellent practice

encompassing a range of bankruptcy issues, including creditors' rights matters.

### Wagner Choi & Verbrugge

**THE FIRM** This group has extensive experience in a range of matters relating to corporate bankruptcy and insolvency. The group comes most recommended for its debtor-side practice, but it also acts for creditors and trustees.
**KEY INDIVIDUALS Chuck Choi's** excellent and wide-ranging practice encompasses creditor and debtor representations in all manner of workouts, bankruptcy and commercial disputes. He regularly undertakes work involving Chapter 7, 11 and 13 cases. **James Wagner's** practice includes undertaking foreclosures, reorganizations and workouts. He is also particularly well versed in Chapter 7 work.

## Band 2

### Ashford & Wriston

**THE FIRM** This well-regarded group advises a range of clients, including creditors, debtors and trustees, in a variety of Chapter 11 reorganizations and distressed transactions.
**KEY INDIVIDUALS Cuyler Shaw** has a broad practice which encompasses bankruptcy, healthcare and M&A work.

### Carlsmith Ball LLP
See profile on p.1127

**THE FIRM** This firm offers considerable expertise across the areas of creditors' rights, bankruptcy, restructurings, foreclosure, workouts and tax. The group recently acted on behalf of the Davidson Family Trust in a Chapter 11 reorganization of Waikiki Hotel.
**KEY INDIVIDUALS Tom Roesser** (see p.1124) is held in considerably high regard. *"He is excellent, and very well respected at the Bar,"* say sources. Others add that *"he is very knowledgeable and does a good job."*

## Gelber, Gelber & Ingersoll, A Law Corporation

**THE FIRM** This group continues to set an excellent standard in its representations of creditors, debtors, lenders, bondholders and trustees.

**KEY INDIVIDUALS Don Gelber** is president of the firm. He brings an extraordinary wealth of experience to the table, and is considered one of the sector's leading authorities.

## Goodsill Anderson Quinn & Stifel

**THE FIRM** This firm's bankruptcy and restructuring group undertakes a diverse cross section of work, including foreclosures, bankruptcy litigation and receiverships. Its high-profile client list includes the Bank of Hawaii and Deutsche Bank.

**KEY INDIVIDUALS Walter Davison** is the head of the firm's creditors' rights and bankruptcy practice group. He leads many of the group's most significant engagements,

and recently represented TGP CW in the $7 million foreclosure on certain real property.

## Moseley Biehl Tsugawa Lau & Muzzi

**THE FIRM** This firm has solid expertise in a wide array of creditor and debtor assignments, undertaking creditors' rights, foreclosures, workouts and distressed transactions.

**KEY INDIVIDUALS Christopher Muzzi** has a broad practice which includes bankruptcy litigation and creditor and debtor representations.

## O'Connor Playdon & Guben

**THE FIRM** This firm offers considerable expertise in all aspects of bankruptcy and corporate reorganizations to clients in the Hawaiian Islands and the Pacific region.

**KEY INDIVIDUALS Jerrold Guben** has a broad-ranging commercial litigation and general business practice, encompassing bankruptcy and reorganizations.

## Rush Moore LLP

**THE FIRM** This group has an excellent creditors' rights litigation practice, and also undertakes workouts and significant debtor cases. The firm has a diverse client base which includes major lenders and banks.

**KEY INDIVIDUALS Susan Tius** offers considerable expertise, particularly in bankruptcy and creditors' rights law and commercial collections. She represents secured creditors, lessors and purchasers.

## Other Notable Practitioners

The highly experienced **James Duca** is of counsel with Lyons, Brandt, Cook & Hiramatsu. He is considered one of the sector's most seasoned authorities.

# CORPORATE/COMMERCIAL

Finance p.1116; Tax p.1116
Commentary about individuals can be found under their firm's paragraph. If the firm has no paragraph (is not ranked) look at Other Notable Practitioners.

### Corporate/Commercial Leading Firms

**Band 1**
Cades Schutte LLP
Carlsmith Ball LLP *
Goodsill Anderson Quinn & Stifel

**Band 2**
Case Lombardi & Pettit *
Chun, Kerr, Dodd, Beaman & Wong
Chun Yoshimoto LLP
McCorriston Miller Mukai MacKinnon LLP
Starn O'Toole Marcus & Fisher *

### Corporate/Commercial Senior Statesmen

**Senior Statesmen: distinguished older practitioners**
Schull E Gunner      Cades Schutte LLP

### Leading Individuals

**Band 1**
| Kim Gregory R | Convergent Law Group LLP (ONP)[†] |
| Pressman Stewart | McCorriston Miller Mukai MacKinnon LLP |
| Reber David J | Goodsill Anderson Quinn & Stifel |

**Band 2**
| Cribley James M | Case Lombardi & Pettit * |
| Starn Peter | Starn O'Toole Marcus & Fisher * |
| Sumida Gerald | Carlsmith Ball LLP * |
| Tanaka Tod | Schneider Tanaka Radovich Andrew (ONP)[†] |

**Up-and-coming individuals**
| Clark Sean K | Goodsill Anderson Quinn & Stifel |

\* Indicates individual with profile.
[†]ONP = Other Notable Practitioner.

## Band 1

## Cades Schutte LLP

**THE FIRM** This leading full-service law firm has expertise in commercial and business disputes, antitrust, securities, corporate finance and M&A matters, among other types of work. Its clients include both Hawaiian-based and international companies and individuals.

**Sources say:** *"This firm understands and appreciates the business side of what we do and what we need to accomplish. The firm acts as a business partner as well as a legal counselor."*

**KEY INDIVIDUALS Vito Galati** has a practice encompassing tax compliance and real estate tax, particularly in relation to energy and housing credits-related matters. The *"very knowledgeable and reasonable"* **Cary Matsushige**'s practice includes finance and real estate development matters. **David Rair** has a practice representing major financial institutions, banks, mortgage lenders and insurance com-

panies, among other parties. **Bernice Littman** concentrates predominantly on real estate transactions, with an emphasis on condominium development, financing, purchases and sales, and conversion. **Gunner Schull** has extensive experience in general corporate and M&A law. Chair of the firm's tax department **Roger Epstein** has a diverse practice encompassing corporate tax law and planning, as well as international tax and international estate planning matters.

## Carlsmith Ball LLP

See profile on p.1127

**THE FIRM** This impressive firm offers a strong network of resources, backed by offices spanning Hawaii, Guam and Los Angeles. As such, the team is renowned for its ability to represent clients in a whole host of cross-border and international matters. The group handles work for a wide range of clients, and is especially recognized for its experience with healthcare, administrative agency and project finance matters involving the energy sector.

**Sources say:** *"This is an extremely reputable firm which has given us solid service. We highly recommend them."*

**KEY INDIVIDUALS Tom Roesser** (see p.1124) chairs the firm's bankruptcy practice and comes highly recommended as a go-to expert in distressed situations. He has been especially active of late in consumer credit-related matters. **David Wong** (see p.1125) has a sterling practice handling the tax aspects of complex commercial transactions. His expertise also covers M&A, workouts and wealth management. Sources praise his *"strong reputation and knowledge of attorneys and regulators."* **Lawrence Okinaga** (see p.1124) is a stalwart in representing major financial institutions. He is praised for being *"skilled in the subject matter."* Chair of the firm's corporate practice group **Gerald Sumida** (see p.1125) produces *"reliable, correct and fast work,"* and has *"very good personal relationships"* with his clients.

## Goodsill Anderson Quinn & Stifel

**THE FIRM** This leading firm offers an extensive range of services covering corporate, regulatory compliance, M&A, securities and bankruptcy issues.

**KEY INDIVIDUALS Lani Ewart** has a focus on financing, largely as it relates to real estate secured lending and general real estate matters, including acquisitions, leases and sales of commercial properties. **Miki Okumura** concentrates her practice on transactional work, including state tax and general business issues. **David Reber** engages in work involving M&A, securities and corporate finance. He also handles corporate governance-related assignments. **Randall Steverson** is an expert in real estate development and financing, including on behalf of financial institutions. **Sean Clark** has a broad-ranging corporate law prac-

tice, undertaking securities and M&A matters, among other types of issues.

## Band 2

### Case Lombardi & Pettit
See profile on p.1128

**THE FIRM** The excellent team at Case Lombardi has a wide-ranging practice encompassing M&A, bankruptcy, finance, tax and real estate. Its key clients include Kahala Senior Living Community, Hawaii BioEnergy and Niu Pia Land Company.

**Sources say:** *"The firm is very professional, and they have a genuine concern for their clients. They are very responsive."*

**KEY INDIVIDUALS James Cribley** (see p.1122) is *"tactful in his dealings with people and always well prepared,"* say sources. He recently represented Kahala Senior Living Community in a major advance bond refunding.

### Chun, Kerr, Dodd, Beaman & Wong

**THE FIRM** This firm handles an array of corporate and general business matters, including corporate governance, formations, compliance, M&A and tax.

**KEY INDIVIDUALS Ray Kamikawa**'s expertise encompasses a wide range of corporate, real estate and tax assignments.

### Chun Yoshimoto LLP

**THE FIRM** This firm has expertise in a broad range of finance and corporate matters, including corporate governance, M&A and tax work.

**KEY INDIVIDUALS Deborah Chun** has a broad practice area encompassing real estate and financing transactions. Sources *"would consider her one of the top attorneys in this sector."*

### McCorriston Miller Mukai MacKinnon LLP

**THE FIRM** In addition to its strength in corporate and commercial matters, this firm has an excellent reputation for undertaking complex commercial litigation and real estate work.

**KEY INDIVIDUALS** The *"very good and capable"* **Stewart Pressman** has a practice covering corporate law, M&A transactions and securities matters.

### Starn O'Toole Marcus & Fisher
See profile on p.1130

**THE FIRM** This Honolulu-based firm is well known for its commercial litigation skills, as well as for its expertise with corporate and real estate issues. Its key clients include CB Richard Ellis Hawaii, Coral Wireless and Hilton Hotels.

**Sources say:** *"An excellent firm. Excellent service and very responsive, with well-trained junior associates. They provide sound commercial advice."*

**KEY INDIVIDUALS** The tremendously experienced **Peter Starn** (see p.1125) has a diverse range of expertise encompassing corporate finance, M&A, real estate and litigation. Among his major engagements is his continued role on behalf of Coral Wireless in the creation of its Oahu cell phone network, and in the development of similar networks on neighboring islands.

### Other Notable Practitioners

**Stephen Gelber** of Gelber, Gelber & Ingersoll, A Law Corporation has a practice covering corporate reorganizations and bankruptcies, as well as tax and litigation. **Ron Heller** of Torkildson, Katz, Moore, Hetherington & Harris is an expert in tax issues and related litigation. **Gregory Kim** of Convergent Law Group LLP is *"a smart guy and a good lawyer,"* according to sources. He has a diverse practice encompassing M&A, securities and corporate matters. **Robert Schneider** of Schneider Tanaka Radovich Andrew & Tanaka, LLLC wins significant recognition from peers. He is an expert in a range of M&A, joint venture and financing matters, among other types of issues. **Jeffrey Scott Piper** of Schlack Ito Lockwood Piper & Elkind, LLLC is best known for his corporate and tax law expertise, particularly as it relates to acting for tax-exempt entities. **Steven Rinesmith** of Rinesmith & Sekiguchi handles tax and business matters. **Ronald Sakamoto** of Char Sakamoto Ishii Lum & Ching has a wealth of experience in taxation, business and corporate matters, as well as M&A engagements. The hugely experienced **Tod Tanaka** of Schneider Tanaka Radovich Andrew & Tanaka, LLLC is described by peers as *"a good transactional lawyer; very practical and hard-working."* **John Aube** heads the banking and real estate group at Watanabe Ing LLP. Peers particularly highlight his extensive experience in financing, real estate and lending work.

# LABOR & EMPLOYMENT

Commentary about individuals can be found under their firm's paragraph. If the firm has no paragraph (is not ranked) look at Other Notable Practitioners.

## Band 1

### Marr Jones & Wang LLLP
See profile on p.1129

**THE FIRM** This leading firm is devoted exclusively to the representation of management in labor and employment law matters, including in labor disputes and employment litigation. In recent highlights, the group acted for Turtle Bay Resort in negotiating a new five-year collective bargaining agreement. Its prestigious client list also includes Hilton Hotels, United Airlines and Safeway.

**Sources say:** "*It is not just the lawyers that are professional, but the support staff are too. They are always courteous, respectful and quick in replying.*"

**KEY INDIVIDUALS Patrick Jones** (see p.1123) has a broad practice in employment-related matters, including defending clients against harassment, wrongful termination and discrimination cases. The tremendously experienced **Barry Marr** (see p.1123) does "*a great job in handling all the complexities,*" say sources; "*he is technically sharp, knows the law and knows employment, but Barry's gift is that he knows how to handle contentious situations with a very nonconfrontational style.*" **Richard Rand** (see p.1124) offers an extensive wealth of experience in labor and employment matters in a wide range of federal and state legal issues, ranging from employment claims to Davis-Bacon Act compliance. **Sarah Wang** (see p.1125) has a strong practice involving the representation of management in labor and employment matters, including in wrongful termination, breach of contract and harassment cases. **Christopher Yeh** (see p.1125) has a practice which includes representing employers in proceedings before private arbitrators as well as the state and federal courts in Hawaii. He is also noted for his expertise in collective bargaining agreements and grievance resolution.

### Torkildson, Katz, Moore, Hetherington & Harris

**THE FIRM** This impressive firm works with large and small US and international employers operating in Hawaii. Its labor and employment group offers extensive advice on matters, including labor practice charges and collective bargaining agreements.

**KEY INDIVIDUALS** The "*excellent*" **Robert Katz** is an expert in a whole host of antitrust, employment and labor, and healthcare transactions, as well as litigation. He works with Hawaii, mainland and international clients in both the private and public sectors, and is especially highlighted for his tax expertise. **John Knorek** has a practice providing advice and representation to large and small employers in all aspects of employment and wrongful discharge law. He also undertakes mediation and arbitration work. **Ernest Moore** is experienced in representing management in matters ranging from alternative dispute resolution to avoiding discrimination and harassment claims.

## Band 2

### Alston Hunt Floyd & Ing Attorneys At Law, A Law Corporation
See profile on p.1126

**THE FIRM** This group provides a comprehensive labor and employment service covering employee benefits, wrongful termination, equal employment opportunities, labor law and wage and hour law matters, among other types of issue. It is also well known for its litigation capabilities. Key clients include DFS Group, Hawaiian Airlines and Louis Vuitton.

**KEY INDIVIDUALS Anna Elento-Sneed** (see p.1122) is described by one particularly impressed client as "*one of the most technically capable labor attorneys in Hawaii.*" While maintaining an excellent and broad-ranging labor and employment practice, she is particularly active in offering strategic planning advice to her clients. **Terry Thomason** (see p.1125) is well known especially for his focus on the labor and employment aspects of government contracts and procurement, and undertakes related wage and hour, EEOC and employee rights issues.

### Cades Schutte LLP

**THE FIRM** The full-service Cades Schutte's highly-respected labor and employment practice group handles an array of issues, including workers' compensation, workplace safety, employee privacy issues, labor relations and business immigration matters.

**Sources say:** "*A superb firm.*"

**KEY INDIVIDUALS** Of counsel **Roger Fonseca** is one of Hawaii's most experienced employee benefits practitioners. Peers commended his all-encompassing benefits knowledge, which includes related tax issues. **Ellen Kawashima** chairs the firm's employee benefits and executive compensation practice. Her extensive expertise covers retirement plans, employee benefits, deferred compensation arrangements, executive compensation and corporate law. **David Banks** leads the firm's corporate team, as well as its employment law and labor relations group. He offers deep experience in preventive counseling, strategic planning, legal compliance and labor and employment issues in M&A transactions.

### Carlsmith Ball LLP
See profile on p.1127

**THE FIRM** Carlsmith Ball's six-partner team has a sterling practice handling wrongful termination and civil rights, wage and hour law, government contracting, and the labor and employment issues relating to business transactions. It also manages an excellent employee benefits and executive compensation workload, and is proficient in ERISA matters. Its key clients include Hawaiian Telcom, Japan Airlines and Bank of Hawaii.

**Sources say:** "*Carlsmith provided excellent client services.*"

KEY INDIVIDUALS **John Khil** (see p.1123) is chair of the firm's tax, estate planning and wealth management practice group. He has an excellent employee benefits and executive compensation practice, and undertakes a variety of profit sharing, tax and pension issues. **James Starshak** (see p.1125) has a broad practice incorporating tax, trusts and estate planning. He is particularly specialized in work pertaining to the formation of qualified pension planning.

## D'Amato & Maloney LLP

THE FIRM This boutique firm specializes in benefits work, and provides ongoing advice to plan fiduciaries on complying with ERISA, the Internal Revenue Code and preparing welfare benefit plans.

KEY INDIVIDUALS **John D'Amato** is best recognized for providing advice on the design and implementation of welfare benefit plans, both qualified and nonqualified pension plans and 401(k) plans. **John Maloney** is an expert in a range of ERISA, executive compensation, benefits and transactional matters. He also represents fiduciaries in benefit claims and ERISA litigation.

## Goodsill Anderson Quinn & Stifel

THE FIRM This full-service firm's solid labor and employment group undertakes a broad-ranging workload representing management, including in wrongful termination, discrimination and harassment cases. Its clients range from individuals to local, national and multinational corporations.

KEY INDIVIDUALS **Barbara Petrus** advises and defends employers across a range of issues, including labor grievances, litigation, unfair labor practices and collective bargaining. Her clients include a variety of Hawaiian-based and international corporations. **Carolyn Wong** undertakes employment discrimination, wrongful termination and unfair labor practice matters, among other areas.

## Band 3

### Kobayashi, Sugita & Goda

THE FIRM This group is respected for its diverse practice handling all manner of grievance, collective bargaining, unfair labor and litigation issue, among other types of work. The team is also highlighted for its expertise with labor and employment matters associated with business transactions.

KEY INDIVIDUALS Peers recommend **Gregory Sato** as "a good lawyer and a good person." A seasoned authority in the sector, he has broad-ranging labor and employment expertise and experience.

## Watanabe Ing LLP

THE FIRM This group focuses predominantly on advising both large and small companies on issues ranging from sexual harassment to wage and hour issues. It also has expertise in unionizing issues and employee benefits.

KEY INDIVIDUALS **Ronald Leong** is the head of the firm's labor, employment and employee benefits group. He has a practice encompassing management labor and general corporate law.

## Other Notable Practitioners

**Perry Confalone** recently left Carlsmith Ball to establish Perry Confalone LLLC. He receives excellent feedback from clients, who value his "good service and legal analysis of issues." He has extensive experience in representing employers in litigation and arbitration proceedings. **Gregory Hansen** (see p.1123) of Case Lombardi & Pettit specializes in the areas of employee benefits, equity incentive plans and employee stock ownership. **Wesley Fujimoto** of Ashford & Wriston has a practice encompassing employment discrimination and harassment, wrongful discharge, wage and hour, and occupational health and safety matters.

# LITIGATION GENERAL COMMERCIAL

Commentary about individuals can be found under their firm's paragraph. If the firm has no paragraph (is not ranked) look at Other Notable Practitioners.

| Litigation: General Commercial Leading Firms |
| --- |
| **Band 1** |
| Alston Hunt Floyd & Ing Attorneys At Law, A Law Corporation * |
| Cades Schutte LLP |
| McCorriston Miller Mukai MacKinnon LLP |
| Starn O'Toole Marcus & Fisher * |
| **Band 2** |
| Bays Lung Rose & Holma |
| Carlsmith Ball LLP * |
| Case Lombardi & Pettit * |
| Goodsill Anderson Quinn & Stifel |
| * Indicates firm with profile. |
| Alphabetical order within each band. Band 1 is the highest. |

## Band 1

### Alston Hunt Floyd & Ing Attorneys At Law, A Law Corporation
See profile on p.1126

THE FIRM This impressive firm has a leading name in complex commercial litigation, real estate litigation, and healthcare and medical malpractice defense. Clients include Marriott Hotels, Bank of Hawaii and Expedia.

Sources say: "This is a well-rounded firm that attracts some of the best attorneys in the State of Hawaii." "The firm has

practice areas that meet all of our needs and we greatly value this. There is good interaction. The paralegals and other staff who interact with us are extremely competent and hardworking."

KEY INDIVIDUALS Clients praise **Paul Alston** (see p.1122) for his "sound business judgment and excellent communication skills." His practice includes large damage claims, commercial litigation, class actions and appellate law. Sources praise **William Hunt** (see p.1123) for "strong knowledge" in the areas of medical malpractice and multi-million-dollar catastrophic injury claims. Of counsel **Sheryl Nicholson** (see p.1124) represents a range of clients, including large hotel owners and developers, in some of the largest and most complex cases litigated in Hawaii. **Ellen Godbey Carson** (see p.1122) is lauded for her "superior analytical ability and practical problem-solving skills." She focuses on representing healthcare providers, healthcare plans and hospitals. **David Nakashima** (see p.1124) is described as "an experienced attorney who is well respected by his peers in the legal industry. He is a negotiator with excellent people skills." **Kenneth Robbins** (see p.1124) is described by peers as "a real talent," particularly in relation to medical malpractice defense.

## Cades Schutte LLP

THE FIRM This leading full-service law firm offers a wealth of experience in matters ranging from antitrust to mediations and arbitrations. The commercial team undertakes litigation in both federal and state courts, and works closely with experts in relevant disciplines.

KEY INDIVIDUALS **Jeffrey Portnoy** "is certainly a talent," say sources. His wide-ranging litigation expertise covers insurance, employment and mass tort-related disputes, among other types of case. **Michael Heihre** is chair of the firm's commercial and real estate litigation and alternative dispute resolution practice group. He is an expert in complex business, construction and contract disputes.

## McCorriston Miller Mukai MacKinnon LLP

THE FIRM This impressive firm undertakes complex commercial litigation, aided by its skill set and resources in e-discovery technology. The team also handles insurance, healthcare and M&A-related disputes, and are adept at carrying out alternative dispute resolution.

Sources say: "Good litigation team."

KEY INDIVIDUALS **William McCorriston** has a diverse practice which includes complex and multidistrict litigation, commercial litigation, professional malpractice, white-collar defense and civil rights matters. The "very capable" **David Minkin** is experienced in a range of civil

## Litigation: General Commercial

### Senior Statesmen

| Senior Statesmen: | distinguished older practitioners |
|---|---|
| Kobayashi Jr Bert T | Kobayashi, Sugita & Goda (ONP)† |

### Leading Individuals

**Star individuals**

| Alston Paul | Alston Hunt Floyd & Ing Attorneys At Law * |
|---|---|
| McCorriston William C | McCorriston Miller Mukai MacKinnon LLP |
| O'Toole Terence J | Starn O'Toole Marcus & Fisher * |

**Band 1**

| Bennett Mark J | Starn O'Toole Marcus & Fisher * |
|---|---|
| Heihre Michael C | Cades Schutte LLP |
| Portnoy Jeffrey | Cades Schutte LLP |

**Band 2**

| Bickerton James J | Bickerton Lee Dang & Sullivan (ONP)† |
|---|---|
| Chang Corlis J | Goodsill Anderson Quinn & Stifel |
| Hunt William S | Alston Hunt Floyd & Ing Attorneys At Law * |
| Lacy John R | Goodsill Anderson Quinn & Stifel |
| Marsh Michael R | Case Lombardi & Pettit * |
| Nishimoto John S | Ayabe, Chong, Nishimoto, Sia (ONP)† |
| Pavey Judith | Starn O'Toole Marcus & Fisher * |
| Price III Warren | Price Okamoto Himeno & Lum (ONP)† |
| Purpura Michael M | Carlsmith Ball LLP * |
| Robbins Kenneth S | Alston Hunt Floyd & Ing Attorneys At Law * |
| Rose Crystal K | Bays Lung Rose & Holma |
| Saffery Edmund K | Goodsill Anderson Quinn & Stifel |
| Zalewski John D | Case Lombardi & Pettit * |

**Band 3**

| Ayabe Sidney K | Ayabe, Chong, Nishimoto, Sia (ONP)† |
|---|---|
| Carson Ellen Godbey | Alston Hunt Floyd & Ing Attorneys At Law * |
| Grimmer Gary | Gary G. Grimmer & Associates (ONP)† |
| Lung Harvey J | Bays Lung Rose & Holma |
| Manaut Pete | Carlsmith Ball LLP * |
| Minkin David J | McCorriston Miller Mukai MacKinnon LLP |
| Munger Lisa Woods | Goodsill Anderson Quinn & Stifel |
| Nakashima David A | Alston Hunt Floyd & Ing Attorneys At Law * |
| Nicholson Sheryl | Alston Hunt Floyd & Ing Attorneys At Law * |
| Park Corey | Law Offices of Corey Y. S. Park (ONP)† |

* Indicates individual with profile.

†ONP = Other Notable Practitioner.

litigation types, including in trial and appellate courts, as well as in arbitration and mediation proceedings.

### Starn O'Toole Marcus & Fisher

See profile on p.1130

**THE FIRM** This prominent group has extensive experience in complex commercial litigation. The team undertakes work in Hawaii, the mainland USA and internationally. In recent highlights, the firm is representing Kalo Student Suites in a dispute over the development and operation of a condominium complex. Other key clients include Bank of Hawaii, Hilton Worldwide and Safeway Stores. **Sources say:** *"A very talented group."*
**KEY INDIVIDUALS** *"Accomplished litigator"* **Terence O'Toole** (see p.1124) is a renowned expert in complex commercial, real estate, wrongful death and personal

injury disputes. Clients commend the *"very capable"* **Mark Bennett** (see p.1122) as a *"a superior trial lawyer."* His practice encompasses commercial, appellate and antitrust cases, as well as government relations. **Judith Pavey** (see p.1124) handles commercial litigation, personal injury, professional negligence and medical malpractice work, among other types of dispute. Sources recommend her as *"a very skilled trial lawyer."*

## Band 2

### Bays Lung Rose & Holma

**THE FIRM** Primarily featuring a strong bench of real estate litigators, this excellent team of attorneys both prosecutes and defends a wide selection of commercial disputes, ranging from commercial real estate litigation to construction litigation. Its client base includes Hawaii-based companies, as well as those in the mainland USA and Japan.
**KEY INDIVIDUALS Crystal Rose** *"is a terrific lawyer,"* remark sources. She undertakes work pertaining to real estate, construction, trusts and commercial litigation. Maintaining his *"good reputation,"* **Harvey Lung** concentrates on construction law, with a particular emphasis on construction contract disputes.

### Carlsmith Ball LLP

See profile on p.1127

**THE FIRM** This group recently represented Pyramid Project Management in its renovation/expansion project for the Grand Wailea Resort and Spa on Maui. This firm engages in litigating, arbitration and mediating disputes pertaining to land use, construction, employment and general commercial matters.
**KEY INDIVIDUALS Michael Purpura** (see p.1124) has a focus on white-collar criminal defense, complex civil litigation and appellate litigation. **Pete Manaut** (see p.1123) *"consistently gets great results – such a pleasure to work with,"* attest sources. They add that he will assist with *"anything we need help on though he is busy."*

### Case Lombardi & Pettit

See profile on p.1128

**THE FIRM** The attorneys within this group represent local, national and international clients before all of the federal and state courts of Hawaii. The team specializes in general commercial litigation matters. In recent highlights, the group defended Ameron International on a claim for additional costs incurred in the construction of a bridge.
**KEY INDIVIDUALS** The *"very talented"* **Michael Marsh** (see p.1123) focuses on dispute resolution and litigation involving construction, development and real estate matters. He led in the aforementioned Ameron case. The *"very pleasant"* **John Zalewski** (see p.1125) handles a range of commercial litigation, including insurance, defense and professional liability cases.

### Goodsill Anderson Quinn & Stifel

**THE FIRM** This firm has a wealth of experience in handling consumer, commercial, business and tort disputes in federal and state courts. The group also offers excellent alternative dispute resolution capabilities. Clients include domestic and foreign entities of all sizes, based both in Hawaii and internationally.
**Sources say:** *"Efficient legal skills."*
**KEY INDIVIDUALS Corlis Chang** focuses on personal injury, product liability, municipal law, malpractice, construction and insurance matters. She has also been particularly active of late in matters involving assisted care homes. Clients praise **John Lacy's** *"excellent knowledge of maritime matters and litigation practices. He has an efficient delivery of services."* He also undertakes an array of civil trial work, including insurance, aviation, IP and malpractice disputes. **Edmund Saffery** is best known for his superb skills in insurance coverage and defense work. He also undertakes a range of other matters, including First Amendment-related and professional malpractice disputes. **Lisa Woods Munger** is *"a very effective and very knowledgeable litigator,"* say sources. She has a broad practice, and is especially recommended for her expertise in environmental law disputes.

### Other Notable Practitioners

**James Bickerton** of Bickerton Lee Dang & Sullivan represents plaintiff and defendant clients in a number of matters, including in commercial and real estate litigation, professional liability of attorneys, and serious personal injury. **Gary Grimmer** of Gary G. Grimmer & Associates has an excellent civil litigation practice. He undertakes a wide range of commercial matters, including torts, real estate and banking finance, and alternative dispute resolution. The *"talented and smart"* **Corey Park** of the Law Offices of Corey Y. S. Park is an expert in business, industrial development and real estate law, as well as in alternative dispute resolution. **Warren Price** of Price Okamoto Himeno & Lum has an *"excellent"* practice encompassing complex and multidistrict litigation, bad faith law and medical malpractice matters. The *"very talented"* **John Nishimoto** of Ayabe, Chong, Nishimoto, Sia & Nakamura comes highly recommended for his work involving insurance and medical malpractice defense. **Sidney Ayabe** of Ayabe, Chong, Nishimoto, Sia & Nakamura undertakes matters encompassing personal injury litigation, real estate and product liability. **Bert Kobayashi** of Kobayashi, Sugita & Goda is a *"well-known and very capable attorney."* His expertise extends to include commercial and construction litigation.

# REAL ESTATE

Commentary about individuals can be found under their firm's paragraph. If the firm has no paragraph (is not ranked) look at Other Notable Practitioners.

## Real Estate
### Leading Firms

**Band 1**
Cades Schutte LLP
Carlsmith Ball LLP *
Goodsill Anderson Quinn & Stifel

**Band 2**
Ashford & Wriston
Belles Graham Proudfoot Wilson & Chun
Case Lombardi & Pettit *
Chun, Kerr, Dodd, Beaman & Wong
Chun Yoshimoto LLP
Mancini Welch & Geiger LLP
McCorriston Miller Mukai MacKinnon LLP
Tom Quitiquit Chee & Watts, LLP
Schlack Ito Lockwood Piper & Elkind, LLLC
Schneider Tanaka Radovich Andrew & Tanaka, LLLC
Starn O'Toole Marcus & Fisher *
Watanabe Ing LLP

## Real Estate: Zoning/Land Use
### Leading Individuals

**Band 1**

| | | |
|---|---|---|
| Belles Michael J | Belles Graham Proudfoot Wilson & Chun |
| Graham Max | Belles Graham Proudfoot Wilson & Chun |
| Ing J Douglas | Watanabe Ing LLP |
| Kudo Benjamin | Ashford & Wriston |
| Mancini Paul | Mancini Welch & Geiger LLP |
| Slovin Gary M | Ashford & Wriston |

## Real Estate: Environment
### Leading Individuals

**Band 1**

| | | |
|---|---|---|
| McHenry Patricia J | Cades Schutte LLP |
| Munger Lisa Woods | Goodsill Anderson Quinn & Stifel |

**Band 2**

| | | |
|---|---|---|
| Bail Lisa A | Goodsill Anderson Quinn & Stifel |
| Sandison Ian Lorne | Carlsmith Ball LLP * |

*\* Indicates firm / individual with profile.*
*† ONP = Other Notable Practitioner.*

## Band 1

### Cades Schutte LLP

**THE FIRM** This leading real estate group offers expertise across all aspects of real estate matters, including acquisitions, development and construction, ground leases and condominium projects. It also undertakes matters involving major hotels and resorts.

**KEY INDIVIDUALS Gino Gabrio** has a broad practice encompassing real estate transactions, commercial leasing and development financing. He regularly serves clients based on the mainland, in the Far East and in Hawaii.

## Real Estate
### Senior Statesmen

**Senior Statesmen: distinguished older practitioners**

| | |
|---|---|
| Chun Ed | Chun, Kerr, Dodd, Beaman & Wong |

### Leading Individuals

**Star individuals**

| | |
|---|---|
| Chun Deborah | Chun Yoshimoto LLP |

**Band 1**

| | |
|---|---|
| Belles Michael J | Belles Graham Proudfoot Wilson & Chun |
| Chang Wesley Y S | Law Offices of Wesley Y S Chang (ONP)† |
| Ewart Lani | Goodsill Anderson Quinn & Stifel |
| Foy Stacey W E | Case Lombardi & Pettit * |
| Gabrio Gino L | Cades Schutte LLP |
| Graham Bruce | Ashford & Wriston |
| Iwamoto Raymond S | Schlack Ito Lockwood Piper & Elkind, LLLC |
| James Eric A | Carlsmith Ball LLP * |
| Kiefer Richard | Kiefer Merchant Garneau LLC (ONP)† |
| Lombardi Dennis M | Case Lombardi & Pettit * |
| MacKinnon D Scott | McCorriston Miller Mukai MacKinnon LLP |
| Mancini Paul | Mancini Welch & Geiger LLP |
| Marcus Kenneth B | Starn O'Toole Marcus & Fisher * |
| Miller Clifford J | McCorriston Miller Mukai MacKinnon LLP |
| Pear Charles | McCorriston Miller Mukai MacKinnon LLP |
| Radovich Scott D | Schneider Tanaka Radovich Andrew |
| Schlack Carl J | Schlack Ito Lockwood Piper & Elkind, LLLC |
| Schneider Robert F | Schneider Tanaka Radovich Andrew |
| Steverson Randall | Goodsill Anderson Quinn & Stifel |
| Welch Thomas | Mancini Welch & Geiger LLP |
| Wong Danton S | Chun, Kerr, Dodd, Beaman & Wong |
| Yuen Leighton | Goodsill Anderson Quinn & Stifel |

**Band 2**

| | |
|---|---|
| Aube John R | Watanabe Ing LLP |
| Ayabe Gail O | Goodsill Anderson Quinn & Stifel |
| Devlin Patricia | Carlsmith Ball LLP * |
| Fisher Duane | Starn O'Toole Marcus & Fisher * |
| Ito Mark | Schlack Ito Lockwood Piper & Elkind, LLLC |
| Littman Bernice | Cades Schutte LLP |
| Quitiquit Bud | Tom Quitiquit Chee & Watts, LLP |
| Shibata David | Rush Moore LLP (ONP)† |
| Starn Peter | Starn O'Toole Marcus & Fisher * |
| Strand Robert | Carlsmith Ball LLP * |
| Tanaka Tod | Schneider Tanaka Radovich Andrew |
| Tom Carl | Tom Quitiquit Chee & Watts, LLP |
| Yoshimoto Janel | Chun Yoshimoto LLP |
| Youngren Nancy | Case Lombardi & Pettit * |

**Up-and-coming individuals**

| | |
|---|---|
| Benck Jennifer | Carlsmith Ball LLP * |
| Bunn Andrew | Chun, Kerr, Dodd, Beaman & Wong |

**Patricia McHenry** works predominantly in environmental and employment law, especially in connection with the OSHA. Clients commend her for the *"marvelous job"* she does. **Bernice Littman** is highlighted in particular for her

expertise in condominium development, financing and real estate transactions. She also regularly delivers seminars on legal subjects ranging from financing to disability laws.

### Carlsmith Ball LLP
**See profile on p.1127**
**THE FIRM** This impressive firm has a leading group in resort, commercial, retail, residential and government projects, among other areas. In recent highlights, the team represented Forest City Hawaii in relation to its Kamakana Villages at Keahuolu project, a mixed-use affordable housing development.

**KEY INDIVIDUALS Eric James** (see p.1123) is *"well regarded for development work,"* and is described by peers as a *"very skilled and knowledgeable lawyer."* He has expertise across a broad range of acquisition, development and sales, as well as in environmental matters. **Patricia Devlin** (see p.1122) undertakes commercial real estate with an emphasis on finance and development. She regularly handles the structuring and documentation of real property transactions, as well as acquisitions and commercial leases. **Ian Sandison** (see p.1124) is lauded for his expertise in environmental law, as well as for his work pertaining to the investigation and cleanup of contaminated real property and lender liability for environmental contamination. **Robert Strand** (see p.1125) is an expert in commercial leasing and complex real estate transactions. His recent highlights include acting for the Ala Moana Shopping Center, the largest open-air shopping center in the world, in commercial lease negotiations. **Jennifer Benck** (see p.1122) is praised by peers for her *"great work ethic, and great inquisitive mind."* She is recognized as an attorney who *"gives good advice."*

### Goodsill Anderson Quinn & Stifel

**THE FIRM** This full-service firm is a leading player in the Hawaii real estate sector. The team works alongside its corporate, taxation and environmental experts in order to take a practical and solution-oriented approach to development, financing, leasing, land title and transactional matters.

**Sources say:** *"They have an excellent real estate and finance department."*

**KEY INDIVIDUALS Lani Ewart** is widely recognized for the financing work she undertakes for both lenders and borrowers. Her practice incorporates credit facilities, loan workouts and leased fee matters. **Lisa Woods Munger** has a broad practice covering a diverse array of sectors, including environmental, antitrust and land use matters. She also represents clients in relation to endangered species and habitat conversion plans. **Leighton Yuen** focuses on real estate development and business law. His real estate practice comprises both commercial, resort and residential transactions, and he also engages in financing arrangements and commercial leasing. **Gail Ayabe** similarly has an impressive practice handling real estate and general business law. She regularly undertakes work pertaining to commercial and industrial developments, affordable housing projects and resort and residential developments. **Lisa Bail** is an expert in a host of environmental, product liability and land use matters. She is especially highlighted for her capabilities in defending litigation involving trail and access issues and right of way issues. **Randall Steverson** has a broad practice which include real estate, development and financing work. He is particularly experienced in representing landlords in leasing transactions and condominium issues.

## Band 2

### Ashford & Wriston

**THE FIRM** This firm represents landowners and developers in a range of matters, including in the development of condominiums, resorts and shopping centers. The real estate group also engages in large mixed-use projects and regularly handles general commercial litigation, arbitration and mediation.

**KEY INDIVIDUALS Bruce Graham** is praised by his peers as a *"very knowledgeable"* attorney. He has a wide-ranging practice handling trust, commercial leasing and land title matters, among other engagements. **Benjamin Kudo** has a practice encompassing land use, zoning and real estate development. He assists developers and landowners with resort, commercial, industrial and residential development throughout Hawaii. **Gary Slovin** is highlighted in particular for his expertise in government affairs. He represents clients before the Hawaii State Legislature and the Honolulu City Council as well as state and county agencies.

### Belles Graham Proudfoot Wilson & Chun

**THE FIRM** This group has an extensive practice in matters ranging from commercial property sales transactions to condominium law. The team handles all stages of the buying and selling real estate process including negotiating real estate agreements, handling land use, zoning and permitting matters. The Kaua'i-based team provides high-quality legal advice on the island, and is especially respected for its entitlement practice.

**KEY INDIVIDUALS Michael Belles** has a practice extending across the areas of administrative law, real estate development, zoning, planning and land use. **Max Graham** is praised as *"the go-to guy there: he knows everything that there is to know about Hawaii."*

### Case Lombardi & Pettit
See profile on p.1128

**THE FIRM** This full-service firm's nine-strong real estate practice group handles any and all types of real estate concern, including real estate acquisitions and sales, commercial financing and loans. The firm represents a diverse array of clients, including Grove Farm Land, Hunt Development and First Hawaiian Bank.

**Sources say:** *"I was very satisfied with their professional attitude and business ethics, and their capability on fulfilling their assignments."*

**KEY INDIVIDUALS** Practice group leader **Stacey Foy** (see p.1123) has extensive experience across a whole host of real estate issues, including matters relating to the conversion of hotels into condominiums. She also represents lenders and borrowers in negotiating and documenting loans for property acquisitions and developments. **Dennis Lombardi** (see p.1123) is described by an impressed client as *"a very knowledgeable and pleasant person to work with."* Peers comment that he maintains the *"highest respect in zoning and land use,"* and is one of the *"top guys in the state."* **Nancy Youngren** (see p.1125) represents both developers and major corporations in matters concerning the acquisition and sale of commercial and residential properties, among other types of engagement.

### Chun, Kerr, Dodd, Beaman & Wong

**THE FIRM** This firm engages in a broad range of work including assisting with real property finance and mortgage matters, condominium development, land use and zoning. Its clients include real estate companies, resort and hotel owners, developers and financial institutions.

**KEY INDIVIDUALS Danton Wong** has an extensive experience across the areas of real estate acquisitions, commercial office buildings and residential condominium projects. He was recently involved in the development of the Honolulu Design Centre. **Ed Chun** has a practice covering the gamut of real estate, corporate, trust and estate law. He routinely assists clients with the purchase and sale of commercial properties. A rising name in the sector, **Andrew Bunn**'s broad real estate practice includes undertaking commercial real estate, general business law, condominium and rental housing development, and work on behalf of ecclesiastical organizations.

### Chun Yoshimoto LLP

**THE FIRM** This boutique firm handles a raft of real estate issues, including acquisitions, development and leasing in conjunction with finance and corporate matters. Peers praise the team's excellent problem-solving capabilities.

**KEY INDIVIDUALS Deborah Chun** is *"very highly regarded"* for her work in commercial real estate financing transactions, and in the acquisition, disposition and development of commercial real estate. **Janel Yoshimoto** is described as *"a fine attorney; responsive, she knows her stuff and is reasonable."* Her practice covers representing buyers and sellers in an array of commercial and residential leasing and real estate due diligence matters.

### Mancini Welch & Geiger LLP

**THE FIRM** Based on the island of Maui, this firm has a broad practice across the areas of corporate and real estate law.

**Sources say:** *"This firm has a very good reputation on Maui."*

**KEY INDIVIDUALS Paul Mancini** is highly respected as the *"go-to guy"* for transactions and municipal and zoning matters. **Thomas Welch** is one of the most senior attorneys

in the area of real estate law. He undertakes work involving municipal, zoning, commercial and probate matters.

### McCorriston Miller Mukai MacKinnon LLP

**THE FIRM** This firm is particularly recognized for its roles on behalf of developers, property owners and investors in the development of hotels, condominiums and residential development matters.

**KEY INDIVIDUALS Scott MacKinnon** works within the areas of real estate financing, leasing, land use, loans and workouts. His recent work includes acting on behalf of the Nauru Tower and the Hawaiki Tower. **Clifford Miller** has a broad practice encompassing residential and commercial real estate development projects. He has also worked on the acquisition and development of office buildings and hotels. **Charles Pear** comes most recommended for his expertise in condominium and timeshare matters. He represents developers and lenders as well as homeowner associations.

### Tom Quitiquit Chee & Watts, LLP

**THE FIRM** The highly respected real estate team at Tom Quitiquit Chee & Watts has expertise across condominium and construction law, land use, zoning and real estate development matters.

**KEY INDIVIDUALS Bud Quitiquit**'s broad real estate expertise includes transactional and condominium law. **Carl Tom** is similarly lauded for his transactional real estate practice.

### Schlack Ito Lockwood Piper & Elkind, LLLC

**THE FIRM** This impressive firm offers a wealth of experience on behalf of developers of commercial and residential real estate in relation to shopping center, office, retail, industrial and hotel matters.

**KEY INDIVIDUALS Raymond Iwamoto** is particularly praised for his skills in relation to condominiums. He also represents individuals as well as local, national and international developers and landowners in a diverse array of real estate matters and business acquisitions. **Carl Schlack** is described by peers as *"a fine attorney."* He is particularly recognized for his work within the areas of commercial leasing, development and financing transactions. **Mark Ito** is *"very well versed in all land court procedures and land registration"* matters, say sources. His broad real estate practice also benefits from his extensive litigation experience.

### Schneider Tanaka Radovich Andrew & Tanaka, LLLC

**THE FIRM** The excellent real estate boutique handles a broad array of matters within real estate and business law, including acquisitions, developments and sales, as well as real estate finance and commercial leasing.

**KEY INDIVIDUALS Scott Radovich** is highly respected for his expertise in condominiums, timeshares and community associations. *"With a long and successful career in real estate,"* **Robert Schneider** is considered one of the sector's most seasoned authorities. **Tod Tanaka** has a broad practice encompassing acquisitions, real estate finance, corporate finance and general corporate law.

## Starn O'Toole Marcus & Fisher

**See profile on p.1130**

**THE FIRM** This seven-strong team assists owners and developers through the process of navigating complex land use and permitting laws. This group is highlighted in particular for its expertise in commercial leasing, land use, zoning and trust matters. Key clients include Hilton Hotels, Morgan Stanley Real Estate Funds and ResortQuest Hawaii.

**KEY INDIVIDUALS** The supremely experienced **Kenneth Marcus** (see p.1123) undertakes work across all areas of commercial real estate development, finance, leasing, purchases and sales. **Duane Fisher** (see p.1122) is a *"very solid corporate and real estate attorney,"* say interviewees. He is further described as a *"go-to guy,"* particularly for construction contracts and related issues. **Peter Starn** (see p.1125) is praised predominantly for his expertise with issues

occurring in the hotel industry. He brings a wealth of experience, and is well versed in the acquisition, development, sale, financing and restructuring of hotels, office buildings and condominiums.

## Watanabe Ing LLP

**THE FIRM** This firm's banking, environment, land use and real estate groups work in conjunction to utilize their expertise in a variety of financings and real estate transactions.

**KEY INDIVIDUALS** Peers commend **Douglas Ing** for being a delight to work with and *"very much a gentleman and a professional."* His practice encompasses government, regulatory law and litigation. Seasoned authority **John Aube** is highlighted as one of the most experienced experts in Hawaii's real estate sector. His clients include major financial institutions and developers.

## Other Notable Practitioners

**Wesley Chang** of Law Offices of Wesley Y S Chang wins plaudits from peers and clients alike, many of whom highlight his superb client-focused and innovative approach to engagements. He recently worked on behalf of Hawaiian Telcom as local counsel in a refinancing transaction. **Richard Kiefer** of Kiefer Merchant Garneau LLC is an expert in a range of commercial, hotel, golf course, residential and land purchases and sales matters. **David Shibata** of Rush Moore LLP specializes in business and real estate matters. He is especially known for his experience in the acquisition and development of hotels and shopping centers.

# Leaders' Profiles in Hawaii

## ALSTON, Paul
Alston Hunt Floyd & Ing Attorneys At Law, A Law Corporation, Honolulu
808 524 1800
palston@ahfi.com
*Featured in Litigation (Hawaii)*
**Practice Areas:** State/federal litigation and ADR for plaintiffs and defendants. Complex business disputes, securities, real property, construction, insurance, civil rights, professional malpractice, First Amendment rights.
**Professional Memberships:** ABA, Hawaii State Bar Association (President 1991-92), American Association of Appellate Attorneys, ABF, Federal Bar Association (President, Hawai`i Chapter, 2012-2013).
**Career:** Special Deputy Attorney General in selected federal matters. Best Lawyers in America 1995-present (Hawai`i Lawyer of the Year: Appellate Law 2013, Real Estate Litigation 2012, Bet-the-Company 2009); Certified Civil Trial Specialist (National Board of Trial Advocacy and Hawai`i Supreme Court); Martindale-Hubbell AV rated. Super Lawyers Pro Bono Award (2012).
**Personal:** USC(JD, 1971)

## BENCK, Jennifer
Carlsmith Ball LLP, Honolulu
808 523 2557
jbenck@carlsmith.com
*Featured in Real Estate (Hawaii)*
**Practice Areas:** Practice encompasses real estate and environmental law emphasizing land use, development and land use entitlements, such as State land use district boundary amendments, conservation district use permits, rezonings and special management area permits, environmental review, and administrative proceedings and related litigation. Represents clients in the purchase and sale of real property, performs due diligence, including pre-closing review of title issues, zoning

and permit compliance, and proposed use reviews.
**Professional Memberships:** Hawaii State Bar Association, Urban Land Institute
**Personal:** JD, cum laude, University of Hawaii, William S. Richardson School of Law, M.Ed., University of Hawaii; BA, US International University

## BENNETT, Mark J
Starn O'Toole Marcus & Fisher, Honolulu
808 537 6100
mbennett@starnlaw.com
*Featured in Litigation (Hawaii)*
**Practice Areas:** Litigation, and as an Arbitrator and Mediator
**Career:** Mark Bennett was Hawaii's appointed Attorney General for eight years, has first-chaired scores of jury trials, is a Fellow of the American College of Trial Lawyers, has argued more than fifty appeals, including twice successfully before the US Supreme Court, and has negotiated complex agreements up to $1 billion. He holds Martindale-Hubbell's AV rating, has been selected by Best Lawyers in America for Commercial and Antitrust Litigation and Appellate Practice, and was named a Top 25 Hawaii Super Lawyer and a Litigation Star by Benchmark Litigation and Appellate.

## CARSON, Ellen Godbey
Alston Hunt Floyd & Ing Attorneys At Law, A Law Corporation, Honolulu
808 524 1800
ecarson@ahfi.com
*Featured in Litigation (Hawaii)*
**Practice Areas:** Healthcare law, alternative dispute resolution, civil rights, constitutional litigation, commercial disputes.
**Professional Memberships:** ABA, Hawaii State Bar Association.
**Career:** Stockholder/Director since 1991.

**Personal:** Harvard Law School (1980, JD, cum laude); University of Tennessee (1976, BA, summa cum laude); Best Lawyers in America for Health Law and Alternative Dispute Resolution (2006-present); Martindale-Hubbell AV rating; President, Hawaii State Bar Association (1996) and recipient of Pro Bono Award for Community Service; President, Hawaii Women Lawyers (1989-90); President, Institute for Human Services (2001-02); YWCA's Outstanding Woman Professional Award (1990); Ronin and counsel for National Council for Japanese American Redress.

## CRIBLEY, James M
Case Lombardi & Pettit, Honolulu
808 547 5400
jcribley@caselombardi.com
*Featured in Corporate/Commercial (Hawaii)*
**Practice Areas:** Director and Head of the firm's Business Group. He advises clients in the areas of general corporate and business law, corporate finance, business acquisitions and real estate law. His clientele includes domestic as well as foreign owners of businesses and properties.
**Professional Memberships:** American Bar Association and Hawaii State Bar Association.
**Career:** Bar Admission: Hawaii State, United States District Court for the District of Hawaii, United States Court of Appeals, Ninth Circuit.
**Personal:** JD, University of Michigan, 1969. BA, Miami University, 1963.

## DEVLIN, Patricia
Carlsmith Ball LLP, Honolulu
808 523 2522
pd@carlsmith.com
*Featured in Real Estate (Hawaii)*

## ELENTO-SNEED, Anna
Alston Hunt Floyd & Ing Attorneys At Law, A Law Corporation, Honolulu
808 524 1800
aes@ahfi.com
*Featured in Labor & Employment (Hawaii)*
**Practice Areas:** Strategic planning, corporate governance, wrongful termination, employment discrimination, labor unions and collective bargaining, wage and hour law, government contracting, benefits, personnel management and training, safety and health, proprietary rights, workplace privacy.
**Professional Memberships:** ABA; Hawaii State Bar Association; Society for Human Resource Management, former Hawai`i State Director; Employment Law Alliance, Hawai`i representative.
**Career:** Stockholder/Director of the firm. Frequent lecturer for universities, business groups, employers. Martindale-Hubbell AV rating. Best Lawyers in America since 2006.
**Publications:** Extensive list includes The Practical Lawyer, Hawaii Bar Journal, and The Pacific Employer.
**Personal:** Boalt Hall School of Law, UC Berkeley (JD).

## FISHER, Duane
Starn O'Toole Marcus & Fisher, Honolulu
808 537 6100
dfisher@starnlaw.com
*Featured in Real Estate (Hawaii)*
**Practice Areas:** Real Estate, Hotels and Resorts, Business Structure and Operations, Commercial Transactions.
**Professional Memberships:** Hawaii State Bar Association, (Member of Real Property and Financial Services Law Section)
**Career:** Duane Fisher has over 20 years of experience in the areas of real estate, hotel and resorts, construction, business structuring and operations and commercial transactional law. Mr Fisher is a

director of the firm and was a founding member. He holds Martindale-Hubbell's highest possible AV rating for his work, reputation and integrity. Mr Fisher is recognized by Best Lawyers in America and Hawaii Super Lawyers in the area of Real Estate Law.

### FOY, Stacey W E
Case Lombardi & Pettit, Honolulu
808 547 5400
sfoy@caselombardi.com
*Featured in Real Estate (Hawaii)*
**Practice Areas:** Real estate acquisitions entitlements, and financing.
**Professional Memberships:** Hawaii State Bar Association.
**Career:** Bar Admission: Hawaii State, United States District Court for the District of Hawaii.
**Personal:** JD, University of San Francisco, 1989, BA, (phi beta kappa) University of California Davis, 1986.

### HANSEN, Gregory
Case Lombardi & Pettit, Honolulu
808 547 5400
ghansen@caselombardi.com
*Featured in Labor & Employment (Hawaii)*
**Practice Areas:** ERISA and related tax and general corporate and business law.
**Professional Memberships:** Hawaii State, California State, Utah State; American Bar Associations; HSBA and ABA Sections on Taxation; ESOP Association Legislative and Regulatory Advisory Committee.
**Career:** Bar Admissions: Hawaii State, California, Utah; United States District Court for the District of Hawaii, United States Tax Court, United States Claims Court.
**Personal:** JD, University of California, Los Angeles, 1973; BS, University of Utah, 1970.

### HUNT, William S
Alston Hunt Floyd & Ing Attorneys At Law, A Law Corporation, Honolulu
808 524 1800
whunt@ahfi.com
*Featured in Litigation (Hawaii)*
**Practice Areas:** Trials in state, federal courts and arbitrations in medical malpractice and personal injury defense, commercial and construction litigation, business disputes, ADR.
**Professional Memberships:** ABA; Hawaii State Bar Association; American Arbitration Association; Defense Research Institute.
**Career:** Hart Leavitt Hall & Hunt 1973-80; Paul Johnson Alston & Hunt 1980-91; Alston Hunt Floyd & Ing 1991-present; Adjunct Professor, University of Hawai'i Law School 1976-77. Best Lawyers in America, Medical Malpractice (2007-present) and Personal Injury Litigation (2005-present). Benchmark Litigation since 2008. Super Lawyers since 2008. Martindale-Hubbell AV rating.
**Personal:** Columbia University School of Law (JD); Colgate University (BA).

### JAMES, Eric A
Carlsmith Ball LLP, Honolulu
808 523 2521
ejames@carlsmith.com
*Featured in Real Estate (Hawaii)*
**Practice Areas:** Practice concentrates on all phases of the acquisition, development and sale of real property, including formation of joint venture entities. Represents developers of master planned communities and condominium projects. Represents landowners in negotiation of long term ground leases. Represents clients in condemnation proceedings, rent re-negotiations, and acquisition and disposition of leased-fee interests in condominiums and cooperatives. Advises clients on environmental laws in leasing and sales transactions.
**Professional Memberships:** Hawaii State and American Bar Associations.
**Career:** Partner at Carlsmith Ball since 1985.
**Personal:** JD, Order of the Coif, UC Hastings; BA, cum laude, Claremont Men's College.

### JONES, Patrick H
Marr Jones & Wang LLLP, Honolulu
808 536 4900
pjones@marrjones.com
*Featured in Labor & Employment (Hawaii)*
**Practice Areas:** Representation of managment. Traditional labor and employment, including collective bargaining, arbitration, unfair labor practices, wrongful termination, discrimination and retaliation claims, FMLA, affirmative action, ADA, WARN and Hawaii Dislocated Workers' laws. Extensive experience in dealing with the EEOC, Hawaii Civil Rights Commission, the Hawaii Department of Labor and Industrial Relations, National Labor Relations Board, and the Office of Federal Contract Compliance Programs.
**Professional Memberships:** Hawaii State Bar Assocation; American Bar Association; Chamber of Commerce of Hawaii (Public Health Committee).
**Career:** Founding Partner (1995). Private practice since 1986.
**Personal:** Georgetown University Law Center (JD, Cum Laude).

### KHIL, John C
Carlsmith Ball LLP, Honolulu
808 523 2512
jck@carlsmith.com
*Featured in Labor & Employment (Hawaii)*
**Practice Areas:** Chair: Tax/Estate Planning/Wealth Management Practice Group. Emphasis: Pensions/Profit Sharing, and employee benefits. Former Attorney: Employee Plans/Exempt Organization Division, IRS Office of Chief Counsel, providing legal opinions, drafting regulations, and assisting in tax legislation. Maintains IRS volume submitter and individually designed retirement plans for clients. Advises on ERISA tax treatment/fiduciary responsibilities for qualified/nonqualified plans, executive compensation matters (409A, SERPs, stock options, stock appreciation, rabbi trust, excess benefit plans, golden parachutes), and ESOP transactions.

**Professional Memberships:** Hawaii State and American Bar Associations.
**Personal:** LL.M Taxation/Georgetown University Law Center; JD/University of San Francisco School of Law; B.S. High Honors/University of Hawaii.

### KLEVANSKY, Simon
Klevansky Piper, LLP, Honolulu
808 237 5541
sklevansky@kplawhawaii.com
*Featured in Bankruptcy/Restructuring (Hawaii)*
**Practice Areas:** Mr Klevansky's practice emphasizes creditor rights and insolvency, in both the federal and state courts and bankruptcy proceedings. He counsels corporate and individual clients upon collection and payment of secured and unsecured claims and judgments, foreclosures and other post-judgment remedies, lien priorities, restructuring and liquidation procedures, and receivership and trusteeship rights and duties, through litigation, arbitration, and less formal procedures. Mr Klevansky is a regular speaker in seminars upon his areas of practice.
**Professional Memberships:** Hawaii State Bar Association (President and Director of Bankruptcy Law Section, 2002-2003); American Bankruptcy Institute (member); American Bar Association (member).

### LOMBARDI, Dennis M
Case Lombardi & Pettit, Honolulu
808 547 5400
dlombardi@caselombardi.com
*Featured in Real Estate (Hawaii)*
**Practice Areas:** Real estate, concentrating in land use and development. Extensive experience in acquisition, permitting, development, financing and sales of master planned residential, resort and commercial communities, shopping centers and hotel projects. He is President of the firm.
**Professional Memberships:** Hawaii State Bar Association, California State Bar Association.
**Career:** Bar Admission: Hawaii State, California State, District of Columbia, United States District Court for the District of Hawaii.
**Personal:** JD (summa cum laude), University of Santa Clara, 1977; BA, University of Hawaii at Manoa, 1974.

### MANAUT, Pete
Carlsmith Ball LLP, Honolulu
808 523 2548
jpm@carlsmith.com
*Featured in Litigation (Hawaii)*
**Practice Areas:** Complex construction, commercial and real property litigation. Representation in all aspects of business litigation, mediation and arbitration, with particular experience in civil litigation; construction disputes; mechanics' lien and bond claims; DROA and real property disputes; lender liability; foreclosures; eminent domain taking cases; equitable and quiet title disputes; insurance defense; toxic tort/asbestos/mold environmental litigation; corporate and partnership litigation; trust and will disputes; copyright infringement; EIS litigation; and federal and state appellate work.

**Professional Memberships:** Hawaii and American Bar Associations; 9th Circuit Court of Appeals; US District Court—Hawaii.
**Personal:** JD, Gonzaga University School of Law; BA, University of Colorado.

### MARCUS, Kenneth B
Starn O'Toole Marcus & Fisher, Honolulu
808 537 6100
kmarcus@starnlaw.com
*Featured in Real Estate (Hawaii)*
**Practice Areas:** Hotels and resorts, commercial real estate, business organizations, corporate and real estate finance, insurance reorganizations.
**Career:** Kenneth Marcus has 37 years of experience in the areas of commercial real estate development, finance, leasing, purchases and sales with particular expertise in the hotel industry. Has extensive experience in the negotiation of hotel management agreements, the formation of partnerships and limited liability companies, corporate finance and mortgage loans. Holds Martindale-Hubbell's highest AV rating for skill and integrity, Vice Chairman of the Stadium Authority of the State of Hawaii, past-chairman of State bar's Real Property Section and International Society of Hospitality Consultants member.

### MARR, Barry W
Marr Jones & Wang LLLP, Honolulu
808 536 4900
bmarr@marrjones.com
*Featured in Labor & Employment (Hawaii)*
**Practice Areas:** Representation of management in labor and employment disputes. Extensive experience in state and federal litigation and in ADR. Substantial experience in labor relations and collective bargaining.
**Professional Memberships:** Fellow, College of Labor and Employment Lawyers; ABA (Labor and Employment Law).
**Career:** Counsel to the Chair of the NLRB (1974-76); Private Practice (1976-present); Special Deputy Attorney General for Hawaii in employment litigation; Adjunct Professor, University of Hawaii School of Law.
**Publications:** Contributing Editor, 'The Developing Labor Law' (BNA).
**Personal:** LLM, Georgetown University Law Center; JD, Albany Law School of Union University; BA, Hobart College; Best Lawyers in America (1993-present).

### MARSH, Michael R
Case Lombardi & Pettit, Honolulu
808 547 5400
MMarsh@caselombardi.com
*Featured in Litigation (Hawaii)*
**Practice Areas:** Commerical litigation; construction, development and real estate litigation and arbitration; copyright and trademark infringement.
**Professional Memberships:** Hawaii State Bar Association.
**Career:** Hawaii State; United States District Court, District of Hawaii; United States Courts of Appeals, Ninth Circuit.
**Publications:** Michael R Marsh, et al. "Doing Business in Hawaii" In Doing Business

in…Handbook (13th,14th & 15th editions). London: Practical Law Company in association with Lex Mundi, 2008-10.

**Personal:** BA, Blackburn University, 1969; JD, George Washington University, 1973.

## NAKASHIMA, David A
Alston Hunt Floyd & Ing Attorneys At Law, A Law Corporation, Honolulu
808 524 1800
DAN@ahfi.com
*Featured in Litigation (Hawaii)*

**Practice Areas:** Business litigation, real property and construction litigation, ERISA and disability insurance litigation. Appearances in Hawai`i state and federal courts, as well as private mediations and arbitrations.

**Professional Memberships:** Hawaii State Bar Association, ABA and Federal Bar Association.

**Career:** Stockholder/Director, 1993-present. Adjunct Professor, University of Hawai`i, William S Richardson School of Law (1997-2001); Adjunct Professor, Kapiolani Community College, Legal Assistant Program (1981-84).

**Personal:** University of Hawai`i, William S Richardson School of Law (JD 1977), University of California at Santa Barbara (BA with honors, 1973). Benchmark Litigation (since 2011); Best Lawyers in America (since 2012); Martindale-Hubbell AV rating.

## NICHOLSON, Sheryl
Alston Hunt Floyd & Ing Attorneys At Law, A Law Corporation, Honolulu
808 524 1800
sln@ahfi.com
*Featured in Litigation (Hawaii)*

**Practice Areas:** Commercial litigation, real property, construction, education.

**Professional Memberships:** Hawaii State Bar Association, American Bar Association, Hawaii Women Lawyers.

**Career:** Best Lawyers in America since 2009, including Hawai`i Bet-the-Company Litigation Lawyer of the Year 2012; Benchmark Litigation; Martindale-Hubbell AV rating.

**Personal:** William S. Richardson School of Law (JD); University of Leeds, England (MA); University of Hawaii (BA).

## OKINAGA, Lawrence S
Carlsmith Ball LLP, Honolulu
808 523 2554
lokinaga@carlsmith.com
*Featured in Corporate/Commercial (Hawaii)*

**Practice Areas:** Financial services, corporate, real estate, trust and administrative/regulatory law. Representation of financial institutions, corporations, partnerships and individuals. Advises clients on business matters and supervises the firm's litigators in client disputes.

**Professional Memberships:** Fellow, American College of Consumer Financial Services Lawyers; Consumer Advisory Council, Board of Governors of the Federal Reserve Board; Advisory Council, Federal Reserve Bank of San Francisco; Member, Federal Savings & Loan Advisory Council to the FHLBB; National Advisory Council, US Small Business Administration.

**Career:** Admitted to practice in 1972. Partner at Carlsmith Ball since 1976.

**Personal:** JD, Georgetown University Law Center; BA, University of Hawaii.

## O'TOOLE, Terence J
Starn O'Toole Marcus & Fisher, Honolulu
808 537 6100
totoole@starnlaw.com
*Featured in Litigation (Hawaii)*

**Practice Areas:** Complex commercial, construction litigation.

**Career:** Terence O'Toole has over forty years experience in commercial and complex litigation. Mr O'Toole is an experienced Trial Attorney and has been named Lawyer of the Year by Best Lawyers in America for Bet-The-Company Litigation and Banking and Finance Litigation. Mr O'Toole has been a Top Listed Hawaii Super Lawyer, and named Litigation Star by Benchmark Litigation. Mr O'Toole is past president of the Federal Bar Association. His practice covers business litigation matters, with emphasis on real estate litigation, hospitality industry related litigation, construction claims and disputes, lender liability and international claims and litigation.

## PAVEY, Judith
Starn O'Toole Marcus & Fisher, Honolulu
808 537 6100
jpavey@starnlaw.com
*Featured in Litigation (Hawaii)*

**Practice Areas:** Commercial Litigation, Personal Injury, Professional Negligence, Substantial Economic Loss/Product Defects, Medical Malpractice

**Career:** Judith Ann Pavey has over 35 years of litigation experience, and is an experienced trial lawyer representing clients in commercial litigation, and plaintiffs in personal injury, medical malpractice and product liability cases. Ms Pavey holds Martindale-Hubbell's highest AV rating and is recognized by Best Lawyers in America. Ms Pavey is a member of the American Board of Trial Advocates and the American Inns of Court. She is past president of the Hawaii Association of Justice and served on the board of the ACLU Hawaii Chapter.

## PETTIT, Ted N
Case Lombardi & Pettit, Honolulu
808 547 5400
tpettit@caselombardi.com
*Featured in Bankruptcy/Restructuring (Hawaii)*

**Practice Areas:** Business reorganization, creditor workouts, commercial foreclosure actions, commercial litigation.

**Professional Memberships:** American Bar Association; Hawaii Bankruptcy Bar Association (President, 2011); Federal Bar Association; American Jurisprudence Society; American Bankruptcy Institute.

**Career:** Bar Admission: Hawaii State, United States District Court for the District of Hawaii, United States Court of Appeals, Ninth Circuit.

**Publications:** Foreclosure Law & Related Remedies: Hawaii, ABA(2d Ed. 2011); Hawaii Collection Law Manual, 2012.

## PIPER, Alika L
Klevansky Piper, LLP, Honolulu
808 237 5542
apiper@kplawhawaii.com
*Featured in Bankruptcy/Restructuring (Hawaii)*

**Practice Areas:** Ms Piper's practice emphasizes business bankruptcy and litigation, financial restructuring and workouts. She counsels a variety of corporate and individual clients on matters related to debt collection, post-judgment remedies, lien priorities, restructuring and liquidation procedures, and receivership and trusteeship rights and duties.

**Professional Memberships:** Hawaii State Bar Association (Current Treasurer and Chair of the Finance Committee); American Bankruptcy Institute (member), American Bar Association (member).

## PURPURA, Michael M
Carlsmith Ball LLP, Honolulu
808 523 2500
mpurpura@carlsmith.com
*Featured in Litigation (Hawaii)*

**Practice Areas:** Practice concentrates on white collar criminal defense, internal investigations, complex civil litigation, and appellate litigation. Represents clients in investigations and prosecutions conducted by Federal and State law enforcement and regulatory agencies. Civil practice encompasses a wide variety of complex litigation, including contract, mass tort, class action, tax, copyright, patent, real property, and securities matters.

**Career:** Previously: Associate Counsel to the President of the United States; Senior Counsel to Deputy Attorney General, US Department of Justice; Assistant United States Attorney, Southern District of New York and District of Hawaii

**Personal:** JD, Columbia Law School; B.S., United States Military Academy

## RAND, Richard M
Marr Jones & Wang LLLP, Honolulu
808 536 4900
rrand@marrjones.com
*Featured in Labor & Employment (Hawaii)*

**Practice Areas:** Exclusively representing management in all facets of labor and employment law. Extensive trial and appellate experience in state and federal court. Represents employers before various administrative agencies. Negotiates and advises clients on administering collective bargaining agreements. Advises employers on labor aspects of large transactions.

**Professional Memberships:** Hawaii State Bar Association; American Bar Association.

**Career:** Partner at Marr Jones & Wang (2007-present). Previously associate/Partner at Torkildson Katz (1980-2007).

**Personal:** Georgetown University Law Center (JD). University of Pennsylvania (BA, Cum Laude).

**Personal:** JD, Richardson School of Law, University of Hawaii, 1986 (Executive Editor, Hawaii Law Review); PhD (medical physiology), University of Hawaii, 1980; MS (veterinary physiology), University of Missouri, 1977.

## ROBBINS, Kenneth S
Alston Hunt Floyd & Ing Attorneys At Law, A Law Corporation, Honolulu
808 524-1800
krobbins@ahfi.com
*Featured in Litigation (Hawaii)*

**Practice Areas:** Commercial litigation, personal injury defense, insurance defense, healthcare, medical malpractice defense, legal malpractice, constitutional and civil rights litigation, appellate law, administrative law.

**Professional Memberships:** Hawaii State Bar Association, American Bar Association, American Board of Trial Advocates, American Academy of Hospital Attorneys.

**Career:** Director of the firm. Best Lawyers in America Personal Injury Defense since 1995, including 2013 and 2010 Hawai`i Lawyer of the Year; Martindale-Hubbell AV rating; Super Lawyers since 2008.

**Publications:** Numerous publications and presentations in various practice areas, including trial practice.

**Personal:** Boston University (JD); Colby College (AB). US Navy, Lieutenant (1966-1970); awarded Bronze Star (1970).

## ROESSER, Tom E
Carlsmith Ball LLP, Honolulu
808 523 2553
ter@carlsmith.com
*Featured in Bankruptcy/Restructuring (Hawaii),*
*Corporate/Commercial (Hawaii)*

**Practice Areas:** Chair, Bankruptcy & Creditors' Rights Practice Group. Advises financial institutions on problem loans, loan workouts, foreclosures, bankruptcy, and lender liability issues. Focuses on commercial lending, security interests and the Uniform Commercial Code, usury and financial services loan regulations. Counsels on consumer credit issues.

**Professional Memberships:** Past President of the Bankruptcy Law Section of the Hawaii State Bar Association. Member, American Bankruptcy Institute and the Business Law Section of the American Bar Association.

**Personal:** JD, Boston University School of Law, cum laude; BA, Northwestern University.

## SANDISON, Ian Lorne
Carlsmith Ball LLP, Honolulu
808 523 2526
ils@carlsmith.com
*Featured in Real Estate (Hawaii)*

**Practice Areas:** Practice concentrates on environmental law. Routinely handles matters involving contested administrative proceedings, environmental impact statements and related permitting, investigation and cleanup of contaminated real property, conventional environmental permitting, negotiation of environmental matters in business and real property transactions, lender liability for environmental contamination, compliance with environmental laws and regulations, and defense of enforcement actions arising from both federal and state laws.

**Professional Memberships:** Hawaii Chamber of Commerce, Chair, Environmental Affairs

Committee; Hawaii State and American Bar Associations; American Society of Civil Engineers.
**Personal:** JD, University of Hawaii, William S. Richardson School of Law; B.S.C.E, University of Hawaii.

### STARN, Peter
Starn O'Toole Marcus & Fisher, Honolulu
808 537 6100
pstarn@starnlaw.com
*Featured in Corporate/Commercial (Hawaii), Real Estate (Hawaii)*
**Practice Areas:** Hotels & Resorts, Commercial Real Estate, Corporate Mergers and Acquisitions, Corporate and Real Estate Finance, International Law
**Career:** Over 40 years experience in commercial real estate development, entitlements and operations. Extensive experience in corporate finance, mergers and acquisitions. Real property practice includes the development, sale, acquisition, financing, and restructuring of hotels, office buildings, condominiums, and shopping centers. Particular expertise in the hotel industry, including hotel management contracts. He also has substantial experience in international transactions. Mr Starn holds Martindale-Hubbell's highest AV rating for skill and integrity. He is a former Naval Aviator and Marine Corps Officer.

### STARSHAK, James L
Carlsmith Ball LLP, Honolulu
808 523 2515
jstarshak@carlsmith.com
*Featured in Labor & Employment (Hawaii)*
**Practice Areas:** Tax, trusts, and estate planning, emphasizing formation of qualified pension plans and estate planning for individuals with substantial amounts in Individual Retirement Accounts and Qualified Plans. Advises charitable trusts on avoiding gains on sale. Represents trustees and beneficiaries in trust litigation matters. Establishes all types of qualified plans, including defined benefit, money purchase pension, profit sharing and 401(k) plans for businesses.
**Professional Memberships:** Hawaii State Bar Association, Taxation Section, Estate and Gift Tax Committee; Hawaii Estate Planning Council; American Bar Association, Taxation Section; Hawaii Chamber of Commerce.
**Personal:** JD, Notre Dame Law School; BBA, University of Notre Dame

### STRAND, Robert
Carlsmith Ball LLP, Honolulu
808 523 2525
rstrand@carlsmith.com
*Featured in Real Estate (Hawaii)*
**Practice Areas:** Practice concentrates on complex real estate transactions, commercial leasing, equipment leasing, water law and public utilities matters. Recently negotiated and documented the acquisition of two resort golf courses on Maui by a foreign national and financing arrangements for a $15 million bank debt facility for a 15.6 MW

wind energy project on the Big Island. Represents shopping centers, developers, banks and utilities.
**Professional Memberships:** International Council of Shopping centers; American Water Works Association.
**Career:** Partner at Carlsmith Ball since 1980.
**Personal:** JD, University of Virginia School of Law; BA, cum laude, Phi Beta Kappa, University of Hawaii

### SUMIDA, Gerald
Carlsmith Ball LLP, Honolulu
808 523 2500
gas@carlsmith.com
*Featured in Corporate/Commercial (Hawaii)*
**Practice Areas:** Chairs Carlsmith's Business, Corporate & Finance Practice Group. Concentrates on business structuring and operations; business acquisitions; sales and mergers; securities law; start-up company and venture capital financing; administrative and public utilities law; energy law, energy project development and finance; antitrust and trade regulation law; federal and state legislative and administrative matters; and international legal matters.
**Professional Memberships:** Hawaii State, American and Inter-Pacific Bar Associations; Hawaii Clean Energy Initiative, Steering Committee, Chair Emeritus
**Career:** Rejoined Carlsmith Ball, 2003, after serving as General Counsel of the Asian Development Bank
**Personal:** JD, Yale Law School; BA, summa cum laude, Princeton University

### THOMASON, Terry E
Alston Hunt Floyd & Ing Attorneys At Law, A Law Corporation, Honolulu
808 524 1800
tthomason@ahfi.com
*Featured in Labor & Employment (Hawaii)*
**Practice Areas:** Government contract labor standards, affirmative action, EEO requirements, drug-free workforce and drug-free workplace procedures, wrongful termination, employment discrimination, labor unions and collective bargaining, personnel management and training, occupational safety and health, workplace privacy.
**Professional Memberships:** ABA (Labor and Public Contracts Sections), Hawaii State Bar Association, Hawaii Procurement Institute, National Contract Management Association.
**Career:** Stockholder/Director of the firm. Best Lawyers in America, Administrative Law (2010-present), including 2013 Hawai`i Lawyer of the Year Administrative/Regulatory Law.
**Personal:** The George Washington University School of Law (LLM in Labor Law); Creighton University School of Law (JD Cum Laude); US Military Academy (BS).

### WANG, Sarah O
Marr Jones & Wang LLLP, Honolulu
808 536 4900
swang@marrjones.com
*Featured in Labor & Employment (Hawaii)*
**Practice Areas:** Representation of management. Labor and employment matters, including federal and state court litigation of wrongful termination, discrimination and harassment, reasonable accommodation, and breach of contract cases; union arbitrations and airline System Boards of Adjustment. Training and guidance for employers on managing personnel issues and complying with various employment laws. Frequent speaker at labor and employment law seminars.
**Professional Memberships:** Hawaii State Bar Association; American Bar Association; Federal Bar Association; Defense Research Institute; Hawaii Women Lawyers.
**Career:** Partner (2001). Private practice since 1995.
**Personal:** University of Virginia School of Law (JD).

### WONG, David W
Carlsmith Ball LLP, Honolulu
808 523 2506
dww.carlsmith.com
*Featured in Corporate/Commercial (Hawaii)*
**Practice Areas:** Strategic, proactive counsel re federal and Hawaii income taxation of individuals and businesses, Hawaii general excise, use and conveyance tax and real property tax. Well regarded for transaction planning, tax controversies, business organization and valuation, entity structuring, inter-generational wealth planning, acquisitions, divestitures, and debt workouts. Deep experience in renewable energy and clean technology industries.
**Professional Memberships:** Hawaii State Bar Association, Section of Taxation; American State Bar Association, Section of Taxation.
**Career:** Admitted: US Federal Courts, US Tax Court; California and Hawaii Bars
**Personal:** JD, Stanford Law School, MBA, Stanford Graduate School of Business; AB, with Distinction, Stanford University

### YEH, Christopher S
Marr Jones & Wang LLLP, Honolulu
808 536 4900
cyeh@marrjones.com
*Featured in Labor & Employment (Hawaii)*
**Practice Areas:** Representation of management concerning labor and employment matters in federal and state court litigation, administrative proceedings and arbitrations. Frequent speaker at labor and employment law seminars.
**Professional Memberships:** Hawaii State Bar Association; American Bar Association.
**Career:** Partner (2003).
**Personal:** Harvard Law School (JD); Harvard University, BA (English and American Literature

and Language). Adjunct Professor at the University of Hawaii William S Richardson School of Law.

### YOUNGREN, Nancy
Case Lombardi & Pettit, Honolulu
808 547 5400
nyoungren@caselombardi.com
*Featured in Real Estate (Hawaii)*
**Practice Areas:** Real estate, including acquisitions and sales of commercial and residential properties, condominium development, registration and conversions, commercial leasing, hotel-resort purchases and sales, and general real estate and land development.
**Professional Memberships:** Hawaii State Bar Association.
**Career:** Bar Admission: Hawaii State, United States District Court for the District of Hawaii.
**Personal:** JD, William S Richardson School of Law, University of Hawaii at Manoa, 1996; MLIS, University of Hawaii at Manoa, 1987; BA, University of Tennessee, 1974.

### ZALEWSKI, John D
Case Lombardi & Pettit, Honolulu
808 547 5400
jzalewski@caselombardi.com
*Featured in Litigation (Hawaii)*
**Practice Areas:** Civil litigation, commercial litigation, defense of officers, directors and professionals, employment practices liability.
**Professional Memberships:** Hawaii State Bar Association, State Bar of Wisconsin, Federal Bar Association, American Bar Association, Defense Research Institute.
**Career:** Bar Admission: State of Hawaii, State of Wisconsin, United States District Court for the District of Hawaii, United States Court of Appeals for the Ninth Circuit. Licensed CPA, State of Hawaii (inactive).
**Personal:** Doctor of Law, University of Wisconsin-Madison, 1986; BS, University of Minnesota-Minneapolis, 1980.

# ALSTON HUNT FLOYD & ING

www.ahfi.com **tel:** 808 524 1800 **fax:** 808 524 4591

**President:** Paul Alston
**Managing Director:** William S Hunt
Number of stockholder/directors: 15   Number of lawyers: 57
Languages: *English, Japanese, Taiwanese, Spanish, Mandarin, Italian, French*

## Firm Overview:

Founded in 1991, Alston Hunt Floyd & Ing (AHFI) is a Hawaii-based firm servicing clients throughout the Pacific region. Known for high-quality, fast, creative and cost-effective service, the firm is the fourth largest in the state.

## Main Areas of Practice:

### Commercial Litigation:

13 director-shareholders; 46 attorneys total
Areas include ADA, antitrust and trade regulation, business torts, communications and media law, constitutional and civil rights, construction, derivative litigation and shareholder disputes, insurance defense and insurance coverage, IP, personal injury, RICO, securities.

- Won appeal of nearly $700 million in transient accommodations taxes assessed to 15 online travel companies by the State of Hawaii
- Represented investment bank defendant in securing dismissal of $700 million breach of contract case before it went to trial
- Won defense verdict in a federal securities fraud trial against investors seeking damages in excess of $500 million from one of Hawaii's largest landowners

**Key Clients:** Expedia, Apple, DFS, Pfizer, Costco, Chevron USA, Hawaiian Electric Industries, Kamehameha Schools.

### Real Property Litigation:

3 director-shareholders; 10 attorneys total
Represent title insurance companies and their insureds in policy coverage issues, quiet title actions, defense of adverse title claims and bad faith claims. Represent clients in disputes involving easements, boundaries, access claims, surveyors' errors, forged deeds, mortgages, landlord-tenant issues.

- Successfully represented class of oceanfront land-owners in an inverse-condemnation suit challenging a Hawaii statute that took away owners' common law property rights in accreted oceanfront land

**Key Clients:** First American Title Company, Fidelity National Title Insurance Company, Old Republic Title Company.

### Real Property & Business Transactions:

2 director-shareholders; 8 attorneys total
Real estate acquisition, disposition, financing, development and construction, leasing. Entity formation, mergers and acquisitions; advise on IP, venture capital financing, licensing and strategic ventures, e-commerce transactions.

- Represented Hawaii developer in obtaining state development permit for $200 million workforce housing project

**Key Clients:** Edmund C. Olson Trust, Office of Hawaiian Affairs (OHA), Chevron USA, Invesco, Ltd., Downtown Capital, LLC.

### Healthcare:

4 director-shareholders; 8 attorneys total
Represent hospitals, health plans, physicians and other healthcare providers in litigation, regulatory compliance, dispute resolution. Advise on risk management.

- Prevailed in contested Certificate of Need proceeding and related lawsuits for healthcare provider client seeking to provide outpatient dialysis services on Maui; projected to save client $5 million a year in lieu of outsourcing

**Key Clients:** Kaiser Permanente, Hawaii Medical Service Association (HMSA), The Queen's Medical Center.

### Banking & Finance:

2 director-shareholders; 7 attorneys total
Advise banks, savings banks, government entities, trustees and judgment creditors on regulatory compliance, lender liability issues, collections, foreclosures and bankruptcy. Represent private lenders in structuring loans, venture capital financing and workout transactions. Advise investment banks and serve as underwriters' counsel in public finance transactions.

- Co-underwriter's counsel for State of Hawaii General Obligation bond sales of $1.28 billion and $867 million, and $300 million airport revenue bond sale

**Key Clients:** Goldman Sachs, Bank of America, Merrill Lynch, Morgan Stanley, Citigroup Capital Markets, Bank of Hawaii, State of Hawaii DBEDT.

### Environmental & Cultural Resources:

2 director-shareholders; 10 attorneys total
Land use and development, endangered species, environmental impact statements, historic site preservation, Native Hawaiian issues, air and water pollution, solid and hazardous waste management, water rights, insurance coverage issues.

- Brought a citizen lawsuit against the City & County of Honolulu for Clean Water Act Violations in its wastewater collection system; settlement created $800,000 in environmental grant funding

**Key Clients:** Office of Hawaiian Affairs (OHA), Sierra Club of Hawaii.

## AREAS OF PRACTICE

Commercial Litigation
Real Property Litigation & Transactions
Healthcare
Banking & Finance
Environmental & Cultural Resources
Labor & Employment
Government Contracts & Grants
Government Relations

## OFFICES

HAWAII

**OAHU:** 1001 Bishop Street, Suite 1800, Honolulu, HI 96813
Tel: 808 524 1800   Fax: 808 524 4591
Email: info@ahfi.com

**BIG ISLAND:** 65-1241 Pomaikai Place, Suite 2, Kamuela, HI 96743
Tel: 808 885 6762   Fax: 808 885 6011
Email: bigislandinfo@ahfi.com

**MAUI:** 2220 Main Street, Suite 521, Wailuku, HI 96793
Tel: 808 244 1160   Fax: 808 442 0794
Email: mauiinfo@ahfi.com

### Labor & Employment:

5 director-shareholders; 11 attorneys total
Advise employers in matters involving wrongful termination, EEO, labor law and collective bargaining, wage and hour law, employee benefits, Taft-Hartley trust funds, business transactions, personnel management, safety and health, immigration, proprietary rights, workplace privacy. Provide management training and strategic planning assistance.
**Key Clients:** Hawaii Pacific University, Starwood Hotels, Hawaiian Airlines, DFS, Louis Vuitton.

### Government Contracts & Grants:

3 director-shareholders; 6 attorneys total
Advise contracting agencies, contractors and subcontractors involved in federal, state and county government contracts and federal grants. Privatization issues, solicitation analysis and bid preparation, protests, contract interpretation and administration, defense of contract terminations, debarment actions, litigation, qui tam actions.

- Prevailed in protest appeal against State of Hawaii Office of Elections, resulting in $1.05 million payment to client, the highest protest payment in the state to date

**Key Clients:** Ameresco, Akimeka, Syncadd.

### Government Relations:

2 director-shareholders; 3 attorneys total
Represent clients before the state legislature, county councils and federal, state and local government agencies. Bill tracking and monitoring, legislative and government relations strategy development, bill drafting, lobbying.
**Key Clients:** American Resort Development Association (ARDA), Pfizer.

# CARLSMITH BALL

www.carlsmith.com   **tel:** 808 523 2500   **fax:** 808 523 0842

**Managing Partners:** Michelle C Imata
Languages: *Filipino, French, German, Ilocano, Italian, Japanese, Romanian, Spanish, Tagalog, Vietnamese*

**Firm Overview:**
Carlsmith Ball, founded in 1857, is one of Hawaii's oldest and largest full service firms and has a reputation for deep experience and skill in a wide variety of practice areas. It strives at all times to provide the highest quality legal work, client service, and assistance in developing business relationships in industry sectors such as banking, real estate, renewable energy, hospitality, retail, manufacturing and distribution, maritime, entertainment, and new media.

## Main Areas of Practice:

**Administrative Law:**
Carlsmith represents US and foreign business clients in their dealings with government agencies and regulatory bodies.

**Admiralty & Maritime:**
The firm maintains a dominant admiralty and shipping practice throughout the Pacific, with an international client base spanning the shipping, maritime, transportation, and marine insurance industries.

**Banking & Finance:**
The firm provides counsel to national, state-chartered, local, and foreign financial institutions in all types of business, regulatory, and litigation matters.

**Bankruptcy & Creditors' Rights:**
Carlsmith represents national, state-chartered and local financial institutions, in enforcing claims and recovering collateral, in workouts and/or restructurings of troubled loans, and in all related tax aspects.

**Corporate, Business & Finance (including Project Finance):**
The firm represents profit and nonprofit, private and public domestic and international clients. Recently, the firm has been at the forefront of a number of complex and sophisticated green energy projects.

**Environmental & Land Use:**
Carlsmith represents clients including major land owners and developers, agribusiness, energy, and banking clients, providing counsel and representation in an extensive array of environmental and land use matters.

**Entertainment & Media:**
Firm attorneys have been inside counsel as well as longtime counselors to the industry. The group's litigation and arbitration experience allows it to provide keen insights into the best strategies for dispute avoidance. Counsel and advice covers non-litigation matters including intellectual property.

**Labor, Employment & Immigration:**
The firm provides proactive and preventive counsel to public and private, for profit and not-for-profit, business and government entities of all types and sizes, and has successfully represented them before government agencies and defended them in litigation.

**Litigation & Dispute Resolution:**
Carlsmith is well regarded and has deep experience at trial in all aspects of litigating, arbitrating, and preventing and mediating business and other disputes. The firm represents the City and County of Honolulu with regard to its rail project. It handles myriad complex commercial and civil disputes and criminal matters.

**Real Estate, Land Use & Hospitality:**
The firm represents domestic and foreign clients in matters involving resort and hotel, commercial, retail, residential, governmental, agricultural and industrial projects. It assists clients in complex real estate matters, including acquisition, disposition, construction, development and financing (including project finance). The firm has deep experience in areas such as land use, entitlement, zoning and planning; leasing and property management; environmental law; Hawaiian land claims; real property valuation and tax challenges; and permitting and licensing.

**Renewable Energy & Clean Technology:**
Carlsmith provides counsel and guidance in all areas related to the structure, operation and finance of energy and clean technology projects, including for some of Hawaii's most important renewable and alternative energy projects: wind, geothermal, solar, waste-to-energy, OTEC, hydroelectric, biofuel, and wave energy.

**Tax: Employee Benefits & Executive Compensation:**
Carlsmith advises businesses and individuals on the tax-efficient structuring of organizations and transactions, and represents clients in tax controversies at all levels. The firm maintains the largest group of attorneys in Hawaii practicing in the highly specialized area of pension law, providing counsel on employee benefit and executive compensation matters for closely held organizations, public corporations, government entities, and profit and nonprofit organizations. Carlsmith provides a full range of estate planning services. It has extensive experience in advising clients in the creation, management, and operation of charities and other tax-exempt organizations.

**White-Collar Crime & Criminal Defense:**
Carlsmith handles white collar criminal defense, internal investigations, complex civil litigation, crisis management, and appellate litigation.

## Clients:

Actus Lend Lease; Aulani, a Disney Resort & Spa; Bank of Hawaii; Borg-Warner Morse Tec; Bradley Pacific Aviation; Central Pacific Bank; City and County of Honolulu; First Wind Energy; General Growth Properties; Government of Guam Retirement Fund; Hawaii Gas; Hawaiian Telcom Communications, Inc.; Horizon Lines, Inc.; James Campbell Company LLC; Japan Airlines; Kalaeola Partners, LP; Kapolei Property Development LLC; Marsh USA; Northwestern Mutual Life Insurance Company; Parker Ranch Foundation Trust; Petco Animal Supplies Stores, Inc.; Puna Geothermal Ventures; Schnitzer Steel; Sempra Energy; Southern California Edison; Trustees of the Estate of Samuel Damon; United Airlines; University of Hawaii; Wavecom Solutions Corporation.

**OFFICES**

HAWAII

**HONOLULU:** ASB Tower, Suite 2200, 1001 Bishop Street, Post Office Box 656, HI 96813
Tel +1 808 523 2500  Fax +1 808 523 0842
Email : mdolan@carlsmith.com

OTHER OFFICES
The firm has offices in Guam, Hilo, Honolulu (main office), Kona, Los Angeles, and Maui.

# CASE LOMBARDI & PETTIT

www.caselombardi.com **tel:** 808 547 5400 **fax:** 808 523 1888

**Executive Committee:** Michael L Lam, Dennis M Lombardi, Lauren R Sharkey
**Managing Director:** Lauren R Sharkey
**President:** Dennis M Lombardi
Number of directors: 14
Number of other lawyers: 9

**OFFICES**

HAWAII

**HONOLULU:** Pacific Guardian Center, Mauka Tower,
737 Bishop Street, Suite 2600, HI 96813
Tel: 808 547 5400   Fax: 808 523 1888
Email: info@caselombardi.com

**Firm Overview:**

Case Lombardi & Pettit, A Law Corporation, is a prominent law firm in Hawaii with a diverse civil practice. The firm's attorneys, legal assistants and support staff are committed to client service and quality representation that is efficient and cost-effective. The firm is located in the Pacific Guardian Center in Honolulu on the island of Oahu. Tracing its roots back to 1888, Case Lombardi & Pettit has a history of providing quality legal services throughout Hawaii. To assure the highest quality of service to its clients, the firm's attorneys, legal assistants and support staff are organized into client service groups. The firm has three multi-faceted client service groups which consist of bankruptcy, business, estate planning and taxation; litigation and dispute resolution; and real estate.

**Main Areas of Practice:**

**Bankruptcy, Business, Estate Planning & Taxation:**
The firm's Bankruptcy practice covers all aspects of creditor-debtor relationships ranging from foreclosure, receivership, collection and enforcement of judgments in state and federal court to reorganization and liquidation in bankruptcy court. The practice also represents secured creditors, unsecured creditor committees and landlords in all aspects of bankruptcy proceedings. The firm has a team of creditor counsel experienced in negotiating workouts and restructurings outside of bankruptcy.
Attorneys in the firm's Business practice assist in the formation and operation of business entities; advise on profit-sharing, pension and other employee benefit plans, with an emphasis on ESOP and ERISA; address opportunities and challenges faced by an ongoing business; and provide advice regarding transactions governed by the UCC, mergers, acquisitions, dissolutions, asset purchases and financings. The firm's corporate attorneys frequently work together with its real estate attorneys to structure, draft and close real estate transactions structured as corporate mergers or stock transfers.
The firm's Estate Planning and Taxation practice serves a broad spectrum of clients, and involves analyzing and implementing plans and transactions to fit a client's circumstances and concerns. Attorneys in the firm's Tax practice advise clients on a variety of federal and state tax matters, including real estate tax issues, business tax planning and resolution of tax disputes.
**Contact:** Ted N Pettit (Bankruptcy), James M Cribley (Business), Estate Planning and Taxation (Lauren R Sharkey).

**Litigation & Dispute Resolution:**
The firm's Litigation and Dispute Resolution Practice Group is led by a team of skillful, experienced and successful litigators and trial attorneys with practice concentrations that include commercial litigation, complex business litigation, real estate litigation,

construction litigation, insurance defense, errors and omissions and professional liability defense, defense of business and non-profit organizations, defense of directors and officers, employment litigation, subrogation actions, trade name and trade mark infringement actions, and other civil disputes and litigation matters, including disputes involving developers, contractors, and design professionals.
The firm's attorneys regularly appear in all federal and state trial and appellate courts in Hawaii and before arbitration tribunals and federal and state administrative and regulatory agencies.
The litigation team engages in creative, conscientious, and effective advocacy to achieve successful outcomes. A focus of the group is the practice of alternative and cost- and time-effective mechanisms to resolve claims and disputes, including mediation, arbitration, and negotiated settlement.
**Contact:** John D Zalewski, Michael L Lam, Michael R. Marsh

**Real Estate:**
The firm's Real Estate Practice Group is sophisticated and diverse. Areas of expertise include the structuring of real estate acquisitions and sales; subdivision; condominium development, formation and registration on state and federal levels; real estate sales and administration; regulatory and licensing compliance; development, land use, zoning and entitlement matters; construction contracting; commercial financing, including complex construction and syndicated loans; loan restructuring; office and retail leasing; community association formation and administration; residential financing; and affordable housing financing, registration and development.
The firm represents landowners, developers, purchasers, investors and lenders in the acquisition, sale and financing of all types of real estate, including undeveloped land, hotels, shopping centers, office buildings and residential and mixed-use developments.
The firm's attorneys in the Real Estate Group take pride

in assisting in the consummation of real estate transactions as well as providing creative and cost-effective solutions to the needs of its clients.
**Contact:** Stacey W E Foy, Esther Han Roberts

**International Affiliation:**
Case Lombardi & Pettit is the exclusive member firm in Hawaii for Lex Mundi – the world's leading network of independent law firms with in-depth experience in 100+ countries worldwide. As part of the Lex Mundi global network, the firm can provide its clients with preferred access to more than 21,000 lawyers around the world – all from a single point of contact.
**Contact:** Nancy J Youngren, Michael L Lam

**Clients:**
The firm's clientele is varied. They include large international, national and local corporations and businesses, financial institutions, trusts and non-profit organizations, real estate developers, sole proprietors and individuals.

CASE LOMBARDI & PETTIT
A LAW CORPORATION
Celebrating 125 YEARS
1888-2013

Member
LexMundi
World Ready

# MARR JONES & WANG LLLP

www.marrjones.com **tel**: 808 536 4900 **fax**: 808 536 6700

**Managing Partner:** Sarah Wang
Number of partners: 11
Number of lawyers: 14
Languages: *English*

## Firm Overview:

In 1995, the founding lawyers of Marr Jones & Wang left Hawaii's two largest law firms to form what is now the largest law firm in the state devoted exclusively to the representation of management in labor and employment law matters. Labor and employment law presents unique issues and requires unique strategies; the firm believes employers are best served by attorneys who have devoted their careers to this area of law.

## Main Areas of Practice:

### Labor & Employment Law:

### Traditional Labor Law:

- Successfully defended Hawaiian Dredging Construction Company in complaint brought by the National Labor Relations Board
- Negotiated labor agreements with the Hawaii Nurses' Association, International Longshore and Warehouse Union Local 142, Unite HERE Local 5, International Brotherhood of Electrical Workers Local 1260 and Teamsters Local 996
- Represented healthcare and hotel clients in negotiating issues with unions arising from acquisitions in Hawaii
- Represented employers in labor arbitrations and grievances to uphold discipline of their bargaining unit employees
- Assisted in responding to union organizing campaigns
- Advised clients who are preparing for a strike by their employees

**Key Clients:** Fresenius Medical Care, Hawaiian Dredging Construction Company, Hawaii Pacific Health, Hilton Worldwide, Inc., Servco Pacific Inc., The Queen's Health Systems

### Employment Litigation:

- Obtained declaratory judgment invalidating state Sick Leave Law on behalf of Hawaii's largest hotels and health care providers
- Successfully defended nine-count employment discrimination suit on behalf of health care client
- Represented major airlines and national hotel chains in federal discrimination lawsuits
- Represented American Samoa Government in lawsuit brought by the Equal Employment Opportunity Commission

- Represented counties of Honolulu, Maui and Kauai in wage and hour collective actions

**Key Clients:** Fresenius Medical Care, Hawaii Pacific Health, Hilton Worldwide, Inc., Kyo-ya Hotels & Resorts, LP, Marriott Hotel Services, Inc., Starwood Hotels & Resorts Worldwide, United Air Lines, Wyndham Worldwide

### Administrative Law:

- Represented clients responding to charges/complaints filed by the Equal Employment Opportunity Commission, Hawaii Civil Rights Commission, National Labor Relations Board, Hawaii Labor Relations Board, Federal Department of Labor, State Department of Labor and Industrial Relations
- Represented clients in unemployment appeals hearings
- Assisted clients in responding to federal and state government audits and investigations

### Advice & Legal Compliance:

Advised clients on issues of legal compliance including:
- Collective bargaining and contract administration
- Wage and hour issues
- Criminal background checks
- Family, medical and pregnancy leave
- Employment discrimination
- Sexual harassment
- Accommodations for disabled employees
- Military leave
- Employee discipline and discharge
- Non-compete agreements
- Occupational safety and health
- Non-compete agreements
- Prepaid Healthcare, Temporary Disability Insurance, and continued health care coverage under COBRA

### Prevention & Risk Management:

- Drafting (or updating) employee handbooks
- Drafting (or updating) employment policies
- Drafting executive contracts
- Training managers on key employment issues
- Training employees on your company's harassment and discrimination policy
- Creating compensation programs
- Auditing employment policies and practices for compliance with federal and state law
- Investigating employee complaints

### Business Transactions & Operations:

- Providing notice under the state Dislocated Workers Act and the federal Worker Adjustment and Retraining Notification Act
- Addressing labor and employment issues that arise in the context of a sale, transfer, acquisition or change of control of a business
- Preparing for and implementing a reorganization or reduction in force
- Implementing severance programs

### Government Employers & Contractors Compliance Assistance:

- Executive Order 11246 (which requires affirmative action programs for government contractors)
- Davis-Bacon (which requires government contractors to pay "prevailing wages" to employees who perform work on government projects)

# STARN O'TOOLE MARCUS & FISHER

**www.**starnlaw.com **tel:** 808 537 6100 **fax:** 808 537 5434

Number of partners: 9
Number of other lawyers: 11

**OFFICES**

HAWAII
**HONOLULU:** 733 Bishop Street, Suite 1900, 96813
Tel: 808 537 6100   Fax: 808 537 5434

## Firm Overview:

Starn O'Toole Marcus & Fisher is a leader among Hawaii's law firms, recognized for its expertise in real estate law, commercial transactions and complex commercial litigation in Hawaii, the US mainland and internationally. Transactional and litigation teams often join forces in complex commercial matters that require both business law and litigation experience. The firm's intellectual power, mental strength and toughness generate winning strategies, strong negotiations and innovative settlements for clients. Above all, the firm's passion for excellence and responsive client service has earned an international reputation for extraordinary client results.
The firm is top-listed by US News & World Report-Best Lawyers® "Best Law Firms and has earned Martindale-Hubbell's® highest, AV Preeminent rating, given by other legal professionals for professional excellence.

## Main Areas of Practice:

### Litigation:

Starn O'Toole Marcus & Fisher's litigation powerhouse has extensive experience, including significant jury and non-jury trial work, in complex commercial litigation encompassing business, corporate, contract and accounting issues related to real estate development, corporate ownership and management, the hotel and hospitality industry, environmental matters, construction claims, lender liability, class actions and personal injury. The litigation team has trial expertise before State and Federal courts in Hawaii and the US mainland, including the US Supreme Court, and the team has served as litigation general counsel before courts in foreign jurisdictions. The team is amongst a handful of select "go-to" attorneys when clients are faced with complex commercial issues.

### Trial Approach:

Victory in the legal environment means triumph: economic satisfaction, a win-win agreement, or sometimes, just being proclaimed right.

The importance of the path to victory-strategies, players and desired outcomes – make the selection of the legal trial team critical for success. The job is to design a roadmap that considers each twist and turn that may be presented. Like a great mystery novel where the reader has skipped to the end to learn the ending, the experience and intellectual brainpower of the client's trial attorneys can predict the end of the story by crafting each move on the battlefield along the way. Starn O'Toole Marcus & Fisher's litigation attorneys

take the fight for every client as if it were their own battle. To be personally responsible and involved is a hallmark of the law firm, which is built on the power of its people.

Law firm litigation attorneys are recognized by Best Lawyers in America®, Hawaii Super Lawyers®, Benchmark Litigation, Benchmark Appellate, Benchmark Plaintiff, Chambers and Partners USA Legal Directory of Leading Lawyers for Business and the Bar Register of Preeminent Lawyers ™.

Firm litigation attorneys are rated AV Preeminent by Martindale-Hubbell®, the highest rating possible given by their peers recognizing their skill, ethics and integrity.

### Transactional:

Starn O'Toole Marcus & Fisher's business attorneys are known for sophisticated case analysis and innovative business solutions for complex matters. The transactional team has significant experience in real estate development and transactions, hotels, hotel management agreements, corporate finance, international transactions, secured transactions, mergers and acquisitions, construction law and complex commercial matters.

The firm's impressive skill and experience in strategic case planning, ingenious solutions and powerful negotiations in all aspects of complex real estate transactions has opened many doors for domestic and international clients, helping them navigate Hawaii's complex land use and permitting laws.

### Transactional Approach:

The transactional attorneys at Starn O'Toole Marcus & Fisher have an innate talent for critical thinking through each complex commercial matter. What's more, solving the pieces of a puzzle, examining the players, unraveling the details of agreements and handshake deals, to identify the keys that give the client the clear advantage, is what they relish.

In today's complex competitive environment, firm transactional attorneys shine when approaching the deal table. Strong, experienced and prepared for every zig and zag, firm attorneys drive for exceptional outcomes for every client.

Law firm transactional attorneys are recognized by Best Lawyers in America®, Hawaii Super Lawyers®, Chambers and Partners USA Legal Directory of Leading Lawyers for Business and the Bar Register of Preeminent Lawyers ™.

Firm transactional attorneys are AV rated by Martindale-Hubbell®, the highest rating possible, given by their peers recognizing their skill, ethics and integrity.

# Idaho

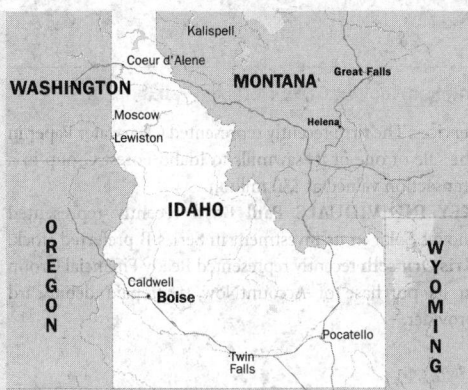

## How lawyers are ranked

Every year we carry out thousands of in-depth interviews with clients in order to assess the reputations and expertise of business lawyers worldwide. The qualities we look for (and which determine rankings) include technical legal ability, professional conduct, client service, commercial awareness/astuteness, diligence, commitment, and other qualities most valued by the client. For details of our research team, see p.5.

# BANKRUPTCY/RESTRUCTURING

Commentary about individuals can be found under their firm's paragraph. If the firm has no paragraph (is not ranked) look at Other Notable Practitioners.

### Bankruptcy/Restructuring
### Leading Firms

**Band 1**
Givens Pursley LLP
Holland & Hart LLP *
Moffatt Thomas Barrett Rock & Fields

### Leading Individuals

**Star individuals**

| | |
|---|---|
| Prince Larry E | Holland & Hart LLP * |

**Band 1**

| | |
|---|---|
| Elsaesser Ford | Elsaesser Jarzabek Anderson Elliott (ONP)† |
| Meier Joseph M | Cosho Humphrey LLP (ONP)† |
| Peterman Randall | Moffatt Thomas Barrett Rock & Fields |

**Band 2**

| | |
|---|---|
| Anderson Bruce | Elsaesser Jarzabek Anderson Elliott (ONP)† |
| Christensen Craig W | Craig W Christensen Chartered (ONP)† |
| Dvorak Thomas E | Givens Pursley LLP |
| Faucher Robert A | Holland & Hart LLP * |
| Kurtz John F | Hawley Troxell Ennis & Hawley LLP (ONP)† |
| Manwaring Jed W | Evans Keane LLP (ONP)† |
| Robinson Brent T | Ling, Robinson & Walker (ONP)† |
| Schwager Sheila R | Hawley Troxell Ennis & Hawley LLP (ONP)† |

**Associates to watch**

| | |
|---|---|
| Geier Judy | Evans Keane LLP (ONP)† |

\* Indicates firm / individual with profile.
Alphabetical order within each band. Band 1 is the highest.

## Band 1

### Givens Pursley LLP

**THE FIRM** This Idaho firm has an active creditors' rights, bankruptcy and workouts group that services a full range of potential client needs. Recent mandates have arisen with respect to a variety of clients including banks, commercial property owners and student loan providers. Notable among the firm's clients are Banner Bank, Agri Beef and A10 Capital.

**Sources say:** "They work tremendously well together."
**KEY INDIVIDUALS** Clients underscore the responsive, personalized service of the "excellent" **Thomas Dvorak**. Recent work highlights include suing a junior judgment lien holder that had sold a bank client's secured collateral.

### Holland & Hart LLP
See profile on p.727
**THE FIRM** This regional powerhouse boasts a full range of expertise in the bankruptcy and financial distress sphere. The bankruptcy and creditors' rights group recently acted for an unsecured creditor on a Chapter 11 action, and for major national banks as creditors on various multimillion-dollar matters. Partners at the firm have experience working on matters in relation to the dairy industry and insurance industry.
**Sources say:** "An exceptionally good experience – their work in Boise couldn't be improved!"
**KEY INDIVIDUALS** The "extremely reasonable, rational and easy to work with" **Larry Prince** (see p.1139) continues to receive considerable praise from peers and clients. Highlights of recent work include numerous Chapter 11 bankruptcy proceedings and high-value workouts. **Robert Faucher** (see p.1139) is described as "a very disciplined thinker" who has experience representing creditors in a variety of industries. He has recently worked on a range of issues in bankruptcy and restructuring for major clients.

### Moffatt Thomas Barrett Rock & Fields
**THE FIRM** This local firm continues to punch above its weight in terms of creditor representation work. Recent work highlights include mandates from international banks and work linked to the manufacturing industry. Other work includes large loan foreclosure action, restructuring and litigation surrounding relevant matters.
**KEY INDIVIDUALS Randall Peterman** is an experienced transactional attorney and litigator. Recent clients include major international lenders and the creditors of a chemical manufacturing plant in Pocatello. One client describes him as "one of the premier bankruptcy attorneys representing banks in Idaho."

## Other Notable Practitioners

**Joseph Meier** of Cosho Humphrey LLP receives significant plaudits, particularly for his work for debtors. "Just excellent," enthused one source. **Jed Manwaring** of Evans Keane LLP enters the rankings this year. Peers note his years of experience and strength across the board, recognizing that he is "very good technically." Pocatello-based **Craig Christensen** of Craig W Christensen Chartered is acknowledged as a key regional practitioner for creditors' rights. "I think really highly of him," states an interviewee. **Brent Robinson** of Ling, Robinson & Walker continues to be a go-to name and is highly regarded for his work in the agricultural sector. Sources relate that he is "so very efficient and great on his feet." **Judy Geier** is a highly rated associate at Evans Keane LLP. Sources highlight her responsiveness and attention to detail. **Ford Elsaesser** of Elsaesser Jarzabek Anderson Elliott & Macdonald, Chtd. maintains a stellar reputation among peers and is widely considered a stalwart in this sector. Commentators report "nothing but the highest respect for him." At the same firm, **Bruce Anderson** receives praise from clients and peers. Clients laud his ability to guide businesses through the bankruptcy process, with one noting that "he does an excellent job." **John Kurtz** of Hawley Troxell Ennis & Hawley LLP has accrued considerable experience across the country. He recently represented Syringa Bank against a lender liability action brought by Ultimate Log. Peers have "nothing but good things to say" about **Sheila Schwager**, also at Hawley Troxell Ennis & Hawley LLP. She was lead partner when the firm acted for Boise Cascade in defense of an action brought by CEI Liquidation Estate.

# CORPORATE/COMMERCIAL

Commentary about individuals can be found under their firm's paragraph. If the firm has no paragraph (is not ranked) look at Other Notable Practitioners.

## Band 1

### Hawley Troxell Ennis & Hawley LLP

**THE FIRM** This firm maintains its excellent reputation for corporate work in Idaho. The firm has a broad range of experience in various corporate matters including entity formation, corporate compliance, joint ventures and acquisitions. Recent highlights include acting for Power Engineers in connection with the acquisition of four strategically located engineering corporations. Other clients include Blue Cross of Idaho and Madison Memorial Hospital.
**Sources say:** "*Consistently good corporate lawyers.*"
**KEY INDIVIDUALS** Chair of the business and finance group **Nicholas Miller** continues to be a prominent figure on the firm's corporate bench. He handles many aspects of securities law and bond transactions and is described by

interviewees as "*a great problem solver.*" **Richard Riley** has a wealth of experience in various corporate matters. Sources describe him as "*technically knowledgeable*" and relate that he is "*really well heeled in Idaho corporate law.*"

### Holland & Hart LLP
See profile on p.727

**THE FIRM** This practice is respected both locally and nationally. Recent work highlights range from high-value asset sales and significant business restructuring to acting as general corporate counsel for a major company in the food and drink industry. Notable clients include IntelliScience and Marlin Equity.
**Sources say:** "*They always provide outstanding work product.*"
**KEY INDIVIDUALS Frederick Mack** (see p.1139) is described as a "*high-caliber, excellent performer.*" His practice encompasses M&A, corporate governance and succession planning. **Brian Hansen** (see p.1139) is noted for his work on the sellers' side of transactions. "*His strength is his pragmatic view, his steady hand under pressure and his capacity to undertake enormous amounts of work in a tight timeframe,*" enthuses one client. The "*outstanding*" **Larry Prince** (see p.1139) achieves high praise for his skills in financial distress issues but is also a keen corporate attorney. His clients include financial institutions and commercial lending companies. Up-and-comer **Nicole Snyder** (see p.1139) impresses clients and peers. She is recognized for her ability in M&A. Sources note that she "*provides excellent legal advice and work product.*"

### Perkins Coie LLP
See profile on p.2548

**THE FIRM** This firm is widely praised for the breadth and depth of its corporate practice. The Boise team is particularly well regarded for its work with business startups and emerging companies, though it has a full range of expertise. Clients include Alpine Investors, Skylight Capital and International Isotopes.
**KEY INDIVIDUALS Stephen Hardesty** is considered to be one of the best lawyers in town by impressed observers. His experience includes fund formations, M&A and private placement offerings. **Melanie Rubocki** is firmwide vice chair of the emerging companies practice and head of the business group for the Boise office. Sources report that she is efficient and aware of how legal needs fit with business practices. Associate to watch **Matthew Purcell** has a broad corporate practice which includes entity formation, M&A, corporate governance and securities. Sources regard him as professional and helpful.

### Stoel Rives LLP

**THE FIRM** This sophisticated practice boasts a wealth of corporate experience and the support of offices across the country. The firm works across a number of industry sectors including mining, forestry, agriculture and finance industries, and has expertise in a variety of transactional

services. The firm recently represented Clearwater Paper in the sale of one of its sawmills to Idaho Forest Group in a transaction valued at $30 million.
**KEY INDIVIDUALS Paul Boyd** recently represented Inovus Solar in its investment in Series B preferred stock. **Kris Ormseth** recently represented Ready Financial Group in its purchase of AccountNow, a prepaid debit card provider.

## Band 2

### Givens Pursley LLP

**THE FIRM** This Idaho firm's corporate practice works closely with its real estate and environmental law practices to offer a holistic service to clients. The team recently represented a holding company in the construction of a manufacturing plant and an energy company in the development and financing of an energy facility. The firm has also acted on various corporate and commercial matters including complex M&A and corporate reorganizations. Clients include TitleOne and Saint Alphonsus Health System.
**Sources say:** "*The firm has the depth and capacity to work quickly when necessary. They did an outstanding job.*"
**KEY INDIVIDUALS William Cole** is noted for his handling of financial matters. He has a broad range of expertise covering commercial lending, securities and M&A. **Judson Montgomery** has broad practice covering a number of corporate and real estate matters and frequently advises clients on asset acquisition and complex transactions. "*He's very good at seeing the whole picture,*" enthuses one client. **Clint Bolinder** is noted for his tax expertise. One client reports: "*He's extremely knowledgeable about tax laws and the associated strategies.*"

### Moffatt Thomas Barrett Rock & Fields

**THE FIRM** This firm's network of Idaho offices ensures that it is well placed to deal with corporate needs across the state. The team features a number of seasoned practitioners with a broad knowledge base. The firm has experience with a number of industries including dairy financing and healthcare. Notable recent corporate work include syndicated credit work and broader acquisition financing.
**Sources say:** "*They certainly know their way around a deal.*"
**KEY INDIVIDUALS David Jensen** has experience in both the real estate and corporate sectors. He is noted for his work with lenders and is described by one source as being "*among the best banking lawyers I know.*" **Christine Nicholas** has long experience in corporate real estate matters. Her broad knowledge base also covers workouts and restructurings. **Michael Roe** is noted for his "*outstanding academic credentials*" and for being "*very, very practical.*" Areas of expertise include entity formation, M&A and finance. **Clayton Gill** routinely advises startup companies in connection with business strategy, in addition to handling M&A and commercial contracts.

# LABOR & EMPLOYMENT

Commentary about individuals can be found under their firm's paragraph. If the firm has no paragraph (is not ranked) look at Other Notable Practitioners.

## Labor & Employment

### Leading Firms

**Band 1**
Hawley Troxell Ennis & Hawley LLP
Moffatt Thomas Barrett Rock & Fields
Stoel Rives LLP

**Band 2**
Givens Pursley LLP
Holland & Hart LLP *
Perkins Coie LLP

### Leading Individuals

**Star individuals**

| | |
|---|---|
| Dale James C | Stoel Rives LLP |

**Band 1**

| | |
|---|---|
| Berenter Steven | Hawley Troxell Ennis & Hawley LLP |
| Husch Gerald T | Moffatt Thomas Barrett Rock & Fields |
| White Robert B | Givens Pursley LLP |

**Band 2**

| | |
|---|---|
| Brailsford Amanda | Andersen Banducci PLLC (ONP)† |
| Hunter Forrest | Perkins Coie LLP |
| Miller Brad P | Hawley Troxell Ennis & Hawley LLP |
| Munther Merrily | Munther Law (ONP)† |
| Olsson Patricia | Moffatt Thomas Barrett Rock & Fields |
| West Kevin | Parsons Behle & Latimer PC (ONP)† |

**Up-and-coming individuals**

| | |
|---|---|
| Heikkila Kara | Hawley Troxell Ennis & Hawley LLP |
| Randolph Scott | Holland & Hart LLP * |

* Indicates firm / individual with profile.
†ONP = Other Notable Practitioner.

## Band 1

### Hawley Troxell Ennis & Hawley LLP

**THE FIRM** This local firm has extensive experience in a range of employment law matters including discrimination, ERISA and employment documentation. The firm has recently represented various clients against allegations of discrimination and has also been involved in class wage action and wrongful discharge claims. The team is also strong on the counseling side, assisting clients in avoiding litigation.
**Sources say:** *"Very fine lawyers."*
**KEY INDIVIDUALS** The *"really good"* **Steven Berenter** chairs the practice and is also managing partner of the firm. He has experience in the full spectrum of employment issues, while sources underscore his solid reputation with local authorities. **Brad Miller** wins the approval of his peers, who say: *"If he tells you something, you can take it to the bank."* Recent work highlights include the defense of his clients against a number of allegations of discrimina-

tion. Rising star **Kara Heikkila** recently joined the firm from Farley Oberrecht Harwood & Burke. She has worked extensively on discrimination cases.

### Moffatt Thomas Barrett Rock & Fields

**THE FIRM** This firm's employment practice maintains respect and recognition across the market. Seasoned practitioners with a broad range of experience in employment issues cement the firm's stellar reputation in Idaho. The team is involved in a range of discrimination claims and also handles noncompetition agreements on behalf of major local employers.
**Sources say:** *"In candor, I would say they're great!"*
**KEY INDIVIDUALS Gerald Husch** continues to be a stalwart of this sector. His wealth of experience impresses peers and clients, who particularly know him for his work on noncompetes. *"He's a quality guy,"* according to sources. **Patricia Olsson** is highlighted for her abilities in litigating employment and medical malpractice disputes. She has deep experience of acting before both federal and state courts, and earns extensive praise from her peers.

### Stoel Rives LLP

**THE FIRM** This regional powerhouse continues to be commended by both its clients and competitors. The group provides both counseling and litigation services on a variety of employment matters. The team has recently acted on behalf of major employers in a range of matters, with recent activity in a class action dispute surrounding unpaid wages. The firm also provides general advice on employment issues across a range of industries including healthcare, mining and telecommunications.
**KEY INDIVIDUALS** Star performer **James Dale** has a deservedly fine reputation in the field. His recent work ranges from providing counsel to major international companies to litigation of sensitive, complex employment issues in Idaho.

## Band 2

### Givens Pursley LLP

**THE FIRM** This pillar of the Idaho legal market has a convincing labor and employment practice. The firm has significant expertise in many aspects of employment law from recruitment and hiring through to employment termination. The firm also provides services related to agricultural employment issues including immigration and farm labor contracting and the defense of agricultural employers.
**KEY INDIVIDUALS Robert White** is described as *"very credible and very easy to work with."* He has accrued a range

of experience in employment issues, and has been active in a number of matters concerning noncompetes.

### Holland & Hart LLP
**See profile on p.727**

**THE FIRM** This firm enters the labor and employment rankings this year following impressive feedback from its clients, who praise the team's high levels of service and deep subject expertise. The group has recently been involved in a range of disputes arising from wrongful termination, noncompetition agreements and fair labor standards. The firm also has a government investigations and white-collar defense practice, as an additional service linked to this sector.
**Sources say:** *"They were outstanding, incredibly reliable, eager to tune to the business and provide the service we needed."*
**KEY INDIVIDUALS Scott Randolph** (see p.1139) has a wealth of experience as a litigator, recently representing both employees and employers. His practice also includes counseling on employment issues. Clients describe him as *"very thorough"* and *"so responsive."*

### Perkins Coie LLP
**See profile on p.2548**

**THE FIRM** The Boise office of this regional practice can draw on national strength to provide high-quality service to its clients. The firm has defended employers against a variety of employee claims and has provided general labor and employment advice to a number of organizations. Notable highlights include the ongoing employment support provided to long-standing local client Boise Cascade.
**KEY INDIVIDUALS Forrest Hunter** is increasingly visible in this sector. Recent work highlights include representing a group of companies against a collective action alleging unpaid wages. He is also lead partner in providing employment counseling to Boise Cascade.

### Other Notable Practitioners

**Merrily Munther** of Munther Law continues to be a key practitioner for employment law in the state. Her practice covers both litigation and counseling on various issues including discrimination, wage and hour matters and occupational health and safety. **Kevin West** (see p.1140) of Parsons Behle & Latimer PC has a wealth of experience in employment law. According to clients, *"Kevin's work product is comprehensively researched, well presented, and has always more than met the requirements of our issue at hand."* Litigator **Amanda Brailsford** of Andersen Banducci PLLC is noted for her experience working on contentious employment issues including noncompetes, nondisclosure, trade secrets and discrimination.

# LITIGATION

Commentary about individuals can be found under their firm's paragraph. If the firm has no paragraph (is not ranked) look at Other Notable Practitioners.

## Litigation: General Commercial
### Leading Firms

**Band 1**
Holland & Hart LLP *
Stoel Rives LLP

**Band 2**
Givens Pursley LLP
Hawley Troxell Ennis & Hawley LLP
Perkins Coie LLP

**Band 3**
Moffatt Thomas Barrett Rock & Fields

### Senior Statesmen

**Senior Statesmen: distinguished older practitioners**

| | |
|---|---|
| Clark Merlyn | Hawley Troxell Ennis & Hawley LLP |
| Greener Richard | Greener Burke Shoemaker PA (ONP)[†] |
| Hall Richard E | Duke Scanlan Hall |
| Hopkins Timothy | Hopkins Roden Crockett Hansen (ONP)[†] |
| Meadows Craig | Hawley Troxell Ennis & Hawley LLP |

### Leading Individuals

**Band 1**

| | |
|---|---|
| Andersen Steven | Andersen Banducci PLLC (ONP)[†] |
| Bithell Walter | Holland & Hart LLP * |
| Farley Donald J | Powers Tolman Farley, PLLC (ONP)[†] |
| Nye Marcus | Racine Olson Nye Budge & Bailey (ONP)[†] |
| Sinclair J Walter | Stoel Rives LLP |
| Squyres Newal | Holland & Hart LLP * |

**Band 2**

| | |
|---|---|
| Bailey John | Racine Olson Nye Budge & Bailey (ONP)[†] |
| Banducci Thomas A | Andersen Banducci PLLC (ONP)[†] |
| Boardman Richard | Perkins Coie LLP |
| Dryden William | Elam & Burke PA (ONP)[†] |
| Duke Keely | Duke Scanlan Hall |
| Geston Mark S | Stoel Rives LLP |
| Lombardi David | Givens Pursley LLP |
| Martin James | Moffatt Thomas Barrett Rock & Fields |
| McLaughlin Alex | Givens Pursley LLP |
| Schossberger Steven | Hawley Troxell Ennis & Hawley LLP |
| Stidham Erik | Holland & Hart LLP * |
| Zarian John N | Parsons Behle & Latimer PC (ONP)[†] * |

**Up-and-coming individuals**

| | |
|---|---|
| Dixon Bradley J | Stoel Rives LLP |
| Hancock Nicole C | Stoel Rives LLP |
| Randolph Scott | Holland & Hart LLP * |

\* Indicates firm / individual with profile.
[†] ONP = Other Notable Practitioner.

## Litigation: Medical Malpractice & Insurance
### Leading Firms

Duke Scanlan Hall
Gjording Fouser PLLC

### Leading Individuals

**Band 1**

| | |
|---|---|
| Brassey Andrew C | Brassey Wetherell Crawford (ONP)[†] |
| Gjording Jack | Gjording Fouser PLLC |
| LaRue James D | Elam & Burke PA (ONP)[†] |
| Powers Raymond D | Powers Tolman Farley, PLLC (ONP)[†] |

**Band 2**

| | |
|---|---|
| Bush John | Comstock and Bush (ONP)[†] |
| Comstock David | Comstock and Bush (ONP)[†] |
| Crawford Nick | Brassey Wetherell Crawford (ONP)[†] |
| Duke Keely | Duke Scanlan Hall |
| Fouser Trudy | Gjording Fouser PLLC |
| Hepworth Charles | Hepworth, Janis & Kluksdal (ONP)[†] |
| Janis John | Hepworth, Janis & Kluksdal (ONP)[†] |
| Tolman Steve | Powers Tolman Farley, PLLC (ONP)[†] |

## Band 1

### Holland & Hart LLP
See profile on p.727

**THE FIRM** This regional powerhouse maintains its preeminent position for litigation work. The Boise office has considerable litigation bench strength, demonstrating a breadth of experience across all manner of industries and legal issues. The team has particular expertise in a number of sectors, including employment, class actions, construction and lender liability. The firm's clients include key companies and organizations in the healthcare, transport and energy industries. Notable among these are Bingham Memorial Hospital, the Idaho Transportation Department and the Ada County Highway District.

**Sources say:** "The knowledge base at the firm is huge - they're absolutely fantastic!"

**KEY INDIVIDUALS** Key litigator **Walter Bithell** (see p.1139) is a stalwart of the Idaho legal market. He has accrued decades of experience in various commercial disputes. "His expertise and breadth are notable strengths," says one source. **Newal Squyres** (see p.1140) also maintains a leading reputation in the state. As well as acting in significant disputes involving lender liability, he has a wealth of experience representing clients in employment litigation. "He has all of the qualities that you look for in a litigator; bright, assertive and a good strategist!" lauds one impressed interviewee. The "very thorough and well-prepared" **Erik Stidham** (see p.1140) has been particularly active in cases with international elements. His litigation expertise encompasses natural resources, real estate and construction. Sources increasingly identify him as a rising name in the sector. **Scott Randolph** (see p.1139) is highlighted as an up-and-coming litigator in the area. He has particular expertise in matters relating to employment law, where he is also developing a name for undertaking noncontentious issues. "He really gets involved and took great care of us," states one client.

### Stoel Rives LLP

**THE FIRM** This firm has near-unparalleled bench strength and breadth of expertise in litigation work in Idaho. The Boise group makes up a key element of the firm's regional litigation practice, and demonstrates experience spanning the agricultural, pharmaceutical and manufacturing industries. The group recently represented St Luke's Regional Medical Center against claims of violation of constitutional and state rights, and also defended Northwest Dairy Association against various contractual claims arising from milk purchase contracts.

**KEY INDIVIDUALS Walter Sinclair** is widely respected as a seasoned litigator. Recent work highlights include his involvement in the aforementioned St Luke's Regional Medical Center matter, and in defending DuPont against mass tort and product liability claims. **Mark Geston** recently led for Timken Alco Aerospace Technologies in a complex product liability matter relating to a helicopter crash. He has also represented clients in the land and pharmaceuticals arenas. **Nicole Hancock** recently represented wine and food distributor TEC Distributing in gaining injunctions to prevent a competitor terminating the client's agreements and transferring its distribution rights. She has also acted in a number of matters involving agricultural clients. The up-and-coming **Bradley Dixon** has acted for a number of major clients of late, including Imperial Oil and Enterprise Rent-A-Car of Utah. Interviewees highlight his client focus and detail-oriented approach.

## Band 2

### Givens Pursley LLP

**THE FIRM** This renowned Idaho firm has an impressive litigation practice. The team works on a wide range of disputes, and is especially active in litigation relating to real estate, environment, healthcare and agriculture. The firm recently acted for developer SilverWing at Sandpoint in a high-value claim against Bonner County regarding runway access rights and depreciation of property value. Other noteworthy litigation clients include Ivy Minerals, Banner Bank and Idaho Press-Tribune. Clients appreciate the firm's experienced bench and breadth of expertise.

**Sources say:** "They were fantastic! Great, efficient communicators that did a top-notch job."

**KEY INDIVIDUALS David Lombardi** is highlighted for his excellent and broad-ranging practice. His recent highlights include successfully enforcing a property claim against the finders of art by Idaho artist James Castle. Lomardi is also highlighted for his work in the healthcare sector. *"He was just excellent,"* enthuses one interviewee. **Alex McLaughlin** enters the rankings this year, having impressed clients and peers across the sector. *"His work was fastidious, extensive, thorough, complete and timely, and presented in a professional and authoritative manner,"* remark sources. McLaughlin recently successfully defended a client against claims of slander of title and abuse of process.

## Hawley Troxell Ennis & Hawley LLP

**THE FIRM** This Idaho firm demonstrates significant capabilities and experience in litigation. The team acts for a range of key clients, including Boise State University, Wells Fargo Bank and URS. A significant feature of the firm's litigation practice is its work involving employment disputes, having recently represented Moreton Insurance and Brown Mackie College on sizable wage claims.

**KEY INDIVIDUALS Steven Schossberger** is frequently involved in high-value litigations, and recently acted for the Idaho Fish and Wildlife Foundation, successfully achieving summary judgment in complaint to grant quiet title. He has significant experience in both state and federal courts. **Merlyn Clark** is a veteran in the dispute resolution arena, and has extensive expertise in mediation and arbitration. Sources respect him for having *"absolutely tons of experience."* **Craig Meadows** is another tremendously experienced practitioner. He is considered by peers to be a *"stalwart of the sector,"* who has tried *"a huge number of cases"* in his time.

## Perkins Coie LLP
### See profile on p.2548

**THE FIRM** This international firm has a compact but extraordinarily effective Idaho litigation practice. The team acts for a range of major clients, including construction and development, real estate and mining companies. The group recently defended a client against antitrust allegations of price-fixing in a multistate dispute. The firm's extensive national presence ensures that the experienced local bench always has the support it needs to act effectively in any dispute.

**KEY INDIVIDUALS Richard Boardman** is renowned for his expertise in all manner of complex business litigation. He is also popular among his peers, who view him as a leading practitioner.

## Band 3

## Moffatt Thomas Barrett Rock & Fields

**THE FIRM** This Idaho firm has experience acting on a range of commercial disputes, and is particularly known for its expertise in litigation involving creditors' rights. The group is widely acknowledged as a key team for lenders, and is also recognized for its work involving employment disputes. The firm also offers clients services in mediation and arbitration.

**KEY INDIVIDUALS** Sources point to **James Martin** as a key litigator at the firm. His practice covers a spectrum of business disputes, including employment and environmental work. *"He's got fantastic common sense and is great on his feet,"* reports one interviewee.

## Medical Malpractice & Insurance

### Duke Scanlan Hall

**THE FIRM** This boutique litigation practice stands out for its work in healthcare and insurance. The firm acts for clients in various disputes in these sectors, including medical device litigation, professional and product liability disputes, and employment law issues. Malpractice cases make up a large part of the firm's work, with a number of its impressive bench boasting expertise in the area. Duke Scanlan Hall also demonstrates great experience in mediating and arbitrating contentious matters.

**Sources say:** *"They really have a lot of potential."*

**KEY INDIVIDUALS Keely Duke** makes regular appearances in the Idaho courts. Described as a *"tenacious attorney who works her tail off,"* she has extensive experience in defending hospitals and other employers in medical malpractice and employment disputes. She is well liked by her peers, with one stating: *"She's one of my favorites."*

**Richard Hall** is a seasoned practitioner in the area, whose depth as a litigator is confirmed by many sources. One interviewee describes him as *"a superb medical malpractice attorney."* He has extensive experience in both medical malpractice and insurance matters.

### Gjording Fouser PLLC

**THE FIRM** This litigation practice group focuses on the malpractice and insurance sectors. The husband and wife-led team is held in high regard across the state for its abundance of jury trial experience. It has acted for businesses, hospitals and professionals, both in the legal and healthcare sectors, in professional liability, insurance defense and other related issues.

**Sources say:** *"An excellent little firm for medical malpractice matters."*

**KEY INDIVIDUALS Jack Gjording** is described as *"one of the best attorneys there is"* by peers. Clients laud his experience, personalized approach and pragmatism. His recent work highlights include acting on complex commercial litigation for an Idaho healthcare provider, as well as malpractice defense for a medical practitioner. *"He's always kindly and available; he tailors every piece of legal advice to what we require,"* says one enthusiastic client. Sources praise the depth of **Trudy Fouser**'s practice, which covers professional liability and insurance disputes. Sources say: *"Her strengths are obvious in her ability to effectively manage litigation and achieve a successful outcome. She has excellent verbal communication skills, along with a gifted ability to persuade and present her point of view."*

## Other Notable Practitioners

**Andrew Brassey** of Brassey Wetherell Crawford & Garrett is identified as *"an excellent court attorney,"* with sources pointing to his skill with juries. A seasoned attorney, he has a broad practice with particular expertise in insurance defense, personal injury and medical malpractice. **Donald Farley** recently joined Powers Tolman Farley, PLLC from Farley Oberrecht West Harwood and Burke, P.A. He is highly regarded for his work in insurance defense and product liability matters. Sources say: *"He's very experienced and always does a good job for his clients."* **Thomas Banducci** of Andersen Banducci PLLC is highlighted by clients as *"an excellent litigator."* Peers identify him as a strategic and focused practitioner, who has a wealth of experience acting for both plaintiff and defendants in complex commercial litigation. **David Comstock** of Comstock and Bush is widely commended by peers, with one source remarking: *"In my opinion, he's one of the finest plaintiff's attorneys in the state."* He has a wealth of experience in representing clients in medical malpractice and personal injury matters. Also at Comstock and Bush, **John Bush** is highlighted for his ability to sensitively deal with clients problems. Sources describe him as *"someone who always does well."* **Nick Crawford** of Brassey Wetherell Crawford & Garrett is another key insurance litigator. Sources describe him as an active practitioner with a broad practice that also covers negligence and product liability work. Seasoned attorney **Richard Greener** of Greener Burke Shoemaker PA is described as *"a classy guy with good jury skills."* Interviewees point to his ability as a negotiator, as well as his standing as a *"key part of the litigation landscape."* **Raymond Powers** of Powers Tolman Farley, PLLC is an experienced practitioner, widely lauded for his work in insurance and medical malpractice defense. Sources praise his ability to command a jury, describing him as *"one of the top defense attorneys"* in the area. Interviewees highly recommend **Charles Hepworth** of Hepworth, Janis & Kluksdal for his plaintiff's work. His expertise covers medical malpractice and personal injury. *"Just excellent!"* enthuses one source. Also at Hepworth Janis, **John Janis** is noted as *"a gentleman and an excellent malpractice attorney."* **John Zarian** (see p.1140) of Parsons Behle & Latimer PC is identified as a key intellectual property attorney. He recently defended RJB Company against patent infringement allegations. He was also lead attorney when the firm acted as sole counsel to Mitt Romney, Rick Santorum and Newt Gingrich in the patent infringement litigation brought against them by EveryMD. **Steve Tolman** of Powers Tolman Farley, PLLC enters the rankings this year. He is a seasoned medical malpractice attorney who is highly commended for his experience. Sources describe him as *"an excellent lawyer."* Interviewees *"have the utmost regard for"* **Timothy Hopkins** of Hopkins Roden Crockett Hansen & Hoopes. This veteran attorney has experience across a number of sectors, litigating on key public law cases and undertaking work on both land use and real estate matters. **James LaRue** of Elam & Burke PA has a broad and highly praised insurance defense practice. *"He's a great trial lawyer,"* say sources. His recent work also includes significant medical malpractice defense engagements. **Marcus Nye** is the managing partner of Racine Olson Nye Budge & Bailey. He is widely accepted as *"a top-notch litigator."* He carries both breadth and depth of experience, having worked on disputes arising in the product liability and insurance sectors. **William Dryden** of Elam & Burke PA is identified as *"the bulldog of defense work."* An extensively experienced attorney, he has superb expertise in litigating and mediating for a range of clients. Litigator and mediator **John Bailey** of Racine Olson Nye Budge & Bailey is noted for his broad practice, which includes healthcare, personal injury and employment litigation. Sources describe him as *"a wonderful lawyer with a straightforward manner."* *"Exceptional trial attorney"*

**Steven Andersen** of Andersen Banducci PLLC is a favorite among peers. His broad practice covers work for both plaintiffs and defendants, as well as product and professional liability, personal injury and intellectual property matters.

## NATURAL RESOURCES & ENVIRONMENT

Commentary about individuals can be found under their firm's paragraph. If the firm has no paragraph (is not ranked) look at Other Notable Practitioners.

### Natural Resources & Environment
### Leading Firms

**Band 1**
Givens Pursley LLP
Holland & Hart LLP *
Perkins Coie LLP
Stoel Rives LLP

**Band 2**
Baird Hanson LLP
Barker Rosholt & Simpson LLP
Moffatt Thomas Barrett Rock & Fields

### Senior Statesmen

Senior Statesmen: distinguished older practitioners
O'Riordan Hugh          *Givens Pursley LLP*

### Leading Individuals

**Band 1**

| | |
|---|---|
| Baird Joseph H | *Baird Hanson LLP* |
| Barker Albert | *Barker Rosholt & Simpson LLP* |
| Beaton Kevin | *Stoel Rives LLP* |
| Feldman Murray | *Holland & Hart LLP* * |
| Fereday Jeffrey | *Givens Pursley LLP* |
| Maynard Robert | *Perkins Coie LLP* |
| McIntyre Krista K | *Stoel Rives LLP* |
| Meyer Christopher | *Givens Pursley LLP* |
| Myers III William G | *Holland & Hart LLP* * |

**Band 2**

| | |
|---|---|
| Allen Gary | *Givens Pursley LLP* |
| Barton Peter | *Givens Pursley LLP* |
| Campbell Scott | *Moffatt Thomas Barrett Rock & Fields* |
| Creamer Michael | *Givens Pursley LLP* |
| Hill Teresa A | *Stoel Rives LLP* |
| Jones Linda B | *Holland & Hart LLP* * |
| Smith Bruce M | *Moore Smith Buxton & Turcke (ONP)* † |

**Up-and-coming individuals**

| | |
|---|---|
| Hall Richard R | *Stoel Rives LLP* |
| Lawrence Dylan B | *Moffatt Thomas Barrett Rock & Fields* |
| Malmen Erika | *Perkins Coie LLP* |

* Indicates firm / individual with profile.
† ONP = Other Notable Practitioner.

### Band 1

#### Givens Pursley LLP

**THE FIRM** Though primarily known for real estate work, this firm has a wealth of experience on key environmental issues. Mining exploration, water law and public access issues have featured heavily in recent work. Givens Pursley also has hands-on experience dealing with legislative and political processes in the context of lobbying. The firm recently acted on a number of environmental matters for Mosquito Consolidated Gold Mines, providing advice on a large copper molybdenum exploration project and defending against challenges to the project.
**Sources say:** *"One of the premier legal houses in the state."*
**KEY INDIVIDUALS Jeffrey Fereday** is described by peers as *"very competent and knowledgeable."* He has broad experience in this sector, and is most noted for his work in water rights. Alongside colleagues, he has represented several cities in respect of municipal water rights matters. He also has extensive experience in mining matters. The *"very good"* **Christopher Meyer** is widely respected for his expertise in water law, though his practice also covers other environmental issues. He recently represented provider United Water Idaho on municipal water rights legislation. **Gary Allen** is noted for his expertise in land use law. He recently advised Hayden Area Regional Sewer Board on litigation and permitting matters. Interviewees laud him for a *"level of skill that is just superb."* Clients single out **Michael Creamer** for praise when it comes to water rights and transfers, describing him as *"exceptional and patient."* His recent work includes acting extensively on the creation, purchase and sale of surface and groundwater rights for Idaho Water Company. Of late, **Peter Barton** has acted for Lactalis American Group on various environmental issues, including those relating to air quality and wastewater discharge. He has a wealth of experience with environmental legislation and has a background in engineering, specifically in relation to this sector. Veteran practitioner **Hugh O'Riordan** is held in high esteem by peers. *"A very creative, highly intelligent lawyer,"* he has accrued vast experience in Clean Air Act, contamination and administrative law issues.

#### Holland & Hart LLP
See profile on p.727

**THE FIRM** This regional powerhouse continues to act at the forefront of environmental issues in Idaho. Practitioners at the firm's Boise office have previously undertaken work on a variety of matters, including environmental compliance, renewable energy, land use, and both air and water quality. Recent highlights include work related to the implementation of wildlife protection measures across the USA and permitting issues within Idaho.
**KEY INDIVIDUALS** *"Really top notch for EPA and endangered species work,"* **Murray Feldman** (see p.1139) impresses sources with extensive knowledge and a wealth of experience in this sector. Feldman has acted on matters across the country and is noted for both regulatory and litigious work. **William Myers** (see p.1139) is noted for a wealth of experience in natural resource, environment and public land issues across the country. He was recently involved in a major environmental litigation impacting on the oil and gas industry. **Linda Jones** (see p.1139) has recently acted on major environmental permitting issues within Idaho. She has a broad practice which also features work in real estate financing. *"I couldn't ask any more of her,"* enthused one client.

#### Perkins Coie LLP
See profile on p.2548

**THE FIRM** This firm's compact Boise office is supported by its extensive network of offices across the USA. The practice has gathered notable experience on renewable energy matters as well as handling traditional energy work. The firm also offers a full spread of services in environmental issues, including water, air, endangered species, forestry and mining matters. Highlights of recent work include acting for the City of Boise on municipal water rights and an associated geothermal heating project.
**KEY INDIVIDUALS Robert Maynard** recently acted for the Mt Ashland Association, defending the expansion of a ski area in a national forest special use permit area against legal challenges. He has also undertaken work relating to mining projects around the country. Rising star **Erika Malmen** has recently acted for the City of Boise in various water rights issues, including settlement negotiations surrounding the Snake River Basin Adjudication.

## Stoel Rives LLP

**THE FIRM** The Boise office of this regional powerhouse demonstrates strength in central issues relating to energy and environmental matters. Leading practitioners in air, water and mining at Stoel Rives undertake work both inside Idaho and across the Northwest. The firm recently represented Hecla Mining Company in water quality and mining issues, and Sunshine Silver Mines Corporation in the reopening of a mine in Kellogg.

**KEY INDIVIDUALS Kevin Beaton** has experience in a broad range of environmental issues, including Superfund and Clean Water Act matters. Recent work highlights include advising major Idaho companies on water quality and cleanup issues. Department head **Krista McIntyre** continues to be a key figure for air quality issues and permitting across the Northwest. A favorite among clients and peers, she provides environmental counsel to major US companies. **Richard Hall** has developed an impressive practice in the mining sector. Recent work includes acting on the sale of the Youngs Creek Coal Mine project for CONSOL energy, in addition to the aforementioned Hecla Mining and Sunshine Silver Mine matters. **Teresa Hill** recently acted for Iberdrola Renewables as lead partner on a sale from its Manzana Wind Power Project. She also has experience in permitting, due diligence and representing clients before administrative agencies.

# REAL ESTATE

Zoning/Land Use p.1138

Commentary about individuals can be found under their firm's paragraph. If the firm has no paragraph (is not ranked) look at Other Notable Practitioners.

| Real Estate |
| --- |
| **Leading Firms** |
| **Band 1** |
| Givens Pursley LLP |
| **Band 2** |
| Hawley Troxell Ennis & Hawley LLP |
| Stoel Rives LLP |
| **Band 3** |
| Holland & Hart LLP * |
| Meuleman Mollerup LLP |
| Moffatt Thomas Barrett Rock & Fields |
| Spink Butler, LLP |
| * Indicates firm with profile. |
| Alphabetical order within each band. Band 1 is the highest. |

## Band 1

## Givens Pursley LLP

**THE FIRM** This group is widely considered the standout firm for real estate work in Idaho. Boasting extensive experience in the arena, Givens Pursley demonstrates considerable strength in a range of related areas, including commercial and environmental work. Recent mandates include acting for Chobani in its development of a state-of-the-art yogurt manufacturing plant in Twin Falls.

## Band 2

## Baird Hanson LLP

**THE FIRM** This boutique firm focuses on mining issues. The compact team has more than 60 years' collective experience serving this industry. The firm also has experience working on endangered species issues.

**Sources say:** *"Probably the most competent mining lawyers around."*

**KEY INDIVIDUALS Joseph Baird** continues to be a stalwart in the mining sector. Working across the West, he has represented a number of important mining companies and is lauded by his peers.

## Barker Rosholt & Simpson LLP

**THE FIRM** This firm has significant expertise in a variety of natural resources and environmental issues. The firm has experience in both water quality and rights issues, and has undertaken work on the Clean Water Act, Endangered Species Act, Superfund and NEPA issues. The team can also handle matters relating to public land issues and mining work.

**KEY INDIVIDUALS Albert Barker** is *"intelligent and produces a good quality product,"* according to sources. He is held in high regard for his work on groundwater contamination issues and acting for mining companies.

**Sources say:** *"We've been so pleased with their service - they continue to be the best!"*

**KEY INDIVIDUALS Christopher Beeson** is widely acknowledged as one of the best real estate attorneys in Idaho. Sources highlight his creativity, direct manner and ability as a negotiator, stating: *"He is the lawyer I respect the most - a consummate professional and fantastic to work with."* His recent work includes major urban renewal projects. **Edward Miller** also receives consistently high praise. In addition to his work for Chobani, he has also undertaken real estate engagements for Millenkamp Cattle. He is *"just excellent,"* reports one client, *"he's always kind and responsive."* Miller's broad real estate practice covers both general real estate transactions and finance. The *"patient, meticulous and responsive"* **Gary Allen** is a client favorite for zoning and land use matters. His recent work highlights include acting in various permitting matters for Mosquito Consolidated Gold Mines and representing national developer The Michaels Organization in a student housing project in Boise. **Deborah Nelson** is also noted for her work in land use. Her recent matters include conducting due diligence of local permitting for three separate wind projects for Atlantic Power Corporation following its acquisition of Ridgeline Energy. She is highly regarded for her forthright pursuit of clients' interests. The *"timely and straightforward"* **Franklin Lee** enters the real estate table

## Moffatt Thomas Barrett Rock & Fields

**THE FIRM** This Idaho firm has extensive expertise in water law, both in respect of water rights and water quality. The team has three locations across the state, enabling it to offer a strong local service to its clients, which include a number of agricultural and mining organizations.

**KEY INDIVIDUALS Scott Campbell** has particular expertise in water law. He acts for clients in the ranching, agriculture and alcohol industries. He is lauded as *"a bright lawyer who knows what he's talking about."* **Dylan Lawrence** continues to impress peers. He has accrued great experience in water rights, but also has undertaken work on alternative energy projects, easements and rights of way, and the Clean Air Act.

## Other Notable Practitioners

**Bruce Smith** of Moore Smith Buxton & Turcke continues to be a noted presence in this sector. His broad practice covers mining, water rights, federal land and endangered species issues.

following a raft of positive client feedback. He recently worked on real estate matters for Saint Alphonsus Health System, and is noted for his expertise in construction contracts and disputes. **Anne Kunkel** has a broad practice covering a wide array of real estate transactions. She also assisted on the aforementioned Chobani and Millenkamp matters. Sources highlight her determination and efficiency.

## Band 2

## Hawley Troxell Ennis & Hawley LLP

**THE FIRM** This stalwart of the Idaho legal market undertakes real estate work across the state. Offices in Boise, Coeur d'Alene and Pocatello ensure both breadth and depth of service. The team's recent work includes acting in the sale of Canyon Park Shopping Center in Twin Falls, as well as for Gardner Company in various real estate and land use issues arising from the development of an 18-story mixed-use office and retail building in Boise.

**Sources say:** *"A great firm with great real estate lawyers!"*

**KEY INDIVIDUALS Brian Ballard** is lauded as *"a thoughtful and experienced attorney"* by sources. He is known for his expertise in commercial transactions, and has worked on numerous significant real estate development projects and financing matters. **Geoffrey Wardle** has a wealth of experience in regulatory and transactional matters. Peers highlight his important work involving impact fee ordinances. Wardle also represented Gardner Company in its construction of a 90,000 sq ft medical office building in Caldwell.

## Stoel Rives LLP

**THE FIRM** This firm is another regional leader with breadth of expertise and the support of offices across the West. While ensuring Idaho-based clients are in safe hands, the firm has also demonstrated deep expertise in regional projects, especially in matters involving the energy sector. Recent work highlights include representing Clearwater Paper Corporation in the sale of its Lewiston, Idaho sawmill to Idaho Forest Group, a transaction valued at approximately $30 million.

**KEY INDIVIDUALS Quentin Knipe** is a key figure for real estate work in Idaho. He recently assisted Coleman Homes in its purchase of land in and around Boise. He has also recently worked on complex leasing transactions and wind energy projects.

## Band 3

### Holland & Hart LLP
**See profile on p.727**

**THE FIRM** This regional firm provides high-caliber service and maintains an enviable reputation. Experience from across the Mountain States ensures client confidence in a range of real estate, zoning and land use matters. The firm recently represented a joint venture entity in a $15 million acquisition of 616 acres of land in Hayden, northern Idaho, for a 'Traditional Neighborhood Design' development, a project involving the construction of leisure, community and residential facilities.

**KEY INDIVIDUALS Matthew Hicks** (see p.1139) acts for various clients in significant real estate matters, including US Bank National Association and major companies in the food and drink industry. He is *"a great attorney - very responsive to all of our needs,"* enthuses one client. Recent arrival at the firm **Laurie Reynoldson** (see p.1139) maintains a solid reputation for work in this sector. She has experience working on commercial and residential developments, as well as land use matters.

### Meuleman Mollerup LLP

**THE FIRM** This local firm is noted for its work for construction companies. Boasting both breadth and depth of expertise, the group offers services to business clients on transactional matters and dispute resolution. Alongside a sterling construction law practice, the firm is well placed to deal with all manner of construction lien claims.

**KEY INDIVIDUALS Kimbal Gowland** is noted for his meticulous approach to transactions. Sources commend his extensive experience in real estate matters, including his expertise in leasing, purchase and sale, development, and transaction financings. Peers highlight the personable nature of **Richard Mollerup**. He continues to be a go-to name for real estate matters, and has significant expertise in escrow law. He is described as *"strong and well-respected lawyer."* **Mike Baldner** is noted for his work on shopping centre developments, and has experience in both transactional and contentious matters. Peers identify him as a *"good, practical attorney."*

### Moffatt Thomas Barrett Rock & Fields

**THE FIRM** This firm boasts experience across both litigious and transactional real estate matters. With offices in Boise, Idaho Falls and Pocatello, Moffatt Thomas is well prepared to undertake work across the southern part of the state. The firm's attorneys undertake matters on behalf of a range of real estate clients, including both commercial and residential developers.

**KEY INDIVIDUALS Robert Burns** has a broad real estate practice encompassing transactional and litigious engagements. Sources praise his creativity and persuasive advocacy, and peers identify him as *"a worthy opponent."* **Christine Nicholas** is respected for her extensive experience in corporate real estate. She is noted as *"a very good, technical lawyer,"* who impresses with her direct yet personable manner and business acumen. Sources underscore the broad range of **David Jensen**'s expertise, describing him as *"a solid attorney and a great financial real estate lawyer."* He is also widely praised for his expertise in real estate finance, particularly on behalf of lenders.

### Spink Butler, LLP

**THE FIRM** Spink Butler is a boutique firm noted for its wealth of expertise in real estate matters. Keen abilities in zoning and land use issues makes it a go-to firm for developers, and its attorneys have experience in title insurance as well as general business transactions and litigation.

**KEY INDIVIDUALS JoAnn Butler** is widely praised for her expertise as a *"personal and persuasive"* land use attorney. Her extensive experience, pragmatism and client focus are also acknowledged by peers, who note: *"She shines when she's on her feet with a city or town council."* Described as *"a very knowledgeable, very creative litigator, "* **Michael Spink** is a key figure for litigious real estate matters. He is also increasingly recognized for his excellent transactional expertise.

### Other Notable Practitioners

**Steve Bradbury** of Williams Bradbury, Attorneys at Law remains popular among peers. He has a wealth of experience working on entitlement matters, and is lauded for his ability in handling land use hearings. Working at her own eponymous firm, **Cynthia Melillo** has a broad practice which includes providing a range of real estate services to commercial real estate development clients. *"It's difficult to say anything negative about her!"* notes an impressed source.

# Leaders' Profiles in Idaho

**BITHELL, Walter**
Holland & Hart LLP, Boise
208 383 3940
wbithell@hollandhart.com
*Featured in Litigation (Idaho)*
**Practice Areas:** Individual and class action tort litigation, including business and commercial, personal injury, products liability, professional liability, commercial, insurance, securities, and general litigation.
**Professional Memberships:** American College of Trial Lawyers, American Inns of Court No. 130, American and Idaho Trial Lawyers Association, University of Idaho Foundation, American Society of Writers on Legal Subjects.
**Career:** Admitted: Idaho Bar, Idaho State and Federal District Courts, US Court of Federal Claims, US Court of Appeals, Ninth Circuit, US Supreme Court. Former Idaho Deputy Attorney General, GC Idaho Department of Insurance, GC Idaho Tax Commission.
**Personal:** University of Idaho: JD (1968), BS (1965).

**FAUCHER, Robert A**
Holland & Hart LLP, Boise
208 383 3941
rfaucher@hollandhart.com
*Featured in Bankruptcy/Restructuring (Idaho)*
**Practice Areas:** Bob Faucher represents clients in complex commercial litigation and transactions, with a specialty in bankruptcy and creditors' rights. He has represented debtors, trustees, secured creditors, creditors' committees, and purchasers of assets in bankruptcy cases. He has represented lenders and other parties in lender liability lawsuits, breach of fiduciary duty cases, breach of contract cases, business torts, and cases involving derivatives. His transactional practice most often involves credit transactions and workouts.
**Personal:** Harvard Law School (JD 1988, cum laude); Yale University (BA 1984, summa cum laude).

**FELDMAN, Murray**
Holland & Hart LLP, Boise
208 383 3921
mfeldman@hollandhart.com
*Featured in Natural Resources (Idaho)*
**Practice Areas:** Represents government, industry, and private clients on endangered species, public lands, transportation and water projects, and permitting. Obtained key rulings in cases on species listing and critical habitat (salmon, polar bear), highway project approvals, and military overflight assessments.
**Professional Memberships:** ABA Section of Environment; Idaho State Bar, Natural Resources Section.
**Career:** Firmwide Partner Responsibility Committee (2011-present); Boise office Administrative Partner (2009-12); Firmwide Environmental Practice Group Manager (2001-03); Partner since 1998.
**Personal:** University of California, Berkeley School of Law (JD 1988); University of Idaho (MS 1985); University of California, Berkeley (BS 1982). Idaho Humanities Council Board Member (2013-present).

**HANSEN, Brian**
Holland & Hart LLP, Boise
208 383 3902
bthansen@hollandhart.com
*Featured in Corporate/Commercial (Idaho)*
**Practice Areas:** Mr Hansen's extensive experience includes mergers, acquisitions, telecommunications, securities, credit agreements, and real estate. He assists clients with operational needs, including license agreements, service and marketing agreements, and purchase and sale agreements.
**Professional Memberships:** Governing Council, Idaho State Bar Business and Corporate Law Section; Idaho State Bar Committee on the Harmonized Uniform Business Organization Code.
**Career:** Before joining Holland & Hart, he served as Sr. Vice President, General Counsel and Corporate Secretary for MPC Computers and as Area Vice President, Legal and Corporate Secretary for Micron Electronics.
**Personal:** University of Virginia School of Law JD 1990.

**HICKS, Matthew**
Holland & Hart LLP, Boise
208 383 3932
mhicks@hollandhart.com
*Featured in Real Estate (Idaho)*
**Practice Areas:** Mr. Hicks focuses on real estate transactions, including acquisitions and sales, financing, commercial leasing, title-related issues, and shopping center, industrial, office and other commercial development. He also represents lenders and borrowers in financing transactions and loan workouts and restructurings.
**Professional Memberships:** Board Member, Board of Advisors, Boise Metro Chamber of Commerce; Member, International Council of Shopping Centers (ICSC)
**Career:** Recipient of Idaho Business Review's Accomplished Under 40 Award for Emerging Business Leaders, 2008
**Personal:** JD, University of Notre Dame (1996); BA, Baylor University (1992).

**JONES, Linda B**
Holland & Hart LLP, Boise
208 34 5000
ljones@hollandhart.com
*Featured in Natural Resources (Idaho)*
**Practice Areas:** Environmental and natural resources law; water, mineral and geothermal rights; project development permits and due diligence; public lands; land use; secured financing; real estate transactions.
**Professional Memberships:** ABA Sections of Environment, Energy and Resources and Business; Idaho State Bar Sections of Environment and Natural Resources (past Chair, Governing Council) and Business-Corporate (past Vice-Chair, Governing Council).
**Career:** Practicing since 1986.
**Publications:** Reporter for Rocky Mountain Mineral Law Foundation Water Law Newsletter (Idaho).
**Personal:** University of California (MPP 1985); University of California Boalt Hall School of Law (JD 1985); San Jose State University (BA 1981, with high distinction).

**MACK, J Frederick**
Holland & Hart LLP, Boise
208 383 3910
fmack@hollandhart.com
*Featured in Corporate/Commercial (Idaho)*
**Practice Areas:** Mr Mack has nearly 30 years of business transactional law experience representing several of Idaho's largest publicly and privately-held companies. He advises clients in contract negotiations, formation/development of corporations, partnerships, limited liability partnerships, and limited liability companies. Mr Mack has extensive experience in mergers, acquisitions, divestitures, share exchanges, protecting proprietary interests and real estate/land use issues. He has been nationally recognized for his work in corporate structure.
**Professional Memberships:** American Bar Association, Section of Business Law; Idaho State Bar Association, Section of Business and Corporate Law.
**Personal:** JD (1972) and BA (1969) - University of Idaho.

**MYERS III, William G**
Holland & Hart LLP, Boise
208 383 3954
wmyers@hollandhart.com
*Featured in Natural Resources (Idaho)*
**Practice Areas:** Public lands, energy, and natural resources law.
**Professional Memberships:** Admitted to practice in Idaho, Wyoming, Colorado and the District of Columbia as well as various federal courts.
**Career:** Held various federal offices including Solicitor of the US Department of the Interior, Deputy General Counsel for Programs for the US Department of Energy, Assistant to the US Attorney General, and Legislative Counsel to US Senator Alan Simpson (WY).
**Publications:** Various publications in academic and popular journals related to his practice areas.
**Personal:** University of Denver College of Law (JD 1981); College of William and Mary (AB 1977).

**PRINCE, Larry E**
Holland & Hart LLP, Boise
208 383 3920
lprince@hollandhart.com
*Featured in Bankruptcy/Restructuring (Idaho), Corporate/Commercial (Idaho)*
**Practice Areas:** Mr Prince specializes in commercial bankruptcy, complex credit transactions, commercial litigation, workout of problem loans and leases, and commercial real estate transactions.
**Professional Memberships:** Member: Idaho and Washington State Bar Associations; US Bankruptcy and District Courts for Idaho and Eastern Washington; American Bankruptcy Institute. Fellow, American College of Bankruptcy; Listed in leading American publications.
**Publications:** Mr Prince has published articles, is a lecturer on bankruptcy and commercial law, and has served as a visiting professor at the University of Idaho School of Law.
**Personal:** University of California, Hastings College of the Law (1975); BA, Boise State College (1972).

**RANDOLPH, Scott**
Holland & Hart LLP, Boise
208 383 3988
serandolph@hollandhart.com
*Featured in Labor & Employment (Idaho), Litigation (Idaho)*
**Practice Areas:** Mr Randolph's practice involves virtually all aspects of litigation, with an emphasis on complex commercial and employment litigation. He has experience with the latest developments in e-discovery and writes regularly on a variety of employment and litigation related topics. Mr. Randolph has successfully represented clients in state and federal courts throughout Idaho as well as in the United States Court of Appeals for the Ninth Circuit.
**Professional Memberships:** Idaho representative, Employment Law Alliance.
**Career:** Law clerk, Hon. N. Randy Smith, U.S. Court of Appeals, 9th Circuit.
**Personal:** JD, The University of Texas (2003); BA, Oregon State University (2000).

**REYNOLDSON, Laurie**
Holland & Hart LLP, Boise
208 489 3035
lreynoldson@spinkbutler.com
*Featured in Real Estate (Idaho)*
**Practice Areas:** Laurie Reynoldson focuses her practice on commercial and real estate transactions. She advises clients on commercial matters including mergers, acquisitions, financing and loan negotiations, loan workouts and restructuring. She assists clients with real estate and development work for commercial and residential projects, including documenting and closing acquisitions and sales, commercial leasing, solving title-related issues, due diligence work, and land use representation on zoning, use and permitting matters for shopping centers, industrial, office, multi-family residential and other commercial development.
**Professional Memberships:** Idaho State Bar; Washington State Bar Association; International Council of Shopping Centers; Urban Land Institute; Idaho Women Lawyers.

## SNYDER, Nicole
Holland & Hart LLP, Boise
208 383 3939
ncsnyder@hollandhart.com
*Featured in Corporate/Commercial (Idaho)*

**Practice Areas:** Ms Snyder's transactional experience extends to general business planning, mergers and acquisitions, debt and equity transactions, corporate governance, and real estate transactions. She also has extensive experience drafting executive employment agreements and negotiating matters related to non-competition covenants.
**Professional Memberships:** Idaho State Bar; Washington State Bar; Idaho State Bar Business and Corporate Law Section; Idaho Women Lawyers.
**Personal:** University of Michigan Law School JD (2001); University of San Diego BA (1997).

## SQUYRES, Newal
Holland & Hart LLP, Boise
208 383 3911
nsquyres@hollandhart.com
*Featured in Litigation (Idaho)*

**Practice Areas:** Complex civil litigation, including False Claims Act, commercial, employment, intellectual property, products liability, construction, insurance coverage and bad faith, and aviation.

**Professional Memberships:** Member, American Bar Association (Litigation Section) and Idaho State Bar (founding Member of ADR Section). President, Idaho State Bar, 2009.
**Career:** Admitted: Texas (1972) and Idaho (1974) Bars; US District Court, District of Idaho (1974); US Court of Appeals, Fifth (1972) and Ninth Circuits (1980). Faculty, University of Idaho Law School, Trial Advocacy Clinic. Mr. Squyres is a frequent speaker on trial preparation and technique.
**Personal:** Texas Tech University: JD (1972 w/high honors), BA (1968).

## STIDHAM, Erik
Holland & Hart LLP, Boise
208 342 3934
efstidham@hollandhart.com
*Featured in Litigation (Idaho)*

**Practice Areas:** Mr Stidham focuses his practice on complex litigation. He has extensive experience litigating disputes involving business torts, real estate development, natural resources and environmental law, construction, employment claims, banking, securities, and fraud.
**Professional Memberships:** American Bar Association, Litigation Section; Idaho State Bar, Litigation Section; Los Angeles County Bar Association.

**Career:** President, Movies for a Cause Foundation; Past Member, Bishop Kelly Foundation; Partner, Stoel Rives LLP, 2000-06.
**Personal:** JD, University of Virginia School of Law (Moot Court Board); BA, Arizona State University (Summa Cum Laude, Phi Beta Kappa).

## WEST, Kevin
Parsons Behle & Latimer PC, Boise
208 562 4908
kwest@parsonsbehle.com
*Featured in Labor & Employment (Idaho)*

**Practice Areas:** Practice emphasizes healthcare and employment law. Experienced trial attorney, particularly in the areas of employment law, commercial litigation, professional malpractice, personal injury and insurance litigation.
**Professional Memberships:** Member, Idaho, Utah and Washington State Bar Associations.
**Career:** Shareholder. Frequent lecturer healthcare issues, insurance law, malpractice prevention and employment law matters. Author of four nationally marketed publications in the healthcare field. Adviser to national companies on healthcare, employment and Medicare matters.
**Personal:** JD, cum laude, Brigham Young University, 1984. BS, Brigham Young University, 1981.

## ZARIAN, John N
Parsons Behle & Latimer PC, Boise
208 562 4902
jzarian@parsonsbehle.com
*Featured in Litigation (Idaho)*

**Practice Areas:** Managing Shareholder, Boise office. Practice emphasizes intellectual property litigation, as well as complex business and commercial litigation. An experienced trial lawyer, he has served as lead counsel in matters involving patents, trademarks, copyrights, trade secrets, right of publicity, unfair competition, e-commerce, cybersquatting, contracts, business torts, antitrust claims, class actions, securities, and other commercial disputes.
**Professional Memberships:** J. Reuben Clark Law Society; Litigation Counsel of America.
**Career:** Practiced law in Southern California, 1989-2005.
**Publications:** Frequent author and lecturer on topics of current legal interest.
**Personal:** JD, University of Southern California Law School, 1989. MS Finance, University of Utah, 1989.

### How lawyers are ranked

Every year we carry out thousands of in-depth interviews with clients in order to assess the reputations and expertise of business lawyers worldwide. The qualities we look for (and which determine rankings) include technical legal ability, professional conduct, client service, commercial awareness/astuteness, diligence, commitment, and other qualities most valued by the client. For details of our research team, see p.5.

## Contents:

# ILLINOIS: An Introduction

## Contributed by Neal, Gerber & Eisenberg LLP

**Illinois Business Climate Improves, but State Still Has a Ways to Go**

The Illinois economy continued its sluggish recovery in 2012. After reaching a high of 11.5% in 2009, the state's unemployment rate was back down at 8.6% in December 2012, but remained above the national average of 7.8%. Real GDP growth continued to trend upward in most sectors of the state's broad and diversified economy, though weighed down by continued high unemployment and foreclosure rates, but the state is underperforming national GDP growth. Economists forecast GDP growth for Illinois of about 3.2% in 2013. The Business Barometer Index for the Great Lakes region for 2013, based on surveys of private sector purchasing managers throughout the region, reflects cautious optimism and continued modest expansion. A similar survey of local conditions conducted by the Federal Reserve Bank of Chicago also identified firming business conditions.

But the general economy is only one piece of the puzzle when it comes to the Illinois business climate. Although many states have budget issues, Illinois has some of the worst in the nation. In 2010, the state's budget shortfall was more than 40% of its general fund, the second-highest of any state. Illinois also has the lowest bond rating of all 50 states, according to Moody's, and approximately $8 billion in unpaid bills. In addition, the state only funded 43% of its pension liability in 2011, the lowest percentage of any state. The 2011 $82.9 billion pension gap is up from $38.6 billion in 2005. These factors, among others, led Moody's Investors Service to downgrade the state's credit rating yet again in January 2013.

Although positive steps have been taken toward fiscal responsibility, many years of financial mismanagement have resulted in a state economic condition that is precarious at best. The temporary increase in the state's income tax rate for individuals and businesses from 3% to 5%, passed early in 2011 and in effect from 2011 through 2014, gave rise to predictions of mass business defections to neighboring states. The combination of tax increases and spending caps enacted in 2011 are working, and have resulted in an estimated budget gap of $2.9 billion in FY 2012, which is down from $5.6 billion in FY 2011. Additionally, there has been no wave of business departures, perhaps partly as a result of a flurry of busi-

ness-friendly tax benefits the legislature created or extended at the end of 2011 in response to grumbling by business leaders. And, despite the 2011 income tax increase, after taking into account the complete array of taxes and the overall burden on business, the pro-business Tax Foundation ranked Illinois 29th out of 50 states on the 2013 State Business Climate Index, well ahead of other major commercial states such as California, New York, Ohio and New Jersey, and only narrowly behind Massachusetts. In fact, savvy executives able to take advantage of the range of tax incentives now on the books in Illinois may find ways to ride the Illinois economy's gathering wave.

Here is a brief summary of some of the recent legislative changes providing or extending tax incentives for doing business in Illinois:

- A 5-year extension of the New Markets Development Program, providing tax credits to those making qualified equity investments in Illinois.
- A 5-year extension of the Small Business Job Creation Tax Credit, with up to $2,500 of credit available per new employee on the payroll in Illinois through the end of the incentive period, which now ends on June 30, 2016.
- A 5-year extension of all exemptions, credits and deductions in the Illinois sales and use tax laws that were otherwise scheduled to expire in 2011, 2012 or 2013.
- The restoration of the previously suspended net operating loss ("NOL") Illinois income tax deduction (initially subject to an annual limit of $100,000, but then available on an unlimited basis beginning with tax years ending on or after December 31, 2014).
- The 5-year extension of the Illinois Research and Development Credit through tax years ending prior to January 1, 2016.

In recent years, Illinois has also established or extended tax incentives targeting specific industries, such as biodiesel and gasohol production, live theater production and nursing homes, and granted substantial tax relief to several specific major employers. However, as of January 1, 2013, the state increased its rate for withholding Illinois Income Tax from 3% to 5%. In 2012, the state took the extraordinary step of establishing a new Independent Tax Tribunal Board to

assuage concerns that the state's Department of Revenue could not fairly adjudicate tax disputes in light of its own pressing need to maximize tax revenues. Also noteworthy are the City of Chicago's surprise decision in March 2012 to rapidly phase out the infamous Chicago $4 per employee per month "head tax," the Cook County Board's vote to roll back the 2008 increase in sales and use tax and increase the tax on a pack of cigarettes by $1, which went into effect in 2013. Finally, high net worth individuals will appreciate the 2011 passage of an increase in the Illinois estate tax exclusion from the former $2 million to $3.5 million for persons dying on or after January 1, 2012 and prior to January 1, 2013, and to $4 million for persons dying thereafter.

Illinois is a centrally located national financial and transportation hub with a diversified service and manufacturing economy, serving as a top connection point for air, rail, highway, telecommunications and internet traffic. While 2013 is certainly not the go-go 1990s and the state is facing some major fiscal challenges, the overall economy looks to be trending upward and the business tax burden is not extraordinary for a large commercial state. With the many tax incentives now available, there are more reasons than ever to give Illinois a second look as a place to establish or grow a business.

# ANTITRUST

Commentary about individuals can be found under their firm's paragraph. If the firm has no paragraph (is not ranked) look at Other Notable Practitioners.

### Antitrust
### Leading Firms

**Band 1**
Kirkland & Ellis LLP *
Mayer Brown LLP *
McDermott Will & Emery LLP *

**Band 2**
Eimer Stahl LLP *
Jones Day *
Sidley Austin LLP *
Winston & Strawn LLP *

**Band 3**
Baker & McKenzie *
Freeborn & Peters LLP *
Freed Kanner London & Millen LLC
Sperling & Slater

**Band 4**
Dentons *
Edwards Wildman Palmer *
Jenner & Block LLP *
McGuireWoods LLP *

*Indicates firm with profile.*
*Alphabetical order within each band. Band 1 is the highest.*

## Band 1

### Kirkland & Ellis LLP
See profile on p.1254

**THE FIRM** Like many of the leading firms in Illinois, this group has a truly national antitrust scope. Within Chicago, it is frequently seen in the largest class action suits and is widely recognized by peers for its formidable bench strength. Among its numerous litigation highlights it has been defending Bain Capital against a putative nationwide class action suit estimated at $10 billion. Other notable cases include acting for Hitachi on the settlement of the TFT-LCD flat panel class action, which alleged price-fixing, and representing the Blue Cross and Blue Shield Association in an ongoing nationwide action that could

potentially impact some 100 million Americans insured by the BCBSA.
**Sources say:** *"Very good lawyers: on the ball, aggressive and smart. They're on everyone's list."*
**KEY INDIVIDUALS** The terrific **James Mutchnik** (see p.1223) is *"very professional, bright and responsive,"* according to sources. In addition to the Bain Capital and Hitachi cases, his extensive recent resume also includes work for Navistar International against an allegation of monopolization of the heavy-duty truck transmission market, and for EVA Airways, which he represents in three separate civil and criminal antitrust matters. **Daniel Laytin** (see p.1217) is described as *"outstanding"* and a *"go-to guy"* who is particularly praised for his *"ability to think and react on his feet while doing an excellent job of staying several steps ahead of the game."* Laytin is taking the lead in the BCBSA case. **Andrew Langan** (see p.1216) is a litigator with wide experience in antitrust work and is currently heavily involved in general commercial litigation on the defense side in the BP Deepwater Horizon case. **David Zott** (see p.1238) has a *"wealth of litigation experience,"* according to one source. Although he practices in a number of areas, he has been heavily involved in plasma derivative antitrust litigation on behalf of Baxter, as well as playing a significant role in the BCBSA case.

### Mayer Brown LLP
See profile on p.1257

**THE FIRM** With a raft of leading names in this field, Mayer Brown's Chicago antitrust practice continues to be among the very best on offer and is able to draw upon the national and international reach of the firm. The group has an excellent reputation for its appellate practice, but is also highly sought for more general antitrust litigation and counseling. It has ongoing work for clients in two of the most significant current price-fixing class action suits, for The Mosaic Company in the potash litigation and for Temple-Inland in the containerboard litigation.
**Sources say:** *"They are real competitors – they cover a lot of ground nationally and locally."*

**KEY INDIVIDUALS Andrew Marovitz** is described as an *"outstanding lawyer"* who is particularly noted for the *"wonderful job"* he does in court and his excellent rapport with clients. Present in nearly all of the firm's recent major work, particular highlights include representing ArcelorMittal in an alleged conspiracy by steel producers to influence prices by reducing output, and defending BASF in a case concerning alleged urethane price-fixing. **Mark McLaughlin** *"continues to do first-rate work"* in antitrust despite having become the firm's general counsel. Although he predominantly focuses on antitrust counseling, he maintains an excellent reputation for his work in litigation. **Britt Miller** is described as a *"very formidable and energetic"* attorney who *"argues and presents well."* Miller has worked with Andrew Marovitz on much of the firm's most significant recent work and has also taken the lead in some notable cases, including being liaison counsel in the potash class action litigation. Commentators also note that she is well liked by clients and judges. **Lee Abrams** continues to amaze his colleagues and peers by showing few signs of slowing down despite some 55 years' experience as a litigator. He maintains a practice in antitrust, franchising and general commercial litigation.

### McDermott Will & Emery LLP
See profile on p.1258

**THE FIRM** This group maintains its place at the top table by virtue of its excellent reputation in litigation and its notable strengths in healthcare work. It has appeared in large class action suits including the sulfuric acid, steel and chocolate litigation, for Koch Industries, Steel Dynamics and Mars respectively. On the healthcare side, it has represented ProMedica Health System in a hospital merger, and Northwestern Lake Forest Hospital in a zoning case.
**Sources say:** *"They are very responsive and, more importantly, the guidance they give is very clear – they are able to synthesize issues in a coherent way so that I can explain it to my clients. They're an excellent resource for me."*
**KEY INDIVIDUALS Joel Chefitz** (see p.1201) is *"one of the top antitrust attorneys I would send people to,"* according

to one impressed peer. A highly adept litigator, he has recently defended National Standard in a patent suit concerning welding wire, and Dairy Farmers of America, a major dairy cooperative, in an alleged monopolization case. Complementing Chefitz's practice is his colleague **David Marx** (see p.1220), a leading attorney whose portfolio has a strong healthcare focus. Sources call him *"insightful, strategic and very bright"* and *"an extraordinary talent"* who is *"very easy to work with."* He has been involved in

two cases of late concerning the alleged depression of nurses' wages by hospitals.

## Band 2

### Eimer Stahl LLP
See profile on p.1245

**THE FIRM** Despite the recent departure of partner Andy Klevorn to Katten Muchin Rosenman, this compact litigation boutique continues to punch above its weight and is routinely sought to handle complex and high-value antitrust disputes. Recent work has seen it involved in class actions in the steel and dairy litigation.

**KEY INDIVIDUALS Nathan Eimer** (see p.1205) is a *"truly fine lawyer"* according to sources, who also comment that *"if there's a big Chicago case, he's usually in it."* One peer simply says: *"He is a star."*

### Jones Day
See profile on p.919

**THE FIRM** Helped by its worldwide presence and with a fine roster of antitrust lawyers, this team remains an excellent choice for antitrust work within Chicago. Recent highlights have seen it involved in some of the major nationwide class action suits including the potash litigation, for Potash Corporation of Saskatchewan, and the packaged ice litigation, for Arctic Glacier.

**Sources say:** *"I was very happy with their willingness to understand our business and to be part of the solution, but at the same time being prepared to tell you what you can and can't do."*

**KEY INDIVIDUALS** Commentators call **Michael Sennett** (see p.1230) a *"superlative"* antitrust attorney who *"understands the regulators, is pragmatic and efficient and offers concrete advice."* He helped to secure a merger clearance for Baxter and is also defending 3D Systems in a monopolization case involving stereolithography equipment. **Pamela Taylor** (see p.1235) focuses on transactional antitrust work and counseled 3D Systems in its acquisition of two other companies. Sources describe her as *"a very practical lawyer who understands antitrust risks but also understands that the client has a business to run."*

### Sidley Austin LLP
See profile on p.1264

**THE FIRM** With a good crop of litigators, this firm remains one of the stronger groups in the Chicago antitrust arena. A substantial proportion of its work comes in pharmaceutical and related IP matters, with recent cases including acting for AstraZeneca against a class action alleging sham patent litigation, and representing GlaxoSmithKline in the sale of various drug rights.

**Sources say:** *"Great firm, great reputation, with a diverse antitrust practice."* *"Excellent – their response time is very good."*

**KEY INDIVIDUALS John Treece** (see p.1236) is a highly experienced attorney who is *"smart, witty and impressive"* and *"good with the big picture,"* according to sources. He recently represented SSAB Swedish Steel in the steel litiga-

tion class action, and AstraZeneca in the sham patent litigation matter. **Jack Bierig** (see p.1199) is an adept litigator with a particular focus on healthcare work, which sees him undertake a wealth of IP work alongside his antitrust caseload. General commercial litigator **Charles Douglas** (see p.1204) is noted for his vast range of antitrust experience and is currently defending AT&T Mobility in a class action relating to the alleged forced use of text message codes to increase revenue. **David Graham** (see p.1209) has recently acted for Citi in a case concerning the alleged setting of Visa and MasterCard fees. In addition to antitrust work, he also has expertise in securities.

### Winston & Strawn LLP
See profile on p.1267

**THE FIRM** This firm maintains one of the largest antitrust presences in the state and is building an impressive practice. It has comprehensive expertise in both civil and white-collar criminal work and also particularly prides itself on its strength in IP-related antitrust matters. In recent highlights it represented JSC International Potash in the potash class action and is also acting for Verizon Wireless on the text messaging litigation.

**Sources say:** *"I've never regretted a penny I've spent on them. They treated us like we were their most important client."*

**KEY INDIVIDUALS** Commentators note that *"there are few antitrust lawyers as knowledgeable"* as **Mark McCareins** (see p.1220), Winston & Strawn's head of department. He is also described as *"a great counsel in terms of his legal mind but also in his ability to approach matters from a non-legal angle."* Among his recent cases, he has represented RockTenn in the containerboard litigation alleging artificial manipulation of the corrugated container market. **Dan Webb** (see p.1236) is *"one of the leading trial lawyers in Chicago"* and maintains a diverse litigation practice which takes in IP, product liability, securities, and white-collar defense work, in addition to antitrust disputes. Of late, he has played active roles in the firm's representation of C.R. Bard in a case alleging anticompetitive practices against hospitals nationwide, and in the text messaging litigation.

## Band 3

### Baker & McKenzie
See profile on p.435

**THE FIRM** This group maintains a solid antitrust presence within Illinois and further benefits from the firm's extensive global reach. Commentators are quick to point to the strength of its healthcare practice, but it also has significant experience in defending class action work and cross-border merger review. Among its recent highlights was securing a notable settlement on behalf of Tatung Company of America in the TFT-LCD antitrust litigation.

**Sources say:** *"Their strengths in antitrust are obvious. They are increasingly global and have people around the world."*

**KEY INDIVIDUALS Roxane Busey** maintains an excellent reputation within the market. She is particularly recognized for her healthcare work, although she has wider antitrust experience, with recent undertakings including counseling for Accenture and merger review for Nidec-Shimpo. **Patrick Ahern** is a practitioner with experience across a wide range of antitrust work. He has been heavily involved in the TFT-LCD litigation for Chunghwa Picture Tubes in addition to acting for Tatung, and also had an instrumental role in a case relating to the alleged price-fixing of eggs for four opt-out plaintiffs. **Thomas Campbell** is held in very high regard by his peers for the breadth and depth of his antitrust experience. Now of counsel at the firm, he is another practitioner whose reputation in healthcare goes before him.

## Freeborn & Peters LLP
See profile on p.1248
**THE FIRM** This medium-sized firm continues to attract big-name clients including Deloitte, Coca-Cola and Nintendo of America, and is particularly well regarded for its counseling services on the civil antitrust side. Litigation highlights include being liaison counsel for the plaintiff class in the plasma derivative protein therapies antitrust suit.
**Sources say:** *"We are repeatedly impressed by them – particularly their legal insight and ability to build client relationships."*
**KEY INDIVIDUALS Jeffery Cross**'s (see p.1203) *"substantial expertise and knowledge"* earn him high praise from commentators, who also praise his practical approach to matters. He is an active antitrust counselor in addition to being a broad commercial litigator. **Eugene Zelek** (see p.1238) is an *"unbelievably responsive"* practitioner who is especially noted for his counseling ability. According to one source he is *"masterful in helping clients understand the issues."* **David Gustman** (see p.1210) is described by sources as *"a very, very skilled litigator."* Another general litigator who undertakes antitrust work, he has been involved in a number of the firm's larger cases recently, including the plasma derivative protein therapies antitrust suit mentioned above.

## Freed Kanner London & Millen LLC
**THE FIRM** This boutique is widely regarded as one of the leading names in the state for plaintiff class action work, with all four named partners practicing in that area. Among its recent case highlights is the automotive wire harness systems antitrust litigation against 22 named wire harness manufacturers.
**KEY INDIVIDUALS** The *"outstanding"* **Michael Freed** remains one of the deans of the plaintiff Bar in the state and garners much praise from the market for his courtroom presence and all-around ability.

## Sperling & Slater
**THE FIRM** This firm maintains a fine reputation for high-stakes antitrust litigation, particularly on the plaintiff side. The group remains an excellent choice for clients in the retail and financial services sectors and, in addition to its contentious antitrust work, also maintains enviable track records in a diverse range of areas, such as bankruptcy and IP.
**Sources say:** *"A terrific firm on the plaintiff side."*
**KEY INDIVIDUALS Paul Slater** has been practicing in antitrust law for over 40 years and this experience is reflected by commentators, who call him a *"wonderful lawyer."* The majority of his practice is in antitrust, although he also undertakes more general commercial work.

## Band 4

### Dentons
See profile on p.449
**THE FIRM** Although this practice predominantly focuses on counseling and antitrust risk management, it also offers effective litigation expertise. Among those to whom it has recently provided antitrust advice are InterContinental Hotels and McDonald's, and it is currently working with Land O'Lakes on distribution and pricing issues.
**Sources say:** *"Efficient, responsive and knowledgeable."*
**KEY INDIVIDUALS Stephen Libowsky** (see p.1218) is recognized by sources for his *"very good underlying knowledge of the law."* Among his recent highlights is advising James Hardie on a significant potential merger. Senior statesman **Alan Silberman** (see p.406) is held in high regard for his experience and ability to *"extemporaneously give you an answer that might take another lawyer weeks to do."* A trusted and respected practitioner, he is the chair emeritus of the nationwide antitrust practice.

### Edwards Wildman Palmer
See profile on p.1520
**THE FIRM** This practice undertakes both civil and criminal antitrust matters, with most of its recent notable cases seeing them acting on the defense side. It continues to represent Belarusian Potash Company in the potash price-fixing litigation, and is also involved in a class action suit alleging market allocation by insurance brokers.
**Sources say:** *"What impressed me was their thoroughness in the way they think about and approach antitrust, particularly their ability to address gray areas."*
**KEY INDIVIDUALS** According to commentators, **Michael McCluggage** (see p.1221) is a *"very practical, thoughtful and knowledgeable"* practitioner. He has particular experience in antitrust matters relating to the insurance industry. *"I can't say enough about his responsiveness and ability,"* an impressed source also notes.

## Jenner & Block LLP
See profile on p.1252
**THE FIRM** Principally known for its general litigation expertise, this group nevertheless takes on a wide range of antitrust work. Increasingly its specialty is in advising and representing clients on the plaintiff side who opt out of class actions.
**Sources say:** *"They're outstanding thinkers and they foster a team approach. This great diversity of thought leads to well-reasoned analysis."*
**KEY INDIVIDUALS John Kinney** (see p.1214) debuts in the rankings this year following strong market support. He has a wealth of antitrust experience and is described by one source as *"diligent and capable."* In addition to his recognized opt-out plaintiff strength, he also undertakes work on the defense side in government investigations.

## McGuireWoods LLP
See profile on p.2519
**THE FIRM** Another firm with a strong litigation department, McGuireWoods takes on both civil and criminal antitrust suits, where it covers a wide variety of cases. Recently it has notably represented Horizon Lines both in a criminal investigation relating to water freight price collusion and in ongoing related civil suits.
**Sources say:** *"They have really impressed us with their professionalism, quality of work and responsiveness."*
**KEY INDIVIDUALS Amy Manning** is a respected practitioner who has left clients *"nothing but impressed"* with her quality of advice, practicality and knowledge. She is the firm's main practitioner in Chicago and has a number of high-profile clients, both domestic and international.

## Other Notable Practitioners

**Laura Keidan Martin** of Katten Muchin Rosenman LLP maintains a fine reputation in healthcare-related work. She is described as *"very accessible and bright."* Also at the firm is **Andrew Klevorn**, who has recently joined from Eimer Stahl. He is an experienced antitrust and general commercial lawyer with expertise in both criminal and civil matters. **James Gardner** (see p.1208) at Neal, Gerber & Eisenberg LLP is regarded as a *"very bright and very personable"* lawyer. He has recently represented UnitedHealthcare in its opposition to a hospital merger. **Randall Hack** (see p.1210) is the key presence in Locke Lord LLP's antitrust department and is described as a *"highly competent and very smart lawyer."* He undertakes both antitrust litigation and counseling.

# BANKING & FINANCE

Commentary about individuals can be found under their firm's paragraph. If the firm has no paragraph (is not ranked) look at Other Notable Practitioners.

| Banking & Finance | |
|---|---|
| **Leading Firms** | |
| **Band 1** | |
| Latham & Watkins LLP * | |
| Sidley Austin LLP * | |
| **Band 2** | |
| Goldberg Kohn Ltd * | |
| Kirkland & Ellis LLP * | |
| Mayer Brown LLP * | |
| Winston & Strawn LLP * | |
| **Band 3** | |
| Jones Day * | |
| Katten Muchin Rosenman LLP * | |
| Skadden, Arps, Slate, Meagher & Flom LLP & Affiliates * | |
| Vedder Price PC * | |
| **Band 4** | |
| Chapman and Cutler LLP * | |
| Greenberg Traurig, LLP * | |
| McDermott Will & Emery LLP * | |
| Reed Smith LLP | |
| Schiff Hardin LLP | |
| Ungaretti & Harris LLP * | |

| Banking & Finance | |
|---|---|
| **Senior Statesmen** | |
| **Senior Statesmen:** distinguished older practitioners | |
| Bernstein H Bruce | Sidley Austin LLP * |

**Leading Individuals**

| **Band 1** | |
|---|---|
| Baptista Robert C | Mayer Brown LLP |
| Clark James | Sidley Austin LLP * |
| Crumbaugh David G | Latham & Watkins LLP |
| Murray Gregory S | Winston & Strawn LLP * |
| Myers Linda K | Kirkland & Ellis LLP * |
| **Band 2** | |
| Barrow Peter H | Neal, Gerber & Eisenberg LLP (ONP) † * |
| Boehrer Charles B | Winston & Strawn LLP * |
| Butler Christopher | Kirkland & Ellis LLP * |
| Gerber Dean N | Vedder Price PC * |
| Gold Michael | Sidley Austin LLP * |
| Jacobson Ronald H | Winston & Strawn LLP * |
| Mason David M | Goldberg Kohn Ltd * |
| Schwartz Donald | Ungaretti & Harris LLP * |
| Shulruff Stuart P | Katten Muchin Rosenman LLP |
| **Band 3** | |
| Bokhari Zulfiqar | Sidley Austin LLP * |
| Doetsch Douglas A | Mayer Brown LLP |
| Doran James | Latham & Watkins LLP |
| Dranoff David | Goldberg Kohn Ltd * |
| Forrester J Paul | Mayer Brown LLP |
| Jacobson Michael A | Katten Muchin Rosenman LLP |
| Jacobson Seth E | Skadden, Arps, Slate, Meagher & Flom * |
| Kohn Richard | Goldberg Kohn Ltd * |
| Kotler Bradley E | Latham & Watkins LLP |
| Lawlor John F | Mayer Brown LLP |

| | |
|---|---|
| Lewin Matthew R | Greenberg Traurig, LLP * |
| McEnroe John T | Vedder Price PC * |
| Meland Creighton | Baker & McKenzie (ONP) † |
| Pickens Scott E | Schiff Hardin LLP |
| Scott Ami G | Schiff Hardin LLP |
| **Band 4** | |
| Boykins Michael L | McDermott Will & Emery LLP * |
| Brown Joel F | Goldberg Kohn Ltd * |
| Cardonick Andrew | Greenberg Traurig, LLP * |
| Coleman Jill A | Fox, Swibel, Levin & Carroll, LLP (ONP) † |
| Cooper Jonathan | Goldberg Kohn Ltd * |
| Des Laurier Victor A | Thompson Coburn LLP (ONP) † |
| Graves Robert | Jones Day * |
| Hernandez Louis | Paul Hastings LLP (ONP) † |
| Kilkenney Michelle | Kirkland & Ellis LLP * |
| McGovern Lynn M | Skadden, Arps, Slate, Meagher & Flom * |
| Moran Jeffrey G | Latham & Watkins LLP |
| Perzek Philip | McGuireWoods LLP (ONP) † |
| Rathgeber David | Latham & Watkins LLP |
| Satyr Allison J | Sidley Austin LLP * |
| Schaider Joel | Reed Smith LLP |
| Sweeney Maureen E | Kirkland & Ellis LLP * |
| Wright Michael D | Kirkland & Ellis LLP * |
| Zussman Gary T | Goldberg Kohn Ltd * |
| **Up-and-coming individuals** | |
| Fisher Frederick | Greenberg Traurig, LLP * |
| Kirsons Mark | Sidley Austin LLP * |

*\* Indicates firm / individual with profile.*
*Alphabetical order within each band. Band 1 is the highest.*

## Band 1

### Latham & Watkins LLP
See profile on p.446

**THE FIRM** Latham & Watkins is singled out by sources for its high-quality work, which sees it frequently undertake transactions of a national and international scope, for clients such as GE Capital. The group is known for its strength in investment finance, including leveraged finance, and handles lender and borrower work for private equity firms and commercial lenders. A key mandate for the group saw it handle the refinancing of the current revolving credit and term facilities for Singer Sewing Machines. Other clients in the group's impressive portfolio include JPMorgan, TransUnion, Koch Industries and Bank of America.

**Sources say:** *"If I were a lender and looking to be not only protected but also to have a good relationship with my borrowers, I'd go to Latham first."*

**KEY INDIVIDUALS** The *"terrific"* **David Crumbaugh** is a *"consummate professional"* who clients *"cannot say enough good things about."* He focuses on securitized lending, which has seen him handle a term loan and revolving credit facility for GE Capital. **James Doran** undertakes work involving the representation of financial institutions in unsecured and secured credit facilities. He enjoys a fine reputation in the market, not least for his hard-working approach to matters. **Bradley Kotler** handles credit facilities for acquisition and working capital matters, and is singled out by observers for his business acumen, negotiating prowess and demeanor. Sources reserve special praise for **Jeffrey Moran**'s skill and work ethic. A recent highlight saw

him lead the team representing GE Capital in the financing of Affymetrix's acquisition of a biotech company. The *"very effective and very knowledgeable"* **David Rathgeber** is well versed in recapitalization work for domestic and international companies. Acquisition finance is also an area of expertise, which has recently led to him representing Arlington Capital Partners in its acquisition of Aero-Metric.

### Sidley Austin LLP
See profile on p.1264

**THE FIRM** Sidley Austin maintains its position as one of the leading banking and finance practices in Illinois. The team acts for lenders, sponsors and borrowers on matters covering the gamut of financing activities and financial instruments. A recent highlight saw it act for JPMorgan Chase as an administrative agent on a $2 billion senior multicurrency revolving credit facility. Wells Fargo, BNP

Paribas, GE Capital and Citi are also counted among the group's distinguished client base.

**Sources say:** *"Always first-class." "Really critical to our success."*

**KEY INDIVIDUALS** In a recent highlight *"fabulous lawyer"* **James Clark** (see p.1202) worked with US Bank as administrative agent on a $450 million acquisition loan facility for Graco. The *"phenomenal"* **Michael Gold** (see p.1209) has expertise in debt restructuring on behalf of debtors and lenders. He is also well versed in matters involving syndicated finance, and recently acted on behalf of GE Capital on $99.5 million of senior secured acquisition financing facilities. **Zulfiqar Bokhari** (see p.1199) focuses on the structure and syndication of senior credit facilities, including recapitalization and bridge credit. *"He's both efficient and practical, and, substantively, he knows his stuff,"* note observers, who go on to say that *"he does a great job of understanding customer service from our perspective."* He led on the JPMorgan Chase matter. **Mark**

Kirsons (see p.1215) handles transactional structured finance, lending and asset securitization for a wide range of clients. He elicits particular praise for his ability to "*adapt very easily,*" and is singled out as "*extremely bright and very accommodating.*" **Bruce Bernstein** (see p.1198) is recognized for his wealth of experience in the banking and finance arena, and in particular for his skill in restructuring work and secured transactions. Sources describe **Allison Satyr** (see p.1230) as "*knowledgeable, creative and always available.*" She represents both borrowers and lenders in a wide range of matters, and recently acted for JPMorgan Chase as an administrative agent on a CAD250 million senior term loan facility.

## Band 2

### Goldberg Kohn Ltd
See profile on p.1249

THE FIRM The team at Goldberg Kohn has a strong mid-market focus and a particular expertise in cross-border asset-based lending. In a recent highlight, it advised the Bank of Montreal on a senior loan facility with secured guarantors in Ireland, Luxembourg and Australia. Its client roster also includes Madison Capital Funding, PNC Bank, Wells Fargo Capital Finance and LBC Credit Partners.
Sources say: "*Very responsive, smart lawyers, who have tons of experience.*"
KEY INDIVIDUALS The "*extremely methodical*" **David Mason** (see p.1220) is singled out by interviewees for being "*good at breaking down an issue, and addressing in a fair manner every aspect of that issue.*" His focus lies within cash flow transactions, restructurings, workouts and consolidation loans. Commercial finance group chair **David Dranoff** (see p.1205) brings a wealth of experience to his practice, which encompasses leveraged buyouts, mezzanine investments and asset-based secured loans. He led on the Bank of Montreal matter. **Richard Kohn** (see p.1215) is a well-known force in the banking and finance community. His practice primarily focuses on asset-based lending, often with a cross-border element. **Joel Brown** (see p.1200) "*brings his expert knowledge to bear*" with high levels of practicality, thoroughness and intellect, sources comment. He undertakes work involving the representation of financial institutions in midmarket lending matters. **Jonathan Cooper** (see p.1203) is a "*thoughtful and detailed lawyer.*" He is particularly appreciated for his ability to remain practical when advising clients, who include borrowers and lenders, on the full spectrum of financial transactions. **Gary Zussman** (see p.1239) focuses on acting for cash flow and asset-based lenders aimed at the midmarket. He elicits much praise from interviewees for his responsiveness and subject matter expertise.

### Kirkland & Ellis LLP
See profile on p.1254

THE FIRM Kirkland & Ellis has a strong client base of borrowers and lenders, which it advises on matters from real estate financing through to hedging devices and alternative pricing mechanisms. The team is seen as one of the first ports of call for large and complex deals, as demonstrated by its representation of Madison Dearborn Partners in its sale of TransUnion to Advent International and GS Capital Partners, a $3 billion deal. Other clients include Six Flags Entertainment, Molson Coors Brewing and Bain Capital.
Sources say: "*Great practical legal advice.*" "*They really do help think about our particular issues and help us as a management team.*"
KEY INDIVIDUALS Debt finance group head **Linda Myers** (see p.1223) "*does an incredible job and is an incredible attorney,*" say sources. Of late, she led the team representing Burlington Coat Factory in the refinancing of a term loan, as well as an asset-based lending facility amendment and restatement of maturity. She also led on the Madison Dearborn Partners matter. **Christopher Butler** (see p.1200) "*knows how lenders think, what they work like, and has a perspective that he brings that many others don't,*" according to interviewees. His practice has a focus on acquisitions and leveraged financings, and in a recent highlight he led the team acting for Infor Global Solutions in the refinancing of its senior debt. Sources also particularly commend his work ethic. **Michelle Kilkenney** (see p.1214) represents borrowers and lenders in all matters relating to secured and unsecured financing transactions. Observers comment that she "*knows how to make a deal,*" and also applaud her practicality, market knowledge and efficiency. **Maureen Sweeney** (see p.1235) is singled out by sources for her well thought-out responses and creative, solution-oriented approach. Her practice covers the gamut of financing transactions, including mezzanine and subordinated debt issues. **Michael Wright** (see p.1237) represents private equity groups and corporate borrowers in a broad range of matters. He recently led the team representing VWR Funding and Madison Dearborn Partners in the amendment and extension of a series of US and European loans and revolving credit, a $1.1 billion deal.

### Mayer Brown LLP
See profile on p.1257

THE FIRM Mayer Brown is praised by sources for the strength and depth of its banking and finance team, as well as for the complex work it undertakes. The group represents borrowers and lenders across a broad spectrum of matters, including energy finance, private equity and securitization work. The team is also known for its strength in cross-border transactions, as illustrated by its work for Prologis in a senior term loan agreement involving multiple currencies and international bodies. It counts Goldman Sachs, Credit Suisse and Bank of America among its high-profile client base.
Sources say: "*Extremely accessible, thorough and thoughtful.*" "*We are able to receive swift, direct, and yet comprehensive responses to every query we address to them.*" "*We always feel safe having Mayer Brown on our side.*"
KEY INDIVIDUALS "*Terrific lawyer*" **Robert Baptista** is a "*consummate draftsman and technician,*" interviewees report. His clients include both borrowers and lenders, who he advises on syndicated financing transactions. A recent highlight is his representation of Bank of America in a $1.45 billion syndicated credit facility. "*Fantastic practi-*

tioner" **Douglas Doetsch** represents clients on a wide range of matters, from acquisition financing to securitization and debt restructuring. He recently acted as counsel to the Steering Committee of Creditors on the debt restructuring of Trinidad Cement. **Paul Forrester** undertakes project finance and structured credit product work, and has a wealth of experience within the energy sector. Sources are particularly appreciative of his accessibility and responsiveness, one stating: "*There's rarely a time when I have a question for him that he hasn't already answered or previously had to consider.*" **John Lawlor** provides advice and representation to borrowers and lenders across a variety of financing matters. In particular he advises private equity and real estate funds, and recently assisted Macquarie Infrastructure Partners with a $375 million financing transaction. Sources reserve particular praise for his negotiation skills and preparation.

### Winston & Strawn LLP
See profile on p.1267

THE FIRM This robust practice undertakes a variety of matters that range from lower and midmarket to big-ticket. The team frequently represents financial institutions that are acting either in a borrower or a lender capacity, as well as multinational companies in a variety of matters. It is also well versed in areas such as asset-based transactions, syndicated credit and cross-border facilities. The team's expertise saw it represent JPMorgan Chase as the administrative agent for a banking syndicate in a $1.8 billion senior secured revolving credit facility for SXC Health Solutions. Other prestigious clients include Ares Capital Corporation, Reyes Holdings and Deutsche Bank.
KEY INDIVIDUALS **Gregory Murray** (see p.1223) centers his practice around commercial lending transactions, recently representing Bank of America in a $2 billion multicurrency revolving and term credit facility for Flextronics. He is regarded as "*superexperienced, smart, and supercommercial.*" The highly regarded **Charles Boehrer** (see p.1199) focuses on leveraged transactions for borrowers and lenders. Of late, he has acted for Deutsche Bank on an $850 million credit facility for Ball Corporation and selected associated subsidiaries. Global finance practice cochair **Ronald Jacobson** (see p.1213) handles matters which include structured finance, private equity and capital markets. He is also well versed in advising clients on all aspects of debt markets. Sources are quick to praise his excellent work product and responsive service.

## Band 3

### Jones Day
See profile on p.919

THE FIRM This team covers the full spectrum of financial transactions, including those with a cross-border element. A key mandate for the group saw it represent Baird Capital Partners in its acquisition and related financing of PC Helps Support. The team also continues to advise Texas Instruments on its high-value acquisition and related financing of National Semiconductor. The group's portfolio includes such big-ticket clients as Koch Industries, Bank of America and Stonehenge Financial Holdings.

**Sources say:** *"Global resources and quality advice."*

**KEY INDIVIDUALS Robert Graves** (see p.1210) handles matters relating to troubled credits, as well as a wide range of senior debt financing arrangements. A recent work highlight saw him lead the team advising Bunge North America on a $48 million synthetic lease. He also played leading roles in the Baird Capital Partners and Texas Instruments matters.

### Katten Muchin Rosenman LLP
See profile on p.1253

**THE FIRM** This group represents a broad base of clients, from junior capital providers to senior lenders. The team has a strong midmarket focus and regularly handles sophisticated work across the USA. The group is particularly strong in matters involving healthcare finance and sports franchises, and is well placed to draw upon the expertise of other departments when required.

**Sources say:** *"They're pragmatic, practical, detail-oriented and client-focused." "Will fully vet every issue with you."*

**KEY INDIVIDUALS Stuart Shulruff** focuses on representing investment funds and financial institutions, and specializes in all aspects of senior and mezzanine credit facilities. Sources value his excellent understanding of law and commercial approach, and go on to praise his clear communication. Commercial finance practice head **Michael Jacobson** has a broad practice that covers healthcare finance as well as first and second lien structures. Observers value his wealth of knowledge, and are also appreciative of his constructive advice.

### Skadden, Arps, Slate, Meagher & Flom LLP & Affiliates
See profile on p.2008

**THE FIRM** This group handles all kinds of financing transactions, from DIP and exit financings to senior and subordinated bridge financings. The team benefits from the firm's global footprint, and undertakes a multitude of work for clients as diverse as merchant banking firms, LBO sponsors and pension funds, both within the USA and internationally.

**Sources say:** *"The quality has been extremely good. They are very thorough and responsive."*

**KEY INDIVIDUALS Seth Jacobson** (see p.1213) heads the banking practice in Chicago and handles complex financing transactions across a broad spectrum of industries. Sources reserve particular praise for his creative approach and ability to get the most complicated of deals done. **Lynn McGovern**'s (see p.1221) practice includes exit financings, asset-based loans and mezzanine financings, which she undertakes for both borrowers and lenders. One source enthuses that she is *"always available, committed to advocating our position, helping us to understand the issues and getting us to the right place."*

### Vedder Price PC
See profile on p.1266

**THE FIRM** Vedder Price has a wealth of expertise in secured and unsecured structures, with a strong asset based finance offering. It also acts for borrowers, lenders and financiers on a wide range of transactions. A large portion of the team's work is cross-border in nature and involves a wide range of jurisdictions, as evidenced by its recent representation of the Export-Import Bank of the United States in the $1.2 billion financing of twelve aircraft for LAN Airlines, which included financings across Africa, Central and South America, Europe and Asia. The group's portfolio includes CIT Group, Bank of America, Ally Commercial Finance and The PrivateBank and Trust Company.

**Sources say:** *"Great technical expertise and good business acumen."*

**KEY INDIVIDUALS Dean Gerber** (see p.319) is a respected figure within the Illinois market for his experience in representing lessors and lessees. A recent highlight saw him act as bankruptcy counsel to a number of creditors on the American Airlines bankruptcy. **John McEnroe** (see p.1221) represents private and public companies across the gamut of financial transactions. Market sources particularly appreciate his efficiency and quick turnaround of work.

### Band 4

### Chapman and Cutler LLP
See profile on p.1244

**THE FIRM** Chapman and Cutler has a strong focus on finance that covers leases, workouts, public finance and bonds. The Chicago group is known within the market for the strength of its banking and finance practice, and sources are appreciative of the practical nature of its advice.

**Sources say:** *"Very responsive, and when there's an issue they listen." "They have some excellent people there."*

**KEY INDIVIDUALS Morrison Warren** is a key contact.

### Greenberg Traurig, LLP
See profile on p.1024

**THE FIRM** Greenberg Traurig is well versed in all matters connected with financial institutions, public finance, and structured finance and derivatives. Of late, the team has represented Wells Fargo Bank in some $19 million of series loans to Cook-Illinois Corporation. Its stable of clients also includes BMO Harris, Bank of America and CNH Capital America.

**Sources say:** *"They devote partner-level attention to all matters, and make themselves available at all times."*

**KEY INDIVIDUALS Matthew Lewin** (see p.1217) principally handles tax-exempt financings for a number of organizations and industries. He also frequently acts as bond and underwriting counsel for municipal financings. Financial institutions practice cochair **Andrew Cardonick** (see p.1201) comes recommended for his expertise in bankruptcy exit financings, lending, and club bank facilities. Sources particularly value his ability to be *"aggressive*

*when he needs to be."* **Frederick Fisher** (see p.1207) has attracted much market recognition due to his work ethic, high level of attention to detail, and understanding of clients' business issues. He focuses on financing transactions for domestic and international clients.

### McDermott Will & Emery LLP
See profile on p.1258

**THE FIRM** This group focuses on the midmarket, within which it represents borrowers and lenders with equal frequency. The team is well suited to deal with a wide range of transactions for both domestic and global financial institutions. A key mandate has seen the firm represent Acushnet Company in a $500 million secured Euro floating rate note offering. A further highlight saw the team represent Novis Pharmaceuticals in a secured revolving loan facility.

**KEY INDIVIDUALS** Illinois banking and finance team head **Michael Boykins** (see p.1199) is recognized for his representation of lenders, borrowers and investors in a broad spectrum of issues. He is also particularly experienced in acting for underwriters and issuers in public offerings and other secured transactions.

### Reed Smith LLP

**THE FIRM** Reed Smith represents lenders and borrowers in domestic and multijurisdictional financial transactions. This expertise has seen the team act as counsel to administrative agent and lender BMO Harris Bank on a $50 million unsecured credit facility. In another highlight the group advised Zell Credit Opportunities Master Fund on a $17 million unsecured mezzanine credit facility to a radio station. Other key clients include GE Capital, PNC Bank National Association and Fifth Third Bank.

**KEY INDIVIDUALS Joel Schaider** deals with transactions that involve corporate financing and lending. He has expertise involving equipment and mezzanine financing, as well as multistate secured credit facilities. He recently advised Wells Fargo Bank on a $150 million secured credit facility.

### Schiff Hardin LLP

**THE FIRM** Schiff Hardin is known for its skill representing financial institutions, particularly banks, on regulatory and enforcement matters. In addition, the group represents borrowers and lenders across the full spectrum of secured lending, and is also noted for its strengths in project and structured finance. A recent highlight saw the team represent John Hancock Life Insurance in the monetization of the value of Bell Canada's investment in the joint sponsorship of the National Hockey League.

**KEY INDIVIDUALS** The highly regarded **Scott Pickens** concentrates on the representation of creditors in financing transactions, and is also sought for his expertise in workouts. **Ami Scott** is noted for her strengths in acquisition and lending transactions, including working capital facilities.

### Ungaretti & Harris LLP
**See profile on p.1265**
**THE FIRM** This practice concentrates on representing lenders in midmarket finance and is known for its strength in asset-based financing. The group is also experienced in refinancings and workouts, and recently handled a Chapter 11 bankruptcy case for Clare Oaks, as well as advising on the restructuring of its long-term debt and the sale of a facility. Other clients in the team's portfolio include Wells Fargo, JPMorgan Chase and Royal Bank of Canada.
**Sources say:** *"I have been very pleased with the work product and responsiveness of Ungaretti & Harris. The team is able to provide appropriate service efficiently without compromising on quality."*
**KEY INDIVIDUALS** Banking and finance department head **Donald Schwartz** (see p.1230) has a wealth of expe-

rience in advising Canadian banks on financings and insolvency cases. *"He understands the importance of client service,"* asserts one interviewee.

### Other Notable Practitioners

The *"very talented"* **Louis Hernandez** of Paul Hastings LLP elicits particular praise for his *"responsiveness, understanding of the market, and work ethic."* A recent highlight saw him lead the team representing Contract Research Solutions in its Chapter 11 bankruptcy. McGuireWoods LLP's **Philip Perzek** concentrates on debt finance and lending transactions. He is well respected by the market, who value his wealth of experience and knowledge. **Peter Barrow** (see p.1197) of Neal, Gerber & Eisenberg LLP is *"extraordinarily thoughtful and wise in his practice of the law, and deeply committed to the well-being of the client,"*

according to one commentator. He represents all sides in a broad practice that includes financing transactions, dispositions and intercreditor arrangements. Baker & McKenzie's **Creighton Meland** represented Bank of America in the closure of a $100 million secured syndicated credit facility. Sources are quick to praise his hands-on approach and *"studied knowledge of past history as it pertains to ever-changing current situations."* **Jill Coleman** recently joined Fox, Swibel, Levin & Carroll, LLP from Neal, Gerber & Eisenberg. Coleman undertakes matters pertaining to commercial lending, and is often called upon to handle military-related joint ventures. The *"very capable"* **Victor Des Laurier** is vice chair of Thompson Coburn LLP's banking and commercial finance practice. He concentrates on credit facilities, both syndicated and single lender, acting for borrowers, lenders and lessors.

# BANKRUPTCY/RESTRUCTURING

Commentary about individuals can be found under their firm's paragraph. If the firm has no paragraph (is not ranked) look at Other Notable Practitioners.

## Bankruptcy/Restructuring
### Leading Firms

**Band 1**
Kirkland & Ellis LLP *
Skadden, Arps, Slate, Meagher & Flom LLP & Affiliates *

**Band 2**
Latham & Watkins LLP *
Sidley Austin LLP *

**Band 3**
Goldberg Kohn Ltd *
Greenberg Traurig, LLP *
Jenner & Block LLP *
Kaye Scholer LLP *
Proskauer Rose LLP *
Shaw Fishman Glantz & Towbin LLC *

**Band 4**
DLA Piper LLP (US) *
Jones Day *
Mayer Brown LLP *
Perkins Coie LLP
Vedder Price PC *
Winston & Strawn LLP *

**Band 5**
Adelman & Gettleman Ltd *
Dentons *
Edwards Wildman Palmer *
Foley & Lardner LLP *
Katten Muchin Rosenman LLP *
Neal, Gerber & Eisenberg LLP *
Schiff Hardin LLP

*\* Indicates firm / individual with profile.*
*Alphabetical order within each band. Band 1 is the highest.*

## Bankruptcy/Restructuring
### Leading Individuals

**Band 1**
| | |
|---|---|
| Butler Jr John Wm | Skadden, Arps, Slate, Meagher & Flom * |
| Conlan James F | Sidley Austin LLP * |
| Heller David S | Latham & Watkins LLP |
| Nyhan Lawrence | Sidley Austin LLP * |
| Sprayregen James HM | Kirkland & Ellis LLP * |

**Band 2**
| | |
|---|---|
| Athanas Josef S | Latham & Watkins LLP |
| Bacon J Douglas | Latham & Watkins LLP |
| Berkoff Mark A | Neal, Gerber & Eisenberg LLP * |
| Fishman Robert M | Shaw Fishman Glantz & Towbin LLC |
| Klein Randall | Goldberg Kohn Ltd * |
| Levy Richard A | Latham & Watkins LLP |
| Marwil Jeff J | Proskauer Rose LLP |
| Panagakis George N | Skadden, Arps, Slate, Meagher & Flom * |
| Peterman Nancy A | Greenberg Traurig, LLP * |
| Sathy Anup | Kirkland & Ellis LLP * |
| Seligman David R | Kirkland & Ellis LLP * |
| Shapiro Keith J | Greenberg Traurig, LLP * |
| Solow Michael | Kaye Scholer LLP * |
| Stempel James A | Kirkland & Ellis LLP * |
| Swett Brian I | Winston & Strawn LLP * |
| Thomas Mark K | Proskauer Rose LLP |
| Towbin Steven B | Shaw Fishman Glantz & Towbin LLC |
| Zazove Daniel A | Perkins Coie LLP |

**Band 3**
| | |
|---|---|
| Adelman Howard | Adelman & Gettleman Ltd * |
| Barliant Ronald | Goldberg Kohn Ltd * |
| Botica Matthew J | Winston & Strawn LLP * |
| Chesley Richard A | DLA Piper LLP (US) * |
| Dickerson Christopher L | DLA Piper LLP (US) * |
| Eaton David L | Kirkland & Ellis LLP * |
| Eidelman Michael M | Vedder Price PC * |
| Erens Brad B | Jones Day * |
| Gettleman Chad H | Adelman & Gettleman Ltd * |
| Jacobson Fruman | Dentons * |

| | |
|---|---|
| Kaplan Harold L | Foley & Lardner LLP |
| Kiriakos Thomas S | Mayer Brown LLP |
| Krakauer Bryan | Sidley Austin LLP * |
| Lazar Vincent | Jenner & Block LLP * |
| Lipke Douglas J | Vedder Price PC * |
| Lyons John K | Skadden, Arps, Slate, Meagher & Flom * |
| Millner Robert B | Dentons * |
| Murray Daniel | Jenner & Block LLP * |
| Neff David M | Perkins Coie LLP |
| Perlman Felicia G | Skadden, Arps, Slate, Meagher & Flom * |
| Peterson Ronald R | Jenner & Block LLP * |
| Smith William P | McDermott Will & Emery LLP (ONP)[†] |
| Solow Alan P | DLA Piper LLP (US) * |
| Steege Catherine L | Jenner & Block LLP * |

**Band 4**
| | |
|---|---|
| Bobo Stephen | Reed Smith LLP (ONP)[†] |
| Coco Nathan F | McDermott Will & Emery LLP (ONP)[†] * |
| Downs Jeremy | Goldberg Kohn Ltd * |
| Fischer David | Edwards Wildman Palmer * |
| Fisher Mark | Schiff Hardin LLP |
| Hammer Aaron | Sugar Felsenthal Grais & Hammer (ONP)[†] * |
| Heroy David | Baker & McKenzie (ONP)[†] * |
| Karcazes Dimitri | Goldberg Kohn Ltd * |
| Lonstein Carmen | Baker & McKenzie (ONP)[†] * |
| Meisler Ron E | Skadden, Arps, Slate, Meagher & Flom * |
| Mesires George | Ungaretti & Harris LLP (ONP)[†] * |
| Messersmith Michael | Kaye Scholer LLP * |
| Molinaro Michael L | Reed Smith LLP (ONP)[†] |
| Nash, Jr Patrick | Kirkland & Ellis LLP * |
| Nurnberg D Tyler | Kaye Scholer LLP * |
| Ottaviano Kenneth | Katten Muchin Rosenman LLP |
| Possinger Paul | Proskauer Rose LLP |
| Sieger John | Katten Muchin Rosenman LLP |
| Solow Sheldon L | Kaye Scholer LLP * |
| Wolf Neal L | Neal Wolf & Associates, LLC (ONP)[†] |
| Young Jonathan | Edwards Wildman Palmer * |

## Band 1

### Kirkland & Ellis LLP
See profile on p.1254

**THE FIRM** Kirkland's Chicago restructuring group maintains its outstanding reputation in the bankruptcy and restructuring arena. The firm has a preeminent debtor-side practice, and a widely respected creditor-side caseload. The team's work representing Apple during Eastman Kodak's bankruptcy in a dispute over patents is a notable example of recent highlights. The firm also acted for Hawker Beechcraft in its Chapter 11 proceedings. The team is also noted for its superb out-of-court restructuring expertise. It has considerable experience in many different industries including aviation, shipping, and a variety of other transportation types, as well as in the energy, media, real estate, oil and gas, and chemical sectors.
**Sources say:** *"Number-one law firm in the world for restructuring." "The most sought-after team in the USA for both debtors and creditors."*
**KEY INDIVIDUALS** Sources recommend **James Sprayregen** (see p.411) for his *"gravitas and wisdom,"* and as a seasoned bankruptcy specialist. He has a formidable presence in the market representing leading companies in complex out-of-court restructurings and bankruptcy situations. He also represents both buyers and sellers of distressed assets in a variety of industry sectors. The *"terrific restructuring lawyer"* **Anup Sathy** (see p.1229) is experienced in acting for a wide range of clients in restructurings, workouts and reorganizations. He has recently worked on some of the group's most significant restructuring matters including its representations of Centerbridge Partners and YRC Worldwide. **Patrick Nash** (see p.1223) has a *"great presence"* in the sector and is described by sources as *"well-rounded and good at everything."* He works with a variety of clients in matters involving debt restructurings, reorganizations, troubled M&A and other financing issues. Nash recently acted for Black Diamond Capital Management on the restructuring of GSC Group. **David Eaton** (see p.1205) represents debtors, financial institutions, bondholders, unsecured creditors and committees in a range of restructuring and bankruptcy-related matters. He is known as a *"quality and driven attorney"* who is able to *"take large cases and manage them with very little support."* **David Seligman** (see p.1230) is noted for his *"extraordinary knowledge and responsiveness."* He regularly becomes involved in the group's most notable cases, including its recent representation of Apple during Eastman Kodak's bankruptcy, and Corus Bankshares in its restructuring matters. **James Stempel** (see p.1234) recently represented Friendly Ice Cream Corporation in its Chapter 11 cases, in which the business emerged from bankruptcy just three months after filing. He is described by observers as a *"wonderful lawyer."*

### Skadden, Arps, Slate, Meagher & Flom LLP & Affiliates
See profile on p.2008

**THE FIRM** Skadden continues to be one of the most highly regarded groups in Chicago, both nationally and internationally, for restructuring and bankruptcy-related matters. The group excels in representing debtors in large and complex Chapter 11 reorganizations but also has expertise in acting for a wide range of other clients including creditors, troubled companies, and investors. Skadden is able to draw upon expertise across the firm utilizing its strengths in tax, M&A, banking, litigation, real estate and securities, among others. Recent representations include Zell Credit Opportunities Master Fund in the Delta Petroleum Chapter 11 case.
**Sources say:** *"Provides a seamless service." "These guys walk on water."*
**KEY INDIVIDUALS Jack Butler** (see p.290) is described as a *"unique individual"* and is considered one of the leading figures in the restructuring and bankruptcy world. His recent representations include his work for DPH Holdings in the company's joint reorganization. **George Panagakis** (see p.1224) has experience of acting for a range of different clients in complex reorganizations and debt restructurings. He is described by sources as *"absolutely first-rate in every respect."* Panagakis recently acted for Nuveen Investments in Northern Berkshire Healthcare's Chapter 11 cases. **John Lyons** (see p.1219) *"communicates very well and does a good job of managing a lot of complex pieces,"* say interviewees. He represents corporations in reorganizations and acquisitions and has expertise in dealing with entities in distressed situations. **Felicia Perlman** (see p.1225) continues to impress sources by being *"very capable, and very determined, with a very flexible mind."* She is also gaining a solid reputation for her work in the healthcare sector. Perlman is currently working on AMR's bankruptcy case representing the unsecured creditors' committee. **Ron Meisler** (see p.1221) *"provides his clients with a competitive advantage"* and is a *"very thoughtful and very creative attorney,"* according to sources. He is currently working on Delta Petroleum's Chapter 11 for Zell Credit Opportunities Master Fund. Meisler has experience of representing a range of clients across a broad range of restructuring and bankruptcy matters both nationally and internationally.

## Band 2

### Latham & Watkins LLP
See profile on p.446

**THE FIRM** Latham's Chicago office continues to grow, as a number of attorneys join the team. The group continues to enjoy an excellent reputation in dealing with a wide range of insolvency matters both within the USA or globally. Notably, the group's work in the airlines, hedge fund and private equity spaces has increased. The team currently acts for GE Capital Aviation Services on the American Airlines bankruptcy, and for GE Capital as agent for the first lien lenders on SP Newsprint's bankruptcy proceedings.
**Sources say:** *"They excel in marrying up bankruptcy strategy with business strategy."*
**KEY INDIVIDUALS David Heller** is chair of the firm's finance practice group. He is praised by sources for being *"one of the top guys in the country,"* and he is *"extremely creative and he always gets results."* He represents both secured and unsecured lenders in workouts and bankruptcy matters. Heller also has a wealth of experience of acting for companies during their restructurings either in or out of court. **Josef Athanas** is very *"hands-on, thoughtful and has a great business mind and commercial understanding of complex corporate and real world challenges,"* according to commentators. He is experienced in representing both debtors, secured creditors and others in bankruptcy and reorganization matters. Athanas and Heller recently acted for Graceway Pharmaceuticals and its subsidiaries in their Chapter 11 cases. **Douglas Bacon** is *"someone who can bring people together to get a deal done,"* say observers. He is leading the case for GE Capital Aviation Services in the American Airlines bankruptcy. Bacon is immensely experienced in acting for a broad range of different entities in a variety of industries in bankruptcy and insolvency matters. The *"phenomenal"* **Richard Levy** is described by sources as *"a black belt in this area."* He has excellent expertise in representing major financial institutions, large corporate debtors and creditors' committees, among others. He recently acted on behalf of GE Capital in the SP Newsprint business bankruptcy.

### Sidley Austin LLP
See profile on p.1264

**THE FIRM** Sidley Austin's growing Chicago-based bankruptcy group has excellent national and international capabilities. The team has earned its reputation as one of the leading firms in restructuring matters by successfully acting for large and mid-sized companies. Recent noteworthy debtor representations include Dynegy Holdings, Tribune Company and RH Donnelley Corporation.
**Sources say:** *"A top-notch, go-to firm"*
**KEY INDIVIDUALS James Conlan** (see p.1202) cochairs the firm's corporate reorganization and bankruptcy group and has been described as a *"very smart, very practical, good all-around lawyer."* He has recently been involved in the group's representation of Dynegy Holdings in its substantial Chapter 11 proceedings, and also represented RH Donnelley. **Bryan Krakauer** (see p.1216) is experienced in all manner of financial restructuring and corporate reorganization. He and Conlan were both involved in the renowned Tribune Company Chapter 11 proceedings. **Lawrence Nyhan** (see p.378) is *"top of the food chain"* and *"one of the best in the business,"* according to clients. He cochairs the practice group alongside Conlan. Nyhan's recent highlights include his representation of Smurfit-Stone Container in its insolvency matters.

## Band 3

### Goldberg Kohn Ltd
See profile on p.1249

**THE FIRM** Goldberg Kohn has an excellent reputation in the bankruptcy and restructuring market, particularly for its representation of secured creditors. The group is noted by commentators for its ability to draw upon expertise from its finance practice, among other departments, to integrate services for its clients. The group recently represented Fifth Third Bank in Giordano's Enterprises Chapter 11 bankruptcy.

**Sources say:** *"I've never not been impressed by them." "Adept at pulling resources from within the firm."*

**KEY INDIVIDUALS** Practice group chair **Randall Klein** (see p.1215) is described by sources as a *"smart lawyer and smart business person."* He recently worked on the Giordano's case acting on behalf of Fifth Third Bank. **Ronald Barliant** (see p.1197) *"has a gravitas and approachability about him,"* according to sources. He is experienced in acting for both debtors and creditors, and recently represented PNC Bank. **Jeremy Downs** (see p.1205) is appreciated for his ability to *"articulate legal issues well to individuals who might not understand the legal ramifications."* He is particularly experienced in representing secured lenders, junior lenders and large unsecured creditors. **Dimitri Karcazes** (see p.1214) has excellent experience in representing lenders in the protection and enforcement of creditors' rights in all manner of bankruptcy and restructuring matters. Sources comment that he is *"good to have on your side"* and *"helps to guide the process towards resolution."*

## Greenberg Traurig, LLP
See profile on p.1024

**THE FIRM** Greenberg Traurig's Chicago-based business reorganization and financial restructuring practice forms an integral part of the firm's respected national presence. Naturally inclined towards representing lenders and other financial institutions, the group is also noted for its excellent expertise in the healthcare sector. In addition it is able to utilize its international resources, having recently drawn on resources from its Shanghai office in a large Chapter 11 matter.

**Sources say:** *"They did an outstanding job." "Absolutely wonderful in every single state that I work with."*

**KEY INDIVIDUALS Nancy Peterman** (see p.1225) chairs the Chicago-based practice group. She is well versed in representing debtors, purchasers of assets, committees and secured creditors in corporate restructurings and bankruptcy matters. She also has expertise in health law. Sources comment that she is a *"great advocate for the client"* and that *"she is on top of everything, like orchestrating a symphony."* **Keith Shapiro** (see p.1231) chairs the group's Chicago office and is cochair of the firm's national business reorganization and financial restructuring practice. He has in-depth experience in a range of restructuring and bankruptcy matters, and typically represents troubled companies, financial institutions, creditors' committees, hedge funds and private equity funds. Sources say that Shapiro is a *"veteran"* who can *"see the full picture from a business perspective."*

## Jenner & Block LLP
See profile on p.1252

**THE FIRM** Jenner & Block maintains its excellent reputation for bankruptcy, workout and reorganization work. It is held in particularly high esteem for its bankruptcy-relat-

ed litigation work. Areas of expertise include sovereign debt matters, the energy sector, and labor and pensions issues. In recent highlights, the group represented the Section 1114 committee of retired employees of American Airlines during the company's Chapter 11 proceedings.

**Sources say:** *"They did a terrific job." "Clear thinkers."*

**KEY INDIVIDUALS Vincent Lazar** (see p.1217) cochairs the firm's bankruptcy litigation practice and is experienced in representing a wide range of clients including debtors, committees and trustees. **Daniel Murray** (see p.1223) chairs the firm's bankruptcy, workout and corporate reorganization practice. He recently acted for Public Service Enterprise Group as a creditor in Dynegy's high-profile Chapter 11 proceedings. **Catherine Steege** (see p.1234) is recognized for her excellent litigation and courtroom skills. One impressed source said: *"She was so clear in her explanation; nothing flusters her."* Steege represents many types of clients including creditors, debtors, creditors' committees and trustees. **Ronald Peterson** (see p.1225) *"has seen it all,"* according to observers, as evidenced by his longstanding reputation and his extensive experience. He regularly represents a range of different entities both in litigation and distressed transactions.

## Kaye Scholer LLP
See profile on p.1984

**THE FIRM** Kaye Scholer's bankruptcy and restructuring department is particularly commended for its work representing lenders, fund clients and creditors. The group benefits from national and international reach through its other global offices. However, the group's most significant highlights have recently included company-side representations, such as its role on behalf of 4Kids Entertainment in its Chapter 11 proceedings. Other key clients include US Bank, Bank of America and Cerberus Partners.

**Sources say:** *"They have unique insight into what investors want to see in a restructuring, and the different opinions and views of banks and institutional investors."*

**KEY INDIVIDUALS Michael Solow** (see p.1233) is the firm's managing partner and cochair of its bankruptcy and restructuring department. He has a wealth of experience working on a wide range of bankruptcy and restructuring matters, and typically represents creditors, trustees and governmental agencies, among other entities. One source commented that Solow is *"a very smooth character and very influential in the way he puts a case forward in negotiations."* He recently acted for GSC Group in its highly litigious Chapter 11 case. **Michael Messersmith** (see p.1222) often acts for lenders, bondholders and other institutional investors. Sources describe him as *"commercially minded"* and say that he *"helps to get a deal across the finish line."* Messersmith recently acted for Cantor Fitzgerald Securities as administrative agent to the senior lenders of Caribe Media. Chicago office managing partner **Tyler Nurnberg** (see p.1224) represents troubled companies, lenders and investment funds, among others. He is noted for his *"business-savvy"* approach, and his ability to *"provide practical solutions to complicated problems."* Nurnberg recently worked on the 4Kids Entertainment bankruptcy. **Sheldon Solow** (see p.1233) is a well-regarded, *"seasoned attorney"*

who represents a wide range of both individual and corporate clients. He is currently representing a large movie production company in a multinational bankruptcy.

## Proskauer Rose LLP
See profile on p.2001

**THE FIRM** Proskauer Rose acts for a variety of entities on bankruptcy, workouts and restructurings. However, the group is particularly revered for its debtor-side representations. The firmwide business solutions, governance, restructuring and bankruptcy practice continues to grow in manpower. The team recently represented Ocala Funding, a subsidiary of Taylor Bean & Whitaker, in its Chapter 11 proceedings. Other key clients include the American Federation of Musicians and Employers' Pension Fund, and Gas City.

**Sources say:** *"Incredibly pragmatic, good businesspeople and good attorneys."*

**KEY INDIVIDUALS Jeff Marwil** co-heads the business solutions, governance, restructuring and bankruptcy group. He has expertise in representing both public and private companies in bankruptcy, restructuring and distress situations. He recently acted as Chapter 11 trustee for Life Funds. **Mark Thomas** also co-heads the business solutions, governance, restructuring and bankruptcy practice group. He handles a wide range of matters in both US and cross-border cases including bankruptcy, restructuring and workout matters. Thomas is described as a *"very strong negotiator, highly pragmatic, very solution-oriented lawyer"* who is *"really imaginative in seeking to achieve goals."* The *"business-savvy"* **Paul Possinger** acts for a range of financially distressed entities and lenders. He recently represented Gas City in its bankruptcy proceedings.

## Shaw Fishman Glantz & Towbin LLC
See profile on p.1263

**THE FIRM** Shaw Fishman is increasingly respected in Chicago as a sterling bankruptcy boutique firm. The group represents trustees in bankruptcies but also acts for a wide variety of other entities on distressed situations, and comes particularly recommended for its bankruptcy litigation prowess.

**Sources say:** *"Very pro-client; they take the time to understand the details."*

**KEY INDIVIDUALS Robert Fishman** is highly experienced in representing many different parties involved in bankruptcy issues in court or out of court. He is described as *"someone who people know and call, from all over the country." "Great tactician"* **Steven Towbin** is an accomplished bankruptcy and restructuring attorney whom many peers highlight for his superb abilities in contentious proceedings; *"he cannot be intimidated."*

## Band 4

## DLA Piper LLP (US)
See profile on p.1971

**THE FIRM** DLA's Chicago office plays a key role in the firm's wider and growing global restructuring practice.

The group is particularly well versed in company and buyer-side representations, and is well placed to handle bankruptcy issues both in the USA and overseas. The team's expertise covers all manner of industry including real estate, hospitality and IP. In recent highlights, it represented PJ Finance in a $500 million debt restructuring.

Sources say: "*They are exceptional communicators.*"

**KEY INDIVIDUALS** Practice group cochair **Richard Chesley** (see p.1201) undertakes both national and international bankruptcy matters, and frequently represents debtors and purchasers of distressed assets. Sources describe him as a "*very tough negotiator*" and praise him for his astute financial and business understanding. He recently acted for Trident Microsystems on its Chapter 11 cases. **Chris Dickerson** (see p.1204) is renowned for representing debtors and purchasers of distressed assets in a variety of cases involving debt restructuring, reorganization and Chapter 11 matters. He is a "*very creative, very aggressive and very smart bankruptcy person,*" say sources. He played a key role in the group's representation of Reddy Ice in its prearranged Chapter 11 filing. The immensely experienced **Alan Solow** (see p.1233) recently represented FDIC in a dispute involving Corus Bankshares. He has a sterling practice acting on behalf of creditors, debtors and other entities on an array of bankruptcy and restructuring matters.

### Jones Day
See profile on p.919

**THE FIRM** Jones Day's solid Chicago-based business restructuring and reorganization group forms an integral part of the firm's leading national and international practice. The team has a strong line in debtor-side representations as well as secured creditor assignments. The group recently acted for premier gifting company Harry & David in its Chapter 11 filing. Other notable clients include HSBC, Wells Fargo, and a special committee of Tribune Company directors.

Sources say: "*A very commercial, big team with a deep bench.*"

**KEY INDIVIDUALS** Brad Erens (see p.1206) manages the firm's Chicago-based business restructuring and reorganization practice. He has extensive experience in a range of restructuring, workout and bankruptcy matters, acting for parties across the spectrum. He recently acted for German American Capital, and continues to act for Harry & David since it emerged from bankruptcy.

### Mayer Brown LLP
See profile on p.1257

**THE FIRM** Mayer Brown is particularly well known for its work representing creditors and lenders. However, the group also has expertise in acting for debtors and investors. In addition, the group has experience in real estate, gaming, manufacturing, food packing, restaurants, and the hotel industries, among others. Recent work highlights include representing Bank of America in a major debt refinancing for Mohegan Tribal Gaming Authority

**KEY INDIVIDUALS Thomas Kiriakos** has a particular strength in representing major banks, insurance compa-

nies and financial institutions, such as JPMorgan Chase Bank and Bank of America.

### Perkins Coie LLP
See profile on p.2548

**THE FIRM** Perkins Coie has quickly developed a sterling reputation for representing a broad range of debtors, creditors, committees and parties in distressed M&A. The group has particular expertise in hotel-related bankruptcies. The team recently concluded its high-profile representation of the owners of the RadLAX Gateway Hotel during Chapter 11 proceedings.

**KEY INDIVIDUALS** Practice group cochair **David Neff** is highly regarded for both his transactional and litigation work, and in particular for his superb expertise in the hospitality and leisure sector. Interviewees are especially impressed with his excellent ability to bring consensus to difficult situations. **Daniel Zazove** has a wealth of experience in representing a wide range of entities involved in bankruptcy issues. Sources note his ability to find practical solutions to any situation and pragmatic approach.

### Vedder Price PC
See profile on p.1266

**THE FIRM** Vedder Price frequently acts for lenders, creditors and trustees, among others. The group has particular expertise in and is recognized for its bankruptcy work in the aviation industry, and benefits from close links with the firm's global transport finance practice. Recent highlights include its representation of numerous lessors and lenders, including Bank of America Leasing & Capital.

**KEY INDIVIDUALS Michael Eidelman** (see p.1205) is cochair of the firm's insolvency, bankruptcy and corporate reorganization group. Sources praise him for his ability to take on and tackle extremely complex proceedings. He acts for a range of different clients such as debtors, creditors, trustees and purchasers of distressed assets. Fellow practice group cochair **Douglas Lipke** (see p.1218) has solid expertise in creditors' rights and secured lender situations. "*He is very straightforward and he gets to the point,*" say sources.

### Winston & Strawn LLP
See profile on p.1267

**THE FIRM** Winston & Strawn's Chicago-based bankruptcy practice is highly regarded among respondents. The group is well versed in representing creditors, large institutional lenders and non-bank lenders, and has been particularly active in municipal bankruptcy cases of late. Its recent highlights include representing ARG Investments and MRR Venture as creditors and minority equity holders of Hartford Computer Hardware.

Sources say: "*Sophisticated and talented.*"

**KEY INDIVIDUALS Matthew Botica** (see p.1199) represents a range of clients across the country, including debtors, lenders, creditors' committees and trustees, and also advises management and fiduciary groups on distressed situations and avoidance. He is currently acting for ARG Investments and MRR Venture on the Hartford Computer matter. **Brian Swett** (see p.1235) is praised for

being "*thoughtful, patient and careful at thinking through all the problems.*" His representations span a wide area, acting for lenders, companies, investors, and sellers and purchasers, among other parties.

## Band 5

### Adelman & Gettleman Ltd
See profile on p.1240

**THE FIRM** This boutique firm enjoys a solid reputation for working on complicated and sophisticated midmarket bankruptcy issues. The group acts for debtors, creditors, as well as purchasers and sellers of business assets, on a variety of bankruptcy, restructuring and workout cases and related litigation.

Sources say: "*Talented and knowledgeable.*"

**KEY INDIVIDUALS Howard Adelman** (see p.1196) and **Chad Gettleman** (see p.1208) come highly recommended and are praised for their effectiveness in complex bankruptcy litigation issues.

### Dentons
See profile on p.449

**THE FIRM** Dentons's Chicago restructuring and insolvency group benefits from the firm's international resources and continues to have a solid reputation in this area. The group works on a wide range of cases including Chapter 11 proceedings, distressed M&A situations, and out-of-court workouts. The group has recently been involved in a number of matters relating to real estate and aviation. The team recently represented Northstar Aerospace (USA) in its Chapter 11 case, and Pension Benefit Guaranty Corporation (PBGC) in the American Airlines bankruptcy.

Sources say: "*I think they gave outstanding service. Extremely pragmatic in their approach.*"

**KEY INDIVIDUALS Fruman Jacobson** (see p.1213) is currently representing PBGC in the bankruptcy cases of American Airlines and Eastman Kodak. He has particular expertise in representing public and private debtors, and cochairs the firm's credit markets and subprime team. The highly "*experienced and talented*" **Robert Millner** (see p.1222) is recommended for his creativity during bankruptcy litigation, particularly on behalf of insurance companies and financial institutions. He recently represented Safeco Insurance Company as insurer in the Chapter 11 proceedings of the Society of Jesus, Oregon Province.

### Edwards Wildman Palmer
See profile on p.1520

**THE FIRM** Edwards Wildman Palmer's successful restructuring and insolvency department is particularly renowned for its expertise in banking-related matters. However, the team has been especially active of late in real estate bankruptcy issues. The group also represents other entities, such as financial institutions, institutional investors and insurers. Recent highlights include representing Old Second Bank as secured creditor in a $10 million defaulted loan secured by an athletics facility in Chicago.

KEY INDIVIDUALS **David Fischer** (see p.1207) chairs the firm's restructuring and insolvency department. His expertise includes real estate, finance, insurance and private equity-related bankruptcy issues. He has experience in representing a diverse range of parties in restructurings, workouts, foreclosures and Chapter 11 liquidations. **Jonathan Young** (see p.1238) is increasingly recognized for being "*very thorough and practical.*" He regularly appears in court, having expertise both in litigation and transactional work.

## Foley & Lardner LLP
See profile on p.2588

THE FIRM The capabilities of Foley & Lardner's bankruptcy and business reorganization practice span a wide range of bankruptcy issues in many different industries, including sport, energy, commodities and healthcare. The group is also recognized for its strong trustee and bondholder representations. Recent highlights include the representation of Computershare Trust Company as indenture trustee of a number of issues of notes issued by Travelport. It also acted for Guggenheim Corporate Funding in the acquisition of equity and assets of Los Angeles Dodgers.

**Sources say:** "*Very good at being able to create a relationship with the other parties in a situation, and to keep adversarial matters collegial and constructive.*"

KEY INDIVIDUALS **Harold Kaplan** leads the firm's corporate trust and bondholders' rights practice group. As such, he has particular expertise in representing bondholders, committees, financial institutions and trustees. Sources say that Kaplan is a "*very knowledgeable and talented attorney,*" who "*sees the big picture and looks way ahead.*"

## Katten Muchin Rosenman LLP
See profile on p.1253

THE FIRM Katten's insolvency and restructuring practice represents a diverse range of lenders and creditors, although the group also undertakes significant debtor work. The team has a solid reputation in sophisticated real estate work and has also been highly active in the healthcare space. The group recently acted for US Bancorp on a matter relating to the largest nursing home chain in Illinois.

**Sources say:** "*Very responsive and attentive to our client needs.*"

KEY INDIVIDUALS **Kenneth Ottaviano** is cochair of the Chicago-based insolvency and restructuring practice group. Sources comment that he "*gets right to the issues at hand,*" and "*always figures out a way to get the job done.*" He recently represented RBS Citizens in an out-of-court restructuring. **John Sieger** represents a diverse set of entities, including lenders, debtors and purchasers of distressed companies and assets. Sources appreciate his "*astute business judgment and litigation strategy.*" He represents the Robert R McCormick and Cantigny Foundations as the former largest shareholders of the Chicago Tribune in litigation centered on fraudulent transfer actions.

## Neal, Gerber & Eisenberg LLP
See profile on p.1260

THE FIRM Neal Gerber's practice group covers a wide spectrum of insolvency and reorganization matters both in and out of court. The team represents debtors, creditors and financially distressed companies. Recent highlights include the group's representation of LNV Corporation in a high-profile appeal in a Chapter 11 filing by River East Plaza.

KEY INDIVIDUALS **Mark Berkoff** (see p.1198) chairs the financial restructuring and bankruptcy practice group. Respondents praise Berkoff for his strong business sense and his focus on achieving objectives cost-effectively. He is currently representing R&M Aviation in Chapter 11 proceedings, and is lead counsel for the Official Committee of Unsecured Creditors for Hartmarx Corporation.

## Schiff Hardin LLP

THE FIRM Longstanding Chicago firm Schiff Hardin is a new entrant in this year's rankings. The group represents a wide range of clients including debtors, lenders and creditors' committees. Recent representations include acting for Amalgamated Bank as indenture trustee on a matter relating to large real estate developments, and Raymond Professional Group in its Chapter 11 proceedings.

**Sources say:** "*Seamless as a team.*"

KEY INDIVIDUALS **Mark Fisher** focuses on acting for a variety of lenders and financial institutions in workouts and reorganizations. Sources describe him as "*a calming influence,*" with one interviewee mentioning: "*He did a great job for us in a complex and nasty situation.*"

## Other Notable Practitioners

**David Heroy** (see p.1212) is cochair of the global financial restructuring and insolvency team at Baker & McKenzie. He is described as "*articulate, strategic, forward-thinking and very well connected.*" Also at Baker & McKenzie, **Carmen Lonstein** (see p.1218) leads the firm's North American financial restructuring, creditors' rights and bankruptcy practice. She is "*client-friendly, responsive, creative and thoughtful,*" say sources, and possesses "*a perfect balance between the legal nuts and bolts and the business requirements of her clients.*" **Stephen Bobo** of Reed Smith LLP is regarded as "*one of the most pragmatic and realistic attorneys in Chicago,*" and a "*trustworthy, solid performer.*" He has a varied practice acting on behalf of both creditors and debtors, and recently represented Warrantech Corporation as creditor in the complex Chapter 11 case of US Fidelis. **Aaron Hammer** (see p.1211) chairs the bankruptcy, reorganization and creditors' rights practice group at Sugar Felsenthal Grais & Hammer LLP. Sources describe him as a "*tenacious, hard-working lawyer, and a zealous advocate for his clients.*" **William Smith** (see p.1232) of McDermott Will & Emery LLP is recommended in particular for his expertise in tax-exempt finance and healthcare-related bankruptcy issues. He is a "*fantastic lawyer; very sophisticated and a pleasure to work with,*" say interviewees. **Nathan Coco** (see p.1202), also of McDermott Will & Emery LLP, is described as "*very intellectual – and he gets great results for his clients.*" Both he and Smith recently represented Pacific Retirement Services in claims and disputes relating to Lehman Brothers. **Neal Wolf** leads Neal Wolf & Associates, LLC, a famed local boutique firm. Wolf and his team undertake a wide variety of bankruptcy and reorganization matters and related litigation. **George Mesires** (see p.1222) of Ungaretti & Harris LLP has "*an acute sense of how to best solve and navigate complex issues related to any matter,*" according to sources. He acts for a range of entities on various insolvency and restructuring matters, and recently represented Clare Oaks and Fairview Ministries in their respective Chapter 11 cases. **Michael Molinaro** recently joined Reed Smith from Loeb & Loeb. He is a seasoned attorney with experience of representing banks, financial institutions, insurance companies and other entities. He is a "*good tough litigator,*" say sources; "*articulate, client-focused, and an attorney who grasps complex topics very easily.*"

# COMMUNICATIONS

## Band 1

### Mayer Brown LLP
See profile on p.1257

**THE FIRM** This preeminent firm maintains its position as a leader in the communications field, with interviewees commending the team's thoroughness of approach, practical knowledge of the business environment and understanding of its clients' best interests. Its attorneys are well versed in handling substantial contentious matters before the FCC, as well as at state and federal court level, and before the US Supreme Court. In recent work it has acted on behalf of key client AT&T on a number of matters, including handling the company's applications for various permits to construct wireless communication facilities. **Sources say:** *"The knowledge, expertise, legal skills and experience they bring to the table have made the firm our first choice for state regulatory advocacy nationwide."*
**KEY INDIVIDUALS Theodore Livingston** is held in high esteem as a leading force in the communications sector. Sources regard him as *"meticulous, aware of all key relevant facts no matter how arcane, and able to apply them creatively."* In the past year he has been acting for AT&T on disputes with competing carriers. The highly organized and

personable **John Muench** attracts widespread praise as a litigation specialist. Sources value his dedication to his clients' cause, noting: *"He has a plan for success and marshals resources to get it accomplished."* He recently played a significant role in the AT&T applications for various wireless communication facilities permits. The *"very talented"* **Christian Binnig** elicits praise from commentators for his skill as a litigator. He continues to maintain a fine track record in regulatory proceedings. Clients benefit from **Dennis Friedman**'s established presence as an expert telecom litigator, with sources drawing particular attention to his *"deep understanding of both the legal and business"* sides. He also comes recommended for the commercial acumen he displays during complex negotiations. Commentators describe **Hans Germann** as *"highly accessible, client-focused, attentive to detail and very analytical."* An impressive breadth of experience sees him in demand in substantial disputes at both trial and appellate level, as well as before the FCC. The *"diligent and practical"* **Demetrios Metropoulos** wins praise for his technical skill and deep understanding of the commercial environment in which clients operate. He also stands out for his prowess in appellate litigation. Recent work highlights include defending AT&T against appeals relating to rates paid to access the networks of local carriers. **Tyson Covey** continues to impress interviewees with the quality of his work and is especially singled out for his efficiency and practical approach to issues. His practice extends across regulatory, trial and appellate matters. The past twelve months have seen him acting on behalf of AT&T on multistate carrier litigation.

## Band 2

### Kelley Drye & Warren LLP
See profile on p.1985

**THE FIRM** This established telecom practice receives praise for the strength of expertise it exhibits across the board. Its team members regularly appear before the FCC, state commissions and federal courts, and market commentators are quick to highlight the attorneys' attention to client needs and commercial awareness. The reputation of the practice attracts both domestic and international industry leaders to the client fold, including DISH Network and Mediacom.
**Sources say:** *"The firm has always been available to provide timely expertise and response regardless of vacation schedules or locations and time zone differences. In other words, they are available whenever you need them."*
**KEY INDIVIDUALS** Practice leader **Henry Kelly** remains a much-respected figure in the telecom industry, with sources singling out his *"depth of regulatory and commercial experience, evenhanded demeanor and willingness to explore alternatives."*

### Sidley Austin LLP
See profile on p.1264

**THE FIRM** Sidley Austin remains a firm of choice for wireless and wireline providers, satellite carriers and broadcasting stations. The communications regulatory practice represents clients on a domestic and international scale, and the group is well known for its work with major television networks. Over the past twelve months its lawyers have represented clients in a series of significant matters relating to the evolution of wireless technology, and they offer a particularly broad expertise in this area. Clients include Merrill Lynch, GE Capital and U.S. Cellular.
**KEY INDIVIDUALS** The excellent **David Carpenter** (see p.1201) remains an outstanding figure in telecom, with peers attesting to the breadth of his regulatory expertise. Sources also note: *"As long as you have David Carpenter you certainly have significant strength."* He is singled out for his stellar appellate practice, which has included representing AT&T in a number of novel matters over the past year.

## Band 3

### Meyer Capel, PC

**THE FIRM** Champaign-based Meyer Capel retains its status as the firm of choice for independent telecom carrier companies. The telecom and public utility regulation practice is singled out for both its longstanding reputation and its high level of activity in this concentrated area. Its attorneys are also notable for their experience in issues surrounding carrier access reform, intercarrier compensation issues and ongoing regulatory compliance.
**Sources say:** *"Quite excellent at what they do."*
**KEY INDIVIDUALS** President of the firm **Joseph Murphy** is noted for the breadth of his practice, which also takes in IP matters. He comes particularly recommended for his work with wireless and wireline carriers, local telephone companies and interexchange resellers. The highly respected **Dennis Muncy** has amassed a wealth of experience during the course of his long career. He is widely recognized as an expert in the telecommunications arena and is commended by market commentators for his deep industry knowledge.

### Schiff Hardin LLP

**THE FIRM** This firm is noted for its strength in the Illinois telecom space, and its team of experienced lawyers impresses with its breadth of expertise in regulatory, contentious and transactional matters. Its attorneys are well versed in acting on behalf of clients before regulatory bodies as well as state and federal courts. The team also offers an in-depth understanding of commercial realities that influence the shape of interconnection agreements.
**KEY INDIVIDUALS Owen MacBride** is a highly regarded figure in the firm's energy and public utilities practice group, and in his work on behalf of telecom carriers he has been involved in a variety of regulatory proceedings and has structured numerous intercarrier agreements.

# CONSTRUCTION

Commentary about individuals can be found under their firm's paragraph. If the firm has no paragraph (is not ranked) look at Other Notable Practitioners.

| Construction Leading Firms |
| --- |
| **Band 1** |
| Schiff Hardin LLP [*] |
| Stein Ray LLP |
| **Band 2** |
| Laurie & Brennan, LLP |
| Lyman & Nielsen |
| Ogletree, Deakins, Nash, Smoak & Stewart, PC [*] |
| **Band 3** |
| Conway & Mrowiec |
| Duane Morris LLP [*] |
| Harris Winick LLP |
| K&L Gates [*] |
| Sabo & Zahn |
| Seyfarth Shaw LLP [*] |
| Vedder Price PC [*] |

| Construction Senior Statesmen | |
| --- | --- |
| **Senior Statesmen:** distinguished older practitioners | |
| Lurie Paul | Schiff Hardin LLP |
| Lyman Bill | Lyman & Nielsen |

| Leading Individuals | |
| --- | --- |
| **Band 1** | |
| Friedlander Mark C | Schiff Hardin LLP |
| Laurie Ty D | Laurie & Brennan, LLP |
| Lewis Charles B | Duane Morris LLP |
| Roberts Kenneth M | Schiff Hardin LLP |
| Shapiro Clifford J | Barnes & Thornburg LLP (ONP) [†] [*] |
| Stein Steven G M | Stein Ray LLP |
| **Band 2** | |
| Altman Ross | Dykema Gossett PLLC (ONP) [†] |
| Bisceglia Joseph G | Jenner & Block LLP (ONP) [†] [*] |
| Brennan Daniel | Laurie & Brennan, LLP |
| Cole Alexandra | Perkins Coie LLP (ONP) [†] |
| Fradin Scott R | Much Shelist, P.C (ONP) [†] |
| Leavitt Josh | K&L Gates [*] |
| Mrowiec John S | Conway & Mrowiec [*] |
| Nielsen Jennifer A | Lyman & Nielsen |
| Pearse Richard W | Vedder Price PC [*] |
| Ray Stephen E | Stein Ray LLP |
| Ruff Randolph E | Ogletree, Deakins, Nash, Smoak & Stewart [*] |
| Slutzky Lorence H | Robbins, Schwartz, Nicholas, Lifton (ONP) [†] |
| **Band 3** | |
| Andre Greg | K&L Gates [*] |
| Bedard Peter | Stein Ray LLP |
| Conway Timothy R | Conway & Mrowiec [*] |
| Dash James | Carlson Dash LLC (ONP) [†] |
| Layng Karen P | Vedder Price PC [*] |
| Newman Margery | Deutsch, Levy & Engel, Chartered (ONP) [†] |
| Ponder Anita | Seyfarth Shaw LLP [*] |
| Sabo Werner | Sabo & Zahn |
| Singer Eric L | Ice Miller LLP (ONP) [†] |
| Winick Jeffrey | Harris Winick LLP |
| Zahn Jim | Sabo & Zahn |

| Up-and-coming individuals | |
| --- | --- |
| Rosenberg Daniel | Sheppard, Mullin, Richter & Hampton (ONP) [†] |

[*] Indicates firm / individual with profile.
Alphabetical order within each band. Band 1 is the highest.

## Band 1

### Schiff Hardin LLP

**THE FIRM** Schiff Hardin continues to have a strong national practice and its attorneys remain active on national and international projects. It is particularly active in the energy and utilities sectors and has specialist lighting knowledge. It was recently retained by Alliant Energy as part of its billion-dollar environmental retrofit projects at four coal-fired power generation facilities spanning several states. Notable clients of the firm also include Kansas City Power & Light, Genon Energy and Constellation/Exelon Power.
**Sources say:** *"They remain at the top of their class." "Even though they are a large firm, they provide a boutique firm experience."*
**KEY INDIVIDUALS** The *"absolutely wonderful"* **Mark Friedlander** is particularly experienced in advising clients on project delivery and construction methods and covers transactional and litigation construction work. He has recently pioneered a popular new business structure for design-build projects. **Kenneth Roberts** specializes in project controls and procurement contracts, with an emphasis on acting for owners in the energy industry. He has a wealth of experience of both alternative dispute resolution and power plant construction. *"Perennial all-star for construction"* **Paul Lurie** is described by market sources as *"one of the seminal leading mentors of the construction industry."* He contributes over 40 years of experience to his dispute avoidance and resolution and contract negotiation assignments.

### Stein Ray LLP

**THE FIRM** This boutique firm focuses principally on the resolution of construction disputes, contract negotiation, transactional work and general legal management of construction projects. It is particularly experienced in dealing with complicated construction-related disputes. Significant clients of the firm include AECOM, Thornton Tomasetti, Clark Construction and Boston Financial.
**KEY INDIVIDUALS Steven Stein** specializes in complex trials and arbitrations of design and construction matters. He is also a trustee of the Chicago Architecture Foundation. **Stephen Ray** is an expert in complex construction and design disputes on a nationwide basis. Observers say that he is *"good to deal with, gets to the point, makes sense; the kind of person you can accomplish things with, with the minimum of time and expense."* **Peter Bedard**

is experienced in issues arising from the design and construction of industrial and commercial properties and is very experienced before both state and federal courts.

## Band 2

### Laurie & Brennan, LLP

**THE FIRM** Laurie & Brennan undertakes the full spectrum of construction matters, and is especially renowned for its expert mediation practice. Since being founded in 2010, the firm has quickly developed into one of the leading players in the state. Recent work saw the firm represent the New Jersey Devils in a design error claim related to the Devils' new arena in Newark, New Jersey. Other key clients include Howard Hughes Medical Institute, McCaffery Interests, Ascher Brothers and DePaul University.
**Sources say:** *"Professional, highly experienced, focused and worked extremely well."*
**KEY INDIVIDUALS Ty Laurie** is an expert in all areas of construction law, and is a qualified arbitrator and mediator. He recently acted for Nestlé, revising the design and consultation forms for all of its US industrial and commercial facilities. *"He's very knowledgeable in the construction area, both the law, but perhaps more importantly, the business side as well,"* say sources. *"He's practical and pragmatic but also thorough and detailed."* **Daniel Brennan** predominantly advises designers, owners and contractors on risk management within the construction process. Sources comment that he is *"bright, professional, personable but tough and also highly knowledgeable."*

### Lyman & Nielsen

**THE FIRM** Lyman & Nielsen remains highly respected by its peers and clients. The firm provides advice across the spectrum of construction matters, including mediation and arbitration when necessary. The team is hailed in particular for being very strong on matters involving subcontractors.
**KEY INDIVIDUALS Jennifer Nielsen** handles transactional and contentious construction work in the public and private sectors. She also undertakes litigation involving mechanics' liens, security bonds and real estate. Sources describe her as *"aggressive and hard-working for her clients."* *"Real gentleman"* **Bill Lyman** is an expert in a broad range of transactional construction matters and frequently acts as an arbitrator and mediator. He is *"one of the first guys that put construction on the map in Chicago,"* according to sources.

### Ogletree, Deakins, Nash, Smoak & Stewart, PC

See profile on p.1110
**THE FIRM** The firm's highly regarded construction practice advises general contractors, design-builders, owners and manufacturers on all legal matters pertaining to both

private and public construction projects. It is active with national and international construction projects. The team recently advised Mechanical Dynamics & Analysis in negotiating engineering, construction and design contracts for a high-speed balance plant. Key clients include Pepper Construction, Formica, The Frederick Quinn Corporation and Abercrombie & Fitch.

**Sources say:** *"They have demonstrated excellent performance."*

**KEY INDIVIDUALS Randolph Ruff** (see p.1229) wins praise for being *"well versed in his area of expertise and he is always accessible."* Observers go on to comment that he is *"a real go-getter"* with the *"highest ethical standards."*

## Band 3

### Conway & Mrowiec

**THE FIRM** This boutique firm provides construction advice on a whole host of public contract law issues and litigation. It is particularly adept at contract drafting, assisting on project administration, and claims prosecution.

**Sources say:** *"Very good lawyers; we have confidence in them."*

**KEY INDIVIDUALS John Mrowiec** (see p.1223) is hailed by sources as a *"great trial lawyer"* who is *"very good technically."* He is eminently experienced in arbitration and mediation engagements. **Timothy Conway** (see p.1202) has a wealth of experience representing clients with projects involving prisons, telecom, libraries, shopping centers and highways on a nationwide basis. Sources single him out for praise due to his deep knowledge.

### Duane Morris LLP
See profile on p.2239

**THE FIRM** This firm's construction practice provides advice across an array of transactional and litigation construction matters. The firm regularly assists private and public owners, design professionals, contractors and suppliers. It is also very active in sureties on a range of project segments and is particularly strong at mediation and arbitration.

**Sources say:** *"Very thorough and extremely knowledgeable in construction matters."*

**KEY INDIVIDUALS** *"One of the best construction attorneys in Chicago,"* **Charles Lewis** is appreciated for being unerringly prompt and knowledgeable in this field. He is especially recommended as one of the state's leading mediators in the construction sector.

### Harris Winick LLP

**THE FIRM** Harris Winick provides advice on the full range of construction transaction, insurance recovery and litigation matters across the USA and internationally. The firm acts for a diverse spread of client types, including universities and REITs, undertaking drafting, design and construction contracts as well as general risk management matters. Key clients include Jones Lang LaSalle, the University of Chicago and Hyatt Hotels.

**Sources say:** *"Sophisticated thinking, deep knowledge of real estate and prompt service."*

**KEY INDIVIDUALS Jeffrey Winick** representS owners, contractors, and design and construction professionals in construction litigation. He also has extensive experience in the negotiating and drafting of design and construction agreements. Winick is hailed for being *"extremely intelligent, hard-working, prompt, efficient, client-focused, result-focused and cost-effective."*

### K&L Gates
See profile on p.2245

**THE FIRM** K&L Gates provides construction advice on contentious and noncontentious matters internationally and nationally. It is particularly praised for its skill in construction litigation and is well placed to complement its construction advice with the expertise of partners in a multitude of other practice areas.

**KEY INDIVIDUALS** *"Creative counsel"* **Josh Leavitt** (see p.1217) is praised for the quality of his scholarship and his knowledge. He provides general litigation construction advice and also possesses expertise across a whole host of transactional construction matters. **Greg Andre** (see p.1196) has a wealth of experience in construction matters, dispute resolution and large-scale projects and land use matters.

### Sabo & Zahn

**THE FIRM** This boutique construction firm wins praise from market observers for its in-depth knowledge, especially of architectural matters. The team provides construction transactional advice to individuals and businesses of all sizes. It also offers construction litigation advice on the gamut of construction concerns, with an emphasis on contract negotiation and dispute avoidance.

**Sources say:** *"They have a very good feel for where the market is."*

**KEY INDIVIDUALS Werner Sabo** is a *"good, smart, practical lawyer,"* renowned for his expertise as an arbitrator and mediator. He also comes highly praised for his knowledge of contract issues. **Jim Zahn**'s deep construction expertise is complemented by his extensive experience as an architect. He is best known for his know-how in nontrial construction matters.

### Seyfarth Shaw LLP
See profile on p.1262

**THE FIRM** The national construction giant maintains a solid offering in Chicago, acting on behalf of developers, contractors, owners and engineering companies. The firm has particular expertise in mechanics' and construction liens and government contracts. The group has also been making inroads into lending-related work. The firm's recent work in the construction arena saw it act for Wisconsin Utility Exposure on an appeal connected with its application for certification eligibility as a women business enterprise.

**Sources say:** *"Very strong and broad in the business arena."*

**KEY INDIVIDUALS Anita Ponder** (see p.1226) specializes in construction matters involving government con-

tract work and wins praise from observers for being *"always well prepared and knowledgeable."*

### Vedder Price PC
See profile on p.1266

**THE FIRM** This group represents a range of manufacturers, contractors and owners in a broad spectrum of construction matters, including drafting contracts for large projects. The team is experienced in handling disputes in federal and state courts and also provides alternative dispute resolution representation. A recent highlight saw the firm acting for Target on obtaining zoning and permitting approvals for multiple urban stores.

**Sources say:** *"They are able to quickly assess the construction issue and attempt to resolve it in an expeditious manner while trying to obtain the best possible outcome for their client."*

**KEY INDIVIDUALS Richard Pearse** (see p.1224) is experienced in dealing with infrastructure projects and their financing, development and construction contracting. Sources are especially impressed by his standout competence and approachability. **Karen Layng** (see p.1217) has extensive experience in complex litigation cases before federal and state courts. Sources praise her *"ability to consistently provide appropriate and good advice."* They also describe her as *"a good lawyer; very aggressive and knowledgeable."*

### Other Notable Practitioners

The *"very meticulous"* **Clifford Shapiro** (see p.1231) of Barnes & Thornburg LLP specializes in construction law and litigation, including insurance coverage litigation. **Alexandra Cole** of Perkins Coie LLP has the respect of peers and clients. She acts for all parties in the construction and development process. She recently represented DiNapoli Capital Partners in the renovation and conversion of Crowne Plaza San Jose to a Hyatt Place. **Margery Newman** of Deutsch, Levy & Engel, Chartered specializes in cases involving complex construction litigation in both the public and private sectors. Sources praise her as a *"strong advocate."* **Ross Altman** of Dykema Gossett PLLC focuses on cases involving design, engineering, procurement and construction matters. He represents contractors, design professionals, owners and lenders. Sources comment that he is *"very knowledgeable, very well thought-of, and very well respected."* **Joseph Bisceglia** (see p.1199) of Jenner & Block LLP is a certified arbitrator and has a well-established construction practice spanning a wide spectrum of construction matters. Clients appreciate his technical prowess and ability to direct a case smoothly. **Lorence Slutzky** of Robbins, Schwartz, Nicholas, Lifton & Taylor, Ltd represents contractors, designers, manufacturers, insurers, and public and private owners and developers. Market observers are appreciative of the fact that he is *"exceptionally strong in terms of understanding complex issues."* **James Dash** of Carlson Dash LLC has over 25 years' experience of construction litigation, and is commended for his expertise in mechanics' lien claims and title insurance defense work. **Eric Singer** of Ice Miller LLP is valued by sources for being *"very competent and very knowledgeable."* His construction practice has a particular emphasis on the representation of contractors, owners, lenders, architects and engineers. **Scott Fradin** of Much Shelist Denenberg Ament & Rubenstein, PC acts on a broad spectrum of construction related matters, including mechanics' lien and breach of contract disputes. He is hailed by sources as an *"excellent attorney,"* who *"always contributes in an insightful way."* The *"very knowledgeable and thorough"* **Daniel Rosenberg** recently joined Sheppard, Mullin, Richter & Hampton LLP from K&L Gates. He is an expert in contract drafting and negotiation, risk management and construction litigation.

# CORPORATE/M&A & PRIVATE EQUITY

Private Equity p.1157

Commentary about individuals can be found under their firm's paragraph. If the firm has no paragraph (is not ranked) look at Other Notable Practitioners.

## Corporate/M&A & Private Equity
### Leading Firms

**Band 1**
Kirkland & Ellis LLP *
Latham & Watkins LLP *
Sidley Austin LLP *
Skadden, Arps, Slate, Meagher & Flom LLP & Affiliates *

**Band 2**
Mayer Brown LLP *
McDermott Will & Emery LLP *
Winston & Strawn LLP *

**Band 3**
DLA Piper LLP (US) *
Jenner & Block LLP *
Jones Day *
Katten Muchin Rosenman LLP *

**Band 4**
Baker & McKenzie *
Greenberg Traurig, LLP *
Neal, Gerber & Eisenberg LLP *
Ungaretti & Harris LLP *
Vedder Price PC *

**Band 5**
Dentons *
Duane Morris LLP *
K&L Gates *
Paul Hastings LLP *
Reed Smith LLP
Schiff Hardin LLP

*\* Indicates firm / individual with profile.*
*Alphabetical order within each band. Band 1 is the highest.*

## Corporate/M&A
### Senior Statesmen

**Senior Statesmen: distinguished older practitioners**

| | | |
|---|---|---|
| Helman Robert A | Mayer Brown LLP | |
| Lubin Donald G | Dentons * | |
| Wander Herbert S | Katten Muchin Rosenman LLP | |

### Leading Individuals

**Star individuals**

| | |
|---|---|
| Cole Thomas A | Sidley Austin LLP * |
| Mulaney Jr Charles W | Skadden, Arps, Slate, Meagher & Flom * |

**Band 1**

| | |
|---|---|
| Falk R Scott | Kirkland & Ellis LLP * |
| Gerstein Mark D | Latham & Watkins LLP |
| Lowinger Frederick C | Sidley Austin LLP * |
| Wall Robert F | Winston & Strawn LLP * |

**Band 2**

| | |
|---|---|
| Choi Paul L | Sidley Austin LLP * |
| Davis Scott J | Mayer Brown LLP |
| Kitslaar Elizabeth C | Jones Day * |
| Qasim Imad I | Sidley Austin LLP * |
| Schreiber Rodd M | Skadden, Arps, Slate, Meagher & Flom * |
| Thomas Frederick B | Mayer Brown LLP |

**Band 3**

| | |
|---|---|
| Aizenstein Neal | DLA Piper LLP (US) * |
| Cullen Gary P | Skadden, Arps, Slate, Meagher & Flom * |
| Duwe Brian W | Skadden, Arps, Slate, Meagher & Flom * |
| Friedli Helen R | McDermott Will & Emery LLP * |
| Froy Michael M | Dentons * |
| Harris Linda C | Dentons * |
| Junewicz James J | Winston & Strawn LLP * |
| Lanznar Howard S | Katten Muchin Rosenman LLP |
| Levenstein Gary | Ungaretti & Harris LLP * |
| Lieberman Peter H | Greenberg Traurig, LLP * |
| Malik Thaddeus | Paul Hastings LLP |
| Melton Timothy J | Jones Day * |

| | |
|---|---|
| Nemeroff Michael A | Vedder Price PC * |
| Pucker Michael A | Latham & Watkins LLP |
| Sperber Marc F | Mayer Brown LLP |
| Toth Bruce A | Winston & Strawn LLP * |
| Weil Andrew L | DLA Piper LLP (US) * |

**Band 4**

| | |
|---|---|
| Barden Larry A | Sidley Austin LLP * |
| David Oscar A | Winston & Strawn LLP * |
| Ferguson Thomas | Kelley Drye & Warren LLP (ONP) [†] |
| Fogel Eric M | Lathrop & Gage LLP (ONP) [†] |
| Gromacki Joseph P | Jenner & Block LLP * |
| Hatcher Merrick | K&L Gates * |
| Kaufman David J | Duane Morris LLP |
| Keim Jr Thomas E | Latham & Watkins LLP |
| Kucera William | Mayer Brown LLP |
| Landsman Stephen A | Greenberg Traurig, LLP * |
| Lee Michael P | Reed Smith LLP |
| Meadows Stanley | McDermott Will & Emery LLP * |
| Roeder Craig A | Baker & McKenzie * |
| Schneidman Edward J | Kirkland & Ellis LLP * |
| Shepro Richard Warren | Mayer Brown LLP |
| Simala Jodi A | Mayer Brown LLP |
| Stone David S | Neal, Gerber & Eisenberg LLP * |
| Theiss Paul W | Mayer Brown LLP |

**Up-and-coming individuals**

| | |
|---|---|
| Faris Bradley | Latham & Watkins LLP |
| Koenigsknecht John K | Neal, Gerber & Eisenberg LLP * |

## Band 1

### Kirkland & Ellis LLP
**See profile on p.1254**

**THE FIRM** This impressive and comprehensive practice remains at the market's vanguard, and handles all aspects of M&A and private equity matters. Recently, the group represented Accel-KKR Capital Partners in the $1 billion sale of Endurance International to Warburg Pincus Private Equity and Goldman Sachs. In a further highlight, the team acted for Bain Capital on its acquisition of Physio-Control, a $487 million deal. The group's stellar client portfolio also includes Sun Capital Partners, Baxter International and The Boeing Company.

**Sources say:** *"Kirkland has knocked my socks off."* *"They have every corner of the market absolutely nailed. They man the corporate market with such force you're never going to ask a question that someone hasn't asked before."*
**KEY INDIVIDUALS Jon Ballis** (see p.1197) handles sophisticated commercial transactions, including private investment in public equity (PIPE) and strategic mergers. *"He does a nice job of bringing all the different pieces together,"* notes one enthusiastic source, who goes on to describe him as *"very practical and very strong in deal work."* The

*"exceptional"* **Scott Falk** (see p.1206) *"is thoughtful and has great judgment."* He is well versed in securities offerings and M&A, and recently led the team acting for Molson Coors Brewing on its agreement to acquire StarBev. The *"obviously terrific"* **Sanford Perl** (see p.1225) has a broad-based practice that encompasses IPOs, debt and equity restructurings, and fund formation. Sources commend him for his ability *"to communicate very complex issues with very few words."* Recently, he acted for KRG Capital Partners on its investment in Ansira Partners. **Stephen**

**Ritchie** (see p.1227) undertakes sophisticated business transactions, within which he places an emphasis on leveraged buyouts, recapitalizations, workouts and M&A. In a recent highlight, he led the team advising GTCR on its high-value acquisition of CAMP Systems International. **Matthew Steinmetz** (see p.1234) handles transactional cases and is noted for his fund formation strengths. Sources appreciate his ability to take a commercial perspective and stay levelheaded in matters. **Douglas Gessner**'s (see p.320) practice includes representing venture capital and private equity sponsors across the spectrum of investment matters, and he comes recommended for his expertise in leveraged buyouts and fund formation matters. He recently acted on behalf of the Friendly Ice Cream Corporation in its Chapter 11 bankruptcy and sale to Sun Capital Partners. **Walter Holzer** (see p.1212) focus-

es on leveraged buyouts, in addition to divestitures and M&A. In a recent highlight, he represented Cardno in its $106 million merger with ATC Group Holdings. Sources single out his *"expertise, common-sense approach and commerciality in the M&A space,"* and also appreciate his ability to understand the needs of the client. Sources are quick to assert the *"impressive"* **Edward Schneidman**'s (see p.1230) *"great judgment."* His practice covers the spectrum of securities and corporate law, and he is sought for his wide-ranging experience in public offering activities for companies with a real estate focus. The seasoned **Jeffrey Hammes** (see p.1211) continues to enjoy an excellent reputation in the market, and is well versed in matters involving the structuring and negotiation of sophisticated commercial transactions.

### Latham & Watkins LLP
See profile on p.446

**THE FIRM** Latham & Watkins's Chicago team remains a force within the corporate/M&A and private equity world, and is supported by the firm's national and international network. The group has a full-service outlook that allows it to provide top-level advice and representation for clients across the spectrum of corporate/M&A matters. The team is well known for its ability to deal with complex M&A transactions for both public and private companies. This expertise recently saw it act for TransUnion, Madison Dearborn Partners and the Pritzker family on the sale of TransUnion to Advent International and Goldman Sachs. The team is also acting for Walgreen's on its purchase of Crescent Healthcare. Other clients in the firm's impressive roster include Citi, The Toro Company and PIMCO.
**Sources say:** *"Tremendous knowledge of the M&A market – tremendous strategic knowledge."* *"They have a clear understanding of the law, but also have a nice practical sense."*
**KEY INDIVIDUALS** Global M&A practice chair **Mark Gerstein** is *"just phenomenal."* His practice encompasses takeover defense and corporate governance, in addition to M&A. He recently led the team advising Phoenix International Freight Services on its sale to C.H.Robinson Worldwide, a $635 million deal. Sources describe him as a *"consummate professional,"* and also single him out as *"great tactically."* **Michael Pucker** has recently handled the sale of nine senior living rental properties by Vi to Senior Housing Properties Trust. He wins particular praise for his ability to get to grips with the details of a transaction. **Thomas Keim** is noted for his expertise in both domestic and cross-border M&A work. Clients view him as *"a true partner,"* and value his *"willingness to find answers to the most obscure questions."* **Bradley Faris** is a rising star in the market and continues to develop his name in M&A work, including takeover defense and conflict of interest counseling.

### Sidley Austin LLP
See profile on p.1264

**THE FIRM** Sidley Austin remains one of the market's most dominant and successful forces, and its team continues to represent clients such as Aon in some of the most complex cases. The group has a successful history of advising private and public entities, including financial sponsors,

boards of directors and committees, on a diverse array of M&A work. In addition, the team also advises clients on a range of private equity transactions, as illustrated by its representation of CHS Capital in its acquisition of Dura-Line. Other recent highlights include its representation of Nationstar Mortgage in the purchase of mortgage servicing assets and corresponding servicing receivables of Residential Capital.
**Sources say:** *"The quality and breadth of expertise is first-rate."* *"Established top-quality corporate firm."*
**KEY INDIVIDUALS** The *"terrific"* **Thomas Cole** (see p.1202) is praised for his communication skills, which are *"inherently calming even in the most tumultuous of situations."* He focuses on corporate governance matters as well as M&A for public companies. He is also described as *"a household name among CEOs,"* principally for his skill in *"helping corporations and boards see a clear path through difficult situations."* The *"supersmart"* **Frederick Lowinger** (see p.1218) is the first port of call for many sources, who reserve particular praise for his understanding of the most complex matters. He recently led the team acting for Central Vermont on its $720 million sale to Gaz Metro. **Sy Peck** (see p.1224) focuses on M&A transactions, and has particular expertise in leveraged buyouts. He recently acted for Prospect Partners on its acquisition of 15 of Culligan International's water treatment dealerships. **Paul Choi** (see p.1201) has a wide-ranging corporate practice that sees him represent clients in debt and equity offerings and all aspects of M&A. He is particularly lauded for his solution-oriented approach to matters. He recently led the team acting for Commercial Metals on the defense of a hostile takeover bid by Icahn Enterprises. The highly regarded **Imad Qasim** (see p.1226) handles matters such as corporate governance, joint ventures and M&A. In a key mandate, he formed part of the team representing ITT in the company's acquisition of YSI Incorporated. Clients appreciate **Jeffrey Smith**'s (see p.1232) *"bright, common-sense"* approach. He focuses on sophisticated commercial transactions, and has a strong background in multijurisdictional and cross-border matters. **Larry Barden** (see p.1197) handles securities, private equity and M&A matters for public and private companies. Sources describe him as *"a steady presence in stressful situations,"* who is *"unflappable in difficult negotiations."*

### Skadden, Arps, Slate, Meagher & Flom LLP & Affiliates
See profile on p.2008

**THE FIRM** This team continues to be renowned for its legal and technical prowess. It ably fulfills an advisory role to financial institutions, private equity funds and businesses that extends across the scope of corporate matters. The heavyweight group stands out in particular for its skill in acting as corporate counsel to public companies in international settings. The practice is also routinely sought for its expertise in securities compliance issues.
**Sources say:** *"We like their responsiveness and quality advice."*
**KEY INDIVIDUALS** **Charles Mulaney** (see p.1223) is a preeminent figure in the market, with many sources quick

to attest to his star ranking. He is noted for his adroit handling of M&A and joint venture work. Corporate transactions group co-head **Peter Krupp** (see p.1216) wins praise from clients and peers alike for his quick responses and high level of creativity. He frequently represents private equity firms and financial investors, and is also singled out for his *"fantastic client communication skills."* **Rodd Schreiber** (see p.1230) focuses on the representation of financial advisers in both domestic and cross-border transactions. *"He consistently provides sound judgment and advice,"* report sources, who also appreciate his ability *"to see the big picture."* **Kimberly deBeers** (see p.1203) is a frequent adviser to private equity firms across a wide variety of corporate and financing transactions, including acquisitions and joint ventures. The *"skilled and practical"* **Gary Cullen** (see p.1203) handles the purchase and sale of public companies at auction, as well as joint ventures and proxy contests, as part of his corporate practice. He elicits particular praise from interviewees for his ability to carefully manage issues in order to get a deal done. Head of the Chicago office **Brian Duwe** (see p.1205) has a varied practice that covers a variety of corporate concerns, from spin-offs to buyouts and divestitures. Commentators single out his courtroom abilities and excellent judgment among his key attributes.

### Band 2

### Mayer Brown LLP
See profile on p.1257

**THE FIRM** This comprehensive M&A practice frequently represents big-name clients across the spectrum of corporate matters. The team is particularly noted for its expertise in cross-border transactions, as evidenced by its representation of Fresenius Kabi in the company's acquisition of Fenwal Holdings. It counts Baxter, UBS, Whirlpool, Yum! Brands, AT&T and Syngenta among its impressive roster of clients.

**Sources say:** *"Their attorneys are dedicated to providing unconditional support under all circumstances." "I am extremely impressed with their work ethic and the work product they produce."*

**KEY INDIVIDUALS** Mergers and acquisition group head **Scott Davis** handles matters involving corporate governance, M&A and securities. Conflicts of interest between directors and shareholders are also an area of expertise. Sources are quick to laud him as *"a lawyer's lawyer,"* and he receives further praise for his *"depth of knowledge of the field."* **John Noell** is a *"great technician"* who is *"very even tempered and really good at negotiations,"* according to interviewees. He undertakes a range of corporate and transactional matters, including the representation of issuers in the private placements of partnership interest. He is also sought for his expertise in joint ventures. **Frederick Thomas** is a *"very savvy corporate counselor with excellent judgment."* He provides clients with general corporate advice in areas such as strategic alliances, tender offers and joint ventures. **Marc Sperber** handles a broad range of matters pertaining to M&A for domestic and

international clients. Observers commend him for *"his ability to provide positive counsel to his clients that extends far beyond a technical knowledge of law."* **William Kucera** primarily concentrates on M&A for public and private companies, and is also called upon for his corporate governance advice. Clients single out his *"ability to provide top-quality legal work, often under tight deadlines, all the while maintaining a practical approach and understanding the business objectives."* **Jodi Simala** heads the corporate and securities practice and handles a broad spectrum of work within those areas. She recently represented Macquarie Infrastructure Partners in its acquisition of WCA Waste Corporation. **Paul Theiss** has a wide-ranging practice that encompasses capital markets and M&A. Sources are enthusiastic about his *"responsiveness, knowledge and practical advice."* **Robert Helman** has over five decades' experience in corporate, M&A and private equity matters, and is renowned as one of the doyens of the Illinois market. **Rick Shepro** is noted as a fine choice of counsel to financial institutions, and focuses on complex acquisitions that frequently have a cross-border element to them.

### McDermott Will & Emery LLP
See profile on p.1258

**THE FIRM** McDermott has carved out a strong niche focusing on healthcare clients, and recently represented the healthcare-focused private equity fund Beecken Petty O'Keefe in its acquisition of Genoa Healthcare Holdings. The team has a focus on the mid to upper end of the corporate and private equity market, and regularly advises clients on a broad range of issues such as leveraged buyouts, dispositions and financings. Other key clients include Mars, Baird Capital Partners, Pfingsten Partners and Glencoe Capital.

**Sources say:** *"McDermott does excellent, thorough work. We are very happy." "The value they place in long-term relationships and responsiveness is what really stands out."*

**KEY INDIVIDUALS Andrew McCune** (see p.1221) focuses on private equity transactions and securities. He also represents sponsors, buyers and sellers in leveraged transactions, and recently acted for CCCC Growth Fund on its acquisition of WNC Insurance Holding. He is praised by sources for his high levels of responsiveness. **Helen Friedli** (see p.1207) is known for her strong corporate skills, and is commonly called upon to handle corporate governance and securities issues. She acted for Actuant on its debt offering of an aggregate $300 million in senior notes. Practice head **Brooks Gruemmer** (see p.1210) receives much praise in the market, and advises public and private companies on all areas of M&A. He counts HIG Capital and Great Point Partners among his key clients. **Stanley Meadows** (see p.1221) recently acted for Heico Holding in its cross-border purchase of Coolcentric from Vette and associated subsidiaries. Sources are quick to highlight his *"great strategic vision."*

### Winston & Strawn LLP
See profile on p.1267

**THE FIRM** Winston & Strawn enjoys a strong reputation for its high-quality work in securities, regulatory and gen-

eral M&A matters. The team is experienced in the representation of high-profile clients such as Guggenheim Partners, which it acted for on the acquisition of the Los Angeles Dodgers. IPOs are also a particular strength of the team, where it represents both underwriters and companies. The group's broad stable of clients also includes Motorola Solutions, Nuveen Investments and Sycamore Partners.

**Sources say:** *"They are truly partners in getting deals done." "I find their legal teams to be extremely responsive and very knowledgeable."*

**KEY INDIVIDUALS Robert Wall** (see p.1236) is a *"driving force"* in the community, and concentrates on M&A and securities. Of late he has acted for the Martin-Brower Company on a matter pertaining to its acquisition of several distribution and logistics businesses belonging to Keystone Foods. **James Junewicz** (see p.1213) is experienced in counseling underwriters and placement agencies regarding debt and equity offerings, such as IPOs and high-yield securities. Sources value his ability to handle complicated situations effectively. **Bruce Toth** (see p.1235) attracts praise from sources, who appreciate his ability to work as a business partner with the client as well as his sage advice and guidance. M&A/securities group head **Oscar David** (see p.1203) is hailed by observers for the responsiveness and high-quality advice he provides to clients. In a key mandate, he represented Motorola Solutions in a high-value share repurchase program.

### Band 3

### DLA Piper LLP (US)
See profile on p.1971

**THE FIRM** DLA Piper acts in an advisory role for clients from a multitude of industries on all areas of corporate, M&A and private equity. The team is ably supported by its impressive global network, for which clients are particularly appreciative. In a recent highlight, it acted for Appleton Papers on a matter relating to a proposed merger with Hicks Acquisition. The team has also advised Groupon on numerous merger and acquisition matters. The group's client portfolio also includes Abbot, Pritzker Capital Management and Experian.

**Sources say:** *"We are incredibly impressed by how quickly they delivered expert service."*

**KEY INDIVIDUALS** Private equity practice chair **Steven Napolitano** (see p.1223) *"knows his stuff and doesn't over-lawyer an issue,"* according to sources. He has a broad-based practice that spans the spectrum of private equity matters, and is routinely sought to advise corporations in governance and fiduciary issues. **Neal Aizenstein** (see p.1196) is *"very practical and willing to work on business solutions,"* and his *"responsiveness is phenomenal,"* assert interviewees. His practice spans acquisitions, dispositions, financing and IPOs. **Andrew Weil** (see p.1237) has wide-ranging experience in matters involving securities, including REITs, in addition to a broad corporate practice. He is particularly commended by market observers for his impressive work ethic.

### Jenner & Block LLP
See profile on p.1252

**THE FIRM** Jenner & Block maintains a solid reputation for its efficient work in corporate governance, securities and M&A. The groups handles cases for public and private clients such as News Corporation/Fox News, Honeywell and Guggenheim Corporate Funding. The team recently acted for General Dynamics on the public offering of an aggregate $2.4 billion of notes, and also acted for Hertz on a secondary offering of common stock.
**Sources say:** "*I've found them to be very effective.*"
**KEY INDIVIDUALS Mark Harris** (see p.1211) cochairs the private equity, hedge fund and investment management practice. He particularly specializes in advising sponsor groups and private equity portfolio companies, and comes highly recommended for his work in the healthcare sector. **Joseph Gromacki** (see p.1210) is chair of the firm's corporate practice. He concentrates on securities and sophisticated M&A transactions. In a key mandate, he recently led the team representing General Motors in its share repurchase transaction, worth $5.5 billion, with the Department of the Treasury.

### Jones Day
See profile on p.919

**THE FIRM** Jones Day is highly respected for the corporate, M&A and private equity advice it provides to key clients such as The Riverside Company, Koch Industries and the Potash Corporation of Saskatchewan. In a key mandate, the team advised Veolia Environment on the sale of its domestic solid waste business to Star Atlantic Waste Holdings. The group has also advised FleetPride on a number of acquisitions throughout the year.
**Sources say:** "*They're fantastic.*"
**KEY INDIVIDUALS** The "*absolutely terrific*" **Elizabeth Kitslaar** (see p.1215) represents domestic and international clients in the full range of M&A and corporate matters. Sources describe her as "*a good partner and a good sounding board.*" **Timothy Melton** (see p.1222) "*has the ability to bring the parties together and to get a deal concluded in an efficient process,*" an impressed interviewee reports. He handles a wide spectrum of work on corporate and M&A matters, from governance to stockholder activism issues.

### Katten Muchin Rosenman LLP
See profile on p.1253

**THE FIRM** This team is renowned for its work in the midmarket and has expertise across a range of industries, including technology, publishing and sports. It is also well placed to draw on the expertise of the firm's bankruptcy and finance groups when required. Of late, the team has represented Standard Parking in its $345 million acquisition of Central Parking, in part facilitated through a new credit facility. Other clients include Sterling Partners, Victory Park Capital and Svoboda Capital Partners.
**Sources say:** "*We like the fact that they are commercial thinkers, who work thoroughly and quickly as the situation requires. I have come to trust their judgment and their participation in our transactions.*"

**KEY INDIVIDUALS** Private equity practice head **Kenneth Miller** acts for private investors on leveraged buyouts, M&A and recapitalizations. He recently led the team representing the equity holders of Double E in their sale of the company to an acquisition vehicle. **Walter Weinberg** "*is smart, thorough and a good counselor with excellent judgment and deal skills,*" according to one highly impressed client. In a key mandate he acted for Nicolet Capital Partners on obtaining a senior debt facility and the company's subsequent acquisition of InterFlex. **Howard Lanznar** handles matters for both buyers and sellers across the full spectrum of commercial transactions. He recently assisted Diamond Resorts International with its acquisition of the majority of Pacific Monarch Resorts's assets out of a Chapter 11 bankruptcy. The seasoned **Herbert Wander** is a much-respected figure in the market and undertakes work on a wide range of business matters, including securities law.

## Band 4

### Baker & McKenzie
See profile on p.435

**THE FIRM** This team is noted for its broad international reach and strong offering in pharmaceutical and healthcare matters. In a recent highlight, the team advised CareFusion on the sale of its international surgical products distribution business. It also assisted Gardner Denver with its EUR152 million acquisition of the entirety of Robuschi's outstanding shares. Other clients on the group's roster include Kellogg, Medtronic and One Equity Partners.
**Sources say:** "*Excellent network of good lawyers.*" "*Baker has provided consistently high-quality work for a fair price.*"
**KEY INDIVIDUALS** The "*very skilled*" **Craig Roeder** (see p.1227) heads the corporate and securities group, and has a wide-ranging practice dealing with domestic and international matters.

### Greenberg Traurig, LLP
See profile on p.1024

**THE FIRM** The team at Greenberg Traurig handles a range of M&A work, and also has a solid offering in transactional private equity. The group also has a dedicated hedge fund practice that sees it represent hedge fund investors in their investment transactions and securities compliance matters. In a recent work highlight, the team represented Brentwood Associates in its purchase of the majority stake in Sundance Holdings Group and Soft Surroundings. Other key clients include Puma Energy, Narrative Science and River Lake Equity Partners.
**Sources say:** "*Very capable and very detail-oriented.*" "*The firm has a broad range of expertise which can be called upon.*"
**KEY INDIVIDUALS Gary Silverman**'s (see p.1231) practice covers the spectrum of M&A and private equity matters. Sources appreciate his commercial outlook, and also describe him as "*a very strong transactional attorney who doesn't miss anything.*" He handled the Brentwood

Associates matter alongside corporate and securities practice cochair **Peter Lieberman** (see p.1218). Lieberman handles a diverse range of M&A and private equity matters, and wins plaudits for his ability to be "*aggressive when he needs to be.*" The "*knowledgeable*" **Stephen Landsman** (see p.1216) comes recommended for his expertise in leveraged recapitalization and joint venture/strategic alliance transactions.

### Neal, Gerber & Eisenberg LLP
See profile on p.1260

**THE FIRM** Neal, Gerber & Eisenberg is known for its broad corporate and securities practice. In a recent key mandate, the group represented Covanta Holding Corporation as securities counsel relating to their $400 million offering of senior secured notes. The group's clients also include Goldcorp, Apex Venture Partners, Model Metrics and YapStone.
**Sources say:** "*They produce high-quality work.*"
**KEY INDIVIDUALS Michael Gray** (see p.1210) focuses on private equity, venture capital, funds and their formation. Sources comment that he "*has an open mind and likes to try to solve problems instead of indicating why something can't be done.*" He recently acted for Model Metrics on the sale of a venture capital-backed company to a client and public company investor. Cross-border practice group cochair **John Koenigsknecht** (see p.1215) "*goes above and beyond*" for clients, and is "*always accessible and responsive.*" In a recent cross-border matter, he represented Grayd Resource in its acquisition by Agnico Eagle Mines, a $275 million deal. Chair of the corporate and securities group **David Stone** (see p.1234) acts for clients on sophisticated transactions involving securities, in addition to handling general corporate matters. In a recent highlight, he acted on behalf of Sandstorm Gold on its SEC registration statement, NYSE listing and offering.

### Ungaretti & Harris LLP
See profile on p.1265

**THE FIRM** The firm is known for its strong emphasis on the midmarket. It is particularly noted for its representation of family offices, and is also sought for its expertise in matters concerning transport and logistics, insurance companies, digital media and healthcare devices. In a key mandate, the team negotiated and documented the sale of assets, as well as the employment agreements, for the sale of ProSource Financial to AJ Gallager. The group's client roster also includes Catamaran Corporation, BMO Harris, Bekin Van Lines and Lab Corp.
**Sources say:** "*Not only were they top-notch in their knowledge and expertise, but we really felt they took a personal interest in our case.*"
**KEY INDIVIDUALS** Department head **Gary Levenstein** (see p.1217) brings a wealth of experience to his practice, which spans M&A, private equity, corporate governance and securities regulation. He wins particular praise for his commitment to client care.

## Vedder Price PC
See profile on p.1266

**THE FIRM** Vedder Price remains an active player within the M&A and private equity worlds, and advises clients of all sizes. Of late, the team has acted for the Clairvest Group on its investment in Centaur Holdings, a $200 million deal. In a further highlight it represented Wynnchurch Capital in its acquisition of Northstar Aerospace and its US and Canadian subsidiaries through a bankruptcy sale. Other key clients include CIT Group, HCI Equity Partners, Victor Park Capital and The Duchossois Group.

**KEY INDIVIDUALS Michael Nemeroff** (see p.1223) is an *"excellent deal attorney"* who is the first port of call at Vedder Price for many market sources. He recently advised Edgewater Funds on its recapitalization and acquisition of the Unitech Composites aerospace business.

## Band 5

## Dentons
See profile on p.449

**THE FIRM** This group deals with a diverse range of matters within the M&A and private equity world, including regulation, financing and privatization. The group handles matters for well-established international clients, and is also noted for its work with startups.

**Sources say:** *"Excellent at representing their clients."*

**KEY INDIVIDUALS Michael Rosenthal** undertakes matters that deal with venture capital, private equity and restructuring, and also comes recommended for his joint venture work. He has particular expertise in the representation of technological companies. **Michael Froy** (see p.1208) focuses on areas including securities offerings and M&A in both a domestic and international context, and is also sought for his expertise in compliance issues. He heads the manufacturing sector team globally, as well as the Chicago office's corporate and business transactions practice. **Linda Harris** (see p.1211) has a broad practice that covers leveraged buyouts, workouts and private equity, acting for both domestic and international clients. **Donald Lubin** (see p.1219) covers the spectrum of corporate matters, including restructurings, M&A and the defense of takeovers. He is particularly noted for his work with senior management and directors.

## Duane Morris LLP
See profile on p.2239

**THE FIRM** Duane Morris acts on a range of M&A and private equity issues, including joint ventures, securities, compliance and corporate governance. The team is well versed in both domestic and international matters, and in a recent highlight it acted for the US subsidiary of CJ CheiJedang in its joint venture with Cargill to build a lysine production facility.

**Sources say:** *"They're very good, and aside from being technically proficient they come up with practical solutions."*

**KEY INDIVIDUALS Brian Kerwin** recently acted on behalf of Avee Laboratories, Screen Tox, and Global Analytical Development on their sale to ATS Laboratories.

Sources reserve particular praise for his communication skills. **David Kaufman** has a general M&A and private equity practice, and handled the joint venture matter for the US subsidiary of CJ CheiJedang. *"He's to the point, his advice is very concise, and he's efficient,"* reports one impressed client. He is also singled out for his responsiveness.

## K&L Gates
See profile on p.2245

**THE FIRM** K&L Gates acts for an impressive client base, including Fitch, Hecla Mining, Boise and Deere & Company across the board of M&A and private equity matters. The group recently represented Mandalay Baseball Properties in a series of transactions including the sale of Staten Island Yankees and Hagerstown Suns as well as the leveraged buyout of Oklahoma City Redhawks.

**Sources say:** *"They give full attention to important matters and never let something slip through the net."*

**KEY INDIVIDUALS Merrick Hatcher** (see p.1211) focuses on securities, M&A and venture capital investments. *"His work was incredibly helpful and insightful from beginning to end. He was the most important voice and adviser for me in the deal,"* asserted one satisfied client. Hatcher led on the Mandalay Baseball Properties matters.

## Paul Hastings LLP
See profile on p.1996

**THE FIRM** Paul Hastings is an established name for its private equity and corporate/M&A work, handling matters for clients such as Cortec Group, Apax Partners and Beecken Petty O'Keefe & Company. In a key mandate, the team acted as counsel to Madison Capital Partners in a complex cross-border case concerning the sale of KraussMaffei and subsidiaries to Onex.

**Sources say:** *"Very hands-on involvement by senior lawyers." "Detail-oriented and focused."*

**KEY INDIVIDUALS** The seasoned **Paul Quinn** is cochair of the private equity practice, and principally concentrates on leveraged acquisitions and dispositions as well as private equity funds focused on distressed work. Department head **Brian Richards** handles M&A and private equity-related matters. He receives much praise for his personable style and technical proficiency. The well-regarded **Thaddeus Malik** focuses on securities, private equity and M&A. In a key mandate, he acted as counsel to Beecken Petty O'Keefe on the formation of a joint venture with KKR. The *"incredibly bright and dynamic"* **Amit Mehta** handles venture capital transactions, restructuring and distressed work, and corporate governance. He recently represented Contract Research Solutions and its subsidiaries in its filing for bankruptcy.

## Reed Smith LLP

**THE FIRM** Reed Smith has a strong midmarket focus that sees it undertake work both across the US and internationally. Of late, the team acted for K.A. Steel Chemicals on its auctioned stock sale to Olin for a cash consideration of $328 million.

**Sources say:** *"Excellent firm with very broad capabilities and very good attorneys."*

**KEY INDIVIDUALS Bradley Schmarak** is a *"very balanced, seasoned attorney"* who is *"very attentive,"* according to sources. He recently represented long-term client Citadel Plastics in its sale to Huntsman Gay Global Capital. He cochairs the private equity group practice with **Seth Hemming**. Hemming has a wealth of experience in private equity transactions, and also led on the K.A. Steel Chemicals matter. Sources single out his *"high-quality work"* and *"diligent"* approach to matters. **Michael Lee** provides sage advice as corporate counsel to both businesses and investors, with a specialty in representing technological companies in IP and IT agreements. He recently acted for Valence Health on a $30 million venture capital financing.

## Schiff Hardin LLP

**THE FIRM** Schiff Hardin has a full-service approach that sees it represent private and public companies in M&A across the gamut of sectors from healthcare to telecoms. The group is particularly known for its capable handling of complex matters and its securities strength.

**KEY INDIVIDUALS Stephen Dragich** is a key contact at the firm.

## Other Notable Practitioners

**Frank Ballantine** (see p.1197) of Clark Hill PLC is a *"very pragmatic lawyer"* who wins praise from sources for his *"exceptional legal services"* and focus on getting a transaction done. He centers his practice on advising investors, boards of directors and management. **James Cruger** is chair of the private equity practice at Perkins Coie LLP, and focuses his practice on fund formation and M&A. Sources particularly praise him for his leadership skills and work ethic on behalf of clients. At the same firm, **Teri Lindquist** handles matters involving fund formation and investment, transactional financing and leveraged M&A. **James Lidbury** of Ropes & Gray LLP handles all areas of M&A and corporate governance issues. He represents big-ticket clients such as Starwood Capital. **Alan Roth** (see p.1228) cochairs the private equity and venture capital practice at Edwards Wildman Palmer. He is recognized for his expertise in SBIC licensing and fund formation. At the same firm, **Craig Bradley** (see p.1200) is a well-known figure in the market who has a broad practice that encompasses debt financings, securities and venture capital. **Thomas Ferguson** of Kelley Drye & Warren LLP is not only *"extremely responsive"* but also has *"intuitive business acumen,"* sources say. He is recognized for his expertise in equity and debt financing and M&A. **Eric Fogel** of Lathrop & Gage LLP is an *"excellent communicator"* who *"leaves no stone unturned in studying problems and analyzing options,"* and also provides *"creative and cost-effective recommendations for his clients."* He is noted for his strengths in debt and equity transactions and fund formation.

# ENERGY & NATURAL RESOURCES

Commentary about individuals can be found under their firm's paragraph. If the firm has no paragraph (is not ranked) look at Other Notable Practitioners.

## Energy & Natural Resources
### Leading Firms

**Band 1**
Rooney Rippie & Ratnaswamy LLP

**Band 2**
Eimer Stahl LLP *
Lueders, Robertson & Konzen
Schiff Hardin LLP
Sidley Austin LLP *

**Band 3**
Foley & Lardner LLP *
Jones Day *

## Energy & Natural Resources: Regulatory
### Leading Individuals

**Band 1**

| | | |
|---|---|---|
| MacBride Owen | Schiff Hardin LLP | |
| Rippie E Glenn | Rooney Rippie & Ratnaswamy LLP * | |
| Robertson Eric | Lueders, Robertson & Konzen | |
| Rooney John E | Rooney Rippie & Ratnaswamy LLP * | |
| Stahl David M | Eimer Stahl LLP * | |

**Band 2**

| | |
|---|---|
| Fosco Carmen L. | Rooney Rippie & Ratnaswamy LLP * |
| Ratnaswamy John | Rooney Rippie & Ratnaswamy LLP * |
| Townsend Christopher | Quarles & Brady LLP (ONP)† * |

**Band 3**

| | |
|---|---|
| Johnson Mark R | Eimer Stahl LLP * |
| Reed G Darryl | Sidley Austin LLP * |

**Up-and-coming individuals**

| | |
|---|---|
| Scarsella Carla | Rooney Rippie & Ratnaswamy LLP * |

## Energy & Natural Resources: Transactional
### Leading Individuals

**Band 1**

| | |
|---|---|
| Astle Richard W | Sidley Austin LLP * |
| Forrester J Paul | Mayer Brown LLP (ONP)† |

*\* Indicates firm / individual with profile.*
*Alphabetical order within each band. Band 1 is the highest.*

## Band 1

### Rooney Rippie & Ratnaswamy LLP

**THE FIRM** This firm continues to be a powerhouse of the Illinois energy and natural resources Bar, with notable expertise in all areas of electric and natural gas regulation. It recently represented AGL Resources, Nicor and Nicor Gas before the Illinois Commerce Commission (ICC) in proceedings to obtain approval for a merger. Other key clients include US Steel and Aqua America.
**Sources say:** *"Their legal acumen, understanding of the regulatory landscape, and unwavering professionalism make them a true pleasure to work with."*

**KEY INDIVIDUALS Glenn Rippie** (see p.1227) has *"superb technical and practical skills,"* according to clients. He counts a number of natural gas and electric industry companies among his clients. **John Rooney** (see p.1227) is praised by clients for both his *"excellent written work product"* and *"relentless focus on obtaining the needed results for his clients."* He represented Nicor Gas before several Illinois regulatory bodies and courts in a potential statutory obligation to enter into a synthetic natural gas sourcing agreement with Chicago Clean Energy. **Carmen Fosco** (see p.1207) recently represented Commonwealth Edison before the ICC in a matter related to the reconciliation of approximately $3.58 billion of expenses and $3.56 billion in revenues under tariff riders. He is particularly highly commended by sources for his cross-examination skills. **John Ratnaswamy** (see p.1226) is praised by sources for his expertise in complex ratemaking and financial issues. He represented The Peoples Gas Light and Coke Company and the North Shore Gas Company in consolidated gas utility rate cases before the ICC. **Carla Scarsella** (see p.1230) has notable expertise in representing clients before regulatory bodies and courts. She is tipped by sources as a rising star.

## Band 2

### Eimer Stahl LLP
**See profile on p.1245**
**THE FIRM** This team continues to attract the respect of market commentators for its strength in representing a range of market participants in the energy sector on litigation, regulatory and restructuring matters.
**KEY INDIVIDUALS David Stahl** (see p.1233) is highly regarded by sources for his litigation expertise. He is a founding partner of the firm. **Mark Johnson** (see p.1213) focuses on utility regulation and restructuring. His areas of expertise include ratemaking, competitive market development and financing.

### Lueders, Robertson & Konzen
**THE FIRM** This Granite City-based firm is held in high esteem for its gas, electricity and water ratemaking, in addition to other regulatory work. It counts a number of corporates and municipalities among its clients.
**KEY INDIVIDUALS** The *"highly knowledgeable"* **Eric Robertson** is praised by sources as *"one of the finest"* in his field. He has expertise in a range of energy and public utilities law matters.

### Schiff Hardin LLP
**THE FIRM** The team at this firm enjoys a longstanding reputation in the Illinois market for its high-quality advice to industry participants on all areas of regulatory law. It recently represented North American Electric Reliability in

developing and filing a revised definition of 'Bulk Electric System' with the Federal Energy Regulatory Commission.
**KEY INDIVIDUALS** The *"very responsive and analytical"* **Owen MacBride** is *"extremely diligent and comprehensive in representing clients before the ICC,"* according to commentators. His recent highlights include representing Rock Island Clean Line on its application before the ICC for certification as a public utility.

### Sidley Austin LLP
**See profile on p.1264**
**THE FIRM** This team is recognized for its transactional work as well as its state and federal regulatory advice to a range of market participants, including energy companies, lenders and investors. Recent highlights include advising Enbridge on the development of pipeline projects to transport Canadian and Bakken Formation oil to Illinois and other markets.
**KEY INDIVIDUALS** *"Terrific lawyer"* **Richard Astle** (see p.1197) recently represented Exelon Generation on investments made by its nuclear decommissioning trust funds. He is a respected option for public utility companies and others on a range of corporate and financing matters. **Darryl Reed** (see p.1226) advised Commonwealth Edison on appeals in the Illinois Appellate Court related to the ICC's order approving an increase of $155.7 million in annual revenue through new electric distribution rates. His clients include a number of electricity, gas and pipeline companies.

## Band 3

### Foley & Lardner LLP
**See profile on p.2588**
**THE FIRM** This team is a respected choice for a range of gas and electric utilities, pipeline and natural gas distributors, and energy lenders. It has recently been representing The Peoples Gas Light and Coke Company and the North Shore Gas Company before the ICC seeking the recovery of costs, additions to rate bases and increases in their rates of return.
**KEY INDIVIDUALS** James Tynion and Bradley Jackson are key contacts at the firm.

### Jones Day
**See profile on p.919**
**THE FIRM** This firm represents a range of utility industry companies and has notable expertise in corporate finance, M&A and federal disclosure obligations. It is also a respected choice when it comes to advising clients on corporate governance matters.
**KEY INDIVIDUALS** Peter Clarke is a key contact.

## Other Notable Practitioners

**Christopher Townsend** (see p.1236) of Quarles & Brady LLP is "*highly smart and tenacious,*" and "*grasps the relevant issues quickly,*" according to impressed clients. He has recently represented Chicago Clean Energy in its efforts to build and operate a $3 billion coal-to-synthetic natural gas facility. "*Highly capable lawyer*" **Paul Forrester** of Mayer Brown LLP is a finance specialist. He represented Alliance Pipeline in the amendment and restatement of its $125 million US credit facility agreement with the Bank of Nova Scotia.

# ENVIRONMENT

Commentary about individuals can be found under their firm's paragraph. If the firm has no paragraph (is not ranked) look at Other Notable Practitioners.

| Environment Leading Firms | | |
| --- | --- | --- |
| **Band 1** | | |
| Jenner & Block LLP * | | |
| Sidley Austin LLP * | | |
| **Band 2** | | |
| Barnes & Thornburg LLP * | | |
| Nijman Franzetti LLP | | |
| Schiff Hardin LLP | | |
| **Band 3** | | |
| Baker & McKenzie * | | |
| Bryan Cave LLP | | |
| Hodge Dwyer & Driver | | |
| Mayer Brown LLP * | | |
| Seyfarth Shaw LLP * | | |
| **Band 4** | | |
| Dentons * | | |
| McDermott Will & Emery LLP * | | |
| Quarles & Brady LLP * | | |
| Winston & Strawn LLP * | | |

*\* Indicates firm / individual with profile.*
*Alphabetical order within each band. Band 1 is the highest.*

| Environment: Litigation Leading Individuals | |
| --- | --- |
| **Band 1** | |
| Bishop Timothy S | *Mayer Brown LLP* |
| Eggert Russell R | *Lathrop & Gage LLP* |
| Franzetti Susan M | *Nijman Franzetti LLP* |
| Nijman Jennifer T | *Nijman Franzetti LLP* |
| Olian Robert | *Sidley Austin LLP* * |
| White Bruce | *Barnes & Thornburg LLP* * |
| **Band 2** | |
| Boyd Eric E | *Seyfarth Shaw LLP* * |
| Madonia Joseph F | *Barnes & Thornburg LLP* * |
| Perellis Andrew H | *Seyfarth Shaw LLP* * |
| Running Andrew R | *Kirkland & Ellis LLP* * |
| Sigel Gabrielle | *Jenner & Block LLP* * |
| Wiener Todd | *McDermott Will & Emery LLP* * |
| **Band 3** | |
| Bonebrake Stephen J | *Schiff Hardin LLP* |
| Comella Philip L | *Seyfarth Shaw LLP* * |
| Lillie Mark S | *Kirkland & Ellis LLP* * |
| Rich Nancy J | *Katten Muchin Rosenman LLP* |
| Selman Russell | *Schiff Hardin LLP* |
| Siros Steven | *Jenner & Block LLP* * |
| Taylor Byron | *Sidley Austin LLP* * |
| Ter Molen Mark R | *Mayer Brown LLP* |
| Zebovitz Lisa S | *Neal, Gerber & Eisenberg LLP* * |
| **Band 4** | |
| Rodriguez Gabriel M | *Schiff Hardin LLP* |
| Skinner Thomas V | *Jones Day* * |

| Environment: Mainly Transactional Leading Individuals | |
| --- | --- |
| **Band 1** | |
| Cipriano Renee | *Schiff Hardin LLP* |
| Fort Jeffrey | *Dentons* * |
| Graham Robert L | *Jenner & Block LLP* * |
| Grayson E Lynn | *Jenner & Block LLP* * |
| Hodge Katherine D | *Hodge Dwyer & Driver* |
| Watson John W | *Baker & McKenzie* |
| **Band 2** | |
| Andes Fredric | *Barnes & Thornburg LLP* * |
| Cahan James N | *Sidley Austin LLP* * |
| Kouimelis Eleni | *Winston & Strawn LLP* * |
| Lyons Francis X | *Bryan Cave LLP* |
| Ohm Michael K | *Bryan Cave LLP* |
| Rieser David | *Much Shelist, P.C* |
| Vidmar Jacqueline M | *Rooney Rippie & Ratnaswamy LLP* * |
| **Band 3** | |
| Harsch Roy M | *Drinker Biddle & Reath LLP* |
| Ketzback Thor W | *Bryan Cave LLP* |
| Landow-Esser Janine | *Quarles & Brady LLP* * |
| Magel Barbara A | *Barnes & Thornburg LLP* * |
| Saines Richard | *Baker & McKenzie* |
| **Up-and-coming individuals** | |
| Brice Susan E | *Bryan Cave LLP* |

## Band 1

### Jenner & Block LLP
See profile on p.1252

**THE FIRM** Jenner & Block maintains its excellent standing in the state, with sources keen to highlight the team's quality across the board on environmental litigation, transactional and compliance matters. It has recently handled several Occupational Safety and Health Administration (OSHA) investigations and enforcement actions on behalf of key client Veolia ES Solid Waste Services. The team has also acted for the Olin Corporation on an indemnification claim and the conducting of internal investigations.
**Sources say:** "*Terrific partners who work with the client and understand their desires and priorities.*"
**KEY INDIVIDUALS** Experienced practitioner **Robert Graham** (see p.1210) is a highly regarded figure in the market. He recently represented a citizen's group opposing a Clean Air Act PSD permit for a refinery in South Dakota, a matter which he led all the way to the South Dakota Supreme Court. **Lynn Grayson** (see p.1210) is commended for her "*knowledgeable and practical*" approach as well as her "*ability to reach a reasonable consensus.*" She has won the admiration and trust of clients through her work on numerous high-profile matters, including the recent acquisition of Metro Machine Corporation by client NASSCO. **Gabrielle Sigel** (see p.1231) is popular with clients, who are eager to note her "*great people skills*" and depth of knowledge. "*She is the consummate professional,*" attests one source. Commonwealth Edison and Exelon Corporation recently benefited from Sigel's excellent representation in litigation concerning a former manufactured gas plant site. Sources emphasize **Steven Siros's** (see p.1232) knowledge and technical experience as his key strengths. He is particularly well recognized for his toxic tort expertise.

### Sidley Austin LLP
See profile on p.1264

**THE FIRM** Offering wide-ranging expertise on environmental matters, this firm is commended as a significant force in the market. The 16-strong Chicago team represents the likes of BP, GE and Jupiter Aluminum across the board on transactional matters, Superfund cleanups, environmental criminal investigations and Clean Air Act litigation.
**Sources say:** "*A leading firm in terms of scope, quality and ability to handle any type of environmental matter.*"
**KEY INDIVIDUALS** Department head **Robert Olian** (see p.1224) inspires confidence from all quarters: "*There's nothing he can't handle, he's great,*" states one observer. He wins respect for his skillful handling of environmental criminal investigations. **James Cahan** (see p.1200) is identified as a "*very good Clean Air Act lawyer.*" He has recently been retained by Solvay Specialty Polymers and Martin Marietta Materials regarding enforcement actions under

the Clean Air Act. **Byron Taylor** (see p.1235) *"is excellent in understanding a variety of potential issues and concerns and then working with me to determine the best course of action,"* notes one impressed interviewee. He is noted for his expertise in environmental litigation.

## Band 2

### Barnes & Thornburg LLP
See profile on p.436

THE FIRM This team has consolidated its strong position in the Illinois market, winning praise for its broad and active environmental practice. It acts on behalf of Ameren Corporation, Honeywell and Precision Brands, utilizing its highly experienced bench to assist across the spectrum of potential matters, including those involving land, water, air and toxic torts.

Sources say: *"They have expanded their presence in the environment market and we see them a lot."*

KEY INDIVIDUALS **Bruce White** (see p.1237) *"would be on my dream team of environmental lawyers,"* comments one source. He is characterized as a *"very good Superfund litigator,"* with a practice that also covers toxic torts and federal and state regulatory matters. The *"terrific"* **Joseph Madonia** (see p.1219) is praised as a gifted litigator, and acts as cochair of the environmental litigation practice group. His strong experience includes the handling of toxic torts and environmental class actions. **Barbara Magel** (see p.1219) has cultivated a reputation as a *"tough, no-non-sense lawyer."* She acts on behalf of corporate, individual and municipal clients with equal skill. **Fredric Andes** (see p.1196) is hailed by one client as an *"absolutely top lawyer."* He works on clean water issues across the state and on a national basis, and has *"developed a niche in terms of quality regulations."*

### Nijman Franzetti LLP

THE FIRM This well-established environment boutique continues to enjoy highly productive relationships with key clients such as Exelon, Fortune Brand and Midwest Generation. A recent mandate saw lawyers acting for the latter on high-value rulemaking proceedings pertaining to the Clean Water Act. Its attorneys are equally comfortable handling matters involving land, water and air as well as litigation defense and matters pertaining to the Clean Air Act.

Sources say: *"Impeccable service – they are always available. I feel like they are never inconvenienced by our needs."*

KEY INDIVIDUALS **Susan Franzetti** is the recipient of resounding endorsements from market observers this year. One source states: *"She is an amazing lawyer – very intelligent and very good at understanding technical issues. She is pragmatic, works hard, and goes above and beyond expectations."* Sources regard **Jennifer Nijman** as an *"outstanding and very well-regarded"* practitioner with a wide-ranging practice that covers enforcement, litigation defense, Superfund issues and matters pertaining to the Clean Air Act.

### Schiff Hardin LLP

THE FIRM This well-reputed team is conversant on all aspects of environmental law, ranging from compliance counseling to toxic tort litigation. The group has attracted the business of clients from a wide range of industry backgrounds, such as real estate development, electric generation and chemical manufacturing. Recent matters include defending Midwest Generation against claims brought by the EPA.

Sources say: *"Excellent responsiveness, really strong client service, and well-credentialed people with great experience."*

KEY INDIVIDUALS **Renee Cipriano** is renowned as an *"excellent advocate."* Her ability to speak in business terms without *"overcomplicating or legalizing matters"* is much appreciated by her clients. **Stephen Bonebrake** has been responsible for some of the team's biggest matters this year, including the successful conclusion of a consent decree negotiation on behalf of client North Indiana Public Service Company. Litigator **Russell Selman** is noted for his broad environmental practice and strong grasp of issues surrounding Superfunds. **Gabriel Rodriguez** heads the environment group, and is well regarded for his representation of gas and electric companies in the region. Observers comment that he is a *"prominent name"* in the Illinois environmental Bar.

## Band 3

### Baker & McKenzie
See profile on p.435

THE FIRM Baker & McKenzie advises a diverse roster of local, national and international clients. Its substantial global presence inspires the confidence of multinational corporations, who benefit from the resources of the whole firm when seeking advice on environmental matters. It has recently been called upon by the Natural Resources Defense Council (NRDC) to act as outside counsel in a Clean Water Act citizen suit against a significant wastewater treatment plant.

KEY INDIVIDUALS Head of the North American environmental practice **John Watson** attracts positive attention from market observers. He provides assured strategic, compliance and transactional advice to national and multinational companies. **Richard Saines** is a *"very well-regarded Clean Air Act regulations lawyer,"* with an excellent industry profile. He advises a host of companies and institutions on carbon and environmental market transactions.

### Bryan Cave LLP

THE FIRM Sources are quick to highlight the caliber and depth of the environmental group at Bryan Cave, emphasizing its ability to add value to transactions. The team is comprised of nine lawyers offering comprehensive coverage of a host of environmental matters. CenterPoint Properties Trust, Dow Chemical and CMS Energy are some of the key client names calling upon the guidance of this team on a regular basis.

KEY INDIVIDUALS Former EPA administrator **Francis Lyons** has substantial experience handling a whole range

of environmental matters, from regulatory compliance to brownfield redevelopment. **Michael Ohm** possesses excellent technical knowledge, and is highlighted by sources as an astute negotiator who is highly respected by regulators. His Superfund cleanup and brownfield redevelopment expertise is held in high esteem by market observers. **Thor Ketzback** enjoys a strong reputation for his command of Clean Air Act regulatory requirements. He is commended by sources for his approach to client service and his responsiveness. **Susan Brice** is highly prized by clients for her excellent negotiation skills. Her business acumen makes her a favorite with clients looking for guidance across the board on environmental matters.

### Hodge Dwyer & Driver

THE FIRM This firm has consistently been a visible player in the region, and earns particular respect for its compact but vibrant team of environmental specialists. The group is well versed in all relevant legislation and regulation and is able to navigate clients through enforcement actions, compliance procedures and investigations with skill. A strong offering in transactional matters is also cited as a key attractive feature of the practice.

Sources say: *"Well known in the community and very good."*

KEY INDIVIDUALS **Katherine Hodge** runs a highly active practice advising clients on compliance, permitting and enforcement matters. Sources praise her *"high level of knowledge"* in Illinois EPA matters.

### Mayer Brown LLP
See profile on p.1257

THE FIRM Mayer Brown has a strong offering in the environmental space, handling complex transactions for large corporations such as Arkema, Cargill and Caterpillar. Its broad global reach means that the team is able to invite mandates from Europe and Asia as well as America. The group recently acted on behalf of Georgia-Pacific on a Supreme Court case regarding the Clean Water Act.

KEY INDIVIDUALS *"Terrific lawyer"* **Timothy Bishop** has recently represented high-profile names such as US Sugar, Georgia-Pacific and Dow Chemical. He is renowned as a talented environmental appellate lawyer. **Mark Ter Molen** acts as cochair of the environmental litigation group at Mayer Brown, and is perceived to be a *"really excellent"* practitioner. He recently acted for Nicor regarding its historic manufactured gas plant liabilities.

### Seyfarth Shaw LLP
See profile on p.1262

THE FIRM Seyfarth Shaw has attracted the business of some key industry players in the chemicals and pharmaceuticals manufacturing and waste disposal sectors. The practice concentrates largely on litigation matters, with transactional and compliance support ably provided as required. The team recently achieved the successful dismissal of all claims against its client Corning in a high-value groundwater contamination case.

KEY INDIVIDUALS **Eric Boyd** (see p.1199) is lauded as a *"pleasure to work with"* by impressed sources. Recent matters include the provision of ongoing support to Rhodia on air, waste and water issues at its manufacturing facilities. Identified as a highly skilled negotiator, **Andrew Perellis** (see p.1225) also wins praise for his *"terrific client service,"* and is described as *"very responsive and well versed in all aspects of CERCLA matters."* Environment practice chair **Philip Comella** (see p.1202) recently acted for Veolia on the expansion of a landfill site and the concurrent remediation of an adjacent Superfund site. Sources confirm his fine reputation.

## Band 4

### Dentons

See profile on p.449

**THE FIRM** This group is noted for its handling of the full spectrum of environmental matters, from litigation to regulatory compliance. The team provides environmental advice to an impressive array of industrial clients, such as Citgo Petroleum and Sterling Valuation Group. Recent work has included several rulemaking and enforcement procedures relating to water quality standards and a proposed wastewater permit.

**KEY INDIVIDUALS** *"Superb practitioner"* **Jeffrey Fort** (see p.1207) has an outstanding reputation, and is hailed for his ability to *"cover a wide range of topics, from policy to transactions to fundraising."*

### McDermott Will & Emery LLP

See profile on p.1258

**THE FIRM** The environmental team at McDermott Will & Emery has maintained a steady portfolio of work, handling a Superfund cleanup case on behalf of National Standard Company as well as asbestos litigation for Honeywell International. The latter case saw Chicago lawyers joining forces with teams from the firm's New York and Washington, DC offices, demonstrating the firm's strong ability to coordinate across the country.

**Sources say:** *"Very knowledgeable and willing to help."*

**KEY INDIVIDUALS Todd Wiener** (see p.1237) is highly rated in the market for his technical knowledge, as well as his work on asbestos litigation and Superfund cleanup matters. Recent notable clients have included Invensys and Syngenta Crop Protection.

### Quarles & Brady LLP

See profile on p.2593

**THE FIRM** This firm is a solid choice for clients seeking environmental law guidance. The group prides itself on its long history of servicing clients such as Wal-Mart and Invensys. A recent highlight saw the team engaged on a Cross-State Air Pollution Rule case for Wisconsin Electric Power.

**Sources say:** *"Good, deep capabilities, and a lot of experience dealing with the EPA."*

**KEY INDIVIDUALS** The *"down-to-earth and practical-minded"* **Janine Landow-Esser** (see p.1216) is well regarded for her valuable contacts at government agencies. This year she has been working on a CERCLA matter for a key client.

### Winston & Strawn LLP

See profile on p.1267

**THE FIRM** Winston & Strawn continues to perform well in the Illinois market. The team recently represented Highstar Capital in environmental issues stemming from its $1.9 billion acquisition of Veolia ES Solid Waste. The matter saw the group coordinating on a multidisciplinary basis with the firm's corporate, labor and employment, energy and tax teams. The firm is also recognized for its handling of environmental litigation and related criminal proceedings.

**KEY INDIVIDUALS Eleni Kouimelis** (see p.1215) is *"highly professional and very competent,"* say sources. She acts as cochair of the environmental law group and handles transactional, compliance and litigation matters on behalf of clients.

## Other Notable Practitioners

**Roy Harsch** of Drinker Biddle & Reath LLP was recently engaged by Alteris International to act on consent decree proceedings concerning its aluminum smelting operations. He is *"thoroughly informed and current"* in his knowledge, and *"enables the client to make informed decisions,"* say sources. Experienced attorney **Russell Eggert** of Lathrop & Gage LLP is commended for his technical excellence and is described as having *"a deep sense of how regulators and regulations work in the environmental area."* **Nancy Rich** continues to impress at Katten Muchin Rosenman LLP. Clients appreciate her *"no-nonsense advice,"* as well as her *"knowledge of the law and ability to explain it in everyday English."* Clients of the environmental practice at Much Shelist, P.C benefit from **David Rieser**'s considerable experience counseling a range of industry groups on complex transactional matters. Chicago-based partners **Andrew Running** (see p.1229) and **Mark Lillie** (see p.1218) are highly active members of Kirkland & Ellis LLP's environmental law team. They frequently handle complex matters for household names such as Dow Chemical, BP and ExxonMobil. *"Excellent lawyer"* **Thomas Skinner** (see p.1232) of Jones Day is praised for his *"very good judgment."* He has substantial experience working for state and federal government, and has served in high-level positions at the EPA. The *"well-regarded"* **Jacqueline Vidmar** (see p.1236) of Rooney Rippie & Ratnaswamy LLP was recently mandated to act on behalf of the United States Steel Corporation on a matter before the Illinois Commerce Commission. **Lisa Zebovitz** (see p.1238) cochairs the environmental practice group at Neal, Gerber & Eisenberg LLP. She has more than three decades' worth of experience in the arena and continues to be much sought after for her expertise in disputes and administrative proceedings concerning solid and hazardous wastes, air, water, and federal procurement.

# HEALTHCARE

Commentary about individuals can be found under their firm's paragraph. If the firm has no paragraph (is not ranked) look at Other Notable Practitioners.

## Healthcare
### Leading Firms

**Band 1**
McDermott Will & Emery LLP *

**Band 2**
Hogan Marren Ltd *
Katten Muchin Rosenman LLP *
McGuireWoods LLP *
Ungaretti & Harris LLP *

**Band 3**
Barnes & Thornburg LLP *
Dentons *
Drinker Biddle & Reath LLP *
The Health Law Consultancy *
Holland & Knight LLP *
Jones Day *
Polsinelli PC *
Proskauer Rose LLP *
Sidley Austin LLP *

## Band 1

### McDermott Will & Emery LLP
See profile on p.1258

**THE FIRM** McDermott Will & Emery remains at the vanguard of healthcare matters in Illinois, with a deep bench of attorneys that covers the gamut of matters. The firm has a strong international presence and continues to represent US clients abroad. The team has been particularly active on M&A matters and advised Underwood Memorial Health System on its auction and merger with South Jersey Health System. The group also includes the Alzheimer's Association, Provena Health, Waud Capital Partners and Central DuPage Health among its impressive client roster. **Sources say:** *"Obviously excellent." "Healthcare has long been a focus for them."*

**KEY INDIVIDUALS** The *"phenomenal"* **Bernadette Broccolo** (see p.1200) handles compliance work for academic medical institutions and is at the forefront of IT matters affecting the healthcare sector. She wins widespread praise from market sources for her depth of knowledge and experience and her ability to communicate effectively. **Michael Peregrine** (see p.1225) is noted for his work with corporations and nonprofit organizations on governance matters and fiduciary duty issues. Sources single him out for praise for his wealth of experience and excellent judgment on matters. **Kerrin Slattery** (see p.1232) undertakes work involving the representation of healthcare providers and investors in healthcare transactions. Observers comment that she is *"very knowledgeable, reasonable, and always a fair person to deal with."* The highly regarded **Ralph DeJong** (see p.1203) handles the full spectrum of work involving executive compensation and benefits for tax-exempt healthcare providers. **Daniel Melvin** (see p.1222) centers his practice around fraud and abuse in

## Healthcare
### Senior Statesmen

**Senior Statesmen: distinguished older practitioners**

| | |
|---|---|
| Anthony Michael F | McDermott Will & Emery LLP * |

### Leading Individuals

**Band 1**

| | |
|---|---|
| Becker Scott | McGuireWoods LLP |
| Broccolo Bernadette | McDermott Will & Emery LLP * |
| Callahan Michael R | Katten Muchin Rosenman LLP |
| Dube Monte I | Proskauer Rose LLP |
| Fahey Thomas M | Ungaretti & Harris LLP * |
| Keidan Martin Laura | Katten Muchin Rosenman LLP |
| Peregrine Michael W | McDermott Will & Emery LLP * |

**Band 2**

| | |
|---|---|
| Davis, Jr W Kenneth | Katten Muchin Rosenman LLP |
| DeJong Ralph E | McDermott Will & Emery LLP * |
| Durso John | Ungaretti & Harris LLP * |
| Glaser D Louis | Katten Muchin Rosenman LLP |
| Griffith Gerald M | Jones Day * |
| Lynn Nicholas J | Duane Morris LLP (ONP) [†] |
| Marren John P | Hogan Marren Ltd |
| Mills Elizabeth M | Proskauer Rose LLP |
| Raskin Richard D | Sidley Austin LLP * |
| Rovner Jack A | The Health Law Consultancy * |
| Rust Mark E | Barnes & Thornburg LLP * |
| Slattery Kerrin | McDermott Will & Emery LLP * |

**Band 3**

| | |
|---|---|
| Babbo Thomas | Hogan Marren Ltd |
| Callahan John M | McDermott Will & Emery LLP * |
| Coffey Patrick S | Whyte Hirschboeck Dudek S.C. (ONP) [†] |
| Gordon Lynn | Ungaretti & Harris LLP * |
| Hogan Carol C | Hogan Marren Ltd |
| Kraft Jeffrey G | Neal, Gerber & Eisenberg LLP (ONP) [†] * |
| McCahill Jane K | Polsinelli PC |
| Melvin Daniel | McDermott Will & Emery UK LLP * |
| Ranalli Clare | Holland & Knight LLP |
| Riley Jr James B | McGuireWoods LLP |
| Roe Kathryn | The Health Law Consultancy * |
| Skinner Honey J | Sidley Austin LLP * |
| Swill Douglas B | Drinker Biddle & Reath LLP * |

**Up-and-coming individuals**

| | |
|---|---|
| DiVarco Sandra | McDermott Will & Emery UK LLP * |
| Guenthner Robert | Dentons * |

* Indicates firm / individual with profile.
Alphabetical order within each band. Band 1 is the highest.

healthcare and is also renowned for his strengths in structuring hospital-physician alignment transactions. He elicits particular praise from sources for his expertise on Stark law. The *"terrific"* **John Callahan** (see p.1200) handles M&A within the life sciences and health services industries and also comes recommended for his knowledge of healthcare regulatory matters. Senior counsel **Michael Anthony** (see p.274) maintains a fine reputation in the market and

has deep experience in handling all healthcare matters, including policy formation. Rising star **Sandra DiVarco** (see p.1204) is described as a *"very hard-working"* and *"well-rounded"* lawyer by sources. She undertakes healthcare transactions and restructurings and represents hospitals and health systems.

## Band 2

### Hogan Marren Ltd
See profile on p.1251

**THE FIRM** This healthcare boutique undertakes the full spectrum of work and has considerable depth of experience upon which to draw. Its work in clinical integration wins widespread praise from market observers and the team has been particularly active in work involving accountable care organizations of late. The team is also noted for its expertise in fraud and antitrust matters concerning the healthcare sector.
**Sources say:** *"A tradition of excellence and availability."*
**KEY INDIVIDUALS John Marren** has over three decades' experience and a particular specialty in hospital and physician alignment schemes. Sources reserve praise for his *"practical and straightforward"* approach to matters and single him out as *"a very intelligent attorney who has the ability to simplify the process and explain it in easy terms."* **Thomas Babbo** maintains a fine track record acting for healthcare professionals on matters related to alignment and integration. He is *"particularly excellent in terms of making himself available to his clients,"* and is *"insightful and sees the big picture,"* note impressed sources. The well-regarded **Carol Hogan** concentrates on regulatory issues and is particularly strong in nonprofit legal matters.

### Katten Muchin Rosenman LLP
See profile on p.1253

**THE FIRM** This practice advises an impressive and diverse client base on all aspects of healthcare law. Recent work has seen the team act for Walgreens on an appeal against the State of Illinois' effort to access confidential information. Other key representative clients include Lahey Clinic, Midwest Alliance for Patient Safety, Northwestern Memorial Hospital and the University HealthSystem Consortium. The team also notably works in tandem with the firm's white-collar litigation group and frequently assists clients under investigation at a local and national level.
**Sources say:** *"Very high-caliber."*
**KEY INDIVIDUALS Michael Callahan** undertakes a wide range of healthcare work and is particularly experienced in matters related to medical staff and integrated delivery systems. He is *"knowledgeable and works hard to meet needs in a timely way,"* note sources. He was lead partner on the Walgreens matter. National healthcare practice chair **Laura Keidan Martin** attracts widespread praise from the mar-

ket. Interviewees single her out as *"very knowledgeable and a very good advocate for her client."* Her practice covers the full healthcare spectrum and she is particularly recommended for corporate integrity and compliance matters. **Kenneth Davis** predominantly concentrates on transaction and compliance matters in corporate healthcare, with an emphasis on the integration of healthcare providers. He elicits praise from sources for his expertise in physician-focused matters. **Louis Glaser** *"is a one-stop shop for transactions because he is able to assess the regulatory and reimbursement issues involved in a deal,"* reports one very impressed client.

## McGuireWoods LLP
See profile on p.2519

**THE FIRM** McGuireWoods handles matters on both a state and nationwide platform and is particularly noted for its strong private equity healthcare practice. It also has an active practice within health systems and frequently undertakes regulatory consulting. In recent work, it has represented Rush University Medical Center in the establishment of a CyberKnife joint venture. The group also acted for Water Street Healthcare on the acquisition of Medical Specialties Distributors.
**Sources say:** *"High quality and very responsive to our needs."*
**KEY INDIVIDUALS** The *"very bright"* **Scott Becker** concentrates on regulatory and transactional matters, and is particularly strong in all concerns relating to ambulatory surgery centers. Healthcare chair **James Riley** is much in demand for his *"prudent advice,"* note sources. He is well versed in corporate healthcare and is recognized for his adept handling of sophisticated transactions, including third-party financing. His practice also includes advising clients on regulatory issues within healthcare.

## Ungaretti & Harris LLP
See profile on p.1265

**THE FIRM** Ungaretti & Harris is consolidating its presence in Illinois and is seen as particularly strong in matters involving nonprofit providers. Other noted areas of expertise include clinical integration and healthcare finance work. In a recent highlight, the team acted for US Renal Care on its expansion into Illinois and the establishment of three new dialysis centers. The group also counts Clare Oaks, IHC Health System, Alexian Brothers Health System and Presence Health among its impressive roster of clients.
**Sources say:** *"They are very thorough, aware of the latest legislation and case law, and have a diverse team that has expertise in many areas."*
**KEY INDIVIDUALS Thomas Fahey** (see p.1206) chairs the healthcare and public finance groups. He is an expert in all areas of corporate healthcare, and is equally adept on both the regulatory and transactional side. He *"is well respected and knowledgeable – he does a really nice job,"* reports one enthusiastic interviewee. **John Durso** (see p.1205) comes particularly recommended for his work concerning long-term care and nonprofit providers. He attracts particular praise for his dynamism and work in

matters related to senior living. As one satisfied client avers, *"he has come to understand the perspective of the client as though he was in-house."* According to sources, **Lynn Gordon** (see p.1209) is *"very innovative and really keeps up to date on the law."* She handles corporate and regulatory healthcare work, principally for healthcare providers.

## Band 3

### Barnes & Thornburg LLP
See profile on p.436

**THE FIRM** This group undertakes a wide range of matters principally for healthcare providers and has developed a niche in the formation and funding of cooperatives under the PPACA. Recently, the team acted for the American Cancer Society, producing the appropriate screening documentation for healthcare centers in Illinois to help establish a grant program to reduce colorectal cancer. It also includes Metrodocs, Oak Mill Medical Associates and HealthyCT among its fine client portfolio.
**Sources say:** *"Very good – responses to questions are always timely."*
**KEY INDIVIDUALS** Chair of the firm's national healthcare department **Mark Rust** (see p.1229) is an expert in regulatory and transactional matters, and has nearly three decades' experience in the healthcare arena.

### Dentons
See profile on p.449

**THE FIRM** The group is well placed to deal with all aspects of healthcare matters and is able to draw on the expertise of other teams when necessary. The team is particularly recognized for its expertise in alignment and partnership matters. In addition, its members are noted for their strengths in healthcare finance, representing healthcare providers and also financial institutions acting as credit providers to nonprofits.
**Sources say:** *"The quality of service I have experienced has been excellent across the board in terms of high legal acumen in every area, prompt response and follow-through."*
**KEY INDIVIDUALS Robert Guenthner** (see p.1210) is an expert in transactional healthcare, fraud and abuse matters. He *"shows a deep knowledge of the rules of the law but is also able to understand our needs,"* reports one happy client.

### Drinker Biddle & Reath LLP
See profile on p.2238

**THE FIRM** The group handles all aspects of healthcare work and comes particularly recommended for its work in hospital affiliation and integration. Recently, the team advised Springfield Clinic on the formation of a subsidiary, Jardogs. The group's impressive client roster also includes GE Healthcare, John Hopkins Health System, Kewanee Hospital and Ottawa Regional Medical Center.
**Sources say:** *"They give us excellent advice and get good results – very good to work with." "They work collaboratively with us to find solutions."*

**KEY INDIVIDUALS Douglas Swill** (see p.1235) is noted for his strengths representing healthcare providers and nonprofit organizations on corporate matters. He also advises on physician integration and compensation. *"He has consistently demonstrated his ability to solve problems by offering his clients options that best fit the situation,"* asserts one impressed market commentator.

### The Health Law Consultancy
See profile on p.1250

**THE FIRM** This boutique firm maintains its position as a solid player in the healthcare space. The group primarily focuses on advising service providers and business associates on a variety of healthcare matters, including affiliations and alliances and government healthcare programs. Data security, privacy and federal law are other notable areas of expertise.
**Sources say:** *"They are extremely adept and knowledgeable."*
**KEY INDIVIDUALS Jack Rovner** (see p.1228) has a well-established reputation among peers and has a broad practice that includes handling healthcare reform work, IT initiatives and joint ventures. He is also noted for his expertise in antitrust and fraud and abuse matters. Clients particularly single out his thorough and detail-oriented approach and also reserve praise for his responsiveness. **Kathryn Roe** (see p.1227) has a wealth of experience handling matters concerning healthcare insurance, information exchange and government health programs, among others. Sources single her out as a *"tireless attorney"* whose *"knowledge and diligence make her a pleasure to work with."*

### Holland & Knight LLP
See profile on p.1028

**THE FIRM** Sophisticated regulatory and transactional matters are at the core of Holland & Knight's healthcare practice. The group also specializes in advising academic medical centers and other providers on health reform. In a recent highlight it represented the Union Associated Physicians Clinic in its restructuring of a new healthcare system designed to service West Central Indiana.
**Sources say:** *"I have never been disappointed with the quality of the work completed or dissatisfied with the cost."*
**KEY INDIVIDUALS** The *"very knowledgeable"* **Clare Ranalli** undertakes corporate and regulatory work for dialysis and ambulatory surgery centers, as well as public and private health organizations. She is *"resourceful and very responsive to our needs,"* reports one happy client.

### Jones Day
See profile on p.919

**THE FIRM** Jones Day is well versed in all areas of transactional, compliance and investigation work. The team also has expertise in healthcare financing, with a particular specialty in tax bond finance work, and has recently worked with Presence Health on its system consolidation. Other recent work has included acting for Loyola University of Chicago on the sale of its affiliates. It also counts Premier Health Partners, The Cleveland Clinic and Regional Health among its key clients.
**Sources say:** *"Very fine lawyers."*

KEY INDIVIDUALS **Gerald Griffith** (see p.1210) is an expert in regulatory compliance and M&A and joint ventures. He also maintains a strong practice in matters involving tax-exempt organizations.

### Polsinelli PC
See profile on p.1641

THE FIRM The team at Polsinelli handles a broad spectrum of healthcare matters, including physician relationships, regulatory compliance and related litigation, and operational issues. Clients include academic medical centers, long-term care facilities, specialty medical groups and hospice providers.

Sources say: "*They deliver high-quality legal support in a very cost-effective manner.*"

KEY INDIVIDUALS **Jane McCahill** attracts praise from sources for her regulatory and reimbursement work, and is also recognized for her expertise acting on behalf of healthcare providers and institutions in corporate transactions.

### Proskauer Rose LLP
See profile on p.2001

THE FIRM Proskauer Rose focuses on representing service providers, particularly on high-end M&A, in addition to acting for nonprofit entities on compliance and governance issues. The team's expertise has recently seen it represent the Colorado Health Foundation in the sale of its equity share in HCA-HealthONE. Other key clients include Sherman Health Systems, Sumner Regional Health Care and the University of Chicago Medical Center.

Sources say: "*Very approachable, excellent results, well respected and they find a way to bring people to a consensus.*"

KEY INDIVIDUALS The "*very thorough and very knowledgeable*" **Elizabeth Mills** is particularly highly regarded for her tax exemption work pertaining to nonprofit organizations, with one highly impressed interviewee commenting: "*She is one of the best healthcare/tax exemption lawyers that I know.*" **Monte Dube** is a well-established figure with over 25 years' experience in the healthcare arena. He provides expert advice to hospitals and private equity firms in all healthcare matters. Sources appreciate that he is "*easy to work with and always available.*"

### Sidley Austin LLP
See profile on p.1264

THE FIRM This 21-strong Chicago team handles work across the board and has particular expertise in pharmaceutical and medical device work. The team's expertise has seen it recently represent GlaxoSmithKline in a DOJ investigation concerning a filed False Claims Act qui tam action. Allergan, Novo Nordisk, Henkel and Sunovion are among the group's other key clients.

Sources say: "*One of our preferred providers – excellent, excellent lawyers.*" "*They're fantastic: we've had a long relationship with them and they've been great.*"

KEY INDIVIDUALS The "*highly skilled and extremely responsive*" **Richard Raskin** (see p.1226) is head of the Chicago healthcare team. He specializes in antitrust, fraud and abuse, and managed care matters and also maintains a fine track record for his work in federal and state investigations. The "*terrific*" **Honey Skinner** (see p.1232) undertakes work involving the representation of healthcare providers before government agencies. She also has a well-established reputation for her expertise in certificate of need matters.

### Other Notable Practitioners

The highly regarded **Nicholas Lynn** of Duane Morris LLP comes recommended for his expertise in pharmaceutical law and long-term care issues. He also advises on healthcare litigation and regulation matters. The "*very effective*" **Patrick Coffey** recently joined Whyte Hirschboeck Dudek S.C. from Locke Lord. He undertakes healthcare-oriented litigation and is well versed in a wide range of matters including antitrust, Stark law investigation and reimbursement. **Jeffrey Kraft** (see p.1216) of Neal, Gerber & Eisenberg LLP is singled out by market observers for his experience and skill in healthcare matters, and is adept in all areas of corporate, transactional and regulatory work.

# INSURANCE

Dispute Resolution: Reinsurance p.1168;   Transactional & Regulatory p.1168

Commentary about individuals can be found under their firm's paragraph.  If the firm has no paragraph (is not ranked) look at Other Notable Practitioners.

| Insurance: Dispute Resolution Leading Firms |
| --- |
| **Band 1** |
| Jenner & Block LLP * |
| Kirkland & Ellis LLP * |
| Reed Smith LLP |
| **Band 2** |
| Bates Carey Nicolaides LLP |
| Dentons * |
| Meckler Bulger Tilson Marick & Pearson LLP |
| Neal, Gerber & Eisenberg LLP * |
| Proskauer Rose LLP * |
| **Band 3** |
| Barnes & Thornburg LLP * |
| Locke Lord LLP * |
| Troutman Sanders LLP |

\* Indicates firm with profile.
Alphabetical order within each band. Band 1 is the highest.

*The editorial is in alphabetical order by firm name.*

### Barnes & Thornburg LLP
See profile on p.436

THE FIRM This Chicago policyholder group has been involved in a number of high-value insurance recovery disputes on behalf of its clients. For example, the team recently acted for General Growth Properties on the recovery of over $100 million losses arising from damage caused by Hurricane Katrina. Other key clients include Georgia-Pacific, First Bank & Trust Co. of Illinois and the City of Chicago.

KEY INDIVIDUALS **Adam Hollander** (see p.1212) takes a lead role on many of the firm's most significant insurance disputes, particularly in professional liability and business interruption claims. He has recently continued his involvement in the firm's high-value representation of Georgia-Pacific.

### Bates Carey Nicolaides LLP

THE FIRM This specialist insurance firm is known and respected for its longstanding representation of the insurance industry on both a domestic and international basis. The team offers expertise across a range of insurance areas including direct insurance, reinsurance and professional liability. The group also has a prominent presence in construction and transport insurance claims.

KEY INDIVIDUALS **Robert Bates** is known as a "*tough, smart and very tenacious lawyer*" among commentators. He handles a range of reinsurance and insurance coverage disputes on behalf of domestic and international clients. Founding partner **Scott Carey** handles coverage, reinsur-

ance and professional liability claims. According to sources, he is "*smart, responsive and an excellent lawyer.*" **Maria Enriquez** has a broad practice which takes in international arbitrations relating to sophisticated Bermuda Form issues as well as general liability and commercial insurance disputes.

### Butler Rubin Saltarelli & Boyd LLP
See profile on p.1243

THE FIRM This firm is known for its deep experience and expertise in reinsurance dispute resolution. The team regularly acts on behalf of various insurers and reinsurers, and has an impressive client list including Argonaut Insurance and CIGNA. It recently resolved a major case on behalf of Clearwater Insurance and Hudson Insurance against a commutation plan. Clients are particularly impressed by the firm's cost-effectiveness and customer service.

Sources say: "*An excellent firm – highly skilled and experienced in reinsurance disputes.*"

KEY INDIVIDUALS Reinsurance expert **James Rubin** (see p.1228) is described as "*one of the deans of this area,*" and has been involved in various complex matters, including the representation of Liberty Mutual in a landmark case against AIG. According to commentators, he has "*very deep knowledge and experience*" and "*conducts himself like a gentleman.*" **Ira Belcove** (see p.1198) has been instrumen-

## Insurance: Dispute Resolution
### Leading Individuals

**Star individuals**

| | |
|---|---|
| Foradas Michael P | Kirkland & Ellis LLP * |
| Gilford Steven R | Proskauer Rose LLP |

**Band 1**

| | |
|---|---|
| Bates Jr Robert J | Bates Carey Nicolaides LLP |
| Berkeley Jill B | Neal, Gerber & Eisenberg LLP * |
| Johnson Robert C | Dentons * |
| Mathias Jr John H | Jenner & Block LLP * |
| Rosenthal Marc | Proskauer Rose LLP |
| Shugrue John | Reed Smith LLP |
| Vishneski John S | Reed Smith LLP |

**Band 2**

| | |
|---|---|
| Boulos Nader | Kirkland & Ellis LLP * |
| Carey Scott | Bates Carey Nicolaides LLP |
| Davis James M | Reed Smith LLP |
| Elbert Angela R | Neal, Gerber & Eisenberg LLP * |
| Langer Paul | Proskauer Rose LLP |
| Litt Paula E | Schopf & Weiss LLP (ONP)† * |
| Marrinson Thomas A | Reed Smith LLP |
| Rosenberg Carolyn | Reed Smith LLP |
| Ross Rebecca L | Troutman Sanders LLP |
| Seaman Scott | Meckler Bulger Tilson Marick & Pearson |
| Vobornik Donna | Dentons * |

**Band 3**

| | |
|---|---|
| Cutter David F | Troutman Sanders LLP |
| Dickinson Christopher C | Jenner & Block LLP * |
| Enriquez Maria G | Bates Carey Nicolaides LLP |
| Hollander Adam K | Barnes & Thornburg LLP * |
| Kallianis James | Meckler Bulger Tilson Marick & Pearson |
| Marick Michael | Meckler Bulger Tilson Marick & Pearson |
| Nardoni Stanley C | Reed Smith LLP |
| Walker-Bright Paul R | Reed Smith LLP |

## Insurance: Dispute Resolution: Reinsurance
### Leading Firms

**Band 1**

Butler Rubin Saltarelli & Boyd LLP *
Sidley Austin LLP *

**Band 2**

Foley & Lardner LLP *
Locke Lord LLP *
Schiff Hardin LLP

### Leading Individuals

**Star individuals**

| | |
|---|---|
| Rubin James I | Butler Rubin Saltarelli & Boyd LLP * |
| Spector David | Schiff Hardin LLP |

**Band 1**

| | |
|---|---|
| DiGiovanni Nick J | Locke Lord LLP * |
| Sneed William M | Sidley Austin LLP * |
| Stone Susan | Sidley Austin LLP * |

**Band 2**

| | |
|---|---|
| Bates Jr Robert J | Bates Carey Nicolaides LLP |
| Belcove Ira J | Butler Rubin Saltarelli & Boyd LLP * |
| Gilford Steven R | Proskauer Rose LLP |
| Haab Eric | Foley & Lardner LLP |
| Hermes Robert N | Butler Rubin Saltarelli & Boyd LLP * |
| Isely Catherine | Butler Rubin Saltarelli & Boyd LLP * |
| Moglin Neal | Foley & Lardner LLP |
| Schwab Stephen W | DLA Piper LLP (US) * |

**Band 3**

| | |
|---|---|
| Burt Antony S | Schiff Hardin LLP |
| Cunningham Thomas | Sidley Austin LLP * |
| Goering Gail | Foley & Lardner LLP |
| LaGory Dennis | Schiff Hardin LLP |
| McCullough Joe | Freeborn & Peters LLP (ONP)† * |
| Neppl Daniel J | Sidley Austin LLP * |
| Rodriguez Aldort Julie | Butler Rubin Saltarelli & Boyd LLP * |
| Snider Teresa | Butler Rubin Saltarelli & Boyd LLP * |

## Insurance: Transactional & Regulatory
### Leading Firms

**Band 1**

Sidley Austin LLP *

**Band 2**

Dentons *
DLA Piper LLP (US) *
Locke Lord LLP *
Mayer Brown LLP *

### Leading Individuals

**Band 1**

| | |
|---|---|
| Goldman Michael P | Sidley Austin LLP * |
| Mendelsohn David | DLA Piper LLP (US) * |
| Schwab Stephen W | DLA Piper LLP (US) * |
| Shwachman Perry | Sidley Austin LLP * |

**Band 2**

| | |
|---|---|
| Biasetti Jon | Locke Lord LLP * |
| Goodman Mark R | Freeborn & Peters LLP (ONP)† * |
| Jones Thomas M | McDermott Will & Emery LLP (ONP)† * |
| Pinsel Michael | Sidley Austin LLP * |
| Waters Paige D | Locke Lord LLP * |
| Wylie Kenneth R | Sidley Austin LLP * |

**Band 3**

| | |
|---|---|
| Best Edward S | Mayer Brown LLP |
| Carr Corinne P | Dentons * |
| Hamilton Larry | Mayer Brown LLP |
| Ribaudo Anthony | Sidley Austin LLP * |

**Up-and-coming individuals**

| | |
|---|---|
| Kallas Jay | Locke Lord LLP * |

\* Indicates firm / individual with profile.
*Alphabetical order within each band. Band 1 is the highest.*

---

tal in several high-value reinsurance matters and has particular skill in arbitrations. Sources say he is *"an excellent, quality lawyer who takes the time to properly understand the specific issues involved, is easily reachable and responsive."* **Robert Hermes** (see p.1212) is known in the field for his expertise in arbitration and litigation. In the past year he steered a plaintiff client through the complexities of its multimillion-dollar case against a reinsurer. **Catherine Isely** (see p.1212) is described by sources as *"a highly skilled professional."* Her extensive experience in reinsurance defense work has cemented her place as an expert litigator and arbitrator in the field. **Julie Rodriguez Aldort** (see p.1227) is commended for her ability to *"cut to the heart of the issue"* and for her commercial approach. She has recently acted for TIG in a reinsurance case against AIU Insurance of more than $22 million. Client favorite **Teresa Snider** (see p.1233) *"is always well briefed and well organized and seems to take inordinate amounts of hard work and planning in her stride."* She notably worked on the Clearwater Insurance and Hudson Insurance reinsurance matter.

### Dentons
**See profile on p.449**

**THE FIRM** The Chicago group at this well-regarded national practice is known for its comprehensive litigation experience in complex matters as well as upholding the firm's longstanding tradition in regulatory issues. The dispute resolution arm has been involved in a range of coverage, mass tort and insurance bad faith claims on behalf of major insurers such as The Travelers Companies and Chartis. On the transactional and regulatory side, the team has dealt with insurance M&A and complex insolvency issues.

**KEY INDIVIDUALS Robert Johnson** (see p.1213) focuses on complex insurance disputes and is regarded by commentators as *"a very tough but reasonable advocate."* He has recently represented MMIC and Chartis in coverage litigation, as well as acting for Travelers on a range of asbestos, toxic tort and environmental cases. Coverage litigator **Donna Vobornik** (see p.1236) has represented insurance companies in a variety of environmental cases across the country, particularly on behalf of major insurer Travelers. Peers respect her expertise in this arena and identify her as

a target for referrals. Transactional and regulatory specialist **Corinne Carr** (see p.1201) regularly represents insurance and reinsurance companies in sophisticated issues. She has recently been involved in a number of regulatory issues on behalf of major insurance brokers and property and casualty insurers.

### DLA Piper LLP (US)
**See profile on p.1971**

**THE FIRM** This household name has a broad insurance and reinsurance practice across the world, with a deep level of transactional and regulatory expertise in Chicago. The team regularly advises industry clients on both local and international insurance and reinsurance regulations. As well as acting for insurers and reinsurers, the firm also advises financial institutions and government officials on regulatory issues.

**Sources say:** *"The firm is excellent; it has done an exemplary job representing us on all transactions to date."*

**KEY INDIVIDUALS Stephen Schwab** (see p.1230) is praised by commentators for being *"very attentive to the client's needs and good on strategy."* He recently worked on behalf of SCOR in the $55 million sale of Investors Insurance Corporation to Athene Holding. *"Excellent lawyer"* **David Mendelsohn** (see p.1222) regularly handles a range of reinsurance transactional and regulatory matters. He also counsels clients on a range of risk management issues and investigations.

### Foley & Lardner LLP
See profile on p.2588

**THE FIRM** This firm's Chicago insurance team is regularly involved in a range of high-stakes insurance and reinsurance disputes. The team has recently been involved in a number of matters on behalf of various members of ACE Group including Century Indemnity and Pacific Employers Insurance. Other key clients include AIG, Munich American Reassurance and Excalibur Reinsurance.

**KEY INDIVIDUALS Eric Haab** is renowned for his skill in litigation and regularly deals with significant insurance cases including issues such as asbestos and silica losses. He is described by sources as *"a very fine reinsurance practitioner."* **Neal Moglin**'s expertise lies in life/health and property/casualty insurance disputes. He is held in high regard by sources, who say: *"You're in safe hands with Neal. He knows what he's doing."* **Gail Goering** maintains an international practice and advises clients on a range of issues, including property/casualty and life/health reinsurance contracts. She has a particularly strong focus on life insurance.

### Jenner & Block LLP
See profile on p.1252

**THE FIRM** This internationally recognized insurance practice has a prominent Chicago presence in coverage claims on behalf of policyholders. The firm has represented both plaintiffs and defendants in various high-value matters in the past year, including working on Fiserv Solutions's case against XL Specialty Insurance. Major clients include American Electric Power and Kellogg.

**Sources say:** *"There is no comparison – they are excellent."*

**KEY INDIVIDUALS** *"Really great lawyer"* **John Mathias** (see p.1220) receives praise from peers and clients for his skill as a trial lawyer. He recently represented Fiserv Solutions in its case against XL Specialty Insurance. **Christopher Dickinson** (see p.1204) has recently worked on behalf of HSBC against Princeton Eagle West relating to a securities fraud case. According to clients, he is *"great at strategy, a great brief writer and very calm against aggressive lawyers on the other side."*

### Kirkland & Ellis LLP
See profile on p.1254

**THE FIRM** This market-leading firm has a wealth of experience in disputes involving sophisticated insurance programs and high-stakes coverage litigation involving a range of professional and product liability claims among other issues. Key policyholder clients include Abbott Laboratories, Boeing and Aon. The practice has recently acted in coverage litigation for Viking Pump against multiple insurers regarding liability claims for asbestos products.

**Sources say:** *"These guys will travel anywhere and do consistently great work."*

**KEY INDIVIDUALS Nader Boulos** (see p.1199) worked on behalf of TOUSA against 12 D&O insurers in a high-value coverage action. Sources recommend him as *"a very skillful litigator and strategist who is extremely smart and creative and very responsive."* **Michael Foradas** (see p.1207) is known for being *"a fantastic lawyer and good litigator who gives good business advice."* He has a specific focus on insurance coverage as part of a broad litigation practice.

### Locke Lord LLP
See profile on p.2443

**THE FIRM** This firm has a large transactional and regulatory practice which demonstrates a capacity to handle the most complex insurance issues. The firm also maintains an impressive dispute resolution group, with deep expertise in both direct insurance and reinsurance. Both arms of the insurance department have a diverse range of clients, including Humana, Berkshire Hathaway and Brit Insurance. The group continues to cultivate its links with the healthcare industry, particularly through its transactional dealings.

**Sources say:** *"The go-to firm for underwriters."*

**KEY INDIVIDUALS Nick DiGiovanni** (see p.1204) chairs the reinsurance and insurance litigation practice in Chicago and remains a firm favorite with insurance clients due to his familiarity with the industry. Sources say: *"Nick is very experienced and has seen all of the problems that the industry has faced. He has tried dozens of cases and his skill set is complete for that. He is accessible and easy to talk to."* Regulatory and transactional insurance group cochair **Jon Biasetti** (see p.1199) recently advised Humana on its acquisition of Arcadian Management Services. He has deep expertise in the full range of corporate issues, while peers commend his good reputation for customer service. **Paige Waters** (see p.1236) specializes in insurance regulation and is held in excellent regard for her handling of the most sophisticated issues. Sources consider her to be *"very good on regulatory insurance and very practical,"* while noting that *"she has good relationships with a lot of regulators."* **Jay Kallas** (see p.1214) works on a broad range of insurance-related transactions and acts on behalf of a variety of clients, including offshore reinsurance companies and property-casualty insurers. Sources comment that *"he is very knowledgeable, has a good work ethic and is motivated."*

### Mayer Brown LLP
See profile on p.1257

**THE FIRM** This large Chicago team is noted for its expertise in transactional and regulatory insurance matters. Links with the firm's international insurance team coupled with extensive expertise in corporate matters means it is equipped to deal with a wide range of complex insurance transactions.

**KEY INDIVIDUALS Edward Best** receives accolades from sources who describe him as *"excellent, a good communicator and an extremely hard worker."* His experience in insurance transactions is backed by his expertise in corporate and capital markets deals. **Larry Hamilton**'s international practice focuses on the regulatory compliance of insurance

companies. Sources commend his attention to detail and deep knowledge of the industry.

### Meckler Bulger Tilson Marick & Pearson LLP
**THE FIRM** This well-established Chicago insurance group centers its practice around insurance dispute resolution, and has a dedicated focus on professional and general liability claims, construction defect matters and reinsurance arbitrations. The firm regularly acts for some of the most prominent insurers in the country including Zurich, Farmers and Allstate.

**Sources say:** *"On the insurance carrier side, a firm that really deserves note is Meckler Bulger. They are just terrific."*

**KEY INDIVIDUALS Michael Marick** focuses on complex insurance coverage cases and appeals. Sources regard him as *"a guy that's worked hard and developed himself into one of the most sophisticated insurance coverage guys in Chicago."* He has recently represented Zurich in various high-value insurance coverage and litigation matters. **Scott Seaman** is respected for his expertise in bad faith and reinsurance matters as well as complex insurance coverage cases. He has recently been involved in a series of significant litigation matters and reinsurance arbitrations. *"Brilliant trial lawyer"* **James Kallianis** is experienced in professional liability cases and has represented a variety of clients including accountants, insurance brokers and lawyers.

### Neal, Gerber & Eisenberg LLP
See profile on p.1260

**THE FIRM** This impressive policyholder practice is held in high regard for its prominent work in contentious matters including litigation, arbitration and mediation. The team regularly acts for clients from a range of industrial sectors, with particular recent activity on behalf of Ameren in the energy industry. Other major clients include ExxonMobil, Waste Management and Alliant Credit Union.

**KEY INDIVIDUALS** Practice chair **Jill Berkeley** (see p.1198) is hailed as *"an outstanding lawyer with encyclopedic knowledge of case law."* She is known for her extensive expertise across the full range of insurance coverage disputes. **Angela Elbert** (see p.1206) is considered by sources to be *"a very tough litigator, but reasonable at the same time. She works hard to find solutions to problems and is very knowledgeable in this area."* She is well versed in all manner of insurance disputes, and has recently acted on behalf of Euromarket Designs and Keeley Asset Management.

### Proskauer Rose LLP
See profile on p.2001

**THE FIRM** The Chicago arm of this large insurance group deals in arbitration and litigation on behalf of policyholders as well as in nonlitigation matters, including advising on risk management, negotiation and insolvency actions. The firm also handles reinsurance claims and has expertise in the niche area of cyber risk coverage. The firm's client list includes Dow Chemical and Union Carbide, and it recently represented Cargill in a coverage litigation case concerning property damage and personal injury claims.

**KEY INDIVIDUALS Marc Rosenthal** has a broad practice which takes in insurance coverage litigation, insurance company formation and M&A. He is noted as a *"very skilled counselor with very strong practice judgment."* **Paul Langer** is hailed by sources as *"a very strong litigator and adviser on policy issues."* He has extensive experience in coverage litigation and in litigation concerning healthcare entities, managed care claims and IP. **Steven Gilford** has been involved in a number of major asbestos matters and has deep experience in all areas of coverage litigation. According to one source, *"Steven must be one of the most sensible people I've ever met. He's got excellent judgment."*

## Reed Smith LLP

**THE FIRM** More than 20 lawyers make up the Chicago arm of this leading international practice, which specializes in representing policyholders in coverage disputes concerning a variety of commercial insurance products. Recent cases have concerned asbestos liability matters, mortgage insurance litigation, property damage and product recall claims. Bank of America/Countrywide is part of the firm's impressive client list and retains the team in high-value mortgage insurance matters.

**Sources say:** *"There's a small community of insurance claims lawyers out there in the market and Reed Smith's are right up there. They know the people involved, know the issues and are responsive and pleasant."*

**KEY INDIVIDUALS** The focus of **John Shugrue**'s practice is on acting for major policyholders, in both domestic and international matters. He has recently been representing Anadarko in ongoing high-value claims concerning the 2010 Gulf oil spill. Sources describe him as *"bright, dedicated and encyclopedic"* in his practice. **James Davis** regularly represents Fortune 500 companies in a range of insurance coverage disputes. He is experienced in handling the intricacies of sophisticated litigation and has expertise in innovative areas including global warming coverage and data privacy. The *"experienced and bright"* **Thomas Marrinson** specializes in professional and fiduciary liability insurance, and first-party property/business interruption insurance. **John Vishneski** *"has drive, is very bright and gets great results in his cases,"* according to continually impressed sources. Complex insurance coverage litigation cases lie at the heart of his nationwide practice and his experience spans environmental and toxic torts liability. **Carolyn Rosenberg** is a *"well-known and respected lawyer"* who specializes in developing areas of insurance coverage, including data privacy and cloud computing. She maintains a strong reputation for her work both in mediation and in litigation. **Stanley Nardoni** is recognized as an experienced professional in coverage litigation with a particular focus on antitrust, IP and environmental claims. **Paul Walker-Bright** works predominantly on behalf of corporate policyholders in complex insurance recovery and litigation. He was recently involved in representing Tribune Company in the insurance aspects of a bankruptcy matter.

## Schiff Hardin LLP

**THE FIRM** This practice focuses on a range of corporate, litigation and regulatory matters within an insurance context, but earns particular recognition in Illinois for reinsurance. The team has recently been involved in a number of reinsurance disputes, especially in the areas of toxic and asbestos torts, workers' compensation and London market arbitrations.

**KEY INDIVIDUALS** Sources say **David Spector** is the person to call on *"if you're looking for someone that can do it all, someone that's bright, articulate and dedicated and who has the complete set of skills."* As well as leading the way in reinsurance, he is also vastly experienced in insurer solvency and coverage litigation. **Antony Burt** has a particular focus on reinsurance and insurance insolvency, but also handles complex litigation including professional liability disputes. **Dennis LaGory** has deep expertise and experience in reinsurance issues as part of a broad practice which also incorporates professional liability and coverage litigation.

## Sidley Austin LLP
See profile on p.1264

**THE FIRM** This international firm has a large reinsurance dispute resolution department which handles a range of domestic and cross-jurisdictional claims. The practice also includes a dedicated insurance and financial services team which acts for a variety of clients on the full range of transactional and regulatory issues. The group is known as a market leader in catastrophe bond transactions, having continued to be involved in a number of such matters recently.

**Sources say:** *"They are fine lawyers who are consistently good."*

**KEY INDIVIDUALS William Sneed** (see p.1233) is known for his methodical and analytical approach to reinsurance disputes, with sources describing him as *"a very effective advocate."* Recently, he successfully defended a claim at trial on behalf of TIG brought by Transport Insurance. The *"brilliant"* **Susan Stone** (see p.413) is known for her strong links with the insurance industry. She has recently been involved in matters for key client Trustmark, in addition to various arbitration cases. **Thomas Cunningham** (see p.1203) is *"energetic with a good demeanor – he has a very strong set of people skills."* He recently succeeded in defending Transatlantic Reinsurance in a matter brought against it by Allstate. **Daniel Neppl** (see p.1224) is commended by sources for being *"very secure in his own skill set and confident without being arrogant – bright, articulate and absolutely committed."* He has been involved in a number of recent reinsurance arbitrations. Insurance and financial services group cochair **Michael Goldman** (see p.1209) is known for being a *"hard-working and bright"* lawyer. In the past twelve months he led the team in a $3.4 billion matter on behalf of Transatlantic surrounding regulatory issues arising from its proposed merger with Allied World Assurance. **Perry Shwachman** (see p.1231) co-heads the insurance

and financial services team. He recently represented Liberty Life Insurance in a reinsurance matter involving $3.1 billion of liabilities. **Michael Pinsel** (see p.1225) represents the insurance industry in a range of transactional and regulatory matters. He has been particularly active in a number of catastrophe bond transactions. *"Fine regulatory lawyer"* **Kenneth Wylie** (see p.1238) is well known for his deep experience across the range of insurance regulatory matters. He has been involved in the firm's advice to the insurance industry on the impact of the Dodd-Frank Act. **Anthony Ribaudo** (see p.1227) recently represented UBS in a $397 million Regulation A-XXX letter of credit solution matter for Pacific Life Insurance. His broad practice also takes in securities, M&A and private equity.

## Troutman Sanders LLP

**THE FIRM** The Chicago office of this established national insurance practice handles a range of disputes on behalf of the industry. It is particularly involved in high-value coverage disputes for major insurance companies including The Travelers Companies, XL and Chubb Group. The team has maintained its longstanding relationship with CNA insurance companies, exemplified by its recent representation of Columbia Casualty in bad faith claims.

**KEY INDIVIDUALS Rebecca Ross** is held in high regard by commentators thanks to her expertise across a range of insurance issues. She took a lead on the firm's bad faith work for Columbia Casualty, and also handles environmental and asbestos mass torts. **David Cutter** remains popular with clients thanks to his broad litigation experience. He recently played a key role in the firm's nationwide representation of XL subsidiary Indian Harbor Insurance.

## Other Notable Practitioners

**Paula Litt** (see p.1218) of Schopf & Weiss LLP frequently represents corporate clients in insurance recovery disputes. According to commentators she is *"savvy, smart and understands the practicality of cases."* **Joe McCullough** (see p.1221) of Freeborn & Peters LLP is known for reinsurance dispute work both locally and internationally. Peers note that *"his business is reinsurance and he has done well in this niche."* Also at Freeborn & Peters, **Mark Goodman** (see p.1209) handles transactional and regulatory insurance matters including large M&A deals on behalf of major insurance companies. Sources describe him as *"a quality lawyer and person."* **Thomas Jones** (see p.1213) of McDermott Will & Emery LLP has a tax background which has informed his successful insurance regulatory practice concerning captive insurance. He acts for a variety of clients, including joint ventures, healthcare providers and trade associations.

# INTELLECTUAL PROPERTY

Commentary about individuals can be found under their firm's paragraph. If the firm has no paragraph (is not ranked) look at Other Notable Practitioners.

## Intellectual Property
### Leading Firms

**Band 1**
Kirkland & Ellis LLP *
Sidley Austin LLP *

**Band 2**
Banner & Witcoff, Ltd *
Brinks Hofer Gilson & Lione *
Leydig, Voit & Mayer, Ltd *
McDermott Will & Emery LLP *
McDonnell Boehnen Hulbert & Berghoff LLP *
Niro, Scavone, Haller & Niro
Winston & Strawn LLP *

**Band 3**
Barnes & Thornburg LLP *
DLA Piper LLP (US) *
Drinker Biddle & Reath LLP *
Fitch, Even, Tabin & Flannery *
Jenner & Block LLP *
Jones Day *
Katten Muchin Rosenman LLP *
Marshall, Gerstein & Borun LLP *
Mayer Brown LLP *
McAndrews, Held & Malloy, Ltd
Neal, Gerber & Eisenberg LLP *
Pattishall, McAuliffe, Newbury, Hilliard & Geraldson LLP

\* Indicates firm / individual with profile.
*Alphabetical order within each band. Band 1 is the highest.*

## Intellectual Property
### Senior Statesmen

| Senior Statesmen: distinguished older practitioners | | |
|---|---|---|
| Gilson Jerome | *Brinks Hofer Gilson & Lione* * | |
| Hilliard David C | *Pattishall, McAuliffe, Newbury, Hilliard* | |
| Katz A Sidney | *Husch Blackwell LLP (ONP)*[†] | |
| McAndrews George P | *McAndrews, Held & Malloy, Ltd.* * | |

### Leading Individuals

| **Band 1** | |
|---|---|
| Adamo Kenneth R | *Kirkland & Ellis LLP* * |
| Addy Meredith Martin | *Steptoe & Johnson LLP (ONP)*[†] |
| Feldman Mark I | *DLA Piper LLP (US)* * |
| Lombardi George C | *Winston & Strawn LLP* * |
| Malloy Timothy J | *McAndrews, Held & Malloy, Ltd* * |
| Mandell Floyd A | *Katten Muchin Rosenman LLP* |
| Niro Raymond | *Niro, Scavone, Haller & Niro* |
| Pritikin David T | *Sidley Austin LLP* * |
| Roper Harry J | *Jenner & Block LLP* * |
| Ropski Gary | *Brinks Hofer Gilson & Lione* * |
| Warnecke Michael O | *Perkins Coie LLP (ONP)*[†] |

| **Band 2** | |
|---|---|
| Boehnen Daniel A | *McDonnell Boehnen Hulbert & Berghoff* * |
| Cederoth Richard A | *Sidley Austin LLP* * |
| Hartmann H Michael | *Leydig, Voit & Mayer, Ltd* * |
| Hurst James F | *Winston & Strawn LLP* * |
| Kozak John W | *Leydig, Voit & Mayer, Ltd* * |
| Levine Russell E | *Kirkland & Ellis LLP* * |
| Lyerla Bradford P | *Jenner & Block LLP* * |
| Streff Jr William A | *Kirkland & Ellis LLP* * |
| Vezeau Timothy | *Katten Muchin Rosenman LLP* |
| Witcoff David L | *Jones Day* * |

| **Band 3** | |
|---|---|
| Browne Robert E | *Neal, Gerber & Eisenberg LLP* * |
| Callahan David K | *Kirkland & Ellis LLP* * |
| Cooperman Marc S | *Banner & Witcoff, Ltd* * |
| Duncan Margaret M | *McDermott Will & Emery LLP* * |
| Martini Christina | *DLA Piper LLP (US)* * |
| Miller Laura Beth | *Brinks Hofer Gilson & Lione* * |
| Nelson Dave | *Quinn Emanuel Urquhart & Sullivan (ONP)*[†] |

| **Band 4** | |
|---|---|
| Fifer Samuel | *Dentons (ONP)*[†] * |
| Frankel William H | *Brinks Hofer Gilson & Lione* * |
| Gabric Ralph J | *Brinks Hofer Gilson & Lione* * |
| Halligan R Mark | *Nixon Peabody LLP (ONP)*[†] * |
| Kriegel Jeremy | *Marshall, Gerstein & Borun LLP* |
| Letchinger John S | *Edwards Wildman Palmer (ONP)*[†] * |
| Mahoney Joseph A | *Mayer Brown LLP* |
| Maloney Timothy P | *Fitch, Even, Tabin & Flannery* * |
| Medansky Keith | *DLA Piper LLP (US)* * |
| Minsker Helen Hill | *Banner & Witcoff, Ltd* * |
| Parr Keith D | *Locke Lord LLP (ONP)*[†] * |

| **Up-and-coming individuals** | |
|---|---|
| Aly Imron | *Winston & Strawn LLP* * |
| Hawkins Brent | *McDermott Will & Emery UK LLP* * |
| Kelly Adam G | *Loeb & Loeb LLP* * |

## Band 1

### Kirkland & Ellis LLP
See profile on p.1254

**THE FIRM** Kirkland & Ellis retains its impressive reputation for patent litigation. The firm's ability to match national firm resources with litigation expertise rivaling specialist IP shops makes it one of the standout practices in the Chicago market. The team recently acted for Pfizer, defending a patent infringement and defeating a temporary restraining order on a pharmaceutical product. Other key clients include IBM, BlackBerry, and Dyson.

**Sources say:** *"A very good firm that you hear a lot of in IP cases. They did a nice job – very professional and very good to work with."*

**KEY INDIVIDUALS** The deeply experienced **Kenneth Adamo** (see p.1196) is *"someone that everyone knows in the IP world,"* with market sources praising his *"great court skills."* His recent highlights include advising IBM on a patent infringement lawsuit brought by Financial Systems Technology. **Russell Levine** (see p.1217) recently represented Coskata in a trade secret and tortious interference dispute with INEOS, reaching an out-of-court settlement after counterclaim. **William Streff** (see p.1234) is known as a *"high-power, recognized individual in the IP community."* He has extensive experience in computer, telecom, semi-

conductor and fuel system technologies. Sources describe **David Callahan** (see p.1200) as *"an excellent lawyer"* with *"a great grasp of the law, coupled with strong litigation instincts both on paper and in the courtroom."* He recently represented Hill-Rom Holdings in a patent infringement suit relating to medical technology patents.

### Sidley Austin LLP
See profile on p.1264

**THE FIRM** Sidley Austin continues to be heralded by sources as a leading firm in the Chicago IP market. Clients particularly praise the firm's dedication to their needs, along with its deep bench of experienced practitioners. The practice is focused on patent litigation in the electronics, computer software, telecom and life sciences sectors, and is also known for its leading appellate group. Key clients include Merck, BlackBerry, and Microsoft.

**Sources say:** *"The level of service and expertise at Sidley are unsurpassed."*

**KEY INDIVIDUALS** Well-regarded patent litigator **Richard Cederoth** (see p.1201) is praised by market commentators as *"a really thorough lawyer."* His practice covers software, computer and semiconductor technologies.

National IP practice chair **David Pritikin** (see p.1226) has extensive experience in patent cases covering software, semiconductor and medical technologies. He enjoys a fine reputation as a *"terrific lawyer."*

## Band 2

### Banner & Witcoff, Ltd
See profile on p.1241

**THE FIRM** This firm earns widespread praise as one of Chicago's leading IP boutiques. The team lists several Fortune 500 companies among its clients, including Allstate, Bank of America, Kimberly-Clark and PepsiCo. Recently, the practice defended sportswear giant Nike against patent infringement claims of $60 million relating to its SasQuatch golf products.

**Sources say:** *"The attorneys of Banner & Witcoff are of consummate quality in the IP law area. They are highly intelligent, quite knowledgeable and thorough in their approach. They are able to give practical, business-sensitive advice."*

**KEY INDIVIDUALS Marc Cooperman** (see p.1203) is well regarded by peers and clients alike. He recently acted as lead counsel for Kimberly-Clark on the protection of 11 patents related to a series of products. He is "*an excellent IP litigator and a practical lawyer with a good sense of strategy.*" **Helen Hill Minsker** (see p.1222) heads the trademark practice group in Chicago and advises clients on trademark, unfair competition and copyright matters. She is described as "*an expert in the trademark area,*" who "*looks for creative solutions to problems.*"

## Brinks Hofer Gilson & Lione
### See profile on p.1242

**THE FIRM** Brinks Hofer enjoys a longstanding reputation as a high-quality boutique that offers a range of IP services. It is particularly noted for its patent prosecution expertise and strong trademark practice, while the litigation group is lauded for its courtroom presence. The team recently represented R.J. Reynolds in a patent infringement litigation brought by Star Scientific; other notable clients include Watson Pharmaceutical, A.P. Moller - Maersk and Yahoo!.

**Sources say:** "*Brinks Hofer has always been and continues to be very strong in the electronic, software and mechanical sectors.*"

**KEY INDIVIDUALS Gary Ropski** (see p.1228) is "*very highly thought-of*" and is known to have built a strong reputation in litigation. His practice covers copyright, trademark and trade secret matters, and he is particularly noted for his patent litigation abilities. **Laura Beth Miller** (see p.1222) chairs the ITC practice at Brinks, and is known for her experience and expertise in both trademark and patent litigation. **Ralph Gabric** (see p.1208) has litigation experience in bench and jury trials covering pharmaceutical, automotive, software and other technologies. He was one of the lead partners in the R.J. Reynolds matter. **William Frankel** (see p.1207) is known to be "*extremely knowledgeable on internet-related issues,*" and also "*a very fine patent litigator.*" He was one of the lead lawyers representing Maersk in a long-running patent infringement claim brought by Transocean Offshore Deepwater Drilling. The deeply experienced **Jerome Gilson** (see p.1209) is a well-respected trademark and unfair competition practitioner. He remains a prominent figure in the IP sector.

## Leydig, Voit & Mayer, Ltd
### See profile on p.1256

**THE FIRM** This firm is a well-established IP boutique with superb counseling, prosecution, licensing and litigation capabilities. The practice covers trademark, copyright and trade secret matters, and is particularly active on patent work. Working with clients such as American Express, Nike, Caterpillar and Human Genome Sciences, the Leydig team houses expertise across the mechanical, electronic, software, chemical and pharmaceutical technology sectors. Life sciences has also been an area of particular activity in recent years.

**Sources say:** "*They provide excellent client service and I would highly recommend them.*"

**KEY INDIVIDUALS Michael Hartmann** (see p.1211) is particularly known for his trade secrets practice, and is active in patent counseling and litigation. He served as lead

counsel for Omron and its subsidiary in a patent infringement suit, which concluded before trial after a successful challenge to the patent in question. Clients praise his business-oriented approach. **John Kozak** (see p.1216) is a "*very experienced and accomplished litigator, and an outstanding attorney.*" Specializing in licensing, patent counseling and patent litigation, Kozak works across the electronic, computer, chemical and mechanical IP sectors.

## McDermott Will & Emery LLP
### See profile on p.1258

**THE FIRM** This established full-service organization has a highly respected IP practice. The firm is known in the market for its strength in patent prosecution and litigation. Recent highlights include representing Tolmar and Sandoz in Hatch-Waxman litigation regarding generic pharmaceutical products. Trademark prosecution, litigation and strategy is also a key practice focus, and the firm advises Hitachi on all US trademark matters. Other key clients include HTC and IKEA.

**KEY INDIVIDUALS** IP team head **Margaret Duncan** (see p.1205) has a wide-ranging practice, incorporating copyright, trade secrets and domain names. Her main focus is in patent litigation, and she successfully represented Extreme Networks in a patent infringement claim relating to computer networks. According to sources, "*she is a fine attorney and a real straight shooter.*" **Brent Hawkins** (see p.1211) is a "*very good litigator*" with a growing reputation in the Chicago IP market, serving as lead and co-counsel on a number of patent cases in the pharmaceutical and e-technology sectors. He handles IP counseling, prosecution and litigation for WKI Holding and World Kitchen.

## McDonnell Boehnen Hulbert & Berghoff LLP
### See profile on p.1259

**THE FIRM** This firm covers the range of IP matters, from patent, trademark and copyright to trade secrets and licensing. The practice is equally known for counseling, prosecution and litigation, acting for both plaintiffs and defendants in disputes. A real strength of the team is in biotech and the life sciences sector, alongside an established electronics and software practice. Key clients include Amgen, Bristol-Myers Squibb, Cochlear and Roche Diagnostics Operations.

**Sources say:** "*The firm is very strategic and very practical.*"

**KEY INDIVIDUALS Daniel Boehnen's** (see p.1199) practice focuses on patent litigation and covers a variety of technologies. Market sources say that, in particular, he is "*a really good pharmaceutical lawyer*" with "*deep experience in that area.*"

## Niro, Scavone, Haller & Niro

**THE FIRM** This well-known boutique is held in excellent regard in the IP arena for its ability to offer clients a broad range of patent, trademark, copyright, trade secrets and unfair competition capabilities. The firm has a unique reputation in the Chicago market thanks to its strong contingency practice and specialization in plaintiff patent litigation.

**Sources say:** "*The first firm that comes to mind if you think of plaintiff work.*"

**KEY INDIVIDUALS Raymond Niro** is described by market sources as "*one of the most preeminent litigators ever,*" and is recognized as a prominent and successful figure in the market. Sources say they "*would refer to Ray because Ray wins big.*"

## Winston & Strawn LLP
### See profile on p.1267

**THE FIRM** This firm's Chicago office is renowned for its patent litigation expertise. The practice covers electronic, telecom and oil and gas technologies but has a particular focus on the pharmaceutical sector and Abbreviated New Drug Application (ANDA) suits. The team successfully represented Hospira in a high-value patent infringement case brought by Sanofi. Clients appreciate the firm's flexibility, efficiency, responsiveness and value for money, as well as its tireless dedication to their needs. Key clients include Dell and Motorola Mobility.

**Sources say:** "*They have the depth of expertise and know-how that extends beyond any one attorney and truly results in a team approach.*"

**KEY INDIVIDUALS George Lombardi** (see p.1218) is a "*phenomenal litigator*" who can "*set forth incredibly passionate arguments that appear indisputable.*" He is highly regarded by peers and clients alike. Specializing in biotech and pharmaceuticals, Lombardi is particularly adept at handling ANDA cases, an area in which clients say he is "*really exceptional.*" IP department head **James Hurst** (see p.1212) has a string of pharmaceutical patent victories to his name, including recent cases for Sun Pharmaceuticals, Caraco and Hospira. He is "*very well respected*" in the pharmaceutical field. **Imron Aly** (see p.1196) is a rising star in Winston & Strawn's IP practice. Clients appreciate his "*mastery of the facts*" and impressive court presence, with sources also lauding his "*excellent command of the courtroom*" and cross-examination abilities.

## Band 3

## Barnes & Thornburg LLP
### See profile on p.436

**THE FIRM** The Chicago practice at this full-service law firm enjoys a healthy profile in the marketplace. It covers a range of IP services, including trade secrets, franchises, licensing, internet issues, and trademark and patent infringement. The firm recently represented Recticel Interiors North America and Recticel Automobilsysteme in a sophisticated patent dispute. Other key clients of the firm include Wahl Clipper, Roche Diagnostics and Nutrimed Biotech.

**Sources say:** "*Barnes & Thornburg's attorneys are very service-oriented, strategic in their approach and straightforward in their representation. Their follow-up has been spot-on and thorough.*"

**KEY INDIVIDUALS Thomas Donovan** is head of the IP department.

## DLA Piper LLP (US)
See profile on p.1971

**THE FIRM** This international, full-service firm is known for its leading trademark and franchising practice. With clients including Amgen (Immunex), Midas International, Omni Hotels and Snap-on Tools, the firm represents companies from a range of sectors such as pharmaceutical, retail, consultancy and hospitality. DLA Piper is particularly active on the transactional side of IP deals, having recently acted on the due diligence of the acquisition of several restaurant chains and manufacturing companies. **Sources say:** "*DLA is our go-to firm for all trademark-related issues. I would highly recommend DLA to other companies who are in need of outstanding legal services.*"
**KEY INDIVIDUALS** Clients are full of praise for **Mark Feldman** (see p.1206), who provides a "*superlative service.*" Regarded as a "*top-notch attorney*" and "*a class act*" by peers, Feldman's practice incorporates trademark, franchise, copyright, competition, advertising, trade dress and transactional work. Clients say **Christina Martini** (see p.1220) is "*skilled, intelligent and business-savvy*" as well as "*a pleasure to work with.*" Her broad practice incorporates trademark portfolio work, transactional due diligence and branding strategy. **Keith Medansky** (see p.1221) is "*truly an expert with great experience and vast knowledge of both trademark law and developments in the trademark area.*" His practice covers litigation, as well as corporate and commercial work in anticounterfeiting, copyright, technology and trademark matters.

## Drinker Biddle & Reath LLP
See profile on p.2238

**THE FIRM** This national firm has a broad practice in Chicago, with litigation, transactional and patent prosecution capabilities. A particular area of growth for the practice is in social media and online technology. The team represents B/E Aerospace in prosecution and enforcement of its patent and trademark portfolios. Key clients include LG Electronics, Samtec and Illinois Tool Works.
**KEY INDIVIDUALS** Darren Cahr is a key contact in the IP department.

## Fitch, Even, Tabin & Flannery
See profile on p.1246

**THE FIRM** Fitch Even is a long-established IP boutique with patent, trademark, copyright, trade secret, advertising and unfair competition expertise. Its practice covers non-contentious work and litigation in a wide range of areas, including online and software, mechanical, chemical and pharmaceutical technologies. The firm recently acted for Boeing on the defense of a patent infringement suit, achieving summary judgment at district level and affirmation of noninfringement in the Federal Court of Appeals.
**Sources say:** "*The firm is knowledgeable and has a great ability to speak in layman's terms. Not only would I recommend them, but I would feel uncomfortable without their services.*"
**KEY INDIVIDUALS Timothy Maloney** (see p.1219) has a growing reputation in IP litigation and is well regarded by both clients and peers. Clients appreciate his "*efficient and incisive analysis*" and "*good command of the law.*"

## Jenner & Block LLP
See profile on p.1252

**THE FIRM** Jenner & Block's Chicago office fields a team of strong litigators with a focus on patent litigation and particular experience in jury trials. The practice covers chemical and life science technologies, as well as semiconductors, software, e-commerce and other technology industries. The team was recently appointed as defense counsel to Amazon.com in a patent infringement action brought against its websites and the Kindle product.
**KEY INDIVIDUALS Bradford Lyerla** (see p.1219) is "*an outstanding litigator*" whose "*strategic thinking, experience and character*" come in for high praise from market sources. He has trial experience in several districts, including Delaware, the Eastern District of Texas and the Southern District of California, and has also achieved victories at the Federal Circuit. **Harry Roper** (see p.1228) is an experienced, well-known and highly regarded patent litigator. His practice covers software, pharmaceuticals, medical technology and biotech.

## Jones Day
See profile on p.919

**THE FIRM** Jones Day has a global presence in IP work, with a strong Chicago offering. The team has been particularly active in patent litigation, with expertise in computer technology, electronics, and online and communications network technology. The firm recently represented IBM in a semiconductor patent infringement action brought against Auburn University. In the Supreme Court, Jones Day represented Myriad Genetics in the patent eligibility of DNA molecules.
**KEY INDIVIDUALS David Witcoff** (see p.1237) has a good reputation as a litigator, with sources describing him as "*very smart*" and "*a great lawyer.*" He was a lead attorney acting for Nikon in consolidated patent lawsuits across several districts.

## Katten Muchin Rosenman LLP
See profile on p.1253

**THE FIRM** The Chicago office of this nationwide firm has a practice focusing on litigation in patent, trademark, unfair competition, copyright and advertising claims. The patent practice is split in two, with one group dedicated to generic pharmaceutical clients and one to software and electronics. The firm recently acted for Microsoft in a trademark infringement case relating to the Kin and Kinect products. Other key clients include Kimberly-Clark, Apotex and Motorola Mobility.
**KEY INDIVIDUALS Floyd Mandell** is "*very practical, knowledgeable and responsive*" and "*is not afraid of a challenge.*" His recent work includes the Microsoft trademark case and advising Dell on the defense of a trademark infringement claim. **Timothy Vezeau** is part of the electronic technology and hi-tech group at Katten. He focuses on patent litigation, but has also represented clients in a variety of other IP disputes.

## Marshall, Gerstein & Borun LLP
See profile on p.▓▓▓▓▓▓▓▓▓▓

**THE FIRM** This dedicated IP firm offers both prosecution and litigation capabilities, with particular strength in patent prosecution. Computer and electronic technologies are an active area of the practice, although the team works across a range of sectors including mechanical, chemical and biotech. Clients include Amgen, InterMune and Merck Serono.
**Sources say:** "*In many ways we think of them as part of us because they know our business well and have a team approach. Their tremendous amount of contacts and history allows them to provide services and opinions that are well-rounded.*"
**KEY INDIVIDUALS Jeremy Kriegel** is well regarded in patent prosecution, with particular experience in mechanical and electronic technologies. Clients say: "*He is very thorough in his consideration of the issues and their potential impact on his client's business.*" He is also praised for his "*innovative insight and creative solutions.*"

## Mayer Brown LLP
See profile on p.1257

**THE FIRM** This full-service, global law firm has an established presence in the Chicago market. The practice has well-regarded IP litigation capabilities, particularly in patent disputes. Notable clients include Bristol-Myers Squibb, Dow Chemical, GlaxoSmithKline and Nestlé.
**KEY INDIVIDUALS Joseph Mahoney**'s practice focuses on chemical, pharmaceutical, biotech and medical device technologies. He works in both counseling and litigation. "*He is very organized and understands the patent appeal process very well,*" according to commentators.

## McAndrews, Held & Malloy, Ltd

**THE FIRM** This specialist IP boutique is particularly known for patent prosecution as well as a respected litigation capacity. The practice handles patent, trademark, copyright and trade secrets matters, among other areas of IP enforcement and protection.
**Sources say:** "*There are some great people at McAndrews. They were and are great lawyers.*"
**KEY INDIVIDUALS Timothy Malloy** (see p.1219) is chair of the firm. He has extensive experience in patent, contract, antitrust and general IP litigation. **George McAndrews** (see p.1220) is well regarded by peers and clients, and is recognized as a leading practitioner at the firm. He advises client on all aspects of patent, trademark, unfair competition and other IP matters, and is experienced in litigation. His key areas of expertise include mechanical, electronic and chemical technologies.

## Neal, Gerber & Eisenberg LLP
See profile on p.1260

**THE FIRM** This full-service firm is based in Chicago and has a broad IP practice, covering litigation, prosecution and counseling work in patent, trademark, copyright and domain name matters. Domestic and international portfolio management is also a key area of practice, and the team represents Beats Electronics in the management of its worldwide trademark and patent portfolio. Other key clients include Lettuce Entertain You Enterprises.

Sources say: "*Extremely capable, very efficient and knowledgeable.*"

KEY INDIVIDUALS The deeply experienced Robert Browne (see p.1200) focuses on patent, trademark, copyright and unfair competition litigation.

## Pattishall, McAuliffe, Newbury, Hilliard & Geraldson LLP

THE FIRM This firm is known as one of Chicago's leading IP boutiques, with a particularly impressive reputation in trademark issues. The practice covers prosecution, due diligence, brand management and international protection strategy, and litigation up to federal court level. The team also has experience in alternative dispute resolution, including mediation.

KEY INDIVIDUALS David Hilliard is "*very active in his trial practice*" and a "*very knowledgeable*" attorney. Sources particularly commend his ability in mediation.

## Other Notable Practitioners

Michael Warnecke of Perkins Coie LLP is known to be a strong player in patent litigation, representing both defendants and plaintiffs. He practices across a range of technologies, including sporting, mechanical and computer areas. With a background in electrical engineering, Dave Nelson of Quinn Emanuel Urquhart & Sullivan, LLP has a strong patent litigation practice in the electronic and software fields. Sources say he is "*becoming a bigger and bigger player in the Chicago market.*" He recently represented Motorola Mobility at the ITC against Microsoft. Mark Halligan (see p.1211) of Nixon Peabody LLP is a "*recognized expert*" in the trade secrets area. He recently acted for multiple defendants on a misappropriation of trade secrets action. John Letchinger (see p.1217) of Edwards Wildman Palmer is "*very practical, gives good advice and knows the client's business very well.*" He recently represented US Gas & Electric in defense of trademark infringement, false advertising and unfair competition claims brought by New York State Electric & Gas. Keith Parr (see p.1224) of Locke Lord LLP is a key part of the firm's Hatch-Waxman litiga-

tion practice. He also works in the biotech, life sciences, agricultural and energy sectors within IP. He recently acted for Apotex on bringing an antitrust and false advertising case against Acorda. Sidney Katz of Husch Blackwell LLP has a broad IP practice and deep experience in counseling, licensing and litigation. A particular area of his focus lies in copyright law relating to computer software and video games. Adam Kelly (see p.1214) of Loeb & Loeb LLP is a well-regarded litigator with a growing profile in the Chicago market. Clients appreciate his creative approach and his "*ability to explain complex issues in a way a layperson can understand.*" Sources are full of praise for Meredith Martin Addy of Steptoe & Johnson LLP. She is an "*outstanding*" litigator with particular experience in taking cases to the Federal Court of Appeals. She recently represented Biogen and Genentech in an appeal against a decision of noninfringement by GlaxoSmithKline. Samuel Fifer (see p.1206) of Dentons handles a range of internet-based matters, and software and licensing issues. He is also experienced in litigation and counseling surrounding the media and entertainment sectors.

# LABOR & EMPLOYMENT

Employee Benefits & Compensation p.1176

Commentary about individuals can be found under their firm's paragraph. If the firm has no paragraph (is not ranked) look at Other Notable Practitioners.

## Labor & Employment
### Leading Firms

**Band 1**
Morgan, Lewis & Bockius LLP *
Seyfarth Shaw LLP *

**Band 2**
Franczek Radelet P.C. *
Jones Day *
Meckler Bulger Tilson Marick & Pearson LLP
Winston & Strawn LLP *

**Band 3**
Jackson Lewis LLP *
Laner Muchin, Ltd *
Littler Mendelson, PC *
Ogletree, Deakins, Nash, Smoak & Stewart, PC *
Sidley Austin LLP *
Vedder Price PC *

**Band 4**
Bryan Cave LLP
FordHarrison LLP *
Holland & Knight LLP *
McGuireWoods LLP *
Neal, Gerber & Eisenberg LLP *
Proskauer Rose LLP *
Schiff Hardin LLP

\* Indicates firm with profile.
Alphabetical order within each band. Band 1 is the highest.

*The editorial is in alphabetical order by firm name.*

## Baker & McKenzie
See profile on p.435

THE FIRM While international employee benefits and executive compensation forms the core of Baker & McKenzie's practice, the group is also well versed in domestic matters. The team defended Safety-Kleen Systems in a collective action regarding the overtime payments of shift workers. The firm has high-profile clients such as American Apparel, Southwest Airlines and Ecolab. Sources say: "*They bring worldwide legal expertise to the client in an accessible manner.*"

KEY INDIVIDUALS Maura Ann McBreen (see p.1220) specializes in designing and drafting tax-qualified retirement plans and is also noted for her experience in employment and benefit issues relating to corporate transactions. Brian Wydajewski (see p.1238) focuses on equity compensation and is well versed in issues arising from cross-border data collection and transfer. Ryan Vann (see p.1236) handles arbitrations and unfair labor practice proceedings including litigating under state discrimination laws, and provides ERISA counsel.

## Bryan Cave LLP

THE FIRM The Bryan Cave team handles the full scope of labor and employment matters, leveraging the firm's national and international capabilities to offer corporate clients a seamless service. The group represented Kimberly-Clark in an age discrimination case, while other

clients include Kraft, BioScrip, and Northeastern Illinois University.

KEY INDIVIDUALS Mary Margaret Moore is experienced in the defense of class and individual actions. She undertakes a wide range of labor and employment matters including noncompete agreements and disciplinary issues. Sources consider her to be very smart and talented. Bill Wortel represents management in litigation matters. Sources comment that he has very good business acumen and makes very practical recommendations in a very clear way.

## Drinker Biddle & Reath LLP
See profile on p.2238

THE FIRM This solid benefits and compensation team is able to deal with transactional matters and is noted for its deep understanding of stock plans and compliance. The group has impressive expertise in the healthcare, manufacturing and retail industries with clients such as Providence Health & Services, Banner Health and Ulta Salon, Cosmetics & Fragrance.

Sources say: "*Not only do they have the level of expertise but they also have a truly warm and caring attitude. They're down-to-earth, friendly and they're hitting all of the marks.*"

KEY INDIVIDUALS Michael Rosenbaum handles all varieties of benefit and compensation work and has particular expertise in the design and compliance of health and welfare plans. Sources single him out for praise, with one interviewee paying tribute to his "*great thought leadership, communication and listening skills.*" Sources say that "*technical and on-the-spot*" David Wolfe is "*just impeccable.*" He

*The editorial is in alphabetical order by firm name.*

| Labor & Employment | | |
| --- | --- | --- |
| **Senior Statesmen** | | |
| Senior Statesmen: distinguished older practitioners | | |
| Brittain Max | Schiff Hardin LLP | |
| Gangemi Jr Columbus R | Winston & Strawn LLP * | |

| Leading Individuals | | |
| --- | --- | --- |
| **Band 1** | | |
| DiNardo Lawrence | Jones Day * | |
| Franczek, Jr James C | Franczek Radelet P.C. * | |
| Jackson Charles C | Morgan, Lewis & Bockius LLP * | |
| Kaplan Joel | Seyfarth Shaw LLP * | |
| Miscimarra Philip A | Morgan, Lewis & Bockius LLP * | |
| Olson Camille A | Seyfarth Shaw LLP * | |
| Piskorski Thomas | Seyfarth Shaw LLP * | |
| Stillman Nina G | Morgan, Lewis & Bockius LLP * | |
| Tilson Joseph | Meckler Bulger Tilson Marick & Pearson | |
| **Band 2** | | |
| Alamuddin Sari M | Morgan, Lewis & Bockius LLP * | |
| Bernstein Howard L | Neal, Gerber & Eisenberg LLP * | |
| Bulger Brian | Meckler Bulger Tilson Marick & Pearson | |
| Cleveland Michael G | Vedder Price PC * | |
| Costello Slovak Patricia | Schiff Hardin LLP | |
| Gagliardo Joseph M | Laner Muchin, Ltd. * | |
| Gray Michael J | Jones Day * | |
| Hartstein Barry A | Littler Mendelson, PC * | |
| Jepson Jr Edward C | Vedder Price PC * | |
| Maatman Jr Gerald L | Seyfarth Shaw LLP * | |
| Sessions Rex L | Winston & Strawn LLP * | |
| Smith Jr Arthur B | Ogletree, Deakins, Nash, Smoak & Stewart * | |
| Torres Joseph J | Winston & Strawn LLP * | |
| Yastrow Joseph | Laner Muchin, Ltd. * | |
| **Band 3** | | |
| Casey Robert P | Ogletree, Deakins, Nash, Smoak & Stewart * | |
| Catlett Steven T | Schiff Hardin LLP | |
| Dolin Kenneth R | Seyfarth Shaw LLP * | |
| Gold Brian J | Sidley Austin LLP * | |
| Golden Gerald A | Neal, Gerber & Eisenberg LLP * | |
| Mazura Adrianne | Quarles & Brady LLP (ONP) † * | |
| McLaughlin Ellen E | Seyfarth Shaw LLP * | |
| Moore Mary Margaret | Bryan Cave LLP | |
| Ritter David B | Barnes & Thornburg LLP (ONP) † * | |
| Zdravecky Amy J | Franczek Radelet P.C. * | |
| **Band 4** | | |
| Anaclerio Nicholas | Ungaretti & Harris LLP (ONP) † | |
| Boggs Craig | Perkins Coie LLP (ONP) † | |
| Doyle Linda | McDermott Will & Emery LLP * | |
| Erf Stephen | McDermott Will & Emery LLP * | |
| Goodman Marcia E | Mayer Brown LLP | |
| Karpeles Michael D | Greenberg Traurig, LLP (ONP) † * | |
| Leffert Kim A | Mayer Brown LLP | |
| McFetridge Jane | Jackson Lewis LLP * | |
| Morris Ralph A | Schiff Hardin LLP | |
| Piell Jeffrey | Quarles & Brady LLP (ONP) † * | |
| Saibert Frank J | Ungaretti & Harris LLP (ONP) † * | |
| Shapiro Mark L | Holland & Knight LLP * | |
| Sheehan Michael J | DLA Piper LLP (US) (ONP) † * | |
| Sparks Kenneth F | Vedder Price PC * | |
| Spitz Joel | McGuireWoods LLP | |
| Thorstenson Craig | FordHarrison LLP * | |
| Vyverberg Robert | Holland & Knight LLP * | |
| Wortel William J | Bryan Cave LLP | |
| **Associates to watch** | | |
| Vann Ryan | Baker & McKenzie * | |

* Indicates individual with profile.
Alphabetical order within each band. Band 1 is the highest.

has particular expertise in benefits work for tax-exempt clients and legal compliance reviews. **Howard Levine** chairs the group's employee benefits and executive compensation practice. He focuses on benefit plans including profit sharing and has a depth of experience in ESOPs.

## FordHarrison LLP
See profile on p.1108

**THE FIRM** The team at FordHarrison handles the full spectrum of labor and employment matters for management clients. The group is experienced in dealing with government agency investigations, collective bargaining, business immigration and employment-related litigation. It recently advised CNH America on union-organizing campaigns at two manufacturing facilities.

**Sources say:** *"Exceptionally high-quality work which is tailored to the specific challenges of our company."*

**KEY INDIVIDUALS Craig Thorstenson** (see p.1235) is an *"experienced litigator who works to understand the company's culture."* He specializes in employment discrimination and actions over restrictive covenants.

## Franczek Radelet P.C.
See profile on p.1247

**THE FIRM** Franczek Radelet has a solid reputation as a high-quality firm and is the first port of call for many in Chicago. The 50-strong team handles the full spectrum of labor and employment and employee benefits matter and represents publicly traded and private companies across the USA.

**Sources say:** *"We find them to be very detailed, very thorough and very methodical. You feel like they're taking a personal interest."*

**KEY INDIVIDUALS** Founding partner **James Franczek** (see p.1207) heads the firm's labor and employment practice and is hailed as *"one of the best-known names in Chicago"* by market observers. He represents public and private sector employers across a range of industries. **Amy Zdravecky** (see p.1238) is particularly noted for her expertise in labor relations matters, and is experienced in NLRB proceedings. In addition, she counsels employers on union avoidance, sexual harassment issues and other compliance matters.

## Holland & Knight LLP
See profile on p.1028

**THE FIRM** This team handles employment law and labor relations for clients such as Ameren Services, Boston Market Corporation, CVS Caremark and Exelon. The group represented Exelon Nuclear Security in a labor arbitration brought against it by a former employee claiming wrongful dismissal.

**Sources say:** *"The firm is very knowledgeable, very professional and gives outstanding customer service and results."*

**KEY INDIVIDUALS Robert Vyverberg** (see p.1236) is *"always willing to roll up his sleeves and help with whatever needs to be done,"* say sources. Observers go on to comment that he is *"low ego and high integrity, a great mix of intellect and practicality."* **Mark Shapiro** (see p.1231) focuses on contract administration and collective bargaining. He is very experienced in litigating proceedings before the NLRB and is described as *"extremely thoughtful and detail-oriented."*

## Jackson Lewis LLP
See profile on p.1982

**THE FIRM** This team has specialist skills in discrimination and harassment matters, as illustrated by its representation of the City of Chicago in a case bought by a police officer alleging civil rights violations. The group also has expertise in benefits litigation and in industries such as gaming, retail and automotive, and it has advised clients such as Karl Knauz Motors and Grand Victoria Casino.

**Sources say:** *"They take each matter personally and partner with us to resolve each dispute, misunderstanding or conflict with grace and dignity."*

**KEY INDIVIDUALS Jane McFetridge** (see p.1221) undertakes work on the gamut of labor and employment issues and has expertise in employee handbook policies. She recently successfully defended Pfizer in Schubert v Pfizer concerning allegations of age discrimination and retaliation.

## Jones Day
See profile on p.919

**THE FIRM** A force in labor and employment, Jones Day has deep trial experience and a broad practice that includes real strength in trade secrets, employee raiding and whistle-blower litigation. The group was retained by the National Railway Labor Conference in a national-level collective bargaining for multiple employers on behalf of some of the largest freight railroads in the USA. Other clients include McDonald's, Verizon, Las Vegas Sands and Abbott Laboratories.

**Sources say:** *"A wonderful firm. We needed their creativity and sophistication."*

**KEY INDIVIDUALS Lawrence DiNardo** (see p.1204) undertakes the gamut of labor and employment work and has deep trial and appellate experience. He led the team in the representation of the National Railway Labor Conference. **Michael Gray** (see p.1210) focuses his practice on the representation of corporate clients in labor and employment litigation. Sources attest that he *"quickly gets down to the nuts and bolts and gets people focused on what's*

*The editorial is in alphabetical order by firm name.*

## Labor & Employment: Employee Benefits & Compensation
### Leading Firms

**Band 1**

Drinker Biddle & Reath LLP *
McDermott Will & Emery LLP *
Winston & Strawn LLP *

**Band 2**

Katten Muchin Rosenman LLP *
Mayer Brown LLP *
Morgan, Lewis & Bockius LLP *
Seyfarth Shaw LLP *
Sidley Austin LLP *
Vedder Price PC *

**Band 3**

Baker & McKenzie *
Dentons *
McGuireWoods LLP *
Neal, Gerber & Eisenberg LLP *

*important – his approach is unique and he gets exceptional results."*

## Katten Muchin Rosenman LLP
See profile on p.1253

**THE FIRM** Katten Muchin Rosenman has a real strength in employee benefit and executive compensation and is particularly well known for its strength in ERISA and ESOP matters. The team advised Cardinal Health on matters pertaining to the compliance, governance and risk mitigation of ERISA plans. An impressive client roster also includes such prominent names as Ball Corporation, RP Donnelley, Verde Holdings and North Star Trust.

**Sources say:** *"Knowledgeable on the subject, great service, and quality relationships with the client."*

**KEY INDIVIDUALS Gregory Brown** is an expert in all matters pertaining to ERISA and ESOP, including litigation. Sources are appreciative of his skill and recognize him as *"one of the leading ESOP lawyers in the state,"* with one impressed interviewee naming him *"the most knowledgeable person I know across the full ERISA spectrum."*

## Laner Muchin, Ltd
See profile on p.1255

**THE FIRM** This firm focuses on the representation of employers in labor and employment matters concerning both public and private companies. The team's client roster spans a range of sectors and includes educational institutions, professional sports teams and restaurant chains.

**Sources say:** *"Their subject matter expertise and experience has been invaluable."*

**KEY INDIVIDUALS Joseph Gagliardo** (see p.1208) chairs the firm's litigation department and also acts as an arbitrator in employment disputes. Sources are particularly appreciative of the in-depth knowledge that he brings to his broad practice. **Joseph Yastrow** (see p.1238) has expertise in employment practices liability insurance, arbitrations and mediations. Sources say quite simply that he is *"tremendous."*

## Labor & Employment: Employee Benefits & Compensation
### Senior Statesmen

| Senior Statesmen: distinguished older practitioners | |
| --- | --- |
| Kaplan Jared | McDermott Will & Emery LLP * |

### Leading Individuals

| Star individuals | |
| --- | --- |
| Baker Pamela | Dentons * |

| Band 1 | |
| --- | --- |
| Brown Gregory | Katten Muchin Rosenman LLP |
| Daley Susan J | Perkins Coie LLP (ONP) † |
| Krueger Herbert W | Mayer Brown LLP |
| Melbinger Michael S | Winston & Strawn LLP * |
| Rosenbaum Michael D | Drinker Biddle & Reath LLP |
| Ryan Priscilla E | Sidley Austin LLP * |
| Stucker Robert J | Vedder Price PC * |
| Weisberg Mark S | Winston & Strawn LLP * |
| Wolfe David L | Drinker Biddle & Reath LLP |

| Band 2 | |
| --- | --- |
| Adams Joe | McDermott Will & Emery LLP * |
| Bakker Jeffrey J | Neal, Gerber & Eisenberg LLP * |
| Cain Patricia S | Neal, Gerber & Eisenberg LLP * |
| Dickstein Beth | Sidley Austin LLP * |
| Hoffman Debra B | Mayer Brown LLP |
| Hood Vicki V | Kirkland & Ellis LLP (ONP) † * |
| Klein Leslie A | Greenberg Traurig LLP (ONP) † * |
| Levine Howard J | Drinker Biddle & Reath LLP |
| McBreen Maura Ann | Baker & McKenzie * |
| Occhino Lennine | Mayer Brown LLP |
| Ross Nancy | McDermott Will & Emery LLP |
| Shepherd Stewart R | Sidley Austin LLP * |
| Wolf Charles B | Vedder Price PC * |

| Band 3 | |
| --- | --- |
| Ackerman David | Morgan, Lewis & Bockius LLP * |
| Andrioff Joni | Littler Mendelson, PC * |
| Compernolle Paul | McDermott Will & Emery LLP * |
| Desmond Thomas P | Vedder Price PC * |
| Kreindler Marla | Morgan, Lewis & Bockius LLP * |
| Simonsen Karen | McDermott Will & Emery LLP * |
| Sirus Richard A | Greenberg Traurig, LLP (ONP) † * |
| Starr Kelly A | Vedder Price PC * |

| Up-and-coming individuals | |
| --- | --- |
| Struve Robin | Latham & Watkins LLP (ONP) † |
| Wydajewski Brian | Baker & McKenzie * |

*\* Indicates firm / individual with profile.*
*Alphabetical order within each band. Band 1 is the highest.*

## Littler Mendelson, PC
See profile on p.688

**THE FIRM** Littler Mendelson's labor and employment group is comprised of 41 lawyers who are well supported by the firm's global network. The team advises clients in the insurance industry such as Nationwide Mutual Insurance, which it recently successfully represented in a class action trial. A further work highlight saw the group represent Whirlpool in a disability discrimination claim.

**Sources say:** *"The team is politically astute, cost-effective and reliable."*

**KEY INDIVIDUALS Barry Hartstein** (see p.1211) represents clients across a wide range of industries and has deep experience of handling individual, class and collective actions. **Joni Andrioff** (see p.1197) *"can take all the technical facts and come to a solution that works,"* say sources. Interviewees relate that her accounting experience enables her to bring a new perspective to benefits and compensation matters.

## Mayer Brown LLP
See profile on p.1257

**THE FIRM** The Mayer Brown employee benefits and executive compensation offering is routinely trusted by large corporate entities on the full range of compliance counseling and transactional work. The group advised Caterpillar on issues arising from its acquisition of, and subsequent integration with, Bucyrus International. Other clients include UBS Global Asset Management, Bristol-Myers Squibb, DuPont Capital Management and Grosvenor Capital Management.

**Sources say:** *"Thorough yet practical, timely, responsive and very knowledgeable."*

**KEY INDIVIDUALS Marcia Goodman** handles the full range of employment matters, including representing employers before the EEOC, NLRB and DOL. Clients comment favorably that *"her advice is practical and she tailors her work to the situation."* **Kim Leffert** is a talented employment litigator with a developing expertise in electronic discovery matters. Market observers comment that she *"excels at being prepared"* and praise her good communication skills. **Herbert Krueger**'s broad practice includes advising on executive compensation, ERISA fiduciary rules and prohibited transaction exemptions. Sources commend him for his exceptional work ethic. **Lennine Occhino** focuses solely on pension investment and ERISA fiduciary matters and is particularly experienced in the representation of clients in matters relating to the DOL. While **Debra Hoffman**'s practice includes the gamut of ERISA matters, she has a particular focus on benefits matters emanating from corporate transactions. Clients single her out for praise, commenting that she is able to make complex issues understandable and that she is *"very levelheaded"* and provides *"honest, straightforward and practical legal advice."*

## McDermott Will & Emery LLP
See profile on p.1258

**THE FIRM** This sizable team has strength and depth in the gamut of labor and employment matters, including an established employee benefits and executive compensation practice group. The group's strength in private equity matters saw it advise Merrick Ventures on the employment matters pertaining to its acquisition of Sun-Times Media Holdings. Sources are also appreciative of the group's expertise in ERISA matters, which saw it victoriously defend Northrop Grumman in a landmark class action suit. Clients include Kaiser Aluminum, Liberty Mutual, BMO Harris Bank and Schneider Electric.

**Sources say:** *"They know what the issues are and can give you feedback immediately."* *"Outstanding performance across all fronts. Industry experts and very professional."*

*The editorial is in alphabetical order by firm name.*

**KEY INDIVIDUALS Stephen Erf** (see p.1206) handles a wide range of matters relating to civil rights and labor and employment, and has particular experience advising on the healthcare sector. He is commended by sources for the efficiency of his work and the trust that he engenders in his clients. *"One to watch,"* **Joe Adams** (see p.1196) is fast establishing a reputation for excellence among peers and clients alike. He undertakes work on executive and incentive compensation programs including 401(k) and ESOPs as well as transaction-related labor and employment issues. **Nancy Ross** is a *"go-to person for ERISA litigation"* according to impressed sources. In addition to her expertise in ERISA matters she also handles class action litigation. Sources comment that **Paul Compernolle** (see p.1202) *"has a knack for breaking down complex issues and explaining them in plain English."* Areas of expertise include ESOPs and 401(k). **Karen Simonsen** (see p.1231) has expertise in fiduciary matters including the design and compliance of plans and policies. She heads the Chicago employee benefits and executive compensation team. **Jared Kaplan** (see p.1214) is considered *"the guru of the stock ownership Bar,"* according to one impressed source. He has the respect of the market and observers comment that he *"can still work his magic: he's seen everything and done everything."* **Linda Doyle** (see p.1205) handles all manner of employment litigation and is singled out by sources who praise her logical approach to an issue, coherent explanation and personable approach.

## McGuireWoods LLP
See profile on p.2519

**THE FIRM** This team covers the full spectrum of labor and employment law, and has notably handled discrimination matters for clients such as Manpower, AT&T and Philips. In addition, the group offers expertise in administrative proceedings, internal investigations and executive compensation. Sources hail the group's litigation skills and comment favorably on its responsiveness.

**Sources say:** *"The main driver for choosing them was their combination of high-quality legal work and affordable rates. The firm is extremely responsive and is full of great lawyers."*
**KEY INDIVIDUALS** The *"practical and knowledgeable"* **Joel Spitz** chairs the firm's labor and employment practice. He has expertise in family medical leave, sexual harassment claims and the representation of clients in investigations conducted by the EEOC.

## Meckler Bulger Tilson Marick & Pearson LLP

**THE FIRM** This boutique firm undertakes all types of labor and employment issues for public, private, educational and nonprofit entities. While it places an emphasis on counseling to avoid litigation, the firm also has deep experience representing employers in individual and class actions on a nationwide basis.

**Sources say:** *"Excellent lawyers with a great understanding of our business."*
**KEY INDIVIDUALS** **Joseph Tilson** handles large, complex labor and employment litigation and arbitration, where he represents employers. He also specializes in large

wage and hour class actions. Sources comment that he is *"a great lawyer who is just very well respected."* **Brian Bulger** undertakes work on a broad range of labor and employment concerns including training and counseling.

## Morgan, Lewis & Bockius LLP
See profile on p.2246

**THE FIRM** Morgan Lewis is at the vanguard of labor and employment matters in Illinois and undertakes a wide range of work for companies in Illinois and nationwide. The group is known for its handling of large, complex matters, a focus that saw it defend GreatBanc Trust in a complex ERISA class action. The team has also defended Walgreens against class claims of national origin discrimination. An impressive client roster also includes Comcast, Deere & Company, The Gap and Hewlett-Packard.

**Sources say:** *"They are detail-oriented, conscientious, available, and have high standards of integrity."*
**KEY INDIVIDUALS Charles Jackson** (see p.339) wins praise from observers for his client-focused work. He centers his practice around class action and ERISA litigation. Sources attest that he *"does a very good job of interacting with the other side and is very effective."* **Philip Miscimarra** (see p.1222) specializes in employment litigation and traditional labor issues. He recently acted for the Coalition for a Democratic Workplace and the US Chamber of Commerce on a successful challenge to new rules introduced by the NLRB. Sources consider **Nina Stillman** (see p.1234) to be *"a truly exceptional attorney who consistently provides top-notch, outstanding and efficient legal services."* Sources go on to comment that *"it is a pleasure to work with her on legal matters."* Areas of focus include litigation and compliance counseling relating to discrimination and occupational safety. Observers are full of praise for **Sari Alamuddin** (see p.1196), with one satisfied client relating that he *"works hard to understand the business and its needs."* He handles work involving class actions and multiplaintiff cases. *"Dynamic and entrepreneurial"* **David Ackerman** (see p.1196) is a recognized expert on all matters pertaining to ESOPs. Recent highlights include representing Appleton Papers in ESOP matters relating to its proposed merger with Hicks Acquisition Company II. **Marla Kreindler** (see p.1216) specializes in tax-qualified retirement plans and the management and investment of employee benefit plan assets. Clients enthuse that she is *"a brilliant thinker."*

## Neal, Gerber & Eisenberg LLP
See profile on p.1260

**THE FIRM** Neal, Gerber & Eisenberg provides advice to clients such as Jack Cooper Transport and Kronos Foods on a diverse range of matters including benefit plans, wage and hour and M&A. The team is known and respected for its good judgment and clear communication.

**Sources say:** *"The people we work with at the firm more than live up to their reputation for technical competency, advocacy and dedication to client service."*
**KEY INDIVIDUALS Howard Bernstein's** (see p.1198) areas of expertise include discrimination, unfair labor practice and injunction proceedings. He has *"a rare talent*

*to blend the common associations of the law"* according to clients, who go on to comment that *"you feel like you're bringing in a heavyweight."* The *"completely unflappable"* **Gerald Golden** (see p.1209) is known for his *"ability to anticipate situations,"* say sources. His practice includes handling noncompetition and nonsolicitation issues as well as collective bargaining. The *"thorough and well-informed"* **Jeffrey Bakker** (see p.1197) handles employee benefits and executive compensation matters and has *"an exceptional knack for formulating benefit plans and compensation packages that work for both the employer and the employee."* **Patricia Cain** (see p.1200) is *"really effective in understanding the right level of approach,"* say sources. She specializes in employee benefits and has expertise in pension and healthcare plans, from inception through to administration.

## Ogletree, Deakins, Nash, Smoak & Stewart, PC
See profile on p.1110

**THE FIRM** The Chicago office of this national employment boutique has a recognized expertise in labor and employment matters, as evidenced by its long-term role as advisers to Hillshire Brands. The team is often noted for its strength in labor relations, and has an impressive depth of experience in handling collective bargaining negotiations for clients in the construction industry. Other clients include JPMorgan Chase, Hospira and Best Buy Stores.

**Sources say:** *"They do a very good job of keeping abreast of the law and pending legislation that may affect employers."*
**KEY INDIVIDUALS Arthur Smith** (see p.1232) focuses his practice on the representation of management from a broad section of industries in labor and employment issues. He also specializes in acting as counsel on collective bargaining negotiations in regulated industries. **Robert Casey** (see p.1201) represents employers in the steel, construction and utilities sectors. Admiring interviewees refer to his *"knowledge, experience, promptness and quality."*

## Proskauer Rose LLP
See profile on p.2001

**THE FIRM** Proskauer Rose undertakes a broad range of labor and employment work and offers specialties in single-plaintiff disputes, class action disputes and trade secret protection. Key work mandates have seen the team represent Lorillard Tobacco in a nationwide FLSA collective action. Clients in the firm's portfolio include Coca-Cola, McDonald's, Forest River, Sientra and Credit Suisse Securities.

**Sources say:** *"I recommend them all the time, without hesitation."*
**KEY INDIVIDUALS Nigel Telman** is a key contact.

## Schiff Hardin LLP

**THE FIRM** This group undertakes work for both private and public companies on the gamut of labor and employment and benefits matters. Sources are appreciative of the firm's interest and commitment to achieving clients' goals.
**Sources say:** *"They provide a wide range of expertise and are always diligent in their work."*

*The editorial is in alphabetical order by firm name.*

**KEY INDIVIDUALS Patricia Costello Slovak** *"provides no-nonsense yet expert advice on a variety of employment and HR issues,"* say sources. She handles labor and employment matters and is praised by sources for her *"deep knowledge, wide-ranging experience and responsiveness."* **Ralph Morris** focuses his practice on advising employers on measures to avoid harassment issues. He is also experienced in the mediation and arbitration of employment issues. **Max Brittain** has expertise representing management before the NLRB and EEOC as well as state and federal agencies. He has handled agency charges for Ameristar Casino and the American Academy of Pediatrics. **Steven Catlett** handles the defense of class action and multiparty litigation in trade secrets claims as well as ERISA, wage and hour and employment matters.

## Seyfarth Shaw LLP
See profile on p.1262

**THE FIRM** This firm has one of the foremost labor and employment practices in Illinois, with expertise that spans the spectrum of matters. The team has undertaken a number of high-profile cases including representing Kaplan Higher Education in a landmark case against the EEOC and its credit practices. Sources are particularly appreciative of the group's expertise in wage and hour litigation. The group's client portfolio includes companies of the caliber of Yum! Brands, United Airlines, Wrigley and Caterpillar.

**Sources say:** *"When it comes to litigation they're the best I've seen: very aggressive and constantly thinking strategically."*

**KEY INDIVIDUALS Joel Kaplan** (see p.1214) undertakes traditional labor and employment work for management bodies and has deep litigation experience. Recent matters include the successful defense of Danaher in an FLSA overtime action. **Camille Olson** (see p.1224) is enthusiastically singled out by market sources for her experience in litigation and focus on complex labor and employment cases. She recently won plaudits for her authoritative handling of two sexual harassment litigation matters on behalf of Aaron's Inc. **Thomas Piskorski** (see p.1225) is a *"tremendous practitioner"* with *"an incredible amount of integrity,"* according to impressed sources. He handles labor and employment matters for management clients before both state and federal courts. Research reveals that **Gerald Maatman** (see p.1219) is *"a compelling presence in the courtroom,"* with a focus on the defense of employers facing wage and hour and discrimination class actions and other lawsuits. **Kenneth Dolin** (see p.1204) has deep experience in traditional labor and employment matters, which saw him advise Caesars Entertainment on a union election matter. He is also very experienced in NLRB cases. **Ellen McLaughlin** (see p.1221) is *"an invaluable resource"* for management clients. Her practice covers the gamut of labor and employment matters and she is noted for her experience in helping clients to avoid litigation.

## Sidley Austin LLP
See profile on p.1264

**THE FIRM** This respected international firm covers a full range of employment, employee benefits and executive compensation matters. It frequently advises clients on issues arising from ESOPs during acquisitions and LBOs. This strength saw the team advise Fortune Brands and its spin-off venture Fortune Brands Home & Security on the implementation of their respective compensation and benefit plans after the spin-off. The team's client roster includes AT&T, Booz Allen Hamilton, eBay and The ServiceMaster Company.

**KEY INDIVIDUALS Priscilla Ryan** (see p.1229) is praised by market observers for her depth of knowledge and client relationship skills. She is noted for her expertise in ERISA litigation and executive compensation. **Stewart Shepherd** (see p.1231) focuses on executive compensation and benefits matters arising from M&A. He has a specialty in transactions prohibited by ERISA and matters relating to committees of 401(k) plans. **Beth Dickstein** (see p.1204) undertakes work on fiduciary matters, frequently advising clients in relation to investment plans and compensation plans. **Brian Gold** (see p.1209) heads the Chicago labor and employment team and handles a broad range of matters including collective bargaining and industrial labor litigation.

## Vedder Price PC
See profile on p.1266

**THE FIRM** The Vedder Price team is particularly focused on equal opportunity law and is known for its solid reputation in executive compensation matters. The team has deep experience working with large public and private companies, as evidenced by a client list which includes Resurrection Health Care, Exel, US Foodservice and Follett. A key matter for the team saw it advise US Foodservice on all aspects of a strike organized by a local union and the subsequent arbitration demands and NLRB charges.

**Sources say:** *"They bring business insights as well as sound legal advice to the table."*

**KEY INDIVIDUALS Robert Stucker** (see p.1234) chairs the executive compensation group and is highly experienced in advising on employment arrangements for CEOs; he advises corporations and financial institutions on a regular basis. Sources remark that his *"strong business and legal knowledge sets him apart."* **Michael Cleveland** (see p.1202) centers his practice on defending employers in employment litigation cases. The representation of employers before administrative agencies is also a noted area of expertise. **Edward Jepson** (see p.1213) contributes over 30 years' experience in labor and employment matters and has a recognized expertise in age discrimination issues. **Charles Wolf** (see p.1237) represents employers and multiple employer funds across a broad range of industries. He also specializes in arbitration proceedings and the design and administration of employee benefit plans. **Thomas Desmond** (see p.1204) cochairs the executive compensation group. He focuses on executive compensation matters affecting corporations and financial institutions. **Kenneth Sparks** (see p.1233) takes a *"no-nonsense approach to providing thorough legal advice,"* according to sources. He has expertise in collective bargaining and union organizing, including matters arising from strikes. **Kelly Starr** (see

p.1234) handles work across the spectrum of employee benefits and has a deep knowledge of her practice. Market observers go on to praise her client service ethic.

## Winston & Strawn LLP
See profile on p.1267

**THE FIRM** Winston & Strawn has a formidable presence in the Illinois employee benefits and executive compensation world. It is noted for its strong focus on executive compensation matters, regularly advising corporation, boards of directors and partnerships such as the Chicago Mercantile Exchange and Financial Services Roundtable. In addition to advising clients on benefits programs it is well placed to advise on problems faced due to ERISA class actions. Other clients include Lear Corporation, FreightCar America, Cantor Fitzgerald and CBOE Holdings.

**Sources say:** *"They handle extraordinarily complex matters with diligence, great competence and creativity."*

**KEY INDIVIDUALS Michael Melbinger** (see p.1222) is global head of the firm's employee benefits and executive compensation practice. He is noted for his exceptional responsiveness and subject matter expertise, while one interviewee lauds his *"ability to think past the tried solutions to meet out-of-the-ordinary needs."* **Mark Weisberg** (see p.1237) handles employee benefit and compensation work for employers such as Lear Corporation, Grant Thornton and Chicago Mercantile Exchange. **Rex Sessions** (see p.1231) handles the gamut of labor and employment matters and has represented a number of high-profile fashion brands such as Marc Jacobs International and LVMH. He recently defended American Airlines in an employment class action alleging age discrimination. **Joseph Torres** (see p.1235) is hailed by clients as a *"very responsive, astute, practical and knowledgeable"* attorney. He has handled a number of automobile cases including labor negotiations between Caterpillar and the International Association of Machinists. **Columbus Gangemi** (see p.1208) contributes deep experience in labor and employment matters to the firm's practice and has advised on domestic and international employment matters.

## Other Notable Practitioners

**Vicki Hood** (see p.1212) of Kirkland & Ellis LLP focuses on matters relating to the reduction and discharge of employee benefits liabilities. She is *"super-responsive"* and very knowledgeable, according to sources. **Susan Daley** of Perkins Coie LLP is knowledgeable in securities, benefits and compensation issues. Clients consider her to be one of the strongest executive compensation attorneys in the country. She handles benefits and compensation matters for clients like Ventas. **Craig Boggs** of Perkins Coie LLP handles restrictive covenants, whistle-blower cases and collective bargaining. **Adrianne Mazura** (see p.1220) of Quarles & Brady LLP is highly thought of by peers for her broad labor and employment practice. **Jeff Piell** (see p.1225) of Quarles & Brady LLP is *"very customer-oriented, responsive, proactive, technically strong and a great business partner,"* sources say. He handles a wide range of labor and

*The editorial is in alphabetical order by firm name.*

employment issues such as workforce reductions, social media and employment contracts. **Michael Sheehan** (see p.1231) of DLA Piper LLP (US) is a labor and employment specialist and *"a strategic thinker, really able to think through how to handle a matter and come up with the right solution for the company,"* say sources. **Nicholas Anaclerio** of Ungaretti & Harris LLP focuses on employment litigation. Clients comment that he *"shows just the right amount of aggression to force and gain position against stiff adversaries."* **Frank Saibert** (see p.1229) of Ungaretti & Harris LLP is known for his *"incredible responsiveness and practicality."* He focuses his practice on NLRB proceedings, discrimination matters and backpay compliance. Sources go on to comment that he is a *"tenacious litigator."* **Robin Struve** of Latham & Watkins LLP focuses on the application of tax, ERISA and securities laws to benefit and compensation plans and matters. Sources hail her creative approach. **Leslie Klein** (see p.1215) of Greenberg Traurig LLP has a broad benefit and compensation practice and *"knows all the underlying law backwards and forwards."* Sources comment that his *"advice is practical. He understands our plans and he remembers."* **Richard Sirus** (see p.1232) of Greenberg Traurig, LLP is an employee benefits and executive compensation specialist. Clients comment that he is *"always available, he is responsive to our needs and makes sure all aspects of the issue are understood and in our best interests."* **Michael Karpeles** (see p.1214) of Greenberg Traurig, LLP defends employers in a plethora of employment issues including sexual harassment, trade secrets and whistle-blower matters. **David Ritter** (see p.1227) of Barnes & Thornburg LLP provides *"practical advice that is directly on point"* on matters such as restrictive covenants, harassment claims and trade secrets. He is also an expert in the representation of clients before governmental agencies, and in contract and statutory employee claims.

# LITIGATION

White-Collar Crime & Government Investigations p.1181

Commentary about individuals can be found under their firm's paragraph. If the firm has no paragraph (is not ranked) look at Other Notable Practitioners.

| Litigation: General Commercial |
| --- |
| **Leading Firms** |
| **Band 1** |
| Bartlit Beck Herman Palenchar & Scott LLP |
| Jenner & Block LLP * |
| Kirkland & Ellis LLP * |
| Sidley Austin LLP * |
| Winston & Strawn LLP * |
| **Band 2** |
| Jones Day * |
| Mayer Brown LLP * |
| **Band 3** |
| Latham & Watkins LLP * |
| McDermott Will & Emery LLP * |
| Skadden, Arps, Slate, Meagher & Flom LLP & Affiliates * |
| **Band 4** |
| Baker & McKenzie * |
| Foley & Lardner LLP * |
| Goldberg Kohn Ltd * |
| Goldman Ismail Tomaselli Brennan & Baum LLP |
| Katten Muchin Rosenman LLP * |
| Neal, Gerber & Eisenberg LLP * |
| Schiff Hardin LLP |
| Schopf & Weiss LLP * |
| **Band 5** |
| Dentons * |
| DLA Piper LLP (US) * |
| Drinker Biddle & Reath LLP * |
| Edwards Wildman Palmer * |
| Freeborn & Peters LLP * |
| McGuireWoods LLP * |
| Reed Smith LLP * |
| Thompson Coburn LLP |

*\* Indicates firm with profile.*
*Alphabetical order within each band. Band 1 is the highest.*

*The editorial is in alphabetical order by firm name.*

## Baker & McKenzie
See profile on p.435

**THE FIRM** The Chicago office of Baker & McKenzie hosts a 40-strong litigation team that covers the full spectrum of litigation concerns. Recent highlights include the representation of Fellowes in a dispute concerning the payment of purchase orders placed with a Chinese manufacturer. The group also defended Pension Consulting Alliance in a $98 million lawsuit concerning breach of fiduciary duty. Other clients in the firm's portfolio include John Crane and Hallstar.
**Sources say:** *"They are extremely collaborative and don't let ego get in the way."*
**KEY INDIVIDUALS Robert Kent** is *"a true gentleman and a real pleasure to work with,"* according to clients. He focuses his practice on compliance, internal investigations and civil and criminal litigation.

## Bartlit Beck Herman Palenchar & Scott LLP
**THE FIRM** The Bartlit Beck litigation team offers clients a recognized degree of excellence in complex commercial litigation, mass tort, class actions and product liability. Clients include RealNetworks, Samsung Electronics and Hewlett-Packard.
**KEY INDIVIDUALS Philip Beck** is a simply outstanding attorney according to sources. He is an expert in product liability cases, mass torts and financial cases, while observers praise his detailed understanding of various areas of the law and excellent oral advocacy skills. **Adam Hoeflich** represents clients in complex, multidistrict litigation. Areas of excellence include matters involving pharmaceutical withdrawals, mass torts and class actions. Sources single **Fred Bartlit** out as a leading figure in the market and hold him in extremely high regard for his widespread experience. Clients include Tyco, Bayer and Tessera.

## Cotsirilos Tighe & Streicker Ltd
**THE FIRM** This established Chicago boutique is known for its strength in white-collar matters. The team focuses on defending individuals and corporations and has experience in high-profile cases involving RICO charges, securities fraud, corruption and environmental regulations.
**KEY INDIVIDUALS** According to sources **James Streicker** is *"extremely good at counseling clients about whether or not to go to trial."* His broad white-collar practice ranges from SEC investigations through to antitrust and government fraud. **Terence Campbell** has impressed peers with his skill in white-collar litigation. He handles cases including bid rigging, drug offenses, perjury and conspiracy. **Theodore Poulos** is singled out by sources for his deep experience. He is very experienced in cases involving kickbacks, drug offenses and bribery charges in federal courts as well as SEC investigations.

## Dentons
See profile on p.449

**THE FIRM** This firm's litigation team has an established reputation for its work in securities litigation, insurance litigation and consumer class action defense. In a recent key mandate the team represented MetLife in a nationwide class action. Sources are particularly appreciative of the team's creative approach toward cases.
**Sources say:** *"Excellent writing, advocacy skills, diligence and client responsiveness."*
**KEY INDIVIDUALS** Roger Heidenreich is head of the US litigation and arbitration practice and a key contact.

## DLA Piper LLP (US)
See profile on p.1971

**THE FIRM** DLA Piper's Chicago office offers a litigation practice that covers all aspects of commercial litigation. Areas of excellence include product liability, class action litigation and insurance litigation. Sources are particularly appreciative of the team's ability to deal with complex commercial litigation and their responsiveness.

The editorial is in alphabetical order by firm name.

## Litigation: General Commercial
### Senior Statesmen
**Senior Statesmen:** distinguished older practitioners

| | | |
|---|---|---|
| Bartlit Jr Fred | Bartlit Beck Herman Palenchar & Scott LLP | |
| Sullivan Thomas P | Jenner & Block LLP * | |

### Leading Individuals

**Star individuals**

| | |
|---|---|
| Webb Dan K | Winston & Strawn LLP * |

**Band 1**

| | |
|---|---|
| Beck Philip | Bartlit Beck Herman Palenchar & Scott LLP |
| Connelly Vincent J | Mayer Brown LLP |
| Filip Mark | Kirkland & Ellis LLP * |
| Godfrey Richard C | Kirkland & Ellis LLP * |
| Reidy Daniel E | Jones Day * |
| Valukas Anton R | Jenner & Block LLP * |

**Band 2**

| | |
|---|---|
| Anderson Kimball R | Winston & Strawn LLP * |
| Berkowitz Sean M | Latham & Watkins LLP |
| Carlson Walter C | Sidley Austin LLP * |
| Conlon William | Sidley Austin LLP * |
| Dockterman Michael | Edwards Wildman Palmer * |
| Hickey Jr John T | Kirkland & Ellis LLP * |
| Kopecky Robert J | Kirkland & Ellis LLP * |
| Nicklin Emily | Kirkland & Ellis LLP * |
| Odorizzi Michele L | Mayer Brown LLP |
| Pope Michael | McDermott Will & Emery LLP * |
| Rosenbloom David | McDermott Will & Emery LLP * |
| Salpeter Alan N | Kaye Scholer LLP (ONP)† * |
| Shapiro Stephen M | Mayer Brown LLP |
| Stone Jeffrey E | McDermott Will & Emery LLP * |

**Band 3**

| | |
|---|---|
| Berberian H Nicholas | Neal, Gerber & Eisenberg LLP * |
| Bradford David | Jenner & Block LLP * |
| Braun Bruce R | Winston & Strawn LLP * |
| Douglas Charles W | Sidley Austin LLP * |
| Durkin Thomas M | Mayer Brown LLP |
| Fisher Scott J | Neal, Gerber & Eisenberg LLP * |
| Graham David F | Sidley Austin LLP * |

| | |
|---|---|
| Ismail Tarek | Goldman Ismail Tomaselli Brennan & Baum |
| Kipp Matthew R | Skadden, Arps, Slate, Meagher & Flom * |
| Levinson Michael | Seyfarth Shaw LLP (ONP)† |
| Nash Gordon B | Drinker Biddle & Reath LLP * |
| Novack Stephen | Novack and Macey LLP (ONP)† |
| Sklarsky Charles B | Jenner & Block LLP * |
| Sperling Robert Y | Winston & Strawn LLP * |
| Stoll R Ryan | Skadden, Arps, Slate, Meagher & Flom * |
| Zarov Herbert L | Mayer Brown LLP |

**Band 4**

| | |
|---|---|
| Alberts Barry S | Schiff Hardin LLP |
| Bishop Martin | Foley & Lardner LLP |
| Chefitz Joel | McDermott Will & Emery LLP * |
| Cimino Jr Thomas P | Vedder Price PC (ONP)† * |
| Collins Joseph | DLA Piper LLP (US) * |
| Colman Jeffrey D | Jenner & Block LLP * |
| Daly James R | Jones Day * |
| Ferguson James R | Mayer Brown LLP |
| Hartsell David | McGuireWoods LLP |
| Hoeflich Adam | Bartlit Beck Herman Palenchar & Scott LLP |
| Jacobs Caryn | Winston & Strawn LLP * |
| Kistenbroker David H | Dechert LLP (ONP) * |
| Rabinowitz Mark A | Cozen O'Connor (ONP)† * |
| Rowden Todd | Thompson Coburn LLP |
| Schopf William G | Schopf & Weiss LLP * |
| Smylie Sallie G | Kirkland & Ellis LLP * |
| Stein Marta | McGuireWoods LLP |
| Tabacchi Tina M | Jones Day * |
| Trela Jr Constantine L | Sidley Austin LLP * |
| Weiss Steven A | Schopf & Weiss LLP * |

**Up-and-coming individuals**

| | |
|---|---|
| Quinn Jonathan | Reed Smith LLP |

\* Indicates individual with profile.
Alphabetical order within each band. Band 1 is the highest.

Sources say: *"They worked extremely hard under difficult conditions and obtained good results."*
**KEY INDIVIDUALS** Joseph Collins (see p.1202) handles matters involving class actions, securities and insurance coverage in his commercial litigation practice.

### Drinker Biddle & Reath LLP
See profile on p.2238
**THE FIRM** This firm's commercial litigation practice handles matters including securities fraud and mass tort claims. Recent matters include the representation of Standard Motor Products in a number of cases arising from exposure to products containing asbestos. Other key clients include Johnson & Johnson, Deloitte, Unicom Investment Bank and Horizon Wind Energy.
Sources say: *"Bright and accomplished attorneys who consistently provide first-rate client service."*
**KEY INDIVIDUALS** Gordon Nash (see p.1223) is noted for his *"high quality"* and *"high reputation."* He is experi-

enced at trial and appellate level in cases concerning securities and general commercial litigation.

### Edwards Wildman Palmer
See profile on p.1520
**THE FIRM** This firm represents large clients such as Credit Suisse, KeyCorp and Motorola in a host of commercial litigation matters. In a key mandate the team represented Toys R Us in a large class action under the Fair and Accurate Credit Transactions Act.
Sources say: *"The team was excellent. They were highly responsive and available whenever needed."*
**KEY INDIVIDUALS** Michael Dockterman (see p.1204) has a broad litigation practice that covers IP, environmental contracts and antitrust. According to one impressed interviewee, *"he's smarter than most people I know. He delivers exactly what I need."*

### Foley & Lardner LLP
See profile on p.2588
**THE FIRM** Foley & Lardner handles big-ticket litigation matters on a state and federal level. Key mandates include the multidistrict defense of JTH Tax in a number of putative class actions. Other clients include WellPoint, LNR Partners, Chinese Yellow Pages and JPMorgan Chase.
Sources say: *"The firm is always quick to give practical advice and does not over-lawyer a file."*
**KEY INDIVIDUALS** The *"consistently professional"* Martin Bishop focuses his practice on complex commercial litigation and has particular expertise in class actions and injunctive relief proceedings.

### Freeborn & Peters LLP
See profile on p.1248
**THE FIRM** This team handles complex commercial litigation matters, frequently involving multijurisdictional disputes. It recently represented Prism Development Corporation to seek primary injunctive relief following its development of the Ritz Carlton Condominium Residences in Chicago. Other clients include Northern Trust and Menard.
Sources say: *"Outstanding. The lawyers pay attention to detail and 'think like a business' to search for solutions."*
**KEY INDIVIDUALS** Joseph Fogel and Todd Ohlms head the litigation practice.

### Goldberg Kohn Ltd
See profile on p.1249
**THE FIRM** The team at Goldberg Kohn handles general commercial litigation matters and has particular expertise in midmarket financial litigation across the USA. Clients include Sun-Times Media, Abbott Laboratories, The University of Chicago and Fender Musical Instruments.
**KEY INDIVIDUALS** Litigation group chair Frederic Klein is a key contact.

### Goldman Ismail Tomaselli Brennan & Baum LLP
**THE FIRM** This Chicago litigation boutique has extensive trial experience in a range of areas including mass tort matters and headline commercial litigation. The team represents a number of Fortune 500 clients such as Bayer HealthCare, Pfizer and Merck. The team acted as lead counsel for Tickets.com, a subsidiary of Major League Baseball Advanced Media, in the defense of a patent infringement action.
Sources say: *"They don't miss a thing. They complement each other's strengths and have different expertise that they put together."*
**KEY INDIVIDUALS** Tarek Ismail is singled out by clients for his honesty and accessibility. He specializes in big-ticket litigation for large US corporations and has acted as lead trial counsel for Merck in the first federal trial of a number of product liability suits.

### Jenner & Block LLP
See profile on p.1252
**THE FIRM** This talented group has an exceptional reputation in the general commercial litigation and white-collar

*The editorial is in alphabetical order by firm name.*

## Litigation: White-Collar Crime & Government Investigations
### Leading Firms

**Band 1**
Jenner & Block LLP *
Stetler, Duffy & Rotert Ltd

**Band 2**
Cotsirilos Tighe & Streicker Ltd
Jones Day *
Katten Muchin Rosenman LLP *
Latham & Watkins LLP *
Mayer Brown LLP *
McDermott Will & Emery LLP *
Perkins Coie LLP
Schiff Hardin LLP
Sidley Austin LLP *
Skadden, Arps, Slate, Meagher & Flom LLP & Affiliates *
Winston & Strawn LLP *

crime arenas. The team's first-rate trial expertise has earned considerable successes in a number of leading cases. It successfully represented Ventas in the US Court of Appeals, resulting in a $227 million recovery in a tortious interference case. The white-collar crime team is equally formidable, scoring a notable victory in winning a new trial for Paul Daugerdas, an attorney convicted for an illegal tax shelter scheme.

**Sources say:** "*I went with Jenner because of the firm's reputation as one of the best litigation firms in the country. Its work is of the highest quality.*"

**KEY INDIVIDUALS** Firm chairman **Anton Valukas** (see p.1236) is "*just fantastic,*" and "*at the top of his game,*" report interviewees. He has an outstanding reputation in commercial litigation and white-collar crime, recently achieving a favorable settlement for Medline in a False Claims Act case. The "*very talented*" **David Bradford** (see p.1199) is cochair of the litigation department and an authority on commercial litigation. He led the team in the Ventas matter. **Jeffrey Colman** (see p.1202) represents law firms and attorneys in professional liability cases and handles both complex civil and criminal matters. **Thomas Sullivan** (see p.1234) contributes a wealth of experience to the firm's white-collar practice. He handles investigations and arbitrations as part of a broad litigation practice. The "*very savvy*" **Charles Sklarsky** (see p.1232) is cochair of the white-collar practice group. He recently led the team acting for a Japanese manufacturer subject to a DOJ investigation. Sources note that he is "*a bright and experienced guy.*"

## Jones Day
### See profile on p.919

**THE FIRM** This firm's esteemed litigation team represents high-profile clients such as Takeda, Woodward and Dow Chemical. The team has real strength in multidistrict, high-stakes cases, acting as lead counsel for R.J. Reynolds in a high-value arbitration matter. The firm's white-collar group has expertise across the board, representing individuals and corporations in a host of government investigations and criminal proceedings.

**Sources say:** "*Top-shelf; I think they're excellent.*"

## Litigation: White-Collar Crime & Government Investigations
### Leading Individuals

| Star individuals | |
| --- | --- |
| Webb Dan K | Winston & Strawn LLP * |

| **Band 1** | |
| --- | --- |
| Berkowitz Sean M | Latham & Watkins LLP |
| Connelly Vincent J | Mayer Brown LLP |
| Duffy Joseph J | Stetler, Duffy & Rotert Ltd |
| Filip Mark | Kirkland & Ellis LLP * |
| Lassar Scott R | Sidley Austin LLP * |
| Monico Michael D | Monico, Pavich & Spevack (ONP) † |
| Reidy Daniel E | Jones Day * |
| Rosenbloom David | McDermott Will & Emery LLP * |
| Safer Ronald S | Schiff Hardin LLP |
| Sklarsky Charles B | Jenner & Block LLP * |
| Stetler David J | Stetler, Duffy & Rotert Ltd |
| Valukas Anton R | Jenner & Block LLP * |

| **Band 2** | |
| --- | --- |
| Fardon Zachary | Latham & Watkins LLP |
| Fitzgerald Patrick | Skadden, Arps, Slate, Meagher & Flom * |
| Rotert Mark L | Stetler, Duffy & Rotert Ltd |
| Soffer Gil M | Katten Muchin Rosenman LLP |
| Stone Jeffrey E | McDermott Will & Emery LLP * |
| Streicker James R | Cotsirilos Tighe & Streicker Ltd |
| Zenner Sheldon | Katten Muchin Rosenman LLP |

| **Band 3** | |
| --- | --- |
| Campbell Terence | Cotsirilos Tighe & Streicker Ltd |
| Collins Patrick | Perkins Coie LLP |
| Crowl Matthew | Schiff Hardin LLP |
| Gair Chris | Gair Law Group, Ltd |
| Gallo John N | Sidley Austin LLP * |
| Holmes Patricia | Schiff Hardin LLP |
| Kent Robert | Baker & McKenzie |
| Margolis Jeremy | Loeb & Loeb LLP (ONP) † * |
| Poulos Theodore T | Cotsirilos Tighe & Streicker Ltd |
| Rao Pravin B | Perkins Coie LLP |
| Scott Zaldwaynaka | Kaye Scholer LLP (ONP) † * |
| Sher Michael D | Neal, Gerber & Eisenberg LLP * |
| Sussman Eric H | Kaye Scholer LLP (ONP) † * |

| **Up-and-coming individuals** | |
| --- | --- |
| Kocoras John | McDermott Will & Emery LLP * |
| Zubairi Junaid A | Vedder Price PC (ONP) † * |

* Indicates firm / individual with profile.
Alphabetical order within each band. Band 1 is the highest.

**KEY INDIVIDUALS Daniel Reidy** (see p.1226) handles both commercial and criminal litigation as well as investigations for plaintiffs and defendants. A key mandate saw him act as lead counsel for Abbott Laboratories on a product liability case. Observers comment that he is "*a very seasoned trial lawyer who reads judges very well.*" **Tina Tabacchi** (see p.1235) handles a broad range of litigation matters including class actions, false claims and consumer fraud. Sources comment favorably that she is "*a very strong lawyer.*" **James Daly** (see p.1203) is "*well organized, client-focused and cost-conscious*" according to sources. He is very experienced in the defense of class action cases.

## Katten Muchin Rosenman LLP
### See profile on p.1253

**THE FIRM** Katten's litigation group has expertise across the board. It is particularly well noted for matters involving the Foreign Corrupt Practices Act (FCPA), compliance programs and internal investigations for corporations. The group's expertise saw it represent the Royal Bank of Canada in a civil case brought against it by the Commodity Futures Trading Commission. The team has also represented I-Flow, a subsidiary of Kimberly-Clark, in a series of product liability claims.

**Sources say:** "*They are able to handle very sophisticated cases but do so incredibly efficiently and cost-effectively.*"

**KEY INDIVIDUALS Gil Soffer** is "*polished and effective*" and "*able to very cogently and persuasively express a client's position.*" He specializes in white-collar litigation, including corporate fraud, healthcare and investigations. The "*exceptional*" **Sheldon Zenner** heads the litigation and dispute resolution group. His practice comprises complex white-collar and civil litigation, with expertise in securities, tax and antitrust matters.

## Kirkland & Ellis LLP
### See profile on p.1254

**THE FIRM** This superb team has a well-earned reputation for its ability to handle difficult, high-profile and high-stakes cases. The team has acted for Abbott Laboratories in a series of cases concerning the drug Humira. In the white-collar crime and government investigations space, Kirkland is one of the firms leading the defense of BP in the plethora of investigations stemming from the Deepwater Horizon disaster. Other A-list clients include ExxonMobil and Dow Chemical.

**Sources say:** "*They are creative and strategic on substantive legal issues.*"

**KEY INDIVIDUALS Mark Filip** (see p.1206) has a key role in Kirkland's defense of BP in the Deepwater Horizon matters. Sources say he is "*one of the brightest people out there.*" Observers go on to praise his strategic thinking and comment that he is just "*terrific.*" **Richard Godfrey** (see p.1209) is also closely involved in the firm's work for BP. He has an outstanding reputation for commercial litigation, including class actions and appellate work. **Robert Kopecky** (see p.1215) recently defended GM and its board of directors in a securities class action. He is seen by some sources as "*one of the leading securities lawyers.*" **John Hickey** (see p.1212) is also active representing BP in the Deepwater Horizon matters. He has expertise in matters relating to consumer fraud, antitrust and product liability. **Emily Nicklin** (see p.1224) well known for her litigation skills. She focuses her practice on torts, employment discrimination, professional liability and contract law. She has represented Medtronic in a securities fraud action. **Sallie Smylie** (see p.1232) specializes in litigation involving pharmaceutical and medical device product liability. She is also very experienced defending corporate clients in a wide range of class actions.

*The editorial is in alphabetical order by firm name.*

## Latham & Watkins LLP
See profile on p.446

THE FIRM Latham's Chicago litigation team is known for its strength in commercial litigation and white-collar matters. The firm represented the NFL Players Association in its $4 billion lockout fund case against the NFL and the 32 team owners. On the white-collar side, the team represented the CEO of STEC, Inc in an insider trading case brought by the SEC. Other clients include GE Capital and Reebok International.

Sources say: *"They provide very strong judgment. I cannot speak highly enough about them."*

KEY INDIVIDUALS **Sean Berkowitz** is global chair of the firm's litigation department. He specializes in complex commercial litigation and investigations including whistleblower allegations and international commercial compliance. Sources describe him as *"an excellent litigator."* **Zachary Fardon** focuses on high-profile commercial litigation, government investigations and white-collar matters. Sources describe him as *"extremely responsive"* and relate that he is *"a very sharp, aggressive advocate."*

## Mayer Brown LLP
See profile on p.1257

THE FIRM The Chicago office of Mayer Brown hosts a team that has deep experience across the litigation spectrum. The group represented Lear Corporation in a series of class actions alleging price fixing. The team also represented Orbit Medical in a simultaneous criminal and civil investigation by the DOJ regarding billing practices. An impressive client portfolio includes BASF, The Bank of New York Mellon, Union Carbide and Dow Chemical.

Sources say: *"Mayer Brown's white-collar and commercial litigation practices are considered formidable and are widely held in high regard."*

KEY INDIVIDUALS **Vincent Connelly**'s *"judgment and demeanor are excellent,"* say sources. He focuses on civil and criminal trial work, with sources believing him to be *"one of the premier litigators here in the city."* **Michele Odorizzi** has a tremendous reputation for brief-writing at trial and appellate litigation. Sources confirm that she is *"an outstanding brief writer who is a very clear thinker and very strong at oral argument."* Substantive areas of expertise include securities litigation and fiduciary duty issues. **Stephen Shapiro** is hailed as a *"brilliantly effective appellate lawyer"* by sources. He recently helped to successfully defend Mayo Collaborative Services in a Supreme Court case alleging patent infringement. **Thomas Durkin** handles cases involving public corruption, fraud and tax issues. Sources enthuse that he *"has a lot of credibility in the community."* **Herbert Zarov** centers his practice on mass tort matters. He also focuses on both commercial and appellate litigation. Observers comment appreciatively that *"he has a great intellect. He's great in terms of brief writing and strategy."* **James Ferguson** is hailed as *"a thinking man's lawyer."* His practice has a strong focus on IP but he is also recognized for his skill in complex commercial litigation as well as arbitrations and internal investigations.

## McDermott Will & Emery LLP
See profile on p.1258

THE FIRM This talented team regularly represents high-end clients in complex litigation that is of local, national or international scope. The commercial litigation team recently represented Orbitz Worldwide in a series of multijurisdictional tax disputes. The white-collar team boasts expertise in international anticorruption and criminal cartel matters as well as internal investigations and SEC matters. The group recently represented biopharmaceutical giant Amgen in a series of whistle-blower suits.

Sources say: *"Outstanding work! Top-notch people with great subject matter expertise."*

KEY INDIVIDUALS Commercial litigator **Michael Pope** (see p.1226) is experienced in dealing with high-stakes disputes. He is particularly noted for his expertise in product liability litigation. **David Rosenbloom** (see p.1228) handles complex commercial and white-collar criminal litigation. Sources refer to his *"broad knowledge of the law,"* and note his *"exceptional ability to assimilate complex facts and build a position based on the facts and the law."* Sources report *"tremendous respect"* for firm cochair **Jeffrey Stone** (see p.1234). He handles civil and criminal matters for corporations, their executives and individuals. **Joel Chefitz** (see p.1201) handles complex commercial matters including antitrust litigation and M&A-related disputes. His expertise has seen him defend CPI in a securities class action brought against the company by its shareholders. **John Kocoras** (see p.1215) is highlighted by observers as a rising star of the Illinois litigation community. He handles matters under the FCPA, including international investigations for firms and corporations across a range of industries.

## McGuireWoods LLP
See profile on p.2519

THE FIRM The McGuireWoods litigation practice represents clients such as Capital One, ARS National Services and Fidelity National Information Services. Recently, the team has acted for CompuCredit on defending a class action alleging violation of the Credit Repair Organizations Act.

Sources say: *"Their work is solid and efficient in every respect."*

KEY INDIVIDUALS **David Hartsell** cochairs the firm's financial services litigation group and has deep experience in the defense of class actions and single-plaintiff lawsuits. Sources report *"unwavering trust"* in his abilities. **Marta Stein** is cochair of the banking litigation group. She represents financial institutions and entrepreneurs in business tort matters and contractual litigation. Interviewees attest that she gives *"wonderfully informed advice"* and is *"an excellent communicator and negotiator."*

## Neal, Gerber & Eisenberg LLP
See profile on p.1260

THE FIRM This firm enjoys a solid reputation in the Chicago commercial litigation arena. The team recently represented American Hardware Manufacturers in a trial arising out of claims of breach of fiduciary duty and fraud.

Other clients include JPMorgan Chase, Citigroup Global Markets and The Carle Foundation.

Sources say: *"The work was very thorough and I felt as though I was very well represented and received excellent advice."*

KEY INDIVIDUALS **Scott Fisher** (see p.1207) is cochair of the litigation group. He provides *"excellent courtroom representation"* and *"can credibly negotiate with opposing parties,"* according to sources. He focuses on complex commercial litigation and has a noted expertise in class actions. **Nicholas Berberian** (see p.1198) handles regulatory and litigation matters for financial services clients, including arbitrations and internal investigations. He recently represented JPMorgan Chase in a Financial Industry Regulatory Authority arbitration relating to auction-rate securities. **Michael Sher** (see p.1231) is *"knowledgeable and well versed in the law,"* say sources. He handles the gamut of commercial and white-collar litigation.

## Perkins Coie LLP
See profile on p.2548

THE FIRM This team impresses for its high-quality white-collar litigation work, often handling big-ticket matters involving enforcement and criminal defense. In a key case the group represented Boeing and two of its senior executives in a high-profile securities class action. The team's impressive portfolio includes clients such as Career Education and Globetrotters.

KEY INDIVIDUALS **Patrick Collins** is held in high regard by commentators as a leading practitioner. He is adept at handling headline cases for both individuals and corporations. **Pravin Rao** is praised by sources for his deep government investigations expertise. He focuses on complex criminal and regulatory matters and is particularly knowledgeable in matters involving the DOJ and SEC.

## Reed Smith LLP

THE FIRM The litigation team at Reed Smith is particularly strong in the manufacturing, healthcare and pharmaceutical sectors. The team acts as long-term counsel to Johnson Controls, which it recently represented in a product liability case. The group also defended Innovative Aftermarket Systems regarding alleged infringement of a warranty act. Clients include York International, SunCoke Energy and WellPoint.

KEY INDIVIDUALS **Jonathan Quinn**'s areas of specialization include securities enforcement and litigation. Sources comment that he *"does not waver and is not intimidated by the opposition."*

## Schiff Hardin LLP

THE FIRM The diverse practice is particularly well known for its white-collar work, offering noted expertise in the representation of clients before state and federal agencies such as the FBI, SEC and DOJ. The commercial litigation team handles a broad range of concerns including class actions, fiduciary matters and trade secrets. Key mandates have seen the team defend breach of contract and copyright infringement claims.

*The editorial is in alphabetical order by firm name.*

Sources say: *"Very smart people working for the best interests of the client."*

KEY INDIVIDUALS **Ronald Safer** is *"a very fine lawyer indeed"* and *"an absolute, consummate gentleman,"* according to sources. He specializes in white-collar defense work and civil litigation mattes. Sources go on to comment that he is *"relentless in his advocacy for clients."* **Patricia Holmes** handles internal investigations and white-collar criminal trials. Sources commend her rapport with clients and several note their *"high regard for her."* **Matthew Crowl** is *"very smart, experienced and knowledgeable"* according to sources. He is also noted for his work pertaining to internal investigations and criminal proceedings. **Barry Alberts** handles civil litigation matters, including professional liability claims and securities fraud. He represents a broad spectrum of clients, including law firms, directors and corporations.

## Schopf & Weiss LLP
See profile on p.1261

THE FIRM Schopf & Weiss represents clients such as AT&T Mobility, Guardsmark, Motorola Solutions and Tyson Foods in business litigation. The team recently represented Helaba in a $150 million insurance coverage case. Areas of expertise include professional liability, insurance coverage and noncompete matters.

Sources say: *"Exceptional quality. They do a great job."*

KEY INDIVIDUALS **William Schopf** (see p.1230) has over 30 years of litigation experience and is particularly noted for his work pertaining to fraud and international trade matters. **Steven Weiss** (see p.1237) heads the general commercial litigation department and is known for his prowess in areas including IP, contract breach and trade secrets.

## Sidley Austin LLP
See profile on p.1264

THE FIRM The Sidley Austin litigation team offers exceptional depth and expertise across the board. A key mandate for the group has been its representation of Microsoft in a high-value breach of contract claim against Motorola. The team also represented SMART Technologies in a putative securities class action. Other clients include Bayer HealthCare and Bank of America.

Sources say: *"They are very effective courtroom advocates who deliver significant courtroom victories."*

KEY INDIVIDUALS **Walter Carlson** (see p.1201) is head of the Chicago financial and security litigation group and an expert in cases involving securities fraud and fiduciary duty issues. He is also experienced in representing corporations and their directors in SEC investigations. Global coordinator of Sidley's complex commercial litigation practice, **William Conlon** (see p.1202) focuses on criminal investigations and civil matters, including class actions. **Charles Douglas's** (see p.1204) areas of focus include antitrust, securities and commercial litigation. Sources speak highly of his commitment to client service and name him *"a power hitter."* Market observers note that **David Graham** (see p.1209) *"has the capacity to understand complicated facts and get right to the heart of the matter extreme-*

*ly quickly and incisively."* He handles matters such as consumer class actions, fiduciary issues and M&A litigation. **Constantine Trela** (see p.1236) is chair of the appellate practice group and part of the Sidley team representing Microsoft in a breach of contract case brought against Motorola Mobility. His practice covers a broad range of commercial arenas. Former US Attorney **Scott Lassar** (see p.1217) handles all aspects of white-collar work, including investigations of companies. Sources report *"tremendous respect"* for his abilities. **John Gallo** (see p.1208) is *"very smart, very deliberate and very good at weighting arguments,"* according to sources. He has represented criminal defendants, institutional clients and clients in grand jury investigations.

## Skadden, Arps, Slate, Meagher & Flom LLP & Affiliates
See profile on p.2008

THE FIRM Skadden's well-respected litigation department handles complex cases across the USA. The sizable team has deep expertise across a range of areas, and is recognized for its strength in commercial and white-collar litigation. Recent highlights include the group's defense of Anheuser-Busch InBev in a lawsuit brought against it by the Oglala Sioux Indian Nation regarding alcohol smuggling. The team also acted for Martin Marietta Materials on a $4.7 billion matter against Vulcan Materials.

Sources say: *"They have done a fine job for us. I think they have very talented people."*

KEY INDIVIDUALS **Matthew Kipp** (see p.1214) is noted for his strength in commercial litigation, including securities, derivatives and M&A-related disputes. Sources relate that he is *"a fine lawyer."* **Ryan Stoll** (see p.1234) focuses his commercial litigation practice on the defense of mass torts. He is also experienced in representing clients in multidistrict proceedings. Recent matters include representing Toyota in state and federal court cases relating to the alleged unintended acceleration of its vehicles. Former US Attorney **Patrick Fitzgerald** (see p.1207) has recently joined private practice. He has extensive trial experience and focuses on internal investigations and government enforcement matters.

## Stetler, Duffy & Rotert Ltd

THE FIRM This white-collar litigation boutique has earned a stellar reputation for its quality of work. The group represents individuals and corporations confronted with matters such as criminal prosecutions, grand jury trials and government regulatory investigations. Market observers hold the group in high regard.

Sources say: *"They are very high-quality."*

KEY INDIVIDUALS **Joseph Duffy** focuses his practice on advising and defending clients in governmental and internal investigations. He also handles jury trials and appeals, both civil and criminal. He is a well-established name within the world of white-collar litigation. **David Stetler** receives phenomenal praise from the market for his white-collar practice. He represents businesses and individuals in criminal trials and government investigations and is hailed by sources as *"a very talented trial lawyer."* **Mark Rotert**

represents individuals, businesses and corporations in criminal and regulatory cases. He brings a wealth of experience to his practice, and is experienced at all levels, including the Supreme Court.

## Thompson Coburn LLP

THE FIRM Thompson Coburn is recognized for its skill in the prosecution and defense of a wide range of matters, from construction disputes through to trade secrets. The team recently defended Federal Signal in a number of consolidated claims brought by Chicago Fire Department firefighters.

Sources say: *"The counsel and support staff with whom I have worked are always responsive, enthusiastic, engaged and committed to doing all that they can to support the objectives of their clients."*

KEY INDIVIDUALS **Todd Rowden** is *"always absolutely prepared to represent his clients,"* according to sources. He has a broad-based practice that includes business torts, injunctions and real estate.

## Winston & Strawn LLP
See profile on p.1267

THE FIRM This firm goes from strength to strength in Illinois. The white-collar group is as active as ever, recently defending John Schulte, the former CEO of Spectranetics, on allegations relating to the use of medical devices. The general commercial litigation team, meanwhile, has scored some remarkable victories and earned outstanding feedback from the market. It notably represented Deloitte & Touche in a federal trial alleging fraud, breach of contract and malpractice. Clients in the group's impressive portfolio include Monsanto, JPMorgan Chase and Magnetar Capital.

Sources say: *"An outstanding, top-flight litigation practice. The lawyers really understand the need to deliver results in a cost-effective way."*

KEY INDIVIDUALS **Dan Webb** (see p.1236) focuses on criminal cases as well as regulatory and complex civil cases. Observers comment that he is *"a great lawyer"* with a *"completely deserved reputation."* He led the team in the John Schulte matter. **Kimball Anderson** (see p.1196) is a commercial litigator with an expertise in class actions, professional liability and product liability. Observers note that he is *"very, very good in the courtroom."* **Bruce Braun** (see p.1200) handles complex commercial litigation, including class actions and multijurisdictional litigation. He played a key role in the Deloitte litigation. **Robert Sperling** (see p.1233) undertakes complex commercial litigation that includes the defense of antitrust and securities actions. He successfully defended Goldman Sachs in a class action alleging violations of the Commodities Exchange Act. **Caryn Jacobs** (see p.1213) focuses on the defense of audit firms, securities litigation and trust law. She was also part of the Winston team that acted for Deloitte & Touche.

## Other Notable Practitioners

**Alan Salpeter** (see p.1229) of Kaye Scholer LLP is hailed by sources as an *"exceptional attorney."* He handles matters

1183

involving financial services litigation and specializes in areas including securities fraud and proxy contests. **Michael Levinson** (see p.1217) of Seyfarth Shaw LLP is a *"consummate professional"* who *"gives real, down-to-earth, practical advice."* He undertakes work involving trade secrets litigation and disputes involving motor vehicle dealers. Sources comment that he is also an *"excellent strategist."* **Stephen Novack** of Novack and Macey LLP has a broad practice that covers professional liability, trust litigation and the defense of class actions. **David Kistenbroker** (see p.1215) of Dechert LLP has *"deep subject matter expertise"* in areas such as SEC investigations, securities class actions and governance disputes. **Mark Rabinowitz** (see p.1226) of Cozen O'Connor is *"very intelligent and very thorough,"* say sources. His practice is centered on the representation of insurance companies and

financial institutions. **Michael Monico** of Monico, Pavich & Spevack is *"the grand don of the white-collar Bar,"* according to highly impressed market observers. He handles headline criminal and regulatory litigation cases. **Jeremy Margolis** (see p.1219) of Loeb & Loeb LLP *"knows the law and law enforcement"* and is *"a great counselor,"* according to sources. He is an esteemed white-collar trial lawyer who is also noted for his handling of internal investigations and compliance. **Zaldwaynaka Scott** (see p.1230) of Kaye Scholer LLP is *"very easy to work with, very practical and very responsive,"* say sources. She has deep trial experience and focuses on white-collar criminal defense and internal investigations. At the same firm, **Eric Sussman** (see p.1235) is hailed by clients as *"a remarkable individual."* He represents individuals and corporations involved in white-collar litigation and is experienced in matters involving

governmental agencies. **Tom Cimino** (see p.1201) of Vedder Price PC *"has a practical, conservative approach to dealing with complex problems,"* say sources. He handles complex commercial litigation, including contentious patent and bankruptcy matters. **Junaid Zubairi** (see p.1239) of Vedder Price PC is commended for his *"high ethics and high quality of client service."* He represents clients in investigations before governmental agencies, whistle-blower allegations and insider trading cases. **Chris Gair** of Gair Law Group, Ltd. recently left Jenner & Block to form his own firm. Gair has a broad practice that covers internal investigations and trial cases. At his former firm he was one of the lead partners on the high-profile Paul Daugerdas tax shelter case.

# MEDIA & ENTERTAINMENT LITIGATION

Commentary about individuals can be found under their firm's paragraph. If the firm has no paragraph (is not ranked) look at Other Notable Practitioners.

| Media & Entertainment: Litigation | |
|---|---|
| **Leading Firms** | |
| **Band 1** | |
| Dentons * | |
| Jenner & Block LLP * | |
| Sidley Austin LLP * | |
| **Band 2** | |
| Lathrop & Gage LLP | |

| Leading Individuals | |
|---|---|
| **Band 1** | |
| Fifer Samuel | Dentons * |
| Klenk James | Dentons * |
| O'Brien Richard | Sidley Austin LLP * |
| Sanders David P | Jenner & Block LLP * |
| **Band 2** | |
| Conway Michael M | Foley & Lardner LLP (ONP) † |
| Kimrey Blaine C | Lathrop & Gage LLP |
| Mandell Steven P | Mandell Menkes (ONP) † |
| Mattson Eric S | Sidley Austin LLP * |
| Spears Natalie | Dentons * |
| **Associates to watch** | |
| Clark Bryan | Lathrop & Gage LLP |

\* *Indicates firm / individual with profile.*
*Alphabetical order within each band. Band 1 is the highest.*

## Band 1

### Dentons
See profile on p.449

**THE FIRM** The collective wealth of knowledge and experience that this team brings to the table has seen it firmly established as a leader in the media litigation space. Clients are especially quick to commend the highly responsive service provided by the group, which regularly represents

newspapers, publishing houses and authors across a range of matters including libel, copyright, trademark and privacy issues. Among its recent highlights, it has been acting on behalf of household names such as NBC and Yahoo!.

**Sources say:** *"Always prepared, always accessible, and never fail to deliver."*

**KEY INDIVIDUALS Samuel Fifer** (see p.1206) continues to be a much-lauded figure in the space and remains a popular choice of counsel for a host of high-profile clients, especially in IP and technology disputes. Recent examples of his work include assisting Al Jazeera with a variety of matters, including cable distribution, and advising Village Voice Media on internet law and other related issues. **James Klenk** (see p.1215) draws particular praise from commentators for his experience, judgment and deep understanding of media and entertainment matters. He is frequently called upon to act on behalf of organizations in the broadcast, digital and print arenas, and is also particularly noted for his aptitude in First Amendment matters. **Natalie Spears** (see p.1233) continues to develop her practice within this strong media and entertainment team, representing a broad range of media entities, such as NBC and Chicago Tribune, in a variety of matters including defamation, privacy and First Amendment rights. Sources are quick to celebrate her responsiveness as well as her ability to understand clients and the marketplace they occupy.

### Jenner & Block LLP
See profile on p.1252

**THE FIRM** This robust media and First Amendment team forms a significant part of Jenner & Block's national litigation practice. The group represents a plethora of traditional and new media entities, advising on libel claims, access to information, privacy, news gathering and copyright. The team is particularly sought to act on behalf of news and other media organizations such as The New York Times,

The Washington Post and Forbes Magazine on libel litigation.

**KEY INDIVIDUALS David Sanders** (see p.1229) is cochair of the firm's media and First Amendment practice and is much valued by clients for his litigation capabilities and wealth of experience in First Amendment and libel cases. *"He is a trusted resource who handles matters quickly and efficiently, and is cost-effective,"* sources note.

### Sidley Austin LLP
See profile on p.1264

**THE FIRM** This litigation powerhouse has established a strong presence within the media and entertainment space, acting for a distinguished roster of clients including Northwestern University, the Chicago Tribune and the Illinois Civil Justice League. Recent highlights have included handling matters involving defamation, First Amendment and copyright infringement litigation. The group is also renowned within the community for providing numerous nonprofit organizations with legal advice on a pro bono basis.

**Sources say:** *"They are a great firm – top-tier! They are very effective and form deep relationships with clients."*

**KEY INDIVIDUALS** Seasoned media and entertainment litigator **Richard O'Brien** (see p.1224) elicits much praise for his experience, efficiency and proactive approach to matters. He recently obtained a victory in the Seventh Circuit Court of Appeals on behalf of longtime client the American Civil Liberties Union. The highly regarded **Eric Mattson** (see p.1220) is particularly noted for his journalistic background, which has afforded him an in-depth understanding of the media arena. In a recent case highlight, he defended Northwestern University in a defamation suit brought against the institution.

## Band 2

### Lathrop & Gage LLP

**THE FIRM** The Chicago office of this nationwide media and entertainment team handles a broad range of matters within this space, including defamation, marketing, First Amendment and IP. The firm currently represents a host of distinguished clients including Scripps Networks, Sharp Entertainment and Encyclopaedia Britannica.

**Sources say:** *"Very responsive; the quality of work is high."* *"Very thorough, very comprehensive – we get good results with Lathrop & Gage and they're very easy to work with."*

**KEY INDIVIDUALS** Commentators are impressed with **Blaine Kimrey**'s *"sophisticated practice"* and he also wins particular plaudits for his advice, range of knowledge and ability to *"get down to the nitty-gritty."* He heads the firm's Chicago office and has recently worked on a number of high-profile IP litigation matters, an example of which is his recent success for Merriam-Webster against a copyright infringement claim. **Bryan Clark** is a highly regarded associate, with sources particularly commending his communication skills and proactive approach to matters. He is especially noted for his digital privacy and media work.

### Other Notable Practitioners

The highly respected **Steven Mandell** of Mandell Menkes has broad experience across an array of areas from media and IT to IP and advertising. He represents clients from all corners of the media and entertainment industry, including film, television, music, radio, print media and book publishing. Sources describe Foley & Lardner LLP's **Michael Conway** as *"an excellent attorney – he is highly skilled and very accessible,"* and also celebrate his *"excellent advice on digital as well as traditional media matters."* Much of his recent work has been in defamation litigation.

# MEDIA & ENTERTAINMENT TRANSACTIONAL

Commentary about individuals can be found under their firm's paragraph. If the firm has no paragraph (is not ranked) look at Other Notable Practitioners.

## Band 1

### Leavens, Strand & Glover, Adler LLC

**THE FIRM** This preeminent boutique is heralded for its expertise in music, TV and film, and is further recommended for its work in entertainment financing and matters concerning new media. Clients span the media industry, ranging from record labels and publishers to film producers and broadcasters.

**Sources say:** *"The whole firm is top-shelf."* *"A preeminent practice."*

**KEY INDIVIDUALS Jerry Glover** has over 30 years' experience acting for companies and individuals, covering the gamut of the media and entertainment industry. He focuses exclusively on transactional matters and is a particularly fine choice of counsel for television and film producers. The seasoned **Thomas Leavens** is well known and much respected within the industry. He covers a wide array of areas including IP, new media, entertainment financing and contracts. **Peter Strand** is recommended for his transactional expertise, and acts for clients ranging from broadcasters and authors to independent record labels and songwriters. He elicits particular praise for his excellent communication skills and personable approach to matters.

### Winston & Strawn LLP
See profile on p.1267

**THE FIRM** Winston & Strawn remains at the top of its field, and gains particular recognition for its work in advertising and marketing. The firm handles a variety of matters, including privacy, promotions and litigation, for a list of enviable clients such as Honda, McDonald's and Wrigley. The team continues to advise Taco Bell on advertising and promotions.

**Sources say:** *"They are efficient and proactive. They go above and beyond in providing their services."*

**KEY INDIVIDUALS** Sources are quick to lavish praise on the *"brilliant"* **Mary Hutchings Reed** (see p.1212), describing her as *"extremely knowledgeable"* and *"extremely intelligent and accessible."* She is particularly renowned for her advertising, marketing and sponsorship work. **Brian Heidelberger** (see p.1211) is applauded for his very practical and efficient approach to transactions, and is also singled out for his *"ability to keep up-to-date with the law."* He advises various companies on branding and marketing, and also represents professional athletes in an array of matters, including endorsements. **Brian Fergemann** (see p.1206) is noted for his expertise in advertising, marketing and promotions, and is currently advising The J.M. Smucker Company on national advertising issues. *"He is very hard-working, focused and very intelligent,"* asserts one impressed interviewee. **Liisa Thomas** (see p.1235) has extensive knowledge of media and entertainment law, including privacy, promotions, data collection and IP law. Current clients include the Chicago Sun-Times and Tyson Foods, both of which she advises on a broad spectrum of issues. She is singled out for her *"encyclopedic mind"* and ability to *"explain issues and get to the heart of the matter."*

## Band 2

### Freeborn & Peters LLP
See profile on p.1248

**THE FIRM** This impressive group maintains a strong name in IP, providing counsel to clients on a whole range of related issues, from copyright and trade mark protection to advertising, internet and computer law. The group provides ongoing counsel to clients such as Nintendo and Canadian National Railroad on licensing matters and trademark registration.

**Sources say:** *"Excellent firm!"*

**KEY INDIVIDUALS Andrew Goldstein** (see p.1209) is a leading figure in IP and counsels various media entities on trade mark and copyright law. He is currently handling matters for Canadian National Railroad. *"Outstanding attorney"* **Eugene Zelek** (see p.1238) receives particular praise for his detail-oriented approach to matters. He is especially recommended for his marketing work, including licensing, branding and product development, and is currently advising Nintendo on licensing and a range of other issues.

## Holland & Knight LLP
See profile on p.1028

**THE FIRM** The entertainment team at Holland & Knight is renowned for its work within film production, and also continues to expand its work in television, music, finance and celebrity branding. It has represented celebrity chefs Anthony Mantuano and Sarah Grueneberg in a variety of matters, and is also acting as production counsel for TinRes Entertainment on an upcoming film.

**Sources say:** *"Fantastic! Very responsive and proactive. They really care and their advice is always to the point and really good."*

**KEY INDIVIDUALS** *"Major film lawyer"* **Robert Labate** (see p.1216) elicits much praise for his range of experience and depth of knowledge. *"He is very helpful, his advice is always terrific and you always get the sense he cares about clients,"* reports one enthusiastic interviewee.

## Band 3

### Bryan Cave LLP
**THE FIRM** The Chicago office of this global law firm provides a broad range of media and entertainment services. The group advises clients on issues including IP, branding and privacy, and is particularly recognized for its work in art and music.

**KEY INDIVIDUALS** A leading art lawyer, **Scott Hodes** has extensive experience within this niche field, acting on behalf of leading artists, dealers and collectors.

## InfoLawGroup

**THE FIRM** This relatively new firm advises clients on the full range of traditional media issues and also maintains a strong reputation for its work in new media matters. Particular areas of expertise include advertising and promotions work, IP and privacy issues, and social media matters. It counts Viacom, Facebook and Paramount Pictures among its distinguished client list.

**Sources say:** *"Their response time is excellent." "A very cohesive team."*

**KEY INDIVIDUALS** The *"very personable"* **Jamie Rubin** (see p.1229) impresses clients with his *"great understanding of law and how it relates to industry."* He is well versed in both traditional and new media matters, and continues to represent major studios, recording artists and companies. **Justine Gottshall** (see p.1209) is especially noted for her work on privacy compliance and is also routinely sought to assist clients with promotions, marketing, social media partnerships and media contracts. *"She is very proactive and very practical in her advice,"* note sources.

## Michael Best & Friedrich LLP
See profile on p.2592

**THE FIRM** This media and entertainment team continues to work with a wide variety of clients, from individual artists and record labels to theaters and sports arenas, handling a range of matters including contract negotiations, licensing, promotions, IP protection and disputes. It is currently acting for Rhymesayers Entertainment, handling a diverse array of issues, including IP advice and artist agreements.

**Sources say:** *"Strong advice, well organized, and quick to answer questions."*

**KEY INDIVIDUALS Luke DeMarte** (see p.1203) impresses on a variety of entertainment issues, and is particularly recommended for his work with record labels and artists, for whom he negotiates and drafts artist agreements and licensing agreements, as well as advising on IP issues. Trademark and copyright practice head **Jeffrey Brown** (see p.1200) works on a broad range of business and IP matters, such as copyright, trade secret and advertising. He is currently advising Soundset on all aspects of the Soundset music festival.

## Other Notable Practitioners

**David Saltiel** of Golan & Christie LLP works with clients across television, film and theater, and is increasingly sought for his expertise in publishing matters. Sole practitioner **Daliah Saper** is recognized for her strengths in IP, entertainment and libel matters, and has recently been engaged on several online defamation cases. **Peter O'Reilly** of boutique practice Lea + O'Reilly continues to impress the market. He acts for an enviable client list, and is particularly renowned for his work concerning promotions issues. **Linda Mensch** is an experienced and well-respected sole practitioner. She works with clients from every corner of the media and entertainment industry on a diverse range of matters, from brand protection and advertising to copyright and trademark issues.

# REAL ESTATE

Real Estate p.1187; Zoning/Land Use p.1188

Commentary about individuals can be found under their firm's paragraph. If the firm has no paragraph (is not ranked) look at Other Notable Practitioners.

## Band 1

### Barack Ferrazzano Kirschbaum & Nagelberg LLP
**THE FIRM** This team has a preeminent and longstanding reputation in the real estate sector, where it continues to have a strong focus. The group has deep experience across the full range of real estate matters including joint ventures, financing and retail leasing. Its attorneys undertake work for pension fund advisers and nonprofit corporations as well as private entrepreneurs and banks. Representative clients include Ventas, Wells Fargo, USAA Real Estate and Alliance Partners.

**Sources say:** *"Thorough, well prepared, aggressive, reliable." "They did an excellent job and I consider them first-tier."*

**KEY INDIVIDUALS** The *"very well-respected"* **Dennis Ferrazzano** is particularly experienced in matters involving office buildings, retail properties, mixed-use and industrial buildings, and multifamily housing. Sources are full of praise and comment that he *"really contributes to the Bar."* **Howard Kirschbaum** is highly experienced in restructurings and financings, and also acts for clients in matters relating to joint ventures. He is *"smart, practical and a deal-doer,"* say sources. **Suzanne Bessette-Smith** is especially knowledgeable when it comes to REITs, build-to-suit projects and other types of commercial development and real estate financing. According to clients she is *"excellent, knowledgeable, practical"* and *"technically strong."* **Howard Nagelberg** is experienced in international real estate and in REIT issues. Clients and peers praise him for his skill and experience. **Mark Beaubien** undertakes complex acquisitions and disposals of a commercial nature, in addition to joint ventures for both private equity funds and publicly traded REITs, among other parties. Sources are consistently impressed with his *"tireless,"* *"extremely bright, client and business-focused"* approach.

### Dentons
See profile on p.449

**THE FIRM** Dentons's real estate practice group provides in-depth advice across the gamut of real estate concerns to clients from all sectors. Of late, the team has been particularly active on tax credit and advantaged work and refinancing matters. The firm is well placed to draw on the relevant expertise of colleagues in other offices across the globe and maintains its reputation as a real estate powerhouse.

**Sources say:** *"A group of well-respected, senior practitioners."*

**KEY INDIVIDUALS** The preeminent **Patrick Moran** (see p.1222) specializes in real estate financing, development, leasing, construction and joint ventures. He has been highly active on multibank revolving credit facilities and specialty leases. Sources have *"high respect for him,"* describing him as *"very steady"* and *"very trustworthy."* **Mark Mehlman** (see p.1221) has a wide-ranging practice

## Real Estate
### Leading Firms

**Band 1**
Barack Ferrazzano Kirschbaum & Nagelberg LLP
Dentons *
DLA Piper LLP (US) *
Katten Muchin Rosenman LLP *
Sidley Austin LLP *

**Band 2**
Dykema Gossett PLLC
Greenberg Traurig, LLP *
Kirkland & Ellis LLP *
Levenfeld Pearlstein LLC
Mayer Brown LLP *
Seyfarth Shaw LLP *

**Band 3**
Goldberg Kohn Ltd *
Holland & Knight LLP *
Jenner & Block LLP *
Jones Day *
Neal, Gerber & Eisenberg LLP *
Quarles & Brady LLP *
Shefsky & Froelich

**Band 4**
Freeborn & Peters LLP *
K&L Gates *
Latham & Watkins LLP *
Locke Lord LLP *
Paul Hastings LLP *
Perkins Coie LLP
Pircher, Nichols & Meeks
Skadden, Arps, Slate, Meagher & Flom LLP & Affiliates *
Winston & Strawn LLP *

## Real Estate
### Senior Statesmen

**Senior Statesmen: distinguished older practitioners**

| | | |
|---|---|---|
| Edwards Charles L | DLA Piper LLP (US) * | |
| Ferrazzano Dennis | Barack Ferrazzano Kirschbaum & Nagelberg | |
| Rosenberg Sheli | Skadden, Arps, Slate, Meagher & Flom * | |

### Leading Individuals

**Band 1**

| | |
|---|---|
| Beard James | DLA Piper LLP (US) * |
| Gearen John J | Mayer Brown LLP |
| Kane Ivan P | Mayer Brown LLP |
| Katz Alvin | Katten Muchin Rosenman LLP |
| Kirschbaum Howard | Barack Ferrazzano Kirschbaum & Nagelberg |
| Lee Robert C | Jones Day * |
| Moran Patrick G | Dentons * |
| Novak Theodore | DLA Piper LLP (US) * |
| Rubin Joel D | Seyfarth Shaw LLP * |

**Band 2**

| | |
|---|---|
| Bessette-Smith Suzanne | Barack Ferrazzano Kirschbaum |
| Cohen Louis | Locke Lord LLP * |
| Fishman Michael T | Greenberg Traurig, LLP * |
| Kurtzon Michael S | Dykema Gossett PLLC |
| Light Corey E | Greenberg Traurig, LLP * |
| Lubelchek Douglas J | Neal, Gerber & Eisenberg LLP * |
| Mehlman Mark | Dentons * |
| Nagelberg Howard | Barack Ferrazzano Kirschbaum & Nagelberg |
| Perlman Daniel J | Kirkland & Ellis LLP * |
| Resnick Donald I | Jenner & Block LLP * |
| Rosenbloom James B | Goldberg Kohn Ltd * |
| Sarasek Peter A | Quarles & Brady LLP * |
| Schiller Eric M | Dentons * |
| Simon Mark C | Katten Muchin Rosenman LLP |
| Small Andrew D | Kirkland & Ellis LLP * |
| Usow Jeffrey A | Mayer Brown LLP |

**Band 3**

| | |
|---|---|
| Aiello Anthony | Sidley Austin LLP * |
| Axelrod Gary | Latham & Watkins LLP |
| Beaubien Mark J | Barack Ferrazzano Kirschbaum & Nagelberg |
| Berger Stephen L | Neal, Gerber & Eisenberg LLP * |
| Berzon David | Levenfeld Pearlstein LLC |
| Buday Robert | Latham & Watkins LLP |
| Budny Terrence | Sheppard, Mullin, Richter & Hampton (ONP) [†] |
| Davidson Steven R | Dentons * |
| Dlugie David | Katten Muchin Rosenman LLP |
| Glickstein David | DLA Piper LLP (US) * |
| Homburger Thomas C | K&L Gates * |
| Jaros Tom | Levenfeld Pearlstein LLC |
| Kozminski Brian | Levenfeld Pearlstein LLC |
| Kruse Alvin | Seyfarth Shaw LLP * |
| Markovic Milos | Greenberg Traurig, LLP * |
| Messerly Robert | Quarles & Brady LLP * |
| Meyer Paul E | Mayer Brown LLP |
| Murtaugh Christopher D | Winston & Strawn LLP * |
| Spitzer Gregory | Paul Hastings LLP |
| White Linda | Dentons * |
| Yi Ted | Quarles & Brady LLP * |

**Band 4**

| | |
|---|---|
| Barbe Jana Cohen | Dentons * |
| Brown Rachel S | Kirkland & Ellis LLP * |
| Bryant David | Katten Muchin Rosenman LLP |
| Cole Alexandra | Perkins Coie LLP |
| Duffy Thomas P | Edwards Wildman Palmer (ONP) [†] * |
| Fernandez Robert L | Dentons * |
| Henning Mark G | Winston & Strawn LLP * |
| Leone Eugene | Pircher, Nichols & Meeks |
| Linton Robert C | Dykema Gossett PLLC |
| Olson Nancy M | Skadden, Arps, Slate, Meagher & Flom * |
| Pearlstein Mark D | Levenfeld Pearlstein LLC |
| Pinchot Dov | Freeborn & Peters LLP * |
| Schrank Charles E | Sidley Austin LLP * |

**Up-and-coming individuals**

| | |
|---|---|
| Rechtin Jr Michael | Quarles & Brady LLP * |

\* Indicates firm / individual with profile.
Alphabetical order within each band. Band 1 is the highest.

encompassing real estate finance, including loan workouts, partnerships, joint ventures and transactions involving the hospitality sector. With more than 30 years' experience in the real estate arena, **Eric Schiller** (see p.1230) has a *"wonderful reputation"* among interviewees. He represents all manner of institutional clients and large corporations in commercial finance and real estate matters. He is particularly experienced in joint ventures, real estate financings, acquisitions, workouts and sales. **Jana Cohen Barbe** (see p.1197) is recommended as an expert in tax credit issues relating to low-income housing, renewable energy credits and historic tax work. **Steven Davidson** (see p.1203) is experienced in handling real estate financing, including loans focusing on securitization, credit enhancement transactions and products concerned with interest rate protection. Sources hold him in high regard and comment that he is *"technically strong."* **Linda White** (see p.1237) represents tenants and landlords in complicated leasing matters involving office and retail units. She attracts praise from market sources for her excellent capabilities, particularly in leasing work. She also has strong expertise in workouts, financing and telecom. Head of the real estate practice **Robert Fernandez** (see p.1206) is *"responsive and patient,"* according to clients. He is experienced in advising institutional lending clients on senior debt, equity financing and leasing issues.

### DLA Piper LLP (US)
See profile on p.1971

**THE FIRM** DLA has a truly international practice and is seen as a go-to firm for large-scale real estate matters. The large Chicago real estate team covers the gamut of matters and has an unrivaled reputation for its expertise in zoning and land use matters. This strength was demonstrated with its representation of the owners of the Wrigley Building in its landmark designation. Additionally, the team recently represented Green Courte Partners in the $230.8 million purchase and financing of The Parking Spot.

**Sources say:** *"Probably the leading team in government affairs and zoning practice."*

**KEY INDIVIDUALS** Chair of the Chicago real estate practice **Richard Klawiter** (see p.1215) specializes in land use and zoning, landmarks and historic preservation issues, and tax increment financing. Sources say that thanks to his knowledge he is frequently a first port of call for zoning and real estate advice. **Theodore Novak** (see p.1224) specializes in land use, zoning, condemnation, development and public incentive work. He is *"one of the outstanding zoning lawyers in the city,"* say sources. He recently represented Chicago Clean Energy in legislative matters relating to the development of a $3 billion clean coal/synthetic natural gas facility on Chicago's South Side. While handling a broad range of real estate matters, the *"wonderful"* **David Reifman** (see p.1226) comes most recommended for his preeminent expertise in zoning, land use, financings, and landmark and historic preservation assignments. The supremely experienced **Charles Edwards** (see p.1205) handles complex commercial real estate transactions. One particularly impressed source said: "*He is one of my favorite lawyers on planet Earth; he has a wonderful combination of intellect and technician, and is probably the most admired real estate lawyer in Chicago.*" **James Beard** (see p.1198) is "*a practical problem solver,*" say interviewees. He has a wealth of experience across a host of commercial real estate issues, representing institutional lenders as well as major developers. He has particular expertise in the restructuring and workout of distressed real estate projects. **David Glickstein** (see p.1209) advises across the board of transactional real estate. Market observers say that he is "*a very fine lawyer; a technician's technician who never misses a thing.*"

## Katten Muchin Rosenman LLP
See profile on p.1253

**THE FIRM** Nearly half of Katten Muchin's 100-strong real estate team practice out of the firm's Chicago office. The group provides its clients with representation across the full spectrum of real estate matters, and particularly stands out for its real estate finance expertise. A recent highlight saw the team advise a Eurohypo syndicate of 13 lenders on a revolving credit facility for a public shopping center REIT. Representative clients also include GE Capital, iStar Financial, Macquarie Bank and ST Residential.
**Sources say:** "*Seriously strong.*" "*A high level of expertise and understanding.*"
**KEY INDIVIDUALS Alvin Katz** has deep experience across the board of real estate matters. Sources comment that he is "*very skilled, very responsive; but he's also a good draftsman and spots all the issues.*" Observers go on to single out his "*exceptional intelligence*" for praise. **Mark Simon** is highly experienced in workouts and real estate owned (REO) sales in particular. He is also highlighted for his expertise in joint ventures focusing on development, and in representing lenders and borrowers in syndicated credit facilities. National head of real estate **David Bryant** principally focuses on commercial real estate, an area in

which he has more than 25 years' experience. He also has expertise in representing real estate fund sponsors, forming joint ventures and other mechanisms concerned with real estate. Chicago head of real estate **David Dlugie** "*has a wealth of experience and is an excellent business attorney with a keen ability to focus on important issues.*" He specializes in representing institutional lenders across a wide range of loan programs, and also represents developers in the acquisition and sale of real estate.

## Sidley Austin LLP
See profile on p.1264

**THE FIRM** Sidley Austin is a truly international firm with an offering of 28 real estate lawyers in its Chicago office. The team has a well-established reputation for excellence within restructuring and workouts, and is also very strong with acquisitions. The group recently acted for Starwood Property Trust on the purchase of 26 mortgage loans from Citibank and Citicorp. Representative clients also include KKR, JPMorgan Chase, Drawbridge (Fortress) and Deutsche Bank.
**Sources say:** "*Comprehensive, thorough, diligent and high-quality. An extremely value-added firm that provides terrific transactional guidance and advice.*"
**KEY INDIVIDUALS Anthony Aiello** (see p.1196) is head of the firm's Chicago real estate group. His practice encompasses workouts and restructurings, as well as leasings, acquisitions and dispositions. He is also active in real estate financing matters, representing a range of lender clients in structured finance matters. **Charles Schrank** (see p.1230) has the respect of his peers and clients, many of whom single out his knowledge and thorough approach. He has expertise in structured finance matters, as well as restructurings, acquisitions, disposals and workouts.

## Band 2

## Dykema Gossett PLLC

**THE FIRM** Dykema's superb practice group is particularly commended for its handling of sophisticated real estate issues and financings relating to major construction projects. The team's recent highlights include representing The John Buck Company in the sale of a premium apartment building asset to a REIT, a deal of some $62 million. The group's client roster also includes Firth Third Bank, Invesco Real Estate, Bang & Olufsen and JT Cullen.
**Sources say:** "*Courteous, respectful and knowledgeable. They know how to counsel you and where to draw the line. They are creative and work toward solving issues*"
**KEY INDIVIDUALS Michael Kurtzon** is an expert in complicated lending cases, including restructurings and loan workouts. Sources are impressed with his excellent subject matter expertise and "*expedient and courteous service.*" **Robert Linton** undertakes real estate matters relating to leasing and development as well as sales, acquisitions and condominium-related matters. Market sources are appreciative of his excellent communication skills and comment that he has "*great attention to detail, and very thorough, deep experience.*"

## Greenberg Traurig, LLP
See profile on p.1024

**THE FIRM** This dynamic team advises on all aspects of real estate law, including financing, investment, development and management on a state, national and international level. The team recently advised the Schottenstein Property Group on its acquisition of the Orchard at Saddleback shopping center for $122 million including the mortgage debt. Key clients of the firm also include Albertson's, Walton Street Capital, Kimco Realty and William Harris Investors.
**Sources say:** "*Fantastic quality, practical and very business-focused.*"
**KEY INDIVIDUALS** Cochair of the real estate practice **Michael Fishman** (see p.1207) is an expert in finance, private equity and fund formation. Sources enthuse that he is "*truly one of the most entrepreneurial lawyers;*" he is "*perfect for giving more than just legal advice.*" **Corey Light** (see p.1218) has an excellent reputation for the transactional side of real estate and real estate development work. He is particularly experienced in representing large retailers, owners and developers. Sources continue to be impressed by his skill. "*Go-getter*" **Milos Markovic** (see p.1220) is particularly recommended for his expertise with REITs and for representing private and public investors in real estate transactions. He also maintains expertise in investments and financings compliant with Shari'a law.

## Kirkland & Ellis LLP
See profile on p.1254

**THE FIRM** Transactional real estate is at the heart of Kirkland & Ellis's practice and the group handles related matters nationwide and internationally. The team specializes in first mortgages, REIT formation and joint ventures of all types, and has a strong line in restructuring work. A recent work highlight for the firm was representing Equity LifeStyle Properties in its acquisition of a large portfolio of home communities, a $1.43 billion deal. Its client portfolio also includes Archstone, Square Mile Capital Management, LaSalle Investment Management and KKR.
**Sources say:** "*Excellent lawyers.*"
**KEY INDIVIDUALS Daniel Perlman** (see p.1225) is an "*effective real estate lawyer,*" say market observers. He has a strong focus on real estate financing of all kinds and advises lenders and borrowers on related matters. **Andrew Small** (see p.1232) focuses his practice on commercial real estate and related financing and development. Sources comment that he is "*a hell of a lawyer*" and are appreciative of his approach. **Rachel Brown** (see p.1200) concentrates on real estate finance and associated matters, including workouts and foreclosures.

## Levenfeld Pearlstein LLC

**THE FIRM** Levenfeld Pearlstein offers real estate advice on a wide range of matters including acquisitions, development, dispositions and tax-deferred exchanges. The team is well placed to deal with complex issues and is supported by other groups within the firm when required. A recent case saw the firm represent Piedmont Office Realty Trust on the negotiations of GE Capital's lease of offices at 500 West

Monroe. Other notable clients include Ryan Companies US, Behringer Harvard and Next Realty.

**Sources say:** *"Very thorough and diligent." "Fast, efficient and extremely high-quality work."*

**KEY INDIVIDUALS Brian Kozminski** is praised for his ability to review a matter carefully, and provide thoughtful advice while working to a deadline. His skill as a negotiator is also particularly appreciated by clients. He concentrates on a broad spectrum of real estate matters and advises developers and owners on a variety of properties. **David Berzon** is highly experienced in commercial real estate and associated equity financings. One client enthuses that he is a *"good person to work with: he understands the issues and works to find a solution."* **Tom Jaros** has a strong focus on the financial side of real estate and advises on difficult mortgage matters and complex nonrecourse financing transactions. He is hailed by market sources for his *"high integrity"* and is described as *"smart, insightful, helpful and responsive." "The dean of the condo,"* **Mark Pearlstein** specializes in condominium property and community associations and is praised by peers and clients for his deep knowledge on the matter: *"He's the guy to go to for complicated condo agreements."*

## Mayer Brown LLP
See profile on p.1257

**THE FIRM** This group has considerable experience in transactional and cross-border work, and represents clients across the range of private and public companies. The group recently represented OptAsia Capital in a $71 million refinancing of the redevelopment and acquisition loan secured by the St. Regis Aspen Hotel. It also benefits from a long-term relationship with Clarion Partners and has advised it on numerous cases. The team's client portfolio also includes The Carlyle Group, McShane Development, GM and GoldenTree InSite.

**Sources say:** *"They made me feel valued as a client from the first day." "Thorough, highly responsive to client needs, and they represent us very well in a competitive and challenging environment."*

**KEY INDIVIDUALS John Gearen** wins praise for his intellect, technical knowledge and style of practice. One client commented: *"He continually acts in the best interests of my company."* He has a sterling practice representing national clients in all matters pertaining to real estate. **Ivan Kane** acts for clients from a wide range of sectors on all manner of development, financing and acquisition matter. He is well respected by peers, many of whom continue to laud his talents as a real estate lawyer. **Jeffrey Usow** attracts praise for his *"complete dedication to the craft."* They are particularly appreciative of his skills in drafting and negotiations, and of his ability to remain calm in tense situations. One source comments that he is *"unflappable."* **Paul Meyer** has tremendous experience in all real estate matters and undertakes work focusing on investors and developers in real estate transactions. Sources comment that he is a *"very sophisticated lawyer"* and highlight his *"knowledge, accessibility, professionalism and ability to get the work done on time."*

## Seyfarth Shaw LLP
See profile on p.1262

**THE FIRM** This highly respected 17-strong team has a broad real estate practice representing major lenders and investors, as well as other parties, from within and outside the USA. The Chicago team is supported by over 110 attorneys nationwide and frequently undertakes work outside Illinois. Members of the team specialize in pension funds, institutional investors, public/private REITs and big-box retail. The team is a long-term counsel to the likes of GK Development, which the group represents in a myriad of real estate matters. The team's client roster includes Colorado Public Employees Retirement Association, The Strive Group, Muvico and Hamilton Partners.

**Sources say:** *"Timely, efficient and cost-conscious."*

**KEY INDIVIDUALS Joel Rubin** (see p.1229) maintains his position as a leader in the real estate field. Clients and peers alike appreciate his intellect, professionalism, accessibility and ability to work to deadlines while effectively managing his team. He has a wealth of experience in developmental financing at all stages of a project and finance structuring. **Alvin Kruse** (see p.1216) handles all types of real estate matters and has deep experience in secured lending. Sources find him to be responsive, experienced and understanding of the business concerns faced by the client.

## Band 3

## Goldberg Kohn Ltd
See profile on p.1249

**THE FIRM** This group advises across a wide range of real estate matters but has particular expertise in pari passu and tranched loan syndications, and special assets. The team also represents financial institutions in midmarket structured mortgage and mezzanine financing. Clients appreciate the team's efficiency and client focus. Recently, the team represented CME Group in the sale of two buildings, which included the negotiation of cross-easement and facilities declaration. Notable clients also include NXT Capital Funding, LBC Credit and Cole Taylor Bank.

**Sources say:** *"The firm is efficient, practical, timely and well informed." "Respectful of the client's time and budget."*

**KEY INDIVIDUALS James Rosenbloom** (see p.1228) is an expert in representing investors in the financing for real estate projects. Sources comment that he is *"able to do exceptional legal work but can also take the business perspective; he has wonderful common sense and straddles the business and legal world."*

## Holland & Knight LLP
See profile on p.1028

**THE FIRM** Holland & Knight wins praise from clients for its work in land use, zoning and government-related real estate work. Additionally, members of the team specialize in representing REITs, investment advisers, and landlords and tenants, on leasing matters. The firm recently represented the Governor of the State of Illinois in a matter involving the development of a third airport in south Chicago. Representative clients also include CVS Realty, Washington Properties, New Trier Partners Development and Poag & McEwen Lifestyle Centers.

**Sources say:** *"What makes them stand out is their ability to get matters completed, and their connections to government and business players in the community." "Highly professional and well researched."*

**KEY INDIVIDUALS** Head of the firm's land use and government practice group, and leader of the firm's Chicago office, **Steven Elrod** (see p.1206) specializes in land use for private and public clients. Sources comment that he is *"incredibly responsive and accessible – Steve has a unique perspective when representing private clients."* **Victor Filippini** (see p.1206) has expertise in municipal law, zoning and land use and is well thought-of by clients and peers alike, many of whom particularly appreciate the thought he puts into matters. Head of real estate **Peter Friedman** (see p.1208) concentrates on representing private equity firms, state and local governments and private sector developers on all matters related to real estate, land use and zoning. Sources comment that his *"work is always very detailed and thorough, with well thought-out recommendations."*

## Jenner & Block LLP
See profile on p.1252

**THE FIRM** The team at Jenner & Block has a broad client base which it represents in the gamut of real estate matters, including multiple property transactions, single asset projects and equity investments. Additionally, the firm's attorneys are experienced in structuring investment vehicles for the acquisition, operation and financing of real estate projects. In recent highlights, the firm represented Equity Residential in the acquisition of a development site, including a joint venture with a condominium developer to develop a luxury residential high-rise building in New York.

**Sources say:** *"Highly sophisticated and also practical in applying the law."*

**KEY INDIVIDUALS Donald Resnick** (see p.1227) is an expert in commercial real estate and has experience covering loans, equity restructurings and workouts related to real estate. Clients enthuse about his skill as an attorney and comment that he *"has particular talent for the dynamics of business, deal-making, negotiation and structuring."*

## Jones Day
See profile on p.919

**THE FIRM** The members of Jones Day's solid Chicago real estate team have expertise in all types of general real estate matter, including secured financing and the representation of institutional investors. The group is particularly well placed to draw on the expertise of attorneys from other teams across the firm's extensive network of offices. The team recently acted for Prime Group Realty Trust on a lease agreement for SmithBucklin's relocation of its Chicago office. Representative clients also include RLJ Capital, LaSalle Investment Management, Navistart and Ohio State University.

Sources say: *"The group has a deep and broad platform, as well as a high-quality customized client service."*

KEY INDIVIDUALS **Robert Lee** (see p.1217) is cochair of the firm's global real estate practice, and head of its real estate funds group. He is experienced in real estate private equity, public and private M&A, fund formation, joint venture agreements and sizable portfolio transactions. Sources comment that *"Bob is particularly sharp and savvy in complicated investments and structures."*

## Neal, Gerber & Eisenberg LLP
### See profile on p.1260

THE FIRM The team at Neal, Gerber & Eisenberg advises across the spectrum of real estate matters, and has expertise in REIT work, condominium ownership and conversion, among other areas. The group also has a specialized real estate tax practice concentrating on state and local property tax, foreclosure and exemption. The firm is praised for its ability to guide transactions from inception through to completion.

Sources say: *"Very practical and won't overnegotiate; they know how to focus on what is important."* *"Very smart and knowledgeable in their field of expertise."*

KEY INDIVIDUALS **Douglas Lubelchek** (see p.1219) represents clients of all kinds in a variety of complex finance and real estate transactions. Sources praise him, saying he *"has the strength to move complex transactions along to a finishing point."* **Stephen Berger** (see p.1198) focuses on the financing and development of hotel, resort, commercial and apartment properties for individuals and companies in real estate. He is particularly praised for his high level of business acumen.

## Quarles & Brady LLP
### See profile on p.2593

THE FIRM This team is highly experienced in all aspects of commercial finance and corporate real estate matters, and is also building its expertise in work involving data center and medical building leasing matters. Its recent highlights include representing Giordano's Enterprises as debtor in multiple restaurant site auctions. Representative clients also include MillerCoors, United Airlines, UBS Realty Advisors and TIAA-CREF.

Sources say: *"Very professional, prompt, quality work."*

KEY INDIVIDUALS **Michael Rechtin** (see p.1226) concentrates on commercial real estate, handling a range of industrial, office and retail leasing, acquisitions, disposals and financings. He has been particularly active in matters relating to data center projects. Interviewees appreciate **Peter Sarasek** (see p.1229) for his intellect, and particularly value his client service. His in-depth expertise covers a wide range of commercial real estate finance, sales and acquisitions and leasing. **Ted Yi** (see p.1238) is an expert in handling commercial lease transactions, and represents both the owners and users of industrial, office and retail properties. He also has significant experience representing large corporations in office relocation matters. Sources find him to be *"incredibly smart; he immediately gets the grasp of complicated issues, and intellectually he works at a higher level."* **Robert Messerly** (see p.1222) recently joined

Quarles & Brady from Dentons and concentrates on large portfolio acquisitions, disposals and leasing. He also has a strong practice involving real estate finance and equity investments.

## Shefsky & Froelich

THE FIRM This team provides advice across the board of commercial real estate matters and undertakes large real estate transactions on a state and nationwide basis. In particular, it is the team's work and expertise in zoning, land use and government contracts that consistently attracts praise from market sources.

KEY INDIVIDUALS **Edward Kus** has a wealth of experience and expertise in real estate development, zoning and municipal land use law. He is widely hailed as an established authority on the subject by his peers. Real estate practice group leader **Anthony Licata** has a strong practice involving private equity, venture capital and major commercial real estate transactions across a variety of sectors. Partner emeritus **Jack Guthman** maintains a well-established reputation as an experienced expert in zoning and land use.

## Band 4

## Freeborn & Peters LLP
### See profile on p.1248

THE FIRM Freeborn & Peters has a practice covering the gamut of real estate matters for clients from all sectors. The team recently acted for Stonewater One North State Funding on the negotiation of a sizable lease with a for-profit college in a downtown campus. The group also recently secured multiple city government approvals on behalf of Prism Development for a planned 40-story residential building in Chicago's 'Magnificent Mile'. The team's client portfolio also includes The Trump Organization, McCaffery Interests, Hilco Industrial and AEW Capital Management.

Sources say: *"They respond quickly and professionally."* *"Excellent business advice."*

KEY INDIVIDUALS The *"highly knowledgeable and responsive"* **Mitchell Carrel** (see p.1201) represents a wide range of public and private clients. He is particularly lauded for his subject area expertise and zoning knowledge. **Dov Pinchot** (see p.1225) has expertise in leasing and subleasing matters and has negotiated contracts for clients in all industry sectors, including retail, culinary services and office developments. One impressed client comments: *"He is a great strategist and I fully trust his counsel."*

## K&L Gates
### See profile on p.2245

THE FIRM The Chicago real estate group at K&L Gates has a wide-ranging practice undertaking matters across the range of zoning, hospitality, financing and distressed real estate matters. The team remains particularly active in Illinois and is well placed to draw on the expertise of other teams due to its sizable global platform.

KEY INDIVIDUALS The *"exceptionally intelligent"* and tremendously experienced of counsel **Thomas Homburger** (see p.1212) is an expert in the financing and development of real estate projects. His experience and skills in the sector win superb praise from market observers.

## Latham & Watkins LLP
### See profile on p.446

THE FIRM Latham's real estate team is well equipped to advise on matters involving complex transactional real estate matters. The group advises a broad range of clients, many of whom enthuse that they have complete confidence in the team's abilities across a range of issues. In recent highlights, the team acted for Walton Street Capital on the formation of multiple joint ventures, and on the joint venture's related acquisition, and subsequent foreclosure, of a mezzanine loan, resulting in acquiring ownership of the Aston Waikiki Hotel.

Sources say: *"The practice group is sophisticated, diverse and very high-quality."*

KEY INDIVIDUALS **Gary Axelrod** is particularly experienced in real estate matters concerning the hospitality industry. He represents owners and operators in a wide spectrum of matters, including issues involving hotel, resort and gaming properties. Sources say he is an *"outstanding transactional attorney with practical solutions to getting a deal done; he is a problem solver."* **Robert Buday** has deep experience in the representation of clients in all aspects of investment vehicles, and is an expert in tax-efficient compensation arrangements. Market observers recommend him for his *"excellent strategic as well as technical advice on direction and transactions."*

## Locke Lord LLP
### See profile on p.2443

THE FIRM The group at Locke Lord is increasingly recognized as a major presence in the real estate market in Chicago, and advises on all commercial real estate concerns. In recent highlights, the group represented Shapack Development and AJ Capital Partners in the acquisition, financing and redevelopment of a property for use as a Soho House Club. The team's client list also includes Pearlmark Real Estate Partners, Hamilton Partners, JPMorgan Chase and Tishman Speyer Properties.

Sources say: *"A high-quality group."*

KEY INDIVIDUALS **Louis Cohen** (see p.1202) chairs the firm's finance, banking and real estate practice group. His practice encompasses commercial real estate transactions, and matters involving professional sports venues and franchises. Sources comment that he is a *"supremely experienced, well thought-of and strategic real estate lawyer."*

## Paul Hastings LLP
### See profile on p.1996

THE FIRM The team at Paul Hastings handles a broad range of complex commercial real estate matters, including zoning, land use and financing transactions, and is also highly experienced in related restructuring matters. The group has a particular advantage in being able to draw on the firm's extensive international resources and talent pool. The group's client portfolio includes notable clients such as Starwood Capital, TPG Capital, Aterian Partners and Citicorp.

**Sources say:** *"They have been fantastic."*

**KEY INDIVIDUALS Gregory Spitzer** has a solid reputation among sources for his real estate work. His expertise includes acquisitions, disposals and financing transactions, and he actively represents private equity firms, as well as public and private companies.

### Perkins Coie LLP
**See profile on p.2548**

**THE FIRM** Perkins Coie's Chicago-based real estate team has a strong line in undertaking major projects on a national and international level involving retail, hotels and offices. The group also has particular expertise in representing CMBS special servicers. Its recent highlights include acting for Maritz, Wolff & Co on the $192 million refinancing and sale of the Fairmont San Francisco hotel. Other key clients include Strategic Hotels & Resorts, DiNapoli Capital Partners and Optima.

**KEY INDIVIDUALS** Client favorite **Alexandra Cole** has expertise in real estate transactions and project finance both domestically and internationally.

### Pircher, Nichols & Meeks

**THE FIRM** This group is well placed to deal with complex real estate problems, and comes highly recommended by peers for its practical approach to sophisticated issues. The team provides advice across the board of real estate concerns, including environmental, tax and land use issues.

**Sources say:** *"They bring a very practical, problem-solving approach to the work that they do."*

**KEY INDIVIDUALS Eugene Leone** is managing partner of the firm's Chicago office. He has broad expertise in all types of commercial real estate matters, including distressed real estate transactions. Sources praise him for being *"very creative, very hard-working and an attorney who thinks outside the box."*

### Skadden, Arps, Slate, Meagher & Flom LLP & Affiliates
**See profile on p.2008**

**THE FIRM** Skadden's solid Chicago real estate group handles a wide range of matters related to real estate and real estate assets, and is noted in particular for its expertise with complex joint venture, partnership and fund formation issues. A recent highlight saw the team advise GIC Real Estate on a joint venture for a sizable investment in industrial real estate properties.

**KEY INDIVIDUALS** Of counsel **Sheli Rosenberg** (see p.1228) brings years of experience in a private real estate investment firm to her practice. She is singled out by peers and clients for her established industry experience and deep knowledge of real estate. **Nancy Olson** (see p.1224) advises clients across the range of real estate matters, including financing and reorganizations. She is also a member of the firm's REIT group.

### Winston & Strawn LLP
**See profile on p.1267**

**THE FIRM** Winston & Strawn's wide-ranging Chicago real estate practice acts on behalf of major institutional clients and developers, undertaking multifamily, commercial and industrial real estate matters, among an array of other issues. Clients are particularly appreciative of the team's thorough and practical approach toward matters.

**KEY INDIVIDUALS Christopher Murtaugh** (see p.1223) is a *"great lawyer and a gentleman; a pleasure to work opposite,"* say sources. His practice encompasses real estate financing, investment and disposal of commercial properties. **Mark Henning** (see p.1212) has a broad real estate practice covering all areas of complex transactions. Sources praise him for his *"knowledge, accessibility, professionalism and his ability to get the work done on time."*

### Other Notable Practitioners

**Langdon Neal** of Neal & Leroy LLC is widely hailed for his excellent practice in the zoning and land use space. Sources laud his *"really wonderful knowledge of zoning and land use in Chicago."* **Terrence Budny** of Sheppard, Mullin, Richter & Hampton LLP recently joined the firm from K&L Gates. He focuses on investment, financing and development of properties on behalf of clients from a variety of industries. **Thomas Duffy** (see p.1205) of Edwards Wildman Palmer is an expert in real estate development matters, including brownfield, zoning, and reciprocal easement agreements. Sources comment that he is a *"good lawyer with great clients; very experienced and respected."*

# TAX

Tax p.1192

Commentary about individuals can be found under their firm's paragraph. If the firm has no paragraph (is not ranked) look at Other Notable Practitioners.

## Band 1

### Kirkland & Ellis LLP
**See profile on p.1254**

**THE FIRM** The Chicago team of this international giant undertakes tax planning on transactions as well as controversy issues challenged by the IRS or overseas state tax entities. In a recent highlight it acted for Bain Capital on its acquisition of Securitas Direct from a private equity firm for $3.4 billion. Other clients in the team's impressive portfolio include Archstone, Constellation Energy, Walton Street Capital and Tronox Incorporated.

**Sources say:** *"Not only are you getting the best expertise and advice, but it's from a group that are enjoyable to work with."*

**KEY INDIVIDUALS Todd Maynes** (see p.1220) enjoys a fine reputation in the market, and is routinely called upon to handle tax litigation, debt restructuring and bankruptcy. According to one impressed interviewee, he is *"one of those standout individuals where you have total faith that*

*he's giving great advice."* The *"excellent"* **Donald Rocap** (see p.1227) handles transactional tax work and is an expert in matters concerning private equity fund formation. He is *"incredibly intelligent and creative in terms of how to tackle problems,"* notes one source. Clients say that **Jeffrey Sheffield** (see p.1231) is *"the consummate tax attorney and has excellent judgment on tax issues."* He is particularly praised by sources for his work involving M&A and tax planning for publicly traded companies. *"Excellent lawyer"* **William Welke** (see p.1237) undertakes work involving sophisticated corporate transactions, and also maintains a fine track record in tax controversy matters. Rising star **Natalie Keller** (see p.344) is well versed in all areas of tax controversy, including IRS matters, and is also noted for her expertise in transfer pricing matters. **Gregory Gallagher** (see p.1208) undertakes work on transactional tax matters in the domestic and international arenas. He recently led the team acting for Bain Capital on its $487 million purchase of Physio-Control.

### McDermott Will & Emery LLP
**See profile on p.1258**

**THE FIRM** This team remains one of the powerhouses in Illinois, and enjoys a fine reputation for its work handling tax matters in domestic and cross-border corporate restructurings and transactions. Of late, the team has advised tax-exempt Underwriters Laboratories on the restructuring of its global operations, and has also acted as tax adviser to Procter & Gamble in its joint venture with Teva Pharmaceutical Industries. Other high-profile clients include Urban Outfitters/Anthropologie, Abbott Laboratories, Hallmark Cards and MasterCard.

**Sources say:** *"They provide us with the highest-quality service."*

**KEY INDIVIDUALS Thomas Borders** (see p.285) is an expert in federal controversy matters, including litigation and audits. Sources describe him as *"a great team leader"* and reserve particular appreciation for his *"knowledge of the inner workings of the IRS."* The highly regarded **Lowell**

Yoder (see p.1238) is head of the US and international tax practice. He is an authority on sophisticated corporate tax planning and structuring, and comes particularly recommended for his cross-border work in these areas. **Roger Jones** is a new addition to the team, having recently joined from Latham & Watkins. He handles tax controversy matters, with a focus on the representation of taxpayers. He garners much acclaim for his work, with one source praising his ability to be *"three steps ahead"* on matters. **Andrea Kramer**'s (see p.1216) forte is in financial products, but she is also consolidating her experience in tax matters concerning the energy sector. Observers single out her *"unbelievable energy"* in matters. Head of state and local tax, **Jane Wells May** (see p.1220) focuses on tax controversy work. Clients reserve particular praise for her tax law knowledge and responsiveness.

## Band 2

### Baker & McKenzie
See profile on p.435

**THE FIRM** The tax practice of this international firm has a long history of advising high net-worth clients and multinational corporations on tax matters. Sources comment favorably on the international dimension of the team's practice, and those within Illinois see it as one of the go-to firms for international pricing cases.

**KEY INDIVIDUALS** *"Tremendous lawyer"* **Gregg Lemein** (see p.354) undertakes work involving federal income taxation in the USA. He is particularly experienced in matters relating to intercompany pricing. The *"really brilliant"* **Richard Lipton** (see p.1218) is noted for his advice regarding federal tax issues, and is also in much demand for expertise concerning REITs. **John McDonald** (see p.1221) is an expert in foreign currency and foreign tax provision. He has a wealth of experience in acquisitions and reorganizations, both in a domestic and international setting.

### Mayer Brown LLP
See profile on p.1257

**THE FIRM** Mayer Brown's team undertakes matters involving all aspects of tax for both multinationals and individuals. It has a solid transactional and controversy practice that is held in high esteem by clients. The team's controversy practice recently successfully represented Consolidated Edison of New York in a case filed in the Court of Federal Claims. The group also acted for Caterpillar in its $8.6 billion acquisition of mining equipment manufacturer Bucyrus International. Other clients among its distinguished portfolio include Abbott Laboratories, ProLogis, Nestlé and JPMorgan Chase.

**Sources say:** *"Mayer Brown's service is of the highest quality. I can always depend on them to do a thorough job analyzing issues and presenting options on the most complex issues."*

**KEY INDIVIDUALS** The superb **Timothy Sherck** is an expert in corporate tax matters and focuses on the tax issues of M&A and dispositions. He also has a specialty in dealing with requests for private letter rulings before the IRS. *"International expert"* **James Barry** represents an excellent choice of counsel on tax-planning work for planned operations by both US and foreign corporations. He played a lead role in Caterpillar's acquisition of Bucyrus. Sources are very appreciative of **George Craven**'s skill as a tax attorney. He handles corporate tax and international planning issues, and is also noted for his expertise in the tax implications of franchising and insurance. **Joel Williamson** is particularly lauded for his tax controversy expertise and elicits praise for his high level of client service, timely work product and attention to detail.

### Sidley Austin LLP
See profile on p.1264

**THE FIRM** This team has a thriving transactions and controversy practice and also comes recommended for its expertise in low-income tax credit matters. In a recent highlight, it handled all the attendant tax issues involved in Western Union's acquisition of the global payments division of Travelex Holdings. Other standout work saw the team advise Takeda Pharmaceutical on its purchase of URL Pharma. Tyson Foods, SXC Health Solutions, Exelon and GE are among the group's other high-profile clients.

**Sources say:** *"The attorneys we use are very knowledgeable. I have recommended them and will continue to do so." "Tremendous as a team."*

**KEY INDIVIDUALS** The *"top-notch"* **Sharp Sorensen** (see p.1233) handles federal tax concerns and transactions, and recently advised McGladrey & Pullen on the tax issues involved in its acquisition of RSM McGladrey. He also led on the Western Union matter. **Jay Zimbler** (see p.1238) also undertakes federal tax matters, but focuses particularly on income tax and contested issues. He recently represented Principal Life Insurance in a tax refund case. **Suresh Advani** (see p.1196) is an expert in federal income tax and has extensive knowledge of asset securitization and securities offerings. Recent work has seen him handle the tax issues involved in GE Healthcare's formation of Caradigm, a medical software joint venture with Microsoft. **Lee Christie** (see p.1201) comes particularly recommended for

his tax work in the insurance arena, and advises on transactions and controversy matters. He assisted Cigna with its recent acquisition of ARG's Great American Supplemental Benefits Group. **Tracy Williams** (see p.1237) is similarly noted for her expertise in tax matters concerning insurance companies, and recently represented Chartis and

Zurich in state insurance retaliatory litigation across the nation.

## Skadden, Arps, Slate, Meagher & Flom LLP & Affiliates
See profile on p.2008

**THE FIRM** This impressive team is well versed in all areas of tax, including transfer pricing, disputes and controversy, and has been particularly busy with large public deals and tax restructuring matters of late. Recent work has seen it advise on tax matters concerning high-profile acquisitions and joint ventures.
**Sources say:** *"Extremely responsive, with substantive and thoughtful responses."*
**KEY INDIVIDUALS Louis Freeman** (see p.1207) is regarded as a *"leading light"* in the tax community. He is a noted authority on federal tax planning, and is also regularly called on to handle spin-offs, restructurings and disputes. *"Good all-around tax attorney"* **David Polster** (see p.1226) is head of the Chicago tax group. He has a diverse tax practice and is a fine choice of counsel for high-value transactions. **John Rayis** (see p.389) enjoys a fine reputation for his expertise in tax matters involving REITs and has been particularly busy of late advising on the formation of several high-value joint ventures. **David Levy** (see p.1217) is developing an excellent name in the tax community and undertakes a broad spectrum of tax work, including foreign investment in real property.

## Band 3

### Jenner & Block LLP
See profile on p.1252

**THE FIRM** This solid mid-market firm covers transactional and controversy tax matters. Subspecialties within the practice include tax advantage programs sold as securities and tax issues concerning real estate securities programs. The group is also routinely sought for its strengths in cross-border and multijurisdictional cases.
**KEY INDIVIDUALS Geoffrey Davis** (see p.1203) is noted for his expertise in transactional and controversy matters, and is also well versed in tax concerns involving investment management and bankruptcy. Chicago tax practice chair **Christian Kimball** (see p.1214) has a broad practice that encompasses all facets of federal income tax, and comes particularly recommended for his work in corporate restructurings.

### Katten Muchin Rosenman LLP
See profile on p.1253

**THE FIRM** Katten Muchin Rosenman's tax group is particularly strong in the M&A and private equity space. Additionally, the practice is singled out for its advice to foreign clients on the US tax concerns of their operations and investments, and vice versa for US clients working abroad.
**Sources say:** *"Responsive, efficient and cost effective. Love their work."*
**KEY INDIVIDUALS Sheldon Banoff** is *"a prince of a guy and a really super lawyer,"* according to clients. He focuses on federal income taxation and excels in real estate, limited liability and partnership tax matters within this area. **Saul Rudo** is recognized for his expertise in tax planning concerning corporate M&A and venture capital, and elicits much praise from clients for his *"brilliant tax advice."*

### Latham & Watkins LLP
See profile on p.446

**THE FIRM** Latham & Watkins provides tax advice on all matters to both public and private companies, including fund sponsors. The team is well known for its advice on tax matters concerning renewable energy projects, and in a recent highlight it advised Morgan Stanley regarding the project financing of the Arlington Valley Solar Energy II project. It also counts AO Smith, GE Capital, Walgreen and Koch Industries among its distinguished group of clients.
**Sources say:** *"They have a solid roster of people here and across the globe." "A very complete firm."*
**KEY INDIVIDUALS** Practice chair **Diana Doyle** is *"tremendous in all aspects"* and *"a pleasure to work with,"* according to sources. She is well versed in both domestic and international work, and counts Hyatt Hotels as a key client. The *"extremely efficient and knowledgeable"* **Alan Van Dyke** is an authority on tax matters concerning fund sponsors and advises on all issues relating to private equity funds. Interviewees are quick to praise his industry and technical know-how, and also single out his fine communication skills. *"The real deal"* **Stephen Bowen** is a key figure in the tax world. He specializes in federal income tax matters, and is noted by sources for his *"long and distinguished career"* in the market.

### Neal, Gerber & Eisenberg LLP
See profile on p.1260

**THE FIRM** The group at Neal, Gerber & Eisenberg has a wide client base, including tax-exempt organizations, individuals and corporations, which it represents on both domestic and international tax matters. The team undertakes a broad spectrum of work, and has particular

strength in tax and business planning and unclaimed property compliance.
**Sources say:** *"Service is exemplary."*
**KEY INDIVIDUALS Robert Bedore** (see p.1198) is a *"creative problem solver"* who focuses on resolving federal tax controversies for private and publicly listed companies, as well as individuals. **John Biek** (see p.1199) handles corporate transactions and controversies and also specializes in tax planning for multistate organizations. Sources reserve particular praise for his extensive subject matter knowledge. **Andrea Despotes** (see p.1204) concentrates on assisting Fortune 500 companies on tax-planning matters, and is well versed in the structuring of tax-free reorganizations and spin-off transactions. **Kenneth Harris** (see p.1211) is well respected by clients and peers for his work on federal tax income matters relating to corporate divestments, planning strategies, and acquisitions. Sources hail his interpersonal skills and approach towards cases.

### Winston & Strawn LLP
See profile on p.1267

**THE FIRM** Winston & Strawn has a broad practice with a particular focus on tax concerns in project finance. The team also undertakes regulatory and compliance work at a federal and state level, for which it wins praise from clients. Recent work has seen it act for Motorola on the company's $1.2 billion sale of its global wireless phone systems to Nokia Siemens. The group was also lead counsel for Thrifty Oil in recent large-scale tax litigation. The team's client portfolio also includes Wealth and Tax Advisory Services, Olympus Partners and Baird Capital.
**Sources say:** *"Very knowledgeable and easy to work with."*
**KEY INDIVIDUALS** The *"really creative"* **James Lynch** (see p.1219) handles corporate tax matters and counts Yum! Brands among his key clients. He co-heads the tax department with **Louis Weber** (see p.1236). Weber focuses on tax matters pertaining to corporate and private equity transactions. Sources say: *"He is very bright – he sees the whole picture and looks for a solution with you."*

### Other Notable Practitioners

The popular and much-recommended **Paul Carman** of Chapman and Cutler LLP concentrates on the tax implications of investment vehicles and financial transactions. **Thomas Stephens** (see p.1234) of Dentons is a *"class act and a really smart guy,"* according to sources. He handles tax planning and transactional structuring work for a broad base of clients.

# TECHNOLOGY & OUTSOURCING

Commentary about individuals can be found under their firm's paragraph. If the firm has no paragraph (is not ranked) look at Other Notable Practitioners.

| Technology & Outsourcing | |
|---|---|
| **Leading Firms** | |
| **Band 1** | |
| Baker & McKenzie * | |
| Mayer Brown LLP * | |
| **Band 2** | |
| Dentons * | |
| DLA Piper LLP (US) * | |
| Kirkland & Ellis LLP * | |
| **Band 3** | |
| Drinker Biddle & Reath LLP * | |
| Edwards Wildman Palmer * | |
| Neal, Gerber & Eisenberg LLP * | |
| Sidley Austin LLP * | |

| Leading Individuals | |
|---|---|
| **Band 1** | |
| Docksey Ross | Dentons * |
| Eisner Rebecca S | Mayer Brown LLP |
| Kirchhoefer Gregg | Kirkland & Ellis LLP * |
| Mensik Michael S | Baker & McKenzie * |
| Peterson Brad L | Mayer Brown LLP |
| Roy Paul J N | Mayer Brown LLP |
| Sanchez Vincent | DLA Piper LLP (US) * |
| Smedinghoff Thomas J | Edwards Wildman Palmer * |
| **Band 2** | |
| George Peter R | Baker & McKenzie * |
| Gullikson Rosemary L | Dentons * |
| Halpern Marcelo | Perkins Coie LLP (ONP) † |
| Hirshman Neil S | Kirkland & Ellis LLP * |
| Kaufmann Mark L | Sidley Austin LLP * |
| Kramer Samuel | Baker & McKenzie * |
| Ryan Michael | Kelley Drye & Warren LLP (ONP) † |
| Weiss Robert M | Neal, Gerber & Eisenberg LLP * |
| **Band 3** | |
| Bennett Michael P | Edwards Wildman Palmer * |
| Gold Stephen | McGuireWoods LLP (ONP) † |
| Hengesbaugh Brian | Baker & McKenzie * |
| Kalina Ira M | Drinker Biddle & Reath LLP * |
| Rang Kevin A | Mayer Brown LLP |
| Rothstein Jeffrey | Sidley Austin LLP * |
| **Up-and-coming individuals** | |
| Lele Sachin A | DLA Piper LLP (US) * |
| Manter Gregory A | Mayer Brown LLP |
| **Associates to watch** | |
| Lewis Dan | Kirkland & Ellis LLP * |
| Swan Tim | Sidley Austin LLP * |

\* Indicates firm / individual with profile.
Alphabetical order within each band. Band 1 is the highest.

## Band 1

### Baker & McKenzie
See profile on p.435

THE FIRM This established practice is singled out for the strength of its technology and outsourcing practice, with both peers and clients recognizing the impact of its international reach on the breadth of its expertise. The practice is regarded as a leader in the field of transformational strategic sourcing, privacy and data management, and also maintains a fine reputation for technology-related M&A transactions. Its enviable client list includes high-profile names such as Bausch & Lomb, Wells Fargo and Hewlett-Packard. **Sources say:** "*They understand the market and are able to negotiate competitive deals.*"

KEY INDIVIDUALS The highly respected **Michael Mensik** (see p.367) cochairs the firm's North American sourcing practice and is regarded by peers as a thought leader and an important member of the legal community. He is best known for his work advising clients on the structure of sourcing arrangements in national and international operations. **Samuel Kramer**'s (see p.1216) practice continues to go from strength to strength, with sources keen to recommend his "*great service and excellent work product.*" He specializes in major IT services and outsourcing deals and offers significant expertise in cyberspace law. **Peter George**'s (see p.1208) deep outsourcing experience and impressive awareness of industry developments is much valued by clients. "*He's a strong but reasonable negotiator and a very creative thinker in dealing with the variety of issues that come up in these sorts of transactions,*" asserts one impressed interviewee. He is particularly noted for his adept handling of cross-border outsourcing transactions. Clients especially benefit from **Brian Hengesbaugh**'s (see p.333) extensive knowledge base and wealth of experience in privacy and data security matters, and he continues to be much in demand for his expertise in the implementation of privacy programs and the management of data collection.

### Mayer Brown LLP
See profile on p.1257

THE FIRM Mayer Brown is universally regarded as a leading player in the technology and outsourcing arena, with market commentators commending the ease with which its lawyers integrate with clients, delivering business-focused advice and guidance. The team specializes in high-value strategic sourcing, cloud computing and facilities management, and offers expertise in the structuring, renegotiation and termination of transactions. It counts CoreLogic and McCain Foods among its key clients. **Sources say:** "*I think the world of them in terms of how they have helped me – I have learned a lot and wouldn't hesitate to go to them on anything.*"

KEY INDIVIDUALS **Brad Peterson** remains a leading practitioner in the outsourcing field, with peers recognizing the impressive quality of his work, spanning licensing and service agreements and outsourcing arrangements.

Sources also acknowledge his outstanding commercial acumen and the results that stem from his vast reserves of knowledge. "*Excellent negotiator*" **Rebecca Eisner** commands respect for her enviably immense knowledge of IT and outsourcing-related transactions. She continues to act on behalf of McCain Foods, recently negotiating a number of IT and business process license and service arrangements. **Paul Roy** enjoys an outstanding reputation, winning plaudits for his ability to present practical solutions with an admirable expediency. He comes particularly recommended for his wealth of experience, acting on behalf of emerging and established companies in business-critical outsourcing transactions. **Kevin Rang** is singled out as a master of facilities management deals and elicits praise for his ability to make clients feel "*100% secure*" on matters. "*He is a savvy negotiator and skilled at finding creative solutions to solve disputes – his ability to collaborate with me and my internal business owners is amazing,*" asserts one happy client. His practice also extends to the full range of BPO transactions. **Gregory Manter** maintains a broad practice, offering experience in a range of outsourcing and licensing transactions, and he is particularly renowned for his prowess in the cloud computing arena. He is currently acting on behalf of CoreLogic during the negotiation of an outsourcing services agreement.

## Band 2

### Dentons
See profile on p.449

THE FIRM Dentons is widely recognized for its leading strategic sourcing practice, with interviewees paying tribute to the depth of experience housed within the team. The practice is focused on customer-side representation, while also employing its previous experience acting on behalf of vendors to the client's advantage. Clients from a range of sectors including energy, healthcare, technology and retail acknowledge the business acumen that backs up the team's technical brilliance.

KEY INDIVIDUALS Established practitioner **Ross Docksey** (see p.1204) is held in the highest regard by members of the legal community. He remains well known for the stellar quality of his work structuring complex outsourcing transactions and strategic alliances. **Rosemary Gullikson** (see p.1210) wins plaudits for her clear understanding of the market place, with interviewees remarking: "*She has a strong ability to get deals done efficiently for her clients and is focused on reaching an agreement in a way that protects her clients.*" She is valued for the experienced and professional manner with which she guides clients through ITO, BPO and technology contracting transactions.

### DLA Piper LLP (US)
See profile on p.1971

THE FIRM DLA Piper's technology sourcing and commercial group maintains a high-profile presence in the market, and is much noted for its breadth of expertise, acting for both vendors and customers across a variety of industries. It counts RBS Citizens and Groupon among its impressive roster of clients.

**Sources say:** *"Good across the board and well coordinated around the world – they really have my trust."*

**KEY INDIVIDUALS** Clients appreciate **Vincent Sanchez**'s (see p.1229) deft management of complex issues and pay tribute to his responsiveness. Commentators also single out his *"ability to absorb and retain large amounts of information."* His practice is focused on large-scale international outsourcing transactions. **Sachin Lele** (see p.1217) *"gets the deal done and is a good negotiator."* He specializes in ITO and BPO transactions, and IP-related strategic alliances and licensing arrangements. He is also recognized for his knowledge of the Indian market, representing both Indian and US clients doing business in India.

## Kirkland & Ellis LLP
See profile on p.1254

**THE FIRM** Kirkland & Ellis is well known as a pioneer in the outsourcing market, and the practice remains a group of choice for companies seeking advice on complex procurement initiatives, supply chain management and ITO and BPO transactions. Its lawyers represent both customers and vendors in matters that arise throughout the outsourcing cycle. Key clients include CIGNA and Goldman Sachs.

**Sources say:** *"They are very smart and very practical. I count on them to deliver great results and they do. They are consummate professionals who listen to, and understand the needs of, their clients."*

**KEY INDIVIDUALS** Practice chair **Gregg Kirchhoefer** (see p.1214) *"has the command of the room and the respect of everyone,"* note interviewees, who also view him as *"a real go-to guy for the tough issues."* He has a keen expertise in technology-related transactions, which builds upon his previous experience in the computer industry. *"Thought leader"* **Neil Hirshman** (see p.334) is applauded for the realistic nature of his advice: *"Some tell the client what they want to hear – he will tell you his honest view and assessment."* He practices at a domestic and international level and is recognized for his expertise in complex outsourcing and licensing and development transactions. Recent work highlights include structuring and completing the last of seven outsourcing transactions for National Grid. **Dan Lewis** (see p.1218) is described as *"the best associate"* by one enthusiastic source. He is building a name for himself in IP and technology-based transactions, with sources commending the quality of his work on strategic alliances, outsourcing deals and licensing agreements.

## Band 3

## Drinker Biddle & Reath LLP
See profile on p.2238

**THE FIRM** This team of skilled technology and IP lawyers is well versed in the concerns that drive both vendor and customer-side transactions. The practice is well known for

its work with small and midsized vendors and also assists customers with the acquisition of services, software and hardware. Additionally, the group offers specialist outsourcing advice on healthcare-related transactions and to emerging technology companies. Clients such as Comcast, B/E Aerospace and the American Hospital Association illustrate the breadth of industry knowledge housed within the team.

**Sources say:** *"They have a high level of customer service."*

**KEY INDIVIDUALS** **Ira Kalina** (see p.1213) continues to make his mark representing high-profile companies in their technology and IP-related transactions. *"He brings very relevant commercial experience into each of our deals and is very creative in deal structure and ideas,"* reports one impressed source.

## Edwards Wildman Palmer
See profile on p.1520

**THE FIRM** Edwards Wildman Palmer wins plaudits across the board, with interviewees commending the strength of its technology and outsourcing practice. Its lawyers enjoy a particularly good reputation for their handling of IP and privacy matters within this space, and are regularly instructed by high-profile organizations such as JPMorgan Chase, Hyatt and Kia. In a recent highlight, it represented Groupon in a series of data collection and security matters.

**Sources say:** *"The firm is very responsive and has the breadth and strength to assist in domestic and international matters."*

**KEY INDIVIDUALS** The *"extremely knowledgeable"* **Thomas Smedinghoff** (see p.1232) is singled out as a leading force in the identity management arena, and has a wealth of experience concerning electronic transactions and digital signatures. Commentators are effusive in their praise of his extensive knowledge base and thoughtful and informative approach. **Michael Bennett**'s (see p.1198) *"client service is at the highest level."* He is noted for his extensive cloud computing experience, which alongside his deep open source knowledge gives him an enviable awareness of the impact of emerging technologies on business development. Recent work highlights include acting on behalf of Kia on a number of technology acquisition, development and outsourcing transactions.

## Neal, Gerber & Eisenberg LLP
See profile on p.1260

**THE FIRM** Neal, Gerber & Eisenberg's technology transactions and services practice maintains a strong reputation for representing clients in the buying, selling and licensing of data, software, hardware and services. It is particularly noted for its expertise across system development and integration, global sourcing and telecom, and represents a particularly fine choice of counsel for clients in the healthcare, hospitality, transport and financial services sectors.

**Sources say:** *"They have taken the time to understand our business and they understand it well."*

**KEY INDIVIDUALS** **Robert Weiss** (see p.1237) is widely recognized as a thought leader in the technology space, and over the course of his career he has developed specialist knowledge that spans BPO, licensing, joint venture and

systems integration and development transactions. *"He has remained very sensitive to our needs and is at the top of the game the entire time,"* said one happy client.

## Sidley Austin LLP
See profile on p.1264

**THE FIRM** Sidley Austin's technology practice offers specialist knowledge in IT procurement and outsourcing, life sciences transactions, and digital media and entertainment. In the past year it has advised GE Healthcare on the formation of its medical joint venture with Microsoft, and also acted on behalf of GlaxoSmithKline in a copromotion agreement with Auxilium Pharmaceuticals.

**Sources say:** *"A firm that offers not only strong legal counsel, but practical business advice as well."*

**KEY INDIVIDUALS** Sources describe **Mark Kaufmann** (see p.1214) as *"an exceptional lawyer who stays on top of the developments in his specialty."* He is noted for his expertise on acquisitions, outsourcing, licensing and infrastructure transactions. Recent work has included representing OneAmerica in the long-term outsourcing of its IT infrastructure and operations to T-Systems. Practice head **Jeffrey Rothstein** (see p.1228) is well known for his strengths in domestic and international transactions and has a wealth of experience in matters relating to medical device, pharmaceuticals, biotech and satellite technology. Interviewees draw attention to his *"deep subject matter expertise, business acumen and superior negotiation skills."* He lead on the GE Healthcare and GlaxoSmithKline matters. Associate **Tim Swan** (see p.1235) is recognized as a rising star and elicits particular praise for his client-friendly attitude and solution-oriented approach. He is noted for his expertise in IP and technology-related transactions, and works with clients from a range of fields, including IT, financial services, telecom and biotech.

## Other Notable Practitioners

The highly respected **Marcelo Halpern** of Perkins Coie LLP offers an impressive breadth of expertise that spans strategic alliances, licensing, outsourcing and data security. Clients range from emerging companies to established global entities. *"Fabulous lawyer"* **Michael Ryan** of Kelley Drye & Warren LLP is commended for his responsiveness, personable demeanor and ability to think outside the box. His practice is focused on complex outsourcing, licensing, development agreements and strategic alliances. Recent work includes handling a series of software and technology agreements on behalf of Guggenheim Capital. **Stephen Gold** of McGuireWoods LLP is vastly experienced in a wide range of transactions including outsourcing, licensing, systems procurement and data security. *"He is very proficient at analyzing an engagement and providing the right mix of resources so that we get the best combination of skills for our needs,"* reports one enthusiastic interviewee.

# Leaders' Profiles in Illinois

## ACKERMAN, David
Morgan, Lewis & Bockius LLP, Chicago
312 324 1170
dackerman@morganlewis.com
*Featured in Labor & Employment (Illinois)*

**Practice Areas:** David Ackerman is a partner in Morgan Lewis's Employee Benefits and Executive Compensation Practice and a leader of the ESOP Practice. He is a nationally recognized ESOP lawyer, having advised hundreds of corporations and their shareholders and directors on using ESOPs in a wide variety of transactions, including leveraged buyouts, corporate stock repurchases, ownership succession transactions, going-private transactions and corporate reorganizations.
**Professional Memberships:** Member of The ESOP Association and The National Center for Employee Ownership.
**Personal:** Mr Ackerman graduated from Harvard Law School (1974, JD) and Princeton University (1971, AB). He is admitted to practice in Illinois.

## ADAMO, Kenneth R
Kirkland & Ellis LLP, Chicago
312 862 2671
kradamo@kirkland.com
*Featured in Intellectual Property (Illinois)*

**Practice Areas:** IP law, including patent, trademark and unfair competition, and trade secrets. Extensive lead trial counsel experience in jury and non-jury matters before state and federal courts and the ITC, as well as ex parte and inter partes experience in the US Patent and Trademark Office and with non-US patent and trademark authorities. Has substantial appellate experience before the Federal Circuit, as well as arbitration and ADR experience.
**Career:** Admitted to Bars of Illinois, New York, Ohio and Texas; USPTO Reg No 27 299.
**Publications:** Frequent lecturer and author on trial, appellate and litigation issues, skills, and training topics.

## ADAMS, Joe
McDermott Will & Emery LLP, Chicago
312 984 7790
jadams@mwe.com
*Featured in Labor & Employment (Illinois)*

**Practice Areas:** Partner in employee benefits department. Concentrates on employee benefits and executive compensation matters for public, private and tax-exempt organizations. Advises clients regarding executive and incentive compensation programs including employment agreements, stock based compensation, nonqualified deferred compensation, SERPs, and compliance with SEC proxy disclosure rules regarding executive compensation. Frequently advises employers with respect to employee benefits and executive compensation matters in mergers and acquisitions and other corporate transactions.
**Personal:** Cornell Law School (JD, cum laude), University of Chicago (BA with honors).

## ADELMAN, Howard
Adelman & Gettleman Ltd, Chicago
312 435 1050
hla@ag-ltd.com
*Featured in Bankruptcy/Restructuring (Illinois)*

**Practice Areas:** Commercial bankruptcy, reorganization and insolvency matters, and commercial litigation. Has been involved in major bankruptcy cases since 1978 representing business debtors, secured creditors, creditors' committees, sureties and other parties in a variety of bankruptcy proceedings.
**Professional Memberships:** Illinois State Bar Association; Chicago Bar Association - Bankruptcy and Reorganization Committee; Missouri Bar Association; 7th Circuit Bar Association.
**Career:** Co-founder, shareholder and Member of Adelman & Gettleman, Ltd. since 1983. Law clerk to the Honorable Robert G Dowd, Chief Judge - Missouri Court of Appeals. Executive Judicial Assistant - Missouri Court of Appeals. Schwartz, Cooper, Kolb & Gaynor, 1978-83, Partner, 1982.
**Personal:** St. Louis University School of Law (cum laude 1977 JD); Illinois State University (1974 BS). He has been listed for more than 20 years in Naifeh and Smith's The Best Lawyers in America, Woodward/White. He is listed as one of the Top 10 Illinois Super Lawyers in 2012 and 2013 regardless of specialty, one of the Top 100 Illinois Super Lawyers for 2006-2013 and one of the Top 100 Business Lawyers in Illinois by the Leading Lawyers Network in 2006-2013. In October of 1999, Chief Justice William Rehnquist appointed Howard L. Adelman to serve as a member of the Judicial Conference Advisory Committee on the Federal Rules of Bankruptcy Procedure. Mr Adelman served on the Advisory Committee from 1999-2005 through the implementation of BAPCPA. Mr Adelman is also a Fellow of the American College of Bankruptcy, as part of its Twelfth Class.

## ADVANI, Suresh
Sidley Austin LLP, Chicago
312 853 2176
sadvani@sidley.com
*Featured in Tax (Illinois)*

**Practice Areas:** Partner in Sidley's Chicago office, practicing in the Tax group with a focus in federal income tax matters. He represents domestic and foreign corporations involved in mergers and acquisitions, partnerships and joint ventures, spin-offs and other divisive transactions, financial products, asset securitizations, restructurings of financially-troubled corporations and partnerships, and foreign and domestic securities offerings.
**Professional Memberships:** Member, American Bar Association Section of Taxation, Chicago Bar Association.
**Personal:** Northwestern University School of Law, JD, 1992, cum laude, Order of the Coif; University of Illinois, BS, 1987, with highest honors. Admission: Illinois.

## AIELLO, Anthony
Sidley Austin LLP, Chicago
312 853 7128
aaiello@sidley.com
*Featured in Real Estate (Illinois)*

**Practice Areas:** Partner in, and the head of, Sidley's Chicago Real Estate Group. Mr Aiello represents a wide variety of clients including financial institutions, REITs, real estate funds, utility companies, banks and developers and has particular experience in real estate acquisition, development, construction, financing, leasing, and disposition, as well as joint venture and preferred equity transactions, including transactions involving office buildings, department stores, industrial facilities and hotels.
**Personal:** DePaul University College of Law, JD, 1986, with honors, Editor of DePaul University Law Review; University of Notre Dame, BBA, 1983. Admission: Illinois.

## AIZENSTEIN, Neal
DLA Piper LLP (US), Chicago
312 368 3435
neal.aizenstein@dlapiper.com
*Featured in Corporate/M&A (Illinois)*

**Practice Areas:** Corporate/M&A
**Career:** He represents purchasers, sellers and investors in public and private acquisitions and disposition transactions and issuers and underwriters in public and private financings, including initial public offerings and Rule 144A offerings of both equity and debt securities. He advises public companies on the Sarbanes-Oxley Act of 2002; prepares and reviews periodic reports, registration statements and proxy statements filed with the Securities and Exchange Commission; and advises boards of directors, board committees and executive officers on day-to-day and extraordinary events.
**Personal:** JD, Northwestern University School of Law, cum laude; BS, CPA, University of Illinois at Urbana-Champaign.

## ALAMUDDIN, Sari M
Morgan, Lewis & Bockius LLP, Chicago
312 324 1158
salamuddin@morganlewis.com
*Featured in Labor & Employment (Illinois)*

**Practice Areas:** Sari M. Alamuddin is a partner in Morgan Lewis's Labor and Employment Practice and is the practice group leader for the Labor and Employment Practice in Chicago. Sari represents clients on a wide range of labor and employment matters. His practice particularly focuses on class-action and multi-plaintiff litigation, including benefits litigation, wage and hour litigation and complex employment litigation. He has served as first and second chair in trials before federal, state, and administrative law judges.
**Personal:** Attended University of Wisconsin Law School, 1993, JD, Cum Laude; Princeton University, 1990, AB.

## ALY, Imron
Winston & Strawn LLP, Chicago
312 558 8929
ialy@winston.com
*Featured in Intellectual Property (Illinois)*

**Practice Areas:** Imron Aly's trial practice is focused on patent infringement suits. He has applied his technical background in matters including pharmaceuticals, medical devices, DNA arrays, computer business methods, and financial trading systems. He has managed high-profile lawsuits that have garnered significant media attention, including a pharmaceutical patent case where the district court found inequitable conduct and the Federal Circuit affirmed the decision. It was the only case where an inequitable conduct finding has been affirmed since the appellate court heightened the standard. He has also led several publicized pro bono matters, including a Seventh Circuit appellate argument.

## ANDERSON, Kimball R
Winston & Strawn LLP, Chicago
312 558 5858
kanderson@winston.com
*Featured in Litigation (Illinois)*

**Practice Areas:** Mr Anderson focuses his practice in intellectual property litigation, professional liability, product liability, insurance coverage, consumer class actions, and arbitrations.
**Career:** Mr Anderson is a nationally recognized trial lawyer with 35 years of experience at Winston & Strawn LLP. He graduated first in class from the University of Illinois College of Law. He has tried many complex commercial cases to verdict in state and federal courts around the country and has argued cases before the federal courts of appeals, including two arguments before the Supreme Court of the United States.

## ANDES, Fredric
Barnes & Thornburg LLP, Washington, DC
312 214 8310
fredric.andes@btlaw.com
*Featured in Environment (Illinois)*

**Practice Areas:** Mr Andes is the Administrator of the Barnes & Thornburg Environmental Department for the Chicago office, and leader of the Water Team. He serves as coordinator for the Federal Water Quality Coalition, which participates in Clean Water Act rulemakings. He also advises clients on water quality matters on the state and federal levels.
**Career:** Admitted in Illinois and Washington, D.C.; District Courts for Northern District of Illinois and Washington, D.C.; Courts of Appeals for First, Second, Third, Fourth, Fifth, Sixth, Seventh, Ninth, Tenth and D.C. Circuits.
**Personal:** JD cum laude, Harvard Law School 1980; BA, Northwestern University, 1977.

## ANDRE, Greg
K&L Gates, Chicago
312 807 4254
greg.andre@klgates.com
*Featured in Construction (Illinois)*

**Practice Areas:** Greg Andre has more than 25 years of experience in design and construction contracts and construction dispute resolution. He has handled a wide variety of projects across the United States, including major urban high-rises, shopping centers, senior living facilities, mixed-use projects, hotels, manufacturing facilities, airports, highways and public utilities. Mr Andre is the author of numerous books and articles on construction law. He is also a member of the Society of Illinois Construction Attorneys and a co-founder of the Illinois Chapter of the Construction Owners Association of America.

**ANDRIOFF, Joni**
Littler Mendelson, PC, Chicago
312 795 3274
jandrioff@littler.com
*Featured in Labor & Employment (Illinois)*
**Practice Areas:** Employee Benefits, Executive Compensation, ERISA, M&A.
**Professional Memberships:** Immediate Past Chair, ABA (Section of Taxation), Employee Benefits Committee; Member, American College of Employee Benefits Counsel; Fellow, American Bar Foundation; Member, Chicago Bar Association Employee Benefits Committee.
**Career:** Ms Andrioff has practiced in the area of employee benefits and executive compensation for 26 years with particular emphasis on ERISA fiduciary matters, M&A, executive compensation, benefit plan design, compliance, and correction. Ms Andrioff's career includes experience in law firm practice, as well as consulting, in both domestic and international benefit contexts. Ms Andrioff started her career as a union representative.

**ANTHONY, Michael F**
McDermott Will & Emery LLP, Chicago
312 984 7635
manthony@mwe.com
*Featured in Healthcare (Illinois), Healthcare (Nationwide)*
See under Nationwide for profile.

**ASTLE, Richard W**
Sidley Austin LLP, Chicago
312 853 7270
rastle@sidley.com
*Featured in Energy & Natural Resources (Illinois)*
**Practice Areas:** Partner in Sidley's Chicago office. He focuses on various corporate and securities matters, including disclosure, compliance and governance questions; contract preparation and review; affiliations, joint ventures, investments, acquisitions and dispositions, including generation plant sales; and financings involving credit facilities and private and public offerings of securities. He advises energy companies, including electric and gas utilities; retail purchasers of energy; manufacturers; and tax-exempt entities, such as universities and cultural institutions.
**Personal:** Georgetown University Law Center, JD, 1980, magna cum laude; University of Pennsylvania, MAcc, 1977, with distinction; University of Pennsylvania, BS, 1977, summa cum laude. Admission: Illinois.

**BAKER, Pamela**
Dentons, Chicago
312 876 8989
pamela.baker@dentons.com
*Featured in Employee Benefits & Executive Compensation (Nationwide), Labor & Employment (Illinois)*
**Practice Areas:** Chair Emerita and Vice Chair of legacy Dentons's Employee Benefits and Executive Compensation practice. Focuses on non-qualified deferred compensation, executive equity arrangements for private and public entities, including not-for-profits, and their treatment in corporate transactions. Represents public company compensation committees, employers and senior executives in employment, change in control, severance arrangements; employers in design and administration of tax-qualified retirement plans; institutional fiduciaries and financial institutions concerning ERISA issues arising in pension fund investing.
**Professional Memberships:** American Bar Association; American College of Employee Benefits Counsel.
**Personal:** University of Wisconsin Law School, JD, managing editor, Wisconsin Law Review; Smith College, AB, with honors.

**BAKKER, Jeffrey J**
Neal, Gerber & Eisenberg LLP, Chicago
312 269 8270
jbakker@ngelaw.com
*Featured in Labor & Employment (Illinois)*
**Practice Areas:** Represents companies in a wide array of executive compensation and employee benefit matters, including: designing and preparing deferred compensation and equity compensation plans; ensuring tax and ERISA compliance of qualified and non-qualified retirement plans; advising clients as to their fiduciary responsibilities with respect to employee benefit plans; and counseling clients on the administration of welfare benefit plans. He also provides assistance in the employee benefits aspects of corporate transactions and preparation of employment and separation agreements.
**Career:** Partner; Employee Benefits & Executive Compensation Practice Group.
**Personal:** Monmouth College (BA, 1990); University of Illinois College of Law (JD, 1997).

**BALLANTINE, Frank D**
Clark Hill PLC, Chicago
312 985 5937
fballantine@clarkhill.com
*Featured in Corporate/M&A (Illinois)*
**Practice Areas:** Corporate Law Corporate Counsel Corporate Governance E-Commerce & Technology Executive Compensation Food & Beverage Mergers & Acquisitions Private Equity Secured Transactions Technology Protection and Transfer.
**Professional Memberships:** Chicago Shakespeare Theater; Board of Directors Chicago Innovations Mentors; Lead Mentor Two Venture Funds; Advisory Board Member The Nature Conservancy in Illinois; Founding Chair; Corporate & Advisory Committee.

**Career:** Frank D. Ballantine is a member of Clark Hill's Corporate Practice Group. He is a trusted advisor and counselor to senior management, boards of directors and investors in public and private companies based in the United States and abroad, across a wide range of industries. Active client sectors include information technology, food, life sciences, manufacturers, lenders and business services. Frank serves innovative and rapidly growing businesses and the investors who fund them. Frank is outside general counsel to numerous businesses and lead transaction counsel to investors and management in venture and private equity investments, mergers and acquisitions, and debt financings. He also assists clients in joint ventures, marketing alliances and licensing. He has served or is serving ex officio on the Boards of over 20 clients, as well as the advisory boards of two technology venture funds. Frank frequently speaks on topics involving private equity and venture capital finance, mergers and acquisitions, securities transactions, and high-growth developmental companies. Frank has been AV Peer Rated by Martindale-Hubbell and recognized by Chambers America's Leading Lawyers. He has been named one of America's leading mergers & acquisitions law attorneys in Best Lawyers and an Illinois Super Lawyer in securities & corporate finance.
**Publications:** •Author, "Paying Up For Management," Private Equity Manager (UK) •Author, "Management Teams Reap Rewards of Endurance," Private Equity News •Author, "Forces Shaping European Buy Outs and Venture Investing," White Paper, University of Chicago International Forum •Author, "The Chicago Shakespeare Theater: An Entrepreneurial Success," Illinois Venture Capital Association News •Author, "Non-Profit Entrepreneurship: The Astoria Motion Picture and Television Center," The Journal of Arts Management and Law.

**BALLIS, Jon A**
Kirkland & Ellis LLP, Chicago
312 862 2332
jon.ballis@kirkland.com
*Featured in Corporate/M&A (Illinois)*
**Practice Areas:** Jon Ballis focuses his practice on private equity related transactions, including leveraged buyouts of private and public companies, strategic acquisitions, divestitures and joint ventures, and growth equity and PIPE investments, with emphasis on corporate, securities, structuring and tax aspects.
**Professional Memberships:** The Vision for Tomorrow Foundation (Founder and Director). Anti-Defamation League (Director).
**Personal:** Harvard Law School (JD, 1994) cum laude; Lehigh University (BA, Soviet Studies, 1991) High Honors.

**BARBE, Jana Cohen**
Dentons, Chicago
312 876 7967
jana.barbe@dentons.com
*Featured in Real Estate (Illinois)*
**Practice Areas:** Member of the Global Board of legacy Dentons, the Global Advisory Committee

and the U.S. Management Committee. Specializes in representing institutional investors on tax-advantaged investments including low income housing tax credits, renewable energy credits, historic tax credits and social investments generally. Representations include proprietary and multi-investor fund investments, and direct investments, along with asset management. Recognized for unique expertise in workouts and bankruptcies involving debt and equity positions in affordable housing and community development transactions or relating to tax credit syndication businesses.

**BARDEN, Larry A**
Sidley Austin LLP, Chicago
312 853 7785
lbarden@sidley.com
*Featured in Corporate/M&A (Illinois)*
**Practice Areas:** Partner in Sidley's Chicago office, member of Executive and Management Committees, and a Global Coordinator of the Securities practice. He focuses on M&A, corporate finance, strategic counseling/corporate governance and private equity/venture capital. He represents buyers and sellers of public and private corporations and counsels boards of directors and financial advisors on acquisition, takeover defense, corporate and financial restructuring and corporate governance-related matters. He represents issuers and underwriters in a variety of securities offerings.
**Personal:** Washington and Lee University School of Law, JD, 1982, magna cum laude, Order of the Coif; Miami University - Oxford, BS, 1978. Admission: Illinois.

**BARLIANT, Ronald**
Goldberg Kohn Ltd, Chicago
312 201 3880
ronald.barliant@goldbergkohn.com
*Featured in Bankruptcy/Restructuring (Illinois)*
**Career:** Ronald Barliant is a principal in the Bankruptcy & Creditors' Rights Group. His debtor representations include a machine tool manufacturing company in a Delaware Chapter 11 case involving significant environmental and mass tort liabilities (plan confirmed with future claimants trust 11 months after filing), a wireless telecommunications carrier in a Chapter 11 case requiring the restructuring of debts owed the FCC for PCS licenses (plan confirmed 5 months after filing), and a home products manufacturing company in a pre-negotiated Chapter 11 case involving a debt-for-equity swap and the issuance of new debt securities (plan confirmed 75 days after filing).

**BARROW, Peter H**
Neal, Gerber & Eisenberg LLP, Chicago
312 269 8479
pbarrow@ngelaw.com
*Featured in Banking & Finance (Illinois)*
**Practice Areas:** Represents lenders, borrowers and third parties in the negotiation and documentation of a wide variety of commercial lending and finance transactions, including private banking, middle-market and large corporate financings, asset-based lending, public finance, secured transactions, syndicated loans, Eurodollar,

multicurrency and cross-border financings, participations, debt subordinations and intercreditor arrangements. Peter has represented lenders and borrowers in debt workouts and restructurings, recapitalization, asset purchases and dispositions and related transactions.
**Career:** Partner; Finance Practice Group.
**Personal:** Syracuse University (JD, 1976) cum laude, Law Review, Notes and Comments Editor; Washington University (BA, 1972), summa cum laude, Phi Beta Kappa.

## BEARD, James
DLA Piper LLP (US), Chicago
312 368 2169
james.beard@dlapiper.com
*Featured in Real Estate (Nationwide), Real Estate (Illinois)*
**Practice Areas:** Real estate, real estate finance, construction, and sports facilities development.
**Career:** He concentrates his practice in commercial real estate law and has represented clients in a wide range of commercial real estate transactions, including acquisitions and dispositions, financing, joint venture formation, construction contract negotiation, lease preparation, and government procurement and contracting. He represents developers and institutional lenders in restructuring and workout of troubled real estate projects.
**Personal:** JD, Chicago-Kent College of Law, Illinois Institute of Technology (with highest honors); BS, University of Illinois at Urbana-Champaign.

## BEDORE, Robert A
Neal, Gerber & Eisenberg LLP, Chicago
312 269 8415
rbedore@ngelaw.com
*Featured in Tax (Illinois)*
**Practice Areas:** Focuses on the resolution of federal tax controversies. Extensive experience representing both corporate and individual clients, including large multinational public and privately held corporations subject to "Large and Mid-Size Business" coordinated examination and industry specialization programs of the IRS. Has represented numerous clients before all administrative levels of the IRS and U.S. Department of the Treasury. Handled and resolved hundreds of federal income, employment, estate and gift tax cases, by trial or negotiated settlement.
**Career:** Partner; Tax Practice Group.
**Publications:** Author, lecturer and adjunct Professor (Loyola University) on tax controversy topics.
**Personal:** DePaul University (JD, 1980; BSC, 1975).

## BELCOVE, Ira J
Butler Rubin Saltarelli & Boyd LLP, Chicago
312 696 4462
ibelcove@butlerrubin.com
*Featured in Insurance (Illinois)*
**Practice Areas:** Business litigation, including reinsurance arbitration and insurance coverage litigation, insurance insolvency, and appellate.
**Professional Memberships:** Ira Belcove is a Member of ARIAS-U.S. He has been a speaker at numerous industry programs, including ARIAS,

Mealey's Insurance Insolvency and Reinsurance Roundtable, Reinsurance Association of America, and American Conference Institute.
**Career:** A Member of the Management Committee at Butler Rubin, Ira has more than 25 years of experience in complex business litigation, and his practice focuses on reinsurance arbitration and insurance coverage litigation. He has tried numerous disputes involving traditional and finite reinsurance, addressing such issues as the consolidation of arbitrations arising out of multiple treaties, the aggregation of asbestos claims and the number of occurrences in other environmental claims, the propriety of cessions of construction defect claims, the insurability of claims for punitive damages, the notice required for termination of an MGA agreement, the interpretation of guaranteed minimum death and income benefit reinsurance agreements, and the interpretation of sublimits, termination clauses, and other provisions found in finite reinsurance treaties. He has also litigated direct coverage disputes, and represents credit insurers in suits brought by or against banks and other lenders. In addition, Ira has testified before the High Court of Justice as an expert witness on aspects of US insurance law. Ira has been recognized as a leading lawyer in insurance law in the 2011-2013 editions of The Best Lawyers in America. In 2005 and 2009-2013, he was named a leader in business litigation by Illinois Super Lawyers. And, as part of the Law Bulletin Publishing Group's 2012 survey of the top lawyers in the state, Ira was designated a "Leading Lawyer" in Illinois in Insurance, Insurance Coverage & Reinsurance Law. He joined Butler Rubin after clerking for the Hon. Bernard M Decker of the US District Court for the Northern District of Illinois, and practicing for several years at Mayer Brown.
**Personal:** JD, University of Chicago Law School, 1987. BA, summa cum laude, Columbia University, 1984.

## BENNETT, Michael P
Edwards Wildman Palmer, Chicago
312 201 2679
mbennett@edwardswildman.com
*Featured in Technology (Illinois)*
**Practice Areas:** Mike Bennett advises companies on the legal issues inherent in existing and emerging technology. He counsels clients on their use of technology and provides strategies to avoid the legal pitfalls that frequently arise from such use. He consults with clients on the use and distribution of software licensed under an open source model, creation of RFID payment systems, data security and privacy issues, and the use of marketing data in a manner that does not violate various federal, state and international laws.
**Personal:** Loyola University of Chicago, JD; University of Notre Dame, BA; DePaul University, Computer Career Program.

## BERBERIAN, H Nicholas
Neal, Gerber & Eisenberg LLP, Chicago
312 269 8005
nberberian@ngelaw.com
*Featured in Litigation (Illinois)*

**Practice Areas:** Represents financial services firms and their employees with respect to a wide range of litigation and regulatory matters. These matters have included securities class actions, mass actions, lawsuits and arbitrations involving investors and employment practices at financial services firms as well as regulatory matters.
**Professional Memberships:** ABA Securities Litigation Committee (Co-Chair, 2003-06); ABA Subcommittee on Broker-Dealer Litigation (Co-Chair, 1993-2003).
**Career:** Partner; Securities and Commodities Litigation Practice Group Chair; Executive Committee (Member).
**Publications:** Annual Survey of Broker-Dealer Litigation (Co-Editor, 1993-2003).
**Personal:** University of Chicago Law School (JD, 1978); University of Chicago (MBA, 1975); Kenyon College (AB, 1974).

## BERGER, Stephen L
Neal, Gerber & Eisenberg LLP, Chicago
312 269 8041
sberger@ngelaw.com
*Featured in Real Estate (Illinois)*
**Practice Areas:** Represents real estate companies and individuals in the acquisition, development and financing of commercial and multi family, as well as hotel, resort and spa properties. Acted as Counsel for a national chain leasing space in over 450 shopping center locations, together with national companies acquiring and operating multifamily properties throughout the US.
**Career:** Partner; Real Estate Practice Group.
**Publications:** Frequent author, commentator and lecturer on various real estate issues.
**Personal:** IIT/Chicago-Kent College of Law (JD, 1970); University of Illinois (BA, 1967).

## BERKELEY, Jill B
Neal, Gerber & Eisenberg LLP, Chicago
312 269 8024
jberkeley@ngelaw.com
*Featured in Insurance (Nationwide), Insurance (Illinois)*
**Practice Areas:** Represents policyholders and claimants in insurance coverage disputes involving toxic torts and hazardous wastes, environmental pollution, construction, products liability, intellectual property, first-party property, business interruption and excess liability matters. Additionally, Jill offers her clients strategic advice on insurance coverage to help manage risk.
**Professional Memberships:** Fellow American College of Coverage and Extracontractual Counsel; Chair, Tort Trial & Insurance Practice Section (TIPS), ABA; Vice-Chair, Insurance Coverage Litigation Committee, TIPS, ABA.
**Career:** Partner; Insurance Policyholder Practice Group Chair.
**Publications:** Author and lecturer on insurance law topics.
**Personal:** Northwestern University School of Law (JD, 1975); University of Michigan (BA, 1972).

## BERKOFF, Mark A
Neal, Gerber & Eisenberg LLP, Chicago
312 269 8072
mberkoff@ngelaw.com
*Featured in Bankruptcy/Restructuring (Illinois)*
**Practice Areas:** Represents debtors and creditors' committees in complex commercial Chapter 11 cases in diverse industries. Handled all aspects of Chapter 11 proceeding from pre-bankruptcy planning through plan confirmation and post-confirmation matters. Experienced in workouts, out-of-court compositions and business reorganizations / restructurings.
**Professional Memberships:** ABA Business Law Section and Bankruptcy Committee; Chicago Bar Association, Bankruptcy and Reorganization Committee; American Bankruptcy Institute; co-chairman, Turnaround Management Association's Education Committee (2001-03).
**Career:** Partner; Financial Restructuring and Bankruptcy Practice Group Chair.
**Publications:** Frequent author, commentator and lecturer on financial restructuring and bankruptcy issues.
**Personal:** University of Chicago (JD, 1986), University of Wisconsin-Madison (BA, 1986).

## BERNSTEIN, H Bruce
Sidley Austin LLP, Chicago
312 853 7635
bbernstein@sidley.com
*Featured in Banking & Finance (Illinois)*
**Practice Areas:** Senior Counsel in Sidley's Chicago office. He concentrates his practice in secured transactions and restructurings on behalf of commercial banks and asset-based lenders.
**Professional Memberships:** Member (Emeritus), National Bankruptcy Conference; Fellow, American College of Bankruptcy; Fellow, American College of Commercial Finance Lawyers; General Counsel, Commercial Finance Association (1995-2001); Past chairman of the Commercial, Banking and Bankruptcy Law Section of the Illinois Bar Association; Past chairman of the Uniform Commerical Code Committee of the Chicago Bar Association.
**Personal:** Harvard Law School, JD, 1968, cum laude; Cornell University, AB, 1965, cum laude. Admission: Illinois.

## BERNSTEIN, Howard L
Neal, Gerber & Eisenberg LLP, Chicago
312 269 8447
hbernstein@ngelaw.com
*Featured in Labor & Employment (Illinois)*
**Practice Areas:** Represents employers throughout the US in labor relations and employment law matters and employment-related litigation, with an emphasis on contract negotiations, arbitrations and injunction proceedings, NLRB election campaigns, unfair labor practice cases and employment discrimination matters.
**Professional Memberships:** ISBA; ABA Labor Law Section Committee on Development of the Law Under the NLRA (Chairman); NLRB (Counsel to the Chairman), 1970-72.
**Career:** Partner; Labor and Employment Practice Group.

**Publications:** Author and lecturer on various labor and employment topics.
**Personal:** University of Texas School of Law (JD, 1968); University of Texas (BBA, 1965).

## BIASETTI, Jon
Locke Lord LLP, Chicago
312 443 1866
jbiasetti@lockelord.com
*Featured in Insurance (Illinois)*
**Practice Areas:** Co-chair of the Insurance Regulatory and Transactional Practice Group. Represents clients on corporate, transactional and insurance regulatory matters. Significant experience structuring, negotiating, documenting and closing reinsurance transactions of various kinds and complexity. Also regularly represents health insurance companies in their marketing alliances and joint ventures with other health insurers and hospital systems.
**Professional Memberships:** ABA.
**Career:** Partner since 1997.
**Personal:** Boston College Law School (JD, magna cum laude, 1987); Boston College (BA, cum laude, 1984).

## BIEK, John A
Neal, Gerber & Eisenberg LLP, Chicago
312 269 8485
jbiek@ngelaw.com
*Featured in Tax (Illinois)*
**Practice Areas:** Represents large publicly traded and privately held businesses in controversies, transactional matters and tax planning involving multistate corporate income/franchise taxes, gross receipts taxes, sales and use taxes, and other business privilege taxes. He has represented clients in state tax audits and litigation before courts, administrative law judges and departments of revenue throughout the United States.
**Professional Memberships:** Fellow of the American College of Tax Counsel; Unclaimed Property Subcommittee of the ABA's Tax Section's State & Local Tax Committee Chair.
**Career:** Partner; Tax Practice Group.
**Personal:** Georgetown University Law Center (JD, 1987); Yale University (BS, 1984).

## BIERIG, Jack R
Sidley Austin LLP, Chicago
312 853 7614
jbierig@sidley.com
*Featured in Antitrust (Illinois)*
**Practice Areas:** Partner in Sidley's Chicago office. Has experience in representation of associations, antitrust matters, litigation challenging government action affecting health care providers, copyright, trademark and trade secret cases, and FDA matters. Represented numerous associations and health care providers in government antitrust and health fraud investigations, in actions brought by the Department of Justice and the Federal Trade Commission, and in private antitrust cases.
**Professional Memberships:** Lecturer, University of Chicago Law School and Harris School of Public Policy.
**Personal:** Harvard Law School, JD, 1972; Brandeis University, AB, 1968, Phi Beta Kappa.

Admissions: Illinois, Supreme Court, Several Courts of Appeals.

## BISCEGLIA, Joseph G
Jenner & Block LLP, Chicago
312 923 2784
jbisceglia@jenner.com
*Featured in Construction (Illinois)*
**Career:** Joseph Bisceglia has extensive experience in a variety of complex civil and criminal litigation in both federal and state trial and appellate courts, including business and corporate litigation of virtually every type. He is Chair of his Firm's Real Estate and Construction Litigation Practice. He has lectured and published extensively regarding federal and state civil practice and procedure, real estate and construction law, trial practice, and alternative dispute resolution. In addition to other activities and honors, he is Past President of the Illinois State Bar Association and listed among the top lawyers in Illinois by all major rating organizations.

## BOEHNEN, Daniel A
McDonnell Boehnen Hulbert & Berghoff LLP, Chicago
312 913 2130
boehnen@mbhb.com
*Featured in Intellectual Property (Illinois)*
**Practice Areas:** Daniel A Boehnen is a founder of McDonnell Boehnen Hulbert & Berghoff LLP. His practice focuses primarily on trials, appeals, opposition proceedings, and all forms of disputed patent matters. Clients seek his counsel on general IP, business, and legal problems. Clients praise him for crafting aggressive strategies to try cases and settle cases while remaining sensitive to the client's business goals. His litigation experience encompasses a wide range of high-tech industries in all levels of the federal court system. He has been involved in many notable and precedent-setting cases.

## BOEHRER, Charles B
Winston & Strawn LLP, Chicago
312 558 5989
cboehrer@winston.com
*Featured in Banking & Finance (Illinois)*
**Practice Areas:** Finance, securities, merger and acquisitions.
**Career:** Mr Boehrer attended the University of Michigan where he served as an editor of the Law Review. He joined Winston & Strawn in 1985 and is currently a Partner specializing in corporate finance. Mr Boehrer's extensive experience includes structuring of senior and subordinated credit facilities, including investment-grade, leveraged, asset-based and mezzanine transactions. He has recently represented leading financial institutions such as BMO/Harris, Deutsche Bank, Bank of America, American Capital and HSBC and borrowers such as Motorola, Lear Corporation, Bucyrus International, Nuveen Investments, Treehouse Foods, Hub International and World Kitchen.

## BOKHARI, Zulfiqar
Sidley Austin LLP, Chicago
312 853 2220
zbokhari@sidley.com
*Featured in Banking & Finance (Illinois)*
**Practice Areas:** Partner in Sidley's Chicago office. He regularly represents, and coordinates the firm's client relationships with, leading commercial and investment banks in the syndicated loan markets. His primary practice involves the structuring and syndication of senior credit facilities, including acquisition, recapitalization, bridge, working capital and other domestic, cross-border and multicurrency financings. His clients include, among others, JPMorgan, Bank of America/Merrill Lynch, BNP Paribas, Morgan Stanley, Deutsche Bank, U.S. Bank and Citigroup.
**Personal:** Notre Dame Law School, JD, 1996; University of Notre Dame, BA, 1993, magna cum laude.

## BORDERS, Thomas
McDermott Will & Emery LLP, Chicago
312 984 7552
tborders@mwe.com
*Featured in Tax (Illinois), Tax (Nationwide)*
See under Nationwide for profile.

## BOTICA, Matthew J
Winston & Strawn LLP, Chicago
312 558 8095
mbotica@winston.com
*Featured in Bankruptcy/Restructuring (Illinois)*
**Practice Areas:** Practice concentration in insolvency, bankruptcy, and business reorganization. More than 35 years experience representing banks, institutional lenders, creditors' committees, trustees, and other creditors in the bankruptcy, reorganization, and claims trading areas.
**Professional Memberships:** American College of Bankruptcy.
**Career:** Prior to joining Winston & Strawn as a Partner in 1999, he was the Chairman of the Bankruptcy Practice at Hopkins & Sutter.
**Publications:** Author of a chapter on chapter 7 'Business Liquidations' in the Illinois Institute for Continuing Legal Education (IICLE) 'Bankruptcy Practice Handbook'.
**Personal:** Boston College, 1972, summa cum laude, Phi Beta Kappa. Harvard Law School, 1975.

## BOULOS, Nader
Kirkland & Ellis LLP, Chicago
312 862 2061
nader.boulos@kirkland.com
*Featured in Insurance (Illinois)*
**Practice Areas:** Litigation partner with extensive trial experience in commercial litigation and insurance coverage litigation and counseling. Has obtained trial and appellate victories in cases involving antitrust, class action, contract, toxic tort and product liability disputes. Has assisted insurance policyholders in recovering hundreds of millions of dollars through trial and pretrial resolution of complex coverage claims under CGL, D&O, EPL, products and first-party policies. Clients include Baxter, Boeing, Dow Chemical, FMC, Motorola, Union Carbide, Visteon and other companies in a diverse range of industries.

**Personal:** Stanford University, AB, 1991. University of Michigan Law School, JD cum laude, 1994.

## BOYD, Eric E
Seyfarth Shaw LLP, Chicago
312 460 5903
eboyd@seyfarth.com
*Featured in Environment (Illinois)*
**Practice Areas:** Environmental.
**Career:** Mr Boyd represents clients in regulatory compliance, litigation and transaction matters. He has represented clients in numerous permit proceedings and administrative and judicial cases involving air, water, waste, wetlands, toxic chemical, underground injection, hazardous material transport, process safety, and chemical security requirements, as well as toxic tort matters involving environmental releases. He also helps clients with sustainability, renewable energy, climate change, and green marketing compliance issues.
**Publications:** Mr Boyd speaks and writes frequently on air, waste and chemical release topics.
**Personal:** JD, Indiana University (1986); BS, Northwestern University (1981).

## BOYKINS, Michael L
McDermott Will & Emery LLP, Chicago
312 984 7599
MBoykins@mwe.com
*Featured in Banking & Finance (Illinois)*
**Practice Areas:** Practice focuses on the corporate finance area, representing both corporate and individual lenders, investors and borrowers in connection with secured and unsecured credit facilities, asset–based lending, acquisition financings, over-the-counter derivatives, insurance industry financings, senior subordinated debt, mezzanine and venture capital transactions.
**Professional Memberships:** Member of Illinois and Wisconsin bars; member of Economic Club of Chicago; fellow in American College of Investment Counsel.
**Personal:** University of Wisconsin Law School, JD, 1990; University of Wisconsin - Madison, BS, 1987.

## BRADFORD, David
Jenner & Block LLP, Chicago
312 923 2975
dbradford@jenner.com
*Featured in Litigation (Illinois)*
**Career:** David J. Bradford is Co-Chair of the Litigation Department and a Fellow of the American College of Trial Lawyers. He is sought after as lead trial and appellate counsel in federal and state lawsuits involving complex commercial and financial transactions and novel constitutional and legal issues. He has defended and prosecuted to verdict a number of nine figure cases. He serves as lead trial counsel for Fortune 500 companies, leading law firms, financial institutions, officers and directors, and bankruptcy constituencies. The National Law Journal recognized him among "winning" litigators who exemplify "the qualities that make a great trial attorney."

## BRADLEY, Craig C
Edwards Wildman Palmer, Chicago
312 201 2606
cbradley@edwardswildman.com
*Featured in Corporate/M&A (Illinois)*

**Practice Areas:** Craig is widely regarded as a go-to corporate attorney for emerging software, life sciences, Internet, communications and other technology companies. He serves as primary outside counsel for many of these companies, advising both on general corporate matters and in connection with angel and capital financing, mergers and acquisitions, IPOs and compensation arrangements. Craig is known in both the business community and venture capital/angel investment communities for playing a valuable role in facilitating connections between companies and investors.

**Personal:** Indiana University School of Law, JD; Elmhurst College, BA.

## BRAUN, Bruce R
Winston & Strawn LLP, Chicago
312 558 5139
bbraun@winston.com
*Featured in Litigation (Illinois)*

**Practice Areas:** Mr Braun's practice focuses on professional liability matters, class action prosecution and defense, multi-district litigation, antitrust litigation, corporate internal investigations, fiduciary duty and contract cases, and intellectual property disputes.

**Career:** Mr Braun is the Global Chair of the firm's Complex Commercial Litigation Group. Prior to joining the firm, Mr Braun served as a law clerk to the Chief Justice of the United States, William H. Rehnquist, and to Judge Joel M. Flaum of the United States Court of Appeals for the Seventh Circuit.

**Personal:** University of Virginia, JD, 1989, Editor in Chief, Virginia Law Review.

## BROCCOLO, Bernadette
McDermott Will & Emery LLP, Chicago
312 984 6911
bbroccolo@mwe.com
*Featured in Healthcare (Illinois), Healthcare (Nationwide)*

**Practice Areas:** Health industry experience: federal tax-exemption, not-for-profit corporate governance, privacy, human subject protection, technology contracting, conflicts of interest, and biomedical research regulatory compliance. Representative engagements: develop and implement complex relationship formation/realignment (joint ventures, governance restructurings, institutional provider-physician relationships); information technology acquisitions; electronic information networks; comprehensive biomedical research program operations/compliance infrastructure; corporate compliance programs.

**Professional Memberships:** Leadership positions for American Health Lawyers Association, American Bar Association, Illinois Association of Healthcare Attorneys. Frequent speaker and author.

**Personal:** University of Notre Dame Law School (JD); Boston College (BSc).

## BROWN, Jeffrey H
Michael Best & Friedrich LLP, Chicago
312 222 5794
jhbrown@michaelbest.com
*Featured in Media & Entertainment (Illinois)*

**Practice Areas:** Jeff Brown counsels clients on corporate and intellectual property matters in the music and entertainment industry. His practice includes trademark, copyright, trade secret, advertising and unfair competition issues. He assists clients in strategizing to protect, exploit and enforce their intellectual property rights and represents them against allegations of infringement. Mr Brown represents well-known independent record labels in connection with their corporate and intellectual property matters, including negotiation of contracts with artists, publishing companies and distributors. He represents bands and performers in the negotiation of recording agreements and merchandising deals and other uses of sound recordings and musical compositions.

## BROWN, Joel F
Goldberg Kohn Ltd, Chicago
312 201 3918
joel.brown@goldbergkohn.com
*Featured in Banking & Finance (Illinois)*

**Career:** Joel Brown is a principal in the firm's Commercial Finance Group. His practice focuses on the representation of banks and non-bank finance companies engaged principally in middle market lending operations. He has extensive experience in structuring, documenting and negotiating both cash-flow and asset-based financing, as well as broad exposure to senior, mezzanine and hybrid lending products. Mr Brown handles mergers and acquisition financings, recapitalization financings, refinancings, and other complex financial arrangements requiring institutional debt. He has been engaged to "trouble spot" deal structures and documentation, particularly in co-lend arrangements, as well as to lead multi-bank/multi-borrower facilities.

## BROWN, Rachel S
Kirkland & Ellis LLP, Chicago
312 862 5275
rachel.brown@kirkland.com
*Featured in Real Estate (Illinois)*

**Practice Areas:** Rachel Brown concentrates her practice in the areas of finance, development, acquisitions, dispositions and venture formation. Her experience includes representing borrowers and lenders of all types including banks, funds and insurance companies in real estate based financing transactions, including first mortgage loans, construction loans, mezzanine loans and other structured financings, and representing both buyers and sellers in the distressed debt market. She also represents real estate developers in acquisitions and dispositions of real estate assets and equity and operating partners in real estate joint venture transactions.

**Personal:** BA, University of Michigan; JD, cum laude, Loyola University Chicago.

## BROWNE, Robert E
Neal, Gerber & Eisenberg LLP, Chicago
312 269 5225
rbrowne@ngelaw.com
*Featured in Intellectual Property (Illinois)*

**Practice Areas:** Represents clients in all aspects of patent, trademark, copyright and unfair competition law and related litigation before the federal district and appellate courts and the ITC; negotiates and drafts patent license, trademark, and merchandise licenses, computer software licenses and development agreements, publishing agreements, technology transfer and development agreements, and video and motion picture distribution agreements.

**Professional Memberships:** Member, Intellectual Property Law Association of Chicago, International Trademark Association, and American Bar Association.

**Career:** Partner; Intellectual Property Practice Group Co-Chair.

**Publications:** Author and lecturer on intellectual property topics.

**Personal:** University of Wisconsin (JD, 1970); University of Notre Dame (BSCE, 1967).

## BUTLER, Christopher
Kirkland & Ellis LLP, Chicago
312 862 2298
christopher.butler@kirkland.com
*Featured in Banking & Finance (Illinois)*

**Practice Areas:** Christopher concentrates in financing transactions for private equity groups and private and public companies with an emphasis on highly leveraged financings, including acquisitions and restructurings. He represents borrowers and lenders in structuring secured and unsecured lending transactions, LBO and acquisition financings, first and second lien financings, subordinated debt transactions, mezzanine and other private issuances, DIP financings and hedging arrangements. Clients include financial sponsors Bain Capital, GTCR, Golden Gate Capital, Summit Partners, Vestar Capital and Welsh Carson, and portfolio companies and major corporations, including Molson Coors and Roundy's Supermarkets.

**Personal:** Fordham University, JD, 1988; University of Pennsylvania, BA, 1984.

## BUTLER JR, John Wm
Skadden, Arps, Slate, Meagher & Flom LLP & Affiliates, Chicago
312 407 0730
jack.butler@skadden.com
*Featured in Bankruptcy/Restructuring (Nationwide), Bankruptcy/Restructuring (Illinois)*
See under Nationwide for profile.

## CAHAN, James N
Sidley Austin LLP, Chicago
312 853 7750
jcahan@sidley.com
*Featured in Environment (Illinois)*

**Practice Areas:** Partner in Sidley's Chicago office. His practice focuses on Clean Air Act regulation, climate change, permitting of major energy and manufacturing projects, environmental crisis response and management, environmental aspects of bankruptcies and transactions and environmental management systems. He represents clients regarding hazardous air pollutants and MACT standards, including participating in rulemakings, petitions for review and enforcement actions under this program.

**Publications:** He has written, lectured and taught on various topics relating to environmental law and management.

**Personal:** Washington University School of Law, JD, 1976; Washington University, BA, 1973. Admissions: District of Columbia, Illinois.

## CAIN, Patricia S
Neal, Gerber & Eisenberg LLP, Chicago
312 269 8032
pcain@ngelaw.com
*Featured in Labor & Employment (Illinois)*

**Practice Areas:** Advises employers on a broad range of employee benefit matters, including counseling employers on the design, implementation and administration of broad-based pension and healthcare plans, executive compensation arrangements and early retirement programs; represents clients in ruling requests and controversies before the IRS, Department of Labor and Pension Benefit Guaranty Corporation; represents clients in litigation arising out of disputes involving benefit plans.

**Career:** Partner; Employee Benefits and Executive Compensation Practice Group Chair; Executive Committee (Member).

**Publications:** Frequent author, commentator and lecturer on various employee benefit issues.

**Personal:** Northwestern University School of Law (JD, 1977); Georgetown University (AB, 1974).

## CALLAHAN, David K
Kirkland & Ellis LLP, Chicago
312 862 2182
david.callahan@kirkland.com
*Featured in Intellectual Property (Illinois)*

**Practice Areas:** Focused on complex litigation involving patents, trademarks, trade secrets, false advertising and unfair competition. Numerous bench and jury trials in Federal Courts, and has argued appeals before the Federal and Seventh Circuits. In patent matters, has worked in a variety of technologies, including medical devices, abrasives, paper products, semiconductors, automotive products, business methods, cellular telephony, building products and agricultural equipment.

**Professional Memberships:** DePaul University Center for Intellectual Property Law and Information Technology Advisory Board, Illinois College President's Advisory Council.

**Personal:** University of Michigan Law School, JD, 1991 ; University of Chicago, AB, 1987; Campbell University, AA, 1984.

## CALLAHAN, John M
McDermott Will & Emery LLP, Chicago
312 984 7553
jcallahan@mwe.com
*Featured in Healthcare (Illinois)*

**Practice Areas:** Head of the international healthcare M&A practice, and focused on mergers and acquisitions in the health services and life sciences industries. Represents private equity firms, academic medical centers and health systems, governmental entities and other healthcare companies in the acquisition and divestiture of businesses and business. Has handled some of the most high-profile US and international transactions within the health sector.

**Professional Memberships:** American Health Lawyers Association; American, Illinois and Chicago Bar Associations.

### CARDONICK, Andrew
Greenberg Traurig, LLP, Chicago
312 456 1073
CardonickA@gtlaw.com
*Featured in Banking & Finance (Illinois)*

**Practice Areas:** Co-Chair of the firm's National Financial Institutions Practice / syndicated, club, and single back asset-based and cash flow credit facilities; business reorganization, financial restructuring.

**Professional Memberships:** Member, Commercial Finance Association, Advisory Board Member; Member, Turnaround Management Association, Past Co-Chair, Public Relations Committee, TMA Chicago Chapter.

**Career:** Listed: Chambers USA Guide, 2010-13; Super Lawyers magazine, 2011-13; Leading Lawyers Network, 2012-13.

**Publications:** Author, 'How Lenders Can Avoid Equitable Subordination,' The Secured Lender, November/December 2008.

**Personal:** JD, with honors, University of Chicago Law School, 1992, University of Chicago Law Review; BS, summa cum laude, Pennsylvania State University, 1989.

### CARLSON, Walter C
Sidley Austin LLP, Chicago
312 853 7734
wcarlson@sidley.com
*Featured in Litigation (Illinois)*

**Practice Areas:** Partner in Sidley's Chicago office, member of the firm's Executive Committee, head of the Chicago Financial and Securities Litigation Group, and head of the firm's M&A/D&O Litigation practice. He regularly serves as lead counsel in federal securities fraud lawsuits and cases in state and federal courts involving corporate control, corporate governance and fiduciary duty issues. He represents corporations and directors in M&A litigation, SEC investigations, derivative lawsuits and fiduciary liability claims.

**Personal:** Harvard Law School, JD, 1978, magna cum laude; Yale University, BA, 1975, magna cum laude, Phi Beta Kappa. Admission: Illinois.

### CARPENTER, David
Sidley Austin LLP, Chicago
312 853 7237
dcarpenter@sidley.com
*Featured in Communications (Illinois)*

**Practice Areas:** Partner in Sidley's Chicago office. His practice focuses on antitrust and regulatory issues in the telecommunications and electric industries and in appellate cases involving all areas of the law. He has argued five cases in the US Supreme Court, over 65 cases in the federal and

state appellate courts, and briefed and argued many dispositive motions in federal and state trial courts.

**Personal:** Boston University School of Law, JD, 1975, magna cum laude; Yale University, BA, 1972, cum laude. Admissions: Illinois, District of Columbia. Law clerk to Justice Willliam Brennan, 1977-78 and to Judge Frank Coffin, 1975-77.

### CARR, Corinne P
Dentons, Chicago
312 876 7477
corinne.carr@dentons.com
*Featured in Insurance (Illinois)*

**Practice Areas:** A partner in Dentons' Insurance Regulatory Practice and head of legacy Dentons's Risk Management practice. Significant transactional and regulatory experience representing corporate risk managers, foreign and domestic insurers and reinsurers, agents, brokers, employee leasing and temporary staffing companies, transportation carriers and other non-industry clients seeking to cross-market insurance, warranty and service contract products. Frequently represents clients in strategic insurance matters related to insurer insolvencies, reinsurance, self-insurance, product development/withdrawal, policyholder collateral, surplus lines coverage, domestic/off-shore captive facilities and market conduct investigations.

**Personal:** University of Notre Dame Law School, JD; St. Mary's College, Notre Dame, BA, Political Science and History.

### CARREL, Mitchell
Freeborn & Peters LLP, Chicago
312 360 6542
mcarrel@freeborn.com
*Featured in Real Estate (Illinois)*

**Practice Areas:** Mr Carrel is a Partner in the Real Estate Practice Group. His practice focuses on representing public and private companies, land owners, developers and investors and helping them secure land use and zoning approvals, public incentives, local regulatory and siting approvals, as well as performing zoning due diligence. Among Mr Carrel's projects, he has helped obtain approvals for the siting of wireless communications facilities and written about the siting process. He represents clients before local plan commissions, zoning boards and city councils. As a member of both the Food and Transportation Teams, Mr Carrel helps companies in these industries secure land use and zoning approvals, public incentives, and local regulatory and siting approvals.

**Personal:** JD, Michigan State University College of Law, cum laude; BS, Miami University, Finance and Marketing.

### CASEY, Robert P
Ogletree, Deakins, Nash, Smoak & Stewart, PC, Chicago
312 558 1250
robert.casey@ogletreedeakins.com
*Featured in Labor & Employment (Illinois)*

**Practice Areas:** Labor and Employment, Collective Bargaining, Labor Arbitration, Construction Industry Labor, Employee Benefits

(including multiemployer pension plan withdrawal liability advice and litigation, delinquent contribution claims, alter ego/single employer litigation, and retiree health benefits litigation).

**Professional Memberships:** American Bar Association, Illinois Bar Association, AGC Labor and Employment Law Council (past Chair), Fellow, The College of Labor and Employment Lawyers.

**Career:** Admitted in Illinois, multiple Federal District Courts (Illinois, Indiana, Michigan), U.S. Court of Appeals (6th, 7th, 10th, 11th, and District of Columbia Circuits), U.S. Supreme Court.

**Personal:** St. Anselm's College (BA, summa cum laude, 1973), DePaul University College of Law (JD, summa cum laude, 1976).

### CEDEROTH, Richard A
Sidley Austin LLP, Chicago
312 853 7026
rcederoth@sidley.com
*Featured in Intellectual Property (Illinois)*

**Practice Areas:** Chicago Partner, focuses his practice on patent litigation, primarily involving software, computers and semiconductors. He has represented major corporations in patent disputes for over 25 years, including many multiple defendant federal court cases and the International Trade Commission, and has taught and lectured on patent and intellectual property law.

**Professional Memberships:** Member, Intellectual Property Section of American Bar Association; American Intellectual Property Law Association; Bradley University Electrical Engineering Alumni Advisory Board.

**Personal:** University of Illinois College of Law, JD, 1983; Bradley University, BS, 1980, magna cum laude, Phi Kappa Phi, Etta Kappa Nu, Tau Beta Pi. Admission: Illinois.

### CHEFITZ, Joel
McDermott Will & Emery LLP, Chicago
312 984 6484
jchefitz@mwe.com
*Featured in Antitrust (Illinois), Litigation (Illinois)*

**Practice Areas:** Accomplished trial and antitrust lawyer and head of Chicago securities litigation practice. Consistent success in complex business litigation.

**Career:** Previously, managing partner of Howrey's Chicago office and trial partner at Kirkland & Ellis; past judicial clerk to Judge Walter Jay Skinner, USDC for District of Massachusetts; received faculty prize as the graduate demonstrating greatest legal scholarship; Note and Case Editor of Boston University Law Review during law school.

**Personal:** Boston University School of Law (JD, magna cum laude), Boston University (AB, with honors).

### CHESLEY, Richard A
DLA Piper LLP (US), Chicago
312 368 3430
richard.chesley@dlapiper.com
*Featured in Bankruptcy/Restructuring (Illinois)*

**Practice Areas:** Bankruptcy, Restructuring.

**Professional Memberships:** American Bankruptcy Institute.

**Career:** He practices primarily in corporate restructuring, with an emphasis on bankruptcy transactions in the US and internationally. He has served as restructuring counsel in a number of chapter 11 proceedings and has led a number of out-of-court restructurings. He comes to DLA Piper from Paul Hastings, where he founded that firm's Chicago office and served as the Chicago managing partner.

**Personal:** JD, University of Cincinnati College of Law; BA, Northwestern University.

### CHOI, Paul L
Sidley Austin LLP, Chicago
312 853 2145
pchoi@sidley.com
*Featured in Corporate/M&A (Illinois)*

**Practice Areas:** Partner in Sidley's Chicago office. His practice focuses on mergers and acquisitions, dispositions, spin-offs, joint ventures, and counseling clients on takeover defense and proxy contests. He represents issuers and underwriters on private and public offerings, IPO's, and subsidiary or 'carve-out' offerings. He advises public company clients on corporate governance and general securities law matters, including Sarbanes-Oxley, Board of Director, fiduciary duty, audit committee, PCAOB, disclosure policy and related issues.

**Personal:** Harvard Law School, JD, 1989, magna cum laude, Sears Prize, Editor of the Harvard Law Review; Harvard College, AB, 1986, magna cum laude, Phi Beta Kappa. Admission: Illinois.

### CHRISTIE, R. Lee
Sidley Austin LLP, Chicago
312 853 3586
lchristie@sidley.com
*Featured in Tax (Illinois)*

**Practice Areas:** Partner in Sidley's Chicago office. He is a tax lawyer whose practice focuses on the insurance industry, including all aspects of federal and state taxation affecting insurance companies and insurance products. He has advised insurance companies and investment banks in financings, restructurings, and acquisitions involving insurance companies, and represents insurance companies in tax controversy matters including both administrative proceedings and litigation in federal and state courts.

**Personal:** Harvard Law School, JD, 1984; Illinois Wesleyan University, BA, 1981.

### CIMINO JR, Thomas P.
Vedder Price PC, Chicago
312 609 7784
tcimino@vedderprice.com
*Featured in Litigation (Illinois)*

**Practice Areas:** Shareholder; Chair, Litigation practice area; Member, Board of Directors; Chairman, Financial Services Litigation practice group. Broad experience in complex commercial litigation, including securities fraud class actions, shareholder disputes, patent infringement and bankruptcy litigation. Appeared in both state and federal trial and appellate courts throughout the US and represented clients in proceedings before the SEC and Commodity Futures Trading Commission.

**Professional Memberships:** Member: Seventh Circuit Bar Association, American Bar Association and Chicago Bar Association.

**Career:** Admitted (IL) 1987.

**Personal:** JD, magna cum laude, Loyola University Chicago School of Law; BA, summa cum laude, Loyola University of Chicago.

### CLARK, James
Sidley Austin LLP, Chicago
312 853 7776
jclark@sidley.com
*Featured in Banking & Finance (Illinois), Banking & Finance (Nationwide)*

**Practice Areas:** Partner in Sidley's Chicago office. He represents clients in a broad range of financing transactions.

**Professional Memberships:** Faculty, University of Chicago Law School, Legal Ethics and Professional Responsibility; Faculty, "Financing Leveraged Buyouts and Acquisitions" held by Practicing Law Institute; Past Member, Board of Contributors of "The Bankruptcy Strategist"; Past Chairman, Acquisition Financing Subcommittee of the Commercial Financial Services Committee of the American Bar Association Business Law Section; Fellow, American College of Commercial Finance Lawyers; American Bar Association.

**Personal:** University of Chicago, JD, 1976; Brown University, AB, 1970, Phi Beta Kappa. Admission: Illinois.

### CLEVELAND, Michael G
Vedder Price PC, Chicago
312 609 7860
mcleveland@vedderprice.com
*Featured in Labor & Employment (Illinois)*

**Practice Areas:** Shareholder in the firm's Labor and Employment practice group. Concentrates on employment litigation and successfully litigates employment cases in state and federal courts, before administrative agencies and in arbitration, including equal employment, ERISA, FLSA and wrongful-discharge matters. Defends employers in all phases of class action litigation, including race discrimination and age discrimination matters that resulted in complete verdicts for the employer defendants. Represents employers in matters before administrative agencies, and advises employers on employment issues and policies and on matters relating to employment agreements.

**Career:** Admitted (IL) 1974.

**Personal:** JD, University of Chicago; BA, Loyola University of Chicago.

### COCO, Nathan F
McDermott Will & Emery LLP, Chicago
312 984 3658
ncoco@mwe.com
*Featured in Bankruptcy/Restructuring (Illinois)*

**Practice Areas:** Focuses his practice on the areas of restructuring and insolvency, including distressed finance and M&A transactions, creditor rights matters and bankruptcy litigation. Represents and advises corporate clients, strategic and financial buyers, institutional investors, public debt holders, indenture trustees and asset based

lenders in connection with distressed credits in the healthcare, retail, energy, manufacturing and derivative financial product sectors. Has particular expertise with respect to financially-distressed public projects and defaulted municipal securities.

**Career:** University of Iowa College of Law, JD, (with distinction), 1996, University of Iowa, BS, 1993.

### COHEN, Louis
Locke Lord LLP, Chicago
312 443 0298
lcohen@lockelord.com
*Featured in Real Estate (Illinois)*

**Practice Areas:** International Chair of the Firm's Finance, Banking & Real Estate Department. He concentrates in transactional real estate matters and the development and use of professional sports venues. His real estate practice involves commercial acquisitions and dispositions, development, venture structuring and formation, leasing, lending, restructuring and workouts. His sports franchise and sports facilities development practice addresses the development, financing, leasing and media/sponsorship/naming of professional sports stadia, as well as the acquisition and disposition of interests in professional sports franchises.

**Career:** Partner at Locke Lord since 2010.

**Personal:** Northwestern University School of Law (JD, 1981); Stanford University (BA 1978).

### COLE, Thomas A
Sidley Austin LLP, Chicago
312 853 7473
tcole@sidley.com
*Featured in Corporate/M&A (Illinois)*

**Practice Areas:** Thomas Cole is a partner in Sidley's Chicago office. In April 2013, he will step down after 15 years as Chair of the firm's Executive Committee. He will continue to advise clients on public company mergers and acquisitions and corporate governance.

**Professional Memberships:** Trustee, The University of Chicago; Chairman - Emeritus, Board of Trustees, Northwestern Memorial HealthCare; Director, World Sport Chicago; Lecturer at The University of Chicago Law School.

**Personal:** The University of Chicago Law School (JD, 1975); Johns Hopkins University (AB, 1970). Admission: Illinois.

### COLLINS, Joseph
DLA Piper LLP (US), Chicago
312 368 2143
joseph.collins@dlapiper.com
*Featured in Litigation (Illinois)*

**Practice Areas:** Litigation

**Career:** He focuses his practice in the areas of complex commercial litigation, class actions, securities litigation, white-collar investigations, consumer fraud litigation and insurance coverage litigation. He has represented a broad range of clients, from start-up ventures to Fortune 100 Companies, in matters pending across the country.

**Personal:** MBA, Kellogg School of Management, Northwestern University; JD, Chicago-Kent College of Law, Illinois Institute of Technology.

### COLMAN, Jeffrey D
Jenner & Block LLP, Chicago
312 923 2940
jcolman@jenner.com
*Featured in Litigation (Illinois)*

**Career:** Jeff Colman is Co-Chair of the Professional Responsibility Practice. A Fellow of the American College of Trial Lawyers, he focuses his career on complex civil and criminal litigation at the trial and appellate levels. He has represented more than 35 law firms in professional liability matters. He has represented plaintiffs and defendants in class action litigation, in the defense of environmental and civil rights litigation, and in commercial matters. Mr Colman serves as Chairman of the Illinois Supreme Court's Commission on Access to Justice, and he is active in pro bono representations and a host of law reform organizations.

### COMELLA, Philip L.
Seyfarth Shaw LLP, Chicago
312 460 5501
pcomella@seyfarth.com
*Featured in Environment (Illinois)*

**Practice Areas:** Focuses on environmental-related litigation, representing waste treatment, recycling and disposal companies; heavy industry; and environmental firms. Also concentrates on negotiation of landfill gas and renewable energy contracts; regulatory counseling; and enforcement action defense.

**Professional Memberships:** Solid Waste Management of North American; National Solid Waste Management Association.

**Career:** Former in-house counsel at national hazardous waste company; twenty five years in private practice.

**Publications:** Prepared Environmental Issues chapter for Practicing Law Institute's book on Acquiring or Selling the Privately Held Company; published articles on landfill gas contracts for SWANA and hazardous waste issues for ELI and Boston College environmental journal.

### COMPERNOLLE, Paul
McDermott Will & Emery LLP, Chicago
312 984 7632
pcompernolle@mwe.com
*Featured in Labor & Employment (Illinois)*

**Practice Areas:** Based in the firm's Chicago office. Focuses on the employee benefits field, advising businesses on a broad range of employee benefits matters, including establishing and administering 401(k) and pension plans and the benefits aspects of acquisitions and sales of businesses.

**Professional Memberships:** Admitted to the Illinois Bar.

**Personal:** University of Illinois College of Law, JD, 1978; Yale University, BA, 1975.

### CONLAN, James F
Sidley Austin LLP, Chicago
312 853 6890
jconlan@sidley.com
*Featured in Bankruptcy/Restructuring (Nationwide), Bankruptcy/Restructuring (Illinois)*

**Practice Areas:** Partner in Sidley's Chicago office, Co-Chair of the firm's Corporate Reorganization and Bankruptcy Group, and member of the firm's Executive Committee. Some representative engagements include: Tribune Company (client, debtor); Dynegy Holdings (client, debtor); RH Donnelley (client, debtor); Smurfit-Stone Container (client, debtor); Merisant (client, debtor); Budget Rent-A-Car Corporation (client, debtor); Meridian Automotive Systems (client, debtor); and Owens Corning (client, debtor). Was selected by Turnarounds & Workouts to its 2009 list of the top dozen outstanding restructuring lawyers in America.

**Personal:** University of Iowa College of Law, JD, 1988, with honors; University of Iowa, BS, 1985, with honors. Admission: Illinois.

### CONLON, William
Sidley Austin LLP, Chicago
312 853 7384
wconlon@sidley.com
*Featured in Litigation (Illinois)*

**Practice Areas:** Partner in Sidley's Chicago office. His trial and appellate experience includes jury and bench trials as well as administrative proceedings in state and federal courts throughout the country. Representative issues have included antitrust, ERISA, securities laws, banking and bank regulatory issues, telecommunications, accountants' liability, insurance and insurance regulatory issues, utilities law, and a variety of complex commercial individual and class action cases.

**Professional Memberships:** Fellow, American College of Trial Lawyers; Board Member, Chicago Board Foundation, Chicago Bar Association.

**Personal:** University of Illinois College of Law, JD, 1970; Indiana University, AB, 1967. Admission: Illinois.

### CONWAY, Timothy R
Conway & Mrowiec, Chicago
312 658 1100
trc@cmcontractors.com
*Featured in Construction (Illinois)*

**Practice Areas:** Construction law.

**Professional Memberships:** American (Member, Fidelity and Surety Law Committee) Bar Association; Builders Association of Chicago; Fox Valley General Contractors Association; Association of Subcontractors and Affiliates; Society of Illinois Construction Lawyers; Leading Lawyers Network.

**Publications:** Co-Author, Chapter 10, BIM and Shared Design Risks for Structural Steel Contractors, "Shared Design" (Aspen 2011); "Requirements for the Original Contractor's Lien on Private Projects", Illinois Institute of Continuing Legal Education, 1994, 2000, 2004, 2007, 2010 eds.; Chapter 11, Scope Changes and Differing Site Conditions, "Construction Litigation Dispute Handbook", Illinois Institute of Continuing Legal Education, 2013.

**COOPER, Jonathan**
Goldberg Kohn Ltd, Chicago
312 201 3980
Jonathan.cooper@goldbergkohn.com
*Featured in Banking & Finance (Illinois)*
**Career:** Jonathan Cooper is a principal in the firm's Commercial Finance Group. He has represented both institutional lenders and borrowers in all facets of commercial finance transactions, including senior secured asset-based and cash-flow transactions, first lien, second lien and mezzanine positions, as well as in workouts and restructurings. Mr Cooper has significant experience conducting international commercial finance transactions for a wide range of clients, primarily focusing on Europe and the Americas. He frequently gives presentations regarding international finance and has written several articles on the subject. He also chairs the American Bar Association Subcommittee on Cross Border and Trade Finance.

**COOPERMAN, Marc S**
Banner & Witcoff, Ltd, Chicago
312 463 5000
mcooperman@bannerwitcoff.com
*Featured in Intellectual Property (Illinois)*
**Practice Areas:** Patent, trademark and copyright litigation; Trademark Trial and Appeal Board proceedings; and alternative dispute resolution.
**Professional Memberships:** ABA, AIPLA, FCBA, INTA.
**Career:** Principal shareholder, Banner & Witcoff. Joined firm in 1989 and elected firm president at age 34 in 1999; spent entire career at the firm.
**Publications:** Authored numerous articles and spoken frequently on intellectual property. Former contributing editor, Federal Circuit Bar Journal; and regular columnist on intellectual property issues affecting the toy industry, Playthings magazine.
**Personal:** BSME, University of Illinois; JD, University of Illinois. Adjunct professor at Northwestern, where he teaches patent and trademark litigation courses.

**CROSS, Jeffery M**
Freeborn & Peters LLP, Chicago
312 360 6430
jcross@freebornpeters.com
*Featured in Antitrust (Illinois)*
**Practice Areas:** Over 35 years of experience representing clients throughout the country on all aspects of antitrust litigation and counseling, including mergers and acquisitions. His experience includes representing BP America in an antitrust jury trial in Los Angeles; representing the Burlington Northern Santa Fe Railway Company in an antitrust case in San Francisco; representation of a Santa Barbara, California textile rental company in an antitrust class action in East St. Louis; representation of the Noranda defendants in the Sulfuric Acid Antitrust Litigation in Chicago; and representation of Falconbridge before the Department of Justice in its investigation of Inco's $17 billion merger with Falconbridge.

**Professional Memberships:** Former Officer, various ABA Antitrust Section Committees; Chair, Illinois State Bar Association Antitrust Law Section Council (1988-89).
**Career:** Freeborn & Peters LLP (1999-present); Adjunct Professor, Antitrust Law, The John Marshall Law School (1999-present).
**Publications:** Two chapters in the Matthew Bender treatise, Antitrust Counseling and Litigation Techniques; and two chapters in the Aspen treatise, Corporate Legal Compliance Handbook; numerous other articles and speeches. For a complete list see www.freebornpeters.com.
**Personal:** JD, magna cum laude: Syracuse University College of Law, Order of the Coif, Research Editor, Syracuse Law Review; BS, cum laude: University of Illinois at Chicago.

**CULLEN, Gary P**
Skadden, Arps, Slate, Meagher & Flom LLP & Affiliates, Chicago
312 407 0680
gary.cullen@skadden.com
*Featured in Corporate/M&A (Illinois)*
**Practice Areas:** Co-head of the Chicago office's Corporate Group. Represents Fortune 500, middle market and emerging companies, investment banking and other financial institutions in M&A and corporate finance transactions. Represents buyers and sellers in auctions involving public companies, other stock and asset acquisitions and dispositions, negotiated and contested takeovers, proxy contests and joint ventures, and issuers and investment banking institutions in initial and other public offerings, private placements of securities and high-yield debt transactions. Advises on corporate governance, disclosure and corporate control issues, and litigation strategy matters.
**Career:** JD, Columbia University School of Law, 1985; BA, University of Illinois, 1982.

**CUNNINGHAM, Thomas**
Sidley Austin LLP, Chicago
312 853 7594
tcunningham@sidley.com
*Featured in Insurance (Illinois)*
**Practice Areas:** Thomas Cunningham is a partner in the Insurance and Financial Services Group. He has extensive experience in insurance and reinsurance disputes. He has represented insurers, ceding companies, reinsurers, receivers and holding companies. Tom is a frequent author and speaker on insurance and reinsurance related topics. He has counseled on matters involving aggregation and allocation of claims, workers' compensation, life, health and medical claims, stable value wraps, finite reinsurance, insurance insolvency, and structuring and unwinding of triple-x structures.
**Personal:** JD, University of Michigan Law School, 1995, cum laude; AB, University of Michigan, 1992, with high honors and high distinction.

**DALY, James R**
Jones Day, Chicago
312 269 4141
jrdaly@jonesday.com
*Featured in Litigation (Illinois)*

**Practice Areas:** Commercial litigator with broad experience in a wide range of areas. Current practice places particular emphasis on defending pharmaceutical companies in multidistrict litigation against private, federal and state plaintiffs alleging improper pricing and promotional practices under Medicare and Medicaid; defense of qui tam actions under state and federal False Claims Acts; defense of consumer class actions; antitrust defense; and representing tobacco company against the states in various matters relating to the Tobacco Master Settlement Agreement. Coordinates litigation practice in Chicago.
**Professional Memberships:** Trial Bar of the US District Court for the Northern District of Illinois; ISBA.

**DAVID, Oscar A**
Winston & Strawn LLP, Chicago
312 558 5745
odavid@winston.com
*Featured in Corporate/M&A (Illinois)*
**Practice Areas:** Chair-Winston & Strawn's mergers and acquisitions, securities & corporate governance practice. Practice also includes private equity and venture capital. Regularly advises senior executives on sensitive challenges arising in these matters. Representative clients include Motorola Solutions, Activision Blizzard, Discover Financial Services, BDT Capital Partners, CIVC Partners, Fulcrum Strategy Partners, Loop Capital Markets LLC and Waud Capital Partners. Guest lecturer, Kellogg Graduate School of Management, Northwestern University.
**Career:** Joined Winston & Strawn in 1987. Elected as Partner in 1995.
**Personal:** JD University of Chicago Law School 1987; BA (economics) George Washington University 1984 (Phi Beta Kappa).

**DAVIDSON, Steven R**
Dentons, Chicago
312 876 8238
steven.davidson@dentons.com
*Featured in Real Estate (Illinois)*
**Practice Areas:** Concentrates his real estate practice in the financing area. Has handled both construction and term loans secured by virtually every type of real estate collateral, including office buildings, hotels, apartment complexes, retail centers and vacant land. Regularly handles syndicated loans, mezzanine loans, and restructurings and workouts. In addition, has non-real estate finance practice, including representing agent banks in unsecured syndicated revolving credit and term credit facilities and facilities secured by other asset types.
**Personal:** Harvard Law School, JD (cum laude); University of Michigan, AB (high honors and high distinction).

**DAVIS, Geoffrey M**
Jenner & Block LLP, Chicago
312 923 8302
gdavis@jenner.com
*Featured in Tax (Illinois)*
**Career:** Geoffrey M. Davis is a member of Jenner & Block's Tax and Tax Controversy Practices. Mr Davis has a broad federal tax practice focusing on

acquisition and divestiture transactions, restructuring and financing transactions and fund formation and related investments. He also routinely handles a wide spectrum of tax controversy matters. Mr Davis is an adjunct professor at John Marshall Law School in Chicago, where he teaches in the Real Estate LLM program, and at Chicago-Kent College of Law, where he teaches taxation of financial instruments.

**DEBEERS, Kimberly A**
Skadden, Arps, Slate, Meagher & Flom LLP & Affiliates, Chicago
312 407 0982
kimberly.deBeers@skadden.com
*Featured in Corporate/M&A (Illinois)*
**Practice Areas:** Concentrates practice in corporate, securities and other aspects of complex business transactions. Represents private equity and hedge funds in acquisitions, dispositions and portfolio company issues. Advises public companies in joint ventures with private equity as well as investments from private equity or hedge funds. Counsels on complicated debt and equity restructurings for distressed and other companies. A frequent speaker on securities law.
**Career:** JD, DePaul University College of Law, 1995 (Managing Editor of Lead Articles, Business Law Journal; Member, Law Review); BS, University of Illinois, 1990.

**DEJONG, Ralph E**
McDermott Will & Emery LLP, Chicago
312 984 6918
rdejong@mwe.com
*Featured in Healthcare (Illinois)*
**Practice Areas:** Particular focus on compensation, executive benefits and employee benefits of tax-exempt organizations, including designing and preparing deferred and incentive compensation arrangements, leading governing boards in independent review and approval of executive and physician compensation arrangements, negotiating and preparing executive and physician employment and severance agreements, and analyzing the private inurement and intermediate sanctions implications of executive and physician compensation and benefit arrangements. Practices in full range of employee benefits issues for various employers, focusing on analyzing and minimizing fiduciary liability of employer plan sponsors.
**Personal:** University of Notre Dame Law School (JD, magna cum laude); Calvin College (BA).

**DEMARTE, Luke W**
Michael Best & Friedrich LLP, Chicago
312 222 5795
lwdemarte@michaelbest.com
*Featured in Media & Entertainment (Illinois)*
**Practice Areas:** Luke DeMarte practices in the areas of trademark, copyright and entertainment law. Mr DeMarte counsels clients in a wide variety of industries including consumer products, hospitality, beverage alcohol, financial services, music, software and more. Mr DeMarte assists clients with the acquisition, enforcement and exploitation of intellectual property rights, such as trademarks and copyrights, both domestically and

abroad. He has experience in general commercial transactions and litigation. Mr DeMarte represents recording artists, producers and record labels in connection with contractual, intellectual property and corporate matters. He also negotiates with talent for endorsements and televised appearances.

### DESMOND, Thomas P
Vedder Price PC, Chicago
312 609 7647
tdesmond@vedderprice.com
*Featured in Labor & Employment (Illinois)*
**Practice Areas:** Shareholder, Chair of the Corporate Practice area and Co-chair of the Executive Compensation practice group. Nationally known for engagements representing corporations, compensation committees, CEOs, management teams and other executives on all aspects of the development and implementation of employment, equity-based compensation, change-in-control and separation arrangements. Practical advisor on related regulatory, proxy and other disclosure considerations and requirements. Also counsels public and private corporations and boards on mergers and acquisitions, corporate finance, fiduciary duty and governance matters.
**Career:** Admitted (IL) 1981.
**Personal:** JD, Northwestern University; BBA, Accountancy, University of Notre Dame.

### DESPOTES, Andrea M
Neal, Gerber & Eisenberg LLP, Chicago
312 269 8480
adespotes@ngelaw.com
*Featured in Tax (Illinois)*
**Practice Areas:** Advises Fortune 500 companies in structuring tax-free reorganizations and spin-off transactions, and counsels mid-sized companies and entrepreneurial concerns in all aspects of tax planning. Has significant experience obtaining private letter rulings from the Internal Revenue Service and advising on the complex federal income tax rules governing consolidated groups, S corporations, real estate investment trusts and partnerships, with a concentration on the federal income tax aspects of corporate divestitures and acquisitions, partnership transactions and tax-planning strategies.
**Career:** Partner; Tax Practice Group.
**Publications:** Author on tax law topics.
**Personal:** Stanford University (BA, 1991); Harvard Law School (JD, 1995).

### DICKERSON, Christopher L
DLA Piper LLP (US), Chicago
312 368 7045
chris.dickerson@dlapiper.com
*Featured in Bankruptcy/Restructuring (Illinois)*
**Practice Areas:** Bankruptcy/Restructuring.
**Professional Memberships:** American Bankruptcy Institute; Turnaround Management Association.
**Career:** He represents a variety of clients in complex business reorganizations, debt restructurings and insolvency matters, including purchasers of and investors in distressed companies and lenders to and creditors of such companies. He has assisted large corporations inside and outside Chapter

11, investors in and acquirors of distressed assets and secured lenders and providers of debtor-in-possession financings. He frequently lectures and writes on restructuring topics.
**Personal:** JD, University of Wisconsin Law School (cum laude, Order of the Coif); MA, Georgetown University (National Security Studies); BS, U.S. Naval Academy.

### DICKINSON, Christopher C
Jenner & Block LLP, Chicago
312 923 2858
cdickinson@jenner.com
*Featured in Insurance (Illinois)*
**Career:** Christopher C. Dickinson is a partner in Jenner & Block's Litigation Department and is a member of the Firm's Insurance Litigation and Counseling Practice. Financial institutions and other corporate policyholders turn to him for help pursuing insurance recovery for high-stakes claims and losses of all kinds. Through litigation, arbitration or negotiation, he has recovered hundreds of millions of dollars for his clients from virtually all of the major insurers in domestic, London and Bermuda markets. He also counsels corporate policyholders on claims review and management; insurance program design; crafting policy language; and insurer insolvencies.

### DICKSTEIN, Beth
Sidley Austin LLP, Chicago
312 853 6093
bdickstein@sidley.com
*Featured in Labor & Employment (Illinois)*
**Practice Areas:** Partner in Sidley's Chicago office focusing on employee benefit matters. Represents companies in the establishment and administration of pension and profit sharing plans, welfare plans, stock purchase plans, incentive compensation plans and non-qualified deferred compensation plans. Also advises investment managers, commodity pool operators and pension plan investors on the application of ERISA to a variety of investment products, including hedge funds. Practice also focuses on benefits issues arising in connection with mergers, acquisitions and financings.
**Personal:** University of Pennsylvania Law School, JD, 1988, cum laude, University of Illinois, BS, 1985, with highest honors. Admission: Illinois.

### DIGIOVANNI, Nick J
Locke Lord LLP, Chicago
312 443 0634
ndigiovanni@lockelord.com
*Featured in Insurance (Illinois)*
**Practice Areas:** Insurance and Reinsurance.
**Career:** Chairs the Firm's Global Reinsurance and Insurance Litigation and Counseling Practice Groups. Trial lawyer with more than 25 years of experience in large commercial cases including national and international litigation, arbitration, insolvency and rehabilitation proceedings. Concentrates on reinsurance, insurance and financial services-related disputes. Named one of America's Leading 500 Lawyers for his accomplishments in reinsurance. Represents many of the world's major insurance and reinsurance compa-

nies and regularly advises them on complex and newly emerging issues in the industry.
**Personal:** University of Notre Dame (JD, cum laude, 1980); Southern Methodist University (BBA, cum laude, 1977).

### DINARDO, Lawrence
Jones Day, Chicago
312 269 4306
lcdinardo@jonesday.com
*Featured in Labor & Employment (Illinois)*
**Practice Areas:** Global Chair of the firm's Labor and Employment Practice. Particular emphasis on employment discrimination litigation, FLSA/wage-hour cases, employee benefits, and executive employment contract disputes. Extensive experience defending employers in class actions and individual cases and representing employers before the NLRB and labor arbitrations and negotiations. He has tried more than 35 cases to verdict before juries around the US and handled an equal number of cases before federal and state appellate courts. Served as a visiting Professor at Notre Dame Law School and guest lecturer at University of Chicago Business School and DePaul University College of Law.

### DIVARCO, Sandra
McDermott Will & Emery UK LLP, London
312 984 2006
sdivarco@mwe.com
*Featured in Healthcare (Illinois)*
**Practice Areas:** Focuses her practice on the representation of hospitals and health systems. Has counseled health care facility and system clients regarding all aspects of health law transactions and health system restructurings. Regularly advises clients on the legal aspects of clinical issues and policy/procedure matters. Additionally has significant experience in assisting clients across the country with regulatory, licensure and accreditation issues, including state-level and CMS survey responses, formulation of successful Plans of Correction, Joint Commission complaint responses and EMTALA/regulatory investigations.
**Personal:** Loyola University Chicago School of Law, JD, (cum laude), 2002, University of Illinois at Chicago, BS (with honors), 1994.

### DOCKSEY, Ross
Dentons, Chicago
312 876 8171
ross.docksey@dentons.com
*Featured in Outsourcing (Nationwide), Technology (Illinois)*
**Practice Areas:** Outsourcing, insourcing and shared services contracting; technology contracting, including systems development, distribution and licensing contracts; mediation and arbitration of disputes arising pursuant to sourcing contracts; development of joint ventures and alliances; structuring and negotiating mergers and acquisitions.
**Professional Memberships:** Sourcing Interests Group.
**Career:** Joined Dentons in 1981.
**Publications:** Why Outsourcing Sometimes Fails, Inside Sourcing, When East Meets West in the Outsourcing World, HRO Europe Dispelling the Myths in Outsourcing, Institutional Investor

News Outsourcing Made Simple, Insight Information The Role of Information Technology Risk Assessment in Enterprise Risk Management, SIG Effective Enterprise Risk Management, SIG.
**Personal:** University of Minnesota, JD. West Point, BS.

### DOCKTERMAN, Michael
Edwards Wildman Palmer, Chicago
312 201 2652
mdockterman@edwardswildman.com
*Featured in Litigation (Illinois)*
**Practice Areas:** Michael concentrates his practice in complex civil and criminal business litigation, securities and derivative litigation, and in advising clients on matters of corporate governance and compliance. He has appeared as principal trial counsel in state and federal courts in over half of the United States, and has tried securities, antitrust, intellectual property, environmental, contract, fraud and product liability cases, and both federal and state white collar criminal cases. He also has represented both corporate and individual interests in grand jury and other government investigations across the country.
**Personal:** Duke University, JD; Yale University, BA.

### DOLIN, Kenneth R
Seyfarth Shaw LLP, Chicago
312 460 5522
kdolin@seyfarth.com
*Featured in Labor & Employment (Illinois)*
**Practice Areas:** Labor and employment law, including NLRB casehandling, collective bargaining, arbitrations, strikes and lockouts, NLRB election campaigns and strategizing on complex labor relations issues; employment litigation, including discrimination and restrictive covenants; and business restructuring such as RIFs, plant closings, work relocations and outsourcings.
**Professional Memberships:** American Bar Association, Labor and Employment Section.
**Career:** Partner at Seyfarth Shaw since 2004; NLRB Attorney, 1982-84.
**Publications:** Associate editor, around "The Developing Labor Law" (BNA); columnist, National Law Journal.
**Personal:** JD, University of Illinois, cum laude (1980); LLM in Labor Law, New York University (1987); Fellow, College of Labor & Employment Lawyers.

### DOUGLAS, Charles W
Sidley Austin LLP, Chicago
312 853 7706
cdouglas@sidley.com
*Featured in Antitrust (Illinois), Litigation (Illinois)*
**Practice Areas:** Mr Douglas is a partner in Sidley's Chicago office, a member of Sidley's Executive Committee and Chairman of Sidley's Management Committee. Has extensive litigation experience in major antitrust, trade regulation, securities, product liability and commercial litigation, and numerous major trials in a variety of complex cases. Former head of the firm's Commercial, Competition, and Securities Litigation group.

**Professional Memberships:** Fellow, American College of Trial Lawyers; Trustee, Chicago Academy of Sciences; Trustee, Chicago Symphony Orchestra; Trustee, Children's Memorial Hospital; Trustee, Northwestern University.
**Personal:** Harvard Law School, JD, 1974; Northwestern University, BA, 1970, Phi Beta Kappa. Admission: Illinois.

### DOWNS, Jeremy
Goldberg Kohn Ltd, Chicago
312 201 3893
jeremy.downs@goldbergkohn.com
*Featured in Bankruptcy/Restructuring (Illinois)*
**Career:** Jeremy Downs is a principal in the firm's Bankruptcy & Creditors' Rights Group. He regularly represents secured lenders in corporate bankruptcies and workouts, and a large portion of his practice involves representing junior lenders and large unsecured creditors. Having successfully navigated several clients through complex automotive restructurings, liquidations and contract disputes, he has developed a particularly strong set of creditors' rights skills related to truck and automotive manufacturing and supply situations. His general bankruptcy experience includes the negotiation, documentation and litigation of debtor-in-possession financing, use of cash collateral, asset sales, relief from the automatic stay, and various related procedural matters.

### DOYLE, Linda
McDermott Will & Emery LLP, Chicago
312 984 6905
ldoyle@mwe.com
*Featured in Labor & Employment (Illinois)*
**Practice Areas:** Represents clients in employment-related litigation, including employment discrimination, executive compensation, whistleblower, wage and hour and benefits litigation. Represents employers in arbitrations under collective bargaining agreements, before National Labor Relations Board and in union organizing campaigns. Conducts internal investigations for corporations. Counsel employees on employment-related issues.
**Professional Memberships:** American Bar Association (Labor and Employment Law Section).
**Publications:** Co-authored "Domestic-Partner Benefit Plans Raise Legal Issues," and "Outside the Title VII Bubble: Other Theories of Employment Liability,". Chapter Editor "How To Take a Case Before The NLRB,".
**Personal:** University of Michigan Law School (JD cum laude), St. Joseph's University (BS).

### DRANOFF, David
Goldberg Kohn Ltd, Chicago
312 201 3939
David.Dranoff@goldbergkohn.com
*Featured in Banking & Finance (Illinois)*
**Career:** David Dranoff is a principal and chairs the firm's Commercial Finance Group, with 28 years of experience representing lenders in negotiating, documenting and closing financing transactions. His experience covers a broad range of commercial finance transactions, including traditional asset-based secured loans; complicated

leveraged buy-out and cash-flow transactions; senior, mezzanine and equity investments; and one-stop banking matters. His practice encompasses the representation of lenders to many manufacturing, wholesale, service and agricultural sectors, as well as to various retail concerns. In addition, he has worked frequently in cross-border lending transactions in North and South America, in Europe and in Asia.

### DUFFY, Thomas P
Edwards Wildman Palmer, Chicago
312 201 2585
tduffy@edwardswildman.com
*Featured in Real Estate (Illinois)*
**Practice Areas:** Tom represents developers in all aspects of real estate development, including real estate acquisitions and dispositions, retail, industrial and mixed use developments and related leasing, construction, permanent and securitized lending, intercreditor agreements, debt restructuring, work-outs and real estate litigation. He provides ongoing counsel to shopping center, multi-family and industrial developers in acquisitions of vacant land and annexation to adjacent municipalities, negotiation of municipal development agreements, zoning, TIF financing, governmental tax rebates and abatements, special service area agreements, ground leases, site development agreements and reciprocal easement agreements.
**Personal:** DePaul University, JD, cum laude; University of Pennsylvania, BA.

### DUNCAN, Margaret M
McDermott Will & Emery LLP, Chicago
312 984 6476
mduncan@mwe.com
*Featured in Intellectual Property (Illinois)*
**Practice Areas:** Head of Chicago intellectual property practice. Focuses on IP litigation, counseling, protection and transactions. Lead counsel in federal district courts in patent, trademark, copyright, unfair competition, right of publicity, domain name and trade secret cases. Represents clients in complex technology areas including chemical formulations, electronic circuitry, methods for conducting financial and business transactions and computer programs.
**Professional Memberships:** Admission: Illinois Bar (1981); US District Courts in Illinois and Wisconsin, US Courts of Appeals, Seventh Circuit and Federal Circuit, US Patent and Trademark Office.
**Personal:** Loyola University of Chicago School of Law (JD); Xavier University (BS); Indiana University (BS).

### DURSO, John
Ungaretti & Harris LLP, Chicago
312 977 4440
jdurso@uhlaw.com
*Featured in Healthcare (Illinois)*
**Practice Areas:** John Durso is a partner in the Healthcare group at Ungaretti & Harris LLP. John concentrates his practice in healthcare law, representing hospitals, long-term care facilities, assisted-living establishments, senior housing, continuing care retirement communities, home community services, and pace accountable care organiza-

tions. He represents religious and not-for-profit healthcare organizations in tax exemption and regulatory issues. His expertise includes affiliations, mergers, acquisitions and financial workout. John serves as a volunteer director for not-for-profit healthcare providers and educational institutions.
**Personal:** Loyola University Chicago School of Law (JD, magna cum laude,1977); Northern Illinois University (BA, 1974).

### DUWE, Brian W
Skadden, Arps, Slate, Meagher & Flom LLP & Affiliates, Chicago
312 407 0816
brian.duwe@skadden.com
*Featured in Corporate/M&A (Illinois)*
**Practice Areas:** Heads the Firm's Chicago office. Focuses on mergers and acquisitions, corporate finance, and general corporate and securities matters. Represents buyers, sellers and their financial advisers in a variety of transactions, including negotiated and contested public acquisitions and divestitures, management buyouts, restructurings, spin-offs, and joint ventures and other strategic alliances. Counsels issuers, selling shareholders and investment banks in public offerings and private placements of debt and equity securities.
**Career:** JD, The University of Chicago Law School, 1987 (associate editor, The University of Chicago Law Review; Order of the Coif; Olin Scholar); BA, Dartmouth College, 1982 (summa cum laude).

### EATON, David L
Kirkland & Ellis LLP, Chicago
312 862 2066
david.eaton@kirkland.com
*Featured in Bankruptcy/Restructuring (Illinois)*
**Practice Areas:** Represents debtors, creditors, committees and purchasers of troubled companies in restructuring and bankruptcy planning, negotiation and litigation. Active cross-border practice drawing from unique experience in turnaround consulting and investment banking. Debtor clients include Collins & Aikman, Sea Containers, YRC Worldwide and Flying J. Investor clients include Oaktree Capital, Versa Capital and Golden Gate Capital.
**Professional Memberships:** ABA, INSOL.
**Career:** Formerly Managing Director of PricewaterhouseCoopers Securities, handling multinational debt restructuring and distressed M&A. Formerly Executive Chairman of LA Gear Inc. after Chapter 11.
**Personal:** University of Illinois College of Law, JD, 1978; University of Michigan, BA, 1974.

### EDWARDS, Charles L
DLA Piper LLP (US), Chicago
312 368 4010
charles.edwards@dlapiper.com
*Featured in Real Estate (Illinois)*
**Practice Areas:** Real estate.
**Professional Memberships:** Member, American College of Real Estate Lawyers and the American College of Mortgage Attorneys.

**Career:** His practice concentrates exclusively in complex commercial real estate transactions, including purchase and sale; mortgage financing; leasing; joint ventures and partnerships; condominiums and co-operatives; general development and all other aspects of commercial real estate practice.
**Personal:** JD, University of Chicago; BBA, University of Wisconsin (the highest honors).

### EIDELMAN, Michael M
Vedder Price PC, Chicago
312 609 7636
meidelman@vedderprice.com
*Featured in Bankruptcy/Restructuring (Illinois)*
**Practice Areas:** Shareholder and Co-chair, Bankruptcy & Creditors' Rights group, and member of the firm's Board of Directors. Has acted as lead counsel for debtors, secured and unsecured creditors, Chapter 7 and 11 trustees, landlords, purchasers of assets, and creditors' and bondholders' committees. Represents companies, creditors, court-appointed receivers and assignees for the benefit of creditors in out-of-court restructurings and liquidations. Represents officers and directors of financially distressed companies.
**Professional Memberships:** Member, Turnaround Management Association and American Bankruptcy Institute.
**Career:** Admitted (IL) 1988.
**Personal:** JD, DePaul University College of Law; B.G.S., University of Michigan.

### EIMER, Nathan P
Eimer Stahl LLP, Chicago
312 660 7601
neimer@eimerstahl.com
*Featured in Antitrust (Illinois)*
**Practice Areas:** Mr Eimer is a trial lawyer who has acted as trial counsel in numerous federal and state courts and arbitration settings. He specializes in complex commercial litigation with emphasis on antitrust litigation. He was named "Antitrust Lawyer of the Year" for 2011 and 2013 by US News & World Report - Best Lawyers, and is the only antitrust lawyer in Illinois and one of only five antitrust lawyers in the United States to receive Chambers & Partners' 'star' rating. Mr Eimer has played a prinicpal role in dozens of grand jury investigations and criminal and civil antitrust cases, including several in which he has been national lead counsel for all defendants. He has represented a large number of major corporations in antitrust matters, including CITGO Petroleum, The Dow Chemical Company, Land O'Lakes, Inc., Ingredion Incorporated, Gerdau Ameristeel, Baxter International Inc., Bank of New York Mellon, Deutsche Bank AG, UBS AG, Praxair, Inc., LG Electronics, Inc., The Art Institute of Chicago, Schreiber Foods, Inc., and City of Kankakee.
**Professional Memberships:** Antitrust and Criminal Sections of the American Bar Association.
**Career:** He was one of the founding members of his firm in July 2000. Prior to that he was a Member of the Executive Committee, General Counsel, Head of the Commercial and Regulatory

Litigation Group, and a Partner of Sidley & Austin. From 1984 until 1990 he was the Head of that firm's New York Litigation Practice.
**Personal:** Born June 26, 1949. Received his JD, cum laude, from Northwestern Universtiy School of Law in 1973, where he was a notes and comments editor for the 'Law Review'. Received a BA, magna cum laude, with Highest Distinction in Economics, from the University of Illinois in 1970.

### ELBERT, Angela R
Neal, Gerber & Eisenberg LLP, Chicago
312 269 5995
aelbert@ngelaw.com
*Featured in Insurance (Illinois)*
**Practice Areas:** Counsels clients on complex risk management and insurance issues. Advises entities and boards of directors on a wide variety of risk management issues. Handles complex insurance coverage litigation, other commercial litigation, mediations and arbitrations, with an emphasis on representing policyholders in insurance coverage disputes nationwide involving virtually every line of insurance.
**Professional Memberships:** ABA Insurance Coverage Litigation Committee (CLE Seminar Co-Chair, 2008); Chicago Bar Association Insurance Committee (Chair, 2009-10).
**Career:** Partner; Litigation Practice Group; Insurance Policyholder Practice Group.
**Publications:** Frequent author and lecturer on insurance topics.
**Personal:** Indiana University (JD, 1996); Hanover College (BA, 1993).

### ELROD, Steven M
Holland & Knight LLP, Chicago
312 578 6565
steven.elrod@hklaw.com
*Featured in Real Estate (Illinois)*
**Practice Areas:** Steven M. Elrod represents both private and public sector clients on a broad range of land use and zoning matters. He chairs Holland & Knight's National Land Use and Government Team, and is the Executive Partner of the firm's Chicago office. He consults with local governments throughout Illinois, and is regularly engaged to secure zoning relief and government entitlements, incentives and approvals for developers and land owners. Mr Elrod lectures throughout the country on land use issues, and teaches State & Local Government Law at Northwestern University Law School.

### ERENS, Brad B
Jones Day, Chicago
312 269 4050
bberens@jonesday.com
*Featured in Bankruptcy/Restructuring (Illinois)*
**Practice Areas:** Oversees the Business Restructuring and Reorganization Practice in Jones Day's Chicago office. His practice focuses on corporate restructuring, workout, and bankruptcy matters. He has substantial experience in representing companies, bank groups, other secured and unsecured creditors, asset purchasers, and other interested parties in a wide variety of matters.

**Professional Memberships:** American Bankruptcy Institute. Turnaround Management Association. Economic Club of Chicago.
**Career:** He is an adjunct Professor at the DePaul University College of Law in Chicago where he teaches corporate reorganizations.
**Personal:** University of Chicago (JD 1991; Order of the Coif); Yale University (BA summa cum laude 1988).

### ERF, Stephen
McDermott Will & Emery LLP, Chicago
312 984 7637
serf@mwe.com
*Featured in Labor & Employment (Illinois)*
**Practice Areas:** Partner in Labor and Employment Group. Concentrates on civil rights and labor/employment counseling and litigation, union organizing, collective bargaining, arbitration, employment discrimination, wrongful discharge, wage and hour and public accommodations. Has worked with clients in a wide range of industries, including energy, healthcare, education, construction, manufacturing, logistics and distribution, finance, service, food, social service, chemical and transportation.
**Personal:** Loyola University of Chicago School of Law (JD, cum laude); University of Illinois (BA).

### FAHEY, Thomas M
Ungaretti & Harris LLP, Chicago
312 977 4376
tmfahey@uhlaw.com
*Featured in Healthcare (Illinois), Healthcare (Nationwide)*
**Practice Areas:** Tom Fahey is the firm's Managing Partner and chairs the Healthcare and Public Finance groups at Ungaretti & Harris LLP. Tom has been responsible for projects involving virtually every type of health law issue, with a special emphasis in transactions and state and federal regulatory issues. In the public finance arena, he has served as counsel to borrowers, underwriters, banks, and issuers in hundreds of transactions in a wide range of taxable and tax-exempt financings.
**Personal:** DePaul University College of Law (JD, 1980); University of Wisconsin (BS, 1974).

### FALK, R Scott
Kirkland & Ellis LLP, Chicago
312 862 2340
scott.falk@kirkland.com
*Featured in Corporate/M&A (Illinois)*
**Practice Areas:** Scott Falk focuses primarily on mergers and acquisitions and securities offerings for public company clients. His broad base of experience includes negotiated mergers, tender and exchange offers, acquisitions and divestitures of subsidiaries and divisions of public companies, private placements and public offerings of securities and securities law counseling. Mr Falk has also structured and negotiated numerous cross-border investments and acquisitions, both in-bound and out-bound.
**Professional Memberships:** Member, American Bar Association Section of Business Law.

**Personal:** Harvard University, AB, 1985; Harvard Law School, JD, 1989.

### FELDMAN, Mark I
DLA Piper LLP (US), Chicago
312 368 7271
mark.feldman@dlapiper.com
*Featured in Intellectual Property (Illinois)*
**Practice Areas:** Intellectual property, trademark, trademark litigation, domain name, and copyrights.
**Career:** He focuses on trademarks, patents, copyrights, trade secrets, and internet and technology law. He has extensive experience counseling clients on domestic and international intellectual property registration, enforcement, and licensing. He has litigated the protectability of color as a trademark; the enhanced scope of protection for famous trademarks; trademark priority disputes; and protection of the interior design and exterior trade dress of franchised restaurants.
**Personal:** JD, Georgetown University Law Center; B.S.I.E., University of Illinois at Urbana-Champaign (with high honors).

### FERGEMANN, Brian
Winston & Strawn LLP, Chicago
312 5588024
bfergemann@winston.com
*Featured in Media & Entertainment (Illinois)*
**Practice Areas:** Mr Fergemann counsels major national consumer product companies and retailers, and their advertising and marketing agencies, on a wide range of advertising, marketing, social media, privacy, and intellectual property issues. He has extensive experience in negotiating agency-client agreements, talent agreements, and sponsorship agreements. He has represented numerous companies in governmental investigations by the FTC and state attorneys general involving allegations of false advertising and deceptive business practices, and in challenges before the National Advertising Division of the Council of Better Business Bureaus.
**Personal:** University of Virginia, JD, 1999; Michigan State University, BA, 1996.

### FERNANDEZ, Robert L
Dentons, Chicago
312 876 7371
robert.fernandez@dentons.com
*Featured in Real Estate (Illinois)*
**Practice Areas:** Legacy Dentons's US Real Estate Practice Leader. Bob focuses on commercial real estate transactions, real estate finance, acquisitions and dispositions, restructurings and workouts, commercial leasing and real estate development. Represents landlords and tenants in commercial lease negotiations covering office, medical, industrial, educational campus and mixed-use properties. Extensive real estate finance experience, including sophisticated senior, mezzanine and equity financings involving investment funds, REITs, bio-medical research facilities, office buildings, shopping center developments and hospitality properties throughout the US.
**Personal:** Northwestern University School of Law, JD; H. Washington Scholar, Editor, NU

Journal of Int'l Law and Business; DePaul University, BA.

### FIFER, Samuel
Dentons, Chicago
312 876 3114
samuel.fifer@dentons.com
*Featured in Intellectual Property (Illinois), Media & Entertainment (Illinois)*
**Practice Areas:** Intellectual property and technology; patent litigation; entertainment/media law; venture capital/emerging growth company group; trademark, copyright and advertising; internet law.
**Professional Memberships:** American Bar Association Forum Committee on Communications Law; International Trademark Association; Board of Editors, Trademark Reporter, mediator member of Panel of Neutrals; member, Media Law Resource Center, Defense Counsel Section Executive Committee.
**Career:** Adjunct Professor, Northwestern University School of Law (1992-present). Teaches "Entertainment Law" seminar.
**Personal:** DePaul University, JD, cum laude, 1974, managing editor, DePaul Law Review; Northwestern University, BS, communications, 1971.

### FILIP, Mark
Kirkland & Ellis LLP, Chicago
312 862 2192
mark.filip@kirkland.com
*Featured in Litigation (Illinois)*
**Practice Areas:** Mark represents Fortune 500 clients in varied industries in complex civil litigation, as well as in criminal cases, internal investigations and corporate integrity matters. He has extensive experience in court and advising boards of directors.
**Career:** Prior to joining Kirkland, Mark was at the U.S. Department of Justice, where he served as Deputy Attorney General of the United States, which is the #2 position at the U.S. Justice Department. He also formerly served as a U.S. District Judge in Chicago.
**Personal:** Harvard Law School, JD, 1992 magna cum laude; Law Clerk to Justice Scalia, U.S. Supreme Court (1993-1994).

### FILIPPINI, Victor P
Holland & Knight LLP, Chicago
312 578 6560
victor.filippini@hklaw.com
*Featured in Real Estate (Illinois)*
**Practice Areas:** Partner in the firm's Chicago Real Estate Section, he practices principally in the areas of state and local government law, as well as land use and development law. He is actively involved in the general representation of the firm's Chicago area local governmental clients, and has provided special counseling and litigation representation for many private sector clients. Filippini has authored or co-authored various articles in law journals and publications, and lectured on annexation, land use, environmental, first amendment, economic development, legal ethics, and zoning matters. He is also an adjunct professor of law at Northwestern University Law School.

## FISCHER, David
Edwards Wildman Palmer, Chicago
312 201 2641
dfischer@edwardswildman.com
*Featured in Bankruptcy/Restructuring (Illinois)*
**Practice Areas:** David is a partner and Chair of the Restructuring and Insolvency Department of Edwards Wildman. With nearly 30 years of experience focused on the interplay of finance and law, David has a reputation of being a skilled strategist who is highly regarded for structuring innovative business deals and workouts. He is experienced in handling financings, workouts, restructuring, foreclosures and Chapter 11 liquidation from virtually every constituent's perspective. David's practice spans many segments with a particular focus on finance, real estate, insurance and private equity.
**Personal:** Boston University, JD, cum laude; Yale University, BA, magna cum laude.

## FISHER, Frederick
Greenberg Traurig, LLP, Chicago
312 456 1042
FisherF@gtlaw.com
*Featured in Banking & Finance (Illinois)*
**Practice Areas:** Banking & Finance. Mr Fisher's practice focuses on the representation of corporate and lending clients in connection with domestic and international financing transactions. He frequently represents lead lenders and agents in structuring loan transactions, including leveraged buyouts, refinancings, cash flow and asset-based financings, add-on acquisitions, cross-border financings, and loan restructurings and workouts.
**Professional Memberships:** Board Member, Open Books.
**Career:** Member, Winning Team, Global M&A Network's 2012 Turnaround Atlas Award for 'Private Equity Turnaround of the Year' for American Laser Skincare; Listed, Illinois Super Lawyers, 'Rising Star', 2012-13.
**Personal:** JD, Northwestern University School of Law; BS, Miami University.

## FISHER, Scott J
Neal, Gerber & Eisenberg LLP, Chicago
312 269 8035
sfisher@ngelaw.com
*Featured in Litigation (Illinois)*
**Practice Areas:** Concentrates his practice on complex commercial litigation, with an emphasis on class actions. Has considerable jury and non-jury trial experience, representing clients in state and federal courts throughout the US and in a wide range of cases and areas of law, including consumer and commercial fraud, antitrust, uniform commercial code and common law contract, business torts, governmental investigations, bankruptcy, health law, ERISA and corporate structure and governance.
**Career:** Partner; Litigation Practice Group Co-Chair.
**Publications:** Author, commentator and lecturer on litigation issues.
**Personal:** Ohio State University (BA, 1993); Chicago-Kent College of Law (JD, 1996).

## FISHMAN, Michael T
Greenberg Traurig, LLP, Chicago
312 476 5075
FishmanM@gtlaw.com
*Featured in Real Estate (Illinois)*
**Practice Areas:** Co-Chair, Chicago Real Estate Practice. Real estate funds.
**Professional Memberships:** Member: Urban Land Institute; United Jewish Communities National Young Leadership Cabinet; Pension Real Estate Association.
**Career:** Selected, Chambers USA Guide, 2005-13; member, Leading Lawyers Network, 2007-13; recommended, PLC Which Lawyer?, 2009-11 Yearbooks; member, Winning Team, 2010 Chambers and Partners USA Award for Excellence in Real Estate.
**Publications:** Co-Author, 'Issues for the Cross-Border Real Estate Lawyer', printed in PLC Cross-border Corporate Real Estate Handbook 2006-07 and The In-House Perspective, January 2007.
**Personal:** JD, Cleveland-Marshall College of Law at Cleveland State University; BA, The Ohio State University.

## FITZGERALD, Patrick
Skadden, Arps, Slate, Meagher & Flom LLP & Affiliates, Chicago
312 407 0508
patrick.fitzgerald@skadden.com
*Featured in Litigation (Illinois)*
**Practice Areas:** Trial lawyer and experienced investigator whose practice focuses on internal investigations, government enforcement matters and civil litigation.
**Professional Memberships:** Fellow, American College of Trial Lawyers; Feirson Distinguished Lecturer at The University of Chicago Law School.
**Career:** U.S. Attorney, Northern District of Illinois, 2001-2012; Assistant U.S. Attorney, Southern District of New York, 1988-2001; JD, Harvard Law School, 1985; BA, Amherst College, 1982 (Phi Beta Kappa).

## FORADAS, Michael P
Kirkland & Ellis LLP, Chicago
312 862 2308
michael.foradas@kirkland.com
*Featured in Insurance (Illinois)*
**Practice Areas:** Extensive trial experience in commercial, insurance coverage, business tort, mass tort and product liability, intellectual property and antitrust matters. Recent trials involving several industries (chemical, financial services, healthcare and insurance), various substantive areas (trade secret, business tort, antitrust, mass tort and product liability) and multiple venues (Illinois, Texas, Florida, California and Massachusetts). Clients include Abbott, Citadel, Dow Chemical, Union Carbide and other Fortune 500 companies.
**Personal:** Fellow, American College of Trial Lawyers. AB, College of William & Mary, 1978 (Phi Beta Kappa). JD, Northwestern University School of Law, 1981 (Editor-in-Chief, Northwestern Law Review; Order of Coif; cum laude).

## FORT, Jeffrey
Dentons, Chicago
312 876 2380
jeffrey.fort@dentons.com
*Featured in Climate Change (Nationwide), Environment (Illinois)*
**Practice Areas:** Works with all environmental media, state and federal agencies and investors. Practice includes renewable energy projects and investment funds, carbon offset credits, internal compliance investigations and designing compliance programs. Experienced in complex air regulatory and permitting matters and evaluating risks associated with chemical exposure in remediation and toxic tort claims. Successfully litigated before all levels of state and federal courts and negotiated with state and federal agencies.
**Career:** Joined Dentons in 1990. Clerked for Illinois Appellate Court Justice John M Karns Jr. Lecturer on environmental topics for professional groups, former Adjunct Professor Northwestern Law School.

## FOSCO, Carmen L.
Rooney Rippie & Ratnaswamy LLP, Chicago
312 447 2800
*Featured in Energy & Natural Resources (Illinois)*
**Practice Areas:** Mr Fosco focuses primarily on representing natural gas, electric, telecommunications and water industry clients before regulatory agencies and state courts. He has extensive experience in rate and procurement proceedings, and proceedings to approve plans for compliance with statutory energy efficiency and demand response requirements. He has represented clients in workshops, collaboratives, and proceedings to develop and consider investment in advanced metering infrastructure and other smart grid technologies.
**Career:** Prior to joining the firm, Mr Fosco spent more than 14 years with the Illinois Commerce Commission, gaining extensive experience and serving as lead counsel in numerous regulatory proceedings including rate, reorganization, procurement, and reconciliation cases.
**Personal:** DePaul University College of Law, JD; Southern Illinois University, BA.

## FRANCZEK, JR, James C
Franczek Radelet P.C., Chicago
312 786 6110
jcf@franczek.com
*Featured in Labor & Employment (Illinois)*
**Practice Areas:** Serves as chief labor counsel for private and public sector clients, including City of Chicago, Chicago Public Schools, Starwood Hotels & Resorts, Hilton Hotels, Midwest Generation, Metropolitan Pier and Exposition Authority, Chicago Park District, City Colleges of Chicago.
**Professional Memberships:** Member, The Commercial Club of Chicago, Economic Club of Chicago, Metropolitan Planning Council's Board of Governors, College of Labor & Employment Lawyers; Board of Directors, Chicagoland Chamber of Commerce, Advance Illinois. Founding member, Institute for Law & the Workplace/Chicago-Kent College of Law.
**Career:** President, Franczek Radelet (1994).

**Personal:** University of Chicago Law School; University of Notre Dame. Ranked No. 71 on Chicago magazine's list of 100 Most Powerful Chicagoans (2013); Best Lawyers: Chicago Lawyer of Year - Employment Law - Management (2012); Crain's Who's Who in Chicago (2009-2012); Distinguished Service Award, Labor & Employment Relations Association (2011).

## FRANKEL, William H
Brinks Hofer Gilson & Lione, Chicago
312 321 7736
wfrankel@usebrinks.com
*Featured in Intellectual Property (Illinois)*
**Practice Areas:** Mr Frankel has over 30 years of IP experience focused on patent, copyright, trademark, trade secret and unfair competition litigation in jury and non-jury cases. He is chair of the firm's Copyright practice group and its Israel task force. Mr Frankel has represented multinational clients in federal courts, before the U.S. Patent and Trademark Office, before the International Trade Commission and in alternative dispute resolution forums in connection with injunction, trial, contempt and appellate proceedings.
**Professional Memberships:** Mr Frankel serves on the Board and is a past President of Lawyers for the Creative Arts.

## FREEMAN, Louis S
Skadden, Arps, Slate, Meagher & Flom LLP & Affiliates, Chicago
312 407 0650
louis.freeman@skadden.com
*Featured in Tax (Illinois)*
**Practice Areas:** Handles federal tax planning and dispute work in corporate acquisitions and dispositions, spin-offs, consolidated groups, financings, joint ventures and partnerships, workouts and restructurings, real estate, financial products and foreign inbound and outbound transactions. Serves as Chair of "Tax Strategies for Corporate Acquisitions, Dispositions, Spin-offs, Joint Ventures, Financings, Reorganizations and Restructurings," Practicing Law Institute.
**Professional Memberships:** ABA Tax Section (former Chair, Committee on Corporate Tax); American College of Tax Counsel; Tax Advisory Group of the ALI Federal Income Tax Project-Subchapter C.
**Career:** LLM (Taxation), New York University, 1972; JD, Harvard Law School, 1966; BBA, University of Cincinnati, 1963.

## FRIEDLI, Helen R
McDermott Will & Emery LLP, Chicago
312 984 7563
hfriedli@mwe.com
*Featured in Corporate/M&A (Illinois)*
**Practice Areas:** Focused on mergers and acquisitions of public and private companies, corporate governance and general corporate counseling. Extensive experience in representing public and privately held corporations in domestic and cross-border mergers, acquisitions and dispositions, including contested takeovers and proxy contests. In addition, counsels public company directors and management on corporate governance and securities law compliance.

**Personal:** Indiana University School of Law (JD); Purdue University, (BSIM).

## FRIEDMAN, Peter
Holland & Knight LLP, Chicago
312 578 6566
peter.friedman@hklaw.com
*Featured in Real Estate (Illinois)*

**Practice Areas:** Peter Friedman is the head of Holland & Knight's Chicago Real Estate, Land Use, and Local Government Group. He represents clients in all phases of real estate acquisition, development, financing, and zoning entitlements. In Illinois, he is Village Attorney for Lake Bluff and Oak Brook, and General Counsel for City of Des Plaines. He represents the State on large public-private partnerships and local and state government entities on real estate and public law. Peter was Legislative Director for US Rep. John Porter (IL-10), Judicial Clerk for Judge Suzanne Conlon (N.D. IL), and a Fellow of Leadership Greater Chicago.

## FROY, Michael M
Dentons, Chicago
312 876 8222
michael.froy@dentons.com
*Featured in Corporate/M&A (Illinois)*

**Practice Areas:** Advises businesses in meeting their strategic objectives focusing on mergers and acquisitions, both public and private, securities offerings, complex commercial transactions, corporate governance and public company compliance. Extensive experience in cross-border, manufacturing, energy and life sciences transactions.
**Career:** Admitted to practice in 1983; joined in 1983, Partner in 1990, and current global head of legacy Dentons's Manufacturing Sector and US head of Mergers and Acquisitions. Previously head of legacy Dentons's US Corporate and Capital Markets.
**Personal:** University of Chicago, JD; University of Michigan, AB, with honors and high distinction.

## GABRIC, Ralph J
Brinks Hofer Gilson & Lione, Chicago
312 321 4253
rgabric@usebrinks.com
*Featured in Intellectual Property (Illinois)*

**Practice Areas:** Mr Gabric is chair of the Litigation Practice Group at Brinks Hofer Gilson & Lione, and focuses on high-stakes patent litigation and related antitrust matters. With over two decades of trial experience, Mr Gabric has substantial first and second chair responsibilities in bench and jury trials. His litigation experience also includes Markman hearings, preliminary injunctions, temporary restraining orders, arbitrations, mediations, and appeals. Mr Gabric has represented clients from a variety of industries, including pharmaceuticals, medical devices, automotive, ecommerce, electronic trading, analytical instrumentation, chemical, and computer software and hardware. He has lectured on the subject of patent litigation, ethics and patent licensing and written about trade dress protection and dispute resolution.

**Professional Memberships:** Illinois Supreme Court; Supreme Court of the United States; Court of Appeals, Federal Circuit; Federal District Court, Western District of Michigan, Southern District of Indiana; Registered Attorney before United States Patent and Trademark Office; Federal District Court, Northern District of Illinois; AIPLA; ABA; FCBA; Intellectual Property Owners Association.
**Personal:** Education: BS, Chemistry, Boston College (1985); JD, DePaul University (1988), Member DePaul Law Review.

## GAGLIARDO, Joseph M
Laner Muchin, Ltd, Chicago
312 467 9800
jgagliardo@lanermuchin.com
*Featured in Labor & Employment (Illinois)*

**Practice Areas:** Mr Gagliardo has over 35 years experience in providing counseling and representation to public and private employers in labor and employment matters, including complex and class action litigation. He also actively practices in the area of alternative dispute resolution, and serves as an arbitrator in employment and commercial disputes. Mr Gagliardo is the Managing Partner of Laner Muchin and is the Chair of the firm's Litigation Department. Mr Gagliardo previously served as First Deputy Corporation Counsel for the City of Chicago.
**Professional Memberships:** Mr Gagliardo is active in many professional organizations and is a past President of the Chicago Chapter of the Federal Bar Association and the Justinian Society of Lawyers. He has also served as Chairperson of the Illinois State Bar Association's Labor-Law Section Council.

## GALLAGHER, Gregory W.
Kirkland & Ellis LLP, Chicago
312 862 2087
gregory.gallagher@kirkland.com
*Featured in Tax (Illinois)*

**Practice Areas:** Greg Gallagher's practice focuses primarily on domestic and international transactional tax matters. In the domestic area, Greg has advised clients on a wide variety of transactions, including mergers and acquisitions, spin-offs, IPOs, joint ventures, debt restructurings, bankruptcy and general tax planning. He also regularly advises clients on tax aspects of complex cross-border transactions.
**Personal:** University of Illinois College of Law, JD, 1997 summa cum laude, Order of the Coif, Harno Fellow Associate Editor, Law Review; University of Illinois, BS, 1994 University Honors (Bronze Tablet).

## GALLO, John N
Sidley Austin LLP, Chicago
312 853 7494
jgallo@sidley.com
*Featured in Litigation (Illinois)*

**Practice Areas:** Partner in the Chicago office, a former federal prosecutor in Chicago. His practice includes conducting internal investigations for institutions, representing criminal defendants and grand-jury targets, and representing parties in complex civil litigation.

**Publications:** The author of "Effective Law-Enforcement Techniques for Reducing Crime," published in The Journal of Criminal Law and Criminology, Vol. 88, No. 4 (Summer 1998), a Northwestern University School of Law publication.
**Personal:** Law Clerk to US District Court Judge Ann C Williams (1986-1988); Harvard Law School, JD, 1986, cum laude; University of Notre Dame, BA, 1983, Phi Beta Kappa, summa cum laude; Admission: Illinois.

## GANGEMI JR, Columbus R
Winston & Strawn LLP, Chicago
847 6641100
chris.gangemi@us.ul.com
*Featured in Labor & Employment (Illinois)*

**Practice Areas:** Senior Partner, Labor and Employment Practice. Concentrates in all areas of labor and employment relations counseling and litigation, representing clients before federal agencies and courts, US Supreme Court, US Congress.
**Professional Memberships:** National Labor Relations Board Practice Committee, American Bar Association, 1976-present; Fellow, College of Labor and Employment Lawyers, 1998-present.
**Career:** Joined firm as associate, 1973. Partner, 1979. National Chair, Labor and Employment Group,1983 to 2005 Member, Executive Committee. Managing Partner, Chicago Office, 2004-06.
**Personal:** Villanova University, AB, 1969; Temple University, Doctoral Fellow-Philosophy, 1970; Villanova University School of Law, JD, 1973, Case & Comments Editor, 'Villanova Law Review'.

## GARDNER, James K
Neal, Gerber & Eisenberg LLP, Chicago
312 269 8030
jgardner@ngelaw.com
*Featured in Antitrust (Illinois)*

**Practice Areas:** Represents clients in complex civil litigation matters, competitive analysis of mergers and acquisitions and enforcement agency challenges to transactions. Experience in antitrust and trade regulation, healthcare litigation, consumer fraud, unfair competition and business torts litigation, particularly class actions. Active trial and appellate practice experience in federal and state courts. Experience in arbitration proceedings and mediation efforts, management and coordination of multidistrict litigation and supervision and management of litigation portfolios.
**Career:** Partner; Antitrust & Trade Regulation Practice Group Chair; Litigation Practice Group Co-Chair; Executive Committee (Member).
**Personal:** Purdue University (BA, 1965); Indiana University School of Law (JD, 1968).

## GEORGE, Peter R
Baker & McKenzie, Chicago
312 861 6587
peter.george@bakermckenzie.com
*Featured in Outsourcing (Nationwide), Technology (Illinois)*

**Practice Areas:** Outsourcing, including business process outsourcing, information technology outsourcing and offshoring, information technology law, complex licensing, intellectual property

and cross-border commercial transactions. Special focus on counseling providers and users in domestic and multi-jurisdictional transformational projects.
**Career:** Admitted in Illinois (1997).
**Publications:** "Renegotiating Supplier Contracts to Bring New Value to the Client" (2012) "Engineering & Design Services Outsourcing" (2008);"Changing Landscape: New Legal Issues in Outsourcing"; "Umbrellas for Clouds: Applying Outsourcing Risk Mitigation Strategies to Cloud Computing"; "Outsourcing Application Development and Maintenance Services - What Makes ADM Unique".
**Personal:** JD, Northwestern University School of Law. BA, University of Michigan.

## GERBER, Dean N
Vedder Price PC, Chicago
312 609 7638
dgerber@vedderprice.com
*Featured in Transportation (Nationwide), Banking & Finance (Illinois), Banking & Finance (Nationwide)*
See under Nationwide for profile.

## GESSNER, Douglas C
Kirkland & Ellis LLP, Chicago
312 862 2140
douglas.gessner@kirkland.com
*Featured in Private Equity (Nationwide), Corporate/M&A (Illinois)*
See under Nationwide for profile.

## GETTLEMAN, Chad H
Adelman & Gettleman Ltd, Chicago
312 435 1050
cgettleman@ag-ltd.com
*Featured in Bankruptcy/Restructuring (Illinois)*

**Practice Areas:** Commercial bankruptcy, reorganization and insolvency matters, and commercial litigation. Has been involved in major bankruptcy cases since 1976 and has confirmed numerous plans of reorganization. Has represented debtors, secured creditors, creditors' committees, sureties and other parties. Bankruptcy case involvement includes Armstrong World Industries, Inc., Outboard Marine Corp., Enron Corp., Federal Mogul Corp. Kaiser Aluminum Corp., Kmart Corp., USG Corp., National Jockey Club, Dennis Bamber, Inc. d/b/a The Woodwind and The Brasswind, and Enesco Groups, Inc.
**Professional Memberships:** American Bar Association - Section on Corporation, Banking and Business Law; Illinois State Bar Association; Wisconsin State Bar Association; Chicago Bar Association - Bankruptcy and Reorganization Committee.
**Career:** Founder and shareholder of Adelman & Gettleman, Ltd. since 1983. Began practicing in 1976 with the United States Securities and Exchange Commission, Branch of Corporate Reorganization.
**Publications:** Co-author, 'Representing the Secured Creditor and Adequate Protection', Business Bankruptcy Practice, 2006 ed., 2008 Supp., Illinois Institute of Continuing Legal Education. Co-author, 'Attracting and Retaining Clients', 2008 ed., Aspatore Books (A Thomson Reuters Business).

**Personal:** Marquette University Law School (JD 1976); University of Illinois (BS - Accounting 1973); Certified Public Accountant (State of Illinois 1974). Named member of Illinois Leading Lawyers Network for Bankruptcy and Workout Lawyers (2004-12); listed in The Best Attorneys Network, and elected as an Illinois Super Lawyer, in the areas of bankruptcy and reorganization (2005-13).

### GILSON, Jerome
Brinks Hofer Gilson & Lione, Chicago
312 321 4205
jg@brinkshofer.com
*Featured in Intellectual Property (Illinois)*
**Practice Areas:** Jerome Gilson is a Senior Partner who has specialized in trademark and unfair competition law for more than 45 years.
**Professional Memberships:** INTA; ABA; IPLAC. Admitted to practice law in US Supreme Court and eight US Courts of Appeals.
**Publications:** Collaborating author with Anne Gilson LaLonde, 'Gilson on Trademarks' (standard treatise, supplemented three times annually) and articles in numerous publications. Co-winner with Gilson LaLonde of four Burton Awards for Excellence. Speaker before ABA, INTA, AIPLA and CBA.
**Personal:** Education: AB, University of Missouri-Columbia (1952); JD, Northwestern University School of Law (1958); Member, Board of Editors, 'Northwestern Law Review'.

### GLICKSTEIN, David
DLA Piper LLP (US), Chicago
312 368 7270
david.glickstein@dlapiper.com
*Featured in Real Estate (Illinois)*
**Practice Areas:** Real estate, real estate finance.
**Professional Memberships:** American College of Real Estate Lawyers.
**Career:** He has extensive experience in a broad range of real estate transactions including acquisitions and dispositions, financing, development, joint ventures and leasing. He represents owners and developers on local, national and international projects and has significant experience representing lenders and borrowers on complex financing transactions and workouts.
**Personal:** JD, Northwestern University; BBA, University of Wisconsin-Madison (with honors).

### GODFREY, Richard C
Kirkland & Ellis LLP, Chicago
312 862 2391
richard.godfrey@kirkland.com
· *Featured in Litigation (Illinois)*
**Practice Areas:** Senior litigation partner and member of the Firm's Management Committee. Has acted as trial and appellate counsel in individual and class action suits involving complex claims in the following areas: antitrust, business torts, consumer fraud, contracts, discrimination, ERISA, environmental contamination, franchise, insurance, products liability, toxic tort, trade secrets and tax disputes.
**Professional Memberships:** Trustee of Boston University and the Chicago Symphony Orchestra. Member, Board of Directors of The Appleseed

Foundation, The Churchill Centre and the National Center for State Courts.
**Personal:** Boston University School of Law, JD, 1979. Augustana College, BA, 1976.

### GOLD, Brian J
Sidley Austin LLP, Chicago
312 853 2064
bgold@sidley.com
*Featured in Labor & Employment (Illinois)*
**Practice Areas:** Partner in Sidley's Chicago office and co-head of the firm's Employment and Labor group. He counsels and litigates on behalf of the Firm's clients on a wide range of labor and employment matters. On behalf of numerous Fortune 500 employers as well as many mid-size manufacturing and service companies, he handles individual and class employment discrimination, employee benefits and wage and hour litigation; as well as industrial labor litigation, NLRB charges, arbitrations, and collective bargaining.
**Personal:** Georgetown University Law Center, JD, 1982, cum laude; Miami University - Oxford, AB, 1979, cum laude, Phi Beta Kappa. Admission: Illinois.

### GOLD, Michael
Sidley Austin LLP, Chicago
312 853 7148
mgold@sidley.com
*Featured in Banking & Finance (Illinois)*
**Practice Areas:** Partner in Sidley's Chicago office. Practices in syndicated commercial finance and debt restructuring representing banks, commercial finance companies and hedge funds as lenders, and representing debtors, including corporations and private equity and hedge funds. Focuses on secured and unsecured syndicated finance, including senior, second lien and mezzanine financing, acquisition and recapitalization financing, cross-border financing, work-outs and debt restructurings, debtor-in-possession financing, bankruptcy exit financing, and on intercreditor, subordination and complex domestic and international collateral security matters.
**Professional Memberships:** Member of American and Illinois Bar Associations.
**Personal:** John Marshall Law School, JD, 1984; University of Illinois, BS, 1981. Admission: Illinois.

### GOLDEN, Gerald A
Neal, Gerber & Eisenberg LLP, Chicago
312 269 8008
ggolden@ngelaw.com
*Featured in Labor & Employment (Illinois)*
**Practice Areas:** Advises employers on compliance with federal and state employment laws such as the National Labor Relations Act, Family and Medical Leave Act, Americans with Disabilities Act, anti-discrimination and wage-hour laws. Extensive experience in collective bargaining, employment contract disputes, noncompetition/non-solicitation matters as well as other issues that arise between employers, their employees and union representatives.
**Professional Memberships:** College of Labor and Employment Lawyers (Fellow).

**Career:** Partner; Labor and Employment Practice Group.
**Publications:** Author and lecturer on labor and employment topics.
**Personal:** DePaul University College of Law (JD, 1972); Northwestern University (MBA, 1968); Washington University in St Louis (AB, 1966).

### GOLDMAN, Michael P
Sidley Austin LLP, Chicago
312 853 4665
mgoldman@sidley.com
*Featured in Insurance (Nationwide), Insurance (Illinois)*
**Practice Areas:** Partner in Sidley's Chicago office, co-chair of the Insurance and Financial Services Group, member of firm's Executive Committee. Focuses on representation of insurers and related entities, with emphasis on acquisitions, divestitures and reorganizations; the formation, capitalization and corporate financing of insurance companies and related ventures; holding company and invested asset regulation; alternative risk finance; transactional reinsurance; insurance distribution systems and risk retention strategies. Also represents investment and commercial banks, private equity funds, investment advisors and derivatives dealers regarding insurance company transactions.
**Personal:** Loyola University Chicago School of Law JD, 1985; University of Illinois BS, 1982. CPA. Admission: Illinois.

### GOLDSTEIN, Andrew
Freeborn & Peters LLP, Chicago
312 360 6438
agoldstein@freebornpeters.com
*Featured in Media & Entertainment (Illinois)*
**Practice Areas:** Intellectual property law, Internet, technology, outsourcing and computer law; entertainment, advertising and promotion law. Listed in The Leading Lawyers Network for Advertising & Media, Arts, Entertainment & Sports Law, and Intellectual Property Law in Illinois; Who's Who Legal: Illinois; and, Illinois Super Lawyers.
**Professional Memberships:** Board of Directors, International Trademark Association (INTA) (1994-95); Board of Directors, Illinois Technology Association (ITA); Former Chair, Chicago Bar Association's Patent, Trademark and Copyright Committee; Former President and Honors Council, Lawyers for the Creative Arts; General Counsel, Publicity Club of Chicago.
**Personal:** University of Illinois: BS, with highest honors; JD, magna cum laude.

### GOODMAN, Mark R
Freeborn & Peters LLP, Chicago
312 360 6729
mgoodman@freebornpeters.com
*Featured in Insurance (Illinois)*
**Practice Areas:** Mark's practice includes advising members of the financial services and insurance industry on corporate, regulatory and transactional matters. He has represented a wide range of clients in complex, high profile matters, including insurance holding companies, insurers, producers, agents and brokers, banks and savings

associations, leasing and financing companies, credit insurers and financial guaranty insurers.
**Professional Memberships:** Insurance Regulator Education Foundation, Lawyers Club of Chicago.
**Personal:** University of Notre Dame Law School, 1983 (JD, cum laude); associate editor of the Notre Dame Law Review. University of Northern Iowa, 1980 (BA, summa cum laude).

### GORDON, Lynn
Ungaretti & Harris LLP, Chicago
312 977 4134
lgordon@uhlaw.com
*Featured in Healthcare (Illinois)*
**Practice Areas:** Lynn Gordon is a partner in the Healthcare Group at Ungaretti & Harris LLP. Her areas of specialty include addressing the transactional, regulatory and operational legal counsel needs of hospitals, health systems and other providers, including mergers and acquisitions; healthcare joint ventures; contract drafting and negotiations; physician integration; Stark, Anti-kickback and IRC 501(c)(3) regulatory compliance; and Medicare and Medicaid recoupment and repayment (self-disclosure) matters.
**Personal:** Loyola University Chicago School of Law (JD, health law concentration, 1996); North Carolina State University (MA, 1991); Michigan State University (BA, 1988).

### GOTTSHALL, Justine
InfoLawGroup, Chicago
312 204 7199
jgottshall@infolawgroup.com
*Featured in Media & Entertainment (Illinois)*
**Practice Areas:** Justine Gottshall focuses on privacy and digital marketing, and the legal issues created by new technologies, including mobile applications, social media campaigns, e-mail and text messages, targeted advertising, viral marketing, and sweepstakes, contests and other promotions. Her practice encompasses counseling, compliance, crafting privacy policies, terms of use and other consumer policies, and drafting and negotiating contracts.
**Professional Memberships:** International Association of Privacy Professionals (IAPP) (including prior service on the IAPP Educational Advisory Board); Certified Information Privacy Professional (CIPP); Promotions Marketing Association.
**Personal:** JD, Stanford Law School; BA, University of Michigan (Phi Beta Kappa).

### GRAHAM, David F
Sidley Austin LLP, Chicago
312 853 7596
dgraham@sidley.com
*Featured in Antitrust (Illinois), Litigation (Illinois)*
**Practice Areas:** Partner in Sidley's Chicago office, member of the Firm's Executive Committee, co-chair of the Securities Litigation and SEC Enforcement practice. Concentrates on complex commercial litigation, at both the trial and appellate levels, with emphasis on defense of securities fraud, antitrust and consumer class actions. Frequently advises boards of directors on fiduciary and other issues, and represents compa-

nies and directors in M&A litigation matters. Has tried numerous matters in variety of settings, including jury trials, bench trials, arbitrations and administrative proceedings.

**Personal:** The University of Chicago Law School, JD, 1978; Haverford College, BA, 1975, with high honors. Admission: Illinois.

## GRAHAM, Robert L
Jenner & Block LLP, Chicago
312 923 2785
rgraham@jenner.com
*Featured in Environment (Illinois)*

**Career:** Robert L Graham is the founder of Jenner & Block's Environmental and Workplace Health & Safety Law Practice and a nationally recognized authority on environmental, health, safety, natural resources, and energy matters. He literally helped "write the book" on these issues, co-authoring an environmental law casebook that is widely used in many of the nation's law schools, Environmental Law and Policy: Nature, Law, and Society. He has represented clients in trial, regulatory, and transactional settings before federal and state courts and agencies nationwide, and has handled appeals before the U.S. Supreme Court and other state and federal appellate courts.

## GRAVES, Robert
Jones Day, Chicago
312 269 4356
rjgraves@jonesday.com
*Featured in Banking & Finance (Illinois)*

**Practice Areas:** Co-chairs Jones Day's Banking and Finance Practice. Practice focuses on financing strategies and transactions and matters pertaining to corporate treasury function. Represents lenders and borrowers in various commercial financial transactions and has structured, negotiated, and documented all types of senior debt financing arrangements. Also focuses on workouts and restructurings of troubled credits, including purchases and sales of distressed debt. Has extensive experience in structured finance and securitization.

**Professional Memberships:** ABA (Business Law Section), New York State Bar Association, and the Economic Club of Chicago.

## GRAY, Michael B
Neal, Gerber & Eisenberg LLP, Chicago
312 269 8086
mgray@ngelaw.com
*Featured in Corporate/M&A (Illinois)*

**Practice Areas:** Concentrates his practice in venture capital, private equity, hedge funds, fund formations, real estate and intellectual property. He represents investors, companies, and executives in venture capital and private equity financings; mergers, acquisitions and restructurings; executive compensation; general contract and intellectual property agreements and the structuring of partnerships, corporations and limited liability companies. He also has extensive experience advising funds on their formation and compliance needs (both on-shore and off-shore).

**Career:** Partner; Fund Formation & Investment Management Practice Group Chair.

**Personal:** Northwestern University School of Law (JD, 1992); University of Illinois (MS, 1988); University of Chicago (BA, 1987).

## GRAY, Michael J
Jones Day, Chicago
312 269 4096
mjgray@jonesday.com
*Featured in Labor & Employment (Illinois)*

**Practice Areas:** Leads the Labor and Employment Practice in Jones Day's Chicago office. His practice focuses on representing clients with complex labor and employment matters, with emphasis on class action and multiplaintiff employment discrimination lawsuits, FLSA and state-law overtime class actions, and restrictive covenant cases. His experience includes representing employers throughout the United States in bench and jury trials in state and federal courts, administrative hearings, arbitrations, and appellate courts.

**Professional Memberships:** Frequent speaker for the Labor & Employment Section of the American Bar Association and the National Employment Law Institute.

## GRAYSON, E Lynn
Jenner & Block LLP, Chicago
312 923 2756
lgrayson@jenner.com
*Featured in Environment (Illinois)*

**Career:** E. Lynn Grayson is Co-Chair of Jenner & Block's Environmental and Workplace Health & Safety Law Practice and Co-Editor of the firm's Corporate Environmental Lawyer Blog. Recognized as one of the country's leading lawyers in the environmental law, she serves as lead environmental counsel in U.S. and international transactions and counsels corporate leadership on management of material environmental risks and liabilities. She advises clients on critical enforcement and regulatory concerns as well as conducting environmental audits at manufacturing operations and has significant experience defending natural resource damage claims and performing environmental due diligence with a focus on water scarcity.

## GRIFFITH, Gerald M
Jones Day, Chicago
312 269 1507
ggriffith@jonesday.com
*Featured in Healthcare (Illinois)*

**Practice Areas:** Represents healthcare clients in a variety of transactions and compliance activities, including fraud and abuse, Stark, and tax considerations for hospital-physician relationships and joint ventures.

**Professional Memberships:** Illinois State Bar Association; State Bar of Michigan; ABA (Health Law Section); Past President of American Health Lawyers Association.

**Career:** Former Partner with Honigman Miller Schwartz and Cohn and Chair of their Healthcare Department.

**Publications:** Co-author of Charity Care for Nonprofit Hospitals: A Legal and Administrative Guide (Aspen 2009); author of Physician Recruitment & Retention: Reconciling Legal Tensions Between Tax Law and Fraud & Abuse (AHLA 3rd Ed. 2010).

## GROMACKI, Joseph P
Jenner & Block LLP, Chicago
312 923 2637
jgromacki@jenner.com
*Featured in Corporate/M&A (Illinois)*

**Career:** Joseph P. Gromacki chairs Jenner & Block's firmwide Corporate Practice, overseeing all transactional practices. He focuses on structuring and negotiating complex M&A and securities transactions and providing counsel on corporate governance, fiduciary and disclosure matters. He regularly represents General Motors in corporate and securities matters, including its historic $23.1 billion IPO and earlier $50+ billion Section 363 sale out of bankruptcy, and has represented global defense contractor General Dynamics in numerous M&A and securities transactions; Sam Zell in the $8.2 billion Tribune Company going-private transaction; and the Chicago Board of Trade in its demutualization and subsequent $200 million IPO.

## GRUEMMER, Brooks B
McDermott Will & Emery LLP, Chicago
312 984 7594
bgruemmer@mwe.com
*Featured in Corporate/M&A (Illinois)*

**Practice Areas:** Broad range of transactional and business counseling experience, with an emphasis on mergers, acquisitions, recapitalizations, joint ventures and the related financing required to fund such transactions. Experience in a wide range of transactions, business ventures and general corporate matters and regularly represents a number of private equity funds in leveraged acquisitions and recapitalizations.

**Professional Memberships:** Admitted to the Bar in the State of Illinois; Member of the American and Illinois Bar Associations.

**Personal:** University of Michigan Law School, JD (cum laude and Order of the Coif), 1990; University of Notre Dame, BBA (with highest honors), 1987.

## GUENTHNER, Robert
Dentons, Chicago
312 876 8961
robert.guenthner@dentons.com
*Featured in Healthcare (Illinois)*

**Practice Areas:** Robert focuses his practice on transactional matters with an emphasis on the health care industry. His expertise includes mergers and acquisitions, divestitures, joint ventures, strategic alliances, equity and debt financings, corporate reorganizations, hospital - physician relationships, accountable care organizations and other innovative delivery arrangements, and other complex commercial transactions. He also regularly advises clients with respect to regulatory matters, including GME Issues, fraud and abuse, certificate of need, licensure and other general regulatory matters.

**Professional Memberships:** AHLA, Co-Chair of Transactions Affinity Group IAHA, Board Member and Co-Chair Quarterly Lecture Committee HFMA.

**Personal:** Washington University, MBA; Washington University, JD; University of Dayton, B.S.

## GULLIKSON, Rosemary L
Dentons, Chicago
312 876 8963
rosemary.gullikson@dentons.com
*Featured in Outsourcing (Nationwide), Technology (Illinois)*

**Practice Areas:** Evaluates, structures, negotiates, and documents BPO and ITO transactions, supply-chain transactions, complex licensing and systems implementations, technology-based strategic alliances and joint ventures, including cross-border transactions. Advises on exit strategies, and structuring seamless sourcing solutions using more than one provider. Counsels clients on privacy and data security issues. Represents a diverse client base in the insurance, financial services and funds, health care, media and entertainment, manufacturing, retail and education sectors.

**Career:** Chair of legacy Dentons's US Strategic Sourcing Group.

**Personal:** Northwestern University, JD, cum laude; Northern Illinois University, BS, summa cum laude.

## GUSTMAN, David C
Freeborn & Peters LLP, Chicago
312 360 6515
dgustman@freebornpeters.com
*Featured in Antitrust (Illinois)*

**Career:** For more than 30 years, he has worked with clients on complex business litigation cases involving antitrust, accounting, banking, bankruptcy, construction, finance, insurance, real estate and securities. David is also an experienced counselor, litigating and providing in-depth strategic and corporate advice on class action litigation, and antitrust and securities law issues.

## HACK, Randall A
Locke Lord LLP, Chicago
312 443 0676
rhack@lockelord.com
*Featured in Antitrust (Illinois)*

**Practice Areas:** Co-chairs the firm's Antitrust Practice Group. Accomplished at defending commercial antitrust class actions, with substantial experience in cases involving allegations of industry-wide collusion. Counsels businesses and associations on antitrust audits and compliance, distribution programs and structuring mergers and joint ventures. Also represents corporate clients in RICO, securities and other complex class action litigation.

**Professional Memberships:** ABA (Antitrust, Business Law and Litigation Sections); Board Member and Past President, The Lawyers Club of Chicago.

**Career:** Partner at Locke Lord since 1993.

**Personal:** University of Michigan Law School (JD, with honors, 1984); University of Notre Dame (BA, with honors, 1981).

**HALLIGAN, R Mark**
Nixon Peabody LLP, Chicago
312 425 3970
rmhalligan@nixonpeabody.com
*Featured in Intellectual Property (Illinois)*
**Practice Areas:** Mark Halligan is a "go-to" practitioner and thought leader in the important area of trade secret protection. An accomplished litigator with over 30 years experience, Mark has been sought out to take on the most complex trade secret matters. These global engagements often involve damages in the hundreds of millions and, even, billions of dollars. He has been a pioneer in helping clients identify, classify, and defend their trade secrets from theft. Mark leads Nixon Peabody's expanding Trade Secret Team in the US, Europe and BRIC countries.
**Personal:** Northwestern University, JD; University of Cincinnati, BA, summa cum laude.

**HAMMER, Aaron**
Sugar Felsenthal Grais & Hammer LLP, Chicago
312 704 2170
ahammer@SugarFGH.com
*Featured in Bankruptcy/Restructuring (Illinois)*
**Practice Areas:** Advisor to Fortune 500 companies and global financial institutions on their most challenging insolvency matters. Cross-border experience includes representing foreign representatives in chapter 15 proceedings, multi-national conglomerates in restructuring their foreign subsidiaries and international financing transactions.
**Career:** Named among '40 Illinois Attorneys Under Forty to Watch' from over 20,000 by publisher of Chicago Lawyer; 2009 'Large Transaction of the Year' award from the Turnaround Management Association; Adjunct Professor, Northwestern University School of Law.
**Personal:** JD, magna cum laude: Northwestern University School of Law, Order of the Coif; BA, with distinction: University of Michigan, James B. Angell Scholar.

**HAMMES, Jeffrey C**
Kirkland & Ellis LLP, Chicago
312 862 2476
jeffrey.hammes@kirkland.com
*Featured in Private Equity (Nationwide), Corporate/M&A (Illinois)*
**Practice Areas:** Mr Hammes concentrates his practice on structuring and negotiating complex business transactions including mergers, acquisitions, leveraged buyouts, going private transactions, and private equity compensation and governance matters.
**Career:** Chairman of Kirkland's Global Management Executive Committee. Founding partner of Kirkland's San Francisco and Palo Alto offices. Led the Firm's expansion into Asia with the opening of the Hong Kong office in 2006 and the Shanghai office in 2010. Mr Hammes was a certified public accountant with Arthur Andersen & Co. from 1980-82.
**Personal:** University of Wisconsin (BBA, 1980); Northwestern University School of Law (JD, 1985). Certified Public Accountant, Illinois.

**HARRIS, Kenneth L**
Neal, Gerber & Eisenberg LLP, Chicago
312 269 8410
klharris@ngelaw.com
*Featured in Tax (Illinois)*
**Practice Areas:** Concentrates his practice on the federal income tax aspects of corporate divestitures and acquisitions, partnership transactions and tax planning strategies; advises companies in structuring tax-free reorganizations, spin-off transactions, partnerships, and LLC joint venture agreements and cross border investments; provides counsel in tax planning.
**Professional Memberships:** American College of Tax Counsel (fellow).
**Career:** Partner; Tax Practice Group Chair; Executive Committee (Member).
**Publications:** 'Standards of Tax Practice' (co-author, 6th Ed. 2004).
**Personal:** New York University School of Law (LLM, 1987); University of Chicago Law School (JD, 1985); Hamilton College (AB, 1982).

**HARRIS, Linda C**
Dentons, Chicago
312 876 7982
linda.harris@dentons.com
*Featured in Corporate/M&A (Illinois)*
**Practice Areas:** Specializes in mergers and acquisitions, joint ventures, leveraged buy-outs, venture capital, restructurings. Represents Fortune 100 and privately-held companies, banks, insurance companies and not for profits. Devotes majority of time helping clients identify, structure, negotiate and consummate successful business transactions. Equally experienced representing buyers and sellers. Services clients in a variety of industries including consumer products, manufacturing, airlines, insurance, higher education, distribution, technology. Represents companies of all stages from startup through expansion stage (including public offerings and debt financings) to sale, and has in-depth expertise in work-outs and bankruptcies.
**Personal:** Catholic University of America, JD; University of Michigan, BA, Phi Beta Kappa.

**HARRIS, Mark A**
Jenner & Block LLP, Chicago
312 923 8484
mharris@jenner.com
*Featured in Corporate/M&A (Illinois)*
**Career:** Mark A. Harris is Co-Chair of the Firm's Private Equity/Investment Funds Practice and a member of its Mergers and Acquisitions Practice. Mr Harris advises public and private companies, private equity funds and management teams on acquisitions, divestitures, reorganizations, corporate financings, spin-offs and other complex transactions, as well as on securities, corporate governance and internal investigation matters. His clients include both well-established healthcare, software, media and industrial businesses and start-up entrepreneurial ventures and technology companies. His significant recent deals include Wrapports' acquisition of the Chicago Sun-Times and various transactions for Merge Healthcare and Health Care Service Corporation.

**HARTMANN, H Michael**
Leydig, Voit & Mayer, Ltd, Chicago
312 616 5600
mhartmann@leydig.com
*Featured in Intellectual Property (Illinois)*
**Practice Areas:** IP litigation, IP counseling, in US and internationally.
**Professional Memberships:** Include ABA; AIPLA; AIPPI; LES.
**Career:** Mr Hartmann is active in all phases of intellectual property law with an emphasis in intellectual property litigation and technology protection and transfer in the United States and internationally. He has acted as trial counsel in jury and bench trials, ITC proceedings, and related pre-trial and appellate proceedings in diverse technical fields, including software; telecommunications; machine vision and semiconductor manufacturing; polymeric soft contact lenses; polymeric membranes; hydrocarbon catalysts and oil-field drilling technology; x-ray film emulsions; and gypsum wall board manufacture. His international experience includes directing legal proceedings in courts in England, Germany, and France, as well as before the European and Japanese Patent Offices. He has participated in a number of domestic and international technology transfer and licensing transactions.
**Personal:** Mr Hartmann was born in Frankfurt, Germany. Prior to joining the firm, he served on the engineering staff of Mobil Oil Corporation (now ExxonMobil) and worked as an intern with a German patent firm. He has lectured before several groups, including AIPLA, the Practicing Law Institute and the Chicago International Trade Association. Mr Hartmann presently serves as the president of the firm.

**HARTSTEIN, Barry A**
Littler Mendelson, PC, Chicago
312 372 5520
BHartstein@littler.com
*Featured in Labor & Employment (Illinois)*
**Practice Areas:** Labor and Employment; Individual, Class Action Claims.
**Professional Memberships:** Former Co-Chair, EEO Committee, Current National Membership Co-Chair, ABA Labor and Employment Section; Cornell University ILR School – Former President, Alumni Association; Dean's Advisory Council, Scheinman Institute – Current Board Member.
**Career:** Previously Managing Partner of the Chicago Office of a major AM Law 100 Firm, where he served as the Chicago head of the labor and employment practice.
**Publications:** Executive Editor, Annual Report on EEOC Developments - FY 2011 and 2012 (Jan. 2012 and 2013); An Employers' Guide to EEOC Systemic Investigations and Subpoena Enforcement Actions (Aug. 2011).

**HATCHER, Merrick**
K&L Gates, Chicago
312 807 4433
merrick.hatcher@klgates.com
*Featured in Corporate/M&A (Illinois)*

**Practice Areas:** Merrick Hatcher represents strategic and private equity buyers in connection with mergers and acquisitions, leveraged buyouts, and other transactional matters. He advises public companies in securities offerings and compliance and early-stage and growth companies in connection with venture capital, private equity, and debt fundraising. He represents closely-held and family-run businesses in commercial and M&A transactions and advises boards of directors, management, and stockholders regarding governance and strategic matters.

**HAWKINS, Brent**
McDermott Will & Emery UK LLP, London
312 984 7764
bhawkins@mwe.com
*Featured in Intellectual Property (Illinois)*
**Practice Areas:** Focuses his practice on intellectual property litigation, counseling and procurement. Has served as lead counsel in numerous patent, trademark, trade dress, unfair competition and copyright matters, representing clients in jurisdictions throughout the country. Represents clients across a wide range of technologies including, most recently, prescription topical pharmaceutical products, internet based technology, consumer electronics hardware and software; photo processing, diesel engine, and consumer housewares.
**Personal:** University of Illinois College of Law, JD, 1997, University of Michigan, BS, 1994.

**HEIDELBERGER, Brian L**
Winston & Strawn LLP, Chicago
312 558 5897
bheidelberger@winston.com
*Featured in Media & Entertainment (Illinois), Advertising (Nationwide)*
**Practice Areas:** Represents: consumer products/packaged goods companies, retailers/restaurants, broadcasters/publishers, e-commerce/new media ventures, advertising/promotions/fulfillment/event marketing agencies and athletes, entertainers and their agents. Practices: advertising law, promotions law, e-commerce/new and social media law, consumer privacy law, mobile marketing, trademark and other intellectual property matters, IP, advertising and entertainment litigation/disputes and sports and entertainment law.
**Career:** Chair, Advertising, Marketing and Privacy Law Practice.
**Publications:** Columnist - Advertising Age "Mini Law Lessons" www.youtube.com/brianheidelberger; Twitter: www.twitter.com/briheidelberger.
**Personal:** BS Marketing, Indiana University (1991). JD Chicago Kent College of Law (1994): Law Review, Kent Legal Scholar.

**HENGESBAUGH, Brian**
Baker & McKenzie, Chicago
312 861 3077
brian.hengesbaugh@bakermckenzie.com
*Featured in Technology (Illinois), Privacy & Data Security (Nationwide)*
See under Nationwide for profile.

## HENNING, Mark G
Winston & Strawn LLP, Chicago
312 558 5793
mhenning@winston.com
*Featured in Real Estate (Illinois)*

**Practice Areas:** Head of firm's Chicago based Real Estate Practice. National practice focused on representing institutional investors, lenders and developers in acquisition, disposition, financing and leasing of commercial real estate and structured financing transactions.
**Professional Memberships:** Fellow of the American College of Real Estate Lawyers and member of the International Council of Shopping Centers.
**Career:** Partner since 1985; Associate 1978-85.
**Publications:** Lease Financing of Real Estate: Equipment Leasing - Leveraged Leasing (Practicing Law Institute, 1999).
**Personal:** Loyola University Chicago (JD cum laude, 1978); University of Illinois (BA, magna cum laude with Distinction in Economics (Phi Beta Kappa), 1975).

## HERMES, Robert N
Butler Rubin Saltarelli & Boyd LLP, Chicago
312 696 4445
rhermes@butlerrubin.com
*Featured in Insurance (Illinois)*

**Practice Areas:** Complex Business and Reinsurance Litigation and Arbitration, including work in the areas of Bankruptcy and Insolvency.
**Professional Memberships:** Robert Hermes is a Member of ARIAS-U.S. and its Forms and Procedures Committee. He was active in developing ARIAS' Practical Guide to Reinsurance Arbitration Procedures. He is a frequent speaker on reinsurance issues and has spoken at AIRROC, Mealey's and ARIAS programs, including co-chairing the Fall 2008 ARIAS-U.S. Conference and Annual Meeting.
**Career:** Bob is one of the original lawyers from Winston & Strawn to join Butler Rubin at its inception. He is Co-Chair of Butler Rubin's Reinsurance Practice Group and a member of the firm's Management Committee. He has more than 30 years of experience as a trial lawyer in all aspects of reinsurance arbitration/litigation and commercial litigation, including jury and bench trials in breach of contract and fraud actions, business torts, real estate transactions, trade secret and restrictive covenants, insurance coverage disputes, antitrust and class actions. His appellate experience includes both state and federal courts. Reinsurance experience includes disputes involving the scope and applicability of arbitration clauses, placement disclosures, claim handling, adherence to underwriting guidelines, retrospectively rated business, obligations to follow settlements, allocation of settlements, obligations under surplus share reinsurance contracts, excess of loss contracts, application of ultimate net loss and net retained line clauses, clash covers, and accounting for premiums and losses. Bob has provided reinsurance advice to insurance company clients who are involved in the large asbestos bankruptcies. Bob was named a leader in insurance law in the 2011-2013 editions of The Best Lawyers in

America. And, as part of the Law Bulletin Publishing Group's 2012 survey of the top lawyers in the state, he was designated as a "Leading Lawyer" in Illinois in Commercial Litigation.
**Personal:** JD, DePaul University Law School, 1979, Editor-in-Chief, DePaul University Law Review, 1978-79. BA, Indiana University, 1976.

## HEROY, David
Baker & McKenzie, Chicago
312 861 3731
David.Heroy@bakermckenzie.com
*Featured in Bankruptcy/Restructuring (Illinois)*

**Practice Areas:** David Heroy co-chairs the firm's restructuring and insolvency practice. A trained corporate lawyer, he also leads bankruptcy and related litigation, including appellate arguments. He has played a leading role in many high-profile, "mega" restructuring and bankruptcy cases in the US, serving as lead counsel for lenders, court-appointed committees of creditors and equity security holders, and purchasers of distressed assets. Recently he has handled numerous cross-border insolvency matters.
**Professional Memberships:** Illinois State Bar Association; New York State Bar Association.
**Publications:** Mr Heroy is well-known for writing and lecturing on insolvency-related issues.

## HICKEY JR, John T
Kirkland & Ellis LLP, Chicago
312 862 2348
john.hickey@kirkland.com
*Featured in Litigation (Illinois)*

**Practice Areas:** Lead Trial Counsel in commercial, intellectual property, environmental, product liability, consumer fraud, securities, shareholder derivative, antitrust, and contract litigation in state and federal courts, arbitrations and administrative proceedings throughout the US.
**Career:** Fellow, American College of Trial Lawyers; Listed in 2006-08 and 2010-12 editions of The Best Lawyers in America; Selected as 2006-12 Illinois Super Lawyer — Named one of the Top 100 Attorneys in Illinois (2008); Named one of Top 100 Business Lawyers in Illinois by Leading Lawyers Network (2009).
**Personal:** Georgetown University, AB, 1974 magna cum laude, Phi Beta Kappa; University of Chicago, JD, 1977.

## HIRSHMAN, Neil S
Kirkland & Ellis LLP, Chicago
312 862 2493
neil.hirshman@kirkland.com
*Featured in Outsourcing (Nationwide), Technology (Illinois)*

See under Nationwide for profile.

## HOLLANDER, Adam K
Barnes & Thornburg LLP, Chicago
312 214 5610
ahollander@btlaw.com
*Featured in Insurance (Illinois)*

**Practice Areas:** Policyholder insurance recovery and counseling involving CGL, D&O, E&O, EPL, M&A, property, and fidelity coverages. Represents chemical, packaging, telecommunications, banking, pharmaceutical, healthcare, real estate, concessions, and manufacturing industry

clients. Experience includes: large scale environmental, toxic tort, antitrust, securities, asbestos, products, wrongful death, intellectual property, false advertising, fiduciary duty, malpractice, hurricane, theft, employment coverage matters; and domestic/international insolvencies.
**Professional Memberships:** 5th Circuit; N.D. Illinois; E.D. Michigan; Illinois.
**Career:** Barnes & Thornburg: 2007-present; Mayer Brown: 1996-2007.
**Personal:** DePaul University College of Law: JD With Honors 1992, Order of the Coif, DePaul Law Review; Extern to Hon. Kenneth Ripple (7th Circuit).

## HOLZER, Walter S
Kirkland & Ellis LLP, Chicago
312 862 2636
walter.holzer@kirkland.com
*Featured in Corporate/M&A (Illinois)*

**Practice Areas:** Walt Holzer is a partner in Kirkland's Chicago office who focuses on complex business transactions, including mergers, acquisitions, buyouts, recapitalizations, divestitures, venture capital and growth equity investing, and executive compensation. He has handled numerous private equity and merger and acquisition transactions in a wide variety of industries for both strategic and financial clients including The Riverside Company, Resilience Capital Partners, Rockwood Equity Partners, Premier Farnell plc, Cardno Limited, Solera Holdings and Benford Capital Partners.

## HOMBURGER, Thomas C
K&L Gates, Chicago
312 807 4267
thomas.homburger@klgates.com
*Featured in Real Estate (Illinois)*

**Practice Areas:** Thomas C. Homburger represents major corporate users of real estate, lenders, borrowers and foreign investors in complex real estate financings, acquisition and disposition of real estate assets and national and international leasing programs. He is nationally recognized for his experience in real estate sale/leaseback transactions, for his use of advanced financing techniques and for his work in title insurance claims. Mr Homburger is the past Chair of the Real Property Law Committee of the Chicago Bar Association.

## HOOD, Vicki V
Kirkland & Ellis LLP, Chicago
312 862 2092
vicki.hood@kirkland.com
*Featured in Labor & Employment (Illinois)*

**Practice Areas:** Vicki Hood is the Head of Kirkland's Employee Benefits Group. Her practice focuses on employee/employee benefits aspects of business transactions and restructuring. Vicki also has experience in advising private equity and real estate funds and other clients regarding Department of Labor plan asset rules, prohibited transactions and other fiduciary compliance issues and responsibilities.
**Professional Memberships:** Chicago Council of Lawyers.
**Personal:** Northwestern University, BA, 1974. Northwestern University Kellogg School of

Management, MBA, 1977. Northwestern University School of Law, JD, 1977.

## HURST, James F
Winston & Strawn LLP, Chicago
312 558 5230
jhurst@winston.com
*Featured in Intellectual Property (Illinois)*

**Career:** Jim Hurst chairs Winston & Strawn's highly acclaimed 500-lawyer litigation department. He serves on the firm's Executive Committee and is a veteran trial lawyer. In 2012, the American Lawyer named him one of eight finalists for Litigator Of The Year. He regularly argues appeals in the federal courts, including precedent-setting cases before the Supreme Court and the Seventh, Ninth, Federal, and DC Circuits. Mr Hurst graduated cum laude from the University of Pennsylvania Law School in 1989.

## HUTCHINGS REED, Mary
Winston & Strawn LLP, Chicago
312 558 5721
mreed@winston.com
*Featured in Media & Entertainment (Illinois)*

**Practice Areas:** Advertising, trademark, copyright, arts and entertainment.
**Professional Memberships:** ABA, Chicago Bar Association, Lawyers for the Creative Arts.
**Career:** Sidley & Austin, associate, 1976-83; Partner, 1983-89; Winston & Strawn, Partner, 1989-93; Of Counsel, 1994 to present.
**Publications:** The IEG Legal Guide to Sponsorship, (International Events Group, 1990); Sponsorship Contracts on Disk, (IEG, 1996); The Legal Guide to Cause Marketing (IEG, 2001);The Copyright Primer for Librarians and Educators (ALA/NEA,1987); Business Torts, Contributing Editor and Author of Chapters, 'Privacy and Publicity' and 'Trademarks' (Matthew Bender, 1989).
**Personal:** BA Brown University, 1973; MA (Economics) Brown University, 1973; JD Yale Law School 1976.

## ISELY, Catherine
Butler Rubin Saltarelli & Boyd LLP, Chicago
312 696 4472
cisely@butlerrubin.com
*Featured in Insurance (Illinois)*

**Practice Areas:** Reinsurance and Complex Commercial Litigation.
**Professional Memberships:** Catherine Isely is an active Member of ARIAS-U.S., presenting at its 2008 Fall Conference and Annual Meeting and co-chairing the Fall 2009 ARIAS-U.S. Conference and Annual Meeting. She has spoken about allocation, aggregation and occurrence issues at a reinsurance claims management seminar held by the Reinsurance Association of America, and she led a panel at the June 2012 AIRROC Chicago Seminar.
**Career:** Catherine is a Partner in Butler Rubin's Reinsurance Practice Group. She has extensive experience before courts and arbitration panels litigating the allocation of environmental and toxic tort settlements, as well as disputes related to claims handling, bad faith allegations, pool membership rights and obligations, retrospectively-rated business, commutations, retrocessional cov-

erage, obligations to follow settlements, obligations to post security and interpretation of ultimate net loss, aggregate limit, definitive statement of loss, net retained lines, prompt notice, access to records, consent to settle and arbitration clauses. Catherine has also litigated and arbitrated numerous credit and mortgage insurance disputes. In addition, she has litigated product liability cases involving toxic torts and business and contract disputes, assisted in jury selection in Madison County asbestos cases and successfully argued before the Illinois Appellate Court. She also served as the firm's Attorney Training Partner and in 2011, served as Adjunct Faculty for the Bartlit Program at the Bluhm Legal Clinic of Northwestern University School of Law. Catherine joined Butler Rubin in 1999, after three years as an associate with Kirkland & Ellis. She is a founding member and co-host of Butler Rubin's annual Women in Reinsurance Program (www.womeninreinsurance.com), an educational and networking series for women arbitrators, business executives, consultants and attorneys operating in the reinsurance industry.
**Personal:** JD, Northwestern University School of Law, 1996, Member, National Trial Team, 1994-96. BA, Duke University, 1988. Admitted to practice in Illinois, and before the U.S. District Court in the Northern District of Illinois (Member, Trial Bar), the U.S. District Court in the Western District of Wisconsin and the 7th Circuit Court of Appeals.

## JACKSON, Charles C
Morgan, Lewis & Bockius LLP, Chicago
312 324 1156
charles.jackson@morganlewis.com
*Featured in ERISA Litigation (Nationwide), Labor & Employment (Illinois)*
See under Nationwide for profile.

## JACOBS, Caryn
Winston & Strawn LLP, Chicago
312 558 6168
cjacobs@winston.com
*Featured in Litigation (Illinois)*
**Practice Areas:** Ms Jacobs is a litigator with over 25 years of experience in defending accountants and auditors in federal securities and common law individual and class cases; defending issuers and financial institutions in ERISA, federal securities, and common law individual and class cases; and handling other complex commercial litigation, arbitrations, and SEC matters. She was a federal prosecutor in Chicago for five years and has been trial counsel in numerous civil trials and arbitrations, including a major federal securities fraud trial for an accounting client and Lexecon v. Milberg (verdicts for client).

## JACOBSON, Fruman
Dentons, Chicago
312 876 8123
fruman.jacobson@dentons.com
*Featured in Bankruptcy/Restructuring (Illinois)*
**Practice Areas:** Founder of and partner in legacy Dentons's Corporate Reorganization and Bankruptcy practice. Fruman has extensive experience representing public and private creditors, debtors, creditors' committees, government agen-

cies, prominent financial advisors, and trustees. Also has substantial experience handling bankruptcy and related litigation including foreclosure, fraud, lender liability and insurance matters. Fruman is currently co-lead counsel for the PBGC in the American Airlines and Kodak bankrpucty cases. While conducting his practice in the states, Fruman also is the Chief Administrative Officer of legacy Dentons's Paris office.

## JACOBSON, Ronald H
Winston & Strawn LLP, Chicago
312 558 5832
rjacobson@winston.com
*Featured in Banking & Finance (Illinois)*
**Practice Areas:** Corporate lending, capital markets, structured finance, and private equity; all aspects of debt markets, across the capital structure; represents leading global commercial and investment banking institutions, non-bank financial institutions, institutional debt investors, senior debt fund managers, onshore and offshore capital markets issuers, corporate borrowers, and equity sponsors.
**Career:** Co-Chair, Global Finance, Corporate Lending and Debt Capital Markets.
**Publications:** Reuters Gold Sheets, Loan Syndications and Trading Association, University of Chicago Booth School of Business, Northwestern Law School, American Banker, Corporate Counselor, Daily Deal, Journal of Structured Finance, and Thomson Reuters.
**Personal:** Also listed in Chambers Global, Legal 500/.

## JACOBSON, Seth E
Skadden, Arps, Slate, Meagher & Flom LLP & Affiliates, Chicago
312 407 0889
seth.jacobson@skadden.com
*Featured in Banking & Finance (Illinois)*
**Practice Areas:** Head of the Chicago office's Banking and Finance Group. Represents both lenders and borrowers in connection with various types of sophisticated financing transactions in a wide variety of industries. Typical transactions include asset-based loans, secured financings and leasing arrangements.
**Career:** JD, University of Michigan Law School, 1988 (cum laude); BA, University of Michigan, 1985 (with high distinction).
**Publications:** Co-author, "Enforcement of Intercreditor Agreements in Bankruptcy," Norton Journal of Bankruptcy Law & Practice, May/June 2011.

## JEPSON JR, Edward C
Vedder Price PC, Chicago
312 609 7582
ejepson@vedderprice.com
*Featured in Labor & Employment (Illinois)*
**Practice Areas:** Shareholder in the firm's Labor and Employment practice group. Has handled many employment litigation matters in federal and state courts and various administrative agencies and has been lead counsel on class-action as well as individual employment cases. Has successfully tried jury cases. Also experienced in traditional labor matters, including arbitration, bar-

gaining and NLRB cases. Frequently lectures on employment law issues and was formerly an Adjunct Professor of Law at DePaul University.
**Career:** Admitted (IL) 1980.
**Publications:** Author of several articles on the Age Discrimination in Employment Act.
**Personal:** JD, Harvard Law School; BA, Knox College.

## JOHNSON, Mark R
Eimer Stahl LLP, Chicago
312 660 7628
mjohnson@EimerStahl.com
*Featured in Energy & Natural Resources (Illinois)*
**Practice Areas:** Practice focuses principally on matters involving utility regulation and restructuring, and also includes substantial experience in the areas of white collar crime and antitrust litigation and counseling. He represents utilities in a variety of regulatory matters and proceedings, including traditional and performance-based formula ratemaking, smart grid, energy efficiency, renewable energy, clean coal, energy procurement, utility restructuring and competitive market development, municipal aggregation, and financing. He also provides counsel regarding the preparation, implementation and interpretation of legislation related to these issues.
**Professional Memberships:** American Bar Association, Sections of Environment, Energy, and Resources and Public Utilities, and Committee on Renewable Energy; Chicago Bar Association, Energy and Communications Law Committee.
**Career:** Admitted to the Illinois Bar, 2002. Admitted to United States District Court for the Northern District of Illinois, 2003. Admitted to the Minnesota Bar, 2005. Associate at Sidley Austin LLP (Chicago), 2002-10. Partner at Eimer Stahl LLP, 2010-Present.
**Publications:** 'Seeing Green: Identifying And Anticipating Regulatory Issues And Risks In The Evolving Energy Efficiency Environment'. Bloomberg Sustainable Energy Law Report, Feb. 2009.
**Personal:** Born: August 16, 1976. Received his JD, with distinction, from the University of Iowa College of Law, 2002. Member, Iowa Law Review. Received his BA from Wheaton College (Illinois), 1999 (Philosophy).

## JOHNSON, Robert C
Dentons, Chicago
312 876 8155
robert.johnson@dentons.com
*Featured in Insurance (Illinois)*
**Practice Areas:** Trial and appellate litigation, with an emphasis on complex insurance and reinsurance litigation and arbitrations. Litigates coverage claims (including environmental, asbestos, product liability and construction defect claims), class actions, insurance bad faith and bankruptcy matters.
**Career:** Head of legacy Dentons's Chicago Litigation practice. Chair of legacy Dentons's national Litigation practice (1996-2006).
**Publications:** Numerous articles, including "The Litigator: Advocate and Counselor" in "Inside the Minds: Leading Litigators."

**Personal:** New York University School of Law, JD; Cornell College, BA, magna cum laude, Phi Beta Kappa.

## JONES, Thomas M
McDermott Will & Emery LLP, Chicago
312 984 7536
tjones@mwe.com
*Featured in Insurance (Nationwide), Insurance (Illinois)*
**Practice Areas:** Practice focuses on federal and state tax, insurance regulatory and legal matters concerning captive insurance and other alternatives to commercial insurance. Works with multinational corporations, private business, taxable and exempt health care providers, trade associations, joint ventures and enterprises of all sizes. Extensive transactional experience in all major US and offshore captive insurance jurisdictions.
**Professional Memberships:** Bar of the State of Illinois; American Bar Association; Chicago Bar Association; International Fiscal Association.
**Personal:** Cornell Law School, JD, 1975; Cornell University, MBA, 1971; University of Illinois at Urbana-Champaign, BA, 1969.

## JUNEWICZ, James J
Winston & Strawn LLP, Chicago
312 558 5257
jjunewicz@winston.com
*Featured in Corporate/M&A (Illinois)*
**Practice Areas:** Represents corporations and investment banks in debt and equity financings, including IPOs, high-yield securities, US offerings by foreign issuers and private placements. Handles major M&A transactions, corporate restructurings and private equity transactions. Particular industry expertise in telecommunications, manufacturing, consumer products, transportation & natural resources.
**Career:** Currently Adjunct Professor of Law at Cornell University Law School (teaching capital markets transactions). Office of the General Counsel, US Securities and Exchange Commission, Washington, DC, 1979-84; Assistant General Counsel, 1982-84. Manuel F. Cohen Award, 1983.

## KALINA, Ira M
Drinker Biddle & Reath LLP, Chicago
312 569 1466
Ira.Kalina@dbr.com
*Featured in Technology (Illinois)*
**Practice Areas:** Technology transactions, information technology, outsourcing, research and development, intellectual property licensing, e-commerce, joint ventures and open source software.
**Career:** Counsels clients from industries including media, financial services, health care, education, consulting and manufacturing. Represents customers, vendors and resellers/distributors worldwide from venture-backed start-ups through public companies. Previously worked as vice president of business development and general counsel of an Internet startup and served as licensing counsel to a leading gaming company and video game developer. Regularly speaks on social media,

cloud services, technology and intellectual property transactions.

**Personal:** The University of Chicago, JD 1994; University of Michigan, BA 1991.

### KALLAS, Jay
Locke Lord LLP, Chicago
312 443 0619
jkallas@lockelord.com
*Featured in Insurance (Illinois)*

**Practice Areas:** Practices in the corporate area, with an emphasis on matters involving insurance regulation, reinsurance and mergers and acquisitions in the insurance industry. Represents clients active in nearly all facets of the insurance industry, from offshore reinsurance companies to motor clubs to traditional life and property-casualty insurers. Regularly advises clients on purchase and sale transactions, including stock and asset deals. Also has extensive experience advising clients on reinsurance matters involving both life and property-casualty risks, as well as alternative risk transfer and surplus relief arrangements.
**Personal:** Northwestern University School of Law (JD, 2000); University of Illinois (BS, 1997).

### KAPLAN, Jared
McDermott Will & Emery LLP, Chicago
312 984 6955
jkaplan@mwe.com
*Featured in Labor & Employment (Illinois)*

**Practice Areas:** Focuses on employee benefits, ERISA, federal tax matters, corporate finance and employee stock ownership plans (ESOPs).
**Career:** Completed a three-year term on board of directors of Family Firm Institute, and in 2003 was named its general counsel. In 2004, elected a fellow of American College of Employee Benefit Counsel.
**Publications:** Co-author of 'Tax Portfolio on Employee Stock Ownership Plans' (ESOPs), and 'Corporate Portfolio on ESOPs in Corporate Transactions', both published by the Bureau of National Affairs. Editor of 'The Best of Law', published by the Family Firm Institute.
**Personal:** Harvard Law School (LLB); University of California-Los Angeles (AB).

### KAPLAN, Joel
Seyfarth Shaw LLP, Chicago
312 460 5821
jkaplan@seyfarth.com
*Featured in Labor & Employment (Illinois)*

**Practice Areas:** Labor and employment.
**Career:** Mr Kaplan has an extensive traditional labor law practice, including significant NLRB case handling experience, collective bargaining, unique arbitration matters, advising employers regarding difficult labor relations issues and Railway Labor Act matters. He also has an extensive litigation practice—particularly in complex labor law and employment matters—in discrimination matters, general employment matters and wage-hour cases.
**Publications:** Mr Kaplan has published numerous articles on labor law and employment law.
**Personal:** JD, University of Chicago Law School.

### KARCAZES, Dimitri
Goldberg Kohn Ltd, Chicago
312 201 3976
dimitri.karcazes@goldbergkohn.com
*Featured in Bankruptcy/Restructuring (Illinois)*

**Career:** Dimitri Karcazes is a principal in the firm's Bankruptcy & Creditors' Rights Group. Mr Karcazes primarily represents lenders in the protection and enforcement of creditors' rights and is involved in all aspects of commercial workouts and bankruptcies, including restructurings, reorganizations, sales and liquidations, as well as out-of-court workouts and assignments for the benefit of creditors. He has considerable experience with high-yield, distressed debt, intercreditor and subordinated debt matters, along with significant expertise with respect to asbestos-related bankruptcies. He has handled transactions and cases throughout the United States and in Canada, Mexico and the European Union.

### KARPELES, Michael D
Greenberg Traurig, LLP, Chicago
312 456 1076
KarpelesM@gtlaw.com
*Featured in Labor & Employment (Illinois)*

**Practice Areas:** Chair, Chicago Labor & Employment Practice. Litigation.
**Professional Memberships:** Member: Chicago Bar Association, Labor and Employment Law Committee; Member, American Bar Association, Litigation Section; Society for Human Resource Management (SHRM); Salvation Army Greater Chicago Advisory Board. President, Salvation Army Correctional Services Program Advisory Council.
**Career:** Fellow, The College of Labor and Employment Lawyers; Selected, Best Lawyers in America, 2008-13; Super Lawyers magazine, 2005-06, 2008-12; a Law360 2011 Employment Practice Group of the Year. Rated, AV® Preeminent™ 5.0 out of 5.
**Personal:** JD, cum laude, Harvard Law School; BA, summa cum laude, Wheaton College.

### KAUFMANN, Mark L
Sidley Austin LLP, Chicago
312 853 2221
mkaufmann@sidley.com
*Featured in Technology (Illinois)*

**Practice Areas:** Partner in Sidley's Chicago office. His practice is primarily in the area of intellectual property and technology-related transactions focusing on outsourcing and infrastructure; acquisition, development and licensing of software, databases, and web-based products and services; and distribution, facilities management, data processing, escrow, hardware lease, consultancy, system integration and services transactions. He also focuses on intellectual property and technology-related issues that occur in the M&A context, including acquisitions, divestitures, mergers, alliances, joint ventures and bankruptcies.
**Personal:** University of Illinois College of Law, JD, 1989, cum laude, Associate Editor, Law Review; University of Illinois, BS, 1986, with high honors.

### KELLER, Natalie
Kirkland & Ellis LLP, Chicago
312 862 2229
natalie.keller@kirkland.com
*Featured in Tax (Illinois), Tax (Nationwide)*
See under Nationwide for profile.

### KELLY, Adam G
Loeb & Loeb LLP, Los Angeles
312 464 3138
akelly@loeb.com
*Featured in Intellectual Property (Illinois)*

**Practice Areas:** Practices intellectual property law including patent and trademark counseling, litigation, and prosecution. Extensive experience in the United States and abroad, including conducting due diligence, providing strategic counseling, procuring new technologies, negotiating licenses, and enforcing or defending against infringement actions in various jurisdictions. Represented clients in prosecution, opposition, and reexamination proceedings before the United States Patent and Trademark Office in Washington, D.C. and the European Patent Office in the Hague, Netherlands.
**Career:** Partner since 2011.
**Personal:** The John Marshall Law School (JD, 2002); Purdue University (MS, 1998, Biology); Indiana University (BA, 1997, Biology).

### KILKENNEY, Michelle
Kirkland & Ellis LLP, Chicago
312 862 2487
michelle.kilkenney@kirkland.com
*Featured in Banking & Finance (Illinois)*

**Practice Areas:** Michelle focuses her practice on debt financing transactions. She represents private equity groups, commercial lending institutions and other private and public companies in connection with the negotiation, structuring and documentation of secured and unsecured financing transactions for both borrowers and lenders, including senior, mezzanine and subordinated debt transactions, acquisition financings, and loan workouts and restructurings, including debtor-in-possession financings. In 2012, Michelle was shortlisted for the Chambers USA Women in Law Awards for finance.
**Personal:** Ohio State University Moritz College of Law, JD, with honors, 2002; Ohio Wesleyan University, BA, summa cum laude, with honors, Phi Beta Kappa, 1999.

### KIMBALL, Christian E
Jenner & Block LLP, Chicago
312 923 2662
ckimball@jenner.com
*Featured in Tax (Illinois)*

**Career:** Christian E. Kimball is Chair of Jenner & Block's Tax Practice. He has extensive experience with all aspects of the federal income tax, including particular experience with corporate and partnership transactions, including mergers and acquisitions, reorganizations, joint ventures and workouts, and with tax controversies. As an Adjunct Professor in the Chicago-Kent College of Law LLM program, he teaches a course on taxation of financial instruments. He has co-authored a book on the tax aspects of forming a corpora-

tion, published articles on the tax treatment of convertible debt and options, and spoken on numerous subjects related to federal income tax.

### KINNEY, John
Jenner & Block LLP, Chicago
312 923 2807
jkinney@jenner.com
*Featured in Antitrust (Illinois)*

**Career:** John F. Kinney concentrates in antitrust, public utility and general commercial litigation. He has led many of the largest and most complex price-fixing cases in the last 35 years, including cases involving ocean shipping, egg, vitamin, carbon dioxide, folding carton, corrugated container and beef industries. Mr Kinney has represented respondents and third parties in investigations by the Federal Trade Commission. He was on the legal team that developed and presented detailed submissions to the Department of Justice in its review of the proposed merger of major global financial exchanges. He also counsels clients on a variety of antitrust-related topics.

### KIPP, Matthew R
Skadden, Arps, Slate, Meagher & Flom LLP & Affiliates, Chicago
312 407 0728
matthew.kipp@skadden.com
*Featured in Litigation (Illinois)*

**Practice Areas:** Concentrates in complex securities litigation and governmental investigations. Experience includes representing clients in federal, state and arbitral tribunals. Representative clients include Baxter International Inc., Hillshire Brands Company, Molex Inc., OfficeMax Inc. and Stryker Corporation.
**Career:** JD, Columbia University School of Law, 1989 (Harlan Fiske Stone Scholar each academic year); BA, Yale University, 1985 (with Honors; recipient of the Charles Heber Dickerman Memorial Prize for best Departmental Essay in Economics).

### KIRCHHOEFER, Gregg
Kirkland & Ellis LLP, Chicago
312 862 2177
gregg.kirchhoefer@kirkland.com
*Featured in Outsourcing (Nationwide), Technology (Illinois)*

**Practice Areas:** Gregg Kirchhoefer is a partner in Kirkland's Chicago office where he is responsible for the IP/technology transactions and outsourcing practices. His practice focuses on IP/technology matters, with particular emphases on outsourcing, strategic alliances, licensing and mergers and acquisitions. His experience in outsourcing spans the globe, dates back more than 28 years, has involved several of the most significant outsourcing transactions in history, and includes several seminal BPO and offshoring transactions. Gregg has represented both customers and service providers in numerous ITO, BPO, supply chain management, contract manufacturing, and ERP system matters. He is a Certified Outsourcing Professional.

**KIRSONS, Mark**
Sidley Austin LLP, Chicago
312 853 6891
mkirsons@sidley.com
*Featured in Banking & Finance (Illinois)*
**Practice Areas:** Partner in Sidley's Global
Finance practice. Represents commercial and
investment banks, finance companies, hedge
funds, private equity funds, insurance companies
and both private and public companies in traditional lending and asset securitization transactions. Represents debtors and creditors in workouts, restructurings and bankruptcies. Covers a
range of industries and market sectors, including
industrial, manufacturing, chemical, construction,
energy, media, telecommunications, retail, gaming, transportation, healthcare, and technology.
Works with agents, arrangers, lenders, borrowers
and sponsors on investment grade, mid-corpo-
rate, and middle market transactions. Structures
cross-border and multicurrency facilities, asset-
based loans, leveraged buyouts, bridge loans, and
regulated industry financings.

**KISTENBROKER, David H**
Dechert LLP, Chicago
312 646 5811
david.kistenbroker@dechert.com
*Featured in Litigation (Illinois)*
**Practice Areas:** Mr Kistenbroker, co-chair of
Dechert's White Collar and Securities Litigation
practice and managing partner of the firm's
Chicago office, represents publicly traded compa-
nies and their directors and officers in securities
class actions, SEC investigations, internal investi-
gations and corporate governance disputes.
**Professional Memberships:** Member, Illinois
and New York Bars; admitted to practice before
the U.S. Supreme Court and numerous federal
courts; member, Board of Directors, University of
Chicago Laboratory Schools.
**Personal:** University of Wisconsin – Whitewater
(B.S., 1975); Marquette University (MA, Foreign
Policy, 1977); Marquette University Law School
(JD, 1980).

**KITSLAAR, Elizabeth C**
Jones Day, Chicago
312 269 4114
ekitslaar@jonesday.com
*Featured in Corporate/M&A (Illinois)*
**Practice Areas:** Oversees Corporate Practice in
Jones Day's Chicago Office. Practice concentrated
in U.S. and international M&A, complex financings and restructuring, and securities law. Serves
as outside counsel to numerous publicly-held
companies and advises on corporate governance
matters, including Sarbanes-Oxley, fiduciary duty,
takeover preparedness, disclosure and related
issues. Recognized in Best Lawyers in America
(2008-2012); Top 10 Women Business Lawyers
(2012); Top 50 Leading Women Business Lawyers
(2009-2011) (Illinois), Leading Lawyers Magazine;
Chambers USA: America's Leading Lawyers for
Business (2007-2012); Illinois Super Lawyers
(2006-2012); PLC Which lawyer? (2007; 2009);
BTI "All Star Team" (2012).

**KLAWITER, Richard F**
DLA Piper LLP (US), Chicago
312 368 7243
richard.klawiter@dlapiper.com
*Featured in Real Estate (Illinois)*
**Practice Areas:** Real estate.
**Career:** He focuses in land use and zoning, multifamily housing, tax increment financing and
other public-private financing transactions, and
transactions involving community and economic
development. His land use, zoning, and government affairs practice concentrates on representing
developers and municipalities in annexation, zoning, and public sector-related matters for complex
commercial, retail, residential, hotel, and office
developments. He concentrates on public-private
development transactions.
**Personal:** JD, Stanford Law School; MA, Harvard
University; BA, St. Olaf College.

**KLEIN, Leslie A**
Greenberg Traurig LLP, Phoenix
602 445 8328
KleinL@gtlaw.com
*Featured in Labor & Employment (Illinois)*
**Practice Areas:** Global benefits and compensa-
tion; tax; DOL and IRS voluntary compliance
programs; DOL, IRS and PBGC employee plan
audits; ERISA fiduciary and prohibited transac-
tion rules; ERISA litigation.
**Professional Memberships:** Fellow, American
College of Employee Benefits Counsel; Member,
American Bar Association, Taxation Section.
**Career:** Selected, Chambers USA Guide, 2009-
13; Best Lawyers in America, 2006-13; Super
Lawyers magazine, 2006, 2008-13; Leading
Lawyers Network, 2007-13. Rated, AV®
Preeminent™ 5.0 out of 5.
**Personal:** JD, with high honors, Chicago-Kent
College of Law, Illinois Institute of Technology;
BS, with honors, Accountancy, University of
Illinois at Urbana-Champaign. Certified Public
Accountant.

**KLEIN, Randall**
Goldberg Kohn Ltd, Chicago
312 201 3974
randall.klein@goldbergkohn.com
*Featured in Bankruptcy/Restructuring (Illinois)*
**Career:** Randy Klein is a principal at Goldberg
Kohn and Chairs the firm's Bankruptcy &
Creditors' Rights Group. He concentrates his
practice in the area of the protection and enforce-
ment of creditors' rights. Mr Klein is recognized
as a leader in his field by his peer selection as a
Fellow in the American College of Bankruptcy. Mr
Klein has written extensively on creditors' rights,
including: "The Pre-Petition Right to Post-
Petition Income Streams and the
Misinterpretation of section 552," Co-author,
American Bankruptcy Institute Journal,
(December 2010); "Majority Rules: Non-Cash
Bids and the Reorganization Sale," Co-author,
American Bankruptcy Law Journal (September
2010).

**KLENK, James**
Dentons, Chicago
312 876 8062
james.klenk@dentons.com
*Featured in Media & Entertainment (Illinois)*
**Practice Areas:** Practice areas include litigation;
media and entertainment; intellectual property
and technology; patent, trademark, copyright and
advertising litigation; sports law.
**Professional Memberships:** Board Member,
Constitutional Rights Foundation of Chicago.
**Career:** Clerked Chief Judge Thomas Fairchild,
United States Court of Appeals, Seventh Circuit,
1974-75. Joined Dentons in 1988.
**Publications:** Co-author of the MLRC Libel
Survey of Illinois Law.
**Personal:** University of Wisconsin Law School,
Order of the Coif, Articles Editor, Wisconsin Law
Review, JD, 1974; Beloit College, Phi Beta Kappa,
BA, magna cum laude, 1971.

**KOCORAS, John**
McDermott Will & Emery LLP, Chicago
312 984 7688
jkocoras@mwe.com
*Featured in Litigation (Illinois)*
**Practice Areas:** Focuses his practice on internal
investigations, white-collar criminal defense mat-
ters including Foreign Corrupt Practices Act
(FCPA) cases and complex litigation.
**Career:** Previously, served for four years as
Managing Director and Regional Counsel of the
global investigations company Kroll, where he
directly supervised investigators, forensic account-
ants and computer forensics professionals on
FCPA matters and other international investiga-
tions. He also served for over five years as an
Assistant United States Attorney in the Northern
District of Illinois.
**Personal:** Loyola University Chicago School of
Law, JD, (cum laude),University of Illinois at
Urbana-Champaign, BA.

**KOENIGSKNECHT, John K.**
Neal, Gerber & Eisenberg LLP, Chicago
312 269 5382
jkoenigsknecht@ngelaw.com
*Featured in Corporate/M&A (Illinois)*
**Practice Areas:** Represents publicly held and
privately held clients in complex corporate, business and securities law matters. Represents clients
involved in public and private mergers and acquisitions, initial and secondary public offerings, debt
offerings, tender offers, joint ventures, cross-border transactions, and private equity and venture
capital matters. He provides representation on a
wide variety of matters arising under federal securities laws, including the Securities Act of 1933,
the Securities Exchange Act of 1934 and the
Sarbanes-Oxley Act of 2002.
**Career:** Partner; Corporate Practice Group and
Cross-Border Practice Co-Chair.
**Personal:** George Washington University Law
School (JD, 1996); Harvard University (AB, 1991).

**KOHN, Richard**
Goldberg Kohn Ltd, Chicago
312 201 3926
Richard.Kohn@goldbergkohn.com
*Featured in Banking & Finance (Illinois)*
**Career:** Richard Kohn is a senior principal and
founder of Goldberg Kohn. He is a member of the
firm's Commercial Finance Group, recognized as
having one of the strongest and most diversified
commercial finance practices in the country.
Selected by Chambers Global 2012 as one of the
leading lawyers in Banking & Finance in the
United States, he also heads up the firm's practice
in cross-border asset-based lending, a field in
which he is widely recognized as a pioneer. He has
served as Co-General Counsel of the Commercial
Finance Association, the principal US trade association for the commercial finance industry, since
2002.

**KOPECKY, Robert J**
Kirkland & Ellis LLP, Chicago
312 862 2084
robert.kopecky@kirkland.com
*Featured in Litigation (Illinois)*
**Practice Areas:** Represents leading US corporations and professional firms, as well as their officers, directors and partners, in securities class
actions, shareholder derivative suits, disputes over
corporate transactions, ERISA class actions, mortgage-backed securities litigation, and business tort
suits. Successful representations include General
Motors, Motorola, Baxter International, Ally
Financial, Abbott Laboratories, McDonald's,
PricewaterhouseCoopers, Allstate, Boeing,
Monsanto and Morgan Stanley. Tried cases in
state and federal courts, and argued appeals in the
US Supreme Court and numerous appellate
courts. Advises on corporate governance and acts
as counsel to special board committees.
**Personal:** Kalamazoo College, BA, 1972;
University of Chicago, JD, 1979.

**KOUIMELIS, Eleni**
Winston & Strawn LLP, Chicago
312 558 5133
ekouimelis@winston.com
*Featured in Environment (Illinois)*
**Practice Areas:** Eleni Kouimelis is Co-Chair of
the firm's Environmental Law Department and
focuses her practice on environmental transactions, compliance counseling, and litigation. Ms
Kouimelis provides compliance counseling to
industrial and manufacturing clients for audit and
sustainability programs, strategic planning, and
permitting and siting approval. She also advises
clients in the remediation and redevelopment of
contaminated properties under both voluntary
and government-mandated cleanups. Ms
Kouimelis represents clients in environmental
enforcement actions brought throughout the
United States. She also provides counseling in corporate and real estate transactions.
**Career:** Ms Kouimelis previously served as an
assistant regional counsel with the USEPA.

## KOZAK, John W
Leydig, Voit & Mayer, Ltd, Chicago
312 616 5600
jkozak@leydig.com
*Featured in Intellectual Property (Illinois)*

**Practice Areas:** Patent litigation and counseling; domestic and international negotiations and licensing.
**Professional Memberships:** Fellow American College of Trial Lawyers, American Bar Association, and American Intellectual Property Law Association.
**Career:** Mr Kozak's practice is focused on intellectual property litigation, licensing and counseling. He has served as Trial Counsel involving diverse technologies, including electrical and fiber optic connectors, telephony, television, semiconductors, numeric controllers, software, adhesives, geophysical surveying, food processing, and air filtration.
**Personal:** Mr Kozak received an Electrical Engineering degree from the University of Notre Dame and a law degree from Georgetown University.

## KRAFT, Jeffrey G
Neal, Gerber & Eisenberg LLP, Chicago
312 269 8009
jkraft@ngelaw.com
*Featured in Healthcare (Illinois)*

**Practice Areas:** Representation of hospitals and academic medical centers, health insurance plans, health insurers and HMOs, and other healthcare businesses with respect to corporate, regulatory and transactional matters; substantial experience in the acquisition and sales of HMOs and hospitals, and in structuring joint ventures, alliances, mergers and systems among healthcare organizations.
**Professional Memberships:** American Health Lawyers Association; Illinois Association of Health Care Attorneys.
**Career:** Partner; Health Law Practice Group Co-Chair.
**Publications:** Author and lecturer on health law topics.
**Personal:** Harvard University (Master's degree in public health, 1977); Case Western Reserve University (JD, 1976).

## KRAKAUER, Bryan
Sidley Austin LLP, Chicago
312 853 7515
bkrakauer@sidley.com
*Featured in Bankruptcy/Restructuring (Illinois)*

**Practice Areas:** Partner in Sidley's Chicago office. Practice includes financial restructurings and reorganizations, and insolvency related litigation. Recent non-court matters include lead counsel in successful restructurings of construction company, boat manufacturer, truck servicing company, national provider of AV services, and rewards marketing company, all with national presence. Sample chapter 11 engagements include acting as counsel to Tribune Company, to PG&E bank lenders, to venture partner in connection with Cajun Electric, and to El Paso Electric Company. International engagements include as counsel to lead lender in Parmalat proceedings.
**Personal:** University of Chicago Law School, JD, 1981; Duke University, AB, 1978.

## KRAMER, Andrea S
McDermott Will & Emery LLP, Chicago
312 984 6480
akramer@mwe.com
*Featured in Tax (Illinois)*

**Practice Areas:** Member of firm's tax department. Practice focus is derivative financial products: their taxation, management, trading, regulation, and documentation. Works with high net worth taxpayers and family offices in managing their derivatives transactions. Represents taxpayers in contested matters with IRS. Has also worked to shape legislative and regulatory policy with respect to derivative products.
**Personal:** Northwestern University School of Law, JD (cum laude), 1978; University of Illinois at Urbana-Champaign, BA (summa cum laude), 1975.

## KRAMER, Samuel
Baker & McKenzie, Chicago
312 861 7960
samuel.kramer@bakermckenzie.com
*Featured in Outsourcing (Nationwide), Technology (Illinois)*

**Practice Areas:** Partner, Information Technology/Commercial Practice Group. Focus: domestic and international technology transactions, including outsourcing, complex licensing, commercial and supply chain.
**Professional Memberships:** Adjunct faculty, John Marshall Law School, Information Technology LLM Program.
**Career:** Partner, Baker & McKenzie. Selected one of the '40 Attorneys under 40' in Illinois to Watch in 2004.
**Publications:** Co-author, "Communications Outsourcing," published by the Practical Law Company in 2010. Author, "Taking an Interest in Carbon: Secured Financing and the Legal Nature of Carbon Credits" in Energy and Environmental Project Finance Law and Taxation (Kramer and Fusaro eds.), published by The Oxford University Press in 2010.

## KREINDLER, Marla
Morgan, Lewis & Bockius LLP, Chicago
312 324 1114
mkreindler@morganlewis.com
*Featured in Labor & Employment (Illinois)*

**Practice Areas:** Marla J. Kreindler is a partner in Morgan Lewis's Employee Benefits and Executive Compensation Practice. She concentrates her practice on the management and investment of employee benefit plan assets and tax-qualified retirement plans and on the establishment of, and investment in, private funds. She is well versed in the application of ERISA's fiduciary standards and prohibited transaction rules and related banking, securities, and state insurance law requirements. She counsels clients on their qualified retirement plans, including 401(k) and defined benefit plans.

## Personal:
Graduated from University of Michigan Law School (1987, JD) and the University of Michigan (1984, BA).

## KRUPP, Peter C
Skadden, Arps, Slate, Meagher & Flom LLP & Affiliates, Chicago
312 407 0855
peter.krupp@skadden.com
*Featured in Corporate/M&A (Illinois)*

**Practice Areas:** Serves as Global Co-head of Skadden's Corporate Transactions Group. Focuses on mergers and acquisitions, private equity and corporate and securities law practice. Represents private equity firms and several of the firm's corporate and investment banking clients on a variety of acquisition transactions, leveraged buyouts, private equity and venture capital transactions, corporate restructurings and recapitalizations, proxy contests, joint ventures and other financing transactions. Advises management and senior executives in connection with acquisitions and various separation events.
**Career:** JD, University of Michigan Law School, 1986 (cum laude); BA, Albion College, 1983.

## KRUSE, Alvin
Seyfarth Shaw LLP, Chicago
312 460 5824
akruse@seyfarth.com
*Featured in Real Estate (Illinois)*

**Practice Areas:** Real estate, real estate and other secured lending, bond financing, healthcare.
**Career:** Alvin Kruse has significant experience as counsel to lenders and borrowers in connection with complex loan transactions, including construction, permanent and mezzanine loans for real estate projects, loan participations and syndications, commercial loans and prominent loan workouts and restructurings. His health care experience includes counseling hospitals, long-term care facilities, physicians and other health care providers in connection with legal health care issues.
**Personal:** JD, Northwestern University School of Law, cum laude (1968, Order of the Coif); BA, Northwestern University, with distinction (1965, Phi Beta Kappa).

## LABATE, Robert J
Holland & Knight LLP, Chicago
312 263 3600
robert.labate@hklaw.com
*Featured in Media & Entertainment (Illinois)*

**Practice Areas:** Mr Labate concentrates his practice in the areas of corporate restructuring and in developing, financing and distributing feature film and television programming. He is an adjunct professor at De Paul University School of Law and annually organizes and teaches film seminars sponsored by Lawyers For the Creative Arts, the Independent Feature Project and Columbia College Film School. Mr Labate's clients include: Bunim Murray Productions (producer of 'Real World'), Yari Film Group, LLC (producer of 'Crash'), Media General, Inc., Steppenwolf Films (a division of Steppenwolf Theatre Company) and Kartemquin Educational Films (producer of 'Hoop Dreams' and 'New Americans').

## LANDOW-ESSER, Janine
Quarles & Brady LLP, Chicago
312 715 5055
janine.landow-esser@quarles.com
*Featured in Environment (Illinois)*

**Practice Areas:** Environmental, Environmental Insurance and Occupational Safety and Health.
**Professional Memberships:** Chicago Bar Association; American Bar Association.
**Career:** Partner and Chair of the Chicago Office Energy and Environmental Law Group since 2000. Represent a wide range of manufacturers, developers, lenders, and other regulated entities in transactions and enforcement actions covering air, water, waste, contaminated land, insurance, and occupational safety and health.
**Publications:** Environmental Compliance Programs and OSHA Compliance Programs for the Corporate Legal Compliance Handbook, Second Edition 2012, published by Wolters Kluwer.
**Personal:** George Washington University Law School (JD with honors, 1976); University of Wisconsin, Madison (BA, 1973).

## LANDSMAN, Stephen A
Greenberg Traurig, LLP, Chicago
312 456 1075
LandsmanS@gtlaw.com
*Featured in Corporate/M&A (Illinois)*

**Practice Areas:** Corporate and securities; mergers and acquisitions; health care; private equity; capital markets.
**Career:** Selected: Chambers USA Guide; Super Lawyers magazine, 2005-06, 2008-13; Leading Lawyers Network, 2012-13. Rated, AV® Preeminent™ 5.0 out of 5. Recipient: The Juvenile Protective Association's Jane Addams Medal of Honor; Anti-Defamation League's Judge Abraham Lincoln Marovitz Civil Rights Award.
**Publications:** Co-Editor, The Mergers & Acquisitions Handbook - First Edition, Bowne & Co., Inc., 2007.
**Personal:** JD, summa cum laude, University of Michigan Law School; BS, University of Pennsylvania Wharton School of Business.

## LANGAN, J Andrew
Kirkland & Ellis LLP, Chicago
312 862 2064
andrew.langan@kirkland.com
*Featured in Antitrust (Illinois)*

**Practice Areas:** Experience as litigation and trial counsel in commercial, antitrust and products liability cases, including class actions and mass torts. Andy has been principal counsel to major corporate clients in high-stakes class actions alleging violations of the antitrust laws, as well as class actions alleging products liability, mass tort and breach of warranty. He has also been principal counsel in high-profile merger investigations and related litigation. He has tried, as lead counsel, seven jury trials, and has been involved in numerous other contested proceedings and appeals.
**Personal:** University of Illinois at Urbana-Champaign, AB, 1979; Harvard Law School, JD, 1982.

## LASSAR, Scott R
Sidley Austin LLP, Chicago
312 853 7668
slassar@sidley.com
*Featured in Litigation (Illinois)*

**Practice Areas:** Partner in Sidley's Chicago office. His practice involves all aspects of white collar criminal defense, including the Foreign Corrupt Practices Act, securities fraud, insider trading, price fixing, environmental crimes, tax fraud, and healthcare fraud.
**Career:** Prior to joining Sidley, Mr Lassar was the United States Attorney for the Northern District of Illinois in Chicago. As the district's top federal law enforcement official, he managed 130 assistant US attorneys, who handled civil litigation and criminal investigations and prosecutions involving white collar fraud, public corruption, narcotics trafficking and violent crime.

## LAYNG, Karen P
Vedder Price PC, Chicago
312 609 7891
kplayng@vedderprice.com
*Featured in Construction (Illinois)*

**Practice Areas:** Shareholder; Chair, Construction Law group; Member, Board of Directors; Chair, Compensation Committee. Trial experience with sophisticated construction cases, including complex defect and delay matters; successfully represents national companies in complex litigation matters before federal and state courts, the AAA and other alternative dispute resolution forums.
**Professional Memberships:** First woman President, Seventh Circuit Bar Association; Member, Board of Directors and Chair, Property Committee, Greater Chicago and Northwest Indiana Girl Scouts; Member, Economic Club of Chicago; Member, AAA Panel of Arbitrators for commercial and construction disputes; Co-Chair, Program Subcommittee of the American Bar Association's Construction Litigation Committee.

## LAYTIN, Daniel E
Kirkland & Ellis LLP, Chicago
312 862 2198
daniel.laytin@kirkland.com
*Featured in Antitrust (Illinois)*

**Practice Areas:** Mr Laytin represents clients in high-profile commercial, antitrust and class action litigation in federal and state courts throughout the United States. In the antitrust area, he regularly litigates conspiracy and monopolization cases arising in both commercial and class action contexts, and counsels clients on distribution, pricing and competitor collaboration issues.
**Professional Memberships:** Past Vice-Chair of the Chicago Bar Association Antitrust Section.
**Personal:** University of Michigan, AB, high honors, Phi Beta Kappa, 1995; University of Michigan Law School, JD, magna cum laude, Order of the Coif, 1998.

## LAZAR, Vincent
Jenner & Block LLP, Chicago
312 923 2989
vlazar@jenner.com
*Featured in Bankruptcy/Restructuring (Illinois)*

**Career:** Vincent E. Lazar is Co-Chair of the firm's Bankruptcy Litigation Practice and a member of its Bankruptcy, Workout and Corporate Reorganization Practice. Mr Lazar represents debtors, trustees, committees, lenders and creditors in high-profile bankruptcies and related litigation, handles corporate governance disputes in distressed situations, and advises clients with respect to asset acquisitions, divestitures and successor liability issues. He is particularly recognized for his expertise in commodity broker bankruptcy situations. He is a Fellow of the American College of Bankruptcy, a contributing author for the leading bankruptcy treatise Colliers on Bankruptcy and a frequent speaker on panels discussing bankruptcy-related topics.

## LEAVITT, Josh
K&L Gates, Chicago
312 807 4316
josh.leavitt@klgates.com
*Featured in Construction (Illinois)*

**Practice Areas:** Josh Leavitt has more than 25 years experience in litigating construction and real estate disputes in court and in ADR proceedings, achieving successful results in numerous multi-million dollar disputes. Mr Leavitt also negotiates all manner of industry contracts, provides risk counseling and leads due diligence efforts in mergers and acquisitions in the construction industry. He is an elected Fellow of the American College of Construction Lawyers and member of the Illinois Society of Construction Attorneys.

## LEE, Robert C
Jones Day, Chicago
312 269 4173
rclee@jonesday.com
*Featured in Real Estate (Illinois)*

**Practice Areas:** Co-chairs Jones Day's Real Estate Practice, and leads the Real Estate Funds Practice. Represents clients in real estate private equity transactions, cross-border real estate investments, and real estate private equity funds and REIT formations. Experienced in joint venture arrangements, preferred equity and debt investments, public and private real estate company mergers and acquisitions, and portfolio transactions. Forms funds and joint ventures to invest in properties, debt, real estate companies and platforms, and distressed assets in the US, UK, Europe, and Asia, using US and non-US collective investment vehicles and tax structures. Counsels fund sponsors in ongoing fund operations.

## LELE, Sachin A
DLA Piper LLP (US), Chicago
312 368 3495
sachin.lele@dlapiper.com
*Featured in Technology (Illinois)*

**Practice Areas:** Technology and Outsourcing.
**Career:** He focuses his practice on complex commercial transactions and technology-related transactions, including joint ventures, strategic alliances, acquisitions and divestitures of technology assets, outsourcing, licensing and other commercial transactions involving intellectual property assets. He works with clients to identify and develop creative solutions for managing key risk allocation issues in complex business and technology related transactions.
**Personal:** MBA, Kellogg School of Management, Northwestern University; JD, University of North Carolina School of Law, with honors; BA, Finance and Political Science, University of Illinois at Urbana-Champaign.

## LEMEIN, Gregg D
Baker & McKenzie, Chicago
312 861 8013
Gregg.Lemein@bakermckenzie.com
*Featured in Tax (Illinois), Tax (Nationwide)*
See under Nationwide for profile.

## LETCHINGER, John S
Edwards Wildman Palmer, Chicago
312 201 2698
jletchinger@edwardswildman.com
*Featured in Intellectual Property (Illinois)*

**Practice Areas:** John is Vice-Chair of Edwards Wildman's Intellectual Property Department. An accomplished trial attorney, he handles intellectual property and related commercial disputes, including patent, trade secret, trademark, and copyright infringement; breach of license, contract and restrictive covenant; and unfair competition, false advertising, electronic commerce and data security cases. Regularly representing industry-leading manufacturers, marketing companies and retailers, John has litigated a wide range of complex disputes. In addition, John is a respected counselor to his clients in complex and multifaceted intellectual property, contracting, business partnering and related matters.
**Personal:** University of Illinois, JD, Northwestern University, BS.

## LEVENSTEIN, Gary
Ungaretti & Harris LLP, Chicago
312 977 4108
gilevenstein@uhlaw.com
*Featured in Corporate/M&A (Illinois)*

**Practice Areas:** Gary I Levenstein chairs the Corporate Department at Ungaretti & Harris LLP. He concentrates his practice in the areas of mergers and acquisitions, private equity, corporate finance, securities regulation and corporate governance. His clients include privately and publicly held corporations, private equity funds, financial institutions, family offices, emerging growth companies and boards of directors. He is a frequent speaker on such topics as mergers and acquisitions, corporate finance, access to the capital markets and corporate governance.
**Personal:** Northwestern University School of Law (JD, 1976); University of Illinois (BA, high honors, 1973); Accreditations: Certified Public Accountant.

## LEVINE, Russell E
Kirkland & Ellis LLP, Chicago
312 862 2466
russell.levine@kirkland.com
*Featured in Intellectual Property (Illinois)*

**Practice Areas:** Trial and ADR: patent infringement matters, disputes involving patent license agreements, and ITC Section 337 proceedings. Appellate: includes Federal Circuit appeals. Licensing: structuring, negotiating licensing-in and -out transactions. ILO Client Choice 2012 Award - Litigation, USA. Member of WIPO Center's List of approved Mediators and Arbitrators; USPTO registered.
**Professional Memberships:** Licensing Executives Society (USA & Canada), President-Elect.
**Publications:** Co-editor (with A. Liberman and P. Chrocziel) of "International Licensing and Technology Transfer: Practice and the Law," Kluwer Law Publishing.
**Personal:** American Heart Association, Chicago Board of Directors; Museum of Science & Industry, Immediate Past Chair of the Presidents Council.

## LEVINSON, Michael
Seyfarth Shaw LLP, Chicago
312 460 5868
mlevinson@seyfarth.com
*Featured in Litigation (Illinois)*

**Practice Areas:** Commercial Litigation.
**Career:** Senior Trial Partner and Member of the Firm's Administrative and Compensation Committees. Former national Chair of the Firm's 180-member Litigation Department. Trial counsel in patent, trade secrets, franchise, contract and commercial lawsuits and arbitrations. Has appeared as lead trial counsel in federal and state courts, arbitrations, or agency proceedings in the last three years in: Illinois, New York, Texas, California, Washington, Utah, D.C., New Jersey, Minnesota and Tennessee.
**Personal:** Claremont McKenna College BA 1976, Harvard Law School JD 1979, University of Chicago Booth School of Business MBA 1995.

## LEVY, David
Skadden, Arps, Slate, Meagher & Flom LLP & Affiliates, Chicago
312 407 0831
david.levy@skadden.com
*Featured in Tax (Illinois)*

**Practice Areas:** Concentrates on tax matters, including partnership transactions, M&A, formation of REITs, UPREIT and DownREIT acquisition transactions, matters arising under FIRPTA, various types of public and private debt and equity financing transactions, restructuring transactions and transactions involving private equity funds, hedge funds, and financial instruments and products.
**Career:** LLM, Georgetown University Law Center, 1998; JD, American University Washington College of Law, 1995; BA, University of Maryland, 1992.
**Publications:** "Wind REITs – The New Tax Equity?", Public Utilities Fortnightly, May 2012; "Tax Issues in Structuring Private Equity and Other Financing Transactions," The 47th Annual Southern Federal Tax Institute, October, 2012.

## LEWIN, Matthew R
Greenberg Traurig, LLP, Chicago
312 456 8458
LewinM@gtlaw.com
*Featured in Banking & Finance (Illinois)*

**Practice Areas:** Public Finance; Education (Charter Schools); Affordable Housing.

**Career:** Listed: Banking and Finance, Chambers USA Guide, 2009-13; The Best Lawyers in America, 2012-13; Leading Lawyers Network, 2008-13.

**Publications:** Co-author, 'Local PHAs Use HUD Capital Grants to Back Bonds', Affordable Housing Finance, May 2003; Author, 'Growing Trend of HUD Capital Grant-Backed Housing Bonds Offer Win-Win for Investors, Communities', Asset Securitization Report, March 10, 2003.

**Personal:** JD, magna cum laude, Indiana University School of Law - Bloomington; MBA, Indiana University Kelley School of Business; BS, summa cum laude, State University of New York at Albany.

### LEWIS, Dan
Kirkland & Ellis LLP, Chicago
312 862 7149
daniel.lewis@kirkland.com
*Featured in Technology (Illinois)*

**Practice Areas:** Focuses on complex transactions involving technology and intellectual property, including outsourcing, joint ventures and strategic alliances, telecommunications, software development, and licensing (software, SaaS, technology, patent, and trademark licenses). Has advised on numerous outsourcing transactions, including with respect to IT (including ADM, infrastructure, hosting, and network monitoring), F&A, call center, and other functions. Practice also includes advising on intellectual property and technology issues in mergers and acquisitions, bankruptcies, and private equity and venture capital transactions.

**Professional Memberships:** Chicago Bar Association.

**Personal:** University of Chicago Law School, JD, 2008; University of Michigan, BSE, 2001 (Mechanical Engineering; Industrial and Operations Engineering).

### LIBOWSKY, Stephen D.
Dentons, Chicago
312 876 2529
stephen.libowsky@dentons.com
*Featured in Antitrust (Illinois)*

**Practice Areas:** Steve has a broad range of antitrust experience counseling and litigating matters, including grand jury/internal investigations, mergers/acquisitions, joint ventures, relationships with competitors, cartels, dominant firm behavior, distribution and unfair competition. He has extensive experience in markets for technology, beef/cattle, newspapers, television stations, information retrieval, health care and pharmaceuticals, sports/entertainment, automobiles and parts, the professions, and many manufacturing industries. Steve also has an active pro bono practice for which he has won many awards.

**Professional Memberships:** ABA, the Illinois Bar and the Sate Bar of Georgia.

**Personal:** University of Georgia School of Law, JD; Vanderbilt University, BA

### LIEBERMAN, Peter H
Greenberg Traurig, LLP, Chicago
312 456 8417
LiebermanP@gtlaw.com
*Featured in Corporate/M&A (Illinois)*

**Practice Areas:** Co-Chair, Chicago Corporate & Securities Practice. Mergers and acquisitions.

**Career:** Selected: Winning Team, Global M&A Network's 2012 Turnaround Atlas Award for 'Private Equity Turnaround of the Year' for the Chapter 11 reorganization and acquisition of American Laser Skincare LLC; Winning Deal Team - Distressed M&A Deal of the Year (Over $100mm), 2011 Turnaround Awards, The M&A Advisor, 2011; Best Lawyers in America, 2007-13; Super Lawyers, 2006-10, 2013; Chambers USA Guide, 2010-13; Leading Lawyers Network, 2005-13.

**Personal:** MPP, John F. Kennedy School of Government, 1988; JD, cum laude, Harvard Law School, 1988; AB, University of Michigan, 1984.

### LIGHT, Corey E
Greenberg Traurig, LLP, Chicago
312 476 5001
LightC@gtlaw.com
*Featured in Real Estate (Illinois)*

**Practice Areas:** Co-Chair, Global Real Estate Practice. Retail industry; real estate investment trusts (REITs); real estate funds; complex commercial real estate transactions including joint ventures, financings, acquisition and disposition of commercial property.

**Professional Memberships:** Member: Illinois State Bar Association; American Bar Association.

**Career:** Member, Winning Team, 2010 Chambers and Partners USA Award for Excellence in Real Estate. Listed: Chambers USA Guide, 2008-13; Legal 500 US, 2007-09, 2011-12; Leading Lawyers Network, 2005-13; Super Lawyers magazine, 2005, 2007-08. Recommended, PLC Which Lawyer?, 2010 Yearbook.

**Personal:** JD, DePaul University College of Law; BS, University of Illinois at Urbana-Champaign.

### LILLIE, Mark S
Kirkland & Ellis LLP, Chicago
312 862 2089
mark.lillie@kirkland.com
*Featured in Environment (Illinois)*

**Practice Areas:** Litigation Partner with over 25 years of experience representing manufacturing/industrial companies in complex commercial matters. Served as lead trial counsel on broad array of cases, including environmental, contract, antitrust, class actions, tort, and supplier/distributor disputes. Trials and appeals in various State and Federal courts throughout the US Licensed in Illinois and Texas.

**Professional Memberships:** Section of Litigation and Section of Environment, Energy and Resources.

**Publications:** "State Price Gouging Legislation: Compliance Difficulties and Counter-productive Overdeterrence," Energy Antitrust News, Fall 2009 (ABA).

**Personal:** University of Denver College of Law, JD 1984, Northwestern University, BS, Environmental Engineering, 1981.

### LIPKE, Douglas J
Vedder Price PC, Chicago
312 609 7646
dlipke@vedderprice.com
*Featured in Bankruptcy/Restructuring (Illinois)*

**Practice Areas:** Shareholder and Co-chair, Bankruptcy and Creditors' & Rights group. Concentrates his practice in workout, bankruptcy and reorganization law. Represents a full range of national and international clients, including secured lenders, debtors, trustees and creditors' committees. Has tried a wide range of large, sophisticated matters that arise in bankruptcy cases. Represents financial institutions in structuring workouts and foreclosures in international equipment, aircraft leasing and equipment financing transactions.

**Professional Memberships:** Member, Bankruptcy Advisory Board for Strafford Publications; Member, American Bankruptcy Institute.

**Career:** Admitted (IL) 1979.

**Personal:** JD, Loyola University Chicago School of Law; B.S., Marquette University.

### LIPTON, Richard
Baker & McKenzie, Chicago
312 861 7590
Richard.Lipton@bakermckenzie.com
*Featured in Tax (Illinois)*

**Practice Areas:** Advises on partnerships, LLCs, other pass-through entities, and real estate transactions for multinational corporations and major owners and investors in real estate.

**Professional Memberships:** Member, Chicago Bar Association (Federal Taxation Committee, Chair, 1991-92) and American Bar Association (section of taxation: Chair, 2001-02; House of Delegates, 2005-); fellow and regent, American College of Tax Counsel (Chair, 2008-2011).

**Career:** Admitted to Illinois Bar and US Tax Court, 1977.

**Publications:** Contributor and editor of 'Journal of Taxation'; 'Journal of Pass-Through Entities'; 'Journal of Real Estate Taxation'. Co-author of two treatises. Author of 200+ articles on partnership and real estate taxation.

### LITT, Paula E
Schopf & Weiss LLP, Chicago
312 701 9317
litt@sw.com
*Featured in Insurance (Illinois)*

**Practice Areas:** Paula Litt is a business litigator who regularly represents corporate clients in disputes with their insurers and insurance brokers. Her clients include financial institutions, governmental entities, manufacturers, and professional services organizations. She has recovered defense costs and indemnification for those clients from their insurers for claims ranging from toxic torts to statutory violations to catastrophic accidents to professional liability. Ms Litt was chosen as one of the Top Ten Super Lawyers in Illinois in 2010.

**Professional Memberships:** Ms Litt is a member of the American Bar Association, the Chicago Bar Association, and The Chicago Network.

**Career:** Schopf & Weiss LLP (1987-present) Partner, Co-Founder and Executive Committee Member; Isham, Lincoln & Beale (1986-87); Reuben & Proctor (1984-86).

**Publications:** Ms Litt is a frequent author and speaker on insurance coverage topics. Her publications include "You've Settled Now What? What the Insured Must Show to Recover Indemnity," "Securing Insurance Coverage for your Corporate Client," and "10 Things Every Illinois Lawyer Should Know About The Duty To Defend."

**Personal:** Harvard Law School (JD); University of Chicago (MA); The Ohio State University (BA).

### LOMBARDI, George C
Winston & Strawn LLP, Chicago
312 558 5600
glombardi@winston.com
*Featured in Intellectual Property (Illinois)*

**Practice Areas:** George Lombardi chairs Winston's IP practice and concentrates primarily on patent and general commercial cases. Law360 recently named him a 2013 IP MVP, based in part on the $1 billion jury verdict he secured for Monsanto in a mammoth patent dispute (which was ranked a Top 3 Verdict of 2012). In his 20 years experience in patent litigation, he has been the lead trial lawyer in cases that resulted in the invalidation of patents covering best-selling drugs as well as other technologies.

**Career:** Member of Winston's Executive Committee.

**Personal:** University of Michigan Law School.

### LONSTEIN, Carmen
Baker & McKenzie, Chicago
312 861 8606
Carmen.Lonstein@bakermckenzie.com
*Featured in Bankruptcy/Restructuring (Illinois)*

**Practice Areas:** Ms Lonstein advises on a wide range of bankruptcy and corporate restructuring matters, including complex issues for distressed investors and creditors seeking to maximize value recoveries. In her broad transactional and litigation practice, she's represented debtors, official and ad hoc committees of creditors and equity holders, secured creditors, bondholders, and asset purchasers.

**Professional Memberships:** International Women's Insolvency & Restructuring Confederation; The American Bankruptcy Institute; Turnaround Management Association; International Bar Association.

**Personal:** Vice Chair, Metropolitan Pier and Exposition Authority; Trustee, Frank Lloyd Wright Foundation; Commissioner, Great Lakes Commission.

### LOWINGER, Frederick C
Sidley Austin LLP, Chicago
312 853 7238
flowinger@sidley.com
*Featured in Corporate/M&A (Illinois)*

**Practice Areas:** Partner in Sidley's Chicago office, co-head of the firm's M&A practice, head of the Chicago office's Corporate group, and

member of Sidley's Executive Committee. Principal areas of practice: mergers and acquisitions, corporate finance and corporate governance.
**Professional Memberships:** Member of the ABA Corporate Laws Committee, the Planning Committee of the Tulane Corporate Law Institute, and the Executive Committee of Northwestern University's Garrett Corporate and Securities Law Institute. Member of the Board of Directors of the Rehabilitation Institute of Chicago Foundation and the Board of Directors of Columbia College Chicago.
**Career:** Mr Lowinger is also a Certified Public Accountant.

### LUBELCHEK, Douglas J
Neal, Gerber & Eisenberg LLP, Chicago
312 269 5255
dlubelchek@ngelaw.com
*Featured in Real Estate (Illinois)*
**Practice Areas:** Represents clients involved in complex real estate and finance transactions, including developers, private real estate companies, publicly traded real estate investment trusts, banks and insurance companies, and management and leasing companies in connection with transactions involving office properties, shopping centers, apartment complexes, industrial sites, hotels, military bases and other government facilities. Handles complex joint venture transactions and represents clients in various portfolio transactions and transactions involving loan assumptions, bond issuances, new construction, sale-leasebacks, residential development, condominium conversions and like-kind exchanges.
**Career:** Partner; Real Estate Practice Group Chair.
**Personal:** University of Chicago (JD, 1987); University of Illinois (1984); CPA.

### LUBIN, Donald G
Dentons, Chicago
312 876 8007
donald.lubin@dentons.com
*Featured in Corporate/M&A (Illinois)*
**Practice Areas:** Counsels boards, management of private and public companies on restructurings, takeover defense, joint ventures, governance, M&A. Represents independent directors or committees.
**Career:** Joined Dentons in 1957. Chairman, 1991-96. Was McDonald's longest serving Director, Executive Committee Member; chaired Nominating and Corporate Governance Committee. Molex: Board Member, chaired audit committee. Chairman, Metropolis Strategies. Vice Chairman, Rush University Medical Center. Trustee, Ronald McDonald House Charities. Former Chairman, New Schools for Chicago, Ravinia Festival Association. Former Director, Smithsonian Institution, National Museum of American History.
**Personal:** Harvard Law School, LLB; University of Pennsylvania, BS.

### LYERLA, Bradford P
Jenner & Block LLP, Chicago
312 923 2613
blyerla@jenner.com
*Featured in Intellectual Property (Illinois)*
**Career:** Bradford P. Lyerla, Co-Chair of the Patent Litigation and Counseling Practice, has more than 30 years of experience in patent, trade secret and antitrust law. He has represented some of America's most prominent corporations in industries including aerospace; applied mathematics; chemical, food and material sciences; communications; computing; consumer products; electrical and software engineering; financial services; internet and cyberlaw; medical devices; nanotechnology; television; and pharmaceuticals. He is Editor-at-Large for the ABA's Intellectual Property Litigation newsletter, contributing author to West Publishing's Patent Claim Construction in the Federal Circuit and a frequent speaker at local and national Bar, trade and industry conferences.

### LYNCH, James M
Winston & Strawn LLP, Chicago
312 558 5935
jlynch@winston.com
*Featured in Tax (Illinois)*
**Practice Areas:** Mr Lynch's practice focuses on US and international tax aspects of mergers and acquisitions, joint ventures, corporate taxation and tax controversies.
**Professional Memberships:** Mr Lynch is a member of the American Bar Association and Chicago Bar Association, American Institute of Certified Public Accountants, American College of Tax Counsel, and is on the University of Chicago's Tax Conference Planning Committee.
**Career:** Mr Lynch received a LLM from Georgetown University, a JD from John Marshall School, and a BS in Business Administration from Xavier University. He is also a Certified Public Accountant. Mr Lynch joined Winston & Strawn in 2000.

### LYONS, John K
Skadden, Arps, Slate, Meagher & Flom LLP & Affiliates, Chicago
312 407 0860
john.lyons@skadden.com
*Featured in Bankruptcy/Restructuring (Illinois)*
**Practice Areas:** Represents domestic and international corporations in complex business reorganizations, acquisitions and divestitures, typically in distressed situations. Has counseled many significant business reorganizations including: The Official Committee of Unsecured Creditors for AMR Corporation; VeraSun Energy Corporation; Delphi Corporation; Interstate Bakeries Corporation; US Airways, Inc.; Exodus Communications, Inc.; Montgomery Ward, LLC; and Einstein/Noah Bagel Corp. Advises on transactions in distressed situations including representation of Verizon Capital, Valens Capital Management and Faurecia N.A.
**Professional Memberships:** Member, American Bankruptcy Institute; Member, Turnaround Management Association.

**Career:** JD, Villanova University School Of Law, 1989 (cum laude); BS, Georgetown University School of Foreign Service, 1986.

### MAATMAN JR, Gerald L
Seyfarth Shaw LLP, Chicago
312 460 5965
gmaatman@seyfarth.com
*Featured in Labor & Employment (Illinois)*
**Practice Areas:** Labor and employment/class action litigation.
**Professional Memberships:** ABA.
**Career:** Mr Maatman's practice focuses on defending companies in employment discrimination class actions, wage/hour collective actions, EEOC pattern or practice lawsuits, and civil rights class actions. He is the editor of the Annual Workplace Class Action Report and Workplace Class Action Blog, and co-chair of the class action defense practice group. He is an experienced, hands-on case litigator and strategist who has confronted virtually every legal and procedural issue that can arise in class actions.
**Publications:** Mr Maatman has authored six books on employment law topics.
**Personal:** JD, Northwestern University.

### MADONIA, Joseph F
Barnes & Thornburg LLP, Chicago
312 214 5611
jmadonia@btlaw.com
*Featured in Environment (Illinois)*
**Practice Areas:** Joe has spent over 25 years defending and counseling clients in a number of environmental matters. He has served as national trial counsel in complex litigation for international chemical companies and has successfully defended large class action suits involving groundwater, air and soil contamination issues in multiple states across the United States. In addition, as a former Deputy Chief of the Illinois Attorney General's Environmental Enforcement Division, Joe tried and supervised many high-profile enforcement and other proceedings in federal and state courts and before various regulatory agencies.
**Personal:** JD, Southern Methodist University; BA, University of Notre Dame.

### MAGEL, Barbara A.
Barnes & Thornburg LLP, Chicago
312 214 4585
barbara.magel@btlaw.com
*Featured in Environment (Illinois)*
**Practice Areas:** Environmental counseling and litigation on water and hazardous materials matters for individuals, companies of all sizes, and governmental entities including State and Federal regulatory compliance, transactional work, negotiations, Superfund committee chairmanships, permitting, and enforcement representations.
**Career:** Worked as counsel and acting assistant regional counsel with U.S. EPA, Region V before moving into private practice primarily with Karaganis, White and Magel LTD and now with Barnes & Thornburg LLP's Chicago office.
**Personal:** Wesleyan University (Bachelor of Arts 1976); University of North Carolina School of Law ( JD 1979).

### MALLOY, Timothy J
McAndrews, Held & Malloy, Ltd, Chicago
312 775 8000
tmalloy@mcandrews-ip.com
*Featured in Intellectual Property (Illinois)*
**Practice Areas:** Trial lawyer IP/Antitrust.
**Professional Memberships:** US and Illinois Supreme Courts and US District and Appellate Courts. Registered USPTO.
**Career:** Numerous multi-million dollar verdicts-settlements, e.g., ACS v Medtronic, Inc (TOP TEN IP DAMAGE AWARDS FOR ALL TIME). Numerous judgments of invalidity and noninfringement, e.g,, ICU v Alaris, Fed. Cir, claims invalid, not infringed, $5 million in fees. Lilly v. Medtronic, US Supreme Court.
**Publications:** E.g., Patent Litigation, PLI, Chapter 6, Cost Control.
**Personal:** BSEE and JD degrees Notre Dame; Strathmore's Who's Who, Top 100 Illinois Super Lawyers, Fellow, Litigation Counsel of America, International Who's Who Patent Lawyers.

### MALONEY, Timothy P
Fitch, Even, Tabin & Flannery, Chicago
312 577 7000
tim@fitcheven.com
*Featured in Intellectual Property (Illinois)*
**Practice Areas:** IP litigation and trial work, IP business strategy, IP transactions, IP risk management.
**Career:** Mr Maloney is managing partner of the firm. His practice entails all aspects of intellectual property enforcement and defense, with an emphasis on representing plaintiffs in patent litigation, often multi-party complex litigation. He is an established trial lawyer with a solid track record in numerous jury and bench trials, including cases involving patent, trade secret, antitrust, trademark, unfair competition, and professional malpractice matters. He has also successfully argued several cases before the U.S. Court of Appeals for the Federal Circuit. In addition, Mr Maloney provides counsel for mergers and acquisitions, technology licenses, patent portfolio sales, and other business transactions. He helps companies implement effective IP risk management programs, and provides legal opinions informed by front-line litigation experience. Mr Maloney represents clients in a wide range of areas including biotechnology, chemicals and chemical engineering, computer software and hardware, consumer and industrial electronics, energy and clean technology, Internet and e-commerce, medical devices, and mechanical systems.
**Personal:** JD, University of Illinois College of Law, 1993, summa cum laude; B.S., Chemical Engineering, University of Illinois, 1988, summa cum laude.

### MARGOLIS, Jeremy
Loeb & Loeb LLP, Chicago
312 464 3167
jmargolis@loeb.com
*Featured in Litigation (Illinois)*
**Practice Areas:** Focuses on complex commercial litigation, white-collar crime and corporate investigations.

**Professional Memberships:** Has lectured extensively at law schools, Bar associations, and civic organizations and has conducted training for state and local prosecutors and law enforcement officers.

**Career:** Assistant US attorney, Illinois Inspector General; director, Illinois State Police; co-chair of the white-collar practice at Sonnenschein Nath & Rosenthal LLP. Joined Loeb as Partner in 2008; white-collar practice co-chair.

**Personal:** Northwestern University School of Law (JD, cum laude, 1973); University of Illinois (BA, 1970).

## MARKOVIC, Milos
Greenberg Traurig, LLP, Chicago
312 456 1041
MarkovicM@gtlaw.com
*Featured in Real Estate (Illinois)*

**Practice Areas:** Real estate; real estate investment trusts (REITs); construction, mezzanine, bridge and permanent financings; restructurings and workouts; partnerships and joint ventures; Shari'ah compliant financings and equity investments; acquisitions and dispositions of all asset classes; build-to-suit leasing transactions.

**Career:** Selected, Chambers USA Guide, 2008-13; member, Winning Team, 2010 Chambers and Partners USA Award for Excellence in Real Estate; Leading Lawyers Network, 2011-13. Team Member, a Law360 'Real Estate Practice Group of the Year', 2011-12.

**Personal:** JD, DePaul University College of Law, 1999; BA, University of Illinois at Chicago, 1993.

## MARTINI, Christina
DLA Piper LLP (US), Chicago
312 368 7025
christina.martini@dlapiper.com
*Featured in Intellectual Property (Illinois)*

**Practice Areas:** Intellectual property, trademarks, copyrights.

**Career:** She is Vice Chair of the Chicago office's IP Practice Group and is a Member of the firm's Policy Committee. She focuses her practice in domestic and international trademark and copyright law, as well as domain name, internet, advertising, unfair competition and entertainment law. She has extensive experience in counseling, prosecution, enforcement, and licensing matters, and in assisting clients in protecting their intellectual property rights through litigation and other means, including the courts and uniform dispute resolution procedures.

**Personal:** JD, Northwestern University School of Law; B.S.I.E., University of Illinois at Chicago.

## MARX, David
McDermott Will & Emery LLP, Chicago
312 984 7668
dmarx@mwe.com
*Featured in Antitrust (Illinois)*

**Practice Areas:** Partner in litigation department. Concentrates practice in civil and criminal antitrust litigation and counseling, and trade regulation matters. Responsible for Chicago antitrust practice. Serves corporate and healthcare industry clients, and individuals who are the subjects or targets of investigations or enforcement proceed-

ings initiated by federal or state antitrust agencies, and in private civil litigation. Develops, implements and monitors antitrust and trade regulation compliance programs for a variety of corporate clients.

**Personal:** Syracuse University College of Law (JD); Amherst College (BA, cum laude).

## MASON, David M
Goldberg Kohn Ltd, Chicago
312 201 3915
David.Mason@goldbergkohn.com
*Featured in Banking & Finance (Illinois)*

**Career:** David Mason is a principal in the Commercial Finance Group with over 20 years' experience, principally representing banks and other commercial lenders in cash-flow transactions that provide for acquisition, working capital, capital expenditure, mezzanine and one-stop financing. Mr Mason also represents asset-based lenders and has been engaged in loan restructurings, bankruptcies and workout matters. He has been involved with industry consolidation loans and purchase order financing. Lenders Mr Mason represents typically service middle market borrowers with average transactions ranging from $20 million to $300 million. His finance practice includes various retail, manufacturing and service industries.

## MATHIAS JR, John H
Jenner & Block LLP, Chicago
312 923 2917
jmathias@jenner.com
*Featured in Insurance (Illinois)*

**Career:** A veteran trial lawyer, John Mathias' practice focuses on representing policyholders in insurance coverage disputes as well as select clients in reinsurance arbitrations. His clients include many leading US publicly traded and privately owned companies in recovery actions involving general liability, property damage, business interruption, D&O, E&O, fidelity, and other specialty lines claims. He was recently appointed to represent the Illinois Director of Insurance in the rehabilitation proceedings of the Lumbermens Insurance companies. An active participant in both the IBA and ABA, he has co-authored over 20 legal publications and is a frequent lecturer on insurance and reinsurance topics.

## MATTSON, Eric S
Sidley Austin LLP, Chicago
312 853 4716
emattson@sidley.com
*Featured in Media & Entertainment (Illinois)*

**Practice Areas:** Partner in Sidley's Chicago office. A former newspaper reporter, his media law practice has ranged from defending defamation, privacy and reporter's privilege cases to pursuing Freedom of Information Act and court access cases. Representative clients include the Chicago Tribune and Northwestern University. His practice also includes class action defense and other commercial litigation.

**Personal:** Northwestern University School of Law, JD, 1994, cum laude; University of Michigan, AB, 1987, with distinction.

## MAY, Jane Wells
McDermott Will & Emery LLP, Chicago
312 984 2115
jmay@mwe.com
*Featured in Tax (Illinois)*

**Practice Areas:** Head of firm's state and local tax practice. Represents businesses in connection with state and local tax controversies at the audit, administrative and judicial levels. Successfully litigated state and local tax matters raising a variety of statutory and constitutional issues. Defended numerous internet sellers in several states against cases brought under state whistleblower statutes alleging fraudulent failures to collect and remit use tax.

**Professional Memberships:** Admitted to practice in Illinois; Taxpayer's Federation of Illinois Policy Committee; Chicago Bar Association's State and Local Tax Committee.

**Personal:** Vanderbilt University Law School (JD), Wittenberg University (BA).

## MAYNES, Todd F
Kirkland & Ellis LLP, Chicago
312 862 2485
todd.maynes@kirkland.com
*Featured in Tax (Illinois), Tax (Nationwide)*

**Practice Areas:** Todd Maynes focuses his practice on the tax aspects of bankruptcy and tax litigation. He was the lead tax lawyer on many of the most significant bankruptcies in recent history, including United Airlines, Conseco, Calpine, Charter Communications and W.R. Grace, and is one of only a few tax attorneys to ever be elected to the National Bankruptcy Conference. He is former chairman of the University of Chicago Federal Tax Conference, former chairman of the Chicago-Kent Federal Tax Institute and is adjunct professor of bankruptcy taxation at Northwestern University.

**Personal:** BYU, JD, 1987; BYU, BA, 1984.

## MAZURA, Adrianne
Quarles & Brady LLP, Chicago
312 715 5213
adrianne.mazura@quarles.com
*Featured in Labor & Employment (Illinois)*

**Practice Areas:** Labor and employment.

**Professional Memberships:** Member, American Bar Association; Life Fellow, American Bar Foundation; Fellow, College of Labor and Employment Lawyers.

**Career:** She has represented employers before the National Labor Relations Board and the Equal Employment Opportunity Commission, as well as before numerous state agencies, courts and arbitration panels. Her work has involved her in every area of employment law including union organizing campaigns, collective bargaining negotiations, and defense of numerous individual and multiparty and class cases throughout the country.

**Personal:** Wayne State University (JD, magna cum laude); University of Michigan (BA, with distinction).

## MCANDREWS, George P
McAndrews, Held & Malloy, Ltd, Chicago
312 775 8000
gmcandrews@mcandrews-ip.com
*Featured in Intellectual Property (Illinois)*

**Career:** George P McAndrews is Chairman Emeritus and a founder of the firm. His practice focus has been on successfully litigating patent, trademark and antitrust cases involving mechanical, electrical, chemical and medical device subject matter, primarily before juries, in federal and state courts throughout the United States. He has been repeatedly praised by federal judges, juries, and clients and has been highly ranked in numerous national and international publications, e.g., National Law Journal, as one of the nation's ten leading litigators, and a patent attorney who uses "artful analogies to win over the jury." His specific profile is at www.mcandrews-ip.com.

## MCBREEN, Maura Ann
Baker & McKenzie, Chicago
312 861 6630
mauraann.mcbreen@bakermckenzie.com
*Featured in Labor & Employment (Illinois)*

**Practice Areas:** Advises on design, implementation, compliance and transactional implications of executive compensation (including equity and equity-based arrangements) and benefit plans, including Code Section 162(m), 280G, 409A and 457A issues.

**Professional Memberships:** Best Lawyers in America; Leading Lawyers Network; American Bar Association; Chicago Bar Association; Board of Contributing Editors and Advisors, Corporate Taxation. Admitted to Illinois bar and U.S. Tax Court.

**Career:** Partner, Baker & McKenzie.

**Publications:** Quarterly column "Compensation and Fringe Benefits," Corporate Taxation.

**Personal:** AB Smith College; JD Harvard Law School.

## MCCAREINS, R Mark
Winston & Strawn LLP, Chicago
312 558 5902
rmccareins@winston.com
*Featured in Antitrust (Illinois)*

**Practice Areas:** Antitrust, trade regulation, intellectual property litigation.

**Professional Memberships:** American, Federal and Seventh Circuit, Illinois, Chicago, and California Bar Associations; American Bar Foundation Fellow; Adjunct Professor of Antitrust, Northwestern University Kellogg School of Management; Board of Regents (Chicago) and National Law Council Washington University; Corporate Secretary, Lawrence Hall Youth Services; General Counsel, Metals Service Center Institute.

**Publications:** "Drafting Agreements to Avoid Antitrust Violations", Law Seminars International, Feb. 2012; "Current State of Patent False Marking Litigation", IPTLJ, May, 2011.

**Personal:** Northwestern University, BA, with honors, 1978; Washington University, JD, 1981, Editor-in-Chief, Washington University Law Quarterly.

## MCCLUGGAGE, Michael L
Edwards Wildman Palmer, Chicago
312 201 2548
mmccluggage@edwardswildman.com
*Featured in Antitrust (Illinois)*
**Practice Areas:** Mike McCluggage has extensive experience in antitrust litigation, government antitrust investigations, internal investigations and antitrust counseling. He has litigated a wide spectrum of substantive antitrust issues, including allegations of price-fixing conspiracies, bid-rigging, monopolization attempts, boycotts and customer allocation claims. His experience encompasses representation of a variety of industries including pharmaceutical manufacturers, insurers, and equipment manufacturers. He has special expertise in the scope or applicability of antitrust exemptions such as the McCarran-Ferguson Act relating to the insurance industry.
**Personal:** University of Chicago, JD; Ohio Wesleyan University, BA.

## MCCULLOUGH, Joe
Freeborn & Peters LLP, Chicago
312 360 6327
jmccullough@freebornpeters.com
*Featured in Insurance (Illinois)*
**Practice Areas:** Joe McCullough is a Partner in the Litigation Practice Group and leads the firm's Reinsurance Practice Group. He is also a member of the Firm's Executive Committee. Mr McCullough has devoted his practice over the past 26 years to counseling insurance and reinsurance companies. He has acted as counsel to insurers and reinsurers in more than 100 arbitrations and court proceedings across the United States, as well as in Bermuda, England and Continental Europe, including some of the highest profile cases in the industry.
**Career:** Prior to joining Freeborn & Peters in July 2010, Mr McCullough was a Partner at Lovells LLP, where he opened the firm's US practice in 1995, was the U.S. Regional Managing Partner for seven years, served as the firm's US Insurance and Reinsurance Practice Group Head and was a member of the firm's International Executive Committee. Mr McCullough began his career at Sidley & Austin in 1983 where he founded the firm's reinsurance practice.
**Personal:** JD, cum laude: Northwestern University, Order of the Coif, Law Review; BA, magna cum laude, Georgetown University; License in European Law, with high honors, University of Gent, Belgium.

## MCCUNE, Andrew W
McDermott Will & Emery LLP, Chicago
312 984 6921
amccune@mwe.com
*Featured in Corporate/M&A (Illinois)*
**Practice Areas:** Focuses on private equity, corporate transactions, corporate financings, and securities matters, representing sponsors, purchasers, and sellers in public and private mergers, acquisitions, and investments in diverse industries and market segments. Private equity experience includes domestic and international leveraged transactions involving financial as well as strategic

parties. Finance and securities experience includes domestic and international public offerings, as well as private placements of debt and equity.
**Personal:** JD, University of Chicago Law School; AB, Washington University in St. Louis (summa cum laude).

## MCDONALD, John D
Baker & McKenzie, Chicago
312 861 8917
john.mcdonald@bakermckenzie.com
*Featured in Tax (Illinois)*
**Practice Areas:** Mr McDonald's practice involves providing advice regarding various international tax issues such as planning in connection with subpart F, foreign tax credit, and hedging issues. He regularly advises on cross-border M&A transactions and joint ventures.
**Professional Memberships:** Mr McDonald belongs to the Chicago Tax Club and the International Fiscal Association.
**Publications:** Mr McDonald regularly publishes a bi-monthly column in CCH's TAXES Magazine. He co-authors a book on international taxation called "U.S. Corporations Doing Business Abroad" published through the Research Institute of America. He has also published articles for Tax Analysts and the Public Law Institute.

## MCENROE, John T
Vedder Price PC, Chicago
312 609 7885
jmcenroe@vedderprice.com
*Featured in Banking & Finance (Illinois)*
**Practice Areas:** Shareholder, Finance and Transactions group. Concentrates his practice in secured transactions, leveraged buyouts, mergers and acquisitions, bankruptcy and business reorganizations, and related areas of the law. Represents public and private companies in acquisitions and divestitures, including structuring and negotiating acquisition documents and procuring, structuring and finalizing the requisite financing. Represents first lien lenders, secured lien lenders and mezzanine debt holders—including traditional banks, finance companies, hedge funds and other financial institutions—in unsecured, asset-based, cash flow and project finance credit facilities.
**Career:** Admitted (IL) 1977.
**Personal:** JD, Yale Law School; B.S., University of Illinois.

## MCFETRIDGE, Jane
Jackson Lewis LLP, Chicago
312 274 6308
mcfetrij@jacksonlewis.com
*Featured in Labor & Employment (Illinois)*
**Practice Areas:** Employment Litigation; Employment law trials; Class/Collective Actions; Advice and Counseling.
**Professional Memberships:** DRI (Employment Law Committee); Chicago Bar Association (Labor and Employment Law Committee); American Bar Association (Labor and Employment Section).
**Career:** Jackson Lewis (Managing Partner, Chicago) 2007 – Present; Fisher & Phillips (Partner) 2000 – 2007; Donohue Brown

Mathewson & Smyth (Partner) 1999 – 2000. Certified Public Accountant (inactive) - Illinois.
**Publications:** Frequent speaker and published on employment law topics.
**Personal:** JD Northwestern University School of Law, BS University of Illinois (James Scholar). Best Lawyers in America, Illinois Super Lawyers, "AV" rated, -by Martindale Hubbell.

## MCGOVERN, Lynn M
Skadden, Arps, Slate, Meagher & Flom LLP & Affiliates, Chicago
312 407 0825
lynn.mcGovern@skadden.com
*Featured in Banking & Finance (Illinois)*
**Practice Areas:** Represents borrowers and financial institutions in a broad range of secured and unsecured financing transactions, including acquisition financings, amend and extend facilities, working capital financings, debtor-in-possession financings, exit financings and restructuring transactions. Has represented financial institutions as agents and investors in a broad range of financial transactions. Has represented numerous corporate clients and private equity clients in various domestic and international financings.
**Career:** JD, The University of Michigan Law School, 1986 (magna cum laude); BA, University of Illinois, 1983 (bronze tablet).

## MCLAUGHLIN, Ellen E
Seyfarth Shaw LLP, Chicago
312 460 5887
emclaughlin@seyfarth.com
*Featured in Labor & Employment (Illinois)*
**Practice Areas:** Labor and employment.
**Professional Memberships:** Fellow, College of Labor and Employment Lawyers.
**Career:** Trusted advisor on high level issues; counseling practice focused on creating compliant HR practices and systems to achieve business purposes and avoid litigation; federal and state court and administrative agency employment litigation. Lecturer on wide variety of employment topics.
**Publications:** Co-authored "A Client's Guide to the ADA, FMLA and Workers' Compensation," The Journal of the American Corporate Counsel Association and "Training Becomes Important Step to Avoid Liability," The National Law Journal; contributing author, Workplace Harassment Law, BNA.
**Personal:** JD, University of Notre Dame Law School.

## MEADOWS, Stanley
McDermott Will & Emery LLP, Chicago
312 984 7570
smeadows@mwe.com
*Featured in Corporate/M&A (Illinois)*
**Practice Areas:** Acquisitions and dispositions of businesses, public and private financings and business counseling. Clients include companies whose securities are publicly traded, buy out funds, entrepreneurs and other buyers of financially distressed companies. Matters include acquisitions and financings of businesses engaged in telecommunications, software development, sports and entertainment, construction and real estate activities. Practice also includes formation

of private equity funds. Counseled purchasers of professional sports franchises, including financing of purchase and development of new sports venues. Represented clients in Asia and Eastern Europe.
**Personal:** University of Illinois (BS); University of Chicago Law School (JD).

## MEDANSKY, Keith
DLA Piper LLP (US), Chicago
312 368 7271
keith.medansky@dlapiper.com
*Featured in Intellectual Property (Illinois)*
**Practice Areas:** Intellectual Property.
**Career:** His concentration in intellectual property includes a full range of transactional and litigation matters pertaining to trademarks, copyrights, software, anti-counterfeiting and technology. He has handled trademark matters in the United States and in over 100 other countries. He has extensive experience managing large intellectual property portfolios for all kinds of businesses and has experience in counseling clients in matters involving the protection of web site content and domain names and in developing cyberspace and copyright policies.
**Personal:** JD, University of Illinois at Urbana-Champaign (magna cum laude); BA, Northwestern University.

## MEHLMAN, Mark
Dentons, Chicago
312 876 8023
mark.mehlman@dentons.com
*Featured in Real Estate (Illinois)*
**Practice Areas:** Practice focuses on all types of sophisticated financing, including conduit lending and multi-property, multi-state facilities, for both major institutional lenders and owners of all types of real estate assets; workouts of troubled loans for borrowers and lenders, including special servicers; the representation of clients active in the hospitality industry, including hotel owners and investors involved in significant transactions and debt and equity placements; and real estate development, acquisitions and dispositions and complex partnership and joint venture relationships.
**Career:** Served on legacy Dentons's Policy and Planning Committee for 18 years.
**Personal:** University of Michigan, LLB; University of Illinois, BA.

## MEISLER, Ron E
Skadden, Arps, Slate, Meagher & Flom LLP & Affiliates, Chicago
312 407 0549
ron.meisler@skadden.com
*Featured in Bankruptcy/Restructuring (Illinois)*
**Practice Areas:** Represents a variety of clients in complex transactions involving company-side reorganizations (in- and out-of-court) and debt restructurings, alternative and special situation investments, including distressed M&A, and creditors' committee representations. He has represented and currently represents debtors, creditors, investors, buyers, sellers and secured lenders in all stages of complex restructuring transactions throughout the globe.

**Professional Memberships:** Member, Turnaround Management Association (TMA); Board Member, TMA; Member, TMA Board's Executive Committee.
**Career:** JD, University of Michigan Law School, 1999; MBA, University of Michigan, 1999; BA, University of Michigan, 1994.

## MELBINGER, Michael S
Winston & Strawn LLP, Chicago
312 558 7588
mmelbinger@winston.com
*Featured in Labor & Employment (Illinois)*
**Practice Areas:** Executive compensation, retirement plans and related tax, securities, ERISA, M&A, and litigation issues.
**Professional Memberships:** NASPP, ABA, American College of Employee Benefits Counsel.
**Career:** Partner and Chair: Executive Compensation and Employee Benefits Department, Winston & Strawn LLP, 1997 - present; Adjunct Professor, Northwestern University Law School, 2003 to present; Adjunct Professor, University of Illinois College of Law, 2007 to present.
**Publications:** Executive Compensation, CCH; Guide to Employee Benefit Trusts, ABA; Melbinger's Compensation Blog; myNQDQ.com; numerous articles on employee benefits and executive compensation topics.
**Personal:** BA University of Notre Dame, 1980; JD University of Illinois College of Law, 1983.

## MELTON, Timothy J
Jones Day, Chicago
312 269 4154
tmelton@jonesday.com
*Featured in Corporate/M&A (Illinois)*
**Practice Areas:** Counsels a diverse range of public and private companies, investment banks and other financial institutions, and their boards of directors, focusing on corporate finance and corporate governance matters. He regularly advises domestic and non-US entities on matters relating to governance, securities regulations, financing strategies and alternatives, mergers and acquisitions, and stockholder activism. He has significant experience advising SEC reporting companies on matters of securities laws and stock exchange rules. He also has significant experience representing financial institutions in connection with public and private financings and various restructuring scenarios.

## MELVIN, Daniel
McDermott Will & Emery UK LLP, London
312 984 6935
dmelvin@mwe.com
*Featured in Healthcare (Illinois)*
**Practice Areas:** Focuses his practice on counseling clients on Federal health care program fraud and abuse, Stark law, and Medicare reimbursement issues. Has substantial experience auditing hospitals and other health care organizations for Medicare and other regulatory compliance, and structuring ambulatory clinical joint ventures, including ambulatory surgery centers, cardiac and vascular labs, imaging centers, radia-

tion therapy centers, sleep labs and in-office physician diagnostic facilities.
**Personal:** DePaul University College of Law, JD, 1995, Azusa Pacific University, BA, 1978.

## MENDELSOHN, David
DLA Piper LLP (US), Chicago
312 368 7272
david.mendelsohn@dlapiper.com
*Featured in Insurance (Illinois)*
**Practice Areas:** Insurance and reinsurance.
**Career:** He focuses in insurance and reinsurance transactional and regulatory matters, representing insurers, reinsurers, brokers, and others on transactions including mergers and acquisitions, complex regulatory and finite, structured risk and reinsurance. He counsels clients on investigations, responding to subpoenas, compliance, and information management, such as records management and retention, money laundering, data privacy and security, E&O risk management, and ethics.
**Personal:** JD, Chicago-Kent College of Law, Illinois Institute of Technology; Lancaster Gate School of Law (with honors); LLB, University College of London (with honors).

## MENSIK, Michael S
Baker & McKenzie, Chicago
312 861 8941
michael.mensik@bakermckenzie.com
*Featured in Outsourcing (Nationwide), Technology (Illinois)*
See under Nationwide for profile.

## MESIRES, George
Ungaretti & Harris LLP, Chicago
312 977 4151
grmesires@uhlaw.com
*Featured in Bankruptcy/Restructuring (Illinois)*
**Practice Areas:** George Mesires co-chairs the Finance and Restructuring group. George concentrates on distressed M&A, corporate restructuring, insolvency, and finance. George also focuses on advising directors and officers on corporate governance and fiduciary duties. He has represented private equity firms, lenders, and debtors in a variety of finance, insolvency and distressed situations. Prior to private practice, George was General Counsel for a telecommunications company, and an Assistant Attorney General in the New York State Attorney General's Office.
**Personal:** Syracuse University College of Law (JD,1995); Syracuse University School of Management (MBA,1995); Colgate University (BA,1991).

## MESSERLY, Robert
Quarles & Brady LLP, Chicago
312 715 5117
robert.messerly@quarles.com
*Featured in Real Estate (Illinois)*
**Practice Areas:** Practice concentrated in equity investments, large portfolio acquisition and disposition, leasing and real estate finance. Represents pre-eminent US institutional real estate investors and lenders on a global, national and local basis. Works on acquisitions and dispositions across the United States, including transactions involving office buildings, apartment complexes, industrial

buildings, hotels and mixed-use buildings. Significant experience in leasing (for both landlords and tenants) and traditional real estate loans as well as mezzanine loans, loan restructurings and Shari'ah compliant financings and ownership structures.
**Personal:** Northwestern University, JD; Xavier University, BA.

## MESSERSMITH, Michael
Kaye Scholer LLP, Chicago
312 583 2374
Michael.Messersmith@kayescholer.com
*Featured in Bankruptcy/Restructuring (Illinois)*
**Practice Areas:** Michael Messersmith is a Partner in the Bankruptcy & Restructuring Department of Kaye Scholer's Chicago office. He represents lenders, bondholders, agents, indenture trustees, hedge funds and other financial institutions, as well as borrowers, in distressed situations, workouts and bankruptcy proceedings throughout the United States. A primary focus of his practice is advising ad hoc groups of lenders and bondholders in restructuring situations.

## MILLER, Laura Beth
Brinks Hofer Gilson & Lione, Chicago
312 321 4715
lmiller@usebrinks.com
*Featured in Intellectual Property (Illinois)*
**Practice Areas:** Ms Miller co-chairs the ITC Practice Group at Brinks Hofer Gilson & Lione. She is a skilled trial attorney with experience in intellectual property law, as well as antitrust and commercial litigation. In addition to representing major Fortune 500 companies in patent and trademark matters in both federal court and the ITC, she is an adjunct professor at The John Marshall Law School.
**Career:** She has been recognized as one of Illinois' leading intellectual property lawyers by Chambers USA, and has been named a Leading Intellectual Property Lawyer and one of the Top 50 Women Business Litigation Lawyers in Illinois by the Leading Lawyers Network.
**Publications:** 'Finding A Common Language With Clients In Patent Litigation: Discussion Points for Foreign Clients and their US-Based Counsel', American Intellectual Property Law Association, January 2008; 'ITC Growing As a Forum for IP Disputes', Intellectual Property Litigation Newsletter (ABA 2007); '337 Actions Before The International Trade Commission', International Trade Commission Basics (ICLE 2007); 'Enforcing and Defending Against Patent Rights Through Litigation', Intellectual Property Law (ICLE 2005 and 2013).
**Personal:** Education: BA, University of Virginia (1982); JD, College of William and Mary (1985). Registered Patent Attorney.

## MILLNER, Robert B
Dentons, Chicago
312 876 7994
robert.millner@dentons.com
*Featured in Bankruptcy/Restructuring (Illinois)*
**Practice Areas:** Practices bankruptcy and commercial litigation. Represents financial institutions and insurance companies in bankruptcy litigation.

Represents lenders, other creditors and debtors in complex reorganization matters. Has handled significant cross-border matters.
**Professional Memberships:** Fellow, American College of Bankruptcy; member, International Insolvency Institute; past Co-Chair, Bankruptcy and Insolvency Committee, Litigation Section of the American Bar Association; chair, Insurance Subcommittee of ABA Business Bankruptcy Committee; honorary overseas member, Commercial Bar Association (London).
**Personal:** University of Chicago, JD, Law Review; Wesleyan University, BA, magna cum laude, Phi Beta Kappa.

## MINSKER, Helen Hill
Banner & Witcoff, Ltd, Chicago
312 463 5000
hminsker@bannerwitcoff.com
*Featured in Intellectual Property (Illinois)*
**Practice Areas:** Trademark counseling, prosecution, registration and enforcement in the US and internationally; trademark, unfair competition and copyright litigation, inter partes proceedings; Internet, domain name issues; copyright law.
**Professional Memberships:** ABA, AIPLA, ECTA, FCBA, and INTA. Served on AIPLA and INTA Board of Directors, former AIPLA Treasurer.
**Career:** Principal Shareholder at Banner & Witcoff. Adjunct Professor of Law at Georgetown University (2001-2011). Bar Admissions: District of Columbia and Illinois.
**Publications:** Editorial board for The Trademark Reporter (2006-09); Co-chair of PLI program and program publication 'Navigating Trademark Practice Before the PTO' (2003-09).
**Personal:** AB, Vassar College; JD, George Washington University.

## MISCIMARRA, Philip A
Morgan, Lewis & Bockius LLP, Chicago
312 324 1165
pmiscimarra@morganlewis.com
*Featured in Labor & Employment (Illinois)*
**Practice Areas:** Philip A. Miscimarra is a partner in Morgan Lewis's Labor and Employment Practice. He represents clients in a wide range of matters, with a focus on traditional labor law and employment litigation. He co-chairs Morgan Lewis/Workforce Change, devoted to employment, labor and benefits issues arising from mergers, acquisitions, workforce reductions, startups and other major business restructuring. He is also a Senior Fellow at the University of Pennsylvania's Wharton School and the Wharton Center for Human Resources.
**Personal:** Attended University of Pennsylvania Law School, 1982, JD; University of Pennsylvania, Wharton School of Business, 1982, M.BA; Duquesne University, 1978, BA.

## MORAN, Patrick G
Dentons, Chicago
312 876 8132
patrick.moran@dentons.com
*Featured in Real Estate (Illinois)*
**Practice Areas:** Handles various commercial real estate and related financing matters, empha-

sizing development, leasing, joint ventures and financing. Has worked with major office landlords and tenants in developing and leasing more than 15 million square feet of office and retail space, with special focus on ground leases. Financing practice focuses on multi-state secured and unsecured term and revolving credit loans to REITs and other real estate companies, along with traditional project loans.
**Career:** Joined Dentons in 1976; former Chair of legacy Dentons's Real Estate Group; Member American College of Real Estate Lawyers.
**Personal:** Georgetown University, JD; Harvard College, BA.

### MROWIEC, John S
Conway & Mrowiec, Chicago
312 658 1100
jsm@cmcontractors.com
*Featured in Construction (Illinois)*
**Practice Areas:** Construction law.
**Professional Memberships:** Chicago (Mechanics Lien) and American (Construction, Public Contracts and Litigation Sections) Bar Associations; Builders Association; Fox Valley Contractors Association; Associated General Contractors; American Institute of Architects; Society of Illinois Construction Attorneys.
**Publications:** Law Columnist, Midwest Construction (McGraw-Hill) (May 2000-10); Instructor: 'Construction Law', Real Estate Center, DePaul University (2002-06); co-author: 'Original Contractor's Lien on Private Projects', Illinois Mechanics Liens, IICLE (1994, 2000, 2004, 2007, 2010 eds.); co-author: 'Pre-Construction Issues for the Contractor or Construction Manager', IICLE (2009 ed.); co-author: 'Changes and Differing Site Conditions', IICLE (2012); 'Changes that Result from Delays and Interferences', Construction Change Order Claims 2d (Aspen, 2005); Author/Speaker, 'Recent Decisions on Perennial Delay Claims Issues', SOICA (2012); 'AIA Contract Documents' (2004-13); 'Public Construction Contracting' (2001-04, 2012); 'Construction Contracts' (2002-06); 'Construction Management and Design-Build' (2002-05); 'Construction Delay Claims' (2000-06); 'Construction Bidding Process' (2008); 'Cumulative Impact Claims' (2007); 'Electronic Discovery in Construction Disputes' (2007, 2005); 'Nelson Energy Project' (2005); 'Drafting Arbitration Agreements', IICLE (2010); 'School and University Delay Claim Decisions' (2008); 'Special Mechanics Lien Issues with Newly Constructed Condominium Buildings' (2008, 2010); 'Impact of Exculpatory Clauses on Delay Claims' (2007).

### MULANEY JR, Charles W
Skadden, Arps, Slate, Meagher & Flom LLP & Affiliates, Chicago
312 407 0500
charles.mulaney@skadden.com
*Featured in Corporate/M&A (Illinois)*
**Practice Areas:** Concentrates on mergers and acquisitions (both friendly and hostile), joint ventures, divestitures and spin-offs, corporate financings, restructurings and general corporate governance. Counsels clients on securities, corporate

and business related matters, including disclosure issues, directors' duties and responsibilities, corporate governance and internal investigations.
**Professional Memberships:** Lecturer, Corporate Counsel Institute of Northwestern University School of Law and the business schools of the University of Chicago, Duke University and Northwestern University; Member, executive committee, Corporate and Securities Law Institute, Northwestern University School of Law.
**Career:** JD, Yale Law School, 1974 (Editor, Yale Law Journal); AB, Georgetown University, 1971 (summa cum laude).

### MURRAY, Daniel
Jenner & Block LLP, Chicago
312 923 2953
dmurray@jenner.com
*Featured in Bankruptcy/Restructuring (Illinois)*
**Career:** Daniel R Murray chairs the Bankruptcy, Workout and Corporate Reorganization Practice. Mr Murray's national practice focuses on commercial law, secured transactions and corporate restructuring. He counsels and represents clients in corporate restructurings in a range of industries, including transportation, manufacturing, retailing, energy, gaming and financial services. He also advises clients in matters relating to commercial law, including secured transactions, sales, leasing, banking law and letters of credit. He has been involved in numerous high-profile matters, including representing General Motors Corporation in its Chapter 11 bankruptcy. He has taught corporate reorganization and written extensively on the Uniform Commercial Code.

### MURRAY, Gregory S
Winston & Strawn LLP, Chicago
31 2558 5669
gmurray@winston.com
*Featured in Banking & Finance (Illinois)*
**Practice Areas:** Syndicated leveraged finance, representing prominent US and foreign lending institutions in senior and subordinated credit facilities, cross-border facilities and structured finance transactions. Extensive experience structuring multi-tiered acquisition and tender facilities. In recent years has represented agents and lead arrangers in US and London-based financings aggregating in excess of US$60 billion.
**Career:** Attended the University of Notre Dame and the University of Virginia Law School. Recognized by Chambers Global, the International Who's Who of Business Lawyers, The Best Lawyers in America and as an Illinois Super Lawyer.

### MURTAUGH, Christopher D
Winston & Strawn LLP, Chicago
312 558 5798
cmurtaugh@winston.com
*Featured in Real Estate (Illinois)*
**Practice Areas:** Partner and former Chairman of the Real Estate Department. More than 35 years' experience focusing on national practice in commercial property acquisition and disposition, real estate development, and lending activities; also involved in active practice in real estate pro bono activities.

**Professional Memberships:** Member of the American College of Real Estate Lawyers, Order of the Coif, Fellow of the American Bar Foundation, Illinois and Florida Bar Associations.
**Career:** Joined as associate, 1974. Partner, 1979.Service on various firm committees.
**Personal:** University of Illinois, 1967. JD, University of Illinois College of Law, 1970.

### MUTCHNIK, James H
Kirkland & Ellis LLP, Chicago
312 862 2350
james.mutchnik@kirkland.com
*Featured in Antitrust (Illinois)*
**Practice Areas:** James Mutchnik represents corporate and individual clients in antitrust, white-collar crime, commercial, bankruptcy and patent litigation in federal and state courts throughout the United States and before a variety of federal and state investigative agencies. In the antitrust area, he litigates various matters, from alleged price fixing to price discrimination, and represents clients in dealing with antitrust aspects of mergers, acquisitions and joint ventures. He counsels a wide range of small and large companies in diverse industries on pricing, marketing, distribution and dealer termination issues.
**Personal:** University of Pennsylvania, B.S., 1986. Northwestern University School of Law, JD, 1989.

### MYERS, Linda K
Kirkland & Ellis LLP, Chicago
312 862 2322
linda.myers@kirkland.com
*Featured in Banking & Finance (Illinois), Banking & Finance (Nationwide)*
**Practice Areas:** Corporate partner who focuses on debt financing transactions for major private and public companies, private equity groups and commercial lending institutions. Linda has been responsible for financings in connection with leveraged buyouts, public offerings, working capital financings/refinancings and restructurings (including out-of-court, debtor-in-possession and exit financing). The transactions she has handled have included senior debt and mezzanine financings, both secured and unsecured, and have ranged in size from several hundred million dollars to several billion dollars. Recent representative clients include Bain Capital, Bristol-Myers Squibb, Dex Corporation, Madison Dearborn Partners, Nuveen Investments, Radio One, SIRVA and Six Flags Entertainment Corporation.

### NAPOLITANO, Steven V
DLA Piper LLP (US), Chicago
312 368 3378
steven.napolitano@dlapiper.com
*Featured in Corporate/M&A (Illinois)*
**Practice Areas:** Corporate/M&A, private equity.
**Career:** He chairs the firm's US Private Equity practice. His national practice spans the full range of private equity representation. He represents private equity funds and portfolio companies in mergers, acquisitions, leveraged buyouts, equity financings, and senior mezzanine debt financings. He has substantial experience with private equity transactions involving both private and public tar-

gets, including management-sponsored going private transactions. He frequently represents equity funds and senior management teams in complex incentive compensation arrangements.
**Personal:** JD, Boston University School of Law; BA, University of Notre Dame.

### NASH, Gordon B
Drinker Biddle & Reath LLP, Chicago
312 569 1384
gordon.nash@dbr.com
*Featured in Litigation (Illinois)*
**Practice Areas:** Partner, Commercial Litigation Group. Focuses on trial and appellate work in white collar criminal defense, securities, antitrust and commercial matters. Frequently engaged to conduct internal investigations and serve as arbitrator/mediator.
**Professional Memberships:** Fellow, American College of Trial Lawyers; Chair, Illinois Supreme Court Commission on Professionalism; Review Board, Attorney Registration Disciplinary Commission, Illinois; Past President, Chicago Bar Association, Chicago Inn of Court; Past Chair, Constitutional Rights Foundation.
**Career:** Previously, Chief of Special Prosecutions Division, U.S. Attorney's Office, Chicago.
**Personal:** JD, Loyola University Chicago School of Law, 1969; BA, University of Notre Dame, 1966.

### NASH, JR, Patrick
Kirkland & Ellis LLP, Chicago
312 862 2290
patrick.nash@kirkland.com
*Featured in Bankruptcy/Restructuring (Illinois)*
**Practice Areas:** Patrick Nash represents a variety of clients in complex business reorganizations, troubled company mergers and acquisitions, debt restructurings and financing matters. He has counseled companies experiencing financial difficulties, purchasers of and investors in distressed companies and lenders to and creditors of such companies. Representative debtor clients include Hawker Beechcraft, Tronox Incorporated, AMF Bowling, U.S. Concrete, Inc. and FGIC Corporation. Representative creditor clients include Black Diamond Capital Management, Angelo Gordon and noteholders of TerreStar Networks.
**Personal:** University of Illinois College of Law, JD, 1996; University of Notre Dame, BA, 1993.

### NEMEROFF, Michael A
Vedder Price PC, Chicago
312 609 7858
mnemeroff@vedderprice.com
*Featured in Corporate/M&A (Illinois)*
**Practice Areas:** President and CEO of Vedder Price P.C.; Shareholder and Chair, Finance and Transactions group. Counsels corporations in merger-and-acquisition transactions and corporate finance matters. Provides private equity firms and hedge funds with experienced direction in leveraged and management buyouts, and guides financial institutions in complex finance transactions. Negotiates and structures executive compensation arrangements for companies, management teams, compensation committees and executives.

**Professional Memberships:** Member, Board of Directors, Oil-Dri Corporation of America; Member, Economic Club of Chicago.
**Career:** Admitted (IL) 1988.
**Personal:** JD, George Washington University Law School; BA, Binghamton University.

### NEPPL, Daniel J
Sidley Austin LLP, Chicago
312 853 7334
dneppl@sidley.com
*Featured in Insurance (Illinois)*
**Practice Areas:** Partner in Sidley's Chicago office. Represents and counsels clients in a wide range of commercial disputes in federal and state courts and arbitrations in the insurance and financial services sectors. Tried numerous bench and jury trials to verdict, and numerous arbitral cases to final award. Successfully briefed and argued appeals in numerous federal and state courts. Emphasis on disputes arising out of commercial agreements, including insurance policies, facultative and treaty reinsurance contracts, structured products, and stable value wrap agreements.
**Personal:** Creighton University School of Law, JD, 1993, cum laude; University of Iowa, BS, 1990, with honors.

### NICKLIN, Emily
Kirkland & Ellis LLP, Chicago
312 862 2387
emily.nicklin@kirkland.com
*Featured in Litigation (Illinois)*
**Practice Areas:** Lead trial counsel in individual and class actions in areas including: professional liability for accountants and consultants, securities, contract, tort (including product liability and personal injury), employment discrimination, constitutional law and municipal law. Jury and bench trials and arbitrations in Arkansas, California, Delaware, Idaho, Illinois, Iowa, Michigan, Missouri, Nevada, New York, Oklahoma, Pennsylvania, Texas, Wisconsin and Washington, DC. Lead counsel for clients in federal and state government investigations, including at the SEC, the NY Attorney General and the Equal Employment Opportunity Commission.
**Personal:** University of Chicago: BA, 1975 (Phi Beta Kappa); JD, 1977 (Order of the Coif).

### NOVAK, Theodore
DLA Piper LLP (US), Chicago
312 368 4037
theodore.novak@dlapiper.com
*Featured in Real Estate (Illinois)*
**Practice Areas:** Real estate, mixed use development.
**Professional Memberships:** ACREL.
**Career:** He chairs the firm's Zoning, Land Use and Condemnation Practice. He has more than 35 years of experience and has handled some of the most significant real estate and land use projects in the Midwest. Has been instrumental in acquisition, disposition, public financing, condemnation, rezoning, and development of all types of property. His clients include the largest stock exchange-listed companies as well as individual property owners and developers.

**Personal:** JD, Chicago-Kent College of Law, Illinois Institute of Technology; BS, University of Illinois.

### NURNBERG, D Tyler
Kaye Scholer LLP, Chicago
312 583 2313
tyler.nurnberg@kayescholer.com
*Featured in Bankruptcy/Restructuring (Illinois)*
**Practice Areas:** Tyler Nurnberg represents lenders, funds, institutional investors and troubled companies in workouts and reorganizations throughout the United States and in cross-border engagements. He advises private equity sponsors in their dealings with distressed portfolio companies. He also represents distressed investors in their acquisition of troubled businesses. Recent cases include representing 4Kids Entertainment in its Chapter 11 case, which was named one of the "Successful Restructurings — 2012" by Turnarounds & Workouts. Tyler is Managing Partner of the firm's Chicago office and admitted to practice in Illinois and New York.

### NYHAN, Lawrence
Sidley Austin LLP, Chicago
312 853 7710
lnyhan@sidley.com
*Featured in Bankruptcy/Restructuring (Nationwide), Bankruptcy/Restructuring (Illinois)*
See under Nationwide for profile.

### O'BRIEN, Richard
Sidley Austin LLP, Chicago
312 853 7283
robrien@sidley.com
*Featured in Media & Entertainment (Illinois)*
**Practice Areas:** Partner in Sidley's Intellectual Property Litigation practice. He has been lead trial counsel in lawsuits involving copyright, trademark, misappropriation of ideas, false advertising, defamation, invasion of privacy, trade secrets, and patent litigation.
**Career:** Mr O'Brien was law clerk to U.S. District Court Judge Abraham L. Marovitz in Chicago.
**Personal:** Georgetown University Law Center, JD, 1979, cum laude; Saint Louis University, BA, 1976, magna cum laude.

### OLIAN, Robert
Sidley Austin LLP, Chicago
312 853 7208
rolian@sidley.com
*Featured in Environment (Illinois)*
**Practice Areas:** Partner in Sidley's Chicago office, head of Chicago's Environmental practice and co-head of the firm's national Environmental practice. He works primarily on contested matters involving compliance and civil or criminal enforcement proceedings. He also has experience in managing complex legal projects, such as environmental impact statement proceedings and the siting of new waste disposal facilities.
**Professional Memberships:** Mr Olian is a Fellow in the American College of Environmental Lawyers.
**Personal:** Harvard Law School, JD, 1977; Harvard Kennedy School - John F Kennedy School of Government, MPP, 1977; Harvard College, AB, 1973, cum laude.

### OLSON, Camille A
Seyfarth Shaw LLP, Chicago
312 460 5831
colson@seyfarth.com
*Featured in Labor & Employment (Illinois)*
**Practice Areas:** Complex Employment Litigation.
**Professional Memberships:** ABA, IBA, SHRM, US Chamber of Commerce Employment Subcommittee, AELC; California and Illinois State Bars.
**Career:** Represents companies nationwide in challenges to their employment practices and in internal investigations and highly sensitive matters. Seyfarth's National Chairperson, Complex Discrimination Litigation Practice Group. Frequently testifies before federal agencies and Congress on pending employment legislation. Named to "Top 50 Employment Lawyers in America" by HRExecutive Magazine.
**Publications:** Authored and edited numerous books and articles, including, "Labor and Employment Law: The 2012 Employer's Compliance Guide" (Thompson).
**Personal:** Graduate, University of Michigan and University of Michigan Law School.

### OLSON, Nancy M
Skadden, Arps, Slate, Meagher & Flom LLP & Affiliates, Chicago
312 407 0532
nancy.olson@skadden.com
*Featured in Real Estate (Illinois)*
**Practice Areas:** Head of Chicago office's Real Estate Group and member of the firm's REIT Group and Chicago REIT Group. Advises on real estate transactions focusing on REIT formations and REIT related transactions, secured and unsecured financings and construction loans, joint venture transactions, private equity and fund investment, real estate fund formation and single asset and portfolio acquisitions and dispositions. Handles leasing, reorganizations and real property development. Represents both lenders and borrowers in connection with real estate finance practice and debt restructuring transactions in and out of bankruptcy.
**Career:** JD, Loyola University School of Law, 1996; BA, Northwestern University, 1993.

### PANAGAKIS, George N
Skadden, Arps, Slate, Meagher & Flom LLP & Affiliates, Chicago
312 407 0638
george.panagakis@skadden.com
*Featured in Bankruptcy/Restructuring (Nationwide), Bankruptcy/Restructuring (Illinois)*
**Practice Areas:** Head of the Chicago office's Corporate Restructuring Group. Represents clients in complex business reorganizations, debt restructurings and insolvency matters. Advises debtors, creditors, investors, sellers, purchasers and other parties in all stages of restructuring transactions, from Chapter 11 reorganizations to out-of-court negotiations, workouts and divestitures.
**Professional Memberships:** Member, American Bankruptcy Institute; Member, Turnaround Management Association.

**Career:** JD, Northwestern University School of Law, 1990; BA, Northwestern University, 1987.
**Publications:** Co-authored a chapter in the 2011 edition of Business Bankruptcy Practice, a book published by the Illinois Institute of Continuing Legal Education.

### PARR, Keith D
Locke Lord LLP, Chicago
312 443 0497
kparr@lockelord.com
*Featured in Intellectual Property (Illinois)*
**Practice Areas:** Chairs the Firm's IP Pharmaceutical Practice Group. Focuses principally in the biotechnology, pharmaceutical, life sciences, agribusiness and energy areas. Acts principally as lead trial counsel in Hatch-Waxman Pharmaceutical Patent Infringement cases. Also tries other patent infringement cases, trademark, copyright infringement and commercial cases. Corporate advisor to clients in project finance (ethanol and biofuels), regulatory compliance (seed, biotech, and pharmaceutical) and antitrust areas.
**Professional Memberships:** ABA; Illinois State Bar Association; Chicago Bar Association; American IP Law Association; American Agricultural Law Association; American Seed Trade Association.
**Career:** Partner since 1990.
**Personal:** University of Illinois (JD, 1981; BS, Agricultural Science, 1978).

### PEARSE, Richard W
Vedder Price PC, Chicago
312 609 7650
rpearse@vedderprice.com
*Featured in Construction (Illinois)*
**Practice Areas:** Shareholder representing international and domestic lenders, owners, manufacturers, OEMs, contractors and engineering firms in project acquisition and loan documents, complex design, engineering, procurement and construction agreements, equipment purchase and sale agreements, supply and off-take agreements, operation and maintenance agreements, power sale/tolling agreements, interconnection agreements, steam agreements, fuel supply and transportation agreements, pipeline leases, joint venture agreements, equity commitments and guaranties, and related project and financing documentation.
**Career:** Admitted (IL) 1984.
**Personal:** JD, Northwestern University; MA, University of Chicago; BA, Boston University.

### PECK, S Michael
Sidley Austin LLP, Chicago
312 853 4150
speck@sidley.com
*Featured in Corporate/M&A (Illinois)*
**Practice Areas:** Partner in Sidley's Chicago office. He concentrates his practice in the areas of leveraged buyouts and other merger and acquisition transactions as well as general corporate, investment and financing matters. His practice consists principally in the representation of private equity funds in their merger and acquisition activity and the portfolio companies they acquire

with respect to acquisitions, divestitures, public offerings, restructurings, recapitalizations and general corporate activities. He has represented numerous Private Equity funds and their portfolio companies.
**Personal:** University of Michigan Law School, JD, 1972, cum laude; University of Chicago, BA, 1969. Admission: Illinois.

**PEREGRINE, Michael W**
McDermott Will & Emery LLP, Chicago
312 984 6933
mperegrine@mwe.com
*Featured in Healthcare (Illinois), Healthcare (Nationwide)*
**Practice Areas:** Represents nonprofit healthcare facilities and systems and other charitable organizations, with focus on corporate, fiduciary duty, tax and charitable trust issues facing such organizations. Experience includes representation of nonprofits in connection with the organization and operation of health care systems, including related governance issues and parent/subsidiary relationships. Has experience with complex business transactions such as mergers, consolidations and acquisitions and related corporate and charitable trust law issues.
**Personal:** Northwestern University School of Law (JD); Texas Christian University (BA).

**PERELLIS, Andrew H**
Seyfarth Shaw LLP, Chicago
312 460 5813
aperellis@seyfarth.com
*Featured in Environment (Illinois)*
**Practice Areas:** Environmental law and environmental litigation.
**Professional Memberships:** American Bar Association.
**Career:** Mr Perellis possesses 30 years of experience focused on environmental law and toxic tort litigation, including interpretation and application of state and federal environmental statutes and regulations; state and federal enforcement actions; administration of complex CERCLA sites; performance of on-site environmental assessments; and counseling regarding land use, environmental aspects of real estate transactions and corporate mergers, acquisitions and divestitures.
**Publications:** Illinois Class Action Rules for Mass Tort Cases (IDF Monograph, Spring 2009).
**Personal:** JD, George Washington University National Law Center; BA, University of Michigan.

**PERL, Sanford E**
Kirkland & Ellis LLP, Chicago
312 862 2291
sanford.perl@kirkland.com
*Featured in Corporate/M&A (Illinois)*
**Practice Areas:** Concentrates on corporate, securities and tax aspects of complex business transactions, including leveraged buy-outs; mergers and acquisitions; venture capital and growth equity investments; IPOs; private equity fund formations; executive compensation; and restructurings. Leads transactions in a variety of industries. Clients include Beecken Petty O'Keefe & Company; Chicago Growth Partners; CHS Capital; ClearLight Partners; Flexpoint Partners;

GTCR; KRG Capital Partners; Lake Capital Partners; Lake Pacific Partners; Madison Dearborn Partners; as well as numerous portfolio companies.
**Personal:** University of Illinois, BS, accountancy, high honors; University of Michigan Law School, JD, magna cum laude, Order of the Coif. Certified Public Accountant.

**PERLMAN, Daniel J**
Kirkland & Ellis LLP, Chicago
312 862 6090
daniel.perlman@kirkland.com
*Featured in Real Estate (Illinois)*
**Practice Areas:** Daniel Perlman is a partner in the Real Estate Group in the Chicago office of Kirkland & Ellis LLP. He has extensive experience in advising pension funds and their advisors, national developers, foreign institutions, public and private REITs as well as investment banks and hedge funds on real estate fund and venture formations, loan workouts, sales and purchases of distressed loans, securitized, conventional and mezzanine financings, commercial development, and commercial acquisitions and dispositions.
**Personal:** University School of Law, JD, 1985; University of Michigan, BA, 1982.

**PERLMAN, Felicia G**
Skadden, Arps, Slate, Meagher & Flom LLP & Affiliates, Chicago
312 407 0758
felicia.perlman@skadden.com
*Featured in Bankruptcy/Restructuring (Illinois)*
**Practice Areas:** Handles business reorganizations, debt restructurings and insolvency matters. Advises debtors, creditors, lenders, investors, sellers, purchasers and other parties-in-interest in restructuring transactions, including Chapter 11 reorganizations, out-of-court negotiations, workouts and acquisitions. Frequent speaker on bankruptcy topics.
**Professional Memberships:** Member, Turnaround Management Association; Member, American Bankruptcy Institute; Member, Board of Directors, Chicago Coalition of Women's Initiatives in Law Firms and Women in Law Empowerment Forum.
**Career:** JD, Northwestern University School of Law, 1992; BSE/BA, Wharton Business School, University of Pennsylvania, 1989.
**Publications:** Author, "Bankruptcy Acquisition/Divestitures," ABI Health Care Insolvency Manual (2012); Editor, Debtor-In-Possession Financing: Funding a Chapter 11 Case (2012).

**PETERMAN, Nancy A**
Greenberg Traurig, LLP, Chicago
312 456 8410
PetermanN@gtlaw.com
*Featured in Bankruptcy/Restructuring (Illinois)*
**Practice Areas:** Chair, Chicago Business Reorganization, Financial Restructuring Practice. Debtor rights; creditors' rights; Health law.
**Professional Memberships:** Board of Directors and Executive committee, American Bankruptcy Institute. Former Chair, Chicago Bar

Association's Bankruptcy & Reorganization Committee.
**Career:** Fellow, American College of Bankruptcy. Listed: Chambers USA Guide, 2006-13; Legal 500 US, 2011-12. Selected, Leading Lawyers Network, 2006-13.
**Publications:** Contributing Author, ABI Health Care Insolvency Manual, Third Edition, June 2012; Assistant Editor, West's Norton Bankruptcy Law & Practice treatise; Assistant Editor, Contributing Author, American Bankruptcy Institute's Health Care Insolvency Manual, December 1997.
**Personal:** JD, University of Michigan Law School; BA, University of Michigan.

**PETERSON, Ronald R**
Jenner & Block LLP, Chicago
312 923 2981
rpeterson@jenner.com
*Featured in Bankruptcy/Restructuring (Illinois)*
**Career:** Ronald R. Peterson, a member of the Bankruptcy, Workout and Corporate Reorganization Practice, concentrates in commercial, insolvency and bankruptcy law, representing debtors, trustees, creditors' committees, landlords and secured lenders in Chapter 11 cases. He has presided over numerous complex commercial cases, including Stotler & Co, the country's 10th largest commodities house, and Lancelot Investment, a $1.7 billion Ponzi scheme. He represented the creditors' committees in the bankruptcies of Anicom Inc. and Keystone Consolidated Industries, Inc. He represented the debtor in the bankruptcies of Harrah's Jazz Company and Armstrong's, Inc. He is a fellow of the American College of Bankruptcy.

**PIELL, Jeffrey**
Quarles & Brady LLP, Chicago
312 715 5216
*Featured in Labor & Employment (Illinois)*
**Practice Areas:** Labor and employment.
**Professional Memberships:** Chicago Bar Association; American Bar Association.
**Career:** Experienced trial lawyer and business advisor in the area of labor and employment law. Advises clients on discrimination claims, wage and hour compliance, reductions in force, enforcement of restrictive covenants, employment contracts and separation agreements, employee selection and discipline, WARN compliance, internal investigations and business transactions. Defends employers in all types of employment litigation before federal and state courts and agencies.
**Personal:** Harvard University (JD, 1991); University of Michigan (BA, 1988).

**PINCHOT, Dov**
Freeborn & Peters LLP, Chicago
312 360 6579
dpinchot@freeborn.com
*Featured in Real Estate (Illinois)*
**Practice Areas:** Dov J. Pinchot co-heads the Real Estate Practice Group and concentrates his practice in the areas of commercial leasing, corporate real estate and property acquisition and sales. Mr Pinchot is commonly regarded as one of the

elite leasing attorneys in the United States. Known for his ability to constructively guide parties through thorny issues, he has been a trusted adviser to clients in negotiating a variety of commercial leases, including office, retail, headquarters relocation, restaurant, sale-leaseback, culinary services and industrial leases, as well as a broad array of subleases. Mr Pinchot has represented many of the country's leading businesses in connection with major leasing, acquisition and development transactions throughout the United States and around the globe.
**Career:** Freeborn & Peters (2009-present); DLA (1999-2009); Lord Bissell & Brook (1994-1999); profiled in Leading Lawyer Magazine (2012).
**Publications:** Mr Pinchot is also a frequent lecturer and a published author on leasing subjects.
**Personal:** JD: The University of Chicago Law School, First Place, Hinton Moot Court Competition; BA, cum laude: Yeshiva University.

**PINSEL, Michael**
Sidley Austin LLP, Chicago
312 853 7103
mpinsel@sidley.com
*Featured in Insurance (Illinois)*
**Practice Areas:** Partner in Sidley's Chicago office, and co-head of the firm's property and casualty alternative risk transfer practice. His practice is concentrated primarily in the corporate and regulatory representation of insurance companies, investors and financial advisors with a focus on alternative risk transfer transactions, including insurance securitization and derivatives transactions; the organization and operation of insurance-linked securities funds; complex reinsurance arrangements; acquisitions, divestitures and corporate reorganizations; the formation, capitalization and corporate financing of insurance companies and related ventures; the regulation of insurance holding company systems; and the regulation of insurance company investment practices, including the use of derivative instruments.

**PISKORSKI, Thomas**
Seyfarth Shaw LLP, Chicago
312 460 5925
tpiskorski@seyfarth.com
*Featured in Labor & Employment (Illinois)*
**Practice Areas:** Management - labor, employment and employee benefits litigation.
**Professional Memberships:** College of Labor & Employment Lawyers.
**Career:** Concentrates on the representation of management in all labor, employment and employee benefits matters, including traditional labor law (collective bargaining, labor contract administration, arbitrations, NLRB proceedings), federal, state and local law employment litigation, ERISA and employee benefits litigation, affirmative action and general counseling.
**Publications:** Published numerous articles on labor and employment law subjects, including the University of Michigan Law Review.
**Personal:** JD, University of Notre Dame; MBA, University of Notre Dame; law clerk to Senior United States District Judge Robert Grant.

**POLSTER, David**
Skadden, Arps, Slate, Meagher & Flom LLP & Affiliates, Chicago
312 407 0736
david.polster@skadden.com
*Featured in Tax (Illinois)*
**Practice Areas:** Head of the Chicago office's Tax Group. Represents clients on a wide range of tax matters, including partnership transactions, mergers and acquisitions, real estate investment trusts, foreign investments in the United States, restructurings, leveraged leases, project financings and financial products. Represents clients in tax-free and taxable acquisitions, dispositions, financings, restructurings and international tax matters. Advises private equity funds and hedge funds in connection with fund formations and restructurings and foreign governments in connection with investments in the United States.
**Career:** JD, Harvard Law School, 1994 (cum laude); BA, Yeshiva University, 1991 (magna cum laude).

**PONDER, Anita**
Seyfarth Shaw LLP, Chicago
312 460 5671
aponder@seyfarth.com
*Featured in Construction (Illinois)*
**Practice Areas:** Government Contracts; Construction.
**Career:** Advising and training government contractors and agencies on procurement regulations and policies; preparing subcontracting plans, bid protests and contract claims; drafting and negotiating contracts; facilitating contract compliance to small business participation requirements; handling certification matters; representing contractors in debarment proceedings; and preparing supplier diversity compliance manuals. Chair of Seyfarth's Government Contractors Business Forum and former Director of Contract Compliance for governmental agency.
**Personal:** Named to Today's Chicago Woman magazine's "100 Women Making a Difference 2011" list; honored by Chicago Lawyer Magazine's Chicago Women in Law 2011; and recognized as Chicago United Business Leader 2009.

**POPE, Michael**
McDermott Will & Emery LLP, Chicago
312 984 7780
mpope@mwe.com
*Featured in Litigation (Illinois)*
**Practice Areas:** Heads international product liability practice, including complex class action lawsuits and consumer fraud actions. Has extensive experience in handling reinsurance disputes, interpretation of excess and umbrella liability insurance policies, and professional liability and complex business litigation.
**Professional Memberships:** Fellow, American College of Trial Lawyers; International Academy of Trial Lawyers; International Society of Barristers; Former President, International Association of Defense Counsel; 7th Circuit Bar Association; Illinois Equal Justice Foundation.

**Personal:** Loyola University of Chicago (BS); Northwestern University School of Law (JD, cum laude).

**PRITIKIN, David T**
Sidley Austin LLP, Chicago
312 853 7359
dpritikin@sidley.com
*Featured in Intellectual Property (Illinois)*
**Practice Areas:** Partner in the Chicago office, chair of the firm's national Intellectual Property practice, and a member of the firm's Executive Committee. David has served as lead counsel in many high profile patent cases involving telecommunications, handsets, software, and medical devices. He has also handled more than a dozen Hatch-Waxman cases involving important pharmaceutical products. His experience includes jury and bench trials in the federal courts as well as trials in the International Trade Commission and arguments before the Court of Appeals for the Federal Circuit.
**Professional Memberships:** Fellow of the American College of Trial Lawyers.

**QASIM, Imad I**
Sidley Austin LLP, Chicago
312 853 7094
iqasim@sidley.com
*Featured in Corporate/M&A (Illinois)*
**Practice Areas:** Partner based in Sidley's Chicago office. His principal areas of practice are mergers and acquisitions, corporate governance, securities offerings, and private equity and joint ventures transactions. Mr Qasim has played a major role in a large number of public company transactions. He regularly advises public companies and their boards of directors on corporate governance and securities law matters. He has extensive private equity and joint venture experience, including investments by strategic investors in public and private companies and the formation and organization of a number of large industry consortiums and B2B exchanges.
**Personal:** Admissions: Illinois, New York.

**RABINOWITZ, Mark A**
Cozen O'Connor, Chicago
312 382 3150
mrabinowitz@cozen.com
*Featured in Litigation (Illinois)*
**Practice Areas:** Mark has substantial experience representing corporations, financial institutions, insurance companies, partnerships, and individuals in a wide array of complex commercial litigation matters. These include copyright infringement, real estate, lender liability, consumer fraud class actions, breach of contract, insurance coverage, reinsurance, securities fraud, probate and violation of the federal Racketeer Influenced and Corrupt Organizations Act.
**Career:** Member; Global Insurance Group.
**Publications:** Author and lecturer on various litigation topics.
**Personal:** Harvard Law School (JD, 1978) University of Illinois (BA, summa cum laude 1975).

**RASKIN, Richard D**
Sidley Austin LLP, Chicago
312 853 2170
rraskin@sidley.com
*Featured in Healthcare (Illinois)*
**Practice Areas:** Partner, co-chair of Sidley's Global Healthcare practice and head of the Chicago Healthcare group. His practice focuses on complex healthcare litigation involving antitrust, fraud and abuse, and reimbursement issues. Frequent speaker and writer. Clients include pharmaceutical manufacturers, device companies, medical groups, hospitals and professional associations. Former officer in Antitrust Section of the American Bar Association.
**Personal:** Law clerk to US District Judge Hubert L Will, 1985-87; University of Cincinnati College of Law, JD, 1985, Order of the Coif; Brown University, AB, 1979, magna cum laude. Admission: Illinois.

**RATNASWAMY, John**
Rooney Rippie & Ratnaswamy LLP, Chicago
312 447 2850
john.ratnaswamy@r3law.com
*Featured in Energy & Natural Resources (Illinois)*
**Practice Areas:** Mr Ratnaswamy is a Partner in the energy and litigation practices. He focuses on regulatory counseling, trials, and appeals involving natural gas and electric industry clients; and business litigation. He has worked on numerous rate cases, investigations, reconciliations, prudence, and other regulatory proceedings. He also teaches legal ethics.
**Professional Memberships:** Energy Bar Association; American Bar Association, former member House of Delegates, Commission on Racial and Ethnic Diversity in the Profession, Standing Committee on Ethics and Professional Responsibility; National Asian Pacific American Bar Association.
**Career:** Clerked for judges of the United States Court of Appeals for the Fourth Circuit and Eastern District of Pennsylvania.
**Personal:** Northwestern University, JD cum laude, Law Review; Northwestern University, B.S. and MA, Communication Studies.

**RAYIS, John D**
Skadden, Arps, Slate, Meagher & Flom LLP & Affiliates, Chicago
312 407 0778
john.rayis@skadden.com
*Featured in Tax (Illinois), Capital Markets (Nationwide)*
See under Nationwide for profile.

**RECHTIN JR, Michael**
Quarles & Brady LLP, Chicago
312 928 6053
michael.rechtin@hklaw/com
*Featured in Real Estate (Illinois)*
**Practice Areas:** Leasing (specializing in data center and corporate headquarters), purchases, sales, financing and development.
**Professional Memberships:** Illinois Bar Association, American Bar Association, North Branch Works (Secretary and Board of Directors Member).

**Career:** Specializes in office, data center, industrial and retail leasing, build-to-suit transactions, acquisitions, dispositions, financings, joint ventures and development. Worked extensively on data centers and understands its many unique features. Represents locally and nationally publicly-traded companies, pension funds and pension fund advisors, investment advisory groups, local and national commercial developers, entrepreneurs and professional services firms.
**Personal:** University of Notre Dame (JD, 1992); M.I.T. (BS 1989).

**REED, G Darryl**
Sidley Austin LLP, Chicago
312 853 7766
greed@sidley.com
*Featured in Energy & Natural Resources (Illinois)*
**Practice Areas:** G. Darryl Reed is counsel in Sidley's Chicago office. Mr Reed's practice includes complex commercial litigation and regulatory counseling. Mr Reed has experience in representing electric utilities, pipeline companies, gas providers, water and sewer companies, railroads and telecommunications providers before various state utility commissions and state courts. Prior to receiving his law degree, Mr Reed served in the United States Marine Corps from 1978-1984.
**Personal:** DePaul University College of Law, JD, 1988; Eastern Illinois University, BA, 1977.

**REIDY, Daniel E**
Jones Day, Chicago
312 269 4140
dereidy@jonesday.com
*Featured in Litigation (Nationwide), Litigation (Illinois)*
**Practice Areas:** Serves as the Partner-in-Charge of the Chicago office. Divides his time evenly between civil and criminal litigation. He has extensive trial and appellate experience as Lead Counsel in civil and criminal matters in state and federal courts. He has handled numerous 'high profile' civil, complex financial crime and corruption cases. He has served as Lead Counsel in nationwide (MDL) matters. He has taught trial practice and has spoken on criminal defence and civil litigation issues at various seminars.
**Professional Memberships:** Fellow, American College of Trial Lawyers and the International Academy of Trial Lawyers.

**REIFMAN, David L**
DLA Piper LLP (US), Chicago
312 368 2162
david.reifman@dlapiper.com
*Featured in Real Estate (Illinois)*
**Practice Areas:** Real estate, land use and development, and affordable housing.
**Career:** He concentrates primarily in land use and zoning, real estate transactions, tax increment financing and other public-private financing transactions, and transactions involving community and economic development. He has extensive experience securing required annexation, development, zoning, and subdivision approvals for complex commercial, retail, residential, hotel, and office developments. He represents developers and property owners in the acquisition and disposi-

tion of property. He has a substantial practice in public-private development transactions.
**Personal:** JD, Northwestern University School of Law; MA, University of Illinois at Urbana-Champaign; BA, University of Illinois at Urbana-Champaign.

### RESNICK, Donald I
Jenner & Block LLP, Chicago
312 923 2656
dresnick@jenner.com
*Featured in Real Estate (Illinois)*
**Career:** Donald I Resnick chairs the Real Estate Practice and co-chairs its Real Estate Securities Practice and Tenant-in-Common Workout Task Force. Mr Resnick's significant experience includes all types of real estate transactions, including financing, joint ventures, development and construction, leasing, loan and equity restructuring and workouts. He represents pension funds, REITS and other institutions regarding secured and unsecured senior and mezzanine credit facilities and construction and permanent financing. He also assists clients with acquisitions and dispositions, capital markets transactions, leasing, joint ventures and like-kind exchanges involving office buildings, multi-family apartment projects, retail projects, hotels and industrial facilities.

### RIBAUDO, Anthony
Sidley Austin LLP, Chicago
312 853 7830
aribaudo@sidley.com
*Featured in Insurance (Illinois)*
**Practice Areas:** Partner in Sidley's Chicago office practicing in the Insurance and Financial Services Group where he heads the Capital Markets and Alternative Risk Transfer (Life) practices. Mr Ribaudo represents insurance companies and financial institutions in all types of corporate transactions involving the insurance industry. He has deep experience in advising the insurance industry in corporate finance matters, alternative risk transfer solutions, M&A transactions, strategic transactions and insurance regulatory matters.
**Personal:** The University of Chicago Law School, JD, 1996; Harvard University, AB, 1993. Admission: Illinois.

### RIPPIE, E Glenn
Rooney Rippie & Ratnaswamy LLP, Chicago
312 447 2828
glenn.rippie@r3law.com
*Featured in Energy & Natural Resources (Illinois)*
**Practice Areas:** Glenn primarily provides strategic counseling to electric and gas industry clients and litigates before state and federal agencies and trial and appellate courts. Recent matters include bundled and delivery rate design and revenue proceedings and pioneering work on state formula rates; wholesale energy supply procurements; siting and licensing new facilities; formulating and implementing Smart Grid strategies and price responsive rates; and prudence and service reliability investigations.
**Professional Memberships:** American Bar Association (Public Utilities, Litigation, and Environment, Energy & Resources Sections); Chicago Bar Association; Energy Bar Association.

**Personal:** Yale Law School, JD, Coker Fellow; Northwestern University, AB highest distinction, MA (mathematics, economics).

### RITCHIE, Stephen L
Kirkland & Ellis LLP, Chicago
312 862 2210
stephen.ritchie@kirkland.com
*Featured in Corporate/M&A (Illinois)*
**Practice Areas:** Mr Ritchie focuses on complex business transactions, with a particular emphasis on structuring, negotiating and managing the legal aspects of mergers, acquisitions, leveraged buyouts, recapitalizations, venture capital and growth equity investments, restructurings and workouts. He has handled private equity, LBO, venture capital and merger and acquisition transactions for clients including GTCR, CHS Capital, Chicago Growth Partners, Evergreen Pacific Partners, Technology Crossover Ventures, Wind Point Partners, and their respective portfolio companies. He is a member of the Firm's 15-person global management committee.
**Personal:** University of Virginia, BA, 1985; University of Chicago, JD, 1988.

### RITTER, David B
Barnes & Thornburg LLP, Chicago
312 214 4862
david.ritter@btlaw.com
*Featured in Labor & Employment (Illinois)*
**Practice Areas:** Extensive nationwide experience in federal and state court litigation in the areas of employment discrimination, including harassment claims, class actions, non-compete, trade secret and restrictive covenants, employment torts and all other litigation related to the employment relationship; special knowledge in training employees in the full-range of employment law issues.
**Professional Memberships:** ABA Labor and Employment Law and Litigation Sections (Member).
**Career:** Partner; Labor and Employment Practice Group Chair; Executive Committee (Member).
**Publications:** Author, commentator and lecturer on various employment law issues.
**Personal:** Case Western Reserve University (JD, 1985); Cornell University School of Industrial and Labor Relations (BS, 1980).

### ROCAP, Donald E
Kirkland & Ellis LLP, Chicago
312 862 2266
donald.rocap@kirkland.com
*Featured in Tax (Illinois)*
**Practice Areas:** Don's practice focuses on the tax aspects of complex business transactions, including mergers, acquisitions, leveraged buyouts, formation of private equity funds, and debt and equity restructurings and workouts. He is a lecturer at the University of Chicago Law School and is a co-author of 'Mergers, Acquisitions, and Buyouts,' by Martin Ginsburg, Jack Levin and Donald Rocap, and of 'Structuring Venture Capital, Private Equity, and Entrepreneurial Transactions,' by Jack Levin and Donald Rocap.
**Personal:** University of Virginia School of Law, JD, 1980; Duke University, BA, 1977.

### RODRIGUEZ ALDORT, Julie
Butler Rubin Saltarelli & Boyd LLP, Chicago
312 696 4478
jaldort@butlerrubin.com
*Featured in Insurance (Illinois)*
**Practice Areas:** Reinsurance and Complex Commercial Litigation.
**Professional Memberships:** Women in Reinsurance; ARIAS-U.S.; Trial Bar of U.S. District Court in the Northern District of Illinois; Member APIW – Association of Professional Insurance Women.
**Career:** Julie Rodriguez Aldort concentrates her practice in complex business disputes, with an emphasis on reinsurance and commercial litigation. Her significant reinsurance experience before courts and arbitration panels includes disputes regarding allocation of latent claims, coverage for punitive damages, allocation of retrospectively-rated premium, and allegations of late notice, bad faith, and poor claims administration. Her reinsurance matters have addressed contracts covering a variety of risks, including workers compensation, builders risk, directors and officers liability, and construction defect. She has also litigated suits and arbitrations regarding credit and mortgage insurance. Julie has been engaged in contract disputes regarding, among other things, investor rights, mortgage seller liability, and commercial leases. She has successfully defended derivative suits and she handles an array of commercial litigation matters, including disputes regarding trademark infringement, trade secrets, and restrictive covenants. Julie began her legal career as a litigation associate at Wilmer Cutler & Pickering in Washington D.C. and then served as Law Clerk to the Hon. Joan B Gottschall, U.S. District Court, Northern District of Illinois. After her clerkship, she worked as a litigation associate at Jenner & Block.
**Publications:** She has published articles in Corporate Counsel Magazine.
**Personal:** JD, cum laude, University of Michigan Law School, 1998, Contributing Editor, Michigan Law Review, 1995-97, Notes Editor, Michigan Journal of Race and Law, 1996-97. MS, Conservation Biology, University of Michigan, 1998, Rackham Merit Fellowship. BA, magna cum laude, Claremont McKenna College, 1994.

### ROE, Kathryn
The Health Law Consultancy, Chicago
312 332 7711
kroe@hlconsultancy.com
*Featured in Healthcare (Illinois)*
**Practice Areas:** Applies health law strategically for business benefit; offers predictable project pricing for assured client budgeting. Core competencies: health reform; health benefit products, markets and exchanges; Medicare, Medicaid and other government health programs; payer/provider value-based contracting; business process outsourcing; health information exchange, privacy, security and transactions.
**Professional Memberships:** American Bar Association; American Health Lawyers Association; International Association of Privacy

Professionals; International Network of Boutique Law Firms.
**Career:** Principal, The Health Law Consultancy. Formerly health law partner, Neal, Gerber & Eisenberg LLP and Michael, Best & Friedrich LLP; health law associate, Katten Muchin Rosenman LLP; compliance attorney, publicly-traded national life and health insurance company.
**Publications:** Frequent author, commenter and lecturer on the strategic application of law to the business of health care.
**Personal:** Northwestern University School of Law (JD); University of Notre Dame (BA, summa cum laude).

### ROEDER, Craig A
Baker & McKenzie, Chicago
312 861 3730
craig.roeder@bakermckenzie.com
*Featured in Corporate/M&A (Illinois)*
**Practice Areas:** Advises clients across a broad range of industries on corporate and securities matters, including public and private cross-border and domestic acquisition and divestiture transactions, joint ventures and strategic alliances.
**Professional Memberships:** American Bar Association - Section on Business Law.
**Career:** Admitted to Illinois (1985).
**Personal:** Boston University School of Law (JD cum laude) (1985); University of Denver (BS) (1982). Mr Roeder serves on the Executive Committee of the Garrett Corporate and Securiites Law Institute of Northwestern University Law School, the board of the Constitutional Rights Foundation Chicago, and the board of the Ted Muller Camp Scholarship Fund.

### ROONEY, John E
Rooney Rippie & Ratnaswamy LLP, Chicago
312 447 2801
john.rooney@r3law.com
*Featured in Energy & Natural Resources (Illinois)*
**Practice Areas:** Mr Rooney focuses primarily on representing natural gas, electric, telecommunications and water industry clients before regulatory agencies and state courts. He works on all aspects of utility regulatory matters and related legislative issues and has successfully represented clients before the Illinois Commerce Commission on complex issues, including rate cases, rulemakings, and audits and investigations. Mr Rooney also represents clients involved in competitive marketplace development issues for energy and telecommunications service providers. Other work includes transactions involving electric generation and transmission assets, energy efficiency programs and pipeline safety.
**Professional Memberships:** Chicago Bar Association - Past Chairman, Public Utilities Law Committee.
**Career:** Former Chief Administrative Law Judge, Illinois Commerce Commission (1992 - 1997).
**Personal:** The John Marshall Law School, JD, Law Review; Loyola University, BBA.

## ROPER, Harry J
Jenner & Block LLP, Chicago
312 923 8303
hroper@jenner.com
*Featured in Intellectual Property (Illinois)*

**Career:** Harry J Roper, Co-Chair of the Patent Litigation and Counseling Practice, is a nationally recognized trial lawyer with extensive experience in complex patent trials. He has been lead counsel in numerous patent infringement bench and jury trials and appeals on behalf of national and international companies, including The Dow Chemical Company, Union Carbide, Johnson & Johnson, and Phillips Petroleum Company. In 2012, he led the successful appeal of a $61.7 million damages award on behalf of Dow. His work has involved chemicals, pharmaceuticals, software, wireless, and printing technologies. He is a Fellow of the American College of Trial Lawyers.

## ROPSKI, Gary
Brinks Hofer Gilson & Lione, Chicago
312 321 4216
gropski@usebrinks.com
*Featured in Intellectual Property (Illinois)*

**Practice Areas:** Gary Ropski has practiced intellectual property law for over 35 years at Brinks Hofer Gilson & Lione and is the immediate past president of the firm. He is a trial and appellate lawyer who has participated in more than 100 IP cases, several of which were jury trials and appeals to various courts, including the Court of Appeals for the Federal Circuit. He has litigated in every federal judicial circuit in the US and in almost all of the top ten districts for patent litigation. He emphasizes the need to make complex topics easily understandable by a jury or judge, and has often used creative visual and computer-generated techniques at trial. He taught classes in Patent and Copyrights for 17 years at Northwestern University School of Law.

**Professional Memberships:** American Intellectual Property Law Association; Federal Circuit Bar Association; Intellectual Property Law Association of Chicago; Intellectual Property Owners Association; International Trade Commission Trial Lawyers Association; International Trademark Association; and Richard Linn American Inn of Court.

**Career:** Mr Ropski has received numerous awards, including recently being named sixth among the Top Ten Business Litigators in Illinois by Leading Lawyers Network, in addition to being a Top Ten Leading Lawyer in Illinois for several years. Chambers USA has also named him as a Leading Illinois Intellectual Property Lawyer for many years. Mr Ropski has also been recognized as an Illinois Super Lawyer in Intellectual Property Litigation and was named one of the Top Ten attorneys in Illinois.

**Publications:** Editor, Butterworths 'Patent Litigation: Enforcing a Global Patent Portfolio'.

**Personal:** Education: BS, Physics, Carnegie-Mellon University (1972); JD (cum laude), Northwestern University School of Law (1976).

## ROSENBERG, Sheli
Skadden, Arps, Slate, Meagher & Flom LLP & Affiliates, Chicago
312 407 0688
sheli.rosenberg@skadden.com
*Featured in Real Estate (Illinois)*

**Practice Areas:** Has extensive board-level corporate experience, in addition to considerable knowledge of real estate law. Represented Real Estate Investment Trusts in initial public offerings and continued business operations, and served on numerous REIT boards. On the board of directors/trustees of many public and private corporations, foundations and community and charitable organizations. Former adjunct professor, Northwestern University's J.L. Kellogg Graduate School of Management and co-founder and previous president of Center for Executive Women at Kellogg School.

**Professional Memberships:** Member, Steering Committee of the Center for Executive Women at Kellogg School.

**Career:** JD, Northwestern University School of Law; BA, Tufts University.

## ROSENBLOOM, David
McDermott Will & Emery LLP, Chicago
312 984 7759
drosenbloom@mwe.com
*Featured in Litigation (Illinois)*

**Practice Areas:** Defends corporations and individuals in connection with criminal and civil government investigations, internal investigations, qui tam litigation, healthcare fraud and abuse compliance counseling, antitrust defense, and class actions and other complex commercial litigation. Extensive experience in representing healthcare providers and manufacturers. Also has advised clients in a variety of other industries, including securities, financial institutions, insurance, manufacturing, and energy.

**Personal:** Harvard Law School (JD, magna cum laude); Colorado College (BA, magna cum laude).

## ROSENBLOOM, James B
Goldberg Kohn Ltd, Chicago
312 201 3925
james.rosenbloom@goldbergkohn.com
*Featured in Real Estate (Illinois)*

**Career:** Jim Rosenbloom is a firm founder and a principal in the Real Estate Group. He has engaged in a broad-gauged practice during his 36-year legal career, encompassing real estate, commercial finance and bankruptcy matters. Mr Rosenbloom's real estate transactional experience includes acquisitions and dispositions, mortgage financing and syndication, renovation and construction financings, commercial leasing, synthetic leasing, sale-leaseback transactions, construction contracting and bankruptcy. Mr Rosenbloom has extensive experience in real estate loan restructurings, foreclosures, workouts, distressed loan sales and intercreditor issues. His commercial finance experience includes structuring secured and cash-flow loans to finance leveraged buyouts and debtors in possession.

## ROTH, Alan B
Edwards Wildman Palmer, Chicago
312 201 2633
aroth@edwardswildman.com
*Featured in Corporate/M&A (Illinois)*

**Practice Areas:** Alan is Co-Chair of Edward Wildman's Business Transactions Department. He is nationally known for his representation of middle-market private equity funds and is one of the few true authorities in the country on the SBIC program. In addition to representing private equity funds in their transactions and general corporate needs, Alan is viewed by clients and other law firms alike as a premier source for SBIC fund formation, licensing and investments.

**Personal:** Washington University, JD; New York University, LLM; Duke University, BA.

## ROTHSTEIN, Jeffrey
Sidley Austin LLP, Chicago
312 853 7260
jrothstein@sidley.com
*Featured in Technology (Illinois)*

**Practice Areas:** Partner in Sidley's Chicago office, co-head of the Firm's global Technology Transactions practice. His practice covers a wide range of intellectual property transactions with emphasis on life sciences and information technology transactions. He advises firms ranging from major pharmaceutical, biotechnology, medical device, agricultural and consumer products companies to emerging companies on licensing, contract manufacturing, development, collaboration and other commercial agreements as well as the intellectual property aspects of joint ventures and M&A transactions. He is recognized by Chambers, PLC, IAM, and Who's Who Legal.

**Personal:** University of Chicago Law School, JD, 1982; Harvard University, AB, 1978. Admission: Illinois.

## ROVNER, Jack A
The Health Law Consultancy, Chicago
312 332 7711
jrovner@hlconsultancy.com
*Featured in Healthcare (Illinois)*

**Practice Areas:** Applies health law strategically for business benefit; offers predictable project pricing for assured client budgeting. Core competencies: health reform; health plans; hospital systems, joint ventures and other strategic alliances; antitrust; fraud and abuse; Medicare, Medicaid and other government health programs; data privacy and security, electronic transactions and health information technology initiatives.

**Professional Memberships:** American Bar Association; American Health Lawyers Association; International Network of Boutique Law Firms.

**Career:** Principal, The Health Law Consultancy. Formerly health law practice co-chair and partner, Neal, Gerber & Eisenberg LLP; Chicago office health law practice leader and partner, Michael, Best & Friedrich LLP; partner, Kirkland & Ellis LLP.

**Publications:** Frequent author, speaker and commenter on current developments and strategic opportunities in health law. Advisory board member, Bloomberg BNA 'Health Law Reporter' (2005-present); advisory board member, AIS 'Guide to Health Insurance Reform: Benefit Design Regulation under Federal Reform' (2010-2012).

**Personal:** Boston University School of Law (JD, cum laude); Brandeis University (BA)

## RUBIN, James I
Butler Rubin Saltarelli & Boyd LLP, Chicago
312 696 4443
jrubin@butlerrubin.com
*Featured in Insurance (Nationwide), Insurance (Illinois)*

**Practice Areas:** Commercial and Reinsurance Litigation and Arbitration.

**Professional Memberships:** James Rubin is a member of the Board of Directors of The AIDA Reinsurance and Insurance Arbitration Society, ARIAS-U.S. He is a frequent speaker on reinsurance issues at industry programs. Jim is a member of the ARIAS Ethics and Publications committees. With two other industry representatives, he co-authored ARIAS' Code of Conduct for Arbitrators.

**Career:** Jim is a trial lawyer, founding partner and co-chair of the firm's Reinsurance Litigation and Arbitration Practice Group. He has tried numerous antitrust, commercial and reinsurance cases and represented insurance and reinsurance companies and brokers in hundreds of complex disputes. He also counsels insurers and reinsurers regarding transactions, reinsurance wordings, and commutations. Jim's experience includes property and casualty and life insurance disputes covering such disparate issues as the proper allocation of losses, fraud, contract interpretation, the authority of agents, the conclusiveness of commutations, guaranteed death and income benefits and claims by and against companies in receivership or operating under schemes of arrangement. He was named the "Global Insurance & Reinsurance Lawyer of the Year 2010" by The International Who's Who of Business Lawyers, in conjunction with the ABA Section of International Law. Also, Jim was identified as being among the world's leading practitioners in The International Who's Who of Insurance & Reinsurance Lawyers (2011-2013), Who's Who in America (2012) and The International Who's Who of Business Lawyers (2013 and 2014). Legal Media Group named Jim one of America's top 25 pre-eminent Insurance & Reinsurance practitioners in its Guide to the World's Leading Lawyers - Best of the Best USA 2011. He was named to the list of the Top 100 Illinois Super Lawyers for 2009-2012 and as a leader in insurance law in The Best Lawyers in America (2006-2013). In 2007 and 2008, Lawdragon named Jim one of America's Leading 500 Lawyers. And, as part of the Law Bulletin Publishing Group's 2012 survey of the top lawyers in the state, he was designated as a "Leading Lawyer" in Illinois in the following fields: Commercial Litigation; Insurance, Insurance Coverage & Reinsurance Law; and International Business & Trade Law.

Personal: JD, Loyola University Law School, 1971, Member, Loyola University Law Review, 1970-71. AB, University of Illinois, 1967.

## RUBIN, Jamie
InfoLawGroup, Chicago
312 286 6030
jrubin@infolawgroup.com
*Featured in Media & Entertainment (Illinois)*

**Practice Areas:** Jamie Rubin works with clients to bring their entertainment, advertising and promotional campaigns from concept to execution. Whether it relates to the launch of a national talent search, a reality television program, negotiating a spokesperson agreement for a new product launch, sweepstakes, user-generated content promotions, use of social network platforms, viral marketing, mobile applications and beyond, Jamie's experience covers the spectrum of new media and entertainment issues.

**Professional Memberships:** Association of Media & Entertainment Counsel - Chair, Chicago Steering Committee; International Association of Privacy Professionals (IAPP); Promotion Marketing Association, Inc.

## RUBIN, Joel D
Seyfarth Shaw LLP, Chicago
312 460 5600
jrubin@seyfarth.com
*Featured in Real Estate (Illinois)*

**Professional Memberships:** American College of Real Estate Lawyers, Pension Real Estate Association.

**Career:** Provides strategic planning and legal advice to pension funds, investment advisors, foreign investors, public and private REITs and real estate companies regarding real estate investments. Has extensive experience planning co-investments, joint ventures and REITs, and acquiring and disposing of income-producing properties. Also advises regarding fiduciary responsibilities of fund managers and advisors and acts as legal counselor to businesses in a variety of areas. In 2012, chaired two of the largest reported US industrial transactions and other prominent transactions.

**Personal:** BS, Wharton School; JD, Northwestern University Law School.

## RUFF, Randolph E
Ogletree, Deakins, Nash, Smoak & Stewart, PC, Chicago
312 558 1220
randolph.ruff@ogletreedeakins.com
*Featured in Construction (Illinois)*

**Practice Areas:** Mr Ruff heads the Construction Practice Group at Ogletree Deakins. National and regional general contractors, subcontractors, specialty contractors and suppliers rely on his expertise to guide them in all phases of the construction process. He manages construction claims, disputes, litigations, arbitrations and mediations, including design and construction defect, delay, acceleration, extra work, and mechanics lien matters.

**Professional Memberships:** Society of Illinois Construction Attorneys (Steering Committee), ABA Construction Industry Forum, CBA

Construction and Mechanics Lien Committee (past chairperson).

**Publications:** Has lectured and written extensively on construction processes and disputes.

**Personal:** University of Colorado (BA, 1981), Valparaiso University (JD, 1986).

## RUNNING, Andrew R
Kirkland & Ellis LLP, Chicago
312 862 2412
andrew.running@kirkland.com
*Featured in Environment (Illinois)*

**Practice Areas:** Extensive experience in environmental, insurance, toxic tort and product liability litigation. He has tried numerous environmental lawsuits involving claims of property damage and alleged regulatory violations, as well as litigation over the allocation of responsibility for the cleanup of hazardous waste sites. He has successfully defended product liability actions involving allegations of hazardous substance contamination. His arbitration experience includes the trial of cases involving commercial breach of contract claims, disputes between international joint venture partners, non-compete clause disputes, biotechnology licensing disputes and reinsurance and insurance fraud claims.

**Personal:** University of Chicago, AB, Economics, 1979. Yale University JD, 1982.

## RUST, Mark E
Barnes & Thornburg LLP, Chicago
312 214 8309
mark.rust@BTLaw.com
*Featured in Healthcare (Illinois)*

**Practice Areas:** Chair, Healthcare Department. Regulatory/business-legal issues affecting hospitals, physician groups and related entities; antitrust, self-referral, tax exemption, governance matters; formation of healthcare CO-OPs, ACO's, integrated organizations committed to clinical management; in-hospital based physician groups, healthcare M&A, organizational responses to healthcare regulatory change.

**Professional Memberships:** Past chair, Illinois State Bar Association's Health Law Section; Chicago Bar Association's Health Law Committee; American Bar Association's Medicine and Law Committee (Tort and Insurance Practice Section).

**Career:** Admitted to practice in Illinois; federal appellate bar, including U.S. Supreme Court.

**Personal:** Loyola University Chicago School of Law (JD, 1989); University of Notre Dame (BA, 1981).

## RYAN, Priscilla E
Sidley Austin LLP, Chicago
312 853 7072
pryan@sidley.com
*Featured in Employee Benefits & Executive Compensation (Nationwide), Labor & Employment (Illinois)*

**Practice Areas:** Partner in Sidley's Chicago office whose practice is concentrated in employee benefits matters. She represents large multinational corporations and domestic corporations with multi-state operations on issues related to the design, implementation and administration of retirement plans, health plans, fringe benefits,

equity-based compensation, deferred compensation and executive compensation. She has represented clients on a variety of matters before the Treasury Department, the Internal Revenue Service, the Department of Labor and the Pension Benefit Guaranty Corporation.

**Personal:** Loyola University Chicago School of Law, JD, 1982; Marquette University, AB, 1969. Admission: Illinois.

## SAIBERT, Frank J
Ungaretti & Harris LLP, Chicago
312 977 4154
fjsaibert@uhlaw.com
*Featured in Labor & Employment (Illinois)*

**Practice Areas:** Frank Saibert is chair of the Labor and Employment Group at Ungaretti & Harris LLP. He represents public and private sector employers throughout the United States in labor relations and employment matters with an emphasis on National Labor Relations Board proceedings, state, federal and local employment discrimination matters, union election campaigns, unfair labor practices, backpay compliance proceedings, wrongful discharge cases, arbitrations, workplace defamation cases, labor contract negotiations, and other miscellaneous employment-related laws and issues.

**Personal:** University of Michigan Law School (JD, cum laude,1983); University of Illinois (BA, summa cum laude, 1980).

## SALPETER, Alan N
Kaye Scholer LLP, Chicago
312 583 2450
alan.salpeter@kayescholer.com
*Featured in Litigation (Illinois)*

**Practice Areas:** Alan Salpeter is Senior Counsel in Kaye Scholer's Complex Commercial Litigation Department. His practice focuses on securities and commercial litigation. He has tried approximately 70 bench and jury trials and argued 20 appeals in federal and state courts throughout the country. He has a great deal of experience in commercial cases focusing on alleged malpractice suits against lawyers, accountants and consultants; alleged securities fraud; multiple kinds of class actions, including shareholder and consumer class actions; disputes over information technology; contested mergers or acquisitions; business torts; and actions involving corporate governance and alleged breach of fiduciary duties.

## SANCHEZ, Vincent
DLA Piper LLP (US), Chicago
312 368 3420
vincent.sanchez@dlapiper.com
*Featured in Outsourcing (Nationwide), Technology (Illinois)*

**Practice Areas:** Outsourcing, technology.

**Career:** He is the Global Co-Chair of the firm's Technology, Sourcing and Commercial practice. He represents companies in acquisitions, divestitures, joint ventures, strategic alliances, equity investments, and licensing arrangements involving technology or intellectual property. He represents companies in outsourcing of business processes and operations and advises companies in legal and regulatory issues and risks regarding the use

and security of data and other information as well as transacting business through the internet or in other networked environments.

**Personal:** MBA, Northwestern University; JD, University of Notre Dame; BA, University of Notre Dame.

## SANDERS, David P
Jenner & Block LLP, Chicago
312 923 2963
dsanders@jenner.com
*Featured in Media & Entertainment (Illinois)*

**Career:** David P. Sanders, co-chair of the Media and First Amendment Practice, counsels clients on defamation, privacy, newsgathering, subpoenas, Internet publishing, Freedom of Information Act, copyright, media insurance and related issues. He has served as regular outside counsel to, among others, a national broadcast network and national publishers, including Crain Communications. He successfully represented numerous other national publishers, broadcasters and others in the news and entertainment businesses, including the Associated Press, NBC Universal, the New York Times Company, the Washington Post Company, Univision Communications, Inc., Emmis Communications and Forbes. He successfully defended media clients in numerous libel and privacy cases.

## SARASEK, Peter A
Quarles & Brady LLP, Chicago
312 715 5035
peter.sarasek@quarles.com
*Featured in Real Estate (Illinois)*

**Practice Areas:** Real estate, financial institutions.

**Professional Memberships:** Fellow, American College of Real Estate Lawyers; Chicago Bar, Illinois State Bar "(Real Property Section)," Wisconsin Bar, American Bar Associations.

**Career:** Partner since 1980; 'Chicago Magazine' "Top 100 Attorneys in Illinois" (2009, 2010, 2011, 2012, 2013). PLI Program Chair: Commercial Real Estate Institute (2004-11); Commercial Real Estate Financing (2005-2012).

**Publications:** 'Buying and Selling a Mortgage Loan in Foreclosure' (Practising Law Institute, 2010); 'Working Out the Troubled Loan' (PLI, 2012).

**Personal:** University of Wisconsin (JD, 1974); Catholic University of America (MA, 1968; BA, 1967).

## SATHY, Anup
Kirkland & Ellis LLP, Chicago
312 862 2046
anup.sathy@kirkland.com
*Featured in Bankruptcy/Restructuring (Nationwide), Bankruptcy/Restructuring (Illinois)*

**Practice Areas:** Anup Sathy is a nationally recognized practitioner in matters relating to corporate restructurings, workouts and Chapter 11 reorganizations. He has substantial experience representing and advising companies, buyers, boards, investors and lenders in all aspects of distressed and insolvency situations. Anup has worked on some of the most complex restructuring matters in the country, including General

Growth Properties, Conseco, YRCW, Chiquita Brands and Zenith Electronics. He has also regularly represented many distressed investors, including Centerbridge, Blackstone and Davidson Kempner.

**Personal:** Northwestern University School of Law, JD, cum laude, 1995; University of Illinois at Urbana-Champaign, BS, finance, highest honors, 1992.

**SATYR, Allison J**
Sidley Austin LLP, Chicago
312 853 4342
asatyr@sidley.com
*Featured in Banking & Finance (Illinois)*

**Practice Areas:** Allison Satyr is a partner with Sidley's Global Finance Group in Chicago. She counsels clients, including commercial banks, finance companies, funds and businesses, with respect to a diverse range of finance matters and transactions. Ms Satyr frequently represents agents, arrangers, lenders, equity sponsors and borrowers in syndicated financings for public and private companies of varying sizes and credit quality, whether secured or unsecured, dollar-denominated or multi-currency.

**Personal:** University of Pennsylvania Law School, JD, 1997; Cornell University, BA, 1994, magna cum laude, Phi Beta Kappa.

**SCARSELLA, Carla**
Rooney Rippie & Ratnaswamy LLP, Chicago
312 447 2804
Carla.Scarsella@R3Law.com
*Featured in Energy & Natural Resources (Illinois)*

**Practice Areas:** Ms Scarsella is a Partner in the energy and litigation practices. She focuses on regulatory counseling, trials, and appeals involving natural gas, electric and water industry clients. She has worked on numerous rate cases, investigations, reconciliations, and other regulatory proceedings.

**Professional Memberships:** Chicago Bar Association; Energy Bar Association; and American Bar Association.

**Career:** Associate with Foley and Lardner LLP; Attorney in the Office of General Counsel, Illinois Commerce Commission; Tax Consultant for eight years; Registered Certified Public Accountant in Illinois.

**Personal:** John Marshall Law School, JD; Loyola University Chicago, BBA, Public Accounting.

**SCHILLER, Eric M**
Dentons, Chicago
312 876 8015
eric.schiller@dentons.com
*Featured in Real Estate (Illinois)*

**Practice Areas:** Partner with 30+ years representing clients in real estate and commercial finance matters. Specializes in financing, workouts and restructurings, joint ventures, real estate acquisitions and sales, including complex multi-state, multi-asset real estate and commercial transactions of office and industrial buildings, shopping centers, hotels and apartment complexes. Counsels lenders in syndication loans.

**Personal:** Northwestern University School of Law, JD, Law Review; Indiana University, BA with

honors. Fellow, American College of Real Estate Lawyers; Adjunct Professor in real estate finance at Northwestern University School of Law.

**SCHNEIDMAN, Edward J**
Kirkland & Ellis LLP, Chicago
312 862 3333
edward.schneidman@kirkland.com
*Featured in Corporate/M&A (Illinois)*

**Practice Areas:** Edward J. Schneidman is a Corporate and Real Estate partner at Kirkland whose experience includes all aspects of corporate and securities laws with a focus on real estate capital markets-related matters. He has extensive experience in public and private mergers and acquisitions, capital formation and public offering activities for REITs and other real estate-oriented companies. He has advised clients on corporate and partnership liquidations and reorganizations, stock and asset acquisitions and divestitures, as well as general corporate governance and compliance.

**Personal:** University of Pennsylvania, BSE, 1977, magna cum laude; Duke University School of Law, JD, 1980, with honors.

**SCHOPF, William G**
Schopf & Weiss LLP, Chicago
312 701 9308
schopf@sw.com
*Featured in Litigation (Illinois)*

**Practice Areas:** William Schopf is a business litigator representing both plaintiffs and defendants. He focuses on international trade, civil RICO, legal malpractice, price-fixing, breach of contract, and deceptive practices matters.

**Professional Memberships:** Mr Schopf is a member of the American Bar Association and the Chicago Bar Association.

**Career:** Schopf & Weiss LLP Founding Partner and Member of the Executive Committee (1987-present), Isham, Lincoln & Beale (1986-87), Reuben & Proctor (1979-86), Price, Cushman, Keck & Mahin (1973-79).

**Publications:** Mr Schopf has authored and co-authored a number of legal publications on topics ranging from discovery to a primer for foreign companies on litigating in the United States. These publications include "Failing Bank Litigation," Discovery in Federal and State Courts in Illinois, and Litigation Risk and Opportunity in the United States.

**Personal:** Cornell Law School (JD); Princeton University (AB).

**SCHRANK, Charles E**
Sidley Austin LLP, Chicago
312 853 4140
cschrank@sidley.com
*Featured in Real Estate (Illinois)*

**Practice Areas:** Partner in Sidley's Chicago office, practicing in real estate. He represents institutional investors, lenders, insurers, developers, retailers, corporations and multi-investor ventures in connection with sales and acquisitions, equity investments, joint ventures, construction and permanent loans, mezzanine loans, preferred equity investments, mortgage origination for commercial mortgage-backed securitization programs,

restructurings and work-outs, sale-leasebacks, and commercial and industrial leasing and development.

**Personal:** University of Wisconsin Law School, JD, 1986; University of Wisconsin, BBA, 1983. Admission: Illinois.

**SCHREIBER, Rodd M**
Skadden, Arps, Slate, Meagher & Flom LLP & Affiliates, Chicago
312 407 0531
rodd.schreiber@skadden.com
*Featured in Corporate/M&A (Illinois)*

**Practice Areas:** Co-head of the Chicago office's Corporate Group. Concentrates in mergers and acquisitions, corporate financings and other corporate and securities matters. Represents corporate clients and financial advisers in a variety of domestic and international transactions, including public and private acquisitions and divestitures, negotiated and contested takeovers, leveraged buyouts, spin-offs, joint ventures and other strategic alliances, and public and private debt and equity financings. Provides counseling to corporate clients regarding general corporate and securities matters, including governance, securities law compliance and disclosure issues.

**Career:** JD, University of Michigan, Ann Arbor, 1987 (cum laude); BA, University of Michigan, 1984 (with distinction).

**SCHWAB, Stephen W**
DLA Piper LLP (US), Chicago
312 368 2150
stephen.schwab@dlapiper.com
*Featured in Insurance (Illinois)*

**Practice Areas:** Insurance.

**Career:** He concentrates in insurance and reinsurance regulation, transactions, dispute resolution, and receiverships. He represents, serves, and advises senior management of domestic and multinational stock, mutual and captive insurers and reinsurers, intermediaries, trade organizations, regulators, receivers and receivership creditors. His experience includes development and presentation of complicated reinsurance claims and organization, prosecution, and defense of complex reinsurance disputes in informal negotiation, formal mediation, arbitration proceedings, and court litigation throughout the world, from trial through appeal.

**Personal:** Harvard Leadership Program; A.Re, Insurance School of Chicago; JD, The Dickinson School of Law of Pennsylvania State University; BA, Northwestern University.

**SCHWARTZ, Donald**
Ungaretti & Harris LLP, Chicago
312 977 4415
dlschwartz@uhlaw.com
*Featured in Banking & Finance (Illinois)*

**Practice Areas:** Don Schwartz co-chairs the Finance and Restructuring group, which focuses on bank finance and related work including distressed transactions, restructuring and bankruptcy. He joined Ungaretti & Harris in July 2010 after retiring from Latham & Watkins, where he was a founder and long-time chair of the Banking group. With 39 years of experience in banking and

finance law, Don is widely recognized for his representation of major banking institutions and for developing creative, business-oriented solutions to banking, corporate finance and insolvency problems.

**Personal:** University of Chicago Law School (JD, 1974); Macalester College (BA, 1971).

**SCOTT, Zaldwaynaka**
Kaye Scholer LLP, Chicago
312 583 2347
z.scott@kayescholer.com
*Featured in Litigation (Illinois)*

**Practice Areas:** Zaldwaynaka (Z) Scott is Kaye Scholer's Chicago Co-Chair of the White Collar Litigation and Internal Investigations practice. Z, a former federal prosecutor and seasoned trial lawyer who has taken more than 40 mostly jury trials to verdict in federal court, concentrates her practice in complex litigation, corporate internal investigations, corporate compliance counseling and representation of corporate clients in government investigations.

**Career:** In 2011, Z was appointed Chair of the Board of the Chicago Housing Authority by Mayor Rahm Emanuel. She is also the Vice Chair of Chicago State University's Board of Trustees.

**SELIGMAN, David R**
Kirkland & Ellis LLP, Chicago
312 862 2463
david.seligman@kirkland.com
*Featured in Bankruptcy/Restructuring (Illinois)*

**Practice Areas:** David concentrates his practice in all aspects of complex corporate restructuring and insolvency, both in and out-of-court, in US domestic and cross-border matters. He primarily advises reorganizing companies, boards and management, but also has significant experience representing investment funds, purchasers and others in restructuring transactions. He has special expertise in the airline, energy and gaming industries, particularly addressing legacy liabilities.

**Professional Memberships:** American Bankruptcy Institute.

**Personal:** London School of Economics, 1991; Hebrew University of Jerusalem, 1992; Dartmouth College, AB, 1993; University of Miami School of Law, JD, 1996.

**SENNETT, Michael**
Jones Day, Chicago
312 269 4243
msennett@jonesday.com
*Featured in Antitrust (Illinois)*

**Practice Areas:** Represents clients on the antitrust aspects of mergers and joint ventures, in antitrust litigation, civil investigations before the US Department of Justice, FTC, and state attorneys general, and in criminal antitrust and grand jury proceedings. Industry experience includes pharmaceuticals, biotechnologies, medical devices, steel, automotive, building products, farm equipment, computers, consumer products, mining and minerals, utilities, water technologies, transportation, financial services, and communications. Writes extensively on antitrust law topics and addresses antitrust law conferences in the US and abroad.

**Professional Memberships:** Adjunct law faculty, Loyola University Chicago (antitrust), Institute for Consumer Antitrust Law Studies and Midwest Antitrust Colloquium.

**SESSIONS, Rex L**
Winston & Strawn LLP, Chicago
312 558 5286
rsessions@winston.com
*Featured in Labor & Employment (Illinois)*
**Practice Areas:** Labor, employment and employee benefits litigation; agreements; labor and employment aspects of corporate mergers, acquisitions and divestitures; trade secrets; non-competition disputes.
**Professional Memberships:** Board of Directors of Junior Achievement of Chicago; Board of Directors and Executive Committee of Chicago Scholars; Board of Directors and Executive Committee, Chicago Childrens Museum; Board of Trustees, Sacred Heart Schools.
**Career:** Chairman of Winston & Strawn's Labor and Employment Relations Department; member of the firm's Diversity Committee and Executive Committee.
**Personal:** BA in 1981 from Northwestern University; JD in 1984 from University of Michigan.

**SHAPIRO, Clifford J**
Barnes & Thornburg LLP, Chicago
312 214 4836
clifford.shapiro@btlaw.com
*Featured in Construction (Illinois)*
**Practice Areas:** Chair, Construction Law Practice Group. Handles claims involving various construction projects – industrial, commercial, municipal, residential, mixed use; complex commercial litigation; alternative dispute resolution (mediation/arbitration); insurance coverage on behalf of construction industry policyholders. Clients: large oil company, large municipality, developers, general contractors, businesses building/expanding facilities. Negotiates construction project documents.
**Professional Memberships:** American College of Construction Lawyers; ABA Forum on the Construction Industry; ABA Construction and Insurance Coverage Litigation Committees; Society of Illinois Construction Attorneys (President); Litigation Counsel of America.
**Personal:** Washington University (BA, Magna Cum Laude); George Washington University Law School (JD, High Honors, Order of the Coif).

**SHAPIRO, Keith J**
Greenberg Traurig, LLP, Chicago
312 456 8405
ShapiroK@gtlaw.com
*Featured in Bankruptcy/Restructuring (Illinois)*
**Practice Areas:** GT VP. Chairman, Chicago Office. National Chairman, Strategic Recruitment. Co-Chair, Business Reorganization, Financial Restructuring.
**Professional Memberships:** Fellow, American College of Bankruptcy; Board of Directors, Turnaround Management Association; Former President/Chairman, American Bankruptcy

Institute; Former Board of Directors, INSOL International.
**Career:** Best Lawyers in America, 2001-13; 'Who's Who in Business', Crain's Chicago Business, 2005-12; Chambers USA Guide, 2005-13, Super Lawyers, 2005-13; Leading Lawyers Network, 2005-13.
**Publications:** Co-Editor-in-Chief, Wiley's Bankruptcy Law Update; Contributing author, West's Norton Bankruptcy Law and Practice treatise, Wiley's Advanced Chapter 11 Bankruptcy Practice treatise.
**Personal:** JD, Emory University School of Law; BS, University of Illinois at Urbana-Champaign.

**SHAPIRO, Mark L**
Holland & Knight LLP, Chicago
312 578 6521
mark.shapiro@hklaw.com
*Featured in Labor & Employment (Illinois)*
**Practice Areas:** Mark Shapiro represents employers in labor and employment litigation and counseling. He has extensive litigation experience, including jury trials and class/collective actions, in federal and state trial and appellate courts, and before the NLRB, arbitrators and administrative agencies. He represents public and private companies nationwide in wage-hour, discrimination, harassment, OSHA, whistleblower/retaliation, non-competes, trade secrets, union avoidance, collective bargaining, accessibility for disabled customers, employee benefits, affirmative action, sensitive internal investigations, executive contracts and separation agreements, and other aspects of federal and state employment laws. His clients are in numerous industries, including manufacturing, construction, restaurants, pharmaceuticals, retail, hotels and technology.

**SHEEHAN, Michael J**
DLA Piper LLP (US), Chicago
312 368 7024
michael.sheehan@dlapiper.com
*Featured in Labor & Employment (Illinois)*
**Practice Areas:** Labor and Employment
**Career:** He leads the firm's US Labor and Employment practice and is Global co-chair of the International Labor, Employment, Benefits and Compensation practices. His litigation experience includes prosecuting and defending unfair competition litigation involving large scale raiding, inevitable disclosure of trade secrets, and breach of non-compete agreements. He provides strategic counseling on protecting employee mobility and trade secrets. He investigates and defends Sarbanes-Oxley whistleblower cases, and handles NASD litigation, including raiding cases and employment matters.
**Personal:** JD, Wake Forest University School of Law; BA Hillsdale College, cum laude.

**SHEFFIELD, Jeffrey T**
Kirkland & Ellis LLP, Chicago
312 862 2454
jeffrey.sheffield@kirkland.com
*Featured in Tax (Illinois)*
**Practice Areas:** Jeffrey Sheffield concentrates his practice in the areas of business planning; mergers, acquisitions and spin-offs; venture capi-

tal investing; and tax planning for public and closely held entities.
**Publications:** He has authored or co-authored several articles, most recently "Corporate Transactions and the Economic Substance Doctrine," 89 Taxes 163 (March 2011).
**Personal:** University of Chicago, BA, Phi Beta Kappa, 1976; Harvard Law School, JD, 1979 (editor, Harvard Law Review).

**SHEPHERD, Stewart R**
Sidley Austin LLP, Chicago
312 853 2654
sshepherd@sidley.com
*Featured in Labor & Employment (Illinois)*
**Practice Areas:** Partner in Sidley's Chicago office, practicing in employee benefits and executive compensation. He represents large employers on employee benefits and executive compensation matters and advises institutional trustees, Boards of Directors and other plan fiduciaries regarding their powers and responsibilities under ERISA and other applicable law. He has experience representing clients in disputes and negotiations with the Internal Revenue Service, Department of Labor and Pension Benefit Guaranty Corporation and in ERISA litigation.
**Personal:** University of Chicago Law School, JD, 1973, with honors, Order of the Coif; Rockford College, BA, 1970, magna cum laude, Phi Beta Kappa. Admission: Illinois.

**SHER, Michael D**
Neal, Gerber & Eisenberg LLP, Chicago
312 269 8085
msher@ngelaw.com
*Featured in Litigation (Illinois)*
**Practice Areas:** Represents clients in complex civil litigation and in business-related criminal investigations, trials and appeals in federal and state judicial and administrative proceedings. Michael is and has been a Lecturer in Law at the University of Chicago Law School, teaching Fourth and Fifth Amendment law, and trial practice.
**Professional Memberships:** American College of Trial Lawyers (Fellow).
**Career:** Partner; Litigation Practice Group; White Collar Criminal, Regulatory & Internal Investigative Services Practice Group.
**Publications:** Author, commentator and lecturer on various issues.
**Personal:** University of Michigan (BA, 1971) with distinction; University of Wisconsin Law School (JD, 1974) cum laude.

**SHWACHMAN, Perry**
Sidley Austin LLP, Chicago
312 853 7061
pshwachman@sidley.com
*Featured in Insurance (Illinois)*
**Practice Areas:** Partner in Sidley's Chicago office, Co-Head of the Global Insurance Group and Member of Sidley's Executive Committee. He regularly represents insurance companies, banks, investment managers and other financial institutions on merger and acquisition, securities, insurance securitization, private equity, lending, derivative, structured product, structured investment

vehicle and stable value transactions. His experience includes advising on life, health, property and casualty, financial guaranty and mortgage insurance matters.
**Personal:** University of Chicago Law School, JD, 1986, cum laude; University of Illinois, BS, 1983, with highest honors. CPA. Admission: Illinois.

**SIGEL, Gabrielle**
Jenner & Block LLP, Chicago
312 923 2758
gsigel@jenner.com
*Featured in Environment (Illinois)*
**Career:** Gabrielle Sigel is Co-Chair of Jenner & Block's Climate and Clean Technology Law Practice and a founding member of its Environmental and Workplace Health & Safety Law Practice. Clients seek her representation in complex environmental statutory, common law, and cost recovery actions, in defense of toxic tort lawsuits, and for advice on climate change regulatory issues. She represents employers in matters concerning work-related injuries and chemical exposures, including OSHA enforcement defense, whistleblower matters, compliance programs, and regulatory interpretation, and counsels corporate clients on environmental and workplace health and safety regulatory and transactional issues throughout the US and Europe.

**SILBERMAN, Alan H**
Dentons, Chicago
312 876 8103
alan.silberman@dentons.com
*Featured in Franchising (Nationwide), Antitrust (Illinois)*
See under Nationwide for profile.

**SILVERMAN, Gary R**
Greenberg Traurig, LLP, Chicago
312 456 8414
SilvermanG@gtlaw.com
*Featured in Corporate/M&A (Illinois)*
**Practice Areas:** Corporate and securities; mergers and acquisitions.
**Career:** Selected: Band 1, Chambers USA Guide; Super Lawyers magazine, 2005-11; Leading Lawyers Network, 2012-13. Rated, AV® Preeminent™ 5.0 out of 5.
**Publications:** Author: 'Avoiding the Pitfalls in Sell-Side Engagement Letters', Buyouts, October 8, 2007; 'Seller Beware', Private Equity Manager, June 2005; 'Venture Capital Investing in the New Economy', The Venture Capital Review, Spring 2000.
**Personal:** JD, magna cum laude, Northwestern University, 1986, Order of the Coif, Law Review Editorial Board; MBA, University of Chicago, 1990, Dean's Honor List; MLA, University of Chicago, 2006; BA, cum laude, Brandeis University, 1983.

**SIMONSEN, Karen**
McDermott Will & Emery LLP, Chicago
312 984 6960
ksimonsen@mwe.com
*Featured in Labor & Employment (Illinois)*
**Practice Areas:** Partner in employee benefits department. Advises on tax-qualified retirement plans, non-qualified deferred compensation, sev-

erance programs, and other employee benefits. Focuses on ERISA fiduciary and plan investment issues. Counsels on investment policy matters, alternative investments, ERISA prohibited transaction issues, investment management agreements, plan expense and plan asset issues, compliance reviews, investment advice products, and administrative services contracts. Advises on plan investments in employer securities. Has represented clients in audits by the IRS, DOL, and PBGC. Counsels clients on employee benefits aspects of corporate transactions, including outsourcing deals.

**Personal:** Northwestern University School of Law (JD), Colorado State University (BA).

## SIROS, Steven
Jenner & Block LLP, Chicago
312 923 2717
ssiros@jenner.com
*Featured in Environment (Illinois)*

**Career:** Steven M Siros's environmental practice focuses on litigation, regulatory and transactional matters. He represents clients in complex CERCLA and RCRA proceedings and regularly defends property damage and personal injury toxic tort claims. He counsels clients on compliance matters relating to a variety of environmental, health and safety statutes including TSCA, CAA, and ATF, and he manages all environmental aspects of complex real estate and corporate transactions involving domestic and international facilities. He frequently speaks at environmental seminars and has written numerous articles concerning environmental law. He is Co-Editor of the Corporate Environmental Lawyer, a blog covering emerging environmental issues.

## SIRUS, Richard A
Greenberg Traurig, LLP, Chicago
312 476 5006
SirusR@gtlaw.com
*Featured in Labor & Employment (Illinois)*

**Practice Areas:** Global benefits and compensation; corporate and securities; tax; corporate and transactional; employee benefits; executive compensation; health law; mergers and acquisitions.
**Professional Memberships:** Member, American Bar Association; member, American Institute of Certified Public Accountants; member, Illinois CPA Society/Foundation.
**Career:** Certified Public Accountant. Selected: Chambers USA Guide, 2010-13; Leading Lawyers Network, 2006-13.
**Personal:** JD, Loyola University Chicago School of Law, 1982; BBA, Loyola University Chicago, 1980.

## SKINNER, Honey J
Sidley Austin LLP, Chicago
312 853 7577
mskinner@sidley.com
*Featured in Healthcare (Illinois)*

**Practice Areas:** Partner in Sidley's Chicago office, practicing in the Healthcare group. She represents healthcare providers before government agencies both in Illinois and Washington, DC. She assists hospitals, health systems and physician practices in gaining government approval for the

expansion of their services and in their efforts to achieve equitable Medicaid reimbursement.
**Professional Memberships:** Director, The Northern Funds.
**Personal:** Northwestern University School of Law, JD, 1981; Harvard University, BA, 1978, cum laude. Admissions: US Supreme Court, District of Columbia, Illinois.

## SKINNER, Thomas V
Jones Day, Chicago
312 782 3939
tskinner@jonesday.com
*Featured in Environment (Illinois)*

**Practice Areas:** Tom Skinner has more than 25 years experience in environmental and general litigation, federal and state civil and criminal enforcement matters, regulatory and permitting issues, and counseling, including response to environmental and corporate crisis situations. Tom previously held a series of high-level governmental positions, including as acting Assistant Administrator for Enforcement and Compliance at the U.S. EPA and as the Director of the Illinois EPA. Tom's practice also has included such high-profile general litigation matters as the impeachment trial of the chief justice of the Illinois Supreme Court and legislative redistricting litigation before the federal district court.

## SKLARSKY, Charles B
Jenner & Block LLP, Chicago
312 923 2904
csklarsky@jenner.com
*Featured in Litigation (Illinois)*

**Career:** Charles B. Sklarsky is a Partner in the Litigation Department and Co-Chair of the White Collar Defense and Investigations Practice. He counsels clients regarding fraud and abuse, conflicts of interest, public corruption, criminal tax matters, criminal antitrust, theft of trade secrets, and securities fraud. He represents individuals and entities in grand jury investigations, SEC investigations, criminal trials, SEC enforcement actions, qui tam litigation, complex civil litigation and appearances before regulatory and legislative bodies. Mr Sklarsky is a former Assistant United States Attorney for the Northern District of Illinois and a former Assistant State's Attorney of Cook County, Illinois.

## SLATTERY, Kerrin
McDermott Will & Emery LLP, Chicago
312 984 7685
kslattery@mwe.com
*Featured in Healthcare (Illinois)*

**Practice Areas:** Represents hospitals and health industry clients in all aspects of health law transactions, including mergers, acquisitions, dispositions, Catholic/non-Catholic affiliations, joint ventures and system restructurings. Advises clients on related regulatory compliance with licensure, accreditation and other state and federal healthcare regulatory matters.
**Professional Memberships:** American Health Lawyers Association; Illinois Association of Healthcare Attorneys.

**Career:** Admitted to Illinois Bar (1996); Partner at McDermott Will & Emery LLP since 2003; joined the firm in 1996.
**Personal:** Loyola University Chicago School of Law (JD); Loyola University Chicago Graduate School of Business (MBA); University of San Diego(BS, BA).

## SMALL, Andrew D
Kirkland & Ellis LLP, Chicago
312 862 5489
andrew.small@kirkland.com
*Featured in Real Estate (Illinois)*

**Practice Areas:** Concentrates in commercial real estate and real estate finance including loan originations (including mezzanine debt), sales and acquisitions of debt portfolios and loan restructurings. His practice also includes commercial real estate development on behalf of real estate investors, funds, sponsors, finance companies and operating companies. He has substantial experience representing clients in connection with the formation of joint ventures to own, operate, finance and develop real estate nationally and internationally.
**Personal:** University of Michigan - Bachelors Degree, Business Administration; University of Chicago Law School - JD, 1989; Completed Certified Public Accountant's examination, 1987.

## SMEDINGHOFF, Thomas J
Edwards Wildman Palmer, Chicago
312 201 2021
tsmedinghoff@edwardswildman.com
*Featured in Technology (Illinois); Privacy & Data Security (Nationwide)*

**Practice Areas:** Tom's practice focuses on information law and electronic transactions, privacy, information security, and online authentication issues from both a transactional and public policy perspective. He is internationally recognized for leadership in addressing legislative and public policy issues relating to information security and electronic signatures.
**Professional Memberships:** US Delegation to UN Commission on International Trade Law; World Customs Organization; Legal Working Group of the UN Center for Trade Facilitation and Electronic Business; ABA Advisor to Drafting Committee on Uniform Electronic Transactions Act (now adopted in 47 states).
**Personal:** University of Michigan, JD; Knox College, BA.

## SMITH, Jeffrey
Sidley Austin LLP, Chicago
312 853 7312
jnsmith@sidley.com
*Featured in Corporate/M&A (Illinois)*

**Practice Areas:** Partner in Sidley's Corporate and Securities practice group. Concentrates in complex business transactions, including mergers, acquisitions, leveraged buyouts, divestitures, financings, debt and equity restructurings, equity investments and joint ventures. Has significant international experience and has led numerous cross-border and multi-jurisdiction transactions. Principally represents private equity funds and investors. Has handled transactions in a wide vari-

ety of industries, including distribution, infrastructure and construction, healthcare, consumer products, industrial products, retailing and service businesses.
**Personal:** Northwestern University School of Law, JD, 1985, cum laude; University of Michigan, BBA, 1982, with high distinction, Phi Beta Kappa, Beta Gamma Sigma; Admission: Illinois.

## SMITH, William P
McDermott Will & Emery LLP, Chicago
312 984 7588
wsmith@mwe.com
*Featured in Bankruptcy/Restructuring (Illinois)*

**Practice Areas:** Practices centers on the restructuring of troubled financial transactions and defaulted securities, especially tax-exempt bonds. Represents indenture trustees, institutional investors, credit enhancers, commercial banks, and debt issuers (principally health care) in resolution of a broad variety of troubled debt financings in the United States, Canada and Germany. Has extensive experience in bankruptcy-related matters. Recognized as one of the leading practitioners on tax-exempt and healthcare-related defaults.
**Personal:** University of Cincinnati College of Law (JD); Cornell University (BA).

## SMITH JR, Arthur B
Ogletree, Deakins, Nash, Smoak & Stewart, PC, Chicago
312 558 1230
arthur.smith@ogletreedeakins.com
*Featured in Labor & Employment (Illinois)*

**Practice Areas:** Labor and employment.
**Professional Memberships:** American Bar Association, New York Bar Association.
**Career:** Admitted to practice in Illinois, New York, US Supreme Court, United States Courts of Appeal (2nd, 5th, 6th, 7th, 11th, and District of Columbia Circuits).
**Publications:** Has authored seven editions of Employment Discrimination Law, Cases & Materials, a casebook for law school instruction and Construction Labor Relations, a reference work widely used by construction managers and labor lawyers. Current Contributing Editor of the ABA's Developing Labor Law Treatise.
**Personal:** Cornell University (BA, 1966), University of Chicago Law School (JD, 1969).

## SMYLIE, Sallie G
Kirkland & Ellis LLP, Chicago
312 862 2421
sallie.smylie@kirkland.com
*Featured in Litigation (Illinois)*

**Practice Areas:** National practice representing companies in mass tort, class action, and multidistrict litigation, with emphasis in the areas of pharmaceutical and medical device products liability litigation, commercial litigation, securities litigation, and employment litigation.
**Career:** In 2012, Sallie was selected as a "Top Ten Woman Business Lawyer in Illinois" by Leading Lawyers Network. In 2011 and 2012, Sallie was selected as a leading litigator in Chambers USA: America's Leading Lawyers for Business.

**Personal:** DePaul University College of Law, JD, 1989, cum laude, Member of Law Review; Salem College, BA, 1977; Adjunct Instructor, The University of Chicago Law School.

### SNEED, William M
Sidley Austin LLP, Chicago
312 853 7899
wsneed@sidley.com
*Featured in Insurance (Illinois)*
**Practice Areas:** Partner in Chicago, practicing in insurance and insurance/reinsurance disputes. He has extensive experience arbitrating and litigating reinsurance disputes on behalf of ceding companies and reinsurers. He has arbitrated dozens of reinsurance disputes, addressing issues such as allocation, aggregation of claims, late notice, ECO/XPL coverage, follow the fortunes, pre-hearing security, cessions of declaratory judgment expenses and retention warranties. He has successfully litigated major reinsurance contract disputes at the trial and appellate levels.
**Personal:** Northwestern University School of Law, JD, 1987, magna cum laude, Order of the Coif; Northwestern University, MM, 1987; Stanford University, AB, 1983. Admission: Illinois.

### SNIDER, Teresa
Butler Rubin Saltarelli & Boyd LLP, Chicago
312 696 4483
tsnider@butlerrubin.com
*Featured in Insurance (Illinois)*
**Practice Areas:** Reinsurance Arbitration, Litigation, and Related Insolvency Issues.
**Professional Memberships:** Teresa Snider is a member of ARIAS-U.S. and the International Association of Insurance Receivers. She is actively involved in AIRROC and has written for various reinsurance publications and Corporate Counsel magazine. Teresa has spoken on reinsurance issues at programs held by ARIAS-U.S, Mealey's/HB Litigation, IAIR, INSOL and ACI's International Forum on Run-Off and Commutations. She also co-chairs Butler Rubin's annual Women in Reinsurance program.
**Career:** Teresa is a partner and member of the Management Committee of Butler Rubin. She has handled numerous arbitration hearings and court cases, including matters related to allocation issues, treaty interpretation, bad faith, misrepresentation and nondisclosure allegations, claim handling, issues arising out of common account excess of loss reinsurance, actuarial standards for calculating IBNR, and agency issues. She also provides counseling on contract wording and coverage issues, assists clients in assessing their rights against insolvent insurers, and drafts commutation and settlement agreements. Teresa represents both ceding insurers and assuming reinsurers. She was named as a leader in insurance law in The Best Lawyers in America (2012-2013). And, in 2005 and 2009-2013, Teresa was named as a leader in business litigation by Illinois Super Lawyers. She joined Butler Rubin in 1994 after a clerkship with Hon. Harry D. Leinenweber, U.S. District Court, Northern District of Illinois.
**Personal:** JD, magna cum laude, University of Michigan Law School, 1992. Executive Editor,

Michigan Journal of International Law, 1991-1992. Order of the Coif. BA, summa cum laude, University of Illinois, 1989. Phi Beta Kappa. Bronze Tablet.

### SOLOW, Alan P
DLA Piper LLP (US), Chicago
312 368 3370
alan.solow@dlapiper.com
*Featured in Bankruptcy/Restructuring (Illinois)*
**Practice Areas:** Bankruptcy and restructuring.
**Career:** He has practiced in bankruptcy and restructuring for more than 30 years. He represents secured and unsecured creditors, including indenture trustees, covering the range of legal services from workout planning through active participation in bankruptcy cases. He is a widely published author and frequent lecturer and has been honored for his contributions to the bankruptcy and insolvency field.
**Personal:** JD, Harvard Law School (cum laude); BA, University of Illinois at Urbana-Champaign (summa cum laude).

### SOLOW, Michael
Kaye Scholer LLP, Chicago
312 583 2310
michael.solow@kayescholer.com
*Featured in Bankruptcy/Restructuring (Illinois)*
**Practice Areas:** Michael Solow, Managing Partner of Kaye Scholer, Co-Chair of the Executive Committee and Co-Chair of the Bankruptcy & Restructuring Department, has over 27 years of experience representing creditors, debtors, trustees and governmental agencies in bankruptcy and insolvency matters throughout the US and involving foreign jurisdictions. He has represented clients in a variety of industries, including healthcare, energy, gaming, finance and manufacturing. He is a frequent author and lecturer on various topics related to dealing with insolvent entities, and serves on numerous boards for both private and public companies.

### SOLOW, Sheldon L
Kaye Scholer LLP, Chicago
312 583 2320
sheldon.solow@kayescholer.com
*Featured in Bankruptcy/Restructuring (Illinois)*
**Practice Areas:** Sheldon Solow represents a variety of constituencies, including secured lenders and bank syndicates, purchasers of businesses, bondholders, fiduciaries, special litigation committees, debtors, and individual clients. Sheldon also represents private equity sponsors and other investors in the acquisition of distressed businesses or assets and in debt restructurings involving portfolio companies. An author and speaker on bankruptcy law topics, he has served on the Subcommittee pertaining to Avoiding Powers for the Bankruptcy Reform Commission. Sheldon is also an adjunct professor at the Loyola University Chicago School of Law and on the faculty of the Harvard Law School Trial Advocacy Workshop.

### SORENSEN, Sharp
Sidley Austin LLP, Chicago
312 853 7151
ssorensen@sidley.com
*Featured in Tax (Illinois)*
**Practice Areas:** Partner in Sidley's Chicago office, a Global Coordinator of the firm's Tax practice and head of the Tax practice in Chicago. He practices in federal tax matters and focuses on representing domestic and foreign entities involved in a wide variety of transactions, including mergers and acquisitions, spin-offs, securitizations and other asset-based financings, partnerships and joint ventures, foreign and domestic securities offerings, leveraged leasing and regulated investment companies.
**Personal:** Northwestern University School of Law, JD, 1985, with honors, Order of the Coif; University of Utah, BS, 1982, magna cum laude. Admission: Illinois.

### SPARKS, Kenneth F
Vedder Price PC, Chicago
312 609 7877
ksparks@vedderprice.com
*Featured in Labor & Employment (Illinois)*
**Practice Areas:** Shareholder with 20+ years' experience in labor and employment matters. Represents and advises private and public employers in complicated labor law and litigation matters nationwide. Concentrates on collective bargaining, union organizing, arbitration and related matters, including development of integrated responses and negotiation tactics, such as strikes and boycotts. Has negotiated first time, concessionary and closure agreements; tried complex NLRB cases; handled organizing and decertification campaigns; managed issues arising from nationwide and local strikes; quelled unlawful secondary boycotts; handled EEO and related employment matters.
**Career:** Admitted (IL) 1997.
**Personal:** JD, University of Michigan; B.S., Massachusetts Institute of Technology.

### SPEARS, Natalie
Dentons, Chicago
312 876 2556
natalie.spears@dentons.com
*Featured in Media & Entertainment (Illinois)*
**Practice Areas:** Litigates cases including marketing and competition-related disputes, intellectual property and media defense, consumer class actions, and commercial and real estate matters.
**Professional Memberships:** Co-chair, MLRC/NAA/NAB, 2010-2012 Media Law Conference; Member, Governing Committee of the ABA Forum on Communications Law, 2006-2009; Chicago Inn of Court, President, 2008-2009; President, Chicago Bar Foundation Board of Directors, 2012-2013.
**Career:** Joined Dentons in 1995.
**Publications:** Co-author, Media Defense Resource Center's annual libel and media privacy law surveys for Illinois and the Seventh Circuit.
**Personal:** University of Michigan Law School, JD, cum laude, 1995; University of Iowa, BA, honors and highest distinction, 1992.

### SPERLING, Robert Y
Winston & Strawn LLP, Chicago
312 558 7941
rsperling@winston.com
*Featured in Litigation (Illinois)*
**Practice Areas:** Complex litigation with an emphasis on securities litigation and commercial litigation, including class actions.
**Professional Memberships:** American Bar Association, Illinois State Bar Association, Chicago Bar Association.
**Career:** Has extensive experience representing financial services clients in securities actions, including class actions. Has represented the directors of various companies in derivative shareholders actions and ERISA actions that related to securities claims filed against those companies. Has extensive experience in national class actions that involved alleged violations of various federal consumer protection statutes.
**Personal:** DePaul University School of Law, JD; DePaul Law Review; University of Illinois, AB in History.

### SPRAYREGEN, James HM
Kirkland & Ellis LLP, Chicago
312 862 2481
james.sprayregen@kirkland.com
*Featured in Bankruptcy/Restructuring (Nationwide), Bankruptcy/Restructuring (Illinois), Bankruptcy/Restructuring (New York)*
See under Nationwide for profile.

### STAHL, David M
Eimer Stahl LLP, Chicago
312 660 7602
dstahl@EimerStahl.com
*Featured in Energy & Natural Resources (Illinois)*
**Practice Areas:** Antitrust, commercial and energy litigation with broad trial experience in state and federal courts and regulatory agencies, and in arbitrations. His practice has encompassed Sherman Act (§ 1 and § 2) and Robinson-Patman Act litigation and counseling, acquisitions, securities litigation, breach of contract, products liability and toxic tort, professional malpractice defense, and a wide variety of electric power litigation. For the last twenty years he has concentrated on energy litigation. He has represented a number of leading firms including, among others, CITGO Petroleum Corporation, Kimberly-Clark Corporation, Praxair, Inc, Abbott Laboratories, Holcim (US) Inc, Midwest Generation EME, LLC, the former Central and South West Corporation (now part of American Electric Power), Northern Illinois Gas, Exelon Corp., Commonwealth Edison and CMS Energy.
**Professional Memberships:** American Bar Association, Litigation and Antitrust Sections; Chicago Bar Association; Chicago Inn of Court.
**Career:** Admitted to the Illinois Bar, 1972. Member of the Trial Bar of the United States District Court for the Northern District of Illinois. Partner at Isham, Lincoln & Beale, 1979-88. Partner at Sidley & Austin, 1988-2000. Head of Regulatory/Litigation Group, 1995-2000. Co-Founder of his firm, 2000.

**Personal:** Born: September 22, 1946. Received his JD, magna cum laude, from the University of Michigan, 1971. Member, Michigan Law Review, Order of the Coif, 1971. Received his MA (History) from the University of Michigan, 1971. Received his BA from the University of Illinois (Chicago), 1968 (History).

## STARR, Kelly. A
Vedder Price PC, Chicago
312 609 7768
kstarr@vedderprice.com
*Featured in Labor & Employment (Illinois)*

**Practice Areas:** Chair, Employee Benefits group. Counsels employers on all aspects of employee benefits law, including design, tax qualification, legal compliance, correction, interpretation, communication and termination of broad-based employee benefit plans. Negotiates and structures executive employment agreements and compensation benefit arrangements, including incentive compensation, deferred compensation, severance agreements and change-in-control programs, on behalf of both individual executives and companies. Experience advising boards of directors on executive compensation issues.

**Professional Memberships:** Member: American Bar Association (Sections on Taxation and Business Law), Chicago Bar Association.

**Career:** Admitted (IL) 1995.

**Personal:** JD, cum laude, University of Illinois College of Law; B.S., Cornell University.

## STEEGE, Catherine L
Jenner & Block LLP, Chicago
312 923 2952
csteege@jenner.com
*Featured in Bankruptcy/Restructuring (Illinois)*

**Career:** Catherine L. Steege is Co-Chair of the Bankruptcy Litigation Practice, and is a fellow of the American College of Bankruptcy. She represented the Section 1114 Committees in the American Airlines, Northwest Airlines and United Airlines Chapter 11 cases. She has handled complex litigation arising out of the bankruptcy filings for LA Dodgers LLP, Tribune Co., Sentinel Management Group, Inc., Emerald Casino Inc., Magnatrax Corporation, National Steel Corp. and Consolidated Industries Corp. She has represented chapter 11 debtors, unsecured creditors committees and significant creditors in many cases. She also was one of the attorneys representing the Lehman Brothers Examiner.

## STEINMETZ, Matthew E
Kirkland & Ellis LLP, Chicago
312 862 2341
matthew.steinmetz@kirkland.com
*Featured in Corporate/M&A (Illinois)*

**Practice Areas:** Matthew Steinmetz, a corporate partner, focuses primarily on complex leveraged and un-leveraged acquisitions and divestitures, including going private transactions, global corporate carve-outs and distressed M&A. His practice also includes all of the traditional areas of corporate law, including private and public equity capital investing, debt and equity restructurings, joint venture activities and management incentive arrangements.

**Personal:** University of Chicago Graduate School of Business, MBA, 1989; University of Notre Dame Law School, JD, 1987; Alma College, BA, 1984.

## STEMPEL, James A
Kirkland & Ellis LLP, Chicago
312 862 2440
james.stempel@kirkland.com
*Featured in Bankruptcy/Restructuring (Illinois)*

**Practice Areas:** James Stempel concentrates his practice in counseling debtors in all aspects of Chapter 11 cases, purchasers of distressed companies and investors in distressed debt inside and outside of bankruptcy, owners, companies and boards of directors in out-of-court workouts and restructurings, and secured and unsecured lenders to insolvent companies. Mr Stempel was named as one of the Outstanding Young Bankruptcy Lawyers of 2002 by Turnarounds & Workouts Magazine.

**Personal:** IIT/Chicago-Kent College of Law, JD, 1989; University of Michigan, BGS, 1985.

## STEPHENS, Thomas M
Dentons, Chicago
312 876 7485
thomas.stephens@dentons.com
*Featured in Tax (Illinois)*

**Practice Areas:** Nationally recognized in partnership taxation and tax credit investing. Head of the Tax Advantaged Investments practice. Focuses on tax planning, transaction structuring and workout restructuring for partnerships, limited liability companies, corporations and individuals, with an emphasis on real estate and tax credit investments.

**Career:** Joined Dentons in 1987. Previously practiced in Connecticut (1983-1986) and had a clerkship in Connecticut Superior Court (1982-1983). Also, served for five years as Adjunct Professor at Chicago Kent College of Law, teaching corporate taxation in the LLM program, and as Adjunct Professor at Northwestern University, teaching partnership taxation in the JD program.

## STILLMAN, Nina G
Morgan, Lewis & Bockius LLP, Chicago
312 324 1150
nstillman@morganlewis.com
*Featured in Labor & Employment (Illinois)*

**Practice Areas:** Nina G. Stillman is a partner in Morgan Lewis's Labor and Employment Practice. Nina focuses on labor and employment, equal employment opportunity, and occupational safety and health law matters. She has successfully represented corporations and institutions in large employment class actions and individual employment, restrictive covenants, and health and safety-related cases. She counsels employers nationwide on cross-border workplace issues and counsels international clients on US employment and workplace safety and health law.

**Personal:** Attended Northwestern University School of Law, 1973, JD, Cum Laude, Order of the Coif; Smith College, 1970, AB, Phi Beta Kappa.

## STOLL, R Ryan
Skadden, Arps, Slate, Meagher & Flom LLP & Affiliates, Chicago
312 407 0780
ryan.stoll@skadden.com
*Featured in Litigation (Illinois)*

**Practice Areas:** Concentrates in complex litigation, complex torts defense, white collar criminal defense and domestic and international arbitration with extensive trial and appellate experience. Previously served in the office of the U.S. Attorney for the Northern District of Illinois and handled a wide variety of cases, including complex racketeering, public corruption and fraud prosecutions. Has been involved in a number of significant civil litigation matters, including federal multidistrict proceedings and other complex state and federal litigations.

**Career:** JD, Harvard Law School, 1990 (Editor, Harvard Law Review); MA, Stanford University, 1987; BA, Stanford University, 1987 (Phi Beta Kappa).

## STONE, David S
Neal, Gerber & Eisenberg LLP, Chicago
312 269 8411
dstone@ngelaw.com
*Featured in Corporate/M&A (Illinois)*

**Practice Areas:** Represents clients in complex corporate and securities transactions and general corporate matters. Has advised both buyers and sellers in connection with numerous negotiated public and private mergers, acquisitions, divestitures and dispositions, and private equity investments. Represents clients involved in public tender offers, public and private mergers and proxy contests. Represents issuers in registered public equity offerings (including initial public offerings, secondary offerings and rights offerings) and public and private placements of equity securities.

**Career:** Partner; Corporate & Securities Practice Group Chair.

**Personal:** University of Michigan (AB, with distinction, 1982); University of Michigan Law School (JD, cum laude, 1985).

## STONE, Jeffrey E
McDermott Will & Emery LLP, Chicago
312 984 2064
jstone@mwe.com
*Featured in Litigation (Illinois)*

**Practice Areas:** Firm co-chair. Concentrates on white-collar criminal defense, complex commercial litigation, internal investigations and RICO. Represents individuals and corporations in criminal prosecutions and complex commercial litigation.

**Professional Memberships:** Fellow, American College of Trial Lawyers; Board of Directors - Northwestern Law School Center on Wrongful Convictions; Board of Governors - American Jewish Committee; National chairman, Stanford Fund.

**Career:** Assistant US attorney (Chicago); law clerk to Chief Judge Robert F Peckham of US District Court, San Francisco.

**Personal:** Stanford University, (BA with honors and distinction); Harvard Law School, (JD, cum laude).

## STONE, Susan
Sidley Austin LLP, Chicago
312 853 2177
sstone@sidley.com
*Featured in Insurance (Nationwide), Insurance (Illinois)*

See under Nationwide for profile.

## STREFF JR, William A
Kirkland & Ellis LLP, Chicago
312 862 2126
wstreff@kirkland.com
*Featured in Intellectual Property (Illinois)*

**Practice Areas:** Bill Streff has been practicing intellectual property law for 40 years, concentrating on patent litigation (including jury trials) and transactions (including international strategic alliances) involving computer hardware, firmware, software and systems; semiconductor processing technology and circuitry, including LEDs, DRAMs, CCDs, MPUs and inverter controllers; optical networks; satellite and cable communications systems; avionics; high definition and satellite television systems; navigation systems; and digitally-controlled fuel systems. He was named a 2013 Client Service All-Star by BTI Consulting. He is one of the leaders of Kirkland's IP Practice Group and the Firm's Japanese Client Practice.

**Professional Memberships:** ABA, FBCA, JASC, IPBA.

## STUCKER, Robert J
Vedder Price PC, Chicago
312 609 7606
rstucker@vedderprice.com
*Featured in Employee Benefits & Executive Compensation (Nationwide), Labor & Employment (Illinois)*

**Practice Areas:** Chairman of the firm and Shareholder in the Executive Compensation group. Advises corporations and financial institutions regarding executive compensation and governance matters. Advisor to compensation, audit, governance and other special committees of the boards of directors of public corporations. Nationally recognized for his representation of corporations, compensation committees and executives regarding recruitment and employment arrangements for CEOs.

**Career:** Admitted (IL) 1970.

**Publications:** Featured in 'The Wall Street Journal,' the 'New York Times' and the 'Chicago Tribune'.

**Personal:** JD, University of Chicago; BA, cum laude, Phi Beta Kappa, Georgetown University.

## SULLIVAN, Thomas P
Jenner & Block LLP, Chicago
312 923 2928
tsullivan@jenner.com
*Featured in Litigation (Illinois)*

**Career:** Thomas P. Sullivan is a Partner in Jenner & Block's Chicago office. With the exception of an almost four-year period (July 1977 to April 1981) when he served as the United States Attorney for the Northern District of Illinois, Mr Sullivan has practiced law at Jenner & Block since 1954.

### SUSSMAN, Eric H.
Kaye Scholer LLP, Chicago
312 583 2442
eric.sussman@kayescholer.com
*Featured in Litigation (Illinois)*

**Practice Areas:** Eric Sussman is the Chicago Co-Chair of Kaye Scholer's White Collar Litigation and Internal Investigations practice. Eric focuses on complex civil and white collar criminal litigation, representing individuals and corporations in proceedings involving the SEC, DOJ and other governmental agencies. He regularly counsels international companies and private equity funds on compliance and regulatory matters, including criminal antitrust and Foreign Corrupt Practices issues.
**Career:** Eric was previously Deputy Chief of the Financial Crimes and Special Prosecutions Section for the US Attorney's Office, Northern District of Illinois, and the Food & Drug Administration Coordinator for the US Attorney's Office.

### SWAN, Tim
Sidley Austin LLP, Chicago
312 853 3421
tswan@sidley.com
*Featured in Technology (Illinois)*

**Practice Areas:** Associate in Sidley's Chicago office who practices in the Technology Transactions group. Mr Swan assists clients with critical license agreements, collaboration agreements, outsourcing transactions, complex transition arrangements, and various other technology, IT and IP matters. He also advises clients on the intersection of technology matters with M&A transactions. His clients range from Fortune 500 companies to emerging firms, and span various industries, with a focus on life sciences, agribusiness, financial services, telecommunications, software and web-based services.
**Personal:** The University of Chicago Law School, JD, 2006, with high honors; Rose-Hulman Institute of Technology, BS, 2003, magna cum laude.

### SWEENEY, Maureen E
Kirkland & Ellis LLP, Chicago
312 862 2190
maureen.sweeney@kirkland.com
*Featured in Banking & Finance (Illinois)*

**Practice Areas:** Maureen Sweeney focuses her practice on debt financing transactions. She represents private equity groups, commercial lending institutions and other private and public companies in connection with the negotiation, structuring and documentation of secured and unsecured financing transactions for both borrowers and lenders, including senior, mezzanine and subordinated debt transactions; acquisition financings; and loan workouts and restructurings, including debtor-in-possession financings.
**Personal:** University of Michigan Law School, JD, cum laude, 1996; University of Michigan, BS, Mathematics, 1993.

### SWETT, Brian I
Winston & Strawn LLP, Chicago
312 558 3716
bswett@winston.com
*Featured in Bankruptcy/Restructuring (Illinois)*

**Practice Areas:** Brian Swett is a Partner in Winston & Strawn's Restructuring and Insolvency Practice. He represents senior secured lenders and other creditors, companies, shareholders, investors, sellers and purchasers in restructurings, bankruptcy cases, out-of-court workouts and distressed and foreclosure transactions. His experience includes a wide range of debtor-in-possession financing and cash collateral matters in numerous industries.
**Professional Memberships:** American Bankruptcy Institute.
**Publications:** Mr Swett's most recent publication was 'Pension Protection Act, New FASB Rule May Put Secured Lenders at Greater Risk of PBGC Liens', American Bankruptcy Institute Journal, December/January 2007 (co-author).

### SWILL, Douglas B
Drinker Biddle & Reath LLP, Chicago
312 569 1270
Douglas.Swill@dbr.com
*Featured in Healthcare (Illinois)*

**Practice Areas:** Managing Partner at the firm; Chair, Health Care Practice Group; represents health systems, hospitals, physician groups and other providers, counsels on healthcare corporate and regulatory matters, acquisitions, affiliations, governance and nonprofit issues, Stark, anti-kickback, tax-exemption law, Medicare and Medicaid compliance program audits, due diligence reviews; counsels hospitals in physician employment, recruitment, hospital-based physician relationships and hospital/physician group joint ventures.
**Career:** Formerly assistant state's attorney, Office of the State's Attorney's Federal Litigation and Hospitals Departments (1990-93).
**Publications:** Frequent lecturer.
**Personal:** Loyola University Chicago School of Law, LLM 1990 (Health Law Fellow), Washington University, JD 1989, Muhlenberg College, BA, 1986.

### TABACCHI, Tina M
Jones Day, Chicago
312 269 4081
tmtabacchi@jonesday.com
*Featured in Litigation (Illinois)*

**Practice Areas:** Tina is a business litigator with a focus on the pharmaceutical and healthcare industries. She has experience in US DOJ, State Attorney General, multidistrict and class action litigation; in False Claims Act/qui tam, RICO, consumer fraud, contract and licensing matters; and in government investigations.
**Career:** Tina is currently acting as national counsel for a Fortune 10 client in a series of State Attorney General and private class action lawsuits. She is also Jones Day's Firmwide Chair of Recruiting.
**Personal:** Named one of "The Most Powerful and Influential Women in Illinois" by the National Diversity Council (March 15, 2012).

### TAYLOR, Byron
Sidley Austin LLP, Chicago
312 853 4717
bftaylor@sidley.com
*Featured in Environment (Illinois)*

**Practice Areas:** Partner and a member of Sidley's Environmental practice group. Practice includes civil litigation, compliance counseling and training, internal investigations, regulatory advocacy, alternative dispute resolution and environmental aspects of transactions. Frequently called upon to defend clients against alleged violations of federal and state environmental laws, and over the past several years, has handled a number of complex Clean Air Act related matters. Also regularly presents on clean air and climate change issues for clients, bar associations and other groups.
**Personal:** The University of Chicago Law School, JD, 1990; Yale University, BA, 1987; Admission: Illinois.

### TAYLOR, Pamela
Jones Day, Chicago
312 269 4327
ptaylor@jonesday.com
*Featured in Antitrust (Illinois)*

**Practice Areas:** Pam Taylor represents companies in antitrust matters. Her practice includes government antitrust investigations and enforcement actions before the Federal Trade Commission and the Department of Justice Antitrust Division.
**Professional Memberships:** Pam is a member of the bars of Illinois and Massachusetts and the American Bar Association's Antitrust Section. She is admitted to practice before various U.S. District Courts and Courts of Appeals.
**Career:** Pam has provided antitrust advice to clients in a broad range of industries, including the pharmaceutical, medical device, biotechnology, health care services, consumer products, automotive, mining, waste management, chemical, and defense industries.

### THOMAS, Liisa
Winston & Strawn LLP, Chicago
312 558 6149
LMthomas@winston.com
*Featured in Media & Entertainment (Illinois)*

**Practice Areas:** Liisa Thomas has created a unique practice, focusing on the cutting-edge convergence of privacy and advertising laws. Liisa provides clients clarity in a sea of confusing legal requirements with practical and efficient advice. She counsels her clients—which include major consumer brands, advertising agencies, and consumer research companies—so that they are able to use emerging advertising and market research techniques while effectively managing their legal risks. Her extensive experience ranges from the development of mobile marketing and online behavioral advertising campaigns, to responding to data breaches and handling international advertising and privacy issues.

### THORSTENSON, Craig
FordHarrison LLP, Chicago
312 960 6116
cthorstenson@fordharrison.com
*Featured in Labor & Employment (Illinois)*

**Practice Areas:** Labor and Employment.
**Career:** Craig Thorstenson concentrates his practice in the litigation of employment disputes and providing related counseling. His experience includes defending numerous WARN Act and Title VII class actions, prosecuting and defending actions over restrictive covenants, and handling complex labor arbitrations. He regularly acts as "in-house" employment counsel for several companies that elect to outsource their employment work. Craig received his JD, magna cum laude, from the University of Illinois College of Law in 1988.

### TORRES, Joseph J
Winston & Strawn LLP, Chicago
312 558 7334
jtorres@winston.com
*Featured in Labor & Employment (Illinois)*

**Practice Areas:** Labor, employment and ERISA litigation before trial and appellate courts; collective bargaining and labor disputes; labor and employment aspects of corporate mergers, acquisitions and divestitures; trade secrets and non-competition disputes.
**Professional Memberships:** Member, American Bar Association, Labor and Employment Section; Chairman, Hispanic Lawyers Scholarship Fund of Illinois.
**Career:** Joined firm in 1990; became Partner, 1998; Chair of firm Hiring Committee; Member of Diversity Committee.
**Publications:** Editor, 'The Developing Labor Law' (BNA).
**Personal:** University of Chicago, 1985; University of Illinois College of Law, 1990.

### TOTH, Bruce A
Winston & Strawn LLP, Chicago
312 558 5723
btoth@winston.com
*Featured in Corporate/M&A (Illinois)*

**Practice Areas:** Mr Toth's practice focuses on securities and M&A. Representative clients include Lear, Danaher, TreeHouse Foods, NGL Energy, Plexus, Excellere, IAC, Federal Mogul, IPG Photonics and American Capital. Recent transactions include $320 million IPO, $5.2 billion merger, $2.4 billion sale, $350 million acquisition, $650 million acquisition, $300 million sale, $150 million purchase, $500 million bond issuance and $900 million spin-out.
**Career:** Joined Winston & Strawn in 1982. Elected as Partner in 1987.
**Publications:** Co-editor of BNA portfolio titled "Board of Directors."
**Personal:** BS, summa cum laude, Georgia Institute of Technology. MBA, and JD, Stanford University.

## TOWNSEND, Christopher
Quarles & Brady LLP, Chicago
312 715 5255
chris.townsend@quarles.com
*Featured in Energy & Natural Resources (Illinois)*
**Practice Areas:** Energy, environmental.
**Career:** He has more than twenty years of experience in all aspects of energy, public utility, and environmental law and regulation and represents commercial and industrial energy users, competitive natural gas and electric providers, as well as local, state, national and international governments in addressing risks and opportunities associated with the restructuring of the gas and electricity industries. He has been involved in a wide variety of regulatory proceedings before the Illinois Commerce Commission and FERC with an emphasis on restructuring the energy industries.
**Personal:** JD, University of Iowa (with honors); BA, Augustana College (cum laude).

## TREECE, John
Sidley Austin LLP, Chicago
312 853 2937
jtreece@sidley.com
*Featured in Antitrust (Illinois)*
**Practice Areas:** A Global Coordinator of the firm's Antitrust/Competition practice, Mr Treece focuses on antitrust, patent, and commercial litigation. He has experience with multidistrict price-fixing class actions (involving cement, paper, pharmaceuticals, steel, and telecommunication services) and monopolization cases (involving medical devices, software, and pharmaceuticals). He has twice won antitrust jury trials named "Defense Verdicts of the Year" by the National Law Journal, and has handled "sham" litigation and "citizen petition" monopolization cases for pharmaceutical clients.
**Professional Memberships:** Member, American and Chicago Bar Associations.
**Personal:** Columbia University School of Law, JD, 1978; Harvard University, BA, 1975, magna cum laude. Admission: Illinois.

## TRELA JR, Constantine L
Sidley Austin LLP, Chicago
312 853 7293
ctrela@sidley.com
*Featured in Litigation (Illinois)*
**Practice Areas:** Partner, chairs the Appellate practice group in the Chicago office and is a global coordinator of Sidley's Appellate practice team. Former law clerk for Justice Stevens, handled matters in the Supreme Court, most US Courts of Appeals and various state courts. Appellate practice covers a range of substantive areas, including patent and other intellectual property, product liability, insurance, commercial, and class action matters.
**Personal:** Northwestern University School of Law, JD, 1979, magna cum laude, Order of the Coif; Northwestern University, BA, 1976, with highest distinction, Phi Beta Kappa. Admission: Illinois.

## VALUKAS, Anton R
Jenner & Block LLP, Chicago
312 923 2903
avalukas@jenner.com
*Featured in Litigation (Nationwide), Litigation (Illinois)*
**Career:** Anton R. Valukas, Chairman of Jenner & Block, is a former United States Attorney. A Fellow of the American College of Trial Lawyers, he has extensive civil litigation experience in the areas of mass tort and class actions; in his white-collar criminal defense practice, his clients have included lawyers, accountants, real estate developers, and corporate executives. He represents Fortune 500 companies with regard to conflicts of interest, ethics violations, internal corporate and SEC investigations and civil securities fraud lawsuits. In 2009-2010, Mr Valukas served as court-appointed Examiner in the Lehman Brothers Holdings bankruptcy, the largest bankruptcy in US history.

## VANN, Ryan
Baker & McKenzie, Chicago
312 861 2588
ryan.vann@bakermckenzie.com
*Featured in Labor & Employment (Illinois)*
**Practice Areas:** Labor and employment litigation and counseling. Has litigated several FLSA and state wage and hour class and collective actions, single-plaintiff discrimination cases, unfair labor practice proceedings and arbitrations. Provides day-to-day counseling regarding labor and employment compliance issues, best practices and risk management.
**Professional Memberships:** American Bar Association; Chicago Bar Association.
**Career:** Admitted in 2006. Joined Baker & McKenzie in 2009.
**Publications:** Chapter Editor - How to Take a Case Before the NLRB (2008-2013); The Developing Labor Law (2012-2013) Author - Compensable Time Best Practices, Practical Law Labor and Employment Journal (October 2011)
**Personal:** Attended Indiana University - Bloomington.

## VIDMAR, Jacqueline M
Rooney Rippie & Ratnaswamy LLP, Chicago
312 447 2802
jacqueline.vidmar@r3law.com
*Featured in Environment (Illinois)*
**Practice Areas:** Ms Vidmar advises clients on a wide range of environmental and safety issues in compliance, transactional and litigation matters. Her practice includes managing Superfund litigation and remediation matters, defense of environmental enforcement claims and citizen suits, assisting in transactions involving complex environmental issues, and representing clients before the Illinois Commerce Commission and the Illinois Pollution Control Board. She advises utilities in permitting and regulatory matters, pipeline safety, and the remediation of former manufactured gas plants.
**Professional Memberships:** Asian American Bar Association of Greater Chicago; Board Member and Former Chair, Chicago Committee on Minorities in Large Law Firms.

**Personal:** Northwestern University School of Law, JD; University of Pennsylvania, BA.

## VOBORNIK, Donna
Dentons, Chicago
312 876 7370
donna.vobornik@dentons.com
*Featured in Insurance (Illinois)*
**Practice Areas:** Head of legacy Dentons's Insurance Litigation practice and a general litigator with extensive experience in complex insurance coverage litigation. Has represented insurance clients in approximately 80 environmental coverage cases in state and federal courts across the US. Also litigates other types of toxic tort coverage claims, including asbestos, Chinese drywall and diacytal. Represents insurers in bankruptcy proceedings where the insured is the debtor, and represented insurers in major subrogation matters. She has extensive experience representing insurers in personal lines class actions, and defendants in consumer class actions.
**Personal:** University of Wisconsin Law School, JD, 1987; Northwestern University, BA, 1984.

## VYVERBERG, Robert
Holland & Knight LLP, Chicago
312 578 6559
robert.vyverberg@hklaw.com
*Featured in Labor & Employment (Illinois)*
**Practice Areas:** National Practice Group Leader for firm's Labor, Employment and Benefits Practice Group. His employment practice involves representing employers in individual and class action litigation, administrative proceedings before federal, state and local agencies, mediations, and arbitrations involving all types of statutory and common law claims. He counsels and trains employers on personnel and compliance matters, including implementation of ADR programs, responses to government inquiries and internal investigations. His national practice includes clients in manufacturing, utility, retail, financial services, distribution, hospitality, technology, transportation, and health care industries. He is a frequent author and lecturer on workplace and employment law issues.

## WALL, Robert F
Winston & Strawn LLP, Chicago
312 558 5699
rwall@winston.com
*Featured in Corporate/M&A (Illinois)*
**Practice Areas:** Senior Partner in Corporate Department. Concentration in mergers and acquisitions, contested battles for control, special committees and corporate finance for public companies. Represented clients in these areas since 1977.
**Professional Memberships:** Member, Editorial Board, Mergers and Acquisitions and Corporate Control Law Reporter; past Chair, Northwestern University's Ray Garrett Securities Institute.
**Career:** Joined firm as associate, 1977. Partner, 1984.
**Personal:** University of Virginia, 1970; Northwestern University, BA, with distinction, 1973; Santa Clara University, JD, summa cum

laude, 1977, comments editor, 'Santa Clara Law Review'.

## WATERS, Paige D
Locke Lord LLP, Chicago
312 443 1815
pwaters@lockelord.com
*Featured in Insurance (Illinois)*
**Practice Areas:** Handles corporate transactional and insurance regulatory matters involving national and international property and casualty, life insurance, surplus line, HMO, reinsurance and healthcare clients. Represents troubled insurers, receivers and creditors in complex insolvency matters; private equity and hedge funds in acquisitions of, and investments in, insurers and similarly-regulated entities. Assists insurers in M&A, entity formations, licensure, market conduct and financial examinations, product development and enforcement actions.
**Professional Memberships:** ABA; International Association of Insurance Receivers; NCOIL; NAIC Working Groups; ARIAS US; AIR-ROC.
**Career:** Joined Locke Lord as Partner in 2011.
**Personal:** Chicago-Kent College of Law (JD, 1989); Miami University (BA, 1986).

## WEBB, Dan K
Winston & Strawn LLP, Chicago
312 558 5856
dwebb@winston.com
*Featured in Antitrust (Illinois), Litigation (Nationwide), Products Liability (Nationwide), Litigation (Illinois)*
**Practice Areas:** National trial practice in the areas of major commercial, civil, regulatory, and white-collar criminal cases.
**Professional Memberships:** Fellow, American College of Trial Lawyers.
**Career:** Joined Winston & Strawn as Partner in 1985. Firm Chairman and Member of the Executive Committee.
**Publications:** Co-author, "Corporate Internal Investigations" (Law Journal Seminars Press).
**Personal:** Western Illinois University, 1967; Loyola University School of Law, JD 1970. Iran-Contra Special Trial Counsel; U.S. Attorney, Northern District of Illinois, 1981-85; Illinois Department of Law Enforcement, 1979-80; Assistant U.S. Attorney, 1970-76.

## WEBER III, Louis J
Winston & Strawn LLP, Chicago
312 558 5627
lweber@winston.com
*Featured in Tax (Illinois)*
**Practice Areas:** Mr Weber advises clients on numerous issues related to both taxable and tax-free mergers and acquisitions on behalf of public and private buyers and sellers, and on behalf of private equity funds and their portfolio companies.
**Career:** Mr Weber is co-chair of the firm's tax practice. He has a significant tax controversy practice including substantial cases involving transfer pricing, defense of tax-free reorganizations, application of step-transaction doctrine, defense of alleged tax shelters, amortization of various fees

and expenses, and section 263A capitalization. Mr Weber joined Winston & Strawn LLP in 1985 and was named Partner in 1993.

## WEIL, Andrew L
DLA Piper LLP (US), Chicago
312 368 3425
andrew.weil@dlapiper.com
*Featured in Corporate/M&A (Illinois)*
**Practice Areas:** Corporate/M&A.
**Career:** With more than 25 years of experience in corporate and securities law, he represents purchasers, sellers and investors in M&A transactions involving public and private companies in a broad range of industries, as well as in cross-border and real estate related transactions; assists private companies and institutional and corporate investors in venture capital, private equity and strategic investment transactions; represents issuers and underwriters in public and private financings, including IPOs; counsels public companies and boards in corporate governance, corporate control/takeover defense, proxy fights, and securities regulatory compliance issues.
**Personal:** JD, Northwestern University School of Law.

## WEISBERG, Mark S
Winston & Strawn LLP, Chicago
312 558 8070
mweisberg@winston.com
*Featured in Labor & Employment (Illinois)*
**Practice Areas:** Design, establishment and administration of retirement benefit, welfare benefit, and non-qualified deferred compensation and equity compensation plans (including compliance with Internal Revenue Code Section 409A). Negotiation and drafting of executive employment agreements on behalf of companies and their compensation committees, individual executives and management teams. ERISA litigation.
**Professional Memberships:** National Association of Stock Plan Professionals.
**Career:** Previous Partner/co-chair of ERISA Group, KMZ Rosenman.
**Personal:** University of Pennsylvania, 1985; University of Pennsylvania Law School, 1988; Trustee, Evanston Police Pension Fund; Board of Managers, Officer, University of Pennsylvania Law School Alumni Society; All Stars Project of Chicago Advisory Committee.

## WEISS, Robert M
Neal, Gerber & Eisenberg LLP, Chicago
312 269 8455
rweiss@ngelaw.com
*Featured in Technology (Illinois)*
**Practice Areas:** Provides legal and strategic advice on commercial IT matters, and represents clients worldwide in a variety of complex technology transactions, including systems integrations, infrastructure and business process outsourcings, technology development and licensing projects, ERP implementations, cloud computing and web hosting arrangements, data center and co-location agreements and telecommunications procurements.
**Professional Memberships:** ITechLaw board of directors for 2007-Present.

**Career:** Partner; Information Technology Practice Group, Chair; named to '40 Under 40' most accomplished Illinois attorneys, Chicago Daily Law Bulletin (2003).
**Publications:** Author and lecturer on information technology law issues.
**Personal:** Stanford Law School (JD, 1990); Dartmouth College (AB, 1987).

## WEISS, Steven A
Schopf & Weiss LLP, Chicago
312 701 9311
weiss@sw.com
*Featured in Litigation (Illinois)*
**Practice Areas:** Steven Weiss is a business litigator focused on representing both plaintiffs and defendants. He is well-known for his work on intellectual property cases, trade secret matters, and large commercial disputes. Mr Weiss was chosen as one of the Top Ten Super Lawyers in 2009 and one of the Top Hundred Super Lawyers from 2005 to 2013. He is Chair of the American Bar Association's Standing Committee on Strategic Communications and is on the Council of the ABA's Litigation Section. He is a on the Board of the Chicago Bar Foundation and the Business Council of the Goodman Theatre.
**Professional Memberships:** Mr Weiss is a member of the American and the Chicago Bar Associations.
**Career:** Schopf & Weiss LLP Chairman, Founding Partner, and Member of the Executive Committee (1987-present); Isham, Lincoln & Beale (1986-1987); Reuben & Proctor (1980-1986).
**Publications:** Mr Weiss's publications include "Thirteen Tips for Being a Better Lawyer," "Cost-shifting for E-discovery," "Non-Competes and Trade Secrets in a High Tech E-World," "Sanctions for Spoliation of Electronic Evidence," and A Trial Lawyer's Guide to Discovery in Federal and State Courts in Illinois.
**Personal:** University of Michigan Law School (JD); Cornell University (BA).

## WELKE, William R
Kirkland & Ellis LLP, Chicago
312 862 2143
william.welke@kirkland.com
*Featured in Tax (Illinois)*
**Practice Areas:** William Welke focuses his practice on the tax aspects of complex business transactions and entities, including mergers, acquisitions and leveraged buyouts; venture capital and other private equity investments; formation of private equity funds; joint ventures and partnerships; debt and equity restructurings; and executive compensation.
**Personal:** University of Michigan Law School, JD, 1983; Massachusetts Institute of Technology, SB, 1980.

## WHITE, Bruce
Barnes & Thornburg LLP, Chicago
312 214 4584
Bwhite@BTLaw.com
*Featured in Environment (Illinois)*
**Practice Areas:** Environmental Law: litigation, arbitration and mediation of environmental dis-

putes, and in administrative permitting and enforcement proceedings, along with environmental aspects of corporate and real estate transactions.
**Professional Memberships:** American Bar Association, Illinois State Bar Association, Chicago Bar Association.
**Career:** Admitted to practice in Illinois; US Supreme Court; 5th, 7th, 9th Circuits; USDC Northern District of Illinois; Member of the Federal Trial Bar.
**Personal:** University of Illinois, 1973 (B.S. Psychology, BA Economics, both with highest distinction); University of Chicago Law School. 1978.

## WHITE, Linda
Dentons, Chicago
312 876 8950
linda.white@dentons.com
*Featured in Real Estate (Illinois)*
**Practice Areas:** Senior Real Estate Partner, member legacy Dentons Financial Management Team Executive Committee. Extensive experience in real estate transactions including work-outs, acquisitions and dispositions, equity investments, financing, leasing (representing both landlords and tenants), sale leasebacks, corporate real estate management and telecommunications.
**Professional Memberships:** Trustees' Council, Penn Women; Northwestern Law Board; Editorial Board, Practical Real Estate Lawyer (American Law Institute - ABA); Practicing Law Institute's Real Estate Law Advisory Committee.
**Publications:** Lectures and writes extensively on commercial lease issues, real estate debt and equity work-outs.
**Personal:** Northwestern University School of Law, JD, 1976; University of Pennsylvania, BA, 1973; Fellow, American Bar Foundation.

## WIENER, Todd
McDermott Will & Emery LLP, Chicago
312 984 7719
twiener@mwe.com
*Featured in Environment (Illinois)*
**Practice Areas:** Focuses on all aspects of environmental law and toxic tort litigation. Significant experience in administrative enforcement proceedings and litigation arising under all major federal environmental laws, including the Comprehensive Environmental Response, Compensation and Liability Act (CERCLA), the Clean Air Act (CAA), the Resource Conservation Recovery Act (RCRA), the Clean Water Act (CWA), the Emergency Planning and Community Right-to-Know Act, the Occupational Safety and Health Act (OSHA) and corresponding state laws.
**Professional Memberships:** Illinois bar; American Bar Association.
**Personal:** Harvard Law School, JD (cum laude), 1986; University of Cincinnati, BA (summa cum laude), 1983.

## WILLIAMS, Tracy D
Sidley Austin LLP, Chicago
312 853 3664
tdwilliams@sidley.com
*Featured in Tax (Illinois)*

**Practice Areas:** Partner in Sidley's Chicago Office. Her practice focuses on federal, international and state taxation of insurance companies and insurance-related transactions. She advises insurance companies, banks and investors in structuring corporate transactions involving insurance companies, and regularly advises insurance company clients on premium, income and retaliatory tax issues. She also represents insurance companies in tax controversy matters and in tax litigation in state and federal courts. She is a member of the Board of Directors of the Insurance Tax Conference.
**Personal:** Harvard Law School, JD, 1994, cum laude; University of Illinois, BA, 1991, magna cum laude.

## WITCOFF, David L
Jones Day, Chicago
312 269 4259
dlwitcoff@jonesday.com
*Featured in Intellectual Property (Illinois)*
**Practice Areas:** Specializes in litigating complex, high-stakes patent and other intellectual property disputes across a broad spectrum of technologies, including semiconductor products, processing and packaging; internet and World Wide Web systems and protocols; computer hardware and software; electronic commerce systems; digital cameras; cellular telephones; paging control systems; optic lens; pharmaceuticals; medical devices; diagnostic equipment; automotive control systems and components; and many other products. Admitted to practice before various US District Courts, the US Court of Appeals for the Federal Circuit, and the US Patent and Trademark Office. Repeatedly recognized in numerous publications as a leading intellectual property litigator.

## WOLF, Charles B
Vedder Price PC, Chicago
312 609 7888
cwolf@vedderprice.com
*Featured in Labor & Employment (Illinois)*
**Practice Areas:** Labor and Employment Shareholder representing clients in a wide range of industries and focusing on labor, employment and employee benefits law and litigation, representing employers and multi-employer funds. Experienced in all aspects of employee benefit plan design and administration, executive compensation, collective bargaining, NLRB and arbitration proceedings, employment discrimination cases and wrongful discharge cases. Recent emphasis includes ERISA litigation and withdrawal liability issues. Lead counsel in several well-known employee benefits cases and has handled the labor and benefits aspects of numerous mergers and acquisitions.
**Career:** Admitted (IL) 1975.
**Personal:** JD, University of Chicago; BA, Brown University.

## WRIGHT, Michael D
Kirkland & Ellis LLP, Chicago
312 862 2243
michael.wright@kirkland.com
*Featured in Banking & Finance (Illinois)*

**Practice Areas:** Michael Wright is a corporate partner who represents private equity groups and corporate borrowers in international, working capital, acquisition, cash flow, asset-based and mezzanine financings, loan restructurings and workouts. The transactions he has handled range in size from several million dollars to more than $1 billion.
**Personal:** Indiana University School of Law - Indianapolis, JD, cum laude, 1988; Purdue University, B.S., Management, 1985.

### WYDAJEWSKI, Brian
Baker & McKenzie, Chicago
312 861 8286
brian.wydajewski@bakermckenzie.com
*Featured in Labor & Employment (Illinois)*
**Practice Areas:** Assists multinational corporations with the design, implementation and operation of global equity plans and other incentive arrangements, particulary on tax, securities, labor/employment and currency issues. Also advises on compensation/benefits, labor/employment, and equity compensation matters arising in global corporate transactions, including mergers/acquisitions, spin-offs, IPOs, reorganizations and redomestications.
**Professional Memberships:** National Association of Stock Plan Professionals. Global Equity Organization. Adjunct Professor, John Marshall Law School (Graduate Employee Benefits Program).
**Personal:** Born 3 February 1966. JD, Loyola University School of Law (1994). Senior Member, Loyola University Law Journal. BS, DePaul University (1988). Married (Anna Maria), 4 children (Christian, Olivia, Brendan, Ariana).

### WYLIE, Kenneth R
Sidley Austin LLP, Chicago
312 853 7157
kwylie@sidley.com
*Featured in Insurance (Illinois)*
**Practice Areas:** Senior Counsel in Sidley's Chicago office. He practices in Insurance with a focus on regulatory matters affecting insurance companies, agents and brokers, and other insurance entities. He provides counseling on corporate, commercial and regulatory matters including organization and acquisition of insurance companies, evaluation of captives, alternative risk transfer vehicles and securitizations. He has extensive experience representing guaranty funds, insureds, reinsurers, reinsureds, claimants and others involved in insurance company insolvencies. Also handles reinsurance arbitrations including reinsurance pools and finite reinsurance disputes.
**Personal:** University of Michigan Law School, JD, 1977; Michigan State University, BS, 1973, with high honors. Admission: Illinois.

### YASTROW, Joseph
Laner Muchin, Ltd, Chicago
312 467 9800
jyastrow@lanermuchin.com
*Featured in Labor & Employment (Illinois)*
**Practice Areas:** Management side labor and employment law. Certified mediator.

**Professional Memberships:** Member and former Chair Chicago Bar Association Labor and Employment Law Committee. Member: American Bar Association, the College of Labor and Employment Lawyers and the American Employment Law Council. Multiple selections to Chambers Guide to America's Leading Business Lawyers, The International Who's Who of Business Lawyers, Illinois' Super Lawyers, Illinois Leading Labor and Employment Attorneys and Best Lawyers In America. AV Martindale-Hubbell rating.
**Career:** Mr Yastrow has exclusively represented employers in labor and employment law matters since 1978 primarily with Laner Muchin where he is a Partner and an Executive Committee Member.
**Personal:** SMU School of Law (JD 1978). Law Review Editor. Dartmouth College (AB 1975).

### YI, Ted
Quarles & Brady LLP, Chicago
312 715 5209
ted.yi@quarles.com
*Featured in Real Estate (Illinois)*
**Practice Areas:** Real estate, commercial landlord leasing, commercial tenant leasing.
**Professional Memberships:** Fellow, American College of Real Estate Lawyers; Member, Lambda Alpha International (Ely Chapter).
**Career:** He concentrates his practice in the area of real estate law. His extensive and varied real estate experience includes a wide range of commercial real estate transactions, with a particular focus on commercial lease transactions representing both owners and users of office, retail and industrial properties.
**Personal:** Harvard Law School (JD, 1982); University of Illinois at Urbana-Champaign (BA and BS, Phi Beta Kappa, 1979).

### YODER, Lowell D
McDermott Will & Emery LLP, Chicago
312 984 7523
lyoder@mwe.com
*Featured in Tax (Illinois)*
**Practice Areas:** Focuses on international tax planning for multinationals. Advises on cross-border acquisitions, dispositions, mergers, joint ventures, and financings.
**Career:** Frequent speaker for Practising Law Institute, Tax Executives Institute and International Fiscal Association; Adjunct Professor of International Tax Law at Northwestern University School of Law; editor-in-chief of 'The International Tax Journal'; board member of 'Tax Management International Journal'.
**Publications:** Author of four treatises on Subpart F (rules applying to foreign operations of US multinationals); author of numerous international tax articles.
**Personal:** University of Illinois College of Law (JD, magna cum laude).

### YOUNG, Jonathan
Edwards Wildman Palmer, Chicago
312 201 2662
jyoung@edwardswildman.com
*Featured in Bankruptcy/Restructuring (Illinois)*

**Practice Areas:** Jonathan Young is experienced in the interplay between the Bankruptcy Code and complex programs of insurance law, and regularly advises insurers in connection with restructuring and insolvency driven disputes. He also has extensive experience advising fiduciaries. In addition, he has represented public and private companies in a variety of restructuring and workout contexts, including advice and representation in connection with the restructuring of numerous complex credit facilities. Jonathan focuses on developing timely, workable strategies that pay equal attention to both the legal and business issues involved.
**Personal:** Northwestern University School of Law, JD; Yale University, BA, cum laude.

### ZDRAVECKY, Amy J
Franczek Radelet P.C., Chicago
312 786 6501
ajz@franczek.com
*Featured in Labor & Employment (Illinois)*
**Practice Areas:** Engages in all areas of traditional labor and employment law; negotiates collective bargaining agreements and administers and enforces these agreements in arbitration; provides training and counseling to clients regarding union avoidance, sexual harassment and compliance with a variety of employment-related statutes including Title VII, ADEA, ADA, FMLA and FCRA.
**Professional Memberships:** Labor and Employment Law section, ABA; Subcommittee on the Development of the Law under the NLRA, ABA.
**Career:** Partner; Labor and Employment Practice Group.
**Publications:** Author, commentator and lecturer on employment law issues.
**Personal:** University of Michigan (BA, 1992); University of Michigan Law School (JD, 1994).

### ZEBOVITZ, Lisa S
Neal, Gerber & Eisenberg LLP, Chicago
312 269 8033
lzebovitz@ngelaw.com
*Featured in Environment (Illinois)*
**Practice Areas:** Represents both the government and private sectors in complex litigation and administrative proceedings involving environmental issues in the areas of solid and hazardous wastes, mold, underground tanks, toxic substances, pesticides, water, air and federal procurement. She is uniquely situated to provide cost-effective and practical counsel given that her many years of in-house corporate and government experience allow her to appreciate issues from the client's perspective, as well as from the government's.
**Career:** Partner; Environmental Practice Group Co-Chair.
**Personal:** Lake Forest College (BA, 1977); DePaul University College of Law (JD, 1980).

### ZELEK, Eugene
Freeborn & Peters LLP, Chicago
312 360 6777
ezelek@freebornpeters.com
*Featured in Antitrust (Illinois), Media & Entertainment (Illinois)*

**Practice Areas:** Extensive counseling, transactional, and litigation expertise in marketing-related law for leading consumer and industrial businesses and consulting firms internationally, in such areas as antitrust, pricing, and supply/distribution, as well as branding, licensing, entertainment, complex contracts, alliances, and advertising.
**Professional Memberships:** For a list of professional memberships, visit: www.freebornpeters.com/attorneyDetail.aspx?aid=129.
**Career:** Chair, Antitrust and Trade Regulation Group; Adjunct Professor, Northwestern University Kellogg School of Management; former product manager, The Quaker Oats Company. Peer Ratings: Super Lawyer, Antitrust, Intellectual Property, and Franchising and Dealership work; Leading Lawyer, Antitrust, Advertising, Intellectual Property, and Entertainment; Leading Individual, Antitrust and Media and Entertainment (Chambers); recognized in Competition/Antitrust Law (PLC Cross-Border Handbook); Best Lawyers in America, Advertising and Entertainment.
**Publications:** For a list of recent published works and more detailed information, visit: www.freebornpeters.com/attorneyDetail.aspx?aid=129.
**Personal:** JD, cum laude: Northwestern University, Executive Editor, Law Review; MBA, Marketing, with Distinction: Northwestern University Kellogg School of Management, Distinguished Scholar; BS, Journalism, with high honors: University of Illinois.

### ZIMBLER, Jay
Sidley Austin LLP, Chicago
312 853 2232
jzimbler@sidley.com
*Featured in Tax (Illinois)*
**Practice Areas:** Partner in Sidley's Chicago office, practicing in tax and tax controversy. He focuses on federal income tax matters with emphasis on contested matters, Subchapter C and the taxation of foreign related transactions. He has handled complex cases with IRS Appeals for a variety of multinational corporations nationwide, as well as litigated cases in the US Tax Court, the US Court of Federal Claims, and the Seventh Circuit Court of Appeals.
**Personal:** Harvard Law School, JD, 1975, cum laude; University of Michigan, BA, 1972, with highest honors. CPA and fellow of the American College of Tax Counsel. Admission: Illinois.

### ZOTT, David J
Kirkland & Ellis LLP, Chicago
312 862 2428
david.zott@kirkland.com
*Featured in Antitrust (Illinois)*
**Practice Areas:** Trial lawyer. Complex commercial and class action litigation, with an emphasis on antitrust, energy and bankruptcy litigation. Lead trial counsel in multidistrict antitrust, distribution and franchise lawsuits. Represents clients in all facets of oil, gas and energy litigation, including exploration, production and marketing. Trials involving business valuation, fraudulent

conveyance and related issues arising from corporate restructurings.

**Professional Memberships:** ABA, Antitrust Section; Institute for Energy Law; Rocky Mountain Mineral Law Foundation.

**Personal:** University of Michigan Law School, JD, magna cum laude, Order of the Coif, 1986; Northwestern University, BA, highest distinction, Phi Beta Kappa, 1983; Virginia Military Institute, 1980.

**ZUBAIRI, Junaid A.**
Vedder Price PC, Chicago
312 609 7720
jzubairi@vedderprice.com
*Featured in Litigation (Illinois)*

**Practice Areas:** Shareholder and Chair of Government Enforcement & Special Investigations group; practices before SEC, U.S. Attorney's Office, CFTC and other agencies. Represents companies and individuals in investigations and securities litigation, conducts internal investigations, advises on investment services matters, counsels during regulatory examinations and on FCPA matters, provides compliance and remediation advice. Successfully represented clients in matters involving financial statement restatements, alleged financial fraud, books/records, internal control violations, whistleblower allegations, board governance, supervision and insider trading. Serves as Co-Chair of ASECA.

**Career:** Admitted (IL) 2002.

**Personal:** JD, Loyola University Chicago School of Law; BA, cum laude, Loyola University of Chicago.

**ZUSSMAN, Gary T**
Goldberg Kohn Ltd, Chicago
312 201 3940
gary.zussman@goldbergkohn.com
*Featured in Banking & Finance (Illinois)*

**Career:** Gary Zussman is a principal in the Commercial Finance Group with more than 20 years of experience representing banks and financial institutions in documenting, negotiating and closing loan transactions, such as refinancings, leveraged buyouts and recapitalizations. The majority of his clients are asset-based and cash-flow lenders who typically service middle market borrowers, with average transactions ranging from $10 million to $100 million. He has experience in securing all types of collateral, such as intellectual property, agricultural products, licensed inventory and investment property. He represents financial institutions that finance various types of industries, including retail, manufacturing, health care products and trucking.

# ADELMAN & GETTLEMAN LTD

**www**.ag-ltd.com  **tel:** 312 435 1050  **fax:** 312 435 1059

**Principal Partners:** Howard L Adelman, Chad H Gettleman, Henry B Merens, Brad A Berish, Mark A Carter, Adam P Silverman, Nathan Q Rugg, Steven B Chaiken and Erich S Buck

## Firm Overview:

Adelman & Gettleman, Ltd. was founded in March, 1983 by Howard L Adelman and Chad H Gettleman, both of whom have devoted their entire professional career to the areas of bankruptcy, corporate reorganization and insolvency, and commercial litigation. The firm presently has nine (9) principals including: Howard L Adelman, Chad H Gettleman, Henry B Merens, Brad A Berish, Mark A Carter, Adam P Silverman, Nathan Q Rugg, Steven B Chaiken and Erich S Buck all of whom have devoted their entire professional careers to the foregoing areas of concentration.

In its 30th year, the firm remains one of the few Chicago Bankruptcy boutique firms recognized annually in Illinois Super Lawyers, Illinois Leading Lawyers Network, Best Lawyers in America, and Chambers and Partners. Two of its attorneys, Chad H Gettleman and Brad A Berish are also non-practicing Certified Public Accountants. Both Howard L Adelman and Chad H Gettleman were listed in the 2012 edition of Chambers USA and are listed again in Chambers USA 2013, America's Leading Lawyers for Business, Chambers & Partners Legal Publishers. Eight (8) of its attorneys are listed in the 2013 edition of Illinois Super Lawyers. Howard L Adelman is listed as one of the Top 10 Illinois Super Lawyers, regardless of specialty in 2012 and 2013, one of the Top 100 Illinois Super Lawyers for 2006-13 and one of the Top 100 Business Lawyers in Illinois by the Leading Lawyers Network in 2006-12. In October of 1999, Chief Justice William Rehnquist appointed Howard L Adelman to serve as a member of the Judicial Conference Advisory Committee on the Federal Rules of Bankruptcy Procedure. Mr Adelman served on the Advisory Committee from 1999-2005 through the implementation of BAPCPA. Mr Adelman is also a Fellow of the American College of Bankruptcy, as part of its Twelfth Class.

## Main Areas of Practice:

**Their speciality:**

In addition to commercial litigation in the State and Federal Courts, the firm has participated in many major bankruptcy and reorganization cases, representing debtors, trustees, secured creditors and committees. Approximately 75% of the firm's matters consist of litigation in the Bankruptcy Courts. The firm has an extensive internal continuing legal education program. Members of the firm participate as speakers in seminars and commercial litigation programs, and offer articles on areas of their concentration.

The firm's bankruptcy and commercial litigation practice is highly regarded and respected in bankruptcy courts throughout Illinois, Indiana, and Wisconsin. The firm seeks innovative approaches and solutions in the workout context, but stands ready to draw upon its substantial litigation experience in complex bankruptcy litigation when necessary. The firm is experienced in resolving the business and legal problems that arise when commercial transactions, credit agreements, business plans, and mortgages fail to proceed as intended. Their bankruptcy attorneys routinely handle the following matters for its clients:

- Advising management, boards of directors, and committees of directors of troubled companies before and during insolvency and reorganization, including counseling financially distressed companies regarding alternatives to the commencement of a Chapter 11 reorganization case.
- Identifying problems and solutions which may or will arise in bankruptcy cases and structuring the potential resolution of same, prior to their emergence.
- Handling cash collateral negotiations and debtor-in-possession financing arrangements.
- Structuring and implementing the purchase and sale of businesses and assets from Chapter 11 debtors.
- Handling complex Chapter 11 plan negotiations and the litigation of contested plan confirmation issues.
- Prosecuting and defending preference litigation and fraudulent conveyance litigation.
- Enforcing the rights of secured creditors.
- Handling single asset real estate partnership cases.
- Providing corporate restructuring advice.

**PRACTICE AREAS**

Insolvency
Bankruptcy & Reorganization Law
Commercial & Corporate Litigation

**OFFICES**

ILLINOIS
**CHICAGO:** 53 West Jackson Blvd., Suite 1050, IL 60604
Tel: 312 435 1050   Fax: 312 435 1059

ADELMAN & GETTLEMAN LTD
established 1983

# BANNER & WITCOFF

**www.**BannerWitcoff.com **tel:** 312 463 5000 **fax:** 312 463 5001

**Managing Partner:** Gary D Fedorochko
Number of partners: 49
Number of lawyers: 85
Languages: *English*

## Firm Overview:

A national law firm with more than 90 attorneys and agents and 90 years of practice, Banner & Witcoff provides legal counsel and representation to the world's most innovative companies. The firm's attorneys are known for having the breadth of experience and insight needed to handle complex patent applications as well as handle and resolve difficult disputes and business challenges for clients across all industries and geographic boundaries.

## Main Areas of Practice:

### Litigation:

Banner & Witcoff is a preferred litigation provider for *Fortune* 500 companies, midlevel companies, and technology-focused start-ups. The firm has a deep bench of seasoned trial and appellate lawyers with industry experience and advanced degrees in engineering and biotechnology fields. Many of the firm's litigators have served as former law clerks to federal judges, and have former in-house counsel experience. The firm has assisted and consulted in connection with enforcement activities worldwide playing key roles in the strategy and coordination of foreign litigation. Banner & Witcoff lawyers try cases before judges and juries in both federal and state courts around the country, at the appellate levels, and before the ITC and the USPTO.
Building on six decades of success in IP infringement bench trials, Banner & Witcoff's litigators have successfully conducted jury trials throughout the United States in wide ranging technical fields, including in such diverse technologies as computer software, recombinant DNA pharmaceuticals, prosthetic hip implants, process industrial controls, automotive components, plastic injection molds and textiles. The firm has successfully represented clients in numerous landmark cases, including several renowned intellectual property decisions including Tasini v. The New York Times, Deepsouth Packing Co. v. Laitram Corp., and Diamond v. Chakrabarty.
**Contact:** Joseph M Potenza **Tel:** 202 824 3000
**Email:** jpotenza@bannerwitcoff.com
**Contact:** Christopher J Renk **Tel:** 312 463 5000
**Email:** crenk@bannerwitcoff.com

### Prosecution:

Banner & Witcoff 's prosecution teams manage large patent portfolios ranging from several hundred to several thousand patents and patent applications and typically including substantial numbers of foreign patents and applications. Many of the firm's patent prosecutors are former US Patent and Trademark Office examiners.
**Contact:** Gary D Fedorochko **Tel:** 202 824 3000
**Email:** gfedorochko@bannerwitcoff.com
**Contact:** Charles L Miller **Tel:** 312 463 5000
**Email:** cmiller@bannerwitcoff.com

### Design Patents:

Banner & Witcoff is widely known as the leader in design patent procurement and design patent procurement strategies. In 2012, Banner & Witcoff procured more design patents than any other firm for the 10th consecutive year. In 2012, Banner & Witcoff procured 660 US design patents on behalf of its clients, bringing the total number of design patents procured by the firm since 2003 to more than 5,700.
**Contact:** Robert S Katz **Tel:** 202 824 3000
**Email:** rkatz@bannerwitcoff.com
**Contact:** Richard S Stockton **Tel:** 312 463 5000
**Email:** rstockton@bannerwitcoff.com

### Trademarks:

Trademark attorneys at Banner & Witcoff have extensive experience with evaluating trademark use and registrability issues, and obtaining trademark registrations efficiently and effectively for US and international clients. Banner & Witcoff attorneys devise overarching brand- and product-oriented trademark strategies, both offensive and defensive for the firm's clients as well as licensing and assigning trademarks to and from their clients. The firm manages and maintains large and complex trademark portfolios for global corporations, and enforces and defends against trademark infringement allegations both domestically and internationally, including through oppositions, cancellations, court litigation, and customs procedures.
**Contact:** Helen Hill Minsker **Tel:** 312 463 5000
**Email:** hminsker@bannerwitcoff.com

## PRACTICE AREAS

Copyrights
Design Patents
Jury Trials
Licensing
Litigation
Patent Prosecution
Trademarks
Trade Secrets

## OFFICES

**DISTRICT OF COLUMBIA**
**WASHINGTON DC:** 1100 13th Street, N.W., Suite 1200
DC 20005
Tel: 202 824 3000   Fax: 202 824 3001

**ILLINOIS**
**CHICAGO:** 10 S. Wacker Drive, Suite 3000, IL 60606
Tel: 312 463 5000   Fax: 312 463 5001

**MASSACHUSETTS**
**BOSTON:** 28 State Street, Suite 1800, MA 02109
Tel: 617 720 9600   Fax: 617 720 9601

**OREGON**
**PORTLAND:** 121 SW Salmon Street, Suite 1100,
OR 97204
Tel: 503 425 6800   Fax: 503 425 6801

BANNER & WITCOFF, LTD.
INTELLECTUAL PROPERTY LAW

# BRINKS HOFER GILSON & LIONE

www.usebrinks.com **tel:** 866 222 0112 **fax:** 312 321 4299

**President:** James R Sobieraj
Number of partners: 81
Number of other lawyers: 65

## Firm Overview:

All IP, all the time – that's Brinks Hofer Gilson & Lione. One of the largest dedicated intellectual property law firms in the US, Brinks is at the cutting edge of IP law, providing services in the US and globally to research-driven clients whose business success depends on developing and protecting innovation.

Brinks manages IP litigation and all aspects of patent, trademark, copyright and trade secrets, unfair competition, and intellectual asset management law, as well as technology and licensing agreements. The firm serves clients in electrical engineering, chemical engineering, the mechanical arts, biotechnology, pharmaceuticals, nanotechnology, and computer sciences. It prosecutes thousands of patents every year; and also has a thriving practice at the International Trade Commission (ITC).

Brinks is repeatedly ranked by *Chambers & Partners* as the #1 IP firm in Chicago and #1 in the Midwest. In 2012 – for the third consecutive year – US News & World Report ranked Brinks as Best Law Firm, National, Intellectual Property Law. The firm has seven offices – including in Chicago and in Washington DC – and the firm is supported by a full complement of scientific advisors, patent agents and paralegals.

## Main Areas of Practice:

### Patents:

Brinks lawyers prosecute patents in every major technical field and help clients obtain and license and protect their patents. The firm's International Patent Group also serves as a full-service resource for global companies by establishing, protecting and enforcing patent portfolios around the world.

In 2012, Managing Intellectual Property magazine named Brinks one of the top Patent Prosecution firms in the Midwest. Legal 500 has listed Brinks as a top law firm for Patent Prosecution in Utility and Design for the last four years.

### Litigation:

Brinks' litigators have earned a reputation nationwide for their success in winning jury verdicts, leveraging a thorough knowledge of technology, their mastery of the nuances of the law, and their commitment to effectively communicating with clients about legal strategies. The firm represents clients at all levels of the judicial system and guides them through alternative means to resolve important disputes.

In 2010, Managing Intellectual Property magazine named Brinks the Patent Litigation Firm of the Year for the Midwest Region and one of the Top 5 Patent Litigation Firms in the US.

### Trademarks & Unfair Competition:

Brinks has been at the forefront of trademark and unfair competition law, trying cases throughout the country and arguing them all the way to the US Supreme Court. Brinks conducts litigation; trademark searches and clearance; application and prosecution; licensing activities including collegiate licensing and sports stadium naming rights licensing; due diligence in acquisitions; mediation and arbitration; and Customs recordal and enforcement.

Brinks International Trademark Group has represented clients in trademark prosecution around the world and actively represents clients in oppositions, consultations and litigation in association with their global network of independent foreign associates.

Brinks was named a Top Trademark Firm in the Midwest for Trademark Contentious – Midwest by Managing Intellectual Property magazine in 2012. IP Today also named the firm a Top 5 Trademark Practice in its annual survey.

### International Trade Commission:

With the globalization of corporations, new technologies, and increasing competition worldwide, holders of intellectual property rights are increasingly turning to the International Trade Commission for its accelerated procedures and powerful remedies. Brinks' ITC Group represents a vast array of clients before the United States International Trade Commission. Recognizing that ITC proceedings are complex and specialized, the Brinks ITC Group uses a team approach to offer clients a unique combination of legal and technical expertise.

### Clients:

Clients include a wide range of major US and international corporations. Representative clients include Ball Corp., Amway, Alticor, Broadcom, Brunswick, Cook, Deere & Co., ESCO Technologies, Herman Miller, Progressive, United Airlines, Visteon and the Wm. Wrigley Jr. Co.

## PRACTICE AREAS

Appellate
Copyright
Intellectual Asset Management
International Patent
International Trade Commission (ITC)
International Trademark
Licensing
Litigation
Patent Prosecution
Trade Secrets
Trademarks & Unfair Competition

## INDUSTRY GROUPS

Biotechnology & Pharmaceutical
Chemicals, Energy & Agriculture
Electrical & Computer
Green Technology
Medical Devices
Nanotechnology

## OFFICES

**ILLINOIS**
**CHICAGO:** NBC Tower, Suite 3600,
455 North Cityfront Plaza Drive, IL 60611-5599
Tel: 312 321 4200
Email: iplaw@usebrinks.com

**DISTRICT OF COLUMBIA**
**WASHINGTON, DC:** Suite 900, 1775 Pennsylvania Ave.,
NW, DC, 20006
Tel: 202 296 8700

**INDIANA**
**INDIANAPOLIS:** Capital Center, Suite 1100,
201 North Illinois Street, IN 46204-4220
Tel: 317 636 0886

**MICHIGAN**
**ANN ARBOR:** 524 South Main Street, Suite 200,
MI 48104-2921
Tel: 734 302 6000

**DETROIT:** 300 River Place Drive, Suite 1775, MI 48207
Tel: 313 393 5400

**NORTH CAROLINA**
**DURHAM:** 4721 Emperor Boulevard, Suite 220, NC
27709-5285
Tel: 919 998 5700

**UTAH**
**SALT LAKE CITY:** 222 South Main Street, Suite 1930,
UT 84101-2194
Tel: 801 355 7900

BRINKS
HOFER
GILSON
& LIONE ®

# BUTLER RUBIN SALTARELLI & BOYD LLP

**www.**butlerrubin.com **tel:** 312 444 9660 **fax:** 312 444 9287

**Managing Partners:** The firm is governed by a four-person management committee.
Number of partners: 21  Number of other lawyers: 15

**OFFICES**

ILLINOIS

**CHICAGO:** 70 West Madison Street. Suite 1800 IL 60602
Tel: 312 444 9660  Fax: 312 444 9287

## Firm Overview:

Formed in 1980, Butler Rubin Saltarelli & Boyd LLP is a Chicago-based litigation boutique with a national reputation in the core practice areas of commercial litigation and reinsurance, including antitrust, competition law and opt-out antitrust litigation; class action; defense of corporate directors and officers; mortgage insurance; credit insurance, insolvency; creditors' rights; and products liability and mass tort matters. The firm works throughout the United States and abroad. From representing clients in international reinsurance disputes in London to representing clients in antitrust cases in the United States, its practice is diverse and its approach innovative.

Butler Rubin is always looking for new and more efficient ways to partner with clients. Whether it is through its award-winning Client Service program or a long-standing policy of not passing internal costs on to clients, Butler Rubin distinguishes itself from other law firms. At its inception, a group of partners from one of the nation's largest law firms left to form a different type of law firm. The original concept continues – a firm where the needs of clients serve as the guiding force, where a smaller environment promotes demonstrated teamwork and true collaboration, and where an elite corps of lawyers practices together.

## Main Areas of Practice:

### Antitrust & Competition Law:

Serving as antitrust counselors as well as litigators for over 30 years, including serving as counsel for the plaintiff in the ground-breaking Spray-Rite v Monsanto case. The firm helps clients successfully resolve a wide variety of disputes with customers, suppliers and distributors and its representation of large purchasers in the burgeoning area of opt-out antitrust litigation have earned Butler Rubin an enviable reputation. The firm's representation of manufacturers who sell their products through distributors has helped those businesses avoid expensive problems when those relationships change.
**Contact:** James A Morsch

### Class Action:

Representing clients in all types of class action disputes. The attorneys have successfully defended insurers and financial institutions in nationwide class action lawsuits brought under the securities and antitrust laws as well as federal consumer protection and state consumer fraud statutes. The firm has also represented manufacturers and distributors in high-stakes class actions, as well as acting as national coordinating counsel and local counsel in class actions at the federal and state courts at the trial or appellate levels.
**Contacts:** Albert E Fowerbaugh, Jr, James A Morsch and Michael R Hassan

### Complex Business Disputes:

Representing clients in large, complex business disputes, including shareholder derivative suits, managed care disputes and employment litigation, throughout the United States. As experienced trial lawyers, the firm's approach to discovery is extremely focused, eschewing battles and discovery that are not essential to trial or favorable settlement. With more than 30 litigators and a sizeable support staff of trained professionals, the firm has the depth and experience to efficiently handle complex disputes throughout the country.
**Contacts:** Robert N Hermes and Gerald G Saltarelli

### Mortgage Insurance & Credit Insurance:

Representing insurers and reinsurers in mortgage insurance and credit insurance disputes regarding breach of contract, rescission, fraud, coverage issues and bad faith disputes. The firm is currently representing a mortgage insurer and a credit insurer in eleven separate litigations throughout the United States against various lenders concerning mortgage and credit insurance policies involving aggregate exposures of hundreds of millions of dollars.
**Contact:** Michael R Hassan

### Reinsurance:

Representing domestic and foreign clients in complex reinsurance disputes involving areas such as underwriting, scope and applicability of arbitration clauses, placement disclosures, claim handling, retrospectively rated business, obligations to follow settlements, allocation of settlements, obligations under surplus share reinsurance contracts, excess of loss contracts, application of ultimate net loss and net retained line clauses, accounting for premiums and losses, agency, insolvency and finite reinsurance, and credit and mortgage insurance and reinsurance. The firm's attorneys are immersed in the intricacies of reinsurance custom and practice and the commercial relationships upon which participants in the industry depend.

In 2004, Butler Rubin created Women in Reinsurance™ (WIR™) to discuss how the reinsurance industry was evolving and how women could play a dynamic role in the future of the field. WIR™ regularly sponsors events of interest to professional women in the reinsurance industry and fosters networking and information sharing ( www.womeninreinsurance.com).
**Contacts:** Robert N Hermes and James I Rubin

### Diversity Efforts:

The firm is a founding member of the Small Firm Diversity Initiative in coordination with the Minority Corporate Counsel Association. The initiative sets forth written standards for promoting diversity in smaller law firms, as well as mentoring and other commitments. In addition, the firm has provided financial support to a number of minority law student groups and awards a $10,000 renewable annual scholarship to a first-year law student, with preference given to diverse candidates.

### Pro Bono:

Since its inception, Butler Rubin has encouraged its lawyers to participate in projects that are pro bono publico, or for the public good. Each year, the firm commits to devoting at least 2% of billable time to pro bono matters and to getting more partners involved in this work. It prides itself on using its noted litigation expertise to satisfy the unmet legal needs of the Chicago community and gives full billable hour credit to time spent by the firm's attorneys on pro bono matters. As one of the few firms its size to sign the Pro Bono Initiative's Statement of Principles, Butler Rubin is proof that no law firm or corporation is too large or too small to make a commitment to the provision of free legal services. Butler Rubin was named to the 2012 Public Interest Law Initiative Pro Bono Recognition Roster.

### International Work:

A substantial portion of the firm's reinsurance matters and clients are international.

### Clients:

Butler Rubin tends to represent larger corporations, both public and private, primarily in the sectors of insurance, manufacturing, real estate and services, and works internationally. Domestically, the firm has represented clients in the courts of over 35 states and before state and federal agencies, commissions and arbitration panels in more than 25 states.

# CHAPMAN AND CUTLER LLP

www.chapman.com

**Chief Executive Partner:** Timothy P Mohan
**Chief Operating Partner:** Daniel L Johnson
Number of partners: 130   Number of other lawyers: 100

## Firm Overview:

Chapman and Cutler was founded in 1913 as a firm focused primarily on banking and bond offering transactions. Although the firm has maintained that focus over the last 100 years, it has also evolved with the financial services marketplace and now represents a broad array of participants in many types of commercial, corporate and public finance transactions. The firm represents nearly 300 foreign and domestic financial services institutions, providing counsel on virtually everything a financial institution does beginning with organization, chartering and funding, to regulation and compliance, commercial lending, corporate finance, consumer financial services, credit enhancements and derivatives transactions, and financial, commercial and other litigation on behalf of financial institutions, including workout, bankruptcy and class action defense.

## Main Areas of Practice:

### Asset Securitization:
The firm represents clients in domestic and cross-border asset-backed and mortgage-backed securities, tax-exempt and CDO transactions. Asset classes financed include traditional receivables and esoteric assets. The firm has a leading practice advising clients on the securities law and bank regulatory aspects of securitization transactions and structures.

### Banking, Bank Regulatory & Consumer Financial Services:
The firm has a comprehensive banking practice, with emphasis on syndicated bank credits, asset-based lending transactions, bank mergers and acquisitions, real estate finance, lease finance, credit enhancement, swaps and derivatives, consumer financial services, bank regulatory compliance and examination activities, cash management, payment systems and technology, outsourcing and securitization of receivables as well as other traditional commercial bank lending activities.

### Bankruptcy, Workouts & Commercial Litigation:
The firm is nationally recognized as one of the leading creditors' counsel in bankruptcy, restructuring and workouts and has been involved in many of the largest bankruptcies in the United States, including major airline, utilities, retail and manufacturing cases. In addition, the firm maintains a strong commercial, financial and consumer finance litigation and dispute resolution practice.

### Corporate Counseling, Employee Benefits & IP:
The firm provides general corporate, employee benefit and intellectual property counseling to a variety of domestic and international corporate clients.

### Corporate Finance & Securities:
The firm represents financial institutions and issuers in connection with public and private offerings of debt and equity securities, including domestic and cross-border private placements and Rule 144A offerings, public offerings, private equity, hedge funds,

mezzanine and project finance. The firm also counsels issuers with respect to disclosure requirements, stock exchange rules and compliance with the requirements of the Sarbanes-Oxley Act.

### Environment, Energy & Resources:
The firm routinely oversees the environmental, energy and natural resource aspects of a large variety of sophisticated transactions, including those involving the acquisition or refinancing of complex real estate, energy, manufacturing and mining portfolios. The firm also has extensive litigation experience in the environmental, commercial and toxic tort areas.

### Investment Companies & Investment Partnerships:
The firm serves as counsel to investment companies, sponsors and advisors to investment companies, and the independent members of investment company boards of directors.

### Lease Finance:
The firm is a market leader in representing a wide range of lessees, lessors, capital providers and underwriters in lease finance transactions with extensive experience with all types of lease finance structures. The firm also represents leasing companies in portfolio management, financing and joint venture transactions.

### Public Finance:
The firm has been one of the country's preeminent law firms in state and municipal finance and for over 25 years consistently served as bond counsel on more municipal bond issues each year than any other law firm in the country.

### Public-Private Partnerships:
The firm has acted as counsel to both public and private sector participants in PPP transactions, making use of its deep experience in mergers and acquisitions, securities, privatization strategies and private and public offerings.

### Tax:
The firm is nationally recognized for its advice on tax issues involved in corporate and municipal finance transactions, with particular emphasis on the representation of state and local governments and financial institutions.

### Trust Counsel & Estate Planning:
The firm represents the corporate and personal trust departments of financial institutions and provides estate and gift planning and probate services.

## International Work:
Chapman and Cutler has extensive experience in structuring cross-border financial transactions and regularly acts as bank counsel and/or investor counsel in structuring LIBOR-based and multicurrency financings involving foreign obligors, foreign collateral and/or foreign note offerings. The firm's Private Placements Group is internationally known as one of the largest and most active of the groups based in the US.

## Clients:
US commercial banks, many of the world's largest foreign banks, insurance companies, investment banks, corporate and governmental issuers, investors and credit providers including: Bank of America, Bank of Montreal, Bank of New York, Bank of Nova Scotia, Bank of Tokyo-Mitsubishi, Bayerische Landesbank, BNP Paribas, BNSF Railway, CalPERS, Capital One, Citizens Financial Group, Credit Agricole, Credit Suisse, Depfa Bank, Deutsche Bank AG, Dexia Credit, First Midwest Bank, First Republic Bank, John Hancock Life Insurance Company (USA), Landesbank Baden-Württemberg, MB Financial, National Australia Bank, New York Life Insurance Company, Norddeutsche Landesbank, PNC, PrivateBank, The Prudential Insurance Company of America, Redwood Trust, Inc., Royal Bank of Canada, Royal Bank of Scotland plc, Sumitomo-Mitsui, SunTrust, Toronto Dominion, Union Pacific, U.S. Bancorp, Wells Fargo, and White Oak Global Advisors, LLC.

**OFFICES**

ILLINOIS
**CHICAGO:** 111 West Monroe Street, IL 60603
Tel: 312 845 3000  Fax: 312 701 2361

CALIFORNIA
**SAN FRANCISCO:** 595 Market Street, CA 94105
Tel: 415 541 0500  Fax: 415 541 0506

DISTRICT OF COLUMBIA
**WASHINGTON DC:** 1717 Rhode Island Avenue NW, DC 20036
Tel: 202 478 6444  Fax: 202 296 4433

NEW YORK
**NEW YORK:** 330 Madison Avenue, NY 10017
Tel: 212 655 6000  Fax: 212 608 7210

UTAH
**SALT LAKE CITY:** 201 South Main Street, UT 84111
Tel: 801 533 0066  Fax: 801 533 9595

# EIMER STAHL LLP

www.eimerstahl.com

**Managing Partner:** Nathan P Eimer
Number of partners: 8
Number of other attorneys: 24

## Firm Overview:

Eimer Stahl LLP engages in complex litigation throughout the United States. The firm is dedicated to providing the highest quality legal and client service. With a commitment to advanced technology and diversity, the firm partners with clients to obtain creative solutions to complex legal problems. The firm is proud to serve as trial counsel to many leading companies and organizations.

## Main Areas of Practice:

The firm concentrates on complex litigation across a variety of subject areas, including antitrust, environmental, securities, utility regulation, energy, unfair competition, product liability, toxic torts, construction, and general commercial disputes. The firm has particular expertise relating to the defense of class action lawsuits, particularly in the antitrust, securities and mass tort fields. Matters on which the firm has recently worked include defense of mass tort claims alleging injuries arising from the use of a fuel additive, defense of price-fixing claims in the steel, electronics, paper and dairy sectors, government investigations and related private suits in the banking and financial sector, and rate cases for leading utilities. The firm also engages in antitrust counseling, including obtaining government antitrust clearance of proposed mergers and acquisitions. Members of the firm have provided advice regarding such matters across a wide variety of industries, including consumer goods, paper, building materials, chemicals, commercial printing, cosmetics, telecommunications, foodstuffs, and automotive parts.

## Clients:

The firm serves clients across a wide array of industries, including CITGO Petroleum, Commonwealth Edison Company, Exelon Generation Company, Ingredion Incorporated, Kimberly-Clark, The Dow Chemical Company, Nicor, Land O' Lakes, Gerdau Ameristeel, Credit Suisse Group AG, Bank of New York Mellon, Deutsche Bank AG, UBS AG, Praxair, Inc., LG Electronics, Inc., The Art Institute of Chicago, Schreiber Foods, Inc., City of Kankakee, and Baxter International Inc. Superior client service is a hallmark of the firm's operating philosophy and principles.

**PRACTICE AREAS**

Antitrust/Securities/Commercial Litigation
Energy/Commercial Litigation

**OFFICE**

ILLINOIS
**CHICAGO:** 224 S. Michigan Avenue, Suite 1100, IL 60604
Tel: 312 660 7600 Fax: 312 692 1718

# FITCH, EVEN, TABIN & FLANNERY LLP

www.fitcheven.com **tel:** 312 577 7000 **fax:** 312 577 7007

**Managing Partner:** Timothy P. Maloney
Number of partners: 33
Number of lawyers: 53
Languages: *Bosnian, Croatian, French, German, Japanese, Mandarin Chinese, Russian, Serbian, Spanish, Taiwanese*

## Firm Overview:

Founded in 1859, Fitch, Even, Tabin & Flannery LLP is a respected leader in intellectual property law. Focusing only on IP matters, Fitch Even offers the high level of technical competence and legal skills needed in this increasingly complex area of law, along with a tradition of providing outstanding, personalized service. The firm is adept at obtaining strong global IP rights and managing global IP portfolios, successfully navigating the intricacies of the varying legal systems involved. The firm's extensive trial experience informs the entire practice. It regularly handles IP and technology-related litigation, with a reputation for delivering outstanding returns on the litigation investment. Fitch Even offer a full range of services to help clients leverage their assets by developing strategic licensing, investment, and other business relationships important to diversification and growth.

## Main Areas of Practice:

### IP Litigation:

Fitch Even's deep experience, strategic approach, vigorous advocacy, and proven trial capabilities have led to a stellar track record of success against top legal teams from the largest US law firms. It has handled cases involving patent infringement, trade secret theft, breach of license, trademark infringement, copyright infringement, unfair competition, antitrust, and other disputes. The firm's litigation teams are led by accomplished trial lawyers with significant experience at the trial court and appellate levels. Litigators' technical backgrounds and patent bar credentials provide the specific mix of legal and technical capabilities needed for each case. The firm regularly represents small and midsized plaintiffs against larger defendants, and has successfully defended infringement cases involving substantial damages exposures through jury verdict and appeal.

### Patent Practice:

Fitch Even lawyers prepare and prosecute patent applications with a clear focus on the larger business objectives of the invention and a keen understanding of the legal principles governing effective patent enforcement around the world. The firm works with clients to develop and exploit strong, defensible patents at each stage – from patent office approval, to monetization in a strategic venture or licensing arrangement, to effective enforcement against infringers. Lawyers are skilled at moving challenging cases through the patent offices, and can also navigate complex post-patent issuance procedures. Fitch Even counsels clients regarding IP risk management, provides solid validity and infringement opinions, and offers in-depth product clearance analysis and freedom-to-operate studies.

### Trademark Practice:

Fitch Even lawyers counsel clients on branding strategies and the initial selection of a mark or design, conduct extensive trademark availability searches, and provide opinions. The firm manages portfolios of hundreds of marks and assist clients in aggressively policing and exploiting their marks globally. It provides day-to-day advice regarding potential infringement of their trademarks as well as avoidance of competitor's trademarks. Fitch Even lawyers know the unique procedural requirements of opposition proceedings, having participated in hundreds of oppositions worldwide to protect our clients' rights. The firm also offers comprehensive services supporting copyright protection and enforcement involving a wide range of traditional to cutting-edge media.

### IP Transactions:

Fitch Even lawyers support, structure, and negotiate complex commercial transactions involving IP, including technology licenses, mergers and acquisitions, joint ventures, patent sales, and litigation-assisted patent licensing. Working closely with the client, Fitch Even approaches each transaction with a keen understanding of the scope and value of the asset involved and the benefits and potential pitfalls of various transaction structures. Proficient in the strategic use of litigation to drive licensing efforts, the firm achieves favorable results for clients in a variety of licensing campaigns. Its patent analysis and enforcement capabilities can better position a portfolio for sale or licensing at attractive valuations.

### Clients:

Fitch Even represents clients ranging from individuals, small businesses, and start-ups to Fortune 500 corporations, universities, hospitals, venture capital firms, and research institutions. The firm has helped numerous high-profile clients protect and exploit innovations in mechanics, electronics, chemistry, advanced materials, physics, computer and software technology, biotechnology, food and agricultural sciences, energy, and other areas. The firm's client base is geographically diverse, spanning the globe. Fitch Even supports clients worldwide through an established network of highly competent associates in over 100 countries.

## PRACTICE AREAS

Advertising, Marketing & Promotions
Copyrights
Entertainment & Media
International IP Protection
Internet & Domain Names
IP Litigation
IP Portfolio Management
IP Strategy Development
IP Transactions
Patent Post-Issuance Proceedings
Patent Preparation & Prosecution
Product Clearance & Legal Opinions
Trademarks & Brands
Trade Secrets

## OFFICES

### ILLINOIS
**CHICAGO:** 120 S. LaSalle Street, Suite 1600, IL 60603-3406
Tel: 312 577 7000  Fax: 312 577 7007
Email: info@fitcheven.com

### DISTRICT OF COLUMBIA
**WASHINGTON, DC:** One Lafayette Centre, 1120 20th Street, NW, Suite 750 South, DC 20036
Tel: 202 419 7000  Fax: 202 419 7007

### CALIFORNIA
**LOS ANGELES:** 21700 Oxnard Street, Suite 1740, CA 91367
Tel: 818 715 7025   Fax: 818 715 7033

**SAN DIEGO:** 9330 Scranton Road, Suite 350, CA 92121
Tel: 858 552 1311  Fax: 858 552 0095

**SAN LUIS OBISPO:** PO Box 512, 1010 Peach Street, CA 93406
Tel: 805 548 1800  Fax: 805 980 3483

### COLORADO
**BOULDER:** 1942 Broadway, Suite 213, CO 80302
Tel: 303 402 6966  Fax: 303 402 6970

# FRANCZEK RADELET P.C.

**www.**franczek.com **tel:** 312 986 0300 **fax:** 312 986 9192

**Managing Partner:** Ronald J Hein, Jr
Number of partners: 35
Number of other lawyers: 16

## Firm Overview:

Founded in 1994 by attorneys from some of Chicago's largest multi-services law firms, Franczek Radelet has grown from 12 to 50 attorneys. Its boutique labor, employment and employee benefits practice focuses exclusively on representing and advising employers in both the private and public sectors.

## Main Areas of Practice:

### Labor Relations:

The firm's labor practice covers every aspect of managing a unionized workforce as well as assisting management with non-unionized workforces when union organizing campaigns arise. Its labor practice handles all aspects of the union-management relationships, including collective bargaining, state and National Labor Relations Board proceedings, contract administration, impasse arbitration proceedings and grievance arbitration proceedings. The firm's unique offering – the combination of its relationships in the marketplace and extensive experience, maximize its clients' achievements and assure the attainment of their labor relations goals. The firm has long-standing relationships with nearly all of the labor unions in Illinois, as well as significant players in the public and private sectors in Chicago, Illinois and the Midwest, and it has the depth to service the largest clients with the most sophisticated and complex labor issues.

- Served as chief labor counsel for Starwood Hotels & Resorts Worldwide, Inc. in high profile, difficult labor negotiations with Unite Here Local 1
- Since 1995, served as chief labor counsel to Navistar International Corp. in its comprehensive, multi-site contracts with the United Auto Workers covering 3,700+ employees around the country
- For 17 years, served as labor counsel on behalf of the City of Chicago negotiating exemplary agreements with the City's police and fire unions, as well as its 40 other unions
- Since 1994, served as labor counsel for Chicago Public Schools. During that period, the firm negotiated three four-year collective bargaining agreements, one three-year agreement and one five-year agreement with the Chicago Teachers Union
- Since 2002, the firm has served as labor counsel for Chicago Automobile Trade Association in the negotiation of Standard Auto Agreements covering approximately 3,000 service technicians and parts workers at approximately 150 Chicago-area new car dealerships

**Key Clients:** Dominick's Finer Foods; Tuthill Corporation; OMNOVA Solutions, Inc.; Metropolitan Pier and Exposition Authority; Midwest Generation EME, LLC; City of Chicago.
**Contact:** James C Franczek, Jr **Tel:** 312 786 6110
**Email:** jcf@franczek.com

### Employment:

Franczek Radelet advises, counsels and represents management in all areas of employment law. The firm has extensive experience counseling on employee discipline and termination, affirmative action, sexual harassment and anti-discrimination training, downsizing and reduction-in-force assistance, wage and hour compliance, workplace safety and employee handbook drafting and review. It has a long and deep track record of representing clients in all aspects of employment litigation and appellate advocacy, including defense of employment discrimination and harassment claims, express and implied employment contract claims, wrongful discharge actions, employment-related torts and enforcement of restrictive covenants. The firm has extensive experience representing employers in individual and class-wide claims before federal and state courts and administrative agencies throughout the US.

- Obtained a significantly favorable judgment for a major national retailer in a race discrimination, whistleblower retaliation and FMLA retaliation case brought by a former human resources director; the New Jersey federal district court dismissed the employee's claims in their entirety and also awarded attorneys' fees in favor of the retailer
- Secured favorable ruling for the University of Chicago in a jury trial where a former PhD student alleged the University violated provisions in its student handbook when it suspended him after he made continuous inappropriate communications to administrators
- Obtained summary judgment in the Seventh Circuit Court on behalf of Morningstar in a highly publicized same sex harassment and retaliation lawsuit
- Obtained summary judgment on behalf of a railway

service industry client in a Family and Medical Leave Act retaliatory discharge case
- Obtained summary judgment after securing dismissal of class claims, for an energy company in a lawsuit alleging that the company violated the Americans with Disabilities Act by demoting allegedly disabled employees for excessive absenteeism
- Resolved 20-plaintiff sexual harassment lawsuit successfully on behalf of large retail employer

**Key Clients:** Chicago Automobile Trade Association; Target Corporation; Northwestern University; Midwest Generation EME, LLC; Dominick's Finer Foods; Southwest Airlines; Supervalu; Career Education Corp.
**Contact:** David P Radelet **Tel:** 312 786 6190
**Email:** dpr@franczek.com

### Employee Benefits:

Franczek Radelet's benefits attorneys counsel employers with respect to virtually every aspect of benefits, pension and health law issues. They have extensive experience amending and restating benefit plan documents, as well as counseling clients on the administration of benefit plans, including 401(k), 403(b) and 457(b) retirement plans, Section 125 plans, including flexible spending arrangements and dependent care assistance programs, educational assistance programs and transportation fringe benefit programs. The firm takes a practical, common sense approach to amending and restating plan documents and summary plan descriptions when legislation and IRS guidance changes.

**Key Clients:** Navistar International Corp.; Regional Transportation Authority; Chicago Automobile Trade Association; MDA (Muscular Dystrophy Association, Inc.); Morningstar; Dwyer Instruments, Inc.; Access Community Health Network; Dominican University.
**Contact:** Michael I Richardson **Tel:** 312 786 6166
**Email:** mr@franczek.com

# FREEBORN & PETERS LLP

**www.freeborn.com tel:** 312 360 6000 **fax:** 312 360 6520

**Chairman:** Peter I Mason
**Managing Partners:** Michael J Kelly, Michael A Moynihan
Number of partners: 71
Number of lawyers: 118
Languages: *English*

## Firm Overview:

Freeborn & Peters LLP is a full-service Midwestern law firm with national and global capabilities headquartered in Chicago, Illinois. Freeborn & Peters is always looking ahead and seeking to find better ways to serve its clients. It takes a proactive approach to ensure its clients are more informed, prepared and able to achieve greater success – not just now, but also in the future. While the firm serves clients across a very broad range of sectors, it has also pioneered an interdisciplinary approach that serves the specific needs of targeted industries, including food, transportation, and insurance and reinsurance. Freeborn & Peters is a firm that genuinely lives up to its core values of integrity, caring, effectiveness, teamwork, and commitment, and embodies them through high standards of client service and responsive action. Its lawyers build close and lasting relationships with clients and are driven to help them achieve their legal and business objectives.

## Main Areas of Practice:

### Litigation:
43 partners; 15 fee earners, all based in Chicago
- With more than 60 litigators, Freeborn's Litigation Practice Group brings both bench strength and deep experience to each client matter. Members of the practice group consider themselves 'litigators first' and their philosophy is to prepare cases to be tried. Even when settlement is appropriate, they believe their trial-ready approach provides the best ultimate outcome
- Each litigator is trained, first and foremost, to understand the client's business and its goals for the litigation. Within the context of their goals, the focus is obtaining the best result possible for their business

**Contact:** David Gustman **Tel:** 312 360 6515
**Email:** dgustman@freeborn.com

### Corporate Law:
16 partners; 8 fee earners, all based in Chicago
- Extensive experience providing strategic counsel on growth-oriented initiatives, including financing, acquisition and joint ventures, as well as essential operational areas including marketing and distribution
- Team includes former CEOs, business executives, and general counsels, allowing the firm to bring significant business experience to its legal solutions

**Contact:** Cynthia A Bergmann **Tel:** 312 360 6652
**Email:** cbergmann@freeborn.com
**Contact:** Jeff Mattson **Tel:** 312 360 6312
**Email:** jmattson@freeborn.com

### Real Estate:
9 partners; 3 fee earners, all based in Chicago
- Capabilities drawn from across all key real estate disciplines to help clients buy, entitle, develop, lease, finance, and sell their assets
- Performs work at the local, regional, and national level

**Contact:** Anne R Garr **Tel:** 312 360 6619
**Email:** agarr@freeborn.com
**Contact:** Richard J Traub **Tel:** 312 360 6605
**Email:** rtraub@freeborn.com

### Bankruptcy & Financial Restructuring:
3 partners, 4 fee earners, all based in Chicago
Offers a broad range of bankruptcy-related services, but with a particular emphasis on:
- Providing legal counsel to unsecured creditors' committees, with one of the most active practices in the Midwest
- Representing plaintiffs and defendants in litigation brought under chapter 5 of the US Bankruptcy Code, including service to liquidating trustees and chapter 7 trustees

**Contact:** Richard S Lauter **Tel:** 312 360 6641
**Email:** rlauter@freeborn.com

### Government & Regulatory Law:
2 partners, one in Chicago, one in Springfield
- One of the very few national law firms with full-service offices in both Springfield and Chicago

### Food:
16 partners; 4 fee earners, all based in Chicago
- Offers a full range of legal services to food processors, manufacturers, suppliers, growers and producers, wholesalers, and distributors to help address the complex challenges facing the food industry

**Contact:** Brian A Smith **Tel:** 312 360 6472
**Email:** bsmith@freeborn.com

### Insurance & Reinsurance:
9 partners; 3 fee earners, all based in Chicago
- Served as the lead counsel for AXA Versicherung AG in an arbitration in which AXA obtained $16.4m award, plus interest and punitive damages
- Submitted amicus brief to the New York Court of Appeals on behalf of Reinsurance Association of America, supporting the opinion that ultimately prevailed in *U.S. Fidelity & Guaranty Co. et al. v. American Re-Insurance Co. et al.*, case number 00784

**Contact:** Joseph McCullough IV **Tel:** 312 360 6327
**Email:** jmccullough@freeborn.com

### Transportation:
13 partners; 3 fee earners, all based in Chicago, bar one in Springfield, IL
- Advised Canadian National on its $300m acquisition of the Elgin, Joliet and Eastern Railway Company, a major link among Class I railroads across Chicago

**Contact:** Cynthia A Bergmann **Tel:** 312 360 6652
**Email:** cbergmann@freeborn.com

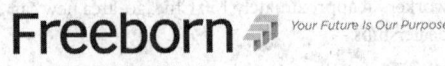

Freeborn *Your Future Is Our Purpose*
FREEBORN & PETERS LLP

# GOLDBERG KOHN LTD

www.goldbergkohn.com **tel:** 312 201 4000

Number of partners: 43  Number of lawyers: 34

## Firm Overview:

Goldberg Kohn is a midsized Chicago firm with a large firm practice. The firm thrives as counsel to clients unwilling to compromise on quality but seeking an alternative to mega-firm billing structures. The distinctive collaborative philosophy at the firm has led to long-term relationships with clients who treat Goldberg Kohn attorneys as integral team members.

## Main Areas of Practice:

### Banking & Finance:

14 Partners; 14 fee earners based in Chicago

- Goldberg Kohn has one of the most highly respected commercial finance practices in the U.S. The firm represents a diverse group of major money-center and regional banks, commercial finance companies, mezzanine lenders and other institutional lenders in structuring and documenting commercial finance transactions. The commercial finance practice runs the gamut of transactions, including revolving working capital facilities (asset-based and cash flow), leveraged acquisitions, loan restructurings, mezzanine loans and debtor-in-possession financings, covering virtually all business sectors.
- The firm has been a pioneer in international asset-based lending, and has one of the most prominent and active international lending practices in the U.S., representing clients in scores of international lending transactions in Europe, Asia and Latin America. The firm also participates actively in projects at the United Nations Commission on International Trade Law (UNCITRAL) to help countries modernise their secured transactions laws.

**Contact:** Richard Kohn  **Tel:**  312 201 3920
**Email:** Richard.kohn@goldbergkohn.com

### Bankruptcy & Creditors' Rights:

5 Partners; 4 fee earners based in Chicago

- The Bankruptcy & Creditors' Rights Group at Goldberg Kohn is known as a creative and highly effective team of bankruptcy experts. The group's foundation rests upon serving the firm's commercial lending clients. Whether or not the firm originally documented a deal, agent banks and individual lenders seek the group's result-driven and efficient approach to troubled credits. Goldberg Kohn lawyers are intimately familiar with the nuances of loan documents, credit policies, market trends and the politics of syndicated credit facilities. Inter- and intra-class lender negotiations and disputes are a particular specialty, as is litigation involving cash collateral, adequate protection and postpetition financing issues.
- Goldberg Kohn supplements its lender representations by advising substantially all other types of creditors, including trustees and debtors in select situations. The

firm has had singular success as counsel to asset purchasers in chapter 11 bankruptcy cases, secondary debt market participants and various constituents of the automotive industry.
**Contact:** Randall Klein  **Tel:** 312 201 3974
**Email:** Randall.klein@goldbergkohn.com

### Litigation:

13 Partners; 10 fee earners based in Chicago

- Goldberg Kohn's litigators combine professional aggressiveness with legal creativity. The firm has expertise in counseling and litigation involving business-to-business disputes, banks, lenders and other financial institutions, complex workouts, corporate restructuring and bankruptcies, intellectual property, trade secret and restrictive covenants, labour and employment issues, the prosecution of substantial claims of defrauding federal and state governments (qui tam claims), insurance and brokerage firms, complex tax issues, real estate development, financing and foreclosures, prosecuting and defending class, collective and multi-district litigation, and federal and state appeals.
- The firm has served as Illinois, Midwest or national litigation counsel to clients ranging from private to *Fortune* 100 companies, as well as domestic counsel to companies headquartered throughout the world. The efforts of Goldberg Kohn's litigators foster long-term client relationships and recognition at the local, state and national level for outstanding litigation achievements, including obtaining the largest verdict and judgment in the history of the U.S. False Claim Act ($334 million).

**Contact:** Fred Klein  **Tel:** 312 201 3908
**Email:** Frederic.klein@goldbergkohn.com

### Corporate:

6 Partners; 3 fee earners based in Chicago

- The Corporate, Securities & Tax Group at Goldberg Kohn is a versatile group of experienced business counselors and advocates. The firm's business clients rely on the group for practical, experience-based advice that has been built up over decades of representing and advising private equity investors, public and private businesses and business owners. Goldberg Kohn's corporate lawyers help to achieve the business objectives of a wide range of business entities spanning

the manufacturing and distribution, financial and professional services, technology, education and not-for-profit sectors.
- Goldberg Kohn works to help its clients grow through all the phases of their life cycle, including capital raising, financing, investing, admitting additional owners, ownership succession and transition, mergers, acquisitions and selling businesses. The firm represents large public companies, mid-sized and emerging businesses, limited and general partners and limited liability companies, serving many clients as general or principal outside counsel. The group works with the firm's secured lending clients in connection with equity co-investing, debt for equity exchanges and foreclosure and bankruptcy sales and acquisitions.

**Contact:** Deni Caplan  **Tel:** 12 201 3901
**Email:** Denise.caplan@goldbergkohn.com

### Real Estate:

6 Partners; 7 fee earners based in Chicago

- Goldberg Kohn's Real Estate Group is respected as one of the best real estate departments in Chicago and is experienced in virtually every aspect of real estate transactions. The depth of the firm's practice encompasses every aspect of commercial property transactions, including acquisitions, dispositions, developments, financings, hotel, retail, office, senior housing, industrial and specialty leasing, construction, sale and leasebacks, synthetic leasing, workouts and bankruptcies and environmental issues.
- The transactions on which Goldberg Kohn's real estate lawyers work are often large and particularly complex, many involving multiple jurisdictions or large 'trophy' commercial properties. The firm's real estate-related clients are especially diverse, including small entrepreneurs to large multinational corporations, such as institutional lenders, developers, pension funds, insurance companies, REITs, landlords, commercial tenants, bondholders, investors and syndicates.

**Contact:** Gary Ruben  **Tel:** 312 201 3907
**Email:** Gary.ruben@goldbergkohn.com

**OFFICES**

ILLINOIS
**CHICAGO:** Goldberg Kohn Ltd., 55 E. Monroe St., Suite 3300, IL 60603
Tel: 312 201 4000 Fax: 312 332 2196
Email: info@goldbergkohn.com www.goldbergkohn.com
International Offices- Goldberg Kohn is proud to be a member of Meritas, a long-standing business alliance of approximately 170 independent  commercial law firms located in over 60 countries.

GOLDBERG KOHN

# THE HEALTH LAW CONSULTANCY

www.hlconsultancy.com **tel:** 312 332 7711 **fax:** 312 332 7722

**Managing Partner:** Kathryn Roe
Number of partners: 2
Number of lawyers: 2
Languages: *English*

**Firm Overview:**

The Health Law Consultancy is a Chicago-based boutique law firm that provides strategic legal counsel for the business of health care. The firm's professionals help health industry participants identify and capitalize on the opportunities and manage the challenges embedded in health law. The firm reinforces its business focus with an innovative business model that offers clients predictable project pricing for assured project budgeting of legal costs.

The Health Law Consultancy's core areas of strategic counsel and legal support include: federal health reform; antitrust and fraud and abuse; data privacy, security, transactions and exchange; Medicare, Medicaid and other government health benefits programs; health insurance exchanges, markets and products; payer-provider joint ventures, affiliations and alliances; health information technology and business process outsourcing.

The Health Law Consultancy is the health law practice member of the Chicago chapter of the International Network of Boutique Law Firms.

**Main Areas of Practice:**

**Healthcare:**

- Antitrust counsel, advice and interaction with federal and state antitrust agencies with respect to various health care arrangements and activities, including agency investigations of provider consolidation and joint negotiation activities; most-favored nation clauses in payer-provider contracting; provider collaborations and joint ventures; and accountable care organization formation and activities.

- Ongoing federal health reform law counsel and guidance for health insurer and state association of health plans for education of and negotiations with governor, relevant state agencies and legislative leaders to identify options and devise plans for establishment and operation of a state-based health insurance exchange.

- Legal support of consumer operated and oriented plan (CO-OP), which has qualified for federal financial assistance under federal health reform law, in structuring, negotiating and documenting business process outsourcing arrangements for key insurance functions and in establishing corporate compliance infrastructure.

- Review of early stage Internet-based care coordination company's collection, use and disclosure of personal health information and assistance in its establishment of data protection program in compliance with applicable law and financing commitments for board approval and company implementation.

- Advice with respect to changing requirements for provider quality reporting and new requirements for accountable care organizations and their implications for client's business, assistance in influencing federal agency's application of those requirements to client's business and updating of client's contract documentation for furnishing provider quality reporting and clinical integration support to respond to evolving health care regulatory environment.

- Strategic counsel and legal analysis for structuring options and seeking fraud and abuse waiver for foundation-funded not-for-profit organization developing—in collaboration with state Medicaid agency and select health care providers—a grant proposal for submission to federal government.

- Strategic counsel and legal analysis for ensuring appropriate protection of personal health information used and disclosed for new initiatives undertaken by association and its member organizations in response to federal health reform.

- Ongoing strategic counsel, advice and interpretation of federal health reform law and implementing regulations governing health plans' offering and sale of commercial health insurance products and participation in government health benefits programs.

**PRACTICE AREAS**

Healthcare

**OFFICES**

ILLINOIS

**CHICAGO:** 20 North State Street, Suite 706
P.O. Box A3351, 60690-3351
Tel: 312 332 7711  Fax: 312 332 7722
Email: kroe@hlconsultancy.com

# HOGAN MARREN LTD

**www.**hmltd.com **tel:** 312 946 1800 **fax:** 312 946 9818

**President:** Edward M Hogan
Number of partners: 11 Number of lawyers: 17

## Firm Overview:

The breadth and depth of the health law experience of the members of Hogan Marren distinguishes them from their competitors. Hogan Marren attorneys have practiced exclusively in the health care area for many years and in a variety of settings. Their experience, both as former in-house counsel and partners at large law firms, provides Hogan Marren with an historical in-depth context for the changes taking place within the health care industry. The firm prides itself on its ability to offer clients solutions to problems from different perspectives and to advise them with respect to industry developments, as well as the legal questions that are transactional or regulatory in nature.

## Main Areas of Practice:

### Advocacy:

The firm represents their clients in investigations and/or seeking approval or opinions in front of various state agencies such as department of insurance, certificate of need agencies, state attorneys general, and Federal agencies such as the U.S. Department of Justice, Federal Trade Commission, the Internal Revenue Service and the Department of Health and Human Services. Their representation related to HHS includes practice before CMS and OIG with respect to issues such as Medicare reimbursement, Stark self-disclosures, RACs and other investigations.

### Clinical Integration, Accountable Care & Physician Alignment:

Hogan Marren has counseled clients extensively in clinical integration matters, and has assisted clients in establishing accountable care organizations through which the independent and employed physicians can develop, implement and coordinate a clinical integration program and engage in joint contracting activities with the government and managed care organizations. Hogan Marren is one of the only firms in the country selected to represent a Pioneer ACO based on their vast experience in clinical integration and accountable care and the firm has also assisted with the formation of numerous ACO's under the Affordable Care Act. As part of its representation Hogan Marren offers its clients a comprehensive menu of clinical integration development tools such as a readiness assessment, network contracting, risk assessment, vendor and consultant selection and retention, clinical integration program formation and evaluation, proper messenger model formation and educational support for executive, board and member levels. The firm also analyzes the compliance of such organizations with other regulatory laws, such as the Medicare Anti-Fraud and Abuse and the Stark law.

### Hospital/Physician/Joint Ventures/Collaborations:

The firm has developed and assisted in the operation of countless hospital/physician joint ventures, including ambulatory surgery centers, medical office buildings, sleep laboratories, diagnostic imaging facilities, hospital/physician employment. Recently, their practice has focused extensively on co-management agreements, pay-for-performance arrangements, gainsharing and other arrangements to promote quality and efficiency.

### Hospital Collaborations:

Hogan Marren has assisted hospitals in collaborating through mergers, asset acquisitions, joint operating agreements, and super-parent models. The firm is expert in the attendant legal issues related to these transactions, including certificates of need, licensure, change of ownership, tax, Medicare and the other regulatory issues which affect complex transactions. The firm has received precedent-setting rulings and opinions in these transactions.

### Antitrust:

Hogan Marren has advised numerous clients regarding the antitrust implications of acquisitions, consolidations, mergers, affiliations and managed care contracting. Most recently, they defended a multi-hospital system and its affiliated physician network against a charge of price fixing brought by a large national health plan, wherein the health plan sought over $250 million in alleged antitrust damages and equitable relief. Following a full trial on the merits, the arbitration panel dismissed all claims against the hospital system and the physician network.

### Management Care:

The firm's attorneys have developed numerous IPAs, PHOs, HMOs, PPOs, Point of Service option plans and specialized risk plans.

### Provider Based Status:

The firm has helped hospitals analyze their current operational structure and obtain provider-based status for appropriate clinic sites.

### Physicians Relations/Medical Staff Development:

The firm's representation includes the development of medical staff bylaws, credentialing plans and medical staff development plans and representation of managed care entities and hospital systems related to selection and rejection of providers. They have also represented hospitals in medical staff bylaw disputes and have assisted individual physicians in peer review hearings. They understand the critical need for positive and honest relationships between the medical staff and hospital.

### Privacy & Security Laws/EHR:

The firm counsels clients, including publicly-traded companies and providers, regarding legal issues arising with acquisition and use of health care information technology, including privacy and security laws. The firm has conducted internal investigations of breaches of protected health information and assisted clients with responding to governmental investigations of alleged violations of HIPAA/HITECH.

### General Corporate:

The firm reviews various business arrangements for its clients, including purchases and leases of equipment, land and supplies, medical director services, employment, management, construction and other types of service agreements. The firm's review ensures such arrangements are structured in compliance with applicable law and prudent business practices in the industry.

### Qui Tam / Whistleblower Cases:

Hogan Marren has represented clients in various federal and state whistleblower lawsuits, including a recent case involving claims brought by former employees of an ambulance transport company under the federal False Claims Act and the Medicare Anti-Kickback Statute.

Hogan Marren is one of the only firms in the country selected to represent a Pioneer ACO based on their vast experience in clinical integration and accountable care and the firm is uniquely qualified having assisted with the formation of many ACO's under the MSSP Regulation.

# JENNER & BLOCK LLP

**www.**jenner.com **tel:** 312 222 9350 **fax:** 312 527 0484

**Managing Partner:** Susan C Levy
**Firm Chairman:** Anton R Valukas
Number of partners: 220
Number of lawyers: 480
Languages: *English, Arabic, Armenian, Chinese/Mandarin, Dutch, Filipino, French, German, Greek, Gujarati, Haitian Creole, Hindi, Italian, Japanese, Korean, Marathi, Polish, Portuguese, Russian, Serbo-Croatian, Shona, Sign Language, Spanish, Tagalog, Taiwanese, Ukrainian, Urdu*

## Firm Overview:

Founded in 1914, Jenner & Block is known for its prominent and successful litigation practice and experience handling sophisticated and high-profile corporate transactions. It represented firm Chairman Anton Valukas as court-appointed Examiner in the Lehman Brothers bankruptcy, the largest bankruptcy in US history. Firm clients include Fortune 100 companies, large privately held corporations, financial services institutions, emerging companies, venture capital and private equity investors. The firm was named to The American Lawyer's 2012 "A-List," which recognizes the 20 most elite law firms across the country for outstanding performance.

## Main Areas of Practice:

### Litigation:

The multidisciplinary litigation practice is comprised of trial lawyers who have won victories in a broad range of complex and challenging civil and criminal cases before federal, state and administrative courts. Jenner & Block has deep strength in the following practice areas: appellate and supreme court; complex commercial litigation; content, media and entertainment; government contracts; insurance litigation and counseling; patent litigation and counseling; professional responsibility; securities litigation and enforcement; and white collar defense and investigations. Recent highlights include:

- Won a record $431 million FINRA award on behalf of STMicroelectronics in an auction-rate securities suit, which was affirmed on appeal
- Won a $227 million recovery for Ventas in a suit for tortious interference arising out of Ventas' acquisition of a publicly traded healthcare REIT, following the appeal of a $101 million federal jury verdict won by the firm and a subsequent settlement on a remanded punitive damages claim
- Won a reversal of a $126 million federal jury verdict against L-3 Communications in a dispute arising out of a joint effort to purchase businesses
- Won a major victory for CRST Van Expedited, Inc., when the 8th Circuit Court of Appeals affirmed an Iowa federal trial court's dismissal of 268 of 270 individual Title VII sexual harassment claims brought by the Equal Employment Opportunity Commission
- Won a major US Supreme Court victory for video game industry client Entertainment Merchants Association in a First Amendment challenge to a California law that would have restricted the sale or rental, to anyone under the age of 18, of video and computer games based on their content
- Won a $61.7 million jury verdict for The Dow Chemical Company in a patent infringement suit in Delaware District Court, which was affirmed on appeal

**Litigation Department Contacts:**
Co-Chair David J Bradford **Tel:** 312 923 2975
**Email:** dbradford@jenner.com
Co-Chair Craig C Martin **Tel:** 312 923 2776
**Email:** cmartin@jenner.com

### Transactional:

Jenner & Block has a sophisticated transactional practice focusing on mergers and acquisitions, securities, corporate finance, corporate governance, private equity and hedge fund formation and investing, and workouts and corporate reorganizations. The firm's corporate attorneys also work closely with attorneys from its regulatory groups to provide comprehensive due diligence and integrated transaction structures. Jenner & Block handles transactional work for a variety of clients, including Fortune 500 companies, middle-market and emerging companies, private equity and hedge funds, and closely held and family businesses. Recent achievements include:

- Represented General Motors in its repurchase of $5.5 billion of GM common stock held by the US Department of the Treasury and represented GM as lead issuer's counsel in GM's $23.1 billion initial public offering (IPO) in 2010 – the largest IPO in history
- Represented General Dynamics in numerous mergers and acquisitions and securities offerings, including its $960 million acquisition of Vangent, its $360 million acquisition of Force Protection, and its multiple public offerings of debt securities totaling more than $8 billion
- Represented Swiss-based Lonza Group in its approximately $1.2 billion acquisition of Arch Chemicals
- Represented Hertz Global Holdings in its $930 million acquisition of Donlen Corporation, its multiple Rule 144A offerings of debt securities totaling more than $3.5 billion and a $780 million underwritten block trade of Hertz common stock by its private equity sponsors
- Represented News Corporation/Fox Networks Group in its acquisition of interests in regional sports networks, including YES Network and Sports Time Ohio; its creation and launch of Fox Sports San Diego, a regional sports network anchored by San Diego Padres games; and its joint venture with Rogers Media for the creation and launch of FX Canada

**Transactional Department Contact:**
Chair Joseph P Gromacki **Tel:** 312 923 2637
**Email:** jgromacki@jenner.com

### Public Service:

Pro bono service is woven into the fabric of the firm. Over the last 20 years, the firm has devoted more than 1,000,000 hours to pro bono matters. The firm's efforts have been recognized by The American Lawyer as the number one pro bono program in the country five times and one of the top 10 programs in the country every year since 1990. The firm's pro bono program provides litigation and transactional services to dozens of organizations and thousands of individuals in a wide range of criminal and civil matters.

## OFFICES

**ILLINOIS**
**CHICAGO:** 353 N. Clark Street, IL 60654-3456
Tel: 312 222 9350  Fax: 312 527 0484

**CALIFORNIA**
**LOS ANGELES:** 633 West 5th Street, Suite 3600, CA 90071-2054
Tel: 213 239 5100  Fax: 213 239 5199

**NEW YORK**
**NEW YORK:** 919 Third Avenue, NY 10022-3908
Tel: 212 891 1600  Fax: 212 891 1699

**DISTRICT OF COLUMBIA**
**WASHINGTON:** 1099 New York Avenue, NW, Suite 900, DC 20001-4412
Tel: 202 639 6000  Fax: 202 639 6066

# JENNER & BLOCK

# KATTEN MUCHIN ROSENMAN LLP

www.kattenlaw.com **tel:** +1 312 902 5200 **fax:** +1 312 902 1061

**Managing Partner:** Vincent A F Sergi
Number of partners: 310
Number of other lawyers: 278

**OFFICES**

USA
Austin, Century City, Chicago, Charlotte, Irving, Los Angeles, New York, Oakland, Orange County, Washington, DC

**INTERNATIONAL**
The firm also has offices in Shanghai, China and London, UK (Katten Muchin Rosenman UK LLP)

**Firm Overview:**

Katten Muchin Rosenman is a full-service law firm with 600 attorneys in locations across the United States and in London and Shanghai. Among the firm's clients are a wide range of public and private companies, including nearly a third of the Fortune 100, as well as a number of government and non-profit organisations and individuals. In addition to the practices listed below, the firm maintains many highly focused practices, including antitrust, customs and international trade, employee benefits and executive compensation, entertainment and media, health care, labour and employment and public finance.

## Main Areas of Practice:

### Litigation:

The firm's trial lawyers handle cases ranging from contract disputes and regulatory matters to securities class action lawsuits, antitrust matters and other complex commercial and criminal litigation. The Securities Litigation Practice is nationally recognised for successfully representing corporations and their officers and directors in shareholder class actions, derivative actions, SEC investigations and federal and state criminal investigations. The White Collar Defense, Internal Investigations and Compliance Practice is led by highly respected former federal prosecutors and law enforcement officers with broad investigative, trial and appellate experience.

### Corporate:

The Corporate Practice provides sophisticated transactional representation and business counseling to national and global companies across a broad range of concentrations. The Mergers and Acquisitions group is involved in all aspects of public and private mergers, acquisitions and divestitures, representing both targets and bidders in negotiated and hostile takeovers. The nationally recognised Private Equity group represents leveraged buyout funds, mezzanine debt funds and venture capital funds in acquisitions, divestitures and financing transactions, and advising in all aspects of private equity fund formation. The Securities group assists clients with public and private offerings of equity and debt securities, tender offers, proxy contests and going private transactions. They also provide corporate governance counseling to public and private companies, boards of directors and board committees.

### Real Estate:

The Real Estate Practice has one of the most extensive and renowned practices in the country and serves clients in virtually every aspect of real estate law, including acquisitions, dispositions, developments and financings, as well as the establishment of joint ventures, real estate investment trusts, real estate opportunity funds and other real estate investment vehicles.

### Financial Services:

The Financial Services Practice regularly advises a broad range of participants in the financial services arena, including broker-dealers, futures commission merchants, investment advisors, finance companies, investment bankers, futures and securities exchanges, commodity trading advisors, pension funds, banks and insurance companies, as well as investment vehicles such as hedge funds, commodity pools, venture capital funds and private equity funds, securitisation vehicles, mutual funds and bank collective investment funds. Attorneys apply an interdisciplinary approach in providing comprehensive legal services, including regulatory and transactional advice, tax and ERISA counsel and domestic and foreign litigation.

### Commercial Finance:

The Commercial Finance Practice represents financial institutions making a wide variety of debt investments of all types and sizes in a broad range of industries. The firm's senior lending practice focuses on the representation of administrative agents, lead arrangers and bookrunners in syndicated asset-based and cash flow financing transactions to support leveraged buyout, recapitalisation, acquisition and refinancing transactions. The firm also represents investors in a wide variety of secured and unsecured mezzanine investments, term B and second lien term loans and other forms of junior capital.

### Insolvency & Restructuring

The Insolvency and Restructuring Practice focuses on managing the risks inherent in the restructuring process, and offering practical and innovative solutions to challenging problems. Clients include banks and other financial institutions, secured and unsecured creditors, hedge funds and private equity funds, debtors and borrowers, agents and participants in syndicated loan transactions, indenture trustees and bondholders, landlords, official and unofficial creditors' committees, equity committees, equipment lessors, shareholders, partners, purchasers of distressed assets, vendors, trade creditors and other interested parties in all manner of insolvency and workout situations. The team also provides front-end counseling of clients in structuring

their commercial transactions to identify and minimise risks related to insolvency and bankruptcy.

### Intellectual Property:

The Intellectual Property Practice secures, protects and enforces patents, trademarks, trade secrets and other intellectual property. They have represented plaintiffs and defendants in some of the most significant intellectual property cases (i.e., patents, trademarks, trade secrets, copyrights and unfair competition) of the last 20 years, for some of the world's most prominent corporations. Attorneys also assist in exploiting intellectual property rights through licensing, joint venture and technology transfer agreements.

### Environmental

The Environmental Practice blends a variety of legal skills–from providing effective advocacy with regulators and legislators on issues such as air quality and climate change, to building strong and effective compliance programs, to litigating cutting-edge matters, to responding to government investigations and enforcement actions. Their team of experienced attorneys and consultants includes public policy advocates and strategic communications professionals who work together to deal with environmental and energy issues that are often controversial.

### Tax:

The Tax Practice handles US and international tax planning and advises clients on the tax aspects of mergers and acquisitions, recapitalisations, reorganisations, spin-offs, venture capital and LBO transactions and financings, investment fund formation, securitisations of debt, equipment leasing, real estate transactions, hedge funds, public and private partnerships, limited liability companies and closely held and multinational corporations.

### Trusts & Estates:

The Trusts and Estates Practice develops and implements sophisticated estate, tax, business succession and charitable plans on the state, federal and international levels. They handle all aspects of the administration of estates and trusts, as well as probate, accounting, tax and other litigation.

# KIRKLAND & ELLIS LLP

www.kirkland.com **tel:** 312 862 2000 **fax:** 312 862 2200

Number of partners: 756  Number of other lawyers: 860

## Firm Overview:

For more than 100 years, Kirkland & Ellis has provided exceptional service to clients around the world in complex corporate, intellectual property, litigation, real estate, restructuring, tax and counseling matters.

## Main Areas of Practice:

Kirkland is a full-service law firm focusing in the following core practice areas:

### Corporate:

Kirkland's corporate lawyers cover the full spectrum of corporate transactions important to businesses in today's global marketplace. Because of the firm's consistently high volume of complex transactional engagements, it has developed a broad vision of the issues that confront business organizations and an aptitude for developing novel, creative and constructive solutions. Kirkland's emphasis on teamwork allows it to synthesize the specialty areas needed to support a top-tier transactional practice for the benefit of its clients. For two years in a row, *Chambers and Partners* named Kirkland as 'Private Equity Law Firm of the Year'. In 2010, Kirkland's Private Funds Group was recognized with an Award for Excellence from *Chambers and Partners*. In 2012, for the second year in a row, Kirkland was ranked No. 1 in Global Buyouts by volume and No. 1 for US M&A by Volume in mergermarket's League Tables of Legal Advisers to M&A for Year End 2012. The firm was also one of five selected M&A 'Practice Groups of the Year' in 2011, and Private Equity 'Practice Groups of the Year' in 2011 and 2012 by Law360.

### Intellectual Property:

Kirkland's Intellectual Property Practice Group is one of the oldest such practices in a full-service firm in the country, having been an integral part of Kirkland since 1925. Located in the firm's Chicago, London, Los Angeles, New York, Palo Alto, San Francisco and Washington, DC offices, Kirkland's intellectual property lawyers are experienced in a variety of technical disciplines and registered to practice before the U.S. Patent and Trademark Office. Kirkland's lawyers have been recognized for their experience in litigation, transactions, counseling and administrative matters involving all areas of intellectual property. In 2008, Kirkland was named one of three finalists in The American Lawyer's 'IP Litigation Department of the Year' survey. In 2009, Kirkland was recognized with an Award for Excellence in the IP Litigation Team category by *Chambers and Partners*. Kirkland was one of five selected IP 'Practice Groups of the Year' by Law360 in 2011.

### Litigation & Arbitration:

Kirkland litigators expect – and are expected – to try cases. The firm believes that the best litigation results happen when the lawyers and client form a team that assumes it will try the case. Because of this trial-ready philosophy, the firm is able to offer clients a deep bench of lawyers who have been taking cases to verdict since the early stages of their careers. Whether in the courtroom, at the bargaining table or helping clients avoid risks without litigation, Kirkland has a long and proven track record of generating successful results for clients in their most high-stakes cases. In 2012, for the 11th consecutive year, Kirkland was named a 'go-to' firm for litigation in the *Corporate Counsel* survey 'Who Represents America's Biggest Companies?'. Kirkland was named as a 2010 finalist and 2008 winner of The American Lawyer 'Litigation Department of the Year' competition. Kirkland's appellate and class action practices were selected as 2012 'Practice Groups of the Year' by Law360.

### Real Estate:

The members of the Real Estate Practice Group pursue an interdisciplinary approach to sophisticated real estate transactions to offer clients flexible and creative solutions to difficult problems across a broad range of transactions in the commercial real estate industry. In the summer of 2011, Kirkland recruited 10 seasoned real estate partners in New York and Chicago to add depth and breadth to several areas that involve important aspects of the real estate market, including joint ventures, complex debt restructurings, workouts and equity recapitalizations, fund formation, first mortgage and mortgage financings, capital markets and tax, in addition to core real estate transactional and development work. In 2011, Kirkland was one of five selected Real Estate 'Practice Groups of the Year' by Law360.

### Restructuring:

By combining sophisticated business advisory and crisis management skills with extensive experience in domestic and international insolvency matters, Kirkland's Restructuring Practice Group navigates clients through the turmoil of situations involving financially troubled companies. The firm has earned a distinguished reputation by achieving positive results for a wide range of global clients in complex corporate restructuring, workout and bankruptcy planning, negotiation and litigation. The practice was named second in 'best in practice' in the 2013 *Vault Guide to the Top 100 Law Firms* and was one of five selected Restructuring 'Practice Groups of the Year' by *Law360* in 2011.

### Tax, Benefits & Estate Planning:

The firm's Tax Practice Group has handled an array of matters for clients in the courtroom and the boardroom, with proven results in the fund formation, merger and acquisition and tax litigation arenas. Kirkland's employee benefits lawyers provide traditional employee benefits counseling and creative approaches to issues arising in the transactional, post-transactional and restructuring settings. Through the firm's trusts and estates lawyers, individual and corporate fiduciaries receive counsel in connection with the preservation, management and transfer of wealth. In 2008, 2009, 2010 and 2012, Kirkland was honored as 'Chicago Tax Firm of the Year', and in 2012 as the 'Americas Tax Restructuring Team of the Year' at the *International Tax Review's* Americas Tax Awards.

Kirkland also has lawyers with significant experience in the areas of antitrust and competition, regulatory, government, internal investigation and white-collar criminal defense, and securities enforcement. Kirkland's competition and securities practices were selected as 2012 'Practice Groups of the Year' by *Law360*.

## OFFICES

**ILLINOIS**

**CHICAGO:** 300 North LaSalle, IL 60654
Tel: 312 862 2000  Fax: 312 862 2200
Email: jeffrey.hammes@kirkland.com

**CALIFORNIA**

**LOS ANGELES:** 333 South Hope Street, CA 90017
Tel: 213 680 8400  Fax: 213 680 8500
Email: mark.holscher@kirkland.com

**PALO ALTO:** 3330 Hillview Avenue, CA 94304
Tel: 650 859 7000  Fax: 650 859 7500
Email: adam.phillips@kirkland.com

**SAN FRANCISCO:** 555 California Street, CA 94104
Tel: 415 439 1400  Fax: 415 439 1500
Email: david.breach@kirkland.com

**DISTRICT OF COLUMBIA**

**WASHINGTON DC:** 655 Fifteenth Street NW, DC 20005
Tel: 202 879 5000  Fax: 202 879 5200
Email: eugene.assaf@kirkland.com

**NEW YORK**

**NEW YORK:** 601 Lexington Avenue, NY 10022
Tel: 212 446 4800  Fax: 212 446 4900
Email: lefkowitz@kirkland.com

## INTERNATIONAL OFFICES

China, Germany, Hong Kong, United Kingdom

# KIRKLAND & ELLIS

# LANER MUCHIN

**www.lanermuchin.com tel:** 312 467 9800 **fax:** 312 467 9479

**Managing Partner:** Joseph M. Gagliardo
**President:** Joseph H. Yastrow
Number of partners: 10 income partners, 16 equity partners
Number of lawyers: 43
Languages: *English*

**OFFICES**

ILLINOIS

**CHICAGO:** 515 N. State Street, Suite 2800, IL 60654
Tel: 312 467 9800   Tel: 312 467 9479
Email: jyastrow@lanermuchin.com

## Firm Overview:

Laner Muchin was founded in 1945 and is one of the oldest law firms in Chicago concentrating exclusively in representing private and public sector employers in the fields of labor relations, employment litigation, employee benefits and business-related immigration. The firm's client base spans the United States, and includes national corporations, sports teams, media organizations and other large and medium-sized companies in virtually every sector of business and industry.

The firm is comprised of 43 attorneys and six paralegals, all of whom concentrate in representing employers in labor and employment matters. Because of the firm's singular focus on labor and employment law, every aspect of its practice is dedicated to providing clients with practical, responsive, cost-effective counseling and representation in all labor and employment matters. Client service is so important to the firm that it adheres to an institutional commitment to return every client call within two hours – a service commitment that is unique to the profession.

## Main Areas of Practice:

The firm's practice includes representation of clients in individual and class action litigation involving issues such as: state and federal civil rights and constitutional claims; retaliation and whistleblower claims; sexual, racial and other unlawful harassment; retaliatory discharge and other tort-based claims; employment discrimination (age, race, sex, disability, national origin, religion, etc.); breach of employment contracts; actions seeking injunctive relief; claims arising under the Family Medical Leave Act; claims arising under the Employee Retirement Income Security Act or otherwise involving employee benefits; claims arising under the Fair Labor Standards Act and other wage claims; covenants not to compete; trade secrets; enforcement of arbitration awards; and prevention of violent or unlawful picketing. Laner Muchin attorneys are experienced in all aspects of litigation ranging from pre-trial discovery and motions, to bench and jury trials and appeals. The firm also represents clients before the Equal Employment Opportunity Commission, National Labor Relations Board, and state and local employment commissions, civil rights agencies and departments of labor.

Further, the firm provides a full range of labor and employee relations services to clients representing a cross-section of private and public sector employers, a number of whom are unionized. The firm's attorneys conduct employee relations audits; provide day-to-day counseling, training and other preventative services; assist in the drafting and implementation of employment manuals and policies; act as spokespersons in collective bargaining negotiations, as well as assisting in labor contract administration; and assisting clients in handling grievances, through the appeal stages, including arbitration.

The firm also represents and provides counsel to employers with respect to all types of qualified retirement, health and welfare and executive nonqualified deferred compensation plans and trusts. This includes the development and design of incentive and other benefits intended to attain specific organizational goals; their documentation, operation and compliance with changing and extensive legal and regulatory requirements under state and federal law; responding to audits; and obtaining governmental agency approvals.

This firm's Immigration Group provides a full range of employment-based immigration services to our clients, including all nonimmigrant and immigrant visa processing procedures, I-9 audits, training and compliance, and immigration and relocation policies and procedures.

## Clients:

Chicago Bulls, McDonald's, The Trump Organization, The State of Illinois, University of Illinois, Corn Products International, True Value Company.

# LEYDIG, VOIT & MAYER, LTD.

www.leydig.com **tel:** 312 616 5600 **fax:** 312 616 5700

**President:** H Michael Hartmann
**Vice President:** Robert F Green
**Treasurer:** Steven P Petersen
**Secretary:** Eley O Thompson
Number of US partners: 50
Number of other US lawyers: 28

## Firm Overview:

Leydig, Voit & Mayer has a singular focus: the practice of intellectual property law. The firm provides intellectual property litigation, prosecution, counseling and licensing services to a wide range of clients worldwide, from individual inventors to multinational corporations. Leydig offers deep litigation and technical expertise in areas critical to business today, including pharmaceuticals, industrial processing chemicals, electronics, software, computers, manufacturing, biotechnology and business methods. Founded in 1893, the firm has over 90 attorneys and technical advisors, along with 100 staff professionals working in five offices in the US and Germany.

## Main Areas of Practice:

### Intellectual Property Litigation:

Throughout its rich history, Leydig has been at the forefront of IP litigation, as that practice has changed in the US and around the world. That tradition continues to this day. Leydig's distinguished and successful courtroom performance derives from its knowledgeable and experienced personnel. The strength of legal and technical experience of the firm's attorneys enables the firm to tailor its services to the unique litigation needs of each client.

### Patent Practice:

At Leydig, patent prosecution standards are exacting. The firm recognizes that the patent itself is the most critical document in patent enforcement and valuation, and works diligently to obtain the best possible protection for each of its clients' inventions. While quality is paramount, Leydig also consistently ranks among the top performers for number of patents prosecuted on behalf of clients worldwide. For international services, Leydig has cultivated an extensive international network of foreign associates, which allows the firm to quickly and efficiently prepare and prosecute patent applications throughout the world, while remaining up to date on the changes in patent law in every country.

### Trademark Practice:

Leydig's trademark services include assisting in name and mark selection, licensing, and counseling – in traditional media, in software, and on the Internet. The firm also handles all phases of trademark enforcement including pre-lawsuit negotiations and litigation before state and federal courts, as well as proceedings before the Trademark Trial and Appeal Board. Clients rely on Leydig for experience in related areas such as antitrust, unfair competition, misappropriation, Internet domain name disputes and trade libel, entertainment law, deceptive trade practices, interference with customer relations, employee pirating, and civil RICO charges.

## Representative Clients:

- Leydig represents American Express Company in trademark matters. 'American Express' is one of the most recognized brands in the world. Leydig works to clear, enforce, and defend American Express' trademarks worldwide.
- Leydig represents Caterpillar Inc. Caterpillar is the world's leading manufacturer of construction and mining equipment, and Leydig handles a significant portion of Caterpillar's patent procurement efforts.
- Leydig represents Google. Leydig prepares and prosecutes patent applications for Google in the area of mobile technology, including the important Android operating system.
- Leydig represents Huawei. Huawei is now the third largest telecommunications company, and among the largest filers of patent applications, in the world. Leydig partners with Huawei to assist in managing their patent portfolios.
- Leydig represents the National Institutes of Health (NIH). Leydig is pleased to represent the NIH with respect to its worldwide patent needs, and to be involved with ground-breaking technological developments in the discrete areas of biotechnology patent prosecution, chemical (pharmaceutical) patent prosecution, biotechnology contested proceedings, chemical (pharmaceutical) contested proceedings, and licensing.
- Leydig represents Sandoz, Inc. Sandoz is the generic pharmaceutical division of Novartis, the second largest pharmaceutical company in the world. Leydig is handling patent litigation matters for Sandoz, all of which relate to pending applications filed by Sandoz with the US FDA, seeking approval to market a wide variety of generic drugs.
- Leydig represents Teva Pharmaceuticals USA. Teva is the largest generic pharmaceutical manufacturer in the United States. Leydig is handling patent litigation matters for Teva that relate to generic pharmaceuticals which Teva plans to launch in the US, pending FDA approval.
- Leydig represents USG. Leydig is one of USG's leading intellectual property law firms and has been responsible for preparing and prosecuting patent applications in a variety of different subject matter areas for USG.
- Leydig represents Walgreen Co. In addition to trademark litigation and US and foreign oppositions, Leydig manages Walgreens' foreign trademark portfolio.

## OFFICES

### ILLINOIS

**CHICAGO:** Two Prudential Plaza, 180 N. Stetson Avenue, Suite 4900, IL 60601-6731
Tel: 312 616 5600  Fax: 312 616 5700
Email: mail@leydig.com

**ROCKFORD:** 6815 Weaver Road, Suite 300, IL 61114-8018
Tel: 815 963 7661  Fax: 815 963 7664
Email: rockmail@leydig.com

### CALIFORNIA

**WALNUT CREEK:** The Atrium Building, 1981 N. Broadway, Suite 310, CA 94596-5083
Tel: 925 482 0100  Fax: 925 482 0110

### DISTRICT OF COLUMBIA

**WASHINGTON DC:** 700 Thirteenth Street, NW, Suite 300, DC 20005-3960
Tel: 202 737 6770  Fax: 202 737 6776
Email: dcmail@leydig.com

## INTERNATIONAL OFFICES

The firm has an office in Frankfurt, Germany

**LEYDIG**

**LEYDIG, VOIT & MAYER, LTD.**
INTELLECTUAL PROPERTY LAW

# MAYER BROWN LLP

www.mayerbrown.com

**Chairman:** Paul W Theiss (Chicago)
**Managing Partner:** Kenneth S Geller (Washington, DC)
Number of lawyers worldwide: approximately 1,450

## Firm Overview:

Mayer Brown is a leading global law firm with 20 offices across the Americas, Europe and Asia. The firm is known for its client-focused approach to providing creative solutions to complex problems on behalf of businesses, governments and individuals. Mayer Brown is particularly renowned for its Supreme Court and appellate, litigation and dispute resolution, corporate and securities, banking and finance, real estate and tax practices. The firm serves many of the world's largest companies, including a significant proportion of the Fortune 100, FTSE 100, DAX and Hang Seng Index companies together with global leaders in major industries.

Mayer Brown provides a global service to its clients through eight offices in Asia, five offices in Europe and seven offices in the United States. In Asia, the firm operates as Mayer Brown JSM as a result of its 2008 combination with JSM (formerly Johnson Stokes & Master), a leading Asian law firm. In Brazil, the firm has an association with Tauil & Chequer Advogados.

## Main Areas of Practice:

### Banking & Finance:
The practice is one of Mayer Brown's signature strengths. Many of the firm's largest clients are bank holding companies, commercial banks, investment banks, insurance companies, asset-based lenders, leasing companies or institutional real estate companies. The Banking and Finance practice also represents numerous finance companies, funds and investors, as well as borrowers operating in many different industries.

### Corporate & Securities:
The lawyers provide a full range of legal services to leading global companies and financial institutions for some of their most important transactions, including complex cross-border deals and industry-specific issues. Key practices within corporate and securities include capital markets, mergers and acquisitions, private equity, and business and technology sourcing.

### Employment & Benefits:
The firm provides sophisticated solutions to the most complex issues in employment, employee benefits, executive compensation, ERISA litigation and pensions, as well as country-by-country knowledge of employment law and practices.

### Financial Services Regulatory & Enforcement:
This practice brings together the full range of sophisticated strategic, regulatory, compliance and enforcement capabilities required by today's leading financial services organizations. The practice includes lawyers experienced in traditional banking, broker-dealer, investment management, cross-border investigations and enforcement and insurance regulation.

### Global Trade:
The Global Trade practice includes some of the most experienced trade professionals and lawyers in the Americas, Europe and Asia, with in-depth knowledge and vast experience with virtually every aspect of international trade and investment, including market access and trade policy, trade remedies, trade compliance, international litigation and dispute settlement, ITC Section 337 investigations and the WTO.

### Government:
Mayer Brown's Government Relations practice draws upon lawyers and professionals located in key business centers throughout the Americas, Asia and Europe to help clients advance their domestic and global public policy goals. Lawyers of the government contracts group help clients from virtually every industry successfully manage all aspects of the government contracting process at the federal, state and local levels.

### Intellectual Property:
Innovators at global multinationals, emerging growth companies and established mid-sized businesses rely on Mayer Brown to protect, preserve and enforce their intellectual property assets. The lawyers assess IP portfolios, perform due diligence for acquisitions, secure patents, trademarks, trade secrets or copyrights, or use litigation to resolve business disputes over infringement or misappropriation.

### Litigation & Dispute Resolution:
Services cover antitrust and competition, commercial litigation, consumer litigation and class actions, electronic discovery and records management, employment and ERISA, environmental, international arbitration, product liability and mass torts, securities enforcement and litigation, and white-collar defense and compliance. The Supreme Court and Appellate practice is consistently ranked as a top-tier practice.

### Real Estate:
The firm is experienced in every stage of the real estate cycle, including acquisition, disposition, construction, leasing, financing, zoning and environmental matters. Clients include commercial banks, real estate investment trusts, institutional investors, pension funds and pension fund advisers, private equity, opportunity funds, governments, statutory bodies, investment banks, industrial banks, insurance companies, real estate holding companies, developers and corporations.

### Restructuring, Bankruptcy & Insolvency:
The firm has extensive experience in cross-border restructuring and formal insolvencies, working closely with colleagues in other regional offices on multi-jurisdictional matters. It represents liquidators, receivers, administrators, bondholders, lenders, liquidity providers, trustees, debtor-in-possession providers, company directors, insurers, pension fund trustees and corporate debtors and creditors on all aspects of restructuring, bankruptcy and insolvency.

### Tax (Tax Controversy, Tax Transactions & Consulting):
Mayer Brown's Tax practice covers every aspect of corporate, partnership and individual taxation, including taxation of cross-border transactions, litigation and state and local issues. The full-service practice includes sub-practices in transactions, consulting and planning, audits, administrative appeals, litigation and international transfer pricing.

### Wealth Management (Trusts, Estates & Foundations):
High-net-worth individuals require legal advice that is as sophisticated as their business and investment interests and never loses sight of their goals. The advice reaches beyond minimizing taxes to ensure practical and effective solutions to complex issues while maintaining flexibility to accommodate unforeseen events and family situations.

## REGIONAL HUBS

**AMERICAS**

**ILLINOIS:** Mayer Brown LLP, 71 South Wacker Drive, Chicago, 60606-4637
Tel: +1 312 782 0600  Fax: +1 312 701 7711
Email: info@mayerbrown.com

**EUROPE**

**UNITED KINGDOM:** Mayer Brown International LLP, 201 Bishopsgate, London EC2M 3AF
Tel: +44 20 3130 3000  Fax: +44 20 3130 3001

**ASIA**

**HONG KONG:** Mayer Brown JSM, 16th - 19th Floors, Prince's Building, 10 Chater Road, Central, Hong Kong
Tel: +852 2843 2211  Fax: +852 2845 9121

## OTHER OFFICES

USA: Charlotte, Houston, Los Angeles, New York, Palo Alto, Washington, DC
Asia: Bangkok, Beijing, Guangzhou, Hanoi, Ho Chi Minh City, Shanghai, Singapore
Europe: Brussels, Dusseldorf, Frankfurt, Paris

MAYER • BROWN

# MCDERMOTT WILL & EMERY LLP

www.mwe.com **tel:** 312 372 2000 **fax:** 312 984 7700

**Co-Chairs:** Jeffrey E Stone, Peter J Sacripanti
Number of partners: 595   Number of other lawyers: 527

**Firm Overview:**

McDermott Will & Emery is an international law firm with more than 1,100 lawyers in eighteen offices. The firm has a strategic alliance with MWE China Law Offices in Shanghai. The firm represents a wide range of industrial, financial and commercial enterprises, both publicly and privately held.

**Main Areas of Practice:**

**Corporate:**

The Corporate Practice represents a wide spectrum of business interests around the world, from Global 50 companies to venture backed start-ups. The corporate lawyers focus on specific areas including mergers and acquisitions, private equity, real estate, restructuring and insolvency, securities and structured finance and derivatives.

**Employee Benefits & Pensions:**

The firm's lawyers advise clients in a variety of employee benefits and compensation matters, including international planning, implementation and administration of a wide range of compensation and benefit plans and programs.

**Energy:**

The firm represents clients in all facets of the US and international energy industry. The energy lawyers advise in the areas structured transactions, federal and state law and regulatory compliance, government investigations and enforcement defense, commercial transactions, mergers and acquisitions, project development and corporate finance, risk management controls and policies, and litigation.

**Finance & Banking:**

The firm has an integrated finance and banking team with recognized experience in all areas of US, UK, European and international corporate finance.

**Health:**

With an over 50-year history of serving the healthcare industry, the firm has one of the United States' largest and most prestigious health law departments. The health lawyers counsel leading organizations in every major sector of the healthcare industry on regulatory and business transaction issues.

**Labor & Employment:**

The practice has considerable experience in all employment-related matters, both contentious and non-contentious. Its lawyers advise on wrongful and unfair dismissal, executive severance, confidentiality and restrictive covenants, breaches of fiduciary duty, fraud by employees, sex/race/disability discrimination, early retirement programs, development of employee manuals, wage-hour compliance, workers' compensation, equal pay, Working Time Regulations, union recognition and works councils, industrial disputes, EU employment law, TUPE, employment aspects of acquisitions.

**Intellectual Property:**

The firm's IP lawyers are uniquely capable of handling intellectual property matters in virtually every technical or scientific discipline. The firm's IP Practice is renowned for its trial and appellate experience. The IP Practice includes client counseling, procurement, and licensing in the patent, trademark, trade dress, copyright, trade secret, and entertainment areas. The firm's IP lawyers have assisted clients with oppositions in the European Patent Office and the Community Trade Mark Office.

**Private Client:**

The firm's Private Client Practice is one of the largest and best-known departments of its kind in the United States. The firm's lawyers represent families and individuals, family offices, closely-held businesses, foundations, estates, trusts and special purpose asset transfer and investment management entities providing a spectrum of estate, succession, gift transfer and wealth planning services.

**Regulatory & Governmental Affairs:**

The firm's lawyers have extensive experience working with state, national and international legislative bodies and administrative agencies. The practice is focused on antitrust and competition law, government strategies, international trade, food and agriculture, alcohol, OSHA and environmental law. The firm is adept at handling government regulations across numerous jurisdictions to meet the challenges faced by global organizations.

**Tax:**

The firm advises clients on all tax-related areas, including corporate, employee benefits, private clients, state and local taxation, and international matters. The core of the tax practice deals with thousands of statutory tax requirements imposed at international, federal, state and local levels. The firm represents more than half of the Fortune 100 companies in tax matters.

## OFFICES

**ILLINOIS**

**CHICAGO:** 227 West Monroe Street, IL 60606-5096
Tel: 312 372 2000   Fax: 312 984 7700

**CALIFORNIA**

**MENLO PARK:** 275 Middlefield Road, Suite 100, CA 94025
Tel: 650 815 7400   Fax: 650 815 7401

**LOS ANGELES:** 2049 Century Park East, 34th Floor, CA 90067-3208
Tel: 310 277 4110   Fax: 310 277 4730

**IRVINE:** 4 Park Plaza, Suite 1700, CA 92614-2559
Tel: 949 851 0633   Fax: 949 851 9348

**DISTRICT OF COLUMBIA**

**WASHINGTON DC:** 500 N Capitol Street, NW, DC 20001
Tel: 202 756 8000   Fax: 202 756 8087

**FLORIDA**

**MIAMI:** 333 Avenue of the Americas, Suite 4500, FL 33131-4336
Tel: 305 358 3500   Fax: 305 347 6500

**TEXAS**

**HOUSTON:** 1000 Louisiana Street, Suite 3900, TX 77002-5005
Tel: 713 653 1700   Fax: 713 739 7592

**MASSACHUSSETTS**

**BOSTON:** 28 State Street, MA 02109-1775
Tel: 617 535 4000   Fax: 617 535 3800

**NEW YORK**

**NEW YORK:** 340 Madison Ave, NY 10017
Tel: 212 547 5400   Fax: 212 547 5444

## INTERNATIONAL OFFICES

The firm also has offices in Brussels, Düsseldorf, Frankfurt, London, Milan, Munich, Paris, Rome and Seoul.

## ALLIANCES

The firm has a strategic alliance with MWE China Law Offices in Shanghai

**Trial:**

The trial lawyers are regularly engaged in all aspects of civil, regulatory and white-collar criminal defense litigation in US and international forums. Experience includes handling emergency situations such as temporary restraining orders and preliminary injunctions, bench and jury trials, arbitrations and alternative dispute resolution, including mediations and summary jury trials.

McDermott
Will & Emery

# MCDONNELL BOEHNEN HULBERT & BERGHOFF LLP

www.mbhb.com **tel:** 312 913 0001 **fax:** 312 913 0002

**Managing Partner:** Marcus J Thymian
Number of partners: 54
Number of lawyers: 80

## Firm Overview:

McDonnell Boehnen Hulbert & Berghoff LLP ("MBHB") provides creative, pragmatic business solutions through a variety of intellectual property services, including litigation, prosecution, and general client counseling. With offices in Illinois, California and North Carolina, MBHB provides comprehensive legal services to obtain and enforce its clients' intellectual property rights, from navigating patent office procedures to litigating complex infringement actions. MBHB attorneys prosecute patent and trademark applications in both the US and abroad, handle intellectual property litigation matters in trial and appellate courts across the country, and counsel clients nationwide and worldwide on the enforcement and defense of their intellectual property rights.

## Main Areas of Practice:

### Intellectual Property:

MBHB attorneys are experienced in the procurement, licensing, enforcement, and defense of patents, trademarks, copyrights, trade secrets, and unfair competition actions in a number of technological disciplines and product categories including:

- Biotechnology
- Business methods
- Chemical
- Electrical
- Mechanical and materials
- Pharmaceuticals and diagnostics
- Software
- Telecommunications

Comprised of 80 attorneys and 13 technical professionals, MBHB provides effective and service-oriented representation on a case-by-case basis. MBHB's client list includes Fortune 100 companies, mid-size companies, start-ups and academic institutions.
MBHB devotes about 50% of its practice to patent and trademark prosecution and counseling. The firm counsels clients on the management and development of their intellectual property assets and craft strategies consistent with their business goals. Likewise, MBHB dedicates about 50% of its practice to litigation. The

firm stands at the forefront of legally complex, highly technical patent litigation. This uniquely balanced focus upon both prosecution and litigation enables MBHB to approach a client's needs from multiple perspectives.
Many MBHB attorneys have both worked and published in their respective industries. MBHB attorneys are admitted to practice law in at least one jurisdiction are registered to practice before the United States Patent & Trademark Office.
At MBHB, the legal and scientific credentials of their professionals are first rate. MBHB professionals speak the languages of law and science – and of the people they serve. One hundred percent of the firm's attorneys and technical advisors hold science or engineering degrees. Of these, nearly 50% of their attorneys and technical advisors hold PhD's or other advanced degrees.
In 2012, MBHB processed 2,638 patent applications for clients (including National Phase Applications filed in 2012), making MBHB well experienced and capable of handling a variety of patent filings. At least half of the firm's clients are prosecution-oriented. In 2012, MBHB assisted in the issuance of 706 US patents for firm clients.
MBHB's singular focus on intellectual property law coupled with their culture of teamwork means clients benefit from the collective knowledge of their entire

firm. This growing base of specific knowledge is of tremendous value to their clients.
Despite MBHB's unsurpassed legal and technical skills, the focus of their professionals remains on clear communication – with judges, juries, patent examiners, other lawyers, and most importantly, with clients. Collaboration with clients comes easily. MBHB attorneys and technical advisors speak the language of the scientists and inventors with whom they work. They are current on today's ways of thinking regarding science and technology. They are up to the minute – and up to speed – on current IP law. The result is a positive, spirited firm culture – one that fosters teamwork and enables their professionals and staff to be more flexible and efficient in meeting client needs.

## PRACTICE AREAS

Copyright
Counseling
Litigation (Intellectual Property)
Patent
Prosecution
Trademark & Unfair Competition

## OFFICES

**ILLINOIS**
**CHICAGO (HEAD OFFICE):** 300 South Wacker Drive, 31st Floor, IL 60606
Tel: 312 913 0001

**CALIFORNIA**
**MOUNTAIN VIEW:** 800 West El Camino Real, Suite 180, CA 94040
Tel: 650 396 3300

**NORTH CAROLINA**
**DURHAM:** 2530 Meridian Parkway, Suite 300, NC 27713
Tel: 919 213 1302

McDonnell Boehnen Hulbert & Berghoff LLP
Intellectual Property Law

# NEAL, GERBER & EISENBERG LLP

**www.**ngelaw.com **tel:** 312 269 8000 **fax:** 312 269 1747

**Managing Partner:** Jerry H Biederman
**Senior Partners:** Marshall E Eisenberg, Phil C Neal
Number of partners: 111 Number of other lawyers: 52

**OFFICES**

ILLINOIS

**CHICAGO:** Two North LaSalle Street, Suite 1700, IL 60602-3801
Tel: 312 269 8000 Fax: 312 269 1747

**Firm Overview:**

Neal, Gerber & Eisenberg LLP serves clients throughout the world, providing legal business solutions to public and private entities in connection with business transactions and litigation. Clients include *Fortune* 100 companies, financial institutions, nonprofits and high net-worth individuals. The firm's steadfast devotion to its single-office concept ensures that clients will never get lost in a shuffle of thousands of lawyers or multiple worldwide offices.

**Main Areas of Practice:**

**Antitrust & Unfair Trade Practices:**
The firm's Antitrust Practice is dynamic and built around highly qualified antitrust lawyers who provide sophisticated, solutions-oriented advice on all aspects of antitrust and trade regulation law.

**Commercial Leasing:**
The firm handles a broad range of leasing and leasing-related matters in the retail, office and industrial areas.

**Corporate & Securities:**
Addressing all areas of business and transactional law, the firm handles complex acquisition and financing transactions and provides general corporate counsel.

**Corporate Governance:**
Be it best practices in corporate governance or defense of potential claims, the firm provides counsel to boards of directors, committees (including audit committees), directors, officers and others with oversight responsibilities.

**Cross-Border & International:**
The firm excels in representing foreign and domestic clients with respect to their US legal needs in connection with cross-border transactional, regulatory and commercial litigation matters throughout the US.

**Employee Benefits & Executive Compensation:**
The firm advises a variety of clients on employee pension plans, executive compensation arrangements, executive employment contracts, severance arrangements and health and welfare plans.

**Environmental:**
The firm has extensive experience in environmental litigation, government enforcement actions, corporate and real estate transactions, solid and hazardous waste landfill regulation, air quality regulation and general regulatory compliance.

**Finance & Lending:**
The firm represents borrowers and lenders of secured and unsecured commercial loans providing a full range of financial legal services.

**Financial Restructuring & Bankruptcy:**
The firm has extensive experience in the full range of insolvency matters, from out-of-court restructurings to formal reorganization and liquidation proceedings.

**Fund Formation & Investment Management:**
The firm represents a broad range of funds, fund managers and investors. Clients include asset management firms, hedge funds, private equity and venture funds, family offices and fund-of-funds.

**General & Commercial Litigation:**
The firm is home to a large group of litigators adept in all types of commercial litigation and alternative dispute resolution, including antitrust, ERISA, health care, product liability, fraud and trusts and estate.

**Healthcare & Life Sciences:**
The firm partners with companies—including those from the medical care, life sciences, pharmaceutical, medical devices and diagnostic sectors—to advance their business interests through counseling, litigation and transactional work.

**Insurance Policyholder:**
The firm represents claimants and corporate policyholders in the defense, negotiation and settlement of first and third-party claims in litigation, arbitration and mediation around the country and world.

**Intellectual Property:**
The firm handles a wide variety of strategic intellectual property counseling, litigation and prosecution matters involving patents, trademarks, service marks, domain names, trade dress, trade secrets, copyrights and advertising claims.

**Labor & Employment:**
The firm advises a myriad of clients on how to encourage a union-free workplace, litigate employment-related claims, develop employee-friendly yet effective employment policies, manage legal risks and liabilities and negotiate contracts.

**Private Wealth Services:**
The firm represents high net worth clients and their families in providing the full range of tax, estate planning and corporate issues.

**Real Estate:**
The firm's client base includes REITs, local and national corporations, partnerships, entrepreneurs, financial institutions, multi-project builders, management companies, operators, developers and individuals.

**Real Estate Tax:**
The firm maintains a significant property tax foreclosure and exemption practice coupled with extensive work in all aspects of state and local property tax, including assessment appeals.

**Securities & Commodities Litigation:**
Representing many of the major national, regional and local broker/dealers and commodities firms, as well as affiliated individuals, the firm advises and defends clients in the full range of customer disputes, employment disputes and regulatory matters.

**Taxation:**
The firm represents clients in domestic and international income tax and business planning, estate, gift and generation-skipping taxation, the tax aspects of executive compensation arrangements and the successful resolution of federal and state tax controversies.

**Technology Transactions & Services:**
The firm serves a wide variety of buyers, sellers, licensors and licensees of software, hardware, data and services in drafting and negotiating complex technology agreements.

**Trade & Professional Associations:**
The firm represents international, national, state and local organizations of all sizes including trade associations, professional societies, educational foundations and charities.

**White-Collar Crime & Investigations:**
Broad investigative, trial and appellate experience provides effective early resolution of potential criminal problems and the ability to deal directly with regulatory and government agencies.

**Clients:**
Examples: Boeing Company; Citigroup Global Markets Inc.; Goldcorp, Inc.; Hyatt International Corp.; JPMorgan Chase & Co.; Tyson Foods, Inc.; UBS; United Healthcare; and United Parcel Service of America, Inc.

# SCHOPF & WEISS LLP

**www.**sw.com   **tel:** 312 701 9300   **fax:** 312 701 9335

**Chairman:** Steven A Weiss
**Managing Partner:** Jason M Rosenthal
Number of partners: 16   Number of other lawyers: 5

## Firm Overview:

Schopf & Weiss LLP was founded in 1987 based on the idea that a small focused team of experienced litigators would provide better, more efficient and more successful representation to clients than the large department store law firms to which businesses traditionally turn. The firm's experience and the results obtained for clients confirm this view. The firm emphasizes responsiveness and service to clients, professional excellence, a commitment to keeping ahead of evolving technology, and the ability to apply creative solutions to complex legal challenges. Schopf & Weiss continually measures success based on client satisfaction.

## Main Areas of Practice:

### General Business Litigation:
The firm represents corporations and business people in sophisticated and complex business disputes throughout the United States. The firm tries more business cases, from antitrust to RICO to intellectual property and contract, than firms many times its size. Schopf & Weiss is forceful in advocacy, creative in approach, tenacious in negotiations, focused on results, and mindful of costs.
**Contact:** Steven A Weiss **Tel:** 312 701 9311
**Email:** weiss@sw.com

### Insurance Coverage:
Schopf & Weiss has sophisticated expertise and nationwide experience in insurance coverage litigation. Clients are exclusively corporations and other businesses involved in coverage disputes against their insurers. Through the firm's efforts, clients have recovered millions of dollars in coverage and defense costs from insurers refusing to pay. The firm will litigate and advise clients concerning coverage issues involving a wide array of subject matters, including environmental contamination, product liability, automobile liability, directors and officers liability, defamation, trademark and patent infringements, technology errors and omissions, 'sick building' claims, and first party claims for property damage and business interruption. Schopf & Weiss's national perspective enriches its practice, enabling it to draw on trends or decisions from one jurisdiction for efforts in others.
**Contact:** Paula E Litt **Tel:** 312 701 9317
**Email:** litt@sw.com

### Securities:
Schopf & Weiss represents clients in securities-related litigation and arbitration, including matters involving alleged securities fraud, commodities and futures transactions, unauthorized trading, and disputes between brokers and brokerage houses over trade secrets and noncompetition or non-solicitation agreements. Clients include large Wall Street firms, foreign investment firms, broker dealers, clearing firms, banks and their investment banking and securities operations, issuers, officers and directors, brokers, traders, investors, and purchasers.
**Contact:** Marcus D Fruchter **Tel:** 312 701 9354
**Email:** fruchter@sw.com
**Contact:** Lesley G Smith **Tel:** 312 701 9329
**Email:** lgsmith@sw.com

### Intellectual Property:
The firm represents a broad range of defendants and plaintiffs in litigation involving copyright, trademark, and patent infringement, as well as in the related areas of trade secret, misappropriation, and unfair competition. The firm has represented companies in pursuing and defending against claims of copyright or trademark infringement of items such as website content, logos, video games, industrial products and instructional manuals. Also, the firm has prosecuted or defended patent infringement cases involving biopsy needles, hemodialysis catheters, nutritional products, cellular phones, automotive torque transfer technology, programmable logic controllers, web server load balancing technology, and post-press collating machines.
**Contact:** Bradley P Nelson **Tel:** 312 701 9313
**Email:** nelson@sw.com

### Antitrust:
The firm has successfully represented corporate clients in many of the largest and most complex antitrust suits filed over the last three decades. The firm has defended clients against claims of price-fixing, monopolization, discriminatory pricing, and other antitrust violations in court and in federal grand jury proceedings. Attorneys have represented clients in a variety of industries including carbon dioxide, industrial gases, beer, cast iron pipe, gypsum wall board, uranium, corrugated containers, real estate, newspaper, records and tapes, and real estate brokers' commissions.
**Contact:** Patrick J Heneghan **Tel:** 312 701 9323
**Email:** heneghan@sw.com

## PRACTICE AREAS

Business Litigation
Alternative Dispute Resolution
Antitrust Litigation
Banking Litigation
Bankruptcy
Class Action
Copyright Litigation
Corporate Governance Litigation
Corporate Investigations
International Business Litigation
Insurance Coverage Litigation
Patent Litigation
Professional Liability
Real Estate Litigation
Securities Litigation
Trademark Litigation
Trade Secret & Noncompete Litigation

## OFFICES

ILLINOIS
**CHICAGO:** One S. Wacker Drive, 28th Floor, IL 60606
Tel: 312 701 9300   Fax: 312 701 9335

### Professional Liability:
Schopf & Weiss has built an extensive practice in the field of professional liability, representing lawyers, accountants, financial advisors, and other professionals against claims of professional malpractice and in related matters. Fellow attorneys at some of the largest and most prestigious firms in the country have turned to Schopf & Weiss to handle significant cases on their behalf.
**Contact:** Robert J Palmersheim **Tel:** 312 701 9319
**Email:** palmersheim@sw.com

### International Litigation:
From its inception, Schopf & Weiss developed a significant range of expertise international litigation. With a client base that includes many large multi-national corporations, and with the globalization of the world economy, the firm regularly handles cases between US companies and their foreign trading partners, competitors, vendors, distributors, and joint venturers.
**Contact:** Peter V Baugher **Tel:** 312 701 9315
**Email:** baugher@sw.com

### Clients:
Representative clients include Sears Holdings Corporation (including subsidiaries Sears Roebuck and Co. & Kmart Corp.), Exelon Corporation, Walgreen Co., Illinois Tool Works, Inc., Air Liquide USA LLC, Motorola Solutions, Inc., Guardsmark, LLC, Tyson Foods, Inc., Goss International, The John Buck Company, Checkpoint Systems, Inc., Kaplan Higher Education, and DeVry University to name a few.

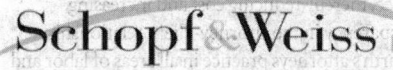

# SEYFARTH SHAW LLP

www.seyfarth.com **tel:** 312 460 5000 **fax:** 312 460 7000

**Managing Partner:** J Stephen Poor
Number of partners: 355  Number of other lawyers: 455

## Firm Overview:

Founded in 1945, Seyfarth Shaw is a full-service international law firm with more than 800 attorneys representing clients in every sector of the global economy. Seyfarth is a legal industry leader in innovative, client-focused solutions for the delivery of value and excellence. The firm client service model, Seyfarth*Lean*, which combines the principles of Lean Six Sigma, technology, knowledge management and project management, has received numerous accolades.

## Main Areas of Practice:

### Corporate:

Offering focused, sophisticated and efficient attention to client matters, delivered with the resources of a full-service national practice, the firm's 105 corporate attorneys effectively blend broad knowledge of corporate law with extensive experience in key practice areas including finance, M&A, securities, tax, and trusts and estates. Representing closely held companies, multinational corporations, private investment funds, financial institutions, investment banking firms and others – on both sides of the deal making table – the firm understands the unique legal, regulatory, economic and competitive forces their clients face.

### Employee Benefits & Executive Compensation:

Seyfarth maintains one of the largest and most prominent Employee Benefits and Executive Compensation Departments in the nation. The department includes nearly 50 attorneys nationwide practicing exclusively in the area of employee benefit and executive compensation regulatory compliance and plan administration. The firm's lawyers are a diverse group with experience as in-house ERISA counsel in large corporations, with national tax and consulting practice experience, and as adjunct professors in graduate-level law programs. This depth and breadth of expertise allows the firm to competently and efficiently resolve a limitless variety of client needs arising out of executive compensation and retirement, health and welfare plans and programs.

### Labor & Employment:

Seyfarth Shaw's Labor and Employment Department is home to over 385 L&E attorneys, representing the Fortune 1000 and other globally-recognized companies in all facets of labor and employment litigation and counseling. Seyfarth's attorneys serve as trusted advisors to their clients, whether litigating "bet-the-company" matters or handling routine L&E litigation and day-to-day counseling advice. Its attorneys combine unparalleled expertise with a commitment to delivering value to the client, focusing on constantly improving its service, thereby reducing cost and increasing transparency in the attorney-client relationship. Seyfarth's attorneys practice in all areas of labor and

employment law and have particular expertise in the following subspecialties: complex discrimination, wage-hour and ERISA complex and class litigation; labor management relations; workplace and employment counseling; OFCCP and affirmative action compliance; international employment law; business immigration and environmental, safety and toxic torts. In addition, Seyfarth Shaw at Work, a subsidiary of the firm, is one of the nation's leading legal compliance and management training companies, providing highly engaging and interactive employment law-related training over a variety of platforms.

### Litigation:

The firm offers a full-service Commercial and Corporate Litigation Practice composed of approximately 175 attorneys and 17 legal assistants across the country. Seyfarth's highly experienced attorneys concentrate in a variety of litigation areas of specialization, including bankruptcy; class action defense; construction; eDiscovery; government contracts; trade secrets, computer fraud and non-competes; intellectual property; product liability; franchise and dealer disputes; and securities. The firm's talented litigators are innovative and aggressive in their pursuit of strategic outcomes, and are prepared to pursue clients' interests in every forum, including traditional jury trials in state and federal courts, guidance throughout the appellate process, and alternative dispute resolution methods.

### Real Estate:

With approximately 125 attorneys in key markets across the US, Seyfarth Shaw is home to a premier, broad-based institutional real estate and real estate finance practice. The firm's real estate lawyers have deep experience in: acquisitions and dispositions, capital markets, development, construction, leasing, financing, restructuring and loan workouts, and joint ventures/partnerships. Clients include real estate developers, management companies, privately held and public companies, pension funds, government entities, landlords, tenants, not-for-profits, REITs, institutional investors, lenders, servicers and those in the retail and hospitality industry. Firm lawyers help clients identify emerging opportunities and challenges in the ever evolving real estate market, and bring to bear a deep

## OFFICES

### CALIFORNIA

**LOS ANGELES - CENTURY CITY:** One Century Plaza, 2029 Century Park East, Suite 3500, CA 90067-3021
Tel: 310 277 7200  Fax: 310 201 5219

**LOS ANGELES - DOWNTOWN:** 333 South Hope Street, Suite 3900, CA 90071-1406
Tel: 213 270 9600  Fax: 213 270 9601

**SACRAMENTO:** 400 Capitol Mall, Suite 2350, CA 95814-4428
Tel: 916 448 0159  Fax: 916 558 4839

**SAN FRANCISCO:** 560 Mission Street, Suite 3100, CA 94105-2930
Tel: 415 397 2823  Fax: 415 397 8549

### DISTRICT OF COLUMBIA

**WASHINGTON DC:** 975 F Street, NW, DC 20004
Tel: 202 463 2400  Fax: 202 828 5393

### GEORGIA

**ATLANTA:** 1075 Peachtree Street, NE, Suite 2500, GA 30309-3962
Tel: 404 885 1500  Fax: 404 892 7056

### ILLINOIS

**CHICAGO:** 131 S Dearborn Street, Suite 2400, IL 60603-5577
Tel: 312 460 5000  Fax: 312 460 7000

### MASSACHUSETTS

**BOSTON:** World Trade Center East, Two Seaport Lane, Suite 300, MA 02210-2028
Tel: 617 946 4800  Fax: 617 946 4801

### NEW YORK

**NEW YORK:** 620 Eighth Avenue, 32nd Floor, NY 10018-1405
Tel: 212 218 5500  Fax: 212 218 5526

### TEXAS

**HOUSTON:** 700 Louisiana Street, Suite 3700, TX 77002-2797
Tel: 713 225 2300  Fax: 713 225 2340

## INTERNATIONAL OFFICES

The firm also has an office in London, UK, and will be opening an office in Shanghai, China, in 2013.

national bench and decades of experience in successfully closing complex transactions and long-term projects.

**Clients:**

Clients include companies in the financial, media, hospitality, insurance, healthcare, manufacturing, professional services, retail, technology and telecommunications industries. The firm also represents a number of federal, state and local governmental and educational entities.

**International Work:**

Seyfarth Shaw's team of international attorneys assist clients with multinational operations in their cross-border legal needs.

# SHAW FISHMAN GLANTZ & TOWBIN LLC

**www.**shawfishman.com **tel:** 312 541 0151 **fax:** 312 980 3888

Number of Members: 17
Number of Associates and Of Counsel: 8

## Firm Overview:

Shaw Fishman focuses on and specializes in three areas of commercial law: bankruptcy and restructuring, litigation, and real estate. Excellence, efficiency and value are the cornerstones of the Shaw Fishman practice, as the boutique firm is committed to providing outstanding representation and counsel in an economical and expeditious manner. Shaw Fishman offers an aggressive but pragmatic approach to solving problems and obtaining results. Its attorneys are leaders in their respective fields and provide clients with big firm depth and experience at small firm rates.

## Main Areas of Practice:

### Bankruptcy:

The firm concentrates its practice on bankruptcy, reorganization, creditors' rights, insolvency, crisis management, and related transactions and litigation. The Bankruptcy and Insolvency Group has depth of experience in all phases of complex bankruptcy and reorganization cases, as well as state and federal court receiverships and out-of-court workouts. The firm has substantial experience in all elements of bankruptcy litigation, including cash collateral and debtor in possession financing issues, modification of the automatic stay, contested plan confirmation hearings, and the prosecution and defense of fraudulent conveyance and preference avoidance actions. Shaw Fishman has extensive experience with respect to the purchase and sale of assets in both formal bankruptcy cases and out-of-court insolvency situations. The firm routinely represents debtors, debtors in possession, trustees, committees, and creditors in large national cases and smaller regional and local situations. In 2012, Ira Bodenstein was appointed the Chapter 7 Trustee of Peregrine Financial Group, Inc. and the firm has been engaged as the Trustee's counsel, handling the multiple investigations, the claims review process, the administration of the case and the numerous pieces of associated litigation. Members of the Bankruptcy and

Insolvency Group are frequent lecturers and authors on numerous bankruptcy and insolvency topics. The co-chairmen of the firm's Bankruptcy and Insolvency Group, Robert M Fishman and Steven B Towbin, are Fellows of the American College of Bankruptcy.

### Commercial Litigation:

The Commercial Litigation Group has experience in all aspects of state and federal commercial and tort litigation, including contract claims, fraud claims, labor and employment disputes, products and premises liability claims, franchise disputes, professional negligence, securities and commodities fraud, insurance coverage disputes (from the policy holder side), partnership and shareholder disputes, mechanics lien actions, and construction and real estate disputes. The Commercial Litigation Group also lends continual support to our Bankruptcy and Insolvency Group through its extensive involvement in the numerous adversary proceedings handled by the firm, such as preference and fraudulent conveyance cases.

### Real Estate:

The Real Estate Group provides representation with respect to all aspects of commercial and residential real estate. The firm has a very significant real estate development practice, involving acquisitions, land use and entitlement, planned developments dispositions, financing and leasing.

### Mediation:

Robert M Fishman is now regularly being retained as a mediator in various bankruptcy disputes across the United States. Mr Fishman was a member of the faculty fo the 2012 American Bankruptcy Institute/St. John's University Law School Bankruptcy Mediation Training Program.

### Clients:

The Bankruptcy and Insolvency Group regularly represents trustees, committees, financial institutions, equity holders, landlords, asset purchasers, plan liquidating and disbursing agents, assignees, and receivers. Clients of the Bankruptcy and Insolvency Group consist of companies from numerous industries throughout the United States, including the manufacturing, healthcare, retail, entertainment, telecommunications, financial and real estate industries. The Commercial Litigation Group represents clients in various jurisdictions across the country, including banks, printing companies, venture capital firms, real estate developers, hotels, manufacturing companies, retailers, and bankruptcy trustees, committees, and estates. Clients of the Real Estate Group include developers of shopping centers, office buildings and residential projects throughout the greater Chicagoland area.

# SIDLEY AUSTIN LLP

www.sidley.com **tel:** 312 853 7000 **fax:** 312 853 7036

**Chairman of Executive Committee:** Carter G Phillips
**Chairman of Management Committee:** Charles W Douglas
Number of partners worldwide: 666
Number of lawyers worldwide: 1747

## Firm Overview:

Sidley Austin is one of the world's premier law firms, with a practice highly attuned to the ever-changing international landscape. The firm has built a reputation for being a powerful adviser for global businesses, with approximately 1700 lawyers in 18 offices worldwide. Sidley maintains a commitment to providing quality legal services wherever they are needed, offering advice in litigation, transactional and regulatory matters spanning virtually every area of law. The firm's lawyers leverage their diversity of knowledge and wide-reaching legal backgrounds with a dedication to teamwork, collaboration and superior client service.

Sidley values the recognition it has received in response to its leadership in its wide cross-section of legal services around the globe. These accolades, which come from professional peers, publications and industry journals and clients in numerous industries, include:

- Received the most first-tier national rankings of any US law firm in the 2013 US News – Best Lawyers 'Best Law Firms' survey for the third consecutive year and each year since the survey's inception
- One of just three firms to have been in the top 10 of the BTI Client Service rankings every year since the inception of those rankings in 2001
- Consistently ranks among the top global capital markets firms in the Thomson Reuters league tables
- Named a finalist in the American Lawyer Litigation Department of the Year 2012
- Received the Most Innovative Gender Diversity Initiative Award at the first Chambers USA Women in Law Awards in 2012
- Received a 'perfect' 100 score on the Human Rights Campaign's 2013 Corporate Equality Index (CEI) report. Sidley has received 'perfect' 100 scores on each report since 2008
- Named as one of the top 25 national corporate law firms in Corporate Board Member magazine's 2012 survey of corporate directors and general counsel
- Named USA Law Firm of the Year for 2011 and 2012 in the Who's Who Legal Awards
- Recognized in four categories of the Law360 Practice Groups of 2012 award series: Appellate, Environmental, International Trade and Life Sciences
- Only law firm with top tier Life Sciences rankings across three continents in the Practical Law Company (PLC) Life Sciences Handbook 2012. Also ranked among the world's top five firms for both its life sciences industry practice and its life sciences regulatory practice

## Main Areas of Practice:

Accountants/Professional Service Firms Liability
Antitrust/Competition
Appellate
Banking & Financial Services
Communications Regulatory
Complex Commercial Litigation
Corporate Governance & Compliance
Corporate Reorganization & Bankruptcy
Emerging Companies & Venture Capital
Employee Benefits
Energy
Environmental
ERISA Litigation
Executive Compensation
Financial Services/Consumer Class Actions
Food, Drug and Medical Device Compliance & Enforcement
Food, Drug & Medical Device Regulatory

Global Finance
Government Strategies
Healthcare
Insurance
Insurance/Reinsurance Disputes
Intellectual Property Litigation
International Arbitration (Commercial and Treaty)
International Trade
Investment Funds, Advisers & Derivatives
Labor, Employment & Immigration
Life Sciences
M&A & D&O Litigation
M&A
Privacy, Data Security & Information Law
Private Equity
Products Liability
Project Finance & Infrastructure
Public Finance

Real Estate
SEC Enforcement
Securities
Securities & Futures Regulatory
Securities Litigation
Tax
Tax Controversy
Technology Transactions
Transportation
Trusts, Estates & Not-for-Profits
White Collar: Government Litigation & Investigations

## OFFICES

### CALIFORNIA
**LOS ANGELES:** 555 West Fifth Street, CA 90013
Tel: 213 896 6000   Fax: 213 896 6600

**PALO ALTO:** 1001 Page Mill Road, Building 1, CA 94304
Tel: 650 565 7000   Fax: 650 565 7100

**SAN FRANCISCO:** 555 California Street, CA 94104
Tel: 415 772 1200   Fax: 415 772 7400

### DISTRICT OF COLUMBIA
**WASHINGTON, DC:** 1501 K Street, NW, DC 20005
Tel: 202 736 8000   Fax: 202 736 8711

### ILLINOIS
**CHICAGO:** One South Dearborn, IL 60603
Tel: 312 853 7000   Fax: 312 853 7036

### NEW YORK
**NEW YORK:** 787 Seventh Avenue, NY 10019
Tel: 212 839 5300   Fax: 212 839 5599

### TEXAS
**DALLAS:** 717 North Harwood, Suite 3400, TX 75201
Tel: 214 981 3300   Fax: 214 981 3400

**HOUSTON:** 1000 Louisiana Street, Suite 6000, TX 77002
Tel: 713 495 4500   Fax: 713 495 7799

## INTERNATIONAL OFFICES

The firm also has offices in Beijing, Brussels, Frankfurt, Geneva, Hong Kong, London, Shanghai, Singapore, Sydney and Tokyo.

SIDLEY AUSTIN LLP
# SIDLEY

# UNGARETTI & HARRIS LLP

**www.uhlaw.com  tel:** 312 977 4400  **fax:** 312 977 4405

**Managing Partner:** Thomas M. Fahey
Number of partners: 70
Number of lawyers: 96
Languages: *French, Italian, Russian, Spanish, Ukrainian*

## Firm Overview:

Ungaretti & Harris LLP is a mid-sized law firm serving clients from offices in Chicago and Springfield, Illinois and Washington, DC. The firm represents clients including *Fortune* 500, mid-market, and small businesses; private equity funds; healthcare providers; energy companies; real estate companies; financial institutions; professional organizations; and government agencies.

## Main Areas of Practice:

### Corporate:

The Corporate Practice is one of the largest and most highly regarded among mid-sized law firms in the Midwest. The Corporate Practice handles mergers and acquisitions, corporate finance transactions, commercial agreements, securities matters, venture capital financings and derivative products.

### Employee Benefits & Executive Compensation:

The Employee Benefits and Executive Compensation Practice handles all aspects of employee benefit plans, executive compensation and ERISA litigation.

### Finance & Restructuring:

The Finance and Restructuring Practice provides lenders, creditors, borrowers and debtors with a full range of legal services for their lending, restructuring and bankruptcy needs.

### Gaming:

The Gaming Practice is widely recognized for their experience in representing gaming industry clients. The practice represents clients in matters involving licensing, suitability and compliance, administrative and disciplinary hearings, corporate and commercial transactions and litigation.

### Government:

The Government Practice provides services including legislative and executive branch counseling, advocacy, negotiation, litigation involving government agencies and officials and representation in hearings and presentations involving legislative and administrative bodies.

### Healthcare:

The Healthcare Practice has earned a national reputation for its representation of healthcare providers. The attorneys represent providers in a wide range of healthcare matters including healthcare regulatory issues; health system financings; mergers, acquisitions and joint ventures; and general business matters.

### Intellectual Property:

The Intellectual Property Practice represents clients worldwide, providing prosecution, litigation and counseling services on matters involving patents, trademarks, trade dress, copyrights, trade secrets, unfair competition, computer technologies, franchising, and licensing.

### Labor & Employment:

The Labor and Employment Practice provides counseling and litigation services on all manner of employment and labor issues, including wage and hour disputes, discrimination and harassment, whistleblower allegations, workplace torts, and organized labor issues.

### Land Use & Zoning:

The Land Use and Zoning Practice has extensive knowledge of economic development incentives, zoning requirements, property tax assessments and municipal code compliance. The practice represents clients regarding licenses and permits, litigation, government hearings, economic incentives, and imminent domain matters.

### Litigation:

The Litigation Practice handles a broad range of disputes for clients ranging from Global 50 to small and mid-sized clients. Services include commercial litigation, products liability and mass tort, bankruptcy, appellate, fiduciary law, constitutional law, environmental litigation and white collar representation.

### Public Finance:

The firm has a nationally recognized Public Finance Practice that typically handles well over $1 billion in bond transactions annually for clients including state and local government agencies, healthcare providers, not-for-profit organizations, municipalities, schools, and other special-purpose districts.

### Real Estate:

The Real Estate Practice assists clients nationwide with property acquisitions and dispositions; lease transactions; loan advice and documentation; development projects; and mortgage workouts, restructurings and foreclosures.

### Tax:

The Tax Practice structures, develops and advises with respect to mergers and acquisitions, various debt and equity financings, mortgage-backed and asset-backed securitizations, leasing transactions and financial products.

### Trusts & Estate Planning:

The Trusts and Estate Planning Practice advises on complex estate, gift, generation-skipping and income tax matters, asset-management matters and related planning devices.

## PRACTICE AREAS

Corporate
Employee Benefits & Executive Compensation
Finance & Restructuring
Gaming
Government
Healthcare
Intellectual Property
Labor & Employment
Land Use & Zoning
Litigation
Public Finance
Real Estate
Tax
Trusts & Estate Planning

## OFFICES

ILLINOIS
**CHICAGO:** Three First National Plaza, 70 West Madison-Suite 3500, IL 60602
Tel: 312 977 4400  Fax: 312 977 4405

**SPRINGFIELD:** 400 East Jefferson Street-Suite 1200, IL 62701
Tel: 217 544 7000  Fax: 217 544 7950

DISTRICT OF COLUMBIA
**WASHINGTON, DC:** 601 Pennsylvania Avenue NW-South Building, Suite 900, DC 20004
Tel: 202 434 8237  Fax: 312 977 4405

# UNGARETTI & HARRIS

# VEDDER PRICE

www.vedderprice.com **tel:** 312 609 7500 **fax:** 312 609 5005

**CEO & President:** Michael A Nemeroff
**Chairman:** Robert J Stucker
Number of partners worldwide: 160   Number of other lawyers worldwide: 115

### Firm Overview:

Vedder Price serves clients of all sizes in virtually all industries with a responsive, results-oriented and cost-effective approach. Vedder Price is an international law firm operating through various separate and distinct entities, including Vedder Price P.C., which operates in the United States, and Vedder Price LLP, which operates in England and Wales and is regulated by the Solicitors Regulation Authority.

### Main Areas of Practice:

**Construction:**
15 Shareholders and 3 Associates
- Successfully represented Target Corporation in more than a dozen shopping and distribution center projects around the US, including obtaining zoning and permitting approvals for urban stores
Contact: Karen P Layng  Tel: 312 609 7891
Email: kplayng@vedderprice.com

**Executive Compensation:**
15 Shareholders and 6 Associates
- Advised major retailer on complex employment arrangements for new CEO
- Counseled a senior executive team in negotiations of investment, employment, compensation and long-term incentive equity arrangements in connection with the $7 billion sale of a health care products company
Contact: Thomas P Desmond  Tel: 312 609 7647
Email: tdesmond@vedderprice.com

**Finance & Transactions:**
53 Shareholders, 1 Counsel and 26 Associates
- Handle complex M&A and private equity transactions for companies nationwide. Representations include Wynnchurch Capital in the $70 million acquisition of Northstar Aerospace and its U.S. and Canadian subsidiaries; North American Coatings, LLC (NAC), a portfolio company of Valor Equity Partners, in Safway Group's 100% acquisition of the membership interests of NAC; and PGI International, a portfolio company of The Edgewater Funds, in its sale to Parker Hannifin Corporation
- Counsel borrowers and lenders regarding a broad array of debt transactions and structures. Representations include Ally Commercial Finance in a $76.1 million revolving and term loan transaction with American Driveline Systems, Inc.; CIT Group as revolving agent in an international $355 million syndicated loan transaction to fund the acquisition of Culligan International Co. by Centerbridge Partners; and CIT Finance LLC in a $190 million revolving and term loan transaction with Wastequip, LLC and its subsidiaries
Contact: Michael A Nemeroff  Tel: 312 609 7858
Email: mnemeroff@vedderprice.com

**Financial Institutions:**
22 Shareholders and 13 Associates
- Members include former senior officials of the Federal Reserve, OCC, OTS, SEC, FINRA and the U.S. Department of Justice
- One of the largest US legal practice groups focusing on the corporate and regulatory representations of financial institutions
Contact: James M Kane  Tel: 312 609 7533
Email: jkane@vedderprice.com
Contact: Daniel C McKay, II  Tel: 312 609 7762
Email: dmckay@vedderprice.com

**Global Transportation Finance:**
19 Shareholders, 5 Counsel/Of Counsel, 2 Partners and 24 Associates
- Represented Export-Import Bank of the United States in the first-of-its-kind prefunded Export Credit Agency-backed capital markets transaction
- Representing Southwest Airlines Co. as lessor in the $1.5 billion subleasing of 88 Boeing 717-200 Aircraft to Delta Air Lines, Inc.
- Secured railcar equipment notes related to railcars and railcar leases for Trinity Industries Leasing Company/TRIP Rail Master Funding LLC; aggregate debt issuance for the securitization and the debt private placement was approximately $1.032 billion
- Represented private equity funds in joint ventures with European shipping managers with aggregate equity commitments in excess of $500 million
Contact: Dean N Gerber  Tel: 312 609 7638
Email: dgerber@vedderprice.com

**Intellectual Property:**
31 Shareholders, 1 Of Counsel, 10 Associates and 1 Patent Agent
- Full-service patent, trademark, copyright, technology law and IP litigation practice in all technical disciplines
- All of the firm's Intellectual Property attorneys are also registered patent agents with experience in the prosecution of patent applications at all levels in the US Patent and Trademark Office
Contact: Angelo J Bufalino  Tel: 312 609 7850
Email: abufalino@vedderprice.com

**Investment Services:**
33 Shareholders and 14 Associates
- Experienced in all aspects of investment company and investment adviser securities regulations, broker-dealer regulatory and compliance matters, derivatives and financial product matters, and ERISA and tax matters
- Clients include mutual fund complexes, ETFs, investment advisers, hedge and other private funds, broker-dealers and independent directors of investment companies
Contact: David A Sturms  Tel: 312 609 7589
Email: dsturms@vedderprice.com

**Labor & Employment:**
21 Shareholders, 1 Of Counsel and 16 Associates
- Advised medical centre on strike and labor planning, collective bargaining, and grievance and arbitration strategy; acted as spokesperson in negotiations
- Provided due diligence advice on labor and employment matters in a successful $700 million acquisition of a national broadline food distributor
Contact: J Kevin Hennessy  Tel: 312 609 7868
Email: khennessy@vedderprice.com

**Litigation & Arbitration:**
44 Shareholders and 32 Associates
- Successfully defended Chairman of a public company in a DOJ investigation and criminal complaint, parallel SEC investigation and federal district court complaint and securities class action arising from alleged misconduct
- Serving as counsel for the Receiver appointed in the bankruptcy case against the founder of Peregrine Financial Group, Inc.
Contact: Thomas P Cimino, Jr  Tel: 312 609 7784
Email: tcimino@vedderprice.com

### OFFICES

**DISTRICT OF COLUMBIA**
**WASHINGTON, DC:** 1401 I Street NW, Suite 1100, DC 20005
Tel: 202 312 3320  Fax: 202 312 3322

**ILLINOIS**
**CHICAGO:** 222 North LaSalle Street, IL 60601
Tel: 312 609 7500  Fax: 312 609 5005

**NEW YORK**
**NEW YORK:** 1633 Broadway, 47th Floor, NY 10019
Tel: 212 407 7700  Fax: 212 407 7799

The firm also has an office in London, UK

# WINSTON & STRAWN

**Managing Partner:** Thomas P Fitzgerald
**Senior Partners:** Dan K Webb (Chairman), James R Thompson (Senior Chairman)
Number of partners in US: 359
Number of other lawyers in US: 463
Number of lawyers worldwide: 925

## Firm Overview:

Winston & Strawn LLP is an international law firm with more than 900 attorneys among 15 offices in Beijing, Charlotte, NC, Chicago, Geneva, Hong Kong, Houston, TX, London, Los Angeles, Moscow, New York, Newark, NJ, Paris, San Francisco, Shanghai, and Washington, DC.

## Main Areas of Practice:

### Litigation:

Corporate America consistently trusts Winston & Strawn with their most high-stakes litigation. Its litigators have tried major jury and bench trials in virtually every significant federal and state venue and assisted with high-profile investigations related to SEC, AG, and other regulatory inquiries. They handle appeals before the US Supreme Court, US Courts of Appeals, and state appellate courts. Winston's international arbitration attorneys have extensive experience with all the major arbitration and international claims institutions and rules, and the firm has locally qualified commercial litigators in Geneva, Hong Kong, Paris and London. Substantive areas of litigation work include: antitrust, securities, product liability, class actions, white-collar, patent/ trademark/ copyright, ERISA, insurance coverage, construction, energy, media and entertainment.

### Corporate & Financial:

Winston's global Corporate Practice provides securities and M&A legal services to multinational companies, investment banks, and other financial services firms. The firm's private equity work encompasses capital raising, investment and divestiture, and operational activities. In the finance area, Winston represents clients in capital markets, corporate lending, securitization, lease finance, and derivatives transactions. The firm's Financial Services Practice assists clients in bank regulatory and compliance, investment management, private funds, broker-dealers, and futures/exchange matters. Winston provides restructuring and insolvency advice to debtors, creditors, committees, purchasers, and other parties in bankruptcy matters.

### Labor & Employment Relations:

Winston has more than 50 partners and associates in the area of labor and employment law. They have appeared in state and federal courts around the country, and before the NLRB, DOL, EEOC, and other local, state, and federal agencies. The firm provides national and international employment law assistance from most US offices, as well as from Paris and London.

### Intellectual Property:

The firm's IP attorneys litigate disputes in federal courts and before the US PTO. The practice includes risk assessment, portfolio management, and prosecution of applications for patents, trademarks, and copyrights, and supervision of global IP enforcement initiatives. Winston IP attorneys assist with patent, trademark, and copyright licenses, product development deals, and advertising, marketing, and promotions.

### Real Estate:

Winston & Strawn's real estate attorneys assist purchasers, sellers, developers, borrowers and lenders in major real estate investment, development, and lending activities. They represent US and international corporations, financial institutions, and other clients in acquisitions, financings, sales, developments, and leasings.

### Tax:

Tax attorneys at the firm provide assistance that ranges from planning through audit, appeals and litigation, as well as legislative and regulatory representation. They help clients resolve significant tax issues through creatively planning transactions, effectively influencing tax policy, and carefully working with the IRS.

### Energy:

For more than 30 years, Winston has helped clients deal with changes in the energy industry, from leading renewable energy projects to advising on nuclear security matters. Energy attorneys handle development, financing, construction, and regulatory matters, and the sale and purchase of energy companies and assets. They also provide litigation, tax and labor advice.

### Environmental:

This practice encompasses all aspects of environmental law, from Superfund actions and toxic tort claims to environmental compliance in transactions to regulatory issues. The Paris Environmental Practice includes regulatory, transactional, and litigation in the European Community.

### Government Relations & Regulatory Affairs:

The Government Relations Practice at Winston is composed of attorneys and advisors adept at using the rules of the legislative process to develop and implement practical solutions. They assist corporate clients with campaign finance issues, and public sector clients with appropriations.

### Employee Benefits & Executive Compensation:

Winston assists employers with the compensation of employees and the planning and administration of employee benefits, as well as all forms of executive compensation plans.

### International Work:

Albemarle Corporation, Alstom Group, Deutsche Bank AG, EDF, FAGE Dairy Industry SA, Foot Locker France, Française des Jeux SA, LVMH, Nestle SA, Philip Morris International, Republic of Ecuador, Rhodia, Soitec SA, Warner Bros. Entertainment.

### Clients:

Abbott Laboratories, American Airlines, Bank of America NA, Calpine Corporation, Dell Inc., Goldman Sachs & Co., JP Morgan Chase Bank, Lear Corporation, Luxottica Group S.p.A., McDonald's Corporation, Microsoft Corporation, Motorola Mobility Inc., Philip Morris USA, Wachovia Bank, Weatherford International, Wyeth.

## How lawyers are ranked

Every year we carry out thousands of in-depth interviews with clients in order to assess the reputations and expertise of business lawyers worldwide. The qualities we look for (and which determine rankings) include technical legal ability, professional conduct, client service, commercial awareness/astuteness, diligence, commitment, and other qualities most valued by the client. For details of our research team, see p.5.

# CORPORATE/M&A

## Corporate/M&A
### Leading Firms

**Band 1**
Barnes & Thornburg LLP *
Faegre Baker Daniels
Ice Miller LLP

**Band 2**
Taft Stettinius & Hollister LLP *

**Band 3**
Bingham Greenebaum Doll LLP *
Bose McKinney & Evans LLP
Krieg DeVault LLP

*\* Indicates firm / individual with profile.*
*Alphabetical order within each band. Band 1 is the highest.*

### Band 1

#### Barnes & Thornburg LLP
See profile on p.436

THE FIRM Barnes & Thornburg's sizable team is spread across four offices throughout Indiana, making it a top choice for large and sophisticated transactions. The firm also benefits from a significant presence throughout the rest of the country, and its broad-based offering includes advice on M&A, joint ventures, corporate governance and private equity financing. Recent highlights include advising Wolverine World Wide on its joint $2 billion agreement to acquire Collective Brands.
**Sources say:** *"They have done an excellent job simultaneously protecting us while getting the deal done."*
**KEY INDIVIDUALS Catherine Bridge** (see p.1276) continues to be a *"significant player"* in the state, lauded for her deep expertise in a wide range of corporate matters. Insurance regulatory issues, securities and M&A transactions are areas of particular strength. She recently counseled Vectren on the $39 million sale of its retail natural gas business Vectren Source, to Direct Energy. Clients laud **Claudia Swhier** (see p.1280) as *"a first-rate adviser for legal issues surrounding financial institutions."* Her highlights include advising Indiana Community Bancorp on its $79.2

## Corporate/M&A
### Leading Individuals

**Band 1**

| | |
|---|---|
| Boeglin Daniel L | *Faegre Baker Daniels* |
| Bridge Catherine L | *Barnes & Thornburg LLP \** |
| Brown J Jeffrey | *Faegre Baker Daniels* |
| Hackman Stephen | *Ice Miller LLP* |
| Hicks Robert J | *Taft Stettinius & Hollister LLP \** |
| Humke Steven | *Ice Miller LLP* |
| Strain James A | *Taft Stettinius & Hollister LLP \** |
| Swhier Claudia V | *Barnes & Thornburg LLP \** |
| Thornburgh John | *Ice Miller LLP* |
| Thrapp Richard | *Ice Miller LLP* |

**Band 2**

| | |
|---|---|
| Cross Patrick | *Faegre Baker Daniels* |
| Densborn Donald | *Taft Stettinius & Hollister LLP \** |
| Greising Robert | *Krieg DeVault LLP* |
| Millard David B | *Barnes & Thornburg LLP \** |
| Prechtel David | *Bingham Greenebaum Doll LLP \** |
| Worrell David | *Faegre Baker Daniels* |

**Band 3**

| | |
|---|---|
| Caruso II Ralph A | *Taft Stettinius & Hollister LLP \** |
| Danz Kristine Camron | *Ice Miller LLP* |
| Hill Jeremy | *Bingham Greenebaum Doll LLP \** |
| Inveiss Roberts E | *Bose McKinney & Evans LLP* |
| Moy Eric R | *Barnes & Thornburg LLP \** |
| Wynne Robert S | *Faegre Baker Daniels* |

**Up-and-coming individuals**

| | |
|---|---|
| Belden Trevor J | *Faegre Baker Daniels* |

million sale to Old National Bank. Department chair **David Millard** (see p.1278) is held in particularly high regard for his work on behalf of emerging businesses. Notable mandates include his recent representation of OnSite Space in its acquisition of Tyson. Clients applaud his wealth of experience and highlight his ability to *"find good solutions during difficult negotiations."* **Eric Moy** (see p.1279) counsels a range of business clients on regulatory, transactional and financing matters, and is commended by

peers for his strong technical skills and *"first-rate mind."* He recently advised Herff Jones on its acquisition of Varsity Brands.

#### Faegre Baker Daniels

THE FIRM This team has a top-drawer reputation in the state, and advises on issues ranging from financing transactions and securities regulation to public and private offerings and takeovers. It is particularly adept at advising clients in the private equity, healthcare, life sciences, insurance, and food and agriculture industries. Recent highlights include advising Circle K Stores on the acquisition of approximately 750 convenience stores across several US states.
**KEY INDIVIDUALS Daniel Boeglin** has an excellent reputation for corporate work in the healthcare and life sciences arenas. In this space, he recently advised Zimmer on its purchase of ExtraOrtho through a reverse triangular merger. Peers praise **Jeffrey Brown** for his hard work on behalf of clients. Sources note his private equity and venture capital expertise, but he also handles acquisitions and corporate governance matters, securities offerings, LBOs and other sophisticated transactions. Like Boeglin, **Patrick Cross** draws praise for his work on behalf of healthcare and life sciences clients. Of late, he advised Indiana University Health on the sale of membership interests in a range of ambulatory surgery centers to an affiliate of Surgical Care Affiliates. **David Worrell** is highlighted for his strength in securities matters. He also undertakes general business transactions, corporate governance issues and executive compensation. His notable work includes counseling Endocyte on its $71.6 million follow-on public offering of common stock. **Robert Wynne**'s broad-based practice covers corporate dispositions, M&A, joint ventures, strategic partnerships and MBOs. He also counsels companies and financial institutions on a comprehensive range of financing transactions. **Trevor Belden** recently assisted Boeglin in the aforementioned representation of Zimmer, and is well known for counseling clients in the IT and logistics space.

## Ice Miller LLP

**THE FIRM** This 16-partner team handles a substantial amount of M&A and private equity work, and is increasingly involved in privatization transactions. It is also well positioned to advise on the tax implications of M&A transactions. It recently represented Citizens Energy Group in its $1.9 billion acquisition of the City of Indianapolis's water and wastewater assets. Other major clients include Vera Bradley, CID Capital and ExactTarget.

**Sources say:** *"It is among the best for expertise, service and value."*

**KEY INDIVIDUALS Stephen Hackman** is lauded as *"one of the very best,"* with a *"top-notch practice"* in the securities space. He recently counseled Symmetry Medical on all aspects of its $165 million acquisition of Codman & Shurtleff's surgical instruments portfolio. The *"very successful"* **Steven Humke** focuses on sophisticated financing and business transactions, frequently advising entrepreneurs and startup companies as well as private equity firms. *"If you ask anyone in town, he will be among their top advisers,"* say sources. Commentators agree that **John Thornburgh** *"has one of the strongest reputations in terms of venture capital and private equity."* He cochairs the firm's business group and chairs its sports and entertainment group. He is therefore a popular choice with entertainment industry clients and universities seeking advice on collegiate sports matters. **Richard Thrapp**'s expertise includes corporate governance, joint ventures, acquisitions and divestitures. Clients praise him as a *"very capable lawyer who does a great job leading his team and reaching compromises."* He was part of the team advising Citizens Energy Group on the aforementioned acquisition. **Kristine Camron Danz** is singled out for her solid general corporate advice, and for her strength in private equity matters. Peers acknowledge her visible presence in the market, and she is well known for advising entrepreneurs and emerging companies.

## Band 2

### Taft Stettinius & Hollister LLP
See profile on p.2130

**THE FIRM** This well-respected group is praised by sources for its work in the private equity space. It maintains an active M&A practice, while also handling a substantial amount of securities work and general corporate matters. The team's impressive client roster includes Melvin Simon & Associates, MH Equity and Emmis Communications.

**Sources say:** *"They are deal-makers, not deal-breakers. The team is very knowledgeable of market and legal trends, very reliable, talented and creative."*

**KEY INDIVIDUALS** *"Star of the team"* and partner-in-charge of the firm's Indianapolis office, **Robert Hicks** (see p.1277) is widely regarded as a first-rate attorney for general business work, private equity and venture capital transactions. Clients laud *"his experience and his ability to see the key issues and work through them to find a good, business-savvy solution."* **James Strain** (see p.1280) is *"highly intelligent,"* and has a fantastic reputation in the state for undertaking corporate governance matters, M&A and securities law. He cochairs the firm's business and finance practice and is also noted for his work as an expert witness. **Donald Densborn** (see p.1276) is *"very professional, knowledgeable and practical in terms of his style and approach."* He has a wealth of experience in acquisitions and fundraising activities, and counsels clients ranging from entrepreneurs and investors to large businesses and financing sources. **Ralph Caruso**'s (see p.1276) clients appreciate *"his experience, his knowledge of the area, and his ability to understand the core of what clients need."* His focus lies on the representation of merchant banking firms, private equity funds and other equity sponsors in relation to acquisitions, divestitures and financing transactions.

## Band 3

### Bingham Greenebaum Doll LLP
See profile on p.1281

**THE FIRM** The team at Bingham Greenebaum Doll provides a comprehensive corporate service to clients from a broad range of industries. Major highlights include assisting the Capital Improvement Board of Managers of Marion County, Indiana in negotiations with the NFL relating to the state's bid to host the Super Bowl.

**Sources say:** *"I rate their responsiveness, quality of work, expertise and practical approach to problem solving."*

**KEY INDIVIDUALS David Prechtel**'s (see p.1279) practice centers around healthcare, M&A, securities and the representation of financial institutions. He recently advised First Merchants Bank on its acquisition of the assets and liabilities of Shelby County Bank through an auction transaction. **Jeremy Hill** (see p.1277) is lauded by interviewees as being *"extremely easy to work with."* His communication skills, responsiveness, and *"superior intellect and practical approach to problem solving"* are highlighted as key strengths.

## Bose McKinney & Evans LLP

**THE FIRM** This team specializes in bank financings, M&A, securities offerings and other business transactions. Observers are impressed with the firm's client service and its strength in explaining complex legal concepts in layman's terms.

**Sources say:** *"It has a wide range of specialists and can assist us across a broad scope of issues."* *"They are able to efficiently and effectively educate us on key issues and resolve them without over-lawyering."*

**KEY INDIVIDUALS** Department head **Roberts Inveiss** is a *"strong advocate"* who focuses on representing clients in the life sciences, publishing, social media, food processing and manufacturing industries.

## Krieg DeVault LLP

**THE FIRM** Krieg DeVault has a solid reputation in Indiana, with its corporate lawyers spread across five offices throughout the state. Peers commend its strength in real estate transactions, securities and matters involving regional banks, and highlight it as a firm to which they happily refer clients.

**KEY INDIVIDUALS Robert Greising** leads the firm's business practice group, providing counsel on issues including M&A, joint ventures and strategic alliances, and secured loan transactions. *"He is an extremely strong attorney for whom I have a lot of respect,"* noted one interviewee.

# ENVIRONMENT

Commentary about individuals can be found under their firm's paragraph. If the firm has no paragraph (is not ranked) look at Other Notable Practitioners.

## Band 1

### Barnes & Thornburg LLP
See profile on p.436

**THE FIRM** This longstanding team offers expertise in matters ranging from environmental litigation and toxic torts to environmental insurance and helping clients with the environmental aspects of business transactions. Sources are also quick to note the group's involvement in developing legislation. **Sources say:** *"An established and well-regarded environmental practice."* **KEY INDIVIDUALS John Kyle** (see p.1278) is a *"masterful lawyer,"* lauded by interviewees as *"delightful, charming and intelligent."* He frequently deals with solid and hazardous waste regulatory matters, contamination issues, and insurance and transactional issues. Sources agree that **Sean Griggs**'s (see p.1277) past as a chemical engineer is a great asset to his practice. An expert in environmental litigation, he has handled matters before state and federal courts and administrative agencies, as well as in appellate tribunals.

### Bose McKinney & Evans LLP

**THE FIRM** This firm's environmental team advises, and provides stellar representation in litigation to, a wide array of clients, including local governments, agricultural and industrial companies. The team recently represented Legget & Platt in a groundwater contamination case, advising on the implementation of a voluntary remediation program. Other major clients include Salina Bank, Fair Oaks Farms and The Store. **Sources say:** *"The lawyers are extremely timely in getting back to you with regards to any questions you might have. They are personable and treat people with respect."* **KEY INDIVIDUALS Daniel McInerny** is lauded for his strength in agricultural law, while also displaying solid expertise in natural resources and a range of environmental matters. Together with **Alex Intermill**, he recently represented New Fashion Pork in its appeal against the Indiana Department of Environmental Management's denial of three Combined Feeding Operations and Concentrated Animal Feeding Operations applications. Intermill is held in high regard by clients: *"Alex has a laid-back style. He shows patience when listening to an issue and then spends time brainstorming potential solutions with me. His main strengths are his integrity and his subject matter knowledge."* The *"very well-regarded"* **Kathleen Lucas** enjoys a particularly strong reputation for administrative law. She was involved in the aforementioned contamination case, acting on behalf of Legget & Platt.

### Hatchett & Hauck LLP

**THE FIRM** This boutique environmental firm is highly regarded in the state and provides its clients with strong representation in litigation, transactions and regulatory compliance. The six-strong team handles highly complex environmental issues, covering water treatment, power generation and biofuels, among others. **Sources say:** *"They specialize and impress."* **KEY INDIVIDUALS David Hatchett**'s breadth of experience allows him to counsel clients on all aspects of environmental law, including litigation, compliance, enforcement and permitting. He is a popular choice with large industrial clients locally and across the country. Sources say he is *"really smart – he is on the cutting edge of this kind of work."*

### Plews Shadley Racher & Braun LLP

**THE FIRM** This firm places strong emphasis on its environmental practice and is able to offer attorneys with impressive industry backgrounds in chemical engineering, biology and geology. The sizable team deals with all aspects of environmental law, advising on cost recovery claims, permitting issues, government enforcement, cleanups and toxic torts. **Sources say:** *"They are one of the strongest – hands down."* **KEY INDIVIDUALS** Name partner **George Plews** is respected across the state for his impressive performance in complex trials and appeals. Throughout his 30-year career, he has facilitated the recovery of hundreds of millions of dollars to fund environmental cleanups. Peers admire his efforts in shaping Indiana legislation. **Amy Romig** is an *"excellent environmental lawyer"* who really *"knows her stuff."* She specializes in the Indiana Administrative Orders and Procedures Act, and also provides environmental and natural resource counseling.

## Band 2

### Bingham Greenebaum Doll LLP
See profile on p.1281

**THE FIRM** This group covers every area of environmental law, with sources particularly quick to highlight the team's work on compliance and regulatory matters. It recently advised longstanding client Duke Energy on a number of matters, including on the renewal of a National Pollutant Discharge Elimination System permit for wastewater discharges from a power plant. **Sources say:** *"Their strongest point is their thoroughness when reviewing a matter."* **KEY INDIVIDUALS** Practice co-head **Andy Bowman** (see p.1276) *"is very thorough and meticulous."* He represents governmental, commercial and industrial clients, and is a Certified Hazardous Materials Manager. Bowman recently advised PPG Industries in connection with investigation and remediation activities, under the Indiana Voluntary Remediation Program, relating to certain legacy sites. **Larry Kane** (see p.1278) is lauded by peers as diligent and easy to work with, and he is widely recognized for his strength in regulatory and permitting matters. He plays a key role in the firm's representation of Duke Energy, and also recently advised Subaru of Indiana Automotive on matters associated with the renewal of a Title V operating permit.

### Ice Miller LLP

**THE FIRM** Ice Miller's team covers the gamut of environmental matters and thus attracts an impressive client list that includes the likes of the City of Indianapolis, Columbus Regional Hospital and Haynes International. Environmental and toxic tort litigation, contamination issues and administrative matters are all skillfully handled by the 11-partner team. **Sources say:** *"I have been totally satisfied with their work. The firm members have been very knowledgeable and communicate the status of projects in an easily understood manner."* **KEY INDIVIDUALS Terri Ann Czajka** *"works hard for her clients,"* and is someone peers frequently see in litigation and property transfer matters. Permitting, administrative enforcement, and federal and state regulation are additional areas of expertise. The *"wonderful"* **Brent Huber** draws praise as *"thorough and analytical in his approach."* Environmental litigation and toxic tort are at the heart of his practice.

## Taft Stettinius & Hollister LLP
See profile on p.2130

**THE FIRM** This 20-strong group enjoys a diverse environmental practice, and has recently been particularly active in toxic tort and hazardous waste cases. In this arena, the team recently represented 46 plaintiffs in a groundwater contamination lawsuit relating to releases of perchloroethylene from a manufacturing plant. Duke Energy, Chevron and Textron Industries also feature on its client list.

**Sources say:** "*They are a comprehensive firm; they cover the gamut of environmental matters.*"

**KEY INDIVIDUALS** Practice cochair **Frank Deveau** (see p.1277) "*is a top-tier person – just wonderful, well regarded and diplomatic.*" An expert in environmental litigation, he recently counseled Textron Industries on two toxic tort litigation matters where plaintiffs alleged personal injury through trichloroethylene contamination to well water.

## Other Notable Practitioners

The "*very responsive*" **Carrie Doehrmann** (see p.1277), in the Indianapolis office of Frost Brown Todd LLC, is highlighted by peers for her expertise in insurance defense matters.

# LABOR & EMPLOYMENT

Commentary about individuals can be found under their firm's paragraph. If the firm has no paragraph (is not ranked) look at Other Notable Practitioners.

| Labor & Employment Leading Firms |
| --- |
| **Band 1** |
| Barnes & Thornburg LLP * |
| Faegre Baker Daniels |
| Ogletree, Deakins, Nash, Smoak & Stewart, PC * |
| **Band 2** |
| Bose McKinney & Evans LLP |
| Ice Miller LLP |
| Littler Mendelson, PC * |

## Band 1

### Barnes & Thornburg LLP
See profile on p.436

**THE FIRM** Barnes & Thornburg remains a leading name in the Indiana labor and employment space, offering depth and breadth in a range of areas including labor relations, employment contracts, trade secret and noncompete claims, and union avoidance. The team also sees itself increasingly involved in class action matters. It recently drafted and successfully defended national arbitration agreements for The Finish Line's stores across the USA.

**Sources say:** "*I have found all of their work to be flat-out excellent.*"

**KEY INDIVIDUALS** Practice chair **Kenneth Yerkes** (see p.1280) is "*excellent for litigation issues.*" He continues to represent The Finish Line, advising it on the aforementioned matter. Enthused clients say: "*He is a rock star and stands out from all the rest. Ken is very bright, energetic and creative.*" **John Maley** (see p.1278) specializes in labor and employment litigation. "*He is an excellent trial attorney, cares about his clients and is amazingly responsive,*" say sources. Together with Yerkes, he serves as national labor and employment and litigation counsel for Hillenbrand. **Peter Morse** (see p.1279) focuses his practice on the representation of employers in the full range of labor and employment matters. He also cochairs the firm's global services practice group. Like Morse, **Anthony Prather**'s (see p.1279) practice covers the gamut of labor and employment matters. His forte is in the area of litigation, and he has defended clients in state and federal courts, as well as before the NLRB. Sources say that **Keith White** (see

| Labor & Employment Senior Statesmen | |
| --- | --- |
| **Senior Statesmen:** distinguished older practitioners | |
| Utken Gregory | Faegre Baker Daniels |

| Leading Individuals | |
| --- | --- |
| **Band 1** | |
| Baldwin Charles B | Ogletree, Deakins, Nash, Smoak & Stewart * |
| Ebert Kim F | Ogletree, Deakins, Nash, Smoak & Stewart * |
| Neighbours John T | Faegre Baker Daniels |
| Pfeiffer Hudnall A | Faegre Baker Daniels |
| Yerkes Kenneth J | Barnes & Thornburg LLP * |
| **Band 2** | |
| Blickman Michael A | Ice Miller LLP |
| Boldt Michael | Ice Miller LLP |
| Boshkoff Ellen | Faegre Baker Daniels |
| Carr David J | Ice Miller LLP |
| Given David A | Faegre Baker Daniels |
| Maley John | Barnes & Thornburg LLP * |
| McDermott Brian L | Ogletree, Deakins, Nash, Smoak & Stewart * |
| McLaughlin Alan L | Littler Mendelson, PC * |
| Padgett Mike | Jackson Lewis LLP (ONP)† * |
| Swider David | Bose McKinney & Evans LLP |
| Terrell Michael | Taft Stettinius & Hollister LLP (ONP)† * |
| Tooley Michael L | Ice Miller LLP |
| **Band 3** | |
| Dale Gregory N | Faegre Baker Daniels |
| Guevara Gregory W | Bose McKinney & Evans LLP |
| Morse Peter A | Barnes & Thornburg LLP * |
| Nierman Todd | Littler Mendelson, PC * |
| Prather R Anthony | Barnes & Thornburg LLP * |
| Sinclair Paul H | Ice Miller LLP |
| White Keith E | Barnes & Thornburg LLP * |
| Wilson Heather L | Frost Brown Todd LLC (ONP)† * |

\* Indicates firm / individual with profile.
†ONP = Other Notable Practitioner.

p.1280) is "*great at traditional labor law.*" He advises clients on training programs, strikes and collective bargaining, and represents them in state and federal court litigation.

### Faegre Baker Daniels

**THE FIRM** The labor and employment team at Faegre Baker Daniels continues to impress clients with its breath of expertise and its fantastic pool of resources. The comprehensive stable of attorneys handles everything from labor management relations and employment litigation to workplace safety, compliance and training. It recently successfully advised Indiana Limestone on long-term concessionary contract negotiations and a related nationally publicized strike.

**KEY INDIVIDUALS** **John Neighbours** is noted for his handling of traditional labor law matters. He continues to counsel Amsted Industries on labor matters in numerous locations throughout the USA. **Hud Pfeiffer** represents public and private employers in the full range of labor and employment matters. His strength in labor issues is highlighted by sources. **Ellen Boshkoff** specializes in the representation of public and private employers, frequently defending class actions. **David Given** handles a range of labor and employment matters, and comes particularly recommended for employment litigation. **Gregory Dale** acts as national OSHA counsel to Colorcon. His areas of focus include employment discrimination litigation and labor arbitration. **Gregory Utken** recently advised Bristol Compressors on labor and employment matters in connection with its reorganization.

### Ogletree, Deakins, Nash, Smoak & Stewart, PC
See profile on p.1110

**THE FIRM** This group maintains its reputation as a key force in the state for a range of labor and employment matters. Its local and national strength attracts an impressive roster of clients that includes the likes of Kraft, Starbucks and Steak 'n Shake. Clients are quick to commend the team's business-savvy approach. Major recent highlights include successfully defending AT&T in a discrimination lawsuit filed by an employee.

**Sources say:** "*Ogletree consistently provides an outstanding service and advice in a variety of situations.*"

**KEY INDIVIDUALS** **Charles Baldwin** (see p.1276) is lauded for his efficient and hard work on behalf of clients. Employment litigation is at the heart of his practice, and he recently successfully defended Kroger in an age discrimination lawsuit filed by a former employee. **Kim Ebert** (see p.1277) currently serves as the firm's managing shareholder. He undertakes solid work in employment litigation, collective bargaining agreements, arbitrations and union matters. His *"professionalism, timeliness, and depth and breadth of knowledge"* are held in high regard by interviewees. **Brian McDermott** (see p.1278) is a *"great guy with an excellent reputation and impressive practice."* He played a key role in the firm's representation of AT&T in the aforementioned discrimination lawsuit.

## Band 2

### Bose McKinney & Evans LLP

**THE FIRM** This eight-strong team is highlighted by interviewees for its strength on employment issues, counseling clients on matters ranging from employee benefits and disciplinary matters, to providing representation before local, state and federal agencies. It continues to handle a substantial amount of noncompete litigation.
**Sources say:** *"They have a wealth of resources and offer great customer service."*
**KEY INDIVIDUALS David Swider** is widely recognized for his work on employment litigation, wage and hour disputes, collective bargaining and employment discrimination. **Gregory Guevara** enjoys a broad-based labor and employment practice, providing counsel to a range of local and national businesses as well as employers. Observers appreciate his common-sense approach, as well as his upfront and honest style toward clients.

### Ice Miller LLP

**THE FIRM** Ice Miller impresses observers with its strong and diverse labor and employment team and a notable client list that includes Haynes International, Purdue University and medical devices company Cook. Its expertise extends from assisting clients with employment contracts and training programs to providing representation in employment litigation and dealing with traditional labor issues.

**Sources say:** *"An excellent group – strong players who provide good representation."*
**KEY INDIVIDUALS** Peers are impressed with **Michael Blickman's** *"great client following and diverse practice."* He is particularly highly regarded for his representation of nonprofit employers, including universities and hospitals, on noncompete matters, union organizing and employment contracts. He is also deemed *"wonderful"* for litigation issues. *"Tremendous lawyer"* **Michael Boldt** is highlighted for his work on behalf of construction industry clients. Management-side labor law is his forte, and in this space he regularly advises on collective bargaining, organizational drives and equal employment opportunity law. **David Carr** chairs the firm's employment litigation group, and is noted by peers for his work on noncompete matters. Wage and hour law, discrimination and employment contracts involving trade secrets are additional areas of expertise. The well-regarded **Michael Tooley** chairs the firm's labor and employment group. He is particularly skilled in administrative proceedings before the EEOC, NLRB and other state and federal agencies, and also handles employment litigation, collective bargaining and arbitration. **Paul Sinclair** focuses on traditional labor law, and provides day-to-day employment counseling and training to a range of clients.

### Littler Mendelson, PC
See profile on p.688
**THE FIRM** The nationwide capabilities of Littler Mendelson's labor and employment team are a major draw for clients. The team is able to handle the full range of labor and employment matters, but has in the last year been particularly active in employment litigation. Its client list includes pharmaceutical, insurance and retail corporations, and it recently achieved the dismissal in federal court of ADA violation, defamation and improper release of medical information claims against client Dow AgroSciences.

**Sources say:** *"They are accessible – I always receive immediate attention and dependable responses."*
**KEY INDIVIDUALS** Clients are full of praise for **Alan McLaughlin's** (see p.1278) practice, describing him as *"a skilled litigator who has great experience and can explain complicated matters to business people."* He was recently involved in the aforementioned case on behalf of Dow AgroSciences. Like McLaughlin, **Todd Nierman** (see p.1279) is lauded for his strong litigation skills. He also handles a substantial amount of union avoidance matters, and is applauded by clients for his *"knowledge, experience and demeanor."*

### Other Notable Practitioners

**Michael Terrell** (see p.1280) of Taft Stettinius & Hollister LLP is admired by clients for his *"practical and effective approach to conflict avoidance and conflict resolution."* He has in the last year represented both Brightpoint and Knauf Insulation in employment litigation. Construction, entertainment, real estate and hi-tech companies all feature on his impressive client list. **Mike Padgett** (see p.1279) of Jackson Lewis LLP is elevated in the rankings on the back of extensive client praise: *"Padgett is very approachable, very open, an excellent communicator and has the ability to make complicated legal matters understandable."* He specializes in traditional labor law and employment litigation, and recently defended TA Operating in a lawsuit brought by a former employee. **Heather Wilson** (see p.1280) of Frost Brown Todd LLC joins this year's rankings, having earned praise for her *"preparedness and courage."* Her forte lies in employment litigation, and she is also well placed to provide general business advice.

# LITIGATION GENERAL COMMERCIAL

Commentary about individuals can be found under their firm's paragraph.  If the firm has no paragraph (is not ranked) look at Other Notable Practitioners.

## Band 1

### Barnes & Thornburg LLP
See profile on p.436
**THE FIRM** Barnes & Thornburg enjoys an outstanding reputation in the Indiana litigation arena. The group offers depth of talent and experience, and has achieved notable victories in some of the most sophisticated cases before both state and federal court. For example, the team successfully represented the State of Indiana in a complex dispute with IBM concerning the implementation of an outsourcing arrangement. Other major clients include Dow AgroSciences and Whirlpool.

**Sources say:** *"I think they are the best firm in Indiana. They are very client focused and they have quality people."*
**KEY INDIVIDUALS John Maley** (see p.1278) led the team in its representation of the State of Indiana, and continues to draw praise from the market. Sources note that he does *"an excellent job"* of representing his clients. The *"wonderfully bright and talented"* **Peter Rusthoven** (see p.1279) is noted for his excellence in appellate level work, which he handles a part of a broader business and litigation practice. Sources describe his courtroom demeanor as *"articulate and persuasive."* **Jan Carroll** (see p.1276) is a *"bright and client-focused"* litigator who is experienced at state and federal level. She handles commercial litigation,

product liability and professional liability disputes. **Larry Mackey** (see p.1278) is noted for his expertise in complex commercial litigation and white-collar criminal defense. **Robert MacGill** (see p.1278) is a commercial litigator with an expertise in defending class actions. Areas of focus include antitrust, trade secrets and insurance litigation. **Andrew Detherage** (see p.1277) is commended by market sources for his *"very practical"* approach to litigation and his *"great business sense."* He handles commercial litigation, toxic torts and insurance coverage litigation. **Anne DePrez** (see p.1276) handles securities and business litigation, often with reference to the financial services sector. Commentators note that she *"has street smarts and works* things aggressively without going over the edge," and pay tribute to her *"extraordinary ability."* The highly experienced **Donald Knebel** (see p.1278) has an excellent reputation in patent litigation and antitrust work. Sources laud him as a *"superb"* practitioner.

## Faegre Baker Daniels

**THE FIRM** This firm's exceptional group of litigators handles a variety of disputes, from antitrust and IP matters to mass torts, insurance issues, and securities derivative suits and class actions. The team represents clients before both state and federal courts, and is adept at handling complex, multijurisdictional litigation. Recent matters include the representation of Zimmer in a complex action surrounding false advertising and defamation, among other claims. **KEY INDIVIDUALS David Herzog** heads the firm's business litigation team. He has a broad litigation practice encompassing contentious contractual, securities and corporate governance issues. **Chris Scanlon** has a broad business and commercial litigation practice that includes business tort, class actions and insurance coverage work. **Robert Stanley** handles litigation and arbitration pertaining to a wide range of commercial disputes. He has recently been involved in a series of significant multidistrict cases on behalf of his clients. **Jay Yeager** is held in high regard by interviewees, who speak particularly highly of his abilities in the courtroom. He recently acted for Zimmer in federal multi-district litigation alleging defects in the NexGen knee replacement system. **Jon Laramore** spearheads the firm's appellate practice in Indiana. He has represented clients in a range of sectors including healthcare, gaming, construction and education.

## Band 2

### Bingham Greenebaum Doll LLP
See profile on p.1281

**THE FIRM** This firm's litigation team enjoys a healthy reputation in the Indiana legal community. The group handles a wide range of commercial disputes on behalf of significant clients such as Ernst & Young, WellPoint and AT&T. Recent matters include acting for Obsidian Enterprises in securities fraud and bankruptcy matters arising from the collapse of Fair Financial Corporation. **KEY INDIVIDUALS** The experienced **Karl Mulvaney** (see p.1279) is noted for his expertise in appellate matters. Sources confirm that he is *"well regarded and highly skilled."* **Wayne Turner** (see p.1280) wins plaudits for his measured and analytical approach to advocacy, with market observers adding that he is *"very collegial and easy to work with."* **Brian Welch** (see p.1280) recently represented an individual with substantial business interests in Indiana following the fraudulent transfer of those interests to a

Russian entity. He represents businesses and individuals in a range of commercial disputes. **David Campbell** (see p.1276) is one of the most experienced figures at the Indiana Bar. Sources confirm that he is *"very well respected."* **David Tittle** (see p.1280) has a *"sterling reputation"* for handling commercial disputes, often with a focus on the financial services sector. He has increasingly handled mediation and alternative dispute resolution of late.

### Ice Miller LLP

**THE FIRM** This team handles antitrust, business and commercial litigation for clients across a range of industry sectors. The group recently represented Spencer County Redevelopment Commission in federal court and tax court litigation concerning a breach of taxpayer agreement by AK Steel. Other key clients include Ontario Systems, Altec Industries and RC2 Corporation.
**Sources say:** *"They are very strong in their trial skills, and that is reflected in their handling of all our work."*
**KEY INDIVIDUALS Philip Whistler** is *"one of the best litigators in town,"* according to impressed sources, who also point to his *"good analytical skills and wonderful judgment."* He led the team in its work on behalf of Spencer County. **James Petersen** has a broad practice which incorporates securities litigation, commercial disputes and insurance coverage matters. The *"impressive"* **Michael Wukmer** handles litigation and arbitration with respect to a wide spectrum of business and commercial disputes.

## Band 3

### Frost Brown Todd LLC
See profile on p.1329

**THE FIRM** Frost Brown Todd maintains its solid reputation for litigation in Indiana. The team handles all aspects of business and commercial litigation, and also represents individuals in white-collar criminal litigation. The group is particularly noted by market observers for its strength in insurance coverage disputes.
**KEY INDIVIDUALS Alan Brown** (see p.1276) chairs the firm's business litigation group. He acts for plaintiffs and defendants in a range of matters, including breach of contract, breach of fiduciary duty and corporate governance disputes. **David Kasper** (see p.1278) is noted for his abilities in insurance litigation, commercial litigation and professional malpractice matters. **Nelson Alexander** (see p.1276) is a rising star of the Indiana litigation arena. Sources note that he is *"a great litigator"* with a focus on the automotive sector. **Nicholas Pappas** (see p.1279) is emerging as a force in the appellate sphere. Interviewees refer to his *"even-keeled, determined and professional approach,"* and note that he is *"strategically savvy and dedicated to client service."*

### Taft Stettinius & Hollister LLP
See profile on p.2130

**THE FIRM** This firm is recognized for its strength in securities litigation, environmental litigation and white-collar criminal defense. Recent matters include representing NH

Environmental Group with respect to alleged violations of the CWA. Other clients include Duke Energy and World Media Group.

**Sources say:** *"A number of very fine lawyers. They are very sophisticated and skilled."*

**KEY INDIVIDUALS Jackie Bennett** (see p.1276) handled the aforementioned matter for NH Environmental Group, and is also noted for his skill in white-collar criminal litigation. Sources refer to him as *"a really good, imaginative lawyer."* **Jonathan Polak** (see p.1279) recently represented Pacific Coast Breaker and PC Systems with respect to allegations of false advertising and unfair competition. He handles complex commercial litigation and IP disputes.

## Other Notable Practitioners

**Irwin Levin** is the managing partner of Cohen & Malad. He handles commercial litigation and class actions, and is described as *"a very skilled, tenacious and effective litigator."* **Linda Pence** of Pence Hensel LLC handles commercial litigation and white-collar criminal defense. Sources respect her tenacious litigation style and confirm that she is *"well regarded"* at the Indiana Bar. The highly experienced **Ronald Elberger** of Bose McKinney & Evans LLP is recognized for his broad litigation expertise. He is particularly associated with the media and entertainment sectors. **Douglas King** (see p.1278) of Wooden & McLaughlin LLP handles civil litigation across a range of areas including product liability, breach of contract and insurance coverage. **Andrew Hull** of Hoover Hull LLP handles commercial litigation as part of a broader litigation practice. Sources

attest that he is *"very persistent and always very well prepared."* **Samuel Laurin** of Bose McKinney & Evans LLP is described as *"a bright and excellent"* advocate with *"really good instincts."* He handles construction and general commercial litigation. **George Plews** of Plews Shadley Racher & Braun LLP is particularly noted for his work in the insurance coverage sphere, with one admiring interviewee remarking that he is *"a wonderful lawyer."* **Michael Wilkins** of Broyles Kight & Ricafort, PC is a *"versatile, smart, practical litigator,"* according to market observers. He applies his respected litigation skills across a range of areas, including media law, construction disputes and business torts. **Bryan Babb** of Bose McKinney & Evans LLP enters the rankings after receiving warm praise for his emerging appellate practice. Sources note that he *"takes a practical approach to legal issues"* and suggest that he is *"a very impressive appellate litigator."*

# REAL ESTATE

Commentary about individuals can be found under their firm's paragraph. If the firm has no paragraph (is not ranked) look at Other Notable Practitioners.

| Real Estate Leading Firms | |
| --- | --- |
| **Band 1** | |
| Faegre Baker Daniels | |
| Ice Miller LLP | |
| **Band 2** | |
| Barnes & Thornburg LLP * | |
| Benesch, Friedlander, Coplan & Aronoff LLP * | |
| Wallack Somers & Haas PC | |
| Wooden & McLaughlin LLP | |
| **Band 3** | |
| Bingham Greenebaum Doll LLP * | |
| Bose McKinney & Evans LLP | |
| Krieg DeVault LLP | |
| Taft Stettinius & Hollister LLP * | |

## Band 1

### Faegre Baker Daniels

**THE FIRM** The consistent breadth and quality of the work undertaken by this firm ensure that it continues to justify its position in the premier tier. The sizable team has recently been involved in a variety of complex, substantial matters, including in the representation of Centre Properties in the River Place development project. It also acted as lead counsel for Silvara Real Estate as it successfully sought zoning and development approval on another project.

**KEY INDIVIDUALS Mary Lisher** has been involved in several sizable property transactions, demonstrating exemplary negotiation skills. **Joseph Scimia** was recently engaged in the Prairie Lakes Apartment joint venture. He represents clients in a range of real estate transactions and financings. **Steven Hardin** acted as lead partner on the River Place matter and was instrumental in obtaining a favorable incentive package for the client.

### Ice Miller LLP

**THE FIRM** This well-staffed firm recently gained national recognition for its handling of real estate issues pertaining to the 2012 Super Bowl. The group demonstrates superb negotiation skills, which it regularly and effectively utilizes in negotiations with the City of Indianapolis. Its eight partners each have their own specific expertise in a number of niche areas, enabling the firm to undertake work across a notably broad spectrum of industries.

**Sources say:** *"The firm has very qualified partners and associates, all of whom are logical, practical and extremely knowledgeable."*

**KEY INDIVIDUALS** Managing partner **Phillip Bayt** is recognized for having a *"broad and sophisticated practice,"* which encompasses a range of commercial real estate. He was part of the team that advised HDG Mansur Investment Services in relation to a number of acquisitions of industrial facilities made throughout 2012. The *"well-regarded"* **Zeff Weiss** has enjoyed a particularly active year, in which he headed the team acting on behalf of the 2012 Super Bowl Host Committee. Weiss is also an integral part of the Indiana Continuing Legal Education forum, and has consequently earned praise as a prolific speaker on a diverse range of legal issues. **Aaron Dixon** is a highly respected practitioner with impressive knowledge of the commercial real estate field. He recently provided counsel for Skjodt-Barrett Foods as it sought to establish its American headquarters in Indiana. Those surveyed identify **Timothy Ochs** as one of the most talented attorneys in the state. His proficiency in virtually all areas of real estate law was apparent in his masterful handling of the Buckingham Companies' mixed-use development project.

| Real Estate Senior Statesmen | | |
| --- | --- | --- |
| **Senior Statesmen:** distinguished older practitioners | | |
| Mitchell Marvin | Mitchell Hurst Jacobs & Dick (ONP) [†] | |
| Warshauer David R | Barnes & Thornburg LLP * | |

| Leading Individuals | |
| --- | --- |
| **Band 1** | |
| Bayt Phillip | Ice Miller LLP |
| Dinwiddie Thomas | Wooden & McLaughlin LLP * |
| Lee Stephen W | Barnes & Thornburg LLP * |
| Lisher Mary | Faegre Baker Daniels |
| Scimia Joseph | Faegre Baker Daniels |
| Weiss Zeff | Ice Miller LLP |
| **Band 2** | |
| Abrams Jeffrey A | Benesch, Friedlander, Coplan & Aronoff * |
| Baxter John B | Krieg DeVault LLP |
| Haas Karl P | Wallack Somers & Haas PC |
| Johnson Dennis A | Barnes & Thornburg LLP * |
| O'Bryan Rory | Harrison & Moberly LLP (ONP) [†] |
| Schwarz James H | Benesch, Friedlander, Coplan & Aronoff * |
| Somers George W | Wallack Somers & Haas PC |
| Wallack Barry Z | Wallack Somers & Haas PC |
| **Band 3** | |
| Dixon Aaron J | Ice Miller LLP |
| Fuson Bradley S | Krieg DeVault LLP |
| Hamilton John W | Wooden & McLaughlin LLP * |
| Hardin Steven D | Faegre Baker Daniels |
| Ochs Timothy E | Ice Miller LLP |
| Ponader Erick | Taft Stettinius & Hollister LLP * |
| Solada Mary E | Bingham Greenebaum Doll LLP * |
| Stephens Angela E | Bose McKinney & Evans LLP |
| Wolenty Barbara A | Robinson Wolenty & Young, LLP (ONP) [†] |

\* Indicates firm / individual with profile.
[†] ONP = Other Notable Practitioner.

## Band 2

### Barnes & Thornburg LLP
See profile on p.436

THE FIRM This full-service firm maintains a strong presence in the Indiana real estate sector. Its team is particularly noted for advising various institutional lenders, as exemplified by its continued representation of Keybank. Recently, the firm has also acted on behalf of Indiana University and the University of Notre Dame, with the representation of the latter pertaining to the proposed development of lands adjacent to the university campus.

KEY INDIVIDUALS **Stephen Lee** (see p.1278) remains one of the leading practitioners in this area. He recently provided counsel to Flaherty & Collins with regards to the financing and development of rental and condominium projects in a number of different states. Sources identify **Dennis Johnson** (see p.1277) as an integral member of the practice, with his strength in the field of real estate lending being cited upon multiple occasions. The *"phenomenal"* **David Warshauer** (see p.1280) has superb strength in the real estate sector. He is able to draw upon vast years of practical experience, and has acted in an advisory capacity throughout the firm's representation of the University of Notre Dame.

### Benesch, Friedlander, Coplan & Aronoff LLP
See profile on p.2120

THE FIRM This active and well-regarded real estate practice exhibits particular strength in general lender representations. Its six partners collaborate closely with their equivalents in the neighboring state of Ohio, enabling the firm to effectively draw upon the expertise of two very talented groups of real estate attorneys. Notable recent clients include BMO Harris Bank and an affiliate of Melvin Simon & Associates.

Sources say: *"The firm is very strong, very experienced and very sophisticated."*

KEY INDIVIDUALS According to sources, **Jeffrey Abrams** (see p.1276) is *"responsive and thorough in documentation,"* in addition to displaying an impressive *"depth of experience and legal expertise in all types of real estate."* He recently assisted Simon Property Group as it sought to release an outlet shopping center. Clients have found **James Schwarz** (see p.1279) to be *"very intelligent, open to suggestions and easy to work with."* A large proportion of his time over the past year was spent advising Solage California Resort and Spa on a complex refinancing matter.

### Wallack Somers & Haas PC

THE FIRM Owing to the aptitude of its lead partners, the resourceful boutique firm of Wallack Somers & Haas continues to thrive. The firm is frequently engaged in a wide variety of commercial real estate matters and its attorneys are noted for their business acumen and their breadth and depth of industry experience.

Sources say: *"Their attorneys are well trained, smart, intelligent and creative."* *"They do very dynamic work."*

KEY INDIVIDUALS **Karl Haas** draws particular praise for his ability to apply his formidable intellect to provide practical real estate solutions. Indeed, one source insisted that Haas is an attorney who one would want on *"complex, challenging deals."* The *"technically strong"* **George Somers** in highly active in the development sector. He is regarded as being extremely *"good to work with,"* and has a reputation for being able to swiftly *"get deals done."* Founding partner **Barry Wallack** is one of the most experienced practitioners in his field. His areas of expertise include real estate acquisition and secured lending, and he possesses the skill set required to assist in a variety of matters.

### Wooden & McLaughlin LLP

THE FIRM This firm's diverse real estate practice ensures that it remains a prominent player in the Indiana legal arena. Its lawyers are renowned for the wealth of transactional experience they have amassed in both the commercial real estate leasing and lending fields.

KEY INDIVIDUALS **Thomas Dinwiddie** (see p.1277) is primarily tasked with representing mortgage lenders, an undertaking which he carries out with an exceptional level of skill and sophistication. Sources are particularly complimentary of his tremendous intelligence. The widely recognized **John Hamilton** (see p.1277) is singled out for praise by numerous commentators, who laud his skillful approach and technical aptitude.

## Band 3

### Bingham Greenebaum Doll LLP
See profile on p.1281

THE FIRM This firm distinguishes itself with the broad range of projects that it effectively undertakes, and is also highlighted for its particular strength in the distressed real estate and land use sectors. In addition to its prominence in the more traditional areas of construction and development, the firm is fast acquiring a reputation for providing advice on a range of renewable energy projects.

Sources say: *"The firm has strong local ties and good market coverage."* *"We always receive very high value."*

KEY INDIVIDUALS The *"well-respected"* **Mary Solada** (see p.1280) is renowned for being a talented zoning attorney. She recently represented E.ON Climate & Renewables as it sought to obtain the relevant permits in a large wind energy development project.

### Bose McKinney & Evans LLP

THE FIRM The ten partners comprising this firm's highly commended real estate practice advise clients on a wide range of issues, ranging from commercial leasing and leasehold financing to the formation of REITs. It is firmly established in the state and continues to offer clients an impressive level of service.

KEY INDIVIDUALS **Angela Stephens** is known and admired for the quality of her commercial leasing work. She is also frequently engaged in advising REITs on all stages of development.

### Krieg DeVault LLP

THE FIRM This full-service firm is a new addition to the rankings, having been increasingly recommended for its prominence in the real estate arena. The firm undertakes an impressive array of work, ranging from commercial leasing and lending to more niche environmental matters.

KEY INDIVIDUALS The prominent **John Baxter** specializes in representing both real estate lenders and commercial developers. **Bradley Fuson** is heralded by sources for being bright and practical. He chairs the firm's real estate lending practice group and, as such, possesses a wealth of relevant knowledge and experience.

### Taft Stettinius & Hollister LLP
See profile on p.2130

THE FIRM The January 2012 merger with Ohio-based Chester Wilcox & Saxbe saw this firm's real estate practice gain both traction and expertise within the real estate sector. The eight-partner team continues to be engaged in a diverse range of matters across a variety of different industries. Clients include The Broadbent Company, Centre Properties and Casa Verde.

KEY INDIVIDUALS Identified by sources as both *"talented"* and *"smart,"* **Erick Ponader** (see p.1279) remains an integral partner at the firm. Moreover, he is said to *"write well, understand issues and negotiate well."*

### Other Notable Practitioners

**Marvin Mitchell** of Mitchell Hurst Jacobs & Dick is one of the state's most experienced and respected attorneys. He is *"well regarded"* by peers and clients alike, and remains an exceptionally strong practitioner. The *"very intelligent"* **Rory O'Bryan** of Harrison & Moberly LLP is extremely active within the real estate field. He is frequently engaged on a broad spectrum of commercial matters. **Barbara Wolenty** of Robinson Wolenty & Young, LLP is an expert in real estate, consistently delivering a high level of service. She is perhaps best known for her tenancy representation expertise.

# Leaders' Profiles in Indiana

**ABRAMS, Jeffrey A**
Benesch, Friedlander, Coplan & Aronoff LLP, Indianapolis
317 632 3232
jabrams@beneschlaw.com
*Featured in Real Estate (Indiana)*
**Practice Areas:** Real estate law. Represents banks and lending institutions, developers, landlords, tenants, builders, contractors and all types of business owners. Has represented companies and lenders in documenting various types of transactions, including acquisition and development of land, shopping centers, office and industrial buildings, acquisition of businesses and development loans.
**Career:** Partner-in-Charge of Indianapolis office and member of firm's Executive Committee.
**Personal:** Indiana University School of Law (JD, cum laude, 1981); Miami University (BS, 1978).

**ALEXANDER, Nelson D**
Frost Brown Todd LLC, Indianapolis
317 237 3265
nalexander@fbtlaw.com
*Featured in Litigation (Indiana)*
**Practice Areas:** Member-In-Charge of Indianapolis office. Devotes significant part of his practice to representation of manufacturers of end goods and components in commercial and product liability litigation. Has devoted remainder of his practice to business litigation involving varied commercial disputes. Has acted as appellate counsel in more than 40 reported appellate decisions.
**Professional Memberships:** Indianapolis Bar Association, American Bar Association.
**Personal:** BA in Economics from Wabash College 1990; JD from University of Chicago Law School 1993. Member, Greater Indianapolis Progress Committee.

**BALDWIN, Charles B**
Ogletree, Deakins, Nash, Smoak & Stewart, PC, Indianapolis
317 916 1300
charles.baldwin@ogletreedeakins.com
*Featured in Labor & Employment (Indiana)*
**Practice Areas:** Employment; Labor; Litigation.
**Professional Memberships:** College of Labor and Employment Lawyers, Best Lawyers in America, Board of Directors, Indiana Chamber of Commerce.
**Career:** Admitted: Indiana; Ohio; various U.S. District Courts and U.S. Courts of Appeals. Selected as Counsel for Amici Curiae 7th Circuit Court of Appeals concerning case of 1st impression under ADA. Labor and Employment Lecturer—Indiana University Law School.
**Publications:** Contributing Author, ABA's Model Jury Instructions—Employment Litigation; Seventh Circuit Editor, ABA's Employment & Labor Relations Litigation Newsletter; Co-Author, Indiana Guide to Preventing Workplace Harassment.
**Personal:** Valparaiso University (BS, 1980), University of Dayton (JD, 1983).

**BENNETT, Jackie**
Taft Stettinius & Hollister LLP, Indianapolis
317 713 3444
jbennett@taftlaw.com
*Featured in Litigation (Indiana)*
**Practice Areas:** White Collar Criminal Defense, Litigation, Securities - Litigation, Patent Litigation, First Amendment & Media Law, Environmental, Campaign & Election Law, FCPA and International Anti-Corruption, Environmental Transactional Services.
**Career:** Mr Bennett represents individuals and corporations in cases expected to go to trial. His practice concentrates in the areas of commercial, civil and white-collar criminal litigation. Mr Bennett served in the Office of Independent Counsel Kenneth W Starr from 1995 to 1999, serving as a senior advisor on the Impeachment Referral of William Jefferson Clinton.
**Personal:** Indiana University - Robert H McKinney School of Law (1983); Hanover College (1980).

**BOWMAN, Andy**
Bingham Greenebaum Doll LLP, Indianapolis
317 686 5210
abowman@bgdlegal.com
*Featured in Environment (Indiana)*
**Practice Areas:** Andy has provided environmental regulatory services to industrial, commercial and governmental clients for over 30 years.
**Professional Memberships:** Indianapolis Bar Association, Environmental Law Section; Indiana State Bar Association, Environmental Law Section; American Bar Association, Section of Environment, Energy and Resources; Indiana Chamber of Commerce; Indiana Manufacturers Association; Indiana State Poultry Association; Air & Waste Management Association; Alliance of Hazardous Materials Professionals; American Agricultural Law Association; Solid Waste Association of North America; Water Environment Federation.
**Personal:** Purdue University, B.S., Economics, 1978; Indiana University Robert H McKinney School of Law, JD, 1982; Indiana University Kelley School of Business, MBA, 1982.

**BRIDGE, Catherine L**
Barnes & Thornburg LLP, Indianapolis
317 231 7255
catherine.bridge@BTLaw.com
*Featured in Corporate/M&A (Indiana)*
**Practice Areas:** Mergers, acquisitions and divestitures; securities offerings including initial public offerings; securities compliance; corporate governance; corporate law; corporate finance; insurance regulation; represents clients in insurance regulatory and other matters including changes in control and redomestications, reinsurance and captive insurance companies.
**Professional Memberships:** American Bar Association and Indiana State Bar Association.
**Career:** Admitted to practice in Indiana and before the US District Court for the Southern District of Indiana.

**Personal:** Fordham University (AB, summa cum laude, 1972); Columbia University School of Law (JD, Kent Scholar, 1975).

**BROWN, Alan**
Frost Brown Todd LLC, Indianapolis
317 237 3841
abrown@fbtlaw.com
*Featured in Litigation (Indiana)*
**Practice Areas:** Business and commercial litigation, including contracts; manufacturing and distribution; financial institutions; ownership, governance and control disputes; securities; restrictive covenants; trade secrets.
**Professional Memberships:** American Bar Association, Federation of Defense and Corporate Counsel (President, FDCC Foundation, Indianapolis Bar Association.
**Career:** Chair of Business Litigation Practice Group; lead trial and appellate counsel in significant decisions in state and federal courts involving injunctions, shareholder rights, fiduciary duty, lender liability, trade secrets, RICO, and contract interpretation and remedies; counselor to businesses on risk management and litigation avoidance.
**Personal:** Director, American Pianists Association and Indiana Soccer Association; past chair, Indy Jazzfest.

**CAMPBELL, David**
Bingham Greenebaum Doll LLP, Indianapolis
317 968 5362
dcampbell@bgdlegal.com
*Featured in Litigation (Indiana)*
**Practice Areas:** Litigation and trial practice, including complex commercial matters, contract, torts, general corporate and business litigation. Skilled in Alternative Dispute Resolution, including commercial and securities arbitration and mediation.
**Professional Memberships:** American College of Trial Lawyers; Defense Trial Counsel of Indiana (President, 1989); Indianapolis Legal Aid Society (President, 1996-2000); American, Indiana (Fellow), Indianapolis (Fellow) Bar Associations.
**Career:** Listed in Best Lawyers in America (Commercial Litigation, Antitrust Litigation, Trusts and Estates Litigation).
**Personal:** Indiana State University (BS, 1971); Indiana University (JD, summa cum laude, 1974); Indiana State University Foundation (Board of Directors, 1989-present; Chair, 2007-09) Indiana State University (Trustee, 2011-15).

**CARROLL, Jan M**
Barnes & Thornburg LLP, Indianapolis
317 231 7265
jan.carroll@BTLaw.com
*Featured in Litigation (Indiana)*
**Practice Areas:** Co-chair, Media Practice Group; commercial litigation; drug and medical device litigation; First Amendment litigation and media law counseling; land-use, eminent domain and historic preservation litigation; marital dissolutions for high net worth individuals.

**Professional Memberships:** Indiana State Bar Association.
**Career:** Admitted to practice in Indiana; before the U.S. Supreme Court, U.S. Courts of Appeals for the Seventh, Eleventh, and Federal Circuits; and the U.S. District Courts for the District of Colorado, and the Northern and Southern Districts of Indiana.
**Personal:** Southern Methodist University (BFA, 1974, magna cum laude); Indiana University School of Law - Indianapolis (JD, 1984, cum laude).

**CARUSO II, Ralph A**
Taft Stettinius & Hollister LLP, Indianapolis
317 713 3463
rcaruso@taftlaw.com
*Featured in Corporate/M&A (Indiana)*
**Practice Areas:** Corporate finance, mergers and acquisitions, private equity and venture capital, gaming, business and finance.
**Career:** Mr Caruso has particular experience in complex business transactions that involve private companies and the divisions of public companies. He also focuses on the representation of private equity funds, their portfolio companies, and other equity sponsors in connection with acquisition, divestiture and financing transactions. In that regard, Mr. Caruso has guided his clients through numerous domestic and international acquisitions and divestitures having an aggregate value of well over $1 billion dollars.
**Personal:** University of Notre Dame Law School (1994); LeMoyne College (1991).

**DENSBORN, Donald**
Taft Stettinius & Hollister LLP, Indianapolis
317 713 4402
ddensborn@taftlaw.com
*Featured in Corporate/M&A (Indiana)*
**Practice Areas:** Mergers and acquisitions, corporate finance, private equity and venture capital, business and finance, emerging companies.
**Professional Memberships:** American, Indiana State and Indianapolis Bar Associations
**Career:** Mr Densborn serves diverse businesses, investors, financing sources and entrepreneurs in an array of fundraising and acquisition transactions. His work includes substantial governance, compliance and consultative aspects. He has experience with commercial and owner-occupied real estate, particularly its financing, leasing, and conveyancing.
**Personal:** Indiana University - Robert H. McKinney School of Law (1976); Indiana University (1973).

**DEPREZ, Anne**
Barnes & Thornburg LLP, Indianapolis
317 231 7264
anne.deprez@BTLaw.com
*Featured in Litigation (Indiana)*
**Practice Areas:** Securities litigation; corporate governance advice and litigation; shareholder disputes; derivative actions; broker-dealer, investment adviser, officer and director representation in regulatory, enforcement and criminal investiga-

tions and actions; arbitration; business litigation; class action defense.

**Professional Memberships:** American and Indiana State Bar Associations.

**Career:** Admitted to practice in Indiana, before the US Circuit Courts of Appeals for the Sixth and Seventh Circuits, the US District Courts for the Northern and Southern Districts of Indiana, the Eastern District of Wisconsin and the Western District of Michigan.

**Personal:** Smith College (BA Economics); Indiana University Maurer School of Law (JD magna cum laude).

### DETHERAGE, Andrew J
Barnes & Thornburg LLP, Indianapolis
317 231 7717
andy.detherage@btlaw.com
*Featured in Litigation (Indiana)*

**Practice Areas:** Co-Chair, Insurance Recovery and Counseling Group, management committee member; insurance coverage for policyholders; insurance bad faith; commercial litigation; complex litigation; toxic tort defense.

**Professional Memberships:** Indiana and California Bar Associations.

**Career:** Admitted to practice in: Indiana, California; 7th Circuit Court of Appeals; U.S. District Courts for the Northern, Southern Districts of Indiana, Northern District of Illinois, Eastern District of Wisconsin, Central District of California.

**Personal:** Indiana University (BA, with highest distinction, 1987); Indiana University School of Law - Indianapolis (JD, summa cum laude, 1990); board member and past president, Big Brothers Big Sisters of Central Indiana.

### DEVEAU, Frank J.
Taft Stettinius & Hollister LLP, Indianapolis
317 713 3520
fdeveau@taftlaw.com
*Featured in Environment (Indiana)*

**Practice Areas:** Litigation, Insurance Law, Environmental Transactional Services, Environmental.

**Professional Memberships:** American, Indiana State and Indianapolis Bar Associations

**Career:** Mr Deveau is Co-Chair of the Environmental group. He represents clients in all aspects of environmental law. He advises and defends clients in relation to environmental litigation involving private parties and federal and state government. He has assisted clients in administrative proceedings, obtaining and maintaining compliance with solid and hazardous waste permits, air permits, water discharge permits, CAFO and CFO permits.

**Personal:** Indiana University - Robert H McKinney School of Law (1980); Indiana University, AB (1976).

### DINWIDDIE, Thomas
Wooden & McLaughlin LLP, Indianapolis
317 639 6151
tdinwiddie@woodmclaw.com
*Featured in Real Estate (Indiana)*

**Practice Areas:** Tom's practice covers a broad range of commercial subjects, with clients involved

in many different businesses and professions. While a significant number of Tom's clients are involved with real estate, real estate finance and real estate development, many are involved with the health care industry. Tom has been involved extensively with the impact of Dodd Frank on commercial banking and mortgage banking. Tom is recognized as an expert on real estate finance and has a great deal of experience with Federal and State mortgage licensing and regulation. He has represented the Indiana Mortgage Bankers Association for over thirty years, drafting some of the most important Indiana mortgage lending statutes. He is a frequent speaker on real estate finance issues. Tom represents mortgage banking companies across the country and is often called upon to advise out of state borrowers and lenders on Indiana law. He also has extensive experience in construction issues and the resolution of business and financial disputes.

**Professional Memberships:** Indianapolis and Indiana State Bar Associations. Named an Indiana Super Lawyer 2005-12.

**Personal:** DePauw University, AB, 1969. Indiana University School of Law – Indianapolis JD, 1973.

### DOEHRMANN, Carrie
Frost Brown Todd LLC, Louisville
317 237 3947
cdoehrmann@fbtlaw.com
*Featured in Environment (Indiana)*

**Practice Areas:** Practice includes representation of clients in environmental litigation, compliance counseling, and due diligence inquiries associated with property transfers. She has represented buyers, sellers and lenders on environmental considerations in real estate and corporate transactions. Included in her related litigation experiences have been negotiations with federal, state and local environmental protection agencies in matters of federal and state environmental law.

**Professional Memberships:** American Bar Association, Indiana and Indianapolis Bar Association.

**Career:** Indiana University School of Law, Indianapolis, JD; DePauw University, BA.

### EBERT, Kim F
Ogletree, Deakins, Nash, Smoak & Stewart, PC, Indianapolis
317 916 1300
kim.ebert@ogletreedeakins.com
*Featured in Labor & Employment (Indiana)*

**Practice Areas:** Represents employers in the full range of labor and employment matters, including litigation, administrative proceedings, collective bargaining, union contract administration and union avoidance.

**Professional Memberships:** ABA (Member, Standing Committee on Continuing Education of the Bar 1997-2000; Past Chair, Employer-Employee Relations Committee, TTIPS), Japan-America Society of Indiana (Board Member).

**Career:** In Best Lawyers in America since 1995. Fellow in College of Labor and Employment Lawyers. Named Distinguished Barrister by Indiana Lawyer in 2007.

**Publications:** Has lectured and written extensively on labor and employment subjects at regional and national programs.

**Personal:** Wabash College (BA cum laude, 1972), Indiana University (JD cum laude, 1976).

### GRIGGS, Sean
Barnes & Thornburg LLP, Indianapolis
317 231 7793
sean.griggs@btlaw.com
*Featured in Environment (Indiana)*

**Practice Areas:** Environmental Litigation; Environmental Law; Appellate Practice; Administrative Law; Alternative Dispute Resolution.

**Professional Memberships:** Indianapolis Bar Association (Senior Distinguished Fellow); Indiana State Bar Association; American Bar Association.

**Career:** US Court of Appeals for the Sixth Circuit; Federal District Courts for the Northern and Southern Districts of Indiana; pro hac vice admissions to numerous state and federal courts.

**Publications:** Indiana Super Lawyers (2012-2013); The Best Lawyers in America (2008-13); Best Lawyers, Lawyer of the Year Honors (2013).

**Personal:** Rose-Hulman Institute of Technology (BS, Chemical Engineering, 1988); Indiana University School of Law-Indianapolis (JD, 1994), magna cum laude.

### HAMILTON, John W
Wooden & McLaughlin LLP, Indianapolis
317 639 6151
jhamilton@woodmclaw.com
*Featured in Real Estate (Indiana)*

**Practice Areas:** John's focus is primarily the representation of institutional investors, commercial banks, finance companies and private developers with respect to a myriad of real estate-related issues; in particular, the representation of lenders and borrowers in commercial lending transactions. John also represents commercial developers in the acquisition, sale and leasing of real estate. John has substantial expertise with regard to tax credit, bond, TIFF and other government-sponsored subsidy programs. John has been listed as one of the leading real estate attorneys in the State of Indiana and as a Best Lawyer in America ®. John is recognized nationally as an expert on multi-family lending and subsidy programs and regularly consults with borrowers and lenders in this area.

**Professional Memberships:** Indianapolis Bar Association; Indiana State Bar Association; and Mortgage Bankers Association.

**Career:** Prior to joining Wooden & McLaughlin LLP, John was an Assistant Vice President of SunTrust Bank and focused upon commercial lending for retail centers, residential developments, and resort developments.

**Personal:** Davidson College (BA, 1986). Washington & Lee University (JD, cum laude, 1993).

### HICKS, Robert J
Taft Stettinius & Hollister LLP, Indianapolis
317 713 3465
rhicks@taftlaw.com
*Featured in Corporate/M&A (Indiana)*

**Practice Areas:** Mergers and acquisitions, tax, business and finance, corporate finance, private equity and venture capital, structured finance, gaming.

**Professional Memberships:** American, Indiana State and Indianapolis Bar Associations.

**Career:** Mr Hicks is a member of the Executive Committee and the Partner-in-Charge of the Indianapolis office. He focuses his practice on complex business and commercial transactions, private equity and venture capital transactions, mergers and acquisitions, structured financings, business advisory services and structural tax matters. He serves as outside counsel for the two largest private equity funds in Indiana.

**Personal:** William and Mary School of Law (1986); Butler University (1984).

### HILL, Jeremy
Bingham Greenebaum Doll LLP, Indianapolis
317 968 5384
jhill@bgdlegal.com
*Featured in Corporate/M&A (Indiana)*

**Practice Areas:** Jeremy's practice focuses in the area of emerging business and financial institutions. Clients turn to him for a range of legal services, especially mergers and acquisitions, securities law compliance, business organization and general business and corporate transactions. He is a member of the firm's Corporate and Transactional Practice Group.

**Professional Memberships:** Drafting Committee for the Indiana Uniform Securities Act; Indianapolis Bar Association: Business Law Section, Past Chair; Indiana and American Bar Associations.

**Personal:** Indiana University - Bloomington (BS with highest distinction, Accounting, Kelley School of Business, 1996); Indiana University Maurer School of Law (JD, magna cum laude, 1999).

### JOHNSON, Dennis A
Barnes & Thornburg LLP, Indianapolis
317 231 7736
dennis.johnson@btlaw.com
*Featured in Real Estate (Indiana)*

**Practice Areas:** Co-Chair, Financial Institutions Practice Group; real estate; commercial finance law; represents construction and permanent real estate lenders, commercial real estate developers, developers of multi-family and single-family residential projects and single-family residential builders.

**Professional Memberships:** Former Chair of the Business Section of the Indianapolis Bar Association and a former Member of the Board of Directors of the Community Organization Legal Assistance Project.

**Career:** Admitted to practice in the state of Indiana.

**Personal:** Indiana University (BS in accounting, 1982); Indiana University School of Law - Indianapolis (JD, cum laude, 1985).

## KANE, Larry
Bingham Greenebaum Doll LLP, Indianapolis
317 968 5390
lkane@bgdlegal.com
*Featured in Environment (Indiana)*

**Practice Areas:** Larry's practice focuses on permitting and enforcement issues under the Clean Air Act and the Clean Water Act, especially in the electric utility and automotive industries. He counsels business and public sector clients on compliance issues under all major environmental laws; has advised clients on remediation projects, brownfields redevelopment and corporate transactions, and legislation; and has defended permitting and toxic tort litigation, having appeared before the Indiana Supreme Court and Court of Appeals.
**Professional Memberships:** American, Indiana State and Indianapolis Bar Associations; Indiana Chamber of Commerce, Indiana Manufacturers Association, Air & Waste Management Association, Indiana Water Environmental Association.

## KASPER, David
Frost Brown Todd LLC, Indianapolis
317 237 3838
dkasper@fbtlaw.com
*Featured in Litigation (Indiana)*

**Practice Areas:** Mr Kasper concentrates his practice in litigation, professional malpractice and insurance services.
**Professional Memberships:** American Bar Association, Seventh Circuit Bar Association, Indianapolis Bar Association, Indiana State Bar Association.
**Career:** Also listed in The Best Lawyers in America (2005-12), The Best Lawyers in America Indianapolis Legal Malpractice Lawyer of the Year (2011-12), Indiana Super Lawyers (2005-12).
**Personal:** Indiana University School of Law, JD; Union College, AB.

## KING, Douglas B
Wooden & McLaughlin LLP, Indianapolis
317 639 6151
dking@woodmclaw.com
*Featured in Litigation (Indiana)*

**Practice Areas:** Doug's practice is almost exclusively civil litigation, typically for the defense. He has successfully tried and defended: Toxic Tort and chemical cases; Drug and Medical Device product liability cases; Asbestos cases; Environmental Suits; Breach of Contract and various commercial claims; and a wide variety of Personal Injury and Wrongful Death claims. Doug has successfully tried numerous jury and bench trials in state and Federal courts throughout the United States, resulting in a number of published decisions and landmark cases. In the products liability area, Doug has defended manufacturers and distributors of a wide variety of products, devices, and substances over the last 30 years.
**Professional Memberships:** American College of Trial Lawyers; International Association of Defense Counsel; Litigation Counsel of America;

Bars of United States Court of Appeals for Seventh and Third Circuits and the United States Supreme Court; Indianapolis and Indiana State Bar Associations; Defense Research Institute; and Defense Trial Counsel of Indiana.
**Personal:** Butler University (BS, 1973). Indiana University (JD, summa cum laude, 1976).

## KNEBEL, Donald E
Barnes & Thornburg LLP, Indianapolis
317 231 7214
donald.knebel@btlaw.com
*Featured in Litigation (Indiana)*

**Practice Areas:** Intellectual property; intellectual property litigation; patent litigation; federal civil litigation; antitrust and trade regulation; unfair trade.
**Professional Memberships:** Fellow, American College of Trial Lawyers; Listed in Best Lawyers in America since 1983 (litigation, intellectual property, bet-the-company litigation, antitrust); Adjunct professor and senior advisor to the Center for Intellectual Property Research at the Indiana University Maurer School of Law.
**Career:** Admitted to practice in Indiana and before the First, Third, Fourth, Sixth, Seventh and Federal Circuits.
**Personal:** Purdue University (BSEE, with highest distinction, 1968); Harvard University (JD, magna cum laude, 1974).

## KYLE, John
Barnes & Thornburg LLP, Indianapolis
317 231 7284
john.kyle@btlaw.com
*Featured in Environment (Indiana)*

**Practice Areas:** Concentrates on remediation projects for soil, groundwater and surface-water contamination under a wide variety of regulatory programs; business transactions involving environmental issues; and insurance coverage for environmentally impaired property. Handles complex environmental litigation before state and federal courts and agencies.
**Career:** Former chair of the firm's Environmental Department.
**Publications:** Has written and lectured extensively on environmental issues; former adjunct professor at Indiana University Maurer School of Law-Bloomington.
**Personal:** Indiana University - Bloomington (BA, 1976) Indiana University - Bloomington (JD, 1979).

## LEE, Stephen W
Barnes & Thornburg LLP, Indianapolis
317 231 7200
stephen.lee@btlaw.com
*Featured in Real Estate (Indiana)*

**Practice Areas:** Real estate; commercial real estate; construction law; zoning; planning and land use; eminent domain; all aspects of commercial real estate acquisition, development, construction, financing, leasing, disposition and related litigation, including condemnation proceedings.
**Professional Memberships:** Indianapolis and Indiana State Bar Associations.
**Career:** Admitted to practice before the Supreme Court of Indiana, the US District Court for the

Southern District of Indiana, the US Court of Appeals for the Seventh Circuit and the Supreme Court of the United States.
**Personal:** Ball State University (BS, 1971); Indiana University (JD, summa cum laude, 1977).

## MACGILL, Robert D
Barnes & Thornburg LLP, Indianapolis
317 231 7223
robert.macgill@btlaw.com
*Featured in Litigation (Indiana)*

**Practice Areas:** Intellectual property and antitrust litigation; commercial litigation; and insurance coverage for policy holders. Represents US and foreign-owned companies in matters litigated in trial and appellate courts throughout the United States.
**Professional Memberships:** Chair, Litigation Department, Barnes & Thornburg LLP (1999-2007); Chair, Board of Indianapolis Tennis Championships, Inc. (1999-2008); Chair, Indiana Secondary Market for Education Loans, Inc. (2001-08).
**Career:** Admitted to practice in the United States Supreme Court, Northern and Southern Districts of Indiana and the Third, Sixth, Seventh, Eighth and Ninth Circuit Courts of Appeals.
**Personal:** Indiana University (BS, with high distinction, 1978; JD, cum laude, 1981).

## MACKEY, Larry A
Barnes & Thornburg LLP, Indianapolis
317 231 7236
larry.mackey@btlaw.com
*Featured in Litigation (Indiana)*

**Practice Areas:** Co-Chair, White-Collar Crime Defense Practice Group; internal investigations; complex litigation. Has tried scores of federal jury trials as prosecutor and defense counsel across the country.
**Professional Memberships:** Fellow, American College of Trial Lawyers; Indianapolis Bar Association.
**Career:** Tried more than 60 federal criminal jury trials across country as defense counsel and federal prosecutor including the government's closing argument in U.S. v Timothy McVeigh. Frequent lecturer on trial practice and conduct of internal investigations.
**Personal:** University of Evansville (BA, summa cum laude, 1973; DHL 1999); Indiana University School of Law - Bloomington (JD, magna cum laude, 1976).

## MALEY, John
Barnes & Thornburg LLP, Indianapolis
317 231 7464
john.maley@BTLaw.com
*Featured in Labor & Employment (Indiana), Litigation (Indiana)*

**Practice Areas:** National trial and appellate practice. Listed in Best Lawyers in America®; top-ranked attorney in several Indiana SuperLawyers® surveys; Best Lawyers "Lawyer of the Year" for Litigation - Labor & Employment; "Lawyer of the Year" for Bet-the-Company Litigation in Indiana.
**Professional Memberships:** Chair, Local Rules Committees S.D. of Indiana; Member, Local Rules Committee, N.D. of Indiana; past-president, Indianapolis Bar Association, Indianapolis Bar Foundation.

**Career:** Law Clerk, US Dist Ct, SD of Ind, 1988-90.
**Publications:** Appellate Handbook for Indiana Lawyers.
**Personal:** University of Notre Dame (BA); Indiana University (MBA); Indiana University School of Law - Indianapolis (JD, summa cum laude).

## MCDERMOTT, Brian L
Ogletree, Deakins, Nash, Smoak & Stewart, PC, Indianapolis
317 916 2170
brian.mcdermott@ogletreedeakins.com
*Featured in Labor & Employment (Indiana)*

**Practice Areas:** Employment law, employment litigation, management labor law, ERISA litigation.
**Professional Memberships:** Indiana Bar Association (Member; Chair, Labor and Employment Section 2003-04), Indianapolis Bar Association (Member; Chair, Labor and Employment Section 2004-05); Society for Human Resource Management.
**Career:** Admitted in Indiana, Iowa. Named as an Indiana Super Lawyer in 2005-13; Best Lawyers 2005-13.
**Publications:** Co-author of various Indiana Chamber of Commerce's publications, including: The Indiana Employer's Guide to the ADA and FMLA and The Interviewing Guide: Designed to Assist Indiana Employers with Hiring and Retaining Employees.
**Personal:** University of Iowa (JD, 1991), with Distinction; Judicial Clerk, U.S. District Judge Donald Porter.

## MCLAUGHLIN, Alan L
Littler Mendelson, PC, Indianapolis
317 287 3600
amclaughlin@littler.com
*Featured in Labor & Employment (Indiana)*

**Practice Areas:** Employment Litigation, including discrimination actions, agency proceedings, arbitrations, class/collective actions, and emergency proceedings involving non-compete agreements, trade secrets, business torts and contracts.
**Professional Memberships:** Indiana State Bar Association (Past Chair, Litigation Section; Federal Judiciary Committee; Employment Section), Indianapolis Bar Association, Seventh Circuit Bar Association, American Bar Association (Litigation and Employment Sections).
**Publications:** "Litigation Skills Series: Employment Litigation Update," Indianapolis Bar Association, 2010; "Compass to the New ADAAA Regulations," ICLEF, December 2009; "Trade Secrets and Covenants Not to Compete: Tactics, Enforceability and Defenses," ICLEF, 2007.
**Personal:** JD, Vanderbilt University, 1982; AB, Wabash College, 1979, summa cum laude, Phi Beta Kappa.

## MILLARD, David B
Barnes & Thornburg LLP, Indianapolis
317 231 7803
david.millard@btlaw.com
*Featured in Corporate/M&A (Indiana)*

**Practice Areas:** Chair of the Corporate Department of Barnes & Thornburg. Corporate law; corporate finance; mergers and acquisitions;

private equity; venture capital and joint ventures. Counsels large-cap, middle market and high-growth businesses in the U.S. and globally, as well as venture capital and private equity funds.
**Professional Memberships:** Served as President of The Venture Club of Indiana and Entrepreneur's Alliance of Indiana and Chairman of the Indiana Chamber of Commerce Business Council and on the Chamber's Board and Executive Committee.

### MORSE, Peter A
Barnes & Thornburg LLP, Indianapolis
317 231 7794
pete.morse@BTLaw.com
*Featured in Labor & Employment (Indiana)*
**Practice Areas:** Full-service traditional labor/employment attorney; national, regional representation. Litigation (wrongful discharge, discrimination, harassment, ERISA, disability, FMLA, wage-hour, class actions). Traditional labor (negotiations, strikes, unfair labor practices, arbitrations, union avoidance campaigns & training). Non-compete. RIFs, WARN. Handbooks, contracts. International labor law. Qui tam. Fraud. Anti-Corruption (FCPA).
**Professional Memberships:** Japan-America Society (Officer); TerraLex (Officer, Co-Chair–International Labour Practice Group, global law firm network).
**Career:** Partner; Administrator of Labor Department; Co-Chair of Japanese and Global Services Practice Groups – "Best Lawyers in America," "SuperLawyer" recognitions. Assisted clients in all 50 states & 20+ foreign countries.
**Personal:** Vanderbilt (JD, 1993); DePauw (BA, 1990).

### MOY, Eric R
Barnes & Thornburg LLP, Indianapolis
317 231 7298
eric.moy@BTLaw.com
*Featured in Corporate/M&A (Indiana)*
**Practice Areas:** Corporate, financing, regulatory, and transactional matters including: mergers and acquisitions, corporate governance, SEC and financial regulation, public offerings, venture capital and private placements, ESOPs, commercial lending, securitization and structured finance, and executive compensation.
**Professional Memberships:** Member of the Federal Regulation of Securities Committee, the Corporate Governance Committee and the Committee on Professional Responsibility of the Business Section of the American Bar Association.
**Career:** Joined Barnes & Thornburg as an associate in 1985 and became a Partner in 1994.
**Personal:** Earlham College (BA, 1982); Columbia Law School (JD, 1985).

### MULVANEY, Karl
Bingham Greenebaum Doll LLP, Indianapolis
317 968 5400
kmulvaney@bgdlegal.com
*Featured in Litigation (Indiana)*
**Practice Areas:** Practices in the areas of appellate, litigation and attorney disciplinary law. Has represented both plaintiffs and defendants in complex appellate matters.

**Professional Memberships:** Indianapolis, Indiana, Seventh Circuit, American Bar Associations; American Academy of Appellate Lawyers.
**Career:** Indiana Supreme Court, Administrator (1984-91), Assistant Administrator (1978-84).
**Personal:** The Ohio State University, (BS, cum laude, 1972); U.S. Army 1972-74; Indiana University (JD, cum laude, 1977); Indiana Bar Foundation, Executive Committee, 2003-2008; Indiana Supreme Court Rules Committee 1992-2003, Chair 1994-2003; Res Gestae Best Article Award, 1989; Indianapolis Bar Association Professionalism Award, 2007; Indiana State Bar Civility Award, 2009; Sagamore of the Wabash.

### NIERMAN, Todd
Littler Mendelson, PC, Indianapolis
317 287 3600
tnierman@littler.com
*Featured in Labor & Employment (Indiana)*
**Practice Areas:** Employment Litigation; Advice, Counseling and Training; Collective Bargaining and Labor Arbitration; Union Avoidance; Wage & Hour.
**Professional Memberships:** Past Chair, American Bar Association/Labor and Employment Section's Federal Labor Standards Legislation Committee; member, United States Chamber of Commerce, Labor Relations Committee, Wage, Hour and Leave Subcommittee; NLRB Region 25 Practice and Procedure Committee.
**Publications:** Contributing author to the Fair Labor Standards Act (BNA Books), Past Editor & Chief, Cumulative Supplement to Age Discrimination in Employment Law (BNA).
**Personal:** University of Michigan, BBA, with distinction, 1983; Vanderbilt University, JD, 1986; Certified Public Accountant, Illinois, 1983.

### PADGETT, Mike
Jackson Lewis LLP, Indianapolis
317 489 6936
PadgettM@jacksonlewis.com
*Featured in Labor & Employment (Indiana)*
**Practice Areas:** Employment litigation, advice, counseling, and labor - contract negotiations, labor arbitrations, and NLRB matters.
**Professional Memberships:** Indianapolis Bar Association (Past Chair, Labor/Employment Committee); Indiana Chamber of Commerce Employment Law Committee; Indy SHRM, Legislative Director.
**Career:** Jackson Lewis (2007 – present); Bingham McHale (1998 – 20070; State of Indiana: Executive Assistant to Governor, Chief Counsel, Department of Labor, Chief Counsel, Department of Workforce Development (1991 – 1998.)
**Publications:** Numerous articles for professional organizations, periodicals and journals.
**Personal:** BS, Mechanical Engineering Technology, Purdue University; J.D., Indiana University School of Law – Bloomington; Four years as mechanical engineer before law school.

### PAPPAS, Nicholas
Frost Brown Todd LLC, Indianapolis
317 237 3888
npappas@fbtlaw.com
*Featured in Litigation (Indiana)*

**Practice Areas:** Chair of Frost Brown Todd Product Liability Practice Group. Concentrates practice in product liability and commercial litigation. Serves as national lead trial counsel for a major construction and agricultural equipment manufacturer.
**Professional Memberships:** Defense Research Institute, Defense Trial Counsel of Indiana, Indianapolis Bar Association, Indianapolis Bar Foundation (Distinguished Fellow, Vice President of the Board of Directors).
**Career:** DRI 2012 Product Liability Seminar Chair; 2010 Defense Lawyer of the Year, Defense Trial Counsel of Indiana; Selected for inclusion in Indiana Super Lawyers® (2011-13); AV® Rated, Martindale-Hubbell®; The Best Lawyers in America® (2010-13).

### POLAK, Jonathan
Taft Stettinius & Hollister LLP, Indianapolis
317 713 3532
jpolak@taftlaw.com
*Featured in Litigation (Indiana)*
**Practice Areas:** Litigation, Patent Prosecution, Trademark, Copyright and Trade Secret, Intellectual Property, Patent Litigation, Sports
**Career:** Mr Polak practices in the areas of complex commercial litigation and intellectual property litigation. He has litigated complex, multi-party cases in state and federal courts around the country. He has also litigated intellectual property infringement claims on behalf of nationally-recognized rights holders. He has established a national practice in the area of the right of publicity, representing such personalities as Marilyn Monroe, Duke Ellington, John Wayne, Rosa Parks and John Dillinger.
**Personal:** Southern Methodist University School of Law (1994); Southern Methodist University (1991)

### PONADER, Erick
Taft Stettinius & Hollister LLP, Indianapolis
317 713 3473
eponader@taftlaw.com
*Featured in Real Estate (Indiana)*
**Practice Areas:** Health and life sciences, trademark, copyright and trade secret, business and finance, real property.
**Career:** Mr Ponader represents clients in commercial law and real estate development, acquisition, sale, leasing and financing. He also advises and represents life science companies in all aspects from start-up forward, including entity structure and formation, financing and operations. He has extensive experience in the sale and purchase of businesses, intellectual property licensing, trademark law, construction law, aviation law and medical device and pharmaceutical law.
**Personal:** Indiana University Maurer School of Law - Bloomington (1985); Indiana University (1982).

### PRATHER, R Anthony
Barnes & Thornburg LLP, Indianapolis
317 231 7435
tony.prather@BTLaw.com
*Featured in Labor & Employment (Indiana)*
**Practice Areas:** Employment law; employment litigation; management labor law; wrongful termi-

nation; experience includes federal and state court litigation involving discrimination, wrongful discharge claims, non-competition agreements, representation in alternative dispute resolution proceedings; supervisor training; and representation in arbitration proceedings. He has a full-service practice representing management interests exclusively in all aspects of labor and employment law and litigation.
**Career:** Admitted to practice before the U.S. Court of Appeals for the Seventh and Eleventh Circuits and several district courts.
**Personal:** Indiana University (BA, 1980); Indiana University School of Law - Bloomington (JD, 1983).

### PRECHTEL, David
Bingham Greenebaum Doll LLP, Indianapolis
317 968 5403
dprechtel@bgdlegal.com
*Featured in Corporate/M&A (Indiana)*
**Practice Areas:** Experienced in the areas of business transactions with an emphasis on mergers and acquisitions, healthcare, financial institutions and securities. Has been involved in numerous mergers and acquisitions, as well as public and private securities offerings. Previously served on the firm's Management Committee and chaired the firm's Corporate and Transactional Practice Group.
**Professional Memberships:** Indianapolis, Indiana, American Bar Associations; American Health Lawyers Association.
**Career:** Named among Best Lawyers in America, 2005-present; Indiana Super Lawyers 2004-present.
**Personal:** Purdue University, Krannert School of Management (BS, with distinction, 1982); Indiana University (JD, cum laude, 1985).

### RUSTHOVEN, Peter J
Barnes & Thornburg LLP, Indianapolis
317 231 7299
peter.rusthoven@btlaw.com
*Featured in Litigation (Indiana)*
**Practice Areas:** Litigation - appellate, trial-level advocacy in constitutional, banking, contract, environmental, labor, utilities, other fields; Business - transactional, corporate governance, change-of-control work for NYSE and other companies; helped draft Indiana's corporation statute and official comments; Governmental services - gaming, alcoholic beverage, other regulatory and legislative services.
**Professional Memberships:** U.S. and Indiana Supreme Courts; U.S. Courts of Appeals for Federal, Third, Fifth, Seventh Circuits; U.S. District Courts for Indiana Northern, Southern Districts.
**Personal:** BA, magna cum laude, Harvard College, 1973; JD, magna cum laude, Harvard Law School, 1976; Associate Counsel to President of the United States, 1981-1985.

### SCHWARZ, James H
Benesch, Friedlander, Coplan & Aronoff LLP, Indianapolis
317 632 3232
jschwarz@beneschlaw.com
*Featured in Real Estate (Indiana)*
**Practice Areas:** Real Estate. Represents real estate developers in the acquisition, development, financing, leasing and sale of real estate.

**Career:** Partner with the firm's real estate and environmental Practice Group.
**Personal:** Indiana University School of Law (JD, summa cum laude, 1980); Indiana University, Bloomington (BS, highest distinction, 1977).

## SOLADA, Mary E
Bingham Greenebaum Doll LLP, Indianapolis
317 968 5412
msolada@bgdlegal.com
*Featured in Real Estate (Indiana)*
**Practice Areas:** Experienced in all aspects of real estate development, zoning and planning law, as well as government services. Has worked on behalf of developers of renewable energy projects, assisting with land use approvals and economic incentives for wind energy projects. Experienced in representing developers of office, industrial and retail projects, including work with redevelopment authorities. Serves as Indianapolis Managing Partner and Real Estate Practice Group Chair.
**Professional Memberships:** American, Indiana, Indianapolis, Florida Bar Associations.
**Career:** Land Planner, City of Indianapolis (1979-81).
**Personal:** Indiana University (BS, 1978; JD, 1982); Named Indianapolis Business Journal Who's Who in Real Estate.

## STRAIN, James A
Taft Stettinius & Hollister LLP, Indianapolis
317 713 3460
jstrain@taftlaw.com
*Featured in Corporate/M&A (Indiana)*
**Practice Areas:** Corporate Governance, Public Offerings, Government Contracts Law, Business & Finance, Public Company, Securities - Corporate
**Professional Memberships:** American, Indiana State, Indianapolis and Seventh Circuit Bar Associations.
**Career:** Mr Strain is Co-Chair of the Business & Finance Group. He practices in the areas of securities law, mergers and acquisitions and corporate governance. He was one of the architects of the Indiana Business Corporation Law and successfully defended its Control Shares Acquisition Chapter before the United States Supreme Court in CTS Corporation v Dynamics Corporation of America.
**Personal:** Indiana University Maurer School of Law - Bloomington (1969); Indiana University (1966).

## SWHIER, Claudia V
Barnes & Thornburg LLP, Indianapolis
317 231 7231
claudia.swhier@BTLaw.com
*Featured in Corporate/M&A (Indiana)*
**Practice Areas:** Banks and banking; securities; mergers and acquisitions; corporate finance; serves publicly traded and private banks, thrifts, and credit unions; provides the full spectrum of legal services in the bank and securities regulatory compliance area; handles public offerings, holding company formations, financings and stock conversions of mutual thrifts for client financial institutions; represents financial institutions with respect to regulatory enforcement agreements.

**Professional Memberships:** Indiana State and Indianapolis Bar Associations.
**Career:** Admitted to practice in the state of Indiana.
**Personal:** Yale University (BA, 1972); Harvard University (JD, cum laude, 1975); Member of Harvard Law Review from 1973-75.

## TERRELL, Michael
Taft Stettinius & Hollister LLP, Indianapolis
317 713 3590
mterrell@taftlaw.com
*Featured in Labor & Employment (Indiana)*
**Practice Areas:** Litigation, College & University Law, Labor and Employment.
**Career:** Mr Terrell is Chief employment counsel for numerous international and domestic companies engaged in various industries, including manufacturing, real estate, banking, construction, entertainment and high tech. He concentrates his practice in all aspects of labor and employment law, with a particular emphasis on prevention and defense of employment litigation. He also counsels clients on personnel issues and provides clients with in-house training on an array of employment matters.
**Personal:** Indiana University - Robert H McKinney School of Law (1984); Indiana University (1981).

## TITTLE, David O
Bingham Greenebaum Doll LLP, Indianapolis
317 968 5418
dtittle@bgdlegal.com
*Featured in Litigation (Indiana)*
**Practice Areas:** Provides representation in commercial litigation, business disputes, financial institutions, product liability, toxic tort, class actions and professional (legal) liability in federal and state courts.
**Professional Memberships:** American College of Trial Lawyers (State Chair, 2010-12); Indiana Defense Trial Counsel, Past President; International Association of Defense Counsel; Fifth, Seventh, Federal Circuit Bar Associations.
**Career:** Voted among the top 10 attorneys in Indiana (2009) and recognized by The Best Lawyers in America® (2010-13).
**Personal:** Indiana University (BS), Indiana University Maurer School of Law (JD, cum laude); Docent, Eiteljorg Museum of Native American Art; Indiana Supreme Court Character & Fitness Committee.

## TURNER, Wayne C
Bingham Greenebaum Doll LLP, Indianapolis
317 968 5526
wturner@bgdlegal.com
*Featured in Litigation (Indiana)*
**Practice Areas:** Represents businesses in federal and state trials and appeals, in securities and corporate governance disputes; breaches of fiduciary duties; defense of class actions involving securities, ERISA and commercial fraud claims; defense of accountants, lawyers and securities broker-dealers; utility regulation litigation; restraint of trade and

antitrust litigation; contract and business tort disputes.
**Professional Memberships:** American, Indiana, Indianapolis, and Seventh Circuit Bar Associations; Indianapolis Law Club.
**Career:** McTurnan & Turner, 1989-2007.
**Personal:** Purdue University (BS, with highest distinction, 1982; GA Ross Outstanding Graduate); Indiana University (JD, magna cum laude, 1985).

## WARSHAUER, David R
Barnes & Thornburg LLP, Indianapolis
317 231 7346
david.warshauer@BTlaw.com
*Featured in Real Estate (Indiana)*
**Practice Areas:** Real estate; zoning; planning and land use; represents a broad range of clients in connection with real estate development, acquisition, and leasing; has worked on real estate issues for some of Indiana's largest projects, including the Subaru-Isuzu automotive facility in Lafayette, Indiana; the Toyota plant in Princeton, Indiana; the steel plant in Hendricks County, Indiana; projects for several universities; and the Village of West Clay, a mixed-use project in suburban Indianapolis.
**Professional Memberships:** American College of Real Estate Lawyers.
**Personal:** Washington University (BA, 1980); Indiana University (JD, magna cum laude, 1984).

## WELCH, Brian
Bingham Greenebaum Doll LLP, Indianapolis
317 686 5208
bwelch@bgdlegal.com
*Featured in Litigation (Indiana)*
**Practice Areas:** Represents business and government clients in complex business litigation and regulatory matters. Also represents professional service providers and post-secondary schools. Has represented both plaintiffs and defendants in complex class action matters.
**Professional Memberships:** Indianapolis, Indiana State and Seventh Circuit Bar Associations; Indianapolis Law Club.
**Career:** Named among Best Lawyers in America, Commercial Litigation.
**Personal:** DePauw University (BA, 1973); Indiana University Robert H. McKinney School of Law (JD, cum laude, 1978); WFYI Foundation, Inc. (Board Member, 1996-present); 2012 Indianapolis Super Bowl Host Committee; Distinguished Fellow, Indianapolis Bar Foundation.

## WHITE, Keith E
Barnes & Thornburg LLP, Fort Wayne
260 425 4770
keith.white@btlaw.com
*Featured in Labor & Employment (Indiana)*
**Practice Areas:** Management labor law; union avoidance; facility/plant closure, WARN, and reductions in force; contract administration and arbitration; management/supervisor training; employment law; employment litigation; non-competition agreements; alternative dispute resolution proceedings.

**Professional Memberships:** American Bar Association, and its Committee on Alternative Dispute Resolution in Labor and Employment Law.
**Career:** US Court of Appeals for the Seventh Circuit, and the Federal District Courts for the Northern and Southern Districts of Indiana.
**Publications:** Chapter Editor, 'How Arbitration Works', Elkouri and Elkouri, (BNA Books, 6th Ed., and 2008 Supp., 2008).
**Personal:** Hanover College (BA, 1980), and Indiana University School of Law-Bloomington (JD, 1983).

## WILSON, Heather L
Frost Brown Todd LLC, Indianapolis
317 237 3805
hwilson@fbtlaw.com
*Featured in Labor & Employment (Indiana)*
**Practice Areas:** Concentrates in employment litigation, representing employers in federal and state courts and before the Seventh Circuit Court of Appeals. Provides employment counseling and training and drafts handbooks, personnel policies and contracts.
**Professional Memberships:** Member of the American, Seventh Circuit, Indiana, and Indianapolis Bar Associations.
**Career:** Became a member of the Firm in 2006. Serves on the firm's Executive Committee. Chairs the Training and Development Committee.
**Publications:** Authored numerous publications on topics such as workplace harassment, interviewing, discipline, hiring, retaliation, social networking, and diversity.
**Personal:** Born in 1969 in Bristol, Tennessee. Attended Indiana University and the Mauer School of Law in Bloomington, Indiana. Enjoys running, reading, and Indiana basketball.

## YERKES, Kenneth J
Barnes & Thornburg LLP, Indianapolis
317 231 7513
ken.yerkes@btlaw.com
*Featured in Labor & Employment (Indiana)*
**Practice Areas:** Management labor law; collective bargaining; arbitration; union avoidance; union elections; employment law; employment litigation; wrongful termination defense; discrimination defense; non-competition agreements; supervisor training.
**Professional Memberships:** Indiana State Bar Association, College of Labor & Employment Lawyers.
**Career:** Admitted to practice in Indiana, Tennessee, Pennsylvania ; US Supreme Court; US Courts of Appeals for the Sixth, Seventh, Eighth, Eleventh, D.C. Circuits and multiple district courts.
**Publications:** The Indiana Guide to Hiring & Firing; Guide to Labor Relations: How to Deal Effectively with Unions in the Workplace.
**Personal:** Earlham College (BA, 1980); Indiana University School of Law (JD, 1983).

# BINGHAM GREENEBAUM DOLL LLP

**www.**bgdlegal.com

**Co-Chairmen:** W Tobin McClamroch, Phillip D Scott
Managing Partners: 4
Number of partners: 140  Number of other attorneys: 85

**Firm Overview:**
Bingham Greenebaum Doll LLP is a regional law firm providing progressive business, litigation and government services to clients ranging from Fortune 500 businesses and Global 1000 companies to small, regionally based organizations across a variety of industries and sectors. The firm is both locally accessible and nationally connected with offices in Indiana, Kentucky and Ohio. In addition to its regional presence, Bingham Greenebaum Doll LLP provides international representation to a multitude of clients and is a member of TerraLex®, an association of independent law firms in nearly 100 countries, providing the firm and its clients with quick access to advice on the laws of foreign jurisdictions.

**Main Areas of Practice:**

**Corporate & Transactional:**
Bingham Greenebaum Doll serves clients in a variety of industries, from domestic start-up companies to multinational corporations located throughout the United States and abroad. Its attorneys are experienced in business planning, negotiating and drafting contracts, preparing public filings, advising clients on intellectual property issues, and working with federal and state regulators. Group members counsel companies in the structuring, negotiating and documentation of mergers, acquisitions, joint ventures, financing and other business transactions.

**Estate Planning:**
The Estate Planning Practice Group's attorneys provide integrated services in estate planning, estate and trust administration, fiduciary representation, tax return preparation, disability planning, family and charitable gifting arrangements, marital agreements, guardianships and adoptions, limited partnerships, business succession planning, drafting and representing qualified and non-qualified employee benefit plans, and the representation of healthcare providers and health insurers.

**Environmental & Natural Resources:**
Bingham Greenebaum Doll's attorneys are experienced in advising businesses, utilities and governments on complex air, water, and waste  permitting and compliance issues, enforcement defense, criminal defense, regulatory and legislative policy development, remediation and environmental due diligence. The group is well known for its representation of the energy industry, including coal mining, environmental, mineral law and transaction matters.

**Labor & Employment:**
The firm's labor and employment attorneys defend employers against all employee claims, including discrimination, harassment, retaliation, wrongful termination, ERISA and employee benefits; wage and hour; OSHA; immigration status; employment contract disputes and covenants not to compete. The group's attorneys also advise employers in union-management relations, responding to union organizing campaigns, collective bargaining, grievance arbitration, severance packages and employment contract negotiations. The group also has a concentration in the representation of highly compensated C-Suite executives with both their entry into and exit from a corporate position.

**Litigation:**
Bingham Greenebaum Doll's attorneys are experienced in all aspects of trial and appellate work in federal and state courts and have substantial experience in alternative dispute resolution matters. The group has extensive experience in corporate governance disputes, intellectual property disputes, securities litigation, white-collar criminal defense, appeals, e-discovery, litigation-avoidance techniques, utility and other regulatory disputes, construction and real estate litigation, business torts, product liability defense, class actions, environmental and toxic tort defense, and First Amendment issues.

**Tax & Finance:**
The firm's skilled, seasoned and connected tax and finance attorneys include individuals who serve on ABI, IRS and American Bar Association advisory groups, have advanced law degrees in taxation and publish on a variety of topics. Their credentials and dedication permit in-depth service to the firm's clients in areas including bankruptcy and workout, commercial and public finance, federal tax, international tax, non-profit and tax exempt organizations, and state and local tax.

**Government:**
Bingham Greenebaum Doll's services include procurements, general regulatory issues, rule-making, economic development, public finance, lobbying, ordinance drafting and review, regulatory enforcement, licensing, permitting and municipal/private utility matters. The firm's attorneys also advise clients on ethics, election laws, acquisition and disposal of property, public contracts, public construction, privatization, public meetings and records laws and annexation. In addition to its representation of private sector clients who interact with various levels of government, the group also serves as special counsel to various state and local government entities.

**Real Estate:**
The firm's real estate attorneys represent real estate developers, buyers and sellers, government entities, utilities and lending institutions, with particular expertise in renewable energy projects, land use matters, tax appeals, construction issues, economic incentives, office, industrial and shopping center leasing, financial restructuring and distressed markets.

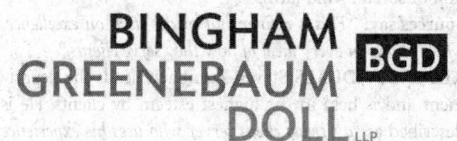

## How lawyers are ranked

Every year we carry out thousands of in-depth interviews with clients in order to assess the reputations and expertise of business lawyers worldwide. The qualities we look for (and which determine rankings) include technical legal ability, professional conduct, client service, commercial awareness/astuteness, diligence, commitment, and other qualities most valued by the client. For details of our research team, see p.5.

## CORPORATE/M&A

Banking & Finance p.1283

Commentary about individuals can be found under their firm's paragraph. If the firm has no paragraph (is not ranked) look at Other Notable Practitioners.

### Corporate/M&A
### Leading Firms

**Band 1**
Belin McCormick PC
Davis, Brown, Koehn, Shors & Roberts, PC
Nyemaster, Goode, West, Hansell & O'Brien

**Band 2**
Bradley & Riley PC
Brown, Winick, Graves, Gross, Baskerville and Schoenebaum
Dickinson, Mackaman, Tyler & Hagen, PC
Lane & Waterman LLP
Shuttleworth & Ingersoll PLC

**Band 3**
Ahlers & Cooney PC
Faegre Baker Daniels
Simmons Perrine Moyer Bergman PLC

*\* Indicates firm with profile.
Alphabetical order within each band. Band 1 is the highest.*

## Band 1

### Belin McCormick PC

**THE FIRM** This Des Moines firm earns wide praise from clients across a range of industries, with particular note given to the diverse range of services offered. The corporate department benefits from the interdisciplinary strengths of its lawyers, which include six CPAs as well as experts in taxation and economics. The firm's recent work covers acquisitions and sales for a range of top companies in Iowa and the Midwest, as well as nationwide. One particular area of growth for the firm is wind energy, where the team represented MidAmerican Energy in its acquisition of several wind farms.

**Sources say:** *"This is a firm that prides itself on excellence, which shows in every facet of how they serve clients."*

**KEY INDIVIDUALS Steven Zumbach** heads the department and is held in the highest esteem by clients. He is described as *"a tireless client server who uses his experience in mergers and acquisitions to effectively guide clients through the multitude of decisions associated with selling a business"* and *"an extremely bright and capable individual."* **Quentin Boyken** is held in high regard by commentators, one of whom said: *"Despite his calm demeanor with clients, Quent is a shrewd negotiator with the opposing attorneys and does a great job of framing important issues during negotiations."* Boyken recently represented Consumer Safety Technology in its acquisition by a California-based venture capital firm. **Garth Adams** acted as lead attorney on Edge Business Continuity Center LLC's sophisticated real estate purchase of a computer data center facility. **Robert Mullen** focuses on counseling banking and finance institutions on a range of transactions, applying his insight into state and federal regulatory bodies. He is described by one client as *"the premier banking attorney in the state of Iowa."* **Thomas Flynn** is a prominent banking and finance attorney, with other areas of expertise including bankruptcy and tax disputes. The *"extremely intelligent and dutiful"* **Wayne Reames** handles structuring and tax issues on a range of transactions. Clients say he is *"very thorough and thoughtful regarding all services provided and how all aspects of our work relate to each other."* **Christian Nelson** focuses on corporate acquisitions for closely held companies. He was recently involved in the representation of LMC Insurance & Risk Management in its acquisition of two insurance agencies in Dubuque. He is described as *"very personable and dedicated."*

### Davis, Brown, Koehn, Shors & Roberts, PC

**THE FIRM** This firm's strong corporate practice engages in the full range of corporate services, including restructuring, finance, bankruptcy and intellectual property across the agriculture, telecom and construction industries, among others. The firm is particularly involved in work with startup business and developing markets, especially renewable energy. Clients include MidAmerican Renewables and Weitz Company.

**Sources say:** *"An organization of talented lawyers who enjoy practicing together, which expands their collective worth to me."*

**KEY INDIVIDUALS** Department head **Frank Carroll** leads on several of the firm's most high-profile deals. His diverse practice includes business organizations and transactions, M&A and tax, and he is appreciated by clients for his extensive experience and business knowledge. He is described as *"a prodigious M&A talent and worker."* The financial institutions department is chaired by senior shareholder **Robert Gamble**, who is known by banking clients to be *"very experienced and an expert in our industry, and readily accessible."* **Beverly Evans** works in corporate organization, M&A and securities law, and has a particular focus on working with startup enterprises and public limited companies. Clients are impressed by **Jason Stone's** *"timely response and turnarounds to meet tight deadlines,"* and by his *"very strong general business knowledge with an ability to state options and associated risk with each."* He is a versatile corporate lawyer, handling all aspects of corporate transactions and administration. *"Proactive, engaging, articulate communicator"* **Susan Freed** practices in healthcare and employee benefits, representing a range of healthcare providers and employers in regulatory, transactional and litigation matters.

### Nyemaster, Goode, West, Hansell & O'Brien

**THE FIRM** This established firm has significant prestige in the market and enjoys long working relationships with several major companies and financial institutions in Iowa and nationwide. The firm is deeply involved in significant finance and M&A transactions, particularly in real estate and agriculture. In addition to these areas, it has growing strength in emerging sectors in Iowa, including renewables, biofuels and intellectual property.

**Sources say:** *"We are very pleased with their work and impressed with their knowledge and abilities."*

**KEY INDIVIDUALS Rod Kubat** is a general corporate law practitioner who has also worked on a range of financial

## Corporate/M&A
### Senior Statesmen

**Senior Statesmen: distinguished older practitioners**

| | |
|---|---|
| Cortesio John | Bradshaw, Fowler, Proctor (ONP)[†] |
| Hansell Edgar | Nyemaster, Goode, West, Hansell & O'Brien |
| Riley Byron | Bradley & Riley PC |

### Leading Individuals

**Star individuals**

| | |
|---|---|
| Zumbach Steven E | Belin McCormick PC |

**Band 1**

| | |
|---|---|
| Adams Garth | Belin McCormick PC |
| Carroll Frank | Davis, Brown, Koehn, Shors & Roberts, PC |
| Gross Doug | Brown, Winick, Graves, Gross, Baskerville |
| Neumann G R | Nyemaster, Goode, West, Hansell & O'Brien |
| Streit Gary J | Shuttleworth & Ingersoll PLC |
| Waterman III Dana | Lane & Waterman LLP |

**Band 2**

| | |
|---|---|
| Berenstein Marvin | Berenstein, Moore, Heffernan (ONP)[†] |
| Blaser Michael R | Brown, Winick, Graves, Gross, Baskerville |
| Boyken Quentin | Belin McCormick PC |
| Brown William | Brown, Winick, Graves, Gross, Baskerville * |
| Dickinson Mark | Nyemaster, Goode, West, Hansell & O'Brien |

**Band 3**

| | |
|---|---|
| Bergstrom Brian D | Shuttleworth & Ingersoll PLC |
| Boyd III Willard L | Nyemaster, Goode, West, Hansell & O'Brien |
| Evans Beverly | Davis, Brown, Koehn, Shors & Roberts, PC |
| Hart Bradley | Bradley & Riley PC |
| Kubat Rod | Nyemaster, Goode, West, Hansell & O'Brien |
| Malm Richard | Dickinson, Mackaman, Tyler & Hagen, PC |
| McCartan William | Bradley & Riley PC |
| Nelson S Christian | Belin McCormick PC |
| Reames Wayne E | Belin McCormick PC |
| Sackett Christopher R | Brown, Winick, Graves, Gross, Baskerville * |
| Scholer Randal J | Simmons Perrine Moyer Bergman PLC |
| Stone Jason M | Davis, Brown, Koehn, Shors & Roberts, PC |
| Van Vooren Scott | Lane & Waterman LLP |
| Ward J Marc | Dickinson, Mackaman, Tyler & Hagen, PC |
| Wilcox Gregory B | Nyemaster, Goode, West, Hansell & O'Brien |

**Band 4**

| | |
|---|---|
| Anderson Andrew | Faegre Baker Daniels |
| Carroll Jr Edmund H | Lane & Waterman LLP |
| Giebelstein Terry M | Lane & Waterman LLP |
| Hintze John | Ahlers & Cooney PC |
| Roy Steven J | Nyemaster, Goode, West, Hansell & O'Brien |
| Slaughter Thomas L | Faegre Baker Daniels |

**Up-and-coming individuals**

| | |
|---|---|
| Freed Susan | Davis, Brown, Koehn, Shors & Roberts, PC |

**Associates to watch**

| | |
|---|---|
| Hertzke Adam | Faegre Baker Daniels |

* Indicates individual with profile.
[†] ONP = Other Notable Practitioner.

## Corporate/M&A: Banking & Finance
### Leading Individuals

**Star individuals**

| | |
|---|---|
| Hagen Howard O | Dickinson, Mackaman, Tyler & Hagen, PC |

**Band 1**

| | |
|---|---|
| Gamble Robert A | Davis, Brown, Koehn, Shors & Roberts, PC |
| Mullen Robert A | Belin McCormick PC |

**Band 2**

| | |
|---|---|
| Burke Thomas H | Whitfield & Eddy, PLC (ONP)[†] |
| Flynn Thomas L | Belin McCormick PC |
| Kubat Rod | Nyemaster, Goode, West, Hansell & O'Brien |
| Page Gregory P | Nyemaster, Goode, West, Hansell & O'Brien |

tion. **Mark Dickinson** practices across a broad range of corporate and transactional law, handling securities, M&A, insurance regulatory matters and franchising for clients of all sizes. He has been a frequent speaker on corporate, franchising and securities law topics. **Gregory Page** is praised by clients as being "very detail-oriented and tenacious. He will fight hard for you to get the client's point across. He's been very personable and understanding to work with." He focuses on regulatory matters for financial institutions, as well as a range of commercial and financial transactions. "Good, solid lawyer" **Gregory Wilcox** handles business transactions for a range of Fortune 500 clients, and is also often requested as counsel for strategic legal and business issues. He is appreciated by clients for his "extremely helpful attitude and well-rounded knowledge of many different areas." **Willard Boyd** works on a range of corporate, commercial and regulatory matters across several industries, and is well regarded by clients, who say "he is personable and professional, and has a sterling reputation. He does an outstanding job of organizing and directing the significant resources of the firm for the benefit of clients." Tax specialist **Steven Roy** focuses on the taxation of NPOs, LLCs and corporate reorganizations. "Steve can quote anything you like in federal tax. He's as good a tax attorney as you'll ever find, in Iowa or nationwide," say sources. **Edgar Hansell** is deeply experienced in a range of corporate fields. He is highly praised by clients for his broad and deep legal expertise, and is known as an expert on the Universal Commercial Code.

### Band 2

### Bradley & Riley PC

**THE FIRM** The 16-strong corporate team at Bradley & Riley's Cedar Rapids practice acts on a diverse range of business matters, handling work in Iowa and interstate transactions. The firm has recently handled a number of high-profile acquisitions, particularly in the manufacturing sector, in which it notably represented a holding company in a $25 million stock acquisition involving a computer hardware and software company. Other clients include United Fire & Casualty Company, Iowa First Capital Fund and Genova Technologies.

**KEY INDIVIDUALS Bradley Hart** heads the transactional team and is highlighted by clients for his practical

approach. One source said: "He is thorough and logical. He thinks through and analyzes all the alternatives, and then will clearly explain this thinking to me. He is fair and looks for the best solution for us." **William McCartan** practices in corporate and business law, securities and broker-dealer arbitration. He recently served as lead counsel to Connectronics in the $7 million sale of its electronics distribution business to a Chicago-based private equity group. **Byron Riley** is a cofounder of the firm and a respected figure in the Cedar Rapids legal community.

### Brown, Winick, Graves, Gross, Baskerville and Schoenebaum PLC

**THE FIRM** This team offers a diverse range of services to clients, including M&A, sales, financing, debtor/creditor work and bankruptcy. The firm has handled a heavy volume of work in agriculture, biofuels and renewable energy of late, with highlights including advising Amaizing Energy on its $80 million sale to The Andersons.

**Sources say:** "I believe it is one of the best firms in the state. They are able to handle matters in all areas of law."

**KEY INDIVIDUALS Doug Gross** is known among peers for his government and politics-related work. His practice chiefly concerns M&A, agriculture and regulatory compliance. He was recently involved in the $18 million sale of two subsidiaries on behalf of Tetra Agrigroup. The firm's agricultural business group is led by **Michael Blaser**. He is well appreciated by clients, one of whom said: "He effectively understands our business inside and out. He understands the important legal issues and doesn't get bogged down with insignificant details that do not pose a legal risk." Tax specialist **William Brown** (see p.1291) has deep experience in the field and focuses on a range of corporate services, including business planning, banking and securities. He is particularly noted for his expertise in S Corp taxation. Managing partner **Christopher Sackett** (see p.1291) counsels clients on a range of legal matters, including corporate planning and environmental law. "He's become a partner in our business. I have a tremendous amount of respect for him," said one client.

### Dickinson, Mackaman, Tyler & Hagen, PC

**THE FIRM** This well-regarded firm handles a large volume of transactions and other corporate services, including restructuring and demutualization. It is best known for its formidable banking practice, which recently acted for the Iowa Capital Investments Board on a $57 million financial restructuring. Major banking clients include Wells Fargo and NorthStar Bank.

**Sources say:** "We are very satisfied. They have experts in every facet of law."

**KEY INDIVIDUALS** Head of banking **Howard Hagen** is recognized as a premier banking lawyer with extensive knowledge of banking regulatory matters. He has led on a number of significant matters, including Iowa Capital Investment Board's restructuring of state obligations. Clients say that he "seems to have a sixth sense." **Marc Ward** heads the business and corporate group, and handles a wide range of corporate matters. He recently represented Farmers Trust & Savings Bank in an acquisition involving

transactions in a variety of industry areas. He earns particular praise from commentators for his extensive knowledge and client-oriented approach. **G R Neumann** is a well-regarded business lawyer practicing on a range of matters. In the past year he has worked on state and local government development incentives and property acquisi-

the purchase of an insurance company. **Richard Malm** *"gives very common-sense, authoritative advice,"* according to clients. He is best known for his work with large financial institutions on a range of acquisitions and regulatory matters.

### Lane & Waterman LLP

**THE FIRM** This longstanding Davenport firm continues to be a leading player in eastern Iowa and regularly serves clients in the Quad Cities area and beyond. The team is active across a wide range of industries, including agriculture, publishing and manufacturing. Recent highlights include representing Lee Enterprises in a $1 billion refinancing; other key clients include Woodward Communications and Genesis Health System.
**Sources say:** *"These guys do this stuff in their sleep. They're so good."*
**KEY INDIVIDUALS** The corporate, M&A and securities group is headed by **Dana Waterman**, who is greatly appreciated among clients, who say: *"Dana has an incredible gift for interpreting complex issues. He asks challenging questions, is forward thinking, and pays attention to the smallest details."* He was the lead partner on Lee Enterprises' refinancing. **Edmund Carroll** is praised by clients as *"responsive and available, very engaging, and very easy to develop a rapport with."* He has recently been involved in high-value sales transactions. **Scott Van Vooren** advises on corporate and M&A law, as well as tax and estates, and is described by one client as *"exceptional – we have worked with him for many years now, and have never once been disappointed for timeliness or quality of work. Just outstanding."* **Terry Giebelstein** works in a wide range of legal areas, including corporate, commercial and regulatory law, as well as litigation. *"The amount of data he gathered and boiled down to the important parts was phenomenal,"* said one client.

### Shuttleworth & Ingersoll PLC

**THE FIRM** Shuttleworth & Ingersoll maintains its reputation as one of the top firms for corporate and business work in the Cedar Rapids area. It represents business clients in the full range of transactions. Peers note that the firm is a significant competitor in the legal marketplace and are quick to single out the team as a top choice for referrals.
**KEY INDIVIDUALS** Firm president **Gary Streit** is well respected among peers and provides services in general business law, including estate planning, tax and employee benefits. Firm vice president **Brian Bergstrom** is chair of the M&A and equity finance group. He regularly handles equity finance, business planning, sales and acquisitions, and is known in the market as *"a talented lawyer."*

## Band 3

### Ahlers & Cooney PC

**THE FIRM** Ahlers & Cooney offers a broad range of services in the corporate/M&A field, and is especially well known among market sources for its robust finance work, including public finance and commercial bonds. The firm's client base includes several major banks, financial institutions, public bodies and NGOs.
**KEY INDIVIDUALS** The corporate, business and tax department is chaired by **John Hintze**, who provides advice and counsel to clients on a range of corporate, commercial and tax issues.

### Faegre Baker Daniels

**THE FIRM** The Des Moines office of this globally reaching firm makes use of its wider network to coordinate the interests of several nationwide clients in Iowa. The team is active across a range of industries and acts for high-profile clients including Wells Fargo, Cargill and Aviva. Recent work highlights include representing Archer Daniels Midland in an $80 million bond financing.

**KEY INDIVIDUALS** The highly experienced **Andrew Anderson** works with a range of corporate clients on the expansion of their business in Iowa. Sources praise his commitment to client service. **Thomas Slaughter** is regarded by market observers as an outstanding business attorney. He has a wealth of experience and counsels on a wide range of transactions and corporate law issues. Corporate associate **Adam Hertzke** counsels public and private clients on a range of corporate law, with a particular emphasis on the food agriculture industry.

### Simmons Perrine Moyer Bergman PLC

**THE FIRM** This Cedar Rapids-based firm has acted on corporate transactions through all stages, as well as serving as corporate counsel. The team has recently handled a number of significant restructurings in Iowa. Key clients include West Side Transport, Modern Piping and Kelly Demolition.
**KEY INDIVIDUALS** Department head **Randal Scholer** handles a wide range of M&A and restructurings. He is warmly received by clients for his diligence and helpful attitude, with one saying: *"Without his counsel none of our successes would have been possible."*

### Other Notable Practitioners

**Marvin Berenstein** of Berenstein, Moore, Heffernan, Moeller & Johnson, L.L.P. in Sioux City has a reputation as a highly regarded corporate and estate lawyer, and *"a dominant lawyer in that community."* **Thomas Burke** of Whitfield & Eddy, PLC represents clients in a wide range of matters, including real estate, litigation and transactional work. He is particularly known for his banking practice, especially as related to real estate foreclosures and workouts. Senior statesman **John Cortesio** is of counsel to Bradshaw, Fowler, Proctor & Fairgrave, PC, and is recognized for his wealth of experience in transactions and disputes.

# LABOR & EMPLOYMENT

Commentary about individuals can be found under their firm's paragraph.  If the firm has no paragraph (is not ranked) look at Other Notable Practitioners.

## Band 1

### Ahlers & Cooney PC

**THE FIRM** Ahlers & Cooney is widely regarded as one of the top employment firms in the state, and is especially highlighted for its work with public sector organizations, particularly academic institutions including school districts and higher education establishments. In addition, the firm has worked on a range of employment disputes in the private sector in FMLA-related lawsuits.
**Sources say:** *"Anyone we've worked with at Ahlers & Cooney has been professional and brilliant and easy to work with."*
**KEY INDIVIDUALS** **Elizabeth Gregg Kennedy** earns unanimous praise from peers in the employment field,

who name her as one of the top lawyers in the practice. One client adds: *"Liz Kennedy is, without exception, the best outside counsel I have ever worked with."* **James Hanks** leads the K-12 education practice, providing representation and counsel to school districts. He is also noted for his expertise in labor law, including the negotiation of union contracts. Clients say he is *"excellent in manner and attitude."* **Nathan Overberg** chairs the employment and labor group, and represents clients in a diverse range of employment litigation at state and federal level. He is known by peers for his employment work in the education sector. **Andrew Bracken** focuses on education-based employment matters, in both counsel and litigation. He is described by clients as *"very easy to work with"* and *"a clear communicator."*

**Amanda Wachuta** debuts in the rankings this year. One client says: *"I've always found her to be very pleasant, very efficient and knowledgeable."*

### Dickinson, Mackaman, Tyler & Hagen, PC

**THE FIRM** This firm's employment and labor law practice is well regarded for its depth of expertise and high levels of client service. The team handles a diverse range of employment matters, including labor relations, litigation and compliance counseling. It recently represented Git N Go in collective action lawsuits relating to compensation under the FLSA. Other key clients include Merit Resources, Veridian Credit Union and Ankeny Community School District.

| Labor & Employment |
|---|
| **Leading Firms** |

| **Band 1** |
|---|
| Ahlers & Cooney PC |
| Dickinson, Mackamann, Tyler & Hagen, PC |
| Nyemaster, Goode, West, Hansell & O'Brien |

| **Band 2** |
|---|
| Belin McCormick PC |
| Bradley & Riley PC |
| Davis, Brown, Koehn, Shors & Roberts, PC |
| Simmons Perrine Moyer Bergman PLC |

| **Band 3** |
|---|
| Brown, Winick, Graves, Gross, Baskerville and Schoenebaum |
| Faegre Baker Daniels |
| Lane & Waterman LLP |
| Shuttleworth & Ingersoll PLC |
| Whitfield & Eddy, PLC |

**Sources say:** *"It has a whole bench full of personable players who are knowledgeable, courteous, dependable, prompt, able to articulate with their clients and dedicated to seeing the job completed."*

**KEY INDIVIDUALS** Practice chair **Russell Samson** draws acclaim as an authority on labor matters, with a practice covering union representation, unfair labor practices, negotiating contracts and union grievances. He recently defended Anderson Erickson Dairy in a suit alleging racial discrimination. **Bridget Penick** practices in all areas of employment litigation, at both the state and federal level. One client noted: *"She makes me think that I am her only customer."* **Ann Holden Kendell** is described by clients as *"smart, resourceful, and always professional."* She practices in all areas of employment law, providing services including dispute resolution and counseling on regulatory compliance, preventive counseling and HR matters. **Jill Jensen-Welch** is praised for her *"solid, uncompromised judgment and decision making,"* and for her ability to relate to and work with clients in various roles. She works with a diverse range of clients on employment law and civil litigation. **Jeffrey Krausman** represents public and private sector bodies in a range of employment matters, including advocacy in grievance disputes. He has recently represented Ankeny Community School District in negotiations with teacher and support staff unions.

### Nyemaster, Goode, West, Hansell & O'Brien

**THE FIRM** This firm continues to be recognized as a leading provider of services in labor and employment law. It is praised by market commentators for its wide range of services and depth of expertise. The team has a bench of well-regarded practitioners who are deeply experienced in representing clients in state and federal courts both in Iowa and out of state. Recent work has included representing employers in contentious matters relating to FLSA compliance, wrongful termination and wage and hour issues.
**Sources say:** *"We have been working with Nyemaster for years and couldn't be more pleased with their guidance, support and direction with our labor law issues."*

| Labor & Employment |
|---|
| **Leading Individuals** |

| **Band 1** | |
|---|---|
| Baier Kelly | Bradley & Riley PC |
| Harty Frank | Nyemaster, Goode, West, Hansell & O'Brien |
| Kennedy Elizabeth Gregg | Ahlers & Cooney PC |
| Muchmore Iris | Simmons Perrine Moyer Bergman PLC |
| Reck Michael | Belin McCormick PC |
| Samson Russell | Dickinson, Mackaman, Tyler & Hagen, PC |
| Swanger James R | Belin McCormick PC |
| Zaiger Mark L | Shuttleworth & Ingersoll PLC |

| **Band 2** | |
|---|---|
| Armentrout Randall | Nyemaster, Goode, West, Hansell & O'Brien |
| Cunningham Thomas | Nyemaster, Goode, West, Hansell & O'Brien |
| Funk Mary E | Nyemaster, Goode, West, Hansell & O'Brien |
| Gilliam James H | Brown, Winick, Graves, Gross, Baskerville * |
| Giudicessi Michael A | Faegre Baker Daniels |
| Hanks James | Ahlers & Cooney PC |
| Harrison Gayla R | Harrison, Moreland & Webber PC (ONP)† |
| Jensen-Welch Jill R | Dickinson, Mackaman, Tyler & Hagen, PC |
| La Suer Gene | Davis, Brown, Koehn, Shors & Roberts, PC |
| Malheiro Sharon | Davis, Brown, Koehn, Shors & Roberts, PC |
| Naylor Greg A | Whitfield & Eddy PLC |
| Penick Bridget R | Dickinson, Mackaman, Tyler & Hagen, PC |
| Samuelson Jaki | Whitfield & Eddy, PLC |
| Tharnish Deborah | Davis, Brown, Koehn, Shors & Roberts, PC |
| Visser Kevin | Simmons Perrine Moyer Bergman PLC |

| **Band 3** | |
|---|---|
| Bracken Andrew J | Ahlers & Cooney PC |
| Cain Hugh | Hopkins & Huebner, P.C. (ONP)† |
| Herrmann Judith | Lane & Waterman LLP |
| Kendell Ann Holden | Dickinson, Mackaman, Tyler & Hagen, PC |
| Knutson Becky S | Davis, Brown, Koehn, Shors & Roberts, PC |
| Krausman Jeffrey A | Dickinson, Mackaman, Tyler & Hagen, PC |
| Overberg Nathan | Ahlers & Cooney PC |
| Shoff Patricia | Belin McCormick PC |
| Wood Nancy | Bradley & Riley PC |

| **Up-and-coming individuals** | |
|---|---|
| Knowles Kelsey J | Belin McCormick PC |
| Schiltz Mikkie | Lane & Waterman LLP |
| Wachuta Amanda G | Ahlers & Cooney PC |

**KEY INDIVIDUALS** Head of department **Frank Harty** is a widely respected *"standout figure"* in labor and employment law. He has impressive trial experience, handling a diverse array of cases including discrimination, ERISA and wrongful discrimination. **Randall Armentrout** is described by clients as *"a good communicator and negotiator,"* and *"creative and open minded."* He has particular expertise in harassment and discrimination claims. **Thomas Cunningham** represents businesses in a range of employment disputes, including wage and hour disputes, OSHA matters and trade secrets and noncompete clauses. **Mary Funk** deals with a variety of employment and labor matters, including litigation, counseling and arbitration, and is recognized among peers as a talented practitioner. According to clients, *"she is always on time and her delivery of legal services is without flaw."* **Neal Westin** practices in business and immigration law. He focuses on temporary

| Labor & Employment: Immigration |
|---|
| **Leading Individuals** |

| **Band 1** | |
|---|---|
| Chesser Lori | Davis, Brown, Koehn, Shors & Roberts, PC |
| Penick Bridget R | Dickinson, Mackaman, Tyler & Hagen, PC |

| **Up-and-coming individuals** | |
|---|---|
| Blankenship Kimberly H | Bradley & Riley PC |
| Westin Neal | Nyemaster, Goode, West, Hansell & O'Brien |

*\* Indicates firm / individual with profile.*
*† ONP = Other Notable Practitioner.*

worker visas and green cards, I-9 employment verification rules and immigration law compliance matters.

## Band 2

### Belin McCormick PC

**THE FIRM** This practice offers the full range of legal services in labor and employment law, and is primarily known for its strong employment defense work on behalf of regional companies. The firm has also been involved in union-related work, as well as labor relations management. The team has recently handled a series of disputes surrounding ADA and FMLA compliance.
**Sources say:** *"They quickly became familiar with our agency and the services we provide, and can therefore give us sound advice and counsel."*
**KEY INDIVIDUALS James Swanger** is particularly active in the food and manufacturing areas, where he represents clients in a range of employment litigation and union matters. Clients say: *"His common-sense attitude in helping us deal with unusual or sensitive employment situations is a huge strength."* **Michael Reck** is appreciated by clients for his depth of knowledge and experience in employment litigation. According to clients, *"Mike Reck's handling of employee issues is top notch. He breaks down employment law issues into practical language that our managers can utilize."* **Patricia Shoff** specializes in employment discrimination defense. She is described by sources as *"extremely thorough and knowledgeable. She takes the time to train and teach rather than only provide legal guidance. We have a very successful employee relations risk history because of working with her."* **Kelsey Knowles** deals with a wide range of employment litigation at all stages. She advises employers on collective bargaining negotiations and arbitrations.

### Bradley & Riley PC

**THE FIRM** This team works from offices in Cedar Rapids and Iowa City, representing clients in the full range of labor and employment matters. Clients include educational institutions, healthcare providers and private companies. Recent work highlights include representing CBE Group in a lawsuit relating to alleged national origin discrimination and retaliation, winning a jury verdict in favor of the defense. The firm also has a substantial immigration practice, particularly related to the H1B process, work visas and green cards.

Sources say: *"Bradley & Riley is a firm that has its clients' best interests in mind and looks for ways to address our concerns in an efficient and timely manner, which we appreciate."*
KEY INDIVIDUALS Kelly Baier is held in the highest regard by peers in the labor and employment field as a *"premier labor lawyer in Cedar Rapids."* He recently defended CBE Group against discrimination claims. Nancy Wood focuses on employment litigation, and is appreciated by sources as being *"very prompt and very knowledgeable in areas of discrimination."* Immigration lawyer Kimberly Blankenship enters the rankings for the first time this year. She handles many of the firm's most significant immigration matters.

## Davis, Brown, Koehn, Shors & Roberts, PC

THE FIRM The attorneys at this Des Moines firm specialize in a range of labor and employment matters. The firm has recently been particularly involved in disputes concerning overtime pay and working hours, discrimination and labor disputes. Key clients include the Civic Center of Greater Des Moines and the Iowa State Education Association.
Sources say: *"From the moment we found them and spoke to a paralegal, it was utterly different from any experience before. They respected me, dealt with me directly, and really made it a priority."*
KEY INDIVIDUALS Lori Chesser is recognized as one of the top lawyers in the state for immigration. Her practice incorporates I-9 visa applications and immigration audits. Gene La Suer has a particular focus on collective bargaining, unfair labor practice proceedings, and wage and hour disputes. Sharon Malheiro receives warm praise from interviewees, with one client saying: *"She was fantastic - professional, prompt, understood the law and respected the client. A phenomenal experience. I've dealt with attorneys in lots of states, and none compare to Sharon."* Deborah Tharnish practices in business litigation and employment law, and regularly counsels clients on preventive measures and regulatory compliance matters. Becky Knutson advises both public and private sector clients. She is also an experienced mediator in sophisticated labor and employment disputes.

## Simmons Perrine Moyer Bergman PLC

THE FIRM This Cedar Rapids firm has a strong local presence in labor and employment matters, representing both employers and employees in sophisticated cases. The firm has been heavily involved in litigation and class actions, particularly regarding discrimination and harassment. Major clients include AEGON, Alliant Energy and GreatAmerica Financial Services.

Sources say: *"The firm has a large number of attorneys who are very strong in their areas of specialization."*
KEY INDIVIDUALS Iris Muchmore is lauded by peers as a top labor and employment attorney in Cedar Rapids. She was involved in the firm's representation of CRST Van Expedited in a sexual harassment class action. Kevin Visser litigates on high-stakes matters, including a diverse variety of labor and employment disputes. According to clients, *"Kevin is a great communicator and always remains cool and calm."* He led the firm's representation of CRST Van Expedited.

## Band 3

## Brown, Winick, Graves, Gross, Baskerville and Schoenebaum PLC

THE FIRM This Des Moines firm handles a range of employment matters. The team is especially active in employment disputes, including trade secrets and non-compete clauses, and in wrongful termination and civil rights suits. In addition to litigation work, the firm counsels clients on matters such as workplace wellness and healthcare plans, labor relations and human resources.
KEY INDIVIDUALS James Gilliam (see p.1291) chairs the practice, working primarily on employment litigation and focusing on wrongful termination.

## Faegre Baker Daniels

THE FIRM The Des Moines office of this global firm handles a broad range of employment matters, covering employment litigation, compliance training, labor relations and immigration, among others. The firm has a national reach, and handles the Iowa interests of national clients such as Wells Fargo and US Bank. Recent work highlights include defending Principal Life Insurance in an alleged age discrimination suit.
KEY INDIVIDUALS Michael Giudicessi is commended for his responsiveness. He handles a variety of employment matters, and is noted for his tenacious advocacy style.

## Lane & Waterman LLP

THE FIRM This firm has a balanced practice between litigation and consulting services, frequently defending clients throughout the Quad Cities area in a wide range of employment lawsuits. Recent work highlights include successfully defending Lincare in a highly complex lawsuit brought by a terminated employee, alleging discrimination on the basis of pregnancy and disability.
Sources say: *"Extremely solid. A good base of resources for a variety of needs."*
KEY INDIVIDUALS Judith Herrmann heads the department, and is a frequent litigator on discrimination cases.

She also provides counseling and education services to clients, including workshops and seminars. New entry Mikkie Schiltz represents clients in a range of matters, particularly relating to pregnancy and disability discrimination. *"She's done a great job helping us in administrative cases and hearings. Her work on those is outstanding,"* said one client.

## Shuttleworth & Ingersoll PLC

THE FIRM Based in Cedar Rapids and Iowa City, this firm has a solid local base from which to represent public and private sector clients in the full spectrum of labor and employment matters. In addition to representation in dispute resolution and counseling clients, the firm provides services including preparation of employer policies and employee handbooks, and drafting and implementing schemes such as drug testing.
KEY INDIVIDUALS *"Standout"* lawyer Mark Zaiger is strongly recommended by peers as one of the top labor and employment attorneys in the state. He is particularly noted for his knowledge in matters relating to technology and social media.

## Whitfield & Eddy, PLC

THE FIRM Whitfield & Eddy offers a broad and full service to clients in labor and employment matters, representing and advising both public and private sector clients. The firm is particularly involved in a range of litigation matters, including unfair dismissal, discrimination, harassment, and wage and hour disputes, in addition to traditional labor and union activity. The firm has also been active on a rising number of noncompetition disputes.
KEY INDIVIDUALS Greg Naylor is a management-side labor attorney, who focuses on counseling clients on regulatory compliance and handling workplace problems and disputes before they reach litigation. He is noted for his union and labor practice. Jaki Samuelson is held in high regard by peers as a strong litigator and employment lawyer. She is a frequent writer and speaker on a range of workplace employment issues.

## Other Notable Practitioners

Gayla Harrison of Ottumwa-based firm Harrison, Moreland & Webber PC is widely acclaimed by her peers in the labor and employment field as one of the stronger practitioners in the state. She is known for the strength of her trial work and case investigations. Hugh Cain of Hopkins & Huebner, P.C. is described as *"very thorough and competent"* by commentators. He practices and teaches seminars on employment law and government practice.

# LITIGATION GENERAL COMMERCIAL

Insurance p.1288

Commentary about individuals can be found under their firm's paragraph. If the firm has no paragraph (is not ranked) look at Other Notable Practitioners.

## Litigation: General Commercial
### Leading Firms

**Band 1**
Belin McCormick PC
Nyemaster, Goode, West, Hansell & O'Brien

**Band 2**
Davis, Brown, Koehn, Shors & Roberts, PC
Faegre Baker Daniels
Lane & Waterman LLP
Simmons Perrine Moyer Bergman PLC

**Band 3**
Ahlers & Cooney PC
Bradley & Riley PC
Brown, Winick, Graves, Gross, Baskerville and Schoenebaum
Dickinson, Mackaman, Tyler & Hagen, PC
Finley, Alt, Smith, Scharnberg, Craig, Hilmes & Gaffney PC
Lederer Weston Craig PLC
Shuttleworth & Ingersoll PLC
Whitfield & Eddy, PLC

\* Indicates firm / individual with profile.
† ONP = Other Notable Practitioner.

*The editorial is in alphabetical order by firm name.*

## Ahlers & Cooney PC

**THE FIRM** This firm is recognized by peers for the strength of its seasoned, trial-experienced attorneys. The firm is proficient in a wide variety of litigation, and also handles jury and bench trials, arbitrations, mediations and administrative proceedings.

**KEY INDIVIDUALS Edward Remsburg** has been involved in both complex commercial and personal injury litigation, and is well regarded by peers as *"a great lawyer who does a very good job."* According to peers, **Wade Hauser** *"is a very strong commercial litigator and has great presence in a courtroom setting."* He has handled more than 350 cases in state, federal and bankruptcy courts throughout his career. **David Luginbill** has a broad litigation practice covering matters such as trademark infringement, product liability and professional liability. He represents national and international clients at state and federal levels. **Randall Stefani** practices in complex commercial and personal injury matters. He is also a certified public accountant.

## Belin McCormick PC

**THE FIRM** This market-leading firm has expertise across all areas of litigation, and is particularly involved in complex commercial disputes and class actions, defending clients across several industries, including Alliant Energy, Mediacom and Wellmark Blue Cross Blue Shield. Recent highlights include representing MetaBank in trial and on appeal in a complex foreclosure action concerning disputed rights to commercial property.
**Sources say:** *"Very professional and a great ally."*

**KEY INDIVIDUALS Mark McCormick** handles a variety of complex commercial litigation. Clients *"greatly value his judgment and expertise,"* and particularly praise his in-court ability: *"He lent our case gravitas before the judge. He was the authority in the courtroom when he spoke."* **David Swinton** focuses on complex commercial litigation, representing clients in trials and appeals in both state and federal courts. **Stephen Eckley** specializes in civil trials, representing plaintiffs and defendants in a wide range of litigation. According to peers, *"he's a very good lawyer."* Rising star **Matt McDermott** has had an active year defending financial institutions, among other organizations, in a variety of disputes. According to clients, he is *"a great strategist"* who *"has the foresight to analyze the other party's representation and outline a plan to overcome any obstacles."*

## Bradley & Riley PC

**THE FIRM** Spread across the Cedar Rapids and Iowa City offices, this firm has a strong presence in east Iowa. The litigation practice covers a broad range of matters, including employment discrimination and noncompetition. The firm has a particularly strong insurance litigation practice, representing securities brokers against their insurers in coverage disputes. Key clients include American Foods Group, Collins Community Credit Union and East Central Iowa Council of Governments.
**Sources say:** *"Excellent legal service."*

**KEY INDIVIDUALS Timothy Hill** is praised by clients for his *"knowledge of insurance law, attention to detail and commitment to clients."* His practice covers a broad range of commercial litigation, including insurance. Iowa City partner **Paul Burns** is particularly well known for his construction litigation practice. According to one peer, *"he delivers cost-effective solutions for clients. I would hire him."* **Donald Thompson** represents clients in commercial and civil disputes, trials and appeals. Peers say he *"has an excellent professional reputation and is an experienced trial lawyer."*

## Bradshaw, Fowler, Proctor & Fairgrave, PC

**THE FIRM** Litigation and trial work forms the largest component of this firm's practice, and the team handles a wide range of civil and commercial cases in mediation and arbitration as well as litigation. The firm is especially noted for its contentious insurance work.

**KEY INDIVIDUALS** Experienced trial lawyer **Mark Tripp** draws resounding praise from clients for his *"consistently excellent work and top-notch service,"* and for his *"responsiveness and practical thinking, which is invaluable for the benefit of the client."* **Michael Figenshaw** is a senior and well-respected figure in insurance law, with a practice primarily covering professional liability and malpractice.

## Litigation: General Commercial
### Senior Statesmen

**Senior Statesmen: distinguished older practitioners**

| | | |
|---|---|---|
| James Dwight W | *The James Law Firm PC (ONP)* † | |

### Leading Individuals

**Band 1**

| | |
|---|---|
| Dutton David J | *Dutton, Braun, Staack & Hellman (ONP)* † |
| Lederer Gregory | *Lederer Weston Craig PLC* |
| McCormick Mark | *Belin McCormick PC* |
| Remsburg Edward W | *Ahlers & Cooney PC* |
| Roby Patrick M | *Elderkin & Pirnie PLC (ONP)* † |
| Sapp Richard | *Nyemaster, Goode, West, Hansell & O'Brien* |
| Tank David | *Dorsey & Whitney LLP (ONP)* † |
| Waterman Jr Robert | *Lane & Waterman LLP* |
| Weinhardt Mark | *Weinhardt & Logan (ONP)* † |

**Band 2**

| | |
|---|---|
| Brown David | *Hansen, McClintock & Riley (ONP)* † |
| Cook Guy | *Grefe & Sidney, PLC (ONP)* † |
| Hauser III Wade | *Ahlers & Cooney PC* |
| Luginbill David H | *Ahlers & Cooney PC* |
| Reynolds Kevin | *Whitfield & Eddy, PLC* |
| Swinton David | *Belin McCormick PC* |
| Tharnish Deborah | *Davis, Brown, Koehn, Shors & Roberts, PC* |

**Band 3**

| | |
|---|---|
| Burns Paul D | *Bradley & Riley PC* |
| Collins Kevin H | *Nyemaster, Goode, West, Hansell & O'Brien* |
| Critelli Jr Nicholas | *Law Chambers of Nicholas Critelli (ONP)* † |
| Draper Hayward L | *Nyemaster, Goode, West, Hansell & O'Brien* |
| Driscoll Kevin J | *Finley, Alt, Smith, Scharnberg, Craig, Hilmes* |
| Hilmes Jack | *Finley, Alt, Smith, Scharnberg, Craig, Hilmes* |
| Houghton Robert | *Shuttleworth & Ingersoll PLC* |
| Pawlosky Mollie M | *Dickinson, Mackaman, Tyler & Hagen, PC* |
| Phipps David | *Whitfield & Eddy, PLC* |
| Rickert Brian P | *Brown, Winick, Graves, Gross, Baskerville* \* |
| Scharnberg Steven K | *Finley, Alt, Smith, Scharnberg, Craig, Hilmes* |
| Stefani Randall | *Ahlers & Cooney PC* |
| Thompson Donald | *Bradley & Riley PC* |
| Thrall Michael W | *Nyemaster, Goode, West, Hansell & O'Brien* |
| Walker Kim J | *Faegre Baker Daniels* |

**Band 4**

| | |
|---|---|
| Abernathy Terry J | *Pickens, Barnes & Abernathy (ONP)* † |
| Bickel John M | *Shuttleworth & Ingersoll PLC* |
| Bylund Jacob | *Faegre Baker Daniels* |
| Combs Terri | *Faegre Baker Daniels* |
| Eckley Stephen R | *Belin McCormick PC* |
| Hanson Thomas D | *Hanson, Bjork & Russell LLP (ONP)* † |
| Holtman Stephen | *Simmons Perrine Moyer Bergman PLC* |
| Johnson Ross W | *Faegre Baker Daniels* |
| Lyford F Richard | *Dickinson, Mackaman, Tyler & Hagen, PC* |
| Pettit Debra | *Davis, Brown, Koehn, Shors & Roberts, PC* |

**Up-and-coming individuals**

| | |
|---|---|
| Linebaugh Jesse | *Faegre Baker Daniels* |
| McDermott Matt | *Belin McCormick PC* |

*The editorial is in alphabetical order by firm name.*

| Litigation: Insurance | |
| --- | --- |
| **Leading Firms** | |
| **Band 1** | |
| Bradley & Riley PC | |
| Bradshaw, Fowler, Proctor & Fairgrave, PC | |
| Finley, Alt, Smith, Scharnberg, Craig, Hilmes & Gaffney PC | |
| Lederer Weston Craig PLC | |

| **Senior Statesmen** | |
| --- | --- |
| **Senior Statesmen:** distinguished older practitioners | |
| Figenshaw Michael H | *Bradshaw, Fowler, Proctor & Fairgrave, PC* |
| Finley Thomas A | *Finley, Alt, Smith, Scharnberg, Craig, Hilmes* |

| **Leading Individuals** | |
| --- | --- |
| **Band 1** | |
| Hill Timothy J | *Bradley & Riley PC* |
| Tripp Mark | *Bradshaw, Fowler, Proctor & Fairgrave, PC* |
| Weston J Michael | *Lederer Weston Craig PLC* |

\* Indicates firm / individual with profile.
*Alphabetical order within each band. Band 1 is the highest.*

## Brown, Winick, Graves, Gross, Baskerville and Schoenebaum PLC

**THE FIRM** This firm regularly appears in courts at both the state and federal levels, and represents clients in a wide range of disputes. It has recently gained momentum in the representation of clients in energy, finance, construction, real estate, insurance and intellectual property litigation. In a recent highlight, the team represented Energy Panel Structures as the defendant in a suit claiming negligence and improper design of four buildings in Iowa, Illinois and South Dakota.
**Sources say:** *"High performing and excellent client representation."*
**KEY INDIVIDUALS Brian Rickert** (see p.1291) is chair of the firm's construction practice and handles a range of complex commercial litigation and business torts. Clients say he is *"always highly responsive and dedicated to ensuring our needs are met."*

## Davis, Brown, Koehn, Shors & Roberts, PC

**THE FIRM** This firm houses a number of specialized attorneys who cover all bases in litigation, including real estate and construction, tax and IP. It remains a trusted choice for clients such as GROWMARK, Energetix and Assured Guaranty. In a recent work highlight, the firm defended Ag Leader Technology in a trademark infringement suit by an international marketer and distributor of agricultural products.
**KEY INDIVIDUALS** Key partner **Deborah Tharnish** is held in high esteem by peers in the litigation field as being *"outstanding"* and *"dedicated to her clients, with a whole lot of common sense."* According to clients, *"her communication skills are excellent; she's very helpful with her expertise."* *"Excellent lawyer"* **Debra Pettit** is chair of the firm's construction practice, with a focus on real estate and construction disputes. She recently defended RDG in a suit brought by the West Des Moines Community School District alleging faults in the design and construction of Hillside Elementary School.

## Dickinson, Mackaman, Tyler & Hagen, PC

**THE FIRM** This firm offers the full range of litigation services, and has particular strength in real estate, technology and intellectual property litigation. The team has also been increasingly involved in alternate dispute resolution, such as representing Briggs Medical in arbitration against Imagetek for failure to design and deliver electronic medical record software to market to Briggs's client base.
**Sources say:** *"Very responsive and proactive on my behalf."*
**KEY INDIVIDUALS Mollie Pawlosky** covers a broad range of litigation, including insurance, construction and contract disputes, and also has an active appellate practice. *"I couldn't ask for a better partner,"* said one client, adding: *"She's done an outstanding job."* **Richard Lyford** has deep experience in litigation and handles a broad range of matters, including contract, tort, antitrust, tax, construction and workout litigation. He is well regarded by peers in the field.

## Faegre Baker Daniels

**THE FIRM** Clients commend this firm for its versatile and wide-ranging litigation capabilities, as well as its engaged client service and relationships. It has been highly active in agribusiness litigation and finance litigation, including securities, regulatory compliance and antitrust. The firm recently defended Wells Fargo and SunTrust Bank against a federal court class action alleging failure to record mortgage documents and pay fees to local county recorders in Iowa.
**KEY INDIVIDUALS Kim Walker** leads the firm's national food and agriculture industry team. Areas of expertise include antitrust, products liability and contract disputes. **Ross Johnson** is best known for his product liability work, including product defects, product contamination, contract disputes and defamation claims. **Jacob Bylund** is commended for the depth of his knowledge of the commodities and agriculture sectors. He handles a broad range of litigious matters pertaining to these industries including IP disputes, products liability and contract disputes. Commercial litigator **Terri Combs** practices primarily in financial services litigation, including securities arbitration and regulatory enforcement defense. Clients appreciate her substantive knowledge and strong client service skills. **Jesse Linebaugh** also practices in financial services litigation, and cochairs the firmwide securities and financial services litigation practice group. His primary area of activity is defending insurance companies, banks and broker-dealers throughout the USA.

## Finley, Alt, Smith, Scharnberg, Craig, Hilmes & Gaffney PC

**THE FIRM** This well-established Iowa firm is best known for its impressive trial practice. The team has a healthy presence in medical and professional malpractice work, in addition to an expanding capability in various general commercial disputes, including employment litigation. The firm is particularly well known for its leading position in insurance litigation.
**KEY INDIVIDUALS** *"Excellent"* lawyer **Kevin Driscoll** maintains an active practice in various types of insurance

and professional malpractice litigation, as well as construction and other commercial matters. **Jack Hilmes**'s primary area of practice is medical malpractice defense. He regularly defends hospitals, clinics and medical professionals statewide. **Steven Scharnberg** represents medical facilities and professionals in a wide range of disputes, including malpractice, licensing and disciplinary issues, business operations and employment matters. **Thomas Finley** covers a broad range of litigation, primarily related to healthcare and insurance. He also lends his services as a mediator in several arbitration proceedings.

## Lane & Waterman LLP

**THE FIRM** Lane & Waterman maintains a powerful position in Davenport and the Quad Cities area. The firm handles a wide range of litigation, including professional malpractice, tortuous negligence, product liability and white-collar crime. It has a burgeoning intellectual property practice, with recent highlights including successfully defending Winegard, the manufacturer of the Carryout portable GPS system, in a patent infringement suit, also winning a patent invalidity countersuit against the plaintiff.
**KEY INDIVIDUALS Robert Waterman** is a leading figure in the litigation field, held in high esteem by peers and clients alike for his work in insurance, professional malpractice and product liability cases. According to sources, *"he just commands the case"* and *"is one of the finest trial lawyers I have ever seen."*

## Lederer Weston Craig PLC

**THE FIRM** This compact Cedar Rapids firm handles all areas of litigation, from trial to appeal, across a wide range of industry areas. The firm's reputation for insurance litigation and medical malpractice defense is particularly strong.
**KEY INDIVIDUALS Gregory Lederer**'s litigation practice is broad in scope, including medical malpractice and business torts as particular areas of repute. Clients are impressed by his strategy and oratory performance in court, saying: *"He is a good writer and is very practical. He knows and understands the goal his client wants to achieve and how to accomplish it. He also represents his client exceptionally well before the court."* **Michael Weston** is a leading figure in the firm and the state for insurance litigation and personal injury defense, as part of a diverse general commercial litigation practice.

## Nyemaster, Goode, West, Hansell & O'Brien

**THE FIRM** This firm maintains a healthy reputation among market sources for its strong full-service litigation practice with significant depth of expertise in a range of areas. The team regularly deals with malpractice, construction, product liability and labor and employment disputes. The firm has also been increasingly involved in intellectual property cases, including infringement, domain name disputes and noncompetition clauses.
**Sources say:** *"I would recommend their services to anyone that asked."*

**KEY INDIVIDUALS Michael Thrall** is noted for his expertise in ERISA litigation and complex tort defense, among other areas. According to clients, "*he's a hard worker – no-nonsense and efficient.*" **Kevin Collins** is a key member of the firm's intellectual property team, and has additional experience in business tort, product liability and construction litigation. "*Immediately after we brought Kevin in, our problem started to get solved. We have a good history with him,*" said one client. "*Smart, tactical and aggressive,*" **Hayward Draper** earns client praise for his tenacity in advocating for their interests in court. He is best known for his medical malpractice work, and for defending civil and criminal charges. **Richard Sapp** has extensive litigation experience, with a focus on product liability, commercial litigation and appellate work. Clients praise his courtroom performance, with one saying: "*Although he is soft-spoken he was clearly a very capable trial lawyer who knew his way around a courtroom and also handled the lawyer on the other side with ease. I truly felt we were in good hands with his representation.*"

## Shuttleworth & Ingersoll PLC

**THE FIRM** This Cedar Rapids firm continues to place an emphasis on its active work in litigation, with a strong bench of experienced trial lawyers who try cases before federal and state courts, regulatory agencies and administrative hearings. The team handles cases from the discovery and investigation phase through to trial and appeals, and also offers representation in alternate dispute resolution, including arbitration and mediation.

**KEY INDIVIDUALS** Senior vice president **Robert Houghton** is highly praised by one peer as "*a good, common-sense lawyer who sees the issues clearly and deals with them efficiently.*" He practices primarily in the areas of medical malpractice defense, commercial litigation and product liability, but is increasingly known for his work in

the IP field as well. **John Bickel** has extensive trial experience and focuses primarily on media law, civil litigation, construction law, workers' compensation and professional liability.

## Simmons Perrine Moyer Bergman PLC

**THE FIRM** This Cedar Rapids firm offers a broad litigation service to both plaintiffs and defendants in a range of industries, including financial services litigation, mass tort and construction. In addition to its litigation practice, the firm is increasingly engaged in arbitration and mediation. Recent work highlights include defending West Side Unlimited in a business tort and RICO arbitration claiming $15 million.

**KEY INDIVIDUALS Stephen Holtman** is singled out as "*an excellent lawyer*" by peers in the field. He handles a wide range of litigation matters, including commercial law, contracts, intellectual property and antitrust.

## Whitfield & Eddy, PLC

**THE FIRM** This firm is best known for litigation in tort and breach of contract cases, with a particular emphasis on the construction industry. It also handles a substantial amount of foreclosures, insurance defense, product liability work and professional liability.

**KEY INDIVIDUALS Kevin Reynolds** is a product liability defense attorney and is well known among peers for his performance in this field. He has represented insurers, wholesalers, distributors and retailers in a litany of products cases. **David Phipps** chairs the insurance law practice at Whitfield & Eddy. As well as insurer defense work, he has defended professionals including CPAs, lawyers and doctors, and is involved in commercial litigation as well as arbitration and appellate matters.

### Other Notable Practitioners

"*Dynamite*" defense attorney **David Dutton** of Cedar Falls-based firm Dutton, Braun, Staack & Hellman PLC has defended clients in a wide range of civil and criminal litigation, in both state and federal courts and administrative hearings. **Dwight James** of The James Law Firm PC is a senior and respected figure in the professional malpractice field, with a long career of trial experience. He is a much sought-after mediator in dispute resolution. **Patrick Roby** of Cedar Rapids-based firm Elderkin & Pirnie PLC is described as "*excellent*" by peers in the field. He practices primarily in employment defense, particularly defense of medical practitioners and other professionals in malpractice suits. **David Brown** of Hansen, McClintock & Riley has an "*excellent reputation in defense of physicians,*" according to interviewees. As well as professional malpractice, he also handles insurance defense and personal injury disputes. **Guy Cook** of Grefe & Sidney, PLC makes waves in Iowa as a dynamic and highly active lawyer. His practice covers all areas of civil and criminal litigation. Founding partner **Nicholas Critelli** of the Law Chambers of Nicholas Critelli PC is known as "*a well-respected, experienced attorney.*" He is particularly praised for criminal defense work. **Thomas Hanson** of Hanson, Bjork & Russell LLP has a wealth of experience on a wide range of commercial disputes, litigating in both federal and state courts. One peer describes him as a "*worthy adversary to tangle with.*" **Mark Weinhardt** of Weinhardt & Logan is recommended by peers as a "*top white-collar crime lawyer.*" **David Tank** of Dorsey & Whitney LLP practices primarily in IP litigation, and draws praise from clients for his "*professionalism and deep knowledge.*" Sources add that "*nothing is more important to him than his clients.*" **Terry Abernathy** of Cedar Rapids-based firm Pickens, Barnes & Abernathy is recognized by peers as an "*excellent*" litigator and trial attorney.

# REAL ESTATE

Real Estate p.1290

Commentary about individuals can be found under their firm's paragraph. If the firm has no paragraph (is not ranked) look at Other Notable Practitioners.

## Band 1

### Belin McCormick PC

**THE FIRM** Belin McCormick's real estate practice maintains top-tier recognition among national and regional clients in a diverse variety of industries, delivering a full range of legal services. The firm is particularly noted for its transactional work, including a strong lending practice, and has been active in the past year on emerging industry areas such as wind energy. The group earns high praise from clients, who laud its high-quality work product, while peers are quick to single out the firm as a target for referrals.

**Sources say:** "*The Belin firm is clearly one of the top business and general law firms in the state of Iowa.*"

**KEY INDIVIDUALS William Bartine** works primarily in commercial real estate transactions and financing. According to an impressed client, "*he knew what issues to focus on and addressed them in a professional and proficient manner.*" **Jeremy Sharpe** is described by one client as "*in my opinion, one of the best real estate attorneys in the state of Iowa.*" He is held in high regard by sources for his extensive expertise in all areas of transactional real estate. **Nathan Barber** focuses on real estate transactions, workouts and foreclosures. "*It seems that he sees nearly every, if not all, angles of real estate contracts and structures,*" say clients.

## Davis, Brown, Koehn, Shors & Roberts, PC

**THE FIRM** This market-leading firm offers a full range of real estate services, and is particularly noted for its transac-

tional, financing and foreclosure work. The firm is a popular choice for corporate clients in a range of industries, and enjoys the patronage of financial institutions such as West Bank and Northwest Bank. Recent work highlights include the representation of Wells Fargo in the handling of debtor-creditor issues throughout Iowa.

**Sources say:** "*We are very happy with them. They're approachable. I never hesitate to pick up the phone and talk to them.*"

**KEY INDIVIDUALS Robert Douglas** represents clients in a wide range of commercial and residential sales and acquisitions, and is held in high esteem for his financial institutions work. Sources say: "*He's very approachable, professional, and understands the law and how to approach it.*" **David Erickson** works with lenders, developers, debtors and cred-

## Real Estate
### Leading Firms

**Band 1**
Belin McCormick PC
Davis, Brown, Koehn, Shors & Roberts, PC
Lane & Waterman LLP
Nyemaster, Goode, West, Hansell & O'Brien

**Band 2**
Dickinson, Mackaman, Tyler & Hagen, PC
Lillis O'Malley Olson Manning Pose & Van Dike LLP

**Band 3**
Bradley & Riley PC
Brown, Winick, Graves, Gross, Baskerville and Schoenebaum
Shuttleworth & Ingersoll PLC
Simmons Perrine Moyer Bergman PLC
Whitfield & Eddy, PLC

## Real Estate
### Statesmen

**Senior Statesmen: distinguished older practitioners**

| | | |
|---|---|---|
| Holcomb | James M | Bradshaw, Fowler, Proctor (ONP)[†] |
| Tyler | Paul | Dickinson, Mackaman, Tyler & Hagen, PC |

### Leading Individuals

**Band 1**

| | | |
|---|---|---|
| Andeweg | Robert | Nyemaster, Goode, West, Hansell & O'Brien |
| Bartine | William | Belin McCormick PC |
| Dettmann | David | Lane & Waterman LLP |
| Douglas | Robert J | Davis, Brown, Koehn, Shors & Roberts, PC |
| Kubicek | David W | Simmons Perrine Moyer Bergman PLC |
| Lillis | William | Lillis O'Malley Olson Manning Pose & Van |
| Moore | Dan | Berenstein, Moore, Heffernan (ONP)[†] |
| Sharpe | Jeremy | Belin McCormick PC |

**Band 2**

| | | |
|---|---|---|
| Colacino | Antonio | Nyemaster, Goode, West, Hansell & O'Brien |
| Erickson | David | Davis, Brown, Koehn, Shors & Roberts, PC |
| Hanson | Mark V | Hanson Law PC (ONP)[†] |
| Pose | Christopher | Lillis O'Malley Olson Manning Pose & Van |
| Sullivan | Jon | Dickinson, Mackaman, Tyler & Hagen, PC |
| Wine | James C | Nyemaster, Goode, West, Hansell & O'Brien |

**Band 3**

| | | |
|---|---|---|
| Austin | Brad | Nyemaster, Goode, West, Hansell & O'Brien |
| Gartin | Timothy L | Hastings & Gartin LLP (ONP)[†] |
| Hastings | Craig R | Hastings & Gartin LLP (ONP)[†] |
| McMenimen | Dennis | Shuttleworth & Ingersoll PLC |
| Myers | Gary M | Davis, Brown, Koehn, Shors & Roberts, PC |
| Neppl | William | Bradley & Riley PC |
| Olson | Eugene E | Lillis O'Malley Olson Manning Pose & Dike |
| Prowell | William | Shuttleworth & Ingersoll PLC |
| Seyfer | Greg | Bradley & Riley PC |

**Band 4**

| | | |
|---|---|---|
| Barber | Nathan J | Belin McCormick PC |
| Davidson | Richard A | Lane & Waterman LLP |
| Gray | Mark R | Whitfield & Eddy, PLC |
| Hamborg | Kelly D | Brown, Winick, Graves, Gross, Baskerville |
| Hogan | Timothy C | Hogan Law Office (ONP)[†] |
| Law | Kathleen K | Nyemaster, Goode, West, Hansell & O'Brien |
| Longnecker | Anthony A | Nyemaster, Goode, West, Hansell & O'Brien |
| Sinnard | Kara M | Whitfield & Eddy, PLC |
| Stevenson | Jill M | Nyemaster, Goode, West, Hansell & O'Brien |
| Wetsch | David L | Wetsch & Abbott PLC (ONP)[†] |

**Associates to watch**

| | | |
|---|---|---|
| Hektoen | Matthew | Simmons Perrine Moyer Bergman PLC |

[*] Indicates firm / individual with profile.

[†] ONP = Other Notable Practitioner.

itors on a range of real estate projects, and is particularly noted for his foreclosures practice. Sources describe him as an *"excellent Iowa practitioner."* **Gary Myers** is chair of the real estate department, with a practice covering land use, leasing, sale, financing and acquisition matters.

## Lane & Waterman LLP

**THE FIRM** This Davenport-based firm is the regional powerhouse for eastern Iowa and one of the most prominent in the Quad City area, with a wide reach throughout Iowa and Illinois. The firm handles a wide range of high-value and complex real estate undertakings, including a large number of acquisitions, refinancings, restructurings and development projects. Recent highlights include the firm's representation of Midwest department store chain Von Maur in relation to five new stores in Iowa, Georgia, Alabama and New York.

**KEY INDIVIDUALS** Department head **David Dettmann** is a highly regarded figure within the firm and the real estate legal fraternity in Iowa. He recently represented University of Iowa Hospitals & Clinics in the development of a major satellite medical facility. **Richard Davidson** is particularly active on real estate-related financial matters, including bankruptcy, financing and refinancing, in addition to his involvement in a range of real estate development projects. He was lead partner in the Von Maur expansion.

## Nyemaster, Goode, West, Hansell & O'Brien

**THE FIRM** This firm's real estate group offers expertise in the full spectrum of real estate transactions and developments, and regularly represents several major nationwide and regional clients, including financial institutions and insurance companies such as Iowa State Bank and Farm Bureau Life Insurance. The firm is particularly active in the green energy sector, handling a high proportion of the state's wind farming transactions.

**Sources say:** *"The firm is very well organized and has a great understanding of the level of comfort that we require as a lender in our loan closings. The attorneys are a pleasure to do business with."*

**KEY INDIVIDUALS Robert Andeweg** provides representation and counsel on a number of high-value real estate transactions, and focuses his service on commercial transactional work. He is known to be *"a very knowledgeable real estate lawyer."* **James Wine** is known for his focus and expertise on advising insurance company lenders on real estate investment and commercial mortgage loans. **Antonio Colacino** practices in real estate transactions and has particularly deep knowledge and expertise in municipal eminent domain law and utilities. **Brad Austin** is held

in high regard for his work on the commercial and financing side of real estate transactions and developments. He handles real estate financing operations including mezzanine financing. The *"excellent"* **Kathleen Law** is recognized as an authority on wind energy, and has represented wind energy developers in the establishment of numerous wind energy plants. **Anthony Longnecker** is well known for his work in real estate financing and acquisitions. Clients say: *"He is very knowledgeable about commercial real estate law in various states, is very helpful in loan document negotiation and is able to handle a large caseload as well."* **Jill Stevenson** garners great praise from clients, who say: *"She makes it a point to keep us as the lender informed and involved with all legal decisions in the closing process at all times and navigates loan document negotiation with great skill."*

## Band 2

### Dickinson, Mackaman, Tyler & Hagen, PC

**THE FIRM** This firm is able to offer its clients services in the full spectrum of real estate law. The practice has particular strength in transactional and financial work for a variety of organizations. As well as its experience in real estate deals, the team also houses expertise in related litigation. Clients include developers, banks and borrowers.

**KEY INDIVIDUALS Jon Sullivan** is recognized by peers for debt and financing work. His practice primarily involves asset-based loan agreements, including workouts and foreclosures. Senior statesman **Paul Tyler** is now of counsel to the firm, and offers clients the benefit of his extensive knowledge and experience of transactional matters, estate planning and trusts.

### Lillis O'Malley Olson Manning Pose & Van Dike LLP

**THE FIRM** This Des Moines firm has a prominent real estate practice, with a particularly healthy market reputation for handling zoning and land use issues. The team regularly interacts with local city councils on the full range of regulatory issues in relation to various real estate developments.

**KEY INDIVIDUALS William Lillis** is heavily involved in municipal law, land use and entitlement, and development and condemnation. He is a deeply experienced player in Iowa's real estate market. **Eugene Olson** focuses on real estate and zoning law, and is well respected by peers, who also describe him as *"very good to work with."* **Christopher Pose**'s focus is on zoning and environmental law. He is praised by peers in the field for his talent in these areas, and for his strong working relationships with public authorities.

## Band 3

### Bradley & Riley PC

**THE FIRM** This full-service Cedar Rapids firm is appreciated by clients for its efficient and well-rounded service on a range of real estate matters. The firm has handled a litany of real estate acquisitions and developments in the past year, and has continued to benefit from a raft of new development work. Recent work highlights include legal services to Nibor LLC regarding the acquisition of a Red Robin restaurant in Davenport valued at $1.4 million.

**Sources say:** *"One of the best I have dealt with in Cedar Rapids."*

**KEY INDIVIDUALS William Neppl** is the chair of the real estate practice group, and was the counsel on the aforementioned Nibor acquisition. Clients say his *"interpretation of intricate property rights issues has been superior."* **Greg Seyfer** practices in real estate and banking and finance law, and is regarded by peers as *"a great attorney."*

## Brown, Winick, Graves, Gross, Baskerville and Schoenebaum PLC

**THE FIRM** The real estate practice group at this firm offers a wide range of transactional and financing services to clients in various industries, and has recently been more active in agriculture, biofuels and green energy. Recent work highlights include the representation of R.E. Properties 1 in a property acquisition in Des Moines worth $1 million. The team has also been involved in a series of restructurings and refinancings.

**Sources say:** *"A solid firm with high-quality attorneys."*

**KEY INDIVIDUALS Kelly Hamborg**'s real estate practice includes acquisitions, development work, finance and leasing. He is described by clients as *"excellent at what he does – very thorough and knowledgeable."*

## Shuttleworth & Ingersoll PLC

**THE FIRM** Shuttleworth & Ingersoll maintains a prominent, full-service real estate practice in Cedar Rapids and the surrounding area. The firm is particularly active in food and agriculture-related transactions and restructur-

ing, as well as multiple-occupant residential developments. The firm also has a robust property tax practice, and serves clients in the tax aspects of real estate transactions, particularly with regards to flood relief.

**KEY INDIVIDUALS Dennis McMenimen**'s real estate practice covers a broad range of matters, including sales and acquisitions, and leasing and lending. He is also involved in matters relating to condominiums and housing cooperatives. **William Prowell**'s practice has a particular niche in tax matters, particularly relating to tax credits for renovation and restoration of historic landmarks.

## Simmons Perrine Moyer Bergman PLC

**THE FIRM** This Cedar Rapids team is active in all areas of real estate law, including transactions, financing, zoning and land use and related litigation. The group represents a diverse range of clients including lenders, developers and brokers, in addition to both public and private organizations.

**KEY INDIVIDUALS** Commercial real estate partner **David Kubicek** comes highly recommended by peers in the field, particularly for his work in title and insurance issues. Sources describe him as *"a superior title attorney."* Associate **Matthew Hektoen** is pointed to by lawyers in the real estate field as a rising star. He focuses on commercial real estate, with a particular focus on purchase transactions, tax credit financing and residential and commercial development.

## Whitfield & Eddy, PLC

**THE FIRM** This team works from offices in Des Moines and Ankeny and handles a range of real estate transactions including M&A and financing deals. The firm works primarily with local developers of residential properties,

including high-value complexes, as well as representing clients in related litigation.

**KEY INDIVIDUALS** Ankeny partner **Mark Gray** chairs the real estate practice and handles a full variety of real estate matters. He also has particular expertise in estate planning and probate matters. Des Moines-based **Kara Sinnard** has a broad practice covering real estate, corporate, banking and municipal law. She counsels on a variety of real estate issues, including dispute resolution and prevention.

## Other Notable Practitioners

**Dan Moore** of Berenstein, Moore, Heffernan, Moeller & Johnson, L.L.P. in Sioux City draws both client and peer recommendation as *"the best in that area of Iowa."* **Mark Hanson** of Hanson Law PC has a broad practice, but is particularly well known for his title opinions on residential transactions. Peers recognize him as a *"good real estate attorney"* who *"does a nice job."* **Craig Hastings** and **Timothy Gartin** of Hastings & Gartin LLP in Ames are jointly named by peers as *"very significant practitioners in real estate issues statewide."* Both have extensive experience in the field and are well respected by their peers. **David Wetsch** of Wetsch & Abbott PLC is recognized by peers as a *"great guy who does complicated work."* He primarily represents lenders in creditor rights, foreclosures and debt collection. **James Holcomb** is of counsel at Bradshaw, Fowler, Proctor & Fairgrave, PC, where he practices real estate law with an emphasis on purchase and sale and lending transactions. Market sources say that he has *"a great reputation in the community."* **Timothy Hogan** of Hogan Law Office is known primarily for his work with real estate developers, and is regarded by peers as a strong player in the market.

# Leaders' Profiles in Iowa

**BROWN, William**
Brown, Winick, Graves, Gross, Baskerville and Schoenebaum PLC, Des Moines
515 242 2412
brown@brownwinick.com
*Featured in Corporate/M&A (Iowa)*
**Practice Areas:** Focuses on a corporate transactional and business planning practice, concentrating on acquisitions, divestitures, capital formation, financing, business succession, and tax and estate planning. Also has been active in legislative matters affecting businesses.
**Professional Memberships:** American Bar Association Section on Taxation, S Corporation Committee; Iowa State Bar Association Section on Taxation.
**Career:** Has been active in a wide variety of civic leadership positions with organizations such as the Iowa Association of Business and Industry, the Iowa Taxpayers Association and the Polk-Des Moines Taxpayers Association. Former Managing Partner of BrownWinick. Past Chair of the Iowa Association of Business and Industry.

**Publications:** "Gift Tax Annual Exclusion", 65 Tax Lawyer 477, 2012; "Dividend Equivalency in Stock Sales to Related Corporations", 132 Tax Notes 415 (2011); "Evaluating a Subchapter S Conversion", 37 Drake Law Review 395, 1989.
**Personal:** BA with honors in psychology 1974, University of Iowa; JD with high distinction 1977, University of Iowa. LLM in Taxation, magna cum laude 2012, University of Alabama.

**GILLIAM, James H**
Brown, Winick, Graves, Gross, Baskerville and Schoenebaum PLC, Des Moines
515 242 2446
gilliam@brownwinick.com
*Featured in Labor & Employment (Iowa)*
**Practice Areas:** General practice including but not limited to labor and employment law, civil rights and discrimination and litigation, including advice to private and public sector employers in collective bargaining and employment transactions of all types.
**Professional Memberships:** ABA and SHRM.
**Career:** US Army Judge Advocate General's Corps (1980-84); Iowa Public Employment

Relations Board, General Counsel (1984-88); BrownWinick (1988 to present), Partner since 1991.
**Personal:** University of Iowa (JD, 1980); University of Iowa (BA, 1977).

**RICKERT, Brian P**
Brown, Winick, Graves, Gross, Baskerville and Schoenebaum PLC, Des Moines
515 242 2457
rickert@brownwinick.com
*Featured in Litigation (Iowa)*
**Practice Areas:** Complex civil and commercial litigation, agribusiness, banking, construction, governmental and regulatory, healthcare, products liability, real estate, shareholder and corporate disputes.
**Professional Memberships:** Iowa State Bar Association; ABA Forum on the Construction Industry; Master Builders of Iowa; AGC of Iowa.
**Career:** Admitted to practice in Iowa, Kansas and Missouri. Also included in Best Lawyers in America and Great Plains Super Lawyers.
**Publications:** Frequent speaker on construction law and litigation.

**Personal:** Drake University Law School (JD, with Honors, 1998); University of Iowa (BBA, Finance, 1995).

**SACKETT, Christopher R**
Brown, Winick, Graves, Gross, Baskerville and Schoenebaum PLC, Des Moines
515 242 2470
sackett@brownwinick.com
*Featured in Corporate/M&A (Iowa)*
**Practice Areas:** Practice focuses primarily on domestic and international business, transactional, corporate and securities matters, including: organization, formation and management; debt and equity financing including public and private securities offerings; mergers and acquisitions; joint ventures and licensing; real estate; and franchise, dealer and distributor issues. Industries served include manufacturing, software and technology, agribusiness (including production livestock operations, dairies, eggs, and food products), private equity, venture capital, investment banking and energy (including generation, transmission, storage and renewable energy).

## How lawyers are ranked

Every year we carry out thousands of in-depth interviews with clients in order to assess the reputations and expertise of business lawyers worldwide. The qualities we look for (and which determine rankings) include technical legal ability, professional conduct, client service, commercial awareness/astuteness, diligence, commitment, and other qualities most valued by the client. For details of our research team, see p.5.

# CORPORATE/M&A

Commentary about individuals can be found under their firm's paragraph. If the firm has no paragraph (is not ranked) look at Other Notable Practitioners.

### Corporate/M&A
### Leading Firms

**Band 1**
Foulston Siefkin LLP *
Stinson Morrison Hecker LLP

**Band 2**
Polsinelli PC *
Triplett, Woolf & Garretson LLC *

**Band 3**
Lathrop & Gage LLP

### Senior Statesmen

Senior Statesmen: distinguished older practitioners

| | | |
|---|---|---|
| Engstrom Eric | Fleeson, Gooing, Coulson & Kitch (ONP)† | |
| Garretson Thomas P | Triplett, Woolf & Garretson LLC * | |
| Triplett Thomas C | Triplett, Woolf & Garretson LLC * | |

### Leading Individuals

**Band 1**

| | |
|---|---|
| Sorensen Harvey | Foulston Siefkin LLP * |
| Swain Lawrence A | Polsinelli PC |
| Wood William | Foulston Siefkin LLP † |

**Band 2**

| | |
|---|---|
| Cupps Terry C | Foulston Siefkin LLP * |
| Marvin Jack | Stinson Morrison Hecker LLP |
| Pishny Lyle D | Lathrop & Gage LLP |
| Trenkle William | Foulston Siefkin LLP * |

**Band 3**

| | |
|---|---|
| Bengtson David E | Stinson Morrison Hecker LLP |
| Caro Frank | Polsinelli PC |
| Dahlgren Jeffery C | Triplett, Woolf & Garretson LLC * |
| Palecki Scott C | Foulston Siefkin LLP * |
| Thengvall Andrew | Foulston Siefkin LLP * |
| Ward Dale | Hinkle Law Firm LLC (ONP)† |
| Willman Steven C | Polsinelli PC |

* Indicates firm / individual with profile.
†ONP = Other Notable Practitioner.

## Band 1

### Foulston Siefkin LLP
See profile on p.1303

**THE FIRM** With offices in both Wichita and Overland Park, Foulston Siefkin has a first-class reputation in Kansas for its corporate and M&A team. The group is adept at handling the full spectrum of issues relating to complex commercial transactions, financing and tax. A particular area of strength is the representation of healthcare clients in corporate matters, as exemplified by the firm's role as outside general counsel for Nueterra Healthcare Management, a national developer and manager of healthcare services. Other key clients include Spirit AeroSystems, Foley Equipment and Fox & Hound Restaurant Group.
**Sources say:** "To successfully lead entrepreneurs is not an easy task. Foulston excelled at this task."
**KEY INDIVIDUALS Harvey Sorensen's** (see p.1300) extensive experience enables him to guide clients through all phases of the business cycle, and he is adept at handling M&A and tax planning issues. He recently acted for the shareholders of Quality Solutions on the sale of the company to private equity firm Gridiron Capital. One satisfied client states: "Harvey Sorensen is world class." **William Wood** (see p.1301) is head of the firm's business group and has a stellar reputation for serving public and private entities on a broad array of corporate matters. Market feedback reflects his impressive knowledge and expertise in corporate law. A notable work highlight was representing the majority owner of Lubbock Heart Hospital in its sale to Symbion Healthcare. **Terry Cupps** (see p.1299) is a talented practitioner in the bankruptcy and creditors' rights domain. He is noted for his representation of a variety of creditors and trustees, and for his expertise in the purchase and disposal of the assets of troubled companies. **William Trenkle** (see p.1301) is a highly experienced business attorney with a reputation for handling complex tax planning issues. He is also well versed in entity formation and varied transactional matters. **Andrew Thengvall** (see p.1301) is

an expert in M&A, general corporate matters and franchise law, and draws praise from clients who consider him to be "very practical." He recently led the firm's representation of Foley Equipment in its purchase of Dean Machinery. **Scott Palecki** (see p.1300) has a strong reputation for his work with healthcare clients on a range of transactional and regulatory issues. He recently advised Pratt Regional Medical Center on a referendum to increase sales tax to help finance the renovation of the medical center. "He does a good share of transactional work. He's excellent," says an impressed commentator.

### Stinson Morrison Hecker LLP

**THE FIRM** This multioffice firm continues to have a market-leading reputation in Kansas for its corporate and M&A work. The firm has a number of excellent attorneys based in its Wichita and Overland Park offices, but is also able to draw on the expertise of those based in Kansas City, Missouri.
**Sources say:** "A top-quality firm."
**KEY INDIVIDUALS** Recognized as an "excellent lawyer," **Jack Marvin** has a focus on representing banks and lending institutions, and has significant experience in financing transactions, corporate workouts, bankruptcy and commercial foreclosure litigation. He also frequently handles corporate matters for clients in the energy and hotel industries. Oil and gas expert **David Bengtson** is adept at handling the full range of issues affecting businesses in the sector. His practice covers transactional work, business litigation and regulatory matters.

## Band 2

### Polsinelli Shughart PC
See profile on p.1641

**THE FIRM** This firm's Overland Park-based attorneys are esteemed for their corporate, M&A and finance work. The team is well known for representing clients in the energy, manufacturing and home-building industries, and for having significant strength in IP-related matters. The team continues to attract an impressive roster of clients, including Tradewind Energy, Carter Energy and Tradenet Publishing.

**Sources say:** *"They were first-rate in all respects: prompt, thorough, amiable and creative."*

**KEY INDIVIDUALS Lawrence Swain** combines expertise in IP and corporate law to provide *"exemplary"* service to clients spanning a variety of industries. His remit includes M&A, business transactions and licensing issues. One satisfied client praises his *"outstanding subject matter knowledge, outstanding responsiveness and outstanding organizational abilities."* **Frank Caro** is a member of the firm's business department and chairs the firm's national energy group, enabling him to provide high-quality corporate advice to clients across the energy and telecommunications industries. **Steven Willman** draws on more than 25 years' experience to serve clients on a diverse range of matters relating to business transactions and M&A. A key area of focus is the representation of clients in the energy sector.

### Triplett, Woolf & Garretson LLC
See profile on p.1304

**THE FIRM** This compact Wichita-based firm is well regarded for its corporate work for clients, which range from small family-owned businesses to public companies. The team is experienced in structuring sophisticated M&A deals, disposals and other transactions.

**Sources say:** *"Triplett, Woolf & Garretson has done a great job for us."*

**KEY INDIVIDUALS Jeffery Dahlgren** (see p.1299) comes recommended in both corporate law and transactional real estate matters. He has a focus on business acquisitions and sales, and is also noted for his knowledge of general contract issues. Senior statesman **Thomas Garretson** (see p.1299) has built up a wealth of experience in securities and corporate law. He continues to advise all players involved in M&A deals, IPOs and other transactional and advisory issues. With over 40 years in private practice, **Thomas Triplett** (see p.1301) is a seasoned business attorney with the ability to handle the full range of corporate matters. He is admired for utilizing his expertise in taxation law to attain optimum results for clients.

### Band 3

### Lathrop & Gage LLP

**THE FIRM** This firm is particularly well known over the state border in Kansas City, Missouri, but its Overland Park office is also home to a solid group of corporate attorneys. The team handles an array of business matters, such as entity formation, M&A, financing and compliance issues.

**KEY INDIVIDUALS Lyle Pishny** maintains a strong reputation for his business practice. He has an LLM in taxation, which he uses to great effect in structuring commercial transactions for clients.

### Other Notable Practitioners

**Dale Ward** of Hinkle Law Firm LLC is admired for his work in both the corporate law and real estate domains. He regularly involved in clients' finance, M&A and tax matters. Industry veteran **Eric Engstrom** of Fleeson, Gooing, Coulson & Kitch, LLC has more than 38 years' experience in a wide range of corporate and transactional work. He is also noted for his representation of creditors and unsecured creditors' committees in bankruptcy matters.

# LABOR & EMPLOYMENT

| Labor & Employment Leading Firms | |
|---|---|
| **Band 1** | |
| Foulston Siefkin LLP * | |
| **Band 2** | |
| Joseph, Hollander & Craft LLC. | |
| Kutak Rock LLP * | |
| Martin, Pringle, Oliver, Wallace & Bauer, L.L.P. | |
| Morris, Laing, Evans, Brock & Kennedy, Chartered | |
| Spencer Fane Britt & Browne LLP | |
| Stinson Morrison Hecker LLP | |

*\* Indicates firm with profile.*
*Alphabetical order within each band. Band 1 is the highest.*

## Band 1

### Foulston Siefkin LLP
See profile on p.1303

**THE FIRM** Foulston Siefkin is widely regarded as the pre-eminent firm in Kansas for labor and employment issues, with an impressive team of 18 attorneys. The group serves clients on the full spectrum of matters, frequently handling wage and hour class actions, OSHA investigations, discrimination claims and wrongful and retaliatory discharge claims. The attorneys are also well versed in advising companies on policies and procedural issues. Key clients include Spirit AeroSystems, Fox & Hound Restaurant Group and Via Christi Health System.

**Sources say:** *"It's comforting to have them on our side."*

**KEY INDIVIDUALS Jay Rector** (see p.1300) heads the labor and employment department in the Wichita office. His practice covers a wide array of employment, labor and

ERISA benefits issues. *"He's strong on the labor side and very pragmatic,"* say clients. **Douglas Stanley** (see p.1301) is an acclaimed employment and labor lawyer, with market sources describing him as *"extraordinary"* and *"a valued leader."* He has recently handled various issues on behalf of Spirit AeroSystems. **Boyd Byers** (see p.1299) is noted for his expertise on personnel policies, compliance issues, employment contracts and severance agreements. He also frequently represents clients in employee relations issues before administrative agencies and federal and state courts. **Douglas Hanisch** (see p.1299) comes highly recommended in the employee benefits domain. A recent work highlight was assisting Foley Equipment with the benefits aspects of the acquisition of Dean Machinery, including welfare benefit plans, retirement plans and 401(k) plans. **Jeffrey Hurt** (see p.1300) is special counsel at the firm's Overland Park office and has a broad practice advising clients on a diverse range of labor, employment and HR issues. He is also experienced in proceedings before state and federal courts and administrative agencies. **Donald Berner** (see p.1299) focuses his practice on employment and immigration law. He regularly assists clients with discrimination, FMLA matters and wage and hour claims. He also advises businesses on nonimmigrant and immigrant visa issues. **Trisha Thelen** (see p.1301) is a talented trial lawyer with a significant focus on employment litigation. She is noted for her representation of clients in class action suits. **Wyatt Wright** (see p.1301) leads the labor and employment team in the Overland Park office. He continues to represent Nueterra Healthcare Management in a variety of employment, termination and personnel issues. **Jason Lacey** (see p.1300) is fast developing a reputation as a prominent employee benefits and executive compensa-

tion attorney. He wins plaudits from clients, with one stating: *"He's very knowledgeable and responsive, and takes into account our business goals."* **Forrest Rhodes** (see p.1300) is another rising star in the labor and employment sphere. He is well versed in discrimination, wage and hour, and health and safety laws. Sources praise his knowledge and say that *"he is always quick to assist in employee-related issues."*

### Band 2

### Joseph, Hollander & Craft LLC.

**THE FIRM** This firm has three offices across Kansas and an impressive reputation for handling employment matters. The team has particular strength in employment law defense, representing employers in a wide array of matters before administrative agencies. It is also noted for advising clients on policies, procedural issues and the evolving legal landscape.

**KEY INDIVIDUALS** Wichita lawyer **Ross Hollander** is a seasoned litigator with a heavy focus on employment law. One commentator says: *"Ross has an outstanding reputation as an employment lawyer. He has a lot of experience."* **Michelle Moe** is an associate at the firm's Wichita office and a talented trial lawyer. A particular area of focus is defending employers against discrimination claims.

### Kutak Rock LLP
See profile on p.1670

**THE FIRM** Kutak Rock's Wichita office wins plaudits for its talented team of employment litigators, who have a reputation for trying cases and offering valuable employment law counsel. The group is known for defending employers in areas such as discrimination, wrongful discharge, whistle-blowing, retaliation and breach of fiduciary duty. The team is also adept at handling class and collective action wage and hour lawsuits.

**Sources say:** *"They do top-flight work in a prompt fashion."*

**KEY INDIVIDUALS Alan Rupe** (see p.1300) is recognized as a highly active trial lawyer in the employment sphere. A recent work highlight was successfully defending American Foods Group to obtain a summary judgment win against a former employee who had alleged sexual harassment, racial discrimination, retaliation and violations of the ADA.

## Martin, Pringle, Oliver, Wallace & Bauer, L.L.P.

**THE FIRM** This impressive regional firm is noted for its proficiency in representing clients before administrative agencies and state and federal courts. The employment group is adept at advising clients on compliance issues and litigation prevention.

**KEY INDIVIDUALS Terry Mann** focuses on employment litigation, handling issues related to the FMLA and the FLSA, and defending employers against discrimination claims. She also has significant expertise in appellate matters.

## Morris, Laing, Evans, Brock & Kennedy, Chartered

**THE FIRM** This team maintains a strong presence in the Kansas market. It is able to handle the full range of labor relations issues, employment litigation and employment counseling.

**Sources say:** *"A good firm that has been around for a long time."*

**KEY INDIVIDUALS Diane Worth** is recognized for her extensive experience of counseling clients on employment relations matters. She also handles employment litigation before federal and state courts.

## Spencer Fane Britt & Browne LLP

**THE FIRM** While this multioffice firm is perhaps better known over the state line in Kansas City, Missouri, its Overland Park office is home to a number of labor and employment experts. The group provides services related to a wide spectrum of labor and employment matters, including employment litigation, traditional labor law, HR counseling, trade secrets issues and employee benefits law.

**KEY INDIVIDUALS Nick Badgerow** is praised by sources as *"first-rate"* in the employment litigation sphere. He focuses on representing employers in discrimination and wrongful termination claims, among other matters. One commentator says: *"He's a guru on a lot of employment matters."*

## Stinson Morrison Hecker LLP

**THE FIRM** This team at this firm's Wichita office is recognized for its strength in traditional labor law but also has a growing presence in the FLSA and wage and hour collective actions domain. The group continues to serve an impressive list of clients, including Cessna Aircraft, Westar Energy and Wolf Creek Nuclear Operating Corporation.

**Sources say:** *"They are excellent in labor negotiations."*

**KEY INDIVIDUALS Robert Overman** recently arrived from Morris, Laing, Evans, Brock & Kennedy, Chartered, bringing expertise accrued over more than 30 years of practice. He wins acclaim for his representation of employers in labor law matters, with sources describing him as *"very knowledgeable"* and a *"great coach on labor issues."* **Stephanie Scheck** heads the firm's employment department and recently led the firm's representation of Cessna Aircraft. She is praised by peers as a *"good lawyer"* who *"does a nice job."*

## Other Notable Practitioners

**Mark Ferguson** of Gates, Shields & Ferguson, PA centers his practice on employment and education issues, advising and representing employers and educational institutions on a wide range of matters. One commentator says: *"I was out-and-out impressed with his ability and knowledge."* **Trinidad Galdean** recently moved to Hinkle Law Firm LLC from Kutak Rock. He concentrates on advising businesses on an array of employment matters and addressing compliance issues related to the ADA, FMLA and other statutes. **Gaye Tibbets** of Hite, Fanning & Honeyman LLP is well respected for her work representing both employers and employees in varied issues. She is highly experienced in litigation and administrative proceedings. **Eric Metz** (see p.1300) of Triplett, Woolf & Garretson LLC is noted as a talented practitioner with a specialty in employment relations. He frequently advises employers on compliance issues, contract drafting, personnel issues and severance agreements, and is experienced in proceedings before administrative agencies and state and federal courts.

# LITIGATION

Commentary about individuals can be found under their firm's paragraph. If the firm has no paragraph (is not ranked) look at Other Notable Practitioners.

## Litigation: General Commercial
### Leading Firms

**Band 1**
Foulston Siefkin LLP *

**Band 2**
Depew Gillen Rathbun & McInteer LC *
Fleeson, Gooing, Coulson & Kitch, LLC
Hinkle Law Firm LLC
Hite, Fanning & Honeyman LLP
Martin, Pringle, Oliver, Wallace & Bauer, L.L.P.
Polsinelli PC *
Stinson Morrison Hecker LLP

**Band 3**
Adams Jones Law Firm, PA
Lathrop & Gage LLP
Morris, Laing, Evans, Brock & Kennedy, Chartered
Triplett, Woolf & Garretson LLC *

## Litigation: General Commercial
### Senior Statesmen

| Senior Statesmen: distinguished older practitioners | |
| --- | --- |
| Hite Richard | Hite, Fanning & Honeyman LLP |

### Leading Individuals

| Band 1 | |
| --- | --- |
| Armstrong James M | Foulston Siefkin LLP * |
| Fowler Jay | Foulston Siefkin LLP * |
| Gillen Dennis L | Depew Gillen Rathbun & McInteer LC |
| Musil Greg L | Polsinelli PC |
| Peterson Ken | Morris, Laing, Evans, Brock & Kennedy |
| Rebein David | Rebein Bangerter PA (ONP)† |
| Stout Mikel | Foulston Siefkin LLP * |

| Band 2 | |
| --- | --- |
| Ayers Gary L | Foulston Siefkin LLP * |
| Badgerow J Nick | Spencer Fane Britt & Browne LLP (ONP)† |
| Campbell Ronald L | Fleeson, Gooing, Coulson & Kitch, LLC |
| Herren Mitch | Hinkle Law Firm LLC |
| Honeyman Richard | Hite, Fanning & Honeyman LLP |
| Millsap Charles E | Fleeson, Gooing, Coulson & Kitch, LLC |
| Oliver James D | Foulston Siefkin LLP * |
| Pigg J Steven | Fisher Patterson Sayler & Smith (ONP)† |
| Rathbun Randall K | Depew Gillen Rathbun & McInteer LC |
| Robinson Jr F James | Hite, Fanning & Honeyman LLP |
| Rupp Anthony F | Polsinelli PC |
| Spahn Jr Jeff C | Martin, Pringle, Oliver, Wallace & Bauer |
| Vines Monte | Adams Jones Law Firm, PA |
| Walker James A | Triplett, Woolf & Garretson LLC * |
| Warta Darrell | Foulston Siefkin LLP * |

| Band 3 | |
| --- | --- |
| Beeler R Scott | Lathrop & Gage LLP |
| Bengtson David E | Stinson Morrison Hecker LLP |
| Chalmers Arthur S | Hite, Fanning & Honeyman LLP |
| Crabtree Daniel D | Stinson Morrison Hecker LLP |
| Gribble II Don D | Hite, Fanning & Honeyman LLP |
| Seely David G | Fleeson, Gooing, Coulson & Kitch, LLC |
| Stout Bradley A | Adams Jones Law Firm, PA |
| Wooding David S | Martin, Pringle, Oliver, Wallace & Bauer |

| Up-and-coming Individuals | |
| --- | --- |
| Bird Geron J | Hinkle Law Firm LLC |

## Litigation: White-Collar Crime & Government Investigations
### Senior Statesmen

| Senior Statesmen: distinguished older practitioners | |
| --- | --- |
| Focht Jack | Foulston Siefkin LLP * |

### Leading Individuals

| Band 1 | | |
| --- | --- | --- |
| Bath Thomas J | Bath & Edmonds, P.A (ONP)† | |
| Monnat Dan | Monnat & Spurrier (ONP)† * | |
| Robison Stephen E | Fleeson, Gooing, Coulson & Kitch, LLC | |

| Band 2 | | |
| --- | --- | --- |
| Joseph Stephen M | Joseph, Hollander & Craft LLC. (ONP)† | |
| Rapp David | Hinkle Law Firm LLC | |
| Shultz Craig | Shultz Law Office PA (ONP)† | |
| Thompson Lee | Thompson Law Firm LLC (ONP)† | |

* Indicates firm / individual with profile.
† ONP = Other Notable Practitioner.

## Band 1

### Foulston Siefkin LLP
See profile on p.1303

**THE FIRM** This firm is at the forefront of litigation across Kansas, with an impressive team of 27 attorneys able to tackle every type of commercial dispute. The group displays a depth of experience, with seven attorneys who are members of the American College of Trial Lawyers. Active clients include Cessna Finance, Koch Industries and Spirit AeroSystems.

**Sources say:** *"Foulston Siefkin is the biggest firm, with great resources and lawyers." "Excellent, without exception."*

**KEY INDIVIDUALS James Armstrong** (see p.1299) enjoys a broad litigation practice, covering areas such as shareholder and breach of fiduciary duty claims, IP, employment and contract disputes. He earns respect as a *"very effective lawyer."* **Jay Fowler** (see p.1299) is recognized as an *"excellent," "very •ctive"* litigator, having tried more than 185 jury cases to verdict. He acts for both plaintiffs and defendants on an array of high-value fiduciary duty and business tort matters. **James Oliver** (see p.1300) is based in the firm's Overland Park office and is noted for his complex business litigation work and outstanding appellate law practice. One impressed source states: *"He's probably the premier appellate lawyer in Kansas."* **Gary Ayers** (see p.1299) is respected for his litigation expertise, with a particularly strong reputation for his work in the healthcare sector. He is also noted for his representation of clients in contract disputes, government investigations and white-collar crime matters. **Darrell Warta** (see p.1301) concentrates on tort defense work and has more than 40 years' experience trying cases. He is involved in large personal injury, product liability and professional liability lawsuits. With more than 50 years of experience, **Jack Focht**

(see p.1299) is recognized as *"an icon"* in the Kansas litigation market, and is particularly known for his white-collar crime work. He is special counsel to Foulston Siefkin's litigation and healthcare teams. Former president of the American College of Trial Lawyers, **Mikel Stout** (see p.1301) continues to actively try cases and draws praise from peers, who agree that he is an *"excellent"* attorney. In addition, he advises clients on alternative dispute resolution.

## Band 2

### Depew Gillen Rathbun & McInteer LC
See profile on p.1302

**THE FIRM** This compact but highly effective firm is acclaimed for its focus on litigation, with a team of attorneys who handle a wide array of civil and criminal disputes. Based in Wichita, the group is particularly noted for its efficacy in business, energy and environmental litigation.

**Sources say:** *"They have real business talent."*

**KEY INDIVIDUALS Dennis Gillen** is known as a *"very good commercial lawyer,"* and has built extensive dispute resolution experience. Currently, his practice is slanted toward the mediation domain, where he is a highly active attorney. Commentators note that *"he's in huge demand."* Sources describe **Randall Rathbun** as a *"respected environmental litigator."* He combines expertise in the courtroom with a vast knowledge of complex environmental laws and regulations. He also represents plaintiffs in an array of employment and product liability cases.

### Fleeson, Gooing, Coulson & Kitch, LLC

**THE FIRM** About half of the attorneys at this respected Wichita-based firm focus their practices on litigation, giving the team a depth of expertise. Although the group is perhaps best known for its outstanding work in the natural resources domain, the firm is also equipped to handle areas such as general commercial litigation and white-collar defense, both civil and criminal.

**Sources say:** *"There are very strong litigators there and they have good experience in oil and gas."*

**KEY INDIVIDUALS Stephen Robison** handles civil, criminal and administrative disputes, with a particularly strong reputation for his work in white-collar defense matters. He is met with glowing praise, with one commentator saying: *"If I were going to crown somebody as the leading white-collar crime lawyer, it would be Steve Robison."* **Charles Millsap** is extremely well regarded for his general business and commercial litigation expertise, but he is also experienced in environmental, construction and health-care-related disputes. Sources laud him as *"a really able individual and very good lawyer."* **Ronald Campbell** is a respected trial attorney, recognized for his work in complex commercial disputes. In addition, he is experienced in a variety of personal injury, product liability and construction cases. *"Veteran lawyer"* **David Seely** is a new addition to the rankings. Market sources agree that he is a highly experienced litigator, and he is particularly well known for his work in oil and gas-related litigation and class actions.

## Hinkle Law Firm LLC

**THE FIRM** This firm serves as a one-stop shop for clients' litigation needs, from complex commercial matters to white-collar crime defense. The team frequently draws on the expertise of attorneys in other departments to address all facets of clients' business objectives.

**KEY INDIVIDUALS Geron Bird**'s practice is rapidly expanding as he establishes an impressive reputation for his product liability defense and commercial litigation work. He also has experience in litigation related to ERISA matters, environmental law and employment. **Mitch Herren** has an impressively varied practice, covering all types of business litigation. Sources describe him as an *"excellent"* attorney. **David Rapp** has more than 30 years' experience practicing law in Wichita, and is noted for handling both criminal and civil cases. He is particularly well regarded for his white-collar crime expertise.

## Hite, Fanning & Honeyman LLP

**THE FIRM** Traditionally renowned for insurance defense work, Hite, Fanning & Honeyman has expanded to cover a full array of general commercial litigation matters. The highly regarded group represents clients in industries such as banking, energy, franchising and IP.

**Sources say:** *"They're an excellent firm."*

**KEY INDIVIDUALS Richard Honeyman**, a founding partner at the firm, has nearly 50 years of experience in dispute resolution. He is noted as an expert in civil litigation and mediation. **James Robinson**'s work includes business litigation, professional liability and product liability. He wins acclaim for his involvement in complex financial disputes, including bankruptcies. Trial lawyer **Don Gribble** is prized for his medical malpractice and personal injury work. He frequently handles high-value cases and has been involved in more than 50 jury trials. Senior statesman **Richard Hite** is described as the *"dean of the Bar in Wichita."* He is exceptionally experienced in commercial litigation, oil and gas matters, arbitration and mediation. One commentator states: *"Hite is a truly wonderful lawyer."* **Arthur Chalmers** centers his practice on civil litigation and insurance coverage litigation. With more than 30 years' experience, he is known as a very talented attorney in the Kansas market. One peer enthuses: *"Chalmers is really good."*

## Martin, Pringle, Oliver, Wallace & Bauer, L.L.P.

**THE FIRM** This firm retains a stellar reputation for its product liability work, but is also known for its expertise in areas such as medical malpractice defense, employment litigation, oil and gas and insurance matters. The group also continues to represent long-standing client Hawker Beechcraft on aviation accident litigation matters.

**KEY INDIVIDUALS** Chair of the product liability practice group, **David Wooding** frequently defends manufacturers and pharmaceutical companies in personal injury and wrongful death claims. With more than 30 years of litigation experience, he has also built up specialties in aviation law and medical malpractice defense. **Jeff Spahn** has tried more than 60 cases in state and federal courts and is an experienced arbitrator. He is well versed in product liability, aviation matters and employment litigation. *"Spahn is a good attorney,"* say sources.

## Polsinelli PC

See profile on p.1641

**THE FIRM** This national firm remains a force in Kansas, particularly via its Overland Park branch. The team of nine litigation attorneys is known for trying jury cases, handling class action lawsuits and antitrust matters, and representing professional services firms. It is also noted for its work with clients in the aviation and telecoms sectors. The group has recently represented companies such as LB Steel, MidniteMonkey.com and Sara Lee.

**Sources say:** *"They do an outstanding job preparing cases."* *"They are thoughtful counselors and skilled advocates."*

**KEY INDIVIDUALS Greg Musil** is an active commercial litigator, mediator and arbitrator. He is well respected by peers and clients, with one source noting: *"He has a lot of patience and a great personality."* He recently represented Shriners Hospitals for Children in a substantial matter regarding the alleged misappropriation of funds intended for the benefit of the hospitals. **Anthony Rupp** is a senior partner at the firm and a highly experienced trial attorney. Areas of focus include commercial litigation, medical malpractice and employment discrimination. *"He goes out of his way to provide an excellent service and keep us informed,"* says an enthusiastic client.

## Stinson Morrison Hecker LLP

**THE FIRM** The Wichita and Overland Park branches of this regional firm are noted for their strength in commercial litigation, acting for clients on a wide range of industries, such as telecoms, banking and finance, and pharmaceuticals. The attorneys are also adept at providing alternative dispute resolution services, and continue to attract an enviable list of clients including Sprint Nextel, Hallmark and Westar Energy.

**Sources say:** *"Stinson is a great firm."*

**KEY INDIVIDUALS David Bengtson** is a respected attorney based in the firm's Wichita office. He is recognized for his expertise in oil and gas-related litigation, product liability matters and general commercial litigation. **Daniel Crabtree** practices in both Kansas and Missouri, and frequently represents businesses in state and federal courts.

He also acts for local governments, as was exemplified by his recent representation of the Unified Government of Wyandotte County/Kansas City, Kansas in opposition to a petition to empanel a citizen grand jury.

## Band 3

## Adams Jones Law Firm, PA

**THE FIRM** This solid team of four partners is perhaps best known for its strength in real estate litigation, but is also equipped to handle wide-ranging commercial matters. The attorneys are experienced in proceedings before state and federal courts and regulatory agencies. Key clients include Intrust Bank, J.P. Weigand & Sons and First American Title Insurance.

**Sources say:** *"They are forthright, prepared and knowledgeable of the law."*

**KEY INDIVIDUALS** Dispute resolution expert **Monte Vines** wins praise for his work in the civil litigation space. He frequently represents entities in the banking and finance, legal and real estate industries, as well as general business clients. *"He is a fine lawyer,"* says one commentator. **Bradley Stout** specializes in the niche area of eminent domain. His expertise has seen him represent landowners in condemnation issues relating to both commercial and residential properties across Kansas. He is also noted for his tax appeal litigation work.

## Lathrop & Gage LLP

**THE FIRM** This national firm's Overland Park, Kansas office houses a team of experienced litigators. The group is able to offer expertise in areas such as complex commercial litigation, antitrust, class actions and white-collar criminal defense. The team regularly represents clients in proceedings before state and federal courts.

**KEY INDIVIDUALS Scott Beeler** is a talented practitioner, capable of handling a full range of business disputes, from complex commercial issues, to land use and real estate, to multiparty matters. He focuses on representing clients in the construction, hospitality and energy industries.

## Morris, Laing, Evans, Brock & Kennedy, Chartered

**THE FIRM** Although this firm recently opened a Chicago office, bolstering its national presence, it is the Wichita branch that is best known for its strength in litigation. The group represents plaintiffs and defendants in all varieties of civil and commercial disputes, and is also noted for its alternative dispute resolution services.

**Sources say:** *"An excellent firm. They're one of the best."*

**KEY INDIVIDUALS** With more than 40 years' experience, **Ken Peterson** is acclaimed as one of Kansas's most talented litigators, with a particular focus on complex business and IP cases. He has represented clients in high-stakes disputes all around the USA. One source states: *"He's the best trial lawyer I've ever seen."*

## Triplett, Woolf & Garretson LLC
See profile on p.1304

**THE FIRM** This Wichita firm is a new addition to the rankings, with sources noting that the firm is up-and-coming in the litigation domain. The team handles all types of commercial litigation and is experienced in proceedings before state, federal and appellate courts.

**Sources say:** "*This firm is going places in the Wichita market.*" "*They do a lot of litigation and have good lawyers.*"

**KEY INDIVIDUALS James Walker** (see p.1301) has practiced in Kansas for more than 34 years. Areas of focus include antitrust class action defense and general commercial matters.

## Other Notable Practitioners

**Thomas Bath** of Bath & Edmonds, P.A has been practicing criminal law for more than 25 years and is one of the leading white-collar attorneys in Kansas. He represents both individuals and businesses on a wide range of matters before state and federal courts and regulatory agencies. **Dan Monnat** (see p.1300), a founding partner of Monnat & Spurrier, is hailed as a "*really good*" criminal defense attorney by market sources. He is recognized as a talented trial and appellate lawyer. **David Rebein** of Dodge City firm Rebein Bangerter PA is recognized as a "*premier western Kansas lawyer,*" and has tried hundreds of cases, with an emphasis on personal injury. One source states: "*Rebein is a great person to have on your team.*" Criminal defense attorney **Stephen Joseph** of Joseph, Hollander & Craft LLC is described as a "*big name*" in the Kansas litigation mar-

ket. With more than 40 years' experience, he is extremely "*well respected and well qualified.*" **Craig Shultz** of Shultz Law Office PA concentrates his practice on personal injury, medical malpractice and criminal defense. One source hails him as an "*excellent*" attorney. **Nick Badgerow** is the partner-in-charge at Spencer Fane Britt & Browne LLP's Overland Park office. He is an expert in business and employment litigation and is also a certified construction arbitrator. **Steven Pigg** is based in the Topeka branch of Fisher Patterson Sayler & Smith LLP and is highly skilled in the defense of constitutional and civil rights claims. Sources recognize him as "*very good,*" with one source being particularly "*impressed with his knowledge and experience.*" **Lee Thompson** is the managing partner of Thompson Law Firm LLC. He is an expert in civil litigation, oil and gas litigation and white-collar criminal defense.

# REAL ESTATE

Commentary about individuals can be found under their firm's paragraph. If the firm has no paragraph (is not ranked) look at Other Notable Practitioners.

| Real Estate Leading Firms | |
|---|---|
| **Band 1** | |
| Adams Jones Law Firm, PA | |
| Foulston Siefkin LLP * | |
| Polsinelli PC * | |
| Triplett, Woolf & Garretson LLC * | |
| **Band 2** | |
| Lathrop & Gage LLP | |
| Stinson Morrison Hecker LLP | |
| **Band 3** | |
| Barber Emerson LC | |
| Hinkle Law Firm LLC | |
| Morris, Laing, Evans, Brock & Kennedy, Chartered | |

| Real Estate Senior Statesmen | |
|---|---|
| **Senior Statesmen: distinguished older practitioners** | |
| Hughey Roger | Adams Jones Law Firm, PA |

| Leading Individuals | |
|---|---|
| **Band 1** | |
| Buckley Mert | Adams Jones Law Firm, PA |
| Harnden Ronald H | Triplett, Woolf & Garretson LLC * |
| Heaven Jr Lewis A | Lathrop & Gage LLP |
| Marvin Jack | Stinson Morrison Hecker LLP |
| Petersen John D | Polsinelli PC |
| Wood William | Foulston Siefkin LLP * |
| **Band 2** | |
| Andersen Mark A | Barber Emerson LC |
| Dahlgren Jeffery C | Triplett, Woolf & Garretson LLC * |
| Shadwick Jay | Duggan, Shadwick, Doerr (ONP)† |
| Stark Stephen | Fleeson, Gooing, Coulson & Kitch (ONP)† |
| Theis Roger L | Morris, Laing, Evans, Brock & Kennedy |
| Voth Blankenship Patricia | Foulston Siefkin LLP * |
| Wigner Jr Harry E | Lathrop & Gage LLP |
| Woodworth Stanley N | Polsinelli PC |
| **Band 3** | |
| Hesse Karl N | Foulston Siefkin LLP * |
| Logan Catherine P | Lathrop & Gage LLP |
| Nolan Andrew J | Foulston Siefkin LLP * |
| Standifer Sabrina | Adams Jones Law Firm, PA |
| Stout Bradley A | Adams Jones Law Firm, PA |
| Ward Dale | Hinkle Law Firm LLC |

| Up-and-coming individuals | |
|---|---|
| Neil Darren B | Polsinelli PC |
| Petersen Curtis J | Polsinelli PC |

*Indicates firm / individual with profile.
†ONP = Other Notable Practitioner.

## Band 1

### Adams Jones Law Firm, PA

**THE FIRM** This thriving team of real estate experts maintains its leading position in the Kansas market. It is equipped to handle all facets of real estate law from transactional matters to tax appeals. It is particularly noted for its work with clients in the wind energy, hospitality, medical, retail and senior housing sectors. The group has recently represented companies such as A.G. Holdings, Osage Capital and Oxford Development Holdings.

**Sources say:** "*The nature and quality of their work are of the highest quality.*"

**KEY INDIVIDUALS Mert Buckley** centers his practice on real estate transactions and financing. He regularly represents clients across the hospitality, wind energy and senior housing industries, and continues to serve regional hotel developer A.G. Holdings. "*He's extremely thorough, diligent and well respected by opposing attorneys,*" says one source. **Sabrina Standifer** regularly represents developers, property owners and lenders on a host of transactional issues. She

is noted by clients for her ability to think through complex problems. **Bradley Stout** specializes in the areas of con-

demnation and tax appeals. According to sources, he exhibits exceptional knowledge in those areas and "*he's very good at representing clients.*" He recently acted for Sedgwick County on a number of real estate issues. Senior statesman **Roger Hughey** is of counsel to the firm and a highly experienced attorney. He has built an excellent reputation representing lenders, developers and other businesses in real estate matters.

### Foulston Siefkin LLP
See profile on p.1303

**THE FIRM** The real estate group at Foulston Siefkin continues to impress with its breadth and depth of expertise. The team provides services on the full spectrum of real estate matters, including leasing, financing, energy-related issues and development. A notable highlight was representing LodgeWorks in the $660 million sale of 20 hotels to Hyatt Hotels. Other clients include Foley Equipment, Value Place and Restaurant Management.

**Sources say:** "*Their work is always timely, thoroughly researched and exceptional.*"

**KEY INDIVIDUALS** Head of the real estate department **William Wood** (see p.1301) is recognized as a multitalented attorney. He has a broad practice which covers business and corporate law as well as real estate issues. Described by one commentator as "*very prompt and very knowledgeable,*" **Patricia Voth Blankenship** (see p.1301) has a well-regarded transactional real estate practice. She recently represented enXco in the development of a number of wind energy projects. **Karl Hesse** (see p.1299) advises companies and nonprofit entities on an array of real estate issues. He continues to serve as real estate counsel to the Catholic Diocese of Wichita. One source says: "*I could not be more pleased with the quality and turnaround time of his work.*" **Andrew Nolan** (see p.1300) is regularly involved in real estate transactions and is particularly noted for his expertise in Section 1031 of the Internal Revenue Code and other tax issues.

## Polsinelli PC

See profile on p.1641

**THE FIRM** This firm has a stellar reputation in Kansas for having one of the state's most capable real estate teams. Clients benefit from the group's versatility and ability to provide services across all facets of real estate law, including transactional matters, tax issues, zoning and land use. Clients include Merrill Companies, MD Management and Sunflower Redevelopment.

**Sources say:** *"Each of the individuals has a can-do attitude, is well respected in the legal community and gets work done efficiently."*

**KEY INDIVIDUALS Stanley Woodworth** is an expert in residential real estate development, frequently advising developers and home builders. He specializes in transactional matters and is also noted for his corporate work. **Darren Neil** is highly regarded for his commercial real estate practice. An area of focus is the wind energy sector in which he recently represented Tradewind Energy in the development, financing, construction and operation of an Oklahoma-based wind project. **Curtis Petersen** is fast gaining a reputation as an excellent real estate lawyer. *"He works extremely hard and is very bright,"* says one source. **John Petersen** focuses his practice on the acquisition, development and financing of real estate projects, with commentators adding that he is *"a very good zoning attorney,"* and is *"knowledgeable in government affairs."* He recently acted for hospital chain HCA on the $70 million expansion of the Overland Park Regional Medical Center.

## Triplett, Woolf & Garretson LLC

See profile on p.1304

**THE FIRM** This Wichita firm provides comprehensive real estate services, covering nearly all elements of investment, development, operations and ownership. The small team's experience stretches from conventional real estate purchases, sales and leasing, to areas such as construction, condominium creation and tax planning.

**Sources say:** *"It's a very good firm for real estate."*

**KEY INDIVIDUALS Ronald Harnden** (see p.1299) has a diverse real estate practice which benefits from his strength in corporate law. He is adept at tackling issues ranging from development projects and financing to purchases and sales. A key area of focus for **Jeffery Dahlgren** (see p.1299) is the representation of both landlord and tenants in large leasing transactions. He also excels in the areas of purchases, sales and financing.

## Band 2

## Lathrop & Gage LLP

**THE FIRM** This firm's real estate attorneys are equipped to tackle all aspects of commercial and residential real estate projects, covering subspecialties such as the creation of incentive packages, planning and zoning, litigation and related environmental issues.

**KEY INDIVIDUALS Lewis Heaven** is noted for his skill in handling land use and zoning matters. He previously served as city attorney for the City of Merriam for 18 years, giving him a deep understanding of both real estate development and governmental issues. Sources say: *"He's excellent."* **Harry Wigner** is well versed in all aspects of residential, commercial and industrial real estate development. He is highly experienced and previously spent a stint on a suburban planning commission and on the Kansas Development Finance Authority, boosting his financing and zoning expertise. **Catherine Logan** offers clients city attorney services, as well as advising both public and private clients on matters relating to tax incentives and financing. She is also experienced in a variety of real estate transactions.

## Stinson Morrison Hecker LLP

**THE FIRM** This team of transactional real estate attorneys continues to impress market observers with its strength in areas such as acquisitions and sales, financing, mortgage lending and tax issues. The group also works with attorneys in other practice areas to creatively address the full range of issues affecting clients. The group has recently represented Kansas Speedway, Unified Government of Kansas City/Wyandotte County and The Allen Group.

**Sources say:** *"I consistently receive outstanding advice and support."*

**KEY INDIVIDUALS Jack Marvin** is particularly well known for handling the real estate aspects of energy finance projects and for his representation of lenders in real estate transactions. He recently acted for Wind Capital on a $376 million wind energy project. *"Jack is quick and concise and looks after our best interests,"* say clients.

## Band 3

## Barber Emerson LC

**THE FIRM** Based in Lawrence, this firm is a top choice for clients in northeastern Kansas. The real estate group continues to warrant recognition for its prowess across a range of commercial and residential issues.

**KEY INDIVIDUALS Mark Andersen** wins plaudits from peers for his real estate work. He is recognized by sources as *"results oriented,"* and is noted as an expert in transactional real estate matters.

## Hinkle Law Firm LLC

**THE FIRM** This compact team offers expertise in both commercial and residential real estate matters. Its attorneys have the capacity to undertake work in areas such as development, acquisitions and sales, leasing, financing and tax.

**Sources say:** *"They're one of the hardcore real estate firms in Wichita."*

**KEY INDIVIDUALS Dale Ward** has an impressive record of assisting clients with zoning, leasing, purchases and sales. He also is noted for his knowledge of financing issues.

## Morris, Laing, Evans, Brock & Kennedy, Chartered

**THE FIRM** This firm maintains a good reputation for its real estate offering, with particular strength in its Wichita office. The attorneys are able to guide clients through all aspects of the purchase and sale of commercial and residential properties. Other areas of expertise include land use, title examination and compliance issues.

**KEY INDIVIDUALS Roger Theis** has a broad practice, which covers general corporate law as well as transactional real estate issues. He is also well regarded for his work in the oil and gas domain.

## Other Notable Practitioners

**Jay Shadwick** of Duggan, Shadwick, Doerr & Kurlbaum, P.C. is an expert in business, banking and real estate matters. He wins praise from peers and clients, who describe him as *"a very competent real estate attorney."* **Stephen Stark** of Fleeson, Gooing, Coulson & Kitch, LLC has wide-ranging experience covering nearly all aspects of real estate law. He is also noted for his expertise in environmental matters.

# Leaders' Profiles in Kansas

**ARMSTRONG, James M**
Foulston Siefkin LLP, Wichita
316 291 9576
jarmstrong@foulston.com
*Featured in Litigation (Kansas)*
**Practice Areas:** Commercial and complex litigation, appellate law, and employment and labor. Mr Armstrong has developed a practice in the areas of major commercial litigation, including securities fraud and other shareholder and breach of fiduciary duty claims, oil and gas, intellectual property, employment, and general contract litigation. He has represented clients in major class actions and False Claims Act cases.
**Professional Memberships:** American Bar Association - Litigation Section; Kansas Bar Association; Wichita Bar Association; Kansas Association of Defense Counsel; Kansas Judicial Council - Civil Code Advisory Committee, Civil Rules Committee.

**AYERS, Gary L**
Foulston Siefkin LLP, Wichita
316 291 9530
gayers@foulston.com
*Featured in Litigation (Kansas)*
**Practice Areas:** Commercial and complex litigation, healthcare, and intellectual property. Mr Ayers has represented clients in state and federal lawsuits involving a wide variety of contract disputes, government investigations (Medicare, Medicaid and Department of Defense), white-collar crime, trade secrets, restrictive covenants, trademark and trade dress, and the corporate practice of medicine. In addition, he has represented clients in the dissolution of their marital estates, which most often involve a variety of valuation issues.
**Professional Memberships:** Kansas and American Bar Associations, Health Law Sections; Kansas Association of Hospital Attorneys; American Association of Health Lawyers; Kansas Bar Foundation, Fellow.

**BERNER, Donald**
Foulston Siefkin LLP, Wichita
316 291 9738
dberner@foulston.com
*Featured in Labor & Employment (Kansas)*
**Practice Areas:** Employment & labor, OSHA, and immigration. Mr Berner represents clients in employment relations matters including employment discrimination claims under Title VII, claims under the Family and Medical Leave Act, wage and hour matters under the FLSA and state laws, labor relations issues under the various federal and state laws, health and safety matters involving OSHA, reduction in force issues, and immigration matters. Mr Berner has represented employers in employment-related disputes in federal and state court, administrative agencies,and a wide range of state and local agencies.
**Professional Memberships:** American, Kansas and Wichita Bar Associations; American Immigration Lawyers Association (AILA).

**BYERS, Boyd**
Foulston Siefkin LLP, Wichita
316 291 9716
bbyers@foulston.com
*Featured in Labor & Employment (Kansas)*
**Practice Areas:** Employment and labor. Mr Byers represents clients in employment relations matters. He provides preventive consultation and helps employers implement personnel policies and comply with employment laws. He prepares and reviews employee handbooks, policy manuals, government contractor affirmative action plans, employment contracts, and severance agreements. He handles litigation before federal and state courts and administrative agencies and represents clients with government agency audits and discrimination charges.
**Professional Memberships:** Kansas Bar Association, Employment Law Section, past President; Journal of the Kansas Bar Association, Board of Editors; Defense Research Institute; Kansas Association of Defense Counsel; Kansas Employment Law Letter, Co-Editor.

**CUPPS, Terry C**
Foulston Siefkin LLP, Wichita
316 291 9504
tcupps@foulston.com
*Featured in Corporate/M&A (Kansas)*
**Practice Areas:** Creditors' rights/bankruptcy, banking and financial services, real estate, general business, and commercial and complex litigation. Mr Cupps has extensive and varied experience representing creditors in bankruptcies, out-of-court workouts of problem credits, receiverships and foreclosures. Mr Cupps represents clients in the acquisition and sale of assets of troubled companies in bankruptcies and receiverships. Mr Cupps has substantial experience in representing trustees in the administration and enforcement of defaulted industrial revenue bonds and represents lenders in documenting secured loan transactions.
**Professional Memberships:** Kansas, and Wichita Bar Associations; American Bankruptcy Institute; Wichita and Topeka Area Bankruptcy Councils; Kansas Bar Foundation, Fellow.

**DAHLGREN, Jeffery C**
Triplett, Woolf & Garretson LLC, Wichita
316 630 8100 ext 291
jcdahlgren@twgfirm.com
*Featured in Corporate/M&A (Kansas), Real Estate (Kansas)*
**Practice Areas:** Real estate leasing, acquisition, and sales; business and corporate law; mergers and acquisitions; financing transactions.
**Professional Memberships:** American Bar Association; Kansas Bar Association; Wichita Bar Association.
**Career:** In his real estate practice, Mr Dahlgren assists both landlord and tenant clients in complex leasing transactions, and represents real estate developers and investors in the acquisition, financing, development and sale of commercial, office and industrial real estate. Additionally, Mr Dahlgren regularly counsels clients concerning

business acquisitions and divestitures and a variety of corporate and business operational matters.

**FOCHT, Jack**
Foulston Siefkin LLP, Wichita
316 291 9519
jfocht@foulston.com
*Featured in Litigation (Kansas)*
**Practice Areas:** Commercial and complex litigation, healthcare law, fraud and abuse, white-collar crime, civil rights, employment law, professional responsibility, government investigations and business litigation. Mr Focht has more than 50 years of legal experience. His practice has ranged from high profile criminal cases to complex civil litigation. Mr Focht has directed the defense of numerous individuals and companies targeted for investigation by state and federal government agencies.
**Professional Memberships:** American Bar Foundation, Fellow; Wichita Bar Association, Past President; Kansas Bar Association, Past President; American College of Trial Lawyers, Fellow; National Association of Criminal Defense Attorneys; Kansas Bar Foundation, Fellow.

**FOWLER, Jay**
Foulston Siefkin LLP, Wichita
316 291 9541
jfowler@foulston.com
*Featured in Litigation (Kansas)*
**Practice Areas:** Commercial and complex litigation, professional malpractice, employment and labor, and product liability. Mr Fowler's trial practice emphasizes trial of lawsuits involving commercial relationships, including representation in fiduciary duty litigation and business torts. He handles complex commercial lawsuits, intellectual property and employment disputes. He has tried high-exposure professional negligence cases and has built an extensive civil litigation practice in state and federal court. He has taken in excess of 185 jury cases to verdict.
**Professional Memberships:** American College of Trial Lawyers, Fellow; Kansas Bar Foundation, Fellow; American and Kansas Bar Associations; Wichita Bar Association, President; Kansas Association for Justice.

**GARRETSON, Thomas P**
Triplett, Woolf & Garretson LLC, Wichita
316 630 8100 ext 218
tpgarretson@twgfirm.com
*Featured in Corporate/M&A (Kansas)*
**Practice Areas:** Securities regulation; mergers and acquisitions; business and corporate law; bond counsel/municipal finance/economic development.
**Professional Memberships:** Member of Advisory Committee to the Kansas Securities Commissioner; member of American, Kansas and Wichita Bar Associations; fellow of Kansas Bar Foundation; former adjunct professor of University of Kansas School of Law teaching Business Planning.

**Publications:** Due Diligence in Mergers and Acquisitions of Private Businesses (Kansas Bar Association seminar); Securities Registrations and Exemptions (Wichita Bar Association seminar); author of Securities Regulation chapter of the Kansas Bar Association's Kansas Corporation Law and Practice Handbook – Fourth and Fifth Editions.

**HANISCH, Douglas L**
Foulston Siefkin LLP, Wichita
316 291 9748
dhanisch@foulston.com
*Featured in Labor & Employment (Kansas)*
**Practice Areas:** Employee benefits and ERISA. Mr Hanisch is well known as an attorney in the benefits community. Mr Hanisch advises a diverse and broad spectrum of clients regarding their employee benefit plans and practices. Areas of emphasis include retirement plans, group insurance plans, flexible benefits and cafeteria plans, and nonqualified deferred compensation arrangements.
**Professional Memberships:** American, Kansas, and Wichita Bar Associations.

**HARNDEN, Ronald H**
Triplett, Woolf & Garretson LLC, Wichita
316 630 8100 ext 292
rharnden@twgfirm.com
*Featured in Real Estate (Kansas)*
**Practice Areas:** Real estate law; business and corporate law; mergers and acquisitions; financing transactions.
**Professional Memberships:** American Bar Association; Kansas Bar Association; Kansas Bar Foundation; Wichita Bar Association.
**Career:** Ron Harnden's practice includes business, commercial and real estate matters. In recent years, he has been heavily involved in representing clients in the purchase, exchange, sale, leasing and development of real estate and real estate improvements, financing transactions, the acquisition and sale of businesses, in a variety of other contract matters, and in analyzing and advising clients concerning many topics pertaining to their business and personal affairs.

**HESSE, Karl N**
Foulston Siefkin LLP, Wichita
316 291 9554
khesse@foulston.com
*Featured in Real Estate (Kansas)*
**Practice Areas:** Real estate, general business, church and school law, and adoption/probate law. He advises both not-for-profit and for-profit businesses including large and small companies, charitable and religious entities. As general counsel to the Catholic Diocese of Wichita, its schools, churches, and related projects, Mr Hesse advises in the areas of real estate, non-profit status, employment law, constitutional and contract law. He has represented clients in both exemption and valuation tax appeals before the Kansas Court of Tax Appeals.

**Professional Memberships:** American, Kansas and Wichita Bar Associations; National Diocesan Attorneys Association; Rocky Mountain Mineral Law Foundation.

## HURT, Jeffrey
Foulston Siefkin LLP, Overland Park
913 253 2165
jhurt@foulston.com
*Featured in Labor & Employment (Kansas)*

**Practice Areas:** Employment and Labor. Mr Hurt has more than 20 years experience in a broad range of employment, traditional labor, and human resource related matters. His practice includes preventive advice to employers on employment law subjects and representation of employers in litigated matters before administrative agencies, including the Department of Labor, the United States Equal Employment Opportunity Commission and similar State agencies, the Occupational Health and Safety Administration, the National Labor Relations Board, and the Kansas Division of Workers Compensation, and claims before arbitrators and state and federal courts.

**Professional Memberships:** Kansas Bar Association,Employment Law Section-past secretary/treasurer.

## LACEY, Jason P
Foulston Siefkin LLP, Wichita
316 267 6371
*Featured in Labor & Employment (Kansas)*

**Practice Areas:** Employee Benefits/ERISA. Mr Lacey practices primarily in the areas of income taxation, ERISA, employee benefits, and executive compensation. He assists taxable and tax-exempt employers with employee benefit and executive compensation issues, including design and administration of welfare benefit plans and qualified and nonqualified pension, retirement savings, and deferred compensation plans. He also represents clients with respect to the tax and business aspects of entity formation, tax-advantaged exchanges and reorganizations, and tax controversies, and has significant practice experience in the areas of estate administration, estate and gift taxation, and the federal tax aspects of municipal finance transactions.

## METZ, Eric B
Triplett, Woolf & Garretson LLC, Wichita
316 630 8100 ext 215
ebmetz@twgfirm.com
*Featured in Labor & Employment (Kansas)*

**Practice Areas:** Employment law; civil rights law; education law; civil and business litigation.

**Professional Memberships:** Kansas Association of Defense Counsel; Defense Research Institute; National Association of College and University Attorneys; American Bar Association; Kansas Bar Association; Wichita Bar Association.

**Publications:** Helping Clients Find the Best Employees and Protect Themselves in the Process: Background Checks and Noncompetition Agreements; Current Developments in Employment Law; Addressing Your Company's Exposure to Employment Related Lawsuits; Kansas Employment Law: Hiring and Firing So

You Won't Get Sued (or Lose if You Do); Conducting a Successful Performance Appraisal; Coaching and Counseling Employees.

## MONNAT, Dan
Monnat & Spurrier, Wichita
316 264 2800
dan.monnat@monnat.com
*Featured in Litigation (Kansas)*

**Practice Areas:** Defense and appellate counselor in the areas of criminal law, white-collar criminal law, and governmental investigations. Federal Court Admissions: U.S. Supreme Court; U.S. Court of Appeals (10th Circuit); U.S. District Courts of Kansas, Nebraska, Colorado and Western District of Missouri. State Court Admissions: Kansas and Nebraska.

**Professional Memberships:** Fellow, International Academy of Trial Lawyers; Fellow, American College of Trial Lawyers; Fellow, Litigation Counsel of America; Past Board Member, National Association of Criminal Defense Lawyers; Past President, Kansas Association of Criminal Defense Lawyers.

**Career:** Mr Monnat has 37 years of extensive litigation experience in high-profile, white-collar, and complex criminal cases. Founded Monnat & Spurrier, Chartered, in 1985. Frequent author on criminal defense topics. Nationwide lecturer whose topics include Crouching Tiger, Hidden Dragon: Kung Fu Strategies for the Courtroom.

**Publications:** Has authored Sentencing, Probation, and Collateral Consequences, a chapter of the 'Kansas Bar Association's Kansas Criminal Law Handbook, 4th edition.'. He recently co-authored How to Free A Guilty Client by Arguing Entrapment by Estoppel, 'NACDL The Champion', December 2010, as well as Unsealing Search Warrant Materials for Uncharged Clients, 'NACDL The Champion', July 2006.

**Personal:** California State University, San Francisco, BA, cum laude; Creighton University School of Law, JD; Gerry Spence's Trial Lawyers College and Graduate Course I.

## NOLAN, Andrew J
Foulston Siefkin LLP, Wichita
316 267 6371
anolan@foulston.com
*Featured in Real Estate (Kansas)*

**Practice Areas:** Taxation, closely-held businesses, real estate, mergers and acquisitions, and general business. Mr Nolan assists investors and developers with a wide range of commercial real estate matters, including forward and reverse like kind exchanges, sales and acquisitions, titles and survey review, leasing, lending, and financing. Mr Nolan also assists closely-held business entities (including corporations, LLCs, and partnerships) and their principals in entity formation, business and tax planning, restructuring, and mergers and acquisitions.

**Professional Memberships:** American Bar Association, Tax Section; Kansas Bar Association, Tax Law Section, Executive Committee; Leadership Wichita, Wichita Area Chamber of Commerce.

## OLIVER, James D
Foulston Siefkin LLP, Wichita
913 253 2145
joliver@foulston.com
*Featured in Litigation (Kansas)*

**Practice Areas:** Commercial and complex litigation, appellate law, securities, antitrust, franchise, general business, and administrative/regulatory. Mr Oliver's knowledge and experience includes a number of registered securities offerings, franchise offerings, mergers and acquisitions, and debt financings. He has devoted much of his time to the trial and appeal of complex business litigation. Mr Oliver is the firm's appellate practice team leader and is partner-in-charge of the firm's Overland Park office.

**Professional Memberships:** American Bar Association, Antitrust and Business Law Sections; Kansas Bar Foundation, past President; Wichita Bar Association, past President; Kansas, Johnson County and Kansas City Metropolitan Bar Associations.

## PALECKI, Scott C.
Foulston Siefkin LLP, Wichita
316 291 9578
spalecki@foulston.com
*Featured in Corporate/M&A (Kansas)*

**Practice Areas:** Health care, taxation, mergers and acquisitions, and general business. Mr Palecki practices primarily in the health care regulatory and health care transactional areas. He works with health care clients on matters relating to operational, regulatory, reimbursement and compliance issues, including the Stark law, fraud and abuse, managed care, tax exemption issues, individual and facility licensure, joint ventures, medical staff bylaws, peer review and credentialing matters, and Medicare and Medicaid certification and reimbursement. He also represents clients in state and local taxation matters.

**Professional Memberships:** American Health Lawyers Association; Kansas Bar Association-Health Law Section, past president; American, Topeka, Wichita Bar Associations.

## RECTOR, Jay
Foulston Siefkin LLP, Wichita
316 291 9722
jrector@foulston.com
*Featured in Labor & Employment (Kansas)*

**Practice Areas:** Employment and labor, employee benefits, and OSHA. Mr Rector is the practice group leader for the firm's labor and employment law litigation team. Mr Rector represents clients in a wide variety of employment, labor and ERISA benefit matters. He has a broad base of experience in labor-management relations, advising employers in specialized and general employment and benefit matters, and in representing employers in labor arbitrations, OSHA investigations, wage and hour disputes and state and federal claims.

**Professional Memberships:** American Bar Association Section of Labor and Employment Law; Kansas Bar Association, Employment Law Section; Wichita Bar Association.

## RHODES JR, Forrest T
Foulston Siefkin LLP, Wichita
316 267 6371
*Featured in Labor & Employment (Kansas)*

**Practice Areas:** Employment and Labor. Mr Rhodes represents employers in a diverse range of employment-related matters, including government audits and private litigation under state and federal employment discrimination laws, the federal and state wage and hour laws, and laws administered by the Occupational Safety and Health Administration. Mr Rhodes assists employers with the review and development of employment policies including the proper handling of situations involving military leave or leave under FMLA. He represents employers on labor-management issues, including union organizing efforts, labor contract negotiations, and responding to unfair labor practice charges filed with the National Labor Relations Board.

## RUPE, Alan L
Kutak Rock LLP, Wichita
316 609 7900
alan.rupe@kutakrock.com
*Featured in Labor & Employment (Kansas)*

**Practice Areas:** Partner and head of firm's National Employment Practice Group. American Board of Trial Advocates Trial Specialist; Advocate in American Board of Trial Advocacy; Best Lawyers; Super Lawyers. Named to BTI's Client Service A-Team 2011. Lead counsel in more than 135 civil jury trials. Litigates employment class and collective actions nationwide. Wide-ranging experience in employment, civil rights and constitutional law. Contributing author, Kansas Employment Law Handbook and Kansas Annual Survey of Law, Civil Rights Section. Provides continuing legal education to attorneys and human resource professionals.

**Career:** Education: BA, University of Kansas (1972); JD, Washburn University School of Law (1975).

## SORENSEN, Harvey
Foulston Siefkin LLP, Wichita
316 291 9774
hsorensen@foulston.com
*Featured in Corporate/M&A (Kansas)*

**Practice Areas:** Taxation, estate planning, mergers and acquisitions, general business, private equity, venture capital, and family business enterprise. Mr Sorensen's practice focuses on mergers and acquisitions, private equity transactions and venture capital investments, income and intergenerational tax planning, and economic development incentives. His practice includes advising family-owned businesses through the life cycle of the business and the family.

**Professional Memberships:** American College of Tax Counsel, Fellow; American Bar Association, Business Law and Tax Sections; Kansas Bar Association, Tax Section, past President; Lex Mundi, Inc., State and Local Tax Committee, past Chair; World Services Group, past Chairman; Integrated Advisory Group International.

**STANLEY, Douglas L**
Foulston Siefkin LLP, Wichita
316 291 9502
dstanley@foulston.com
*Featured in Labor & Employment (Kansas)*
**Practice Areas:** Employment and labor. Mr Stanley is the firm's Managing Partner. He has served as chief negotiator of numerous collective bargaining agreements and advised employers in union attempts to organize groups of employees. Mr Stanley also has extensive experience in responding to unfair labor practice charges, wage and hour disputes, and employment discrimination charges before state and federal administrative agencies. Mr Stanley has tried numerous employment arbitrations in both union and non-union settings.
**Professional Memberships:** The College of Labor & Employment Lawyers, Fellow; American, Kansas and Wichita Bar Associations; Employment Law Section of the Kansas Bar Association, past President.

**STOUT, Mikel**
Foulston Siefkin LLP, Wichita
316 291 9516
mstout@foulston.com
*Featured in Litigation (Kansas)*
**Practice Areas:** Commercial litigation, environmental law, employment and labor, and mediation/dispute resolution. Mr Stout handles employment and complex commercial cases. He specializes in high exposure litigation with an emphasis on trial practice. He is one of the most well-known trial lawyers in Kansas and has tried many of the region's high profile employment, environmental and commercial cases. His practice includes consultation on litigation problem solving and alternative dispute resolution.
**Professional Memberships:** American College of Trial Lawyers, past President, Fellow and Board of Regents; Wichita Bar Association, past President; Kansas Bar Foundation, past President; Kansas Association of Defense Counsel, past President.

**THELEN, Trisha A**
Foulston Siefkin LLP, Wichita
316 291 9586
tthelen@foulston.com
*Featured in Labor & Employment (Kansas)*
**Practice Areas:** Ms Thelen's practice is divided between commercial and employment litigation, as well as counseling employers on how to avoid or resolve disputes with employees. She represents clients in industries ranging from aviation, oil and gas, construction, manufacturing and retail. Ms Thelen has litigated cases in state and federal courts as well as AAA arbitrations. She has exten-

sive experience in class actions. Ms Thelen leads the firm's Electronic Discovery Committee and advises clients on best practices for the retention and production of e-mail and electronic files.
**Professional Memberships:** The Sedona Conference Working Group on Electronic Document Retention and Production.

**THENGVALL, Andrew**
Foulston Siefkin LLP, Wichita
316 291 9765
athengvall@foulston.com
*Featured in Corporate/M&A (Kansas)*
**Practice Areas:** General business, mergers & acquisitions, franchise, private equity & venture capital, securities, and banking & financial services. Mr Thengvall's practice includes an emphasis on mergers and acquisitions, franchise, general business law and corporate practice. Mr Thengvall represents start-up and established franchisors with state and federal compliance issues and general business concerns. Mr Thengvall also represents many public and private companies in mergers and acquisitions, securities transactions, private equity transactions, tax credit financing, venture capital investments, financing, contract negotiations and preparation, creation and termination of business entities, business entity ownership issues, and general business matters.

**TRENKLE, William**
Foulston Siefkin LLP, Overland Park
913 253 2150
btrenkle@foulston.com
*Featured in Corporate/M&A (Kansas)*
**Practice Areas:** Corporate, general business, taxation, banking and financial services, estate planning and probate, and health law. Mr Trenkle practices as a general business lawyer with an emphasis in taxation. Businesses he represents range from large agri-business enterprises to a multi-state retailer. This representation includes commercial transactions, entity formation, tax planning, estate planning, and succession planning.
**Professional Memberships:** American, Southwest Kansas, and Johnson County Bar Associations; Kansas Bar Association, Tax Section - Executive Committee and past President, Corporation and Banking Section - past President; Kansas Judicial Council Special Committee on Inheritance Tax; Kansas Supreme Court Client Protection Fund Commission.

**TRIPLETT, Thomas C**
Triplett, Woolf & Garretson LLC, Wichita
316 630 8100 ext 221
tctriplett@twgfirm.com
*Featured in Corporate/M&A (Kansas)*

**Practice Areas:** Business and corporate law; taxation; mergers and acquisitions; estate planning - wills, trusts and probate; financing transactions.
**Professional Memberships:** American Bar Association; Kansas Bar Association; Wichita Bar Association; Past President of the Tax Section of The Kansas Bar Association; Fellow of The American College of Tax Counsel.

**VOTH BLANKENSHIP, Patricia**
Foulston Siefkin LLP, Wichita
316 291 9767
pvoth@foulston.com
*Featured in Real Estate (Kansas)*
**Practice Areas:** Real estate, general business, agribusiness, and wind energy. Ms Voth Blankenship assists clients with commercial, agricultural and residential real estate matters, focusing her practice on real estate law. Representative areas of her real estate practice include: sales and acquisitions, development, lending and financing, wind farm agreements, Section 1031 tax-deferred exchanges, leasing, owners' associations and covenants, and title and survey review.
**Professional Memberships:** American Bar Association, Real Property Section and Business Section Member; Kansas Bar Association, Real Estate Title Standards Committee, and Real Estate Section Member; Wichita Bar Association, Real Estate Committee, past Chair; Wichita Women Attorneys Association.

**WALKER, James A**
Triplett, Woolf & Garretson LLC, Wichita
316 630 8100 ext 239
jawalker@twgfirm.com
*Featured in Litigation (Kansas)*
**Practice Areas:** Civil and business litigation; class action defense; antitrust; higher asset divorce litigation.
**Professional Memberships:** Fellow of the Litigation Counsel of America; Wesley E. Brown Inn of Court; American Bar Association; Kansas Bar Association; Wichita Bar Association.
**Publications:** Contributing author, "A Practitioner's Guide to Class Actions", ABA Publication (2010).

**WARTA, Darrell**
Foulston Siefkin LLP, Wichita
316 291 9514
dwarta@foulston.com
*Featured in Litigation (Kansas)*
**Practice Areas:** Commercial and complex litigation, professional malpractice, products liability, and mediation/dispute resolution. Mr Warta has spent over 35 years successfully trying civil lawsuits in Wichita and throughout the state of Kansas. Mr Warta is lead trial counsel specializing

in defending high exposure personal injury, product liability and professional liability jury trials.
**Professional Memberships:** American College of Trial Lawyers, Fellow; Federation of Defense and Corporate Counsel; Kansas Association of Defense Counsel; American, Kansas and Wichita Bar Associations.

**WOOD, William**
Foulston Siefkin LLP, Wichita
316 291 0772
bwood@foulston.com
*Featured in Corporate/M&A (Kansas), Real Estate (Kansas)*
**Practice Areas:** Mergers and acquisitions, securities, real estate, franchise, banking, private equity, venture capital, and general business. Mr Wood is the firm's General Business Practice Group leader and represents public and private companies in mergers and acquisitions, real estate, securities, franchising, private equity, venture capital, financing, contract negotiations and preparation, creation and termination of business entities, business entity ownership issues, and general business matters.
**Professional Memberships:** American Bar Association, member Franchise Forum and Section of Business Law Legal Opinions Committee; Kansas Bar Association, Corporate Banking & Business Law Section, member and Past President of Executive Committee, and Wichita Bar Association.

**WRIGHT, Wyatt**
Foulston Siefkin LLP, Overland Park
913 253 2152
wwright@foulston.com
*Featured in Labor & Employment (Kansas)*
**Practice Areas:** Employment and labor, education/public entity, and product liability. Mr Wright's employment law and litigation practice includes civil rights litigation, breach of employment contracts, wrongful and retaliatory discharge, and constitutional claims involving public entity employers. He defends employers involving harassment and discrimination claims. He works with employers with employment and employee discipline issues and represents management in negotiating employee severance agreements. He works with healthcare providers regarding employment and labor issues, as well as risk management and peer review matters.
**Professional Memberships:** Kansas City Metropolitan and Johnson County Associations; Defense Research Institute; Kansas Association of Defense Counsel.

# DEPEW GILLEN RATHBUN & MCINTEER, LC

www.depewgillen.com **tel:** 316 262 4000 **fax:** 316 265 3819

**Managing Partner:** Charles C Steincamp
Number of partners: 7   Number of other lawyers: 2

**OFFICE**

KANSAS

**WICHITA:** 8301 East 21st Street North, Suite 450, KS
67206
Tel: 316 262 4000   Fax: 316 265 3819
Email: dg@depewgillen.com

## Firm Overview:

Depew Gillen Rathbun & McInteer, LC is a mid-size general practice law firm in Wichita, Kansas. With the firm's roots tracing back to 1885, the firm has built a highly-respected firm practicing administrative, environmental, aviation, business, energy, estate and trust planning, civil practice, litigation and mediation. Attorneys are individually known on a state and national-level for their expertise, skills and ethical practices. Many firm members have backgrounds and experience in non-legal professions such as geology, biology, chemistry, business administration and aviation that inform and complement our ability to provide legal services. Depew Gillen Rathbun & McInteer brings a very high level of experience to client issues in a variety of fields. The firm's small size enables it to maintain personal involvement with its clients. Depew Gillen Rathbun & McInteer is dedicated to serving its clients with integrity and the best representation.

## Main Areas of Practice:

### Litigation:
The firm's lawyers are not only skilled in the traditional areas of litigation such as personal injury and product liability, but also in advocating in the areas of environmental law, oil and gas, employment and other matters that affect the personal and business affairs of clients. Randy Rathbun leads the litigation efforts. As a former United States Attorney and Fellow of the American College of Trial Lawyers, his experience allows the firm to engage in complex litigation of all types. Dennis Gillen is responsible for the firm's commercial and business litigation.

### General Business:
Depew Gillen Rathbun & McInteer's lawyers have the experience and skill to represent a business through any stage of its existence from formation through expansion, succession planning, and, if necessary, contraction or restructuring. The firm's lawyers are familiar with the statutory, legal, financial and tax consequences involving sole proprietorship, joint ventures, partnerships, limited partnerships, business trusts, the various types of corporations (general, close, non-profit, professional, 'C,' 'S,' etc.) and limited liability companies and partnerships, and the firm can guide its clients through the negotiation and structuring necessary to achieve the best possible results.

### Aviation:
The Federal Aviation Administration, Department of Transportation and National Transportation Safety Board each have jurisdiction-often overlapping-over areas of aviation. The firm regularly represents clients before each of these agencies and before comparable agencies throughout the UK and the ECC and many other countries. Lawyers have a working knowledge of the various international conventions and treaties governing aviation.

### Employment:
Employment relationships are heavily regulated by numerous federal and state agencies. Depew Gillen Rathbun & McInteer regularly represent employers and employees in employment matters before the State and Federal Courts, Equal Employment Opportunity Commission, the Occupational Safety and Health Administration, the Department of Labor and other applicable federal and state agencies.

### Energy:
The firm represents numerous regional oil and gas independent operators and investors on their various leasing, exploration, development and financing transactions and certain major oil and gas companies on selected transactions. The firm frequently appears before the Kansas Corporation Commission and has general familiarity with the laws and regulations of other states with significant energy production

### Environmental:
Depew Gillen Rathbun & McInteer represent individuals, business entities and political bodies, before various state and federal agencies including the United States Environmental Protection Agency, the Kansas Department of Health and Environment, other state environmental agencies and various local and regional health and environmental agencies. This representation has included among other things: violations representation, compliance issues, permitting, clean-up, regulatory inspections, investigations, toxic torts and wind energy.

### Healthcare:
The firm has been involved with formation and business needs of numerous healthcare providers. Depew Gillen Rathbun & McInteer consult on a regular basis with those clients in the ever-changing administrative interpretations of rules and regulations governing the healthcare industry, keeping abreast of these changes to meet the needs of its clients. The firm also appears before the Health Care Financing Administration (HCFA), Social and Rehabilitation Services (SRS) and the Kansas Department of Health.

### Estate & Trust Planning:
Personal and business succession planning, protection and care of children and other loved ones, and the ever present and impending tax consequences, require that the client have the best and most current assistance available. Throughout its existence Depew Gillen Rathbun & McInteer has assisted its clients to fulfill this need.

### Mediation & Arbitration:
The firm is committed to alternate dispute resolution. Today's litigation may involve costs which can become unreasonable or even prohibitive. Depew Gillen Rathbun & McInteer has participated in and administered various forms of alternate dispute resolution including: binding and non-binding arbitration, mediation, negotiation and nonjudicial trial. Dennis Gillen provides over 30 years of experience in this field.

### Mergers & Acquisitions:
Depew Gillen Rathbun & McInteer has assisted hundreds of businesses in their mergers, acquisitions, sales and reorganizations. Clients have varied from small family companies to large publicly traded institutions. The deals have been structured using stock, cash, other assets and techniques to achieve the business and tax goals clients desired.

### Clients:
Advanced PT, LLC; Aero Controls, Inc.; Ahavath Achim-Hebrew Congregation; Anadarko Petroleum Corporation; Anderson Energy, Inc.; Associated Material & Supply Co., Inc.; Bachus & Son, Inc. dba The Yard Store; CITGO Petroleum Corp.; Custom RX; Downing & Lahey, Inc.; Dugan Truck Line; EOG Resources, Inc.; Evenson Auctioneers, Inc.; Globe Engineering, Inc.; Heartland Cardiology, P.A.; Heckendorn Manufacturing Co., Inc.; J.P. Morgan Chase Bank, N.A.; Kansas Foundation for Medical Care, Inc.; Kansas Surgery and Recovery Center, LLC; McCoy Petroleum Corporation; Murfin Drilling, Inc.; Pintal Petroleum, Ltd.; Professional Insurance Management, Inc.; Range Oil Company, Inc.; Ritchie Exploration, Inc.; Sauerwein Construction Co.; Spurrier Chemical Cos.; Stannard Construction Co., Inc.; Sullivan Higdon & Sink, Inc.; Trans Pacific Oil; Walz, Harman & Huffman Construction, Inc.; Great Plains Manufacturing, Inc.; Shell Exploration & Production Co.; ConocoPhillips.

# FOULSTON SIEFKIN

**www.**foulston.com **tel:** 316 267 6371 **fax:** 316 267 6345

**Managing Partner:** Douglas L Stanley
Number of partners: 59   Number of other attorneys: 30

### Firm Overview:
Foulston Siefkin LLP is the largest, and one of the oldest law firms in Kansas, tracing its origins to 1919. Today the firm has over 85 attorneys, and has offices in Wichita, the state's largest city; Topeka, the state's capital; and Overland Park, the heart of commerce in the Kansas City area. Foulston Siefkin is the only Kansas member of Lex Mundi, Integrated Advisory Group International, State Law Resources, and World Services Group.

### Main Areas of Practice

**Administrative & Regulatory:**
The firm represents companies, before the Kansas Corporation Commission, the Kansas Racing and Gaming Commission and other agencies.

**Appellate:**
Foulston Siefkin attorneys have a reputation for incisive legal writing and determined advocacy and have been counsel of record in more reported federal and state cases in Kansas than any other firm.

**Banking, Financial Services & Bankruptcy:**
Foulston Siefkin is experienced representing lenders, financial institutions and other creditors in lending transactions, disputes, securities issues, loan enforcement, creditors' rights and bankruptcy litigation.

**Commercial & Complex Litigation:**
The firm handles every variety of commercial litigation from the simple contract dispute to complex litigation, including class action, qui tam and white collar criminal defense cases. The litigation group includes seven members of the American College of Trial Lawyers.

**Construction:**
Foulston Siefkin attorneys assist construction industry clients with a wide range of construction projects, from conception through completion, and any dispute resolution.

**Employment, Labor & Workers Compensation:**
Over 20 employment law attorneys advise and represent employers in the full range of issues arising from the employer/employee relationship. The firm's labor lawyers are experienced in responding to union organizing efforts, representing employers in unfair labor practice proceedings and negotiating collective bargaining agreements.

**Energy:**
Foulston Siefkin attorneys understand the complex issues involved in the oil & gas, electric, ethanol, biofuel and biomass, wind and nuclear sectors, and provide service in the areas of exploration, financial and commercial transactions, purchase and sales, operational production issues, title matters, leasing, marketing, transportation, regulatory compliance and litigation.

**Environmental & Water Rights:**
Foulston Siefkin is experienced in all areas of environmental law, related toxic tort litigation, regulatory and transactional areas and water rights issues in Kansas. Their attorneys have relationships with regulators and consultants on local, state, and national levels. The team includes a Fellow of the American College of Environmental Lawyers.

**Franchise:**
The firm has represented local, regional and national franchisors, franchisees and franchise associations, including some of the best known franchise names, in the full range of franchise law issues.

**General Business:**
The firm's experience in representing a diverse range of business clients, ranging from industry leading companies, to private equity firms, to sole proprietors, in local, state, regional, national and international transactions provides a wide-ranging perspective allowing the business attorneys to find creative and resourceful solutions to business issues.

**Health Law & Senior Care:**
The firm's health law and senior care practice groups are experienced in handling complex government regulations and government investigations and are knowledgeable in Kansas and federal health care matters, including the Stark law, fraud and abuse and tax laws.

**Insurance Defense:**
Foulston Siefkin's insurance defense attorneys have decades of experience and one of the most active trial practices in the region, defending medical malpractice actions, product liability and personal injury claims.

**Life Science & Biotechnology:**
The firm actively represents bioscience clients throughout Kansas. The firm handles legal issues ranging from the formation of a company to its commercialization and continued success.

**Mergers & Acquisitions:**
The firm's depth and experience in the structuring, financing and successful completion of acquisitions, divestitures, joint ventures and other business transactions rivals that of any law firm in the region.

### OFFICES

KANSAS

**WICHITA:** 1551 N. Waterfront Parkway, Suite 100, KS 67206
Tel: 316 267 6371  Fax: 316 267 6345
Email: info@foulston.com

**OVERLAND PARK:** 9225 Indian Creek Parkway, 32 Corporate Woods, Ste 600, KS 66210
Tel: 913 498 2100  Fax: 913 498 2101

**TOPEKA:** 534 S. Kansas Ave., Bank of America Tower, Ste 1400, KS 66603
Tel: 785 233 3600  Fax: 785 233 1610

**Real Estate:**
Foulston Siefkin's real estate attorneys provide legal services on all types of real estate transactions. Real estate clients include developers, investors, lenders, borrowers, sellers, purchasers, landlords, tenants, landowners, businesses and entrepreneurs.

**Taxation & Employee Benefits:**
The team assists individuals and businesses interpret, apply and utilize the rules of ERISA, the Internal Revenue Code and state laws. Foulston Siefkin's taxation services include representation before the IRS, Kansas Department of Revenue and other taxing authorities and agencies, including all matters of tax litigation. Seven team attorneys hold an LLM. in taxation.

**Clients:**
The firm represents a broad range of clients, including major financial institutions, corporations, public utilities, insurance companies, health care providers, bioscience companies, manufacturers, franchisors and franchisees, agricultural and natural resource producers and processors, professional entities, construction companies and contractors and service providers. Clients include: All American Adoptions, AVIVA, Bank of America, N.A, The Boeing Company, Bombardier Aerospace Learjet, Cargill Meat Solutions Corporation, Catholic Diocese of Wichita, Cessna Aircraft Company, The Coleman Company, Inc., Commerce Bank, Cox Communications, Delta Dental Plan of Kansas, Inc., Envision, Inc., enXco, Fox and Hound Restaurant Group, Freddy's Frozen Custard, LLC, Galichia Medical Group, P.A., Hawker Beechcraft Corp., Hays Medical Center, Iberdrola Renewables, ICM, Inc., Invista, KCAMP, Koch Industries, Inc., KU Medical Center Research Institute, Larksfield Place, Neuterra Healthcare, Newman University, Schaefer Johnson Cox Frey Architecture, Spirit AeroSystems, Inc., Stormont-Vail HealthCare, Inc., Value Place, LLC, Via Christi Health System, Viega LLC, Wichita Metro Chamber of Commerce, and Wichita State University.

# TRIPLETT WOOLF & GARRETSON LLC

www.twgfirm.com **tel:** 316 630 8100 **fax:** 316 630 8101

**Managing Partner:** Tad Patton
Number of partners: 16
Number of associates: 5

**OFFICES**

KANSAS

**WICHITA:** 2959 N. Rock Road, Suite 300, KS 67226
Tel: 316 630 8100   Fax: 316 630 8101
Email: twg@twgfirm.com

## Firm Overview:

Since its formation in 1985, TWG has been recognized as a full service law firm providing its clients with consistent, high quality legal representation and results. Large enough to provide comprehensive legal advice in a prompt and thorough manner, yet small enough to maintain personal contact between senior attorneys and clients, TWG is a diverse, innovative law firm, actively assisting its clients in business, in court, and in their personal legal needs.

## Main Areas of Practice:

### Business Organization & Financing:

TWG assists its clients in all facets of business formation, acquisition, reorganization, liquidation, mergers, stock and asset purchases and dispositions, and related tax consequences.
**Contact:** Jeff Dahlgren

### Civil & Business Litigation:

TWG attorneys provide aggressive representation in business and commercial litigation, construction, OSHA investigations, employment disputes, environmental, energy and oil and gas-related matters.
**Business Litigation Contact:** Jim Walker
**Civil Litigation Contact:** John Woolf

### Construction:

TWG represents developers, contractors and sub-contractors in contract negotiation and drafting, as well as litigation, arbitration and alternative dispute resolution.
**Contact:** Jeff Leonard

### Employment Law:

The firm has expertise in compliance and preventive measures, wage and hour issues, contract drafting (including employment, non-competition, confidentiality and similar agreements), defense and prosecution of administrative charges, employment litigation, including discrimination ADA, FMLA and ERISA.
**Contact:** Eric Metz

### Estate Planning:

TWG's knowledgeable estate planning attorneys design plans uniquely suited to each client and incorporate TWG tax experts to assist in handling the most complicated estate plans.
**Contact:** Tad Patton

### Fiduciary Litigation:

TWG represents financial institutions, individual fiduciaries, beneficiaries and heirs in all forms of disputes related to trusts, decedent's estates and conservatorships.
**Contact:** Rachael Pirner

### Intellectual Property:

TWG has expertise in the protection and enforcement of trademarks, service marks, trade secrets and copyright applications. TWG is experienced in software development, licensing and confidentiality agreements.
**Contact:** Andrew Kovar

### Municipal Finance:

TWG represents cities, counties and other municipalities, as well as underwriters and conduit borrowers, in the issuance of municipal bonds and other specialized debt obligations, both taxable and tax-exempt, including the issuance of industrial revenue bonds by municipalities.
**Contact:** J T Klaus

### Natural Resources Law:

TWG counsels individuals, companies and utilities which own, produce, transport and market various natural resources – particularly oil and gas.
**Contact:** Tim McKee

### Real Estate Law:

The firm represents developers in the purchase, sale, leasing and development of both residential and commercial properties, in addition to landlords and tenants in leasing transactions, and lenders and borrowers with respect to real estate financing, contracts, deeds, leases, zoning matters, code compliance, foreclosures and property tax assessments and appeals.
**Contact:** Ron Harnden

### Securities:

TWG represents both issuers and underwriters in the private placement and registration of securities, as well as broker/dealers, investment advisers, brokerage firms and others, appearing before the NASD and Kansas Securities Commissioner.
**Contact:** Tom Garretson

### Taxation:

TWG assists businesses and individuals with tax planning and all tax-related issues including resolution of tax disputes with local, state and federal bodies and participates extensively in corporate and commercial transactions.
**Contact:** Tom Triplett

## Clients:

Abengoa Bioenergy Corporation; Ablah Enterprises, Inc.; ATT Corp.; British American Tobacco Co.; City of Andover, KS; City of Emporia, KS; City of Garden City, KS; City of Mulvane, KS; City of Wichita, KS; Cobalt Boats, LLC; Coca-Cola Enterprises, Inc.; Commerce Bank;  Davidson Securities; Dean & DeLuca, Inc.; Devlin Enterprises, Inc.; Devon Energy Corporation; Dondingler & Sons Construction Co., Inc.; Emprise Bank; Equity Bank; Fireman's Fund Insurance Co.; Flint Hills Residential Development, L.L.C.; Friends University; IPC Retail Properties Mgmt.; Intrust Bank, N.A.; Jay Russell Companies; Kansas Humane Society; Key Construction, Inc.; LDF Support Group, Inc.; Lario Oil and Gas Co.; Larson Operating Company; Marketplace Properties, L.L.C.; Mega Manufacturing Inc.; National Plastics Color, Inc.; Newman University; Nies Builder, Inc.; Osborn Heirs Company; Pioneer Exploration, Ltd.; Quik Trip Corporation; Ritchie Development Corp.; Sedgwick County, KS; Spirit AeroSystems, Inc.; The Travelers Companies; Southwestern Energy Co.; Star Lumber & Supply Co., Inc.; USD #259, Sedgwick Co., KS; Valero Energy Corporation; Vantage Point Properties, Inc.; Via Christi Health, Inc.; VISA U.S.A., Inc.; Woolsey Petroleum Corporations; Zenith Drilling Corp.

# Kentucky

## How lawyers are ranked

Every year we carry out thousands of in-depth interviews with clients in order to assess the reputations and expertise of business lawyers worldwide. The qualities we look for (and which determine rankings) include technical legal ability, professional conduct, client service, commercial awareness/astuteness, diligence, commitment, and other qualities most valued by the client. For details of our research team, see p.5.

**Contents:**

## CORPORATE/M&A

Commentary about individuals can be found under their firm's paragraph. If the firm has no paragraph (is not ranked) look at Other Notable Practitioners.

| Corporate/M&A |
| --- |
| **Leading Firms** |
| **Band 1** |
| Frost Brown Todd LLC * |
| Stites & Harbison PLLC * |
| Stoll Keenon Ogden PLLC * |
| Wyatt, Tarrant & Combs, LLP * |
| **Band 2** |
| Bingham Greenebaum Doll LLP * |
| Reed Weitkamp Schell & Vice PLLC |

### Band 1

#### Frost Brown Todd LLC
See profile on p.1329

**THE FIRM** Frost Brown Todd provides market-leading expertise across the full range of transactional, financing and compliance-related matters. It advises public and private companies on regional, national and international deals, and has extensive experience of representing buyers, sellers, strategic investors and financial institutions. The firm is well known for its work in the energy sector, and has recently expanded its corporate healthcare practice.

**Sources say:** *"An excellent corporate practice."* *"Outstanding."*

**KEY INDIVIDUALS** Leading practitioner **Edward Glasscock** (see p.1318) handles a variety of corporate/M&A matters and is noted for his work with startup companies. Clients appreciate his business expertise as much as his legal knowledge. **Scott Dolson** (see p.1318) is regarded as *"one of the top corporate lawyers in the region"* and is highly respected for his prowess across a broad spectrum of business matters, spanning transactional and tax issues. **Alan MacDonald** (see p.1321) represents public companies in general corporate matters, including transactions, governance and compliance. Clients value his *"responsiveness, competency and timeliness."* **James Straus** (see p.1325) counsels clients on complex transactions, franchising and antitrust law. He is particularly known for

| Corporate/M&A | | |
| --- | --- | --- |
| **Senior Statesmen** | | |
| Senior Statesmen: distinguished older practitioners | | |
| Conner Stewart | *Wyatt, Tarrant & Combs, LLP* * | |
| **Leading Individuals** | | |
| **Star individuals** | | |
| Glasscock C Edward | *Frost Brown Todd LLC* * | |
| **Band 1** | | |
| Brinkman Scott W | *Stoll Keenon Ogden PLLC* * | |
| Dolson Scott | *Frost Brown Todd LLC* * | |
| Helm III Kennedy | *Stites & Harbison PLLC* * | |
| Lyndrup Peggy B | *Bingham Greenebaum Doll LLP* * | |
| MacDonald Alan | *Frost Brown Todd LLC* * | |
| Straus R James | *Frost Brown Todd LLC* * | |
| Weitkamp Gary R | *Reed Weitkamp Schell & Vice PLLC* | |
| Williams Ernest W | *Stoll Keenon Ogden PLLC* * | |
| Young Cynthia W | *Wyatt, Tarrant & Combs, LLP* * | |
| **Band 2** | | |
| Bradley Jr C Craig | *Stites & Harbison PLLC* * | |
| Giesel James A | *Frost Brown Todd LLC* * | |
| Halbleib Jr W Thomas | *Stites & Harbison PLLC* * | |
| Hallos Jeffrey L | *Frost Brown Todd LLC* * | |

| | |
| --- | --- |
| Diamond Ivan M | *Bingham Greenebaum Doll LLP* * |
| Steenrod Ralston W | *Stites & Harbison PLLC* * |
| Lester R David | *Stoll Keenon Ogden PLLC* * |
| Mattingly Patrick W | *Wyatt, Tarrant & Combs, LLP* * |
| Mckenzie Jeffrey A | *Bingham Greenebaum Doll LLP* |
| Seiffert James C | *Stites & Harbison PLLC* * |
| Strench William G | *Frost Brown Todd LLC* * |
| **Band 3** | |
| Beck Jr Robert M | *Stites & Harbison PLLC* * |
| Fisher Daniel E | *Fultz Maddox Hovious & Dickens PLC* |
| Herrington Jr Alex P | *Stites & Harbison PLLC* * |
| Jelsma Franklin | *Wyatt, Tarrant & Combs, LLP* * |
| Keeton Charles R | *Frost Brown Todd LLC* |
| King June N | *Bingham Greenebaum Doll LLP* * |
| Rutledge Thomas E | *Stoll Keenon Ogden PLLC* * |
| Smith, Jr J David | *Stoll Keenon Ogden PLLC* * |
| Terry Joseph H | *Dinsmore & Shohl LLP* |
| Welsh Patrick J | *Bingham Greenebaum Doll LLP* * |

*Indicates firm / individual with profile.*
*Alphabetical order within each band. Band 1 is the highest.*

his work with financial institutions. *"Standout lawyer"* **James Giesel** (see p.1318) is chair of the firm's investment management practice group and cochair of its public companies and securities group. **Jeffrey Hallos** (see p.1319) leads the firm's business department and is noted for the breadth and profile of his M&A practice, as well as his experience in securities transactions and national and international financing. Clients report that **William Strench** (see p.1325) is *"incredible when it comes to the numerous issues relating to startup companies."* Additional areas of expertise include M&A, securities and healthcare. **Charles Keeton** undertakes a range of transactional and financial restructuring work, with a particular focus on internet commerce.

#### Stites & Harbison PLLC
See profile on p.1331

**THE FIRM** Stites & Harbison's experienced corporate group impresses clients with its technical abilities and level of service. The practice encompasses M&A, private equity, venture capital, corporate governance, employee stock ownership plans and financial regulatory matters, with a focus on the banking, insurance, healthcare, equine and municipal finance sectors.

**KEY INDIVIDUALS** Chairman emeritus of the firm, **Kennedy Helm** (see p.1320) is recognized for his banking, finance and transactional work, as well as his expertise in airport law. *"Trusted adviser"* **Thomas Halbleib** (see p.1319) *"provides a broad range of business expertise with a* *common-sense approach.*" He concentrates his practice on M&A and is particularly noted for his work with airports. **Robert Beck** (see p.1316) is one of the premier equine transactional lawyers in the region. He also advises businesses on general corporate matters. **Craig Bradley** (see p.1316) focuses on banking, securities and corporate governance matters. Clients appreciate his thorough preparation and responsiveness. "*Highly regarded*" practitioner **James Seiffert** (see p.1324) has substantial experience in the fields of entrepreneurial services and taxation. Senior statesman **Ralston Steenrod** (see p.1325) advises clients from a variety of industry sectors on corporate/M&A issues. He has a particular interest in contest transactions. **Alex Herrington** (see p.1320) is singled out for his municipal finance expertise. Clients describe him as "*absolutely brilliant.*"

## Stoll Keenon Ogden PLLC
### See profile on p.1332

**THE FIRM** This firm commands significant respect for its M&A, banking and municipal finance work. The lawyers' work ethic, experience and aptitude for seeking creative solutions have secured them an appreciative client base of financial institutions, healthcare providers, manufacturers and distilleries. The team also has considerable expertise in equine matters. In the past year it acted for Brown-Forman on the $234 million sale of Feltzer Vineyards, for Baptist Healthcare on a $140 million bond issue, and for Farmers Capital Bank on a $30 million stock auction.

**Sources say:** "*Their strengths are their depth of knowledge and level of expertise.*"

**KEY INDIVIDUALS** Chair of the firm's M&A practice, **Ernest Williams** (see p.1326) has represented Brown-Forman in a number of substantial acquisitions and disposals. Clients value his analytical approach and industry knowledge. **Scott Brinkman** (see p.1316) spearheads the firm's public finance group and recently served as bond counsel to the Fayette County School District. **David Lester** (see p.1321) handles issues relating to healthcare law, the Uniform Commercial Code and M&A. Clients commend his insight into the nuances of sale and purchase agreements. **Thomas Rutledge** (see p.1323) is another highly praised practitioner. His practice concentrates on M&A and banking litigation. **David Smith** (see p.1324)

cochairs the business services practice and is a new entry into the rankings this year. He is recommended for his client-focused approach and his talent for looking beyond the technical details to the business implications of a transaction.

## Wyatt, Tarrant & Combs, LLP
### See profile on p.1333

**THE FIRM** Wyatt, Tarrant & Combs provides a multiservice corporate practice with particular expertise in matters relating to healthcare, financial institutions and natural resources. It recently represented Heaven Hill Distilleries in the purchase of Admiral Nelson Brands, acted for NarrowCast on its sale to QuinStreet, and advised The Learning House on its sale to Weld North. Clients admire the attorneys' dexterity in balancing attention to detail with an appreciation of the wider commercial context.

**KEY INDIVIDUALS Patrick Mattingly** (see p.1322) specializes in corporate issues relating to mineral transactions and entrepreneurial business. Clients prize his attentiveness and his ability to manage transactions smoothly. "*Phenomenal M&A lawyer*" **Cynthia Young** (see p.1326) is described by clients as "*very thorough,*" "*pragmatic,*" and "*a good negotiator.*" She cochairs the firm's financial services team. The "*extremely competent*" **Franklin Jelsma** (see p.1321) is "*adept at negotiating sophisticated sale and purchase transactions.*" His practice focuses on M&A, corporate finance and general business matters. Another eminent practitioner at the firm, **Stewart Conner** (see p.1317) undertakes a range of corporate work, with a focus on finance, banking and securities issues.

## Band 2

## Bingham Greenebaum Doll LLP
### See profile on p.1327

**THE FIRM** This firm is traditionally known for the strength of its coal and natural resources M&A practice, and also has substantial experience in the manufacturing and bourbon industries. The corporate and transactional group advises on a broad spectrum of business matters and has developed a noteworthy reputation in the fields of

franchising, distribution agreements and economic development incentives. Recent clients include LG&E and KU Energy, Chatham Imports and KFC National Council and Advertising Co-operative.

**KEY INDIVIDUALS** Clients value **Peggy Lyndrup**'s (see p.1321) "*incredible business strength*" and commitment to protecting their interests. She represents clients in domestic and international transactions, and has a particular interest in the service and manufacturing sectors. **June King** (see p.1321) advises public and private companies on issues relating to banking, finance and securities law. **Patrick Welsh** (see p.1325) is prominent at the firm for his product distribution and franchising expertise. He also counsels clients on M&A. New addition to the rankings **Jeffrey Mckenzie** is highly regarded for his work with Kentucky's bourbon industry. Clients describe him as "*very business-oriented,*" with "*tremendous judgment.*" Distinguished attorney **Ivan Diamond** (see p.1318) focuses on finance, securities and M&A transactions within the banking sector.

## Reed Weitkamp Schell & Vice PLLC

**THE FIRM** Clients praise this Louisville firm's work product and diligence. It has extensive expertise in a variety of corporate matters, including M&A, finance, securities, tax and compliance, and advises publicly and privately held companies, partnerships and professional practice groups from a range of industries. Res-Care and Jordan Holding Company are recent clients.

**Sources say:** "*They're just excellent in every way.*"

**KEY INDIVIDUALS Gary Weitkamp** impresses clients with his knowledge and attention to detail. He handles a range of business issues and has substantial experience of transactions in the healthcare and coal sectors.

## Other Notable Practitioners

**Joseph Terry** of Dinsmore & Shohl LLP is recognized for his M&A, securities and corporate governance practice. **Daniel Fisher** of Fultz Maddox Hovious & Dickens PLC advises on finance matters, M&A and strategic alliances, and has particular expertise in the healthcare industry. Clients describe him as a "*great lawyer and great resource.*"

# ENVIRONMENT, NATURAL RESOURCES & UTILITIES

## Band 1

### Bingham Greenebaum Doll LLP
See profile on p.1327

**THE FIRM** Bingham Greenebaum Doll continues to impress with its performance across a broad range of regulatory, transactional and contentious matters, and enjoys an especially strong reputation for its permitting work. Clients highlight its lawyers' environmental expertise, approachability and talent for negotiation. In the past year they have advised Hitachi Automotive on an unexpected release and discharge, Kentucky Syngas on a permit challenge defense and Ramaco on an acquisition of coal reserves. **Sources say:** "*They have a statewide reputation for high quality.*" **KEY INDIVIDUALS Jack Bender** (see p.1316) represents companies in environmental compliance disputes and is well versed in issues relating to the CWA. Clients value his engineering background and his aptitude for grasping the various facets of an argument or issue. Chair of the firm's environmental and natural resources practice group, **Carolyn Brown** (see p.1316) is particularly noted for her air permitting experience. Clients report that "*she is always very practical and looks out for our best interests.*" Transactional expert **Bruce Cryder** (see p.1318) is admired for his ability to "*distill deals down to larger issues.*" He undertakes a range of corporate work, with a focus on the coal industry. **Bradley Dillon** (see p.1318) concentrates on counseling chemical operations and distilleries on environmental and compliance concerns, in addition to issues arising out of transactions. He is described as "*outstanding in terms of the environmental issues concerning distilleries.*" **Kelly Bartley** (see p.1315) commands respect for her grasp of the environmental issues arising from solid waste, wastewater and air emissions. Clients identify her as "*exceedingly knowledgeable,*" "*easy to work with*" and "*thorough.*"

### Frost Brown Todd LLC
See profile on p.1329

**THE FIRM** This highly regarded Kentucky firm places a heavy emphasis on environmental compliance, liability and litigation. While it remains prominent for its experience in the coal sector, it has recently enjoyed an expansion in its natural gas capabilities. Its talented practitioners represent clients from a variety of backgrounds, encompassing utilities, healthcare providers and commercial real estate developers. The firm also handles transactional matters and dispute resolution for companies in the fields of utilities and minerals. **Sources say:** "*They have a tremendous amount of expertise.*" **KEY INDIVIDUALS** Clients prize **Timothy Hagerty**'s (see p.1319) environmental knowledge. He acts for natural resources companies in matters concerning regulatory compliance, and has a particular interest in water law. Much-admired practitioner **Dennis Conniff** (see p.1317) is described by clients as "*approachable*" and "*well versed.*" His practice focuses on environmental liability and related transactional issues, as well as waste, water and air permitting. **Warren Hoffmann** (see p.1320) is another highly regarded attorney. He handles transactional matters for clients in the coal and electric utility industries. **Philip Schworer** (see p.1324) is commended for his ability to provide clients with viable business options within a legal framework. Areas of concentration include environmental compliance and litigation, and toxic torts. **Patrick Northam** (see p.1322) recently joined the firm from Bingham Greenebaum. He has significant expertise in utilities and natural resources. "*A good communicator and very patient,*" clients also commend his dexterity in overseeing complex transactions: "*Patrick did a fantastic job. On an incredibly complicated matter, he kept it all organized and negotiated good outcomes.*"

## Band 2

### Dinsmore & Shohl LLP

**THE FIRM** Dinsmore & Shohl is best known for the strength of its natural resources transactional practice. Its team counsels clients on all aspects of sale and purchase, financing, extraction and transportation, with a focus on the region's signature mining industry. The group is also well placed to advise on compliance and liability issues and represents businesses in a variety of civil actions, including contractual, environmental, safety and employment disputes.

**KEY INDIVIDUALS** Chair of the firm's natural resources practice group **Chauncey Curtz** handles both corporate and contentious matters. Clients report that he is "*a really strong negotiator*" and "*very attuned to the business of coal mining.*" **John Rhorer** focuses on transactional and financing undertakings, primarily within the coal sector.

### Stites & Harbison PLLC
See profile on p.1331

**THE FIRM** Clients admire Stites & Harbison's talented attorneys and regional clout. Its environment, natural resources and energy group is equipped to provide a broad spectrum of transactional, compliance and litigation services to clients from a variety of industry sectors. The team is particularly noted for its mineral transactional experience, which encompasses coal, oil and gas, sand and gravel, and limestone. It is also singled out for its expertise in mining company bankruptcy and mine reclamation.

**KEY INDIVIDUALS** Outstanding lawyer **Patrick Stallard** (see p.1325) counsels businesses on environmental compliance and disputes relating to air, water and waste. Practice group leader **William Gorton** (see p.1319) tackles the business and regulatory aspects of natural resources transactions. Clients consider him to be *"extremely smart, very hard-working and very personable."* Another prominent practitioner is **Mark Overstreet** (see p.1322). He specializes in the regulation of utilities, including water, gas and electricity. Senior statesman **David Brown** (see p.1317) is highly esteemed in the area of electric energy and utilities regulation.

## Stoll Keenon Ogden PLLC
See profile on p.1332

**THE FIRM** This firm remains a leading presence in the utilities arena. Its utility and energy group is recognized for its transactional work within the sector, as well as its role in significant rate increase cases. The firm also advises on environmental compliance, permitting and litigation, and has seen an increase in its mineral portfolio, particularly in natural gas. Notable clients include Kentucky Utilities, Westlake Chemical and Delta Natural Gas.

**KEY INDIVIDUALS** Leading lawyer **Kendrick Riggs** (see p.1323) acts for energy and telecoms clients in complex disputes concerning rate mechanisms, corporate issues and energy activities. **Robert Watt** (see p.1325) is another prominent figure at the firm. He focuses on utilities regulatory compliance and litigation. **Kent Hatfield** (see p.1320) wins respect for his experience prosecuting antitrust cases in the natural gas and electric power industries. He also advises utility companies on corporate matters.

## Wyatt, Tarrant & Combs, LLP
See profile on p.1333

**THE FIRM** This much-admired mineral and energy group handles a wide range of transactional and contentious work for coal producers, industrial businesses and oil and gas companies, as well as advising on environmental compliance, liability and litigation. The attorneys are also expe-

rienced in the area of toxic torts. In the past year they have acted for GE, Masonite and Rockwell Automation.

**Sources say:** *"They are top-quality. The work that they do is high-caliber and they are good at strategic thinking."*

**KEY INDIVIDUALS** Clients describe **Karen Greenwell** (see p.1319) as *"fantastic,"* adding that *"she has a great legal mind and really knows how to distill complicated issues."* She focuses on litigating complex property disputes within the oil and gas sector. **Carl Horneman** (see p.1320) concentrates his practice on air compliance and permitting. Clients view him as *"a fantastic resource"* and admire his pragmatism in achieving economic business solutions. *"Accomplished"* attorney **Patrick Mattingly** (see p.1322) is recognized as an authority on mineral and energy transactions.

# INTELLECTUAL PROPERTY

| Intellectual Property Leading Firms | |
|---|---|
| **Band 1** | |
| Middleton Reutlinger PSC | |
| Stites & Harbison PLLC * | |
| **Band 2** | |
| Frost Brown Todd LLC * | |
| King & Schickli | |
| Wyatt, Tarrant & Combs, LLP * | |
| **Band 3** | |
| Bingham Greenebaum Doll LLP * | |
| Dinsmore & Shohl LLP | |
| Stoll Keenon Ogden PLLC * | |

\* Indicates firm / individual with profile.
Alphabetical order within each band. Band 1 is the highest.

| Intellectual Property Leading Individuals | |
|---|---|
| **Band 1** | |
| Beres Joel T | Stites & Harbison PLLC * |
| Higgins Jr James R | Middleton Reutlinger PSC |
| Schickli Warren D | King & Schickli |
| **Band 2** | |
| Barr P Douglas | Stoll Keenon Ogden PLLC * |
| Berge Amy B | Bingham Greenebaum Doll LLP * |
| Duvall Scot A | Middleton Reutlinger PSC |
| Everett Denise M | Dinsmore & Shohl LLP |
| Gregory Julie Ann | Middleton Reutlinger PSC |
| Hall Stephen C | Wyatt, Tarrant & Combs, LLP * |
| Hollander William H | Wyatt, Tarrant & Combs, LLP * |
| Nagle Jr David W | Stites & Harbison PLLC * |
| O'Brien III Thomas P | Frost Brown Todd LLC * |
| Salazar John F | Middleton Reutlinger PSC |
| Stewart Cynthia L | Frost Brown Todd LLC * |
| Wheat Jack A | Stites & Harbison PLLC * |
| **Up-and-coming individuals** | |
| Williams Matthew | Wyatt, Tarrant & Combs, LLP * |

## Band 1

### Middleton Reutlinger PSC

**THE FIRM** Middleton Reutlinger has a reputation for fielding some of the strongest IP lawyers in the state. Its dedicated team advises national and international businesses on all areas of IP law, with particular strength in the patent and trademark arenas. In the past year it acted for Biomet on a substantial patent dispute and for Community Trust Bancorp on a trademark infringement appeal.

**Sources say:** *"They've become very knowledgeable on our product categories and they have great follow-up. They understand our business model and what we need."*

**KEY INDIVIDUALS** Celebrated practitioner **James Higgins** handles IP litigation, with a focus on patent and trademark disputes. **Scot Duvall** concentrates on trademark prosecution and litigation. He has a strong reputa-

tion for dealing with matters at an appellate level and is described by clients as *"a teacher and a guide."* **Julie Ann Gregory** is highly regarded for her trademark prosecution work in the fields of sport and healthcare. *"Excellent patent attorney"* **John Salazar** specializes in electronic and computer issues. Clients commend his ability to understand the technical aspects of their products and communicate with inventors.

## Stites & Harbison PLLC
See profile on p.1331

**THE FIRM** This acclaimed practice covers patent and trademark applications, copyright counseling and litigation. It represents a diverse mix of regional and national companies within the manufacturing and consumer product sectors, and is particularly known for handling patent prosecutions on behalf of universities.

**KEY INDIVIDUALS** **Jack Wheat** (see p.1325) is a much-admired attorney with extensive experience of trademark prosecution and litigation. He possesses special expertise in IP issues affecting sororities and fraternities. *"Top-tier"* practitioner **Joel Beres** (see p.1316) is a highly respected patent litigator. He represents plaintiffs and defendants in the state and federal courts at trial and appellate level. Another leading patent expert, **David Nagle** (see p.1322) focuses on prosecution for food service, manufacturing and software companies. He is also well versed in licensing law.

## Band 2

### Frost Brown Todd LLC
See profile on p.1329

**THE FIRM** Frost Brown Todd's skilled attorneys concentrate on brand management and the protection of IP rights. They have noteworthy experience in handling trademark and copyright matters, and litigation and licensing issues, and are able to draw on the traditional IP strength of the firm's Cincinnati office.

**KEY INDIVIDUALS** **Thomas O'Brien** (see p.1322) litigates IP disputes nationally. He acts for significant clients in the telecoms and consumer products sectors. *"Fabulous* *attorney*" **Cynthia Stewart** (see p.1325) has a wealth of experience in information technology and software licensing and acquisitions. Clients appreciate her panoramic understanding of IP issues and her talent for negotiation.

### King & Schickli
**THE FIRM** This highly regarded Lexington IP boutique is recognized for its strength in patent prosecution in a variety of industries, including biotechnology, animal science, and electrical, chemical and mechanical engineering. It also deals with domestic and international trademark and copyright issues.
**KEY INDIVIDUALS** Standout individual **Warren Schickli** deals with patent, trademark and copyright issues.

### Wyatt, Tarrant & Combs, LLP
See profile on p.1333
**THE FIRM** This firm continues to demonstrate capabilities across a broad spectrum of IP issues, and has strengthened its patent prosecution practice with the addition of new talent. Core client sectors include spirits, consumer products and restaurants. The group also has growing expertise in dealing with IP matters as they relate to corporate transactions. Heaven Hill Distilleries, Cracker Barrel Old Country Store and AAF-McQuay are all recent clients.
**Sources say:** "*It exemplifies all the qualities you look for in a professional law firm that does sophisticated work for clients with a national focus.*"
**KEY INDIVIDUALS Stephen Hall** (see p.1319) handles patent prosecution and litigation. Clients observe: "*He's really easy to work with; he's conscientious of time and effort, and is direct and informative so we know where we stand.*" Managing partner **William Hollander** (see p.1320) has a

strong reputation in the market for trademark and copyright counseling and litigation. He has substantial experience of Kentucky's signature bourbon and racing industries. **Matthew Williams** (see p.1326) has a broad practice, encompassing patent and trademark prosecution and litigation. He is praised by clients for his technical knowledge and attentiveness.

### Band 3

### Bingham Greenebaum Doll LLP
See profile on p.1327
**THE FIRM** This well-rounded practice represents clients in patent and trademark prosecution, copyright issues, licensing and IP litigation. It benefits from special expertise in the manufacturing, healthcare and technology domains, and has seen an increase in biotechnology and university work. It has recently provided IP advice to Atria Senior Living, Churchill Downs and Clark Material Handling.
**Sources say:** "*An excellent firm – very conscientious.*"
**KEY INDIVIDUALS Amy Berge** (see p.1316) impresses clients with her diligence, efficiency and passion for her work. She focuses on trademark and copyright law, with a particular interest in the manufacturing and healthcare domains.

### Dinsmore & Shohl LLP
**THE FIRM** Dinsmore & Shohl's IP team is particularly well known for its work in the biotechnology and pharmaceutical areas. Its attorneys have specialist expertise in the Hatch-Waxman Act and FDA regulatory compliance, as

well as considerable experience of internet-based business paradigms, Kentucky's bourbon industry and the restaurant business. In the past year, the firm has acted for Roche Diagnostics, Mylan Pharmaceuticals and Advanced Cancer Therapeutics.
**Sources say:** "*I'm exceptionally pleased. They worked really hard and overcame some big obstacles.*"
**KEY INDIVIDUALS** Clients applaud **Denise Everett**'s "*deep and thorough scientific insight,*" and appreciate her personable and involving manner. She is noted for her patent prosecution work for national and international pharmaceutical companies.

### Stoll Keenon Ogden PLLC
See profile on p.1332
**THE FIRM** Stoll Keenon Ogden advises clients on a broad range of IP issues, and displays notable strength in dealing with contentious matters. Areas of growth include biotechnology, alternative energy and medical devices. The firm continues to act for printing giant Lexmark in complex patent litigation, and recently defended a consortium of retail clients in a trademark and copyright infringement dispute.
**Sources say:** "*They had a good customer-service focus and were willing to take time out to learn the issues from a business perspective.*"
**KEY INDIVIDUALS Douglas Barr** (see p.1315) tackles patent, trademark and trade secrets litigation, with a concentration on technology and spirits. Clients respect his knowledge and identify him as "*an excellent guy to work with.*"

## LABOR & EMPLOYMENT

Commentary about individuals can be found under their firm's paragraph. If the firm has no paragraph (is not ranked) look at Other Notable Practitioners.

| Labor & Employment Leading Firms |
|---|
| **Band 1** |
| Fisher & Phillips LLP * |
| Frost Brown Todd LLC * |
| **Band 2** |
| Bingham Greenebaum Doll LLP * |
| Dinsmore & Shohl LLP |
| Littler Mendelson, PC * |
| Smith & Smith Attorneys * |
| Stoll Keenon Ogden PLLC * |
| Wyatt, Tarrant & Combs, LLP * |
| * Indicates firm with profile. |
| Alphabetical order within each band, Band 1 is the highest. |

### Band 1

### Fisher & Phillips LLP
See profile on p.1107
**THE FIRM** This national labor and employment firm continues to enjoy a prominent position in the market by virtue of its specialist expertise in the automotive and healthcare sectors, as well as its impressive OSHA and collective bargaining experience. The group has recently represented Toyota Motor & Engineering, Humana and Baptist Healthcare.
**Sources say:** "*They are able to anticipate and adapt to our ever-changing needs.*"
**KEY INDIVIDUALS** Managing partner **Thomas Birchfield** (see p.1316) divides his time between employment counseling and traditional labor matters. Clients "*trust him implicitly. He has an excellent understanding of what our business is and offers advice that is pertinent.*" **Raymond Haley** (see p.1319) is best known for his work within the traditional labor arena. He represents employers in labor arbitration and litigation, as well as employ-

ment and civil rights disputes. Chair of the firm's automotive manufacturing group, **Jeffrey Savarise** (see p.1324) focuses on labor and employment work within this sector. He is noted for his involvement in ADA disputes and wage and hour class actions. "*Exceptional*" associate **Laurel Cornell** (see p.1317) wins praise from clients for her talent in the field of employment litigation.

### Frost Brown Todd LLC
See profile on p.1329
**THE FIRM** Frost Brown Todd's highly regarded labor and employment group represents employers in a broad spectrum of matters, including wage and hour, union avoidance, discrimination and harassment, OSHA and non-compete claims. It is especially distinguished for the depth of its traditional labor practice, and has noteworthy experience in the distribution, automotive, manufacturing and healthcare industries.
**Sources say:** "*An excellent group of lawyers with vast experience in the field.*"

**KEY INDIVIDUALS** "Outstanding" practitioner **John Lovett** is described by clients as "diligent, practical and personable." He handles employment counseling and litigation, union avoidance and negotiations, and unfair competition issues. **Richard Cleary** (see p.1317) has an excellent reputation in the field of traditional labor law. His practice concentrates on collective bargaining, labor arbitration and litigation within the automotive manufacturing sector. Respected advocate **James Cockrum** (see p.1317) advises on liability prevention, collective bargaining and union avoidance, and defends employers in related litigation. Clients say: "He does an extremely good job of interpreting the law for us so that we can understand it and make a decision." Clients identify **Patton Pelfrey** (see p.1323) as being "good at seeing the big picture and bringing us to the nexus of the problem." He has wide-ranging experience in both labor and employment issues. **Tony Coleman** (see p.1317) is one of the region's leading labor lawyers, with expertise in the Railway Labor Act. Clients report that "he has a lot of institutional knowledge, which is a huge asset to us as we deal with different matters." **Laurence Woods** (see p.1326)

is commended for his litigation practice, which covers all types of employment disputes under state and federal law. Another esteemed practitioner at the firm, **Robert Hudson** (see p.1321) undertakes employment litigation and advises employers on managing employee and union relationships.

## Band 2

### Bingham Greenebaum Doll LLP
See profile on p.1327

**THE FIRM** Bingham Greenebaum Doll earns particular praise for its litigation practice. The team advises clients on a range of labor and employment matters, including avoidance and liability, as well as supervisor training. It has significant experience of the hospitality industry, automotive manufacturers and healthcare providers, and has recently acted for Global Fitness, The Kroger Company and Humana.
**Sources say:** "They have a focus on pushing matters towards resolution."
**KEY INDIVIDUALS** Group cochair **Philip Eschels** (see p.1318) continues to focus on noncompete and trade secret issues. He also counsels employers on risks relating to social media in the workplace. Clients describe him as "personable" and "attentive," commenting that "he's done a fantastic job at negotiating." Employment lawyer **Wendy Becker** (see p.1316) is highly esteemed. She concentrates on litigation, including wrongful discharge, discrimination and EEOC matters.

### Dinsmore & Shohl LLP

**THE FIRM** This firm provides both labor and employment counsel to clients from a number of different sectors, including healthcare, media and governmental agencies. Its labor expertise spans union avoidance, strike planning and unfair labor practice charges and, within the sphere of employment litigation, it is distinguished by its experience of taking discrimination cases to trial.
**Sources say:** "They are very knowledgeable in what they do and are very effective litigators."
**KEY INDIVIDUALS** **Donna Perry** is regarded as a "leading expert" in labor and employment litigation. Clients describe her as an "extremely well-rounded attorney with a broad base of knowledge" and an "effective negotiator." The "excellent" **Kathryn Quesenberry** handles employment litigation defense, with a specialization in EEOC class action cases.

### Littler Mendelson, PC
See profile on p.688

**THE FIRM** The Lexington office of this national labor and employment powerhouse demonstrates noteworthy strength in the fields of labor and employment litigation. Its attorneys also advise executives, supervisors and human resources managers on employment policy and liability prevention. Recent clients include Amazon, Ecolab and Charter Communications.

**Sources say:** "The firm's resources and experienced lawyers are very beneficial."
**KEY INDIVIDUALS** Managing shareholder **Susan Sears** (see p.1324) deals with a wide variety of employment issues, including litigation. Clients appreciate that "she's always passionate about what she does," and admire her ability to "develop a great action plan." "Excellent associate" **Emily Morris** (see p.1322) is recommended for her client-oriented approach and impressive knowledge of employment matters.

### Smith & Smith Attorneys
See profile on p.1330

**THE FIRM** This Louisville boutique is greatly admired for the excellence of its select group of attorneys. It counsels clients on labor relations, collective bargaining, wage and hour disputes, OSHA matters and general employment-related issues.
**KEY INDIVIDUALS** **Kevin Smith** is a well-respected practitioner and handles both labor and employment matters. The "universally highly regarded" **James Smith** is hailed as one of the top attorneys in the field. Clients value him as a "great counselor."

### Stoll Keenon Ogden PLLC
See profile on p.1332

**THE FIRM** The labor and employment group at Stoll Keenon Ogden is held in high esteem for its work with employers from Kentucky's bourbon and equine industries, and provides representation to some of the state's most illustrious businesses. It advises clients on a broad spectrum of labor and employment issues, including employee benefits and executive compensation. Lexmark, Jim Bean Brands and Papa John's are among its key clients.
**Sources say:** "The employment department is extremely strong. Customer service: A+."
**KEY INDIVIDUALS** Leading practitioner **Richard Griffith** (see p.1319) is sought after for his labor and employment litigation prowess. He counsels clients from a wide variety of sectors, and is particularly prominent for his expertise in the distilled spirits industry. Clients describe **Walter Sales** (see p.1323) as "fantastic" and "very detail-oriented." He is best known for his traditional labor practice and has significant experience of union-organizing campaigns and strikes. Experienced attorney **Thomas Williams** (see p.1326) provides advice on a number of employment issues, including terminations. He also handles litigation and acts as an employment law mediator. **Joseph Beavin** (see p.1316) specializes in employee benefits and executive compensation. He is commended by clients for his knowledge, diligence and commitment to keeping them informed of changes in the law. **John Sheller** (see p.1324) is impressive in the fields of complex employment litigation and labor management. Clients value his deep understanding of their businesses.

### Wyatt, Tarrant & Combs, LLP
See profile on p.1333

**THE FIRM** Wyatt, Tarrant & Combs fields an experienced ensemble of attorneys with command of a comprehensive range of labor and employment matters, encompassing litigation defense, NLRB representation, ongoing employee education and counseling, and labor issues relating to corporate transactions. During the past year, the group has enjoyed significant success in a number of wage and hour disputes. Notable clients include GE, American Red Cross and Georgetown College.

**Sources say:** *"First-class service and deep experience."*

**KEY INDIVIDUALS** *"Excellent"* attorney **Edwin Hopson** (see p.1320) is viewed as a specialist in labor arbitration and negotiations. Clients prize his exceptional knowledge

and experience in the area. **Debra Dawahare** (see p.1318) is lauded for her strategic thinking, advocacy and draftsmanship. She represents businesses in employment litigation and is an authority on the law as it relates to colleges and universities. Another key individual at the firm is **George Miller** (see p.1322). He has a broad employment law practice which encompasses litigation and health and safety matters.

## Other Notable Practitioners

**Shannon Antle Hamilton** (see p.1320) of Stites & Harbison PLLC is a skilled litigator with a wealth of experience across a broad portfolio of employment issues, including noncompetes, confidentiality, sexual harassment and age discrimination. *"Outstanding young attorney"* **Loren Prizant** of Middleton Reutlinger PSC is recognized for his potential in labor and employment litigation. Clients note that *"he is very smart and knows his subject matter really well."*

# LITIGATION

Construction p.1312;  Tort & Insurance Defense p.1312

Commentary about individuals can be found under their firm's paragraph.  If the firm has no paragraph (is not ranked) look at Other Notable Practitioners.

## Litigation: General Commercial
### Leading Firms

**Band 1**
Stites & Harbison PLLC *
Stoll Keenon Ogden PLLC *

**Band 2**
Dinsmore & Shohl LLP
Frost Brown Todd LLC *
Wyatt, Tarrant & Combs, LLP *

**Band 3**
Bingham Greenebaum Doll LLP *
Fultz Maddox Hovious & Dickens PLC
Middleton Reutlinger PSC
Reed Weitkamp Schell & Vice PLLC
Tachau Meek PLC

*\* Indicates firm with profile.*
*Alphabetical order within each band. Band 1 is the highest.*

## Band 1

### Stites & Harbison PLLC
**See profile on p.1331**

**THE FIRM** This group continues to be recognized as one of the leading dispute resolution practices in Kentucky and the Southeast. Its multiservice litigation department is particularly well known for handling banking, construction and product liability work, and fields dedicated tort and class action teams. It acts for a variety of domestic and international clients, with a focus on the distilled spirits, financial, healthcare and manufacturing sectors.

**KEY INDIVIDUALS** *"Super litigator"* **Charles Cronan** (see p.1318) is widely acknowledged as a *"star individual."* He focuses on complex commercial litigation within the healthcare sector. Esteemed litigator **Philip Collier's** (see p.1317) practice encompasses antitrust, environmental and contract disputes, as well as business torts. **Robert Connolly** (see p.1317) leads the firm's litigation section and handles product liability, contract, construction and OSHA disputes. Trial lawyer **Marc Murphy** (see p.1322) handles white-collar criminal litigation, with a particular focus on healthcare fraud and environmental crimes.

**Robert Griffith** (see p.1319) is an experienced commercial litigator, whose practice covers lender liability, environmental, land use and noncompete matters. **Joseph Hamilton** (see p.1319) defends clients against consumer class actions nationally and specializes in disputes relating to the insurance sector. Leading construction specialist **Anne Gorham** (see p.1318) is well versed in all phases of major construction projects, including contract negotiation, permitting and litigation. *"Premier lawyer"* **Buckner Hinkle** (see p.1320) is also a construction expert. He advises clients on contract negotiation and drafting, and handles a broad range of commercial litigation. *"Top attorney"* **David Ratterman** (see p.1323) is an authority on construction issues relating to the fabricated structured steel industry. The *"excellent"* **William Geisen** (see p.1318) is singled out as one of Kentucky's most talented construction specialists. He handles contract negotiation and litigation, and is also sought as a *"knowledgeable and authoritative"* mediator and arbitrator.

### Stoll Keenon Ogden PLLC
**See profile on p.1332**

**THE FIRM** This impressive group of litigators maintains an excellent reputation across a broad spectrum of complex commercial issues, encompassing shareholder, insurance coverage and banking disputes. It is also well versed in environmental, land use and professional liability litigation, and has noteworthy expertise in antitrust and equine matters. Recent clients include the Bank of Oklahoma, the American Saddlebred Horse Association and Kentucky American Water.

**Sources say:** *"I've been very happy with the knowledge base they bring."*

**KEY INDIVIDUALS** *"Excellent"* practitioner **Douglas Ballantine** (see p.1315) chairs the firm's business torts group. His practice spans general commercial, product liability, medical malpractice and personal injury litigation. Head of the tort, trial and insurance services team, **Gregory King** (see p.1321) specializes in medical malpractice, hospital and personal injury defense. **Samuel Hinkle** (see p.1320) is a highly regarded litigator. He has wide-ranging experience in a number of areas, including com-

plex commercial and bankruptcy litigation, as well as environmental, equine and land use disputes. **David Royse** (see p.1323) has a strong reputation for handling commercial, medical negligence and employment litigation. Senior statesman **John Ballantine** (see p.1315) has a wealth of experience in defending medical malpractice and professional negligence cases.

## Band 2

### Dinsmore & Shohl LLP

**THE FIRM** Dinsmore & Shohl's litigation department handles a variety of commercial matters, and is particularly well known for its natural resources and energy expertise. The group also deals with shareholder disputes and fiduciary issues, as well as medical malpractice, product liability and insurance coverage litigation. Louisville Gas and Electric, the University of Kentucky and Anheuser-Busch are among its key clients.

**Sources say:** *"They do a superb job at trial."*

**KEY INDIVIDUALS** *"One of the most distinguished litigators in the state,"* **Barbara Edelman** has an excellent reputation in the complex commercial arena. Clients value her experience, responsiveness and ability to communicate. **Richard Clay** handles general business litigation, with a strong focus on representing banks and trust companies in fiduciary issues. *"Phenomenal lawyer"* **Jon Fleischaker** is a highly respected appellate attorney and an expert in First Amendment law. **David Monohan** is another notable practitioner. He has a broad practice encompassing commercial litigation, railroad defense, hospital defense and professional malpractice cases. **Colin Lindsay** represents clients in commercial and intellectual property litigation. He is particularly noted for dealing with contractual disputes.

### Frost Brown Todd LLC
**See profile on p.1329**

**THE FIRM** This experienced team of litigators represents clients in a diverse range of contentious matters, including disputes related to banking, construction, product liability

## Litigation: General Commercial

### Senior Statesmen

| Senior Statesmen: distinguished older practitioners | |
| --- | --- |
| Ballantine John T | Stoll Keenon Ogden PLLC * |

### Leading Individuals

**Star individuals**

| Cronan IV Charles J | Stites & Harbison PLLC * |
| --- | --- |

**Band 1**

| Collier Philip W | Stites & Harbison PLLC * |
| --- | --- |
| Cox Donald | Lynch, Cox, Gilman & Mahan, P.S.C. |
| Edelman Barbara B | Dinsmore & Shohl LLP |
| Haynes Greg | Wyatt, Tarrant & Combs, LLP * |
| Hovious R Gregg | Fultz Maddox Hovious & Dickens PLC |
| Reed John S | Reed Weitkamp Schell & Vice PLLC |
| Snyder Sheryl | Frost Brown Todd LLC * |

**Band 2**

| Clay Richard H C | Dinsmore & Shohl LLP |
| --- | --- |
| Connolly Robert M | Stites & Harbison PLLC * |
| Fleischaker Jon | Dinsmore & Shohl LLP |
| Fultz Benjamin C | Fultz Maddox Hovious & Dickens PLC |
| Hinkle IV Samuel D | Stoll Keenon Ogden PLLC * |
| Jakubowicz Janet P | Bingham Greenebaum Doll LLP * |
| Leet Byron E | Wyatt, Tarrant & Combs, LLP * |
| Maddox Victor | Fultz Maddox Hovious & Dickens PLC |
| Miller Winston | Frost Brown Todd LLC * |
| Monohan David | Dinsmore & Shohl LLP |
| Murrell Dennis D | Middleton Reutlinger PSC |
| Pitt M Stephen | Wyatt, Tarrant & Combs, LLP * |
| Tachau David | Tachau Meek PLC |

**Band 3**

| Ballantine Douglas C | Stoll Keenon Ogden PLLC * |
| --- | --- |
| Coryell II Cornelius E | Wyatt, Tarrant & Combs, LLP * |
| Ison Eric | Bingham Greenebaum Doll LLP * |
| Lindsay Colin Hugh | Dinsmore & Shohl LLP |
| Snell Virginia | Wyatt, Tarrant & Combs, LLP * |

**Band 4**

| Ely III Hiram | Middleton Reutlinger PSC |
| --- | --- |
| Greenwell Charles D | Goldberg Simpson LLC |
| Griffith Robert W | Stites & Harbison PLLC * |
| Keane Margaret E | Bingham Greenebaum Doll LLP * |
| Meek Dustin | Tachau Meek PLC |
| Robinson III Wm T | Frost Brown Todd LLC * |
| Royse David T | Stoll Keenon Ogden PLLC * |
| Smith Raymond G | Boehl Stopher & Graves, LLP * |

and insurance coverage. The group has a prominent environmental practice and regularly acts for energy and utility companies in complex commercial litigation. It also attracts praise for its personal injury work and is singled out for its experience of handling fire and explosion cases. **Sources say:** "*I am impressed with the entire team. They are good about deadlines and good on developing case strategy.*" **KEY INDIVIDUALS** "*Terrific lawyer*" **Winston Miller** (see p.1322) handles tort and business litigation. Clients say: "*He is very approachable, he communicates clearly and he has great experience and legal knowledge.*" Experienced appellate litigator **Sheryl Snyder** (see p.1324) is highly respected in the field of complex commercial disputes. **William Robinson** (see p.1323) is well versed in commer-

## Litigation: Construction

### Leading Individuals

**Band 1**

| Blandford David B | Ackerson & Yann PSC |
| --- | --- |
| Geisen William | Stites & Harbison PLLC * |
| Gorham Anne E | Stites & Harbison PLLC * |
| Grundy J Mark | Bingham Greenebaum Doll LLP * |
| Hinkle, Jr. Buckner | Stites & Harbison PLLC * |
| Ratterman David B | Stites & Harbison PLLC * |
| Shull III C Michael | Frost Brown Todd LLC * |
| Stovall Gerald L | Hall, Render, Killian, Heath & Lyman, PSC |

cial, environmental, medical malpractice, product liability and antitrust litigation at trial and appellate levels. Construction lawyer **Michael Shull** (see p.1324) counsels contractors, subcontractors and design firms on a range of contentious and noncontentious matters.

### Wyatt, Tarrant & Combs, LLP
See profile on p.1333

**THE FIRM** This broad business litigation practice has a particular emphasis on the financial, healthcare and energy sectors. It represents public and private companies, government bodies and professional firms in complex commercial litigation, professional negligence, product liability and insurance coverage cases. Recent clients include Henderson Municipal Power & Light and Owensboro Medical Health System.
**Sources say:** "*They provided an excellent strategy for approaching the litigation.*" "*The resources at the firm are of outstanding quality.*"
**KEY INDIVIDUALS** **Greg Haynes** (see p.1320) is acknowledged as one of Kentucky's premier litigators. His practice is concentrated on complex commercial disputes, including securities, class action and shareholder litigation. **Cornelius Coryell** (see p.1317) is known for representing financial institutions in banking, commercial and UCC litigation. He also has a distinguished class action practice. Cochair of the firm's litigation and dispute resolution service team, **Byron Leet** (see p.1321) is a talented advocate, whose varied client roster includes financial institutions, healthcare companies and public authorities. "*Well-respected*" attorney **Stephen Pitt** (see p.1323) handles commercial, toxic tort and environmental litigation. He has a particular interest in the coal industry. **Virginia Snell** (see p.1324) is a highly regarded appellate practitioner. Clients report that she is "*responsive and logical,*" and "*comes up with creative ideas of how to approach the problem.*"

**Band 3**

### Bingham Greenebaum Doll LLP
See profile on p.1327

**THE FIRM** This group undertakes a variety of commercial matters, with a strong focus on corporate and tax litigation, and is also noted for its environmental and toxic tort capabilities. The team has considerable experience representing utilities, alcohol companies, automobile manufacturers and major restaurant chains. It has recently acted for

## Litigation: Tort & Insurance Defense

### Leading Firms

**Band 1**

| Boehl Stopher & Graves, LLP * | |
| --- | --- |

### Leading Individuals

**Star individuals**

| Stopher Edward H | Boehl Stopher & Graves, LLP * |
| --- | --- |

**Band 1**

| Ballantine Douglas C | Stoll Keenon Ogden PLLC * |
| --- | --- |
| Connolly Robert M | Stites & Harbison PLLC * |
| Fenzel Mark S | Middleton Reutlinger PSC |
| Hamilton Joseph L | Stites & Harbison PLLC * |
| Keane Margaret E | Bingham Greenebaum Doll LLP * |
| King W Gregory | Stoll Keenon Ogden PLLC * |
| Miller Winston | Frost Brown Todd LLC * |
| Murphy Marc S | Stites & Harbison PLLC * |
| Oldham William K | Middleton Reutlinger PSC |
| Stopher Robert E | Boehl Stopher & Graves, LLP * |
| Thompson B Todd | Thompson Miller & Simpson PLC |

*Indicates firm / individual with profile.*
*Alphabetical order within each band. Band 1 is the highest.*

Chatham Imports, Global Fitness and Louisville Gas and Electric.
**Sources say:** "*The practice is focused and efficient.*" "*They had excellent command of the legal matters.*"
**KEY INDIVIDUALS** Clients describe **Janet Jakubowicz** (see p.1321) as "*practical, knowledgeable and a pleasure to deal with.*" She handles a range of commercial disputes, with a particular emphasis on securities litigation and class action defense. **Eric Ison** (see p.1321) is another well-respected litigator at the firm and has wide-ranging business litigation experience. "*Excellent litigator*" **Margaret Keane** (see p.1321) focuses on product liability defense in the pharmaceutical sector. She is also called upon to assist in general commercial and employment litigation. Construction expert **Mark Grundy** (see p.1319) represents owners and contractors in a wide array of contentious and noncontentious matters, including real estate-related disputes. He also handles general business litigation.

### Fultz Maddox Hovious & Dickens PLC
**THE FIRM** This Louisville firm has established a national reputation for healthcare litigation and counseling, and represents a number of large healthcare providers, including Pharmerica, Ventas and Rehabcare. The group also handles commercial, employment and personal injury disputes, as well as significant public interest litigation.
**Sources say:** "*They're very responsive and extremely knowledgeable about the healthcare industry.*"
**KEY INDIVIDUALS** **Gregg Hovious**'s broad-based commercial litigation practice commands significant respect in the Kentucky market. Clients value his knowledge and attentiveness, describing him as "*very talented*" and "*very responsive.*" "*Tremendous attorney*" **Benjamin Fultz** is singled out by clients as a healthcare expert with strong business acumen and a good head for risk management. "*Outstanding*" individual **Victor Maddox** deals primarily

with complex accounting and business disputes. He is also well versed in constitutional litigation.

### Middleton Reutlinger PSC

**THE FIRM** Middleton Reutlinger's business litigation group acts for clients on a range of contentious matters, including shareholder disputes, noncompete issues and commercial fraud. It also places a heavy emphasis on insurance defense and healthcare litigation, and has significant experience in the fields of professional negligence and nursing home defense. Biomet, CNA Insurance and Norton Healthcare are among its key clients.

**Sources say:** *"They're quick to respond, good communicators and accessible."*

**KEY INDIVIDUALS Mark Fenzel** chairs the firm's insurance litigation practice group and defends professional negligence, personal injury and employment-related claims. Clients admire his *"proactive handling and management of cases."* Leader of the firm's healthcare practice group, **William Oldham** is an experienced litigator of administrative cases and malpractice actions. Clients prize his diligent preparation and logical approach. **Dennis Murrell** is praised by clients for his ability to *"cut through all the distraction and get to the heart of the issue."* He handles a broad range of commercial matters, including breach of contract, commercial fraud and intellectual property litigation. Clients report that **Hiram Ely** is *"bright, responsive, highly experienced in litigation strategies and successful in their execution."* He has a varied practice that encompasses product liability, environmental, securities, antitrust and tax litigation.

### Reed Weitkamp Schell & Vice PLLC

**THE FIRM** This Louisville firm receives high praise for the excellence of its small but distinguished team of litigators. The group has a strong focus on business litigation, particularly within the healthcare sector, and its experience includes business torts, antitrust, patent litigation and trade secret matters. Recent clients include Diageo, First Capital Bank of Kentucky and Connected Learning Network.

**Sources say:** *"Skilled and savvy litigators."*

**KEY INDIVIDUALS** Highly regarded practitioner **John Reed** is known for handling antitrust, trade secret and contractual disputes. Clients describe him as *"very analytical"* and *"very objective."*

### Tachau Meek PLC

**THE FIRM** This much-admired litigation boutique has a good reputation across a broad spectrum of commercial disputes. Areas of expertise include unfair competition, trust and estate, construction, professional negligence, employment and bet-the-company litigation.

**KEY INDIVIDUALS** *"Tenacious advocate"* **David Tachau** focuses on general commercial, employment, trust and estate, and insurance, litigation. **Dustin Meek** handles lender liability, land use, insurance coverage, employment discrimination and ERISA litigation. Her clients are drawn primarily from the banking and healthcare sectors.

### Band 1

### Boehl Stopher & Graves, LLP
See profile on p.1328

**THE FIRM** Boehl Stopher & Graves is preeminent in the state for its tort action and insurance defense expertise. Its highly regarded civil litigation team is well equipped to represent clients in a range of matters, including general insurance, wrongful death, personal injury, professional negligence and product liability. It also has significant experience with railroad and nursing home defense. CSX Railroad, Ford and Ohio Casualty are all recent clients.

**KEY INDIVIDUALS** *"Outstanding lawyer"* **Edward Stopher** (see p.1325) is described by peers as a *"star."* He defends insurance carriers and corporate clients against negligence, malpractice and product liability claims. **Robert Stopher** (see p.1325) focuses on insurance defense, product liability and professional negligence matters, with a particular interest in personal injury and wrongful death litigation. **Raymond Smith** (see p.1324) is an experienced appellate lawyer. He has a broad practice encompassing antitrust, insurance coverage and professional malpractice litigation.

### Other Notable Practitioners

**Donald Cox** of Lynch, Cox, Gilman & Mahan PSC is described by peers as *"absolutely brilliant."* He handles commercial litigation, with a particular interest in intellectual property. Highly respected practitioner **Todd Thompson** of Thompson Miller & Simpson PLC specializes in commercial, healthcare and product liability litigation. **Charles Greenwell** of Goldberg Simpson LLC is an esteemed commercial litigator, with a focus on fiduciary, governance and financial services-related litigation. **David Blandford** of Ackerson & Yann PSC is an expert in construction law. Sources describe him as *"even-keeled,"* with *"impeccable judgment."* **Gerald Stovall** of Hall, Render, Killian, Heath & Lyman PSC is also singled out as a leading construction attorney. He provides construction and engineering-related representation to owners, contractors, designers, suppliers and lenders.

# REAL ESTATE

Commentary about individuals can be found under their firm's paragraph. If the firm has no paragraph (is not ranked) look at Other Notable Practitioners.

### Band 1

### Frost Brown Todd LLC
See profile on p.1329

**THE FIRM** Frost Brown Todd's much-admired real estate group offers broad expertise across a spectrum of commercial matters, including acquisition, finance, development, land use and zoning, and CMBS. Its clients include institutional lenders, developers, investors, owners and real estate professionals, and its attorneys have recently advised on significant projects within the healthcare and hospitality sectors.

**Sources say:** *"They're easy to work with and very creative."* *"The firm has global insight into what my company needs."*

**KEY INDIVIDUALS** *"Market leader"* **Timothy Martin** (see p.1322) is in the vanguard of the Kentucky real estate market. His work ranges from leasing and conveyancing to zoning, development and financing. The *"well-respected"* **Dale Ahearn** (see p.1315) is described as *"a good communicator."* He represents borrowers and institutional lenders in retail developments, asset-based lending and project finance issues. Another leading practitioner at the firm is *"excellent lawyer"* **Barry Hines** (see p.1320). He represents lenders in real estate finance transactions and has a nationwide CMBS practice. **Glenn Price** (see p.1323) is distinguished in the fields of zoning and land use. He assists businesses and developers with securing approvals, permits and variances, in addition to tackling any related litigation. Clients identify **Geoff White** (see p.1325) as *"very smart, very creative and very adaptable."* He is called upon to represent lenders, developers and investors in real estate transactions, financings and workouts.

### Stites & Harbison PLLC
See profile on p.1331

**THE FIRM** Stites & Harbison is widely regarded as a leading firm for Kentucky real estate. The team is well versed in a wide range of real estate transactional matters and has considerable experience of representing lenders in real estate financings and troubled loan workouts. In the past year it has advised on new markets tax credits and affordable housing transactions, and has expanded its hospitality group.

**KEY INDIVIDUALS** Sources describe *"top-tier"* practitioner **William Haden** (see p.1319) as *"very smart"* and a *"great advocate."* He focuses on advising banks on special assets, letters of credit and commercial lending. **Gregory Ehrhard** (see p.1318) advises on a variety of real estate matters, including lending, leasing and condominiums. He also devotes a significant portion of his practice to zoning housing and land use. **Robert Vice** (see p.1325) is highly recommended for his commercial real estate expertise. He has a well-developed practice concentrated on affordable housing.

## Band 2

### Middleton Reutlinger PSC

**THE FIRM** This group of attorneys recently acted for the purchaser on the $36 million acquisition of historic thoroughbred breeding and training estate Calumet Farm. The firm provides a comprehensive range of real estate services to development companies, financial institutions and investors, and has prominent clients in the healthcare and hospitality industries. In the past year it has represented Norton Healthcare, Dow Corning and Musselman Hotels. **Sources say:** *"Their work is outstanding."*
**KEY INDIVIDUALS Michael Tigue** is one of Kentucky's leading zoning and land development attorneys. Clients report: *"He's great at making an argument and making it understandable."* Experienced practitioner **Gregory Compton** is held in high esteem for his commercial and residential real estate development acumen. Clients value **Gregory Mayes**'s *"calm and collected"* negotiation skills. He is particularly well known for his work with housing initiative organizations and institutional lenders. **Thomas Ice** receives glowing reviews for his transaction-focused real estate practice. Clients describe him as *"exceptional"* and admire his energy, intellect and *"great interpersonal skills."*

### Reed Weitkamp Schell & Vice PLLC

**THE FIRM** Reed Weitkamp Schell & Vice is preeminent in the state for its real estate tax and finance practice. Its talented attorneys are well equipped to provide advice on acquisitions, leasing, development and redevelopment, and loan documentation.
**KEY INDIVIDUALS** Clients value the much-praised **Robert Vice**'s industry knowledge and business acumen. He handles commercial real estate finance matters for developers and lenders, with a concentration on affordable housing tax credits. **Jeffrey Hamilton** represents lenders in the financing of commercial real estate projects and has specialist knowledge of mortgage warehouse lending. Clients prize his diplomacy and identify him as negotiating with *"finesse."*

### Stoll Keenon Ogden PLLC
See profile on p.1332

**THE FIRM** This multiservice Lexington firm is one of Kentucky's foremost providers of eminent domain expertise. It is also particularly active in the commercial real estate development arena, with recent highlights including retail and student housing projects. Other areas of emphasis are lending, leasing, and zoning and land use. PBI Bank, Brown-Forman and JH Properties are all key clients.
**Sources say:** *"A well-rounded firm with a lot of talent and a lot of expertise."*
**KEY INDIVIDUALS** Admired practitioner **Frank Wilford** (see p.1326) has a strong focus on transactional, finance and banking-oriented real estate issues. Chair of the firm's real estate practice, **Richard Nunnelley** (see p.1322) has a wealth of experience across finance and commercial leasing matters. He is especially noted for his expertise in equine transactions, and recently assisted Capall Stables with the purchase of a 168-acre horse farm in Woodford County, Kentucky. Clients describe **Anthony Schnell** (see p.1324) as an *"experienced and very insightful attorney,"* observing that *"he has a keen intellect that's useful in negotiating complex transactions."* He is based in the firm's Louisville office and handles real estate finance, acquisition and leasing.

### Wyatt, Tarrant & Combs, LLP
See profile on p.1333

**THE FIRM** This real estate practice continues to enjoy a strong regional presence. Its distinguished attorneys act for owners, developers, investors and tenants on a multitude of transactional matters, complex financings, developments and zoning issues. Notable clients include 3rd Street Development and Republic Bank & Trust Company.
**KEY INDIVIDUALS Deborah Bilitski** (see p.1316) is viewed as a leading authority on zoning and land use in the state of Kentucky. She recently assisted Horizon Group Properties with the development of an outlet mall in Simpsonville, Kentucky. Highly regarded practitioner **Mark Burton** (see p.1317) is based in the firm's Lexington office. He has a wide-ranging real estate practice and is regularly called on to represent institutional lenders in loan workout negotiations. Clients appreciate **Arthur Rouse**'s (see p.1323) business sense. His practice has a heavy focus on commercial lending and loan workouts. **Michael Vincenti** (see p.1325) is recognized for his experience in the fields of leasing, development and lending. **Leo Camp** (see p.1317) is another key practitioner at the firm. He advises national clients on issues relating to liquor licensing law. **David Seewer** (see p.1324) impresses clients with his experience in real estate transactional matters, financing, development and leasing. Up-and-coming individual **Clifford Ashburner** (see p.1315) has developed a noteworthy reputation for his zoning and land use expertise.

and land use. **David Saffer** (see p.1323) continues to represent developers and institutional lenders in commercial lending transactions. *"Market leader"* **Alfred Joseph** (see p.1321) is an experienced transactional lawyer. His practice covers all areas of real estate law, with a focus on affordable

## Band 3

### Bingham Greenebaum Doll LLP
See profile on p.1327

THE FIRM This firm is best known for handling high-end real estate transactions, commercial developments and real estate matters relating to corporate M&A. The team counsels developers, financial institutions, government bodies and utilities on a range of projects, including multiuse developments, stadiums and retail centers. Global Fitness Holdings, Heaven Hill Distilleries and Dominion Homes are among its key clients.
KEY INDIVIDUALS Skilled practitioner **Tandy Patrick** (see p.1322) has distinguished herself in the fields of leasing, acquisitions and real estate development.

### McBrayer, McGinnis, Leslie & Kirkland, PLLC

THE FIRM This Lexington-based firm is recognized for its zoning and land use experience. It has an impressive track record in assisting developers with gaining approval for developments on underutilized and vacant properties. The team also advises on a broad range of residential and commercial real estate transactions, and has recently acted for Lexington Trots Breeders, Kentucky Eagle Beer and Oak Grove Village.
**Sources say:** *"I was thrilled with their performance."*
KEY INDIVIDUALS The *"brilliant"* **James Frazier** handles all phases of real estate development, including acquisition, zoning and leasing.

### Weber & Rose, PSC

THE FIRM Weber & Rose's real estate group acts for owners, developers and lenders at every stage of commercial real estate developments. The attorneys are particularly well known for representing institutional lenders in financing transactions, and are also equipped to advise on loan workouts, zoning and land use, leasing, eminent domain and municipal housing. The practice counts banks, healthcare providers and quasi-governmental agencies among its clients.
**Sources say:** *"They do a very good job of protecting their clients' interests and are proactive in making deals work."*
KEY INDIVIDUALS **Joseph Gathright** wins respect for his command of real estate finance. He has a particular interest in workouts of troubled projects and issues relat-ing to condominiums. Clients hail **James Lobb** as an *"excellent real estate attorney,"* who is *"very detail-oriented."* He is best known for advising developers on retail projects, medical facilities and office complexes. **Sharon Hardy** focuses on asset-based lending and real estate workouts. She is praised by clients for her diligence, approachability and common-sense approach.

### Other Notable Practitioners

The *"talented"* **Andrew Fleischman** of Miller Wells PLLC continues to build an impressive reputation for his activities in the real estate lending arena. He is particularly well known for representing coal mining companies. **Daniel Walter** of Ackerson & Yann PSC attracts praise for his high-quality insight, informed by his accounting background. He acts for owners, developers and tenants on transactional and finance-related real estate matters. Zoning and land use expert **Paul Whitty** of Goldberg Simpson LLC is noted in the market for his prowess in commercial and residential development, adaptive real estate projects and land use litigation.

# Leaders' Profiles in Kentucky

### AHEARN, Dale
Frost Brown Todd LLC, Louisville
502 568 0275
dahearn@fbtlaw.com
*Featured in Real Estate (Kentucky)*
**Practice Areas:** Complex commercial transactions, focusing on commercial real estate, asset based lending and project finance. Represents institutional lenders and borrowers in structuring, documenting and closing complex transactions on a national and international basis. Represents clients involving a wide variety of other real estate transactions, including high-rise office buildings, campus housing, condominiums, senior living, and industrial properties.
**Career:** Included in the Best Lawyers in America since 2000 and Kentucky Super Lawyers since 2008. Lead counsel in the development of over 100 regional shopping centers during the past 20 years.
**Personal:** JD, University of Michigan Law School, 1977.

### ASHBURNER, Clifford
Wyatt, Tarrant & Combs, LLP, Louisville
502 562 7107
chashburner@wyattfirm.com
*Featured in Real Estate (Kentucky)*
**Practice Areas:** Cliff Ashburner, LEED AP, represents developers and other property owners before planning commissions, boards of zoning adjustment, city councils and courts. He is proficient in sustainable development issues, including the LEED certification process, brownfield redevelopment and other land uses.
**Professional Memberships:** Kentucky Bar Association; United States Green Building Council, Board of Directors.
**Career:** LEED Accredited Professional (First Kentucky attorney to obtain the accreditation); Recipient of the SPIRE Award for having "the greatest positive impact on Kentucky commercial real estate in 2011."
**Personal:** University of Kentucky (JD 1998); James Madison University (BA 1995).

### BALLANTINE, Douglas C
Stoll Keenon Ogden PLLC, Louisville
502 560 4247
douglas.ballantine@skofirm.com
*Featured in Litigation (Kentucky)*
**Practice Areas:** Concentration in commercial, intellectual property, and environmental litigation, including superfund and toxic tort matters. Experience with professional negligence litigation, especially defense of medical malpractice cases, and defense of personal injury and products liability actions.
**Professional Memberships:** American, Kentucky (Member, Board of Governors), and Louisville Bar Associations; Past member, Advisory Committee on Local Rules of United States Court of Appeals for Sixth Circuit; Past member, Kentucky Supreme Court Civil Rules Committee; Defense Research Institute; Kentucky Defense Counsel, Inc.
**Personal:** Indiana University (Bloomington) (JD, 1988); American University (BA, 1984). Listed in 'Best Lawyers in America,' and 'Super Lawyers,' Business Litigation.

### BALLANTINE, John T
Stoll Keenon Ogden PLLC, Louisville
502 560 4213
john.ballantine@skofirm.com
*Featured in Litigation (Kentucky)*
**Practice Areas:** Civil litigation with concentration on professional liability and medical malpractice defense cases; mediation and arbitration of all types of civil cases and claims.
**Professional Memberships:** Fellow, American College of Trial Lawyers; Life Member, Judicial Conference of U.S. Court of Appeals, Sixth Circuit; Kentucky Defense Counsel, Inc.
**Personal:** Harvard Law School (LLB, 1957); University of Kentucky (AB, Phi Beta Kappa, high distinction, 1952). Listed in 'Best Lawyers in America,' Personal Injury Litigation; recipient of Kentucky Bar Association Outstanding Lawyer Award (2003) and Louisville Bar Association Judge Shobe Civility and Professionalism Award (2006).

### BARR, P Douglas
Stoll Keenon Ogden PLLC, Lexington
859 231 3046
douglas.barr@skofirm.com
*Featured in Intellectual Property (Kentucky)*
**Practice Areas:** Mr Barr has focused his practice in Complex Business Litigation, including Intellectual Property Litigation. He has successfully litigated matters in numerous jurisdictions ranging from patent infringement, trademark and copyright infringement, trade secret misappropriation and internet disputes (including domain name disputes). Also, Mr Barr has successfully represented clients in complex antitrust cases, business torts and contract disputes, ERISA matters and class action suits.
**Professional Memberships:** American, Kentucky, Fayette County, Ohio and Cincinnati Bar Associations.
**Personal:** University of Kentucky (BA, with high distinction, 1980); Ohio State University (JD, with honors, 1983).

### BARTLEY, Kelly D
Bingham Greenebaum Doll LLP, Lexington
859 288-4641
kbartley@bgdlegal.com
*Featured in Environment (Kentucky)*

**Practice Areas:** As a member of the Environmental and Natural Resources Practice Group, Kelly's practice at Bingham Greenebaum Doll LLP involves consulting with and representing firm corporate clients with respect to a broad range of state and federal environmental law compliance, permitting and litigation issues, including issues relating to air emissions, solid and hazardous waste, and wastewater treatment.
**Professional Memberships:** Fayette County Bar Association, Kentucky Bar Association.
**Publications:** Editor, Bingham Greenebaum Doll Air Quality Letter, published quarterly; Associate Editor, Kentucky Environmental Law Handbook, 3d ed., Government Institutes 2001.
**Personal:** Attended University of Kentucky College of Law.

## BEAVIN, C Joseph
Stoll Keenon Ogden PLLC, Lexington
859 231 3074
joseph.beavin@skofirm.com
*Featured in Labor & Employment (Kentucky)*
**Practice Areas:** Concentration in areas of ERISA, employee benefits and deferred compensation. Regularly counsels employers in employee benefit and related employment law matters and represents employers before the Internal Revenue Service and the Department of Labor.
**Professional Memberships:** Fayette County, Kentucky and American (Member, Labor and Employment Law Section) Bar Associations.
**Personal:** University of Kentucky (B.S., Accounting with high distinction, 1973); University of Kentucky College of Law (JD, with high distinction, 1983; editor, Kentucky Law Journal; Order of the Coif). AV® Preeminent™ Peer Review Rated by Martindale-Hubbell® and named to Kentucky's Top Rated Lawyers; listed in "Best Lawyers in America".

## BECK JR, Robert M
Stites & Harbison PLLC, Lexington
859 226 2336
rbeck@stites.com
*Featured in Corporate/M&A (Kentucky)*
**Practice Areas:** Business practice with emphasis in equine, corporate, finance, mergers and acquisitions.
**Professional Memberships:** Admitted to practice in Kentucky (1975). Member of American, Kentucky and Fayette County Bar Associations; Fellow, Former President, Founder and Director, American College of Equine Attorneys; listed in Best Lawyers In America, Chambers USA and Kentucky SuperLawyers; Chairman, Kentucky Horse Racing Commission.
**Career:** Member, Stites & Harbison.
**Publications:** Co-author, 'Business Combinations Non-Tax Considerations', University of Kentucky CLE publications, 2009; Co-author, 'Multiple Ownership Arrangements for Investing in the Horse Business', University of Kentucky CLE publications, 2003.
**Personal:** JD, Vanderbilt University, 1975; BA, Economics, Vanderbilt University, 1971.

## BECKER, Wendy
Bingham Greenebaum Doll LLP, Lexington
859 288 4701
wbecker@bgdlegal.com
*Featured in Labor & Employment (Kentucky)*
**Practice Areas:** Wendy represents employers in all phases of employment law. Her practice includes the litigation of employment discrimination and wrongful discharge cases, representation of employers before the EEOC, state and local Human Rights Commissions, and general counseling to employers on hiring, firing, wage-hour and other day to day employment matters.
**Professional Memberships:** President, Fayette County Bar Association Labor and Employment Section, 2006-2007; President, Fayette County Bar Association Women Lawyer's Association, 2006; Kentucky Bar Association, Labor and Employment Law Section.
**Publications:** "Workplace Harassment," UK CLE Employment Law Handbook, 2000, 2007, 2012.
**Personal:** Attended University of Kentucky College of Law.

## BENDER, Jack
Bingham Greenebaum Doll LLP, Lexington
859 288 4607
jbender@bgdlegal.com
*Featured in Environment (Kentucky)*
**Practice Areas:** Jack's practice involves consulting and representing the firm's clients in litigation with respect to air, solid and hazardous waste, and wastewater compliance and permitting issues. He has negotiated Consent Decrees with U.S. EPA on behalf of industry and municipal clients, and successfully defended clients in citizen suits. He's a frequent speaker at Business and Trade Group meetings on environmental issues. He also serves as assistant editor of his firm's quarterly newsletter on Kentucky air regulations - Kentucky Air Quality Review.
**Personal:** BS, Mining Engineering, Pennsylvania State University State University, 1978; JD, University of Kentucky College of Law, 1987.

## BERES, Joel T
Stites & Harbison PLLC, Louisville
502 681 0324
jberes@stites.com
*Featured in Intellectual Property (Kentucky)*
**Practice Areas:** Litigates patent, trademark and copyright infringement actions; prosecutes trademark and copyright applications; consults regarding software and technology licensing agreements.
**Professional Memberships:** Admitted in Kentucky and California. American, California, Kentucky and Louisville Bar Associations; International Trademark Association; Federal Circuit Bar Association.
**Career:** Member, Stites & Harbison. Regional Counsel to Microsoft Corp. Handled one of the biggest mark transfers ever for ELECTROLUX.
**Publications:** 'Protecting Trade Secrets', Louisville Bar Association, May 2004; 'IP Law for Design-Build Professionals', Half-Moon Publications, March 2008.
**Personal:** JD, University of California at Los Angeles, 1986; AB, Stanford University, 1983.

## BERGE, Amy B
Bingham Greenebaum Doll LLP, Louisville
502 587 3707
aberge@bgdlegal.com
*Featured in Intellectual Property (Kentucky)*
**Practice Areas:** Practices in the areas of US and international trademark, copyright, advertising and internet law. Also concentrates on licensing, privacy and computer and technology agreements. Assists clients in obtaining and maintaining registrations with the relevant trademark and copyright offices, negotiates agreements, and litigates before the US Trademark Trial and Appeal Board and before federal and state courts.
**Professional Memberships:** International Trademark Association, Louisville Bar Association, Kentucky Bar Association, The Advertising Federation of Louisville.
**Career:** Admitted in Kentucky, 1988.
**Publications:** Co-Author, Kentucky Chapter, State Trademark and Unfair Competition Law.
**Personal:** Attended University of Louisville School of Law.

## BILITSKI, Deborah A
Wyatt, Tarrant & Combs, LLP, Louisville
502 562 7297
dbilitski@wyattfirm.com
*Featured in Real Estate (Kentucky)*
**Practice Areas:** Ms. Bilitski leads Wyatt's Real Estate & Lending Service Team. Represents clients in securing zoning, subdivision, and other development approvals, handles land use litigation and appeals.
**Professional Memberships:** Kentucky Bar Association; Florida Bar Association; U.S. District Court - Western District of Kentucky; U.S. Circuit Court - Sixth Circuit, Homebuilders Association of Louisville Board of Directors; Louisville Downtown Management District Vice Chair/Board of Directors.
**Career:** Served as counsel to Louisville Metro Planning Commission, Metro Board of Zoning Adjustment, Metro Council, and Louisville/Jefferson County Environmental Trust.
**Personal:** University of Louisville School of Law (JD 1995); University of Pittsburgh (BA 1992).

## BIRCHFIELD, Thomas J
Fisher & Phillips LLP, Louisville
502 561 3960
tbirchfield@laborlawyers.com
*Featured in Labor & Employment (Kentucky)*
**Career:** Thomas Birchfield is Managing Partner of the Louisville office. He advises employers on the development and implementation of preventive labor relations programs to avoid charges and lawsuits, protection of trade secrets, and resolution of disputes. Birchfield counsels employers during union representation elections, decertifications, corporate campaigns, collective bargaining negotiations, strikes, and lockouts. He handles employment-related litigation and arbitrations before state and federal courts and administrative agencies involving claims of discrimination, wrongful discharge and other statutory claims.

## BRADLEY JR, C Craig
Stites & Harbison PLLC, Louisville
502 681 0411
cbradley@stites.com
*Featured in Corporate/M&A (Kentucky)*
**Practice Areas:** Business Service Group. Practice emphasis in securities and corporate finance, mergers and acquisitions and corporate governance.
**Professional Memberships:** Admitted to practice in Kentucky (1980). Member of American, Kentucky and Louisville Bar Associations, Kentucky Securities Law Legislative Advisory Committee and Drafting Committee for Kentucky Business Corporation Act.
**Career:** Member of Stites & Harbison. With the firm since 1980.
**Publications:** 'The Roles and Motivations of Key Players in Corporate Governance Cases', Aspatore Books, 2007.
**Personal:** JD, University of Kentucky, 1980; BA, University of Virginia, 1977.

## BRINKMAN, Scott W
Stoll Keenon Ogden PLLC, Louisville
502 560 4244
scott.brinkman@skofirm.com
*Featured in Corporate/M&A (Kentucky)*
**Practice Areas:** Mr Brinkman practices primarily in public finance and secured lending, business acquisitions, capital formation, general corporate law and commercial real estate. He represents issuers of taxable and tax-exempt securities and commercial banks in secured loan transactions; both buyers and sellers of businesses, whether structured as asset acquisitions, stock acquisitions, mergers or share exchanges; issuers of securities in private offerings under federal and state securities laws; and real estate developers.
**Professional Memberships:** American, Kentucky, Louisville Bar Associations. State Representative, Kentucky House of Representatives, 2001-2010.
**Personal:** University of Notre Dame (BA, cum laude, 1977); University of Cincinnati (JD, 1980).

## BROWN, Carolyn M
Bingham Greenebaum Doll LLP, Lexington
859 288 4614
cbrown@bgdlegal.com
*Featured in Environment (Kentucky)*
**Practice Areas:** Carolyn is managing partner of the firm's Lexington office and chair of the firm's Environmental and Natural Resources Practice Group. Her practice focuses on all areas of environmental law and includes advice and counseling on regulatory requirements, permitting and transactional issues as well as environmental litigation.
**Professional Memberships:** Kentucky Bar Association (Environment, Energy & Resources Section), Texas Bar Association, American Bar Association.
**Career:** Admitted in Kentucky (1985) and Texas (1982).
**Publications:** Frequent presenter on environmental law topics for the Kentucky Chamber of Commerce, Manufacturers' Education Council and other groups.

**Personal:** Attended University of Kentucky College of Law.

## BROWN, David C
Stites & Harbison PLLC, Louisville
502 681 0421
dbrown@stites.com
*Featured in Environment (Kentucky)*

**Practice Areas:** Kentucky Public Service Commission Practice, commercial and business transactions and energy regulatory transactions. Certified Mediator, Private Adjudication Center, Duke University School of Law, 2002.

**Professional Memberships:** Admitted to practice in Kentucky. Member of American, Kentucky and Louisville Bar Associations.

**Career:** Counsel, Stites & Harbison. Former Managing Partner. With the firm since 1964.

**Personal:** JD, University of Virginia, 1964; BA, Kenyon College, 1961.

## BURTON, J Mark
Wyatt, Tarrant & Combs, LLP, Lexington
859 288 7407
mburton@wyattfirm.com
*Featured in Real Estate (Kentucky)*

**Practice Areas:** Partner-in-Charge of Lexington office, Co-Partner-in-Charge of Finance for the Firm. Concentrates practice in the areas of real estate and commercial lending, with an emphasis in commercial lending, real estate conveyancing, IRC §1031 transactions, real estate development, commercial loan work-outs and foreclosures.

**Professional Memberships:** Fayette County and Kentucky Bar Associations; Vice President of the Fayette County Bar Foundation; Lifetime Member of the Board of the Lexington Speech and Hearing Center.

**Career:** Best Lawyers in America® Real Estate Law, 2007-13; AV Rating by Martindale-Hubbell.

**Personal:** University of Kentucky, JD, 1980; Roanoke College, BA, 1977.

## CAMP, Leo
Wyatt, Tarrant & Combs, LLP, Louisville
502 562 7552
lcamp@wyattfirm.com
*Featured in Real Estate (Kentucky)*

**Practice Areas:** Mr Camp regularly represents sellers and buyers of commercial and industrial properties, lessors and lessees of office, retail and industrial properties, and borrowers and lenders in commercial lending transactions. In addition, Mr Camp represents individuals and entities in liquor licensing matters.

**Professional Memberships:** Louisville, Kentucky and American Bar Associations. International Council of Shopping Centers, Kentucky representative in the Alliance of Alcohol Industry Attorneys and Consultants.

**Career:** Recognized by Woodward/White's The Best Lawyers in America® Real Estate Law, 2013; AV rated by Martindale-Hubbell; Real Estate Law "Top Lawyers" by Louisville Magazine, 2012; Kentucky Super Lawyers 2012.

## CLEARY, Richard S
Frost Brown Todd LLC, Louisville
502 779 8562
rcleary@fbtlaw.com
*Featured in Labor & Employment (Kentucky)*

**Practice Areas:** Represents employers exclusively in employment and wage-hour litigation, collective bargaining, arbitration and before the National Labor Relations Board and other federal and state administrative agencies. Practice emphasis is on the labor relations implications of corporate restructurings.

**Professional Memberships:** Council Member, ABA Labor and Employment Law Section 2008-present; Co-Chair, Committee on the Development of the Law Under the NLRA 1999-2002.

**Publications:** Kentucky Employment Law Letter, M Lee Smith Publishing Co, editor, 1991-present.

**Personal:** JD Georgetown University 1981; Washington and Lee University 1978 (cum laude). Born in New York; married to Helen Bragg Curtin; two children.

## COCKRUM, James
Frost Brown Todd LLC, Louisville
502 568 0317
jcockrum@fbtlaw.com
*Featured in Labor & Employment (Kentucky)*

**Practice Areas:** Mr Cockrum practices management-side labor and employment law representing employers before federal and state courts and administrative agencies.

**Professional Memberships:** Kentucky Bar Association; Louisville Bar Association.

**Career:** Mr Cockrum has been a Member of Frost Brown Todd LLC since its inception. He joined Brown, Todd & Heyburn in 1987.

**Publications:** Mr Cockrum has authored private seminar publications for seminars sponsored by the Kentucky Chamber of Commerce, the University of Louisville, the University of Kentucky and other organizations.

**Personal:** JD - Indiana University (Bloomington) 1987. BA - Kentucky Wesleyan College (cum laude) 1980.

## COLEMAN, Tony C
Frost Brown Todd LLC, Louisville
502 568 0354
tcoleman@fbtlaw.com
*Featured in Labor & Employment (Kentucky)*

**Career:** Tony Coleman has practiced labor and employment law, representing management exclusively, since becoming a lawyer in 1983. His practice includes handling all types of labor issues under both the National Labor Relations Act (NLRA) and Railway Labor Act (RLA). He has handled organizing campaigns, unfair labor practice charges, litigation and administrative proceedings under the statutory frame of both the NLRA and RLA. He has also served as counsel for management in numerous airline and transportation related labor contracts.

**Personal:** University of Louisville, BA, 1980, summa cum laude; University of Louisville, Louis D Brandeis School of Law, JD, 1983.

## COLLIER, Philip W
Stites & Harbison PLLC, Louisville
502 681 0415
pcollier@stites.com
*Featured in Litigation (Kentucky)*

**Practice Areas:** Business, insurance and class action defense litigation.

**Professional Memberships:** Admitted to practice in Kentucky and United States Supreme Court. Member of American and Kentucky Bar Associations.

**Career:** Member, Stites & Harbison. Presented oral arguments before United States Supreme Court in Itel Containers International Corp. v Huddleston, 113 S.Ct. 1095 (US 1993). Appellate arguments before Kentucky Court of Appeals, Tennessee Supreme Court and United States Court of Appeals for the 6th Circuit.

**Publications:** Lecturer, Kentucky Bar Association Convention, 'Disputes in Closely Held Businesses', June 2003.

**Personal:** JD, University of Kentucky, 1979; BA, with high distinction, University of Kentucky, 1976.

## CONNER, Stewart
Wyatt, Tarrant & Combs, LLP, Louisville
502 562 7223
sconner@wyattfirm.com
*Featured in Corporate/M&A (Kentucky)*

**Practice Areas:** Stewart Conner is the former Chair of the Firm's Executive Committee and a member of the Corporate & Securities Service Team. Concentrates practice in the general corporate, corporate finance, securities and banking areas.

**Professional Memberships:** Board of Directors of Louisville Water Company; Chair of Executive Board of Boy Scouts of America, Lincoln Heritage Council; Director of DNP Select Income Fund; Fellow of the American and Kentucky Bar Foundations.

**Publications:** He has authored numerous articles and handbooks for practitioners.

**Personal:** Received BSC degree in 1963 and JD degree (cum laude) in 1966 from the University of Louisville.

## CONNIFF, Dennis J
Frost Brown Todd LLC, Louisville
502 568 0398
dconniff@fbtlaw.com
*Featured in Environment (Kentucky)*

**Practice Areas:** Environmental Law. Work includes advising clients on compliance with the waste, air and water programs, and litigation of environmental liability issues.

**Professional Memberships:** Chair, Greater Louisville, Inc. Air Toxics Task Force; Vice-Chair, American Bar Association Section of Environment, Energy and Resources, Waste and Resource Recovery Committee.

**Career:** Admitted to practice in Kentucky (1979). Joined Brown, Todd & Heyburn, now Frost Brown Todd LLC (Member, 1995). Also admitted to the federal courts for the Eastern and Western Districts of Kentucky, and the Sixth Circuit Court of Appeals.

**Personal:** Born February 2, 1953. Attended University of Louisville School of Law.

## CONNOLLY, Robert M
Stites & Harbison PLLC, Louisville
502 681 0424
rconnolly@stites.com
*Featured in Litigation (Kentucky)*

**Practice Areas:** Product liability and business litigation. Over 80 trials and numerous appellate arguments.

**Professional Memberships:** Admitted to practice in Kentucky, US 1st, 6th and 7th U.S. Appellate Circuits. Member of American, Kentucky Bar Associations, Louisville Bar Foundation, Inc., DRI, Kentucky Defense Council.

**Career:** Member, Stites & Harbison. Chair, Litigation Section.

**Publications:** Reported cases: Marley Cooling Tower v Caldwell Energy & Environmental, Inc., 280 F.Supp.2d 651 (W.D. Ky. 2003); Southeastern United Medigroup, Inc. v Hughes, et al., Ky., 952 S.W.2d 195 (1997); and others.

**Personal:** JD, Washington and Lee University, 1980. BA, Dartmouth College, Government (Honors), magna cum laude with high distinction, 1977.

## CORNELL, Laurel
Fisher & Phillips LLP, Louisville
502 561 3987
lcornell@laborlawyers.com
*Featured in Labor & Employment (Kentucky)*

**Career:** Laurel Cornell is an associate in the Louisville office. Her practice involves representing employers in litigation of employment disputes involving Title VII, the FMLA, retaliation, breach of contract, and wrongful termination claims. She also has experience advising and representing employers in administrative actions. While in law school, Laurel was a member of the Kentucky Law Journal.

## CORYELL II, Cornelius E
Wyatt, Tarrant & Combs, LLP, Louisville
502 562 7376
ccoryell@wyattfirm.com
*Featured in Litigation (Kentucky)*

**Practice Areas:** Corky Coryell is a member of the Firm's Litigation and Dispute Resolution Service Team. He concentrates his practice in the areas of commercial litigation, banking litigation, UCC litigation, and consumer class action litigation.

**Professional Memberships:** Louisville and Kentucky Bar Associations; Defense Research Institute member.

**Career:** Woodward/White's Best Lawyers in America® 2006-13 in the area of commercial litigation; recognized as Local Litigation Star by Benchmark Litigation 2013; named in Kentucky Super Lawyers 2012 in the area of business litigation.

**Personal:** University of Kentucky College of Law, JD, 1987; University of Louisville, BS BA (Finance), with high honors, 1984.

## CRONAN IV, Charles J
Stites & Harbison PLLC, Louisville
501 681 0430
ccronan@stites.com
*Featured in Litigation (Kentucky)*
**Practice Areas:** Business litigation. General civil, medico-business and products liability litigation.
**Professional Memberships:** Admitted to practice in Kentucky (1970). Fellow of the American College of Trial Lawyers, Member of Federation of Defense and Corporate Counsel and Defense Research Institute, Member of American, Kentucky and Louisville Bar Associations, and Kentucky Bar Foundation.
**Career:** US Navy Judge Advocate General's Corps, 1970-74. Joined Stites & Harbison in 1974. Managing Partner, 1994-97. Listed in The Best Lawyers in America, 1989-present.
**Personal:** JD, cum laude, University of Louisville, 1970. BA, Government, Wesleyan University, 1967. Married, four grown children.

## CRYDER, Bruce E
Bingham Greenebaum Doll LLP, Lexington
859 288 4623
bcryder@bgdlegal.com
*Featured in Environment (Kentucky)*
**Practice Areas:** Bruce is a member of the Environmental and Natural Resources Practice Group. His practice focuses on mineral, energy and natural resources law, with a particular emphasis on the coal industry. He represents coal producers, utilities, investors, lenders and others in connection with acquisitions and dispositions, mineral leasing, and commercial transactions of every nature. He also represents clients in commercial litigation matters.
**Professional Memberships:** Board of Trustees, Energy and Mineral Law Foundation; Kentucky Bar Association; Ohio Bar Association; Fayette County Bar Association.
**Personal:** Attended The Ohio State University Law School.

## DAWAHARE, Debra
Wyatt, Tarrant & Combs, LLP, Lexington
859 288 7617
ddawahare@wyattfirm.com
*Featured in Labor & Employment (Kentucky)*
**Practice Areas:** Debra Dawahare is member of the Firm's Labor & Employment Service Team. She regularly counsels employers about all employment issues, such as handbooks, policies, hiring, discipline and discharge, and compliance with anti-discrimination laws. Trains managers and workforce. A seasoned litigator; has tried a wide variety of statutory and employment tort cases, including harassment, retaliation, defamation, and breach of contract claims.
**Professional Memberships:** Kentucky State Bar; U.S. District Court, Eastern and Western Districts of Kentucky; U.S. Court of Appeals, Sixth Circuit; U.S. Supreme Court.
**Personal:** University of Kentucky (JD 1983); University of Kentucky (MA 1979); Centre College (BA 1976).

## DIAMOND, Ivan M
Bingham Greenebaum Doll LLP, Louisville
502 587 3534
idiamond@bgdlegal.com
*Featured in Corporate/M&A (Kentucky)*
**Practice Areas:** Ivan is a member of the Corporate and Transactional Practice Group. An attorney with the Securities and Exchange Commission in Washington, DC, prior to joining the firm, Ivan has represented various companies in connection with the numerous public and private offerings of equity and debt securities and mergers and acquisitions. He counsels boards of directors on corporate governance and Sarbanes-Oxley Act compliance and has advised financial institutions in over 100 acquisitions and restructuring.
**Professional Memberships:** American, Florida, Louisville and Kentucky Bar Associations.
**Personal:** Attended University of Florida College of Law.

## DILLON, Bradley E
Bingham Greenebaum Doll LLP, Louisville
502 587 3668
bdillon@bgdlegal.com
*Featured in Environment (Kentucky)*
**Practice Areas:** Bradley is a member of the Environmental and Natural Resources Practice Group and a certified risk manager. He represents businesses in dealing with state, local and federal agencies in securing permits and maintaining compliance with those permits, in the areas of air emissions, hazardous waste and water, including developments associated with wetlands and flood plain areas. He also represents clients in Brownfields redevelopment projects.
**Professional Memberships:** Kentucky Chapter of Hazardous Material Managers, Kentucky Bar Association.
**Career:** Admitted in Kentucky, 1976.
**Publications:** Kentucky Chamber of Commerce, Environmental Justice Update.
**Personal:** Attended University of Louisville School of Law.

## DOLSON, Scott
Frost Brown Todd LLC, Louisville
502 568 0203
sdolson@fbtlaw.com
*Featured in Corporate/M&A (Kentucky)*
**Practice Areas:** Mergers and acquisitions; tax; corporate law. He is a deal lawyer with extensive background in business and tax issues for pass-through entities.
**Publications:** Author, "Dolson's Limited Liability Company Forms"; Managing Editor and Co-Author of "Kentucky Limited Liability Companies" and "Business Succession Planning"; Co-Author of "Professional Practice Entities"; Author of articles published in the Kentucky Bar magazine on "Fiduciary Duty Issues for Kentucky LLCs" and "Dissenters rights of Kentucky LLCs".
**Personal:** JD, University of Virginia Law School, 1982; AB, Harvard College, 1979.

## EHRHARD, T Gregory
Stites & Harbison PLLC, Louisville
502 681 0492
gehrhard@stites.com
*Featured in Real Estate (Kentucky)*
**Practice Areas:** Land use and zoning, real estate finance, real estate practice.
**Professional Memberships:** American Bar Association, Kentucky Bar Association, Louisville Bar Association.
**Career:** Member, Stites & Harbison. Represents lenders, developers and municipalities in many areas of commercial real estate law, including zoning, leasing, lending and transfers.
**Personal:** Indiana University School of Law - Bloomington, JD, cum laude, 2001.

## ESCHELS, Philip
Bingham Greenebaum Doll LLP, Louisville
502 587 3665
peschels@bgdlegal.com
*Featured in Labor & Employment (Kentucky)*
**Practice Areas:** Phil is the Co-Chair of the Labor and Employment Practice Group. He represents employers in defending against employment-related claims in administrative agencies and both federal and state courts. He also represents clients involving covenants not to compete and the protection of trade secrets and provides counseling and training in all areas of traditional labor and employment law.
**Professional Memberships:** Sections of Labor and Employment in American, Indiana, Kentucky and Louisville Bar Associations.
**Publications:** "How to Avoid Legal Pitfalls in Hiring and Firing in Kentucky," Bingham Greenebaum Doll, LLP, Seventh Edition, 2013.
**Personal:** Attended Indiana University School of Law.

## GEISEN, William
Stites & Harbison PLLC, Lexington
859 226 2276
wgeisen@stites.com
*Featured in Litigation (Kentucky)*
**Practice Areas:** Construction law, construction contracts, dispute resolution and litigation.
**Professional Memberships:** Admitted to practice in Kentucky and Ohio. American College of Construction Lawyers (Fellow); Allied Construction Industries (Board of Directors); American Bar Association (Forum on the Construction Industry); Kentucky Bar Association (Construction and Public Contract Law Section, Member and Former Chair); Construction Users Roundtable; Midwest/Midsouth Construction Law Institute (Chair, Planning Committee); Construction Owners Association of the Tri-State.
**Career:** Member, Stites & Harbison.
**Personal:** JD, University of Kentucky College of Law, 1982.

## GIESEL, James A
Frost Brown Todd LLC, Louisville
502 568 0307
jgiesel@fbtlaw.com
*Featured in Corporate/M&A (Kentucky)*
**Practice Areas:** Mr Giesel represents clients in public offerings, mergers and acquisitions, strate-

gic corporate planning, private placements, investment adviser compliance, takeover battles, periodic reporting by public companies and other matters in the general corporate law field.
**Professional Memberships:** American Bar Association, Kentucky Bar Association, Louisville Bar Association, Louisville Bar Foundation.
**Career:** Chair, Firm's Business Combinations and Capital Markets Practice Group; Best Lawyers, 2012; Super Lawyers, 2012; Frequent speaker and author on corporate law issues.
**Personal:** Harvard Law School, JD, cum laude; Yale University, BA, magna cum laude.

## GLASSCOCK, C Edward
Frost Brown Todd LLC, Louisville
502 568 0230
eglasscock@fbtlaw.com
*Featured in Corporate/M&A (Kentucky)*
**Practice Areas:** Co-Chairman of Mergers and Acquisitions Section. Has extensive experience in mergers and acquisitions, joint ventures and venture capital transactions.
**Professional Memberships:** Admitted to practice in Kentucky (1969); Chambers & Partners, Chambers USA, ranked Number One Corporate/M&A attorney in Kentucky, and the only 'star attorney' listed in Corporate/M&A in Kentucky; selected and listed in Naifeh and Smith, The Best Lawyers in America (1991-2013) (selected as Lawyer of the Year in Corporate/M&A Law - 2010, 2012); selected and listed in Kentucky Super Lawyers (2007-2013); Kentucky Bar Association, Past Chairman, Corporations, Banking and Business Law Section; American Bar Association, Member, Mergers and Acquisitions Committee; Louisville Bar Association, Past Chairman, Corporations, Banking and Business Law Section.
**Career:** Joined Frost Brown Todd (FBT), formerly Brown, Todd & Heyburn, 1969; Member, 1974; Managing Partner, Brown, Todd & Heyburn, 1977-2001; Co-Managing Member, FBT (2001-08); Chairman Emeritus, FBT (present).
**Personal:** JD with high distinction, University of Kentucky, 1969; Order of The Coif; Kentucky Law Journal, Member of Staff; Recipient, Outstanding Student Award, University of Kentucky, Phi Delta Phi, Graduate of the Year; BS Civil Engineering, 1966.

## GORHAM, Anne E
Stites & Harbison PLLC, Lexington
859 226 2308
agorham@stites.com
*Featured in Litigation (Kentucky)*
**Practice Areas:** Construction contracts and construction dispute resolution, and energy & power projects.
**Professional Memberships:** American Bar Association (Forum on the Construction Industry, Governing Committee); American College of Construction Lawyers; American Bar Foundation (Fellow).
**Career:** Member, Stites & Harbison.
**Publications:** Contributing author, 'Navigating Construction Contracts: Comparison and Risk Allocation of Standard Forms,' Aspatore Books, May 2009; contributing author, 'AIA and

ConsensusDOCS: Which Contract Forms are Best for Your Project', Lorman Education Services, August 2012.

**Personal:** JD, University of Kentucky College of Law, 1991. Former member of the firm's Management Committee, member and former Chair of the Construction Service Group.

### GORTON, William T
Stites & Harbison PLLC, Lexington
859 226 2241
wgorton@stites.com

*Featured in Environment (Kentucky)*

**Practice Areas:** Environmental, natural resources, agriculture, energy and surety law, environmental audits and due diligence related to environmentally sensitive commercial transactions.

**Professional Memberships:** Admitted to practice in Kentucky, Pennsylvania and federal courts. Member of American, Kentucky and Pennsylvania Bar Associations.

**Career:** Member, Stites & Harbison. University of Kentucky, Assistant Professor in Environmental Law, College of Agriculture, Natural Resources Conservation, 1998-present. Associate, Buchanan-Ingersoll, Philadelphia, 1989-93. Manager, Skelly and Loy Engineers - Consultants, 1976-85.

**Publications:** 'A Primer for Engineering and Technical Professionals Regarding Reclamation and Environmental Surety Bonds'.

**Personal:** JD, with distinction, University of Kentucky, 1988; BS, Pennsylvania State University, 1976.

### GREENWELL, Karen J
Wyatt, Tarrant & Combs, LLP, Lexington
859 288 7636
kgreenwell@wyattfirm.com

*Featured in Environment (Kentucky)*

**Practice Areas:** Karen Greenwell is a member of the firm's Executive Committee and a Co-Team Leader of the Natural Resources & Environmental Service Team. She concentrates her practice in the areas of mineral, energy and property law, and commercial litigation.

**Professional Memberships:** Fellow of the Institute for Mining and Mineral Research; Trustee, Energy and Mineral Law Foundation; Advisory Board, Institute for Energy Law; Member, Kentucky Oil and Gas Association; Member, Energy Bar Association; and Adjunct Professor at the University of Kentucky College of Law.

**Personal:** University of Kentucky (JD 1985); University of Kentucky (BA 1976).

### GRIFFITH, Richard G
Stoll Keenon Ogden PLLC, Lexington
859 231 3036
richard.griffith@skofirm.com

*Featured in Labor & Employment (Kentucky)*

**Practice Areas:** Concentration in the area of labor and employment law. He regularly counsels employers and litigates all types of employment law disputes and is Chair of the firm's Employment Law Practice Group.

**Professional Memberships:** Fayette County, Kentucky and American (Member, Labor and Employment Law Section) Bar Associations.

**Personal:** University of Kentucky (BA, History with distinction, 1980; Phi Beta Kappa); University of Kentucky College of Law (JD, 1983; staff member, Kentucky Law Journal; Moot Court Board). Listed in 'Best Lawyers in America', Labor and Employment and 'Super Lawyers', Employment and Labor.

### GRIFFITH, Robert W
Stites & Harbison PLLC, Louisville
502 681 0422
rwgriffith@stites.com

*Featured in Litigation (Kentucky)*

**Practice Areas:** Business Litigation Service Group. Focus on corporate, commercial and real estate litigation.

**Professional Memberships:** Admitted to practice in Kentucky and New York. Member of American, Kentucky and Louisville Bar Associations.

**Career:** Member of Stites & Harbison. With the firm since 1982.

**Personal:** JD, University of Kentucky, 1977; MA, University of Pennsylvania, 1974; BA, Centre College, 1968.

### GRUNDY, J Mark
Bingham Greenebaum Doll LLP, Louisville
502 587 3628
jgrundy@bgdlegal.com

*Featured in Litigation (Kentucky)*

**Practice Areas:** Mark concentrates his practice in business litigation and dispute resolution. He has broad experience in contract, commercial, estate, real estate, trade secret, employee benefit and products liability law. Mark significantly concentrates his practice in construction law, representing owners, developers, general contractors, subcontractors, and suppliers. Chambers USA, Kentucky Super Lawyers and Louisville Magazine have recognized Mark as a leading lawyer in his field of practice.

**Professional Memberships:** American Bar Association, Construction Law Section; Kentucky Bar Association, Construction and Public Contract Law Section; USLAW Network, Construction Law Committee; Defense Research Institute.

### HADEN JR, William H
Stites & Harbison PLLC, Louisville
502 681 0473
bhaden@stites.com

*Featured in Real Estate (Kentucky)*

**Practice Areas:** Real estate lending, commercial leasing, tax exempt financings.

**Professional Memberships:** Admitted to practice in Kentucky. Member of American and Kentucky Bar Associations; National Association of Bond Lawyers; International Council of Shopping Centers.

**Career:** Member, Stites & Harbison. Law clerk, Kentucky Supreme Court, 1972-73.

**Publications:** 'Limited Liability Company Annotated Forms Compendium', 1995; Contributing Editor, Kentucky, 'State By State

Guide to Commercial Real Estate Leases', Aspen Publishers, 2006; 'Implied Covenants of Continuous Operation in Percentage Leases: Was Charles Dickens Right', Commercial Leasing Law & Strategy, November 1999.

**Personal:** JD, University of Kentucky, 1972. BA, History, University of Kentucky, 1969.

### HAGERTY, Timothy J
Frost Brown Todd LLC, Louisville
502 568 0268
thagerty@fbtlaw.com

*Featured in Environment (Kentucky)*

**Practice Areas:** Environmental, focusing on natural resources, water and wetlands. Includes extensive permitting and compliance counseling, and litigation and transactional expertise. Experience with coal mining, electric power generation and transmission, industrial facilities, pipelines, oil and gas production, commercial and residential development, transportation.

**Professional Memberships:** Director, Kentucky Chamber of Commerce; Chair, Environment and Energy Committee, Greater Louisville, Inc.

**Publications:** 'The Clean Water Act Two-Step', 30 Energy & Min. L. Inst. ch. 6 (2009); 'Beyond Section 404: Corps Permitting and the National Environmental Policy Act', Environmental Law Reporter (July 2002).

**Personal:** JD, Yale Law School, 1994; BA, Univ. of Louisville, 1991.

### HALBLEIB JR, W Thomas
Stites & Harbison PLLC, Louisville
502 681 0447
thalbleib@stites.com

*Featured in Corporate/M&A (Kentucky)*

**Practice Areas:** Business and finance with substantial experience representing airport sponsors, governmental agencies and other tax exempt organizations, commercial lenders, and buyers and sellers of assets and businesses.

**Professional Memberships:** Admitted to practice in Kentucky. Member of the American Bar Association, Kentucky Bar Association, and Louisville Bar Association.

**Career:** He is a member of Stites & Harbison, PLLC, whose Business & Finance Service Group he leads.

**Personal:** JD, University of Kentucky College of Law, with high distinction, Order of the Coif, 1991; BS, Miami University, cum laude, 1987.

### HALEY III, Raymond
Fisher & Phillips LLP, Louisville
502 561 3986
rhaley@laborlawyers.com

*Featured in Labor & Employment (Kentucky)*

**Career:** Ray Haley is Of Counsel in the Louisville Office. He has practiced labor and employment law for almost 30 years. Ray represents employers in a variety of industries, including healthcare, manufacturing, transportation and rehabilitative services. His representation of clients involves defense of all forms of civil rights and wrongful discharge claims in state and federal courts, labor litigation before state and federal agencies and courts, as well as arbitration of labor disputes. Ray

regularly advises clients concerning compliance with virtually all employment-based state and federal mandates, and union related matters.

### HALL, Stephen C
Wyatt, Tarrant & Combs, LLP, Louisville
502 562 7355
schall@wyattfirm.com

*Featured in Intellectual Property (Kentucky)*

**Practice Areas:** Stephen Hall concentrates his practice in the areas of patents and litigation involving medical technology, life sciences, and chemical products and inventions. Mr Hall advocates for the interests of clients and their technology before the United States Patent and Trademark Office and in the federal and state courts, and he regularly advises clients on legal risk management.

**Professional Memberships:** Kentucky Bar Association; U.S. Patent and Trademark Office; American Bar Association; Louisville Bar Association; American Chemical Society.

**Personal:** University of Louisville (BA, Chemistry, Magna Cum Laude, 1988); University of Cincinnati College of Law (JD, 1992).

### HALLOS, Jeffrey L
Frost Brown Todd LLC, Lexington
859 244 3256
jhallos@fbtlaw.com

*Featured in Corporate/M&A (Kentucky)*

**Practice Areas:** Chair of the firm's Business Department. Advises clients regarding mergers and acquisitions, corporate finance transactions, domestic and international financing transactions, and private equity investments.

**Professional Memberships:** Admitted to practice in California (1989) (currently inactive), District of Columbia (1991), Kentucky (1996).

**Career:** Joined Frost Brown Todd LLC, 1996; Member, 1998. Previously practiced in the Los Angeles, Washington DC and Hong Kong offices of Latham & Watkins.

**Personal:** Born 18 July 1963; JD (cum laude) Cornell Law School, 1988; BA Bucknell University (magna cum laude, Phi Beta Kappa), 1985.

### HAMILTON, Joseph L
Stites & Harbison PLLC, Louisville
502 681 0433
jhamilton@stites.com

*Featured in Litigation (Kentucky)*

**Practice Areas:** Business litigation, with an emphasis in class action defense.

**Professional Memberships:** Admitted in Kentucky and before the United States Supreme Court. Member, American, Federal, Kentucky and Louisville Bar Associations.

**Career:** Member, Stites & Harbison. Defend clients in class actions on a regional and national basis, having appeared in the state and/or federal courts of over 25 states. Defended nearly 100 class actions.

**Publications:** Example: 'HMO Class Action Update', American Bar Association, Annual Meeting, July 2000; numerous additional class action publications.

**Personal:** JD, University of Louisville School of Law, 1977; BA, Williams College, 1973.

## HAMILTON, Shannon Antle
Stites & Harbison PLLC, Louisville
502 681 0469
shamilton@stites.com
*Featured in Labor & Employment (Kentucky)*
**Practice Areas:** Employment Law Service Group (Co-Chair). Emphasis in litigation of complex employment law issues.
**Professional Memberships:** Admitted to practice in Kentucky. Member of American, Kentucky and Louisville Bar Associations.
**Career:** Member of Stites & Harbison. Chair, Diversity Committee. Lead trial counsel experience in employment litigation, and has tried numerous employment cases to verdict. Kentucky Super Lawyer 2007/08.
**Publications:** 'Update on Discrimination and Harassment in the Workplace', 19th Annual Kentucky Human Resources Update, Kentucky Chamber of Commerce, Louisville, Ky., June 6-7, 2007, and Lexington, Ky., June 20-21, 2007.
**Personal:** JD, University of Louisville, 1988; BSBA, University of Louisville, 1985.

## HATFIELD, C Kent
Stoll Keenon Ogden PLLC, Louisville
502 568 5745
kent.hatfield@skofirm.com
*Featured in Environment (Kentucky)*
**Practice Areas:** Concentration in antitrust and trade regulation, energy, public utility law, telecommunications, and corporate law and litigation. Corporate practice involves mergers, acquisitions, financing, restructuring, corporate valuations and shareholder disputes. Corporate secretary to large manufacturing joint venture. Principal outside counsel to many corporations and LLCs.
**Professional Memberships:** Louisville, Kentucky, American and Energy Bar Associations.
**Personal:** University of Kentucky (B.S., 1970); University of Kentucky College of Law (JD, with high distinction, 1973); Trial Attorney, Antitrust Division, U.S. Department of Justice, Washington, D.C., 1973-78. Listed many years in Best Lawyers, Chambers USA, Kentucky Super Lawyers.

## HAYNES, Greg
Wyatt, Tarrant & Combs, LLP, Louisville
502 562 7363
ghaynes@wyattfirm.com
*Featured in Litigation (Kentucky)*
**Practice Areas:** Concentration in commercial litigation, lead counsel and case management responsibility in class actions, shareholders derivative and securities cases involving multiple parties and counsel.
**Professional Memberships:** Louisville Bar Association/Past President; Kentucky Bar Association, Kentucky Court of Appeals; Kentucky Supreme Court; United States District Courts of Kentucky; United States Court of Appeal for the Sixth Circuit; United States Supreme Court.
**Career:** Local Litigation Star recognition by Benchmark Litigation 2013; Best Lawyers® 2012 Louisville Litigation-Securities "Lawyer of the Year;" Best Lawyers® 2010 Louisville "Bet-the-Company Litigation Lawyer of the Year; "Best

Lawyers in America® Business Litigation 1989-present; AV Rating by Martindale-Hubbell.

## HELM III, Kennedy
Stites & Harbison PLLC, Louisville
502 681 0449
khelmiii@stites.com
*Featured in Corporate/M&A (Kentucky)*
**Practice Areas:** Business, airport law, project finance, transportation law and university law. Lead counsel to the $780 million Louisville Airport Improvement Program.
**Professional Memberships:** Admitted, Kentucky (1968) and United States Supreme Court. Member of American, Kentucky and Louisville Bar Associations. Listed in Best Lawyers in America, Outstanding Lawyers of America, Kentucky Super Lawyers.
**Career:** Member of Stites & Harbison. Chairman Emeritus of Stites & Harbison. Joined the firm in 1974.
**Publications:** Guest Lecturer, Aviation Law, Embry-Riddle Aeronautical University, 2000-04.
**Personal:** JD, University of Virginia, 1974; Order of the Coif. MA, Indiana University, 1970. BA, cum laude, Yale University, 1968.

## HERRINGTON JR, Alex P
Stites & Harbison PLLC, Louisville
502 681 0494
mherrington@stites.com
*Featured in Corporate/M&A (Kentucky)*
**Practice Areas:** Business & corporate services, public finance law, securities, municipal bonds, tax-exempt debt financing, and economic development.
**Professional Memberships:** Louisville, Kentucky and American Bar Associations; National Association of Bond Lawyers; Listed National Directory of Municipal Bond Dealers; National Association of Investment Counsel.
**Career:** Member, Stites & Harbison.
**Publications:** Mr Herrington has written and spoken on many corporate and banking matters.
**Personal:** JD, magna cum laude, University of Kentucky College of Law, 1978.

## HINES, Barry A
Frost Brown Todd LLC, Louisville
502 779 8578
bhines@fbtlaw.com
*Featured in Real Estate (Kentucky)*
**Practice Areas:** Real estate financing; general real estate law.
**Professional Memberships:** Chair of the Capital Markets Committee for the American College of Real Estate Lawyers; Mortgage Bankers Association of America.
**Career:** Member, Frost Brown Todd LLC, 2011-present; Stites & Harbison, 1993-2011.
**Publications:** "What's New for CMBS 2.0 Loan Originations and Why?", The ACREL Papers, Fall 2011; "Commercial Real Estate Financing," Kentucky Real Estate Law and Practice, Chapter 8, 3d Ed., 2008; and "Service Contracts: Protecting Real Estate Lenders," Probate and Property, March/April 1997.
**Personal:** JD, cum laude, University of Louisville, 1993. BS, University of Kentucky, 1987.

## HINKLE IV, Samuel D
Stoll Keenon Ogden PLLC, Louisville
502 568 5709
sam.hinkle@skofirm.com
*Featured in Litigation (Kentucky)*
**Practice Areas:** Commercial Litigation Practice Group Chair. Mr Hinkle's practice focuses on contracts and commercial matters, corporate governance and breach of fiduciary duty litigation, environmental law, bankruptcy issues, unfair competition, fraud and lender liability and equine law. He has experience with federal and state regulatory agencies, including United States Department of Justice, United States Federal Trade Commission and United States Environmental Protection Agency.
**Professional Memberships:** Louisville, Kentucky and American Bar associations.
**Personal:** Washington & Lee University (B.A., 1969) summa cum laude, Phi Beta Kappa; Yale Law School (JD, 1972). Listed in 'Best Lawyers in America' and 'Kentucky Super Lawyers.'

## HINKLE, JR., Buckner
Stites & Harbison PLLC, Lexington
859 226 2334
bhinkle@stites.com
*Featured in Litigation (Kentucky)*
**Practice Areas:** Construction contracts, construction litigation and dispute resolution and business litigation.
**Professional Memberships:** American Bar Association (Forum on the Construction Industry, Public Contract Law and Litigation); American College of Construction Lawyers.
**Career:** Private practice since 1974 devoted to construction industry and business disputes.
**Publications:** 'Dealing with the Cumulative Effects of Requests for Information, Change Order Requests and Change Directives,' 2007; 'Discovery by Interrogatories,' Discovery Deskbook for Construction Disputes, 2006.
**Personal:** Chair of firm's Construction Service Group; Chair of Governing Committee, ABA Forum on the Construction Industry, 2000-2001.

## HOFFMANN, Warren
Frost Brown Todd LLC, Lexington
859 244 3220
whoffmann@fbtlaw.com
*Featured in Environment (Kentucky)*
**Practice Areas:** Corporate and commercial law emphasizing coal and electric utility industries.
**Professional Memberships:** Admitted to practice, Kentucky, 1984. Energy and Mineral Law Foundation (Trustee); Kentucky Coal Association; Generation and Transmission Lawyers' Association; Western Kentucky Coal Association; Coal Operators and Associates; Cincinnati Coal Exchange; Lexington Coal Exchange.
**Career:** Joined firm in 1984. Expertise regarding acquisitions and dispositions of coal companies; electricity generation, transmission and distribution; sales and leases of coal reserves; coal supply agreements and related transportation matters; coal company reorganizations, permitting, financing, and other operational issues.

**Personal:** Born: Newark, New Jersey, 1957; University of Kentucky, JD, 1984; BA, 1979.

## HOLLANDER, William H
Wyatt, Tarrant & Combs, LLP, Louisville
502 562 7318
whollander@wyattfirm.com
*Featured in Intellectual Property (Kentucky)*
**Practice Areas:** Managing Partner, Chair of Executive Committee. He concentrates his practice in the areas of intellectual property and litigation regarding trademarks, copyrights, trade secrets, patents, unfair competition and privacy.
**Professional Memberships:** International Trademark Association; Kentucky and Louisville Bar Associations (former Chair of Louisville Intellectual Property Section); Leadership Louisville, Chair. Admitted in Kentucky and Indiana.
**Publications:** Numerous articles on a variety of intellectual property matters, including several publications in The Federal Lawyer, Bench & Bar magazine, and Business First of Louisville.
**Personal:** Harvard College, AB (cum laude), 1975; Indiana University-Bloomington, JD (summa cum laude), 1984.

## HOPSON, Edwin
Wyatt, Tarrant & Combs, LLP, Louisville
502 562 7360
ehopson@wyattfirm.com
*Featured in Labor & Employment (Kentucky)*
**Practice Areas:** Labor and Employment Law. Experience in employment discrimination, wrongful discharge and related tort cases, FMLA matters and litigation, class action litigation, union organizing campaigns, NLRB litigation, collective bargaining negotiations, strike preparation/planning, strike/injunction litigation, arbitrations, mediations, OSHA and wage-hour matters.
**Career:** Attorney in the Office of the Solicitor, U.S. Department of Labor, Washington, D.C.; Field Attorney with National Labor Relations Board, Baltimore, Maryland.
**Publications:** Co-author of numerous books/articles, including contributing Chapter Editor to BNA's How Arbitration Works, Discipline and Discharge in Arbitration, Employment Law in Kentucky, The Developing Labor Law; and monthly contributor to KY OSHA Journal.

## HORNEMAN, H Carl
Wyatt, Tarrant & Combs, LLP, Louisville
502 562 7192
chorneman@wyattfirm.com
*Featured in Environment (Kentucky)*
**Practice Areas:** Concentrates practice in the areas of compliance counseling, permitting, environmental liabilities in business transactions and litigation, strong emphasis on defending government enforcement actions, and cost recovery and toxic tort claims. Also focuses on compliance counseling and defending enforcement actions related to worker safety and health laws.
**Career:** Senior Counsel, Environmental Law and EHS Practice Group Leader for the General Electric Company's Consumer & Industrial business; Law Clerk to Honorable Pierce Lively, Chief

Judge - United States Sixth Circuit Court of Appeals; Director of Enforcement for the Division of Waste Management, Kentucky Natural Resources and Environmental Protection Cabinet.

### HUDSON, Robert D
Frost Brown Todd LLC, Florence
859 817 5909
rhudson@fbtlaw.com
*Featured in Labor & Employment (Kentucky)*
**Practice Areas:** Labor and employment, representing management. Including: client consulting, training, labor negotiations, non-competes, trade secrets, and defending employment claims.
**Professional Memberships:** Former-Chair, Northern Kentucky Chamber of Commerce and Covington Business Council; Past President, Northern Kentucky SHRM.
**Career:** Admitted: Ohio (1987); Kentucky (1988). Current Member, Frost Brown Todd LLC, labor and employment practice. Former-Member, Greenebaum Doll & McDonald PLLC (1995-2009).
**Publications:** Author, "A Better Tomorrow; Fighting for Capitalism and Jobs in the Heartland".
**Personal:** Born Owensboro, Kentucky, May 24, 1962. University of Kentucky, BS (Accounting), JD Wife, Melissa Hudson, Pharmacist, with two children, residing in Villa Hills, Kentucky.

### ISON, Eric
Bingham Greenebaum Doll LLP, Louisville
502 587 3564
eison@bgdlegal.com
*Featured in Litigation (Kentucky)*
**Practice Areas:** Concentrates practice in commercial litigation, in state and federal courts, at the trial and appellate levels. Has been selected for inclusion in The Best Lawyers in America, Chambers USA America's Leading Lawyers for Business and Kentucky Super Lawyers in the category of commercial litigation.
**Professional Memberships:** American Bar Association, Kentucky Bar Association, Louisville Bar Association; Chair, Kentucky Board of Bar Examiners.
**Personal:** Attended Vanderbilt School of Law.

### JAKUBOWICZ, Janet P
Bingham Greenebaum Doll LLP, Louisville
502 587 3664
jjakubowicz@bgdlegal.com
*Featured in Litigation (Kentucky)*
**Practice Areas:** Janet is a member in the Litigation Practice Group and managing partner of the firm's Cincinnati office. Her practice focuses on business and commercial litigation, with an emphasis in the areas of financial institutions, securities and RICO litigation and arbitration and class action litigation.
**Professional Memberships:** American Bar Association, Kentucky Bar Association, Louisville Bar Association, Louis D. Brandeis American Inn of Court, Kentucky Defense Trial Lawyers Association.
**Publications:** 'Juries', Kentucky Civil Practice at Trial, 3d Edition Handbook, 2008; 'The Executive

Branch Code of Ethics', Election Law in Kentucky (1995).
**Personal:** Attended University of Kentucky College of Law.

### JELSMA, Franklin
Wyatt, Tarrant & Combs, LLP, Louisville
502 562 7285
fjelsma@wyattfirm.com
*Featured in Corporate/M&A (Kentucky)*
**Practice Areas:** Franklin Jelsma is Partner in Charge of Wyatt's Louisville office. He concentrates his practice in the areas of general business law, mergers and acquisitions, corporate finance and venture capital transactions.
**Professional Memberships:** Louisville and Kentucky Bar Associations.
**Career:** Highest professional ratings by Martindale-Hubbell Law Directory; Woodward/White's The Best Lawyers in America® 2007-13 in the areas of corporate, securities and mergers and acquisitions.
**Personal:** University of Kentucky, Associate Editor for the Kentucky Law Journal (JD 1991); Princeton University (AB 1986).

### JOSEPH III, Alfred S
Stites & Harbison PLLC, Louisville
502 681 0465
fjoseph@stites.com
*Featured in Real Estate (Kentucky)*
**Practice Areas:** Real estate law.
**Professional Memberships:** Admitted to practice in Kentucky (1968). Member of American, Kentucky and Louisville Bar Associations and American College of Real Estate Lawyers. Listed in 'The International Who's Who of Business Lawyers'.
**Career:** Counsel, Stites & Harbison. Listed in the 'Real Estate Lawyers' and 'Land Use' sections of The Best Lawyers in America.
**Publications:** Author, Kentucky Chapter, State-By-State Guide to Commercial Real Estate Leases, Mark Senn, editor, 2004; co-author, 'Certificates of Insurance: The Illusion of Protection,' Probate & Property, Jan/Feb 1995.
**Personal:** JD, University of Michigan, 1968. BA, cum laude and Honors, Wesleyan University, 1965.

### KEANE, Margaret E
Bingham Greenebaum Doll LLP, Louisville
502 587 3641
mkeane@bgdlegal.com
*Featured in Litigation (Kentucky)*
**Practice Areas:** Litigation Practice Group and leader of the Beverage Alcohol team. Practice focuses on defense of products liability actions, general commercial litigation, healthcare litigation, defending employers in employment actions and representing parties in family law actions.
**Professional Memberships:** Kentucky Bar Association (Past President); Louisville (Past President) and American Bar Associations.
**Career:** Admitted in Kentucky, 1982; U.S. District Court, Western District of Kentucky, 1982; U.S. District Court, Eastern District of Kentucky, 1983; U.S. Court of Appeals for the Sixth Circuit, 1984; U.S. Court of Federal Claims,

1991; U.S. Court of Appeals for the Federal Circuit, 1992; U.S. Supreme Court, 1993.

### KING, June N
Bingham Greenebaum Doll LLP, Louisville
502 587 3637
jking@bgdlegal.com
*Featured in Corporate/M&A (Kentucky)*
**Practice Areas:** June's practice focuses on US and state securities laws compliance, Sarbanes-Oxley Act and corporate governance issues, and financial institution regulatory matters. She advises clients with respect to private and public securities offerings, compliance with securities laws and regulations, preparation of securities law reports and filings, design of corporate governance compliance programs, financial institution regulatory issues, and financial institution mergers and acquisitions.
**Professional Memberships:** Kentucky Bar Association, Louisville Bar Association.
**Publications:** "SEC Guidance on Use of Websites, Emails and Blogs," 15th Biennial Midwest/Midsouth Securities Law Conference.
**Personal:** Attended University of Kentucky College of Law.

### KING, W Gregory
Stoll Keenon Ogden PLLC, Louisville
502 560 4284
greg.king@skofirm.com
*Featured in Litigation (Kentucky)*
**Practice Areas:** Concentration in defense of medical malpractice, and product liability, as well as will and trust contests, and general civil litigation. Has extensive jury trial experience, including defense of professional negligence, and plaintiff's personal injury and business fraud.
**Professional Memberships:** American, Kentucky, and Louisville Bar Associations (President, 2000; Distinguished Service Award, 2005); Kentucky Justice Association; Kentucky Defense Counsel, Inc.; Defense Research Institute.
**Personal:** University of Kentucky (JD, 1982); Kentucky Wesleyan College (B.A., 1979). Listed in 'Best Lawyers in America;' Board Certified, National Board of Trial Advocates.

### LEET, Byron E
Wyatt, Tarrant & Combs, LLP, Louisville
502 562 7354
bleet@wyattfirm.com
*Featured in Litigation (Kentucky)*
**Practice Areas:** Byron Leet is a member of Wyatt's Executive Committee and Co-Chair of its Litigation & Dispute Resolution Service Team. Byron has nearly 30 years of experience in state and federal court handling jury trials, bench trials, and injunction hearings in several states.
**Professional Memberships:** Member of the Defense Research Institute, Federalist Society, and the Louisville and Kentucky Bar Associations.
**Career:** Woodward/White's The Best Lawyers in America® 2006-2013 in the area of commercial litigation; Kentucky Super Lawyers ® 2007-2012; Highest Professional AV Rating by Martindale-Hubbell Law Directory.
**Personal:** Vanderbilt University (1983 JD); University of Louisville (1980 BA, cum laude).

### LESTER, R David
Stoll Keenon Ogden PLLC, Lexington
859 231 3082
david.lester@skofirm.com
*Featured in Corporate/M&A (Kentucky)*
**Practice Areas:** Practices in areas of corporate, business acquisitions, Uniform Commercial Code and healthcare.
**Personal:** Western Kentucky University (B.S., 1970); University of Kentucky College of Law (JD, with high distinction, 1975). AV® Preeminent™ Peer Review Rated by Martindale-Hubbell®. Listed in Best Lawyers in America® and "Kentucky Super Lawyers". Named 'Best Lawyers' 2009 Lexington Corporate Lawyer of the Year and 'Best Lawyers' 2011 Lexington Mergers and Acquisitions Lawyer of the Year. Participated in Kentucky Bar Association Joint Subcommittee on Limited Liability Company Legislation and Kentucky Bar Association Committee to draft Chapter 271B (business corporations).

### LYNDRUP, Peggy B
Bingham Greenebaum Doll LLP, Louisville
502 587 3626
plyndrup@bgdlegal.com
*Featured in Corporate/M&A (Kentucky)*
**Practice Areas:** Peggy is co-chair of the Corporate and Transactional Practice Group. She works extensively in the areas of mergers and acquisitions, product distribution, real estate leasing, advertising contracts, endorsements and licensing and international law. She represents publicly and privately held corporations in US and international transactions.
**Professional Memberships:** Louisville Bar Association (Past President), Kentucky Bar Association, American Bar Association (Antitrust Section and Business Law Section), International Bar Association.
**Career:** Former VP and General Counsel - Meidinger, Inc.
**Personal:** Attended University of Louisville School of Law (summa cum laude and valedictorian); Harvard Law School Program of Instruction for Lawyers.

### MACDONALD, Alan
Frost Brown Todd LLC, Louisville
502 568 0277
amacdonald@fbtlaw.com
*Featured in Corporate/M&A (Kentucky)*
**Practice Areas:** Business combinations, capital transactions, corporate governance, securities regulation.
**Professional Memberships:** Kentucky Bar (admitted 1985). Member, American Bar Association, Section on Corporation, Banking and Business Law; Kentucky Bar Association, Business Law Section (Chair 2000-2002); Louisville Bar Association, Business Law Section (Chair 1997).
**Career:** Joined Frost Brown Todd, 1985; member 1993.
**Publications:** Co-Author: Kentucky Corporate Law (1997); Limited Liability Companies in Kentucky (2nd ed. 2000); Business Succession Planning (1998).

**Personal:** Born 8 June 1955. JD, Vanderbilt University, 1985; AB, Dartmouth College, 1977.

## MARTIN, Timothy
Frost Brown Todd LLC, Louisville
502 568 0274
tmartin@fbtlaw.com
*Featured in Real Estate (Kentucky)*

**Practice Areas:** Acquisition, zoning, land use, financing, leasing and development of commercial, retail, residential, industrial and office properties.
**Professional Memberships:** Admitted to practice in Kentucky (1972). Member, American College of Real Estate Lawyers; International Council of Shopping Centers; American, Kentucky and Louisville Bar Associations.
**Career:** Joined Brown, Todd & Heyburn (now Frost Brown Todd LLC), 1972; became Partner, 1979; Chair of Real Estate Practice Group.
**Publications:** 'Federal Regulations Affecting Real Estate' published by University of KY ('Kentucky Real Estate Law and Practice Handbook').
**Personal:** Born April 9, 1947. JD, University of Kentucky, 1972; BA, University of Kentucky, 1969.

## MATTINGLY, Patrick W
Wyatt, Tarrant & Combs, LLP, Louisville
502 562 7294
pmattingly@wyattfirm.com
*Featured in Corporate/M&A (Kentucky), Environment (Kentucky)*

**Practice Areas:** Represents entrepreneurs, management teams and privately owned businesses in mergers and acquisitions, exit and succession planning, corporate governance, raising debt and equity capital and strategic partnerships. He advises private equity and venture capital firms with their investments in such businesses, including diligence, deal structure, negotiation, documentation and closing of transactions. Works extensively with clients on transactional matters relating to mineral and energy businesses and properties, including mergers, stock and asset acquisitions and the financing of such transactions.
**Professional Memberships:** Louisville, Kentucky, American Bar Associations; Institute for Energy Law Advisory Board; Energy and Mineral Law Foundation; Energy Bar Association.

## MILLER, George
Wyatt, Tarrant & Combs, LLP, Lexington
859 288 7640
gmiller@wyattfirm.com
*Featured in Labor & Employment (Kentucky)*

**Practice Areas:** Mr Miller concentrates his practice in labor and employment law and eminent domain law.
**Professional Memberships:** Fayette County and Kentucky Bar Associations; Past Secretary and President of Labor and Employment Law Section of Kentucky Bar Association; Past Member of Kentucky Bar Association House of Delegates; Coordinator for American Bar Association Labor & Employment Section Law Student Outreach Program at University of Kentucky College of Law (2003-present).

**Publications:** 'Responsive Pleadings', Ch. 8, Kentucky Civil Practice Before Trial, 3rd ed. (University of Kentucky, 2008); 'Labor Law Issues', Ch. 16, Employment Law in Kentucky, 3rd ed. (University of Kentucky, 2007).

## MILLER, Winston
Frost Brown Todd LLC, Louisville
502 568 0296
wmiller@fbtlaw.com
*Featured in Litigation (Kentucky)*

**Practice Areas:** Civil litigation including diversified experience in products liability, mass tort, fire and explosion, employment and business litigation.
**Professional Memberships:** American, Kentucky and Louisville Bar Associations and Defense Research Institute.
**Career:** Defending complex multi-party cases arising out of catastrophic losses and serial litigation. Examples (San Juan DuPont Plaza Hotel Fire, The Breast Implant Litigation and the West Pharmaceutical Fire, NC). Represents manufacturers of various products, devices, drugs, appliances, and materials. Represents area's largest employer in employment and business litigation.
**Personal:** JD University of Kentucky. Prior experience as a Trial Attorney with the US Department of Justice.

## MORRIS, Emily
Littler Mendelson, PC, Lexington
859 317 7978
emorris@littler.com
*Featured in Labor & Employment (Kentucky)*

**Practice Areas:** Discrimination and Harassment; Leaves of Absence and Disability Accommodation; Whistleblowing and Retaliation.
**Professional Memberships:** Member, Kentucky and Fayette County Bar Associations; Chair, Girls on the Run Central Kentucky Board of Directors; Member, Transylvania University Alumni Board; Member, Central Christian Church Childcare Center Board of Directors.
**Career:** Emily H Morris advises and represents employers in a broad range of employment matters, appearing in state and federal courts. She regularly handles discrimination, harassment and retaliation issues. Emily also has experience advising clients in connection with the increasing number of social media issues which employers face in the employment context.

## MURPHY, Marc S
Stites & Harbison PLLC, Louisville
502 681 0536
mmurphy@stites.com
*Featured in Litigation (Kentucky)*

**Practice Areas:** Jury trial and commercial litigation. Practice emphasis on white-collar criminal litigation and complex commercial and class action defense.
**Professional Memberships:** Admitted to practice in Indiana (1984) and Kentucky (1988). Member of American, Kentucky and Louisville Bar Associations.
**Career:** Member of Stites & Harbison. Former military prosecutor, Judge Advocate General's Corps; former Commonwealth's Attorney. Joined

the firm in 1997. Seasoned trial lawyer with over 20 years of courtroom experience handling challenging, high-profile, and complex commercial and white-collar criminal cases.
**Personal:** JD, University of Louisville, 1984. BA, cum laude, University of Notre Dame, 1981.

## NAGLE JR, David W
Stites & Harbison PLLC, Louisville
502 681 0321
dnagle@stites.com
*Featured in Intellectual Property (Kentucky)*

**Practice Areas:** Registered U.S. Patent Attorney. Extensive experience prosecuting domestic and foreign patent applications covering a wide range of subject matter, including consumer goods, mechanical devices, and software-related inventions. Also counsels clients on trademark and copyright issues, and regularly negotiates and prepares license agreements and other contracts implicating intellectual property rights.
**Professional Memberships:** Louisville (Member, Intellectual Property Law Section), Kentucky and American Bar Associations; Licensing Executives Society International; American Intellectual Property Law Association; International Trademark Association.
**Career:** Member, Stites & Harbison. Co-Chair, IP&T Group.
**Personal:** University of Louisville, JD, 1998; University of Louisville (B.S., Engineering, 1994; M.Eng., 1995).

## NORTHAM, Patrick
Frost Brown Todd LLC, Louisville
502 779 8170
pnortham@fbtlaw.com
*Featured in Environment (Kentucky)*

**Practice Areas:** Represents numerous public and privately-owned industrial, commercial and service businesses in connection with mergers, divestitures, acquisitions, partnerships and joint ventures, intellectual property licenses, recourse and non-recourse financings, executive employment and compensation plans, and general corporate and commercial matters, including in the areas of fossil fuel and renewable energy services, natural gas, coal, chemicals, aluminum production, steel tank fabrication, sporting goods, distilled spirits, telecommunications, paints and coatings, engineering and public works, aluminum production, newspapers, franchised restaurants and commercial graphics.
**Personal:** Attended University of Louisville School of Law.

## NUNNELLEY, Richard A
Stoll Keenon Ogden PLLC, Lexington
859 231 3957
Richard.Nunnelley@skofirm.com
*Featured in Real Estate (Kentucky)*

**Practice Areas:** Mr Nunnelley is the Chair of the Real Estate Finance and Development Practice Group. His practice focuses on commercial real estate transactions, business transactions and equine law. He has substantial experience representing buyers, sellers, developers and lenders in complex real estate transactions, including commercial acquisitions, development, financing, leas-

ing, construction and condominium formation. Mr Nunnelley also has substantial experience representing foreign interests.
**Professional Memberships:** American, Kentucky and Fayette County Bar Associations.
**Personal:** Transylvania University (BA, 1988); University of Louisville (JD, cum laude, 1991).

## O'BRIEN III, Thomas P
Frost Brown Todd LLC, Louisville
502 568 0205
tobrien@fbtlaw.com
*Featured in Intellectual Property (Kentucky)*

**Practice Areas:** Intellectual Property litigation, including patent, trademark, copyright infringement, trade secrets; complex commercial litigation, including telecommunications; federal appellate.
**Professional Memberships:** Bars: Supreme Courts of the United States and Kentucky, United States Courts of Appeals for the Fourth, Sixth, Seventh, Tenth and Federal Circuits. Kentucky, American, Louisville and Federal Bar Associations. Chambers USA (2008-13); Kentucky Super Lawyers (2007-08, 2010-12); Benchmark Litigation (2011).
**Career:** Member, Frost Brown Todd (2000); associate, Middleton Reutlinger (1993-2000); Judicial Law Clerk, Hon Frederick P Stamp, Jr, USDC, NDW Va (1991-93).
**Personal:** Born 31 October 1966. Washington and Lee University, BA, Magna cum laude, 1988; JD, 1991.

## OVERSTREET, Mark R
Stites & Harbison PLLC, Frankfort
502 209 1219
moverstreet@stites.com
*Featured in Environment (Kentucky)*

**Practice Areas:** Civil and administrative litigation with emphasis on business litigation, representation of utilities and other businesses before administrative agencies.
**Professional Memberships:** Admitted to practice in Kentucky. Member of American Bar Association.
**Career:** Member, Stites & Harbison. Trial practice before state and federal courts in Kentucky. Appellate arguments before Supreme Court of Kentucky, Court of Appeals of Kentucky and US Court of Appeals for the 6th Circuit.
**Publications:** 'Preclusive Effect of Administrative Agency Determinations in Subsequent Court Proceedings', Kentucky Bar Association's Bench & Bar, March 2004.
**Personal:** JD, University of Kentucky, 1980; BA, University of Kentucky, 1976.

## PATRICK, Tandy
Bingham Greenebaum Doll LLP, Louisville
502 587 3512
tpatrick@bgdlegal.com
*Featured in Real Estate (Kentucky)*

**Practice Areas:** Tandy is a partner in the firm's Real Estate Practice Group. Her practice focuses on the leasing, acquisition, development and financing of commercial real estate, including retail, office, warehouse and multi-family projects, with a particular emphasis on shopping centers,

condominium and mixed use projects, restaurants and entertainment venues. She is also involved in various general business and commercial transactions.
**Professional Memberships:** American College of Real Estate Lawyers; Certified Commercial Investment Managers (Director, 2005-2008); International Council of Shopping Centers; Commercial Property Association of Lexington (Director, 2006-10); Home Builders Association of Louisville.
**Personal:** Attended University of Louisville School of Law.

**PELFREY, D Patton**
Frost Brown Todd LLC, Louisville
502 568 0252
ppelfrey@fbtlaw.com
*Featured in Labor & Employment (Kentucky)*
**Practice Areas:** Founding Chair, Frost Brown Todd's Labor and Employment Department specializing in representing management.
**Career:** Vast experience negotiating collective bargaining agreements, handling union avoidance campaigns and litigating various employee relations issues. Former National Labor Relations Board trial attorney.
**Publications:** Authored chapters, various editions, The Developing Labor Law (considered most authoritative treatise in the field of labor relations); Contributor- Labor Arbitration Cases and Materials for Advocates.
**Personal:** Included in all 'The Best Lawyers in America' editions; Kentucky Super Lawyers Top 50; Fellow, College of Labor and Employment Lawyers; received University of Louisville's Brandeis School of Law's Distinguished Alumnus Award.

**PITT, M Stephen**
Wyatt, Tarrant & Combs, LLP, Louisville
502 562 7372
mspitt@wyattfirm.com
*Featured in Litigation (Kentucky)*
**Practice Areas:** Focuses practice on major commercial, toxic tort, coal supply contract, CERCLA, environmental, antitrust and criminal litigation matters. Mr Pitt has acted as lead counsel in, and has tried, a number of complex cases in both federal and state courts.
**Professional Memberships:** Life Member of the Sixth Circuit Judicial Conference and various state and federal Bars.
**Career:** Recognized by Woodward/White's The Best Lawyers in America® in the areas of Commercial Litigation, Antitrust Litigation, and Environmental Litigation, 2005-2013; Recognized as a Local Litigation Star by Benchmark Litigation 2013; and by his peers as one of the Kentucky Super Lawyers.

**PRICE JR, Glenn A**
Frost Brown Todd LLC, Louisville
502 779 8511
gaprice@fbtlaw.com
*Featured in Real Estate (Kentucky)*
**Practice Areas:** Land use, zoning and land development law; land use litigation.

**Professional Memberships:** Kentucky, Louisville and American Bar Associations; Urban Land Institute; CCIM; Homebuilders Association of Louisville; Louisville Real Estate Group.
**Career:** University of Louisville Instructor, Land Use Law, Brandeis School of Law 1987, 1995, 2010; Land Use Law, School of Urban and Public Affairs 2002-03; Louisville Metro Planning Commission 1978-80 (Chair 1979-1980); Mayor's Housing Task Force 2005-06; Bingham Fellows 2008.
**Publications:** Price & Murphy, Land Use and Zoning Law in Kentucky, University of Kentucky (4th ed., 2011); Co-author, "Financing Capital Improvements Through Impact Fees: An Option in Kentucky?" 14 State Tax Notes 1111 (April 6, 1998).

**RATTERMAN, David B.**
Stites & Harbison PLLC, Louisville
502 681 0539
dratterman@stites.com
*Featured in Litigation (Kentucky)*
**Practice Areas:** Construction law with particular emphasis on the fabricated structural steel industry.
**Professional Memberships:** Fellow and former Member of the Board of Governors, American College of Construction Lawyers; Life Fellow, American Bar Foundation; Member: Engineers Without Borders, American Society of Civil Engineers, Society of Construction Law, International Steelwork Contractors Group; Society of American Military Engineers.
**Career:** Structural design and fabricated steel construction; Secretary & General Counsel, American Institute of Steel Construction; Engineering Officer, United States Navy (Commander, USNR-Retired).
**Publications:** Multiple publications and presentations on construction law and steel industry issues.

**RIGGS, Kendrick R**
Stoll Keenon Ogden PLLC, Louisville
502 560 4222
kendrick.riggs@skofirm.com
*Featured in Environment (Kentucky)*
**Practice Areas:** Practice Areas Firm: Vice-Chair, Board of Directors; Chair, Energy and Utility Practice Group. Thirty years representing energy and telecommunications clients before state and federal regulatory agencies and courts involving rates, mergers and acquisitions, power facilities and commercial disputes.
**Professional Memberships:** Kentucky Bar Association; Virginia State Bar Association; Energy Bar Association, Greater Louisville Inc.
**Personal:** University of Kentucky (JD, 1982); Wittenberg University (B.A., cum laude, 1979). 'Best Lawyers in America,' Public Utility Law, since'97; Martindale-Hubbell AV Rating since '96; since '06 Louisville Magazine "Top Lawyer"; Only Kentucky attorney listed 2012 and 2013 BTI Client Service All-Star.

**ROBINSON III, Wm. T**
Frost Brown Todd LLC, Florence
859 817 5901
wrobinson@fbtlaw.com
*Featured in Litigation (Kentucky)*
**Practice Areas:** Civil litigation at the trial and appellate levels has been the primary focus of Bill's law practice of over forty years, with extensive experience in commercial litigation, class actions, product liability defense, environmental litigation and medical malpractice defense.
**Professional Memberships:** American Bar Association, American Academy of Appellate Lawyers, American Law Institute, International Association of Defense Counsel, International Society of Barristers, Product Liability Advisory Council, Uniform Law Commission.
**Career:** Member-in-Charge, Frost Brown Todd's Florence office; President, American Bar Association (2011-12).
**Personal:** University of Kentucky College of Law, JD; Thomas More College, BA.

**ROUSE, Arthur**
Wyatt, Tarrant & Combs, LLP, Louisville
502 562 7508
arouse@wyattfirm.com
*Featured in Real Estate (Kentucky)*
**Practice Areas:** Arthur Rouse is a member of the Firm's Real Estate & Lending Service Team and is Chair of the Professional Personnel Committee. Mr Rouse concentrates his practice in the areas of commercial lending. He regularly represents institutional lenders in making all types of commercial/industrial, commercial real estate/construction and syndicated loan financings and in pre-litigation loan workout negotiations and documentation.
**Professional Memberships:** Louisville and Kentucky Bar Associations; Kentucky CCIM Chapter.
**Personal:** St. John's University School of Law (JD 1982); New York University (MBA 1978); Florida State University (BA, magna cum laude, Phi Beta Kappa, 1971).

**ROYSE, David T**
Stoll Keenon Ogden PLLC, Lexington
859 231 3681
david.royse@skofirm.com
*Featured in Litigation (Kentucky)*
**Practice Areas:** Mr Royse's practice includes commercial litigation, fiduciary obligations, equine law, personal injury and wrongful death. He is also regularly involved in eminent domain and planning and zoning matters. He served as Plaintiffs' Liaison Counsel in the litigation regarding the crash of Comair 5191 in Lexington. He has been appointed by the Governor as a Special Justice on the Kentucky Supreme Court.
**Professional Memberships:** Kentucky and American Bar Associations. Eastern and Western Districts of Kentucky and 6th Circuit.
**Personal:** Birmingham-Southern College, University of Kentucky College of Law, Order of the Coif.

**RUTLEDGE, Thomas E**
Stoll Keenon Ogden PLLC, Louisville
502 560 4258
thomas.rutledge@skofirm.com
*Featured in Corporate/M&A (Kentucky)*
**Practice Areas:** Business and securities law with a focus on the law of business organizations.
**Professional Memberships:** ABA Committee on LLCs, Partnerships and Unincorporated Entities (incoming Chair – 2013). Advisor to the Revised Uniform LLC Act and the Uniform Statutory Trust Act. Member of American Law Institute.
**Publications:** A national authority on business entity law, his publications include in the Kentucky Law Journal, Journal of Taxation, The Business Lawyer, and Delaware Journal of Corporate Law.
**Personal:** University of Kentucky (JD, 1990); Saint Louis University (BA cum laude, 1985); University of Notre Dame, Graduate Fellow, Medieval History.

**SAFFER, David**
Stites & Harbison PLLC, Louisville
502 681 0547
dsaffer@stites.com
*Featured in Real Estate (Kentucky)*
**Practice Areas:** Concentrates practice in real estate and lending and regularly represents institutional lenders and borrowers in all types of commercial loan transactions including complex conduit-lending transactions.
**Professional Memberships:** Member of the Louisville, Kentucky, and American Bar Associations. Member of the American College of Mortgage Attorneys.
**Career:** Member, Stites & Harbison. Joined the firm in 2004.
**Publications:** Co-author, 'Mortgages', UK/CLE Kentucky Real Estate and Practice Handbook, 2d Ed., 1996.
**Personal:** JD, cum laude, University of Louisville, 1995; BLS, summa cum laude, University of Evansville, 1992.

**SALES, Walter L**
Stoll Keenon Ogden PLLC, Louisville
502 560 4252
walter.sales@skofirm.com
*Featured in Labor & Employment (Kentucky)*
**Practice Areas:** Concentration in labor and employment and commercial litigation in cases contesting the enforcement of covenants-not-to-compete, breach of fiduciary duty, and breach of confidentiality. Tried many cases including class action employment discrimination cases for age, race and sex discrimination, sexual harassment, Equal Pay Act, and ADA cases. Represents employers in resisting union organizing drives. Regularly appears in federal and state appellate courts.
**Professional Memberships:** American, Kentucky, and Louisville Bar Associations.
**Personal:** University of Kentucky (JD, 1973); Washington & Lee University (B.A., 1970). 'Best Lawyers in America,' Labor and Employment.

Recognized as one of Kentucky's Super Lawyers for Appellate Litigation.

## SAVARISE, Jeffrey A
Fisher & Phillips LLP, Louisville
502 561 3965
jsavarise@laborlawyers.com
*Featured in Labor & Employment (Kentucky)*

**Career:** Jeff Savarise is a Partner in the Louisville office and Chair of the firm's Automotive Manufacturing Practice Group. Jeff practices exclusively in the areas of labor and employment law on behalf of employers, where he handles cases in a number of state and federal jurisdictions. He also provides a variety of preventive maintenance and employment training programs especially geared to the automotive industry. Jeff received the "Distinguished Alumni Award" given to alumni of the University of Akron Law School who have demonstrated significant achievement in the field of law and have made significant contributions to their community.

## SCHNELL, Anthony L
Stoll Keenon Ogden PLLC, Louisville
502 560 4219
anthony.schnell@skofirm.com
*Featured in Real Estate (Kentucky)*

**Practice Areas:** Concentration in the area of commercial real estate law including real property acquisitions and development, financing, leasing, planning and zoning consultation, title examinations and title insurance, and real estate litigation. In an international context, has represented local businesses acquiring and leasing property in foreign countries.
**Professional Memberships:** American, Kentucky and Louisville Bar Associations.
**Personal:** University of Louisville School of Law (JD, Cum Laude 1989); Bellarmine University (BA, Summa Cum Laude 1986); St. Xavier High School, Louisville, KY (Summa Cum Laude 1983).

## SCHWORER, Philip
Frost Brown Todd LLC, Florence
859 817 5903
pschworer@fbtlaw.com
*Featured in Environment (Kentucky)*

**Practice Areas:** Practice includes environmental, health and safety litigation, chemical exposure litigation, corporate transaction due diligence, compliance auditing, and compliance counseling. Included in his related litigation experiences have been negotiations with federal, state and local environmental protection agencies management of Superfund PRP settlements.
**Professional Memberships:** American Bar Association, Ohio, Kentucky, Cincinnati and Northern Kentucky Bar Association.
**Career:** Northern Kentucky University, honorary Doctor of Laws; Northern Kentucky University, Salmon P. Chase College of Law, JD; University of Cincinnati, BS-biology, MS- environmental science/engineering.

## SEARS, Susan C
Littler Mendelson, PC, Lexington
859 317 7977
ssears@littler.com
*Featured in Labor & Employment (Kentucky)*

**Practice Areas:** Employment Defense Litigation & Management Counseling/Training.
**Career:** Susan C. Sears has a regional and national employment defense law practice exclusively focused on representing management in connection with the employee-employer relationship. Highly respected by the bench and bar, she has an excellent record of litigation success, defending employers in state and federal court against alleged statutory claims of discrimination, harassment, and retaliation, in addition to all other employment issues. Susan is a highly effective teacher, presenter and trainer on employment law topics on a state and national level, regularly conducting in-house training sessions for clients on employment litigation avoidance.

## SEEWER, David
Wyatt, Tarrant & Combs, LLP, Louisville
502 562 7586
dseewer@wyattfirm.com
*Featured in Real Estate (Kentucky)*

**Practice Areas:** David Seewer concentrates his practice in the areas of real estate, commercial lending and leasing, and municipal zoning law. He represents developers in residential and commercial developments from the zoning stage through the acquisition and financing stages. He also represents local and regional lenders in connection with acquisition and development financing for residential and commercial developments.
**Professional Memberships:** Louisville and Kentucky Bar Associations; Kentucky Chapter of the Certified Commercial Investment Managers (CCIM); International Council of Shopping Centers (ICSC).
**Personal:** University of Kentucky (JD 1981), staff member of the Kentucky Law Journal; Eastern Kentucky University (BS 1978).

## SEIFFERT, James C
Stites & Harbison PLLC, Louisville
502 681 0519
jseiffert@stites.com
*Featured in Corporate/M&A (Kentucky)*

**Practice Areas:** Mergers and acquisitions, corporate, taxation.
**Professional Memberships:** Admitted to practice in Kentucky and Iowa. Member of American, Kentucky and Iowa Bar Associations.
**Career:** Member of Stites & Harbison.
**Publications:** 'Physicians Beware! Dealing with Tax-Exempt Healthcare Organizations Can be Hazardous to One's Financial Health,' Journal of Kentucky Medical Association, February 1998; 'Man-O-War Restaurants, Inc. v John Martin, Jr, Ky. Supreme Court Deals a Severe Blow to Compensatory Restricted Stock Arrangement,' Louisville Bar Association Bar Briefs, May 1997.
**Personal:** JD, with high distinction, University of Louisville, 1980. LLM, Taxation, University of Miami, 1981. BA, American History, University of Iowa, 1977.

## SHELLER, John
Stoll Keenon Ogden PLLC, Louisville
502 560 4288
john.sheller@skofirm.com
*Featured in Labor & Employment (Kentucky)*

**Practice Areas:** Concentration in areas of labor and employment law. He counsels employers and litigates all types of employment disputes. He is responsible for creating legal precedent entitling employers to secure indemnity from other parties in civil rights cases and holding that a claim for outrage is preempted by statute.
**Professional Memberships:** Louisville, Kentucky, Indiana and Texas Bar associations; Federalist Society.
**Personal:** AV® Preeminent™ Peer Review Rated by Martindale-Hubbell® and honored as a Best Lawyer. National Multiple Sclerosis Society, board member; Disabled American Veterans Supporter; Sunrise Children's Services Contributor; Christian Legal Society Contributor/Supporter; SPOT Board Member; LHA President.

## SHULL III, C Michael
Frost Brown Todd LLC, Louisville
502 568 0239
mshull@fbtlaw.com
*Featured in Litigation (Kentucky)*

**Practice Areas:** Practice focuses on all aspects of the construction industry, from pre-construction acquisition and procurement through project completion and dispute resolution. Drafts, reviews and negotiates contracts in excess of $800 million. Past representation includes ENR 400 contractors and owners/developers in disputes involving projects over $250 million. Experience involves representation of clients in court or in ADR proceedings in Alabama, California, Colorado, Georgia, Florida, Kentucky, Nevada, North Carolina, and elsewhere. Clients include contractors, suppliers and owners from most US States, the Republic of Ireland, and Switzerland.
**Professional Memberships:** ABA Forum on the Construction Industry, Construction Financial Managers Association, Kentucky Association of Highway Contractors.
**Career:** Practice history involves tenures with large national firms in Atlanta and Denver prior to relocating to Louisville. Admitted in Georgia (2000), Colorado (2005) and Kentucky (2009). Former research engineer in civil engineering with the Kentucky Transportation Center prior to studying law.
**Publications:** Contributing author to Construction Business Handbook (Aspen), Common Sense Construction Law (Wiley), and the ABA's A State-by-State Guide to Construction & Design Law.
**Personal:** Born in Owensboro, KY in 1974. Attended University of Kentucky College of Engineering (BS Civil Engineering, 1996) and University of Kentucky College of Law (JD, 2000).

## SMITH, Raymond G
Boehl Stopher & Graves, LLP, Louisville
502 589 5980
rsmith@bsg-law.com
*Featured in Litigation (Kentucky)*

**Practice Areas:** Appellate Practice, Legal Malpractice Defense Litigation.
**Professional Memberships:** Mr Smith is a Member of the Louisville Bar Association, Kentucky Bar Association, Association of Defense Trial Attorneys. He is listed in The Best Lawyers in America 2006-2013.
**Career:** Mr Smith was Law Clerk to Chief Justice John S Palmore, Supreme Court of Kentucky, 1977-78. He joined Boehl Stopher & Graves, LLP in 1978 and became Partner in 1982.
**Personal:** BA, DePauw University, 1970; JD, Southern Methodist University, 1977.

## SMITH, JR, J David
Stoll Keenon Ogden PLLC, Lexington
859 231 3062
david.smith@skofirm.com
*Featured in Corporate/M&A (Kentucky)*

**Practice Areas:** Mr Smith serves as Co-Chair of the Business Services Practice Group and his practice concentrates on corporate and banking law, mergers and acquisitions, securities and equine law.
**Personal:** Mr Smith is AV® Preeminent™ Peer Review Rated by Martindale-Hubbell® and is listed in The Best Lawyers in America® for his many legal accomplishments. He serves as a director for many organizations throughout Kentucky, including Delta Dental of Kentucky, The Kentucky Historical Society Foundation, LexArts, Louisville Fund for the Arts and Keeneland Association. Mr Smith graduated Order of the Coif from the University of Kentucky College of Law.

## SNELL, Virginia
Wyatt, Tarrant & Combs, LLP, Louisville
502 562 7366
vsnell@wyattfirm.com
*Featured in Litigation (Kentucky)*

**Practice Areas:** Chair of firm's Appellate Advocacy Practice; representing clients in all kinds of cases in appellate/lower courts likely to proceed to appellate level.
**Professional Memberships:** Member, Bar Admission Committee; Master, Bar of Court; Chair, LBA Appellate Section; 2009-10 Chair, KBA Appellate Advocacy Section; member, Louisville Public Media; member, Litigation Committee, Kentucky Chamber of Commerce; member, The Law Club.
**Personal:** BA, University of Texas Plan II Honors Program with highest honors; Phi Beta Kappa; JD with honors, University of Texas; Member, Order of the Coif, Articles Editor, Texas Law Review.

## SNYDER, Sheryl
Frost Brown Todd LLC, Louisville
502 568 0247
ssnyder@fbtlaw.com
*Featured in Litigation (Kentucky)*

**Practice Areas:** Complex business litigation, appellate practice, constitutional law, state and federal.
**Professional Memberships:** Bars of the Supreme Courts of the United States, Kentucky, Tennessee, Texas, and Missouri; United States Courts of Appeals for the Third, Fourth, Sixth, Seventh, Eighth, Tenth and Eleventh Circuits. Past President, Kentucky and Louisville Bar Associations.
**Career:** Joined Frost Brown Todd (then Brown, Todd & Heyburn) 1994. Executive Vice President

and General Counsel, ICH Corporation (1990-94). Wyatt Tarrant & Combs (1973-90).
**Publications:** Co-author, Appellate Practice, Vol. 19, Kentucky Practice Series (Thomson/West).
**Personal:** Born 11 October 1946. University of Kentucky, BA 1968, JD 1971.

### STALLARD, W Patrick
Stites & Harbison PLLC, Louisville
502 681 0507
pstallard@stites.com
*Featured in Environment (Kentucky)*
**Practice Areas:** Environmental, natural resources and energy law.
**Professional Memberships:** Admitted, Kentucky. American, Kentucky, Louisville Bar Associations; Louisville Metro Brownfields Working Group; Chairman, Metro Solid Waste Advisory Committee; West Louisville Economic Alliance Advisory Committee; Greater Louisville, Inc., Environmental Committee.
**Career:** Member, Stites & Harbison, 1983-present. Member, Prichard Stallard & Shepherd, 1978-83; Assistant Attorney General, Kentucky, 1974-78.
**Publications:** 'Environmental Considerations in Real Estate Transactions' (Chapter), Co-author, Kentucky Real Estate Handbook, University of Kentucky, 3d Edition, 2007.
**Personal:** JD, University of Kentucky, 1974; BA, University of Kentucky, 1971.

### STEENROD, Ralston W
Stites & Harbison PLLC, Louisville
502 681 0436
rsteenrod@stites.com
*Featured in Corporate/M&A (Kentucky)*
**Practice Areas:** Practice includes corporate mergers, taxable acquisitions, tax-free reorganizations, contested takeovers and general corporate. Also includes bank holding company formations, rights of dissenting shareholders and securities registration and exemptions.
**Professional Memberships:** Admitted to practice in Kentucky. Member of the American, Kentucky and Louisville Bar Associations.
**Career:** Member of Stites & Harbison. Joined the firm in 1971.
**Personal:** JD, University of Louisville, 1968; AB, cum laude, English, Princeton University, 1959.

### STEWART, Cynthia L
Frost Brown Todd LLC, Louisville
502 568 0225
cstewart@fbtlaw.com
*Featured in Intellectual Property (Kentucky)*
**Practice Areas:** Ms Stewart focuses her practice in the software and technology field, spending most of her time negotiating deals for the license of health care and financial industry software/technology and for the implementation of IT networks. She also does trademark and copyright related work.
**Professional Memberships:** American Bar Association, Kentucky Bar Association, Louisville Bar Association, Women Influencing Louisville, Best Lawyers in Technology and Intellectual Property Law for 2003-2011.

**Career:** Began practice in 1985; engaged in bank transactional work for 10 years, then focused practice on Intellectual Property.
**Personal:** Attended University of Kentucky Law School and Morehead State University.

### STOPHER, Edward H
Boehl Stopher & Graves, LLP, Louisville
502 589 5980
estopher@bsg-law.com
*Featured in Litigation (Kentucky)*
**Practice Areas:** Civil litigation and Trial Practice with emphasis on corporate law, insurance law, product liability, legal malpractice and negligence matters.
**Professional Memberships:** Mr Stopher is a Member of the Louisville Bar Association; Kentucky Bar Association; American Bar Association; Fellow, American College of Trial Lawyers; Fellow, International Society of Barristers; Association of Defense Trial Attorneys; Fellow, American Bar Foundation; Fellow, International Academy of Trial Lawyers; National Association of Railroad Trial Counsel; Kentucky Defense Counsel; The Law Club; The Lawyers Club. He is listed in 'The Best Lawyers in America' 1989-2013.
**Career:** Mr Stopher was Law Clerk to Hon James F Gordon, United States Judge Western District of Kentucky, 1968-69. He joined Boehl Stopher & Graves, LLP, in 1969 and became Partner in 1970.
**Personal:** BA with Honors, Davidson College, 1965; JD, University of Virginia, 1968.

### STOPHER, Robert E
Boehl Stopher & Graves, LLP, Louisville
502 561 9402
rstopher@bsg-law.com
*Featured in Litigation (Kentucky)*
**Practice Areas:** Civil Litigation and Trial Practice, with emphasis on tort and insurance defense, product liability, and professional liability.
**Professional Memberships:** Mr Stopher is a Fellow of the American College of Trial Lawyers and a member of the International Association of Defense Counsel. He has been listed in 'The Best Lawyers in American' every year since 2003.
**Career:** Mr Stopher joined Boehl Stopher as an associate in 1977, becoming a partner in 1979. He has served on the firm's Executive Committee from 1999 to date.
**Personal:** BA, cum laude, Davidson College, 1974; JD University of Virginia School of Law 1977.

### STRAUS, R James
Frost Brown Todd LLC, Louisville
502 568 0221
jstraus@fbtlaw.com
*Featured in Corporate/M&A (Kentucky)*
**Practice Areas:** Firm Practice Chair, Financial Institutions and Franchising. Has extensive experience in banking, distribution, purchasing groups and mergers and acquisitions.
**Professional Memberships:** Admitted to practice in Kentucky (1974). Member of American Bar Association Sections on Business, Banking and Antitrust Law, and Forum on Franchising.

**Career:** Joined Frost Brown Todd 1974, became Partner, 1980. Business Law Department Chair.
**Personal:** Born 17 August 1946. JD, University of Chicago, 1974; BA, Yale University (cum laude), 1968; Captain USMC, Vietnam Veteran; Legal Aide Society Board of Directors.

### STRENCH, William G
Frost Brown Todd LLC, Louisville
502 568 0207
wstrench@fbtlaw.com
*Featured in Corporate/M&A (Kentucky)*
**Practice Areas:** Business and securities law with a focus on venture capital, private equity, executive compensation and mergers and acquisitions.
**Professional Memberships:** Admitted to practice in Kentucky (1989); American Bar Association (Corporation, Banking and Business Law Section). Selected and listed in Kentucky Super Lawyers since 2007 and Best Lawyers in America since 2005.
**Personal:** Vanderbilt University, BA, 1980, summa cum laude; Yale Law School, JD, 1983.

### VICE JR, Robert B
Stites & Harbison PLLC, Louisville
502 681 0636
rvice@stites.com
*Featured in Real Estate (Kentucky)*
**Practice Areas:** General real estate, real estate finance, tax credit finance, and corporate general services.
**Professional Memberships:** Member - Louisville, Kentucky and American Bar Associations.
**Career:** Associate, Stites & Harbison.
**Personal:** JD, University of Kentucky College of Law, 2005. LEED Accredited Professional.

### VINCENTI, Michael
Wyatt, Tarrant & Combs, LLP, Louisville
502 562 7518
mvincenti@wyattfirm.com
*Featured in Real Estate (Kentucky)*
**Practice Areas:** Extensive experience in real estate leasing, development and lending law, particularly transactions involving multiple components. Vincenti is Co-Chair of Wyatt's Business Law Department and former member of Wyatt's Executive Committee.
**Professional Memberships:** American College of Real Estate Lawyers; American College of Mortgage Attorneys; International Council of Shopping Centers; American Land Title Association; CREL; KYLTA; CCIM; American, Kentucky and Louisville Bar Associations.
**Publications:** Frequent lecturer on commercial leasing, title insurance, loan documentation, workouts and real estate development matters; Instructor for Kentucky Real Estate Commission.
**Personal:** New York University School of Law (JD 1975); Johns Hopkins University (BA 1972).

### WATT III, Robert M
Stoll Keenon Ogden PLLC, Lexington
859 231 3043
robert.watt@skofirm.com
*Featured in Environment (Kentucky)*

**Practice Areas:** Member of the business litigation, utilities and equine law practice groups, concentrating on utility regulation and equine law. Areas of particular substantive focus include utility rate and other regulation, contract disputes, intentional torts, corporate law disputes, and equine administrative, litigation and transactional matters.
**Professional Memberships:** American, Kentucky and Fayette County Bar Associations.
**Personal:** Duke University (B.A., 1969); University of Kentucky College of Law (JD, with distinction, 1973).

### WELSH, Patrick J
Bingham Greenebaum Doll LLP, Louisville
502 587 3679
pwelsh@bgdlegal.com
*Featured in Corporate/M&A (Kentucky)*
**Practice Areas:** Member of the Corporate and Transactional Practice Group. Involved in the day-to-day activities of the firm's clients, and advises them with respect to mergers and acquisitions, contractual issues, real estate and other business related topics. He represents several manufacturing companies and distributors, advising them on issues related to product distribution.
**Professional Memberships:** Louisville Bar Association, Kentucky Bar Association, American Bar Association (Section of Corporation, Banking and Business Law, Health Law Section).
**Career:** Admitted in Kentucky, 1984.
**Publications:** Distribution of Goods-Drafting the Distribution Agreement, Louisville Bar Association.
**Personal:** Attended University of Louisville School of Law, graduating magna cum laude.

### WHEAT, Jack A
Stites & Harbison PLLC, Louisville
502 681 0323
jwheat@stites.com
*Featured in Intellectual Property (Kentucky)*
**Practice Areas:** Concentration in infringement litigation. Served as Lead Counsel in intellectual property disputes in nearly 30 states. Experience includes the ultimately successful representation of Tennessee-based manufacturer of nationally-marketed foam athletic pads in patent case argued before US Supreme Court. Nelson v. Adams USA, Inc., 529 US 460 (2000).
**Professional Memberships:** Admitted, Kentucky. Member, American, Kentucky and Louisville Bar Associations.
**Career:** Member, Stites & Harbison since 2000. Formerly with Wheat, Smith & Beres. Adjunct Professor of Intellectual Property, Louis D Brandeis School of Law at University of Louisville.
**Personal:** JD, University of Louisville, 1979; BA, Hanover College, 1976.

### WHITE, Geoff
Frost Brown Todd LLC, Louisville
502 568 0202
gwhite@fbtlaw.com
*Featured in Real Estate (Kentucky)*
**Practice Areas:** Represents lenders, special servicers, regional and national developers and real estate investment trusts (REITs) in the financing,

workout, servicing, purchase, sale, leasing, development and management of commercial real estate properties.

**Professional Memberships:** Member of the International Conference of Shopping Centers (ICSC) and Mortgage Bankers Association (MBA).

**Career:** Licensed in Ohio in 2003 and Kentucky in 2006. Joined Frost Brown Todd LLC in 2008.

**Personal:** Graduated cum laude from University of Michigan Law School in 2003 and magna cum laude from Mary Washington College in 2000.

### WILFORD, Frank L
Stoll Keenon Ogden PLLC, Lexington
859 231 3013
frank.wilford@skofirm.com
*Featured in Real Estate (Kentucky)*

**Practice Areas:** Practices in the areas of banking and commercial real estate. Has substantial experience advising banks and representation of buyers and sellers of real estate interests, real estate development and construction and commercial financing. Serves as a bank director.

**Professional Memberships:** American, Kentucky and Fayette County Bar Associations.

**Personal:** University of Kentucky (BA, 1970, JD 1974).

### WILLIAMS, Ernest W
Stoll Keenon Ogden PLLC, Louisville
502 560 4243
ernest.williams@skofirm.com
*Featured in Corporate/M&A (Kentucky)*

**Practice Areas:** Concentration in the area of business acquisitions with regular representation of both buyers and sellers of businesses, including asset acquisitions, stock acquisitions, mergers, supply and distribution agreements, employment agreements, service agreements, and business planning for closely-held businesses. In an international context, has represented local businesses acquiring businesses or establishing joint venture arrangements in foreign countries, as well as representing foreign businesses seeking to acquire or establish local operations.

**Professional Memberships:** Kentucky and Louisville Bar Associations.

**Personal:** Harvard Law School (JD, 1975); Murray State University (B.A., 1972). Listed in 'Best Lawyers in America,' and 'Kentucky Super Lawyers.'

### WILLIAMS, Matthew
Wyatt, Tarrant & Combs, LLP, Louisville
502 562 7378
mwilliams@wyattfirm.com
*Featured in Intellectual Property (Kentucky)*

**Practice Areas:** Matt, a registered patent attorney, focuses his practice on intellectual property law. Matt's practice includes prosecution of patent and trademark applications, litigation, transaction support, and licensing. Matt has experience with a wide-range of technologies including consumer products, appliances, statistical process and quality control, and manufacturing machinery.

**Career:** Before law school, Matt spent ten years at G.E. Appliances as an engineer, manufacturing supervisor, and purchasing agent.

**Personal:** 2004 - JD, summa cum laude, Brandeis School of Law at the University of Louisville: Valedictorian; 1992 - B.S. (Engineering Science), with highest honors, Speed Scientific School at the University of Louisville.

### WILLIAMS, Thomas M
Stoll Keenon Ogden PLLC, Louisville
502 560 4279
tom.williams@skofirm.com
*Featured in Labor & Employment (Kentucky)*

**Practice Areas:** Concentration in the area of labor and employment law. He regularly counsels employers and litigates all types of employment law disputes.

**Professional Memberships:** American Bar Association (Employment Rights and Responsibilities Subcommittee since 1999); Louisville Bar Association (Past President, Board of Directors,); Louisville Society for Human Resources Management (Past Labor Relations Chair).

**Personal:** University of Cincinnati (JD, 1990); College of William & Mary (BA, 1986). Listed in 'Best Lawyers in America, and Super Lawyers Labor and Employment; 2002 Award for Professional Excellence from Louisville Society for Human Resources Management; 2010 Board Chair, Leadership Louisville.

### WOODS III, C Laurence
Frost Brown Todd LLC, Louisville
502 568 0288
lwoods@fbtlaw.com
*Featured in Labor & Employment (Kentucky)*

**Practice Areas:** Mr Woods practices labor and employment law, representing management exclusively.

**Career:** Mr Woods has broad experience handling employment litigation. This includes actions under Title VII of the Civil Rights Act of 1964 and 1991, Age Discrimination in Employment Act, Fair Labor Standards Act, Americans with Disabilities Act, local anti-discrimination laws, and RICO. His practice also includes all types of labor issues under the National Labor Relations Act (NLRA), and arbitrations and collective bargaining agreements.

**Personal:** University of Louisville, JD, 1976, cum laude; University of Kentucky, MBA, 1970; University of Kentucky, BS, 1969.

### YOUNG, Cynthia W
Wyatt, Tarrant & Combs, LLP, Louisville
502 562 7292
cyoung@wyattfirm.com
*Featured in Corporate/M&A (Kentucky)*

**Practice Areas:** Cindy Young is a co-leader of the Firm's Financial Institutions practice. She concentrates her practice in the areas of mergers and acquisitions; securities transactions; and advising public and private clients on corporate, corporate governance, corporate finance, securities, strategic planning, banking and insurance matters.

**Career:** Past President of the Louisville Bar Association and has taught securities law at the University of Louisville Law School. She worked previously as corporate counsel to I.C.H. Corporation, an insurance holding company.

**Personal:** University of Louisville, Valedictorian (JD, summa cum laude, 1982); Indiana University (BA Mathematics, with high distinction, 1978).

# BINGHAM GREENEBAUM DOLL LLP

**www.**bgdlegal.com

**Co-Chairmen:** W Tobin McClamroch, Phillip D Scott
Managing partners: 4
Number of partners: 140  Number of other attorneys: 85

## Firm Overview:

Bingham Greenebaum Doll LLP is a regional law firm providing progressive business, litigation and government services to clients ranging from *Fortune* 500 businesses and *Global* 1000 companies to small, regionally based organizations across a variety of industries and sectors. The firm is both locally accessible and nationally connected with offices in Indiana, Kentucky and Ohio. In addition to its regional presence, Bingham Greenebaum Doll LLP provides international representation to a multitude of clients and is a member of TerraLex®, an association of independent law firms in nearly 100 countries, providing the firm and its clients with quick access to advice on the laws of foreign jurisdictions.

## Main Areas of Practice:

### Corporate & Transactional:

Bingham Greenebaum Doll serves clients in a variety of industries, from domestic start-up companies to multinational corporations located throughout the United States and abroad. Its attorneys are experienced in business planning, negotiating and drafting contracts, preparing public filings, advising clients on intellectual property issues, and working with federal and state regulators. Group members counsel companies in the structuring, negotiating and documentation of mergers, acquisitions, joint ventures, financing and other business transactions.

### Estate Planning:

The Estate Planning Practice Group's attorneys provide integrated services in estate planning, estate and trust administration, fiduciary representation, tax return preparation, disability planning, family and charitable gifting arrangements, marital agreements, guardianships and adoptions, limited partnerships, business succession planning, drafting and representing qualified and non-qualified employee benefit plans, and the representation of healthcare providers and health insurers.

### Environmental & Natural Resources:

Bingham Greenebaum Doll's attorneys are experienced in advising businesses, utilities and governments on complex air, water, and waste permitting and compliance issues, enforcement defense, criminal defense, regulatory and legislative policy development, remediation and environmental due diligence. The group is well known for its representation of the energy industry, including coal mining, environmental, mineral law and transaction matters.

### Labor & Employment:

The firm's labor and employment attorneys defend employers against all employee claims, including discrimination, harassment, retaliation, wrongful termination, ERISA and employee benefits; wage and hour; OSHA; immigration status; employment contract disputes and covenants not to compete. The group's attorneys also advise employers in union-management relations, responding to union organizing campaigns, collective bargaining, grievance arbitration, severance packages and employment contract negotiations. The group also has a concentration in the representation of highly compensated C-Suite executives with both their entry into and exit from a corporate position.

### Litigation:

Bingham Greenebaum Doll's attorneys are experienced in all aspects of trial and appellate work in federal and state courts and have substantial experience in alternative dispute resolution matters. The group has extensive experience in corporate governance disputes, intellectual property disputes, securities litigation, white-collar criminal defense, appeals, e-discovery, litigation-avoidance techniques, utility and other regulatory disputes, construction and real estate litigation, business torts, product liability defense, class actions, environmental and toxic tort defense, and First Amendment issues.

### Tax & Finance:

The firm's skilled, seasoned and connected tax and finance attorneys include individuals who serve on ABI, IRS and American Bar Association advisory groups, have advanced law degrees in taxation and publish on a variety of topics. Their credentials and dedication permit in-depth service to the firm's clients in areas including bankruptcy and workout, commercial and public finance, federal tax, international tax, non-profit and tax exempt organizations, and state and local tax.

### Government:

Bingham Greenebaum Doll's services include procurements, general regulatory issues, rule-making, economic development, public finance, lobbying, ordinance drafting and review, regulatory enforcement, licensing, permitting and municipal/private utility matters. The firm's attorneys also advise clients on ethics, election laws, acquisition and disposal of property, public contracts, public construction, privatization, public meetings and records laws and annexation. In addition to its representation of private sector clients who interact with various levels of government, the group also serves as special counsel to various state and local government entities.

### Real Estate:

The firm's real estate attorneys represent real estate developers, buyers and sellers, government entities, utilities and lending institutions, with particular expertise in renewable energy projects, land use matters, tax appeals, construction issues, economic incentives, office, industrial and shopping center leasing, financial restructuring and distressed markets.

## PRACTICE AREAS

Corporate & Transactional
Estate Planning
Environmental & Natural Resources
Labor & Employment
Litigation
Tax & Finance
Government
Real Estate

## OFFICES

### INDIANA

**INDIANAPOLIS:** 2700 Market Tower, 10 West Market Street, IN 46204-4900
Tel: 317 635 8900  Fax: 317 236 9907

**EVANSVILLE:** 25 NW Riverside Drive, Suite 100, IN 47708
Tel: 812 437 0200  Fax: 812 437 6717

**JASPER:** 212 West 6th Street, IN 47546
Tel: 812 482 5500  Fax: 812 482 2017

**VINCENNES:** 312 Main Street, IN 47591
Tel: 812 882 0222  Fax: 812 437 6717

**VINCENNES:** 112 North 7th Street, IN 47591
Tel: 812 886 9970  Fax: 812 886 0776

### KENTUCKY

**LOUISVILLE:** 3500 National City Tower, 101 South Fifth Street, KY 40202-3197
Tel: 502 589 4200  Fax: 502 587 3695

**FRANKFORT:** 229 West Main Street, Suite 205, KY 40601
Tel: 859 231 8500  Fax: 859 255 2742

**LEXINGTON:** 300 West Vine Street, Suite 1100, KY 40507
Tel: 859 231 8500  Fax: 859 255 2742

### OHIO

**CINCINNATI:** 2350 First Financial Center, 255 East Fifth Street, OH 45202
Tel: 513 455 7600  Fax: 513 455 8500

# BOEHL STOPHER & GRAVES LLP

**www.**BSG-Law.com **tel:** 502 589 5980 **fax:** 502 561 9400

**Executive Committee:** Richard W Edwards, Robert E Stopher, Raymond G Smith, David T Klapheke, Jeffrey L Hansford, Richard L Walter and Tom Anderson
Number of partners: 26
Number of lawyers: 50

## Firm Overview:

Since 1895, Boehl Stopher & Graves LLP, has represented a wide variety of businesses all across Kentucky in State and Federal Courts. The firm's philosophy is simple: though the firm is highly effective in the courtroom, it is more concerned with bringing matters to a satisfactory conclusion, whether it be through negotiation, mediation, arbitration, or litigation. From insurance to energy, from workers' compensation to mergers and acquisitions, the diversity of the firm's experience in civil litigation has given it depth and breadth in the areas in which it practices.

## Main Areas of Practice:

### Civil Litigation:

The firm represents clients in civil matters in just about every arena. The majority of its work has focused on product liability, toxic torts, contract disputes, corporate disputes, employment disputes, professional negligence, facility negligence, intellectual property law, and personal injury.
**Contact:** Edward H Stopher

### Workers' Compensation:

The firm represents clients in the defense of workers' compensation claims.
**Contact:** Philip J Reverman, Jr

### Corporate:

The firm represents buyers and sellers in various transactions including mergers, buy-outs, and other business combinations.
**Contact:** Jefferson K Streepey

### Trust & Estates:

The firm represents individuals in the area of trust and estate planning, will preparation, execution and probate.
**Contact:** Jefferson K Streepey

## Clients:

Boehl Stopher & Graves LLP has successfully defended corporations such as Eli Lilly and Company, CSX Transportation, Bristol-Myers Squibb, Ford, PolyOne Corporation, and NCAA in high-risk, high-visibility cases. The firm has successfully defended insurance companies such as AIG, Coregis, Old Republic Companies, State Farm, and Ohio Casualty. Boehl Stopher & Graves, LLP has also defended individuals and non-profit organizations.

## US Offices:

### New Albany

**Managing Partner:** Jeffrey L Hansford
Number of lawyers: 6
**Office Profile:** The New Albany, Indiana office is an integral part of the Greater Louisville metropolitan area providing defense representation of medical malpractice, products liability, workers' compensation, personal injury, professional liability and other litigation matters.

### Lexington

Number of lawyers: 5
**Office Profile:** The Lexington office is strategically located 20 minutes from the state capital, Frankfort, Kentucky, and approximately 75 miles from both Louisville and Cincinnati. The office has provided a broad range of trial and appellate services since 1943.

### Paducah

**Managing Partner:** Richard L Walter
Number of lawyers: 6
**Office Profile:** The Paducah office has an active practice in western Kentucky and southern Illinois, including all State and Federal Courts in both jurisdictions. The Paducah office handles a wide variety of litigation, including professional liability, construction, personal injury and maritime matters.

## OFFICES

### KENTUCKY

**LOUISVILLE:** 2300 AEGON Center, 400 W. Market Street, KY 40202
Tel: 502 589 5980   Fax: 502 561 9400
Email: Louisville@bsg-law.com

**LEXINGTON:** 444 West Second Street, KY 40507
Tel: 859 252 6721   Fax: 859 253 1445
Email: Lexington@bsglex.com

Paducah: 410 Broadway, KY 42001
Tel: 270 442 4369   Fax: 270 442 4689
Email: rwalter@bsgpad.com

**PIKEVILLE:** 137 Main Street, Suite 200, PO Box 1139, KY 41502
Tel: 606 432 9670   Fax: 606 432 9680
Email: tanderson@bsgeast.com

### INDIANA

**NEW ALBANY:** Elsby East - Suite 204, 400 Pearl Street, IN 47150
Tel: 812 948 5053   Fax: 812 948 9233
Email: Indiana@bsg-in.com

### Pikeville

**Managing Partner:** Tom Anderson
Number of lawyers: 3
**Office Profile:** The Pikeville office handles a significant amount of workers' compensation defense cases in the heart of eastern Kentucky's coal mining region. This office's practice also includes auto and coal truck defense, school board matters and professional, products and premises liability cases.

BOEHL STOPHER & GRAVES, LLP

# FROST BROWN TODD LLC

**www.**frostbrowntodd.com **tel:** 502 589 5400 **fax:** 502 581 1087

**Chairman:** John R Crockett III
**Managing Member:** George E Yund
Number of partners: 303
Number of lawyers: 463

## Firm Overview:

Frost Brown Todd is a full-service law firm serving some of America's top corporations and emerging companies. With attorneys regularly identified by clients, peers and industry organizations as leaders in their practice areas, the firm advises and protects clients in business transactions and litigation in industries including healthcare, insurance, financial institutions, manufacturing, transportation, real estate, construction, and energy. Its attorneys in Indiana, Kentucky, Ohio, Tennessee and West Virginia provide unparalleled service to meet clients' needs; deliver the insights and solutions available only from a diverse group of professionals; and support the communities in which they operate.

## Main Areas of Practice:

### Litigation:

The firm counsels and represents corporations and individuals in every aspect of civil, commercial and white-collar criminal litigation. The firm's litigators blend skill and insight, sophisticated legal savvy and a deep roster of partners across disciplines to meet challenges across numerous industries and business situations. Frost Brown Todd serves as national counsel for a variety of companies on complex and potentially large exposure matters. The firm also counsels and represents a variety of international, national, regional and local corporations and has extensive experience in complex litigation, multi-party cases and class actions. The firm has defended public companies in hostile takeover battles, and pharmaceutical companies and medical device manufacturers in class action product liability suits. Frost Brown Todd also defends accountants and medical facilities in malpractice claims. The firm's litigators defend and prosecute complex litigation involving RICO violations, securities violations, fraud, trade secrets, covenants not to compete, dealer terminations, antitrust matters, intellectual property, breach-of-contract and breach of fiduciary duties. Frost Brown Todd has a long record of success in the courtroom and features many nationally-recognized litigators. While the firm frequently tries cases to judges and juries, its trial attorneys regularly resolve disputes out of court through negotiation, arbitration, mediation, mini-trials and other alternative dispute resolution methods.
**Contact:** Adam P Hall

### Business & Corporate:

With the combined efforts of over 70 attorneys with focused business and regulatory knowledge, Frost Brown Todd has created a powerful team with virtually unlimited knowledge and resources to answer your questions, provide insight and guide you along the right path. Frost Brown Todd attorneys are trusted legal counsel for some of America's best-known companies, completing over $9 billion in mergers/acquisitions over the past two years. The firm's business law section covers the full spectrum of transactions important to US business, utilizing the different disciplines that must be brought to bear in complex transactions. The firm leverages technical, industry and legal knowledge and experience to serve a diverse client base, ranging from global multinationals to small entrepreneurial companies. Frost Brown Todd handles large-scale corporate deals and matters of every type including: Mergers/Acquisitions, Entrepreneurial Business, Public Companies/Securities, Venture Capital, Employee Benefits/Executive Compensation, Tax Law, Intellectual Property, Franchise/Distribution, International Business and Mutual Funds/Hedge Funds.
**Contact:** Jeffrey L Hallos

## OFFICES

### KENTUCKY

**LOUISVILLE:** 400 West Market Street, Suite 3200, KY 40202-3363
Tel: 502 589 5400  Fax: 502 581 1087
Email: info@fbtlaw.com

**LEXINGTON:** Lexington Financial Center, Suite 2800, 250 West Main Street, KY 40507-1749
Tel: 859 231 0000 Fax: 859 231 0011

**FLORENCE:** 7310 Turfway Road, Suite 210, KY 41042
Tel: 859 817 5900 Fax: 859 283 5902

### OHIO

**CINCINNATI:** 3300 Great American Tower, 301 East Fourth Street, OH 45202
Tel: 513 651 6800  Fax: 513 651 6981

### INDIANA

**INDIANAPOLIS:** 201 North Illinois Street, Suite 1900, P.O. Box 44961, IN 46204
Tel: 317 237 3800 Fax: 317 237 3900

### OHIO

**COLUMBUS:** One Columbus, Suite 2300, 10 West Broad Street, OH 43215-3484
Tel: 614 464 1211 Fax: 614 464 1737

**WEST CHESTER:** 9277 Centre Pointe Drive, Suite 300, OH 45069
Tel: 513 870 8200 Fax: 513 870 0999

### TENNESSEE

**NASHVILLE:** 1900 The Pinnacle at Symphony Place, 150 Third Ave South, TN 37201
Tel: 615 251 5550 Fax: 615 251 5551

### WEST VIRGINIA

**CHARLESTON:** Laidley Tower, Suite 401, 500 Lee Street East, WV 25301-3207
Tel: 304 345 0111 Fax: 304 345 0115

# SMITH & SMITH ATTORNEYS

www.smithandsmithattorneys.com **tel:** 502 587 0761 **fax:** 502 589 5345

**Managing Partner:** Oliver B Rutherford
Number of partners: 4
Number of other attorneys: 2

**OFFICES**

KENTUCKY

**LOUISVILLE:** 400 North, First Trust Centre, 200 South Fifth
Street, KY 40202
Tel: 502 587 0761   Fax: 502 589 5345
Email: firm@smithandsmithattorneys.com

## Firm Overview:

Founded in 1946, Smith & Smith Attorneys is well known for representing and counseling employers on employment and labor matters throughout the Kentuckiana region. Whether through litigation, negotiation or arbitration, Smith & Smith seeks the most cost-effective resolution to a wide array of legal challenges facing small, mid-size and large employers. When necessary, Smith & Smith is prepared to litigate vigorously. But more often, a desirable outcome can be identified and ultimately achieved through negotiation or alternative dispute resolution.

Smith & Smith Attorneys also is a proud member of the Worklaw® Network, a nationwide network of independent law firms practicing exclusively in labor and employment law. With a network of 34 firms with offices in 26 US states plus Australia, China, Europe, India, and Mexico, members are able to share substantive information concerning work product, creative strategies and research. Smith & Smith's relationship with Worklaw® Network enables it to address clients' legal needs throughout the United States and internationally.

## Main Areas of Practice:

### Labor Relations:

Smith & Smith has a strong and established history of representing and advising management-side clients regarding all manner of labor issues. Smith & Smith has advised and assisted non-union clients with all facets of employee organizing campaigns. In representing unionized clients, Smith & Smith attorneys routinely practice before the National Labor Relations Board, providing representation in unfair labor practice cases, certification and decertification petitions, and other myriad issues under the jurisdiction of the Board.

In addition, Smith & Smith has significant experience in matters of labor arbitration. It has arbitrated various issues for employers, including 'just cause' discharge, contract interpretation issues, strike misconduct and interest arbitration. Smith & Smith has practiced in front of arbitrators who serve on the panels of the Federal Mediation and Conciliation Service and the American Arbitration Association.

### Collective Bargaining:

Smith & Smith Attorneys has advised and acted on behalf of employers in countless collective bargaining negotiations, with a high rate of success of achieving clients' bargaining goals. Smith & Smith has experience in all sectors of the workforce, but has particular experience in negotiations involving healthcare, the service sector, manufacturing, construction and printing and binding.

Smith & Smith also has substantial experience in counseling employers on strike prevention and preparedness for those times when collective bargaining negotiations do not yield agreement on a contract. With over 100 years of collective experience in dealing with these issues, Smith & Smith offers sound advice during challenging periods for employers and the employer-employee and employer-union relationship.

### Employment Litigation:

A large part of Smith & Smith's practice involves complex employment litigation, including Title VII discrimination and harassment claims, Americans with Disabilities Act claims, Family Medical Leave Act claims, and state and local civil rights claims, among others. Smith & Smith also has substantial experience litigating employment tort and contract claims, including those dealing with trade secrets and covenants not to compete. Its attorneys have practiced such cases in the state courts and state appellate court, including the Kentucky Supreme Court, federal courts and courts of appeal, including the Sixth and Seventh Circuit Courts of Appeal, and in front of administrative bodies such as the Equal Employment Opportunity Commission and the Kentucky Commission on Human Rights. Smith & Smith also has significant experience seeking injunctive relief for violations of covenants not to compete, as well as labor matters. Smith & Smith routinely practices in front of other state and federal agencies on employment matters, including the Department of Labor, the Kentucky Labor Cabinet, the federal and state Occupational Safety and Health Administrations, and the Kentucky Unemployment Insurance Commission. The firm has achieved success in all of these forums, either through summary judgment or other dispositive motion, jury verdict, or administrative decision.

Smith & Smith also provides counseling services to employers regarding employment issues. This includes advising clients with respect to pre-employment testing, advertising for positions, drafting enforceable employment contracts, severance matters and releases, Older Worker Benefit Protection Act, and the WARN Act, just to name a few. Smith & Smith has broad-based knowledge and skill in tailoring severance agreements and employee layoff or discharge plans that best fit the needs of its clients. Smith & Smith also offers preventative education to the managers, supervisors, and employees of its clients.

### Clients:

Clients include: Abel Construction Co., Advance Ready Mix Concrete, Inc., Appalachian Regional Healthcare, Inc., Arch Chemicals, Inc., Associated Builders & Contractors, Inc., Beach Mold and Tool, Inc., The Brown Hotel, Bruce Fox, Inc., Campbell Tobacco Rehandling, Cardinal Aluminum Company, Inc., Carrier Vibrating Equipment, Inc., Churchill Downs, Inc., Clariant Corporation, Conco, Inc., Cummins Crosspoint, LLC, David Engineering, Delta Dental of Kentucky, Inc., 84 Lumber, Fabricated Metals, LLC, FireKing Security Group, Flexible Materials, Inc., GCH International, Inc., Goodwill Industries, Hall Contracting of Kentucky, Inc., Gray Construction Co., Kelley Construction Company, Lindsey Wilson College, Mattingly Foods, Inc., MedVenture Corporation, nth/Works, Inc., Neill-LaVielle Supply Co., Ralcorp, Inc., R.C. Bigelow, Inc., Republic Diesel, Robert Bosch Tool Corporation, Sandvik, Inc., Stock Yards Bank & Trust Co., Sypris Solutions, Wehr Constructors, Inc., Whayne Supply Company.

# STITES & HARBISON, PLLC

**www.**stites.com **tel:** 502 587 3400 **fax:** 502 587 6391

**Chair:** Kenneth R Sagan (ksagan@stites.com)
Number of partners: 131
Number of lawyers: 231
Languages: *Arabic, English, French, German, Mandarin Chinese, Spanish, Urdu, Yoruba*

## Firm Overview:

Stites & Harbison, PLLC, is a pre-eminent law firm based in strategic Southeastern locations and sought by business and institutional clients nationwide for sophisticated transactions, difficult litigation and complex regulatory matters. Stites & Harbison is a full-service firm practicing through departmental groupings with specialty and industry teams whose nine locations function as a single law office.

## Main Areas of Practice:

**Business & Corporate Services:**
**Contact:** W Thomas Halbleib, Jr
**Tel:** 502 681 0447
**Email:** thalbleib@stites.com

**Business Litigation:**
**Contact:** Phillip W Collier
**Tel:** 502 681 0415
**Email:** pcollier@stites.com

**Construction:**
**Contact:** Buckner Hinkle, Jr
**Tel:** 859 226 2334
**Email:** bhinkle@stites.com

**Creditors' Rights & Bankruptcy:**
**Contact:** Elizabeth Lee Thompson
**Tel:** 859 226 2389
**Email:** ethompson@stites.com

**Employment Law:**
**Contact:** Shannon Antle Hamilton (Louisville)
**Tel:** 502 681 0469
**Email:** shamilton@stites.com
**Contact:** Stephen H Price (Nashville)
**Tel:** 615 782 2232
**Email:** stephen.price@stites.com

**Environmental, Natural Resources & Energy:**
**Contact:** William T Gorton III
**Tel:** 859 226 2241
**Email:** bgorton@stites.com

**Equine:**
**Contact:** Robert M Beck, Jr
**Tel:** 859 226 2366
**Email:** rbeck@stites.com

**Healthcare:**
**Contact:** Jennifer Landrum Elliot
**Tel:** 502 681 0682
**Email:** jlelliot@stites.com

**Insurance Regulatory:**
**Contact:** Janet A Craig
**Tel:** 859 226 2377
**Email:** jcraig@stites.com

**Intellectual Property & Technology:**
**Contact:** David W Nagle, Jr (Louisville)
**Tel:** 502 681 0321
**Email:** dnagle@stites.com
**Contact:** B Aaron Schulman (Alexandria)
**Tel:** 703 837 3907
**Email:** bschulman@stites.com

**Sustainability & Emerging Technologies:**
**Contact:** Jamie L Cox
**Tel:** 502 681 0576
**Email:** jcox@stites.com

**Torts & Insurance Practice:**
**Contact:** John M Famularo (Lexington)
**Tel:** 859 226 2335
**Email:** jfamularo@stites.com
**Contact:** John L Tate (Louisville)
**Tel:** 502 681 0460
**Email:** jtate@stites.com

**Trusts & Estate Planning:**
**Contact:** J David Porter
**Tel:** 859 226 2310
**Email:** dporter@stites.com

**Real Estate & Banking:**
**Contact:** Julian L Bibb
**Tel:** 615 782 2227
**Email:** julian.bibb@stites.com

## Clients:

Aegon USA; AFL Telecommunications LLC; Akebono Brake Corporation; Alcan Aluminum Corporation; Alstom Power; American Electric Power Service Corporation (Kentucky Power Co.); American General Corporation; American Institute of Steel Construction, Inc.; American Optical Corporation; Anthem Inc.; Bank of America, NA; Bank One, Kentucky, N.A.; Baptist Healthcare System; Blue Grass Airport; Branch Banking & Trust Company; Bridgestone Americas Holdings, Inc.; Bridgestone Americas Tire Operations, LLC; Brown-Forman Corporation; Caldwell Tanks, Inc.; LLC; CHA HMO, Inc.; Community & Southern Bank; Dynegy Inc.; E.I. du Pont de Nemours and Company; Fifth Third Bank; GE Capital Corporation; GlaxoSmithKline; Gray Construction; Holder Construction Company; International Port of Kentucky; JPMorgan Chase Bank, N.A.; KFC Corporation; Lexington Clinic; Lin R. Rogers Electrical Contractors; Louisville Regional Airport Authority; M.A. Mortensen Company; Microsoft; National Health Investors, Inc.; LLC; New York Department of Insurance; Northern Life Insurance Company; Presco Steel, Inc.; Purdue Pharma LP; Regions Bank; ReliaStar Life Insurance Company; Southern Land Company; Steel Technologies, Inc.; Stock Yards Bank & Trust Co.; Stryker Corporation; SunTrust Bank; Synaxis Group, Inc.; Tempur-Pedic International, Inc.; The Goodyear Tire & Rubber Company; Tyson Foods, Inc.; University Medical Center, Inc.; University of Kentucky; University of Louisville; United Community Banks, Inc; Vanderbilt University; Windstream Communications; Whayne Supply Company; Zurich American Insurance Companies.

## OFFICES

### KENTUCKY
**COVINGTON:** 100 East RiverCenter Blvd., Suite 450, KY 41011
Tel: 859 226 2276  Fax: 859 425 7966
Email: general@stites.com

**FRANKFORT:** 421 W. Main St., KY 40602
Tel: 502 223 3477  Fax: 502 223 4124

**LEXINGTON:** 250 W. Main St., Suite 2300, KY 40507
Tel: 859 226 2300  Fax: 859 253 9144

**LOUISVILLE:** 400 W. Market St., Suite 1800, KY 40202
Tel: 502 587 3400  Fax: 502 587 6391

### GEORGIA
**ATLANTA:** 303 Peachtree St., NE, 2800 SunTrust Plaza, GA 30308
Tel: 404 739 8800  Fax: 404 739 8870

### INDIANA
**JEFFERSONVILLE:** 323 E. Court Ave, IN 47130
Tel: 812 282 7566  Fax: 812 284 5519

### TENNESSEE
**FRANKLIN:** 604 West Main Street, TN 37064
Tel: 615 595 0636  Fax: 615 599 6012

**NASHVILLE:** 401 Commerce Street, Suite 800, TN 37219
Tel: 615 782 2200  Fax: 615 782 2371

### VIRGINIA
**ALEXANDRIA:** 1199 N. Fairfax St., Suite 900, VA 22314
Tel: 703 739 4900  Fax: 703 739 9577

## STITES & HARBISON PLLC
**ATTORNEYS**

# STOLL KEENON OGDEN

www.skofirm.com **tel:** 502 333 6000 **fax:** 502 333 6099

**Managing Director:** William M Lear, Jr
Number of lawyers: 145

## Firm Overview:

With more than 145 attorneys in seven cities in Kentucky, Indiana, and Pennsylvania, SKO is an established law firm representing clients on local, state, national, and international levels. Tracing their history back to 1897, SKO's commitment to client service is demonstrated by enduring relationships built on honest, experienced, and trusted counsel.

SKO's scope of service is diverse – from environmental and mineral law to business, finance and litigation to regulatory and administrative law – and their attorneys are ranked as some of the highest in their fields. The BTI Consulting Group named SKO a "Client Service A-Team" in both 2012 and 2013. SKO prides themselves on raising the practice of law to an art form, and client success is always at the core of the firm's mission.

## Main Areas of Practice:

### Business Litigation:

SKO's Business Litigation practice provides strategic advice to businesses and professionals faced with disputes, lawsuits, arbitration and other conflicts. They help manage disputes on the front end with guidance on sound business practices, and for conflicts that could not be resolved early, they help clients through even the most complex, high-stakes disputes with a careful, focused and strategic approach.

SKO's litigation practice experience includes matters involving antitrust, trade regulation and franchise; appellate; banking litigation; bankruptcy and financial restructuring; business torts; class action; construction law; criminal law; eminent domain and real estate litigation; environmental litigation; equine litigation; healthcare litigation; securities litigation; tort, trial and insurance services and trust and estate litigation.
**Contact:** Samuel D Hinkle IV  **Tel:** 502 568 5709
**Email:** sam.hinkle@skofirm.com

### Business Services:

SKO's Business Services practice combines skilled practitioners, decades of experience and innovative business practices to help clients excel in a complicated and turbulent marketplace. From local to international levels, the firm represents clients involved in a broad range of business activities and has the personnel and experience to help achieve their legal objectives.

The SKO Business Services practice is comprised of several related practices which allow them to take a comprehensive approach to the legal needs of clients. This structure encourages multi-level collaboration among all attorneys to help ensure efficient and favorable legal outcomes for the firm's clients and includes the following practices: banking; corporate finance and lending; equine transactional; healthcare transactional; immigration; intellectual property;

mergers and acquisitions; public finance; real estate; securities and corporate governance; state and federal tax and trusts, estates and family law.
**Contact:** Scott W. Brinkman  **Tel:** 502 560 4244
**Email:** scott.brinkman@skofirm.com
**Contact:** J David Smith Jr  **Tel:** 859 231 3062
**Email:** david.smith@skofirm.com

### Labor, Employment & Employee Benefits:

SKO's Labor, Employment & Employee Benefits practice has a proven record of being trusted advisors and effective advocates. They help employers solve their problems through proactive counseling, employee training and, where possible, cost-efficient litigation, including alternative dispute resolution. They know the employment laws thoroughly, and make it their goal to acquire a comprehensive knowledge of their clients and their business so the firm can provide tailored solutions for each of their needs.
**Contact:** Richard G Griffith  **Tel:** 859 231 3036
**Email:** richard.griffith@skofirm.com

### Utility & Energy:

SKO's Utility & Energy practice works with a host of utility businesses on regulation and operation issues, from day-to-day procedures to major mergers and acquisitions. Their attorneys have extensive experience in the field that includes the representation of clients before the Federal Energy Regulatory Commission, the Federal Communications Commission, Kentucky Public Service Commission and other state and federal regulatory bodies, including trial and appellate courts. SKO's Utility & Energy practice scope of services includes rate adjustments; transfers of control; financing and construction applications; consumer complaint proceedings; mergers and acquisitions; employment issues; securities; antitrust and compliance; market entry; inter-carrier relations and legislative affairs.

SKO also has a strong Mineral & Environmental practice with a regional presence and renowned experience in the industry. Their attorneys are pledged to supplying prompt and proficient services in all substantive categories of the practice area, including but not limited to transactions, due diligence, environmental compliance, litigation and regulatory disputes.
**Contact:** Kendrick R Riggs  **Tel:** 502 560 4222
**Email:** kendrick.riggs@skofirm.com
**Contact:** John H Henderson  **Tel:** 812 759 3802
**Email:** john.henderson@skofirm.com

## Clients:

Representative clients include: Brown-Forman Corporation, LG&E and KU Energy LLC, Lexmark International, Inc., Keeneland Association, Baptist Healthcare System, Central Bank, Fifth Third Bank, Farmers Bank and Capital Trust Company, Caterpillar, Inc., ISCO Industries, Inc., Kentucky American Water Company, Alliance Energy and University of Louisville.

STOLL KEENON OGDEN PLLC

# WYATT, TARRANT & COMBS, LLP

www.wyattfirm.com **Tel:** 502 589 5235 **Fax:** 502 589 0309

**Managing Partner:** William H Hollander

## Firm Overview:

With approximately 200 attorneys in six offices, Wyatt, Tarrant & Combs, LLP offers a full range of legal services in Kentucky, Tennessee, Mississippi and Indiana. By leveraging the firm's rich heritage and tradition of excellence, the Wyatt firm has been able to continually attract top legal talent and grow its business. Attorneys in the Wyatt firm adhere to their core principles of integrity, zealous representation and absolute loyalty to clients. This discipline, combined with an overriding dedication to client service, an uncompromising commitment to quality legal work and an old fashioned work ethic are hallmarks of the firm.

## Main Areas of Practice:

### Business Law:

Wyatt has active practices in the areas of banking, tax, public finance, venture capital, environment, real estate and lending, securities compliance, executive compensation, employee benefit plans and labor law. Wyatt counsels its clients over the entire life of the business – from selecting the form of business entity, to raising capital and financing growth (both public and private offerings), to taxation issues, to acquisition and sale transactions and other exit strategies. The firm represents directors, officers, majority/minority owners and entrepreneurs in connection with a wide range of business issues.

### Litigation & Dispute Resolution:

Wyatt handles all types of business litigation, including class actions, multi-district litigation and other complex litigation as well as more routine matters of business litigation in both jury and non-jury settings. The firm regularly represents the interests of major businesses, individuals, professional firms and governmental entities in all varieties of disputes, including those involving contracts, antitrust, fiduciary duties, toxic torts, tortious interference with contracts, franchises, unfair competition, regulatory law, bankruptcy and creditors' rights.

### Healthcare:

Wyatt has significant experience in all aspects of the healthcare industry including: (i) regulatory, administrative and accreditation matters such as certificates of need, licensure, HIPAA, Medicare, Medicaid and third-party reimbursement, (ii) planning and implementation regarding corporate structure, joint ventures, sales and acquisitions and tax-exempt status, and (iii) hospital / physician / patient relationships.

### Natural Resources & Environmental:

Wyatt represents owners, producers and distributors of coal, oil and gas, energy facility operators and those who provide financing, technical assistance, equipment and insurance to mineral and energy industries. The firm handles a broad range of matters such as:

acquisitions and divestitures; mineral leasing; supply contracts; real and personal property issues; labor and employment; taxes; mining agreements; and disaster response consultation. The firm also frequently handles litigation matters in these areas before state and federal courts and regulatory agencies.

### Labor & Employment:

Wyatt's labor and employment lawyers litigate for its employer clients in all areas of labor and employment law, including defending employment discrimination and wrongful discharge claims, wage and hour class and collective actions, FMLA and ADA claims, OSHA investigations and litigation and False Claims Act retaliation cases. The firm's labor lawyers also handle all aspects of union representation elections including litigating representation petition issues and unfair labor practice charges before the National Labor Relations Board, collective bargaining negotiations, and arbitrations. The firm also represents employers and their employees in immigration matters. The firm also deals with questions concerning the administration of affirmative action plans, OFCCP compliance and employer policies under federal, state and local government law. A great deal of time is spent by the firm's lawyers providing advice and counsel in all areas of labor and employment law.

### Intellectual Property:

The firm's intellectual property attorneys are responsible for matters related to the registration and licensing of trademarks and infringements of rights thereto; counseling and negotiation and documentation of transactions related to technology licensing, transfer and franchising; and patents and related matters including counseling inventors and company management on invention protection, drafting and prosecution of patent applications, infringement avoidance and litigation.

### International Trade:

The firm also has experience with international business negotiations, acquisitions and joint ventures, as well as multinational sales, distribution and licensing arrangements, protection of intellectual property and tax issues related to the foregoing.

## PRACTICE AREAS

Business Law
Litigation & Dispute Resolution
Healthcare
Natural Resources & Environmental
Labor & Employment
Intellectual Property
International Trade
Real Estate

## OFFICES

**KENTUCKY**
**LOUISVILLE:** 500 West Jefferson Street, Suite 2800, KY 40202
Tel: 502 589 5235   Fax: 502 589 0309

**LEXINGTON:** Lexington Financial Center, 250 West Main Street, Suite 1600, KY 40507
Tel: 859 233 2012  Fax: 859 259 0649

**TENNESSEE**
**MEMPHIS:** 1715 Aaron Brenner Drive, Suite 800, TN 38120
Tel: 901 537 1000  Fax: 901 537 1010

**NASHVILLE:** 2525 West End Avenue, Suite 1500, TN 37203
Tel: 615 244 0020  Fax: 615 256 1726

**INDIANA**
**NEW ALBANY:** 120 West Spring Street, 3rd Floor, IN 47150
Tel: 812 945 3561  Fax: 812 949 2524

**MISSISSIPPI**
**JACKSON:** 4450 Old Canton Road, Suite 210, MS 39211
Tel: 601 987 5300   Fax: 601 987 5353

### Real Estate:

The firm's real estate attorneys have considerable experience in all aspects of real estate development and finance, including both commercial and construction lending. The firm represents developers of real estate projects ranging in size from a few million dollars to mixed-use, multi-phased developments costing in excess of $100,000,000. The firm also regularly serves as primary or local counsel for borrowers and lenders in real estate financings.

### Clients:

Representative clients include: Churchill Downs Incorporated; E.I. duPont de Nemours; General Electric Company; Heaven Hill Distilleries; Houchens Industries, Inc., Interlock Industries; International Paper Company; JPMorgan Chase Bank N.A.; Regions Financial Corporation; Smith & Nephew, Inc.; Thorntons Inc.

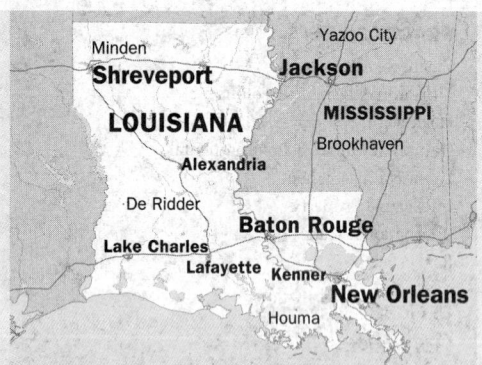

## How lawyers are ranked

Every year we carry out thousands of in-depth interviews with clients in order to assess the reputations and expertise of business lawyers worldwide. The qualities we look for (and which determine rankings) include technical legal ability, professional conduct, client service, commercial awareness/astuteness, diligence, commitment, and other qualities most valued by the client. For details of our research team, see p.5.

## LOUISIANA: An Introduction

### Contributed by Fishman Haygood Phelps Walmsley Willis & Swanson, L.L.P.

**Introduction** – Louisiana has a civil law system that is based primarily on the French, but also the Roman and Spanish systems. This renders Louisiana unique in the United States but much like most of the world's other legal systems. Louisiana's principal businesses are its oil, gas and petrochemical industries, shipping, agriculture, entertainment, and service industries. Louisiana's economy was relatively resilient during the recent economic downturn, and is experiencing significant growth in the manufacturing arena mainly due to inexpensive and available energy supplies. Tourism levels are also back near their historic highs. Louisiana's business climate has improved with reduced regulation, lowered taxes, and improved government ethics standards. Through its motion picture and film tax credit program, Louisiana has become the third-largest state for movie productions.

**Business Organizations** – Louisiana recognizes common forms of business entities, including corporations, limited liability companies, limited partnerships, and general partnerships. Partnership agreements must be in writing for a partnership to own real property in Louisiana; otherwise, the individual partners are deemed to own the property. Limited partnerships must register with the Secretary of State for the limited partners to enjoy limited liability.

**Contracts** – The law of contracts is based on provisions of the Louisiana Civil Code. There is a strict public records doctrine whereby persons, even with actual knowledge to the contrary, are not bound by the contents of documents affecting real property unless those documents are properly recorded in the public records. Generally, parties have ten years to sue for breaches of contracts, and specific performance is a favored remedy.

**State Courts** – Louisiana does not have courts in equity. Its trial courts are state district courts, the decisions of which are appealable to a circuit court of appeal. With very limited exceptions, courts of appeal decisions may be reviewed only if the Louisiana Supreme Court accepts the case.

**Creditors' Rights and Secured Transactions** – Louisiana's laws are generally lender-friendly. There are no usury restrictions for commercial transactions. Louisiana is a mortgage lien state, and has adopted Articles 8 and 9 of the Uniform Commercial Code for personal property secured transactions. Financing statements are filed locally but indexed centrally. Most creditors'

remedies require judicial action; self help is prohibited as to tangible personalty. There is no bulk sales law. Generally, creditors have five years to sue on promissory notes and three years to sue on open accounts. Attorneys' fees are not recoverable unless provided for by statute or contract.

**Oil and Gas** – Louisiana has extensive oil, natural gas and petrochemical industries with production extending into federal waters of the Gulf of Mexico. The methods of conveying and granting security interests in oil and gas properties are well developed. Louisiana does not recognize separate estates in minerals. Instead, third parties can obtain rights to explore for or produce minerals and, once captured, to convey and dispose of the minerals. Mineral rights, if owned separate from the land, may not be owned in perpetuity. Generally, an owner of mineral rights will lose them if there is no production for a period of ten years.

**Property** – Louisiana property law is uniquely civilian, and does not recognize common law estates in property. It is based on the concept of full ownership with rights of limited duration being permitted charges on full ownership. Generally one cannot own limited interests in property in perpetuity or grant continued rights on property for more than one generation. Examples include leases, mortgages, usufructs (similar to life estates), servitudes (similar to common law easements), and rights of use. Most rights are lost if not used within a ten year period. Louisiana strictly limits agreements not to partition jointly owned property.

**Sales** – Louisiana has not adopted UCC Article 2; rather, sales are governed by the Civil Code. Louisiana does not recognize common law conditional sales whereby title is retained by a vendor until payment is made. A sale is perfected when there is agreement as to the thing and the price. Unpaid sellers protect themselves by obtaining security. Also, unpaid sellers have a vendor's privilege (lien) and right to dissolve the sale if the property remains in the vendee's possession. Louisiana law imposes two general warranties in all sales: a general warranty of title and a warranty that the property is free of redhibitory (latent) defects. Both warranties can be limited through careful drafting.

**Taxation** – Louisiana has a state income tax, state and local sales taxes, mineral severance taxes, and a corporate franchise tax. The franchise tax includes borrowed capital in its calculation. There are no parish (county) or municipal income taxes or mortgage taxes in Louisiana (other than a nominal document transaction tax in New Orleans). There are numerous local and state tax incentive programs, including for low income housing, historic structures, film and theater development, new economic enterprises, Go Zone and new market tax credits.

**Torts** – Generally, claims for damages to persons and property based on tort must be filed within one year of the accident. Also, except for certain claims usu-

ally involving hazardous materials, Louisiana courts will not award punitive or exemplary damages.

**Trusts and Estates** – Louisiana does not recognize common law trusts or constructive trusts. All donations, wills, and trusts must comply with strict requirements as to form and content. Louisiana has a forced heirship doctrine requiring that children up to a certain age or having a specified condition receive a minimum amount of an estate.

# BANKING & FINANCE

Commentary about individuals can be found under their firm's paragraph. If the firm has no paragraph (is not ranked) look at Other Notable Practitioners.

| Banking & Finance |
| --- |
| **Leading Firms** |
| **Band 1** |
| Jones Walker LLP * |
| Phelps Dunbar LLP * |
| **Band 2** |
| Fishman Haygood Phelps Walmsley Willis & Swanson, L.L.P. * |
| Liskow & Lewis * |
| McGlinchey Stafford PLLC * |
| **Band 3** |
| Carver, Darden, Koretzky, Tessier, Finn, Blossman & Areaux |
| Foley & Judell LLP |
| Pettiette, Armand, Dunkelman, Woodley, Byrd & Cromwell |

| Banking & Finance | |
| --- | --- |
| **Senior Statesmen** | |
| **Senior Statesmen:** distinguished older practitioners | |
| Claverie Sr Philip deV | Phelps Dunbar LLP |
| **Leading Individuals** | |
| **Band 1** | |
| Cromwell David | Pettiette, Armand, Dunkelman, Woodley |
| Rubin Michael H | McGlinchey Stafford PLLC * |
| Stuckey James A | Phelps Dunbar LLP |
| **Band 2** | |
| Lelong Rivers | Jones Walker LLP * |
| Page Marshall | Jones Walker LLP * |
| Talley Susan G | Stone Pigman Walther Wittmann (ONP)† |
| Tessier Frank A | Carver, Darden, Koretzky, Tessier, Finn |
| Willis Sterling Scott | Fishman Haygood Phelps Walmsley Willis * |
| Wogan John D | Liskow & Lewis |
| **Band 3** | |
| Bennett Wm Blake | Liskow & Lewis |
| Brown Laura | McGlinchey Stafford PLLC * |
| Richard P Ragan | Phelps Dunbar LLP |
| Weinstock Marion | Gordon, Arata, McCollam, Duplantis (ONP)† * |
| Werner John D | Fishman Haygood Phelps Walmsley Willis * |
| **Up-and-coming individuals** | |
| Scafidel Amy Garrity | Jones Walker LLP * |
| **Associates to watch** | |
| Bernard G Wogan | Chaffe McCall, LLP (ONP)† * |

| Banking & Finance: Marine Finance | |
| --- | --- |
| **Leading Individuals** | |
| **Band 1** | |
| Arnold III Edward H (Hank) | Baker, Donelson, Bearman (ONP)† * |
| Bennett Wm Blake | Liskow & Lewis |
| Broders John J | Jones Walker LLP * |
| Duncan J Kelly | Jones Walker LLP * |
| King Henry A | King, Krebs and Jurgens PLLC (ONP)† |
| Roussel James H | Baker, Donelson, Bearman (ONP)† * |

| Banking & Finance: Public Finance | |
| --- | --- |
| **Leading Individuals** | |
| **Band 1** | |
| Chevalier Fred | Jones Walker LLP * |
| Cornelius O Ray | Adams and Reese LLP (ONP)† * |
| Hathorn Meredith L | Foley & Judell LLP |
| Leibowitz Richard D | Breazeale, Sachse & Wilson, LLP (ONP)† |
| Weeks Susan | Foley & Judell LLP |

\* Indicates firm / individual with profile.
†ONP = Other Notable Practitioner

## Band 1

### Jones Walker LLP
**See profile on p.1378**

**THE FIRM** This practice is one of the undisputed heavyweights of the Louisiana banking and finance world, and offers a comprehensive service which includes advising on corporate credit facilities, public note offerings, bonds and marine finance. Its lawyers regularly counsel state institutions, public and private companies, commercial and investment banks and other lenders. In a recent highlight it represented CenturyLink as lead counsel in a $2 billion syndicated revolving loan transaction.
**Sources say:** "The work is efficient, managed in a timely manner and gets to the heart of the subject; they understand the business side and the practicalities."
**KEY INDIVIDUALS John Broders** (see p.1358) is recognized by sources for his well-developed marine finance practice, which covers transactions, maritime liens and enforcement of mortgages. Commentators describe him as "attentive, responsive, very capable and always a pleasure to work with." **Kelly Duncan** (see p.1361) comes recommended his expertise in the maritime sector, where he undertakes mandates including maritime lien enforcement, charter parties and acquisitions. His practice also includes a strong gaming element and he is noted for operating effectively at the intersection of maritime and gaming in relation to Louisiana's riverboat casinos. Sources say: "He is a gentleman: very capable and always a pleasure to

work with." **Fred Chevalier** (see p.1359) has an active Baton Rouge-based bond practice and maintains a fine track record acting for a range of public organizations. **Marshall Page** (see p.1367) runs the firm's business and commercial transactions group. He is well versed in private equity investments and new market tax credits, as well as project finance, credit facilities and structured finance. Interviewees are quick to single him out as "very detail-oriented and very responsive." **Rivers Lelong** (see p.1365) excels in the areas of secured finance and real estate finance, regularly representing private companies, banks and real estate developers in lending and financing matters. **Amy Garrity Scafidel** (see p.1369) acts as the firm's lead lawyer when it comes to credit facility work and public note deals on behalf of publicly traded companies.

Recent work includes acting as lead counsel for Ruth's Hospitality Group on its negotiation of a $100 million senior secured credit facility. Sources describe her as "tremendous: experienced, exceptionally responsive and very knowledgeable."

### Phelps Dunbar LLP
**See profile on p.1383**

**THE FIRM** This banking and finance team is able to draw on a wealth of experience gained from its work throughout the region, representing banks, private and public companies, developers and utilities, across a vast array of financing and transactions. The group is noted for its experience throughout project finance, credit facilities, and public and structured finance, and is also known for its expertise with new market tax credits. In addition, it represents an excellent choice of counsel for clients within oil and gas, real estate, gaming and maritime.
**Sources say:** "I like the fact that they have individual specialists. We had a team of four lawyers on our transaction, all with a specific specialty."

**KEY INDIVIDUALS Philip Claverie** has an enviable reputation among both fellow attorneys and the wider Louisiana business community. He has a great deal of experience representing banks and has also carved out an impressive practice in the field of new market tax credits. *"He doesn't get caught up in chasing rabbits down holes; he knows the issues and knows what to focus on,"* asserts one highly impressed commentator. **James Stuckey** is *"a very, very good attorney who is very smart and very knowledgeable."* He maintains a fine track record for his work in banking, project finance and real estate finance. Interviewees reserve special praise for his unparalleled knowledge of Louisiana's UCC, which he has helped develop in his capacity as a member of the Louisiana State Law Institute. **Ragan Richard** is well versed in real estate finance and project finance, and is also noted for his credit facilities expertise. Sources say: *"His enthusiasm and knowledge of the business can't be duplicated and he is one hell of a negotiator."*

## Band 2

### Fishman Haygood Phelps Walmsley Willis & Swanson, L.L.P.
See profile on p.1375

**THE FIRM** This firm's strong banking practice represents both lenders and borrowers in financing transactions and is also recognized for its tax credits expertise, including new market tax credits. Among its recent highlights is its representation of Whitney Bank in the redevelopment of Saenger Theatre in New Orleans, the financing of which included handling federal tax credits, community development grant funds and Louisiana musical and theatrical production tax credits. It also counts IberiaBank, Capital One, the State of Louisiana and First Guaranty Bank among its key clients.

**KEY INDIVIDUALS Scott Willis** (see p.1371) has a focus on real estate financing and commercial finance and elicits warm praise from clients for his ability to get a transaction completed in an efficient manner. Recent work has seen him act for IberiaBank in a number of transactions involving elements such as film and historic tax credit financing. **John Werner** (see p.1371) acts for a variety of banks, investment funds, private equity firms and state institutions in financings for projects that include community health clinics and retirement homes. Recent work includes handling two Florida-based investments on behalf of Jefferson Capital Partners, a mezzanine lender which provides subordinated debt to middle-market companies. Sources say: *"He does a good job of understanding what the real practical drivers are in getting a deal done."*

### Liskow & Lewis
See profile on p.1381

**THE FIRM** Liskow & Lewis is traditionally seen as an energy powerhouse, and energy and maritime transactions have continued to be the main drivers for growth in the banking and finance department. The firm acts for a raft of banks and private equity groups and is particularly known for its expertise across credit facilities, equity and debt financings and credit restructurings.

**KEY INDIVIDUALS Blake Bennett** has an active banking and finance practice with a very strong marine finance element, and enjoys a fine reputation for his work in real estate lending, energy financing and secured transactions. *"He is a deal guy who brings a very practical approach to transactions,"* notes one impressed source. **John Wogan** remains a well-regarded figure in the Louisiana legal community and is recognized for his experience in corporate finance, project finance and bank regulatory matters. He also represents a fine choice of counsel for securitized lending transactions.

### McGlinchey Stafford PLLC
See profile on p.1382

**THE FIRM** The banking team at this firm is well known for its strengths in banking regulatory issues and consumer finance. Recent work includes advising Whitney Bank on a variety of consumer lending and banking issues, including regulatory compliance with state and federal law on loan documentation. It counts First National Bankers Bank, First NBC Bank and Harland Financial Solutions among other key clients.

Sources say: *"They are very attuned to the actual needs of banks and are familiar with both the commercial and consumer issues."*

**KEY INDIVIDUALS Michael Rubin** (see p.1369) is based in Baton Rouge and is well regarded for his deep knowledge of Louisiana banking and business law. Sources say: *"He has a great mind and understands how the law fits together and how changes in the law impact on other provisions."* **Laura Brown** (see p.1358) comes highly recommended for her banking and consumer finance expertise and regularly advises banks and other financial institutions on these issues in Louisiana and throughout the Southeast. Recent work has seen her take a leading role in Whitney Bank's matters. *"The advice we get from her is extremely practical,"* notes one satisfied client.

## Band 3

### Carver, Darden, Koretzky, Tessier, Finn, Blossman & Areaux LLC

**THE FIRM** This practice is recognized by peers for the significant amount of commercial banking work and real estate financing it carries out in New Orleans and throughout the state. Its attorneys are particularly noted for their expertise in the areas of security devices, loan agreements and debt enforcement, as well as financing transactions.

**KEY INDIVIDUALS Frank Tessier** regularly counsels banks and other lenders on a variety of transactions throughout the state and the wider region. Sources say: *"He is a gent: thorough, experienced, and a pleasure to work with."*

### Foley & Judell LLP

**THE FIRM** This boutique is home to a coterie of experienced attorneys who focus on providing clients with advice on all facets of public finance and bond issues. The group is particularly noted for its strengths in the structuring of bond issues, capital improvement financings and tax-exempt bond issues. It acts for public bodies throughout the state, including port commissions, parishes, municipalities, school boards and levee boards, in addition to acting as underwriter counsel for investment banks.

Sources say: *"They are very knowledgeable and responsive and know exactly what needs to be done going through the tax laws and various state laws."*

**KEY INDIVIDUALS Susan Weeks** is highly commended by interviewees, who consistently cite her excellent technical skills and her vast knowledge of bond issues, with one source noting: *"She is the most organized and efficient bond counsel in the state – she is preeminent."* **Meredith Hathorn** is based in Baton Rouge and is similarly highly regarded for expertise in bond matters. She elicits particular praise for her responsiveness and excellent people skills.

### Pettiette, Armand, Dunkelman, Woodley, Byrd & Cromwell LLP

**THE FIRM** This firm's banking and finance practice is considered to be one of the foremost in north Louisiana and is widely commended by its peers. It continues to be highly regarded for its expertise in real estate finance and is also highly sought for its strengths in debt collection and security agreement matters.

**KEY INDIVIDUALS David Cromwell** is widely regarded as one of the top banking lawyers in the state. *"He has an incredible memory: he is like a walking computer, he remembers the smallest details and is really good at homing in on the issues that you are after,"* notes one impressed source, who goes on to add: *"He is the kind of guy that looks for solutions – he is not 'the law doesn't let you do that,' more 'how can I solve this problem?'"*

## Other Notable Practitioners

**Hank Arnold** (see p.1357) of Baker, Donelson, Bearman, Caldwell & Berkowitz, PC has a varied practice which includes a strong element of marine financing and he regularly acts for lenders, shipyards and owners on the financing and operation of boats. Sources reserve particular praise for his calm approach to matters. **Henry King** of King, Krebs and Jurgens PLLC is active in the marine financing sector, where he has a wealth of experience representing lenders, buyers and sellers in the acquisition of companies and vessels. Commentators particularly single out his excellent client relationships. **James Roussel** (see p.1369) at Baker, Donelson, Bearman, Caldwell & Berkowitz, PC handles financing, transactions and litigation in the marine sector and regularly acts for both lenders and sellers. Sources say: *"He is one of those guys that make it all look easy."* Breazeale, Sachse & Wilson, LLP's **Richard Leibowitz** is based in Baton Rouge and is particularly commended for handling bond work for issuers, including local agencies, public trusts and political entities, in addition to acting as underwriter counsel for investment banks. **Susan Talley** is cochair of Stone Pigman Walther Wittmann LLC's real estate group, and her involvement in the banking and finance sector often stems from her active real estate lending practice. Sources describe her as *"very much an excellent lawyer"* and add that she is *"very smart, very organized and very hard-working."* Chaffe McCall, LLP's **Wogan Bernard** (see p.1358) is regarded by sources as *"a real up-and-comer"* and much of his practice involves representing lenders and developers in the financing, acquisition and sale of real estate. Sources say: *"He is focused and very responsive."* **Marion Weinstock** (see

p.1371) of Gordon, Arata, McCollam, Duplantis & Eagan LLC is highly regarded for her expertise in oil and gas financings, and financings for manufacturing groups and economic development projects. *"She catches the smallest things in documents and her work ethic is unbelievable – she can take a 300-page document and will work all night to get it done in 24 hours,"* notes one impressed interviewee. Adams and Reese LLP's **Ray Cornelius** (see p.1360) is head of the firm's public finance team and has represented

numerous public and private organizations in negotiating economic incentives and PPP. Additionally, he regularly acts as bond counsel and underwriters' counsel on bond financings. Recent highlights include acting as bond counsel for the Louisiana Utilities Restoration Corporation Project on the issuing of a $900 million Louisiana Public Facilities Authority revenue bonds.

# BANKRUPTCY/RESTRUCTURING

Commentary about individuals can be found under their firm's paragraph. If the firm has no paragraph (is not ranked) look at Other Notable Practitioners.

## Bankruptcy/Restructuring
### Leading Firms

**Band 1**
Gordon, Arata, McCollam, Duplantis & Eagan LLC *
Heller, Draper, Patrick & Horn, LLC
Jones Walker LLP *

**Band 2**
Adams and Reese LLP *
Liskow & Lewis *
McGlinchey Stafford PLLC *

**Band 3**
Carver, Darden, Koretzky, Tessier, Finn, Blossman & Areaux
Beirne, Maynard & Parsons, L.L.P *
Phelps Dunbar LLP *

## Bankruptcy/Restructuring
### Senior Statesmen

| Senior Statesmen: | distinguished older practitioners |
|---|---|
| Schiff Gerald H | *Gordon, Arata, McCollam, Duplantis* * |

### Leading Individuals

**Band 1**

| | |
|---|---|
| Draper Douglas S | *Heller, Draper, Patrick & Horn, LLC* * |
| Jones Jr Philip K | *Liskow & Lewis* |
| Patrick III William H | *Heller, Draper, Patrick & Horn, LLC* * |
| Phillips Louis | *Gordon, Arata, McCollam, Duplantis* * |
| Rubin David S | *Kantrow Spaht Weaver & Blitzer (ONP)†* |
| Steffes William E | *Steffes, Vingiello & McKenzie LLC (ONP)†* |
| Vance R Patrick | *Jones Walker LLP* * |

**Band 2**

| | |
|---|---|
| Aguilar Richard A | *McGlinchey Stafford PLLC* * |
| Cerone Rudy | *McGlinchey Stafford PLLC* * |
| Cheatham Robin B | *Adams and Reese LLP* † |
| Duck John M | *Adams and Reese LLP* † |
| Forsyth J David | *Sessions, Fishman & Nathan LLP (ONP)†* |
| Futrell Elizabeth J | *Jones Walker LLP* * |
| Goodman Alan H | *Breazeale, Sachse & Wilson, LLP (ONP)†* |
| Hayden Jan M | *Baker, Donelson, Bearman (ONP)† *|
| Hebert Joseph P | *Liskow & Lewis* |
| Hootsell III Sessions Ault | *Phelps Dunbar LLP* |
| Johnson Jr Patrick | *Beirne, Maynard & Parsons, L.L.P* * |
| Kuebel III Omer F (Rick) | *Locke Lord LLP (ONP)† *, † |
| Peck Stewart F | *Lugenbuhl, Wheaton, Peck, Rankin (ONP)†* |
| Waguespack David F | *Carver, Darden, Koretzky, Tessier, Finn* |

**Band 3**

| | |
|---|---|
| Barriere Brent B | *Fishman Haygood Phelps (ONP)† *, † |
| Finn William | *Carver, Darden, Koretzky, Tessier (ONP)†* |
| Furr Brett P | *Taylor, Porter, Brooks & Phillips, LLP* |
| Landis John M | *Stone Pigman Walther Wittmann (ONP)†* |
| Manthey Tristan E | *Heller, Draper, Patrick & Horn, LLC* * |
| Strohschein Stephen P | *McGlinchey Stafford PLLC* * |

\* *Indicates firm / individual with profile.*
† *ONP = Other Notable Practitioner*

## Band 1

### Gordon, Arata, McCollam, Duplantis & Eagan LLC
See profile on p.1377

**THE FIRM** This firm's bankruptcy practice is based on the bedrock provided by its two ex-bankruptcy judges who both get accolades from the Louisiana legal community for their skills and experience in this sector. The firm has offices in New Orleans, Lafayette and Baton Rouge and regularly handles large bankruptcies throughout the state and further afield, including before the busy Delaware bankruptcy court. The firm's large team is experienced in every facet of the bankruptcy code and has handled large Chapter 11 bankruptcies across a great many industries.
**Sources say:** *"They are outstanding."*
**KEY INDIVIDUALS Louis Phillips** (see p.1368) is considered by sources to be one of the dominant figures in the market, particularly in Baton Rouge and the western district of Louisiana. His practice includes representing both creditors and debtors and acting as a trustee, and he is described by sources as *"a very bright and creative thinker."* The well-respected **Gerald Schiff** (see p.1369) is a qualified mediator and much of his current practice involves utilizing his long experience in the bankruptcy sector to mediate cases, both in Louisiana and throughout the nation.

### Heller, Draper, Patrick & Horn, LLC
**THE FIRM** This boutique firm is unanimously considered to be the leading debtor representation group in the state. It acts for local and national companies on Chapter 11

bankruptcies and has a reputation for taking on the biggest cases in the state. It acts for a range of clients drawn from gaming, energy, financial services and real estate.
**Sources say:** *"The firm has a great reputation down in New Orleans and throughout the state."*
**KEY INDIVIDUALS Douglas Draper** (see p.1360) is cited by sources as one of the leading bankruptcy lawyers in the Gulf South, with a practice that spans creditor work and debtors' rights matters. His practice takes him around the country and sources point to a particular niche he has developed in bankruptcies involving franchises. *"Doug is just one of the most creative lawyers in the area and always does a good job,"* notes one impressed source. **William Patrick** (see p.1367) is a debtors' lawyer and focuses on issues such as litigation stemming from insolvency, restructuring debt and business reorganizations. Interviewees particularly praise him for his knowledge of bankruptcies in the casino industry. According to interviewees, *"he understands more than just the law, he understands how business operates,"* and he *"has an innate ability to develop relationships across the table."* Rising star **Tristan Manthey** (see p.1366) continues to establish himself as an important part of the firm's excellent bankruptcy practice. Sources describe him as *"smart, aggressive and hard-working,"* and add that *"he is easy to work with and doesn't pick arguments for the sake of arguments."*

### Jones Walker LLP
See profile on p.1378

**THE FIRM** This firm has offices in New Orleans, Baton Rouge and Lafayette and serves its clients across the state and in bankruptcy courts throughout the country. The lawyers at this firm take on a wide variety of work, representing clients from across the board, and are particularly noted for their work with debtors in the oil and gas and marine support industries. Market sources also recognize the firm for its strong creditor representation practice, where it acts on behalf of an impressive roster of banks and financial institutions.
**Sources say:** *"Excellent lawyers who do an excellent job."*
**KEY INDIVIDUALS Patrick Vance** (see p.1371) is respected across the region for his work in the bankruptcy arena. His practice is heavily based on creditor representa-

tion and he has been engaged by a multitude of banks and financial institutions in this area. According to his peers, *"as an opposing counsel, he is fair, courteous and analyzes issues well."* **Elizabeth Futrell** (see p.1362) is highly rated by sources, who praise her technical skills and loyalty to clients. Her practice encompasses both representing creditors and debtors, and she is frequently called as an expert witness in this area. Sources say: *"She is very meticulous – if there is an issue there she has found it."*

## Band 2

### Adams and Reese LLP
See profile on p.1372

**THE FIRM** This New Orleans-based firm has a well-regarded bankruptcy practice that extends throughout the region. The firm's lawyers are primarily known in the market for their creditor representation in commercial bankruptcies, in which they regularly represent secured creditors and trustees under bond, including banks and other financial institutions. However, the group also comes highly recommended for its strong debtor work, particularly in the oil and gas arena.
**Sources say:** *"They are super guys: good lawyers and worthy opponents."*
**KEY INDIVIDUALS Robin Cheatham** (see p.1359) is an experienced bankruptcy attorney with a strong suit in oil and gas work. He represents debtors and creditors and receives warm praise from the market for his industry knowledge and thoughtful approach to matters. **John Duck** (see p.1361) is viewed by his peers as a courteous and knowledgeable lawyer who undertakes both debtor and creditor work, although he is perhaps better known for expertise on the latter. *"He is a very talented guy who is always well prepared,"* notes one impressed commentator.

### Liskow & Lewis
See profile on p.1381

**THE FIRM** This firm operates from offices in New Orleans and Lafayette and carries out a great deal of bankruptcy work on behalf of creditors throughout Louisiana and beyond. The group acts on creditor cases, where its clients include banks, for which it also carries out large seven and eight-figure collections on commercial loans. Additionally, a large part of the group's creditor practice involves representing major oil entities following the bankruptcies of independent oil and gas companies and ancillary companies, such as marine support groups.
**Sources say:** *"They are extremely well versed in the law, extremely thorough and well prepared, very well connected and good to work with."*
**KEY INDIVIDUALS Philip Jones** has a primarily creditor-side representation practice and is praised by sources for both his writing and negotiating skills as well as for his abilities in the courtroom. *"His best attribute is that he can find a deal even when involved in a very acrimonious situation,"* reports one impressed source. Creditor lawyer **Joseph Hebert** is based in Lafayette and is recognized for

his strong understanding of the oil and gas industry. Interviewees praise his analytical and communication skills, and his ability to manage cases and clients.

### McGlinchey Stafford PLLC
See profile on p.1382

**THE FIRM** McGlinchey Stafford has offices in Baton Rouge and New Orleans, from where its attorneys handle bankruptcy cases throughout Louisiana and across the Gulf South. The firm's attorneys are largely known for creditor representation, particularly of banks and financial institutions, in addition to helping clients acquire assets out of bankruptcies. In one recent case, the firm represented IberiaBank in loans to a real estate developer of $20 million, which involved coordinating five separate foreclosures across Mississippi and Louisiana. The firm also counts HSBC, Wells Fargo and Hancock Bank among its enviable client roster.
**Sources say:** *"I am very pleased with the overall performance of the firm."*
**KEY INDIVIDUALS Stephen Strohschein** (see p.1370) is based in the firm's Baton Rouge office and largely deals with secured lender work. He represented C-3 Asset Management in a case against a franchisor after it allegedly failed to recognize the rights of its lender client in the foreclosure of a hotel. According to one impressed source, *"he is just always insightful and it doesn't take him long to grasp what is really involved in the matter and get to the heart of it."* The *"very knowledgeable"* **Rudy Cerone** (see p.1359) focuses on the representation of lenders and is regularly engaged by HSBC to defend it in multiple class actions brought by trustees and debtors. **Richard Aguilar** (see p.1357) concentrates on creditors' rights matters and comes recommended for his work on behalf of secured and unsecured creditors in bankruptcies related to a diverse array of sectors, including real estate, energy and transport. *"He is a tenacious litigator, who works extremely hard on behalf of his clients,"* reports one enthusiastic interviewee.

## Band 3

### Carver, Darden, Koretzky, Tessier, Finn, Blossman & Areaux LLC

**THE FIRM** This firm is home to a number of individuals who have the experience and ability to handle a range of bankruptcy cases on behalf of the firm's diverse client base. It mostly has a reputation as a creditor representation practice, although its lawyers are also well versed in defending debtors in convoluted Chapter 11 reorganizations and attendant litigation proceedings.
**KEY INDIVIDUALS David Waguespack** is well regarded by his peers for his creditor representation practice and interviewees cite his willingness to go out and find creative solutions for his clients as a particular strength. One source said: *"He is a very smart, capable guy. If you hire David you are going to be well represented."* **William Finn** is based in the firm's Baton Rouge office and maintains a reputation as a strong bank lawyer who appears in the bankruptcy

arena on behalf of his bank clients in creditor cases. Sources say: *"He is a good lawyer who tries to bring practicalities to the table."*

### Beirne, Maynard & Parsons, L.L.P
See profile on p.2428

**THE FIRM** This practice focuses on representing lenders, particularly banks and other financial institutions, and maintains a fine track record acting on behalf of unsecured and secured creditors, and lessees and lessors, on large Chapter 11 and Chapter 12 cases. The practice is well versed in bankruptcy matters concerning gaming, healthcare, real estate, and leisure and hospitality; in a recent highlight it acted for Colonial Finance, which was a secured lender in the bankruptcy of a country club. The group also counts Capital One, PNC Bank and US Bank among its distinguished client list.
**Sources say:** *"They respect the entire process and everyone in the process, not just the client but the opposing counsel and judges; they are all around a great firm."*
**KEY INDIVIDUALS Patrick Johnson** (see p.1364) is predominantly known for representing banks and other financial institutions and is respected for his abilities both in and outside the courtroom. He represented Capital One in a farm bankruptcy under Chapter 12 of Title 11 of the US Code and filed an action outside the bankruptcy court against the guarantors of the farm. *"He is a very good lawyer: very detail-oriented; he understands the bankruptcy code very well and thinks through complex problems very methodically,"* asserts one impressed commentator.

### Phelps Dunbar LLP
See profile on p.1383

**THE FIRM** This practice continues to enjoy a fine reputation in the region, despite the recent departure of partner Brent Barriere. From offices in Baton Rouge and New Orleans, it handles bankruptcy and related litigation across the Gulf South. It predominantly focuses on the representation of creditors, including banks and noninstitutional lenders, and is noted for its work on behalf of trustees and creditors bringing claims against officers and directors for breaches of fiduciary duties.
**KEY INDIVIDUALS Sessions Ault Hootsell** *"knows what he's doing"* when it comes to handling a bankruptcy matter in court, report interviewees. He principally acts on behalf of creditors and elicits much praise for his wealth of knowledge.

## Other Notable Practitioners

**David Rubin** of Kantrow Spaht Weaver & Blitzer is based in Baton Rouge and represents clients across the board, including secured and unsecured creditors, trustees, bondholders and debtors, in Chapter 11 bankruptcy cases and related litigation. *"He is the whole package – definitely a first-rate lawyer,"* reports one commentator, while another was quick to afford him praise for his drive to recover assets for creditor clients, saying: *"He is like a dog that won't let go of your ankle."* **William Steffes** of Steffes, Vingiello & McKenzie LLC is described by sources as the leading debtors' lawyer in Baton Rouge. He handles Chapter 11 bankruptcies and reorganizations in Louisiana and in courts across the country, as well as undertaking creditor committee work. According to one interviewee, "*he is smart, creative, and he is aggressive without coming across as aggressive.*" **Jan Hayden** (see p.1363) of Baker, Donelson, Bearman, Caldwell & Berkowitz, PC is well versed in handling matters for both debtors and creditors, and comes particularly recommended for her assistance with reorganizations following Chapter 11 bankruptcies. "*She is a really good courtroom manager and has a good negotiating style; she gets deals done with the minimum acrimony,*" notes one impressed source. Sessions, Fishman & Nathan LLP's **David Forsyth** is a well-known creditors' lawyer based in New Orleans. He handles work on behalf of unsecured creditors and lessors and has developed a particular niche in dealing with shopping center bankruptcies. As one source reports: "*He is very thoughtful, has very good emo-*

*tional control and is very comfortable in resolving issues.*" **Alan Goodman** of Breazeale, Sachse & Wilson, LLP is particularly noted for secured lender work, but is also routinely called upon to handle trustee issues, unsecured creditor representation and large debtor cases. "*Experience is his strongest suit,*" asserts one interviewee, who adds: "*He has handled a lot of large bankruptcies and has seen most everything you could see and always has a ready solution to problems.*" Locke Lord LLP's **Rick Kuebel** (see p.1365) is an experienced creditors' lawyer with a deep understanding of the oil and gas industry. Sources say: "*He knows the code and is a superb negotiator.*" The "*very talented*" **John Landis** of Stone Pigman Walther Wittmann LLC is noted for his wealth of experience, serving as debtors' and lenders' counsel on behalf of clients involved in Chapter 11 bankruptcies and in the litigation that can ensue. Creditors' lawyer **Brett Furr** of Taylor, Porter, Brooks & Phillips, LLP represents clients such as banks and other financial institutions in

bankruptcies and foreclosures and is regarded by sources as "*a very knowledgeable and experienced lawyer in this arena.*" **Stewart Peck** of Lugenbuhl, Wheaton, Peck, Rankin & Hubbard is based in New Orleans and has a fine reputation as a debtors' lawyer. He is particularly well known for his work in the oil and gas industry and receives praise for his strategy, attention to detail and doggedness on matters. **Brent Barriere** (see p.1357) has recently joined Fishman Haygood Phelps Walmsley Willis & Swanson, L.L.P. from Phelps Dunbar. He practices in the area of creditors' rights, where he has developed a particular niche representing trustees and creditors in bringing claims against company executives in the aftermath of bankruptcies. According to one impressed source, "*he is a good lawyer who knows where the bankruptcy court is and knows what he is doing when he is there.*"

# CONSTRUCTION

Commentary about individuals can be found under their firm's paragraph. If the firm has no paragraph (is not ranked) look at Other Notable Practitioners.

| Construction |
| --- |
| **Leading Firms** |
| **Band 1** |
| Baker, Donelson, Bearman, Caldwell & Berkowitz, PC * |
| Krebs, Farley & Pelleteri PLLC * |
| **Band 2** |
| Breazeale, Sachse & Wilson, LLP |
| Deutsch, Kerrigan & Stiles LLP |
| Jones Walker LLP * |
| Phelps Dunbar LLP * |
| Simon, Peragine, Smith & Redfearn |
| **Band 3** |
| Adams and Reese LLP * |
| Gordon, Arata, McCollam, Duplantis & Eagan LLC * |

* Indicates firm / individual with profile.
Alphabetical order within each band. Band 1 is the highest.

| Construction | | |
| --- | --- | --- |
| **Leading Individuals** | | |
| **Star individuals** | | |
| Shaw Danny | Baker, Donelson, Bearman, Caldwell * | |
| **Band 1** | | |
| Brennan Terrence L | Deutsch, Kerrigan & Stiles LLP | |
| Shreves Bruce | Simon, Peragine, Smith & Redfearn | |
| Tyler Richard J | Jones Walker LLP * | |
| **Band 2** | | |
| Bergeron Keith J | Deutsch, Kerrigan & Stiles LLP | |
| Botnick Michael | Gordon, Arata, McCollam, Duplantis * | |
| Clary Albert Dale | Long Law Firm LLP (ONP)† * | |
| Foster, III Murphy J | Breazeale, Sachse & Wilson, LLP | |
| Franco Philip A | Adams and Reese LLP * | |
| Hunt Michael D | Phelps Dunbar LLP | |
| Krebs David J | Krebs, Farley & Pelleteri PLLC * | |
| Kurtz David | Baker, Donelson, Bearman, Caldwell * | |
| Loeb Steven B | Breazeale, Sachse & Wilson, LLP | |
| Puente Denise | Simon, Peragine, Smith & Redfearn | |
| Shields Lloyd N | Shields Mott Lund L.L.P. (ONP)† | |
| **Up-and-coming individuals** | | |
| Andrishok John T | Breazeale, Sachse & Wilson, LLP | |
| Funes Kelsey | Phelps Dunbar LLP | |
| Mercante Mark W | Baker, Donelson, Bearman, Caldwell * | |

†ONP = Other Notable Practitioner

**Sources say:** "*They have an excellent construction practice and they know how to get to an efficient resolution of very complex matters.*"

**KEY INDIVIDUALS Danny Shaw** (see p.1369) is the preeminent construction litigator in Louisiana. He has a strong construction background and is a licensed profes-

## Band 1

### Baker, Donelson, Bearman, Caldwell & Berkowitz, PC
See profile on p.2313

**THE FIRM** This top-notch construction practice is home to a number of highly experienced litigators who are praised by sources for their legal skills and technical knowledge of the construction industry. The bench strength of the practice and the experience of its leading partners give the team the ability to handle large and intricate litigation cases on a nationwide basis. Particular areas of strength include design professional liability and insurance defense and coverage.

sional engineer, which gives him an additional insight into the technical aspects of cases. As one source says: "*He is one of the most engaging and friendliest people you could ever meet. A terrific personality coupled with great skill.*" The highly regarded **David Kurtz**'s (see p.1365) practice combines traditional construction litigation with post-Katrina litigation, involving issues such as representing contractors in disputes and injury cases and making claims for contractors against insurers. **Mark Mercante** (see p.1366) is an up-and-coming construction litigator based in the firm's Mandeville office. Sources say: "*His grasp of construction issues is excellent. He is very responsive, very efficient and effective,*" asserts one enthusiastic interviewee.

### Krebs, Farley & Pelleteri PLLC
See profile on p.1380

**THE FIRM** This New Orleans firm is unanimously regarded as the leading surety bond defense practice in the state. The firm counsels surety clients in claims made against them, and its lawyers are recognized as highly adept litigators on their behalf. Areas of particular expertise include dealing with bond claims following construction defaults, Miller Act litigation and interpreting the bond rights of the various parties in a project.

**Sources say:** "*A top-notch firm of very good surety lawyers.*"
**KEY INDIVIDUALS David Krebs** (see p.1365) enjoys a fine reputation as a surety lawyer and elicits much praise from the market for his knowledge of the construction industry. "*The characteristics that make him a particularly effective surety lawyer are that he is a very effective communicator and he recognizes that the greatest benefit he can provide is to help folks avoid litigation,*" says one highly impressed commentator.

## Band 2

### Breazeale, Sachse & Wilson, LLP

THE FIRM Breazeale Sachse is seen as particularly strong in its Baton Rouge heartland but covers the whole state from additional outposts in New Orleans and Covington. Clients are impressed by the firm's ability to prevent matters reaching litigation through contract negotiation, contract review and the provision of training and advice. The firm's lawyers are equally adept in litigation, and recently won $3 million in damages for its client, M. Matt Durand, a contractor which sued over a cardinal change in estimated quantities needed for a project. The firm's client list includes ISC Constructors, Baton Rouge Metropolitan Airport, Chenevert Architects and the City of Alexandria. Sources say: "We find that attention to detail is very good." "Breazeale's attorneys are knowledgeable in the different areas of expertise which allows for quick responses."

KEY INDIVIDUALS Murphy Foster is noted for his reputation in the sector representing contractors and contractors' associations. In one recent highlight, he represented a contractor who had built a water treatment plant and was bringing claims against the owner and engineer of the plant. After a jury trial the court found the engineer liable for $1 million in damages. "He is a very astute guy. His approach is: this is the problem and these are the solutions and let's move on," asserts one impressed source. Steven Loeb is a well-regarded construction litigator who is particularly respected for his deep technical knowledge and detail-oriented approach, as well as for his ability as a negotiator and a courtroom lawyer. He is a trained architect and, as such, a great deal of his practice involves representing architects in litigation. John Andrishok is a construction litigator who regularly pursues and defends claims against contractors in issues such as contract disputes and construction defect claims. He was involved in Millennium Partners v Millennium Construction, in which the practice negotiated a $5 million settlement over a construction project in North Dakota. Sources say: "He is an excellent, excellent construction lawyer with a good temperament for the practice."

### Deutsch, Kerrigan & Stiles LLP

THE FIRM This firm has offices in New Orleans and Monroe and has long been considered a leading light among the firms that handle construction litigation in Louisiana. Sources point to the firm's large portfolio of traditional commercial construction work, which includes matters such as bid and contract disputes, Miller Act claims and architect and design error cases. In addition to longstanding experience of construction litigation, a number of the firm's lawyers have relevant qualifications and experience in fields such as architecture and engineering. Sources say: "I am very impressed with them. They have a lot of technical knowledge, which can be even more important than the legal knowledge in construction matters."

KEY INDIVIDUALS Terrence Brennan's peers speak highly of his knowledge and experience and consider him to be one of the best construction litigators in the state. He acts on behalf of architects, owners, surveyors, contractors

and suppliers in both pure construction litigation and in construction surety matters. Sources say: "He is a phenomenally good lawyer. He is the whole package; he knows the industry from the technical side as well as the lawyer side." Keith Bergeron worked as a mechanical engineer prior to practicing law, which is experience that has stood him in good stead for his construction law practice, where he has a particular niche in design professional malpractice cases. He receives much praise for his preparation when it comes to matters.

### Jones Walker LLP
See profile on p.1378

THE FIRM This firm, one of the largest in the state, has offices in Lafayette, New Orleans and Baton Rouge and handles transactional and litigation matters for its construction clients on a regional basis. Clients are impressed by the technical knowledge of the firm's attorneys and the scope and depth of the legal research they carry out. Jones Walker's construction clients include oil and gas companies, commercial construction companies, and industrial and electrical contractors.

Sources say: "They are very knowledgeable and they don't get intimidated by the other side."

KEY INDIVIDUALS Richard Tyler (see p.1370) is the head of the firm's construction team and takes the lead on transactional and litigation matters for its clients. Sources say: "He is very intelligent, highly qualified, his attention to detail is great and he understands the law and how it applies to business very well."

### Phelps Dunbar LLP
See profile on p.1383

THE FIRM This firm's Baton Rouge office is known for its construction litigation practice, which regularly handles matters such as bid disputes, industrial construction matters and the negotiation of construction contracts. The practice acts for clients from across the industry, including owners, contractors, subcontractors, insurers and design professionals. The firm represented the defendant in Kinder Morgan Louisiana Pipeline v AMEC Paragon, a dispute over an interstate oil pipeline where the plaintiff claimed damages for alleged engineering and construction errors. Key clients include Excel, W.G. Yates & Sons Construction and Breckenridge Group.

Sources say: "They know the business very well and are very able opponents."

KEY INDIVIDUALS Michael Hunt is based in Baton Rouge and handles construction litigation and transactional matters. He acted for the defendant in Americas Styrenics v Excel, a dispute over damages after a gas supply line to a factory was damaged during construction activity. The plaintiff sued for the economic loss occasioned by the shutdown of the plant and the case was settled prior to trial. He draws particular praise for his "thorough and detail-oriented" approach to matters. Kelsey Funes is noted by sources as an up-and-coming construction litigator who is on her way to becoming a real player in the Louisiana construction sector. Her practice ranges over the entirety of the construction sector, including claims

involving construction defects, lien claims, inefficiency claims and an increasing amount of public bid protest work. Sources say she is "very easy to deal with, very knowledgeable and very straightforward."

### Simon, Peragine, Smith & Redfearn

THE FIRM This firm's construction practice is strong in both transactional and dispute resolution matters, acting for a wealth of clients across the country including owners, contractors, insurers and designers. The team is based in New Orleans and its lawyers advise clients on all aspects of the construction process, from contract negotiations to post-completion litigation. The group is particularly noted for its expertise in disputes, ranging from defect and inefficiency claims to delay and professional negligence cases.

KEY INDIVIDUALS Bruce Shreves is seen as one of the leading lights of the Louisiana construction Bar. Much of his practice is based on alternative dispute resolution in construction cases and he is widely respected as an arbitrator and a mediator. "He approaches legal matters from an intellectual standpoint and is a fine, fine lawyer," note sources. Denise Puente represents owners and contractors in transactional matters in the surety and construction fields. Additionally, she litigates on behalf of clients in matters such as public bid disputes. "She is a phenomenally good transactional lawyer. She is very, very good at contract development, negotiation and dispute avoidance," notes one impressed commentator.

## Band 3

### Adams and Reese LLP
See profile on p.1372

THE FIRM This firm has offices in New Orleans and Baton Rouge from which its lawyers handle transactional and dispute resolution construction matters throughout the region. The group represents a wide range of clients in the sector including municipalities, developers, contractors and subcontractors, architects, engineers and owners. In one recent matter, the firm acted for Olshan Foundation Repair in an arbitration after a plaintiff claimed damages for the subsidence of a building, allegedly caused by the faulty underpinning of a wall. The firm's client was found to be without fault, no damages were awarded and partial underpinning of a wall was deemed an acceptable practice. Among its other key clients are Siemens, Humana Insurance, Hard Rock Construction and Entergy Louisiana.

KEY INDIVIDUALS The highly regarded Philip Franco (see p.1361) is representing Cajun Elevation & Shoring in an administrative hearing before the state's Office of Community Development on an alleged violation of the rules concerning home elevations. He also led on the Olshan Foundation Repair matter.

## Gordon, Arata, McCollam, Duplantis & Eagan LLC

See profile on p.1377

**THE FIRM** Gordon Arata has offices in New Orleans, Baton Rouge and Lafayette and counsels clients on contract negotiation and dispute resolution in construction cases. The team represents a number of large public and private entities as well as smaller construction and architectural groups. Its attorneys are able to oversee the entire legal process of construction projects from initial document preparation through arbitration, mediation and, if necessary, litigation.

**Sources say:** *"I like the level of expertise and their practical approach; they always have our interests at heart."*

**KEY INDIVIDUALS Michael Botnick** (see p.1358) is noted for his construction litigation strengths on behalf of clients in the public and private sectors. Peers praise his pragmatic approach to disputes and his focus on reaching the best solution for clients, whether by a negotiated settlement or litigation. Sources say: *"He is very good at breaking it down, anticipating issues before they happen and coming up with practical solutions that avoid wasting time and money."*

### Other Notable Practitioners

**Albert Clary** (see p.1360) of Long Law Firm LLP is based in Baton Rouge and has a construction litigation practice which is heavily focused on representing engineers and designers. Sources say: *"He is a good pragmatic lawyer, he knows the business, he knows the law, he can be a bulldog when he needs to be but can also serve his clients by being a facilitator."* At Shields Mott Lund L.L.P. the highly regarded **Lloyd Shields** is noted for his expertise in surety law, construction contracts, insurance defense and professional defense. He handles alternative dispute resolution cases in addition to practicing in court, where he has a reputation as an aggressive and effective litigator.

# CORPORATE/M&A

Commentary about individuals can be found under their firm's paragraph. If the firm has no paragraph (is not ranked) look at Other Notable Practitioners.

## Corporate/M&A
### Leading Firms

**Band 1**
Fishman Haygood Phelps Walmsley Willis & Swanson, L.L.P. *
Jones Walker LLP *

**Band 2**
Kantrow Spaht Weaver & Blitzer
Stone Pigman Walther Wittmann LLC

**Band 3**
Baker, Donelson, Bearman, Caldwell & Berkowitz, PC *
Kean Miller LLP *
Liskow & Lewis *
McGlinchey Stafford PLLC *
Phelps Dunbar LLP *

*Indicates firm / individual with profile.*
*Alphabetical order within each band. Band 1 is the highest.*

## Corporate/M&A
### Senior Statesmen

**Senior Statesmen: distinguished older practitioners**

| | |
|---|---|
| Haygood Paul M | Fishman Haygood Phelps Walmsley Willis * |

### Leading Individuals

**Band 1**

| | |
|---|---|
| Fishman Louis Y | Fishman Haygood Phelps Walmsley Willis * |
| Fullmer Mark A | Phelps Dunbar LLP |
| Hearn Curtis R | Jones Walker LLP * |
| Kantrow Lee | Kantrow Spaht Weaver & Blitzer |

**Band 2**

| | |
|---|---|
| Caverly Joseph L | Stone Pigman Walther Wittmann LLC |
| Clark Blane | Kean Miller LLP * |
| Norton William N | Baker, Donelson, Bearman, Caldwell * |
| Rousseau Dionne M | Jones Walker LLP * |
| Walmsley Robert | Fishman Haygood Phelps Walmsley Willis * |
| Whittaker Scott T | Stone Pigman Walther Wittmann LLC |

**Band 3**

| | |
|---|---|
| Aguilar Jr Rodolfo J | McGlinchey Stafford PLLC * |
| Fantaci James M | Chehardy, Sherman, Ellis, Murray (ONP)[†] |
| Najder Kenneth | Jones Walker LLP * |
| Reymond III Leon J | Liskow & Lewis |
| Robinson Michael | Kantrow Spaht Weaver & Blitzer |
| Wogan John D | Liskow & Lewis |
| Wolfe Richard | Jones Walker LLP * |

**Band 4**

| | |
|---|---|
| DiLeo Anthony M | Anthony M DiLeo (ONP)[†] |
| Miller Jr Ben R | Kean Miller LLP * |
| Perrault Jean-Paul | McGlinchey Stafford PLLC * |
| Werner John D | Fishman Haygood Phelps Walmsley Willis * |

**Up-and-coming individuals**

| | |
|---|---|
| Chenevert Scott D | Jones Walker LLP * |
| Gershanik Maureen | Fishman Haygood Phelps Walmsley Willis * |
| Rieveschl David | Baker, Donelson, Bearman, Caldwell * |

## Corporate/M&A: Tax
### Leading Individuals

**Star individuals**

| | |
|---|---|
| Casey Robert | Jones Walker LLP * |

**Band 1**

| | |
|---|---|
| Backstrom William | Jones Walker LLP * |
| Dicharry Christopher | Kean Miller LLP * |
| Exnicios James C | Liskow & Lewis |
| Klein Steven | Sher Garner Cahill Richter Klein (ONP)[†] |
| Ramelli Rudolph R | Jones Walker LLP * |

**Band 2**

| | |
|---|---|
| Angelico Robert S | Liskow & Lewis |
| Cassidy David R | Breazeale, Sachse & Wilson, LLP (ONP)[†] |
| Koonce Jeffrey | Phelps Dunbar LLP |

[†]*ONP = Other Notable Practitioner*

## Band 1

### Fishman Haygood Phelps Walmsley Willis & Swanson, L.L.P.

See profile on p.1375

**THE FIRM** This firm's corporate group is regarded as one of the best in the region for handling complex M&A transactions and for providing public and private companies with strategic corporate advice. Its lawyers have been particularly active in corporate and transactional matters with elements of tax credit financing, most notably in film, theater, digital media and renewable energy. Its lawyers advised Home Bancorp on its expansion in Louisiana and acquisition of Guaranty Savings Bank in New Orleans. The group also counts Capital One Southcoast, Louisiana Sports and Entertainment District, Genesis Offshore and Rouses Supermarkets among its key clients.

**Sources say:** *"The work is meticulous and we always recommend them for transactions."*

**KEY INDIVIDUALS Louis Fishman** (see p.1361) is one of the most well-known and well-respected transactional attorneys in Louisiana. He has advised Sanderson Farms on a wide range of matters, including financing, securities law compliance, corporate governance and risk management. Sources say: *"He has a ton of experience – he is a* hard-working guy and a practical lawyer." *"Top transactional lawyer"* **Robert Walmsley** (see p.1371) practices widely in the business sphere, advising clients on financing, securities and general business matters. He advised SMG on the negotiation of the lease of the Mercedes-Benz Superdome by the New Orleans Saints and the lease of the New Orleans Arena to New Orleans Hornets. **John Werner** (see p.1371) is a noted transactional and corporate lawyer, who has of late been particularly active advising private equity funds and their clients on the negotiation and structuring of private equity transactions. Sources highlight his ability to *"come up with practical solutions"* and also praise his advice, which *"is always sound from a practical business standpoint."* Of counsel **Paul Haygood** (see p.1363) is esteemed by peers for his long track record, advising businesses on issues such as corporate law, M&A transactions and securities, among others. *"He will help you find a way to solve your problems rather than creating problems,"* reports one interviewee. Rising star **Maureen Gershanik** (see p.1362) advises clients on corporate restructuring, public and private offerings of debt and equity, and securities regulatory compliance. She is the lead partner in the firm's relationship with Capital One Southcoast, which she has counseled on a range of issues relating to FINRA and SEC regulatory matters.

## Jones Walker LLP

See profile on p.1378

**THE FIRM** Peers view this firm as a leader in the state by virtue of the volume and quality of the corporate and transactional work handled by its business department. The firm represents a number of publicly traded companies in corporate and securities matters, in addition to acting as corporate, securities and general counsel to privately held companies throughout the Gulf South. The firm is very active in the transactional arena, and represents clients such as buyers from out-of-state looking to acquire Louisiana businesses, public companies looking to acquire or dispose of assets, and privately held companies looking to make acquisitions, particularly in the energy sector. **Sources say:** *"It is probably the law firm with the best public company practice in the state."*

**KEY INDIVIDUALS Robert Casey** (see p.1359) is well respected for his work advising clients on federal, state and local tax matters. He also has a fine reputation for dealing with the tax aspects of M&A, with one source noting: *"He just quotes the tax code off his head."* State and local tax group head **William Backstrom** (see p.1357) is regularly involved in advising clients on tax planning, the use of business incentives, and litigation against the state. In addition to advising clients and handling litigation, his practice has a strong lobbying and government relations aspect, and he regularly lobbies on behalf of clients with concerns about the impact of proposed taxes on their industries. *"He is considered to be a leading state and local sales tax attorney in this state and he sure proved it with us,"* notes one satisfied client. **Curtis Hearn** (see p.1364) heads the corporate and securities group and regularly represents corporations, lenders, private equity and venture capital firms in all aspects of M&A transactions. One happy client asserts: *"He wants what is best for our company and sees our company's success as an extension of his own success."* The *"very talented"* **Rudolph Ramelli**'s (see p.1368) practice centers on corporate and partnership federal income tax issues. Sources say: *"He is a leader in the Bar as far as working to make sure that tax issues and tax changes are properly handled by the state of Louisiana."* **Dionne Rousseau** (see p.1368) is based in the firm's Baton Rouge office and provides corporate and securities advice to public and private companies. She has a broad corporate and securities practice, which includes advising on transactional matters and assisting clients with issues such as corporate governance and securities regulatory compliance. Sources praise her responsiveness and strong subject matter experience. **Kenneth Najder** (see p.1367) is a corporate and securities lawyer and is renowned for his meticulous understanding of the subject. His main spheres of activity include corporate finance, venture capital transactions, joint ventures, corporate governance and M&A. *"Ken does a really good job of playing devil's advocate with the client, putting on the opposition hat and giving you a touch of reality when you are trying to put together a deal,"* notes one impressed client.

**Richard Wolfe** (see p.1371) practices in the area of corporate and securities law and is well versed in M&A transactions, venture capital transactions, tender offers and public equity offerings. *"Rising star"* **Scott Chenevert** (see p.1359) recently acted for Superior Energy Services on its $320 million acquisition of Complete Productions Services. *"He is responsive and very businesslike, and I enjoy working with him,"* notes one interviewee.

## Band 2

## Kantrow Spaht Weaver & Blitzer

**THE FIRM** Kantrow Spaht's corporate and business department impresses interviewees with its high-quality work. This Baton Rouge firm is home to 21 attorneys, with a great depth of expertise in matters such as M&A, general corporate law and securities law. The group maintains a fine track record acting for both public and private companies, most notably in healthcare, banking, insurance and construction.

**KEY INDIVIDUALS Lee Kantrow** is viewed as the driving force behind the corporate group and is respected by sources for his calm approach to issues. He is noted for his corporate and securities advice to healthcare organizations, telecom companies, banks and insurers, among other clients. Sources say: *"He is very thorough and he doesn't practice without a full range of knowledge as to what he is dealing with."* **Michael Robinson** is singled out by peers as one of the firm's key lawyers, and is noted for his experience in M&A and securities matters. *"He is a calm, level-headed guy, who is practical about what needs to get done and doesn't take unreasonable positions,"* notes one impressed commentator.

## Stone Pigman Walther Wittmann LLC

**THE FIRM** This corporate team advises public and private companies on the full range of legal issues in areas such as securities law, M&A, corporate restructurings, and stock and asset sales. In one recent highlight the firm acted as Louisiana counsel for Chicago Bridge & Iron on its $2 billion purchase of the Shaw Group. Other key clients include Capital Health Services, Pelican Finance, Star Enterprises and Taste Buds.

**Sources say:** *"They don't throw legalese at me – they help me understand things in basic business terms, so that I can make good decisions based upon their recommendations."*

**KEY INDIVIDUALS Joseph Caverly** chairs the corporate and securities practice and elicits praise from sources for his personable and meticulous approach to matters. One impressed interviewee noted: *"He does a really good job of thinking forward and pointing out the potential ramifications down the road. This gives me a degree of comfort when making long-term decisions."* **Scott Whittaker** is noted for his strength in M&A, private equity and venture capital transactions, and is also recommended for his expertise in corporate structuring matters. In one recent transaction he represented the owners of a number of healthcare facilities in the sale of the controlling interest in those businesses to private equity firm Elm Creek Partners. *"He always tries to*

*find a way to make things happen; he is a 'can do' kind of lawyer and clients like that about him,"* asserts one enthusiastic commentator.

## Band 3

## Baker, Donelson, Bearman, Caldwell & Berkowitz, PC

See profile on p.2313

**THE FIRM** This firm services its corporate clients in Louisiana from offices in Baton Rouge, New Orleans and Mandeville. The team handles a plethora of issues, including stock purchases, stock offerings, and the disposal of assets and subsidiaries. Clients include Our Lady of the Lake Regional Hospital, Hall-deGravelles, Entergy, and CSX.

**KEY INDIVIDUALS** Of counsel **William Norton** (see p.1367) is based in the New Orleans office and is much sought for his expertise in M&A, capital formation, business reorganizations and takeover defense. Sources say: *"He is a really smart guy and a good negotiator; he is a good thinker and he is able to work his way through problems and come up with common-sense solutions."* **David Rieveschl** (see p.1368) is an up-and-coming lawyer in the firm's corporate department and is noted for his strengths in M&A and in issues concerning securities law compliance.

## Kean Miller LLP

See profile on p.1379

**THE FIRM** This firm serves clients from its Baton Rouge headquarters and additional outposts in Lake Charles and New Orleans. The firm's corporate and transactional team is noted for its expertise in M&A, securities work, corporate structuring, joint ventures and entity formation. Its recent work has included helping industrial clients with capital expansion, and handling acquisitions of companies and assets for public and private organizations. The group is particularly recommended for its knowledge and experience across a diverse range of industries, including oil and gas, banking, advertising, and food and agriculture.

**KEY INDIVIDUALS Christopher Dicharry** (see p.1360) has a good reputation at the bar for his state and local tax work, representing clients in the state courts and before the Louisiana Tax Commission and the Louisiana Board of Tax Appeals. Additionally, sources highlight his abilities as a lobbyist and particularly value his connections with decision makers at the Department of Revenue. Department head **Blane Clark** (see p.1360) has a varied practice covering M&A, sales of stocks and shares, among other areas, and helping companies to expand their capital base. Sources say: *"He is calm and thoughtful, and a good lawyer to work with to get things done."* Firm founding member and of counsel **Ben Miller** (see p.1367) practices law in Baton Rouge with a focus on M&A, commercial lending transactions, and the provision of general corporate advice.

## Liskow & Lewis
See profile on p.1381

**THE FIRM** This firm has offices in Lafayette and New Orleans, from where it advises clients on the full spectrum of business issues including tax, corporate structure, M&A, and securities. It is particularly strong in the energy and maritime areas, and is also noted for its work in heavy industry.

**KEY INDIVIDUALS** The well-regarded **James Exnicios** concentrates on federal, state and local tax issues. He regularly provides tax advice to businesses and continues to be much in demand for his litigation expertise, providing representation in the courts and before the IRS and the State of Louisiana Department of Revenue. **Robert Angelico** is chair of the state and local tax group and has a fine reputation in the market assisting clients with Louisiana tax matters. He is also routinely called upon for his skills in tax-based disputes and appeals. The *"very skilled and knowledgeable"* **John Wogan** has a broad-based practice that spans banking, real estate and corporate work. He is particularly recommended for his expertise in corporate restructurings. **Leon Reymond** recently joined the firm from Stone Pigman Walther Wittman. He handles a wide variety of work in the corporate sphere, including M&A, corporate structuring and private equity transactions.

## McGlinchey Stafford PLLC
See profile on p.1382

**THE FIRM** This firm services its clients from offices in Baton Rouge, New Orleans and Monroe. It is particularly well known for its consumer finance and insurance regulatory practices, and a great deal of the corporate and transactional work that the firm handles involves elements of these practice areas. The firm acted for GM on setting up an aftermarket sales division, which involved structuring the new program before its nationwide rollout. Other key clients include Boyd Gaming, Louisiana Sugar Refining, DePuy Orthopedics and Toyota Financial Services.

**Sources say:** *"What I have appreciated is that you can call them and they give you general thoughts quickly and off the cuff – they don't require extensive research because they are so familiar with the subject matter."*

**KEY INDIVIDUALS** Managing partner **Rodolfo Aguilar** (see p.1357) represented Bossier Casino Venture in a $200 million casino development, handling issues including corporate structuring, financing and contract negotiation. *"He's the easiest attorney I have ever worked with in a deal and he knows how to cut to the core issues,"* noted one impressed interviewee. **Jean-Paul Perrault** (see p.1367) is noted for his insurance regulatory expertise, in addition to his general corporate work. He has recently advised clients such as Mercedes-Benz Financial Services and GM Financial on corporate and regulatory issues. According to one satisfied client, *"he was very approachable and responsive, his baseline knowledge was very good and he was able to field my questions and help me through nuances in the law that I wasn't clear about."*

## Phelps Dunbar LLP
See profile on p.1383

**THE FIRM** This firm operates from bases in New Orleans and Baton Rouge, and handles corporate and tax work for clients in industries such as banking, oil and gas and software. Recent work includes representing LLOG Exploration Company in its acquisition of a $500 million semi-submersible floating platform from a seller in Belgium. Other key clients include Technip Offshore International, Investar Bank, Schedulist.com and Audubon Capital.

**Sources say:** *"They do an excellent job: whatever you get dragged into they always pull really good, competent guys out who can deal with all the issues."*

**KEY INDIVIDUALS Mark Fullmer** is an M&A and securities attorney who is held in high regard by clients and peers alike. Among his recent work, he represented M.G. Maher & Co in its $20 million sale to Livingston International. Sources praise his ability to close difficult deals, with one noting: *"Mark has a knack for defusing the tension and getting transactions to work – he is a lawyer that makes it happen."* Tax lawyer **Jeffrey Koonce** focuses on federal taxation, and commercial transactions and business formations. A recent highlight saw him oversee the tax issues in Investar Bank's $12 million acquisition of South Louisiana Business Bank. *"He is very knowledgeable – he gets the answers when I need them and they are good answers,"* reports one happy client.

### Other Notable Practitioners

**David Cassidy** of Breazeale, Sachse & Wilson, LLP in Baton Rouge maintains a fine reputation among peers for his state and local tax work. In addition to advising on tax matters, he assists clients with administrative claims and litigation. Sole practitioner **Anthony DiLeo** is based in New Orleans and focuses on corporate transactions, arbitration and litigation. *"In any complex matter where the issues are not completely crystal clear, he is always my first choice because of his ability to see through the issues and find a solution,"* asserts one source. **Steven Klein** of Sher Garner Cahill Richter Klein & Hilbert LLC is a well-regarded tax lawyer based in New Orleans. Commentators particularly praise his federal taxation practice, and note his knowledge of Subchapter S laws. The *"very knowledgeable"* **James Fantaci** of Chehardy, Sherman, Ellis, Murray, Recile, Griffith, Stakelum & Hayes LLP is a corporate and transactional attorney who operates out of Metairie. Sources reserve particular praise for his documentation work and ability to handle complex concepts.

# ENERGY & NATURAL RESOURCES

Commentary about individuals can be found under their firm's paragraph. If the firm has no paragraph (is not ranked) look at Other Notable Practitioners.

## Energy & Natural Resources
### Leading Firms

**Band 1**
Gordon, Arata, McCollam, Duplantis & Eagan LLC *
Liskow & Lewis *

**Band 2**
Baker, Donelson, Bearman, Caldwell & Berkowitz, PC *
Bradley Murchison Kelly & Shea *
Carver, Darden, Koretzky, Tessier, Finn, Blossman & Areaux
Jones Walker LLP *
Kean Miller LLP *
Phelps Dunbar LLP *
Stone Pigman Walther Wittmann LLC

## Energy & Natural Resources: Oil & Gas
### Senior Statesmen

Senior Statesmen: distinguished older practitioners

| | |
|---|---|
| Carver M Hampton | Carver, Darden, Koretzky, Tessier, Finn |
| McCollam John M | Gordon, Arata, McCollam, Duplantis * |

### Leading individuals

**Band 1**

| | |
|---|---|
| Darden M Taylor | Carver, Darden, Koretzky, Tessier, Finn |
| Duplantis Bob J | Gordon, Arata, McCollam, Duplantis * |
| Hunter Jonathan A | Liskow & Lewis |
| Rosenblum Carl D | Jones Walker LLP * |
| Simon Jr Lawrence P | Liskow & Lewis |

**Band 2**

| | |
|---|---|
| Hayne Jr C Peck | Gordon, Arata, McCollam, Duplantis * |
| Revels, Jr Richard W | Liskow & Lewis |

**Band 3**

| | |
|---|---|
| Hunter David | Jones Walker LLP * |
| Klemm Kenneth | Baker, Donelson, Bearman, Caldwell * |
| O'Connor Scott A | Gordon, Arata, McCollam, Duplantis * |
| Ottinger Patrick S | Ottinger Hebert |
| Shea, Jr Joseph L | Bradley Murchison Kelly & Shea * |
| Slattery Jr Gerald | Slattery, Marino & Roberts A Professional |
| Songy Randall | Onebane Law Firm |
| Taggart David R | Bradley Murchison Kelly & Shea * |

**Up-and-coming individuals**

| | |
|---|---|
| Lapeze James | Liskow & Lewis |

## Band 1

### Gordon, Arata, McCollam, Duplantis & Eagan LLC
See profile on p.1377

THE FIRM This oil and gas powerhouse is universally considered one of the best energy firms in Louisiana. From bases in New Orleans, Lafayette and Baton Rouge, its lawyers provide a full energy service and are much noted for their wealth of transactional and litigation expertise. They are adept at dealing with every type of dispute, including contentious matters between operators and

## Energy & Natural Resources: Utilities
### Leading Individuals

**Band 1**

| | |
|---|---|
| Bergin Edward H | Jones Walker LLP * |
| Fontham Michael R | Stone Pigman Walther Wittmann LLC |
| Gilliam Robert S | Wilkinson, Carmody & Gilliam |
| Guerry David L | Long Law Firm LLP * |
| King Katherine | Kean Miller LLP * |
| Shirley John O | Phelps Dunbar LLP |
| Wolf Alan C | Phelps Dunbar LLP |
| Zimmering Paul L | Stone Pigman Walther Wittmann LLC |

**Band 2**

| | |
|---|---|
| Marionneaux Kyle | Kyle Marionneaux LLC |
| Shelton Dana | Stone Pigman Walther Wittmann LLC |
| Young J Randy | Kean Miller LLP * |

* Indicates firm / individual with profile.

†ONP = Other Notable Practitioner

nonoperators, legacy suits and litigation with the state pertaining to severance taxes.

Sources say: *"They try to put the right attorney with the right talents to the task and then they go from there. They have a lot of experience and do a great job."*

KEY INDIVIDUALS **Bob Duplantis** (see p.1361) is regarded as one of the top attorneys in the energy field and is particularly recognized for his unitization work, regularly representing clients before the Louisiana Department of Natural Resources and the Louisiana Office of Mineral Resources. He is much noted for his wide industry experience, having previously worked as an engineer in oil exploration and production, and as in-house counsel for an oil company. *"He brings a good background-oriented skill set and is very bright and insightful in his approach,"* notes one commentator. **Peck Hayne** (see p.1364) is equally well respected for his litigation and transactional abilities. Sources praise his personable style and say he is *"studied in his responses and very analytical."* **Scott O'Connor** (see p.1367) has a fine reputation among fellow oil and gas attorneys, and is particularly known for his commercial litigation practice, which has included defending oil and gas companies in statewide and nationwide class actions. Sources reserve particular praise for his practical approach to matters and his ability to zero in on the main issues. The *"very bright and eloquent"* **John McCollam** (see p.1366) is universally regarded as the dean of the energy Bar and is well versed in transactions, litigation and regulatory work.

### Liskow & Lewis
See profile on p.1381

THE FIRM This highly respected oil and gas firm has handled some of the most significant and high-profile matters in the sector over the past year for a client list that includes a number of international oil companies. Interviewees praise the firm's capacity in all areas of oil and gas legal work, including onshore and offshore matters, transac-

tional work, litigation and regulatory representation. A number of the firm's lawyers are regarded as experts in their fields, with well-attested links to government and industry figures.

Sources say: *"It has a great deal of expertise in offshore matters and is one of the preeminent firms in that area."*

KEY INDIVIDUALS **Jonathan Hunter** is lauded by peers and industry sources for his expertise across litigation, transactions and regulatory matters. He is particularly noted for his strengths in upstream oil and gas issues, and is also recommended for his federal practice, having won a number of significant cases against the government on behalf of his clients. *"He is really smart as hell – he is very creative, writes well and presents well in front of judges. A top-shelf guy, he'd be on my list for a high-dollar case,"* asserts one enthusiastic source. The highly regarded **Richard Revels** is considered a statewide leader in the unitization and conservation space, and is noted for his innovative approach to matters in this area. He regularly handles cases before the Commissioner of Conservation and the State Mineral Board, and is also sought to deliver title opinions on behalf of clients. The *"superb"* **Lawrence Simon** is a well-regarded oil and gas litigator based in Lafayette. He has litigated in state and federal courts throughout Louisiana, and has much experience acting for clients before the Department of Conservation. Sources say: *"He has a way of synthesizing what can be highly technical information so that it is understandable, and he has a manner which is very effective both in deposition and in presentation of cases."* Rising star **James Lapeze** *"is a younger lawyer who in due course will be right up there with his partners,"* asserts one impressed commentator. An oil and gas litigator, Lapeze focuses primarily on representing oil companies in issues stemming from upstream oil and gas production.

## Band 2

### Baker, Donelson, Bearman, Caldwell & Berkowitz, PC
See profile on p.2313

THE FIRM This firm represents oil companies in litigation and transactional matters on a statewide basis from offices in New Orleans and Baton Rouge. It represents clients in a range of litigation, from blowouts and damage claims to legacy suits and trespass claims. The group is also well versed in matters concerning oil and gas leases, the negotiation of production payment purchase agreements, and the negotiation of master service agreements.

KEY INDIVIDUALS **Kenneth Klemm** (see p.1365) is a well-regarded oil and gas litigator with a varied practice in the field. His clients include oil and gas production entities, oil field cleanup companies and insurance organizations. Sources say: *"He's got good skills and is personable and easy to work with."*

## Bradley Murchison Kelly & Shea
See profile on p.1374

**THE FIRM** This oil and gas practice operates out of Shreveport, in the heart of the Haynesville Shale. Its lawyers handle energy cases related to lignite mining and upstream and midstream oil and gas production, for clients including independent and publicly traded oil and gas companies. The team handles the full range of transactional and litigation matters, from acquisitions of mineral producing land and production companies to legacy suits, class action defense and appeals to the Louisiana Office of Conservation.

**Sources say:** *"They are very responsive, they are knowledgeable about our company, and they are willing to put in whatever it takes in terms of time and effort to get the job done."*

**KEY INDIVIDUALS Joseph Shea**'s (see p.1369) varied practice includes a significant proportion of oil and gas litigation and transactional work. His work in the sector has included defending clients in legacy cases, lease termination suits, title disputes, and mineral rights and mineral contract litigation. *"He is very thorough and does a very good job of presenting our positions,"* said one satisfied client. **David Taggart** (see p.1370) has a broad litigation practice spanning oil and gas work and utility regulatory matters, particularly in the midstream oil and gas sector. He has been heavily involved in litigation surrounding pipeline and gas gathering construction, legacy suits and regulatory issues. Sources say: *"He is a very intelligent guy and able to connect with the decision-makers and present our case in a common-sense manner."*

## Carver, Darden, Koretzky, Tessier, Finn, Blossman & Areaux LLC

**THE FIRM** This New Orleans firm represents producers and landowners in a broad range of litigation and transactional matters. It regularly handles oil and gas contract disputes, land and title opinions, and the representation of buyers and sellers of mineral producing properties. Its experienced attorneys are also routinely sought to act on behalf of clients in royalty and lease termination disputes.

**KEY INDIVIDUALS** *"Effective oil and gas litigator"* **Taylor Darden** is of counsel at the firm, and is well versed in operational disputes, expropriation, royalty collection and mineral leasing. **Hampton Carver** is a well-respected energy and mineral law attorney, with much of his practice focused on offshore matters. He is particularly noted for his work in disputes related to outer continental shelf leases and regulations. *"He is a fine, fine lawyer,"* remarks one impressed source.

## Jones Walker LLP
See profile on p.1378

**THE FIRM** This firm's oil and gas practice has become increasingly prominent over the past few years, and interviewees agree that the effort the firm has made to build its practice in the area has been successful. The full-service energy practice covers not only upstream, midstream and downstream oil and gas work, but also mining, power generation and utility regulatory matters. The firm's attorneys handle a wide array of work, including transactional mat-

ters, litigation, regulatory compliance and enforcement action representation.

**KEY INDIVIDUALS** The highly respected **Edward Bergin** (see p.1358) is recognized by sources for his utility regulation expertise. He regularly represents clients including water and electric companies, industrial clients and telecom organizations before the Louisiana Public Service Commission (LPSC). **Carl Rosenblum** (see p.1368) is singled out by peers for his involvement in a number of recent high-profile oil and gas cases. His practice involves representing clients in disputes which have included oil and gas leases, drilling contracts, exploration agreements and contentious royalty matters. Sources say: *"He is a smart, aggressive litigator who produces good results."* **David Hunter** (see p.1364) is a noted energy attorney based in New Orleans. He concentrates on transactional matters such as the acquisition and disposal of mineral-bearing real estate and associated infrastructure, and the purchase and sale of mineral leases. He is also routinely called upon to advise on the import and export of LNG.

## Kean Miller LLP
See profile on p.1379

**THE FIRM** This firm owes its reputation in the energy sector to its state-leading utilities regulation practice. The team regularly represents a diverse client base drawn from telecom, electricity generation and heavy industry sectors, among others, in regulatory proceedings before the LPSC. **Sources say:** *"They represent their clients excellently."*

**KEY INDIVIDUALS** The *"formidable"* **Katherine King** (see p.1364) is recommended by peers for her work representing clients before the LPSC, and is particularly noted for representing the end users of electricity suppliers. Sources say: *"She is the total package – effective lawyering and very hard-working as well."* **Randy Young** (see p.1371) has a fine reputation for acting on behalf of telecom companies and large electricity users, among other clients, before the LPSC and the FERC.

## Phelps Dunbar LLP
See profile on p.1383

**THE FIRM** This firm is acknowledged in the market for its utilities regulation practice, which operates from Baton Rouge and New Orleans. The firm's lawyers regularly represent Cleco Power before the LPSC and the FERC in issues such as wholesale electric power transactions, acquisition of natural resources and ratemaking.

**KEY INDIVIDUALS John Shirley** focuses on representing clients from a range of utilities, including electricity, water and telecom, before the LPSC. Recent matters include representing CenterPoint Energy before the Commission in a number of actions relating to fuel audits and ratemaking. Sources say: *"He is a very effective lawyer before the commission and has good relationships with the commissioners."* Utilities and energy practice chair **Alan Wolf** is the firm's lead partner in its relationship with the Wind Capital Group, and also led in the Cleco Power matters. *"He is an excellent lawyer: he is levelheaded, very good on his feet and very effective in negotiations,"* notes one impressed commentator.

## Stone Pigman Walther Wittmann LLC

**THE FIRM** This group is noted by sources for the quality of its utility regulation practice and maintains a fine track record acting on behalf of clients including industrial energy consumers, gas entities and pipeline companies in regulatory matters before the LPSC. Additionally, the firm has been engaged as special counsel to the commission in selected ratemaking cases.

**KEY INDIVIDUALS Michael Fontham** and **Paul Zimmering** are both highly recommended for their utilities regulation expertise. Sources describe Fontham as *"a very able litigator, and very well versed in the technicalities of the federal law issues,"* while commentators single out Zimmering as being *"absolutely five-star! He is a great lawyer and a great person to work with."* The *"very well-respected"* **Dana Shelton** is similarly well regarded in the market for her utilities regulation practice and, like Fontham and Zimmering, has much experience acting for the LPSC in matters before the FERC.

## Other Notable Practitioners

**Robert Gilliam** of Wilkinson, Carmody & Gilliam is a noted litigator with an established utility regulation practice, and *"has an amazing relationship with the commissioners at the Public Service Commission,"* note sources. *"True oil and gas litigator"* **Patrick Ottinger** of Ottinger Hebert is a much-respected energy lawyer and operates out of Lafayette. Sole practitioner **Kyle Marionneaux** regularly represents clients before the LPSC, including electricity generating entities, gas utilities and motor carrier companies. Sources say: *"He has a more casual approach with the commissioners in his argument – it is more of a conversational approach, which works well with the Commission."* **Gerald Slattery** is a member of well-respected New Orleans boutique Slattery Marino & Roberts and focuses on oil and gas litigation. His practice includes cases related to drilling contracts, legacy suits, lease disputes, trespass matters and well blowouts. *"He is extremely knowledgeable in oil and gas litigation. He is a superbright guy and very thorough and diligent,"* reports one source. Long Law Firm LLP's **David Guerry** (see p.1362) is particularly recognized for his work representing electric and telecom utility clients before the LPSC. Sources say: *"He has very good relationships with the commissioners and is very good in negotiations and bringing parties together in settlement."* The *"exceptional"* **Randall Songy** of Onebane Law Firm is based in Lafayette and is noted for his wealth of experience in the oil and gas arena. Commentators particularly admire his knowledge of unitization and conservation work.

# ENVIRONMENT

Commentary about individuals can be found under their firm's paragraph. If the firm has no paragraph (is not ranked) look at Other Notable Practitioners.

## Environment
### Leading Firms

**Band 1**

Jones Walker LLP *
Kean Miller LLP *
Liskow & Lewis *
Phelps Dunbar LLP *
Taylor, Porter, Brooks & Phillips, LLP

**Band 2**

Adams and Reese LLP *

### Leading Individuals

**Band 1**

| | |
|---|---|
| Crochet Anne J | Taylor, Porter, Brooks & Phillips, LLP |
| Dicharry Paul | Taylor, Porter, Brooks & Phillips, LLP |
| Harbourt Maureen N | Kean Miller LLP * |
| Holden Robert E | Liskow & Lewis |
| Kilgore III Leonard L | Kean Miller LLP * |
| Levine Steve J | Phelps Dunbar LLP |
| McNeal Robert B | Liskow & Lewis |

**Band 2**

| | |
|---|---|
| Bryan Boyd A | Jones Walker LLP * |
| Diaz Daria B | Stone Pigman Walther Wittmann (ONP)† |
| Hardy Timothy | Roedel Parsons Koch Blache (ONP)† |

**Band 3**

| | |
|---|---|
| Buatt Louis | Jones Walker LLP * |
| Jarrell Eric E | King, Krebs and Jurgens PLLC (ONP)† |
| Johnson Greg L | Liskow & Lewis |
| Jones Jerald N | Bradley Murchison Kelly & Shea (ONP)† * |
| Pilie Glen M | Adams and Reese LLP * |

## Band 1

### Jones Walker LLP
See profile on p.1378

**THE FIRM** This firm is particularly known for its strengths in environmental disputes and regulatory enforcement throughout the region. Its lawyers have a great deal of experience with regulatory agencies, including the Louisiana Department of Environmental Quality (LDEQ) and the EPA, and often counsel clients in regulatory enforcement matters and environmental prosecutions. Additionally, the group is renowned for its expertise in permitting matters and environmental due diligence concerning commercial transactions.

**Sources say:** "I like the communication between them and us as the client: they keep us informed of what is going on and seek our input on any major decisions. Their drafting of briefs is very good and I have found them very good to work with."

**KEY INDIVIDUALS Boyd Bryan** (see p.1358) is much sought for his expertise in enforcement, permitting and environmental disputes. He elicits particular praise from sources for his substantive knowledge of federal and state law, as well as the regulatory landscape. Special counsel

## Environment: Litigation
### Senior Statesmen

**Senior Statesmen:** distinguished older practitioners

| | |
|---|---|
| McCowan Charles | Kean Miller LLP * |

### Leading Individuals

**Band 1**

| | |
|---|---|
| Kanner Allan | Kanner & Whiteley, LLC (ONP)† * |

**Band 2**

| | |
|---|---|
| Levine Steve J | Phelps Dunbar LLP |
| McNeal Robert B | Liskow & Lewis |
| Spansel Mark J | Adams and Reese LLP * |

**Band 3**

| | |
|---|---|
| Hand, Jr Albert M. | Cook, Yancey, King & Galloway (ONP)† * |
| Jones, III Gladstone N | Jones, Swanson, Huddell (ONP)† |
| Manard, Jr John P | Phelps Dunbar LLP |
| Monk William | Stockwell, Sievert, Viccellio (ONP)† |
| Pilie Glen M | Adams and Reese LLP * |
| Pitre Loulan | Gordon, Arata, McCollam (ONP)† * |

**Up-and-coming individuals**

| | |
|---|---|
| Lapeze James | Liskow & Lewis |

\* Indicates firm / individual with profile.

†ONP = Other Notable Practitioner

**Louis Buatt** (see p.1358) is noted for his experience working for the state, including a period spent as general counsel to the LDEQ. Sources describe him as "very knowledgeable and very practical in his approach to dealing with regulatory matters."

### Kean Miller LLP
See profile on p.1379

**THE FIRM** Kean Miller supports its clients across the full range of environmental regulatory and litigation issues. Its attorneys regularly defend their clients in state and federal environmental prosecutions, in addition to liaising with regulatory agencies, applying for permits and carrying out due diligence in transactions. Additionally, the attorneys are recognized in the market for their presence in defending energy companies in legacy litigation suits brought by landowners alleging environmental damage in past oil and gas production and transport.

**Sources say:** "They are really good practitioners: they are aggressive, smart and hard-working, and they understand the politics of the litigation."

**KEY INDIVIDUALS Maureen Harbourt** (see p.1362) is an environmental regulatory lawyer with a superb reputation; she is particularly recognized by her peers for her knowledge of the CAA. She is described as "one of the most preeminent regulatory lawyers in the state: she really knows her stuff and she has a great network of contacts in industry and at the regulators." **Leonard Kilgore** (see p.1364) is a litigator who possesses a great deal of experience in environmental matters. He has been particularly prominent recently defending energy companies in legacy cases and

additionally he is known for his involvement in Superfund-related work. "He is very thoughtful and pragmatic and he is effective at conveying technical arguments in a way that laypeople are able to understand," asserts one interviewee. **Charles McCowan** (see p.1366) is an experienced litigator whose practice involves a strong element of environmental work. He is particularly recognized in the market for his work representing chemicals manufacturers in regulatory issues.

### Liskow & Lewis
See profile on p.1381

**THE FIRM** This firm has a broad practice that encompasses litigation, environmental cleanup work, and regulatory liaison and compliance. It has a stellar list of energy companies on its client roster and its lawyers regularly act for these entities on a variety of regulatory matters and environmental cases, including legacy suits.

**KEY INDIVIDUALS** Practice head **Robert Holden** remains much admired for his regulatory capabilities and is particularly renowned for his expertise in offshore regulatory matters. "He is good in terms of coming up with innovative strategies and taking a bigger-picture view of issues," asserts one impressed interviewee. **Robert McNeal**'s experience working as a trial lawyer for one of the major oil companies has stood him in good stead for his heavily oil and gas-related environmental practice. Commentators regard him as a "go-to legacy lawyer" and single out his strengths in the courtroom, reserving particular praise for his thoroughness and ability to take a strategic view on matters. The "very knowledgeable" **Greg Johnson** is well versed across the full spectrum of environmental work, including regulatory, litigation and transactional matters. Prior to working as an attorney, Johnson worked as an environmental engineer, giving him invaluable experience in the technical aspects of the practice. **James Lapeze** is recognized for his representation of oil and gas companies in numerous legacy suits. Sources say: "He is on top of what is going on in the case, very knowledgeable of the subject and a great advocate for the position."

### Phelps Dunbar LLP
See profile on p.1383

**THE FIRM** Phelps Dunbar is home to attorneys who are adept at handling every aspect of environmental law, including providing regulatory compliance advice, acting for clients on litigation and carrying out due diligence in transactions. The firm acted for Vanguard Synfuels on challenging a decision by the LDEQ to issue a water permit to the company's biodiesel manufacturing facility. Other clients include Union Pacific, Zurich and Rubicon.

**Sources say:** "The Phelps Dunbar team has helped our company achieve its goals in the matters that they have been engaged in."

**KEY INDIVIDUALS Steve Levine** regularly counsels his clients in a variety of litigation and regulatory enforcement cases. Interviewees also value his efficient, targeted approach to cases and ability *"to see the situation from an overall, holistic angle so that we are not leaving anything that can still be negotiated on the table."* **John Manard** is a litigator who is active in the environmental sphere. A significant proportion of his practice in the area involves representing clients after accidents or spillages in mass tort or class action suits that ensue.

### Taylor, Porter, Brooks & Phillips, LLP

**THE FIRM** This Baton Rouge firm provides its clients with a full environmental service covering litigation, regulatory compliance and enforcement and transactional matters. Its lawyers are well versed in all areas of environmental permitting, and are routinely sought to handle mass tort, class action and Superfund defense work.

**KEY INDIVIDUALS Anne Crochet** comes recommended for her regulatory and litigation strengths and routinely represents clients in enforcement actions brought by the LDEQ and the EPA. As one source notes, *"she is very good at what she does: good with clients and good with regulators."* **Paul Dicharry**'s practice covers a wide spectrum of areas, including compliance, permitting and environmental audits. He is also recognized for his expertise in enforcement matters and environmental disputes.

### Band 2

### Adams and Reese LLP

See profile on p.1372
**THE FIRM** Adams and Reese's Louisiana environment practice is part of a larger firmwide group that serves its clients in environmental matters across the Gulf South. Its

lawyers are well versed in all areas of environmental work, from permitting and due diligence provision in transactions to litigation and regulatory enforcement defense. **Sources say:** *"They know what they are doing, are properly staffed to handle claims, respond very well and they know the law."*

**KEY INDIVIDUALS** The experienced **Mark Spansel** (see p.1370) enjoys a diverse practice that involves a strong element of environmental litigation. Sources say: *"He is excellent to work with, he knows the right questions to ask and he knows how to tackle the cases, and does a good job of it."* His partner **Glen Pilie** (see p.1368) is a seasoned attorney who is similarly well versed in environmental litigation, most notably mass toxic tort disputes.

### Other Notable Practitioners

**Allan Kanner** (see p.1364) of Kanner & Whiteley, LLC is a well-known plaintiff litigator who practices in the environmental sector and continues to be an excellent choice of counsel for large class actions and multidistrict litigation. **Daria Diaz** of Stone Pigman Walther Wittmann LLC is well known at the environment Bar for her practice which includes environmental regulatory matters and litigation. Her work has included representing American Sugar Refining in a number of LDEQ enforcement matters centered on alleged air and water infringements. **Timothy Hardy** of Roedel Parsons Koch Blache Balhoff & McCollister is a Baton Rouge-based attorney who wins particular plaudits for his strong regulatory and political background as well as for his deep knowledge of the environment sector. As one source notes, *"he is incredibly capable, very hard-working and has a great relationship with the regulators."* King, Krebs and Jurgens PLLC's **Eric Jarrell** is noted for his heavy involvement in legacy litigation and is also sought by clients facing enforcement action from the

LDEQ, the EPA and the Department of Natural Resources. **Gladstone Jones** of Jones, Swanson, Huddell, & Garrison, LLC is a well-regarded plaintiff litigator whose practice includes environment litigation, with a particular focus on legacy cases. He commands much respect from his peers, not least for his ability to take a broad, strategic view of matters. The experienced **William Monk** of Stockwell, Sievert, Viccellio, Clements & Shaddock operates out of Lake Charles and maintains a varied practice that includes a strong element of environment litigation. *"He is somebody who is just excellent at representing the interests of his clients,"* asserts one impressed commentator. **Albert Hand** (see p.1362) of Cook, Yancey, King & Galloway, A Professional Law Corporation is a litigator based in Shreveport who practices in the environmental sector. Sources say: *"He is very knowledgeable, does a good job for his clients and he wants to get to a resolution rather than to fight for the sake of fighting."* **Loulan Pitre** (see p.1368) of Gordon, Arata, McCollam, Duplantis & Eagan LLC is a well-respected litigator who represents a fine choice of counsel on legacy litigation as well as traditional environment disputes. He elicits particular praise for his *"thorough, fully considered opinions"* on matters. Shreveport-based **Jerald Jones** (see p.1364) of Bradley Murchison Kelly & Shea has a broad practice which includes handling air and water permitting issues and representing clients in matters before the LDEQ and in the courts. *"He can mentor you and keep you from doing something that will cost you a lot of money; he truly wants the best outcome for his client,"* asserts one impressed source.

# GAMING & LICENSING

Commentary about individuals can be found under their firm's paragraph. If the firm has no paragraph (is not ranked) look at Other Notable Practitioners.

## Gaming & Licensing
### Leading Firms

**Band 1**
Baker, Donelson, Bearman, Caldwell & Berkowitz, PC *
Jones Walker LLP †

**Band 2**
Adams and Reese LLP *
Breazeale, Sachse & Wilson, LLP
McGlinchey Stafford PLLC *
Phelps Dunbar LLP *
Stone Pigman Walther Wittmann LLC

### Leading Individuals

**Star individuals**

| | |
|---|---|
| West Paul | Baker, Donelson, Bearman, Caldwell * |

**Band 1**

| | |
|---|---|
| Duncan J Kelly | Jones Walker LLP * |

**Band 2**

| | |
|---|---|
| Barbin Jeffrey M | Phelps Dunbar LLP |
| Benjamin Thomas M | Breazeale, Sachse & Wilson, LLP |
| Harkins Deborah | McGlinchey Stafford PLLC * |
| Orlansky C Lawrence | Stone Pigman Walther Wittmann LLC |

**Band 3**

| | |
|---|---|
| Boles Janet | The Boles Law Firm (ONP) † |
| Brantley IV Joseph P | Brantley & Associates, APLC (ONP) † |
| Colomb P. Kevin | Gordon, Arata, McCollam, (ONP) † * |
| Easterling Richard B | Taylor, Porter, Brooks & Phillips (ONP) † |
| Rester Daniel K | Adams and Reese LLP * |

\* Indicates firm / individual with profile.

†ONP = Other Notable Practitioner

## Band 1

### Baker, Donelson, Bearman, Caldwell & Berkowitz, PC
See profile on p.2313

**THE FIRM** This state-leading gaming practice is heavily involved in regulatory and transactional matters on behalf of its client list of well-known gaming companies. The firm represents a wide array of gaming groups including casino operators, gaming manufacturers, horse racing tracks, gaming investors and gaming suppliers.
**KEY INDIVIDUALS** The *"very talented"* **Paul West** (see p.1371) maintains a leading reputation on both a state and national level. His practice is predominantly focused on representing casino companies and gaming operators in regulatory matters. Sources are quick to describe him as *"personable, attentive and efficient,"* and he is also singled out by interviewees as *"somebody who can come in and get things done effectively."*

### Jones Walker LLP
See profile on p.1378

**THE FIRM** This regional firm has a strong gaming practice in the state and advises its clients on a full range of gaming-related issues including regulatory compliance, licensing and transactional matters. In Louisiana the firm is particularly recognized for representing land-based and riverboat casino developers and operating companies.
**KEY INDIVIDUALS Kelly Duncan** (see p.1361) is a leading Louisiana gaming attorney with a national reputation in the industry, and is particularly noted for his experience in the maritime sector as it relates to riverboat gaming regulatory issues. Sources say: *"He is just great: he knows the laws, has great relationships with the regulators and is very well respected, which is important in this area."*

## Band 2

### Adams and Reese LLP
See profile on p.1372

**THE FIRM** This longstanding gaming and licensing practice operates out of offices in Baton Rouge and New Orleans. The group acts for a diverse range of gaming and licensing clients, including truck stop gaming companies, bars and restaurants, and comes particularly recommended for its expertise in obtaining video poker and alcohol licenses.
**Sources say:** *"They understand Louisiana law and just get it done quickly and for a reasonable fee."*
**KEY INDIVIDUALS Daniel Rester** (see p.1368) maintains a varied practice and is noted for his expertise in gaming regulatory matters. He is *"very knowledgeable about the politics and the sensibilities of the regulators that we deal with,"* notes one impressed client.

### Breazeale, Sachse & Wilson, LLP

**THE FIRM** This firm is a relative newcomer to the Louisiana gaming and licensing market, but has already established itself as a practice well-equipped to handle all manner of regulatory, legislative and transactional matters for a number of gaming operators, developers and equipment manufacturers within the state. In a recent highlight, it represented Redman Gaming of Louisiana and Riverbend Truckstops & Palace Casinos in a $3.8 million sale of a video poker truck stop and video gaming machines to another operator. Other clients include AAA Gaming, Cane Row Casino and American Gaming.
**KEY INDIVIDUALS Thomas Benjamin** is an experienced litigator and regulatory lawyer whose practice includes a strong gaming element, both in Louisiana and throughout the country. In addition to handling the Redman Gaming matter, he also recently acted for a startup, Illinois Gaming Investments, on a series of investments and sales in the video poker market in Illinois. Sources say: *"He steps back*

*from the problem and tries to look at what will fit the client's need and what are the long-term and short-term impacts of decisions."*

### McGlinchey Stafford PLLC
See profile on p.1382

**THE FIRM** This practice is noted for its representation of a number of gaming clients in regulatory and legislative lobbying matters across the state. Recent work has seen it act for Bossier Casino Venture on a variety of concerns relating to the development of the new Margaritaville Hotel and Casino in Lake Charles. It also counts Landry's Restaurants, Wincor Nixsdorf and Apollo Management among its key clients.
**KEY INDIVIDUALS Deborah Harkins** (see p.1363) remains well regarded by sources for her experience in lobbying, regulatory and licensing matters. She is particularly noted for the fine relationships she maintains with the state police and the Attorney General's office.

### Phelps Dunbar LLP
See profile on p.1383

**THE FIRM** This firm supports its gaming clients in regulatory and transactional matters throughout Louisiana, as well as in Mississippi and other gaming jurisdictions. The firm has advised DeAgostini, an Italian company that owns a controlling interest in GTECH, on regulatory compliance matters throughout the USA. Other key clients include Isle of Capri Casinos, Spielo Manufacturing and the first lien lenders group of Legends Gaming.
**KEY INDIVIDUALS Jeffrey Barbin** is a well-respected Baton Rouge gaming practitioner, and handles regulatory and licensing work for clients including casino operator El Dorado Resorts, which he has represented in hearings before the Louisiana Gaming Control Board. Clients describe him as *"an absolute gent and a joy to work with"* and he is also particularly valued for his ability *"to translate issues into regulatory parlance and apply regulatory frameworks to practical problems."*

### Stone Pigman Walther Wittmann LLC

**THE FIRM** This practice is noted for its representation of gaming operators, suppliers and lenders in regulatory and litigation matters. The group is particularly known in the market for its relationship with Pinnacle Gaming, which holds four of the 15 riverboat gaming licenses in the state, and which it has acted for on numerous regulatory matters before the Louisiana Gaming Control Board. In other recent work, it has acted for a variety of lenders and gaming suppliers on licensing matters involving the Gaming Enforcement Division of the Louisiana State Police.
**Sources say:** *"An excellent firm with a great reputation."*
**KEY INDIVIDUALS Lawrence Orlansky** is recognized by peers for his gaming regulatory and litigation work. In addition to his work for Pinnacle Gaming, he is advising

the secured creditors of a gaming company on regulatory matters pertaining to a Chapter 11 reorganization bankruptcy. As one impressed source notes, *"his knowledge of the applicable laws is superb and he gives timely, relevant advice."*

### Other Notable Practitioners

**Joseph Brantley** of Brantley & Associates, APLC is based in Baton Rouge and represents clients in gaming transaction-al and regulatory matters. Commentators note: *"He is effective, works well with the regulators and is well respected by the guys in the Attorney General's office."* The well-regarded **Janet Boles** of The Boles Law Firm enjoys a varied practice, which includes elements of gaming regulatory law. Sources are quick to note her wealth of experience in the sector and particularly value her *"great relationships with the regulators."* The much admired **Kevin Colomb** (see p.1360) at Gordon, Arata, McCollam, Duplantis & Eagan LLC has a great deal of experience in gaming, regulatory and administrative law, having previously worked as a US Assistant Attorney and an in-house gaming lawyer. **Richard Easterling** recently joined Taylor, Porter, Brooks & Phillips, LLP from Adams and Reese. He has a government relations and regulatory practice which focuses on alcohol and gaming licensing for clients throughout the state. Sources reserve particular praise for his understanding of the technical side of the licensing process.

# LABOR & EMPLOYMENT

Employee Benefits & Compensation p.1350

Commentary about individuals can be found under their firm's paragraph. If the firm has no paragraph (is not ranked) look at Other Notable Practitioners.

**Labor & Employment**
**Leading Firms**

**Band 1**
Fisher & Phillips LLP *
Jones Walker LLP *
The Kullman Firm PLC
Phelps Dunbar LLP *

**Band 2**
Adams and Reese LLP *
Baker, Donelson, Bearman, Caldwell & Berkowitz, PC *
Breazeale, Sachse & Wilson, LLP
Coats Rose Yale Ryman Lee
Kean Miller LLP *
Liskow & Lewis *
Proskauer Rose LLP *

*Indicates firm with profile.*
*Alphabetical order within each band. Band 1 is the highest.*

## Band 1

### Fisher & Phillips LLP
See profile on p.1107

**THE FIRM** The New Orleans outpost of this national firm has an excellent reputation for acting for management clients across the full spectrum of labor, employment and ERISA cases. Among its recent work, the group represented Boise Cascade in arbitration and a Louisiana Supreme Court case concerning unjust termination, subcontracting, and wage and hour issues. Other clients include Glazer's, Aetna Life Insurance, Enterprise Rent-A-Car and SEACOR Marine.

**Sources say:** *"Their people are specialists and they've just been very effective."*

**KEY INDIVIDUALS** The *"outstanding"* **Sandra Feingerts** (see p.1361) is an ERISA and employee benefits attorney. She is particularly recognized for her extensive knowledge of the tax issues and regulations in the area, and for her ability to communicate this knowledge effectively to her clients. Labor attorney **Keith Pyburn** (see p.1368) is recommended by sources for his hands-on approach and *"get-it-done"* attitude. He represented Entergy in negotiations with a union to renew a three-year contract for the operators and maintenance staff of a power plant, and also led on the Boise Cascade matter. **Timothy Scott** (see p.1369) focuses on employment litigation, in addition to handling labor negotiations and arbitrations. *"There is no scenario that he hasn't seen before and that experience is very useful. He can give me advice on any issue that I raise and I trust his advice due to his experience and knowledge,"* asserts one enthusiastic client. The well-regarded **Edward Harold** (see p.1363) concentrates on employment litigation. He recently represented GEC Development in a wrongful termination case, winning a summary judgment in favor of his client which was affirmed by the Fifth Circuit Court of Appeal. *"He is an excellent lawyer, as smart as a whip,"* note sources. **Michael Mitchell**'s (see p.1367) practice centers on unfair labor practices, collective bargaining and arbitration, among other areas. In a recent highlight he represented Austal USA before the NLRB in unfair labor practice charges related to a union-representation election. Sources describe **Robert McCalla** (see p.1366) as the *"dean of all employment litigators in Louisiana."* In addition to his employment disputes practice, he is also a much-respected and highly skilled traditional labor attorney.

### Jones Walker LLP
See profile on p.1378

**THE FIRM** Jones Walker's labor and employment group offers a full service to clients, including litigation, labor relations, employee benefits, and training and compliance advice. Additionally, the firm regularly represents clients before state and federal bodies including the NLRB, the OSHA, the EEOC and the Wage and Hour Division of the US Department of Labor. It counts National Oilwell Varco, Superior Energy Services, Turner Industries and the Ralph Brennan Restaurant Group among its key clients.

**Sources say:** *"Their attorneys are all very good and they have a great reputation in the community. They have depth within the department which conveys solidity and the ability to cover everything."*

**KEY INDIVIDUALS** Labor and employment group head **Sidney Lewis** (see p.1366) is based in New Orleans and is a noted labor attorney with a great deal of experience in labor-organizing campaigns, contract negotiations and labor arbitrations. He also practices in the employment sector, regularly handling litigation and providing counseling and compliance training to companies. *"When it comes to strategy I would trust no one else – he knows what is going to happen a couple of moves ahead,"* reports one enthusiastic client. **Mark Adams** (see p.1357) is a well-known and respected employment lawyer with a practice based on providing companies with compliance advice and training, in addition to handling employment litigation. Sources say: *"He is always polite, but he is very aggressive and assertive in defending his clients."* Employment litigator **Jennifer Anderson** (see p.1357) is based in the firm's Baton Rouge office. Her recent highlights include defeating a putative class action and obtaining a number of summary judgments in the courts on behalf of clients. Sources say: *"She is good, smart and aggressive."* **Cornelius Heusel** (see p.1364) is a well-regarded employment litigator whose experience includes stints at the FBI and the US Attorney General's office. He regularly handles employment and labor cases for his clients, before both the courts and various state and federal administrative bodies.

### The Kullman Firm PLC

**THE FIRM** This firm focuses exclusively on representing management clients in labor and employment matters from its offices in New Orleans and Baton Rouge. The practice covers labor and employment law, and includes litigation, representation before government agencies, advice on compliance, and management training. Market sources praise the firm's capacity in labor matters and its ability to handle affirmative action reporting requirements for public bodies.

**Sources say:** *"They have a stellar reputation and very good lawyers over there."*

**KEY INDIVIDUALS Ernest Malone** is an experienced labor and employment attorney who advises companies on employment policies and strategies, and represents management in disputes and negotiations with unions. He is highly regarded among peers, and his ability to provide clients with strategic advice and guidance is praised. According to one commentator, *"he is a fantastic attorney: very pragmatic and a very good consultant, and good at taking a client's issues and walking them through it."* **Samuel Zurik** has a thriving employment litigation practice and is

| Labor & Employment | |
| --- | --- |
| **Senior Statesmen** | |
| **Senior Statesmen:** distinguished older practitioners | |
| Heusel Cornelius | *Jones Walker LLP* * |
| McCalla Robert | *Fisher & Phillips LLP* * |

| **Leading Individuals** | |
| --- | --- |
| **Band 1** | |
| Alessandra M Nan | *Phelps Dunbar LLP* |
| Jacob Clyde | *Coats Rose Yale Ryman Lee* * |
| Lewis Sidney | *Jones Walker LLP* * |
| Malone Jr Ernest | *The Kullman Firm PLC* |
| McGoey II Thomas | *Liskow & Lewis* |
| Pyburn Jr Keith M | *Fisher & Phillips LLP* * |
| **Band 2** | |
| Adams H Mark | *Jones Walker LLP* * |
| Anderson Jennifer | *Jones Walker LLP* * |
| Beiser Stephen P | *McGlinchey Stafford PLLC (ONP)† * |
| Boyle Kim M | *Phelps Dunbar LLP* |
| Cancienne Phyllis G | *Baker, Donelson, Bearman, Caldwell* * |
| Christy Walter W | *Coats Rose Yale Ryman Lee* * |
| Crochet Vicki | *Taylor, Porter, Brooks & Phillips (ONP)†* |
| Duncan III Brooke | *Adams and Reese LLP* * |
| Furr Susan W | *Phelps Dunbar LLP* |
| Hartmann Melanie | *Kean Miller LLP* * |
| Kiggans Thomas H | *Phelps Dunbar LLP* |
| Koretzky I Harold | *Carver, Darden, Koretzky, Tessier (ONP)†* |
| Lanusse Leslie A | *Adams and Reese LLP* * |
| Mallery Mark N | *Ogletree, Deakins, Nash, Smoak (ONP)† * |
| Moore Christopher | *Ogletree, Deakins, Nash, Smoak (ONP)† * |
| Murov Ellis B | *Deutsch, Kerrigan & Stiles LLP (ONP)†* |
| **Band 3** | |
| David Jr Robert J | *Juneau David (ONP)†* |
| Desmond Susan | *Jackson Lewis LLP (ONP)† * |
| Foster, III Murphy J | *Breazeale, Sachse & Wilson, LLP* |
| Griffith, Jr Steven F | *Baker, Donelson, Bearman, Caldwell* * |
| Hardin, Jr A Edward | *Kean Miller LLP* * |
| Harold Edward F | *Fisher & Phillips LLP* * |
| Koch Amelia W | *Baker, Donelson, Bearman, Caldwell* * |
| Linzy Howard S | *The Kullman Firm PLC* |
| Masinter Eve B | *Breazeale, Sachse & Wilson, LLP* |
| Mitchell Michael S | *Fisher & Phillips LLP* * |
| Preis Jr E Fredrick | *Breazeale, Sachse & Wilson, LLP* |
| Scott Timothy H | *Fisher & Phillips LLP* * |
| Seemann Charles | *Jackson Lewis LLP (ONP)† * |
| Wisdom Rachel Wendt | *Stone Pigman Walther Wittmann (ONP)†* |
| Zurik III Samuel | *The Kullman Firm PLC* |

| Labor & Employment: | | |
| --- | --- | --- |
| **Employee Benefits & Compensation** | | |
| **Leading Individuals** | | |
| **Star individuals** | | |
| Shapiro Howard | | *Proskauer Rose LLP* |
| **Band 1** | | |
| Feingerts Sandra Mills | | *Fisher & Phillips LLP* * |
| Thorne René | | *Jackson Lewis LLP (ONP)† * |
| **Band 2** | | |
| Armstrong Jane E | | *Phelps Dunbar LLP* |
| Conklin Katherine | | *McGlinchey Stafford PLLC (ONP)† * |
| Littauer Dwayne O | | *The Kullman Firm PLC* |
| Rachal Robert | | *Proskauer Rose LLP* |
| Seemann Charles | | *Jackson Lewis LLP* * |
| Snyder Randye C | | *Liskow & Lewis* |

*\* Indicates individual with profile.*

*†ONP = Other Notable Practitioner*

as union-organizing drives, collective bargaining and wage and hour disputes, as well as in a large variety of cases before the NLRB.

## Phelps Dunbar LLP
### See profile on p.1383

**THE FIRM** From offices in Baton Rouge and New Orleans, this regional firm advises employment, labor and employee benefits matters. The group is particularly noted for its work on behalf of government bodies, educational organizations and state agencies, in addition to handling matters in the private sector. Key clients include Edison Chouest Offshore, Louisiana Lottery, Gulf Coast Pharmaceutical Specialty and Franklin Templeton.
**Sources say:** *"What I like about the firm is that they have a specialist in everything I come across: labor, EEOC, personnel issues – they have an attorney for each element of the system."*
**KEY INDIVIDUALS** The *"very diligent and very bright"* **Nan Alessandra** has a fine reputation in the market for her expertise in employment litigation, arbitration and alternative dispute resolution. She is also much in demand for compliance and general employment advice. **Jane Armstrong** is noted by sources for her skills in the employee benefits area. She advises companies and directors on the design and implementation of employee benefit plans, including 401(k) plans and employee stock ownership plans. Sources say: *"She is very good at making difficult or complex subjects understandable."* *"High-profile"* attorney **Kim Boyle** is well versed in a broad range of employment disputes and has handled litigation concerning workplace harassment, discrimination, EEOC claims and retaliation cases. Baton Rouge-based **Susan Furr** has represented businesses in a wide variety of cases, including EEOC cases and claims related to workplace harassment, discrimination and retaliation. *"She is very thorough, knowledgeable and levelheaded, and gives good advice,"* asserts one impressed interviewee. Interviewees claim that **Thomas Kiggans** instills confidence in his clients due to his broad experience in the labor and employment arena and his practical, decisive approach to litigation. He is routinely called upon to handle claims regarding sexual harassment

and discrimination, union issues, wage and hour cases and ERISA matters. According to one commentator, Kiggans *"is down-to-earth and real easy to talk to, and can meet and talk to anyone in the company, from the president down."*

## Band 2

### Adams and Reese LLP
### See profile on p.1372

**THE FIRM** This full-service Southeastern firm provides labor and employment advice and representation to clients from offices in Baton Rouge and New Orleans. The team advises clients on the full spectrum of labor, employment and employee benefits matters. Recent work has seen it advise the Air Conditioning Contractors of America, a trade association, on providing an online service answering queries from association members on labor and employment matters.
**Sources say:** *"They always answer my questions within 24 hours."*
**KEY INDIVIDUALS** New Orleans-based labor attorney **Brooke Duncan** (see p.1361) is well respected by clients and peers alike. Sources praise his strategic approach and note his skillful advocacy in the courts and in matters before the NLRB. He is lead lawyer on the Air Conditioning Contractors of America matter. **Leslie Lanusse** (see p.1365) is an experienced labor and employment litigator noted by sources for her meticulous preparation. She has handled a large range of cases, including claims arising from the FLSA, ERISA litigation and matters before the EEOC. *"She understands what you need to do to be successful in a labor defense situation,"* notes one satisfied client.

### Baker, Donelson, Bearman, Caldwell & Berkowitz, PC
### See profile on p.2313

**THE FIRM** This Southeastern powerhouse has offices in New Orleans, Baton Rouge and Mandeville, and is home to a number of well-respected labor and employment litigators. The firm's lawyers advise clients on compliance and policy issues, in addition to representing them in litigation before the courts and various state and federal administrative bodies.
**KEY INDIVIDUALS** *"Methodical and well prepared,"* **Phyllis Cancienne** (see p.1359) is based in Baton Rouge and has a fine reputation in the market. She advises clients on policy and strategic issues, in addition to representing them in litigation in the courts and before federal bodies such as the EEOC and the NLRB. **Steven Griffith**'s (see p.1362) labor and employment practice focuses on defending class actions brought on wage and hour and FLSA grounds. *"He is a diligent, bright young lawyer, and very capable and competent,"* reports one impressed commentator. **Amelia Koch** (see p.1365) *"is a knowledgeable attorney and knows her labor and employment law,"* sources say. She is a well-liked litigator with a varied practice that includes labor and employment work and antitrust litigation.

described by sources as *"one of the key players"* at the firm. He has represented clients in a wide variety of litigation and arbitration matters, including wage and hour and wrongful termination claims, and cases relating to discrimination, harassment and breach of contract. *"He is a very conscientious and competent professional and he does a good job for his clients,"* report sources. **Dwayne Littauer** is noted for his advice on employee benefits plans and also acts for clients in litigation, perhaps most notably in ERISA suits. The very experienced **Howard Linzy** is a labor lawyer of vast experience. He has represented clients in issues such

## Breazeale, Sachse & Wilson, LLP

**THE FIRM** This group operates out of Baton Rouge and New Orleans, and has the necessary expertise to undertake a wide variety of tasks, including benefits litigation, personnel policies, defense of EEOC charges and NLRB work. The team is also well versed in collective bargaining negotiations and responding to harassment and discrimination claims. It represents a wide range of clients from sectors such as energy, education and healthcare.

**Sources say:** *"We find their attention to detail is very good and once on assignment our staff has little follow-up to do – status updates are well timed and provide relevant information."*

**KEY INDIVIDUALS Murphy Foster** is a well-known practitioner in this arena and represents companies in response to class actions and wage and hour suits, cases under the whistle-blower statute, and the defense of discrimination and harassment claims. *"He provides prompt, knowledgeable responses to our needs,"* reports one happy client. New Orleans-based employment litigator **Eve Masinter** is noted for her prowess in the courtroom. Sources say: *"She is a good lawyer, knowledgeable in this area and is respected by clients and peers."* **Fredrick Preis** is an experienced attorney who maintains a fine reputation in the market for his expertise in traditional labor matters.

## Coats Rose Yale Ryman Lee

**THE FIRM** The New Orleans branch of this Texas firm has a reputation that belies its compact size. The quality and experience of its labor and employment lawyers is well recognized by market commentators. The group is noted for its strengths in discrimination claims, wage and hour cases and matters before the NLRB, and also continues to be called on to handle collective bargaining negotiations and the creation of affirmative action programs.

**KEY INDIVIDUALS Clyde Jacob** (see p.1364) is an experienced and well-regarded attorney who focuses on traditional labor matters, in addition to advising companies on employment policies. He is well versed in NLRB cases, collective bargaining negotiations and responding to union-organizing campaigns. Sources say: *"He is a very thoughtful, careful and smart lawyer."* The *"very knowledgeable"* **Walter Christy** (see p.1359) is a well-respected labor and employment litigator, much noted for his wealth of trial experience. He predominantly concentrates on employment litigation, including claims concerning discrimination, harassment and wage and hour cases.

## Kean Miller LLP
### See profile on p.1379

**THE FIRM** This practice is based in Baton Rouge and also operates out of New Orleans and Lake Charles, advising clients on a variety of issues including personnel policies, and the defense of discrimination and retaliation cases. The group is also much sought for its strengths in EEOC claims and Department of Labor investigations. It draws its diverse client base from a variety of fields including energy, chemicals, heavy industry, advertising and the hospitality sector.

**Sources say:** *"They are well versed in substantive legal matters and are able to relate their expertise, not just to me, but to our staff."*

**KEY INDIVIDUALS Edward Hardin** (see p.1363) handles employment litigation and advisory work, as well as traditional labor matters. *"He is always available, well versed in the law and practical in his advice,"* note commentators. **Melanie Hartmann** (see p.1363) is an experienced and well-respected employment litigator based in the firm's Baton Rouge office. Her practice includes advising clients on policy and compliance with statutes, as well as representing them in court and in EEOC and Department of Labor matters. *"She is very easy to deal with, and has a good presence and the ability to relate to our staff and managers,"* note enthusiastic clients, who also praise her negotiating skills.

## Liskow & Lewis
### See profile on p.1381

**THE FIRM** The key drivers behind this firm's labor and employment practice are its clients in the energy and heavy industry arenas. The firm has offices in New Orleans and Lafayette, and is particularly noted for its defense of wage and hour class actions brought under the FLSA. In addition, the group routinely handles labor arbitrations with unions, and has a fine track record in Title VII race discrimination lawsuits and ERISA cases.

**KEY INDIVIDUALS Thomas McGoey** is a widely respected employment litigator highlighted by sources for his effective advocacy in the courtroom. His varied experience includes advising clients on personnel matters and policy, and providing representation in state and federal courts and before government bodies. Sources say: *"He is very thoughtful and does a great job for his client, really taking the time to understand the entire picture in order to provide cogent advice."* The *"accomplished"* **Randye Snyder** is an employee benefits and ERISA attorney who is particularly recommended for her advice on employee benefits programs.

## Proskauer Rose LLP
### See profile on p.2001

**THE FIRM** The New Orleans office of this international firm is recognized for its expertise in employee benefits and ERISA litigation, in addition to its general labor and employment work. In one notable matter, the firm represented an entrepreneur in a putative class action that claimed an employee stock ownership plan had overpaid by $500 million in the purchase of a hotel owned by his company; the case was settled before trial for $15 million. The group counts Foot Locker, Honeywell International, Fidelity Management Trusts, Met Life Insurance and Chevron among its distinguished client base.

**Sources say:** *"They are very creative and strategic-minded, always thinking of alternative ways to approach litigation in order to get the best results."*

**KEY INDIVIDUALS Howard Shapiro** is a nationally renowned employee benefits attorney described as *"the ERISA guru and Mr New Orleans."* His ERISA litigation practice includes defending clients in cases related to 401(k) matters and fiduciary misrepresentation claims. Sources say: *"Everyone in the ERISA arena knows Howard Shapiro – just having his name on a pleading means a ton."* Clients highly praise **Robert Rachal**'s abilities as an ERISA litigator, with one interviewee commenting: *"He has an encyclopedic knowledge of ERISA litigation and he is very good at the economics of a case."* Rachal's practice also covers employment and traditional labor matters. In a recent highlight, he represented Cajun Sugar Co-Operative in grievance and collective bargaining negotiations.

## Other Notable Practitioners

ERISA litigator **René Thorne** (see p.1370) is managing partner of Jackson Lewis LLP's New Orleans office and is *"very well organized and very articulate."* In a recent case, she successfully represented a pension fund in a class action claim of more than $100 million for alleged breaches of ERISA and other claimed failings. The court dismissed the claims in a summary judgment and awarded $50,000 in attorney fees against the plaintiffs' counsel. At the same firm, **Susan Desmond** (see p.1360) handles labor and employment law in Mississippi and Louisiana. *"She is very quick to respond to my concerns and is always available to support me,"* notes one satisfied client. **Stephen Beiser** (see p.1358) of McGlinchey Stafford PLLC is an employment litigator who maintains a fine reputation among peers, with sources describing him as *"calm and cool under pressure,"* and *"very good in terms of strategy."* **Katherine Conklin** (see p.1360) is also at McGlinchey Stafford PLLC and is an ERISA and employment lawyer whose primary focus is on assisting clients with employee benefits plans and compliance. Sources say: *"She is available at all time for the client's questions and inquiries."* The *"excellent"* **Vicki Crochet** of Taylor, Porter, Brooks & Phillips, LLP advises clients on personnel policies and strategies, in addition to litigating in the courts and before government bodies such as the EEOC. *"Always very impressive,"* **Harold Koretzky** of Carver, Darden, Koretzky, Tessier, Finn, Blossman & Areaux LLC is a labor and employment attorney based in New Orleans. He is recommended for his expertise in collective bargaining negotiations, mediations, and matters before government administrative bodies. Deutsch, Kerrigan & Stiles LLP's **Ellis Murov** is an experienced attorney who represents clients in employment, labor and ERISA cases. *"He sees the issues that no one else sees,"* report impressed interviewees. **Rachel Wendt Wisdom** of Stone Pigman Walther Wittmann LLC is an employment attorney whose practice includes both litigation and advisory work. In a recent case she obtained a summary judgment dismissal on behalf of Kansas City Southern Railway in an EEOC case alleging race discrimination that sought $5 million in claims. One client praised *"her responsiveness, practical business sense, and ability to get me the answer I need without spending a bunch of money."* **Robert David** of Juneau David is a Lafayette-based labor and employment attorney who has developed a fine reputation among peers. Sources say: *"He is very good on his feet and comfortable in court."* **Mark Mallery** (see p.1366) is managing partner of the New Orleans office of Ogletree, Deakins,

Nash, Smoak & Stewart, PC. His practice covers traditional labor matters, such as collective bargaining and union-organizing campaigns, as well as employment matters, including claims brought by the EEOC and whistle-blower cases. "*He is always well prepared and methodical, and*

*gets good results,*" asserts one impressed commentator. At the same firm, **Christopher Moore** (see p.1367) is developing a fine reputation in the Louisiana market. He is equally adept in employment litigation and traditional labor matters. Employment and ERISA litigator **Charles**

**Seemann** (see p.1369) has recently joined Jackson Lewis LLP from Proskauer Rose. "*He has an incredible knowledge of ERISA; I can call him up and mention section 408 of ERISA and he can recite it right back to me,*" said one impressed interviewee.

## LITIGATION

Commentary about individuals can be found under their firm's paragraph. If the firm has no paragraph (is not ranked) look at Other Notable Practitioners.

### Litigation: General Commercial
#### Leading Firms

**Band 1**
Baker, Donelson, Bearman, Caldwell & Berkowitz, PC *
Barrasso Usdin Kupperman Freeman & Sarver LLC *
Jones Walker LLP *
Liskow & Lewis *
Stone Pigman Walther Wittmann LLC

**Band 2**
Fishman Haygood Phelps Walmsley Willis & Swanson, L.L.P. *
Gordon, Arata, McCollam, Duplantis & Eagan LLC *
Phelps Dunbar LLP *

**Band 3**
Breazeale, Sachse & Wilson, LLP
Gainsburgh, Benjamin, David, Meunier & Warshauer, L.L.C.
Herman, Herman & Katz LLC
Kean Miller LLP *
McGlinchey Stafford PLLC *
Sher Garner Cahill Richter Klein & Hilbert LLC
Taylor, Porter, Brooks & Phillips, LLP

### Litigation: Securities
#### Leading Individuals

**Band 1**
| | |
|---|---|
| Freeman III George C | Barrasso Usdin Kupperman Freeman * |
| Swanson James R | Fishman Haygood Phelps Walmsley Willis * |
| Tulley Frederick R | Taylor, Porter, Brooks & Phillips, LLP |

### Litigation: White-Collar Crime & Government Investigations
#### Leading Individuals

**Band 1**
| | |
|---|---|
| Becker Walter F | Chaffe McCall, LLP (ONP)† * |
| Hardin Pauline | Jones Walker LLP * |
| Polite Jr Kenneth Allen | Liskow & Lewis |
| Rosenberg Harry | Phelps Dunbar LLP |

### Litigation: General Commercial
#### Senior Statesmen

**Senior Statesmen:** distinguished older practitioners
| | |
|---|---|
| Lund Daniel | Montgomery Barnett (ONP)† * |
| McCowan Charles | Kean Miller LLP * |

#### Leading Individuals

**Star individuals**
| | |
|---|---|
| Wittmann Phillip A | Stone Pigman Walther Wittmann LLC |

**Band 1**
| | |
|---|---|
| Abaunza Donald R | Liskow & Lewis |
| Barrasso Judy Y | Barrasso Usdin Kupperman Freeman * |
| Barriere Brent B | Fishman Haygood Phelps Walmsley Willis * |
| Cheatwood Roy C | Baker, Donelson, Bearman, Caldwell * |
| Eagan Ewell | Gordon, Arata, McCollam, Duplantis * |
| Herman Russ M | Herman, Herman & Katz LLC |
| Lee Wayne J | Stone Pigman Walther Wittmann LLC |
| Meunier Gerald E | Gainsburgh, Benjamin, David, Meunier |
| Sarver Richard E | Barrasso Usdin Kupperman Freeman * |
| Stanley Richard | Stanley Reuter Ross Thornton (ONP)† |
| Swanson James R | Fishman Haygood Phelps Walmsley Willis * |
| Vance R Patrick | Jones Walker LLP * |

**Band 2**
| | |
|---|---|
| Brown James | Liskow & Lewis |
| Garner James | Sher Garner Cahill Richter Klein & Hilbert |
| Hardin III Harry S | Jones Walker LLP * |
| Kupperman Stephen H | Barrasso Usdin Kupperman Freeman * |
| Mince Loretta G | Fishman Haygood Phelps Walmsley Willis * |
| Philips Harry | Taylor, Porter, Brooks & Phillips, LLP |

| | |
|---|---|
| Rosenberg Harry | Phelps Dunbar LLP |
| Sinor Howard | Gordon, Arata, McCollam, Duplantis * |
| Usdin Steven W | Barrasso Usdin Kupperman Freeman * |

**Band 3**
| | |
|---|---|
| Aguilar Richard A | McGlinchey Stafford PLLC * |
| Ashe Barry W | Stone Pigman Walther Wittmann LLC |
| Beebe Mark | Adams and Reese LLP (ONP)† * |
| Bezet Gary A | Kean Miller LLP * |
| Degan Nancy | Baker, Donelson, Bearman, Caldwell * |
| Geary Covert J | Jones Walker LLP * |
| Goodman Alan H | Breazeale, Sachse & Wilson, LLP |
| Haycraft Donald | Liskow & Lewis |
| Jarrett R Keith | Liskow & Lewis |
| Kerrigan Jr Robert E | Deutsch, Kerrigan & Stiles LLP (ONP)† |
| Lambert Kent A | Baker, Donelson, Bearman, Caldwell * |
| Lipsey Christine | McGlinchey Stafford PLLC * |
| Reynaud, Jr Claude F | Breazeale, Sachse & Wilson, LLP |

**Up-and-coming individuals**
| | |
|---|---|
| Giarrusso III, Joseph I | Liskow & Lewis |

**Associates to watch**
| | |
|---|---|
| Burge Jason | Fishman Haygood Phelps Walmsley Willis * |

* Indicates firm / individual with profile.
†ONP = Other Notable Practitioner

## Band 1

### Baker, Donelson, Bearman, Caldwell & Berkowitz, PC
See profile on p.2313

**THE FIRM** This large Southeastern firm is well represented in Louisiana, with offices in Baton Rouge, New Orleans and Mandeville. Its litigators are known and respected throughout the state and are seen as formidable opponents in a wide array of commercial litigation areas. The team regularly defends clients in cases in state and federal court, and is adept at handling class actions and large jury trials. Baker Donelson's attorneys are experienced in areas such as securities litigation, traditional energy litigation, legacy cases, construction litigation and financial services cases. **Sources say:** "*It is a very good and highly respected firm in the commercial litigation area.*"

**KEY INDIVIDUALS** Peers in New Orleans consider **Roy Cheatwood** (see p.1359) to be "*one of the top senior litigators in the city.*" He has wide experience and has recently handled cases in areas including securities fraud, traditional energy litigation, oil field legacy cases, and banking and finance. Sources say: "*He is a very polished and tenacious*

*lawyer,*" and a "*terrific jury trial advocate.*" **Nancy Degan** (see p.1360) is a well-known commercial litigator who practices from New Orleans. She has handled a plethora of cases including securities fraud, oil and gas disputes, banking litigation and franchise litigation. Sources say: "*She is very detail-oriented, well organized and hard-working.*" **Kent Lambert** (see p.1365) is "*an up-and-coming younger lawyer,*" with a profile that "*will continue to rise.*" He has a varied commercial litigation practice that has includes cases in the banking sector, directors and officers matters, mortgage fraud and consumer class action defense.

## Barrasso Usdin Kupperman Freeman & Sarver LLC
See profile on p.1373

**THE FIRM** This consistently excellent boutique fields a number of state-leading litigators, and is well equipped to handle the largest and most complicated litigation cases in the state and throughout the region. Particular areas of expertise include disputes concerning trade secrets and franchises, and contentious matters in the energy sector. Securities litigation is another area of strength, and the firm regularly represents clients in state and federal courts, and before regulatory bodies such as the Financial Industry Regulatory Authority (FINRA).

**Sources say:** "They are experienced and extremely capable litigators."

**KEY INDIVIDUALS Judy Barrasso** (see p.1357) has a reputation as a formidable trial lawyer and she has handled a diverse selection of cases, including class action and insurance defense, and securities fraud. Sources say: "The word that comes to mind is tough; you know it is not going to be easy if she is on the other side." **George Freeman** (see p.1361) is a securities litigator whose practice includes representing clients in class actions and regulatory enforcement actions by FINRA and SEC. He is recognized by peers for his "academic, scholarly knowledge of securities law," but his abilities in the courtroom are also widely praised, with one source commenting: "As a litigator, he is cool, calm and analytical, and he has superb judgment." **Richard Sarver** (see p.1369) is particularly noted for his work in product liability cases and toxic torts. Sources agree that he is "a superb trial lawyer – extremely persuasive and well prepared." **Stephen Kupperman** (see p.1365) is a well-respected commercial litigator singled out by market sources for his abilities in securities litigation, and for his understanding of the mechanics of class actions. "He is incredibly bright, very intuitive, and relentless," reports one impressed commentator. Accomplished trial lawyer **Steven Usdin** (see p.1370) is well versed in energy litigation, class actions, insurance coverage cases and IP disputes. According to one interviewee, "he has a way of taking simple business communications and weaving them into a very methodical legal argument and making it look easy."

## Jones Walker LLP
See profile on p.1378

**THE FIRM** This Louisiana powerhouse has offices in Baton Rouge, Lafayette and New Orleans, and has an enviably deep bench of experienced litigators. Consequently, the practice has the capacity to deal with the full spectrum of litigation matters. Its lawyers are particularly experienced in class actions, either on a statewide level or a national platform. The group is also recommended for its expertise in litigation concerning securities, insurance coverage, and in the energy and financial services arenas.

**KEY INDIVIDUALS Patrick Vance** (see p.1371) leads the firm's business litigation group and is regarded as a "polished, intelligent and determined" lawyer with wide-ranging trial experience. Sources also reserve particular praise for his superb judgment. **Harry Hardin** (see p.1363) is "a very good litigator: competent and experienced, and very good

with the jury." He is much noted for his expertise in insurance, trademarks, breach of contract, antitrust and professional conduct, among other matters. **Covert Geary** (see p.1362) "is a seasoned litigator who understands complex litigation," asserts one well-placed market commentator. Geary is well respected by peers and is noted for his experience in significant commercial cases which have covered oil and gas disputes, insurance coverage and defense work, and ERISA litigation, among others. **Pauline Hardin** (see p.1363) is a widely noted criminal litigator, who is regarded by sources as "very knowledgeable and savvy" and also singled out for her "very good judgment."

## Liskow & Lewis
See profile on p.1381

**THE FIRM** This Louisiana firm practices across the Southeast from offices in Lafayette and New Orleans. The engine of the firm has traditionally been its energy department, and its commercial litigators regularly handle cases for blue-chip energy clients. However, the firm has strength in several other areas, particularly professional liability defense work and legal malpractice cases. Other standout areas of expertise include securities and antitrust litigation, and white-collar criminal defense.

**Sources say:** "The attorneys are smart, creative and efficient. We feel confident in the hands of Liskow & Lewis."

**KEY INDIVIDUALS** "Top-flight guy" **Donald Abaunza** is recommended for high-stakes litigation and is particularly noted for his focus on maritime disputes. He is also recognized for his expertise in cases related to energy matters, breach of contract, product liability and insurance. **Kenneth Polite** is a white-collar crime defense attorney with noted experience, having previously practiced at the US Attorney's Office where he prosecuted and investigated a wide variety of cases. As one source notes, "he brings knowledge of the US Attorney's Office and has a good rapport with the Louisiana US Attorney's Office." **James Brown** is popular with clients, who say that "dealing with him is a pleasure." He is predominantly recognized for his professional liability and legal malpractice defense practice, although he also handles cases in areas such as banking, trusts and estates, and antitrust. Sources say: "He is excellent to work with – he is responsive, provides solid advice, and has excellent judgment." **Donald Haycraft** "is a really good stand-up trial lawyer," according to sources. His practice includes class action defense, toxic tort and wrongful death cases, and he maintains a fine track record in multidistrict litigation. **Joseph Giarrusso** is a well-regarded younger litigator, whose practice focuses on commercial and energy-related disputes. "He is a really good guy and he displays a lot of attention to detail," report interviewees. Managing partner **Keith Jarrett** focuses on representing energy companies in admiralty cases, in addition to handling traditional energy matters and legacy litigation. An impressed commentator asserts: "He is so experienced in the industrial accidents crisis area and he knows people in the industry and judges. He has a big-picture view of litigation and he can put things in context."

## Stone Pigman Walther Wittmann LLC

**THE FIRM** This strong and well-respected commercial litigation practice has offices in New Orleans and Baton Rouge, and handles a vast array of litigation. The group has a fine track record in disputes related to land, mineral interests, securities fraud and zoning issues, and its lawyers are well versed in defending class actions and running multistate litigation. In one recent case, the firm represented the NFL and the New Orleans Saints in a trademark dispute with a plaintiff alleging ownership of the phrase 'Who Dat?'.

**Sources say:** "They are considered one of the very best in New Orleans"

**KEY INDIVIDUALS** Sources describe **Phillip Wittmann** as "a leader of the Louisiana Bar and a dean of the Louisiana trial Bar." He is leading the team in the firm's representation of R.J. Reynolds in a number of tobacco lawsuits in the state. "He is very effective in court, he has a great voice and presence in the courtroom, and the jurors react well to him," note commentators. **Wayne Lee** focuses on insurance suits and has handled a wide variety of cases in this area, including class actions. In one recent case, he was part of the team that successfully defended healthcare product manufacturer Respironics after it was accused of antitrust and civil rights breaches. Sources say: "He stays on top of the details and is a great lawyer to work with because he can see both sides of the issues and come up with unique approaches of how to handle things." Sources describe **Barry Ashe** as a "very thoughtful advocate" and further praise his excellent brief writing. He concentrates on defending clients in class actions and product liability cases.

## Band 2

## Fishman Haygood Phelps Walmsley Willis & Swanson, L.L.P.
See profile on p.1375

**THE FIRM** This boutique has a great deal of firepower and a number of experienced and highly skilled litigators. It represents plaintiffs and defendants in areas such as complex commercial litigation, contentious securities matters and arbitration. It is also noted for its expertise in disputes concerning the media and product liability. The firm represented a putative class of purchasers of Lloyds Banking Group American depositary receipts (ADRs), which claimed that the bank made misleading statements concerning the financial condition of Halifax Bank in 2009, leading to purchasers of Lloyds ADRs paying an inflated price. Other key clients include Metropolitan Bank, The Times Picayune, West Virginia University Hospitals and the Louisiana Department of Revenue.

**Sources say:** "A very talented group of lawyers, producing high-quality legal product on a timely basis; they deliver what they say they are going to, when they say they are going to."

**KEY INDIVIDUALS** Managing partner **James Swanson** (see p.1370) is recommended for his expertise in disputes concerning securities, tax and the media. Sources say: "He is a very capable lawyer – aggressive and well prepared. In *court he is a formidable opponent."* Swanson was lead partner alongside **Loretta Mince** (see p.1367) in the Lloyds Banking Group matter. Mince is a commercial litigator who, like Swanson, is noted for her strength in securities, media and tax litigation. *"She fully researches and understands the complex ins and outs of litigation, and she becomes a passionate advocate for the interests of her clients,"* assert impressed interviewees. Associate **Jason Burge** (see p.1359) is *"practicing beyond his years,"* according to interviewees, who also say: *"He is incredibly smart and incredibly driven, and produces a great work product."* The *"really top-notch"* and *"very creative"* **Brent Barriere** (see p.1357) is a recent addition to the firm's litigation group from Phelps Dunbar. He is noted for his work on behalf of plaintiffs and has a proven track record in a number of high-profile cases. He draws much praise from the market and is described as a *"polished"* and *"tenacious"* advocate with excellent instincts and an industrious work ethic.

## Gordon, Arata, McCollam, Duplantis & Eagan LLC
See profile on p.1377

**THE FIRM** This Louisiana firm has three offices in the state, in New Orleans, Lafayette and Baton Rouge. The main driver of the firm's litigation practice is its representation of energy companies in a wide range of matters, including title disputes, breach of contract claims and royalty litigation. Additionally, the team is a good choice of counsel for representation in class actions in areas such as securities, antitrust and franchise litigation, shareholder disputes and breach of fiduciary duty cases.

**KEY INDIVIDUALS Ewell Eagan** (see p.1361) *"is a very bright, experienced trial lawyer with excellent instincts,"* and is highlighted as *"one of the deans of the Bar."* His wide trial experience includes representing clients in class actions and multidistrict litigation in fields including securities, energy and IP. **Howard Sinor** (see p.1370) is a commercial litigator *"well regarded for his writing and analysis."* He has handled a wide spectrum of cases, including environmental, antitrust, IP litigation and product liability claims. Sources say: *"He is able to see the key issues in a case and spends his time getting those key issues resolved."*

## Phelps Dunbar LLP
See profile on p.1383

**THE FIRM** Phelps Dunbar has offices in New Orleans and Baton Rouge, and handles litigation on behalf of both plaintiffs and defendants. The group is well versed in disputes concerning antitrust, energy, media, professional malpractice and securities, and also has a fine track record in white-collar crime litigation. In a recent highlight, the group successfully defended American Traffic Solutions in a case that challenged the constitutionality of an automated traffic camera system installed in New Orleans. Other clients include SE Property Holdings and St. Paul Fire & Marine Insurance.

**KEY INDIVIDUALS** Commercial litigator **Harry Rosenberg** is particularly recognized in the market for his white-collar crime practice. Sources single him out for his skills as *"a planner and a strategist,"* with one peer adding:

*"When I am working with him I know I am in good shape because he is a very sound thinker and a good lawyer."*

## Band 3

### Breazeale, Sachse & Wilson, LLP

**THE FIRM** This Louisiana firm of great pedigree is centered in Baton Rouge, with additional offices in New Orleans and Covington. Its litigation team has handled cases in a wide array of areas, including shareholder disputes, oil and gas cases, antitrust, insurance coverage, contract disputes and professional malpractice. In one recent case, the group defended a municipality in a putative class action brought by its ratepayers.

**Sources say:** *"They are very good, competent and timely attorneys. They respect their clients, work closely with them, and get excellent results."*

**KEY INDIVIDUALS Alan Goodman** is an experienced litigator who practices out of the firm's New Orleans office. He has a notable bankruptcy practice, and additionally handles matters such as securities fraud, insurance coverage litigation, product liability cases and contract disputes. **Claude Reynaud** is based in Baton Rouge and represents clients in areas such as intellectual property, securities, lender liability, fiduciary duties cases and general contract disputes. Sources say: *"He is very prepared and articulate, respectful to the court and to other counsel, but effective in making his argument."*

### Gainsburgh, Benjamin, David, Meunier & Warshauer, L.L.C.

**THE FIRM** This plaintiff-focused firm is respected throughout the state. It has offices in New Orleans and New Roads, and represents clients in a wide array of litigation, including class actions, toxic torts, product liability and real estate. It is cited as an excellent choice of counsel for clients in disputes related to major disasters, such as Hurricane Katrina and the Macondo oil spill.

**Sources say:** *"An excellent plaintiff firm. If you see them you know they are going to be bringing a good claim to court."*

**KEY INDIVIDUALS Gerald Meunier** is *"one of the top plaintiff lawyers in New Orleans."* Sources highlight his leading role in the multidistrict litigation related to FEMA's provision of trailers containing formaldehyde to victims of Hurricane Katrina. *"He is very aggressive, but well regarded, credible with the judges and active in the bar,"* sources note.

### Herman, Herman & Katz LLC

**THE FIRM** This New Orleans plaintiff's firm is recognized in the market for its ability to handle large and complex cases with great success. The firm's lawyers are adept in class actions and multidistrict litigation, and are particularly noted for their abilities in mass disaster tort cases.

**KEY INDIVIDUALS Russ Herman** is a *"top-notch trial lawyer,"* respected among the legal community as *"one of the deans of the plaintiff Bar."*

### Kean Miller LLP
See profile on p.1379

**THE FIRM** This firm operates out of offices in Baton Rouge, New Orleans and Lake Charles, and represents clients in a wide variety of litigation matters. It is well versed in class action defense and maintains a fine track record for trial work concerning the energy sector, including oil and gas, pipeline and legacy litigation. The group is also recommended for its expertise in product liability disputes.

**Sources say:** *"A very fine firm."*

**KEY INDIVIDUALS** Sources praise **Gary Bezet** (see p.1358) for his ability in the areas of toxic tort litigation and product liability disputes. He represents a fine choice of counsel for energy companies, product manufacturers and petrochemical producers. Of counsel **Charles McCowan** (see p.1366) is based in the firm's Baton Rouge office and elicits market praise for his strategic approach in litigation and his ability to provide a big-picture view of a case.

### McGlinchey Stafford PLLC
See profile on p.1382

**THE FIRM** This firm offers representation throughout the state, with offices in New Orleans, Baton Rouge and Monroe. The group is well versed in class action defense and has a strong track record in disputes concerning the financial services and insurance sectors. In a recent highlight, it acted for Morgan Buildings & Spas on a class action brought by a group of plaintiffs alleging they had been exposed to formaldehyde while staying in temporary accommodation provided by FEMA in the aftermath of Hurricane Katrina. The firm was successful in having 211 of 230 cases against its client dismissed; a successful settlement of the remaining cases is currently being documented.

**Sources say:** *"They are creative and very responsive, and they keep me updated."*

**KEY INDIVIDUALS Christine Lipsey** (see p.1366) is an experienced commercial litigator based in the firm's Baton Rouge office. She has represented clients in multiparty and multidistrict litigation in areas such as trade secrets, insurance, banking and contract disputes. Sources say: *"She can simplify a very complex situation in a way that lay people can understand."* New Orleans-based **Richard Aguilar** (see p.1357) is recommended for his work in bankruptcy litigation. *"He is a tenacious litigator who works extremely hard on behalf of clients,"* report impressed interviewees.

### Sher Garner Cahill Richter Klein & Hilbert LLC

**THE FIRM** This New Orleans-based firm provides litigation services in a wide range of sectors. Its attorneys are experienced in matters such as toxic torts, professional liability, oil and gas, unfair competition and banking litigation.

**KEY INDIVIDUALS** The highly regarded **James Garner** is well versed in class action work, representing both plaintiffs and defendants in areas such as noise pollution, banking and the energy sector.

## Taylor, Porter, Brooks & Phillips, LLP

**THE FIRM** This Baton Rouge firm represents clients in a wide array of litigation scenarios. Its lawyers have extensive experience in defending class actions and multidistrict litigation, and are recommended for their expertise in cases concerning securities, professional malpractice, toxic torts and energy.

**KEY INDIVIDUALS** *"Smart, capable lawyer"* **Frederick Tulley** is noted by peers for his wide-ranging litigation experience, but is principally recognized for his ability in securities cases. **Harry Philips** is seen as one of the leading litigators in Baton Rouge and maintains a fine reputation for his work in insurance, banking and product liability disputes, and general commercial litigation. Sources say: *"He is very smooth, very polished in court and good at interacting with jurors; he has all the qualities of a good trial lawyer."*

## Other Notable Practitioners

Former Assistant US Attorney **Walter Becker** (see p.1358) is now head of Chaffe McCall, LLP's white-collar crime section. He is well respected in the New Orleans legal world and is described as *"a very diligent and knowledgeable white-collar crime attorney."* **Richard Stanley** of Stanley Reuter Ross Thornton & Alford LLC is perhaps best recognized in the market for his knowledge of professional liability work, and is widely considered one of the leading Louisiana-based practitioners in that field. He is also sought for his expertise in securities and product liability suits. *"He is absolutely superb: I have seen him argue and he is very analytical, persuasive and creative,"* reports one impressed commentator. **Robert Kerrigan** of Deutsch, Kerrigan & Stiles LLP is an experienced litigator recommended for his work defending personal injury claims,

toxic torts, professional liability cases and insurance coverage disputes. Sources note: *"He is an excellent trial lawyer and he has a terrific way with juries."* Montgomery Barnett's **Daniel Lund** (see p.1366) is noted for his strengths in disputes concerning banking, securities, antitrust and oil and gas, as well as contract litigation. He is particularly recognized by legal sources for his legal malpractice defense work, and sources say: *"He is a very capable trial lawyer, has a great presence and is very smart; if you were in trouble he would be on your list."* The well-regarded **Mark Beebe** (see p.1358) at Adams and Reese LLP concentrates on litigation related to antitrust and securities, and is also much in demand for his expertise in contractual disputes and directors and officers cases.

# REAL ESTATE

Commentary about individuals can be found under their firm's paragraph. If the firm has no paragraph (is not ranked) look at Other Notable Practitioners.

**Real Estate**
**Leading Firms**

### Band 1
Jones Walker LLP *
Phelps Dunbar LLP *
Sher Garner Cahill Richter Klein & Hilbert LLC
Stone Pigman Walther Wittmann LLC

### Band 2
McGlinchey Stafford PLLC *
The Steeg Law Firm, LLC

### Band 3
Adams and Reese LLP *
Kean Miller LLP *
Liskow & Lewis *

*Indicates firm / individual with profile.*
*Alphabetical order within each band. Band 1 is the highest.*

| **Real Estate** **Leading Individuals** | |
| --- | --- |
| **Band 1** | |
| Claverie Sr Philip deV | *Phelps Dunbar LLP* |
| Colvin R Keith | *Jones Walker LLP *  |
| Roussel Randy P | *Phelps Dunbar LLP* |
| Sher Leopold | *Sher Garner Cahill Richter Klein & Hilbert* |
| Steeg Robert M | *The Steeg Law Firm, LLC *  |
| Talley Susan G | *Stone Pigman Walther Wittmann LLC* |
| **Band 2** | |
| Adams Marguerite L | *Liskow & Lewis* |
| Bacot Samuel A | *McGlinchey Stafford PLLC *  |
| Cahill Jr Elwood | *Sher Garner Cahill Richter Klein & Hilbert* |
| Cromwell David | *Pettiette, Armand, Dunkelman (ONP)[†]* |
| Gregorie Jr Isaac McPherson | *Kean Miller LLP *  |
| Landry Charles | *Jones Walker LLP *  |
| Reymond Jr Leon J | *Liskow & Lewis* |
| Schneider Michael R | *Stone Pigman Walther Wittmann LLC* |
| Willis Sterling Scott | *Fishman Haygood Phelps Walmsley (ONP)[†] *  |
| **Band 3** | |
| Crosby E Howell | *Chaffe McCall, LLP (ONP)[†] *  |
| Gray Jeffry W | *Jones Walker LLP *  |
| Kling Neal | *Sher Garner Cahill Richter Klein & Hilbert* |
| LeBreton Rose | *Lugenbuhl, Wheaton, Peck, Rankin (ONP)[†]* |
| Leyens, Jr Jon F | *Baker, Donelson, Bearman, Caldwell (ONP)[†] *  |
| Meyer Malcolm A | *Adams and Reese LLP *  |
| Moore Marie | *Sher Garner Cahill Richter Klein & Hilbert* |
| Quinn Jr Louis S | *Jones Walker LLP *  |
| Richard P Ragan | *Phelps Dunbar LLP* |
| Schmidt Justin B | *Adams and Reese LLP *  |
| Tessier Frank A | *Carver, Darden, Koretzky, Tessier (ONP)[†]* |
| Tyler Susan M | *Jones Walker LLP *  |

[†]*ONP = Other Notable Practitioner*

## Band 1

### Jones Walker LLP
See profile on p.1378

**THE FIRM** This premier practice represents clients throughout the state and beyond from offices in New Orleans, Lafayette and Baton Rouge. The team handles every stage of real estate work for its clients, from financing and development to acquisition, sales and leasing, and is also recommended for its expertise in securitization, land use and title issues. A recent focus for the firm has been in the area of housing, and it has been involved in projects across the USA, developing student, low income and public housing. Clients include developers, banks, nonprofits, industrial companies, public bodies and healthcare groups.

**Sources say:** *"They are excellent."*

**KEY INDIVIDUALS** Commercial real estate attorney **Keith Colvin** (see p.1360) represents lenders, developers

and owners, and has worked on a wide variety of matters, from housing projects to industrial developments. Sources say: *"He knows what he is doing and tries to make things*

*move forward. He is a good, careful lawyer and a good person to work with."* **Charles Landry** (see p.1365) is popular with clients, winning much praise for his work ethic, advocacy skills and ability to keep up to date with developments in the law. Landry is based in Baton Rouge and represents a fine choice of counsel on land use and zoning issues, as well as real estate development and financing. **Louis Quinn** (see p.1368) is noted for his wealth of experience in real estate transactions, financing, development and leasing, and elicits praise from peers for his practical, reasonable approach to matters. Interviewees also praise *"his expertise with complex commercial real estate documents and his willingness to dive down into the weeds on those projects."* **Susan Tyler** (see p.1370) is a well-respected attorney who focuses on real estate financing and lending. *"She is very detail-oriented and has good business sense,"* sources note. **Jeffry Gray** (see p.1362) has a broad-based practice that takes in land use, zoning work, financing and lending, in both the commercial and industrial space. Additionally, he is very experienced in title work and is an authorized title agent. *"He is easy to work with because he is a 'try to get a deal done' kind of guy,"* notes one impressed commentator.

### Phelps Dunbar LLP
See profile on p.1383

**THE FIRM** This fine team is equipped to handle the full spectrum of real estate work, and counsels commercial and industrial clients on issues ranging from land use to financing. The group acts for a range of clients, including restaurant chains, real estate developers, transport groups, energy companies and public bodies. In recent work, it acted for a leading real estate development and investment firm on the refinancing of four apartment complexes worth $150 million.

**Sources say:** *"We see those guys a lot and they are good real estate lawyers."*

**KEY INDIVIDUALS** Sources regard **Philip deV Claverie** as *"one of the preeminent attorneys in the community."* He elicits much praise from the market for his work with developers, and also for his strengths in real estate finance. **Randy Roussel** is a business attorney who is particularly recommended for his work on the development side as well as on title matters. **Ragan Richard** has a varied business practice and regularly counsels clients on real estate transactions, developments and financing matters. Sources say: *"He represents clients very well and knows how to get a transaction closed."*

## Sher Garner Cahill Richter Klein & Hilbert LLC

**THE FIRM** This firm is recognized by sources in the New Orleans legal community for its wide-ranging capabilities in this field. It handles an array of matters including transactions, zoning, financing and disputes. The team represents organizations and individuals, and has a fine reputation for its work on projects including convention centers, office buildings and housing developments.

**KEY INDIVIDUALS** The well-respected **Leopold Sher** has a varied business practice with a strong focus on finance and commercial real estate. He has a strong track record in representing banks, REITs, insurance companies and real estate developers. **Elwood Cahill** is a *"practical and business-oriented attorney"* focusing on commercial real estate, financing and general business law. *"He is smart and he can work towards finding a reasonable solution to something while still representing his client well,"* asserts one impressed interviewee. **Neal Kling** has a mixed business practice which includes real estate transactional, leasing and finance work. Sources praise his courteous approach, and say: *"He is knowledgeable and very practical in his understanding of clients' strengths and weaknesses."* Business and real estate lawyer **Marie Moore** has developed an excellent reputation in the commercial leasing area. Sources reserve particular praise for her deep knowledge of the real estate environment.

## Stone Pigman Walther Wittmann LLC

**THE FIRM** This Louisiana firm has offices in New Orleans and Baton Rouge and has developed a strong reputation in the real estate and real estate financing space. Its attorneys regularly arrange complex financings from sources such as bank loans, tax credits and government grants. The firm's clients include industrial companies, banks and other lenders, construction companies, energy companies and restaurant groups. In one recent matter, the firm represented the New Orleans Hornets in negotiating its lease on the New Orleans Arena.

**Sources say:** *"They are very knowledgeable and good at helping us to pause and take in the bigger picture."*

**KEY INDIVIDUALS Susan Talley** has a fantastic reputation in the market and is singled out as a *"very thorough and detail-oriented lawyer,"* and *"like white on rice, she is on top of absolutely everything."* Her practice includes real estate financing, development, leasing and transactions. She recently acted for Kemira Chemicals on its sale of a decommissioned plant in Shreveport to another chemicals

group. **Michael Schneider** is noted for his strengths in real estate financing and development, and also has a fine reputation in the market for his adept handling of transactions. In one matter he represented a West Coast REIT in its purchase of a New Orleans hotel. *"He is knowledgeable, he is a good analyzer and is able to present us with good options,"* asserts one satisfied client.

## Band 2

### McGlinchey Stafford PLLC
See profile on p.1382

**THE FIRM** This firm has offices in New Orleans, Baton Rouge and Monroe, and advises clients on the full spectrum of real estate matters. Clients include lenders, developers and title insurance companies. The team has recently handled significant real estate matters in fields such as healthcare, gaming, student housing and retail.

**Sources say:** *"It's a great service; they are so knowledgeable and always get back to you quickly."*

**KEY INDIVIDUALS** Baton Rouge-based **Samuel Bacot** (see p.1357) is recommended for his land use and zoning work, and is also well versed in commercial leasing, real estate litigation and transactions. Sources say: *"He goes above and beyond – if he can't figure out a solution at first, he goes away and thinks, and always figures it out for us."*

### The Steeg Law Firm, LLC

**THE FIRM** This New Orleans firm offers a comprehensive real estate service covering financing and transactional work, among other areas. The group is recommended for its work with condominium owners and on title insurance matters, and is also particularly noted for its expertise in developing multifamily dwellings.

**KEY INDIVIDUALS Robert Steeg** (see p.1370) is recognized for his experience in transactional and financing matters related to projects such as industrial developments, condominium developments, hotels, apartment buildings and nursing homes. He elicits particular praise for his ability to quickly get up to speed on matters.

## Band 3

### Adams and Reese LLP
See profile on p.1372

**THE FIRM** This firm operates from New Orleans and Baton Rouge, and handles real estate finance, transactions, title work, and zoning and land use matters. In a recent highlight, the team has represented Regions Bank in a number of cross-state matters, including several real estate-related transactions. Other key clients include Louisiana REALTORS, Taco Bell, Old Republic National Title Insurance Company and Iberia Bank.

**KEY INDIVIDUALS Malcolm Meyer** (see p.1367) is noted in the market for his title work and active transactional practice. Sources say: *"He is very knowledgeable and is a deal-doer."* Meyer is based in the firm's New Orleans office alongside fellow partner **Justin Schmidt** (see

p.1369), who is particularly recommended for his expertise in land use and zoning work.

## Kean Miller LLP
See profile on p.1379

**THE FIRM** This real estate practice is centered in Baton Rouge and is particularly notable for the work it carries out for the firm's industrial and energy clients. It also represents developers, investors, landlords and tenants in a wide variety of real estate-related issues, including transactions, land use, zoning and title matters.

**KEY INDIVIDUALS Isaac McPherson Gregorie** (see p.1362) is based in Baton Rouge and has a mixed business practice covering real estate transactions, leasing and financing. He wins much praise from the market, with one source singling him out as being *"highly responsive, detail-oriented and a problem solver."*

## Liskow & Lewis
See profile on p.1381

**THE FIRM** This firm has offices in New Orleans and Lafayette, and is particularly recognized for its real estate work for energy and chemical companies. The group has a fine track record working with developers and lenders, and continues to be much sought for its advice to commercial tenants on leases.

**KEY INDIVIDUALS Marguerite Adams** acts for lenders and developers and is well versed in acquisitions and sales, as well as real estate financing matters. Additionally, she is much in demand for her title opinion work. The *"terrific"* **Leon Reymond** is a business lawyer whose real estate practice focuses on representing clients in the sale and leasing of real estate and mineral-bearing properties. Sources reserve particular praise for his hard-working approach to matters.

## Other Notable Practitioners

**David Cromwell** of Pettiette, Armand, Dunkelman, Woodley, Byrd & Cromwell LLP is well versed in acquisitions, leasing and lending, and is also sought for his expertise in asset-based financing and loan workouts. *"He spots issues very quickly and is very focused on the critical components in a particular matter – he homes in immediately on what is essential,"* notes one impressed source. Chaffe McCall, LLP's **Howell Crosby** (see p.1360) is a noted transactional attorney who practices in the areas of real estate and general business law. He has a fine reputation for acting for developers and lenders on a wide variety of projects, including housing, shopping centers and hotel developments. According to sources, *"he is thorough and represents his clients very well."* **Rose LeBreton** of Lugenbuhl, Wheaton, Peck, Rankin & Hubbard is recommended for her strengths in title defense work, an area that *"she knows backwards and forwards,"* say interviewees. She is also commonly sought for her expertise in development and transactions, as well as land use, title work and leasing. **Frank Tessier** at Carver, Darden, Koretzky, Tessier, Finn, Blossman & Areaux LLC focuses on financing and transactional work, and is recognized for his strengths in development, lease negotiation, zoning and land use, and real estate disputes. *"Practical, results-oriented lawyer"* Sterling Scott Willis (see p.1371) of Fishman Haygood Phelps Walmsley Willis & Swanson, L.L.P. has a varied corporate and real estate practice. *"He makes you feel like you are his*

*only client: it seems like he is always there when you need him and he responds almost immediately,"* reports one enthusiastic client. Jon Leyens (see p.1366) is based in the New Orleans office of Baker, Donelson, Bearman, Caldwell & Berkowitz, PC. He concentrates on real estate and business

financing, acting for developers and lenders on matters such as commercial leasing, real estate transactions, asset-based financing and bond loans.

# Leaders' Profiles in Louisiana

## ADAMS, H Mark
Jones Walker LLP, New Orleans
504 582 8258
madams@joneswalker.com
*Featured in Labor & Employment (Louisiana)*
**Practice Areas:** Senior Partner and founder of Jones Walker's Labor and Employment Practice. For more than 30 years has represented and counseled employers in all aspects of labor relations and employment law and regulatory compliance.
**Professional Memberships:** American Bar Association, Labor and Litigation Sections; Louisiana and Mississippi State Bars; also admitted: United States Supreme Court; United States Courts of Appeal, Second, Fifth, Sixth, Eighth, and Eleventh Circuits; all United States District Courts in Louisiana and Mississippi. Louisiana representative to Employers Counsel Network, an association of leading labor and employment law firms in the United States and Canada.
**Career:** Joined Jones Walker, 1981; Partner since 1986; Member of firm's Executive Committee from 2001 to 2006; chaired firm's Labor Relations and Employment Practice until 2006.
**Publications:** Editor, 'Louisiana Employment Law Letter' (the leading Louisiana authority on developments and emerging trends in labor and employment law), since 1992.

## AGUILAR, Richard A
McGlinchey Stafford PLLC, New Orleans
504 596 2884
raguilar@mcglinchey.com
*Featured in Bankruptcy/Restructuring (Louisiana), Litigation (Louisiana)*
**Practice Areas:** Commercial and business litigation; bankruptcy, reorganization and creditors' rights; real estate.
**Professional Memberships:** Association for Corporate Growth; Commercial Finance Association's Southwest Chapter; Equipment Leasing and Finance Association; Louisiana State University Greater New Orleans Advisory Board; Turnaround Management Association.
**Career:** Has extensive experience in the areas of high-consequence commercial and business litigation, including disputes involving lender liability, construction contracts, estate and trust disputes, real estate contracts and leases, other contractual and unfair trade practices claims, and issues concerning shareholder's rights, claims against officers and directors, and derivative actions. Also handles bankruptcy, creditors' rights, the enforcement of loan and lease obligations, and foreclosures.
**Personal:** Louisiana State University Paul M. Hebert Law Center, JD (1986); Louisiana State University, BS, Finance (1983).

## AGUILAR JR, Rodolfo J
McGlinchey Stafford PLLC, Baton Rouge
225 382 3625
rudyaguilar@mcglinchey.com
*Featured in Corporate/M&A (Louisiana)*
**Practice Areas:** Commercial finance, construction law, corporate law, insurance regulatory law, mergers and acquisitions.
**Professional Memberships:** Louisiana State Bar Association, Baton Rouge Bar Association.
**Career:** Managing Member of the firm; maintains a corporate, business, and insurance regulatory practice; handles corporate transactions, commercial financing transactions, transactions relating to real estate development and general business matters; represents physician groups and organizations in their internal corporate structure, joint ventures and healthcare related matters; represents clients in the acquisition and formation of health, property, casualty and life insurance companies; represents insurers in various regulatory, corporate and financial matters; represents developers and owners in the negotiation, documentation, acquisition, financing, construction and management of various mixed use developments including hotel, retail and condominium development.
**Personal:** Speaks conversational Spanish, Member of the Baton Rouge Rotary Club, Member of Board of Directors of City Year Baton Rouge, Past Member of Board of Governors of the Baton Rouge Community College Foundation.

## ANDERSON, Jennifer
Jones Walker LLP, Baton Rouge
225 248 2040
janderson@joneswalker.com
*Featured in Labor & Employment (Louisiana)*
**Practice Areas:** Partner in Jones Walker's Labor and Employment Practice representing employers in the litigation and trial of employment-related claims, including FLSA claims and collective actions, discrimination, harassment, and retaliation claims under various state and federal laws, and restrictive covenant and contract disputes. Regularly provides management training, conducts compliance audits, and counsels employers in the development of policies and practices for complying with, and minimizing claims under, labor and employment laws.
**Professional Memberships:** Louisiana State Bar Association; Texas Bar Association; Louisiana representative to Employers Counsel Network, an association of leading labor and employment law firms in the United States and Canada.
**Career:** Admitted in Texas in 2005; admitted in Louisiana in 1995; Louisiana State University (JD, 1995, BA 1990).

**Publications:** Editor, 'Louisiana Employment Law Letter' (the leading Louisiana authority on developments and emerging trends in labor and employment law), since 1999.

## ARNOLD III, Edward H (Hank)
Baker, Donelson, Bearman, Caldwell & Berkowitz, PC, New Orleans
504 566 5204
harnold@bakerdonelson.com
*Featured in Banking & Finance (Louisiana)*
**Practice Areas:** Extensive experience in commercial, marine and energy finance and real property acquisitions and leases. Represents owners, shipyards and lenders regarding construction, financing and operation of documented vessels. Represents creditors, bankruptcy trustees and official committees before bankruptcy courts in Louisiana, Texas and Mississippi. Assists developers, lenders and licensed vendors regarding finance and regulatory matters in riverboat gaming, video gaming and casino industries.
**Professional Memberships:** Former National Board of Directors Member and Louisiana Chapter Board Member, Turnaround Management Association. Member, American Bankruptcy Institute, Louisiana Bankers Association, Maritime Law Association, American, Federal and Louisiana Bar Associations.
**Career:** Licensed in Louisiana, 1988.

## BACKSTROM, William
Jones Walker LLP, New Orleans
504 582 8228
bbackstrom@joneswalker.com
*Featured in Corporate/M&A (Louisiana)*
**Practice Areas:** State and local tax; economic development; tax and estates; tax and fiduciary litigation; tax policy.
**Professional Memberships:** American Bar Association (Member and Vice-Chair, 2010–2011, Section of Taxation, Committee on State and Local Taxes); Louisiana State Bar Association (Member, Section of Taxation); The Mississippi Bar (Member, Section of Taxation).
**Career:** Leads the firm's Tax & Estates Practice Group. For more than 30 years, he has focused primarily on state and local tax matters in Louisiana and on a multistate basis, including tax and business planning, utilization of tax and business incentives, audits, government relations, administrative appeals, judicial appeals, and legislative matters. He is a Board-Certified Tax Specialist as certified by the Louisiana Board of Legal Specialization.
**Publications:** He is a frequent lecturer and author on a variety of tax topics, including all aspects of Louisiana state and local taxation, as

well as state and local tax issues relating to multi-state and multinational operations.
**Personal:** New York University School of Law, LLM in Taxation, 1980; The University of Mississippi School of Law, JD, 1979; Mississippi State University, BS in Accounting, 1976. Admitted to practice in Louisiana and Mississippi.

## BACOT, Samuel A
McGlinchey Stafford PLLC, Baton Rouge
225 382 3650
sbacot@mcglinchey.com
*Featured in Real Estate (Louisiana)*
**Practice Areas:** Commercial real estate, related land use and zoning law, commercial and multi-family leasing, corporate and business law.
**Professional Memberships:** American Bar Association, Baton Rouge Bar Association, Baton Rouge Growth Coalition Incorporated, Greater Baton Rouge Association of Realtors, International Council of Shopping Centers, Louisiana Bar Foundation.
**Personal:** Louisiana State University, LLM, 1973, Louisiana State University, BS, 1969.

## BARRASSO, Judy Y
Barrasso Usdin Kupperman Freeman & Sarver LLC, New Orleans
504 589 9700
JBarrasso@BarrassoUsdin.com
*Featured in Litigation (Louisiana)*
**Practice Areas:** Ms Barrasso represents clients in complex commercial litigation matters, including unfair trade practices, trade secret, professional liability, securities and banking, class actions, insurance coverage and insurance bad faith claims.
**Career:** Founding Member of Barrasso Usdin Kupperman Freeman & Sarver. Louisiana's Litigator of the Year 2012-Benchmark Litigation; Top 10 Louisiana Super Lawyers; 'Best Lawyers in America'.
**Personal:** JD, summa cum laude, Tulane University 1981; Order of the Coif; Articles Editor, Tulane Law Review; a Fellow of the American College of Trial Lawyers and International Society of Barristers; Tulane University Law School Trial Advocacy Adjunct faculty (1993 - present).

## BARRIERE, Brent B
Fishman Haygood Phelps Walmsley Willis & Swanson, L.L.P., New Orleans
504 584 9210
barriereb@phelps.com
*Featured in Bankruptcy/Restructuring (Louisiana), Litigation (Louisiana)*
**Practice Areas:** Brent Barriere is a Partner and the Practice Coordinator of the Commercial Litigation Group in the New Orleans office. He represents clients in a wide variety of commercial

disputes, including bankruptcy and creditors' rights, securities litigation, breach of contract, business valuation disputes, and class actions. He has been named one of Louisiana's top 10 litigators by the National Law Journal.

**Personal:** Tulane University, JD, magna cum laude, 1981. Hamilton College, BA, with honors, 1977.

### BECKER, Walter F
Chaffe McCall, LLP, New Orleans
504 585 7046
becker@chaffe.com
*Featured in Litigation (Louisiana)*

**Practice Areas:** White-collar Criminal Defense, Maritime Criminal Law, Select Civil Litigation, Internal Corporate Investigations, Corporate Compliance Programs.

**Professional Memberships:** American Bar Association, Louisiana State Bar Association, State Bar of Texas, Federal Bar Association, Fifth Circuit Bar Association.

**Career:** Assistant District Attorney, Orleans Parish (1983-87); Assistant United States Attorney, EDLA (1987-2001) (Chief, Criminal Division, First Assistant United States Attorney); Associate Independent Counsel, Washington, DC (1996).

**Publications:** How to Use a Jury Consultant: A Guide for Trial Attorneys, Louisiana Bar Journal, Volume 50, Number 6; Recent Trends in Magic Pipe Cases, The Maritime Advocate Online, Issue 376, December 9, 2008,

**Personal:** Tulane University, BA, 1978; Tulane School of Law, JD, 1982.

### BEEBE, Mark
Adams and Reese LLP, New Orleans
504 581 3234
mark.beebe@arlaw.com
*Featured in Litigation (Louisiana)*

**Practice Areas:** Litigation, agricultural chemicals, antitrust, d&o/professional liability, education, errors and omissions, franchise/distribution, health care, maritime/offshore, securities.

**Professional Memberships:** Louisiana Bar Foundation, International Association of Defense Counsel, Litigation Counsel of America Fellow.

**Career:** Represents Goldman Sachs, Credit Suisse First Boston, Salomon Smith Barney, First Investors INVESCO and US Trust. Advises boards of Jazz Casino Corporation and New Orleans Center for the Creative Arts - Riverfront, the Algiers Charter School Association and Crescent City Charter School Association.

**Personal:** JD, Tulane University Law School, 1989; BA, Tulane University, 1986.

### BEISER, Stephen P
McGlinchey Stafford PLLC, New Orleans
504 596 2756
sbeiser@mcglinchey.com
*Featured in Labor & Employment (Louisiana)*

**Practice Areas:** Labor and employment; employee benefits; employment litigation and arbitration; appellate litigation; regulatory law.

**Professional Memberships:** American Bar Association; Louisiana Association of Defense Counsel; Louisiana State Bar Association; The New Orleans Bar Association.

**Career:** Experienced litigator in labor and employment law representing management interests before state and federal courts as well as regulatory agencies. Also maintains a commercial litigation and regulatory law practice.

**Personal:** Tulane University Law School, JD (1984); Tulane University, BA (1980).

### BERGIN, Edward H
Jones Walker LLP, New Orleans
504 582 8222
nbergin@joneswalker.com
*Featured in Energy & Natural Resources (Louisiana)*

**Practice Areas:** Antitrust and trade regulation; business and commercial litigation; class action defense; disaster recovery client team; economic development; energy; FEMA and SBA assistance; insurance and litigation; tax and fiduciary litigation; telecommunications and utilities.

**Professional Memberships:** American Bar Association; Louisiana State Bar Association; New Orleans Bar Association.

**Career:** Mr Bergin's practice focuses on commercial litigation with emphasis on utility regulation, complex and class action litigation, contract litigation, energy litigation, and antitrust.

**Personal:** University of Virginia School of Law, JD, 1979; University of Virginia, BA, 1972, with distinction; Omicron Delta Kappa; Raven Society; Echols Scholar; NROTC Scholarship.

### BERNARD, G Wogan
Chaffe McCall, LLP, New Orleans
504 585 7289
bernard@chaffe.com
*Featured in Banking & Finance (Louisiana)*

**Practice Areas:** Business and Taxation, Real Estate.

**Professional Memberships:** Louisiana State and American Bar Associations; Vice-Chair of the ABA Real Property, Trust and Estate Law Section Committee on Mortgage Lending; Co-Vice Chair of the Young Lawyers Network of the ABA Section of Real Property, Trust and Estate Law; Louisiana Bankers Association.

**Career:** Mr Bernard has represented lenders and developers with the acquisition, divestiture, development, leasing and financing, loan workouts, and distressed asset assistance of office buildings, apartments, condominiums, restaurant, low-income housing, and hotel developments. He has also assisted clients in the areas of planning, zoning, subdivision, and permitting requirements on the state and local level.

**Personal:** Washington & Lee University, BA, 2003; Louisiana State University, Paul M. Hebert Law Center, JD, B.C.L., 2006 (Senior Editor - Louisiana Law Review).

### BEZET, Gary A
Kean Miller LLP, Baton Rouge
225 387 0999
gary.bezet@keanmiller.com
*Featured in Litigation (Louisiana)*

**Practice Areas:** Litigation and Toxic Tort Defense.

**Professional Memberships:** Baton Rouge, Louisiana State, and American Bar Associations; Louisiana Association of Defense Counsel.

**Career:** Gary Bezet is a founding member of Kean Miller LLP. He served as the firm's managing partner for 9 years. Gary represents industrial and energy industry clients in cases involving toxic tort, chemical exposure, pipeline expropriation, products liability, and class action defense. Gary is a respected litigation strategist having handled thousands of cases for some of the nation's most prominent energy and petrochemical companies.

### BOTNICK, Michael
Gordon, Arata, McCollam, Duplantis & Eagan LLC, New Orleans
504 582 1111
mbotnick@gordonarata.com
*Featured in Construction (Louisiana)*

**Career:** Michael Botnick is a member in the Litigation section and has 38 years of experience in construction, litigation, transactions, real estate, contracts and corporate law, and trust and estates. Michael served as Deputy City Attorney for the City of New Orleans and handled the negotiation, drafting and preparation of all public bid, professional and personal service contracts. Michael also served as Director of Economic Development for the City and as Lead Counsel for the 1988 Republican National Convention, the Pope John Paul II visit, the Harrah's Casino project, and in various complex and high-profile state and federal litigation.

### BRODERS, John J
Jones Walker LLP, New Orleans
504 582 8172
jbroders@joneswalker.com
*Featured in Banking & Finance (Louisiana)*

**Practice Areas:** Senior Partner concentrating in all aspects of maritime and marine energy related matters with an emphasis on marine transactions, including construction of vessels, charters, services agreements, acquisitions and sales, financing and mortgages, flagging and manning, marine insurance and arbitration and related matters. In addition, he represents owners of mega yachts in all aspects of construction, purchase, sale and ownership.

**Career:** Joined Jones Walker in 1971, Partner in 1976, Senior Partner in 2000.

**Personal:** Tulane University (BA 1971, JD 1971).

### BROWN, Laura
McGlinchey Stafford PLLC, New Orleans
504 596 2787
lbrown@mcglinchey.com
*Featured in Banking & Finance (Louisiana)*

**Practice Areas:** Banking and consumer finance law.

**Professional Memberships:** American Bar Association: Business Law Section, Banking Law Committee, Deposit Products and Payment Systems subcommittee (Chairman 2012, Vice Chairman 2008-2011), Consumer Financial Services Committee, Uniform Commercial Code Committee; 2014 Louisiana Bankers Association; Louisiana Bar Association; Mortgage Bankers Association; Industrial Development Board of the City of New Orleans.

**Career:** Laura Brown is a member of the firm's Consumer Financial Services Group, concentrat-ing her practice on banking and consumer finance law. She represents local, regional and national banks and financial institutions in connection with matters relating to deposits and payment systems, bank operations, vendor management and varied aspects of consumer finance, including residential mortgage banking, credit card law and regulatory and compliance matters. Ms Brown publishes reguarly and frequently speaks to national and regional audiences on topics regarding banking and consumer lending regulation and compliance.

**Personal:** Loyola University New Orleans College of Law, JD, (cum laude, Law Review); Jacksonville State University, BA, English, (with honors).

### BRYAN, Boyd A
Jones Walker LLP, Baton Rouge
225 248 2134
bbryan@joneswalker.com
*Featured in Environment (Louisiana)*

**Practice Areas:** Environmental; energy; green law and sustainability; real estate: land use, development and finance.

**Professional Memberships:** Louisiana State Bar Association (Immediate Past Chairman, Council Member, Section of Environmental Law); American Bar Association (Member, Section of Environment, Energy and Resources); Louisiana Chemical Industry Alliance (Jones Walker, member); Louisiana Oil and Gas Association; Louisiana Mid-Continent Oil and Gas Association.

**Career:** Mr Bryan has represented clients in a broad range of environmental matters, including permitting, regulatory advice, environmental due diligence and risk allocation in transactions, defense of agency enforcement actions, and environmental litigation. He has extensive experience in permitting of industrial facilities and resolving issues before the Louisiana Department of Environmental Quality, the Louisiana Department of Natural Resources, the US EPA, the US Army Corps of Engineers, and other regulatory agencies.

**Publications:** Mr Bryan is a frequent author and speaker on environmental issues. His publications include "Environmental Due Diligence in Mineral Property Transactions: Emerging Risks, Requirements, and Strategies," Published by the Rocky Mountain Mineral Law Foundation in the Proceedings of the 51st Annual Rocky Mountain Mineral Law Institute (2005).

**Personal:** Paul M Hebert Law Center, Louisiana State University, JD, 1987; University of Southwestern Louisiana, BS, 1984.

### BUATT, Louis
Jones Walker LLP, New Orleans
504 582 8237
lbuatt@joneswalker.com
*Featured in Environment (Louisiana)*

**Practice Areas:** Energy; energy, environment and natural resources; real estate: land use, development and finance; water law.

**Professional Memberships:** Louisiana Oil and Gas Association (Board of Directors 2011-Present); Louisiana Mid-Continent Oil and Gas Association (2011-Present); Louisiana State Bar

Association (1989 to date); Atchafalaya Basin Research and Promotion Board (Chairman, 1989 to date); Coastal Protection and Restoration Authority (2008–2011); Coastal Protection and Restoration Finance Corporation (Ex Officio Member, 2008–2011); Gulf of Mexico Alliance (2008–2010); Louisiana Environmental Education Commission (2008–2011).

**Career:** Former Assistant Secretary and General Counsel, Louisiana Department of Environmental Quality; Former Assistant Secretary of the Louisiana Department of Natural Resources; Acting Secretary of the Mineral and Energy Board.

**Publications:** "Oil and Gas Operators Must Pay to Use Running Water: A Critique of the Attorney General Opinions", LOGA Industry Report, Winter 2013; "The 2012 Legacy Lawsuit Legislation: Making the Most of the DNR Public Hearing", LOGA Industry Report, Fall 2012; "Are You Minding Your Section 404 Permits?" LOGA Industry Report, Winter 2012; "OCM Reduces Permit Times" LOGA Industry Report, Fall 2011.

**Personal:** University of Houston Law Center, LLM in Energy and Environmental Law, 1995; Southern University Law Center, JD, magna cum laude; moot court board, 1989; Louisiana State University, BS in Geology, 1986.

### BURGE, Jason
Fishman Haygood Phelps Walmsley Willis & Swanson, L.L.P., New Orleans
504 586 5241
jburge@fishmanhaygood.com
*Featured in Litigation (Louisiana)*

**Practice Areas:** Mr Burge represents clients in commercial and securities litigation. Recent litigation clients include Rouse's Enterprises, LLC, Wampold Companies, Inc., municipal and health care issuers of Auction Rate Securities.

**Career:** Mr Burge graduated magna cum laude from Ohio State University, summa cum laude from Loyola University New Orleans College of Music, magna cum laude from New York University School of Law, where he was selected to the Order of the Coif. Following graduation, clerked for the Honorable Jerry E. Smith on the United States Court of Appeals for the Fifth Circuit.

**Personal:** Father of Jonathan, 4, and Simon, 2.

### CANCIENNE, Phyllis G
Baker, Donelson, Bearman, Caldwell & Berkowitz, PC, Baton Rouge
504 566 5200
pcancienne@bakerdonelson.com
*Featured in Labor & Employment (Louisiana)*

**Practice Areas:** Ms Cancienne has 24 years of experience representing employers before federal and state courts and governmental agencies in all areas of labor and employment law including discrimination, harassment, medical leave, disability, non-competition and wage and hour litigation. She counsels employers on HR compliance, conducts workplace training and drafts personnel policies and procedures.

**Professional Memberships:** Louisiana, American and Federal Bar Associations, Louisiana

representative for the Employment Law Alliance, a global alliance of leading L&E firms.

**Career:** Licensed in Louisiana, 1989. AV-Rated, Martindale-Hubbell; Louisiana Super Lawyers (2010, 2011, 2012).

**Personal:** Louisiana State University Law Center, JD-1989; Louisiana State University, BA-1985.

### CASEY, Robert
Jones Walker LLP, Baton Rouge
225 248 2090
rcasey@joneswalker.com
*Featured in Corporate/M&A (Louisiana)*

**Practice Areas:** Tax (international, federal, state and local); trusts, estates and personal planning.

**Professional Memberships:** American College of Tax Counsel (past Member of Council, 2006-2012); American Bar Association (Member, Section on Taxation; past Chairman, Committee on Partnerships, 1982-84; past Member of Council, 1985-88; past Secretary, Section on Taxation, 1988-89; past Vice-Chair, Section on Taxation, 1989-91); Louisiana Law Institute; Louisiana State Bar Association (past Chair, Section on Taxation, 1978-79).

**Career:** Mr Casey's practice is predominately transactional, dealing with acquisitions of businesses, sales of businesses, tax advices to businesses and individuals, and estate planning. He occasionally is involved in tax controversy administrative work and litigation. He concentrates on federal, Louisiana, and local income, estate, gift, and sales taxation. Mr Casey is a Board-Certified Tax Specialist as certified by the Louisiana Board of Legal Specialization. Mr Casey was named one of Worth magazine's 100 Top Attorneys serving affluent families for 2005 and 2006.

**Personal:** New York University School of Law, LLM in Taxation, 1973, Harry Rudnick Award; Tulane University Law School, JD, 1971, Tulane Law Review, Order of the Coif; University of Notre Dame, BBA in Accounting, 1968, magna cum laude.

### CERONE, Rudy
McGlinchey Stafford PLLC, New Orleans
504 596 2786
rcerone@mcglinchey.com
*Featured in Bankruptcy/Restructuring (Louisiana)*

**Practice Areas:** Bankruptcy, reorganization and creditors rights litigation; collections; gaming; business and commercial litigation.

**Professional Memberships:** American College of Bankruptcy (2001-present); American Bankruptcy Institute (Secretary, 2010-present; Board of Directors, 2004-present; Advisory Board of Southwest Bankruptcy Conference, 2003-2011), American Bar Association, American Board of Certification (former Chair, President and Board Member), Bar Association of the Fifth Federal Circuit, State Bar of California, Louisiana State Bar Association, New Orleans Bar Association.

**Career:** Primary emphasis in business and complex consumer finance bankruptcy and commercial litigation; certified as a specialist in Business Bankruptcy Law by the American Board of Certification (1993) and by the Louisiana State Bar Association Board of Legal Specialization

(1997). Mr Cerone has been a lecturer on bankruptcy issues for more than 20 years.

**Personal:** Boston College Law School, JD, cum laude (1979); University of California at San Diego, BA, summa cum laude (1976).

### CHEATHAM, Robin B
Adams and Reese LLP, New Orleans
504 585 0411
robin.cheatham@arlaw.com
*Featured in Bankruptcy/Restructuring (Louisiana)*

**Practice Areas:** Partner: commercial restructuring and bankruptcy, energy and environmental, bankruptcy, oil and gas contracts, construction law, commercial litigation.

**Professional Memberships:** American Bankruptcy Institute, Mid-Continent Law Association, Commercial Law League of America.

**Career:** Experienced in commercial litigation, construction law, asset acquisitions, general business counseling and complex commercial financial transactions as well as various aspects of oil and gas transactions. He has appeared on behalf of creditors, committees and trustees and has also litigated various construction law issues.

**Personal:** JD Loyola University New Orleans School of Law, 1979; BS University of New Orleans, 1976.

### CHEATWOOD, Roy C
Baker, Donelson, Bearman, Caldwell & Berkowitz, PC, New Orleans
504 566 5266
rcheatwood@bakerdonelson.com
*Featured in Litigation (Louisiana)*

**Practice Areas:** Practice focused in commercial litigation including corporate/securities, banking/financial services, oil/gas, energy/minerals, construction, trade secrets and legal malpractice. Represents local, national and international concerns before trial and appellate courts, regulatory bodies and ADR forums.

**Professional Memberships:** Member, LSBA CLE committee, DRI, IADC; American, Federal, Louisiana State and New Orleans Bar Associations. Former Member, Louisiana Board of Legal Specialization. Former faculty, National Institute for Trial Advocacy, Trial and Deposition Programs. Master Barrister, Tulane Inn of Court. Co-author, Louisiana Courtroom Evidence.

**Career:** Louisiana license. Served US Army (First Lieutenant, Infantry).

**Personal:** Tulane University, JD. University of South Florida, BA.

### CHENEVERT, Scott D
Jones Walker LLP, Baton Rouge
225 248 2116
schenevert@joneswalker.com
*Featured in Corporate/M&A (Louisiana)*

**Practice Areas:** Corporate & Securities; Mergers & Acquisitions; Business & Commercial Transactions; Venture Capital & Emerging Companies.

**Professional Memberships:** American Bar Association; Baton Rouge Bar Association; District of Columbia Bar; Louisiana State Bar Association.

**Career:** Mr Chenevert is a partner in the firm's Corporate & Securities Practice Group. He represents public and private companies in the energy, technology, construction and engineering, and professional services industries and has extensive experience in public and private offerings of equity and debt securities, and routinely structures and negotiates acquisitions and financing transactions for public and private companies. He also provides corporate and boardroom advice to a variety of public and private companies, including compliance with U.S. Securities and Exchange Commission (SEC) disclosure laws; preparing proxy materials; implementing anti-takeover defenses, including stockholder rights plans; drafting contracts; and assisting clients with corporate governance matters.

**Personal:** Washington and Lee University School of Law (JD 1997); Louisiana State University (BS 1994).

### CHEVALIER, Fred
Jones Walker LLP, Baton Rouge
225 248 2046
fchevalier@joneswalker.com
*Featured in Banking & Finance (Louisiana)*

**Practice Areas:** Public Finance; Economic Development; Business & Commercial Transactions; Government Relations & Legislative Advocacy; Tax Credit Programs.

**Professional Memberships:** Louisiana State Bar Association; National Association of Bond Lawyers; International Economic Development Council; Louisiana Industrial Development Executives Association; Southern Economic Development Council.

**Career:** Mr Chevalier is a partner in the firm's Business & Commercial Transactions Practice Group. He served as Assistant Attorney General for Public Finance for the State of Louisiana and Chief of the Public Finance Section from 1973–1980, in which he represented the LA State Treasury Department and the State Bond Commission as Bond Counsel to the State. He was later appointed Assistant State Treasurer, and was responsible for the investment of state funds. He also served as in-house counsel to the Louisiana State Treasurer's Office and the State Bond Commission. He has represented numerous private clients in negotiation of incentive packages pending site selections and has developed varied experience in economic development matters.

**Personal:** Louisiana Tech University BA 1971; Louisiana State University Law Center JD 1971; Best Lawyers in America, 2012-2013.

### CHRISTY, Walter W
Coats Rose Yale Ryman Lee, New Orleans
504 299 3073
wchristy@coatsrose.com
*Featured in Labor & Employment (Louisiana)*

**Practice Areas:** Walter Christy specializes in the representation of management in labor and employment matters, including the areas of employment discrimination, state and federal employment claims against employers, employee relations, contract negotiations, arbitration, OSHA, wage and hour cases, the development and implementation of drug and contraband control programs, government contractor obligations, as well as practice before the National Labor Relations Board.

**Career:** Mr Christy has practiced as a litigator in state and federal courts around the country, including several of the federal courts of appeals and the United States Supreme Court. He was inducted as a Fellow of The College of Labor and Employment Lawyers.

## CLARK, Blane
Kean Miller LLP, Baton Rouge
225 387 0999
blane.clark@keanmiller.com
*Featured in Corporate/M&A (Louisiana)*

**Practice Areas:** Transactions and Business Planning - Corporate, Oil and Gas, Health Care.
**Professional Memberships:** Baton Rouge, Louisiana State, and American Bar Associations.
**Career:** Blane Clark is the managing partner at Kean Miller LLP. He has more than 28 years of experience in handling complex industrial, commercial and health care transactions. In addition to handling transactions for clients, Blane works with planning their overall corporate structure and in helping with day-to-day issues that surface in the operation of their businesses. He has also advised many shareholders and partners on the relative rights of holders of a majority or minority equity position.

## CLARY, Albert Dale
Long Law Firm LLP, Baton Rouge
225 922 5110
adc@longlaw.com
*Featured in Construction (Louisiana)*

**Practice Areas:** Practices: Insurance Defense; Professional Liability; Construction Litigation; Arbitration & Settlement Counsel.
**Professional Memberships:** American Bar Association (Litigation Section, Construction Litigation Committee, Professional Liability Subcommittee; Torts and Insurance Practice Section; Forum on the Construction Industry; Professionals', Officers', and Directors' Liability Law Committee; Business Tort Committee) American Institute of Architects;Louisiana Association of Defense Counsel Baton Rouge Bar Association (Law Office Expo, Past Chair; Law Day Committee, Past Chair; Civil Court Liaison Sub Committee, Past Chair).
**Career:** Mr Clary is one of the few attorneys in the state of Louisiana who specializes in professional liability, primarily representing architects, engineers, land surveyors, and accountants. He also handles construction and commercial litigation. He has handled cases from the smallest surveying snafu to multi-million dollar claims by owners, contractors, and injured persons. He received a bachelor of science degree from Louisiana State University and his juris doctorate from the Paul M. Hebert Law Center at LSU. He is an affiliate member of the American Institute of Architects. Projects range in value from $5,000 to multi-millions dollars.
**Publications:** Tenth Amendment Revisited: The Enumerated Powers Clause, Around the Bar, New

Anti-Indemnity Act for Design Professional and Contractors in Louisiana: La.R.S. 9:2780.1.

## COLOMB, P. Kevin
Gordon, Arata, McCollam, Duplantis & Eagan LLC, New Orleans
504 582 1111
kcolomb@gordonarata.com
*Featured in Gaming & Licensing (Louisiana)*

**Career:** Kevin Colomb is a member in Gordon Arata's New Orleans office. He focuses primarily in the areas of gaming, oil and gas and business, where he represents clients concerning licensing, transfers and acquisition of interests and administrative actions. Before Gordon Arata, he established the Law Department of Harrah's Entertainment in New Orleans as V.P. and General Counsel of Louisiana properties. He handled all legal aspects of the gaming businesses including contract negotiation and preparation; the development and implementation of rules and policies concerning local, state and federal rules and regulations; and representation of Harrah's before regulatory and governmental agencies.

## COLVIN, R Keith
Jones Walker LLP, New Orleans
504 582 8524
kcolvin@joneswalker.com
*Featured in Real Estate (Louisiana)*

**Practice Areas:** Commercial real estate, commercial finance; represents developers, owners, and lenders in projects including industrial plants, shipyards and docks, shopping centers and malls, apartment complexes, hotels, office buildings, condominiums, townhomes and timeshare developments, and golf course and resort developments. Licensed title insurance agent.
**Professional Memberships:** American College of Mortgage Attorneys, President; Lex Mundi, North American Regional Vice-Chair of the Real Estate Practice Group; American College of Real Estate Lawyers, Past Chairman, Title Insurance Committee; International Council of Shopping Centers; Urban Land Institute, Executive Committee; Coalition to Restore Coastal Louisiana, Past Chairman; New Orleans Regional Leadership Institute, Past Chairman; New Orleans, Louisiana State and American Bar Associations.
**Publications:** Author and editor of the initial working draft of the Louisiana Uniform Title Standards as Chairman of the Uniform Title Standards Committee of the Louisiana State Bar Association, 1991-94. The Louisiana Uniform Title Standards were published by the Louisiana State Bar Association in 2000 after a period of promulgation and discussion.
**Personal:** LSU Law School, JD (1979), Managing Editor, 'Louisiana Law Review', Volume 39; LSU, BS (1976).

## CONKLIN, Katherine
McGlinchey Stafford PLLC, New Orleans
504 596 2876
kconklin@mcglinchey.com
*Featured in Labor & Employment (Louisiana)*

**Practice Areas:** Employment law, including employee benefits and employment law compliance; taxation; estate planning.
**Professional Memberships:** American, Louisiana and New Orleans Bar Associations, Association of Employee Benefits Planners, New Orleans Estate Planning Council, Gulf Coast Area TE/GE Liaison Council (alumni member).
**Career:** Practice focuses on employee benefits in both the welfare and retirement benefit areas and advising clients on employment law compliance and tax law. Board Certified Tax Specialist and Board Certified Estate Planning and Administration Specialist (Certified by the Louisiana Board of Legal Specialization).
**Personal:** Tulane University Law School, JD (1983); Louisiana State University, BA (1980).

## CORNELIUS, O Ray
Adams and Reese LLP, New Orleans
504 581 3234
ray.cornelius@arlaw.com
*Featured in Banking & Finance (Louisiana)*

**Practice Areas:** Partner: public finance, banking/finance, governmental relations, economic development and business incentives.
**Professional Memberships:** Louisiana State Bar Association; Arkansas State Bar Association; American Bar Association; National Association of Bond Lawyers.
**Career:** O Ray Cornelius is the Public Finance Practice Team Leader for the firm. He is also a Member of the Banking and Finance Team and the Governmental Relations Team. His practice is devoted primarily to public finance, economic development and business incentives, banking and finance.
**Personal:** JD, University of Arkansas, 1979; BA, University of Arkansas, 1976.

## CROSBY, E Howell
Chaffe McCall, LLP, New Orleans
504 585 7212
crosby@chaffe.com
*Featured in Real Estate (Louisiana)*

**Practice Areas:** Business and Taxation, Real Estate.
**Professional Memberships:** American College of Mortgage Attorneys (Past President); American College of Real Estate Lawyers; Fellow - American Bar Foundation; Louisiana State Bar Association.
**Career:** Chaffe McCall, 1985 - Present; District A Council Member, New Orleans City Council, 1999 - 2000; New Orleans Former Member, Industrial Development Board; New Orleans Alcohol Beverage Control Board (Vice Chair); and New Orleans Human Relations Committee.
**Personal:** Tulane University, BSM, 1981; the AB Freeman School of Business, MBA, 1984; and Tulane School of Law, JD, 1985.

## DEGAN, Nancy
Baker, Donelson, Bearman, Caldwell & Berkowitz, PC, New Orleans
504 566 5249
ndegan@bakerdonelson.com
*Featured in Litigation (Louisiana)*

**Practice Areas:** Trial and appellate commercial litigation: oil and gas, shareholder/securities,

breach of contract and business torts cases. Mediation and arbitration.
**Professional Memberships:** American Bar Association, Section of Litigation: Revenue Officer and Vice Chair Nominee.
**Career:** The Best Lawyers in America (9 years); Louisiana Super Lawyers Top 10 Attorneys in Louisiana (2010–2012); "Leader in the Law" and "Women of the Year" member, CityBusiness Magazine.
**Personal:** Shareholder and leader of firm's Business Litigation Group; member of firm's Board of Directors. Loyola University, JD, 1983, magna cum laude (Articles Editor, Loyola Law Review). University of New Orleans, BA, 1979, cum laude.

## DESMOND, Susan
Jackson Lewis LLP, New Orleans
504 208 1755
Susan.Desmond@jacksonlewis.com
*Featured in Labor & Employment (Louisiana)*

**Practice Areas:** Labor and Employment law for management. Advices and litigation.
**Professional Memberships:** American Bar Association, Mississippi Bar Association, Louisiana Bar Association, Society for Human Resource Management, Republican Professional Women.
**Career:** Before Jackson Lewis, she was a shareholder with Watkins Ludlam Winter & Stennis, P.A. Prior to that, Ms Desmond was a partner with Phelps Dunbar LLP.
**Publications:** Contributing author, Legal Aspects of Doing Business in North America, 2012 and 2013 ed: Juris Publishing, Inc.); Contributing author, Complying with Employment Regulations, 2011 ed: Aspature Books.
**Personal:** University of Tennessee School of Law (JD 1985); University of Mississippi (BA 1982).

## DICHARRY, Christopher
Kean Miller LLP, Baton Rouge
225 387 0999
chris.dicharry@keanmiller.com
*Featured in Corporate/M&A (Louisiana)*

**Practice Areas:** State and Local Tax, Governmental, Legislative and Administrative Law.
**Professional Memberships:** Louisiana State and American Bar Associations.
**Career:** Chris Dicharry is a partner at Kean Miller LLP. He has been certified by the Louisiana Board of Legal Specialization as a Board Certified Tax Attorney. Chris represents local, state and national clients in the area of Louisiana state and local taxation. In addition to representing clients before the Louisiana Board of Tax Appeals, the Louisiana Tax Commission, and the Louisiana courts, he has experience representing taxpayers in tax issues before the Louisiana Legislature.

## DRAPER, Douglas S
Heller, Draper, Patrick & Horn, LLC, New Orleans
504 299 3333
ddraper@hellerdraper.com
*Featured in Bankruptcy/Restructuring (Louisiana)*

**Practice Areas:** Managing Member and practices primarily in the creditor and debtor rights area. His practice involves an equal mix of litigation and business negotiation, reorganization, construction and finance law.

**Professional Memberships:** A Fellow of the American College of Bankruptcy since 1999. He is a Member of the American, Louisiana, Illinois, Colorado and Federal Bar Associations. Has been a member since 1989 in 'Best Lawyers in America', was recently recognized as one of the top 50 'Super Lawyers in Louisiana'. He has Chaired the ABI Unsecured Trade Creditor's Committee.

**Career:** Received his BA, in 1971 from Syracuse University, then received his JD in 1975 from Tulane University. He received a LLM in Taxation in 1978 from New York University.

**Publications:** He has lectured for the Louisiana Bar Association, American Bar Association, Mississippi Bankruptcy Conference, Commercial Law League, Practicing Law Institute, Tulane Tax Institute, Loyola Estate Planning Counsel, AB Freeman School of Business (Tulane University) Executive MBA program, and the William O'Neil Great Lake Region Program in Ohio. He has served as Educational Chairman for the National Conference of Bankruptcy Judges and as Co-Chairman for the American Bankruptcy Insitutue Unsecured Creditors' Committee.

**Personal:** Born May 31, 1950 in New York, NY.

### DUCK, John M
Adams and Reese LLP, New Orleans
504 585 0226
john.duck@arlaw.com
*Featured in Bankruptcy/Restructuring (Louisiana)*

**Practice Areas:** Corporate/securities/mergers and acquisitions, commercial restructuring/bankruptcy, banking/finance, general business/transactions.

**Professional Memberships:** American, Louisiana, and Fifth Federal Circuit Bar Associations, Louisiana Bar Foundation, American Bankruptcy Institute, Chairman Urban League of New Orleans Nominating Committee, Executive Committee New Orleans Ballet, Vice-Chair Committee for a SECURE Louisiana, Committee of 100 and Committee for Economic Development for Louisiana.

**Career:** Partner: Complex corporate restructuring matters both bankruptcy and non-bankruptcy contexts. Advises/represents clients in connection with the acquisition/disposition of corporate assets, commercial lending matters, including debtor-in-possession financing transactions.

**Personal:** JD, Tulane University Law School, 1980; BS, University of Southern Mississippi, 1977.

### DUNCAN, J Kelly
Jones Walker LLP, New Orleans
504 582 8218
kduncan@joneswalker.com
*Featured in Gaming & Licensing (Nationwide), Gaming & Licensing (Louisiana), Banking & Finance (Louisiana)*

**Practice Areas:** Member of the firm's Admiralty and Maritime and Business and Commercial Transactions Practice Groups. Firm's Gaming Practice Chair concentrating in the representation of major casino companies, domestic and international manufacturers and suppliers, and financial institutions in connection with licensing, compliance, statutory and regulatory interpretation, administrative hearings, acquisitions, operations and financings. Over 30 years of experience in handling acquisitions, financings, contracts, constructions, lien enforcement and foreclosure, and customs rulings with particular emphasis on marine related matters.

**Professional Memberships:** Member of the following: International Masters of Gaming Law (President); International Association of Gaming Advisors; American Bar Association — Sections on Admiralty and Maritime Law and Business Law - Maritime Financing and Gaming Law Committees; Maritime Law Association of the United States - Maritime Financing; New Orleans Maritime Seminar Advisory and Planning Committees; and Past Chairman of the New Orleans Bar Association Maritime and International Law Committee.

**Career:** Member of Jones Walker's Board of Directors.

**Publications:** Member, Editorial Board, Gaming Law Review; Member, Board of Editors, UNLV Gaming Law Journal.

**Personal:** Born, New Orleans, Louisiana, February 22, 1954; Georgetown University (AB, cum laude, 1976); Tulane University (JD, 1979).

### DUNCAN III, Brooke
Adams and Reese LLP, New Orleans
504 585 0220
brooke.duncan@arlaw.com
*Featured in Labor & Employment (Louisiana)*

**Practice Areas:** Partner: labor relations, management counseling, collective bargaining, employment discrimination - agency practice, OSHA.

**Professional Memberships:** Louisiana State Bar; American Bar Association; Chair, Louisiana State Police Commission; Louisiana Civil Service League.

**Career:** Proactive consulting with managers on problematic labor and employment issues to achieve positive employee relations. Counsels on union-free status, defends discrimination claims, wage-hour issues, OSHA, reduction-in-force questions, mergers/acquisitions, compliance with regulations, and state law issues. Represents management before National Labor Relations Board, defends union grievances, and negotiates contracts.

**Personal:** JD, Tulane University Law School, 1986; AB, Vassar College, 1974.

### DUPLANTIS, Bob J.
Gordon, Arata, McCollam, Duplantis & Eagan LLC, Lafayette
337 237 0132
bduplantis@gordonarata.com
*Featured in Energy & Natural Resources (Louisiana)*

**Career:** Bob Duplantis is a member in the oil and gas section of Gordon Arata's Lafayette office. His practice focuses on oil and gas regulation and he routinely argues contract disputes affecting the energy industry, including lease interpretation and operational issues, joint operating agreements, oil and gas marketing/sales issues, and forced pooling issues. He represents clients before various state agencies and frequently addresses industry groups, such as the Mineral Law Institute. He is a former in-house counsel and lobbyist, and also worked as a chemical engineer in exploration and production throughout Louisiana, Texas, California, and New York.

### EAGAN, Ewell
Gordon, Arata, McCollam, Duplantis & Eagan LLC, New Orleans
504 582 1115
eeagan@gordonarata.com
*Featured in Litigation (Louisiana)*

**Career:** Tim Eagan is a member in Gordon Arata's New Orleans office. He enjoys a diverse legal practice concentrating on complex commercial litigation in trial and appellate courts in state and federal court systems. He has represented business clients in a range of industries including energy, securities, exploration, health care, banking, and construction. Tim has served as lead counsel in national and state class actions, and has frequently defended consumer class actions. He represents exploration companies pursuing and defending claims for breach of contract involving hundreds of millions of dollars. He is also experienced in construction law.

### FEINGERTS, Sandra Mills
Fisher & Phillips LLP, New Orleans
504 529 3836
sfeingerts@laborlawyers.com
*Featured in Labor & Employment (Louisiana)*

**Career:** Sandra Feingerts is a Partner in the New Orleans office and a Member of the firm's Employee Benefits Practice Group. Her practice is focused primarily on ERISA and employee benefits law. She was recognized by New Orleans City Business as one of the City's 50 "Outstanding Lawyers," and has been listed in The Best Lawyers in America since 1995.

### FISHMAN, Louis Y
Fishman Haygood Phelps Walmsley Willis & Swanson, L.L.P., New Orleans
504 586 5252
lfishman@fishmanhaygood.com
*Featured in Corporate/M&A (Louisiana)*

**Practice Areas:** Louis Fishman has since 1966 represented a variety of business clients in numerous transactions that have included mergers and acquisitions and public and private offerings of securities. He also counsels clients on business, securities and corporate law matters, including corporate governance and family business issues.

**Career:** Louis has been listed as a top corporate lawyer in a leading legal publication in America, since that publication's first edition in 1983. In 2009, that publication named Louis as its first corporate lawyer of the year for New Orleans. In 2010, it named him as its first mergers and acquisitions lawyer of the year for New Orleans. Another leading publication in America named him in 2011 to its "500" and called him "without question one of the very best corporate transactional attorneys in the South." Louis was a Founder in 1988 of Tulane's Corporate Law Institute and still serves on its Planning Committee. He has served since 1991 as a Member of the Advisory Board of Editors of the 'Tulane Law Review'. He has held several key posts, including Chairman, of the Louisiana State Bar Association's Section on Corporation and Business Law and has served as a Member of that Section's Corporate Laws Committee. Louis teaches 'Corporate Governance From Enron to Hollinger to Disney' at Tulane Law School, and has taught 'Judaism and Christianity' at a Presbyterian church in New Orleans.

**Personal:** Louis received his Undergraduate Degree in Business Administration from Tulane University in 1963. He received his LLB Degree in 1965 from Tulane Law School, where he was a Member of the Order of the Coif and Editor-in-Chief of the 'Tulane Law Review'. He earned a Master of Laws Degree in 1966 from Yale Law School, where he was a Sterling Fellow.

### FRANCO, Philip A
Adams and Reese LLP, New Orleans
504 585 0291
philip.franco@arlaw.com
*Featured in Construction (Louisiana)*

**Practice Areas:** Partner: Construction/real estate, commercial dispute resolution.

**Professional Memberships:** Member: Louisiana, Texas and District of Columbia Bar Associations, licensed to practice in all courts in Louisiana, Texas and the District of Columbia, as well as the Eleventh Circuit Court of Appeals and the United States Supreme Court.

**Career:** Focus has been on cases that are high profile, involve significant risks to the client, and/or include particularly contentious opponents, more recently in the areas of construction, real estate, and commercial dispute resolution.

**Personal:** JD, Loyola University New Orleans School of Law, 1978; BA, Loyola University, 1975.

### FREEMAN III, George C
Barrasso Usdin Kupperman Freeman & Sarver LLC, New Orleans
504 589 9700
GFreeman@BarrassoUsdin.com
*Featured in Litigation (Louisiana)*

**Practice Areas:** Mr Freeman has represented clients in litigation, arbitration and regulatory proceedings in a wide variety of complex commercial matters but, in recent years, has focused his practice primarily on securities and other financial cases.

**Professional Memberships:** American Law Institute; American Bar Association; Louisiana Bar Association.

**Career:** Mr Freeman is a Founding Member of Barrasso Usdin Kupperman Freeman & Sarver, L.L.C. Prior to entering private practice, Mr Freeman was a law clerk for the Hon. Albert Tate on the United States Court of Appeals for the Fifth Circuit and for the Hon Henry Mentz on the United States District Court for the Eastern District of Louisiana.

**Personal:** JD, MA, University of Virginia (1982); BA, Oxford University (1977, Rhodes Scholar); BA, Emory University (1975); Listed in 'Best Lawyers in America' and 'Louisiana Super Lawyers'. Adjunct Faculty, Tulane University School of Law (Securities).

## FUTRELL, Elizabeth J
Jones Walker LLP, New Orleans
504 582 8260
efutrell@joneswalker.com
*Featured in Bankruptcy/Restructuring (Louisiana)*
**Practice Areas:** Ms Futrell concentrates her practice in bankruptcy, restructuring and creditors debtors rights and business and commercial litigation.
**Professional Memberships:** Mississippi and Louisiana State Bar Associations; American Bankruptcy Institute; Fellow, American College of Bankruptcy (since 1999); Fellow, Litigation Counsel of America.
**Career:** Ms Futrell has been a Partner at the firm since 1986 and is a former Member of its Board of Directors (2006-2012). She currently serves on the Board of the Louisiana Diversity Council. A frequent public speaker, some of her speaking engagements include: "Can You Really Confirm This Plan? An Analysis of Various Plan Provisions from Real Chapter 11 cases," Louisiana State Bar Association (December, 2012); "From Proofs to Payment: (Almost) Everything You Want to Know About Claims," American Bar Association Section of Business Law 2010 Fall Meeting Joint Program of National Conference Of Bankruptcy Judges and the Business Bankruptcy Committee (October, 2010); "Individual Chapter 11 Issues: This Stuff is Pretty Hard," Panelist, 16th Annual LSU Bankruptcy Seminar (2010); "Problems and Challenges When Your Client Has Distressed Collateral," Louisiana Bankers Bank Counsel Conference (2009).
**Personal:** University of Tennessee (BA, with high honors, 1978); University of Mississippi (JD, with honors, 1981); Comment Editor, Mississippi Law Journal, 1980-81.

## GEARY, Covert J.
Jones Walker LLP, New Orleans
504 582 8276
cgeary@joneswalker.com
*Featured in Litigation (Louisiana)*
**Practice Areas:** Complex Commercial and Class Action Litigation; Insurance Coverage; Life, Health and Disability Insurance and ERISA; Energy Litigation; Disaster Recovery.
**Professional Memberships:** International Association of Defense Counsel; American Bar Association (former Chair of Life Insurance Law Committee); Defense Research Institute; Federal Bar Association; Rocky Mountain Mineral Law Institute; Louisiana Association of Defense Counsel; American Bar Foundation.
**Career:** Mr Geary's practice focuses on business and commercial litigation with emphasis on energy litigation, insurance coverage including life, health and disability insurance coverage, ERISA litigation, and class actions. In 2006, he received a New Orleans CityBusiness Leadership in Law

Award. Prior to joining Jones Walker, he clerked for a US District Judge in New Orleans, and was employed by a global public accounting firm.
**Personal:** Louisiana State University (JD, 1984); Louisiana Law Review; Washington and Lee University (BS, Administration and Accounting, cum laude, 1980); Omicron Delta Kappa; Chancellor, Episcopal Diocese of Louisiana (2003-present).

## GERSHANIK, Maureen
Fishman Haygood Phelps Walmsley Willis & Swanson, L.L.P., New Orleans
504 586 5278
mgershanik@fishmanhaygood.com
*Featured in Corporate/M&A (Louisiana)*
**Practice Areas:** Ms Gershanik regularly represents clients in public and private offerings of debt and equity securities, acquisition transactions and corporate restructuring transactions. She also advises the boards of directors of public and private companies on matters of securities law compliance, corporate governance and executive compensation and advises public companies with respect to on-going SEC reporting requirements.
**Professional Memberships:** Ms Gershanik is a member of the Corporations Committee of the Louisiana Law Institute, Treasurer of the Corporate and Business Law section of the Louisiana State Bar Association, and a member of the Business Law section of the American Bar Association.
**Personal:** Ms Gershanik received her JD degree from Louisiana State University in 2000, where she was class valedictorian, editor-in-chief of the Louisiana Law Review and a member of the Order of the Coif. She received her BSFS degree, cum laude, from Georgetown University in 1992. She was also law clerk to the Honorable John M. Duhé, Jr., senior judge of the United States Court of Appeals for the Fifth Circuit, from 2000 to 2001.

## GRAY, Jeffry W
Jones Walker LLP, Baton Rouge
225 248 2044
jgray@joneswalker.com
*Featured in Real Estate (Louisiana)*
**Practice Areas:** Business & Commercial Transactions; Commercial Lending & Finance; Disaster Preparedness & Recovery; Real Estate: Land Use, Development & Finance.
**Professional Memberships:** American Land Title Association; Baton Rouge Property Lawyers Association; International Council of Shopping Centers (Louisiana Government Relations Committee Chair, 2010 to date); Louisiana Land Title Association.
**Career:** Mr Gray has practiced law for more than 29 years and is a partner in the firm's Real Estate Practice Group. He concentrates in the areas of commercial and industrial real estate development, the development of energy related infrastructure, land use and zoning, as well as all types of commercial financings. Mr Gray is Vice President of the firm's title company and has written billions of dollars of title insurance for all types of commercial real estate properties.

## GREGORIE JR, Isaac McPherson
Kean Miller LLP, Baton Rouge
225 387 0999
mack.gregorie@keanmiller.com
*Featured in Real Estate (Louisiana)*
**Practice Areas:** Business and Corporate Transactions, Commercial and Industrial Real Estate, Finance.
**Professional Memberships:** Baton Rouge, Louisiana State, and American Bar Associations; American College of Mortgage Attorneys; Council of the Louisiana State Law Institute.
**Career:** Mack Gregorie is a partner at Kean Miller LLP. He represents major international petrochemical clients, worldwide energy producers, banks and financial institutions, buyers and sellers, landlords and tenants, and lenders. A Certified Public Accountant, Mack lectures frequently on real estate topics such as sales, leases, property law, purchase and sale agreements, and recent developments in real estate law.

## GRIFFITH, JR, Steven F
Baker, Donelson, Bearman, Caldwell & Berkowitz, PC, New Orleans
504 566 5225
sgriffith@bakerdonelson.com
*Featured in Labor & Employment (Louisiana)*
**Practice Areas:** Shareholder who practices in the area of employment and business litigation with a focus on clients facing wage and hour issues. Considerable experience in defending nationwide collective actions brought under the Fair Labor Standards Act, as well as related class actions across the country under state law.
**Professional Memberships:** Federal Bar (Board Member, New Orleans Chapter), Louisiana State Bar, American Bar, Fifth Circuit Bar and New Orleans Bar Associations.
**Career:** Licensed in Louisiana, 2001.
**Personal:** Loyola School of Law, JD, 2000, magna cum laude. Rhodes College, BA, 1997, cum laude.

## GUERRY, David L
Long Law Firm LLP, Baton Rouge
225 922 5110
dlg@longlaw.com
*Featured in Energy & Natural Resources (Louisiana)*
**Practice Areas:** His practice is focused in the areas of litigating business structure matters, general corporate and business claims, regulatory litigation (including issues related to telecommunications, energy and electricity), banking litigation, and construction claims.
**Professional Memberships:** Louisiana State Bar Association-Founding Chair of the Public Utilities Section (2002-2003), Chair (second appointment) (2007-2009); Chair of the Law Office Practice and Professional Economics Committee (1989-1992) Louisiana Bar Foundation- Sustaining Fellow; Federal Bar Association- 5th Circuit Vice President (2005-present); Member, National Council (2001-present); Chair, Bench Bar Committee 2011; President of the Baton Rouge Chapter (2001-2002); Foundation of the Federal Bar Association-National President (2005-2006);Lifetime Sustaining Fellow;Secretary (2004);Member Board

of Directors (2003- present); Fellows Chair (2006-2008) Fifth Federal Circuit Bar Association- Serves on Judicial Liaison Committee of the 5thCircuit; American Arbitration Association- Approved member of the construction, commercial and large complex case panels; Serves on the Panel of Mediators : Instructor, AAA Arbitration Advocacy Program, November, 2002; Louisiana Trial Lawyers Association-Member of President?s Advisory Council; Louisiana Airport Authority-Member (2004-2007).
**Career:** Mr Guerry is a litigation partner with over 25 years trial experience. His legal practice specifically includes representation in the fields of telecommunications and electric regulatory transactions and litigation; acquisitions and other business transactions and related litigation, banking litigation, general, corporate and franchise structure related business litigation. Mr Guerry has also served as Special Counsel to the Louisiana Utilities Restoration Corporation and as litigation counsel to the Louisiana Housing Finance Authority. Mr Guerry is also a member of the American Arbitration Association, serving on the large, complex, commercial, construction and mediation panels.
**Publications:** Co-Author: Louisiana Banking Law with Forms, Claitors, 1989.
**Personal:** Mr Guerry is a graduate of, and former president of, the Board of Directors of Leadership of Greater Baton Rouge and is also an alumnus of Leadership Louisiana. Mr Guerry is active as a volunteer and fundraiser for Junior Achievement, YMCA, the United Way, the Hospice Foundation, the American Red Cross,the American Heart Association and others. Mr Guerry is a Member of St. Luke's Episcopal Church.

## HAND, JR., Albert M.
Cook, Yancey, King & Galloway, A Professional Law Corporation, Shreveport
318 227 7727
al.hand@cookyancey.com
*Featured in Environment (Louisiana)*
**Practice Areas:** Products Liability Environmental Toxic Tort Litigation.
**Professional Memberships:** American Bar Association, Louisiana Bar Association, Shreveport Bar Association, DRI, and Louisiana Association of Defense Counsel.
**Career:** Leads the firm's Environmental Practice Group. For more than 30 years, he has focused his practice on Toxic Tort Litigation, Environmental Law and Products Liability.
**Personal:** He is AV rated by Martindale-Hubbell. He attended Vanderbilt University and received his undergraduate, masters, and law degrees from Louisiana State University.

## HARBOURT, Maureen N
Kean Miller LLP, Baton Rouge
225 387 0999
maureen.harbourt@keanmiller.com
*Featured in Environment (Louisiana)*
**Practice Areas:** Environmental Law.

**Professional Memberships:** Baton Rouge, Lousiana State, and American Bar Associations; Air and Waste Management Association.
**Career:** Maureen Harbourt is a partner at Kean Miller LLP. She represents clients in a variety of substantive environmental areas. Maureen works with several trade associations and individual clients with regard to environmental permitting and project planning, as well as rulemaking and legislative issues. She advises clients with regard to compliance issues. She has particular experience in creating in-plant environmental training programs. Maureen also works extensively with other members of the firm on energy and alternative energy development projects.

### HARDIN, Pauline
Jones Walker LLP, New Orleans
504 582 8110
phardin@joneswalker.com
*Featured in Litigation (Louisiana)*
**Practice Areas:** Commercial litigation, corporate compliance, white collar crime and related civil and regulatory parallel proceedings.
**Professional Memberships:** Louisiana State and American Bar Associations; American College of Trial Lawyers; Louisiana Association of Criminal Defense Lawyers.
**Career:** Ms Hardin has been a Partner in Jones Walker's Litigation Practice since 1990. She has over 35 years of experience litigating criminal matters and over 25 years of experience litigating business and commercial matters. She served as former Head of the firm's Litigation Section for four years. Prior to joining Jones Walker, she served as both First Assistant United States Attorney and Chief of the Criminal Division at the United States Attorney's Office for the Eastern District of Louisiana. Prior to that, she served as an Assistant District Attorney in charge of the Orleans Parish Fraud and White-Collar Crime Unit. Listed in The Best Lawyers in America® 2013 (Copyright 2012 by Woodward/White, Inc., Aiken, SC) in the areas of Commercial Litigation and Criminal Defense: White Collar (listed annually since 2005.) Named to New Orleans CityBusiness' 2009 Leadership in Law.
**Personal:** Admitted to bar, 1974, Louisiana; Loyola University of New Orleans (BA, 1971); Tulane University (JD, 1974). Instructor, Trial Advocacy, Tulane University Law School.

### HARDIN III, Harry S
Jones Walker LLP, New Orleans
504 582 8170
hhardin@joneswalker.com
*Featured in Litigation (Louisiana)*
**Practice Areas:** Senior Partner concentrating in commercial business litigation, contract, antitrust, trademark, copyright, professional responsibility, environmental law, and mediation.
**Professional Memberships:** Fellow, American College of Trial Lawyers; American Bar Association: American Bar Insurance Board of Directors; Chair, Operations & Communications Committee (2007-08); Executive Committee (2007-08); Board of Governors (2005-08), Louisiana State Delegate (1994-2003), Fifth

Circuit Representative to Standing Committee on Federal Judiciary (1998-2002), sections of litigation, antitrust, patent, trademark and copyright, tort and insurance practice; Louisiana State Bar Association, past President, LSBA Ethics 2000 Committee, Chair; Louisiana Bar Foundation, past President; American Judicature Society Board of Directors (2003-06); International Association of Defense Counsel; President - Louisiana Appleseed (2007-10).
**Career:** 1971 Jones Walker, (1973-77 1st Lt JAG US Army), Partner, 1976; mediator; speaks on ethics, professionalism and malpractice avoidance; Louisiana Supreme Court: Chair, Judicial Campaign Oversight Committee, Advisory Committee for Revision of Code of Judicial Conduct. Listed annually in The Best Lawyers in America® (Copyright by Woodward/White, Inc.) in Commercial Litigation since 2003.
**Publications:** Managed Care and Antitrust: The PPO Experience, ABA Press (contributing author); 'Pitfalls for In-House Counsel', The Brief, ABA Press.
**Personal:** BA Harvard (cum laude); JD Tulane University.

### HARDIN, JR, A Edward
Kean Miller LLP, Baton Rouge
225 387 0999
edward.hardin@keanmiller.com
*Featured in Labor & Employment (Louisiana)*
**Practice Areas:** Labor and Employment.
**Professional Memberships:** Baton Rouge, Louisiana State, and American Bar Associations.
**Career:** Ed Hardin, Jr is a partner at Kean Miller LLP. He represents and advises employers on a variety of issues including employee handbooks and contracts, non-compete and non-solicitation agreements, wrongful termination claims, discrimination and harassment claims, and issues involving wage payment, drug testing, and employee leave. Ed also represents and advises management on labor relations issues including union representation of employees, union representation elections, arbitration of collective bargaining agreement grievances, unfair labor practice charges, and collective bargaining agreements with unions.

### HARKINS, Deborah
McGlinchey Stafford PLLC, New Orleans
504 596 2799
dharkins@mcglinchey.com
*Featured in Gaming & Licensing (Louisiana)*
**Practice Areas:** Gaming, government relations, education, banking, commercial finance, healthcare, insurance regulation and compliance.
**Professional Memberships:** American and Louisiana Bar Associations, Check this name International Association of Gaming Advisors, State Law Resources Board Member, American Association of Political Consultants, Association of Louisiana Lobbyists, Louisiana Association of Health Plans, New Orleans Chamber of Commerce, World Trade Center New Orleans.
**Career:** Ms Harkins has more than 30 years of legal experience representing the gaming industry, during which time she has been instrumental in

passing key regulatory and legislative matters on behalf of her gaming clients. She works closely with the Gaming Division of the Attorney General's office, the Gaming Division of the Louisiana State Police, and the Louisiana State Racing Commission. Over the last year, she has worked extensively with the Louisiana Gaming Control Board developing a new casino in the Shreveport/Bossier City area. Ms Harkins is currently actively engaged in gaming acquisitions and refinancing with a number of clients. She represents both publicly-held and private companies on licensing and tax issues relating to riverboats and racetracks. She also works in the Indian Gaming arena, negotiating compacts and other related matters.
**Personal:** Ms Harkins has been named "Woman of the Year" by New Orleans CityBusiness multiple times and has earned the publication's "Leadership in Law" Award. She was appointed by the Governor to the Louisiana Endowment for the Humanities Board and serves in multiple leadership capacities for many community organizations in the Greater New Orleans area. Last year she was elected to the board of the New Orleans Jazz & Heritage Festival and Foundation and was the author and editor of the WWOZ cookbook "That Sounds Good!". Additionally, Louisiana Super Lawyers and Best Lawyers in America directories continue to name Ms Harkins to their annual lists of leading gaming and government relations lawyers.

### HAROLD, Edward F
Fisher & Phillips LLP, New Orleans
504 592 3801
eharold@laborlawyers.com
*Featured in Labor & Employment (Louisiana)*
**Career:** Ed Harold is a Partner in the New Orleans office and chair of the firm's Retail Industry Practice Group. He devotes his practice to counseling employers about issues arising every day in the workplace including counseling, disciplining and terminating employees. He has also worked very closely with employers in the development of attendance and leave of absence issues that comply with the FMLA and the ADA. He has successfully defended cases brought under the ADA, the FMLA, the Age Discrimination in Employment Act, Title VII, ERISA, Louisiana Employment Discrimination Law and Louisiana Wage Payment statute.

### HARTMANN, Melanie
Kean Miller LLP, Baton Rouge
225 387 0999
melanie.hartmann@keanmiller.com
*Featured in Labor & Employment (Louisiana)*
**Practice Areas:** Labor and Employment.
**Professional Memberships:** Baton Rouge, Louisiana State, American, and Federal Bar Associations.
**Career:** Melanie Hartmann is a partner at Kean Miller LLP. She leads the labor and employment practice area. With 24 years of experience in employment law, she serves as lead counsel in employment litigation; represents clients in bench and jury trials; represents employers in charges

before the EEOC; provides advice to employers regarding a variety of employment-related issues and personnel decisions; and gives speeches on employment law topics such as the ADA, FMLA, Title VII, conducting investigations, termination issues and employment policies.

### HAYDEN, Jan M
Baker, Donelson, Bearman, Caldwell & Berkowitz, PC, New Orleans
504 566 8645
jhayden@bakerdonelson.com
*Featured in Bankruptcy/Restructuring (Louisiana)*
**Practice Areas:** Shareholder in the Bankruptcy & Restructuring group, with a practice concentrated in reorganizations under Chapter 11 of the U.S. Bankruptcy Code.
**Professional Memberships:** Member: Louisiana, New Orleans, American and Federal Bar Associations. Fellow: the Louisiana and American Bar Foundations and American College of Bankruptcy. Vice Chair of The Pro Bono Project. One of the top ten lawyers in Super Lawyers in Louisiana since inception. Recipient - International Women's Insolvency & Restructuring Federation 2011 Woman of the Year and Louisiana State Bar Association 2009 Pro Bono Publico Award.
**Career:** Louisiana, 1979.
**Personal:** Louisiana State University, JD, 1979.

### HAYGOOD, Paul M
Fishman Haygood Phelps Walmsley Willis & Swanson, L.L.P., New Orleans
504 586 5263
phaygood@fishmanhaygood.com
*Featured in Corporate/M&A (Louisiana)*
**Practice Areas:** Mr Haygood is now Of Counsel to the firm. His practice has been in the areas of mergers and acquisitions, corporate law, securities law, probate, estate planning and trust law. He has represented clients in a variety of corporate finance and planning matters, including representing numerous financial institutions in connection with acquisition transactions involving more than $1 billion in assets; acting as Lead Outside Counsel in connection with the corporate and securities aspects of the reorganization of a large publicly-held enterprise in what was the largest financial reorganization up to that time of a Louisiana-based company; acting as Lead Outside Counsel in connection with the financial and corporate restructuring of a Louisiana-based, publicly-traded entity with assets in excess of $500 million; representation of an international oil and gas service company in connection with the acquisition of assets located on three different continents and totaling in excess of $40 million; and structuring estate plans for individuals having an estimated combined net worth in excess of $150 million.
**Career:** Like partners Louis Fishman and Robert Walmsley, Mr Haygood is a former Chairman of the Corporate and Business Law Section of the Louisiana State Bar Association. He also chaired for many years the Association's Bar Admission Committee that prepares the Louisiana corporation law portion of the Louisiana Bar

Examination, as well as chairing for ten years the Association's Corporate Laws Committee, which monitors the Louisiana Business Corporation Law and makes recommendations to the Louisiana Legislature with respect to changes in the Louisiana Business Corporation Law.

**Publications:** Mr Haygood is listed in a leading legal publication in America as one of the best lawyers in America in the area of corporate law. He has retained that listing since 1983, when that publication was first published.

**Personal:** Mr Haygood graduated from Louisiana State University in 1964 and received his LLB from Harvard Law School in 1967. In addition to the practice of law, Mr Haygood also has played an active role in the civic affairs of New Orleans and Louisiana, having served as President of the Council for a Better Louisiana, as President of the New Orleans Bureau of Governmental Research, and as an active Board Member of a number of philanthropic organizations. In 1991 he chaired the New Orleans Conference on North American Free Trade. Mr Haygood also is a Former Member of the Board of Supervisors of Louisiana State University and a Former Member of the Board of Advisors of the National Trust for Historic Preservation.

### HAYNE JR, C Peck
Gordon, Arata, McCollam, Duplantis & Eagan LLC, New Orleans
504 569 1858
phayne@gordonarata.com
*Featured in Energy & Natural Resources (Louisiana)*

**Career:** Peck Hayne is a member in Gordon Arata's New Orleans office where he practices oil and gas, pipeline and other energy-related transactions and regulation and on federal appellate litigation. He regularly negotiates drafts and advises clients on complex purchase/sale agreements, operating agreements, mineral leases, right-of-way agreements, transportation and interconnection agreements, gas storage agreements and settlement agreements in complex litigation and other disputes. He also frequently renders title opinions on complex petroleum titles in Louisiana and on the Outer Continental Shelf offshore Louisiana and Texas and assists both lenders and borrowers in the financing of onshore and offshore energy properties.

### HEARN, Curtis R
Jones Walker LLP, New Orleans
504 582 8308
chearn@joneswalker.com
*Featured in Corporate/M&A (Louisiana)*

**Practice Areas:** Mergers and acquisitions; public company representation; private equity transactions; venture capital; health care transactions; corporate governance.

**Professional Memberships:** Member of Business Law Section of American Bar Association; Member of Negotiated Acquisitions Task Force of Business Law Section.

**Career:** Practice Group Leader of Corporate and Securities Practice Group.

**Personal:** Adjunct Professor of Law, Mergers and Acquisitions, Tulane University Law School.

### HEUSEL, Cornelius
Jones Walker LLP, New Orleans
504 582 8148
nheusel@joneswalker.com
*Featured in Labor & Employment (Louisiana)*

**Practice Areas:** Senior Partner in Jones Walker's labor and employment and white-collar crime and corporate compliance practices.

**Career:** Mr Heusel served as a Special Agent with the Federal Bureau of Investigation, and later as Executive Assistant District Attorney in charge of capital cases for the New Orleans District Attorney's office. He joined the US Attorney's Office in New Orleans, and served as Criminal Division Chief and First Assistant US Attorney. He later headed the Department of Justice Organized Crime Strike Force and served as Assistant Special Prosecutor to investigate allegations of corruption by a member of the White House staff. Mr Heusel has been a guest lecturer at the Department of Justice Trial Advocacy Institute and in the Tulane University Trial Advocacy Program. In 1975 he was awarded the US Attorney General's Exceptional Service Award, the highest award given by the Justice Department. He has represented management in labor relations litigation as lead trial counsel in 35 states.

**Personal:** Native of New Orleans; Loyola University (BBA, 1967; JD, 1967).

### HUNTER, David
Jones Walker LLP, New Orleans
504 582 8366
dhunter@joneswalker.com
*Featured in Energy & Natural Resources (Louisiana)*

**Practice Areas:** Primarily offshore oil and gas development. Mr Hunter's representations include buyers and sellers of mineral properties and pipeline facilities, lenders, underwriters, and borrowers in mineral-based financings, and investors and joint-venturers participating in mineral development programs. He provides advice on BOEM-RE lease obligations, bonding and abandonment requirements, and other elements of regulatory compliance under the federal scheme. Mr Hunter negotiates all forms of agreements used in mineral development, including operating agreements, agreements creating net profits interests, production handling agreements, and gas storage agreements, among others.

**Professional Memberships:** Louisiana State Bar Association, Energy Bar Association, Rocky Mountain Mineral Law Foundation.

**Career:** Partner, Phelps Dunbar (1992). Partner, Jones Walker (2008).

**Publications:** Some Unresolved Business From the Take-Or-Pay Decade (Louisiana Bar Journal, 1989); OCS Due Diligence (Rocky Mountain Mineral Law Foundation, 1998); Penalty Issues Arising From Offshore Operations (Rocky Mountain Mineral Law Foundation, 2002); Doing the Deal: Buying and Selling Offshore Properties (Texas Oil and Gas Law Journal (LexisNexis), 2009).

**Personal:** Yale University (BA, 1977); LSU Law School (JD, 1982), Law Review; Adjunct Professor, Tulane Law School (Advanced Oil and Gas, 2010-2012).

### JACOB, Clyde
Coats Rose Yale Ryman Lee, New Orleans
504 299 3072
cjacob@coatsrose.com
*Featured in Labor & Employment (Louisiana)*

**Practice Areas:** Clyde Jacob represents employers in response to union organizing, boycotts, National Labor Relations Board representation cases, and corporate campaigns. He also focuses on employment relations, including defense of discrimination claims, development of affirmative action programs, defense of wage/compensation claims, and counseling of corporations.

**Career:** Mr Jacob has prepared corporate executives for testimony, and personally testified before Congress as a labor law expert. He regularly speaks to employers and associations nationwide. His professional recognitions include Martindale Hubbell, Chambers USA, Best Lawyer and Super Lawyers. The College of Labor & Employment Lawyers inducted Mr Jacob as a Fellow in 2011.

### JOHNSON JR, Patrick
Beirne, Maynard & Parsons, L.L.P, New Orleans
504 584 9417
pjohnson@bmpllp.com
*Featured in Bankruptcy/Restructuring (Louisiana)*

**Practice Areas:** Patrick Johnson has over thirty years of experience counseling clients in matters relating to bankruptcy, loan restructuring, and business litigation. He has represented numerous banks and bank groups, as well as creditors, lessors and other parties in bankruptcy court and in district and appellate courts, both state and federal.

**Professional Memberships:** Mr Johnson is a member of the American Bankruptcy Institute; American Bar Association, Business Bankruptcy Committee, Chapter 11 and Secured Creditors Subcommittees; Louisiana Bankers Association; Louisiana Bar Foundation; Louisiana State Bar Association; and the New Orleans Bar Association.

**Career:** He is admitted to the Louisiana Bar, 1980; U.S. District Courts for the Eastern, Middle, and Western Districts of Louisiana; U.S. Supreme Court, 1985; and the U.S. Court of Appeals for the 5th and 11th Circuits.

### JONES, Jerald N
Bradley Murchison Kelly & Shea, Shreveport
225 490 5000
jjones@bradleyfirm.com
*Featured in Environment (Louisiana)*

**Practice Areas:** Jerald N. Jones is a partner in the Baton Rouge office who's practice includes assisting private and public entities with local, state, and federal governmental regulation; zoning; environmental; utility and municipal franchise agreements; public works contracts; contract negotiations, disputes and administration; business litigation; energy, oil & gas; and public utility law. Jerry served as Shreveport City Attorney for eight years prior to returning to private practice. He currently serves as Chairman, Louisiana Board of Commerce and Industry, and is a former member of the Government and Fiscal Reform Transition Committee, both positions appointed by Louisiana Governor Bobby Jindal.

### KANNER, Allan
Kanner & Whiteley, LLC, New Orleans
a.kanner@kanner-law.com
*Featured in Environment (Louisiana)*

**Career:** Allan Kanner of Kanner & Whiteley, LLC, a national law firm based in New Orleans, specializes in complex litigation, class actions and trials, handling substantial matters throughout the US. He is especially well known for his commercial, toxic tort, environmental, natural resource damages, Medicaid fraud and first-party insurance cases. He currently represents Louisiana in the BP Oil Spill litigation. He has served as an adjunct professor at Tulane, Duke, Yale and University of Texas Law Schools. He is the author of two books and over 80 scholarly articles. He is a member of the American Law Institute.

### KILGORE III, Leonard L
Kean Miller LLP, Baton Rouge
225 387 0999
len.kilgore@keanmiller.com
*Featured in Environment (Louisiana)*

**Practice Areas:** Environmental Law, Litigation.

**Professional Memberships:** Baton Rouge, Louisiana State, and American Bar Associations; Defense Research Institute; Louisiana Association of Defense Counsel; Louisiana Bar Foundation; LSU Paul M. Hebert Law Center Chancellor's Council; LSU Law Center Board of Trustees.

**Career:** Len Kilgore is a founding member of Kean Miller LLP and has over 30 years of experience in environmental law, including all aspects of state and federal environmental regulations. He also has extensive experience in complex litigation, including environmental, toxic tort, energy, mass joinder, and class action litigation. Len represents local, national and international commercial, energy and industrial clients in litigation involving toxic tort claims, personal injury, property damage claims, and class actions.

### KING, Katherine
Kean Miller LLP, Baton Rouge
225 387 0999
katherine.king@keanmiller.com
*Featured in Energy & Natural Resources (Louisiana)*

**Practice Areas:** Energy, Telecommunications, Utilities Regulation.

**Professional Memberships:** Baton Rouge, Louisiana State, and American Bar Associations; Association of Energy Engineers.

**Career:** Katherine King is a partner at Kean Miller LLP. She has extensive experience before the Louisiana Public Service Commission with a focus on the regulation of Louisiana's electric, telecommunications and pipeline industries. Katherine has provided project development and electric regulatory advice with respect to a number of generation projects, including renewables. She advises industrial clients on electric supply contracts, interconnection and generation project structures that satisfy client needs while complying with both Federal energy regulatory law and LPSC requirements.

## KLEMM, Kenneth
Baker, Donelson, Bearman, Caldwell &
Berkowitz, PC, New Orleans
504 566 5258
kklemm@bakerdonelson.com
*Featured in Energy & Natural Resources (Louisiana)*
**Practice Areas:** Shareholder and Co-Chair of
Oil & Gas Industry Service Team. Primarily
defends clients in energy, oil and gas and mar-
itime litigation.
**Professional Memberships:** Co-Chair, Energy
Litigation Committee, ABA Section of Litigation;
Federal Bar Association; Advisory Board, Institute
for Energy Law; Member, Louisiana Oil & Gas
Association and Louisiana Mid-Continent Oil and
Gas Association; Proctor Member, Maritime Law
Association of the U.S.
**Career:** Licensed in Louisiana, New York, New
Jersey. Captain, Battalion Intelligence Officer,
Louisiana ARNG (1990-92; active duty in
Operation Desert Shield/Desert Storm);
Lieutenant, Military Intelligence, ARNG (1986-
90).
**Personal:** Fordham University School of Law
(JD-1990). Dartmouth College (BA-1986).

## KOCH, Amelia W
Baker, Donelson, Bearman, Caldwell &
Berkowitz, PC, New Orleans
504 566 5200
akoch@bakerdonelson.com
*Featured in Labor & Employment (Louisiana)*
**Practice Areas:** Shareholder in the Labor and
Employment Department, she has substantial
experience in all aspects of employment litigation
and counseling, including the Fair Labor
Standards Act, the Family Medical Leave Act, the
American with Disabilities Act, Title VII, the Age
Discrimination in Employment Act, covenants
not to compete, personnel policies and manuals,
state discrimination and wage statutes, and
employment and severance agreements.
**Professional Memberships:** Listed: Best
Lawyers in America; Louisiana Super Lawyers.
Named Best Lawyers' 2013 New Orleans
Litigation - Antitrust "Lawyer of the Year".
**Career:** Licensed: Louisiana.
**Personal:** University of Virginia, J.D; University
of Georgia, BA.

## KREBS, David J.
Krebs, Farley & Pelleteri PLLC, New Orleans
504 299 3570
dkrebs@kfplaw.com
*Featured in Construction (Louisiana)*
**Practice Areas:** His practice concentrates on
commercial litigation, particularly in the areas of
construction law, fidelity and surety law, contracts,
lease and property litigation, and insurance coverage.
**Professional Memberships:** He was a member
of Tulane Law Review in 1982, and was admitted
to the Order of the Coif that same year. He is currently a member of the Louisiana State Bar
Association, the Texas State Bar Association, the
American Bar Association, (serving as Chair of
the Fidelity and Surety Committee of the Tort and
Insurance Practice Section from 2009-2010) the

Federal Bar Association and the New Orleans Bar
Association.
**Career:** He was admitted to practice in Louisiana
in 1982, and worked as an associate at the law
firm of Phelps, Dunbar from 1982-1987. He was
admitted to partnership at that firm in 1988, and
remained there in that capacity through 1991,
when he co-founded the firm of Preaus, Roddy &
Krebs, where he was a partner from 1991 through
2001. Since 2001, he has been managing partner
of Krebs, Farley & Pelleteri. He was admitted to
practice in Texas in 2007.
**Publications:** Mr Krebs has authored several
publications, including: Performance Bond
Manual, "Louisiana," American Bar Association,
2006; Annotated Financial Institution Bond,
American Bar Association, 2004, Chapter 5
Section 5 – General Agreement (E) – Joint
Insured and Chapter 6, Section 4 – Limit of
Liability, co-authored by David J. Krebs and Diane
L. Matthews; Does a Surety Have to Issue a
Performance Bond for a Contractor after
Furnishing a Bid Bond?, Performance Bonds, edit-
ed by Steven Strawbridge and Larry Lerner (ABA
Monograph 1998); Judicial Rescission of Fidelity
Coverage, The Fidelity Law Journal, Vol. VII, co-
authored by David J. Krebs and Diane L.
Matthews, October 2001; Recent Developments in
Fidelity and Surety Law, Tort & Insurance Law
Journal, Volume 33, Number 2 (Winter 1998).
**Personal:** Mr Krebs was heavily involved in
Qatar's Treme/Laffitte Corridor Revitalization
Project, which rehabilitated 100 homes in the his-
toric Treme neighborhood following Hurrican
Katrina. His other pro bono activities have
brought him the Distinguished Service Award for
Pro Bono Project, 2002 and 2004. He also served
on the Client Protection Committee of the
Louisiana State Bar Association, and was
Chairman of the Pro Bono Project in 2005 and
2006.

## KUEBEL III, Omer F (Rick)
Locke Lord LLP, New Orleans
504 558 5155
rkuebel@lockelord.com
*Featured in Bankruptcy/Restructuring (Louisiana)*
**Practice Areas:** Bankruptcy, restructuring,
creditors' rights and business litigation. Vast experience representing parties in oil, gas and energy-
related bankruptcies, restructurings and corporate
reorganizations and has represented creditor committees in complex bankruptcy reorganizations.
Substantial experience in financial risk management in the energy sector, commercial collection
litigation, property litigation, enforcement of
security rights and bankruptcy litigation.
**Professional Memberships:** American
Bankruptcy Institute; Turnaround Management
Association; Federal Bar Association; Institute for
Energy Law (Advisory Board Member); active in
several financial risk and restructuring trade
organizations.
**Career:** Partner since 2001.
**Personal:** Loyola University School of Law (JD,
1992); Tulane University (BA, Economics 1986).

## KUPPERMAN, Stephen H
Barrasso Usdin Kupperman Freeman &
Sarver LLC, New Orleans
504 589 9700
SKupperman@BarrassoUsdin.com
*Featured in Litigation (Louisiana)*
**Practice Areas:** Mr Kupperman has over 35
years experience representing clients in commer-
cial litigation and arbitration, including securities,
class actions, fraud and other complex matters.
**Career:** Mr Kupperman is a founding Member
of Barrasso Usdin Kupperman Freeman & Sarver.
He is named one of the 'Best Lawyers in America'
and Top 50 among Louisiana's Super Lawyers. He
has served on the adjunct faculty at Tulane Law
School for almost 25 years, and written numerous
articles.
**Personal:** JD, Tulane University, 1977; Order of
the Coif; Board of Editors and Articles Editor,
Tulane Law Review; BA, magna cum laude, Duke
University, 1974.

## KURTZ, David
Baker, Donelson, Bearman, Caldwell &
Berkowitz, PC, New Orleans
504 566 5259
dkurtz@bakerdonelson.com
*Featured in Construction (Louisiana)*
**Practice Areas:** Construction litigator and
shareholder with experience representing owners,
contractors, subcontractors, architects and others.
Court-appointed contractor liaison counsel in the
multi-district litigation, In Re FEMA Trailer
Formaldehyde Products Liability Litigation. Has
appeared before state and federal courts, both at
trial and appellate levels, as well as before arbitration panels and regulatory bodies.
**Professional Memberships:** Editor of
Construct!, the newsletter of the ABA Section of
Litigation Construction Litigation Committee.
Member: New Orleans, Louisiana State, Federal
and American Bar Associations.
**Career:** Louisiana, 1995.
**Personal:** Duke University School of Law, JD,
1995; Tulane University, BS (mathematics), BA
(history), 1992.

## LAMBERT, Kent A
Baker, Donelson, Bearman, Caldwell &
Berkowitz, PC, New Orleans
504 566 5252
klambert@bakerdonelson.com
*Featured in Litigation (Louisiana)*
**Practice Areas:** Practice concentrated in the
area of commercial litigation. Emphasis upon civil
trial work, including all aspects of complex litigation practice, with state and intermediate federal
court appellate experience. Works with domestic
and international concerns in various industries,
including financial, banking, manufacturing, tech-
nology, telecommunications, hospitality, and construction. Chair of Firm's eDiscovery and
Information Management group.
**Professional Memberships:** American Bar
Association (Chair, Trial Evidence Committee);
Louisiana State Bar, US Fifth Circuit; US District
Courts for the Eastern, Middle & Western
Districts of Louisiana.
**Career:** Licensed in Louisiana, 1993.

**Personal:** Tulane University, JD, 1993, cum
laude. Denison University, BA, 1990.

## LANDRY, Charles
Jones Walker LLP, Baton Rouge
225 248 2020
clandry@joneswalker.com
*Featured in Real Estate (Louisiana)*
**Practice Areas:** Real Estate; Zoning and Land
Use; Project Development and Finance.
**Professional Memberships:** LSU Foundation;
Urban Land Institute; Council for a Better
Louisiana; EBR Parish Planning Commission
Zoning Ordinance Task Force; Pennington
Biomedical Foundation. Baton Rouge Area
Chamber. Lafayette Chamber of Commerce.
**Career:** Charles Landry's practice includes real
estate development and finance, land use, zoning,
and business law. He represents numerous parties
in a wide range of real estate transactions and
land use matters, which include residential devel-
opments (including Traditional Neighborhood
Developments), office buildings, shopping centers,
hotels, medical facilities, golf course communities,
and industrial developments. He was instrumental
in establishing the Louisiana Technology Park and
is General Counsel to the Research Park
Corporation. Since 1993, he has been listed in The
Best Lawyers in America® (Copyright
Woodward/White, Inc. Aiken, SC). Baton Rouge
Business Report named him 2006 Businessperson
of the Year and to the 2007 Power Book Top 10
list of the most influential people in the Baton
Rouge Region. Since 2006, he has been selected to
Louisiana Super Lawyers in Real Estate.
**Publications:** 'The Foreign Investor's Guide to
the Legal Aspects of Doing Business in Louisiana',
Co-Editor.
**Personal:** Louisiana State University Law School
(JD, 1977); (BS, Business, 1975).

## LANUSSE, Leslie A
Adams and Reese LLP, New Orleans
504 585 0298
leslie.lanusse@arlaw.com
*Featured in Labor & Employment (Louisiana)*
**Practice Areas:** Labor and employment litigation, management counseling, employment discrimination, agency and litigation, affirmative
action plan design and defense.
**Career:** She has more than two decades of experience in the representation of management in all
phases of employee relations, including defending
claims of discrimination before the EEOC and the
Louisiana Commission on Human Rights; handling claims arising under the Fair Labor
Standards Act and state compensation commissions; defense of OSHA and environmental
whistleblower claims before administrative agencies; and other employment matters.
**Personal:** JD, Loyola University New Orleans
School of Law, 1984; BS, University of New
Orleans, 1976.

## LELONG, Rivers
Jones Walker LLP, New Orleans
504 582 8378
rlelong@joneswalker.com
*Featured in Banking & Finance (Louisiana)*

**Practice Areas:** Mr Lelong's practice involves a variety of commercial transactions involving secured finance, real estate, acquisitions and divestitures of privately held companies and their assets, and the negotiation of sophisticated commercial contracts.

**Professional Memberships:** Louisiana State Bar Association.

**Career:** Admitted to Bar, 1990, Louisiana; Partner at Jones Walker since 1998; Member of Jones Walker's Board of Directors.

**Personal:** Born New Orleans, Louisiana, February 14, 1965; Amherst College (BA, summa cum laude, 1987); Stanford Law School (JD 1990).

## LEWIS, Sidney
Jones Walker LLP, New Orleans
504 582 8352
slewis@joneswalker.com
*Featured in Labor & Employment (Louisiana)*

**Practice Areas:** Mr Lewis is a Senior Partner and Practice Group leader of the firm's Labor and Employment Law Practice Group. He is an experienced litigator in federal, state and administrative judicial forums. A large part of his practice is devoted to advising and counseling employers with respect to union organizing drives and in the development, maintenance and administration of personnel policies, procedures and employee relations to minimize exposure to litigation and union organizing. Mr Lewis regularly conducts supervisor and management training programs. He is a frequent speaker for human resource associations, and has authored numerous articles for professional journals and other publications on a wide range of labor and employment law topics.

**Professional Memberships:** Louisiana State Bar Association; New Orleans Bar Association, Labor & Employment Committee Chair.

**Career:** Admitted in Louisiana, 1985; Joined Jones Walker as Partner in 1999; Tulane School of Law (JD, 1985); University of Alabama (BA, 1982).

**Publications:** 'Jones Walker Labor and Employment E-Bulletins' (electronic newsletter) (editor).

**Personal:** Native of New Orleans, Louisiana.

## LEYENS, JR, Jon F
Baker, Donelson, Bearman, Caldwell & Berkowitz, PC, New Orleans
504 566 8628
jleyens@bakerdonelson.com
*Featured in Real Estate (Louisiana)*

**Practice Areas:** Shareholder in the Real Estate/Finance group. Focuses practice on commercial real estate leasing and development, business financing and land use. Experience with a variety of commercial and public-private transactions.

**Professional Memberships:** Fellow: American College of Real Estate Lawyers. Chair: American Bar Association's Ground Leasing Committee. Frequent speaker and panelist on leasing, land use, financing and sustainable building issues.

**Career:** Louisiana, 1993. Texas, 2007.

**Personal:** Harvard Law School, JD, 1993.

## LIPSEY, Christine
McGlinchey Stafford PLLC, Baton Rouge
225 382 3683
clipsey@mcglinchey.com
*Featured in Litigation (Louisiana)*

**Practice Areas:** Commercial and class action/mass joinder litigation.

**Professional Memberships:** American Bar Association, Business Torts Committee; Commercial & Business Litigation Committee; and Professional Liability Litigation Committee; Bar Association of the Fifth Federal Circuit; Louisiana Bar Foundation; Louisiana State Bar Association, Committee on Rules of Professional Conduct; Wex S. Malone American Inn of Court; Louisiana State Bar Association, Board of Governors, Disciplinary Board, House of Delegates (former member); Louisiana Supreme Court's Mandatory Continuing Legal Education Committee (former member); Louisiana Law Institute's Prescription (statute of limitations) Committee; and Capital Area CASA (Court Appointed Special Advocates) Association Board of Directors.

**Career:** Member of McGlinchey Stafford's Commercial Litigation Practice Group and focuses on business, insurance, and class action/mass joinder litigation. Clients include banks and other lenders, insurers, manufacturers, technology and telecommunications companies, and state agencies. Frequently lectures and publishes in areas of business litigation, corporate governance, and legal ethics and professionalism.

**Personal:** Louisiana State University Paul M. Hebert Law Center adjunct faculty and Alumni Board of Trustees member.

## LUND, Daniel
Montgomery Barnett, New Orleans
504 585 7640
dlund@monbar.com
*Featured in Litigation (Louisiana)*

**Practice Areas:** Engaged in general civil practice with concentration in trial and appellate practice in lawyers' professional liability litigation and broad array of business litigation.

**Professional Memberships:** Fellow, American College of Trial Lawyers, American Bar Association, Louisiana State Bar Association, Louisiana Association of Defense Counsel, International Association of Defense Counsel, Federation of Defense and Corporate Counsel, and American Arbitration Association.

**Career:** Partner, Montgomery Barnett, L.L.P.

**Personal:** Born in Washington, D.C. Attended Tulane University School of Law, New Orleans.

## MALLERY, Mark N
Ogletree, Deakins, Nash, Smoak & Stewart, PC, New Orleans
504 648 3840
mark.mallery@ogletreedeakins.com
*Featured in Labor & Employment (Louisiana)*

**Practice Areas:** Mr Mallery has spent 25 years in Louisiana practicing law in all areas of labor relations, employment law and human resource management.

**Professional Memberships:** Louisiana State Bar Association. Fellow, College of Labor and Employment Lawyers. American Bar Association. Co-Chair, ABA Labor and Employment Section CLE Conference. (Chicago, November 2010). Section Publications Chair (2011-present).

**Career:** Admitted in Louisiana; US Fifth Circuit Court of Appeals; US Supreme Court.

**Publications:** Regional Editor, Employment At Will, BNA/ABA 2011; Editor-in-Chief, Employment Termination - Rights and Remedies, BNA/ABA, 2003 Supplement.

**Personal:** Mississippi State University (BBA, 1983), University of Mississippi (JD, 1986). Member, Mississippi Law Journal.

## MANTHEY, Tristan E
Heller, Draper, Patrick & Horn, LLC, New Orleans
504 299 3314
tmanthey@hellerdraper.com
*Featured in Bankruptcy/Restructuring (Louisiana)*

**Practice Areas:** Concentration in chapter 11 reorganizations, workouts, debt structure negotiations, insolvency litigation and creditor's rights.

**Professional Memberships:** Licensed to practice in the states of Louisiana and Texas. He is included in Louisiana Super Lawyers, Top Attorneys in Louisiana (Louisiana Life and New Orleans Magazines); certified Business Bankruptcy Specialist by the American Board of Certification; Certified Public Accountant; Chairman of the Bankruptcy Section for the Louisiana State Bar Association(LSBA) and Board Member for the Bankruptcy Section for the Federal Bar Association; Member or the LSBA House of Delegates, the Louisiana and Federal Bar Associations, the American Bankruptcy Institute and the Turnaround Management Association.

**Career:** Received his BA in Accounting and Science from University of New Orleans in 1992. He graduated Cum Laude with a Juris Doctorate from Loyola University in 1996.

**Publications:** Author of Recent Developments for the bankruptcy section in the Louisiana Bar Journal; a CLE speaker at the following seminars: Bankruptcy Law and Practice in Louisiana (2001); Bankruptcy after the 3 Disasters - Katrina, Rita and the Bankruptcy Reform Act (2006); Recent Developments Under the Almost New Bankruptcy Law; A View From the Bench and the Bar (2007); and Landlord - Tenant Law in Louisiana (2009).

**Personal:** Born in New Orleans, LA on November 9, 1970.

## MCCALLA, Robert
Fisher & Phillips LLP, New Orleans
504 522 3303
rmccalla@laborlawyers.com
*Featured in Labor & Employment (Louisiana)*

**Career:** Bob McCalla is a Senior Partner in the New Orleans office. He has over 35 years of experience as a labor and employment lawyer. He has extensive trial experience in both jury and non-jury discrimination cases and he has handled many pieces of complex litigation. He also has an extensive practice in labor relations, including negotiating collective bargaining agreements. He

has advised companies on negotiations, strikes and corporate campaigns. He also has advised companies in connection with their efforts to remain union free and handled the representation and unfair labor practice proceedings arising out of union organizational efforts.

## MCCOLLAM, John M
Gordon, Arata, McCollam, Duplantis & Eagan LLC, New Orleans
403 482 1113
jmccollam@gordonarata.com
*Featured in Energy & Natural Resources (Louisiana)*

**Career:** John McCollam is a member in Gordon Arata's New Orleans office. For over 50 years, he has had a diverse practice ranging from complex commercial and energy transactions and litigation across the globe to energy regulatory matters, products liability, toxic tort and environmental cases, telecommunications, and intellectual property law. He is best known for litigating complex, high-stakes oil and gas disputes, including those arising from take-or-pay gas purchase/sale contracts, onshore and offshore operating agreements, mineral leases, gas balancing agreements, farmout agreements, preferential purchase rights, purchase/sale agreements, pipeline transportation agreements, and unit agreements.

## MCCOWAN, Charles
Kean Miller LLP, Baton Rouge
225 387 0999
charles.mccowan@keanmiller.com
*Featured in Environment (Louisiana), Litigation (Louisiana)*

**Practice Areas:** Litigation, Toxic Tort and Environmental Law.

**Professional Memberships:** American College of Trial Lawyers; American Board of Trial Advocates; Dean Henry George McMahon American Inn of Court; International Society of Barristers.

**Career:** Charles McCowan is a founding member of Kean Miller LLP. He has more than 40 years of experience and represents local, regional, national and international petrochemical, industrial, healthcare, and corporate clients in a wide variety of disputes. His experience includes class action litigation, toxic tort defense, construction litigation, environmental litigation, and commercial disputes.

## MERCANTE, Mark W
Baker, Donelson, Bearman, Caldwell & Berkowitz, PC, Mandeville
985 819 8410
mmercante@bakerdonelson.com
*Featured in Construction (Louisiana)*

**Practice Areas:** Shareholder who concentrates practice in the areas of construction law and commercial litigation. Represents owners, developers, contractors, subcontractors and design professionals in all aspects of construction, including contract negotiation and drafting, pre-claim counseling, and disputes before courts and arbitration panels.

**Professional Memberships:** American, Federal, Louisiana, New Orleans and Covington Bar Associations. Member: ABA Forum on the

Construction Industry Division 3-Design Steering Committee.

**Career:** Louisiana, 1995. U.S. Fifth Circuit Court of Appeals and U.S. District Courts for the Eastern, Middle and Western Districts of Louisiana (1995).

**Personal:** Loyola University School of Law, JD, 1995, cum laude.

### MEYER, Malcolm A
Adams and Reese LLP, New Orleans
504 585 0196
Malcolm.A.Meyer@arlaw.com
*Featured in Real Estate (Louisiana)*

**Practice Areas:** Partner: real estate, transactions, construction, banking, estate and wealth planning, litigation and tax.

**Professional Memberships:** American Bar, Louisiana Bar, New Orleans Bar, Board of Regents, American College of Mortgage Attorneys, Louisiana Law Institute.

**Career:** More than 30 years in real estate, banking and finance, corporate law and business counseling; qualified as an expert witness in Ethics and Real Estate; his book, "Meyer's Manual on Louisiana Real Estate," is the acknowledged treatise on Louisiana real estate law; Daily Point of Light Award, Points of Light Institute, 2011.

**Personal:** JD, Tulane University Law School, 1971; BA, Tulane University, 1968.

### MILLER JR, Ben R
Kean Miller LLP, Baton Rouge
225 387 0999
ben.miller@keanmiller.com
*Featured in Corporate/M&A (Louisiana)*

**Practice Areas:** Commercial and Industrial Transactions, Real Estate, Tax and Corporate Law.

**Professional Memberships:** Baton Rouge, Louisiana State, and American Bar Associations; Louisiana Bar Foundation; Captain, U.S. Army Reserves.

**Career:** A founding member of Kean Miller LLP, Ben Miller has more than 50 years of experience in commercial and industrial transactions, real estate, tax and corporate law. Ben served as the firm's managing partner for 15 years. His experience in Louisiana corporate and business law enables him to recognize the specialized issues involved in commercial and industrial acquisitions, mergers and acquisitions, and real estate matters.

### MINCE, Loretta G
Fishman Haygood Phelps Walmsley Willis & Swanson, L.L.P., New Orleans
504 586 5273
lmince@fishmanhaygood.com
*Featured in Litigation (Louisiana)*

**Practice Areas:** Ms Mince regularly represents various media outlets including The Times-Picayune, CNN, The New York Times, and ProPublica, on First Amendment issues, including defamation cases brought against reporters and disputes regarding the media's right of access in criminal and civil cases. She also handles a variety of securities fraud and other commercial litigation matters for local and national clients and regularly

represents the Louisiana Department of Revenue in corporate tax litigation.

**Professional Memberships:** Ms Mince is a Member of the Louisiana State, Federal and American Bar Associations. She is also a member of Omicron Delta Kappa and the Louisiana Bar Foundation.

**Career:** Ms Mince graduated cum laude from Tulane University in 1992, and obtained her JD, magna cum laude, from Loyola University School of Law in 1998. She was a Member of Loyola Law Review, and is the author of 'Louisiana Smoked Products, Inc. v Savoie & Sausage and Food Products, Inc.: If You Like Laws and Sausages'. She was selected as a member of the New Orleans CityBusiness Leadership in Law Class of 2010. She teaches a course in media law at Tulane Law School, and is on Board of Directors of St. George's Episcopal School.

### MITCHELL, Michael S
Fisher & Phillips LLP, New Orleans
504 529 3830
mmitchell@laborlawyers.com
*Featured in Labor & Employment (Louisiana)*

**Career:** Mike Mitchell is a Partner in the New Orleans office. His practice emphasizes traditional labor law matters such as union avoidance, collective bargaining, arbitration, and unfair labor practice proceedings before the NLRB. With more than 30 years of experience, he has successfully argued major cases in the Third, Fourth, Fifth, and Seventh Circuit US Courts of Appeals. Mitchell performs preventive training and has addressed conferences and trade associations across the country on labor and employment topics.

### MOORE, Christopher
Ogletree, Deakins, Nash, Smoak & Stewart, PC, New Orleans
504 648 3840
christopher.moore@ogletreedeakins.com
*Featured in Labor & Employment (Louisiana)*

**Practice Areas:** Moore is an advocate for employers. His litigation practice includes single-plaintiff discrimination cases, complex contractual matters, multiple-plaintiff class and collective actions (including FLSA claims), and the defense and prosecution of restrictive covenant and trade secrets cases. Moore also handles traditional labor matters and administrative matters before governmental agencies.

**Career:** Moore has been a featured speaker in employment-law programs for HR professionals and attorneys. He has been identified in the prestigious publication Best Lawyers in America for many years and has received an "AV" Peer Review rating by Martindale-Hubbell.

**Personal:** Rhodes College, BA, 1992, University of Memphis, JD, 1996.

### NAJDER, Kenneth
Jones Walker LLP, New Orleans
504 582 8386
knajder@joneswalker.com
*Featured in Corporate/M&A (Louisiana)*

**Practice Areas:** Corporate and securities; mergers and acquisitions; telecommunications

and utilities; venture capital and emerging companies.

**Professional Memberships:** American Bar Association; Association for Corporate Growth – Louisiana Chapter (a Director since 2008 and currently an Officer); Louisiana State Bar Association.

**Career:** Ken Najder is a Partner in the firm's Corporate and Securities Practice Group. He joined Jones Walker in 1985 and became a Partner in 1992. Mr Najder represents public and private companies regarding a variety of corporate and securities law matters, with an emphasis on mergers and acquisitions, corporate finance, venture capital transactions, and corporate governance.

**Personal:** University of Virginia School of Law, JD, 1985; University of Virginia, BA and BS, 1982, summa cum laude.

### NORTON, William N
Baker, Donelson, Bearman, Caldwell & Berkowitz, PC, New Orleans
504 566 5297
wnorton@bakerdonelson.com
*Featured in Corporate/M&A (Louisiana)*

**Practice Areas:** Practices in corporate and business transactions, mergers and acquisitions and finance. He has concentrated his practice in the areas of entity formation, capital formation, acquisitions of financial institutions, service companies and energy concerns, defense of unwanted takeovers, business reorganizations and financings.

**Professional Memberships:** Former Chair, Louisiana Bar Association and New Orleans Bar Association, Corporate and Business Law Sections. Board of Directors, Louisiana Bar Foundation, Finance and Budget Committee. Member, American Bar Association, Negotiated Acquisitions Committee and Small Business Committee.

**Career:** Licensed in Mississippi since 1972 and in Louisiana since 1977.

### O'CONNOR, Scott A
Gordon, Arata, McCollam, Duplantis & Eagan LLC, New Orleans
504 569 1860
soconnor@gordonarata.com
*Featured in Energy & Natural Resources (Louisiana)*

**Career:** Scott O'Connor is a member in Gordon Arata's New Orleans office. His practice focuses on oil and gas and complex commercial litigation. He has litigated and arbitrated numerous disputes involving onshore and offshore operating agreements, royalty claims, gas balancing agreements, farmout agreements, preferential purchase rights, operator removal, joint interest accounting and audit rights, lease and servitude maintenance, environmental contamination, and purchase and sale agreements. He has defended national and state class actions involving oil and gas pricing practices including antitrust litigation, and has represented oil and gas clients as creditors and debtors in bankruptcy proceedings.

### PAGE, Marshall
Jones Walker LLP, New Orleans
504 582 8248
mpage@joneswalker.com
*Featured in Banking & Finance (Louisiana)*

**Practice Areas:** Mr Page primarily handles investment transactions and related financings, including venture capital investments, joint ventures, project development and the strategic and financial acquisition and disposition of businesses and assets. Financing transactions include senior and mezzanine debt facilities, rated/ structured transactions, equity fund formation and project finance. Chair of the International Section of the Louisiana State Bar Association, Mr Page has handled transactions on six continents, in a large percentage of the US states and in the Commonwealth of Puerto Rico.

**Professional Memberships:** Louisiana State Bar Association (Chairman, International Section).

**Career:** Joined Jones Walker in 1988; Partner since 1996; leader of the firm's Business and Commercial Transactions Practice Group.

**Personal:** University of Virginia (JD, 1988; BA, with distinction, 1985), Virginia Law Review; Jefferson Scholar (one of twelve full-tuition, merit based scholarships awarded that year); Echols Scholar; one of 50 fourth year students to live on the Lawn; Omicron Delta Kappa; listed in The Best Lawyers in America (Woodward/ White, Inc.) in the areas of Banking and Finance Law, Corporate Law, International Trade and Finance Law, and Venture Capital Law; City Business Leadership in Law award, 2008.

### PATRICK III, William H
Heller, Draper, Patrick & Horn, LLC, New Orleans
504 299 3345
wpatrick@hellerdraper.com
*Featured in Bankruptcy/Restructuring (Louisiana)*

**Practice Areas:** Concentration is in business work-outs, debt restructure negotiations, insolvency litigation and corporate bankruptcy.

**Professional Memberships:** Fellow, American College of Bankruptcy, included in 'Best Lawyers in America', 'Louisiana Super Lawyers' (Top 50 attorneys), and 'Best Attorneys'. Member of Louisiana Law Review, Order of the Coif, and Phi Kappa Phi.

**Career:** Graduated in an accelerated undergraduate-law program from Louisiana State University with a JD in 1977.

**Publications:** Author 'Enforcement of Judgments Against Public Entities, The New Sovereign Immunity,' 37 Louisiana Law Review 982, 1977. Co-authored: 'The Work of Louisiana Legislature for the 1977 Regular Season,' 38 Louisiana Law Review 51, 1977.

**Personal:** Born December 5, 1954 in Baton Rouge, Louisiana.

### PERRAULT, Jean-Paul
McGlinchey Stafford PLLC, Baton Rouge
225 382 3641
jperrault@mcglinchey.com
*Featured in Corporate/M&A (Louisiana)*

**Practice Areas:** Corporate Law, construction law, insurance regulation and compliance, business litigation.
**Career:** Managing Member of the firm's Baton Rouge office. Advises business clients, including small businesses, developers, lenders, insurance companies and producers regarding general business, corporate, commercial, insurance regulation and compliance issues. Also represents clients in construction law and business litigation.
**Personal:** Loyola University New Orleans College of Law, JD, 1997 (cum laude); Loyola University New Orleans, MBA, 1997 (summa cum laude); Louisiana State University, BS, 1991.

### PHILLIPS, Louis
Gordon, Arata, McCollam, Duplantis & Eagan LLC, Baton Rouge
225 381 9643
lphillips@gordonarata.com
*Featured in Bankruptcy/Restructuring (Louisiana)*
**Practice Areas:** Louis Phillips is a member of the Gordon Arata Baton Rouge office and serves as the leader of the Bankruptcy/Debtor-Creditor/Insolvency practice. He provides legal representation and consultation for debtors, creditors, and trustees over a broad practice area, including transaction and business structuring and restructuring, bankruptcy reorganization, and bankruptcy and commercial litigation. He was the U.S. Bankruptcy Judge for the Middle District of Louisiana from May 1988 through May 2002, where he authored numerous opinions that have been adopted by the Fifth Circuit and other courts. He is an adjunct professor of Law and often speaks and publishes on bankruptcy matters.

### PILIE, Glen M
Adams and Reese LLP, New Orleans
504 585 0260
glen.pilie@arlaw.com
*Featured in Environment (Louisiana)*
**Practice Areas:** Partner: environmental and toxic tort, energy and environmental, environmental regulatory and litigation.
**Professional Memberships:** Mid Continent Oil and Gas Association, American Society of Civil Engineers, Louisiana Society of Professional Engineers.
**Career:** Centers around environmental issues, Co-Chaired industry committee formed under the Mid Continent Oil and Gas Association to review/comment on General Environmental Impact Statement addressing offshore oil and gas operations in coastal waters, varied permitting/compliance issues, EPA remediations, and complex PSD air permitting.
**Personal:** JD, Loyola University New Orleans School of Law, 1982; MS, University of New Orleans, 1977; BSCE University of Southwestern Louisiana, 1973.

### PITRE, Loulan
Gordon, Arata, McCollam, Duplantis & Eagan LLC, New Orleans
lpitre@gordonarata.com
*Featured in Environment (Louisiana)*
**Career:** Loulan Pitre's practice focuses on environmental issues, most often in the context of oil and gas exploration and production. A native of Cut Off, Louisiana, Loulan is a graduate of Harvard Law School and a former member of the Louisiana House of Representatives. He has represented and advised oil and gas companies, oilfield service companies, industrial and construction firms, engineering firms, financial institutions, real estate developers, public agencies, and non-profit organizations. He has defended several dozen "legacy" lawsuits asserting environmental damage, often involving claims of hundreds of millions of dollars. He frequently writes and speaks on environmental issues.

### PYBURN JR, Keith M
Fisher & Phillips LLP, New Orleans
504 522 3303
kpyburn@laborlawyers.com
*Featured in Labor & Employment (Louisiana)*
**Career:** Keith Pyburn is the Managing Partner in the New Orleans office. He has represented management in labor relations and employment law since 1975. A former Chairman of the Labor and Employment Section of the Louisiana State Bar Association and a fellow of the College of Labor and Employment Lawyers, he is a contributing editor to Employment Discrimination Law, published by the American Bar Association's Section of Labor and Employment Law. Pyburn received a JD from Louisiana's Tulane Law School.

### QUINN JR, Louis S
Jones Walker LLP, Baton Rouge
225 248 2054
lquinn@joneswalker.com
*Featured in Real Estate (Louisiana)*
**Practice Areas:** Real Estate Development and Finance; Commercial Leasing; Business and Commercial Transactions; Public Finance; and Commercial Loans.
**Professional Memberships:** American Bar Association; Baton Rouge Bar Association; The Florida Bar; Louisiana Society of Certified Public Accountants; Louisiana State Bar Association; National Association of Bond Lawyers.
**Career:** Leads the firm's Real Estate Practice Group.
**Personal:** Paul M Hebert Law Center, Louisiana State University, JD, 1983; Georgia State University, MS in Community Counseling, 1990; Louisiana State University, BS in Accounting, 1978. Admitted to practice in Florida and Louisiana.

### RAMELLI, Rudolph R
Jones Walker LLP, New Orleans
504 582 8206
rramelli@joneswalker.com
*Featured in Corporate/M&A (Louisiana)*
**Practice Areas:** Banking and financial services; corporate and securities; employee benefits, erisa and executive compensation; health care; tax and estates; transactional tax (federal and international).
**Professional Memberships:** American Bar Association (Chair, Section of Taxation); American College of Tax Counsel; American Tax Policy Institute; American Institute of Certified Public Accountants; Board-Certified Tax Specialist as Certified by the Louisiana Board of Legal Specialization; Certified Public Accountant; Louisiana Society of Certified Public Accountants; Louisiana State Bar Association.
**Career:** He is a partner in the firm's Tax & Estates Practice Group and a member of the firm's board of directors. He has been practicing tax law for more than 25 years. His practice concentrates on corporate and partnership federal income tax issues. In addition, Mr Ramelli represents tax-exempt institutions, particularly tax-exempt health care entities.
**Publications:** He speaks frequently at national and state tax seminars, and is a professor of law at Tulane University Law School and an adjunct professor at the University of New Orleans.
**Personal:** New York University School of Law, LLM in Taxation, 1978, Tax Law Review; Tulane University Law School, JD, 1977, order of the coif; Loyola University, BA, 1974, summa cum laude. Admitted to practice in Louisiana.

### RESTER, Daniel K
Adams and Reese LLP, Baton Rouge
225 336 5200
daniel.rester@arlaw.com
*Featured in Gaming & Licensing (Louisiana)*
**Practice Areas:** Partner: gaming, commercial litigation, general corporate, energy and environmental, real estate, forestry law.
**Professional Memberships:** International Association of Gaming Attorneys, Louisiana Land Title Association, Rotary Club.
**Career:** Practice has been predominately in business, commercial, real estate transactional and construction litigation, including emphasis on gaming and entertainment law and financial transactions. His current representation of clients includes ongoing gaming licensing and financial transactions, commercial lease negotiations, corporate and partnership matters, various commercial loan transactions, construction and commercial litigation, and pipeline right-of-way negotiations and condemnations.
**Personal:** JD, Tulane University Law School, 1971; BS, Louisiana State University, 1969.

### RIEVESCHL, David
Baker, Donelson, Bearman, Caldwell & Berkowitz, PC, New Orleans
504 566 8660
drieveschl@bakerdonelson.com
*Featured in Corporate/M&A (Louisiana)*
**Practice Areas:** Concentrates his practice in the areas of corporate, mergers and acquisitions and securities law. Practice includes representation of publicly traded and privately held clients in complex merger, stock and asset purchase transactions. Also regularly counsels emerging companies on issues affecting legal structure, intellectual property rights and venture capital financing.
**Professional Memberships:** Tulane Association of Business Alumni; ACG Louisiana; American Bar Association.
**Career:** Louisiana (2003); Georgia (2007); District of Columbia (1998); New York (1998).
**Personal:** Tulane Law School, JD, 1997, magna cum laude.

### ROSENBLUM, Carl D
Jones Walker LLP, New Orleans
504 582 8296
crosenblum@joneswalker.com
*Featured in Energy & Natural Resources (Louisiana)*
**Practice Areas:** Mr Rosenblum devotes his time primarily to the representation of parties involved in significant oil and gas related disputes. For nearly three decades, he has represented independent producers, major producers, pipeline companies, oilfield service companies, seismic exploration companies, oil and gas management companies, financial institutions, and significant landowners. He has handled hundreds of disputes concerning the rights and obligations of parties to joint operating agreements, oil and gas leases, royalty matters, exploration agreements, gas purchase contracts, drilling contracts, pipeline right-of-way agreements, farmout agreements, gas balancing agreements, and seismic permitting and exploration agreements. Mr Rosenblum led the team of lawyers who successfully enjoined the United States Government's deepwater drilling moratorium. He regularly appears in Federal and State Courts in Louisiana and Texas.
**Professional Memberships:** Admitted to the State Bars of Louisiana and Texas; American Bar Association; Louisiana State Bar Association; Texas State Bar Association.
**Career:** Jones Walker, 1983; Partner.
**Personal:** Born 1955; married, two daughters; resident of New Orleans since 1983.

### ROUSSEAU, Dionne M
Jones Walker LLP, Baton Rouge
225 248 2026
drousseau@joneswalker.com
*Featured in Corporate/M&A (Louisiana)*
**Practice Areas:** Ms Rousseau is the lead outside Corporate and Securities Counsel for seven public companies, and is the boardroom lawyer for three of those companies. She has more than 20 years of experience handling public and private capital raising and mergers and acquisitions transactions for public and private companies. Transactions handled include a $750 million at-the-market common stock offering for a Fortune 500 company; a $1 billion debt refinancing, including $300 million senior subordinated notes and a $200 million debt tender offer; a $40 million acquisition by a public company of private company assets; a management leveraged buyout of a publicly traded company. She also represents companies and funds in private equity transactions.
**Career:** Joined Jones Walker in 1990; investment banker with Paine Webber Capital Markets, New York, 1985-87; listed in The Best Lawyers in America® 2013 (Copyright 2012 by Woodward/White, Inc., Aiken, SC) in the areas of corporate law and securities law (annually since 1998); selected by New Orleans CityBusiness as one of the leading 50 attorneys in New Orleans (2005, 2007); 2013 BTI Client Service All-Star.
**Personal:** University of Chicago (JD 1990, Order of the Coif); Georgetown University (BA 1985, Phi Beta Kappa).

**ROUSSEL, James H**
Baker, Donelson, Bearman, Caldwell &
Berkowitz, PC, New Orleans
504 566 5278
jroussel@bakerdonelson.com
*Featured in Banking & Finance (Louisiana)*
**Practice Areas:** Senior Counsel in the New
Orleans office. Practices areas include: marine
finance, marine insurance coverage disputes, cargo
damage claims, maritime allisions and collisions,
maritime commercial transactions, ship construction, salvage, drilling and sales contracts, and
charter agreements, and litigating matters arising
from these transactions. Represents general liability, marine, and P and I underwriters in regard to
coverage issues involving a broad range of marine,
energy, general liability, excess and umbrella forms
of coverage, including representation of underwriters interest in litigation arising out of coverage
disputes.
**Personal:** Tulane University, JD, 1964; Phi Delta
Phi; Dartmouth College, AB in History-1961.

**RUBIN, Michael H**
McGlinchey Stafford PLLC, Baton Rouge
225 382 3617
mrubin@mcglinchey.com
*Featured in Banking & Finance (Louisiana)*
**Practice Areas:** Banking, finance, appellate law,
commercial litigation, real estate.
**Professional Memberships:** Past President:
American College of Real Estate Lawyers; U.S.
Fifth Circuit Bar Association; Louisiana State Bar
Association. Member: American Law Institute;
Commissioner, National Conference of Uniform
State Law Commissioners; Member: American
Academy of Appellate Lawyers; American College
of Mortgage Attorneys; Anglo-American Real
Property Institute; and LSU Law School National
Board of Trustees; National Conference of Bar
Presidents (past member of Executive Council);
Commissioner.
**Career:** Handled groundbreaking financial, real
estate, commercial and constitutional cases.
Awards: Distinguished Alumnus, LSU Law School
(2007); Burton Award at the Library of Congress
(outstanding legal writing); Winner of
Foundation for the Improvement of Justice Award
(Atlanta)for simplifying the law.
**Publications:** Author, co-author, and contributing writer of 13 books and more than 30 law
review articles and periodicals. His publications
on finance have been cited as authoritative by
state and federal appellate courts, and his publications on both finance and ethics have been used
by many law schools.
**Personal:** In demand as a public speaker to legal
and non-legal groups. Presented over 375 papers
throughout the US, Canada and the UK on
finance, real estate, appellate litigation, and legal
ethics, and has taught for more than three decades
as Adjunct Professor of finance, real estate, and
legal ethics at LSU and Tulane Law Schools.

**SARVER, Richard E**
Barrasso Usdin Kupperman Freeman &
Sarver LLC, New Orleans
504 589 9700
RSarver@BarrassoUsdin.com
*Featured in Litigation (Louisiana)*
**Practice Areas:** Mr Sarver specializes in
defending toxic tort, environmental and product
liability cases. He serves as lead counsel for the
welding industry in national MDL trials, and has
won defense verdicts in every welding case,
including 10 plaintiffs in 3 different states. His
experience includes work as lead trial counsel in
numerous class actions and mass joinder cases
involving products liability and environmental
issues, including representing CITGO in cases
stemming from the second largest oil spill in the
continental United States.
**Career:** Mr Sarver is a founding Member of
Barrasso Usdin Kupperman Freeman & Sarver,
LLC and a former trial attorney for the US
Department of Justice. He has served as lead trial
counsel in jury trials in thirteen different states.
**Personal:** JD magna cum laude, University of
Michigan School of Law, 1982, Order of the Coif,
Michigan Law Review. LLM, University of
Virginia Law School, 1990.

**SCAFIDEL, Amy Garrity**
Jones Walker LLP, New Orleans
504 582 8462
ascafidel@joneswalker.com
*Featured in Banking & Finance (Louisiana)*
**Practice Areas:** Business and commercial
transactions, commercial lending and finance,
corporate and securities, investment management
legal services, and real estate finance.
**Professional Memberships:** Louisiana State
and New Orleans Bar Associations; Louisiana
Land Title Association; Licensed as a Louisiana
Title Insurance Agent; Approved Agent for First
American Title Insurance Company and Fidelity
Insurance Company; Louisiana Banker's
Association.
**Career:** Ms Scafidel joined Jones Walker in 2001
and is a partner in the firm's Business and
Commercial Transactions Practice Group. She is
Co-Chair of the firm's Hiring Recruitment
Committee, and a member of the its Diversity
Committee. She was named a "Rising Star" in the
area of Business/Corporate in the 2013 edition of
Louisiana Super Lawyers (also in 2012). In 2012,
she was honored with a CityBusiness Women of
the Year Award. She was also mentioned in The
American Lawyer's article entitled, "Big Suits," on
February 28, 2007, along with other Jones Walker
attorneys in connection with the acquisition of
Phelps Dodge Corporation by Freeport-
McMoRan Copper & Gold Inc. for $25.9 billion
in cash and stock.
**Personal:** Louisiana State University, (BS in
Finance, 1998); Paul M. Hebert Law Center,
Louisiana State University (JD, 2001), Order of
the Coif, Louisiana Law Review, Chancellor's List.

**SCHIFF, Gerald H**
Gordon, Arata, McCollam, Duplantis &
Eagan LLC, Lafayette
337 237 0132
gschiff@gordonarata.com
*Featured in Bankruptcy/Restructuring (Louisiana)*
**Career:** Gerald Schiff is a member in the
Lafayette office of Gordon Arata where he prac-
tices in the areas of Mediation and
Bankruptcy/Debtor-Creditor law. He is a former
U.S. Bankruptcy Judge for the Western District of
Louisiana (August 1992—September 2006). His
practice embodies bankruptcy law from all per-
spectives—debtor, creditor, trustee, and creditors'
committees, and he is familiar with all of the
Bankruptcy Code. He has mediated bankruptcy
and non-bankruptcy cases in both State and
Federal Courts. Additionally, he has served as a
Special Master in both State and Federal Courts,
and currently serves as a Chapter 11 Trustee.

**SCHMIDT, Justin B**
Adams and Reese LLP, New Orleans
504 585 0361
justin.schmidt@arlaw.com
*Featured in Real Estate (Louisiana)*
**Practice Areas:** Partner: transactions and cor-
porate advisory services.
**Professional Memberships:** New Orleans and
Louisiana State Bar Associations, American Bar
Association, Real Property, Probate and Trust
Section, International Council of Shopping
Centers, YMCA of Greater New Orleans, Putnam
Cultural Endowment, and Louisiana Children's
Museum.
**Career:** Focuses on real estate, emphasis on land
use and zoning matters and includes commercial
transactions, business developments and land-
lord/tenant negotiations. Represents
lenders/developers with acquisition, divestiture,
development, leasing and financing of shopping
centers, office buildings, apartments, condominiums, low-income housing, restaurant and hotel
developments.
**Personal:** JD, LSU Paul M Hebert Law Center
1998; BBA, University of Mississippi, 1992.

**SCOTT, Timothy H.**
Fisher & Phillips LLP, New Orleans
504 529 3834
tscott@laborlawyers.com
*Featured in Labor & Employment (Louisiana)*
**Career:** Tim Scott is a partner in the New
Orleans office. His practice emphasizes employment litigation, particularly the defense of harassment and discrimination claims. Tim has successfully handled a number of jury trials as well as
cases before the courts of appeals. Tim also advises employers on a day-to-day basis on issues relating to compliance with the various state and federal laws applicable to employers. Tim handles
traditional labor law matters before the National
Labor Relations Board, as well as arbitration of
disputes involving collective bargaining agreements.

**SEEMANN, Charles**
Jackson Lewis LLP, New Orleans
504 208 1755
Charles.Seemann@jacksonlewis.com
*Featured in Labor & Employment (Louisiana)*
**Practice Areas:** ERISA and Employee Benefits
Litigation and Counseling, Employment
Litigation and Counseling, Defense of Regulatory
Investigations.
**Professional Memberships:** American Bar
Association; International Foundation of
Employee Benefits Plans; ESOP Association;
Bloomberg BNA Pensions & Benefits Advisory
Board.
**Career:** Partner. Best Lawyers in America 2007-
present. Included in Chambers USA: Louisiana:
Labor and Employment, Employee Benefits &
Compensation. Recognized in Louisiana Super
Lawyers since 2010. Named "Top Lawyer" by New
Orleans Magazine. AV-Rated by Martindale
Hubbell.
**Personal:** LSU Law, JD, 1995; Emory University,
BA, 1992.

**SHAW, Danny**
Baker, Donelson, Bearman, Caldwell &
Berkowitz, PC, Mandeville
985 819 8401
dshaw@bakerdonelson.com
*Featured in Construction (Louisiana)*
**Practice Areas:** Licensed professional civil engi-
neer, with focus on commercial litigation, alterna-
tive dispute resolution and dispute avoidance.
Experienced in construction, design professional
liability and insurance coverage and defense and
ADR Neutral.
**Professional Memberships:** Fellow, American
College of Construction Lawyers; American Bar
Association; Louisiana State Bar Association;
American Society of Civil Engineers, National
Society of Professional Engineers; American
Arbitration Association (National Panel of
Construction Arbitrators and Mediators).
**Career:** Licensed in Louisiana, 1977; District of
Columbia (inactive).
**Personal:** Georgetown University, JD, 1977.
Louisiana Tech University, BS Civil Engineering,
1970, cum laude. US Navy, Civil Engineer Corps
(LT, CEC, USN).

**SHEA, JR, Joseph L**
Bradley Murchison Kelly & Shea, Shreveport
318 227 1131
jshea@bradleyfirm.com
*Featured in Energy & Natural Resources (Louisiana)*
**Practice Areas:** Joseph L "Larry" Shea, Jr is a
partner in the Shreveport office and has 30+ years
experience, including litigation in matters from
environmental complaints and oil field operations
to contract disputes and ownership issues. His
transactional experience includes oil and gas leasing and operating agreements and exploration
and production joint ventures. He represents businesses matters including corporate structure,
shareholder issues, and acquisitions. Larry actively
pursues improvements in the legal profession,
having served as Chairman of the Louisiana
Attorney Disciplinary Board and was recently

elected Louisiana State Bar Association President. He will assume the office in June 2014.

## SINOR, Howard
Gordon, Arata, McCollam, Duplantis & Eagan LLC, New Orleans
504 582 1117
hsinor@gordonarata.com
*Featured in Litigation (Louisiana)*

**Career:** Howard Sinor's practice is focused on commercial litigation and corporate counseling. He has represented clients in cases involving corporate and securities, environmental, contract, intellectual property, banking, health care, zoning, products liability, construction and antitrust claims. Significant areas of concentration include construction, land use and zoning, industrial contracting, environmental and occupational safety, antitrust and trade regulation. He has extensive trial and appellate experience, having handled cases at all levels of the federal and state judicial systems, including the United States and Louisiana Supreme Courts. His experience includes class action, multi-district, and other complex litigation and alternative dispute resolution.

## SPANSEL, Mark J
Adams and Reese LLP, New Orleans
504 585 0215
mark.spansel@arlaw.com
*Featured in Environment (Louisiana)*

**Practice Areas:** Partner, Executive Committee Member: environmental, toxic tort, maritime/offshore, oil/gas, class action and commercial litigation.
**Professional Memberships:** Louisiana and American Bar Associations, Louisiana Association of Defense Counsel, Defense Research Institute, and Proctor Member of Maritime Law Association of the US Serves on Board of Directors, Executive Committee, and as General Counsel to Jefferson Parish Chamber of Commerce.
**Career:** Practice concentrates in defense and litigation. Frequently lectures at professional and industry seminars. Listed in Best Lawyers in America, Louisiana Super Lawyers, and AV Peer Review Rated by Martindale-Hubbell.
**Personal:** JD, Tulane University Law School, 1978; Tulane University, 1975.

## STEEG, Robert M
The Steeg Law Firm, LLC, New Orleans
504 582 1199
rsteeg@steeglaw.com
*Featured in Real Estate (Louisiana)*

**Practice Areas:** Over 30 years experience as a commercial real estate attorney. Practice areas: commercial real estate, secured transactions, landlord/tenant law, title law and title litigation, ad valorem taxation, zoning and land use. Particular experience: office and retail leases; purchase or sale of commercial property, including office and retail developments and unimproved land; management of multi-site retail acquisitions; easements, waterfront rights, zoning and land use; and representation of lenders in asset-based or real estate financing. Honors: The Best Lawyers in America, top real estate lawyers, Louisiana (1995-

present); Chambers & Partners America's Leading Lawyers for Business, one of top six real estate lawyers, Louisiana (2004-present); New Orleans CityBusiness Leadership in Law Class of 2010; Super Lawyers – Real Estate; New Orleans Magazine – Top Lawyers in Real Estate.
**Professional Memberships:** Member, New Orleans City Planning Commission; Member, International Conference of Shopping Centers; Member, ABA Section of Real Property, Trust, and Estate Law; Member New Orleans Bar Association Real Estate Law Committee.
**Career:** Bar admissions: Louisiana (1978), Texas (2007).
**Personal:** Boston College Law School (Order of the Coif), JD, 1978. Annenberg School of Communications, University of Pennsylvania, MS, 1975. University of Pennsylvania, BA, 1973.

## STROHSCHEIN, Stephen P
McGlinchey Stafford PLLC, Baton Rouge
225 382 3634
sstroh@mcglinchey.com
*Featured in Bankruptcy/Restructuring (Louisiana)*

**Practice Areas:** Bankruptcy, reorganization and creditors' rights; commercial finance; commercial litigation.
**Career:** Holds more than 30 years' experience in commercial lending, providing assistance to lenders of all types – real estate, floor plan, asset based and small business – both with regard to litigating lending issues, handling workouts, foreclosures, collections and bankruptcy matters and also frequently provides assistance with lending transactions, structure and documentation. Certified by the American Board of Certification as a specialist in the area of Business Bankruptcy Law. Served as a law clerk to the Honorable LeRoy Smallenberger, United States Bankruptcy Court for the Western District of Louisiana from 1981 to 1982.
**Personal:** Louisiana State University Paul M. Hebert Law Center, JD (1981); Louisiana State University, BS, Business (1978).

## SWANSON, James R
Fishman Haygood Phelps Walmsley Willis & Swanson, L.L.P., New Orleans
504 586 5267
jswanson@fishmanhaygood.com
*Featured in Litigation (Louisiana)*

**Practice Areas:** Mr Swanson is the firm's Managing Partner. He represents clients in a broad range of business litigation matters, including many that involve the securities laws. He regularly represents The Times-Picayune Publishing Corporation, SMG, the State of Louisiana and others.
**Career:** Mr Swanson teaches at Loyola Law School and serves as the Vice-Chairman of the Choice Foundation, a non-profit charter management organization that holds the charters for four open enrollment schools serving inner city students. He is also the treasurer of The Innocence Project New Orleans.
**Personal:** Mr Swanson received his JD, magna cum laude, from Tulane Law School, where he was

a Member of the Order of the Coif and an associate editor of the 'Tulane Law Review'.

## TAGGART, David R
Bradley Murchison Kelly & Shea, Shreveport
318 227 1131
dtaggart@bradleyfirm.com
*Featured in Energy & Natural Resources (Louisiana)*

**Practice Areas:** David R. Taggart is a partner in the Shreveport office and practices principally in the areas of energy, oil & gas, construction law, public utility law, and a heavy emphasis on complex commercial litigation. In recent years, he has represented several major natural gas transmission and gathering companies on a variety of infrastructure expansion projects, including interstate transmission line construction projects, including multi-state, large diameter transmission line projects with the associated compressor station construction and expansion projects. David has negotiated multiple gas processing plant purchases and installation projects involving amine treatment and cryogenic gas processing.

## THORNE, René
Jackson Lewis LLP, New Orleans
504 208 1755
ThorneR@jacksonlewis.com
*Featured in Labor & Employment (Louisiana)*

**Practice Areas:** Employee benefits litigation, including representation of employers, plans, plan fiduciaries, service providers, and trustees.
**Professional Memberships:** ABA Employee Benefits Subcommittee.
**Career:** Managing Partner, New Orleans.
**Publications:** Conkright v. Frommert- One Year Later: Are Courts Getting It Right?, BNA Pension & Benefits Reporter (May 19, 2011); Two Years Later: The Legacy Of Larue, BNA Pension & Benefits Reporter (March 10, 2010); Rising Tide of Complex ERISA Litigation, BNA P&B Reporter (September 18, 2009); "When is Class Action Appropriate,?" ERISA Litigation (BNA 2d, 3d and 4th ed. and supps.).
**Personal:** Loyola University, JD 1993; BA, 1990.

## TYLER, Richard J
Jones Walker LLP, New Orleans
504 582 8266
rtyler@joneswalker.com
*Featured in Construction (Louisiana)*

**Practice Areas:** Commercial litigation, with a primary emphasis in construction law and alternative dispute resolution. His construction practice involves both dispute resolution and transactional work on a variety of projects and delivery systems. He has litigated, arbitrated, and mediated on behalf of owners, contractors, subcontractors, and suppliers on projects ranging from condominiums to petrochemical plants. His transactional experience involves the negotiation and drafting of design and construction agreements for commercial and industrial projects.
**Professional Memberships:** Admitted Louisiana (1983), Texas (2004), and District of Columbia (1981). American Bar Association Forum on the Construction Industry (Governing Committee 2009-12; Division Chair 2006-08). American Arbitration Association (National

Roster of Neutrals, 2004-present). Dispute Resolution Board Foundation, 2012- present. Litigation Counsel of America (Fellow, 2009).
**Career:** Joined Jones Walker, 1982; Partner since 1986.
**Publications:** Mr Tyler frequently writes and speaks on a variety of topics of interest to industry and legal organizations. Co-editor, Construction Defects (ABA 2012). Contributing author, Construction Law (ABA, 2009); Construction Litigation, Representing the Contractor, 3d Ed. (Aspen, 2001); and, Fifty State Monograph on the Enforceability of "No Damages for Delay Clauses" (ABA, 1998).
**Personal:** Born 1956; married, two sons. Georgetown University (AB 1978); Georgetown University Law Center (JD 1981).

## TYLER, Susan M
Jones Walker LLP, New Orleans
504 582 8298
styler@joneswalker.com
*Featured in Real Estate (Louisiana)*

**Practice Areas:** Real estate: land use, development and finance; banking and financial services.
**Professional Memberships:** American College of Mortgage Attorneys (Fellow); American Bar Association (Member, Commercial Law and Real Estate Property Sections); Florida State Bar Association; Louisiana State Bar Association (Assistant Bar Examiner, Business Entities and Negotiable Instruments, 1998-2003); Texas State Bar Association.
**Career:** Represents lenders and business clients in construction and secured financings, including new market, affordable and historic tax credit transactions, and other commercial developments, including multi-family, industrial, retail, hospital, oil and gas, agricultural, and timber projects.
**Publications:** Louisiana Editor, Trigild Guide to Receiverships & Foreclosure (1st, 2nd, 3rd and 4th Editions), published by Trigild, Inc., San Diego, California.
**Personal:** Tulane Law School (JD, 1986); Georgetown University (BS, Accounting); licensed to practice in Florida, Louisiana, and Texas; licensed title insurance agent; Certified Public Accountant.

## USDIN, Steven W
Barrasso Usdin Kupperman Freeman & Sarver LLC, New Orleans
504 589 9721
SUsdin@BarrassoUsdin.com
*Featured in Litigation (Louisiana)*

**Practice Areas:** Mr Usdin has over 30 years of experience in all types of commercial litigation, including insurance coverage and oil and gas. He has extensive experience in representing clients in class actions and complex litigation.
**Career:** Mr Usdin is a founding Member of Barrasso Usdin Kupperman Freeman & Sarver. He has been named one of the Best Lawyers in America since 2001 and is a fellow in the American College of Trial Lawyers.
**Personal:** JD, University of Virginia School of Law, 1980; Clerk, Honorable Adrian G Duplantier,

United States District Court, Eastern District of Louisiana.

## VANCE, R Patrick
Jones Walker LLP, New Orleans
504 582 8194
pvance@joneswalker.com
*Featured in Bankruptcy/Restructuring (Louisiana), Litigation (Louisiana)*

**Practice Areas:** Commercial litigation, bankruptcy, and creditors-debtors rights. As a trial lawyer he has handled over three hundred plus commercial disputes in a wide variety of practice areas: antitrust, RICO, copyright infringement, securities litigation, class actions, foreclosures, fraud, lender liability, ERISA, dealer-distributor disputes, successions, legal malpractice, expropriation, partnership and utility regulation. He has over 70 reported decisions. He regularly represents debtors, secured and unsecured creditors in all types of business bankruptcy cases involving lenders, telecommunications, utilities, maritime, oil and gas, the music industry, casinos and insurance companies.
**Professional Memberships:** American College of Trial Lawyers; American College of Bankruptcy; Vice Chair, National Bankruptcy Conference; American Law Institute; Past Chairman, New Orleans Bar Association; President, American College of Bankruptcy Foundation.
**Career:** Louisiana State University (BA, 1970; JD 1975); Phi Beta Kappa Faculty Group Award; Louisiana Law Review, 1973-75; admitted to Bar, 1975, Louisiana; practice group leader, business and commercial litigation.
**Publications:** Mr Vance has authored 70-plus articles on topics involving commercial litigation, lender liability and bankruptcy.
**Personal:** Born Birmingham, Alabama, 1948.

## WALMSLEY, Robert
Fishman Haygood Phelps Walmsley Willis & Swanson, L.L.P., New Orleans
504 586 5261
rwalmsley@fishmanhaygood.com
*Featured in Corporate/M&A (Louisiana)*

**Practice Areas:** Mr Walmsley practices in the areas of corporate law, securities law, mergers and acquisitions and commercial law. He has represented various public and private company clients, banks and bank holding companies in securities offerings, mergers and acquisitions and corporate transactions. He has also represented the Louisiana Superdome and the New Orleans Arena in their transactions with the New Orleans Saints, the New Orleans Hornets, the New Orleans VooDoo, the Sugar Bowl and other sports and entertainment companies. He has represented numerous banks and bank holding companies in acquisitions of public and private banking organizations and represented John Swire & Sons affiliates in three recent acquisitions.
**Career:** Mr Walmsley currently serves as a Member of the Corporate Laws Committee of the Business Law Section of the American Bar Association, on which he previously served as a Member from 1986-92. He is a former Chairman of the Corporate Practice Committee of the

Business Law Section of the American Bar Association and former Chairman of the Section on Corporation and Business Law of the Louisiana Bar Association. He is also a Member of the American Law Institute.
**Publications:** He has been the editor of the Louisiana Corporate Newsletter. He was one of the authors of the Corporate Directors Guidebook (3rd ed.). He is listed as a leading corporate governance lawyer in Who's Who Legal and as a leading lawyer in America in the area of corporate law in another leading legal publication.
**Personal:** Mr Walmsley was graduated from Princeton University with a BA in 1968 and received his law degree from the University of Virginia in 1974 where he was a Member of the Editorial Board of the Virginia Law Review. He has also served as President of the Arts Council of New Orleans.

## WEINSTOCK, Marion
Gordon, Arata, McCollam, Duplantis & Eagan LLC, New Orleans
504 569 1833
mweinstock@gordonarata.com
*Featured in Banking & Finance (Louisiana)*

**Career:** Marion Weinstock is a member in Gordon Arata's New Orleans office. Her practice covers a wide range of commercial transactions. She has handled and closed real estate purchases/sales of apartment complexes, warehouses, shopping centers and commercial properties and has negotiated and prepared commercial leases, purchase agreements, condominium documents, servitude agreements, and many other types of contracts and agreements. She also documented and closed financings involving all types of collateral including real estate, state and offshore oil and gas leases, equipment, accounts receivable, securities, ships, vessels, partnership interests, rights-of-way, pipelines and letters of credit, and negotiated loan work-outs.

## WERNER, John D
Fishman Haygood Phelps Walmsley Willis & Swanson, L.L.P., New Orleans
504 586 5265
jwerner@fishmanhaygood.com
*Featured in Banking & Finance (Louisiana), Corporate/M&A (Louisiana)*

**Practice Areas:** Mr Werner handles financing transactions, including acquisitions, private equity and tax credit financings. He represents the State of Louisiana and various lenders, borrowers and investors in public and private financings involving tax credits, and is involved in the early stage financings of numerous entrepreneurial businesses that attract outside capital.
**Career:** Member of Louisiana and American Bar Associations and Partner since 2001.
**Personal:** Duke University in 1988, worked in finance in Hong Kong and New York before attending Tulane Law School, graduated in 1994. Served as law clerk to the Hon Donald E Walter, US District Court, WD LA.

## WEST, Paul
Baker, Donelson, Bearman, Caldwell & Berkowitz, PC, Baton Rouge
225 381 7018
PWest@bakerdonelson.com
*Featured in Gaming & Licensing (Nationwide), Gaming & Licensing (Louisiana)*

**Practice Areas:** Shareholder who concentrates his practice in the area of gaming law. Represents casino owners, operators, suppliers and financiers in all areas of gaming law, from regulatory to transactional to litigation. Adjunct Professor of Gaming Law, LSU Law School.
**Professional Memberships:** International Association of Gaming Advisors (President - 2010); American, Baton Rouge and Louisiana State Bar Associations; Louisiana State University Paul M Hebert Law Center Board of Trustees.
**Career:** Licensed in Louisiana, 1980.
**Personal:** Louisiana State University Paul M Hebert Law Center, JD, 1980 (Phi Kappa Phi). Louisiana State University, MBA, 2005. Louisiana State University, BA, 1977.

## WILLIS, Sterling Scott
Fishman Haygood Phelps Walmsley Willis & Swanson, L.L.P., New Orleans
504 586 5264
swillis@fishmanhaygood.com
*Featured in Real Estate (Louisiana), Banking & Finance (Louisiana)*

**Practice Areas:** Mr Willis practices primarily in the areas of commercial transactions, secured lending, energy and commercial real estate. Mr Willis has counseled business clients in a variety of matters, including a $3 billion bank note securitization; numerous secured energy credit facilities; the acquisition, merger and sale of numerous private and public companies; a $400 million high yield bond offering; the acquisition of the Canal Place mixed-use development in New Orleans; Stirling Properties' acquisition of the Pan American Life Building, Rouses Enterprise's acquisition of the Southern division of A&P Grocery Stores; numerous grocery store, multi-family housing, hotel and shopping center acquisitions, developments and financings; and underground fuel storage facility developments and financings.
**Career:** Mr Willis is a Member of the New Orleans, Louisiana State and American Bar Associations. He is the Past Chair of the ABA Real Property Section's Committee on Legal Opinions, current Vice-Chair of ACREL's Attorney's Opinions Committee, and Vice-Chair of the ABA Real Property Section's Standing Committee on CLE. Mr Willis is Past Chairman of the Louisiana Bankers Association Bank Counsel Committee and the Bureau of Governmental Research. He is a Fellow of the American College of Real Estate Lawyers, an inaugural member of the ABA Working Group on Legal Opinions, the LSU Law School Alumni Board of Trustees, and listed in The International Who's Who of Real Estate Lawyers and Best Lawyers in America.
**Publications:** Mr Willis authored 'Article 9 Remedies' in 'West's Louisiana Code of Civil Procedure' and was a Member of the Drafting

Group for the ABA/ACREL Real Estate Opinion Letter Guidelines.
**Personal:** Mr Willis graduated from Louisiana State University (BA 1980, JD 1983), was a Member of the Order of the Coif and associate editor of the 'Louisiana Law Review.'

## WOLFE, Richard
Jones Walker LLP, New Orleans
504 582 8182
rwolfe@joneswalker.com
*Featured in Corporate/M&A (Louisiana)*

**Practice Areas:** Mr Wolfe's concentration is in corporate and securities law, particularly mergers and acquisitions He has over 40 years' experience in corporate matters, including representing issuers and underwriters in initial and subsequent public equity offerings and advising public and private companies in matters involving tender offers, proxy contests, venture capital transactions, spinoffs, private offerings of securities, special litigation committees in derivative stockholder suits, foreign joint ventures, and related matters. 'A lawyer's area of practice as stated here is one to which (s)he devotes a substantial portion of his/her professional practice and should not be considered a 'specialization' unless certified by the Louisiana Board of Legal Specialization (or similar body in any other state in which such lawyer is licensed to practice)'.
**Career:** Joined Monroe & Lemann, New Orleans, in 1963, Partner in 1968, headed Corporate Department 1974-96; joined Jones Walker LLP as Partner, 1997; Partner as of January 2013.
**Personal:** Princeton University (AB, magna cum laude, 1959); Harvard University (JD 1962); Tulane University (M Civ L 1965); Phi Beta Kappa.

## YOUNG, J Randy
Kean Miller LLP, Baton Rouge
225 387 0999
randy.young@keanmiller.com
*Featured in Energy & Natural Resources (Louisiana)*

**Practice Areas:** Energy, Telecommunications, Utility Regulation, Pilotage Regulation, Environmental Litigation.
**Professional Memberships:** Baton Rouge, Louisiana State, and American Bar Associations.
**Career:** Randy Young is a partner at Kean Miller LLP. He represents industrial manufacturing, refining and related companies, before the Louisiana Public Service Commission and the Federal Energy Regulatory Commission. Randy also represents independent generation companies and telecommunications companies in regulatory proceedings. He represents industry groups before the Louisiana Pilotage Fee Commission. Randy has experience in complex toxic tort litigation, class action proceedings and settlements, and related insurance claims litigation, and has represented clients in environmental remediation claims and litigation.

# ADAMS AND REESE LLP

www.adamsandreese.com  tel: 504 581 3243  fax: 504 581 3234

**Managing Partner:** Charles P Adams, Jr
Number of partners: 183
Number of other lawyers: 128
Total number of lawyers: 311

## Firm Overview:

Adams and Reese is a multidisciplinary, regional law firm with attorneys and advisors in 14 offices throughout the southern United States and Washington, DC. By offering legal services on a regional basis, this AmLaw 200, NLJ 250 firm provides its clients with localized control over their legal matters, and access for clients to multiple markets where they have interests. The firm Adams and Reese was named by American Lawyer Media as a Go-To Law Firm for Litigation and Leading Financial Services Companies. Adams and Reese strives to foster a working environment of inclusion, understanding, respect and opportunity for all. Enriched by a diversity of backgrounds and experiences within the firm, Adams and Reese attorneys and staff are committed to helping improve the communities where they live and work. The firm dedicates time, talent and financial resources to many community outreach projects as well as to civic and professional organizations. In recognition of these efforts, the firm has received multiple community service and pro bono awards from state bar associations across the firm's regional footprint. Adams and Reese has also ranked first in 'Encouraging Diversity' by the *Birmingham Business Journal* and was named by *MultiCultural Magazine* as one of the 'Top 100 Law Firms for Diversity' and by *Women 3.0 Magazine* as one of the 'Top 100 Law Firms for Women.'

## Main Areas of Practice:

### Litigation:

Both of the firm's founding partners were widely respected litigators involved in some of the most momentous court decisions of their time. As the firm grew, Adams and Reese earned a national reputation for outstanding trial work. Adams and Reese represents its clients before all courts, governmental regulatory bodies, tribunals, as well as alternate dispute resolution, including arbitration and mediation. The firm is experienced in an ever-increasing variety of litigation matters ranging from the simplest forms of court action, to multidistrict litigation, complex/class action claims, and mass tort litigation. Adams and Reese litigators represent clients in the following areas: commercial disputes; banking and financial matters; professional liability/D&O; antitrust and unfair competition; products liability; asbestos; pharmaceuticals; insurance; pesticides; energy and environmental; maritime; health care; transportation; real estate and construction; technology and telecommunications; state and local taxation; class action; appellate; arbitration and alternate dispute resolution. The firm's land use attorneys obtain critical land use approvals for clients, including federal, state, regional, local land use plan amendments and zonings. Adams and Reese also recently strengthened its long-term care practice, representing one of the nation's largest diversified providers of post-acute care services.

### Corporate/Transactions:

Adams and Reese provides advice to privately and publicly held business organizations including corporations, general partnerships, limited partnerships, limited liability companies, limited liability partnerships and proprietorships. The firm counsels clients in all phases of business development and continuation, such as business organization, choice of entity, choice of jurisdiction, organizational documentation, state and federal filings, general securities and tax issues bearing upon these types of entities. The firm's corporate practice areas include: banking and finance; tax; general corporate; securities; mergers and acquisitions; bankruptcy and commercial restructuring; public finance; economic development; forestry; and real estate. The firm's Governmental Relations Team of attorneys and advisors constantly follows developments in Washington DC and they, together with other members of our Stimulus Team, are assisting clients in efforts to capitalize on the relatively unique opportunities provided by the Act.

### Special Business Services:

Adams and Reese attorneys partner with their clients to develop and execute creative and insightful strategies that will assist in accomplishing the goals of the organization. On the labor and employment front, Adams and Reese clients turn to the firm to tailor policies and procedures specific to their organization. The firm represents management in all areas of employment and traditional labor law, including employee benefits and compensation; litigation;

administrative proceedings; contract compliance; and labor/management relations. The firm's Intellectual Property Team is experienced in handling all of the following: copyrights; commercial litigation; contractual negotiation, development and litigation; computer and software protection; software technology; communications law; entertainment; internet and cyberspace issues; patents; international protection; trademarks; and trade secrets.

# BARRASSO USDIN KUPPERMAN FREEMAN & SARVER, L.L.C.

**www.**BarrassoUsdin.com **tel:** 504 589 9700 **fax:** 504 589 9701

**Managing Partner:** Steven W. Usdin
Number of partners: 16
Number of other lawyers: 18

## Firm Overview:

Barrasso Usdin is comprised of lawyers with decades of experience litigating complex civil cases throughout the country. The firm provides the high quality representation expected from large firms together with responsive and efficient services provided by top tier small firms. More than half of the firm's lawyers have served as members of law reviews and journals or clerked for federal judges, either at the appellate or district court levels.

## Main Areas of Practice:

**Class Actions & Complex Litigation:**
- Representation of homeowner insurer in putative state-wide class action filed in Missouri state court
- Defense of lead paint class action proceeding
- Representation of insurers in numerous class actions and mass actions filed after Hurricane Katrina

**Key Clients:** Allstate, Liberty Mutual, Scottsdale Insurance Company
**Contact:** Steven W Usdin **Tel:** 504 589 9721
**Email:** SUsdin@BarrassoUsdin.com

**Commercial Litigation:**
- Representation of several drug manufacturers in pricing litigation
- Representation of major law firms in malpractice claims

**Key Clients:** Blanchard & Co., Hoffmann LaRoche Inc.
**Contact:** Stephen H Kupperman **Tel:** 504 589 9728
**Email:** SKupperman@BarrassoUsdin.com

**Construction:**
- Representation of numerous contractors and subcontractors in construction disputes, including both residential and commercial disputes and litigation, arbitration and mediation

**Key Clients:** A&A Mechanical, Inc., Boes Ironworks, Inc., LaGreca Services, Rush Masonry, Inc.
**Contact:** H Minor Pipes, III **Tel:** 504 589 9726
**Email:** MPipes@BarrassoUsdin.com

**Environmental:**
- Represented a major oil company in the first-ever trial under the civil-penalty provisions of the Oil Pollution Act where the result was penalty constituting less than 3% of what the US DOJ sought
- Defending a major oil company in personal injury and property damage claims related to refinery oil spill
- Defending a major oil company against hundreds of personal-injury and property-damage claims related to two separate air releases
- Representation of an international energy company in connection with a pipeline rupture and oil spill
- Representing energy companies in complex oil field legacy litigation

**Key Clients:** CITGO Petroleum Corp., Hilcorp, Chevron
**Contact:** Richard E Sarver **Tel:** 504 589 9733
**Email:** RSarver@BarrassoUsdin.com
**Contact:** Craig Isenberg **Tel:** 504 589 9753
**Email:** CIsenberg@BarrassoUsdin.com

**Insurance Coverage & Bad Faith:**
- Representation of several homeowner and CGL insurers in federal MDL and Louisiana state cases involving an estimated thousands of claims allegedly exceeding $10 billion arising out of use of defective product; also served as Insurer Liaison Counsel pursuant to the court's appointment
- Representation of multiple insurers against claims by a national self-storage company for approx. $300 million in alleged business interruption losses
- Representation of excess insurer with $50 million policy coverage litigation arising out of BP Oil Spill and MDL litigation
- Representation of excess liability insurer in coverage dispute involving environmental claims arising out of New Mexico uranium mine

**Key Clients:** Allied World Assurance, Allstate, Chubb, Homesite, Liberty Mutual, OIL, Inc., Certain Underwriters of Lloyds
**Contact:** Judy Y Barrasso **Tel:** 504 589 9720
**Email:** JBarrasso@BarrassoUsdin.com

**Product Liability & Toxic Tort:**
- National trial counsel for manufacturers and distributors of welding consumables in MDL – the firm has tried six separate cases that resulted in defense verdicts against all ten plaintiffs
- National trial counsel for Johnson & Johnson in cases pending in the DePuy Hip MDL and Illinois consolidated proceedings

**Key Clients:** Johnson & Johnson, Monsanto
**Contact:** Richard E Sarver **Tel:** 504 589 9733
**Email:** RSarver@BarrassoUsdin.com
**Contact:** Celeste Coco-Ewing **Tel:** 504 589 9725
**Email:** CCoco-Ewing@BarrassoUsdin.com

**Securities Litigation & Regulation:**
- Representation of Morgan Keegan in over 350 cases arising out of 2007-08 market meltdown
- Regularly represents the financial-services industry, and brokerage and investment banking firms nationwide
- Represents firms and employees who are subjects of regulatory inquiries, investigations and actions

**Key Clients:** Ameriprise Financial Services, Bank of America Merrill Lynch, Morgan Keegan, Morgan Stanley Smith Barney, Securities America, UBS Financial Services, and Wells Fargo
**Contact:** George C Freeman, III **Tel:** 504 589 9732
**Email:** GFreeman@BarrassoUsdin.com
**Contact:** Thomas A Roberts **Tel:** 504 589 9731
**Email:** TRoberts@BarrassoUsdin.com

BARRASSO
USDIN
KUPPERMAN
FREEMAN
SARVER, L.L.C.

# BRADLEY MURCHISON KELLY & SHEA LLC

www.bradleyfirm.com **tel:** 318 227 1131 **fax:** 318 227 1141

**Managing Partners:** Kay C Medlin, Dwight C Paulsen III
Number of partners: 19
Number of lawyers: 35
Languages: *English*

## Firm Overview:

Bradley Murchison Kelly & Shea was formed in 2009 by a group of lawyers from Shreveport and New Orleans, Louisiana, many of whom have decades of nationally recognized practices. They found common ground in their dedication to high standards of professionalism and in the quality of service they are able to deliver to their clients. Since the firm's inception, client needs in the state's capital have steadily grown, resulting in an office expansion into Baton Rouge in January 2013.

## Main Areas of Practice:

### Energy:

Bradley Murchison energy attorneys have built a longstanding tradition of providing quality legal representation in many facets of the oil and gas business in the region. Attorneys have served as advisors and advocates for clients in oil and gas exploration contracts, drilling contracts, operating agreements, processing agreements, midstream and gathering agreements, transportation and marketing agreements, pipeline construction agreements, regulatory matters, expropriation, new resource project development and finance, lignite surface mining title examination, and joint surface use agreements between competing mineral interests. The firm has advised long-time clients as well as many new clients in connection with issues and opportunities created by the discovery of the Haynesville Shale.

### Environmental:

The environmental litigation and regulatory compliance practice includes attorneys from numerous disciplines that work with firm clients to navigate the complex environmental issues that have evolved over the past few decades. The firm represents clients in critical negotiation and, if necessary, litigation involving various regulatory agencies and private citizens. The firm's goal and primary focus is creative resolution of issues that satisfy the economic concerns of our clients and the regulators' permitting and compliance goals, while ensuring good stewardship of the environment.

### Litigation:

As a full-service firm with multiple locations and a client base consisting of corporate entities, governmental agencies and individuals, the firm maintains a diverse practice. Litigation services include focus areas in class actions, complex litigation, construction, environmental and energy, regulatory compliance, labor and employment, healthcare and rail transportation. The firm's attorneys have experience in the defense of personal injury and property damage claims, medical malpractice claims against physicians, hospitals and their insurers, chemical and product exposure issues facing manufacturers and health care providers, and other healthcare litigation issues faced by hospitals, insurers, and businesses. The firm has received national recognition for their work in all aspects of the rail industry. Their experience includes expropriation and right-of-way disputes, grade crossing accidents, trespasser, pedestrian and other third party injuries, FELA actions, track usage disputes, derailments and hazardous material releases resulting in both ordinary and class action proceedings. The transportation law practice also includes representation of over-the-road common carriers in a variety of litigation issues. The firm's attorneys are also practiced in mediations and arbitrations.

### Transactional:

Bradley Murchison regularly represents and provides corporate transactional services to a large number of corporations, limited liability companies, partnerships and other business entities, in a number of industries. Attorneys advise clients on corporate structure, management and operation, in the negotiation of mergers, acquisitions, joint ventures and divestitures of their business interests, business and succession planning, ownership and management issues, corporate governance, incentive compensation and commercial law matters. They assist clients in connection with emerging businesses on financing transactions, assist in determining if companies are eligible for federal and state tax subsidies and incentives, and aid in various employment related issues, including designing and implementing executive compensation plans and employee benefit arrangements. The transactional group includes Intellectual Property and Technology lawyers who regularly provide representation to a variety of clients such as artists, authors, software developers, inventors, corporate entities, and production and movie studios. The focus of this practice includes patent, federal trademark and copyright registration and review; preparation of sales agreements; preparation and negotiation of licensing and royalty agreements and software licenses; smart phone applications; intellectual property rights enforcement and defense litigation; confidentiality non-replication agreements; ownership agreements; and numerous other business matters.

## PRACTICE AREAS

Alternative Dispute Resolution
Casualty Litigation
Class Actions
Commercial Litigation
Complex Litigation
Construction Contracts & Litigation
Creditor Protection, Creditor's Rights & Commercial Debts
Emerging Businesses
Energy & Natural Resources
Entertainment Law
Environmental Regulation & Regulatory Compliance
General Corporate Representation
Government & Regulatory Affairs
Health Care Law
Insurance Issues
Intellectual Property
Labor & Employment
Mass Torts
Products Liability
Professional Liability
Real Estate
Transportation Law
Trusts, Probate & Estate Planning

## OFFICES

LOUISIANA

**BATON ROUGE:** 301 Main Street, Suite 2100, 70825
Tel: 225 490 5000   Fax: 225 490 5001
Email: jjones@bradleyfirm.com

**NEW ORLEANS:** 1100 Poydras Street, Suite 2700, 70163
Tel: 504 596 6300   Fax: 504 596 6301
Email: tpaulsen@bradleyfirm.com

**SHREVEPORT:** 401 Edwards Street, Suite 1000, 71101
Tel: 318 227 1131   Fax: 504 227 1141
Email: kmedlin@bradleyfirm.com

BRADLEY MURCHISON
KELLY & SHEA LLC

# FISHMAN HAYGOOD PHELPS WALMSLEY WILLIS & SWANSON, LLP

**www.**fishmanhaygood.com **tel:** 504 586 5252 **fax:** 504 586 5250

**Managing Partner:** James R Swanson
Number of partners: 11
Number of other lawyers: 14

## Firm Overview:

The firm was founded in the mid-1990s by leading business and litigation lawyers from three of the largest firms in Louisiana. National and regional publications have repeatedly recognized the firm's lawyers as among the best. The firm's business lawyers regularly represent public and private companies in a variety of matters including securities transactions and compliance, corporate, real estate, commercial finance, banking, bank regulation and general contractual matters. The firm's litigators handle a variety of complex commercial matters, including securities litigation and arbitration, commercial litigation, media law, First Amendment law, and tax litigation.

## Main Areas of Practice:

### Corporate, Securities & M&A:
- Ongoing representation of Sanderson Farms, Inc. in financing and securities matters, including its recent $120,000,000 public equity offering
- Ongoing representation of Gulf Coast Energy Resources, LLC in financing and securities matters, including two separate private equity offerings totalling $375,000,000
- Ongoing representation of SMG, manager of the Mercedes-Benz Superdome, New Orleans Arena, Baton Rouge Centroplex and other sports and entertainment facilities in Louisiana and Alabama
- Previously represented Rouses Supermarkets in its acquisition of 21 stores from A&P and continued representation in Rouses' ongoing expansion

**Key Clients:** Sanderson Farms, Inc., SMG, Home Bancorp, Inc., Rouse's Enterprises, LLC, Chaffe & Associates, Swire Oilfield Services, LLC, Chaffe Securities, Inc., Laitram LLC, Carbo-Chlorination Technologies LLC, TurboSquid, Inc., New Orleans Startup Fund, Inc., LongueVue Capital, Gulf Coast Energy Resources.

**Contact:** Louis Y Fishman **Tel:** 504 586 5252
**Email:** lfishman@fishmanhaygood.com

### Real Estate:
- CMBS cross-collaterized refinancing of six retail shopping centers located in four states
- Ongoing representation of Stirling Properties in its joint-venture acquisition, corporate restructuring, development and financing of Fremaux Town Center in Slidell, Louisiana
- $30,000,000 acquisition and development by Stirling Properties of Mid City Market in New Orleans
- $25,000,000 acquisition and financing of a 287-unit

condominium project in Baton Rouge, Louisiana
- Ongoing representation of Equity Office, an affiliate of The Blackstone Group, in commercial office and retail leases for its New Orleans-area Class A office buildings

**Key Clients:** Stirling Properties, LLC, Rouses Supermarkets, Equity Office, Biltmore Property Group, LLC.

**Contact:** Sterling Scott Willis **Tel:** 504 586 5264
**Email:** swillis@fishmanhaygood.com

### Banking & Finance:
- $37,000,000 financing of a mixed-use residential and commercial building, the first in the country to combine federal and state new markets and historic tax credits with an FHA-insured loan
- $53,000,000 financing of the Saenger Theatre in New Orleans, including new markets, federal, and state historic tax credits, Louisiana musical and theatrical production tax credits, community development grants, and bridge financing
- Ongoing representation of the State of Louisiana in its investment of over $75,000,000 of Community Development Block Grants in real estate financings, including a $78,000,000 hospital and medical office complex in St. Bernard Parish

**Key Clients:** IberiaBank, Whitney Bank, State of Louisiana, AMCREF Community Capital, LLC, Jefferson Capital Partners II, L.P.

**Contact:** John D Werner **Tel:** 504 586 5265
**Email:** jwerner@fishmanhaygood.com

### Litigation & Arbitration:
- **Securities Arbitration & Litigation:** Representation of municipal bond issuers against investment banks and underwriters that misrepresented and omitted material facts about the auction rate securities market
- Defense of public companies, including US Unwired

and Amedisys, in securities class actions
- Representation of the Louisiana Firefighters' Retirement System, as class representative, in class action litigation against Northern Trust Investments, N.A. and Northern Trust Company
- Representation of hundreds of individual investors against their brokers or investment advisors (the firm has recovered tens of millions of dollars for these clients)
- **First Amendment & Media Law:** Representation of media outlets and individuals in defamation cases and public record and access disputes, including cases for The Times-Picayune, Cable News Network, The New York Times, ProPublica, Wick Communications, The Nation Institute, The Daily, and GateHouse Media
- **Tax Litigation:** Representation of the Louisiana Department of Revenue to recover corporate and franchise taxes from corporate taxpayers (the firm has recovered tens of millions of tax dollars, including a $26,000,000 jury award believed to be the largest award of taxes and penalties in Louisiana history)
- **Commercial:** General commercial litigation matters, including contract disputes of various kinds such as options, purchase agreements, leases, employment agreements, and insurance policies

**Key Clients:** The Times Picayune, L.L.C., Berk-Cohen Associates, L.L.C., Wampold Companies, SMG, ASCO Group, Ltd., Louisiana Stadium & Exposition District, Louisiana Firefighters' Retirement System, Municipal Employees' Retirement System, Louisiana Department of Revenue, Wallace C. Drennan, Inc., JMH Realty, L.L.C.

**Contact:** James R Swanson **Tel:** 504 586 5267
**Email:** jswanson@fishmanhaygood.com

## PRACTICE AREAS

Banking & Finance
Corporate, Securities & M&A
Litigation & Arbitration
Real Estate

## OFFICES

LOUISIANA

**NEW ORLEANS:** 201 St. Charles Avenue, Suite 4600, LA 70170
Tel: 504 586 5252
Email: jswanson@fishmanhaygood.com

# FOWLER RODRIGUEZ

**www.frfirm.com** **tel:** 504 523 2600 **fax:** 504 523 2705

**Managing Partners:** George J Fowler, III and Antonio J Rodriguez
Number of partners: 30
Number of lawyers: 60
Languages: *English, Spanish, French, Italian*

## Firm Overview:

Fowler Rodriguez is based on the US Gulf and in South Florida, with a strong international focus. While much of the firm's work is in the maritime, energy, banking, pollution, immigration, insurance law, and commercial and civil litigation areas, the firm's lawyers provide paramount advocacy and dispute resolution in almost any area of law. Fowler Rodriguez is one of the leading maritime law firms in the United States, and it is the largest based on the Gulf of Mexico. The firm's white-collar criminal law practice is headed by a former Assistant United States Attorney with extensive experience in the field. Additionally, the firm's corporate immigration practice helps foreign entities and businesses invest in the US through EB5 or "Investor Visas."
The attorneys are recipients of several prestigious awards including the "Best Lawyers", "Super Lawyers", "Leadership In Law" and the "Top Lawyers" awards.

## Main Areas of Practice:

### Admiralty & Maritime:

Fowler Rodriguez is internationally renowned in the maritime community. The firm represents shipowners and charterers, Protection & Indemnity associations, marine and other insurers, and major energy companies. The firm has guided clients in the development of major marine casualty and pollution response plans; and the firm has a long established legal organization to respond to shipping casualty and pollution incidents. The firm also has extensive experience with shipbuilding and repair, both contracting and dispute resolution. Some of the firm's attorneys are professional mariners.

### Liability Defense:

Excellence in litigation is the cornerstone of the firm's effectiveness in defense of liabilities. Fowler Rodriguez attorneys are skilled litigators and negotiators, having favorably resolved countless cases on behalf of clients before, during or after a trial. The firm's attorneys are experienced in the efficient and cost-effective disposition of all types of potential liability including:

- Construction claims
- Defense of municipalities
- Defense of personal injury claims
- Employment related claims
- Labor law violations
- Manufacturers' and retailers' product liability
- Motor vehicle claims
- Pipeline owners' exposures
- Premises liability
- Professional malpractice
- Toxic tort and environmental liability

### Environmental & Regulatory Compliance:

Fowler Rodriguez is internationally known for coordination of pollution and casualty response efforts, including cleanup, firefighting, salvage, interfacing with federal and state authorities, natural resource damages and their assessment, and other efforts to minimize client exposure. By keeping updated on the latest legislation, Fowler Rodriguez attorneys are authorities on:

- Counseling regarding national and international environmental requirements
- Defense of enforcement actions by federal and state agencies
- Environmental litigation work
- Participation in rule making proceedings, and strategic defense of clients charged with environmental crimes
- Pre-incident response planning

## Clients:

The American Club, The Britannia Steam Ship Insurance Association Limited, BP America Inc., BP Exploration & Production, Inc., Carnival Corporation, Carnival Cruise Lines, Inc., Chubb Insurance, Crystal Cruise Lines, Cunard Cruise Lines, ED&F Man Holdings Limited, Edison Chouest Offshore, ENSCO, Florida Crystals, Forum Oilfield Technologies Inc., Gard Service AS, Halliburton, Hornbeck Offshore Services L.L.C., MasTec Corporation, Noble Corporation, Northeast Construction, North of England P&I Association Limited, Pan-American Life, Rowan Companies Inc., Royal Caribbean Cruises, Ltd., The Steamship Mutual Underwriting Association (Bermuda), Limited, John W. Stone Oil Distributors, LLC, Tidewater Marine, Underwriters at Lloyd's, London, The United Kingdom Mutual Steam Ship Assurance Association (Bermuda), Limited

## PRACTICE AREAS

Admiralty & Maritime
Banking & Financial Services
Business Counseling & Transactions
Commercial & Civil Litigation
Construction Law
Corporate Practice
Energy Law
Environmental & Regulatory Compliance
Foreign Corrupt Practices Act & Compliance
Government Investigations & White Collar Criminal Defense
Immigration & Naturalization Law
International Criminal Law
International Litigation
International Transactions
Labor & Employment Law
Liability Defense
Maritime Criminal Defense
Real Estate Law
Tax and Estate Planning

## OFFICES

**LOUISIANA**
**NEW ORLEANS:** 400 Poydras Street, 30th Floor, 70130
Tel: 504 523 2600   Fax: 504 523 2705

**TEXAS**
**HOUSTON:** Four Houston Center, 1331 Lamar Street, Suite 1560, 77010
Tel: 713 654 1560   Fax: 713 654 7930

**FLORIDA**
**MIAMI:** 355 Alhambra Circle, Suite 801, Coral Gables, 33134
Tel: 786 364 8400   Fax: 786 364 8401

**ALABAMA**
**MOBILE:** 56 St. Joseph Street, Suite 1301, Post Office Box 40008 (36640), 36602
Tel: 251 344 4721   Fax: 251 343 7503

**MISSISSIPPI**
**GULFPORT:** 2505 14th Street, Suite 500, Post Office Box 4080 (39502), MS 39501
Tel: 228 822 9340   Fax: 228 822 9343

## INTERNATIONAL OFFICES

The firm also has offices in Bogotá and Cartagena, Colombia

FOWLER RODRIGUEZ
Counselors at Law

# GORDON ARATA MCCOLLAM DUPLANTIS & EAGAN

**www.**gordonarata.com **tel:** 504 582 1111 **fax:** 504 582 1121

**Management Committee Chairman:** Ewell E Eagan, Jr
Number of attorneys: 59

## Firm Overview:

Gordon Arata is among the most highly respected firms of the Gulf South region. With offices in New Orleans, Baton Rouge, and Lafayette, Louisiana, as well as Houston, Texas, the firm delivers excellent legal service, even in the most complex matters, efficiently and with a personal touch. Gordon Arata's firm culture is distinct because the firm comprises a diverse group of people who, in addition to being bright, are creative, down-to-earth, and business-savvy. As a result, the firm's clients consistently experience service that is better, more practical, and more responsive.

## Main Areas of Practice:

### Oil & Gas:

Gordon Arata is synonymous with the oil and gas legal practice in the Gulf South region. The firm regularly handles oil and gas financing transactions, equity offerings secured by oil and gas assets, production-based financings, specialized acquisition and divestiture of oil and gas properties, mineral leasing, operating agreements, farm-out agreements, unitization, pooling, and title opinions for properties in and offshore Louisiana and Texas. Gordon Arata's Energy Practice also encompasses all forms of dispute resolution including state and federal litigation, mediation and arbitration, as well as administrative and regulatory proceedings before local, state, and federal agencies such as the Bureau of Ocean Energy Management, the Bureau of Safety and Environmental Enforcement, the Federal Energy Regulatory Commission, the Louisiana State Mineral and Energy Board, the Louisiana Commissioner of Conservation, the Louisiana Public Service Commission, and the Louisiana Department of Environmental Quality.

### Litigation:

Gordon Arata is recognized as a leader in commercial litigation and represents clients at every level of the state and federal court systems, as well as before administrative bodies, and in mediation and arbitration. Gordon Arata has extensive experience in complex class action litigation involving a wide array of industries, including tobacco, pharmaceuticals, vitamins, securities, oil and gas, insurance, public utilities, and telecommunications. The firm also enjoys a strong Appellate Practice, up to and including state and US Supreme Courts. Gordon Arata's litigators have represented clients in cases involving anti-trust and unfair business practices, civil RICO, banking, environmental and toxic torts, construction, products liability, corporate and securities, real estate and financing, public utilities, insurance, professional liability, intellectual property, taxation, and telecommunications. The firm's lawyers also represent clients in connection with regulatory investigations.

### Bankruptcy:

Gordon Arata offers one of the largest, most experienced bankruptcy practices in its region. Its Bankruptcy Practice Group includes two former federal bankruptcy judges. From the use of bankruptcy as a business strategy and guiding clients through the benefits and risks associated with bankruptcy proceedings, to representation of clients in preference and fraudulent transfer proceedings, asset acquisitions, or out-of-court workout arrangements, Gordon Arata possesses extensive experience dealing with the insolvency-related issues that arise in business. It regularly represents debtors and creditors, debtor-in-possession lenders, purchasers of assets, and bankruptcy trustees; it also acts as trustee of bankruptcy estates and of non-bankruptcy liquidations.

### Corporate/Transactions:

Gordon Arata attorneys service the business needs of a wide array of clients, from emerging issuers to public companies, from community and regional businesses to global giants. The firm provides such clients with advice and representation in all aspects of their business, including business formation and structure, mergers and acquisitions, reorganizations, tender offers and proxy contests, private offerings and placements of equity and debt securities, securitization of assets, loan and credit facility financings, and compliance with federal securities laws. The firm's experience also runs the gamut of real estate transactions, including construction and development, leasing transactions, acquisition and sale, financing and condominium law. In addition, Gordon Arata possesses extensive experience in trusts, wills, and estate planning and administration.

**OFFICES**

LOUISIANA

**BATON ROUGE:** One American Place, Suite 1600, 301 Main Street, LA 70801-1916
Tel: 225 381 9643   Fax: 225 336 9763

**LAFAYETTE:** 400 East Kaliste Saloom Road, Suite 4200, LA 70508-8517
Tel: 337 237 0132   Fax: 337 237 3451

**NEW ORLEANS:** 201 St. Charles Avenue, 40th Floor, LA 70170-4000
Tel: 504 582 1111   Fax: 504 582 1121

TEXAS

**HOUSTON:** 1980 Post Oak Boulevard, Suite 1800, TX 77056
Tel: 713 333 5500   Fax: 713 333 5501

### Employment & Labor:

Gordon Arata counsels employers and represents them in disputes/litigation involving a broad range of employment and labor issues arising under Title VII, the Family and Medical Leave Act (FMLA), the Americans with Disabilities Act (ADA), the Age-Discrimination in Employment Act (ADEA), the Fair Labor Standards Act (FLSA), the Labor-Management Relations Act (LMRA), the Uniformed Services Employment and Reemployment Rights Act (USERRA), the Occupational Safety and Health Act (OSHA), and other federal and state laws affecting the employment relationship. The firm also advises clients on employee benefit plans, employment agreements, and executive severance agreements.

### Environmental:

Gordon Arata's environmental law practice is a natural complement to its oil and gas practice, given the rising profile of environmental issues in the oil and gas industry. The firm defends against high-stakes legacy environmental claims by landowners alleging environmental damage arising from oil and gas exploration and production operations. The firm also regularly represents and advises clients in the defense of enforcement and investigatory actions by regulatory agencies alleging violations of environmental laws, and with respect to environmental issues arising in complex transactions, permitting and compliance issues, and toxic tort claims by individuals claiming their illnesses were caused by exposure to hazardous substances. The firm has broad experience dealing with many of the key environmental laws, such as the Clean Air Act, the Clean Water Act, NEPA, CERCLA, and related state laws.

# JONES WALKER LLP

**www.joneswalker.com  tel:** 504 582 8000  **fax:** 504 582 8583

**Managing Partner:** William H Hines
Number of partners: 193  Number of other lawyers: 184

## Firm Overview:

Jones Walker is among the largest 250 law firms in the United States, and is one of the largest law firms in the southeastern United States, serving a full range of local, regional, national and international business interests with more than 375 attorneys located in Alabama, Arizona, California, the District of Columbia, Florida, Georgia, Louisiana, Mississippi, New York and Texas.

## Main Areas of Practice:

Antitrust and trade regulation; appellate litigation; aviation; banking and financial services; bankruptcy, restructuring and creditors-debtors rights; business and commercial litigation; business and commercial transactions; class action defense; commercial lending and finance; construction; corporate and securities; corporate compliance and white-collar defense; economic development; employee benefits, ERISA and executive compensation; energy; environmental and toxic torts; gaming; government relations; healthcare; insurance; intellectual property; international; labor and employment; maritime and admiralty; mergers and acquisitions; products liability; professional liability; project development and finance; public finance; real estate: land use, development and finance; tax and estates; telecommunications and utilities; venture capital and emerging companies.

## Clients:

Banking, insurance and finance; communications and technology; energy, environmental and mining; healthcare; maritime; media/advertising; manufacturing/industrial; public sector; sports, entertainment and gaming; real estate; transportation; wholesale/retail/service industries, public and large privately-held companies.

## International Work:

Jones Walker has handled international transactions on five continents, with a concentration in Latin America, Europe and Asia. Jones Walker's experience includes international construction projects, cross-border mergers and acquisitions and international joint ventures and has successfully closed project financings related to large international infrastructure projects, including major development projects, joint ventures, investments and/or asset acquisitions, service agreements, engineering, procurement and construction contracts throughout the world. Through its more than ten-year partnering relationship with an international metals and mining company and its subsidiaries, the firm has gained extensive experience representing US-

based companies operating in foreign countries. This unique partnering relationship involves the handling of virtually all of the client's international business matters, providing representation with respect to all major acquisitions, joint venture arrangements, privatization transactions, product sales agreements, drilling and earthworks projects, offshore and onshore engineering, procurement, construction and maintenance contracts, strategic alliance agreements (relative to the outsourcing of facility operations), transportation agreements and other operating agreements relative to its mining and smelting operations.

The firm's Admiralty and Maritime Practice includes charter party and cargo transactions, international marine sales contracts, international vessel acquisitions, as well as financings and flagging of vessels. Jones Walker has significant experience handling international maritime and commercial litigation and arbitration matters, as well as permitting for off-site drilling.

In the international tax area, the firm regularly structures overseas operations in connection with cross-border mergers and acquisitions to minimize foreign tax liabilities and overall worldwide tax rates, including the use of hybrid financing techniques and foreign entities. Jones Walker has particular experience in the area of counseling financial services businesses including insurers, banks, mutual funds and producers. The firm represents local and regional banks on transactions, litigation and government affairs, and has advised multinational insurance company clients on company formation, foreign regulatory issues with respect to variable life, annuity and health insurance products, foreign laws governing authorization, licensing, marketing practices, agents and brokers, and bancassurance, the drafting and interpretation of insurance policies. It has also advised foreign governments in connection with insurance and pension reform legislation.

Jones Walker regularly represents clients in UNCITRAL and ICC arbitrations and has overseen litigation filed with foreign tribunals. The firm regularly advises clients with respect to the Foreign Corrupt Practices Act, the

Foreign Assets Control Regulations administered by OFAC, the USA Patriot Act, the Homeland Security Act, US anti-boycott legislation and the Sarbanes-Oxley Act. Jones Walker also advises international clients on the General Agreement on Trade in Services (GATS), US bilateral investment treaties with foreign countries, NAFTA and DR-CAFTA.

## OFFICES

### ALABAMA

**BIRMINGHAM:** One Federal Place, 1819 5th Avenue North, Suite 1100, AL 35203
Tel: 205 244 5200  Fax: 205 244 5400
Email: info@joneswalker.com

**MOBILE:** 254 State Street, AL 36603
Tel: 251 432 1414  Fax: 251 433 4106

### ARIZONA

**PHOENIX:** 333 North Central Avenue, AZ 85004
Tel: 602 366 7889  Fax: 504 589 8722

### DISTRICT OF COLUMBIA

**WASHINGTON DC:** 499 South Capitol Street, SW, Suite 600, DC 20003
Tel: 202 203 1000  Fax: 202 203 0000

### FLORIDA

**MIAMI:** 201 S. Biscayne Blvd, Ste 2600, FL 33131
Tel: 305 679 5700  Fax: 305 679 5710

### GEORGIA

**ATLANTA:** 1360 Peachtree St, NE, Suite 1030, GA 30309
Tel: 404 870 7500  Fax: 404 870 7501

### LOUISIANA

**BATON ROUGE:** 8555 United Plaza Boulevard, LA 70809
Tel: 225 248 2000  Fax: 225 248 2010

**LAFAYETTE:** 600 Jefferson Street, Suite 1600, LA 70501
Tel: 337 593 7600  Fax: 337 593 7601

**LAFAYETTE:** 1200 Camellia Boulevard, Suite 203, LA 70508
Tel: 337 593 7700  Fax: 337 993 2557

**NEW ORLEANS:** 201 St. Charles Avenue, Suite 5100, LA 70170-5100
Tel: 504 582 8000  Fax: 504 582 8583

### MISSISSIPPI

**JACKSON:** 190 East Capitol Street, Suite 800, MS 39201
Tel: 601 949 4900  Fax: 601 949 4804

**GULFPORT:** 2510 14th St., Suite 1125, MS 39501
Tel: 228 864 3094  Fax: 228 864 0516

**OLIVE BRANCH:** 6897 Crumpler Blvd, Suite 100, MS 38654
Tel: 662 895 2996  Fax: 662 895 5480

### NEW YORK

**NEW YORK:** 590 Madison Ave, 18th Floor, NY 10022
Tel: 212 759 7025

### TEXAS

**HOUSTON:** 1001 Fannin St, Ste 2450, TX 77002
Tel: 713 437 1800  Fax: 713 437 1810

**THE WOODLANDS:** 10001 Woodloch Forest Drive, Suite 350, TX 77380
Tel: 281 296 4400  Fax: 281 296 4404

# KEAN MILLER LLP

**www.**keanmiller.com **tel:** 225 387 0999 **fax:** 225 388 9133

**Managing Partner:** Blane Clark
Number of partners: 78
Number of attorneys: 137

**OFFICES**

LOUISIANA

**BATON ROUGE:** 400 Convention Street, Suite 700, PO Box 3513 (70821-3513), LA 70802
Email: client_services@keanmiller.com

**BATON ROUGE:** 5035 Bluebonnet Boulevard, Suite B, LA 70809

**NEW ORLEANS:** 909 Poydras Street, Suite 1400 LA 70112

**LAKE CHARLES:** One Lakeshore Drive, Suite 1150 LA 70629

## Firm Overview:

Kean Miller is the largest law firm in Louisiana's Capital Region, and one of the largest in the state. From the boardroom to the courtroom, the firm combines the talents and expertise of its lawyers into multi-disciplinary client teams. These teams are comprised of seasoned legal professionals from a variety of disciplines who are equipped to identify the legal and business needs of the client and to develop superior service strategies that provide unmatched support. Whether the firm is helping clients defend lawsuits, raise capital, comply with regulatory requirements, enter new markets, obtain or defend intellectual property rights, develop and distribute products and services, or acquire or divest businesses, the attorneys understand it is the client's goals that are paramount. Kean Miller has a particular dedication to working closely with Louisiana-based businesses and *Fortune* 500 companies with significant operations in the Gulf South – ensuring that they have the legal resources required to grow into leaders in the region.

## Main Areas of Practice:

**Business & Corporate:**
Kean Miller's corporate and business team has counseled clients in mergers, acquisitions, dispositions and agreements with aggregate transaction values in the tens of billions. The firm handles complex transactions, including entity formation and joint ventures, affiliations, mergers and acquisitions, private placements, securities, strategic alliances, real estate development, lease and financing. This experience, combined with the firm's intellectual property and tax expertise, provides clients with full-service business advice.

**Business Litigation:**
Kean Miller aggressively seeks creative solutions to client's commercial and contract disputes. Kean Miller's business litigation team has specific experience in trade secrets and non-competition agreements, software and licensing disputes, insurance coverage, bankruptcy and workouts, finance litigation, and construction matters.

**Economic Development:**
The Kean Miller economic development team is comprised of attorneys from a variety of disciplines, including: governmental affairs and lobbying; state and local tax incentives and economic development incentives; business and corporate; labor and employment; real estate; construction; utilities regulation; and environmental regulation and permitting. The firms has played an instrumental role in the successful development of numerous projects in Louisiana and in the nine-parish Capitol Region.

**Environmental Regulation:**
Kean Miller's environmental team represents clients in water issues, air permitting and Title V compliance; ozone non-attainment regulation; climate change issues; release reporting; RCRA/HSWA issues, TSCA;

TMDLs, OPA; SPCC; RECAP (state remediation program); DNR oilfield waste remediation programs; Corps of Engineers dredging and wetland matters; radiation and NORM issues; stratospheric ozone regulation; underground injection issues; permitting of commercial saltwater disposal wells and E&P facilities; carbon sequestration and enhanced oil recovery; compliance audits; advice on environmental management systems; Safe Drinking Water Act programs; environmental assessments or impact statements for new or expansion projects; and in due diligence for mergers and acquisitions. The environmental team has extensive experience in Superfund issues, RCRA, and the remediation of all types of hazardous and non-hazardous waste.

**Labor & Employment:**
Kean Miller's labor and employment team has more than 150 years of combined experience in labor and employment law. The labor team has represented some of the world's largest corporations as well as successful local businesses. The firm performs three main labor and employment services for clients:
(1) preventive counseling and training, and assistance in drafting and revising employment policies, handbooks, and procedures;
(2) defense of lawsuits and administrative proceedings;
(3) assistance in labor management (union) relations.

**Real Estate:**
Kean Miller represents many of Louisiana's most prominent and successful companies in the acquisition of real estate, raw land for petrochemical and refining plant sites, and commercial property. The firm's real estate experience includes acquisitions and sales, title insurance, tax, real estate finance, zoning, annexation, environmental matters, land use and property rights, expropriation, subdivision and development ordinances, zoning statutes, and public improvement districts.

**Utilities Regulation:**
Kean Miller represents industrial consumers of power and selected public utilities in proceedings before the Louisiana Public Service Commission, the Federal Energy Regulatory Commission, and other state and federal agencies and courts. The utilities regulation team provides advice to clients on electric contract disputes and rate cases, electric transmission access and regulation, the restructuring of the electric and telecommunications markets, the development of electric power projects and related contractual negotiations, the negotiation of electric service agreements, state and federal regulatory compliance, obtaining of operating certificates and approvals of acquisitions and mergers.

**Additional Practice Areas:**
Admiralty and Maritime, Banking and Finance, Bankruptcy and Reorganization, Chemical Exposure Litigation, Class Action Litigation, Construction, Estate Planning, Health Law, Insurance Coverage Litigation, Intellectual Property, Legislative and Administrative Lobbying, Medical Malpractice, Permitting, Probate, Products Liability, Oil and Gas, Patent Infringement, State and Local Tax, and Toxic Tort Defense.

## Clients:

Kean Miller serves clients in numerous industries including Maritime, Energy, Petrochemicals, Drilling, Exploration, Technology, Telecommunications, Media, Advertising, Film and Entertainment, Retail, Food and Beverage, Construction, Contracting, Banking, Financial Services, Shipping and Transportation, Gaming, Education, Healthcare, Manufacturing, Refining and Real Estate.

KEAN | MILLER LLP
ATTORNEYS AT LAW

*People First*

# KREBS, FARLEY & PELLETERI PLLC

www.kfplaw.com **tel:** 504 299 3570 **fax:** 504 299 3582

**Managing Partner:** David J Krebs
Number of partners: 10
Number of lawyers: 22

## Firm Overview:

Krebs, Farley & Pelleteri is a litigation firm in the Gulf South whose lawyers are consistently recognized for their excellence. The firm is renowned for its expertise in construction law; surety and fidelity law; bankruptcy and creditor's rights; class action defense; directors and officers liability; life, health and disability insurance; and professional malpractice. Since 2001, Krebs, Farley & Pelleteri has delivered innovative, market-leading solutions to its national clients and successfully advocated for advancements in the law to benefit its clients' interests.

## Main Areas of Practice:

### Bankruptcy & Creditors' Rights:

Krebs, Farley & Pelleteri represents creditors and sureties in a comprehensive range of bankruptcy and creditors' rights matters, including workouts, insolvency proceedings, Chapter 11 reorganizations, preference and fraudulent transfer litigation, claim-related bankruptcy litigation, and commercial disputes involving insurance coverage, labor contracts, employee benefits, and guarantees.

### Class & Mass Action Litigation:

Krebs, Farley & Pelleteri's attorneys are experienced in developing national case strategies, coordinating multi-stage discovery processes, obtaining Lone Pine rulings, and trying cases in pivotal jurisdictions. The firm has handled a variety of class and mass actions involving Hurricane Katrina-related insurance claims, personal injury and products liability claims, and more than 150 RICO, rescission, and securities-based claims arising out of the alleged misdeeds of insurance agents.

### Complex Commercial Litigation:

The firm's complex commercial litigation attorneys have achieved favorable results in multi-party, multi-issue, and multi-jurisdictional construction disputes, insurance coverage claims, commercial real estate and personal property disputes, commercial class actions, professional malpractice claims, business tort claims, and securities lawsuits.

### Construction Law:

Krebs, Farley & Pelleteri has a depth of knowledge and experience in litigating construction-related disputes on behalf of owners, developers, contractors, engineers, architects, sureties, and lenders. The firm specializes in resolving conflicts on public and private construction projects, including those relating to site acquisition and development, defective work or design, withheld payments, liens, delay damages, and personal injury claims.

### Directors & Officers Litigation:

The firm has a distinguished practice defending corporate directors and officers in actions involving corporate governance, breach of fiduciary duties, bad faith and negligence, securities fraud, shareholder derivative suits, and insider trading. Several multinational insurers routinely retain Krebs, Farley & Pelleteri to represent them in directors' and officers' insurance coverage litigation.

### Fidelity Law:

The firm is a leader in mediating and litigating financial institution bond and commercial crime coverage claims. Its lawyers are particularly skilled in resolving claims relating to loan losses, employee dishonesty insurance, computer fraud, the direct loss requirement, the fictitious collateral issue, Insuring Agreements (D) and (E), termination of coverage, the potential income exclusion, fraud by the insured, and bad faith.

### Labor & Employment Litigation:

Krebs, Farley & Pelleteri litigates various employment-based disputes, including wrongful termination, sexual harassment, hostile work environment, whistle blower retaliation, and defamation actions. Additionally, the firm's attorneys represent clients in collective bargaining arenas and grievance arbitration, and provide counsel on compliance, preparing employee contracts, and negotiating separation and termination agreements.

### Life, Health & Disability Insurance Litigation:

The firm has a thriving practice representing life, health and disability insurers in matters arising under individual and group policies. The firm regularly defends clients against claims prompted by health or employee benefit denials, including bad faith and fraudulent insurance claims. Often times, the firm's attorneys also serve in an advisory capacity, counseling clients on regulatory issues, the drafting and interpretation of insurance policies, and healthcare financing.

### Professional Malpractice Litigation:

Krebs, Farley & Pelleteri has developed a solid reputation for representing clients in claims of professional malpractice, including the defense of attorneys, engineers, tax professionals, and accounting firms. The firm routinely handles cases involving legal malpractice, breach of fiduciary duty, conflict of interest, negligent advice, and real estate transactions.

### Surety Law:

Krebs, Farley & Pelleteri is a national leader in surety law. The firm's attorneys have achieved notable success representing sureties in contract default situations, and through all phases of litigation and appeals on bonds issued on federal, state and private projects. When major contract defaults lead to bankruptcy or reorganization proceedings, the firm also represents surety clients through the ensuing negotiations, reorganization, planning, and assumption and completion of bonded obligations. The firm's attorneys also have extensive experience litigating commercial surety matters, including license and permit bond claims, and court bonds and public official bonds.

## PRACTICE AREAS

Bankruptcy & Creditors' Rights
Class & Mass Action Litigation
Complex Commercial Litigation
Construction Law
Directors & Officers Litigation
Fidelity Law
Labor & Employment Litigation
Life, Health & Disability Insurance Litigation
Professional Malpractice Litigation
Surety Law

## OFFICES

**LOUISIANA**
**NEW ORLEANS:** 400 Poydras Street, Suite 2500, LA 70130
Tel: 504 299 3570   Fax: 504 299 3582

**ALABAMA**
**BIRMINGHAM:** 1950 Stonegate Drive, Suite 225, AL 35242
Tel: 205 968 4009   Fax: 205 968 7343

**MISSISSIPPI**
**JACKSON:** 188 E. Capitol Street, Suite 900, MS 39201
Tel: 601 968 6710   Fax: 601 968 6708

**TEXAS**
**HOUSTON:** 5100 Westheimer, Suite 200, TX 77056
Tel: 713 588 4488   Fax: 713 588 4489

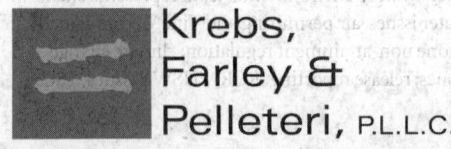

Krebs, Farley & Pelleteri, P.L.L.C.

# LISKOW & LEWIS

www.liskow.com **tel:** 504 581 7979 **fax:** 504 556 4108

**Managing Partner:** R Keith Jarrett
Number of partners: 63
Number of lawyers: 120
Languages: *English*

## Firm Overview:

Liskow & Lewis was established in 1935 when Cullen Liskow and Austin Lewis formed their law partnership. Long recognized for its contribution to the development of Louisiana's mineral law, the firm has grown and diversified to meet the evolving demands of its clients. Today, with offices in New Orleans, Lafayette and Houston, the firm pursues a wide-ranging litigation and transactional practice. Firm lawyers regularly handle cases of statewide and national interest in both state and federal courts throughout Louisiana and Texas, as well as in other venues and before state and federal administrative agencies.

## Main Areas of Practice:

**Appellate Practice:**
US Supreme Court, US Fifth Circuit, Louisiana and Texas Supreme Courts and appellate courts.
**Contact:** Joe B Norman **Tel:** 504 556 4143
**Email:** jbnorman@liskow.com

**Aviation, Toxic Tort & Environmental Litigation:**
Toxic tort, environmental and worker exposure cases involving personal injury and/or property damage.
**Contact:** Don K Haycraft **Tel:** 504 556 4128
**Email:** dkhaycraft@liskow.com
**Contact:** Scott C Seiler **Tel:** 504 556 4026
**Email:** scseiler@liskow.com

**Complex Business, Bankruptcy & Utility Litigation:**
Business reorganizations under Chapter 11, as well as litigation relating to all aspects of a bankruptcy case.
**Contact:** Philip K Jones Jr **Tel:** 504 556 4132
**Email:** pkjones@liskow.com

**Business Law:**
Banking, business transactions, gaming, M&A, real estate, securities, utility regulation.
**Contact:** Robert S Angelico **Tel:** 504 556 4112
**Email:** rsangelico@liskow.com

**Business Litigation:**
Complex business/commercial litigation; class actions, multidistrict proceedings, multiparty litigation.
**Contact:** James A Brown **Tel:** 504 556 4116
**Email:** jabrown@liskow.com

**Construction Law & Litigation:**
Industrial and maritime construction law and litigation; architects' and engineers' liability, disputes, defective construction, mold, insurance coverage.
**Contact:** R Keith Jarrett **Tel:** 504 556 4133
**Email:** rkjarrett@liskow.com

**Employee Benefits:**
Design, operation, and restructuring of employee benefits and executive compensation plans.
**Contact:** Randye C Snyder **Tel:** 504 556 4123
**Email:** rcsnyder@liskow.com

**Energy & Natural Resources Law:**
Clients in domestic production, processing, sale and/or distribution of oil/natural gas, onshore and offshore.
**Contact:** Jonathan A Hunter **Tel:** 504 556 4131
**Email:** jahunter@liskow.com

**Energy Litigation:**
Upstream exploration/production to downstream refining/marketing functions. Has represented industry clients in landmark state and federal cases.
**Contact:** Joe B Norman **Tel:** 504 556 4143
**Email:** jbnorman@liskow.com

**Environmental Law:**
Permitting, regulatory, compliance and transactional matters, as well as environmental litigation. Experience in all areas of federal and state environmental law.
**Contact:** Robert E Holden **Tel:** 504 556 4130
**Email:** reholden@liskow.com

**Governmental Investigations & White-Collar Defense:**
Compliance issues, grand jury/other investigations, criminal trials, qui tam actions, parallel proceedings.
**Contact:** Kenneth Allen Polite, Jr **Tel:** 504 556 4088
**Email:** kapolite@liskow.com

**Labor & Employment:**
Human resources issues and labor and employment litigation and claims in federal and state courts, arbitrations and agency proceedings.
**Contact:** Thomas J McGoey II **Tel:** 504 299 6101
**Email:** tjmcgoey@liskow.comiskow.com

**Maritime, Oilfield & Insurance:**
Major oil companies, international corporations, insurance companies, local and river industry entities in maritime law matters.
**Contact:** David W Leefe **Tel:** 504 556 4137
**Email:** dwleefe@liskow.com

## PRACTICE AREAS

Appellate Practice
Aviation
Toxic Tort & Environmental Litigation
Complex Business, Bankruptcy & Utility Litigation
Business Law
Business Litigation
Construction Law & Litigation
Employee Benefits
Energy & Natural Resources Law
Energy Litigation
Environmental Law
Government Investigations & White-Collar Defense
Labor & Employment
Maritime, Oilfield & Insurance
Real Estate Law
Tax
Trusts & Estates

## OFFICES:

**TEXAS**
**HOUSTON:** 1001 Fannin, Suite 1800, TX 77002
Tel: 713 651 2900 Fax: 713 651 2908

**LOUISIANA**
**LAFAYETTE:** 822 Harding Street, PO Box 52008, LA 70505
Tel: 337 232 7424 Fax: 337 267 2399

**NEW ORLEANS:** One Shell Square, 701 Poydras Street, Suite 5000, LA 70139
Tel: 504 581 7979 Fax: 504 556 4108

**Real Estate:**
Property acquisitions, industrial plants, office buildings, hotels, hospitals, condominiums, residential subdivisions.
**Contact:** Wm Blake Bennett **Tel:** 504 556 4133
**Email:** wbbennett@liskow.com

**Tax:**
Federal, state, and local tax planning, financing transactions, tax-free reorganization transactions.
**Contact:** James C Exnicios **Tel:** 504 556 4034
**Email:** jexnicios@liskow.com

**Trusts & Estates:**
Individual and corporate executors, beneficiaries of successions, trustees and trust beneficiaries in administration of estates and trusts.
**Contact:** Marguerite L Adams **Tel:** 504 556 4142
**Email:** mladams@liskow.com

LISKOW&LEWIS

# MCGLINCHEY STAFFORD

**www.**mcglinchey.com

**Managing Partner:** Rodolfo J Aguilar, Jr
Number of partners: 83
Number of other lawyers: 91

## Main Areas of Practice:

### Commercial & Business Litigation:

Represents clients in state and federal matters involving commercial disputes; business fraud; trusts, estates, and fiduciary duty; securities and brokers/dealers; landlord/tenant disputes; director and officer liability; ERISA; professional liability; lender liability; antitrust and trade regulation laws; pricing, product distribution; dealer terminations; unfair competition; deceptive acts and practices; advertising; patent abuse; franchising; complex multi-district and class action litigation; RICO; DOJ and FTC investigations.

### Banking & Commercial Finance:

Represents financial institutions in matters involving federal and state banking laws/regulations; asset-based lending; equipment leasing; commercial loan closings;workouts; bankruptcies; loan and deposit account agreements; real estate and personal property security interests; bank holding company formations; M&A; trust powers; investment and securities activities; new product development; bank-sponsored mutual funds; insurance and annuity products.

### Consumer Financial Services:

Counsels financial institutions on federal and state consumer finance laws and regulations. Services include multi-state legal surveys; design of mortgage, automobile and manufactured housing finance credit products and agreements; ompliance audits; due diligence reviews for public offerings; training; licensing of consumer lenders, mortgage lenders and sales finance companies; defense of regulatory enforcement actions and consumer credit litigation, including class actions. Affiliate MS&YA serves the residential mortgage lending industry offering outsourcing of mortgage banking functions.

### Class Action Defense & Consumer Finance Litigation:

Defends banks; consumer finance companies; mortgage companies; specialty and non-prime equity lenders; retailers; credit card issuers; credit insurers; property and casualty insurers; life insurers; consumer leasing companies; payday lenders; auto finance companies; insurance premium finance companies; service companies; and other consumer financial services providers in class action and multidistrict litigation involving the entire range of causes of action and emerging legal theories.

### Labor & Employment Law:

Representation includes affirmative action; arbitration; collective bargaining; communications and employee motivation; compensation and benefits; compliance audits; discrimination; contracts; immigration compliance; labor disputes including industry-wide,multi-state strike; management training; OSHA; personnel policies and practices; strikes and labor injunctions; unfair labor practice proceedings before the NLRB; union organizing and election proceedings; wage and hour investigations; and wrongful discharge.

### Healthcare:

Represents clients in matters involving compliance with federal and state healthcare laws and regulations, including fraud and abuse, Stark and false claims; hospital operational and medical staff issues; licensing, including Board matters; contract matters; M&A; Medicare and other third party payor reimbursement issues; legislation/ regulation; litigation, including professional liability, risk management and loss control, and managed care.

### Real Estate:

Represents developers; landlords; tenants; lenders; individual and corporate landowners; financial institutions; insurance and mortgage companies, and institutional investors. Transactions involve historical renovation and low income housing tax credits. Projects include industrial plants; merchant power and cogeneration plants; office buildings; gaming; retail and restaurant chains;wireless network sites; hotels; golf course developments; planned unit, condominium, and timeshare. Owns MACSTAM Title Company LLC, a licensed title insurance agency, and provides title abstract services through its subsidiary, Abstracts by Godail, LLC.

### Products Liability:

Defends foreign and domestic insurers; manufacturers and distributors in manufacturer and design liability cases involving motor vehicles, electrical appliances, and chemical and industrial products. Coordinates products liability litigation for businesses regionally and nationally.

## PRACTICE AREAS

Commercial & Business Litigation
Financial Services
Products Liability, Pharmaceutical & Medical Devices
Class Action Defense & Consumer Finance Litigation
Labour & Employment Law (Defense)
Healthcare
Real Estate (Commercial)
Insurance Regulation, Compliance & Defense
Admiralty
Bankruptcy
Environmental Law
Government Contracts/Relations/Public Law
Estate/Probate/Trust
Corporate & Business Transactions
Taxation
Casino Gaming

## OFFICES

**FLORIDA**

**FORT LAUDERDALE:** 101 NE Third Avenue, Suite 1500, FL 33301
Tel: 954 703 2126  Fax: 954 333 3847

**JACKSONVILLE:** 10407 Centurion Parkway North, Suite 200, FL 32256
Tel: 904 224 4449  Fax: 904 214 1784

**LOUISIANA**

**BATON ROUGE:** 301 Main Street, 14th Floor, LA 70825
Tel: 225 383 9000  Fax: 225 343 3076

**MONROE:** 1811 Tower Drive, Suite A, LA 71201
Tel: 318 651 0807  Fax: 318 651 0809

**NEW ORLEANS:** 12th Floor, 601 Poydras Street, LA 70130
Tel: 504 586 1200  Fax: 504 596 2800

**MISSISSIPPI**

**JACKSON:** 200 South Lamar Street, Suite 1100, City Centre, MS 39201
Tel: 601 960 8400  Fax: 601 960 8406

**NEW YORK**

**ALBANY:** 194 Washington Avenue, Suite 600, NY 12210 (Albany Co.)
Tel: 518 432 1200  Fax: 518 432 8711

**OHIO**

**CLEVELAND:** 25550 Chagrin Boulevard, Suite 406, OH 44122-4640
Tel: 216 378 9905  Fax: 216 378 9910

**TEXAS**

**DALLAS:** 2711 N. Haskell Ave, Suite 2700, LB 25, TX 75204
Tel: 214 257 1700  Fax: 214 257 1818

**HOUSTON:** 1001 McKinney, Suite 1500, TX 77002
Tel: 713 520 1900  Fax: 713 520 1025

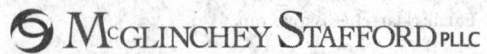

# PHELPS DUNBAR

www.phelpsdunbar.com **tel:** 504 566 1311 **fax:** 504 568 9130

**Managing Partner:** Michael D Hunt
Number of partners: 118

### Firm Overview:

With offices positioned along the Gulf Coast from Houston to Tampa, Phelps Dunbar is a regional law firm of more than 270 attorneys uniquely equipped to serve clients in the major commercial centers of the burgeoning "Third Coast" of the United States. Locations in New Orleans and Baton Rouge, Louisiana; Jackson, Tupelo and Gulfport, Mississippi; Houston, Texas; Tampa, Florida; Mobile, Alabama as well as Raleigh, North Carolina; and London, England enable Phelps Dunbar to serve clients not only along the Third Coast, but also the South, nationwide and abroad. Phelps Dunbar is recognized for its expertise in providing admiralty, business, employment, insurance and litigation services as well as creative solutions tailored to achieving the goals of a diverse clientele, from individuals to small businesses to Fortune 500 companies. Its attorneys and professional staff work together to advance clients' interests by providing excellent, effective and efficient legal services across all areas of practice.

### Main Areas of Practice:

Admiralty, Antitrust and Trade Regulation, Appellate Litigation, Bankruptcy and Creditors' Rights, Business and Finance, Commercial Litigation, Construction, Corporate and Securities, Employee Benefits/Executive Compensation, Energy and Utilities, Environmental, Franchise and Distribution, Gaming, Government Contracts, Health Care, Health Care Litigation, HIPAA Compliance, Immigration, Insurance and Reinsurance, Intellectual Property, International, Labor and Employment, Legislative and Governmental Relations, Oil and Gas, Petroleum Marketing, Products Liability, Professional Liability, Public Finance, Railroad, Real Estate, Regulatory and Governmental Matters, Tax, Tort Litigation, Toxic Tort Litigation, Trusts and Estates, White Collar Criminal Defense.

### US Office Contacts:

**NEW ORLEANS**
**Office Profile:** As the firm's headquarters, the New Orleans office is the largest of Phelps' regional legal practices. Over 80 attorneys represent clients in a wide range of practice areas within six key groups: admiralty, business, commercial litigation, employment law, insurance and reinsurance, and tort litigation.

**BATON ROUGE**
**Office Profile:** The firm's Baton Rouge office was the first regional office of Phelps Dunbar, opening in 1984. With over 50 attorneys, the Baton Rouge office has become one of the largest law offices in the state capital. The firm's attorneys support clients with a full-service litigation and business practice, as well as counseling on employment, regulatory, legislative lobbying, environmental and intellectual property matters.

**JACKSON**
**Office Profile:** The Jackson office opened in 1986, and now, with nearly 30 attorneys, provides full-service litigation, labor and employment, and traditional business practice for a diverse clientele.

**GULFPORT**
**Office Profile:** Phelps Dunbar opened its Gulfport office in 2000. The office handles business litigation, construction, real estate, financing, products liability, insurance, admiralty, environmental, tort litigation, gaming, and transportation.

**TUPELO**
**Office Profile:** Phelps Dunbar is the only law firm with substantial offices in Tupelo, Jackson, and Gulfport, Mississippi. The offices co-ordinate projects for many clients with legal business throughout the state. As the center of the firm's thriving healthcare practice, the Tupelo office represents hospitals, physicians, managed care organizations and other healthcare providers throughout the Southeast as counsel on corporate, tax and health law matters. In addition, it maintains a business and a litigation practice.

**MOBILE**
**Office Profile:** Enhancing its regional presence along the gulf coast of the United States, Phelps Dunbar's Mobile, Alabama office opened in 2010 as the result of 25 attorneys from the firm Lyons, Pipes and Cook joining Phelps Dunbar. The office handles a variety of practice areas within six key groups: admirality, business, commercial litigation, employment law, insurance and reinsurance, and tort litigation.

**HOUSTON**
**Office Profile:** Opened in 1990, the Houston office has attorneys with extensive trial, appellate and business experience. Practices include business and finance, real estate, admiralty and tort litigation, insurance and reinsurance, commercial litigation, and labor and employment.

**TAMPA**
**Office Profile:** Phelps Dunbar extended its legal services from Texas to Florida by opening its eighth office in Tampa in 2001. The Tampa office, with over 45 attorneys, handles admiralty and tort litigation, business, real estate, franchise and distribution, commercial litigation, construction, insurance and reinsurance, labor and employment, intellectual property, and petroleum marketing litigation.

**RALEIGH**
**Office Profile:** Phelps Dunbar's newest office opened in November 2011 in Raleigh. Attorneys in the office represent clients in the areas of insurance and reinsurance, commercial litigation and labor and employment.

### Clients:

Clients include public and private companies, financial institutions, insurance companies, healthcare systems, educational institutions, partnerships, estates, governmental agencies and individuals.

### OFFICES

**LOUISIANA**
**NEW ORLEANS:** Canal Place, 365 Canal Street, Suite 2000, LA 70130-6534
Tel: 504 566 1311  Fax: 504 568 9130
Email: info@phelps.com

**BATON ROUGE:** II City Plaza, 400 Convention Street, Suite 1100, LA 70802-5618
Tel: 225 346 0285  Fax: 225 381 9197

**ALABAMA**
**MOBILE:** 2 N. Royal Street, AL 36602
Tel: 251 432 4481  Fax: 251 433 1820

**NORTH CAROLINA**
**RALEIGH:** GlenLake One, 4140 ParkLake Avenue, Suite 100, NC 27612
Tel: 919 789 5300  Fax: 919 789 5301

**MISSISSIPPI**
**GULFPORT:** NorthCourt One, 2304 19th Street, Suite 300, MS 39501
Tel: 228 679 1130  Fax: 228 679 1131

**JACKSON:** 4270 I-55 North, MS 39211-6391
Tel: 601 352 2300  Fax: 601 360 9777

**TUPELO:** One Mississippi Plaza, 201 S. Spring Street, Seventh Floor, MS 38804
Tel: 662 842 7907  Fax: 662 842 3873

**TEXAS**
**HOUSTON:** Bank of America Center, 700 Louisiana Street, Suite 2600, TX 77002
Tel: 713 626 1386  Fax: 713 626 1388

**FLORIDA**
**TAMPA:** Wells Fargo Center, 100 South Ashley Drive, Suite 1900, FL 33602-5311
Tel: 813 472 7550  Fax: 813 472 7570

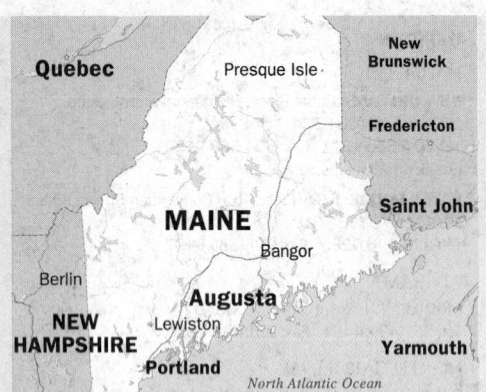

Québec
Presque Isle
New Brunswick
Fredericton
MAINE
Saint John
Bangor
Berlin
Augusta
NEW HAMPSHIRE
Lewiston
Yarmouth
Portland
North Atlantic Ocean

## How lawyers are ranked

Every year we carry out thousands of in-depth interviews with clients in order to assess the reputations and expertise of business lawyers worldwide. The qualities we look for (and which determine rankings) include technical legal ability, professional conduct, client service, commercial awareness/astuteness, diligence, commitment, and other qualities most valued by the client. For details of our research team, see p.5.

## Contents:

## MAINE: An introduction

### Contributed by Pierce Atwood LLP

#### Why Should I Do Business in Maine?

Maine business owners, executives and key decision-makers have cited the natural environment, favorable quality of life and the work ethic of Mainers as the state's greatest assets as a place to do business. Maine offers employers an attractive wage base and offers employees an affordable cost of living.

#### What Should I Know Before Relocating to Maine or Expanding My Maine Business?

The state has implemented a host of incentive programs in an effort to attract businesses to Maine and to encourage the expansion of existing businesses. The following list contains just a few examples of the incentives available to Maine businesses:

*Tax reimbursement, credits and exemptions*

Tax credits, such as the Research Expense Credit, the Maine Seed Capital Tax Credit and the High-Technology Investment Tax Credit, are among the many tools used by Maine policymakers to encourage and support investment in Maine businesses.

In addition, the Pine Tree Development Zone Program, which was once available in only selected geographical locations, has been expanded to cover the entire state. The Program is targeted at particular industries, including biotech, composite materials technology, advanced technologies for forestry and agriculture, IT, aquaculture and marine technology, environmental technology, manufacturing and financial services. Program benefits include up to a 100% Maine income tax credit for five years, a 50% Maine income tax credit for the next five years, an insurance premiums tax credit, increased employment tax increment financing, sales and use tax exemptions and access to reduced electricity rates.

Lastly, the Business Equipment Tax Exemption provides a 100% exemption from Maine personal property tax for certain eligible business equipment.

*State financing*

Through Employment Tax Increment Financing, businesses that add a minimum number of qualified jobs in Maine are reimbursed for a portion of their new employees' state income tax withholdings. Maine businesses also receive grants and awards from the Maine Technology Institute to fund R&D projects and activities leading to commercialization, as well as loans to support job creation and job retention through Economic Development Business Assistance grants provided under the Community Development Block Grant program.

To help Maine businesses access commercial credit, the Finance Authority of Maine's (FAME) Loan Insurance Program insures portions of loans to businesses made by participating financial institutions. The Small Enterprise Growth Fund provides Maine companies and entrepreneurs access to sources of venture capital.

*Local financing*

Through Tax Increment Financing (TIF), a municipality may reimburse a private sector business for a portion of incremental property taxes generated from the business's investment in a local project.

*Marketing*

The Maine Products Marketing Program helps build recognition for hundreds of Maine-made products through producer profiles on www.mainemade.com, product identification labels and trade show participation.

*Intellectual property*

The Maine Patent Program provides technical assistance to inventors and small businesses to identify and protect their IP.

*Technical assistance*

The state's various technical assistance programs offer support to Maine businesses in a wide range of areas, including international trade, farming, small business management, state licensing, energy conservation, manufacturing and compliance with environmental regulation. Though not an exhaustive list, the above-described programs continue to spur the growth of businesses in Maine. See www.econdevmaine.com for more information.

*New Initiatives*

Since 2010, Maine's political leaders have maintained a keen focus on economic development and supporting businesses. In 2011, the Maine Legislature enacted sweeping regulatory reform and created the position of Small Business Advocate within the Secretary of State's Office. The Administration has created Account Executives within the Department of Economic and Community Development and the Governor has created a program to certify qualifying municipalities as "business-friendly communities."

### What Does the Future of Maine Look Like?

While there are local issues affecting the cost of doing business in Maine resulting from the state and local tax burden, government regulation, healthcare costs and energy costs, there are certainly positive indicators that businesses must consider when looking at Maine. The debate during the last gubernatorial campaign centered on the cost of doing business in Maine and what could be done to grow business and, ultimately, jobs in the State. This remains the focus of policy mak-

ers in Maine. In April of 2011, Ernst & Young LLP in conjunction with the Council on State Taxation released a report on the competitiveness of state and local business taxes on new investment, ranking Maine first in the nation. These bright spots truly make Maine a state to consider.

Energy costs are another concern of business that has been at the top of the political agenda. Maine's electricity costs do track lower than the rest of New England, though the region is still known for its high energy costs. Maine's costs, however, have been trending down while costs in the rest of the nation have been trending up – putting Maine closer and closer to median energy costs nationwide.

In 2013, the Maine Legislature created a Joint Select Committee to look at specific issues affecting Maine's economy. This Committee is charged with addressing issues associated with workforce development. In addition, this Committee will look at downtowns as economic engines, and State support of small businesses. Policy makers remain focused on the future of Maine's economy and business attraction.

## CORPORATE/M&A

Commentary about individuals can be found under their firm's paragraph. If the firm has no paragraph (is not ranked) look at Other Notable Practitioners.

| Corporate/M&A Leading Firms |
| --- |
| **Band 1** |
| Bernstein Shur * |
| Pierce Atwood LLP * |
| Verrill Dana, LLP * |
| **Band 2** |
| Drummond Woodsum & MacMahon * |
| **Band 3** |
| Eaton Peabody |
| Preti Flaherty Beliveau & Pachios, LLP * |
| Rudman Winchell |
| **Band 4** |
| Pearce & Dow LLC |
| Perkins Thompson |

* Indicates firm / individual with profile.

†ONP = Other Notable Practitioner.

| Corporate/M&A Leading Individuals | |
| --- | --- |
| **Star individuals** | |
| Googins Mark K | Verrill Dana, LLP * |
| High Michael E | Drummond Woodsum & MacMahon * |
| Zimpritch James B | Pierce Atwood LLP * |
| **Band 1** | |
| Carpenter John L | Bernstein Shur |
| Champoux David | Pierce Atwood LLP * |
| Fryer Gregory | Verrill Dana, LLP * |
| Howard Christopher E | Pierce Atwood LLP * |
| McKay Daniel G | Eaton Peabody |
| **Band 2** | |
| Coggeshall Bruce A | Pierce Atwood LLP * |
| Eaton II George F | Rudman Winchell |
| LoGiudice Susan E | Preti Flaherty Beliveau & Pachios, LLP * |
| MacEwan Alan D | Verrill Dana, LLP * |
| Marcus Benjamin E | Drummond Woodsum & MacMahon * |
| Saunders Eric F | Bernstein Shur |
| **Band 3** | |
| Austin David M | Eaton Peabody |
| Draeger Scot | Bernstein Shur |
| Graceffa Charles M | Pierce Atwood LLP * |
| McLoon Christopher | Verrill Dana, LLP * |
| Pratt Aaron | Drummond Woodsum & MacMahon * |

| Corporate/M&A: Bankruptcy Leading Individuals | |
| --- | --- |
| **Star individuals** | |
| Keach Robert J | Bernstein Shur |
| **Band 1** | |
| Clement Jr Roger A | Verrill Dana, LLP * |
| Fagone Michael A | Bernstein Shur |
| Geller Jay S | Law Office of Jay S Geller (ONP)† |
| Manheimer Jacob A | Pierce Atwood LLP * |
| Marcus Benjamin E | Drummond Woodsum & MacMahon * |
| Marcus George J | Marcus, Clegg & Mistretta PA (ONP)† |
| **Band 2** | |
| Anderson Sam | Bernstein Shur |
| Bopp III Fred W | Perkins Thompson |
| Creswell Randy | Perkins Thompson |
| Pearce Michael J | Pearce & Dow LLC |
| **Band 3** | |
| Dow Joshua R | Pearce & Dow LLC |
| Piampiano Jeffrey T | Drummond Woodsum & MacMahon * |
| **Associates to watch** | |
| Fischer Jeremy R | Bernstein Shur |
| Hull Nathaniel | Verrill Dana, LLP * |

### Band 1

#### Bernstein Shur
See profile on p.1406

**THE FIRM** Bernstein Shur's business law group boasts an international footprint and attracts high-profile clients such as Citibank and American Financial Group. The team is known for its strength in areas such as traditional M&A, venture capital and private equity deals, financial services and securities. The firm's business reorganization and insolvency group is also extremely well regarded, with particular expertise in business bankruptcy and Chapter 11 cases. It represents both debtors and purchasers of assets.

**Sources say:** "*They understand how businesses operate and ask the right questions.*" "*I'd put Bernstein Shur against any of the big boys I've dealt with in New York City.*"
**KEY INDIVIDUALS** Star individual **Robert Keach** is cochair of Bernstein Shur's business reorganization and insolvency group and is well known nationally. Described as "*very knowledgeable*" and as having "*earned a reputation*

*and name for himself,*" Keach has recently served as the court-appointed fee examiner for the Chapter 11 bankruptcy cases of American Airlines and its affiliated debtors. **John Carpenter** provides advice on a wide range of corporate and commercial issues, such as M&A, business start-ups, fiduciary and governance matters, and debt and equity financing. Peers describe him as "*very practical*" and "*a problem solver.*" The "*tenacious*" **Michael Fagone** cochairs the business reorganization and insolvency group, and is much admired for his technical expertise. He recently represented the committee of unsecured creditors appointed in the Chapter 11 case of New England Building Materials. An impressed client describes him as *"one of the most respected bankruptcy lawyers."* **Eric Saunders** has wideranging experience in business law, with a particular focus on the healthcare industry. He is experienced in areas such as partnership and shareholder disputes, corporate takeovers and general business law. One client states: *"I have a lot of confidence in him."* **Sam Anderson** is a member of the business reorganization and insolvency group, and concentrates his practice on representing debtors in Chapter 11 reorganization proceedings. Clients cite his *"good understanding of business principles."* **Scot Draeger**'s practice focuses on the financial services and securities industry, covering a broad range of regulatory, compliance, enforcement and transactional issues. In a recent highlight, he acted for Huntington Strategy Shares on a project to launch two actively managed exchange-traded funds on the NYSE. **Jeremy Fischer** concentrates on restructuring distressed businesses and insolvency-related litigation. One source says: *"Jeremy is as fine a young lawyer as I have worked with anywhere."*

### Pierce Atwood LLP
See profile on p.1408

**THE FIRM** This firm draws praise for the strength of its business group, which has expertise in areas such as business formation and venture capital, loan transactions, M&A, capital markets transactions and corporate governance. In a recent highlight it represented Spinnaker Trust in its merger with Ram Trust Company, creating a combined financial services firm with some $1.2 billion in assets under management. The team harnessed its legal and business skills to take the overall lead in the structuring and execution of the transaction.
**Sources say:** *"There's a great breadth and depth. They can handle anything."*
**KEY INDIVIDUALS** Described as *"the dean of corporate law in Maine,"* **James Zimpritch** (see p.1405) focuses his practice on corporate transactions and governance. He represents businesses of all sizes and types, including banks and bank holding companies, insurance companies and agencies. According to one source, he is *"a very wise guy and clearly should be considered a star."* Clients recognize **David Champoux** (see p.1398) for his *"breadth of knowledge"* and ability to provide *"good, practical business advice."* He focuses on areas such as M&A, business formation, corporate governance, financing transactions and commercial contracts. **Christopher Howard** (see p.1400) is head of Pierce Atwood's business practice group and is lauded by clients for his business acumen. He is considered to be *"very bright"* and *"a great adviser."* A recent work highlight was representing Cate Street Capital and its subsidiary Sunlight Partners in the sale of a number of solar energy projects to Australian private equity fund Capital Dynamics. **Bruce Coggeshall** (see p.1398) is of counsel at Pierce Atwood and is an experienced corporate and commercial law adviser. He also acts as outside general counsel for a number of businesses, and as bond counsel for several Maine municipalities. He recently played a central role

in the acquisition of Webber Energy Fuels by Dead River Company, a petroleum sales and distribution company. **Charles Graceffa** (see p.1400) has expertise in corporate and securities law. He impresses both clients and peers with the quality of his work and is praised for his *"deep experience in negotiations and nice bedside manner."* **Jacob Manheimer** (see p.1402) specializes in financially distressed situations, creditors' rights and commercial transactions. He frequently acts for secured creditors, trade creditors and landlords on a wide range of matters, and sources describe him as a *"great guy and really smart."*

### Verrill Dana, LLP
See profile on p.1410

**THE FIRM** Verrill Dana's business law group handles a wide range of corporate matters, covering areas such as M&A, securities, private equity, tax and regulated businesses. The group also serves an extensive array of companies as primary outside counsel. One work highlight for the group was representing Maine Drilling & Blasting Group in the sale of a minority equity interest to Dyno Nobel and, in a complementary transaction, the purchase of the Northeast assets of Dyno Nobel. The firm's bankruptcy and creditors' rights group acts for both creditors and debtors, and has experience in Chapter 11 business reorganizations, Chapter 7 business liquidations and Chapter 13 cases. Active clients include Bank of America, Spinglass Management and Montreal Maine & Atlantic.
**Sources say:** *"They appreciate what an entrepreneur has had to go through in building a business."*
**KEY INDIVIDUALS Gregory Fryer** (see p.1399) specializes in securities and corporate law, and has also acted as outside general counsel to a variety of companies. He recently represented Border Trust Company in the sale of its assets and certain liabilities to Bar Harbor Bank & Trust, and in the resolution of related regulatory issues. *"Savvy deal guy"* **Mark Googins** (see p.1399) focuses his practice on commercial finance and commercial transactions. He also acted for Woodland Pulp on the purchase of an international railroad. The deal involved regulatory issues in both the USA and Canada. **Alan MacEwan** (see p.1401) represented nonprofit organization Youth Alternatives Ingraham on its merger with The People's Regional Opportunity Program of Cumberland County to create one of the largest social service agencies in Maine and northern New England. One source states: *"I think entrepreneurs feel very comfortable with him. He has an awareness of how significant the sale of a business is to people."* **Christopher McLoon** (see p.1402) applies his tax law and policy expertise to corporate transactions spanning a number of industries, including renewable energy, timber, and real estate investment and development. One source states: *"He's very good for tax advice and very thorough."* **Nathaniel Hull** (see p.1400) is well regarded for his work in business restructurings, avoidance litigation and bankruptcy-related appellate work. Praised by peers as a *"good young lawyer,"* he has gained experience in representing Chapter 11 and Chapter 7 trustees. Described as a *"formidable bankruptcy lawyer,"* **Roger Clement** (see p.1398) focuses on matters related to financially distressed busi-

nesses and insolvency. He chairs the firm's bankruptcy and creditors' rights group and frequently represents creditors' committees, secured creditors, Chapter 11 trustees and debtors-in-possession. A recent work highlight was acting for Fund of Jupiter, the primary secured creditor of both Irvine Tanning Company and Prime Tanning Company, each of which filed for Chapter 11 bankruptcy.

## Band 2

### Drummond Woodsum & MacMahon
See profile on p.1407

**THE FIRM** This team represents businesses across a broad range of industries, with expertise spanning areas such as business formation, joint ventures, M&A, tax planning, financing work and bankruptcy. The firm is also well known for its expertise in Native American Law.
**Sources say:** *"There is an amazing depth and intellect at the firm."* *"They seem to have a cadre of uniformly competent specialists that can be brought to bear when required."*
**KEY INDIVIDUALS Michael High** (see p.1400) chairs the firm's business and commercial services group, and is described as exhibiting *"great competence and sound business judgment."* He is well respected for his experience in corporate and commercial matters, and frequently represents companies, investors, lenders and borrowers across Maine and New England. One client reports: *"He's very thoughtful and always watching to cover our backs."* **Benjamin Marcus** (see p.1402) is admired for his broadbased practice, which covers both bankruptcy and corporate/M&A law. He has experience in representing a range of clients, from Maine-based commercial lenders to Canadian companies doing business in Maine. **Jeffrey Piampiano** (see p.1403) specializes in bankruptcy law. He has experience acting for clients in business reorganizations and in the purchase and sale of assets out of bankruptcy estates. *"Mr Piampiano is an outstanding attorney. He has my best interests at heart,"* says one enthusiastic client. **Aaron Pratt**'s (see p.1403) practice focuses on the representation of businesses, nonprofit organizations, investors, creditors and Native American tribes in corporate and commercial matters.

## Band 3

### Eaton Peabody

**THE FIRM** This team offers a full range of business services, assisting clients in areas such as finance, M&A, commercial disputes and bankruptcy. The firm frequently represents clients in the technology, aquaculture and timberland industries, along with Canadian companies setting up US operations.
**Sources say:** *"Eaton Peabody is dominant in the northern part of the state."*
**KEY INDIVIDUALS** Hailed as *"very talented,"* **Daniel McKay** focuses his practice on representing clients in a wide range of transactional matters. He also advises clients on antitrust issues and matters relating to US-Canada

cross-border trade. He serves as general outside counsel to a variety of businesses. The *"very thorough"* and *"always thoughtful"* David Austin chairs the firm's business law group. He concentrates on corporate and securities law. Austin's expertise spans areas such as M&A, debt and equity financings, commercial contracts and shareholder relations.

## Preti Flaherty Beliveau & Pachios, LLP
See profile on p.1409

THE FIRM This firm's business law team has expertise in a full range of corporate and insolvency matters, covering mergers and acquisitions, securities offerings and commercial contracts. The team represents clients in all stages of their development.

KEY INDIVIDUALS Susan LoGiudice (see p.1401) is well respected for her expertise in M&A and complex corporate transactions. She represents businesses of all sizes and acts as general counsel to a range of corporate clients.

## Rudman Winchell

THE FIRM This Bangor-based firm handles a broad spectrum of business and corporate matters, ranging from M&A and the sale of companies to negotiating and structuring contracts. It represents both lenders and borrowers in all types of financing transactions.

Sources say: *"They are a capable, reliable firm."* *"Good transactional business lawyers."*

KEY INDIVIDUALS George Eaton impresses both peers and clients with his corporate expertise. One source states: *"He's a smart guy and asks a lot of good questions."* He has also served on a number of nonprofit boards.

## Band 4

## Pearce & Dow LLC

THE FIRM This boutique focuses on representing clients in transactional, advisory and bankruptcy matters. The team is experienced in representing a wide variety of clients, from large corporations and municipalities to individuals and families.

KEY INDIVIDUALS Michael Pearce has a broad practice, but is particularly well known for his work in the areas of bankruptcy and debtor and creditor rights. Sources say that he is *"good at getting deals done"* and *"a really diligent, hard-working guy."* Joshua Dow is recognized by peers for his expertise in the bankruptcy sphere. He is well versed in areas such as debtor and creditor rights, insolvency and corporate reorganizations.

## Perkins Thompson

THE FIRM This firm handles corporate/M&A as well as bankruptcy work. The business group offers services relating to formation, transactions, and contractual and regulatory issues. Its bankruptcy team is experienced in a wide array of bankruptcy, insolvency and recovery law issues.

KEY INDIVIDUALS Fred Bopp chairs the firm's bankruptcy group and focuses on issues relating to bankruptcy, insolvency and debtor and creditor rights. He frequently advises Chapter 11 creditors' committees, Chapter 7 bankruptcy trustees, and both secured and unsecured creditors. Sources say that he is *"a fine lawyer"* and *"very detailed in what he does, and excellent in research."* Randy Creswell has a wealth of experience representing parties in bankruptcy and insolvency matters. Clients include financial institutions, Chapter 7 and 11 debtors, secured and unsecured creditors, creditors' committees and individual executives.

## Other Notable Practitioners

Sole practitioner Jay Geller is recommended by peers and clients as *"an outstanding bankruptcy lawyer."* He has extensive experience in significant Chapter 11 cases, bankruptcy litigation, corporate reorganizations and out-of-court workouts. He is also of counsel to Chicago-based firm Shaw Fishman Glantz & Towbin LLC. George Marcus, a senior partner at Marcus, Clegg & Mistretta PA, is an expert in Chapter 11 proceedings and bankruptcy. He is recognized as a *"highly skilled"* practitioner and is a fellow of the American College of Bankruptcy.

# ENERGY & NATURAL RESOURCES

Commentary about individuals can be found under their firm's paragraph. If the firm has no paragraph (is not ranked) look at Other Notable Practitioners.

| Energy & Natural Resources |
| --- |
| **Leading Firms** |
| **Band 1** |
| Bernstein Shur * |
| Pierce Atwood LLP * |
| Preti Flaherty Beliveau & Pachios, LLP * |
| Verrill Dana, LLP * |

*\* Indicates firm with profile.*
*Alphabetical order within each band. Band 1 is the highest.*

## Band 1

## Bernstein Shur
See profile on p.1406

THE FIRM This highly praised team is noted for its knowledge of issues related to electrical generation and distribution. Clients include IPPs, banks and financial institutions, contractors and subcontractors, large consumers of electricity and municipalities. The group recently advised First Wind on matters relating to a number of wind energy projects, and also represented the company before the Maine Public Utilities Commission (MPUC) to obtain approval for a joint venture with Emera.

Sources say: *"I've been very satisfied with their performance."*

KEY INDIVIDUALS Gordon Grimes has more than 30 years' experience acting for clients in the power generation industry, and is known internationally and nationally, as well in Maine. He is admired for his energy-related dispute resolution work, which includes mediation, arbitration, administrative hearings and litigation. Patrick Scully specializes in energy-related contract and regulatory issues. He represents the owners and developers of wind, biomass, hydroelectric, oil and natural gas facilities. He recently advised Statoil on its plans to develop the first commercial floating offshore wind energy project in the USA. *"He's very calm and even-tempered, and when he speaks at a hearing, commissioners listen,"* says one peer. James Broder has expertise in project finance, permitting, contract law, and regulatory elements of electric transmission infrastructure projects. He recently acted for Hudson Transmission Partners on the development and financing of a high-voltage direct current transmission line between New Jersey and Manhattan. One client states: *"He knew the industry very well, did very good work and I would heartily recommend him."*

## Pierce Atwood LLP
See profile on p.1408

THE FIRM Pierce Atwood's energy group advises on a host of matters, with comprehensive expertise in electricity regulation, energy litigation, natural gas matters and renewable energy project development. The team maintains a national and international presence advising financial institutions and governmental bodies on energy-related matters. Active clients include Central Maine Power, Iberdrola and Unitil.

Sources say: *"They're very commercial, easy to deal with, well informed and they know how to get deals done."*

KEY INDIVIDUALS Jared des Rosiers (see p.1399) specializes in energy litigation and regulatory matters. He recently represented Central Maine Power in an investigation initiated by the MPUC into the transmission planning standards used by Maine electric utilities. One impressed client says: *"He's excellent. First-rate."* John Gulliver (see p.1400) is well versed in regulatory energy matters, and has acted for clients before the MPUC, FERC, the US Department of Energy and state public utility commissions. Sources note that he has *"very good cross-border experience,"* as was illustrated by his recent work with the National Electric Power Company of Jordan, K&M Engineering & Consulting LLC and the Jordanian Ministry of Energy & Mining Resources in connection with two new IPP projects in Jordan. Head of the firm's renewable energy practice, **William Hewitt** (see p.1400) has expertise in a range of policy, project development and renewable energy issues. He recently represented Xpress Natural Gas and XNG Maine in the regulatory approvals required for the development of a Maine-based compressed natural gas facility. **Timothy Schneider** (see p.1404) is a well-regarded associate at the firm, having gained experience in both energy-related transactional work and a variety of regulatory issues. One interviewee says: *"He really understands business, understands how to create a legal solution within the context of doing business, and is very pragmatic."*

## Preti Flaherty Beliveau & Pachios, LLP
### See profile on p.1409

**THE FIRM** This group offers a broad array of services, ranging from rulemaking before the FERC to representing energy clients in the acquisition and development of electric generation projects. The firm also has a presence in the renewable energy space and provides comprehensive services linked to clean technology-related project development and transactions. Clients include power producers, consumers and trade associations such as the American Forest & Paper Association.
**Sources say:** *"They have developed an expertise in terms of working between clients and government. They are very good at it."*
**KEY INDIVIDUALS** Chair of the firm's energy group, **Anthony Buxton** (see p.1397) maintains a reputation as a leader in energy and utilities matters. He advises on a wide range of issues related to project purchase, sale and development. He serves as general counsel to the Industrial Energy Consumer Group, representing large electricity consumers in the region. **Joseph Donahue** (see p.1399) is an expert in energy and telecommunications, representing telephone companies on an array of regulatory, transactional and business matters. He was formerly general counsel to the MPUC. **Donald Sipe** (see p.1404) draws on his past experience as chair of New England Power Pool and as an in-house attorney at the MPUC to assist energy and utilities clients. He represents a range of entities before the FERC, state commissions and stakeholder bodies in regional transmission organizations. **Andrew Landry** (see p.1401) is of counsel at the firm and previously served as general counsel to Bangor Hydro Electric. He is particularly recognized for his experience handling energy-related regulatory issues.

## Verrill Dana, LLP
### See profile on p.1410

**THE FIRM** Known to have excellent breadth and depth in the energy domain, Verrill Dana frequently handles complex permitting and development work for new wind generation, electric transmission and natural gas projects. The team is respected for its extensive experience representing clients before the MPUC and FERC, and is noted for its

expertise in energy-related M&A and litigation. The group continues to attract an impressive array of clients, including Emera Energy, Summit Utilities and TransCanada.
**Sources say:** *"They have great lawyers and great rates."* *"Verrill Dana has an excellent energy practice."*
**KEY INDIVIDUALS** Recognized as a leader in his field, **William Harwood** (see p.1400) acts for a vast array of clients from the electric, gas, water and telecoms industries. A key work highlight was representing Emera before the MPUC to obtain approval for both the acquisition of a minority stake in Algonquin Power & Utilities and a joint venture with First Wind. **James Cohen** (see p.1398) has a broad practice with a significant focus on utilities regulation. He represents transmission and distribution utilities, natural gas utilities, wood pellet heat providers and energy aggregators in a broad array of transactional, regulatory and legislative proceedings. He has recently served clients such as Bangor Hydro Electric and Summit Utilities. **Nora Healy** (see p.1400) is fast gaining a reputation for her talent in handling regulatory matters. She frequently appears before the MPUC and recently represented Gaz Métro in successfully obtaining approval for its acquisition of Central Vermont Public Service Corporation. Associate **Katie Gray** (see p.1400) has broad-ranging experience in energy law and is developing an expertise in the natural gas field. One peer states: *"We've been consistently impressed with Katie's professionalism and understanding."*

## Other Notable Practitioners

**Alan Stone** of Skelton, Taintor & Abbott, A Professional Corporation is an experienced trial attorney with a focus on public utilities and energy law. He frequently appears before the MPUC and serves as general counsel to Bangor Gas Company. **James Costello** of Curtis Thaxter LLC has a varied practice, a large component of which involves public utilities matters. He is recognized by peers as a *"very skilled practitioner."* **Charles Micoleau** of Curtis Thaxter LLC has a wealth of experience lobbying for the energy sector. He has served as counsel to a wide array of clients, ranging from nonprofit entities to independent transmission lines.

# ENVIRONMENT

## Band 1

## Pierce Atwood LLP
### See profile on p.1408

**THE FIRM** This group continues to be a leader in the Maine market and has advised on a range of environmental matters since 1970. The team is particularly recognized for its experience in areas such as land use, natural resources, remediation and toxic tort issues. Recently the group acted for a coalition of municipalities and businesses on an intervention in litigation brought by the Penobscot Indian Nation regarding the scope of its territory and its right to regulate a stretch of the Penobscot River.

**Sources say:** *"They work very effectively with their colleagues in providing appropriate levels of staffing and expertise."* *"A solid reputation."*
**KEY INDIVIDUALS Thomas Doyle** (see p.1399) is noted for his experience across a wide range of environmental and land use matters. He recently represented Irving Woodlands in hearings before the Maine legislature over plans to develop a new statute to allow metallic mineral mining in the state. Sources describe him as *"well respected."* **Kenneth Gray** (see p.1400) specializes in hazardous substance and hazardous waste matters, where his knowledge is praised as *"outstanding."* According to one source he is *"exceptionally good at what he does."* Practice group

chair **Matthew Manahan** (see p.1401) focuses on environmental regulations surrounding energy projects. He is also experienced in litigation relating to hydropower and land use matters. **Dixon Pike** (see p.1403) is noted for his focus on state and federal air laws, pollution prevention and toxin reduction requirements. He recently advised Sappi Fine Paper on the development of a compliance plan concerning the CAA. One peer states: *"Dixon is unparalleled in terms of air expertise."* **William Taylor** (see p.1404) concentrates on water law, waste discharge and natural resource and wetland licensing, and represents clients at both the state and federal level. He is considered by sources to be *"very knowledgeable."* **Philip Ahrens** (see p.1397) is of counsel at the firm. He has more than 30 years' experience in environmental law, and advises clients on a broad range of licensing and enforcement issues. **Brian Rayback** (see p.1404) is fast gaining prominence in Maine's environmental law market and has recently acted for clients such as We Care Cleaners and Verso Paper.

## Band 2

### Preti Flaherty Beliveau & Pachios, LLP
See profile on p.1409

**THE FIRM** This group, home to 11 environmental attorneys, is highly regarded for its litigation work and success in obtaining state and federal permits for development projects. The group has represented a diverse array of clients, from Fortune 500 companies to small manufacturers and local businesses. Key names among its portfolio of clients include Chevron, Covidien and Texas Instruments. **Sources say:** *"Incredible knowledge and expertise in environmental matters."* *"They're friendly and easy to work with."*

**KEY INDIVIDUALS David Van Slyke** (see p.1405) is chair of the group and has particular expertise in dealing with hazardous wastes and materials. He also has broader experience in compliance counseling, project permitting and environmental audits. One client states: *"He's highly personable, responsive and has a great knowledge of Maine environmental law."* As a former trial attorney in the Environmental Enforcement Section at the DOJ, **Jeffrey Talbert** (see p.1404) is a *"very accomplished environmental litigator,"* according to sources. He has recently served as counsel to clients such as BB Development, ConAgra Grocery Products and Mallinckrodt. **Sharon Newman** (see p.1402) is a CWA expert with a particular focus on the regulation of storm water. She recently advised the City of Bangor on negotiations with the government regarding alleged combined sewer overflow violations. Clients describe her as *"outstanding"* and *"a good organizer and leader."*

### Verrill Dana, LLP
See profile on p.1410

**THE FIRM** This firm's environment practice maintains an excellent reputation for its expertise in permitting, compliance and litigation. It is also celebrated for its track record in development, in particular its success in wind energy projects. The group continues to attract a roster of high-profile clients such as First Wind, TransCanada and Verizon Wireless.

**Sources say:** *"They have a very deep understanding of processes and the law. They make it understandable for us, and they are good communicators."*

**KEY INDIVIDUALS Juliet Browne** (see p.1397) chairs the firm's environmental group and is particularly commended for her expertise in wind power matters. She recently represented TransCanada in the development and permitting of its Maine-based wind power projects. One source states that *"she is extremely well versed in environmental law."* **Kelly Boden** (see p.1397) has expertise in a broad range of transactional, permitting and regulatory compliance issues. She recently acted for DCP Midstream Partners on applying for permits to operate a 23 million

gallon LPG storage tank. **Scott Anderson** (see p.1397) has extensive experience in environmental permitting, compliance and litigation. Recent work includes representing Plum Creek Timberlands in an appeal of the company's concept plan for the Moosehead Lake Region, a proposal that affects around 400,000 acres of land.

## Band 3

### Bernstein Shur
See profile on p.1406

**THE FIRM** This firm handles a wide range of environmental matters, assisting individuals, businesses and municipalities on litigation, compliance, land use and permitting matters. The team recently handled numerous issues on behalf of ReEnergy Holdings in connection with the purchase of four biomass plants.

**KEY INDIVIDUALS Katherine Joyce** is much admired for her environmental permitting and compliance work. She focuses on areas such as power generation, renewables, remediation, air pollution, solid waste and water issues. She is described as *"personable"* and the *"mainstay of environmental law at Bernstein Shur."*

### Drummond Woodsum & MacMahon
See profile on p.1407

**THE FIRM** This firm's environmental group acts for clients from a variety of industries including manufacturing, energy and education. It offers a broad range of services from due diligence and litigation to criminal enforcement cases.

**KEY INDIVIDUALS Joanna Tourangeau** (see p.1405) represents clients on land use, permitting, compliance and enforcement matters. Peers say that she is *"an excellent attorney"* with a *"sophisticated"* practice. Industry veteran **James Kilbreth** (see p.1401) recently joined the team from Verrill Dana. He concentrates on commercial and regulatory litigation, bringing experience of a variety of environmental concerns. **William Plouffe** (see p.1403) draws on decades of experience to provide representation across a wide range of environmental and land use issues. He is also town attorney to a number of municipalities in Maine.

### Eaton Peabody

**THE FIRM** Headquartered in Bangor, this firm provides counsel and representation on a variety of environmental and land use matters. It acts for both companies and municipal clients in areas such as environmental due diligence, permitting, litigation and compliance. **Sources say:** *"An excellent environmental law division."*

**KEY INDIVIDUALS** Practice chair **Andrew Hamilton** provides advice on environmental compliance and responding to actions by regulatory authorities. Here, *"Andy is at the top of his field in our state,"* asserts one client.

# LABOR & EMPLOYMENT

Commentary about individuals can be found under their firm's paragraph. If the firm has no paragraph (is not ranked) look at Other Notable Practitioners.

## Labor & Employment
### Leading Firms

**Band 1**
Fisher & Phillips LLP *
Pierce Atwood LLP *
Verrill Dana, LLP *

**Band 2**
Bernstein Shur *
Drummond Woodsum & MacMahon *

**Band 3**
Eaton Peabody
Rudman Winchell
Wakelin, Hallock & O'Donovan LLP

**Band 4**
Preti Flaherty Beliveau & Pachios, LLP *
The Bennett Law Firm PA

### Leading Individuals

**Band 1**

| | | |
|---|---|---|
| LePage Margaret Coughlin | Pierce Atwood LLP * |
| McGill Linda D | Bernstein Shur |
| Moon Richard G | Verrill Dana, LLP * |
| Shapiro Jonathan | Fisher & Phillips LLP * |

**Band 2**

| | |
|---|---|
| Brooks Robert C | Verrill Dana, LLP * |
| Caterine Melinda J | Fisher & Phillips LLP * |
| Currier Douglas P | Verrill Dana, LLP * |
| Erwin James R | Pierce Atwood LLP * |
| Hewey Melissa | Drummond Woodsum & MacMahon * |
| McGuire Frank | Rudman Winchell |
| Messerschmidt Michael G | Preti Flaherty Beliveau & Pachios * |
| Pringle Harry R | Drummond Woodsum & MacMahon * |
| Rose Daniel | Drummond Woodsum & MacMahon * |
| Uhl Eric J | Fisher & Phillips LLP * |

**Band 3**

| | |
|---|---|
| Bennett Peter | The Bennett Law Firm PA |
| Coupe Bradford W | Verrill Dana, LLP * |
| Einsiedler Jr Charles S | Pierce Atwood LLP * |
| Finberg Frederick | The Bennett Law Firm PA |
| Israel Glenn | Bernstein Shur |
| Moss Philip J | Fisher & Phillips LLP * |
| O'Brien Timothy J | Libby O'Brien Kingsley, LLC (ONP)† |
| Payne Clare Hudson | Eaton Peabody |
| Peard Patricia A | Bernstein Shur |

**Up-and-coming individuals**

| | |
|---|---|
| Olivier Elizabeth | Preti Flaherty Beliveau & Pachios * |
| Rand Katharine I | Pierce Atwood LLP * |

* Indicates firm / individual with profile.
† ONP = Other Notable Practitioner.

## Labor & Employment: Employee Benefits & Compensation
### Senior Statesmen

**Senior Statesmen:** distinguished older partners

| | |
|---|---|
| Ginn Gregg H | Verrill Dana, LLP * |

### Leading Individuals

**Band 1**

| | |
|---|---|
| Bachelder Stephan G | Bachelder & Dowling, PA (ONP)† |
| Meeker Suzanne | Verrill Dana, LLP * |
| Wakelin David S | Wakelin, Hallock & O'Donovan LLP |

**Band 2**

| | |
|---|---|
| Altholz Eric | Verrill Dana, LLP * |
| Feibel Edward | Eaton Peabody |

**Band 3**

| | |
|---|---|
| Boehm Lisa | Verrill Dana, LLP * |
| Couch Kimberly S | Verrill Dana, LLP * |
| Einsiedler Jr Charles S | Pierce Atwood LLP * |
| Hallock Leslie C | Wakelin, Hallock & O'Donovan LLP |
| Shapiro Jonathan | Fisher & Phillips LLP * |

## Labor & Employment: Immigration
### Leading Individuals

**Band 1**

| | |
|---|---|
| Derosby Anthony R | Pierce Atwood LLP * |

## Band 1

### Fisher & Phillips LLP
See profile on p.1107

**THE FIRM** National labor and employment outfit Fisher & Phillips draws praise for its management-side expertise across a full range of services. It represents clients in industries such as financial services, media and publishing, hospitality, healthcare and education. A recent work highlight for the group was acting for TD Bank in a collective action lawsuit in which a number of call center employees alleged that they had been required to undertake unpaid labor for the bank before and after their scheduled shifts.

**Sources say:** "It's an excellent firm and is well respected throughout the state." "It's our go-to employment firm."

**KEY INDIVIDUALS Jonathan Shapiro** (see p.1404) has a broad practice covering the full spectrum of employment issues, including employee benefits and compensation. A recent highlight was representing Charming Shoppes in an alleged violation of ERISA requirements. Interviewees emphasize his high levels of client service. **Melinda Caterine** (see p.1398) is lauded by clients and peers for her work in discrimination, sexual harassment and wrongful termination claims. She recently advised Capital Pizza Huts in a sexual harassment and retaliation lawsuit. According to one source, her excellent reputation is due to "clients retaining her and trusting her with significant matters" and the fact that "she's really skilled and capable." **Eric Uhl** (see p.1405) advises employers and managers on a wide range of matters. He has recently represented clients such as LKQ and Sweetser. Clients report he is "excellent both in the courtroom and with the negotiating aspect." **Philip Moss** (see p.1402) is of counsel at the firm's New England and Boston offices. Having focused exclusively on labor and employment law since 1975, he is a highly experienced practitioner.

### Pierce Atwood LLP
See profile on p.1408

**THE FIRM** This sizable team is well regarded for its comprehensive labor and employment services. It acts for clients across all aspects of employment law and can call upon its employee benefits group for specialized expertise in areas such as executive compensation and health, life and disability plans. Clients include Wright Express, MaineGeneral Medical Center and Nestlé Waters North America.

**Sources say:** "There's a great breadth and depth. They can handle anything."

**KEY INDIVIDUALS** Praised as a "very strong" practitioner, **Margaret LePage** (see p.1401) has a wealth of experience as both an adviser and a litigator. She counsels independent schools and colleges on school law, employment and student rights, and has deep expertise in areas such as sexual harassment, disability discrimination and family medical leave. **Anthony Derosby** (see p.1399) leads the firm's immigration practice. He serves as general outside immigration counsel for a number of large multinational corporations and healthcare organizations, and advises clients on matters relating to international personnel. Peers single him out as a "very creative immigration lawyer." **James Erwin** (see p.1399), chair of the firm's employment group, is praised for his "specialized knowledge" and ability to give "good, practical business advice." He has considerable litigation experience in areas such as sexual harassment, defamation, wage and hour, retaliation and discharge. Considered to be a "great attorney" and "exceptionally experienced," **Charles Einsiedler** (see p.1399) is chair of the firm's employee benefits group. He acts for clients on a diversity of labor and employment matters. **Katharine Rand** (see p.1403) was recently promoted to partner at Pierce Atwood and is fast developing a reputation among peers and clients as an "outstanding" lawyer. She concentrates on discrimination, harassment, retaliation, and wage and hour issues, and has litigated cases in both the state and federal courts.

### Verrill Dana, LLP
See profile on p.1410

**THE FIRM** Verrill Dana is held in high esteem for its dominance in the employee benefits and executive compensation space, as well as its strength in traditional labor and employment matters. The impressive team has recently acted for clients such as Saint Raphael Healthcare System, Kris-Way Truck Leasing and Mid-State Machine Products. **Sources say:** *"They really do connect with our employees and with our cases."*

**KEY INDIVIDUALS** Chair of the employee benefits and compensation group, **Suzanne Meeker** (see p.1402) is well respected for her knowledge in areas such as qualified and nonqualified retirement plans, benefit plans in M&A, and health and welfare plans. One peer says: *"She's excellent, I think very highly of her."* **Richard Moon** (see p.1402) draws on more than 30 years of experience to advise clients on healthcare reform, discrimination claims, class action wage and hour claims, and union-related matters. A recent work highlight was successfully defending Mid-State Machine Products in an age discrimination and whistle-blowing case. He is regarded as a *"smart, seasoned lawyer"* and a *"formidable opponent for anyone on the other side in a trial."* **Eric Altholz** (see p.1397) specializes in employee benefits and executive compensation work, particularly in the areas of retirement plans, deferred compensation plans, fiduciary compliance and matters relevant to tax-exempt employers. One source praises him for his *"expertise in very nebulous areas of ERISA and benefits programs"* and his ability to *"navigate complex legal structures."* **Robert Brooks** (see p.1397) often acts for clients in the healthcare, manufacturing, transportation and utilities industries. He has successfully represented clients at all levels of the state and federal court systems. One source describes him as an *"excellent employment attorney."* **Douglas Currier** (see p.1399) is chair of Verrill Dana's labor and employment group, and represents clients on a broad spectrum of issues. One interviewee applauds his *"responsiveness, legal knowledge and understanding of the client's goals."* **Lisa Boehm** (see p.1397) has an exclusive focus on the employee benefits and compensation domain. She frequently advises clients on issues relating to ERISA fiduciary duties, 401(k) retirement saving plans, and IRS correction programs for retirement plans. Market feedback suggests she is *"extremely well versed"* in legislative matters. **Kimberly Couch** (see p.1398) is a member of the employee benefits and compensation group. She is experienced in issues related to the Internal Revenue Code and ERISA, as well as the design, drafting, implementation and termination of qualified retirement plans. **Bradford Coupe** (see p.1398) has a niche focus on construction industry labor matters. He is described by clients as a premier project labor attorney in the state and beyond, and interviewees further note his *"extremely broad perspective of what's going on in the industry."* Industry veteran **Gregg Ginn** (see p.1399) recently transitioned to senior counsel status at the firm. He is particularly valued for his experience in ERISA-related work and the provisions of the Internal Revenue Code. One commentator asserts: *"Gregg Ginn is the top ERISA lawyer in the state, if not the region."*

## Band 2

### Bernstein Shur
See profile on p.1406

**THE FIRM** Bernstein Shur brings considerable expertise to a full range of employment matters, and is particularly well known for its work with educational, corporate, municipal and healthcare clients. Key clients include the Bank of Maine, University of New England and Walmart. **Sources say:** *"It's a very fine firm and it has an excellent roster of lawyers."*

**KEY INDIVIDUALS Linda McGill** impresses peers and clients with her *"outstanding"* work representing clients such as Maine Community College System and the City of Saco. According to one source, *"Linda has excelled on the municipal law side."* **Glenn Israel** is known for his litigation and arbitration work on a variety of labor, employment and business issues. Market opinion suggests that he provides *"excellent labor and employment counsel."* A recent work highlight was assisting Everett J. Prescott, a waterworks distributor, on the design of an apprenticeship program and obtaining approval for it from the Maine Department of Labor. **Patricia Peard** specializes in employment issues relating to private schools, colleges and universities. She has acted for clients such as the University of Maine System and a number of independent schools. One satisfied client states: *"She is good to work with, very responsive and very knowledgeable."*

### Drummond Woodsum & MacMahon
See profile on p.1407

**THE FIRM** This renowned group routinely handles a broad range of labor and employment matters and is particularly prominent in the educational and municipal arenas. The team is recognized for its expertise in the design and implementation of HR systems, policies and handbooks, and its practical approach. **Sources say:** *"They're down-to-earth and understand our business very well."* *"I think they have a genuine interest in the people who they're working with."*

**KEY INDIVIDUALS Melissa Hewey** (see p.1400) is a member of the firm's trial services group and has a focus on employment law. She is regarded as being *"extremely knowledgeable and well respected in Maine,"* and is particularly well known for her work with municipalities, schools and higher education-related clients. **Harry Pringle** (see p.1403) is admired for his experience in employment litigation, labor negotiations, arbitrations, and proceedings with the NLRB and the Maine Labor Relations Board. According to one commentator, *"he has very polished interpersonal skills and is well respected and liked, even by his opposition."* **Daniel Rose** (see p.1404) represents private and public sector employers and Indian tribes nationally. His expertise spans areas such as discrimination, wrongful discharge, employee compensation, and wage and hour matters. One client states: *"I think he has a tremendous amount of knowledge and has a realistic approach."*

## Band 3

### Eaton Peabody

**THE FIRM** Eaton Peabody advises clients on a diverse range of labor and employment matters, and is experienced in employment litigation in both the federal and state courts. The team also has a presence in the employee benefits and compensation space, with expertise in areas such as ERISA, executive compensation plans, employee benefit design, and the implementation, operation and benefits issues arising out of M&A. **Sources say:** *"I feel confident to divert more and more work toward Eaton Peabody."*

**KEY INDIVIDUALS Edward Feibel** is a member of Eaton Peabody's employee benefits and executive compensation team. He exhibits a talent for resolving compliance issues under ERISA and the Internal Revenue Code, and is praised by peers for his ability to *"translate complex ERISA requirements into understandable English."* He also focuses on executive compensation arrangements, retirement plans, and welfare and fringe benefit programs. **Clare Payne** frequently advises private, public and nonprofit employers and is adept at handling wage and hour, sexual harassment, discharge and FMLA issues. Clients praise her for being *"very responsive"* and *"very thorough,"* with one source adding: *"I could not imagine having better advice."*

### Rudman Winchell

**THE FIRM** Rudman Winchell's labor and employment attorneys display dexterity in areas such as alternative dispute resolution, the OSHA, administrative law and workers' compensation. Based in Bangor, the well-regarded group frequently serves public, private and municipal clients. **Sources say:** *"In northern Maine it's the go-to firm."*

**KEY INDIVIDUALS** Hailed as a *"very good litigator,"* **Frank McGuire** regularly represents clients on a broad range of employment and personnel matters before state and federal courts and agencies.

### Wakelin, Hallock & O'Donovan LLP

**THE FIRM** Boutique firm Wakelin, Hallock & O'Donovan is considered preeminent in the employee benefits space. The group frequently advises clients on areas such as ERISA, deferred and executive compensation and severance agreements, as well as retirement and medical plans. The group has recently undertaken a significant amount of work relating to the Patient Protection and Affordable Care Act.

**KEY INDIVIDUALS David Wakelin** is respected by peers for his top-quality employment work. One source states: *"He's a great, smart guy, and highly competent."* Recognized as a *"heavyweight"* in the employee benefits domain, **Leslie Hallock** also draws praise for the strength of her specialized practice.

## Band 4

### Preti Flaherty Beliveau & Pachios, LLP
See profile on p.1409

**THE FIRM** This solid labor and employment group serves both businesses and individuals on a vast range of matters. The team regularly defends employers in state and federal courts, and advises clients on the successful development, implementation and communication of workplace policies.

**Sources say:** *"They're very accessible." "Quality work – you can trust them."*

**KEY INDIVIDUALS Michael Messerschmidt** (see p.1402) is chair of the firm's labor and employment practice group. He advises both public and private sector employers on issues such as hiring and employee retention, termination, wage and hour, collective bargaining agreements and compliance with employment discrimina-

tion laws. According to an impressed client, he is *"very thorough and well versed in labor law."* **Elizabeth Olivier** (see p.1402) is regarded as extremely knowledgeable as well as *"very likable and personable."* She specializes in both employment and health law, and regularly advises healthcare clients on employment matters.

### The Bennett Law Firm PA

**THE FIRM** This niche firm draws praise for its strength in employment litigation and traditional labor law. The team focuses on developing preventive policies and procedures, avoiding unionization, resolving employment disputes, negotiating collective bargaining agreements, and providing general labor relations and employment guidance.

**Sources say:** *"Small boutique firm with a solid reputation, lots of clients and a long history."*

**KEY INDIVIDUALS** Sources describe firm president **Peter Bennett** as *"very talented"* and *"highly knowledge-*

*able."* His practice concentrates on labor and employment relations and litigation. Peers hail **Frederick Finberg** as *"very practical, reasonable and solution oriented."* His practice covers labor and employment law, civil litigation and administrative law.

### Other Notable Practitioners

**Stephan Bachelder** of Bachelder & Dowling, PA is best known for his executive compensation work, but also has expertise in employee benefits. One peer asserts that he *"is probably the most sophisticated executive compensation lawyer in northern New England."* **Timothy O'Brien** of Libby O'Brien Kingsley, LLC is an experienced litigator and handles employment issues such as wrongful termination, discrimination, wage and hour claims and whistle-blower claims. He is described as *"a good lawyer and a nice guy."*

# LITIGATION

Commentary about individuals can be found under their firm's paragraph. If the firm has no paragraph (is not ranked) look at Other Notable Practitioners.

### Litigation: General Commercial
### Leading Firms

**Band 1**
Pierce Atwood LLP *

**Band 2**
Bernstein Shur *
Drummond Woodsum & MacMahon *
Norman, Hanson & DeTroy, LLC
Preti Flaherty Beliveau & Pachios, LLP *

**Band 3**
Eaton Peabody
Friedman Gaythwaite Wolf & Leavitt LLP
Richardson, Whitman, Large & Badger
Rudman Winchell
Verrill Dana, LLP *

*\* Indicates firm / individual with profile.*
*Alphabetical order within each band. Band 1 is the highest.*

## Litigation: General Commercial
## Band 1

### Pierce Atwood LLP
See profile on p.1408

**THE FIRM** This impressive team maintains a strong reputation nationally and is equipped to handle all varieties of litigation, with experience spanning commercial disputes, class actions and personal injury cases. Pierce Atwood's attorneys frequently appear before state and federal trial courts, appellate courts and agencies. Recently the group

represented TD Bank in a series of nationwide class actions in which the plaintiffs allege that the bank charged unlawful overdraft fees.

**Sources say:** *"It's certainly a very good litigation shop. I have nothing but good things to say about it." "They provide high-quality service at reasonable rates."*

**KEY INDIVIDUALS William Kayatta** (see p.1401) has been nominated to serve as a judge on the United States Courts of Appeals for the First Circuit. He is considered by sources to be a star litigator, and has experience trying cases before the Supreme Court of the United States. *"His record of success speaks for itself,"* says one peer. **Peter Culley** (see p.1398) has a broad practice covering general commercial litigation, product liability, professional liability and environmental litigation. He is deemed an extremely accomplished attorney who has built extensive trial experience throughout his career. **Jeffrey White** (see p.1405) is of counsel at the firm and advises on complex commercial litigation, IP disputes, antitrust and unfair competition issues. He has significant trial and arbitration experience. **Robert Stier** (see p.1404) has a particular focus on technology and science-related litigation, covering issues such as biotechnology patents, embryonic stem cell issues and cloning technology. One source states: *"He's a strategist, a good adviser and a great communicator."* **David Barry** (see p.1397) is chair of the firm's litigation group and also heads the firm's government investigations and white-collar criminal defense team. He handles both complex commercial cases and government enforcement and compliance matters. *"He is incredibly smart and very well spoken,"* say impressed clients. **Clifford Ruprecht** (see p.1404) is

particularly well regarded for his defense of class actions. He recently represented Hannaford Bros in multidistrict litigation, consolidating a number of class actions over a data breach surrounding an electronic payment system. According to one client, *"his advocacy skills are outstanding."* **Catherine Connors** (see p.1398) specializes in civil and criminal appellate litigation, in which she represents both business clients and individuals. She frequently appears within the United States Courts of Appeals system and before the Maine Supreme Judicial Court. Peers and clients praise **Margaret O'Keefe** (see p.1402) for her expertise in intellectual property disputes, describing her as *"very smart, capable and knowledgeable."* She draws on her wide-ranging experience to advise clients in industries such as design, software and music. She recently represented home furnishings design company Angela Adams Licensing in a copyright infringement case against Homestead Holdings, Walmart and others. Described by peers as an *"icon,"* **Ralph Lancaster** (see p.1401) is of counsel at Pierce Atwood. He continues to be an important figure at the firm, with experience across a wide range of civil and criminal cases.

## Litigation: General Commercial
## Band 2

### Bernstein Shur
See profile on p.1406

**THE FIRM** This sizable team of 22 partners offers great breadth, granting it the flexibility to represent both defen-

## Litigation: General Commercial
### Senior Statesmen and Eminent Partners

**Senior Statesmen:** distinguished older partners

| | |
|---|---|
| Lancaster Jr Ralph I | *Pierce Atwood LLP* * |
| Simmons Jack | *Berman & Simmons* |

### Leading Individuals

**Star individuals**

| | |
|---|---|
| Kayatta Jr William | *Pierce Atwood LLP* * |

**Band 1**

| | |
|---|---|
| Culley Peter | *Pierce Atwood LLP* * |
| DeTroy Peter | *Norman, Hanson & DeTroy, LLC* |
| Petruccelli Gerald | *Petruccelli Martin & Haddow LLP (ONP)* † |
| Rubin Peter J | *Bernstein Shur* |
| White Jeffrey M | *Pierce Atwood LLP* * |

**Band 2**

| | |
|---|---|
| Crouter Jerrol A | *Drummond Woodsum & MacMahon* * |
| Dilworth George Toby | *Drummond Woodsum & MacMahon* * |
| Friedman Harold | *Friedman Gaythwaite Wolf & Leavitt LLP* |
| Gaythwaite Martha | *Friedman Gaythwaite Wolf & Leavitt LLP* |
| Hewey Melissa | *Drummond Woodsum & MacMahon* * |
| Kilbreth James | *Drummond Woodsum & MacMahon* * |
| Kubetz Bernard J | *Eaton Peabody* |
| Piper Jonathan S | *Preti Flaherty Beliveau & Pachios, LLP* * |
| Stier Jr Robert H | *Pierce Atwood LLP* * |
| Whitman John S | *Richardson, Whitman, Large & Badger* |

**Band 3**

| | |
|---|---|
| Barry David | *Pierce Atwood LLP* * |
| Chaiken Paul | *Rudman Winchell* |
| Connors Catherine | *Pierce Atwood LLP* * |
| Frawley Alfred | *Law Office of Alfred Frawley (ONP)* † |
| Goggin James G | *Verrill Dana, LLP* * |
| Hansel Greg | *Preti Flaherty Beliveau & Pachios, LLP* * |
| Langer Leonard W | *Thompson & Bowie (ONP)* † * |
| Large Wendell G | *Richardson, Whitman, Large & Badger* |
| McDonald Paul | *Bernstein Shur* |
| Montgomery III John H | *Bernstein Shur* |
| O'Keefe Margaret Minister | *Pierce Atwood LLP* * |
| Pierce Russell | *Norman, Hanson & DeTroy, LLC* |
| Pratt Neal F | *Eaton Peabody* |
| Ruprecht Clifford H | *Pierce Atwood LLP* * |
| Schutz Sigmund | *Preti Flaherty Beliveau & Pachios, LLP* * |

* Indicates individual with profile.
† ONP = Other Notable Practitioner.

## Litigation: Medical Malpractice & Insurance
### Leading Individuals

**Star individuals**

| | |
|---|---|
| Lavoie Mark G | *Norman, Hanson & DeTroy, LLC* |

**Band 1**

| | |
|---|---|
| Garmey Terrence D | *Terry Garmey & Associates* |
| Nyhan Christopher D | *Preti Flaherty Beliveau & Pachios, LLP* * |
| Poliquin James | *Norman, Hanson & DeTroy, LLC* |
| Silin Steven | *Berman & Simmons* |
| Sweet Julian | *Berman & Simmons* |
| Wolf Karen Frink | *Friedman Gaythwaite Wolf & Leavitt LLP* |

**Band 2**

| | |
|---|---|
| Brogan Jonathan | *Norman, Hanson & DeTroy, LLC* |
| Coffin Philip M | *Lambert Coffin (ONP)* † |
| Hovermale Kenneth | *Hovermale Law (ONP)* † |
| King David C | *Rudman Winchell* |
| Large Wendell G | *Richardson, Whitman, Large & Badger* |
| Nofsinger Jodi L | *Berman & Simmons* |
| Rapaport Dan | *Preti Flaherty Beliveau & Pachios, LLP* * |
| Wade Stephen B | *Skelton, Taintor & Abbott (ONP)* † |
| Whitman John S | *Richardson, Whitman, Large & Badger* |

**Band 3**

| | |
|---|---|
| Bloch Emily | *Norman, Hanson & DeTroy, LLC* |
| Druary William | *Marden Dubord Bernier & Stevens (ONP)* † |
| Gideon Benjamin | *Berman & Simmons* |
| Gould Edward | *Gross Minsky & Mogul PA (ONP)* † |
| Martemucci James | *Germani, Martemucci, Riggle & Hill (ONP)* † |
| Taintor Christopher | *Norman, Hanson & DeTroy, LLC* |

## Litigation: Mainly Plaintiff
### Leading Firms

**Band 1**

Berman & Simmons

### Leading Individuals

**Band 1**

| | |
|---|---|
| Garmey Terrence D | *Terry Garmey & Associates (ONP)* † |
| Robitzek William | *Berman & Simmons* |

**Band 2**

| | |
|---|---|
| Gideon Benjamin | *Berman & Simmons* |
| Nofsinger Jodi L | *Berman & Simmons* |
| Silin Steven | *Berman & Simmons* |
| Sweet Julian | *Berman & Simmons* |
| Wade Stephen B | *Skelton, Taintor & Abbott* |

dants and plaintiffs in matters ranging from business disputes to criminal matters. The group represents clients such as Oxford Networks, Topsham Hydro Partners and Maine Municipal Association.

**Sources say:** *"They are very knowledgeable, take a practical approach and are responsive." "It has some very fine lawyers."*

**KEY INDIVIDUALS** Firm president **Peter Rubin** focuses on product liability, business litigation, malpractice and personal injury. One interviewee notes that *"he is highly experienced and diligent, and his judgment is excellent."* **Paul McDonald** chairs the litigation group and is an expert in complex commercial and business cases. He represented Oxford Networks in the successful appeal of the award of a $32 million contract – to replace the state's emergency call system – to a rival bidder. **John Montgomery** is a highly

regarded litigator with experience of energy, insurance, construction and environmental cases. He also chairs the firm's energy and environmental practice group.

### Drummond Woodsum & MacMahon
**See profile on p.1407**

**THE FIRM** This firm handles the full spectrum of civil and criminal litigation, from commercial disputes to personal injury cases to white-collar criminal defense. The team has a particularly good reputation for its work in the education industry and in cases related to Native American tribal rights. Attorneys regularly appear before federal and state courts, administrative agencies and domestic and international arbitration panels.

**Sources say:** *"We are extremely pleased with the service – it's a terrific firm and knows what it's doing."*

**KEY INDIVIDUALS** Clients and peers consider **George Dilworth** (see p.1399) to be a *"very capable lawyer and very talented."* He is an expert in white-collar defense and internal company investigations, and also handles general commercial litigation. **Jerrol Crouter** (see p.1398) is an experienced civil trial attorney, mediator and arbitrator. His expertise includes higher education, construction and employment issues. One client reports: *"His responsiveness is pretty incredible – I've called at 3am and he's responded!"* **Melissa Hewey** (see p.1400) concentrates on school and higher education issues, employment law, insurance defense and general commercial disputes. Her skills as a trial lawyer are singled out for praise by sources. **James Kilbreth** (see p.1401) joined the team from Verrill Dana in 2012 and focuses on commercial and regulatory litigation, with a strong emphasis on environmental concerns. One source describes him as *"an outstanding litigator."*

### Norman, Hanson & DeTroy, LLC

**THE FIRM** This is widely touted as one of Maine's leading firms for insurance defense and medical malpractice work, and also excels in areas such as general commercial litigation and criminal defense cases. The team frequently represents clients in both state and federal courts.

**Sources say:** *"They seem to be evolving and strengthening into all areas of litigation. Their lawyers are all very talented."*

**KEY INDIVIDUALS** **Mark Lavoie** is recognized as being *"preeminent"* in the medical malpractice defense domain. He also represents businesses and individuals in insurance, commercial and employment claims. *"He's an excellent defense lawyer,"* say peers. *"Tremendous"* **Peter DeTroy** frequently handles matters for businesses, insurance companies, individuals and families. He is known as an excellent litigator, arbitrator and mediator. One source states that *"he's got wisdom and common sense."* **James Poliquin** concentrates on resolving insurance coverage disputes. Sources pick him out as one of the best in his field in Maine, identifying him as an *"outstanding attorney."* Practice chair **Jonathan Brogan** focuses mainly on medical malpractice and personal injury defense, as well as a healthy number of product liability cases. According to one interviewee, he is *"a great trial lawyer and a great guy."* **Emily Bloch** earns recognition for her work representing the interests of healthcare providers over licensing and medical malpractice matters. **Russell Pierce** has a varied litigation practice, including complex commercial disputes, professional negligence and environmental claims. He acts for individuals, businesses and nonprofit organizations. Much of **Christopher Taintor**'s practice is focused on medical malpractice cases, where he frequently represents healthcare providers and professionals. He also advises individuals on insurance coverage disputes.

### Preti Flaherty Beliveau & Pachios, LLP
**See profile on p.1409**

**THE FIRM** With more than 30 attorneys in its litigation team, Preti Flaherty offers an understanding of a wide range of disputes. The group has expertise in areas such as antitrust, construction, environmental matters and medical malpractice, as well as significant strength in general commercial litigation.

**Sources say:** *"This is a firm that provides really good value and expertise." "They've done an excellent job."*

**KEY INDIVIDUALS Christopher Nyhan** (see p.1402) is an imposing presence in the medical malpractice domain, and also tackles issues relating to antitrust, employment disputes and product liability. He is applauded by peers for his success in a large number of cases. **Dan Rapaport** (see p.1403) handles cases relating to personal injury, medical malpractice defense, insurance defense and workers' compensation. Sources describe him as a *"highly skilled"* defense attorney and say he is regularly involved in *"very high-level work."* Managing partner **Jonathan Piper** (see p.1403) is an expert in litigation and arbitration, and represents clients in a wide range of commercial matters. **Greg Hansel** (see p.1400) is particularly well regarded for his involvement in complex antitrust matters. He recently recovered $18.5 million for a group of ready-mix concrete buyers in an antitrust class action concerning price fixing. **Sigmund Schutz** (see p.1404) is a talented litigator with a strong understanding of areas such as environmental and media law. He recently represented MaineToday Media in a high-profile case involving a dance instructor accused of turning her studio into a brothel. Sources praise his *"strong negotiation skills."*

## Litigation: General Commercial
## Band 3

### Eaton Peabody

**THE FIRM** Eaton Peabody's litigation team offers the full range of dispute resolution services. It acts for both individuals and businesses from Maine, the continental USA and Canada, and has particular experience in representing insurance companies before courts and regulatory agencies.

**Sources say:** *"Their strengths are responsiveness, thoroughness and a real focus on the client's needs."*

**KEY INDIVIDUALS** Sources describe **Bernard Kubetz** as an *"outstanding"* trial attorney. He focuses his practice on commercial litigation, personal injury and product liability cases. **Neal Pratt** recently joined Eaton Peabody from Preti Flaherty, bringing significant expertise in complex civil litigation to the group. Peers note that *"he has a good reputation"* and *"people respect him."*

### Friedman Gaythwaite Wolf & Leavitt LLP

**THE FIRM** This boutique firm is home to a substantial team of experienced trial lawyers. The group is equipped to handle complex cases across a wide variety of areas, including product liability, personal injury, environmental disputes, insurance litigation and general commercial litigation. The group also specializes in being brought into cases that are very close to going to trial.

**Sources say:** *"A top trial outfit."*

**KEY INDIVIDUALS Karen Wolf** is prized as one of the state's leading medical malpractice defense attorneys. *"She does an excellent job,"* say enthusiastic sources. **Harold Friedman** is well regarded for his work across a variety of catastrophic loss, professional liability and commercial cases. One source describes him as a *"terrifically capable lawyer."* **Martha Gaythwaite** is a seasoned litigator who has proven her mettle in a variety of cases, including product liability defense, commercial litigation, personal injury and professional malpractice. One interviewee states: *"She's acutely smart, well organized and a very effective advocate in front of the jury."*

### Richardson, Whitman, Large & Badger

**THE FIRM** Based in Portland and Bangor, this well-regarded firm has 12 attorneys with a focus on commercial and civil litigation. The group frequently represents individuals, businesses and insurance companies across the state.

**KEY INDIVIDUALS John Whitman** is an esteemed practitioner with particular strength in legal malpractice defense and insurance litigation. Interviewees say that he is *"very strong in insurance"* and *"an excellent lawyer and a good guy."* **Wendell Large** is an experienced trial attorney with expertise in professional liability, product liability, commercial transportation and personal injury cases. One source states: *"He has a wonderful command of the court."*

### Rudman Winchell

**THE FIRM** This Bangor-based group handles a broad array of civil and criminal matters for clients ranging from individuals to large international corporations. The team is skilled in guiding clients through all elements of pre-trial counseling and information gathering, and has significant expertise in trying cases.

**KEY INDIVIDUALS David King** chairs the group and is particularly well regarded for his work in insurance litigation. He is a highly experienced attorney with a track record of trying cases to a successful verdict in state and federal courts. **Paul Chaiken** adds further strength to the team, drawing on his previous experience as a president of the Maine Bar Association. One source says that he is *"very confident and thoughtful."*

### Verrill Dana, LLP
See profile on p.1410

**THE FIRM** This accomplished group impresses with its ability to handle a wide range of disputes, offering a solid presence in product liability, toxic tort and franchise litigation. The team is equipped to provide alternative dispute resolution services, and is accomplished in litigating at both state and federal courts. Notable clients include Kardex Remstar, Bowdoin College and Verizon Wireless.

**Sources say:** *"Verrill Dana has a very strong and sophisticated practice." "A strong quality-to-value proposition and outstanding expertise."*

**KEY INDIVIDUALS James Goggin** (see p.1399) excels at intellectual property litigation, in which he handles matters relating to trade marks, patents, copyright infringement and trade secret disputes. He recently represented

jewelry manufacturer JewelPops in a lawsuit against Royal Chain alleging copyright infringement.

## Litigation: Mainly Plaintiff
## Band 1

### Berman & Simmons

**THE FIRM** Operating out of offices in Portland, Bangor and Lewiston, Berman & Simmons is widely recognized as the leading plaintiffs' personal injury and medical malpractice firm in the state. The group is hailed for its excellent track record in trying cases, and covers a comprehensive array of matters involving personal injury and negligence. Clients include individuals and families, injured workers and some small businesses.

**Sources say:** *"An outstanding firm – clearly at top of the pile in terms of the kind of work that they do." "They are terrific lawyers with a unique skill set."*

**KEY INDIVIDUALS Steven Silin** is well respected as a highly experienced litigator, specializing in claims involving medical malpractice, personal injury and product liability. Peers describe him as *"an outstanding lawyer"* and *"immensely talented."* **William Robitzek** has a reputation as a leading trial attorney in Maine, offering a wealth of experience in the personal injury domain. He is known for handling complex cases spanning areas such as wrongful death and catastrophic injury. **Jodi Nofsinger** is a talented personal injury and medical malpractice attorney with a background in biology and medical issues. She is noted for her active practice and has represented clients in counties across Maine. **Benjamin Gideon** has a broad practice covering areas such as product liability, malpractice and nursing home negligence. He is known for his success trying cases in both state and federal courts. **Jack Simmons** has been admitted to practice for over four decades and remains an important figure at the firm. He is a seasoned litigator with experience in a broad range of complex tort and medical malpractice cases. **Julian Sweet** applies his wide-ranging trial experience to personal injury and medical malpractice cases. He is characterized by one source as *"the best malpractice lawyer in the state on the plaintiff side."*

### Other Notable Practitioners

**Terrence Garmey** of Terry Garmey & Associates is a standout attorney in the fields of medical malpractice, product liability and personal injury. He brings a national reputation to his work on plaintiff cases. **Gerald Petruccelli** of Petruccelli Martin & Haddow LLP is a highly experienced litigator and appellate attorney. He also serves as an adjunct professor at the University of Maine School of Law Faculty. **Philip Coffin** of Lambert Coffin has developed a reputation as an extremely talented attorney. *"He is very skilled in medical malpractice defense. He knows this field very well,"* reports one interviewee. Coffin has more than 25 years' experience trying cases before both federal and state courts. **Kenneth Hovermale** focuses his practice on medical malpractice and personal injury work. One source states that *"he understands medicine and does a good job."*

Stephen Wade of Skelton, Taintor & Abbott draws on more than 30 years of experience to represent both defendants and plaintiffs in an array of medical malpractice, personal injury and product liability cases. *"Charismatic"* William Druary of Marden Dubord Bernier & Stevens enters the rankings this year, backed by a raft of glowing feedback. He is best known for taking an array of insurance and medical malpractice cases to trial. Sole practitioner Alfred Frawley focuses on intellectual property disputes and complex business litigation. He is able to offer businesses of all sizes guidance on a variety of trademark, licensing and copyright disputes. Leonard Langer (see p.1401) is of counsel at Thompson & Bowie, and is particularly well respected for his expertise in admiralty and maritime law. Edward Gould of Gross Minsky & Mogul PA has a broad practice with a significant focus on insurance defense and personal injury law. Sources consider him to be a significant presence in the Maine market. James Martemucci of Germani, Martemucci, Riggle & Hill is highlighted for his grasp of criminal law, and also represents clients in medical malpractice and civil litigation suits. *"He's really arrived on the scene"* and is *"making his name"* in medical malpractice defense, says an enthusiastic source.

# REAL ESTATE

Commentary about individuals can be found under their firm's paragraph. If the firm has no paragraph (is not ranked) look at Other Notable Practitioners.

## Real Estate
### Leading Firms

**Band 1**

Bernstein Shur *

Pierce Atwood LLP *

Verrill Dana, LLP *

**Band 2**

Drummond Woodsum & MacMahon *

Jensen Baird Gardner & Henry

**Band 3**

Eaton Peabody

Preti Flaherty Beliveau & Pachios, LLP *

Rudman Winchell

\* *Indicates firm / individual with profile.*

† *ONP = Other Notable Practitioner.*

## Real Estate
### Senior Statesmen and Eminent Partners

**Senior Statesmen: distinguished older partners**

| | |
|---|---|
| Oestreicher Charles R | Verrill Dana, LLP * |

### Leading Individuals

**Band 1**

| | |
|---|---|
| Keeler Dennis C | Pierce Atwood LLP * |
| Miller Charles E | Bernstein Shur |
| Schwartz Jaimie Paul | Bernstein Shur |
| Smith Nathan H | Bernstein Shur |

**Band 2**

| | |
|---|---|
| Calcagni Anthony M | Verrill Dana, LLP * |
| Fowler Donald | Donald A. Fowler, Jr. (ONP)† |
| Hanson Tom S | Bernstein Shur |
| Lowry Leslie | Jensen Baird Gardner & Henry |
| Shinay Richard | Drummond Woodsum & MacMahon * |
| Welch William M | Bernstein Shur |
| Woodbury Judith Fletcher | Pierce Atwood LLP * |

**Band 3**

| | |
|---|---|
| Adams Eben | Pierce Atwood LLP * |
| Anderson Drew | Murray, Plumb & Murray (ONP)† |
| Huber Karen A | Eaton Peabody |
| Pietropaoli Paul D | Perkins Thompson (ONP)† |
| Prentice Richard D | Pierce Atwood LLP * |
| Smith Richard | Bernstein Shur |
| Van Hemel Peter | Bernstein Shur |

**Band 4**

| | |
|---|---|
| Crowell C Wesley | Bergen & Parkinson LLC (ONP)† |
| Galgay David | Verrill Dana, LLP * |
| Lane Michael L | Preti Flaherty Beliveau & Pachios * |
| Palmer James C | Verrill Dana, LLP * |
| Pelletier Raymond A | Verrill Dana, LLP * |
| Vogel Gary | Drummond Woodsum & MacMahon * |

**Up-and-coming individuals**

| | |
|---|---|
| Greenfield Rebecca | Pierce Atwood LLP * |

**Associates to watch**

| | |
|---|---|
| Strait Hawley | Bernstein Shur |

## Real Estate: Timberland/Conservation
### Leading Individuals

**Band 1**

| | |
|---|---|
| Beaupain Dean | Dean A. Beaupain (ONP)† |
| Hanson William H | Rudman Winchell |
| Huber Karen A | Eaton Peabody |
| Nolan Eliza M Cope | Bernstein Shur |
| Selser Jeffrey T | Verrill Dana, LLP * |

**Band 2**

| | |
|---|---|
| Pelletier Raymond A | Verrill Dana, LLP * |
| Scannell J Gordon | Perkins Thompson (ONP)† |

**Associates to watch**

| | |
|---|---|
| Katz-Leavy Charlie | Verrill Dana, LLP * |

## Band 1

### Bernstein Shur
See profile on p.1406

**THE FIRM** With an outstanding real estate team of 25 attorneys, Bernstein Shur remains a key player in Maine, and is commended for its breadth, depth and client-focused approach. In addition to its strength in traditional real estate development work, the group is active in advising energy clients on the real estate elements of wind power, hydropower and transmission projects. Key clients include The Haughey Company, Bluefin Investors and First Wind.

**Sources say:** *"They focus on what's important for their clients." "They are very, very thorough, as you must be in the world of real estate and titles."*

**KEY INDIVIDUALS Charles Miller** is Bernstein Shur's CEO as well as a member of the real estate group. He is admired for his broad multistate practice, which covers a comprehensive array of real estate matters. Commentators praise his ability to offer advice on *"bigger-picture issues."* **Eliza Cope Nolan** maintains an esteemed real estate conservation practice. Clients include natural resource-based companies, land conservation organizations, wind power developers and individuals. Group chair **Jaimie Schwartz** is well equipped to serve clients on a variety of real estate matters and has an excellent reputation for his work on energy developments and projects. Areas of focus include complex deal structuring and title insurance coverage. One interviewee describes him as *"very pleasant and very professional."* **Nathan Smith** has more than 28 years' experience in real estate law. He is particularly well respected for handling large-scale development projects and complex energy-related transactions. **Tom Hanson** is well known for his proficiency in handling commercial real estate transactions. A source asserts: *"Tom Hanson is one of the best lawyers in finance law and loan workouts in Maine."* Deemed *"highly competent and nice to work with,"* **William Welch** concentrates on areas such as leasing, acquisitions, sales, financing and title insurance. One satisfied client says: *"He's the best real estate attorney in town."* **Peter Van Hemel**'s practice covers areas such as commercial lease negotiations, real estate transactions and energy-related project development. He also has experience working with clients in the casino and gaming sector. Sources praise him as *"very precise, detail-oriented, efficient and knowledgeable."* Admitted to practice in both Maine and New Hampshire, **Richard Smith** has a wealth of experience in real estate, and has a particular focus on the retail and energy sectors. *"He is pleasant to work with, fair and conscientious,"* says one observer. **Hawley Strait** is an associate at the firm and is rapidly developing an excellent reputation among peers and clients. He frequently represents banking institutions, real estate developers and individuals. *"He's very quick to respond to my needs,"* says an impressed client.

### Pierce Atwood LLP
See profile on p.1408

**THE FIRM** Pierce Atwood remains one of the most prominent firms in Maine for real estate work, with expertise spanning all areas of real estate development and management. The group continues to attract an impressive array of clients such as Central Maine Power, the Dead River Company and Nestlé Waters North America. Recently, the firm's attorneys highlighted their dexterity in the real estate domain with the opening of their new offices in Merrill's Wharf, Portland, which required the complex redevelopment and leasing of a large, underutilized warehouse.

**Sources say:** *"One thing I love about the firm is that I can call the direct line to any attorney." "They did a magnificent job."*

**KEY INDIVIDUALS Dennis Keeler** (see p.1401) focuses on complex permitting and development work. He recently advised Hannaford Bros. on the development and lease arrangements of a number of its stores across New England and New York state. Head of Pierce Atwood's real estate group, **Judith Fletcher Woodbury** (see p.1405) is a highly experienced attorney. She has a fantastic reputation for tackling the real estate elements of complex projects around New England. One highlight was assisting Cate Street Capital with the acquisition, disposal and financing of a number of its portfolio companies. **Eben Adams** (see p.1397) receives excellent feedback from both peers and clients, who agree that *"he's a high-quality lawyer."* He has a broad practice, covering the full range of real estate issues. *"He is wonderful. He's so mindful of our money,"* says an impressed client. **Richard Prentice** (see p.1403) is best known for his leasing and franchise work. He continues to act for two franchisees of Five Guys Enterprises to negotiate leases for Five Guys Burgers & Fries restaurants across the USA. One commentator reports: *"He's a very competent guy, good value and capable."* **Rebecca Greenfield** (see p.1400) was recently promoted to partner and has established a well-respected practice, with a focus on transactional real estate work. Peers agree that she is *"up-and-coming"* in the field.

## Verrill Dana, LLP
See profile on p.1410

**THE FIRM** This leading firm handles the full range of real estate matters, taking center stage for its frequent representation of energy clients and its much-admired timberlands practice group. The group is able to draw on the expertise of attorneys in other practice areas for a seamless service. Key clients include First Wind and Maine Governmental Facilities Authority, and on the timberlands side, Huber Resources and Plum Creek Timber.

**Sources say:** *"The quality of drafting at Verrill Dana is excellent."*

**KEY INDIVIDUALS Jeffrey Selser** (see p.1404) is chair of the firm's timberlands group and has been involved in a variety of transactions across the USA and Latin America. He recently played a key role in multiple noteworthy deals, including the largest timberland sale in the USA since 2005. **Anthony Calcagni** (see p.1398) is frequently involved in high-value real estate projects. A recent work highlight was representing First Wind in the real estate aspects of a 34 MW wind power project in Hancock County. One source states: *"He's an excellent attorney; prac-*

*tical, reasonable and very bright."* **Raymond Pelletier** (see p.1403) is a member of both the real estate and the timberlands teams. According to an impressed client, he has a *"nearly encyclopedic knowledge of timberland in Maine."* He recently acted for J.M. Huber on a number of complex timberlands purchases and sales totaling some $192 million. Experienced real estate attorney **James Palmer** (see p.1403) regularly represents lenders and developers in a range of transactions. He recently advised GHK Company on a $7.75 million refinancing of a multitenant property. One client states: *"His leases are clear and concise. He's a deal-maker, not breaker."* **David Galgay** (see p.1399) enters the rankings this year, with clients and peers agreeing that he is *"a very capable transactional lawyer."* He has significant expertise in the commercial lending area and is vice chair of the real estate group. A work highlight was advising Maine Governmental Facilities Authority on a new courthouse to be built in Augusta. With more than 40 years' experience at the firm, **Charles Oestreicher** (see p.1402) remains a leading authority in the real estate domain. He is senior counsel at the firm and adept in solving complex real estate problems. **Charlie Katz-Leavy** (see p.1401), an associate at the firm, has an excellent reputation in the timberlands sector. He has gained experience in some highly significant timberlands transactions, and is developing an expertise in both commercial and residential real estate.

## Band 2

### Drummond Woodsum & MacMahon
See profile on p.1407

**THE FIRM** This respected firm continues to expand its real estate practice, handling all aspects of permitting, purchase, development and sales. The group frequently represents clients regionally and nationally, as well as Canadian clients with US operations. The team is well known for advising municipal and educational clients.

**KEY INDIVIDUALS Richard Shinay** (see p.1404) concentrates on real estate, land use and land conservation law. His wide-ranging expertise spans areas such as title and conveyancing matters, title insurance underwriting, conservation easements, and condominium and planned unit development projects. **Gary Vogel** (see p.1405) has a broad practice with a significant focus on commercial real estate and affordable housing transactions. He has experience acting for a wide array of clients, including real estate developers, banks and nonprofit organizations.

### Jensen Baird Gardner & Henry

**THE FIRM** This reputable midsized firm is capable of advising clients on a broad range of real estate matters, from residential closures to large commercial transactions. Clients include developers, lenders, commercial landlords and tenants as well as private individuals.

**KEY INDIVIDUALS** Described by sources as a *"great attorney,"* **Leslie Lowry** has significant expertise in areas such as leasing, commercial transactions, and title and

conveyancing issues. He is also experienced in appearing before municipal, state and federal regulatory entities.

## Band 3

### Eaton Peabody

**THE FIRM** This firm is held in high regard for its real estate and timberlands services. The team is able to draw on the strength of Eaton Peabody's other practice areas, such as tax, environmental and land use, and litigation, to cover the full range of issues facing clients.

**KEY INDIVIDUALS Karen Huber** is chair of the firm's timberlands group, and is experienced in complex commercial and timberlands transactions. She receives glowing feedback, with sources describing her as *"a great, highly practical, very smart lawyer"* as well as *"very thorough and thoughtful."*

### Preti Flaherty Beliveau & Pachios, LLP
See profile on p.1409

**THE FIRM** This group continues to impress with its commercial real estate services, covering areas such as acquisitions, easements, permitting and commercial lending. The team often collaborates with the firm's litigation department to tackle real estate disputes.

**Sources say:** *"They're able to handle whatever we throw at them."*

**KEY INDIVIDUALS Michael Lane** (see p.1401) has experience in a diversity of real estate and land use issues, including some timberlands matters. Clients praise his *"no-nonsense approach"* and say he is *"very efficient."*

### Rudman Winchell

**THE FIRM** This Bangor-based outlet is recognized by sources for its strong timberlands background. In addition to clients in the timber industry, the firm represents an array of banks, developers, municipalities and individuals.

**Sources say:** *"They are a Northern powerhouse."*

**KEY INDIVIDUALS William Hanson** is lauded by sources for his dexterity in the timberlands domain. One commentator notes that he is *"very thorough and reasonable."*

### Other Notable Practitioners

Sole practitioner **Dean Beaupain** wins praise for his outstanding timberlands practice. *"He's dynamite!"* says one commentator. *"He's so much more than a lawyer for his clients. He's a valued confidant."* Kingfield-based sole practitioner **Donald Fowler** is widely lauded as one of the leading real estate lawyers in the state. Clients have highlighted his consummate professionalism and personal warmth. In the past five years, **Gordon Scannell** of Perkins Thompson has been involved in a wide variety of timberlands transactions totaling some $200 million. He also frequently advises individuals, businesses, lenders, borrowers and municipalities on real estate matters. Commercial real estate attorney **Drew Anderson** serves as managing director of Murray, Plumb & Murray, and has a varied practice, covering both corporate and real estate law. He receives warm praise for his *"detail-oriented"* approach. **Paul Pietropaoli** is chair of Perkins Thompson's real estate department and focuses on commercial, residential and industrial issues. He also assists clients on brownfield redevelopment and

general business law. **Wesley Crowell** of Bergen & Parkinson LLC is noted for his expertise in a diverse range of real estate matters, as well as his significant experience in business planning and finance issues.

# Leaders' Profiles in Maine

### ADAMS, Eben
Pierce Atwood LLP, Portland
207 791 1175
eadams@pierceatwood.com
*Featured in Real Estate (Maine)*
**Practice Areas:** Eben's practice includes all aspects of real estate law with a focus on commercial and residential development, acquisitions, sales and leasing. Eben has extensive experience representing developers of condominium projects including residential, commercial and mixed-use condominiums. Eben regularly assists energy companies with real estate matters including wind power leases and transmission corridors.
**Career:** Prior to joining Pierce Atwood in 2000, Eben served as a law clerk to the United States District Court Judge Gene Carter.

### AHRENS, Philip FW
Pierce Atwood LLP, Portland
207 791 1298
pahrens@pierceatwood.com
*Featured in Environment (Maine)*
**Practice Areas:** Has concentrated on environmental matters almost exclusively since 1977. Counsels clients on complex and high visibility permitting and enforcement matters before the Maine Department of Environmental Protection, the Maine Land Use Regulation Commission, and other state and federal environmental agencies.
**Professional Memberships:** ABA, Section of Environment, Energy and Resources; Maine Bar Association; American College of Environmental Lawyers.
**Career:** Deputy Attorney General and Chief, Natural Resources Section, Maine Attorney General's Office (1977-90).
**Publications:** Maine Environmental and Land Use Statutes Deskbook.
**Personal:** JD, University of Michigan Law School, 1975; BA, Amherst College (cum laude), 1968; US Navy, 1968-72.

### ALTHOLZ, Eric
Verrill Dana, LLP, Portland
207 774 4000
ealtholz@verrilldana.com
*Featured in Labor & Employment (Maine)*
**Practice Areas:** Employee benefits and executive compensation, healthcare, tax exempt organizations.

**Career:** Mr Altholz counsels employers in a wide variety of employee benefit and executive compensation matters, with special emphasis on executive compensation, deferred compensation plans, fiduciary compliance and the special issues that are of concern to tax-exempt employers. He also maintains an active corporate practice in the health care industry, serving as general counsel to private medical groups and advising them on corporate transactions, physician employment and compensation matters.
**Personal:** Education: University of Chicago (JD, 1987); Columbia University (BS, 1982; MIA 1983).

### ANDERSON, Scott
Verrill Dana, LLP, Portland
207 774 4000
sanderson@verrilldana.com
*Featured in Environment (Maine)*
**Practice Areas:** Environmental, energy, timberlands, administrative law.
**Career:** Mr Anderson's practice is focused on representing parties in environmental matters in administrative, regulatory and litigation proceedings. He is experienced in assisting individuals and corporations in obtaining and defending federal, state and local environmental and land use permits, and has litigated matters in state and federal court involving state natural resource laws, local land use regulations, and federal environmental laws, including CERCLA, the Clean Water Act, and the Federal Power Act.
**Personal:** Education: University of Massachusetts (BA, 1992); Boston College Law School (JD, 1999).

### BARRY, David
Pierce Atwood LLP, Portland
207 791 1376
dbarry@pierceatwood.com
*Featured in Litigation (Maine)*
**Practice Areas:** Dave is Chair of the firm's Litigation Group and heads its Government Investigations and White Collar Criminal Defense practice. He regularly manages complex business litigation in federal and state courts and he has extensive experience assisting clients with government enforcement and compliance matters involving potential criminal penalties. Dave's practice includes representing corporate and indi-

vidual clients in connection with internal investigations and federal and state criminal and regulatory investigations and enforcement matters.
**Professional Memberships:** Member, Maine State Bar Association; Member, Maine Trial Lawyers Association.
**Personal:** University of Notre Dame Law School, JD, cum laude, (1986); Williams College, BA, (1982).

### BODEN, Kelly
Verrill Dana, LLP, Portland
kboden@verrilldana.com
*Featured in Environment (Maine)*
**Practice Areas:** Environmental, timberlands, energy, telecommunications.
**Career:** Kelly represents individual and corporate clients in a variety of transactional, permitting and regulatory compliance matters, including project permitting under federal, state, and local laws. She works with developers of several large scale energy infrastructure projects, including multiple wind power projects under active development and/or construction, as well as the proponent of a recent expansion of existing interstate natural gas pipeline facilities. In addition, she represents individuals and companies in municipal land use proceedings involving site plan review and shoreland zoning.
**Personal:** Education: Vermont Law School (JD, 2000); Bowdoin College (AB, 1996).

### BOEHM, Lisa
Verrill Dana, LLP, Portland
207 774 4000
lboehm@verrilldana.com
*Featured in Labor & Employment (Maine)*
**Practice Areas:** Employee benefits and executive compensation.
**Career:** Ms Boehm's practice focuses exclusively in the areas of employee benefits and executive compensation, with a particular emphasis on the design and operation of 401(k) plans, IRS correction programs for qualified retirement plans, and ERISA fiduciary duties and responsibilities.
**Personal:** Education: Hamilton College (BA, magna cum laude, Phi Beta Kappa 1985); Duke University School of Law (JD, 1988).

### BROOKS, Robert C
Verrill Dana, LLP, Portland
207 774 4000
rbrooks@verrilldana.com
*Featured in Labor & Employment (Maine)*
**Practice Areas:** Construction, labor and employment.
**Career:** Mr Brooks's practice is focused on providing advice and representation to management on all aspects of the employment relationship. He has successfully handled matters related to union organizing campaigns, collective bargaining, unfair labor practice charges, strikes and arbitration. He has significant experience handling claims for wrongful discharge, discrimination, unpaid wages and breach of non-compete and non-solicitation agreements.
**Personal:** Education: Harvard University (AB, 1987); University of Maine School of Law (JD, 1991).

### BROWNE, Juliet T
Verrill Dana, LLP, Portland
207 774 4000
jbrowne@verrilldana.com
*Featured in Environment (Maine)*
**Practice Areas:** Energy, environmental, timberlands.
**Career:** As Chair of the firm's Environmental Law Group and Co-Chair of the Energy Group, Ms Browne's practice encompasses all aspects of environmental law, including permitting under federal, state and local laws, compliance with federal and state environmental laws, litigation in state and federal courts, redevelopment of contaminated properties and transactional matters. Ms Browne has extensive experience in the development and permitting of energy facilities, including wind power, transmission lines, interstate natural gas pipelines, and landfill gas-to-energy facilities.
**Personal:** Education: University of Michigan (BA, 1984); University of California Boalt Hall School of Law (JD, 1990).

### BUXTON, Anthony
Preti Flaherty Beliveau & Pachios, LLP, Portland
207 623 5300
abuxton@preti.com
*Featured in Energy & Natural Resources (Maine)*

**Practice Areas:** Energy Law and Policy before Federal agencies, Regional Transmission Organizations, State Utility Commissions and Congressional and Legislative bodies; Strategic Infrastructure Development such as pipelines and quarries; Complex Energy Asset Transactions, Large Manufacturer Energy Representation on Grid Access, Demand Response, energy purchases and sales, renewable energy projects, behind the meter generation protection, Climate Strategy development, including renewable energy and RGGI credits; complex compliance strategies, Legislative representation on energy issues.

**Professional Memberships:** Admitted in Maine; US Courts of Appeals for the First Circuit and District of Columbia Circuit. Member of the Maine State Bar Association and American Bar Association. Best Lawyers in America; New England Super Lawyers, Energy and Natural Resources.

**Career:** Chair of Energy and Telecommunications Law Group, Co-Chair of Climate Strategy Group. Advises on major energy and other infrastructure development. Structures entities to finance, construct and/or operate energy projects. Advises clients on tax, corporate and other legal implications of energy project purchases, sale and development and energy efficiency implementation. Assists businesses and telecommunications, government and NGO's on greenhouse gas policy development.

**Personal:** University of New Hampshire School of Law (Franklin Pierce Law Center), JD, 1978; Bowdoin College, BA, 1968; Kents Hill School, 1964; Law Clerk, Hon. Hugh Bownes, US Court of Appeals for the First Circuit, 1979-80; Co-Founder, The Energy Law Institute.

## CALCAGNI, Anthony M
Verrill Dana, LLP, Portland
207 774 4000
acalcagni@verrilldana.com
*Featured in Real Estate (Maine)*

**Practice Areas:** Real estate.

**Career:** Mr Calcagni practices Real Estate Law, with an emphasis on sales and leasing of commercial property, easements and title matters, zoning and land use, and community associations. Since joining Verrill Dana in 1994, Mr Calcagni has represented individuals and businesses, including a number of the State's water districts and electric, gas, and wind energy companies, in a wide range of real estate matters.

**Personal:** Education: Washington University (BS, 1991); University of Pennsylvania (JD, 1994).

## CATERINE, Melinda J
Fisher & Phillips LLP, Portland
207 774 6001
mcaterine@laborlawyers.com
*Featured in Labor & Employment (Maine)*

**Career:** Melinda Caterine is a Partner in the Portland, Maine and Boston offices. She has practiced labor and employment law on behalf of management for more than twenty years. Melinda has practiced in the federal and state courts of Maine, New Hampshire, and Massachusetts, as well as before a number of federal and state agen-

cies in several New England states where she has litigated numerous sexual harassment, employment discrimination, wrongful discharge and employment contract dispute cases. She has also served as an Adjunct Professor at the University of Maine School of Law where she taught a course on Employment Discrimination.

## CHAMPOUX, David
Pierce Atwood LLP, Portland
207 791 1364
DChampoux@PierceAtwood.com
*Featured in Corporate/M&A (Maine)*

**Practice Areas:** Corporate, finance, and general transactional representation, including all aspects of corporate, securities, and commercial law, focusing on representing corporations and individuals in a wide variety of transactional settings. Experience includes: securities law; special purpose entities such as limited liability companies; M&A; venture capital financing; SEC reporting and compliance.

**Professional Memberships:** New York Bar (1985); Maine Bar (1987); Massachusetts Bar (2009).

**Career:** Partner, (1993-). Listed in a leading legal publication, 2003-12 editions, for corporate, M&A, and securities.

**Personal:** University of Virginia School of Law, JD 1984; Editor, Virginia Law Review; Harvard College, AB(cum laude) 1981.

## CLEMENT JR, Roger A
Verrill Dana, LLP, Portland
207 774 4000
rclement@verrilldana.com
*Featured in Corporate/M&A (Maine)*

**Practice Areas:** Bankruptcy and commercial law, international law.

**Professional Memberships:** American Bankruptcy Institute.

**Career:** As Chair of the firm's Bankruptcy and Commercial Law Department, Mr Clement's practice focuses on representing debtors and creditors in business bankruptcies, commercial litigation, commercial restructurings, and other matters relating to financial distress and insolvency. He has extensive experience in representing Chapter 11 debtors-in-possession, Chapter 11 trustees, creditors' committees, secured creditors and landlords in local, regional and national Chapter 11 cases.

**Personal:** Education: Bowdoin College (AB, 1986); University of Maine School of Law (JD, 1991).

## COGGESHALL, Bruce A
Pierce Atwood LLP, Portland
207 791 1234
bcoggeshall@pierceatwood.com
*Featured in Corporate/M&A (Maine)*

**Practice Areas:** Bruce's practice spans a broad range of corporate and commercial disciplines, including corporate governance, commercial finance, mergers and acquisitions and public finance. He also has many years of experience in business formation, drafting and interpreting contracts, handling complex financial and M&A transactions.

**Professional Memberships:** Member of the Cumberland County, Maine State, and American Bar Associations; National Association of Bond Lawyers; National Conference of Commissioners on Uniform State Laws; Maine Bar Foundation; American Bar Foundation; and American Law Institute.

**Personal:** AB, Dartmouth College; LLB, Cornell University. Member, Maine Economic Development Incentive Commission. Board Member, Maine and Company.

## COHEN, James I.
Verrill Dana, LLP, Portland
207 774 4000
jcohen@verrilldana.com
*Featured in Energy & Natural Resources (Maine)*

**Practice Areas:** Banking and financial services; energy; government and public relations; telecommunications; water and wastewater; mediation and facilitation.

**Career:** Mr Cohen chairs Verrill Dana's Banking Group, and serves as a Director of Maine Street Solutions, Verrill Dana's government relations arm. MrCohen also chairs the firm's Telecommunications Group, and he is a member of the firm's Energy, Water and Wastewater, and Alternative Dispute Resolution Groups. Mr Cohen helps clients with regulatory and legislative matters before the Maine PUC, the Maine Legislature, and other state agencies.

**Personal:** Princeton University (AB, 1987); Columbia University (JD, 1991) Former Mayor, City of Portland, Maine.

## CONNORS, Catherine
Pierce Atwood LLP, Portland
207 791 1389
cconnors@pierceatwood.com
*Featured in Litigation (Maine)*

**Practice Areas:** Cathy practices primarily in the area of appellate litigation - both civil and criminal - in the federal and state courts, including petitions for review of administrative decisions. She has argued over 100 appeals, primarily in the United States Courts of Appeals and the Maine Supreme Judicial Court.

**Professional Memberships:** Elected as a fellow of the American Academy of Appellate Lawyers in 2005. Fellow of the Maine Bar Foundation. Member of the First Circuit Advisory Committee on Rules.

**Personal:** BA, Northwestern University (Phi Beta Kappa). JD, Northwestern University School of Law (Order of the Coif).

## COUCH, Kimberly S
Verrill Dana, LLP, Portland
207 774 4000
kcouch@verrilldana.com
*Featured in Labor & Employment (Maine)*

**Practice Areas:** Employee benefits and executive compensation.

**Professional Memberships:** Committee on Employee Benefits, Taxation Section, American Bar Association.

**Career:** Ms Couch's practice covers the areas of employee benefits and executive compensation, with special expertise in defined benefit pension

plans, COBRA compliance, self-insured health plans and all aspects of employee benefit plans of tax-exempt employers.

**Personal:** University of Vermont (BA, 1981); George Washington University (JD, 1984).

## COUPE, Bradford W
Verrill Dana, LLP, Portland
207 774 4000
bcoupe@verrilldana.com
*Featured in Labor & Employment (Maine)*

**Practice Areas:** Labor law

**Career:** Mr Coupe's practice is concentrated in labor law and labor relations in a variety of industries with particular emphasis on the construction industry. He handles labor negotiations and advises clients in all facets of the labor-management collective bargaining relationship, including advice on interpretation/administration of labor agreements, representation in enforcement of rights and defense of claims arising out of the collective bargaining relationship, and in response to labor disruption.

**Personal:** New York University School of Law (LLM, 1971); Marshall-Wythe School of Law, College of William and Mary (JD, 1966); University of Rhode Island (BSME, 1963).

## CROUTER, Jerrol A
Drummond Woodsum & MacMahon, Portland
207 772 1941
jcrouter@dwmlaw.com
*Featured in Litigation (Maine)*

**Practice Areas:** Complex civil litigation in state and federal courts involving commercial matters, including shareholder disputes, construction disputes, lender liability cases, and unfair trade practices. Substantial experience in mediation and arbitration, both as a litigator and neutral.

**Professional Memberships:** Maine Trial Lawyers Association, Maine State Bar Association, Cumberland County Bar Association. Treasurer, Maine Equal Justice Project and 2007 Campaign Chair of Maine's Campaign for Justice.

**Career:** Drummond Woodsum & MacMahon, 1984-Present. Weil Gotschal & Manges, 1983-84.

**Personal:** JD, National Law Center of George Washington University (Order of the Coif), 1983; BA, Colby College, 1978.

## CULLEY, Peter
Pierce Atwood LLP, Portland
207 791 1288
pculley@pierceatwood.com
*Featured in Litigation (Maine)*

**Practice Areas:** Extensive experience in representing corporate interests in jury trials in all courts. Represents manufacturers, financial institutions, and professional service firms in a broad range of matters, including business litigation, professional liability and product liability actions.

**Professional Memberships:** Fellow, American College of Trial Lawyers.

**Career:** Jacobson v Raytheon Aircraft Company: Judgment for defendant client in air-crash case; Haines, et al. v Great Northern Paper Company: Successful defense of one of Maine's largest landowners in breach of contract claim seeking

unlimited access to 600,000 acres of Maine forest lands.
**Personal:** Boston University, JD 1968; University of Maine, AB 1965.

### CURRIER, Douglas P
Verrill Dana, LLP, Portland
207 774 4000
dcurrier@verrilldana.com
*Featured in Labor & Employment (Maine)*
**Practice Areas:** Labor and employment, higher education, immigration and global migration.
**Career:** As Chair of the firm's Labor and Employment Group, Mr Currier's practice focuses on traditional labor law, and employment law and litigation, representing management. He provides counsel to management on all aspects of employment and immigration related issues, and has made employer education and initiatives a priority.
**Personal:** Education: Middlebury College (BA, 1982); Ohio State University College of Law (JD, 1985).

### DEROSBY, Anthony R
Pierce Atwood LLP, Portland
207 791 1343
aderosby@pierceatwood.com
*Featured in Labor & Employment (Maine)*
**Practice Areas:** Directs firm's Immigration Practice Group. Practice includes all aspects of employment and immigration law. Extensive experience in business and employment immigration as well as DOL, WHA, OSHA, and IRCA compliance, inspections and enforcement.
**Professional Memberships:** Admitted in Maine (1988) and Massachusetts (1995). Member of American Bar Association, Labor and Employment Law Committee; American Immigration Lawyers Association; Massachusetts State Bar Association, Employment Law Section; and Maine State Bar Association, Employment Law Committee.
**Personal:** JD (cum laude), University of Maine School of Law, 1988; University of North Carolina, Chapel Hill, 1980-81; BA (cum laude), Bates College, 1980.

### DES ROSIERS, Jared S.
Pierce Atwood LLP, Portland
207 791 1390
jdesrosiers@pierceatwood.com
*Featured in Energy & Natural Resources (Maine)*
**Practice Areas:** Jared's practice focuses on complex energy related regulatory and litigation matters before FERC, state regulatory Commissions, and the courts, concerning, among other issues, transmission siting, power contract disputes, utility ratemaking, power market design and RTO participation.
**Professional Memberships:** Member of the Cumberland County and Maine State Bar Associations, the American Bar Association and the Energy Bar Association. Regional Director, Notre Dame Law Association (2007-present).
**Personal:** BS and JD, University of Notre Dame.

### DILWORTH, George Toby
Drummond Woodsum & MacMahon, Portland
207 772 1941
tdilworth@dwmlaw.com
*Featured in Litigation (Maine)*
**Practice Areas:** Complex civil litigation including issues involving contracts, torts, trade secrets, administrative matters; white collar defense; internal investigations.
**Professional Memberships:** Maine State, Cumberland Bar Associations; Board member, Maine Association, Criminal Defense Lawyers, Board member, Maine Bar Journal Advisory Committee.
**Career:** Assistant US Attorney, District of Maine (1991-2005); Adjunct Faculty, University of Maine Law School (1995-2005); Law Clerk, US District Judge Gene Carter (1987-1988); Special Assistant, US Senator Paul Tsongas (1980-1984).
**Publications:** "The Economic Espionage Act of 1996: An Overview"; United States Attorneys' Bulletin (May 2001).
**Personal:** Boston College Law School, JD 1987; Yale College, 1980; Yarmouth School Committee (2002-2008).

### DONAHUE, Joseph G
Preti Flaherty Beliveau & Pachios, LLP, Portland
207 623 5300
jdonahue@preti.com
*Featured in Energy & Natural Resources (Maine)*
**Practice Areas:** Telecommunications, energy, administrative and business law.
**Professional Memberships:** Admitted in Maine, Massachusetts, Member of Maine State Bar Association, Administrative Law Section and Federal Communications Bar Association.
**Career:** Three decades of experience in utility law, including twenty years as counsel to telecommunications companies and seven years as General Counsel to the Maine Public Utilities Commission. Focuses on regulatory, transactional and business issues for both traditional telephone companies and emerging competitive telecommunications providers. Involved in many significant telecommunications, energy and economic policy matters affecting citizens and businesses.
**Personal:** Boston University School of Law, JD, 1977; Bowdoin College, AB, 1974.

### DOYLE, Thomas R
Pierce Atwood LLP, Portland
207 791 1214
tdoyle@pierceatwood.com
*Featured in Environment (Maine)*
**Practice Areas:** Environmental and land use law, including complex adjudicatory proceedings and corporate transactions.
**Professional Memberships:** Vice-Chair, ABA's Environmental Transactions and Brownfields Committee.
**Career:** Lead environmental counsel in many high profile matters, involving energy, renewable energy, manufacturing, semiconductor fabrication, innovative commercial-scale greenhouses, and waste management facilities.

**Publications:** 'A Developer's Dream or Nightmare: Maine's Site Location, Storm Water, and Traffic Permitting Laws', MSBA; co-author: 'Listing Distinct Population Segments of Endangered Species: Has it Gone Too Far?', ABA's Natural Resources & Environment.
**Personal:** Yale University, BA; Suffolk University Law School, JD (cum laude).

### EINSIEDLER JR, Charles S
Pierce Atwood LLP, Portland
207 791 1388
ceinsiedler@pierceatwood.com
*Featured in Labor & Employment (Maine)*
**Practice Areas:** Chair, Employee Benefits Team. Extensive experience in all aspects of labor, employment and employee benefits law. Represents employers in contract negotiations, union election campaigns, strikes, railway labor matters, and in proceedings before the NLRB, OSHA, EEOC and other agencies.
**Professional Memberships:** Bar admissions: ME and NH; First and DC Circuit Courts of Appeals; ABA Railway Labor Act Committee; ABA Labor and Employment Law Committee; ME and NH Bar Association Employment Law Sections; frequent speaker and author.
**Career:** Associate (1978-83); Partner, (1984-) Pierce Atwood LLP.
**Personal:** Boston University, JD (cum laude), 1978; Williams College, BA (cum laude) 1975.

### ERWIN, James R
Pierce Atwood LLP, Portland
207 791 1237
jerwin@pierceatwood.com
*Featured in Labor & Employment (Maine)*
**Practice Areas:** Jim Erwin leads the Employment Group. He has extensive state and federal litigation experience in a wide range of substantive areas at the trial, appellate, administrative and arbitration levels. His practice involves the defense at agencies and in court of all forms of employment discrimination.
**Professional Memberships:** Member, U. S. Chamber of Commerce Labor Relations Committee, 2007-present; Member, American Bar Association Litigation Section, Labor Relations Committee.
**Career:** Assistant Attorney General, Maine (major prosecutions) (1978-83); Commissioner, Maine Human Rights Commission (1985-87).
**Publications:**
**Personal:** Boston University School of Law, JD; Dartmouth College, AB (cum laude, High Distinction).

### FRYER, Gregory
Verrill Dana, LLP, Portland
207 774 4000
gfryer@verrilldana.com
*Featured in Corporate/M&A (Maine)*
**Practice Areas:** Business law, securities law.
**Career:** Mr Fryer's practice includes corporate law, mergers and acquisitions, public and private offerings of securities, SEC regulation and reporting and venture capital.
**Personal:** Education: Dartmouth College (AB, 1976); Cornell University (JD, 1979).

### GALGAY, David
Verrill Dana, LLP, Portland
207 774 4000
dgalgay@verrilldana.com
*Featured in Real Estate (Maine)*
**Practice Areas:** Real Estate, Commercial Lending, Hospitality
**Career:** Mr Galgay concentrates his practice in the commercial lending area, representing lenders and borrowers in a broad range of asset-based and real estate based loans, bond transactions and other complex commercial loan facilities. In addition, Mr Galgay has substantial experience in real estate acquisitions, commercial leases and condominium developments.
**Personal:** Vermont Law School (JD, 1987) New Mexico State University (BA, 1984).

### GINN, Gregg H
Verrill Dana, LLP, Portland
207 774 4000
gginn@verrilldana.com
*Featured in Labor & Employment (Maine)*
**Practice Areas:** Employee Benefits and Executive Compensation.
**Career:** Mr Ginn's practice focuses on the Employee Retirement Income Security Act of 1974 ("ERISA") and the provisions of the Internal Revenue Code relating to retirement benefits, welfare benefits, deferred compensation and executive compensation. He has extensive experience advising clients on fiduciary standards under ERISA and tax qualification requirements under the Code; drafting plans, committee charters, investment policy statements and executive compensation arrangements; and occasionally representing clients in ERISA litigation.
**Personal:** US Air Force Academy (BS, 1971); Columbia University (MA, 1976); Harvard Law School (JD, 1981).

### GOGGIN, James G
Verrill Dana, LLP, Portland
207 774 4000
jgoggin@verrilldana.com
*Featured in Litigation (Maine)*
**Practice Areas:** Mr Goggin's practice is concentrated on intellectual property litigation and bench and jury trials, including trademark, broadcast licensing fee agreements, copyright infringements, trade secrets and patent litigation.
**Professional Memberships:** American Intellectual Property Law Association, Maine Bar Association.
**Career:** Partner, Verrill Dana LLC Litigation Department.
**Personal:** Education: Georgetown University (BA, 1975); Stanford University (JD, 1979).

### GOOGINS, Mark K
Verrill Dana, LLP, Portland
207 774 4000
mgoogins@verrilldana.com
*Featured in Corporate/M&A (Maine)*
**Practice Areas:** Business law, commercial lending, energy, timberlands, banking and financial services.
**Career:** Mr Googins's practice is concentrated in the areas of mergers and acquisitions, complex

commercial negotiations, and in a wide variety of lending transactions, including equipment leasing, leveraged buyouts and sale-leasebacks.
**Personal:** Education: Tufts University (BA, 1977); New York University School of Law (JD, 1982).

### GRACEFFA, Charles M
Pierce Atwood LLP, Portland
207 791 1300
cgraceffa@pierceatwood.com
*Featured in Corporate/M&A (Maine)*
**Practice Areas:** Chuck has a general corporate and securities law practice concentrated in the areas of private equity, emerging company representation, public and private mergers and acquisitions, and securities law compliance. Chuck also has experience in commercial real estate transactions.
**Personal:** University of Virginia School of Law, JD; Amherst College, BA.

### GRAY, Katie
Verrill Dana, LLP, Portland
207 774 4000
kgray@verrilldana.com
*Featured in Energy & Natural Resources (Maine)*
**Practice Areas:** Energy, Water & Wastewater Utilities
**Career:** Ms Gray advises clients on all aspects of energy law and regulatory practice before the Maine Public Utilities Commission and other administrative agencies and state courts. She has done significant work in the natural gas field, including obtaining regulatory authorizations for a new gas utility, and has experience in utility rate cases, drafting energy-related contracts, and licensing energy self-suppliers.
**Personal:** Boston University School of Law (JD, 2008) University of Maine (BA, 2005).

### GRAY, Kenneth F
Pierce Atwood LLP, Portland
207 791 1212
kgray@pierceatwood.com
*Featured in Environment (Maine)*
**Practice Areas:** Ken concentrates on counseling and enforcement issues related to hazardous substance and hazardous waste management, cleanup, and liability, including toxic tort matters; chemical safety requirements under a variety of laws including the Occupational Safety and Health Act; product regulation including toxic substance manufacturing and processing; emergency planning, response, and community right-to-know requirements; groundwater and drinking water regulation; and transactional matters related to environmental concerns.
**Professional Memberships:** American Bar Association; Maine State Bar Association; American College of Environmental Lawyers.
**Personal:** BA, College of William and Mary (1976); JD, Santa Clara University School of Law (Magna Cum Laude), 1979.

### GREENFIELD, Rebecca
Pierce Atwood LLP, Portland
207 791 1246
rgreenfield@pierceatwood.com
*Featured in Real Estate (Maine)*

**Practice Areas:** Commercial real estate and corporate law, focusing upon project finance, acquisitions, dispositions, development and land use. Represents a variety of commercial entities, including developers of retail centers, resort properties and office buildings, a prominent supermarket chain, a major spring water company, educational institutions and utilities. Experience with registration of subdivisions under Interstate Land Sales Disclosure Act and defeasance of securitized loans.
**Professional Memberships:** Admitted in ME,NH; President (2010), Cumberland County Bar Association, Maine Real Estate & Development Association, Secretary, Avesta Housing Development Corporation.
**Personal:** BA, Amherst College; JD, Boston University School of Law.

### GULLIVER, John W
Pierce Atwood LLP, Portland
207 791 1296
jgulliver@pierceatwood.com
*Featured in Energy & Natural Resources (Maine)*
**Practice Areas:** John enjoys a broad range of substantive experience in energy and utilities law and focuses on energy project development and finance, transmission, regulatory issues, renewable energy, investments, privatization, international and cross-border transactions.
**Professional Memberships:** Energy Bar Association; ABA, Section of International Law; International Bar Association; Maine State Bar Association; Boards of Trustees – the American University in Bulgaria, Maine International Trade Center, University of Maine Board of Visitors, New England Canada Business Council, and World Affairs Council of Maine. John also is a member of the Yale Chernobyl Forest Committee.
**Personal:** BA, Yale University; JD, Yale Law School.

### HANSEL, Greg
Preti Flaherty Beliveau & Pachios, LLP, Portland
207 791 3000
ghansel@preti.com
*Featured in Litigation (Maine)*
**Practice Areas:** Complex business litigation, antiturst, class actions, international, mass torts, securities and products liability. Lead trial counsel in $19 million 2011 federal jury verdict.
**Professional Memberships:** American Bar Association, Section on Antitrust Law.
**Career:** Best Lawyers in America for Commercial Litigation, Antitrust Law and Mass Tort Litigation; AV rated, Martindale Hubbell; New England Super Lawyers for Business Litigation.
**Publications:** Extreme Litigation: An Interview with Judge Wm. Terrell Hodges, Chairman of the Judicial Panel on Multidistrict Litigation, Maine Bar Journal.
**Personal:** BA, Harvard University magna cum laude, 1981; JD, University of Virginia School of Law, 1986.

### HARWOOD, William
Verrill Dana, LLP, Portland
207 774 4000
wharwood@verrilldana.com
*Featured in Energy & Natural Resources (Maine)*
**Practice Areas:** Energy, telecommunications, water and wastewater utilities.
**Career:** As Co-Chair of the firm's Energy Group, Mr Harwood specializes in representing public utilities before state and federal regulatory agencies. He has represented energy and utility companies in more than 50 major cases before the Maine Public Utilities Commission and Federal Energy Regulatory Commission. He also counsels utilities on proactive strategies to both anticipate regulatory developments and efficiently manage the regulatory process.
**Personal:** Education: Harvard College (AB, 1974); Fordham University (JD, 1978).

### HEALY, Nora R.
Verrill Dana, LLP, Portland
207 253 4720
nhealy@verrilldana.com
*Featured in Energy & Natural Resources (Maine)*
**Practice Areas:** Energy, water and wastewater utilities.
**Career:** Ms Healy's practice is focused on representing electric and water utilities in state regulatory proceedings. She has significant experience in a variety of issues involving utility mergers, rate proceedings, rulemakings and renewable energy generators. Ms Healy also represents utilities in appellate proceedings.
**Personal:** Education: Oberlin College (BA, 1993); University of Maine School of Law (JD, magna cum laude, 2002).

### HEWEY, Melissa
Drummond Woodsum & MacMahon, Portland
207 772 1941
mhewey@dwmlaw.com
*Featured in Labor & Employment (Maine), Litigation (Maine)*
**Practice Areas:** Complex civil litigation including school law and employment matters, discrimination defense, sexual harassment, civil rights claims and commercial disputes in Maine and New Hampshire.
**Professional Memberships:** Fellow, American College of Trial Lawyers; Member, Maine Trial Lawyers Association and Maine State and Cumberland County Bar Associations; serves on Local Rules Committee, US District Court.
**Career:** Joined firm, 1987. Current Chair, Trial Services Group.
**Publications:** Wrote and published several training videos for schools; co-author, Maine School Law, 4th Edition.
**Personal:** University of Maine School Law (magna cum laude) JD 1987; Wesleyan University, BA 1980.

### HEWITT, William
Pierce Atwood LLP, Portland
207 791 1337
whewitt@pierceatwood.com
*Featured in Energy & Natural Resources (Maine)*

**Practice Areas:** Bill is the head of Pierce Atwood's Renewable Energy Practice. He focuses his practice on renewable energy, policy and project development, as well as complex regulatory, litigation and appellate matters in state and federal courts and administrative tribunals.
**Professional Memberships:** Member of the Energy Bar Association, and the Northeast Chapter of the Energy Bar Association, where he currently serves on its board of directors and holds the office of vice president.
**Personal:** BS, cum laude, in robotic engineering technology from Lake Superior State University (1987); JD, cum laude, from the University of Maine School of Law (1995).

### HIGH, Michael E
Drummond Woodsum & MacMahon, Portland
207 772 1941
mhigh@dwmlaw.com
*Featured in Corporate/M&A (Maine)*
**Practice Areas:** Represents business entities, investors, lenders and borrowers in a wide range of corporate and commercial matters, including mergers and acquisitions, corporate finance, shareholder matters, private placements, venture capital financings, loan transactions, technology licensing and transfers and other intellectual property matters.
**Professional Memberships:** Massachusetts Bar Association, 1983; Maine Bar Association, 1985; listed in several practice areas in leading US legal publication.
**Career:** Chair of the firm's Business and Commercial Services Group.
**Personal:** Cornell Law School (1983).

### HOWARD, Christopher E
Pierce Atwood LLP, Portland
207 791 1335
choward@pierceatwood.com
*Featured in Corporate/M&A (Maine)*
**Practice Areas:** Chris' forte is in managing complex commercial transactions and development projects in time-sensitive environments, and in accessing all sectors of the capital markets. He focuses his practice on three areas: the resort and hospitality industry, corporate finance and transactional representation, and general counsel representation.
**Professional Memberships:** Chris is a Member of the Maine State and American Bar Associations.
**Personal:** BA Degree in English, magna cum laude, from Bates College (1979); JD, magna cum laude, from Cornell Law School (1982), where he was editor of the Cornell International Law Journal.

### HULL, Nathaniel
Verrill Dana, LLP, Portland
207 774 4000
nhull@verrilldana.com
*Featured in Corporate/M&A (Maine)*
**Practice Areas:** Bankrupcty & Creditors' Rights
**Career:** Mr Hull's practice focuses on corporate restructurings, avoidance litigation and bankruptcy-related appellate work. He regularly publishes

articles on commercial bankruptcy issues and practice, including the role mediation can play as a cost-effective alternative to traditional bankruptcy litigation.
**Personal:** JD, University of Maine School of Law; BA, The Evergreen State College.

### KATZ-LEAVY, Charlie
Verrill Dana, LLP, Portland
ckatzleavy@verrilldana.com
*Featured in Real Estate (Maine)*
**Practice Areas:** Real estate, timberlands, commercial lending, Hospitality.
**Career:** Mr Katz-Leavy represents a variety of clients, including landlords, tenants, developers, lenders, investors, timberland companies, telecommunications companies, wind power companies, hotels, and retail establishments. He has helped clients acquire, finance, sell, and lease properties. He negotiates and drafts easements and contracts, analyzes due diligence items, including title reports and zoning and land use ordinances, and advises clients on tax and financing issues.
**Personal:** Education: Boston College Law School (JD, 2006); Columbia University (2002).

### KAYATTA JR, William
Pierce Atwood LLP, Portland
207 791 1100
wkayatta@pierceatwood.com
*Featured in Litigation (Maine)*
**Practice Areas:** Complex civil litigation; class actions.
**Professional Memberships:** Regent, American College of Trial Lawyers; Member, American Law Institute.
**Career:** Bill has been nominated by President Obama to serve as a judge on the US Court of Appeals for the First Circuit. As he awaits a Senate vote on his nomination, he is currently serving by appointment of the US Supreme Court as Special Master in Kansas v. Nebraska and Colorado, No. 126, Original (U.S.S.Ct).
**Personal:** Harvard Law School, 1979; Amherst College, 1976; clerk, Chief Judge Frank Coffin, US 1st Circuit Court of Appeals (1980).

### KEELER, Dennis C
Pierce Atwood LLP, Portland
207 791 1331
dkeeler@pierceatwood.com
*Featured in Real Estate (Maine)*
**Practice Areas:** Practice focuses on real estate development; with emphasis on representing developers and owners of retail centers, office buildings, commercial projects and large residential/resort developments throughout New England and the East Coast. Served as US counsel to UK developer and marketer of US resort properties.
**Professional Memberships:** Colorado Bar; Maine Bar; New Hampshire Bar; Secretary and Member, Executive Committee and Board of Directors of Maine Real Estate Development Association; Member, International Council of Shopping Centers.
**Career:** Partner (1990-). Included in a leading legal publication, (2003-), for real estate law.

**Personal:** University of Denver, JD; University of Maryland, BA.

### KILBRETH, James
Drummond Woodsum & MacMahon, Portland
207 772 1941 ext. 555
jkilbreth@dwmlaw.com
*Featured in Environment (Maine), Litigation (Maine)*
**Practice Areas:** Energy, environmental, higher education.
**Career:** Jamie Kilbreth focuses his practice on complex commercial and regulatory litigation, including antitrust, securities, officer and director liability, class actions, bid award challenges, insurance coverage disputes, environmental and energy matters, and higher education issues. Jamie was the lead lawyer for the State of Maine in its litigation against the tobacco industry, securing a $1.5 billion recovery, the largest in State history.
**Personal:** Education: Harvard College (AB, 1970); Northeastern University (MA, 1974); American University School of Law (JD, 1976).

### LANCASTER JR, Ralph I
Pierce Atwood LLP, Portland
207 791 1260
rlancaster@pierceatwood.com
*Featured in Litigation (Maine)*
**Practice Areas:** Ralph's practice includes civil and criminal matters. His cases have included admiralty, airplane crashes, corporate controversies, income tax evasion, murder, wrongful death, white-collar crime, real estate, eminent domain, products liability, and other complex matters. Ralph has an active trial practice, focusing, for the most part, on complex commercial and personal injury cases for both plaintiffs and defendants.
**Professional Memberships:** Past President of the American College of Trial Lawyers; Honorary member of the Canadian Bar Association.
**Personal:** BA, College of the Holy Cross; LLB, Harvard Law School. Honorary Degree of Doctor of Laws from Saint Joseph's College.

### LANDRY, Andrew
Preti Flaherty Beliveau & Pachios, LLP, Portland
207 623 5300
alandry@preti.com
*Featured in Energy & Natural Resources (Maine)*
**Practice Areas:** Energy and telecommunications law; climate strategy; economic stimulus law.
**Professional Memberships:** Admitted to practice in Maine. Member of Maine and Penobscot County Bar Associations.
**Career:** Former General Counsel to Bangor Hydro-Electric Company. Experienced in representing utility and consumer clients before regulatory agencies, such as the Maine PUC and FERC. Experienced in renewable energy project development.
**Personal:** University of Maine, JD, 1987; Syracuse University , BS, 1983.

### LANE, Michael L
Preti Flaherty Beliveau & Pachios, LLP, Augusta
207 623 5300
mlane@preti.com
*Featured in Real Estate (Maine)*
**Practice Areas:** Real Estate; land use and zoning; environmental; land conservation. Manages complex real estate development projects. Forest products and timberlands. Title and conveyancing in complex timberland transactions, underwriting timberland titles. LURC development, compliance and permitting. Tree Growth, Open Space, and Forest Practices Act compliance.
**Professional Memberships:** Maine State Bar (Title Standards subcommittee) and New Hampshire State Bar. Maine Forest Products Council, Forest Resources Association.
**Personal:** University of Maine School of Law, cum laude, 2001; University of Maine, BA, summa cum laude, 1996, Phi Beta Kappa.

### LANGER, Leonard W
Thompson & Bowie, Portland
lwlanger@thompsonbowie.com
*Featured in Litigation (Maine)*
**Practice Areas:** Admiralty and Maritime Law, Insurance Defense
**Professional Memberships:** Cumberland County Bar Association, Maine State Bar Association, American Bar Association, United States Maritime Law Association
**Career:** Admitted to practice in the State of Maine, the United States District Court for the District of Maine, the First Circuit Court of Appeals, the Third Circuit Court of Appeals, and the United States Supreme Court.
**Publications:** Editor, University of Maine Law Review, 1977-1978. Author: Comment, "The Validity of the Restrictions on the Modern Advisory Opinion," 29 Maine Law Review 305, 1978.
**Personal:** Born Atlanta, Georgia, March 9, 1951, Education: Colgate University (BA cum laude, 1973); University of Maine (JD cum laude, 1978), Law Clerk to Hon. Charles A. Pomeroy, Associate Justice, Maine Supreme Judicial Court, 1978-1979.

### LEPAGE, Margaret Coughlin
Pierce Atwood LLP, Portland
207 791 1382
mlepage@pierceatwood.com
*Featured in Labor & Employment (Maine)*
**Practice Areas:** Partner in Employment Group. Representation of management in federal and state courts and administrative agencies; counseling on employment policy development and preventative practices; management training on employment law; general representation of private schools and colleges; representation of state high school interscholastic athletic association.
**Professional Memberships:** Cumberland County and Maine State Bar Associations; Member of CASA Judicial Advisory Board (2003-).
**Career:** Partner, Pierce Atwood LLP (1992-). Frequently speaks on sexual harassment, ADA and FMLA; conducts worksite trainings on sexual harassment prevention.

**Personal:** University of Michigan Law School, JD (cum laude), 1983; Dartmouth College, AB (magna cum laude, High Distinction).

### LOGIUDICE, Susan E
Preti Flaherty Beliveau & Pachios, LLP, Portland
207 791 3000
sel@preti.com
*Featured in Corporate/M&A (Maine)*
**Practice Areas:** Concentrates practice in business organizations and commercial transactions, including mergers and acquisitions, entity formation and governance, corporate finance, joint ventures, private placements and venture capital financings. She also advises family owned and closely held businesses through the life cycle of the business and on succession planning.
**Professional Memberships:** Admitted to practice in Maine (1985); Maine State Bar Association, Corporate Law Section; American Bar Association, Business Law Section.
**Career:** Joined Preti Flaherty in 1985. Became Partner, 1992.
**Personal:** Born 22 November 1957. Northeastern University JD (1985), State University of New York at Binghamton (1979).

### MACEWAN, Alan D
Verrill Dana, LLP, Portland
207 774 4000
amacewan@verrilldana
*Featured in Corporate/M&A (Maine)*
**Practice Areas:** Business law.
**Professional Memberships:** ABA Negotiated Acquisitions Committee; Editorial Committee, ABA Model Stock Purchase Agreement Revision Task Force.
**Career:** As Chair of the firm's Business Law Group, Mr MacEwan's practice covers the areas of business acquisitions and sales, corporate general counsel representation, contracts, and corporate finance.
**Personal:** Education: Colby College (BA, 1978); Syracuse University (JD, 1981).

### MANAHAN, Matthew
Pierce Atwood LLP, Portland
207 791 1189
mmanahan@pierceatwood.com
*Featured in Environment (Maine)*
**Practice Areas:** Environmental and land use law, including complex adjudicatory proceedings and corporate transactions, with a focus on environmental regulation of energy projects.
**Professional Memberships:** National Hydropower Association (Regulatory Affairs Committee); ABA (Hydropower Committee); MSBA (former chair of Natural Resources Section); NHBA.
**Career:** Concentrated on environmental law since 1989; leader of Environmental Practice Group since 2009; lead environmental counsel in many high profile energy permitting matters.
**Publications:** "Water Quality Certification and Relicensing: Sharing Legal Strategies," Hydro Review Magazine; "FERC and Dam Decommissioning," Natural Resources and Environment Journal.

Personal: Bowdoin College, AB (cum laude); Cornell Law School, JD (cum laude).

## MANHEIMER, Jacob A
Pierce Atwood LLP, Portland
207 791 1338
jmanheimer@pierceatwood.com
*Featured in Corporate/M&A (Maine)*

Practice Areas: Jack devotes his practice primarily to financially distressed situations, creditors' rights and commercial transactions, focusing on creditor-side representation. He regularly represents secured creditors, trade creditors and landlords in Chapter 11 reorganizations, Chapter 7 liquidations and Chapter 13 wage earner cases, out-of-court workouts, and collection matters. Professional Memberships: American Bankruptcy Institute; Maine State Bar Association. Career: Associate, Fried Frank Harris Shriver & Jacobson (1983-86); associate, Pierce Atwood (1986-90); Partner, Pierce Atwood (1991-date). Personal: Fordham University School of Law, JD 1983; Dartmouth College, AB 1978.

## MARCUS, Benjamin E
Drummond Woodsum & MacMahon, Portland
207 772 1941
bmarcus@dwmlaw.com
*Featured in Corporate/M&A (Maine)*

Practice Areas: Representation of purchasers and investors in business acquisitions with particular experience in the acquisition of troubled enterprises in/out of formal reorganization proceedings. Representation of troubled companies in reorganization proceedings. General outside counsel to numerous businesses in the following industries: pulp and paper, light manufacturing, hospitality, aquaculture, insurance, insurance agency, automative sales. Representation-secured lenders in loan originations/restructurings, enforcement actions. Professional Memberships: Maine Bar Association; American College of Bankruptcy. Career: Firm Managing Director; Clerk, Honorable Joseph L Tauro, Chief Judge, US District Court, District of Massachusetts; joined Drummond Woodsum, 1987. Personal: Cornell Law School (magna cum laude)1986.

## MCLOON, Christopher
Verrill Dana, LLP, Portland
207 774 4000
cmcloon@verrilldana.com
*Featured in Corporate/M&A (Maine)*

Practice Areas: Business law, energy, tax, timberlands. Career: Mr McLoon's practice focuses on the tax and business aspects of forming, acquiring, operating, reorganizing, disposing of and liquidating business entities, principally unincorporated business entities such as partnerships and limited liability companies. Personal: Education: University of Maine (BA, 1991); Vermont Law School (JD, 1994); New York University School of Law (LLM, 1995).

## MEEKER, Suzanne
Verrill Dana, LLP, Portland
207 774 4000
smeeker@verrilldana.com
*Featured in Labor & Employment (Maine)*

Practice Areas: Employee benefits and executive compensation, higher education. Career: Ms Meeker chairs the firm's Employee Benefits and Executive Compensation Department and belongs to its Higher Education industry group. Her practice spans all aspects of ERISA and US employee benefits law, including retirement plans, health and welfare plans, benefits in mergers and acquisitions, fiduciary matters, multiemployer plans, fringe benefits, and executive compensation arrangements. Ms Meeker advises global, national, and regional businesses, as well as tax-exempt educational, church and other institutions within and outside New England. Personal: Education: Yale Law School (JD, 1981); Duke University (AB, summa cum laude, 1977)).

## MESSERSCHMIDT, Michael G
Preti Flaherty Beliveau & Pachios, LLP, Portland
207 791 3000
mmesserschmidt@preti.com
*Featured in Labor & Employment (Maine)*

Practice Areas: Chair of Labor and Employment Law Practice Group. Focuses practice on employment discrimination, harassment, civil rights claims, and litigation. Extensive experience in EEO compliance and risk management issues. Has handled numerous arbitrations under collective bargaining agreements. Professional Memberships: College of Labor and Employment Lawyers; Admitted to practice in ME (1978), NH (2007); ME and NH State Bar Associations, Labor and Employment Section; ABA, Labor and Employment Law Section. Career: Assistant Attorney General, State of ME (Criminal Division) (1978-80). Joined Preti Flaherty 1980. Managing Partner 1991-92. Personal: Born 22 June 1953. University of Maine School of Law, JD, 1978; Harvard College, BA (Cum Laude), 1975.

## MOON, Richard G
Verrill Dana, LLP, Portland
207 774 4000
rmoon@verrilldana.com
*Featured in Labor & Employment (Maine)*

Practice Areas: Labor and employment, immigration. Professional Memberships: College of Labor and Employment Lawyers. Career: Mr Moon's practice focuses on labor and employment law, including advising on and litigation and trial of all employment issues, class actions, collective bargaining, arbitrations and preventative labor relations. He has extensive experience representing financial and other service industries, including retail sales and health care, and industrial sectors including aerospace, warehousing, and paper companies. He has taught trial tactics to over 4500 attorneys. He also special-

izes in H1-B and related business immigration compliance and litigation. Personal: Dartmouth College (AB, 1969); University of Michigan (JD, 1974).

## MOSS, Philip J
Fisher & Phillips LLP, Portland
207 774 6001
pmoss@laborlawyers.com
*Featured in Labor & Employment (Maine)*

Career: Philip Moss is Of Counsel in the Portland, Maine and Boston offices. He has practiced in the area of employment law and labor relations since 1975. Phil's experience encompasses all facets of labor and employment law, including advice to employers on union election campaigns and preventive labor relations; defense of unfair labor practice charges, wrongful discharge suits, and complaints of discrimination; advice and representation of employers in OSHA investigations and defense of OSHA citations; prosecution of suits against unions for injunctive relief and damages under Sections 301 and 303 of the LMRA; and collective bargaining negotiations and grievance arbitration.

## NEWMAN, Sharon
Preti Flaherty Beliveau & Pachios, LLP, Portland
207 791 3000
snewman@preti.com
*Featured in Environment (Maine)*

Practice Areas: Environmental compliance, remediation, and permitting; defense of governmental enforcement actions (Clean Water Act, CERCLA, RCRA and SARA); strategic risk evaluation and environmental due diligence in complex transactions; municipal and industrial stormwater permitting and compliance. Professional Memberships: Member, American, Maine and Massachusetts bar associations. Career: Partner, Preti Flaherty; private practice in Cleveland, OH and Seattle, WA; Assistant Regional Counsel, US Environmental Protection Agency, Region 10 (Hazardous Waste Division); Law Clerk, Chief Justice Jay Rabinowitz, Supreme Court of Alaska. Personal: Stanford Law School (1984); Barnard College, Columbia University (magna cum laude, Phi Beta Kappa, 1978).

## NYHAN, Christopher D
Preti Flaherty Beliveau & Pachios, LLP, Portland
207 791 3000
cnyhan@preti.com
*Featured in Litigation (Maine)*

Practice Areas: Chair of the firm's Medical Liability Group. Extensive experience in complex medical, antitrust and products liability. Tried over 100 jury trials in state and federal courts. Has argued over 20 cases to Maine Supreme Court. Professional Memberships: Admitted in ME (1976), Dist of Columbia (1998) and various federal trial and appellate courts. Maine State Bar Assn. Liaison to Model Professional Liability Demonstration Project of Maine State Legislature.

Career: Joined firm in 1976, became Partner in 1980. Member or Chair, Management and Hiring Committees. Frequent lecturer to medical and professional risk associations throughout New England. Listed in 'The Best Lawyers in America.' Personal: Born 4 February 1946; JD, University of San Francisco (1976); MA, University of California, Berkeley (1973); BA, Boston College (1968).

## OESTREICHER, Charles R
Verrill Dana, LLP, Portland
207 774 4000
coestreicher@verrilldana.com
*Featured in Real Estate (Maine)*

Practice Areas: Real estate. Professional Memberships: American College of Real Estate Lawyers. Career: Mr Oestreicher's practice covers most areas of real estate, with emphasis on real estate brokerage, land use and zoning, easements, title matters, conservation easements and timberland acquisitions and sales. Personal: Education: Indiana University of Pennsylvania (BS, 1964); Case Western Reserve University (JD, 1968).

## O'KEEFE, Margaret Minister
Pierce Atwood LLP, Portland
207 791 1351
mokeefe@pierceatwood.com
*Featured in Litigation (Maine)*

Practice Areas: Margaret focuses on a mix of strategic business and legal advice for clients in the creative worlds of design, music, consumer products, software, and biotech industries. Margaret's practice focuses on copyrights and trademarks, brand and product licensing, software and new technology licensing, privacy and data security, intellectual property asset management, and intellectual property protection and enforcement. Professional Memberships: Elected Member, American Law Institute, 2006-present; Member, Justice Action Group, 2010-present; Chair, Advisory Committee of Providers (of legal aid), 2010-present. Personal: Harvard Law School, JD; Bowdoin College, AB, summa cum laude; Phi Beta Kappa.

## OLIVIER, Elizabeth
Preti Flaherty Beliveau & Pachios, LLP, Portland
207 791 3000
eolivier@preti.com
*Featured in Labor & Employment (Maine)*

Practice Areas: Employment and health law. Extensive experience counseling employers on discrimination laws, compliance and risk management, contracting, and noncompetition; and defending employment disputes before administrative agencies and courts. Professional Memberships: Admitted in Maine and First Circuit. Maine and American Bar Associations (Labor and Employment and Health Law Sections); American Health Lawyers Association

**Career:** Joined firm in 1987, became partner in 1995. Best lawyers for Employment 2012 and 2013.

**Personal:** Born Leominster, Massachusetts; JD, Suffolk University Law School (cum laude), 1987; BS, University of Maine, 1978.

### PALMER, James C
Verrill Dana, LLP, Portland
207 774 4000
jpalmer@verrilldana.com
*Featured in Real Estate (Maine)*

**Practice Areas:** Real estate, commercial lending.

**Career:** Mr Palmer's practice is concentrated in the areas of development, acquisition and leasing of office, retail and industrial properties and real estate lending. He has extensive experience with complex loan transactions and in the drafting and negotiation of leases and subleases.

**Personal:** Education: Bowdoin College (AB, 1978); University of Pennsylvania (JD, 1981).

### PELLETIER, Raymond A
Verrill Dana, LLP, Portland
207 253 4512
rpelletier@verrilldana.com
*Featured in Real Estate (Maine)*

**Practice Areas:** Real Estate, Timberlands, Telecommunications, International.

**Career:** Mr Pelletier's Real Estate practice focuses on all aspects of commercial development, including site acquisition and leasing, governmental licensing and permitting, construction and financing. His timberlands experience covers a wide variety of matters, including purchases and sales involving hundreds of thousands of acres. Mr Pelletier has provided real estate and zoning expertise in the build out and reconfiguration of hundreds of telecommunications sites. His international practice provides transactional expertise to foreign as well as domestic clients.

**Personal:** Education: Boston College Law School (JD, 1983); Georgetown University (BS, 1973).

### PIAMPIANO, Jeffrey T
Drummond Woodsum & MacMahon, Portland
207 772 1941
jtp@dwmlaw.com
*Featured in Corporate/M&A (Maine)*

**Practice Areas:** Representing debtors and creditors in Chapter 11 reorganization and other insolvency proceedings, including bankruptcy-related litigation and asset sales; representing creditors in enforcing rights and remedies under state law; complex civil litigation involving commercial matters.

**Professional Memberships:** Maine State Bar Association; Oregon State Bar Association; American Bankruptcy Institute; Turnaround Management Association.

**Career:** Clerk, Honorable Rick T. Haselton, Oregon Court of Appeals (2000–02); joined Drummond Woodsum in 2002.

**Personal:** JD, Northwestern School of Law of Lewis & Clark College (2000); MS, University of Maine (1996); AB, Colgate University (1993).

### PIKE, Dixon P
Pierce Atwood LLP, Portland
207 791 1374
dpike@pierceatwood.com
*Featured in Environment (Maine)*

**Practice Areas:** Dixon has extensive experience assisting clients with environmental permitting, compliance, and enforcement defense issues. He focuses primarily on state and federal air laws, including involvement in hundreds of air permitting matters, numerous federal and state rulemakings, state and federal enforcement actions, PSD/GHG/BACT/BART/MACT strategies and compliance counseling. Has served as environmental counsel to Maine Pulp and Paper Association for over 15 years.

**Publications:** Frequently writes and lectures on air quality control regulations. Co-author of 'The Maine Air Permitting Handbook', 1996.

**Personal:** BA, political science (1983) Williams College; JD (cum laude, 1987), Boston University School of Law.

### PIPER, Jonathan S
Preti Flaherty Beliveau & Pachios, LLP, Portland
207 791 3000
jpiper@preti.com
*Featured in Litigation (Maine)*

**Practice Areas:** Managing Partner of the firm. Extensive experience in complex litigation, international and domestic arbitration, commercial litigation, securities litigation, and libel defense work for the media.

**Professional Memberships:** Admitted to practice in Maine (1976); United States District Court, District of Maine (1976); United States Court of Appeals, First Circuit and Third Circuit. Fellow, Maine Bar Foundation (since 1996); Fellow, American Bar Foundation (since 2009); Counsel Member of Media Law Resource Center; Maine Civil Rules Advisory Committee (1999-2000).

**Career:** Law Clerk, Honorable Edward S Godfrey, Maine Supreme Judicial Court, 1976-77. Joined Preti Flaherty, 1977; became Partner, 1982. Managing Partner, 1995-99, 2008-.

**Publications:** Comment, The Repair Rule: Maine Rule of Evidence 407(a) and the Admissibility of Subsequent Remedial Measures in Proving Negligence, 27 Maine Law Review 255 (1975); Article, Subpoenas on the Press: The Constitutional Privilege Not to Produce, Maine Bar Journal, Vol. 2, No. 2 (1987); Contributor: Annual 50-State Survey of Libel and Privacy, Media Law Resource Center (1986 through present); 'How to Avoid Covering Your Own Trial,' Maine State Bar Association Media/Law Guide (1990).

**Personal:** Born 7 April 1950; JD, University of Maine School of Law (Portland), 1976; BA (magna cum laude), Bowdoin College, 1972.

### PLOUFFE, William
Drummond Woodsum & MacMahon, Portland
207 772 1941
wplouffe@dwmlaw.com
*Featured in Environment (Maine)*

**Practice Areas:** Extensive experience in land use, zoning and environmental permitting at local, state levels. Representation before courts and administrative agencies.

**Professional Memberships:** Maine State Bar Association; has briefed and argued before the United States Supreme Court.

**Career:** Joined firm 1984, former Managing Director.

**Publications:** Numerous pieces in association with lectures on land use and environmental law issues; author of "Forty Years after First Iowa: A Call for Greater State Control of River Resources," 71 Cornell Law Review, Number 4 (May 1986).

**Personal:** University of Connecticut School of Law (with honors, 1974); College of the Holy Cross (1969).

### PRATT, Aaron
Drummond Woodsum & MacMahon, Portland
207 772 1941
apratt@dwmlaw.com
*Featured in Corporate/M&A (Maine)*

**Practice Areas:** Representation of businesses, non-profit organizations, investors, lenders and Indian tribes in a wide range of corporate, partnership and commercial matters, including mergers and acquisitions, corporate finance, shareholder and partner matters, private placements, venture capital financing and Tribal finance and economic development matters.

**Professional Memberships:** American Bar Association Business Section, Maine Bar Association, New Hampshire Bar Association, Co-Chair of Maine State Bar Association's Limited Liability Company Act Drafting Committee (new act effective on July 1, 2011).

**Career:** Joined Drummond Woodsum in 2001.

**Personal:** JD, Wake Forest University School of Law (2001); BA, Bowdoin College (1996) (cum laude).

### PRENTICE, Richard D
Pierce Atwood LLP, Portland
207 791 1356
rprentice@pierceatwood.com
*Featured in Real Estate (Maine)*

**Practice Areas:** Real estate.

**Professional Memberships:** Maine State Bar Association; International Council of Shopping Centers.

**Career:** Dick has practiced real estate law for more than 30 years. He focuses his practice on the sale and purchase of real estate and the leasing of office, warehouse, industrial, and retail properties. His practice includes the negotiation of purchase and sale agreements, leases, subleases, easement agreements, brokerage agreements, and other related agreements.

**Personal:** A 1976 graduate of Dartmouth College, Dick holds a JD from Fordham Law School (1979). Dick is admitted to practice in Maine, New York, and New Jersey.

### PRINGLE, Harry R
Drummond Woodsum & MacMahon, Portland
207 772 1941
hrpringle@dwmlaw.com
*Featured in Labor & Employment (Maine)*

**Practice Areas:** Extensive experience in employment litigation, labor negotiations, NLRB and MLRB proceedings, Title VII litigation, discrimination cases before the courts and all administrative agencies.

**Professional Memberships:** Former member, Board of Directors, NSBA Council of School Board Attorneys. Listed in labor/employment law in leading US legal publication for over 15 years. Fellow, College of Labor and Employment Lawyers.

**Career:** Joined firm, 1973. Frequent lecturer, employment law issues.

**Publications:** Author, numerous articles on employment law issues and Editor of Maine School Law, 4th Edition 2012.

**Personal:** Harvard Law School (1973 cum laude); Princeton University (1968 magna cum laude, Phi Beta Kappa).

### RAND, Katharine I
Pierce Atwood LLP, Portland
207 791 1267
krand@pierceatwood.com
*Featured in Labor & Employment (Maine)*

**Practice Areas:** Katy's work primarily involves employment law, with a focus on discrimination, harassment, retaliation, and wage / hour issues. Katy has litigated a number of employment cases in state and federal court, and routinely represents employers before the Maine Human Rights Commission. In addition, she advises employers on employment related matters including employee relations issues, performance management, leaves of absence, and the reasonable accommodation process.

**Professional Memberships:** Chair, Maine Labor Relations Board; Member, Maine Bar Association; Member, American Bar Association.

**Personal:** BA, Davidson College; JD, University of Maine School of Law.

### RAPAPORT, Dan
Preti Flaherty Beliveau & Pachios, LLP, Portland
207 791 3000
drapaport@preti.com
*Featured in Litigation (Maine)*

**Practice Areas:** In his 35th year with Preti, has concentrated in trial work and litigation. Litigation Practice Group Chair. Tried 175+ cases (jury, non-jury and administrative hearings). Regularly appears before state regulatory agencies. Has arbitrated and mediated 500+ cases in all areas of civil litigation. Member of the International Association of Defense Counsel and named one of the USA's Best Lawyers, America's Top Lawyers and New England Super Lawyers.

**Professional Memberships:** Admissions: ME and MA; US District Court, District of ME; US Court of Appeals, First Circuit.

**Personal:** JD, Cornell Law School, 1978; BA, Colby College, Phi Beta Kappa, 1974.

### RAYBACK, Brian
Pierce Atwood LLP, Portland
207 791 1188
brayback@pierceatwood.com
*Featured in Environment (Maine)*

**Practice Areas:** Environmental and land use law, with a focus on natural resources, stormwater, wastewater, and air issues, as well as appellate and enforcement matters.
**Professional Memberships:** Vice Chair, State and Regional Environmental Cooperation Committee of the ABA's Section of Environment, Energy, and Resources; and Maine State Bar Association's Continuing Legal Education Committee.
**Personal:** JD, Georgetown University Law Center (Magna Cum Laude, Order of the GIF); BA, Colby College (Summa Cum Laude, Phi Beta Kappa).

### ROSE, Daniel
Drummond Woodsum & MacMahon, Portland
207 772 1941
drose@dwmlaw.com
*Featured in Labor & Employment (Maine)*

**Practice Areas:** Represents private and public entities in employment/labor matters, including compliance with discrimination laws, wrongful discharge, wage/hour issues, workers' compensation discrimination, litigation and negotiations. Represents employers before the courts and all administrative agencies.
**Professional Memberships:** Vice-Chair, Employer-Employee Relations Committee for the ABA; past Co-Chair, Labor and Employment Section, Maine Bar Assn.
**Career:** Lectures frequently on employment topics; law course lead instructor at two universities.
**Publications:** Publications: Author, numerous articles on employment law; editor, 'Litigating the Employment Tort Case', ABA publication.
**Personal:** Boston College Law School; Hamilton College.

### RUPRECHT, Clifford H
Pierce Atwood LLP, Portland
207 791 1186
cruprecht@pierceatwood.com
*Featured in Litigation (Maine)*

**Practice Areas:** Cliff's practice involves litigation in both the state and federal courts at the trial and appellate levels, and before both state and federal agencies, with a focus on complex commercial litigation and class-action defense.
**Professional Memberships:** Member, Cumberland County Bar Association; Maine State Bar Association; American Law Institute.
**Personal:** BA, Williams College; PhD, The University of Chicago Divinity School; JD, University of Pennsylvania Law School.

### SCHNEIDER, Timothy
Pierce Atwood LLP, Portland
207 791 1433
tschneider@pierceatwood.com
*Featured in Energy & Natural Resources (Maine)*

**Practice Areas:** Energy. Tim has worked on a wide range of matters before state and federal regulators, in addition to energy-related transactions. He is currently handling a number of proceedings, including eminent domain and transmission line siting cases, before the Maine Public Utilities Commission.
**Personal:** New York University School of Law, JD; Harvard University, BA.

### SCHUTZ, Sigmund
Preti Flaherty Beliveau & Pachios, LLP, Portland
sschutz@preti.com
*Featured in Litigation (Maine)*

**Practice Areas:** Complex commercial, First Amendment and media, environmental, land use, and securities litigation and arbitration.
**Professional Memberships:** Fellow, Maine Bar Foundation; Listed, Benchmark Litigation, Super Lawyers New England, Best Lawyers in America; Board Member, New England First Amendment Coalition, Maine Freedom of Information Coalition; Admitted, Maine, New Hampshire, New York.
**Career:** Sig represents Fortune 500 companies, news media, regional businesses, insurers and entrepreneurs in resolving their thorniest disputes.
**Publications:** Media Law Resource Center, Reporters Committee for the Freedom of the Press, Maine Bar Journal, and Maine Law Review.
**Personal:** Cornell Law School, 1997; Colby College, cum laude, 1994.

### SELSER, Jeffrey T
Verrill Dana, LLP, Portland
207 774 4000
jselser@verrilldana.com
*Featured in Real Estate (Maine)*

**Practice Areas:** Timberlands, real estate, environmental, energy.
**Professional Memberships:** Forest Landowners Association.
**Career:** Mr Selser is one of the most active timberland lawyers in the United States, representing clients in matters involving land in most US states and several Latin American countries. His work involves some of the largest and most complex timberland transactions in US history, and his practice ranges from multi-million acre deals to assisting owners of small woodlots. Mr Selser also has experience assisting timberland owners with conservation easements, mitigation banks and other eco-system services agreements.
**Personal:** Old Dominion University (BS, 1994); University of Richmond (JD, 1998).

### SHAPIRO, Jonathan
Fisher & Phillips LLP, Portland
207 774 6001
jshapiro@laborlawyers.com
*Featured in Labor & Employment (Maine)*

**Career:** Jonathan Shapiro is the Managing Partner of the Portland, Maine office and a partner in the Boston office. He practices in all aspects of employment, labor and employee benefits law and litigation on behalf of management. He has represented management before state and federal courts throughout New England, New York, New Jersey, Illinois, Maryland, Oregon, Virginia and Texas. Jonathan regularly counsels employers on a broad range of business and employment matters, including designing personnel policies, overseeing the hiring and termination of employees, negotiating severance packages for executives, conducting internal corporate audits and investigations, and safeguarding corporate property and information.

### SHINAY, Richard
Drummond Woodsum & MacMahon, Portland
207 772 1941
rshinay@dwmlaw.com
*Featured in Real Estate (Maine)*

**Practice Areas:** Represents clients in acquisition, development, financing and sale of real estate and land conservation.
**Professional Memberships:** ABA; Maine State Bar Association; Maine Title Standards Subcommittee; ABA Committee on Condominiums, Cooperatives and Associations and Real Property, Probate and Trust Law Section; American Land Title Association; Maine Real Estate and Development Association.
**Career:** Drummond Woodsum (1985-); past Chair, South Portland Planning Board; Scarborough Planning Board; past Co-Chair, Scarborough Open Space, Scarborough Growth/Services Committee; Co-Chair, Scarborough Comprehensive Plan Revision Committee; Trustee, Scarborough Land Conservation Trust.
**Personal:** University of Maine School of Law, 1980; Boston College, 1977.

### SIPE, Donald J
Preti Flaherty Beliveau & Pachios, LLP, Portland
207 791 3000
dsipe@preti.com
*Featured in Energy & Natural Resources (Maine)*

**Practice Areas:** Energy and telecommunications law.
**Professional Memberships:** Admitted to practice in Maine.
**Career:** Skilled in the complex interrelation between law, regulation and economics in the electric markets. Helps clients address the challenges of the shifting energy and utility landscape. Served for ten years as Vice Chair of the New England Power Pool (NEPOOL) and was elected for two terms as chair of that organization. Before joining Preti Flaherty, he worked for eight years as a staff attorney with the Maine Public Utilities Commission.
**Publications:** Recognized by the publication Public Utilities Fortnightly as a "2009 Groundbreaking Attorney."

### STIER JR, Robert H
Pierce Atwood LLP, Portland
207 791 1163
rstier@pierceatwood.com
*Featured in Litigation (Maine)*

**Practice Areas:** Jury trials of cases involving complex scientific or technical subject matter, particularly patent litigation and products liability defense, but also copyright, trademark, trade secret and other complex commercial litigation.
**Professional Memberships:** American Law Institute; AIPLA; Products Liability Advisory Council (Sustaining Member); state bar associations in Maine, Massachusetts and Virginia.
**Career:** For over 30 years he has successfully handled patent litigation nationwide at the trial and appellate levels for a wide variety of clients.
**Personal:** Harvard College, AB (honors) 1975; University of Gothenburg, Sweden (non-degree) 1977; Harvard Law School, JD (honors) 1980.

### TALBERT, Jeffrey
Preti Flaherty Beliveau & Pachios, LLP, Portland
207 791 3000
jtalbert@preti.com
*Featured in Environment (Maine)*

**Practice Areas:** Environmental litigation, permitting, compliance, environmental aspects of corporate transactions involving range of environmental statutes.
**Professional Memberships:** Admissions: Maine, Massachusetts, District of Columbia, Hawaii, American Bar Association Member of Environment and Litigation Sections.
**Career:** White & Case LLP (2000-2004); Trial Attorney, US Department of Justice, Environmental Enforcement Section (2004-08); Preti Flaherty, Boston, MA and Portland, ME (2008 – Present). Of Counsel 2008-2011. Partner 2012.
**Personal:** JD, University of Michigan Law School; BA, Kalamazoo College (Cum Laude). Awards include: several DOJ Special Achievement Awards, DOJ Environmental Enforcement Section Attorney General Award nomination, 2010 EPA Gold Medal Award for Exceptional Service.

### TAYLOR, William E
Pierce Atwood LLP, Portland
207 791 1213
wtaylor@pierceatwood.com
*Featured in Environment (Maine)*

**Practice Areas:** Partner, Environmental Practice Group. Represents clients before administrative agencies. Practice is devoted to matters related to water law, waste discharge, and natural resource licensing and compliance counseling.
**Professional Memberships:** Commissioner, New England Interstate Water Pollution Control Commission; Member, Maine Agricultural Water Management Board; and the American and Maine State Bar Associations Natural Resources Sections.
**Publications:** 'A Wetlands Primer', Natural Resources & Environment, 1992; 'The Watershed Protection Approach', Natural Resources & Environment, 1996; and 'Water and Water Rights', Matthew Bender, 2007.
**Personal:** Vermont Law School, JD and Masters in Environmental Law 1983; University of Massachusetts, BA (cum laude) 1980.

**TOURANGEAU, Joanna B.**
Drummond Woodsum & MacMahon,
Portland
207 772 1941
jtourangeau@dwmlaw.com
*Featured in Environment (Maine)*
**Practice Areas:** Represents multiple Maine
businesses in obtaining local, state, federal permits
for contested proposals to construct multiple spe-
cialized facilities. Represented "potentially respon-
sible parties" in resolving liability under state and
federal "Superfund" laws including acting as a co-
chair of a group of over 100 such PRPs at one site.
Audited numerous facilities in Maine and New
Hampshire for compliance with environmental
laws.
**Professional Memberships:** Admitted in
Maine, Massachusetts, New Hampshire
**Career:** Listed in New England Super Lawyers
directory "Rising Star" - category of
Environmental Law.
**Personal:** JD, The National Law Center at
George Washington University (2000) (with hon-
ors).

**UHL, Eric J**
Fisher & Phillips LLP, Portland
207 774 6001
euhl@laborlawyers.com
*Featured in Labor & Employment (Maine)*
**Career:** Eric Uhl is a Partner in both the
Portland, Maine and Boston offices. He concentrates his practice in employment law, advising
and defending management in all aspects of the
workplace and employer-employee relations. Uhl
provides counsel and representation to management before state and federal courts and administrative agencies in a wide range of matters, including discrimination, wrongful termination, wage
and hour issues, restrictive covenants and non-
competition agreements, employment agreements, and intellectual property. Uhl also is an
experienced mediator. He has defended management in courts nationwide.

**VAN SLYKE, David**
Preti Flaherty Beliveau & Pachios, LLP,
Portland
207 791 3000
dvanslyke@preti.com
*Featured in Environment (Maine)*
**Practice Areas:** Chair of firm's Environmental
Law Practice Group and Co-Chair of Climate
Strategy Group. Practice areas include environ-
mental aspects of corporate strategic planning,
environmental litigation, due diligence in business
and lending transactions, environmental risk
management and compliance counseling, and
defense of governmental enforcement actions and
toxic tort suits.
**Professional Memberships:** Admitted to prac-
tice: District of Columbia (1982), Maine (1992),
US District Court (DC 1982, Maine 1992), US
Court of Appeals (First Circuit 1998). Member:
Maine State Bar Association (and Natural
Resources Section), ABA (and Environment,
Energy and Resources Section). State Law Editor -
BNA Environmental Due Diligence Guide. Fellow
- American College of Environmental Lawyers.
**Career:** Booz-Allen & Hamilton 1982-83; US
EPA: Enforcement Attorney 1983-87, Section
Chief 1987-89, Deputy Director - Hazardous
Waste Division 1989-90, Director - Superfund
Division 1990-91. Preti Flaherty: Of Counsel
1991-94, Partner 1994, Environmental Practice
Group Chair 1995, Climate Strategy Group Co-
Chair 2009.
**Personal:** Born 21 September 1954; JD, Syracuse
University Law School 1981; BS, St. Lawrence
University 1976. EPA awards: Department of
Justice Commendation for Outstanding Service
(1991); Assistant Administrator's Enforcement
Award for Excellence (1990); Special Achievement
Silver (1990) and Bronze Medals (1986 and 1988);
six Superior Performance and Outstanding
Achievement Awards (1984-89).

**VOGEL, Gary**
Drummond Woodsum & MacMahon,
Portland
207 772 1941
gvogel@dwmlaw.com
*Featured in Real Estate (Maine)*
**Practice Areas:** Corporate/commercial law,
commercial real estate, mergers/acquisitions,
secured transactions, real estate acquisition, development, construction, financing. Represents
developers, investors, public housing authorities,
lenders in affordable housing transactions, complex financing transactions including transactions
utilizing Federal Low Income Housing Tax Credit,
New Market Tax Credits, State-Federal Historic
Tax Credits. Represents companies at all stages
from formation to succession planning and exit
strategies and financial institutes in loan transactions and as general counsel.
**Professional Memberships:** Maine State Bar
Association; Board Member/Chair of Legislative
Committee, Maine Real Estate & Development
Association, Maine Affordable Housing Coalition.
**Personal:** Albany Law School (cum laude) 1985.

**WHITE, Jeffrey M**
Pierce Atwood LLP, Portland
207 791 1292
jwhite@pierceatwood.com
*Featured in Litigation (Maine)*
**Practice Areas:** Complex, commercial,
antitrust, trade secret, trade regulation and intel-
lectual property litigation.
**Professional Memberships:** Fellow, Maine Bar
Foundation; former Chair, Maine Bar Association
CLE Committee and Director, NE Bar
Association.
**Career:** US v American Skiing Company (merger
litigation); FPL Energy v CMP (defense judgment
on $846 million asset purchase contract); Maine v
Sears Roebuck & Co.(defense judgment on Unfair
Trade Practice claims involving service agreements
and sales practices); Net 2 Press v 58 Dix Ave.
Corp. (defense judgment on business sale contract
and fraud claims); Colt Defense v Bushmaster
Firearms (successful trademark litigation defense).

**WOODBURY, Judith Fletcher**
Pierce Atwood LLP, Portland
207 791 1386
jwoodbury@pierceatwood.com
*Featured in Real Estate (Maine)*
**Practice Areas:** Judy is the Real Estate Practice
Group Leader for the firm. Her broad, general real
estate practice includes complex commercial asset
and financing transactions and all aspects of title
matters.
**Professional Memberships:** Leadership Gift
Co-Chair, Campaign for Justice; Maine Bar
Foundation Fellow; Maine State Bar Association:
Real Estate (past Chair), Women's Law Sections;
Cumberland Bar Association; Maine Land
Conservation Attorney's Network; Maine Society
of Land Surveyors.
**Career:** Assistant Attorney General, Maine;
Lawyers Title Insurance Corporation.
**Personal:** Friends of Casco Bay, Vice President
for Board of Directors. University of Maine Law
School, JD; University of Maine, BA.

**ZIMPRITCH, James B**
Pierce Atwood LLP, Portland
207 791 1270
jzimpritch@pierceatwood.com
*Featured in Corporate/M&A (Maine)*
**Practice Areas:** Broad corporate experience.
Active M&A practice. Extensive experience in corporate and securities, banking, insurance, shareholder disputes, director duties, structuring
investments and general commercial law. Involved
in nearly every takeover fight in Maine in last 20
years. Represents emerging, middle-market, and
large publicly held companies.
**Professional Memberships:** American Law
Institute (1991-); ABA Corporate Laws
Committee (1986-92, 2002-08, Secretary 2009-);
Maine: Chair, Corporate Law Revision Committee
(2000-); past Chair, Business Law Section; fre-
quent lecturer.
**Career:** Partner, Pierce Atwood LLP.
**Publications:** 'Maine Corporation Law &
Practice', the definitive treatise.
**Personal:** Duke Law School, JD; 'Duke Law
Journal'; Dartmouth College, AB.

# BERNSTEIN SHUR

www.bernsteinshur.com **tel:** 207 774 1200 **fax:** 207 774 1127

**CEO:** Charles E Miller
**Senior Shareholder:** Leonard M Nelson
Number of shareholders: 64  Number of lawyers: 107

**Firm Overview:**
Bernstein Shur is one of northern New England's largest multi-service law firms, with more than 100 attorneys in Maine and New Hampshire. Founded in 1915, Bernstein Shur is known for providing practical and innovative counsel. The firm is recognized for its superior technical competence, seasoned judgment, responsiveness, and cost-effective solutions.

**Main Areas of Practice:**

**Business Law:**
Bernstein Shur is a leader in structuring ownership perpetuation plans and related contractual arrangements and financing strategies. Group attorneys represent bidders, targets, investors making financial acquisitions, company founders, financial advisers, and other parties in privately negotiated transfers of securities or assets, leveraged buyouts, public-company combinations, and takeovers. Bernstein Shur is also home to one of the largest and most experienced tax practices in northern New England, providing practical solutions for complicated state, federal, and international tax issues.

**Business Restructuring & Insolvency:**
Bernstein Shur's Business Restructuring and Insolvency Practice is the largest in northern New England. The group's attorneys provide counsel in complex reorganizations and liquidations under Chapter 11 and Chapter 7, large commercial insolvencies, and related litigation. The group's lawyers are active in state, federal, and bankruptcy courts in Maine, New Hampshire, Massachusetts, and many other districts in the United States. Bob Keach, co-chair of the practice group, is past president of the American Bankruptcy Institute.

**Construction Law:**
The firm's construction attorneys handle all aspects of construction law from contract drafting, negotiation, and competitive bidding issues to the development and presentation of claims, mediation, arbitration and litigation, mechanics' liens, and insurance coverage issues.

**Energy & Environmental:**
The firm's energy attorneys represent regional and international clients on energy generation and distribution issues. Its clients are independent power producers, small power producers, co-generators that produce electricity from renewable resources, financial institutions, and large consumers of electricity. The group's environmental attorneys represent individuals, businesses, and municipalities trying to comply with or enforce local, state, or federal environmental and land use laws, as well as acquiring other businesses or large land parcels.

**Financial Services & Securities:**
The firm's financial services and securities lawyers represent the full spectrum of securities regulatory, compliance, and transactional matters, including counseling on capital structure, key governance matters, fiduciary responsibilities, no-action and exemptive relief, and defense of SEC investigations and enforcement matters. The group has expertise handling matters involving public and private issuers, banks, mutual funds, hedge funds, investment advisers, broker-dealers, fund industry service providers, and diversified financial institutions. The group's attorneys include former senior staff members of the US Securities and Exchange Commission and former in-house attorneys for some of the world's largest financial institutions.

**Intellectual Property & Technology:**
The firm's intellectual property attorneys help clients obtain, manage, license, and enforce intellectual property rights. The group handles matters involving utility and design patents, trademarks and service marks, copyrights, and trade secrets. Technology attorneys focus on issues surrounding today's developing business and consumer technologies. The group represents technology developers and parties using new technologies to improve business processes.

**Labor & Employment:**
The Labor and Employment Practice Group represents and counsels private and public employers, including colleges, universities and private secondary schools, throughout northern New England in all aspects of employment law and regulation. Group attorneys help clients address legal issues in the workplace and find practical solutions that fit the business environment and work force.

**Litigation:**
The firm's litigation attorneys represents plaintiffs and defendants in areas including commercial disputes, securities litigation, antitrust, business torts, taxation, energy, products liability, personal injury, transportation, real estate transactions, education, intellectual property infringement, criminal cases, constitutional issues, healthcare, insurance, and environmental matters.

**Municipal, Legislative & Regulatory Law:**
The firm's municipal attorneys serve as general or special counsel to governmental entities including towns, cities, counties, school districts, sanitary and sewer districts, regional planning commissions, and quasi-municipal agencies. The firm's legislative and regulatory attorneys represent clients before the Maine Legislature, state and federal agencies.

**Real Estate:**
The Real Estate Practice Group, the largest of its kind in northern New England, has expertise in all aspects of commercial real estate and a record of finding practical solutions to complex transactional issues. The firm negotiates and closes development and value-added transactions for privately and publicly held businesses, individuals, trusts, subsidized housing projects and investment partnerships involving public and private land ownership.

**Trusts & Estates:**
The firm's trusts and estates attorneys advise clients on estate planning and on the administration, oversight, and settlement of trusts and estates. The group provides counsel on personal and tax planning strategies, business planning, and succession planning.

**International Work:**
Bernstein Shur's attorneys engage in dispute resolution, commercial negotiation, and government relations throughout the industrial and developing world. As Maine's exclusive member of Lex Mundi, the world's leading association of independent law firms, the firm is able to call on the resources, expertise, and local knowledge of member firms worldwide.

**OFFICES**

MAINE
**PORTLAND:** 100 Middle Street, PO Box 9729, ME 04104-5029
Tel: 207 774 1200  Fax: 207 774 1127
Email: info@bernsteinshur.com

**AUGUSTA:** 146 Capitol Street, ME 04330
Tel: 207 623 1596  Fax: 207 626 0200

NEW HAMPSHIRE
**MANCHESTER:** Jefferson Mill Building, 670 North Commercial Street, Suite 108, PO Box 1120, NH 03104
Tel: 603 623 8700  Fax: 603 623 7775

**BERNSTEIN SHUR**

COUNSELORS AT LAW

# DRUMMOND WOODSUM

**www.**dwmlaw.com **tel:** 207 772 1941

**Managing Director:** Benjamin E Marcus
Number of attorneys: 63  Number of consultants: 5

## Firm Overview:

Founded in 1965, Drummond Woodsum has grown into one of the most respected law firms in Northern New England. From their offices in Portland, Maine, and Portsmouth and Manchester, New Hampshire, the firm provides a full spectrum of legal and consulting services for clients across the country. The firm serves some of the nations' largest corporations, small start-up companies, financial institutions, Indian nations and tribal enterprises, municipalities, school districts and individuals. No matter the size of the client, the firm's attorneys take great pride in delivering superior legal advice in a timely and cost-efficient manner. Their goal is to provide clients with services that address the clients' immediate legal needs while taking into account their long-term needs and objectives. The firm's attorneys and consultants never forget that every client is different, and effective legal solutions are never one size fits all. By drawing upon the expertise of individual attorneys and consultants within the firm's service groups, Drummond Woodsum efficiently and creatively responds to the unique needs of every client.

## Main Areas of Practice:

### Business Services:

The Business Group handles a full range of corporate, commercial, corporate finance and securities matters, advising clients on mergers and acquisitions, corporate tax planning and financing, multi-state financings, venture capital and private placements, and international trade. Attorneys in the firm are approved 'Red Book' bond counsel and have extensive experience in public utility law, franchising, executive compensation and bankruptcy, as well as other areas of corporate and business law. The firm also has extensive experience in the area of low income housing tax credits, representing both lenders and developers in these matters.
**Contact:** Michael E High  **Email:** mhigh@dwmlaw.com

### Labor & Employment Services:

The Employment Group is a team of attorneys and highly skilled consultants who counsel private and public employers on the full range of employment issues and manage employment-related risks. The practice includes substantial litigation in federal and state courts, and representation before federal and state agencies, including the National Labor Relations Board and the Maine Labor Relations Board, Human Rights Commissions and other administrative bodies.
**Contact:** Daniel J Rose  **Email:** drose@dwmlaw.com

### Trial Services:

The firm is involved in every type of civil litigation in federal and state courts and administrative agencies, including the United States Supreme Court. Recent cases fall into a broad range of areas including business and commercial litigation, employment, securities, intellectual property, antitrust, real estate and land use, construction disputes, product liability, white-collar criminal defense, bankruptcy and Native American tribal rights.
**Contact:** David S Sherman  **Email:** dsherman@dwmlaw.com

### Indian Law:

Drummond Woodsum's nationally recognized Indian Law Group provides the highest quality legal services to Indian nations, their enterprises and financial institutions, investors and companies that do business with tribes across the country. The firm's Indian practice brings top tier legal, business and transactional experience to its work with some of the country's most successful Indian nations and enterprises. The Indian law attorneys work with clients to address their immediate concerns in ways that are consistent with their long-term economic and governmental objectives. With this flexibility, the firm is able to provide tailored legal services to meet the particular needs of all their tribal clients.
**Contact:** Kaighn Smith Jr  **Email:** ksmith@dwmlaw.com

### Immigration Services:

Drummond Woodsum's Immigration Practice Group is the largest in Northern New England, representing businesses, individuals and families on all aspects of immigration law and procedures throughout New England and the country. The immigration attorneys assist businesses with H-1B visas, labor certification, permanent residence status for key alien employees, and employment compliance including I-9 compliance reviews, trainings and defense in ICE enforcement matters. They also have experience in the complex area of export control licensing and its interaction with immigration law – an area of heightened scrutiny by the federal government. In addition, the Drummond Woodsum immigration attorneys represent scores of individuals and families seeking marriage-based permanent residence, naturalization or family reunification. The firm's world-class expertise is enhanced by a state-of-the-art technology platform which allows it to automate filing preparation and provides real-time access to case updates and report generation for their clients – all within a cost-effective fee structure with no surprises.
**Contact:** Mona Movafaghi
**Email:** mmovafaghi@dwmlaw.com

### School & Local Government Services:

The firm offers expertise in municipal and school law in areas including labor relations, employment matters, special education, finance, construction, employee benefits and litigation, and has litigated numerous precedent-setting cases on behalf of public sector clients. The school practice is the largest on the East coast and is widely recognized as pre-eminent in Maine with a growing presence in New Hampshire. The firm's school law website (www.schoollaw.com) is nationally known.
**Contact:** Melissa A Hewey  **Email:** mhewey@dwmlaw.com

### International Work:

The firm is the only Maine firm to be a member of Meritas, a worldwide organization that offers high quality legal services through an integrated, yet independent, group of full-service law firms. As a member of Meritas, the firm is able to provide clients with legal expertise wherever their needs may arise throughout the US and around the world.

### Clients:

Clients include *Fortune* 500 and private businesses throughout the US and Canada, insurance companies, commercial banks and other financial institutions, public utilities, municipalities, Native American tribes and their business entities, colleges and universities, and public and private schools.

**OFFICES**

MAINE
**PORTLAND:** 84 Marginal Way, Suite 600, ME 04101-2480
Tel: 207 772 1941
Email: info@dwmlaw.com
Websites: www.dwmlaw.com; www.ServingSchools.com

NEW HAMPSHIRE
**PORTSMOUTH:** 100 International Drive, Suite 340, NH 03801
Tel: 603 433 3317

**MANCHESTER:** 66 Hanover Street, Suite 302, NH 03104
Tel: 800 727 1941

**Drummond**Woodsum

# PIERCE ATWOOD LLP

**www.**pierceatwood.com **tel:** 207 791 1100 **fax:** 207 791 1350

**Managing Partner:** Gloria A Pinza
**Senior Partner:** Peter W Culley
Number of partners: 82  Number of other lawyers: 51

## Firm Overview:

Pierce Atwood LLP is a leading New England law firm, recognized nationally and internationally for expertise in complex and class action litigation, energy law, mergers and acquisitions, business and information technology, intellectual property and consumer and bank regulatory law. Current clients range from entrepreneurs to members of the *Fortune* 500 to foreign governments and span a variety of traditional and emerging business sectors. Clients derive superior value based upon the firm's efficient and cost effective service structure coupled with its sophistication, responsiveness and industry knowledge.

## Main Areas of Practice:

### Bankruptcy & Creditors' Rights:

The firm represents secured creditors, landlords, trade creditors, trustees, debtors and committees in complex Chapter 11 reorganizations, business liquidations, out of court workouts, collection matters and avoidance actions, and often represents buyers of businesses out of bankruptcy in Section 363 transactions and pursuant to Chapter 11 plans.
**Contact:** Jacob A Manheimer

### Business:

The firm's Business Group is a leader in acquisitions and sales of businesses, venture capital, banking and finance services, private equity and other financing transactions, entity formation and representation of owners, directors and officers. The firm offers teams specifically focused on family businesses and start-up ventures.
**Contact:** Christopher E Howard

### Employment:

The group seeks to build expertise in its clients through counseling and training. It offers representation of management in state and federal trial, appellate, administrative and ADR proceedings; in matters arising under the NLRA and RLA (bargaining, arbitrations, board proceedings, organizing and labor disputes); in specialty areas such as immigration, benefits, FLSA, OSHA, and workers compensation; and in government relations.
**Contact:** James R Erwin

### Energy:

The firm has built a national and international reputation serving domestic utilities, deregulated enterprises such as major merchant plants, and state and foreign governments' need for energy regulatory and market expertise. Clients are regional, national (utilities, independent project developers, lenders and investors in over 20 states), and international, including foreign governments and international financial institutions. The firm is also known for its strong capability in the development and regulation of renewable energy technologies such as wind, hydroelectric and tidal power.
**Contact:** Randall S Rich

### Environmental:

The firm is the regional leader with national clients in all areas of environmental law and regulation, including land use, wastewater discharge, air emissions, solid waste, hazardous waste, chemical disclosure, wetlands, endangered species and all other natural resources law.
**Contact:** Matthew D Manahan

### Governmental Relations:

The firm's Government Relations Group combines substantive legal expertise, access to governmental leader- ship and a comprehensive, integrated array of comple- mentary services such as public relations, traditional lobbying, media relations, campaigns and stakeholder education, all designed to further clients' public policy initiatives.
**Contact:** John D Delahanty

### Intellectual Property:

The firm has a far reaching intellectual property and technology practice that includes IP diligence, licensing, copyright, patent, trademark, e-commerce, data privacy and internet-related matters for emerging and established companies with national and international business interests. The firm manages national and international patent and trademark portfolios and litigates claims of infringement and misappropriation.
**Contact:** Peter Guffin

### Litigation:

The firm has a national and regional practice in business litigation including energy, intellectual property, white-collar, products liability, class actions, environmental, ERISA, insurance and many other areas. Members include the two most recent Chief Justices of the Maine Supreme Judicial Court, a former Independent Counsel, and a past President and four Fellows of the American College of Trial Lawyers.
**Contact:** David E Barry

### Privacy & Data Security:

The firm offers a cross-disciplinary team with both legal and industry expertise to provide clients with the best practical advice on complex issues such as record retention, breach notification, privacy policies, information safeguarding, e-discovery, consumer identification and other privacy and data security issues.
**Contact:** Peter Guffin

### Real Estate:

The firm's Real Estate Group has a sophisticated commercial practice that includes development, financing, entity creation, taxation leasing, land use permitting and conveyancing of retail, commercial, industrial and energy facilities and timberlands.
**Contact:** Judy F Woodbury

### Tax:

The firm's expertise covers corporate structuring, M&A and other transactions, business planning, succession and estate planning and IRS controversies, as well as all forms of taxation, including personal and corporate income tax, sales and use tax, property tax, excise tax, multistate taxation and related services such as tax controversies, transactional advice, planning, ruling requests and legislative.
**Contact:** Jonathan A Block

### International Work:

The firm's international work encompasses multilateral transactions; cross-border financings; enterprise restructuring; energy and environmental law; EU compliance; regulatory reform and compliance; competition; privatization; litigation; arbitration; cross-border boundary dispute resolution; intellectual property licensing and transfer; defense and litigation. Attorneys have worked in 50 countries.

### Clients:

Angela Adams Design, Anthem Blue Cross & Blue Shield, Backyard Farms, Barber Foods, Brookfield Renewable Power, California Department of Water Resources, Casella Waste Systems, Calypte Biomedical Corporation, Central Maine Power Company, Cianbro Corporation, City of Portland, Dead River Company, DuPont, Environmental Power Corporation, Fairchild Semiconductor, Fraser Paper, Georgia Pacific Corporation, Hannaford Bros. Co., IDEXX Laboratories, Immucell Corporation, J.D. Irving, Ltd., KeyBank N.A., Mercy Hospital, Nestle Waters N.A./Poland Spring, RBS Citizens, N.A., Sappi Fine Paper N.A., Sprague Energy Corporation, State of California, TD Bank, N.A., The Timberland Company, Tom's of Maine/Colgate-Palmolive, University of New England, Unum, USAID, Verizon, Verso Paper Corp., World Bank, WEX, Inc.

## OFFICE

**MAINE**

**PORTLAND:** Merrill's Wharf, 254 Commercial Street, ME 04101
Tel: 207 791 1100  Fax: 207 791 1350
Email: info@pierceatwood.com

**MASSACHUSETTS**

**BOSTON:** 100 Summer Street, 2250, MA 02110
Tel: 617 488 8100  Fax: 617 824 2020

# PRETI FLAHERTY BELIVEAU & PACHIOS LLP

**www.**preti.com **tel:** 207 791 3000 **fax:** 207 791 3111

**Managing Partner:** Jonathan S Piper
Number of partners: 61
Number of other lawyers: 41

### Firm Overview:
Preti Flaherty answers the call of a diverse business community with a sophisticated practice, international reach and multistate experience. One of northern New England's largest law firms, it is known for high-powered legal talent and exceptional credentials working with federal, state and local governments.

### Main Areas of Practice:

**Business Law:**
Preti Flaherty advises clients in every stage of business development including business formation, securities offerings, technology protection and venture capital financing. The firm can also adroitly counsel clients on technology licensing, executive compensation, debt financing and counseling boards. Those businesses that find themselves poised to move into the regional, national or global level also turn to Preti Flaherty for counsel on mergers and acquisitions, franchising, joint ventures and strategic alliances, international transactions, commercial contracts, and tax planning.

**Real Estate:**
Preti Flaherty represents buyers, sellers, lenders and developers on a broad range of complex commercial real estate matters. From negotiating acquisitions, easements, land use issues and commercial leases to securing tax exempt and tax increment financing, the firm is involved with some of northern New England's largest and most complex real estate and land use projects.

**Energy:**
Preti Flaherty is a national leader in the rapidly evolving US-Canada energy marketplace. The firm counsels industrial consumers, energy project developers, energy cooperatives and aggregators, and others on the reduction of risk and cost through deregulation. The firm provides counsel on rate reductions, special rate contracts, cost of service, rate structures, customer relations and competitive relationships with, from and among utilities, energy suppliers and customers. Preti attorneys also assist in the structuring of entities to finance, build, license and operate renewable and natural gas powerplants and large and small transmission lines. The firm is the national leader in the development of Regional Transmission Organizations and Independent System Operators which are responsive to the needs of customers and consumer groups.

**Environmental:**
Preti Flaherty has one of the region's largest and most diverse environmental practices. The firm's environmental litigators, transactional attorneys and regulatory specialists advise clients on legal issues related to all aspects of environmental regulation, compliance and due diligence, including air and water pollution, hazardous waste, chemical regulation and land use controls. The firm offers in-depth experience in all phases of federal, state and local administrative and civil judicial enforcement proceedings.

**Health Law:**
Preti Flaherty counsels hospitals, nursing homes, home health agencies, rehabilitation centers and other health care facilities, as well as insurers and individual practitioners. The firm has encompassing experience dealing with emerging health care issues and their legal ramifications and works hard to adjust regulations and advance laws and interpretations in support of its clients' interests. Preti Flaherty provides extensive services to institutions facing increasingly complex state regulatory issues. It has represented hospitals at hearings and proceedings before the Department of Human Services and the Federal Provider Reimbursement Review Board.

**Intellectual Property:**
The firm works with clients to develop creative and cost-effective strategies for securing, maintaining, exploiting, and enforcing a company's intellectual property assets and has significant experience in technical fields and represent clients with IP matters including patents, trademarks and copyrights, dispute resolution, trade secrets, unfair competition, licensing, M&A, entertainment, multimedia and software law.

**Labor & Employment:**
Preti Flaherty helps businesses, both in non-union and unionized settings, avoid potentially damaging situations by developing, implementing and communicating sound workplace policies and strategies. In addition to the counseling and risk prevention work the group provides, it also has extensive experience litigating claims in state and federal courts, representing management in National Labor Relations Board proceedings and arbitrations under collective bargaining agreements, and defending charges of discrimination before the Equal Employment Opportunity Commission and the Maine Human Rights Commission.

**Government Affairs:**
Preti Flaherty has an extensive legislative/regulatory practice. The firm's inside knowledge of public policy and the legislative process, combined with legal skills both traditional and groundbreaking, combine to create a wide range of approaches to resolving issues and influencing legislation. Many of the firm's attorneys have actively participated in the legislative process at both state and federal levels.

**Litigation:**
Preti Flaherty boasts one of the largest and most respected litigation groups in northern New England. Recognizing that success is often the result of pre-litigation counseling, the Litigation Group is nonetheless equipped to advocate for its clients wherever necessary, including consensual or mandatory mediation, domestic or international arbitration, and trials in state or federal court. The group's experience is varied and extensive, including noteworthy successes in such matters as toxic tort litigation, securities claims, professional liability litigation, construction claims, lender liability claims, injunction of governmental agencies on constitutional grounds, and libel defense of national publications. Members of the litigation group are licensed in more than a dozen states and numerous federal courts.

**International Work:**
Preti Flaherty works with foreign-based companies seeking to do business in the United States whether it is a straightforward joint venture or a more complex acquisition. The firm helps companies navigate the local, state and federal legal and regulatory landscape.

### OFFICES

**MAINE**
**PORTLAND:** One City Center, PO Box 9546, ME 04112-9546
Tel: 207 791 3000  Fax: 207 791 3111
Email: info@preti.com
**AUGUSTA:** 45 Memorial Circle, PO Box 1058, ME 04332-1058
Tel: 207 623 5300  Fax: 207 623 2914

**NEW HAMPSHIRE**
**CONCORD:** 57 North Main Street, PO Box 1318,
NH 03302-1318
Tel: 603 410 1500  Fax: 603 410 1501

**MASSACHUSETTS**
**BOSTON:** Ten Post Office Square, MA 02109
Tel: 617 226 3800  Fax: 617 226 3801
**SALEM:** 27 Congress Street, Suite 305-8, MA 01970
Tel: 978 740 9200  Fax: 978 740 0300

**WASHINGTON, DC**
**WASHINGTON, DC:** 601 Pennsylvania Ave, NW Suite 900,
South Building,  20004
Tel: 202 220 3166  Fax: 202 639 8238

**NEW JERSEY**
**BEDMINSTER:** 90 Washington Valley Road, NJ 07921
Tel: 908 234 9394

# VERRILL DANA, LLP

www.verrilldana.com **tel:** 207 774 4000

**Managing Partner:** Keith C Jones
Number of partners: 47
Number of other lawyers: 58

### Firm Overview:

Verrill Dana, LLP is a mid-sized firm with a strong regional presence. The firm is able to handle the most complex legal needs of clients with interests around the globe, staffing each matter with experienced counsel, ready to address the individual concerns of each client with personal attention and understanding of each client's business needs.

## OFFICES

**MAINE**
**AUGUSTA:** 45 Memorial Circle, ME 04332
**PORTLAND:** One Portland Square, ME, 04101

**CONNECTICUT**
**STAMFORD:** 243 Tresser Boulevard, 17th Floor, CT 06901

**DISTRICT OF COLUMBIA**
**WASHINGTON DC:** 400 North Capitol Street NW, Suite 585, DC 20001-1511

**MASSACHUSETTS**
**BOSTON:** One Boston Place, Suite 1600, MA 02108-4407

### Main Areas of Practice:

#### Bankruptcy & Creditors' Rights:

Verrill Dana's Bankruptcy Group has represented clients in virtually every significant bankruptcy case in Maine for over 20 years. It is known for its highly efficient staffing and effective advocacy, and has represented trustees, debtors and creditors in all phases of Chapter 11 reorganization and handled many other bankruptcy and creditors' rights matters.
**Contact:** Roger A Clement **Tel:** 207 253 4412
**Email:** rclement@verrilldana.com

#### Benefits & Compensation:

With the leading practice in northern New England, the group advises employers around the country on compliance with ERISA and Internal Revenue Code as applicable to retirement plans, health plans and executive compensation. Its attorneys have counseled public and private companies (as well as large tax-exempt organizations) in a wide variety of employee benefits and executive compensation plan issues and have extensive experience in fiduciary compliance and transactional matters.
**Contact:** Suzanne E Meeker **Tel:** 207 253 4906
**Email:** smeeker@verrilldana.com

#### Business Law:

Respected for its deep knowledge and broad experience in M&A, tax, securities, commercial finance, banking, intellectual property and corporate law, Verrill Dana's Business Law Group serves as primary outside counsel to public and private companies throughout New England. The group has represented buyers and sellers in a wide variety of corporation transactions and also serves as general counsel for businesses in many different industries.
**Contact:** Alan D MacEwan **Tel:** 207 253 4410
**Email:** amacewan@verrilldana.com

#### Energy Law:

Focusing on local, state and federal regulation of energy suppliers and users of energy throughout New England, this group represents wind, natural gas, hydro and other energy clients on regulatory, environmental, real estate, finance, tax and governmental relations issues.

**Contact:** William S Harwood **Tel:** 207 253 4702
**Email:** wharwood@verrilldana.com

#### Environmental Law:

Verrill Dana is known as the most successful firm in Maine for the permitting, compliance, development and litigation needs of large infrastructure and other development projects, including one of the largest and most creative river restoration projects in our nation's history and the permitting and/or development of nearly 700 MW of wind energy.
**Contact:** Juliet T Browne **Tel:** 207 253 4608
**Email:** jbrowne@verrilldana.com

#### Labor & Employment:

Highly adept at managing all aspects of the employer/employee relationship, Verrill Dana's Labor & Employment Group is nationally recognized for cutting-edge labor relations strategies and experience, including multi-state arbitrations and Project Labor Agreements.
**Contact:** Douglas P Currier **Tel:** 207 253 4450
**Email:** dcurrier@verrilldana.com

#### Healthcare:

The recent addition of experienced healthcare attorneys to the Boston office has significantly increased Verrill Dana's capacity to serve healthcare providers throughout New England. Together with attorneys in other related practices, the group has recovered millions of dollars from Medicare and has completed several significant hospital/medical center affiliations in the past year.
**Contact:** Jeffrey L Heidt **Tel:** 617 309 2605
**Email:** jheidt@verrilldana.com

#### Litigation & Trial:

Among the most experienced legal teams in the region, Verrill Dana's Litigation & Trial Group is comprised of dedicated, savvy and successful trial and commercial litigators who have years of experience advocating for their clients in a wide variety of tribunals. Recent significant matters have involved intellectual property, transportation, and franchise/dealership issues.
**Contact:** A Robert Ruesch **Tel:** 207 253 4610
**Email:** rruesch@verrilldana.com

#### Real Estate:

A major player in the region's wind and hydroelectric energy development and timberland acquisition, the firm's Real Estate Group is also involved in many of the largest commercial development projects in the state, including industrial property leasing, telecommunications permitting and site acquisition, permitting, leasing, construction and financing for office buildings, multi-building commercial/industrial complex, and mixed-use development projects.
**Contact:** Anthony M Calcagni **Tel:** 207 253 4516
**Email:** acalcagni@verrilldana.com

#### Timberlands & Conservation:

Verrill Dana's Timberlands Group has represented clients on deals involving millions of acres of land in 27 U.S. states and four Latin American countries, including some of the largest and most complex land transactions in U.S. history. It is well known for its broad base of experience and its highly efficient representation, tailored to each client's individual needs.
**Contact:** Jeffrey T Selser **Tel:** 207 253 4528
**Email:** jselser@verrilldana.com

## How lawyers are ranked

Every year we carry out thousands of in-depth interviews with clients in order to assess the reputations and expertise of business lawyers worldwide. The qualities we look for (and which determine rankings) include technical legal ability, professional conduct, client service, commercial awareness/astuteness, diligence, commitment, and other qualities most valued by the client. For details of our research team, see p.5.

## MARYLAND: An introduction

### Contributed by Miles & Stockbridge PC

Foreign businesses from dozens of countries have chosen Maryland to launch their operations in the USA. Maryland offers an attractive location in the mid-Atlantic, a skilled and highly educated work force and proximity to the nation's capital. In addition to being an attractive place to locate US operations, Maryland's laws make it an attractive jurisdiction for organizing US business entities.

### Good location and legal benefits

Maryland offers proximity to Washington, DC and the opportunity to be near the decision and policy makers of the federal government. Maryland is home to federal agencies, such as the National Institutes of Health, the National Institute of Standards and Technology, the National Security Agency, the U.S. Food and Drug Administration, the Social Security Administration and the National Aeronautics & Space Administration. These agencies, plus world-class healthcare and research institutions, make Maryland fertile ground for successful companies in life sciences and IT businesses, as well as government contractors. Quality schools and higher education institutions produce a skilled and motivated workforce. A concentration of IT workers supports the dramatic growth of Maryland's cyber security industry. The state also has a rich history of manufacturing that continues today in a variety of industries. Maryland enjoys an excellent power and telecoms infrastructure and a strong transportation system.

Maryland's location on the East Coast permits easy access to financial institutions, as well as the private capital offered by private equity and venture funds in the region. Numerous technology transfer and business development financing programs are offered through state and local agencies, including the Department of Business and Economic Development and the Maryland Technology Development Corporation. A variety of tax credits for businesses, based on activity, industry and geographic location, and a network of business incubators and accelerators at facilities around the region, are available to foreign-owned businesses.

Maryland's Business and Technology Case Management Program enables its trial courts to handle business and technology disputes in an efficient manner. Maryland's was the first business court in the country to expressly include technology disputes in its jurisdiction. The program emphasizes judicial education, permitting litigants to have more confidence in the courts because judges will have a better understanding of business and technology issues. The program also offers a specialized forum for alternative dispute resolution.

Maryland's statutes authorizing formation of limited liability business entities, including corporations, real estate investment trusts, statutory trusts, and limited liability companies, offer flexibility in governance and capitalization. Maryland courts have been vigilant in upholding the presumption that managers of business entities act in good faith in managing affairs of business entities. That presumption, or the "business judgment rule", is embedded in statute with respect to directors of Maryland corporations.

In addition to the business judgment rule, the Maryland General Corporation Law (the 'MGCL') offers a statutory framework permitting directors of Maryland corporations the ability to make business decisions in all circumstances without undue concern about personal liability. Directors of Maryland corporations are held to a statutory standard of care pursuant to which they must act in good faith, in a manner they reasonably believe to be in the best interest of the corporation and with ordinary care. The MGCL includes a presumption that a director has met that standard of care and confers immunity from liability if the standard is met. The statute also provides flexibility for corporations to exculpate directors from liability to the corporation or its stockholders from money damages.

When directors of a Maryland corporation find themselves confronted with a possible sale of the company, whether friendly or hostile, the MGCL provides protections to the directors as extensive as any state. By statute, directors are expressly entitled to 'just say no,' and their actions related to such a transaction will not be subject to greater scrutiny than is applied in any other context. The MGCL also offers structural impediments to unsolicited takeover attempts – the Maryland Business Combination Act and the Maryland Control Share Acquisition Act – applicable to corporations having 100 stockholders or more.

Under the Maryland Business Combination Act, certain business combinations between a Maryland corporation and a stockholder owning 10% or more of the voting power of the corporation's stock, or affiliates of that stockholder, are prohibited for five years. Those business combinations include mergers, consolidations and, in certain circumstances, transfers of assets and other transactions. After the five-year moratorium, any such business combination must be approved by a supermajority of voting stockholders, unless stockholders receive a minimum price or 'fair value.'

The Maryland Control Share Acquisition Act provides that stock of the corporation acquired by any person in excess of certain ranges of voting power will have no voting rights unless approved by a vote of two-thirds of the corporation's outstanding voting stock, excluding stock owned by the acquirer. Any person who has made or proposes to make a controlling share acquisition may seek a stockholders' vote to consider the voting rights of the shares. If the voting rights are not approved by the stockholders, then, subject to certain conditions, the corporation may redeem the control shares.

## Conclusion

Maryland's corporate laws and anti-takeover statutes enable directors to carefully evaluate a sale of the company and to protect the company from unwanted advances. That protection, and the statutory protections for officers and directors of Maryland corporations afforded by the MGCL, indicate the favorable climate that Maryland offers for new and established businesses.

# CORPORATE/M&A

Commentary about individuals can be found under their firm's paragraph. If the firm has no paragraph (is not ranked) look at Other Notable Practitioners.

| Corporate/M&A |
| --- |
| **Leading Firms** |
| **Band 1** |
| DLA Piper LLP (US) * |
| Hogan Lovells US LLP |
| Venable LLP * |
| **Band 2** |
| Miles & Stockbridge PC * |
| **Band 3** |
| Ballard Spahr LLP * |
| Duane Morris LLP * |
| Lerch, Early & Brewer, Chartered * |
| Ober Kaler Grimes & Shriver * |
| Whiteford, Taylor & Preston LLP * |

## Band 1

### DLA Piper LLP (US)
**See profile on p.1971**

**THE FIRM** This excellent team comes recommended for its expertise in securities and corporate governance work. The group is also noted for its expertise in venture capital and financing transactions and shareholder disputes. Work in the past year includes acting for Human Genome Sciences on its acquisition by GlaxoSmithKline, resulting in a negotiated merger agreement. Other key clients include T. Rowe Price, Deltek, Laureate Education and West Pharmaceutical Services.
**Sources say:** *"They are very responsive, resourceful and diligent. They work with us to find solutions and solve problems. With one phone call or e-mail I can get DLA to focus its global resources on any challenge."*
**KEY INDIVIDUALS Jay Smith** (see p.1433) is noted for his strengths in securities and M&A, and is also routinely sought to advise on corporate governance issues. *"He is one of the best corporate lawyers I've ever dealt with,"* reports one well-placed commentator. Smith led on the Human Genome Sciences matter, alongside **Jason Harmon** (see p.1427). Harmon is recognized for his work with technology and emerging growth companies and REITs. A source says: *"His work, as always, has been stellar. He has provided exemplary service to me."* **David Chalk** (see p.1425) is well

versed in public offerings of equity and debt securities, and public and private M&A, and splits his time between the firm's Baltimore and Washington, DC offices. Recent work includes acting for Desire2Learn Incorporated on a multi-million-dollar strategic round of financing from New Enterprise Associates and OMERs Ventures, which resulted in the largest single venture capital investment in Canadian software history. Rising star **Kelly Tubman Hardy** (see p.1427) acts for public and private companies and investors on both domestic and cross-border financing and business transactions. In a recent highlight, she represented West Pharmaceuticals in a $173 million tender offer and a $168 million private placement of senior debt securities. *"She is tireless and extremely talented; you can call her anytime about anything,"* notes one enthusiastic interviewee.

### Hogan Lovells US LLP

**THE FIRM** This superb practice comes recommended for its strengths in M&A, private equity, securities and tax matters, acting for a diverse group of domestic and international clients. It is particularly renowned for its expertise in the defense, energy and life sciences arenas, and is also regularly sought to handle work in the education and financial services sectors. It counts Lockheed Martin, Wabash National, Accenture and ABS Capital among its impressive client roster.
**Sources say:** *"They're excellent – I recommend them whenever I can. They're a smart, very quick and efficient high-end firm."*
**KEY INDIVIDUALS** The highly regarded **Henry Kahn** is an expert in M&A, securities and investment management matters, and represents a fine choice of counsel for clients in the financial services space. The *"terrific"* **Glenn Campbell** enjoys a fine reputation in the market for his strengths in M&A and is also routinely sought for his private equity expertise. He maintains an excellent track record for his work with government contractors and pharmaceutical clients. **Michael Silver** acts for a diverse client base drawn from, among other areas, the technology, manufacturing and healthcare sectors, advising on M&A, private equity and venture capital investment, and corporate restructuring. *"He's the most efficient lawyer I've ever seen: responsive, prompt, and extremely broad in his*

| Corporate/M&A | |
| --- | --- |
| **Senior Statesmen** | |
| Senior Statesmen: distinguished older practitioners | |
| Lohr Jr Walter | *Hogan Lovells US LLP* |
| **Leading Individuals** | |
| **Band 1** | |
| Cook Bryson | *Venable LLP* * |
| Hanks, Jr James J | *Venable LLP* * |
| Kahn Henry D | *Hogan Lovells US LLP* |
| Silver Michael J | *Hogan Lovells US LLP* |
| Smith Jr Jay | *DLA Piper LLP (US)* * |
| **Band 2** | |
| Baader Michael | *Venable LLP* * |
| Campbell Glenn C | *Hogan Lovells US LLP* |
| Chalk Wm David | *DLA Piper LLP (US)* * |
| Curran Robert | *Whiteford, Taylor & Preston LLP* * |
| Frisch John B | *Miles & Stockbridge PC* * |
| Moran Charles R | *Ballard Spahr LLP* * |
| Webb Thompson | *Miles & Stockbridge PC* * |
| **Band 3** | |
| Abel Kenneth | *Ober Kaler Grimes & Shriver* |
| Cameron Patrick K | *Ober Kaler Grimes & Shriver* |
| Fox Douglas M | *Ballard Spahr LLP* * |
| Harmon Jason C | *DLA Piper LLP (US)* * |
| Hill Eva H | *Whiteford, Taylor & Preston LLP* * |
| Rosso Anthony J | *Venable LLP* * |
| Washburne Thomas | *Venable LLP* * |
| **Band 4** | |
| Carlson William | *Shapiro Sher Guinot & Sandler (ONP)* [†] |
| Cohen Jay G | *Duane Morris LLP* |
| McGowan Patricia | *Venable LLP* * |
| Morton Jr Charles J | *Venable LLP* * |
| Poliakoff Abba | *Gordon Feinblatt LLC (ONP)* [†] |
| Sherbill, Esq Raymond J | *Lerch, Early & Brewer, Chartered* * |
| **Up-and-coming individuals** | |
| Hardy Kelly Tubman | *DLA Piper LLP (US)* * |
| **Associates to watch** | |
| Howard Douglas P | *Duane Morris LLP* |

\* Indicates firm / individual with profile.
[†]ONP = Other Notable Practitioner.

*knowledge,*" a satisfied client reports. *"Good, strategic thinker*" Walter Lohr is of counsel at the firm and a well-known figure in the community, advising on M&A, joint ventures, and public and private offerings of securities.

## Venable LLP
See profile on p.927

**THE FIRM** This premier practice is among the largest corporate teams in the state and represents public and private companies in both domestic and cross-border M&A. The group maintains a fine reputation for its work in securities and equity investment. Its impressive roster of clients is drawn from Fortune 100 companies, family businesses, international and regional entrepreneurs and venture capitalists, among others, and includes Allegis, HSBC Capital, Ilex Consumer Products Group and JPB Enterprises.

**Sources say:** *"The firm is value-oriented and timely, offering concise feedback."*

**KEY INDIVIDUALS** The highly regarded Bryson Cook (see p.1425) maintains a fine reputation for his finance, tax and transactional work, in addition to his general corporate advice, and acts for a range of public and private companies. James Hanks (see p.329) wins much praise from peers and represents a fine choice of counsel in capital markets transactions, governance matters and securities offerings. Michael Baader (see p.1425) is the partner in charge of the firm's Baltimore office. In addition to general corporate planning, he focuses on private equity and venture capital investments, M&A and joint ventures, acting for a range of clients including technology and emerging growth companies. Anthony Rosso (see p.1431) is noted for his expertise both in domestic and cross-border M&A, and is also well versed in equity and debt financings and corporate restructurings. He is regularly called upon to advise middle-market clients from the energy, retail and manufacturing sectors. The *"efficient and extremely responsive"* Patricia McGowan (see p.365) is a younger member of the team and comes recommended for her work concerning spin-offs, restructurings and securities offerings, in addition to her M&A expertise. Thomas Washburne (see p.1433) continues to be sought for his advice on M&A and equity and debt offerings and can also be relied upon for his counsel on takeover defenses and shareholder relations. His client list is predominantly drawn from the financial services and technology sectors. Corporate practice cochair Charles Morton (see p.1430) is recognized for his strengths in all areas of equity investment. A client says: *"He was great – he had a really effective manner about him and the way he handled the negotiation was absolutely masterful."* He splits his time between the firm's Baltimore and Washington, DC offices.

## Band 2

### Miles & Stockbridge PC
See profile on p.1438

**THE FIRM** Miles & Stockbridge's practice comes particularly recommended for its wide-ranging corporate expertise, and has particular strengths in the manufacturing and real estate arenas, as well as in government contracting issues. Recent work includes acting for Blue Sky Factory on its sale to What Counts. Stanley Black & Decker, Fortress International Group, Telos Corporation and US Foods are among the group's other key clients.

**Sources say:** *"Very responsive, practical, with business-minded attorneys."*

**KEY INDIVIDUALS** The much-respected John Frisch (see p.1426) is chairman and CEO of the firm and maintains a fine reputation for his expertise in handling M&A and securities matters on behalf of public and private companies. Thompson Webb (see p.1433) is noted for his corporate work with financial institutions and REITs. Clients say: *"He is very knowledgeable about every corporate regulation in Maryland. He assists us in all our complex technology contracts and has provided exemplary service to us."*

## Band 3

### Ballard Spahr LLP
See profile on p.2234

**THE FIRM** This practice maintains a fine track record in M&A, public and private financings and corporate planning and governance matters. It is also much in demand for its expertise in federal and state securities law issues. The group acts for a range of local, national and cross-border clients and has developed a particular niche handling work in the real estate and life sciences arenas. Key clients include Osiris Therapeutics, TESSCO Technologies, HCP and Red Mortgage Capital.

**Sources say:** *"They are extraordinarily responsive, do thorough research, and take time to ensure they offer an answer which is practical from a business standpoint."*

**KEY INDIVIDUALS** Charles Moran (see p.1430) is well versed in corporate issues concerning the life sciences and technology space and is also regularly called upon to handle private equity and securities matters. *"He has a great business sense and we trust him completely with our large transactions,"* asserts one satisfied client. Douglas Fox (see p.1426) is similarly noted for his strengths in life sciences, as well as in securities, IP and trade marks, in addition to his general corporate expertise. He recently served as primary outside securities counsel to Osiris Therapeutics, a leading player in the adult stem cell therapeutics arena. An impressed client says of him: *"He does excellent work and gives us not just a textbook answer, but something that is readily understandable."*

### Duane Morris LLP
See profile on p.2239

**THE FIRM** This practice is noted for its strengths advising corporate clients in the formation of business entities and regulatory compliance. It also comes recommended for handling succession planning matters, and for its work regarding the rights and relationships of owners and stockholders. Recent work includes counseling Metropolitan Regional Information Systems in restructurings, investments and acquisitions in other companies.

**Sources say:** *"Their approach to client management and engagement sets them apart from other firms." "They are strong and experienced. If they don't have the answer at their fingertips, they know where to go."*

**KEY INDIVIDUALS** Jay Cohen maintains a particularly fine track record handling venture capital and private equity investments. *"Jay is as important to me, if not more, than a key member of my management team or board member. Client service is his strength!"* notes one enthusiastic client. Senior associate Douglas Howard is routinely called upon to advise on corporate governance, securities law and equity and debt financing, in addition to his expertise in M&A. According to one client, Howard is *"very capable and detail-oriented and has a good grasp of the business environment."*

### Lerch, Early & Brewer, Chartered
See profile on p.1437

**THE FIRM** This practice is noted for handling corporate matters facing midsized organizations and startup companies, and is particularly recognized for its M&A and succession planning work. In addition, the team is well versed in all areas of federal and state tax controversies, including administrative appeals and tax court litigation. The group has a diverse client base, but enjoys an especially strong reputation for its work with manufacturers, petroleum companies and government contractors.

**Sources say:** *"They offer great judgment and a clear understanding of the issues, as well as business interests."*

**KEY INDIVIDUALS** Raymond Sherbill (see p.1432) chairs the firm's business and taxation practice group and is well versed in financial and tax-related matters, in addition to handling litigation and general corporate transactional work. Clients speak highly of him and particularly single out his responsiveness on matters.

### Ober Kaler Grimes & Shriver
See profile on p.1439

**THE FIRM** This group is well versed in advising on all areas of the business life cycle, from formation and operation to growth and sale, and is recognized for its counsel to middle-market and emerging growth companies, as well as to larger and more established organizations. The team maintains a particularly fine track record for its work on behalf of clients from a diverse range of sectors, including financial services, technology, healthcare, education and retail.

**KEY INDIVIDUALS** Kenneth Abel cochairs the business group and comes recommended for his expertise in M&A and securities matters. He is also regularly called upon to draft and negotiate all manner of business contracts, including stockholder and venture capital financing agreements. Patrick Cameron represents a good choice of counsel for asset-based lending clients and financial institutions and is especially recognized for his transportation-based financing work.

## Whiteford, Taylor & Preston LLP
See profile on p.1442

**THE FIRM** This team is well versed in a diverse range of corporate work and comes recommended for its strengths in M&A and public and private financing. In addition, it is regularly sought by a varied client base, including energy and healthcare companies, to assist with corporate formation, succession planning and securities issues.

**Sources say:** *"They provide spot-on guidance, instruction and counsel. They consider the best courses of action appropriate for us, and make the best recommendation based on the legal situation and our business interests."*

**KEY INDIVIDUALS Robert Curran** (see p.1426) is much in demand for his taxation and private capital work, in addition to his expertise in M&A. He is also renowned for his strengths in corporate structuring and succession plans. **Eva Hill** (see p.1428) excels in matters concerning corporate reorganizations and is also noted for her wide-ranging M&A experience, which has seen her handle transactions in a variety of fields, including healthcare, IT, retail and energy.

### Other Notable Practitioners

**Abba Poliakoff** is chairman of Gordon Feinblatt LLC's securities practice and is noted for his experience acting for large corporations and emerging growth companies on venture capital and IP matters, as well as in general corporate and securities work. *"He is our lead counsel – he is very responsive, very personable, and we get great advice from him,"* notes one happy client. Senior partner **William Carlson** (see p.1425) is president of Shapiro Sher Guinot & Sandler and the chair of its business department. He is recognized for his expertise in M&A, joint ventures and equity and debt financings, and maintains a fine track record for his work with biotech companies. Sources say: *"He is outstanding and a delight to work with."*

# EMPLOYEE BENEFITS & EXECUTIVE COMPENSATION

Commentary about individuals can be found under their firm's paragraph. If the firm has no paragraph (is not ranked) look at Other Notable Practitioners.

### Employee Benefits & Executive Compensation
#### Leading Firms

**Band 1**
Venable LLP *

**Band 2**
DLA Piper LLP (US) *
Miles & Stockbridge PC *
Whiteford, Taylor & Preston LLP *

#### Leading Individuals

**Band 1**

| | | |
|---|---|---|
| Adkins Edward J | Miles & Stockbridge PC * | |
| Hoffman Kenneth R | Venable LLP * | |
| Kamantauskas-Holder Katrina | Holder Law Group LLC (ONP)† | |
| Madden Paul W | Whiteford, Taylor & Preston LLP * | |
| Schlaff Barbara E | Venable LLP * | |
| Smith III Henry A | Smith & Downey PA (ONP)† | |

**Band 2**

| | |
|---|---|
| Atlas Harry I | Venable LLP * |
| Chesshire Mary Claire | Whiteford, Taylor & Preston LLP * |
| Johnson Thora A | Venable LLP * |
| Mellin Matthew P | Gordon Feinblatt LLC (ONP)† |
| Muedeking Mark | DLA Piper LLP (US) * |
| St. Ville Thomas J | Miles & Stockbridge PC * |
| Thomas Linda Marotta | DLA Piper LLP (US) * |

* Indicates firm / individual with profile.
† ONP = Other Notable Practitioner.

## Band 1

### Venable LLP
See profile on p.927

**THE FIRM** This superb group advises on the full spectrum of employee benefits and executive compensation matters and is particularly sought for its strengths in single-employer retirement plans and multiemployer pension funding and liability. The team also maintains a fine tax-exempt practice, handling the full range of benefits issues for employers including charity, healthcare and educational organizations. In addition, the group is also well versed in the fiduciary and tax qualification aspects of ESOPs.

**Sources say:** *"Broad knowledge, flexible availability, and thought leadership with real-world application." "Venable is a first-rate law firm and working with it is a true partnership."*

**KEY INDIVIDUALS Barbara Schlaff** (see p.1431) is *"a seasoned benefits professional, highly knowledgeable in all aspects of retirement issues,"* according to sources, who also describe her as *"highly organized and detail-oriented"* and an *"engaging personality and creative thinker."* She comes recommended for her expertise in qualified and nonqualified deferred compensation retirement plans and also represents a fine choice of counsel for clients on tax and ERISA-related matters. The highly regarded **Thora Johnson** (see p.1428) excels in the tax-exempt arena, acting for a variety of organizations, including charities, private foundations, trade associations and title holding companies. She also comes recommended for her advice on health and welfare benefits plans. **Kenneth Hoffman** (see p.1428) and **Harry Atlas** (see p.1424) are both applauded for their wealth of experience in all areas of retirement plans. Hoffman is further singled out by commentators as *"a technical expert – flexible and solutions-oriented,"* while interviewees are quick to heap praise on Atlas's *"thorough and highly organized"* approach to matters.

## Band 2

### DLA Piper LLP (US)
See profile on p.1971

**THE FIRM** This fine team covers the gamut of employee benefits and executive compensation issues, including the design and implementation of qualified retirement plans and advising clients on ERISA regulatory compliance. The group is also regularly sought for its expertise in ESOP transactions and welfare benefit plan matters. Its diverse client roster ranges from publicly traded organizations and large privately held businesses to government institutions, trade associations and tax-exempt entities.

**KEY INDIVIDUALS** In addition to his wealth of experience in employee benefits and executive compensation matters, **Mark Muedeking** (see p.1430) comes much recommended for his expertise in ERISA disputes work, acting on behalf of a diverse clientele that includes public and private organizations, as well as trade associations, tax-exempt charities and foundations. **Linda Marotta Thomas** (see p.1433) is recognized for her strengths concerning stock options and restricted stock programs and is also frequently called upon to assist with long-term incentive and performance award plans.

### Miles & Stockbridge PC
See profile on p.1438

**THE FIRM** This robust practice is particularly noted for its advice concerning healthcare and retirement plans and also maintains a fine track record of counseling clients on ERISA compliance issues. Alongside this, the team is well versed in all aspects relating to the establishment and maintenance of ESOPs and stock bonus plans, and is also routinely called upon to assist government entities, as well as profit and nonprofit organizations, on matters concerning tax-deferred plans. Its key clients include GEA North America, Stanley Black & Decker, Fila USA and Frederick Memorial Hospital.

**Sources say:** *"The firm is dedicated to providing great service first and foremost, and is always looking out for our best interests."*

**KEY INDIVIDUALS Edward Adkins** (see p.1424) acts for a diverse roster of clients, from small businesses to large multinationals, as well as government entities, healthcare institutions and tax-exempt organizations. He receives warm praise from sources for his abilities to handle the most complex of benefits and compensation matters and is also applauded for the thoroughness of his advice. **Thomas St. Ville** (see p.1433) comes recommended for his assistance on tax-qualified pension and savings plans and is also noted for his expertise in executive deferred compensation, acting for a wide array of public and private companies and nonprofit organizations. Sources single him out for his attentive approach to matters and fine customer service.

## Whiteford, Taylor & Preston LLP
See profile on p.1442

**THE FIRM** This excellent team has made a particular name for itself acting on behalf of state and local government entities on the design and implementation of retirement and welfare plans, but also enjoys a fine reputation handling benefits and compensation matters for a range of private sector companies, and tax-exempt and nonprofit clients. Among its key clients are Howard County, Idaho

Public Employees Retirement System, McDaniel College and Harford Mutual Insurance.

**Sources say:** *"For large, complex matters we refer to Whiteford."*

**KEY INDIVIDUALS Paul Madden** (see p.1429) is a senior partner at the firm and has vast experience in designing, drafting and providing advice on all kinds of employee benefit and executive compensation programs. He continues to be particularly sought for his expertise in qualified pension and 401(k) plans and nonqualified deferred compensation matters. **Mary Claire Chesshire** (see p.1425) has more than three decades of experience in the employee benefits arena, advising an array of emerging and already established businesses, nonprofit organizations and government entities.

## Other Notable Practitioners

**Katrina Kamantauskas-Holder** of Holder Law Group LLC excels in the area of tax-qualified retirement plans, including matters concerning 401(k) administration, and is also recommended for her advice to clients on welfare plan compliance, such as COBRA and severance issues. Smith & Downey PA's **Henry Smith** is noted for the wealth of experience he has in the design and implementation of benefit and compensation plans and remains much in demand for his expertise in both tax-qualified and non-tax-qualified deferred compensation and retirement programs. **Matthew Mellin** at Gordon Feinblatt LLC is noted for his work with healthcare and financial institutions and continues to be highly sought for assistance with multiemployer benefit plans, ESOPs and deferred compensation programs.

# HEALTHCARE

Commentary about individuals can be found under their firm's paragraph. If the firm has no paragraph (is not ranked) look at Other Notable Practitioners.

### Healthcare
### Leading Firms

**Band 1**
Ober Kaler Grimes & Shriver *
Venable LLP *

**Band 2**
Gallagher, Evelius & Jones, LLP
Gordon Feinblatt LLC

**Band 3**
Adelman, Sheff & Smith LLC
Hogan Lovells US LLP
Lerch, Early & Brewer, Chartered *

### Leading Individuals

**Band 1**

| | |
|---|---|
| Baker Constance H | Venable LLP * |
| Immelt Stephen | Hogan Lovells US LLP |
| Rosen Barry F | Gordon Feinblatt LLC |
| Teplitzky Sanford V | Ober Kaler Grimes & Shriver |
| Tranter Jack C | Gallagher, Evelius & Jones, LLP |

**Band 2**

| | |
|---|---|
| Adelman S Allan | Adelman, Sheff & Smith LLC |
| Haines Sigrid | Lerch, Early & Brewer, Chartered * |
| Holden S Craig | Ober Kaler Grimes & Shriver |
| Matricciani Rose M | Whiteford, Taylor & Preston LLP (ONP) †* |
| Parvis Peter P | Venable LLP * |
| Sollins Howard L | Ober Kaler Grimes & Shriver |

**Band 3**

| | |
|---|---|
| Martin Catherine | Ober Kaler Grimes & Shriver |
| Sherman Davis VR | Venable LLP * |

\* Indicates firm / individual with profile.
† ONP = Other Notable Practitioner.

### Healthcare: Medical Malpractice
### Leading Firms

**Band 1**
Goodell, DeVries, Leech & Dann, LLP *

### Leading Individuals

**Band 1**

| | |
|---|---|
| DeVries Jr Donald L | Goodell, DeVries, Leech & Dann, LLP * |

**Band 2**

| | |
|---|---|
| McSherry M Natalie | Kramon & Graham, PA (ONP) †* |
| Merkle Craig | Goodell, DeVries, Leech & Dann, LLP * |
| Monahan Jr Thomas V | Goodell, DeVries, Leech & Dann, LLP * |
| Preston Susan T | Goodell, DeVries, Leech & Dann, LLP * |

## Band 1
## Healthcare

### Ober Kaler Grimes & Shriver
See profile on p.1439

**THE FIRM** This superb practice acts for academic and community hospitals, health systems and long-term care facilities, and is also known for its work on behalf of clinical laboratories, individual healthcare providers and physician organizations. The group maintains particular expertise in fraud and abuse cases and also continues to develop its work on behalf of biotechnology clients, pharmacies, and healthcare management and billing companies. It counts Quest Diagnostics, Pfizer, HCA and Cardinal Healthcare Renown Health among its impressive roster of clients.

**Sources say:** *"They are really good at Medicare issues."*

**KEY INDIVIDUALS** *"High-quality attorney"* **Sanford Teplitzky** cochairs the firm's health law group. He comes recommended for his work in fraud and abuse matters, acting for large healthcare companies before federal and state investigations. He is additionally recognized for his expertise in regulatory and legislative matters. **Howard**

**Sollins** has over three decades' experience in the healthcare arena and is sought for his strengths in corporate compliance, Medicare and Medicaid, as well as federal and state regulation matters. He is also commonly called upon to advise on e-health issues and ambulance regulation. The *"excellent"* and *"highly regarded"* **Craig Holden** is the firm's president and is particularly known for his work on behalf of clients on Medicare and Medicaid fraud and abuse issues. He is also sought for advice on general compliance matters. **Catherine Martin** is recognized for her expertise in regulatory matters and has assisted healthcare clients in a wide range of matters, including physician recruitment, Medicare and Medicaid reimbursement, and compliance matters. She recently moved from Adelman, Sheff & Smith LLC to Ober Kaler Grimes & Shriver.

### Venable LLP
See profile on p.927

**THE FIRM** Venable's healthcare team is well equipped to assist clients on a broad range of matters from M&A, joint ventures and strategic planning to state and federal reimbursement compliance and governance issues. Recent work includes acting on behalf of a hospital on its negotiation with the Office of Inspector General for the Department of Health & Human Services concerning the imposition of monetary penalties for employing a provider who had been excluded from participation in federal healthcare programs. Key clients include CareFirst Blue Cross Blue Shield, Johns Hopkins University and Frederick Memorial Hospital.

**Sources say:** *"In all areas of expertise, Venable attorneys have proven to be very knowledgeable and have great expertise in their specific areas of focus." "They offer concise, timely and complete analyses on regulatory matters."*

**KEY INDIVIDUALS Constance Baker** (see p.1425) is well versed in advising hospitals, health systems, healthcare professionals and pharmacies on a broad array of issues, and is particularly known for her representation of healthcare providers on regulatory compliance matters. *"I am very satisfied with the work she has done for us because of the consistently high quality she produces,"* asserts one impressed client. **Peter Parvis** (see p.1431) comes recommended for his regulatory compliance work, acting on behalf of hospitals and other institutional providers and physicians, among others. A client says: *"He is responsive, thorough, has a strong work ethic and offers well-regarded advice."* **Davis Sherman** (see p.1432) handles tax-exempt bond financing for capital projects, acting for hospitals and other tax-exempt corporations. He is also noted for his expertise in M&A and project financing.

## Band 2
## Healthcare

### Gallagher, Evelius & Jones, LLP

**THE FIRM** This team is noted for its expertise in healthcare transactions, planning and regulatory compliance, and is also sought for its litigation expertise. Its clients include hospitals and hospital systems, academic medical centers and multispecialty physician groups, and it also maintains a strong reputation for work with home health and hospice agencies, long-term care facilities, and continuing care retirement communities.

**KEY INDIVIDUALS Jack Tranter** continues to be in much demand for his expertise across regulatory compliance, disputes and healthcare-related antitrust matters, acting for hospitals, nursing homes, individual professionals such as physicians and nurses, and other healthcare providers.

### Gordon Feinblatt LLC

**THE FIRM** Gordon Feinblatt's practice has extensive experience in joint ventures, M&A and corporate reorganizations in the healthcare space. It is also well versed in third-party reimbursement, physician contracting, hospital rate setting and certificates of need. It represents a fine choice of counsel for hospitals, professional associations and nursing homes, and also maintains an active practice representing physicians, dentists and continuing care retirement communities.

**Sources say:** *"The group offers quick responses to issues, and depth of expertise in healthcare and business."*

**KEY INDIVIDUALS Barry Rosen** is chairman and CEO of the firm and also heads its healthcare practice. He maintains an active M&A and joint venture practice and is also recognized for his work in healthcare-related antitrust counseling and litigation. *"He is always accessible and responsive,"* a satisfied client reports.

## Band 3
## Healthcare

### Adelman, Sheff & Smith LLC

**THE FIRM** Adelman, Sheff & Smith is well known for its work concerning credentialing, hospital-physician relationships, corrective action and fair hearings, as well as contracts and other medical staff matters. The group is also noted for its expertise in matters related to Health Insurance Portability and Accountability Act (HIPAA) policies and program implementation, patient care, consent to and the withholding of treatment, and medical records issues.

**KEY INDIVIDUALS Allan Adelman** has over three decades' experience in the healthcare arena and is commonly called upon to act as general counsel to several acute care hospitals in the state. He comes particularly recommended for his work in credentialing, peer review and hospital-physician issues and also maintains an active medical malpractice defense practice.

### Hogan Lovells US LLP

**THE FIRM** Hogan Lovells' healthcare team is singled out for its advice to providers and suppliers of healthcare products and also comes highly regarded for its expertise in regulatory matters. Its clients range from startups to multinational companies from every area of the healthcare arena, and it maintains a particularly fine reputation for its work on behalf of manufacturers of pharmaceuticals and medical devices.

**Sources say:** *"Expert knowledge of the medical regulatory environment – great strategists."*

**KEY INDIVIDUALS** The *"excellent"* **Stephen Immelt** is the global co-head of the firm's litigation, arbitration and employment practice, and is noted for his expertise in government investigations and complex enforcement cases. He divides his time between the firm's Washington, DC and Baltimore offices.

### Lerch, Early & Brewer, Chartered
See profile on p.1437

**THE FIRM** This group is known for its regulatory compliance strengths, advising hospitals and physicians on all manner of federal and state laws, including HIPAA and the Emergency Medical Treatment and Active Labor Act (EMTALA). In addition, it is regularly called upon to advise on physician credentialing and licensing matters, patient care and payor investigations.

**Sources say:** *"The firm's strongest points are the availability of legal counsel with expertise and knowledge of the healthcare environment, their accessibility and quick response to requests for assistance."*

**KEY INDIVIDUALS Sigrid Haines** (see p.1427) is noted for her work on behalf of hospital clients, advising on contract disputes and negotiations, patient care, and fraud and abuse investigations, among other areas. She is *"extremely responsive, easy to work with and consistently produces a high-quality work product,"* asserts one impressed client.

## Band 1
## Healthcare: Medical Malpractice

### Goodell, DeVries, Leech & Dann, LLP
See profile on p.1435

**THE FIRM** This firm is well known for its stellar medical malpractice group. It frequently tries high-profile negligence cases in both state and federal courts and its enjoys a fine reputation for its appellate practice. It acts for a diverse range of clients, from regional hospitals, academic medical centers and long-term care facilities, to individual professionals such as physicians, nurses and other healthcare providers.

**KEY INDIVIDUALS Donald DeVries** (see p.1426) is a seasoned trial lawyer with a proven track record in medical negligence defense litigation. **Craig Merkle** (see p.1430) is well versed in hospital litigation and professional disciplinary actions, in addition to medical malpractice defense. He is also sought for his trial experience in matters relating to medical devices. **Thomas Monahan** (see p.1430) comes recommended for his experience in handling negligence cases before state and federal courts and before arbitration panels. His client base ranges from hospitals and long-term care facilities to individual healthcare practitioners, such as physicians and nurses. **Susan Preston** (see p.1431) is, in addition to her widely noted professional negligence practice, routinely called upon to handle product liability cases against medical device manufacturers.

## Other Notable Practitioners

**Rose Matricciani** (see p.1429) of Whiteford, Taylor & Preston LLP is well known for her representation of healthcare providers, including physicians, nurses, dentists, physical therapists and psychologists, before multiple licensure boards. She is also sought for her expertise in hospital-physician group strategic alliances and Medicare matters. **Natalie McSherry** (see p.1430) of Kramon & Graham, PA has over three decades' experience in the healthcare arena and comes recommended for her malpractice defense work. She is also noted for her advice on issues concerned with credentialing and medical staff by-laws.

# LABOR & EMPLOYMENT

Commentary about individuals can be found under their firm's paragraph. If the firm has no paragraph (is not ranked) look at Other Notable Practitioners.

## Labor & Employment
### Leading Firms

**Band 1**
Jackson Lewis LLP *
Shawe Rosenthal LLP *
Venable LLP *

**Band 2**
Kollman & Saucier PA

**Band 3**
DLA Piper LLP (US) *
McGuireWoods LLP *
Miles & Stockbridge PC *
Saul Ewing LLP *
Whiteford, Taylor & Preston LLP *

### Leading Individuals

**Band 1**

| | |
|---|---|
| Ayres Jeffrey P | Venable LLP * |
| Hafets Richard J | Jackson Lewis LLP * |
| Horn Todd J | Venable LLP * |
| McGuire J Michael | Shawe Rosenthal LLP* |
| Paltell Eric | Kollman & Saucier PA |
| Shawe Stephen D | Shawe Rosenthal LLP * |

**Band 2**

| | |
|---|---|
| Abramson Gil | Jackson Lewis LLP * |
| Ames Robert | Venable LLP * |
| Eidelman Gary B | Saul Ewing LLP |
| Gardner Russell H | DLA Piper LLP (US) * |
| Harrison Bruce S | Shawe Rosenthal LLP * |
| Kellner Robert | Gordon Feinblatt LLC (ONP)† |
| McGee Jr Emmett F | Jackson Lewis LLP * |
| Pontone Kathleen | Miles & Stockbridge PC |
| Seegull Larry | Jackson Lewis LLP * |
| Silvestri Stephen | Jackson Lewis LLP * |
| Simpler Gary | Shawe Rosenthal LLP * |
| Taylor Ronald W | Venable LLP * |
| VanDeusen Darrell R | Kollman & Saucier PA |

**Band 3**

| | |
|---|---|
| Amiot Brooks R | Jackson Lewis LLP * |
| Cooperman Harriet E | Saul Ewing LLP |
| Eastman Hope | Paley, Rothman, Goldstein (ONP)† |
| Gillece Jr James P | Whiteford, Taylor & Preston LLP |
| Guattery Peter | Whiteford, Taylor & Preston LLP * |
| Hedian Victoria | Abato, Rubenstein and Abato, PA (ONP)† |
| Kollman Frank L | Kollman & Saucier PA |
| McCormick Kevin C | Whiteford, Taylor & Preston LLP * |
| Quinn Lawrence J | Tydings & Rosenberg LLP (ONP)† |
| Torphy-Donzella Elizabeth | Shawe Rosenthal LLP * |

### Associates to watch

| | |
|---|---|
| Clements Lynn | Jackson Lewis LLP * |

*Indicates firm / individual with profile.*
†*ONP = Other Notable Practitioner.*

## Band 1

### Jackson Lewis LLP
See profile on p.1982

**THE FIRM** The Baltimore office of this highly regarded national boutique is well versed in all forms of labor and employment law and maintains its excellent reputation for work on the management side. The group also comes recommended for its expertise in labor and employment-related disputes and issues concerning OSHA, EEOC and affirmative action. It counts WellCare Health Plans, Perdue Farms, Dunbar Armored, Verizon Services and New World Pasta among its key clients.

**Sources say:** *"The firm's strongest points are its responsiveness, knowledge and a practical approach to issue resolution."* **KEY INDIVIDUALS Gil Abramson** (see p.1424) is the labor practice group coordinator for the Baltimore office. He excels in management-side work, advising on matters including wrongful discharge and restrictive covenants, and is also routinely called upon to counsel clients in issues concerning workplace harassment, employment policies, drug and alcohol matters and training programs. **Brooks Amiot** (see p.1424) maintains a fine track record in employment disputes, including discrimination and wage and hour litigation. He also represents a fine choice of counsel for whistle-blower claims and ADA and FMLA cases. *"Superb lawyer"* **Richard Hafets** (see p.1427) is managing partner of the Baltimore office and acts for Fortune 500 companies, healthcare institutions and charities, among others, on all areas of labor and employment law. He is particularly noted for his expertise in traditional labor/management and union avoidance issues, as well as employment litigation. *"He is incredibly responsive and very proactive in his review of our practices and policies,"* notes one satisfied client. **Emmett McGee** (see p.1429), in addition to advising on the gamut of labor and employment matters, has a wealth of experience in employment litigation, representing clients in cases concerning discrimination and wage and hour issues, before state and federal courts, administrative agencies and arbitration panels. According to one impressed interviewee, *"he is an outstanding lawyer who provides efficient comprehensive responses to all of our questions."* **Larry Seegull** (see p.1432) acts for both public and private sector employers on all aspects of labor and employment law and comes highly regarded for his work concerning compliance and litigation avoidance. He also represents a fine option for clients in employment-related arbitration and agency investigations. **Stephen Silvestri** (see p.1432) recently joined the firm from Miles & Stockbridge. He has over three decades' experience in labor and employment litigation and is recognized for his strengths in disputes concerning employee benefits, union avoidance and restrictive covenants. He is *"timely and responsive, and takes the time to understand our business and the practicalities of what we need,"* reports one impressed interviewee. **Lynn Clements** (see p.1425) assists

employers with OFCCP and EEOC issues and is also regularly called upon to advise them on investigations and enforcement activities by local, state and federal government agencies. A client says: *"She is a trusted adviser and wonderful advocate for our company."*

### Shawe Rosenthal LLP
See profile on p.1441

**THE FIRM** This fine practice is much noted for its experience representing employers before federal and state courts, the NLRB, EEOC and other administrative agencies, as well as in arbitrations. Its attorneys have extensive expertise in matters pertaining to unfair labor practice cases and collective bargaining agreements, and continue to be much in demand for their strengths in discrimination and wrongful termination litigation. The practice has a diverse client base, ranging from small businesses and nonprofits to Fortune 100 companies, and maintains a fine track record for its work on behalf of organizations in the financial services, manufacturing and healthcare sectors, among others.

**KEY INDIVIDUALS** The seasoned **Stephen Shawe** (see p.1432) has more than four decades' experience in the labor and employment arena and maintains a fine reputation for his work in the retail and manufacturing industries. Managing partner **Bruce Harrison** (see p.1428) has more than 30 years of experience acting for management clients and is noted for his expertise in cases relating to the FLSA, as well as sex, race and other discrimination matters, and abuse and wrongful discharge matters. **Michael McGuire** (see p.1429) comes recommended for his work concerning collective bargaining agreements, union representation and unfair labor practice cases. He is also well versed in acting for employers on sexual harassment, discrimination and wrongful termination cases, before both state and federal courts. **Gary Simpler** (see p.1432) is renowned for his knowledge of NLRB and union organizational matters, and also comes recommended for his strengths in collective bargaining negotiations. **Elizabeth Torphy-Donzella** (see p.1433) is highly sought for her expertise in employment disputes, and has notable experience in cases of racial and sexual harassment.

### Venable LLP
See profile on p.927

**THE FIRM** This robust team remains a go-to practice for midsize and large private, public and nonprofit employers, and is well equipped to handle all manner of labor and employment law. The group is particularly noted for its work concerning collective bargaining, M&A-related labor matters, union avoidance and ERISA issues. In addition, it is recognized for strengths in employment disputes, defending clients against claims of discrimination and harassment, and EEOC and OSHA matters. Key clients include Anne Arundel County, National Aquarium Institute, Textron Systems and WMATA.

**Sources say:** *"The overall caliber of the attorneys from Venable is excellent."*

**KEY INDIVIDUALS** The highly regarded **Jeffrey Ayres** (see p.1424) remains much in demand by clients in the financial services, healthcare, education and technology sectors for his complex civil litigation counsel. He is especially well regarded for his handling of ERISA and discrimination cases. The *"brilliant"* **Todd Horn** (see p.1428) excels in class action wage and hour disputes under the FLSA and also comes highly recommended for his strengths in litigation concerning discrimination, sexual harassment, compensation, wrongful discharge and whistle-blowing. *"He is very quick on his feet, and is quick to get at the heart of an issue,"* notes one well-placed market commentator. **Robert Ames** (see p.1424) has extensive experience acting for public and private sector organizations on labor and employment disputes. *"I would highly recommend Robert Ames. He is a real expert who has produced very positive results,"* reports one satisfied client. **Ronald Taylor** (see p.1433) heads the firm's Maryland labor and employment practice. He is recognized for his expertise in cases concerning OSHA, wage and hour, and discrimination, acting for a diverse range of clients drawn from the private, public and nonprofit arenas. According to one impressed client, Taylor is *"very personable, easily reachable and understands our needs."*

## Band 2

### Kollman & Saucier PA

**THE FIRM** This practice is well placed to handle the entire range of labor and employment matters, from cases regarding the EEOC, NLRB and OSHA to ERISA litigation and collective bargaining. The group continues to be noted for its work on behalf of state and local government organizations in their negotiations with labor unions and remains a go-to choice of firm for clients in the construction, healthcare and education sectors. It is also readily sought for its training on matters related to employment policies and practices.

**KEY INDIVIDUALS Eric Paltell** is noted for his disputes work, acting on behalf of public and private sector clients on cases concerning ADA and FMLA, discrimination and sexual harassment, wrongful discharge and wage and hour matters. He is also recognized for his expertise in NLRB proceedings and collective bargaining negotiations. Paltell is a *"fantastic lawyer,"* reports one impressed peer, who goes on to say: *"I would have no hesitancy in sending him work of any kind."* The much-respected **Darrell VanDeusen** is much in demand among employers for his training on matters including avoiding sexual harassment claims and managing a diverse workforce. **Frank Kollman** comes much recommended for his labor and employment work, acting for a wide range of clients, and represents a good choice of counsel for healthcare institutions, construction companies and trade associations.

## Band 3

### DLA Piper LLP (US)
See profile on p.1971

**THE FIRM** This practice is looked to by national and multinational clients to handle a broad range of labor and employment issues. It remains a go-to practice for employment and labor disputes, and is also commonly called upon to advise on ERISA, C-level management transitions and labor-management relations. In addition, the practice maintains a fine track record for its EEOC and OSHA-related work.

**Sources say:** *"An excellent firm!"*

**KEY INDIVIDUALS** The highly respected **Russell Gardner** (see p.1426) is recognized for his strengths in employment discrimination and OSHA matters, and also maintains a fine reputation for his work on ERISA and union avoidance issues.

### McGuireWoods LLP
See profile on p.2519

**THE FIRM** This group advises employers on all areas of employer/employee relationship matters, including compliance, internal investigations, traditional law issues and executive compensation. It acts for a diverse client base including small businesses, Fortune 500 companies, government entities and nonprofits, on a local, national and international platform.

**KEY INDIVIDUALS Elena Marcuss** is a key contact.

### Miles & Stockbridge PC
See profile on p.1438

**THE FIRM** This team is home to a diverse range of employment attorneys, specializing in matters concerning labor, immigration, benefits, workplace safety and employment-related disputes. It maintains a fine track record for its work in financial services, retail, manufacturing, education and healthcare, and counts Bank of America, Town of Ocean City, Rite Aid, Stanley Black & Decker and Brown Capital Management among its key clients.

**Sources say:** *"The firm's strongest points are its litigation and its collective bargaining. I am very satisfied with their work in all areas of representation."*

**KEY INDIVIDUALS** The *"very thorough and knowledgeable"* **Kathleen Pontone** heads the firm's labor and employment, benefits, immigration and environmental practice. She represents a good choice of counsel for clients in the education, financial services, manufacturing and hospitality sectors, advising on cases related to discrimination, sexual harassment and compensation.

### Saul Ewing LLP
See profile on p.2249

**THE FIRM** This group comes recommended for its adept handling of employment-related disputes, labor relations, and employee benefits and executive compensation matters. The team is noted for its strengths in cases concerning discrimination, sexual harassment, wage and hour and wrongful discharge, among other areas, and is also frequently called upon to advise on OSHA, NLRA and ERISA issues. It maintains a fine track for its work within the

healthcare, manufacturing, construction, food, retail and hospitality sectors.

**Sources say:** *"Its partners are very knowledgeable."* *"They have been superb: fast-acting and efficient."*

**KEY INDIVIDUALS** The *"extremely attentive and responsive"* **Gary Eidelman** acts for employers in cases concerning discrimination, workplace harassment, disability, wrongful discharge and wage and hour and is also recognized for his expertise in OSHA and employee benefits matters. *"He is tough, smart and thorough; an excellent litigator who I go to for delicate matters,"* reports one well-placed commentator. **Harriet Cooperman** cochairs the labor, employment and employee benefits practice. She represents management-side clients on a national and international scale and comes recommended for her expertise in NLRA, discrimination, sexual harassment, wage and hour and ERISA matters.

### Whiteford, Taylor & Preston LLP
See profile on p.1442

**THE FIRM** This group acts for a broad client base, including Fortune 500 companies, small businesses, nonprofits and state and local government entities in employment-related disputes, arbitration and contract negotiations, as well as providing general employment and labor counseling to these clients. Recent work includes successfully guiding a software solutions provider into an asset sale while defending several employment-related claims against the client.

**Sources say:** *"Strengths are knowledge of the law, negotiation strategy and execution."*

**KEY INDIVIDUALS** The excellent **James Gillece** is much recognized for his litigation strengths, not least in disputes regarding breaches of contract, RICO and other contentious corporate-related matters. *"He has a stellar work ethic and capabilities – he made himself available 24/7 and deftly helped handle a delicate employment situation to our satisfaction,"* reports one impressed client. **Peter Guattery** (see p.1427) maintains a fine reputation acting for public and private clients in employment and discrimination-related cases, across state and federal courts and agencies, and in courts of appeal throughout the Mid-Atlantic region. **Kevin McCormick** (see p.1429) is noted for handling work across all areas of the employment relationship, advising clients on issues concerning compliance and disputes. He is also recognized for his expertise in union-organizing matters and for his work with healthcare clients. He elicits particular praise for his communication skills.

## Other Notable Practitioners

**Victoria Hedian** of Abato, Rubenstein and Abato, PA has over 30 years of experience acting for local and international unions and employees in arbitrations, negotiations and administrative hearings. She is particularly noted for her expertise in collective bargaining agreements. **Robert Kellner** chairs Gordon Feinblatt LLC's employment law practice and comes recommended for his strengths in matters concerning discrimination, contracts, restrictive covenants, wrongful discharge and wage and hour law. He is also well versed in a broad range of employee benefits matters and enjoys a fine reputation in issues connected with collective bargaining and the NLRA. **Hope Eastman** chairs the employment law group at Paley, Rothman, Goldstein, Rosenberg, Eig & Cooper, Chartered. She has

more than three decades' experience in the employment law arena, and has particular expertise in matters before federal agencies including the EEOC, OFCCP and DOL. **Lawrence Quinn** chairs Tydings & Rosenberg LLP's litiga-

tion department. He represents a fine choice of counsel in stockholder claims and employment disputes, acting for clients in the healthcare, financial services, construction and real estate sectors, among others.

# LITIGATION

Commentary about individuals can be found under their firm's paragraph. If the firm has no paragraph (is not ranked) look at Other Notable Practitioners.

## Litigation: General Commercial
### Leading Firms

**Band 1**

DLA Piper LLP (US) *

Hogan Lovells US LLP

Kramon & Graham, PA *

**Band 2**

Miles & Stockbridge PC *

Rosenberg Martin Greenberg, LLP

Venable LLP *

Zuckerman Spaeder LLP

**Band 3**

Ballard Spahr LLP *

Gallagher, Evelius & Jones, LLP

Lerch, Early & Brewer, Chartered *

Whiteford, Taylor & Preston LLP *

*The editorial is in alphabetical order by firm name.*

## Ballard Spahr LLP
### See profile on p.2234

**THE FIRM** This team operates out of Bethesda and Baltimore and enters the rankings this year following a raft of praise from market sources. The group is frequently sought by clients in the energy, financial services, healthcare, and life sciences and pharmaceuticals arenas, and also maintains a fine reputation for disputes concerning retail, communications and professional sports. In addition, it is frequently sought to advise state and local governments and their entities.

**Sources say:** *"The group developed an excellent defensive strategy from the outset, and then very successfully executed that strategy in the litigation."*

**KEY INDIVIDUALS** Robert Scott is a key contact at the firm.

## DLA Piper LLP (US)
### See profile on p.1971

**THE FIRM** This team maintains a fine reputation for large-scale disputes and bet-the-company litigation, representing a raft of local companies, as well as many of the firm's national and global clients. Recent work includes acting for Transamerica Life Insurance, a subsidiary of AEGON, on a series of lawsuits consolidated in the Municipal Derivative Multidistrict Litigation in the Southern District of New York. Other key clients include Constellation Energy, Lockheed Martin, Marriott International, Johns Hopkins University and M&T Bank.

## Litigation: General Commercial
### Senior Statesmen

**Senior Statesmen:** distinguished older practitioners

| | |
|---|---|
| Rosenberg Benjamin | Rosenberg Martin Greenberg, LLP * |

### Leading Individuals

**Band 1**

| | |
|---|---|
| Dilloff Neil | DLA Piper LLP (US) * |
| Gately Mark | Hogan Lovells US LLP |
| Graham Andrew Jay | Kramon & Graham, PA * |
| Mathias Robert J | DLA Piper LLP (US) * |
| Murphy William | Zuckerman Spaeder LLP |
| Scheeler Charles P | DLA Piper LLP (US) * |
| Ulwick James P | Kramon & Graham, PA * |

**Band 2**

| | |
|---|---|
| Coe III Ward B | Gallagher, Evelius & Jones, LLP |
| Himeles Martin | Zuckerman Spaeder LLP |
| Immelt Stephen | Hogan Lovells US LLP |
| Ingerman Brett | DLA Piper LLP (US) * |
| Kemp Paul F | Ethridge, Quinn, Kemp, McAuliffe (ONP)[†] |
| Martin Gerard P | Rosenberg Martin Greenberg, LLP * |
| Sandler Paul Mark | Shapiro Sher Guinot & Sandler * |
| Strain Paul | Venable LLP * |

**Band 3**

| | |
|---|---|
| Barley Steven F | Hogan Lovells US LLP |
| Bonsib Robert | Marcus & Bonsib (ONP)[†] |
| Bourgeois John A | Kramon & Graham, PA * |
| Caiola Paul S | Gallagher, Evelius & Jones, LLP |
| Cleary Lauri E | Lerch, Early & Brewer, Chartered * |
| Gray James | Venable LLP * |
| Mathias James D | DLA Piper LLP (US) * |
| Monk II Charles O | Saul Ewing LLP |
| Reed Stanley J | Lerch, Early & Brewer, Chartered * |
| Robbins, Jr E Hutchinson | Miles & Stockbridge PC * |
| Shea James | Venable LLP * |
| Wright Jefferson V | Miles & Stockbridge PC * |

**Up-and-coming individuals**

| | |
|---|---|
| Hroblak Kevin G | Whiteford, Taylor & Preston LLP * |
| Moffet Brian | Gordon Feinblatt LLC (ONP)[†] |

**Sources say:** *"Top-notch legal services – DLA Piper is excellent at partnering with clients." "Strong strategists, good listeners regarding client concerns – true business partners."*
**KEY INDIVIDUALS** The highly regarded **Robert Mathias** (see p.1429) is joint global leader and US chair of the firm's litigation practice. He specializes in class action and IP disputes, and is also sought for assistance with white-collar criminal matters affecting corporate clients. He took a leading role in the Transamerica Life Insurance matters. **Charles Scheeler** (see p.1431) concentrates on internal

## Litigation: Bankruptcy
### Leading Firms

**Band 1**

Whiteford, Taylor & Preston LLP *

**Band 2**

Miles & Stockbridge PC *

Shapiro Sher Guinot & Sandler *

### Leading Individuals

**Band 1**

| | |
|---|---|
| Donhauser Linda V | Miles & Stockbridge PC * |
| Nussbaum Paul M | Whiteford, Taylor & Preston LLP * |
| Sher Joel I | Shapiro Sher Guinot & Sandler * |

**Band 2**

| | |
|---|---|
| Dame Thomas C | Gallagher, Evelius & Jones, LLP |
| Fletcher Martin T | Whiteford, Taylor & Preston LLP |
| Goldberg Richard M | Shapiro Sher Guinot & Sandler * |
| Grochal Alan M | Tydings & Rosenberg LLP (ONP)[†] |
| Kremen Richard M | DLA Piper LLP (US) * |
| Monk II Charles O | Saul Ewing LLP (ONP)[†] |

**Up-and-coming individuals**

| | |
|---|---|
| Hroblak Kevin G | Whiteford, Taylor & Preston LLP * |
| Misken Ken | Miles & Stockbridge PC * |

* Indicates firm / individual with profile.

[†] ONP = Other Notable Practitioner.

investigations and white-collar criminal defense, as well as commercial litigation. Representative work includes serving as lead counsel to Senator George Mitchell in his independent investigation of performance-enhancing substance use in Major League Baseball. A client says: *"He has represented us in litigation for years, and is a wonderful and superior attorney."* **Neil Dilloff** (see p.1426) is noted for his expertise in disputes concerning insurance, construction and professional malpractice, as well as other commercial litigation. He also acts as claims counsel to the firm. **Brett Ingerman** (see p.1428) is routinely called upon to handle sophisticated commercial litigation and lender liability matters. A client says: *"The quality of his legal advice can hardly be improved; he is excellent."* **Richard Kremen** (see p.1429) has extensive litigation experience at both the trial and appellate levels, handling lender liability cases and contract disputes. He is also noted for expertise in bankruptcy-related matters. **James Mathias** (see p.1429) is chair of the Baltimore litigation practice and cochair of the firm's financial services litigation group. He comes recommended for his strengths in disputes concerning securities and financial services, as well as trade secrets, unfair competition and real estate. *"The legal advice and the work*

*The editorial is in alphabetical order by firm name.*

*results provided by Jim are of a very high quality. He has an aim-oriented approach which was highly appreciated by our mutual client,"* notes one impressed source.

## Gallagher, Evelius & Jones, LLP

**THE FIRM** This team is well versed in a broad range of disputes, including litigation covering bankruptcy, employment and general contentious business matters. The group is also sought for its strengths in appellate litigation and in class action defense work. In addition to regularly handling litigation before federal and state courts, the group is frequently called upon to act on behalf of clients before arbitrators, mediators and other alternative dispute tribunals.

**Sources say:** *"It is a very good, capable firm."*

**KEY INDIVIDUALS** The highly regarded **Ward Coe** has more than three decades of litigation experience and is much in demand for his expertise in disputes relating to antitrust, IP, ERISA and land use litigation. **Thomas Dame** focuses on receivership issues and financial restructuring in addition to handling bankruptcy litigation and general business disputes. He represents a good choice of counsel for clients in the financial services, healthcare, construction, real estate, retail and energy sectors. **Paul Caiola** comes recommended for his expertise in sophisticated commercial disputes and real estate litigation, acting on behalf of entities and individuals at federal and state levels.

## Hogan Lovells US LLP

**THE FIRM** This group handles a diverse range of disputes, from securities and fraud allegations, product liability and consumer protection cases to RICO claims, contract litigation and white-collar and corporate investigations. In a recent highlight, the team represented AngioScore in a whistle-blower case alleging that the company had suppressed adverse reports of injuries and incidents involving its scoring balloon catheter, successfully achieving a federal declination of the investigation and a district court dismissal of the allegations. Other key clients include Medtronic, Millennium Laboratories of California and Boston Scientific.

**Sources say:** *"Hogan's breadth of expertise is a strong point. A second strong point is the quality of the team they have established. We are working with top-tier professionals in many of their practice areas. This firm is extremely knowledgeable, responsive and credible."*

**KEY INDIVIDUALS** The highly esteemed **Mark Gately** comes recommended for his strengths in disputes covering antitrust, product liability and securities fraud, and is also routinely sought to act on behalf of clients on hostile takeover litigation and professional malpractice cases. *"High-quality attorney"* **Stephen Immelt** is the global co-head of the firm's litigation, arbitration and employment practice, and divides his time between its Washington, DC and Baltimore offices. Recent work includes successfully representing Millennium Laboratories of California in a qui tam action filed in the District of Massachusetts by a relator who was a compliance officer for Calloway Laboratories. **Steven Barley** has extensive experience in professional negligence cases and securities litigation, and

remains a fine choice of counsel for class action defense work.

## Kramon & Graham, PA
### See profile on p.1436

**THE FIRM** This excellent litigation boutique acts for a wide range of corporate clients, government and municipal organizations, and professional service firms, and has significant experience acting before federal and state trial and appellate courts, as well as administrative agencies. Particular areas of strength include commercial, insurance, IP and criminal disputes.

**KEY INDIVIDUALS** *"Fabulous attorney"* **Andrew Graham** (see p.1427) remains a go-to choice of counsel for bet-the-company disputes and white-collar criminal defense work, and is also routinely called upon for his strengths in alternative dispute resolution. **James Ulwick** (see p.1433) is well versed in acting for clients before state and federal courts and comes recommended for his expertise in personal injury, professional negligence and construction-related disputes. He is also regularly instructed to handle complex litigation concerning the financial services and real estate sectors. **John Bourgeois** (see p.1425) has substantial experience in litigation concerning IP, personal injury and professional malpractice.

## Lerch, Early & Brewer, Chartered
### See profile on p.1437

**THE FIRM** This Bethesda-based practice is highly regarded for its expertise in disputes concerning contracts, shareholders, fraud, breach of fiduciary duty and unfair competition. The group also maintains a very active white-collar crime defense practice and has established itself as a go-to practice for attorneys and healthcare providers in professional responsibility-related litigation. It counts Adventist Health Care, Euro Motorcars and Fidelity National among its key clients.

**Sources say:** *"They have taken the time to understand us as a client and handle our cases in line with our philosophy as an organization."*

**KEY INDIVIDUALS** **Lauri Cleary** (see p.1425) is recognized for her adept handling of disputes concerning employment, insurance and white-collar crime, as well as complex commercial litigation. A client says: *"Her representation of our needs is second to none. She knows our business inside out."* **Stanley Reed** (see p.1431) heads the firm's litigation group in Bethesda. He is particularly noted for his work with lawyers and healthcare providers in professional malpractice matters, and also comes recommended for his white-collar criminal defense work.

## Miles & Stockbridge PC
### See profile on p.1438

**THE FIRM** This broad-ranging practice is well versed in all areas of commercial litigation, and is particularly sought for its expertise in financial institution and business practice and regulation disputes. Other key areas of litigation strength include manufacturing, distribution and real estate. It counts Stanley Black & Decker, US Foods,

Verizon, Bank of America, Citi and JPMorgan Chase among its impressive client base.

**Sources say:** *"The firm's lawyers are very easy to work with and they always approach issues from a practical point of view."*

**KEY INDIVIDUALS** The *"very talented"* **Linda Donhauser** (see p.1426) comes particularly recommended for her expertise in bankruptcy litigation. A satisfied client describes her as a *"top-notch attorney: smart, responsive and able to find alternative solutions to matters."* **Hutchinson Robbins** (see p.1431) is head of the firm's commercial and business litigation practice. He has substantial experience in all aspects of state and federal trial and appellate work. In a recent highlight, he successfully defended MultiPlan in a claim brought by United Medical Laboratories. Litigation department head **Jefferson Wright** (see p.1434) is a good choice of counsel for sophisticated business disputes and has substantial experience in a wide range of industries, including IT and telecom, real estate, manufacturing, financial services and insurance. He is also noted for his commercial arbitration work. **Ken Misken** (see p.1430) continues to be much sought for his expertise across all aspects of bankruptcy, including litigation. Sources describe him as *"very easy to work with"* and also praise his ability to *"approach issues from a practical point of view."*

## Rosenberg Martin Greenberg, LLP

**THE FIRM** This excellent local firm is a go-to practice for commercial litigation and white-collar criminal work at both state and federal levels. It also has extensive experience in mediation and alternative dispute resolution.

**KEY INDIVIDUALS** **Gerard Martin** (see p.1429) remains a well-known figure at the Maryland trial Bar and is much noted for his experience in white-collar criminal litigation and civil cases. **Benjamin Rosenberg** (see p.1431) is chairman of the firm and continues to be recognized as one of the senior figures in the state's litigation community. He is a fine choice for complex cases before state and federal trial courts and is also highly regarded for his appellate work.

## Shapiro Sher Guinot & Sandler
### See profile on p.1440

**THE FIRM** This firm has established itself as one of the leading practices in the state for bankruptcy-related litigation. In addition, its experienced team is routinely called upon to handle disputes concerning professional liability, antitrust and employment matters. It is also highly regarded for its appellate work and representation in white-collar crime cases.

**Sources say:** *"The firm is a result-oriented, intelligent band of principled street fighters who have the ability to slay a Goliath adversary for a David client."*

**KEY INDIVIDUALS** **Richard Goldberg** (see p.1427) handles bankruptcy, creditors' rights and workouts, in addition to his work in commercial litigation. A source describes him as *"aggressive, tough, smart and a zealous advocate."* **Paul Sandler** (see p.1431) is often sought for his substantial experience in trial and appellate court, and he also maintains a fine track record in mediation and arbitration. *"Mr Sandler is a truly gifted trial lawyer with deep* experience in all areas of civil litigation and criminal defense work. His understanding of all aspects of courtroom presentation is extraordinary," reports one enthusiastic source. Firm chair **Joel Sher** (see p.1432) is an accomplished bankruptcy litigator, acting for debtors, creditors and creditors' committees in Chapter 11 cases. He is also noted for his counsel to clients in out-of-court workouts and commercial disputes. *"He is flat-out good at what he does,"* asserts one well-placed commentator.

## Venable LLP
### See profile on p.927
**THE FIRM** The attorneys in this group have significant experience at trial and appellate level in both state and federal courts and the US Supreme Court. Its diverse client base ranges from small and emerging business companies to Fortune 100 entities, and also includes nonprofit organizations and governmental institutions. Particular areas of expertise include disputes in securities, IP, antitrust, real estate, tax controversy and healthcare law. The group is also noted for its considerable experience in alternative dispute resolution.
**Sources say:** *"They think very strategically and act quickly. I believe we've been a step ahead of the lender's counsel at all points in the process."*
**KEY INDIVIDUALS** Firm chair **James Shea** (see p.1432) concentrates on corporate disputes and related issues. A happy client says: *"He knows how to get to the bottom of issues and get them resolved."* **Paul Strain** (see p.1433) is particularly sought to represent clients in litigation concerning sophisticated technology and science-based issues. He is well versed in handling cases before the US Supreme Court, federal circuits and state high courts, as well as in federal or state courts across the country. **James Gray** (see p.1427) has over three decades' litigation experience in commercial, IP, insurance coverage and product liability disputes. He is also recognized for his appellate work and frequently advises clients on litigation avoidance.

## Whiteford, Taylor & Preston LLP
### See profile on p.1442
**THE FIRM** This excellent team is particularly known for its strength in bankruptcy disputes, acting for a diverse roster of clients, from Fortune 500 companies and government entities to individuals, trusts and nonprofit organizations. The group is also well versed in a wide variety of other disputes, including construction, environment and IP. In a recent highlight, it represented Ford in asbestos and toxic tort litigation. Union Carbide, Property & Casualty Insurance Guaranty, Rothschild Capital Partners and Papa John's are also included among its key clients.
**Sources say:** *"The team is responsive, smart, analytical, client-focused and pragmatic."*
**KEY INDIVIDUALS** The *"smart and creative"* **Paul Nussbaum** (see p.1430) is much in demand for his expertise in bankruptcy disputes, but also maintains a fine reputation for business litigation and alternative dispute resolution. He heads the firm's business reorganization and bankruptcy practice. Managing partner **Martin Fletcher** is similarly well regarded for his strengths in bankruptcy litigation, and also comes recommended for his reorganization and restructuring work. Rising star **Kevin Hroblak** (see p.1428) cochairs the firm's litigation services department. He is routinely called upon to handle professional and product liability, construction, environmental, IP, technology and labor and employment-related disputes, in addition to bankruptcy litigation. *"He is very easy to work with and practical,"* notes one impressed peer.

## Zuckerman Spaeder LLP
**THE FIRM** This fine litigation group is well versed in complex civil disputes and commercial litigation, and also maintains a fine track record for its class action work. Particular areas of strength include handling disputes in healthcare, real estate, entertainment and professional services. Its client base covers public and private companies on both a regional and national scale, as well as individuals such as executives and directors.

**Sources say:** *"The team has great understanding of complex legal and regulatory issues and a great understanding of our business needs."*
**KEY INDIVIDUALS William Murphy** is a seasoned trial lawyer with much experience handling civil and criminal litigation in state and federal courts, and is also sought for his expertise in commercial arbitrations and appellate matters. A client says: *"He has a calmness about him that exudes confidence and works exceptionally well in the courtroom and with any personality type."* The *"terrific"* **Martin Himeles** is managing partner of the Baltimore office and maintains a fine track record for civil and criminal trial work, as well as for his adept handling of federal and state appellate matters.

## Other Notable Practitioners

**Charles Monk** is managing partner of Saul Ewing LLP's Baltimore office and is recognized for his strengths in IP, antitrust and securities disputes, in addition to general business litigation. **Paul Kemp** of Ethridge, Quinn, Kemp, McAuliffe, Rowan & Hartinger is particularly renowned for his white-collar and general criminal defense work. In addition, he is also commonly called upon to handle civil litigation, commercial disputes and SEC investigations. Marcus & Bonsib's **Robert Bonsib** is well known for his wealth of experience in criminal defense work at local and federal trial and appellate levels. **Alan Grochal** of Tydings & Rosenberg LLP has over three decades' experience in bankruptcy and restructuring matters, including litigation. Sources say he is *"very knowledgeable on how to get the best results in the shortest amount of time while keeping within budget."* **Brian Moffet** is head of the commercial litigation practice at Gordon Feinblatt LLC. He represents a fine choice of counsel for financial services disputes. Sources reserve particular praise for his *"dependability and creative approach to problems."*

# REAL ESTATE

Commentary about individuals can be found under their firm's paragraph. If the firm has no paragraph (is not ranked) look at Other Notable Practitioners.

## Real Estate
### Leading Firms

**Band 1**
Ballard Spahr LLP *
Venable LLP *

**Band 2**
DLA Piper LLP (US) *
Gallagher, Evelius & Jones, LLP
Gordon Feinblatt LLC
Lerch, Early & Brewer, Chartered *
Whiteford, Taylor & Preston LLP *

**Band 3**
Linowes and Blocher LLP
Miles & Stockbridge PC *
Rosenberg Martin Greenberg, LLP
Shulman, Rogers, Gandal, Pordy & Ecker, PA

## Real Estate
### Senior Statesmen

**Senior Statesmen: distinguished older practitioners**

| | |
|---|---|
| Fishman David | Gordon Feinblatt LLC |

### Leading Individuals

**Band 1**

| | |
|---|---|
| Barbuti Thomas | Whiteford, Taylor & Preston LLP * |
| Levin Edward J | Gordon Feinblatt LLC |
| Levine Richard E | DLA Piper LLP (US) * |
| Oliver James | Lenrow, Kohn & Oliver (ONP)[†] |
| Pollak Mark | Ballard Spahr LLP * |
| Shepherd Kevin | Venable LLP * |
| Truitt Raymond G | Ballard Spahr LLP * |
| Winston Roger D | Ballard Spahr LLP * |
| Wright James | Venable LLP * |

**Band 2**

| | |
|---|---|
| Chriss Timothy | Gordon Feinblatt LLC |
| Greenberg Barry C | Rosenberg Martin Greenberg, LLP * |
| Kochanski David | Shulman, Rogers, Gandal, Pordy & Ecker |
| Shulman Lawrence A | Shulman, Rogers, Gandal, Pordy & Ecker |

**Band 3**

| | |
|---|---|
| Brennan J Michael | Miles & Stockbridge PC |
| DeTar Richard | Miles & Stockbridge PC |
| Flynn Guy E | DLA Piper LLP (US) * |
| Goldstein Andrew M | Linowes and Blocher LLP * |
| Keener Mark P | Gallagher, Evelius & Jones, LLP |
| Ritzer Lonnie M | Shapiro Sher Guinot & Sandler (ONP)[†] * |

**Band 4**

| | |
|---|---|
| Goodrich James E | Saul Ewing LLP (ONP)[†] |
| Lewis Thomas B | Gallagher, Evelius & Jones, LLP |
| Mezzanotte Joseph J | Whiteford, Taylor & Preston LLP * |
| Spell Cynthia L | Rosenberg Martin Greenberg, LLP * |
| Totten Thomas L | Duane Morris LLP (ONP)[†] |
| Wilson Jane A | Semmes, Bowen & Semmes (ONP)[†] |

**Up-and-coming individuals**

| | |
|---|---|
| Evans III Edward S | Venable LLP * |
| Shapiro-Cyr Lila | Ballard Spahr LLP * |

## Real Estate: Land Use
### Leading Individuals

**Band 1**

| | |
|---|---|
| Brewer Jr Robert G | Lerch, Early & Brewer, Chartered * |
| Sears Barbara | Linowes and Blocher LLP * |

**Band 2**

| | |
|---|---|
| Fine Stanley S | Rosenberg Martin Greenberg, LLP * |
| Harris Robert Roland | Lerch, Early & Brewer, Chartered * |
| Hoffman Robert | Venable LLP * |
| Kominers William | Lerch, Early & Brewer, Chartered * |
| Laria Jon M | Ballard Spahr LLP * |

**Band 3**

| | |
|---|---|
| Harris Patricia A | Lerch, Early & Brewer, Chartered * |

* Indicates firm / individual with profile.
[†] ONP = Other Notable Practitioner.

## Band 1

### Ballard Spahr LLP
See profile on p.2234

**THE FIRM** This premier practice advises clients throughout the USA and internationally through every phase of a real estate transaction, from acquisition, development and financing to leasing, sale and restructuring. The group is also highly sought for its expertise in due diligence, land use and construction issues and maintains a fine reputation for its work concerning distressed properties. In a recent highlight, the group acted for Under Armour on negotiating leases for several major new distribution centers in California and Maryland. It also assisted the company in its $325 million credit facility and in securing entitlements for a doubling of its campus in Baltimore.
**Sources say:** *"Excellent client service."*
**KEY INDIVIDUALS Mark Pollak** (see p.1431) is particularly noted for his public financing work on sophisticated and large-scale real estate projects and sports stadiums and has more than three decades' experience in the field. He led on the Under Armour matters. He is described by one enthusiastic client as *"an excellent and experienced attorney who handles negotiations and drafting very well."* **Raymond Truitt** (see p.1433) continues to be commonly called upon to assist clients with high-profile commercial financing, leasing and development work and is also highly regarded fo

ing environmental law, and in the hospitality and leisure sector. Key clients include AEGON USA Realty Advisors, Liberty Property Trust, CIM Group and Prudential Real Estate Investors.

**Sources say:** *"They are all extremely intelligent. They know how to not put their clients at risk. They are also all outside-the-box thinkers, and always come up with a solution to problems."*

**KEY INDIVIDUALS** The *"outstanding"* **Richard Levine** (see p.1429) comes recommended for his tax planning strengths in complex real estate transactions, acting on behalf of entrepreneurs, investors and developers, among others. He wins particular acclaim for his creative thinking and solution-oriented approach, and for his ability to handle the most complex of tax-related real estate matters. Real estate practice chair **Guy Flynn** (see p.1426) is well versed in all manner of acquisitions and development, joint ventures, leasings, sales, workouts and foreclosures, acting for a range of lenders, borrowers, underwriters, institutional investors and pension funds.

## Gallagher, Evelius & Jones, LLP
**THE FIRM** This excellent group handles all aspects of residential, industrial, mixed-use and other commercial real estate projects, acting for lenders, developers and equity investors, among others. The team is recommended for its work concerning low-income housing, and federal and state historic tax, new markets tax, and also maintains a strong reputation for real estate matters related to health systems, colleges and universities.

**KEY INDIVIDUALS Mark Keener** has much experience in residential, industrial, mixed-use, as well as other commercial real estate development projects. He also continues to be commonly called upon by developers to assist with the formation of condominium and homeowner associations. **Thomas Lewis** is adept in all areas of real estate acquisitions, financings and sales, and is recognized for his strengths in real estate work concerning mixed-use redevelopment projects, affordable and market rate housing developments, and senior housing and assisted living communities.

## Gordon Feinblatt LLC
**THE FIRM** This fine team handles all manner of real estate work for an array of developers, owners, lenders and investors. The group is frequently sought for its expertise in issues relating to the formation of entities and the preparation of reciprocal easement and operating agreements. In addition, it remains a fine choice for clients seeking zoning, land use, and other governmental approvals.

**Sources say:** *"The practice's strength lies in the depth and breath of services provided on a timely basis by friendly, practical and knowledgeable counsel."*

**KEY INDIVIDUALS Edward Levin** has over 30 years of experience in the real estate arena, and is adept in all areas of financing, leasing, acquisitions and sales. He also remains much in demand for his strengths in workouts and foreclosure. **Timothy Chriss** principally handles transactions concerning office buildings, shopping centers, warehouse and industrial properties, and residential devel-

opments, acting for a broad range of lenders, developers and governmental entities. The seasoned **David Fishman** is chairman of the firm's real estate group and has nearly 50 years of real estate experience. He is recognized for his expertise in financing and foreclosure work.

## Lerch, Early & Brewer, Chartered
See profile on p.1437

**THE FIRM** The recent acquisition of Holland & Knight's practice has established this firm as a leading player in both Montgomery County and throughout the state. The group is particularly known for its mixed-use development work and also has substantial expertise in the land use and zoning arena. Among its distinguished group of clients are McDonald's, Adventist Health Care, Safeway and Maisel Development.

**Sources say:** *"The practice offers great judgment based on thorough research and a clear understanding of the issues and business interests."*

**KEY INDIVIDUALS Robert Brewer** (see p.1425) concentrates on land use and zoning work, and has a particular niche in acting for hospitals and other healthcare institutions on land use matters. Brewer, alongside **Robert Harris** (see p.1428), receives praise from clients for being *"engaged, knowledgeable and insightful."* Harris is similarly noted for his land use and zoning work, frequently appearing on behalf of residential and commercial landowners before planning commissions and governmental agencies on land use rights protection and to obtain development approvals. **William Kominers** (see p.1428) has over three decades' experience in real estate and the land use and zoning arena, and is noted for his strengths in issues concerned with land development and administrative and municipal law. He is also sought to assist with issues concerning development projects such as traffic mitigation and density limitations. **Patricia Harris** (see p.1427) is recognized for her expertise concerning mixed-use development projects, in addition to advising property owners and developers on securing development approvals, including site plans, special exceptions, historic preservation and master plan recommendations. She also maintains a fine reputation acting for large-scale clients, such as Costco, TD Bank and McDonald's.

## Whiteford, Taylor & Preston LLP
See profile on p.1442

**THE FIRM** This group offers an extensive range of expertise across real estate-related transactions, bankruptcy and litigation. The group comes recommended for its expertise in commercial and residential development and is additionally well versed in complex easement agreements and multiform purchase and sales agreements. Sources are quick to also commend the practice's strength in land use and zoning matters and it is frequently sought for advice on condemnation and eminent domain issues.

**Sources say:** *"Quality of service and attention to detail are excellent."*

**KEY INDIVIDUALS Thomas Barbuti** (see p.1425) enjoys a broad practice in real estate and is recognized for his work in matters related to green building and sustainability. Sources value his ability to *"stay focused on the issues and*

*negotiate well."* **Joseph Mezzanotte** (see p.1430) assists clients with zoning and land use work, as well as financing, taxation and environmental aspects concerning real estate matters. *"He always looks after our best interests and we are very satisfied with his work,"* a client reports.

## Band 3

### Linowes and Blocher LLP
**THE FIRM** Linowes and Blocher is well versed in all forms of commercial transactions, handling both single-asset and multiproperty portfolios. Its clients range from developers and builders to financial institutions and life insurance companies, and it maintains a fine reputation for work with tax-exempt organizations, universities and government agencies.

**KEY INDIVIDUALS** The highly regarded **Barbara Sears** (see p.1432) is head of the land use group and assists a variety of local, regional and national clients with land use and administrative and municipal law issues. She continues to be frequently called upon to advise on building and other construction permits and approvals, variances, special exceptions and the other aspects of the development process. Real estate transaction practice leader **Andrew Goldstein** (see p.1427) is experienced across all aspects of acquisitions, dispositions, commercial leasing and real estate finance. He is particularly recognized for his expertise in land development issues and remains a fine choice of counsel for institutional users of real property, as well as developers, builders and tenants.

### Miles & Stockbridge PC
See profile on p.1438

**THE FIRM** This team offers the gamut of real estate services, assisting clients on work ranging from transactional matters and land use issues to regulatory, litigation and environmental concerns. It counts Bank of America, Black Oak Properties, Manekin and Fidelity National Title Insurance among its impressive client roster.

**Sources say:** *"The firm's strongest points are its advocacy and knowledge of land use matters."* *"Great work product and great service."*

**KEY INDIVIDUALS Michael Brennan** handles real estate, corporate and other transactional work for a client base of developers, financial institutions and other commercial entities. His work also includes acting for clients on property tax appeals and matters relating to land trusts and environmental issues. A client is quick to praise his approach, noting that he knows *"that we have a high standard for customer service and response time, and he delivers."* **Richard DeTar** chairs the real estate litigation team and is also managing principal of the Easton and Cambridge offices. He comes recommended for his broad-ranging expertise in real estate and land use-related disputes, with sources describing him as *"extremely knowledgeable"* and *"very effective in litigation strategy and execution."*

## Rosenberg Martin Greenberg, LLP

**THE FIRM** This team handles the full spectrum of commercial real estate matters, acting for a diverse client base that ranges from developers, lenders, and institutional and private investors to home builders, title companies, and shopping center and apartment building owners. The group is routinely called upon to advise on land use and zoning work, and also represents a fine choice of counsel to assist with the formation of commercial condominium regimes and homeowner associations.

**KEY INDIVIDUALS** The highly experienced **Stanley Fine** (see p.1426) continues to be in much demand for his advice to developers and businesses regarding land use and zoning work, in addition to providing counsel on general real estate and corporate matters. Founder and managing partner of the firm **Barry Greenberg** (see p.1427) also serves as the chair to its real estate practice. He is particularly well versed in advising clients on issues concerning home-building, residential development and commercial condominiums, and is also noted for his strengths in commercial leasing and lending. **Cynthia Spell** (see p.1433) is recognized for her work on behalf of institutional lenders in real estate-based loans, in addition to representing major developers in sophisticated transactions, ranging from acquisitions and sales to leasing and the formation of commercial condominiums.

## Shulman, Rogers, Gandal, Pordy & Ecker, PA

**THE FIRM** This group has broad-ranging experience of commercial and residential real estate matters, ranging from acquisitions and financing to commercial lending and leasing. The group also maintains a strong reputation for work in land use, construction and home building, and is also called upon regularly to advise on green building, distressed assets, residential settlements and foreclosures.

**KEY INDIVIDUALS David Kochanski** is an experienced real estate specialist and is regularly called upon to handle transactions relating to office buildings, shopping centers and industrial properties, apartment complexes and undeveloped land. Founding partner **Lawrence Shulman** remains a significant player in the Maryland real estate community and continues to be sought for his commercial leasing strengths.

## Other Notable Practitioners

**James Oliver** of Lenrow, Kohn & Oliver A Professional Corporation comes particularly recommended for his strengths in condominium work and leasing. Duane Morris LLP's **Thomas Totten** specializes in real estate development and finance, and is well versed in acquisitions, sales, leasing and financing. He is also known for expertise in construction and land use issues and maintains a fine track record for work on behalf of healthcare institutions. **Lonnie Ritzer** (see p.1431) of Shapiro Sher Guinot & Sandler remains a good choice of counsel for commercial real estate clients and nonprofit organizations in sophisticated real estate, financing and other corporate transactions. In addition to his domestic work, he is also known for handling cross-border transactions in Australia and Europe. The *"very responsive and attentive"* **James Goodrich** of Saul Ewing LLP acts for local and national clients on a broad range of commercial real estate transactions, and is well versed in sales, purchases and leases, as well as construction contracts and other real estate agreements. **Jane Wilson** of Semmes, Bowen & Semmes is particularly known for her handling of construction and permanent commercial real estate loan transactions, acting on behalf of commercial banks, life insurance companies and other institutional lenders.

# Leaders' Profiles in Maryland

## ABRAMSON, Gil
Jackson Lewis LLP, Baltimore
410 415 2023
Gil.Abramson@JAcksonlewis.com
*Featured in Labor & Employment (Maryland)*
**Practice Areas:** All areas of labor and employment law, traditional labor-management relations, EEO litigation, arbitration, non-competition/trade secrets litigation, OSHA, FLSA. Counsels on employment practices and policies, preventative litigation strategy, union avoidance, collective bargaining, and workplace safety.
**Professional Memberships:** American, Federal Maryland Bar Associations, Labor and Employment Law Sections.
**Career:** Prior to joining Jackson Lewis, he was a partner at Hogan & Hartson LLP. Former Senior Counsel to Chairman of NLRB.
**Personal:** Boston University School of Law (JD 1969); State University of New York at Buffalo (BA 1966).

## ADKINS, Edward J
Miles & Stockbridge PC, Baltimore
410 385 3500
eadkins@milesstockbridge.com
*Featured in Employee Benefits & Executive Compensation (Maryland)*
**Practice Areas:** Member of the Employee Benefits and Executive Compensation Practice Group, specializing in ESOPs; ERISA fiduciary responsibility and plan asset management; health and welfare plans/HIPAA; deferred and executive compensation, plans for governments and non-profit organizations and pension, profit-sharing & 401(k) plans. Represents businesses in the US and internationally; benefits for US subsidiaries of international companies.
**Professional Memberships:** ABA, DC Bar; Maryland Bar; Listed in Best Lawyers in America.
**Career:** Venable, Baetjer & Howard; Miles & Stockbridge P.C.
**Personal:** Born: October 18, 1947, Annapolis, Maryland. JD Degree, 1972, University of Maryland; AB Degree, University of North Carolina, 1969. Married.

## AMES, Robert
Venable LLP, Baltimore
410 244 7448
rgames@Venable.com
*Featured in Labor & Employment (Maryland)*
**Professional Memberships:** Mr Ames is a Member of the American Bar Association, Labor Law Section.
**Career:** For more than 30 years, Mr Ames has represented public and private sector employers with regard to all aspects of labor and employment law. He is experienced as a chief negotiator and strategist in collective bargaining negotiations, as well as lead counsel in labor arbitrations, employment discrimination, and wage and hour litigation.
**Personal:** JD., with honors, The National Law Center, George Washington University, 1973; BBA, Temple University, 1970.

## AMIOT, Brooks R
Jackson Lewis LLP, Baltimore
410 415 2005
Brooks.Amiot@jacksonlewis.com
*Featured in Labor & Employment (Maryland)*
**Practice Areas:** Represents employers in all areas of labor and employment law, including litigation of employment claims; appeals, traditional labor relations; and charges of discrimination. Counsels employers on practices and policies, preventative litigation strategies, and union avoidance issues.Primary labor counsel to one of the largest national poultry companies.
**Career:** Founding partner of Baltimore office. Prior to joining Jackson Lewis, partner at DLA Piper.
**Publications:** Contributing Editor, The Developing Labor Law.
**Personal:** JD, George Washington Law School (Member, Moot Court Board); BA, University of Utah (cum laude); Best Lawyers in America, Maryland Super Lawyer, AV rating by Martindale-Hubbell.

## ATLAS, Harry I
Venable LLP, Baltimore
410 528 2848
hiatlas@Venable.com
*Featured in Employee Benefits & Executive Compensation (Maryland)*
**Practice Areas:** Harry Atlas handles a broad range of employee benefit and executive compensation matters, including the implementation, operation and termination of all types of employee benefit plans. He counsels clients regarding qualified 403(b) and 457 plans, and health and welfare arrangements. In the executive compensation area, Mr Atlas' practice encompasses nonqualified retirement plans, equity compensation arrangements and golden parachute issues. Mr Atlas also handles employee benefit aspects of M&A transactions, and PBGC negotiations.
**Personal:** JD, with honors, University of Maryland, 1997; Order of the Coif, Ner Israel Rabbinical College, 1994.

## AYRES, Jeffrey P
Venable LLP, Towson
410 494 6282
jpayres@Venable.com
*Featured in Labor & Employment (Maryland)*
**Practice Areas:** Jeffrey Ayres concentrates his practice in the area of complex civil litigation, focusing upon labor and employment law, civil rights cases, ERISA, state tort and contract matters, and discrimination issues. Industries in which he has represented clients include high technology/science, education, banking and finance, and healthcare. He is Chair of Venable's Ethics Committee.
**Career:** Past Chair, Maryland State Bar Association, Labor and Employment Section; Commissioner, Maryland Attorney Grievance Commission; Chancellor, Episcopal Diocese of Maryland.
**Personal:** JD, magna cum laude, The National Law Center, George Washington University, 1977;

Order of the Coif; BA, cum laude, Harvard College, 1974.

## BAADER, Michael
Venable LLP, Baltimore
410 244 7708
mjbaader@Venable.com
*Featured in Corporate/M&A (Maryland)*
**Practice Areas:** Michael Baader is the Partner-in-Charge of Venable's Baltimore office. His practice centers on all aspects of corporate planning and business advisory services to corporate clients. He focuses on mergers and acquisitions, private equity, venture capital, corporate finance, joint ventures, and representation of technology and growth companies.
**Professional Memberships:** Mr Baader is Chairman of the Board of Directors of the Economic Alliance. He is also a board member of the Greater Baltimore Committee, the Living Classrooms Foundation, BioHealth Innovation, Inc., and the UMBC Tech Center.
**Personal:** JD, College of William and Mary, 1985; BS, University of Virginia, 1980.

## BAKER, Constance H
Venable LLP, Baltimore
410 244 7535
chbaker@Venable.com
*Featured in Healthcare (Maryland)*
**Practice Areas:** Healthcare law, including hospital medical staff issues, regulatory compliance, physician peer review, the Emergency Medical Treatment and Labor Act, and representation of healthcare professionals before state licensing boards. Counseling and representation of independent schools, including regulatory compliance and corporate governance.
**Professional Memberships:** American Health Lawyers Association; American Bar Association; Maryland State Bar Association.
**Career:** Former prosecutor and Assistant Attorney General, Maryland Board of Physicians.
**Publications:** Publications on healthcare and independent school law topics, including New England Journal of Medicine and National Association of Independent Schools.
**Personal:** JD, Catholic University, 1975; BA, summa cum laude, Vassar College, 1969.

## BARBUTI, Thomas
Whiteford, Taylor & Preston LLP, Baltimore
410 347 8719
tbarbuti@wtplaw.com
*Featured in Real Estate (Maryland)*
**Practice Areas:** Sophisticated, transactional commercial real estate, including purchase and sale agreements, leases, subleases, covenants, conditions and restrictions, easements, reciprocal easements, development agreements, construction contracts and financing with a concentration in development, construction, retail and mixed-use projects.
**Professional Memberships:** American College of Real Estate Lawyers; US Green Building Council; International Council of Shopping Centers; National Association of Industrial and Office Properties; Maryland State Bar Association (Chair, 2005-06, Section of Real Property,

Planning and Zoning). Admitted in Maryland and Washington, DC.
**Personal:** JD, Rutgers University, 1974; BA, University of Maryland, 1970; LEED AP, 2009.

## BOURGEOIS, John A
Kramon & Graham, PA, Baltimore
410 752 6030
jbourgeois@kg-law.com
*Featured in Litigation (Maryland)*
**Practice Areas:** General commercial, criminal, and administrative litigation.
**Professional Memberships:** Mr Bourgeois was past Chair of the Judicial Administration Section Council of the Maryland State Bar Association. He also was appointed a member of the Criminal Justice Act Felony Panel of the United States District Court for the District of Maryland. Mr Bourgeois is a Member of the American, Maryland State, Baltimore City, Baltimore County, and District of Columbia Bar Associations, the American Association for Justice, Trial Lawyers for Public Justice, and the National Association of Criminal Defense Attorneys. He is admitted to practice in Maryland, the District of Columbia, the United States District Court for the Districts of Maryland and the District of Columbia, the United States Courts of Appeals for the Fourth Circuit and the District of Columbia Circuit, and the Supreme Court of the United States.
**Career:** Before becoming an attorney, Mr Bourgeois worked as a human rights officer and assistant director of the Robert F Kennedy Memorial in Washington, DC. He graduated from the University of Maryland in 1987 and from the Georgetown University Law Center in 1993. He is a Member of the Board of Directors of Maryland Lawyers for the Arts, Inc.

## BREWER JR, Robert G
Lerch, Early & Brewer, Chartered, Bethesda
301 657 0165
rgbrewer@lerchearly.com
*Featured in Real Estate (Maryland)*
**Practice Areas:** Real estate development, land use and healthcare.
**Professional Memberships:** Maryland and District of Columbia Bar Associations; Urban Land Institute; Maryland-National Capital Building Industry Association; American Health Lawyers Association.
**Career:** Serves on Montgomery County Zoning Advisory Panel, Montgomery County Business Development Corporation and Music Center at Strathmore boards. Served as Law Clerk to Judge Richard B. Latham from 1976-77 before joining the firm in 1977. Past President: Bethesda-Chevy Chase Chamber of Commerce; Imagination Stage.
**Personal:** JD with honors, University of Maryland, 1976. BA, Hamilton College, 1973. Best Lawyers in America 1990-present.

## CARLSON, William
Shapiro Sher Guinot & Sandler, Baltimore
410 385 4205
wec@shapirosher.com
*Featured in Corporate/M&A (Maryland)*

**Practice Areas:** Corporate and Securities; Technology Transactions; Trademarks and Copyrights.
**Professional Memberships:** Mid Atlantic Venture Association; ABA; Maryland State Bar Association Section of Business Law (Chair, 2012-13).
**Career:** Advises clients in mergers and acquisitions, equity and debt financings, joint ventures, technology transfer and licensing, employment and consulting arrangements, and general corporate planning. Counsels biotech companies in their formation, IP planning and revising, fundraising, clinical trial and CRO contracting, and governance. Provides SEC "Maryland counsel" services to other law firms and is listed in The Bond Buyer's "Red Book" as a nationally recognized bond counsel.

## CHALK, Wm David
DLA Piper LLP (US), Baltimore
410 580 4120
david.chalk@dlapiper.com
*Featured in Corporate/M&A (Maryland)*
**Practice Areas:** Corporate/M&A, capital markets, private equity.
**Career:** He practices corporate and securities law emphasizing on public and private mergers and acquisitions, public offerings of equity and debt securities including IPOs and follow-on public offerings and Rule 144A offerings, tender offers, going private transactions, PIPE transactions, venture capital investments, and other private placements of securities. He advises public companies on disclosure and corporate goverance issues, shareholder relations, and compliance with Sarbanes-Oxley, and the rules and regulations of the SEC.
**Personal:** JD, University of Maryland (with honors); BS, University of Baltimore (summa cum laude).

## CHESSHIRE, Mary Claire
Whiteford, Taylor & Preston LLP, Baltimore
410 347 9465
mchesshire@wtplaw.com
*Featured in Employee Benefits & Executive Compensation (Maryland)*
**Practice Areas:** Partner in the firm's Employee Benefits Practice Group. Substantial experience advising organizations of all sizes with respect to retirement, welfare and executive compensation plan design and ERISA and Internal Revenue Code compliance. Experience also includes fiduciary training and counseling and guiding clients through government agency audits and correction programs. Practice extends to advice regarding employee benefit matters in bankruptcy, litigation and corporate transactions.
**Professional Memberships:** Maryland State Bar Association; National Association of Public Pension Attorneys.
**Personal:** JD (with honors), University of Baltimore School of Law, 1993; BA, The Johns Hopkins University, 1989.

## CLEARY, Lauri E
Lerch, Early & Brewer, Chartered, Bethesda
301 657 0176
lecleary@lerchearly.com
*Featured in Litigation (Maryland)*
**Practice Areas:** Complex commercial litigation: employment, tort, insurance, title insurance, white collar criminal defense. Significant experience representing religious organizations and auto dealerships.
**Professional Memberships:** Maryland, Virginia, DC Bars; Director, Montgomery County Bar Foundation
**Career:** Joined firm in 1986. Judicial law clerk to the Honorable Howard S. Chasanow, Maryland Court of Appeals (Retired), then an Associate Judge of Circuit Court for Prince George's County; co-host "Law School for the Public" Bar Foundation public service cable television program since 2007.
**Personal:** Unversity of Maryland: JD, 1985; BA, English, 1982. Awards: Daily Record's Leadership in Law (2009), Bar Foundation of Montgomery County's Community Service (2009), John Carroll Society's Pro Bono Legal Service(2007). Elected to the Montgomery County Bar Foundation's Bar Leaders (2007).

## CLEMENTS, Lynn
Jackson Lewis LLP, Baltimore
410 415 2009
Lynn.Clements@jacksonlewis.com
*Featured in Labor & Employment (Maryland)*
**Practice Areas:** Labor and employment. Emphasis on affirmative action, EEO, disability leave management compliance.
**Professional Memberships:** BILG, MAAAO, NAPW, ABA.
**Career:** Senior Policy Advisor to the Assistant Secretary for Employment Standards, U.S. DOL, 2008 – 2009; Acting Director of Policy, OFCCP, 2006 – 2009; Special Assistant to the Vice Chair and Legal Counsel, U.S. EEOC, 2001 – 2006.
**Publications:** ACC InfoPak: Managing Family and Medical Leaves of Absence: Statutory Entitlement, Employer Commitments, and Reasonable Accommodations, September 2012.
**Personal:** Maryland Super Lawyer and Rising Star; Georgetown University Law Center, J.D, cum laude, 1997; Wilkes University, BA, BS, magna cum laude, 1994.

## COOK, Bryson
Venable LLP, Baltimore
410 244 7522
blcook@Venable.com
*Featured in Corporate/M&A (Maryland)*
**Practice Areas:** Bryson Cook provides corporate, tax, finance and transactional advice to private and public companies and their owners and key executives. Recent significant matters include assisting a large international hotel and resort chain with its relationship change and conversion to a REIT; restructuring of the governance structure of a major healthcare insurer; succession planning and restructuring for a major real estate developer and general representation of one of the largest U.S. construction companies.

**Personal:** JD, cum laude, University of Pennsylvania Law School, 1973; MBA, Wharton School of Finance and Commerce, 1973; AB, magna cum laude, Princeton University, 1970.

## CURRAN, Robert
Whiteford, Taylor & Preston LLP, Baltimore
410 347 9472
rcurran@wtplaw.com
*Featured in Corporate/M&A (Maryland)*

**Practice Areas:** Business and corporate law; M&A ranging in size from $1,000,000 to $500 million; leveraged buyouts; formation and structuring of business entities; corporate succession planning; ESOP transactions; and executive compensation.
**Professional Memberships:** American Bar Association, Maryland State Bar Association (Chair, Section of Taxation 1987-88). Admitted in Maryland.
**Career:** Partner, Corporate and Securities Department.
**Publications:** Co-author: Tax Planning Forms for Business and Individuals, Warren, Gorham & Lamont (1985).
**Personal:** JD, with Honors (Order of the Coif), University of Maryland School of Law, 1974; BA, University of Delaware, 1971.

## DEVRIES JR, Donald L
Goodell, DeVries, Leech & Dann, LLP, Baltimore
410 783 4000
dld@gdldlaw.com
*Featured in Healthcare (Maryland)*

**Practice Areas:** Medical malpractice; drugs and medical devices; professional liability; drug and medical device litigation; product liability.
**Professional Memberships:** Fellow, International Academy of Trial Lawyers, 2005-Present; Fellow, American College of Trial Lawyers, 2000-Present; American Board of Trial Advocates (President, Maryland Chapter, 1992-95); International Society of Barristers; Association of Defense Trial Attorneys; American Bar Association; Maryland State Bar Association (Chair, Committee on Law Reform, 2011-Present); The Bar Association of Baltimore City; Member, International Association of Defense Counsel, 1985-Present (Vice Chairman, Medical Malpractice, Committee for Newsletters, 1989-90, Program Chairman,1990-92, Chairman, Medical Malpractice Committee, 1992-1995, Chairman, Defense Counsel Committee, 1997-99, Board of Directors, 1999-2002); Maryland Association of Defense Counsel; Defense Research Institute; Chairman, Maryland's Emergency Medical Services Board, 1993-Present.
**Career:** Founding Partner of Goodell, DeVries, Leech & Dann, LLP, 1988; Managing Partner 1998-2004; Semmes, Bowen & Semmes, Associate (1973-80) and Partner (1980-88), Chairman, Medical Malpractice Department.
**Publications:** 'Wrongful Life, Wrongful Birth, and Wrongful Pregnancy: Judicial Divergence in the Birth Related Torts', The Forum, Volume XX, Number 2, Winter 1985. Contributing Author — Textbook — Medical and Hospital Negligence,

Volume III, Chapter 39, Defendant's Voir Dire (1988). Ian Gallacher, Bruce R. Parker and Donald L. DeVries, Jr., 'Back to the Future? Product Liability Class Actions and Proposed Rule 23 Changes', Defense Counsel Journal, April 1997, Vol. 64, No. 2. Donald L DeVries, Jr and Ian Gallacher, 'Medical Monitoring in Drug and Medical Device Cases: Taking the Temperature of a New Theory', Defense Counsel Journal, April 2001, Vol. 68, No. 2. Mr DeVries also widely lectures to legal and medical professionals, has frequently served as Faculty for the Maryland Institute for Continuing Professional Education for Lawyers (MICPEL), and serves as moderator and program planner for many legal seminars.
**Personal:** University of Maryland, JD, with honors, 1973; Dartmouth College, BA, 1969.

## DILLOFF, Neil
DLA Piper LLP (US), Baltimore
410 580 4138
neil.dilloff@dlapiper.com
*Featured in Litigation (Maryland)*

**Practice Areas:** Litigation, insurance litigation and coverage, class action, professional liability.
**Career:** His practice includes significant experience in insurance, professional malpractice, construction litigation, and large, complex commercial litigation matters. He has tried more than 100 cases in state and federal courts and has won two of the largest plaintiffs' verdicts in Maryland history. He has achieved over a dozen recoveries in excess of $1 million. He has written more than 30 articles and books on a variety of subjects in various legal journals.
**Personal:** JD, Georgetown University; BA, University of North Carolina.

## DONHAUSER, Linda V
Miles & Stockbridge PC, Baltimore
410 385 3684
ldonhauser@milesstockbridge.com
*Featured in Litigation (Maryland)*

**Practice Areas:** Representation of secured creditors, trade creditors and other interested parties in insolvency proceedings throughout the United States. She also represents secured lenders in all phases of the restructuring process and in formulating creative workout strategies in and outside of bankruptcy cases.
**Professional Memberships:** Admitted to practice in the state and federal courts of Maryland, the United States District Court for the District of Columbia, and the United States Court of Appeals for the Fourth Circuit. Ms Donhauser is a member of the American Bankruptcy Institute, where she serves on the Advisory Board for the Mid-Atlantic Bankruptcy Conference, and has co-chaired the Conference in 2010, 2011, 2012 and 2013. She is a member of the International Women's Insolvency and Restructuring Confederation, where she serves co- chair and a member of the Board of the Greater Maryland Network.
**Career:** Ms Donhauser became a principal of Miles & Stockbridge in 1998, and has served as the Chair of the Creditors' Rights and Bankruptcy Group since 2004.

**Personal:** University of Baltimore School of Law (JD 1989, Magna Cum Laude and Heuisler Honor Society). Ms Donhauser lives in Fallston, Maryland with her family, and is involved in various sports and other community events.

## EVANS III, Edward S
Venable LLP, Baltimore
410 244 7855
esevans@Venable.com
*Featured in Real Estate (Maryland)*

**Practice Areas:** Real Estate, Finance
**Professional Memberships:** American Bar Association, Maryland State Bar Association
**Career:** Mr Evans concentrates his practice on complex real estate matters, including land acquisition, development, leasing, management and disposition, with a focus on hospitality and medical office facilities, as well as equity investments and commercial finance. Recognized as Baltimore's Legal Elite by BaltimoreCEO Magazine.
**Publications:** "Maryland Taxes — Taxes Imposed Upon Recordation of Instruments Conveying Title to Real and Personal Property"
**Personal:** JD, magna cum laude, University of Baltimore School of Law, Heiusler Honor Society; BS, magna cum laude, University of Delaware.

## FINE, Stanley S
Rosenberg Martin Greenberg, LLP, Baltimore
410 727 6600
sfine@rosenbergmartin.com
*Featured in Real Estate (Maryland)*

**Practice Areas:** Land use and zoning; real estate development and transactions; administrative law.
**Professional Memberships:** Maryland State Bar Association.
**Career:** Partner, Rosenberg Martin Greenberg, LLP (1997 to present); Best Lawyers Land Use & Zoning Lawyer of the Year (2011-2013); Best Lawyers in America - Land Use & Zoning (2007-13); Maryland Super Lawyers - Land Use and Zoning (2007-13); Baltimore City Planning Commission Member (1984-85); Maryland State Lottery Agency - Director (1974-78); Maryland State Lottery Commission - Chairman (2007-09).
**Personal:** Johns Hopkins University, BA, 1965; University of Maryland School of Law, JD, 1969.

## FLYNN, Guy E
DLA Piper LLP (US), Baltimore
410 580 4149
guy.flynn@dlapiper.com
*Featured in Real Estate (Maryland)*

**Practice Areas:** Real estate, corporate, finance.
**Career:** He focuses on commercial real estate development and finance, representing institutional investors, pension funds, developers, lenders, borrowers, underwriters, and other public and private business entities in various commercial transactions, including joint venture, acquisition and development, leasing, commercial finance, purchase and sale, workout foreclosure, and syndication transactions. He counsels clients with respect to land use regulation, taxation, environmental, corporate, and bankruptcy issues.
**Personal:** JD and BA, University of Virginia.

## FOX, Douglas M
Ballard Spahr LLP, Baltimore
410 528 5505
foxd@ballardspahr.com
*Featured in Corporate/M&A (Maryland)*

**Practice Areas:** Douglas M. Fox is Practice Leader of the Life Sciences/Technology Group. He practices corporate, securities, and technology law. Clients include public and private traditional businesses, life sciences, alternative energy, other technology companies, and the investment banks and others that provide them with capital. He represents REITs and other companies on matters of Maryland corporation law, including corporate governance and takeover defenses.
**Professional Memberships:** Maryland State Bar Association Past Chair, Committee on Representing Emerging Companies Maryland Judicial Institute, Instructor, Business and Biotechnology Law.
**Career:** Admissions: Maryland.
**Personal:** University of Baltimore School of Law (JD 1985) University of Maryland (BS Civil Engineering 1979).

## FRISCH, John B
Miles & Stockbridge PC, Baltimore
410 385 3507
jfrisch@milesstockbridge.com
*Featured in Corporate/M&A (Maryland)*

**Practice Areas:** The Chairman and Chief Executive Officer of the firm, he specializes in mergers and acquisitions, securities and other business transactions. He has been responsible for acquisitions and dispositions of businesses by public and private enterprises, including substantial international businesses. He provides general business counseling to businesses and their officers and directors, including counseling concerning fiduciary duty, corporate governance and related matters.
**Professional Memberships:** ABA, MSBA.
**Career:** Principal since 1990.
**Publications:** No Such Thing As a Perfect Deal: Components of an M&A Transaction; Inside the Minds: M&A Negotiations (2006).
**Personal:** University of Maryland (JD, 1983); Dickinson College (BA, 1980).

## GARDNER, Russell H
DLA Piper LLP (US), Baltimore
410 580 4154
russell.gardner@dlapiper.com
*Featured in Labor & Employment (Maryland)*

**Practice Areas:** Labor and employment, class action.
**Career:** His practice encompasses all areas of management-side labor and employment discrimination. He regularly advises on union-avoidance matters, including representation before the National Labor Relations Board, employment discrimination and OSHA matters, and defense of employment claims, including ERISA claims, in state and federal courts across the nation. He has experience in drafting and enforcing employment agreements and non-competition agreements. He has written and lectured extensively on a variety

of employment topics, particularly for the Americans with Disabilities Act.

**Personal:** JD, Syracuse University; BA, Alfred University.

## GOLDBERG, Richard M
Shapiro Sher Guinot & Sandler, Baltimore
410 385 4274
rmg@shapirosher.com
*Featured in Litigation (Maryland)*

**Practice Areas:** Corporate reorganization; creditors' rights; bankruptcy litigation; commercial litigation.

**Professional Memberships:** Bankruptcy Bar Association for the District of Maryland (President); Turnaround Management Association; American Bankruptcy Institute.

**Career:** Represents financial institutions, developers, retailers, home builders, commercial landlords, specialty-lending institutions, trustees, and government agencies in Chapter 11 liquidations and reorganizations, and in large Chapter 7 liquidations. Assists parties in acquiring assets from bankruptcy estates, and represents insurance companies as creditors in bankruptcy/workout situations. Also assists parties in commercial litigation, including disputes regarding commercial transactions and the Uniform Commercial Code, in state and federal courts.

## GOLDSTEIN, Andrew M
Linowes and Blocher LLP, Bethesda
301 961 5154
agoldstein@linowes-law.com
*Featured in Real Estate (Maryland)*

**Practice Areas:** Real estate transactions.

**Professional Memberships:** American Bar Association, Real Property Section, Commercial Leasing Committee. Maryland State Bar Association. International Council of Shopping Centers.

**Career:** Concentrates in the areas of real estate acquisitions and sales, commercial leasing and real estate finance. Represents builders, developers, tenants and institutional users of real property with particular experience in land development matters. Has also represented national and regional retailers in site acquisition and leasing activities in the Washington/Baltimore region.

**Personal:** BA, University of Pennsylvania; JD, Washington College of Law, American University.

## GRAHAM, Andrew Jay
Kramon & Graham, PA, Baltimore
410 752 6030
agraham@kg-law.com
*Featured in Litigation (Maryland)*

**Practice Areas:** Mr Graham practices in the areas of business litigation, securities litigation, general civil litigation, professional liability matters, white-collar criminal litigation, trade secrets litigation, antitrust litigation, and mediation.

**Professional Memberships:** Mr Graham is a fellow of the American College of Trial Lawyers, and was its Maryland State Chairman from 1996-98. He is presently a Member of the Maryland federal court's Magistrate Judges' Merit Selection Panel, and the Association of Professional Responsibility Lawyers. He is a fellow of the

American Bar Foundation. Mr Graham has held various offices, board and committee positions with the American Bar Association, the Federal Bar Association, and the Maryland and Baltimore City Bar Associations. He was the Chairman of the Maryland Bar Ethics 2000 Committee. He is a permanent Member of the Fourth Circuit Judicial Conference. He is a founding member and immediate past President of ADR Maryland, a forum for alternative dispute resolution. He has been the co-chairman of Maryland Legal Aid's Equal Justice Council since 2004.

**Career:** Mr Graham served as a law clerk to the Honorable Alexander Harvey, II of the United States District Court for the District of Maryland. He was an Assistant United States Attorney for the District of Maryland from 1971-74. Mr Graham is an active Member of the Bars of MD, NY and the District of Columbia. He is admitted to practice before the United States Supreme Court, the United States Court of Appeals for the Fourth Circuit, and the United States District Courts for the District of Columbia, the District of Maryland, the Eastern District of New York, and the Southern District of New York. Mr Graham is listed by the 2007-2012 and 2013 Maryland 'Super Lawyers' magazine in 'The Top Ten' Attorneys, and he appears in 'The Best Lawyers in America' in four practice areas. He graduated from Yale University (BA 1965) and received his law degree from the New York University School of Law (JD 1968).

## GRAY, James
Venable LLP, Baltimore
410 244 7471
jegray@Venable.com
*Featured in Litigation (Maryland)*

**Practice Areas:** For more than four decades Jim Gray has maintained a diverse and successful trial and appellate practice focusing on complex litigation involving commercial disputes, insurance coverage, intellectual property, and product liability. He has tried over 100 cases to verdict in federal and state courts in Maryland and throughout the country. He also counsels clients on litigation avoidance and complex litigation management.

**Professional Memberships:** His election to the American College of Trial Lawyers by his peers recognizes him as one Maryland's leading trial lawyers.

**Personal:** JD, University of Maryland, 1970; BA, University of Maryland, 1967.

## GREENBERG, Barry C
Rosenberg Martin Greenberg, LLP, Baltimore
410 727 6687
bgreenberg@rosenbergmartin.com
*Featured in Real Estate (Maryland)*

**Practice Areas:** Real estate development and finance; commercial leasing; banking and finance; bank workouts and foreclosures; business law; contracts and contract disputes.

**Career:** Managing Partner, Rosenberg Martin Greenberg, LLP. Listed in 'Best Lawyers in America' (2004-current) Chambers USA (2005-current) and appeared in Baltimore Magazine's

'Best Lawyers in Maryland.' Adjunct Professor, University of Maryland School of Law, Modern Real Estate Transactions (1993-2005).

**Personal:** Haverford College, BA, 1979; University of Maryland School of Law, JD, with honors, 1984.

## GUATTERY, Peter
Whiteford, Taylor & Preston LLP, Baltimore
410 347 9431
pguattery@wtplaw.com
*Featured in Labor & Employment (Maryland)*

**Practice Areas:** Counsels employers in labor, employment and immigration law, including defense of discrimination, harassment and other employment claims; employer compliance, DOL and other agency investigations, employment of foreign nationals, employment documentation and drafting of contracts, employment litigation.

**Professional Memberships:** Maryland State Bar Association; ABA; AILA, Maryland Bar Foundation. Admitted in Maryland and District of Columbia. Chair MSBA Labor & Employment Section Council 2008-2010.

**Publications:** Limits and License in Rule 35 Examinations, Maryland Bar Journal, 2002; Turn and Face the Strain - New PERM Regulations, Maryland Bar Journal, 2005.

**Personal:** JD, University of Pennsylvania, 1987; BA, Johns Hopkins University, 1984.

## HAFETS, Richard J
Jackson Lewis LLP, Baltimore
410 415 2002
Richard.Hafets@jacksonlewis.com
*Featured in Labor & Employment (Maryland)*

**Practice Areas:** Labor and employment, class action.

**Career:** Practices in all areas of labor and employment law, including union avoidance, traditional labor-management relations, employment litigation, EEO and affirmative action, OSHA, and general personnel. He is primary labor counsel to many Fortune 500 companies, healthcare institutions, charities, and civic organizations, and represents many of the firm's significant clients. He is Managing Partner of the firm's Baltimore office. Prior to joining Jackson Lewis, he was a Partner at DLA Piper and headed the labor practice in the Baltimore office.

**Personal:** JD, American University (magna cum laude); BS, American University (summa cum laude).

## HAINES, Sigrid
Lerch, Early & Brewer, Chartered, Bethesda
301 657 0152
schaines@lerchearly.com
*Featured in Healthcare (Maryland)*

**Practice Areas:** Healthcare, Elder Law. Represent hospitals, foundations, healthcare systems, nursing homes, home health agencies and physicians. Counsel hospitals on contract disputes/negotiations; privileges and credentials; patient care; accreditation and regulatory matters; HIPAA issues; medical staff bylaws; and fraud/abuse investigations and litigation. Advise physicians on privileging/credentialing; licensing; payor issues; contracts; and peer review activities.

Represent individuals and institutions in guardianship matters.

**Professional Memberships:** Maryland State Bar Assn (Board of Governors, Health Law Section Chair), American Health Lawyers Assn

**Career:** Former hospital management consultant.

**Personal:** JD, Case Western Reserve, 1984 (Student Editor, Health Matrix Law Journal); BSBA in Accounting, Bucknell, 1981.

## HANKS, JR, James J
Venable LLP, Baltimore
410 244 7500
jhanks@Venable.com
*Featured in Corporate/M&A (Maryland), Capital Markets (Nationwide)*
See under Nationwide for profile.

## HARDY, Kelly Tubman
DLA Piper LLP (US), Baltimore
410 580 4169
kelly.hardy@dlapiper.com
*Featured in Corporate/M&A (Maryland)*

**Practice Areas:** Corporate/M&A.

**Career:** She practices corporate and securities law, including mergers and acquisitions, public and private offerings of securities, corporate governance, securities compliance and general business law. As Global Desk Partner for the Baltimore office, she has worked on numerous international financings and transactions and is responsible for the flow of work between the firm's Baltimore office and its international offices.

**Personal:** Harvard Leadership Program 2006; JD, University of Maryland School of Law 1996 with honors; Order of the Coif; Associate Editor, University of Maryland Law Review, 1995-1996. MBA, University of Maryland 1996 BA, University of Pennsylvania 1990 cum laude.

## HARMON, Jason C
DLA Piper LLP (US), Baltimore
410 580 4170
jason.harmon@dlapiper.com
*Featured in Corporate/M&A (Maryland)*

**Practice Areas:** Corporate/M&A, private equity, capital markets, life sciences.

**Career:** He focuses on corporate and securities law, including public and private equity and debt offerings, mergers and acquisitions, and other corporate matters. His practice emphasizes high technology and emerging growth companies, including internet, communications, and biotech companies. His merger and acquisition experience includes both serving as buyer's counsel and seller's counsel. In his equity offering and debt offering experience, he has been both company counsel and banker's counsel.

**Personal:** JD, Washington and Lee University (magna cum laude); BA, University of Pittsburgh (summa cum laude).

## HARRIS, Patricia A
Lerch, Early & Brewer, Chartered, Bethesda
301 841 3832
paharris@lerchearly.com
*Featured in Real Estate (Maryland)*

**Practice Areas:** Patricia Harris is a land use and zoning attorney representing developers and property owners to secure approvals needed to develop their properties, including site plans, special exceptions, subdivision approvals, historic preservation, local map amendments, zoning text amendments, master plan recommendations and building permits in Montgomery County, Maryland. She is experienced in transit-oriented development and other issues related to smart growth development. Pat represents national corporations, local development companies, churches and schools. Her clients include companies such as McDonald's, Costco, The JBG Companies and Federal Realty Investment Trust.

### HARRIS, Robert Roland
Lerch, Early & Brewer, Chartered, Bethesda
301 841 3826
rrharris@lerchearly.com
*Featured in Real Estate (Maryland)*

**Practice Areas:** Robert Harris is a partner at Lerch, Early & Brewer in Bethesda, Maryland. His practice includes zoning, land use, real estate, and municipal affairs. Bob has experience with a number of issues including Smart Growth, traffic management, adequate public facilities controls, public infrastructure, mixed-use planned development, environmental issues, urban design, affordable housing, and historic preservation. He has served on numerous boards, committees and task forces advising the government on matters ranging from airport development to water and sewer service. He has authored articles and spoken at conferences and seminars on topics affecting the real estate and development industry.

### HARRISON, Bruce S
Shawe Rosenthal LLP, Baltimore
410 752 1040
harrison@shawe.com
*Featured in Labor & Employment (Maryland)*

**Practice Areas:** Employment discrimination litigation; employment tort and contract litigation; wage and hour laws; class action litigation; family and medical leave act (FMLA); employment agreements, policies, and procedures.
**Professional Memberships:** Bar Admissions: Maryland; District of Columbia; Pennsylvania; US Courts of Appeals for the 1st, 2nd, 3rd, 4th, 5th, 9th, 11th, and DC Circuits. Professional Associations: Fellow, College of Labor and Employment Lawyers, 1999-present; American Bar Association; Maryland State Bar Association.
**Career:** Before joining the firm in 1971, Bruce served as a senior attorney at the Equal Employment Opportunity Commission's headquarter offices.
**Publications:** Bruce is Editor of the 'Employment Law Deskbook' and 'Corporate Counsel Solutions: Disciplining, Discharging and Discrimination Polices' (Lexis/Matthew Bender) and has also co-authored three monographs published by Matthew Bender: 'Avoiding Employment Discrimination Charges', 'Employer Discipline and Discharge', and 'Responding to Employment Discrimination Charges'. Other publications include: 'Sexual Harassment and Related Torts: The Employer's Perspective', American Bar Association. Contributing Author: 'Age

Discrimination: A Legal and Practical Guide for Employers', BNA Special Report. Contributor: 'Workplace Privacy', Thompson Publishing Group. Case Note Editor and Contributing Author: 'Sexual Harassment & Discrimination Reporter', James Publishing, Inc. Board of Editors: 'Model Jury Instructions: Employment Litigation', Section of Litigation, American Bar Association. Contributor: 'Employment Litigation Handbook', Section of Litigation, American Bar Association. Member of Editorial Board and Contributor: Bender's Labor & Employment Bulletin, Matthew Bender, Publishers; Contributing Editor: Maryland and Federal Employment Law Manual, American Chamber of Commerce Publishers. Contributor: 'Workplace Privacy', Thompson Publishing.
**Personal:** George Washington University School of Law, JD, cum laude, 1971; LLM Labor Law, 1975; Case Western Reserve University, BA, 1967.

### HILL, Eva H
Whiteford, Taylor & Preston LLP, Baltimore
410 347 8798
ehill@wtplaw.com
*Featured in Corporate/M&A (Maryland)*

**Practice Areas:** M&A; business and corporate law; corporate governance; succession planning; executive compensation; structuring of business entities; equipment leasing; and commercial contracting. Representation of buyers and sellers in corporate reorganizations and M&As ranging from $100,000-$200 million in the petroleum, homeland defense, equipment leasing, healthcare, IT, retail sales, wholesale distribution, professional services, and publishing industries.
**Professional Memberships:** American, Maryland, and Baltimore City Bar Associations.
**Career:** Co-chair of Corporate and Securities Department.
**Personal:** University of Maryland School of Law (JD, Order of the Coif, 1990); Loyola University of New Orleans (BA, magna cum laude, 1987).

### HOFFMAN, Kenneth R
Venable LLP, Baltimore
410 244 7771
krhoffman@Venable.com
*Featured in Employee Benefits & Executive Compensation (Maryland)*

**Practice Areas:** Executive compensation, retirement plans, collective bargaining, multiemployer plans, worker classification issues, M&A benefit issues, representation before Congress.
**Professional Memberships:** ABA Section of Taxation/Labor & Employment; MSBA Section of Taxation (past Chair).
**Career:** Tax Advisory Committee, Congressman Benjamin Cardin (former member); National Aquarium in Baltimore Foundation (former member); Maryland Comptroller's Task Force to Study Impact of Tax Reform Act of 1986; University of Baltimore Graduate Tax Program (former adjunct); CollegeBound Foundation (past Chair), Pro Bono Action Center (former member/Chair); NCCMP Retirement Income Security Review Commission.

**Personal:** JD, University of Maryland School of Law (Coif); BS, Frostburg State College.

### HOFFMAN, Robert
Venable LLP, Towson
410 494 6200
rahoffman@Venable.com
*Featured in Real Estate (Maryland)*

**Practice Areas:** Land Use, Zoning, State and Local Government.
**Career:** Rob Hoffman has practiced law in Baltimore County for over 30 years, forging relationships with local decision-makers, forming a wealth of institutional knowledge, and earning a reputation as one of the premier state and local government law attorneys in the area. He counsels clients on zoning matters, intercedes and resolves issues with government leaders, and provides a broad range of advice and services from the conceptual stages of the development process through final close-out and permitting.
**Personal:** JD, University of Maryland; BS/BA, Washington University

### HORN, Todd J
Venable LLP, Baltimore
410 244 7709
thorn@Venable.com
*Featured in Labor & Employment (Maryland)*

**Practice Areas:** Todd Horn has extensive experience defending employers successfully in class action discrimination and wage and hour cases, as well as in complex litigation and internal investigations involving "whistleblower" claims, sexual harassment, retaliation, disability accommodations, non-compete agreements, wrongful discharge and defamation.
**Publications:** Mr Horn is co-author of Maryland Employment Law, the principal publication in its field.
**Personal:** JD, William and Mary, Marshall-Wythe School of Law, 1987; BS Economics, Mary Washington University, 1984.

### HROBLAK, Kevin G
Whiteford, Taylor & Preston LLP, Baltimore
410 347 9405
khroblak@wtplaw.com
*Featured in Litigation (Maryland)*

**Practice Areas:** Complex business litigation nationally, including fraud, director and officer claims, professional malpractice, and fraudulent transfers.
**Professional Memberships:** American Bankruptcy Institute, NACD, National Association Bankruptcy Trustees.
**Career:** Co-chair, Litigation. Recognitions: Martindale-AV; Benchmark Litigation, Benchmark Plaintiff Litigation-"Litigation Star"; SuperLawyers; Legal 500-leading bankruptcy lawyers in Northeast ("considerable expertise in...malpractice and professional liability claims").
**Publications:** "The Missing Piece of Accountability: Agency Liability for Corporate Officers" ABI Journal (2012); "Keeping Fiduciary Duties in the Crosshairs When Your Company is in Financial Distress" Association of Corporate Counsel (2011); "The Fifth Amendment and the Bankruptcy Code" Maryland Bankruptcy Bar.

**Personal:** Volunteer, Board: Rebuilding Together Baltimore.

### INGERMAN, Brett
DLA Piper LLP (US), Baltimore
410 580 4177
brett.ingerman@dlapiper.com
*Featured in Litigation (Maryland)*

**Practice Areas:** Business and commercial litigation and arbitration.
**Career:** His focuses on complex commercial disputes and lender liability issues. He has significant experience in corporate investigations and compliance involving criminal, quasi-criminal, and administrative agencies. He worked with Senator George Mitchell in connection with his independent investigation of performance enhancing substance use in Major Leagues Baseball.
**Personal:** JD, University of Maryland School of Law (with honors); BA, Tufts University.

### JOHNSON, Thora A
Venable LLP, Baltimore
410 244 7747
tajohnson@Venable.com
*Featured in Employee Benefits & Executive Compensation (Maryland)*

**Practice Areas:** Ms Johnson focuses her practice on employee benefits and executive compensation matters. She provides counsel to clients on issues regarding qualified and non-qualified deferred compensation plans, and health and welfare benefit plans. She also routinely reviews and drafts employee benefit plans, summary plan descriptions, and other employee communications, and negotiates vendor contracts. She also structures HIPAA compliance programs and advises employers on how health care reform affects their health plans.
**Personal:** JD, with honors, University of Maryland School of Law, 1996; MA, Middlebury College, 1993; BA, magna cum laude, Phi Beta Kappa, Brown University, 1992.

### KOMINERS, William
Lerch, Early & Brewer, Chartered, Bethesda
301 841 3829
wkominers@lerchearly.com
*Featured in Real Estate (Maryland)*

**Practice Areas:** William Kominers navigates governmental processes to help companies use their properties. He practices in the areas of land use, land development, zoning, real estate, development documentation and municipal law. For more than 30 years, Bill has represented developers and businesses before administrative agencies and courts in Maryland, including administrative law appeals. He has particular experience representing large-scale mixed-use developments through the full range of planning, zoning and regulatory processes. He also represents large office and industrial parks and biotech companies in general land use and legislative matters, including master/site planning, text amendments and regulatory appeals.

**KREMEN, Richard M**
DLA Piper LLP (US), Baltimore
410 580 4191
richard.kremen@dlapiper.com
*Featured in Litigation (Maryland)*
**Practice Areas:** Bankruptcy.
**Professional Memberships:** Fellow, American College of Bankruptcy.
**Career:** He concentrates his practice in the area of bankruptcy, commercial lending, title litigation and complex commercial litigation, including defense of lender liability suits and contract litigation. He regularly represents financial institutions and has substantial litigation experience at both the trial and appellate levels. For over 25 years, he has been a member of the Panel of Bankruptcy Trustees. He has served as a Chapter 11 trustee in many operating and nonoperating Chapter 11 cases.
**Personal:** JD, George Washington University (with honors); BA, Oberlin College (with honors).

**LARIA, Jon M**
Ballard Spahr LLP, Baltimore
410 528 5506
laria@ballardspahr.com
*Featured in Real Estate (Maryland)*
**Practice Areas:** Jon M. Laria is Managing Partner of the firm's Baltimore office. He represents owners, developers, and lenders in all types of commercial real estate transactions, including development, finance, acquisition, and leasing. Through his land use and zoning practice, he has provided counsel for some of Baltimore's most prominent development projects. Mr Laria is also Chair of the Maryland Sustainable Growth Commission.
**Professional Memberships:** American Bar Association District of Columbia Bar Association Maryland Bar Association Urban Land Institute
**Career:** District of Columbia Maryland.
**Personal:** University of Maryland School of Law (JD 1992) Johns Hopkins University (BA 1985).

**LEVINE, Richard E**
DLA Piper LLP (US), Baltimore
410 580 4400
rich.levine@dlapiper.com
*Featured in Real Estate (Maryland)*
**Practice Areas:** Real estate, corporate and securities, business tax.
**Professional Memberships:** Fellow of American College of Tax Counsel.
**Career:** His practice focuses on real estate, tax, and partnership matters in representing real estate entrepreneurs, investors, developers, and homebuilders in the Baltimore-Washington area and elsewhere in the United States. He is particularly well known for his creativity in structuring complex transactions, with specific emphasis on tax sensitive issues.
**Personal:** JD, University of Maryland; LLM, Georgetown University Law Center; BS, Mechanical Engineering, Bucknell University.

**MADDEN, Paul W**
Whiteford, Taylor & Preston LLP, Baltimore
410 347 8742
pmadden@wtplaw.com
*Featured in Employee Benefits & Executive Compensation (Maryland)*
**Practice Areas:** Regularly advises employers with respect to retirement, welfare and executive compensation plan design and ERISA and Internal Revenue Code compliance. Experience includes fiduciary training and counseling and guiding clients through government agency audits and correction programs. Provides advice regarding employee benefit matters in bankruptcy, litigation and corporate transactions.
**Professional Memberships:** Maryland State Bar Association, Employee Benefits Subcommittee (chairman 1995-96); Co-Chairman: IRS Employee Benefits Conference (1994-2002) National Association of Public Pension Attorneys.
**Personal:** University of Pennsylvania (JD 1975). Catholic University of America (AB, magna cum laude 1969; MA 1970).

**MARTIN, Gerard P**
Rosenberg Martin Greenberg, LLP, Baltimore
410 727 6600
gmartin@rosenbergmartin.com
*Featured in Litigation (Maryland)*
**Practice Areas:** Complex civil litigation, white-collar criminal defense, RICO, federal multi-district litigation, professional ethics and liability issues.
**Professional Memberships:** Fellow, American College of Trial Lawyers and Maryland Bar Foundation; Member and past Chair, Maryland State Bar Association Ethics Committee; Board Member, Maryland Criminal Defense Attorney's Association.
**Career:** Partner, Rosenberg Martin Greenberg, LLP since 2003. Managing Partner, Martin Snyder & Bernstein 1993-2003. Named one of Maryland's top white-collar criminal defense attorneys in 'Best Lawyers in America'; appeared in Baltimore Magazine's 'Best Lawyers in Maryland'; Chambers USA.
**Personal:** BS John Carroll University, 1966; JD St Louis University, cum laude, 1970.

**MATHIAS, James D**
DLA Piper LLP (US), Baltimore
410 580 4208
james.mathias@dlapiper.com
*Featured in Litigation (Maryland)*
**Practice Areas:** General Commercial Litigation
**Career:** A trial lawyer who engages in a general corporate, securities and business litigation practice. He is chair of the Baltimore Litigation department, co-chair of the firm's Financial Services Litigation group and a member of the firm's Policy Committee. He focuses on litigation concerning securities and financial services, class actions, complex financial transactions, fraud, internal corporate and compliance investigations, trade secrets, unfair competition and real property disputes.

**Personal:** JD, Georgetown University Law Center, magna cum laude; BA, Amherst College, magna cum laude

**MATHIAS, Robert J**
DLA Piper LLP (US), Baltimore
410 580 4209
robert.mathias@dlapiper.com
*Featured in Litigation (Maryland)*
**Practice Areas:** Litigation, class action, securities litigation, international arbitration, white-collar.
**Professional Memberships:** American College of Trial Lawyers, Fellow, Complex Litigation Committee.
**Career:** He is the Joint Global Leader and US Chair of the firm's Litigation practice. He focuses on business, class action, and intellectual property litigation, white-collar criminal advice and investigations for corporate clients. His white-collar litigation practice includes representing corporations and individuals in all stages of federal and state civil and criminal proceedings, as well as internal investigations, legislative proceedings, and regulatory enforcement proceedings.
**Personal:** JD, Harvard Law School; BA, Yale University (cum laude).

**MATRICCIANI, Rose M**
Whiteford, Taylor & Preston LLP, Baltimore
410 347 9476
rmatricciani@wtplaw.com
*Featured in Healthcare (Maryland)*
**Practice Areas:** Health and corporate law, representing group practices, individual practioners, health care systems, and retirement communities (CCRCs). Advised multi-hospital system in merger and joint venture arrangements and multi-state change of ownership of health care facilities. Corporate and health law counsel in CCRC change of ownership and submissions.
**Professional Memberships:** American Health Lawyers Association; American, Maryland, Baltimore City and Baltimore County Bar Associations; Chesapeake Nurse Attorneys; American Association of Nurse Attorneys.
**Publications:** Contributing Editor to numerous publications on domestic violence.
**Personal:** University of Maryland (JD, 1989); Loyola College (BA, 1983); Essex Community College (AA Nursing, 1973); Registered Nurse.

**MCCORMICK, Kevin C**
Whiteford, Taylor & Preston LLP, Baltimore
410 347 8779
kmccormick@wtplaw.com
*Featured in Labor & Employment (Maryland)*
**Practice Areas:** Provides counsel to employers on all phases of the employment relationship to ensure compliance with applicable laws and, when necessary, successfully defends against individual and/or governmental challenges to those employment policies.
**Professional Memberships:** Employers Counsel Network; Lexwork; Meals on Wheels of Central Maryland.
**Career:** Trial Attorney, Office of the Solicitor, U.S. DOL, Partner, Whiteford,Taylor & Preston, LLP, Co-Chair Labor/Employment Section.

**Publications:** Editor, Maryland Employment Law Letter, The Employment Law Strategist, Author of numerous employment publications.
**Personal:** Georgetown University (LLM 1984); Marshall-Wythe School of Law, College of William & Mary (JD, 1979); University of Notre Dame (BA, 1976).

**MCGEE JR, Emmett F**
Jackson Lewis LLP, Baltimore
410 415 2003
McGeeE@jacksonlewis.com
*Featured in Labor & Employment (Maryland)*
**Practice Areas:** Labor and employment.
**Career:** He represents employers in all aspects of employment law and human resource management, including employment discrimination, wage and hour issues and affirmative action planning. His practice includes litigation in state and federal courts throughout the United States, as well as before administrative agencies and arbitration panels. He has extensive experience in areas of employment contracts, trade secrets and restrictive covenants, and related litigation, as well as wage and hour class and collective action litigation.
**Personal:** JD, University of Virginia; BA, Johns Hopkins University (Phi Beta Kappa).

**MCGOWAN, Patricia**
Venable LLP, Baltimore
410 244 7539
pmcgowan@venable.com
*Featured in Corporate/M&A (Maryland), Capital Markets (Nationwide)*
See under Nationwide for profile.

**MCGUIRE, J Michael**
Shawe Rosenthal LLP, Baltimore
410 843 3461
mcguire@shawe.com
*Featured in Labor & Employment (Maryland)*
**Practice Areas:** Labor-management relations; practice before the National Labor Relations Board; collective bargaining and labor arbitration representing management; employment discrimination litigation; human resources advice and counsel; employment agreements; employment tort and contract litigation; employment handbooks, policies, and procedures; wage and hour laws; occupational safety and health acts.
**Professional Memberships:** Bar Admissions: Maryland (State and Federal); US Court of Appeals for the 4th, 9th and 11th Circuits. Professional Associations: American Bar Association; Maryland State Bar Association; Chair, Labor and Employment Law Section of Maryland State Bar Association (2004-06 Term); Maryland Association of Defense Trial Counsel; American Bar Association (EEO and NLRB Practice and Procedure Committees).
**Publications:** Michael has co-authored two books, 'Employee Discipline and Discharge', and 'An Employer's Guide to the Occupational Safety and Health Act', both published by Lexis/Matthew Bender, and numerous articles for the Maryland Bar Journal including 'Jury Trial Waivers' (Vol 38, #4); 'Acquiring a Unionized Facility' (Vol 33, #3), and 'Sex Harassment Investigations' (Vol 35, #1).

**Personal:** University of Maryland School of Law, JD, cum laude, 1978 recipient, Joseph Bernstein Prize (Notes and Comments Editor, Int'l Trade Law Journal); University of Maryland (Economics Honors Program), BA 1975.

## MCSHERRY, M Natalie
Kramon & Graham, PA, Baltimore
410 752 6030
nmcsherry@kg-law.com
*Featured in Healthcare (Maryland)*

**Practice Areas:** Litigation - commercial, medical malpractice, licensing and credentialing.
**Professional Memberships:** Fellow, American College of Trial Lawyers. Member, Maryland ADR Services, Inc.
**Career:** Listed by 2012 and 2013 Maryland 'Super Lawyers' magazine in 'the top 10', and appears in 'The Best Lawyers in America'. Adjunct Faculty, University of Maryland School of Law. 2007, 2009, 2011. Maryland Task Force on Discipline of Health Care Professionals and Improved Patient Care in 2008. Manhattanville College (BA 1971); University of Maryland School of Law (JD, with honors, 1974).

## MERKLE, Craig
Goodell, DeVries, Leech & Dann, LLP, Baltimore
410 783 4007
cbm@gdldlaw.com
*Featured in Healthcare (Maryland)*

**Practice Areas:** Professional Liability - Mr Merkle has represented physicians and healthcare providers in virtually every medical specialty as well as community hospitals and academic medical centers. He has tried to verdict numerous medical malpractice cases throughout the State of Maryland. Privileging and Hospital Litigation - Mr Merkle has represented academic and community healthcare systems in matters involving privileging and employment disputes, impaired physicians, boundary violations, and breach of professional and fiduciary obligations. Pharmaceutical and Medical Device Litigation - Mr Merkle has been actively involved in the firm's medical drug and device practice. He has been lead trial counsel for multiparty trial groups in the diet drug litigation in the Court of Common Pleas in Philadelphia, Pennsylvania.
**Professional Memberships:** Fellow, American College of Trial Lawyers (ACTL); Member, American Board of Trial Advocates (ABOTA); International Association of Defense Trial Counsel (IADC); Fourth Circuit Judicial Conference; Maryland Association of Defense Trial Counsel; Maryland Society for Healthcare Risk Management.
**Career:** Goodell, DeVries, Leech & Dann, LLP, 1988-present. Founding Partner. Semmes, Bowen & Semmes, 1982-88. Associate and senior associate. Judicial law clerk, 1981-82, The Honorable Norman P Ramsey, United States District Court for the District of Maryland.
**Publications:** Mr Merkle has frequently been an invited speaker on a broad range of topics in trial practice, risk management, and the application of

legal and ethical principles to scientific and medical advances.
**Personal:** Western Maryland College (BA, Summa Cum Laude, 1978); Duke University School of Law (JD, with distinction, 1981); Order of the Coif; Duke Law Journal 1979-81.

## MEZZANOTTE, Joseph J
Whiteford, Taylor & Preston LLP, Baltimore
410 347 9441
jmezzanotte@wtplaw.com
*Featured in Real Estate (Maryland)*

**Practice Areas:** Complex commercial real estate transactions and development matters, including acquisitions (purchase and sale agreements, complex easement and title matters), dispositions, financings, leasing (office, warehouse, retail, ground leases and subleases) and the development of commercial, residential, mixed-use and retail projects.
**Professional Memberships:** ICSC; NAIOP; American Bar Association (House of Delegates, 1999-2001); Maryland State Bar Association (Executive Committee and Board of Governors, 1998-99); Maryland Chamber of Commerce (Board of Directors); Howard County Chamber of Commerce (Chairman of the Board, 2009-10); Fellow, American Bar Foundation; Fellow, Maryland Bar Foundation.
**Personal:** University of Baltimore (JD, cum laude, 1989); Boston College (BA, 1986).

## MISKEN, Ken
Miles & Stockbridge PC, Tysons Corner
703 610 8693
kmisken@milesstockbridge.com
*Featured in Litigation (Maryland)*

**Practice Areas:** Bankruptcy and Litigation.
**Professional Memberships:** Admitted in state and federal courts in Virginia, New Jersey and the District of Columbia; admitted in New York and the Southern District of New York; American Bankruptcy Institute; Congressman Walter Chandler Inn of Court.
**Career:** Wide range of experience in all aspects of bankruptcy matters and litigation, including representing corporate debtors and creditors committees in chapter 11 cases. Obtain an LLM from Georgetown University in International and Comparative Law.
**Publications:** Numerous publications in the American Bankruptcy Institute Journal.
**Personal:** Ken coaches youth travel softball and youth baseball.

## MONAHAN JR, Thomas V
Goodell, DeVries, Leech & Dann, LLP, Baltimore
410 783 4000
tvm@gdldlaw.com
*Featured in Healthcare (Maryland)*

**Practice Areas:** Mr Monahan has over 30 years of experience defending physicians, nurses, hospitals, long-term care facilities and related health care providers in medical negligence cases in Maryland, Virginia, and the District of Columbia. He has tried more than 75 medical malpractice cases. Additionally, he has maintained a general litigation practice with experience in commercial

litigation, insurance coverage and the representation of professionals in non-medical fields.
**Professional Memberships:** Fellow, American College of Trial Lawyers; Maryland Defense Counsel (President, 1997-98); Virginia Association of Defense Attorneys; Defense Research Institute; American Bar Association; Maryland Bar Association; Virginia State Bar; District of Columbia Bar Association; Baltimore City Bar Association; Fourth Circuit Judicial Conference, Member.
**Career:** Goodell, DeVries, Leech & Dann, LLP, 1988-present (one of the founding partners); Semmes, Bowen & Semmes, partner 1988, associate 1979-85, 1987-88; McGuire, Woods, associate, 1985-87.
**Publications:** "Punitive Damages Update" The Defense Line, Winter 1993. "Court of Appeals Adopts New Standard For Punitive Damages" The Defense Line, Spring 1992. "Do Ex Parte Interviews Threaten Patient Privacy" The Brief, Vol. 12, No. 1, Fall 1987.
**Personal:** Princeton University (AB 1976, cum laude); University of Virginia (JD 1979).

## MORAN, Charles R
Ballard Spahr LLP, Baltimore
410 528 5689
moran@ballardspahr.com
*Featured in Corporate/M&A (Maryland), Capital Markets (Nationwide)*

**Practice Areas:** Charles R. Moran represents public and private companies, equity funds, investment banks, and institutional lenders in a variety of corporate, business, and finance matters. He has significant experience in the representation of real estate investment trusts. He has acted as special corporate counsel to acquirers and targets, as well as to boards of directors and committees thereof, in connection with numerous mergers, acquisitions, restructurings, and other extraordinary transactions.
**Professional Memberships:** American Bar Association Maryland State Bar Association
**Career:** Admissions: District of Columbia Maryland.
**Personal:** University of Maryland School of Law (JD 1971) University of Maryland (BS ChE 1968).

## MORTON JR, Charles J
Venable LLP, Baltimore
410 244 7716
cjmorton@Venable.com
*Featured in Corporate/M&A (Maryland)*

**Practice Areas:** Co-chair, Corporate practice (Venable's largest practice); founder, Junior Capital/Mezzanine practice. National practice representing entrepreneurs, investors and private equity groups. Focuses on mergers and acquisitions and multi-tiered financings, including subordinated loans and related equity investments.
**Professional Memberships:** Chairman, Global Board of Directors, Association for Corporate Growth; adjunct faculty, Johns Hopkins University; Vice-Chair, Technology Development Corporation of Maryland; General Counsel, Maryland Chamber of Commerce.

**Career:** Clerk, Magistrate Judge Deborah Chasanow and District Court Judge Joseph C. Howard, U.S. District Court for the District of Maryland.
**Personal:** JD, University of Maryland School of Law, 1990; BA, University of Vermont, 1987.

## MUEDEKING, Mark
DLA Piper LLP (US), Washington, DC
202 799 4240
mark.muedeking@dlapiper.com
*Featured in Employee Benefits & Executive Compensation (Maryland)*

**Practice Areas:** Employee benefits and executive compensation.
**Career:** He concentrates primarily in the area of employee benefits and executive compensation, business and tax, and sports law. His employee benefits and executive compensation practice covers all aspects of plan design, operation, assets, audits, and litigation. His business and tax practice includes representation of public and private companies in acquisitions and divestitures. His sports law practice focuses on trademark licensing and enforcement, sponsorship contracts, athlete eligibility, insurance coverage, franchise acquisition, and enforcement of anti-doping regulations.
**Personal:** JD, University of Notre Dame; LLM, Georgetown University; BA, St John's University (cum laude).

## NUSSBAUM, Paul M
Whiteford, Taylor & Preston LLP, Baltimore
410 347 8794
pnussbaum@wtplaw.com
*Featured in Litigation (Maryland)*

**Practice Areas:** Chapter 11 business reorganizations. Bankruptcy trustee representation. Creditors committee representation. Bankruptcy and related commercial litigation. Special counsel litigation services.
**Professional Memberships:** Benchmark Litigation, "Best bankruptcy lawyer in Maryland" (2010); Maryland Super Lawyers, "Top 10 Maryland lawyers" (2008); Maryland Super Lawyers (2007 to present); Legal 500 (2009); Best Lawyers in America (2001 to present); American Bar Association American Bankruptcy Institute; Bankruptcy Bar Association, District of Maryland. Admitted Maryland, New Jersey, New York.
**Career:** Chair of Business Reorganizations and Bankruptcy Litigation Practice; Head, Special Counsel Services.
**Publications:** Co-Author: "Considerations for Existing and Potential Directors and Officers of Financially Distressed Companies," Corporate Board Member Magazine (March 2012); Presentations: "Exit Strategies in a Business Chapter 11," Bankruptcy Bar for the District of Maryland (May 2012), IQPC's Global Distressed Debt Investor Forums (2007, 2008 and 2009).
**Personal:** California Western School of Law (JD 1984, cum laude); Fairleigh Dickinson University (BA, 1980).

**PARVIS, Peter P**
Venable LLP, Baltimore
410 244 7644
ppparvis@Venable.com
*Featured in Healthcare (Maryland)*
**Practice Areas:** Pete Parvis has 35 years' experience working with healthcare clients including hospitals and systems, long-term care entities, pharmaceutical entities, physician groups, and insurance entities. He is a corporate lawyer skilled in helping clients achieve desired results while complying with regulatory and business matters affecting heath care entities.
**Professional Memberships:** Listed, The Best Lawyers in America, Health Care, 1993-present.
**Career:** Venable LLP, 1977-present.
**Publications:** What are ACOs? - HFMA Journal, Introduction to Compliance - AAPI Journal, Constitutionality of ACA - HFMA Journal.
**Personal:** JD, University of Maryland, 1977; BA, University of Maryland, 1968.

**POLLAK, Mark**
Ballard Spahr LLP, Baltimore
410 528 5563
pollakm@ballardspahr.com
*Featured in Real Estate (Maryland)*
**Practice Areas:** Mark Pollak is co-partner-in-charge of the Real Estate Development Group. He has practiced for more than 30 years with a focus on the public financing of complex real estate projects and sports stadiums. He has experience creating public-private partnerships to develop central business districts. He represents local institutions and companies, national corporations, major real estate developers, and investors in the mid-Atlantic area.
**Professional Memberships:** American College of Real Estate Lawyers.
**Career:** Admissions: Maryland.
**Personal:** University of Pennsylvania Law School (JD 1972) University of Pennsylvania (M.C.P. 1972) Brooklyn College, City University of New York (B.A 1968).

**PRESTON, Susan T**
Goodell, DeVries, Leech & Dann, LLP, Baltimore
410 783 4025
stp@gdldlaw.com
*Featured in Healthcare (Maryland)*
**Practice Areas:** Civil litigation, representing a wide array of medical and nursing specialties, and academic and community hospitals in professional malpractice claims before The Circuit Courts of Maryland, Superior Court of Washington, DC, and in the United States District Courts for the Districts of Columbia and Maryland.
**Professional Memberships:** Fellow, American College of Trial Lawyers (State Committee, 2006-10); Associate, American Board of Trial Advocates; Maryland Defense Counsel (President, 1993-94; Executive Committee, 1993-98); Maryland Society for Healthcare Risk Management (President, 2000-01; President-Elect, 1999-2000; Chairman, Legislative Committee, 1996-99; Member at Large, 1997-99); Maryland Volunteer Lawyers Service (Board of Directors 2008-Present; Vice President,

2009-11; Chair Fundraising Committee, 2009-11); Maryland State Bar Association; Defense Research Institute; Bar Association of Baltimore City.
**Career:** Semmes, Bowen & Semmes, 1981 - 1988; Goodell, DeVries, Leech & Dann, LLP, 1988 - Present.
**Publications:** Medical Malpractice: Law Theory and Practice for Attorneys, Physicians, and Risk Managers, Evaluation of a Claim, Settlement and Settlement Negotiations and Structured Settlements, American Bar Association National Institute on Medical Malpractice, Tort &; Insurance Section (1987). Ms Preston has also widely lectured on subjects of professional liability.
**Personal:** American University, BA cum laude 1973; The University of Baltimore, JD, magne cum laude, 1979; law clerk to the Honorable Lawrence F. Rodowsky, Court of Appeals of Maryland, 1980-81.

**REED, Stanley J**
Lerch, Early & Brewer, Chartered, Bethesda
301 657 0177
sjreed@lercheraly.com
*Featured in Litigation (Maryland)*
**Practice Areas:** Complex civil litigation; white-collar criminal defense; and professional responsibility matters.
**Professional Memberships:** Maryland Bar; D.C. Bar; U.S. District Courts, Maryland and D.C.; U.S. Courts of Appeals, Fourth Circuit, D.C.; U.S. Supreme Court; Board of Governors, Federal Bar Association (MD Chapter).
**Career:** 1984-present: Lerch, Early & Brewer, Chtd; Partner(1987-present); Chair, Litigation Department (2001-present); 1990-92: Adjunct Professor, Columbus School of Law, Catholic University; 1979-84: District of Maryland, Assistant Federal Public Defender; 1977-79: Law Clerk for the Honorable Harold H. Greene, U.S. District Court for D.C.
**Personal:** JD (Cum Laude), University of Michigan Law School 1977; BA (Magna Cum Laude), Brandeis University 1974; elected to Phi Beta Kappa (1974).

**RITZER, Lonnie M**
Shapiro Sher Guinot & Sandler, Baltimore
410 385 4221
lmr@shapirosher.com
*Featured in Real Estate (Maryland)*
**Practice Areas:** Tax; Real Estate; Sports Law; Corporate and Securities; Banking and Financial Services
**Professional Memberships:** American Bar Association, Maryland State Bar Association (former Chair, Tax Study Group), Bar Association of Baltimore City
**Career:** Heads the tax practice at Shapiro Sher Guinot & Sandler. Concentrates in tax law, partnership and corporate transactions, real estate planning, mergers, and acquisitions. Experienced in the structuring of complex corporate and real estate transactions, and in counseling non-profit organizations. His real estate experience includes the development of sports facilities, office parks,

and shopping centers. He also handles contract and endorsement planning for sports figures.

**ROBBINS, JR, E Hutchinson**
Miles & Stockbridge PC, Baltimore
410 385 3408
erobbins@milesstockbridge.com
*Featured in Litigation (Maryland)*
**Practice Areas:** Commercial and business litigation, with an emphasis on financial institutions litigation. Mr Robbins is the Leader of the Commercial and Business Litigation Practice Group at Miles & Stockbridge.
**Professional Memberships:** American Bar Association, Maryland State Bar Association, Defense Research Institute. Mr. Robbins is admitted to the Supreme Court of the United States, the United States Court of Appeals for the Fourth Circuit, the United States District Court for the District of Maryland, and the Maryland Bar.
**Career:** Mr. Robbins began his legal career at Miles & Stockbridge in 1993, and has been a principal of the firm since 2002.
**Personal:** Duke University (JD, with Honors, 1993); Trinity College (BA, with Honors, 1988). Mr. Robbins lives in Annapolis, Maryland with his wife and two sons.

**ROSENBERG, Benjamin**
Rosenberg Martin Greenberg, LLP, Baltimore
410 727 6600
brosenberg@rosenbergmartin.com
*Featured in Litigation (Maryland)*
**Practice Areas:** Litigation of business disputes in federal and state courts, appellate litigation in all disciplines.
**Professional Memberships:** Fellow, American College of Trial Lawyers; Fellow, Maryland Bar Foundation; former Member Board of Governors, Maryland State Bar Association.
**Career:** Chairman, formerly Managing Partner of Rosenberg Martin Greenberg, LLP since 1987. Partner, Venable Baetjer and Howard, 1977-87. Named one of 'Ten Best Maryland Lawyers' in Baltimore Magazine. Member, Board of Directors, Enoch Pratt Free Library. Former Trustee, The Walters Art Museum, Bryn Mawr School.
**Personal:** BA Johns Hopkins University, 1965; JD University of Maryland Law School, 1969.

**ROSSO, Anthony J**
Venable LLP, Baltimore
410 244 7543
ajrosso@venable.com
*Featured in Corporate/M&A (Maryland)*
**Practice Areas:** Mr. Rosso represents public and private companies, entrepreneurs and investors in a broad range of business transactions including mergers and acquisitions, equity and debt financings, joint ventures and corporate restructurings. He frequently represents owners of closely-held companies in the sale of their businesses to strategic buyers and private equity investors. Anthony serves as outside general corporate counsel to a variety of businesses and utilizes his CPA background.
**Professional Memberships:** Board member, Greater Baltimore Technology Council.

**Personal:** JD, magna cum laude, University of Baltimore, 1994, Heuisler Honor Society; BBA, Loyola University of Maryland, 1989.

**SANDLER, Paul Mark**
Shapiro Sher Guinot & Sandler, Baltimore
410 385 4272
pms@shapirosher.com
*Featured in Litigation (Maryland)*
**Practice Areas:** Commercial litigation; employment litigation; white-collar criminal defense; appeals; product liability; personal injury.
**Professional Memberships:** American College of Trial Lawyers (Fellow); American Bar Association Section of Litigation (Secretary, 2004-2008); Maryland State Bar Association (Founder and first Chair of Litigation Section); Association of Trial Lawyers of America.
**Career:** Represents defendants in white-collar criminal cases and plaintiffs in civil lawsuits, including personal injury, employment, and product liability cases, as well as appeals. Also defends corporations in wrongful discharge, race and sex discrimination, breach of contract, trademark infringement, and antitrust cases, among other matters. Has authored numerous books on trial advocacy.

**SCHEELER, Charles P**
DLA Piper LLP (US), Baltimore
410 580 4250
charles.scheeler@dlapiper.com
*Featured in Litigation (Maryland)*
**Practice Areas:** Litigation, arbitration, class action, securities litigation, white-collar.
**Career:** He focuses on commercial litigation, internal investigation, and white collar criminal defense practice. His trial experience includes over 25 jury trials and dozens of bench trials and arbitrations. He served as lead counsel to Senator George Mitchell in connection with his independent investigation of performance enhancing substance use in Major League Baseball.
**Personal:** JD, Harvard Law School (cum laude); BS, University of North Carolina at Chapel Hill.

**SCHLAFF, Barbara E**
Venable LLP, Baltimore
410 244 7494
beschlaff@Venable.com
*Featured in Employee Benefits & Executive Compensation (Maryland)*
**Practice Areas:** Barbara Schlaff focuses her practice on qualified and nonqualified deferred compensation retirement plans, executive compensation, welfare plans and other benefit programs. Ms Schlaff designs and drafts employee benefit plans; advises clients on administrative, tax and ERISA issues, including fiduciary rules pertaining to the plans; interfaces on behalf of clients with various governmental agencies such as the Internal Revenue Service, Department of Labor and the Pension Benefit Guaranty Corporation; works with Venable's Corporate Group in acquisitions and mergers; and partners with the firm's litigators in ERISA lawsuits.
**Personal:** JD, Boston College Law School, 1974; BA, Brandeis University, 1971

## SEARS, Barbara
Linowes and Blocher LLP, Bethesda
301 961 5157
bsears@linowes-law.com
*Featured in Real Estate (Maryland)*
**Practice Areas:** Land use.
**Career:** Partner in charge of Land Use Practice Group. Represents land owners, developers and builders in land use, real estate, administrative and municipal law matters before administrative boards and agencies, legislative bodies and state and federal courts. Assists clients in complex matters involving zoning, subdivision, special exceptions, variances, building and other construction permits and approvals, and related facets of the development process. Handles litigation arising from these areas, including administrative appeals and condemnation. Former Associate General Counsel of the Maryland-National Capital Park and Planning Commission.
**Personal:** MA, Catholic University, Urban and Regional Planning; JD, Catholic University.

## SEEGULL, Larry
Jackson Lewis LLP, Baltimore
410 415 2004
Larry.Seegull@jacksonlewis.com
*Featured in Labor & Employment (Maryland)*
**Practice Areas:** Labor and employment, class action.
**Career:** He represents employers in all areas of labor and employment law. He advises clients on compliance, litigation avoidance, and limiting liability with respect to the full complement of employment decisions. He defends clients in all types of employment-related litigation, arbitration and agency investigations, including claims of discrimination and sexual harassment, claims under the ADA and FMLA, and claims for wages and overtime, breach of contract, and employment-related torts. He defends employers with respect to all aspects of union issues.
**Personal:** JD, University of Michigan; BA, Michigan State University (with honors).

## SHAPIRO-CYR, Lila
Ballard Spahr LLP, Baltimore
410 528 5624
shapirocyr@ballardspahr.com
*Featured in Real Estate (Maryland)*
**Practice Areas:** Lila Shapiro-Cyr is a partner in the Real Estate Department and a member of the Housing, Real Estate Development, and Real Estate Leasing Groups. Ms Shapiro-Cyr represents clients in connection with real estate acquisitions, development, leasing, and financing.
**Professional Memberships:** Downtown Partnership of Baltimore's Business and Economic Development Committee, American Bar Association, Maryland State Bar.
**Career:** Admissions: Maryland.
**Personal:** Education: Haverford College (BA 1995) and the University of Maryland School of Law (JD, with honors, 1999).

## SHAWE, Stephen D
Shawe Rosenthal LLP, Baltimore
410 752 1040
sshawe@shawe.com
*Featured in Labor & Employment (Maryland)*
**Practice Areas:** Labor-management relations and NLRB proceedings; collective bargaining; employment discrimination; human resources advice and counsel; employment tort and contract litigation; employment handbooks, policies, and procedures; wage and hour laws; affirmative action programs; Family and Medical Leave Act; Worker Adjustment and Retraining Notification Act; appellate litigation; class actions; alternative dispute resolution.
**Professional Memberships:** Bar Admissions: Maryland; US Court of Appeals for the 4th Circuit; Supreme Court of the United States. Professional Associations: American Bar Association; Maryland State Bar Association; Fellow, College of Labor and Employment Lawyers.
**Career:** Before joining the Firm in 1966, Stephen served as law clerk to Chief Judge Simon Sobeloff of the United States Court of Appeals for the Fourth Circuit. In 1967, he briefly left the firm when he was appointed an Assistant United States Attorney for the District of Maryland. He held that position until 1970 when he was selected to be the first General Counsel of the Maryland Commission on Human Relations.
**Publications:** Stephen has authored numerous articles on labor and employment matters, including 'An Employer's Duty to Bargain Over a Decision to Subcontract' for the Harvard Legal Commentary. He was co-author of 'Avoiding Employment Discrimination Charges' for Matthew Bender & Co., Inc., and he has also written articles for the University of Baltimore Law Review on subjects ranging from concession bargaining to employment discrimination.
**Personal:** Education: Harvard Law School, LLB, 1965; Williams College, BA, cum laude,1962.

## SHEA, James
Venable LLP, Baltimore
410 244 7734
jlshea@venable.com
*Featured in Litigation (Maryland)*
**Practice Areas:** Commercial trial and appellate litigation.
**Professional Memberships:** American College of Trial Lawyers.
**Career:** As Venable's Chair, he maintains an active practice, litigating before courts and agencies in Maryland, DC and elsewhere. Chair, Board of Regents, University System of Maryland; member, Governor O'Malley's Transition Team, Federal Judicial Nominating Committee. Former Maryland Assistant Attorney General.
**Personal:** JD, University of Virginia School of Law, Order of the Coif, 1977; AB, Princeton University, cum laude, 1974.

## SHEPHERD, Kevin
Venable LLP, Baltimore
410 244 7772
klshepherd@Venable.com
*Featured in Real Estate (Maryland)*
**Practice Areas:** Kevin Shepherd is a senior partner in the firm's Real Estate Practice Group. Mr. Shepherd represents pension funds, REITs and institutional investors in a wide range of complex real estate transactions, including financing, acquisitions and dispositions, and leasing.
**Professional Memberships:** Past Chair, ABA Real Property, Trust and Estate Law Section; Past President, American College of Real Estate Lawyers; Fellow, American College of Mortgage Attorneys; Member, ABA House of Delegates; Chair, ABA Task Force on Gatekeeper Regulation and the Profession; Governor, Anglo-American Real Property Institute.

## SHER, Joel I
Shapiro Sher Guinot & Sandler, Baltimore
410 385 4277
jis@shapirosher.com
*Featured in Litigation (Maryland)*
**Practice Areas:** Corporate reorganization; creditors' rights; bankruptcy litigation; commercial litigation.
**Professional Memberships:** American Bankruptcy Institute; Bankruptcy Bar Association for the District of Maryland (past Chair); Maryland State Bar Association.
**Career:** Chairman of Shapiro Sher Guinot & Sandler, Mr. Sher heads the Firm's Bankruptcy and Financial Restructuring Practice. He represents debtors, creditors, and creditors' committees in Chapter 11 bankruptcy cases, and counsels clients in complex out-of-court workouts. He is experienced in a range of industries, including financial services, real estate development, construction management, health care, retail, governmental contracting, manufacturing, and telecommunications.

## SHERBILL, ESQ, Raymond J
Lerch, Early & Brewer, Chartered, Bethesda
301 347 1275
rjsherbill@lercheary.com
*Featured in Corporate/M&A (Maryland)*
**Practice Areas:** Corporate law, mergers and acquisitions, domestic and international business transactions, US government contracting, general business counseling and advocacy, dispute resolution.
**Professional Memberships:** Maryland Bar, District of Columbia Bar, U.S. Tax Court, U.S. Court of Federal Claims, Federal Courts of Maryland and DC.
**Career:** 2007-Present: Lerch, Early & Brewer, Chtd., Partner, Chair of Business and Taxation Group; 1990–2007: Ridberg, Sherbill & Aronson, LLP, Partner; 1982-90: Leva, Hawes, Mason & Martin, Partner (1989-90), Associate (1982-89).
**Personal:** George Washington University National Law Center, JD, with honors,1982; Boston University, BA, American History, Magna Cum Laude, 1979.

## SHERMAN, Davis VR
Venable LLP, Baltimore
410 244 7810
dvsherman@Venable.com
*Featured in Healthcare (Maryland)*
**Practice Areas:** Healthcare, finance, tax-exempt organizations, education, nonprofits.
**Career:** Davis Sherman concentrates his practice in advising hospitals, colleges and other tax-exempt corporations and underwriters in the arranging of tax-exempt bond financing for capital projects. He also represents clients in project financings and corporate mergers and acquisitions. A regular participant in tax-exempt revenue bond financings in various settings, he efficiently manages the complex interface between the multiple players in a major capital project financing.
**Personal:** JD, Columbia University School of Law, 1985; AB, magna cum laude, Harvard College, 1980; law clerk, Hon. John C. Eldridge, Court of Appeals of Maryland 1985-1986.

## SILVESTRI, Stephen
Jackson Lewis LLP, Baltimore
410 415 2006
Stephen.Silvestri@jacksonlewis.com
*Featured in Labor & Employment (Maryland)*
**Practice Areas:** Labor negotiations and strategic advice representing private and public sector employers, NLRB charges and hearings, labor arbitrations and jury and court trials in employment discrimination claims, WARN and ERISA benefits cases. Chief labor and employment counsel for domestic and foreign corporations.
**Professional Memberships:** American Bar Association, Maryland State Bar Association, Former Chair, Section of Labor Law, MSBA.
**Career:** Former Law Clerk, John H. Fanning, Chairman, NLRB, Partner joining Jackson Lewis in 2011,1992-2011, principal and head of labor practice, Miles and Stockbridge, PC, and formerly partner in Semmes, Bowen and Semmes.
**Publications:** Lectures and publishes extensively

## SIMPLER, Gary
Shawe Rosenthal LLP, Baltimore
410 752 1040
simpler@shawe.com
*Featured in Labor & Employment (Maryland)*
**Practice Areas:** Labor-management relations; union avoidance, collective bargaining; employment discrimination; human resources advice and counsel; employment tort and contract litigation; covenants not-to-compete litigation; intellectual property and trade secret litigation; wage and hour laws; Family and Medical Leave Act (FMLA); Worker Adjustment and Retraining Notification act (WARN); employment agreements, employment handbooks, policies, and procedures; appellate litigation.
**Professional Memberships:** Bar Admissions: Maryland; US Courts of Appeals for the 3rd and 4th Circuits. Professional Associations: American Bar Association; Maryland State Bar Association, Member, Labor Law Section.
**Publications:** Gary is a contributing author to the 'Employment Law Deskbook' and 'NLRA Law

& Practice', both published by Lexis/Matthew Bender.

**Personal:** University of Maryland School of Law, JD, with honor, 1985; University of Maryland, BA, cum laude, 1979, Omicron Delta Epsilon, Phi Kappa Phi. Member - Employment Law Alliance and Worklaw Network.

### SMITH JR, Jay
DLA Piper LLP (US), Baltimore
410 580 4266
jay.smith@dlapiper.com
*Featured in Corporate/M&A (Maryland)*

**Practice Areas:** Corporate/M&A, life sciences, corporate governance, private equity.

**Career:** He is Co-Chair of the Corporate and Finance Practice and focuses on public and private offerings of debt and equity securities, mergers and acquisitions, and general representation of public and private companies. He represents issuers and underwriters in the sale of securities by existing public companies, and represents emerging companies in the technology, biology and real estate industries in the initial public offering of securities.

**Personal:** JD, University of Maryland School of Law (with honors); BS, The Wharton School of Finance, University of Pennsylvania (magna cum laude).

### SPELL, Cynthia L
Rosenberg Martin Greenberg, LLP, Baltimore
410 649 4984
cspell@rosenbergmartin.com
*Featured in Real Estate (Maryland)*

**Practice Areas:** Cynthia L. Spell has over 25 years of experience representing major developers in all aspects of complex real estate transactions, including acquisitions, sales, financings, leasing, and the creation of commercial condominiums. She also represents institutional lenders in real estate-based loans.

**Professional Memberships:** Maryland State Bar Association; American Bar Association; Commercial Real Estate Women - Baltimore (CREW); NAIOP.

**Career:** Partner, Rosenberg Martin Greenberg, LLP since 2006.

**Personal:** St. Mary's College of MD, BS, 1979; University of Maryland School of Law, JD, with honors, 1985.

### ST. VILLE, Thomas J.
Miles & Stockbridge PC, Baltimore
410 385 3735
tstville@milesstockbridge.com
*Featured in Employee Benefits & Executive Compensation (Maryland)*

### STRAIN, Paul
Venable LLP, Baltimore
410 244 7717
pfstrain@Venable.com
*Featured in Products Liability (Nationwide), Litigation (Maryland)*

**Practice Areas:** Paul Strain concentrates on litigation involving complex issues of technology and science. He serves as national or regional counsel for Fortune 100 clients and represents pharmaceutical companies and other manufacturers in

product liability, bad faith, intellectual property litigation, and has tried or argued cases in the Supreme Court, Federal Circuit and District Courts, and numerous state trial and appellate courts. He has been the chief litigator for the State of Maryland, Deputy Attorney General of Maryland, and is a Fellow of the American College of Trial Lawyers.

**Personal:** JD, Yale University, 1972; BS, United States Naval Academy, 1966.

### TAYLOR, Ronald W
Venable LLP, Baltimore
410 244 7654
rwtaylor@Venable.com
*Featured in Labor & Employment (Maryland)*

**Practice Areas:** Ron Taylor heads Venable's OSHA and Maryland Labor and Employment practices. He advises employers on and litigates a wide variety of labor and employment law matters, including discrimination, wage and hour, WARN, wrongful discharge, whistleblowing, non-compete agreements, collective bargaining and labor arbitration, and occupational safety and health matters.

**Professional Memberships:** Fellow, College of Labor and Employment Lawyers; member, American Bar Association's Occupational Safety and Health Committee.

**Publications:** Published and spoken extensively in the areas of employment and occupational safety and health law.

**Personal:** JD, College of William and Mary, 1981; BA, University of Virginia, 1977, Echols Scholar.

### THOMAS, Linda Marotta
DLA Piper LLP (US), Baltimore
410 580 4271
linda.thomas@dlapiper.com
*Featured in Employee Benefits & Executive Compensation (Maryland)*

**Practice Areas:** Employee benefits.

**Career:** She counsels companies and individuals in equity-based and incentive compensation arrangements and has extensive experience advising clients regarding stock-based and cash compensation programs. She develops compensation strategies that best position companies in recruiting and retaining executives and other personnel. She is experienced in mergers and acquisitions relative to employee benefits, stock options, and other compensation arrangements. She counsels plan sponsors and fiduciaries in designing and operating tax-qualified retirement plans.

**Personal:** JD, University of Baltimore (summa cum laude); LLM, University of Baltimore (with distinction); BS, University of Dayton (summa cum laude).

### TORPHY-DONZELLA, Elizabeth
Shawe Rosenthal LLP, Baltimore
410 843 3458
etd@shawe.com
*Featured in Labor & Employment (Maryland)*

**Practice Areas:** Employment discrimination litigation; employment tort and contract litigation (including covenants not to compete); Family and Medical Leave Act; human resources advice and

counsel; employment law training; employment handbooks, policies and procedures; appellate litigation; alternative dispute resolution.

**Professional Memberships:** Bar Admissions: Maryland; District of Columbia; US Courts of Appeals for the 3rd, 4th and DC Circuits. Professional Associations: American Bar Association; Maryland State Bar Association; District of Columbia Bar.

**Publications:** Editor of the General Employment Law Volume of the Matthew Bender Treatise, Employment and Labor Law, and contributing editor to the Employment Law Deskbook, also published by Matthew Bender. Articles include 'Davis, et al v Coca-Cola Bottling Company Consolidated: Or What Happens When A Court Takes Aim At 'Shotgun Litigation,'' Bender's Labor & Employment Bulletin, April 2007; 'Supreme Court Adopts Liberal Definition of Title VII Retaliation,' Bender's Labor & Employment Bulletin, August 2006; 'NLRB's Strict Definition of 'Union Discrimination' Finds Little Court Support,' Employment Law Strategist, November 2002.

**Personal:** Georgetown University Law Center, JD, cum laude, 1992; associate editor, Georgetown Journal of Legal Ethics; University of North Carolina, BA, cum laude, 1985.

### TRUITT, Raymond G
Ballard Spahr LLP, Baltimore
410 528 5629
truitt@ballardspahr.com
*Featured in Real Estate (Maryland)*

**Practice Areas:** Raymond G. Truitt is a partner in the Real Estate Department. He concentrates his practice in commercial real estate financing, leasing, development, and restructuring.

**Professional Memberships:** American Bar Association Maryland State Bar Association Past chair, Real Property Section; past chair, Code Revision Committee American College of Real Estate Lawyers International Council of Shopping Centers, Law Conference Program Committee Johns Hopkins University Business School, Edward St. John Real Estate Program Advisory Board, former adjunct faculty.

**Career:** Admissions: Maryland.

**Personal:** University of Virginia Law School (JD 1982) Loyola College (BA 1979, magna cum laude).

### ULWICK, James P
Kramon & Graham, PA, Baltimore
410 752 6030
julwick@kg-law.com
*Featured in Litigation (Maryland)*

**Practice Areas:** Mr Ulwick's Litigation Practice is wide-ranging, including criminal and civil litigation of all kinds. Mr Ulwick has tried many cases in state and federal courts, including: banking, criminal defense, class actions, contracts, personal injury, legal and medical malpractice, RICO, construction, equal employment, real estate, securities, toxic tort, and other cases. He has extensive experience in complex cases, and he frequently appears in multidistrict litigation. He frequently briefs and argues appeals in both federal and state

courts of appeals. He is listed in more than 625 published cases.

**Professional Memberships:** Mr Ulwick is a fellow in the American College of Trial Lawyers and a permanent Member of the Judicial Conference for the United States Court of Appeals for the Fourth Circuit. He is a Member of the Bars of Maryland and the District of Columbia, and is admitted in numerous federal courts.

**Career:** Mr Ulwick served as a judicial clerk for The Honorable Edward S Northrop, Chief Judge, United States District Court for the District of Maryland. Mr Ulwick then spent six years as a federal prosecutor; three years as an Assistant United States Attorney for the District of New Jersey (1978-81) and three years as an Assistant United States Attorney for the District of Maryland (1981-84). He is a 1974 graduate of the University of Massachusetts, and a 1977 graduate of the Columbus School of Law, Catholic University of America.

### WASHBURNE, Thomas
Venable LLP, Baltimore
410 244 7744
twashburne@Venable.com
*Featured in Corporate/M&A (Maryland)*

**Practice Areas:** Tuck Washburne's practice focuses on financial institutions and technology providers in the defense and intelligence community. He advises on mergers and acquisitions, joint ventures, securities and corporate law, corporate governance and financing. With a background in law and management, he assists clients in developing integrated business and legal strategies. Mr. Washburne represents clients in strategic transactions, public and private equity, and debt offerings; and counsels public companies on disclosure and governance issues.

**Personal:** JD, Vanderbilt University; BA, Middlebury College.

### WEBB, Thompson
Miles & Stockbridge PC, Baltimore
410 385 3501
twebb@milesstockbridge.com
*Featured in Corporate/M&A (Maryland)*

**Practice Areas:** Topper Webb represents publicly and privately held entities in a general business and transactional practice, including mergers and acquisitions, joint ventures, a variety of financial transactions and private equity. He frequently counsels boards of directors of reits and other publicly held companies organized under Maryland law, as well as special committees of boards, regarding capitalization, corporate governance issues, antitakeover defenses and Maryland corporate laws generally.

**Personal:** Williams College (AB, 1977); University of Virginia (JD, 1980).

### WINSTON, Roger D
Ballard Spahr LLP, Bethesda
301 664 6201
winstonr@ballardspahr.com
*Featured in Real Estate (Maryland)*

**Practice Areas:** Roger D. Winston is Managing Partner of the Bethesda office and Practice Leader of the Planned Communities and Condominiums

Group. He represents developers, investors, and lenders in the development and restructuring of all forms of common-interest projects, including residential, mixed-use, commercial, and conversion condominiums.

**Professional Memberships:** American Bar Association, Past Chair, Real Property, Trust and Estate Law Section American College of Real Estate Lawyers, Fellow and Board of Governors; Past Chair, Membership Development Committee.

**Career:** Admissions: District of Columbia Maryland.

**Personal:** University of Maryland School of Law (JD 1979) Georgetown University Law Center (LLM 1983) University of Maryland (BA 1976).

---

**WRIGHT, James**
Venable LLP, Baltimore
410 244 7422
jdwright@Venable.com
*Featured in Real Estate (Maryland)*

**Practice Areas:** James Wright represents clients in the structuring, negotiation and documentation of complex real estate transactions, including acquisitions, dispositions, financing and leasing of real estate. Mr. Wright has more than 30 years of experience in sophisticated real estate transactions throughout the U.S. He possesses a thorough knowledge of how to structure real estate transactions to minimize taxes and legal liabilities.

**Professional Memberships:** Mr. Wright is a member of the American College of Real Estate Lawyers.

**Personal:** JD, Harvard University, 1969; BA, University of Delaware, 1966.

---

**WRIGHT, Jefferson V**
Miles & Stockbridge PC, Baltimore
410 385 3600
jwright@milesstockbridge.com
*Featured in Litigation (Maryland)*

**Practice Areas:** Commercial and business litigation and arbitration of complex disputes involving bet-the-company disputes, business contracts and torts, class actions, securities and other fraud claims, intra-corporate and partnership disputes, internal corporate investigations, claims against or among financial institutions (lender liability, enforcement actions, inter-creditor disputes, and claims under consumer protection statutes), privacy claims, fiduciary claims, constitutional challenges involving land use issues. He also advises lawyers on matters relating to professional ethics and liability and businesses on corporate responsibility and liability, and occasionally serves as an expert on matters relating to business litigation and professional ethics or responsibility.

**Professional Memberships:** Admitted to practice in the state and federal courts of Maryland

(1981), the United States Court of Appeals for the 4th Circuit (1981) and the US Supreme Court (1995). Mr. Wright is a Member of the American Bar Association, Maryland State Bar Association (Chair, Committee on Ethics, 1985), Bar Associations of Baltimore City and Baltimore County. Member, Judicial Nominating Commission of Maryland (2002-2006), as well as various professional organizations and societies. He is currently a co-chair of the Law Firm Campaign for The Equal Justice Council, the fundraising arm of Maryland Legal Aid.

**Career:** As of January 1, 2013, Mr. Wright became general counsel and executive vice president for the firm's client, Telos Corporation. He remains part of Miles & Stockbridge P.C. in an of counsel role.

**Personal:** Georgetown University Law Center (JD, 1980, with honors); Tufts University (BA, 1977, with honors). Mr Wright has served as a Member of his firm's Board of Directors for many years. Mr. Wright served as a member of the firm's Board of Directors for many years.

# GOODELL, DEVRIES, LEECH & DANN, LLP

www.gdldlaw.com

**Managing Partner:** Linda S Woolf **Senior Partner:** Charles P Goodell Jr
Number of partners: 36 Number of other lawyers: 29

## Firm Overview:

Goodell DeVries was formed in 1988 by 16 attorneys who left one of Baltimore's largest firms to practice in an environment that fosters the highest-quality legal representation, client service, collegiality and professionalism. The firm has since expanded with offices in Baltimore and Philadelphia and to over 60 attorneys without sacrificing these values. Goodell DeVries has a depth of experience in the trial and management of complex litigation that is found in few other firms. Since the firm's inception, its attorneys have been involved in the defense and trial of pharmaceutical, medical device, healthcare, and commercial actions (including class actions and mass tort litigation) on behalf of national, regional and local clients. The firm's "litigation only" practice allows it to avoid many of the conflicts of interest that arise in firms with extensive corporate and transactional practices. Goodell DeVries has trial attorneys admitted to practice in Maryland, Virginia, the District of Columbia, New York, New Jersey, Pennsylvania, Tennessee, West Virginia, Ohio and California.

The firm's attorneys frequently appear in court in numerous jurisdictions throughout the United States. Corporate clients frequently request that the firm staff trial teams in complex national litigation. Goodell DeVries counsels clients when sensitive business issues intersect with the client's interest in defending itself in court. The firm has been instrumental in helping its clients protect and achieve their business objectives in the course of litigation related to the acquisition or divestiture of businesses, and in disputes involving directors and officers, shareholders, contracts, insurance and similar matters. From its earliest days, Goodell DeVries invested significant resources and technology in order to streamline the practice of law and enhance the communications between client and counsel. Goodell DeVries' Information Service Department supports the firm's attorneys with advances in technology that extend the "office" to wherever its attorneys need to manage large volumes of information and documents. In sum, Goodell DeVries' wealth of trial experience, central East Coast location and utilization of technology enable it to field a team of attorneys uniquely suited to achieving excellent results for its corporate clients in a cost-effective manner.

## Main Areas of Practice:

### Pharmaceutical & Medical Device Litigation:

The firm's attorneys have represented major pharmaceutical and medical device companies in product liability, class action and mass tort litigation since the 1970s. The firm has been responsible for developing successful defense strategies and nationally recognized experts in the fields of drug safety, biostatistics, health economics, epidemiology, engineering and metallurgy, protein biochemistry, hematology, toxicology, regulatory affairs and labelling. Members of the firm have served as national counsel in litigation involving pacemakers, pacemaker leads, defibrillators, HIV-tainted blood products, Hepatitis C, Cipro/Avelox and other mass tort claims. They have served as regional counsel in litigation involving the Dalkon Shield, Rezulin, hormone replacement therapy medications, artificial knees, hips, and spinal devices and HIV-tainted blood products. The firm's attorneys have served on national trial teams in litigation involving breast implants, the Dalkon Shield, heart valves, Rezulin, hormone replacement therapy, Neurontin, Baycol and diet drugs.
**Contact:** Charles P Goodell, Jr, Richard M Barnes

### Medical Institutions & Medical Malpractice Litigation:

Goodell DeVries represents health systems, academic centers and individual hospitals on a regional and local basis. Its work for these institutions includes defending claims of professional negligence, credentialing disputes and commercial matters. The firm has been retained to represent hospital leadership and medical staffs in litigation over termination of hospital privileges. The firm's attorneys have represented healthcare providers in every medical speciality involving claims of medical negligence, and have tried numerous cases to verdict. In addition, several of its attorneys have been designated as regional birth trauma counsel and handle claims alleging brain damaged infants and catastrophic loss.
**Contact:** Donald L DeVries, Jr, Craig B Merkle

### Commercial & Business Tort Litigation:

The firm's attorneys have represented local, national and international clients in litigation arising from the sale of subsidiaries and business units, antitrust, unfair competition and deceptive trade practices, noncompetition agreements, theft of technology, shareholder derivative suits, claims against corporate directors and officers, trustees, securities brokers, and fiduciaries, ERISA class actions, defamation, tortuous interference with contract, government procurement disputes, and other business torts. The firm regularly represents national and international insurers in complex insurance coverage disputes involving directors and officers, errors and omissions, excess and surplus lines, and other insurance products. The firm also represents securities brokers/dealers and registered representatives in NASD proceedings and SEC audits.
**Contact:** Linda S Woolf, Richard M Barnes, K Nichole Nesbitt

### Clients:

The firm represents the largest pharmaceutical companies in the United States on a national and regional basis. It also represents medical systems and individual medical institutions in a variety of litigation contexts. The firm represents international, national and local corporations in commercial litigation and international and national insurance companies in coverage litigation. Finally, it represents numerous national and local companies in toxic tort litigation.

### International Work:

The firm serves as international counsel for a medical device manufacturer, Accufix Research Institute, Inc. (ARI), formally Telectronics Pacing Systems, Inc. The international defense of ARI by the firm has included a class action and other isolated cases pending in Canada (working with Fraser Milner Casgrain LLP), a defibrillator case in the United Kingdom (working with Taylor Wessing) and many product liability matters in France (working with Bouckaert Ormen Passemard Sportes and Proskauer Rose LLP). The firm has also assisted ARI in matters pending in Hong Kong, Israel, Japan and Australia (working with Phillips Fox and Freehills). Finally, the firm advised the officers of ARI in connection with negotiations involving agreements entered into by ARI with related corporations. The firm has represented Pacific Dunlop Limited (n/k/a Ansell Limited), an Australian corporation, in litigation arising from the sale of certain worldwide subsidiaries, including litigation in Illinois state court, federal court and bankruptcy court. The firm represents both an international mining company and one of the world's largest producers of cement and ready-mix products in connection with asbestos liabilities throughout the United States. The firm represented Fireman's Fund Insurance Company in a multi-million dollar fidelity bond claim brought in Greece by a Greek subsidiary of Marriott Corporation.

1435

# KRAMON & GRAHAM, P.A.

www.kramonandgraham.com

**Managing Principal:** David J Shuster
Number of members: 22
Number of other lawyers: 12

## Firm Overview:

Kramon & Graham, P.A., was founded by two former Assistant United States Attorneys to handle complex litigation in 1975. As the firm has grown, its practice now includes commercial real estate, corporate, insurance coverage, employment, serious personal injury, defense of legal and other professional malpractice claims, and administrative law matters. Kramon & Graham attorneys are consistently recognized, year after year, by SuperLawyers, Best Lawyers (including "Bet the Company" litigation), Benchmark Litigation, in addition to many regional and industry-specific rankings. Kramon & Graham lawyers are actively involved in civic, cultural, charitable, and political activities, and serve in leadership roles on a wide range of outside boards and committees.

## Main Areas of Practice:

### Civil Litigation:

A major portion of Kramon & Graham's practice is business litigation, a field in which the firm is pre-eminent. The firm's lawyers have extensive trial and appellate experience at all levels of the federal and state court systems, and before administrative agencies. They have tried innumerable significant matters, involving virtually every kind of business and commercial issue, including: disputes concerning government and private contracts, securities, fiduciary duty, unfair competition, employment, commercial construction and residential development, trademark and copyright, trade secret, professional malpractice, technology, and attendant matters. Four of the firm's members are Fellows in the American College of Trial Lawyers; three are former Assistant United States Attorneys; and three other members are former Assistant Attorneys General for the State of Maryland.
**Contact:** Andrew Jay Graham

### Real Estate:

The firm represents developers, builders and entrepreneurs in complex real estate transactions, large scale development projects, zoning and land use issues, financings, environmental issues, lending matters, and related litigation.
**Contact:** Jeffrey H Scherr

### Insurance Coverage & Advice:

The firm's national insurance practice includes coverage disputes and advice concerning general liability, D&O, E&O, excess, and umbrella policies. Kramon & Graham represents insurers in matters arising out of construction, environmental, products liability, professional liability, and other commercial disputes. The firm has represented national property and casualty insurers in disputes involving more than $1 billion. The firm also represents insurance carriers, agents and brokers in regulatory matters before state insurance departments.
**Contact:** Lee H Ogburn

### Government Contracts & Administrative Law:

The firm's longstanding clients include entities that do business with state and local governments. Several of the firm's principals are former Assistant Attorneys General with extensive knowledge of, and familiarity with, state agencies, that regulate the professions and agencies that award contracts for privatized services, construction work, and the supply of goods and materials. The firm routinely represents clients before various state agencies in licensing and regulation matters, and before the Maryland State Board of Contract Appeals, which has exclusive jurisdiction over bid protests, state contract claims, and related procurement disputes.
**Contact:** Philip M Andrews

### Corporate/Commercial:

The firm represents various international, national, and local businesses and entrepreneurs in matters of corporate law and business transaction. The firm represents architectural firms, law firms, medical practices, real estate services, internet services firms, wholesale distributors, manufacturers, and retail companies. The firm handles transactions that concern equity investments in businesses and real estate ventures. Kramon & Graham lawyers also do a significant amount of corporate legal planning, particularly for family and closely-held businesses.
**Contact:** Cynthia A Berman

### Criminal Litigation:

The firm frequently represents companies, or their officers and directors, involved in federal and state criminal investigations in Maryland and other jurisdictions. Since the firm's founding, Kramon & Graham lawyers have served as lead defense counsel in many of the largest white-collar criminal investigations and trials conducted in federal and Maryland courts.
**Contact:** John A Bourgeois

### Professional Liability:

The firm regularly represents attorneys and self-insured law firms, both local and national, in the defense of professional liability and grievance claims. The firm's attorneys are experienced in accountant and auditor malpractice claims. The firm frequently represents physicians and hospitals in medical malpractice and credentialing actions, and has in-depth experience in regulatory and OIG investigations. Kramon & Graham lawyers also advise professionals in a variety of other industries – including financial services professionals, law school and college professors, fiduciaries, and public officials – both in malpractice claims and before governing and credentialing boards.
**Contact:** James P Ulwick or M Natalie McSherry (Health Care)

## Clients:

Kramon & Graham's clientele includes pre-eminent members of nearly every industry, including medicine, law, insurance, construction, real estate, government, business and finance. Kramon & Graham has lawyers admitted to practice in Maryland, the District of Columbia, New York, New Jersey, California, Illinois, Massachusetts, and Minnesota, as well as federal courts including nearly every Circuit Court of Appeals, the US Court of Federal Claims, and the US Supreme Court.

KRAMON & GRAHAM PA

# LERCH, EARLY & BREWER, CHTD

**www.**lerchearly.com **tel:** 301 986 1300 **fax:** 301 986 0332

**Chairman & Managing Partner:** Arthur F Lafionatis
Number of partners: 41
Number of lawyers: 62
Languages: *English*

**Firm Overview:**
Lerch, Early & Brewer is the go-to firm for representation in the Maryland suburbs of Washington, DC, particularly in the areas of real estate and land use, litigation, corporate law, health care and employment. The Bethesda-based firm has served businesses, nonprofit organizations and individuals since 1950, and is the Washington, DC area's fourth-largest suburban firm.

**Main Areas of Practice:**

**Real Estate & Land Use:**
16 partners; 7 fee earners based in Bethesda, Maryland
The firm's real estate and land use attorneys help clients acquire, develop, finance and invest in real estate. Its commercial transactions practice is diverse and sophisticated, and includes the representation of developers and investors throughout Maryland, D.C. and Virginia in office, warehouse and retail transactions, mixed-use developments, condominiums, exchanges and commercial leasing. Entrepreneurial investors and developers of commercial real estate projects use the real estate attorneys' knowledge and experience in connection with the acquisition, sale, development, financing, and leasing of commercial, retail, industrial and multi-family residential properties. The firm's reputation as one of Montgomery County's premier land use and zoning law firms comes from helping obtain the highest and best uses for their project sites for more than 40 years. The firm's land use attorneys know the lay of the land – literally and figuratively – in and around the county, from Friendship Heights to downtown Bethesda and Silver Spring to White Flint, Gaithersburg, Germantown and beyond.

- Representation of Adventist HealthCare, Inc. in sale of six skilled nursing facilities to Genesis HealthCare
- Representation of multiple stakeholders in redevelopment of White Flint under the new sector plan, including Lerner Enterprises, The Tower Companies and The JBG Companies

**Key Clients:** Washington Adventist Hospital, The JBG Companies, Lerner Enterprises, McDonald's, Costco, Ruppert Companies, Inc.
**Contact:** Steven A Robins **Tel:** 301 657 0747
**Email:** sarobins@lerchearly.com

**Litigation:**
11 partners; 7 fee earners based in Bethesda, Maryland
The firm's litigation attorneys take on a broad variety of complex commercial litigation for trial and appeal, including employment matters, business and contract disputes, trade secret and breach of fiduciary duty cases and lending and construction disputes. The group's clients are corporations, family-owned businesses, individuals, health care providers, attorneys, banks, real estate developers and builders, petroleum marketers and religious institutions. The group also represents corporate executives, professionals and individuals in professional liability and white collar criminal matters, from grand jury investigations through trial and appeal. The firm frequently is retained as co-counsel or local counsel for matters requiring sophisticated e-discovery and extensive knowledge of the Maryland court system.
**Key Clients:** Adventist HealthCare, Euro Motorcars, Inc. and Austrian Motors Corp., Fidelity National Title Insurance Company, MedStar Health
**Contact:** Stanley J Reed **Tel:** 301 657 0177
**Email:** sjreed@lerchearly.com

**Corporate/M&A:**
8 partners; 1 fee earner based in Bethesda, Maryland
The group's experience includes general corporate, transactional, legal compliance, governance, dispute resolution, and tax matters. Attorneys assist clients to form and structure new entities, set up shareholder agreements and executive compensation plans, negotiate and document business relationships, implement complex transactions, buy and sell companies, resolve difficult commercial or corporate disputes, assure compliance with applicable federal, state, and local laws and regulations, and manage and mitigate various business and liability risks. The group also practices in business and individual tax planning, and in resolving tax controversies with the IRS, and other tax authorities.
**Key Clients:** Eastland Food Corporation, Strategic Pharmaceutical Advisors, Inc., Thrustmaster of Texas, Inc.
**Contact:** Raymond J Sherbill **Tel:** 301 347 1275
**Email:** rjsherbill@lerchearly.com

## PRACTICE AREAS

Commercial Lending
Community Associations
Corporate/M&A
Creditors' Rights & Bankruptcy
Elder Law
Estate Planning & Probate
Family Law
Health Care
Labor & Employment
Land Use & Zoning
Litigation
Real Estate

## OFFICES

MARYLAND
**BETHESDA:** 3 Bethesda Metro Center, Suite 460, MD 20814
Tel: 301 986 1300  Fax: 301 986 0332
Email: info@lerchearly.com

**Labor & Employment:**
3 partners; 3 fee earners based in Bethesda, Maryland
The firm's employment and labor attorneys represent management in all matters concerning the employment relationship and the workplace. Their goal is to empower employers to effectively and properly hire, direct, compensate, discipline, and if necessary, terminate employees to the fullest extent permitted by law. They also advise employers in matters involving union avoidance and negotiation of collective bargaining agreements.
**Contact:** Richard G Vernon **Tel:** 301 907 2818
**Email:** rgvernon@lerchearly.com

**Health Care:**
5 partners; based in Bethesda, Maryland
The firm represents hospitals, physicians and other professionals, nursing homes, home health agencies, physician practice groups, health care networks and ventures, and several medical and health-related foundations in a wide variety of health care-related matters. These include hospital general counsel and special counsel representation; advice on patient issues, physicians and medical staff; licensure, surveys, certification and accreditation; and legislative and regulatory issues.
**Key Clients:** Adventist HealthCare, Montgomery Hospice, Inc.
**Contact:** Sigrid C Haines **Tel:** 301 657 0152
**Email:** schaines@lerchearly.com

LERCH
EARLY &
BREWER

# MILES & STOCKBRIDGE P.C.

www.milesstockbridge.com  **tel:** 410 727 6464  **fax:** 410 385 3700

**Chairman:** John B Frisch
Number of partners: 115  Number of lawyers firm wide: 206

## Firm Overview:

Miles & Stockbridge P.C. is a leading full-service law firm with more than 200 lawyers practicing in eight offices located within the mid-Atlantic region. Founded in 1932, the firm represents businesses of various sizes, from national and global companies to local and emerging businesses.

## Main Areas of Practice:

Miles & Stockbridge's comprehensive business and litigation experience comprises 18 practice areas, more than 100 practice focus areas and 15 industries, including manufacturing and distribution, real estate and finance.

## Manufacturing & Distribution:

Miles & Stockbridge has extensive experience in protecting and advancing the interests of manufacturers, distributors and wholesalers, and representing businesses offering a broad range of consumer and industrial products. Its representation includes a variety of matters, such as litigation, product liability, insurance recovery and risk management, labor and employment issues, distribution and supply contracts, leasing, asset-based lending and other forms of financing, real estate, sales and income taxation.

## Real Estate:

Miles & Stockbridge assists owners, developers, lenders, landlords, tenants, operators, contractors and others on matters related to the acquisition, sale, zoning, development, construction, leasing, management, finance, taxation and disposition of new and existing properties. The firm also regularly handles real estate-related litigation and work to resolve controversy, including zoning, land use and property tax appeals, environmental claims, and bankruptcy and reorganization issues. Using unsurpassed market knowledge and close working relationships with governmental entities and commercial finance institutions, the firm brings added value to its representation of real estate clients.

## Finance:

For more than 70 years, Miles & Stockbridge has represented large international, national and regional commercial banks, asset-based lenders, private equity and venture capital investors, commercial credit companies, mortgage companies, credit card companies, institutional investors, and many other commercial finance organizations. The firm's primary focus is representation in financing transactions, but it also represents finance clients in dispute resolution (ranging from bankruptcy and creditors' rights issues to class action litigation defense to workouts), regulatory matters, labor and employment and general corporate matters.

## International Work:

Miles & Stockbridge advises US and multinational corporations on their transactional, investment and trade concerns worldwide, and has long-standing relationships representing non-US companies in direct investment and general business activities within the United States and throughout North America. Miles & Stockbridge is a member of TerraLex®, a worldwide network of top independent law firms. TerraLex has 155 member firms and 17,000 attorneys in 100 countries. The member firms provide a broad range of business and legal counsel, and are well recognized and respected in their local jurisdictions, as well as internationally. The firm's membership in TerraLex allows its lawyers to serve the business and personal interests of clients whose requirements transcend state and national borders.

## PRACTICE AREAS

Alternative Dispute Resolution
Banking & Finance
Commercial & Business Litigation
Corporate & Securities
Creditors' Rights and Bankruptcy
Employee Benefits & Executive Compensation
Environmental, Health & Safety
Estates, Trusts & Elder Law
Family Law & Private Clients
Government Contracts
Insurance Recovery & Risk Management
Intellectual Property & Technology
Labor & Employment
Life Sciences, Biotechnology & Pharmaceutical
Mass Torts
Products Liability
Real Estate Transactions, Land Use & Development
Tax

## OFFICES

### MARYLAND

**BALTIMORE:** 10 Light Street, MD 21202
Tel: 410 727 6464  Fax: 410 385 3700

**CAMBRIDGE:** 300 Academy Street, MD 21613
Tel: 410 228 4545  Fax: 410 228 5652

**EASTON:** 101 Bay Street, MD 21601
Tel: 410 822 5280  Fax: 410 822 5450

**FREDERICK:** 30 West Patrick Street, MD 21701
Tel: 301 662 5155  Fax: 301 662 3647

**ROCKVILLE:** 11 North Washington Street, MD 20850
Tel: 301 762 1600  Fax: 301 762 0363

**TOWSON:** 1 West Pennsylvania Ave, MD 21204
Tel: 410 821 6565  Fax: 410 823 8123

### VIRGINIA

**TYSONS CORNER:** 1751 Pinnacle Drive, VA 22102
Tel: 703 903 9000  Fax: 703 610 8686

### DISTRICT OF COLUMBIA

**WASHINGTON DC:** 1801 K Street NW, STE. 421L, DC 20006
Tel: 202 737 9600

## MILES & STOCKBRIDGE P.C.

# OBER|KALER

www.ober.com **tel:** 410 685 1120 **fax:** 410 547 0699

**Chairman:** John Anthony Wolf

## Firm Overview:

Ober|Kaler provides regulatory, transactional and litigation services to financial, health care, construction and other business clients throughout the US. With more than 130 attorneys and offices in Baltimore, Maryland and Washington, DC, the firm offers clients across the country its knowledge of regulatory and transactional issues, leading skills in dispute resolution and deep resources in other key areas of the law.

## Main Areas of Practice:

### Business:

The Business Group at Ober|Kaler knows the importance of identifying and delivering the services clients need to resolve the challenges encountered at each stage of the business lifecycle. The firm delivers services on a wide range of legal issues frequently encountered by a company in connection with formation, operation, growth and sale. Its Business Group attorneys work closely with clients as they establish, expand and profit from their ventures. The firm's clients represent a broad cross-section of private and publicly traded companies, entrepreneurs, investors, nonprofits and others. These include financial services, technology, health care, media, communications, education, entertainment, advertising, wholesale/distribution, construction and retail. Its practice is organized with an emphasis in five areas: general counsel services; Maryland corporation law; mergers and acquisitions; private funds, venture capital and advisors; and securities.

### Construction:

Ober|Kaler's Construction Group, one of the largest and most prominent in the nation, serves clients involved in a wide range of domestic and international projects, from the largest single construction venture in the Washington, DC area to water treatment facilities in the Middle East. Its clients are involved in many facets of the design, development, engineering, and management aspects of the construction process, and include private companies and manufacturers; utilities; economic development authorities; public entities; institutional owners; developers; condominium associations and boards of directors; contractors and government agencies.

The firm's services include project formation and implementation; contract negotiation; insurance coverage counselling and policy recovery; disputes avoidance; federal, state and local procurement, government contracts, procurement and bid disputes; construction defects and design issues; contract financing and payments; litigation; and arbitration, mediation and other forms of alternative dispute resolution.

### Finance:

Over the course of the last four decades, Ober|Kaler Finance Group attorneys have built a national reputation in the complex and continually evolving finance arena by efficiently and effectively serving the country's premier financial institutions, equipment finance companies and investors.

Whether involved in a financing syndication, interpreting the newest accounting changes or evaluating credit or collateral exposures, the firm's attorneys help clients structure deals in both challenging and booming economic climates.

The firm's Finance Group's primary areas of focus include equipment finance; general commercial and asset-based loans; transportation financing; real estate financing; health care financing; vacation resort financing; public finance; international financing; and mezzanine and equity financing.

### Health:

The origins of Ober|Kaler's Health Law Group date back nearly 35 years, to the beginnings of Health Law as a recognized practice area. The firm is a leader in providing premier legal services to academic and community hospitals, health systems, long-term care facilities, clinical laboratories, institutional pharmacies, physicians and physician organizations. Its growing and evolving practice now includes representation of ancillary service providers, pharmacy and biotechnology companies, health care management and billing companies, and health care trade organizations. Ober|Kaler's Health Law Group is particularly effective because many of its attorneys bring the perspective gained from working in the federal government, at associations, in hospitals and private practice, and with health care organizations in the public and private sector.

The firm's Health Law Group's primary areas of focus include accountable care organizations; business; facility and professional regulation and operation; federal contracts; fraud and abuse; government investigations and white collar defense; antitrust counselling and litigation; health care construction; health care litigation and alternative dispute resolution; health information technology; and Medicare and Medicaid payment and certification.

## PRACTICE AREAS

Admiralty & Maritime
Antitrust & Competition
Business
Construction
Creditors' Rights, Workouts & Bankruptcy
Employment
Estates & Trusts
Finance
Financial Institutions
Food & Agriculture
Government Investigations & White Collar Defense
Health
Intellectual Property
Litigation
Nonprofit Organizations & Associations
Policyholder Insurance
Real Estate
Tax

## OFFICES

**MARYLAND**
**BALTIMORE:** 100 Light Street, MD 21202
Tel: 410 685 1120  Fax: 410 547 0699
Email: info@ober.com

**DISTRICT OF COLUMBIA**
**WASHINGTON, DC:** 1401 H Street, NW, Suite 500, DC 20005
Tel: 202 408 8400  Fax: 202 408 0640
Email: info@ober.com

### Litigation:

Large and small businesses across a range of industries, non-profits and individuals turn to Ober|Kaler to handle a variety of matters that include civil litigation in business disputes; power industry, government contract, commercial and residential construction disputes; contractual disputes; protection of trade secrets and enforcement of restrictive covenants and non-competition agreements; employee recruitment and defection disputes; antitrust proceedings; trust and estate-related fiduciary litigation disputes; employment disputes; creditors' rights proceedings; white collar criminal defense; intellectual property disputes; environmental disputes; disputes regarding commercial leases; licensing and regulatory proceedings; Medicare/Medicaid fraud proceedings; arbitration, mediation and negotiation; E-discovery and electronic record retention practices; tort claims; and RICO.

# SHAPIRO SHER GUINOT & SANDLER

**www.**shaprosher.com **tel:** 410 385 0202 **fax:** 410 539 7611

**Chairman:** Joel I Sher
**President:** William E Carlson

### Firm Overview:

The companies and individuals who rely on Shapiro Sher Guinot & Sandler receive the close attention of deeply experienced attorneys. With offices in Baltimore and Washington, DC, the firm's lawyers concentrate in banking, bankruptcy and creditors' rights litigation, corporate law, civil litigation, real estate, tax, technology law, biotechnology law, and white-collar criminal defense. Since its founding in 1972 by Ronald M Shapiro, Shapiro Sher Guinot & Sandler has represented large corporations, emerging growth businesses, governments, non-profits, and individuals.

### Main Areas of Practice:

#### Bankruptcy & Financial Restructuring:

The firm's Bankruptcy and Financial Restructuring Department represents debtors, secured and unsecured creditors, creditors' committees, and financial institutions in reorganization and bankruptcy proceedings, workouts, refinancings, and restructurings. The practice, headed by Joel I Sher, is enhanced by the firm's robust capabilities in banking, real estate, corporate, and tax law, as well as litigation. Lawyers from multiple practice groups work in concert to help clients emerge from bankruptcy proceedings in strong financial condition. The firm's efforts have consistently led to outstanding results for a variety of debtor and creditor clients.

#### Banking & Financial Services:

Chaired by Scott W Foley, the Banking and Financial Services Group represents regional banks, community banks, credit unions, insurance companies, pension funds, and other financial institutions in Maryland and throughout the Mid Atlantic. Because the group has extensive experience in the origination of loans and in workout situations, it is prepared to provide efficient representation at every stage in the commercial lending process.

#### Commercial Litigation:

Shapiro Sher Guinot & Sandler represents regional, national, and international clients and their officers, directors, and employees in commercial litigation. In complex commercial actions, the firm provides both the capacity to take cases to trial and win, as well as the experience necessary to resolve matters favorably in settlement or through arbitration or mediation. The Litigation Department, chaired by Paul Mark Sandler, is experienced in a variety of commercial disputes, including breach of contract claims, copyright infringement, professional liability, securities law claims, antitrust, and other areas.

#### Corporate & Securities:

The firm's corporate attorneys represent a variety of clients ranging from large corporations to small privately-held entities. Headed by William E Carlson, the Business Law Department has experience in finance, mergers, acquisitions, dispositions, spin-offs, and reorganizations, and frequently works in the technology and life sciences sectors. It has worked with many financing mechanisms, including venture capital, issuance of high-yield debt instruments, debt and equity financing, and mezzanine financing. The firm represents clients in private sales of securities and serves as counsel to issuer companies in Reg. A and Maryland intra-state offerings. The group also provides 'Maryland General Corporation Law' guidance to out-of-state law firms.

#### Employment Law:

Shapiro Sher Guinot & Sandler handles all forms of employment litigation, including actions to enforce noncompetition and non-solicitation agreements, claims alleging breach of employment agreement, breach of fiduciary duty, wrongful discharge, sexual harassment, and violations of federal and state anti-discrimination laws. The firm also provides informed litigation avoidance counsel and assists companies in enacting policies that deter potential employment litigation.

#### Real Estate:

Headed by Ann Clary Gordon and Lonnie M Ritzer, the firm's Real Estate Group is at the heart of major transactions throughout the Mid Atlantic. Major developers and commercial lenders turn to the firm for representation in all aspects of acquisitions and sales, development, leasing, real estate finance, property management, and joint ventures. On behalf of developers, the firm has helped bring about skyscrapers, office parks, mixed-use land development, shopping centers, apartment buildings, stand-alone build-to-suits, and commercial condominiums. In addition, the firm's Litigation Department is experienced in the representation of construction and real estate clients, and can help resolve or avoid contractual disputes.

#### Tax:

Chaired by Lonnie M Ritzer, who assisted in drafting the LLC legislation for the state of Maryland, Shapiro Sher Guinot & Sandler's Tax Law Group represents businesses ranging from large public corporations to small and mid-size companies. The group supports and enhances all the practice areas of the firm to ensure that transactions are handled in the most efficient tax manner possible, and also assists clients with income tax-related matters.

#### Technology Transactions:

Inventors, start-ups, emerging businesses, and major corporations turn to Shapiro Sher Guinot & Sandler for guidance in a range of technology-related transactional matters. The firm advises science and technology companies on technology transfer, financing, research collaboration, employment issues, executive compensation, trade-secret regimens, nondisclosure agreements, and privacy strategies.

#### White-Collar Criminal Defense:

The firm's Litigation Department represents private individuals and public officials in white-collar criminal cases, including those involving bribery, bank fraud, Medicaid fraud, wire fraud, election law, environmental crimes, and RICO. The firm has successfully represented many individuals in high stakes trials in state and federal courts.

## PRACTICE AREAS

Bankruptcy & Financial Restructuring
Business Law
Litigation

## OFFICES

**MARYLAND**
**BALTIMORE:** 36 S. Charles Street, Suite 2000, MD 21201
Tel: 410 385 0202

**DISTRICT OF COLUMBIA**
**WASHINGTON, DC:** 1025 Vermont Avenue, NW, Suite 300, DC 20005
Tel: 202 331 0200

SHAPIRO
SHER
GUINOT &
SANDLER

# SHAWE & ROSENTHAL LLP

www.shawe.com   **tel:** 410 752 1040   **fax:** 410 752 8861

**Managing Partners:** Stephen D Shawe, Bruce S Harrison
Number of partners: 13
Number of lawyers: 16
Languages: *English*

## Firm Overview:

One of the first law firms in the country devoted exclusively to the representation of management in labor and employment matters, Shawe Rosenthal LLP was founded in 1947 by Earle K Shawe. Shawe Rosenthal's practice involves both traditional labor and employment law matters, including claims brought under the Civil Rights Act, Age Discrimination in Employment Act, and the Americans with Disabilities Act. The firm defends claims involving employment discrimination, wrongful termination, defamation, ERISA, wage and hour, and occupational safety and health matters before state and federal agencies and in the courts. The firm represents management in NLRB hearings, representation campaigns and collective bargaining negotiations. The firm provides advice and assistance in the formulation of covenants not to compete and trade secret protection commitments, and is active in litigation associated with disputes over restrictive covenants and trade secrets. The firm also provides advice and counsel in the creation of affirmative action plans and compliance with OFCCP regulations. From its inception in 1947, Shawe Rosenthal decided to remain a boutique practice (16 labor and employment attorneys), select and centralized rather than expand into regional offices. This philosophy has contributed to a professional excellence that has attracted clients from across the nation. The firm has for decades represented many *Fortune* 500 companies, including some of the country's largest manufacturing, public utility, retail, healthcare and insurance concerns. The firm has handled a labor case in the United States Supreme Court (Allentown Mack v NLRB, 118 S.Ct. 818 (1998)).

Shawe Rosenthal is an efficient, well-managed organization, and is therefore able to provide clients with uniform and consistent advice, greater efficiencies in rendering services, and greater capabilities in providing short and long-term strategic planning. All of the firm's clients are represented in their general business affairs by other law firms, indeed some of the largest law firms in the country. Many of these other law firms now have their own labor law sections. The firm's clients have, nonetheless, continued to turn to Shawe Rosenthal for advice and counsel in the labor and employment field because of the firm's specialized knowledge and experience, and capability to provide advice quickly and efficiently. Members of the firm have written many publications in the employment field, including the 'Employment Law Deskbook' (1989-present), two chapters in 'NLRA Law & Practice' (1991) and 'Corporate Counsel Solutions: Employment Policies and Practices', published by LexisNexis Matthew Bender. The firm also wrote the 'Maryland and Federal Employment Law Manual' (2001-present), published by the American Chamber of Commerce Publishers.

## Main Areas of Practice:

### Labor & Employment:

Employment law including defense of statutory and common law employment discrimination claims; labor management relations including collective bargaining, and proceedings before the NLRB; human resources advice and counsel; employment tort and contract litigation; covenants not-to-compete litigation; intellectual property and trade secret litigation; wage and hour laws (FLSA, Portal to Portal Act); Occupational Safety and Health Act (OSHA); Affirmative Action Programs (AAPs); Family and Medical Leave Act (FMLA);Workers' Adjustment and Retraining Act (WARN); Employee Benefits/ERISA; employment policy and document review and drafting, including employment agreements, employment handbooks, policies and procedures; appellate litigation; class action defense.

## Clients:

The firm represents clients in all sectors of the economy including The Baltimore Orioles Baseball Club; major manufacturing concerns such as Danaher Corporation and Pepsi Bottling, Inc.; hospitals and other healthcare providers including and Genesis HealthCare Corporation; service industry corporations including McDonald's Corporation and Sylvan Learning Center; business and financial services such as GEICO and Legg Mason; power industry leaders including NRG Energy, Inc. and Calpine Corporation and hospitality services including Hay-Adams Hotel. Shawe Rosenthal also represents numerous midsize and smaller employers in each of these sectors.

## PRACTICE AREAS

Employment Litigation
Employment Discrimination & Harassment
Administrative Charges
Wage & Hour Litigation
Class Action
Occupational/Workplace Safety
Workplace Investigations
Employment & Severance Contracts
Workplace/Human Resources Advice & Counseling
Employment Law Training
OFCCP & Affirmative Action Compliance
Workplace Policies & Handbooks
Employment Audit
Labor-Management Relations
NLRB Proceedings
Collective Bargaining /Labor Contract Negotiations
Labor Arbitrations & Grievances
Union Avoidance
Strikes & Picketing
Alternative Dispute Resolution (Arbitration & Mediation)
Whistleblower Actions

## OFFICES

MARYLAND

**BALTIMORE:** 20 S. Charles Street, Suite 1102, MD 21201
Tel: 410 752 1040   Fax: 410 752 8861
The firm has a blog at www.laboremploymentreport.com

**SHAWE ROSENTHAL** LLP

# WHITEFORD, TAYLOR & PRESTON, L.L.P.

www.wtplaw.com **tel:** 410 347 8700 **fax:** 410 752 7092

**Managing Partner:** Martin T Fletcher
Number of partners: 103
Number of other lawyers: 60

## Firm Overview:

Closing a transaction, resolving a dispute, litigating or settling a claim, planning a company's future – clients come to Whiteford, Taylor & Preston for representation and guidance on a wide range of issues critical to achieving their business goals. With over 160 lawyers, WTP is one of Maryland's largest law firms. With offices in Maryland, as well as Wilmington, Delaware, Washington, DC, and northern Virginia, the firm serves clients throughout the mid-Atlantic region, as well as national companies and law firms needing representation locally or nationally. Community oriented and culturally diverse, the firm's attorneys practice in every area of law that is important to its clients. In business matters ranging from acquisitions to real estate, and litigation ranging from antitrust to bankruptcy to zoning, Whiteford, Taylor & Preston assert their clients' rights and advance their interests through vigorous and creative legal action. The firm receives exemplary rankings in both US and foreign publications that research lawyers and law firms.

## Main Areas of Practice:

### Business & Corporate:
The firm's services range from starting a business – such as choosing the appropriate form of entity – to those needed at the end of its life, such as succession planning, sale of business, or liquidation. The firm also handles everything in between, including mergers and acquisitions, financings, securities offerings, stockholder and employment agreements, stock incentive programs and tax planning.
**Contact:** Deborah H Diehl, Frank S Jones, Jr

### Bankruptcy & Business Reorganization:
The firm's Bankruptcy Group is well recognised for its cases that are national in stature. The firm represents debtors and debtors in possession, creditors and creditors' committees, lenders and trustees in all types of debt restructuring and bankruptcy reorganization proceedings, including out-of-court workouts. The firm has worked in industries as diverse as real estate development, retail and wholesale, transportation, healthcare, manufacturing, telecommunications, agri-business and a host of other industries. The members of the group include a former Justice Department litigator, Chapter 7 and 11 trustees, career Chapter 11 specialists and a former in-house counsel of a financial institution.
**Contact:** Paul M Nussbaum

### Litigation:
The firm's Litigation Department practices before a wide range of tribunals, including all state and federal trial and appellate courts in the region as well as a wide variety of courts across the nation, administrative agencies, and alternative dispute resolution forums. One of the strengths of the firm is the substantial 'in-court' trial experience of its attorneys. The firm's extensive trial experience greatly enhances its ability to evaluate a case, develop it in a manner that will appeal to a judge and/or jury, and, if appropriate, ultimately go to trial with the confidence and skill that only comes with actual trial experience.
**Contact:** Kevin G Hroblak, William F Ryan, Jr

### Labor & Employment:
The firm helps its clients create a practical platform on which to base labor and employee relations decisions. The team includes attorneys formerly with the Department of Labor and the National Labor Relations Board, along with those whose careers have been devoted to representing and counseling management in labor relations issues. Clients represent virtually every area of business and industry, and range in size from *Fortune* 500 companies with thousands of employees in various locations to small, closely held businesses.
**Contact:** Steven E Bers

### Real Estate & Land Use:
The firm's lawyers have extensive experience in virtually all types and variations of complex commercial real estate matters, including commercial and residential development, commercial leasing, complex easement agreements, sales agreements, condominium development, construction contracts, environmental, real estate finance, and zoning and land use.
**Contact:** John Gontrum (Towson), Joseph Mezzanotte (Columbia)

### Intellectual Property & Technology:
The firm's Intellectual Property and Technology Group handles a full range of technology and intellectual property matters for its clients, including domestic and foreign patents, trademark and copyright applications and related opinion matters, domestic and international technology and content licenses, research and development agreements, technology transfer agreements, strategic alliances, joint ventures and other innovative 'partnering' agreements; and a wide range of software, computer and internet law matters, including web site audits, e-commerce issues, domain names, database protection matters, ASPs, open source and other innovative distribution models.
**Contacts:** Gregory M Stone, Steven E Tiller

### Clients:
Clients range from Fortune 500 companies to small businesses and start-up enterprises. They are engaged in technology and e-commerce, finance, healthcare, insurance, transportation, communications, real estate, securities and manufacturing.

### International Work:
With 20 lawyers, the International Group at WTP helps companies, governments, and industry associations meet the legal and economic challenges of globalization in Asia, Europe, the Middle East and South America. The team focuses on strategic business services (international business advice, finance, transactions and investment, technology and intellectual property, trade policy and government relations, compliance and ethics, crisis management and public affairs), dispute resolution (including unfair trade litigation), regulatory guidance (customs, export controls, other sanctions, Foreign Corrupt Practices Act, immigration, maritime, American harbors and transportation) and development assistance (fair trade, intellectual asset protection, legal reform, microfinance and nongovernmental organizations).
**Contact:** Alexander Koff, Enayat Qasimi (Washington, DC)

## OFFICES

**MARYLAND**
**BALTIMORE:** 7-St. Paul Street, MD 21202-1636
Tel: 410 347 8700  Fax: 410 752 7092

**TOWSON:** One West Pennsylvania Avenue, Suite 300, MD 21204-5025
Tel: 410 832 2000  Fax: 410 832 2015

**COLUMBIA:** 10500 Little Patuxent Parkway, MD 21044-3585
Tel: 410 884 0700  Fax: 410 884 0719

**BETHESDA:** 7501 Wisconsin Ave, Suite 700W, MD 20814
Tel: 301 804 3610  Fax: 301 804 3640

**DELAWARE**
**WILMINGTON:** 405 King Street, Suite 500, DE 19801
Tel: 302 353 4144  Fax: 302 661 7950

**DISTRICT OF COLUMBIA**
**WASHINGTON DC:** 1025 Connecticut Avenue, NW, DC 20036-5405
Tel: 202 659 6800  Fax: 202 331 0573

**MICHIGAN**
**DEARBORN:** 290 Town Center Drive, Suite 324, MI 48126
Tel: 313 406 5659  Fax: 313 406 5840

**VIRGINIA**
**FALLS CHURCH:** 3190 Fairview Park Drive, VA 22042
Tel: 703 573 0351  Fax: 703 573 1287

## INTERNATIONAL OFFICES

**AFGANISTAN**
**KABUL:** Tel: +93 785 120 888

VERMONT
NEW HAMPSHIRE
North Adams
Lawrence
Beverly
**MASSACHUSETTS**
Westfield
**Springfield**
**Boston**
**Brockton**
Taunton
**CONNECTICUT**
**Providence**
Norwich
Newport
Danbury
**RHODE ISLAND**

### How lawyers are ranked

Every year we carry out thousands of in-depth interviews with clients in order to assess the reputations and expertise of business lawyers worldwide. The qualities we look for (and which determine rankings) include technical legal ability, professional conduct, client service, commercial awareness/astuteness, diligence, commitment, and other qualities most valued by the client. For details of our research team, see p.5.

## MASSACHUSETTS: An introduction

### Contributed by Keith H. McCown and Robert P. Joy of Morgan, Brown & Joy, LLP

Massachusetts businesses are watching several trends and developments in 2013 – 2014. The economy is improving, but to make improvements in education and transportation, the Governor and the legislature are actively considering a slate of new taxes. The healthcare sector is a major part of the Massachusetts economy, and healthcare costs are always foremost in the minds of the business community. The legislature recently imposed a regulatory cap on the rate of healthcare cost growth, a fiat aimed at maintaining the viability of Massachusetts' 2006 "universal" healthcare system and at improving conditions for business and consumers generally – but a serious challenge for healthcare employers.

As the economy slowly improves after the recession there are many favorable signs that Massachusetts businesses are moving into a healthy rebound. Massachusetts small businesses (fewer than 500 employees) are hiring, adding jobs at an increasing rate since mid-2012. Job creation among small businesses has always been a key part of the American economy and Massachusetts is no exception, with small businesses tending to generate about 65 percent of all new jobs. Favorable trends in housing and retail auto sales are said to be among the prime drivers of job growth in the small business community.

The Massachusetts housing market is also showing signs of recovery after a long and dismal slump. The situation is hardly like the frenzied sellers' market that Massachusetts saw in the 1990's – characteristic of a housing balloon doomed to burst. Some prognosticators say that when demand rises in this fashion it naturally tends to spread into other communities as buyers broaden their searches. This is good news for the many businesses tied to the housing market, such as building supplies, home repairs, landscapers, garden supplies, and so on.

Perhaps sensing that a rising economy presents an opportunity, Massachusetts Governor Deval Patrick proposed in his January 2013 State of the Commonwealth address a plan for a major "investment" in the state's education system and transportation infrastructure – a series of tax increases aimed at raising $1.9 billion in new revenue. The Governor has proposed a 1 percent increase in the state income tax, from 5.25 to 6.25 percent, and a decrease in the state sales tax, from 6.25 percent down to 4.5 percent. To fund the initiatives in transportation and education, the Governor proposed dedicating the state sales tax to major transportation projects and repairs across the state, while dedicating the increased income tax revenue to education initiatives from pre-school to college. The Governor's proposal is far-reaching, but the legislature might act favorably on more modest tax increases.

Like employers everywhere, Massachusetts businesses are eying and trying to comprehend the looming changes of the federal Affordable Care Act (ACA), with its individual mandates, individual and employer penalties, "Cadillac Plan" taxes, and so on. Massachusetts' 2006 state legislation was the model for the ACA, and thus the state has been an incubator for healthcare reform ideas. Last year the Massachusetts legislature passed Chapter 224 of the Acts of 2012, an effort to impose a legislated cap on healthcare cost growth that was not part of the ACA scheme, but may yet serve as a model for additional legislation outside of Massachusetts.

Governor Patrick hailed Chapter 224 as a "landmark measure that will lower the costs and make quality, affordable care a reality for all Massachusetts residents." But an essential motive for this new healthcare reform legislation was the need to control healthcare cost increases to keep the state's seven-year-old "universal" healthcare system viable. A principal feature of the law is a requirement for "healthcare entities" (clinics, hospitals, ambulatory surgical centers, physician organizations, accountable care organizations and more) to rein in healthcare costs and hit state-created "benchmarks" for cost growth starting in 2015. A healthcare entity that exceeds the benchmark may have to file and implement a performance improvement plan, and cooperation is backed by the possibility of large fines. There are complicated new incentives for healthcare entities to move to alternative payment methodologies and fade away from fee-for-service arrangements and, of course, new filing requirements, record-keeping requirements, and new bureaucratic oversight.

Large parts of the business sector may view Chapter 224 with relief. The healthcare sector, on the other hand, is at the epicenter of the changes. Planning and cost-cutting efforts are well underway to meet the challenge of hitting cost growth benchmarks by 2015. The benchmarks will be tied to the rate of growth in the Massachusetts economy, which may not even cover the fixed cost increase levels within some healthcare entities. The Boston Business Journal recently documented the huge pension liabilities borne by many of the state's hospitals, often involving alarming levels of unfunded liability. Unionized hospitals commonly have wage scales that include annual step increases at the 5 percent level. The new bureaucracy will be issuing regulations throughout 2013, so there is much more to be learned about the impact of the law.

Finally, the innovation sector of the Commonwealth's economy, primarily biotechnology and technology, which has remained relatively healthy, has seen a surge in legal activity associated with covenants not to compete as creative talent is in constant demand. This has triggered legislative initiatives aimed at limiting the enforceability of such covenants, although as yet none have become law.

# ANTITRUST

Commentary about individuals can be found under their firm's paragraph. If the firm has no paragraph (is not ranked) look at Other Notable Practitioners.

## Antitrust

### Leading Firms

**Band 1**

Bingham McCutchen LLP *

WilmerHale *

**Band 2**

Choate Hall & Stewart LLP *

Ropes & Gray LLP *

### Leading Individuals

**Band 1**

| | | |
|---|---|---|
| Berkowitz William N | Bingham McCutchen LLP * | |
| Buchanan Jr Robert M | Choate Hall & Stewart LLP * | |
| Burling James | WilmerHale * | |
| Goldberg Daniel L | Bingham McCutchen LLP * | |
| Miller Michelle | WilmerHale * | |
| Scott Thane D | Bingham McCutchen LLP * | |

**Band 2**

| | |
|---|---|
| Martland David A | Nixon Peabody LLP (ONP)† * |
| Savrin Daniel S | Bingham McCutchen LLP * |
| Willis Jane E | Ropes & Gray LLP |

**Band 3**

| | |
|---|---|
| Conde Kathryn Keough | Nutter McClennen & Fish LLP (ONP)† * |
| Downey Alicia L | Downey Law LLC (ONP)† |
| Johnson Deidre | Ropes & Gray LLP |
| Wood Lisa C | Foley Hoag LLP (ONP)† * |

\* Indicates firm / individual with profile.

†ONP = Other Notable Practitioner.

## Band 1

### Bingham McCutchen LLP

See profile on p.1515

**THE FIRM** The team at Bingham McCutchen continues to earn a sterling reputation for its litigation work, with sources commenting on the exceptional bench strength and the consistently high quality of its representation. Recent successes on behalf of Nissan Japan, defeating a class action alleging price-fixing, and on behalf of Tempur-Pedic International, in a minimum resale pricing case brought by the New York Attorney General, underline the firm's strength in class action and government investigation work.

**Sources say:** "They are a fantastic and diverse firm with wide, deep experience."

**KEY INDIVIDUALS William Berkowitz** (see p.1484) is a longstanding member of the firm who has received plaudits for his role in the Tempur-Pedic case mentioned above and is "right up there at the very top," according to commentators. He is particularly credited by one source for the quality of his written briefs. In addition to antitrust, he concentrates on merger, franchise and distribution work. **Daniel Goldberg** (see p.1493) is a "big name" in the market who is "well respected" by peers and clients alike for his broad commercial practice, in which antitrust litigation features heavily. He has recently been acting for Daimler Trucks North America in a class action alleging monopolization of the market for truck transmissions. The "very creative" **Thane Scott** (see p.1509) is a "terrific lawyer" who is noted for his ability to "quickly and succinctly explain the relevant issues to the client." Of late, he has represented Genzyme in a case relating to distribution rights for medical products. Sources are particularly impressed by **Daniel Savrin's** (see p.1508) "very sharp, strategic mind" and his knowledge of case law. Often seen as part of a team on cases with Daniel Goldberg, Savrin was heavily involved in the Nissan Japan matter mentioned above, as well as acting for Ahold USA in a case brought under the Federal False Claims Act.

### WilmerHale

See profile on p.930

**THE FIRM** Renowned for its IP-oriented antitrust practice, this team has outstanding proficiency both in litigation and counseling, acting for a raft of high-profile clients. Recent highlights have included representing Braintree Laboratories in a putative class action relating to the drug Miralax, and advising SkillSoft on various acquisitions.

**Sources say:** "From the get-go they've helped us manage our business – their commercial awareness is very good." "They really know what we need to be careful of."

**KEY INDIVIDUALS James Burling** (see p.1486) is a leading light in Massachusetts antitrust who "everybody recognizes as a go-to guy." He has particular expertise in IT and pharmaceutical work. Enjoying a similarly excellent reputation to Burling, **Michelle Miller** (see p.1502) is a lawyer who is "always available and always in sync," according to one source. She has recently represented Wyeth LLC in a patent infringement counterclaim.

## Band 2

### Choate Hall & Stewart LLP

See profile on p.1517

**THE FIRM** This group can call upon substantial experience in merger notification, healthcare, insurance and pharmaceutical cases. It also has expertise in media antitrust, as demonstrated by a prominent recent case in which it acted for Sunbeam Television, which alleged monopolistic practices by Nielsen Media Research.

**Sources say:** "They did a fantastic job." "Bright and talented lawyers – very high-quality and intelligent folks."

**KEY INDIVIDUALS** Practice group head **Robert Buchanan** (see p.1486) is sought after by clients for his "encyclopedic knowledge" of the antitrust environment. He recently counseled both Harvard Pilgrim Health Care and Tufts Health Plan in their high-profile merger talks. According to one source, "he always has the answer at his fingertips."

### Ropes & Gray LLP

See profile on p.1528

**THE FIRM** This group remains a robust antitrust outfit, despite the retirement of leading light and former co-head Cary Armistead. The team undertakes the full spectrum of antitrust work, with a strong focus on M&A and related counseling. Recent cases in that area include representing NSTAR in its $21.5 billion merger with Northeast Utilities and acting for Timberland in its sale to VF Corporation.

**Sources say:** "They are very much an efficient and effective organization."

**KEY INDIVIDUALS Jane Willis** wins plaudits from sources for being *"very smart, practical and effective."* She is the key player on the litigation side of the practice group, recently acting for Hitachi-LG Data Services in the defense of a price-fixing class action. **Deidre Johnson** has represented clients in a plethora of M&A matters, including Blackstone Capital Partners in its $2.2 billion purchase of Emdeon. She is particularly skilled in counseling clients and preparing filings in Hart-Scott-Rodino Antitrust Improvement Act cases.

## Other Notable Practitioners

**Kathryn Conde** (see p.1488) of Nutter McClennen & Fish LLP is an experienced practitioner with a particular emphasis on healthcare antitrust. She often works with associations of medical professionals on legislative issues. Another attorney with a healthcare focus is **David Martland** (see p.1501) of Nixon Peabody LLP, although he maintains a broad antitrust practice including frequent advising on distribution issues. He is described by sources as a *"down-to-earth, clear communicator"* who *"knows his way around the US antitrust world."* **Lisa Wood** (see p.1514) of Foley Hoag LLP enjoys *"a very good reputation"* for her varied practice, which includes antitrust, securities and complex commercial litigation. **Alicia Downey** of Downey Law LLC is particularly *"highly regarded"* by sources for her counseling ability, although she also has extensive experience as a litigator. She recently left Bingham McCutchen.

# BANKING & FINANCE

Corporate & Regulatory p.1446;    Public Finance p.1446

Commentary about individuals can be found under their firm's paragraph.  If the firm has no paragraph (is not ranked) look at Other Notable Practitioners.

| Banking & Finance Leading Firms | |
|---|---|
| **Band 1** | |
| Proskauer Rose LLP * | |
| Ropes & Gray LLP * | |
| **Band 2** | |
| Bingham McCutchen LLP * | |
| Choate Hall & Stewart LLP * | |
| Edwards Wildman Palmer LLP * | |
| Goulston & Storrs | |
| Morgan, Lewis & Bockius LLP * | |
| Riemer & Braunstein LLP | |
| **Band 3** | |
| Goodwin Procter LLP * | |
| Nixon Peabody LLP * | |
| Nutter McClennen & Fish LLP * | |
| Sullivan & Worcester LLP * | |

\* *Indicates firm / individual with profile.*
† *ONP = Other Notable Practitioner.*

*The editorial is in alphabetical order by firm name.*

## Bingham McCutchen LLP
### See profile on p.1515

**THE FIRM** This practice maintains a strong creditor focus, representing banks, institutional investors and alternative lenders in the midmarket range. The group prides itself on the international scope of its work, and is readily able to draw on resources in the firm's European and Asian offices. Industry expertise in the fields of energy, transport and retail gives the team diverse experience in the finance space. Regular clients include GE Capital, Ares Capital and HSBC.

**Sources say:** *"They are responsive, have a high level of competency and are able to bring industry expertise around the nuances of financing in the sector I work in."*

**KEY INDIVIDUALS Edwin Smith** (see p.1510) is enthusiastically described by commentators as *"the dean of the commercial lending Bar"* and continues to impress, particularly in relation to UCC matters. He represents a number of prominent financial institutions, and is well known in

| Banking & Finance Leading Individuals | | |
|---|---|---|
| **Star individuals** | | |
| Smith Edwin E | *Bingham McCutchen LLP* * | |
| **Band 1** | | |
| Berman David | *Riemer & Braunstein LLP* | |
| Draper Thomas B | *Ropes & Gray LLP* | |
| Ellis Steven M | *Proskauer Rose LLP* | |
| Herman Philip A | *Goulston & Storrs* | |
| Kyle Amy L | *Bingham McCutchen LLP* * | |
| Palladino Peter M | *Choate Hall & Stewart LLP* * | |
| **Band 2** | | |
| Antoszyk Peter J | *Proskauer Rose LLP* | |
| Boyko Stephen A | *Proskauer Rose LLP* | |
| Furlong Matthew | *Morgan, Lewis & Bockius LLP* * | |
| Ruediger David L | *Edwards Wildman Palmer LLP* * | |
| Siebert Susan E | *Jones Day (ONP)* † * | |
| **Band 3** | | |
| Choi Byung | *Ropes & Gray LLP* | |
| Creem Gary | *Proskauer Rose LLP* | |
| Fiszman Sula | *Morgan, Lewis & Bockius LLP* † | |
| Lerner James | *Goulston & Storrs* | |
| Maloney MacKenzie Pamela | *Goulston & Storrs* | |
| Mills Craig | *Nixon Peabody LLP* * | |
| Patterson Stephen J | *Nutter McClennen & Fish LLP* * | |
| Rosenblatt Philip R | *Nutter McClennen & Fish LLP* * | |
| Sibble Edward Matson | *Goodwin Procter LLP* * | |
| Simard Kevin J | *Choate Hall & Stewart LLP* * | |
| Ticknor George | *Edwards Wildman Palmer LLP* * | |
| **Up-and-coming individuals** | | |
| Hickey Andrew | *Choate Hall & Stewart LLP* | |
| Lee Michael | *Ropes & Gray LLP* | |

the Boston and New York markets. **Amy Kyle** (see p.1499) receives effusive praise from interviewees, and her leveraged finance practice is highly regarded in the market. She has particular expertise in the transportation sector, and has notably represented Bank of America as lender to an international shipping group. Clients appreciate her ability to get deals done, saying: *"What sets her above others is her combination of business sense and negotiating ability. She*

*is able to come into a contentious negotiation and help everybody reach an agreement and move the deal forward."* **Neal Curtin** (see p.1489) is revered in the corporate and regulatory arena. He has impressive international experience, advising numerous non-US financial institutions in their governance and transactional practices.

## Choate Hall & Stewart LLP
### See profile on p.1517

**THE FIRM** This team is a firm client favorite and, while maintaining a robust and varied practice, has particular strength in the retail and sports industries, and can offer litigation expertise alongside transactional prowess. It represents both lenders and borrowers, and is known for its experience in advising alternative lenders. Salus Capital, MassMutual and Wells Fargo are typical clients, and the team has recently represented Bank of America as lender in a high-value syndicated credit facility for the GSI Group. Clients appreciate the superlative client service provided by the group, and are confident in both the team's bench strength and its proficiency as a one-stop shop.

**Sources say:** *"Ultimately, their team is a true extension of our team. We rely on them as a valued partner, and their availability is very consistent."*

**KEY INDIVIDUALS Peter Palladino** (see p.1504) remains a popular choice for corporate financing matters. Recent work includes the representation of Webster Bank in a private equity-sponsored acquisition, and he continues to be a key partner for Bank of America. He is admired for his *"strong business skills and practical approach."* Up-and-comer **Andrew Hickey** (see p.1495) is making a name for himself in the banking and finance field, and combines skill and experience in both financing and restructuring work. Clients say: *"He is technically proficient and has the ability to communicate both to members of my team and to prospective borrowers."* **Kevin Simard** (see p.1510) also enters the rankings this year on the strength of his reputation, particularly in the retail financing space. Market opinion commends both his loan documentation skills and his strong insolvency experience. *"It was comforting,"* says one source, *"that he could help us in troubled times. He offers real-world practical advice on what to look out for at*

*The editorial is in alphabetical order by firm name.*

*the beginning because he knows the bankruptcy process so well."*

## Edwards Wildman Palmer LLP
See profile on p.1520

**THE FIRM** This highly regarded team has an impressive and well-developed practice, serving as bond counsel for state and local governments across New England. Its recent workload includes century bonds for educational institutions and the prominent $3 billion Accelerated Bridge Program deal. The group also has a robust practice in banking and finance work, and is celebrated for its strength in lender-side representations.
**Sources say:** *"An excellent firm – they have a very good reputation and my personal experience with them has been excellent."*
**KEY INDIVIDUALS Walter St. Onge** (see p.1510) continues to serve as bond counsel to the Commonwealth of Massachusetts and other New England states, as well as public bodies including the Massachusetts Water Pollution Abatement Trust. Interviewees comment: *"He is very smart and thinks around the entire transaction, not solely for his clients but also what's best for the deal. He's a pleasure to work with."* **David Ruediger** (see p.1508) is a renowned business lawyer whose expertise is rated highly by both peers and clients. He has a wealth of experience in transactional and debt financing work. **George Ticknor** (see p.1512) continues to impress market commentators with his dexterity in the public debt and financing arena, and he is active in the technology, media and telecoms sectors. **Stephanie Massey** (see p.1501) enters the rankings this year on the strength of her burgeoning reputation in the bond market. She represented MassHousing in its bond financing to provide single-family housing.

## Goodwin Procter LLP
See profile on p.1522

**THE FIRM** This Boston institution enjoys a solid reputation as a corporate and regulatory go-to firm for financial institutions and private equity investors as both lenders and borrowers. The team is well equipped to handle a broad range of matters in an advisory, transactional and litigious capacity and has experience handling credit facilities for clients in the tech space. Regular clients include Bank of America, Brookline Bancorp and TD Bank.
**Sources say:** *"They're really up to speed with changes in regulation and they are able to translate those changes to fit our business needs."*
**KEY INDIVIDUALS** Cochair of the banking practice **Lynne Barr** (see p.278) is a financial services expert whose vast experience in consumer finance matters has established her as a leader in the field. Clients say: *"She is able to talk from the gut in a way that lawyers typically don't. She can anticipate and plan ahead, and tell you which way the wind is blowing."* **William Mayer** (see p.1501) is a seasoned practitioner who, according to interviewees, is *"very effective at dealing with a board or executive management, resolves problems in a sensible way and takes a balanced approach."* He has recently assisted Brookline Bancorp on numerous corporate matters, and continues to represent Harbor One Credit Union. **Eric Fischer** (see p.1491) focuses his practice on regulatory matters and is an authority on Office of Foreign Assets Control compliance issues. Recent work highlights include serving as regulato-

ry counsel to Manulife Asset Management in its establishment of a nondepository trust company. **Edward Matson Sibble** (see p.1509) is a well-known name in the leveraged finance market and commands a high degree of respect from observers, who say: *"He is extremely proactive, practical and knowledgeable. He does a terrific job representing us."* His clients include Bank of America and RBS Citizens, as well as numerous private equity sponsors and venture capital firms. Up-and-comer **Samantha Kirby** (see p.1498) makes her debut in the rankings this year. Her skill in advising financial institutions on a wide variety of transactional and regulatory matters has impressed clients, with one saying: *"She knows that you can't operate in a vacuum and that sometimes the business decision overrules the legal decision. She is very measured in her approach."*

## Goulston & Storrs

**THE FIRM** This Boston stalwart has a substantial presence in both the Massachusetts and New York markets, and concentrates its practice in the midmarket. It typically represents premier national and international financial institutions on the lender side, and has significant experience on the borrower side, with specific reference to the manufacturing, energy, environmental and commercial real estate sectors. The team frequently undertakes work for Bank of America and JPMorgan Chase on everything from syndicated loans to multijurisdictional financing.
**Sources say:** *"They provide a degree of local flavor which makes dialog and negotiation on certain deals more expedited. It is the personal touch that makes them stand out."*
**KEY INDIVIDUALS Philip Herman** is deemed to be a leader of the commercial lending bar and his vast experience in this space brings clients readily to his door. *"He has a high degree of professional acumen that makes us very comfortable with him being lead counsel on our transactions. He knows what we require from a legal and a business standpoint."* He has undertaken substantial private equity sponsored financings on behalf of Abacus Finance Group, and represented HSBC in its dealings with a lending syndicate for New Balance Athletic Shoe. Director **James Lerner** concentrates his practice on commercial real estate lending, and in this capacity has represented JPMorgan Chase, Bank of America and TD Bank. **Pamela Maloney MacKenzie** maintains a broad practice, representing both lenders and borrowers in the commercial and real estate financing space. She works on big-ticket financings for Merrill Lynch and KeyBank. Clients attest to her pragmatism, saying: *"She comes at it from a very practical approach. She tries to handicap the risks appropriately and is not overly concerned about obscure risk."*

## Greenberg Traurig, LLP
See profile on p.1024

**THE FIRM** This team remains a go-to group for public finance work, and its practice is especially noteworthy in the education and healthcare sectors. This group boasts an impressive international dimension, with significant financing expertise in Puerto Rico, Europe and the Far East. Its client list includes South Shore Hospital, Barclays Capital and the Commonwealth of Puerto Rico, for whom it has served as bond counsel for numerous bond refinancings.

Sources say: *"They are a global firm and we always go to them because they have that key knowledge globally."*

KEY INDIVIDUALS **Jean DeLuca** (see p.1490) cultivates a diverse financing practice, and has plentiful experience serving as disclosure counsel and representing issuers and borrowers. She has an expertise in dealing with Puerto Rican clients and handles financing work for their government, infrastructure and port authorities. *"She is very organized, thinks through everything and is very easy to work with."*

## K&L Gates
See profile on p.2245

THE FIRM This team focuses its practice predominantly on corporate regulatory and governance matters, advising on everything from securitizations, to mergers, to regulatory developments under Dodd-Frank. It typically represents smaller, community banks, and has a stellar reputation in this arena.

Sources say: *"They have an outstanding mix of accessibility and resources, and the individuals we work with are accomplished and knowledgeable."*

KEY INDIVIDUALS **Stanley Ragalevsky** (see p.1506) is a high-quality community bank and loan specialist. He warrants effusive praise from clients and peers, who have described him as *"the patron saint of community banking."* He served as primary counsel to Salem Five Bancorp in its acquisition of Stoneham Savings Bank, and handles regulatory matters for the Co-operative Central Bank. Junior partner **Sean Mahoney** (see p.1500) is building an impressive practice in financial services regulation and has this year assisted on several community bank mergers, including that of the Community Bank and Eastern Bank.

## McCarter & English, LLP
See profile on p.1759

THE FIRM This team continues to make waves in the public finance space, and is deemed to be eminently accomplished in complex transactions at local and state level throughout New England. The group impresses as both bond and underwriter's counsel for a robust base of significant clients, including the Massachusetts Water Resources Authority and the New Hampshire Housing Agency.

Sources say: *"They are not stuffed shirts but 'real' people who relate well to our issues. They are sincere, have the ability to answer fully and have a high level of patience."*

KEY INDIVIDUALS **Barbara Kroncke-Moore** (see p.1499) cuts an impressive figure in the market and is known for her bond work for nonprofit institutions. She continues to be very active in this space, with clients praising her superior responsiveness and collaborative approach, and one interviewee commenting: *"She is an asset to any deal team and she is a great team player."* **Thomas Collins** (see p.1488) enters the rankings this year as a firm client favorite. He enhances public finance transactions with crucial tax expertise, and specializes in housing bond work. Clients readily appreciate his rare ability to

translate esoteric legal principles into comprehensible terms.

## Mintz Levin Cohn Ferris Glovsky and Popeo PC
See profile on p.1523

THE FIRM The Boston office of this firm has long been revered for the strength of its public finance practice. The 15-strong group has an enviable reputation not only in the traditional finance practice representing borrowers and issuers, but also in the municipal bankruptcy market. It is adept at representing clients as bond, underwriter's and disclosure counsel, and regular clients include Massachusetts Housing Agency, Wells Fargo and the Vermont Municipal Bank.

Sources say: *"It's a very well-oiled machine; they are outstanding, professional and very thorough."*

KEY INDIVIDUALS Top-drawer public bond lawyer **Meghan Burke** (see p.1486) receives glowing praise from clients and competitors alike. *"She's just a very talented woman. Very thorough in her analysis of the problems and well respected,"* says one respondent. Notable work includes her representation of Massachusetts Bay Transportation Authority to develop a new nonprofit structure to issue tax-exempt debt. **John Regier** (see p.1506) specializes in public agency representation. He represented the Commonwealth of Massachusetts in a second issue of special obligation revenue bonds connected to its Accelerated Bridge Program. The *"absolutely outstanding"* **Richard Moche** (see p.1502) represents a broad client base in tax-exempt bond transactions. He served as counsel to Wells Fargo, the indenture trustee in a continuing care retirement community restructuring, and assisted on a complex M&A transaction in the healthcare sector. **Gregory Sandomirsky** (see p.1508) is a seasoned public bond practitioner who has vast experience in both borrower and lender representation. His practice is national in scope, and he handled a complex project finance transaction in Texas. Clients say: *"He is interested in getting the transaction done, rather than negotiating for the sport of it. He's very creative in coming up with solutions."* Associate **Colin McNiece** (see p.1501) is quickly making a name for himself in the public finance market and is touted by clients as a rising star. He assists on a broad caseload, including a complex rental housing transaction on behalf of Massachusetts Housing Agency.

## Morgan, Lewis & Bockius LLP
See profile on p.2246

THE FIRM This highly rated team is perceived to be especially strong in midmarket deals, mezzanine financing, and syndications in the retail and entertainment industries. The practice has expanded in recent years to provide clients in the banking sector with a more comprehensive full-service package and the resources of a well-developed bench.

Sources say: *"They think more like businesspeople and they are decisive in giving options."*

KEY INDIVIDUALS **Matthew Furlong** (see p.1492) is a renowned specialist in security transactions and big-ticket

financing matters. He assists Bank of America in its financing for Harvard Universitym and Mast Capital Management in relation to several of its loans. Clients say: *"He has the uncanny ability when dealing with a situation to get through the nonsense and to the point, in order to keep the process moving."* **Sula Fiszman** (see p.1491) combines a transactional financing practice with a noted strength in insolvencies and workouts. She continues to assist on complex secured finance transactions.

## Nixon Peabody LLP
See profile on p.1526

THE FIRM This group is praised highly for its banking and public finance practices. It demonstrates particular strengths in state finance, housing finance and social impact bonds. The finance team can count on the support of an accomplished tax team to cover all bases of work for clients in this space, at both state and national level.

Sources say: *"They always meet – and often exceed – my expectations. They are simply a fantastic team that I would highly recommend to all my colleagues."*

KEY INDIVIDUALS Chair of the firm's global finance group, **Craig Mills** (see p.1502) garners praise for the quality of his commercial transaction work and is noted for the clarity of his advice, with one client saying: *"He has not only a great deal of tech expertise but also real-world experience, which he can convey sensibly and in a relevant way."*

## Nutter McClennen & Fish LLP
See profile on p.1527

THE FIRM This commercial finance group has a core expertise in both transactional and regulatory matters, and is able to advise on deals in their entirety, from documentation to restructuring. Their client base is diverse and includes national banks and equipment leasing companies.

Sources say: *"The Nutter team is proactive in its thought process, creative in structuring agreements, and forward-thinking in terms of making us aware of regulation and how it may impact us. We believe this approach is indicative of a true partner."*

KEY INDIVIDUALS Co-head and transactional lawyer **Kenneth Ehrlich** (see p.1490) enjoys a sterling reputation in general finance matters. He has particular expertise in community bank mergers and formations, having this year represented the Adams Community Bank, the Mechanics Co-operative Bank and the Haverhill Bank in this area. Interviewees note that *"he is clearly passionate about his profession and he truly cares about doing what is right for his clients."* Accomplished M&A lawyer **Michael Krebs** (see p.1499) marries his transactional practice with a strong record in corporate and regulatory matters. Clients roundly applaud his dedication to their case, saying: *"His knowledge is superior and he's a really hard worker. He looks at things from every angle and you feel that nothing will be overlooked."* **Philip Rosenblatt** (see p.1507) is applauded for his ability to handle complex transactions expediently, and he regularly handles commercial financing matters for big-ticket national and global banks. **Stephen Patterson** (see p.1505) is an expert in equipment leasing transactions

*The editorial is in alphabetical order by firm name.*

and Dodd-Frank matters. He regularly represents a number of high-profile financial institutions.

## Proskauer Rose LLP
See profile on p.2001

THE FIRM This team has one of the premier practices in Boston for multitranche financing, and clients seek it out for its renowned expertise in mezzanine debt matters. The work of the team extends beyond state level and is truly a national and international practice. It regularly represents such prominent clients as Sankaty, Barclays Capital and Morgan Stanley. Interviewees say they appreciate the breadth and depth of expertise the team can offer.

Sources say: *"They're partners, not just a service provider. They tell us the situation then help us whittle the options down until we get a workable solution."*

KEY INDIVIDUALS Steven Ellis is held in high regard by market commentators. Sources are quick to emphasize his extensive experience in the junior capital space, saying: *"He's very in tune to market developments, so if we're negotiating he can bring his experience to bear and apply the trends to current deals."* Peter Antoszyk combines a successful bankruptcy and restructuring practice with finance work to provide clients with comprehensive and strategic counsel. Notable recent work includes his representation of TPG in a high-value unitranche financing in the healthcare space. The specialties of Stephen Boyko are numerous and his practice covers acquisition financing, LBOs and junior capital. He works with Morgan Stanley on mezzanine loan work. Gary Creem makes his debut in the rankings this year, and has worked with Sankaty on a complex financing project. Market opinion attests to his calming and patient demeanor: *"He never gets flustered and he never gets mad at anybody; he's reasonable. Just what we need to get the deal done."*

## Riemer & Braunstein LLP

THE FIRM This respected group has a particularly strong reputation in the retail sector, and is known to be talented in the area of small tech financings.

KEY INDIVIDUALS David Berman is noted as one of the primary figures in the banking and finance arena. His practice focuses on asset-based loans and retail finance, and he is highly respected by both peers and clients in this space.

## Ropes & Gray LLP
See profile on p.1528

THE FIRM A well-established leader in the Massachusetts legal market, Ropes fields an impressive team in the banking and finance space. The group handles the full range of work for private equity sponsors and other investment funds at state, national and international level, and is building a robust practice in mezzanine lending. The team is also known in the public finance space. Regular clients include Audax, Bain Capital and TPG Capital.

Sources say: *"They have a good understanding of market trends and of financing more broadly, so they have a very current take on what's happening. Other firms have capability and market awareness, but Ropes is up there as a firm that really gets it."*

KEY INDIVIDUALS Transactional lawyer Thomas Draper remains active in the market and is known for his skills in mezzanine lending work. Highly respected by peers and popular with clients, he brings his practical approach to the table in a broad range of financings. Interviewees say: *"He knows the market, has the ability to be reasonable and to see the forest for the trees. He does not comment on theoretical points but gets deals done and protects us from risk."* Eminent practitioner Anne Phillips Ogilby has a wealth of experience of financings in the healthcare, non-profit and educational sectors, and her acumen in this space is attested to by market commentators. Co-head of the finance group, Byung Choi focuses his practice on

leveraged transactions for an impressive list of private equity clients, including Silver Lake Partners, Bain Capital and TPG, which he recently advised in relation to its high-value financing for the acquisition of Immucor. Michael Lee makes his debut in the rankings this year in recognition of his standing in the market and his impressive caseload. He served as counsel to Audax in a complex refinancing to support its portfolio company, Phoenix Children's Academy. Clients say: *"He's good at conceptualizing what these agreements mean and what the salient points are in layman's terms."*

## Sullivan & Worcester LLP
See profile on p.1534

THE FIRM This team primarily represents bank and alternative lenders in all aspects of lending work. The group is active in the debt financing community. Recent work highlights include the closing of a revolving credit facility for Five Star Quality Care and the negotiation of an unsecured term loan on behalf of Government Properties Income Trust.

Sources say: *"The firm has knowledge and expertise in specialist areas which are normally the preserve of much larger firms. They are responsive and provide a good service at a reasonable cost."*

KEY INDIVIDUALS William Levine is a key contact for the team.

## Other Notable Practitioners

Talented transactional attorney Susan Siebert (see p.1509) of Jones Day has a wealth of experience across a wide range of work, including M&A, restructurings and debt financing. She receives abundant praise for her practical focus, with one interviewee commenting: *"She is very client friendly and knows how to make sure the other side feels well served and respected as well as her own client. She knows how to put a transaction together successfully."*

# BANKRUPTCY/RESTRUCTURING

Commentary about individuals can be found under their firm's paragraph. If the firm has no paragraph (is not ranked) look at Other Notable Practitioners.

| Bankruptcy/Restructuring |
| --- |
| **Leading Firms** |
| **Band 1** |
| Goodwin Procter LLP * |
| Mintz Levin Cohn Ferris Glovsky and Popeo PC * |
| Murphy & King, P.C. * |
| Ropes & Gray LLP * |
| WilmerHale * |
| **Band 2** |
| Brown Rudnick LLP * |
| Choate Hall & Stewart LLP * |
| Goulston & Storrs |
| **Band 3** |
| Bingham McCutchen LLP * |
| Duane Morris LLP * |
| **Band 4** |
| Foley Hoag LLP * |
| Holland & Knight LLP * |
| Jager Smith PC |
| Sullivan & Worcester LLP * |

| Senior Statesmen | |
| --- | --- |
| **Senior Statesmen:** distinguished older practitioners | |
| Levine Richard L | *Nelson Kinder + Mosseau, PC (ONP)[†]* |

| Leading Individuals | | | | |
| --- | --- | --- | --- | --- |
| **Star individuals** | | | | |
| Glosband Daniel M | *Goodwin Procter LLP* * | | Martin D Ross | *Ropes & Gray LLP* |
| Mikels Richard | *Mintz Levin Cohn Ferris Glovsky* * | | Morrier John | *Casner & Edwards, LLP (ONP)[†]* |
| Murphy Harold B | *Murphy & King, P.C.* * | | Ricotta Paul J | *Mintz Levin Cohn Ferris Glovsky* * |
| **Band 1** | | | Schwartz Andrew | *Foley Hoag LLP* * |
| Baldiga William R | *Brown Rudnick LLP* | | Sigel John | *WilmerHale* * |
| Cohn Daniel C | *Murtha Cullina LLP (ONP)[†]* | | Ventola John F | *Choate Hall & Stewart LLP* * |
| Dale III Charles A | *K&L Gates (ONP)[†] * | | Wilton Jim | *Ropes & Gray LLP* |
| Glerum Charles L | *Edwards Wildman Palmer LLP (ONP)[†] * | | **Band 3** | |
| Gooding Douglas R | *Choate Hall & Stewart LLP* * | | Bostwick Janet E | *Janet E Bostwick PC (ONP)[†]* |
| Hoort Steven T | *Ropes & Gray LLP* | | Dinardo Patrick P | *Sullivan & Worcester LLP* * |
| Monaghan John J | *Holland & Knight LLP* * | | Ehrlich Gayle | *Pierce Atwood LLP (ONP)[†] * |
| Moore Paul D | *Duane Morris LLP* | | Jeffery D Ethan | *Murphy & King, P.C.* * |
| Pappone Michael J | *Goodwin Procter LLP* * | | Jenkins Dennis L | *WilmerHale* * |
| Rosner Douglas | *Goulston & Storrs* | | Leonetti Kenneth | *Foley Hoag LLP* * |
| Smith Edwin E | *Bingham McCutchen LLP* * | | Lizotte Andrew G | *Murphy & King, P.C.* * |
| Wallack James F | *Goulston & Storrs* | | Martin Gina Lynn | *Goodwin Procter LLP* * |
| **Band 2** | | | Panos Christopher J | *Craig and Macauley PC (ONP)[†]* |
| Appelbaum Mitchel | *WilmerHale* * | | Smith Bruce | *Jager Smith PC* |
| Bennett Jr Charles R | *Murphy & King, P.C.* * | | Sternklar Jeffrey | *Duane Morris LLP* |
| Berman Mark N | *Nixon Peabody LLP (ONP)[†] * | | Walsh Kevin J | *Mintz Levin Cohn Ferris Glovsky* * |
| Bleck Daniel | *Mintz Levin Cohn Ferris Glovsky* * | | Willett Sabin | *Bingham McCutchen LLP* * |
| Goldberg Michael | *Casner & Edwards, LLP (ONP)[†]* | | **Up-and-coming individuals** | |
| Kannel William | *Mintz Levin Cohn Ferris Glovsky* * | | Walker Adrienne K | *Mintz Levin Cohn Ferris Glovsky* * |
| Lynch Christine D | *Goulston & Storrs* | | **Associates to watch** | |
| | | | Kaden Greg | *Goulston & Storrs* |

*\* Indicates firm / individual with profile.*

*[†]ONP = Other Notable Practitioner.*

## Band 1

### Goodwin Procter LLP
See profile on p.1522

**THE FIRM** The capabilities of this Boston institution are broad-reaching on both the domestic and the international scene. The team is able to advise on bankruptcy litigation, out-of-court settlements and Chapter 11 matters, and has a wealth of experience representing debtors, creditors and committees. As one of the premier insolvency practices in the state, clients seek Goodwin out for its combination of innovative legal advice and superlative client service.

**Sources say:** *"They are a preeminent bankruptcy firm. They have the resources for large, sophisticated cases, but they can also handle the smaller matters. They just have outstanding bankruptcy people."*

**KEY INDIVIDUALS Daniel Glosband** (see p.1493) is truly a leader in the restructuring space and he has plentiful experience in international insolvency work, having served as an adviser to the American Law Institute and the US State Department. This year he has notably served as counsel to the court-appointed receiver for a Madoff feeder fund. Peers and clients are quick to praise his talents, with one describing him as *"a guru"* and another as *"my go-to guy for particularly thorny issues."* **Michael Pappone** (see p.1504) is also highly regarded in the insolvency sphere, and is as comfortable working on a high-stakes corporate restructuring as he is with smaller clients. He has had a string of success representing clients in the retail industry, and has particular flair in matters relating to the technology sector. He has recently represented BRIKOR, BuyWithMe and Exit41. **Gina Lynn Martin** (see p.1501) is described as *"a top-flight bankruptcy lawyer"* who is highly accomplished in the market. She has particular strength in

financial restructuring matters and is an experienced insolvency litigator. She continues to handle work for the Educational Resources Institute following its Chapter 11 proceedings.

### Mintz Levin Cohn Ferris Glovsky and Popeo PC
See profile on p.1523

**THE FIRM** This team is very well established in the state market and has a depth of resources to draw on nationwide. It handles the full range of business bankruptcy matters, and this is combined with a leading tax-exempt bond practice which gives them the edge in Chapter 9 work. The group is at home representing both creditors and debtors from a wide range of industries, including the healthcare and life sciences industries.

**Sources say:** *"They are a terrific firm and a powerhouse in Boston and New York."*

**KEY INDIVIDUALS** Star individual **Richard Mikels** (see p.1502) is a revered practitioner with a name for debtor representation in complex restructurings. Clients speak at length about his calming presence during negotiations and his pragmatism, saying: *"He has a unique ability to identify*

*issues that should be negotiated as opposed to hard fought, and he always finds a good compromise. He has the respect of everybody that he deals with."* **Daniel Bleck** (see p.1485) is best known for his work in the healthcare space and is an expert on cases involving continuing care retirement communities, although his practice is more broad in scope and covers the full range of bankruptcy and restructuring work. Clients praise him highly, remarking: *"He has common sense, he looks for solutions and takes the time required to get a deep understanding of the transaction."* **Paul Ricotta** (see p.1506) is described as being *"very practical, and he knows when to hit hard and when to find a compromise."* He brings an air of business-minded authority to his work for clients in the banking space by virtue of his experience as in-house counsel at M&T Bank. He has recently worked on a high-value workout in the gaming field, and is a celebrated litigator. **William Kannel** (see p.1497) is lauded as a masterful negotiator and concentrates his practice on nationwide Chapter 9 municipal bankruptcies. Clients say: *"He is very good at bringing disparate parties together and reaching consensus."* **Kevin Walsh** (see p.1512) has a broad insolvency practice, and this year he has represented the liquidating trustee in a high-value Chapter 11 case as well as various creditors' committees. Clients praise his practical business focus, saying: "*He is not afraid of a fight, but he understands that the goal is to resolve money for the creditors and he is very capable in achieving that.*" Up-and-comer **Adrienne Walker** (see p.1512) is accomplished in Chapter 9 and 11 proceedings, and has experience in both bankruptcy litigation and out-of-court restructurings. She has handled healthcare bond bankruptcies throughout the USA.

## Murphy & King, P.C.
See profile on p.1525

**THE FIRM** This Boston institution retains its dominant position in the Massachusetts market and is highly regarded by both clients and competitors. The team predominantly undertakes debtor-side Chapter 11 work across a range of industries, including the telecom, construction and pharmaceutical sectors. The firm stands out as being a top-tier firm offering competitive rates and outstanding client service, with a well-developed geographical reach which extends beyond the confines of New England into the New York and Delaware markets.
**Sources say:** "*Murphy & King has a large bankruptcy practice and has some of the best insolvency lawyers in the city.*"
**KEY INDIVIDUALS** An undisputed champion of the New England bankruptcy Bar, **Harold Murphy** (see p.1503) is a widely recognized leader for midmarket debtor cases. Competitors are readily prepared to refer both debtor and creditor work to him, and they shower him in praise for his work: "*He continues to be tremendous. He's really a king of this practice.*" **Charles Bennett** (see p.1484) is revered for his skills as both an adviser and a litigator. This year he has led a reorganization for a global health club client and has been a dominant figure on local filings. **Ethan Jeffery** (see p.1496) is a gifted attorney for both debtor and creditor representations in the bankruptcy and restructuring space. Recent work highlights include acting as lead counsel for a major telecoms provider and representing the lead creditor in a New Hampshire construction company case. **Andrew Lizotte** (see p.1500) is equally well regarded as an all-around insolvency practitioner who is very active on Chapter 11 work and out-of-court restructurings.

## Ropes & Gray LLP
See profile on p.1528

**THE FIRM** The Boston headquarters of this international firm continues to impress the market with its strong foothold on insolvency matters both at home and abroad. The firm's strength in private equity work permeates the bankruptcy practice, and the team is able to offer a truly comprehensive service package to investment funds and advisers on both the creditor and debtor side. The team is at the forefront of healthcare-related restructurings and insolvencies within the energy sector. The group maintains an impressive client base including Bain Capital as well as Deutsche Bank and Wells Fargo.
**Sources say:** "*Ropes is very much a top-tier New England firm.*"

**KEY INDIVIDUALS Steven Hoort** is a commanding figure in the market and focuses his practice on bankruptcies in the healthcare industry. In the last year he has undertaken significant work concerning tax-exempt bond restructuring for Northern Berkshire Healthcare, and has handled a Chapter 11 proceeding in Delaware for Pyxis Capital. **Ross Martin** provides robust insolvency advice to private equity sponsors and institutional investors. Notable work highlights of the last twelve months include the defense of a group of big-ticket higher education institutions in a claim for recovery of funds. He remains a key player in the ongoing Lehman Brothers creditor disputes. **Jim Wilton** remains a popular choice with clients for bankruptcy and restructuring work. He has been involved in the Lehman Brothers creditor cases and has successfully negotiated a high-value out-of-court settlement on behalf of a prominent pharmaceutical client.

## WilmerHale
See profile on p.930

**THE FIRM** This team prides itself on its defense practice in bankruptcy litigation, and typically works for creditors and acquirers in insolvency proceedings. The group boasts depth in both the Boston and the New York office, and has the resources of a nationwide practice at its disposal. It recently represented Kodak in a Section 363 patent sale and represented the unsecured creditors' committee for Getty Petroleum.
**Sources say:** "*They did an excellent job of representing the committee, protecting our rights while at the same time keeping a fractious bondholder group together. Their efforts enabled us to achieve a successful resolution to the negotiation.*"
**KEY INDIVIDUALS Mitchel Appelbaum** (see p.1483) is respected for "*his ability to point out real, as opposed to theoretical, business risks.*" With established expertise in Chapter 11 proceedings, he is valued counsel for debtors, creditors and bondholders groups. With specialist knowledge of UCC matters and distressed finance transactions, **John Sigel** (see p.1509) has a broad practice which reflects both financing and restructuring experience. This year he has assisted with the negotiation of high-value credit facilities for a diverse client base. **Dennis Jenkins** (see p.1496) has recent experience in the representation of unsecured creditors, and is widely praised by market commentators for his strength in "*advising the steering committee of the group's broader position while still maintaining everyone's confidentiality.*"

## Band 2

## Brown Rudnick LLP
See profile on p.437

**THE FIRM** This group maintains a strong presence in both Boston and New York, and is well versed in sophisticated restructuring issues. The team has developed a collective specialty in complex intercreditor agreements, and is known for its work in the energy sector. Clients include Beacon Power, ATP Oil & Gas and Pinnacle Airlines.

**Sources say:** "*They're very strong advocates and litigators, and they will fight to the death for their clients. If it's going to be a big fight, they're the guys I want.*"
**KEY INDIVIDUALS** Clients say of **William Baldiga:** "*His legal brilliance, strategic thinking and communication skills are top-notch. He is inarguably excellent.*" His reputation as a bankruptcy litigator goes before him, and he has recently represented Beacon Power in its Chapter 11 proceedings.

## Choate Hall & Stewart LLP
See profile on p.1517

**THE FIRM** This Boston-based firm fields an impressive bankruptcy team at both state and federal level. It is particularly distinguished in its representation of insurers during insolvency proceedings, but maintains a good balance of work for both creditors and debtors. The team recently served as bankruptcy counsel for Gordon Brothers in a New Jersey court action.
**Sources say:** "*Outstanding bankruptcy people. They can provide one-stop shopping for whatever issues I have.*"
**KEY INDIVIDUALS Douglas Gooding** (see p.1493) is an accomplished insolvency practitioner who is admired for his litigation skills. "*He's a good adversary,*" sources say; "*forceful but reasonable.*" He regularly represents Bank of America, and has undertaken significant recovery work for Hudson Advisors. **John Ventola** (see p.1512) acts as counsel for John Hancock and Bank of America. Clients value his collaborative approach, with one saying: "*He takes the time to learn our business so that he can be a better lawyer for us, and he takes a keen interest in helping us develop our team through legal training.*"

## Goulston & Storrs

**THE FIRM** This stalwart of the Boston legal scene has a solid reputation for real estate restructuring work, although market commentators are keen to emphasize that the practice is broader in scope. The team routinely handles midmarket creditors' committee work, as well as Chapter 11 proceedings and distressed M&A transactions. Clients include Rogge Global Partners, Audax and JPMorgan Chase.
**Sources say:** "*They're great to work with. It's been a smooth and easy process dealing with them.*"
**KEY INDIVIDUALS Douglas Rosner** is a real market leader and took a prominent role in representing Rogge Global in relation to the Lehman Brothers collapse. With experience in creditor, debtor and trustee work, he has this year represented Betsy Johnson as lead debtor-in-possession counsel throughout its Chapter 11 bankruptcy proceedings. **James Wallack** is an accomplished bankruptcy litigator whose clients put a premium on his extensive courtroom experience. He has recently been involved in the Pilgrim's Pride bankruptcy case, and has represented Audax in relation to the Madoff proceedings. Clients describe him as "*a very direct and very businesslike lawyer.*" **Christine Lynch** continues to cut an impressive figure in the bankruptcy market and is known for her prowess in creditors' rights matters. She remains lead counsel to the unsecured creditors' committee in the Elephant & Castle Chapter 11 proceedings. **Greg Kaden** has been a key mem-

ber of the team supporting Rogge Global Partners, Lehman Brothers and other high-profile clients. Commentators remark: "*He is very responsive and a pleasure to work with.*"

## Band 3

### Bingham McCutchen LLP
See profile on p.1515

THE FIRM This team has drawn on a traditional strength in bankruptcy litigation to carve out a niche in the representation of litigation trusts, and is accomplished in work involving troubled energy projects. This creditor-focused group prides itself on the well-established cross-border capabilities of its members, and has recently represented Bank of America in connection to a complex restructuring involving multiple jurisdictions for debtor-in-possession TBS International.
Sources say: "*One of the finest players nationally for bankruptcy litigation work.*"
KEY INDIVIDUALS **Edwin Smith** (see p.1510) is a celebrated practitioner of the bankruptcy Bar and this year has been active in representing a prominent investment fund in its settlement of substantial avoidance claims. Market commentators have said: "*If you have a banking problem it doesn't get better than him.*" **Sabin Willett** (see p.1513) has an established reputation as a bankruptcy litigator, and has recently represented Evergreen Solar in a Delaware Chapter 11 case. Clients remark on his "*strong presence in the courtroom,*" and say "*he is very knowledgeable and is able to negotiate very favorable resolutions.*"

### Duane Morris LLP
See profile on p.2239

THE FIRM This team has established a name for itself in debtor representation, but also undertakes significant creditors' committee and potential acquirers work. The practice is national in scope, and the team has strong capabilities in the bankruptcy hubs of New York and Delaware. The team continues to represent the unsecured creditors' committee in the Quincy Medical Center Chapter 11 case.
Sources say: "*They have great geographical coverage. They are very competent attorneys and very responsive.*"
KEY INDIVIDUALS **Paul Moore** is a masterful and much-admired attorney in the bankruptcy space. Impressed observers comment: "*When he's on the other side from you, you know you're going to have your hands full!*" He continues to represent CrossHarbor Capital in connection with a Chapter 7 filing. **Jeffrey Sternklar** is renowned for committee work. He continues to serve as counsel to the unsecured creditors' committee in the Quincy Medical Center case, and successfully negotiated a substantial recovery for the unsecured creditors. "*He represents his clients' interests in an intelligent way and is forceful when necessary. He always moves toward a consensual resolution.*"

## Band 4

### Foley Hoag LLP
See profile on p.1521

THE FIRM This respected team is very active regionally, and covers a broad range of insolvency and restructuring matters for both creditors and debtors. The group has experience of cross-border work, and is able to capitalize on the strength of its European office to provide a comprehensive and far-reaching service to non-US clients.
KEY INDIVIDUALS **Andrew Schwartz** (see p.1509) is a talented bankruptcy litigator who is much admired by both peers and clients for his courtroom prowess. He is well versed in guiding international clients through the complexities of US securities law. **Kenneth Leonetti** (see p.1500) is regarded as a strong player in the bankruptcy space, with particular reference made to his experience in Chapter 11 work.

### Holland & Knight LLP
See profile on p.1028

THE FIRM Midmarket companies facing financial distress form the key client base for the Boston branch of this firm, which uses its expertise in asset disposition and in-house counseling to great effect. The team maintains a strong hold over local filings as well as an impressive caseload for international borrowers. This year the group has successfully represented Silver Sun Partners as trial counsel in a contested confirmation hearing, as well as handling the more general aspects of the Chapter 11 proceedings.
KEY INDIVIDUALS National practice group leader **John Monaghan** (see p.1502) remains a leading figure of the state and federal bankruptcy Bar. His practice has a strong international dimension, particularly in the maritime and hospitality industries. He has recently secured a substantial victory for client Haymarket Capital in relation to its loans to Planet Fitness.

### Jager Smith PC

THE FIRM This local firm has an established expertise in bankruptcy work and can harness the strength of its New York office to provide comprehensive coverage in the key insolvency markets. The team is known for its strength in committee representation and is well versed in bankruptcy litigation.
Sources say: "*My experience with the firm has been very positive – they are superb counsel in the bankruptcy area.*"
KEY INDIVIDUALS Founding partner and group head **Bruce Smith** is a multitalented attorney with extensive experience of corporate insolvency and bankruptcy litigation.

### Sullivan & Worcester LLP
See profile on p.1534

THE FIRM This team is highly regarded in the Massachusetts market for its work in creditor representation in the context of both litigation and out-of-court settlements. The group also has a specialty in restructuring aircraft financing transactions and represents several airlines in Chapter 11 proceedings.

Sources say: "*They are a very engaging group of people. All my experiences with them have been positive and I always received very prompt advice.*"
KEY INDIVIDUALS Head of the practice group **Patrick Dinardo** (see p.1490) is praised by clients for his effective communication skills and his practical approach. "*He really understands the client's objectives,*" says one interviewee. "*He tailors his representation accordingly and he is very realistic about what is achievable.*" Notable work this year includes his representation of Staples in matters stemming from the Kodak bankruptcy.

## Other Notable Practitioners

**Christopher Panos** of Craig and Macauley PC commands the highest degree of respect from market commentators. One peer remarks: "*He is very well rounded, and has a personality that clients really appreciate.*" **Charles Dale** (see p.1489) of K&L Gates is a lawyer of choice when it comes to insolvency work and his practice covers the full range of bankruptcy and restructuring work. He is described as being "*very smart, very personable and very practical.*" Sole practitioner **Janet Bostwick** is held in high esteem by her peers in the Massachusetts market. She is accomplished in all areas of insolvency work and her practice focuses on assisting financially distressed companies. **Richard Levine** of Nelson Kinder + Mosseau, PC remains one of the foremost authorities of the state bankruptcy Bar and has been a guiding influence in the development of bankruptcy administration nationwide. **Gayle Ehrlich** (see p.1490) of Pierce Atwood LLP has a masterful command of insolvency work within the telecoms sector, and in this capacity has represented clients including American Tower and a prominent European bank. "*She gives tactical advice, and is assertive and decisive in her negotiating style. That's what we need to represent our interest.*" **John Morrier** of Casner & Edwards, LLP is a go-to attorney for both creditors and debtors in the market, who have commented on his ability to translate the law into business strategy: "*He was invaluable in helping our CFO to keep things moving day to day. He was very collaborative.*" Of the same firm, **Michael Goldberg** has a broad base of experience in insolvency-related matters. He has carved out a niche in real estate financing transactions and restructurings. The highly lauded **Charles Glerum** (see p.1493) of Edwards Wildman Palmer LLP has long been a clear favorite for creditor-side representation. He has recently represented clients including NewStar Financial in a wide variety of bankruptcy matters. "*He keeps his head screwed on tight, is good at getting parties who aren't in a negotiating mood to negotiate, and is able to move the process forward,*" says one interviewee. "*We left every meeting having accomplished something.*" **Daniel Cohn** of Murtha Cullina LLP is a revered debtor-side attorney, although his practice is broader in scope and encompasses the full range of insolvency work. Recent highlights include a substantial recovery for Harvard University when a biotech company it had sponsored made a Chapter 7 filing. **Mark Berman** (see p.1484) of Nixon Peabody LLP is a highly experienced bankruptcy and restructuring lawyer, who this year has represented a large number of high-profile clients in connection with the Lehman Brothers Chapter 11 cases.

# CORPORATE/M&A

Commentary about individuals can be found under their firm's paragraph. If the firm has no paragraph (is not ranked) look at Other Notable Practitioners.

## Corporate/M&A
### Leading Firms

**Band 1**

| | |
|---|---|
| Goodwin Procter LLP * | |
| Ropes & Gray LLP * | |
| WilmerHale * | |

**Band 2**

| | |
|---|---|
| Skadden, Arps, Slate, Meagher & Flom LLP & Affiliates * | |
| Weil, Gotshal & Manges LLP * | |

**Band 3**

| | |
|---|---|
| Bingham McCutchen LLP * | |
| Choate Hall & Stewart LLP * | |
| Edwards Wildman Palmer LLP * | |
| Foley Hoag LLP * | |
| Latham & Watkins * | |
| Mintz Levin Cohn Ferris Glovsky and Popeo PC * | |
| Nixon Peabody LLP * | |

## Corporate/M&A: Capital Markets
### Leading Individuals

**Band 1**

| | |
|---|---|
| Higgins Keith F | Ropes & Gray LLP |
| Menna Gilbert G | Goodwin Procter LLP * |

**Band 2**

| | |
|---|---|
| Haggerty John | Goodwin Procter LLP * |
| Handrinos Peter N | Latham & Watkins |
| Kinsella Paul M | Ropes & Gray LLP |
| Kravetz Jonathan | Mintz Levin Cohn Ferris Glovsky * |
| O'Brien Patrick | Ropes & Gray LLP |
| Santucci Ettore A | Goodwin Procter LLP * |

## Band 1

### Goodwin Procter LLP
See profile on p.1522

THE FIRM This Boston institution is well versed in all aspects of corporate M&A work, with particular attention given to its prowess in public offerings, joint ventures and REIT work. The team is especially prominent in the technology and life sciences arenas. Clients have confidence in the firm's well-developed and reliable bench. Notable recent work includes Avila's acquisition by Celgene and a significant public offering for REIT client, Archstone.
Sources say: *"Goodwin has a unique team of specialists who work as a multidisciplinary, responsive team to achieve the client's goals."*
KEY INDIVIDUALS Eminent practitioner **Stuart Cable** (see p.1487) focuses on the life sciences and technology space, and is spearheading the firm's expansion into the Asian market. *"His intellect, experience, sensitivity to clients and responsiveness are unparalleled. Stuart is a businessman who understands how to make challenging decisions in the domain of risk,"* remarks one satisfied client. REIT practice cochair **Gilbert Menna** (see p.367) continues to impress in

the capital markets field. He notably served as one of the primary attorneys on Archstone's aforementioned IPO. Clients say: *"I go to him as a sounding board – I value his judgment, and there's nothing more valuable than that."* **Mark Bettencourt** (see p.1484) maintains a broad business practice, and is noted for his expertise in advising international technology companies on aspects of their US-based business. He recently facilitated the high-value sale of Endeca Technologies to Oracle, as well as iRobot's acquisition of Evolution Robotics. **Mark Burnett** (see p.1487) is regarded as a strong figure in the private equity space, bringing that experience to bear in his work for a host of public and private companies. He has experience in cross-border transactions and has recently served as counsel to JMI Equity, implementing an active buyout and acquisition programme. **John Haggerty** (see p.1494) has built an impressive corporate and securities practice, with a particular emphasis on REITs. He notably represented Sonesta International Hotels in its recent acquisition by a NYSE-traded hospitality REIT. Capital markets practitioner **Ettore Santucci** (see p.399) is an expert in leveraged transactions for complex REITs. He represented a group of global banks as underwriters for Digital Realty's $830 million common stock offering. The well-regarded **Joseph Johnson** (see p.1496) chairs the firm's corporate governance practice, and typically represents buyers and sellers in the technology sector. He has notable experience in the defense and pursuit of proxy contests. **John Egan** (see p.1490) comes much recommended for his work related to technology companies. He recently represented Admeld in its high-value sale to Google. **Mitchell Bloom** (see p.1485) specializes in representing public and private life sciences companies, and investors with an interest in the life sciences field. He has served as lead counsel in Warp Drive Bio's strategic partnership with pharmaceutical giant Sanofi. **William Schnoor** (see p.1508) is known for his work in the technology arena, and recently represented Brightcove in its substantial initial public offering.

### Ropes & Gray LLP
See profile on p.1528

THE FIRM Massachusetts stalwart Ropes remains a prominent name in this field and has ample experience representing buyers, sellers and advisers on a number of sophisticated transactions. The team provides comprehensive services to clients on a national and global level, and it counts Covidien, Dunkin' Brands and NSTAR among its impressive client network. Among its recent highlights is its handling of a series of acquisitions for Zynga Game Network.
Sources say: *"High-quality, excellent lawyers who know what they are doing with national practices and profiles."*
KEY INDIVIDUALS The much-admired **David Chapin** has solid experience in joint venture, acquisition and buyout matters, and is well regarded in the market. He represented the special committee of Ness Technologies in its

## Corporate/M&A
### Senior Statesmen

| | |
|---|---|
| **Senior Statesmen:** distinguished older practitioners | |
| Keller Stanley | Edwards Wildman Palmer LLP * |
| Malt R Bradford | Ropes & Gray LLP |

### Leading Individuals

**Band 1**

| | |
|---|---|
| Borden Mark | WilmerHale * |
| Brown Margaret A | Skadden, Arps, Slate, Meagher & Flom * |
| Cable Stuart M | Goodwin Procter LLP * |
| Chapin David C | Ropes & Gray LLP |
| Goodman Louis A | Skadden, Arps, Slate, Meagher & Flom * |
| Redlick David E | WilmerHale * |

**Band 2**

| | |
|---|---|
| Asher Jr William B | Choate Hall & Stewart LLP * |
| Bettencourt Mark T | Goodwin Procter LLP * |
| Bothwick Jay | WilmerHale * |
| Browne Steven C | Bingham McCutchen LLP * |
| Burnett Mark | Goodwin Procter LLP * |
| Jones Julie H | Ropes & Gray LLP |
| Leibowitz Hal J | WilmerHale * |
| Rosenblum Peter | Foley Hoag LLP * |
| Utzschneider John R | Bingham McCutchen LLP * |
| Wiesen Jeffrey M | Mintz Levin Cohn Ferris Glovsky * |

**Band 3**

| | |
|---|---|
| Basile Joseph | Weil, Gotshal & Manges LLP * |
| Egan III John J | Goodwin Procter LLP * |
| Goldstein Jane D | Ropes & Gray LLP |
| Johnson III Joseph L | Goodwin Procter LLP * |
| Kolb William R | Foley Hoag LLP * |
| Naughton Laurence P | Choate Hall & Stewart LLP * |

**Band 4**

| | |
|---|---|
| Bloom Mitchell S | Goodwin Procter LLP * |
| Brigham Johan V | Latham & Watkins |
| Cohen Margaret R | Skadden, Arps, Slate, Meagher & Flom * |
| Feinberg David | Feinberg Hanson LLP (ONP) [†] |
| Feldman Roger D | Fish & Richardson PC (ONP) [†] |
| Haddad Mark | Foley Hoag LLP * |
| Jahrling III Robert V | Choate Hall & Stewart LLP * |
| Schnoor William J | Goodwin Procter LLP * |
| Stokes James C | Bingham McCutchen LLP * |
| Westenberg David | WilmerHale * |
| Williams Samuel P | Brown Rudnick LLP (ONP) [†] |
| Wolfman Jonathan | WilmerHale * |

**Up-and-coming individuals**

| | |
|---|---|
| Follansbee Daniel | Mintz Levin Cohn Ferris Glovsky * |
| Harlev Shayla K | Weil, Gotshal & Manges LLP * |
| O'Shaughnessy Gregory | Nixon Peabody LLP * |
| Robinson Graham | Skadden, Arps, Slate, Meagher & Flom * |

*\* Indicates firm / individual with profile.*
*† ONP = Other Notable Practitioner.*

sale to Citi Venture Capital. The *"terrific"* **Keith Higgins** commands a high degree of respect from peers and clients in the capital markets field. Recent work has seen him act for Zynga Game Network in a series of purchases, as mentioned above. **Julie Jones** has vast experience in the representation of public companies, and is well versed in governance and compliance issues, as well as transactional M&A work. **Paul Kinsella** focuses his securities and public company practice on the pharmaceutical and biotech arenas. He has recently represented Cubist Pharmaceuticals in its acquisition of Adolor Corporation and Covidien in its acquisition of Maya Medical. **Patrick O'Brien** has a significant securities and public companies practice. He is well-honed in sales, acquisitions and offerings, and has represented clients including Alexion Pharmaceuticals in these matters. **Jane Goldstein** is head of the retail and consumer brand practice, and is especially adept on transactional and compliance matters. Regular clients include Green Mountain Coffee Roasters, Party City Holdings and Timberland. Seasoned practitioner **Bradford Malt** is much admired in the market, and is particularly revered as a leader in the private equity space. He specializes in fundraising and investment matters for a diverse client base.

## WilmerHale
### See profile on p.930

**THE FIRM** This team has a much noted strength in public company transactional work, but also offers governance and restructuring advice. It is this breadth and depth of expertise which makes it first choice as general outside counsel for a substantial number of publicly traded companies in the USA. Recent work has seen it act for Thermo Fisher Scientific in its acquisition of One Lambda and Kiva Systems in its sale to Amazon.
**Sources say:** *"They have lots of very good corporate and IP people. For corporate and business development, they are at the top."*
**KEY INDIVIDUALS Hal Leibowitz** (see p.1499) is revered as a *"tenacious negotiator,"* and recently represented Enobia Pharmaceuticals in its competitive auction sale to Alexion, and Thermo Fisher Scientific in its aforementioned purchase of One Lambda. **Mark Borden** (see p.1485) is an outstanding practitioner in the corporate field. In notable recent work, he served as outside counsel for Demandware during its initial public offering, and as company counsel for State Street in an offering of preferred stock. *"First-rate lawyer"* **David Redlick** (see p.390) has considerable experience in the M&A arena. Recent case highlights include leading Stromedix through its acquisition by Biogen, and representing OvaScience on a variety of matters. M&A group cochair **Jay Bothwick** (see p.1485) is highly respected for his down-to-earth approach, with interviewees commenting: *"He provides outstanding customer service and is able to explain complex legal language in business terms."* He represents Sonus Networks and ISTA Pharmaceuticals. **David Westenberg** (see p.1513) maintains a practice that is national in scope, and which has a particular focus on assisting companies in going public. He recently acted for Kiva Systems in its sale to Amazon men-

tioned above. Also making his entry into the rankings this year is **Jonathan Wolfman** (see p.1513), who impresses the market with his prowess in corporate securities matters. Clients say: *"He is always even keeled and objective, with a good sense of humor. He is someone who earns the trust of the smartest, most seasoned business leader."*

## Band 2

## Skadden, Arps, Slate, Meagher & Flom LLP & Affiliates
### See profile on p.2008

**THE FIRM** This corporate stalwart continues to impress market commentators with its strength in transactions and restructurings, joint ventures and distressed M&A work. The firm has a wide geographical reach, and the Boston office is able to tap into a substantial network of resources to service both domestic and international clients. Notably, the group represented Northeast Utilities in its $9.5 billion merger with NSTAR in 2012.
**Sources say:** *"They're one of the most accommodating firms I've ever dealt with, and their turnaround time is unparalleled – we described something as 'Skadden-quick' if it is done very quickly!"*
**KEY INDIVIDUALS** Practice group head **Margaret Brown** (see p.1486) is described as *"quick, practical, tenacious and incredibly effective in negotiations."* She combines this prowess with acumen in governance and compliance issues when representing clients such as Northeast Utilities and LPL Investment Holdings. First-rate attorney **Louis Goodman** (see p.1493) is a go-to adviser on a broad range of transactional work. As one source notes: *"He's got reason, knowledge and experience, and gives you safe, practical advice that is hard to match."* In a recent matter, he handled the acquisition of Sonesta International Hotels by Sonesta Acquisition. **Margaret Cohen** (see p.1488) maintains a broad corporate practice, and, in a recent highlight, worked on the IPO of Select Income REIT. Clients appreciate her ability to *"get the job done timely and professionally."* Up-and-comer **Graham Robinson** (see p.1506) continues to establish himself in the Massachusetts market, and is noted as a specialist in the life sciences space. *"He projects a good manner in negotiations – he doesn't hesitate, he gives a solid response and he stands behind it. His good instinct and judgment engenders a lot of trust,"* reports one impressed interviewee.

## Weil, Gotshal & Manges LLP
### See profile on p.2015

**THE FIRM** This team manages a robust national and international M&A practice, and it maintains a fine track record in the areas of distressed M&A, board level engagements and crisis management. Recent highlights include representing AmSafe Global Holdings in its $750 million acquisition, and Thomas H Lee Partners in its acquisition of a Brazilian steakhouse chain. It also counts Medicis Pharmaceutical, Sanofi and Advent International among its distinguished client roster.

**Sources say:** *"The team anticipated potential issues so there were no surprises and they did a great job on a very difficult negotiation. They served as a buffer between us and the other side to get us through some of the harder issues."*
**KEY INDIVIDUALS** Managing partner of the Boston office, **Joseph Basile** (see p.1484) has significant international M&A experience, and specializes in distressed M&A transactions. He regularly represents French company Sanofi, and is a lead partner for Medicis Pharmaceutical. *"He is not someone who is agitated in a crisis – he is very calm, very steady, and has good judgment in the middle of a lot of frantic activity,"* notes one impressed source. **Shayla Harlev** (see p.1495) enters the rankings this year, and comes recommended for her robust M&A expertise alongside the much-noted competitive international dimension of her practice. She has worked on numerous substantial M&A projects, including the aforementioned AmSafe Global Holdings and Thomas H Lee Partners matters.

## Band 3

## Bingham McCutchen LLP
### See profile on p.1515

**THE FIRM** This firm enjoys an established presence in the corporate M&A midmarket, and prides itself on the strength of its representation of clients in the technology sector. Notable recent work includes the $100 million initial public offering of Kayak Software Corporation. The team also advised TD Bank on the sale of TD Insurance.
**Sources say:** *"They offer practical legal advice that is fitted to how we run as a business – they understand what we're looking for and they don't waste our time."*
**KEY INDIVIDUALS** *"Superb lawyer"* **John Utzschneider** (see p.1512) is highly regarded for all aspects of his corporate work. Notable recent work includes his representation of Tempur-Pedic in its acquisition of Sealy Corporation, and advising TD Bank in the aforementioned sale of TD Insurance. **Steven Browne** (see p.1486) is experienced in the acquisitions and dispositions arena, and is key to the firm's relationship with Oracle. He has recently advised Citrix and Sapient on a variety of matters. **James Stokes** (see p.1510) is a renowned expert in cross-border matters, with a particular focus on Latin American and Caribbean M&A transactions.

## Choate Hall & Stewart LLP
### See profile on p.1517

**THE FIRM** This team is well regarded for its financing and transactional work in the technology and healthcare sectors. Clients particularly appreciate the group's capacity to call on experts in other departments, including litigation and tax, to provide a thorough and comprehensive service. Its client roster includes Summit Partners and NaviNet.
**KEY INDIVIDUALS** The highly regarded **William Asher** (see p.1483) is cochair of the business and technology practice, and represents a fine choice of counsel for corporate work in the life sciences arena. Fellow business and technology cochair **Laurence Naughton** (see p.1503) is a well-known figure in the market, and in a recent highlight

he represented SR One Limited in a $35 million Class C financing investment in Canadian company Thrasos Innovation. **Robert Jahrling** (see p.1496) specializes in capital markets matters in addition to his general corporate work, and is particularly noted for his strengths in the areas of alternative energy and clean technology.

## Edwards Wildman Palmer LLP
See profile on p.1520

**THE FIRM** This team is a prominent feature of the Boston corporate arena and maintains a fine track record for its work in the midmarket. The group is well versed across the whole gamut of corporate matters, and enjoys a fine reputation for its work with clients in the fields of life sciences, financial services and insurance.

**KEY INDIVIDUALS** *"Securities guru"* **Stanley Keller** (see p.1498) is a stalwart of the corporate Bar, and is much noted for his experience in M&A, corporate governance and financing, as well as other general corporate work.

## Foley Hoag LLP
See profile on p.1521

**THE FIRM** This strong Boston outfit excels at general corporate counseling and transactional work in the midmarket. Its practice is well balanced between buy and sell work. In addition, the group is noted for its significant international experience and is frequently sought after to handle work throughout the Southern Hemisphere, Canada and Europe.

**Sources say:** *"They have a balance of both legal and business perspectives – they are very in-tune on the business side and therefore they understand the risk factors in a lot of deals. There is a strong level of consistency in the value they add."*

**KEY INDIVIDUALS** Cochair of the group **Peter Rosenblum** (see p.1507) is an eminent practitioner in this space. Notable work includes his representation of Advion BioSciences throughout its sale to Quintiles. **William Kolb** (see p.1499) is co-managing partner of the Boston office and is well versed in all aspects of corporate work. He assisted InforMed throughout its acquisition by Conifer Health Solutions. The well-respected **Mark Haddad** (see p.1494) combines a fine transactional practice with much

sought-after expertise with regard to regulatory and compliance matters. He represented Alere in several recent acquisitions.

## Latham & Watkins
See profile on p.446

**THE FIRM** This group is relatively new to the Boston market, but is already impressing with its strong market share and well-developed bench. The team can harness the strength of its offices nationwide to provide very comprehensive coverage in the general corporate space, and it is accomplished in international M&A transactions. It counts American Superconductor and Boston Scientific Corporation among its key clients.

**KEY INDIVIDUALS Peter Handrinos** is a recognized specialist in corporate and venture capital transactions in the tech and life sciences industries. In a recent highlight, he handled the common stock offering on behalf of client A123 Systems, and a warrant offering for American Superconductor. **Johan Brigham** combines strong practices in both private equity and corporate M&A to the benefit of his clients, who comment: *"He is very proactive and ahead of the curve."* He has counseled Boston Scientific Corporation through several acquisitions recently.

## Mintz Levin Cohn Ferris Glovsky and Popeo PC
See profile on p.1523

**THE FIRM** This team is well known for its work in M&A, divestitures and reorganizations, as well as other corporate matters, and also maintains a fine track record for its securities work. Additionally, it is routinely sought after for its expertise in technology and life sciences.

**Sources say:** *"In terms of quality they are very good, and we like them for their client service."*

**KEY INDIVIDUALS** The highly regarded **Jeffrey Wiesen** (see p.426) is well versed across a diverse array of transactions, including private and public finance, strategic alliances and joint ventures, acting for clients ranging from emerging startups to large public companies. He is particularly noted for his expertise within the life sciences space. **Jonathan Kravetz** (see p.350) is similarly noted for his

work in life sciences, and is highly sought after for his expertise acting on behalf of European entities in financing and M&A transactions. Up-and-comer **Daniel Follansbee** (see p.1491) enters the rankings this year following effusive client praise, and is lauded for his general all-round corporate expertise.

## Nixon Peabody LLP
See profile on p.1526

**THE FIRM** This client favorite is noted for its representation of lower and midmarket clients in corporate M&A transactions, and also comes recommended for its expertise with regard to leveraged buyouts and private equity and venture capital financings. The group maintains a particularly fine track record for its work in the healthcare, energy and consumer products arenas.

**Sources say:** *"They are willing to help on anything and everything. Their general availability is fantastic, and the quality of the work and advice we get is extremely on point from a business perspective."*

**KEY INDIVIDUALS Gregory O'Shaughnessy** (see p.1504) enters the table this year as a much-admired young practitioner. His practice focuses on the retail, life sciences, and food and beverage sectors. *"He does a phenomenal job of blending the legal issues with the business reality,"* note sources.

## Other Notable Practitioners

**Samuel Williams** is head of the corporate and capital markets department at Brown Rudnick LLP, and is a well-known practitioner in this space. He represented Origis Energy USA in its acquisition of several solar farm projects. Feinberg Hanson LLP's **David Feinberg** is widely regarded as a go-to attorney for corporate M&A work, especially for emerging companies. He served as issuer's counsel to Boston-Power in its preferred stock financing. **Roger Feldman** of Fish & Richardson PC is widely regarded as a strong all-round practitioner for transactional M&A work.

# EMPLOYEE BENEFITS & EXECUTIVE COMPENSATION

Commentary about individuals can be found under their firm's paragraph. If the firm has no paragraph (is not ranked) look at Other Notable Practitioners.

## Employee Benefits & Executive Compensation
### Leading Firms

**Band 1**
Goodwin Procter LLP *
Ropes & Gray LLP *

**Band 2**
Bingham McCutchen LLP *
McDermott Will & Emery LLP *
Mintz Levin Cohn Ferris Glovsky and Popeo PC *
WilmerHale *

**Band 3**
Brown Rudnick LLP *
Parker Brown & Macaulay, P.C.
Proskauer Rose LLP *

### Leading Individuals

**Band 1**

| | |
|---|---|
| Bianchi Alden J | Mintz Levin Cohn Ferris Glovsky * |
| Chimento George L | Davis, Malm & D'Agostine, P.C. (ONP)† * |
| Cleary John J | Goodwin Procter LLP * |
| Guadagnoli David A | Sullivan & Worcester LLP (ONP)† * |
| Isaia Russell E | Bingham McCutchen LLP * |
| Liazos Andrew C | McDermott Will & Emery LLP * |
| Marathas Peter J | Proskauer Rose LLP |
| Meyers Arthur S | Choate Hall & Stewart LLP (ONP)† * |
| Rosenberg Peter N | Ropes & Gray LLP |
| Tse Marian A | Goodwin Procter LLP * |
| Zorn Jonathan M | Ropes & Gray LLP |

**Band 2**

| | |
|---|---|
| George Natascha S | Bingham McCutchen LLP * |
| Greene Thomas M | Mintz Levin Cohn Ferris Glovsky * |
| Hauser James | Brown Rudnick LLP |
| Hugg Joseph A | DLA Piper LLP (US) (ONP)† * |
| McCord Thomas | Nixon Peabody LLP (ONP)† * |
| Null Amy A | WilmerHale * |
| Webster Scott A | Goodwin Procter LLP * |
| Wethly Kimberly B | WilmerHale * |

**Band 3**

| | |
|---|---|
| Ferrari Renata | Ropes & Gray LLP |
| Macaulay Jr Robert C | Parker Brown & Macaulay, P.C. |
| Richard Loretta | Ropes & Gray LLP |
| Slavin Leslie | Lourie & Cutler (ONP)† |

* Indicates firm / individual with profile.
†ONP = Other Notable Practitioner.

## Band 1

### Goodwin Procter LLP
See profile on p.1522

**THE FIRM** This robust practice occupies a leading position in the market. It operates across a wide range of sectors, most notably in the financial services, private equity and life sciences industries. Its core competencies include fiduciary matters, collective and common trust funds, and issues pertaining to corporate M&A transactions. The team represents Boston Properties, Hasbro and Brookline Bancorp, among other high-profile clients.
**Sources say:** "*They have an outstanding practice in this area.*"
**KEY INDIVIDUALS Marian Tse** (see p.1512) brings her extensive experience to bear on a large variety of compensation and benefits work, and chairs the firm's ERISA and executive compensation practice. Her recent work includes handling a complex M&A transaction on behalf of Brookline Bancorp, and working with other key clients such as Boston Properties. Impressed sources comment: "*I can't say enough good things about her – she's a top person in Boston.*" **Scott Webster** (see p.1513) focuses his practice on the financial services industry, and has particular expertise in collective investment vehicles and new investment products. His work as ongoing ERISA counsel for Russell Investments sees him handle a host of retirement and pension plan matters. Eminent practitioner **John Cleary** (see p.1488) marries solid substantive knowledge with a seasoned understanding of the business objectives of his clients, who appreciate that "*he doesn't sit on the fence. He provides very valuable advice to help you move ahead and he provides it quickly.*" State Street Bank and AEW Capital Management are among his regular clients.

### Ropes & Gray LLP
See profile on p.1528

**THE FIRM** This team has a deservedly strong reputation in the field of benefits and compensation. It is also particularly noted for its broad geographical reach, having represented private equity clients in the UK, Switzerland and Asia. It is a recognized expert in hedge funds, ERISA matters and traditional benefits plans, and is expanding in the healthcare space. Its clients include TPG Capital, Bain Capital Venture Partners and Genzyme.
**Sources say:** "*The leadership team at the firm is very good at translating legal issues into business terms for us, so when I speak to them they can answer the questions that we're trying to solve from a business perspective.*"
**KEY INDIVIDUALS Peter Rosenberg** is a renowned ERISA expert, and is well versed in the design, compliance and administration of a wide variety of plans. He works with many of the firm's leading clients and has recently advised Bain Capital on issues pertaining to the creation of a $600 million investment fund. **Renata Ferrari** is highly regarded by market commentators for her expertise in executive compensation. She has recently handled matters for Becton Dickinson, TPG and Satélites Mexicanos, and is described as "*highly competent, very qualified and extremely responsive.*" **Loretta Richard** is a go-to tax and benefits counsel for TPG and other private equity clients. She is sought out for her experience and strength in transactional work in this area. **Jonathan Zorn** leads the firm's ERISA group, and brings his comprehensive tax expertise to bear across a broad range of benefits and compensation matters. His clients include Genzyme, Green Mountain Coffee Roasters and Advent International.

## Band 2

### Bingham McCutchen LLP
See profile on p.1515

**THE FIRM** This group is recognized as a leading firm for matters relating to the financial services industry, and is noted for its strength in fiduciary matters and ERISA-related issues. It handles a broad range of benefits and compensation work, including transactions, designs and compliance. The team is also highlighted for its ability to offer tailored plans to clients in the private equity space. Clients particularly praise the business-centric approach and practical attitude of the team.
**Sources say:** "*I think really highly of Bingham; they have really smart attorneys who just get it. They are as practical as they can be and get results for the client.*"
**KEY INDIVIDUALS Russell Isaia** (see p.1495) is an established figure in the benefits and compensation space, and can apply his extensive knowledge of tax, securities and issues arising under ERISA to a wide range of transactions. Clients praise his creativity and innovative approach, stating that "*he's very good when you're structuring a deal – he can think outside the box and come up with alternative solutions that get you where you need to be.*" **Natascha George** (see p.1492) is an expert in a variety of plan work and pension benefit guarantee corporation issues. She commands a great deal of respect from both clients and peers, who highlight her personable demeanor and pragmatic approach: "*She is able to look at an issue and distill it down very succinctly for someone who doesn't have that expertise, which is hugely helpful. She is phenomenal.*"

### McDermott Will & Emery LLP
See profile on p.1258

**THE FIRM** The Boston branch of the firm's benefits and compensation practice works in close conjunction with its offices across the USA and overseas on a wide array of matters. It has a flourishing healthcare practice and particular strength in ERISA litigation. The group is able to call on its deep firmwide bench to offer a full service to its corporate clients. Of late, the team has worked on matters for Demoulas Supermarkets, Liberty Mutual and DaVita.
**Sources say:** "*They are really looking for the solution and so they spend time with the client as objective advisers, working through the pros and the cons of each action.*"
**KEY INDIVIDUALS Andrew Liazos** (see p.1500) is lauded for his unshakable work ethic and commitment to his clients, who describe him as "*a calm negotiator who understands where we're going and is effective in getting there.*" He recently defended State Street in a claim by former Chrysler executives for unpaid plan benefits.

### Mintz Levin Cohn Ferris Glovsky and Popeo PC
See profile on p.1523

**THE FIRM** This team has a highly respected benefits and compensation practice, and is comprised of recognized specialists in welfare plans and healthcare reform. It works with clients such as Leavitt Partners, DaVita and Adecco, and is able to offer a significant network of global resources. Its recent work includes counseling the American Staffing Association on matters related to the Patient Protection and Affordable Care Act.

**Sources say:** *"I was very satisfied with the responsiveness, knowledge, guidance and support provided. The Mintz team always came across as extremely knowledgeable, well prepared and highly effective in delicate negotiations."*

**KEY INDIVIDUALS** Preeminent healthcare expert **Alden Bianchi** (see p.1485) has an impressive knowledge of healthcare reform and its impact on businesses and corporations. Clients note that he *"always responds promptly and thoroughly to questions raised, and is a pleasure to deal with."* **Thomas Greene** (see p.1494) is well versed in sophisticated executive compensation and benefits matters, and has recently been involved in several major transactions representing clients such as Caliper Life Sciences, DaVita and Informa USA. One client comments: *"I have never posed a question to him that he did not have a current answer to. He keeps up to date and provides excellent guidance as to what might happen down the road."*

## WilmerHale
See profile on p.930

**THE FIRM** This team offers the full range of benefits and compensation work and is able to draw on the parallel expertise of its tax and M&A teams to assist on large transactions for corporate clients. It is well versed in the design, compliance and administration of benefit plans, and its notable clients include PerkinElmer and Disney.

**Sources say:** *"The team could not have been more client-focused! All the partners in the different departments were seamless and integrated; everyone was on the same page."*

**KEY INDIVIDUALS Kimberly Wethly** (see p.1513) is a respected executive compensation and tax specialist who has recently counseled clients through a number of high-profile transactions. One source comments: *"She went above and beyond to make the client experience transparent, clear and helpful."* **Amy Null** (see p.1504) has a highly respected benefits practice and is well placed to guide her clients through a range of ERISA-related issues. Market

commentators hold her in high regard as a strong practitioner who can be relied upon for solid, practical advice.

## Band 3

### Brown Rudnick LLP
See profile on p.437

**THE FIRM** This group has a strong focus on representing boards of directors and compensation committees in executive compensation matters. The Boston-based practitioners work closely with their counterparts in New York to provide a comprehensive service for their financial institution clients. The firm is also able to offer an international scope to its practice, with offices in the UK and Ireland.

**Sources say:** *"The team is easy to work with and looks at things from a holistic business perspective, rather than just looking at the specific matter at hand."*

**KEY INDIVIDUALS James Hauser** covers a broad range of ERISA and executive compensation matters. He recently advised Motricity's compensation committee on several key issues, including severance terms related to the exit of four senior executives. Clients confirm that *"he is able to find pathways to deliver the result you need."*

### Parker Brown & Macaulay, P.C.

**THE FIRM** Parker Brown is a dedicated employee benefits boutique firm, and spans an impressive range of related matters in its respected practice. It has primarily made its name in the representation of smaller corporations and nonprofit clients. Market commentators particularly highlight the deep expertise that its practitioners bring to this arena.

**KEY INDIVIDUALS Robert Macaulay** is a highly experienced attorney in this field whose widespread knowledge covers welfare benefits, matters pertaining to disability and health insurance plans.

### Proskauer Rose LLP
See profile on p.2001

**THE FIRM** This team is held in high esteem for its nationwide ERISA litigation practice and offers particular expertise in matters related to healthcare reform. It has recently

undertaken extensive plan work on behalf of key clients such as EMC and Eaton Vance.

**Sources say:** *"They always have the talent and capacity to advise on new developments – we know that we can rely on what they tell us."*

**KEY INDIVIDUALS Peter Marathas** impresses commentators with his unparalleled knowledge of the Affordable Care Act and its implications for businesses. He has been described as *"an outstanding lawyer whose expertise and demeanor make him stand out,"* and garners particular praise for his client-centered approach.

## Other Notable Practitioners

**Arthur Meyers** (see p.1502) of Choate Hall & Stewart LLP is described as *"an encyclopedia of equity and executive compensation issues."* He offers particular strength in matters relating to the formatting of non-US companies while maintaining a broad-based practice in the field. *"Rockstar attorney"* **George Chimento** (see p.1487) of Davis, Malm & D'Agostine, P.C. has a solid reputation among financial investor clients. He brings his substantial knowledge of tax, ERISA issues and retirement plans to his respected practice. **Joseph Hugg** (see p.1495) of DLA Piper LLP (US) is a specialist in private equity fund formation for hedge funds and large investment pools, and is revered by commentators as *"a superb lawyer who certainly deserves recognition."* **Leslie Slavin** of Lourie & Cutler is renowned for her expertise in employee benefits work and is highly respected by her peers in this area. **Thomas McCord** (see p.1501) of Nixon Peabody LLP is held in high esteem for his experience in ERISA litigation. Impressed market commentators note that he *"communicates clearly, concisely and for the benefit of the client."* **David Guadagnoli** (see p.1494) of Sullivan & Worcester LLP is an eminent practitioner in the employee benefits space. Clients readily appreciate his relaxed demeanor and note that *"he is always there when we need him. He gets us through some of the anxious times and his unflappability is great – he never gets flustered."*

# ENVIRONMENT

Commentary about individuals can be found under their firm's paragraph. If the firm has no paragraph (is not ranked) look at Other Notable Practitioners.

## Band 1

### Foley Hoag LLP
See profile on p.1521

**THE FIRM** Foley Hoag is recognized as a true market leader in the environmental field. The team displays an impressive breadth of expertise at both state and federal level, supported by solid substantive knowledge. It has particular strength in the energy generation sector, with clients including Covanta Energy, Cornell-Dubilier Electronics and GDF Suez North America/FirstLight Power Resources, the latter of which it is currently representing in the relicensing of the largest hydroelectric facility on the Eastern seaboard.

**Sources say:** *"Excellent lawyers doing excellent work." "They are very responsive, think strategically, and look for ways to keep costs down."*

**KEY INDIVIDUALS Adam Kahn** (see p.1497) is lauded as *"a good strategist and effective negotiator,"* and *"eminently enjoyable to work with."* He has been highly active of late in several compliance cases in South America, as well as handling state and federal regulatory issues. He also has expertise in the renewable energy sector, and led in the aforementioned matter for GDF Suez North America/FirstLight Power Resources. **Seth Jaffe** (see p.1496) is highly respected as the head of Foley Hoag's environment department. He has a strong reputation in Clean Water Act work, and recently defended NextEra in a citizen suit relating to the alleged harm to endangered salmon caused by hydroelectric dams. He is also active in negotiations with the EPA regarding the cleanup of the Wells G&H Superfund site. *"Formidable environmental litigator"* **Robert Sanoff** (see p.1508) is lead counsel for MPM Silicones in its federal case against Union Carbide, and also represented Cornell-Dubilier Electronics in a high-value environmental insurance recovery case. **Doug McGarrah** (see p.1501) is *"a consummate professional with a clear command of the issues."* In keeping with his expertise in development and infrastructure matters, he recently assisted the City of Malden, Massachusetts, in the redevelopment of National Grid land into a minor league baseball stadium.

## Band 2

### Goodwin Procter LLP
See profile on p.1522

**THE FIRM** Goodwin Procter's environmental team is favored for its multidisciplinary approach and its attorneys' broad-ranging expertise in remediation, permitting, compliance, regulation and litigation. The group is a leading authority on the Clean Water Act and soil vapor intrusion work, and represents a diverse range of clients across the manufacturing, conventional and renewable energy, educational, and real estate investment and development sectors. In a recent highlight, the group represented envi-

ronmental advocacy group the Buzzards Bay Coalition in the initiation of a public investigation into aspects of nitrogen pollution reports by the University of Massachusetts at Dartmouth.

**Sources say:** *"They are very capable and have considerable expertise."*

**KEY INDIVIDUALS** Chair of the environment practice **Gregory Bibler** (see p.1485) commands a high degree of respect from peers. He has recently brought his considerable vapor intrusion expertise to bear in a regulatory investigation and cleanup of the largest vapor intrusion site in Massachusetts, as well as securing a successful conclusion to an EPA investigation of vapor issues at the Wells G&H Superfund site. **Elise Zoli** (see p.1514) is a highly regarded lawyer with strong expertise in energy work, especially in the fields of cleantech and climate change, and is at the cutting edge of environmental insurance coverage. She recently represented Entergy Corp in the Supreme Court in licensing and permitting matters across several states, and has been integral to the development of the first voluntary public carbon-reduction program.

### Goulston & Storrs

**THE FIRM** This group is able to draw on the considerable strength of its real estate department to offer comprehensive support and expertise to its environmental clients, giving it notable strength in permitting matters. The team also undertakes a good deal of corporate work, litigation and government enforcement actions, and is developing a strong practice in environmental insurance. Its clients include JPMorgan Chase and Harvard University, among a variety of educational and financial institutions and real estate developers.

**Sources say:** *"Their responsiveness and quality is excellent." "Goulston & Storrs know how to make a business deal."*

**KEY INDIVIDUALS** The *"unstoppable"* **William Seuch** inspires the confidence of his clients with his straightforward and calm demeanor: *"He tells it to you straight, and when he says something you believe him – he has a proven track record of accomplishments."* His recent work has included matters involving the acquisition of contaminated sites for a broad variety of clients, including developers and educational institutions. **Ned Abelson** is lauded by commentators as *"responsive, enormously attentive to detail, pleasant, consistent, and an expert in his field."* He is a stalwart of the environmental group, and couples his extensive knowledge of brownfield sites and environmental insurance with exceptional people skills to provide the best results for his clients. **Jonathan Pearlson** is carving out a name for himself in environmental insurance and is a driving force behind policy in this area. *"His work is fantastic,"* say sources; *"he covers every base."* His clients include JPMorgan Chase, Audax Private Equity and other property developers. Highly regarded associate **Kate Velasquez-Heller** is building a strong reputation in the environmental sphere. She brings her environmental engineering background to bear in contaminated sites and general compliance issues, among other things.

## Mackie Shea O'Brien, PC

**THE FIRM** Peers see this boutique environmental firm as a strong competitor, with an established expertise in solid waste work and an emerging strength in renewable energy. The team is able to draw on its considerable experience with federal and state regulators to assist clients with permitting, licensing and enforcement defense. The group's recent cases include special permitting for the development of commercial wind turbines, and an agreement with the Department of Defense relating to the large-scale cleanup of a munitions production site.
**Sources say:** *"They knew everyone in the state environment organizations very well, they knew all of the appropriate experts, and were meticulous in preparing opposition." "They are supportive, attentive and professional."*
**KEY INDIVIDUALS** *"Fearless litigator"* **Michelle O'Brien** receives nothing but praise from her clients, who include Future Generation Wind, National Coating Corporation and Steelcase. She is described as *"an excellent and patient attorney."* She handles a significant amount of land use and development work, and is experienced in environmental enforcement. The diplomatic **John Shea** is described as a *"dean of the environment Bar"* who *"senses what is appropriate, what your philosophy and goals are, and then works with you to come to a win-win situation."* He undertakes a wide range of environmental work, and has particular expertise in stormwater and coastal erosion cases. He recently defended a public interest lawsuit dealing with alleged violations of the Clean Water Act. **Thomas Mackie** is *"good at understanding the technical complexities of the project; he really digs in and gives the issues a lot of thought."* He has a strong reputation in solid waste work, but is equally adept in renewable energy. He recently represented Palmer Renewable Energy in its $150 million biomass energy plant construction project.

## Mintz Levin Cohn Ferris Glovsky and Popeo PC
### See profile on p.1523

**THE FIRM** This influential national practice is widely regarded for its broad scope of environmental expertise and its strength in regulatory work. The team is able to utilize this extensive regulatory experience to advise clients on complex compliance strategies that are innovative and up to date. The group regularly advises GE, NorthEast Utilities, Colony Realty Partners and Cargill on all aspects of regulation, permitting and sustainable development matters.
**Sources say:** *"They go above and beyond. The work product has been uniformly excellent."*
**KEY INDIVIDUALS** The preeminent **Jeffrey Porter** (see p.1506) recently represented GE in relation to one of the most high-profile Superfund matters in the US, securing a cost recovery of unprecedented value for his client. Sources praise him for his *"innovative and holistic approach to problem solving."* The *"extremely well-regarded"* **Ralph Child** (see p.1487) comes highly recommended by both peers

and clients. He recently advised NorthEast Utilities in high-value environmental issues stemming from its merger with NSTAR, and also provided permitting counsel for Spectra Energy in relation to its natural gas pipelines. **Susan Phillips** (see p.1505) serves as nationwide general outside counsel for CVS Caremark, leading a team on a variety of matters relating to compliance, due diligence and portfolio management of brownfield sites.

### Band 3

## Anderson & Kreiger LLP

**THE FIRM** This solid environmental boutique has impressively broad capabilities and considerable expertise in remediation and litigation. The group undertakes all manner of compliance, enforcement and permitting issues, and is also known for its sterling work on behalf of plaintiffs.
**Sources say:** *"They are terrific and I have a lot of respect for them."*
**KEY INDIVIDUALS William Lahey** is recognized by commentators as a leader in environmental permitting and land use work, and is developing a strong practice in the alternative energy sector. He has experience in both state and federal courts, and serves as general counsel to several towns and municipalities within Massachusetts. Renowned litigator **Arthur Kreiger** has impressive experience in the environmental sector, especially with zoning and land use matters. He litigates, counsels and mediates on a broad range of issues.

## Beveridge & Diamond PC
### See profile on p.907

**THE FIRM** The Boston offering of this national environmental boutique provides highly technical compliance, regulation and litigation representations. It has particular expertise in Clean Air Act compliance and enforcement and solid waste management. The group also undertakes acquisition due diligence matters, including permitting and the establishment of compliance structures. Notable clients include Bayer Crop Science, Siemens and Chevron.
**Sources say:** *"They're excellent lawyers."*
**KEY INDIVIDUALS Stephen Richmond** (see p.1506) is praised for his ability to understand industry-specific commercial goals and apply his substantial legal knowledge to achieve them. One impressed client said: *"He really looks out for our interests and he's prepared to discuss all the options."* He is highly active in regulatory compliance, permitting and enforcement matters. Of counsel **Jeanine Grachuk** (see p.1494) is regarded as a savvy tactician by her clients, and is appreciated for her *"strong grasp of both the law and the practical aspects of the case."* She has extensive experience in brownfield site development and the management of risk through environmental insurance.

## Nixon Peabody LLP
### See profile on p.1526

**THE FIRM** This group has a solid base in the Massachusetts market and covers the whole spectrum of

environmental work. It has a strong tradition of serving clients in the renewable energy sector, drawing on the firm's considerable construction and engineering expertise to handle high-value cases for energy producers. The practice also undertakes regulation, compliance, land use and zoning matters, as well as litigation. The group's client base includes municipalities, banks and energy producers.
**Sources say:** *"Very high-caliber work in terms of quality of thinking. Presentation of arguments has been crisp and well thought out. Implementation has been persuasive and well received."*
**KEY INDIVIDUALS** The *"very knowledgeable and very down-to-earth"* **Ruth Silman** (see p.1510) is an eminently respected environmental lawyer, well known for her expertise in Clean Air Act matters as well as energy permitting, compliance and regulatory matters, and affordable housing development. **Donald Cooper** (see p.1488) brings his engineering background to bear on a broad range of environmental work, from wetlands and Clean Water Act issues to Superfund matters and environmental litigation. Commentators note that he is extremely personable, taking *"a genuine interest in the project and a collaborative approach to working with a huge variety of professional disciplines."*

## Nutter McClennen & Fish LLP
### See profile on p.1527

**THE FIRM** This practice is widely regarded as a major player in the environmental litigation arena, undertaking industry-specific compliance and enforcement work within the petroleum and energy sectors, among other areas. It is equally adept in project development and permitting work, and is able to call on the firm's well-established real estate group to offer counsel on these projects. The group undertakes sophisticated and challenging work relating to the Clean Water Act, and is very active in representing cities in complex negotiations and agreements linked to publicly owned water systems.
**Sources say:** *"The lawyers have a talent for facilitating meetings that are not adversarial."*
**KEY INDIVIDUALS Mary Ryan** (see p.1508) has a superb reputation for environmental litigation work, and is highlighted for her experience of Superfund-related issues. Her recent work includes representing AVX Corporation in various Superfund, CERCLA, remediation and litigation matters. She has also been involved in the South Shore Tri-Town former naval air base development regarding a unique range of permitting and cleanup issues. The talented **Michael Leon** (see p.1500) commands a great deal of respect from both clients and adversaries, and enjoys a reputation as *"a deal-maker, not a deal-breaker; a problem solver, not a problem creator. He is willing to go the extra step to facilitate a solution."* He is actively engaged in clean air and water compliance and enforcement, and counts several municipalities among his clients.

## WilmerHale
### See profile on p.930

**THE FIRM** WilmerHale's Massachusetts environment group plays an integral part in the firm's national practice, and is distinguished by its experience in Superfund, regulation and litigation matters. The group undertakes work in traditional solid waste management and Clean Water Act matters, and is particularly noted for its representation of clients in the energy sector. Key clients include Casella Waste Systems, Urban Green Technologies and the Vermont Public Service Department.

**KEY INDIVIDUALS Robert Kirsch** (see p.1498) is highlighted for his *"phenomenal"* environment litigation and Superfund expertise. His recent highlights include representing BBA Aviation in challenging claims of drinking water contamination at Burbank California Airport. Impressed clients report that *"his strengths are his openness, fairness, and problem solving through thorough research, legal and factual."*

## Other Notable Practitioners

**Lisa Goodheart** (see p.1493) of Sugarman, Rogers, Barshak & Cohen, PC is highly regarded by peers as *"an outstanding practitioner doing very sophisticated work."* She undertakes the full range of environmental work and is particularly known for her strength in litigation. **Robert Cox** of Bowditch & Dewey LLP represents a number of educational institutions and real estate developers, and has a strong reputation in land use and zoning litigation, regulatory work and Superfund matters. Commentators describe him as a *"terrific lawyer"* with a strong hold on the market outside of Boston. **Hamilton Hackney** (see p.1494) of Greenberg Traurig, LLP is recommended for his expertise in Clean Water Act and storm water issues, and for his

strong abilities across the full range of environmental work. Clients appreciate his flawless knowledge of both technical and statutory issues: *"His advice is right on, and he's very knowledgeable about the technical aspects of environment law."* The *"very helpful and responsive"* **Leigh Gilligan** (see p.1492) of McCarter & English, LLP has a solid and broad-ranging environment and land use practice. She recently represented the Massachusetts Department of Transportation in relation to the acquisition of ground and air leases for a mixed-use development project.

# HEALTHCARE

Commentary about individuals can be found under their firm's paragraph. If the firm has no paragraph (is not ranked) look at Other Notable Practitioners.

| Healthcare |
| --- |
| **Leading Firms** |
| **Band 1** |
| Foley & Lardner LLP * |
| McDermott Will & Emery LLP * |
| Ropes & Gray LLP * |
| **Band 2** |
| Mintz Levin Cohn Ferris Glovsky and Popeo PC * |
| **Band 3** |
| Ankner & Levy |
| Foley Hoag LLP * |
| Nixon Peabody LLP * |
| *\* Indicates firm with profile.* |
| *Alphabetical order within each band. Band 1 is the highest.* |

## Band 1

### Foley & Lardner LLP
See profile on p.2588

**THE FIRM** This team is 16 strong in Massachusetts, and is able to call on its impressive bench strength across the country when working with its notable client base. The group handles a broad range of work in the healthcare space, and its focus includes compliance matters, strategic planning and healthcare transactions. The team represented the West Clinic in its affiliation with Methodist Health System in one of the largest conversion transactions in the US in recent times.

**KEY INDIVIDUALS Lawrence Vernaglia** is highly respected for his broad and impressive practice, and in recent years has distinguished himself as a go-to name for compliance issues relating to federal healthcare reform. He is described as being *"of the highest quality in terms of knowledge, responsiveness and business effectiveness."* **Michael Blau** maintains his reputation as one of the top healthcare lawyers in Massachusetts. He largely focuses on

transactional matters, and has a wealth of experience in assisting private equity clients wishing to enter the healthcare space. One peer acknowledges him as being *"so good it's frustrating!"* Antitrust expert **Mark Waxman** is a highly regarded practitioner in the healthcare field. Clients praise his knowledge of the space and his practical approach, stating that *"he brings a broad experience and understanding of the operations of the biggest institutional healthcare clients."* The highly respected **Alan Einhorn** is a transactional attorney with additional expertise in compliance and regulatory matters. He works closely with a wide range of clients, including hospitals, clinics and provider networks. **Lawrence Litwak** is an eminent practitioner in the field, and has an impressive grasp of the implications of federal and state healthcare reform for his clients. One peer commented: *"I refer to him even when there is no conflict, especially for transactional work. He is wonderful."*

### McDermott Will & Emery LLP
See profile on p.1258

**THE FIRM** The Boston branch of this highly respected national practice is well placed to advise on all aspects of healthcare law, and is sought out by an impressive portfolio of clients. The team maintains a strong transactional platform for joint venture and M&A work, and works with both private equity clients and healthcare providers in this space. It is also noted for its strong litigation capabilities, as demonstrated by its recent representation of the Foundation for Seacoast Health in a contractual dispute with HCA.

**Sources say:** *"They have a very deep history and experience of the healthcare landscape from all perspectives – it is hard to find a firm that can rival them."*

**KEY INDIVIDUALS Christopher Jedrey** (see p.1496) is described as *"an incredibly creative transactional lawyer,"* and leads the Boston-based practice. Steward Healthcare System is a key client of his, and he recently represented it

in a number of significant hospital and physician group acquisitions. **Stephen Bernstein** (see p.1484) leads the firm's international healthcare practice, and offers extensive experience in handling transactional and regulatory matters. He has particular strength in privacy and information protection within the healthcare space, and continues to work with clients such as Emdeon and Cardinal Health. **Charles Buck** (see p.1486) maintains his reputation as an expert in joint venture and transactional work. His recent work includes advising MedFusion on a number of matters, including on the creation of laboratories which allow for highly focused testing. Source praise his *"strategic direction and exceptional negotiating skills."* **Jerome Tichner** (see p.1511) is a new entry to the rankings, and handles a range of regulatory and transactional matters for clients. One source stated: *"He demystifies very complex business and legal landscapes into understandable concepts, and has a good grasp on what we're trying to achieve."* **Monica Neuman** (see p.1503) is noted for her expertise in handling a range of corporate and regulatory matters. She offers particular experience in working with clients on the compliance and contractual issues related to research involving human and animal subjects.

### Ropes & Gray LLP
See profile on p.1528

**THE FIRM** The highly regarded Boston-based healthcare offering of Ropes & Gray draws on the widespread strength of the firm to provide a comprehensive package for its diverse client base. The team's expertise is broad in scope, and includes the full spread of regulatory, transactional and litigation-related matters. Its recent work includes working with Partners Healthcare System in settling an enforcement action brought against Massachusetts General Hospital by the Office of Civil Rights.

**Sources say:** *"They managed and created an efficient process in an area that is extremely detailed, navigating the regula-*

tory landscape with common sense and a practical approach."

**KEY INDIVIDUALS Anne Phillips Ogilby** has a particular focus on public finance matters within the healthcare space, and is considered "the best healthcare bond lawyer in Boston." She has recently been involved in a number of corporate affiliations for clients such as the Western Connecticut Health Network and the Lahey Clinic. The widely acclaimed **Michele Garvin** offers extensive expertise in a wide range of areas, including healthcare regulation, compliance and governance matters. She is considered a leading attorney in this market, with one source noting: "She is a fantastic, standout lawyer." **Eve Brunts** is praised by clients for her diligence and dedication, with one commenting: "She's an excellent partner and really has my interests at heart." She recently worked with Yale

University and Yale-New Haven Hospital in creating a research program in collaboration with a for-profit research institute. **Nancy Forbes** is highly regarded for her expertise in representing clients including children's hospitals and academic medical centers in a range of matters. Her recent work includes acting for Lifespan Corporation in its internal restructuring, and she is praised for her "smart, experienced and practical" approach. **William Knowlton** handles issues pertaining to corporate transactions and regulation for a number of clients within the healthcare space. He serves as a key partner for Stamford Health System and the Controlled Risk Insurance Company.

## Band 2

### Mintz Levin Cohn Ferris Glovsky and Popeo PC
See profile on p.1523

**THE FIRM** This highly regarded national group occupies a strong position in the Massachusetts healthcare market. Its broad practice encompasses the key areas of growth in the space, including ACO formation, hospital consolidation and regulatory concerns related to recent reforms. Clients also benefit from its ability to work seamlessly with other practice area groups in order to offer a more comprehensive service. The team's recent work includes acting for Lowell General Hospital and LGH Corporation in a system merger with Saints Medical Center.
**Sources say:** "Mintz stands out because healthcare is a 24/7 operation, and if there is an issue arising out of office hours, I can always get someone within a matter of minutes. The ability to have immediate assistance adds tremendous value."
**KEY INDIVIDUALS Ellen Janos** (see p.1496) handles a wide range of healthcare work for clients such as hospices, pharmaceutical manufacturers and hospitals. She is highly regarded for the breadth of her expertise in this area, and recently advised Kindred Healthcare on a number of regulatory matters. Healthcare practice chair **Stephen Weiner** (see p.1513) has well-established expertise in matters relating to healthcare mergers and acquisitions. His recent work includes representing New England Sinai Hospital in the sale of the majority of its assets. He is characterized by one source as "a real guru's guru in the healthcare area," and is "very thorough and responsive." **Deborah Daccord** (see p.1489) is highly experienced in all manner of transactions within this arena, and represents a number of high-profile clients. Her focus also extends to regulatory matters. Clients particularly praise her creativity and efficiency when working on deals. **Daria Niewenhous** (see p.1504) handles both transactional and regulatory matters for clients within this space, and has recently worked on several ACO-related issues for clients. Her clients include Winchester Hospital and Affiliates, and she is characterized by one source as "not only superbly smart and knowledgeable, but also very practical."

## Band 3

### Ankner & Levy
**THE FIRM** This dedicated healthcare boutique maintains its strong reputation and handles a wide range of regulatory and transactional matters for its clients. It plays a key role in increasing consolidation activity in the healthcare space, and recently represented a community hospital in its merger with a large hospital system.
**KEY INDIVIDUALS Sally Levy** is respected in the field for her competence in all areas of healthcare law. Her expertise in this area is enhanced by her additional expertise in tax-related matters. **Lianne Ankner** offers impressive experience across a broad range of healthcare work, and works with clients such as physician groups, clinics and hospitals.

### Foley Hoag LLP
See profile on p.1521

**THE FIRM** This group is well positioned within the market to offer advice across a range of healthcare matters to its clients. In addition to its expertise in advising on policy compliance within the changing regulatory landscape, it handles an array of other issues for clients, including corporate transactions, litigation and reimbursement-related matters.
**Sources say:** "I need a firm that can handle the demand of understanding policy and then has the contacts to act on it – Foley Hoag can do this."
**KEY INDIVIDUALS Thomas Barker** (see p.1484) is an expert in issues relating to healthcare reform, and is praised as someone who can translate specialist substantive knowledge. One client stated: "He really dives down and gets to grips with the issue, and can advise accordingly. He delivers on his promises and his expertise is second-to-none." **Colin Zick** (see p.1514) handles a wide range of litigation and advisory work for clients, drawing on his notable expertise in compliance-related matters. His recent work includes handling cases involving alleged healthcare fraud and antikickback statutes for a diverse range of clients.

### Nixon Peabody LLP
See profile on p.1526

**THE FIRM** This Boston-based team is recognized for its significant expertise across the board in the healthcare arena, and seamlessly draws on the wider capabilities of the firm when working with clients. Its recent work has seen it act at the forefront of developments in healthcare payment systems.
**KEY INDIVIDUALS Carolyn Jacoby Gabbay** (see p.1492) is respected for her experience in a range of regulatory compliance matters, and offers particular expertise in matters related to reimbursement and payment systems. **Regina Rockefeller** (see p.1507) is highlighted for her expertise in physician disciplinary matters and her broader work acting for physicians. She also focuses on a range of other regulatory and transactional issues within the healthcare space.

## Other Notable Practitioners

**Christine Savage** (see p.1508) of Choate Hall & Stewart LLP is highly regarded for her broad-based expertise in healthcare-related matters. Commentators remark that *"she has a deep knowledge of the law and very good judgment in terms of understanding what the regulators are interested in."* **Paul Shaw** (see p.1509) of K&L Gates is a respected healthcare litigator, and has extensive expertise in fraud and abuse matters. Clients say of him: *"He has the credibility that makes dealing with third parties much more direct and straightforward."* **Lynn Coe** (see p.1488) is a respected practitioner based in the Boston office of Jones Day, and is particularly experienced in the area of tax-exempt bond financings. His recent work includes acting for Baptist Health South Florida in relation to a public offering. **David Szabo** (see p.1511) of Edwards Wildman Palmer LLP is highly regarded by sources as an expert in the field of healthcare IT, and offers expertise across a broader spread of regulatory and transactional matters. **Jeffrey Heidt** (see p.1495) of Verrill Dana, LLP remains a leading lawyer in the healthcare space, and offers experience across a range of regulatory compliance and transactional matters. His recent highlights include acting as counsel to Beth Israel Deaconess Medical Center during its affiliation with Milton Hospital. He is described as *"responsive, a problem solver and very pleasant to work with."*

# HEDGE & MUTUAL FUNDS

## Band 1

### Bingham McCutchen LLP
See profile on p.1515

**THE FIRM** This group is an institution in the Massachusetts registered and mutual fund market, and can harness the strength of offices in Europe and Asia to complement the impressive bench strength of the Boston group. Its solid fund practice is supported by a robust grounding in regulatory, compliance and enforcement matters. The group represents some of the largest fund managers in the USA, and regular clients include Legg Mason Funds, State Street and Bank of America Alternative Investments. Notable work this year includes the acquisition of a Hong Kong-based asset management fund on behalf of local client Gottex.
**Sources say:** *"They just get on with practicing law in an imaginative way."*
**KEY INDIVIDUALS Richard Goldman** (see p.1493) is an experienced and knowledgeable lawyer in this market. He has recently represented SCS Capital Management in the launch of a fixed-income fund of funds, and Hayman Capital of Dallas in various negotiations with UBS concerning its distribution platform. *"Uniquely wonderful lawyer"* **Roger Joseph** (see p.1496) heads the department and is an expert in mutual fund work. This year he set up a zero-fee feeder fund to act as an investment vehicle on behalf of a prominent fund manager, and has assisted another client in the strategic reduction of the number of fund boards on its roster. **Lea Anne Copenhefer** (see p.299) remains an active player in the mutual funds market and is well versed in issues pertaining to independent boards of funds. She has recently helped clients in this space downgrade money fund investments as well as transform their asset management strategy into one which is compatible in non-US jurisdictions.

### Dechert LLP
See profile on p.1969

**THE FIRM** This highly regarded team is particularly well known in the market for its strength in mutual funds work and independent board issues. It utilizes the collective expertise of its 20-strong Boston group to represent global asset management groups and investment managers across a broad range of mutual and hedge fund matters. The group also has particular acumen in regulation and compliance matters as well as cross-border transactions.
**Sources say:** *"Dechert takes the time to tailor its advice to our particular circumstances instead of just telling us what everybody else is doing in response to a new regulation or ruling."*
**KEY INDIVIDUALS Christopher Harvey** (see p.1495) maintains a robust regulation and compliance practice alongside transactional work. He continues to impress peers and clients, with one commenting: *"Chris consistent-*ly provides practical and flexible advice, and is a master at finding the right middle ground when balancing business objectives and the multiple regulatory schemes in which we operate."* Equally well regarded in the market is **Geoffrey Kenyon** (see p.1498). He serves as fund counsel to a leading global asset manager, overseeing a wide variety of matters relating to a complex series of funds. *"He takes a broad view of investment management legal issues. He is able to give you wise counsel, and applies his good judgment and experience to the issues,"* notes one impressed source. **Joseph Fleming** (see p.314) has a diverse client base and is accomplished in all aspects of fund work. He is particularly well versed in issues relevant to Canadian asset managers. **John O'Hanlon** (see p.379) routinely represents boards of directors, managers and funds, and has recently been advising clients in connection with both US and non-US compliance matters. Sources reserve particular praise for his responsiveness and attention to client needs.

### Ropes & Gray LLP
See profile on p.1528

**THE FIRM** This linchpin of the Massachusetts legal market boasts a strong regulated funds practice at state, national and international level. The team consists of 35 Boston-based lawyers who can draw on a deep bench nationwide to deliver superlative client service and innovative legal advice across the spectrum of fund work. Regular clients include Blackstone, Allianz Global and Putnam Funds among a host of significant US and international financial institutions.
**Sources say:** *"Ropes responds immediately to our needs and provides top-shelf service and advice."*
**KEY INDIVIDUALS John Loder** continues to be an authority on complex fund matters, and is particularly singled out for his knowledge and expertise in Investment Adviser Act matters. He provides ongoing representation to the Schwab and Laudus funds and is admired by clients for his practical nature: *"He can extrapolate from prior experience and provide business-oriented advice."* The *"helpful and attentive"* **Gregory Sheehan** is highly rated for the strength of his regulatory work. He regularly undertakes work for MFS and its independent trustees. *"He is possessed of an unusual combination of brilliance and humility – he informs and advises us but does not direct us,"* reports one happy client. The much-respected **Thomas Hiller** contin-

ues to represent Bracebridge Capital in connection with fund restructurings, contemplated offerings and regulatory matters. **John Gerstmayr** remains busy advising and representing Putnam Funds and its trustees. *"He has an extraordinary ability to look at legal and business issues. It is not simply a conversation that puts up legal walls around a problem – he is able to look at the broader ramifications,"* asserts one interviewee. The highly regarded **Timothy Diggins** has recently represented State Street in its acquisition of a Goldman Sachs hedge fund administrator, and covers all aspects of RS Investments' product and regulatory work.

## Band 2

### Foley Hoag LLP
See profile on p.1521

**THE FIRM** This well-established practice focuses exclusively on hedge fund work and is a dominant player in this field. While a streamlined team in comparison to its competitors, the Boston group has made a number of significant client wins in the last twelve months, including AJO

# INTELLECTUAL PROPERTY

Licensing p.1463

Commentary about individuals can be found under their firm's paragraph. If the firm has no paragraph (is not ranked) look at Other Notable Practitioners.

| Intellectual Property |
| :--- |
| **Leading Firms** |
| **Band 1** |
| Fish & Richardson PC |
| Goodwin Procter LLP * |
| WilmerHale * |
| **Band 2** |
| Foley Hoag LLP * |
| Proskauer Rose LLP * |
| Ropes & Gray LLP * |
| Wolf, Greenfield & Sacks PC * |
| **Band 3** |
| Choate Hall & Stewart LLP * |
| Clark & Elbing |
| Finnegan, Henderson, Farabow, Garrett & Dunner LLP * |
| Foley & Lardner LLP * |
| McCarter & English, LLP * |

## Band 1

### Fish & Richardson PC

**THE FIRM** This national IP firm is recognized as one of the leaders in the market, with a number of highly regarded attorneys among the 63 practitioners in the Boston office. A real strength of the practice is patent litigation, with particular emphasis on Abbreviated New Drug Application pharmaceutical disputes. The team works across the life sciences, medical device, electrical, software

Partners, Garelick Capital and True Hedge. The team is especially noted for its frequent cross-border work for non-US managers who want to offer funds in the USA. **KEY INDIVIDUALS** The highly regarded **Jeffrey Collins** (see p.1488) is practice co-head, and has recently served as counsel to Garelick Capital Partners and True Hedge in relation to their respective hedge fund launches in Delaware.

### Goodwin Procter LLP
See profile on p.1522

**THE FIRM** This team receives praise for its strength in mutual funds and has an equally well-developed hedge funds practice. It comes particularly recommended for its expertise in regulatory and compliance matters. Among its recent work is acting as general outside counsel to the independent trustees of Eaton Vance, which has included handling a class action dispute concerning auction rate preferred shares.

**KEY INDIVIDUALS** Practice head **Elizabeth Shea Fries** (see p.1492) is highly commended for her hedge fund work, and is noted for her advice to clients regarding the development of compliance strategies and the negotiation

and mechanical technology industry sectors, acting for a prestigious roster of clients including Adobe Systems, FUJIFILM Dimatix, Procter & Gamble and Boston Scientific.

**Sources say:** *"Fish & Richardson is a top-tier patent litigation firm with good depth and many skilled attorneys."*

**KEY INDIVIDUALS** The *"outstanding"* **Frank Porcelli** is a much-revered litigator, with particular experience in appellate work in the patent and trade secret spheres. Porcelli recently represented the plaintiff in the Federal Circuit appeal of Gaylord v United States of America, a copyright infringement case relating to a commemorative stamp. **Frank Scherkenbach** is an experienced trial lawyer specializing in software, medical devices and semiconductor technology. He recently represented Adobe Systems in a patent infringement action brought by Tarkus Imaging, resulting in a jury verdict of no infringement. **Robert Hillman** is a highly experienced patent litigator, and is particularly noted for his expertise in electronics and biotechnology.

### Goodwin Procter LLP
See profile on p.1522

**THE FIRM** The Boston IP practice notably benefits from the resources of this full-service, national firm, and receives particular praise from clients for its deep bench and thorough approach to matters. The team offers a range of IP services, including transactional, litigation and counseling work, with particular strength in the pharmaceutical and software technology sectors. Teva, Boston Scientific, Cisco Systems and GE are among its key clients.

of acquisitions. **Philip Newman** (see p.1504) is a well-regarded figure in the mutual fund space, and as counsel for a broad range of funds and investors undertakes the full gamut of work in this field. He represents the independent trustees of Van Eck Funds. **Derek Steingarten** (see p.1510) continues to impress as a younger partner in the fund space. He has recently conducted work on behalf of the independent trustees of Eaton Vance, and he regularly advises the Russell Investment Group.

### K&L Gates
See profile on p.2245

**THE FIRM** This client-focused team maintains a fine presence in Boston, in addition to its national and global reach. It typically serves a broad base of investment managers, and is well positioned to cover a vast assortment of complex fund work. Eaton Vance, John Hancock and Salient Capital are among its key clients.

**KEY INDIVIDUALS Mark Goshko** (see p.1494) is a renowned practitioner in the closed-end fund market. Recent work has served as special counsel to Loomis, Sayles & Company and Eaton Vance.

**Sources say:** *"They are, in my view, as good as there is in patent litigation."*

**KEY INDIVIDUALS** The much-admired **Paul Ware** (see p.1513) predominantly focuses on litigation, particularly patent and trade secret disputes. He recently represented Teva in a patent jury trial against Novartis and Sandoz. Clients say that **Anthony Downs** (see p.1490) is *"outstanding at trial"* and *"greatly skilled in making complex technical arguments understandable to lay persons."* He is chair of the IP litigation practice at Goodwin Procter, specializing in patent cases in district courts and at the ITC. **Edmund Pitcher** (see p.1505) is a seasoned IP attorney with a very broad practice, ranging from portfolio development and patentability analysis to patent litigation. He works across the chemical and life sciences industry sectors, and a recent highlight includes strategy, preparation, prosecution and litigation advisory work for Serenity Pharmaceuticals in relation to a new drug. **Duncan Greenhalgh** (see p.1494) focuses on patent procurement and enforcement in the life sciences field. He also offers strategic advice with regard to IP development, finance and transactions. **Douglas Kline** (see p.1498), chair of the IP group at Goodwin Procter, is a general IP litigator with particular expertise in patent disputes. Recent work includes representing Eloqua as defendant in patent infringement litigation concerning automated marketing software. **John Englander** (see p.1491) principally concentrates on patent, trade secret and copyright litigation. His patent practice covers mechanical, pharmaceutical, biotechnology and hi-tech matters, such as telecoms and software architecture. He recently repre-

## Intellectual Property
### Senior Statesmen

**Senior Statesmen: distinguished older practitioners**

| | | | |
|---|---|---|---|
| Clark Paul T | Clark & Elbing | Hillman Robert | Fish & Richardson PC |

### Leading Individuals

**Star individuals**

| | |
|---|---|
| Lee William F | WilmerHale * |

**Band 1**

| | |
|---|---|
| Bauer Steven M | Proskauer Rose LLP |
| Bromberg Lee C | McCarter & English, LLP * |
| Frank Jr Robert S | Choate Hall & Stewart LLP * |
| Myers Louis | Lando & Anastasi, LLP (ONP)† |
| Porcelli Frank P | Fish & Richardson PC |
| Ware Donald | Foley Hoag LLP * |
| Ware Jr Paul F | Goodwin Procter LLP * |

**Band 2**

| | |
|---|---|
| Arnold Beth E | Foley Hoag LLP * |
| Columbia Sarah Chapin | McDermott Will & Emery LLP (ONP)† * |
| DeConti Jr Giulio A | Lathrop & Gage LLP (ONP)† |
| Dichiara Peter M | WilmerHale * |
| Downs J Anthony | Goodwin Procter LLP * |
| Frank Steven J | Bingham McCutchen LLP (ONP)† * |
| Gordon Dana M | Foley Hoag LLP * |
| Greenhalgh Duncan | Goodwin Procter LLP * |
| Hanley Elizabeth A | McCarter & English, LLP * |
| Jarrell Brenda H | Choate Hall & Stewart LLP * |
| Kelly Edward J | Ropes & Gray LLP |
| Kline Douglas J | Goodwin Procter LLP * |
| Laporte Claire | Foley Hoag LLP * |
| Pirozzolo Lisa J | WilmerHale * |
| Scherkenbach Frank E | Fish & Richardson PC |
| Stoner Wayne L | WilmerHale * |

**Band 3**

| | |
|---|---|
| Black Edward | Ropes & Gray LLP |
| Brook David | Hamilton, Brook, Smith & Reynolds (ONP)† |
| Capraro Jr Joseph A | Proskauer Rose LLP |
| Davis Steven G | McCarter & English, LLP * |
| DeFranco Denise W | Finnegan, Henderson, Farabow, Garrett * |
| Elbing Karen L | Clark & Elbing |
| Elrifi Ivor R | Mintz Levin Cohn Ferris Glovsky (ONP)† * |
| Engellenner Thomas J | Pepper Hamilton LLP (ONP)† * |
| Englander John C | Goodwin Procter LLP * |
| Gates Edward R | Wolf, Greenfield & Sacks PC |
| Honeyman Jason M | Wolf, Greenfield & Sacks PC |
| Krumholz Joshua C | Holland & Knight LLP (ONP)† * |
| Lanza John D | Foley & Lardner LLP |
| Lowrie Matthew | Foley & Lardner LLP |
| Marandett Eric J | Choate Hall & Stewart LLP * |
| McGurk Michael R | Finnegan, Henderson, Farabow, Garrett * |
| Meyers Thomas | Brown Rudnick LLP (ONP)† |
| Pitcher Edmund R | Goodwin Procter LLP * |
| Steinberg Donald R | WilmerHale * |
| Swain Philip C | Foley Hoag LLP * |
| Turano Thomas A | K&L Gates (ONP)† * |

**Up-and-coming individuals**

| | |
|---|---|
| Mollaaghababa Reza | Pepper Hamilton LLP (ONP)† * |
| Rader Michael | Wolf, Greenfield & Sacks PC |
| Underwood Robert H | McDermott Will & Emery LLP (ONP)† * |

### Intellectual Property: Licensing
### Leading Individuals

**Band 1**

| | |
|---|---|
| Bevilacqua Michael J | WilmerHale * |
| Copenhaver Karen F | Choate Hall & Stewart LLP * |

\* Indicates individual with profile.

† ONP = Other Notable Practitioner.

---

sented Aereo in a copyright litigation brought by a number of major television broadcast networks.

## WilmerHale
**See profile on p.930**

THE FIRM WilmerHale is a full-service firm with an international presence and an outstanding Boston IP practice. While offering the full range of IP services, including prosecution, strategy and counseling, the group is particularly known for its patent litigation practice, which covers a broad spread of technologies. It counts Pfizer, Intel, Novartis and Harvard University among its impressive group clients.

**Sources say:** *"WilmerHale is a firm of the highest caliber. Excellent."*

KEY INDIVIDUALS Market sources describe **William Lee** (see p.353) as *"one of the pillars of IP here in Boston."* An experienced litigator, he represents clients from the hi-tech, electrical engineering and pharmaceutical industries at the ITC, Federal Circuit and district courts. He recently represented Cree in litigation against SemiLEDS, in which eight Cree patents relating to high-brightness LED chips were alleged to have been infringed. **Michael Bevilacqua** (see p.1485) enjoys an excellent reputation in the market and specializes in licensing, development and joint venture agreements. His practice also covers patents and trademarks, with particular focus on software technology. Sources are quick to applaud **Peter Dichiara's** (see p.1490) command of the patent prosecution process as well as his *"world-class"* expertise in the nanotechnology space. His practice also covers electronics and electrical engineering, wireless communication and semiconductors. He also played a key role in the above matter for Cree, alongside Lee. **Wayne Stoner** (see p.1510) is a patent litigator whose practice covers medical devices, semiconductors, electro-chemistry and telecoms, among other technologies. He recently acted for A123 Systems, achieving the settlement of long-term multiforum litigation relating to the licensing of lithium ion battery technology. **Lisa Pirozzolo** (see p.1505) is cochair of the IP litigation practice at WilmerHale. She focuses on patent infringement, and contractual and licensing disputes in life sciences and electronics. The *"very talented"* **Donald Steinberg** (see p.1510) is renowned among commentators for *"working hard for his client."* He is chair of WilmerHale's IP group, with a personal practice focus on trademark and patent protection. He worked with Research In Motion on a patent case relating to wireless technology, resulting in a $150 million settlement before trial.

## Band 2

### Foley Hoag LLP
**See profile on p.1521**

THE FIRM Foley Hoag has a strong reputation in Boston, with peers naming the practice as part of the 'go-to' group of IP firms. The team has notable strength in patent litigation, particularly in the biotechnology and biopharmaceutical fields. The practice also covers broader IP work, including trademark and licensing matters. Key clients include Biogen Idec, Dana Farber Cancer Institute and Johns Hopkins University School of Medicine.

**Sources say:** *"They handle difficult contentious matters that require higher-level thinking and creative solutions."*

KEY INDIVIDUALS **Donald Ware** (see p.1513), chair of Foley Hoag's IP department, is much admired for his litigation skills. His practice covers a range of biotechnologies, including recombinant DNA matters, research tools and medical devices. He recently represented Biogen Idec in a consolidated patent infringement case brought by Sanofi, obtaining district court judgment of noninfringement. The highly regarded **Beth Arnold** (see p.1483) is experienced in pharmaceutical and biotechnology patent protection. Her practice also encompasses development and commercialization agreements, patent counseling, and IP due diligence on M&A. **Claire Laporte** (see p.1499) is a well-regarded trial lawyer with a particular focus patent litigation in the life sciences field and in computer technologies. She recently represented GI Dynamics as defendant in a patent action brought by WL Gore & Associates, relating to a medical device for the treatment of obesity and diabetes. **Dana Gordon** (see p.1493) is *"a recognized name in the IP community,"* specializing in patent preparation and prosecution. His practice also includes patent and trade secret protection strategy, and patent portfolio due diligence analysis. **Philip Swain** (see p.1511) is an experienced patent litigator, appearing in district and Federal Circuit appeal cases. His practice is largely focused on telecom, computer technology and medical devices.

## Proskauer Rose LLP
**See profile on p.2001**

THE FIRM The Boston office of this international, multiservice firm is known for its strength in patent litigation. The practice also offers patent portfolio development, patent prosecution, counseling and transactional services. Areas of particular focus include the life sciences field and hi-tech industries, such as telecoms and software. T-Mobile USA, MobileMedia Ideas and Viacom are counted among its distinguished client base.

Sources say: *"One of the reasons I continue to send work to them is because I can rely on them and can be confident the work will be done well and in a timely manner."* **KEY INDIVIDUALS Steven Bauer** is a dedicated IP litigator, who practices across patent, trademark, copyright and trade secret matters. *"He is a very intelligent guy with a good grasp of the technical issues that are important to us,"* an impressed client notes, while other market commentators mention his tenacity and fine tactical approach to matters. He recently represented MobileMedia Ideas in litigation against Apple, which was found to have infringed three of the plaintiff's patents. **Joseph Capraro** is *"a very responsive, thoughtful and efficient counselor,"* according to one happy client. His broad practice covers a range of industries and technologies, including medical devices, alternative energy, semiconductors and financial services.

## Ropes & Gray LLP
See profile on p.1528

**THE FIRM** This Boston-based global giant is noted for the strength of its transactional practice, and also maintains a fine track record for patent work in both prosecution and litigation. Recent standout work includes handling patent prosecution and portfolio strategy matters for Google. Other key clients include Genzyme and Bristol-Myers Squibb.

**KEY INDIVIDUALS Edward Kelly** is a well-regarded attorney whose practice focuses on strategic advice as well as trademark, copyright and patent prosecution. He is particularly noted for his work in the hi-tech, semiconductor and medical device technologies, and recently played a central role in the aforementioned matters for Google. **Edward Black** is head of the IP transactions practice and specializes in IP asset creation and management. Clients praise him as *"responsive and smart,"* appreciate his *"clear advice"* and comment that he is *"an expert in his field."* He recently worked with TPG Capital on the IP elements of its investment transactions, as well as on brand protection matters.

## Wolf, Greenfield & Sacks PC
See profile on p.1535

**THE FIRM** Wolf Greenfield is a well-known and respected IP boutique based in Boston. The team offers full IP services and is particularly known in the market for its patent prosecution capabilities. Clients are also full of praise for its trademark and patent litigation work, and additionally single out its strengths on transactional matters. The practice covers technologies as diverse as acoustics, robotics, bio-sequencing, pollution reduction and ceramics.

**Sources say:** *"They provide high-quality legal work while maintaining a commitment to client service."*

**KEY INDIVIDUALS Edward Gates** is a *"very talented lawyer"* with *"very good business sense."* Recent work includes assisting Shire, a biopharma company, in negotiating exclusive worldwide rights to a technology used to investigate curative therapies for hemophilia. Market sources also add: *"He is a purist in his attention to his clients and his focus on protecting their interests."* The highly regarded **Jason Honeyman** comes recommended for his

work across a wide range of IP matters, including patent and trademark litigation, as well as portfolio management, technology-related due diligence and technology licensing. *"He is very diligent and knowledgeable,"* asserts an impressed interviewee. **Michael Rader** is a *"very strong advocate"* whose practice covers patent, trademark and copyright matters in a variety of technologies and industries. These have included hi-tech products like LCD screens, semiconductors, medical devices and transgenic mice. Sources describe him as *"extremely responsive, very creative and imaginative."*

## Band 3

### Choate Hall & Stewart LLP
See profile on p.1517

**THE FIRM** This group offers the full range of IP services, from trademark and copyright issues to patent, unfair competition and trade secret matters. The practice is particularly active in the biotechnology, pharmaceuticals, computer and electrical engineering fields. Key clients include Shire, Momenta Pharmaceuticals, Hewlett-Packard and Celgene.

**Sources say:** *"They are the most responsive law firm I've worked with. I have a high degree of confidence in the quality of their thinking and I have a real partnership with them."* **KEY INDIVIDUALS** The highly regarded **Karen Copenhaver** (see p.1489) specializes in licensing and technology transfer, and also comes recommended for her expertise in open source software issues. **Robert Frank** (see p.1492) is noted for his experience in IP disputes and patent litigation, and elicits praise from sources for his *"very dedicated, focused and very client-centered"* approach to matters. He recently represented Insulet in a patent infringement case relating to medical instruments for the treatment of diabetes. **Brenda Jarrell** (see p.1496) is a seasoned practitioner in the life sciences and chemical IP arenas. Her expertise spans litigation, licensing and transactional work, and she is particularly renowned by sources for doing an *"excellent job"* on the prosecution of patents. **Eric Marandett** (see p.1500) is a *"fantastic attorney"* and much-respected litigator, with particular experience in the biotechnology, pharmaceutical and technology spheres.

### Clark & Elbing

**THE FIRM** Clark & Elbing is a highly regarded patent boutique based in Boston, offering portfolio management and strategy, M&A due diligence work, technology licensing and freedom-to-operate analysis. Sources particularly note the firm's excellence in patent prosecution. Biotechnology, pharmaceuticals and chemistry are the key areas of practice.

**Sources say:** *"They are very good at helping you build your IP position to the point where it creates additional value for the company."*

**KEY INDIVIDUALS** *"Very, very high-caliber"* attorney **Karen Elbing** is noted for her litigation expertise, and her practice also covers strategy, prosecution and in-licensing patent matters. Additionally, she comes much recom-

mended for her knowledge of the life sciences arena. The excellent **Paul Clark** has extensive experience in the biotechnology sphere and maintains a fine track record working with clients on prosecution and licensing matters.

### Finnegan, Henderson, Farabow, Garrett & Dunner LLP
See profile on p.912

**THE FIRM** The Cambridge office of this national IP firm offers the full range of services, including prosecution, litigation, reexaminations, strategy and transactional work. The practice covers trade secret, trademark, copyright and patent matters in a variety of industry sectors, from life sciences and chemicals to software, telecoms and the internet. It counts Boston Scientific, Caterpillar, Genzyme and Walmart among its impressive roster of clients.

**Sources say:** *"They are absolutely top-notch in terms of their expertise."*

**KEY INDIVIDUALS Denise DeFranco** (see p.1489) is an experienced trial and appellate court litigator, specializing in life science and hi-tech matters. She recently represented Boston Scientific in a patent infringement action brought against three competitors, asserting ten patents relating to digestive stents. Clients appreciate that she is *"easy to work with"* and praise her *"high competency."* **Michael McGurk** (see p.1501) is managing partner of the Cambridge office. His practice covers licensing, and transactional and strategic work, as well as litigation, interference and reexamination proceedings. Clients say he is *"practical, smart and able to really focus on the important issues."*

### Foley & Lardner LLP
See profile on p.2588

**THE FIRM** The Boston office of this national, full-service firm is well regarded by clients, who particularly note the strength of the litigation practice. The team also has prosecution, counseling and transactional capabilities. Key clients include Google, Sony and MIT.

**KEY INDIVIDUALS John Lanza** specializes in strategic advice on IP enforcement and transactional matters. *"He is incredibly well organized, very accurate and has great responsiveness,"* reports one happy client. He works with Citrix Systems as ongoing lead counsel on the development and management of its IP portfolio. **Matthew Lowrie** is chair of the firm's IP litigation group and specializes in patent litigation, covering IT, telecom, and medical device and semiconductor technologies. Clients reserve particular praise for his *"very strategic"* approach to matters. He defended Sun Life Assurance in a longrunning patent infringement suit, obtaining Federal Circuit affirmation of an invalidity judgment.

### McCarter & English, LLP
See profile on p.1759

**THE FIRM** McCarter & English is a full-service firm with a growing profile in the Boston market. The practice covers the range of IP services, including trademark, copyright and patent litigation, and it is also frequently called upon to handle patent prosecution, portfolio management and brand management. The team is particularly known for its work in the pharmaceutical and biotechnology sectors, with key clients including GlaxoSmithKline, Novartis, Sanofi and Abbott Laboratories.

**KEY INDIVIDUALS Lee Bromberg** (see p.1486) is an experienced litigator who sources describe as *"one of the best and brightest in Boston – and he has been for years."* His practice covers patent infringement disputes as well as other IP litigation. Peers also add: *"He is a great lawyer and a first-class guy."* The excellent **Elizabeth Hanley** (see p.1494) heads McCarter & English's IP and IT group. Her practice covers prosecution, patentability, licensing and due diligence work in chemical and biotechnology patent law. **Steven Davis** (see p.1489) specializes in patent prosecution, portfolio management and licensing issues. Chemistry, biotechnology and pharmaceuticals are areas of particular expertise. Clients say: *"He is a highly skilled attorney – very strategic and a real problem solver."*

### Other Notable Practitioners

**Thomas Meyers** of Brown Rudnick LLP is an experienced counselor and patent prosecutor in the biotechnology, pharmaceutical, medical device and chemical technology fields. He is particularly well regarded in relation to genomics work, and receives particular praise from clients for his responsive approach to matters. At Lathrop & Gage LLP, the very well-respected **Giulio DeConti** focuses on prosecution, portfolio development, counseling and licensing across the biotechnology, pharmaceutical and chemical arenas. The terrific **Thomas Turano** (see p.1512)

at K&L Gates has a particular focus on the medical device, diagnostics, software, electronics and optics fields. His practice covers prosecution of patents and trademarks, as well as licensing, due diligence, litigation and counseling. **David Brook** at Hamilton, Brook, Smith & Reynolds, P.C. has *"an unbelievable clientele and reputation,"* according to market sources, who add that he is *"a real creative thinker in biotechnology IP strategy."* Along with biotechnology, his practice covers chemistry, chemical engineering and medical devices. The excellent **Louis Myers** of Lando & Anastasi, LLP specializes in biotechnology, pharmaceutical and chemical patent matters. He is particularly known for his prosecution practice, also offering portfolio acquisition and development, transactional due diligence, licensing and analysis opinion services. **Sarah Chapin Columbia** (see p.1488) is head of the IP litigation group at McDermott Will & Emery LLP. Her practice incorporates patent, copyright, trademark and trade secret matters, particularly within the life sciences, computer and electronics fields. She represents Sandoz as defendant in a Hatch-Waxman patent infringement case against Teva, Amphastar and Watson. Sources say: *"She is the whole package; a very good courtroom lawyer and an exceptional counselor outside the courtroom."* At the same firm, **Robert Underwood** (see p.1512) has an impressive range of expertise within the fields of life sciences and chemicals. Clients say: *"We leave our interactions with Bob both educated and confident that we are proceeding on a positive course of action."* Underwood works with Novartis Vaccines & Diagnostics on strategic counseling, due diligence and patent prosecution matters. Bingham McCutchen LLP's

**Steven Frank** (see p.1491) has a practice focus on transactional due diligence, patent prosecution and analysis, in addition to handling copyright matters and licensing agreements. Sources regard him as *"extremely dependable and contactable."* The very experienced **Ivor Elrifi** (see p.309) of Mintz Levin Cohn Ferris Glovsky and Popeo PC is noted for his patent prosecution, licensing and enforcement capabilities, and specializes in life sciences, including medical devices, genetics and novel therapeutics. *"Tremendous strategic thinker"* **Joshua Krumholz** (see p.1499) is a patent litigator and chair of the IP practice at Holland & Knight LLP. He works in the computer ware, chemical products, air jet and consumer goods areas. Clients appreciate his *"common-sense approach to solving business problems,"* as well as his *"responsiveness, availability to answer questions, organizational skills and efficiency."* **Thomas Engellenner** (see p.1490) of Pepper Hamilton LLP has *"the depth and knowledge needed, as well as a superb service attitude to his clients,"* according to market sources. He focuses on patent and licensing in biotechnology, pharmaceuticals and medical devices. He recently arrived from Nutter McClennen & Fish. Clients say **Reza Mollaaghababa** (see p.1502) of Pepper Hamilton LLP is *"creative and effective at getting to the heart of the matter."* His practice covers patent and trademark prosecution, as well as counseling. His expertise includes such technologies as medical devices, computer ware, nanotechnology and optics. He is another new arrival from Nutter McClennen & Fish.

# LABOR & EMPLOYMENT

Commentary about individuals can be found under their firm's paragraph. If the firm has no paragraph (is not ranked) look at Other Notable Practitioners.

### Band 1
### Labor & Employment

#### Goodwin Procter LLP
See profile on p.1522

**THE FIRM** This highly regarded group offers a leading labor and employment practice with a strong reputation in counseling and transactional advice. The team also handles high-stakes litigation and investigations conducted by the DOL. Its client base is diverse and spans a wide range of sectors, demonstrating the breadth of the team's expertise. Its recent work includes representing Hewlett-Packard in noncompete litigation.

**Sources say:** *"The attorneys I work with are smart, thoughtful and analytical, while at the same time practical and considerate of business imperatives."*

**KEY INDIVIDUALS Robert Hale** (see p.1494) is an expert in employment litigation, and offers particular experience in matters involving the Family and Medical Leave Act. Clients say he is *"very articulate and really understands the issues,"* while highlighting his *"extraordinary attention to*

*detail and client needs."* **Wilfred Benoit** (see p.1484) is highly experienced in representing clients in a wide range of disputes, including claims of employment discrimination and unfair practice. His recent work includes acting for clients in whistle-blower claims arising from the Sarbanes-Oxley Act. **James Nagle** (see p.1503) maintains his leading reputation in the field, and has a particular focus on defending clients against claims of discrimination. His expertise also extends to disputes involving senior executive termination. Clients praise his approach, stating: *"He knows just the right balance between being an effective, strong advocate without being overly aggressive."* **Bradford Smith** (see p.1510) is a respected practitioner with experience in a range of litigation and counseling matters. His recent work includes successfully defending Henley Enterprises in response to various claims of discrimination.

#### Morgan, Brown and Joy LLP
See profile on p.1524

**THE FIRM** This highly respected Boston-based boutique has a very deep and well-developed bench, and handles an impressive range of disputes and advisory matters for clients. Its practice is truly national in scope, and its recent work has seen the team handle cases for clients such as Walgreens, General Dynamics and Macy's across the country. Clients admire and appreciate the firm's dedication to top-quality service and legal advice at competitive rates.

**Sources say:** *"They give a great deal of attention to us and are very thorough and value oriented."*

**KEY INDIVIDUALS** *"Excellent litigator"* **Robert Joy** (see p.1497) is a highly regarded labor and employment lawyer in Massachusetts. His recent work includes handling the negotiations for a labor contract for over 14,000 employees across New England. *"Outstanding lawyer"* **William Joy** (see p.1497) is a respected practitioner in the labor space, with a strong reputation for representing management in that area. His recent work includes working with clients such as Bloomingdale's on contract negotiation. **Jaclyn**

## Labor & Employment
### Leading Firms

**Band 1**
- Goodwin Procter LLP *
- Morgan, Brown and Joy LLP *
- Ropes & Gray LLP *
- Seyfarth Shaw LLP *

**Band 2**
- Foley Hoag LLP *
- Littler Mendelson, PC *

**Band 3**
- Bello, Black & Welsh LLP
- Jackson Lewis LLP *
- Mintz Levin Cohn Ferris Glovsky and Popeo PC *
- Nixon Peabody LLP *
- Ogletree, Deakins, Nash, Smoak & Stewart, PC *
- Proskauer Rose LLP *

**Band 4**
- Davis, Malm & D'Agostine, P.C. *
- Edwards Wildman Palmer LLP *
- Hirsch Roberts Weinstein LLP
- Holland & Knight LLP *
- Skoler, Abbott & Presser, PC *
- WilmerHale *

\* Indicates firm / individual with profile.
† ONP = Other Notable Practitioner.

## Labor & Employment
### Senior Statesmen

**Senior Statesmen: distinguished older practitioners**

| | |
|---|---|
| Jacobs Neil | WilmerHale * |
| Weinstein Jerome N | Hirsch Roberts Weinstein LLP |

### Leading Individuals

**Band 1**

| | |
|---|---|
| Alfred Richard | Seyfarth Shaw LLP * |
| Benoit Wilfred J | Goodwin Procter LLP * |
| Bucking James W | Foley Hoag LLP * |
| Casey David | Littler Mendelson, PC * |
| Damon Lisa J | Seyfarth Shaw LLP * |
| Gordon Robert B | Ropes & Gray LLP |
| Hale Robert | Goodwin Procter LLP * |
| Nagle James W | Goodwin Procter LLP * |
| Patrick Diane | Ropes & Gray LLP |
| Telegen Arthur | Seyfarth Shaw LLP * |

**Band 2**

| | |
|---|---|
| Batten Mark W | Proskauer Rose LLP |
| Ebb Peter L | Ropes & Gray LLP |
| Faust Scott | Proskauer Rose LLP |
| Joy Robert | Morgan, Brown and Joy LLP * |
| Joy William | Morgan, Brown and Joy LLP * |
| Mandel David M | Ropes & Gray LLP |
| Pickett Andrew | Jackson Lewis LLP * |
| Rizzotti Anthony D | Littler Mendelson, PC * |
| Rodriques Louis A | Bingham McCutchen LLP (ONP) † * |
| Schwartz Sara Goldsmith | Schwartz Hannum PC (ONP) † * |
| Shirley Thomas E | Choate Hall & Stewart LLP (ONP) † * |
| Smith Bradford J | Goodwin Procter LLP * |
| Sunshine Ilene Robinson | Sullivan & Worcester LLP (ONP) † * |
| Welsh John F | Bello, Black & Welsh LLP |

**Band 3**

| | |
|---|---|
| Abbott Jr Ralph F | Skoler, Abbott & Presser, PC |
| Cohen Bret A | Mintz Levin Cohn Ferris Glovsky * |
| Cudkowicz Ariel D | Seyfarth Shaw LLP * |
| Davis Joshua M | Goulston & Storrs (ONP) † |
| Donoghue Laurence J | Morgan, Brown and Joy LLP * |

| | |
|---|---|
| Forman Adam | Littler Mendelson, PC * |
| Gault Robert M | Mintz Levin Cohn Ferris Glovsky * |
| Hirsch Jeffrey L | Hirsch Roberts Weinstein LLP |
| Keating Gregory C | Littler Mendelson, PC * |
| Kugell Jaclyn L | Morgan, Brown and Joy LLP * |
| Rosen Michael | Foley Hoag LLP * |
| Rosenthal David S | Nixon Peabody LLP * |
| Whitham Michele A | Foley Hoag LLP * |

**Band 4**

| | |
|---|---|
| Ambash Joseph W | Fisher & Phillips LLP (ONP) † * |
| Bannon Patrick | Seyfarth Shaw LLP * |
| Beck Russell | Beck Reed Riden LLP (ONP) † |
| Bello Kenneth | Bello, Black & Welsh LLP |
| Black Josiah M | Bello, Black & Welsh LLP |
| Boyle Philip G | Morgan, Brown and Joy LLP * |
| Clark Lori R | Schwartz Hannum PC (ONP) † * |
| Feldman Gary M | Davis, Malm & D'Agostine, P.C. * |
| Fentin Susan G | Skoler, Abbott & Presser, PC * |
| Hannum III William E | Schwartz Hannum PC (ONP) † * |
| Kaitz Nathan | Morgan, Brown and Joy LLP * |
| Kaplan Tamsin R | Davis, Malm & D'Agostine, P.C. * |
| McCourt Terence | Greenberg Traurig, LLP (ONP) † * |
| McKendall Miriam | Holland & Knight LLP * |
| Musiker Jean | Sugarman, Rogers, Barshak (ONP) † * |
| Oberstein Gary J | Nixon Peabody LLP * |
| Rosenfeld Jonathan | WilmerHale * |
| Schroeder Donald W | Mintz Levin Cohn Ferris Glovsky * |
| Sussman Heather Egan | McDermott Will & Emery LLP (ONP) † * |
| Van Dyck Timothy P | Edwards Wildman Palmer LLP * |

**Up-and-coming individuals**

| | |
|---|---|
| Cooper Jenny | Bingham McCutchen LLP (ONP) † * |

**Kugell** (see p.1499) is a recognized expert in FMLA and ADA matters, and is viewed by clients as a go-to attorney for advice in these areas. **Laurence Donoghue** (see p.1490) is a popular choice with clients in the labor and employment space, and has a broad-based practice. His recent work includes forming part of the team which represented Verizon Wireless in labor actions stemming from a strike. **Philip Boyle** (see p.1485) is an experienced practitioner in this space, and works with private and public sector clients in a range of disputes. He recently acted for Phoenix Light Rail Transit in negotiating its new labor contract. **Nathan Kaitz** (see p.1497) has a nationwide practice which is broad in scope. He offers experience in a wide range of litigation and arbitration matters on behalf of employers.

## Ropes & Gray LLP
### See profile on p.1528

**THE FIRM** This highly regarded group undertakes an impressive range of labor and employment work for its clients, including compliance counseling, high-stakes negotiations and discrimination litigation. The team has extensive experience of collective bargaining, and has recently represented both Wellesley College and Jordan Hospital in significant union negotiations.
**Sources say:** *"When I know they're on the case I'm relieved – I know I'll get the right answers. They are so incredibly responsive, and their client service is a cut above."*
**KEY INDIVIDUALS Diane Patrick** is highly a regarded labor and employment practitioner whose extensive expertise in representing nonprofit clients is particularly highlighted. She is described as *"practical and solution oriented"* by one client, and is praised for her ability to *"put complex issues in understandable terms."* **Robert Gordon** garners significant praise for his employer defense practice, and is recognized as a *"fabulous litigator"* by one source. He offers experience in having tried numerous cases at state and federal level, and his recent work includes acting for EnerNOC in the enforcement of a noncompete agreement. **Peter Ebb** heads the firm's labor and employment practice, and has established a broad practice with a particular emphasis on working with education and healthcare clients. He is characterized as *"knowledgeable, responsive and problem solving."* *"Outstanding litigator"* **David Mandel** handles a wide range of matters related to unions, and offers significant experience in acting for healthcare clients.

## Seyfarth Shaw LLP
### See profile on p.1262

**THE FIRM** This leading group is highly praised for its superior wage and hour class actions and audit work. Its practice is nationwide in scope, and includes a well-developed trial team able to handle a range of employment disputes. It is also highly experienced in workplace compliance and counseling, and works with clients such as Verizon, Target and Staples.
**Sources say:** *"I feel really comfortable with them, and if there is a pressing issue there is definitely the quick response that is needed."*
**KEY INDIVIDUALS Richard Alfred** (see p.1483) is a leading attorney in Massachusetts for high-stakes wage and hour class action work, and is well versed in handling a range of other disputes for clients. He is held in high esteem by peers and clients for his expertise in the field. **Lisa Damon** (see p.1489) chairs the firm's national practice, and offers extensive experience in both multiple and single plaintiff claims litigation on behalf of management. She is highly regarded by commentators for her strong labor and employment capabilities, and is praised by one client as being *"exceptionally good at delivering value."* **Arthur Telegen** (see p.1511) is a highly respected attorney in the labor and employment space, and has recently served as lead counsel to Verizon in a case dealing with unlawful activities during a strike. **Ariel Cudkowicz** (see

p.1489) is carving out a niche specialty in wage and hour tips cases within the hospitality sector. He is also highly respected for his litigation capabilities. **Patrick Bannon** (see p.1483) recently joined the Seyfarth team, and brings with him notable strength in complex wage and hour cases. His practice is national in scope, and he is highly regarded by both peers and clients.

## Band 2
## Labor & Employment

### Foley Hoag LLP
See profile on p.1521

THE FIRM This full-service firm continues to impress with the depth of resources it can deploy when working with its diverse client base. The team is held to be particularly strong in labor relations, but also covers traditional employment issues. The group is also noted for its proven capacity for trial and litigation success. The team regularly represents clients such as CVS Caremark, Starbucks and Dominion Energy.

Sources say: *"They deliver on what they say they are going to do – the work product is done well and on time."*

KEY INDIVIDUALS **Michael Rosen** (see p.1507) is particularly well versed in issues facing technology companies, and is a specialist in noncompete and nondisclosure litigation. Sources say: *"He's so easy to work with – he's always accessible, and gives very clear and good advice in terms of how to handle and navigate certain situations."* **Michele Whitham** (see p.1513) combines a strong traditional employment practice with her expertise in data security and privacy in the workplace. She has impressive litigation experience, and is described as *"a tough negotiator and a*

*real savvy litigator."* Chair of the firm's labor and employment group **James Bucking** (see p.1486) is respected by both peers and clients. He handles a wide range of matters across the country, and has a particular focus on union-related issues. He is praised for his *"straightforward and practical"* approach, as well as his *"good business sense."*

### Littler Mendelson, PC
See profile on p.688

THE FIRM This firm fields an impressive team of 24 lawyers from its Boston office, and is well placed to offer comprehensive labor and employment advice to a broad range of clients. It was recently engaged by Patheon Pharmaceutical to assist with its global employment matters, undertaking audits in several international jurisdictions.

Sources say: *"It is a national firm with offices everywhere, and has the ability to provide you with detailed, concise advice in a short timeframe and cost effectively."*

KEY INDIVIDUALS **David Casey** (see p.1487) is highly regarded as a *"preeminent trial lawyer"* in this space. His recent work includes the representation of CIGNA in a nationwide gender discrimination class action. **Anthony Rizzotti** (see p.1506) handles both labor and employment matters, and is widely admired in the field. *"He's very efficient, very smart, and has a good way with people – he always maintains good relationships,"* say clients. **Adam Forman** (see p.1491) is well versed in employment law on both a national and international scale. His recent work includes leading the global representation of Patheon Pharmaceutical referred to above. **Gregory Keating** (see p.1497) has a robust whistle-blower and retaliation practice. He is characterized by one source as someone who *"is very good at explaining options and weighing risks. He can look at all sides of an issue and present several solutions."*

## Band 3
## Labor & Employment

### Bello, Black & Welsh LLP

THE FIRM This local firm offers notable strength in employment litigation and labor management relations. The firm has a nationwide reach, with the team handling litigation matters across various states. The team also provides training and affirmative action programs for clients spanning a range of industries, including publishing and biotech.

Sources say: *"They have a seasoned team of partners who have been doing this a long time with all the judgment, perspective and knowledge base that brings."*

KEY INDIVIDUALS **John Welsh** is a talented litigator, and has notable experience in state, federal and appellate courts. He impresses commentators with his practical approach, and *"gets sensible solutions in a straightforward manner."* **Kenneth Bello** handles a wide range of labor and employment matters, and is highly experienced in this field. He works with clients from a broad spread of industries across the nation. **Josiah Black** is a skilled employ-

ment litigator, and is regularly called upon by clients to offer compliance and governance counseling.

### Jackson Lewis LLP
See profile on p.1982

THE FIRM This versatile nationwide firm is highly praised by sources, who admire the strength of the Boston office and its dedicated approach to client service. The team handles the full range of employment and labor matters, and counts among its specialties discrimination and harassment claims and class action litigations. Its broad client base includes Hyatt Hotels, Aspen Technology and Liberty Mutual.

Sources say: *"They are a good group of attorneys, and provide really strong client service."*

KEY INDIVIDUALS Managing partner of the Boston office **Andrew Pickett** (see p.1505) is highly regarded by sources. He offers notable expertise in counseling and litigating employment law matters.

### Mintz Levin Cohn Ferris Glovsky and Popeo PC
See profile on p.1523

THE FIRM This team is identified as a particularly strong group for labor and employment litigation. The team draws on the strengths of the firm to provide robust coverage to employers in the biotech and life sciences space. It handles a range of matters for its clients, and has a particular expertise in noncompete cases and the effects of state healthcare legislation on employers

Sources say: *"They are agile, responsive, creative and flexible – they have accommodated 100% of our needs."*

KEY INDIVIDUALS **Robert Gault** (see p.1492) has significant expertise in executive employment agreements, in particular those pertaining to foreign companies establishing themselves in the USA. Clients comment: *"You really want him on your side – he's tough, but also very thorough and realistic. He did a great job at being my advocate."* **Bret Cohen** (see p.1488) is praised for his skills as a *"great litigator,"* and offers significant expertise in handling disputes related to matters such as executive compensation, wrongful termination and noncompetition agreements. **Donald Schroeder** (see p.1509) has proven strength in matters involving labor relations, and also offers broader expertise in the employment arena. His recent highlights include leading negotiations for Cooley Dickinson Hospital in complex union contract discussions. He is praised as being a *"very good, practical guy,"* and is highly valued by clients for his commitment to cases.

### Nixon Peabody LLP
See profile on p.1526

THE FIRM This robust team is well placed to cover a broad range of labor and employment matters. It houses an experienced group of litigators, and recently handled numerous wage and hour class actions and whistle-blower cases. Clients span a wide range of industries, and are quick to highlight the firm's nationwide capabilities and experience.

Sources say: *"I have a great confidence in their knowledge of the law and their experience working within it – they understand the challenges that are unique to us. Their national scope is also very helpful."*

KEY INDIVIDUALS David Rosenthal (see p.1507) is a renowned employment litigator who is praised for his track record of trial success and pragmatic advice. Clients describe him as *"a counselor rather than just an adviser."* Gary Oberstein (see p.1504) heads the national wage and hour practice at Nixon, and is very active in assisting clients in affirmative action educational programs. He garners praise for his broad-based expertise in employment law matters.

## Ogletree, Deakins, Nash, Smoak & Stewart, PC
See profile on p.1110

THE FIRM This national labor and employment boutique attracts praise within the Massachusetts market for its deep resources and expertise. The firm's scope is global, and clients value its ability to handle their international employment needs. Its client base is diverse, with seasoned attorneys representing employers in the transport, retail and pharmaceutical industries. The team also has experience in representing government bodies such as the City of Boston.

Sources say: *"They have excellent subject matter experts in all areas of labor and employment law. They are one of the few firms in the country that can offer one-stop shopping for all HR issues."*

KEY INDIVIDUALS Michael Clarkson heads the labor and employment department, and is also the managing partner of the Boston office.

## Proskauer Rose LLP
See profile on p.2001

THE FIRM This team's practice is truly national in scope and continues to expand throughout the USA, and is highly skilled in litigation work. It also offers notable expertise in collective bargaining and employee benefits matters. Clients include Steward Health Care System, The Boston Globe and the Hearst Corporation. Recent work highlights include representing RBS Americas in a number of lawsuits concerning alleged violations of overtime payment agreements.

KEY INDIVIDUALS Mark Batten is a seasoned litigator with impressive experience in a wide range of employment law disputes. He has a nationwide class and collective action practice, and leads the RBS work referred to above. Peers praise his ability to *"get great results,"* and characterize him as *"a consummate negotiator."* Scott Faust is an authority on the representation of unionized employers in traditional labor and employment matters. He has particular experience in representing industrial and manufacturing clients on a nationwide basis. He is highly praised for his practical approach, with one interviewee stating: *"He knows how to convey issues and guide us through the more complex ones. He is very approachable and available, and understands our business."*

## Band 4
## Labor & Employment

### Davis, Malm & D'Agostine, P.C.
See profile on p.1519

THE FIRM This team offers expertise across the full range of employment law matters, and has the capabilities to represent both management and employees. The group is highly experienced in workplace counseling, and also offers expertise in litigating precedent-setting cases before state, federal and appellate courts.

Sources say: *"The attorneys are very client oriented, knowledgeable and proactive. They provide excellent representation."*

KEY INDIVIDUALS Gary Feldman (see p.1491) is a new entry to the rankings, and is an experienced employment litigator. His recent work includes representing a former employee of HEI Hospitality in an age discrimination case. His trial skills are particularly praised by clients, as is his *"knowledge of employment law and the pitfalls that need to be avoided."* Tamsin Kaplan (see p.1497) is new to the firm, and brings with her notable experience across a broad range of employment matters. Clients particularly value her strength in counseling and management training, praising her as being *"very thorough in her work."*

### Edwards Wildman Palmer LLP
See profile on p.1520

THE FIRM This team prides itself on its expertise in noncompete covenants and nondisclosure agreements. It also routinely handles a range of other matters, including discrimination claims and internal investigations. Notable clients include CVS Caremark, Bank of America and Steward Healthcare.

Sources say: *"This is a large firm with exceptional personal service. They have the staff to manage a full range of organizational needs, and have offices in multiple locations, so can facilitate the full range of issues that may emerge."*

KEY INDIVIDUALS Cochair of the labor and employment group Timothy Van Dyck (see p.1512) is a new entry to the rankings. He offers significant experience in employer representation, and is praised for his strong litigation capabilities.

### Hirsch Roberts Weinstein LLP

THE FIRM This well-known Boston boutique has a particular focus on litigation within the labor and employment space. The team covers a broad scope of workplace issues in its counseling practice, and also handles a range of union matters. It recently developed a specialist data security team to address the new regulations surrounding protection of personal information.

KEY INDIVIDUALS Jeffrey Hirsch has widespread experience in representing a diverse client base of employers. He has worked on wage and hour litigations, labor relations, and a range of statutory claims. Seasoned labor and employment attorney Jerome Weinstein is highly experienced in representing clients from a wide range of industries. His practice focuses on both litigation and counseling.

### Holland & Knight LLP
See profile on p.1028

THE FIRM The expertise of this Boston team is far reaching, and includes civil rights claims, OSHA, whistle-blower cases and noncompete cases. Its attorneys handle labor-related matters and litigation in employment with equal aplomb. The firm has particular expertise in representing clients drawn from the healthcare, technology and education sectors, while still maintaining a broader client base.

Sources say: *"They take the time to really get to know our business. Regardless of how big or small the issue may be, they ask the right questions and get the right results."*

KEY INDIVIDUALS Miriam McKendall (see p.1501) focuses her practice on the education sector. She has recently worked on cases involving allegations of discrimination, sexual harassment and violations of the Family Medical Leave Act. Sources state that she is *"responsive, an excellent problem solver, and a partner throughout the process."*

### Skoler, Abbott & Presser, PC
See profile on p.1533

THE FIRM This management-side boutique is well positioned in the New England market to cater to employers' needs. The team has a notable strength in labor relations, but is also well versed in the full range of labor and employment issues. The group represents clients drawn from a wide range of industries.

Sources say: *"They are patient and have an ability to explain complex legal matters to non-legal individuals, and they have good commercial awareness."*

KEY INDIVIDUALS Ralph Abbott is a leading figure in the firm, and is well known in the market. Clients reap the benefits of his extensive experience, with one commentator saying: *"He's heard almost every trick and situation before, so he rarely gets surprised – he always gives measured responses."* He has significant expertise in matters related to labor relations. Susan Fentin (see p.1491) offers extensive experience in handling employment litigation and counseling. One commentator characterizes her as *"extremely talented, and someone who has a great style in relating to people. She has always provided solid advice."*

### WilmerHale
See profile on p.930

THE FIRM This national team offers an impressive scope, both geographically and in terms of depth of expertise. It offers significant experience in employment law matters, and provides clients with specifically adapted training programs. It works with clients including the Museum of Science and Bose Corporation.

KEY INDIVIDUALS Jonathan Rosenfeld (see p.1507) is a respected practitioner in the employment space, and is a member of the Dodd-Frank whistle-blower working group. His experience extends to labor-related matters, including collective bargaining negotiations. Neil Jacobs (see p.1496) is a senior figure in the labor and employment Bar, and has a wealth of experience in collective bargaining negotiations. He works with clients from a wide range of industries, and is an experienced litigator.

## Band 1
## Labor & Employment: Mainly Plaintiffs Representation

### Shilepsky Hartley Robb Casey Michon LLP
**See profile on p.1532**

**THE FIRM** This boutique firm is dedicated to plaintiff-side representation, for which it is generally acknowledged to be a leader in the Massachusetts market. Its practice is particularly focused on executive representation in matters ranging from enforcement of employment contracts to change in control and departure agreements. Clients appreciate the team's personal and dedicated approach. **Sources say:** *"They are terrific advocates, and are also fair and balanced. They are realistic in setting expectations, and incredibly diligent about following through with them."*
**KEY INDIVIDUALS James Hartley** (see p.1495) is a highly respected employment adviser and litigator, whose practice focuses largely on executive representation. He is praised by commentators for his longstanding experience in the field, and for his *"calm demeanor"* and creative approach to disputes. **Nancy Shilepsky** (see p.1509) is revered in this space for her expertise in executive representation. Her practice is broad, and covers complex employment disputes as well as high-profile discrimination claims. She is praised for her unwavering dedication to her clients, and has a *"very down-to-earth, practical mindset."* **Katherine Michon** (see p.1502) is highly regarded for her prowess in executive transition matters. Clients clearly appreciate her practical approach: *"She puts you at ease, and is able to put the situation in clear, logical terms so that you can evaluate your options."*

## Band 2
## Labor & Employment: Mainly Plaintiffs Representation

### Lichten & Liss-Riordan, P.C.
**THE FIRM** This boutique firm is particularly strong in wage and hour class action work, with a team dedicated to plaintiff and union representation in this space. The firm has considerable arbitration, trial and appellate experience, and is particularly well versed in plaintiff tips cases and employment issues relating to immigrant workers.
**KEY INDIVIDUALS Shannon Liss-Riordan** is considered a leader of the wage and hour litigation Bar, where she is described by peers as *"the reigning plaintiff's champion."* She has a nationwide practice, and is highly experienced in cases involving tipped employees. **Harold Lichten** is held in high esteem for his expertise as a seasoned litigator, with a wealth of experience in state, federal and appellate courts.

He has particular expertise in representing police and firefighter unions.

### Messing, Rudavsky & Weliky PC
**THE FIRM** This boutique firm retains its position as one of the most prominent plaintiff's firms in Massachusetts. Its three partners are well positioned to handle a broad range of labor and employment matters for clients employed in both the private and public sector.
**KEY INDIVIDUALS Ellen Messing** is one of the key partners based at the firm.

### Segal Roitman LLP
**THE FIRM** This talented boutique continues to impress clients with its work in the labor and employment space, which includes discrimination claims, compensation disputes and union representation. Its reputation in labor matters is particularly outstanding, and it regularly represents unions in a wide range of sectors.
**KEY INDIVIDUALS Donald Siegel** is a key contact at the firm.

## Other Notable Practitioners

**Jody Newman** of Collora LLP is a renowned practitioner at the plaintiff's Bar, who has the skill and expertise to handle a wide variety of matters for employees. She has a specialty in representing clients in government service and national defense. **Thomas Shirley** (see p.1509) chairs the labor, employment and benefits group at Choate Hall & Stewart LLP. He is respected in the market as a highly experienced litigator in the employment space, and also offers expertise in labor work. He is described by one peer as *"effective, sensible and practical"* in his approach. **Joseph Ambash** (see p.1483) of Fisher & Phillips LLP is considered *"an invaluable and indispensable resource for advocacy and advice."* He regularly represents clients including the City of Boston, the University of Massachusetts and Brown University. **Terence McCourt** (see p.1501) of Greenberg Traurig, LLP is a new entry to the rankings, and is highly respected by market commentators. He has a strong reputation for labor relations work, and also handles employment matters. Sources praise him as being *"collaborative, business-minded and always thoughtful."* **Anne Josephson** of Kotin, Crabtree & Strong, LLP has a broad practice in employment law, with a particular focus on litigation matters. She offers notable experience in representing employees and employers from a range of industries. Her colleague at Kotin, Crabtree & Strong, LLP, **Sharen Litwin**, is equally respected, and has the skill and experience to undertake a variety of cases in the employment field. **Heather Sussman** (see p.1511) of McDermott Will &

Emery LLP is a talented employment lawyer with a particular strength in workplace privacy and data security issues. Her clients are impressed with her *"invaluable knowledge of employment laws,"* and praise her as being *"exceptionally responsive."* The *"phenomenal"* **Ilene Robinson Sunshine** (see p.1511) of Sullivan & Worcester LLP is a venerable expert in a wide range of employment law matters. Her practice encompasses noncompetition, discrimination litigation and employee discipline. **Jean Musiker** (see p.1503) of Sugarman, Rogers, Barshak & Cohen, PC is a well-established employment attorney who is highly respected by commentators. She is described as *"an excellent lawyer who is very smart and pragmatic."* **Louis Rodriques** (see p.1507) of Bingham McCutchen LLP is an experienced litigator who handles a range of labor and employment matters. Clients praise his pragmatic and collaborative approach, highlighting *"his depth of knowledge in the employment space."* He recently represented CleanNet in a class action suit concerning various violations of the rights of independent contractors. **Jenny Cooper** (see p.1488) is also at Bingham McCutchen LLP, and is a new entry to the rankings. She undertakes significant amounts of counseling work on behalf of her growing client base, and is building up a robust litigation portfolio. Clients praise her impressive approach to handling sensitive matters. **Ellen Zucker** of Burns & Levinson LLP is a highly respected plaintiff-side litigator, whose trial experience includes discrimination, harassment and breach of contract cases. She is singled out by commentators for her strong advocacy skills. **Joshua Davis** recently returned to Goulston & Storrs, and is held in high regard by sources for his experience in labor and employment matters. His business-oriented approach impresses clients, with one commenting: *"He is very willing to offer pragmatic advice and help the client work out what to do, without just telling them what the law is."* **Russell Beck** of Beck Reed Riden LLP is respected by commentators for his skills as a litigator. His areas of specialty include noncompete and trade secrets matters. **Sara Goldsmith Schwartz** (see p.1509) is the president of Schwartz Hannum PC, and offers extensive experience in the representation of employers on a nationwide scale. *"She has the ability to really listen to you, and boil down whatever your particular issues are in a very quick and succinct way,"* stated one client. At the same firm, **William Hannum** (see p.1494) is adept at handling high-profile employment matters, and is praised for his ability to work with all parties to find the best solution. Clients comment: *"He is respectful and responsive, and people respond to that."* **Lori Clark** (see p.1487), also of Schwartz Hannum PC, recently arrived from Hinckley, Allen & Snyder. She has a management-side practice, and is highly experienced in a range of litigation and counseling matters.

## LITIGATION

White-Collar Crime & Government Investigations p.1471

Commentary about individuals can be found under their firm's paragraph. If the firm has no paragraph (is not ranked) look at Other Notable Practitioners.

### Litigation: General Commercial

#### Leading Firms

**Band 1**
Bingham McCutchen LLP *
Goodwin Procter LLP *
Ropes & Gray LLP *
Skadden, Arps, Slate, Meagher & Flom LLP & Affiliates *
WilmerHale *

**Band 2**
Choate Hall & Stewart LLP *
Collora LLP *
Foley Hoag LLP *
McDermott Will & Emery LLP *
Mintz Levin Cohn Ferris Glovsky and Popeo PC *
Nutter McClennen & Fish LLP *

**Band 3**
Foley & Lardner LLP *
Goulston & Storrs
Nixon Peabody LLP *

### Senior Statesmen

**Senior Statesmen: distinguished older practitioners**

| | |
|---|---|
| Keating Michael | Foley Hoag LLP * |
| Montgomery John T | Ropes & Gray LLP |
| Muldoon Jr Robert J | Sherin and Lodgen LLP (ONP) [†] |
| Popeo R Robert | Mintz Levin Cohn Ferris Glovsky * |
| Renehan Richard | Goulston & Storrs |
| Todd Owen | Todd & Weld LLP (ONP) [†] |

### Leading Individuals

**Band 1**

| | |
|---|---|
| Carroll James R | Skadden, Arps, Slate, Meagher & Flom * |
| Donovan John D | Ropes & Gray LLP |
| Hanify John D | Jones Day (ONP) [†] * |
| Kociubes Joseph L | Bingham McCutchen LLP * |
| Lukey Joan | Ropes & Gray LLP |
| Ware Jr Paul F | Goodwin Procter LLP * |
| Zielinski Richard M | Goulston & Storrs |

**Band 2**

| | |
|---|---|
| Albano Jonathan M | Bingham McCutchen LLP * |
| Frank Jr Robert S | Choate Hall & Stewart LLP * |
| Goldberg Daniel L | Bingham McCutchen LLP * |
| Harshbarger Scott | Proskauer Rose LLP (ONP) [†] |
| Mungovan Timothy W | Proskauer Rose LLP (ONP) [†] |
| Parsigian Kenneth J | Latham & Watkins (ONP) [†] |
| Poss Stephen D | Goodwin Procter LLP * |
| Tuteur Michael | Foley & Lardner LLP |

**Band 3**

| | |
|---|---|
| Arrowood Lisa G | Arrowood.Peters LLP (ONP) [†] |
| Cahill Mark D | Choate Hall & Stewart LLP * |
| Feldman Paul L | Davis, Malm & D'Agostine, P.C. (ONP) [†] * |
| Felter John Kenneth | Ropes & Gray LLP |
| Gleason Daniel J | Nutter McClennen & Fish LLP * |
| Kaler Robert | McCarter & English, LLP (ONP) [†] * |
| O'Connor Kevin | Hinckley, Allen & Snyder LLP (ONP) [†] |
| O'Flaherty Kevin | Goulston & Storrs |
| O'Toole Patrick | Weil, Gotshal & Manges LLP (ONP) [†] * |
| Swirbalus Mark | Goulston & Storrs |
| Weld Chris | Todd & Weld LLP (ONP) [†] |
| Wolkoff Harvey J | Ropes & Gray LLP |

**Up-and-coming individuals**

| | |
|---|---|
| Sablone Jonathan | Nixon Peabody LLP * |

### Litigation: Securities

#### Leading Individuals

**Star individuals**

| | |
|---|---|
| Donovan John D | Ropes & Gray LLP |
| Dougherty Thomas J | Skadden, Arps, Slate, Meagher & Flom * |
| Rudman Jeffrey | WilmerHale * |

**Band 1**

| | |
|---|---|
| Bodner Randall W | Ropes & Gray LLP |
| Dittmar James S | Goodwin Procter LLP * |
| Hershman Jordan D | Bingham McCutchen LLP * |
| Paine William H | WilmerHale * |
| Pastuszenski Brian E | Goodwin Procter LLP * |
| Poss Stephen D | Goodwin Procter LLP * |
| Robinson Andrea J | WilmerHale * |

**Band 2**

| | |
|---|---|
| Batter III John F | WilmerHale * |
| Boland Beth | Bingham McCutchen LLP * |
| Hemr Kurt Wm | Skadden, Arps, Slate, Meagher & Flom * |
| Jones Robert | Ropes & Gray LLP |
| Steinberg Laura | Sullivan & Worcester LLP (ONP) [†] * |
| Sylvia Jack | Mintz Levin Cohn Ferris Glovsky * |

* Indicates firm / individual with profile.
[†] ONP = Other Notable Practitioner.

## Band 1

### Bingham McCutchen LLP
See profile on p.1515

**THE FIRM** This litigation team is firmly established as a leader at both state and national levels. It has the resources and bench strength to bring top-notch expertise to the full range of litigation matters, and is often sought out for its experience in complex, high-stakes cases. The firm's list of high-profile clients includes GM, Bank of America, JPMorgan Chase, Starbucks, Daimler and the Boston Globe.
**Sources say:** "*I would rate the firm as being at the top for trial capacity, issue identification, written product, pragmatism and talent in negotiations.*"
**KEY INDIVIDUALS Jordan Hershman** (see p.1495) cochairs the securities group, and has been very active as lead defense counsel to Freddie Mac in a series of securities fraud class actions, recently securing a landmark win. He is so admired by his peers that he has on occasion been engaged by his opposing counsel to represent them – a testament to his presence and prowess in the field. **Joseph Kociubes** (see p.1498) is a well-respected commercial trial litigator with experience in both domestic and international arbitration. Notably, he represented MassMutual in a class action relating to the Madoff Ponzi scheme, and has a strong track record in complex jury trials. "*I have great confidence in him and his ability to assess risk in a matter. He is truly great in a trial – I haven't seen anyone who can equal him,*" one source enthused. **Mark Robinson** (see p.1507) is a leading figure in the white-collar sphere. He is particularly well known for his work in regulatory enforcement and corporate crisis management, undertaking both litigation and preventive work for high-profile clients. He is

described as "*a strong strategic thinker who focuses on the best outcome for the company. He is very client focused and articulate.*" **Jonathan Albano** (see p.1483) is deputy chair of the firm's litigation practice and has extensive experience in jury, bench and appellate trials. He represents financial service companies, educational institutions, high-profile individuals and newspapers, including the Boston Globe, in a broad range of commercial and constitutional cases. **Daniel Goldberg** (see p.1493) has a broad national practice in commercial litigation. Of note, he recently secured a substantial win in state court for the New

England Patriots in their dispute with the Kraft Group. "*He is very smart and resourceful,*" say sources. **Beth Boland** (see p.1485) advises on securities litigation and corporate governance, and represents an impressive list of clients, including JPMorgan Chase, Starbucks and companies in the investment management field. Clients turn to her for her experience assisting companies facing inquiries from regulatory bodies, saying: "*Her extremely detailed and in-depth knowledge is invaluable. She has a good sense of how things work on the ground.*"

### Goodwin Procter LLP
See profile on p.1522

**THE FIRM** This practice group operates to a high standard at the state, federal and international levels, handling significant anti-corruption work overseas and high-stakes litigation across a broad range of industries within the USA. Clients include Teva Pharmaceutical, Nomura Securities, Bruker and the Children's Hospital of Boston.
**Sources say:** "*They are deeply experienced thinkers and strategists, first-rate writers and superb trial lawyers.*"
**KEY INDIVIDUALS Brian Pastuszenski** (see p.1504) specializes in shareholder litigation and is described by clients as "*a dean of the class action Bar.*" He serves as national defense counsel for Countrywide Financial Corporation and has represented it in a large number of cases, including multidistrict litigation involving 30 securities suits. **James Dittmar** (see p.1490) is a leading figure in the securities field and is hailed by clients as "*a superb trial lawyer.*" He frequently represents financial services providers and

## Litigation: White-Collar Crime & Government Investigations
### Leading Individuals

#### Band 1

| | |
|---|---|
| Cinquegrana Jack | Choate Hall & Stewart LLP * |
| Keefe Robert D | WilmerHale * |
| Levy Joshua S | Ropes & Gray LLP |
| McPhee Joan | Ropes & Gray LLP |
| O'Connor Brien T | Ropes & Gray LLP |
| Pearlstein Mark W | McDermott Will & Emery LLP * |
| Robinson Mark E | Bingham McCutchen LLP * |
| Savage Joseph F | Goodwin Procter LLP * |
| Theodorou Nicholas C | Foley Hoag LLP * |

#### Band 2

| | |
|---|---|
| Burroughs Allison | Nutter McClennen & Fish LLP * |
| Collora Michael A | Collora LLP |
| Cronan Todd | Goodwin Procter LLP * |
| Fee Michael K | Ropes & Gray LLP |
| Frongillo Thomas C | Weil, Gotshal & Manges LLP (ONP) † * |
| Kendall Michael | McDermott Will & Emery LLP * |
| Kettlewell William H | Collora LLP |
| Lloyd Diana K | Choate Hall & Stewart LLP * |
| Loucks Michael | Skadden, Arps, Slate, Meagher & Flom * |
| Miner Tracy A | Mintz Levin Cohn Ferris Glovsky * |
| Murphy Martin F | Foley Hoag LLP * |
| Pollack Barry S | Sullivan & Worcester LLP (ONP) † |
| Rehnquist James C | Goodwin Procter LLP * |
| Tuteur Michael | Foley & Lardner LLP * |
| Ullmann Robert L | Nutter McClennen & Fish LLP * |

* Indicates individual with profile.
† ONP = Other Notable Practitioner.

asset management companies in litigation and enforcement proceedings. **Stephen Poss** (see p.1506) routinely represents high-profile business and private equity clients in securities matters, and counsels directors on compliance issues. He is currently representing several leading financial institutions in MBS-related litigation. **Joseph Savage** (see p.1508) is revered for his expertise in white-collar and government investigations. *"He has incredible judgment and has the ability to distill complex facts down to simple elements."* **Paul Ware** (see p.1513) is an *"excellent trial lawyer"* with substantial experience in white-collar defense and commercial litigation. He was recently appointed independent counsel for an investigation of the state's probation department by the Massachusetts Supreme Court. **James Rehnquist** (see p.1506) is described as *"one hell of an attorney"* and brings his experience as a federal prosecutor to bear in his white-collar defense practice. He also has substantial experience advising on civil litigation. **Todd Cronan** (see p.1489) is lead outside counsel for GE, and represents numerous financial services providers and investors. Clients appreciate his calm and professional demeanor, as well as his *"ability to gain everyone's confidence with just the right amount of persuasion. He has good intuition."*

## Ropes & Gray LLP
See profile on p.1528

**THE FIRM** This highly respected firm is recommended for its representation of both public and private companies in complex, high-stakes matters, including securities, shareholder and insurance litigation, data breach matters and class actions. Its impressive client roster includes Bain Capital, Genzyme and the Timberland Company, among many other high-profile organizations.

**Sources say:** *"They are outstanding – one of the best in Boston. They're successful, responsive and good at rightsizing jobs."*

**KEY INDIVIDUALS** The experienced **John Donovan** is *"as good as it gets"* in securities litigation. He represents clients in the mutual fund and financial services industry, and has significant experience in shareholder litigation. Recent highlights include work for Blackstone Capital and NSTAR. **Joan Lukey** adds depth to the firm's complex business litigation practice. She has notably represented the novelist Patricia Cornwell and her company, Cornwell Entertainment, in a variety of business disputes and civil litigation matters. Securities litigation practice group leader **Randall Bodner** represents clients in a broad range of industries. Peers say: *"You don't want to have him as an adversary, but you respect him as a lawyer, an intellect and an advocate."* **Joshua Levy** is recognized for his expertise in cases relating to the healthcare and pharmaceutical industries. His practice focuses on white-collar defense and investigations, and interviewees highlight his ability to achieve *"absolutely stunning results."* **Joan McPhee** is a key member of the white-collar group and recently represented a client who had been implicated in the high-profile Gulf of Mexico oil disaster. She is also co-lead counsel for Medical Information Working Group, an association of leading pharmaceutical companies. *"World-class white-collar lawyer"* **Brien O'Connor** is a hugely experienced and well-respected litigator who delivers both quality service and quality results. **Michael Fee** has a strong reputation in the healthcare sector. He has represented Medtronic, IASIS Healthcare and UMass Memorial Healthcare in a wide range of matters over the past year. IP expert **John Kenneth Felter** maintains his reputation in this area and has significant experience at the state, federal and appellate court level. **Robert Jones** is a strong securities and general business litigator and has a wealth of experience in matters relating to SEC investigations for public company and private equity clients. *"He can speak the business language while also being an extraordinary litigator; he has such integrity and is very persuasive."* **Harvey Wolkoff** is an accomplished business litigator at both the state and federal level. He is developing expertise in data breach litigation, and represents such high-profile clients as State Street Bank and Ameriprise Financial Services. **John Montgomery** is a leading figure in the firm and has represented numerous pharmaceutical clients in several significant court victories.

## Skadden, Arps, Slate, Meagher & Flom LLP & Affiliates
See profile on p.2008

**THE FIRM** This highly respected group has a strong reputation both in Boston and nationwide, and is revered for the scope and strength of its global reach. With competencies covering the spectrum of litigation, the team has particular strength in private securities and SEC work, and has represented clients in a number of class and derivative actions. Its diverse client base covers the hi-tech, insurance, financial and healthcare sectors. Notable clients include Guardian Life Insurance, Roth Capital Partners and Aspen Technology.

**Sources say:** *"It's an outstanding firm that get things done overnight. I call it the A-Team, and I would choose no one else."*

**KEY INDIVIDUALS** The eminent **Thomas Dougherty** (see p.1490) is a highly regarded securities litigator. He has successfully represented Guardian Life Insurance in a series of cases, including the dismissal of a class action. He also won a mandatory injunction on behalf of EMC. **James Carroll** (see p.1487) is *"an outstanding litigator"* who has a wealth of experience representing clients in the financial and insurance sectors in SEC investigations and government enforcement proceedings. **Kurt Wm Hemr** (see p.1495) is a securities expert who enjoyed significant trial success in 2012, including a $10 million contractual dispute in Texas and a London-based arbitration. Clients describe him as *"thorough and a great researcher; there were tough times, but he put everything into perspective and told us what all our options were."* **Michael Loucks** (see p.1500) is a new addition to the group, bringing expertise in healthcare litigation. He specializes in foreign corrupt practice and false claims work, and has strong international experience. Commentators say: *"He is literally feared by his opposition because he is so stinking good."*

## WilmerHale
See profile on p.930

**THE FIRM** WilmerHale undertakes prominent trial work throughout the USA and, with more than 126 litigation specialists in Boston, has unparalleled bench strength in this field. It is recommended for its strength in general commercial, securities and white-collar matters, catering to a diverse range of clients and industries. The team has impressive trial experience and maintains its reputation as a top choice for tough cases.

**Sources say:** *"They were just very, very good – they always made us feel comfortable and they really understood what the issues were."* *"We would go to them for a big-ticket class action."*

**KEY INDIVIDUALS** Practice stalwart **Jeffrey Rudman** (see p.1507) is a revered securities litigator who routinely handles high-profile matters with unique issues at stake. Clients and peers view him as a leader in the field. Market commentators hail **William Paine** (see p.1504) as one of the top commercial litigators in the state. His reputation has been further cemented by recent high-profile work for prominent financial sector clients. **John Batter** (see p.1484) is a white-collar expert whose clients say he is *"great at breaking down the case – we are always very happy with his analysis."* He has a strong profile in the technology space. **Robert Keefe** (see p.1497) has considerable experience handling criminal investigations, and has been active representing clients in cases involving the theft of trade secrets and violations of the antikickback statute. *"He brought a tremendous credibility on our behalf – he was great at shepherding us through an unfamiliar process and dealing with our concerns,"* one client said. **Andrea Robinson** (see p.1506) is a go-to lawyer in the securities space. She is equally adept in litigation and regulatory enforcement, and her practice has a large focus on issues facing the financial services sector.

## Band 2

### Choate Hall & Stewart LLP
See profile on p.1517

THE FIRM This well-respected Boston-based group has a thriving national practice, driven by its expertise in white-collar crime. The team also has particular strength in IP and healthcare matters, and advises on bankruptcy and private equity-related litigation. Notable clients include Akamai, Hewlett-Packard and Samsung.

Sources say: *"It's a good firm with great resources."*

KEY INDIVIDUALS **Robert Frank** (see p.1492) is a seasoned litigator accustomed to handling high-profile commercial and IP cases. In recent highlights, he represented Hewlett-Packard in a $4 billion contract dispute with Oracle. Clients describe him as *"endlessly professional and relentless."* **Jack Cinquegrana** (see p.1487) is highly regarded as a white-collar specialist with an established profile in the pharmaceutical and healthcare sectors. He recently advised Merck in relation to a seven-year investigation regarding the drug VIOXX, and has represented various other high-profile clients in sensitive matters. **Diana Lloyd** (see p.1500) is lauded for her substantial expertise in the white-collar world, with a practice that covers a range of healthcare and securities fraud work. Commentators praise her calm manner and her strategic approach: *"She's intuitive about where things are headed, and can see around corners. She's very smart but she doesn't wear it on her sleeve."* General commercial litigator **Mark Cahill** (see p.1487) specializes in representing insurance companies, and in private equity and M&A-related cases. Clients appreciate that *"he is thorough and very quick to understand the situation, and has a fantastic ability to dig deep into all the relevant areas."*

### Collora LLP
See profile on p.1518

THE FIRM This boutique firm handles an impressive range of litigation in both the civil and criminal spheres, and is very highly regarded by clients and competitors alike. Areas of practice include healthcare advocacy, business and employment litigation, alternative dispute resolution and appellate law.

Sources say: *"An exceptional firm for litigation – it has great expertise in representing both individuals and companies."*

KEY INDIVIDUALS **William Kettlewell** is described as *"a top-notch lawyer"* with a strong reputation for white-collar defense work. **Michael Collora** enjoys an equally strong reputation within the market, and is known for his involvement in complex litigation.

### Foley Hoag LLP
See profile on p.1521

THE FIRM This group advises on a broad range of high-profile litigation at the state, federal and international levels. It is highlighted for its strength in professional liability and malpractice cases, as well as business torts, corporate governance, white-collar defense and insurance recovery litigation. Notable clients include PwC, the Massachusetts Port Authority and KPMG.

Sources say: *"I have been incredibly impressed with their commitment and the quality of their work."*

KEY INDIVIDUALS Accomplished white-collar litigator **Nicholas Theodorou** (see p.1511) chairs the firm's business crimes and government investigations group. He is described as *"outstanding, thorough and a good judge of the situation."* **Martin Murphy** (see p.1503) maintains a strong reputation in the white-collar world. He recently brought a high-value investment fraud case to a successful conclusion. *"Extraordinary talent"* and department chair **Michael Keating** (see p.1497) advised on a seminal case in the Massachusetts Supreme Court defending the right of the judiciary not to disclose details of their judicial deliberations. He has also acted on several other high-profile public interest cases over the past year.

### McDermott Will & Emery LLP
See profile on p.1258

THE FIRM This Boston group is renowned for its leading healthcare and securities litigation practices, both in Massachusetts and across the country. Recent highlights include representing Goldman Sachs in relation to allegations of securities fraud. The firm also acted for Premier, an alliance of hospitals and health systems, on a claim concerning allegations of trade libel. Other clients include State Street, US Bank and Concentra.

Sources say: *"I really appreciate their responsiveness and breadth of knowledge. The lawyers there have a great deal of experience."*

KEY INDIVIDUALS **Mark Pearlstein** (see p.1505) specializes in the defense of SEC charges and internal investigations. He recently successfully defended former State Street executive Sean Flannery against allegations relating to subprime mortgage fraud. **Michael Kendall** (see p.1498) has significant experience with both national and cross-border litigation. Recent work includes advising on the resolution of a $1 billion whistle-blower suit relating to alleged Medicare fraud, and representing the Demoulas Super Market chain in a variety of matters, including a pension case. Clients benefit from his meticulous preparation, with one commentator remarking: *"His cross-examination was astonishing – he had prepared every possible question and answer."*

### Mintz Levin Cohn Ferris Glovsky and Popeo PC
See profile on p.1523

THE FIRM This team handles the full range of litigation work, with a strong focus on SEC investigations and complex business litigation, including bet-the-company work. The firm represents a notable roster of high-profile senior executives, CEOs, public officials and politicians. Other key clients include Teva, Quest Diagnostics and Liberty Mutual.

Sources say: *"They are not presumptuous in the way they manage a matter. They work with, consult and respect the client."* *"They have a great bench – they can put together a great team, day or night."*

KEY INDIVIDUALS **Tracy Miner** (see p.1502) is a respected white-collar specialist with a strong track record. She has worked with a number of high-profile clients on sensitive matters. Established securities practitioner **Jack Sylvia** (see p.1511) impresses commentators with his experience representing a broad client base in trials and arbitrations. He is also recognized for his deep knowledge of regulatory law. **Robert Popeo** (see p.1505) is an eminent litigator who is well known in the Massachusetts market. Clients and peers regard him as one of the most distinguished figures in the field.

### Nutter McClennen & Fish LLP
See profile on p.1527

THE FIRM This Boston law firm operates a broad litigation practice and has particular strength in product liability litigation, business torts and government enforcement. Clients include Stryker Biotech, Delta Dental of Massachusetts and Safeco Insurance.

KEY INDIVIDUALS **Allison Burroughs** (see p.1487) is recognized for her expertise in white-collar crime and government investigations at both the state and federal level. She has significant experience representing clients in the life sciences industry. Former federal prosecutor **Robert Ullmann** (see p.1512) has an established white-collar practice. He recently secured the dismissal of healthcare fraud allegations against the former national sales director of Stryker Biotech. **Daniel Gleason** (see p.1493) focuses on intellectual property, life sciences and insurance litigation. Commentators describe him as *"very smart and seasoned, with good judgment."*

## Band 3

### Foley & Lardner LLP
See profile on p.2588

THE FIRM The Boston arm of this national firm is home to a well-respected litigation department, and is especially well regarded for its healthcare practice. The team regularly represents individuals as well as corporate clients, such as Wireless Properties and AIG.

Sources say: *"We always use them for litigation – it's an excellent firm with great lawyers."*

KEY INDIVIDUALS **Michael Tuteur** has a strong litigation practice which is national in scope. Sources say: *"He is* *very good on his feet and he never skips a beat – he has a very strong ability and reputation."*

## Goulston & Storrs

**THE FIRM** This firm is renowned for its real estate practice and stands out for its expertise in related litigation. The Boston litigation department also has a strong reputation for its involvement in professional liability and medical malpractice cases. Its diverse client base includes the Dana-Farber/Harvard Cancer Center, New England Development and the Attorney's Liability Assurance Society.

**Sources say:** *"The expertise is outstanding."*

**KEY INDIVIDUALS Richard Zielinski** is revered for his courtroom skills. *"He is very comfortable in briefing and arguing cases, has a good vision as to strategy and tactics, and takes a long-term view of the case,"* say sources. He recently defended Cynosure in a high-value class action concerning alleged violations of the Telephone Consumer Protection Act. **Mark Swirbalus** has a substantial probate and client trust practice, and is an experienced litigator in that area. His clients include individuals, financial institutions and charities, and his practice is national in scope. **Kevin O'Flaherty** is admired for his calm demeanor and straightforward, practical approach: *"He does everything without ego or resistance. He's a consummate professional."* He recently represented the O'Connor Group in its successful defense of a challenge against its permits relating to a large-scale multifamily development project. The distinguished **Richard Renehan** has a solid reputation built on years of experience. Recent work highlights include defending a national law firm in a professional malpractice suit.

## Nixon Peabody LLP

See profile on p.1526

**THE FIRM** This group has established a strong reputation in the healthcare and financial services sectors, in which it is well equipped to handle both litigation and government investigations. Recent highlights saw the firm win a $3 billion healthcare fraud settlement on behalf of GlaxoSmithKline. Other notable clients include Credit Suisse, Boston Capital and AT&T.

**KEY INDIVIDUALS Jonathan Sablone** (see p.1508) is recognized for his specialization in private funds disputes, e-discovery and digital evidence. He recently represented Credit Suisse in MBS-related litigation.

## Other Notable Practitioners

**Lisa Arrowood** of Arrowood Peters LLP has a strong reputation in the personal injury space. Her practice also covers employment law and business litigation. **Paul Feldman** (see p.1491) of Davis, Malm & D'Agostine, P.C. is highlighted for his expertise in environmental matters. He also advises on insurance and business disputes. *"He's an excellent litigator,"* say sources. **John Hanify** (see p.1494) is one of the key litigation partners at the new Boston office of Jones Day, and has extensive experience across the spectrum of litigation matters. Clients say: *"He has great judgment and is a great trial lawyer."* **Robert Kaler** (see p.1497) of McCarter & English, LLP is a go-to litigator for clients in the hi-tech and IP space. Sources say: *"He immerses himself in the case and understands every technical detail – he really becomes an expert in the subject matter."* **Timothy Mungovan** of Proskauer Rose LLP is sought after for his *"excellent legal knowledge and business acumen."* Sources also highlight his cross-border expertise. Also at Proskauer, **Scott Harshbarger** is described by clients as *"an aggressive advocate and a great balancing force."* He represents a diverse client base within the general commercial space. **Barry Pollack** of Sullivan & Worcester LLP is an authority on white-collar crime and government investigations. He has undertaken a great deal of work stemming from the Madoff Ponzi scheme. At the same firm, **Laura Steinberg** (see p.1510) operates a practice which is national in scope, focusing on securities and financial services litigation. She is described as an *"extremely bright, knowledgeable and practical lawyer"* who understands the business goals of her clients. **Chris Weld** of Todd & Weld LLP specializes in high-profile commercial litigation and is regarded by peers as a talented lawyer who is highly effective in court. Also at Todd & Weld is **Owen Todd**, who is described as *"a force of nature"* in the courtroom and is highly regarded by peers and clients alike. **Thomas Frongillo** (see p.1492) is the head of the litigation department at Weil, Gotshal & Manges LLP and specializes in white-collar criminal defense. *"He is one of the smartest people I've ever met and he's humble about it,"* said one client, adding: *"He brings a very calming influence."* At the same firm, **Patrick O'Toole** (see p.1504) is described by clients as *"the whole package – excellent on paper, in person and in court. He is an earnest advocate who exudes quiet confidence and expertise."* **Kenneth Parsigian** of Latham & Watkins is renowned for his expertise in product liability litigation and is lauded by his competitors as a standout lawyer in this area. **Robert Muldoon** of Sherin and Lodgen LLP is a stalwart of the Massachusetts Bar, and is highly respected by peers for his many and varied courtroom achievements. **Kevin O'Connor** joined Hinckley, Allen & Snyder LLP in 2012. He handles complex business disputes, and is admired by clients for his pleasant demeanor and strategic approach. *"He takes a personal interest in the outcome of the case, but doesn't get emotional or argue for the sake of arguing,"* say sources.

## PRIVATE EQUITY BUYOUTS & VENTURE CAPITAL INVESTMENT

Commentary about individuals can be found under their firm's paragraph. If the firm has no paragraph (is not ranked) look at Other Notable Practitioners.

### Private Equity: Buyouts

**Leading Firms**

**Band 1**
Ropes & Gray LLP *
Weil, Gotshal & Manges LLP *

**Band 2**
Goodwin Procter LLP *

**Band 3**
Choate Hall & Stewart LLP *
Edwards Wildman Palmer LLP *

**Senior Statesmen**

**Senior Statesmen:** distinguished older practitioners
Malt R Bradford — Ropes & Gray LLP *

**Leading Individuals**

**Band 1**

| | | |
|---|---|---|
| Chapin David C | Ropes & Gray LLP | |
| Hodges Taylor Laura C | Goodwin Procter LLP * | |
| LeClaire John R | Goodwin Procter LLP * | |
| Stillwell R Newcomb | Ropes & Gray LLP | |

**Band 2**

| | |
|---|---|
| Cohen Stephen M L | Choate Hall & Stewart LLP * |
| Curley James M | Goodwin Procter LLP * |
| Meredith Stephen O | Edwards Wildman Palmer LLP * |
| Peck Steven | Weil, Gotshal & Manges LLP * |
| Rose Alfred O | Ropes & Gray LLP |

**Band 3**

| | |
|---|---|
| Basile Joseph | Weil, Gotshal & Manges LLP * |
| Burnett Mark | Goodwin Procter LLP * |
| French Marilyn | Weil, Gotshal & Manges LLP * |
| Jones Julie H | Ropes & Gray LLP |
| Kendall Michael J | Goodwin Procter LLP * |
| Marcus Craig | Ropes & Gray LLP |
| Sullivan Kevin J | Weil, Gotshal & Manges LLP * |
| Temel Alexander B | Latham & Watkins |

**Up-and-coming individuals**

| | |
|---|---|
| Shields William M | Ropes & Gray LLP |

*The editorial is in alphabetical order by firm name.*

### Choate Hall & Stewart LLP
See profile on p.1517

THE FIRM This group handles work in both the buyouts and venture capital markets for clients operating primarily in the midmarket space. It has a strong focus on transactions in the tech industry, and has particular experience of cross-border work in Canada and Ireland. A recent highlight saw it act on behalf of IZI Medical, a portfolio company of Riverside Partners, in regard to its sale to Landauer, valued at $93 million.
**Sources say:** *"They are terrific and I think very highly of them. Having good counsel makes an enormous difference, and they are very good value."*

### Private Equity: Venture Capital Investment

**Leading Firms**

**Band 1**
Goodwin Procter LLP *

**Band 2**
Foley Hoag LLP *
Gunderson Dettmer Stough Villeneuve Franklin & Hachigian
Latham & Watkins *
WilmerHale *

**Band 3**
Choate Hall & Stewart LLP *
Cooley LLP
Morse, Barnes-Brown & Pendleton PC

**Leading Individuals**

**Band 1**

| | |
|---|---|
| Borden Mark | WilmerHale * |
| Chory John | Latham & Watkins |
| Egan III John J | Goodwin Procter LLP * |
| Rosenblum Peter | Foley Hoag LLP * |
| Schnoor William J | Goodwin Procter LLP * |

**Band 2**

| | |
|---|---|
| Hachigian Jay | Gunderson Dettmer Stough Villeneuve |
| Lenihan Brian P | Choate Hall & Stewart LLP * |
| Macenka Mark | Goodwin Procter LLP * |

**Band 3**

| | |
|---|---|
| Bain Michael D | WilmerHale * |
| Broadwin David | Foley Hoag LLP * |
| Mazur Susan L | Latham & Watkins |
| Mitchell Patrick | Cooley LLP |
| Nevo Itai | DLA Piper LLP (US) (ONP)† * |
| Pravda Susan | Foley & Lardner LLP (ONP)† |

**Band 4**

| | |
|---|---|
| Barrett James | Edwards Wildman Palmer LLP * |
| Dupré Marc F | Gunderson Dettmer Stough Villeneuve |
| Fagen Lester J | Cooley LLP |
| Martland David A | Nixon Peabody LLP (ONP)† * |

\* Indicates firm / individual with profile.
† ONP = Other Notable Practitioner.

KEY INDIVIDUALS Private equity cochair **Stephen Cohen** (see p.1488) continues to make a favorable impression on the market. Clients say: *"He has a wealth of experience, and is able to apply that experience to help us understand the market positions and shape our negotiating strategy."* **Brian Lenihan** (see p.1500) is a strong practitioner in the buyouts space and has considerable expertise in cross-border matters in Canada. *"He's a really talented, very likable guy who is good at advising us as well as interfacing with management teams and opposing counsel,"* notes one satisfied client.

### Cooley LLP

THE FIRM This firm is well known on a national stage for its representation of emerging growth companies in the

venture capital market. The Boston team has close links with the firm's West Coast headquarters, offering a streamlined nationwide service to clients.
KEY INDIVIDUALS **Patrick Mitchell** regularly advises clients on leveraged acquisitions and investments, and is a renowned figure in the venture capital space. **Lester Fagen** maintains a broad practice, encompassing private equity, venture capital and matters pertaining to emerging growth businesses.

### Edwards Wildman Palmer LLP
See profile on p.1520

THE FIRM This buyout team is well regarded by both peers and clients, and concentrates its expertise in the communications, IT and life sciences arenas.
KEY INDIVIDUALS **Stephen Meredith** (see p.1502) commands a high degree of respect from market commentators, who describe him as *an excellent adviser."* He is particularly noted for his negotiation skills. **James Barrett** (see p.1484) is cochair of the private equity and venture capital group, and remains a fine choice of counsel for venture capital and private equity funds, as well as clients in the the technology and life sciences space.

### Foley Hoag LLP
See profile on p.1521

THE FIRM This group garners praise for the strength of its esteemed venture capital group, which manages matters for clients from early to late-stage venture financing transactions. The practice has a heavy focus on representing clients in the life sciences, energy and technology sectors, where its attorneys have considerable expertise. The team is regularly appointed counsel by angel investors, who value its experience in this area. Clients include CommonAngels, Polaris Ventures and Highland Capital.
**Sources say:** *"They are thorough and have a great grasp of business issues. They respond to me in a timely manner, irrespective of the time of year."*
KEY INDIVIDUALS **Peter Rosenblum** (see p.1507) cuts an authoritative figure in the venture capital space and commands respect from his impressive client base. He has recently advised Adage Capital Management on its investment in Puma Biotechnology and GMZ Energy in a Series C preferred stock offering. Interviewees assert: *"He is crazy smart. He is an adviser as much as a lawyer, and he gets into the nitty-gritty of the deal documents."* The Waltham-based **David Broadwin** (see p.1486) leads the firm's emerging enterprise center and has particular expertise in PIPE transactions.

### Goodwin Procter LLP
See profile on p.1522

THE FIRM This firm remains at the forefront of the Massachusetts venture capital space, with a sterling reputation for serving midmarket private equity clients in late-stage venture matters. The team handles joint ventures, recapitalizations and LBOs, and industry-specific areas of expertise include life sciences, consumer products and clean energy. The Boston office also fields a strong buyouts team, and has a grasp on the full range of private equity work in New York, California and Asia. Recent clients include TA Associates, JMI Equity and Goldman Sachs. **Sources say:** *"They are able to get the transaction done efficiently, professionally and smoothly with our interests in mind. They are gold standard."*

**KEY INDIVIDUALS Laura Hodges Taylor** (see p.1495) is a renowned negotiator in the buyouts space, and clients are moved to say: *"She excels at negotiations by finding unique ways to solve the problems that are presented."* Notable recent work highlights include the representation of Nova Capital Management in a series of acquisitions. **John Egan** (see p.1490) is cochair of the technology companies group and continues to impress on the venture capital side of the private equity field. He covers a comprehensive range of early to late-stage venture financings, focusing on the life sciences, tech and software industries. He recently represented Fidelis Security Systems in its sale to General Dynamics. The *"phenomenally smart"* **John LeClaire** (see p.1499) cements his position as a leading figure in the buyouts market. He handles minority investments at home and abroad, as well as LBOs and recapitalizations. Goldman Sachs and TA Associates remains key clients of his. **William Schnoor** (see p.1508) enjoys a well-established and much-respected venture capital practice. He is known for his representation of blue-chip venture-backed projects, involving IPOs, acquisitions and cross-border work. *"He is exactly what a deal-oriented lawyer should be: smart, practical and looks at things from a client's perspective,"* notes one impressed source. **James Curley** (see p.1489) continues to make waves in the private equity space and maintains a broad corporate practice in a number of sectors, including education, retail and manufacturing. He notably represented Leeds Equity Partners on a variety of deals and acquisitions. **Mark Macenka** (see p.1500) has an impressive private equity practice, encompassing acquisitions, securities matters and cross-border financing. He recently acted for Mimecast in its Series C financing. **Mark Burnett** (see p.1487) covers a wide array of matters for early and late-stage private equity companies, and has of late handled an impressive range of work on behalf of regular client JMI Equity. The *"thorough, productive and intelligent"* **Michael Kendall** (see p.1498) is a clear client favorite, and recent work includes his representation of Mobilitie in its high-value sale of numerous wireless tower sites throughout Central America.

### Gunderson Dettmer Stough Villeneuve Franklin & Hachigian

**THE FIRM** This group is particularly known for its strong West Coast presence, but continues to develop its name in the Boston market and remains a popular option for clients in the emerging companies space, who place a particular premium on the team's experience in this area. **KEY INDIVIDUALS** Founding partner **Jay Hachigian** receives plaudits for his practical, business-oriented

approach. His practice focuses on the life sciences, pharmaceutical and software domains. **Marc Dupré** is a recognized venture capital practitioner who combines strong technical acumen with a pleasant, client-friendly demeanor.

### Latham & Watkins
See profile on p.446

**THE FIRM** The Boston offering of this national powerhouse continues to gain traction in the local market and is viewed as a significant competitor in the venture capital space. The team places emphasis on its expertise in the cleantech, life sciences and technology arenas, and is well equipped to offer an extensive global service to clients.

**KEY INDIVIDUALS John Chory** is an accomplished corporate practitioner whose venture capital work for emerging companies is particularly highly regarded. He has recently assisted ActiFio in a preferred stock financing, and has handled Series E and F financings for Basho Technologies. **Susan Mazur** continues to make waves in the venture capital field and has particular experience representing clients in the startup community. She has managed numerous transactions on behalf of regular client Care.com. **Alexander Temel** has worked on significant transactions for Goldman Sachs, Great Hill Partners and Bregal Sagemount.

### Morse, Barnes-Brown & Pendleton PC

**THE FIRM** This Waltham-based team is recognized in the venture capital market for its strength in representing early-stage companies. The team remains known for offering excellent value for money.

**KEY INDIVIDUALS** Mary Beth Kerrigan and Jonathan Gworek are key contacts at the firm.

### Ropes & Gray LLP
See profile on p.1528

**THE FIRM** This private equity powerhouse dominates the local and national buyouts markets. Typically representing high-profile private equity funds and sponsors, the team is best known for its excellence in large transactions across the capital structure. The team continues to represent Bain Capital and TPG on a variety of private equity matters, and it recently advised Blackstone on its $3 billion acquisition of Emdeon. **Sources say:** *"They work tirelessly and will do whatever it takes to get the job done."*

**KEY INDIVIDUALS** Managing partner **David Chapin**'s reputation as an accomplished buyouts attorney precedes him. He is applauded for his representation of public companies, and has handled a range of transactional matters for Berkshire Partners and Blackstone in the last year. **Newcomb Stillwell** enjoys a strong national reputation for his buyouts practice. Bain Capital and TPG are major clients, and he has managed a variety of matters for them in recent times. The highly regarded **Alfred Rose** is head of the firm's private equity transactions group, and has particular expertise in go-private transactions and structured financial products. He notably represented 3i in a transaction with Fraser Sullivan. **Craig Marcus** has hit the ground

running and established a thriving buyouts practice both locally and nationally. He handles M&A, securities offerings and LBOs and is noted for his robust regulatory counsel. Clients include Thomas H Lee Partners and Bain Capital. **Bradford Malt** is the undisputed godfather of the buyouts space. He has extensive knowledge and experience of the private equity arena, and counsels clients on virtually every aspect of their transactional and regulatory needs. Up-and-comer **William Shields** manages a sophisticated portfolio of clients, including private equity sponsors and other corporate clients. His recent work saw him taking a leading role in Bain Capital's high-value acquisition of GenPac, as well as TPG's acquisition of Par Pharmaceuticals. **Julie Jones** enters the rankings this year in recognition of her dual strengths in the corporate M&A and private equity fields. She is particularly known for her adroit handling of public company and securities work, and her clients have the utmost confidence in her: *"People here love her. She brings a unique perspective to transactions and is very hands-on, so we feel like we're getting the top-level advice."*

### Weil, Gotshal & Manges LLP
See profile on p.2015

**THE FIRM** This team maintains a preeminent practice in the buyouts space and is a first choice for clients seeking assistance with substantial transactions. The group particularly stands out for the scope of its practice, offering clients representation at state, national and international level. The team has a diverse client base including Summit Partners, Advent International and Thomas H Lee Partners.

**KEY INDIVIDUALS** The highly regarded **Steven Peck** (see p.1505) continues to represent Summit Partners and recently served as counsel to it in its acquisition of Help/Systems. **Joseph Basile** (see p.1484) is managing partner of the Boston office and continues to maintain a fine reputation in the buyouts market. Recent work includes his representation of Hopkins Manufacturing in its Section 363 acquisition of F3 Brands. **Marilyn French** (see p.1492) handles work for both public and private companies and private equity sponsors. Advent International is a regular client and she has recently managed a number of transactions on its behalf. **Kevin Sullivan** (see p.1511) led the team handling Guggenheim Partners' acquisition of Dick Clark Productions and has served as counsel to the organic grocery chain Earth Fare in its buyout by Oak Hill Capital Partners.

### WilmerHale
See profile on p.930

**THE FIRM** This team is regarded as a key player in the venture capital market and also supports clients across the full range of private equity matters, from seed stage to exit. The team is noted for its deep bench and is able to draw on the collective strengths of over 100 venture capital lawyers nationwide. Its client roster includes Agios Pharmaceuticals, Demandware and North Bridge Venture Partners.

**Sources say:** *"WilmerHale provides a high degree of personalized service. While they have the resources of a large firm, their commitment to each client – no matter how small – is exemplary."*
**KEY INDIVIDUALS** Chair of the corporate practice, **Mark Borden** (see p.1485) retains his leading position in the venture capital field. He receives warm praise from both peers and clients alike, with one source commenting: *"He is a very strong lawyer and he handles clients well."* **Michael Bain** (see p.1483) is cochair of the emerging companies and venture capital group, and an active member of the private equity team. He represented Matrix Partners

and North Bridge Venture Partners in a Series C financing, and assisted in the sale of Rhythmia Medical to Boston Scientific.

## Other Notable Practitioners

**Itai Nevo** (see p.1503) of DLA Piper LLP (US) is a highly regarded practitioner in the venture capital field. He focuses on serving technology companies and growth and private equity investors. As one interviewee asserts, *"he is extraordinarily responsive and thorough. He is an aggressive defender of our interests and yet is able to get deals done."*

**Susan Pravda** of Foley & Lardner LLP retains her reputation as a strong venture capital specialist, and she commands a high level of respect from her loyal client base. *"She is consistently competent, knowledgeable and effective. She is unquestionably my most trusted adviser,"* notes one satisfied client. **David Martland** (see p.1501) is leader of the global business and transactions team at Nixon Peabody LLP, and counsels clients on a full range of venture capital matters. Clients say: *"He doesn't get caught up on past problems, he works on moving forward. He helps to save a lot of deals and I feel we are well protected by him. He is an accomplished, intelligent attorney."*

# PRIVATE EQUITY FUND FORMATION

Commentary about individuals can be found under their firm's paragraph. If the firm has no paragraph (is not ranked) look at Other Notable Practitioners.

| Private Equity: Fund Formation Leading Firms |
| --- |
| **Band 1** |
| Proskauer Rose LLP * |
| Ropes & Gray LLP * |
| **Band 2** |
| Goodwin Procter LLP * |
| Weil, Gotshal & Manges LLP * |
| **Band 3** |
| Bingham McCutchen LLP * |
| Choate Hall & Stewart LLP * |
| Nixon Peabody LLP * |
| WilmerHale * |

| Private Equity: Fund Formation Leading Individuals | |
| --- | --- |
| **Star individuals** | |
| Painter Robin A | Proskauer Rose LLP |
| **Band 1** | |
| Finkelman Daniel P | Proskauer Rose LLP |
| Milner Ann L | Ropes & Gray LLP |
| Rothermel Sarah | WilmerHale * |
| Rowe Larry Jordan | Ropes & Gray LLP |
| **Band 2** | |
| Beals John P | Nixon Peabody LLP * |
| Beaudoin Thomas A | Goodwin Procter LLP * |
| Kreisler David | Weil, Gotshal & Manges LLP * |
| Nicholls III Malcolm B | Proskauer Rose LLP |
| Tegeler David W | Proskauer Rose LLP |
| Watson David W | Goodwin Procter LLP * |
| **Band 3** | |
| Beber Howard J | Proskauer Rose LLP |
| Hill Sean J | Proskauer Rose LLP |
| Kaplan-Gross Kimberley | Cooley LLP (ONP) [†] |
| Kehoe Gerald J | Bingham McCutchen LLP * |
| King Rufus C | Goodwin Procter LLP * |
| Mears Stephen | Proskauer Rose LLP |
| Robbins Brett A | Ropes & Gray LLP |
| Rosenblum Howard S | DLA Piper LLP (US) (ONP) [†] * |
| Taylor Jr Andrew E | Choate Hall & Stewart LLP * |
| **Up-and-coming individuals** | |
| Harris Kari K | Nixon Peabody LLP * |

## Band 1

### Proskauer Rose LLP
See profile on p.2001
**THE FIRM** This team is an institution in the Massachusetts private equity market, and comes particularly recommended for its strength in limited partner and secondary fund representation. The Boston team is able to draw on the resources and bench strength of the firm's US and international offices to offer a comprehensive and far-reaching service for its impressive client list, which includes JPMorgan, Ares Management and Charles River Ventures, among others.
**Sources say:** *"They are by far and away the most experienced fund formation team I've dealt with. That translates into them being very practical and focused on getting things done. They also have a really good sense of the market, so you can really trust their advice."*
**KEY INDIVIDUALS** *"Total rockstar"* **Robin Painter** remains a luminary in the fund formation market. She advises long-term client Charles River Ventures on all aspects of its fund projects, and recently helped to raise a $375 million fund on its behalf. **Daniel Finkelman** is regarded as an expert in multinational fund formation and assisted New Enterprise Associates in relation to one of the largest global funds ever raised. The highly regarded **Sean**

**Hill** is co-head of the private investment funds group and continues to make waves in the fund formation market. **Malcolm Nicholls** is described by clients as *"very practical in his approach, pleasant to work with and very responsive."* Adams Street Partners remains a key client of his. Seasoned practitioner **David Tegeler** *"is very good in an advisory capacity due to his excellent experience, and we like him on a personal level, too,"* notes one enthusiastic client. He advises Boston-based Falcon Investment Advisers on its fund structuring projects. **Howard Beber** continues to cut an impressive figure in the fund formation landscape and is known for his expertise in advising investors on alternative

investments. Sources say: *"He focuses on getting a deal done and he has a great sense of 'client comes first'."* He advises Ridgemont Equity Partners in the structuring of its funds. **Stephen Mears** maintains a robust fund formation practice and played a leading role in the aforementioned work for New Enterprise Associates.

### Ropes & Gray LLP
See profile on p.1528
**THE FIRM** This group is the cornerstone of the New England private equity scene, and it enjoys a stellar reputation in fund formation work. The team typically represents high-profile funds, investors and sponsors, who sing the praises of the group's breadth and depth of expertise. The Boston office is supported by a well-established global network of resources which puts it in a good position to handle multinational fund work. Summit Rock Advisors, the Rockefeller Foundation and Columbia University are fixtures on the team's impressive client roster.
**Sources say:** *"They have been a real go-to firm for us. They answer questions any time we have them, and they also have really good judgment on the market."*
**KEY INDIVIDUALS Ann Milner** is an experienced practitioner with a firm handle on the fund market. She inspires loyalty and admiration from clients, who say: *"She is an unbelievable lawyer: she has great style, great presence and is very easy to work with."* **Larry Rowe** represents Harvard University on a variety of matters relating to its fund activity, and he continues to serve as counsel to Goldman Sachs Asset Management on a variety of funds. **Brett Robbins** commands respect in the market for his robust fund formation practice. He regularly advises MIT on its alternative investments, and serves as counsel to the Bill & Melinda Gates Foundation.

## Band 2

### Goodwin Procter LLP
See profile on p.1522
**THE FIRM** This highly regarded team excels in real estate fund work, but also offers clients a broad base in private equity fund expertise. The team represents Advent

International, Abingworth and Khosla Ventures on a wide array of fund formation matters.

**KEY INDIVIDUALS Thomas Beaudoin** (see p.1484) is new to the Goodwin team this year, and brings with him a well-established and much-admired fund practice. He has a particular focus on venture capital fund work and serves as counsel to Pitango Venture Capital, Israel's leading venture capital fund. Private investment funds practice chair **David Watson** (see p.1513) is an experienced fund attorney who is widely respected by peers and clients. He represented JMI Realty in the formation of a joint venture for hotel investment. **Rufus King** (see p.1498) has a respected practice which is truly national in scope. He advises Russian investment fund DST Global in both fund formation and transactional matters.

## Weil, Gotshal & Manges LLP
See profile on p.2015

**THE FIRM** This compact but much-admired group is well known for its representation of private equity sponsors operating in the midmarket, and maintains strong national and international links, working at close quarters with its New York office. It counts Caledon Capital Management, OceanBridge Capital Partners and Saudi Aramco among its key clients.

**KEY INDIVIDUALS** Key partner **David Kreisler** (see p.1499) retains his position as a prominent fund attorney, and comes much recommended for his work with private equity fund sponsors. In recent work, he continues to advise Berkshire Partners and has also served as counsel to the Gores Group in the formation of Gores Small Capitalization Partners.

## Band 3

## Bingham McCutchen LLP
See profile on p.1515

**THE FIRM** This team has significant expertise in international fund formation, representing a large number of US investors with offshore commitments. The firm's notable presence in Asia gives the team excellent access to these markets, much to the benefit of its impressive institutional and alternative investor client base.

**KEY INDIVIDUALS Gerald Kehoe** (see p.1498) is praised for his unwavering practical approach. He continues to represent long-term client EIF Management on a variety of fund investments in the energy sector, and advises State Street on its fund activity.

## Choate Hall & Stewart LLP
See profile on p.1517

**THE FIRM** This group is known for its representation of limited and general partners, and handles formation matters on a variety of funds. In a recent highlight, it acted as lead counsel for Riverside Partners in the formation of the $561 million private equity Riverside Fund V. Other key clients include Tudor Ventures and Spectrum Equity.

**KEY INDIVIDUALS Andrew Taylor** (see p.1511) continues to be a leader in the Boston fund formation space, and is also sought after by private organizations for his general strategic business advice and assistance with corporate governance issues.

## Nixon Peabody LLP
See profile on p.1526

**THE FIRM** This team is renowned in the market for its strength in limited partner representation, and has a strong client base consisting of state and institutional investors. The group also has experience representing investors in global markets.

**Sources say:** *"They're a fine group."*

**KEY INDIVIDUALS John Beals** (see p.1484) is particularly noted for his public pension funds work. *"With John, we are covered in terms of making sure everything is in order and we have the right provisions and protections,"* notes one impressed client. **Kari Harris** (see p.1495) is a new addition to the table this year and has become an emerging force in the fund space. Interviewees say: *"She's really knowledgeable in what she does for us; she is proactive and she works with our businesspeople to make sure the deal is implemented."*

## WilmerHale
See profile on p.930

**THE FIRM** This team enjoys a solid reputation for private equity fund work, including venture capital and growth equity funds. The group is also able to offer clients sound regulatory and compliance advice on all aspects of the fund administration process.

**KEY INDIVIDUALS** Chair of the fund formation group **Sarah Rothermel** (see p.1507) is a celebrated venture capital specialist and counts Greylock, Matrix Partners, Flagship Ventures and Xander Group among her key clients.

## Other Notable Practitioners

**Kimberley Kaplan-Gross** of Cooley LLP continues to impress with her fund formation work, and is noted for her expertise in secondary transactions and governance issues. **Howard Rosenblum** (see p.1507) of DLA Piper LLP (US) is described as *"sage, calm and savvy,"* and he maintains a robust formation practice. He represents numerous Israeli clients, and continues to represent TrueBridge Capital.

# REAL ESTATE

Zoning/Land Use p.1478

Commentary about individuals can be found under their firm's paragraph. If the firm has no paragraph (is not ranked) look at Other Notable Practitioners.

| Real Estate |
| --- |
| **Leading Firms** |
| **Band 1** |
| DLA Piper LLP (US) * |
| Goodwin Procter LLP * |
| Goulston & Storrs |
| **Band 2** |
| Mintz Levin Cohn Ferris Glovsky and Popeo PC * |
| Nutter McClennen & Fish LLP * |
| WilmerHale * |
| **Band 3** |
| Edwards Wildman Palmer LLP * |
| Holland & Knight LLP * |
| Nixon Peabody LLP * |
| Ropes & Gray LLP * |

*Indicates firm with profile.*

*Alphabetical order within each band. Band 1 is the highest.*

## Band 1

## DLA Piper LLP (US)
See profile on p.1971

**THE FIRM** This group enjoys a strong presence at state, federal and international levels. It is equally strong in real estate development, investment and financing, and is renowned for its ability to bring innovative solutions to complex commercial real estate matters nationwide. Notable clients include Millennium Partners, Fan Pier Development and Clarion Partners.

**Sources say:** *"A mature and excellent real estate practice."*

**KEY INDIVIDUALS John Rattigan** (see p.1506) is a well-known name in major development work, with recent highlights including the redevelopment of the former Ritz Carlton, and an $800 million joint venture development which, at 1.1 million sq ft, constitutes the largest leasing project in Massachusetts. Clients say: *"He is exceedingly cre-* *ative in solving business problems."* The eminent **Richard Rudman** (see p.1508) recently represented National Development of New England and Charles River Realty Fund in the formation of a joint venture for the development of a life science research building on the Harvard University Medical Area. **John Sullivan** (see p.1511) leads the firm's Boston-based real estate group. His recent highlights include representing AEW Capital Management in its $167 million acquisition of the National Press Building. He is also highly active in commercial real estate work on behalf of pension funds and private equity investors. Clients admire his hands-on approach and laud him as *"simply an excellent attorney."* Managing partner of the firm's Boston office **Elliot Surkin** (see p.1511) brings his formidable experience and knowledge of real estate financing and taxation to bear, and maintains strong relationships with major commercial developers and investors.

## Real Estate
### Senior Statesmen

Senior Statesmen: distinguished older practitioners

| | | | | | | | |
|---|---|---|---|---|---|---|---|
| Krasnow Jordan | Goulston & Storrs | | Rottenberg Alan | Goulston & Storrs | | Surkin Elliot M | DLA Piper LLP (US) * |

### Leading Individuals

| Band 1 | | | Zabowsky Michael D | Nutter McClennen & Fish LLP * | | Litwin Frank | Goulston & Storrs |
|---|---|---|---|---|---|---|---|
| Bachman Katharine E | WilmerHale * | | **Band 3** | | | Lynch Matthew | Nixon Peabody LLP * |
| Fishman Robert A | Nutter McClennen & Fish LLP * | | Ayoub Paul | Nutter McClennen & Fish LLP * | | McDougall Lorne W | Edwards Wildman Palmer LLP * |
| Glazer Michael H | Goodwin Procter LLP * | | Barker Christopher B | Goodwin Procter LLP * | | Milton Christopher H | Greenberg Traurig, LLP (ONP)† * |
| Rattigan Jr John | DLA Piper LLP (US) * | | Boulger Sean T | WilmerHale * | | Moynihan Carla M | Robinson & Cole LLP (ONP)† * |
| Rudman Richard D | DLA Piper LLP (US) * | | Bouton Paul E | Nixon Peabody LLP * | | Pearlstein Andrew M | Seyfarth Shaw LLP (ONP)† * |
| Sullivan John L | DLA Piper LLP (US) * | | Broderick James M | Goodwin Procter LLP * | | Phillips Thomas | Brown Rudnick LLP (ONP)† |
| **Band 2** | | | Freeman Eric | Mintz Levin Cohn Ferris Glovsky * | | Pittaro Frederick | Mintz Levin Cohn Ferris Glovsky * |
| Cooper Scott | Holland & Knight LLP * | | Friedenberg Peter | Sherin and Lodgen LLP (ONP)† | | Robinson Deirdre | Murtha Cullina LLP (ONP)† |
| Green Barry D | Goulston & Storrs | | Gaquin Dan | Mintz Levin Cohn Ferris Glovsky * | | Rodgers Dave | Edwards Wildman Palmer * |
| Kay Minta E | Goodwin Procter LLP * | | Glincher Andrew | Nixon Peabody LLP * | | Schwartz Paul D | Goodwin Procter LLP * |
| Keliher Cynthia | McCarter & English, LLP (ONP)† * | | Gordet Richard E | Ropes & Gray LLP | | Stern Andrew | Foley & Lardner LLP (ONP)† |
| McCabe III Walter | Ropes & Gray LLP | | Horwitz Debbie | Goulston & Storrs | | Sucoff Andrew | Goodwin Procter LLP * |
| Mitchell Beth H | Nutter McClennen & Fish LLP * | | Jakubowski Paul | WilmerHale * | | Toelke Richard A | Bingham McCutchen LLP (ONP)† * |
| Notopoulos Philip | Holland & Knight LLP * | | Kwasnick Raymond | Goulston & Storrs | | Weinstein Steven J | Riemer & Braunstein LLP (ONP)† |
| O'Reilly Jr William R | WilmerHale * | | Lapatin Philip | Holland & Knight LLP * | | **Up-and-coming individuals** | |
| Urban Andrew | Mintz Levin Cohn Ferris Glovsky * | | Laudano Paul | Brown Rudnick LLP (ONP)† | | Burton Doug | WilmerHale * |

## Real Estate: Zoning/Land Use
### Leading Individuals

| Band 1 | | |
|---|---|---|
| Fishman Robert A | Nutter McClennen & Fish LLP * | |
| Healy Martin R | Goodwin Procter LLP * | |
| Husid Douglas M | Goulston & Storrs | |
| Kiefer Matthew J | Goulston & Storrs | |
| **Band 2** | | |
| Blaesser Brian | Robinson & Cole LLP (ONP)† * | |
| Kaplan Lawrence | Goodwin Procter LLP * | |
| Lee Rebecca A | Edwards Wildman Palmer LLP * | |
| Nylen Jr Richard A | Lynch DeSimone & Nylen LLP (ONP)† | |
| Twohig John E | Goulston & Storrs | |

* Indicates individual with profile.

† ONP = Other Notable Practitioner.

### Goodwin Procter LLP
**See profile on p.1522**

THE FIRM This group retains its place among the elite of the Massachusetts real estate space, and cultivates a leading practice in the nationwide hospitality and leisure industry. Known for its strengths in complex corporate financing, joint ventures and REIT work, this group is able to match substantive knowledge in both financing and acquisitions with superlative client service. Notable clients include AEW Capital, Beacon Capital, BlackRock Realty and Gallus BioPharmaceuticals.

Sources say: *"They're one of the best; their partners are incredibly capable and have a great group of associates."*

KEY INDIVIDUALS Michael Glazer (see p.1493) is an esteemed commercial real estate attorney, specializing in joint ventures, financing and leasing within the hospitality industry. He recently represented Four Seasons Hotel in a joint venture development, and regularly undertakes high-profile acquisitions and disposals. *"His balanced perspective*

on commercial endeavors was a great resource for us."* Chair of the development and permitting practice Martin Healy (see p.1495) is described as *"simply a fantastic development guy"* whose expertise lies in environmental permitting for major development projects. His key roles include advising the Massachusetts Port Authority on environmental compliance matters. Financing specialist Minta Kay (see p.1497) has a wealth of experience in REIT-related work, and represents debt and equity investors in sophisticated acquisitions and developments. James Broderick (see p.1486) is the head of the firm's real estate investment management practice group, and works extensively on behalf of institutional investors. Clients appreciate the manner in which *"he gets to the heart of the matter."* Commentators hail Christopher Barker (see p.278) as a solid lawyer in the real estate space. He has firm experience in joint venture hotel development projects. Paul Schwartz (see p.1509) is singled out as *"a dean of the real estate investment space,"* who has been highly active in working on sophisticated fund formation matters. Andrew Sucoff (see p.1510) is cochair of the firm's real estate, REITs and real estate capital markets practice group. He has been highly active in numerous retail acquisitions for Kimco Realty and other commercial investors, and also has great experience in the development of multifamily and assisted living space. Lawrence Kaplan (see p.1497) has particular strength in zoning and land use, and recently undertook a mixed-use development project for New Balance Athletic Shoe incorporating office and hotel space alongside sports facilities.

### Goulston & Storrs

THE FIRM Goulston & Storrs is renowned for its real estate strength, and for its capabilities in providing a full service to commercial developer clients in this space. Its attorneys are well placed to handle a range of transaction-

al work, from acquisitions and disposals to financing and development. The team is particularly highlighted for its expertise in the structuring of syndicated transactions. Key clients include Avalon Bay Communities, MIT and CrossHarbour Capital.

Sources say: *"We have always been impressed by the quality of work delivered by Goulston & Storrs."*

KEY INDIVIDUALS Douglas Husid is a leading zoning and land use practitioner. He is noted, among other areas, for his expertise in permitting, which he recently brought to bear in his work on a large-scale mixed-use development for long-term client Samuels & Associates. He is joined in this area by urban planning expert Matthew Kiefer, whose recent highlights include assisting in the representation of MS Boston Seaport in relation to a 23-acre joint venture development in the Seaport District of Boston. Practice stalwart Jordan Krasnow is admired for his proactive, deal-making approach, and for his impressive real estate knowledge. He is highly regarded by both peers and clients: *"He's great at getting people around the table and finding a solution; he is diplomatic, knowledgeable and gets the right people involved."* Barry Green is a strong player both in Boston and nationally. He was lead counsel in the acquisition and financing of the Ohio Marriott hotel portfolio. He is described as *"very responsive to clients; very bright and very personable."* Clients of established leasing lawyer Frank Litwin benefit from his considerable experience and expertise in development projects. He was lead counsel in the aforementioned Boston Seaport joint venture between Morgan Stanley and Boston Global Investors. Debbie Horwitz has experience across a diverse range of real estate matters. She recently represented a publicly traded REIT, Federal Realty Investment Trust, in the acquisition of a controlling interest in a 381,000 sq ft shopping center in El Segundo, California. The seasoned authority Alan Rottenberg has built an established and respected practice in the Massachusetts real estate sector. He has an impressive track record across a broad range of complex real estate matters and brings this experience to bear on behalf of a diverse client base. Zoning and land use expert **John Twohig** recently acted for a joint venture between New England Development, National Development and Eastern Development in the acquisition of a 60-acre mixed-use development site from a hedge fund. **Raymond Kwasnick** is renowned for his strength in complex leasing, and clients commend him for his skill and tenacity in leasing negotiations. *"Ray is spectacular in negotiations,"* say sources; *"his knowledge of the area is great."*

## Band 2

### Mintz Levin Cohn Ferris Glovsky and Popeo PC
See profile on p.1523

**THE FIRM** Mintz Levin has a strong and expanding development practice, supported by a public financing section, operating locally and nationally. Clients are continually impressed with the team's dedication and professionalism on some of the most high-profile and groundbreaking developments in the state. A host of Fortune 500 companies choose Mintz Levin to represent them in acquisitions, dispositions, leasings and developments, such as Wells Fargo, CVS Caremark and Bristol-Myers Squibb.
**Sources say:** *"The team is very good at adapting to changes and being flexible, and working to find solutions."*
**KEY INDIVIDUALS Andrew Urban** (see p.1512) is an expert when it comes to sophisticated financing and structuring. He represents longstanding client CVS Caremark in a range of high-value sale and leaseback transactions. *"I like him because he's straightforward, works with us to understand our goals and isn't afraid to roll up his sleeves to get the transaction completed,"* say sources. **Dan Gaquin** (see p.1492) is a go-to attorney for real estate investment, and is leading the team on major developments in the gaming space. He has worked on numerous transactions for a number of leading private real estate investors, such as Colony Realty Partners. **Frederick Pittaro** (see p.1505) is vastly experienced and well respected for his work involving sophisticated real estate matters. He recently led on behalf of The First Church of Christ, Scientist in relation to the 14-acre renovation plan for its headquarters in the Back Bay of Boston. **Eric Freeman** (see p.1492) undertakes a great deal of high-value acquisitions and dispositions, among other types of matter, on behalf of various private owners, operations and investors, such as Colony Realty. *"He has gone out of his way to understand me and my firm,"* said one impressed client; *"he's a fine lawyer."*

### Nutter McClennen & Fish LLP
See profile on p.1527

**THE FIRM** This superb group has a diverse client base and expertise covering financing and development work. The team is able to call on support from its tax, bankruptcy and litigation groups to provide a truly comprehensive package for its owner, developer and lender clients. The group's

recent highlights include representing the City of Quincy in the negotiation and drafting of a land disposition agreement for the redevelopment of the Quincy Center.
**Sources say:** *"They are outstanding as a firm; extremely knowledgeable, very responsive and efficient."*
**KEY INDIVIDUALS Robert Fishman** (see p.1491) is a strong all-arounder with a solid reputation in both real estate and zoning and land use issues. He led in group's representation of the City of Quincy in the aforementioned land disposition agreement drafting and negotiation. **Michael Zabowsky** (see p.1514) has a highly regarded practice with an emphasis on financing. He represents extensive asset portfolios in loan restructuring and other matters. *"He represented us very well,"* said one impressed client, *"creating a smooth, efficient transaction that everyone was happy with."* **Beth Mitchell** (see p.1502) works both locally and nationally, and has played a crucial role in development projects in the region. Commentators praise her for her *"superb understanding of the law and her ability to navigate the bureaucratic waters."* **Paul Ayoub** (see p.1483) is an experienced practitioner with the ability to handle the most sophisticated deals. He counts several financial institutions among his clients and is praised for his leadership skills in getting a deal done.

### WilmerHale
See profile on p.930

**THE FIRM** WilmerHale's real estate practice, while national in scope, is praised for its firm grasp of local real estate, land use and development issues. Core areas of its expertise include senior living, retail and life sciences. In the fallout of the financial crisis, the group has also been a reliable go-to for distressed investments. Notable clients include Benchmark Senior Living, Eaton Vance and Trinity Financial.
**Sources say:** *"They have great reputations and they have good clients."*
**KEY INDIVIDUALS** The preeminent **Katharine Bachman** (see p.1483) *"knows the intricacies of complicated and sensitive matters,"* say sources, *"and is an excellent resource, leading clients through with good, practical advice."* She recently represented Alexandria Real Estate Equities in leasing transactions relating to life sciences projects. The highly respected **William O'Reilly** (see p.1504) is praised for his wide-ranging real estate expertise. His recent work includes undertaking the workout of a mixed-use development, representing a high-profile retailer in major acquisitions and dispositions, and advising on the development of an ambitious new lab facility for Novartis. Chair of the practice group **Paul Jakubowski** (see p.1496) is an expert in complex, high-value lease transactions and has nationwide experience in loan workouts and foreclosures. One impressed source said: *"He understands what we as a client are looking for; he has a great skill set and is always available."* **Doug Burton** (see p.1487) covers all aspects of financing and development work, and has been actively involved in mixed-use developments and senior and affordable housing projects across the country. **Sean Boulger** (see p.1485) is an expert in senior housing joint ventures and multifamily housing projects, among other

types of matter. *"When I work with him, I always find that the transaction goes smoothly,"* said one happy client; *"he's a good-quality, careful lawyer who is a pleasure to deal with."*

## Band 3

### Edwards Wildman Palmer LLP
See profile on p.1520

**THE FIRM** This well-respected and broad-ranging real estate group makes its entry into the rankings this year on the back of high praise for its expertise in land use and construction matters, and for its cross-disciplinary strengths in tax credits and public financing. The team's recent highlights include acting for the Massachusetts Convention Center Authority in various brownfields remediation issues relating to the Boston Convention and Exhibition Center phase II development area.
**Sources say:** *"They are very responsive and able to grasp and dissect very complex matters in a very short period of time."*
**KEY INDIVIDUALS Rebecca Lee** (see p.1499) is described by her clients as *"a real force, doing brilliant work,"* primarily in the land use and permitting space. Her work highlights include advising on a high-value campus development for the Winsor School, and a $230 million built-to-suit development for AREA Property Partners. **Lorne McDougall** (see p.1501) undertakes sophisticated real estate work and is a powerful advocate for his clients during negotiations. *"Nothing gets by him, yet he's very easy to deal with,"* say interviewees; *"even difficult clients like him – he masterfully defuses potentially explosive negotiations."* **Dave Rodgers** (see p.1507) has a broad range of real estate skills, and is particularly highlighted for his expertise in relation to construction projects. *"He is brilliant, methodical and meticulous,"* say sources.

### Holland & Knight LLP
See profile on p.1028

**THE FIRM** This team is held in high esteem for its strength in financing, representing lenders in syndication and lease work, as well as for its growing practice in development work. The group also has experience in multifamily and mixed-use projects.
**Sources say:** *"The team has creativity combined with attention to detail and knowledge of how the client likes to work."*
**KEY INDIVIDUALS** Head of the Boston real estate group **Scott Cooper** (see p.1488) is a well-respected financing expert who represents financial institutions in complex transactional work. *"He's just a fantastic financing lawyer who really knows his stuff,"* say interviewees. **Philip Notopoulos** (see p.1504) offers expert guidance in acquisition and easement work, and recently worked on a significant rail expansion project. One impressed source said: *"Phil has always been right on top of very complex zoning, permitting and financing processes – I always feel I'm getting the best advice from him."* **Philip Lapatin** (see p.1499) is a well-regarded commercial leasing expert, representing both landlords and tenants. Client praise for him is high: *"He has done a superb job; we couldn't have asked for better."*

## Nixon Peabody LLP
See profile on p.1526

**THE FIRM** Nixon Peabody's Boston group is well known for its expertise in the nationwide affordable and senior housing industries and the related field of tax credit financings, among other areas. Its real estate investment finance team is well placed to provide services in loan restructuring and workouts. Its recent highlights include representing Boston Tea Party Ship in the negotiation of a loan and grant for the construction of the Boston Tea Party Ship Museum.

**Sources say:** "*They have a very good working knowledge of the industry.*"

**KEY INDIVIDUALS Paul Bouton** (see p.1485) is an expert in affordable housing financing and development. Clients admire his quiet but effective professionalism: "*He's able to rise above the fray, keeping his eye on the ball; his balanced approach makes him a very good advocate for his client.*" Firm CEO and managing partner **Andrew Glincher** (see p.1493) "*has a unique ability to be a crossover between a business lawyer and a litigator,*" said an impressed source. He is commended as both a leader and a front-line advocate, with strength in loan recovery and restructuring. **Matthew Lynch** (see p.1500) is a respected lawyer with a broad practice, covering all aspects of real estate work. "*I like working with him because he understands my business, how I work and where I want to get to,*" according to one client.

## Ropes & Gray LLP
See profile on p.1528

**THE FIRM** This widely acclaimed national and international practice occupies a firm position in the Boston market. The group has a reputation for providing strong real estate financing support to its corporate and private equity clients, which include APG Asset Management, Siguler Guff and Verizon Investment.

**Sources say:** "*They're extremely responsive, and their work is very high quality.*"

**KEY INDIVIDUALS** Eminent real estate practitioner **Walter McCabe** is a go-to lawyer for sophisticated structuring and finance work. "*He's the kind of guy you want on a complex transaction,*" say observers; "*great at thinking outside the box and coming up with solutions.*" **Richard Gordet** has a strong reputation in counseling private equity investors, and is particularly commended for his expertise in joint ventures. One client said: "*He is extremely interested in making sure that everyone understands all the options – he is an extremely strong lawyer and adds a lot of value for us.*"

## Other Notable Practitioners

**Thomas Phillips** of Brown Rudnick LLP has broad-ranging expertise, and is highlighted in particular for his strength in retail leasing issues. He recently represented MGM Resorts in its western Massachusetts casino development. He also handles nationwide lease negotiation work for Ulta Beauty. **Paul Laudano**, also of Brown Rudnick LLP, is lead counsel on the $2.5 billion development of the Revel resort and casino project. Clients appreciate that he is "*calm and thorough in his approach – totally attentive and amazingly helpful.*" **Christopher Milton** (see p.1502) of Greenberg Traurig, LLP undertakes a range of complex real estate issues, including acquisitions, dispositions, leases and financing. He recently served as special counsel to MetLife in relation to an $80 million loan to the owner of a condominium unit at Reservoir Woods Main Campus. **Andrew Stern** of Foley & Lardner LLP is a recognized expert in commercial real estate and office leasing. He regularly represents the likes of Snyder Properties and the Potpourri Group, among other commercial clients, and is described as "*sincere, caring, committed and always available.*" **Steven Weinstein** of Riemer & Braunstein LLP has a solid reputation in Boston for representing banks in complex real estate transactions, and for his particular strength in workouts and loan restructurings. **Cynthia Keliher** (see p.1498) of McCarter & English, LLP is a revered negotiator, bringing her skills to bear on behalf of landlords and tenants in relation to major developments. Her recent highlights include representing the Massachusetts Bay Transportation Authority in connection with ground lease and air rights dispositions. She is described as "*generous, selfless and always engaging.*" **Brian Blaesser** (see p.1485) of Robinson & Cole LLP manages an excellent and broad-ranging transactional and litigious real estate practice. "*He does excellent work,*" say sources; "*he's really knowledgeable, and an engaging and personable guy to deal with.*" **Carla Moynihan** (see p.1503), also of Robinson & Cole LLP, is a respected drafter and negotiator who works on complex projects for clients such as Distinctive Hospitality, Mica Creek Sagamore and Guardian Life Insurance. One impressed client said: "*She takes a personal interest in accomplishing the mission and is a strong advocate for my interests.*" Seyfarth Shaw LLP's **Andrew Pearlstein** (see p.1505) has a reputation for being "*a very pleasant guy who goes out of the way to help his client and give a consistently good product.*" He represents financial institutions, developers and owners on sophisticated commercial work. **Peter Friedenberg** of Sherin and Lodgen LLP is highly commended by his clients. He recently represented the Massachusetts Department of Transportation in the negotiation of a ground lease to a private developer as part of the 'Big Dig' project. "*His work is always flawless and perfectly formulated,*" say sources. **Deidre Robinson** is chair of the affordable housing practice group at Murtha Cullina LLP. She has a reputation as "*a superwoman of an attorney,*" who handles commercial leasing, financing and developing matters, as well as affordable housing assignments. **Richard Toelke** (see p.1512) is cochair of the real estate practice group at Bingham McCutchen LLP. He has a broad-based practice, with a particular emphasis in recent years on multifamily acquisitions and dispositions. He is praised for his collaborative approach and his "*understanding of the business goals.*" **Richard Nylen** of Lynch DeSimone & Nylen LLP is a well-regarded practitioner whose expertise in land use helps his clients to bridge the gap between real estate and environmental law at both local and federal level.

# TAX

Commentary about individuals can be found under their firm's paragraph. If the firm has no paragraph (is not ranked) look at Other Notable Practitioners.

## Tax
### Leading Firms

**Band 1**
Goodwin Procter LLP *
Ropes & Gray LLP *

**Band 2**
Bingham McCutchen LLP *
Sullivan & Worcester LLP *
WilmerHale *

**Band 3**
Choate Hall & Stewart LLP *
Proskauer Rose LLP *

### Leading Individuals

**Band 1**

| | |
|---|---|
| Brown John S | Bingham McCutchen LLP * |
| Cubell Howard A | Goodwin Procter LLP * |
| Elfman Esq Eric M | Ropes & Gray LLP |
| Johnston Susan A | Ropes & Gray LLP |
| Leich Christopher M | Ropes & Gray LLP |
| Ponda Ameek Ashok | Sullivan & Worcester LLP * |
| Watson Rom P | Ropes & Gray LLP |
| Whitledge William H | Goodwin Procter LLP * |

**Band 2**

| | |
|---|---|
| Abrams Donald-Bruce | Bingham McCutchen LLP * |
| Burke Robert | WilmerHale * |
| Caporizzo A William | WilmerHale * |
| Davis Michael M | Sullivan & Worcester LLP * |
| Kirshenbaum Mark | Goodwin Procter LLP * |
| Marett Louis J | Choate Hall & Stewart LLP * |
| May Arnold P | Proskauer Rose LLP |
| Newberg Joseph H | Weil, Gotshal & Manges LLP (ONP)† * |
| Ritt Roger M | WilmerHale * |

**Band 3**

| | |
|---|---|
| Eichel Steven P | Choate Hall & Stewart LLP * |
| Flanagan Christopher M | Edwards Wildman Palmer LLP (ONP)† * |
| Giuliani Richard W | WilmerHale * |
| Jones Richard L | Sullivan & Worcester LLP * |
| Jones Scott S | Proskauer Rose LLP |
| Mooney Michael E | Nutter McClennen & Fish LLP (ONP)† * |
| Nagle David J | Sullivan & Worcester LLP * |
| Robbins Brett A | Ropes & Gray LLP |
| Sandford H Neal | Goodwin Procter LLP * |
| Schnall Matthew D | Bingham McCutchen LLP * |

## Tax: Estate Planning
### Leading Individuals

**Band 1**

| | |
|---|---|
| Cohen Kimberly | Ropes & Gray LLP |
| Levitan Shari | Holland & Knight LLP (ONP)† * |
| Sloan David Scott | Holland & Knight LLP (ONP)† * |
| Wand Barbara Freedman | Bingham McCutchen LLP * |

**Band 2**

| | |
|---|---|
| Connolly Sarah | Nixon Peabody LLP (ONP)† * |
| Mair George P | Bingham McCutchen LLP * |

\* Indicates firm / individual with profile.

†ONP = Other Notable Practitioner.

## Band 1

### Goodwin Procter LLP
See profile on p.1522

**THE FIRM** This team retains its position as one of the premier tax practices in Boston. It covers all aspects of tax work at state, federal and international level, and market commentators identify REIT and private equity-related tax as areas of particular strength. The group is well versed in cross-border matters, and is rightly proud of its capacity for global work in the tech sector. The team provides regular counsel to a diverse client base, including DCT Industrial Trust and Prudential Real Estate Investors.

**Sources say:** "*They bring exceptional legal expertise, sound business judgment, great responsiveness and a real sense of how to assess risk.*"

**KEY INDIVIDUALS** Private equity specialist **Howard Cubell** (see p.1489) continues to impress the market with his innovative approach to developing tax structures. He has substantial experience representing clients in tax controversy cases in state and federal courts, and is no stranger to sophisticated cross-border matters. The excellent **William Whitledge** (see p.1513) chairs the firm's tax practice and maintains a broad practice in this field. He also demonstrates particular flair in the structuring of both domestic and international transactions and funds. Market sources are full of praise for **Mark Kirshenbaum** (see p.1498), who is described as "*a clear communicator and a great problem solver.*" His expertise is weighted toward the real estate and technology sectors, and he counts Brookfield among his key clients. **Neal Sandford** (see p.1508) continues to excel in tax work concerning real estate matters. In a recent highlight, he advised Retail Properties of America regarding its initial listing on the NYSE.

### Ropes & Gray LLP
See profile on p.1528

**THE FIRM** This well-established and highly respected practice is notable for its expertise in issues relating to M&A transactions and joint ventures. The group is also regarded as a leader in planning, controversies and the representation of tax-exempt organizations. The team has advised NSTAR on its high-profile merger with Northeast Utilities, and served as counsel to State Street in its acquisition of Goldman Sachs Administrative Services.

**KEY INDIVIDUALS Eric Elfman** is an established practitioner in both the Massachusetts and New York tax markets. He has ample experience in tax issues relating to complex M&A transactions, and a strong reputation in the field of tax controversy. He notably advised Cubist Pharmaceutical in connection with its Adolor merger. **Susan Johnston** has particular expertise in the taxation of regulated investors, and is described by interviewees as "*the ultimate professional.*" Sources particularly single out her timely advice and practical approach to matters. Tax department head **Christopher Leich** maintains his position as one of the leading figures in tax matters pertaining to private equity funds, with private equity sponsors forming the bulk of his client base. He continues to represent Bain Capital, having recently advised on the company's stake purchase in Genpact. **Rom Watson** is a revered international tax specialist who focuses his impressive practice on supporting multinational corporations. He regularly advises prominent financial institutions on aspects of cross-border securities lending. "*He is very helpful, very technical and very practical,*" notes one impressed source. **Brett Robbins** focuses on tax-exempt organizations and hedge funds, and is particularly adept at tax matters related to the natural resources and real estate arenas. **Kimberly Cohen** excels in the estates planning field and serves a variety of private clients, including high net worth individuals, private equity partners and venture capitalists.

## Band 2

### Bingham McCutchen LLP
See profile on p.1515

**THE FIRM** This team retains its sterling reputation in the tax space and is particularly dominant in tax controversy matters. Its industry-specific capabilities extend to the medical device, consumer products and financial services arenas, and the competence of the group's estate planning division is widely recognized. The team has notably advised Union Bank in the tax aspects of its acquisition of the Smartstreet unit of PNC Bank.

**KEY INDIVIDUALS** Eminent practitioner **John Brown** (see p.1486) places particular emphasis in his practice on state and local tax matters. He has extensive experience in the courtroom handling tax controversies, and his skill in this arena is attested to by clients and peers alike. **Barbara Freedman Wand** (see p.1513) is a dominant figure in the local estate planning Bar, and wins much praise for her ability to translate legal principles into layman's terms. Clients also add: "*She is compassionate and understanding,*" and "*what distinguishes her from others is her superb interpersonal skills and ability to work effectively with multiple generations.*" The highly regarded **Matthew Schnall** (see p.1508) maintains a broad tax practice in transactions, regulation and controversies, and has been active on a number of high-profile litigations. **George Mair** (see p.1500) is another celebrated member of the trusts and estates team, who combines his private client practice with a healthy track record in tax controversy work. **Donald-Bruce Abrams** (see p.1483) cultivates a robust tax practice with particular expertise in the energy sector.

## Sullivan & Worcester LLP

See profile on p.1534

**THE FIRM** This team maintains a thriving transactional and tax controversy practice. The group leads the way in the field of international taxation, advising US businesses on foreign investments, as well as counseling foreign investors in US tax regulations. Its REIT practice continues to garner praise in the market, and the group is considered a go-to firm for tax matters with constitutional or civil rights elements. A recent highlight included advising the government of Israel on various tax matters relating to Israeli government employees resident in the USA. American Tower, Iron Mountain and Government Properties Income Trust are among its other key clients.

**KEY INDIVIDUALS** Head of the tax department **Ameek Ashok Ponda** (see p.1505) receives warm praise from market commentators, who assert: *"He is outstanding in his craft and brings an awful lot to the table."* His practice is strongly based in REIT matters, and recent highlights include his representation of American Tower, Iron Mountain and Equinix in their REIT conversions. **Michael Davis** (see p.1489) continues to impress with his work in the tax space, and is particularly singled out for his acumen on complex estate planning and income tax matters. The highly regarded **Richard Jones** (see p.1496) has a robust state tax litigation and transactional practice, but is noted for his capacity for cases with an international element. Recent work included playing a lead role in the aforementioned matters for the government of Israel. He also continues his active role in the team's efforts as tax counsel to challenge the constitutionality of the federal Defense of Marriage Act – a case which is currently appealed to the US Supreme Court. **David Nagle** (see p.1503) is an expert in state and local tax matters, and has plentiful experience representing individuals in landmark tax cases before the IRS and the state courts. Recent work has seen him handle a dispute regarding the deductibility of medical expenses for gender reassignment surgery.

## WilmerHale

See profile on p.930

**THE FIRM** The Boston arm of this international firm comes highly recommended for the strength of its broad tax practice. It covers a wide array of transactional matters at both state and national level, and is noted for its prominence in matters relating to tax-exempt organizations. Recent highlights include acting for Thermo Fisher Scientific in its acquisition of One Lambda.

**Sources say:** *"They are very wise counselors – they offer strategic, practical advice on solving the matter expeditiously."*

**KEY INDIVIDUALS Robert Burke** (see p.1486) is an expert in tax matters relating to partnerships and liability companies and has a well-established transactional practice. He played a leading role in the aforementioned acquisition for Thermo Fisher Scientific. Chair of the tax group **William Caporizzo** (see p.1487) is particularly singled out for his M&A and cross-border restructuring work. In a recent matter, he is providing tax advice to Dean Ford in connection with its separation from its subsidiary WhiteWave Foods. **Roger Ritt** (see p.1506) is known for his M&A-related work and his strength in tax controversies before state and federal courts. **Richard Giuliani** (see p.1492) has a broad advisory and transactional tax practice, with experience representing clients in tax controversies. Recent highlights include serving as counsel to the Oneida Indian Nation on numerous tax matters.

## Band 3

## Choate Hall & Stewart LLP

See profile on p.1517

**THE FIRM** This Boston office fields a quality federal tax team, which serves as counsel to numerous private equity clients. It has a well-developed international tax capability, and has represented Chase Corporation in its acquisition of NEPTCO Holdings and its Chinese subsidiary.

**KEY INDIVIDUALS Louis Marett** (see p.1501) has extensive experience in tax issues relating to private equity fund formation, and recently represented Mainsail Partners in the formation of its third fund, as well as Riverside Partners in the formation of an offshore fund in various European jurisdictions. **Steven Eichel** (see p.1490) is equally adept in cross-border work as a supplement to his flourishing local practice. In recent work he assisted MassHousing in a portfolio restructuring.

## Proskauer Rose LLP

See profile on p.2001

**THE FIRM** This team is known for its skills in federal tax matters and private equity work, including fund formation and related tax issues. Regular clients include Ares Management, Lexington Partners and Ridgemont Equity Partners.

**Sources say:** *"Proskauer Rose continues to put its best foot forward on all matters."*

**KEY INDIVIDUALS Arnold May** is lauded by clients as a creative, solution-oriented attorney. Sankaty and Ridgemont Equity Partners are among his regular clients. **Scott Jones** undertakes fund structuring work for Adams Street Partners both in the USA and globally.

## Other Notable Practitioners

**Christopher Flanagan** (see p.1491) of Edwards Wildman Palmer LLP is admired for the strength of his transactional and restructuring practice, and is considered by market commentators to be a strong, technically proficient attorney. Holland & Knight LLP's **Shari Levitan** (see p.1500) is highly regard in trusts and estate planning circles, and is well versed in all matters falling under this category, including breach of fiduciary duty and consequences to family trusts following the dissolution of marriage. At the same firm, **David Scott Sloan** (see p.1510) is a clear client favorite for estates planning work. One interviewee remarked: *"He was outstanding in his ability to think through the chessboard and understand the players' motivations and likely moves, vulnerabilities and areas of compromise."* **Sarah Connolly** (see p.1488) of Nixon Peabody LLP is an experienced estate planning practitioner who routinely handles sophisticated matters on behalf of high net worth individuals. **Michael Mooney** (see p.1503) at Nutter McClennen & Fish LLP commands much respect from the market. He advises businesses across the full spectrum of tax matters, and is noted for his experience representing clients in tax controversies. **Joseph Newberg** (see p.1503) of Weil, Gotshal & Manges LLP retains his position as one of the most established tax practitioners in the state, and continues to impress both clients and competitors.

# Leaders' Profiles in Massachusetts

**ABRAMS, Donald-Bruce**
Bingham McCutchen LLP, Boston
617 951 8584
don.abrams@bingham.com
*Featured in Tax (Massachusetts)*
**Practice Areas:** Co-leader of Bingham's Tax Group. Practice is primarily devoted to advising corporations, partnerships and individuals on federal, state and international tax controversy and transactional tax planning matters. Transactional practice includes providing advice to clients on the structuring and negotiation of mergers and acquisitions; equity and debt financing transactions; project finance; leveraged lease and structured finance transactions; transactions involving the structuring, formation and operation of specialized investment entities; bankruptcy and restructuring transactions; spin-offs; and general operational matters.
**Personal:** Harvard Law School, JD, magna cum laude, 1987; Massachusetts Institute of Technology, MBA, 1984; Massachusetts Institute of Technology, BS, 1982.

**ALBANO, Jonathan M**
Bingham McCutchen LLP, Boston
617 951 8360
jonathan.albano@bingham.com
*Featured in First Amendment Litigation (Nationwide), Litigation (Massachusetts)*
**Practice Areas:** Managing partner of Bingham's Boston office. Focuses on constitutional, commercial and appellate litigation. Commercial litigation experience includes representation of financial institutions and private and public companies in multimillion-dollar litigation claims. Has represented clients on constitutional issues, including free speech rights; the public's right of access to information; and privacy, defamation and equal protection claims.
**Career:** Contributing author to the Survey of Privacy and Related Claims Against the Media, the Massachusetts Tort Handbook, and the Massachusetts Journalists' Court and Legal Handbook.
**Personal:** Boston College Law School, JD, magna cum laude, 1982; Boston College, BA, magna cum laude, 1979.

**ALFRED, Richard**
Seyfarth Shaw LLP, Boston
617 946 4802
ralfred@seyfarth.com
*Featured in Labor & Employment (Massachusetts)*
**Practice Areas:** National Chair Wage-Hour Litigation Practice Group; Boston Office Chair Labor and Employment Group. Defense of complex wage/hour lawsuits.
**Professional Memberships:** College of Labor & Employment Lawyers; Past Chair, First Circuit Credentials Committee; ABA, Employment Rights Responsibilities, Complex Litigation, Co-Chair.
**Publications:** Senior Editor, Wage-Hour Collective and Class Litigation (LJP 2012); Co-authored: "Impact of Dukes on Wage Hour Collective Actions," ABA ERR (2012);

"Continuous Confusion: Defining the Workday in the Modern Economy," ABA Journal of L&E Law (2011). Testified, US House of Reps., Comm. on Education and Workforce, Subcom. Workforce Protections (2011).
**Personal:** JD, Harvard Law School; BA, Harvard College.

**AMBASH, Joseph W**
Fisher & Phillips LLP, Boston
617 532 9320
jambash@laborlawyers.com
*Featured in Labor & Employment (Massachusetts)*
**Career:** Joe Ambash is the managing partner of the Boston office. His practice includes all aspects of employment law, including labor-management relations, employment discrimination and wrongful discharge litigation, and preventive labor relations. He also has an extensive practice training managers in all areas of employment law compliance. Joe represents management in a broad range of industries, including health care, higher education, financial services, retail, media, sports and state and local government. Joe's experience in labor-management relations extends over several decades and involves representing management in representation cases, unfair labor practice cases, strikes and other labor disputes.

**APPELBAUM, Mitchel**
WilmerHale, Boston
617 526 6713
mitchel.appelbaum@wilmerhale.com
*Featured in Bankruptcy/Restructuring (Massachusetts)*
**Practice Areas:** Practice focuses on financial restructuring of corporate clients including the use of Chapter 11, secured lending, and other commercial transactions. Advises variety of clients on acquisition of troubled companies and distressed and troubled assets, and has counsels creditors with respect to bankruptcy, workout and restructuring matters.
**Professional Memberships:** Turnaround Management Association; American Bankruptcy Institute; Association of Insolvency & Restructuring Advisors; American and Boston Bar Associations; Board of Directors, Project Bread Walk for Hunger.
**Career:** Admitted to Massachusetts Bar. Joined firm in 1991.
**Personal:** Boston University School of Law (JD); Brandeis University (BA).

**ARNOLD, Beth E**
Foley Hoag LLP, Boston
617 832 1294
barnold@foleyhoag.com
*Featured in Intellectual Property (Massachusetts)*
**Practice Areas:** Beth E Arnold, a Partner and Co-Chair of the firm's Life Sciences Practice Group, is a US registered patent attorney with more than 20 years of experience in obtaining worldwide patent protection on biomedical products and technologies. Ms Arnold also has extensive experience in performing patent due diligence

in connection with public and private financings and mergers and acquisitions, and with negotiating and drafting patent license and commercialization agreements. Ms Arnold was a former in-house counsel at Genzyme Corporation, a Technology Transfer Officer at the Massachusetts General Hospital and a pharmaceutical researcher.
**Personal:** Boston University, MS in Molecular Biology; Northeastern University School of Law, JD; University of Rhode Island, BS in Biology.

**ASHER JR, William B**
Choate Hall & Stewart LLP, Boston
617 248 5087
washer@choate.com
*Featured in Corporate/M&A (Massachusetts)*
**Practice Areas:** Mr Asher counsels companies, their founders, executives and boards from start-up through public offering and acquisition on matters including financing, M&A, strategic alliances, executive compensation, securities law compliance and corporate governance. He works primarily with clients in technology and life sciences. Mr Asher also represents VC firms, underwriters and financial advisors with respect to private and public capital market transactions. Mr Asher has extensive experience counseling clients on cross-border financing and acquisitions and on US-based activities for companies headquartered in Canada and Israel.
**Personal:** JD cum laude Harvard Law School (1974); BA cum laude Harvard College (1970).

**AYOUB, Paul**
Nutter McClennen & Fish LLP, Boston
617 439 2270
payoub@nutter.com
*Featured in Real Estate (Massachusetts)*
**Practice Areas:** Paul Ayoub is a partner in the Real Estate and Finance Department and serves on the firm's Executive Committee. He has thirty years of experience representing clients in the acquisition, sale, leasing, financing and development of commercial real estate throughout the country. Paul represents local and national lending institutions and private lenders in construction, permanent and mezzanine loans as well as in complex workouts and debt reorganizations nationally. Paul serves on the Board of Directors of the Real Estate Finance Association. Among many philanthropic activities, Paul is Vice-Chair of the ALSAC/St. Jude Children's Research Hospital Board of Directors.

**BACHMAN, Katharine E**
WilmerHale, Boston
617 526 6216
katharine.bachman@wilmerhale.com
*Featured in Real Estate (Massachusetts)*
**Practice Areas:** Partner in WilmerHale's Real Estate Practice. Practice covers broad spectrum of real estate development and financial transactions; including representation of investors and developers in office, industrial, R&D facilities and residential developments. Represents institutional lenders in loan collection matters, landlords and tenants

in commercial leasing matters (including high technology and biotechnology facilities). Special interest in projects involving public/private partnerships and affordable housing.
**Professional Memberships:** American College of Real Estate Lawyers; National Association of Office and Industrial Parks, Boston Bar Association.
**Career:** Admitted to Massachusetts Bar.
**Personal:** New York University School of Law (JD); Dickinson College, (BA, summa cum laude).

**BAIN, Michael D**
WilmerHale, Waltham
781 966 2027
michael.bain@wilmerhale.com
*Featured in Private Equity (Massachusetts)*
**Practice Areas:** Specializes in counseling entrepreneurs and companies. Advises on formation and governance issues, equity and compensation matters, initial through late-stage venture capital financings, mergers and acquisitions, technology licensing and securities laws. Counsels companies in a range of industries, including software, telecommunications and wireless, storage, semiconductors, network security, web services, energy and clean tech, and life sciences.
**Career:** Partner-in-Charge of Waltham office; Co-Chair of WilmerHale's Emerging Company Practice; and Co-Chair of its Cleantech and Energy Group. Admitted to the Massachusetts Bar. Joined firm in 1993.
**Personal:** Boston University School of Law (JD); Providence College (BA).

**BANNON, Patrick**
Seyfarth Shaw LLP, Boston
617 946 4987
pbannon@seyfarth.com
*Featured in Labor & Employment (Massachusetts)*
**Practice Areas:** Defense and avoidance of wage/hour claims, including class and collective actions; enforcement and challenging enforcement of non-competition, non-solicitation and non-disclosure agreements; defense of age, disability, gender and race discrimination and retaliation claims.
**Professional Memberships:** ABA, L&E Section (speaker and member); Massachusetts Bar Association, Vice-Chair, L&E Section (2003-2004).
**Publications:** "OT for IT: Which Information Technology Employees Are Entitled to Overtime Pay?" 42 Compensation & Benefits Review 142 (2010); "Bill Would Allow Unions to Expand At All Costs," Boston Globe 1/18/09.
**Personal:** JD, Stanford Law School, with distinction, 1992; AB, Harvard College, Phi Beta Kappa, Magna Cum Laude, 1989.

**BARKER, Christopher B**
Goodwin Procter LLP, Boston
617 570 1462
cbarker@goodwinprocter.com
*Featured in Leisure & Hospitality (Nationwide), Real Estate (Massachusetts)*
See under Nationwide for profile.

## BARKER, Thomas
Foley Hoag LLP, Boston
202 261 7310
tbarker@foleyhoag.com
*Featured in Healthcare (Massachusetts)*
**Practice Areas:** Thomas Barker advises employers and potential Exchange business partners on implementing the 2010 federal health care reform law and complex federal/state health care regulatory matters. He handles Medicare and Medicaid reimbursement and coverage challenges for pharmaceutical companies and provides advice for Medicare providers and health plans. He served as acting General Counsel of the US Department of Health and Human Services and as General Counsel of the Centers for Medicare & Medicaid Services, playing a key role in implementing health care initiatives of the Bush Administration.
**Personal:** Suffolk University Law School, JD, magna cum laude; Jacksonville University, BA.

## BARR, Lynne B
Goodwin Procter LLP, Boston
617 570 1610
lbarr@goodwinprocter.com
*Featured in Financial Services Regulation (Nationwide), Banking & Finance (Massachusetts)*
See under Nationwide for profile.

## BARRETT, James
Edwards Wildman Palmer LLP, Boston
617 239 0385
jbarrett@edwardswildman.com
*Featured in Private Equity (Massachusetts)*
**Practice Areas:** As the co-chair of the Firm's Private Equity & Venture Capital Group, Jim Barrett is a business and securities lawyer who represents life sciences and other technology companies as well as venture capital and private equity funds. He regularly counsels Boards of Directors and General Partners on corporate governance matters and guides their businesses through all stages of development.
**Personal:** University of Pennsylvania Law School, JD, University of Pennsylvania, BA, magna cum laude.

## BASILE, Joseph
Weil, Gotshal & Manges LLP, Boston
617 772 8834
joseph.basile@weil.com
*Featured in Corporate/M&A (Massachusetts), Private Equity (Massachusetts)*
**Practice Areas:** Joe Basile is Managing Partner of Weil's Boston office. He has over 30 years of experience representing sophisticated corporations and private investment funds in complex international transactions, including cross-border M&A, control and minority investments, joint ventures and strategic alliances in the United States, Canada, Europe, Asia and Latin America. His experience also includes distressed M&A transactions and financial restructurings. In addition, Joe advises publicly held companies regarding securities law issues, disclosure and compliance matters and corporate governance.

**Personal:** Stonehill College (AB 1974, summa cum laude); Harvard Law School (JD 1977, cum laude).

## BATTER III, John F
WilmerHale, Boston
617 526 6754
john.batter@wilmerhale.com
*Featured in Litigation (Massachusetts)*
**Practice Areas:** Partner in WilmerHale's Securities and Litigation Departments. Mr Batter focuses on the defense of public and private companies and their directors and management against breach of fiduciary duty and securities fraud allegations, including those arising out of IPOs and in SEC investigations.
**Professional Memberships:** Mr Batter has served on Massachusetts Continuing Legal Education programs, is a Director of the New England Legal Foundation and is a visiting teacher at MIT's Sloan School of Management, co-teaching since 1984 'Business Law for Entrepreneurs'.
**Career:** Joined the firm in 1982. Admitted to Massachusetts Bar.
**Personal:** Harvard Law School (JD); MIT (SB).

## BEALS, John P
Nixon Peabody LLP, Manchester
603 628 4056
jbeals@nixonpeabody.com
*Featured in Private Equity (Massachusetts), Corporate/Commercial (New Hampshire)*
**Practice Areas:** John focuses his practice on private investment fund structuring, formation and investments, mergers and acquisitions, joint ventures, financings, and other general corporate matters. His clients include a number of fund sponsors, funds of funds and public pension plans. He has represented these clients in over 500 investments in leading leveraged buyout and venture capital private equity partnerships, both domestically and internationally. He also has an active transactional practice representing buyers and sellers of technology, manufacturing, professional services, hospitality and service businesses.
**Personal:** Suffolk University Law School, JD, magna cum laude; University of New Hampshire, BS, summa cum laude.

## BEAUDOIN, Thomas A
Goodwin Procter LLP, Boston
617 570 1580
tbeaudoin@goodwinprocter.com
*Featured in Private Equity (Massachusetts)*
**Practice Areas:** Mr Beaudoin is a leader in the field of fund formation, he advises venture capital and private equity funds, and his clients include premier venture capitalists in the United States, Israel and other technology centers, as well as small and mid-sized private equity funds. He also represents institutional investors in the United States and abroad in their investments in all types of private investment funds.
**Professional Memberships:** American Bar Association; Massachusetts Bar Association; Boston Bar Association.
**Personal:** JD, George Washington University Law School, 1986; BA, Boston University 1978 (cum laude).

## BENNETT JR, Charles R
Murphy & King, P.C., Boston
617 423 0400
crb@murphyking.com
*Featured in Bankruptcy/Restructuring (Massachusetts)*
**Practice Areas:** Complex commercial litigation involving financial institutions and corporations, including directors' and officers' claims and insolvency. The current focus of his practice is on rights and remedies for debtors and creditors in corporate Chapter 11 cases. Mr Bennett has substantial experience in banking and lending litigation representing both borrowers and banking institutions in commercial disputes. He has tried numerous jury and jury-waived cases concerning business torts, unfair trade practices, and insolvency issues.
**Professional Memberships:** American Bankruptcy Institute, Massachusetts and Boston Bar Associations.
**Career:** Massachusetts Bar, New Hampshire Bar, Rhode Island Bar.
**Personal:** JD, Boston College Law School (1974); BA, cum laude, Boston College (1970).

## BENOIT, Wilfred J
Goodwin Procter LLP, Boston
617 570 1155
wbenoit@goodwinprocter.com
*Featured in Labor & Employment (Massachusetts)*
**Practice Areas:** Mr Benoit has represented management in all types of labor and employee relations disputes since 1975. He also has extensive employment litigation and alternative dispute resolution experience. He has successfully defended companies across a broad spectrum of industries in suits involving a wide variety of wrongful discharge and employment discrimination issues, including disparate treatment, sexual and racial harassment, equal pay, reasonable accommodation of disabilities and age discrimination claims arising out of reductions in force.
**Personal:** JD, University of Michigan Law School, 1973 (cum laude); BA, University of Notre Dame, 1970 (cum laude).

## BERKOWITZ, William N
Bingham McCutchen LLP, Boston
617 951 8375
bill.berkowitz@bingham.com
*Featured in Antitrust (Massachusetts)*
**Practice Areas:** Former co-chair of the firm's Antitrust and Trade Regulation Practice Group. Focuses on antitrust, mergers and acquisitions, distribution, franchise, and other commercial litigation. Represents clients before the Department of Justice, Federal Trade Commission, the Federal Reserve Board and a number of state agencies. Routinely consults with parties to mergers and acquisitions on compliance with federal and state antitrust laws, state franchise laws, the Hart-Scott-Rodino Act, and foreign premerger notification laws.
**Personal:** University of Michigan Law School, JD, cum laude, 1984; University of Pennsylvania, BS, cum laude, 1981.

## BERMAN, Mark N
Nixon Peabody LLP, Boston
617 345 6037
mberman@nixonpeabody.com
*Featured in Bankruptcy/Restructuring (Massachusetts)*
**Practice Areas:** Mr Berman is a Partner in the firm's Financial Restructuring and Bankruptcy Practice Group working out of its Boston and New York City offices. He supports the firm's Securitization and Structured Finance Team, the Global and Leveraged Finance Teams, the Infrastructure Team, the Sports and Entertainment Team, the Private Equity Group and the Public Finance Group. Using his experience over 37 years of practice, Mr Berman solves problems either when a transaction is first negotiated or when a business slips into workout or bankruptcy.
**Personal:** Boston College, JD; Northwestern University, BA.

## BERNSTEIN, Stephen W
McDermott Will & Emery LLP, Boston
617 535 4062
sbernstein@mwe.com
*Featured in Healthcare (Massachusetts), Healthcare (Nationwide)*
**Practice Areas:** Head of health industry advisory practice group. Specializes in health information, e-health, privacy/security/HIPAA/EU data protection, electronic health records, clinical trials, product and disease registries as well as healthcare merger/acquisitions, affiliations and joint ventures. Works with pharmaceutical/biotech companies, healthcare providers and insurers, and universities concerning uses of health information and tissue samples for clinical and database research, post-market approval observational registries and marketing matters.
**Personal:** Boston College Law School (JD, cum laude), Duke University (AB, magna cum laude).

## BETTENCOURT, Mark T
Goodwin Procter LLP, Boston
617 570 1091
mbettencourt@goodwinprocter.com
*Featured in Corporate/M&A (Massachusetts)*
**Practice Areas:** Mr Bettencourt concentrates his practice on general corporate and securities law and has extensive experience in mergers and acquisitions, public offerings, private placements of debt and equity securities, securities law compliance, and technology transfer and licensing. He represents start-up, private and public companies in a wide range of industries, including software, hardware, networking equipment, information services and healthcare. He has worked with numerous companies from their initial financing through successful initial public offerings or acquisitions.
**Personal:** JD, New York University School of Law, 1994 (cum laude); BA, University of Notre Dame, 1991 (with high honors).

**BEVILACQUA, Michael J**
WilmerHale, Boston
617 526 6448
michael.bevilacqua@wilmerhale.com
*Featured in Intellectual Property (Massachusetts)*
**Practice Areas:** Partner, Intellectual Property and Transactional Departments. Practice focuses primarily on technology-related agreements, such as license agreements, development agreements, collaboration agreements, distribution agreements and joint venture agreements. Has a considerable trademark practice, which includes the management of several thousand US and foreign trademark and service mark registrations.
**Career:** Massachusetts, New York, US Patent and Trademark Office Bar Admissions. Joined firm in 1987.
**Personal:** JD, Boston College Law School; MS, State University of New York at Stony Brook; BS, University of Scranton.

**BIANCHI, Alden J**
Mintz Levin Cohn Ferris Glovsky and Popeo PC, Boston
617 348 3057
ajbianchi@mintz.com
*Featured in Employee Benefits & Executive Compensation (Nationwide), Employee Benefits & Executive Compensation (Massachusetts)*
**Practice Areas:** Alden advises corporate, not-for-profit, governmental and individual clients on executive compensation and employee benefits issues, including qualified and non-qualified retirement plans, stock and stock-based compensation arrangements, ERISA fiduciary and prohibited transaction issues, benefit-related aspects of mergers and acquisitions, health and welfare plans.
**Professional Memberships:** Fellow, American College of Employee Benefits Counsel; Board of Directors, New England Employee Benefits Council.
**Career:** Advised Romney Administration in connection with the 2006 Massachusetts health care reform law. Testified before the Senate Finance Committee on the subject of healthcare reform.
**Publications:** Author of seven books and over 100 benefits-related articles.

**BIBLER, Gregory A**
Goodwin Procter LLP, Boston
617 570 1621
gbibler@goodwinprocter.com
*Featured in Environment (Massachusetts)*
**Practice Areas:** Mr Bibler works with clients to develop and implement creative strategies for addressing and resolving environmental risks. His practice includes litigation, corporate compliance, contaminated site management, and business transactions. Mr Bibler's expertise includes cost recovery and environmental tort litigation, environmental auditing and management systems, SEC reporting of environmental liabilities, and complex or 'mega' sites, particularly those involving coal tar, contaminated sediment, vapor intrusion, or DNAPL migration and remediation.
**Personal:** JD, Harvard Law School, 1985 (magna cum laude); AB, Harvard College, 1981 (summa

cum laude); Christ's College, Cambridge University (John Knox Fellow), 1981-82.

**BLAESSER, Brian**
Robinson & Cole LLP, Boston
617 557 5970
bblaesser@rc.com
*Featured in Real Estate (Massachusetts)*
**Practice Areas:** Brian Blaesser practices in the areas of commercial real estate development, leasing, multifamily residential development, environmental law, renewable energy, public-private partnerships using public financing mechanisms, and litigation. Mr Blaesser represents real estate owners, investors, and developers in securing entitlements from state and local governments, and negotiating development agreements. He has extensive experience in state and federal courts in land use litigation, including the takings issue and appeals of permit denials. He is co-author of the books, Federal Land Use Law & Litigation (Thomson-Reuters: 2012) and Redevelopment (ABA: 2008), and is a LEED Accredited Professional.

**BLECK, Daniel**
Mintz Levin Cohn Ferris Glovsky and Popeo PC, Boston
617 348 4498
dsbleck@mintz.com
*Featured in Bankruptcy/Restructuring (Massachusetts)*
**Practice Areas:** Bankruptcy, restructuring and commercial law.
**Professional Memberships:** Northeast Region of the Turnaround Management Association (Board Member), American Bankruptcy Institute, and Boston Bar Association.
**Career:** Significant experience representing indenture trustees, institutional bondholders, debtors, borrowers in out-of-court workouts, and purchasers of assets in distressed sale transactions.
**Publications:** Author of various articles and lecturer on numerous subjects at various forums, most recently the Northeast American Bankruptcy Institute conference.
**Personal:** Admitted to practice in Massachusetts, the United States District Court for the District of Massachusetts and New Hampshire. BA, cum laude, Boston College; JD, cum laude, Boston University School of Law.

**BLOOM, Mitchell S**
Goodwin Procter LLP, Boston
617 570 1055
mbloom@goodwinprocter.com
*Featured in Corporate/M&A (Massachusetts)*
**Practice Areas:** Mr Bloom represents public and private life science companies, as well as venture capital firms and investment banks in this sector, including biotechnology, medical devices, diagnostics and healthcare information technology. In addition to corporate counseling and strategic advice, he handles a variety of major business transactions, including venture capital financings on behalf of companies and investors, private placements and public offerings on behalf of companies and leading investment banking firms, mergers and acquisitions, joint ventures and other

strategic collaborations and commercial transactions.
**Personal:** JD, Boston College Law School, 1989; BS, Suffolk University, 1986 (cum laude).

**BOLAND, Beth**
Bingham McCutchen LLP, Boston
617 951 8143
beth.boland@bingham.com
*Featured in Litigation (Massachusetts)*
**Practice Areas:** Concentrates on consumer/shareholder class actions, corporate governance and securities issues. Represents clients in SEC and attorney general investigations, shareholder disputes and derivative actions, and fraudulent sales practice class actions and privacy issues in a variety of industries, including financial services, high-tech and manufacturing/retail. Also represents special committees of corporate boards in connection with executive compensation and stock option internal investigations, whistleblower claims over accounting write-downs and major strategic transactions such as a sale of the company.
**Personal:** The University of Chicago Law School, Juris Doctor, 1988; The University of Chicago, Artis Baccalaureate, With Honors (Highest Academic Ranking), 1985.

**BORDEN, Mark**
WilmerHale, Boston
617 526 6675
mark.borden@wilmerhale.com
*Featured in Corporate/M&A (Massachusetts), Private Equity (Massachusetts)*
**Practice Areas:** Partner and Chair of the firm's Corporate Practice Group. Mr Borden's practice concentrates primarily in the areas of securities law, corporate finance and acquisitions; has over 30 years experience in representing public companies; represented companies and underwriters in over 100 public offerings; has extensive experience both in structuring acquisitions and in designing defenses against unsolicited takeovers.
**Career:** Admitted to Massachusetts Bar. Joined firm in 1976.
**Publications:** Co-author of 'Start-up Companies - Planning, Financing and Operating the Successful Business,' published by Law Journal Seminars Press.
**Personal:** Harvard Law School (JD); Yale University (BA, summa cum laude).

**BOTHWICK, Jay**
WilmerHale, Boston
617 526 6526
jay.bothwick@wilmerhale.com
*Featured in Corporate/M&A (Massachusetts)*
**Practice Areas:** As chair of WilmerHale's M&A Group, Mr Bothwick's practice focuses on mergers and acquisitions. He advises public and private companies, both domestically and overseas, in mergers and acquisitions (including through bankruptcy proceedings), tender and exchange offers, and proxy contests. He has significant experience in venture capital and corporate finance transactions, including public and private offerings.

**Professional Memberships:** American, Massachusetts and Boston Bar Associations; Negotiated Acquisitions Committee of the Business Law Section of the American Bar Association.
**Career:** Admitted to Massachusetts Bar. Joined firm in 1981.
**Personal:** Columbia Law School (JD); Bowdoin College (AB).

**BOULGER, Sean T**
WilmerHale, Boston
617 526 6870
sean.boulger@wilmerhale.com
*Featured in Real Estate (Massachusetts)*
**Practice Areas:** Vice chair, Real Estate Practice Group. Practice covers a variety of real estate transactions and development projects. Represents investors, developers and operators in joint ventures, acquisitions, developments, leases and financing transactions across a broad spectrum of real estate asset classes. Areas of expertise include senior housing, retail, industrial, leasing and design and construction contracts.
**Career:** Clients include not-for-profit corporations, including Pine Street Inn, and Allston Brighton Community Development Corporation and Fields Corner Community Development Corporation, which develop affordable housing in Allston, Brighton and Dorchester, Massachusetts.
**Personal:** Co-leader of the firm's public interest partnership with Cathedral High School.

**BOUTON, Paul E**
Nixon Peabody LLP, Boston
617 345 1240
pbouton@nixonpeabody.com
*Featured in Real Estate (Massachusetts)*
**Practice Areas:** Paul Bouton focuses his practice in the area of multifamily housing finance and development, primarily representing owners, developers and syndicators of affordable housing developments.
**Professional Memberships:** Paul is a member of the American and Boston bar associations. Previously he has served as chair of his community's Finance Committee, as vice-chair of the Housing Partnership Committee, and town moderator.
**Personal:** Boston College Law School, JD; University of Connecticut, MBA; University of Massachusetts, BBA.

**BOYLE, Philip G**
Morgan, Brown and Joy LLP, Boston
617 788 5006
PBoyle@morganbrown.com
*Featured in Labor & Employment (Massachusetts)*
**Practice Areas:** Mr Boyle's practice concentrates on collective bargaining, including arbitration and related agency and court litigation in the public and private sectors. He has a particular concentration in the transportation sector: transit, railroad, airport and shipping. He has extensive experience in interest arbitration in the transit, railroad and public safety environment.
**Professional Memberships:** American Bar Association, Massachusetts Bar Association, Boston Bar Association, American Arbitration

Association, Panel of Arbitrators, College of Labor and Employment Attorneys, Fellow.
**Career:** Morgan Brown & Joy LLP, Partner 1998 to present; Sherin and Lodgen, Partner 1994-98; Law Office of Philip G. Boyle, 1985-1994; Holland Crowe and Drachman, Partner 1981-85; General Cinema Corporation, Theatre Division Labor Counsel 1977-1981; City of Boston Assistant Corporation Counsel 1976-77.
**Personal:** Suffolk University Law School, JD 1975 Yale University, BA 1971.

## BROADWIN, David
Foley Hoag LLP, Boston
781 895 5905
dbroadwin@foleyhoag.com
*Featured in Private Equity (Massachusetts)*
**Practice Areas:** Dave Broadwin is a member of the Firm's Executive Committee and Co-Chair of the Emerging Enterprise and Venture Capital Group. He focuses on representation of venture-financed technology companies as well as buyers and sellers of public and private companies. Dave counsels clients across a broad range of business transactions, including mergers and acquisitions, venture capital financings, public offerings, private placements, PIPE (private investment in public equity) transactions, and bank financings. Dave is the author of Negotiating and Documenting Business Acquisitions, 1997 American Law Institute.
**Personal:** Yale Law School, JD; University of Chicago, MA; New York University, BA.

## BRODERICK, James M
Goodwin Procter LLP, Boston
617 570 1969
jbroderick@goodwinprocter.com
*Featured in Real Estate (Massachusetts)*
**Practice Areas:** Mr Broderick represents real estate investment advisors and institutional investors in real estate transactions, with particular emphasis on structuring and implementing equity joint venture and debt investments on behalf of institutional tax-exempt investors, their advisors and investment funds. He also has significant experience in the formation of commingled real estate investment funds and in structuring subscription secured credit facilities on behalf of institutional investment funds. He also represents developers and noninstitutional investors in real estate acquisition, financing, development, zoning and land use matters.
**Personal:** JD, Cornell Law School, 1990 (cum laude); BS, Providence College, 1983 (magna cum laude).

## BROMBERG, Lee C
McCarter & English, LLP, Boston
617 449 6538
lbromberg@mccarter.com
*Featured in Intellectual Property (Massachusetts)*
**Career:** Mr Bromberg has tried cases throughout the US and has extensive experience in intellectual property litigation (patent, copyright, trademark, trade secret and unfair competition) and business litigation. He is skilled at presenting complex technical and scientific subject matter to courts and juries. He has handled cases involving phar-

maceuticals, medical devices, software, computers and electronics and obtained numerous multimillion-dollar recoveries. His expertise also includes client counseling, negotiation and alternative dispute resolution. He has served as a court-appointed discovery master in federal court litigation and as an expert witness on patent litigation and trademark law and practice. For full bio: http://www.mccarter.com/Lee-C-Bromberg/.

## BROWN, John S
Bingham McCutchen LLP, Boston
617 951 8252
john.brown@bingham.com
*Featured in Tax (Massachusetts)*
**Practice Areas:** Practice devoted primarily to federal and state tax matters. Handles tax controversies involving both administrative proceedings and litigation. Provides tax-planning advice in connection with structuring organizations and transactions.
**Career:** Served as special assistant to the assistant attorney general in the Tax Division of the US Department of Justice. Spent four years as a professor at Cornell University Law School. Has taught classes at Harvard Law School, Boston University School of Law and Northeastern University Graduate School of Professional Accounting.
**Personal:** Cornell Law School, LLB, with distinction, 1965; Villanova University, BS, 1957.

## BROWN, Margaret A
Skadden, Arps, Slate, Meagher & Flom LLP & Affiliates, Boston
617 573 4815
Margaret.Brown@skadden.com
*Featured in Corporate/M&A (Massachusetts)*
**Practice Areas:** Head of the firm's Boston office and the Boston-based Mergers and Acquisitions Group. Works on a wide variety of corporate and securities matters, including mergers and acquisitions and capital markets transactions. Counsels clients on a broad range of business-related matters, including directors' duties and responsibilities and other aspects of corporate governance, disclosure issues, corporate compliance matters and internal investigations. Recognized by The American Lawyer as "Dealmaker of the Week" in 2009, and "Dealmaker of the Year" in 2008.
**Career:** JD, Boston College Law School, 1979 (cum laude, Articles Editor, Boston College Law Review) BA, Holy Cross College, 1976.

## BROWNE, Steven C
Bingham McCutchen LLP, Boston
617 951 8124
steven.browne@bingham.com
*Featured in Corporate/M&A (Massachusetts)*
**Practice Areas:** Co-chairs Bingham's Corporate Practice Group. Extensive experience in M&A, leveraged buyouts, corporate finance, private equity financing transactions, public offerings, SEC compliance, and technology transfer and licensing. Serves as general counsel to public and privately held companies in many industries. Represents technology companies, from startup to global public company. Represents private equity firms in complex structured finance transactions.

Serves as counsel to boards of directors on corporate governance and related matters.
**Personal:** Cornell Law School, JD, cum laude, 1988; University of Rhode Island, BA, cum laude, 1985.

## BUCHANAN JR, Robert M
Choate Hall & Stewart LLP, Boston
617 248 5027
rbuchanan@choate.com
*Featured in Antitrust (Massachusetts)*
**Practice Areas:** Provides antitrust counsel in strategic transactions and litigation. Represents companies in pre-merger review and other antitrust matters before the FTC, US Justice Department and various states. Represents technology companies, energy companies, health plans, hospitals and others in antitrust litigation and other major commercial disputes, including defending consumer class actions. Recent matters: joint counsel advising merger discussions for two of state's three largest health plans; winning dismissal of Section One complaint against manufacturer/retailer (first such case to address private-label brand).
**Personal:** JD cum laude Harvard Law School (1985); AB magna cum laude, Phi Beta Kappa Harvard University (1982).

## BUCK, Charles
McDermott Will & Emery LLP, Boston
617 535 4151
cbuck@mwe.com
*Featured in Healthcare (Massachusetts)*
**Practice Areas:** Partner specializing in healthcare transactions, strategic affiliations, and joint ventures; federal and state regulatory matters, including anti-kickback and Stark law; health privacy and HIPAA; federal tax-exemption; and state insurance law.
**Career:** Professional Staff of the United States Senate Finance Committee, with responsibility for Medicare Part A (1994-96); law clerk to the Honorable Charles R Breyer, Northern District of California (2001-02).
**Personal:** Stanford Law School (JD, order of the coif), Middlebury College (BA, magna cum laude).

## BUCKING, James W
Foley Hoag LLP, Boston
617 832 1182
jbucking@foleyhoag.com
*Featured in Labor & Employment (Massachusetts)*
**Practice Areas:** James W. Bucking, Partner and Chair of the Labor and Employment Practice, advises and represents corporations and other employers in union disputes, wage/hour, discrimination, and other labor and employment matters. Mr Bucking has extensive experience representing management at the bargaining table in union negotiations and litigating labor disputes in court, before arbitrators, and at the National Labor Relations Board. In the field of employment law, he represents clients in court and before the Massachusetts Commission Against Discrimination defending discrimination complaints. He has represented many clients in actions initiated by the US Department of Labor, the state

Attorney General's Office, and private attorneys on various wage/hour issues. Mr Bucking is a frequent speaker on a variety of labor and employment law topics and recently authored the primer 'Massachusetts Wage and Hour Laws: What Every Manager Needs to Know'.
**Personal:** University of Pennsylvania Law School, JD; Northeastern University, BS.

## BURKE, Meghan
Mintz Levin Cohn Ferris Glovsky and Popeo PC, Boston
617 348 1663
MBBurke@mintz.com
*Featured in Banking & Finance (Massachusetts)*
**Practice Areas:** Meghan is a member in the firm's Boston office and practices in the Public Finance Section. She has extensive experience in public finance and public agency representation serving as bond counsel, and as counsel to underwriters, borrowers, trustees, and purchasers in connection with tax-exempt and taxable general obligation and revenue financings related to transportation, higher education, health care, economic development, project finance, water, and wastewater. She also has vast experience with interest rate swaps and hedging transactions for governmental, 501(c)(3), and corporate clients.
**Professional Memberships:** Member, National Association of Bond Lawyers.
**Personal:** BA, Oberlin College; JD, Northeastern University.

## BURKE, Robert
WilmerHale, Boston
617 526 6470
robert.burke@wilmerhale.com
*Featured in Tax (Massachusetts)*
**Practice Areas:** Practice concentrates on the taxation of partnerships and limited liability companies engaged in investment activities (including real estate, venture capital and 'hedge fund' activities) and business operations as well as on corporate restructurings, acquisitions, and dispositions and the taxation of financial instruments.
**Professional Memberships:** Member of the American Bar Association's Section on Taxation; serves on its Committee on Partnerships and Subcommittee on Partnership Allocations.
**Career:** Admitted to Massachusetts Bar.
**Personal:** Williams College (BA, magna cum laude, Phi Beta Kappa); Cornell University Law School (JD, magna cum laude); Boston University School of Law (LLM in taxation).

## BURLING, James
WilmerHale, Boston
617 526 6416
james.burling@wilmerhale.com
*Featured in Antitrust (Massachusetts)*
**Practice Areas:** Partner, Antitrust and Competition Practice. Concentrates in antitrust litigation and merger clearance for high technology clients, particularly in computer, telecom, internet, biotech and pharmaceutical industries. Represents clients in private litigation, in responding to government antitrust investigations, and before the Department of Justice and Federal

Trade Commission in Hart-Scott-Rodino review of mergers and acquisitions.
**Professional Memberships:** American Bar Association Antitrust Section; Boston Bar Association Antitrust Committee; Massachusetts Bar Association.
**Career:** Admitted to Massachusetts Bar; United States Supreme Court. Joined firm in 1978 after two years with the Federal Trade Commission.
**Personal:** Harvard Law School (JD); Grinnell College (AB).

### BURNETT, Mark
Goodwin Procter LLP, Boston
617 570 1031
mburnett@goodwinprocter.com
*Featured in Private Equity (Nationwide), Corporate/M&A (Massachusetts), Private Equity (Massachusetts)*
**Practice Areas:** Mr Burnett works in the firm's corporate, private equity, M&A/ corporate governance and technology companies groups, focusing on business, corporate and securities law matters, mergers and acquisitions, buyouts, and corporate finance and venture capital transactions. His clients include public and private companies in a range of industries (including software, Internet services, telecommunications services, healthcare services and water purification), venture capital and private equity firms and investment banks. He has extensive experience representing public and private companies in mergers, acquisitions and corporate finance transactions.
**Personal:** JD, George Washington University School of Law, 1983; BA, Union College, 1980 (cum laude).

### BURROUGHS, Allison
Nutter McClennen & Fish LLP, Boston
617 439 2684
aburroughs@nutter.com
*Featured in Litigation (Massachusetts)*
**Practice Areas:** Allison Burroughs, an experienced trial lawyer, focuses her practice on white collar criminal defense and government investigations, with particular emphasis on the life sciences industry, computer crimes, intellectual property matters and other complex litigation. She represents companies and individuals in state and federal court, in all phases of litigation, from internal investigation through grand jury and trial. Allison spent 16 years as an Assistant US Attorney in Philadelphia and then Boston. In Boston, during eight years in the Economic Crimes Unit, she served terms as the Office's Senior Litigation Counsel and ran the Computer Crime and High Technology Section.

### BURTON, Doug
WilmerHale, Boston
617 526 6270
douglas.burton@wilmerhale.com
*Featured in Real Estate (Massachusetts)*
**Practice Areas:** Mr Burton is a partner in the Real Estate Practice Group. His practice focuses on all aspects of real estate law, including private equity investment, development, acquisitions, dispositions and leasing. He serves as counsel for a broad range of clients, including investment man-

agers and advisors, Fortune 50 corporations, developers and non-profit institutions.
**Professional Memberships:** Pension Real Estate Association; International Council of Shopping Centers; American, New York State, Massachusetts and Boston Bar Associations.
**Personal:** JD, magna cum laude, Cornell University Law School, 1996, Order of the Coif; BA, magna cum laude, Amherst College, 1992.

### CABLE, Stuart M
Goodwin Procter LLP, Boston
617 570 1322
scable@goodwinprocter.com
*Featured in Corporate/M&A (Massachusetts)*
**Practice Areas:** Mr Cable represents as outside general counsel a wide array of public and private companies involved in diverse businesses, including technology, software, life sciences, professional and business services, alternative energy and financial services. He also represents private equity sources investing in such companies. His transactional practice is focused on mergers and acquisitions, private equity recapitalizations, venture capital private placements and public offerings.
**Personal:** JD, Columbia Law School, 1979 (Harlan Fiske Stone Scholar); MBA, Tuck School of Business Administration at Dartmouth College, 1976; AB, Dartmouth College, 1975 (magna cum laude).

### CAHILL, Mark D
Choate Hall & Stewart LLP, Boston
617 248 5033
mcahill@choate.com
*Featured in Litigation (Massachusetts)*
**Practice Areas:** Mr Cahill represents public and private companies and VC/PE firms in complex financial, intellectual property, class action and contract litigation. He is experienced in insurance coverage, bad faith, extra-contractual claims and reinsurance issues. He has tried numerous jury and bench cases in federal/state courts, and arbitrations in various alternative dispute resolution forums. He has argued appeals before the Massachusetts Supreme Judicial Court and Appeals Court, and the US Court of Appeals, and regularly handles matters in courts throughout the country.
**Personal:** JD with highest honors Drake University Law School (1984), Order of the Coif; AB Rutgers University (1980).

### CAPORIZZO, A William
WilmerHale, Boston
617 526 6411
william.caporizzo@wilmerhale.com
*Featured in Tax (Massachusetts)*
**Practice Areas:** Chair of Tax Practice Group. Practice concentrates on the taxation of domestic and international funds engaged in investment activities (including venture capital and buy out funds) and partnership and limited liability companies engaged in business activities. Mr Caporizzo also advises companies on domestic and cross-border mergers, acquisitions and dispositions, and companies and individuals on the taxation of non-US investment structures, including

foreign trusts and offshore investment holding companies.
**Personal:** JD, magna cum laude, Boston University School of Law; BS, magna cum laude, University of Pennsylvania.

### CARROLL, James R
Skadden, Arps, Slate, Meagher & Flom LLP & Affiliates, Boston
617 573 4801
james.carroll@skadden.com
*Featured in Litigation (Massachusetts)*
**Practice Areas:** Experience in mutual fund, annuity, insurance and securities class action defense and complex civil litigations. Regularly represents individuals and corporations in SEC and CFTC enforcement matters. Has tried securities fraud, theft of trade secrets and covenant-not-to-compete cases to verdict. Current engagements include defense of lender in subprime matters, defense of an investment bank in an antitrust class action and defense of qui tam actions. Mr Carroll regularly represents clients in contested matters against the Massachusetts Attorney General's office and Massachusetts Securities Division.
**Career:** JD, Harvard University, 1989; BA, Niagara University, 1986 (summa cum laude; Presidential Scholar).

### CASEY, David
Littler Mendelson, PC, Boston
617 378 6000
dcasey@littler.com
*Featured in Labor & Employment (Massachusetts)*
**Practice Areas:** Complex Litigation and Jury Trials Competition and Trade Secret Law Discrimination and Harassment Class Actions Appellate Practice.
**Professional Memberships:** Massachusetts and Boston Bar Associations.
**Career:** Mr Casey focuses on the litigation of discrimination, non-competition, common law and wage and hour actions. He has extensive experience defending management in all aspects of employment law.
**Personal:** JD, Northeastern University, 1979; BA, English & American Literature, Brown University, 1976.

### CHILD, Ralph
Mintz Levin Cohn Ferris Glovsky and Popeo PC, Boston
617 348 3021
RChild@mintz.com
*Featured in Environment (Massachusetts)*
**Practice Areas:** Ralph represents owners and developers of energy and manufacturing facilities concerning environmental issues.
**Professional Memberships:** Ralph chaired the Environmental Law Section of the Boston Bar Association. He is an invited member of the American College of Environmental Lawyers.
**Career:** Ralph served as General Counsel to the Massachusetts Department of Environmental Protection and as an Assistant US Attorney.
**Personal:** He graduated from Dartmouth College and Harvard Law School, where he was an editor of the Harvard Law Review. He was a Luce

Scholar in Indonesia and clerked for the US Court of Appeals for the 1st Circuit.

### CHIMENTO, George L
Davis, Malm & D'Agostine, P.C., Boston
617 589 3847
gchimento@davismalm.com
*Featured in Employee Benefits & Executive Compensation (Massachusetts)*
**Practice Areas:** Employee benefit and deferred compensation plans for public, private, non-profit, and governmental entities, including multiemployer plans. Represented industries include higher education, hospital, physician care, mutual and credit union banking, governmental public transit, and basic industrial. Serves as PBGC-appointed trustee for insolvent multiemployer plans. Representation in audits and contested procedures.
**Professional Memberships:** American, Boston, and New Hampshire Bar Associations.
**Career:** Admitted: Massachusetts and New Hampshire (active) and Rhode Island (inactive).
**Personal:** JD, University of California, Berkeley, Boalt Hall School of Law (1973); AB, Brown University (1970).

### CINQUEGRANA, Jack
Choate Hall & Stewart LLP, Boston
617 248 4002
rjcinquegrana@choate.com
*Featured in Litigation (Massachusetts)*
**Practice Areas:** Represents companies/individuals in civil and criminal litigation and investigations involving government agencies. Served as President of the Boston Bar Association, an Assistant US Attorney and Chief Trial Counsel in the Boston District Attorney's Office, and is a Fellow of the American College of Trial Lawyers and the International Academy of Trial Lawyers. Recent matters: defense of major pharmaceutical companies in investigations regarding marketing practices; companies/corporate officers in SEC investigations; hospitals/insurers in antitrust and False Claims Act matters; Special Counsel to Massachusetts Supreme Judicial Court for independent inquiry.
**Personal:** JD Boston College Law School (1978); BA Cornell University (1974).

### CLARK, Lori R
Schwartz Hannum PC, Andover
978 623 0900
lclark@shpclaw.com
*Featured in Labor & Employment (Massachusetts)*
**Practice Areas:** Lori Rittman Clark's practice focuses on labor and employment law. She represents companies of all sizes in federal and state courts and before administrative agencies regarding a variety of employment-related claims. Lori also regularly counsels businesses on employment issues ranging from reasonable accommodations to severance agreements. Finally, Lori represents clients in traditional labor proceedings, including collective bargaining and grievance arbitration.
**Personal:** JD, cum laude, Western New England College School of Law, 1997; Note Editor, Western New England Law Review; Law Clerk, Honorable Alfred V. Covello, United States District Court,

District of Connecticut; BA, University of Connecticut.

## CLEARY, John J
Goodwin Procter LLP, Boston
617 570 1199
jcleary@goodwinprocter.com
*Featured in Employee Benefits & Executive Compensation (Nationwide), Employee Benefits & Executive Compensation (Massachusetts)*
**Practice Areas:** Mr Cleary specializes in all aspects of ERISA and employee benefits, representing numerous employers in connection with their employee benefit requirements, including qualified and non-qualified retirement plans, welfare plans and executive compensation. He has particular experience with respect to issues arising in connection with corporate and real estate transactions and under Title I of ERISA, including fiduciary, investment and prohibited transaction matters. He has been extensively involved in establishing and operating numerous collective investment fund vehicles for institutional investors.
**Personal:** JD, Harvard Law School, 1974 (magna cum laude); MA, Yale University, 1970; BS, Massachusetts Institute of Technology, 1968.

## COE, Lynn
Jones Day, Boston
617 449 6884
llcoe@jonesday.com
*Featured in Healthcare (Massachusetts)*
**Practice Areas:** Experienced in the areas of tax-exempt health care and education financing and tax-exempt industrial development revenue bonds in multiple states as well as Puerto Rico. For more than 35 years he has worked as Bond Counsel, Underwriter's Counsel, Issuer's Counsel, Borrower's Counsel, Purchaser's Counsel, and Bond Insurer's Counsel in both tax-exempt and taxable health care transactions. These transactions have entailed a wide variety of document structures, including multimodal transactions, imbedded derivatives, forward commitments and swaps, and FHA and GNMA credit enhancement as well as pooled financings.
**Professional Memberships:** American College of Bond Counsel. American Health Lawyers Association.

## COHEN, Bret A
Mintz Levin Cohn Ferris Glovsky and Popeo PC, Boston
617 348 3089
BCohen@mintz.com
*Featured in Labor & Employment (Massachusetts)*
**Practice Areas:** Wage and Hour, whistleblower, non-competition agreement and trade secret, employment related breach of contract and tort employment claims, discrimination, employment counseling, and the creation of and the litigation of employment agreements.
**Professional Memberships:** Fellow: Mass Bar Association and ABA; BBA's Labor and Employment Section Council
**Publications:** Editor of Employment Law chapter of the ABA's Annual Review of the Developments in Business and Corporate litigation (2004 – 2010), contributor to Trade Secret

chapter in same book (2009 to present); Editor of the Annual Review (2010 to present).
**Personal:** BA University of Illinois (1989), JD St. Louis University (1993).

## COHEN, Margaret R
Skadden, Arps, Slate, Meagher & Flom LLP & Affiliates, Boston
617 573 4859
margaret.cohen@skadden.com
*Featured in Corporate/M&A (Massachusetts)*
**Practice Areas:** Focuses on mergers and acquisitions, public and private debt and equity financings, commercial contracts and other corporate and securities law matters. Representative clients include CommonWealth REIT, Sonesta Acquisition Corp., TravelCenters of America LLC, Textron Inc., UGL Limited, Government Properties Income Trust, Select Income Reit, Novell Inc. and BJ Services Co.
**Career:** Before joining Skadden, Ms Cohen worked as deputy director, international markets, at the Ontario Securities Commission and in private practice in Canada. At the OSC, she helped develop the US/Canadian Multijurisdictional Disclosure System. LLB, Queen's University; BS, Acadia University.

## COHEN, Stephen M L
Choate Hall & Stewart LLP, Boston
617 248 5050
scohen@choate.com
*Featured in Private Equity (Massachusetts)*
**Practice Areas:** Mr Cohen represents private equity funds in merger, acquisition and investment activities, fund formation and ongoing portfolio company matters. Engagements include: acquisition of premier media properties (including The Hollywood Reporter and Billboard Magazine), formation of Riverside Fund V, LP (domestic and offshore), sale of national healthcare business (Buyouts Magazine Deal of the Year) and formation of renewable energy integrator (M&A Advisor Green/Environmental Deal of the Year).
**Personal:** JD Cornell Law School (1980), Law Review; BA cum laude Harvard College (1977).

## COLLINS, Jeffrey D
Foley Hoag LLP, Boston
617 832 1265
jcollins@foleyhoag.com
*Featured in Investment Funds (Massachusetts)*
**Practice Areas:** Jeffrey Collins, Co-Head of the Investment Advisers and Private Investment Funds Group and Chair of the Business Department, helps investment advisers comply with federal and state registration and regulatory standards. He has extensive experience in the formation of onshore and offshore hedge funds and other private funds, and has experience in structuring management companies for private fund managers in order to achieve optimal business and tax results. Recently he advised a number of hedge fund managers overseas on US regulatory, securities and tax matters.
**Personal:** Duke University School of Law, JD; Brown University, BA.

## COLLINS, Thomas
McCarter & English, LLP, Boston
617 449 6570
tcollins@mccarter.com
*Featured in Banking & Finance (Massachusetts)*
**Career:** Mr Collins has over 30 years of experience in tax-exempt financing. His practice includes structuring financings to qualify for tax-exempt status, advising public authorities on post-bond-issuance tax compliance issues, and counseling corporate and individual clients on numerous business tax issues. Mr Collins coauthored the chapter on "Tax Exempt Bonds" in CCH's Federal Tax Service. He has presented seminars on the low-income housing tax credit, the impact of the unrelated business income tax on the activities of exempt organizations, and the requirements for obtaining and maintaining exempt organization status and tax-exempt financing opportunities for 501(c)(3) organizations. For full bio: http://www.mccarter.com/Thomas-G-Collins/.

## COLUMBIA, Sarah Chapin
McDermott Will & Emery LLP, Boston
617 535 4074
scolumbia@mwe.com
*Featured in Intellectual Property (Massachusetts)*
**Practice Areas:** Head of IP litigation practice. Focuses on intellectual property litigation including patent, trademark, copyright and trade secret matters. Extensive experience in representing clients in private arbitration proceedings under the rules and procedures of the International Chamber of Commerce, Swiss Chamber of Commerce, World Intellectual Property Organization, American Arbitration Association and other organizations.
**Professional Memberships:** Admitted to practice in Massachusetts, US Courts of Appeal for Federal Circuit, First Circuit, Second Circuit, Ninth Circuit and the Supreme Court.
**Personal:** Harvard Law School (JD, magna cum laude); John F. Kennedy School of Government (MPP); Wesleyan University (BA).

## CONDE, Kathryn Keough
Nutter McClennen & Fish LLP, Boston
617 439 2420
kconde@nutter.com
*Featured in Antitrust (Massachusetts)*
**Practice Areas:** Kathryn Conde is a partner in the Litigation Department and chairs the Antitrust practice group. Her experience includes counseling and litigation in civil and criminal matters and ranges from large-scale class actions in multi-district litigation to suits affecting local and regional companies. Companies rely on her advice to reduce antitrust risk in all areas of their business - including pricing and distribution, joint ventures, mergers and compliance. She also represents companies and individuals in civil and criminal antitrust investigations by the state and federal governments.

## CONNOLLY, Sarah
Nixon Peabody LLP, Boston
617 345 6075
sconnolly@nixonpeabody.com
*Featured in Tax (Massachusetts)*

**Practice Areas:** Sarah concentrates her work in the area of estate planning and estate administration, including handling sophisticated gift, estate, and income tax issues. Sarah also frequently serves as trustee of clients' trusts and as executor of their wills.
**Professional Memberships:** Board member, Family Service of Greater Boston, Inc.; Chair, Redeemer Lutheran Church Charitable Foundation.
**Personal:** New York University School of Law, JD; Georgetown University, AB, magna cum laude (Phi Beta Kappa).

## COOPER, Donald D
Nixon Peabody LLP, Boston
617 345 6077
dcooper@nixonpeabody.com
*Featured in Environment (Massachusetts)*
**Practice Areas:** Don practices in the areas of environmental law, land use law and construction law. He is a Registered Professional Civil Engineer in Massachusetts and New Hampshire. He has a broad-based environmental and land use law practice, including providing advice to utilities and energy generators. Don also advises construction firms, owners and developers on construction contract issues and has substantial experience in construction litigation.
**Professional Memberships:** Don is General Counsel to the Massachusetts Licensed Site Professional Association, and is Chairman of the Andover, Massachusetts Conservation Commission. He is on the Board of Directors of the Massachusetts Audubon Society.

## COOPER, Jenny
Bingham McCutchen LLP, Boston
617 951 8473
jenny.cooper@bingham.com
*Featured in Labor & Employment (Massachusetts)*
**Practice Areas:** Represents employers in litigation alleging claims of disability, age, race, sex and sexual orientation discrimination; retaliation; harassment; breach of contract; defamation; unpaid wages; and unfair competition. Has successfully represented clients in state and federal courts as well as before administrative agencies. Advises clients on a wide range of employment issues, including wage and hour compliance, workplace investigations, employee discipline, terminations, leaves of absence, employee benefits, employment agreements, noncompete agreements, and the drafting of employee handbooks.
**Personal:** University of Michigan Law School, Juris Doctor, 2000; University of Michigan, Bachelor of Arts, English, 1997.

## COOPER, Scott
Holland & Knight LLP, Boston
617 305 2052
scott.cooper@hklaw.com
*Featured in Real Estate (Massachusetts)*
**Practice Areas:** Scott Cooper is head of the firm's Real Estate Practice Group in the Boston office and past chair of the National Real Estate Finance Team. Practicing in the areas of banking, finance and real estate law, he has extensive experience representing major US and foreign banks

and other financial institutions in real estate financing transactions, including acquisition, construction and permanent financing of office, retail, hotel, condominium and multi-family projects throughout the United States. This experience includes Fannie Mae and Freddie Mae multi-family loan programs, loan participations and syndicated loan transactions, loan sales, and work-outs and foreclosures.

### COPENHAVER, Karen F
Choate Hall & Stewart LLP, Boston
617 248 4825
kcopenhaver@choate.com
*Featured in Intellectual Property (Massachusetts)*
**Practice Areas:** Ms Copenhaver counsels business and technology clients in technology transfer and licensing of intellectual property, particularly in the areas of patent licensing and software licensing and open source business models. Ms Copenhaver is director of intellectual property strategy for the Linux Foundation and is also only the 5th lawyer ever to receive Mass High Tech's prestigious "Mass High Tech All-Stars Award," which honors thought leaders and innovators throughout the New England technology sector.
**Personal:** JD Dickinson School of Law (1979); BA Dickinson College (1976).

### COPENHEFER, Lea Anne
Bingham McCutchen LLP, Boston
617 951 8515
leaanne.copenhefer@bingham.com
*Featured in Investment Funds (Nationwide), Investment Funds (Massachusetts)*
See under Nationwide for profile.

### CRONAN, Todd
Goodwin Procter LLP, Boston
617 570 1389
tcronan@goodwinprocter.com
*Featured in Litigation (Massachusetts)*
**Practice Areas:** Mr Cronan is chair of the Securities Litigation & White Collar Defense Group and has a national business litigation and corporate investigative practice, concentrating in the areas of securities class action defense, SEC investigations and enforcement actions, Foreign Corrupt Practices Act investigations, M&A related litigation, and complex business litigation and arbitration matters. He also regularly advises boards of directors on strategies to avoid disruptive and costly litigation and provides training sessions for clients on corporate governance issues.
**Personal:** JD, Harvard Law School, 1983 (cum laude); BA, Princeton University, Wilson School of Public and International Affairs, 1980.

### CUBELL, Howard A
Goodwin Procter LLP, Boston
617 570 1560
hcubell@goodwinprocter.com
*Featured in Tax (Massachusetts)*
**Practice Areas:** Mr Cubell's practice focuses on the development of innovative tax strategies for various domestic and international business transactions and collective investment vehicles, with particular emphasis on representing private equity sponsors in acquiring, disposing of and recapitalizing portfolio companies. He has been at the forefront in developing creative structures for private equity funds to use in doing leveraged buyouts overseas and for making investments in domestic pass-through entities such as Subchapter S corporations, partnerships and LLCs.
**Personal:** JD, Boston University School of Law, 1973; BA, University of Michigan, 1970; New York University Graduate Tax Program.

### CUDKOWICZ, Ariel D
Seyfarth Shaw LLP, Boston
617 946 4884
acudkowicz@seyfarth.com
*Featured in Labor & Employment (Massachusetts)*
**Practice Areas:** National co-chair, Employment Litigation & Counseling practice group; wage and hour litigation and compliance.
**Professional Memberships:** American, Massachusetts, and Boston Bar Associations. Fellow, College of Labor & Employment Lawyers.
**Career:** Associate managing partner of the Boston office. Focuses on employment litigation with a particular emphasis on wage and hour collective and class actions, complex single-plaintiff employment discrimination litigation and workplace counseling. Specializes in representing retail clients in FLSA collective actions, and hospitality clients in class actions challenging the distribution of tips and service charges.
**Personal:** JD, Georgetown University Law Center (1987); BA, University of Rochester (1984).

### CURLEY, James M
Goodwin Procter LLP, Boston
617 570 8186
jcurley@goodwinprocter.com
*Featured in Private Equity (Massachusetts)*
**Practice Areas:** Mr Curley's practice focuses primarily on corporate finance, mergers and acquisitions and the general representation of private equity firms, venture capital firms and early and later stage growth companies. He has represented a number of leading private equity and venture capital firms, as well as a wide range of early and later stage growth companies in various industries, including financial services, healthcare, manufacturing, retail and technology.
**Personal:** JD, Boston University School of Law, 1996 (magna cum laude; distinguished scholar); BA, Brandeis University, 1993 (magna cum laude; Phi Beta Kappa).

### CURTIN, Neal J
Bingham McCutchen LLP, Boston
617 951 8437
neal.curtin@bingham.com
*Featured in Banking & Finance (Massachusetts)*
**Practice Areas:** Co-head of Bingham's Financial Institutions Corporate and Regulatory Group. Focuses on financial institutions. Experience in corporate, bank holding company and bank mergers, acquisitions, conversions, and restructurings. Has led international transactions in sub-Saharan Africa, South America and the Caribbean. Guides banks and other international companies establishing operations or making acquisitions in the United States. Regulatory experience involves practice before all of the federal bank regulatory agencies as well as the Office of the Commissioner of Banks of the Commonwealth of Massachusetts.
**Personal:** Fordham University School of Law, JD; Harvard College, BA.

### DACCORD, Deborah
Mintz Levin Cohn Ferris Glovsky and Popeo PC, Boston
617 348 4716
dadaccord@mintz.com
*Featured in Healthcare (Massachusetts)*
**Practice Areas:** Deborah specializes in health industry transactions, representing clients nationally in complex joint ventures, strategic alliances, mergers, acquisitions, unwinds and divestiture transactions.
**Professional Memberships:** Admitted to practice in Massachusetts. Member of the American Health Lawyers Association, the Boston Bar Association, and Women Business Leaders of the US Health Care Industry Foundation (WBL).
**Career:** Serves as a director on the boards of WBL, Big Sister Association of Greater Boston and Brookline Community Mental Health.
**Publications:** Deborah speaks and publishes on a variety of topics.
**Personal:** ALB, cum laude, Harvard University; JD, cum laude, Harvard Law School.

### DALE III, Charles A
K&L Gates, Boston
617 261 3112
chad.dale@klgates.com
*Featured in Bankruptcy/Restructuring (Massachusetts)*
**Practice Areas:** Charles Dale III, a partner in the restructuring and bankruptcy practice group, has extensive experience representing troubled companies, equity investors, creditor committees, trustees and receivers in connection with out-of-court restructurings, bankruptcy proceedings and receiverships. He also represents purchasers of financially distressed businesses both in and out of court. A member of the American Bankruptcy Institute, Turnaround Management Association, and the Boston Bar Association, he has been recognized as one of the top 100 lawyers in New England since 2008.

### DAMON, Lisa J.
Seyfarth Shaw LLP, Boston
617 946 4880
ldamon@seyfarth.com
*Featured in Labor & Employment (Massachusetts)*
**Practice Areas:** Labor and employment.
**Career:** Ms Damon represents management in the area of employment law. Her practice has an emphasis on litigation of claims of sex, race and age discrimination and harassment in the context of multiple-plaintiff claims and single-plaintiff actions. She advises companies nationwide on issues of diversity and conducts privileged and non-privileged audits and assessments of the workplace. Ms Damon is accountable for Seyfarth's lean six sigma efforts with clients and is a certified GreenBelt. Ms Damon was named Employment Lawyer of the Year at the inaugural Chambers USA Women in Law Awards.
**Personal:** JD, Fordham University.

### DAVIS, Michael M
Sullivan & Worcester LLP, Boston
617 338 2848
mdavis@sandw.com
*Featured in Tax (Massachusetts)*
**Practice Areas:** Michael M Davis is a tax partner and concentrates his practice in income tax and estate planning, particularly for owners of closely held businesses and real estate and holders of substantial liquid assets. He counsels numerous corporations, partnerships and limited liability companies, and he has established grantor retained annuity trusts for clients with substantial holdings of real estate and S corporation stock.
**Professional Memberships:** Fellow, American College of Tax Counsel; Assistant Treasurer, National Board of Governors and Executive Council, American Jewish Committee.
**Personal:** LLM, Boston University School of Law; LLB, Yale Law School; BA and ScB, Brown University.

### DAVIS, Steven G
McCarter & English, LLP, Boston
617 449 6580
sdavis@mccarter.com
*Featured in Intellectual Property (Massachusetts)*
**Career:** Dr Davis' practice focuses on patent prosecution, portfolio strategy and management, freedom to operate assessments, infringement analysis, patent issues related to IPOs, and intellectual property licensing. He assists universities, start-ups and major pharmaceutical corporations with protecting technologies in the areas of chemistry, pharmaceuticals and biotechnology, with a particular emphasis in organic chemistry. Of particular interest is advising venture capital investors with due diligence investigations and advising other clients prior to acquiring intellectual property assets. Dr Davis has practiced patent law for 19 years and is committed to the promotion of early-stage technologies. For full bio: http://www.mccarter.com/Steven-G-Davis/

### DEFRANCO, Denise W
Finnegan, Henderson, Farabow, Garrett & Dunner LLP, Washington, DC
617 646 1670
denise.defranco@finnegan.com
*Featured in Intellectual Property (Massachusetts)*
**Practice Areas:** Represents companies in patent infringement litigation in federal trial and appellate courts. She has successfully litigated cases involving a wide range of technologies, including biotechnology, medical devices, pharmaceuticals, telecommunications, electronics, and software. She has written briefs in high-profile patent cases before the US Supreme Court and the US Court of Appeals for the Federal Circuit. These cases have included Bilski (statutory subject matter); Merck v. Integra (271(e)(1)); Phillips (claim construction); Festo (doctrine of equivalents); and Pfaff (on sale bar).
**Personal:** Tulane University (BSE, Biomedical Engineering, 1985); George Washington University, National Law Center (JD, with honors, 1991).

**DELUCA, Jean M.**
Greenberg Traurig, LLP, Boston
617 310 6271
DeLucaJ@gtlaw.com
*Featured in Banking & Finance (Massachusetts)*
**Practice Areas:** Public finance; global energy and infrastructure; public project procurement; education.
**Professional Memberships:** Member: National Association of Bond Lawyers; American Bar Association; Massachusetts Bar Association.
**Career:** Jean M DeLuca has served as bond counsel, issuer's counsel, underwriter's counsel, disclosure counsel and purchaser's counsel in numerous tax-exempt and taxable financing transactions. She has represented general obligation bond issuers and infrastructure revenue bond issuers, as well as hospitals, nursing homes, assisted living facilities, public and private colleges, private and charter schools and cultural institutions.
**Personal:** JD, Boston University School of Law; BA, Brandeis University.

**DICHIARA, Peter M**
WilmerHale, Boston
617 526 6466
peter.dichiara@wilmerhale.com
*Featured in Intellectual Property (Massachusetts)*
**Practice Areas:** Chair, Nanotechnology Practice Group. Practice focuses on obtaining and enforcing intellectual property rights, with emphasis on nanotechnology, electronics, communications, storage and computer industries. Has litigated patents and trade secrets relating to communication systems, computer software, storage systems, digital cameras, electronic security, hard disk drive testing technology, wireless communications, electronic circuits and semiconductor manufacturing equipment. Has prepared infringement and validity opinions; has advised clients on portfolio strategy, risk assessment and design-around strategies.
**Career:** Admitted to Massachusetts Bar, United States Patent and Trademark Office. Joined firm in 1997.
**Personal:** Boston University School of Law (JD); Boston University (BS, Computer Engineering).

**DINARDO, Patrick P**
Sullivan & Worcester LLP, Boston
617 338 2817
pdinardo@sandw.com
*Featured in Bankruptcy/Restructuring (Massachusetts)*
**Practice Areas:** Patrick P Dinardo is a partner in the Litigation Department and the leader of the firm's Bankruptcy & Restructuring Group. Mr Dinardo focuses his practice on the litigation and resolution of business disputes, including disputes involving bankruptcy and creditors' rights. He has almost 30 years of experience representing various parties in complex contract, trust, real estate, and insolvency-related matters in State and Federal court.
**Professional Memberships:** Co-Chair, Bankruptcy Section Pro Bono Committee, Boston Bar Association; American Bankruptcy Institute.
**Personal:** JD, University of Chicago Law School; BA, magna cum laude, Georgetown University.

**DITTMAR, James S**
Goodwin Procter LLP, Boston
617 570 1944
jdittmar@goodwinprocter.com
*Featured in Litigation (Massachusetts)*
**Practice Areas:** Mr Dittmar focuses his practice on complex business litigation with particular emphasis on securities litigation; civil litigation, regulatory investigations and enforcement proceedings involving asset management and other capital markets financial services; civil litigation, regulatory investigations and enforcement proceedings under ERISA; and corporate transaction, control, and governance disputes. He has specific expertise in class actions, derivative actions, and multi-proceeding litigations including federal multi-district litigation and simultaneous federal and state court actions.
**Personal:** JD, Harvard Law School, 1972 (cum laude); MS, London School of Economics, 1967; BA, Amherst College, 1966 (magna cum laude).

**DONOGHUE, Laurence J**
Morgan, Brown and Joy LLP, Boston
617 788 5003
ldonoghue@morganbrown.com
*Featured in Labor & Employment (Massachusetts)*
**Practice Areas:** Labor and employment law - management; litigation.
**Professional Memberships:** American, Massachusetts and Boston Bar Associations.
**Career:** Massachusetts Bar (1980); Partner, Morgan, Brown & Joy (1988).
**Publications:** Contributing author" 'National Labor Relations Act: Law & Practice', Matthew Bender & Co., 1991; author: Massachusetts Employment Law Sourcebook, MCLE, 2001-2013.
**Personal:** JD, Boston College Law School, 1980 magna cum laude; BA, University of Massachusetts, 1977, magna cum laude.

**DOUGHERTY, Thomas J**
Skadden, Arps, Slate, Meagher & Flom LLP & Affiliates, Boston
617 573 4820
Dougherty@skadden.com
*Featured in Securities (Nationwide), Litigation (Massachusetts)*
**Practice Areas:** Heads Skadden's Boston Litigation Department. Active in major control contests and other court and SEC challenges to company disclosures and officer/director conduct. Litigates key jury trials and injunction cases that have fashioned the standards by which subsequent cases have been governed, including cases involving AspenTech, Citigroup, Computervision, Continental Cablevision, EMC, Ernst & Young, GE, Guardian, Hycor, Instron, Interco, John Hancock Advisers, Lotus, MassMutual, Polaroid, Prospect Street, State Street Funds, Stratus and Unitrode.
**Career:** JD, Harvard University, 1976 (cum laude); BPhil Economics, Oxford University, 1973 (Marshall Scholar); BA, Holy Cross College, 1970 (magna cum laude).
**Publications:** "The Directors' Handbook."

**DOWNS, J Anthony**
Goodwin Procter LLP, Boston
617 570 1929
jdowns@goodwinprocter.com
*Featured in Intellectual Property (Massachusetts)*
**Practice Areas:** Mr Downs is Chair of the firm's Intellectual Property Litigation Practice. He focuses in intellectual property litigation, with a specialization in patent matters, and has experience in antitrust/competition law, securities and other complex commercial litigation. He has extensive trial experience and regularly uses arbitration and other alternative dispute resolution procedures. He also has considerable appellate experience, and has briefed or argued cases in the US Supreme Court, the Federal Circuit, the First, Second and Ninth Circuits, and in state appellate courts.
**Personal:** JD, University of Chicago Law School, 1986 (cum laude); AB, Princeton University, 1982 (magna cum laude).

**EGAN III, John J**
Goodwin Procter LLP, Boston
617 570 1514
jegan@goodwinprocter.com
*Featured in Investment Funds (Nationwide), Corporate/M&A (Massachusetts), Private Equity (Massachusetts)*
**Practice Areas:** Mr Egan is Co-Chair of the firm's Technology Companies Group. His practice involves early and late-stage venture financings, leveraged recapitalizations and buyouts, IPOs, mergers and acquisitions, joint ventures, strategic licensing and the general representation of public and private emerging growth companies in industries ranging from enterprise software, networking, security and business services to communications, media and life sciences. He also represents numerous venture capitalists, private equity investors and investment banks and has extensive experience in intellectual property and licensing issues.
**Personal:** JD, Boston University School of Law, 1984; AB, Brown University, 1981.

**EHRLICH, Gayle**
Pierce Atwood LLP, Boston
617 488 8135
gehrlich@pierceatwood.com
*Featured in Bankruptcy/Restructuring (Massachusetts)*
**Practice Areas:** Gayle has practiced in the areas of litigation, business law and restructuring for more than 25 years, representing lenders, indenture trustees, bondholders, committees and other creditors, borrowers and trustees in matters throughout the United States.
**Professional Memberships:** Executive Committee International Turnaround Management Association, 2006-10 and Chair of Awards Committee, 2010. Board Member, Northeast Chapter Turnaround Management Association 1998-2005 and President, 2003-05.
**Career:** Chambers USA, Leading Lawyer in Bankruptcy/Restructuring (2010); Massachusetts Super Lawyers (2004-10); Charter Fellow, Litigation Counsel of America.

**Personal:** BA, Sarah Lawrence College; JD, Cardozo School of Law.

**EHRLICH, Kenneth**
Nutter McClennen & Fish LLP, Boston
617 439 2989
kehrlich@nutter.com
*Featured in Banking & Finance (Massachusetts)*
**Practice Areas:** Kenneth Ehrlich is a partner in the Business Department and co-chair of the firm's Banking and Financial Services practice group. He serves as corporate and regulatory counsel to banks, savings institutions, and other financial institutions. He has practiced extensively before the Federal Reserve, FDIC, OCC, OTS, and the Massachusetts Division of Banks. Ken addresses a wide range of banking clients' needs, including new bank formations, mergers and acquisitions, holding company formations, conversions, interstate expansion, the introduction of new products and services, including securities, insurance and trust services, and electronic banking.

**EICHEL, Steven P**
Choate Hall & Stewart LLP, Boston
617 248 4923
seichel@choate.com
*Featured in Tax (Massachusetts)*
**Practice Areas:** Mr Eichel specializes in tax consulting and business law, including domestic and cross-border M&A, international tax planning, complex joint venture formations and domestic/international equity and debt financing, structuring and restructuring. Mr Eichel, fluent in French, advises French-based companies (and other non-US companies) on the legal and tax aspects of investing and conducting operations in the US.
**Personal:** LLM Boston University School of Law (1991); JD Columbia University School of Law (1985); BA, Summa cum Laude, Phi Beta Kappa, University of Tennessee (1982); Baccalauréat Centre Scolaire St. Marc (Lyon, France) (1978).

**ELRIFI, Ivor R**
Mintz Levin Cohn Ferris Glovsky and Popeo PC, Boston
617 348 1747
IRElrifi@mintz.com
*Featured in Life Sciences (Nationwide), Intellectual Property (Massachusetts)*
See under Nationwide for profile.

**ENGELLENNER, Thomas J**
Pepper Hamilton LLP, Boston
617 204 5189
engellennert@pepperlaw.com
*Featured in Intellectual Property (Massachusetts)*
**Practice Areas:** Partner. Practice includes patents, licensing, trademarks, copyrights and litigation with expertise in the fields of biotechnology, pharmaceuticals and medical devices. More than twenty-five years experience in prosecuting and litigating patents and advising clients on intellectual property strategies. Litigation experience includes patent infringement cases in US federal courts, Canada, Tokyo District Court in Japan and the Dusseldorf Federal Court in Germany, as well as opposition and validity challenges hearings

before the Japanese, European and German patent offices.

**Career:** Former Trial Attorney, US Environmental Protection Agency.

**Personal:** JD Boston University School of Law; MS and BS Rensselaer Polytechnic Institute.

### ENGLANDER, John C
Goodwin Procter LLP, Boston
617 570 1268
jenglander@goodwinprocter.com
*Featured in Intellectual Property (Massachusetts)*

**Practice Areas:** Mr Englander's practice focuses on complex commercial litigation, with an emphasis on patent and other IP litigation. An engineer by training, he has been trial counsel in patent infringement cases involving, among other products, semiconductor manufacturing tools, stem cell technology and generic drugs. He also has extensive experience in banking and financial services litigation, including in particular class action defense. In addition, Mr Englander has litigated cases involving all manner of commercial disputes, business torts and unfair trade practices claims.

**Personal:** JD, Boston University Law School, 1983; BS, Cornell University, 1980.

### FELDMAN, Gary M
Davis, Malm & D'Agostine, P.C., Boston
617 589 3874
gfeldman@davismalm.com
*Featured in Labor & Employment (Massachusetts)*

**Practice Areas:** Advises employers and business executives on all aspects of employment-related issues and policies. Regularly litigates employment issues before the Equal Employment Opportunity Commission, the Massachusetts Commission Against Discrimination, and in federal and state courts. Regularly negotiates executive employment agreements, noncompetition agreements, intellectual property agreements, and severance agreements. Represents individuals, stockholders, and private and public corporations before federal and state trial courts, appellate courts, arbitration panels, and alternative dispute forums throughout Massachusetts and New England. Extensive experience in a wide variety of business and commercial litigation matters.

**Publications:** 'Pay Equity After "Goodyear": Can Employers Afford to Relax?' Massachusetts Lawyers Weekly. 'Jumping the Gun on Weight Discrimination,' The Boston Globe. 'Workplace Privacy,' Human Resources. 'Massachusetts Same-Sex Marriage Ruling Creates Groundbreaking Issues in the American Workplace,' Employee Relations Law Journal.

**Personal:** JD, Boston University School of Law (Edward F Hennessey Scholar), 1982. BA, Washington University, 1979.

### FELDMAN, Paul L
Davis, Malm & D'Agostine, P.C., Boston
617 589 3831
pfeldman@davismalm.com
*Featured in Litigation (Massachusetts)*

**Practice Areas:** Litigation matters involving contract disputes, insurance coverage, business disputes, and environmental cost recovery claims.

Real estate and environmental work includes representation in transactions throughout the United States, including acquisition, leasing, permitting, financing, contamination matters, environmental permitting, and litigation related thereto. Clients include individuals and public, private, Fortune 100, and NYSE-listed companies.

**Professional Memberships:** Massachusetts and Boston Bar Associations.

**Career:** Admitted: Massachusetts, US District Court for the District of Massachusetts, US Court of Appeals for the First Circuit.

**Personal:** JD (cum laude), Boston University (1982); BA (magna cum laude), State University of New York at Albany (1979).

### FENTIN, Susan G
Skoler, Abbott & Presser, PC, Springfield
413 737 4753
sfentin@skoler-abbott.com
*Featured in Labor & Employment (Massachusetts)*

**Practice Areas:** Partner. Defends charges of employment discrimination, representing exclusively management. Advises employers on policies and practices, and conducts extensive supervisor trainings. Teaches Master Classes on FMLA, ADA, and Wage and Hour Law for BLR and numerous webinars on a wide variety of labor and employment topics.

**Professional Memberships:** Member of Worklaw Network, nationwide organization of boutique management labor and employment firms. Member of Employers' Counsel Network, national organization of editors of Employment Law Letters. Admitted to state and federal courts in Massachusetts and Connecticut. Member Massachusetts, Connecticut, and Hampden and Franklin County Bar Association.

**Career:** Admitted to Connecticut Bar in 1996 and Massachusetts Bar in 1997. Clerked for the Honorable John M. Greaney, Associate Justice of the Massachusetts Supreme Judicial Court, 1996-1997. Joined Skoler, Abbott & Presser as Associate in 1999.

**Publications:** Editor, Massachusetts Employment Law Letter; Contributing Author, Workplace Privacy; Editor-in-Chief, Western New England College Law Review, 1995-1996; "The False Claims Act — Finding Middle Ground Between Opportunity and Opportunism: The Original Source Provision of 13 USC 3730(e)(4)" 17 W. New Eng. L. Rev. 255.

**Personal:** Born 16 October 1949. Graduate of Wellesley College and Western New England College School of Law (magna cum laude).

### FISCHER, Eric R
Goodwin Procter LLP, Boston
617 570 1522
efischer@goodwinprocter.com
*Featured in Banking & Finance (Massachusetts)*

**Practice Areas:** Mr Fischer focuses on bank regulatory matters including issues concerning mergers and acquisitions of financial institutions, bank corporate governance, director and officer liability, the bank regulatory process, banking operations and security matters, bank risk management and safety, soundness and examination

matters, capital raising initiatives, securities and insurance activities of banks, and financial institution formation and reorganization transactions. Mr Fischer also advises financial institutions with respect to anti-money laundering and OFAC compliance issues.

**Personal:** LLM, Boston University School of Law, 1982; JD, Stanford Law School, 1971; MBA, Stanford University, 1971; BA, University of Pennsylvania, 1967.

### FISHMAN, Robert A
Nutter McClennen & Fish LLP, Boston
617 439 2204
rfishman@nutter.com
*Featured in Real Estate (Massachusetts)*

**Practice Areas:** Robert Fishman is a partner in the Real Estate and Finance Department and chairs the firm's Land Use Practice Group. His practice focuses on development, financing, acquisition and disposition, leasing and land use/environmental permitting. Bob represents developers, lenders, corporate, institutional, municipal and nonprofit clients involved in the development and financing of mixed-use projects, downtown office buildings, suburban industrial and office parks, shopping centers, hotels, multi-family housing, senior assisted living housing and community facilities.

### FISZMAN, Sula
Morgan, Lewis & Bockius LLP, Boston
617 341 7730
sfiszman@morganlewis.com
*Featured in Banking & Finance (Massachusetts)*

**Practice Areas:** Sula Fiszman represents a wide variety of financial institutions, private equity funds and other companies in connection with debt financings, structured financings and workouts. Ms Fiszman's practice concentrates on complex senior secured finance transactions, subordinated and second lien lending transactions, workouts, and bankruptcies. She manages transactions across a broad range of industries including media and communications, restaurants and hospitality, oil and gas, retail service station operations, convenience store chains, and manufacturing. Ms Fiszman regularly represents private equity funds and their portfolio companies in connection with their various financing needs, often in the context of merger and acquisition transactions.

### FLANAGAN, Christopher M
Edwards Wildman Palmer LLP, Boston
617 239 0485
cflanagan@edwardswildman.com
*Featured in Tax (Massachusetts)*

**Practice Areas:** Christopher M Flanagan is a partner in Edwards Wildman's Tax Department. He has particular experience in representing public and private companies in taxable and tax-free acquisitions and divestitures of corporate subsidiaries and divisions, and in reorganizations and restructurings. Mr Flanagan also represents companies in the structuring and formation of major corporate joint ventures, limited liability companies, and large venture-capital partnerships, as well as advising companies on the tax issues atten-

dant to both public and private debt and equity offerings.

**Personal:** LLM, Taxation, New York University School of Law; JD, Boston University School of Law; BS, cum laude, Villanova University.

### FLEMING, Joseph R
Dechert LLP, Boston
617 728 7161
joseph.fleming@dechert.com
*Featured in Investment Funds (Nationwide),
Investment Funds (Massachusetts)*
See under Nationwide for profile.

### FOLLANSBEE, Daniel
Mintz Levin Cohn Ferris Glovsky and Popeo PC, Boston
617 348 4474
DHFollansbee@mintz.com
*Featured in Corporate/M&A (Massachusetts)*

**Practice Areas:** Daniel's practice involves all aspects of corporate and transactional law and general business representation, including mergers and acquisitions; equity, debt, and convertible debt financings; and general business counseling. He represents both public and private US companies in a wide variety of industries on an ongoing basis. He also represents foreign companies with respect to US acquisitions and securities laws.

**Career:** Before joining the firm, Daniel served as associate general counsel for a public information technology company and its public and private controlled subsidiaries.

**Personal:** BS, Bentley College; MBA, Boston College; JD, Boston College.

### FORMAN, Adam
Littler Mendelson, PC, Boston
617 378 6000
aforman@littler.com
*Featured in Labor & Employment (Massachusetts)*

**Practice Areas:** Discrimination and Harassment Leaves of Absence and Disability Accommodation Complex Litigation and Jury Trials Competition and Trade Secret Law Training

**Professional Memberships:** American Bar Association; Massachusetts Bar Association; Boston Bar Association

**Career:** Mr Forman advises and represents employers in the litigation of discrimination, harassment, retaliation and wrongful discharge claims, as well as non-competition and trade secret matters.

**Publications:** Mr Forman has written for a variety of publications, including CCM: The American Lawyer's Corporate Counsel magazine, the National Law Journal and the Venture Capital Review.

**Personal:** JD, Georgetown University Law Center, cum laude, 1987; Bachelor's degree, Pennsylvania State University, with high distinction, 1984.

### FRANK, Steven J
Bingham McCutchen LLP, Boston
617 951 8770
steven.frank@bingham.com
*Featured in Intellectual Property (Massachusetts)*

**Practice Areas:** Co-leader of Bingham's Intellectual Property Transactions and

Development Initiative. Focuses on advising clients in all areas of intellectual property law, with emphasis on strategic IP transactions, patent prosecution, analysis of infringement and related issues, copyright questions, and the drafting and negotiation of agreements relating to the transfer or license of intellectual property. Has significant experience with general IP diligence, both in investment and M&A contexts. Has negotiated multimillion-dollar domestic and cross-border licenses as well as technology-transfer agreements involving leading universities and research institutions.

**Personal:** Harvard Law School, JD, cum laude, 1986; Brown University, ScB, magna cum laude, 1983.

## FRANK JR, Robert S
Choate Hall & Stewart LLP, Boston
617 248 5207
rfrank@choate.com
*Featured in Intellectual Property (Massachusetts), Litigation (Massachusetts)*

**Practice Areas:** Mr Frank counsels clients with respect to commercial, intellectual property, antitrust and varied business disputes. In 2008, he obtained a jury verdict of over $45 million in a patent case involving delivery of Internet content. Recent engagements as lead counsel involve a variety of patent/copyright infringement, trade secret misappropriation, legal malpractice and complex contract cases in environments as diverse as computer technology, pharmaceuticals, insurance products and law firm defense. He is a member of the American College of Trial Lawyers.
**Personal:** LLB cum laude Harvard Law School (1967); AB cum laude, Phi Beta Kappa Bowdoin College (1964).

## FREEMAN, Eric
Mintz Levin Cohn Ferris Glovsky and Popeo PC, Boston
617 348 3072
EFreeman@Mintz.com
*Featured in Real Estate (Massachusetts)*

**Practice Areas:** Eric's practice focuses on general real estate matters. He is particularly experienced with counseling institutional and private clients in their acquisition, disposition, and financing of their real property and partnership interests, including office buildings, shopping centers, multifamily communities, and industrial and warehouse facilities across the United States. Since joining Mintz Levin, Eric has represented public and private real estate funds and operating companies in more than 100 transactions accounting for more than $4 billion of commercial, industrial, office, and multi-family real estate.
**Personal:** BA, Bates College; JD, Boston College.

## FRENCH, Marilyn
Weil, Gotshal & Manges LLP, Boston
617 772 8319
marilyn.french@weil.com
*Featured in Private Equity (Massachusetts)*

**Practice Areas:** Marilyn French is a partner in Weil's Private Equity Practice. Ms French has a diverse practice which focuses on private equity transactions, including leveraged buyouts, minori-

ty investments and public-to-private transactions, and mergers and acquisitions. She represents several of the country's leading private equity firms, including Advent International, Berkshire Partners and Thomas H. Lee Partners. She also regularly represents companies in connection with corporate counseling, acquisitions and dispositions.
**Personal:** Hofstra University (BA, 1987 magna cum laude); Boston College Law School (JD, 1990, cum laude, Order of the Coif).

## FRIES, Elizabeth Shea
Goodwin Procter LLP, Boston
617 570 1559
efries@goodwinprocter.com
*Featured in Investment Funds (Nationwide), Investment Funds (Massachusetts)*

**Practice Areas:** Ms Fries chairs the firm's Hedge Funds Practice. She advises on a broad range of investment management, fund, broker-dealer, banking and other financial services matters. She is experienced in the public and private offering of interests in open-end and closed-end management investment companies and other collective investment vehicles or pools, such as offshore investment funds, investment limited partnerships, private REITs, CDOs, group trusts, common and collective funds and investment trusts. She works with institutional investors, fund managers, sponsors, distributors and other service providers.
**Personal:** JD, Columbia University School of Law, 1989; AB, Dartmouth College, 1986 (magna cum laude).

## FRONGILLO, Thomas C
Weil, Gotshal & Manges LLP, Boston
617 772 8335
thomas.frongillo@weil.com
*Featured in Litigation (Massachusetts)*

**Practice Areas:** Thomas Frongillo, a former federal prosecutor, represents clients in high-stakes white collar criminal prosecutions, corporate and regulatory investigations and complex litigation involving complicated legal issues. He is widely-known for his strategic analysis and stellar courtroom skills. In 2009, he obtained a stunning acquittal of a senior executive of W.R. Grace in a landmark, three-month criminal jury trial, United States v. W.R. Grace, in which his client was vindicated on charges of knowing endangerment under the Clean Air Act and defrauding the US. The US DOJ characterized the case as the most significant criminal enviromental prosecution in US history.

## FURLONG, Matthew
Morgan, Lewis & Bockius LLP, Boston
617 341 7740
mfurlong@morganlewis.com
*Featured in Banking & Finance (Massachusetts)*

**Practice Areas:** Matthew Furlong is a partner in the Business & Finance Practice and represents leading banks, finance companies, hedge funds and borrowers in a range of finance and business matters, including domestic and international debt financings, debt restructurings, asset-based credit facilities, second lien credit facilities, acquisition and retail finance, and multinational credit facilities. He has worked extensively in the retail,

restaurant, manufacturing, and transportation industries. He has counseled clients on sports finance matters, in which he has advised borrowers (including major-league baseball, football, and hockey teams) and lenders in financings and restructurings.

## GABBAY, Carolyn Jacoby
Nixon Peabody LLP, Boston
617 345 6112
cgabbay@nixonpeabody.com
*Featured in Healthcare (Massachusetts)*

**Practice Areas:** Advises hospitals, physicians and providers on regulatory compliance, transactions and strategic initiatives, managed care contracts, Accountable Care Organizations and Medicare/Medicaid reimbursement as general, special or transaction counsel. Represents clients before federal and state agencies and review panels. Advises on corporate compliance, licensure and accreditation, Stark Law, federal anti-kickback restrictions and 'safe harbors', and standards for tax-exempt organizations. Counsels clients on acquisitions/reorganizations, joint ventures and joint operating agreements, practice group formation, physician recruitment and incentive compensation systems, management services contracts.
**Personal:** Boston University School of Law, JD, cum laude; Boston University, BA, summa cum laude (Phi Beta Kappa).

## GAQUIN, Dan
Mintz Levin Cohn Ferris Glovsky and Popeo PC, Boston
617 348 1874
DOGaquin@mintz.com
*Featured in Real Estate (Massachusetts)*

**Practice Areas:** Dan is a member in the firm's Boston office, where he practices in the Real Estate Section. His experience covers all aspects of commercial real estate, including acquisitions and sales, development, permitting, leasing, and financing. Dan represents developers and investors in development projects and operating properties, including joint ventures and other shared investment vehicles and complex financing arrangements. He also has extensive experience with major project permitting in and around Boston.
**Professional Memberships:** Member, Boston Bar Association; Member, Massachusetts Bar Association.
**Personal:** BA, College of the Holy Cross; JD, Boston College.

## GAULT, Robert M
Mintz Levin Cohn Ferris Glovsky and Popeo PC, Boston
617 348 1643
RGault@mintz.com
*Featured in Labor & Employment (Massachusetts)*

**Practice Areas:** Bob regularly counsels employers on all facets of employment law including hiring, disciplinary and termination issues, layoffs, policies, codes of conduct, disability and leave issues, and harassment, and regularly drafts and negotiates executive employment agreements and separation agreements for both employers and

executives. He has represented employers in reductions in force, severance arrangements, wrongful termination and discrimination suits, union organizing campaigns, arbitrations, mediation and litigation arising from employment disputes. He has also represented private schools in various areas, including alleged student and faculty/administrator misconduct.
**Personal:** Williams College, BA; University of Michigan Law School, JD, with honors.

## GEORGE, Natascha S
Bingham McCutchen LLP, Boston
617 951 8330
natascha.george@bingham.com
*Featured in Employee Benefits & Executive Compensation (Massachusetts)*

**Practice Areas:** Advises clients with respect to all aspects of employee benefits and compensation, including retirement plans, health plans, stock option plans and executive compensation. Also practices in the area of promotion, marketing and advertising law. Practice includes advising on all aspects of consumer and trade promotions, sweepstakes, skill contests and games of chance; self-liquidating offers; sampling and other event-based programs; and rebate, coupon and discount programs.
**Career:** Immediate past vice president, National Institute of Pension Administrators, Massachusetts Chapter.
**Personal:** Boston University, Master of Public Health, 1996; Boston University School of Law, JD, 1995; University of Missouri/Kansas City, BA, 1992.

## GILLIGAN, Leigh A
McCarter & English, LLP, Boston
617 449 6520
lgilligan@mccarter.com
*Featured in Environment (Massachusetts)*

**Career:** Ms Gilligan has extensive experience in many aspects of environmental and land use law, including licensing and permitting, compliance counseling, and representation in connection with business and lending transactions as well as real estate development. Ms Gilligan represents parties involved in federal and state hazardous waste sites, including legal proceedings, private cost recovery actions and dealings with governmental agencies. She has extensive experience in environmental issues involved in transactions for the purchase and sale of land and businesses, including confirming and securing liability protections and economic incentives in connection with brownfields redevelopment. For full bio:
http://www.mccarter.com/Leigh-A-Gilligan/.

## GIULIANI, Richard W
WilmerHale, Boston
617 526 6435
richard.giuliani@wilmerhale.com
*Featured in Tax (Massachusetts)*

**Practice Areas:** Experienced in all areas of tax law including federal and state income taxation and state sales and use taxes. Handles corporate, partnership and individual federal and state tax matters; tax dispute advocacy in administrative and judicial forums; tax planning. Represented

clients before the Internal Revenue Service Appeals Office; US Tax Court; Massachusetts Appellate Tax Board; Massachusetts courts.
**Professional Memberships:** Extensive work with Boston Bar Association, Massachusetts Taxpayers Foundation, Massachusetts Department of Revenue in connection with proposed legislation and regulations.
**Career:** Admitted to Massachusetts Bar. Joined firm in 1970.
**Personal:** Harvard Law School (JD); Harvard College (BA, cum laude).

### GLAZER, Michael H
Goodwin Procter LLP, Boston
617 570 1420
mglazer@goodwinprocter.com
*Featured in Real Estate (Nationwide), Real Estate (Massachusetts)*

**Practice Areas:** Mr Glazer specializes in real estate, commercial finance, joint ventures and leasing. He has developed special expertise advising and representing real estate investment managers, real estate funds and institutional investors in connection with their investment opportunities. These investments often target the special needs of tax exempt investors including pension funds, endowments and foreign investors. He also has extensive real estate transactional experience managing some of the largest real estate acquisition, disposition and joint venture transactions in the United States.
**Personal:** JD, Boston University Law School, 1973; BS, in Economics, Wharton School, University of Pennsylvania, 1970.

### GLEASON, Daniel J
Nutter McClennen & Fish LLP, Boston
617 439 2233
dgleason@nutter.com
*Featured in Litigation (Massachusetts)*

**Practice Areas:** Daniel Gleason is co-chair of the Intellectual Property Litigation practice group. With over 30 years of experience, Dan's trial practice focuses on civil litigation and spans a wide range of business cases that he has handled as lead trial counsel including intellectual property (principally patent, copyright and trademark disputes); non-competition agreements; business torts; partnership dissolution; class actions in accounting, securities, and insurance litigation; First Amendment media defense; Superfund and environmental insurance coverage cases; civil rights; and product liability defense. While he primarily focuses on trials, Dan also has substantial appellate experience on federal and state court appeals.

### GLERUM, Charles L
Edwards Wildman Palmer LLP, Boston
617 239 0516
cglerum@edwardswildman.com
*Featured in Bankruptcy/Restructuring (Massachusetts)*

**Practice Areas:** Charles' practice focuses on creditor representation in which he has represented secured creditors, subordinated creditors and unsecured creditors in all phases of workouts, from the response to the first defaults under loan agreements to the negotiation of workout and for-

bearance agreements through litigation and bankruptcy. He also focuses on transactions with insolvency issues and has extensive experience in all aspects of complicated debt restructurings, workouts, debt acquisitions and asset recovery transactions, as well as the purchase and sale of assets in insolvency situations.
**Personal:** University of Michigan Law School, JD, Brown University, AB.

### GLINCHER, Andrew
Nixon Peabody LLP, Boston
617 345 1222
aglincher@nixonpeabody.com
*Featured in Real Estate (Massachusetts)*

**Practice Areas:** Andrew Glincher is the Managing Partner and CEO. He focuses his practice in representation of institutional and individual owners, developers and managers of real estate; business owners; professional service firms; institutional lenders in financing, loan recovery and restructuring; and various parties in the negotiation and resolution of business and real estate disputes. Andrew is nationally known for his consensus-building, problem-solving and negotiation skills, including his ability to structure successful and creative resolutions to disputes of all types.
**Personal:** Northeastern University School of Law, JD; Boston College Carroll School of Management, BS, Finance, cum laude.

### GLOSBAND, Daniel M
Goodwin Procter LLP, Boston
617 570 1930
dglosband@goodwinprocter.com
*Featured in Bankruptcy/Restructuring (Massachusetts)*

**Practice Areas:** Mr Glosband's primary areas of practice are insolvency and reorganization. He represents secured and unsecured creditors, committees and debtors in workouts and proceedings under the Bankruptcy Code. He has acted as an adviser to the US State Department and the American Law Institute on international insolvency projects. In addition, he has represented lenders and debtors in major real estate, retail and technology oriented reorganizations; parties to significant contracts with debtors in reorganization; purchasers of assets from debtors in insolvency proceedings; and defendants in complex Bankruptcy Court litigation.
**Personal:** JD, Cornell University, 1969; BA, University of Massachusetts, 1966.

### GOLDBERG, Daniel L
Bingham McCutchen LLP, Boston
617 951 8327
daniel.goldberg@bingham.com
*Featured in Antitrust (Massachusetts), Litigation (Massachusetts)*

**Practice Areas:** Focuses on antitrust, intellectual property and franchise cases in his commercial litigation practice. National and regional litigation counsel experience in complex franchise matters. IP litigation experience includes successful prosecution and defense of copyright claims and protection of team logos for the New England Patriots and Boston Red Sox. Has also counseled

clients extensively on antitrust and trade regulation matters.
**Career:** Has authored numerous articles on distribution and franchising, antitrust, unfair competition, and a variety of other topics. Primary draftsman of the Massachusetts Antitrust Act.
**Personal:** Harvard Law School, JD, cum laude, 1971; Trinity College, BA, cum laude, 1968.

### GOLDMAN, Richard A
Bingham McCutchen LLP, Boston
617 951 8851
rich.goldman@bingham.com
*Featured in Investment Funds (Nationwide), Investment Funds (Massachusetts)*

**Practice Areas:** Represents US and international hedge funds and funds of funds, advising them on a broad range of issues such as formation and structure, strategic and seed capital arrangements, succession planning, marketing and solicitation arrangements, separately managed accounts, and all types of trading and operational issues. Advises clients on registration as investment advisers with the SEC, regulatory reporting and compliance matters, equity swaps and other derivatives, and private placements of securities.
**Personal:** University of Virginia School of Law, JD, 1988; University of Massachusetts/Amherst, BBA, 1982.

### GOODHEART, Lisa
Sugarman, Rogers, Barshak & Cohen, PC, Boston
617 227 3030
goodheart@srbc.com
*Featured in Environment (Massachusetts)*

**Practice Areas:** Lisa concentrates in environmental, real estate and general business litigation. She has extensive experience in cost recovery cases, permitting appeals, land use disputes, enforcement actions, insurance coverage disputes, design and construction matters, and a broad range of business litigation matters.
**Professional Memberships:** Boston Bar Foundation (Grants Committee; Society of Fellows Committee; Trustee); Boston Bar Association (former President; former Executive Committee and Council Member; former Treasurer; former Co-Chair, Environmental Law Section); New England Women in Real Estate (NEWIRE) (former President; former Steering Committee Member; former Co-Chair, Programs and Seminars Committee); Women's Bar Association of Massachusetts; American Bar Association (former Standing Committee on Environmental Law Member; Co-Chair, 2007 National Law and Policy Conference on Global Warming).
**Career:** Sugarman, Rogers, Barshak & Cohen, PC (2005-); DLA Piper US LLP, Boston, MA (2003-05); Hill & Barlow, P.C., Boston, MA (1988-2003); Drinker Biddle & Reath LLP (1985-88). Member, Supreme Judicial Court Committee to Study the Code of Judicial Conduct (2012-); Chair, Judicial Nominating Commission, by appointment of Massachusetts Governor Deval L. Patrick (2007-10); Member, Massachusetts Department of

Environmental Protection's Wetlands Appeals Streamlining Task Force (2007).
**Personal:** University of Pennsylvania Law School (JD, cum laude); Williams College (BA, cum laude, Phi Beta Kappa). Lelia J. Robinson Award recipient, Women's Bar Association of Massachusetts (2010). In addition to her legal practice, Lisa is an active supporter of the arts community. She has served as a Director and officer of several non-profit corporations operating modern and jazz dance companies, including DanceFusion, Inc., Backyard Dance Theatre, Inc., Impulse Dance Company, Inc., and, currently, Rainbow Tribe, Inc., of which she is also a former assistant artistic director. From 2001-08, Lisa was a Member of the Board of Overseers of Celebrity Series of Boston, Inc., the major presenting organization for the performing arts in New England.

### GOODING, Douglas R
Choate Hall & Stewart LLP, Boston
617 248 5277
dgooding@choate.com
*Featured in Bankruptcy/Restructuring (Massachusetts)*

**Practice Areas:** Mr Gooding is chair of the Finance & Restructuring Group and immediate past co-chair of the Boston Bar Association Bankruptcy Section, with over 20 years' experience in corporate finance, restructuring, bankruptcy and related litigation. He advises lenders (senior, second lien, mezzanine) and insurers in workout, restructuring and bankruptcy matters throughout the country. He advises boards of directors, troubled companies and individual creditors, including software licensors. Recent engagement: representation of lender owed more than $400 million in real estate restructuring.
**Personal:** JD cum laude Duke University School of Law (1991); AB cum laude University of California at Berkeley (1987).

### GOODMAN, Louis A
Skadden, Arps, Slate, Meagher & Flom LLP & Affiliates, Boston
617 573 4830
Louis.Goodman@skadden.com
*Featured in Corporate/M&A (Massachusetts)*

**Practice Areas:** Senior partner in Skadden's Boston office. Advises on a wide range of corporate matters, from acquisitions and financings to restructurings and crisis management. For many years, has represented clients in some of their most significant transactions - many that have industry-wide and sometimes worldwide significance.
**Career:** JD, Harvard Law School, 1969; MA, Harvard University, 1966; AB, Columbia College, 1965.

### GORDON, Dana M
Foley Hoag LLP, Boston
617 832 1765
dgordon@foleyhoag.com
*Featured in Intellectual Property (Massachusetts)*

**Practice Areas:** Dr Gordon, Deputy Chair of Foley Hoag's IP Department, prepares and prosecutes US, international and foreign patent applications in the area of life sciences for leading universities, pharmaceutical companies, and medical device companies. He also prepares opinions in connection with R&D planning, risk assessment and ANDA litigation, advises on patent and trade secret protection, due diligence assessments of patent portfolios, and negotiates and drafts agreements.

**Personal:** Boston College Law School, JD; Harvard University, Post-doctoral Fellow in Chemistry; Yale University, PhD in Organic Chemistry; University of California, Los Angeles, BS in Chemistry, magna cum laude with Departmental Highest Honors.

### GOSHKO, Mark
K&L Gates, Boston
617 261 3163
mark.goshko@klgates.com
*Featured in Investment Funds (Massachusetts)*
**Practice Areas:** Mark Goshko, a partner in the investment management, hedge funds, and alternative investments practice group, focuses on investment management law and represents registered open- and closed-end investment companies, investment company directors, unregistered hedge funds, investment advisers, broker-dealers, and banks. He deals regularly with the SEC, FINRA, Commodity Futures Trading Commission, New York Stock Exchange and other regulatory agencies and organizations. He also serves as the lead partner in representing several mutual fund complexes; counsels hedge funds and advisers on a broad range of issues; and works with investment advisers in contract management.

### GRACHUK, Jeanine L G
Beveridge & Diamond PC, Wellesley
781 416 5713
jgrachuk@bdlaw.com
*Featured in Environment (Massachusetts)*
**Practice Areas:** Practice includes environmental compliance counseling, environmental permitting of brownfields redevelopment projects, and advice on managing environmental risk in complex transactions. Ms Grachuk has extensive experience in matters related to air, wastewater, remediation, and release reporting under state and federal laws. Ms Grachuk's clients include companies in the chemicals, oil and gas, solid waste, recycling, pipeline, and manufacturing industries. Ms Grachuk is a frequent lecturer and author on managing liability for releases of hazardous materials.

### GREENE, Thomas M
Mintz Levin Cohn Ferris Glovsky and Popeo PC, Boston
617 348 1886
TMGreene@mintz.com
*Featured in Employee Benefits & Executive Compensation (Massachusetts)*
**Practice Areas:** Tom advises corporate, tax-exempt, governmental and individual clients on tax, executive compensation and employee benefits matters, including ERISA, mergers and acquisitions, deferred compensation, retirement, equity arrangements, welfare plans and bankruptcy.
**Career:** Tom has counseled clients on hundreds of transactions and has represented a number of

high profile executives in sensitive contract and severance negotiations. He has provided expert commentary in publications such as USA Today, The Boston Globe, The National Law Journal and Corporate Counsel Magazine.
**Publications:** Contributor to Working with ERISA: An Eight Step Guide for Trustees and Advisors, multiple articles and seminar related materials for MCLE.

### GREENHALGH, Duncan
Goodwin Procter LLP, Boston
617 570 1299
dgreenhalgh@goodwinprocter.com
*Featured in Intellectual Property (Massachusetts)*
**Practice Areas:** Dr Greenhalgh focuses his practice on the procurement and enforcement of intellectual property rights, especially patent rights, for clients in life sciences. He counsels clients on intellectual property matters including the strategic development of patent and trademark portfolios; technology licensing; risk assessment, for example, via clearance surveys; non-infringement and invalidity analyses; and the enforcement of patent and trademark rights. Dr Greenhalgh has an extensive science background in biochemistry and biotechnology.
**Personal:** JD, Suffolk University Law School, 1998 (magna cum laude); PhD in Biochemistry, University of Leeds, UK, 1989; BSc in Biotechnology, University of Leeds, UK, 1985 (with honors).

### GUADAGNOLI, David A
Sullivan & Worcester LLP, Boston
617 338 2938
dguadagnoli@sandw.com
*Featured in Employee Benefits & Executive Compensation (Massachusetts)*
**Practice Areas:** David A Guadagnoli concentrates in the employee benefits area and is experienced in the design, implementation and administration of welfare and fringe benefit arrangements and qualified retirement plans for large and small employers, retirement distribution planning and the design and implementation of nonqualified deferred compensation and equity compensation arrangements for public and private employers.
**Professional Memberships:** National Association of Stock Plan Professionals; New England Employee Benefits Council; National Center for Employee Ownership.
**Personal:** LLM, Taxation, Boston University School of Law; JD, cum laude, Boston University School of Law; MBA, cum laude, Boston University; BA, George Washington University.

### HACKNEY, Hamilton H
Greenberg Traurig, LLP, Boston
617 310 6090
HackneyHa@gtlaw.com
*Featured in Environment (Massachusetts)*
**Practice Areas:** Real estate; environmental; global energy and infrastructure.
**Professional Memberships:** Chair, NAIOP National Environment and Infrastructure Subcommittee; Member, ABA, Energy, Environment and Resources Section.

**Career:** Rated, AV® Preeminent™ 5.0 out of 5. Awarded 2010 President's Award, Massachusetts Chapter of National Association of Industrial and Office Properties. Selected: Super Lawyers of Massachusetts 2004-12; Best Lawyers in America, 2007-13.
**Publications:** 'Managing Risks of PCBs In Building Caulking', Law360, December 21, 2009; 'EPA's Policy Encourages New Owners to Disclose Environmental Violations', Stone, Sand and Gravel Review, September/October 2009
**Personal:** JD, University of Utah College of Law; BA, cum laude, Middlebury College.

### HADDAD, Mark
Foley Hoag LLP, Waltham
617 832 1724
mhaddad@foleyhoag.com
*Featured in Corporate/M&A (Massachusetts)*
**Practice Areas:** Mark Haddad's practice includes a client base ranging from investment funds, startup and portfolio companies and public companies. His transactional practice focuses on representing buyers and sellers in mergers and acquisitions, joint ventures and other strategic transactions. Mark represents startup/early stage companies, primarily those in the cleantech, high tech and life sciences sectors, on corporate formation, founder arrangements and financings. He represents private equity, venture capital and angel investors in portfolio investments. Mark guides publicly-held companies with corporate, compliance, finance and defensive measures.
**Personal:** Harvard Law School, JD; University of Buffalo, BA, summa cum laude, Phi Beta Kappa.

### HAGGERTY, John
Goodwin Procter LLP, Boston
617 570 1526
jhaggerty@goodwinprocter.com
*Featured in Corporate/M&A (Massachusetts)*
**Practice Areas:** Mr Haggerty, a Partner in Goodwin Procter's Business Law Department, is a member of its M&A/Corporate Governance Practice and its nationally recognized Real Estate, REITs and Real Estate Capital Markets Practice. Mr Haggerty works on a wide variety of corporate and securities matters, including public and private mergers and acquisitions, public and private offerings of equity and debt securities by public companies, corporate governance and other matters of general corporate and securities law.
**Personal:** JD, Boston College Law School, 1994 (magna cum laude, Order of the Coif); BA, Bucknell University, 1991.

### HALE, Robert
Goodwin Procter LLP, Boston
617 570 1252
rhale@goodwinprocter.com
*Featured in Labor & Employment (Massachusetts)*
**Practice Areas:** Mr Hale's practice involves representation of clients in employment litigation, including non-competition, discrimination, wrongful discharge, FLSA and ERISA litigation. He has obtained successful results for employers at all stages of litigation. He has successfully represented employers before administrative agencies and in labor arbitrations. His practice includes

counseling in numerous areas of labor and employment law, including disability discrimination, sexual harassment and other discrimination matters; non-competition agreement and other restrictive covenants; downsizing; employment agreements; wage and hour compliance; collective bargaining; and personnel policy development and administration.
**Personal:** JD, Boston University, 1983 (magna cum laude); BS, Cornell University, 1980.

### HANIFY, John D
Jones Day, Boston
617 449 6906
jhanify@jonesday.com
*Featured in Litigation (Massachusetts)*
**Practice Areas:** Complex, commercial litigation practice including partnership and shareholder disputes, leveraged buyout defense, claims involving business fraud, trustee and director fiduciary duty, financial litigation involving GAAS, GAAP and class action claims and breaches of warranties in connection with the purchase and sale of businesses.
**Professional Memberships:** American, Boston and Massachusetts Bar Associations; Catholic Lawyers' Guild.
**Career:** Former Assistant US Attorney for the District of Massachusetts; Appointment (2002), Special Assistant Attorney General.
**Personal:** Harvard College; Boston College Law School; Member, Overseers to Boston College Law School; President, Boston College Law School Alumni Board (2009).

### HANLEY, Elizabeth A
McCarter & English, LLP, Boston
617 449 6510
ehanley@mccarter.com
*Featured in Intellectual Property (Massachusetts)*
**Career:** Ms Hanley is the Practice Leader for IP. She began her career as an Examiner at the US Patent and Trademark Office in the fields of biotechnology and chemistry. While employed by the Patent Office, she received specialized biotechnology training at the National Institutes of Health. She has extensive experience in representing early-stage companies and working with them interactively to strategically build their patent portfolios. She also represents many of the leading pharmaceutical companies building and managing complex patent portfolios, protecting blockbuster biotech and small-molecule drugs, and developing global strategic plans. For full bio: http://www.mccarter.com/Elizabeth-A-Hanley/.

### HANNUM III, William E
Schwartz Hannum PC, Andover
978 623 0900
hannum@shpclaw.com
*Featured in Labor & Employment (Massachusetts)*
**Practice Areas:** Labor and Employment Lawyers Guiding Management. Counseling. Litigation. Labor Relations. Collective Bargaining. Training. Education. Compliance. SHPC is an invaluable ally to organizations looking to effect positive employee relations and resolve disputes. Working with local and national businesses in industries ranging from financial services to

healthcare, the Firm also provides guidance and advocacy to distinguished educational and non-profit organizations. The Firm's practice is characterized by responsiveness, confidence, creativity and candor. Our services are delivered by a team of seasoned professionals who have established the Firm as a leading provider of thoughtful, results-oriented legal counsel. The Firm's growth and success reflects our long-standing commitment to help organizations address their employment-related challenges in a responsible and proactive manner.
**Professional Memberships:** ABA, American Employment Law Council, BBA, MBA, NYSBA, NHBA, National Association of Independent Schools, National Business Officers Association, and SHRM.
**Career:** Managing Partner. Previously with Morgan, Lewis & Bockius LLP.
**Publications:** Frequent speaker and author.
**Personal:** University of Virginia, JD 1992, Earle K. Shaw Labor Relations Award. Amherst College, BA Economics and English, magna cum laude, 1986. Rutgers University, MA English, 1989, Marion Johnson Fellow. Admitted to Bars of Massachusetts, New Hampshire and New York.

### HARLEV, Shayla K.
Weil, Gotshal & Manges LLP, Boston
617 772 8344
shayla.harlev@weil.com
*Featured in Corporate/M&A (Massachusetts)*
**Practice Areas:** Ms Harlev has a diverse transactional and corporate counseling practice with an emphasis on representing private equity sponsors in connection with acquisitions and dispositions and other complex transactions. She has extensive experience with leveraged buyouts and dispositions of public and private companies, as well as going-private transactions, minority investments, and joint ventures. Ms Harlev also counsels private equity sponsor portfolio companies on a variety of corporate and strategic matters.
**Personal:** Ms Harlev is fluent in English, Turkish, and Hebrew. Tel-Aviv University (LLB, 1997).

### HARRIS, Kari K.
Nixon Peabody LLP, New York
*Featured in Private Equity (Massachusetts)*
**Practice Areas:** Kari Harris specializes in the representation of private investment funds in connection with their fundraising and regulatory compliance and of institutional investors in connection with their alternative investments. Ms Harris has substantial experience in structuring and organizing offshore funds and solving complex problems relating to structuring internal management of private investment fund sponsors. Ms Harris also has extensive experience regarding relevant securities and investment company law and regulation, including advising private investment advisers regarding registration under the Investment Advisers Act of 1940 and applicable state law, as well as a significant amount of tax, ERISA, and industry knowledge.

### HARTLEY, H James
Shilepsky Hartley Robb Casey Michon LLP, Boston
617 723 8000
jhartley@shilepsky.com
*Featured in Labor & Employment (Massachusetts)*
**Practice Areas:** Executive and professional advocacy, employment law, litigation.
**Professional Memberships:** Massachusetts Bar Association, Boston Bar Association.
**Career:** Founding Partner, Shilepsky Hartley Robb Casey Michon LLP.
**Publications:** Co-author, Negotiating Executive Severance: Five Factors for a Better Package; Author, Taking Stock of the Implied Covenant of Good Faith & Fair Dealing; Co-author, Monitoring and Controlling Inappropriate Behavior in the E-Workplace: Strategies for Avoiding Potential Liability; Co-author, Selected Issues and Answers from the Perspective of an Executive's Employment Lawyer.
**Personal:** University of Massachusetts at Amherst, BA, cum laude; Boston College Law School, JD, cum laude.

### HARVEY, Christopher P
Dechert LLP, Boston
617 728 7167
christopher.harvey@dechert.com
*Featured in Investment Funds (Nationwide), Investment Funds (Massachusetts)*
**Practice Areas:** Mr Harvey focuses his practice on securities and financial services. He represents open and closed-end investment companies, other US and international pooled investment vehicles, and investment advisers in transactional and regulatory matters, including registration and proxy statements, and requests for exemptive and no-action relief from the SEC. He advises mutual funds and their boards on Rule 12b-1 fees and distribution arrangements and counsels companies on "inadvertent investment company" status concerns.
**Professional Memberships:** Member, Massachusetts Bar
**Personal:** Boston College (BA, 1983, summa cum laude); Boston College Law School (JD, 1986, magna cum laude, editor, Boston College Law Review).

### HEALY, Martin R
Goodwin Procter LLP, Boston
617 570 1371
mhealy@goodwinprocter.com
*Featured in Real Estate (Massachusetts)*
**Practice Areas:** Mr Healy's practice concentrates on providing acquisition, due diligence and permitting advice for complex development projects. His current/past projects include acting as lead outside counsel for a billion dollar international airport capital plan, the representation of the developers of a $400 million mixed-use 1,300,000 square foot development on Boston Common and acting as legal advisor to the permitting team for the $12 billion Central Artery/Third Harbor Tunnel project. He is the editor of and a contributing author for the Massachusetts Zoning Manual.

**Personal:** JD, Boston College Law School, 1975 (cum laude); BA, Boston College, 1972 (summa cum laude).

### HEIDT, Jeffrey L
Verrill Dana, LLP, Boston
617 309 2605
jheidt@verrilldana.com
*Featured in Healthcare (Massachusetts)*
**Practice Areas:** For more than 30 years he has represented hospitals, health systems, academic medical centers and health insurers on complex financial, regulatory and strategic issues including Medicare and Medicaid payment appeals, state and federal fraud and abuse investigations, physician disciplinary matters, mergers and acquisitions and related governance matters.
**Career:** Massachusetts Bar (1970); Choate, Hall & Stewart (1970); Partner, Ropes & Gray (2005)
**Personal:** JD, Harvard Law School (1970); AB, cum laude, high honors in Philosophy, Brown University (1967).

### HEMR, Kurt Wm
Skadden, Arps, Slate, Meagher & Flom LLP & Affiliates, Boston
617 573 4833
khemr@skadden.com
*Featured in Litigation (Massachusetts)*
**Practice Areas:** Focuses on securities and financial product litigation, particularly life insurance. Extensive experience with shareholder derivative suits, corporate governance disputes, trade secret and intellectual property disputes, and other forms of complex civil litigation. Has represented individual and corporate clients in proceedings before the US Securities and Exchange Commission and other regulators. Has represented clients in trials, arbitrations, and mediations. Also admitted to practice in federal and state courts in New York.
**Career:** JD, Harvard Law School, 1994 (cum laude); AB, University of Michigan, 1991 (with distinction, and with highest honors in Classical Languages and Literatures)

### HERSHMAN, Jordan D
Bingham McCutchen LLP, Boston
617 951 8455
jordan.hershman@bingham.com
*Featured in Litigation (Massachusetts)*
**Practice Areas:** Co-chair of Bingham's Securities and Financial Institutions Litigation Group. Focuses on securities litigation defense, complex business litigation and intellectual property matters. Currently serving as lead counsel to Freddie Mac in several high-profile securities class action and derivative action cases. Has successfully represented the following companies, among others: Battery Ventures, Cambridge Technology Partners, Deloitte & Touche, Digital Equipment Corp., Gulf South Medical Supply, Investors Financial, Kopin Corp., LCA Vision, Moldflow Corp., Novell, SeaChange International, TempurPedic, and Teradyne.
**Personal:** George Washington University Law School, JD, Order of the Coif, 1986; University of Pennsylvania, BA, cum laude, 1982.

### HICKEY, Andrew
Choate Hall & Stewart LLP, Boston
617 248 5267
ahickey@choate.com
*Featured in Banking & Finance (Massachusetts)*
**Practice Areas:** Mr Hickey counsels clients in all aspects of corporate finance transactions, such as public bond issuances, senior credit facilities and mezzanine and second lien financings. He also represents clients with respect to corporate and securities matters, such as public equity offerings, tender offers, mergers and acquisitions, going private transactions and 34 Act reporting.
**Personal:** JD cum laude Suffolk University Law School (1998), Law Review; BA cum laude Syracuse University (1994).

### HODGES TAYLOR, Laura C
Goodwin Procter LLP, Boston
617 570 1536
lht@goodwinprocter.com
*Featured in Private Equity (Massachusetts)*
**Practice Areas:** Ms Hodges Taylor focuses on corporate finance and securities law, representing a range of investment management firms, including private equity firms, hedge fund managers and investment advisors, often as outside general counsel. She works with businesses in a variety of industries, including life sciences, technology, traditional industry and business services, and investment banking firms in connection with financings and mergers and acquisitions. Her company practice focuses on transactions such as public and private offerings of equity and debt and acquisitions, as well as general business and securities advice.
**Personal:** JD, Harvard Law School, 1982; BA, Wellesley College, 1977.

### HUGG, Joseph A
DLA Piper LLP (US), Boston
617 406 6052
joseph.hugg@dlapiper.com
*Featured in Employee Benefits & Executive Compensation (Massachusetts)*
**Practice Areas:** Tax, employee benefits and ERISA.
**Career:** He concentrates his practice on tax and ERISA issues affecting venture capital and private equity funds and their investors. He advises clients on domestic and international tax aspects of fund formations and assists funds in structuring portfolio investments to minimize taxes and ensure compliance with US and foreign tax laws. He has substantial experience dealing with ERISA plan assets and other fiduciary issues.
**Personal:** LLM, New York University School of Law (Taxation); JD, Harvard Law School; BA, Georgetown University.

### ISAIA, Russell E
Bingham McCutchen LLP, Boston
617 951 8427
russell.isaia@bingham.com
*Featured in Employee Benefits & Executive Compensation (Massachusetts)*
**Practice Areas:** More than 20 years of experience practicing in the area of executive compensation and employee benefits. Substantial experience

advising on the securities, ERISA and tax implications of the design, implementation, administration and termination of all forms of benefit programs for executives and other employees.
**Personal:** Harvard Law School, JD, 1980; University of Illinois/Urbana-Champaign, BA, 1977.

## JACOBS, Neil
WilmerHale, Boston
617 526 6970
neil.jacobs@wilmerhale.com
*Featured in Labor & Employment (Massachusetts)*
**Practice Areas:** Extensive experience in negotiation and administration of collective bargaining agreements; employment and labor law litigation in state and federal courts; and administrative proceedings before state and federal fair employment agencies. Lead trial or appellate counsel in major employment litigation involving ERISA litigation; unfair labor practice proceedings before the National Labor Relations Board and in US Courts of Appeals; predatory hiring cases; employee theft of trade secrets; wrongful discharge litigation; and discrimination litigation.
**Professional Memberships:** American Bar Association's Developing Labor Law Committee.
**Career:** Admitted to Massachusetts Bar. Joined firm in 1977.
**Personal:** Harvard Law School (JD); Harvard College (AB).

## JAFFE, Seth D
Foley Hoag LLP, Boston
617 832 1203
sjaffe@foleyhoag.com
*Featured in Environment (Massachusetts)*
**Practice Areas:** Seth Jaffe represents clients in permitting/licensing of new facilities and compliance work, including matters under federal and state Clean Air Acts, Clean Water Acts, RCRA, MEPA/NEPA. He has expertise in development, permitting, and compliance for energy facilities, as well as matters under federal and state Superfund laws, including representing clients in defense of proceedings brought by the government or private parties and representing plaintiffs seeking recovery of response costs or property damage. He is currently the President-elect of the American College of Environmental Lawyers.
**Personal:** Yale Law School, JD; Harvard University, MPP; Massachusetts Institute of Technology, SB.

## JAHRLING III, Robert V
Choate Hall & Stewart LLP, Boston
617 248 5148
rjahrling@choate.com
*Featured in Corporate/M&A (Massachusetts)*
**Practice Areas:** Mr Jahrling has over 30 years' experience representing publicly-held as well as family-owned, venture-backed and other privately-held companies. He counsels companies (and boards of directors/board committees) on strategic business matters, securities offerings, domestic/international mergers and acquisitions, corporate governance, SEC reporting/compliance, strategic partnerships/joint ventures and executive compensation matters. He represents companies

across many industries, including enterprise software, telecommunications, market research, medical devices, healthcare services and alternative energy. He also represents venture capital and private equity firms in connection with minority investments, buyouts and leveraged recapitalizations.
**Personal:** JD University of Virginia School of Law (1983); AB Dartmouth College (1979).

## JAKUBOWSKI, Paul
WilmerHale, Boston
617 526 6948
paul.jakubowski@wilmerhale.com
*Featured in Real Estate (Massachusetts)*
**Practice Areas:** Mr Jakubowski is the chair of the Real Estate Practice Group. His national practice focuses on all aspects of real estate law. He counts numerous real estate groups among his clients, including REITs, foreign investors in US real estate, national retailers and private equity real estate funds. His practice is national and covers all property types. He works frequently with WilmerHale's tax, corporate, bankruptcy, financial institutions, litigation and fund formation groups.
**Professional Memberships:** Member of the Boston, Massachusetts and American Bar Associations, the Real Estate Finance Association, and the National Association of Industrial and Office Properties.

## JANOS, Ellen L
Mintz Levin Cohn Ferris Glovsky and Popeo PC, Boston
617 348 1662
EJanos@mintz.com
*Featured in Healthcare (Massachusetts)*
**Practice Areas:** Ellen provides regulatory and strategic advice to health care clients of all types including web based health companies. She handles billing investigations and audits and advises clients on corporate compliance programs, privacy and security, telemedicine and fraud and abuse laws.
**Professional Memberships:** Advisory Committee of the Massachusetts Health Information Exchange Council.
**Career:** Former Massachusetts Assistant Attorney General. Successfully argued two cases before the US Supreme Court.
**Publications:** Ellen writes and speaks frequently on board governance, compliance, physician-hospital relationships, drug pricing and HIPAA.
**Personal:** Simmons College, BA with honors; New England School of Law, JD, magna cum laude.

## JARRELL, Brenda H
Choate Hall & Stewart LLP, Boston
617 248 5175
bjarrell@choate.com
*Featured in Intellectual Property (Massachusetts)*
**Practice Areas:** Dr Jarrell helps clients structure creative and ambitious IP strategies in Life Sciences industries, including: protecting life-saving medicines (even when agents are well known or products of nature), navigating competitors' or collaborators' IP portfolios, and evaluating IP assets and risks of potential target opportunities

for investors. Her extensive technical expertise, relentless focus on practical relevance, and articulate and precise presentation ensure that she provides the highest value counsel to her clients.
**Personal:** JD cum laude Harvard Law School (1998); PhD University of California at San Francisco (1993); MA, AB both magna cum laude Harvard University (1988).

## JEDREY, Christopher M
McDermott Will & Emery LLP, Boston
617 535 4405
cjedrey@mwe.com
*Featured in Healthcare (Massachusetts), Healthcare (Nationwide)*
**Practice Areas:** Partner-in-charge of Boston health industry practice, and national co-chairman of academic medical centers practice. Represents providers and HMO clients in mergers, acquisitions, and joint ventures, sales of non-profit assets and operations to for-profit companies, and conversions from taxable to tax-exempt status. Represents academic medical centers for a variety of matters, including strategic affiliations, clinical research and faculty practice plans.
**Personal:** Boston College Law School (JD); Harvard University (PhD, MA); University of Massachusetts (BA).

## JEFFERY, D Ethan
Murphy & King, P.C., Boston
617 226 3410
dej@murphyking.com
*Featured in Bankruptcy/Restructuring (Massachusetts)*
**Practice Areas:** Practice focuses on representing debtors, creditors' committees, creditors and trustees in complex bankruptcies, non-bankruptcy workouts and other related insolvency proceedings. Mr Jeffery also represents parties in commercial litigation matters relating to the debtor-creditor relationship.
**Professional Memberships:** American Bankruptcy Institute, Turnaround Management Association; Boston Bar Association.
**Personal:** JD Villanova Law School (1991); BS University of New Hampshire (1987).

## JENKINS, Dennis L
WilmerHale, Boston
617 526 6491
dennis.jenkins@wilmerhale.com
*Featured in Bankruptcy/Restructuring (Massachusetts)*
**Practice Areas:** Partner, Corporate and Transactional and Intellectual Property Departments; Member, Bankruptcy and Financial Restructuring Practice Group. Mr Jenkins has represented debtors, creditors' committees, individual creditors, and other interested parties in highly contested, US and international corporate restructurings and bankruptcy cases. He has also represented lenders, borrowers and lessors in connection with some of the most complex and innovative debt financing facilities and transactions.
**Publications:** Co-Author, One Creditor or Many? Bondholder Standing in Foreign Insolvencies; Co-Author, Corporate

Reorganisations in Mexico: A Cramdown Alternative.
**Personal:** JD, Boston College Law School; BA, magna cum laude, Brigham Young University.

## JOHNSON III, Joseph L
Goodwin Procter LLP, Boston
617 570 1633
jjohnson@goodwinprocter.com
*Featured in Corporate/M&A (Massachusetts)*
**Practice Areas:** Mr Johnson chairs Goodwin Procter's M&A/Corporate Governance Practice and has substantial experience in the merger and acquisition area, representing both buyers and sellers. Mr Johnson frequently advises investment funds and institutional investors concerning their investments in public and private issuers and with respect to issues in the corporate governance area. He also represents companies in connection with proxy contests.
**Personal:** JD, Boston College Law School, 1986 (summa cum laude); BA, Vassar College, 1983 (cum laude).

## JONES, Richard L
Sullivan & Worcester LLP, Boston
617 338 2482
rjones@sandw.com
*Featured in Tax (Massachusetts)*
**Practice Areas:** Richard L Jones, tax partner, focuses on state tax litigation and transactional planning involving corporate, franchise, personal income and sales/use tax matters. He represents taxpayers in disputes before the Massachusetts Appellate Tax Board, Supreme Judicial Court, various state Departments of Revenue and the Internal Revenue Service on a range of issues, including corporate nexus, apportionment, manufacturing classification, step transaction, unitary reporting and domicile.
**Professional Memberships:** Boston Bar Association, Co-Chair, State and Local Tax Committee; Past Co-Chair, Tax Controversies Committee.
**Personal:** LLM, Taxation, Boston University School of Law; JD, Boston University School of Law; BA, cum laude, Clark University.

## JOSEPH, Roger P
Bingham McCutchen LLP, Boston
617 951 8247
roger.joseph@bingham.com
*Featured in Investment Funds (Nationwide), Investment Funds (Massachusetts)*
**Practice Areas:** Co-chairs Bingham's Financial Services Area, heads the Investment Management Group and is a member of the Management Committee at Bingham. Practice encompasses both publicly offered and private investment funds. Has participated in many innovative developments in the investment management industry, including heading up the legal team that developed the master/feeder legal structure and shepherding the first funds using that structure through the US registration process. Also led the investment management team in the legal structuring of the first principal-protected, actively managed mutual funds.

**Personal:** Columbia University School of Law, JD, 1976; Cornell University, BA, 1973.

## JOY, Robert
Morgan, Brown and Joy LLP, Boston
617 788 5007
rpjoy@morganbrown.com
*Featured in Labor & Employment (Massachusetts)*
**Practice Areas:** Chairman of Management Committee of region's largest management side employment and labor law boutique. Experienced litigator who has represented clients in numerous federal and state trial and appellate courts and agencies. Advises and defends employers on every aspect of employment and labor law.
**Professional Memberships:** Fellow, College of Labor and Employment Lawyers; Member, Board of Overseers of Boston College Law School; Member, American, Massachusetts and Boston Bar Associations; Member, Dartmouth Lawyers Association.
**Career:** Massachusetts Bar, 1975; Partner, Morgan, Brown & Joy, 1982.
**Publications:** Senior Editor, 'How to Take a Case Before The NLRB', BNA.
**Personal:** JD, Boston College Law School, 1975; AB cum laude, Dartmouth College, 1971.

## JOY, William
Morgan, Brown and Joy LLP, Boston
617 788 5051
wjoy@morganbrown.com
*Featured in Labor & Employment (Massachusetts)*
**Practice Areas:** Labor-management relations and related litigation; collective bargaining; labor arbitration; NLRB proceedings.
**Professional Memberships:** American, Massachusetts and Boston Bar Associations.
**Career:** Massachusetts Bar (1975); Partner, Morgan, Brown & Joy (1982).
**Personal:** JD Boston College (1975); AB College of the Holy Cross (1969); 1st Lt US Army 10th Special Forces Group (1969-72); Colonel, USAR (1972-93).

## KAHN, Adam
Foley Hoag LLP, Boston
617 832 1206
akahn@foleyhoag.com
*Featured in Environment (Massachusetts)*
**Practice Areas:** Adam Kahn has expertise in matters involving renewable and conventional energy, project permitting, land use/development, and Brownfields redevelopment. His practice extends to environmental disputes; compliance; siting, permitting, development; and the remediation, redevelopment and reuse of contaminated property. He counsels clients on emerging issues ranging from climate change and greenhouse gas regulation to environmental sustainability and corporate social responsibility initiatives. Along with his extensive US practice, Adam actively works in the arena of international environmental law, including representing clients on environmental matters before the International Court of Justice in The Hague.
**Personal:** Harvard University, JD; Brown University, AB.

## KAITZ, Nathan
Morgan, Brown and Joy LLP, Boston
617 788 5014
nkaitz@morganbrown.com
*Featured in Labor & Employment (Massachusetts)*
**Practice Areas:** Labor-Management Relations and litigation in public and private sector; collective bargaining; labor arbitration; NLRB proceedings.
**Professional Memberships:** Boston (Member, Labor Law Section), Massachusetts and American (Member, Labor and Employment Law Section) Bar Associations.
**Career:** Massachusetts Bar (1977); Partner, Morgan, Brown & Joy (1988); Field Attorney, National Labor Relations Board, 1978-1981
**Publications:** Author, Massachusetts Chapter, Employment At Will, A State-by-State Survey.
**Personal:** JD, Catholic University, 1977; BA, cum laude, University of Massachusetts, 1974.

## KALER, Robert
McCarter & English, LLP, Boston
617 449 6507
rkaler@mccarter.com
*Featured in Litigation (Massachusetts)*
**Career:** Mr Kaler represents publicly traded and privately held corporations, banks and financial institutions, public authorities and agencies, and private organizations and individuals in commercial litigation, including jury trials, arbitrations, class actions and appeals. His practice encompasses disputes in the areas of corporate governance; commercial and international transactions and contracts; fraud, antitrust and unfair competition law; securities fraud and shareholder derivative claims; intellectual property rights; products liability; information technology; and major project construction and engineering. He is a member of the Massachusetts, New York and District of Columbia bars and has extensive trial and appellate experience. For full bio: http://www.mccarter.com/Robert-J-Kaler/.

## KANNEL, William
Mintz Levin Cohn Ferris Glovsky and Popeo PC, Boston
617 348 1665
BKannel@mintz.com
*Featured in Bankruptcy/Restructuring (Massachusetts)*
**Practice Areas:** Bankruptcy, restructuring and bankruptcy litigation.
**Professional Memberships:** American College of Bankruptcy, Former Chair Bankruptcy Section of the Boston Bar Association, American Bankruptcy Institute. Trade group lecturer for the ABI, Turnaround Management Association and National Federation of Municipal Analysts.
**Career:** Admitted to practice Massachusetts, United States District Court for the District of Massachusetts, Courts of Appeal for the First, Second and Seventh Circuits, United States Supreme Court. Significant experience representing institutional lenders, indenture trustees, bondholders.
**Publications:** Numerous, including Co-Editor in Chief of ABI Healthcare Insolvency Manual.

**Personal:** AB Wesleyan University; JD, cum laude, Boston University School of Law.

## KAPLAN, Lawrence
Goodwin Procter LLP, Boston
617 570 1423
lkaplan@goodwinprocter.com
*Featured in Real Estate (Massachusetts)*
**Practice Areas:** Mr Kaplan represents institutions, owners, developers and tenants during the permitting, acquisition and financing process. In addition to his land use and development expertise, he has considerable experience and expertise in construction and permanent lending on behalf of lending institutions and in hazardous waste law and liability. His clients include several universities and colleges, insurance companies, department store chains, a REIT that develops upscale retail outlet centers, supermarket chains, multifamily development owners and developers, a major athletic shoe manufacturer and retailer, and healthcare institutions.
**Personal:** JD, Boston University School of Law, 1968; BS, Boston University, 1965.

## KAPLAN, Tamsin R
Davis, Malm & D'Agostine, P.C., Boston
617 589 3892
tkaplan@davismalm.com
*Featured in Labor & Employment (Massachusetts)*
**Practice Areas:** Represents businesses and executives on employment-related issues, including recruitment, hiring, discrimination, negotiating agreements, contract breach, discipline, termination, employment audits, and workplace policies. Conducts workplace investigations and trainings. Litigates employment issues. Provides alternative dispute resolution services.
**Professional Memberships:** American, Massachusetts, Boston, and Women's Bar Associations; American Arbitration Association Expedited Commercial Panel.
**Publications:** 'Wal-Mart' and What it Means for Future Class Actions,' Massachusetts Lawyers Weekly. 'Employment Agreements' Advising a Massachusetts Business, Chapter 4, Massachusetts Continuing Legal Education. 'Employee Handbooks in Massachusetts: Benefits, Pitfalls and Preserving At-Will Employment,' Massachusetts Continuing Legal Education.
**Personal:** Massachusetts Continuing Legal Education: Labor and Employment Curriculum Advisory Committee.

## KAY, Minta E
Goodwin Procter LLP, Boston
617 570 1877
mkay@goodwinprocter.com
*Featured in Real Estate (Massachusetts)*
**Practice Areas:** Ms Kay is a partner in the firm's nationally recognized Real Estate, REITs & Real Estate Capital Markets Group. She regularly represents institutional investors, tax-exempts, real estate funds and owner/operators in a variety of real estate transactions. She has extensive experience with the formation and restructuring of joint ventures; the origination, acquisition and restructuring of debt, including in complex capital stacks; portfolio roll-up and similar transactions;

real estate development transactions; and property sales and acquisitions.
**Personal:** JD, Columbia University School of Law, 1986; BA, Barnard College, 1983 (magna cum laude).

## KEATING, Gregory C
Littler Mendelson, PC, Boston
617 378 6000
gkeating@littler.com
*Featured in Labor & Employment (Massachusetts)*
**Practice Areas:** Whistleblowing and Retaliation, Healthcare, Class Actions, Discrimination and Harassment, Competition and Trade Secret Law.
**Professional Memberships:** Management Representative, Whistleblower Protection Advisory Committee; Board of Advisors,National Employment Law Institute; Editorial Advisory Board,ADA Compliance Guide; Editorial Advisory Board,Individuals with Disabilities Education Act Newsletter; Editorial Advisory Board, Leave and Disability Coordination Handbook; Editorial Advisory Board,Section 504 Compliance Handbook; Editorial Advisory Board, Special Education Advisor.
**Publications:** Mr Keating wrote a national treatise entitled "Retaliation and Whistleblowing: A Guide for Human Resources Professionals and Counsel," Lexis Nexis, 4th Edition, 2012.
**Personal:** JD, Boston College Law School, 1993 cum laude BA, Trinity College, 1987.

## KEATING, Michael
Foley Hoag LLP, Boston
617 832 1136
mkeating@foleyhoag.com
*Featured in Litigation (Massachusetts)*
**Practice Areas:** Michael B. Keating is one of the firm's principal trial attorneys and is past Chairman of the Litigation Department. He represents corporate and individual litigants in a range of complex litigation in both federal and state courts and serves as both counsel and as arbitrator in commercial arbitration disputes. He was appointed Special Counsel by the Massachusetts Supreme Judicial Court to the Commission on Judicial Conduct and Chairman of the Court Management Advisory Board to advise the Court on all matters of judicial administration.
**Personal:** Harvard Law School, LLB; Williams College, BA.

## KEEFE, Robert D
WilmerHale, Boston
617 526 6334
robert.keefe@wilmerhale.com
*Featured in Litigation (Massachusetts)*
**Practice Areas:** Partner, Investigations and Criminal Litigation Group, with a litigation practice that includes internal corporate investigations, extensive white-collar criminal defense work and complex commercial litigation.
**Professional Memberships:** Admitted to practice before the Supreme Judicial Court of Massachusetts; the US Court of Appeals for the First, Second, Fifth, Sixth, Seventh and Ninth Circuits; the US District Court of the District of

Massachusetts, and all state courts in the Commonwealth of Massachusetts.

**Career:** Attorney in the Criminal Division of the Department of Justice before joining the firm in 1974.

**Personal:** Boston College Law School (JD); Harvard College (BA).

### KEHOE, Gerald J
Bingham McCutchen LLP, Boston
617 951 8593
gerald.kehoe@bingham.com
*Featured in Private Equity (Massachusetts)*

**Practice Areas:** Focuses on private investment funds. Represents US and non-US institutional investors and fund sponsors in connection with master/feeder, leveraged feeder and many other types of private fund structures employing investment strategies in energy, clean technology, clean energy, money management, hospitality, venture capital and other sectors. Experience in domestic and offshore fund formation and fundraising transactions for private equity and hedge fund clients. Advises on debt and equity private placements and public offerings for US and European clients.

**Personal:** Temple University James E. Beasley School of Law, JD, 1986; Cornell University, BS, 1983.

### KELIHER, Cynthia
McCarter & English, LLP, Boston
617 449 6527
ckeliher@mccarter.com
*Featured in Real Estate (Massachusetts)*

**Career:** Ms Keliher's practice involves all aspects of real estate law, including leasing, financing, zoning, development, permitting, tax abatement, foreclosures, and commercial and residential condominiums. Ms Keliher focuses a great deal of her practice on leasing, representing landlords and tenants in ground, retail, office and data center leases. Significant representations include representation of public authority in connection with five ground leases for a mixed-use development, a proposed marina, a shipyard, and residential apartments and condominiums and representation of the Commonwealth of Massachusetts in the disposition of three former state hospitals, including rezoning, permitting and subdivision approvals. For full bio: http://www.mccarter.com/Cynthia-B-Keliher/.

### KELLER, Stanley
Edwards Wildman Palmer LLP, Boston
617 239 0217
stanley.keller@edwardswildman.com
*Featured in Corporate/M&A (Massachusetts)*

**Practice Areas:** Stan has extensive experience in business and securities law matters involving emerging and public companies; representing issuers, underwriters and investors in financial transactions; and mergers and acquisition transactions. He advises companies, boards and board committees on corporate governance issues, transactional matters and special investigations.

**Professional Memberships:** American Bar Association, Boston Bar Association.

**Publications:** Stan has written many articles and treatises on corporate and securities law matters and chaired programs on these subjects. These include articles on SEC regulation and corporate law and governance.

**Personal:** Harvard Law School, LLB, magna cum laude; Columbia University, AB.

### KENDALL, Michael
McDermott Will & Emery LLP, Boston
617 535 4085
mkendall@mwe.com
*Featured in Litigation (Massachusetts)*

**Practice Areas:** Based in the Firm's Boston office. He represents clients in criminal and civil regulatory matters and business litigation. A significant part of his practice involves representing health care companies and representing clients in cross border disputes.

**Career:** From 1989 to 1996, Mike served as an Assistant United States Attorney in the District of Massachusetts. In 1992, he was the Deputy Associate Attorney General and Counselor in the United States Department of Justice.

**Personal:** Harvard Law School, JD, 1984, John F. Kennedy School of Government, MPP, 1984, Harvard College, AB, (magna cum laude), 1979.

### KENDALL, Michael J
Goodwin Procter LLP, Boston
617 570 1765
mkendall@goodwinprocter.com
*Featured in Private Equity (Massachusetts)*

**Practice Areas:** Mr Kendall focuses his corporate finance and securities practice on representing private equity and venture capital firms in connection with early and later stage investments, leveraged recapitalizations and buyouts, as well as counseling a variety of emerging companies. He has substantial experience representing issuers and underwriters in initial and follow-on public offerings, public and private mergers and acquisitions, and advising public companies on SEC reporting and other general corporate matters.

**Personal:** JD, Boston University School of Law, 1993 (magna cum laude); MBA, Boston University Graduate School of Management, 1994; BA, Tufts University, 1990.

### KENYON, Geoffrey
Dechert LLP, Boston
617 728 7126
geoffrey.kenyon@dechert.com
*Featured in Investment Funds (Nationwide), Investment Funds (Massachusetts)*

**Practice Areas:** Mr Kenyon focuses his practice on the investment management industry, working with investment managers, financial institutions, and independent mutual fund directors. He has experience in all sectors of the US market, including Securities and Exchange Commission (SEC)-registered open- and closed-end funds, non-registered funds, and separately managed accounts. He also has significant international experience, working with funds offered to other major world markets and advising non-US investment managers on their US activities.

### Professional Memberships:
Member, Massachusetts Bar; International Bar Association; American Law Institute.

**Personal:** Northwestern University (BA, 1980); Columbia Law School (JD, 1984, Harlan Fiske Stone Scholar).

### KING, Rufus C
Goodwin Procter LLP, Boston
617 570 1880
rking@goodwinprocter.com
*Featured in Private Equity (Massachusetts)*

**Practice Areas:** Mr King represents venture capital and other private equity funds, both in fund organization and in investment transactions. He has also represented public and private high-technology companies in all aspects of corporate operation and development. He has acted as issuers' and underwriters' counsel in public offerings. Mr King represents a wide range of private investment funds, both in the United States and internationally. He has successfully completed more than 100 fund formation projects since 1986.

**Personal:** JD, Harvard Law School, 1986 (cum laude); BPH, Oxford University, 1979; AB, Dartmouth College, 1977 (summa cum laude).

### KIRBY, Samantha
Goodwin Procter LLP, Boston
617 570 8794
skirby@goodwinprocter.com
*Featured in Banking & Finance (Massachusetts)*

**Practice Areas:** Ms Kirby advises financial institutions on a variety of corporate, securities, bank regulatory and transactional matters. She serves as corporate and regulatory counsel to a number of the firm's banking and financial services clients and has experience in public and private offerings of debt and equity securities, financial institution mergers and acquisitions, de novo bank chartering, holding company formations, conversions of thrift institutions from mutual to stock form and operating subsidiary formation and activities.

**Personal:** JD, Georgetown University Law Center, 2001; MSFS Georgetown University, School of Foreign Service, 2001; BA Wellesley College, 1997 (magna cum laude).

### KIRSCH, Robert
WilmerHale, Boston
617 526 6779
rob.kirsch@wilmerhale.com
*Featured in Environment (Massachusetts)*

**Practice Areas:** Partner, Regulatory and Litigation Departments and Environmental Group. Mr Kirsch represents clients in adversarial, counseling and permitting contexts; and pursues and defends cost recovery, including defense contractor claims. He has defended against criminal, civil and administrative investigations and litigation, and counsels in all major areas of compliance, including CAA, RCRA, TSCA, CERCLA and nanotechnology.

**Professional Memberships:** American, Boston and New Hampshire Bar Associations.

**Career:** Admitted: Supreme Court, Massachusetts, New Hampshire. Joined firm in

1983. Massachusetts Lawyers Weekly Lawyer of the Year - 2008.

**Personal:** Cornell Law School (cum laude); Middlebury College (cum laude, Phi Beta Kappa).

### KIRSHENBAUM, Mark
Goodwin Procter LLP, Boston
617 570 1305
mkirshenbaum@goodwinprocter.com
*Featured in Tax (Massachusetts)*

**Practice Areas:** Mr Kirshenbaum focuses on the structuring and other tax aspects of commercial transactions including domestic and international investments, mergers, acquisitions, divestitures, joint ventures and partnership transactions for clients including public and private corporations, private equity funds, real estate funds, financial institutions and REITs. His experience includes tax matters related to the formation and operation of private equity, real estate and other collective investment vehicles and fund of funds and their investors, as well as financial products and securities transactions.

**Personal:** LLM, New York University School of Law, 2003; JD, Columbia School of Law, 1998; BA, Cornell University, 1995.

### KLINE, Douglas J
Goodwin Procter LLP, Boston
617 5701209
dkline@goodwinprocter.com
*Featured in Intellectual Property (Massachusetts)*

**Practice Areas:** Mr Kline concentrates his practice on intellectual property litigation, particularly patent infringement matters and disputes related to the enforcement of intellectual property rights. He advises inventors, companies, investors and underwriters concerning patent enforcement and infringement risks. He advises clients regarding technology transfer, including the negotiation and drafting of all forms of related agreements such as patent licenses and technology development and license agreements. Mr Kline also works with clients to develop patent portfolio development strategies, and oversees the preparation and prosecution of patent applications.

**Personal:** JD, Suffolk University Law School, 1990 (magna cum laude); BS, Tufts University, 1984.

### KOCIUBES, Joseph L
Bingham McCutchen LLP, Boston
617 951 8337
joe.kociubes@bingham.com
*Featured in Litigation (Massachusetts)*

**Practice Areas:** Focuses on civil litigation, including commercial, licensing, energy, financial services, real estate, securities, insurance and constitutional litigation, as well as domestic and international arbitrations. Tries cases in state and federal courts around the US and appears before administrative and regulatory agencies.

**Career:** Fellow, American College of Trial Lawyers and the International Academy of Trial Lawyers. Past president, Boston Bar Association. Served on more than two dozen faculty of Massachusetts Continuing Legal Education and Boston Bar Continuing Legal Education programs.

**Personal:** Harvard Law School, JD, cum laude, 1974; University of Pittsburgh, BA, 1969.

### KOLB, William R
Foley Hoag LLP, Boston
617 832 1209
wkolb@foleyhoag.com

*Featured in Corporate/M&A (Massachusetts)*

**Practice Areas:** William R Kolb, is member of the firm's Executive Committee, Co-Managing Partner, and Chair of the Mergers and Acquisitions Group. He advises clients in corporate reorganizations, completing divestitures, participating in public company acquisitions, "going private" transactions, merger agreements and related intercompany and employment agreements. He also represents companies seeking governmental and third party approvals as a result of a planned change in control. He also represents high growth and emerging companies seeking venture capital and strategic investments and technology companies on licensing matters.
**Personal:** Georgetown University Law Center, JD, magna cum laude; Marquette University, BS, magna cum laude.

### KRAVETZ, Jonathan
Mintz Levin Cohn Ferris Glovsky and Popeo PC, Boston
617 348 1674
JLKravetz@mintz.com

*Featured in Life Sciences (Nationwide), Corporate/M&A (Massachusetts)*

See under Nationwide for profile.

### KREBS, Michael
Nutter McClennen & Fish LLP, Boston
617 439 2288
mkrebs@nutter.com

*Featured in Banking & Finance (Massachusetts)*

**Practice Areas:** Michael Krebs is a partner in the Business Department and co-chair of the Banking and Finance practice group. Michael's areas of expertise include complex mergers and acquisitions, corporate finance and corporate governance. He serves as corporate, regulatory and securities counsel to a variety of banks, savings institutions, insurance companies, underwriters and other financial institutions. He has represented clients before various federal and state regulatory agencies, including the Federal Reserve, OCC, FDIC, the Massachusetts Division of Banks, the New Hampshire Banking Department, and the California Department of Financial Institutions.

### KREISLER, David
Weil, Gotshal & Manges LLP, Boston
617 772 8340
david.kreisler@weil.com

*Featured in Private Equity (Massachusetts)*

**Practice Areas:** David Kreisler regularly represents private equity sponsors and their investment funds in connection with their organization and administration as well as the acquisition, disposition and financings of their investments. He represents institutional investors and has been involved in the acquisition of private equity firms and advises clients on the formation of limited and general partnerships and limited liability companies. His clients include Thomas H. Lee

Partners, Berkshire Partners, The Gores Group, HM Capital, Kainos Capital and Quantum Energy Partners.
**Personal:** Princeton University (AB, 1988); Syracuse University College of Law (JD magna cum laude, 1991, Order of the Coif.).

### KRONCKE-MOORE, Barbara J.
McCarter & English, LLP, Boston
617 449 6571
bkroncke@mccarter.com

*Featured in Banking & Finance (Massachusetts)*

**Career:** Ms Kroncke is experienced in all aspects of public finance and serves as bond counsel, disclosure counsel, issuer's counsel, underwriter's counsel, credit enhancement counsel, purchaser's counsel and borrower's counsel on a variety of transactions for a multitude of issues. Ms Kroncke has served as counsel for bond issues involving water authorities; states and cities; housing bonds; industrial development bonds for industrial and commercial enterprises; and bonds issued on behalf of not-for-profit institutions, including hospitals, colleges and universities, secondary schools, cultural institutions, and behavioral services institutions within and outside the Commonwealth of Massachusetts. For full bio: http://www.mccarter.com/Barbara-J-Kroncke-Moore/.

### KRUMHOLZ, Joshua C
Holland & Knight LLP, Boston
617 573 5820
joshua.krumholz@hklaw.com

*Featured in Intellectual Property (Massachusetts)*

**Practice Areas:** Practice Group Leader for the firm's Intellectual Property Group. Mr Krumholz focuses primarily upon intellectual property litigation, with a particular focus on patent litigation. His practice covers a variety of technologies and jurisdictions. Over the past ten years, Mr Krumholz has been successful in all cases he has taken to trial, including successful jury verdicts in the Eastern District of Texas, Illinois, Massachusetts and New Jersey. Technologies that Mr Krumholz has handled include, among other areas, telecom, software, hardware, electronics, computer chip wafer processes, pesticides, air jet technology and consumer goods.

### KUGELL, Jaclyn L
Morgan, Brown and Joy LLP, Boston
617 788 5054
JKugell@morganbrown.com

*Featured in Labor & Employment (Massachusetts)*

**Practice Areas:** Ms Kugell's practice concentrates on employment litigation, and the representation of mangement in various federal and state courts, and administrative agencies across the country. Ms Kugell's practice also focuses on employment law training. She regularly conducts training for employers on a variety of employment law topics.
**Professional Memberships:** American, Massachusetts and Boston Bar Associations. Massachusetts Women's Bar Association.
**Career:** Massachusetts Bar (1992); Partner, Morgan, Brown & Joy (1999).

**Publications:** Continuing Author, "Massachusetts Employment Law", 1999-2011.
**Personal:** JD, Northeastern University (1992); BA, Brandeis University, 1989, cum laude.

### KYLE, Amy L
Bingham McCutchen LLP, Boston
617 951 8288
amy.kyle@bingham.com

*Featured in Banking & Finance (Massachusetts)*

**Practice Areas:** Co-chair of Bingham's Transactional Finance practice group and a member of the firm's Diversity Executive Committee. Represents leading financial institutions in connection with a broad range of finance-related matters, with a particular focus on the transportation industry. Experience also includes loan workouts and debt restructurings. Actively involved in leveraged finance transactions. Experience includes senior and mezzanine financing of private acquisitions and leveraged recapitalizations, including platform companies and roll ups, public mergers, and tender offer transactions.
**Personal:** Columbia University School of Law, JD, 1983; Princeton University, BA, 1980.

### LAPATIN, Philip
Holland & Knight LLP, Boston
617 573 5869
philip.lapatin@hklaw.com

*Featured in Real Estate (Massachusetts)*

**Practice Areas:** Partner in the Boston office of Holland & Knight, Philip Lapatin is the author of the Standard Forms Guide as well as The Real Estate Legal Desk Book and The Massachusetts Landlord Survival Guide, all published by the Greater Boston Real Estate Board. His practice focuses primarily on commercial leasing as well as the purchase and sale of investment property. Mr Lapatin authors a monthly column for the Rental Housing Association, lectures frequently and serves as case commentator for the Massachusetts Real Estate Bar Association, which in 2008 honored him with its Richard B. Johnson lifetime achievement award.

### LAPORTE, Claire
Foley Hoag LLP, Boston
617 832 1210
claporte@foleyhoag.com

*Featured in Intellectual Property (Massachusetts)*

**Practice Areas:** Claire Laporte tries patent cases relating to biotechnology, medical devices, pharmaceuticals and software. She has tried cases in federal district court and in the International Trade Commission. Notable trials include an ITC trial on behalf of a Chinese biotechnology company in which she won a ruling of invalidity of the plaintiff's two US patents, and a case in which she won a jury verdict of willful infringement. She has filed patent-related amicus briefs in the Federal Circuit and the US Supreme Court.
**Personal:** Harvard Law School, JD; Princeton University's Woodrow Wilson School of Public and International Affairs, AB.

### LECLAIRE, John R
Goodwin Procter LLP, Boston
617 570 1144
jleclaire@goodwinprocter.com

*Featured in Private Equity (Nationwide), Private Equity (Massachusetts)*

**Practice Areas:** Mr LeClaire, Chair of the firm's Private Equity Group, focuses his practice on leveraged recapitalizations, buyouts and minority investments, both in later stage situations and earlier stage ventures, for leading private equity firms throughout the country. He also specializes in the representation of emerging growth companies in sectors such as technology and information services, healthcare, financial services and consumer products. His work with these companies involves strategic counsel, mergers and acquisitions, equity and executive compensation programs, and going-private transactions.
**Personal:** JD, Boston University School of Law, 1982 (magna cum laude); AB, Brown University, 1979 (magna cum laude).

### LEE, Rebecca A
Edwards Wildman Palmer LLP, Boston
617 239 0225
rlee@edwardswildman.com

*Featured in Real Estate (Massachusetts)*

**Practice Areas:** Rebecca represents clients in a wide range of real estate matters, including land use and development permitting, financing, leasing and condominium creation. Rebecca has represented developers in encompassing site assembly and acquisition, obtaining all of the necessary entitlements, construction and permanent financing, including tax-exempt financing, condominium creation and other exit strategies, and leasing.
**Professional Memberships:** New England Women in Real Estate, Asian American Lawyers Association of Massachusetts, National Asian Pacific American Bar Association.
**Personal:** Yale Law School, JD, 1991; Harvard University, MPA, 1979; Brandeis University, BA, 1976.

### LEE, William F
WilmerHale, Boston
617 526 6556
william.lee@wilmerhale.com

*Featured in International Trade (Nationwide), Life Sciences (Nationwide), Litigation (Nationwide), Intellectual Property (Massachusetts)*

See under Nationwide for profile.

### LEIBOWITZ, Hal J
WilmerHale, Boston
617 526 6461
hal.leibowitz@wilmerhale.com

*Featured in Corporate/M&A (Massachusetts)*

**Practice Areas:** Vice Chair of WilmerHale's Transactional Department and a Senior Member of the Mergers and Acquisitions Group. Mr Leibowitz's practice focuses on corporate and securities law matters for companies in the technology, life sciences and services industries, with an emphasis on mergers and acquisitions and public company counseling. He routinely advises clients and their boards of directors on a wide range of merger and acquisition transactions,

including acquisitions and dispositions of public and private companies, tender offers, exchange offers and going private transactions.
**Career:** Joined firm in 1985.
**Personal:** Suffolk University Law School (JD); Brandeis University (BA).

### LENIHAN, Brian P
Choate Hall & Stewart LLP, Boston
617 248 4929
blenihan@choate.com
*Featured in Private Equity (Massachusetts)*
**Practice Areas:** Mr Lenihan, Private Equity co-chair, represents PE and VC funds in financing transactions including leveraged buyouts, majority/minority recapitalizations and growth equity investments. He advises private technology companies in M&A, VC financings and cross-border transactions, primarily US-Canada. Recent engagements: represented Spectrum Equity in connection with acquisitions of HealthMEDX and NetHealth; represented Accel Partners in investment in Lightspeed Retail; represented Symmetric Capital in sale of TekLinks to Pamlico Capital; and represented Century Capital in sale of Digital Risk to MphasiS (HP subsidiary).
**Personal:** JD summa cum laude Boston College Law School (1993); BA cum laude Dartmouth College (1989).

### LEON, Michael
Nutter McClennen & Fish LLP, Boston
617 439 2815
mleon@nutter.com
*Featured in Environment (Massachusetts)*
**Practice Areas:** Michael Leon chairs the firm's Environmental Law practice. He represents numerous business entities and public bodies in oil and hazardous materials, air quality, water and waste water, solid waste and other regulatory matters, including the reuse of contaminated property. He counsels commercial and industrial clients, primarily in the energy and petroleum sectors, in all aspects of environmental regulation, including rulemaking and policy development as well as enforcement and litigation matters. Michael maintains an active land use practice focusing on waterfront permitting and development and has extensive involvement in permitting significant public and private development and infrastructure projects.

### LEONETTI, Kenneth
Foley Hoag LLP, Boston
617 832 1271
kleonetti@foleyhoag.com
*Featured in Bankruptcy/Restructuring (Massachusetts)*
**Practice Areas:** Kenneth Leonetti focuses on complex financial litigation, bankruptcy and restructuring, software and licensing disputes, and valuation litigation. His bankruptcy practice concentrates on Chapter 11 proceedings in the healthcare, technology and real estate industries, and advising venture-backed companies and hedge funds in workouts and restructurings. He represented the creditors committee in the confirmed Chapter 11 of Malden Mills case; debtors in Radianse, Foss Manufacturing and Charles

River Hospital; equity holders in the International Place reorganization; and Media/Communications Partners in a year-long trial against the US Department of Justice.
**Personal:** Columbia University School of Law, JD; Dartmouth College, AB.

### LEVITAN, Shari
Holland & Knight LLP, Boston
617 854 1405
shari.levitan@hklaw.com
*Featured in Tax (Massachusetts)*
**Professional Memberships:** Fellow, American College of Trust and Estate Counsel.
**Career:** Shari Levitan leads Holland & Knight's Private Wealth practice in Boston. Admitted to practice in both Massachusetts and Arizona, Ms Levitan's work involves counseling high-net-worth individuals, developing and implementing tax-efficient wealth transfer strategies, advising private company owners and public company executives in business matters related to their personal planning, and representing trustees in disputes with co-fiduciaries and beneficiaries. She has extensive experience advising clients in the areas of bioethics issues related to estate planning issues involving children born through assisted reproductive technologies (ART), and planning for same-sex couples.

### LIAZOS, Andrew C
McDermott Will & Emery LLP, Boston
617 535 4038
aliazos@mwe.com
*Featured in Employee Benefits & Executive Compensation (Nationwide), Employee Benefits & Executive Compensation (Massachusetts)*
**Practice Areas:** Heads the firm's executive compensation group and the Boston employee benefits practice. Represents public companies, large closely held businesses and compensation committees on tax and securities aspects of executive compensation, ERISA fiduciary matters, employee benefits in business transactions and bankruptcy, and employee stock ownership plans. He also counsels executives in employment agreement and joint venture negotiations.
**Professional Memberships:** Admitted to practice in Massachusetts (1990), Maine (1993), and the United States Tax Court (1990).
**Personal:** Suffolk University Law School, JD (cum laude), 1990; University of Massachusetts Amherst, BS (cum laude), 1987.

### LIZOTTE, Andrew G
Murphy & King, P.C., Boston
617 226 3415
agl@murphyking.com
*Featured in Bankruptcy/Restructuring (Massachusetts)*
**Practice Areas:** Shareholder in Murphy & King's Bankruptcy and Financial Restructuring Group. Specializes in bankruptcy and commercial law including representation of debtors, creditors committees, and trustees.
**Professional Memberships:** American Bankruptcy Institute, Boston Bar Association.
**Career:** Shareholder in Murphy & King's Bankruptcy and Financial Restructuring Group.

Law Clerk to Hon. James F Queenan, US Bankruptcy Court, Certified Public Accountant.
**Personal:** JD, Suffolk University Law School (1991); BSBA, Bryant University (1986).

### LLOYD, Diana K
Choate Hall & Stewart LLP, Boston
617 248 5163
dlloyd@choate.com
*Featured in Litigation (Massachusetts)*
**Practice Areas:** Ms Lloyd has over 20 years of experience in federal and state government enforcement matters, internal investigations and related business and securities litigation. A tenacious and aggressive trial and appellate attorney, she has also had considerable success dissuading governmental agencies from pursuing any enforcement or criminal action against her clients. As an Assistant US Attorney in Boston, she received numerous awards for excellence from the US Attorney and various federal law enforcement agencies.
**Personal:** JD, MA New York University School of Law (1989), Law Review Editor in Chief; BA Valedictorian, summa cum laude St Lawrence University (1984).

### LOUCKS, Michael
Skadden, Arps, Slate, Meagher & Flom LLP & Affiliates, Boston
617 573 4840
michael.loucks@skadden.com
*Featured in Litigation (Massachusetts)*
**Practice Areas:** Nationally recognized health care fraud prosecutor with 25 years in public service. Currently represents companies in government criminal investigations, in False Claims Act and other civil litigation, in regulatory matters with the FDA and the Office of Inspector General, and in FCPA investigations.
**Career:** Former acting US attorney and first assistant US attorney for the District of Massachusetts. Led major criminal and civil investigations, as well as many of the most high-profile health care fraud prosecutions of the past two decades.
**Personal:** JD, University of Virginia School of Law, 1980; BA, Harvard College, 1977 (magna cum laude).

### LYNCH, Matthew
Nixon Peabody LLP, New York
*Featured in Real Estate (Massachusetts)*
**Practice Areas:** Matthew Lynch focuses his practice in the areas of purchase and sale of office, industrial and retail properties, leasing of office, industrial and retail properties, acquisition and construction real estate lending, office, industrial and retail development, land use and environmental permitting, and asset and property management.
**Professional Memberships:** Boston Bar Association; Real Estate Bar Association of Massachusetts; National Association of Industrial and Office Properties; Real Estate Finance Association; and Holy Cross Club of Greater Boston. In addition, Matthew is a member of the Board of Directors of the Lawyers' Committee for Civil Rights in Boston.

### MACENKA, Mark
Goodwin Procter LLP, Boston
617 570 1145
mmacenka@goodwinprocter.com
*Featured in Private Equity (Massachusetts)*
**Practice Areas:** Mr Macenka focuses his practice in the areas of business and securities law, mergers and acquisitions, venture capital and corporate finance. He represents public and private growth oriented companies in emerging and high technology industries, as well as venture capital firms and investment banks. His experience includes business counseling, domestic and international mergers and acquisitions, public and private financing, domestic and international software, Internet, telecommunications and technology licensing and distribution, and strategic partnerships and joint ventures.
**Personal:** JD, Harvard Law School, 1983; AB, Georgetown University, 1980 (magna cum laude).

### MAHONEY, Sean P
K&L Gates, Boston
617 261 3202
sean.mahoney@klgates.com
*Featured in Banking & Finance (Massachusetts)*
**Practice Areas:** A partner whose practice focuses in the areas of corporate law and financial services regulation, Sean Mahoney handles corporate transactions including mergers, acquisitions, public and private securities offerings, debt financings, non-controlling investments in regulated organizations, and bank and holding company formations. He advises clients in the financial services industry on regulatory issues at the state and federal level, including capital requirements, risk management and issues arising under the Federal Reserve Act, Bank Holding Company Act, Federal Deposit Insurance Act, Home Owners' Loan Act, Federal Credit Union Act, Fair Credit Reporting Act, and state information security laws.

### MAIR, George P
Bingham McCutchen LLP, Boston
617 951 8423
george.mair@bingham.com
*Featured in Tax (Massachusetts)*
**Practice Areas:** Concentrates on international tax, financial instruments, estate planning and other tax-related matters, including controversy work for both individuals and corporations.
**Career:** Taught at Harvard Law School. Spoke at the Federal Tax Institute of New England and at various programs sponsored by the Boston Bar Association, Massachusetts Continuing Legal Education and other organizations. Authors numerous publications on tax-related matters.
**Personal:** Harvard Law School, JD, 1978; Harvard College, BA, 1975.

### MARANDETT, Eric J
Choate Hall & Stewart LLP, Boston
617 248 5287
emarandett@choate.com
*Featured in Intellectual Property (Massachusetts)*
**Practice Areas:** Mr Marandett, co-chair of Intellectual Property Litigation, represents biotech, pharmaceutical and technology compa-

nies in high stakes patent litigation and other intellectual property and commercial disputes. Mr Marandett also advises his clients on strategies for protecting and maximizing the value of their most important intellectual property assets. He has been a frequent author and speaker on topics including Hatch-Waxman litigation strategies, Biosimilars legislation, and critical developments in intellectual property law at the Federal Circuit and Supreme Court.
**Personal:** JD University of Pennsylvania Law School (1992); BA magna cum laude Tufts University (1988).

### MARETT, Louis J
Choate Hall & Stewart LLP, Boston
617 248 5091
lmarett@choate.com
*Featured in Tax (Massachusetts)*
**Practice Areas:** Mr Marett advises clients on structuring and negotiating public and private mergers and acquisitions, and other corporate and partnership financings and restructurings, many of them cross-border. He focuses on fund formation and acquisition/disposition of target companies for buyout, venture and hedge funds, including the formation of the first ever long-short/market neutral hedge fund. He guides clients through the various tax issues related to stock options, restricted stock, golden parachutes and deferred compensation arrangements in connection with corporate and partnership transactions.
**Personal:** JD cum laude Harvard Law School (1972); AB magna cum laude Harvard College (1968).

### MARTIN, Gina Lynn
Goodwin Procter LLP, Boston
617 570 1330
gmartin@goodwinprocter.com
*Featured in Bankruptcy/Restructuring (Massachusetts)*
**Practice Areas:** Ms Martin is a member of the firm's financial restructuring and leveraged finance practices. She focuses her work on corporate restructurings, debt financings and acquisitions of distressed businesses. She is active in all aspects of in- and out-of-court restructurings of financially distressed businesses, including the representation of corporate debtors, asset based lenders, hedge funds and purchasers of distressed businesses.
**Professional Memberships:** The Boston and American Bar Associations; the American Bankruptcy Institute.
**Personal:** JD, Fordham University School of Law, 1995; BS, St. Michael's College, 1992 (cum laude).

### MARTLAND, David A
Nixon Peabody LLP, Boston
617 345 6145
dmartland@nixonpeabody.com
*Featured in Antitrust (Massachusetts), Private Equity (Massachusetts)*
**Practice Areas:** David Martland is the Practice Group Leader of Nixon Peabody's Global Business and Transactions Practice Group. His practice is focused in two areas: corporate and antitrust. He

represents a variety of venture and private equity funds and private and public companies on the full range of corporate matters. He also advises substantial corporate and healthcare clients on all aspects of antitrust, including representing them in state and federal merger and non-merger related antitrust investigations.
**Personal:** Yale Law School, JD; Senior Editor, Yale Law Journal; Princeton University, BA; Clerked for Walter Mansfield (2d Cir.)

### MASSEY, Stephanie H.
Edwards Wildman Palmer LLP, Boston
617 239 0558
smassey@edwardswildman.com
*Featured in Banking & Finance (Massachusetts)*
**Practice Areas:** Stephanie Massey serves as bond counsel, underwriter's counsel and borrower's counsel in several states in connection with the issuance of tax-exempt and taxable revenue bonds for governmental entities and in conduit issuer transactions (including pooled borrowings) for nonprofit institutions including hospitals, colleges, private secondary schools and cultural and other institutions. Ms Massey frequently represents borrowers in connection with the bond counsel role.
**Personal:** Boston College Law School, JD (Executive Editor, Boston College International and Comparative Law Review), Cornell University, AB (Cornell National Scholar).

### MAYER, William P
Goodwin Procter LLP, Boston
617 570 1534
wmayer@goodwinprocter.com
*Featured in Financial Services Regulation (Nationwide), Banking & Finance (Massachusetts)*
**Practice Areas:** Mr Mayer serves as corporate and regulatory general counsel for several publicly held financial institutions, financial institution holding companies, and community banking organizations, where he advises banking organizations and their boards on a range of corporate, regulatory, governance and transactional matters. He has handled mergers, acquisitions, public and private offerings of debt and equity securities, stock conversions, bank and holding company formations and reorganizations of financial institutions and holding companies.
**Personal:** JD, Virginia Law School, 1977; MS, University of Dar es Salaam, Tanzania, 1974; AB, Dartmouth College, 1973 (summa cum laude).

### MCCORD, Thomas
Nixon Peabody LLP, Boston
617 345 1337
tmccord@nixonpeabody.com
*Featured in Employee Benefits & Executive Compensation (Massachusetts)*
**Practice Areas:** Thomas McCord's practice deals with all aspects of employee benefits, including retirement plans, ERISA fiduciary issues, employee stock ownership plans, health and flexible benefit programs, investment and transactional issues, and equity and non-equity executive compensation arrangements.
**Publications:** He has spoken before the Boston and Massachusetts Bar Associations as well as at

live and broadcast seminars nationally, and is the author of articles in Employee Benefits News and other publications.
**Personal:** Harvard University, JD, cum laude; Yale University, BA, summa cum laude.

### MCCOURT, Terence
Greenberg Traurig, LLP, Boston
617 310 6246
McCourtT@gtlaw.com
*Featured in Labor & Employment (Massachusetts)*
**Practice Areas:** Labor and Employment Law.
**Professional Memberships:** Co-Chair, Boston Bar Association, Labor and Employment Law Section. Member: American Bar Association; Boston Bar Association.
**Career:** Managing Shareholder, Greenberg Traurig Boston Office. Chair, Labor and Employment Group. Super Lawyers Magazine, Massachusetts Super Lawyers, 2005-12. Law360 'Employment Practice Group of the Year', 2011. Guberman Fellowship for Legal Studies, Brandeis University. George F. Baker Scholar, Georgetown University. Catholic University Law Review. AV® Preeminent™ 5.0 out of 5. Former Deputy Chief Legal Counsel to Governor of Massachusetts.
**Personal:** JD, The Catholic University of America, Columbus School of Law; BA, magna cum laude, Georgetown University.

### MCDOUGALL, Lorne W
Edwards Wildman Palmer LLP, Boston
617 239 0100
lmcdougall@eapdlaw.com
*Featured in Real Estate (Massachusetts)*
**Practice Areas:** Lorne McDougall advises lenders, developers, entrepreneurs, funds and investors in connection with the acquisition, disposition, ownership, use, financing, development, construction, and leasing of commercial real estate. He also represents owners, prime and trade contractors, and design professionals in all types of design and construction contracts and agreements, deal structuring and financing.
**Personal:** New York University School of Law, LLM, Queen's University, LLB, University of New Haven, BA.

### MCGARRAH, Doug
Foley Hoag LLP, Boston
617 832 1217
DMM@foleyhoag.com
*Featured in Environment (Massachusetts)*
**Practice Areas:** Douglas McGarrah, Co-Chair of the Real Estate/Development group, helps clients navigate the intersection of business and government. He advises on managing government regulations and completing major development and infrastructure projects. He leads multidisciplinary teams focused on expedited permitting and development of large-scale academic facilities and commercial centers. He provides counsel for emissions approvals under NEPA, MEPA, wetlands, waterways, highway access, historic preservation and zoning-based reviews. He has expertise in transit-oriented development projects, and has an extensive record advising public authorities on projects involving creative solutions to address regulatory compliance.

**Personal:** Trinity College, BA, 1977; Georgetown University Law Center, JD, 1986.

### MCGURK, Michael R
Finnegan, Henderson, Farabow, Garrett & Dunner LLP, Washington, DC
617 646 1619
michael.mcgurk@finnegan.com
*Featured in Intellectual Property (Massachusetts)*
**Practice Areas:** Managing partner of Finnegan's Boston, Massachusetts office. He has over 25 years of experience in IP matters involving all aspects of patent law, primarily in pharmaceutical, chemical, medical device, and mechanical technologies. He works with a range of clients including startups and Fortune 100 companies. His practice includes due diligence investigations, opinions, global patent portfolio management and analysis, as well as litigation, interferences and reexaminations.
**Personal:** University of Delaware (BS, Chemical Engineering, 1983); George Washington University, National Law Center (JD, 1988).

### MCKENDALL, Miriam
Holland & Knight LLP, Boston
617 573 5846
miriam.mckendall@hklaw.com
*Featured in Labor & Employment (Massachusetts)*
**Practice Areas:** Ms McKendall is co-chair of the Education Team and concentrates her practice in employment law, education law and related litigation. She counsels clients proactively on employment issues, such as investigation of workplace discrimination complaints; development of disability and reasonable accommodations policies; wage and hour compliance; and development of workplace policies and preventative strategies for containment of potential employee claims. She defends employers in employment claims at agency and court levels. She advises clients in workplace matters unique to higher education, including faculty governance. Ms McKendall presents on workplace compliance issues and conducts trainings for managers and executive teams.

### MCNIECE, Colin
Mintz Levin Cohn Ferris Glovsky and Popeo PC, Boston
617 348 1788
CMcNiece@mintz.com
*Featured in Banking & Finance (Massachusetts)*
**Practice Areas:** Colin's practice focuses on public finance matters such as tax-exempt and taxable financings. Serving as bond counsel, borrower's counsel, underwriter's counsel, and bank counsel, Colin has advised clients on financings related to housing, transportation, higher education, health care, economic development, and project finance.
**Career:** Before attending law school, Colin served as the Director of Economic Development for the City of Lowell, Massachusetts, from 2002 to 2004, and as its Chief Planner from 1998 to 2002.
**Personal:** BS, Iowa State University; MSCRP, Iowa State University; JD, Roger Williams University.

**MENNA, Gilbert G**
Goodwin Procter LLP, Boston
617 570 1433
gmenna@goodwinprocter.com
*Featured in Capital Markets (Nationwide), Corporate/M&A (Massachusetts)*
See under Nationwide for profile.

**MEREDITH, Stephen O**
Edwards Wildman Palmer LLP, Boston
617 951 2233
smeredith@edwardswildman.com
*Featured in Private Equity (Massachusetts)*
**Practice Areas:** Steve's experience includes private equity and venture capital financings, M&A, joint ventures, fund formations, buyouts, securities offerings, debt facilities, restructurings and litigation oversight.
**Professional Memberships:** European Venture Capital Association, American Bar Association, Massachusetts Bar Association, Boston Bar Association, Rhode Island Bar Association.
**Publications:** Steve has authored a number of articles on private equity and corporate finance and has been quoted in various business publications, including the Wall Street Journal, Venture Capital Journal, The Deal, Private Equity Analyst, and Bloomberg News.
**Personal:** University of Iowa, JD, 1978; Brown University, AB, 1974.

**MEYERS, Arthur S**
Choate Hall & Stewart LLP, Boston
617 248 4808
ameyers@choate.com
*Featured in Employee Benefits & Executive Compensation (Massachusetts)*
**Practice Areas:** Mr Meyers advises senior executives and boards on all matters relating to executive compensation, including employment, severance and change in control arrangements. He also advises public and closely held entities on tax, corporate, employment and securities law aspects of equity compensation plans. Additionally, Mr Meyers counsels profit and not-for-profit employers on the design, implementation and administration of tax-qualified retirement plans, nonqualified deferred compensation plans and welfare benefit plans, and he serves as ERISA counsel to plan fiduciaries and private funds.
**Personal:** JD University of Michigan Law School (1981); BA University of Michigan (1977).

**MICHON, Katherine J**
Shilepsky Hartley Robb Casey Michon LLP, Boston
617 723 8000
kmichon@shilepsky.com
*Featured in Labor & Employment (Massachusetts)*
**Practice Areas:** Executive and professional advocacy, employment law, litigation.
**Professional Memberships:** Boston Bar Association, Massachusetts Bar Association, Women's Bar Association.
**Career:** Founding Partner of Shilepsky Hartley Robb Casey Michon LLP; Top Women of Law 2012 by Massachusetts Lawyers Weekly.
**Publications:** Co-author, Employment Law 101; Co-author, Selected Issues and Answers from the

Perspective of an Executive's Employment Lawyer; Co-author, Employee Leave: The Essentials Behind What You Have to Do and What You Should Do to Retain Top Management.
**Personal:** University of Massachusetts, Amherst, BA (1986); New England School of Law, JD (1992).

**MIKELS, Richard**
Mintz Levin Cohn Ferris Glovsky and Popeo PC, Boston
617 348 1691
REMikels@mintz.com
*Featured in Bankruptcy/Restructuring (Massachusetts)*
**Practice Areas:** Richard E Mikels serves as Chairman of Mintz Levin's Bankruptcy and Restructuring Department.
**Professional Memberships:** Vice president of the American College of Bankruptcy, member of the College's national board of directors and chairman of the Educational Programs Committee of the American College of Bankruptcy; American Bankruptcy Institute; Turnaround Management Association; Association of Commercial Finance Attorneys; Commercial Law League of America; Boston Bar Association.
**Career:** Adjunct Professor at Boston University Law School.
**Publications:** Contributing editor of the American Bankruptcy Institute Journal and has published numerous bankruptcy related articles. He has also written or edited chapters in numerous legal texts.

**MILLER, Michelle**
WilmerHale, Boston
617 526 6116
michelle.miller@wilmerhale.com
*Featured in Antitrust (Massachusetts)*
**Practice Areas:** Co-Chair, Antitrust and Competition Group. Concentration: antitrust litigation and advising clients on antitrust compliance and merger clearance. Litigation matters include direct and indirect purchaser class actions under the antitrust laws, antitrust counterclaims to patent infringement suits, including cases involving standards-essential patents and Hatch-Waxman Act litigation involving challenges to patent settlements. Litigates in federal and state courts; represents clients before the Federal Trade Commission and Antitrust Division of the Department of Justice.
**Professional Memberships:** ABA Antitrust and Litigation Sections; Former Co-Chair, BBA Antitrust Committee.
**Personal:** Boston College Law School (JD magna cum laude).

**MILLS, Craig**
Nixon Peabody LLP, Boston
617 345 1219
cmills@nixonpeabody.com
*Featured in Banking & Finance (Massachusetts)*
**Practice Areas:** Craig's practice is concentrated primarily in the areas of debt finance, equipment finance, general corporate counseling, business strategy and planning and other business matters.

He regularly represents financial institutions, investors as well as issuers located throughout the United States and Europe in a wide range of domestic and international commercial loan, asset-based and structured finance matters. Craig also represents providers of equity and other capital in aircraft, maritime, rail and other hard asset transactions.
**Personal:** Boston University School of Law, JD; Bucknell University, BA. Trustee at Bucknell University.

**MILTON, Christopher H**
Greenberg Traurig, LLP, Boston
617 310 6280
MiltonC@gtlaw.com
*Featured in Real Estate (Massachusetts)*
**Practice Areas:** Real estate, development, zoning, environmental, land use, gaming, infrastructure, finance, workouts and foreclosures, operations, tax abatements, takings, acquisitions, dispositions and leasing.
**Professional Memberships:** NAIOP. ULI. Massachusetts Bar Association. Boston Bar Association. Real Estate Bar Association. Board of Ambassadors, Home for Little Wanderers. President and Board of Directors, Wellesley Country Club. Gala Committee, Discovering Trustee. Long-Range Planning Committee, Wellesley Country Club. Breakfast Committee, United Way Real Estate & Building Industry Breakfast.
**Career:** Selected: Best Lawyers in America, 2010-13; Chambers USA Guide, 2009-13; Super Lawyers 2011-12; Member, Winning Team, 2010 Chambers and Partners USA Award for Excellence in Real Estate. Rated, AV® Preeminent™ 5.0 out of 5.
**Personal:** JD, University of Michigan Law School; AB, cum laude, English, Princeton University.

**MINER, Tracy A**
Mintz Levin Cohn Ferris Glovsky and Popeo PC, Boston
617 348 1694
TMiner@mintz.com
*Featured in Litigation (Massachusetts)*
**Practice Areas:** Tracy is the Chair of the firm's White Collar Criminal Defense group. She represents many major corporations, financial institutions, public officials, corporate executives and other high-profile individuals in state and federal investigations and prosecutions. She has tried several white collar cases.
**Professional Memberships:** Board Member of NACDL, Past President of MACDL, ABA
**Publications:** Frequent author, speaker and media commentator.
**Personal:** Admitted to practice in Massachusetts, New Hampshire, and the First Circuit and the District of Columbia Circuit Court of Appeals.

**MITCHELL, Beth H**
Nutter McClennen & Fish LLP, Boston
617 439 2309
bmitchell@nutter.com
*Featured in Real Estate (Massachusetts)*

**Practice Areas:** Beth Mitchell is a partner in the Real Estate & Finance Department and co-chair of the Commercial Finance practice group. She represents financial institutions, investors, developers and other public and private entities in real estate financing, development, leasing, troubled debt restructuring, and other transactions locally, regionally and nationally. Beth graduated with honors from Yale College and Northwestern University School of Law. She is a member of numerous professional and trade groups, a past president of the Real Estate Finance Association, and a fellow of the American College of Real Estate Lawyers and the American College of Mortgage Attorneys.

**MOCHE, Richard**
Mintz Levin Cohn Ferris Glovsky and Popeo PC, Boston
617 348 1696
RMoche@mintz.com
*Featured in Banking & Finance (Massachusetts)*
**Practice Areas:** Rich is a member in Mintz Levin's Boston office. He heads the firm's Public Finance Section and is a member of the firm's governing policy committeeHe primarily represents mutual funds, indenture trustees, hedge funds, and insurance companies in tax-exempt bond transactions, focusing in the area of high-yield securities in both workout and new money transactions. His practice encompasses numerous sectors, including senior living, health care, multi-family housing, assessment districts, charter schools, solid waste disposal, and hospitality facilities.
**Personal:** BA, Brown University; JD, University of Chicago.

**MOLLAAGHABABA, Reza**
Pepper Hamilton LLP, Boston
617 204 5168
mollaaghababar@pepperlaw.com
*Featured in Intellectual Property (Massachusetts)*
**Practice Areas:** Partner. Practice focuses on all aspects of intellectual property law, including preparation and prosecution of patent and trademark applications, and preparation of patentability, infringement, validity and clearance opinions. Has represented clients in post-grant proceedings before the US Patent and Trademark Office, such as re-examination and re-issue. Has prepared and prosecuted patent applications in fields of technology, including photonics/optics, nanotechnology, medical devices, semiconductor processing, lithography, telecommunications, magnetic resonance, and computer hardware/software.
**Personal:** JD, magna cum laude, Suffolk University Law School; PhD and MS Harvard University; BS, summa cum laude, State University of New York at Stony Brook.

**MONAGHAN, John J**
Holland & Knight LLP, Boston
617 523 2700
john.monaghan@hklaw.com
*Featured in Bankruptcy/Restructuring (Massachusetts)*
**Practice Areas:** Practice Group Leader of the firm's National Bankruptcy and Creditors' Rights

Group. His bankruptcy practice has involved representation of a wide range of clients, including Chapter 11 debtors, creditors' committees, equity committees, lenders, landlords, licensors, trustees, parties to prepetition contracts and leases, defendants in adversary proceedings and unsecured creditors. He is particularly focused on representing major case participants in complex commercial Chapter 11 cases. He advises clients on business aspects of bankruptcy and workouts, and represents clients in matters in the Bankruptcy Court and state and federal courts. He is a Fellow of the American College of Bankruptcy.

### MOONEY, Michael E
Nutter McClennen & Fish LLP, Boston
617 439 2342
mmooney@nutter.com
*Featured in Tax (Massachusetts)*

**Practice Areas:** Michael Mooney is Nutter's Chairman. Michael maintains an active tax and business practice, representing businesses in a broad range of domestic and international tax issues. He advises clients on all aspects of complex business acquisitions, combinations and divestitures, including joint ventures, taxable and tax-free reorganizations and spin-offs. Michael also assists high net worth individuals with personal tax planning and works with businesses and individuals in designing and implementing executive compensation programs. He has handled many successful tax controversies before the Internal Revenue Service and the Massachusetts Department of Revenue.

### MOYNIHAN, Carla M
Robinson & Cole LLP, Boston
617 557 5940
cmoynihan@rc.com
*Featured in Real Estate (Massachusetts)*

**Practice Areas:** Carla Moynihan focuses her practice on the disposition, acquisition, development, and financing of commercial real estate. Ms Moynihan represents institutions, developers, retailers, investors, lenders, hospitals, medical professionals, hotels, and public entities in all aspects of commercial transactions including negotiating and drafting letters of intent to purchase or lease, term sheets for financing, purchase and sale agreements, land disposition agreements, development agreements, leases for retail, office, medical office or industrial landlords or tenants, and CMBS/CRE loan documents for lenders or borrowers. Ms Moynihan also represents clients throughout the federal, state and local land use/zoning permitting processes.
**Career:**

### MURPHY, Harold B
Murphy & King, P.C., Boston
617 226 3414
hbm@murphyking.com
*Featured in Bankruptcy/Restructuring (Massachusetts)*

**Practice Areas:** Leads Murphy & King's Bankruptcy and Financial Restructuring Group. Specializes in bankruptcy and commercial law including the representation of debtors, creditors' committees, trustees and creditors in Chapter 11

reorganizations and Chapter 7 liquidations. Mr Murphy has been appointed as trustee, examiner and receiver in various bankruptcy and non-bankruptcy corporate restructurings and liquidations. He has had considerable experience in the areas of commercial finance and litigation as well as matters involving secured lending, mergers and acquisitions, and the Uniform Commercial Code.
**Professional Memberships:** American, Boston and Massachusetts Bar Associations; Turnaround Management Association; American Bankruptcy Institute; and American College of Bankruptcy.
**Career:** Founder and Director of Murphy & King's Bankruptcy and Financial Restructuring Group.
**Personal:** JD, Suffolk University Law School (1981); AB, cum laude, Harvard College (1977).

### MURPHY, Martin F
Foley Hoag LLP, Boston
617 832 1213
mmurphy@foleyhoag.com
*Featured in Litigation (Massachusetts)*

**Practice Areas:** Martin Murphy practices in criminal defense, regulatory investigations, and high-stakes civil litigation. He has tried over 30 cases to completion before state and federal courts and arbitration panels, and argued dozens of federal and state appeals. He represents companies and individuals and conducts investigations for corporate boards and committees in areas that are the focus of government enforcement actions, including issues in the healthcare, medical device, securities, financial services, technology, and government contracting industries. He is a fellow of the American College of Trial Lawyers.
**Personal:** Harvard Law School, JD, cum laude; Princeton University, AB, summa cum laude.

### MUSIKER, Jean
Sugarman, Rogers, Barshak & Cohen, PC, Boston
617 227 3030
musiker@srbc.com
*Featured in Labor & Employment (Massachusetts)*

**Practice Areas:** With over 30 years of trial and litigation experience, Jean represents individuals and management in labor and employment matters including, discrimination and wrongful termination claims, wage and hour disputes, employee benefit matters and issues arising in unionized work settings. Jean also represents clients in matters involving housing and public accommodation discrimination. She has substantial experience in both the federal and state courts as well as before the Massachusetts Commission Against Discrimination, the Department of Labor, the EEOC, the Department of Housing and Urban Development and the Architectural Access Board. In addition to litigation, Jean counsels clients on their employment practices and serves as a neutral, providing mediation and arbitration.
**Professional Memberships:** Women's Bar Association (Member); Boston Bar Association (former Chair, Labor & Employment Section); Massachusetts Bar Association (former member, Labor and Employment Law Section Council)

**Career:** Jean is a Partner and Co-Chair of the Employment Law Group at Sugarman, Rogers, Barshak & Cohen, PC. She is a former General Counsel to the Massachusetts Commission Against Discrimination and a former Assistant District Attorney for Middlesex County, Massachusetts. Prior to that, she maintained a civil rights litigation practice in Rhode Island.
**Personal:** University of Pennsylvania Law School (JD, cum laude, Order of the Coif); Boston University (BA, cum laude). College of Labor and Employment Lawyers (Fellow).

### NAGLE, David J
Sullivan & Worcester LLP, Boston
617 338 2873
dnagle@sandw.com
*Featured in Tax (Massachusetts)*

**Practice Areas:** David J. Nagle is a partner in S&W's Tax Department. His practice involves both transactional tax planning and representing taxpayers in disputes before the Internal Revenue Service and the Massachusetts Department of Revenue.
**Professional Memberships:** American Bar Association; Boston Bar Association; Massachusetts Department of Revenue (DOR) Advisory Council (2013-present); Greater Boston Chamber of Commerce; Independent SALT Alliance (President, 2012-present; Board Member, 2010-present); Adjunct faculty member, Boston University School of Law, 2000.
**Personal:** LLM, Taxation, Boston University School of Law; JD, cum laude, Harvard Law School; MA, University of Michigan; BA, with Honors, University of Virginia.

### NAGLE, James W
Goodwin Procter LLP, Boston
617 570 1233
jnagle@goodwinprocter.com
*Featured in Labor & Employment (Massachusetts)*

**Practice Areas:** Mr Nagle, Chair of the firm's Labor and Employment Practice, focuses on defending corporations against claims made by employees. He practices in state and federal courts, as well as before a variety of administrative agencies. He is experienced in litigating complex age, sex, race and disability discrimination claims, and in defending whistle-blower, civil rights, employee privacy and drug-testing cases. He also has experience negotiating and litigating issues related to the termination of highly compensated executives.
**Personal:** JD, Georgetown University Law Center, 1980 (magna cum laude); MPA, American University, 1976; BA, Georgetown University, 1974 (magna cum laude).

### NAUGHTON, Laurence P
Choate Hall & Stewart LLP, Boston
617 248 4878
lnaughton@choate.com
*Featured in Corporate/M&A (Massachusetts)*

**Practice Areas:** Mr Naughton counsels growth-oriented companies regarding initial formation, financings, licensing/strategic partnerships, acquisitions and corporate governance. He also represents VC and PE firms and investment banks. He

has deep expertise in representing European-based clients in connection with US activities. Recent engagements: US VC firm in financing of healthcare-IT company; publicly-traded company in strategic partnership with Fortune 500 company; European-based company in reorganization and growth equity financing; PE firm in disposition of multiple portfolio companies.
**Personal:** JD magna cum laude Boston College Law School (1997), Boston College Law Review editor; BA College of the Holy Cross (1993).

### NEUMAN, Monica
McDermott Will & Emery UK LLP, London
617 535 4079
mneuman@mwe.com
*Featured in Healthcare (Massachusetts)*

**Practice Areas:** Focuses her practice on the representation of a wide range of clients, including tax-exempt hospital systems, academic medical centers, pharmaceutical companies, and physician practice groups. She provides regulatory and transactional representation to such clients in connection with acquisitions, joint ventures, strategic affiliations, conversions to tax-exempt status, and other transactional matters.
**Personal:** Northwestern University School of Law, JD, 2000, Brandeis University, BA, (cum laude), 1997.

### NEVO, Itai
DLA Piper LLP (US), Boston
617 406 6015
itai.nevo@dlapiper.com
*Featured in Private Equity (Massachusetts)*

**Practice Areas:** Private Equity: Venture Capital Investment.
**Career:** He represents clients from many different sectors in a wide range of corporate and securities law matters, primarily focusing on emerging and mature technology companies and venture capital, growth equity and private equity investors. He is fluent in Hebrew and has represented numerous Israeli technology companies and investors. He has been named Massachusetts Rising Star by Law & Politics and Boston magazines.
**Personal:** MBA, Boston University; JD, Boston University School of Law (cum laude); BA, Brandeis University (cum laude).

### NEWBERG, Joseph H
Weil, Gotshal & Manges LLP, Boston
617 772 8350
joseph.newberg@weil.com
*Featured in Tax (Massachusetts)*

**Practice Areas:** Joseph Newberg focuses his practice on the sophisticated problems of private equity funds and fund managers and has particular experience in the international aspects of private equity transactions. He has advised on the formation of private equity funds with over $30 billion of capital commitments, and he has advised such funds and fund sponsors on investment transactions and on the internal aspects of their operations, ownership and structure.
**Personal:** University of Michigan (BA, 1969, with high distinction); Harvard Law School (JD,

1972, magna cum laude); Boston University Graduate Tax Program (LLM, 1976).

## NEWMAN, Philip
Goodwin Procter LLP, Boston
617 570 1558
pnewman@goodwinprocter.com
*Featured in Investment Funds (Nationwide), Investment Funds (Massachusetts)*

**Practice Areas:** Mr Newman chairs the firm's Investment Management Practice. He works with registered investment companies, independent directors of investment companies, registered and unregistered investment advisers, banks and financial services institutions in the investment management industry. He counsels numerous mutual funds and their sponsors, and interfaces with SEC staff on a broad range of regulatory matters, including exemptive order applications, no-action letters, registration statements and examination inquiries. Mr Newman has extensive boardroom experience, including the representation of independent directors of mutual funds.
**Personal:** JD, Cornell Law School, 1981 (magna cum laude); BA, State University of New York at Buffalo, 1975.

## NIEWENHOUS, Daria
Mintz Levin Cohn Ferris Glovsky and Popeo PC, Boston
617 348 4865
DNiewenhous@mintz.com
*Featured in Healthcare (Massachusetts)*

**Practice Areas:** Daria's practice ranges from transactional matters to general counsel services. She has experience with the merger and acquisition of hospitals, long-term care facilities, clinics, home health and hospice programs, group practices, and other provider entities. She provides counsel in contracting, risk management, and adverse events and guides clients through the regulatory aspects of capital projects and strategic initiatives. Daria advises clients on ACOs, clinical integration and affiliation, and similar arrangements.
**Professional Memberships:** Chair: American Health Lawyers Association ACO Taskforce State Regulatory Issues Subcommittee.
**Personal:** BA, Salem State College; MA, Villanova University; JD, New England School of Law.

## NOTOPOULOS, Philip
Holland & Knight LLP, Boston
617 573 5844
philip.notopoulos@hklaw.com
*Featured in Real Estate (Massachusetts)*

**Practice Areas:** Partner in the firm's Real Estate Section, he concentrates his practice in commercial real estate sales and acquisitions, financing, leasing and development. He has substantial experience in land use law and property development, including office and residential condominiums, office, retail and industrial buildings, residential subdivisions, industrial parks, medical office buildings, churches and mixed-use projects for institutional clients. He has appeared before numerous zoning boards of appeal, planning

boards, conservation commissions and city councils.

## NULL, Amy A
WilmerHale, Boston
617 526 6541
amy.null@wilmerhale.com
*Featured in Employee Benefits & Executive Compensation (Massachusetts)*

**Practice Areas:** Ms Null is a Partner in WilmerHale's Tax Practice. She has broad experience advising financial institutions, benefit plan service providers and employers on ERISA, federal income tax law and other rules and regulations applicable to employee benefit plans.
**Professional Memberships:** Former Chair of the American Bar Association Tax Section's Subcommittee on Government Plans and past Chair of the Boston Bar Association's ERISA Committee.
**Career:** Prior to joining the firm in 2001, Ms Null was an attorney advisor for the US Department of the Treasury, Office of Tax Policy.
**Personal:** Harvard Law School (JD, cum laude); Haverford College (BA).

## OBERSTEIN, Gary J
Nixon Peabody LLP, Boston
617 345 1231
goberstein@nixonpeabody.com
*Featured in Labor & Employment (Massachusetts)*

**Practice Areas:** Gary Oberstein counsels and assists clients concerning the many, complex employment law obligations they face. These include preventing discrimination and harassment; issues concerning employee hire, retention, discipline and discharge; employment agreements; handbooks and policy manuals; wage-hour, privacy; drug testing; safety; non-competition agreements; lift-outs; reductions in force; workforce restructuring; and labor and employment implications of mergers and acquisitions. He conducts training programs concerning workplace sexual harassment, performance management, and other employment issues. He serves as Managing Partner of the Boston office and Chair of the Wage-Hour Team.
**Personal:** Boston College Law School, JD, cum laude; Vassar College, AB, Honors.

## O'HANLON, John V
Dechert LLP, Boston
617 728 7111
john.ohanlon@dechert.com
*Featured in Investment Funds (Nationwide), Investment Funds (Massachusetts)*
See under Nationwide for profile.

## O'REILLY JR, William R
WilmerHale, Boston
617 526 6210
william.o'reilly@wilmerhale.com
*Featured in Real Estate (Massachusetts)*

**Practice Areas:** Former chair of the firm's Real Estate Practice Group. Practice focuses on all aspects of real estate law, including land use and development, distressed properties, and investments. Serves as counsel for a broad range of clients, including private equity investors, develop-

ers, large retailers, corporations and non-profit institutions.
**Professional Memberships:** Fellow, The American College of Real Estate Lawyers.
**Career:** Admitted to Massachusetts Bar. Joined the firm in 1980.
**Personal:** Georgetown University Law Center (JD,1980, magna cum laude); Tufts University (BA, 1977, summa cum laude with Special Honors). Vice Chair, Board of Trustees, Tufts University.

## O'SHAUGHNESSY, Gregory
Nixon Peabody LLP, New York
617 345 1343
goshaughnessy@nixonpeabody.com
*Featured in Corporate/M&A (Massachusetts)*

**Practice Areas:** Gregory O'Shaughnessy works in the area of mergers and acquisitions, including representing public and private strategic buyers as well as financial buyers and sellers of privately held businesses. He has advised clients in connection with merger and acquisition transactions having an aggregate value in the billions of dollars. Gregory serves as outside general counsel to a variety of companies in the high-tech, life sciences, food and beverage, retail, and cleantech sectors. His work for these companies covers all aspects of their legal needs, including corporate formation, venture capital financing, executive compensation, general corporate matters, and intellectual property issues.

## O'TOOLE, Patrick
Weil, Gotshal & Manges LLP, Boston
617 772 8365
patrick.otoole@weil.com
*Featured in Litigation (Massachusetts)*

**Practice Areas:** Patrick O'Toole, a partner in Weil's Complex Commercial Litigation and White Collar Defense and Investigations practices, concentrates on business torts, misappropriation, fraud, and unfair trade practice claims, corporate and partnership disputes, government and internal investigations, compliance programs, corporate control and governance, and white collar criminal matters. He has substantial appellate practice experience.
**Career:** Law Clerk to the Honorable Frances J. Boyle of the US District Court for the District of Rhode Island and Honorable Neil L. Lynch of the Massachusetts Supreme Judicial Court; Special Assistant District Attorney.
**Personal:** Stonehill College (BS); Suffolk University Law School (JD, cum laude).

## PAINE, William H
WilmerHale, Boston
617 526 6134
william.paine@wilmerhale.com
*Featured in Litigation (Massachusetts)*

**Practice Areas:** Partner, Securities Department. Mr Paine represents public companies, financial services companies and financial institutions, and their officers and directors, nationwide in securities, derivative and ERISA litigation, and SEC investigations and enforcement proceedings. Mr Paine also conducts internal investigations for corporations and their directors. Subject matters

include securities fraud, accounting, public offerings, insider trading, ERISA, insider trading, foreign exchange, mergers and acquisitions, governance, compliance and mutual funds. Mr Paine has extensive experience in SEC investigations and class and derivative actions.
**Personal:** Boston University School of Law (JD cum laude 1987); Amherst College (BA cum laude 1983).

## PALLADINO, Peter M
Choate Hall & Stewart LLP, Boston
617 248 2132
ppalladino@choate.com
*Featured in Banking & Finance (Massachusetts)*

**Practice Areas:** Extensive commercial finance experience across a range of industries including media, technology, healthcare, sports and retail. Cash flow and asset based structuring/documentation, acquisition, workout, debtor-in-possession and emergence financing. Representative engagements: restructuring media holding company facility including debt to equity conversion; representing Agent in national franchise roll-up transaction; representing Agent in syndicated multi-currency facility for international software consulting firm.
**Professional Memberships:** Chairman, Choate's Business Department (since 1999); past Chair, BBA Commercial Finance Section. Commercial Finance Association (CFA); Turnaround Management Association (TMA); Association for Corporate Growth (ACG).
**Personal:** JD Boston University School of Law (1985); BA Colgate University (1982).

## PAPPONE, Michael J
Goodwin Procter LLP, Boston
617 570 1940
mpappone@goodwinprocter.com
*Featured in Bankruptcy/Restructuring (Massachusetts)*

**Practice Areas:** Mr Pappone concentrates in commercial insolvency and reorganization law. His practice spans the spectrum of representing principal parties in large corporate reorganizations to out-of-court workouts for smaller entrepreneurial companies, including representation of equipment lessors, landlords, asset acquirers, creditors' committees or committee members, court-appointed trustees and entities involved in leveraged buyouts. He also advises clients on commercial and insolvency issues arising in corporate restructurings, financings and securitization transactions.
**Professional Memberships:** American College of Commercial Finance Lawyers: Member; American Bar Foundation: fellow; American College of Bankruptcy: fellow.
**Personal:** JD, Harvard Law School, 1973; AB, University of California, Berkeley, 1970.

## PASTUSZENSKI, Brian E
Goodwin Procter LLP, Boston
617 570 1094
bpastuszenski@goodwinprocter.com
*Featured in Securities (Nationwide), Litigation (Massachusetts)*

**Practice Areas:** Mr Pastuszenski has achieved national prominence in the defense of securities class action and shareholder litigation matters and proceedings brought by the SEC and other regulatory organizations, and the related insurance and indemnification issues that such matters involve. His practice is concentrated in the areas of securities class action and shareholder litigation defense, defense of SEC proceedings, internal corporate investigations, corporate governance and compliance matters, merger and acquisition-related litigation, and other high-stakes business litigation.
**Personal:** JD, Cornell Law School, 1981 (magna cum laude, Order of the Coif); BA, Dartmouth College, 1978 (summa cum laude).

### PATTERSON, Stephen J
Nutter McClennen & Fish LLP, Boston
617 439 2827
spatterson@nutter.com
*Featured in Banking & Finance (Massachusetts)*
**Practice Areas:** Stephen Patterson is a partner in the Business Department. His practice focuses on commercial finance and he represents major financial institutions and companies in complex, multi-party financings, agented credit facilities, and capital formation transactions, with a significant emphasis on equipment lease syndication and origination transactions, asset-based/commercial lending, and tax credit and mortgage warehouse facilities.

### PEARLSTEIN, Andrew M
Seyfarth Shaw LLP, Boston
617 946 4965
apearlstein@seyfarth.com
*Featured in Real Estate (Massachusetts)*
**Practice Areas:** Real Estate, Real Estate Finance, Real Estate Restructuring and Loan Workouts
**Career:** Andrew Pearlstein concentrates his practice in the representation of banks, financial institutions, investment managers, funds, developers, and real estate owners in complex commercial real estate transactions, including financings, acquisitions, dispositions and leasing matters, involving multi-family, hotel, shopping center, retail, office and industrial properties. Andrew is well known for his capital markets expertise and represents financial institutions, special servicers and others in the restructuring, workout, and foreclosure of real estate loans.
**Personal:** JD, Temple University Law School; BA, University of Pennsylvania (Magna Cum Laude, Phi Beta Kappa).

### PEARLSTEIN, Mark W
McDermott Will & Emery LLP, Boston
617 535 4425
mpearlstein@mwe.com
*Featured in Litigation (Massachusetts)*
**Practice Areas:** Concentrates on white-collar criminal defense, the defense of actions brought by the SEC, complex commercial litigation, arbitration and internal investigations. Experience in corporate criminal investigations.
**Career:** Served as Acting US Attorney responsible for negotiating what was then the largest resolution of a healthcare fraud case. Litigated a range of civil and criminal matters and tried a number

of complex white-collar crime cases. Received the Attorney General's Award for Exceptional Service, the highest award presented by the Department of Justice.
**Personal:** University of Michigan (AB, Phi Beta Kappa), Harvard Law School (JD, cum laude).

### PECK, Steven
Weil, Gotshal & Manges LLP, Boston
617 772 8344
steven.peck@weil.com
*Featured in Private Equity (Massachusetts)*
**Practice Areas:** Mr Peck's practice is focused on private equity execution and administration matters and corporate mergers and acquisitions. He represents various parties - acquirors, target companies and management teams - primarily in middle market and large cap transactions. He regularly represents the firm's private equity clients and their portfolio companies in these transactions, which involve both public and private target companies.
**Personal:** Duke University (BA, cum laude, 1984); Boston University School of Law (JD, cum laude, 1987).

### PHILLIPS, Susan P
Mintz Levin Cohn Ferris Glovsky and Popeo PC, Boston
617 348 1713
SPhillips@mintz.com
*Featured in Environment (Massachusetts)*
**Practice Areas:** Susan's practice involves the full range of federal, state, and local environmental and land use regulations. She focuses on evaluating and allocating environmental risks in connection with real estate and corporate transactions, and advising national retail chains on acquisition, development and financing of Brownfields nationwide.
**Professional Memberships:** Board of Directors, Elizabeth Stone House; member of ICSC and various environmental organizations.
**Career:** Involved in ASTM environmental standard-setting: co-chaired Drafting Committee, member of Legal Committee for Vapor Intrusion Standard; member of Phase I Task Group.
**Publications:** Frequent author/commentator in industry publications.
**Personal:** BA, Cornell University; JD, University of Chicago.

### PICKETT, Andrew
Jackson Lewis LLP, Boston
617 367 0025
PickettA@jacksonlewis.com
*Featured in Labor & Employment (Massachusetts)*
**Practice Areas:** Managing Partner, Boston. Employment litigation, including discrimination, "pattern and practice" class actions , RIF's, ADA and FMLA leaves, non-competes, ERISA litigation.
**Professional Memberships:** Boston, Massachusetts, Vermont, American Bar Associations. Co-Chair, Labor and Employment Law Section, Boston Bar Association, 2000-02.
**Career:** AV Rated. Voted Top 100 Attorneys in Massachusetts in 2010, 2011. Law Clerk, Hon. Albert W. Coffrin, USDC VT 1986-87; Ropes &

Gray, Boston, MA, 1987-96; Special Assistant District Attorney, Cambridge, MA, 1990-91.
**Publications:** Employment Law Guide, Co-Author. Boston Bar Association Press, 2007.
**Personal:** Cornell Law, JD, cum laude, 1986; Princeton University, AB, Magna cum laude, 1983.

### PIROZZOLO, Lisa J
WilmerHale, Boston
617 526 6388
lisa.pirozzolo@wilmerhale.com
*Featured in Intellectual Property (Massachusetts)*
**Practice Areas:** Partner in Litigation/Controversy Department; Co-Chair of the firm's Intellectual Property Litigation Practice, and member of the Appellate and Supreme Court Litigation Practice Group.
**Career:** Joined the firm in 1993 and has represented clients in patent infringement, licensing, and contract disputes involving a wide variety of technologies, including medical devices and pharmaceutical products. Experience handling all phases of litigation, as well as arbitration and mediation proceedings.
**Personal:** JD, cum laude, Cornell University Law School; BA, Classics, Yale University.

### PITCHER, Edmund R
Goodwin Procter LLP, Boston
617 570 1780
epitcher@goodwinprocter.com
*Featured in Intellectual Property (Massachusetts)*
**Practice Areas:** Mr Pitcher has over 30 years of experience in intellectual property law as counsel to companies exploiting biological, pharmaceutical, chemical, and medical technologies, and to their private and public investors. He has advised operating companies, venture capital limited partnerships, and securities analysts on intellectual property matters, risks, and strategies. Mr Pitcher has been involved with domestic and foreign patent portfolio development, technology transfers, patent enforcement litigation, patent defense litigation, IP diligence, freedom to operate risk assessments, patentability assessments and IP valuations.
**Personal:** JD, Suffolk University Law School, 1974 (magna cum laude); AB, Chemistry and Biology, Hamilton College, 1968.

### PITTARO, Frederick
Mintz Levin Cohn Ferris Glovsky and Popeo PC, Boston
617 348 1714
FJPittaro@mintz.com
*Featured in Real Estate (Massachusetts)*
**Practice Areas:** Fred chairs Mintz Levin's Real Estate Section. He has served as lead attorney in some of the most significant developments in the Boston area and represents developers and investors in all aspects of real estate development as well as acquisition and sale of operating properties including joint ventures and sophisticated multi-party financing transactions. Notable projects: the ongoing 14-acre Revitalization Plan for the Christian Science Plaza, Battery Wharf, Exchange Place, Devonshire Towers, 400,000 s.f. intermodal cargo facility on the Boston waterfront and Cloverleaf Apartments in Natick.

**Personal:** BS with honors, Providence College. JD, Georgetown University.

### PONDA, Ameek Ashok
Sullivan & Worcester LLP, Boston
617 338 2443
aponda@sandw.com
*Featured in Capital Markets (Nationwide), Tax (Massachusetts)*
**Practice Areas:** Ameek Ashok Ponda is director of S&W's Tax Department and on the firm's Management Committee. He concentrates his practice in structuring corporate mergers and acquisitions, advising emerging companies on financing and business issues, designing REIT transactions and financial instruments and working on cross-border financings and acquisitions.
**Professional Memberships:** American Law Institute; American, Massachusetts, and Boston Bar Associations; National Association of Real Estate Investment Trusts; International Fiscal Association; National Tax Association; Lecturer on Law, Harvard Law School.
**Personal:** LLM, Taxation, valedictorian, Boston University School of Law; JD, magna cum laude, Harvard Law School; BA, summa cum laude, Harvard College.

### POPEO, R Robert
Mintz Levin Cohn Ferris Glovsky and Popeo PC, Boston
617 348 1716
RRPopeo@mintz.com
*Featured in Litigation (Massachusetts)*
**Practice Areas:** Bob is Chairman and President of Mintz Levin, and practices in the firm's Litigation Section. He is nationally recognized as a leading trial attorney, and represents major corporations and their CEOs, as well as well-known political and media figures, throughout the country.
**Professional Memberships:** President, New England Chapter of the National Association of Corporate Directors; Member, American, Massachusetts, DC and Boston Bar Associations and Practising Law Institute. Fellow, American College of Trial Lawyers. Former Chair, Boston Bar Association task force convened to reform the Massachusetts court system.
**Career:** Bob's distinguished career in the public and private sector spans four decades. After serving as a law clerk to a federal judge, he became a Special Assistant Attorney General and was appointed as a United States Commissioner (later known as United States Magistrate Judge). He has also served as an instructor at Boston University Law School and a guest lecturer at other law schools. Bob has been named a Best Lawyers in America annually since 1987, and a Best Lawyers' Lawyer of the Year for Criminal Defense: White Collar in 2011.
**Personal:** Board Member, National Conference of Christians and Jews, Massachusetts Mental Health Research Corporation, Catholic Charitable Bureau, Glover Memorial Hospital, American Cancer Society and United Way of Massachusetts Bay. Member, Board of Overseers, Northeastern University; Board of Advisors, Birmingham

Business School; Trustee, Boston College; and former Trustee, Newton Country Day School. Member, Executive Committee, Massachusetts Business Round Table. AB, Northeastern University. JD, Boston College Law School.

**PORTER, Jeffrey R**
Mintz Levin Cohn Ferris Glovsky and Popeo PC, Boston
617 348 1711
JPorter@mintz.com
*Featured in Environment (Massachusetts)*
**Practice Areas:** Jeff leads Mintz Levin's Environmental Section. With 25 years of experience, he advises clients on complex environmental litigation and permitting matters including Superfund, air/water discharges, treatment, storage and disposal of hazardous waste, and Brownfield redevelopment.
**Professional Memberships:** Board Member and Former Chair, Massachusetts Board of Trustees, The Nature Conservancy; board member and former Vice-Chair, Boston Harbor Island Alliance; NAIOP; ABA; BBA.
**Career:** MADEP Bureau of Waste Site Clean Up Advisory Committee; advised Massachusetts Legislature drafting landmark Brownfield legislation.
**Publications:** Author/commentator in The Wall Street Journal, Law360 and other publications.
**Personal:** BA, Bates College, cum laude; JD, Cornell University.

**POSS, Stephen D**
Goodwin Procter LLP, Boston
617 570 1886
sposs@goodwinprocter.com
*Featured in Litigation (Massachusetts)*
**Practice Areas:** Mr Poss has a national business litigation and corporate counseling practice, focusing on securities class action defense, SEC investigations and enforcement actions, SEC disclosure issues, corporate governance, internal investigations, complex business litigation and arbitration, mergers and acquisitions, private equity and venture capital disputes, post-closing disputes, and contests for corporate control. Client work includes defending securities class action suits, SEC Enforcement and stock exchange investigations, conducting internal investigations and special committee work, and complex business litigation and arbitrations.
**Personal:** JD, University of Chicago Law School, 1981; BA, Amherst College, 1978 (magna cum laude).

**RAGALEVSKY, Stanley V**
K&L Gates, Boston
617 951 9203
stan.ragalevsky@klgates.com
*Featured in Banking & Finance (Massachusetts)*
**Practice Areas:** A partner in K&L Gates' Boston office, Stanley Ragalevsky represents financial institutions in business and regulatory matters including mergers and acquisitions, compliance, charterings, capital formation and assistance, compensation, enforcement actions, examinations, risk management, succession, and governance issues. A frequent lecturer to financial serv-

ice industry organizations, Mr Ragalevsky often writes on financial services issues affecting the banks and credit unions.

**RATTIGAN JR, John**
DLA Piper LLP (US), Boston
617 406 6057
john.rattigan@dlapiper.com
*Featured in Real Estate (Massachusetts)*
**Practice Areas:** Real estate, real estate finance, landlord leasing, land use and development.
**Career:** He is counsel to developers and investors in the acquisition, development, sale, and leasing of large-scale real estate projects. He has extensive experience in development of facilities in airports, most recently the new Terminal A in Boston's Logan Airport and major fueling systems at Logan and in Oakland, California. He has represented banks and investors in a wide variety of real estate loans, acquisitions, and investments.
**Personal:** JD, University of Virginia School of Law; AB, Merrimack College (summa cum laude).

**REDLICK, David E**
WilmerHale, Boston
617 526 6434
david.redlick@wilmerhale.com
*Featured in Life Sciences (Nationwide),*
*Corporate/M&A (Massachusetts)*
See under Nationwide for profile.

**REGIER, John**
Mintz Levin Cohn Ferris Glovsky and Popeo PC, Boston
617 348 1720
JRRegier@mintz.com
*Featured in Banking & Finance (Massachusetts)*
**Practice Areas:** John's practice focuses on public finance and public agency representation, particularly regarding the legislative process and the Massachusetts Constitution. Since 1984, he has been principally responsible for all legal services rendered by the firm to the State Treasurer of Massachusetts, including service as bond counsel and disclosure counsel. He's acted as bond counsel or underwriter's counsel in a variety of tax-exempt bond transactions, including financings for public higher education, transportation, public schools, and water treatment.
**Professional Memberships:** Member, American, Massachusetts, and Boston Bar Associations; Member, National Association of Bond Lawyers.
**Personal:** BA, University of Kansas; JD, Yale University.

**REHNQUIST, James C**
Goodwin Procter LLP, Boston
617 570 1820
jrehnquist@goodwinprocter.com
*Featured in Litigation (Massachusetts)*
**Practice Areas:** Mr Rehnquist is a former federal prosecutor who specializes in white-collar criminal defense, including the representation of clients in SEC and other governmental and regulatory investigations. He has represented corporations and individuals in securities fraud, healthcare fraud, public corruption and money laundering prosecutions and investigations. Mr Rehnquist has also represented various businesses in a wide

variety of civil cases, including patent, antitrust, trade secrets, fraud, corporate governance and contracts matters. He has a substantial criminal and civil appellate practice, in both state and federal courts.
**Personal:** JD, Boston University School of Law, 1987; BA, Amherst College, 1977.

**RICHMOND, Stephen M**
Beveridge & Diamond PC, Wellesley
781 416 5710
srichmond@bdlaw.com
*Featured in Environment (Massachusetts)*
**Practice Areas:** Environmental practice focuses on complex regulatory, permitting and transactional matters involving air, waste, hazardous substance and climate change issues under the federal Clean Air Act, Resource Conservation and Recovery Act, Clean Water Act, Comprehensive Environmental Response, Compensation and Liability Act, Emergency Planning and Community Right-to-Know Act, and analogous state laws. Extensive experience in the drafting and negotiation of environmental provisions in transactional documents. Mr Richmond's clients include companies in the chemicals, hazardous waste, solid waste, recycling, refining, pipeline, power generation, manufacturing and biotech industries. He also represents trade associations and coalitions on environmental regulatory and policy matters.

**RICOTTA, Paul J**
Mintz Levin Cohn Ferris Glovsky and Popeo PC, Boston
617 348 1752
PJRicotta@mintz.com
*Featured in Bankruptcy/Restructuring (Massachusetts)*
**Practice Areas:** Commercial bankruptcy and workouts, federal and state commercial litigation, banking law, commercial debt financing. Paul is also a Uniform Commercial Code expert.
**Professional Memberships:** Fellow, American College of Bankruptcy; Board of Trustees, Massachusetts Continuing Legal Education Association (MCLE); Board of Directors, Association of Commercial Finance Attorneys.
**Career:** Advised Massachusetts Legislature regarding Uniform Commercial Code; Chairman, educational programs for Massachusetts Continuing Legal Education Association; General Counsel, M&T Bank.
**Publications:** Frequent author for American Bar Association; Massachusetts Continuing Legal Education Association; American Bankruptcy Institute; and Thomson-Reuters/Aspatore.
**Personal:** BS, Dartmouth College; JD/MBA, State University of New York.

**RITT, Roger M**
WilmerHale, Boston
617 526 6475
roger.ritt@wilmerhale.com
*Featured in Tax (Massachusetts)*
**Practice Areas:** Practice focuses on taxable and tax-free mergers and acquisitions, spin-offs, federal and state tax controversies, executive compensation and § 280G golden parachutes, and bank-

ruptcies and workouts. Successfully represented many clients at US Tax Court, IRS appeals, Supreme Judicial Court of Massachusetts, Massachusetts Appellate Tax Board and Massachusetts Department of Revenue.
**Professional Memberships:** Elected to the American College of Tax Counsel Board of Regents for the First Circuit. Former chair, Corporate Tax Committee, ABA's Section on Taxation. Fellow, ACTC.
**Career:** Admitted to Massachusetts Bar.
**Personal:** Boston University School of Law (JD, LLM); University of Pennsylvania (BA, with Honors).

**RIZZOTTI, Anthony D**
Littler Mendelson, PC, Boston
617 378 6000
arizzotti@littler.com
*Featured in Labor & Employment (Massachusetts)*
**Practice Areas:** Healthcare, Labor Management Relations, Discrimination and Harassment, Wage and Hour, Training.
**Professional Memberships:** Massachusetts Bar; New York Bar; Rhode Island Bar; Former Chair, Boston Bar Association's Labor and Employment Law Section.
**Career:** Represents a wide range of employers, including healthcare systems, hospitals, and life sciences companies in collective bargaining, negotiations, contract administration, labor arbitrations, union elections, non-compete and trade secret litigation, and wage and hour matters.
**Personal:** JD, Boston College Law School, cum laude, 1992; BA, Boston College, 1989.

**ROBINSON, Andrea J**
WilmerHale, Boston
617 526 6360
andrea.robinson@wilmerhale.com
*Featured in Litigation (Massachusetts)*
**Practice Areas:** Partner, Litigation/Controversy Department; Vice Chair, Securities Department. Focus: securities, financial services, and other commercial litigation, including SEC, FINRA and other regulatory enforcement matters. Experience handling derivative actions and class actions, numerous cases involving alleged accounting improprieties, insider trading, market manipulation and insurance, annuity and other sales practice misconduct. Regulatory practice includes alleged insider trading, accounting issues, revenue sharing, market timing, late trading, 12b-1 fees, failures to supervise and/or disclose, sales practice, suitability issues.
**Personal:** JD, University of Virginia School of Law, Virginia Law Review, Order of the Coif; AB, magna cum laude, Harvard University, Phi Beta Kappa.

**ROBINSON, Graham**
Skadden, Arps, Slate, Meagher & Flom LLP & Affiliates, Boston
617 573 4850
graham.robinson@skadden.com
*Featured in Corporate/M&A (Massachusetts)*
**Practice Areas:** Graham Robinson focuses his practice on mergers, acquisitions and other transactions in the pharmaceutical, medical device and

technology industries in the US and internationally. He also regularly represents both private equity funds and hedge funds on a wide range of matters.

**Professional Memberships:** Member of the American Bar Association.

**Personal:** JD, Harvard Law School, 1999; BA, American History, University of Pennsylvania, 1996.

## ROBINSON, Mark E
Bingham McCutchen LLP, Boston
617 951 8018
mark.robinson@bingham.com
*Featured in Litigation (Massachusetts)*

**Practice Areas:** Co-chair of Bingham's White Collar Investigations and Enforcement Group. Represents many high-profile clients both in federal and state court in connection with regulatory enforcement, commercial litigation, white collar defense and crisis management matters. Background is a combination of senior legal, government and private sector business experience. Has helped some of the leading public and private companies in the world design state of the art compliance and best practices regimes in different markets.

**Personal:** Boston University School of Law, Juris Doctor, Law Review Editor, 1979; Duke University, Bachelor of Arts, Magna Cum Laude, 1976.

## ROCKEFELLER, Regina S
Nixon Peabody LLP, Boston
617 345 6182
rrockefeller@nixonpeabody.com
*Featured in Healthcare (Massachusetts)*

**Practice Areas:** Regina Rockefeller, a partner in the Health Services group, focuses her law practice on the representation of health care providers, and charitable and for-profit organizations in the health care and educational fields. Regina represents and advises hospitals, physicians, group medical practices, accountable care organizations, captive insurers, faculty medical practice plans, continuing care retirement communities and other health care providers. She advises health care providers on cost-effective compliance with HIPAA, HITECH and state data breach laws. Regina defends health care professionals before state licensing boards.

**Personal:** Boston College Law School, JD, cum laude; Tufts University, BA, magna cum laude

## RODGERS, Dave
Edwards Wildman Palmer, Providence
617 239 0362
drodgers@edwardswildman.com
*Featured in Real Estate (Massachusetts)*

**Practice Areas:** David Rodgers concentrates his practice on design, construction and procurement for commercial, institutional and public sector development. His practice also includes zoning and land use, leasing and general commercial real estate matters.

**Professional Memberships:** American Bar Association, Construction Industry Forum and Public Contract Law Section.

**Personal:** New York University School of Law, JD; University of Wisconsin-Madison, BA, cum laude.

## RODRIQUES, Louis A
Bingham McCutchen LLP, Boston
617 951 8340
louis.rodriques@bingham.com
*Featured in Labor & Employment (Massachusetts)*

**Practice Areas:** Co-chair of Bingham's Labor and Employment Practice Group. Practice involves counseling on human resource matters; the development and administration of personnel and human resource policies and employee benefit plans; compliance with statutory and regulatory requirements; development and implementation of affirmative action plans; conducting internal harassment and other investigations; drafting and enforcing non-competition and confidentiality agreements, employment agreements, and executive contracts and compensation plans; developing litigation-avoidance strategies; harassment, diversity and performance management training; and advising on government audits, labor-management relations, mediation and arbitration.

**Personal:** Yale Law School, JD, 1978; Yale University, BA, 1975.

## ROSEN, Michael
Foley Hoag LLP, Boston
617 832 1231
mrosen@foleyhoag.com
*Featured in Labor & Employment (Massachusetts)*

**Practice Areas:** Michael Rosen represents employers in a wide-range of litigation matters, including wage/hour actions, discrimination and retaliation claims, and executive departure disputes. He has expertise enforcing and defending against non-competition, non-solicitation and non-disclosure agreements, as well as unfair competition, theft of trade secrets and breach of fiduciary duty. He counsels on a variety of workplace matters, including harassment investigations, leave-of-absence and accommodation issues, government investigations, workplace privacy, among others. He is a frequent speaker and writer on labor and employment law topics.

**Personal:** New York University School of Law, JD, cum laude; University of Miami, BA, magna cum laude.

## ROSENBLATT, Philip R
Nutter McClennen & Fish LLP, Boston
617 439 2806
prosenblatt@nutter.com
*Featured in Banking & Finance (Massachusetts)*

**Practice Areas:** Philip Rosenblatt is chair of, and a partner in, the firm's Business Department and co-chair of the firm's Commercial Finance practice group. He has extensive experience in complex finance, syndication and securitization transactions. He represents major lending institutions and companies in complex, multi-party financings, agented/syndicated credit facilities and capital formation transactions. This area of his practice has a significant emphasis on equipment finance syndications, as well as on mortgage warehouse and investor bridge lines, asset-based/commercial lending, venture capital and leveraged loans.

## ROSENBLUM, Howard S
DLA Piper LLP (US), Boston
617 406 6050
howard.rosenblum@dlapiper.com
*Featured in Private Equity (Massachusetts)*

**Practice Areas:** Corporate, investment funds.

**Career:** He concentrates in the areas of formation of and investments by domestic and international private equity funds, and provides general representation to emerging growth enterprises. His private equity experience includes advising fund managers on a broad range of issues. He counsels companies in all aspects of their operations from start-up through public offerings and/or acquisitions. He has advised companies across a diverse range of businesses. He has significant involvement with the representation of Israeli and Israel-related companies and venture capital funds.

**Personal:** JD, Boston College Law School; BA, University of Pennsylvania.

## ROSENBLUM, Peter
Foley Hoag LLP, Boston
617 832 1151
pmr@foleyhoag.com
*Featured in Corporate/M&A (Massachusetts), Private Equity (Massachusetts)*

**Practice Areas:** Peter Rosenblum Co-Chairs the Mergers & Acquisitions and Investment Advisors/Funds practice groups. He represents public/private clients in technology, energy, life sciences and investment management industries and advises investors/issuers in connection with private placements of equity and debt for early and later-stage private equity investments. Peter has structured buyouts, recapitalizations, joint ventures and strategic alliances involving complex applications of debt and equity securities. He has expertise in developing transaction-specific off-shore and cross-border structures, LLCs and other passthrough vehicles. He counsels leadership in significant transactions.

**Personal:** Harvard University, JD, cum laude; Yale University, MA; Amherst College, BA, summa cum laude.

## ROSENFELD, Jonathan
WilmerHale, Boston
617 526 6941
jonathan.rosenfeld@wilmerhale.com
*Featured in Labor & Employment (Massachusetts)*

**Practice Areas:** As Chair of WilmerHale's Labor and Employment Practice Group, Mr Rosenfeld has extensive experience in representing employers in all aspects of labor and employment law. He has litigated cases of discrimination, wrongful discharge, non-competes, employee benefit claims and other matters in state and federal court. He also trains employers on performance management and employment law compliance.

**Professional Memberships:** Admitted to Massachusetts, Connecticut and California bars and federal court of Massachusetts, Connecticut and N.D. of California, and US Court of Appeals for the First and Ninth Circuits.

**Personal:** Boston University School of Law (JD); Brandeis University, (AB, cum laude).

## ROSENTHAL, David S
Nixon Peabody LLP, Boston
617 345 6183
drosenthal@nixonpeabody.com
*Featured in Labor & Employment (Massachusetts)*

**Practice Areas:** David Rosenthal's practice focuses on the representation of employers in employment litigation matters, such as breach of contract, wrongful termination, enforcement of noncompetition provisions, discrimination litigation, and defense of wage-hour and other employment-related class actions, in state and federal courts in Massachusetts and nationally, and before the Massachusetts Commission Against Discrimination and the Equal Employment Opportunity Commission. David also counsels employers in a variety of non-litigation matters, including policy creation and enforcement, statutory compliance, and a variety of other human resources decisions.

**Personal:** Georgetown University Law Center, JD, 1976; Trinity College, BA, cum laude (Phi Beta Kappa), 1972.

## ROTHERMEL, Sarah
WilmerHale, Boston
617 526 6512
sarah.rothermel@wilmerhale.com
*Featured in Investment Funds (Nationwide), Private Equity (Massachusetts)*

**Practice Areas:** Partner-in-Charge of WilmerHale's Boston Office and member of the Fund Formation Practice Group. Advises fund clients on all aspects of organization, management, operation and regulatory compliance. Represents principally private investment entities, including venture capital funds. Also represents LLCs, partnerships, joint ventures and closely-held non-corporate businesses engaged in all types of business activities.

**Professional Memberships:** American Bar Association; Massachusetts Bar Association; Boston Bar Association; Private Equity CFO Organization (Advisory Board Member).

**Career:** Admitted to Massachusetts Bar. Joined the firm in 1981.

**Personal:** Boston University School of Law (JD, magna cum laude); Wellesley College (BA).

## RUDMAN, Jeffrey
WilmerHale, Boston
617 526 6912
jeffrey.rudman@wilmerhale.com
*Featured in Securities (Nationwide), Litigation (Massachusetts)*

**Practice Areas:** Nationally recognized authority on defending shareholder class, derivative actions and the related tasks of defending SEC investigations and pursuing directors' and officers' insurance coverage. Formerly Co-Chair of the Securities Litigation and Enforcement Group.

**Professional Memberships:** Chairman of the Board of Trustees, Boston Public Library; appointed Trustee of the Museum of Fine Arts; served on charitable boards, including Board of Directors of the Association of American Rhodes

Scholars; Boston Public Library Foundation; and WGBH Community Advisory Board.
**Career:** Admitted to Massachusetts Bar. Joined firm in 1975.
**Personal:** Harvard Law School (JD); Oxford University (BA, Rhodes Scholar); Columbia College (AB).

### RUDMAN, Richard D
DLA Piper LLP (US), Boston
617 406 6027
richard.rudman@dlapiper.com
*Featured in Real Estate (Massachusetts)*
**Practice Areas:** Real estate.
**Career:** He focuses on real estate development and finance, property acquisition, leasing, land use and environmental regulation, joint venture arrangements, construction loans, and construction and design agreements. He has been the lead lawyer on major development projects, including downtown office towers, suburban office parks, urban and suburban multi-family residential projects, hotels, and medical research/laboratory buildings. He has extensive experience in build-to-suit developments and projects with complicated phasing arrangements, environmentally contaminated sites, contentious permitting issues, and public/private development agreements.
**Personal:** JD, Harvard University (cum laude); BA, Yale College (summa cum laude with distinction in History and Economics).

### RUEDIGER, David L
Edwards Wildman Palmer LLP, Boston
617 239 0266
druediger@edwardswildman.com
*Featured in Banking & Finance (Massachusetts)*
**Practice Areas:** A Co-Chair of the firm's Business Law Department, David represents banks, finance companies, public and private investment funds, equity sponsors and other investors in syndicated lending transactions, mergers and acquisitions, private equity and debt financings, distressed debt investments, restructurings, workouts, and bankruptcies.
**Professional Memberships:** Association for Corporate Growth Boston Chapter, Boston Bar Association.
**Personal:** Boston College Law School, JD, cum laude; University of New Hampshire, BS.

### RYAN, Mary K
Nutter McClennen & Fish LLP, Boston
617 439 2212
mryan@nutter.com
*Featured in Environment (Massachusetts)*
**Practice Areas:** Mary Ryan is a partner in the Litigation Department and a member of the Environmental Law practice group. Her practice includes substantial trial and appellate cases in state and federal courts, particularly in environmental litigation, as well as administrative hearings and proceedings. Mary has significant expertise in federal and state hazardous waste litigation, including CERCLA and Ch. 21E (federal and state Superfund) cases and related insurance coverage matters, as well as various land use issues. Mary has held leadership roles in many bar and civic

associations, and is a fellow of the American College of Environmental Lawyers.

### SABLONE, Jonathan
Nixon Peabody LLP, Boston
617 345 1342
jsablone@nixonpeabody.com
*Featured in Litigation (Massachusetts)*
**Practice Areas:** Jonathan Sablone founded and chairs Nixon Peabody's Private Funds Dispute Group. He represents a broad array of clients in the alternative investment space including hedge, private equity, venture, tax credit and real estate funds, as well as institutional limited partner investors, trustees and liquidators both onshore and offshore in the Cayman Islands and British Virgin Islands. In addition to Jonathan's private funds practice, he maintains an active complex commercial trial practice which includes his role as founder and chair of Nixon Peabody's Electronic Discovery and Digital Evidence Team.
**Personal:** Boston College Law School, JD; Harvard College, AB.

### SANDFORD, H Neal
Goodwin Procter LLP, Boston
617 570 1632
nsandford@goodwinprocter.com
*Featured in Capital Markets (Nationwide), Tax (Massachusetts)*
**Practice Areas:** Mr Sandford specializes in structuring tax-sensitive commercial transactions. His practice includes the organization and operation of REITs, investment funds and other collective investment arrangements; corporate mergers and acquisitions; asset acquisitions and dispositions; the organization and operation of partnerships and joint ventures; transactions involving S corporations; investments by tax-exempt and foreign investors; corporate and partnership restructurings; real estate transactions; equity-based compensation arrangements; international tax issues; and workouts.
**Professional Memberships:** Mr Sandford is a Member of the Boston and American Bar Associations.
**Personal:** JD, University of Virginia School of Law, 1987; BA, Yale University, 1983 (magna cum laude).

### SANDOMIRSKY, Gregory A.
Mintz Levin Cohn Ferris Glovsky and Popeo PC, Boston
617 348 1730
GASandomirsk@mintz.com
*Featured in Banking & Finance (Massachusetts)*
**Practice Areas:** Greg has had extensive experience with debt financing, new enterprise formation, and governmental and corporate reorganization. He provides bond counsel and general advice to major public and private institutions involved in transportation, energy, water and sewer service, housing, health care, education, resource recovery, economic development, and lending. He has substantial experience with project finance in US markets and with private/public joint ventures and cooperations in areas such as solid waste disposal, wastewater and water treatment, energy

generation, health care, subsidized housing, transportation, and parking.
**Personal:** BS, Harvard University; JD, University of Pennsylvania.

### SANOFF, Robert
Foley Hoag LLP, Boston
617 832 1152
rsanoff@foleyhoag.com
*Featured in Environment (Massachusetts)*
**Practice Areas:** Robert Sanoff is a partner in the Environmental and Insurance groups and the immediate past Managing Partner. He focuses on insurance, complex commercial disputes, land use, and environmental litigation as well as alternative dispute resolution. He has served as lead trial counsel, common counsel, and mediator in high-stakes cases around the country. He has worked on more than 50 separate federal and state Superfund matters and handled insurance recovery claims on behalf of policyholders. He is a frequent speaker at conferences on environmental law.
**Personal:** University of Pennsylvania Law School, JD; University of Virginia, PhD; Hamilton College, BA.

### SANTUCCI, Ettore A
Goodwin Procter LLP, Boston
617 570 1531
esantucci@goodwinprocter.com
*Featured in Capital Markets (Nationwide), Corporate/M&A (Massachusetts)*
See under Nationwide for profile.

### SAVAGE, Christine G
Choate Hall & Stewart LLP, Boston
617 248 4084
csavage@choate.com
*Featured in Healthcare (Massachusetts)*
**Practice Areas:** Ms Savage represents healthcare organizations, handling complex regulatory problems and developing practical business solutions. She defends False Claims Act and off-label marketing cases, and advises PE/VC firms on applying industry and regulatory requirements to proposed ventures with healthcare companies. Engagements include: represented pharmaceutical companies/employees in healthcare fraud investigations; represented hospital in first-in-nation settlement under new Stark law self-disclosure protocol; managed federal/state disclosures and dispute resolutions following hospital data loss; advised universities and medical centers in connection with research misconduct allegations.
**Personal:** JD cum laude Harvard Law School (1995); BA cum laude University of Massachusetts at Amherst (1992).

### SAVAGE, Joseph F
Goodwin Procter LLP, Boston
617 570 1204
jsavage@goodwinprocter.com
*Featured in Litigation (Massachusetts)*
**Practice Areas:** Mr Savage concentrates his practice on complex civil litigation, white-collar criminal defense and governmental investigations. His practice involves representing individuals and companies in a variety of fraud, tax, public corruption, healthcare, securities, environmental and

other investigations by federal, state and local law enforcement and government regulators. He has handled sophisticated trade secret, Lanham Act, RICO, consumer fraud and other civil litigation, including multi-district class action litigation, and has experience in litigating complex white-collar criminal matters.
**Personal:** JD, University of Virginia School of Law, 1981 (Order of the Coif); BA, Harvard College, 1978 (magna cum laude).

### SAVRIN, Daniel S
Bingham McCutchen LLP, Boston
617 951 8674
daniel.savrin@bingham.com
*Featured in Antitrust (Massachusetts)*
**Practice Areas:** Focuses on a wide range of antitrust, white collar defense and complex commercial litigation matters. Leading litigator and counselor in handling and trying civil and criminal matters. Litigates and resolves disputes with governmental agencies and among private parties. Practice includes the representation of individuals and corporations in criminal antitrust matters; civil enforcement matters; individual and class action civil litigation; merger-related proceedings and litigation; and counseling on trade regulation, distribution, and merger and acquisition issues.
**Career:** Frequent speaker and author on antitrust subjects.
**Personal:** University of Virginia School of Law, JD, 1989; Union College, BA, 1984.

### SCHNALL, Matthew D
Bingham McCutchen LLP, Boston
617 951 8419
m.schnall@bingham.com
*Featured in Tax (Massachusetts)*
**Practice Areas:** Represents clients in tax controversies, transactional planning, administrative practice and tax regulatory compliance. Extensive experience with corporate and partnership tax issues, international taxation, and state and local taxation. Transactional work includes merger and acquisition transactions, financings, fund formations, liquidations, and workouts. Handles controversies involving federal income; employment and estate taxes and state income; corporate, sales and use, and property taxes; and constitutional issues. Practices before various state trial and appellate tribunals. Speaks frequently on topics in federal, state and international taxation.
**Personal:** Harvard Law School, JD, cum laude, 1993; Harvard College, BA, magna cum laude, 1990.

### SCHNOOR, William J
Goodwin Procter LLP, Boston
617 570 1020
wschnoor@goodwinprocter.com
*Featured in Corporate/M&A (Massachusetts), Private Equity (Massachusetts)*
**Practice Areas:** Mr Schnoor, co-chair of the firm's Technology Companies Group and one of the leaders of Goodwin Procter's interdisciplinary practice focusing on investments in alternative energy and clean technologies, concentrates in the areas of business and securities law, private equity and acquisitions. He represents start-ups and

other private and public companies in a wide range of industries and has worked with numerous companies from their initial financing through initial public offerings or acquisitions, and has advised numerous public companies and their boards of directors.

**Personal:** JD, Yale Law School, 1983; BA, Yale University, 1980 (summa cum laude).

### SCHROEDER, Donald W
Mintz Levin Cohn Ferris Glovsky and Popeo PC, Boston
617 348 3077
dschroeder@mintz.com
*Featured in Labor & Employment (Massachusetts)*

**Practice Areas:** Don is a member in the firm's Employment, Labor and Benefits Section. He has extensive trial experience in state and federal courts representing Fortune 500 clients on a wide range of employment matters, including restrictive covenant litigation, wage and hour class actions and single plaintiff discrimination cases. In addition, Don regularly handles traditional labor matters (management-side) for clients including but not limited to union avoidance training, unfair labor practice proceedings, union elections, mass picketing and 10(j) injunction proceedings, labor arbitrations and collective bargaining negotiations.

**Personal:** BA, College of the Holy Cross; JD, Catholic University.

### SCHWARTZ, Andrew
Foley Hoag LLP, Boston
617 832 1155
aschwartz@foleyhoag.com
*Featured in Bankruptcy/Restructuring (Massachusetts)*

**Practice Areas:** Andrew Schwartz is a Partner and member of the firm's Executive Committee whose practice lies at the intersection of litigation and bankruptcy law. He concentrates his practice on complex commercial and financial matters, often but not exclusively involving insolvency issues. In litigation matters, his clients span many industries, and include foreign governments. He has extensive experience representing debtors, committees, secured and unsecured creditors, buyers, investors and other constituencies in bankruptcy cases. Mr Schwartz has tried business cases in courts across the country.

**Personal:** Boston University School of Law, JD, magna cum laude; Brown University, AB.

### SCHWARTZ, Paul D
Goodwin Procter LLP, Boston
617 570 1422
pschwartz@goodwinprocter.com
*Featured in Real Estate (Massachusetts)*

**Practice Areas:** Mr Schwartz concentrates on private market finance with emphasis on real estate, including collective investment vehicles for institutional investors, joint ventures, participating and mezzanine debt, and REIT investments. He is familiar with integrating the UBTI, REIT and other tax, ERISA, Investment Company Act, and other securities law aspects of investments by ERISA plans and registered investment companies.

**Professional Memberships:** Pension Real Estate Association: Voting Member; National Advisory Committee of the Union of Concerned Scientists: Member.

**Personal:** JD, Harvard Law School, 1978 (magna cum laude); Masters in Architecture, MIT, 1976; BA, Connecticut College, 1973 (magna cum laude).

### SCHWARTZ, Sara Goldsmith
Schwartz Hannum PC, Andover
978 623 0900
schwartz@shpclaw.com
*Featured in Labor & Employment (Massachusetts)*

**Practice Areas:** Labor And Employment Lawyers Guiding Management. Counseling. Litigation. Labor Relations. Training. Immigration. Education. Compliance. For over 15 years, Schwartz Hannum has been an invaluable ally to organizations looking to effect positive employee relations and resolve disputes. A management-side labor and employment law firm that works with local and national businesses in industries ranging from financial services to healthcare, the Firm also provides guidance and advocacy to educational and non-profit organizations. The Firm's practice is characterized by responsiveness, confidence, creativity and candor, and our services are delivered by seasoned professionals who have established the Firm as a leading provider of thoughtful, results-oriented legal counsel. Schwartz Hannum's growth and success reflects our long-standing commitment to help organizations address employment-related challenges in a responsible, proactive manner.

**Professional Memberships:** American Bar Association, American Employment Law Council, Boston Bar Association, Commonwealth Institute, Massachusetts Bar Association, National Association of Independent Schools, National Business Officers Association, Society of Human Resources Management.

**Career:** Firm founder (1995), President, Managing Partner. Began career with Ropes & Gray.

**Publications:** Frequent speaker at seminars for attorneys, HR professionals and educational leaders. Selected as Massachusetts Super Lawyer for six (6) consecutive years.

**Personal:** Cum laude graduate of Yale College and Harvard Law School.

### SCOTT, Thane D
Bingham McCutchen LLP, Boston
617 951 8040
thane.scott@bingham.com
*Featured in Antitrust (Massachusetts)*

**Practice Areas:** Concentrates on matters involving antitrust and trade regulation. Has more than 30 years of experience counseling industry leaders and litigating prominent cases that define modern antitrust law. Has served as lead or liaison counsel in numerous multidistrict, complex and class action cases. Defends business and consumer class actions involving antitrust and business tort claims, including class certification issues, and has successfully concluded well over 100 government investigations of mergers and other coordinated

conduct involving national and international companies.

**Personal:** Boston College Law School, JD, cum laude, 1980; State University of New York/Albany, BA, summa cum laude, 1974.

### SHAW, Paul W
K&L Gates, Boston
617 261 3111
paul.shaw@klgates.com
*Featured in Healthcare (Massachusetts)*

**Practice Areas:** A partner in K&L Gates' regulatory enforcement area, Paul Shaw has a national health care fraud and abuse practice, and has represented numerous health care clients involved in criminal fraud and abuse investigations and civil False Claims Act litigation throughout the United States. In addition, he has an active government investigations, civil litigation and white collar criminal defense practice, having successfully tried numerous cases in state and federal courts involving healthcare, securities and insurance fraud, product liability, and breach of contract claims.

### SHILEPSKY, Nancy S
Shilepsky Hartley Robb Casey Michon LLP, Boston
617 723 8000
nshilepsky@shilepsky.com
*Featured in Labor & Employment (Massachusetts)*

**Practice Areas:** Executive and professional advocacy, employment law, litigation.

**Professional Memberships:** Fellow, The College of Labor and Employment Lawyers; Co-founder, Amicus Group; Women's Leadership Initiative Task Force, WBA; MCAD Advisory Committee.

**Career:** Founding and Co-managing Partner, Shilepsky Hartley Robb Casey Michon LLP.

**Publications:** Co-author, Negotiating Executive Severance: Five Factors for a Better Package; Co-author, Representing a Plaintiff in a Wrongful Termination Case; Co-editor, Massachusetts Employment Law; Author, Avoiding the At Will Doctrine: Three Practical Strategies for Massachusetts Employees and Their Lawyers.

**Personal:** Boston University School of Law, JD (1978); Tufts University, BA, magna cum laude (1974).

### SHIRLEY, Thomas E
Choate Hall & Stewart LLP, Boston
617 248 5145
tshirley@choate.com
*Featured in Labor & Employment (Massachusetts)*

**Practice Areas:** Mr Shirley represents clients in all aspects of employment litigation, including non-compete and fiduciary duty claims, wage and hour claims, employment discrimination and sexual harassment, wrongful termination, defamation and ERISA. He counsels companies on the full range of applicable state and federal employment law issues as well as employment agreements, compensation and benefit matters. Recent matters include extensive noncompetition counseling and litigation engagements and the successful defense of clients in a variety of employment discrimination and wrongful termination matters.

**Personal:** JD University of Virginia School of Law (1980); BA highest distinction University of Virginia (1977).

### SIBBLE, Edward Matson
Goodwin Procter LLP, Boston
617 570 1480
esibble@goodwinprocter.com
*Featured in Banking & Finance (Massachusetts)*

**Practice Areas:** Mr Sibble, Chair of Goodwin Procter's Leveraged Finance Practice, specializes in financing transactions, representing major regional, national and international banks, as well as private equity sponsors, venture capital firms and their portfolio companies. Mr Sibble's practice includes tax-exempt financings, both as nationally recognized bond counsel and as counsel to underwriters and other participants in public offerings.

**Professional Memberships:** Mr Sibble is a member of the American College of Investment Counsel and the National Association of Bond Lawyers.

**Personal:** JD, Georgetown University Law Center, 1976; AB, Harvard University, 1973 (magna cum laude).

### SIEBERT, Susan E
Jones Day, Boston
617 449 6883
ssiebert@jonesday.com
*Featured in Banking & Finance (Massachusetts)*

**Practice Areas:** Involved in all aspects of commercial finance, including representation of banks, financial institutions, hedge funds, and public and private companies in senior and subordinated debt facilities, and creditors in workouts and restructurings. Extensive experience in leveraged finance and other syndicated, multibank senior credit facilities; asset-based and structured finance facilities; asset securitizations; sponsor acquisition financings; letter of credit facilities; cross border and foreign currency facilities; tender offer financings; and debtor-in-possession financings.

**Professional Memberships:** Commercial Finance Association (Syndicated ABL Committee), Loan Syndications and Trading Association, Turnaround Management Association.

**Personal:** Emory University Law School, JD; Wheaton College (IL), BA, high honors.

### SIGEL, John
WilmerHale, Boston
617 526 6728
john.sigel@wilmerhale.com
*Featured in Bankruptcy/Restructuring (Massachusetts)*

**Practice Areas:** Chair of WilmerHale's Bankruptcy and Financial Restructuring Practice Group. Commercial law focus, advising clients on secured and unsecured lending and debt issuance, Chapter 11 reorganizations and Uniform Commercial Code. Expert in matters relating to debt financings of public and private companies and acquisitions and sales of distressed companies. Represented clients in negotiating credit facilities with institutional lenders, including private placement of debt securities; advised corporate clients in connection with public offering of debt securities.

**Professional Memberships:** Massachusetts and Boston Bar Associations.

**Personal:** Cornell Law School (JD); Middlebury College (BA).

### SILMAN, Ruth
Nixon Peabody LLP, New York

*Featured in Environment (Massachusetts)*

**Practice Areas:** Ruth Silman concentrates her practice on complex environmental and land use matters. She leads Nixon Peabody's Climate Change Team, a group of lawyers and environmental scientists/engineers who are assisting the firm's energy, industrial, and financial clients to meet the challenges and seize the opportunities emerging from legislative, regulatory, and judicial responses to the issue of climate change. Ruth represents clients concerning the land use implications of complex real estate transactions, including zoning, environmental impacts, permitting, and compliance. Her extensive environmental experience includes addressing air quality, hazardous waste assessment and remediation, brownfields redevelopment, wetlands protection, and water quality issues.

### SIMARD, Kevin J
Choate Hall & Stewart LLP, Boston
617 248 4086
ksimard@choate.com

*Featured in Banking & Finance (Massachusetts)*

**Practice Areas:** Mr Simard has extensive experience in connection with all aspects of secured financing transactions, including structuring, documentation, intercreditor issues, work out and restructuring and bankruptcy. He regularly represents agents and lenders in connection with large syndicated loan transactions, club deals and single lender transactions. Mr Simard represents lenders with respect to revolving credit and term loan facilities, as well as unitranche transactions and other complex capital structures. He has particular experience in asset based transactions, especially in the retail finance industry.

**Personal:** JD cum laude Boston College Law School (1989); BA College of the Holy Cross (1986).

### SLOAN, David Scott
Holland & Knight LLP, Boston
617 573 5803
davidscott.sloan@hklaw.com

*Featured in Tax (Massachusetts)*

**Practice Areas:** Estate Planning, Business Succession Planning, Private Equity

**Professional Memberships:** Fellow, American College of Trust and Estate Counsel

**Career:** David Scott Sloan works closely with clients to design and implement sophisticated strategies that are integral to family wealth planning. Principals of private equity, venture capital and hedge funds, executives of private and public companies, entrepreneurs and owners of closely held businesses, turn to Mr Sloan for advice in all aspects of succession, tax and wealth transfer planning. He understands the needs of wealthy families and creates plans that address their financial and philanthropic goals while also minimizing transfer taxes.

### SMITH, Bradford J
Goodwin Procter LLP, Boston
617 570 1256
bsmith@goodwinprocter.com

*Featured in Labor & Employment (Massachusetts)*

**Practice Areas:** Mr Smith primarily represents management and institutional clients. His practice includes employment discrimination proceedings before state and federal courts and agencies, wrongful discharge litigation, proceedings before the National Labor Relations Board, labor arbitrations and actions arising under the Occupational Safety and Health Act. He counsels clients on employment-related issues such as employee discipline and termination, development of affirmative action programs and personnel policies, compliance with wage-hour regulations, development and enforcement of employee noncompetition and confidentiality agreements, and compliance with state and federal employment laws and regulations.

**Personal:** JD, Boston University, 1987 (cum laude); BA, University of Pennsylvania, 1980.

### SMITH, Edwin E
Bingham McCutchen LLP, Boston
617 951 8615
edwin.smith@bingham.com

*Featured in Bankruptcy/Restructuring (Massachusetts), Banking & Finance (Nationwide), Banking & Finance (Massachusetts)*

**Practice Areas:** Former co-chair of Bingham's Financial Services Area. Concentrates on general corporate and commercial law, debt financings, structured financings, workouts, bankruptcies, and international transactions. Actively participated in the drafting of a number of recent revisions to the Uniform Commercial Code. Spent nearly four years in Bingham's London office, where he concentrated on international financing and commercial transactions.

**Career:** Past president, American College of Commercial Finance Lawyers. Faculty lecturer, Secured Transactions, Harvard Law School and Northeastern University Law School, among others.

**Personal:** Harvard Law School, JD, 1974; Yale University, BA, 1968.

### ST. ONGE, Walter
Edwards Wildman Palmer LLP, Boston
617 239 0389
wstonge@edwardswildman.com

*Featured in Banking & Finance (Massachusetts)*

**Practice Areas:** Walter St. Onge serves as bond counsel or counsel to underwriters throughout New England and elsewhere for financings by states, municipalities and public authorities for transportation, housing, health care, educational, solid waste, industrial development and general governmental purposes.

**Professional Memberships:** Boston Bar Association, National Association of Bond Lawyers, American College of Bond Counsel.

**Personal:** Columbia University School of Law, JD; Yale University, BA, cum laude.

### STEINBERG, Donald R
WilmerHale, Boston
617 526 6453
don.steinberg@wilmerhale.com

*Featured in Intellectual Property (Massachusetts)*

**Practice Areas:** Chair of WilmerHale's Intellectual Property Department. Practice focuses on advising clients on intellectual property issues, developing intellectual property strategies, obtaining patent and trademark protection, and intellectual property litigation. Has extensive experience with computer software, processors, and systems; electronic devices and circuits; telecommunications; Internet-based applications; and medical devices.

**Professional Memberships:** Intellectual Property Owners Association's Software and Business Methods Committee:

**Career:** Admitted to Massachusetts Bar and United States Patent and Trademark Office. Joined the firm in 1994.

**Personal:** Harvard Law School (JD, cum laude); Princeton University (BSE, magna cum laude, Phi Beta Kappa).

### STEINBERG, Laura
Sullivan & Worcester LLP, Boston
617 338 2867
lsteinberg@sandw.com

*Featured in Litigation (Massachusetts)*

**Practice Areas:** Laura Steinberg is a litigation partner. Her practice consists of federal and state civil (commercial) litigation and arbitrations throughout the United States, with an emphasis on complex regulatory and fiduciary issues. She has extensive experience in disputes involving shareholder and investor rights and relationships; application of the business judgment rule; and fiduciary disclosures, compliance and enforcement issues.

**Professional Memberships:** Boston Bar Association; Board Member, Lawyers Committee for Civil Rights under Law, 1999-present.

**Personal:** JD, cum laude, Harvard Law School; Special Career Fellow, University of California at Berkeley; BA, magna cum laude, Bryn Mawr College.

### STEINGARTEN, Derek
Goodwin Procter LLP, Boston
617 570 1220
dsteingarten@goodwinprocter.com

*Featured in Investment Funds (Massachusetts)*

**Practice Areas:** Mr Steingarten focuses his practice on investment management and financial services matters, including hedge funds, mutual funds and other investment structures, financial services merger and acquisition transactions and regulatory compliance. He has significant experience advising registered and unregistered investment advisers, banks and other institutions, as well as independent directors of mutual funds, on a wide variety of financial services matters. He also has particular expertise with public and private investment vehicles, including mutual funds, onshore and offshore hedge funds, CDOs and other structures.

**Personal:** LLB, University of Ottawa, 2000 (magna cum laude); BA, McGill University, 1997 (first-class honors).

### STOKES, James C
Bingham McCutchen LLP, Boston
617 951 8222
james.stokes@bingham.com

*Featured in Corporate/M&A (Massachusetts)*

**Practice Areas:** Co-chair of Bingham's Latin America practice. Focuses primarily on mergers, acquisitions and corporate finance matters for clients covering a broad range of industries. Has represented both private and public companies and equity and debt financing sources. Has also served as special counsel to boards of directors on corporate governance and related matters. Significant portion of practice is devoted to cross-border transactions. Spent five years as resident partner in Bingham's London office.

**Career:** Former chairman, Boston Bar Association, International Law Section.

**Personal:** Boston College Law School, JD, 1975; College of the Holy Cross, BA, 1966.

### STONER, Wayne L
WilmerHale, Boston
617 526 6863
wayne.stoner@wilmerhale.com

*Featured in Intellectual Property (Massachusetts)*

**Practice Areas:** Partner in the firm's Litigation/Controversy Department, Intellectual Property Litigation and Appellate Practice Group. Practice focuses on patent litigation and strategy. Has represented a broad range of clients, including many jury and bench trials and appeals, in diverse technologies such as lasers, medical devices, semiconductor processing, integrated circuits, electrochemistry, software and telecommunications. Has practiced in courts nationwide and before the US International Trade Commission.

**Professional Memberships:** Faculty, Harvard Law School Trial Advocacy Program, 2003-2009.

**Career:** University of Pennsylvania Law School(JD); Admitted to Massachusetts, Western District of Texas, Federal Circuit Bars; Chair of WilmerHale Intellectual Property Litigation Practice Group, 2000-07.

### SUCOFF, Andrew
Goodwin Procter LLP, Boston
617 570 1995
asucoff@goodwinprocter.com

*Featured in Real Estate (Massachusetts)*

**Practice Areas:** Mr Sucoff represents REITs, institutional investors and lenders, pension fund advisors, underwriters, commercial and retail tenants, developers, commercial banks, and owners and operators of commercial real estate on complex commercial real estate matters throughout the country. He has extensive experience on transactions involving shopping centers, office buildings, multi-family properties, assisted living facilities, industrial properties and hotels. He has represented clients with multi-state acquisition, leasing, financing and disposition programs and also represents corporate clients on a wide range of real estate related matters.

**Personal:** JD, Boston University School of Law, 1989 (cum laude); BA, Hobart College, 1986 (cum laude).

### SULLIVAN, John L
DLA Piper LLP (US), Boston
617 406 6029
john.sullivan@dlapiper.com
*Featured in Real Estate (Massachusetts)*
**Practice Areas:** Real estate.
**Career:** He chairs the firm's Real Estate Practice Group in Boston. His broad-ranging practice encompasses all aspects of commercial real estate, with particular emphasis on public and private pension plans, opportunity funds, investment advisors, and other sophisticated investors in debt, equity, hybrid, and joint venture transactions throughout North America. He has significant experience representing US fund sponsors of US and European real estate funds. He represents lenders and borrowers in complex real estate loan workouts and restructurings throughout the United States.
**Personal:** JD, Cornell University (cum laude); BA, College of the Holy Cross (summa cum laude).

### SULLIVAN, Kevin J
Weil, Gotshal & Manges LLP, Boston
617 772 8348
kevin.sullivan@weil.com
*Featured in Private Equity (Massachusetts)*
**Practice Areas:** Kevin Sullivan is a partner in the Private Equity Practice of Weil, Gotshal & Manges. He joined the firm in 2002 and has a diverse transactional and corporate counseling practice with emphasis on leveraged buyouts, mergers and acquisitions, and growth equity investments. He regularly represents private equity investors in leveraged buyouts and minority investments. He also has broad M&A experience counseling corporate clients on a variety of general corporate and compliance matters, including corporate governance, securities, employment and strategic matters.
**Personal:** Boston College (summa cum laude, 1993); Georgetown University Law Center (JD, cum laude, 1996).

### SUNSHINE, Ilene Robinson
Sullivan & Worcester LLP, Boston
617 338 2928
isunshine@sandw.com
*Featured in Labor & Employment (Massachusetts)*
**Practice Areas:** Ilene Robinson Sunshine is the co-leader of S&W's Employment & Benefits Group where she represents and counsels employers in employment-related matters including employment discrimination, sexual harassment, employee discipline and discharge, handbooks and policy development, drafts executive contracts, and conducts training for managers and employees. She is a certified civil mediator in the Commonwealth of Massachusetts.
**Professional Memberships:** International Association of Privacy Professionals; Former Co-Chair, Labor and Employment Law Section, Boston Bar Association; Former Chair, Labor and

Employment Law Section, Massachusetts Bar Association.
**Personal:** JD, cum laude, New England School of Law; BA, University of Wisconsin.

### SURKIN, Elliot M
DLA Piper LLP (US), Boston
617 406 6030
elliot.surkin@dlapiper.com
*Featured in Real Estate (Massachusetts)*
**Practice Areas:** Real estate.
**Professional Memberships:** Member of the American College of Real Estate Lawyers.
**Career:** He concentrates his practice on real estate development, finance and taxation. He has acted as general counsel to the developers and owners of many of the most significant office, mixed-use and retail projects in the greater Boston area. He has taught courses in real estate development and finance throughout his career.
**Personal:** LLB, Harvard Law School (magna cum laude); AB, Princeton University (magna cum laude).

### SUSSMAN, Heather Egan
McDermott Will & Emery LLP, Boston
617 535 4177
hsussman@mwe.com
*Featured in Labor & Employment (Massachusetts)*
**Practice Areas:** Based in firm's Boston office. Helps clients successfully navigate the many state and federal laws that govern the workplace, including laws covering payment of wages, fair employment practices, reasonable accommodations, discrimination and harassment, family and medical leave, reductions in force. Negotiates executive employment agreements and enforceable restrictive covenants, and helps multinational clients establish worksites throughout the United States.
**Professional Memberships:** Boston Bar Association; American Bar Association; Massachusetts Bar; Bar of the United States District Court, District of Massachusetts.
**Personal:** Boston College Law School, JD, 2000; University of Massachusetts Dartmouth, BA, 1996.

### SWAIN, Philip C.
Foley Hoag LLP, Boston
617 832 1150
PCS@foleyhoag.com
*Featured in Intellectual Property (Massachusetts)*
**Practice Areas:** With more than 26 years' experience, Phil Swain has represented clients in intellectual property litigation throughout the country in both trials and appeals. He has tried copyright and trademark infringement, trade secret misappropriation and unfair competition cases, and uses this experience to deliver cost-effective service in complex litigation. His focus is primarily on clients in advanced technology applications, including telecommunications and information technology, computer software and medical devices. He has also handled intellectual property litigation involving mechanical devices, sporting goods and healthcare products.

**Personal:** Northwestern University School of Law, JD; Tufts University, BA and BS in Mechanical Engineering.

### SYLVIA, Jack
Mintz Levin Cohn Ferris Glovsky and Popeo PC, Boston
617 348 1820
JSylvia@mintz.com
*Featured in Litigation (Massachusetts)*
**Practice Areas:** Jack is a seasoned trial attorney and Co-Chair of the Securities Litigation Practice Group.
**Career:** Jack has a proven track record in the courtroom defending clients in both civil and criminal proceedings, including a National Law Journal top defense verdict. Outside the courtroom, Jack has handled numerous internal investigations and represented both corporate and individual clients in connection with investigations and enforcement proceedings conducted by the SEC and other government regulatory agencies.
**Publications:** Jack has appeared on CNBC, FOX News, BBC and been quoted in the Wall Street Journal, the New York Times, Financial Times and BusinessWeek.

### SZABO, David S
Edwards Wildman Palmer LLP, Boston
617 239 0414
dszabo@edwardswildman.com
*Featured in Healthcare (Massachusetts)*
**Practice Areas:** Dave represents hospitals, integrated delivery systems, home care companies, pharmaceutical companies and healthcare technology ventures. He has extensive experience in healthcare licensing and regulation, reimbursement, fraud and abuse compliance matters, and the structuring of joint ventures between taxable and tax-exempt entities. He has assisted healthcare clients in structuring complex transactions, including tax-exempt financings. His practice also includes the privacy and information security law applicable to healthcare, e-commerce, and financial service organizations.
**Professional Memberships:** Healthcare Financial Management Association, Health Information and Management Systems Society.
**Personal:** Boston University School of Law, JD; University of Rochester, BA, cum laude.

### TAYLOR JR, Andrew E
Choate Hall & Stewart LLP, Boston
617 248 5097
ataylor@choate.com
*Featured in Private Equity (Massachusetts)*
**Practice Areas:** Mr Taylor represents firms in fund formation, portfolio company investments, restructuring and recapitalizations of existing investments and exit transactions. He advises private companies on strategic business matters, contract negotiation and corporate governance matters, as well as mergers & acquisitions, equity financings, private placements and exit transactions. Recent engagements include: formation of $900 million healthcare fund, formation of $150 million environmental fund, formation of energy fund, $175 million equity acquisition financing of

pharmaceutical company, acquisition of software company, sale of snack food company.
**Personal:** JD Stanford Law School (1973); BA cum laude University of Rochester (1970).

### TELEGEN, Arthur
Seyfarth Shaw LLP, Boston
617 946 4949
atelegen@seyfarth.com
*Featured in Labor & Employment (Massachusetts)*
**Practice Areas:** Labor and employment.
**Professional Memberships:** College of Labor and Employment Lawyers, Fellow; Greater Boston Legal Services, Board of Directors.
**Career:** Arthur Telegen has over 35 years experience representing clients in labor law and employment litigation. He also represents corporate clients in the labor and employment aspects of corporate transactions, including the combination of union and non-union employers. He is listed in The Best Lawyers in America (2010 Boston Labor & Employment Lawyer of the Year), Massachusetts Super Lawyers, and is ranked as a leading lawyer by Chambers USA.
**Personal:** JD, Harvard Law School; AB, Brandeis University.

### THEODOROU, Nicholas C
Foley Hoag LLP, Boston
617 832 1163
ntheodorou@foleyhoag.com
*Featured in Litigation (Massachusetts)*
**Practice Areas:** Nicholas Theodorou, Chair of the Business Crimes and Government Investigations group, focuses in the areas of complex white-collar investigations and proceedings. He represents corporations, officers, directors and other individuals in criminal, civil and regulatory investigations and complex civil litigation. He has counseled national and regional medical device companies, financial institutions, technology companies, pharmaceutical companies, manufacturers, government contractors and healthcare providers and their officers, directors and employees in a variety of criminal and civil investigations and related trial and administrative proceedings for over 20 years.
**Personal:** University of Chicago Law School, JD; Dartmouth College, BA, summa cum laude.

### TICHNER, Jerome B
McDermott Will & Emery UK LLP, London
617 535 4094
jtichner@mwe.com
*Featured in Healthcare (Massachusetts)*
**Practice Areas:** Maintains a general health law practice, focusing on the representation of hospitals, health systems and other health care clients. Jerry has experience representing pharmaceutical companies, durable medical equipment companies and medical device manufacturers. He regularly provides regulatory and transactional representation to such clients in connection with acquisitions, joint ventures, strategic affiliations, conversions to tax-exempt status and other transactional matters.
**Personal:** Boston University School of Law, JD, 1998, University of Rochester, BA, 1993.

## TICKNOR, George
Edwards Wildman Palmer LLP, Boston
617 239 0357
gticknor@edwardswildman.com
*Featured in Banking & Finance (Massachusetts)*
**Practice Areas:** George represents banks, finance companies, public and private investment funds, and other financial institutions in financings with emphasis on financing buyouts and recapitalizations. He also represents transactionally active public companies and private equity and other investor groups making investments and acquisitions. His experience also encompasses public and 144A debt and convertible note issues and restructurings, and securitizations, second lien, and mezzanine financings. George has particular industry experience in media and communications.
**Professional Memberships:** American Bar Association, Boston Bar Association.
**Personal:** Harvard University, BA, magna cum laude, 1977; University of Virginia School of Law, JD, 1983.

## TOELKE, Richard A
Bingham McCutchen LLP, Boston
617 951 8830
richard.toelke@bingham.com
*Featured in Real Estate (Massachusetts)*
**Practice Areas:** Deputy co-chair of Bingham's Real Estate Practice Group. Has represented developers, institutional property owners, pension fund advisers, REITs, lenders, and other owners and operators of real estate in all aspects of transactional real estate practice. Has worked on a wide variety of transactions regionally and nationally, including acquisitions and dispositions of office, industrial, R&D and multifamily properties; leasing transactions; financing arrangements; joint ventures; and development projects.
**Personal:** Villanova University School of Law, JD, 1989; Boston College, BA, 1986.

## TSE, Marian A
Goodwin Procter LLP, Boston
617 570 1169
mtse@goodwinprocter.com
*Featured in Employee Benefits & Executive Compensation (Nationwide), Employee Benefits & Executive Compensation (Massachusetts)*
**Practice Areas:** Ms Tse is chair of the firm's ERISA & Executive Compensation Practice, focusing primarily on executive compensation and employee benefits matters. She has represented clients in the design, implementation and administration of many types of executive compensation programs and broad-based employee benefit plans, as well as the treatment of equity and employee benefits in hundreds of corporate mergers and acquisitions. She is well-versed in tax, accounting and securities laws affecting executive compensation, as well as governance issues raised by institutional shareholders.
**Personal:** JD, Columbia Law School, 1979; BA, Vassar College, 1976 (cum laude).

## TURANO, Thomas A
K&L Gates, Boston
617 261 3148
thomas.turano@klgates.com
*Featured in Intellectual Property (Massachusetts)*
**Practice Areas:** Thomas Turano is a partner in the international firm of K&L Gates and a former leader of the firm's Intellectual Property practice area, focusing on intellectual property counseling, patent and trademark prosecution, licensing, opinions, transactional due diligence, and litigation. He counsels both international and US clients on creating patent portfolios that will maximize the business value of a company's intellectual property in the individual jurisdictions of interest. He practices in the biological, medical and the tech-related areas. Much of his practice is directed toward startup and emerging companies.

## ULLMANN, Robert L
Nutter McClennen & Fish LLP, Boston
617 439 2262
rullmann@nutter.com
*Featured in Litigation (Massachusetts)*
**Practice Areas:** Robert Ullmann, a veteran trial lawyer and former federal prosecutor, has one of New England's most extensive practices in defending criminal and civil government enforcement cases. Bob has counseled clients ranging from Fortune 100 companies and their top officers to non-profit entities and government officials. He has successfully tried healthcare and securities fraud cases of national import, and a wide range of other matters. Bob's career at Nutter followed more than ten years with the Justice Department, including stints as the First Assistant US Attorney and Chief of the Criminal Division in the US Attorney's Office in Boston.

## UNDERWOOD, Robert H
McDermott Will & Emery LLP, Boston
617 535 4093
runderwood@mwe.com
*Featured in Intellectual Property (Massachusetts)*
**Practice Areas:** Practice focused on patent portfolio development and management, patent prosecution, opinions, licensing, due diligence and related counseling. Also assists with product planning matters as they relate to intellectual property, patent life-cycle management and the acquisition and divestment of intellectual property assets. Extensive experience creating and evaluating intellectual property protection in the areas of life sciences and chemistry.
**Professional Memberships:** Registered patent attorney; American Bar Association; American Intellectual Property Law Association; Boston Patent Law Association.
**Personal:** Suffolk University Law School, JD, (cum laude), 2005; Tufts University, PhD, 1998; University of New Hampshire, BS 1989.

## URBAN, Andrew
Mintz Levin Cohn Ferris Glovsky and Popeo PC, Boston
617 348 1750
AUrban@mintz.com
*Featured in Real Estate (Massachusetts)*
**Practice Areas:** Andy is Vice Chairman of Mintz Levin; Member of the Firm's governing Policy Committee and the former Managing Partner of the Firm. Advises clients in real estate acquisition, development/finance and general corporate finance. Represents corporate and institutional clients in national transactions, multi-state retail acquisition, leasing/sale leaseback transactions, joint ventures, structuring and negotiation of acquisitions and financings of office projects, shopping centers, R&D facilities, industrial properties. Counsels Fortune 500 companies on financing, design/implementation of creative acquisition, leasing, financing programs for national and international corporate real estate portfolios.
**Personal:** AB, Dartmouth; MBA, Wharton School; JD, University of Pennsylvania Law School.

## UTZSCHNEIDER, John R
Bingham McCutchen LLP, Boston
617 951 8852
john.utzschneider@bingham.com
*Featured in Corporate/M&A (Massachusetts)*
**Practice Areas:** Co-chair of Bingham's Corporate Area, head of the firm's initiatives in financial services M&A and CleanTech, and a member of the Management Committee at Bingham. Focuses primarily on mergers and acquisitions and corporate finance, including debt restructurings. Represents both private and public companies, equity and debt financing sources, and underwriters in mergers and acquisitions, leveraged buyouts, joint ventures, private and public offerings, and restructurings. Also represents public companies and boards of directors on securities, corporate governance and related matters.
**Personal:** New York University School of Law, JD, 1986; Dartmouth College, BA, 1982.

## VAN DYCK, Timothy P
Edwards Wildman Palmer LLP, Boston
617 951 2254
tvandyck@edwardswildman.com
*Featured in Labor & Employment (Massachusetts)*
**Practice Areas:** Tim Van Dyck counsels telecommunications companies, financial institutions, insurers, retailers, manufacturers, and construction companies, among others, against employment related claims. He also advises employers on the entire spectrum of employment issues, including sexual harassment investigations, employment counseling and terminations, retaliation claims, FLSA, FMLA and ADA issues, and reductions in force.
**Personal:** Boston College Law School, JD, cum laude; Boston College, BA summa cum laude, Phi Beta Kappa.

## VENTOLA, John F
Choate Hall & Stewart LLP, Boston
617 248 5085
jventola@choate.com
*Featured in Bankruptcy/Restructuring (Massachusetts)*
**Practice Areas:** Represents clients in loan workouts, financing transactions and restructurings/bankruptcies, including post-petition financings, cash collateral disputes, equitable subordination/recharacterization, Section 363 sales and contested plans of reorganization. Experience includes transactions for secured lenders, hedge funds, and institutional investors, including asset-based, debtor-in-possession, cash flow, Tranche B, second-lien, and mezzanine loans, and junior capital investments. Recent matters: counsel to DIP Agent in Chapter 11 case of two national retailers; represent international pharmaceutical company in complex out-of-court restructuring; counseling lenders in multiple workout/restructuring matters.
**Personal:** JD Boston College Law School (1994), Order of the Coif; BS Boston College (1990); both magna cum laude.

## WALKER, Adrienne K
Mintz Levin Cohn Ferris Glovsky and Popeo PC, Boston
617 348 1612
AWalker@mintz.com
*Featured in Bankruptcy/Restructuring (Massachusetts)*
**Practice Areas:** Bankruptcy, restructuring and commercial law.
**Professional Memberships:** American Bankruptcy Institute, International Women's Insolvency & Restructuring Confederation (IWIRC), and former co-chair of the Bankruptcy Section at the Boston Bar Association.
**Career:** Significant experience representing secured creditors, indenture trustees, institutional lenders, and debtors in court and out-of-court workouts. Admitted to practice in Massachusetts, the United States District Court, District of Massachusetts. Adrienne also teaches bankruptcy law at New England Law Boston.
**Publications:** Frequent author for the American Bankruptcy Institute Journal; Massachusetts Continuing Legal Education.
**Personal:** BA, with honors from Simmons College, JD, magna cum laude from Suffolk University Law School.

## WALSH, Kevin J
Mintz Levin Cohn Ferris Glovsky and Popeo PC, Boston
617 348 1622
KWalsh@mintz.com
*Featured in Bankruptcy/Restructuring (Massachusetts)*
**Practice Areas:** Kevin's practice focuses on corporate bankruptcy and commercial law, workouts, restructurings, and commercial lending transactions. He represents corporate debtors, secured and unsecured lenders, trustees, bondholders, committees, lessors and lessees and other entities in out-of-court restructuring and bankruptcy proceedings. He has experience in distressed acquisitions and divestitures, complex commercial transactions and business litigation.
**Publications:** Frequent author and lecturer on topics related to bankruptcies, restructurings and commercial finance.
**Personal:** BA, Economics, Trinity College; JD, magna cum laude, New York Law School. Massachusetts Super Lawyer and Best Lawyers in

America: Bankruptcy and Creditor Debtor Rights/Insolvency and Reorganization Law.

### WAND, Barbara Freedman
Bingham McCutchen LLP, Boston
617 951 8614
barbara.wand@bingham.com
*Featured in Tax (Massachusetts)*
**Practice Areas:** Concentrates practice in the areas of sophisticated estate planning; estate and trust administration; and advising individuals, families and businesses on the development and implementation of philanthropic goals. Serves as managing director of Bingham Charitable Advisers and counsels private foundations and public charities on governance, compliance and planned giving programs. Assists clients with estate administration, including preparation of federal and state estate tax returns and service as executor. Trained mediator available to mediate family law, family business, probate and employment disputes.
**Personal:** Indiana University School of Law/Bloomington, JD, summa cum laude, 1979; Brandeis University, BA, magna cum laude, 1972.

### WARE, Donald
Foley Hoag LLP, Boston
617 832 1167
dware@foleyhoag.com
*Featured in Intellectual Property (Massachusetts)*
**Practice Areas:** Donald Ware, Partner and Chair of the firm's Intellectual Property Department, has over 25 years' experience in intellectual property litigation, licensing, and counseling. He has litigated patent disputes for global biopharmaceutical, medical device, and high technology companies, and for major universities and hospitals. He is experienced in alternative dispute resolution, including mediation and arbitration. He has expertise in life sciences patent litigation, including recombinant DNA, RNA interference, monoclonal antibodies, biosimilars, molecular diagnostics, research tools, and medical devices. He advises venture capitalists and institutional investors on patent litigation and due diligence.
**Personal:** Harvard Law School, JD; Yale College, AB.

### WARE JR, Paul F
Goodwin Procter LLP, Boston
617 570 1280
pware@goodwinprocter.com
*Featured in Litigation (Nationwide), Intellectual Property (Massachusetts), Litigation (Massachusetts)*
**Practice Areas:** Mr Ware's practice has included substantial commercial, financial and intellectual property litigation. He represents companies in a wide spectrum of commercial and business disputes, including breach of contract actions, civil RICO, and sophisticated commercial litigation. He served as Trial Counsel for the Office of Independent Counsel for the Iran Contra investigation, Special Counsel to the Massachusetts Commission on Judicial Conduct, and as Special Assistant Attorney General (Massachusetts) to serve as Special Prosecutor for the criminal inves-

tigation of the Central Artery Tunnel collapse in Boston's 'Big Dig'.
**Personal:** LLB, University of Pennsylvania, 1969; AB, University of Notre Dame, 1966.

### WATSON, David W
Goodwin Procter LLP, Boston
617 570 1888
dwatson@goodwinprocter.com
*Featured in Private Equity (Massachusetts)*
**Practice Areas:** Mr Watson's practice focuses on public and private securities offerings, private fund formation, partnership law, public and private mergers and acquisitions, securities law compliance for public companies and general corporate matters. His experience in the fund formation area includes establishing private funds through US and international securities offerings, organizing fund manager and sponsor entities, advising fund managers and sponsors in establishing compensation structures and internal operating policies, representing funds and investors and restructuring the terms of existing investment funds.
**Personal:** JD, Harvard Law School, 1988 (cum laude); BA, University of Maine, 1985 (salutatorian).

### WEBSTER, Scott A
Goodwin Procter LLP, Boston
617 570 8229
swebster@goodwinprocter.com
*Featured in Employee Benefits & Executive Compensation (Massachusetts)*
**Practice Areas:** Mr Webster represents numerous financial service organizations and other fiduciaries concerning issues arising in connection with the investment of employee benefit plan assets, including fiduciary, investment and prohibited transaction matters. He has been extensively involved in establishing and operating collective investment vehicles, including VCOCs and REOCs, as well as developing a variety of new investment products. Mr Webster works closely with public and private companies in structuring, implementing and administering equity-based compensation, incentive compensation and other employee benefit plans and arrangements.
**Personal:** JD, University of Pennsylvania Law School, 1996; BA, Boston University, 1993 (summa cum laude, with distinction).

### WEINER, Stephen M
Mintz Levin Cohn Ferris Glovsky and Popeo PC, Boston
617 348 1757
SWeiner@mintz.com
*Featured in Healthcare (Massachusetts)*
**Practice Areas:** Steve chairs Mintz Levin's National Health Law Practice. He has served as policymaker, educator and attorney. He counsels providers on strategic affiliations, significant corporate transactions, ACO development and regulatory and reimbursement matters, etc.
**Professional Memberships:** ABA, Massachusetts, Boston Bar Associations, AHLA.
**Career:** Counseling major health system deals, implementing health reform and HITECH legislation; structuring Dubai HealthCare City's regulatory system;; representation on military health

care; medical travel. Chaired Massachusetts Rate Setting Commission. Chair, HealthWell Foundation.
**Publications:** Yale Journal, Health Policy, Law and Ethics: Payment Reform after PPACA.
**Personal:** Healthcare and cultural organization boards. Harvard College; Yale Law School.

### WESTENBERG, David
WilmerHale, Boston
617 526 6626
david.westenberg@wilmerhale.com
*Featured in Corporate/M&A (Massachusetts)*
**Practice Areas:** Mr Westenberg has focused on the software, Internet and information technology industries for more than twenty years. In addition to advising industry pioneers and world leaders, he has counseled start-up clients from formation through venture financing and on to successful acquisitions or IPOs.
**Publications:** Mr Westenberg writes frequently on the IPO, M&A and venture capital markets. He is author of Initial Public Offerings: A Practical Guide to Going Public (Practising Law Institute), a comprehensive yet practical guide to the IPO process, and blogs on IPOs at wilmerhale.com/IPOBlog.

### WETHLY, Kimberly B
WilmerHale, Boston
617 526 6481
kimberly.wethly@wilmerhale.com
*Featured in Employee Benefits & Executive Compensation (Massachusetts)*
**Practice Areas:** Partner, Tax Practice Group; member, FinTech Group. Extensive experience in all aspects of executive compensation: applicable tax, corporate securities and accounting issues. Represented public and privately held companies' boards of directors, compensation committees and corporate executives. Advises clients concerning compensation issues arising in mergers and acquisitions, spin offs, formation, financings, restructurings and public offerings. Expertise encompasses equity compensation, nonqualified deferred compensation, incentive plans, and executive, retention and severance agreements. Advised financial institutions on TARP executive compensation rules and Federal Reserve's guidance on incentive compensation.
**Career:** Joined firm in 1997.
**Personal:** JD, Boston College Law School; BA, Boston College.

### WHITHAM, Michele A
Foley Hoag LLP, Boston
617 832 1239
mwhitham@foleyhoag.com
*Featured in Labor & Employment (Massachusetts)*
**Practice Areas:** Michele Whitham represents employers in complex, high-risk workplace situations. She defends employers against wage/hour class actions, helps enforce non-competition/non-solicitation agreements, litigates executive wrongful termination and severance claims, and defends against employee EEO, ERISA, tort and contract claims. She helps protect employers from abuse of their computer systems, respond to threats of workplace violence, and implement workplace

security systems and statistical monitoring programs. She co-founded the firm's Security and Privacy group, which provides remediation for data, security and privacy breaches in the workplace.
**Personal:** Cornell University, JD, Order of the Coif (and graduate Degrees in Education and Human Development).

### WHITLEDGE, William H
Goodwin Procter LLP, Boston
617 570 1056
wwhitledge@goodwinprocter.com
*Featured in Tax (Massachusetts)*
**Practice Areas:** Mr Whitledge, chair of the firm's Tax Practice, specializes in corporate, partnership, foreign and general business taxation. He spends a substantial amount of time structuring international and domestic business transactions, including mergers, acquisitions, financings, dispositions, reorganizations and other business restructurings, and venture capital investments. He also has extensive experience in structuring collective investment vehicles with tax-exempt, foreign and domestic investors, including RICs, REITs and pension investments from an unrelated business taxable income perspective.
**Personal:** LLM, New York University, 1985; JD, Columbia University, 1980; BA, Michigan State University, 1976.

### WIESEN, Jeffrey M
Mintz Levin Cohn Ferris Glovsky and Popeo PC, Boston
617 348 1759
JWiesen@mintz.com
*Featured in Life Sciences (Nationwide), Corporate/M&A (Massachusetts)*
See under Nationwide for profile.

### WILLETT, Sabin
Bingham McCutchen LLP, Boston
617 951 8775
sabin.willett@bingham.com
*Featured in Bankruptcy/Restructuring (Massachusetts)*
**Practice Areas:** Practices commercial and bankruptcy litigation. Experienced in complex commercial disputes and the representation of lenders and other institutional creditors in lender liability cases and complex Chapter 11 disputes as well as general commercial litigation. Has tried jury trials and numerous bench or "issues to court" trials.
**Personal:** Harvard Law School, JD, cum laude 1983; Harvard College, BA, magna cum laude 1979.

### WOLFMAN, Jonathan
WilmerHale, Boston
617 526 6833
jonathan.wolfman@wilmerhale.com
*Featured in Corporate/M&A (Massachusetts)*
**Practice Areas:** Jonathan Wolfman co-chairs WilmerHale's Public Company Counseling Group. He represents public companies on a wide variety of disclosure, governance and compensation matters, including compliance with SEC and stock exchange rules and understanding and

addressing the impact of new and emerging disclosure and governance practices.

**Professional Memberships:** ABA's Committee on Federal Regulation of Securities (former Co-chair, Subcommittee on Disclosure and Continuous Reporting).

**Publications:** Co-editor, The Practitioner's Guide to the Sarbanes-Oxley Act published by the ABA. Author, corporate governance chapter in PLI's Initial Public Offerings: A Practical Guide to Going Public.

## WOOD, Lisa C
Foley Hoag LLP, Boston
617 832 1117
lwood@foleyhoag.com
*Featured in Antitrust (Massachusetts)*

**Practice Areas:** Lisa Wood, Litigation Department Chair, handles complex litigation matters involving antitrust, securities fraud, auditor defense and business tort claims. She counsels clients on antitrust issues, including mergers, joint ventures, information exchanges, distribution and marketing practices, pricing strategies, IP, Noerr Pennington, standard setting and competitive strategies including non-competes, employee raid-

---

ing, and competitive intelligence. She has represented companies in government investigations by the SEC, DOJ, FTC, IRS, PCAOB and State Attorney General. Her experience spans several industries, including technology, specialty chemical, retail, pharmaceutical, real estate, financial services, accounting and trade associations.

**Personal:** Boston College Law School, JD; Kenyon College, AB.

## ZABOWSKY, Michael D
Nutter McClennen & Fish LLP, Boston
617 439 2721
mzabowsky@nutter.com
*Featured in Real Estate (Massachusetts)*

**Practice Areas:** Michael Zabowsky is a partner in the Real Estate and Finance Department and has experience in real estate transactions both locally and nationally. He represents, among other clients, financial institutions, real estate investment and pension funds, banks, life insurance companies, landowners, developers, landlords, tenants, limited liability companies, corporations and real estate trusts. He primarily handles leasing transactions, financings, acquisitions, dispositions and workouts. Mike's projects include downtown

---

office buildings, suburban office buildings and office parks, shopping centers, mixed-use developments, retail complexes and residential properties.

## ZICK, Colin
Foley Hoag LLP, Boston
617 832 1275
czick@foleyhoag.com
*Featured in Healthcare (Massachusetts)*

**Practice Areas:** Colin Zick's practice focuses on health care and compliance issues, often at the intersection of administrative proceedings or litigation. Co-chair of the firm's Health Care Practice Group, Mr Zick's work emphasizes compliance issues and defense before state and federal licensing and regulatory entities related to allegations of kickbacks, overpayments, and billing and coding problems. His practice includes transactional and employment agreements, creating compliance programs, and advising on information privacy and security matters including HIPAA, and state and federal data security laws and regulations.

**Personal:** University of Michigan School of Law, JD; University of Michigan, BA.

---

## ZOLI, Elise N
Goodwin Procter LLP, Boston
617 570 1612
ezoli@goodwinprocter.com
*Featured in Environment (Massachusetts)*

**Practice Areas:** Ms Zoli specializes in the areas of energy, environmental and development law. She has extensive experience in the transfer, permitting and development of energy projects, particularly electric-generating and natural-gas-pipeline facilities. Examples of her energy work include strategic development and acquisition advice, compliance counseling and litigation services on behalf of nuclear-powered, fossil-fuel and wind-turbine electric-generating stations and strategic counseling for a leading 'Green tag' provider. She has done work on the assessment and permitting of redevelopment projects involving complex sites, including former nuclear assets.

**Personal:** JD, University of Pennsylvania Law School, 1990; BA, Duke University, 1987 (magna cum laude).

# BINGHAM MCCUTCHEN LLP

**www.**bingham.com  **tel:** 617 951 8000  **fax:** 617 951 8736

**Chairman:** Jay S Zimmerman
Number of partners: 423
Number of lawyers: 1,000

## Firm Overview:

Bingham's market-leading practices are focused on global financial services firms and *Fortune* 100 companies. The firm has approximately 1,000 lawyers in the US, Europe and Asia.

## Main Areas of Practice:

### Corporate:

Bingham's corporate lawyers serve clients ranging from small and emerging entrepreneurial businesses to the world's largest multinational corporations. Strengths span M&A; government affairs; energy and project finance; real estate; structured transactions; tax; and telecommunications, media and technology.
**Contact:** Reed D Auerbach  **Tel:** 212 705 7400
**Contact:** Steven C Browne  **Tel:** 617 951 8124
**Contact:** John R Utzschneider  **Tel:** 617 951 8852
**Contact:** Richard J Welch  **Tel:** 213 229 8510

### Financial Services:

Bingham's financial services area provides a full range of transactional, regulatory, compliance, enforcement and litigation legal services to financial services clients on a global basis. Strengths span broker-dealer, financial restructuring, investment management, Japanese practice, London finance and transactional finance.
**Contact:** Timothy P Burke  **Tel:** 617 951 8620
**Contact:** Frederick F Eisenbiegler  **Tel:** 212 705 7745
**Contact:** Roger P Joseph  **Tel:** 617 951 8247

### Litigation:

Bingham's litigators and trial lawyers represent businesses that seek assistance with sophisticated, difficult problems. Strengths span antitrust; appellate; entertainment, media and communications; environmental, land use and natural resources; intellectual property; labor and employment; real estate, project finance and construction; securities and financial institutions litigation; and white collar.
**Contact:** Robert M Dombroff  **Tel:** 212 705 7757
**Contact:** Geoffrey M Howard  **Tel:** 415 393 2485
**Contact:** Donn P Pickett  **Tel:** 415 393 2082

## PRACTICE AREAS

Corporate
Financial Services
Litigation

## OFFICES

### CALIFORNIA

**ORANGE COUNTY:** 600 Anton Boulevard, Suite 1800
Costa Mesa, CA 92626-7653
Tel: 714 830 0600  Fax: 714 830 0700

**LOS ANGELES:** 355 South Grand Avenue, Suite 4400, CA 90071-3106
Tel: 213 680 6400  Fax: 213 680 6499

**SILICON VALLEY:** 1117 S. California Avenue, Palo Alto, CA 94304-1106
Tel: 650 849 4400  Fax: 650 849 4800

**SAN FRANCISCO:** Three Embarcadero Center, CA 94111-4067
Tel: 415 393 2000  Fax: 415 393 2286

**SANTA MONICA:** The Water Garden, Suite 2050 North, 1601 Cloverfield Boulevard, CA 90404-4082
Tel: 310 907 1000  Fax: 310 907 2000

### CONNECTICUT

**HARTFORD:** One State Street,  CT 06103-3178
Tel: 860 240 2700  Fax: 860 240 2800

### DISTRICT OF COLUMBIA

**WASHINGTON:** 2020 K Street NW, DC 20006-1806
Tel: 202 373 6000  Fax: 202 373 6001

### MASSACHUSETTS

**BOSTON:** One Federal Street, MA 02110-1726
Tel: 617 951 8000  Fax: 617 951 8736

### NEW YORK

**NEW YORK:** 399 Park Avenue, NY 10022-4689
Tel: 212 705 7000  Fax: 212 752 5378

## INTERNATIONAL OFFICES

The firm also has offices in Beijing and Hong Kong, China; Frankfurt, Germany; Tokyo, Japan; and London, UK

# BINGHAM

# CAMPBELL CAMPBELL EDWARDS & CONROY

www.campbell-trial-lawyers.com **tel:** +1 617 241 3000 **fax:** +1 617 241 5115

**Managing Partners:** James M Campbell, Richard P Campbell
**Senior Partners:** William J Conroy, Brian P Voke, Bryan D McElvaine
Number of Partners: 17
Number of Lawyers: 40

## Firm Overview:

Campbell Campbell Edwards & Conroy Professional Corporation is recognized nationally and internationally for delivering results in state and federal courts throughout the United States. Campbell Trial Lawyers have successfully tried hundreds of large-value, high-exposure, technically complex cases to verdict and combine the power of a winning team with the agility to respond quickly and incisively to every problem. As one of the most mentioned firms nationally for Tort Litigation in Corporate Counsel's 2011 "Who Represents America's Biggest Companies" survey, the firm is honored to be considered among the "Litigation Kings" by America's Fortune 100 businesses. The firm is also one of only six shortlisted for the 2012 *Chambers* USA Awards for Excellence in Product Liability. The firm's attorneys are well connected throughout the profession offering clients the advantage of an international network of relationships, access to courts across the country, and world-class trial experience.

Campbell Campbell Edwards & Conroy Professional Corporation provides advice, counseling and representation during all stages of a dispute, ranging from the time before the filing of a lawsuit through the final appeal. The American College of Trial Lawyers, widely considered to be the premier professional organization of trial lawyers in the United States, has acknowledged the exceptional skill and highest standards of ethical conduct demonstrated by the firm's attorneys. James Campbell, Richard Campbell, and William Conroy are Fellows of the College. James Campbell is a Diplomate of the American Board of Trial Advocates, recognizing the trial of more than 100 cases. Many of the firm's lawyers hold or have held leadership positions in local and national bar associations, regularly present educational programs and contribute to professional publications. James Campbell is also a past President of the International Association of Defense Counsel.

## Main Areas of practice

The defense of product liability claims has been a mainstay of the firm's practice since its inception in 1983. The firm serves as local, regional and national counsel to a variety of product manufacturers including those in the automotive, transportation, pharmaceutical, medical device, chemical, heavy equipment, commercial equipment, consumer product and many other industries. Campbell Trial Lawyers defend:

- Pharmaceutical companies and medical device manufacturers in all types of product defect litigation, which generally involve exposures in the millions of dollars and include the defense of mass tort actions
- Clients in the transportation industry that include not only vehicle manufacturers and motor carriers, but also domestic and foreign airlines and their insurers, aircraft manufacturers and component part suppliers, airport authorities and ground handling companies

- A number of major industrial and construction equipment manufacturers
- Cases arising in a wide variety of commercial contexts in jurisdictions across the country, including domestic and international contract actions, construction litigation, corporate and partnership disputes, directors and officers, unfair competition and defamation and shareholder actions
- Commercial property owners, managers, agents, contractors and tenants against claims of alleged negligence on premises ranging from restaurants and hotels to construction sites, retail stores to industrial plants, and healthcare facilities to airports
- Claims of toxic torts, including asbestos related cases, environmental contamination and chemical exposure

**Contact:** James M Campbell
**Tel:** 617 241 3060
**Email:** jmcampbell@campbell-trial-lawyers.com

## PRACTICE AREAS

Appellate Practice
Asbestos
Aerospace/Aviation
Business & Commercial
Construction
Directors' & Officers' Liability
Employment
Environmental
Fraud/Bad Faith
Insurance Coverage
Insurance Defense
Intellectual Property
Legal Malpractice
Medical Malpractice
Personal Injury/Negligence
Pharmaceutical/Medical Devices
Premises Liability
Product Liability
Professional Liability
Toxic Torts/Mass Torts
Transportation/Trucking

## OFFICES

**MASSACHUSETTS**
**BOSTON:** One Constitution Center, Third Floor, MA 02129
Tel: 617 241 3000   Fax: 617 241 5115

**PENNSYLVANIA**
**BERWYN:** 1205 Westlakes Drive, Suite 330, PA 19312
Tel: 610 964 1900   Fax: 610 964 1981

# CHOATE HALL & STEWART

**www.**choate.com **tel:** 617 248 5000 **fax:** 617 248 4000

**Co-Managing Partners:** William P Gelnaw, Jr, John A Nadas
Number of equity partners: 65

**OFFICES**

MASSACHUSETTS

**BOSTON:** Two International Place, MA 02110
Tel: 617 248 5000   Fax: 617 248 4000
Email: info@choate.com

### Firm Overview:

One of the nation's premier law firms, Choate has chosen to be distinctly different in a number of important respects from the firms with which it competes. The firm believes those differences materially benefit clients. Like a handful of leading Wall Street firms, Choate conducts its national and international practice through a single office model. The firm is all under one roof. Lawyers know each other well and work in teams every day. That familiarity, proximity and continuity allows them to communicate quickly, share knowledge easily and respond to clients' needs not just efficiently, but seamlessly and immediately.

### Main Areas of Practice:

#### Private Equity/M&A:

Choate formed one of the first private equity funds in 1983 and has been a leader in private equity ever since, representing clients in over $30 billion in M&A and investment transactions in the past five years. Choate represents clients across a range of transaction sizes, but has particular expertise and knowledge of market terms and industry best practices in middle market transactions ranging from $25 million to $1 billion. The firm provides in-depth deal coverage – acquisitions and sales, minority investments and recapitalizations, fund formation and capital raising, and tax structuring. In recent years Choate has closed transactions in over 45 states and 27 foreign countries.

#### Technology, IP & Related Litigation:

The firm represents technology companies in their entire life-cycle from start-up to strategic alliances to public company to M&A. Firm lawyers have organized thousands of emerging companies, have completed M&A transactions with proceeds over $50 billion and have been involved in public company securities offerings with proceeds over $18 billion, since 2000. The firm's deep technology team brings IP and industry strategy resources to bear on corporate clients. Choate's IP group provides leading companies and institutions with sophisticated IP strategies for the acquisition and enforcement of IP rights throughout the world. The IP team, many with PhDs and other advanced degrees, uses its scientific and strategic expertise and practical business judgment to represent market-leading technology and life sciences companies in their mission critical, high-value transactions and strategies. Choate's trial lawyers litigate complex IP cases across the US for leading technology and life sciences companies. The trial lawyers bring partner-level intensity to each case, working with a closely integrated team of technical specialists to achieve clients' goals, including pre-litigation and due diligence counseling, and outcome-driven litigation and trial strategies.

#### Finance & Restructuring:

Choate represents leading financial institutions, institutional investors, borrowers and issuers in a full range of financings – senior syndicated, second lien, mezzanine/subordinated and debtor-in-possession. The team has completed financings with proceeds over $20 billion across the US and in 27 foreign countries over the last five years, and has particular expertise in M&A and financings in numerous industries, including healthcare, media, retail, sports, energy and technology. Choate also has significant experience in corporate restructurings, workouts, distressed asset and debt acquisitions and bankruptcy proceedings from both the company and creditor perspective.

#### Complex Commercial Litigation:

Choate has deep expertise in significant complex commercial litigation, with a particular focus on representing clients with respect to their most challenging and complex matters involving financial/business disputes, tort defense and class action defense as well as antitrust, trade secret and securities litigation matters. Choate litigators are actual "trial lawyers" who have extensive experience appearing before federal and state courts (at last count, 41 states) and government agencies and in trial and arbitrations across the US and abroad.

#### Government Enforcement & Compliance:

The government enforcement team is expert in advising and defending companies and individuals who are subjects of government investigations and prosecution. The team has deep experience in the full range of criminal/civil enforcement actions, investigations and prosecutions, with particular expertise handling matters involving pharmaceutical/healthcare fraud and financial fraud as well as advising public and private companies with respect to actual or suspected FCPA violations and internal investigations. With significant prosecutorial backgrounds, the group is focused on resolving matters at the earliest possible stage before indictment or trial and without publicity.

#### Insurance & Reinsurance:

Choate represents national and multinational insurers, reinsurers and intermediaries across the nation and abroad in the UK, Bermuda and other off-shore locales. The reinsurance group works with large cedents, reinsurers and intermediaries in arbitration, trial and appellate matters, counseling clients with respect to underwriting matters, bad faith claims and audits. The firm's coverage litigation experts have appeared in more than 200 cases and arbitrations concerning coverage litigation and bankruptcy proceedings involving environmental, asbestos, non-products, Chinese Drywall, E&O/D&O, implant and toxic tort claims.

#### Wealth Management:

Choate's wealth management group offers integrated services to high net worth individuals and families, with sophisticated financial, tax and estate planning all in one place. The group provides expert counsel to a wide range of clients from multiple generations of families to public and private company CEOs and partners in private equity funds to estates, foundations and trusts. Together with Choate's registered investment advisory subsidiary, Choate Investment Advisors, the group delivers a suite of sophisticated and comprehensive wealth management services to clients. Their collaboration provides a multi-family office, integrating highly sophisticated legal, investment, tax and trust administration expertise – a seamless "one-stop" approach to wealth management.

#### International Work:

The firm has preeminent US-Canada and US-Europe cross-border transactional practices. The corporate teams represent clients in cross-border activities and works with numerous companies headquartered in the EU on expansion into the US. Choate litigators have arbitrated and litigated disputes throughout the world.

#### Clients:

Choate represents market leading "Best of Breed" clients in each of its practice areas. Those clients range from Fortune 500 institutions, to private equity funds, to leading public and private companies, to wealthy families/individuals. Clients include: Akamai, Hewlett-Packard, RIM, Teradyne, Bank of America, John Hancock, Riverside Partners, The Hartford, BV Investment Partners, Liberty Mutual, Shinogi, Travelers, Cabot Corporation, MassMutual, Shire, Wells Fargo, EMC, MIT, Spectrum Equity, Fidelity, Momenta Pharmaceuticals, Summit Partners, Harvard University, NV Energy, Takeda.

# COLLORA LLP

**www.**collorallp.com **tel:** 617 371 1000 **fax:** 617 371 1037

**Managing Partner:** William J Lovett
Number of partners: 12   Number of lawyers: 25
Languages: *English, French, German*

## Firm Overview:

Founded in 1988, Collora LLP is a litigation boutique that represents individual and corporate clients in complex civil and white-collar criminal cases. The firm's first commitment is to its clients. The firm dedicates itself to serving as their allies, advocates and defenders. Service begins with assessing each client's needs and helping set each client's goals. Collora LLP tailors investigative strategies to meet those objectives. Attorneys have tenacity, creativity, versatility and experience to fight the most challenging battles and resolve the most complex disputes.

## Main Areas of Practice:

### Appellate:

Collora LLP is uniquely equipped to assist clients not only with the preparation and argument of a successful appeal, but with the preparation and presentation of a trial that will create a solid foundation for that appeal. Appellate victories require proper preservation of legal issues. One of the ways the firm can shape fate for a client is by examining all of the pertinent facts and legal theories at the outset, so that they can design a legal strategy that can facilitate success at any stage of a proceeding. The firm's early and intense focus on facts and legal theories not only improves a client's chances for ultimate vindication by the highest court of review. Also it can convince authorities not to proceed with charges, it can force a favorable settlement and it can win trials.
**Contact:** Hon Christopher Armstrong (Ret)

### Business Litigation:

Collora LLP has successfully represented clients in many different industries as advocates for their business-related complaints and defenders of their business-related interests. The firm's goal is to solve problems and to obtain the client's desired remedy or objective without the necessity of trial. However, if a case must go to trial, clients can rely upon the firm's tenacity and skillful representation in the courtroom. Collora LLP has represented a broad range of clients in general business litigation, such as corporations, partnerships and closely held businesses, financial service and insurance companies, non-profit organizations, professional corporations and professional service firms, foreign governmental entities, doctors, lawyers, brokers, engineers and other professionals.
Clients have come from different industries, including health care, financial services and insurance, waste and energy management, entertainment and media, food and beverage, employment and staffing and computers, both hardware and software.
**Contact:** Daniel J Cloherty

### Employment:

The firm has deep experience in employment-related litigation representing individuals and employers in a broad range of industries from administrative proceedings through appeal. Attorneys have expertise in Massachusetts common law claims and state and federal statutory claims and have successfully litigated ground-breaking rulings in Massachusetts employment law. The firm is also skilled in assisting clients in the prevention and investigation of potential employment liabilities before they turn into lawsuits. Collora LLP solves clients' employment problems with efficiency, expertise, and vigor.
**Contact:** Jody L Newman

### Heath Care:

The Health Care team provides effective legal advocacy on behalf of health care institutions and professionals in matters such as fraud and abuse investigations, false claims actions in state and federal courts, audits, as well as disciplinary and other administrative agency proceedings. Firm attorneys frequently represent health care professionals before the Board of Registration in Medicine and other licensing authorities, and have often represented physicians in hospital-based peer-review proceedings.  In addition, the health care team has represented health care institutions and providers involved in a variety of commercial and regulatory matters, including Medicare, Medicaid and other third-party administrator audits. Members of the health care practice have extensive experience in providing guidance and counsel regarding developments in health law and regulatory compliance.
**Contact:** Paul Cirel

### Securities Litigation:

Collora LLP has appeared as counsel of record in many civil actions arising out of the purchase or sale of securities, successfully representing both plaintiffs and defendants in a variety of securities-related disputes. Attorneys have represented individuals and corporations in state and federal courts, as well as private arbitration forums, dealing with a host of legal issues related to class actions, registration statements, disclosure statements, fraud, insider trading, and shareholder derivative actions including investigations by the SEC and state security offices.
**Contact:**  Michael A Collora

### White Collar Criminal Defense:

Collora LLP responds swiftly and effectively to government inquiries and enforcement actions. On behalf of clients, the firm maintains one of New England's largest and most recognized practices in the field of government enforcement. The firm is staffed with many well-known former state and federal prosecutors. The firm has successfully defended both corporations and individuals in many of the region's most significant state and federal probes and prosecutions. The firm has defended clients against a wide array of administrative and criminal charges such as financial, wire, securities, health care or tax fraud. Clients have often retained the firm prior to any charge when they first learned they were under investigation. Early intervention has enabled attorneys to persuade government prosecutors to drop all charges or negotiate settlements that protect clients while also protecting their licenses, permits and reputations. Although non public resolutions have drawn little public attention, Collora LLP has always valued them among its greatest achievements. Because of the firm's acquired acumen in the government enforcement arena, it is able to provide clients with effective advice and service for internal investigations and compliance review. Attorneys are equipped to handle parallel civil and criminal proceedings when they arise because many lawyers are cross-trained in business litigation, regulatory proceedings and government enforcement actions. They understand how an adverse regulatory or criminal action can influence a potential civil action, and vice versa. They are committed not only to producing a good result in the case they are handling for clients, but a result that will prevent collateral damage to clients' business.
**Contact:** William H Kettlewell
**Contact:** Kathy B Weinman

## PRACTICE AREAS

Appellate
Business Litigation
Employment Law
Health Care Law
Securities
White Collar Defense

## OFFICE

MASSACHUSETTS
**BOSTON:** 100 High Street, 20th Floor, 02110
Tel: 617 371 1000   Fax: 617 371 1037

# DAVIS, MALM & D'AGOSTINE, PC

**www**.davismalm.com  **tel:** 617 367 2500  **fax:** 617 523 6215

**Managing Partner:** Thomas S Fitzpatrick
**Executive Committee:** J Gavin Cockfield, Paul L Feldman
Number of Partners: 28  Number of Other Lawyers: 11

**OFFICES**

MASSACHUSETTS
**BOSTON:** One Boston Place, 201 Washington Street,
MA 02108
Tel: 617 367 2500  Fax: 617 523 6215

## Firm Overview:

Founded in 1979, Davis Malm is a premier mid-sized, full-service New England firm. The firm provides sophisticated, cost-effective legal services and represents local, national and international public and private businesses, institutions and individuals in a wide spectrum of industries. The attorneys at the firm practice at the top level of the profession. The firm delivers successful results to clients through direct partner involvement, responsive client service and practical and creative problem solving. Since 2011, the firm has had the distinct honor of being a member of the International Lawyers Network (ILN), representing Massachusetts and northern New England. ILN is an association of over 5,000 lawyers in 66 countries. ILN membership has enhanced the firm's already robust international services to clients doing business globally.

## Main Areas of Practice:

### Business:

Davis Malm's skilled business attorneys represent public and privately held businesses in a wide range of industries, including manufacturing, pharmaceutical, biotech, software, environmental management, internet commerce, service, distribution and medical, among others. The firm is known for its representation of buyers, sellers and lenders in connection with the full range of merger, acquisition and sale transactions. The breadth of experience of Davis Malm's business attorneys allows the firm to represent business clients in all areas of corporate and securities law, from initial organization through the entire range of business transactions over the life of the business.

### Commercial Lending & Real Estate Finance:

The commercial lending and real estate finance attorneys at Davis Malm have extensive expertise in both complex and routine commercial lending and real estate finance transactions, including term loans, revolving credit facilities, equipment financing, real estate acquisition financing, and fee and leasehold construction financing. The firm has particular expertise in the areas of floor plan and healthcare facility financing as well as closing and servicing US Small Business Administration loan transactions. Private equity bond financing and public finance transactions have been a specialty at Davis Malm since its founding. Two of the firm's shareholders drafted enabling legislation authorizing the issuance of tax-exempt special assessment bonds to finance local municipal infrastructure, which was enacted in 2012 as Chapter 23L of the Massachusetts General Laws. Since 1981, Davis Malm has had the distinction of being listed as bond counsel in The Bond Buyer's Municipal Marketplace, the industry's comprehensive reference source.

### Compensation & Benefits:

The firm's compensation and benefits attorneys consult regularly with business entities and their human resources professionals, corporate counsel, plan administrators and trustees on the complex rules—ERISA, tax, securities, insurance and accounting—that regulate benefits and compensation. Clients include NYSE-, AMEX- and NASDAQ-listed companies, senior officers, financial institutions, hospital and group medical practices, multi-employer pension plan boards, ESOP trustees, closely held businesses, benefit brokers, and organizations devoted to higher education, governmental purposes and charitable endeavors.

### Employment:

The firm regularly represents employers, executives and employees in all aspects of employment law, including discrimination law, breach of contract matters, noncompetition, trade secret and confidential information cases. Davis Malm's employment attorneys are experienced trial lawyers with a strong record of success who are prepared, when necessary, to negotiate, mediate, arbitrate and litigate employment issues in all administrative and judicial forums.

### Litigation:

Davis Malm's litigators have extensive experience handling civil controversies of all sizes and complexity for all types of clients. The firm resolves large and complex litigation for major, publicly traded companies and handles "bet the company" litigation for smaller, privately held enterprises and individuals. The litigation team handles each controversy, regardless of the size, with the same zealous dedication to victory and attention to the client. The attorneys work closely with clients to reduce their litigation risks and resolve disputes outside the courtroom arena whenever possible. The firm's commitment to dispute resolution demonstrates the importance the firm places on preserving its clients' management, human and financial resources.

### Real Estate & Environmental:

Davis Malm has a complete and varied real estate development, land use and transactional practice. The firm's practice involves all aspects of residential, commercial and industrial development, including acquisition, financing, permitting, appeals, land use litigation, conveyancing, commercial leasing, creation of condominium documents, representing condominium associations and performing foreclosures. Environmental compliance and contamination matters are also areas in which the firm has extensive experience and a strong record of success.

### Trusts & Estates:

Davis Malm's trusts and estates attorneys have extensive experience in counseling individuals and families to accomplish their financial and charitable goals, and to plan the orderly disposition of their assets. The firm advises clients on charitable giving, sophisticated estate and gift taxation issues, and the effective administration of estates and trusts. For clients who own interests in privately held businesses, the firm provides succession planning geared toward a smooth, tax-efficient transfer of ownership of the business at retirement or death. The firm has developed a concentrated expertise in four specialized areas: Wealth Transfer and Business Succession Planning, Planning for Persons with Disabilities, Planning for Nontraditional Families, and Planning for Personal Injury Settlements.

### Clients:

Clients include Bernardi Auto Group, Brook Venture Partners, LLC, Clean Harbors, Inc., Comfort Foods, Inc., Conroy Development Corporation, Eastern Bank, Equity LifeStyle Properties, Inc., ESS Group, Inc., Exeter Hospital, Fabrico, Inc., First Student, Inc., F.W. Webb Company, Handa Pharmaceuticals, LLC, Hannaford Bros., International Fund for Animal Welfare, Maggiore Construction Corporation, Massachusetts Development Finance Agency, Massachusetts Laborers Pension Fund, Materials Systems, Inc., Medicalis, Inc., M&T Bank, N.A., New England Office Supply, Inc., Northern Bank & Trust Company, Optikos Corporation, Pulte Homes, Inc., Pure Hockey, LLC, Rockland Trust, Stonehill College, Inc., Trigen-Boston Energy Corporation, Tufts Medical Center, UniFirst Corporation, Versatile Club Technologies, Inc., Wendy's International, Inc., Wentworth-Douglass Hospital.

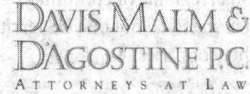

# EDWARDS WILDMAN PALMER LLP

www.edwardswildman.com **tel:** 617 239 0100 **fax:** 617 227 4420

**Chairman:** Alan J Levin
**Managing Partner:** Robert L Shuftan
Number of partners: 295   Number of total lawyers: 629

## Firm Overview:

Edwards Wildman is a 125-year-old full-service, business-minded, Am Law 100 firm whose lawyers work with *Fortune* 500 and FTSE 250 clients and start-up companies alike, throughout a range of industries across three continents. The firm's lawyers are known internationally for their work in private equity, venture capital, corporate and finance transactions, complex litigation, insurance and reinsurance and intellectual property. Their clients know them as trusted legal and business advisers, providing the strategic, collaborative and client-focused counsel that helps protect and advance their business goals. Creative yet pragmatic, Edwards Wildman lawyers bring deep industry knowledge and take the time to develop an intimate understanding of their clients' businesses, to help them effectively navigate risk, regulatory issues and the diverse challenges of a competitive marketplace, in the boardroom or the courtroom.

## Main Areas of Practice:

### Business Law:
The firm's Business Law Department handles billions of dollars of private equity, venture capital and debt finance transactions, mergers and acquisitions and public offerings for clients, with particularly deep experience in telecommunications, media and broadcasting, healthcare, life sciences, technology, banking and financial services, and insurance and reinsurance. Edwards Wildman is consistently ranked as a most active law firm based on the number of deals closed annually.

### Insurance & Reinsurance:
Globally, the firm has one of the largest Insurance and Reinsurance Departments, dedicated to the business of insurance. The firm's clients include the world's largest insurance and reinsurance companies, which it represents in corporate, transactional and regulatory matters, in reinsurance arbitrations and litigation, and in sophisticated claims and coverage matters.

### Intellectual Property:
The Intellectual Property Department is composed of lawyers and patent agents holding degrees in technology and scientific disciplines, including many with PhD degrees in engineering, life sciences and chemistry. The firm is consistently ranked among the leading US firms for number of patents prosecuted to issuance each year and is widely recognized for achieving excellent results in patent litigation and interferences.

### Litigation:
The Litigation Department represents a broad range of clients across many industries and has represented clients as national, regional or coordinating counsel in matters in 47 US states, all but one US territory, the UK and several other countries.

Edwards Wildman litigators frequently handle national class-action cases involving antitrust/competition, asset tracing, intellectual property, securities, employment, environment, construction, white-collar defense, products liability and various commercial litigation.

### Private Client:
The firm's Private Client Department provides advice and representation to individuals and families in the world of tax law and finance. This group is one of the largest and most experienced in the country.

### Public Finance:
For over a century, the firm's nationally recognized public finance practice has assisted state and local governments in accessing capital markets to finance major public projects and programs.

### Public Policy & Government Relations:
The firm's public policy and government relations professionals have the demonstrated experience and capability to prepare successful government relations strategies in high pressure, complex, and time sensitive situations.

### Real Estate:
The Real Estate Department handles matters ranging from complex public/private development relationships, sophisticated financing structures and local, state and federal regulatory and permitting schemes.

### Restructuring & Insolvency:
The Restructuring and Insolvency Department regularly advises premier financial institutions, institutional investors, debt investors, finance companies, insurers and sureties to enforce creditors' rights and to achieve strategic goals in the context of structured transactions, commercial litigation, loan workout, debt restructurings and bankruptcy.

## OFFICES

**CALIFORNIA**
**LOS ANGELES:** 1901 Avenue of the Stars, CA 90067
Tel: 310 860 8700  Fax: 310 860 3800

**ORANGE COUNTY:** 3 Park Plaza, CA 92614
Tel: 949 423 2100  Fax: 949 423 2101

**CONNECTICUT**
**HARTFORD:** 20 Church Street, CT 06103
Tel: 860 525 5065  Fax: 860 527 4198

**STAMFORD:** One Canterbury Green, CT 06901
Tel: 203 975 7505  Fax: 203 975 7180

**DISTRICT OF COLUMBIA**
**WASHINGTON DC:** 1255 23rd Street, NW, DC 20037
Tel: 202 478 7370  Fax: 202 478 7380

**FLORIDA**
**FORT LAUDERDALE:** 500 W. Cypress Creek Road, FL 33309
Tel: 561 833 7700

**WEST PALM BEACH:** 525 Okeechobee Blvd, FL 33401
Tel: 561 833 7700  Fax: 561 655 8719

**ILLINOIS**
**CHICAGO:** 225 West Wacker Drive, IL 60606
Tel: 312 201 2000  Fax: 312 201 2555

**MASSACHUSETTS**
**BOSTON:** 111 Huntington Avenue, MA 02199-7613
Tel: 617 239 0100  Fax: 617 227 4420

**NEW JERSEY**
**MADISON:** One Giralda Farms, NJ 07940
Tel: 973 520 2300  Fax: 973 520 2600

**NEW YORK**
**NEW YORK:** 750 Lexington Avenue, NY 10022
Tel: 212 308 4411  Fax: 212 308 4844

**RHODE ISLAND**
**PROVIDENCE:** 2800 Financial Plaza, RI 02903
Tel: 401 274 9200  Fax: 401 276 6611

## INTERNATIONAL OFFICES
The firm also has offices in London, Hong Kong and Tokyo.

**Tax & Benefits:**
The attorneys in the firm's Tax and Benefits Department assist clients in structuring a wide variety of transactions, including mergers and acquisitions, corporate finance, and formation of, or investment in, pass-through entities.

# FOLEY HOAG LLP

**www.foleyhoag.com tel:** 617 832 1000 **fax:** 617 832 7000

**Co-Managing Partners:** Adam P Kahn, William R Kolb
Number of partners: 95
Number of lawyers: 210

## Firm Overview:

Foley Hoag is a dynamic law firm that represents public and private clients in a wide range of disputes and transactions worldwide. The firm has expertise in industries such as life sciences and healthcare, technology, energy and renewables, investment management and professional services. It also offers clients market-leading international litigation and arbitration and corporate social responsibility services. From offices in Boston, Washington, D.C. and Paris, and the Emerging Enterprise Center in Waltham, Massachusetts, its lawyers provide strategic legal advice that is tailored to each of its clients' unique goals. Foley Hoag combines powerful regional, national and international practices that share a common emphasis on client service and are focused on helping clients succeed through the delivery of exceptional legal service.

## Main Areas of Practice:

### Industry Focus:

Foley Hoag recognizes the importance of understanding its clients' industries and partnering with them to meet day-to-day challenges and opportunities. The firm's long-standing focus on high-growth industries enables its lawyers to provide creative but practical solutions for clients in the life sciences, healthcare, technology, energy, clean technology and financial and professional services sectors. To serve companies in these rapidly changing industries, Foley Hoag brings an understanding of its clients' products and services and related intellectual property value, combined with the insight of political and regulatory issues, unique financial aspects, or environmental concerns affecting their businesses. This multidisciplinary approach draws on the support of lawyers who have been scientists, engineers and researchers and have held senior-level positions in presidential administrations, on Capitol Hill, in regulatory agencies and with industry trade organizations. Particularly important to clients in the life sciences sector, the firm features a full complement of lawyers and professionals in government strategies and FDA/reimbursement practices. The firm also is an essential partner to technology clients. Its lawyers have a deep understanding of the sector, having been involved in many important industry milestones, including the IPO of the first software company listed on the New York Stock Exchange and the largest merger in the software industry.

### Litigation:

Foley Hoag's highly respected Litigation Department is a cornerstone of the firm, handling complex and novel dispute resolution cases on a global scale, with prominent experience in the areas of intellectual property litigation, securities litigation, accountants professional liability, business crimes and government investigations and public international law. Foley Hoag lawyers have unique experience in handling complex state-to-state disputes, investor-state arbitration and international commercial and construction arbitration. Foley Hoag provides clients with a range of services aimed at resolving disputes, including preventive counseling, pre-litigation investigation, prosecution and defense of claims at the trial level and representation in post-trial and appellate proceedings. In addition to traditional courtroom trials, it represents clients in arbitration proceedings, before administrative tribunals and in alternative dispute resolution settings.

### Intellectual Property:

Ideas and designs are as important to corporate success as financial and operational expertise. The firm's Intellectual Property Group is comprised of more than 80 professionals, including lawyers, scientists, engineers, medical doctors and others experienced in patent prosecution, patent litigation, IP due diligence and strategy, licensing and strategic alliances, and trademark, copyright and unfair competition counseling. Together they provide a strategic global approach to managing clients' intellectual property portfolios.

### Business:

Foley Hoag's Business Department provides strategic advice in a cost-efficient and responsive manner. Members of the group regularly counsel clients in transactions involving initial and follow-on public offerings, secondary offerings, PIPE transactions, private placements and resales of restricted securities, business combinations involving equity, cross-border transactions, proxy and consent solicitations, tender and exchange offers, going private transactions, fund formations and reorganizations in bankruptcy. Foley Hoag provides its clients with sophisticated guidance on complying with securities regulation matters, including corporate governance, insider trading, public company reporting and disclosure, exchange and NASDAQ rules and equity compensation plans. The firm's Investment Advisers and Private Investment Funds Group counsels investment advisers, hedge funds, and other private investment funds, including those with alternative asset strategies, in addressing their complex structural, financial, regulatory and compliance issues.

Clients include managers forming their first funds and mature investment groups managing billions of dollars in multiple domestic and international strategies.

## OFFICES

### MASSACHUSETTS

**BOSTON:** Seaport West, 155 Seaport Blvd., MA 02210-2600
Tel: 617 832 1000  Fax: 617 832 7000

**WALTHAM:** Emerging Enterprise Center at Foley Hoag, Bay Colony Corporate Center, 1000 Winter Street, Suite 2000, MA 02451
Tel: 781 895 5900  Fax: 781 895 5999

### DISTRICT OF COLUMBIA

**BOSTON:** 1875 K Street, NW, Suite 800, DC 20006-1238
Tel: 202 223 1200  Fax: 202 785 6687

## INTERNATIONAL OFFICES

The firm also has an office in Paris.

# GOODWIN PROCTER LLP

**www.**goodwinprocter.com **tel:** 617 570 1000 **fax:** 617 523 1231

**Chairman:** Regina M Pisa
**Managing Partner:** Robert S Insolia

## Firm Overview:

Goodwin Procter is one of the nation's leading law firms, with offices in Boston, Hong Kong, London, Los Angeles, New York, San Diego, San Francisco, Silicon Valley and Washington, DC. Excelling at complex and sophisticated transactional work and precedent-setting, bet-the-company litigation, the firm combines in-depth legal knowledge with practical business experience to help clients maximize opportunities, manage risk and move their business forward. The firm hires talented, motivated people committed to excellence, innovation and client service, and believes that every attorney and staff member deserves a supportive, meritocratic environment in which people of all backgrounds are given the opportunity to excel and thrive. It is one of only a handful of comparably sized law firms in the United States with a woman serving as chairman. The firm takes seriously its obligations as a corporate citizen and is dedicated to community service. Through its extensive and longstanding pro bono program, Goodwin Procter encourages its legal staff to assist those unable to afford legal representation.

## Main Areas of Practice:

Goodwin Procter provides corporate law and litigation services to clients ranging from emerging companies to *Fortune* 500 multinationals, with a focus on matters involving private equity; technology companies and life sciences; real estate, REITs and real estate capital markets; financial institutions; intellectual property; products liability and mass torts; and securities litigation and white-collar defense.

## Business Law:

The firm's business law attorneys specialize in transactional work and are respected for their ability to structure, negotiate and close deals that balance clients' immediate objectives with long-term strategic advantages. Primary areas of industry focus are financial services, technology, life sciences, media and communications, energy, manufacturing, consumer products and real estate. Services range from counseling, financing, fund and insolvency work to structuring complex mergers and acquisitions, joint ventures, private equity deals and capital markets transactions.

## Litigation:

Goodwin Procter's litigation matters are factually and legally complex. Its litigators are engaged in high stakes cases across the country, conducting trials, arbitrations, mediations and negotiations, and counseling on litigation avoidance and risk management. These matters primarily involve consumer financial services, intellectual property, products liability and mass torts, white collar defense, securities litigation, commercial litigation, labor and employment, environmental litigation, ERISA and antitrust. Clients include companies in the software, technology, manufacturing, mining, defense, consumer products, life sciences, communications, real estate, healthcare and financial services industries.

## Clients:

Goodwin Procter represents a diverse client base, with clients ranging from entrepreneurial emerging companies to established multinationals. The firm's clients present complex issues and expect cost-effective results to be delivered under tight deadlines. Client service begins with knowing the clients, knowing their business and knowing their competitors. With this information, the firm's attorneys leverage their specialized skills and expertise to deliver responsive, knowledgeable and practical legal advice. The firm maximizes its practice efficiency by focusing on effective use of technology and knowledge management.

## PRACTICE AREAS

Business Law
Financial Institutions
Intellectual Property
Litigation
Private Equity
Product Liability & Mass Torts
Real Estate, REITs & Real Estate Capital Markets
Securities Litigation & White-Collar Defense
Technology Companies & Life Sciences

## OFFICES

### MASSACHUSETTS

**BOSTON:** Exchange Place, MA 02109
Tel: 617 570 1000   Fax: 617 523 1231
Email: rpisa@goodwinprocter.com

### CALIFORNIA

**LOS ANGELES:** 601 S Figueroa Street, CA 90017
Tel: 213 426 2500   Fax: 213 623 1673
Email: lfeldman@goodwinprocter.com

**MENLO PARK:** 135 Commonwealth Drive, CA 94025
Tel: 650 752 3100   Fax: 650 853 1038
Email: amccusker@goodwinprocter.com

**SAN DIEGO:** 4365 Executive Drive, CA 92121
Tel: 858 202 2700   Fax: 858 457 1255
Email: dkleinfeld@goodwinprocter.com

**SAN FRANCISCO:** Three Embarcadero Center, CA 94111
Tel: 415 733 6000   Fax: 415 677 9041
Email: bbugdano@goodwinprocter.com

### DISTRICT OF COLUMBIA

**WASHINGTON DC:** 901 New York Avenue, NW, DC 20001
Tel: 202 346 4000   Fax: 202 346 4444
Email: whanlon@goodwinprocter.com

### NEW YORK

**NEW YORK:** The New York Times Building, 620 Eighth Avenue, NY 10018
Tel: 212 813 8800   Fax: 212 355 3333
Email: asolecki@goodwinprocter.com

### INTERNATIONAL OFFICES

The firm also has offices in Hong Kong and London.

# GOODWIN

# PROCTER

# MINTZ, LEVIN, COHN, FERRIS, GLOVSKY AND POPEO

**www.**mintz.com **tel:** 617 542 6000 **fax:** 617 542 2241

**Chairman:** R Robert Popeo
**Vice Chairman:** Andrew R Urban
**Managing Member:** Robert I Bodian

**Firm Overview:**
Mintz Levin's 450 attorneys counsel major public corporations, privately held businesses, entrepreneurs, emerging growth companies, investors and underwriters, directors and officers, medical and academic institutions and public agencies.

## Main Areas of Practice:

### Antitrust & Federal Regulation:
Spans the full spectrum, encompassing counseling clients through antitrust issues that affect business relationships, including joint ventures and competitor collaborations, shepherding transactions through the merger review process and litigating antitrust cases, including criminal matters.

### Bankruptcy & Restructuring:
Represents all parties and interests involved in restructurings, including acquisitions of insolvent companies. Mintz Levin is well known for its representation of debtors and creditors in Chapter 11 cases and out-of-court restructurings. The firm is one of the best known in the country for representing tax-free bond holders in workouts and reorganizations.

### Communications:
Advises and represents clients in a broad range of regulatory, legislative and litigation matters before the FCC, Congress, state public utility commissions, Executive Branch agencies and federal and state courts, as well as on domestic and international business transactions.

### Corporate & Securities:
Advises clients internationally, from start-ups with little more than an idea to large multinational companies, venture capital firms and investment banks, and research organizations and institutions, in all stages of the capital-raising process (from start-up funding, to initial public offerings, to continuing debt and equity finance needs, including private placements and public offerings), corporate governance and compliance, licensing and collaborations, and mergers and acquisitions.

### Employment, Labor & Benefits:
Advises employers and their executives on complex labor and employment law issues, relating to government agency investigations and litigation, HR policies and procedures, retirement, welfare and other benefit plans, employment and executive compensation agreements, and representing management in collective bargaining negotiations and other labor issues.

### Energy & Clean Technology:
Mintz Levin was one of the first law firms to establish a dedicated clean technology practice. The group works with start-ups to established companies and financing sources, and is one of the only law firms that counts its Energy & Clean Technology Practice among its top industry practices. The practice serves more than 300 clients, and since 2006 has completed more than 300 transactions in this sector totaling over $7 billion.

### Environmental:
Represents the nation's most sophisticated corporations in high profile environmental matters, including the prosecution and defense of complex claims under federal and state environmental laws, the permitting of major energy and infrastructure projects and the remediation and redevelopment of Brownfields. All of its partner level lawyers are individually recognized in Chambers USA.

### Health Law:
Represents public, private and non-profit healthcare providers and suppliers, payors, investors, pharmaceutical, biotech and medical device companies in all stages of commercial development. Attorneys provide a variety of transactional, litigation and regulatory services and advise clients on issues involving accreditation, licensing and certification; antitrust; clinical trials and FDA regulations; corporate governance; fraud and abuse; healthcare compliance, reimbursement and other regulatory matters; HIPAA and other laws governing health information privacy and security; and government investigations.

### Intellectual Property:
Focuses on protecting, licensing and enforcing intellectual property rights, and on matters relating to trade secrets and unfair competition. Counsel clients in a wide range of industries and represents them before the U.S. Patent and Trademark Office, the European Patent Office and other regulatory and administrative agencies and tribunals and in all aspects of intellectual property litigation.

### Life Sciences:
Mintz Levin has served as one of the leading law firms to the life sciences industry since the industry's birth in the 1970s. Today, the firm advises life science companies of every size, from start-ups looking for their first funding to public companies with products on the market, as well as venture capital firms, investment banks, research and academic institutions and others engaged in the life sciences ecosystem.

### Litigation:
Focus on antitrust, bankruptcy, construction, corporate compliance and internal investigations, employment, environmental, foreign corrupt practices act, insurance and reinsurance, intellectual property, product liability and complex tort litigation, securities, white collar defense and real estate and land use. Clients include closely-held corporations, *Fortune* 100 companies and multinational corporations, including businesses in the financial services, technology, construction, healthcare, and life sciences industries.

### Public Finance:
Serve as bond, borrower's and underwriter's counsel for numerous tax-exempt bond financings annually, generally ranking among the top firms in the Northeast in these categories. The firm is nationally recognized for its expertise in tax and disclosure issues relative to tax exempt bonds. In addition, the firm has a nationally pre-eminent practice representing bondholders and their trustees in maximizing capital recovery on defaulted transactions. The firm also has an active practice in resolving tax controversies and post-issuance compliance.

### Real Estate:
Represent owners, developers, public and private agencies, lenders, tenants and landlords across the country in sophisticated real estate acquisitions, dispositions, developments, financings and leasing transactions. The Real Estate Group also advises corporations with facilities around the world.

---

## OFFICES

**CALIFORNIA**
**LOS ANGELES:** Tel: 310 586 3200  Fax: 310 586 3202
**SAN DIEGO:** Tel: 858 314 1500  Fax: 858 314 1501
**SAN FRANCISCO:** Tel: 415 432 6000  Fax: 415 432 6001

**CONNECTICUT**
**STAMFORD:** Tel: 203 388 8464  Fax: 203 658 1701

**DISTRICT OF COLUMBIA**
**WASHINGTON, DC:** Tel: 202 434 7300  Fax: 202 434 7400

**MASSACHUSETTS**
**BOSTON:** Tel: 617 542 6000  Fax: 617 542 2241

**NEW YORK**
**NEW YORK:** Tel: 212 935 3000  Fax: 212 983 3115

## INTERNATIONAL OFFICES
The firm also has an office in London, United Kingdom, and a liason office in Israel.

# MORGAN, BROWN & JOY, LLP

www.morganbrown.com

**Managing Partner:** Robert P Joy
Number of partners: 17
Number of other lawyers: 14

**OFFICES**

MASSACHUSETTS
**BOSTON:** 200 State Street, MA 02109-2605
Tel: 617 523 6666 Fax: 617 367 3125

## Firm Overview:

Founded in 1923, Morgan, Brown & Joy is New England's oldest and largest management-side employment law firm. The firm's continued longevity and success can be credited to its ability to respond rapidly to changes in the law and the workplace and to the value and return on investment that it provides employers. The firm represents clients before courts at all levels, including the United States Supreme Court as well as state and federal agencies. Clients range from *Fortune* 100 corporations to small businesses and across all sectors of the economy including retailing, technology, biotechnology, healthcare, colleges and universities, utilities, insurance, banking, government and manufacturing. Morgan, Brown & Joy's focus is on anticipating and finding solutions to the ever-expanding range of employment-related legal issues in order to avoid the time and cost of litigation. When litigation becomes necessary, the firm aggressively defends its clients and has a proven record of litigation success.

## Main Areas of Practice:

### Labor & Employment:

Morgan, Brown & Joy's services include advice on all aspects of work place discrimination, harassment or retaliation issues; collective bargaining and labor-management relations; reductions in force and terminations; FLSA; NLRA; FMLA; ERISA; OFCCP; worker's compensation; business tort and contract litigation including trade secrets, non-competition agreements and individual employment contracts.

### Employment Counsel & Legal Advice:

Morgan, Brown & Joy focuses on anticipating and finding solutions to the ever-expanding range of employment-related legal issues in an effort to avoid the time and cost of litigation. Its services include: advice on all aspects of workplace discrimination, harassment or retaliation issues; comprehensive counsel on labor-management relationships; advice on reductions in force, terminations and handling employee complaints; expertise on changes in business operations and labor contracts due to mergers and acquisition; counsel on FMLA, wage and hour issues, workers' compensation claims and ERISA, and the ever-increasing list of employment-related laws; guidance on the complex set of laws and regulations governing employee illness, injury, disability and medical leaves; business tort and contract litigation including trade secrets, non-competition agreements and individual employment contracts.

### Litigation:

Morgan, Brown & Joy attorneys are not only expert advisors in employment law, but also experienced litigators. When the same team of attorneys handles the case from inception to the courtroom, they bring complete knowledge of the case along with skills in negotiation, mediation and alternative dispute resolution that can help minimize the most abrasive and expensive litigation. When litigation becomes necessary, the firm aggressively defends its clients in all of the employment areas about which they provide advice and counsel.

### Prevention & Training:

Morgan, Brown & Joy emphasizes the importance of seeking legal advice at the earliest possible time.Because the prevention of claims is preferable to the defense of claims, they offer the following services: its Audit and Training Team reviews clients' policies and practices and provides training to the workforce on how to avoid litigation or other adverse legal consequences; human resource support includes employee handbooks and counsel on a range of personnel policies.

### Labor Law:

Resolution of labor disputes is its primary objective, and they support employers with counsel and litigation related to: unfair labor practice charges; negotiations of collective bargaining agreements; grievance and arbitration; National Labor Relations Act (NLRA) and state labor law matters, including union organizing issues and union avoidance strategy.

### Employment Law Leadership:

Morgan, Brown & Joy holds the distinction of having two partners who have served as Chairman of the Labor and Employment Law Section of the American Bar Association. Its attorneys are active in the American Bar Association and the Massachusetts Bar Association, as well as national organizations in specific industries such as the National Association of College and University Attorneys and the National Retail Federation. Its attorneys frequently serve as faculty members of educational programs sponsored by these and other organizations. Morgan, Brown & Joy attorneys are members of multiple state bars including California, Connecticut, Georgia, Massachusetts, New Hampshire, New York, Ohio, Pennsylvania, Rhode Island and Vermont.

### Clients:

Representative clients include MACY'S, Inc.,Home Depot U.S.A., Inc., General Electric Company,Harvard University, NSTAR Electric and Gas Corp.,CVS Corporation, Oracle Corporation, Entergy Nuclear Operations, Inc., Federal Express Corporation, Massport, MBTA, Liberty Mutual Ins. Co, WHDH-TV, City of Boston, University of Vermont, University of New Hampshire, Shaw's Supermarkets, Inc., General Dynamics, Boston College, Providence College, Brandeis University, MIT, Nordstrom, Inc., Boston Medical Center, Walgreen Co., Delaware North Companies, Stop & Shop Co., Morgan Stanley, BJ's Wholesale Club, Inc.

# MURPHY & KING PROFESSIONAL CORPORATION

**www.**murphyking.com **tel:** 617 423 0400 **fax:** 617 423 0498

**Managing Partner:** James Coyne King
**Executive Director:** Robert J Perry
Number of partners: 13  Number of lawyers: 29

**OFFICES**

MASSACHUSETTS

**BOSTON:** One Beacon Street, 21st Floor, MA 02108-3107
Tel: 617 423 0400   Fax: 617 423 0498

NEW YORK

**NEW YORK:** 590 Madison Avenue, 35th Floor, NY 10022
Tel: 212 631 0223   Fax: 212 624 0223

## Firm Overview:

Since 1980 Murphy & King P.C. has met the legal needs of individuals, small businesses and large corporations by delivering on-target solutions in a focused and cost-effective manner. Murphy & King attorneys represent clients in areas ranging from commercial litigation, bankruptcy and financial restructuring to business formation and labor and employment. Clients include private and public corporations, investment partnerships, government agencies, *Fortune* 500 companies, individuals and non-profit organizations. Murphy & King's sensible approach to legal guidance is embodied in its 13 partners and 16 associates and reflected in its ongoing investment in the most current technology available to the legal profession. This commitment to technology allows Murphy & King attorneys to build evidentiary databases and offer interactive documents that allow for immediate access to critical case information, thereby truncating the time between the onset of a client's problem and its resolution. Exceptional legal talent and catered client service have earned Murphy & King a reputation as a top-notch mid-sized firm.

## Main Areas of Practice:

### Litigation:

Litigation is Murphy & King's largest practice area, and its attorneys appear before state and federal courts and administrative agencies with an 'at trial' success rate of 85 percent or higher. Several cases tried by Murphy & King attorneys have set legal precedents in areas such as intellectual property, business fraud, bankruptcy, leveraged buyouts, professional malpractice and employment. The firm's litigation attorneys led by David Lee Evans and Daniel J Lyne, work with clients outside the courtroom as well, guiding them through critical cost/ benefit decisions. The wide-ranging Civil Litigation Practice Group offers expertise in the following areas: financial representations, warranty and fraud claims, business divorce and intra-entity disputes, real estate development, ownership and construction disputes, labor and employment, intellectual property claims, insolvency, public and administrative law and fiduciary duty and professional liability claims.
**Contact:** David Lee Evans, Daniel J Lyne

### Bankruptcy & Financial Restructuring:

The Bankruptcy and Financial Restructuring Group represents debtors, creditors and creditors' committees, estate fiduciaries, investors in formal insolvency proceedings and out-of-court workouts throughout the United States. Led by Harold B Murphy, recognized in two leading legal publications, Chambers USA and America's

Leading Business Lawyers, Murphy & King bankruptcy lawyers have been nationally recognized for delivering superior results in a timely and cost-effective manner. Members of the group include former law clerks to bankruptcy judges and attorneys with the Office of the United States Trustee. Murphy & King's Bankruptcy Practice is regularly called upon to serve as estate representatives and counsel in Chapter 7 and 11 cases. The group has represented clients in all types of businesses including real estate, hospitality, healthcare, technology, telecommunications, manufacturing and retail.
**Contact:** Harold B Murphy

### Corporate:

The Corporate Practice at Murphy & King represents clients in mergers and acquisitions and in the purchase and sale of business assets. Murphy & King's corporate attorneys provide counsel to owners and investors in the sale, acquisition, development, zoning, and leasing of commercial real estate. James Coyne King and Robert E Richards, Jr head this practice area and have compiled a team of professionals who are able to negotiate complex transactions and navigate due diligence reviews, debt and equity structures, licensing or transfer of intellectual property, business organization and commercial loans. The group also counsels both public and private sector employers to ensure that the myriad legal requirements concerning personnel practices do not distract them from achieving their business objectives.
**Contact:** James Coyne King, Robert E Richards, Jr

### Alternative Dispute Resolution:

Murphy & King's Alternative Dispute Resolution Practice stems from the firm's expertise inside the courtroom. Murphy & King's attorneys are experienced trial attorneys, however, they understand that not all cases need to be settled in court. The firm encourages clients involved in cases with potential or actual litigation to explore the benefits of alternative dispute resolution. The Alternative Dispute Resolution Group, headed by David Lee Evans, has settled countless business disputes through mediation, arbitration or other informal dispute resolution proceedings, bringing conflicts to a quick and less expensive resolution. Attorneys at Murphy & King have served in more than 100 cases for the American Arbitration Association's Commercial and Large Complex Case Panels. The firm also co-founded the Technology Company Mediation Program for the Massachusetts Software and Internet Council. Murphy & King's Alternative Dispute Resolution Group has successfully handled the legal needs of deadlocked corporations, professional malpractice and intellectual property claims and complex business disputes.
**Contact:** David Lee Evans

# NIXON PEABODY LLP

www.nixonpeabody.com **tel:** +1 617 345 1000 **fax:** 617 345 1300

**CEO & Managing Partner:** Andrew I. Glincher
Number of lawyers: 700

## Firm Overview:

Nixon Peabody sees 21st century law as a tool to help shape its clients' futures. The firm's role is to navigate its clients through the unbelievably exciting and challenging times we live in—foreseeing obstacles and opportunities in their space, smoothing the way, and ensuring they are equipped to innovate and deploy winning legal strategies. The qualities that drive the firm are extreme understanding of its clients and their industries, a future-leaning orientation, and a culture that taps collective intelligence to create value for clients. As a Global 100 firm, Nixon Peabody provides counsel on the full range of corporate transactions, disputes, and regulatory challenges.

## Main Areas of Practice:

### Affordable Housing:
National leaders representing developers of government financed and assisted multifamily housing projects, housing authorities, state housing finance agencies, and financiers and equity syndicators of these projects.

### Business & Finance:
200 business lawyers who collaborate on the full range of mergers and acquisitions, investments, joint ventures, licensing, and strategic transactions for both private and public clients.

### Energy:
Counsel on traditional and renewable energy financing, development, siting and permitting, regulatory compliance, M&A, divestitures, and operating agreements.

### Government Investigations & White-Collar Defense:
Extensive counseling, investigation, and litigation experience in all forms of government inquiry. The firm manages matters from investigation through grand jury process, trial and, if necessary, appeal, and collateral proceedings.

### Health Services:
Services for health care providers and companies including: corporate transactions, regulatory, reimbursement, privacy, development, financing, litigation, and strategic planning.

### Intellectual Property:
A full range of patent prosecution, IP litigation, trademark, licensing, copyright, brand management, and trade secret protection.

### Labor & Employment:
Comprehensive labor and employment resources, including advice and counseling, strategic planning, training, administrative response, and civil litigation.

### Products: Class Action, Trade & Industry Representation:
Experienced counsel for high stakes, multi-jurisdictional cases involving products liability and complex tort litigation.

### Life Sciences:
Highly integrated, cross-practice team recognized for transactional, regulatory, and litigation services for pharmaceutical, biotechnology, and medical device companies.

### Litigation & Dispute Resolution:
More than 300 litigators representing clients in federal and state courts, the US Supreme Court, and the US Courts of Appeals, as well as in mediation, arbitration, and other methods of alternative dispute resolution. From early case assessment to verdict or settlement, the firm handles matters ranging from complex commercial disputes and disruptive contractual situations to bet-the-company class actions.

### M&A:
Honored as "Dealmakers of the Year" by American Lawyer. In 2012, recognized by the Association for Corporate Growth (ACG) and M&A Advisor as the legal advisor of the "Middle Market Deal of the Year" as well as the "Cross-Border Deal of the Year."

### Private Equity & Investment Funds:
A national leader in advising institutional investors, private equity funds, and portfolio companies, particularly in the middle market. Ranked among the most active law firms for private equity and venture capital transactions, as well as for fund formation and investments.

### Public Finance:
One of the largest public finance practices in the U.S., regularly ranked among the 10 most active bond and underwriter counsels in dollar value of bonds issued.

### Real Estate:
Nationally ranked in real estate finance, restructuring and workouts, acquisition, and development of commercial real estate.

### Tax Credit Finance & Syndication:
A national leader in advising on transactions involving the new markets tax credit, and tax credits leveraged for historic rehabilitation, renewable energy projects, and development of low-income housing.

## OFFICES

### CALIFORNIA
**LOS ANGELES:** Gas Company Tower, 555 West Fifth Street, CA 90013
Tel: 213 629 6000  Fax: 213 629 6001

**SAN FRANCISCO:** One Embarcadero Center, CA 94111
Tel: 415 984 8200  Fax: 415 984 8300

**PALO ALTO:** 2 Palo Alto Square, 3000 El Camino Real, CA 94306
Tel: 650 320 7700  Fax: 650 320 7701

### DISTRICT OF COLUMBIA
**WASHINGTON DC:** 401 Ninth Street NW, Suite 900, DC 20004
Tel: 202 585 8000  Fax: 202 585 8080

### ILLINOIS
**CHICAGO:** 300 South Riverside Plaza, IL 60606
Tel: 312 425 3900  Fax: 312 425 3909

### MASSACHUSETTS
**BOSTON:** 100 Summer Street, MA 02110
Tel: 617 345 1000  Fax: 617 345 1300

### NEW HAMPSHIRE
**MANCHESTER:** 900 Elm Street, NH 03101
Tel: 603 628 4000  Fax: 603 628 4040

### NEW YORK
**ALBANY:** 677 Broadway, NY 12207
Tel: 518 427 2650  Fax: 518 427 2666

**BUFFALO:** Key Towers, 40 Fountain Plaza, Suite 500, NY 14202
Tel: 716 853 8100  Fax: 716 853 8109

**LONG ISLAND:** 50 Jericho Quadrangle, Jericho, NY 11753
Tel: 516 832 7500  Fax: 516 832 7555

**NEW YORK:** 437 Madison Avenue, NY 10022
Tel: 212 940 3000  Fax: 212 940 3111

**ROCHESTER:** 1300 Clinton Square, NY 14604
Tel: 585 263 1000  Fax: 585 263 1600

### RHODE ISLAND
**PROVIDENCE:** One Citizens Plaza, RI 02903
Tel: 401 454 1000  Fax: 401 454 1030

### INTERNATIONAL OFFICES:
The firm also has offices in Beijing, Hong Kong, London and Shanghai.

**NIXON PEABODY** LLP
ATTORNEYS AT LAW

# NUTTER McCLENNEN & FISH LLP

**www.**nutter.com **tel:** +1 617 439 2000 **fax:** +1 617 310 9000

**Co-Managing Partners:** Deborah J Manus, William C Geary III
**Chairman:** Michael E Mooney
Number of partners: 76
Number of lawyers: 146

**OFFICES**

MASSACHUSETTS:
**BOSTON:** Nutter McClennen & Fish LLP, Seaport West, 155 Seaport Boulevard, MA 02210
Tel: +1 617 439 2000 Fax: +1 617 310 9000
Email: kgormley@nutter.com

## Firm Overview:

Nutter McClennen & Fish LLP is a firm of top quality lawyers representing clients who include leading global corporations, major banks and other public and private businesses, innovative emerging growth companies, entrepreneurs and capital sources, as well as medical and educational institutions, charitable foundations and families. The attorneys of Nutter provide expertise in a range of practice areas that include business and finance, litigation, intellectual property, real estate, tax, and trusts and estates. Numerous Nutter partners in many areas of legal practice have been selected for inclusion in the Chambers USA directory. In addition, the firm has repeatedly received top tier national rankings and top tier Boston rankings in the US News & World Report/Best Lawyers survey. Twenty-five Nutter attorneys are designated Best Lawyers and 45 are recognized annually as Massachusetts Super Lawyers. The firm has ranked first in the nation for mid-level associate satisfaction in The American Lawyer survey for the last five years. Nutter has a track record of executing high quality work with efficiency and pragmatism. The firm adheres to a service model of close partner involvement and lean staffing that allows flexibility in addressing client needs and results in cost effectiveness. In continuous practice for over 130 years since its founding in 1879, Nutter is dedicated to collaborating closely with clients through relationships characterized by trust, responsiveness and respect.

Detailed information including attorney profiles, representative clients and case studies, publications and practice descriptions is available on the firm's web site at www.nutter.com.

## Main Areas of Practice:

### Life Sciences:

Nutter's international roster of life sciences clients is involved in many sophisticated technologies and includes leading US and multinational medical device, biotechnology and pharmaceutical companies, renowned medical institutions and research universities, health care providers, emerging growth companies, angel and venture capital firms, and entrepreneurs.

The firm has a long track record of working with companies throughout the enterprise lifecycle to meet their legal and strategic needs. Nutter attorneys practicing in these industries understand how critical it is to know a client's business and the unique regulatory and financial pressures driving it. They provide legal counsel in intellectual property, licensing, clinical trial programs, government regulation and investigation including off-label marketing issues and white collar defense, product liability litigation, financing, mergers, acquisitions and joint ventures, among others. Nutter represents clients in an array of technologies and products, from medical devices such as orthopedic implants, surgical instruments, and diagnostic and therapeutic products, to research instrumentation and tools, to biopharmaceuticals ranging from functional genomics and immunology to diagnostics and gene therapy.

### Banking & Financial Services:

Nutter's banking and financial services practice represents national and global banks as well as publicly held, family-owned and mutual banks, thrift institutions, insurance companies, investment firms, pension funds, real estate investment trusts and leasing companies.

Clients rely on the firm's expertise in regulatory, compliance, corporate and transactional matters as well as its depth in real estate finance, equipment leasing, restructurings and workouts, and bankruptcy. Using knowledge of the market, the players and the law, Nutter helps clients to address a range of needs – from reorganizing mutual bank charters into mutual holding companies and defending banks against threatened regulatory enforcement action; to equipment lease transactions, syndication and sales; to real estate financings, mezzanine financings and portfolio transactions.

Nutter also handles sophisticated litigation matters for the banking and financial services industry, including government investigations in the areas of securities fraud and insider trading, and mutual fund late trading and market timing, as well as cases involving accounting issues, suspicious transactions and money laundering, broker/dealer disputes and claims involving investment advisory firms.

### Real Estate:

With one of the largest and most established real estate practices in the Northeast, Nutter represents national and international clients across the country in all aspects of sophisticated real estate transactions and development. These transactions range from financing and acquisitions to leasing, dispositions, zoning, permitting, redevelopment projects, environmental compliance and regulatory matters, and litigation. The firm also represents numerous institutional lenders in creditor matters such as financings, loan restructurings, workouts, foreclosures and bankruptcy.

Nutter's real estate and environmental clients include major developers and corporations, key investors, lenders and debt providers, cities and towns, and real estate owners in diverse industries. The firm has represented parties in over $10 billion of real estate transactions in the last decade and has been involved in some of the most notable large scale redevelopment and land use projects in the region, in addition to many of Boston's signature commercial buildings.

### Emerging Companies:

Nutter works with a wide range of technology entrepreneurs, startup and emerging growth companies to provide the end-to-end legal solutions they need to create their businesses and realize their visions. Nutter supports ventures across the innovation economy with a value proposition built on deep engagement in and understanding of the technology, life sciences and consumer products markets; a full service platform to support growth through commercialization, scaling and exits, including intellectual property, commercial technology, corporate, securities, litigation, employment, real estate, tax, and estate planning services; and understanding of market terms for financing, outsourcing, hiring, etc., in the early stage venture arena.

# ROPES & GRAY LLP

www.ropesgray.com **tel:** 617 951 7000 **fax:** 617 951 7050

**Chairman:** R Bradford Malt
**Managing Partner:** David C Chapin
Number of partners: 300
Number of lawyers: 1,000 (includes associates, partners, counsel, career associates and hourly associates)

**Firm Overview:**

Ropes & Gray is one of the world's most highly respected law firms, with offices in key business and financial capitals in the United States, the United Kingdom and Asia. The firm's network of over 1,000 lawyers and professionals provides the highest quality legal advice for the world's leading businesses on their most critical legal and business issues.

## Main Areas of Practice:

### Private Equity:

- TPG Capital: $3 billion acquisition of J.Crew; $1.97 billion acquisition of Immucor; $1.9 billion acquisition of Par Pharmaceutical Companies; $1.6 billion acquisition of Ontex
- TPG Growth: acquisition of iMDsoft
- Bain Capital: acquisition of MYOB; $3 billion acquisition of Skylark; $1 billion acquisition of Genpact; acquisition of 50 percent of Jupiter Shop Channel
- Berkshire Partners: $1.1 billion acquisition of SkillSoft
- Blackstone Group: $3 billion acquisition of Emdeon
- BlackRock: acquisition of Swiss Re Private Equity

**Contact:** Al Rose **Tel:** 617 951 7372
**Email:** alfred.rose@ropesgray.com

### M&A:

- Alexion Pharmaceuticals: $1.08 billion acquisition of Enobia Pharma
- NStar: $7 billion sale to Northeast Utilities
- Becton Dickinson: $730 million sale of Discovery Labware
- Timberland: VF Corp's $2 billion acquisition of Timberland
- State Street: $550 million acquisition of Goldman Sachs Administration Services
- Party City: $2.64 billion sale to Thomas H. Lee Partners
- URL Pharma: $800 million sale to Takeda Pharmaceutical of Japan

**Contact:** Paul Kinsella **Tel:** 617 951 7921
**Email:** paul.kinsella@ropesgray.com
**Contact:** Patrick O'Brien **Tel:** 617 951 7527
**Email:** patrick.obrien@ropesgray.com

### Finance:

- Liberty Global: financing for €3.16 billion acquisition of Germany's third-largest cable TV operator Kabel BW Erste Beteiligungs GmbH, from private equity group EQT Partners AB and others
- Dunkin'Brands Inc: in structuring, and obtaining $1.975 billion of aggregate financing, including senior credit facilities and high yield notes, to refinance

'whole business securitisation' and fund shareholder dividend
- TPG Capital: $200 million global IPO of its portfolio company China NT Pharma Group in Hong Kong
- Zynga, LinkedIn, China Zenix Auto International, Dunkin'Brands and TRIA Beauty in IPOs
- Pachinko operator DYNAM: IPO on the Hong Kong Stock Exchange, the first for a Japanese company
- China GrenTech Corp.: privatisation of leading provider of radio and wireless products and services

**Contact:** Jay Kim **Tel:** 212 497 3626
**Email:** jay.kim@ropesgray.com
**Contact:** Byung Choi **Tel:** 617 951 7277
**Email:** byung.choi@ropesgray.com

### Bankruptcy/Restructuring:

- Committee of mezzanine lenders to the KCA Deutag Group, including funds and accounts managed by BlackRock, EIG and GoldenTree, in connection with KCA's financial restructuring

**Contact:** Mark Bane **Tel:** 212 841 8808
**Email:** mark.bane@ropesgray.com
**Contact:** Alyson Allen **Tel:** 617 951 7483
**Email:** alyson.allen@ropesgray.com

### Investment Management:

- Significant industry participants, including Allianz, Ameriprise, BlackRock, DWS, MFS, Natixis, PIMCO, Putnam
- Start-ups, including DoubleLine Funds, one of the fastest-growing mutual fund complexes
- ETFs and their sponsors, including ProShares
- BlackRock (acquisition of Swiss Re's fund of fund business), SteelPath Fund Advisors (sale to Oppenheimer Funds), H.I.G. Capital (acquisition of Arctic Glacier Income Fund), DST Systems (acquisition of ALPS Fund Services)

**Contact:** Bryan Chegwidden **Tel:** 212 497 3636
**Email:** bryan.chegwidden@ropesgray.com
**Contact:** John Loder **Tel:** 617 951 7405
**Email:** john.loder@ropesgray.com

### Hedge Funds:

- PIMCO: formation of numerous hedge funds, including various tail risk funds and several overlay strategy programs and related separate account

## PRACTICE AREAS

Private Equity
Mergers & Acquisitions
Finance
Hedge Funds
Investment Management
Life Sciences
Health Care
Intellectual Property
Business & Securities Litigation
Tax & Benefits
Antitrust
Bankruptcy
Government Enforcement/FCPA
Privacy & Data Security
Securities & Public Companies
Labor & Employment
Real Estate
Private Client
Sports Law

## OFFICES

**MASSACHUSETTS**
**BOSTON:** Prudential Tower, 800 Boylston Street, MA 02199-3600
Tel: 617 951 7000  Fax: 617 951 7050

**CALIFORNIA**
**EAST PALO ALTO:** 1900 University Avenue, 6th Floor, CA 94303-2284
Tel: 650 617 4000  Fax: 650 617 4090

**SAN FRANCISCO:** Three Embarcadero Center, CA 94111-4006
Tel: 415 315 6300  Fax: 415 315 6350

**DISTRICT OF COLUMBIA**
**WASHINGTON DC:** One Metro Center, 700 12th Street, NW, Suite 900, DC 20005-3948
Tel: 202 508 4600  Fax: 202 508 4650

**ILLINOIS**
**CHICAGO:** 191 North Wacker Drive, 32nd Floor, IL 60606-4302
Tel: 312 845 1200  Fax: 312 845 5500

**NEW YORK**
**NEW YORK:** 1211 Avenue of the Americas, NY 10036-8704
Tel: 212 596 9000  Fax: 212 596 9090

products
- Blackstone: formation of a hybrid private equity/hedge fund vehicle that seeds third-party hedge fund managers
- UBS Global Asset Management: structure open-end real estate funds of funds and investments by those funds

**Contact:** Laurel FitzPatrick **Tel:** 212 497 3610
**Email:** laurel.fitzpatrick@ropesgray.com

### Private Investment Funds:

- Represent fund sponsors in fundraising, general sponsor and regulatory matters: ArcLight Capital Partners, Bain Capital, CITIC Private Equity, Greenpark Capital, Neuberger Berman, Nordic Capital, PIMCO, RRJ Capital, TPG Capital and others
- Represent institutional investors in fund investment

# ROPES & GRAY LLP CONT'D

projects: AlpInvest, Temasek, Harvard and Stanford Universities, Makena Capital Management and others

In last 6 years acted as counsel:

- to organise 530 separate funds, with aggregate capital commitments of approximately $450 billion
- for 100+ investors in connection with investments in approximately 2,250 private funds

**Contact:** John Ayer **Tel:** 617 951 7937
**Email:** john.ayer@ropesgray.com
**Contact:** Raj Marphatia **Tel:** 617 951 7538
**Email:** raj.marphatia@ropesgray.com

## Life Sciences:

- MedImmune LLC: establishment of its landmark biologics joint venture with a Chinese life sciences company that is publicly traded in the US
- Biogen Idec: $300 million j.v. to develop and market biosimilars with Korea-based Samsung Biologics
- Janssen Pharmaceutical NV: sale of all US patents and other US and Canadian intellectual property for Bystolic® (nebivolol) to Forest Laboratories Holdings

**Contact:** Greg Levine **Tel:** 202 508 4831
**Email:** gregory.levine@ropesgray.com
**Contact:** Marc Rubenstein **Tel:** 617 951 7826
**Email:** marc.rubenstein@ropesgray.com

## Health Care:

- West Penn Allegheny Health System: representation as lead transaction counsel in West Penn's affiliation with the largest Blue Cross Blue Shield insurer in PA, WV, MD and DE. The affiliation resulted in the creation of an insurer/provider healthcare delivery and financing system described by the Wall Street Journal as a "game changer"
- Liberty Dialysis: representation of Liberty Dialysis and its principal private equity sponsors, KRG Capital & Bain Capital, in the $1.7 billion sale of Liberty Dialysis to Fresenius Medical Care
- NYU Langone Medical Center: representation in connection with NYU's proposed affiliation with Continuum Health Partners, Inc. This affiliation would unite two of the most prominent health care systems in New York

**Contact:** Anne Ogilby **Tel:** 617 951 7472
**Email:** anne.ogilby@ropesgray.com
**Contact:** Stephen Warnke **Tel:** 212 841 0681
**Email:** stephen.warnke@ropesgray.com

## Intellectual Property:

- Microsoft v. Motorola: Represent Motorola in ITC and multijurisdictional District Court disputes with Microsoft over patents related to video game

operating systems and software

- Abbott Laboratories and Therasense v. Becton, Dickinson and Company and Nova Biomedical Corp: Achieved a decisive victory for BD and Nova in one of 2011's most significant patent infringement decisions before the Northern District of California and the Federal Circuit
- AstraZeneca PLC: Represent internationally on complex IP due diligence matters, patent opinions; due diligence support in connection with numerous transactions
- Zynga: Negotiation of strategic relationship with Hasbro to extend Zynga's virtual game success into traditional board games and toys

**Contact:** Edward Black (IP transactions)
**Tel:** 617 951 7984
**Email:** ed.black@ropesgray.com
**Contact:** Joseph Guiliano (IP rights management)
**Tel:** 212 596 9081
**Email:** joseph.guiliano@ropesgray.com
**Contact:** Anita Varma (IP rights management)
**Tel:** 617 951 7796
**Email:** anita.varma@ropesgray.com
**Contact:** Gene Lee (IP litigation) **Tel:** 212 596 9053
**Email:** gene.lee@ropesgray.com
**Contact:** Rick McCaulley (IP litigation)
**Tel:** 312 845 1313
**Email:** richard.mccaulley@ropesgray.com

## Government Enforcement/FCPA:

- Secured dismissal of all 13 felony charges against Stryker Biotech following opening statements in exchange for a fine and a plea to a single misdemeanor, and secured dismissal of all charges against the former company president and three sales directors in a trial involving alleged off-label marketing
- Represented a global medical device company in connection with a DOJ and SEC industrywide FCPA investigation and secured a deferred prosecution agreement with the DOJ and a consent agreement with the SEC, settling the government's charges

**Contact:** Brien O'Connor **Tel:** 617 951 7385
**Email:** brien.o'connor@ropesgray.com
**Contact:** Colleen Conry **Tel:** 202 508 4834
**Email:** colleen.conry@ropesgray.com

## Litigation:

- Sony Computer Entertainment America: global coordinating counsel with respect to litigation, including 65 putative class actions, and government investigations related to criminal cyberattacks
- Carter's Inc. (global clothing retailer): secured first

non-prosecution agreement with SEC; won dismissal without prejudice of two securities fraud class actions claims with aggregate exposure of nearly half a billion dollars
- Jones v. Harris: representation of Harris Associates (manager of Oakmark mutual funds), and Ameriprise (manager of Columbia and RiverSource mutual funds) in a related case, after prevailing for client and mutual funds industry in 9-0 victory at US Supreme Court using innovative argument and setting desired standard of how so-called 'excessive fees' are litigated

**Contact:** Randy Bodner **Tel:** 617 951 7776
**Email:** randall.bodner@ropesgray.com
**Contact:** Harvey Wolkoff **Tel:** 617 951 7522
**Email:** harvey.wolkoff@ropesgray.com

## Privacy & Data Security:

- Heartland Payment Systems: won a motion to dismiss for payment card processor Heartland in the pending class action litigation facing the company relating to its computer system intrusion
- Sony Computer Entertainment America LLC: representation as global coordinating counsel with respect to the multiple litigations and government investigations that have arisen from the recent criminal cyber-attacks on certain of Sony's computer networks
- Massachusetts General Hospital: representation in connection with the negotiation and settlement of the first significant federal enforcement action relating to the loss of protected health information by an employee

**Contact:** Douglas Meal **Tel:** 617 951 7517
**Email:** douglas.meal@ropesgray.com
**Contact:** Tim McCrystal **Tel:** 617 951 7278
**Email:** timothy.mccrystal@ropesgray.com

## Tax & Benefits:

- Genzyme: advised on tax matters related to its sale pursuant to an exchange offer and merger with Sanofi-Aventis
- Dunkin' Brands Group: advised on executive and equity compensation issues relating to its IPO
- PIMCO: advise on their hedge funds' ongoing operations and administration relating to ERISA compliance

**Contact:** Christopher M Leich (Tax) **Tel:** 617 951 7279
**Email:** christopher.leich@ropesgray.com
**Contact:** Loretta R Richard (Benefits) **Tel:** 617 951 7271
**Email:** loretta.richard@ropesgray.com

# SCHWARTZ HANNUM PC

www.shpclaw.com **tel:** 978 623 0900 **fax:** 978 623 0908

Managing partners: 2
Number of partners: 5
Number of other lawyers: 10

## Firm Overview:

Established in 1995 by its President and Managing Partner, Sara Goldsmith Schwartz, Schwartz Hannum PC (a certified woman-owned business) is a labor, employment and immigration firm that represents businesses and non-profit organizations in a wide variety of industries. The firm is committed to providing high quality legal representation with excellent client service at cost effective rates. Attorneys in the firm are members of the bars of numerous states, including: Connecticut, District of Columbia, Florida, Maine, Massachusetts, New Hampshire, New Jersey, New York, several associated U.S. District Courts, and the United States Supreme Court.

## Main Areas of Practice:

### Employment Litigation:
The firm provides employers with a full range of representation in employment litigation before state and federal courts, government agencies and arbitration panels, involving claims of discrimination and retaliation and other statutory claims.
**Key Clients:** Assumption College, Calloway Laboratories, Inc., Dassault Systems SolidWorks Corp., HP Hood, LLC, Nationwide Mutual Insurance Company, New York Life Insurance Company

### Labor Relations:
The firm represents unionized and non-unionized employers in a broad range of labor relations matters, including representation campaigns and elections, collective bargaining, arbitrations, strikes, decertifications and unfair labor practice charges for employers in numerous industries, including airlines, construction, distribution, education, healthcare, manufacturing, retail, social services and trucking, and have negotiated industry-wide, company-wide and site-specific collective bargaining agreements.
**Key Clients:** HP Hood LLC, Heywood Hospital

### Counseling:
The firm provides counseling with respect to innumerable labor and employment law issues, including hiring, discipline and termination decisions, workplace investigations, reductions in force, plant closings, separation agreements, employment applications and employment and independent contractor agreements.
**Key Clients:** Copyright Clearance Center, Inc., HP Hood, LLC, Nashoba Brooks School, Smith & Wesson, Waste Management, Inc., Worldwide TechServices

### Compliance:
The firm conducts a full range of proactive and preventative human resources audits of policies and procedures to evaluate compliance with all applicable state and federal labor and employment laws. The firm counsels employers regarding classification as government contractors, and/or subcontractors, and assists employers in complying with any government contractor obligations, including drafting, implementing and updating affirmative action plans. The firm drafts and reviews employee handbooks, managers' guides, human resources manuals, employment policies, employment applications and other employment-related forms for small businesses and multi-state employers. The firm provides training for managers and employees on a variety of human resources topics.
**Key Clients:** Calloway Laboratories, Inc., Cynosure, Inc., The Governor's Academy, Smith & Wesson

### Education:
The firm provides comprehensive guidance to independent schools, colleges and universities, and is available to address the myriad issues that arise for school administrators, such as student and employee disciplinary matters; promotions and tenure; internal grievances; internal investigations; risk management; regulatory compliance; layoffs; and employee terminations. The firm prepares a wide range of documents for its school and education clients, including: faculty and staff offer letters; employment contracts; admissions documents; student enrollment agreements; school board bylaws; bullying prevention and intervention plans; data security compliance programs; student/parent handbooks, including disciplinary procedures and codes of conduct; employee handbooks; and faculty handbooks.
**Key Clients:** The Armand Hammer United World College Of The American West, Assumption College, Belmont Hill School, Berkshire School, Dexter School – Southfield School, Eaglebrook School, Fessenden School, The Governor's Academy, Haleakala Waldorf School, Harvard University, Nashoba Brooks School, Shady Hill School, Tufts University, Westtown School

## PRACTICE AREAS

Employment Litigation
Labor Relations
Counseling
Compliance
Education
Mediation & Arbitration
Government Audits & Investigations
Immigration Law

## OFFICES

**MASSACHUSETTS**
**ANDOVER:** 11 Chestnut Street, Andover, MA 01810
Tel: 978 623 0900 Fax: 978 623 0908
Email: schwartz@shpclaw.com
Website: www.shpclaw.com

### Mediation & Arbitration:
The firm represents employers in binding and voluntary alternative dispute resolution efforts such as mediation and arbitration, both with respect to employment and labor disputes.
**Key Clients:** Dassault Systems SolidWorks Corp., Island Airlines, LLC, Longfellow's Wayside Inn

### Government Audits & Investigations:
The firm represents employers in a broad range of government audits and investigations arising in labor and employment law, and with respect to unemployment compensation appeals and investigations of public accommodation issues before state and federal discrimination agencies and state architectural access boards.
**Key Clients:** Eastern Bank

### Immigration Law:
The firm assists employers with preparing and processing applications for permanent residence, as well as all types of temporary visa applications, counsels employers regarding I-9 procedures and audits by the Department of Labor and USCIS, and handles the special concerns of foreign nationals in planning and executing reductions in force.
**Key Clients:** Cynosure, Inc., Exony Ltd., GenomeQuest, Inc., Worldwide TechServices

### Clients:

Other Representative Clients: Affiliated Managers Group, Inc., Brown Brothers Harriman & Co., Longfellow's Wayside Inn, The Vineyard Golf Club, The Westmoor Club

SCHWARTZ HANNUM PC
Labor and Employment Lawyers Guiding Management

# SHERIN AND LODGEN LLP

www.sherin.com

**Managing Partner:** Ronald W Ruth
Number of partners: 25
Number of other lawyers: 16

**OFFICES**

MASSACHUSETTS
**BOSTON:** 101 Federal Street, MA 02110
Tel: 617 646 2000   Fax: 617 646 2222

## Firm Overview:

Leading businesses rely on Sherin and Lodgen LLP to handle complex transactions, difficult litigation and challenging regulatory issues in real estate, litigation, and business law. With nearly 50 attorneys, the firm handles large, complicated matters while providing responsive, senior-level attention to every matter. Clients receive sophisticated analysis and effective, efficient and focused representation. The firm is committed to providing legal services of unsurpassed quality at reasonable expense and giving the highest value to clients. By design, the firm is not a general practice. Instead, the focus is on what they do best, attracting talented, experienced attorneys in specific practice areas. Sherin and Lodgen LLP is affiliated with Lexwork International, a strategic global alliance of mid-sized law firms, including providing representation in all 50 states and 36 countries.

## Main Areas of Practice:

### Life Sciences Litigation:
Represents pharmaceutical companies and medical device manufacturers in a variety of cases, including government enforcement actions for Medicaid and Medicare fraud, false claims, patent disputes, licensing disputes, licensing and assignment disputes, product liability, contractual disputes and antitrust.
**Contact:** Debra Squires-Lee

### Litigation/General Commercial:
Represents publicly-traded and other businesses in complex commercial litigation throughout the country to resolve contract claims, product liability claims, strategic real estate litigation, construction, employment claims, insurance coverage disputes, intellectual property litigation, professional liability litigation, and general business disputes.
**Contact:** John C La Liberte

### Real Estate:
Developers, property owners and managers seek Sherin and Lodgen's assistance with land acquisition and site assembly; permitting before local, state and federal authorities; negotiation of contracts with contractors, architects and other design professionals; debt and equity financings for both construction and permanent financing; retail, office, industrial, warehouse, R&D

leasing; acquisition and disposition of assets; multi-property portfolio sales; national disposition programs; and sale-leaseback transactions.
**Contact:** Peter Friedenberg

### Environmental:
Represents developers, manufacturers and property owners with environmental issues, including contaminated properties (brownfields), compliance/enforcement, cost recovery actions, and LEED/Green development. Five attorneys are LEED Accredited Professionals.
**Contact:** Joshua M Alper

### Bankruptcy/Restructuring:
Commercial landlords, tenants, and lenders turn to Sherin and Lodgen for complex and sophisticated insolvency proceedings relating to retail, commercial and/or industrial real estate for secured, unsecured, and trade creditor representation in litigation and insolvency disputes.
**Contact:** John C La Liberte

### Professional Liability:
Represented over 100 law firms over 25 years, including several Am Law firms. Also represents professional liability insurers and attorneys in Bar disciplinary matters.
**Contact:** Robert J Muldoon, Jr

### Corporate/General Business:
Represent businesses and non-profits with entity formation, financing, contracts and licensing, distribution, employment, executive compensation, real estate, IP, joint ventures, M&A, ownership structure, private placements, venture capital, shareholder issues, sale of assets/stock, and tax law. Extensive experience with closely-held and emerging businesses.
**Contact:** C Forbes Sargent III

### Banking & Finance:
Represent national and local banks, life insurance companies, mezzanine lenders, governmental agencies and other conventional and non-conventional financing sources.
**Contact:** Gary M Markoff

# SHILEPSKY HARTLEY ROBB CASEY MICHON LLP

www.shilepsky.com

**Managing Partner:** Nancy S Shilepsky, Barbara A Robb
Number of partners: 5
Number of other lawyers: 5

**OFFICE**

MASSACHUSETTS

**BOSTON:** 155 Seaport Boulevard, 11th Floor, MA 02210
Tel: 617 723 8000   Fax: 617 447 2800

## Firm Overview:

Shilepsky Hartley Robb Casey Michon LLP concentrates in Executive Advocacy, Employment Law and Litigation and is founded by some of the Nation's most accomplished attorneys in these fields. The attorneys of Shilepsky Hartley Robb provide counseling, negotiation and litigation services to executives and professionals, as well as to corporate clients in a broad range of industries. The firm serves its clients in a variety of ways: as retained advisors, in negotiations and mediation, before government agencies, in independent and industry arbitration and in federal and state trial and appellate courts. The heart of Shilepsky Hartley Robb's practice is protecting the interests of their clients and advocating for those clients' rights. Effective representation and successful advocacy can take many forms, which is why the firm offers three core services: counseling, negotiation and litigation. Clients draw from one or multiple service areas to maximize options and obtain favorable results. Shilepsky Hartley Robb's transactional lawyers provide benchmarking and sophisticated analysis showing that the clients' interests are aligned with those of shareholders, while the firm's experienced trial lawyers have the strategic acumen and resources necessary to achieve success. Shilepsky Hartley Robb's track record in the courtroom and before regulatory bodies often spurs resolution before disputes reach the litigation stage of the process. The firm's seasoned team of trial lawyers zealously pursues and protects their clients' rights and interests, and has secured several precedent-setting decisions, particularly in the areas of executive advocacy and workplace discrimination.

## Main Areas of Practice:

### Employment Law & Litigation:

Shilepsky Hartley Robb's attorneys are nationally recognized as leaders in the field of employment law and litigation. The firm's partners have been at the forefront of developing the law – literally writing the books upon which other attorneys rely and bringing cutting-edge cases that have re-written how discrimination claims are handled. Their unparalleled experience and understanding of the nuances of these laws gives the firm's individual and corporate clients a tremendous advantage in conflict resolution. This area of practice includes: breach of contract claims; discrimination claims; sexual harassment claims; maternity and pregnancy claims; reasonable accommodation claims; wrongful termination claims; whistleblower, Sarbanes-Oxley, and Dodd-Frank claims; Family and Medical Leave Act claims; non-competition and non-solicitation disputes; compensation claims; workplace misconduct investigations and representation; and expert advice on equitable resolution of workplace disputes.

### Executive & Professional Advocacy:

Shilepsky Hartley Robb's attorneys pioneered the area of executive advocacy, a practice that focuses on the unique legal needs of executive level and professional individuals, and offers them a powerful combination of sophisticated transactional services and aggressive, effective trial capabilities. The firm's attorneys bring the experience and savvy needed to handle complex employment matters with finesse. They understand the underlying business issues, and often provide behind-the-scenes counsel to help clients obtain preemptive business solutions for what might otherwise become future legal problems. This practice area includes: change-of-control and severance protections; defense of employment when termination has been threatened, including corporate founders being forced out; assisting executives and partners of firms in transition; protection of incentive compensation arrangements; defeat of overbroad non-competition agreements and other career restrictions; employment issues of expatriated executives and professionals, domestically and abroad; contractual protections for both long-term and newly hired executives.

### Mediation & Arbitration:

Shilepsky Hartley Robb represents both employees and employers in binding and alternative dispute resolution efforts in a variety of employment disputes, including at AAA and JAMS, obtaining six and seven figure resolutions on behalf of their clients.

### Clients:

Due to confidentiality concerns, Shilepsky Hartley Robb cannot share the names of its specific clients. The firm's individual and executive clients come from a wide range of industries, including, financial and other professional services, information technology, medical, broadcasting, energy, manufacturing, and professional sports.

Shilepsky | Hartley | Robb | Casey | Michon

*Executive Advocacy, Employment Law and Litigation*

# SKOLER, ABBOTT & PRESSER, PC

www.skoler-abbott.com

**Managing Partner:** Ralph Abbott
**Partner:** Susan G Fentin
Number of partners: 6  Number of other attorneys: 4

**OFFICES**

MASSACHUSETTS
**SPRINGFIELD:** One Monarch Place, MA 0114
Tel: 413 737 4753  Fax: 413 787 1941

**Firm Overview:**

For over 40 years, Skoler, Abbott & Presser has practiced exclusively labor and employment law, representing exclusively management. With offices in Springfield and Worcester, Massachusetts, Skoler Abbott is one of the largest law firms in New England specializing in the practice of labor relations and employment law exclusively for management. The firm has been rated "AV" in the Martindale-Hubbell Law Directory and has also been recognized in the Martindale-Hubbell Bar Register of Preeminent Lawyers in the Labor and Employment Law Section. Four of its attorneys are listed among the "Best Lawyers in America" for Labor and Employment Law, and five partners are consistently rated as among Massachusetts' "Super Lawyers".

Skoler Abbott has a long history of strength in labor relations, where it has assisted employers in matters arising under the National Labor Relations Act, including representation elections and collective bargaining, as well as defending unfair labor practice charges before the National Labor Relations Board and State Labor Relations agencies and helping maintain their union-free status.

From its original roots as a management-side, labor relations firm, Skoler Abbott has grown over the years into a full service employment law firm, representing employers in all forms of employment litigation and advising on compliance with the full panoply of state and federal laws, including the FLSA, Title VII, the ADA, the ADEA, the FMLA, ERISA, and the Vocational Rehabilitation Act. Attorneys are admitted to practice in state courts in Massachusetts, Connecticut and New York, as well as federal courts in these and other jurisdictions, including the United States Supreme Court. Skoler Abbott has extensive experience in defending employers at proceedings before administrative agencies across the country, in addition to defending litigation in federal and state courts throughout New England. It is also experienced in defending employers and their managers against state common law claims, including breach of contract, libel and slander, interference with contract, infliction of emotional distress, and wrongful discharge. The firm drafts, defends, and enforces non-compete and confidentiality agreements for clients and assists in the preparation, documentation, and revision of Affirmative Action Plans, as well as compliance reviews and complaint investigations by the OFCCP. Where workplace safety issues arise, the firm provides representation during investigations and administrative enforcement proceedings under OSHA, including retaliation claims and providing advice on compliance with OSHA safety standards.

The underpinning of Skoler Abbott's successful relationship with its clients is the firm's "preventive maintenance" philosophy. Careful employment practices can improve the likelihood of successful employment litigation and even lessen the likelihood that litigation will ensue. Accordingly, the firm provides counseling and training in a wide variety of employment-related areas, including sexual harassment, wage and hour law, the intersection among the ADA, FMLA and state workers compensation statutes, proper documentation, performance improvement plans and evaluations, and how to lawfully hire, fire, and discipline employees. The firm regularly helps clients develop, review, and update policies, procedures, and employee handbooks and conducts formal audits of personnel practices, including in-depth analyses of employers' personnel policies and practices in action.

Skoler Abbott has been able to translate its extensive experience with union arbitration into its litigation practice by effectively and appropriately utilizing Alternate Dispute Resolution as an alternative to costly and time consuming litigation where appropriate. It also partners with its clients to facilitate low risk reductions-in-force or layoffs within the constraints of the WARN Act, drafting separation agreements and releases, and developing voluntary separation programs. Legal advice in the specialized ERISA area is available from the firm's ERISA specialist, Wendy L. Grabel, who is of counsel to the firm and who assists Skoler Abbott clients in drafting cafeteria plans, retirement plans, 401(k) plans, stock and other benefit and compensation plans, as well as advice on all ERISA issues.

Skoler Abbott believes that a timely answer to a pressing problem can sometimes prevent costly litigation, so it specializes in prompt response to client e-mail and telephone questions. It also routinely provides its clients with updates of significant employment law developments through e-mail alerts. Skoler Abbott attorneys write and edit the Massachusetts Employment Law Letter, one of the best read employment law newsletters in the country, and have taught master classes for the publisher on labor relations, the ADA, Wage and Hour law, and the FMLA. In addition, attorneys at the firm conduct webinars on a variety of labor and employment law topics and speak frequently to employers' associations and personnel groups, as well as bar associations and Continuing Legal Education programs. Skoler Abbott is also a member of the Employers' Counsel Network, which consists of editors of the various Employment Law Letters throughout the country, and a founding firm in the Worklaw Network®, a nationwide consortium of management side, boutique, labor and employment law firms, giving the firm the ability to handle employment law problems for its clients in all 50 states.

**Main Areas of Practice:**

State and Federal employment law including statutory and common law employment discrimination claims; labor/management relations including collective bargaining, and proceedings before the NLRB; human resources advice and counsel; employment tort and contract litigation; covenants not-to-compete; wage and hour laws (FLSA, Portal to Portal Act); OSHA compliance and defense; Affirmative Action Programs; FMLA administration and defense; WARN; employee benefits/ERISA; employment policy and document review and drafting, including employment agreements, employment handbooks, policies and procedures; appellate litigation; class action defense.

**Clients:**

Skoler Abbott represents clients in all sectors of the economy, including some of the largest employers in Massachusetts, as well as employers with locations across the country and many small and midsize employers. The firm's access to the Worklaw Network as well as to the Employers' Counsel Network gives Skoler Abbott attorneys the ability to solve problems and defend employment related claims in all 50 states, while preserving the convenience and cost-efficiency of a centralized, Massachusetts-based law firm. Skoler Abbott clients include health care providers and not-for-profit organizations, including Baystate Health Systems, Danbury Hospital, and The Boston Medical Center HealthNet Plan; recreational and retail corporations including Six Flags New England, and National Amusements; major manufacturing companies, including Yankee Candle, Smith and Wesson, and U.S. Tsubaki.

# SULLIVAN & WORCESTER LLP

www.sandw.com **tel:** +1 617 338 2800 **fax:** +1 617 338 2880

**Managing Partners:** Joel R Carpenter, William J Curry
Number of attorneys: 175

## Firm Overview:

Sullivan & Worcester LLP is a leading corporate law firm providing counsel to domestic and international clients ranging from Fortune 500 companies to emerging businesses. With more than 175 lawyers in Boston, New York and Washington, DC, the firm offers services in a wide range of areas, including corporate finance, securities, litigation, mergers and acquisitions, tax, real estate, private equity and venture capital, bankruptcy, environment and natural resources, renewable energy and water resources and employment and benefits. Sullivan & Worcester is also recognized for its representation of REITs and its deep experience in mutual fund law.

## Main Areas of Practice:

**Banking & Finance:**
Contact: William A Levine   Tel: 617 338 2921
Email: wlevine@sandw.com

**Bankruptcy & Restructuring:**
Contact: Patrick P Dinardo   Tel: 617 338 2817
Email: pdinardo@sandw.com

**Corporate:**
Contact: Susan M Barnard   Tel: 617 338 2473
Email: sbarnard@sandw.com
Contact: Jon M Jenkins   Tel: 212 660 3016
Email: jjenkins@sandw.com

**Employment & Benefits:**
Contact: David A Guadagnoli   Tel: 617 338 2938
Email: dguadagnoli@sandw.com
Contact: Ilene Robinson Sunshine   Tel: 617 338 2928
Email: isunshine@sandw.com

**International & Cross-Border Transactions:**
Contact: J Truman Bidwell, Jr   Tel: 212 660 3032
Email: jtbidwell@sandw.com

**Environment & Natural Resources:**
Contact: Jeffrey M Karp   Tel: 202 370 3921
Email: jkarp@sandw.com

**Government Investigations & White Collar Defense:**
Contact: Paul E Summit   Tel: 617 338 2488
Email: psummit@sandw.com

**Intellectual Property:**
Contact: Kimberly B Herman   Tel: 617 338 2943
Email: kherman@sandw.com

**Investment Management:**
Contact: David C Mahaffey   Tel: 202 775 1207
Email: dmahaffey@sandw.com

**Litigation:**
Contact: Andrew T Solomon   Tel: 212 660 3023
Email: asolomon@sandw.com

**Mergers & Acquisitions:**
Contact: Carol G Wolff   Tel: 617 338 2877
Email: cwolff@sandw.com

**Private Investment Funds:**
Contact: Martha F Coultrap   Tel: 212 660 3014
Email: mcoultrap@sandw.com

**Real Estate:**
Contact: John G Balboni   Tel: 617 338 2438
Email: jbalboni@sandw.com
Contact: John M Steiner   Tel: 617 338 2902
Email: jsteiner@sandw.com

**REITs:**
Contact: Ameek Ashok Ponda   Tel: 617 338 2443
Email: aponda@sandw.com

**Securities & Corporate Governance:**
Contact: Howard E Berkenblit   Tel: 617 338 2979
Email: hberkenblit@sandw.com

**Securitization:**
Contact: Duncan T O'Brien   Tel: 617 338 2949
Email: dobrien@sandw.com

**Tax:**
Contact: Ameek Ashok Ponda   Tel: 617 338 2443
Email: aponda@sandw.com

**Trusts & Estates:**
Contact: Cornelius J Murray III   Tel: 617 338 2931
Email: cmurray@sandw.com

## International Work:

The firm has built its international capability carefully, by forging relationships with the best non-US law firms, many of which they have worked with for decades. For example, the firm has relationships with several law firms in London, allowing transactions to be structured under New York or English law. The relationships vary depending on the country; the firm focuses on finding the best arrangement possible for clients within the economic and cultural context of the particular country.

## PRACTICE AREAS

Banking & Finance
Bankruptcy & Restructuring
Corporate
Employment & Benefits
Environment, Energy & Natural Resources
Government Investigations & White-Collar Defense
Intellectual Property
International & Cross-Border Transactions
Investment Management
Litigation
Mergers & Acquisitions
Private Investment Funds
Real Estate
REITs
Securities & Corporate Governance
Securitization
Tax
Trusts & Estates

## OFFICES

**MASSACHUSETTS**
**BOSTON:** One Post Office Square, MA 02109
Tel: 617 338 2800 Fax: 617 338 2880
Email: info@sandw.com

**NEW YORK**
**NEW YORK:** 1633 Broadway, NY 10019-6708
Tel: 212 660 3000 Fax: 212 660 3001

**DISTRICT OF COLUMBIA**
**WASHINGTON DC:** 1666 K Street, NW, DC 20006
Tel: 202 775 1200 Fax: 202 293 2275

## INTERNATIONAL OFFICES

The firm also has a joint venture with Zysman, Aharoni, Gayer & Co. (ZAG/S&W), an Israeli law firm.

ZAG/S&W, the firm's joint venture with one of Israel's top law firms, advises Israeli companies and US companies with Israeli interests in securities and other corporate transactions as well as litigation matters.

## Clients:

Representative clients include: American Tower Corporation; Bank of America; CommonWealth REIT; Deutsche Bank AG, New York; Ernst & Young U.S. LLP; Fidelity Management & Research Company; The Governor and Company of the Bank of Ireland PLC; HSBC Bank USA, N.A.; IBRC (formerly known as Anglo Irish Bank Corporation); Iron Mountain Incorporated; John Hancock Financial Services; Konarka Technologies; J. W. Childs Equity Partners, L.P.; Lloyds Banking Group; Raytheon Company; The Robert Wood Johnson Foundation; Staples, Inc.; Wells Fargo Bank.

# WOLF, GREENFIELD & SACKS, P.C.

www.wolfgreenfield.com   **tel:** 617 646 8000   **fax:** 617 646 8648

**Managing Partner:** Timothy J Oyer
**Chairman:** Edward R Gates
Number of partners: 34   Number of lawyers: 72
Languages: *Arabic, Cantonese, Dutch, French, German, Hebrew, Japanese, Khmer, Korean, Mandarin, Russian, Spanish*

### Firm Overview:

Wolf Greenfield is the largest New England-based law firm focused solely on intellectual property (IP) law. For over 85 years, the firm has protected and defended the IP rights of clients ranging from startups to Fortune 500 companies to major research institutions. In 2012, the firm filed 3,017 patents and 848 trademarks in the US and over 130 countries. A recent survey of key clients confirmed the firm's reputation as the go-to firm for complex IP matters. Clients noted the firm's solid, carefully planned research and work product. They also value the firm's responsiveness, attention to detail, and ability to provide the right strategic guidance for achieving their business goals in a cost-effective manner.

## Main Areas of Practice:

### Biotechnology:

17 attorneys, patent agents, and technology specialists; 16 with PhDs or MDs
Largest biotechnology group in New England.
Main areas of expertise include biochemistry; biodefense; bioinformatics; biomechanics; biophysics; cell biology; genetics; imaging; medical devices; medical disciplines; microbiology; molecular biology; molecular biophysics; nanotechnology; neuroscience/neurobiology; nutraceuticals; physiology; plant biology; sequencing technologies; stem cell biology and systems biology.
**Key Clients:** Biogen Idec, Dyax, GTC Biotherapeutics, Lantheus Medical Imaging, Massachusetts General Hospital, and Shire Pharmaceuticals.
**Contact:** John R Van Amsterdam **Tel:** 617 646 8233
**Email:** jvanamsterdam@wolfgreenfield.com

### Chemical & Materials Technologies:

10 attorneys and technology specialists; 9 with PhDs
Main areas of expertise include biochemistry; chemical engineering; chemistry; cleantech; energy storage technologies; materials technologies; medical devices and technologies; nanotechnology and pharmaceuticals.
**Key Clients:** DEKA Research & Development; Harvard University, Luminus Devices, MIT, and Sion Power.
**Contact:** Robert H Walat **Tel:** 617 646 8291
**Email:** rwalat@wolfgreenfield.com

### Electrical & Computer Technologies:

21 attorneys, patent agents, and technology specialists; 15 have advanced degrees
Main areas of expertise include acoustics; bioinformatics; business methods; communications; defense; e-commerce and internet; electronics/computers; image processing; information content; medical technologies; nanotechnology; networking technologies; robotics; semiconductors; software and storage technology.
**Key Clients:** EMC, L-3 Communications, Nuance, Sony, and STMicroelectronics.

**Contact:** Richard F Giunta **Tel:** 617 646 8232
**Email:** rgiunta@wolfgreenfield.com

### Litigation:

20 attorneys, many with technical backgrounds
Argued cases before US Supreme Court, Federal Circuit and other circuit courts of appeal, IP dispute forums including US Patent Board of Appeals and Interferences, International Trade Commission, Trademark Trial and Appeal Board, US Court of Federal Claims, various district courts, and arbitration tribunals including National Arbitration Forum, American Arbitration Association, World Intellectual Property Organization. The firm represents both plaintiffs and defendants in virtually every kind of IP action: patent infringement; patent interference; trademark infringement; reexaminations and post grant proceedings; trade secret, nondisclosure, and non-competition disputes; Internet and domain name disputes and arbitration; copyright disputes; breach of contract claims; IP licensing and other transactional disputes; antitrust and unfair competition claims; ANDA litigation; joint ownership issues; university/corporate collaborations and alternative dispute resolution.
**Key Clients:** C.R.Bard, Charms, E-Ink, EMC, Euro-Pro, Infineon, Keurig, MStar Semiconductor, Nuance, Sony, and Staples.
**Contact:** Michael A Albert **Tel:** 617 646 8240
**Email:** malbert@wolfgreenfield.com

### Mechanical Technologies:

11 attorneys and patent agents
Industry experience includes: apparel and footwear; automotive; communications systems; consumer products; diagnostic equipment; electrical connectors; electromechanical devices; environmental technologies; imaging and control systems; manufacturing and industrial equipment; medical devices; microfluidic devices; optics; sensors; sporting goods and recreational equipment and textiles.
**Key Clients:** Burton Snowboards, C.R. Bard, Euro-Pro

Operating, Husky Injection Molding Systems, Keurig, and Staples.
**Contact:** Neil P Ferraro **Tel:** 617 646 8267
**Email:** nferraro@wolfgreenfield.com

### Pharmaceutical:

6 attorneys and patent agents; 5 with PhDs
Main areas of expertise: bioinformatics; biopharmaceuticals; chemistry; drug discovery; generic drug issues; Hatch-Waxman issues; lifecycle management; Orange Book listings and strategies; patent term extensions; pharmacogenomics and toxicology.
**Key Clients:** Harvard University, Progenics Pharmaceuticals, Shire Pharmaceuticals, and Synta Pharmaceuticals.
**Contact:** C Hunter Baker **Tel:** 617 646 8281
**Email:** c.hunter.baker@wolfgreenfield.com

### Trademark & Copyright:

4 members; filed 848 trademarks in 2012
Annually listed by NameProtect among top US trademark firms
Recognized for excellence by World Trademark Review, US World & News Report, and Best Lawyers
Representative industries include: apparel and fashion accessories; athletic equipment; chemical technologies; computer hardware; computer software; consumer electronics; electronic components; financial services; fluid treatment and purification equipment; food, beverages and restaurants; footwear; hospitals; infant and children's products; Internet technologies; kitchen and houseware products; medical devices; office supplies; personal care products; pharmaceuticals; publishing; semiconductors and toys.
**Key Clients:** Burton Snowboards, Keurig, Staples, Teradyne, THQ, and Tootsie Roll Industries.
**Contact:** Douglas R Wolf **Tel:** 617 646 8260
**Email:** dougwolf@wolfgreenfield.com

**Wolf Greenfield**
SPECIALISTS IN INTELLECTUAL PROPERTY LAW

## How lawyers are ranked

Every year we carry out thousands of in-depth interviews with clients in order to assess the reputations and expertise of business lawyers worldwide. The qualities we look for (and which determine rankings) include technical legal ability, professional conduct, client service, commercial awareness/astuteness, diligence, commitment, and other qualities most valued by the client. For details of our research team, see p.5.

# BANKING & FINANCE

Commentary about individuals can be found under their firm's paragraph. If the firm has no paragraph (is not ranked) look at Other Notable Practitioners.

### Banking & Finance
### Leading Firms

**Band 1**
Bodman PLC *

**Band 2**
Dickinson Wright PLLC *
Honigman Miller Schwartz and Cohn LLP
Miller, Canfield, Paddock and Stone, P.L.C. *

**Band 3**
Barnes & Thornburg LLP *
Warner Norcross & Judd LLP

### Leading Individuals

**Star individuals**
Shulman Larry R            Bodman PLC *

**Band 1**
Kochanek Joseph J          Bodman PLC *
Shield Jr William P         Dickinson Wright PLLC *

**Band 2**
Campbell Michael G         Barnes & Thornburg LLP *
Shevnock Colleen M         Dickinson Wright PLLC *
Zabriskie Wendy L          Bodman PLC *

**Band 3**
Breay James                Warner Norcross & Judd LLP
Gyorke Scott P             Bodman PLC *
Hammond Craig              Dickinson Wright PLLC *
Hickey Kathleen O'Callaghan  Bodman PLC *
McLeod David K             Varnum LLP (ONP) †
Riback Ronald H            Miller, Canfield, Paddock and Stone *
Taylor Trent               Miller, Canfield, Paddock and Stone *
Watson Daniel C            Bodman PLC *

\* Indicates firm / individual with profile.
† ONP = Other Notable Practitioner

### Banking & Finance: Bankruptcy
### Leading Individuals

**Band 1**
Diehl Jr Robert J          Bodman PLC *
Green Jonathan S           Miller, Canfield, Paddock and Stone, P.L.C. *
McDowell Ralph E           Bodman PLC *

**Band 2**
Baty Donald                Honigman Miller Schwartz and Cohn LLP
Howell Steven G            Dickinson Wright PLLC *
Mears Patrick E            Barnes & Thornburg LLP *
Plemmons James             Dickinson Wright PLLC *
Skilton III Robert H        Warner Norcross & Judd LLP
Sylwestrzak Theodore       Dickinson Wright PLLC *

**Band 3**
Roach Steven A             Miller, Canfield, Paddock and Stone, P.L.C. *
Sable E Todd               Honigman Miller Schwartz and Cohn LLP

## Band 1

### Bodman PLC
**See profile on p.1557**

**THE FIRM** This Michigan firm is known for fielding the premier banking team in the state. Its practice encompasses a wide variety of commercial lending and regulatory matters, including bankruptcy and restructuring issues, and it has significant experience of transactions relating to the automotive, healthcare and environmental services sectors. The group recently represented Comerica Bank in the creation of a $400 million syndicated secured multicurrency credit facility. Bank of America, Wells Fargo and Huntington National Bank are also key clients.

**Sources say:** "*I trust them with my business because deadlines are always met and the quality of work is strong.*"

**KEY INDIVIDUALS Larry Shulman** (see p.1555) is widely regarded as "*the gold standard*" banking attorney in Michigan. Clients prize his "*pragmatic business approach*" and ability to deal with the most complex matters, **Ralph**

**McDowell** (see p.1552) is also considered "*one of the finest attorneys in town.*" He is a commercial bankruptcy and workout specialist, with a particular interest in the automotive and manufacturing sectors. The "*incredibly smart*" **Robert Diehl** (see p.1549) is a bankruptcy expert with notable experience in the real estate, construction and automotive sectors. Clients observe that "*he understands the requirements from a business perspective, as well as the legal ramifications in bankruptcies and workouts.*" **Joseph Kochanek** (see p.1551) is recognized as a leading practitioner in the field of loan origination and is known for dealing with syndicated credit arrangements. Clients report that he is "*very focused on the business issues*" and "*does a good job at managing multiple parties.*" **Wendy Zabriskie** (see p.1556) has a strong reputation for handling commercial and real estate loans. Clients say: "*She has a good business sense in addition to good legal sense, and she's very responsive.*" Clients admire **Scott Gyorke**'s (see p.1550) knowledge, responsiveness and creativity. He is adept at handling a broad range of matters relating to loan origination. Interviewees describe him as "*knowledgeable, responsive and creative.*" **Kathleen O'Callaghan Hickey** (see p.1550) advises lenders on secured transactions, workouts, liability and loan structuring. She has well-established expertise in the healthcare arena and is described by clients as "*very knowledgeable and very responsive.*" **Daniel Watson** (see p.1556) impresses clients with the quality and timeliness of his work product. He represents financial institutions in a range of loan origination matters, with a heavy emphasis on real estate transactions.

## Band 2

### Dickinson Wright PLLC
**See profile on p.1561**

**THE FIRM** Dickinson Wright has a strong reputation across a broad range of banking-related matters, including syndicated lending, asset-based finance and cross-border financings. The group receives glowing praise for its loan documentation expertise and is well equipped to represent lenders in workouts and bankruptcy litigation. JPMorgan Chase, PNC Bank and Fifth Third Bank are all recent clients.

**Sources say:** *"They are able to protect our interests and do a good job, but are also realistic in working with our prospects and realizing that there must be some give and take to keep a transaction moving along. They have a very good business sense about them."*

**KEY INDIVIDUALS Steven Howell** (see p.1551) is described by clients as *"not only a good lawyer, but a good businessman."* He represents financial institutions in loan workouts and restructurings. **James Plemmons** (see p.1554) receives high praise for his commitment to client service. His practice is focused on bankruptcy litigation and workouts, and he has significant clients in the automotive industry. **Colleen Shevnock** (see p.1555) represents institutional lenders in a wide variety of loan transactions, including syndicated, cross-border and multicurrency credit facilities. Clients value her *"balanced approach to loan documentation."* The *"outstanding"* **William Shield** (see p.1555) has a top-tier reputation in the field of syndicated credit facilities. Clients prize his *"speed, efficiency and quality of loan documentation"* and his deep understanding of the business issues. Clients admire **Theodore Sylwestrzak**'s (see p.1555) *"exceptional draftsmanship,"* *"good business sense"* and negotiation skills. He advises lenders on bankruptcy, workouts and secured lending. New entry to the rankings **Craig Hammond** (see p.1550) represents institutional lenders in loan financings and bond issuances. Clients characterize him as *"a superstar for bond deals"* and highlight his *"knowledge, responsiveness and comprehensiveness."*

### Honigman Miller Schwartz and Cohn LLP

**THE FIRM** This highly regarded group is best known for its expertise in bankruptcy, workouts and secured finance. It is also well versed in a wide range of finance-related matters, with an emphasis on commercial transactions and real estate finance. The team has recently been called upon to represent Capitol Bancorp in a Chapter 11 reorganization. Other notable clients include GM, Valeo and Citizens Bank.

**Sources say:** *"Honigman is a Detroit legal powerhouse; it is well known for the level of sophistication of its work product, as well as the pedigree of its attorneys."*

**KEY INDIVIDUALS Todd Sable** is a bankruptcy specialist, with a particular interest in the automotive and manufacturing industries. Clients report that *"he gives you answers that allow your business people to understand the risks and make informed decisions."* The well-respected **Donald Baty** has extensive banking and finance experience, spanning loan origination, bankruptcy, and issues relating to troubled suppliers. He recently advised GM with respect to its position as a major customer to a number of troubled suppliers at home and abroad.

### Miller, Canfield, Paddock and Stone, P.L.C.
See profile on p.1563

**THE FIRM** Miller Canfield's banking group handles a diverse range of matters, including construction, real estate and aircraft finance, as well as bankruptcy and restructuring within the automotive industry. The firm is particularly well known for its experience in the public finance arena and recently acted as bond counsel to the City of Detroit in a bond issuance of more than $133 million. It counts Citigroup Global Markets, JPMorgan Securities and Wayne County Airport Authority among its key clients.

**Sources say:** *"They're responsive, smart and practical."*

**KEY INDIVIDUALS Jonathan Green** (see p.1550) is singled out as one of the most distinguished bankruptcy lawyers in the state. He is particularly well known for working with automotive manufacturers and troubled suppliers. He receives outstanding plaudits from the market, with one interviewee professing that *"he's one of the finest lawyers I've ever worked with."* **Ronald Riback** (see p.1554) concentrates his practice on healthcare lending, loan origination and workouts. He is also known for his activities within the real estate lending arena. **Steven Roach** (see p.1554) has a strong reputation in the field of bankruptcy litigation. The *"astute"* **Trent Taylor** (see p.1556) advises institutional lenders on construction, equipment, real estate and working capital finance. Clients describe him as *"very issue-oriented and very results-oriented."*

## Band 3

### Barnes & Thornburg LLP
See profile on p.436

**THE FIRM** Barnes & Thornburg's finance, insolvency and restructuring team has notable experience in the fields of syndicated financing and real estate lending. It is also recognized for its bankruptcy and workout capabilities, par-

ticularly within the automotive and real estate sectors. Its client roster comprises of a number of major financial institutions, including Huntington National Bank, Fifth Third Bank and JPMorgan Chase.

**Sources say:** *"Their lawyers are knowledgeable and understand how to apply that knowledge in unique circumstances. They have handled cases of all sizes and complexity for us and we are impressed with their consistent execution."*

**KEY INDIVIDUALS Michael Campbell** (see p.1548) focuses his practice on commercial and real estate lending. Clients report that *"he consistently homes in on the most important issues."* **Patrick Mears** (see p.1553) has a broad banking and finance practice, with a heavy emphasis on real estate restructuring work. Clients value his bankruptcy expertise and attention to detail.

### Warner Norcross & Judd LLP

**THE FIRM** This well-respected banking group undertakes a wide range of transactional, commercial lending and regulatory matters on behalf of an impressive portfolio of clients from the finance sector. Its restructuring and insolvency group has a similarly broad base of experience, including litigation, supply chain management and receiverships, with a particular focus on the automotive industry. Clients include Fifth Third Bank and Huntington National Bank.

**Sources say:** *"In terms of service they are amazing, and they have a very high level of expertise."*

**KEY INDIVIDUALS Robert Skilton** is experienced in matters relating to bankruptcy and creditors' rights. Clients admire his *"encyclopedic knowledge of bankruptcy law."* **James Bready** handles a range of banking work, with a focus on finance, secured transactions and regulatory issues. He is currently serving as counsel to the Michigan Bankers Association.

## Other Notable Practitioners

Highly regarded attorney **David McLeod** of Varnum LLP is called upon to advise institutional lenders on commercial finance and real property acquisitions.

## CORPORATE/M&A

Commentary about individuals can be found under their firm's paragraph. If the firm has no paragraph (is not ranked) look at Other Notable Practitioners.

### Corporate/M&A
### Leading Firms

**Band 1**
Honigman Miller Schwartz and Cohn LLP

**Band 2**
Bodman PLC *
Dykema Gossett PLLC
Miller, Canfield, Paddock and Stone, P.L.C. *

**Band 3**
Barnes & Thornburg LLP *
Dickinson Wright PLLC *
Foley & Lardner LLP *
Warner Norcross & Judd LLP

**Band 4**
Butzel Long
Clark Hill PLC *
Miller Johnson
Varnum LLP

### Leading Individuals

**Band 1**

| | |
|---|---|
| Damschroder Timothy R | Bodman PLC * |
| Foltyn David | Honigman Miller Schwartz and Cohn LLP |
| Klimko Justin | Butzel Long |
| Kunz Donald | Honigman Miller Schwartz and Cohn LLP |
| Larsen Tracy T | Barnes & Thornburg LLP * |
| Minkus Daniel H | Clark Hill PLC |

**Band 2**

| | |
|---|---|
| Ammon Jeffrey S | Miller Johnson |
| Bernard J Michael | Dykema Gossett PLLC |
| Deitch Laurence B | Bodman PLC * |
| Miziolek Aleksandra A | Dykema Gossett PLLC |
| Parsigian David N | Honigman Miller Schwartz and Cohn LLP |

**Band 3**

| | |
|---|---|
| Alam Joel | Jaffe Raitt Heuer & Weiss, PC (ONP)† |
| Bolton Richard M | Dickinson Wright PLLC * |
| Cambridge James | Kerr, Russell & Weber, PLC (ONP)† |
| Doogal Daljit | Foley & Lardner LLP |
| DuBay Michael D | Honigman Miller Schwartz and Cohn LLP |
| High Mark R | Dickinson Wright PLLC * |
| Kaye Barbara | Honigman Miller Schwartz and Cohn LLP |
| Koh Jin-Kyu | Dykema Gossett PLLC |
| Lark Eric I | Kerr, Russell & Weber, PLC (ONP)† |
| Lewand F Thomas | Bodman PLC * |
| Lukas Edwin J | Bodman PLC * |
| Schwartz Alan S | Honigman Miller Schwartz and Cohn LLP |
| Waterbury Stephen C | Warner Norcross & Judd LLP |

**Up-and-coming individuals**

| | |
|---|---|
| LaBine Jeffrey L | Miller, Canfield, Paddock and Stone * |
| Leahy Carrie | Bodman PLC * |

**Associates to watch**

| | |
|---|---|
| Daly Erik | Barnes & Thornburg LLP * |

\* Indicates firm / individual with profile.
†ONP = Other Notable Practitioner

### Band 1

#### Honigman Miller Schwartz and Cohn LLP

**THE FIRM** This group is singled out as Michigan's market-leading corporate practice, and is highly recommended across a broad spectrum of transactional and regulatory specialties. The team has a strong focus on the private equity sector and is also active in the fields of public M&A, corporate governance and venture capital. Recent clients include Quicken Loans, Tecumseh Products and Taubman. **Sources say:** "They are exceptional, extremely high quality and have a great reputation."

**KEY INDIVIDUALS** The "terrific" **David Foltyn** is chief executive of the firm. He has extensive experience in a range of corporate matters, including M&A, public offerings and private equity transactions. **Donald Kunz** is also held in high esteem. He is known for his public company expertise and has notable experience of handling corporate finance-related matters. **David Parsigian** is recognized as one of the state's leading venture capital and hi-tech sector specialists. Clients report that "he is great to work with and very diligent." "Very strong practitioner" **Michael DuBay** is noted for handling private equity transactions. Clients highlight his "good commercial instincts" and "deep transactional experience." **Barbara Kaye** is another key player at the firm. She focuses her practice on private equity and corporate finance. Well-respected practitioner **Alan Schwartz** counsels private businesses on a range of corporate issues, including business planning and transactional matters.

### Band 2

#### Bodman PLC
See profile on p.1557

**THE FIRM** This firm has a highly regarded corporate finance and M&A practice, with a focus on the automotive and manufacturing sectors. The group is also increasingly active in the areas of private equity, securities transactions and hi-tech venture capital, and has impressive cross-jurisdictional experience. It has recently provided corporate counsel to Lear Corporation, Fruedenberg-NOK and Grede Holdings.
**Sources say:** "It is a conscientious and accessible group, with a good understanding of our business and our business needs."

**KEY INDIVIDUALS** Leading transactional attorney **Timothy Damschroder** (see p.1549) handles M&A and corporate finance, with significant experience of the automotive, energy and emerging technologies sectors. Clients describe him as being "almost without comparison; he's really very good at identifying particular problems and helping to work through them with good pragmatic solutions." "Really good lawyer" **Laurence Deitch** (see p.1549)

impresses clients with his experience, creative thinking and "execution-oriented" approach. He focuses on transactions within the automotive and private equity arenas. **Thomas Lewand** (see p.1552) is called upon to handle public-private partnerships and municipal bond financings. Clients value his experience and talent for project management. Up-and-coming attorney **Carrie Leahy** (see p.1552) concentrates on securities matters. Clients describe her as "a superb technician and eminently practical," and appreciate that "she really attempts to understand what we're dealing with and help us make the best decisions." **Edwin Lukas** (see p.1552) also focuses on securities and corporate finance. Clients admire his document development skills and characterize him as a "conscientious" and "thoughtful" practitioner.

#### Dykema Gossett PLLC

**THE FIRM** This widely praised practice places a heavy emphasis on M&A within the automotive, energy and financial services sectors, and was recently engaged to advise Citizens Republic Bancorp on its $1.3 billion merger with FirstMerit Bank. It is also well equipped to advise on corporate governance and a broad range of finance-related issues. Other key clients include Flagstar Bank, Alta Gas and Asterand.
**Sources say:** "Our overall impression is very positive and we would highly recommend them to those who want to get the job done right."

**KEY INDIVIDUALS** Well-regarded practitioner **Michael Bernard** is particularly active in the M&A arena and has significant clients in the manufacturing industry. **Jin-Kyu Koh** handles M&A and financing work. He has notable experience in the area of biotechnology, and recently acted for Asterand on its $9 million sale to Stemgent. **Aleksandra Miziolek** has extensive experience of the automotive industry. Her practice encompasses M&A, securities and governance issues.

#### Miller, Canfield, Paddock and Stone, P.L.C.
See profile on p.1563

**THE FIRM** This highly respected group is best known for its automotive expertise and is well versed in a range of M&A, governance and finance issues. The team is increasingly advising on cross-border transactions and has experience handling matters with Canadian and Mexican elements. It recently acted for Canadian insurance rating company Compu-Quote on its sale to Bain Capital. In the past year, it has also provided corporate counsel to Ford, Cypher Systems Group and Bartech.
**Sources say:** "We were extremely pleased with how they represented our interests."

**KEY INDIVIDUALS** Up-and-coming attorney **Jeffrey LaBine** (see p.1552) focuses on M&A and syndicated financing. Clients prize his "good business sense," "conscien-

*tious"* approach and the *"excellent"* quality of his work. He handled the aforementioned matter for Compu-Quote.

## Band 3

### Barnes & Thornburg LLP
See profile on p.436

**THE FIRM** Barnes & Thornburg's corporate group counsels clients on a wide variety of matters, with a focus on M&A within the automotive and aviation sectors. The team is known for advising on the acquisition side and recently represented Wolverine World Wide, one of three buyers in the multibillion-dollar purchase of Collective Brands. Other key clients include NetJets, Meijer and SRA International.

**Sources say:** *"They have been not only very responsive, but also have been very efficient in providing the advice that we need without extraneous memos and research. They are good value for money."*

**KEY INDIVIDUALS Tracy Larsen** (see p.1552) is recognized as a leading M&A and corporate finance practitioner, and was lead counsel to Wolverine World Wide in the acquisition described above. Clients describe him as *"deeply knowledgeable," "supremely responsive"* and a *"good business and legal adviser."* Associate-to-watch **Eric Daly** (see p.1549) impresses sources with his M&A expertise. Clients value his *"prompt turnaround and attention to detail."*

### Dickinson Wright PLLC
See profile on p.1561

**THE FIRM** This firm is known for its corporate finance work and has considerable experience of private equity fund formation and restructuring matters. It is also active in the fields of M&A, stock and asset acquisitions, joint ventures and bond financing. Clients include HMA Capital Partners, Active Interests Media and Mercantile Bank.

**Sources say:** *"They do outstanding work."*

**KEY INDIVIDUALS** Clients describe **Richard Bolton** (see p.1548) as *"very experienced, even-keeled and solution-oriented."* His practice focuses on private equity organizations, and he recently represented Peninsula Capital Partners in the organization and closing of a $389 million private equity fund. **Mark High** (see p.1550) is also well regarded in the market. He handles M&A matters for clients from a diverse range of industries.

### Foley & Lardner LLP
See profile on p.2588

**THE FIRM** This practice places an emphasis on private equity and M&A transactions, in addition to general corporate counseling. It is particularly active in the automotive arena and is noted for its venture capital experience. Recent work highlights include representing Wynnchurch Capital in the $100 million acquisition of US Pipe. Other clients include Ficosa North America, Fabco Automotive and Fisker.

**Sources say:** *"They have always made themselves available to us and have done an excellent job representing us through the acquisition."*

**KEY INDIVIDUALS Daljit Doogal** divides his practice between debt restructuring, M&A and private equity funds. Sources describe him as *"a very good lawyer."*

### Warner Norcross & Judd LLP

**THE FIRM** This Michigan-focused firm has notable experience handling M&A, joint ventures, stock and asset transactions, public offerings and other corporate finance-related matters. Its client roster comprises a variety of heavy manufacturing, automotive and pharmaceutical companies, including Stryker, Perrigo and East Jordan Iron Works.

**Sources say:** *"They give excellent advice and they're prompt."*

**KEY INDIVIDUALS Stephen Waterbury** is chair of the firm's M&A group, and focuses on transactional matters. Sources describe him as *"very smart from both a legal and business perspective,"* observing that *"he does a terrific job at providing pragmatic, real-world advice."*

## Band 4

### Butzel Long

**THE FIRM** This practice continues to be recognized for its automotive expertise and represents a number of the region's key manufacturers and suppliers. It has also seen an increase in work arising from the technology, healthcare and defense sectors. The group's recent experience includes M&A, joint ventures and shareholder disputes. In the past year it has acted for TK Holdings, MB Aerospace and Diplomat Specialty Pharmacy.

**Sources say:** *"They are knowledgeable and responsive."*

**KEY INDIVIDUALS Justin Klimko** is a leading M&A and corporate governance practitioner. Clients admire his document craftsmanship, negotiation skills and intellectual dexterity. One source reports: *"He was very thorough in his approach and very practical."*

### Clark Hill PLC
See profile on p.1559

**THE FIRM** This firm is known for its activities in the automotive sector and has particular experience of acting for supply chain companies. It is equipped to handle a range of corporate matters, including M&A, asset sales and joint ventures, and has a notable track record of advising on Canadian transactions. Recent clients include Arizona Automobile Dealers Association, Avondale Automotive and Faurecia.

**KEY INDIVIDUALS Daniel Minkus** is a *"great lawyer"* with *"an excellent reputation in the market,"* say sources. He continues to handle a broad range of transactional matters.

### Miller Johnson

**THE FIRM** This group advises clients on a variety of business issues, including M&A, corporate finance, private equity, venture capital, joint ventures and general contractual matters. The team is particularly active in the medical sector and continues to act for medical device and equipment manufacturer Stryker. It has offices in Grand Rapids and Kalamazoo.

**KEY INDIVIDUALS** Experienced practitioner **Jeffrey Ammon** is noted for his activities in the medical arena. His practice also focuses on economic development incentives.

### Varnum LLP

**THE FIRM** This Michigan firm is recommended for its transactional capabilities. It advises public and private companies on a diverse selection of corporate and commercial matters, including M&A, joint ventures and tax, in addition to contractual and UCC issues. The group has particular experience in the manufacturing sector.

**Sources say:** *"I find their corporate support to be very responsive, and they are very diligent in their research and assessment of the situation."*

**KEY INDIVIDUALS** Scott Huizenga is a key contact in the firm's corporate services group.

## Other Notable Practitioners

Well-regarded attorney **Eric Lark** of Kerr, Russell & Weber, PLC has extensive experience of a variety of corporate matters, including transactional, securities and private equity-related issues. Experienced practitioner **Joel Alam** of Jaffe Raitt Heuer & Weiss, PC focuses his practice on M&A work. He is also well versed in securities matters. Highly respected lawyer **James Cambridge** of Kerr, Russell & Weber, PLC has a broad practice encompassing corporate finance and real estate matters.

# EMPLOYEE BENEFITS & EXECUTIVE COMPENSATION

Commentary about individuals can be found under their firm's paragraph. If the firm has no paragraph (is not ranked) look at Other Notable Practitioners.

## Employee Benefits & Executive Compensation
### Leading Firms

**Band 1**
Miller, Canfield, Paddock and Stone, P.L.C. *
Stevenson Keppelman Associates
Warner Norcross & Judd LLP

**Band 2**
Butzel Long
Dykema Gossett PLLC
Honigman Miller Schwartz and Cohn LLP
Maddin, Hauser, Wartell, Roth & Heller PC
Miller Johnson

### Leading Individuals

**Band 1**

| | |
|---|---|
| Bruinsma James | Miller Johnson |
| Brustad Orin D | Miller, Canfield, Paddock and Stone * |
| Hunter Margaret Adams | Dykema Gossett PLLC |
| Keppelman Nancy | Stevenson Keppelman Associates |
| Larson Mary Jo | Warner Norcross & Judd LLP |
| Lax Charles | Maddin, Hauser, Wartell, Roth & Heller PC |
| Stevenson Robert B | Stevenson Keppelman Associates * |
| Zimmer Lisa B | Warner Norcross & Judd LLP |

**Band 2**

| | |
|---|---|
| Bauman Mary V | Miller Johnson |
| Friedman Michael J | Honigman Miller Schwartz and Cohn LLP |
| Joswick Theresa C | Dawda, Mann, Mulcahy & Sadler (ONP) † * |
| Kolenic Jr Anthony | Warner Norcross & Judd LLP |
| McKendry Jr John H | Warner Norcross & Judd LLP |
| McMican Christopher A | Miller, Canfield, Paddock and Stone * |
| Schermerhorn Gregory R | Honigman Miller Schwartz and Cohn LLP |
| Schreier Jordan | Dickinson Wright PLLC |
| Whitfield George L | Warner Norcross & Judd LLP |

**Band 3**

| | |
|---|---|
| Berrodin Frank | Miller Johnson |
| Buydens Robert | Butzel Long |
| Christen Amy M | Dykema Gossett PLLC |
| Hammond Edward | Clark Hill PLC (ONP) † * |
| Remer Gary | Maddin, Hauser, Wartell, Roth & Heller PC |
| Stumpff Andrew | Stevenson Keppelman Associates |
| Thompson Deborah W | Stevenson Keppelman Associates * |
| Walters David B | Bodman PLC (ONP) † * |
| Widmayer Warren | Ferguson & Widmayer (ONP) † |
| Wise Marc S | Maddin, Hauser, Wartell, Roth & Heller PC |

* Indicates firm / individual with profile.

† ONP = Other Notable Practitioner

## Band 1

### Miller, Canfield, Paddock and Stone, P.L.C.
See profile on p.1563

**THE FIRM** This practice is widely acknowledged as one of the preeminent employee benefits and executive compensation groups in the state. It continues to be busy in the area of pension plans and is increasingly called upon to advise on matters stemming from healthcare reform. The team also has considerable experience of issues arising from corporate transactions, particularly ESOP matters. It represents a range of domestic and international clients, including a significant number of governmental employers.

**Sources say:** *"High quality, very helpful."*

**KEY INDIVIDUALS Orin Brustad** (see p.1548) is a *"very well-renowned"* Michigan lawyer. He handles qualified retirement plans, executive compensation, health and welfare benefits and ERISA counseling and litigation, and is an expert on Asian pension systems. **Christopher McMican** (see p.1553) has wide-ranging experience of numerous benefits-related matters. Clients say: *"He's very knowledgeable and considerate, and wants the best results for his clients."*

### Stevenson Keppelman Associates

**THE FIRM** This Ann Arbor boutique has a decidedly national outlook. It counsels clients on the full range of employee benefits and executive compensation matters, and is praised for the quality of its advocates. The group represents a wide variety of domestic and international employers, including automotive manufacturers and suppliers, healthcare providers, governmental entities and professional firms. ThyssenKrupp, L'Oréal and Cooper-Standard Automotive are among its recent clients.

**Sources say:** *"They are specialists – they really focus on this area of the law, they are really passionate about protecting the interests of their clients and they know their business very deeply."*

**KEY INDIVIDUALS Nancy Keppelman** is well known for her expertise in the fields of qualified retirement plans and qualified domestic relations orders. Clients value her detailed understanding of the practice area. **Robert Stevenson** (see p.1555) is regarded as one of the foremost authorities on ERISA law. Clients report that he is *"extremely passionate"* about what he does and communicates *"generously and carefully."* **Deborah Thompson** (see p.1556) is another key practitioner. She advises on a diverse portfolio of employee benefit matters. The well-respected **Andrew Stumpff** (see p.1555) focuses his practice on executive compensation and matters relating to corporate transactions.

### Warner Norcross & Judd LLP

**THE FIRM** This group is highly recommended for its broad base of employee benefits and executive compensation experience. Areas of focus include qualified and non-qualified retirement plans, health and welfare plans, and ERISA issues. The team is also sought after to represent employers in audits and disputes. Dow Corning, PulteGroup and Christian Schools International are among its key clients.

**Sources say:** *"They're bright and responsive. I get immediate feedback on my questions; they are very customer service-focused."*

**KEY INDIVIDUALS Mary Jo Larson** is described by clients as *"very knowledgeable."* She concentrates her practice on retirement plans and executive compensation. **Anthony Kolenic** is the leader of the firm's employee benefits group, and has significant experience of representing governmental and tax-exempt entities. Sources name him *"an excellent attorney."* **John McKendry** is *"highly regarded"* throughout the state for handling retirement and welfare plans. Clients appreciate the fact that *"he truly loves his work."* **George Whitfield** is identified by clients as *"an extremely accomplished attorney who is very well versed in the retirement plan arena."* **Lisa Zimmer** advises on a wide variety of retirement plans and executive compensation arrangements. Clients value her knowledge and attentiveness.

## Band 2

### Butzel Long

**THE FIRM** This versatile practice advises on all aspects of employee benefits law, including executive compensation, health and welfare plans, and qualified retirement plans. It is increasingly called upon to counsel employers on the legal aspects of healthcare reform. The group is also recognized for the strength of its fiduciary compliance practice. Its clients are drawn primarily from automotive, aerospace and other manufacturing backgrounds.

**Sources say:** *"The level of knowledge and experience provided is first rate."*

**KEY INDIVIDUALS Robert Buydens** has a broad employee benefits background. He has particularly distinguished himself in the fields of retiree healthcare and pension plans.

### Dykema Gossett PLLC

**THE FIRM** This group handles a wide range of employee benefit and executive compensation issues, and has a strong reputation for assisting with retirement plans. It places a notable emphasis on providing benefit plan advice to government bodies, and has recently advised the State of Michigan on a variety of matters. The team is also active in the area of welfare plans, with a focus on the Health Insurance Portability and Accountability Act (HIPAA) and retiree medical benefits. Recent clients include Ford, TRW Automotive and Citizens Republic Bancorp.

**KEY INDIVIDUALS Margaret Adams Hunter** heads the firm's employee benefits practice, and specializes in Section 409A executive compensation matters. Clients praise her dexterity in providing *"creative solutions to complex issues."* Clients describe **Amy Christen** as *"responsive,"* *"knowledgeable"* and *"thorough."* She is head of the firm's healthcare and welfare team, and focuses on HIPAA and retiree medical benefits.

## Honigman Miller Schwartz and Cohn LLP

**THE FIRM** This firm has a broad-based employee benefits practice, encompassing executive compensation, tax-qualified retirement plans, welfare benefit plans, ERISA compliance, issues arising from corporate transactions and the litigation of related disputes. It has significant experience of advising government bodies, automotive manufacturers and financial institutions. Ally Financial, Crain Communications and the Detroit Institute of Arts are all key clients.

**KEY INDIVIDUALS** The well-respected **Michael Friedman** has a varied employee benefits practice, with a focus on welfare and healthcare. **Gregory Schermerhorn** is another of the group's notable attorneys. He focuses his practice on retirement benefit programs and executive compensation issues.

## Maddin, Hauser, Wartell, Roth & Heller PC

**THE FIRM** This much-praised practice is based in Southfield and has a strong Michigan presence. The team's core expertise covers qualified retirement plans and welfare benefits, including 401(k) plans, new federal healthcare law and the representation of employers in controversy matters. It acts for manufacturing, automotive, health-

care and nursing home clients, and has a notable track record of acting for professional employer organizations.

**Sources say:** *"They are very professional, and have a high level of ethics and integrity."*

**KEY INDIVIDUALS Charles Lax** is widely regarded as one of the leading qualified retirement plan experts in the state. Clients prize *"his ability to understand problems and come up with practical solutions."* **Gary Remer** has also distinguished himself in the field of qualified retirement plans. He has a particular interest in matters relating to IRS plan audits. **Marc Wise**'s practice places a heavy emphasis on welfare benefits and healthcare plans. Clients value his reputation, knowledge and responsiveness.

## Miller Johnson

**THE FIRM** Miller Johnson's employee benefits and executive compensation group operates from offices in Grand Rapids and Kalamazoo. It handles a comprehensive range of qualified retirement, health benefit and welfare benefit plans, with notable expertise in healthcare reform and ERISA litigation. The team has also seen an increase in issues arising from corporate acquisitions. It continues to be known for representing healthcare providers, and counts Bronson Healthcare and Spectrum Health System among its clients.

**KEY INDIVIDUALS** Group leader **Mary Bauman** advises on a wide variety of benefits-related matters, with a notable focus on new federal healthcare law. **Frank**

**Berrodin** concentrates his practice on qualified and non-qualified retirement plans. He has significant experience of representing employers in disputes with the IRS and the Department of Labor. The highly regarded **James Bruinsma** has recently been called upon to advise employers on benefit-related issues arising from major corporate transactions.

## Other Notable Practitioners

The *"outstanding"* Jordan Schreier recently joined Dickinson Wright PLLC from Butzel Long. Schreier handles ERISA, benefits and compensation work. Clients value his proactivity, tailored approach and *"excellent response time."* **Theresa Joswick** (see p.1551) of Dawda, Mann, Mulcahy & Sadler PLC has extensive experience of advising clients on executive compensation, welfare and retirement plans. Sources name her *"an excellent practitioner."* **Edward Hammond** (see p.1550) of Clark Hill PLC is recognized as a *"very skilled attorney."* He is an expert on benefits issues arising from bankruptcy. **David Walters** (see p.1556) of Bodman PLC is described by peers as a *"very fine benefits lawyer."* He focuses his practice on ESOP, retirement and health plans, and has a notable track record of representing clients from the healthcare sector. **Warren Widmayer** of Ferguson & Widmayer is *"well respected within the benefits community,"* say sources. He is an expert in qualified retirement plans.

# LABOR & EMPLOYMENT

Commentary about individuals can be found under their firm's paragraph. If the firm has no paragraph (is not ranked) look at Other Notable Practitioners.

| Labor & Employment Leading Firms |
| --- |
| **Band 1** |
| Kienbaum Opperwall Hardy & Pelton, P.L.C. * |
| Vercruysse Murray & Calzone, PC * |
| **Band 2** |
| Clark Hill PLC * |
| Miller, Canfield, Paddock and Stone, P.L.C. * |
| Miller Johnson |
| Nemeth Burwell, PC * |
| **Band 3** |
| Bodman PLC * |
| Butzel Long |
| Dickinson Wright PLLC * |
| Dykema Gossett PLLC |
| Honigman Miller Schwartz and Cohn LLP |
| Ogletree, Deakins, Nash, Smoak & Stewart, PC * |
| Varnum LLP |

*\* Indicates firm with profile.*
*Alphabetical order within each band. Band 1 is the highest.*

## Band 1

### Kienbaum Opperwall Hardy & Pelton, P.L.C.
See profile on p.1562
**THE FIRM** This much-admired boutique has one of the leading labor and employment practices in the state. It is well equipped to provide advice on a comprehensive range of issues and its clients range from local businesses to international corporations. The team has recently seen an increase in labor-related matters and notably represented Ford in an arbitration concerning approximately $400 million of claims. Other key clients include Aon, Comcast and the Detroit Tigers.

**Sources say:** *"They are extremely accessible and responsive, and they have a practical approach to these matters that addresses the reality of the situation directly."*

**KEY INDIVIDUALS Thomas Kienbaum** (see p.1551) handles labor and employment matters, with a focus on litigation at trial and appellate levels, and is noted for his experience in class action defense. He has an outstanding reputation in the state, and attracts a level of feedback appropriate for a recognized leader of the employment Bar. In the words of one source, *"I personally know of no*

*other lawyer who has the full package of understanding that really comes through when you listen to him talking."* Sources report that **Elizabeth Hardy** (see p.1550) *"shines"* in the arena of employment litigation: *"She has tremendous people skills and understands how to examine witnesses."* **Theodore Opperwall** (see p.1553) is particularly recommended for his deft handling of labor arbitrations. Clients report that *"he has a very good manner in terms of how he approaches the arbitrators and the witnesses and he has a logical and effective approach."* **William Forrest** (see p.1550) is a well-regarded employment litigator, with particular experience of discrimination and ERISA cases. Clients observe that **Eric Pelton** (see p.1554) *"is smart, applies a common-sense approach to the cases and is an effective and efficient litigator."* He concentrates his practice on employment litigation and traditional labor law.

### Vercruysse Murray & Calzone, PC
See profile on p.1566
**THE FIRM** This eminent Birmingham boutique has extensive experience across a broad spectrum of labor and employment matters. It is particularly prominent in the field of traditional labor law and is regularly engaged to

advise on strikes and other union issues. The group is also active in the ERISA arena and was recently called upon to defend American Axle against $36 million of ERISA and benefits-related claims. It has significant clients in the automotive, media and public sectors, and has recently provided counsel to Faurecia, Gannett and Central Michigan University.
**Sources say:** *"They are excellent attorneys."*

**KEY INDIVIDUALS David Calzone** is an expert in FMLA and ADA matters and recently defended Faurecia against a disability discrimination claim at the Sixth Circuit Court of Appeal. *"Fine attorney"* **Gregory Murray** is praised by clients for his *"legal knowledge and common-sense approach to dispute resolution in negotiations."* He focuses his practice on employment litigation. *"Excellent"* practitioner **Robert Vercruysse** is well versed in a range of employment and ERISA litigation and comes particularly recommended for his incisive approach. *"He got right to the core of what the problem was and I really value that,"* relates one impressed client.

## Band 2

### Clark Hill PLC
See profile on p.1559

**THE FIRM** This well-regarded group has experience handling a wide variety of labor and employment issues. It places a heavy emphasis on litigation and has recently defended a number of class actions. In addition to this, the group is regularly sought after to represent businesses in NLRB bargaining and negotiations. It acts for a considerable number of healthcare, automotive and construction clients, including Trinity Health, Severstal Dearborn and Champion, Inc.

**KEY INDIVIDUALS** Practice group leader **Thomas Brady** divides his practice between employment litigation and traditional labor matters. He is increasingly occupied with benefit disputes. Highly regarded attorney **Daniel Bretz** also handles employment litigation and traditional labor matters. He is particularly active in the healthcare arena. **Thomas Hathaway** is another key player. He focuses his practice on employment litigation and has a particular interest in discrimination cases.

### Miller, Canfield, Paddock and Stone, P.L.C.
See profile on p.1563

**THE FIRM** This practice has wide-ranging experience with labor and employment matters, including collective bargaining, discrimination, FMLA, ERISA and harassment issues. The group has a prominent focus on the public sector and was recently called upon to defend Detroit Public Schools against a discrimination claim in excess of $3 million. It has also recently advised Chubb Group, DTE Energy and the City of Detroit.
**Sources say:** *"They are knowledgeable and productive in their responses."*

**KEY INDIVIDUALS** *"Excellent attorney"* **Megan Norris** (see p.1553) is held in high regard in the market. She specializes in FMLA and ADA, and was recently successful in defending Quikrete against an FMLA interference claim. Experienced practitioner **Leonard Givens** (see p.1550) continues to be respected as a talented labor and employment lawyer. Market commentators note that he is *"a very good lawyer"* who is *"recognized as an expert in employment law."* **Richard Seryak** (see p.1554) is another key player at the firm. He concentrates his practice on litigation and recently prevailed at trial on behalf of the University of

Michigan Law School, which was subject to a discrimination claim of over $1 million. Well-regarded attorney **Adam Forman** (see p.1549) handles employment defense litigation and labor negotiations. He is an expert in social media-related issues. **Jerome Watson** (see p.1556) is also a respected practitioner. He has extensive experience of employment litigation and has recently been active in the defense of discrimination claims. Senior statesman **Charles Mishkind** (see p.1553) focuses his practice on employment and employee benefit-related litigation.

## Miller Johnson

**THE FIRM** This multiservice labor and employment group has offices in Grand Rapids and Kalamazoo. It is particularly known for its labor expertise and has recently been active in the area of collective bargaining. The team has a number of key clients within the healthcare, construction, manufacturing and furniture production sectors, including Spectrum Health System, Douglas Autotech and American Seating.
**Sources say:** *"The firm has an excellent reputation. The people I've dealt with from Miller Johnson are all very strong performers and eager to serve."*

**KEY INDIVIDUALS** Clients have been impressed with **Peter Kok**'s *"keen intellect"* and *"deep understanding of labor and employment law."* He is well equipped to handle both labor and employment issues. **Jon March** is an experienced employment litigator with a focus on discrimination, wrongful dismissal and trade secret matters.

## Nemeth Burwell, PC
See profile on p.1564

**THE FIRM** Nemeth Burwell is a Detroit labor and employment boutique with a good reputation in the local market. It represents a broad range of employers, with a focus on healthcare providers, governmental entities, insurers and casinos. Recent work highlights include defending the City of Detroit against an alleged breach of the Whistleblower Protection Act. In the past year, the group has also provided advice to Motor City Casino, Medilodge and Chubb Group.
**Sources say:** *"I am impressed by the breadth of their knowledge and practical resolutions to business issues, as well as the timeliness of the legal service provided."*

**KEY INDIVIDUALS** Clients report that **Linda Burwell** (see p.1548) is an *"extremely savvy"* representative in employment matters. She handles litigation, arbitration and mediation, in addition to general labor and employment advice. **Patricia Nemeth** (see p.1553) is well versed in a variety of labor and employment issues and comes particularly recommended for employment counseling. Clients describe her as *"extremely bright."*

## Band 3

### Bodman PLC
See profile on p.1557

**THE FIRM** This group places a particular emphasis on its traditional labor practice and is regularly engaged to advise on collective bargaining and union avoidance. It has also seen an increase in employment litigation defense work relating to discrimination and wrongful termination claims. The group has notable experience of representing healthcare, nonprofit, banking and automotive clients, including the Roman Catholic Archdiocese of Detroit, Comerica, Spectrum Health and Lear Corporation.

**Sources say:** *"Their client service is excellent: very attentive, very timely."*

**KEY INDIVIDUALS Karen Piper** (see p.1554) is a respected counselor and litigator, with significant experience of FMLA matters. Clients value her thoroughness, sensitivity and knowledge of the relevant issues. New entry to the rankings **John Cashen** (see p.1548) handles labor matters, including litigation, with a strong focus on issues arising in the automotive sector. Clients report that he is *"extremely knowledgeable about union issues and kept us one step ahead of all the issues that arose."*

## Butzel Long

**THE FIRM** Butzel Long has a multiservice labor and employment group, with particular expertise in the areas of wage and hour, noncompete, whistle-blowing and employment issues relating to higher education institutions. Its client roster encompasses a considerable number of governmental entities, universities, automotive suppliers and healthcare providers. Recent work highlights include representing the City of Detroit in an unfair labor practice proceeding.

**Sources say:** *"They understand their clients' needs and how we would like our cases to be handled."*

**KEY INDIVIDUALS John Hancock** is a collective bargaining and union avoidance specialist. Clients report that *"he has an ability to work within the complex areas of labor law and the practical realities of labor relations."* **Robert Boonin** is an expert in wage and hour defense. Clients value his detailed understanding of the labor relations market, observing that *"he knows the field inside and out."* Clients appreciate the fact that **Daniel Tukel** is *"very thorough in preparing his cases"* and *"very responsive."* His practice focuses on employment litigation and counseling, in addition to traditional labor matters.

## Dickinson Wright PLLC

**See profile on p.1561**

**THE FIRM** Dickinson Wright has a broad labor and employment practice, and represents a range of employers from the automotive, food and restaurant, healthcare and manufacturing sectors. The group's recent experience encompasses sexual harassment, FMLA, ADA, EEOC, whistle-blower, and wage and hour issues. Notable clients include Little Caesar Enterprises, Ford and AT&T.

**Sources say:** *"I find them to be a very valued resource and, overall, they are just extraordinarily well prepared."*

**KEY INDIVIDUALS** Clients identify **Timothy Howlett** (see p.1551) as a *"very good litigator."* He focuses on employment matters.

## Dykema Gossett PLLC

**THE FIRM** This firm is equipped to advise clients on a wide variety of labor and employment matters, with a focus on ERISA litigation, ADA concerns and matters relating to the FLSA. The group is also known for its trade secret practice and was recently engaged to represent MSC Software in a claim of approximately $60 million against certain former employees and their new employer, Altair Engineering. Other clients include Citizens Republic Bancorp, Sears and TRW Automotive.

**Sources say:** *"Extremely professional, competent and client-focused."*

**KEY INDIVIDUALS** Clients describe **Joseph Ritok** as an *"excellent negotiator"* and an *"authentic voice of reason."* He is well versed in labor and employment matters, and has a particular interest in issues relating to the FLSA. Well-regarded attorney **Patrick Hickey** devotes the majority of his practice to trade secret disputes. He also handles ERISA litigation and contractual claims. **John Entenman** is a traditional labor specialist. He has noteworthy experience in the fields of union negotiations and public sector representation. **Martin Jay Galvin** is another leading member of the group. He is singled out for his ADA expertise and has a growing gaming and hospitality practice.

## Honigman Miller Schwartz and Cohn LLP

**THE FIRM** This firm is recognized for its traditional labor practice and is regularly called upon to handle FLSA, NLRB, and wage and hour issues, in addition to labor negotiations and collective bargaining. The group is also experienced in noncompete, discrimination and general employment matters. Recent clients include Quicken Loans, AutoAlliance and CVS Caremark.

**KEY INDIVIDUALS** Clients prize **William Sargent**'s *"wealth of experience."* He has a broad practice, encompassing wage and hour, military leave and wrongful discharge litigation.

## Ogletree, Deakins, Nash, Smoak & Stewart, PC

**See profile on p.1110**

**THE FIRM** This national boutique has established a notable presence in Michigan. Its Detroit Metro office has experience of advising a diverse range of clients on labor negotiations, ERISA issues, complex terminations, non-

compete agreements, EEOC complaints and litigation, in addition to general labor and employment counseling.

**Sources say:** *"They're quick, they give good legal and business advice, they are really creative when it comes certain types of risk and, on the litigation side, they've been phenomenal."*

**KEY INDIVIDUALS Thomas Cattel** (see p.1548) impresses clients with his knowledge, practicality and quick turnaround. He focuses his practice on employment counseling and litigation.

## Varnum LLP

**THE FIRM** Varnum's labor and employment group is known for handling traditional labor work, and is experienced in collective and class action matters. It is also active in the field of employment litigation and counseling, and represents clients from the retail, healthcare and food processing sectors, in addition to manufacturing and automotive companies.

**Sources say:** *"They are practical in their approach; they understand business and they understand their clients' needs."*

**KEY INDIVIDUALS** Well-regarded attorney **Richard Hooker** is singled out for his traditional labor practice. He also provides employment advice and is an experienced litigator. **David Khorey** is described by clients as *"a great strategist and an outstanding labor lawyer."* He also advises on employment issues. *"Very good attorney"* **Lawrence Murphy** focuses his practice on employment litigation. His experience includes wrongful discharge, discrimination and harassment, in addition to contractual disputes.

## Other Notable Practitioners

**Robert Sikkel** (see p.1555) of Barnes & Thornburg LLP is described by clients as *"good at giving choices and articulating a risk."* He is a sought-after labor and employment counsel, and is particularly active in the fields of collective bargaining and labor negotiations. Clients report that **Michael Snapper** (see p.1555), also of Barnes & Thornburg LLP, is always *"responsive, timely, informative and helpful."* His practice places a heavy emphasis on traditional labor law, including training and strategy counseling. **Charles DeWitt** (see p.1549) of Littler Mendelson, PC impresses clients with his ability to be *"both detail-oriented and a big-picture thinker."* He has a strong reputation in the market for handling employment defense litigation. **Maurice Jenkins** (see p.1551) of Jackson Lewis LLP is also a well-respected practitioner. He deals with a diverse range of labor and employment issues and is called upon to litigate, in addition to providing compliance advice.

# LITIGATION

Commentary about individuals can be found under their firm's paragraph. If the firm has no paragraph (is not ranked) look at Other Notable Practitioners.

## Litigation: General Commercial
### Leading Firms

**Band 1**
Honigman Miller Schwartz and Cohn LLP
Miller, Canfield, Paddock and Stone, P.L.C. *

**Band 2**
Barris, Sott, Denn & Driker, PLLC
Bodman PLC *
Dickinson Wright PLLC *
Dykema Gossett PLLC
Warner Norcross & Judd LLP

**Band 3**
Brooks Wilkins Sharkey & Turco, PLLC *
Butzel Long
Miller Johnson
Rhoades McKee *
Varnum LLP

## Band 1

### Honigman Miller Schwartz and Cohn LLP
**THE FIRM** This group is regarded as one of Michigan's finest litigation practices. It handles a diverse range of commercial disputes and has distinguished itself most notably in the areas of antitrust, securities, corporate governance, e-discovery and real estate tax appeals. It is also known as one of the leading IP litigation teams in the state, and recently defended EMI against a copyright infringement claim concerning a rhythmic motif sampled in a rap song. Other clients include Taubman, Meijer and JPMorgan Chase.
**Sources say:** *"They have been practical and pragmatic in their approach and good in their judgment of when to push and when to settle."*
**KEY INDIVIDUALS Norman Ankers** is a *"great communicator"* with a reputation for being someone who *"takes the toughest cases and takes them to trial."* His practice encompasses securities litigation, shareholder disputes and class action defense. **Joseph Aviv** is also very highly regarded. He is known for handling securities, class action and corporate governance litigation. White-collar specialist **Richard Zuckerman** is experienced in the fields of tax fraud and securities fraud. He represents clients in a host of industry sectors before both state and federal courts. **Raymond Henney** is cochair of the firm's securities and corporate governance litigation group. He is another experienced and well-respected practitioner. **I W Winsten** is described by peers as *"phenomenally talented."* He litigates a broad range of issues, with a focus on contractual disputes and breach of fiduciary duty claims.

### Miller, Canfield, Paddock and Stone, P.L.C.
See profile on p.1563
**THE FIRM** This talented group of attorneys is viewed as having one of the premier litigation practices in the state.

## Litigation: General Commercial
### Senior Statesmen

**Senior Statesmen:** distinguished older practitioners

| | |
|---|---|
| Driker Eugene | Barris, Sott, Denn & Driker, PLLC |
| Muth Jon R | Miller Johnson |
| von Ende Carl H | Miller, Canfield, Paddock and Stone, P.L.C. * |

### Leading Individuals

**Band 1**

| | |
|---|---|
| Ankers Norman C | Honigman Miller Schwartz and Cohn LLP |
| Aviv Joseph | Honigman Miller Schwartz and Cohn LLP |
| Brooks Keefe A | Brooks Wilkins Sharkey & Turco, PLLC * |
| Feeney James | Dykema Gossett PLLC |
| Kessler Philip J | Thompson & Knight LLP (ONP) † * |
| Miller E Powell | The Miller Law Firm PC (ONP) † |
| Pappas Edward H | Dickinson Wright PLLC * |
| Sankbeil William A | Kerr, Russell & Weber, PLC (ONP) † |
| Woods Sharon M | Barris, Sott, Denn & Driker, PLLC |
| Young Rodger D | Young & Associates (ONP) † |

**Band 2**

| | |
|---|---|
| Dozeman Douglas A | Warner Norcross & Judd LLP |
| Haffey Dennis M | Dykema Gossett PLLC |
| Hickey Patrick F | Dykema Gossett PLLC |
| Kay Richard A | Warner Norcross & Judd LLP |
| Kronk Edward M | Brooks Wilkins Sharkey & Turco, PLLC * |
| McNeill Thomas G | Dickinson Wright PLLC * |
| Pozza Jr Clarence L | Miller, Canfield, Paddock and Stone, P.L.C. * |

**Band 3**

| | |
|---|---|
| Branigan Thomas P | Bowman and Brooke LLP (ONP) † * |
| Curtner Gregory L | Schiff Hardin LLP (ONP) † |
| Henney Raymond W | Honigman Miller Schwartz and Cohn LLP |
| McCarthy Paul | Rhoades McKee * |
| McIntyre Kenneth J | Dickinson Wright PLLC * |
| Neckers Bruce | Rhoades McKee * |
| Oostema John R | Smith Haughey Rice & Roegge (ONP) † |
| Shannon Joseph J | Bodman PLC * |
| Sharkey Dan | Brooks Wilkins Sharkey & Turco, PLLC * |
| Winsten I W | Honigman Miller Schwartz and Cohn LLP |

It is well equipped to advise clients on a variety of contentious matters and is particularly active in the fields of securities, intellectual property and class action litigation. The team continues to be recognized for its automotive expertise and has also seen a growth in its international arbitration practice. Ford, Meritor and Valassis are among its recent clients.
**Sources say:** *"Miller Canfield's litigation group is among the best in the state. It has some of the best litigation and trial lawyers."*
**KEY INDIVIDUALS** The *"excellent"* **Thomas Cranmer** (see p.1549) is a preeminent white-collar criminal defense lawyer who also handles complex commercial litigation. Sources highlight him as *"a wonderful gentleman."* Sources describe **Carl von Ende** (see p.1556) as a *"very good lawyer."* He represents clients in corporate governance,

## Litigation: White-Collar Crime & Government Investigations
### Leading Individuals

**Band 1**

| | |
|---|---|
| Cranmer Thomas W | Miller, Canfield, Paddock and Stone, P.L.C. * |
| DuMouchel David F | Butzel Long |

**Band 2**

| | |
|---|---|
| Fink Neil | Law Offices of Neil H Fink, PC (ONP) † |
| Harrison Robert | Robert Harrison & Associates (ONP) † |
| Leitman Matthew | Miller, Canfield, Paddock and Stone, P.L.C. * |
| Zuckerman Richard | Honigman Miller Schwartz and Cohn LLP |

\* Indicates firm / individual with profile.

†ONP = Other Notable Practitioner

intellectual property and antitrust disputes, and is regularly called upon to act as an arbitrator and mediator. The *"high-quality"* **Matthew Leitman** (see p.1552) is acknowledged as a talented white-collar defense attorney, and is also an experienced antitrust litigator. The respected **Clarence Pozza**'s (see p.1554) practice is focused on finance, securities and insurance litigation.

## Band 2

### Barris, Sott, Denn & Driker, PLLC
**THE FIRM** This Detroit firm is known for fielding high-quality advocates. The group handles a range of business disputes and has notable experience with construction, legal malpractice and tax fraud litigation. Other areas of focus include class actions, antitrust, employment discrimination, intellectual property and securities issues.
**Sources say:** *"They represented us well and looked for solutions sooner rather than later."*
**KEY INDIVIDUALS Sharon Woods** continues to be highly respected. Her practice is concentrated on complex commercial litigation, including construction and professional malpractice issues. The *"outstanding"* **Eugene Driker** handles a range of contract, antitrust and tort disputes. Sources refer to him as a *"legend"* of the Michigan Bar.

### Bodman PLC
See profile on p.1557
**THE FIRM** This highly regarded group handles a wide range of contentious matters, with a focus on complex commercial disputes within the financial, automotive and insurance sectors. It has also seen an expansion of its healthcare litigation practice. The team recently defended Blue Cross Blue Shield of Michigan against claims of over $100 million in a case concerning insurance access fees. Other key clients include Comerica, Lear Corporation and Meridian Health Plan.
**Sources say:** *"I have been impressed with the breadth of knowledge and expertise available at the firm."*

KEY INDIVIDUALS **Joseph Shannon** (see p.1554) is described by clients as *"smart"* and *"articulate."* His practice places a heavy emphasis on disputes within the automotive industry.

## Dickinson Wright PLLC
See profile on p.1561

THE FIRM Dickinson Wright's litigation group continues to be held in high esteem. It has a broad base of experience, encompassing intellectual property, shareholder dispute, breach of fiduciary duty, antitrust and white-collar criminal litigation. Class actions remain a significant area of expertise and the team has been active defending Dow Chemical against putative allegations of property contamination. Other clients include Microsoft, American Axle and Mitsubishi.

Sources say: *"They have high-profile, high-quality commercial litigators."*

KEY INDIVIDUALS *"Fine trial lawyer"* **Edward Pappas** (see p.1554) is recognized as being *"very skilled in the field of business tort litigation."* He also handles construction, noncompete and product liability disputes. Sources admire his diligence and talent for advocacy. *"Excellent lawyer"* **Thomas McNeill** (see p.1553) is viewed as *"authoritative and well prepared."* He concentrates his practice on consumer class actions, business torts and securities litigation. Clients describe **Kenneth McIntyre** (see p.1553) as *"a very good courtroom litigator."* His practice is focused on antitrust litigation, class actions and manufacturing supply chain disputes.

## Dykema Gossett PLLC

THE FIRM This much-praised group is well versed in handling a range of contentious matters. It places particular emphasis on commercial and product liability disputes within the automotive and pharmaceutical sectors, and has extensive experience of financial services litigation. The team was recently called upon to act for Ford in a complex breach of contract case. Other notable clients include Flagstar Bank, Rehmann and Great Lakes Transportation.

Sources say: *"They have been very shrewd and pragmatic in their approach."*

KEY INDIVIDUALS Clients prize **James Feeney's** *"realistic and practical advice."* He is best known for defending product liability claims. *"Brilliant litigator"* **Dennis Haffey** has a diverse practice covering complex commercial matters, securities fraud and professional malpractice. **Patrick Hickey** is admired by clients for his ability to communicate effectively with witnesses. He handles general business disputes, with particular interest in noncompete, trade secret and employment issues.

## Warner Norcross & Judd LLP

THE FIRM This Grand Rapids firm has a strong focus on litigation. It is well equipped to advise clients on a wide range of contentious matters, and is particularly known for its activities within the automotive sector. The group also has significant experience of litigating environmental claims, product liability cases and insurance coverage disputes.

KEY INDIVIDUALS *"Stellar legal adviser"* **Douglas Dozeman** devotes a considerable portion of his practice to intellectual property matters. Additional areas of expertise include inverse condemnation issues and contractual disputes. **Richard Kay** is another key player at the firm. He has a broad base of experience, which encompasses intellectual property, product liability and general business litigation.

## Band 3

## Brooks Wilkins Sharkey & Turco, PLLC
See profile on p.1558

THE FIRM This litigation and bankruptcy boutique has a reputation for tackling high-risk, high-profile cases. It litigates a variety of business issues, with a strong focus on automotive supply chain disputes and automotive product warranty claims. The group also has notable experience in the healthcare, higher education, financial and technology sectors.

KEY INDIVIDUALS *"Top-drawer"* attorney **Keefe Brooks** (see p.1548) has distinguished himself in the fields of professional malpractice defense and complex commercial litigation. He also acts as an arbitrator and mediator. *"Premier lawyer"* **Edward Kronk** (see p.1551) is known for handling automotive supply chain disputes and product liability cases. **Dan Sharkey** (see p.1555) has a particularly strong reputation in the supply chain dispute arena. He also represents clients in class actions, construction matters and franchise-related cases.

## Butzel Long

THE FIRM Butzel Long's litigation group places a heavy emphasis on disputes within the automotive and manufacturing industries, and recently represented component supplier Whitesell in a $35 million breach of contract case. It also advises on social and digital media issues, and is recognized for its expertise in general media and First Amendment law. Key clients include ThyssenKrupp Budd, Dura Automotive Systems and Michigan Press Association.

KEY INDIVIDUALS **David DuMouchel** is unanimously regarded as one of the leading white-collar experts in the area. Sources refer to him as *"top drawer"* and *"a leading light"* of the Michigan Bar.

## Miller Johnson

THE FIRM This group handles a broad range of contentious matters, including contractual disputes, business torts, environmental claims, product liability, professional malpractice defense and appellate matters. It has notable experience representing clients in shareholder disputes, trade secrets litigation and healthcare reimbursement cases. The firm has offices in Grand Rapids and Kalamazoo.

KEY INDIVIDUALS The venerated **Jon Muth** has wide-ranging litigation experience, encompassing complex commercial, securities, malpractice and environmental matters. He currently devotes a significant portion of his practice to acting as an arbitrator and mediator.

## Rhoades McKee
See profile on p.1565

THE FIRM This Grand Rapids firm acts for clients in a range of disputes, with a focus on general commercial, shareholder and professional malpractice defense matters. It has notable experience of handling cases that involve complex business valuation issues. Recent clients include the Michigan Professional Insurance Exchange and Bell's Brewery.

Sources say: *"They are really good to work with because of the breadth of their knowledge and services, and their team approach."*

KEY INDIVIDUALS **Paul McCarthy** (see p.1552) is held in *"high regard"* in the market as a business valuation specialist. Clients characterize him as a *"pragmatic"* attorney, who *"not only highlights the issues but also the solutions."* *"Outstanding trial attorney"* **Bruce Neckers** (see p.1553) earns client praise for his *"ability to interact on a client level in a practical and easy to understand manner."* He has a broad practice, encompassing complex commercial and personal injury litigation.

## Varnum LLP

THE FIRM This Michigan-focused group is based in Grand Rapids, with local offices in Metro Detroit, Kalamazoo, Grand Haven and Lansing. It has particular strength in the fields of banking litigation and insurance coverage disputes. Additional areas of knowledge include environmental, construction, product liability and complex commercial disputes. The team has experience of acting for a wide range of public and private companies, governmental agencies and individuals.

Sources say: *"Their understanding is excellent so the strategy that they put together for litigation is off the chart."*

KEY INDIVIDUALS **William Rohn** is chair of the firm's trial practice group.

## Other Notable Practitioners

*"Grade-A"* litigator **Philip Kessler** (see p.1551) of Thompson & Knight LLP focuses his practice on complex commercial litigation and intellectual property disputes. He divides his time between Detroit and New York. **Powell Miller** of The Miller Law Firm PC is a highly regarded practitioner. He is a talented business litigator, with particular experience with plaintiff representation. **William Sankbeil** of Kerr, Russell & Weber, PLC is described by clients as *"smart"* and *"practical."* He handles complex commercial litigation and has notable expertise in antitrust issues. **Rodger Young** of Young & Associates is known for his broad civil litigation practice, which encompasses antitrust matters, trade secret cases and shareholder disputes. **Neil Fink** of Law Offices of Neil H Fink, PC is a well-respected white-collar defense specialist. His offices are based in Birmingham. **Thomas Branigan** (see p.1548) of Bowman and Brooke LLP is an admired product liability defense lawyer. He is also experienced in a range of complex commercial matters. Experienced trial lawyer **Gregory Curtner** leads Schiff Hardin LLP's sports practice and antitrust group. His clients include educational institutions, sporting organizations and athletic equipment

manufacturers. **John Oostema** of Smith Haughey Rice & Roegge, P.C. is recognized as one of the leading legal malpractice experts in the state. He is also adept at handling insurance coverage disputes. **Robert Harrison** of Robert Harrison & Associates is a highly esteemed white-collar defense litigator.

# REAL ESTATE

Commentary about individuals can be found under their firm's paragraph. If the firm has no paragraph (is not ranked) look at Other Notable Practitioners.

## Real Estate
### Leading Firms

**Band 1**
Honigman Miller Schwartz and Cohn LLP

**Band 2**
Bodman PLC *
Dickinson Wright PLLC *
Miller, Canfield, Paddock and Stone, P.L.C. *

**Band 3**
Barris, Sott, Denn & Driker, PLLC
Clark Hill PLC *
Dawda, Mann, Mulcahy & Sadler PLC *
Dykema Gossett PLLC
Jaffe Raitt Heuer & Weiss, PC
Maddin, Hauser, Wartell, Roth & Heller PC

\* Indicates firm / individual with profile.
Alphabetical order within each band. Band 1 is the highest.

## Band 1

### Honigman Miller Schwartz and Cohn LLP

**THE FIRM** This group is widely regarded as Michigan's preeminent real estate practice. It is well equipped to provide market-leading advice on a comprehensive range of real estate matters, and has particular expertise in the retail, affordable housing and hospitality sectors. The team recently acted for Pebblebrook Hotel Trust on the $750 million financing of two luxury hotels, and for Rock Ventures on the $100 million acquisition of multiple properties in Detroit. Other notable clients include GM, Kellogg and Kojaian Properties.
**Sources say:** *"A very high-class and high-level sophisticated practice."*
**KEY INDIVIDUALS** Star individual **Lawrence McLaughlin** is considered *"one of the most knowledgeable attorneys in the market"* by impressed sources. He is experienced at handling transactional, finance and land use-related issues. Highly respected practitioner **Howard Luckoff** handles a range of real estate development and finance matters, including incentives, land use, joint ventures and restructuring. **Richard Burstein** is also recognized as one of the leading real estate attorneys in the state. He was recently called upon to advise Ramco-Gershenson on a significant series of real estate acquisitions, dispositions and financings. **Greg DeMars** concentrates his practice on real estate finance, with a strong emphasis on workouts, foreclosures and multifamily financing. He is considered a *"dominant"* presence in the market. **Denise Lewis** is also a key player at the firm. She represents developers in a broad range of projects and has additional experience in the realm of real estate finance. **Adam Rothstein** acts for

owners and operators in major real estate transactions. He has notable experience of advising on retail, hotel and office building projects.

## Band 2

### Bodman PLC
**See profile on p.1557**

**THE FIRM** This much-praised team has an impressive reputation in the field of real estate finance. It is also well versed in development and tax incentives, and manages real estate portfolios for notable clients within the automotive industry. The team recently represented Detroit Manufacturing Systems in the $29 million development of a new manufacturing facility. Comerica, Lear Corporation and the Roman Catholic Archdiocese of Detroit are also key clients.
**Sources say:** *"Ultimately, they are looking out for our best interests and they put a lot of effort into understanding what our issues are and making certain we're protected."*
**KEY INDIVIDUALS David Hipp** (see p.1551) has a broad real estate practice encompassing finance, acquisitions and dispositions, leases and litigation. Clients appreciate that *"he has a lot of experience on all sides of the transactions."* *"Excellent"* attorney **Andrew Spilkin** (see p.1555) has a transactional real estate practice, often serving the interests of clients in the automotive industry. Sources report: *"He is extremely timely and tactful, he has a wealth of experience, and he drives solutions, not issues."* **Nicholas Scavone** (see p.1554) is particularly active in the field of loan origination and has experience of advising on the financing of retail, leisure, residential, office and manufacturing facilities. Clients praise the quality of his work output.

### Dickinson Wright PLLC
**See profile on p.1561**

**THE FIRM** Dickinson Wright's talented real estate team has a broad base of experience, handling acquisition, sale and financing transactions, as well as development, zoning and tax issues. It has a noteworthy track record of representing institutional lenders, automotive manufacturers and commercial developers. Recent clients include Detroit Lank Bank Authority, Chrysler Group and the Grand Hotel Company.
**Sources say:** *"I am thrilled with their expertise, knowledge and general understanding of our business."*
**KEY INDIVIDUALS** Clients describe *"superb negotiator"* **James Candler** (see p.1548) as *"a very engaging, thoughtful and incredibly articulate individual."* He has wide-ranging experience of numerous real estate matters, including finance, leasing, foreclosures, tax appeals and zoning.

## Senior Statesmen

**Senior Statesmen: distinguished older practitioners**

| | | |
|---|---|---|
| Bromberg Stephen A | Butzel Long (ONP)[†] | |
| Dunn William | Clark Hill PLC * | |

## Leading Individuals

**Star individuals**

| | |
|---|---|
| McLaughlin Lawrence | Honigman Miller Schwartz and Cohn LLP |

**Band 1**

| | |
|---|---|
| Barris William G | Barris, Sott, Denn & Driker, PLLC |
| Burstein Richard | Honigman Miller Schwartz and Cohn LLP |
| Dawda Edward C | Dawda, Mann, Mulcahy & Sadler PLC * |
| Luckoff Howard N | Honigman Miller Schwartz and Cohn LLP |
| Palms Stephen G | Miller, Canfield, Paddock and Stone, P.L.C. * |
| Salesin Lowell D | Maddin, Hauser, Wartell, Roth & Heller PC |

**Band 2**

| | |
|---|---|
| Candler James | Dickinson Wright PLLC * |
| Dawson Stephen E | Dickinson Wright PLLC * |
| Fazio Joseph M | Miller, Canfield, Paddock and Stone, P.L.C. * |
| Hipp David W | Bodman PLC * |
| Krysinski Mark | Jaffe Raitt Heuer & Weiss, PC |
| Maddin Michael | Maddin, Hauser, Wartell, Roth & Heller PC |
| Nix II Robert R | Kerr, Russell & Weber, PLC (ONP)[†] |
| Piggott Cameron H | Dykema Gossett PLLC |
| Simpson James A | Miller, Canfield, Paddock and Stone, P.L.C. * |
| Spilkin Andrew Z | Bodman PLC * |
| Zussman Richard | Jaffe Raitt Heuer & Weiss, PC |

**Band 3**

| | |
|---|---|
| Cameron John | Dickinson Wright PLLC * |
| Deems Nyal | Varnum LLP (ONP)[†] |
| DeMars Greg | Honigman Miller Schwartz and Cohn LLP |
| Hauberg Kyle R | Dykema Gossett PLLC |
| Hauser Mark R | Maddin, Hauser, Wartell, Roth & Heller PC |
| Hodess Ronald E | Miller, Canfield, Paddock and Stone, P.L.C. * |
| Karbowski Patrick A | Butzel Long (ONP)[†] |
| Kickham Edward F | Kickham Hanley PC (ONP)[†] |
| Koltun Timothy | Clark Hill PLC * |
| Labe Monica | Dickinson Wright PLLC * |
| Lewis Denise | Honigman Miller Schwartz and Cohn LLP |
| Mulcahy Michael D | Dawda, Mann, Mulcahy & Sadler PLC * |
| Page Brian J | Dykema Gossett PLLC |
| Rothstein Adam | Honigman Miller Schwartz and Cohn LLP |
| Rubenfire Mark | Jaffe Raitt Heuer & Weiss, PC |
| Scavone Jr Nicholas P | Bodman PLC * |
| Share Daniel M | Barris, Sott, Denn & Driker, PLLC |
| Winokur Laurence | Dickinson Wright PLLC * |
| Zelenock Katheryne L | Dickinson Wright PLLC * |

**Up-and-coming individuals**

| | |
|---|---|
| Lewis Leslee | Dickinson Wright PLLC * |

[†]ONP = Other Notable Practitioner

Stephen Dawson (see p.1549) is another leading individual. He focuses on real estate acquisitions, financing and development, and has particular expertise in lender representation. He recently advised Mercedes-Benz Financial on its national mortgage loan program. John Cameron (see p.1548) has a strong reputation for handling real estate transactions and litigation. His expertise spans development, construction, title and leasing issues. His clients include Whirlpool and University of Michigan. Monica Labe (see p.1552) impresses clients with her *"deep real estate experience"* and *"top-quality"* work product. She has a broad practice and acts as real estate counsel to major automotive manufacturers and suppliers. Well-respected practitioner Laurence Winokur (see p.1556) concentrates his practice on real estate finance, development, leasing and investment trusts. Katheryne Zelenock (see p.1556) advises institutional lenders on commercial mortgages. Her experience includes office, retail, nursing home and manufactured housing communities, and she receives particular praise for her adept handling of multifamily loan closings. Leslee Lewis (see p.1552) leads the firm's real estate practice. She handles development, finance and leasing matters, and has a notable specialism in LEED-certified green projects. Clients prize her responsiveness and business acumen.

## Miller, Canfield, Paddock and Stone, P.L.C.
See profile on p.1563

THE FIRM This firm's diverse real estate practice is best known for advising on workouts and foreclosures, corporate real estate transactions and economic development incentives. The team also has significant experience in the fields of development and construction. Key clients include Siemens, Wells Fargo and CWCapital.

KEY INDIVIDUALS Highly esteemed practitioner Stephen Palms (see p.1554) counsels clients on a broad range of real estate matters, including acquisition, financing, development and leasing. Sources confirm: *"He is very well thought of."* Joseph Fazio (see p.1549) also has a strong reputation in the market. His practice spans acquisitions, development, leasing and foreclosures. He recently represented C-III Asset Management in the foreclosure of a $36 million mortgage loan. Well-regarded attorney James Simpson (see p.1555) is regularly called upon to represent institutional lenders in financings, workouts and foreclosures. He leads the firm's capital markets lending team and has significant experience in CMBS and portfolio loan origination. Clients report that Ronald Hodess (see p.1551) has an *"excellent command of knowledge"* and is *"extremely sensitive"* to business considerations. He leads the firm's real estate practice group and is particularly well known for his work pertaining to construction projects.

### Band 3

## Barris, Sott, Denn & Driker, PLLC

THE FIRM This distinguished Detroit firm is known for assisting lenders, developers and governmental entities in the financing, development and zoning of commercial and residential properties. It is also experienced at handling workouts and real estate tax appeals. Kojaian, RBS Citizens and Burton-Katzman are among its recent clients.

Sources say: *"It has a reputation for being a high-quality law firm."*

KEY INDIVIDUALS William Barris has a sterling reputation for advising lenders and developers on a diverse range of commercial projects. Sources note that *"he's a dealmaker rather than a deal-breaker,"* and add that *"everybody seems to get along with Bill."* New entry to the rankings Daniel Share represents property owners in both transactional and contentious real estate matters. Sources praise his intellect, attentiveness and talent for negotiation.

## Clark Hill PLC
See profile on p.1559

THE FIRM This versatile group handles a broad range of real estate matters for retail and residential developers, automotive suppliers, and educational institutions. It recently acted for the Tractor Supply Company on the purchase of a number of stores across the USA; other clients include Faurecia, Dunkin' Donuts and Lombardo Homes. The team is also recognized for its expertise in securing economic development incentives for its clients.

Sources say: *"A fantastic firm. I have nothing but outstanding regard for their entire operation."*

KEY INDIVIDUALS Well-regarded attorney Timothy Koltun (see p.1551) has wide-ranging real estate experience, encompassing the acquisition, development, leasing and sale of residential, retail and other commercial properties. He handled the aforementioned matter for the Tractor Supply Company. Senior statesman William Dunn (see p.1549) focuses on providing real estate finance and development counsel to borrowers and lenders.

## Dawda, Mann, Mulcahy & Sadler PLC
See profile on p.1560

THE FIRM This Bloomfield Hills-based group advises on a diverse range of real estate matters, including sale and acquisition, leasing, financing, development and zoning. In the past year it has acted for an impressive roster of banking, retail, residential and healthcare clients.

KEY INDIVIDUALS *"Excellent lawyer"* Edward Dawda (see p.1549) is considered a *"stalwart"* of the Michigan real estate community. He has extensive experience of handling commercial, industrial and retail projects, and is a shopping center development specialist. Michael Mulcahy (see p.1553) is also a prominent attorney. He undertakes real estate transactional matters, with a focus on commercial development.

## Dykema Gossett PLLC

THE FIRM Dykema's Michigan real estate group is engaged to handle a wide variety of matters, with a particular emphasis on financing and development issues, including tax incentives, land use, restructuring and workouts. The team was recently called upon to oversee the due diligence and financing of a $40 million office and affordable housing development in Detroit. Sears, the Neighborhood Service Organization and Crown Castle International are among its key clients.

KEY INDIVIDUALS Cameron Piggott focuses on commercial and residential development projects. He was recently called on to advise M-1 Rail on the financing, design and construction of a railway system in Detroit. Kyle Hauberg is known for representing developers within the retail and healthcare sectors. Clients say: *"He's attentive and understands the pulse of our transactions."* Brian Page specializes in real estate financing and is co-leader of the firm's national lending team. His expertise encompasses workouts and restructuring, economic incentives and land use.

## Jaffe Raitt Heuer & Weiss, PC

THE FIRM This group is well equipped to advise on a broad range of real estate issues from its offices in Southfield, Detroit and Ann Arbor. It has considerable experience of handling real estate transactions, financing, development, workouts, land use and leasing, and is particularly known for representing developers.

KEY INDIVIDUALS *"Outstanding lawyer"* Mark Krysinski concentrates his practice on commercial real estate development and leasing, and is noted for his condominium and land use expertise. Richard Zussman is another key practice member. He handles a broad range of development work, with an emphasis on multifamily housing matters. Real estate group coordinator Mark Rubenfire is particularly active in the areas of real estate finance, workouts and sales and acquisitions.

## Maddin, Hauser, Wartell, Roth & Heller PC

THE FIRM This multiservice real estate group is based in Southfield. It represents clients in relation to sales, acquisitions, financing, development, zoning, leasing and tax appeals, and has experience of acting for developers, lenders and tenants, in addition to a wide variety of real estate professionals.

KEY INDIVIDUALS Highly regarded practitioner Lowell Salesin *"has a great reputation"* in the market. He focuses on real estate development and finance, and is particularly active in the fields of acquisitions and lease restructuring. *"Terrific"* attorney Michael Maddin concentrates his real estate practice on transactional matters, with an emphasis on acquisitions. Mark Hauser is also held in high esteem. He represents investors and developers in sales, acquisitions and financings, and is recognized for his knowledge of the manufactured housing sector.

### Other Notable Practitioners

Clients describe Patrick Karbowski of Butzel Long as *"a very thorough, very conscientious, well-experienced lawyer"* and *"a very valuable resource."* He focuses his practice on sales and acquisitions, often in connection with the automotive industry. Stephen Bromberg, also of Butzel Long, handles transactional and contentious matters. Areas of focus include development, zoning, construction and workouts. Robert Nix of Kerr, Russell & Weber, PLC is viewed as having *"terrific real estate skills."* He has distinguished himself in the fields of lending, development and leasing, and serves as an arbitrator in real estate disputes. **Nyal Deems** of Varnum LLP is experienced in the develop-ment, zoning, leasing and financing of residential, retail and other commercial properties. Much-admired practi-tioner **Edward Kickham** of Kickham Hanley PC repre-sents developers and investors in the acquisition, financing and development of retail, residential, office and manufac-tured housing projects.

## Leaders' Profiles in Michigan

### BOLTON, Richard M
Dickinson Wright PLLC, Detroit
313 223 3648
rbolton@dickinson-wright.com
*Featured in Corporate/M&A (Michigan)*
**Practice Areas:** Managing Director of the Firm's Equity Practice. Serves as counsel to: private equity fund sponsors for fund organization, capitalization & administration; private equity funds & other entities in merger, acquisition, LBO, MBO, "going private," recapitalization & divestiture transactions; funds in mezzanine finance transactions; companies, Boards of Directors & committees regarding all kinds of corporate finance transactions; companies, issuers & underwriters in registered public offerings.
**Professional Memberships:** Board of Directors & Program Committee, Association for Corporate Growth; Michigan Bar Association; named as Crain's Detroit Business Dealmaker of the Year 2010 (Advisor).
**Publications:** Co-author of "Chapter 15, Private Equity Fund and Portfolio Company Investment," Private Equity, History, Governance and Operations; frequent lecturer & panelist on a wide variety of corporate finance issues.
**Personal:** JD, Northwestern University School of Law; BA, Michigan State University.

### BRANIGAN, Thomas P
Bowman and Brooke LLP, Minneapolis
248 687 5316
tom.branigan@bowmanandbrooke.com
*Featured in Litigation (Michigan)*
**Practice Areas:** Tom Branigan is a trial lawyer who has spent his entire career in the courtroom engaged in trials and litigation on behalf of some of the world's largest publicly traded companies, product manufacturers, financial institutions and franchisors. His practice is primarily focused on the defense of complex product liability matters involving catastrophic exposure and commercial litigation.
**Career:** Admitted in Michigan, Ohio and Illinois, he has tried scores of cases in both state and federal courts and he has acted as lead trial counsel and national coordinating counsel in more than 22 states. Mr Branigan is a member of his firm's six person Executive Committee.
**Personal:** Mr Branigan was named a 2012 Michigan Leader in the Law by Michigan Lawyers Weekly. He is a Michigan Super Lawyer, a "Top Lawyer" by DBusiness Magazine, an "Irish Legal 100," a "Michigan Leader in the Law" by Michigan Lawyers Weekly, and in 2002, was a "40 under 40" by The National Law Journal.

### BROOKS, Keefe A
Brooks Wilkins Sharkey & Turco, PLLC, Birmingham
248 971 1710
brooks@bwst-law.com
*Featured in Litigation (Michigan)*
**Practice Areas:** Practice confined to litigation with emphasis on business/commercial matters, insurance coverage, professional responsibility and business torts.
**Professional Memberships:** Fellow of the American College of Trial Lawyers; Fellow of the International Society of Barristers.
**Career:** 29 Years as at Butzel Long. Member of the Firm's Board of Directors (1997-2007). Formed current firm in early 2009.
**Publications:** Civil Procedure Before Trial, West Group Michigan Practice Guides, Thompson/West (2003).
**Personal:** University of Michigan, BA with High Distinction, (1977); University of Michigan Law School, Juris Doctor - Magna Cum Laude, (1980).

### BRUSTAD, Orin D
Miller, Canfield, Paddock and Stone, P.L.C., Detroit
313 496 7605
brustad@millercanfield.com
*Featured in Employee Benefits & Executive Compensation (Michigan)*
**Practice Areas:** Federal tax and employee benefits; pension and other benefit plans and executive compensation, representing public and private sector clients in connection with qualified retirement plans, retirement incentives, fiduciary liability, nonqualified deferred compensation arrangements for executives, plans involving transfer of employer stock to employees, governmental retirement and deferred compensation plans, employment contracts, cafeteria plans, and various self-insured and insured welfare plans.
**Professional Memberships:** American Bar Association, State Bar of Michigan, Fellow, American College of Employee Benefits.
**Career:** Joined firm 1968; Principal 1975.
**Personal:** JD, Harvard Law School, 1968; MA, Yale University, 1964; BA, Yale University, 1963.

### BURWELL, Linda G
Nemeth Burwell, PC, Detroit
313 567 5921
lburwell@nemethburwell.com
*Featured in Labor & Employment (Michigan)*
**Practice Areas:** Management labor law and employment litigation; nationally recognized speaker and author on employment issues.
**Professional Memberships:** Fellow, American Bar Foundation; Board Member, NAMWOLF; DRI, Employment Law Section; State Bar of Michigan, Labor and Employment Section; AAA,
Advisory Panel Member, Employment Law Committee.
**Career:** Co-founder of Nemeth Burwell, the largest woman-owned law firm in Michigan exclusively representing management in the prevention, resolution and litigation of labor and employment disputes. Expertise: Complex and Multi-plaintiff Employment Litigation. Industries served include, Financial, Insurance and other Professional Services, Health Care and Manufacturing.

### CAMERON, John
Dickinson Wright PLLC, Detroit
616 336 1010
jcameron@dickinsonwright.com
*Featured in Real Estate (Michigan)*
**Practice Areas:** Practices in the areas of real estate and construction law. Admitted to practice in Michigan, Illinois, Colorado, and North Carolina.
**Professional Memberships:** Elected Member, American Law Institute and American College of Real Estate Lawyers; Full Member, Urban Land Institute; Real Estate Law Advisor, ALI-ABA; National Board of Editors of The Practical Real Estate Lawyer; Member, State Bar of Michigan Professional Ethics Committee; Member, Land Title Standards Committee.
**Publications:** Written numerous chapters and articles and, in addition to writing Michigan Real Property Law: Principles and Commentary (ICLE 3d ed), is the author of the five-volume treatise Michigan Real Estate Forms & Practice (Aspen Publishers 1998) and A Practitioner's Guide to Construction Law (ALI-ABA).
**Personal:** Wayne State University Law School (JD, 1974); Albion College (BA, 1971); United States Naval Academy

### CAMPBELL, Michael G
Barnes & Thornburg LLP, Grand Rapids
616 742 3975
michael.campbell@BTLaw.com
*Featured in Banking & Finance (Michigan)*
**Practice Areas:** Represents lenders in commercial loans (direct and syndicated) including asset based lending, real estate and construction lending and acquisition financing. Also represents lenders in tax exempt bond financing.
**Professional Memberships:** Member of the State Bar of Michigan.
**Career:** Co-Chair, Lending and Structured Finance Practice Group.
**Personal:** University of Notre Dame (BBA in Finance); University of Michigan (JD); Michigan State University (MBA in Finance).

### CANDLER, James
Dickinson Wright PLLC, Detroit
313 223 3513
jcandler@dickinson-wright.com
*Featured in Real Estate (Michigan)*
**Practice Areas:** Real estate aquisition, development, construction, financing, leasing and disposition, entity formation and governance.
**Professional Memberships:** State Bar of Michigan, Real Property Law Section Council; American College of Real Estate Lawyers; International Association of Attorneys and Executives in Corporate Real Estate.
**Publications:** Lorman Education Services, "Condominiums, Planned Communities and Urban Development"; American Land Title Association, "Casino Financing"; ICLE, "Real Estate Management Agreements" and "Commercial Leases"; State Bar of Michigan, "Commercial Leases"; CLE International, "Commercial Leases"; National Business Institute, "Construction Lending" and "Mortgage Foreclosure".
**Personal:** JD University of Michigan; AB, Princeton University.

### CASHEN, John C
Bodman PLC, Troy
248 743 6077
jcashen@bodmanlaw.com
*Featured in Labor & Employment (Michigan)*
**Practice Areas:** Represents employers facing charges of discrimination, sexual harassment, wrongful discharge, Whistleblowers' Act violations and similar claims in federal and state courts, administrative proceedings and arbitration hearings. Has extensive trial and arbitration experience. Also advises clients in labor management relations, from union election issues and collective bargaining to representation before the NLRB.
**Professional Memberships:** State Bar of Michigan, Oakland County Bar Association, Macomb County Bar Association, Michigan Defense Trial Counsel.
**Personal:** JD, cum laude, University of Michigan; BA and BS, magna cum laude, Aquinas College. Member, Alumni Leadership Committee, Aquinas College.

### CATTEL, Thomas A
Ogletree, Deakins, Nash, Smoak & Stewart, PC, Birmingham
248 723 6123
thomas.cattel@ogletreedeakins.com
*Featured in Labor & Employment (Michigan)*
**Practice Areas:** Represents employers in manufacturing, health care, financial services and retail industries. Mr Cattel has successfully defended claims of discrimination, harassment, retaliation and constructive discharge at trial. He also regularly represents employers in grievance arbitra-

tions and has negotiated collective bargaining agreements in the private and public sector.
**Professional Memberships:** American Bar Association, Section of Labor and Employment Law; Michigan Bar Association, Labor and Employment Law Section; Macomb County and Rochester Bar Associations.
**Career:** Admitted in Michigan; US Court of Appeals (Sixth Circuit); and US Supreme Court.
**Personal:** JD, Detroit College of Law, summa cum laude, 1981; BS, Wayne State University.

**CRANMER, Thomas W**
Miller, Canfield, Paddock and Stone, P.L.C., Troy
313 496 7651
cranmer@millercanfield.com
*Featured in Litigation (Michigan)*
**Practice Areas:** Representing individual and corporate clients in white-collar criminal defense, corporate compliance, and complex commercial civil litigation, including income tax evasion, fraud, food and drug investigations, criminal OSHA, MIOSHA and state/federal environmental matters, criminal antitrust investigations, customs violations, securities violations, public corruption, police corruption and misconduct, RICO violations, and false claims.
**Professional Memberships:** Fellow, American College of Trial Lawyers, Fellow, International Academy of Trial Lawyers, Fellow, International Society of Barristers; State Bar of Michigan President, 2005-06, Criminal Defense Attorneys of Michigan.
**Career:** Joined firm as Principal 2005.
**Personal:** JD, Ohio Northern University, 1975; BA, University of Michigan, 1972.

**DALY, Erik**
Barnes & Thornburg LLP, Grand Rapids
*Featured in Corporate/M&A (Michigan)*
**Practice Areas:** Corporate, M&A, Securities.
**Professional Memberships:** American Bar Association, State Bar of Michigan, Illinois State Bar Association.
**Career:** Mr Daly focuses his practice on mergers and acquisitions, joint ventures and securities law matters. Mr Daly earned his JD cum laude from Harvard Law School in 2007. He received his BS summa cum laude from New York University's Stern School of Business in 2004, where he studied finance and economics and was valedictorian of his class. Mr Daly previously worked as an associate for Jenner & Block in Chicago.
**Personal:** Mr Daly resides with his wife and son in Michigan.

**DAMSCHRODER, Timothy R**
Bodman PLC, Ann Arbor
734 930 0230
tdamschroder@bodmanlaw.com
*Featured in Corporate/M&A (Michigan)*
**Practice Areas:** Mr Damschroder advises clients on matters regarding private equity and venture capital financing, mergers and acquisitions, joint ventures, commercial loans, business transactions (domestic and international), business formation (corporation, limited liability company, and partnership), and corporate gover-

nance. His active involvement with client transactions starts with pre-letter of intent negotiations and continues through to final closing. His primary value to clients is working to close transactions efficiently and effectively. He is a "get the deal done" lawyer.
**Professional Memberships:** State Bar of Michigan (past Chair, Business Law Section); American Bar Association.
**Personal:** JD, University of Detroit-Mercy; AB, University of Michigan.

**DAWDA, Edward C**
Dawda, Mann, Mulcahy & Sadler PLC, Bloomfield Hills
248 642 8696
edawda@dmms.com
*Featured in Real Estate (Michigan)*
**Practice Areas:** Real Estate, Shopping Center Law; Advisor to clients in retail, commercial and industrial development projects; counsel to several of the country's largest retailers and developers on all facets of shopping center and land development; serves as counsel to borrowers in securing long term multi-million dollar construction, permanent, term and revolving loans. Transactions.
**Professional Memberships:** State Bar of Michigan - Business & Real Property Law Sections; Oakland County Bar Association; Illinois State Bar Association; American Bar Association - Real Property, Probate & Trust Law, Business Law Sections; Michigan State Bar Foundation; Oakland County Bar Foundation; International Council of Shopping Centers 1986-Present.
**Career:** Founding and a managing member of firm 1995 to present; Mr Dawda's honors include "Best Lawyers in America" Lawyer of the Year 2011, Real Estate Law-Detroit Area; "Best Lawyers in America" since 2004; "America's Leading Lawyers for Business-2010"; "Michigan Top 100 Super Lawyer" since 2007; "Michigan Super Lawyer-Corporate Counsel" 2009; "Top Lawyer in Metro Detroit" since 2010 by DBusiness Magazine; Midwest Real Estate News Hall of Fame-2012.
**Personal:** JD, cum laude, Michigan State University College of Law, 1977; BA, with high honors, Michigan State University, 1974.

**DAWSON, Stephen E**
Dickinson Wright PLLC, Troy
248 433 7214
sdawson@dickinsonwright.com
*Featured in Real Estate (Michigan)*
**Practice Areas:** Commercial real estate lending and leasing; real estate loan workouts and foreclosures; real estate development.
**Professional Memberships:** State Bar of Michigan, Real Estate and Business Law Sections, and Land Title Standards Committee; Fellow, American College of Real Estate Lawyers; American Bar Association, Real Estate, Probate and Trust Law Sections; Fellow, Michigan State Bar Foundation.
**Publications:** "A Potential Danger for Lessees and Leasehold Mortgagees: The Precision Industries Case," State Bar of Michigan Real Property Law Section Journal.

**Personal:** JD and MA, University of Michigan; BA, Michigan State University.

**DEITCH, Laurence B**
Bodman PLC, Detroit
313 392 1055
ldeitch@bodmanlaw.com
*Featured in Corporate/M&A (Michigan)*
**Practice Areas:** Practice concentrated in corporate law and government relations. Heads Bodman's Automotive/Industrial Team. Substantial experience in corporate governance, mergers and acquisitions (including numerous cross-border transactions), and structuring domestic and international joint ventures. Represents numerous clients based in Asia in connection with mergers, acquisitions and joint ventures in the US and represents US-based companies doing business in Asia. Authored the ballot proposal, later enacted into law, which authorized casino gaming in the City of Detroit.
**Professional Memberships:** State Bar of Michigan.
**Personal:** JD and BA, University of Michigan; Member, University of Michigan Board of Regents.

**DEWITT, Charles**
Littler Mendelson, PC, Detroit
313 446 6401
cdewitt@littler.com
*Featured in Labor & Employment (Michigan)*
**Practice Areas:** Labor and Employment Relations, Employment Litigation, Retail, Discrimination and Harassment, Alternative Dispute Resolution
**Professional Memberships:** State Bar of Michigan, Federal Bar Association, American Bar Association.
**Career:** Mr DeWitt is a founding member and the office-managing shareholder at Littler Mendelson's Detroit office. He has been listed in Best Lawyers in America for over 10 consecutive years. Prior to Joining Littler, Mr DeWitt was a founding shareholder of DeWitt, Balke & Vincent in Detroit, where he practiced for 13 years.
**Personal:** JD, Detroit College of Law, cum laude, 1976; BA, Western Michigan University, 1973

**DIEHL JR, Robert J**
Bodman PLC, Detroit
313 393 7597
rdiehl@bodmanlaw.com
*Featured in Banking & Finance (Michigan)*
**Practice Areas:** Specializes in complex commercial transactions with a focus on banking, debtor-creditor rights and bankruptcy. Represents lenders in out-of-court workouts and in bankruptcy proceedings involving all types of businesses and collateral, especially automotive, real estate and construction. Documents complex, high risk financial transactions, highly leveraged financings and asset-based loans. Counsels lenders on loan structure and lender liability issues. Defends lender liability claims.
**Professional Memberships:** State Bar of Michigan; Detroit Metropolitan Bar Association; American Bar Association; Turnaround Management Association.

**Personal:** JD, magna cum laude and AB, with high honors and high distinction, University of Michigan.

**DUNN, William**
Clark Hill PLC, Grand Rapids
313 965 8510
wdunn@clarkhill.com
*Featured in Real Estate (Michigan)*
**Practice Areas:** Real estate; professional responsibility.
**Professional Memberships:** American Bar Association, Section of Real Property, Trust and Estate Law, past Chair; Standing Committee on Ethics and Professional Responsibility, past Chair; American College of Real Estate Lawyers, Fellow and past President; Association of Professional Responsibility Lawyers; Best Lawyers in America; Chambers USA America's Leading Business Lawyers; Euromoney's Guide to the World's Leading Real Estate Lawyers; An International Who's Who of Real Estate Lawyers; State Bar of Michigan, Professional Ethics Committee, past Chair; Real Property Law Section, past Chair.
**Personal:** JD, University of Michigan, 1964. BA, Muskingum College, 1961.

**FAZIO, Joseph M**
Miller, Canfield, Paddock and Stone, P.L.C., Ann Arbor
734 663 7633
fazio@millercanfield.com
*Featured in Real Estate (Michigan)*
**Practice Areas:** Complex commercial real estate development transactions including acquisition of vacant and improved land; real estate financing including 'securitized loans'; subdivision and condominium development and condominium conversion; resort development; entity formation, including syndication; ground leasing; commercial leasing; industrial revenue bond financing (borrower); 1031 exchanges; and sale/lease-back transactions.
**Professional Memberships:** American Bar Association, State Bar of Michigan (Real Property Law Section).
**Career:** Joined firm 1998; Principal 2000; Deputy Leader, Real Estate Practice Group, 2004-present; Managing Director 2009-present.
**Personal:** JD, Wayne State University Law School; BA, University of Michigan.

**FORMAN, Adam**
Miller, Canfield, Paddock and Stone, P.L.C., Detroit
313 496 7654
forman@millercanfield.com
*Featured in Labor & Employment (Michigan)*
**Practice Areas:** Practice focuses on defending claims of wrongful discharge, discrimination, harassment, retaliation and wage and hour issues. He also represents management in labor arbitrations, unfair labor practice charges and collective bargaining. Adam frequently writes and lectures on issues related to technology in the workplace and trains workforces on how to conduct a workplace investigation.
**Professional Memberships:** American Bar Association, Labor and Employment Law Section

State Bar of Michigan, Labor and Employment Law Section, Detroit Metropolitan Bar Association, Labor and Employment Law Section Oakland County Bar Association.
**Career:** Principal
**Personal:** JD, Syracuse University College of Law; BA, Michigan State University.

## FORREST, III, William B.
Kienbaum Opperwall Hardy & Pelton, P.L.C., Birmingham
248 645 0000
wforrest@kohp.com
*Featured in Labor & Employment (Michigan)*
**Practice Areas:** Employment litigation; employee benefits law; class action defense.
**Professional Memberships:** State Bar of Michigan
**Career:** Mr Forrest has litigated employment disputes for Fortune 500 and Forbes Global 2000 companies, and other clients in the automotive, energy, financial services, big-box retail, and entertainment industries. He has successfully defended those enterprises against a broad spectrum of claims, including discrimination, harassment, retaliation, breach of contract, "whistleblowing," and defamation. He also has extensive experience litigating class action disputes over ERISA welfare and pension benefits.

## GIVENS, Leonard D
Miller, Canfield, Paddock and Stone, P.L.C., Detroit
313 496 7505
givens@millercanfield.com
*Featured in Labor & Employment (Michigan)*
**Practice Areas:** Labor, employment, and school law, including unfair labor practices, jurisdictional disputes, CBAs, mediation, arbitrations, FLSA, OSHA, wrongful discharge, IEP hearings, teacher tenure, FOIA, and student rights to privacy. Also counsels organizations on minority business issues.
**Professional Memberships:** American Bar Association, State Bar of Michigan, National Bar Association, American and National Labor and Employment Council. Fellow, College of Labor and Employment Lawyers and Michigan State Bar Foundation.
**Career:** Joined firm 1971; Principal, 1978; Labor and Employment Group Leader 1982-92, deputy leader 2006-present; Chief Executive Officer, 1991-94.
**Personal:** JD, Howard University School of Law, 1971; BS, Mansfield College, 1965.

## GREEN, Jonathan S
Miller, Canfield, Paddock and Stone, P.L.C., Detroit
313 496 7997
greenj@millercanfield.com
*Featured in Banking & Finance (Michigan)*
**Practice Areas:** Bankruptcy and debtor-creditor law, representing secured and unsecured creditors, creditors' committees, trustees, debtors, and other interested parties in their debtor-creditor relationships with others. He has extensive experience in automotive and troubled-supplier restructurings inside and outside of bankruptcy, includ-

ing the negotiation and documentation of supply protection and lender support agreements. He also has industry expertise in automotive and commercial lending.
**Professional Memberships:** American Bar Association, State Bar of Michigan, and Detroit Metropolitan Bar Association.
**Career:** Principal since 1992; Leader of Bankruptcy and Workout Practice Group.
**Personal:** JD, Cornell University School of Law, 1981; BA, University of Michigan, 1977.

## GYORKE, Scott P
Bodman PLC, Detroit
313 393 7509
sgyorke@bodmanlaw.com
*Featured in Banking & Finance (Michigan)*
**Practice Areas:** Represents lenders in loan originations, including leveraged buyout and leveraged recapitalization loans, asset-based loans, real estate financing, letters of credit, bankers acceptance facilities and multi-rate, multi-currency loans and facilities.
**Professional Memberships:** State Bar of Michigan; American Bar Association.
**Personal:** JD and BA, with high distinction, University of Michigan; AA, Florida State University. Member, Board of Trustees, Leukemia and Lymphoma Society of America-Michigan Chapter.

## HAMMOND, Craig
Dickinson Wright PLLC, Detroit
248 433 7256
chammond@dickinsonwright.com
*Featured in Banking & Finance (Michigan)*
**Practice Areas:** Focuses practice on banking and finance. Bond counsel and underwriter's counsel on hundreds of tax exempt private activity bond issues for financing of manufacturing, health care, educational, cultural, senior housing, and solid waste disposal facilities.
**Professional Memberships:** State Bar Association; National Association of Bond Lawyers.
**Publications:** "Managing OPEB Liabilities Under GASB 45", State Bar of Michigan, Public Corporation Law Quarterly, Fall 2006; Client Alert: IRS Releases Guidance and Allocations for New Recovery Zone Bonds, June 16, 2009; Client Alert: American Recovery and Reinvestment Tax Act Expands Tax-Exempt Bond Provisions, February 2009; "New Economic Stimulus Bonds for US Indian Tribes," International Masters of Gaming Law, 2009 Spring Conference; "Stimulus Plan: Build America Bonds, Recovery Zones and Other Economic Development Financing Tools for Counties," Michigan Association of County Administrative Officers, 2009 Spring Conference "Basics of Bond Finance," CDFA Michigan Financing Round-table 2010 Economic Development Finance Conference, March 2010.
**Personal:** BA, Williams College; JD, University of Michigan.

## HAMMOND, Edward
Clark Hill PLC, Detroit
248 988 1821
ehammond@clarkhill.com
*Featured in Employee Benefits & Executive Compensation (Michigan)*
**Practice Areas:** Employee Benefits / ERISA Services Labor & Employment Law Tax Tax Exempt Organizations.
**Professional Memberships:** American Bar Association, Taxation and Business Law Sections American Society of Pension Professionals and Actuaries Oakland County Bar Association, Taxation and Business Law Sections State Bar of Michigan, Taxation Section
**Career:** Edward C. Hammond is a member of the Oakland County and American Bar Associations (taxation and business law sections), and the State Bar of Michigan (taxation section). His practice primarily involves employee benefits and executive compensation. It includes drafting, implementing, analyzing and terminating defined benefit pension plans and defined contribution, profit sharing and 401(k) plans, as well as Section 403(b) plans (tax sheltered annuities). Ed also develops, designs, and implements non-qualified deferred compensation plans, 457 plans, stock option plans and other incentive plans. Clients also seek his assistance with welfare plan, cafeteria plan and fringe benefit plan design, implementation and compliance. Ed advises clients regarding Department of Labor, Pension Benefit Guaranty Corporation, and Internal Revenue Service audits, and also advises clients regarding Department of Labor and Internal Revenue Service correction programs, including correction program submissions and negotiation of closing agreements. He has substantial experience dealing with client benefits issues in bankruptcy and with the interrelationship of federal bankruptcy law and ERISA. He also advises clients regarding ERISA litigation matters. In addition to all Michigan Courts, Edward is admitted to practice before the United States Sixth Circuit Court of Appeals and the United States Supreme Court.
**Personal:** JD, cum laude, Tulane University Law School, 1987 BA, University of Virginia, 1981.

## HARDY, Elizabeth P
Kienbaum Opperwall Hardy & Pelton, P.L.C., Birmingham
248 645 0000
ehardy@kohp.com
*Featured in Labor & Employment (Michigan)*
**Practice Areas:** Employment litigation, preventive counseling and appellate work.
**Professional Memberships:** Fellow, American College of Trial Lawyers (2012-); Member, American Board of Trial Advocates (2011-); Member, Judicial Qualifications Committee, State Bar of Michigan (2011-; 1996-04; 1991-94); Co-Chair 1998-04); Member, Board of Law Examiners (Michigan Supreme Court appointee) (2008-11); Fellow, College of Labor and Employment Lawyers (2005); Member, Committee on Model Civil Jury Instructions (Michigan Supreme Court appointee) (2005-).

**Career:** George Washington University (BA, with high honors, 1978); Wayne State University Law School (JD, 1984); Editor-in-Chief, Wayne Law Review (1983-84); Best Lawyers in America (2005-); named "Power Lawyer" by Crain's Detroit Business (2008); named Lawyer of the Year, Michigan Lawyers Weekly (2004); named 'One of Detroit's Most Influential Women', Crain's Detroit Business (1997). Member 1991-06, Chair 1995-97, Wayne State University Board of Governors; Member 2001-03, State Board of Canvassers. Partner, Dickinson Wright, 1990-97; Founding Partner, Kienbaum Opperwall Hardy & Pelton, PLC, 1997-present.
**Publications:** Numerous papers and lectures presented on behalf of the National Employment Law Institute and the Michigan State Bar Labor & Employment Law Section.
**Personal:** Born in Traverse City, Michigan; married to Thomas G Kienbaum.

## HICKEY, Kathleen O'Callaghan
Bodman PLC, Detroit
313 393 7506
khickey@bodmanlaw.com
*Featured in Banking & Finance (Michigan)*
**Practice Areas:** Represents lenders in loan originations. Practice encompasses secured transactions, loan workouts, and counseling on lender liability and loan structure issues. Particular expertise in middle market lending, letters of credit, standby bond purchase, bank qualified tax exempt bond and other liquidity facilities to health care, educational institutions and not-for-profit entities, private lending, real estate financing, multi-rate, multi currency loans and facilities and agented and syndicated loan facilities.
**Professional Memberships:** State Bar of Michigan, American Bar Association and Detroit Metropolitan Bar Association.
**Personal:** JD, cum laude, University of Detroit; BA, Michigan State University.

## HIGH, Mark R
Dickinson Wright PLLC, Detroit
313 223 3650
mhigh@dickinsonwright.com
*Featured in Corporate/M&A (Michigan)*
**Practice Areas:** Counsel to buyers and sellers in mergers or acquisitions in hi-tech, manufacturing, retail, real estate, automotive, defense industries; counsel to domestic operations of foreign businesses; experienced in corporate governance and shareholder dispute issues.
**Professional Memberships:** State Bar of Michigan, Former Chair, Business Law Section; Business Law Advisory Board, Institute of Continuing Legal Education; President, Canada-US Business Association (Detroit/Windsor Chapter).
**Publications:** "Drafting Buy-Sell Provisions in Shareholder Agreements: Can We 'Insure' Compliance," Volume 19, Business Law Today, American Bar Association, No. 5 (May/June 2010); "Disney Directors Survive Attack on Magic Kingdom," Business Law Today; "Looking Under the Rocks: Due Diligence After Sarbanes-Oxley," Business Law Today; "The Many Faces of

Corporate Governance," Michigan Business Law Journal.
**Personal:** JD, Duke University School of Law; BA, The College of Wooster, Ohio.

### HIPP, David W
Bodman PLC, Troy
248 743 6022
dhipp@bodmanlaw.com
*Featured in Real Estate (Michigan)*
**Practice Areas:** All aspects of real estate and real estate finance. Represents lenders and borrowers in commercial loan originations, workouts and restructuring, purchases and sales of real estate, leasing, construction and development. Representative projects include transactions involving multi-million dollar hotels, apartment complexes and shopping centers. Negotiates and drafts commercial leases for both lessors and lessees. Primary outside counsel for the Roman Catholic Archdiocese of Detroit in real estate and construction matters.
**Professional Memberships:** State Bar of Michigan, American Bar Association.
**Personal:** JD, magna cum laude, Wayne State University; BA, University of Michigan.

### HODESS, Ronald E
Miller, Canfield, Paddock and Stone, P.L.C., Troy
248 267 3236
hodess@millercanfield.com
*Featured in Real Estate (Michigan)*
**Practice Areas:** Commercial real estate, acquisitions and dispositions, real estate finance, leasing, workouts and foreclosures, title issues, zoning and land use, and all aspects of commercial development. Procurement, negotiation, and consulting for state and local economic development incentives and tax abatements relating to real and personal property. Construction law, construction risk management, construction contracts, architect agreements, construction claims and liens, bonding, surety law, insurance issues and bidding issues.
**Professional Memberships:** American Bar Association, State Bar of Michigan.
**Career:** Principal, 1996; Leader, Real Estate, Construction and Economic Development Incentives.
**Personal:** JD, Georgetown University Law School, 1985; BBA, University of Michigan, 1982.

### HOWELL, Steven G
Dickinson Wright PLLC, Detroit
313 223 3033
showell@dickinsonwright.com
*Featured in Banking & Finance (Michigan)*
**Practice Areas:** Practice Department Manager: Banking & Finance, Creditors' Rights, Municipal Finance; specializing in banking, restructuring, bankruptcy law.
**Professional Memberships:** State Bar of Michigan; American Bar Association; Federal Bar Association, Eastern District of Michigan; American Bankruptcy Institute; Turnaround Management Association.
**Publications:** Turnaround Management Association/Detroit Chapter: 2009 Automotive

Conference, speaker, "Insolvency & Restructuring: A View from the Trenches;" Tenth Annual Conference on Distressed Investing, speaker, "Buying Automotive Suppliers"; American Bankruptcy Institute Central States Workshop, speaker on Buying & Selling Assets; Turnaround Management Association/Detroit Chapter, speaker on Debtor-in-Possession Financing Issues.
**Personal:** JD, Wayne State University Law School (magna cum laude); BGS, University of Michigan with High Distinction.

### HOWLETT, Timothy
Dickinson Wright PLLC, Detroit
313 223 3662
thowlett@dickinsonwright.com
*Featured in Labor & Employment (Michigan)*
**Practice Areas:** Labor and Employment Practice Leader; practices in labor and employment with emphasis on employment litigation and counseling.
**Professional Memberships:** Fellow, College of Labor and Employment Lawyers; Chairperson, Labor and Employment Law Section, State Bar of Michigan; Arbitrator, American Arbitration Association; American Employment Law Council; ICLE Labor and Employment Law Advisory Board; CPR, Employment Law Committee; Master, DMBA American Inn of Court.
**Publications:** Chapter Chair, Lindemann and Grossman, Employment Discrimination Law, 4th Ed.; Chapter Author, Employment Litigation in Michigan, 2nd Ed. (ICLE), "Discrimination Claims".
**Personal:** JD, University of Michigan; BA, Kalamazoo College.

### JENKINS, Maurice
Jackson Lewis LLP, Detroit
248 936 1900
Jenkinsm@jacksonlewis.com
*Featured in Labor & Employment (Michigan)*
**Practice Areas:** Management-side labor and employment law counseling, training, litigation.
**Professional Memberships:** Fellow, American College of Trial Lawyers and Michigan State Bar; Faculty, MI State Bar ICLE; Wolverine, Oakland County and American Bar Associations.
**Career:** General Motors Legal Staff (1981-92); Partner 1992-present; Martindale Hubbell — "Preeminent."
**Publications:** "Winning Trial Strategies", "Internal Investigations & Compliance", "Beyond Restrictive Covenants: Protecting Trade Secrets and Confidential Information in Today's Virtual Workplace" (ICLE); ABA-CLE, "Depositions in Harassment Cases"; ABA, President's Showcase "Anatomy of a Sex Harassment Trial"; Judge, ABA National Trial Competition (2013).
**Personal:** JD, BA, Michigan State University; Univ. of Chicago GSB, Executive Certificate

### JOSWICK, Theresa C
Dawda, Mann, Mulcahy & Sadler PLC, Bloomfield Hills
248 540 8092
tjoswick@dmms.com
*Featured in Employee Benefits & Executive Compensation (Michigan)*

**Practice Areas:** Advises on all aspects of employee benefits issues involving pension, profit sharing, 401(k) and 403(b) plans, welfare plans (such as medical, dental, cafeteria and severance pay), and executive benefit plans for both for-profit and tax-exempt organizations. Counsels clients in compliance matters, including IRS and DOL audits and advises on benefit issues in connection with business mergers, acquisitions and dispositions.
**Professional Memberships:** State Bar of Michigan, Oakland County Bar Association, American Bar Association.
**Career:** Member, Dawda, Mann, Mulcahy & Sadler, PLC; Ms Joswick's honors include Best Lawyers in America since 1997; Michigan Super Lawyers since 2007; Top 50 Women Michigan Super Lawyers, 2008-11; Top Lawyer in Metro Detroit since 2010 by DBusiness Magazine; Top 50 Women Attorneys in Michigan 2011; named in Chambers USA since 2006.
**Publications:** Author, Employee Benefits Chapter in "Employment Law in Michigan, An Employer's Guide," The Institute of Continuing Legal Education.
**Personal:** JD, University of Detroit Mercy School of Law, 1985; AB, University of Michigan, 1976.

### KESSLER, Philip J
Thompson & Knight LLP, Detroit
248 258 7901
Philip.Kessler@tklaw.com
*Featured in Litigation (Michigan)*
**Practice Areas:** Business disputes including antitrust, audit malpractice, contracts, control contests, false advertising, healthcare, pharmaceuticals, international arbitration, intellectual property litigation (copyright, trademark, trade secrets, patents), probate/trust, and securities fraud.
**Professional Memberships:** Fellow, Executive Committee Member, American College of Trial Lawyers (Regent, 2005-2009); Fellow, International Society of Barristers; International Academy of Trial Lawyers; American and Michigan State Bar Foundations; Trustee, Secretary, Executive Committee Member, US Supreme Court Historical Society.
**Career:** Mr Kessler leads the Firm's Michigan and New York operations.
**Personal:** The University of Michigan (AB, with distinction,1969); School of Law, University of California at Berkeley (JD, 1972).

### KIENBAUM, Thomas G
Kienbaum Opperwall Hardy & Pelton, P.L.C., Birmingham
248 645 0000
tkienbaum@kohp.com
*Featured in Labor & Employment (Michigan)*
**Practice Areas:** Employment litigation with emphasis on class or other complex actions; traditional labor relations.
**Professional Memberships:** State Bars: Michigan, Illinois; College of Labor and Employment Lawyers; Executive Committee, National Employment Law Institute; Former President of the State Bar of Michigan and Metropolitan Detroit Bar Association; Chair,

Michigan Attorney Discipline Board; and Chair, Wayne State University Law School Board of Visitors.
**Career:** With over 40 years' experience, Mr Kienbaum has extensive trial experience, having practiced before the US Supreme Court, federal trial and appellate courts, and state courts. He represents clients before federal and state administrative agencies and in traditional labor relations matters. He is a long-time member of the College of Labor and Employment Lawyers, and has been listed in Best Lawyers in America for over 25 years. BA, University of Michigan, 1965; JD, Magna Cum Laude (Order of the Coif) Wayne State University Law School, 1968. Before co-founding Kienbaum Opperwall Hardy & Pelton, PLC, he headed the Labor and Employment Department of Detroit-based Dickinson Wright, P.L.L.C.
**Publications:** Papers presented to industry groups, the National Employment Law Institute and the Institute of Continuing Legal Education.
**Personal:** Born in Berlin, Germany, 1942; fluent in German; married to Elizabeth Hardy.

### KOCHANEK, Joseph J
Bodman PLC, Detroit
313 393 7505
jkochanek@bodmanlaw.com
*Featured in Banking & Finance (Michigan)*
**Practice Areas:** Represents agent banks and other lenders in secured and unsecured loan originations, including multi-currency loan facilities, syndicated credit arrangements and loans secured by stock and other assets located outside the US, principally in Europe, Mexico, South America and the Pacific Rim. Substantial experience in commercial mortgage financings and other real estate transactions; represents foundations, community development corporations and other charitable organizations in public/private partnerships and urban revitalization projects.
**Professional Memberships:** State Bar of Michigan, American and Detroit Metropolitan Bar Associations.
**Personal:** JD, magna cum laude and BA, with high distinction, University of Michigan.

### KOLTUN, Timothy
Clark Hill PLC, Detroit
313 965 8326
tkoltun@clarkhill.com
*Featured in Real Estate (Michigan)*
**Practice Areas:** Construction; real estate.
**Professional Memberships:** American Bar Association; State Bar of Michigan, Real Property Law Section, Condominiums, PUDs and Cooperatives Committee; The Best Lawyers in America; Michigan Super Lawyers.
**Personal:** JD, magna cum laude, University of San Diego School of Law, 1984. BA, Ohio Wesleyan University, 1980.

### KRONK, Edward M
Brooks Wilkins Sharkey & Turco, PLLC, Birmingham
kronk@bwst-law.com
*Featured in Litigation (Michigan)*

**Practice Areas:** Product liability defense litigation, automotive regulatory counseling and litigation and commercial litigation.
**Professional Memberships:** State Bar of Michigan; Faculty of the Michigan Institute for Continuing Legal Education; Faculty of the National Institute of Trial Advocacy; Member and Past President of the Eastern District of Michigan Chapter of the Federal Bar Association; Member and Past President of the Michigan Defense Trial Counsel; Member Product Liability Advisory Council; Fellow of the American College of Trial Lawyers; and listed in Best Lawyers in America.
**Career:** Shareholder, Butzel Long.
**Personal:** University of Michigan (JD 1971); College of the Holy Cross (AB 1968).

### LABE, Monica
Dickinson Wright PLLC, Troy
248 433 7226
MLabe@dickinsonwright.com
*Featured in Real Estate (Michigan)*
**Practice Areas:** Extensive expertise as lead real estate counsel to multi-national corporations (including an OEM and one of world's leading tier one automotive suppliers), developers, real estate investment companies and lenders in the acquisition, development, leasing, financing (including workouts and foreclosures) and disposition of multi-million dollar industrial, office, retail, mixed-use and entertainment projects throughout the US.
**Professional Memberships:** State Bar of Michigan and California; State Bar of Michigan - Real Property Law Section; Michigan Land Title Standards Committee; Fellow, Oakland Bar Foundation; Member, Leadership Detroit XVIII; Prior Board Member: CREW Detroit. Ms Labe is a speaker at a variety of real estate forums in Michigan and nationally.
**Career:** Firm's Management Group (2011-current); Practice Department Manager for Real Estate, Environmental and Energy and Sustainability Practice Groups (2008-10).
**Personal:** JD, Northwestern University; BA, University of Michigan.

### LABINE, Jeffrey L
Miller, Canfield, Paddock and Stone, P.L.C., Ann Arbor
734 668 8801
labine@millercanfield.com
*Featured in Corporate/M&A (Michigan)*
**Practice Areas:** Mergers and acquisitions, venture capital and commercial financing, private equity and debt offerings and general corporate law, including transactions throughout North America, Europe, India, South America and Australia.
**Professional Memberships:** American Bar Association (Business Law Section, Mergers and Acquisitions Committee, Private Equity and Venture Capital Committee; Model Joint Venture Agreement Summaries of International Law Supplement, Editorial Board Member; International Law Section); State Bar of Michigan, Business Section; State Bar of New York, Business

Section Michigan Venture Capital Association, Member MichBio, Corporate Member.
**Career:** Principal.
**Personal:** JD, Wayne State Law School; BBA, Detroit College of Business; AAS, Schoolcraft College.

### LARSEN, Tracy T
Barnes & Thornburg LLP, Grand Rapids
616 742 3931
tracy.larsen@btlaw.com
*Featured in Corporate/M&A (Michigan)*
**Practice Areas:** Mergers and acquisitions, corporate finance, securities law and corporate governance. Has acted as lead counsel in tens of billions of dollars of merger, acquisition and corporate finance transactions; significant cross-border experience; significant experience in private equity sponsored transactions.
**Career:** Co-Chair - Corporate Department, Barnes & Thornburg, LLP; Office Managing Partner - Michigan; Member, Firmwide Management Committee.
**Personal:** Hope College (BA, summa cum laude, Economics, 1981; Phi Beta Kappa); Indiana University School of Law (JD, magna cum laude, 1984; Order of the Coif; Executive Editor, 'Indiana Law Journal'); Chairman Emeritus, Business Law Section, State Bar of Michigan.

### LEAHY, Carrie
Bodman PLC, Ann Arbor
734 930 0120
cleahy@bodmanlaw.com
*Featured in Corporate/M&A (Michigan)*
**Practice Areas:** Counsels established and emerging businesses on complex corporate transactions, mergers, acquisitions, compliance with securities regulations, and venture capital funding. Has experience in M&A transactions ranging up to $1 billion. Advises clients on entity formation, corporate governance, public and private securities offerings, and preparing registration statements and other disclosure documents. Has advised corporate boards on a broad range of issues. Has extensive experience representing start-up and spinoff companies, including those that have licensed technology from the University of Michigan.
**Professional Memberships:** State Bar of Michigan; State Bar of Illinois.
**Personal:** JD, Chicago-Kent College of Law; BA, University of Michigan.

### LEITMAN, Matthew
Miller, Canfield, Paddock and Stone, P.L.C., Troy
248 267 3294
leitman@millercanfield.com
*Featured in Litigation (Michigan)*
**Practice Areas:** Principal practice areas are complex commercial litigation, criminal defense, and appellate litigation. Experience includes trial practice before state and federal trial courts and numerous appeals before state and federal appellate courts. He has been involved in high-profile trials and argued several significant appeals that led to important, precedent-setting rulings. of federal law and Michigan law.

**Professional Memberships:** American Bar Association; State Bar of Michigan; Oakland County Bar Association; Federal Bar Association, Eastern District of Michigan Chapter, Co-Chair, Criminal Law Committee; National Association of Criminal Defense Attorneys
**Career:** Principal
**Personal:** Harvard Law School, JD; University of Michigan, BA.

### LEWAND, F Thomas
Bodman PLC, Detroit
313 393 7573
tlewand@bodmanlaw.com
*Featured in Corporate/M&A (Michigan)*
**Practice Areas:** Represents corporations and municipalities in complex economic development transactions. Has negotiated numerous public-private partnerships, including a $400M stadium complex in Detroit, $300M NASCAR track in Kansas and $50M municipal-assisted Detroit Medical Center restructuring. As Special Master to US District Judge John Feikens on operation of the Detroit Water and Sewer System, negotiated complex intergovernmental agreement resolving 30-year dispute involving the system's seven-county service region.
**Personal:** JD, magna cum laude, Wayne State University; BA, University of Detroit-Mercy; Director, Michigan EDC; Director, Wayne County EDC; Treasurer, Governor's Residence Foundation; Director, Mackinac Island Affordable Housing Corporation; Former Trustee, University of Detroit-Mercy.

### LEWIS, Leslee
Dickinson Wright PLLC, Detroit
616 336 1042
llewis@dickinsonwright.com
*Featured in Real Estate (Michigan)*
**Practice Areas:** Practice Department Manager for Real Estate, Environmental, Energy and Sustainability. Acts as outside general corporate counsel to national, regional and emergent businesses and health care nonprofits in daily contracts and affairs, organization, financing, transactions and governance. Represents banks in syndicated loan originations and REO properties. Experience in all aspects of real estate and banking including green building and leasing, sustainability and wind farms.
**Professional Memberships:** Elected Member, American Law Institute; National Editorial Board, ALI-ABA's The Practical Real Estate Lawyer; Member Consultative Group, ALI Principles of the Law of Nonprofit Organizations; Chairperson, Residential Transactions Committee, State Bar of Michigan Real Property Law Section; Member, State Bar of Michigan; Member, Grand Rapids Bar Association.
**Publications:** Presenter, "Real Estate Documents: Drafting for Success", ALI-ABA, 2012; Presenter and Organizer, "Residential Transactions Boot Camp," State Bar of Michigan, 2012; Presenter, "Current Asset Dispositions: Note and REO Sales and Purchases," State Bar of Michigan, 2011; Presenter, "Green Building Basics" State Bar of Michigan ICLE, 2008; "Understanding Green

Office Leases," ALI-ABA's The Practical Real Estate Lawyer, 2009; "Green Building Basics," ALI-ABA's The Practical Real Estate Lawyer.
**Personal:** JD, Notre Dame Law School (1995); BA, Alma College (1992).

### LUKAS, Edwin J.
Bodman PLC, Detroit
elukas@bodmanlaw.com
313 393 7523
*Featured in Corporate/M&A (Michigan)*
**Practice Areas:** Specializes in corporate and commercial law, public and private equity offerings, compliance with securities law, mergers and acquisitions, and other complex business matters. Has structured joint ventures, strategic alliances, and a number of international transactions. Has successfully negotiated economic development incentive agreements in various jurisdictions. Former in-house counsel to Ford Motor Company. Immediate Past Chairperson of the Business Law Section of the State Bar of Michigan.
**Professional Memberships:** State Bar of Michigan.
**Personal:** JD, University of Detroit School of Law; BA, University of Pennsylvania.

### MCCARTHY, Paul
Rhoades McKee, Grand Rapids
616 233 5133
mccarthy@rhoadesmckee.com
*Featured in Litigation (Michigan)*
**Practice Areas:** Paul litigates the value of privately held business in a host of contexts, including shareholder/member disputes and high networth matrimonial matters. Paul also represents clients in commercial litigation matters, often including complex accounting or financial issues, and he defends attorneys and accountants in malpractice actions.
**Professional Memberships:** State Bar of Michigan, International Society of Barristers, Litigation Council of America, Best Lawyers of America, Michigan Super Lawyers
**Career:** Joined firm in 1992.
**Personal:** JD, Marquette University (cum laude); MBA, Marquette University; BBA, University of Michigan Ross School of Business (with distinction).

### MCDOWELL, Ralph E
Bodman PLC, Detroit
313 393 7592
rmcdowell@bodmanlaw.com
*Featured in Banking & Finance (Michigan)*
**Practice Areas:** Practice focused on commercial bankruptcy, debtor-creditor rights and workouts in all industries, especially automotive and real estate. Represents banks and other financial institutions in pre-bankruptcy workouts, commercial bankruptcy cases, troubled credit situations, sale of debt, foreclosures, liquidation of assets and forbearance arrangements. Assists in structuring and documenting complex commercial loan transactions. Chairman of Bodman PLC.
**Professional Memberships:** State Bar of Michigan, Detroit Metropolitan Bar Association.

Personal: JD, magna cum laude, University of Detroit-Mercy School of Law; BA, Kalamazoo College.

### MCINTYRE, Kenneth J.
Dickinson Wright PLLC, Detroit
313 223 3556
kmcintyre@dickinsonwright.com
*Featured in Litigation (Michigan)*
Practice Areas: Focuses practice on litigation, including civil and criminal antitrust, franchise and distribution, commercial and financial, consumer protection, and class actions.
Professional Memberships: American Law Institute, ABA Antitrust and Litigation Sections, Michigan State Bar Association Litigation Section, Antitrust and Trade Regulation Section (former chairperson) and Federal Bar Association.
Publications: "The Top Ten Things for a Supplier to Consider in Terminating a Distributor" (Mondaq: Litigation, Mediation & Arbitration, 2011).
Personal: JD, University of Michigan Law School; BA, University of Michigan.

### MCMICAN, Christopher A
Miller, Canfield, Paddock and Stone, P.L.C., Detroit
313 496 7922
mcmican@millercanfield.com
*Featured in Employee Benefits & Executive Compensation (Michigan)*
Practice Areas: Federal tax and employee benefits with an emphasis on ERISA compliance; qualified retirement plans, nonqualified deferred compensation, and health and welfare benefits.
Professional Memberships: American Bar Association, Tax Section and Employee Benefits Committee, State Bar of Michigan, Taxation Section, Oakland County Bar Association, Employee Benefits Committee-Vice Chair, 2006-07, The ESOP Association, and The National Association of Health Underwriters.
Career: Principal
Personal: LLM, University of Florida, 1995; JD, cum laude, University of Detroit-Mercy School of Law, 1994, MBA, University of Detroit-Mercy College of Business Administration, 1994; BS, summa cum laude, University of Detroit, 1991.

### MCNEILL, Thomas G
Dickinson Wright PLLC, Detroit
313 223 3632
tmcneill@dickinsonwright.com
*Featured in Litigation (Michigan)*
Practice Areas: Focuses practice in commercial and financial litigation, including class action defense and individual actions in securities, mergers and acquisitions, accounting, banking, private equity, gaming, consumer protection and business torts.
Professional Memberships: Co-Chair, ABA Litigation Section, Securities Class Action Subcommittee; President, Federal Bar Association, Eastern District of Michigan Chapter; Board member, Federal Litigation Section, National Federal Bar Association; Chair, Merit Selection Panel for US Magistrate Judge position (2011); Member, Foundations of the State Bar of

Michigan and the Oakland County Bar Association; Member, State Appellate Defender Commission (appointed by the Governor).
Publications: Co-author, Michigan Business Torts (2003, 2007, 2009); Presenter, "The Definitive Covenant Not to Compete," 2011, Institute of Continuing Legal Education (University of Michigan); Presenter, "Cross Examining Financial Experts in Bankruptcy Court", 2011, Federal Bar Association; Presenter, "Pre-filing Pitfalls, Initial Disclosure and Discovery, 2009, 2010 and 2011, Federal Bar Association; Presenter, "Financial Litigation in Federal Court" 2007, 2008, Federal Bar Association; multiple federal and state publications and presentations in E-Discovery, E-Data and related technical issues.
Personal: JD, University of Virginia (1984); BA, University of Notre Dame (1981).

### MEARS, Patrick E
Barnes & Thornburg LLP, Grand Rapids
616 742 3936
patrick.mears@BTLaw.com
*Featured in Banking & Finance (Michigan)*
Practice Areas: Co-Chair, New York Practice Group. Handles insolvency, Uniform Commercial Code, bankruptcy cases. Negotiates real estate and commercial finance transactions, workouts.
Professional Memberships: American Law Institute; American College of Bankruptcy; Chair, Uniform Commercial Code Committee, State Bar of Michigan.
Career: Milbank, Tweed, Hadley & McCloy (1976-80); Warner, Norcross & Judd (1980-91); Dykema Gossett (1991-2002); Dickinson Wright (2002-04); Barnes & Thornburg (2004-).
Publications: Co-Author: Interrupted!: Understanding Bankruptcy's Effects on Manufacturing Supply Chains (ABI 2012); Strategies for Secured Creditors (ALI-CLE 2012); Receiverships in Michigan (Michigan ICLE 2013); Contributor, Collier Bankruptcy Practice Guide.
Personal: University of Michigan (BA, 1973; JD, 1976).

### MISHKIND, Charles S
Miller, Canfield, Paddock and Stone, P.L.C., Grand Rapids
616 776 6307
mishkind@millercanfield.com
*Featured in Labor & Employment (Michigan)*
Practice Areas: Labor, employment and benefit matters, and related litigation on a state and nationwide basis.
Professional Memberships: Fellow in American College of Labor and Employment Lawyers and American College of Employee Benefits Counsel, American Bar Association, State Bar of Michigan, National Employment Law Institute Advisory Board, American Employment Law Council, US Chamber of Commerce Labor Law Committee, National Retail Federation Committee on Employment Law, and Co-chair, National Finance Industry Labor Law Committee.
Career: Principal since 1985.

Personal: MML, New York University Law Center, 1972; JD, University of Arizona Law School, 1971; BA, University of Arizona, 1966.

### MULCAHY, Michael D
Dawda, Mann, Mulcahy & Sadler PLC, Bloomfield Hills
248 642 8688
mmulcahy@dmms.com
*Featured in Real Estate (Michigan)*
Practice Areas: Commercial real estate law representing owners, developers, lenders and tenants in the acquisition, development, leasing, sale and financing (including workouts) of office, retail and industrial projects.
Professional Memberships: State Bar of Michigan - Real Estate and Business Law Sections.
Career: Founding and a managing member of firm 1995 to present. Honors include: named in Best Lawyers in America since 2003, Michigan Super Lawyers since 2007, top 100 Michigan Super Lawyers 2009-10 and Chambers USA since 2004.
Personal: JD, cum laude, University of Michigan Law School, 1972; Associate Editor Law Reivew, University of Michigan Law School, 1970-72.

### NECKERS, Bruce
Rhoades McKee, Grand Rapids
616 233 5217
bwneckers@rhoadesmckee.com
*Featured in Litigation (Michigan)*
Practice Areas: Having recently completed over 500 mediation cases, Bruce Neckers is a very experienced trial lawyer and certified mediator. His practice experience includes representation of plaintiffs and defendants in significant cases in both state and federal court. He specializes in business, health care, real estate, employment and commercial cases. He also defends attorneys in malpractice cases
Professional Memberships: State Bar of Michigan, Past President; Grand Rapids Bar Association, Past President; Federal Bar Association for the Western District of Michigan, Past President
Career: Bruce led the firm's Executive Committee from 2001-2007 as President managing the firm's day to day operational and strategic direction. He has been consistently recognized by his peers in the American College of Trial Lawyers, Best Lawyers of America® ( Bet the Company Litigation, Commercial Litigation, Personal Injury Litigation & Mediation), International Society of Barristers and Super Lawyers.
Personal: The Ohio State University College of Law (Juris Doctor, 1968), Hope College (Bachelor of the Arts, 1965).

### NEMETH, Patricia
Nemeth Burwell, PC, Detroit
313 567 5921
pnemeth@nemethburwell.com
*Featured in Labor & Employment (Michigan)*
Practice Areas: Management labor and employment litigation; certified mediator.
Professional Memberships: State Bar of Michigan, Labor and Employment Law Section

and International Law Section; American Arbitration Association.
Career: Founder of what is now Nemeth Burwell, the largest woman-owned law firm in Michigan to exclusively represent management in the prevention, resolution and litigation of labor and employment disputes. JD and Masters of Labor Law from Wayne State University; Bachelor's Degree from the University of Michigan. Expertise includes RIFs/layoffs, discrimination, workplace harassment, wrongful discharge, union organizing activities, multi-party and complex lawsuits. Industries served include healthcare, gaming, retail, insurance, and government entities.

### NORRIS, Megan P
Miller, Canfield, Paddock and Stone, P.L.C., Detroit
313 496 7594
norris@millercanfield.com
*Featured in Labor & Employment (Michigan)*
Practice Areas: All aspects of employment and labor, concentrating in the areas of Americans with Disabilities Act, defamation, and employment litigation, including wrongful discharge, sexual harassment, discrimination, and workers' compensation.
Professional Memberships: American Bar Association, State Bar of Michigan, Detroit Metropolitan Bar Association (past President), City of Detroit Board of Police Commissioners (past Chair), Detroit Barristers' Association (past President), Institute of Continuing Legal Education Labor Advisory Board.
Career: Joined firm 1986; Principal, 1995; Leader, Labor and Employment Group, 2003-present.
Personal: JD, University of Michigan Law School, 1986; BA, Wesleyan University, 1983.

### OPPERWALL, Theodore
Kienbaum Opperwall Hardy & Pelton, P.L.C., Birmingham
248 645 0000
topperwall@kohp.com
*Featured in Labor & Employment (Michigan)*
Practice Areas: Labor and employment; employee benefits law; appellate practice.
Professional Memberships: American Bar Association; State Bar of Michigan.
Career: With 40 years' experience in the field, Mr Opperwall specializes in representing management clients throughout the United States in all facets of traditional labor law, including union organizing, collective bargaining and contract administration, labor arbitration, and proceedings before the National Labor Relations Board. He represents a number of clients nationally. A former examiner for the NLRB, Mr Opperwall has a keen understanding of unfair labor practice and union election issues. Listed in Best Lawyers in America and a Fellow of the College of Labor and Employment Lawyers, Mr Opperwall also has extensive experience in wrongful discharge, civil rights, labor injunction, and employee benefits litigation. He is an experienced appellate advocate, admitted to practice before the US Supreme

Court and the US Courts of Appeals for the Sixth Circuit and the District of Columbia Circuit. Founding Partner, Kienbaum Opperwall Hardy & Pelton, PLC, 1997-present.

**Publications:** Contributing Author of 'Employment Law in Michigan: An Employer's Guide', and 'Buying and Selling a Business in Michigan', published by the Institute of Continuing Legal Education.

**Personal:** Born in Grand Rapids, Michigan, 1951.

## PALMS, Stephen G
Miller, Canfield, Paddock and Stone, P.L.C., Ann Arbor
734 668 7118
palms@millercanfield.com
*Featured in Real Estate (Michigan)*

**Practice Areas:** Commercial real estate law representing owners, developers, lenders and tenants in all aspects of office, retail, light industrial and residential projects.

**Professional Memberships:** American Bar Association, State Bar of Michigan, Detroit Metropolitan Bar Association; Chair, Board of Directors, Oakland Community College Foundation; Executive Board, Boy Scouts of America, Detroit Area Council.

**Career:** Joined firm in 1976; Principal, 1983; Managing Director, 1991-93 and 2000-03; and Leader, Real Estate Practice Group, 2002-04. Former Adjunct Professor at Wayne State University Law School.

**Personal:** JD, magna cum laude, University of Michigan Law School, 1976; AB, University of Michigan, 1973.

## PAPPAS, Edward H
Dickinson Wright PLLC, Detroit
248 433 7228
epappas@dickinsonwright.com
*Featured in Litigation (Michigan)*

**Practice Areas:** Focuses practice in commercial and business litigation, arbitration and mediation.

**Professional Memberships:** Co-Chairman and Client Service Director, Dickinson Wright PLLC; former President, State Bar of Michigan; Fellow, International Society of Barristers; mediator and facilitator, Oakland County Circuit Court; American Arbitration Association Roster of Neutral Commercial Litigation Arbitrators; Fellow, American College of Civil Trial Mediators; Fellow, Litigation Counsel of America; Master, Oakland County Bar Association's Inn of Court.

**Publications:** Michigan Business Torts (ICLE), co-author; Trade Secrets: Protection and Remedies (BNA), co-author, Michigan Law of Damages (ICLE), co-author of chapter; Michigan Causes of Action Formbook (ICLE), co-editor, contributing author.

**Personal:** JD and BBA, University of Michigan.

## PELTON, Eric J
Kienbaum Opperwall Hardy & Pelton, P.L.C., Birmingham
248 645 0000
epelton@kohp.com
*Featured in Labor & Employment (Michigan)*

**Practice Areas:** Employment litigation and traditional labor relations.

**Professional Memberships:** College of Labor and Employment Lawyers; Michigan Board of Law Examiners (2011 - present); Executive Committee, Federalist Society Labor and Employment Practice Group (2008 - present); State Bar of Michigan, Board of Commissioners (2007-09);

**Career:** Mr Pelton represents management clients throughout the United States. He has tried numerous jury cases in the state and federal courts of Michigan and other jurisdictions, and has arbitrated and mediated dozens of cases around the country. As an appellate advocate, Mr Pelton has argued cases before the Michigan Supreme Court and the US Courts of Appeals for the Sixth, Seventh, and DC Circuits. Mr Pelton has served as an adjunct faculty member at Wayne State University Law School, and has special expertise in election law, having served as vice chair of the Michigan Board of State Canvassers. Mr Pelton holds a BA from Michigan State University and a JD/MPA from Syracuse University, where he served as an Executive Editor of the Law Review. He is a Founding Partner, Kienbaum Opperwall Hardy & Pelton, PLC, 1997-present.

**Publications:** Author of ICLE and NELI publications.

**Personal:** Born in Royal Oak, Michigan, 1962; married to Connie Pelton.

## PIPER, Karen L
Bodman PLC, Troy
248 743 6025
kpiper@bodmanlaw.com
*Featured in Labor & Employment (Michigan)*

**Practice Areas:** Advises employers on employment issues, including hiring, discipline/discharge, ADA/FMLA, discrimination, harassment and retaliation, and wage/hour issues. Counsels employers on development of employee handbooks and policies. Represents employers in discrimination and wrongful discharge litigation. Particular expertise representing financial institutions and nonprofit and religious organizations.

**Professional Memberships:** State Bar of Michigan and the Detroit Metropolitan, Federal and American Bar Associations; Member, Society of Human Resources Management; Chair, Legal Affairs Committee, Detroit SHRM and National Catholic Education Association.

**Personal:** JD, cum laude, University of Michigan; BA, with distinction, Wayne State University; Adjunct Professor, Madonna University.

## PLEMMONS, James
Dickinson Wright PLLC, Detroit
313 223 3106
JPlemmons@dickinsonwright.com
*Featured in Banking & Finance (Michigan)*

**Practice Areas:** Practices in the areas of bankruptcy, commercial litigation, real estate foreclosure and commercial workouts and his practice focuses on troubled automotive supplier matters, where he represents an OEM and numerous auto suppliers.

**Professional Memberships:** Michigan Bar Association; Federal Bar Association for the Eastern District of Michigan; American Bankruptcy Institute; Tennessee Bar Association.

**Publications:** Strategies for Secured Creditors in Workouts and Foreclosures; Closing, Reorganizing or Selling the Business (ICLE),co-author.

**Personal:** JD, American University's Washington College of Law; BA, Michigan State University.

## POZZA JR, Clarence L
Miller, Canfield, Paddock and Stone, P.L.C., Detroit
313 496 7556
pozza@millercanfield.com
*Featured in Litigation (Michigan)*

**Practice Areas:** Litigation and dispute resolution. Emphasis on commercial, corporate, securities and insurance litigation, regulatory representations, alternative dispute resolution, and preventative and compliance counseling. Experience includes complex trial and appellate work in federal and state courts.

**Professional Memberships:** Fellow, American College of Trial Lawyers, American Bar Association, State Bar of Michigan, Federal Bar Association, Detroit Metropolitan Bar Association, National Association of Securities Dealers, American Arbitration Association, and Midwest Securities Institute.

**Career:** Joined firm 1974; Principal, 1981; Litigation Group Leader, 2000-08; Managing Director, 1992-00.

**Personal:** JD, cum laude, University of Michigan Law School, 1974; BS, University of Michigan, 1971.

## RIBACK, Ronald H
Miller, Canfield, Paddock and Stone, P.L.C., Troy
248 267 3233
riback@millercanfield.com
*Featured in Banking & Finance (Michigan)*

**Practice Areas:** Corporate and securities practice focusing on banking, mergers and acquisitions, commercial and real estate lending transactions, general corporate/business services.

**Professional Memberships:** American Bar Association, Business Law Section, State Bar of Michigan, Corporate and Banking and Real Estate sections.

**Career:** Principal, 1990-present.

**Personal:** JD, De Paul University College of Law, 1971; BA, University of Michigan, 1968.

## ROACH, Steven A
Miller, Canfield, Paddock and Stone, P.L.C., Detroit
313 496 7933
roach@millercanfield.com
*Featured in Banking & Finance (Michigan)*

**Practice Areas:** Commercial litigation with particular emphasis on creditors' rights, including equipment leases, real estate leases, notes, guaranties, mortgages, UCC Articles 2, 2A and 9, and pre-judgment and post-judgment remedies. Other areas of commercial litigation include property disputes, commercial product liability, shareholder disputes, professional negligence defense, includ-

ing legal malpractice, accounting malpractice, fiduciary negligence, bankruptcy trustee negligence, and business torts.

**Professional Memberships:** American Bar Association, State Bar of Michigan, Detroit Metropolitan Bar Association.

**Career:** Joined firm 1986; Principal, 1994; Leader, Financial Institutions and Transactions Group.

**Personal:** JD, University of Michigan Law School, 1986; AB, University of Michigan, 1983.

## SCAVONE JR, Nicholas P
Bodman PLC, Detroit
313 393 7580
nscavone@bodmanlaw.com
*Featured in Real Estate (Michigan)*

**Practice Areas:** All aspects of real estate and real estate finance, including acquisitions, land contracts, leasing, construction and development, and commercial loans, workouts, and foreclosures, involving residential developments, shopping centers, apartment projects, office buildings, manufacturing facilities, golf courses, gas stations and other commercial properties.

**Professional Memberships:** American Bar Association and State Bar of Michigan; Member, Council of the Real Property Section of the State Bar of Michigan; Member, Michigan Land Title Standards Committee.

**Personal:** JD, cum laude, Indiana University Law School, Bloomington (1992); BA, University of Michigan, Ann Arbor (1989). Associate Editor (1990-91) and Notes Editor (1991-92), Indiana Law Journal.

## SERYAK, Richard J
Miller, Canfield, Paddock and Stone, P.L.C., Detroit
313 496 7501
seryak@millercanfield.com
*Featured in Labor & Employment (Michigan)*

**Practice Areas:** Labor and employment practice covers wrongful discharge and employment discrimination civil litigation, NLRB, MERC, EEOC, and Michigan Department of Civil Rights proceedings. Served as lead counsel in numerous reported labor and employment decisions. He also is a Member of the firm's Automotive Group.

**Professional Memberships:** Michigan, Ohio, and Federal Bar Associations, Fellow, College of Labor and Employment Lawyers, Michigan Public Employer Labor Relations Association (MPELRA), former Co-Chair of the Labor and Employment Section of the Federal Bar Association (Detroit Chapter).

**Career:** Joined firm 1978; Principal, 1985.

**Personal:** JD, George Washington University, 1975; BA, University of Notre Dame, 1972.

## SHANNON, Joseph J
Bodman PLC, Detroit
313 393 7549
jshannon@bodmanlaw.com
*Featured in Litigation (Michigan)*

**Practice Areas:** Represents corporate clients involved in large commercial and construction litigation matters and alternative dispute resolution proceedings. Has significant experience represent-

ing clients in the automotive and heavy industry sectors. Experienced in employment and traditional labor law matters.
**Professional Memberships:** State Bar of Michigan, American Bar Association, Detroit Metropolitan Bar Association (Litigation Section Chair), American Arbitration Association, Catholic Lawyers Society (Director), Irish/American Lawyers Association, Notre Dame Law School Advisory Board (Director).
**Personal:** JD, University of Notre Dame; BA, University of Southern California; Leadership Detroit XIX; Crain's Detroit Business "40 Under 40".

### SHARKEY, Dan
Brooks Wilkins Sharkey & Turco, PLLC, Birmingham
sharkey@bwst-law.com
*Featured in Litigation (Michigan)*
**Practice Areas:** Concentrates in supply-chain contacts and commercial litigation. Significant experience in class actions, franchises, environmental, construction, real estate, securities, creditors' rights, and sales representatives. Tried more than 60 cases in US District, Bankruptcy, Military, and State courts, and is also licensed in Ohio.
**Career:** Judge Advocate General's Corps and Special Assistant US Attorney, 1995-1999; Associate and Shareholder, Butzel Long, 1999-2009; Co-Founded Firm in 2009.
**Publications:** Several published articles and dozens of presentations regarding supply-chain contracts and disputes.
**Personal:** Vanderbilt University School of Law (Juris Doctor, 1995), The University of Notre Dame (BBA, cum laude, 1992), married with three daughters.

### SHEVNOCK, Colleen M
Dickinson Wright PLLC, Detroit
734 623 1665
cshevnock@dickinsonwright.com
*Featured in Banking & Finance (Michigan)*
**Practice Areas:** Extensive experience as counsel to banks and other institutional lenders in commercial lending matters. Negotiation and documentation of wide-range of loan transactions ranging from smaller uncommitted working capital facilities to counsel as agent in connection with large syndicated credit facilities. Experience with foreign currency facilities, acquisition facilities, working capital financing and letters or credit. Secured lending experience in all types of real and personal property. Counsel to corporations and entities, such as borrowers, in connection with various financing transactions.
**Personal:** Wayne State University Law School (JD cum laude, Order of the Coif, 1989); Michigan State University (BA, 1986).

### SHIELD JR, William P
Dickinson Wright PLLC, Detroit
313 223 3602
wshield@dickinsonwright.com
*Featured in Banking & Finance (Michigan)*
**Practice Areas:** Lead Counsel to the agent bank and arranger in syndicated credit facilities and cross-border financings; lead Counsel to senior

lenders, subordinated lenders and borrowers in public and private acquisition financings, debt restructurings, bridge financings, mezzanine financings and other leveraged financings and general commercial lending transactions; extensive experience in asset based and other secured lending and specialized collateral transactions.
**Professional Memberships:** State Bar of Michigan; Metropolitan Detroit Bar Association.
**Publications:** Contributing author, ICLE, "Lender vs. Creditors in a Difficult Economic Environment".
**Personal:** JD, University of Michigan Law School; BSEE, University of Michigan.

### SHULMAN, Larry R
Bodman PLC, Detroit
313 393 7503
lshulman@bodmanlaw.com
*Featured in Banking & Finance (Michigan)*
**Practice Areas:** Represents lenders in loan originations and counsels lenders on lender liability issues. Commercial lending experience encompasses leveraged buyout and leveraged recapitalization loans, asset-based loans, letter of credit and bankers acceptance facilities and multi-rate, multi-currency loan facilities. Extensive experience representing lenders providing credit enhancements for commercial paper back-up facilities and municipal bonds.
**Professional Memberships:** State Bar of Michigan; Detroit Metropolitan Bar Association.
**Personal:** JD, cum laude and BA, University of Michigan. Board of Trustees, JARC Foundation.

### SIKKEL, Robert W
Barnes & Thornburg LLP, Grand Rapids
616 742 3978
robert.sikkel@BTLaw.com
*Featured in Labor & Employment (Michigan)*
**Practice Areas:** Management labor law; represents employers on a regional and national basis on labor and employment law matters including: collective bargaining, grievance arbitration, union organizing, NLRB proceedings, labor strategies for mergers and acquisitions; healthcare labor matters; affirmative action/OFCCP; covenants not to compete/trade secrets. Author, speaker and trainer on labor and employment issues.
**Professional Memberships:** State Bar of Michigan, American Bar Association; past Chair: Labor and Employment Law Section, State Bar of Michigan.
**Career:** Partner, Barnes & Thornburg LLP.
**Personal:** Hope College (BA, cum laude, 1971); Indiana University School of Law - Bloomington (JD, summa cum laude, 1974).

### SIMPSON, James A
Miller, Canfield, Paddock and Stone, P.L.C., Troy
248 267 3323
simpson@millercanfield.com
*Featured in Real Estate (Michigan)*
**Practice Areas:** Experienced in all lending products and real estate. Designed loan processes and documentation for national lending programs; closing or supervising counsel on 1,500+ securitized commercial mortgage loans in all 50

states. Real estate portfolio experience over $4 billion, representing owners, developers, contractors, syndicators, landlords and tenants.
**Professional Memberships:** American Bar Association, State Bar of Michigan, Mortgage Bankers' Association of America, Commercial Mortgage Securities Association.
**Career:** Joined firm 2003, Principal, 2006, Leader, Capital Markets Lending Group.
**Personal:** JD, Wayne State University, 1968; BA, Michigan State University, 1965.

### SNAPPER, Michael
Barnes & Thornburg LLP, Grand Rapids
616 742 3947
mike.snapper@BTLaw.com
*Featured in Labor & Employment (Michigan)*
**Practice Areas:** Labor and Employment Law consultation and representation for management, including union relations and strategic planning; mergers and acquisitions; union avoidance; representation in collective bargaining, arbitration, work relocation, strikes and corporate campaigns; NLRB charges and litigation. Also, extensive experience in reductions in force, EEOC and OFCCP matters.
**Professional Memberships:** ABA, member of the Developing Labor Law Sub-Committee, 1987-present; Michigan State Bar (Labor and Employment Law Committee Member).
**Career:** Administrative Department Chair, Labor Department, Barnes & Thornburg's Michigan office; listed in Best Lawyers of America since 1997; AV rated by Martindale Hubbell; 2011 BTI Client Service All-Star National Recognition.

### SPILKIN, Andrew Z
Bodman PLC, Troy
248 743 6029
aspilkin@bodmanlaw.com
*Featured in Real Estate (Michigan)*
**Practice Areas:** Primary real estate counsel for large corporate clients, including Tier-1 automotive suppliers, in matters involving real estate purchases and sales, development of new facilities, leasing of industrial and office space, and general day-to-day real estate activities. Represents buyers, sellers, landlords and tenants in commercial, office, industrial and residential leases, loans, and purchase and sale transactions ranging from single family homes to multi-million dollar complex transactions.
**Professional Memberships:** State Bar of Michigan; CoreNet Global.
**Personal:** JD, cum laude and BBA, with high distinction, University of Michigan; Salvation Army Advisory Council for the Southeast Michigan Adult Rehabilitation Center.

### STEVENSON, Robert B
Stevenson Keppelman Associates, Ann Arbor
734 747 7050
bob@skalaw.com
*Featured in Employee Benefits & Executive Compensation (Michigan)*
**Practice Areas:** ERISA; full range of employee benefits. Involved in significant M&A activity and fiduciary overhauls. Negotiated fee reductions and

fiduciary updgrades in large 401(k) plans. Frequent activity with PBGC. A leader in cash balance plans.
**Professional Memberships:** Michigan Bar and ABA (employee benefits committees of each). Past Chairperson, Michigan Bar Employee Benefits Committee. Charter Fellow, American College of Employee Benefits Counsel. Listed in every edition, Best Lawyers in America and Michigan Superlawyers.
**Publications:** Various books, journal articles and seminars.
**Personal:** BA Michigan State University, 1973, LLM University of Michigan Law, 1976. Previous Head Men's and Women's Lacrosse Coach, Michigan State University. Past President US Lacrosse Michigan Chapter.

### STUMPFF, Andrew
Stevenson Keppelman Associates, Ann Arbor
734 747 7050
andrew@skalaw.com
*Featured in Employee Benefits & Executive Compensation (Michigan)*
**Practice Areas:** All areas of benefits and executive compensation law; particular expertise in fiduciary issues, executive compensation, and VEBAs.
**Professional Memberships:** Fellow, American College of Employee Benefits Counsel. Former Co-Chair, Employee Benefits Committee, NY Bar Association. Member, ABA and Michigan Bar (Employee Benefits Subcommittees). Admitted New York and Michigan.
**Career:** Lecturer, Universities of Michigan and Alabama Law Schools. Former Partner, Davis Polk & Wardwell (New York). Assistant Branch Chief, IRS Chief Counsel, 1991-95.
**Publications:** Law school casebook, 'Employee Benefits and Executive Compensation' (Foundation, 2011); BNA Tax Management Portfolio, 395-3rd T.M., 'VEBAs and Other Welfare Benefit Funding Arrangements' (2011).
**Personal:** JD 1986, University of Michigan (Article Editor, Law Review); AB 1983, Washington University, St. Louis.

### SYLWESTRZAK, Theodore
Dickinson Wright PLLC, Detroit
313 223 3036
TSylwestrzak@dickinsonwright.com
*Featured in Banking & Finance (Michigan)*
**Practice Areas:** Lead Counsel to agents and lenders in asset-based lending; automotive workouts and bankruptcies; loan workouts and bankruptcy; loan originations; factoring; secured lending; extensive experience in workouts, bankruptcy, and asset-based lending.
**Professional Memberships:** Turnaround Management Association; Detroit Metropolitan Bar Association, Committee on Debtor/Creditor Rights; State Bar of Michigan; American Bar Association; Association for Corporate Growth.
**Personal:** JD, Wayne State University Law School (magna cum laude; Order of the Coif; Associate Survey Editor, Wayne Law Review); BS, Northern Michigan University (summa cum laude).

## TAYLOR, Trent
Miller, Canfield, Paddock and Stone, P.L.C., Detroit
616 776 6302
taylort@millercanfield.com
*Featured in Banking & Finance (Michigan)*

**Practice Areas:** Represents national, regional and local financial institutions in real estate, construction, working capital and equipment financing, including syndicated transactions, letter of credit-backed bond financings, tax credit supported financings and asset-based lending.
**Professional Memberships:** American Bar Association; State Bar of Michigan; Grand Rapids Bar Association
**Career:** Principal
**Personal:** JD, University of Michigan Law School; BA, Gustavus Adolphus College

## THOMPSON, Deborah W
Stevenson Keppelman Associates, Ann Arbor
734 747 7050
deb@skalaw.com
*Featured in Employee Benefits & Executive Compensation (Michigan)*

**Practice Areas:** ERISA, with special emphasis on defined benefit plans, 401(k) plans, cafeteria plans, and employee benefit issues in M&As. Recent work on executive compensation.
**Professional Memberships:** ABA; State Bar of Michigan, Past Chair, Employee Benefits Committee; Charter Fellow, American College of Employee Benefits Counsel; Past-Chair, Michigan Employee Benefits Conference; Listed in Best Lawyers in America and Michigan Superlawyers.
**Career:** Joined firm in 2009 from Miller Canfield, where she was a Principal and of Counsel.
**Publications:** Frequesnt author and lecturer on employee benefits.
**Personal:** JD, cum laude, Wayne State University Law School, 1978; BA, with high honor, Michigan State University, 1964.

## VON ENDE, Carl H
Miller, Canfield, Paddock and Stone, P.L.C., Detroit
313 496 7618
vonende@millercanfield.com
*Featured in Litigation (Michigan)*

**Practice Areas:** Litigation and dispute resolution, with an emphasis on trials and appeals relating to intellectual property, corporate control,

securities, banking, taxation, and constitutional litigation.
**Professional Memberships:** State Bar of Michigan, Detroit Metropolitan Bar Association (President 1987-88), American College of Trial Lawyers (Fellow 1994-present, State Chair 1998-99), Faculty Member, Mandatory Continuing Legal Education Program, Michigan Supreme Court, Group Leader, University of Michigan Advocacy Institute, Instructor, American Arbitration Association.
**Career:** Joined firm 1968; Principal, 1975; Litigation Practice Group Leader, 1990-99.
**Personal:** JD, University of Michigan Law School, 1968; AB, University of Michigan, 1964.

## WALTERS, David B
Bodman PLC, Troy
248 743 6052
dwalters@bodmanlaw.com
*Featured in Employee Benefits & Executive Compensation (Michigan)*

**Practice Areas:** Represents clients in employee benefits, corporate law and estate planning. Extensive experience in the establishment, revision, modification, merger and termination of pension, money purchase, stock bonus, ESOP and profit sharing plans (including all types of 401(k) plans), group health plans, health care reimbursement plans, cafeteria plans and dependent care arrangements. Assists health care professionals with general corporate and employment matters.
**Professional Memberships:** State Bar of Michigan (Employee Benefits Committee; Tax Section), American Bar Association (Employee Benefits Committee), Great Lakes Area TE/GE Council (EP Coordinator).
**Personal:** JD, University of Detroit School of Law; BS, cum laude, Central Michigan University.

## WATSON, Daniel C
Bodman PLC, Detroit
313 392 1076
dwatson@bodmanlaw.com
*Featured in Banking & Finance (Michigan)*

**Practice Areas:** Represents financial institutions in commercial, real estate and construction lending transactions. Negotiates and documents commercial real estate loans, secured line of credit facilities, equipment finance facilities, letters of credit, acquisition term loans, syndicated loans, construction loans, and end loans involving businesses in a broad range of industries. Served as in-house counsel to a major bank for 25 years.

**Professional Memberships:** State Bar of Michigan (Business Law and Real Estate sections; Mortgage and Security Devices Subcommittee of Real Property Section).
**Personal:** JD, Wayne State University; BA, Michigan State University.

## WATSON, Jerome R
Miller, Canfield, Paddock and Stone, P.L.C., Detroit
313 496 7552
watson@millercanfield.com
*Featured in Labor & Employment (Michigan)*

**Practice Areas:** Labor law and litigation, primarily defending employers in discrimination, harassment, breach of contract, wrongful discharge, and retaliation cases. Also experienced in FOIA, OMA, workplace violence, and defending constitutional challenges and employment class actions.
**Professional Memberships:** College of Labor and Employment Lawyers Fellow, American Bar Association, State Bar of Michigan, Federal Bar Association, Wolverine Bar Association, National Bar Association. Served as spokesman for Michigan Region of the American Bar Association's Minority Partners in Majority Firms Program.
**Career:** Joined firm 1976; Principal, 1983; Managing Director 2000-2010
**Personal:** JD, University of Michigan Law School, 1976; BA, University of Michigan, 1972.

## WINOKUR, Laurence
Dickinson Wright PLLC, Detroit
248 433 7263
lwinokur@dickinsonwright.com
*Featured in Real Estate (Michigan)*

**Practice Areas:** Real estate development, real estate finance and mortgage lending and leasing; has represented various developers in acquisition, development and leasing of projects.
**Professional Memberships:** American Bar Association; State Bar of Michigan Real Property Section and Business Law Section; frequent lecturer at real estate seminars throughout the nation.
**Personal:** JD, University of Michigan Law School; BA, University of Michigan.

## ZABRISKIE, Wendy L
Bodman PLC, Troy
248 743 6046
wzabriskie@bodmanlaw.com
*Featured in Banking & Finance (Michigan)*

**Practice Areas:** Represents financial institutions in structuring, negotiating and documenting complex, multimillion dollar real estate and commercial loan origination and workout transactions, including construction loans, mortgage loans, acquisition and mezzanine facilities, working capital arrangements, agented and syndicated transactions, restructures, commercial foreclosures, deed in lieu arrangements and distressed loan sales.
**Professional Memberships:** State Bar of Michigan; Commercial Real Estate Development & Ownership Committee, Real Property Law Section.
**Personal:** JD, magna cum laude, Wayne State University; BA, Michigan State University. Member, City of Birmingham Brownfield Redevelopment Authority. Former vice chair, Royal Oak Zoning Board of Appeals.

## ZELENOCK, Katheryne L
Dickinson Wright PLLC, Troy
248 433 7384
kzelenock@dickinsonwright.com
*Featured in Real Estate (Michigan)*

**Practice Areas:** Real estate and commercial finance. Representing national and regional lenders, mortgage bankers and loan servicers, emphasis on capital markets, conduit, and bank financing. Litigation counsel to businesses, principally related to real estate and corporate finance matters.
**Professional Memberships:** American Bar Association, State Bar of Michigan, Mortgage Bankers' Association of America, Commercial Real Estate Finance Council; American College of Mortgage Attorneys; Mortgage Industry Standards Maintenance Organization, Commercial Real Estate Women of Detroit.
**Career:** Joined firm 2009 as Principal; Previously: Co-founder and President, 1998-2003 e-Cognita Technologies, Inc.; Co-leader, Capital Markets Lending Group, Miller Canfield Paddock and Stone PLC (2003-2009).
**Personal:** JD, University of Notre Dame Law School, 1991; BA, University of Michigan, 1987.

# BODMAN PLC

**www.**bodmanlaw.com **tel:** 313 259 7777 **fax:** 313 393 7579

**Chairman, Executive Committee:** Ralph E McDowell
Number of members: 95
Number of other lawyers: 59

## Firm Overview:

Bodman clients demand the best. Bodman attorneys, in turn, are laser-focused on providing the highest quality legal services to clients in Michigan, across the United States and around the world. The firm's clients are businesses, individuals and institutions with big ideas and big achievements. For more than 80 years, they have trusted Bodman to serve as a strategic business partner. In exchange, the firm offers them the insight, experience and value they need to succeed.

Bodman values long-term client relationships above short-term gain, and it nurtures those relationships carefully. Bodman attorneys work to understand their clients' businesses and the markets within which they operate. This enables them to provide both strategic advice and preventative counsel to address potential issues efficiently and discreetly before they become significant and expensive problems. They deliver on their promises with quality, integrity and knowledge.

The power of Bodman's approach is clear in the extraordinarily long-term relationships it has maintained. For example, Bodman has represented the interests of the Ford family continuously since 1929. It has represented Comerica Incorporated and its predecessor, Manufacturers National Bank of Detroit, since it helped found Manufacturers in 1933. Other significant relationships have endured for more than 50 years.

Bodman's extensive pro bono program includes active participation with both Michigan Community Resources and Legal Aid and Defender Association (LAD) to provide free legal services to worthy community organizations and indigent individuals. According to LAD, which has honored Bodman with its Law Firm Pro Bono Award, the firm has provided pro bono services to more indigent individuals than any other law firm in the history of Michigan. The State Bar of Michigan has admitted Bodman to its Pro Bono Circle of Excellence.

## Main Areas of Practice:

The firm's primary areas of practice are: automotive and industrial; banking; business/corporate; construction; debtor-creditor rights and bankruptcy; enterprise procurement; environmental; healthcare; individual clients; insurance; intellectual property; litigation and alternative dispute resolution; municipal law and finance; real property; tax; and workplace law.

## International Work:

Bodman represents many international clients with business interests in Michigan and elsewhere within the United States. Bodman attorneys have substantial expertise in cross-border transactions involving companies and people located in India, Japan, Korea, Europe and Latin America.

## Clients:

Bodman has a diverse client base that includes individuals and businesses in a variety of industries, with emphasis on financial services, automotive, real estate, non-profit and charitable institutions, hi-tech, healthcare, general manufacturing and other sectors.

Representative clients include: AIG/American General; Archdiocese of Detroit; Bank of America; Bharat Forge Limited; Blue Cross and Blue Shield of Michigan; Caraco Pharmaceuticals Ltd., Carmeuse Lime and Stone; CBS Outdoor; Charles Stewart Mott Foundation; City of Ann Arbor; City of Grosse Pointe Park; Comcast Cablevision; Comerica Bank; Crittenton Hospital Medical Center; CSX Transportation, Inc.; The Detroit Lions, Inc.; Fannie Mae; Financial Institutions Compliance Cooperative; Flagstar Bank F.S.B.; Ford Estates; Foster Blue Water Oil Co., Inc.; Foster Energy Services; Freudenberg-NOK; Grede Holdings LLC; The Huntington National Bank; Independent Bank; International Automotive Components Group; Key Plastics, LLC; Lamar Advertising; Lear Corp.; Memorial Healthcare; Monroe Bank & Trust; PNC Bank; PricewaterhouseCoopers LLP; Primerica Financial Services; Pulte Homes of Michigan; RBS Citizens, N.A.; Saga Communications, Inc.; Sparton Corporation; St. Marys Cement Corporation; Stahl's Inc.; Sun Pharmaceutical Industries; Titan International, Inc.; Wayne County; Wells Fargo Bank.

## PRACTICE AREAS

Automotive & Industrial
Banking
Business/Corporate/M&A
Construction
Debtor-Creditor Rights & Bankruptcy
Enterprise Procurement
Environmental
Healthcare
High Tech
Individual Clients/Trusts & Estates
Insurance
Intellectual Property
Litigation & ADR
Municipal Law & Finance
Real Property
Tax
Workplace Law

## OFFICES

**MICHIGAN**

**ANN ARBOR:** Suite 400, 201 South Division, MI 48104
Tel: 734 761 3780  Fax: 734 930 2494

**CHEBOYGAN:** 229 Court Street, PO Box 405, MI 49721
Tel: 231 627 8000  Fax: 231 627 2802

**DETROIT:** 6th Floor at Ford Field, 1901 St. Antoine Street, MI 48226
Tel: 313 259 7777  Fax: 313 393 7579
Email: info@bodmanlaw.com

**TROY:** Suite 500, 201 West Big Beaver Rd., MI 48084
Tel: 248 743 6000  Fax: 248 743 6002

The firm also has an affiliate office in Dallas, Texas.

# bodman
### ATTORNEYS & COUNSELORS

# BROOKS WILKINS SHARKEY & TURCO PLLC

**www.**bwst-law.com **tel:** 248 971 1800 **fax:** 248 971 1801

**Managing Member:** Keefe Brooks
**Senior Members:** Matthew Wilkins, Daniel Sharkey, Michael Turco, Herbert Donovan

## Firm Overview:

Brooks Wilkins Sharkey & Turco is a nationally respected law firm that focuses on three areas: litigation, bankruptcy and supply chain counseling. They serve sophisticated clients worldwide, from Fortune 100 companies to prominent individuals. They leverage a lean business model and emphasize timely, clear and candid communication so that their clients can make informed and effective litigation, bankruptcy and supply decisions.

## Main Areas of Practice:

### Business & Commercial Litigation:

Multinational corporations, local businesses and prominent individuals regularly turn to Brooks Wilkins Sharkey & Turco for business and commercial litigation services in matters ranging from failed business transactions to bet-the-company disputes involving hundreds of millions of dollars in potential damages.

Brooks Wilkins Sharkey & Turco does not try to be all things to all potential clients. Instead, they have assembled a distinguished group of top-flight, highly acclaimed business and commercial litigators with extensive trial and arbitration experience focused on the following areas: business torts; construction disputes; contract disputes; UCC claims; shareholder/member disputes; securities claims; professional liability; dealership litigation; insurance coverage; trade secret/non-competition disputes; D&O liability; financial institutions; supply chain disputes; student loans and warranty, recall and product liability claims.

**Contact:** Keefe Brooks
**Email:** brooks@bwst-law.com
**Contact:** Michael Turco
**Email:** turco@bwst-law.com

### Bankruptcy, Workout & Insolvency Practice:

From taking on insolvent automotive suppliers who have threatened to shut down their client's plants throughout the country, to multimillion-dollar acquisitions of assets out of bankruptcies, to high-stakes bankruptcy litigation, to complex real estate workouts, their attorneys have time and again proven themselves able to develop creative and practical solutions in order to deliver high satisfaction results to their clients.

The firm's clients appreciate the training and experience of their insolvency attorneys gained at larger firms, tempered by the practical experience and focus they have obtained from starting and managing their own firm. This combination of backgrounds translates well to the clients they represent: clients who want and need "large firm" expertise, but in a leaner, more focused and responsive firm.

Being a boutique litigation and bankruptcy firm has been no barrier to the firm's involvement in exceptionally large and complex matters. For example, recent engagements include:

- Representation of the Liquidation Trustee of a bankruptcy estate with $600 million in liabilities, involving international litigation against various affiliates
- Representation of the purchaser of assets of one of the largest solar power companies in the country
- Representation of a large not-for-profit hospital in its restructuring and sale
- Representation of many real estate developers in working out their substantial lender obligations
- Representation of a significant creditor in one of the largest municipal bankruptcy cases in the United States

Beyond these high-profile cases, one of their core competencies is the representation of Tier One and Tier Two automotive suppliers. Their work for Tier One clients involves representing them when their Tier Two suppliers experience financial distress. Here they work to negotiate agreements that enable their clients to either efficiently exit the relationship or provide them assurance of supply on a long-term basis.

**Contact:** Matthew Wilkins
**Email:** wilkins@bwst-law.com

### Contract & Supply Chain Counseling:

The firm's lawyers have decades of experience negotiating and counseling on thousands of supply chain contracts. They understand the complex challenges and risks faced by automotive suppliers and other manufacturers. Because of this special expertise, their lawyers have been invited to present at dozens of events for the Original Equipment Suppliers Association, Precision Metalforming Association, Industrial Fasteners Institute, Precision Machined Parts Association, and other industry trade groups, covering issues such as supply contracts, purchase orders, terms and conditions, warranty, warranty sharing and recall management, financially distressed suppliers and customers, raw material cost management, tooling and molding statutes, contract duration and termination issues, sales representative commission issues, commercial impracticability, force majeure, volume fluctuations, quantity, and requirements contracts. Their in-depth knowledge equips their specialized teams to provide practical, detailed advice to clients ranging from the world's largest and most sophisticated manufacturers to independent tool makers and molders.

**Contact:** Daniel Sharkey
**Email:** sharkey@bwst-law.com
**Contact:** Herbert Donovan
**Email:** Donovan@bwst-law.com

## Clients:

American Axle & Manufacturing, Inc.; Air Center, Inc.; Beaumont Health Systems; MacLean Vehicle Systems; Continental Automotive Systems; Continental Tire the Americas; Delphi Automotive Systems; Michigan Motion Picture Productions; TRW Automotive; T-Systems North America; University of Michigan; Visteon Corporation; Volkswagen Group of America, Inc; Wells Fargo Bank, N.A.

## PRACTICE AREAS

Business & Commercial Litigation
Bankruptcy, Workout & Insolvency
Contract & Supply Chain Counseling

## OFFICE

MICHIGAN

**BIRMINGHAM:** 401 S. Old Woodward, Suite 400, MI 48009
Tel: 248 971 1800  Fax: 248 971 1801

# CLARK HILL PLC

www.clarkhill.com

**Chief Executive Officer:** John J Hern, Jr

Number of attorneys: 220

## Firm Overview:

Clark Hill PLC is an entreprenuerial full service law firm that provides business legal services, government and public affairs, and personal legal services to its clients throughout the country. With offices in Arizona, Illinois, Michigan and Washington, DC, Clark Hill has more than 200 attorneys and professionals. For more information on the firm and its services, visit www.clarkhill.com.

## Main Areas of Practice:

### Corporate Law:

Through representation of many clients in service and manufacturing industries, the firm's attorneys and other professionals advise clients on complex transactions and also routinely counsel businesses on virtually all of the legal problems they face. In addition, the firm's attorneys and other professionals represent clients before a wide array of government agencies at all levels. Reflecting the increasing internationalization of business, the firm's attorneys and other professionals often represent clients in transactions touching numerous Asian, European and Latin American countries. Clark Hill PLC also represents foreign based businesses establishing operations in the United States. As one of the leading providers of legal services to businesses and nonprofit organizations, the firm recognizes the importance of understanding its clients business and providing comprehensive counsel with the perspective to identify and overcome obstacles. The firm accomplishes this through:

- A full-service responsive approach
- An experienced and knowledgeable team
- Knowing its clients' business

### Labor & Employment Law:

Clark Hill's Labor and Employment Practice Group has more than 35 labor and employment attorneys who represent management in all aspects of labor and employment law. The firm's mission is to provide clients with practical, cost-effective, winning solutions to their labor and employment issues. It deploys experienced legal talent with a strong emphasis on prompt and open communication with clients. The firm delivers optimal results through intelligent and effective management of litigation and non-litigation matters. The firm's practice is divided into five departments: Employment counseling and training; litigation; traditional labor law; employment benefits; and immigration. "We Are Unique". Law firms and lawyers are much like people. While everyone shares some characteristics in common, each nonetheless have their own unique qualities which distinguishes them and makes them who they are: an individual's DNA, finger prints, gifts and personalities, if you will. So, when looking for a lawyer, it's important to find not only a skilled attorney, but an ethical counselor who understands both the law and your business, and who focuses on providing the particular results you need. Clark Hill takes this seriously. The Clark Hill Labor and Employment Team is carefully composed of attorneys and counselors who not only understand the law, but know business. When Clark Hill represents your interests, expect not only skilled lawyers to represent your interests, but also wise counselors who think through your issues, provide you with sage advice and achieve the right results.

### Real Estate Services:

Real Estate Practice at Clark Hill is focused on those services a client needs when investing in, owning, leasing, developing, constructing, financing and disposing of real estate related assets - delivered by a talented and diverse group of professionals who have well developed and recognized skills in the broadest spectrum of real estate activities. The firm's delivery of services is driven by its dedication to achieve client goals in a practical and solution-directed manner. The Real Estate Services Group brings together skills in areas such as project finance, public private partnerships, litigation, construction, eminent domain, property tax management, energy and telecommunications, environmental, tax planning, and public support of residential and commercial development. Clark Hill's professionals know the real estate industry, and have demonstrated ability to guide clients through the complexity of modern real estate transactions and litigation. Clark Hill's Real Estate Services Practice serves a diverse range of clients - including private developers, corporate owners, borrowers and lenders, pension funds, investors, landlords, tenants, contractors, public institutions, governmental agencies and municipalities.

## PRACTICE AREAS

Corporate
Labor & Employment Law
Real Estate Law

## OFFICES

### MICHIGAN

**DETROIT:** 500 Woodward Avenue, Suite 3500, MI 48226-3435
Tel: 313 965 8300 Fax: 313 965 8252

**BIRMINGHAM:** 151 S Old Woodward, Suite 200, MI 48009
Tel: 248 642 9692 Fax: 248 642 2174

**LANSING:** 212 East Grand River Avenue, MI 48906
Tel: 517 318 3100 Fax: 517 318 3099

**GRAND RAPIDS:** 200 Ottawa NW, Suite 500, MI 49503
Tel: 616 608 1100 Fax: 616 608 1199

### ARIZONA

**SCOTTSDALE:** 14850 N.Scottsdale Rd, Suite 500, AZ 85254
Tel: 480 684 1100 Fax: 480 684 1199

### DISTRICT OF COLUMBIA

**WASHINGTON:** 601 Pennsylvania Ave., North Building, Suite 1000, DC 20004
Tel: 202 772 0909 Fax: 202 772 0919

### ILLINOIS

**CHICAGO:** 150 N Michigan Avenue, Suite 2700, IL
Tel: 312 985 5900 Fax: 312 985 5999

## CLARK HILL

Legal and Professional Services

# DAWDA, MANN, MULCAHY & SADLER, PLC

**www.dawdamann.com tel:** 248 642 3700 **fax:** 248 642 7791

Managing partners: 5
Number of partners: 29
Number of lawyers: 38
Languages: *English, French, German, Spanish*

## Firm Overview:

Dawda Mann is dedicated to helping businesses and the individuals who own them. The firm's clients include *Fortune* 500 companies, financial institutions, publicly and privately owned companies of varied sizes, tax-exempt entities and emerging businesses located throughout the world.

Dawda Mann has one of the largest real estate development practices in the Midwest; its commercial real estate practice exceeds that of most large firms. In addition, Dawda Mann's attorneys have practiced in the complex area of energy and environmental law since the early 1980s.

## Main Areas of Practice:

### Automotive:
9 partners; 10 fee-earners based in Michigan
Dawda Mann's client roster includes original equipment manufacturers, Tier 1 and Tier 2 suppliers, automotive dealerships and specialty automotive suppliers. The firm serves companies conducting business operations throughout the world. Its automotive practice attorneys represent clients in mergers and acquisitions; supply and services agreements; purchase order disputes; organizational guidance; contract negotiations; complex litigation; labor and employee matters; and tax and economic incentives for business development.
**Contact:** William L Rosin **Tel:** 248 642 3685
**Email:** wrosin@dmms.com

### Banking:
13 partners; 13 fee-earners based in Michigan
Dawda Mann's commercial loan attorneys are leaders in representing banks with loan documentation; commercial loan work-outs; bankruptcy; lender liability defense; Uniform Commercial Code transactions; bank fraud; and real estate transactions. The firm represents both developers and institutional investors in structuring complex financial transactions, including lending transactions, syndications and joint ventures.
**Contact:** Wayne S Segal **Tel:** 248 642 6656
**Email:** wsegal@dmms.com

### Business & Corporate:
13 partners; 15 fee-earners based in Michigan
Dawda Mann handles all aspects of business law for for-profit and tax-exempt entities, including corporate formation, mergers, acquisitions and divestitures; contract negotiations; joint ventures and strategic alliances; shareholder meetings and corporate governance; environmental matters; federal, state and local tax issues; estate planning for management; and litigation.
**Contact:** Robert P Anderson **Tel:** 248 642 1483
**Email:** randerson@dmms.com

### Environment, Energy & Sustainability:
3 partners; 4 fee-earners based in Michigan
Dawda Mann's attorneys have worked in the complicated and ever-changing area of energy and environmental law since the early 1980s. The firm's attorneys were involved in the first Superfund sites and have handled environmental permitting, compliance and litigation matters before the US Environmental Protection Agency and various state and federal regulatory authorities.
**Contact:** Susan J Sadler **Tel:** 248 642 8685
**Email:** ssadler@dmms.com

### Labor / Employment & Employee Benefits:
5 partners; 5 fee-earners based in Michigan
The firm assists business owners with creating employment policies and procedures, handling employee discipline and terminations, preparing release and severance agreements, designing and documenting employee benefits, advising on Employee Retirement Income Security Act (ERISA), IRS and DOL benefits requirements, and conducting labor and benefits compliance reviews. In the event of litigation or a government agency complaint or investigation on labor or benefits matters, Dawda Mann's highly experienced attorneys assist clients in resolving federal and state labor law claims (e.g., wage and hour, FMLA, ADA, discrimination, harassment, health and safety), as well as claims involving noncompetition, non-solicitation, confidentiality agreements, breach of contract and IRS and DOL investigations involving employee benefit plans.
**Contact (Labor/Employment):** Suanne Tiberio Trimmer
**Tel:** 248 642 8695 **Email:** strimmer@dmms.com
**Contact (Employee Benefits/ERISA):** Theresa Joswick
**Tel:** 248 540 8092 **Email:** tjoswick@dmms.com

## PRACTICE AREAS

Automotive
Banking
Business & Corporate
Employee Benefits
Environment, Energy & Sustainability
Estate & Succession Planning
Labor & Employment Relations
Litigation
Mergers & Acquisitions
Real Estate
Tax

## OFFICES

MICHIGAN
**BLOOMFIELD HILLS:** 39533 Woodward Ave., Suite 200, MI 48304-5103
Tel: 248 642 3700  Fax: 248 642 7791
Email: edawda@dmms.com

### Litigation:
14 partners; 16 fee-earners based in Michigan
Dawda Mann's dedicated team of trial lawyers is experienced in all types of litigation and in the major fields of law where disputes occur, including real estate; business and tax; environmental; trusts; estate planning and probate; labor and employment relations; and commercial disputes. The firm has the capability to cost-effectively staff and manage large and small cases, including complex, multi-party cases.
**Contact:** Kenneth A Flaska **Tel:** 248 642 7791
**Email:** kflaska@dmms.com

### Real Estate:
12 partners; 14 fee-earners based in Michigan
Dawda Mann's real estate attorneys work with retailers, developers, owners, property managers, financial institutions and investors in all types of real estate transactions. The firm's clientele includes the world's largest retail companies, *Fortune* 500 companies, financial institutions and mid-size and emerging businesses throughout the world. The firm has one of the largest residential development practices in the Midwest.
**Contact:** Edward C Dawda **Tel:** 248 642 8696
**Email:** edawda@dmms.com

# DICKINSON WRIGHT PLLC

www.dickinsonwright.com **tel:** 313 223 3500 **fax:** 313 223 3598

**Chief Executive Officer:** William T Burgess
Members: 240
Other attorneys: 105

## Firm Overview:

Dickinson Wright PLLC, founded in 1878, has nearly 350 attorneys and is a full-service law firm with more than 40 practice areas, with primary offices located in Michigan; Columbus, OH; Las Vegas, NV; Nashville, TN; Phoenix, AZ; Washington DC; and Toronto, Canada. It provides corporate, commercial litigation, real estate, intellectual property and employment services, among others, to clients ranging from the Fortune 500 to mid-sized and start ups. The firm is one of the largest operating in Michigan and offers legal assistance locally, regionally, nationally and internationally. Dickinson Wright's attorneys are regularly listed in compendiums of leading firms. The firm is a leader in diversity and has been nationally recognized for its commitments in this area.

## Main Areas of Practice:

### Banking & Financial Services:
The firm provides representation and complete transaction planning advice to both lenders and borrowers in virtually all types of transactions. The firm also offers sophisticated services in commercial bankruptcy, including workouts, insolvency litigation, and refinancing.

### Commercial & Business Litigation:
The firm regularly represents clients in all aspects of litigation, including defense in commercial disputes, class actions and other types of complex litigation, including mass tort and multidistrict litigation.

### Corporate:
The firm offers clients attorneys who are seasoned, talented and exceptionally well versed in all areas related to corporate transactions. Its lawyers handle, on a regular basis, complex issues including mergers and acquisitions, private equity transactions, financings, debt restructurings, joint ventures, securities offerings, and other commercial transactions. The firm also handles SOX-related compliance, corporate governance, SEC and regulatory compliance, and all types of entity formation and contractual arrangements.

### Labor & Employment:
The firm's capabilities extend to areas including employment counseling, immigration, employee benefits and executive compensation, complex employment and employee benefits litigation, wage and hour counseling, non-competition agreements and related obligations, labor management relations and disputes, and ESOP's.

### Real Estate:
The firm represents clients in a full array of real estate transactions, including acquisitions and sales, joint ventures, permanent financing, construction, development, leasing transactions and real estate management for clients ranging from financial institutions and developers to schools and corporations.

### International Law:
To assist its clients in meeting the challenges of the global business environment, Dickinson Wright draws on the resources of all of its practice areas to provide integrated solutions to business opportunities and problems. Dickinson Wright attorneys regularly handle cross-border matters and represent numerous international clients, both domestically and abroad. The firm has established an international task force to identify issues that may affect its international clients and find effective and creative ways to address these issues. The firm is regularly recommended by international publications surveying top firms in the United States.

### Gaming:
The firm regularly represents casino operators, casino developers and casino equipment manufacturers, suppliers and employees, as well as Indian tribes and municipalities invested in developing casino projects.

### Additional Practice Specialties:
Alternative dispute resolution; antitrust and trade regulation; appellate litigation; bankruptcy; biotechnology; business criminal defense/investigations; business technology; construction; corporate finance; corporate governance; employee benefits; energy and public utilities; environmental; estate planning and trusts; family and matrimonial; immigration; insurance; intellectual property; labour and employment relations; medical malpractice defense; mergers and acquisitions; minority business enterprises; municipal law and finance; private capital; product liability litigation; railroads and transportation; regulatory and administrative law; risk management; schools and educational institutions; securities; taxation; telecommunications.

### Clients:
Representative clients include JP Morgan Chase Bank NA, Ford Motor Company, Blue Cross Blue Shield of Michigan, MGM Mirage, AT&T Michigan, State of Michigan, E.I. duPont Nemours & Company, Inc.,

## OFFICES

### MICHIGAN
**DETROIT (HEAD OFFICE):** 500 Woodward Avenue, Suite 4000, Detroit, MI 48226
Tel: 313 223 3500  Fax: 313 223 3598

**ANN ARBOR:** 350 S Main Street, Suite 300, Ann Arbor, MI 48104
Tel: 734 623 7075  Fax: 734 623 1625

**GRAND RAPIDS:** 200 Ottawa Avenue, NW, Suite 1000, Grand Rapids, MI 49503-2427
Tel: 616 458 1300  Fax: 616 458 6753

**LANSING:** 215 S Washington Square, Suite 200, Lansing, MI 48933-1816
Tel: 517 371 1730  Fax: 517 487 4700

**SAGINAW:** 4800 Fashion Square Blvd, Saginaw, MI 48604
Tel: 989 791 4646  Fax: 989 791 4633

**TROY:** 2600 W Big Beaver Road, Suite 300, Troy, MI 48084-3312
Tel: 248 433 7200  Fax: 248 433 7274

### ARIZONA
**PHOENIX:** 2901 N Central Avenue, Suite 200 Phoenix, AZ 85012
Tel: 602 285 5000  Fax: 602 285 5001

### DISTRICT OF COLUMBIA
**WASHINGTON, DC:** International Square, 1875 Eye St NW, Suite 1200, Washington, DC 20006
Tel: 202 457 0160  Fax: 202 659 1559

### NEVADA
**LAS VEGAS:** 7201 West Lake Mead Boulevard, Suite 503, Las Vegas, NV 89128
Tel: 702 541 7888  Fax: 702 541 7899

### OHIO
**COLUMBUS:** 150 E Gay Street, Suite 2400, Columbus, OH 43215
Tel: 614 744 2570  Fax: 248 433 7274

### TENNESSEE
**NASHVILLE:** 424 Church Street, Suite 1401, Nashville, TN 37219
Tel: 615 244 6538  Fax: 615 256 8386

## INTERNATIONAL OFFICES

The firm also has an office in Toronto, Canada.

Chrysler Group, Goodyear Tire & Rubber Company, W.Y.Campbell & Company, Goldman Sachs & Co., Compuware Corporation, Wal-Mart Stores, Inc., Kellogg Company, Magna International Inc., Bank of America, Royal Bank of Scotland, Sumitomo Wiring Systems, Aristocrat Technologies, Inc., Bally Technologies, Inc., Shuffle Master, Inc., Federal-Mogul Corporation; Carharrtt, Inc., Johnson Controls, Inc.

DICKINSON WRIGHT PLLC

# KIENBAUM OPPERWALL HARDY & PELTON, P.L.C.

www.kohp.com **tel:** 248 645 0000 **fax:** 248 645 1385

**Managing Partner:** Thomas G Kienbaum
**Administrative Partner:** Eric J Pelton
Number of members: 5
Number of partners: 3
Number of other lawyers: 8

**OFFICES**

MICHIGAN

**BIRMINGHAM:** 280 North Old Woodward Avenue,
Suite 400, MI 48009
Tel: 248 645 0000   Fax: 248 645 1385
Email: kohpinfo@kohp.com

**DETROIT:** 1001 Woodward Avenue,
Suite 1100, MI 48226
Tel: 313 961 3926   Fax: 313 961 3945

## Firm Overview:

Working in partnership with its clients, Kienbaum Opperwall Hardy & Pelton specializes in guiding employers through the challenges of the contemporary workplace. From wrongful discharge claims to traditional union-management matters to preventive advice, the firm's attorneys are all skilled in representing management's interests and perspectives. The firm draws on its attorneys' individual talents, diversity, and wide-ranging experiences in the employment and labor field to deliver large-firm effectiveness at small-firm cost. In addition to competitive hourly rates, the firm derives other efficiencies – which are passed on to clients – from its specialized boutique practice.

The firm was formed in May 1997 by members Thomas G Kienbaum, Theodore R Opperwall, Elizabeth Hardy, and Eric J Pelton. All were previously partners at a major Detroit law firm, where Mr Kienbaum headed the labor and employment law department. In January 2010, William B Forrest III became the fifth member of the firm. The firm is based in downtown Birmingham, Michigan, with an office in downtown Detroit.

For many years, Kienbaum Opperwall Hardy & Pelton has been designated in Chambers USA's Client Guide to America's Leading Business Lawyers as one of the top employment and labor law practices in Michigan. Among the firm's lawyers are some of the region's most recognized and successful employment and labor attorneys. A number of the firm's lawyers have been selected by their peers to be listed among the 'Best Lawyers in America' and have been inducted as Fellows of the College of Labor and Employment Lawyers. The firm's lawyers are frequent lecturers for the prestigious National Employment Law Institute and other business education programs.

The firm's practice spans all aspects of employment and labor law. It provides proactive services – counseling employers on avoiding wrongful discharge claims, employment discrimination suits, and all of the potential employee claims that can arise under a myriad of federal and state statutes. Through their in-house seminars, the firm educates management so that sensitive situations can be prevented or properly handled. The firm conducts on-site investigations of troublesome workplace problems and advises employers on how to deal successfully with the results. But when it becomes necessary, their litigators provide a vigorous defense, based on years of experience before federal and state courts and administrative tribunals. A sizable segment of their practice consists of complex multi-state litigation including class actions. They represent many clients on a regional or national basis, and count many law firms and courts among their clientele. They also have a substantial appellate practice and have been instrumental in establishing legal principles of major significance to employers in Michigan and elsewhere.

The firm's distinctive boutique practice style and philosophy offer their clients a highly focused, proactive, strategic, and resource-conscious approach to avoiding if possible, confronting when necessary, and efficiently resolving the many complex workplace issues facing American employers today. All of the firm's lawyers have devoted their careers to this specialized field, and do not have to 'reinvent the wheel' with each new representation.

## Main Areas of Practice:

Kienbaum Opperwall Hardy & Pelton provides employment and labor law services in the following areas:

### Preventive Counseling:

Personnel policies and handbooks; workforce reductions; sexual harassment claims; employee discipline and terminations; workplace investigations; affirmative action; supervisory training; employment contracts; covenants not to compete and trade secrets; arbitration procedures; wage and hour compliance; disability and family leave issues; drug and alcohol issues.

### Employment Litigation:

Wrongful discharge and discrimination suits; defamation and other workplace torts; injunction suits; non-compete and trade secret litigation; class actions; administrative claims; appeals; alternative dispute resolution.

### Traditional Labor Relations:

Union organizing; collective bargaining; contract administration and arbitration; NLRB matters; specialized labor injunctions; interest arbitrations.

### Clients:

Representative clients include: Amazon.com; American Axle & Manufacturing, Inc.; Aon Corporation; Auto Club of Michigan; Avis Budget Group; Beaumont Health System; College for Creative Studies; Comau, Inc.; Comcast Corporation; Crain Communications, Inc.; DaVita Inc.; Daimler Trucks North America; Deloitte & Touche; Delphi Corporation; Federal-Mogul Corporation; Ford Motor Company; Kinder Morgan, Inc.; L'Oreal USA; Mercedes Benz Financial Services; RadioShack; Robert W. Baird & Co.; Sodexo USA; UBS Financial Services; Verizon Wireless; Walgreen Company; Wayne State University.

# KIENBAUM OPPERWALL HARDY & PELTON, P.L.C.
## ATTORNEYS AND COUNSELORS

# MILLER, CANFIELD, PADDOCK AND STONE, P.L.C.

www.millercanfield.com **tel:** 313 963 6420 **fax:** 313 496 7500

**Chief Executive Officer:** Michael W Hartmann

Attorneys: 330

Legal assistants: 50+

Support staff: 240

## Firm Overview:

Founded in 1852, Miller Canfield is one of the largest and longest established law firms in Michigan and provides a broad range of integrated services to meet the needs of clients. Working together with the US offices, the Poland offices expand the firm's reach to clients throughout Eastern Europe. The Toronto and Windsor, Ontario and Monterrey, Mexico offices broaden the firm's ability to offer clients seamless cross-border representation to organizations interested in doing business in North America. The firm's office in Shanghai, China serves both North American and European companies doing business in China and Chinese companies interested in doing business in North America and the EU. Firm attorneys belong to prestigious American Colleges including the College of Labor and Employment Lawyers, and the American Colleges of Bond Counsel, Employee Benefits, Mortgage, Real Estate, Tax Counsel, Trial Lawyers, and Trust and Estate Counsel.

## Main Areas of Practice:

Bankruptcy; corporate; environmental and regulatory; federal tax and employee benefits; financial institutions/transactions; intellectual property and information technology; international trade and export controls; labor and employment; litigation, including dispute resolution, product safety, and state and local tax; personal services; public law; and real estate. Other specialty areas include antitrust and trade regulation; appellate; automotive; aviation and transportation; capital markets lending; climate change; construction; criminal defense; economic development incentives; electronic discovery and records management; entertainment, sports and multimedia; energy, telecom and public utilities; estate planning, family law, federal government contracts; franchise and distribution; governmental entities; immigration; insurance; life sciences and biotechnology; nonprofit and charitable organizations; professional firms; public-private partnerships; schools; securities and venture and technology. For contact information, visit www.millercanfield.com or the firm's Chinese site at www.millercanfield.cn.com

## International Work:

The firm has dedicated an entire practice group, the International Business Group, to provide legal services to US and foreign multinational companies, banks, and other clients whose business affairs are tied to the increasingly interdependent world economy. The firm handles work in Arabic, Armenian, Chinese, Dutch, English, French, German, Greek, Hebrew, Hindi, Italian, Mandarin, Polish, Portuguese, Punjabi, Russian, Spanish, Swedish, Taiwanese and Urdu.

## Clients:

The firm represents clients diverse in size and character. Attorneys represent individuals in their personal and business concerns, trusts and estates, publicly traded and multinational companies, and many start-up, small and medium-sized businesses. Clients also include public bodies such as the state of Michigan and many of its agencies, authorities and universities, cities, counties, townships, school and community college districts, and special authorities throughout the state. The firm represents many non-profit, tax-exempt institutions, such as hospitals, charitable corporations and professional associations.

## OFFICES

### MICHIGAN

**DETROIT:** 150 W. Jefferson, Suite 2500, MI 48226
Tel: 313 963 6420  fax: 313 496 7500
Email: hartmann@millercanfield.com

**ANN ARBOR:** 101 North Main Street, 7th Floor, MI 48104
Tel: 734 663 2445  fax: 734 747 7147
Email: fazio@millercanfield.com

**GRAND RAPIDS:** 99 Monroe Avenue, NW, Suite 1200, MI 49503
Tel: 616 454 8656  fax: 616 776 6332
Email: taylort@millercanfield.com

**KALAMAZOO:** 277 S Rose Street, MI 49007
Tel: 269 381 7030  fax: 269 382 0244
Email: baylor@millercanfield.com

**LANSING:** One Michigan Avenue, Suite 900, MI 48933
Tel: 517 487 2070  fax: 517 374 6304
Email: danhof@millercanfield.com

**TROY:** 840 West Long Lake Road, Suite 200, MI 48098
Tel: 248 879 2000  fax: 248 879 2001
Email: konop@millercanfield.com

### FLORIDA

**TAMPA:** 10150 Highland Manor Drive, Suite 246, Fl 33610
Tel: 813 314 2188
Email: schluter@millercanfield.com

### ILLINOIS

**CHICAGO:** 225 W Washington, Suite 2600, IL 60606
Tel: 312 460 4200  fax: 312 460 4201
Email: senica@millercanfield.com

### NEW YORK

**NEW YORK:** 500 Fifth Avenue, Suite 1815, NY 10110
Tel: 212 704 4400  fax: 212 704 4410
Email: labine@millercanfield.com

### OHIO

**CINCINNATI:** 1900 Fifth Third Center, 511 Walnut Street,
Tel: 614 203 7800  fax: 248 879 2001
Email: perry@millercanfield.com

## INTERNATIONAL OFFICES

The firm also has offices in Toronto and Windsor, Ontario, Canada, Monterrey, Mexico, Shanghai, China and in Gdynia, Warsaw, and Wroclaw, Poland.

# NEMETH BURWELL PC

www.nemethburwell.com **tel:** 313 567 5921 **fax:** 313 567 5928

**OFFICES**

MICHIGAN

**DETROIT:** 200 Talon Centre Drive, Suite 200, MI 48207
Tel: 313 567 5921  Fax: 313 567 5928

## Firm Overview:

With specialties in employment litigation, traditional labor law, mediation and management consultation for private and public sector employers, Nemeth Burwell, P.C. is Detroit-based but nationally recognized. As a reflection of its reputation, Nemeth Burwell, the largest woman-owned law firm in Michigan to exclusively represent management in the prevention, resolution and litigation of labor and employment disputes, is the law firm of choice when members of the legal profession need counsel on their own employment matters.

Since its founding in 1992, Nemeth Burwell has flourished through client referrals and recommendations from business, community and government leaders who know the firm's passion for management side labor and employment law.

**Firm Leadership:** Founding partners Patricia Nemeth and Linda G Burwell have received numerous national and regional honors for their expertise in employment law and law firm development. Ms Nemeth is a member of the Michigan Bar Association – Labor and Employment Section and International Section, and the American Bar Association – Labor Section and Alternative Dispute Resolution Section. She is a litigator and a certified mediator. Among her many honors, Ms Nemeth was named to the edition of the Best Lawyers in America® for the years 2010-2013 in the area of labor and employment and was also recognized as one of Michigan's 25 Leaders in the Law in 2009. She has received the highest possible AV rating by Martindale-Hubbell.

Ms Burwell is an ABA Foundation Fellow and a Board member, NAMWOLF. She is a member of the American Arbitration Association's Employment Law Advisory Panel and a volunteer mediator for the Attorney Grievance Commission. She is a regular presenter on employment law and risk management topics, serving as a legal expert throughout the US and recently testified before the Equal Employment Opportunity Commission. Among her many honors, Ms Burwell was named to the 2011-13 edition of the Best Lawyers in America® in the area of labor and employment and was also recognized as one of Michigan's 25 Leaders in the Law in 2010.

**Firm Philosophy & Approach:** Nemeth Burwell promotes a team-centered collegial atmosphere where clients are "firm clients" and not solely the responsibility of one attorney. When clients engage with Nemeth Burwell, they gain a collaborative partner, a team of labor and employment experts devoted to preventing, resolving and litigating employment disputes. The firm provides services with a client-friendly fee structure. Moreover, Nemeth Burwell generally has more attorneys dedicated solely to this specialized area than large full service law firms, where employment attorneys may also practice in areas unrelated to employment.

Given its diverse private and public sector experience, the firm knows that what works in one industry may be disastrous in another. Nemeth Burwell respects its clients' right to be guided by their own business approach and philosophy when it comes to employment matters and collaborates with clients to create and implement legally sound workplace policies and practices that complement their particular workplace.

## Main Areas of Practice:

### Legal Focus:

Nemeth Burwell provides training on a broad range of subjects, including: sexual harassment, hiring and firing, evolving technology issues in the workplace and compliance with FMLA, FLSA, the Americans with Disabilities Act and other discrimination laws as well as union and NLRA issues.

Nemeth Burwell effectively resolves employment disputes through arbitration and other alternative dispute resolution techniques.

When litigation is required, Nemeth Burwell vigorously defends clients against all forms of employment litigation. The firm has defended employers in arbitrations, mediations and trials before state and federal agencies, state and federal courts, and appellate courts.

Nemeth Burwell has a strong traditional labor law practice and is the go-to firm for employers seeking to understand Right to Work laws, avoid unionization or navigate the challenges of a unionized workplace.

Nemeth Burwell represents private companies in front of the National Labor Relations Board and public entities before the Michigan Employment Relations Commission. The firm offers expertise in all areas of traditional labor law, including grievance arbitrations, contract negotiations, strikes/walk-outs/wildcats and unfair labor practices.

Nemeth Burwell attorneys regularly serve as mediators in employment and civil matters to help individuals reach a resolution. Even when litigation cannot be prevented, there are points during the litigation process when the parties involved can resolve their differences through mediation. Mediation can also be employed prior to the commencement of litigation if the individuals seek an alternative dispute option. Mediation services provided by Nemeth Burwell can mean a more amicable, lower cost resolution for the individuals involved.

## Clients:

Nemeth Burwell serves employers of all sizes, including Fortune 500 companies and companies involved in complex multi-plaintiff litigation. Industries and service sectors served include: agriculture, automotive, professional service firms, associations, casinos, commercial real estate, courts, employment agencies, financial institutions, governmental units, a broad spectrum of healthcare providers including hospitals, nursing homes, assisted living facilities and home health, hospitality, insurance, manufacturing, medical supplies, packaging, pharmaceutical, retail, transportation and utilities.

# RHOADES MCKEE PC

www.rhoadesmckee.com **tel:** 616 235 3500 **fax:** 616 459 5102

**Managing Partner:** Robert C Shaver
Number of partners: 36
Number of lawyers: 50

## Firm Overview:

Originally founded in 1960, Rhoades McKee is a full-service, comprehensive law firm with nearly 50 attorneys with offices in Grand Rapids and Grand Haven, Michigan. Rhoades McKee represents numerous large and small companies, both publicly and privately held, hospitals and other healthcare institutions, licensed professionals, financial institutions, real estate developers, municipalities and insurance companies.

Several Rhoades McKee attorneys also have a CPA designation, which provides the legal team with additional insight into business transactions and disputes. All attorneys are assisted by a support staff that includes former agents of the Internal Revenue Service. The insurance defense, wrongful death and personal injury attorneys are assisted by paralegals with nursing backgrounds. The Real Estate and Environmental Practice Group contains a LEED Accredited attorney and licensed real estate brokers. These support specialists enhance the delivery of complete and practical legal services.

## Main Areas of Practice:

### Business & Corporate Law:

Rhoades McKee Business and Corporate Law Practice Group represents all business entities in business formation and financing, business valuation litigation, commercial finance law, commercial lending, commercial transaction law, corporate dissolution and bankruptcy, merger acquisitions, non-profit organizations, property taxation and tax law.

Rhoades McKee provides extensive services in all manufacturing and service industry organizations; the firm represents clients in agriculture, banking and healthcare industry services.

**Contact:** Anthony A Pearson  **Tel:** 616 233 5180
**Email:** apearson@rhoadesmckee.com

### Labor & Employment Law:

The labor and employment attorneys specialize in employee benefits and compensation, employment litigation, FLMA/ADA solutions, union-management relations and wage and hour laws.

**Contact:** Mary L Tabin  **Tel:** 616 233 5174
**Email:** mltabin@rhoadesmckee.com

### Litigation:

Rhoades McKee's Litigation Practice Group is best known for complex business, commercial and shareholder litigation. The firm leverages the talents of four JD/CPAs who practice in the business group as well as another attorney who holds an LLM. Further, the firm's commercial trial lawyers have developed unique specializations, including litigation of complex business valuation matters as well as complex financial and accounting matters.

In addition, Rhoades McKee has a robust professional malpractice defense team representing doctors, lawyers and accountants.

**Contact:** Brian K Lawson  **Tel:** 616 233 5234
**Email:** bklawson@rhoadesmckee.com

### Real Estate, Environmental & Construction:

The Real Estate Practice Group provides comprehensive services in all areas of traditional real estate, environmental, green building and construction law. It assists clients in the acquisition, construction, financing, leasing and disposition of real estate. It assists developers, contractors, realtors and investors with analysis and acquisition of parcels of land for all types of projects.

The firm represents clients including retail centers, industrial and office complexes, automobile dealerships, residential site condominium and plat developments, title insurance companies, commercial and residential real estate brokerage firms and senior and multi-family housing throughout the West Michigan region.

The environmental lawyers counsel and represent clients regarding a broad spectrum of environmental issues on a regular basis. They have significant experience with environmental due diligence in business and real estate acquisitions and divestitures, permitting, regulatory compliance, litigation, Brownfield redevelopment, financing opportunities and cleanups. The Real Estate Group at Rhoades McKee also has extensive experience in representing governmental entities and land owners in connection with condemnation proceedings.

**Contact:** Scott J Steiner  **Tel:** 616 233 5206
**Email:** sjsteiner@rhoadesmckee.com

Rhoades McKee PC
*attorneys & counselors*

# VERCRUYSSE MURRAY & CALZONE, P.C.

www.vmclaw.com **tel:** 248 540 8019 **fax:** 248 540 8059

**Managing Directors:** Robert M Vercruysse, President; Gregory V Murray, Vice President/Treasurer; David B Calzone, Secretary
Number of Shareholders: 13

**OFFICES**

MICHIGAN

**DETROIT:** 31780 Telegraph Road, Suite 200, Bingham Farms, MI 48025-3469
Tel: 248 540 8019   Fax: 248 540 8059

## Firm Overview:

Founded in 1996, the firm quickly established itself both locally and nationally as one of the country's pre-eminent management labor, employment and ERISA litigation law practices. In addition, its commercial litigation, immigration and real property practices allow the firm to assist clients with a wide array of employment, business and personnel legal issues. The firm's national reputation has grown along with its size. Robert Vercruysse, Gregory Murray, David Calzone and Susan Hartmus Hiser have been selected by their peers from across the United States as members of the American Bar Association's College of Labor and Employment Lawyers. Vercruysse, Murray, Calzone and Hiser are also members of the American Employment Law Council. Vercruysse, Murray, Calzone, Dorothy Hanigan Basmaji, Hiser, Debra Auerbach Clephane and Kathleen Poppenger are listed in various editions of The Best Lawyers in America. Vercruysse, Murray, Calzone, Basmaji, Hiser, Clephane, and William Altman were named 2012 Michigan Super Lawyers, with Murray named among the Top 100 Super Lawyers in Michigan. Vercruysse and Calzone have previously served as Chair of the Labor and Employment Section of the State Bar of Michigan, and Hiser currently serves on the section's Governing Council. Basmaji has previously served as the Chair, Vice-Chair and Treasurer of the Michigan Chapter of the American Immigration Lawyers Association. The firm's attorneys have a number of publications to their credit, including the monthly Michigan Employment Law Letter, several articles in legal periodicals, and chapter contributions and/or book editing responsibility for the following books: Employment Litigation in Michigan (ICLE 2011); Employment Discrimination Law 3d Ed.(BNA 2002); Age Discrimination in Employment Law (BNA 1999), Michigan Wrongful Discharge and Employment Discrimination Law, 2d Ed. (ICLE 1994); Employment Law in Michigan: An Employer's Guide, 2d Ed. (ICLE 2012); and The Handbook of Fraud Deterrance (2006). Several attorneys have shared their expertise by teaching classes at The University of Michigan Law School, Wayne State Law School and the University of Detroit – Mercy Law School. The firm's attorneys are also frequently featured speakers at American Bar Association, state and local bar association and Institute for Continuing Legal Education programs.

## Main Areas of Practice:

### Labor & Employment Law - Litigation:

The firm has extensive experience representing employers in state and federal courts in all forms of discrimination litigation, non-compete and trade secrets litigation as well as in affirmative action and discrimination matters before administrative agencies such as the Equal Employment Opportunity Commission, state civil rights departments, and the Office of Federal Contract Compliance Programs. The firm also represents employers before state and federal departments of labor, and the State Civil Rights Commission; has successfully defended both private and public employers in class action and complex litigation brought in both federal and state court; and is heavily involved in the defense of wrongful discharge cases, including contract and commission claims, implied employment contract claims, slander and libel claims, negligence and negligent retention claims, and whistleblower claims. Trial experience in both judge and jury trials is extensive.

### Labor & Employment Law-Traditional Labor:

In the traditional labor practice, the firm has extensive experience in negotiating collective bargaining agreements on behalf of employers and multi-employer associations. The firm has handled the two largest strikes in the US in the last decade. In addition, the firm has defended employers before the National Labor Relations Board throughout the United States and the Michigan Employment Relations Commission in both representation and unfair labor practice proceedings, represented employers in wage and hour, OSHA and MIOSHA matters before both the US and Michigan Departments of Labor, and has represented employers in arbitration matters throughout the US.

### Labor & Employment Law - Training & Advice:

Vercruysse Murray & Calzone's attorneys have significant experience in counseling employers in a wide variety of human relations and personnel matters such as the Family Medical Leave Act, the Americans with Disabilities Act and force reduction planning. The firm assists employers in the development of personnel policies and procedures, affirmative action plans, disciplinary policies, employee handbooks, drug and alcohol testing programs, and labor and employment issues in sales, mergers and acquisitions.

### ERISA Law & Litigation:

The firm's ERISA law and litigation practitioners have extensive experience providing all facets of ERISA litigation services, from pre-litigation counseling to partnering with in-house ERISA lawyers before and during ERISA litigation. The firm has successfully defended individual and class actions involving challenges to plan design, administration and interpretation, allegations of breach of fiduciary duty, claims of wrongful benefit denial and interference with the attainment of ERISA-governed benefits, and challenges to reductions in welfare benefits by current and former participants or retirees.

### Immigration:

Vercruysse Murray & Calzone's Immigration Law Practice is devoted to I-9 and immigration matters, with an emphasis on business immigration. The firm provides guidance to US and non-US employers who seek to employ foreign nationals in the US, as well as facilitating the employment of US workers abroad. The firm provides on-site employer training to human resource personnel on issues such as temporary work classifications, student employment, national interest waivers, 'special handling' for university professors, extraordinary ability and outstanding researcher petitions, permanent residence procedures, use of contract employees, I-9 compliance, NAFTA, and IRCA discrimination matters.

### Real Property:

The firm's Real Property group has extensive experience in eminent domain and condemnation law, including obtaining substantial multimillion dollar results on behalf of property owners in state and federal courts. The firm also represents property owners and developers seeking land use and zoning approvals, including litigation when necessary.

### Additionally:

The firm has also distinguished itself in the following areas: general litigation; executive compensation agreements; securities arbitration; constitutional law; commercial litigation; unfair competition litigation; and trade secret and tortious interference litigation.

### Clients:

A.F.L. Web Printing, American Axle & Manufacturing, American Red Cross, Campbell Ewald Advertising, Central Michigan University, Chrysler LLC, Daimler AG, Detroit Diesel Corporation, Detroit Media Partnership, Faurecia Automotive, Gannett Co., Inc., Guardian Industries, H&R Block Financial Advisors, Inc., HP Pelzer, Inergy Automotive Systems (USA), LLC, ITC Transmission, Lake Superior State University, Mueller Industries, Oakwood Healthcare, Inc., Penske Corporation, Pollard Banknote Limited, SPX Corporation, Toyota Motor Sales, Toyota Motor Engineering & Manufacturing, TRW Inc., Unique Fabricating, and Walbridge Aldinger Company.

## How lawyers are ranked

Every year we carry out thousands of in-depth interviews with clients in order to assess the reputations and expertise of business lawyers worldwide. The qualities we look for (and which determine rankings) include technical legal ability, professional conduct, client service, commercial awareness/astuteness, diligence, commitment, and other qualities most valued by the client. For details of our research team, see p.5.

# CONSTRUCTION

Commentary about individuals can be found under their firm's paragraph. If the firm has no paragraph (is not ranked) look at Other Notable Practitioners.

### Construction
### Leading Firms

**Band 1**
Fabyanske, Westra, Hart & Thomson PA
Faegre Baker Daniels

**Band 2**
Briggs and Morgan *
Dorsey & Whitney LLP *
Heley, Duncan & Melander, PLLP
Leonard, Street and Deinard Professional Association
Maslon Edelman Borman & Brand, LLP

## Band 1

### Fabyanske, Westra, Hart & Thomson PA

**THE FIRM** This sizable Minneapolis practice is considered one of Minnesota's premier construction groups. It is best known for representing contractors and subcontractors, in addition to developers and designers. The team is active in both the public and private sectors and is experienced at advising on a wide range of project types, including roads, buildings, tunnels and bridges.
**KEY INDIVIDUALS Marvin Fabyanske** is an extremely experienced and highly regarded construction specialist. His practice places a particular emphasis on ethanol plant projects. **Kyle Hart** is another key member of the practice. He is noted for his experience in the field of changed condition litigation. Highly esteemed attorney **Dean Thomson** focuses his practice on highway and procurement matters. One impressed market source comments: *"I'd put him right at the top of my list of best construction attorneys."* **Gregory Spalj** is also well respected. He is frequently called upon to advise clients on energy projects and underground civil improvements. Clients describe him as *"marvelous and really smart."*

### Faegre Baker Daniels

**THE FIRM** Faegre Baker Daniels has an excellent reputation across the broad spectrum of construction matters. It

### Senior Statesmen

**Senior Statesmen: distinguished older practitioners**
Noteboom Lowell     *Leonard, Street and Deinard Professional*

### Leading Individuals

**Band 1**

| | |
|---|---|
| Bistram Gregory | *Briggs and Morgan* * |
| Champlin Steve | *Dorsey & Whitney LLP* |
| Coleman Jeffrey | *The Coleman Law Firm, LLC (ONP)†* |
| Fabyanske Marvin | *Fabyanske, Westra, Hart & Thomson PA* |
| Hart Kyle | *Fabyanske, Westra, Hart & Thomson PA* |
| Knoll Jocelyn | *Dorsey & Whitney LLP* |
| O'Connor James | *Maslon Edelman Borman & Brand, LLP* |
| O'Connor Patrick J | *Faegre Baker Daniels* |
| Thomson Dean | *Fabyanske, Westra, Hart & Thomson PA* |

**Band 2**

| | |
|---|---|
| Halls Peter C | *Faegre Baker Daniels* |
| Harens John | *Harens Mediation Center, LLC* |
| Hartnett IV James J. | *Faegre Baker Daniels* |
| Heley Mark | *Heley, Duncan & Melander, PLLP* |
| Huber Robert | *Leonard, Street and Deinard Professional* |
| Hull William D | *The Coleman Law Firm, LLC (ONP)†* |
| Killian James | *Maslon Edelman Borman & Brand, LLP* |
| Lapicola Michael | *Faegre Baker Daniels* |
| Lindemann Steven R | *Leonard, Street and Deinard Professional* |
| Spalj Gregory | *Fabyanske, Westra, Hart & Thomson PA* |
| Sullivan Timothy | *Best & Flanagan LLP (ONP)† *￼* |
| Torgerson Robert | *Leonard, Street and Deinard Professional* |

**Up-and-coming individuals**

| | |
|---|---|
| Ruzicka Eric | *Dorsey & Whitney LLP* |

* Indicates firm / individual with profile.
Alphabetical order within each band. Band 1 is the highest.

has extensive experience of acting for contractors, owners and engineers, and has notable knowledge of the utilities sector. The firm continues to act as construction counsel to the $1.7 billion CapX2020 high-voltage power line project. Other key clients include Xcel Energy, Target and Essar Constructions.

**KEY INDIVIDUALS** Highly regarded attorney **Patrick O'Connor** handles contract negotiation and construction litigation. He recently represented RCI Systems in a dispute stemming from the design and implementation of a fire suppression system in an elder care center. **Michael Lapicola** has a vibrant and varied construction practice, and was recently called upon to advise Essar on a $1.6 billion manufacturing project. Clients value his responsiveness and knowledge. **Peter Halls** has extensive experience in representing domestic companies abroad and is particularly recommended for his knowledge of operating in Russia. Clients admire **James Hartnett**'s business insight. He focuses on litigation and recently represented Xcel Energy in a complex series of claims and counterclaims concerning project delays and cost overruns.

### Band 2

#### Briggs and Morgan
**See profile on p.1581**

**THE FIRM** This Twin Cities firm has a highly respected construction practice. It is well equipped to provide advice on a wide variety of projects and has particular experience of acting for trade and professional associations, financial institutions, residential developers and utilities. The group also handles construction dispute resolution. Donlar Construction, CHS and Pulte are among its recent clients.
**KEY INDIVIDUALS Gregory Bistram** (see p.1578) is widely acknowledged as a talented construction lawyer and preeminent mediator and arbitrator. Sources name him *"one of the best construction lawyers in town."*

#### Dorsey & Whitney LLP
**See profile on p.1583**

**THE FIRM** This well-regarded group has wide-ranging construction expertise, with a particular focus on the representation of construction and engineering companies. Its recent experience encompasses energy and utilities, infrastructure and educational projects. The team is also well versed in the niche field of data center construction. Notable clients include URS, UnitedHealth Group and Kraus Anderson Construction.

**Sources say:** *"Fantastic lawyers. They are a top firm in the region and they are extremely well respected."*

**KEY INDIVIDUALS Steve Champlin** is considered *"one of the best construction lawyers in the country."* He recently defended Aker Kvaerner against over $200 million of claims arising from project delays and cost overruns. Clients describe **Jocelyn Knoll** as *"smart, conscientious and extremely client-focused."* She was recently called upon to act for Aker Kvaerner in the pursuit of over $220 million in claims relating to the construction of a coal-fired power plant. *"Talented litigator"* **Eric Ruzicka** is an up-and-coming construction litigator. He was recently engaged to advise Enclos on a complex multiparty dispute.

## Heley, Duncan & Melander, PLLP

**THE FIRM** This firm has a strong focus on construction law. It is known for representing architects and insurers in construction defect matters, in addition to its distinguished arbitration and mediation practice. It also handles disputes arising from project delays. The group is based in Minneapolis.

**KEY INDIVIDUALS Mark Heley** is viewed as *"one of the premier mediators in the state."* He also advises clients on construction transactions and litigation.

## Leonard, Street and Deinard Professional Association

**THE FIRM** This firm continues to have a good reputation across a wide variety of construction matters, encompassing both transactional and contentious issues. It has a particularly strong track record of handling delay and impact claims, earthwork contracting issues and energy savings performance contracts. The team was recently called upon to defend Bossardt against over $40 million of contractual and tort claims. Other key clients include Siemens, Honeywell and Atlantic Power.

**KEY INDIVIDUALS Robert Huber** is recognized as one of the state's leading dirt law specialists. He is active as a litigator, arbitrator and mediator. Clients value **Steven Lindemann**'s knowledge, responsiveness and ability to think on his feet. He was recently engaged to defend Architectural Resources against a Data Practices Act request. **Lowell Noteboom** is also singled out for his knowledge and responsiveness. He has a notable interest in matters relating to energy savings performance contracts. *"Quality lawyer"* **Robert Torgerson** handles a range of construction litigation, including delay and defect law suits. Clients say: *"He was just unbelievably good. He knew the case inside and out."*

## Maslon Edelman Borman & Brand, LLP

**THE FIRM** This firm handles a broad range of construction matters. Its expertise includes alternative fuel projects,

the representation of contractors in default cases and the defense of claims relating to design issues. The team is also active in the niche area of defective construction insurance coverage and was recently engaged to advise Shaw on two competing lawsuits relating to an insurance coverage dispute.

**KEY INDIVIDUALS James O'Connor** is described by sources as *"an intelligent, tenacious and effective advocate."* He was recently called upon to represent Strata Corporation in a number of multimillion-dollar disputes. **James Killian** is known for advising power companies on environmentally preferable products contracts and representing bondholders in construction financings.

## Other Notable Practitioners

**Timothy Sullivan** (see p.1580) of Best & Flanagan LLP is a *"very good lawyer,"* according to market sources. He concentrates his practice on the representation of owners, contractors and subcontractors, and has significant experience in the healthcare arena. **John Harens** of Harens Mediation Center, LLC is considered a *"fantastic arbitrator and mediator"* in Minnesota construction circles. **Jeffrey Coleman** of The Coleman Law Firm, LLC is best known for the representation of design professionals. He has a particular interest in concrete construction. At the same firm, **William Hull** is also recommended for his construction mediation and arbitration practice.

# CORPORATE/M&A

Commentary about individuals can be found under their firm's paragraph. If the firm has no paragraph (is not ranked) look at Other Notable Practitioners.

| Corporate/M&A |
| --- |
| **Leading Firms** |

| **Band 1** |
| --- |
| Dorsey & Whitney LLP * |
| Faegre Baker Daniels |

| **Band 2** |
| --- |
| Briggs and Morgan * |
| Fredrikson & Byron PA * |
| Kaplan, Strangis & Kaplan |
| Leonard, Street and Deinard Professional Association |
| Lindquist & Vennum LLP * |
| Oppenheimer Wolff & Donnelly LLP |

| **Band 3** |
| --- |
| Gray Plant Mooty * |
| Maslon Edelman Borman & Brand, LLP |

*\* Indicates firm with profile.*
*Alphabetical order within each band. Band 1 is the highest.*

## Band 1

### Dorsey & Whitney LLP
**See profile on p.1583**

**THE FIRM** Dorsey & Whitney's corporate group is viewed as one of Minnesota's premier M&A practices. It is particularly active in the medical and healthcare arenas, and recently represented medical device manufacturer Synovis Life Technologies in its $325 million sale to Baxter International. Other key clients include UnitedHealth Group, U.S. Bancorp and Land O'Lakes.

**Sources say:** *"A very efficient, effective, knowledgeable and ethical firm."*

**KEY INDIVIDUALS** *"Top-notch lawyer"* **Kenneth Cutler** recently acted for Jobs2Web on its $110 million sale to SuccessFactors. Clients say he *"is always up to date, informed and practical, and exhibits maturity and wisdom."* **Robert Rosenbaum** is an *"experienced and astute transactional attorney,"* say sources. Clients report that he is *"a very effective negotiator,"* who *"really understands business objectives."* Clients appreciate that **Matthew Knopf** is *"reasonable and practical in his thinking," "responsive"* and *"always*

*very well prepared."* He leads the firm's M&A practice and has notable experience in the healthcare sector. **Timothy Hearn** was lead counsel to Synovis on the disposal described above. Clients say he is *"very knowledgeable about legal issues associated with acquiring and being acquired by a third party company,"* and value his *"ability to communicate clearly and effectively."* **John Marsalek** is also well regarded in the market. He recently acted for Best Buy on its $167 million acquisition of mindSHIFT Technologies.

### Faegre Baker Daniels

**THE FIRM** Faegre Baker Daniels has an excellent reputation across a broad range of corporate and transactional matters. It places a particular emphasis on its strategic M&A and private equity practices, and advises clients from a diverse range of industry sectors. Recent work highlights include acting for HB Fuller on its acquisition of Forbo Group for approximately $394 million. In the past year, it has also provided corporate counsel to 3M, Archer Daniels Midland and General Mills.

**KEY INDIVIDUALS Bruce Engler** is one of Minnesota's preeminent M&A lawyers. He is noted for his private equity expertise and counts Norwest Equity Partners among his recent clients. **Morgan Burns** was lead counsel to HB Fuller on the acquisition described above. He also handles public offerings and recently advised Proto Labs on its $79.1 million IPO. **Steven Kennedy** is known for counseling public companies on securities and corporate governance matters. **Michael Stanchfield** is another key player

at the firm. He was recently called upon to represent 3M in its $550 million acquisition of Avery Dennison. **Amy Seidel** leads the firm's public companies and securities practice group. She was recently involved in the firm's representation of Graco Inc. with respect to its acquisition of Illinois Tool Works. Senior statesman **Philip Garon** is widely considered a figurehead of the Minnesota corporate Bar. He was recently engaged to act as Minnesota counsel to Pentair on its merger with a spun-off subsidiary of Tyco International.

## Band 2

### Briggs and Morgan
See profile on p.1581

**THE FIRM** This well-regarded group places a heavy emphasis on M&A and private equity work, and is increasingly acting for mezzanine finance groups. Recent highlights include representing Crispinian in its sale of two beverage companies to MillerCoors. Other clients include Northstar Capital, Pohlad Companies and Private Capital Management.

**Sources say:** *"They work with us as a team to accomplish what we want."*

**KEY INDIVIDUALS** *"Top-notch"* attorney **Brian Wenger** (see p.1580) represents public companies in sizable corporate transactions. Clients note that he is *"always absolutely prepared,"* and value his ability to anticipate a question and *"initiate thinking on different issues."* Up-and-coming individual **Dennis Knoer** (see p.1579) is identified as a corporate lawyer who *"keeps his eye on the business prize."* Clients admire his *"preparation, approach and style."*

### Fredrikson & Byron PA
See profile on p.1584

**THE FIRM** This much-admired group has impressive M&A, corporate governance and financing expertise, with significant clients in the private equity, manufacturing, financial services and life sciences sectors. Recent work highlights include acting as bond counsel to Medtronic on a $1 billion bond issuance, and advising the same company on its $525 million acquisition of Salient Surgical. The group has also advised Titan Machinery, Western Bank and Techne on corporate matters.

**Sources say:** *"A very robust and diverse practice."*

**KEY INDIVIDUALS** Clients value **Thomas Garton's** knowledge and experience. He assisted Medtronic in the bond issuance mentioned above. Impressed clients speak highly of his *"knowledge and experience,"* and relate that he *"adds value to all dealings."* **Melodie Rose** was lead counsel in the Medtronic bond issuance. She heads up the firm's corporate practice group and is noted for her public companies and securities expertise. Experienced practitioner **John Satorius** is another key player at the firm. He handles a broad range of M&A and corporate finance matters, with a focus on private equity transactions. A new entry to the rankings, **Sean Kearney** has developed a strong reputation in the market. He is a *"talented lawyer"* with significant experience in the private equity sector. Senior statesman

**Keith Libbey** is also highly regarded. He has a distinguished M&A practice, encompassing public and private company matters.

### Kaplan, Strangis & Kaplan

**THE FIRM** This well-respected M&A boutique has a strong focus on midmarket and lower midmarket transactions within the private equity and entrepreneurial arenas. Its clients include private companies and financial institutions, and it has significant experience of representing businesses from the agricultural sector.

**KEY INDIVIDUALS James Melville** is a highly regarded M&A practitioner. He has extensive experience of advising private investors on domestic and international transactions. Senior statesman **Ralph Strangis** is a highly esteemed deal lawyer and corporate adviser.

### Leonard, Street and Deinard Professional Association

**THE FIRM** This group is well equipped to represent clients in a variety of corporate matters, including M&A, securities, private equity and project finance. It has significant experience in the healthcare and energy sectors, and recently acted as US counsel to Atlantic Power on its acquisition of Capital Power Income for over $1.8 billion. Other clients include Two Harbors Investment, Midcontinent Media and Canadian Pacific Railway.

**Sources say:** *"Their lawyers are very practical and have a good common-sense approach."*

**KEY INDIVIDUALS** Clients say **Stephen Quinlivan** is *"extremely intelligent,"* with *"a high level of business acumen."* He focuses on M&A and securities transactions, and recently advised Two Harbors Investment on a number of public common stock offerings. **Thomas Sanders** is known for handling M&A and private equity matters, and has notable experience in the medical device sector. *"He brings a lot of strategic positives and is a very good negotiator,"* say clients. **Jill Radloff** chairs the firm's corporate and securities team, and was also a lead partner in the Two Harbors Investment stock offering. Clients admire her ability *"to understand and communicate risks."* **Mark Weitz** is another key player at the firm. He handles a range of transactional matters, and has notable experience of financing in the medical device sector. Senior statesman **Morris Sherman** is a distinguished and admired Minnesota attorney. He has extensive experience of advising public and private companies on a broad range of corporate transactions.

### Lindquist & Vennum LLP
See profile on p.1587

**THE FIRM** This corporate group has a strong reputation in the Minnesota market. It is well versed in a range of corporate issues, and is particularly active in the areas of M&A and private equity transactions. The group also has notable experience of public debt, securities and corporate governance matters. Key clients include Cushman & Wakefield, Upsher-Smith Laboratories and Norwest Equity Partners.

**Sources say:** *"They are practical, proactive and smart, and have a good sense of my business and its needs."*

**KEY INDIVIDUALS** Well-regarded practitioner **Frank Bennett** continues to be recognized for handling M&A transactions within the private equity arena. *"Outstanding lawyer"* **Charles Moorse** impresses clients with his general corporate counseling. Sources report that he has *"excellent vision, perspective and insight,"* and *"is very practical through every issue."* He regularly advises on M&A matters. **Robert Tunheim** is another key player at the firm. He is noted for his private equity expertise and handles a wide range of M&A and finance-related issues. **Kevin Costley** cochairs the firm's financial institutions team and is well known for handling M&A and regulatory matters within the banking sector.

### Oppenheimer Wolff & Donnelly LLP

**THE FIRM** This much-praised firm has extensive experience of representing public and private companies in M&A and securities transactions. It is particularly prominent in the medical technology arena, and recently represented Hemosphere in its sale to CryoLife. It also has a number of significant manufacturing clients, including Toro and Honeywell International.

**Sources say:** *"They understand our strategic imperatives and objectives."*

**KEY INDIVIDUALS Bruce Machmeier** is a *"top-notch securities lawyer"* who is admired by clients for his *"depth of knowledge and expertise."* Sources report that *"he's also practical and understands the business realities."* Clients are impressed by **Tom Letscher**'s attentiveness and service-ori-

ented approach. He specializes in transactions within the medical technology sector, and was lead counsel to Hemosphere on the transaction described above. **William Kaufman** is also noted for his medical technology expertise, and recently acted as US M&A counsel to superDimension on its sale to Covidien. The *"terrific"* **Tim Scallen** focuses on providing M&A and strategic corporate advice to businesses within the manufacturing and software technology sectors. Clients admire his hands-on approach to transactions. **Amy Culbert** concentrates on securities matters. Clients report that she is *"knowledgeable,"* *"very thorough in reviewing documents and making suggestions,"* and *"easy to work with."*

## Band 3

### Gray Plant Mooty
See profile on p.1585

**THE FIRM** Gray Plant Mooty's M&A group is best known for its franchising expertise, and recently acted for franchisor Smoothie King on its sale to a Korean-based franchisee. It also has notable experience of advising on a range of corporate matters, including M&A, stock and asset and private equity transactions. Its diverse client roster features auto-repair franchisor ABRA, International Dairy Queen and Granite Equity Partners.

**Sources say:** *"A professional firm with a service first approach. We have always been pleased and highly satisfied."*

**KEY INDIVIDUALS John Brower** is known for his knowledge of franchise M&A and was lead counsel to Smoothie King on the transaction described above.

### Maslon Edelman Borman & Brand, LLP

**THE FIRM** This group provides general corporate counsel to clients from a variety of industry sectors, encompassing manufacturing, retail, agriculture, financial services, hospitality and gaming. The team recently represented Jacobs Trading in the $170 million sale of assets to Liquidity Services. Other clients include Miller Milling, Redstone Grill and Raven Industries.

**KEY INDIVIDUALS** The well-respected **Martin Rosenbaum** is noted for his securities expertise. He recently advised Valspar on a $400 million public offering in senior notes. **Alan Gilbert** is a notable transactional lawyer, with significant securities experience. He recently acted alongside Rosenbaum to advise GWG Holdings on a public offering.

### Other Notable Practitioners

**Timothy Barnett** (see p.1578) of Winthrop & Weinstine, PA is particularly active in the area of franchising, and recently advised franchisee No Limits on the sale of its restaurant operations in Missouri and Illinois. Sources admire his *"strong business knowledge"* and *"interpersonal communication skills."*

# LABOR & EMPLOYMENT

Commentary about individuals can be found under their firm's paragraph. If the firm has no paragraph (is not ranked) look at Other Notable Practitioners.

| Labor & Employment |
|---|
| **Leading Firms** |
| **Band 1** |
| Briggs and Morgan * |
| Dorsey & Whitney LLP * |
| Felhaber, Larson, Fenlon & Vogt, PC |
| **Band 2** |
| Faegre Baker Daniels |
| Fredrikson & Byron PA * |
| **Band 3** |
| Gray Plant Mooty * |
| Leonard, Street and Deinard Professional Association |
| Littler Mendelson, PC * |
| Maslon Edelman Borman & Brand, LLP |
| Ogletree, Deakins, Nash, Smoak & Stewart, PC * |

* *Indicates firm with profile.*
*Alphabetical order within each band. Band 1 is the highest.*

## Band 1

### Briggs and Morgan
See profile on p.1581

**THE FIRM** Briggs and Morgan has an excellent reputation across a broad spectrum of labor and employment matters. Its talented lawyers handle a variety of counseling and litigation, and have notable experience in the fields of harassment, discrimination, noncompete and whistleblowing issues, in addition to labor negotiations and NLRB representation. The team is also called on to advise on executive compensation and employee benefits. Its client roster includes the Minnesota Twins, Albany International and Caribou Coffee.

**Sources say:** *"I love the fact that they are very proactive. They stay on top of things and keep me informed of changes in the law."*

**KEY INDIVIDUALS Ann Huntrods** (see p.1579) is a highly regarded employment counselor and litigator. She advises employers on a wide variety of issues, including internal investigations, discrimination and whistle-blowing. Chair of the firm's employment law counseling group,

**Michael Miller** (see p.1579) is described as *"very smart and extremely thorough."* Clients report that *"he gives excellent advice and is good at assessing situations from all angles."* His experience ranges from the negotiation of executive employment contracts to advising on discrimination claims. **Gregory Stenmoe** (see p.1580) focuses his practice on employment litigation. Sources name him *"the prefect counselor"* and report that he *"inspires confidence in what he's saying."* **Ira Friedrich** (see p.1579) impresses clients with his regulatory knowledge and proactive approach. He is leader of the firm's employee benefits and executive compensation team, and recently oversaw the reorganization of an equity incentive plan on behalf of a public company. Senior statesman **Scott Davies** (see p.1578) is an experienced employment litigator. He is also called upon to mediate employment disputes.

### Dorsey & Whitney LLP
See profile on p.1583

**THE FIRM** This group is considered one of Minnesota's leading labor and employment practices. It is noted for its extensive class action experience, which encompasses numerous wage and hour and discrimination claims. The team is also active in the areas of trade secret litigation, collective bargaining, workforce reduction and transactional issues. Recent highlights include defending 3M against a nationwide age discrimination class action. In the past year, it has also provided labor and employment counsel to Allianz Life Insurance, Canon and Ameriprise.

**Sources say:** *"On a scale of one to ten, I'd give the Dorsey firm an 11."*

**KEY INDIVIDUALS** *"Outstanding"* practitioner **Douglas Christensen** is singled out for his *"command"* of the law. Clients describe him as *"extremely knowledgeable and extremely well prepared."* In addition to wage and hour class actions, his practice is increasingly focused on traditional labor matters. *"Excellent lawyer"* **Melissa Raphan** is a well-regarded employment litigator. Her experience includes discrimination, Equal Pay Act and harassment matters. **Joseph Hammell** is another much-praised attorney, with one interviewee commenting: *"I can't say enough good things about him."* Hammell is regularly called upon to represent clients in class action-related litigation. Sources identify **Roy Ginsburg** as a *"good choice for a thorny issue involving senior executives or any high-profile litigation matter."* He recently defended Edwards Lifesciences against a number of trade secret, contractual and tortious interference claims.

## Felhaber, Larson, Fenlon & Vogt, PC

**THE FIRM** This firm's labor and employment group has an outstanding reputation in Minnesota. The practice places a heavy emphasis on traditional labor law, and has impressive experience of labor relations, arbitrations and NLRB representations. It handles a variety of employment litigation, and recently defended Fairview Health Services against an age discrimination claim. Its client roster includes a number of other healthcare providers, in addition to the Archdiocese of St Paul and Minneapolis, the Greater Metropolitan Automobile Dealers Association of Minnesota and Kwik Trip.

**Sources say:** *"They take the time not only to inform us of the law, but also to understand how it will impact our organization on a cultural level."*

**KEY INDIVIDUALS** Leading individual **James Dawson** has an excellent reputation for handling labor relations, with a particular focus on the healthcare sector. Sources attest that *"his historical knowledge and strategic skills are unmatched in this market."* **Sara McGrane** impresses clients with her *"consistently high-quality work."* Her practice is concentrated on employment litigation, and she is particularly recommended for her healthcare expertise. **Penelope Phillips** assists employers with a wide variety of employment issues, including contentious matters. Clients describe her as *"exceptionally talented and knowledgeable,"* and report that she *"relates well to directors and managers."* *"Excellent"* attorney **Paul Zech** is singled out for his labor relations and employment litigation expertise. One interviewee reports: *"He does a great job of directing and guiding me on some very difficult situations."* **Thomas Trachsel** has a strong reputation in the Minnesota market. He focuses on labor relations and NLRB matters.

## Band 2

### Faegre Baker Daniels

**THE FIRM** Faegre Baker Daniels has a broad employment practice, with specialist litigation, immigration and compliance teams. It has a notable track record of handling complex contentious matters, including wage and hour class actions, in addition to ERISA, discrimination and noncompete litigation. The group is also well versed in employment matters arising from corporate transactions, and advises 3M on its acquisition and integration strategy. Other recent clients include Allina Health System, Augsburg Fortress and Boston Scientific.

**KEY INDIVIDUALS** Highly regarded attorney **Kathlyn Noecker** handles a broad range of employment law counseling. Sources characterize her as a thorough and responsive practitioner. **Charles Knapp** focuses on employment litigation and has significant experience of class action and discrimination claims. Clients value his diligence and strategic thinking.

## Fredrikson & Byron PA
See profile on p.1584

**THE FIRM** This group has a diverse labor and employment practice, with notable expertise in the fields of FMLA and ADA compliance. It is also well equipped to handle wage and hour class actions and trade secret litigation, and recently defended Northland Systems against a noncompete claim. The group acts for a considerable number of clients from the healthcare and financial services sectors, including Children's Hospitals and Clinics of Minnesota, North Memorial Health Care and Lockton Companies.

**Sources say:** *"They take time to understand the business aspect of an issue."*

**KEY INDIVIDUALS** *"Terrific"* attorney **Robert Boisvert** focuses on discrimination defense litigation and general employment counseling. Clients describe him as *"extremely grounded and practical,"* and highlight his healthcare expertise. **Richard Ross** is another key player in the practice. He has extensive experience of numerous labor and employment matters, and recently acted for Select POS & Peripherals on a Minnesota Human Rights Act discrimination suit. Highly regarded adviser and litigator **Anne Radolinski** is well versed in a broad range of employment law issues. **Karen Schanfield** represents businesses in both labor and employment matters, and has a particular focus on the healthcare sector. Clients praise her ability to *"understand the business aspects of the decision making that must take place."*

## Band 3

### Gray Plant Mooty
See profile on p.1585

**THE FIRM** This group has a varied labor and employment practice covering NLRB and union organization matters, in addition to discrimination and whistle-blower litigation. It also has experience handling internal audits and advising on issues arising from corporate restructurings. It has notable clients in the educational and manufacturing sectors, including St Olaf College, HNI Corporation and National American University.

**Sources say:** *"Excellent work, terrific client services, and very timely, practical and accurate information."*

**KEY INDIVIDUALS** *"Top-notch"* practitioner **Judith Bevis Langevin** is an experienced employment litigator.

She also handles general employment counseling and training.

### Leonard, Street and Deinard Professional Association

THE FIRM This firm provides clients with labor and employment advice on a wide range of issues. It has considerable experience of FMLA, ADA and noncompete matters, in addition to labor negotiations, FLSA class actions and collective bargaining. The group also handles employee benefits negotiations and litigation. It has recently acted for Basin Electric Power Cooperative, Bobcat and Domino's Pizza.

Sources say: *"They have lots of experience and a practical approach, and are helpful with risk analysis on matters that do not have a clear path."*

KEY INDIVIDUALS Distinguished practitioner **Ellen Sampson** continues to have a good reputation in the market. She has extensive employment law experience and is regularly engaged to act as a mediator. *"Skilled negotiator"* **Joel Abrahamson** handles employment litigation and traditional labor matters. Clients report that he *"gets to the heart of the matter quickly,"* and *"leaves no stone unturned."* *"Well-respected"* attorney **Dominic Cecere** is singled out for his labor expertise. Clients admire his approach to dealing with union-related matters and describe him as *"practical,"* *"approachable"* and *"responsive."* **Robert Zeglovitch** recently rejoined the firm. He has particular experience in the fields of internal investigations and employment litigation.

### Littler Mendelson, PC
See profile on p.688

THE FIRM The Minneapolis office of this national boutique acts for clients across a broad spectrum of labor and employment matters, including labor negotiations, collective bargaining, employment terminations, wage and hour, and other class actions. Recent work highlights include representing Nationwide Mutual in a class action suit concerning FLSA overtime requirements. Other clients include Riverland Ag, Minnesota Vikings and Del Monte.

Sources say: *"Littler has done a superb job on every matter it has handled for us."*

KEY INDIVIDUALS **Marko Mrkonich** (see p.1579) has a strong reputation in the market. He is recognized for his employment litigation talent, in addition to his experience of traditional labor matters. **Kate Wilson** (see p.1580) is a *"well-established and well-respected"* employment litigator and counselor. She is noted for her ADA, FMLA and discrimination expertise. **John Polley** (see p.1580) is singled out as a health and safety specialist. He recently defended Riverland Ag against approximately $3 million OSHA citations. Sources note that he is a *"very good, very solid lawyer."* **Mark Schneider** (see p.1580) is a highly esteemed labor practitioner. One impressed client reports that *"his knowledge of the local union representatives and negotiation skills are the best I've ever seen."*

### Maslon Edelman Borman & Brand, LLP

THE FIRM This Minneapolis firm advises clients on a variety of labor and employment matters, with a focus on noncompete issues. It also handles traditional labor law and general employment counseling, and has significant experience of discrimination defense, OSHA, employee benefits and ERISA litigation. Recent clients include Clockwork Active Media Systems, Hennepin Home Health Care and SafetyCall International.

Sources say: *"They are sophisticated, understand our business really well and are responsive."*

KEY INDIVIDUALS Well-regarded practitioner **Howard Tarkow** has a broad labor and employment practice. His expertise includes discrimination defense litigation and NLRB matters. Leader of the firm's labor and employment group **Jessica Pecoraro** concentrates her practice on employment counseling and has a particular focus on wage and hour, ADA and FMLA issues.

### Ogletree, Deakins, Nash, Smoak & Stewart, PC
See profile on p.1110

THE FIRM The Minneapolis office of this national labor and employment firm has a diverse practice, with experience in discrimination defense, noncompete, contractual, FMLA and OSHA matters, as well as traditional labor law. Recent work highlights include representing U.S. Steel in a case brought under the Worker Adjustment Retraining and Notification Act. In the past year, the team has also acted for Wells Fargo, Sterling Jewelers and Life Time Fitness.

Sources say: *"Quick response time, very knowledgeable, a lot of depth in the bench and really great follow through."*

KEY INDIVIDUALS *"Highly regarded"* attorney **Patrick Martin** (see p.1579) is regularly called upon to handle employment litigation. He recently prevailed on behalf of Sara Lee in a complex contractual dispute involving a $1.5 million pension claim. Employment litigator **Cynthia Bremer** (see p.1578) has a strong reputation in the market. Clients describe her as *"thoughtful, creative and innovative,"* and particularly value her responsiveness.

### Other Notable Practitioners

*"Excellent"* practitioner **Barbara D'Aquila** (see p.1578) of Fulbright & Jaworski LLP is recommended for her litigation and mediation expertise. **Doug Seaton** of Seaton, Peters & Revnew, P.A. is a well-respected traditional labor lawyer, with extensive experience of labor relations, compliance counseling and contentious matters. Duluth-based **Joseph Roby** of Johnson Killen & Seiler is a highly regarded attorney, who focuses his practice on employment litigation and traditional labor work. Employment litigator and counselor **Tina Syring-Petrocchi** (see p.1580) of Barnes & Thornburg LLP receives glowing praise for her knowledge, commercial acumen and service-oriented approach. One client reports: *"Her extensive business experience has helped guide our company on many of our business-related decisions."*

# LITIGATION

Commentary about individuals can be found under their firm's paragraph. If the firm has no paragraph (is not ranked) look at Other Notable Practitioners.

## Litigation: General Commercial
### Leading Firms

**Band 1**
Dorsey & Whitney LLP *
Faegre Baker Daniels
Robins, Kaplan, Miller & Ciresi LLP *

**Band 2**
Briggs and Morgan *
Maslon Edelman Borman & Brand, LLP
Winthrop & Weinstine, PA *

**Band 3**
Anthony Ostlund Baer & Louwagie P.A.
Bassford Remele, A Professional Association
Fredrikson & Byron PA *
Gray Plant Mooty *
Greene Espel PLLP
Leonard, Street and Deinard Professional Association
Lindquist & Vennum LLP *
Meagher & Geer, P.L.L.P.

## Band 1

### Dorsey & Whitney LLP
**See profile on p.1583**

**THE FIRM** This talented group continues to be considered one of Minnesota's premier litigation practices. It provides market-leading expertise across a broad spectrum of commercial disputes, with a particular focus in the areas of construction, banking, healthcare, energy and agriculture. The team recently prevailed at the Supreme Court on behalf of the National Meat Association in a challenge to provisions of the California Penal Code 599f. Its client roster also includes US Bank, UnitedHealth Group and international engineering company Kvaerner.

**Sources say:** *"I have been pleased with their knowledge, expertise and good customer service – all-around high-quality legal work."*

**KEY INDIVIDUALS Peter Carter** is a *"terrific commercial litigator"* who is *"very reasonable"* and *"very effective,"* according to sources. He is cochair of the firm's securities litigation and enforcement practice. **Steve Wells** leads the firm's global trial team and is recognized as an impressive advocate with particular expertise in professional malpractice and franchise litigation. He led the team in the aforementioned Supreme Court case for the National Meat Association. **Paul Klaas** also has a strong reputation in the market. Recent work highlights include securing a favorable settlement for major potash supplier Mosaic in a complex contractual dispute. The *"much-admired"* **Roger Magnuson** continues to lead the firm's national strategic litigation group. He has an impressive track record for handling high-profile and challenging cases in a broad range of areas, including class actions, securities litigation and white-collar criminal litigation. **George Eck** is a *"great*

## Litigation: General Commercial
### Senior Statesmen

Senior Statesmen: distinguished older practitioners

| | |
|---|---|
| Fruth Terence | *Fruth, Jamison & Elsass (ONP)†* |
| Magnuson Roger | *Dorsey & Whitney LLP* |

### Leading Individuals

**Band 1**

| | |
|---|---|
| Anthony Joseph | *Anthony Ostlund Baer & Louwagie P.A.* |
| Carter Peter W | *Dorsey & Whitney LLP* |
| Ciresi Michael V | *Robins, Kaplan, Miller & Ciresi LLP* * |
| Fraser Thomas S | *Fredrikson & Byron PA* |
| Kelly Timothy | *Kelly P.A. (ONP)†* |
| Luger Andrew | *Greene Espel PLLP* |
| Pentelovitch William | *Maslon Edelman Borman & Brand, LLP* |
| Remele Jr Lewis A | *Bassford Remele* |
| Webber Charles F | *Faegre Baker Daniels* |
| Weinstine Robert R | *Winthrop & Weinstine, PA* * |

**Band 2**

| | |
|---|---|
| Fleming Terrence J | *Lindquist & Vennum LLP* |
| Greene Clifford M | *Greene Espel PLLP* |
| Jarpe Geoffrey P | *Maslon Edelman Borman & Brand, LLP* |
| Noteboom Todd | *Leonard, Street and Deinard* |
| Ostlund Richard | *Anthony Ostlund Baer & Louwagie P.A.* |
| Thornton Timothy | *Briggs and Morgan* * |
| Volling James L | *Faegre Baker Daniels* |
| Wells Steve | *Dorsey & Whitney LLP* |

**Band 3**

| | |
|---|---|
| Daley Annamarie | *Barnes & Thornburg LLP (ONP)† *  |
| Eck George G | *Dorsey & Whitney LLP* |
| Ihrig Richard | *Lindquist & Vennum LLP* |
| Kahnke Randall E | *Faegre Baker Daniels* |
| Karpenko Gregory | *Fredrikson & Byron PA* |
| Klaas Paul B | *Dorsey & Whitney LLP* |
| Louwagie Vincent | *Anthony Ostlund Baer & Louwagie P.A.* |
| Moos Rebecca E | *Bassford Remele* |
| Rogers Charles | *Briggs and Morgan* * |
| Schnell, Jr Robert L | *Faegre Baker Daniels* |
| Schultz David | *Maslon Edelman Borman & Brand, LLP* |
| Simonson James S | *Gray Plant Mooty* |
| Wildung Wendy J | *Faegre Baker Daniels* |
| Wind Todd A | *Fredrikson & Byron PA* |

*lawyer"* who concentrates his practice on complex commercial litigation and tort litigation. Areas of expertise include insurance coverage, product liability and environmental cases.

### Faegre Baker Daniels

**THE FIRM** This leading litigation group has demonstrated its excellence in a wide range of contentious matters. It is particularly active in the financial services, securities, energy and trade secret arenas, and has considerable experience in white-collar, antitrust and franchising litigation. The firm is also known for its IP expertise and recently

## Litigation: Appellate
### Senior Statesmen

Senior Statesmen: distinguished older practitioners

| | |
|---|---|
| Hanson Samuel | *Briggs and Morgan* * |

### Leading Individuals

**Band 1**

| | |
|---|---|
| Boyd Thomas H | *Winthrop & Weinstine, PA* * |
| Hart William | *Meagher & Geer, P.L.L.P.* |
| Herr David | *Maslon Edelman Borman & Brand, LLP* |
| Magnuson Eric | *Briggs and Morgan* * |
| Webber Charles F | *Faegre Baker Daniels* |

**Band 2**

| | |
|---|---|
| Lillehaug David | *Fredrikson & Byron* |
| Spevacek Charles | *Meagher & Geer, P.L.L.P.* |
| Van Oort Aaron D | *Faegre Baker Daniels* |

**Up-and-coming individuals**

| | |
|---|---|
| Lorentz Brent A. | *Winthrop & Weinstine, PA* * |

## Litigation: Intellectual Property
### Leading Individuals

**Band 1**

| | |
|---|---|
| Allgeyer David A | *Lindquist & Vennum LLP* |
| Boyd Felicia | *Barnes & Thornburg LLP (ONP)† *  |
| Carlson Alan G | *Carlson, Caspers, Vandenburgh (ONP)†* |
| Ciresi Michael V | *Robins, Kaplan, Miller & Ciresi LLP* * |
| Florey Michael | *Fish & Richardson PC (ONP)†* |
| Gross David JF | *Faegre Baker Daniels* |
| Kahnke Randall E | *Faegre Baker Daniels* |
| Liebman Kenneth A | *Faegre Baker Daniels* |
| Lueck Martin | *Robins, Kaplan, Miller & Ciresi LLP* * |
| McDonald Daniel | *Merchant & Gould PC (ONP)†* |
| Schutz Ronald J | *Robins, Kaplan, Miller & Ciresi LLP* * |
| Singer Jonathan E | *Fish & Richardson PC (ONP)†* |

* Indicates firm / individual with profile.
† ONP = Other Notable Practitioner.

won a significant defense victory for Seagate Technology in its long-standing patent infringement dispute with Siemens. Other key clients include Novartis Pharmaceuticals, Cargill and 3M.

**KEY INDIVIDUALS David Gross** is a noted expert in IP litigation, and recently won a jury verdict in a patent infringement case on behalf of Coloplast. **Randall Kahnke** is a highly recommended trade secret specialist, and also handles general commercial and IP litigation. His clients have included Allianz, Honeywell and Wells Fargo. **Kenneth Liebman** is also a leading IP litigator. He focuses his practice on IT and medical technology patents. **Charles Webber** is well regarded by observers for his broad litigation expertise. He has tried a diverse range of contract, tort and fiduciary matters. **James Volling** is singled out for his antitrust, securities and white collar criminal litigation expertise. He heads the firm's business litigation group.

**Wendy Wildung** represents corporations, directors and officers in litigation stemming from IPOs or allegations of fraud or false reporting. **Robert Schnell** has distinguished himself in the field of financial markets and securities litigation. His clients include investment banks, broker-dealers and financial institutions. **Aaron Van Oort** is a skilled appellate attorney. His clients have included Seagate and the National Football League.

### Robins, Kaplan, Miller & Ciresi LLP
See profile on p.1588

**THE FIRM** This firm is widely considered to field one of Minnesota's premier IP litigation practices, and recently represented Personal Audio in a patent infringement dispute with Apple, securing $8 million in damages. The group is also recommended for its adroit handling of internal investigations and compliance matters, and has significant experience of antitrust, fiduciary, product liability and class action litigation.

**Sources say:** *"It is a top-notch firm. It is very responsive to our needs and delivers results."*

**KEY INDIVIDUALS** *"Great advocate"* **Michael Ciresi** (see p.1578) continues to be held in high regard as a complex commercial, product liability and IP litigator. Clients value the way he *"focuses on the really critical issues,"* and highlight his *"great presence in a courtroom or meeting."* **Martin Lueck** (see p.1579) is another well-regarded IP litigator. Clients praise his *"intellect,"* *"communication"* and focus on *"understanding client needs and client culture, and adapting to it."* *"Tremendous trial lawyer"* **Ronald Schutz** (see p.1580) focuses his practice on patent litigation. Clients report that he *"manages a case incredibly well."* He led the team in the aforementioned matter for Personal Audio.

## Band 2

### Briggs and Morgan
See profile on p.1581

**THE FIRM** This well-respected Minnesota firm has offices in Minneapolis and St Paul. Its diverse litigation practice encompasses banking, securities, IP, telecommunications, environmental and product liability work. The group is also noted for the strength of its appellate practice. Recent work highlights include achieving victory through summary judgment for BMO Harris Bank in a complex contractual dispute. Other notable clients include NFL Players Association, Xcel Energy and Canadian Pacific Railway.

**Sources say:** *"A great law firm."*

**KEY INDIVIDUALS Eric Magnuson** (see p.1579) has an excellent reputation for appellate work. He handles appeals pertaining to a wide spectrum of legal areas, including business contracts, insurance law and corporate fraud. **Timothy Thornton** (see p.1580) is known for handling labor disputes and mass tort actions. He recently acted for BNSF on defending claims for nuisance and negligence damages. Well-regarded practitioner **Charles Rogers** (see p.1580) focuses his practice on commercial, banking and environmental litigation. He led the team in the matter for BMO Harris Bank. Experienced appellate advocate

**Samuel Hanson** (see p.1579) remains an influential presence. He is particularly active in the field of utilities regulation.

### Maslon Edelman Borman & Brand, LLP

**THE FIRM** This much-praised Minneapolis litigation group is well equipped to represent clients in a variety of contentious matters. It has considerable experience of handling environmental and product liability litigation, and recently defended 3M in a high-value environmental action brought by the state of Minnesota. Other key clients include American Medical Systems, Taylor Corporation and Altria.

**Sources say:** *"I have been extremely impressed with the litigation group as a whole. They are quick to assess a case and are extremely realistic about the likelihood of success. When they engage in litigation, they are outcome-focused."*

**KEY INDIVIDUALS** Clients are impressed by **David Herr**'s appellate expertise and describe his advice as *"consistently spot-on."* He recently represented Philip Morris following a class action seeking damages from the sale of 'light' cigarettes. *"Exceptionally gifted litigator"* **William Pentelovitch** is characterized by clients as *"extremely practical."* He concentrates his practice on noncompete, trade secret, IP and corporate governance disputes. **Geoffrey Jarpe** is another prominent member of the practice. He has a broad base of experience and has particularly distinguished himself in the field of securities litigation. New entry to the rankings **David Schultz** is recommended for his product liability prowess. Clients value his *"in-depth knowledge"* of their product lines, his *"terrific negotiation skills"* and his *"deft touch at managing the litigation"* to meet their goals. He is also active in the fields of fraud, healthcare and IP litigation.

### Winthrop & Weinstine, PA
See profile on p.1589

**THE FIRM** This well-regarded firm advises clients on a broad range of commercial disputes. It has a strong IP offering and has recently handled a number of trademark infringement cases. The group also has significant experience of legal malpractice defense and product liability litigation. Notable clients include Alliant Techsystems, FutureCeuticals and wine importer CIV.

**Sources say:** *"The firm has a consistently exceptional performance record."*

**KEY INDIVIDUALS** The *"well-respected"* **Thomas Boyd** (see p.1578) is viewed by sources as *"one of the state's best appellate lawyers."* His areas of excellence include contract law, tort law and insurance coverage disputes. *"Creative and strategic thinker"* **Robert Weinstine** (see p.1580) receives particular praise from clients for his *"tactical capability."* His practice encompasses professional negligence, product liability and IP matters, in addition to general commercial litigation. Sources describe rising star **Brent Lorentz** (see p.1579) as *"highly analytical and careful, a good writer and very client service-oriented."* He handles IP, employment and complex commercial litigation.

## Band 3

### Anthony Ostlund Baer & Louwagie P.A.

**THE FIRM** This Minneapolis litigation boutique has a strong reputation in the state. It focuses exclusively on business litigation, with a heavy emphasis on securities, shareholder and commercial disputes. The group is also equipped to represent clients in professional negligence, employment, real estate and IP cases.

**Sources say:** *"An excellent litigation firm."*

**KEY INDIVIDUALS** Highly regarded practitioner **Joseph Anthony** has a diverse practice encompassing securities, fraud, antitrust, real estate and employment litigation. **Richard Ostlund** is another key player at the firm. His practice is concentrated on corporate and shareholder disputes, IP litigation and employment matters. **Vincent Louwagie** is a new entry to the rankings and is described by sources as a *"very good lawyer."* He has a broad commercial litigation practice, with a focus on disputes arising from financial transactions.

### Bassford Remele, A Professional Association

**THE FIRM** This well-respected litigation boutique is based in Minneapolis and is particularly recommended for its insurance defense expertise. The group also handles a range of general commercial litigation, including contract, ERISA, employment and IP matters. It is notably active in the field of unfair competition and recently represented Seagate Technology in a $630 million trade secret arbitration. St Jude Medical, Allina Health System and Minnesota Lawyers Mutual are also counted among its clients.

**KEY INDIVIDUALS** Medical malpractice expert **Rebecca Moos** is admired by clients for her adept approach to *"navigating and dealing with challenging opponents,"* as well as her advocacy skills and responsiveness. Clients describe *"premier litigator"* **Lewis Remele** as a *"phenomenal trial lawyer and incredibly savvy mediator."* He has extensive experience of complex commercial and tort litigation.

### Fredrikson & Byron PA
See profile on p.1584

**THE FIRM** This practice has diverse litigation experience encompassing healthcare issues, corporate tax disputes and condemnation cases, in addition to a range of general commercial and tort matters. The firm is also known for its IP capabilities, and recently acted for Medtronic in a patent license dispute. Other notable clients include Mayo Foundation, Hormel and Xcel Energy.

**Sources say:** *"The entire Fredrikson firm has an excellent reputation in the Twin Cities legal community. I have a very favorable impression of them."*

**KEY INDIVIDUALS** Talented attorney **Thomas Fraser** is well versed in a variety of complex commercial litigation, including shareholder and partnership disputes. He is also an admired arbitrator. **Gregory Karpenko** is recommended for his medical malpractice expertise. Clients report that *"he has demonstrated impressive instincts, judgment and courtroom skills."* **Todd Wind** is cochair of the firm's litigation team. He has a broad practice encompassing antitrust, business tort and product liability matters. **David Lillehaug** focuses on white-collar defense and the representation of governmental entities in complex disputes. Sources characterize him as *"a smart, careful, thorough lawyer,"* and he has a strong reputation in the Twin Cities.

## Gray Plant Mooty
### See profile on p.1585

**THE FIRM** Gray Plant Mooty's dispute resolution team is best known for its internationally renowned franchise and distribution expertise. Additional areas of focus include business, antitrust, trust and estate, IP, product liability and white-collar crime litigation.

**KEY INDIVIDUALS** Well-respected practitioner **James Simonson** concentrates his practice on product liability, antitrust and securities disputes.

## Greene Espel PLLP

**THE FIRM** This Minneapolis litigation boutique is singled out for the quality of its trial lawyers. The group handles a wide variety of commercial litigation, ranging from breach of contract to business torts, accounting negligence and white-collar defense. It also has significant medical malpractice expertise, and has acted as coordinating counsel for Nevada Mutual on defending a series of individual and class action suits exceeding $1 billion in total claims. Other key clients include Graco, League of Minnesota Cities and Deloitte & Touche.

**Sources say:** *"It is an extremely high-quality litigation boutique. The lawyers have excellent credentials and experience, and are very responsive."*

**KEY INDIVIDUALS** *"Great lawyer"* **Andrew Luger** is held in high esteem in the Minnesota market. His practice is concentrated on white-collar criminal defense and business litigation. Clients admire **Clifford Greene**'s *"ability to organize approaches to complex and politically sensitive matters"* and highlight his *"excellent judgment"* and advocacy skills. His practice includes product liability, constitutional and general commercial litigation.

## Leonard, Street and Deinard Professional Association

**THE FIRM** This well-regarded firm is equipped to advise clients on a broad range of contentious matters, including banking, bankruptcy, labor and employment litigation. The group also handles class actions, and recently defended Walgreens against a putative suit alleging the taking of illegal profits on the sale of prescription drugs. Other clients include JPMorgan Chase, State Farm Mutual Automobile Insurance and Canadian Pacific Railway.

**Sources say:** *"One of their primary strengths is their ability to research the case law and facts and come up with reasons why or why not to pursue a particular tack."*

**KEY INDIVIDUALS** *"Fantastic"* attorney **Todd Noteboom** is known for handling securities and financial services-related litigation.

## Lindquist & Vennum LLP
### See profile on p.1587

**THE FIRM** This group has wide-ranging commercial litigation experience, with a focus on financial institution, workout, fraud and collection litigation. It is also well versed in product liability, IP, noncompete and construction matters. The firm is based in Minneapolis.

**Sources say:** *"An outstanding group of lawyers."*

**KEY INDIVIDUALS** Highly regarded attorney **Terrence Fleming** is cochair of the firm's litigation group. His practice focuses on securities issues, fraud litigation and corporate disputes. **Richard Ihrig** is another key player at the firm. His practice places a heavy emphasis on antitrust litigation. IP expert **David Allgeyer** handles a range of patent, trademark, copyright and trade secret litigation. He is also an active mediator.

## Meagher & Geer, P.L.L.P.

**THE FIRM** This litigation boutique is particularly noted for its strength in insurance defense and insurance coverage disputes, and is much admired for its appellate practice. Recent highlights include successfully defending Scottsdale Indemnity Company against insurance coverage claims of over $50 million. CNA, Federated Insurance and State Farm are also key clients.

**Sources say:** *"The appellate department of Meagher & Geer is a first-class operation."*

**KEY INDIVIDUALS** **William Hart** is widely regarded as an *"excellent appellate lawyer."* He heads the firm's appellate practice and recently represented the Good Samaritan Society in a case relating to the alleged abuse of nursing home residents. **Charles Spevacek** is an insurance coverage specialist. Clients are *"impressed with his ability to simplify the complex and to communicate persuasively orally and in writing,"* with one adding: *"He was integral to us coming up with a successful strategy."*

## Other Notable Practitioners

**Alan Carlson** of Carlson, Caspers, Vandenburgh, Lindquist & Schuman, P.A. is an IP expert. He handles patent, trademark and copyright litigation and is described as *"a strong lawyer."* **Michael Florey** of Fish & Richardson PC is also a leading IP litigator. His practice encompasses patent, trademark, copyright, trade secret and unfair competition litigation. **Jonathan Singer** is head of Fish & Richardson PC's life sciences department and a leading authority on the Hatch-Waxman Act. Clients describe him as *"astonishingly good."* **Daniel McDonald** of Merchant & Gould PC is another notable IP practitioner. He has a strong focus on computer technology and electronics. **Timothy Kelly** of Kelly P.A. continues to be one of Minnesota's leading business litigators. Areas of focus include contract law, business torts and corporate governance disputes. **Terence Fruth** of Fruth, Jamison & Elsass is a highly experienced business litigator. His practice encompasses shareholder disputes, in addition to securities, healthcare and employment issues. Clients characterize **Felicia Boyd** (see p.1578) of Barnes & Thornburg LLP as *"thorough, knowledgeable and strategic,"* and report that *"she is very smart and often has innovative ideas on how to resolve matters."* She focuses her practice on IP litigation. *"Outstanding attorney"* **Annamarie Daley** (see p.1578) of Barnes & Thornburg LLP splits her practice between complex commercial, antitrust and IP litigation.

# REAL ESTATE

Commentary about individuals can be found under their firm's paragraph. If the firm has no paragraph (is not ranked) look at Other Notable Practitioners.

## Real Estate
### Leading Firms

**Band 1**
Faegre Baker Daniels

**Band 2**
Dorsey & Whitney LLP *
Fredrikson & Byron PA *
Leonard, Street and Deinard Professional Association

**Band 3**
Briggs and Morgan *
Fabyanske, Westra, Hart & Thomson PA
Felhaber, Larson, Fenlon & Vogt, PC
Oppenheimer Wolff & Donnelly LLP
Winthrop & Weinstine, PA *

### Leading Individuals

**Star individuals**

| | |
|---|---|
| Ferrell Charles S | Faegre Baker Daniels |
| Hamel Mark | Dorsey & Whitney LLP |

**Band 1**

| | |
|---|---|
| Christy Angela M | Faegre Baker Daniels |
| Koneck John | Fredrikson & Byron PA |
| Westra Mark W | Fabyanske, Westra, Hart & Thomson PA |
| Wheaton John R | Faegre Baker Daniels |

**Band 2**

| | |
|---|---|
| Anderegg Scott A | Faegre Baker Daniels |
| Guthrie LB | Lindquist & Vennum LLP (ONP)[†] |
| Hoganson Jon J | Winthrop & Weinstine, PA * |

**Band 3**

| | |
|---|---|
| Armour Jonathan W. J. | Winthrop & Weinstine, PA * |
| Berrie Peter | Faegre Baker Daniels |
| Bray Thomas | Briggs and Morgan * |
| Finley Joseph M | Leonard, Street and Deinard |
| Haynor Charles | Briggs and Morgan * |
| Kelley David | Leonard, Street and Deinard |
| Kepple Lloyd | Oppenheimer Wolff & Donnelly LLP |
| Martin Kathleen | Malkerson Gunn Martin LLP (ONP)[†] |
| Massopust Richard | Oppenheimer Wolff & Donnelly LLP |
| Mayerle Thomas M | Thomas M Mayerle Law PLLC (ONP)[†] |
| Olson Robert J | Dorsey & Whitney LLP |
| Ranum Mary S | Fredrikson & Byron PA |
| Schwert James J | Oppenheimer Wolff & Donnelly LLP |
| Stoltman Thomas P. | Larkin Hoffman Daly & Lindgren (ONP)[†] |

**Up-and-coming individuals**

| | |
|---|---|
| Drewes Julie | Briggs and Morgan * |

\* Indicates firm / individual with profile.
[†]ONP = Other Notable Practitioner.

## Real Estate: Zoning/Land Use
### Leading Individuals

**Band 1**

| | |
|---|---|
| Herman John H | Faegre Baker Daniels |
| Lindgren Jay | Dorsey & Whitney LLP |
| Malkerson Bruce | Malkerson Gunn Martin LLP (ONP)[†] |
| Sellergren David | Fredrikson & Byron PA |

## Band 1

### Faegre Baker Daniels

**THE FIRM** Faegre Baker Daniels is singled out as Minnesota's leading real estate firm. It places a particular emphasis on corporate real estate and handles the acquisition, financing, development and leasing of properties, in addition to the negotiation and structuring of complex joint ventures. Recent work highlights include advising Life Time Fitness on the $109 million purchase of a number of health clubs in Florida and Minnesota. The team has also acted as real estate counsel to Aeon, Cargill and Target. **KEY INDIVIDUALS** Star individual **Charles Ferrell** is praised as one of Minnesota's leading real estate practitioners. He continues to act for corporate clients and developers, and recently represented Opus in a multimillion-dollar office development in Minneapolis. Highly regarded attorney **Angela Christy** is recognized for her expertise in low income housing matters. She recently advised Project for Pride in Living on the financing of a rental development with tax credits, municipal loans and funds granted by the Affordable Housing Program. **John Herman** is an eminent zoning and development specialist. He recently advised the Minnesota Orchestral Association on the $52 million improvement of its Minneapolis performance space. **John Wheaton** handles the full range of real estate matters for clients such as buyers, sellers, developers and lenders. **Scott Anderegg** is regularly called upon to represent the borrower in real estate loan originations. He was lead counsel to Life Time Fitness in the acquisitions described above. **Peter Berrie** has distinguished himself in the fields of tax credits and financing. Recent matters include representing Lyrical-Antheus Realty Partners II with respect to its renovation of Chicago's historic Shoreland Hotel using federal historic tax credits.

## Band 2

### Dorsey & Whitney LLP
See profile on p.1583

**THE FIRM** This highly regarded group is well equipped to assist clients with a variety of real estate matters. Its practice encompasses acquisition, development, leasing, and sale-and-leaseback transactions, and it has considerable experience advising on office developments. The firm is also recognized for its economic incentive expertise, and recently advised the City of Wayzata on the redevelopment of a retail mall, involving $22 million of tax incentive financing. It also has a number of significant clients in the healthcare sector, including Fairview Health Services. **Sources say:** *"Good attorneys and very business-oriented."* **KEY INDIVIDUALS** Star individual **Mark Hamel** is widely regarded as one of Minnesota's leading real estate experts. Clients observe that he is a *"good listener and proactive communicator."* *"Terrific"* attorney **Jay Lindgren** has a wealth of experience in real estate development and tax incentives. He was lead counsel to the City of Wayzata on the project described above, and also advised the City of Coralville on a $100 million brownfield redevelopment. **Robert Olson** is another well-respected attorney. He handles a broad range of real estate matters, with a particular focus on the healthcare sector.

### Fredrikson & Byron PA
See profile on p.1584

**THE FIRM** This much-praised firm represents a variety of retailers, developers, healthcare providers and corporate entities. The group is regularly engaged to counsel businesses on the acquisition, disposition, development and leasing of retail and office properties. Recent highlights include advising Aldi on its Minnesota, Wisconsin and Iowa properties. The team also provides nationwide real estate representation to Buffalo Wild Wings, and counts Liberty Property Trust and Twin Cities Orthopedics among its key clients. **Sources say:** *"Fredrikson & Byron is an excellent business-oriented law firm."* **KEY INDIVIDUALS** Experienced practitioner **David Sellergren** is a leading land use attorney. He also handles real estate development and financing. **Mary Ranum** handles a range of real estate transactions on behalf of retailers, developers and financial institutions. Clients report that she has *"excellent judgment,"* and add that she *"comes up with viable alternatives and provides sound legal advice."* She continues to act for Carlson Real Estate and Buffalo Wild Wings. The highly regarded **John Koneck** has extensive experience of real estate transactions and litigation. Clients admire his *"incredibly broad base of legal and business knowledge,"* and describe him as *"an excellent draftsman of documentation and a tough, effective litigator."*

### Leonard, Street and Deinard Professional Association

**THE FIRM** This esteemed practice acts for significant clients in the healthcare, energy, retail and hospitality sectors. It handles a wide variety of real estate matters, including acquisitions, financing and development, in addition to condemnation and brownfield redevelopment. Recent highlights include advising Atlantic Power on the real estate due diligence relating to its purchase of over $1 billion of power projects in the USA and Canada. In the past year, the team has also provided real estate counsel to Target, Buffalo Wild Wings and HealthPartners.

**Sources say:** *"They have very solid individuals in the real estate practice. It is good to know that if you need back up then the back up is also strong. I would and have recommended them."*

**KEY INDIVIDUALS** Well-respected practitioner **Joseph Finley** has extensive experience of a broad range of real estate matters, including acquisitions, financings and public developments. **David Kelley** is primarily known for advising lending institutions. His expertise encompasses letters of credit, asset-based lending, troubled loans, and affordable housing matters.

## Band 3

### Briggs and Morgan
See profile on p.1581

**THE FIRM** This Twin Cities firm has notable experience in commercial real estate and construction financing. It is also well versed in a range of development matters, including acquisition, disposition, land use and leasing, and has advised on retail, office, residential, student housing and mixed-use properties. The group has recently provided real estate counsel to Welsh Property Trust, PepsiCo and Founders Properties.

**Sources say:** *"A team of very talented attorneys."*

**KEY INDIVIDUALS Thomas Bray** (see p.1578) focuses his practice on real estate acquisition and development issues, including zoning. Clients say: *"He has a remarkable ability to understand and process a significant amount of disparate and complex information."* *"Strong negotiator"* **Charles Haynor** (see p.1579) is known for representing developers and institutional lenders in real estate acquisitions, dispositions and financings. Clients describe **Julie Drewes** (see p.1579) as *"very bright and very thorough."* She is known for representing developers and financial institutions in a wide range of real estate transactions, and has significant experience of advising on mixed-use, office and student housing projects.

### Fabyanske, Westra, Hart & Thomson PA

**THE FIRM** This Minneapolis firm brings a wealth of construction finance expertise to its real estate endeavors. It handles a broad range of matters, including acquisitions, financings, development and leasing, and is equipped to advise developers, owners, contractors and other real estate professionals. The group is particularly noted for its lending work, and acts for a significant number of financial institutions.

**KEY INDIVIDUALS Mark Westra** has an excellent reputation in Minnesota. He advises lenders and developers on commercial real estate and construction financing.

### Felhaber, Larson, Fenlon & Vogt, PC

**THE FIRM** This Twin Cities firm is particularly active in the acquisition and leasing of residential complexes and business premises, and is noted for its condominium expertise. It advises a variety of developers, construction firms, owners and other real estate professionals on matters including asset-based financings, development and dispositions. It also has significant experience in handling retail and mixed-use projects. Recent clients include Ron Clark Construction and Design, Highland Management Group and First & First.

**Sources say:** *"They really care about their clients."*

**KEY INDIVIDUALS** Catherine Sjoberg is a key contact.

### Oppenheimer Wolff & Donnelly LLP

**THE FIRM** This group has a significant focus on multi-family lending, and acts for a considerable number of institutional lenders. It is also experienced in handling acquisitions, dispositions, sale-and-leaseback transactions and joint ventures relating to residential, healthcare, office and manufacturing properties. The group recently advised Travelers on the $50 million purchase of an office building in Los Altos. Other key clients include Dougherty Funding, KeyCorp Real Estate Capital Markets and Oak Grove Commercial Mortgage.

**Sources say:** *"Their primary focus is doing a good job and completing the task in hand with the complete satisfaction of their client."*

**KEY INDIVIDUALS Lloyd Kepple** is an experienced real estate finance practitioner and was lead counsel to Travelers on the acquisition described above. Clients report that he *"facilitates negotiations by maintaining lines of communication and providing practical advice."* The well-regarded **Richard Massopust** is a notable lenders' lawyer. He is particularly active in the area of commercial mortgage lending. **James Schwert** focuses on multifamily lending and is described as *"conscientious, reliable and hardworking."* Clients observe that *"he is very good at getting to the point and helping us find solutions when we need them."*

### Winthrop & Weinstine, PA
See profile on p.1589

**THE FIRM** This group has significant experience of advising lenders and developers on residential and multi-use development projects. It is also equipped to provide counsel on a range of real estate matters, including acquisition, tax credits, workouts and land use. The team recently represented Wells Fargo as the lender in a $70 million residential development. Other clients include Bremer Bank, Midcountry Bank and Surly Brewing Company.

**Sources say:** *"They are talented, entrepreneurial and pragmatic."*

**KEY INDIVIDUALS Jon Hoganson** (see p.1579) frequently represents banking clients in commercial real estate financings. Clients describe him as *"very customer-oriented,"* and value his *"common-sense"* approach. **Jonathan Armour** (see p.1578) is also known for his lending work, and receives glowing praise from clients for his diligence, insight and commercial acumen. Clients refer to him as *"a highly organized, highly detailed attorney"* who is able to offer *"fantastic advice and insight into how we can do things better."*

### Other Notable Practitioners

**Thomas Mayerle** of Thomas M Mayerle Law PLLC is a respected practitioner. He is particularly noted for his retail and corporate real estate experience. **Thomas Stoltman** of Larkin Hoffman Daly & Lindgren, Ltd. is well regarded in the market. He handles commercial real estate transactions relating to a range of property types, with a focus on hotels and offices. **Bruce Malkerson** of Malkerson Gunn Martin LLP is widely regarded as one of Minnesota's leading zoning and land use attorneys. He has extensive litigation experience. Well-respected real estate attorney **LB Guthrie** of Lindquist & Vennum LLP is recognized for his litigation and transactional capabilities. **Kathleen Martin** of Malkerson Gunn Martin LLP is highly regarded. Her practice covers a variety of commercial real estate and financing matters, and she is particularly noted for her securitized finance expertise.

# Leaders' Profiles in Minnesota

## ARMOUR, Jonathan W. J.
Winthrop & Weinstine, PA, Minneapolis
612 604 6742
jarmour@winthrop.com
*Featured in Real Estate (Minnesota)*
**Practice Areas:** Jon represents businesses, developers and institutional clients in commercial financing, construction and real estate lending and secured transactions, distressed debt, commercial bankruptcy, and creditors' remedies. Jon is involved throughout the lending process, from advising on financing structures to documenting, negotiating and closing transactions.
**Professional Memberships:** Minnesota State, Wisconsin State, American, Ramsey and Hennepin County bar associations; US Court of Appeals for the 7th and 8th Circuits; National Association of Office and Industrial Properties; Association for Corporate Growth; Board of Directors, SPEDCO and NiceRide.
**Career:** JD, Hamline University School of Law, cum laude; BA, University of Minnesota.

## BARNETT, Timothy M
Winthrop & Weinstine, PA, Minneapolis
612 604 6653
tbarnett@winthrop.com
*Featured in Corporate/M&A (Minnesota)*
**Practice Areas:** Corporate transactions; mergers and acquisitions; franchise financing and acquisition; emerging companies; construction law.
**Professional Memberships:** American, Minnesota State and Hennepin County bar associations.
**Career:** Tim is corporate and transactional counsel to national, regional, and local companies in the aerospace, construction, manufacturing, software development and licensing, real estate, quick service restaurants, and franchised business industries. Blending his legal and CPA backgrounds, he counsels on complex transactions, including acquisitions and sales, venture capital investments, strategic alliances, and debt and equity financings.
**Personal:** JD (magna cum laude) and CPA, University of Minnesota Law School; BBA, University of Notre Dame, highest honors.

## BISTRAM, Gregory
Briggs and Morgan, Minneapolis
612 977 8241
gbistram@briggs.com
*Featured in Construction (Minnesota)*
**Practice Areas:** Construction law, commercial litigation, eminent domain, mediation and arbitration.
**Career:** Greg's construction practice involves mediation, arbitration, litigation and counseling for entities and individuals – including owners, sureties, general contractors, subcontractors and suppliers, design professionals, construction managers and insurance carriers – involved in the area of construction both nationally and internationally. He is a qualified neutral and arbitrator by the Minnesota Supreme Court and regularly counsels and represents clients involved in state and federal OSHA investigations. Greg also regularly represents condemning authorities or owners in eminent domain cases.
**Personal:** JD, Oklahoma City University School of Law.

## BOYD, Felicia
Barnes & Thornburg LLP, Minneapolis
*Featured in Litigation (Minnesota)*
**Practice Areas:**
Patent/Trademark/Copyright/Trade Secret Litigation, Trademark Prosecution, Unfair Competition and False Advertising, Advertising/Marketing, Trade Dress, International IP Litigation.
**Professional Memberships:** American Intellectual Property Law Association, International Trademark Association, Minority Corporate Counsel Association, Intellectual Property Owners Association.
**Career:** Admitted to practice in Minnesota, US Court of Appeals for the Eighth Circuit, US Court of Appeals for the Federal Circuit, USPTO.
**Publications:** Intellectual Property Magazine – "The end of John Doe copyright suits in the US?"; Law360 – "Avoiding the Hidden Franchise"; Patent World – "Skillful Navigation Required to Avoid Disaster".
**Personal:** St. Olaf College (BA); University of Minnesota Law School (JD).

## BOYD, Thomas H
Winthrop & Weinstine, PA, Minneapolis
612 604 6505
tboyd@winthrop.com
*Featured in Litigation (Minnesota)*
**Practice Areas:** Appellate; business and commercial litigation.
**Professional Memberships:** MSBA Appellate Practice Section; Eighth Circuit Bar Association; Federal Bar Association; American Law Institute; American Bar Foundation; Minnesota Supreme Court Historical Society; Ramsey County Historical Society.
**Career:** Tom's cases include contracts, torts, probate and trust matters, employment, IP, eminent domain and land use, product liability, and insurance disputes.
**Publications:** Published on numerable legal topics, including in the Iowa, William Mitchell, Hamline, DePaul, Drake, Gonzaga and Missouri law reviews.
**Personal:** JD, University of Iowa College of Law; Note and Comment Editor, Iowa Law Review; MA and BA, University of Iowa.

## BRAY, Thomas
Briggs and Morgan, Minneapolis
612 977 8285
tbray@briggs.com
*Featured in Real Estate (Minnesota)*
**Practice Areas:** Real estate development, common interest communities, commercial real estate sales and acquisitions, commercial leasing, land use and zoning, real estate finance and workouts and foreclosures.

**Career:** Tom represents corporate and individual clients in real estate acquisition, financing, development, leasing and sale transactions. He has significant experience in residential and mixed-use condominium and planned community developments, including condominium conversions. In his work with lenders and creditors, Tom has been involved in numerous workouts and foreclosures. He is chair of the governing counsel of the Real Property Law Section of the MSBA.
**Personal:** JD, University of Minnesota Law School.

## BREMER, Cynthia
Ogletree, Deakins, Nash, Smoak & Stewart, PC, Minneapolis
612 339 1818
cynthia.bremer@ogletreedeakins.com
*Featured in Labor & Employment (Minnesota)*
**Practice Areas:** Cynthia Bremer defends employers in discrimination, harassment, and/or retaliation lawsuits under federal and state employment laws, as well as noncompete agreements. Cynthia also advises on employment-related topics.
**Professional Memberships:** Member, Federal Practice Committee; HCBA; MN, ND, IL, and MO state bar associations.
**Career:** Admitted in Minnesota, North Dakota, Missouri, and Illinois; US District of Minnesota and other federal courts; served as Missouri Assistant Attorney General before private practice.
**Personal:** Carleton College (BA, 1990) (cum laude); Washington University School of Law (JD, 1994) (Order of the Barristers); moot court winner/ board chair); Orono city council member; Board chair, HIRED.

## CIRESI, Michael V
Robins, Kaplan, Miller & Ciresi LLP, Minneapolis
612 349 8500
mvciresi@rkmc.com
*Featured in Products Liability (Nationwide), Litigation (Minnesota)*
**Practice Areas:** Trial Lawyer - product liability, intellectual property, and complex commercial litigation.
**Professional Memberships:** AAJ, IBA, Inner Circle of Advocates, International Academy of Trial Lawyers, American Board of Trial Advocates, American College of Trial Lawyers.
**Career:** Chairman of the Board 1995-2008. Named "Ten of the National Top Trial Lawyers," NLJ (1989, 1993); "100 Most Influential Lawyers in America," NLJ (1997, 2000, 2006); "Ellis Island Medal of Honor," NECO (2002).
**Personal:** Honorary Degree of Doctor of Laws, Southwestern University School of Law; University of Minnesota Law School, JD; University of St. Thomas, BA.

## DALEY, Annamarie
Barnes & Thornburg LLP, Minneapolis
612 367 8749
annamarie.daley@btlaw.com
*Featured in Litigation (Minnesota)*

**Practice Areas:** Complex Commercial Litigation, Intellectual Property Litigation, Antitrust, Regulatory (CPSC Recalls, Rulemaking, Section 15 Reports, Defect Investigations), Class Actions, Distributor/Dealer/Franchisor Litigation.
**Professional Memberships:** ABA Intellectual Property, Antitrust, Franchise and Distribution sections.
**Career:** Minnesota Federal Local Practice Committee (2000-2007; 2012-present), Governing Council of MSBA Section of Litigation (2009-present), Minnesota Supreme Court Historical Society (treasurer), Minnesota Judicial Selection Commission (1999-2007).
**Publications:** Chapter Author, Minnesota Courtroom Evidence Deskbook, "Rule 803: Hearsay – Availability Immaterial".
**Personal:** Marshall Scholar – University of Reading, England (Postgraduate Diploma 1981); Truman Scholar – University of Minnesota (JD 1984) (BA and Bachelor of Agricultural Business Administration 1980).

## D'AQUILA, Barbara
Fulbright & Jaworski LLP, Minneapolis
612 321 2201
bdaquila@fulbright.com
*Featured in Labor & Employment (Minnesota)*
**Professional Memberships:** MSBA Certified Labor & Employment Law Specialist; Council Member, ABA Labor and Employment Section; Fellow, College of Labor and Employment Lawyers.
**Career:** Partner, Fulbright & Jaworski; Manages Minneapolis's Litigation Department; Handles class, collective, and complex business and employment/labor actions in federal and state courts, agencies, arbitration; handles government-related investigations; broad-based litigation experience (business, discrimination, whistleblowing, wage/hour, ERISA); provides high-level counseling. Clients: FORTUNE 500 companies.
**Personal:** JD, cum laude, University of Minnesota Law School (1979) (International Moot Court); BBA, magna cum laude, University of Notre Dame (1977) (various honor societies); Law Clerk, Minnesota Supreme Court; CPA Inactive License (Minnesota).

## DAVIES, Scott
Briggs and Morgan, Minneapolis
612 977 8409
sdavies@briggs.com
*Featured in Labor & Employment (Minnesota)*
**Practice Areas:** ADR, employment, litigation.
**Career:** Scott has more than 40 years of experience in general litigation, with a focus on defending corporations in all aspects of employment litigation. He now focuses his practice on mediating employment disputes, including class actions. A fellow of the American College of Trial Lawyers, Scott has been an active member of state and federal bar committees and is former chair of the Minnesota State Bar Association Committee on Labor and Employment Law. He has been a frequent lecturer and course chair of continuing legal education programs.

**Personal:** JD, University of Minnesota Law School.

## DREWES, Julie
Briggs and Morgan, Minneapolis
612 977 8635
jdrewes@briggs.com
*Featured in Real Estate (Minnesota)*
**Practice Areas:** Commercial real estate acquisitions and dispositions, commercial real estate finance and telecommunications and utility services.
**Career:** Julie is head of the Investment Real Estate Practice Group at Briggs and Morgan. She represents real estate development companies, REITs and funds in a variety of commercial real estate and finance transactions. Her focus is on real estate acquisitions, dispositions and financings involving multi-property, multi-state portfolios.
**Personal:** JD, University of Minnesota Law School.

## FRIEDRICH, Ira
Briggs and Morgan, Minneapolis
612 977 8465
ifriedrich@briggs.com
*Featured in Labor & Employment (Minnesota)*
**Practice Areas:** Benefits and employment.
**Career:** Ira is head of the firm's Employee Benefits and Executive Compensation Practice Group and has significant experience with design and implementation of all types of tax-qualified plans, including 401(k) plans, 403(b) plans, 457 plans and defined benefit plans, welfare benefit plans, executive compensation plans and equity compensation plans. He also has extensive experience with negotiation and due diligence related to benefit plans in business mergers, initial public offerings, acquisitions and dispositions, including multiemployer withdrawal liability, as well as ERISA litigation and HIPAA privacy and security.
**Personal:** JD, Case Western Reserve University.

## HANSON, Samuel
Briggs and Morgan, Minneapolis
612 977 8525
shanson@briggs.com
*Featured in Litigation (Minnesota)*
**Practice Areas:** Arbitration and mediation, complex civil litigation, appellate law, public utility regulation.
**Career:** Sam has worked closely with several major corporate clients, including telephone, gas and electric utilities, insurance companies, financial institutions, and multinational manufacturing and service corporations. He has extensive experience in both the state and federal courts in Minnesota, as well as courts in many other states in the region, and he rejoined the firm after serving on the Minnesota Court of Appeals for two years and the Minnesota Supreme Court for five years. He is a former firm president.
**Personal:** JD, William Mitchell College of Law.

## HAYNOR, Charles
Briggs and Morgan, Minneapolis
612 977 8512
chaynor@briggs.com
*Featured in Real Estate (Minnesota)*
**Practice Areas:** Real estate, banking, creditors' rights and commercial law.
**Career:** For over 35 years, Chuck has represented clients in negotiating and documenting a variety of

sophisticated commercial and real estate financing transactions, including revolving credit facilities, term loans, asset-based loans, syndicated construction and permanent and CMBS real estate loans. His experience includes representing a national real estate development company and its affiliated investment partnerships and joint ventures in private placements, real estate acquisitions, financings, development, leasing and sales. He also has extensive experience representing banks, insurance companies and other financial institutions.
**Personal:** JD, University of Iowa College of Law.

## HOGANSON, Jon J
Winthrop & Weinstine, PA, Minneapolis
612 604 6745
jhoganson@winthrop.com
*Featured in Real Estate (Minnesota)*
**Practice Areas:** Banking and finance; commercial lending; real estate; construction; tax credits; general corporate.
**Professional Memberships:** Minnesota State Bar Association; Ramsey County Bar Association; Hennepin County Bar Association; American College of Mortgage Attorneys.
**Career:** Jon is a shareholder practicing in the areas of banking, real estate and general corporate law. In addition to representing countless financial and institutional lenders, Jon has also acted as developer's counsel in connection with the acquisition, development, financing, leasing and sale of all types of commercial real estate holdings.
**Personal:** JD, University of Minnesota Law School, cum laude; BS, Carroll College, magna cum laude.

## HUNTRODS, Ann
Briggs and Morgan, Minneapolis
612 977 8249
ahuntrods@briggs.com
*Featured in Labor & Employment (Minnesota)*
**Practice Areas:** Employment litigation and employment law counseling and training.
**Career:** Ann has more than 25 years of experience in employment law and litigation, handling cases in state and federal courts. She is a Minnesota State Bar Association Certified Labor & Employment Specialist. Ann has extensive experience in selecting and working with experts on behalf of employers to defend against disability and age discrimination and sexual harassment claims and frequently assists employers in responding to charges brought before the Minnesota Department of Human Rights and EEOC.
**Personal:** JD, University of Minnesota; MA and PhD coursework, University of Minnesota.

## KNOER, Dennis L.
Briggs and Morgan, Minneapolis
612 977 8744
dknoer@briggs.com
*Featured in Corporate/M&A (Minnesota)*
**Practice Areas:** Corporate transactions, mergers and acquisitions, corporate governance, risk management, business contracts, finance and shareholder conflict resolution.
**Career:** Dennis is head of the Emerging Companies Practice Group and represents private equity funds in connection with the acquisition

and divestiture of portfolio companies in numerous industries. He also represents investment banks and issuers in connection with the offer and sale of securities. Dennis serves as outside general counsel to a variety of private companies, assisting them in addressing the full range of their legal needs.
**Personal:** JD, Georgetown University Law Center.

## LORENTZ, Brent A.
Winthrop & Weinstine, PA, Minneapolis
612 604 6481
alorentz@winthrop.com
*Featured in Litigation (Minnesota)*
**Practice Areas:** Brent represents corporations, small businesses and individuals in complex litigation and other legal issues, including disputes involving intellectual property, contracts and insurance, employment, securities, and constitutional issues. Brent has experience in state and federal district courts, appeals courts, and arbitration forums.
**Professional Memberships:** MSBA; US District Court for the District of Minnesota; US Court of Appeals for the Federal Circuit; US District Court for the Western District of Wisconsin.
**Career:** JD, Duke University School of Law; BS, University of North Dakota, Mechanical Engineering, summa cum laude.
**Publications:** Editor/Contributor, www.duets-blog.com

## LUECK, Martin
Robins, Kaplan, Miller & Ciresi LLP, Minneapolis
612 349 8500
mrlueck@rkmc.com
*Featured in Litigation (Minnesota)*
**Practice Areas:** Trial lawyer experienced in civil trial and appeals, arbitration and administrative hearings in commercial litigation, patent, antitrust, and competition law.
**Professional Memberships:** Fellow, International Academy of Trial Lawyers; Fellow, American College of Trial Lawyers; IBA; FCBA; AIPLA; ABA.
**Career:** Chairman of the Executive Board. Selected one of the "Top Rated Lawyers in International Law & International Trade," American Lawyer Media (2012); Named "Minneapolis Patent Law Lawyer of the Year," Best Lawyers (2012); Named a "Top Patent Litigator in the World," IAM (2011).
**Personal:** William Mitchell College of Law, JD, cum laude; Winona State University, BS.

## MAGNUSON, Eric
Briggs and Morgan, Minneapolis
612 977 8788
emagnuson@briggs.com
*Featured in Litigation (Minnesota)*
**Practice Areas:** Appellate law, business litigation.
**Career:** With over 30 years experience, Eric has handled hundreds of appeals in state and federal courts around the country, regarding issues such as the constitutionality of the public school finance system, employment law, trust and probate matters, trade secrets, business contracts, corporate fraud, insurance law and professional liability. As former Chief Justice of the Minnesota Supreme

Court, Eric brings a unique perspective to a full range of appellate consulting services, from evaluating appeals and procedural issues, to reviewing and critiquing briefs, providing moot court review, and fully briefing and arguing cases himself.
**Personal:** JD, William Mitchell College of Law.

## MARTIN, Patrick
Ogletree, Deakins, Nash, Smoak & Stewart, PC, Minneapolis
612 336 6870
pat.martin@ogletreedeakins.com
*Featured in Labor & Employment (Minnesota)*
**Practice Areas:** Pat Martin defends employers in lawsuits involving Title VII, MHRA, ADEA, WARN, ADA, Sarbanes-Oxley, FLSA, FMLA, Chapter 181, discrimination, harassment, whistleblowing, retaliation, and non-competes. Pat also provides employment counseling.
**Professional Memberships:** Federal Bar Association, former President of the Minnesota Chapter (second largest chapter, with 900 members); MSBA; HCBA; and ISBA.
**Career:** Admitted in Minnesota, Eighth Circuit, and Iowa, and clerked for the Minnesota Court of Appeals.
**Personal:** Mankato State University (BA, 1991) (varsity hockey, second in NCAA small college, 3-time winner of "Best Hustle Award"); University of Minnesota (JD, 1995) (cum laude, trial practice); youth hockey coach.

## MILLER, Michael
Briggs and Morgan, Minneapolis
612 977 8515
mmiller@briggs.com
*Featured in Labor & Employment (Minnesota)*
**Practice Areas:** Employment law compliance, employment law counseling and employment litigation.
**Career:** Michael is head of the firm's Employment Law Counseling and Compliance practice group. He has 25+ years experience counseling employers to prevent unwanted litigation and advises companies of ongoing changes in federal, state and local employment law. Michael advises employers in all areas of employment law including discipline and discharge, leaves of absence, wage and hour compliance, non-compete and confidentiality agreements, affirmative action plans, background checking, drug/alcohol testing and executive agreements and separation agreements. He addresses employment law issues in transactional matters and assists in litigation.
**Personal:** JD, William Mitchell College of Law.

## MRKONICH, Marko
Littler Mendelson, PC, Minneapolis
612 630 1000
mmrkonich@littler.com
*Featured in Labor & Employment (Minnesota)*
**Practice Areas:** Employment Litigation, Employment Counseling and Training, Arbitration Proceedings and Negotiations, Class Action Litigation.
**Professional Memberships:** American Bar Association (Litigation and Labor and Employment Law Sections); Minnesota State, Hennepin County, and Wisconsin Bar

Associations; Corporate Board of Fraser Community Services, Inc., Minnesota Management Attorneys Association; Board member of the Noper Foundation.

**Career:** Immediate Past President and Managing Director of Littler Mendelson. Before joining Littler, Mr Mrkonich served as chairperson of the Labor and Employment Practice Group at Oppenheimer Wolff & Donnelly, where he practiced for 17 years.

**Personal:** JD, Harvard University, 1980; AB, Harvard College, 1977.

## POLLEY, John W

Littler Mendelson, PC, Minneapolis
612 313 7649
jpolley@littler.com

*Featured in Labor & Employment (Minnesota)*

**Practice Areas:** Labor Management Relations and Workplace Safety and Health (OSHA).

**Professional Memberships:** Member, ABA Committee on Practice and Procedure under the National Labor Relations Act (NLRA), 1994-present; Committee on the Development of the Law under the NLRA, 2002-present; and Committee on Occupational Safety and Health Law, 2004-present.

**Career:** Mr Polley has practiced traditional labor law for 29 years and successfully opposed more than 90 organizing campaigns. His bargaining experience includes multiemployer bargaining, first-contract bargaining, rewriting multiple, inter-related contracts, multi-employer pension fund withdrawals, and strike planning and response.

**Publications:** Contributing author, How Arbitration Works; Contributing editor, The Developing Labor Law.

## ROGERS, Charles

Briggs and Morgan, Minneapolis
612 977 8446
crogers@briggs.com

*Featured in Litigation (Minnesota)*

**Practice Areas:** Litigation, including: banking, real estate foreclosure, commercial real estate and construction defect, unfair competition and antitrust, shareholder, partnership and closely-held business, environmental, professional liability, trademark and copyright infringement, energy industry, class action, fiduciary and fidelity bond and general complex commercial.

**Career:** Charlie has more than 30 years of successful litigation experience, representing numerous banks and lending institutions, commercial builders and developers, and various businesses in commercial disputes. He also defends industrial clients with respect to environmental claims.

**Personal:** JD, University of Minnesota Law School.

## SCHNEIDER, Mark

Littler Mendelson, PC, Minneapolis
612 630 1000
mschneider@littler.com

*Featured in Labor & Employment (Minnesota)*

**Practice Areas:** Labor & Employment.

**Professional Memberships:** Member, Committee on the Development of the Law Under the National Labor Relations Act - ABA; Member, Commerce Clearing Houses Human Resource Management Advisory Board

**Career:** Mr Schneider has represented the interests of management in labor law, and labor relations matters for over 35 years. His international practice includes advising clients on mergers/acquisitions, restructuring, and other strategic planning, collective bargaining, contract administration and labor arbitration, matters of all types before the NLRB and DOL, and counsels clients, globally, concerning positive employee relations in creating and maintaining a positive union free environment.

## SCHUTZ, Ronald J

Robins, Kaplan, Miller & Ciresi LLP, Minneapolis
612 349 8500
rjschutz@rkmc.com

*Featured in Litigation (Minnesota)*

**Practice Areas:** IP Litigation trial lawyer.

**Professional Memberships:** Fellow: American College of Trial Lawyers, AIPLA, Past Chair, Minnesota Commission on Judicial Selection.

**Career:** Chair, National IP Litigation Group; Regional Managing Partner, NY office; executive board member. Named a "Top 10 Winning Attorney," NLJ (2008); Named a "Life Science Star," LMG Life Sciences (2012); "Minneapolis Intellectual Property Lawyer of the Year," Best Lawyers (2011); Named a "Litigation Star," Benchmark Litigation (2011-2013); Listed in "500 Leading Lawyers in America," Lawdragon (2010, 2011).

**Personal:** University of Minnesota Law School, JD, with honors, member of Law Review; Marquette University, magna cum laude, Mechanical Engineering.

## STENMOE, Gregory

Briggs and Morgan, Minneapolis
612 977 8448
gstenmoe@briggs.com

*Featured in Labor & Employment (Minnesota)*

**Practice Areas:** Employment litigation, non-compete agreements and restraining orders, employment law counseling and training, internal corporate investigations, workforce reductions and reorganizations.

**Career:** Greg is a trial lawyer and chair of Briggs' Litigation Department. Greg has been involved in groundbreaking cases and affirmations of employer rights in courts throughout the United States. He counsels high-profile clients and closely held businesses on discipline and discharge issues, and on management and cost-containment. Greg serves as a corporate trainer on issues such as litigation prevention, sexual harassment, and also serves as a corporate investigator on employment issues.

**Personal:** JD, William Mitchell College of Law.

## SULLIVAN, Timothy

Best & Flanagan LLP, Minneapolis
612 341 9725
tsullivan@bestlaw.com

*Featured in Construction (Minnesota)*

**Practice Areas:** Timothy A Sullivan is a Partner at Best & Flannagan, LLP located in Minneapolis, Minnesota. Tim is a member of the firm's Litigation and Dispute Resolution practice area. His practice focuses on complex civil litigation and appeals, primarily in the areas of construc-

tion, commercial, employment, shareholder, probate and real estate disputes. Tim also represents hospitals, physicians and clinics and has served as general counsel to LifeSource (the Upper Midwest Organ Procurement Organization) since its inception. He has worked on many bid disputes, commercial and construction cases, and litigation involving cities, counties, and states.

**Professional Memberships:** Association of General Contractors, Litigation Counsel of America.

**Career:** Timothy received his law degree from the University of Minnesota in 1979 and his BA from Carleton College in 1975. He joined the Law firm of Best & Flanagan LLP in 1988.

## SYRING-PETROCCHI, Tina A.

Barnes & Thornburg LLP, Minneapolis
612 367 8705
tina.syring-petrocchi@btlaw.com

*Featured in Labor & Employment (Minnesota)*

**Practice Areas:** Employment defense litigation; non-competition agreements and litigation; prevailing wage and FLSA compliance; executive compensation agreements; advising compensation committees; whistleblower advice and litigation; due diligence regarding mergers and acquisitions.

**Professional Memberships:** American Bar Association; Defense Research Institute; Minnesota Defense Lawyers Association.

**Career:** Minnesota, North Dakota and Wisconsin State Bar Associations; US District Court for the District of Minnesota; US District Court for the District of North Dakota; and US District Court for the Western District of Wisconsin.

**Publications:** Contributor to Inside Counsel and BT Currents Employment Law blog.

**Personal:** Indiana State University; Hamline University School of Law (JD 1994).

## THORNTON, Timothy

Briggs and Morgan, Minneapolis
612 977 8550
tthornton@briggs.com

*Featured in Litigation (Minnesota)*

**Practice Areas:** Complex litigation, mass torts, toxic torts, labor and employment, land use, environmental, transportation, contracts, class actions, securities, corporate, partnerships, shareholder relations and corporate governance, interstate commerce and federal preemption, fire and explosions, insurance coverage, the Railway Labor Act and non-compete enforcement and ERISA litigation.

**Career:** In addition to being a leading litigator, Tim has served as both executive vice president and general counsel for a prominent airline, giving him dual perspectives on the value and cost of legal services. He also has represented the NFL Players Association.

**Personal:** JD, Florida State University College of Law.

## WEINSTINE, Robert R

Winthrop & Weinstine, PA, Minneapolis
612 604 6613
rweinstine@winthrop.com

*Featured in Litigation (Minnesota)*

**Practice Areas:** Antitrust and trade regulation; business and commercial litigation; construction

litigation; securities litigation; directors and officers liability litigation; products liability litigation.

**Career:** Mr Weinstine is a nationally known trial attorney securing some of the largest awards in Minnesota business history. A Founding Partner of Winthrop & Weinstine, Mr Weinstine has been key in building a successful, dynamic law firm and the top-notch litigation department for which Winthrop & Weinstine is known.

**Personal:** JD, University of Minnesota Law School, cum laude, Order of the Coif, Board of Editors, Minnesota Law Review, research editor; BA, University of Minnesota, Phi Beta Kappa.

## WENGER, Brian

Briggs and Morgan, Minneapolis
612 977 8573
bwenger@briggs.com

*Featured in Corporate/M&A (Minnesota)*

**Practice Areas:** Strategic corporate transactions, mergers and acquisitions, professional sports teams, corporate governance, special board counsel, securities law, bankruptcy counsel, corporate finance, mezzanine debt and family estate planning.

**Career:** Brian is Briggs and Morgan's chair and concentrates his practice in complex business and commercial transactions, representing public and privately held companies and their boards of directors in a wide variety of matters. His high-profile clients include the world's largest beverage company, national sports teams, premier mezzanine capital providers and ultra-high net worth families. He was awarded "Attorney of the Year" by Minnesota Lawyer in 2009.

**Personal:** JD, Villanova University.

## WILSON, Kate

Littler Mendelson, PC, Minneapolis
612 313 7603
kwilson@littler.com

*Featured in Labor & Employment (Minnesota)*

**Practice Areas:** Employment litigation defense; compliance advice regarding FMLA/ADA and performance management; retail, manufacturing, transportation and financial industries.

**Professional Memberships:** ABA (Labor/Employment); Member Littler's Board of Directors; Co-Chair Littler's Retail Practice; Women's Leadership Initiative - Steering Committee; Board Member Minnesota Boychoir

**Career:** Kate has successfully litigated cases in both federal and state courts nationally. Kate practices before administrative agencies, including EEOC and state FEP agencies, OSHA, and the DOL.

**Personal:** Kate was one of the founding shareholders of Littler's Chicago and Minneapolis offices, and served a term as Minneapolis Office Managing Shareholder. She lives in Minnetrista with her family.

# BRIGGS AND MORGAN, P.A.

**www.briggs.com  tel:** 612 977 8400  **fax:** 612 977 8650

**Chair:** Brian Wenger
**Managing Partner:** Alan Maclin
Number of shareholders: 102  Number of associates: 43
Number of other lawyers: 32  Total number of attorneys: 177
Languages: *English, French, Russian, Spanish*

**Firm Overview:**
Briggs and Morgan, Professional Association is a trusted name in business law and litigation services. For more than 125 years, Briggs and Morgan has been dedicated to providing superior client service. Clients benefit from Briggs' depth of experience and ability to anticipate the rapidly changing legal needs of businesses, communities, institutions and individuals. Briggs ranks among The NLJ 250 as one of the nation's largest firms and has received numerous accolades, including recognition by the publishers of Corporate Counsel and top *Fortune* 500 clients as a 'Go-To Law Firm®' in the areas of litigation, corporate transactions, corporate governance, and labor and employment. Briggs and Morgan offers a broad range of legal services to *Fortune* 500 corporations, business startups, commercial enterprises, non-profit and charitable institutions, utilities, public bodies, and individual clients. Slightly more than half of the firm's attorneys concentrate their practices in litigation and other forms of dispute resolution, while the remainder focus on commercial and transactional law.

**Main Areas of Practice:**

**Banking & Finance:**
The Banking and Finance Group represents major financial institutions in commercial banking and finance transactions of all sizes, nationally. They provide advice on state and federal bank regulatory issues, commercial and consumer lending transactions, mortgage banking, loan workouts and restructurings, bankruptcy, M&A, and other organizational and corporate matters.
**Contact:** Peter Rue  **Tel:** 612 977 8638
**Email:** prue@briggs.com

**Complex Business Litigation:**
The firm's litigators offer more jury trial experience than most at other Twin Cities law firms. National areas of strength include energy litigation, telecommunications, complex financial markets litigation, class action defense, banking, real estate litigation, insurance, mortgage banking, appellate, employment and ERISA litigation, antitrust and franchise litigation, product liability defense, environmental litigation, ADR, and medical malpractice/professional liability defense.
**Contact:** Thomas Basting  **Tel:** 612 977 8406
**Email:** tbasting@briggs.com
**Contact:** Philip Schenkenberg  **Tel:** 612 977 8246
**Email:** pschenkenberg@briggs.com

**Corporate Law:**
In recent years, the firm's Corporate Practice has represented public company clients in acquisitions valued from $50 million to $750 million. Briggs attorneys have represented public and private companies in several financing transactions in excess of $50 million. The practice concentrates heavily on M&A, public offerings and private placements.
**Contact:** Charles Johnson  **Tel:** 612 977 8680
**Email:** cjohnson@briggs.com

**Estate Planning/Administration:**
Briggs represents diverse clients in connection with sophisticated estate planning and charitable giving, including owners of closely held businesses and high net worth individuals. The firm's attorneys assist individual and corporate fiduciaries in the administration of trusts and estates, represent taxpayers in gift and estate tax audits, and handle trust and estate litigation.
**Contact:** Terry Slye  **Tel:** 651 808 6580
**Email:** tslye@briggs.com

**Intellectual Property:**
The firm's established IP Practice serves global clients with their business needs, including assistance with foreign and domestic patent, trademark and copyright prosecution; litigation and international arbitration; TTAB proceedings; technology agreements and due diligence; IP clearance and opinions; IP audits; and policing and enforcement.
**Contact:** Michael Lafeber  **Tel:** 612 977 8472
**Email:** mlafeber@briggs.com

**Employment, Benefits & Labor:**
Briggs maintains one of the largest employment and benefits groups in the Midwest, offering a full-service practice in employment counseling and litigation, employee benefits, executive compensation, ERISA litigation, noncompetition litigation, and labor law.
**Contact:** Neal Buethe  **Tel:** 612 977 8248
**Email:** nbuethe@briggs.com

**Public Finance:**
Serving numerous municipalities and governmental agencies throughout the Midwest, the Public Finance Group assists issuers, underwriters, borrowers, trustees and financial institutions. They have extensive experience assisting clients engaged in infrastructure improvements, privatization, economic development, tax increment financing and housing development.
**Contact:** Mary Ippel  **Tel:** 651 808 6620
**Email:** mippel@briggs.com

**Real Estate:**
With significant local and national reach, the firm's real estate attorneys have substantial experience in the purchase, sale and exchange of various property types; real estate financing; handling lease arrangements and title examinations; facilitating the arrangement of partnerships, joint ventures or syndications; and handling real estate tax and assessment issues.
**Contact:** Tom Bray  **Tel:** 612 977 8285
**Email:** tbray@briggs.com

# DADY & GARDNER, PA

www.dadygardner.com **tel:** 612 359 9000 **fax:** 612 259 3507

**Managing Partner:** Ronald K Gardner
**Senior Partner:** J Michael Dady
Number of partners: 8
Number of other lawyers: 2

**OFFICES**
MINNESOTA
**MINNEAPOLIS:** 5100 IDS Center, 80 South 8th Street, MN 55402
Tel: 612 359 9000  Fax: 612 359 3507
Email: contact@dadygardner.com

## Firm Overview:

Since Dady & Gardner was founded in 1994, the firm's mission has been to help franchisees, dealers and distributors effectively and efficiently resolve their disputes, and to preserve and enhance the value of their businesses in the process. The firm only represents franchisees, dealers and distributors. With this focused concentration, the firm has been able to build a powerhouse of knowledge, skill and proficiency that has been used to obtain practical results for its clients through negotiation, mediation, arbitration and litigation. Dady & Gardner's franchise attorneys have represented a wide array of clients, from quick-service restaurant franchisees to farm and industrial equipment distributors, and have successfully resolved disputes against more than 400 different franchise and supply systems, essentially all of which are listed on the firm's website.

## Main Areas of Practice:

### Termination:
Dady & Gardner franchise attorneys have enjoyed many successes battling franchisors and suppliers over their attempts to terminate franchisees when there is not good cause, sometimes winning court orders preventing the termination, sometimes winning money damages for terminations that took place that the firm was able to prove were not justified.

### Refusal to Renew:
Franchisors and suppliers sometimes attempt to achieve the same results as termination through a refusal to renew the franchise or dealer agreement at the end of its term. Many statutes prevent the franchisor from doing so and allow the franchisee or dealer to continue in business so long as the franchisee is capably performing. Dady & Gardner has been able to obtain compensation for dealers and franchisees whose suppliers or franchisors have refused to renew them without good cause and have been able to obtain court orders preventing such non-renewals and keeping the business alive.

### Changes in Policies:
Dady & Gardner views a franchisor's change in policy that has a detrimental effect on the franchisee or dealer as a serious matter: it may amount to breach of contract, a fraud, or simply bad business that ought to be corrected. The firm has had significant success in addressing these changes in policy through litigation, negotiation, mediation, and the organization of associations of franchisees or dealers to address them.

### Franchisee Association Representation:
Dady & Gardner has a long history of helping nationwide groups of franchisees to organize into associations, and to effectively work with franchisee leaders to obtain long-term positive changes in their relationships with their franchisors on matters such as improved product pricing, more effective use of marketing funds, return-on-investment based capital spending, increased uniformity and reasonableness in store inspection protocols, and more effective, more efficient, and more fair dispute resolution processes, all of which are designed to preserve and enhance the value of the individual franchisees' businesses.

### Territorial Protection & Expansion:
Dady & Gardner franchise attorneys have a proud history of fighting franchisors and suppliers on issues of encroachment and denial of expansion rights. The firm was a pioneer in fighting a franchisor's attempt to encroach on franchisees through the use of the Internet, and obtained an injunction against a franchisor using the Internet to take away sales from its franchisee.

### Fraud & Misrepresentation:
The firm has won substantial verdicts and achieved large settlements for franchisees and dealers who bought their businesses on the basis of misrepresentations or who were not told the whole truth when they were signed up.

### Breach of Contract:
When a franchisor fails to perform its obligations to a franchisee, Dady & Gardner can provide legal assistance to insure that the franchisee does not forfeit any of its rights. The firm's franchise attorneys have been very successful in making sure that franchisors deliver what they promise or in obtaining compensation for franchisees when franchisors do not perform.

**Contacts:** J Michael Dady, Ronald K Gardner, Scott E Korzenowski, John D Holland, Jeffery S Haff, Barbara Bagdon, Kristy L Zastrow, Mark Dady

**DADY & GARDNER, P.A.**
TRIAL LAWYERS
*Lawyers for franchisees...*

# DORSEY & WHITNEY LLP

www.dorsey.com **tel:** 612 340 2600 **fax:** 612 340 2868

**Managing Partner:** Ken Cutler
Number of US partners: 250  Number of other US lawyers: 256

## Firm Overview:

Dorsey supports clients in a wide range of industries and sectors including healthcare and life sciences, energy, natural resources, agribusiness, manufacturing, financial services, technology and retail.

## Main Areas of Practice:

### Corporate:

Dorsey provides an array of corporate legal and transaction services to clients ranging from start-ups to multinational corporations. For over a decade, the firm has been ranked among the top ten US law firms by Thomson Financial for completed M&A transactions. Dorsey's M&A clients include a range of Fortune 500 companies including UnitedHealth Group, U.S.Bancorp, Canon, General Mills, and Hormel Foods. The firm's expertise also includes assisting clients with capital raising such as complex registered debt offerings. International activities include Canadian cross-border transactions as well as US securities work on offerings overseas. The firm provides securities compliance and corporate governance counsel to numerous public companies. Dorsey's emerging companies practice represents numerous medical device and other technology companies and the firm's Energy Group supports financings for a variety of alternative energy facilities as well as traditional energy producers and distributors. The Bankruptcy and Restructuring Group has extensive experience representing debtors, creditors, lenders, and other participants in reorganization, liquidation and workout proceedings. Dorsey has a focus on heathcare legal issues and is positioned to provide unique deep knowledge perspective with important clients in key segments of healthcare including medical technology and services, payor organizations, care providers, and venture and early stage investors.

### Litigation:

The Litigation Practice represents a wide range of businesses and organizations including multinational corporations, medical institutions, small businesses, government, and individuals in all forms of dispute resolution. The firm's attorneys have broad experience in litigation, arbitration, mediation and negotiation in matters involving financial institutions, construction and real estate, employment, commercial, environmental, ERISA, franchise, fraud, health law, intellectual property, international disputes, product liability, securities, tax, and white-collar crime. Dorsey has a long history of success for its clients across a wide range of forums and jurisdictions.

### Labor & Employment Law:

More than 70 attorneys in the United States, Europe and China offer an array of services including employment law training, alternative dispute resolution, labor-management relations advice and litigation, administrative audit and crisis management consulting, and immigration law counsel. The firm also provides advice and counsel on executive and employment compensation law, M&A employment support, employee benefits, ERISA compliance, and taxation law. The firm's lawsuit defense experience crosses a wide range of litigation matters including class action lawsuits, sexual harassment and employment discrimination, wage and hour collective actions, trade secret protection and non-compete enforcement.

### Intellectual Property:

Dorsey's Patent Prosecution, Portfolio Strategy and Management Group is staffed with attorneys skilled in technical fields, with many holding PhD and/or EE degrees. It helps clients protect and leverage critical intellectual property. Clients rely on Dorsey's Trademark, Copyright, Advertising and Brand Management Group to select, protect and enforce trademarks, copyrights and domain names. Both groups work with clients to build and protect strategic intellectual property portfolios and aggressively defend them against competitors including through litigation when necessary. Dorsey represents clients in courtrooms and before regulatory bodies in patent infringement, trade secret, trademark infringement and dilution, unfair competition, trade dress protection and copyright infringement cases.

### International Work:

In over 60 countries, Dorsey provides clients with expertise on matters including cross-border transactions, corporate advice, complex litigation, capital markets, M&A, joint ventures, intellectual property, immigration, tax litigation and arbitration, export controls, licensing agreements and international treaties.

## OFFICES

### MINNESOTA

**MINNEAPOLIS:** 50 South Sixth Street, Suite 1500, MN 55402-1498
Tel: 612 340 2600  Fax: 612 340 2868
Email: minneapolis@dorsey.com

### ALASKA

**ANCHORAGE:** 1031 West Fourth Avenue, Suite 600, AK 99501-5907
Tel: 907 276 4557  Fax: 907 276 4152
Email: anchorage@dorsey.com

### CALIFORNIA

**PALO ALTO:** 305 Lytton Avenue, CA 94301
Tel: 650 857 1717  Fax: 650 857 1288
Email: paloalto@dorsey.com

**COSTA MESA:** Plaza Tower, 600 Anton Boulevard, Suite 2000, CA 92626
Tel: 714 800 1400  Fax: 714 800 1499
Email: socal@dorsey.com

### COLORADO

**DENVER:** Suite 400, 1400 Wewatta St., CO 80202-5549
Tel: 303 629 3400  Fax: 303 629 3450
Email: denver@dorsey.com

### DELAWARE

**WILMINGTON:** 300 Delaware Ave, Suite 1010, DE 19801
Tel: 302 425 7171  Fax: 302 425 7177
Email: delaware@dorsey.com

### IOWA

**DES MOINES:** 801 Grand, Suite 4100, IA 50309-2790
Tel: 515 283 1000  Fax: 515 283 1060
Email: desmoines@dorsey.com

### NORTH DAKOTA

**FARGO:** 3203 32nd Avenue South, Suite 103, PO Box 1344, ND 58107-1344
Tel: 701 235 6000  Fax: 701 235 9969
Email: fargo@dorsey.com

### MONTANA

**MISSOULA:** 125 Bank Street, Suite 600, MT 59802-4407
Tel: 406 721 6025  Fax: 406 543 0863
Email: missoula@dorsey.com

### NEW YORK

**NEW YORK:** 51 West 52nd Street, NY 10019-6119
Tel: 212 415 9200  Fax: 212 953 7201
Email: newyork@dorsey.com

### UTAH

**SALT LAKE CITY:** 136 South Main Street, Suite 1000, UT 84101-1685
Tel: 801 933 7360  Fax: 801 933 7373
Email: saltlakecity@dorsey.com

### WASHINGTON

**SEATTLE:** Columbia Center, 701 Fifth Ave, Suite 6100, WA 98104-7043
Tel: 206 903 8800  Fax: 206 903 8820
Email: seattle@dorsey.com

### DISTRICT OF COLUMBIA

**WASHINGTON DC:** 1801 K Street NW, Suite 750, DC 20006
Tel: 202 442 3000  Fax: 202 442 3199
Email: washingtondc@dorsey.com

Dorsey also has international offices in Toronto, Vancouver, London, Sydney, Shanghai and Hong Kong.

# FREDRIKSON & BYRON PA

www.fredlaw.com  **tel:** 612 492 7000  **fax:** 612 492 7077

**President:** John M Koneck
Number of shareholders: 149
Number of lawyers: 274

### Firm Overview:

Fredrikson & Byron's 274 attorneys serve clients in more than 30 practice and industry areas in six offices in the US, China, and Mexico. Fredrikson has built a reputation as the firm "where law and business meet" by bringing business acumen and entrepreneurial thinking to its work with clients, and by operating as business advisors and strategic partners as well as legal counselors. With a headquarters in Minneapolis, and teams in North Dakota and Iowa, the firm's Midwest locations provide equivalent expertise at a great value compared to law firms on the coasts – all with an exceptional dedication to excellence and client service.

Fredrikson provides a wide range of corporate, litigation, intellectual property, banking, real estate and employment services to publicly and privately held businesses, financial institutions, municipalities, professional corporations, limited liability companies, nonprofits, trade associations, partnerships, and individuals. Clients include new ventures, small and medium-sized companies, family businesses, and national and international companies traded on world stock exchanges.

### Main Areas of Practice:

### Corporate:

Fredrikson's Corporate Group offers substantial experience to its clients over the entire history of the business, from start-up to capital raising, financing growth and M&A deals. Attorneys represent clients in securities compliance, financings, venture capital, private equity, and transactions of all sizes and types, from individuals acquiring a business for the first time to complex deals of *Fortune* 500 companies.

### Mergers & Acquisitions:

Fredrikson's attorneys represent buyers and sellers, as well as management, special board committees, M&A lenders and financial advisors. The firm has handled domestic and international transactions in a wide range of industries, and is experienced in all aspects of M&A work.

### Tax Planning & Business Organization:

Fredrikson's attorneys offer practical counsel in the day to day aspects of business operations and particular proficiency in the formation, purchase, merger, sale and termination of businesses, as well as tax-related issues, tax disputes and tax planning. They represent closely-held businesses, profesisonal corporations, financial institutions, individuals, limited liability companies, partnerships and public companies.

### Intellectual Property:

The firm's Intellectual Property Group has a robust team of attorneys with specialized technical degrees who focus on securing and enforcing patents, trademarks and copyrights, and advising clients regarding trade secret protection. Many of the firm's attorneys are admitted to practice before the United States Patent and Trademark Office.

### Commercial Litigation & Arbitration:

With over 80 attorneys, the firm's Litigation Group is one of the largest and most experienced in the Upper Midwest. It handles all types of business litigation in state and federal courts, including class actions, multi-district litigation and other complex cases. Its attorneys also appear before domestic and international arbitration tribunals and administrative agencies.

### Banking & Financial Services:

Fredrikson attorneys have experience in regulatory and enforcement matters, mergers and acquisitions, financings, governance and securities, tax issues and litigation.

### Employment & Labor:

Fredrikson attorneys litigate on behalf of its employer clients in all areas of employment and labor law, as well as provide employment advice and counsel related to labor issues.

### Energy & Renewable Energy:

Fredrikson's attorneys are experienced in representing electric utilities, independent power producers, gas and oil pipeline and exploration companies, wind developers, ethanol and biodiesel producers, and other participants in the energy sector, with substantial experience in managing the development, construction, financing, acquisition, and divestiture of large energy assets.

### Health Law:

Attorneys in Fredrikson's Health Law Group have significant experience in all aspects of the healthcare industry including business formation and transactions such as corporate structure, joint ventures, acquisitions and divestitures, and tax-exempt status. The group also advises clients on regulatory, administrative and accreditation matters, and relationships among providers and between providers and patients. The health litigation team has extensive experience with investigations and resolving civil and criminal disputes.

### Real Estate:

The firm's attorneys have over 60 years of experience offering a comprehensive range of services involving: purchases and sales, financing, workouts and foreclosures, construction, land use and environmental, leasing, multifamily housing and real estate tax planning and litigation.

### International Work:

Attorneys in the International Group are experienced in handling commercial and financial transactions, cross-border mergers and acquisitions, foreign real estate, finance, acquisitions and development, immigration, distribution of goods, franchising, as well as strategic alliances and company formations. The firm also counsels clients on intellectual property, marketing, distribution and sales contracts, licensing agreements and taxation.

### OFFICES

**IOWA**

**WEST DES MOINES:** 1200 Valley West Drive, Suite 304-4, IA 50266
Tel: 515 224 6706  Fax: 612 492 7077

**MINNESOTA**

**MINNEAPOLIS:** (Head Office) 200 South 6th Street, Suite 4000, MN 55402-1425
Tel: 612 492 7000  Fax: 612 492 7077
Email: email@fredlaw.com

**NORTH DAKOTA**

**BISMARCK:** 200 North Third Street, Suite 150, ND 58501-3879
Tel: 701 221 4020  Fax: 701 221 4040

**FARGO:** 51 Broadway, Suite 402, ND 58102-4970
Tel: 701 237 8200  Fax: 701 237 8220

### INTERNATIONAL OFFICES

The firm also has offices in Monterrey, Mexico and Shanghai, China.

# GRAY PLANT MOOTY

**www.**gpmlaw.com **tel:** 612 632 3000 **fax:** 612 632 4444

**Chairman:** Bruce W Mooty
**Managing Partner:** David C Bahls
Number of partners: 114
Number of other lawyers: 50

## Firm Overview:

Gray Plant Mooty (GPM) is recognized as one of the leading corporate law firms in Minnesota and one of the top franchise firms globally. GPM's roots go back to 1866. Today, it is a full-service firm with offices in Minneapolis and St. Cloud, Minnesota and Washington, DC. GPM attorneys and staff provide exceptional client service and value to clients, and directly or through its Multilaw global network and other affiliations, the firm provides comprehensive legal services on a regional, national and global basis.

## Main Areas of Practice:

### Franchise & Distribution:

One of the world's leading franchise and distribution law practices. A group of 34 lawyers and paralegals in the Minneapolis and Washington, DC, offices serve franchisors at all stages of their development, in the US and throughout the world. Has an expansive and seasoned group of franchise litigation specialists who represent franchisors in system-wide disputes, enforcement of non-compete obligations, and supply chain and antitrust matters. Offers clients a wide range of experience in virtually every facet of international and domestic franchising.

### Corporate & Business:

Handles corporate transactions important to businesses, with strength in corporate finance, entrepreneurial services, M&A, private equity, securities and corporate governance, tax and technology. Clients range from start-ups and middle-market companies to multinational and *Fortune* 500 companies.

### Health Law:

Resolves complex regulatory issues for health care organizations throughout the Midwest and proactively implements sensible plans for the future in an ever-shifting regulatory landscape. Clients range from large multistate delivery systems and health plans to solo rural practitioners. Areas of deep expertise include health care compliance and regulatory matters, health care transactions and health care litigation.

### Trust, Estate & Charitable Planning:

One of the largest and most prestigious trust and estate practices in the Upper Midwest. Works closely with families and their advisors to prepare and administer estate plans that pass on family values, provide for the care and support of family members and friends, transfer assets, transition family businesses, benefit charities and minimize income, estate and gift taxes.

### Nonprofit & Tax-exempt Organizations:

Combines genuine appreciation for its nonprofit clients' work with expertise in the highly specialized, complex and dynamic legal environment in which they operate. Provides legal counsel to colleges, universities and schools; health care organizations; human services programs; community foundations; political organizations; private foundations; start-up nonprofit organizations; and social enterprise nonprofits.

### Intellectual Property, Technology & Privacy:

Provides clients with comprehensive domestic and cross-border IP solutions, specializing in trademark and brand management, copyright, software and technology licensing, information security and privacy, trade secrets and internet and e-commerce.

### Employment & Labor:

Offers clients experience in every aspect of employment and labor law, from defending employers in litigation of all kinds and representing unionized employers in collective bargaining and grievance arbitration to advising employers on personnel situations. Clients include large corporations, small businesses, nonprofits and public entities.

### Litigation:

Has more than 50 litigators offering expertise across a range of practice areas. Areas of strength include antitrust, employment, financial services, franchise, general commercial, government investigations, health care, IP, products liability, real estate, shareholder disputes, trust and estate and white collar defense.

### Employee Benefits & Executive Compensation:

Has one of the most robust employee benefits and executive compensation practices in the Upper Midwest. With clients including *Fortune* 500 companies, closely held businesses, nonprofit organizations and governmental entities, GPM attracts employers nationwide seeking the highest level of expertise on employee benefits and executive compensation issues.

### Financial Services & Bankruptcy:

Has considerable expertise in commercial lending, bond financing, payment systems, consumer finance and regulation and reorganizations and bankruptcy. Represents creditors, including banks and other lenders, creditors' committees and indenture trustees.

### Agribusiness & Food:

Represents national trade organizations, producers, processors and lenders, providing expert counsel in state and federal laws and commercial transactions in the agricultural and food industries. Supports agribusiness and food clients on a wide array of matters, including finance, animal welfare, environmental and food safety issues.

### Real Estate, Environmental Law & Land Use:

Represents developers, government agencies, lenders, public and private corporations, builders, contractors, and investors with real estate legal needs of all types, including development/construction, financing, acquisitions and sales, environmental law and land use management.

# LARKIN HOFFMAN DALY & LINDGREN LTD

www.larkinhoffman.com **tel:** 952 835 3800 **fax:** 952 896 3333

**President:** William C Griffith
**Board of Directors:** Joseph J Fittante, Jr, Daniel T Kadlec, Paul B Plunkett, Gary A Renneke, Tamara O'Neill Moreland, Thomas J Oppold
**Chief Financial Officer:** Daniel T Kadlec
**Chief Operating Officer:** Richard A Knutson
**General Counsel/Secretary:** Jon S Swierzewski
Number of shareholders: 47
Number of other attorneys: 29

## Firm Overview:

Larkin Hoffman Daly & Lindgren Ltd. has proudly served the legal and business counseling needs of clients since 1958. The firm is committed to providing clients with practical solutions to business issues. The firm offers a full range of legal services in the areas of real estate and land use, environmental law, corporate law and government relations, business and intellectual property litigation, franchise and distribution law, technology and intellectual property law, labor and employment law, and personal legal services such as family law, and tax, trusts and estates. The firm's 77 lawyers serve clients ranging from individuals to emerging companies and Fortune 500 corporations located throughout Minnesota, the United States, and the world. Larkin Hoffman is a member of the State Capital Group, a global network of more than 140 of the profession's pre-eminent independent law firms.

## Main Areas of Practice:

### Corporate:
Banking and finance, bankruptcy, employment, health law, international, mergers and acquisitions, securities.
**Contact:** William G Thornton

### Franchise & Distribution:
Clients range from start-up franchisors to sophisticated multinationals. Advise on a wide range of franchising issues – from questions about the benefits and disadvantages of franchising, to preparation and registration of franchise documents, to counseling on franchise relationship issues. Clients benefit from the practice's 35 years of experience and extensive knowledge of the law, supplemented by a deep knowledge of the business issues inherent in franchising.
**Contact:** Charles S Modell

### Government Relations:
Business and non-profits, energy, health care, land development.
**Contact:** Julie L Perrus

### Intellectual Property, Technology & Internet:
Patent procurement, trademark procurement, copyright procurement, internet and e-commerce, technology transfer and licensing, litigation.
**Contact:** Thomas J Oppold

### Litigation:
Business litigation, bankruptcy, employment, family law, intellectual property, product liability, real estate.
**Business Litigation Contact:** Christopher J Harristhal

### Real Estate:
Construction law, environmental regulation, land use, litigation, renewable energy, sustainable development, transactions, eminent domain and inverse condemnation, property tax appeals.
**Contact:** Peder A Larson

### Tax, Trusts & Estates:
Advise individuals, families, professionals and closely held entities regarding estate planning, financial, tax and general business legal matters on an ongoing basis and with special projects.
**Contact:** Michael J Smith

### International Work:
Advise on a full range of international matters - from business transactions to regulatory compliance - including compliance with customs regulations, business immigration issues, compliance with export control regulations, international growth strategies, compliance with international laws and regulations applicable to franchises, and business organizations and governance of foreign business operations. Interface with US and foreign governments to assist in customs, export control, tax and regulatory matters relating to clients' business operations.

### Clients:
Representative clients include: Anytime Fitness, Inc.; BP Amoco Corporation; Burger King Corporation; Chubb Group of Insurance; Digital River, Inc.; Ecowater; Edward Kraemer and Sons; Enbridge Energy Company; Gillette Childrens Speciality Healthcare; Harmon Glass Company; Hilton Inns, Inc.; Home Depot; Mall of America Company; Medicap Pharmacies, Inc.; Minneapolis Radiation Onocology; Mills Fleet Farm; Oppidan Investment Company; Outdoor Advertising Association of Minnesota; Polar Fab; Realife, Inc.; Ritchie Bros. Auctioneers, Ltd.; Robert Half International; Room & Board, Inc.; Shuffle Master Inc.; Silverleaf Resorts, Inc.; Skyline Displays, Inc.; Starwood Hotels and Resorts Worldwide, Inc.; Taco Bell Corp.; Uponor, Inc.; United States Steel; Wal-Mart Stores, Inc.; Zeller Realty Corporation.

## OFFICES

**MINNESOTA**

**MINNEAPOLIS:** 7900 Xerxes Avenue South, 1500 Wells Fargo Plaza, MN 55431
Tel: 952 835 3800   Fax: 952 896 3333
Email: info@larkinhoffman.com

# LINDQUIST & VENNUM LLP

www.lindquist.com **tel:** 612 371 3211 **fax:** 612 371 3207

**Managing Partner:** Dennis M O'Malley
Number of partners: 141   Number of lawyers: 184
Languages: *English, French, German, Spanish*

## Firm Overview:

Lindquist & Vennum is a business-oriented, general practice law firm with offices in Minnesota, Colorado and South Dakota. The firm is known for its extensive bankruptcy, corporate finance, real estate, M&A, private equity and commercial litigation practices, as well as for groups focused on financial institutions, intellectual property, renewable energy and health law. Also of note are its practices in product liability, insurance recovery, and securities and financial litigation.

## Main Areas of Practice:

**Bankruptcy:**
- Representation of the Chapter 11 trustee in the Petters Co., Inc. et al. Ponzi scheme cases, including the prosecution of clawback actions seeking in excess of $15 billion and several multimillion dollar settlements
- Representation of the Chapter 7 trustee for the Polaroid Corporation in obtaining a summary judgment in fraudulent transfer litigation subsequent to representing Polaroid in Chapter 11 and its $87.6 million Section 363 sale
- Representation of American Bank on appeal in defending the $13.6 million jury verdict that the firm obtained against TD Bank for aiding and abetting and conspiracy to commit loan fraud, perpetuated by Louis J Perlman and triggered by his bankruptcy filing

**Key Clients:** Doug Kelley, Chapter 11 Trustee; John Stoebner, Chapter 7 Trustee; American Bank, Polaroid.
**Contact:** James A Lodoen **Tel:** 612 371 3234
**Email:** jlodoen@lindquist.com

## Commercial Litigation:
- Representation of United Credit Recovery, achieving a significant jury verdict and complete absolution of plaintiff claims in connection with a commercial sale of charged-off accounts
- Successful representation of a corporate trustee in a surcharge action against claims of breach of duties of loyalty, communication and prudent investment
- Obtained injunctive relief in federal court on behalf of a participant bank in $100 million credit after servicer attempted to extend credit without obtaining unanimous consent of voting participants
- Successful defense of Ritrama, Inc. against claims for breach of a non-solicitation provision in a manufacturing agreement, misappropriation of trade secrets, and interference with contractual and business relations

**Key Clients:** First Premier, Wells Fargo, The Valspar Corporation.
**Contact:** Randall J Pattee **Tel:** 612 371 3250
**Email:** rpattee@lindquist.com

## Corporate Finance, M&A & Private Equity:
- Representation of Airborne, Inc. in $150 million sale to Schiff Nutrition International, Inc.
- Representation of Performance Food Group, Inc., a portfolio company of The Blackstone Group, in multiple acquisitions, including its purchase of Institution Food House, Inc., a $600 million foodservice distributor
- Representation of Baytex Energy Corp. in sale of North Dakota oil and gas assets to Magnum Hunter Resources Corporation for $312 million
- Representation of Pentair Ltd. in acquisition of Aquatic Eco-Systems, Inc. and Aquatic Habitats, Inc.

**Key Clients:** Norwest Equity Partners, Upsher-Smith Laboratories, Inc., Cushman & Wakefield, Stone Arch Capital, Tonka Bay Equity Partners.
**Contact:** Joseph J Humke **Tel:** 612 371 2453
**Email:** jhumke@lindquist.com

## Real Estate:
- Represented a Fortune 50 national retailer in dispositions and acquisitions of multiple sites nationwide
- Representation of one of the country's 10 largest banks in its lease negotiation for nearly 500,000 sqf office space as part of a consolidation of multiple offices
- Representation of a major national sporting goods retailer in numerous financing and lease matters, including a multi-property sale leaseback transaction in excess of $45 million
- Representation and counsel to the legal and real estate departments of a national motor carrier in connection with its real estate purchases, sales, leases, land use and site development matters

**Key Clients:** Target Corporation, Cushman & Wakefield/NorthMarq Real Estate Services, United Properties, Sportsman's Warehouse, Life Time Fitness, Inc., Opus Development Corporation, Trammell Crow Company, Bechtel Corporation.
**Contact:** LB Guthrie **Tel:** 612 371 3942
**Email:** lguthrie@lindquist.com

## Financial Institutions:
- Represented buyers or sellers in 15 branch sale or whole bank transactions announced in 2012, including the acquisition of a Florida bank by a Minnesota bank holding company, and the joint acquisition of assets of a liquidating Wisconsin bank by two acquirers

- Assisted a nationwide card issuer with the development and implementation of a tax-related secured credit card product, including negotiation of ancillary servicing agreements with one of the nation's largest income tax preparers and its franchisees
- Represented the administrator in connection with the establishment of national mobile wallet and prepaid card programs, including negotiation of contracts with issuing banks, service providers and marketing vendors
- Represented a secured creditor in an $80 million complex financing transaction involving a pledge of securities by an Indian tribe

**Key Clients:** Wells Fargo, First Premier Bank, Merchants Bank, Central Bank.
**Contact:** Steven J Johnson **Tel:** 612 371 3548
**Email:** sjohnson@lindquist.com

## International Work:

The firm regularly assists clients with international activities involving strategic alliances (including joint ventures for product development and distribution); foreign distributors; foreign manufacturing operations; OEM manufacturing; private-label manufacturing; raw-materials supply; dispute resolution; and acquisition of foreign companies and product lines. The firm's reach is extended globally through its membership in TAGLaw, a

# ROBINS, KAPLAN, MILLER & CIRESI LLP

www.rkmc.com **tel:** 612 349 8500 **fax:** 612 339 4181

**Chairman:** Martin R Lueck
**Managing Partner:** Steven A Schumeister
Number of partners: 99  Number of lawyers: 237

## Firm Overview:
Founded in 1938, Robins, Kaplan, Miller & Ciresi LLP represents large corporations, insurance companies, other businesses and individuals as both plaintiffs and defendants. The firm is frequently engaged in high stakes, complex litigation.

## Main Areas of Practice:

### Antitrust & Trade Regulation:
Extensive experience bringing and defending private antitrust cases including price-fixing and other conspiracy claims, monopolization, unfair competition, Walker-Process claims, and Noerr-Pennington defenses. Fully fluent in all areas of antitrust, the group represents clients from a wide range of industries and is adept at handling antitrust allegations arising from complex business disputes, as well as matters involving the intersection of antitrust and intellectual property laws. Significant retentions include the defense of *Fortune* 500 companies against private Sherman Act allegations and the prosecution of a class action against Visa, MasterCard and financial institutions for price-fixing of merchant charges.

### Business Litigation:
This group handles complex, high-stakes litigation, as well as bottom-line-sensitive matters for businesses of every size. Practice areas include antitrust, class actions, corporate criminal defense, distributorships and dealer/franchising, entertainment, financial, healthcare, intellectual property, and special business situations. The group represents Fortune 500 companies, Midwest multi-nationals, governments, individuals and members of the food and beverage, retail and manufacturing industries.

### Entertainment & Media Litigation:
Represents the talent side of film, television, and music industry clients. Litigates matters in Federal and State Court, and arbitrations and proceedings before the entertainment guilds, the California Labor Commissioner, and the American Film and Marketing Association. Represents actors, directors, producers, writers, musicians, entertainment executives, performing rights organizations, independent motion picture and television distribution companies, talent agencies, personal managers, commercial and music video production companies, advertising agencies, and other owners of copyrights, trademarks, publicity rights and other intellectual property.

### Financial Litigation:
Represents institutional investors, mutual funds, insurance companies, venture capital funds, and hedge funds as plaintiffs and as defendants. Cases involved issues relating to residential mortgage-backed securities and other structured finance products, alleged manipulation in the futures and derivatives markets, alleged misrepresentations in securities offerings, alleged financial statement misrepresentations, alleged misrepresentations regarding the success of mergers, SEC investigations, disputes among shareholders in closely-held corporations, disputes between the general and limited partners in investment partnerships, and ERISA fiduciary duty litigation.

### Insurance:
National and international reputation for excellence in handling and trying property and liability insurance coverage matters, bad-faith claims, subrogation recovery claims, negligent inspection claims, reinsurance claims, challenges to insurance market practices, and other tort, contract, and class-action claims against insurers. Has handled some of the most complex cases the insurance industry has known, including cases arising out of the World Trade Center attack, Hurricane Katrina, Northridge earthquake, Big Dig, and the Tohoku earthquake and tsunami.

### Intellectual Property Litigation:
Nationally recognized IP litigation practice. Firm has won several high profile patent infringement trials, including three judgments over $100 million. The firm has also successfully monetized several patent portfolios. Nine times the firm has monetized a patent portfolio in an amount exceeding $100 million. The firm has also successfully defended against patent infringement suits.

### Life Sciences & Hatch-Waxman Intellectual Property Litigation:
The Life Sciences & Hatch-Waxman Litigation Group represents companies in the pharmaceutical, biopharmaceutical, biotechnology, and medical device industries in patent, trade secret, and other intellectual property disputes. The group combines extensive litigation and trial experience - including Hatch-Waxman Act actions on behalf of generic pharmaceutical companies - with significant legal, business and scientific depth.

### Mass Tort:
Represents consumers injured by defective drugs and medical devices, individuals injured or killed in accidents and environmental disasters, and consumers harmed by unfair business practices. Representation includes property owners injured by the recalled Imprelis herbicide, the State of Minnesota and Blue Cross and Blue Shield in their historic suit against big tobacco, and individuals in their claims regarding the recalled St. Jude "Silzone" heart valves, Vioxx, the Parkinson disease drug Mirapex, the smoking cessation drug Chantix and recalled DePuy hip systems.

### Trademark & Advertising Disputes:
Represents both plaintiffs and defendants in trademark and trade dress disputes including those involving product color, shape, and packaging; trademark dilution, tarnishment and disparagement; internet "Key Word" advertising; internet domain name disputes involving domain "tasting," "parking" and "typo-squatting"; rights of publicity; and enforcement of co-existence and trademark licensing agreements. Also represents clients in advertising disputes arising under the federal Lanham Act and applicable state laws.

### Real Estate Litigation & Franchise Litigation:
Represents clients in real estate litigation matters including, but not limited to, lending disputes, investor disputes, partnership disputes, contractor disputes, disputes involving brokerage commissions, and disputes involving technical development and construction obligations. Represents franchisors, licensors and suppliers in franchise litigation.

## OFFICES

**MINNESOTA**
**MINNEAPOLIS:** 2800 LaSalle Plaza, 800 LaSalle Avenue, MN 55402
Tel: 612 349 8500  Fax: 612 339 4181

**GEORGIA**
**ATLANTA:** One Atlantic Center, 1201 West Peachtree Street, GA 30309
Tel: 404 760 4300  Fax: 404 233 1267

**MASSACHUSETTS**
**BOSTON:** 800 Boylston, 25th Floor, MA 02199
Tel: 617 267 2300  Fax: 617 267 8288

**CALIFORNIA**
**LOS ANGELES:** 2049 Century Park East, Suite 3400, CA 90067
Tel: 310 552 0130  Fax: 310 229 5800

**FLORIDA**
**NAPLES:** 711 Fifth Avenue South, Suite 201, FL 34102
Tel: 239 430 7070  Fax: 239 213 1970

**NEW YORK**
**NEW YORK:** 601 Lexington Avenue, 34th Floor, NY 10022
Tel: 212 980 7400  Fax: 212 980 7499

ROBINS, KAPLAN, MILLER & CIRESI LLP

# WINTHROP & WEINSTINE, P.A.

**www.**winthrop.com **tel:** 612 604 6400 **fax:** 612 604 6800

**Managing Partner:** Scott J Dongoske
Number of partners: 70
Number of lawyers: 106

## Firm Overview:

Winthrop & Weinstine, P.A., is an established and successful law firm focused on client results and building strong client relationships. The firm is practical in its approach, responsive to clients and highly competitive. Attorneys rely on innovation rather than outmoded tradition – creativity rather than standard formulas. The firm enjoys steady growth by meeting the diverse needs of clients ranging from individuals and emerging-growth businesses to Fortune 100 companies. The firm is a member of the Law Firm Alliance, an international network of mid-size law firms.

## Main Areas of Practice:

Winthrop & Weinstine's full spectrum of practice areas, team approach, in-depth experience, cost-effective service, and passionate attention to details ensure the firm meets the particular needs of its clients.

### Banking & Finance:

The firm represents bank holding companies, national banking associations, state banking institutions, trust companies, mortgage lenders, insurance companies, asset-based lenders, and governmental entities with mortgage loan programs. Whether it is state and federal bank regulatory issues, mergers, acquisitions and dispositions, commercial lending transactions, construction and bridge loans, corporate restructures, bankruptcy, or credit transaction issues, Winthrop & Weinstine offers unparalleled service and advice.

### Business & Commercial Litigation:

The firm's exceptional trial lawyers tackle complex litigation, representing clients from Fortune 100 organizations to closely held businesses and partnerships. With extensive experience in products liability, shareholder disputes, employment law, construction litigation, insurance, financial services, securities, fraud, intellectual property, real estate, antitrust and unfair business practices, and white-collar crime, a trusted team directs the best course of action.

### Corporate & Transactions:

Winthrop & Weinstine provides legal and business counsel to all sizes and varieties of businesses, representing entrepreneurs and established companies, both privately held and publicly traded. The firm's attorneys are highly experienced in structuring, negotiating and closing sophisticated business transactions, including mergers, acquisitions and dispositions, joint ventures, private equity debt investment, and other strategic relationships. Winthrop & Weinstine securities attorneys have national experience assisting issuers and underwriters on initial and secondary public offerings, SEC, FINRA and marketplace compliance issues, private placements, and equity and debt financings.

### Health:

Winthrop & Weinstine has its finger on the pulse of today's evolving health care industry for regulatory or compliance issues, and representation before state and federal agencies, at the legislature, or in the courtroom. The firm represents a variety of health care providers, including hospitals and clinics; home health care organizations and systems; physician groups; nursing homes; imaging centers; dentists, specialists, pharmacists, other health professionals; trade associations; and others. In addition, the firm's expertise extends to medical devices, pharmaceutical, and life sciences companies on general business, patent, trademark, and liability issues.

### Intellectual Property:

Winthrop & Weinstine offers a full range of intellectual property services, encompassing IP and patent litigation, patent prosecution, trademark and brand management, copyrights, Internet and domain name issues, and technology issues. While Winthrop & Weinstine's IP attorneys are intensely focused on enforcing and defending their clients' rights and commercial competitiveness, they are equally intense in efforts to help avoid disputes and counsel about infringing upon the rights of other companies. The firm's IP attorneys also perform intellectual property audits to assist clients in prioritizing their resources and maximizing the value of their intellectual property assets.

### Legislative & Regulatory:

Winthrop & Weinstine has one of the best-known practices of this nature in Minnesota. The firm's attorneys have built key relationships over 35 years of successfully securing legislative and regulatory outcomes for local, state, and national clients, representing them before the Minnesota Legislature and state regulatory agencies, including the Minnesota Public Utilities Commission, Department of Commerce, Department of Transportation, Department of Revenue, Environmental Quality Board, and the Pollution Control Agency. At the federal level, the firm represents clients before the EPA, FERC, and FCC.

## PRACTICE AREAS

Appellate
Banking & Finance
Business & Commercial Litigation
Corporate Law & Transactions
Emerging Companies & Entrepreneurial Services
Employment
Estate Planning & Business Succession Planning
Franchise
Health
Insurance
Intellectual Property & Brand Management
Legislative & Regulatory
Mergers & Acquisitions
Patent & Technology
Real Estate
Securities & Corporate Finance
Tax

## OFFICES

MINNESOTA

**MINNEAPOLIS:** Capella Tower, 225 South Sixth Street, Suite 3500
Tel: 612 604 6400   Fax: 612 604 6800
Email: sdongoske@winthrop.com

### Real Estate & Tax:

The firm represents local and national clients in all aspects of real estate development, investment, and operations, including land development, common interest communities, affordable housing, land use/eminent domain, financing (both construction and permanent), tax credit syndication, commercial leasing, golf courses, hotels, real estate investment funds, 1031 exchanges, joint ventures, tax exempt organizations, and more. The firm is nationally known for its expertise in real estate development and finance transactions involving state and federal tax credits, including Low-Income Housing Tax Credits, Historic Rehabilitation Tax Credits, and New Markets Tax Credits. Clients are large and small, and include for-profit and non-profit developers, investors, lenders, housing authorities, cities, and builders. In addition to the real estate tax representation, the firm's tax representation includes corporate (both C and S corporations) and partnership tax planning, tax structuring for mergers and acquisitions, and tax disclosure for securities offerings.

WINTHROP W WEINSTINE
ATTORNEYS AND COUNSELORS AT LAW

A firm difference®

## How lawyers are ranked

Every year we carry out thousands of in-depth interviews with clients in order to assess the reputations and expertise of business lawyers worldwide. The qualities we look for (and which determine rankings) include technical legal ability, professional conduct, client service, commercial awareness/astuteness, diligence, commitment, and other qualities most valued by the client. For details of our research team, see p.5.

## MISSISSIPPI: An Introduction

### Contributed by Butler, Snow, O'Mara, Stevens & Cannada, PLLC

Mississippi has made significant strides to provide an environment that is conducive to the growth of existing and new businesses. These factors include: a continued focus on improving the state's public education system; an ample state and local tax structure including relatively low income and franchise taxes; economic incentives of new businesses; a quality workforce subject to balanced labor and employment laws; a central-US location with direct access to Mississippi River and Tennessee-Tombigbee River Waterway ports and two deepwater ports located on the Gulf of Mexico; a solid rail and highway transportation infrastructure; and a balanced legal system vastly improved with the passage of major tort reform.

### Economic Development Incentives

Tax-exempt financing programs in Mississippi offer eligible companies below-market borrowing costs and other incentives. These programs are administered at two levels: statewide through the Mississippi Business Finance Corporation (MBFC) and the Mississippi Development Authority (MDA), and locally through cities, counties, regional planning and development districts, and economic development authorities.

The MBFC is a statewide financing source that offers tax-exempt variable and fixed rate financing and flow-through taxable financing. MBFC tax-exempt financing can also be used in designated areas along with state and federal new markets tax credits. It also provides certain related tax incentives, avoidance of contractor's tax using structured purchasing procedures and sales/use tax exemptions for project purchases with bond proceeds; a bond amortization income tax credit; and, with municipal and county approval, abatement of a portion of property taxes on the project.

Property tax exemptions, with certain approvals, are also available for all types of inventories. Projects over $100 million qualify for a special negotiated fee-in-lieu of property taxes instead of an exemption. Various new jobs and other income tax credits and new jobs income tax rebates are also available.

MDA administers the Community Development Block Grant Program (CDBG) to fund publicly owned infrastructure to aid with the construction, renovation or expansion of businesses and industrial facilities.

Mississippi cities and counties may issue tax increment financing (TIF) bonds to encourage development within designated areas by financing public infrastructure improvements for public or private projects without issuing general obligation bonds. Developers may also utilize a special public improvement district to finance various public infrastructure improvements that are repaid with tax assessments levied on real property within the district.

### Labor and Employment Laws

Mississippi is a both a right-to-work state and an at-will employment state. Absent a contract to the contrary and subject to narrow and limited exceptions, the employer is free to terminate an employee's employment.

### Corporate Income and Franchise Taxes

The Mississippi Corporate Income Tax applies to the entire net income of a corporation if its business activity occurs only in Mississippi. The income of a multistate corporation operating in Mississippi is allocated or apportioned to Mississippi for income tax purposes depending upon where the production of income takes place and whether it is classified as either business or nonbusiness.

The "business income" of a multi-state corporation consists of (1) income arising from activities or transactions in the ordinary course of the taxpayer's trade or business (the "transactional test"); and (2) income from the acquisition, management and/or disposition of tangible or intangible property provided such acquisition, management and/or disposition constitutes an integral part of the taxpayer's regular trade or business operations (the "functional test").

A multi-state corporation with business income must use applicable apportionment formulas to determine the portion of its business income that is subject to Mississippi income tax. The nonbusiness income of a multistate corporation is generally allocated to the state where the income is earned.

Mississippi income tax law contains exclusion for any gain resulting from the sale of equity interests in certain domestic corporations, limited partnerships (except limited liability partnerships) or limited liability companies held for more than one year.

Mississippi income tax law follows federal income tax law regarding corporate reorganizations, to the extent they are consistent with Mississippi law.

The Mississippi Corporate Franchise Tax is an excise tax on the privilege of doing business as a business corporation. This tax is imposed on corporations, associations, joint-stock companies, and partnerships treated as corporations for tax purposes. Organizations that are exempt from this tax include mutual savings banks, many nonprofit organizations, and business and civic leagues.

The corporate franchise tax is calculated at the rate of $2.50 for each $1,000 of the value of the taxable capital of the corporation. Taxable capital is measured by the sum of the corporation's outstanding stock, paid-in capital, retained earnings and surplus and also includes deferred taxes, deferred gains and deferred income, as well as contingent liabilities and all true reserves. It generally does not include reserves for bad debts, accumulated depreciation, debts or other obligations of the corporation. Taxable capital of a parent corporation does not include

the capital of its subsidiaries provided the parent corporation meets the statutory definition of a holding company. A multistate corporation operating in Mississippi must apportion taxable capital among or between states in which it operates using a two-factor formula consisting of the real and tangible personal property ratio and the gross receipts ratio.

**Legal System**

Mississippi has enacted major tort reform that includes reasonable limits on noneconomic and punitive damages and venue provisions more favorable to potential defendants. These reforms, combined with the Mississippi Supreme Court's decision to return to traditional plaintiff joinder rules, have significantly decreased mass tort litigation and so enhanced the state's business environment.

# CORPORATE/COMMERCIAL

Commentary about individuals can be found under their firm's paragraph. If the firm has no paragraph (is not ranked) look at Other Notable Practitioners.

## Corporate/Commercial
### Leading Firms

**Band 1**

Baker, Donelson, Bearman, Caldwell & Berkowitz, PC *

Butler, Snow, O'Mara, Stevens & Cannada, PLLC *

Watkins & Eager PLLC *

Jones Walker LLP *

**Band 2**

Brunini, Grantham, Grower & Hewes, PLLC *

Phelps Dunbar LLP *

Wise Carter Child & Caraway, Professional Association

### Leading Individuals

**Band 1**

| | |
|---|---|
| Cannada R Barry | Butler, Snow, O'Mara, Stevens & Cannada * |
| Chatham Jr Henry E | Wise Carter Child & Caraway, Professional |
| Painter William S | Baker, Donelson, Bearman, Caldwell * |

**Band 2**

| | |
|---|---|
| Bush III F M | Phelps Dunbar LLP |
| Fair George R | Watkins & Eager PLLC * |
| Hafter Jerome C | Phelps Dunbar LLP |
| Houston III Jamie G | Watkins & Eager PLLC * |
| Mendenhall William | Baker, Donelson, Bearman, Caldwell * |
| Weems Walter S | Brunini, Grantham, Grower & Hewes, PLLC |
| Wilson Stephen M | Bradley Arant Boult Cummings LLP (ONP)[†] |

**Band 3**

| | |
|---|---|
| Hodge Jr E Clifton | Baker, Donelson, Bearman, Caldwell * |
| Jacobs Gina | Jones Walker LLP * |
| Johnson III Charles F | Butler, Snow, O'Mara, Stevens & Cannada * |
| Martin David L | Jones Walker LLP * |

\* Indicates firm / individual with profile.
[†]ONP = Other Notable Practitioner.

## Corporate/Commercial: Banking & Finance
### Leading Individuals

**Band 1**

| | |
|---|---|
| Fair George R | Watkins & Eager PLLC * |
| Harrison J Clifford | Butler, Snow, O'Mara, Stevens & Cannada * |
| Landrum Craig | Jones Walker LLP * |
| Parrott Charles N | Adams and Reese LLP (ONP)[†] * |
| Tate Granville | Brunini, Grantham, Grower & Hewes, PLLC |
| Wilmesherr Edward A | Butler, Snow, O'Mara, Stevens & Cannada * |

## Corporate/Commercial: Bankruptcy
### Leading Individuals

**Band 1**

| | |
|---|---|
| Geno Craig M | Harris Jernigan & Geno PLLC (ONP)[†] |
| Henderson Derek | Derek A Henderson Attorney (ONP)[†] |
| Maddux Christopher R | Butler, Snow, O'Mara, Stevens & Cannada * |
| O'Mara James W | Phelps Dunbar LLP |
| Rosenblatt Stephen W | Butler, Snow, O'Mara, Stevens & Cannada * |

## Corporate/Commercial: Gaming & Licensing
### Leading Individuals

**Band 1**

| | |
|---|---|
| Andress Scott | Balch & Bingham LLP (ONP)[†] |
| Hise Daniel G | Butler, Snow, O'Mara, Stevens & Cannada * |
| McDaniel Jr Dan M | Baker, Donelson, Bearman, Caldwell * |
| Shepherd III Thomas B | Jones Walker LLP * |

## Corporate/Commercial: Municipal Finance
### Leading Individuals

**Star individuals**

| | |
|---|---|
| Lazarus Robert | Jones Walker LLP * |

**Band 1**

| | |
|---|---|
| Clark Jr Donald | Butler, Snow, O'Mara, Stevens & Cannada * |
| Taylor Zachary | Jones Walker LLP * |

**Band 2**

| | |
|---|---|
| Edds Steve | Baker, Donelson, Bearman, Caldwell * |
| England John F | Butler, Snow, O'Mara, Stevens & Cannada * |
| Varner Thad W | Butler, Snow, O'Mara, Stevens & Cannada * |
| Wall Randall | Jones Walker LLP * |

## Band 1

### Baker, Donelson, Bearman, Caldwell & Berkowitz, PC
See profile on p.2313

**THE FIRM** This firm enjoys an excellent reputation for corporate and transactional work in Mississippi, and routinely handles high-profile and high-value matters. The team is active in a variety of work, including gambling, mergers and acquisitions, financing and municipal bonds. An impressive client roster includes financial institutions, as well as telecom and gaming companies.

**KEY INDIVIDUALS** Peers describe **Dan McDaniel** (see p.1606) as *"the preeminent gaming lawyer in Mississippi."* He handles corporate and regulatory compliance matters for the firm's largest gaming clients. **William Painter** (see p.1606) specializes in corporate work such as administrative matters and restructurings, often with respect to the

healthcare sector. He also advises clients in connection with mergers and acquisitions and general corporate matters. **Steve Edds** (see p.1602) has considerable expertise in the public finance sphere, routinely advising local and state entities in connection with municipal bonds. He handles bond issuances, refinancings and government debt. **William Mendenhall** (see p.1606) continues to garner praise for a broad practice which includes general corporate counsel, mergers and acquisitions, real estate transactions and other developments. Sources confirm that he is *"a very good lawyer."* **Clifton Hodge** (see p.1604) recently joined the firm from Wise Carter. He has a general corporate practice, including mergers and acquisitions as well as business structuring and planning.

## Butler, Snow, O'Mara, Stevens & Cannada, PLLC
See profile on p.1613

**THE FIRM** This market-leading firm is known for its impressive breadth of expertise and bench strength. It is held in the highest regard for its large transactional practice, and regularly services clients in the oil and gas, gaming, real estate and commercial sectors. The team recently acted as transactional counsel to Willmut Oil and Gas Company in a stock sale to EnergySouth.
**Sources say:** *"They have everything there. A high-quality firm."*
**KEY INDIVIDUALS Barry Cannada** (see p.1602) leads the firm's business services team and is highly regarded for his transactional work. He also counsels corporate clients on business structuring and operations matters. **Donald Clark** (see p.1602) specializes in municipal finance, and is regarded by sources as *"without question one of the movers and shakers"* in the field. He advised the State Bond Commission on a series of high-value general obligation bonds. Experienced practitioner **Clifford Harrison** (see p.1603) is described by market sources as *"a great banking lawyer."* He advises a number of regional financial institutions on a range of regulatory compliance matters. **Daniel Hise** (see p.1604) is an experienced gaming law specialist, and is highly regarded for his in-depth knowledge of regulatory and administrative matters. Sources attest that he is *"very capable"* and *"a very good lawyer."* *"Excellent lawyer"* **Christopher Maddux** (see p.1605) specializes in bankruptcy law. He handles the full range of bankruptcy litigation and restructuring matters. **Stephen Rosenblatt** (see p.1607) is another of the firm's specialist bankruptcy attorneys. He frequently advises clients on Chapter 7 and Chapter 11 matters, and has represented First Commercial Bank in a number of loan workout and restructuring matters. **Edward Wilmesherr** (see p.1610) is noted for his handling of banking regulatory matters. He leads the firm's work advising 46 regional and community banks on compliance with the Dodd-Frank Act and Consumer Finance Protection Bureau regulations. **John England** (see p.1602) has extensive experience in municipal finance matters and is head of the firm's public finance and incentives group. He acted as co-underwriter's counsel to Piper Jaffray in the Metropolitan Government of Nashville and Davidson County's $227 million issuance of general obligation refunding bonds. **Thad Varner** (see p.1609) is also a member of the firm's public finance practice. He acted as bond counsel to Mississippi Development Bank in an advanced refunding of highway construction bonds. **Charles Johnson** (see p.1604) has a broad corporate practice with a focus on the healthcare sector. He also handles mergers and acquisitions as well as general corporate matters.

## Watkins & Eager PLLC
See profile on p.1617

**THE FIRM** This compact corporate practice is recognized for the strength of its corporate, transactional, banking and municipal finance work. The team continues to represent key clients Regions Bank and Trustmark National Bank in large corporate loans. Its impressive client roster also includes American Honda Services, BancorpSouth Bank and Chevron.

**KEY INDIVIDUALS** *"Fantastic lawyer"* **George Fair** (see p.1603) is renowned for his expertise in banking and corporate matters. He frequently represents financial institutions and public utilities before the Mississippi Public Services Commission. **Jamie Houston** (see p.1604) is recognized for his expertise in tax matters. He has represented multinational oil and chemical companies before the Department of Revenue to resolve a number of tax issues. He has also acted on behalf of various individuals and corporations in tax-related matters.

## Jones Walker LLP
See profile on p.1378

**THE FIRM** The team at Jones Walker handles a wide range of corporate matters, including public finance, private equity, banking, gaming regulatory and transactional matters. The firm supplements its broad expertise with an excellent geographical reach across the East and South East of the USA.
**KEY INDIVIDUALS Craig Landrum** (see p.1605) receives excellent feedback from market sources for his banking and finance expertise. One interviewee describes him as *"the top banking regulatory lawyer in the state."* **Robert Lazarus** (see p.1605) is widely considered the preeminent public finance lawyer in the state. Sources praise his innovative approach to municipal finance work, with interviewees describing him as *"a magician"* and *"a fantastic lawyer."* Sources describe **Thomas Shepherd** (see p.1608) as *"very knowledgeable,"* and note that *"the gaming law of Mississippi is his specialty."* He handles a range of matters on behalf of major casino companies, including corporate and real estate matters. **Zachary Taylor** (see p.1609) specializes in public finance work, particularly on behalf of state and local government entities. Sources highlight his commercial awareness and substantial experience in the field, naming him *"a very fine lawyer."* Special counsel **Randall Wall** (see p.1610) is another of the firm's public finance specialists. He acts as bond counsel, issuer's counsel and developer's counsel to a range of school districts, municipal bodies, state entities and universities. *"Excellent lawyer"* **Gina Jacobs** (see p.1604) has a general practice which includes commercial finance, mergers and acquisitions, and business planning and transactions. **David Martin** (see p.1605) is recognized for his representation of insurance industry clients in a broad range of matters. He also handles securities and banking work.

## Band 2

### Brunini, Grantham, Grower & Hewes, PLLC
See profile on p.1611

**THE FIRM** The corporate team at this firm offers clients a broad range of expertise in tax, banking, mergers and acquisitions, and general commercial matters. The group represents clients from a variety of sectors, including telecoms, media, retail and healthcare. The firm has a recognized statewide presence, with offices in Jackson, Biloxi and Columbus.
**Sources say:** *"Excellent value for money."*
**KEY INDIVIDUALS** Banking specialist **Granville Tate** advises financial institutions in connection with mergers

and acquisitions, regulatory compliance and general corporate matters. He acts for a number of regional and community banks. **Walter Weems** is experienced in a wide range of corporate matters, including transactions, regulatory compliance, entity formation and business structuring. Key clients include entities from the media, timber, hospitality and manufacturing industries.

## Phelps Dunbar LLP
See profile on p.1383

**THE FIRM** This solid corporate practice handles a broad range of matters, including bankruptcy, mergers and acquisitions, public finance and gaming. The firm recently served as bond counsel to the City of Louisville, Yazoo City and the Wayne County School District. The firm has an impressive reach across the state, with offices in Tupelo, Jackson and Gulfport.
**KEY INDIVIDUALS James O'Mara** is considered *"preeminent"* in the bankruptcy sphere for his expertise in Chapter 11 and corporate reorganization matters. Clients appreciate his responsiveness and diligence. Clients praise **Jerome Hafter** for his *"deep understanding of the law"* and *"high-quality work."* He is recognized for his broad corporate practice and handling of high-value mergers and acquisitions. **Mike Bush** handles a wide spectrum of corporate work for clients in the banking, healthcare and manufacturing industries. He is also noted for his handling of corporate and municipal finance matters.

## Wise Carter Child & Caraway, Professional Association

**THE FIRM** This firm has significant capabilities in a variety of corporate matters, including mergers and acquisitions, entity formation, joint ventures, and business planning and structuring. The team is based primarily in the firm's Jackson office, and advises a wide range of public and private sector clients, financial institutions and construction companies.
**KEY INDIVIDUALS Henry Chatham** offers a broad and highly rated corporate practice. He advises clients on business structuring, mergers and acquisitions, contract negotiations and bankruptcy.

## Other Notable Practitioners

**Scott Andress** has a specialist gaming practice at Balch & Bingham LLP. He handles a variety of transactional and regulatory matters for a number of major casino companies. **Stephen Wilson** of Bradley Arant Boult Cummings LLP is active in a broad range of securities and general corporate matters. Key clients come from the natural resources and agriculture sectors, among others. Jackson-based **Charles Parrott** (see p.1607) is head of the banking and finance practice at Adams and Reese LLP. He is highly regarded for his years of experience advising financial institutions. **Craig Geno** of Harris Jernigan & Geno PLLC is described as the *"best bankruptcy lawyer in this state"* by one commentator. He handles the full range of bankruptcy and restructuring matters. **Derek Henderson** of Derek A Henderson Attorney is another of Mississippi's most highly regarded bankruptcy specialists. He frequently represents trustees in insolvency cases.

# ENERGY & NATURAL RESOURCES

Commentary about individuals can be found under their firm's paragraph. If the firm has no paragraph (is not ranked) look at Other Notable Practitioners.

## Energy & Natural Resources
### Leading Firms

**Band 1**
Adams and Reese LLP *
Brunini, Grantham, Grower & Hewes, PLLC *
Copeland Cook Taylor & Bush, A Professional Association

**Band 2**
Blair & Bondurant, PA

**Band 3**
Biggs, Ingram, Solop & Carlson, PLLC
Jones & Nix PLLC
Wise Carter Child & Caraway, Professional Association

### Leading Individuals

**Band 1**

| | | |
|---|---|---|
| Blair William | Blair & Bondurant, PA | |
| Bondurant Si Morgan | Blair & Bondurant, PA | |
| Montjoy II R Wilson | Butler, Snow, O'Mara, Stevens (ONP) [†] | |
| Stewart Jefferson | Adams and Reese LLP * | |
| Taylor Glenn | Copeland Cook Taylor & Bush | |

**Band 2**

| | |
|---|---|
| Bush Glenn | Copeland Cook Taylor & Bush |
| Halford James L | Brunini, Grantham, Grower & Hewes, PLLC |
| Jones Roger | Jones & Nix PLLC |
| Sheldon Jerry | Adams and Reese LLP * |
| Ueltschey Watts | Brunini, Grantham, Grower & Hewes, PLLC |

**Band 3**

| | |
|---|---|
| Hall Henderson | Wise Carter Child & Caraway |
| Ingram Stan | Biggs, Ingram, Solop & Carlson, PLLC |
| Miller Dennis | Jones Walker LLP (ONP) [†] |
| Nix James | Jones & Nix PLLC |
| Trotter Jeffrey | Adams and Reese LLP * |

* Indicates firm / individual with profile.
[†] ONP = Other Notable Practitioner.

## Band 1

### Adams and Reese LLP
See profile on p.1372

**THE FIRM** This market-leading firm has a long history in the oil and gas industry as transactional, regulatory and litigation counsel. The firm acted as local counsel to Macquarie Infrastructure Partners II in the acquisition of midstream energy facility Leaf River Energy from NGS Energy. The team represents numerous clients before the Mississippi State Oil and Gas Board (MSOGB).
**Sources say:** *"They are well recognized in the exploration and production area. An excellent firm."*
**KEY INDIVIDUALS** Experienced practitioner **Jefferson Stewart** (see p.1608) offers clients expertise in a broad range of oil and gas exploration and production matters, including litigation, contract drafting and representation before the MSOGB. **Jerry Sheldon** (see p.1607) enjoys a strong market reputation for title work for oil and gas

companies, as well as having significant regulatory expertise. His practice also extends into real estate and forestry matters. Sources name him *"the preeminent title attorney in Mississippi."* Energy and environmental team leader **Jeffrey Trotter** (see p.1609) has a general energy practice. He is active in both contentious and noncontentious work in the oil and gas sector, and has experience with mergers and acquisitions and financing for energy projects.

### Brunini, Grantham, Grower & Hewes, PLLC
See profile on p.1611

**THE FIRM** This firm is a well-established player in the energy regulatory and litigation arenas. The team advises on energy project development, and routinely represents clients before various state bodies, such as the MSOGB, the Mississippi Department of Environmental Equality and the Mississippi Public Service Commission.
**KEY INDIVIDUALS James Halford** is highly regarded for his expertise in natural gas pipeline matters. He has noted experience in Public Service Commission matters, and is also acknowledged for his work in the electricity field. **Watts Ueltschey** has extensive experience of the oil and gas industry, including title matters, contracts, regulatory compliance and litigation.

### Copeland Cook Taylor & Bush, A Professional Association

**THE FIRM** This firm handles a broad range of work for clients in the oil and gas sector in Mississippi. The team has a wealth of experience in title work, litigation, transactions and regulatory matters, including representation before the MSOGB and other state bodies. The firm also has a strong showing in environmental matters, including permitting and regulatory compliance and enforcement.
**Sources say:** *"They are very well known and highly regarded for work in the exploration and production area."*
**KEY INDIVIDUALS** Sources describe **Glenn Taylor** as *"meticulous, with a complete grasp of oil and gas matters from A to Z."* He is highly regarded for both his energy litigation practice and strengths as a courtroom lawyer. **Glenn Bush** specializes in regulatory and title work for the oil and gas sector. He represents numerous clients in MSOGB matters, as well as handling transactional and contentious work.

## Band 2

### Blair & Bondurant, PA

**THE FIRM** This boutique energy firm offers clients significant expertise in oil and gas regulations and title work. The four-lawyer team handles the full gamut of contentious and noncontentious work for its clients, including litigation and representation at both state and federal level.
**Sources say:** *"A niche practice that does a great job."*
**KEY INDIVIDUALS William Blair** is active in both the regulatory and litigation spheres for a number of oil and

gas companies, routinely representing clients before the MSOGB. The *"excellent"* **Si Morgan Bondurant** focuses on title work for oil and gas companies, and has experience in energy-related real estate matters.

## Band 3

### Biggs, Ingram, Solop & Carlson, PLLC

**THE FIRM** The energy practice at this firm covers a broad range of areas, including regulatory compliance, oil and gas title work, and litigation. The firm is well regarded for its expertise in the exploration and production in fossil fuels projects. The team is also active before the MSOGB.
**KEY INDIVIDUALS Stan Ingram** *"is known and well regarded in the exploration and production area,"* according to one commentator. Ingram handles oil and gas work as part of a broader regulatory practice.

### Jones & Nix PLLC

**THE FIRM** This boutique firm specializes in oil and gas regulatory and title work. The two-partner team is well respected for its representation of clients before the MSOGB. The firm is based in Jackson.
**Sources say:** *"Really excellent title lawyers."*
**KEY INDIVIDUALS Roger Jones** focuses on title matters for companies in the oil and gas and broader energy industry. He is also well regarded for his work in real estate. Fellow principal **James Nix** also specializes in title work for energy companies. Nix is highly regarded in the market for his regulatory expertise.

### Wise Carter Child & Caraway, Professional Association

**THE FIRM** The energy and natural resources practice at this three-office firm provides regulatory compliance advice to a number of large clients in the energy industry. The firm frequently represents clients before the Mississippi Public Service Commission and the Federal Energy Regulatory Commission.
**KEY INDIVIDUALS Henderson Hall** *"enjoys a great reputation"* for administrative and public service commission work. He also represents energy clients in contentious matters and commercial litigation.

## Other Notable Practitioners

**Wilson Montjoy** (see p.1606) of Butler, Snow, O'Mara, Stevens & Cannada, PLLC offers a broad energy practice, including litigation, regulatory and natural gas pipeline work. Key clients include the Southern Natural Gas Company. **Dennis Miller** (see p.1606) of Jones Walker LLP has a respected energy practice primarily focused on regulatory matters, including extensive experience before the Public Service Commission. Alongside his work with the Commission, he handles governmental relations matters

# ENVIRONMENT

Commentary about individuals can be found under their firm's paragraph. If the firm has no paragraph (is not ranked) look at Other Notable Practitioners.

| Environment |
| --- |
| **Leading Firms** |

**Band 1**
Brunini, Grantham, Grower & Hewes, PLLC *
Butler, Snow, O'Mara, Stevens & Cannada, PLLC *

**Band 2**
Balch & Bingham LLP *
Corlew Munford & Smith PLLC

**Band 3**
Baker, Donelson, Bearman, Caldwell & Berkowitz, PC *
Watkins & Eager PLLC *

| **Leading Individuals** | |
| --- | --- |

**Band 1**
| Milner John | Brunini, Grantham, Grower & Hewes, PLLC |
| Munford Virginia | Corlew Munford & Smith PLLC |
| Wyly Teri | Balch & Bingham LLP |

**Band 2**
| Blackwood Kelly | Bradley Arant Boult Cummings LLP (ONP)† |
| Caples Michael D | Butler, Snow, O'Mara, Stevens & Cannada * |
| Corlew John | Corlew Munford & Smith PLLC |

**Band 3**
| Allen Trudy B | Butler, Snow, O'Mara, Stevens & Cannada * |
| Brunini John | Brunini, Grantham, Grower & Hewes, PLLC |
| Dawkins Michael | Baker, Donelson, Bearman, Caldwell * |
| Fox Betty Ruth | Watkins & Eager PLLC * |
| Palmer, Jr James I | Butler, Snow, O'Mara, Stevens & Cannada * |
| Turner Keith | Watkins & Eager PLLC * |

**Up-and-coming individuals**
| Zmitrovich Gretchen | Baker, Donelson, Bearman, Caldwell * |

\* Indicates firm / individual with profile.
† ONP = Other Notable Practitioner.

## Band 1

### Brunini, Grantham, Grower & Hewes, PLLC
See profile on p.1611

**THE FIRM** This firm has an impressive reputation at the top of the market for its range of expertise in both regulatory compliance and contentious matters. Key clients come from the public and private sectors, including a number of municipalities. The team has considerable expertise in wastewater and air pollution regulations.
**Sources say:** *"They do a good job with clients and get cases resolved."*
**KEY INDIVIDUALS** Experienced practitioner **John Milner** has a wealth of experience in the environment sector, including air pollution, wastewater, and oil and gas regulatory matters. He represents clients before the EPA and DOJ in both contentious and noncontentious matters. **John Brunini** advises clients on EPA compliance regulations, particularly wastewater issues. He also represents

clients in permitting matters, including surface coal mining and wetlands matters.

### Butler, Snow, O'Mara, Stevens & Cannada, PLLC
See profile on p.1613

**THE FIRM** This leading firm continues to be a major presence in the environmental law market. The team has considerable expertise in a broad range of regulatory compliance and permitting matters, including solid and hazardous waste and brownfield development. The firm's impressive client roster includes the City of Jackson, Hancock Country Utility Authority and FMC.
**Sources say:** *"One of the top firms." "All strong attorneys with a good environmental background."*
**KEY INDIVIDUALS** Head of department **Michael Caples** (see p.1602) advises both public and private clients on a variety of noncontentious matters. He advised FMC on EPA protocol regarding the movement of pesticides. **Trudy Allen** (see p.1601) advises clients on development and property regulations, including groundwater contamination and permitting matters. She also handles environment-related issues in construction and real estate law. **James Palmer** (see p.1606) is highly regarded for his technical expertise, having previously held a position working at the EPA and the Mississippi Department of Environmental Quality (MDEQ). One commentator notes his ability to *"see both the big and small picture"* when advising his clients.

## Band 2

### Balch & Bingham LLP
See profile on p.475

**THE FIRM** This regional firm's Gulfport office is well regarded for its representation of utilities companies, and for its work on behalf of public entities. The team has provided counsel to the MDEQ on its environmental assessment of the Deepwater Horizon oil spill in the Gulf of Mexico.
**KEY INDIVIDUALS** **Teri Wyly** is head of the firm's Gulfport office and specializes in providing regulatory advice to utilities companies and state bodies. She has a strong market presence and leads the team advising the MDEQ.

### Corlew Munford & Smith PLLC

**THE FIRM** This specialist firm offers clients expertise in both litigation and environmental regulatory compliance issues. The team has considerable experience in the areas of solid waste management, wetlands, and air and water pollution, as well as handling permitting matters.
**KEY INDIVIDUALS** *"Fabulous litigator"* **John Corlew** is well known for his representation of clients in contentious

environmental matters. His litigation work extends to include a significant appellate practice. **Virginia Munford** is recognized for being very active at the state's environmental Bar. She specializes in regulatory and administrative work.

## Band 3

### Baker, Donelson, Bearman, Caldwell & Berkowitz, PC
See profile on p.2313

**THE FIRM** This nine-lawyer team is active in representing a number of municipalities and public bodies in both regulatory compliance and contentious matters. Recent work highlights include overseeing the environmental audit of the University of Mississippi Medical Center.
**KEY INDIVIDUALS** **Michael Dawkins** (see p.1602) has experience guiding a number of private and public clients through environmental investigations and advising on regulatory compliance issues. His environmental practice stretches to include transactional and white-collar criminal elements. Up-and-comer **Gretchen Zmitrovich** (see p.1610) has a strong regulatory background, having previously worked with the MDEQ. She works closely with Dawkins on a number of the firm's most high-profile instructions.

### Watkins & Eager PLLC
See profile on p.1617

**THE FIRM** Watkins & Eager advises clients on state and federal environmental issues, including air and water quality, brownfields and wetlands. The team has considerable regulatory expertise and relationships with the DOJ and MDEQ.
**Sources say:** *"Very easy to work with – they know their jobs and are highly skilled."*
**KEY INDIVIDUALS** **Keith Turner** (see p.1609) has *"broad regulatory knowledge,"* according to interviewees. He is popular with clients, who regard him as a *"very calm, logical, clear thinker."* **Betty Ruth Fox** (see p.1603) is well respected for her deep knowledge of both federal and state environmental regulations. She is also known for her skill regarding brownfields projects.

## Other Notable Practitioners

**Kelly Blackwood** of Bradley Arant Boult Cummings LLP is held in high regard by peers, particularly for her regulatory expertise. Key clients include numerous local municipalities.

# LABOR & EMPLOYMENT

Commentary about individuals can be found under their firm's paragraph. If the firm has no paragraph (is not ranked) look at Other Notable Practitioners.

## Labor & Employment
### Leading Firms

**Band 1**
Balch & Bingham LLP *
Phelps Dunbar LLP *

**Band 2**
Butler, Snow, O'Mara, Stevens & Cannada, PLLC *
Ogletree, Deakins, Nash, Smoak & Stewart *
Watkins & Eager PLLC *

**Band 3**
Baker, Donelson, Bearman, Caldwell & Berkowitz, PC *
The Kullman Firm A Professional Law Corporation
Jones Walker LLP *
Wise Carter Child & Caraway, Professional Association

### Leading Individuals

**Star individuals**

| | |
|---|---|
| Moeller Jr Armin J | Balch & Bingham LLP |
| Smith Taylor | The Kullman Firm |

**Band 1**

| | |
|---|---|
| Ardelean Paula Graves | Butler, Snow, O'Mara, Stevens & Cannada * |
| Crutcher Jr Robert Pepper | Balch & Bingham LLP |
| Friedman Gary E | Phelps Dunbar LLP |
| Siler Jr W Thomas | Phelps Dunbar LLP |

**Band 2**

| | |
|---|---|
| Brand Walter J | Watkins & Eager PLLC * |
| Eason Brooks | Baker, Donelson, Bearman, Caldwell * |
| Irby Peyton | Jones Walker LLP * |
| Lindsay Timothy W | Ogletree, Deakins, Nash, Smoak & Stewart * |
| Milam Kenneth E | Watkins & Eager PLLC * |
| Threadgill Timothy M | Butler, Snow, O'Mara, Stevens & Cannada * |
| Walker Jeffrey A | Butler, Snow, O'Mara, Stevens & Cannada * |
| Wallace Barbara C | Wise Carter Child & Caraway |

**Band 3**

| | |
|---|---|
| Keith James A | Adams and Reese LLP (ONP)† * |
| Patterson J Randall | Baker, Donelson, Bearman, Caldwell * |
| Vance Alison | Butler, Snow, O'Mara, Stevens & Cannada * |

\* Indicates firm / individual with profile.
†ONP = Other Notable Practitioner.

## Band 1

### Balch & Bingham LLP
See profile on p.475

THE FIRM This market-leading labor and employment practice receives plaudits for the strength and experience of its four-partner team. The firm demonstrates a broad range of expertise in employee discrimination litigation and Equal Employment Opportunity Commission (EEOC) matters, as well as conventional labor law issues. The firm's impressive stable of clients includes Transport America, the Mississippi Hospital Association and Parkway Properties.
**Sources say:** *"A top-notch firm."*

KEY INDIVIDUALS *"Excellent lawyer"* **Armin Moeller** is described by peers as *"very knowledgeable"* in both labor and employment matters. He has recently overseen the dismissal of a number of EEOC charges on behalf of Telapex. Experienced practitioner **Pepper Crutcher** has been equally involved in the aforementioned work for Telapex. He is praised for his expertise in handling employee discrimination disputes in addition to employment litigation and arbitration.

### Phelps Dunbar LLP
See profile on p.1383

THE FIRM The highly regarded team at this regional firm offers clients a wealth of experience in labor and employment matters. The firm's three-partner Mississippi team handles labor relations issues, employee discrimination litigation, immigration and employee benefits matters. The firm represents a number of private and public companies and can call upon resources from across the firm's numerous offices in the South East.
**Sources say:** *"They are professional and highly competent in the areas in which they practice. They keep commitments, and are timely in performing services requested."*
KEY INDIVIDUALS **Gary Friedman** is highly regarded for his skills as a trial lawyer and for his breadth of knowledge in employment litigation. He also has experience of traditional labor matters and the National Labor Relations Act. Head of department **Thomas Siler** *"brings a wealth of legal knowledge and experience,"* say sources. He is a highly experienced employment litigator and a noted counselor in labor relation issues.

## Band 2

### Butler, Snow, O'Mara, Stevens & Cannada, PLLC
See profile on p.1613

THE FIRM The well-respected labor and employment team at this firm has an active and broad practice. The firm is recognized for its strength in defending employers against accusations of employee discrimination, and has a noted strength in compliance counseling and human resources training. Clients include Baxter Healthcare Corporation, Ergon and Unified Brands.
**Sources say:** *"Their level of professionalism is great."*
KEY INDIVIDUALS Clients choose **Paula Graves Ardelean** (see p.1601) because she has a *"strong work ethic and is practical, smart and thorough."* She is lauded for her skill and experience in defending management clients in employment litigation. Head of department **Timothy Threadgill** (see p.1609) receives praise for his excellent presentational style and strength in employment litigation. Key clients come from the petroleum, healthcare and manufacturing industries, among others. Experienced litigator

**Jeffrey Walker** (see p.1610) is recognized for his proven track record in employment disputes. Clients praise his *"very good sense of strategy through litigation"* and thorough preparation. **Alison Vance** (see p.1609) is described by one client as *"excellent, analytic, very thorough in her work and determined."* She has a broad practice, including contentious and noncontentious employment matters.

### Ogletree, Deakins, Nash, Smoak & Stewart
See profile on p.1110

THE FIRM This national labor and employment boutique advises clients on a wide range of issues, from traditional labor matters to employee discrimination and wage and hour disputes. The Jackson-based team has recently successfully defended a number of clients against race discrimination allegations, as well as claims made under ADA and EEOC legislation. Key clients include Trustmark National Bank, Tropicana Entertainment and the Mississippi Band of Choctaw Indians.
**Sources say:** *"They work to put themselves in the clients' shoes and they have a good understanding."*
KEY INDIVIDUALS Managing partner **Timothy Lindsay** (see p.1605) handles a full range of employment disputes, and was lead partner acting for both Walgreens and Atlantic Industrial services. One client reports: *"The information he provided was easy to understand. He doesn't get caught up in legalese and lays out the pros and cons, which I like."*

### Watkins & Eager PLLC
See profile on p.1617

THE FIRM This well-established firm enjoys an active labor and employment practice and is recognized in the market for its wealth of experience in employment litigation. The firm frequently acts for clients addressing issues and disputes under the FMLA and ADA, as well as accusations of employee discrimination. Clients include Savings Oil Company and Mid-South Industries.
**Sources say:** *"They are very responsive to the company's needs. I can honestly think of no improvements that they could make."*
KEY INDIVIDUALS **Walter Brand** (see p.1601) *"has demonstrated a depth of knowledge and expertise that is impressive,"* according to clients. He has experience in a broad range of employment disputes, and frequently represents pharmaceutical and insurance companies. Seasoned practitioner **Kenneth Milam** (see p.1606) is well respected for his depth of experience in contentious and regulatory employment law. His client roster includes Mississippi Baptist Health Systems, Greenwood Utilities and Hunter Engineering.

## Band 3

### Baker, Donelson, Bearman, Caldwell & Berkowitz, PC

See profile on p.2313

**THE FIRM** This firm regularly acts for employers from a variety of sectors in both employment litigation and regulatory compliance matters. The team is experienced in defending companies against accusations of employee discrimination, as well as in wage and hour and benefits disputes. Clients include Huntington Ingalls and Entergy Services.

**Sources say:** *"I have yet to have a bad experience with any members of Baker Donelson. Hands downs, Baker Donelson remains well ahead of any of the other firms that have represented this company."*

**KEY INDIVIDUALS Brooks Eason** (see p.1602) is highly regarded for his representation of clients in employment litigation. He is particularly adept in defending employers against accusations of discrimination and wrongful dismissal. Head of department **Randall Patterson** (see p.1607) handles both contentious and noncontentious employment matters, including ERISA and EEOC-related litigation.

### The Kullman Firm A Professional Law Corporation

**THE FIRM** This boutique labor and employment firm offer employers expertise in labor relations matters as well as administrative and contentious employment cases. The team that advises clients is experienced in ADA and FMLA regulatory matters, as well as in advising clients before the EEOC.

**KEY INDIVIDUALS** *"Well-respected"* lawyer **Taylor Smith** practices from the firm's Columbus office. He is experienced in traditional labor work and employment litigation, including employment discrimination and federal wage and hour cases.

### Jones Walker LLP

See profile on p.1378

**THE FIRM** This firm's solid employment practice represents a number of public and private companies in the full range of employment law matters. The team advises clients on regulatory matters including wage and hour and OSHA issues, as well as providing support in litigation. The firm's regional presence allows it to call upon resources from offices across the South and Eastern USA.

**KEY INDIVIDUALS Peyton Irby** (see p.1604) is held in high esteem for his *"strong presence"* in the market and dependable counsel. He has experience in handling a broad range of employment matters, including regulatory compliance and disputes.

### Wise Carter Child & Caraway, Professional Association

**THE FIRM** Wise Carter advises clients in a broad range of employment matters, including regulatory compliance and litigation before state and federal bodies. The firm regularly assists employers in drafting employee guidelines, policies and handbooks, and defends clients against accusations of employment discrimination.

**KEY INDIVIDUALS** *"Excellent lawyer"* **Barbara Wallace** is widely regarded as the firm's leading light in employment regulatory and litigation work. She is held in high regard among her peers for her impressive depth of knowledge and *"astounding skills"* as a trial lawyer.

## Other Notable Practitioners

**James Keith** (see p.1604) of Adams and Reese LLP specializes in representing educational institutions and school districts in a variety of employment matters. He has represented clients before state and federal court.

# LITIGATION

Commentary about individuals can be found under their firm's paragraph. If the firm has no paragraph (is not ranked) look at Other Notable Practitioners.

## Litigation: General Commercial
### Leading Firms

**Band 1**
Baker, Donelson, Bearman, Caldwell & Berkowitz, PC *
Bradley Arant Boult Cummings LLP *
Brunini, Grantham, Grower & Hewes, PLLC *
Butler, Snow, O'Mara, Stevens & Cannada, PLLC *
Forman Perry Watkins Krutz & Tardy LLP *
Watkins & Eager PLLC *

**Band 2**
Copeland Cook Taylor & Bush, A Professional Association
Mitchell, McNutt & Sams PA *
Jones Walker LLP *
Wise Carter Child & Caraway, Professional Association

**Band 3**
Adams and Reese LLP *
Balch & Bingham LLP *
Carroll Warren & Parker PLLC *
Corlew Munford & Smith PLLC
McGlinchey Stafford PLLC *
Phelps Dunbar LLP *
Wells Marble & Hurst PLLC

## Litigation: Appellate
### Leading Individuals

| Band 1 | |
| --- | --- |
| Drinkwater Wayne | *Bradley Arant Boult Cummings LLP* |
| Munford Luther T | *Butler, Snow, O'Mara, Stevens & Cannada* * |
| Wallace Michael B | *Wise Carter Child & Caraway* |

| Band 2 | |
| --- | --- |
| Banks Jr Fred L | *Phelps Dunbar LLP* |
| Henegan John C | *Butler, Snow, O'Mara, Stevens & Cannada* * |
| Perry Alan W | *Forman Perry Watkins Krutz & Tardy LLP* * |

| Band 3 | |
| --- | --- |
| Jacobs Donna Brown | *Butler, Snow, O'Mara, Stevens & Cannada* * |
| Robertson James | *Wise Carter Child & Caraway* |

\* Indicates firm / individual with profile.
†ONP = Other Notable Practitioner.

## Band 1

### Baker, Donelson, Bearman, Caldwell & Berkowitz, PC

See profile on p.2313

**THE FIRM** This firm is recognized for its strong presence in the Mississippi litigation market. The team is known for its strength in a number of areas, including breach of contract, products liability and antitrust cases. A stellar client roster includes Chevron, ExxonMobil and Philip Morris.

## Litigation: Construction
### Leading Individuals

| Band 1 | |
| --- | --- |
| Mockbee David | *Mockbee Hall Drake & Hodge (ONP)* † |
| Purdy William R | *Bradley Arant Boult Cummings LLP* |

| Band 2 | |
| --- | --- |
| Abernethy Phil B | *Butler, Snow, O'Mara, Stevens & Cannada* * |
| Kelly Samuel | *Brunini, Grantham, Grower & Hewes, PLLC* |

| Band 3 | |
| --- | --- |
| Carson Dorsey | *Burr & Forman LLP (ONP)* † |
| Gatlin Cheri | *Burr & Forman LLP (ONP)* † |
| Herbert Mark D | *Jones Walker LLP* * |

**Sources say:** *"This firm is uniquely calibrated to address any condition in any county in Mississippi, and presents cases in a way that engages that particular arena."*

**KEY INDIVIDUALS Bill Jones** (see p.1604) is described by a client as *"very experienced and knowledgeable,"* as well as *"a gentlemen of the first order."* He specializes in products liability and insurance defense, and has experience at trial and appellate level. Experienced litigator **Scott Welch** (see p.1610) is *"very active and really strong,"* according to peers. He focuses on representing clients in commercial litigation, business tort and personal injury defense. *"Fine trial lawyer"* **Bill Reed** (see p.1607) handles class action, antitrust and complex commercial litigation for clients which include pharmaceutical companies, insurance

## Litigation: General Commercial
### Senior Statesmen

**Senior Statesmen:** distinguished older practitioners

| | | |
|---|---|---|
| Goodman Jr William F | Watkins & Eager PLLC * | |

### Leading Individuals

**Star individuals**

| | | |
|---|---|---|
| Drinkwater Wayne | Bradley Arant Boult Cummings LLP | |
| Jones Christy D | Butler, Snow, O'Mara, Stevens & Cannada * | |
| Perry Alan W | Forman Perry Watkins Krutz & Tardy LLP * | |

**Band 1**

| | |
|---|---|
| Corlew John | Corlew Munford & Smith PLLC |
| Jones Walker (Bill) | Baker, Donelson, Bearman, Caldwell * |
| Kaufman David | Brunini, Grantham, Grower & Hewes, PLLC |
| Sams Jr L F | Mitchell, McNutt & Sams PA |
| Shapley Christopher | Brunini, Grantham, Grower & Hewes, PLLC |
| Thames Lee Davis | Butler, Snow, O'Mara, Stevens & Cannada* |
| Thomas Stephen L | Bradley Arant Boult Cummings LLP |
| Ulmer Michael | Watkins & Eager PLLC * |
| Wallace Michael B | Wise Carter Child & Caraway |
| Welch W Scott | Baker, Donelson, Bearman, Caldwell * |

**Band 2**

| | |
|---|---|
| Ayers David L | Watkins & Eager PLLC * |
| Bass Jr Ross F | Phelps Dunbar LLP |
| Campbell Roy | Bradley Arant Boult Cummings LLP |
| Copeland Greg | Copeland Cook Taylor & Bush |
| Galloway Robert C | Butler, Snow, O'Mara, Stevens & Cannada * |
| Krutz Fred | Forman Perry Watkins Krutz & Tardy LLP * |
| Raulston Keith R | Jones Walker LLP * |
| Reed William N (Bill) | Baker, Donelson, Bearman, Caldwell * |
| Stephenson III Paul H | Watkins & Eager PLLC * |
| Watkins Jr Walter G | Forman Perry Watkins Krutz & Tardy LLP * |

**Band 3**

| | |
|---|---|
| Abernethy Phil B | Butler, Snow, O'Mara, Stevens & Cannada * |

| | |
|---|---|
| Boschert Neville H | Jones Walker LLP * |
| Carroll James L | Carroll Warren & Parker PLLC * |
| Cowan H Mitchell | Jones Walker LLP * |
| Dove Luke | Dove and Chill (ONP)† |
| Ford Barry W | Baker, Donelson, Bearman, Caldwell * |
| Goodman III Will | Watkins & Eager PLLC * |
| Henegan John C | Butler, Snow, O'Mara, Stevens & Cannada * |
| Latham William Larry | William Larry Latham, PA (ONP)† |
| Manuel J William | Bradley Arant Boult Cummings LLP |
| Minor J Douglas | Bradley Arant Boult Cummings LLP |
| Parker Myles A | Carroll Warren & Parker PLLC * |
| Ray William F | Watkins & Eager PLLC * |
| Robinson III E Barney | Butler, Snow, O'Mara, Stevens & Cannada * |
| Sykes Phillip S | Forman Perry Watkins Krutz & Tardy LLP * |
| Tardy III Thomas W | Forman Perry Watkins Krutz & Tardy LLP * |
| Thompson Jr J Carter | Baker, Donelson, Bearman, Caldwell * |
| Twiford Hunter | McGlinchey Stafford PLLC * |
| Warren Jim | Carroll Warren & Parker PLLC * |

**Band 4**

| | |
|---|---|
| Bell Lewis | Watkins & Eager PLLC * |
| Bey Sheryl | Baker, Donelson, Bearman, Caldwell * |
| Dyal Jonathan | Balch & Bingham LLP |
| Hatten Eric | Burr & Forman LLP (ONP)† |
| Hembree G. Dewey | McGlinchey Stafford PLLC * |
| Smith William L | Balch & Bingham LLP |
| Stone Ben H | Balch & Bingham LLP |
| Wheeler John | Mitchell, McNutt & Sams PA |
| Willson Walter | Wells Marble & Hurst PLLC |

* Indicates individual with profile.

† ONP = Other Notable Practitioner.

providers and financial institutions. **Barry Ford** (see p.1603) has a highly regarded practice in products liability and commercial litigation. Sources name him *"a top-notch lawyer."* **Carter Thompson** (see p.1609) specializes in pharmaceutical and medical device products liability defense, and has wealth of experience representing clients from the healthcare sector. One interviewee comments: *"He's a lawyer who's really tried cases and takes a practical, cost-effective approach to litigation."* **Sheryl Bey** (see p.1601) has a broad practice that includes insurance coverage, personal injury defense and commercial litigation. She recently took the lead in a breach of contract litigation for Caldwell Tanks and the Great American Insurance Company.

### Bradley Arant Boult Cummings LLP
See profile on p.476

**THE FIRM** This firm is well known for the depth of its bench and its broad range of expertise. The team is active in products liability, personal injury, business tort and intellectual property matters, and is also experienced in handling class action and appellate cases. Key clients include Chevron and The Pantry, while the department continues to have close ties to the healthcare and banking sectors.

**KEY INDIVIDUALS Wayne Drinkwater** is both an *"outstanding trial lawyer and outstanding in trial strategy,"* say sources, who also note that he is *"one of the best appellate lawyers in Mississippi."* He has a broad practice which includes commercial litigation, white-collar crime and business tort. Sources praise *"superb lawyer"* **William Purdy** for his *"dedicated, dogged representation"* of clients. He is considered one of the market's foremost construction litigation experts. Respected litigator **Stephen Thomas** receives praise from peers as an excellent advocate. He recently defended AstraZeneca against claims brought by the Attorney General regarding the sale of antipsychotic drug Seroquel. *"Top-notch"* trial lawyer **Roy Campbell** has a wealth of expertise in the insurance, products liability and personal injury defense spheres. He is highly regarded for his proven track record in court, as well as his *"insightful"* advocacy. **William Manuel** advises clients on a broad range of contentious matters, and is highly regarded for his handling of commercial and

employment litigation. **Douglas Minor** regularly represents clients in contentious financial services matters. He is also experienced in employment litigation and general commercial litigation.

### Brunini, Grantham, Grower & Hewes, PLLC
See profile on p.1611

**THE FIRM** This firm maintains its highly respected presence in the litigation market and draws considerable plaudits for its adept team of trial lawyers. The team is active in a broad range of business disputes, including antitrust, toxic tort, contracts and securities matters. Clients have included C Spine Wireless, Rockwell Automotive and Lincoln Electric Company.

**Sources say:** *"Extraordinarily well prepared, cost effective and extremely responsive to the needs of clients."*

**KEY INDIVIDUALS** *"Very fine trial lawyer"* **David Kaufman** garners praise for his meticulous preparation and skills as an advocate. He frequently leads the firm in some of its highest-profile appointments. **Christopher Shapley** is a well-established player in the market, and has amassed a wealth of experience in commercial business litigation, products liability and insurance coverage matters. **Samuel Kelly** specializes in representing clients from the construction industry, and is also highly regarded in insurance coverage matters. Market sources note: *"He is easy to deal with but represents his clients zealously."*

### Butler, Snow, O'Mara, Stevens & Cannada, PLLC
See profile on p.1613

**THE FIRM** This firm is highly regarded in the market for its formidable trial expertise and deep bench. The team is active in a variety of industry sectors, including financial services and pharmaceuticals, handling a broad range of matters such as antitrust and products liability disputes. The team recently defended Eli Lilly & Company in a case alleging violations of the Medicaid Fraud Control Act and the Mississippi Consumer Protection Act.

**Sources say:** *"They are experienced and well prepared. They're good in both written submission and oral presentation in court."*

**KEY INDIVIDUALS** Star litigator **Christy Jones** (see p.341) is *"as good a lawyer as you'll ever see,"* according to market sources. She focuses on products liability and pharmaceutical cases. Recent clients include the University of Mississippi Medical Center. **Luther Munford** (see p.1606) recently joined the team from Phelps Dunbar. He is described by one commentator as the *"preeminent appellate lawyer in the state."* *"Top-notch practitioner"* **Lee Thames** (see p.1609) garners praise for his expertise in products liability and mass tort. Market sources laud his *"vast experience in court"* and fine legal strategies. **Phil Abernethy** (see p.1601) is highly regarded for his experience and expertise in disputes pertaining to the construction sector, while he also handles a range of commercial and insurance matters. Recent work highlights include defending Higher One Holdings against accusations concerning its marketing of financial products to students. **Robert Galloway** (see p.1603) has an active commercial disputes and products liability practice. He was part of the team that defended State Farm Fire and Casualty Company following allegations made under the Federal False Claims Act. Peers note **John Henegan**'s (see p.1604) skill at both trial and appellate level. His broad practice includes antitrust, intellectual property, media defense and telecoms disputes. **Donna Jacobs** (see p.1604) focuses on appellate work, pharmaceutical products liability defense and media defense. She worked alongside colleague Jones representing the University of Mississippi Medical Center. **Barney Robinson** (see p.1607) is regarded by clients as *"a go-to guy"* for financial services litigation. He is highly regarded for his skills as a trial lawyer.

## Forman Perry Watkins Krutz & Tardy LLP
See profile on p.1615

**THE FIRM** The litigation team at this regional firm handles a full range of disputes, including commercial business litigation, contentious real estate and appellate work. Recent work highlights include representing GE on a number of consolidated asbestos-related wrongful death cases. Other clients include CVS Pharmacy and Georgia-Pacific. **Sources say:** *"Very good work. They're very thorough, and no stone is left unturned."*

**KEY INDIVIDUALS** *"Outstanding lawyer"* **Alan Perry** (see p.1607) focuses on complex business litigation and appellate matters. Specific areas of expertise include antitrust, insurance and professional liability disputes. **Fred Krutz** (see p.1605) recently led the successful defense of a number of companies in a complex multiplaintiff silica case. He has a proven track record in mass tort cases, including asbestos litigation, and complex commercial disputes. Sources report that **Walter Watkins** (see p.1610) has *"a very sophisticated view of litigation."* He handles a broad range of disputes, including commercial, construction and environmental litigation. **Phillip Sykes** (see p.1608) specializes in financial services litigation, with clients benefiting from his expertise in accountancy matters. Key clients include Infrasource, which he represented in the complex dismissal of its former president. Seasoned advocate **Thomas Tardy** (see p.1608) handles a broad scope of contentious matters, including personal injury, professional liability and environmental litigation. He is experienced with asbestos cases, and led the team on the aforementioned case for GE.

## Watkins & Eager PLLC
See profile on p.1617

**THE FIRM** This firm is lauded for its expert handling of complex commercial and business litigation, while the group is also active in products liability cases, securities litigation and fraud matters. The team recently represented Bayer Crop Science in complex litigation relating to allegations that the commercial rice supply contained genetically engineered rice. An illustrious client roster also contains Pfizer, Honda North America and Kia Motors. **Sources say:** *"Excellent writers, great communicators and the most responsive attorneys I've ever dealt with."*

**KEY INDIVIDUALS** **Michael Ulmer** (see p.1609) offers clients a wealth of talent and experience in products liabil-

ity and commercial litigation. He acts across a broad range of industries, and peers praise his pragmatic and thorough approach. **David Ayers** (see p.1601) is highly regarded for his excellent skills as a trial lawyer and ability to address a jury. He has experience in defending automotive companies in products liability cases. Clients describe **Paul Stephenson** (see p.1608) as *"a very bright and conservative lawyer. He protects our interests very carefully."* His practice covers a broad range of contentious matters, including financial disputes, oil and gas controversies, and complex class actions. **William Ray** (see p.1607) is highly regarded for his representation of banks and other financial institutions in complex securities and class action cases. Recent work highlights include defending Trustmark National Bank in two putative class action cases brought in federal court. **Will Goodman** (see p.324) specializes in defending pharmaceutical companies in complex class action and personal injury cases. He led the team in the aforementioned matter for Bayer Crop Science. **Lewis Bell** (see p.1601) recently acted alongside colleague Ulmer in representing a number of manufacturers of welding consumables in a complex personal injury case. He handles a broad range of matters, including products liability, toxic tort and general commercial litigation. **William Goodman Jr** (see p.1603) is described by clients as a *"formidable force in trial and a skilled litigator."* He specializes in banking litigation, class actions and complex commercial disputes.

## Band 2

## Copeland Cook Taylor & Bush, A Professional Association

**THE FIRM** This firm enjoys a fine reputation in litigation, particularly for its work in insurance defense cases. The team has experience in a broad range of contentious matters, including business tort, healthcare and natural resources, and frequently represents clients before both state and federal courts. The firm boasts a wide geographical reach, with offices in Biloxi, Hattiesburg and Ridgeland.

**KEY INDIVIDUALS** **Greg Copeland** is *"about as good as they come"* in insurance defense matters, according to one market source. His broad practice covers oil and gas disputes and commercial litigation.

## Mitchell, McNutt & Sams PA
See profile on p.1616

**THE FIRM** This firm's litigation department is highly regarded for its handling of a broad range of contentious matters. Areas of expertise include professional liability, medical products liability and white-collar criminal defense matters. The firm is also recognized for its strength in multijurisdictional and appellate litigation.

**KEY INDIVIDUALS** Seasoned litigator **Sandy Sams** is highly regarded by the Mississippi market. His practice focuses on professional and products liability work, and he is also active in business and commercial litigation. Head of litigation **John Wheeler** specializes in professional lia-

bility defense work, as part of a broader litigation practice which includes products liability and railroad matters.

## Jones Walker LLP
See profile on p.1378

**THE FIRM** This firm is active in a broad range of litigations, including insurance defense, products liability, complex commercial disputes and bankruptcy. The team recently represented PepsiCo in a high-value termination of contract dispute with a major distributor. Other major clients come from the financial, retail and healthcare sectors.

**KEY INDIVIDUALS** Highly regarded advocate **Keith Raulston** (see p.1607) brings his extensive experience of insurance and financial services litigation to the team. He is also active in class actions and commercial business disputes. **Neville Boschert** (see p.1601) has an expert knowledge of products liability matters, particularly those pertaining to the medical and pharmaceutical industries. He also led the team's representation of PepsiCo in the matter detailed above. **Mitchell Cowan** (see p.1602) focuses on contentious financial services matters, as well as handling insurance coverage, banking, consumer and products liability litigations. **Mark Herbert** (see p.1604) has a specialty practice in the construction sector. He is recognized for his expertise in handling insurance and security matters for large-scale construction projects.

## Wise Carter Child & Caraway, Professional Association

**THE FIRM** This firm retains a strong presence in the litigation market, and acts for clients from a variety of industry sectors. The team offers expertise in medical malpractice defense and pharmaceutical products liability, as well as complex commercial, employment and railroad litigation. The firm also has a successful and highly regarded appellate practice.

**Sources say:** *"They have a number of very skilled lawyers and do an excellent job."*

**KEY INDIVIDUALS** *"Outstanding litigator"* **Michael Wallace** is described by clients as *"a good trial lawyer, and widely recognized as a great appellate lawyer."* He focuses on commercial litigation, public utilities cases and appellate work. Former Supreme Court Justice **James Robertson** specializes in appellate cases. He continues to handle appeals in a broad range of legal areas.

## Band 3

## Adams and Reese LLP
See profile on p.1372

**THE FIRM** This Ridgeland firm continues to be recognized for its close ties with its traditional energy sector client base, while it also has a notable presence in the real estate and insurance sectors. The firm is active in commercial, contract, intellectual property and bankruptcy disputes.

**KEY INDIVIDUALS** **William Brabec** is a key contact for the firm and head of the commercial disputes practice.

## Balch & Bingham LLP
See profile on p.475

**THE FIRM** This firm's litigation team is known for its strength in disputes affecting regulated industries such as the energy, healthcare and gaming sectors. The group has handled a number of matters for Kinder Morgan Energy Partners, including litigation stemming from a $2.8 billion pipeline project. Other clients include Atmos Energy, Gulf South Pipelines and International Game Technology.
**Sources say:** *"Their knowledge of the law and everything involved was the most impressive thing to me."*
**KEY INDIVIDUALS** Sources praise **Jonathan Dyal** for his commitment to client service, as well as his familiarity with litigation proceedings in regulated industries. Clients appreciate his technical expertise, in addition to his dedicated and amenable approach. **William Smith** has represented a number of gas pipeline companies in various high-profile domain lawsuits related to the construction of new pipelines across Mississippi. **Ben Stone** is highly regarded for his strong advocacy skills. He recently represented the Mississippi Power Company in proceedings before the Mississippi Public Service Commission concerning the construction of a clean coal facility.

## Carroll Warren & Parker PLLC
See profile on p.1614

**THE FIRM** This compact litigation boutique covers a broad range of matters, including insurance, products liability and construction litigation. It is also recognized for its experience in alternative dispute resolution. The Jackson-based team is active both in Mississippi and across the South, with additional offices in Texas and Florida.
**KEY INDIVIDUALS** Senior counsel **James Carroll** (see p.1602) is a recognized authority in complex insurance litigation. His practice includes international insurance litigation matters. **Myles Parker** (see p.1606) handles a wide range of litigation work including insurance defense, energy and natural resources, and real estate disputes. He also has experience in alternative dispute resolution. Experienced litigator **Jim Warren** (see p.1610) handles both plaintiff and defense-side work. He has a wealth of experience in the energy sector, particularly relating to utilities and refineries.

## Corlew Munford & Smith PLLC

**THE FIRM** This three-partner boutique firm specializes in trial and appellate work, and enjoys an impressive reputation for its work in the administrative and environmental law sectors. The team represents clients before a number of courts and administrative bodies, ranging from county and municipal governing bodies to the US Supreme Court.
**KEY INDIVIDUALS** Firm principal **John Corlew** has an *"outstanding reputation,"* according to market sources. He is held in high esteem for his experience in commercial litigation, appellate and administrative law matters.

## McGlinchey Stafford PLLC
See profile on p.1382

**THE FIRM** This firm is well regarded for its work in complex banking and financial services disputes. The firm recently represented Bank of America and FIA Card Services in an antitrust case concerning the marketing, selling and administering of fee-based products related to credit cards. The team also acts in bankruptcy, foreclosure and class action matters.
**KEY INDIVIDUALS Hunter Twiford** (see p.1609) specializes in defending financial institutions in a broad range of matters. He led the team acting on behalf of Bank of America and FIA Card Services, and is praised by observers for his trial advocacy. **Dewey Hembree** (see p.1603) enjoys a broad practice including commercial litigation and consumer finance matters. He recently acted for Bank of America in a challenge to the bank's authority to foreclose on real property.

## Phelps Dunbar LLP
See profile on p.1383

**THE FIRM** This firm's litigation team is noted for its handling of a wide range of matters, including products liability, antitrust and tax disputes for telecoms, insurance and municipal clients. The firm also has a significant capacity in appellate matters, and recently represented Eaton Corporation and the City of Pasagoula before the Mississippi Supreme Court.
**Sources say:** *"I have enjoyed working with Phelps Dunbar immensely, and feel certain as well as comfortable that their team has helped our company achieve its goals."*

**KEY INDIVIDUALS** Former Mississippi Supreme Court Justice **Fred Banks** is recognized for the strength of his appellate practice. He was closely involved in the aforementioned matters for Eaton Corporation and the City of Pasagoula. **Ross Bass** frequently acts on behalf of financial institutions in complex commercial disputes, class actions and mass tort cases.

## Wells Marble & Hurst PLLC

**THE FIRM** This firm is highly regarded for its work in insurance defense, particularly for blue-chip life insurance companies. The team also handles a broad range of litigation matters, including disputes pertaining to antitrust, products liability, employment and securities law. Clients include Assurant and the Liberty Mutual Insurance Company.
**KEY INDIVIDUALS: Walter Willson** is recognized for his expertise in insurance litigation, and has experience in the defense of insurance companies, banks and other financial institutions.

## Other Notable Practitioners

**David Mockbee** of Mockbee Hall Drake & Hodge is regarded as *"the preeminent"* construction lawyer in Mississippi. One market source describes him as *"a top-notch attorney."* **Dorsey Carson** of Burr & Forman LLP is well regarded for his advocacy skills and expertise in construction matters. He is active on both the plaintiff and defense side of disputes. At the same firm, head of litigation **Cheri Gatlin** is a recognized construction law specialist. She handles a broad range of work for major construction companies, including litigation and commercial matters. Fellow Burr & Forman attorney **Eric Hatten** is recognized for his work in insurance defense. He recently acted for Allstate Insurance in a dispute involving $18 million in bond debt following a major residential development in Madison, Mississippi. **Luke Dove** handles complex commercial litigation at the compact Dove and Chill firm. He enjoys a strong reputation among market observers. **William Larry Latham** of William Larry Latham, PA is described by sources as the *"premier mediator in the state."* He specializes in alternative dispute resolution as well as general commercial litigation.

# REAL ESTATE

Commentary about individuals can be found under their firm's paragraph. If the firm has no paragraph (is not ranked) look at Other Notable Practitioners.

## Band 1

### Butler, Snow, O'Mara, Stevens & Cannada, PLLC
See profile on p.1613

**THE FIRM** This firm is highly regarded for its expertise in large real estate transactions, often with respect to commercial and retail properties, and for its work in real estate financing, leasing and development. The team has close ties to the industrial, agricultural and timber sectors, while key clients include Executive Holdings and Action Properties.

**KEY INDIVIDUALS Don Cannada** (see p.1602) is widely regarded to be one of the foremost real estate attorneys in the state and is "very involved in the cutting edge" of real estate law, according to one commentator. Clients appreciate his extensive experience of the property market in Mississippi. Associate **Matthew Grenfell** (see p.1603) is well respected in the market as "a very knowledgeable and even-tempered" attorney. He frequently advises clients in connection with lease agreements and refinancing work.

### Watkins & Eager PLLC
See profile on p.1617

**THE FIRM** This impressive 13-lawyer team has a sterling market reputation, and enjoys a strong relationship with a number of regional financial institutions. Key banking sector clients include Trustmark National Bank, Regions Bank and BankFirst, while the firm has also represented a number of developers. Recent matters include acting for BancorpSouth Bank in connection with the financing of a medical facility, nursing home and church properties.
**Sources say:** "They were very responsive and always on time with documents."
**KEY INDIVIDUALS** Highly regarded practice group head **Paul Gunn** (see p.1603) has a wealth of experience in multifamily housing projects, tax credits work and commercial lending. One client says: "He knows the law, has good practical sense, and he's easy to get along with." "Excellent lawyer" **William Smith** (see p.1608) has a well-regarded transactional real estate practice, regularly acting for clients from a wide range of industries, including retail and healthcare. He is also experienced in zoning and land use law. **Binford Williams** (see p.1610) has a broad real estate practice with a focus on multifamily projects, office developments and condominiums. He frequently represents banks and lenders, including Trustmark Bank, in high-value real estate financings.

## Band 2

### Baker, Donelson, Bearman, Caldwell & Berkowitz, PC
See profile on p.2313

**THE FIRM** This firm is active in acquisitions, development and financing for clients in a variety of industry sectors, including healthcare, housing, agriculture and retail. Clients benefit from the firm's impressive geographical reach across the South East of the USA.
**KEY INDIVIDUALS** Clients choose **William Mendenhall** (see p.1606) "for his knowledge, expertise and negotiating skills in the complex areas of commercial real estate law." He represents developers and banks in a range of matters, including financings, foreclosures and dispositions. **David Rueff** (see p.1607) "is excellent at project management," praises one interviewee. Rueff focuses on commercial real estate development and lending.

### Jones Walker LLP
See profile on p.1378

**THE FIRM** This well-established real estate practice is active in a variety of transactional, financing, zoning and land use work. The team handles work for a wide range of clients, including water utilities, timber and retail companies. The firm also has close ties with the education sector, having handled a number of matters for universities and community colleges.
**KEY INDIVIDUALS Mark Davis** (see p.1602) assists clients in the acquisition, leasing and financing of large commercial developments and mixed-use facilities. He is particularly active in matters pertaining to the manufacturing, retail and healthcare sectors. Special counsel **Jim Tohill** (see p.1609) advises public and private sector clients on the financing and development of a broad range of projects. He has experience working in the automotive, energy and retail sectors, among others.

## Band 3

### Adams and Reese LLP
See profile on p.1372

**THE FIRM** The regional firm has a broad real estate practice that encompasses litigation, commercial transactions, real estate financing and foreclosures. The group has assisted in a number of acquisitions and financings for clients in the timber industry, and has notable experience in major housing developments.
**KEY INDIVIDUALS Powell Ogletree** (see p.1606) has a significant niche practice in forestry, specializing in a number of leasing and sale agreements for timber companies. Ogletree is the "top timber guy in the state," says one source.

### Brunini, Grantham, Grower & Hewes, PLLC
See profile on p.1611

**THE FIRM** This firm serves clients in a broad range of real estate matters, including acting as transactional counsel to both buyers and sellers and advising on tax matters. The team has substantial experience in real estate finance, routinely advising financial institutions in connection with high-value real estate lending facilities. The group also has significant experience in zoning and land use law.
**KEY INDIVIDUALS** David Andress is a key contact for the practice.

### Forman Perry Watkins Krutz & Tardy LLP
See profile on p.1615

**THE FIRM** This well-established real estate practice is active in a broad range of financings, acquisitions and disposals. The team has handled a number of matters for long-standing clients Parkway Properties and East Group Properties, while it has also acted for the Gulfport Redevelopment Commission and BancorpSouth Bank.

KEY INDIVIDUALS **Steven Hendrix** (see p.1603) is well regarded for his commercial real estate practice. One satisfied client notes: "*We could not ask for more from a legal relationship. We think very highly of him.*"

### Phelps Dunbar LLP
See profile on p.1383

THE FIRM This solid real estate team is adept at handling a wide range of matters, including the acquisition, financing, leasing and development of commercial, industrial and residential properties. In addition, the firm is noted for its expertise in title insurance and land use matters. Clients include large landowners, developers, landlords and tenants.

KEY INDIVIDUALS **Bridgforth Rutledge** is well regarded for his expertise in real estate financing, leasing and conveyances. Sources attest to his tenacious style of representation, and comment that he is "*very knowledgeable*" in real estate law.

### Other Notable Practitioners

**Rodney Clement** of Bradley Arant Boult Cummings LLP has a broad commercial real estate practice, including transactions, financings and sale, and leaseback agreements. His experience includes projects in the retail, healthcare and industrial sectors. Ridgeland-based **David Ash** of Taggart, Rimes & Usry, PLLC handles a range of real estate matters, including transactions, lending, taxation and developments. **John Shows** of ShowsPowell PLLC is well regarded for his expertise in real estate transactions and litigation. He is active in commercial and residential real estate matters.

# Leaders' Profiles in Mississippi

### ABERNETHY, Phil B
Butler, Snow, O'Mara, Stevens & Cannada, PLLC, Ridgeland
601 985 4536
phil.abernethy@butlersnow.com
*Featured in Litigation (Mississippi)*

**Practice Areas:** Construction law and litigation; commercial litigation; product liability law; business tort law.
**Professional Memberships:** American Bar Association (Construction Committee and Forum Committee of Litigation section); International Association of Defense Counsel (Construction Litigation and Fidelity and Surety Committees); American Arbitration Association.
**Career:** AV-rated, Martindale-Hubbell; Best Lawyers in America (Commercial Litigation and Construction Law); Mid-South Super Lawyers (Construction Litigation); former instructor at National Trial Academy of International Association of Defense Counsel; Top Lawyers, Annual Guide To Commercial Litigation American Lawyer/Corporate Counsel; Certified Arbitrator by National Arbitration Forum.
**Personal:** Mississippi State University, BS, 1972; University of Mississippi, JD, cum laude, 1978.

### ALLEN, Trudy B
Butler, Snow, O'Mara, Stevens & Cannada, PLLC, Ridgeland
601 985 4531
trudy.allen@butlersnow.com
*Featured in Environment (Mississippi)*

**Practice Areas:** Business and Commercial Transactions; Construction Contracting Energy Law; Energy, Environment & Natural Resources; Environmental Law Toxic Torts; Government Contracting; Real Estate and Development Law
**Professional Memberships:** State Water Resources Advisory Council; Title V Air Advisory Committee; The Mississippi Bar Association, Section on Natural Resources; Mississippi Manufacturers Association, Committee on Environment; Environment Protection Counsel;Central Data Processing Authority Council.
**Career:** Mid-South Super Lawyers (Environmental); The Best Lawyers in America®

2012 (Environmental Law and Natural Resources Law).
**Personal:** Tulane University, JD, 1980; Louisiana State University, BS, 1977

### ARDELEAN, Paula Graves
Butler, Snow, O'Mara, Stevens & Cannada, PLLC, Ridgeland
601 985 4537
paula.ardelean@butlersnow.com
*Featured in Labor & Employment (Mississippi)*

**Practice Areas:** Employment litigation; employment training and counseling; compliance advice; non-competition agreements.
**Professional Memberships:** American Bar Association (Labor and Employment section; Employer Co-Chair of Employment Rights and Responsibilities Committee); Mississippi Bar (Board of Commissioners, 1993-95; President of Young Lawyer Division, 1993-94); Capital Area Bar Association (Board of Commissioners 1991-92).
**Career:** AV-rated, Martindale-Hubbell; Best Lawyers in America (Labor and Employment); 50 Leading Business Women, (Mississippi Business Journal, 2009); American Bar Association (Fellow);College of Labor and Employment Lawyers (Fellow); Fellow of Young Lawyers Division of Mississippi Bar and awarded President's Award for Public Service.
**Personal:** University of Mississippi, JD, cum laude, 1986.

### AYERS, David L
Watkins & Eager PLLC, Jackson
601 965 1981
dayers@watkinseager.com
*Featured in Litigation (Mississippi)*

**Practice Areas:** Extensive experience in general civil litigation; emphasis on product and premises liability defense, commercial litigation.
**Professional Memberships:** American College of Trial Lawyers, Product Liability Advisory Counsel, Bar Association of the Fifth Federal Circuit, Mississippi Bar, DRI.
**Career:** Admitted to practice in all state and federal courts in Mississippi, and Fifth Circuit Court of Appeals. Pro hac vice admissions in Arkansas, California, Florida, Georgia, Kentucky, Louisiana,

Oklahoma, South Carolina, Tennessee; Best Lawyers in America (Personal Injury, Product Liability Litigation); Mid-South Super Lawyers (Personal Injury Defense: Products, General; General Litigation).
**Personal:** Vanderbilt University (BA, 1980); University of Mississippi (JD, 1983).

### BELL, Lewis
Watkins & Eager PLLC, Jackson
601 965 1977
lbell@watkinseager.com
*Featured in Litigation (Mississippi)*

**Practice Areas:** Extensive experience in product liability (tobacco, tire, automotive, industrial, construction and consumer products), personal injury, commercial and franchise litigation.
**Professional Memberships:** The Mississippi Bar and the Bar Association of the Fifth Circuit.
**Career:** Trial and appellate practice since 1987 in state and federal courts throughout Mississippi. Listed in Best Lawyers in America (Product Liability Litigation) and in Mid-South Super Lawyers (Personal Injury Defense: Products).
**Personal:** Hampden-Sydney College (BA, 1979), University of Mississippi School of Law (JD, 1987)

### BEY, Sheryl
Baker, Donelson, Bearman, Caldwell & Berkowitz, PC, Jackson
601 351 2490
sbey@bakerdonelson.com
*Featured in Litigation (Mississippi)*

**Practice Areas:** Shareholder who concentrates her practice in complex commercial litigation, business litigation involving mortgage lending and servicing industries and litigation regarding real estate issues. Experienced in bad faith insurance defense, insurance coverage and disputes.
**Professional Memberships:** Fellow: American Bar Foundation. Member: Mississippi, Capital Area, Louisiana, American and Federal Bar Associations. Member: Maritime Law Association of the US.
**Career:** Mississippi, 1993. Louisiana, 1989. US Court of Appeals for the First and Fifth Circuits (2001, 1989), US Supreme Court (1994). Mississippi Band of Choctaw Indians Tribal Courts (2000).

**Personal:** Loyola University, JD, 1988.

### BOSCHERT, Neville H
Jones Walker LLP, Jackson
601 949 4703
nboschert@joneswalker.com
*Featured in Litigation (Mississippi)*

**Practice Areas:** Commercial litigation, insurance litigation, product liability and personal injury, antitrust and business tort litigation, medical device product liability.
**Professional Memberships:** Medical Device Subcommittee of the Products Liability Committee of the ABA Section of Litigation; American Bar Association, Defense Research Institute; Mississippi and Federal Bar.
**Career:** Seminars Taught: Current Issues in Medical Device Litigation - Off-Label Use, False Claims Act and Consumer Fraud Actions; Warnings and Proximate Causation Issues;Current Issues in Medical Device Litigation; Duels For The Company Jewels: Non-competition and Trade Secret Litigation; From Scalpel to Gavel: Medical and Business Litigation Involving Doctors and Hospitals.
**Publications:** The Restatement Sections Specifically Applicable to Pharmaceutical and Medical Device Cases in State Court: A 50-State Survey; Fifty State Survey of Challenging Expert Witnesses in Pharmaceutical and Medical Device Cases in State Court; Fifty State Survey of FDCA - Related Tort Causes of Action; Defenses to the Enforcement of a Non-Competition Agreement.

### BRAND, Walter J
Watkins & Eager PLLC, Jackson
601 965 1900
wbrand@watkinseager.com
*Featured in Labor & Employment (Mississippi)*

**Practice Areas:** Employment litigation; commercial litigation; ADR.
**Professional Memberships:** Mississippi Bar (Employment Law Committee); Defense Research Institute (Joint Monograph Sub-committee Chair (EPLI issues), 1999; regional newsletter editor, 1999-2008); American Inns of Court, Charles Clark Chapter (Barrister), 1999-2001; Invited Member, American Employment Law Council, 2009-present.

**Career:** Employer defense in Title VII, ADEA, FMLA, FLSA, ADA, workplace harassment, wrongful termination, employment contract, tort litigation; employer representation in restrictive covenant litigation;whistle blower; Best Lawyers in America (2007-2013 Labor and Employment Law); Mid-South Super Lawyers (2010-2012 Employment litigation defense; Employment and Labor).

**Personal:** University of Mississippi (BBA, 1984; JD, cum laude, 1987).

## CANNADA, Don B
Butler, Snow, O'Mara, Stevens & Cannada, PLLC, Ridgeland
601 985 4510
don.cannada@butlersnow.com
*Featured in Real Estate (Mississippi)*

**Practice Areas:** Real estate law; commercial law and lending; mergers and acquisitions.

**Professional Memberships:** American Bar Association (Property Tax Committee of Real Property, Probate and Trust Section, Business Law Section); Mississippi Bar (Real Estate and Business Law Sections); International Council of Shopping Centers; American Land Title Association; Tri-County Real Estate Association (former President); Dixie Land Title Association; Capital Area Bar Association.

**Career:** Chair, Butler Snow Business Department; AV-rated, Martindale-Hubbell; American College of Real Estate Lawyers; Best Lawyers in America; Mid-South Super Lawyers; and Who's Who Legal: USA (Real Estate); Fellow, Mississippi Young Lawyers.

**Personal:** Vanderbilt University, JD, 1978.

## CANNADA, R Barry
Butler, Snow, O'Mara, Stevens & Cannada, PLLC, Ridgeland
601 985 4535
barry.cannada@butlersnow.com
*Featured in Corporate/Commercial (Mississippi)*

**Practice Areas:** Business planning and operations; mergers and acquisitions; business structure and capitalization.

**Professional Memberships:** American Bar Association; National Lawyers Association; Mississippi Bar Association; Capital Area Bar Association .

**Career:** AV-rated, Martindale-Hubbell; Best Lawyers in America (Corporate Law, Mergers and Acquisitions)and Lawyer of the Year, Mergers and Acquisitions Law; Mid-South Super Lawyers (Business/Corporate).

**Personal:** University of Mississippi, BBA, Accounting, magna cum laude, 1977; JD, cum laude, 1980.

## CAPLES, Michael D
Butler, Snow, O'Mara, Stevens & Cannada, PLLC, Ridgeland
601 985 4412
michael.caples@butlersnow.com
*Featured in Environment (Mississippi)*

**Practice Areas:** Environmental law; government relations.

**Professional Memberships:** American Bar Association; Air and Waste Management Association; Mississippi Manufacturers Association (Environmental Committee); Mississippi Bar (Natural Resource, Energy and Environmental Law section).

**Career:** AV rated, Martindale-Hubbell; The Best Lawyers in America (Government Relations Law); member of Hazard Mitigation Council; "Mississippi Gulf Coast Regional Utility Authority Act" codified as Miss. Code. Ann. §49-17-701 et.seq.; Mississippi Association of Supervisors, Environmental counsel.

**Personal:** University of Mississippi; BS, chemical engineering, cum laude, 1987; JD, 1994.

## CARROLL, James L
Carroll Warren & Parker PLLC, Jackson
601 592 1010
jcarroll@cwplaw.com
*Featured in Litigation (Mississippi)*

**Practice Areas:** General civil litigation, product liability litigation, commercial litigation, insurance coverage litigation, personal injury litigation, large loss subrogation and municipal litigation.

**Professional Memberships:** American Bar Association, The Mississippi Bar, Hinds County Bar Association, Bar Association of the Fifth Federal Circuit, International Association of Defense Counsel, Mississippi Defense Lawyers Association, American Board of Trial Advocates, Mississippi Bar Foundation, Defense Research Institute and Member, ARIAS-US.

**Career:** Senior Counsel: Carroll Warren & Parker PLLC present; Member: Carroll Warren & Parker PLLC 2002-08; Partner: Mitchell, McNutt & Sams 1994-2001; Partner: Watkins & Eager 1975-94.

**Publications:** A list of publications is available upon request.

**Personal:** Millsaps College, BA 1967; University of Mississippi, JD, 1972; Omicron Delta Kappa-National Leadership Honorary; Phi Kappa Delta-National Forensic Honorary; Who's Who in American College and Universities; United States Army-Captain-Active Duty 1969-72.

## CLARK JR, Donald
Butler, Snow, O'Mara, Stevens & Cannada, PLLC, Ridgeland
601 985 4586
don.clark@butlersnow.com
*Featured in Corporate/Commercial (Mississippi)*

**Practice Areas:** Municipal bonds; government relations; public finance; economic development incentives.

**Professional Memberships:** American Bar Association (State and Local Government Section); National Association of Bond Lawyers; Mississippi Bar; Mississippi Association of County Board Attorneys; Capital Area Bar Association.

**Career:** Chair of Butler Snow; AV-rated, Martindale-Hubbell; The Best Lawyers in America (Public Finance Law); former Special Assistant Attorney General for Mississippi; served on Finance Committee of Governor's Commission on Recovery, Rebuilding and Renewal (following Hurricane Katrina); Mid-South Super Lawyers (Bonds/Government Finance).

**Personal:** University of Mississippi, JD, 1973; University of Southern Mississippi, BS, 1971.

## COWAN, H Mitchell
Jones Walker LLP, Jackson
601 949 4713
mcowan@joneswalker.com
*Featured in Litigation (Mississippi)*

**Practice Areas:** Commercial litigation, insurance litigation, product liability and personal injury, banking, mortgage and lender liability, appellate practice.

**Professional Memberships:** American Bar Association; The Mississippi Bar; Mississippi Defense Lawyers Association; Defense Research Institute.

**Career:** Law Clerk to Judge E. Grady Jolly, US Court of Appeals for the Fifth Circuit, 1984; Editor-in-Chief, Mississippi Law Journal, 1983. Honors and Awards: Listed in The Best Lawyers in America® 2013 (Copyright 2012 by Woodward/White, Inc., Aiken, SC) in the area of Commercial Litigation, Insurance Law, Litigation - Antitrust, Litigation - Banking & Finance, and Litigation - Bankruptcy (listed annually since 1995); Listed in Mid-South Super Lawyers (Personal Injury Defense: Products, 2009; Insurance Coverage 2010).

## DAVIS, Mark
Jones Walker LLP, Jackson
601 949 4909
markdavis@joneswalker.com
*Featured in Real Estate (Mississippi)*

**Practice Areas:** Business planning and operations, real estate transactions, real property contract law, commercial law, foreclosure law.

**Professional Memberships:** The Mississippi Bar, Real Property Section, Past-Chairman; Mortgage Bankers Association of America; Mississippi Mortgage Bankers Association; International Council of Shopping Centers.

**Career:** Honors: The Best Lawyers in America® 2012 (Copyright 2011 by Woodward/White, Inc., Aiken, SC), Real Estate; Corporate Counsel: Best Lawyers in Real Estate; Top 50 Mississippi Lawyers in Mid-South Super Lawyers; AV® Peer Review Rating in Martindale-Hubbell; Adjunct Professor, Mississippi College, Real Estate Law; Speaker: Foreclosure Law in Mississippi; Alternatives to Foreclosure.

**Publications:** Alternatives to Foreclosure and Foreclosure of a Construction Loan, University of Mississippi.

**Personal:** Cumberland School of Law, JD, 1984, summa cum laude; Samford University, BA, 1981, magna cum laude.

## DAWKINS, Michael
Baker, Donelson, Bearman, Caldwell & Berkowitz, PC, Jackson
601 351 2428
mdawkins@bakerdonelson.com
*Featured in Environment (Mississippi)*

**Practice Areas:** Shareholder with concentration in white collar criminal defense, environmental law and in conducting internal investigations. Defends individuals and companies undergoing government investigations. His environmental law practice has focused on defending companies and individuals subject to civil or administrative environmental enforcement proceedings, criminal investigations and prosecutions for crimes against the environment. Has extensive experience with civil Federal False Claims Act litigation, including trial experience.

**Professional Memberships:** Fellow of the American Bar Foundation.

**Career:** Licensed in Mississippi, 1988; Alabama, 1999; Tennessee, 2008. Certified Public Accountant, 1984. Listed in Best Lawyers in America in Environmental Law.

## EASON, Brooks
Baker, Donelson, Bearman, Caldwell & Berkowitz, PC, Jackson
601 969 4673
beason@bakerdonelson.com
*Featured in Labor & Employment (Mississippi)*

**Practice Areas:** Practice concentrated on complex business litigation and employment disputes. Has successfully defended clients in numerous employment matters, including class and collective actions and individual suits alleging discrimination on the basis of race, gender, age, religion, and disability as well as claims of sexual and racial harassment and suits under the FLSA. Has served as lead counsel for employment litigation for the largest employer in Mississippi for more than 20 years.

**Professional Memberships:** Member, American, Federal, Mississippi and Hinds County Bar Associations.

**Career:** Licensed in Mississippi.

**Personal:** University of Mississippi, BA, 1979; Duke University School of Law, JD, 1982.

## EDDS, Steve
Baker, Donelson, Bearman, Caldwell & Berkowitz, PC, Jackson
601 969 4660
sedds@bakerdonelson.com
*Featured in Corporate/Commercial (Mississippi)*

**Practice Areas:** Practice concentrated in public finance, structured finance, government relations. Experienced in reviewing, analyzing and structuring a variety of tax exempt and taxable municipal and corporate financings. Has served as Bond Counsel to state's largest conduit issuer and Lead Counsel on majority of recent state financings. Regularly serves as trustee's Counsel to a number of nationwide banks. Experienced in combining various business and tax incentives for economic development projects.

**Professional Memberships:** Member, American and Mississippi Bar Associations, National Association of Bond Lawyers.

**Career:** Licensed in Mississippi since 1973.

**Personal:** University of Mississippi, BA, 1971, JD, 1973.

## ENGLAND, John F
Butler, Snow, O'Mara, Stevens & Cannada, PLLC, Ridgeland
601 985 4563
john.england@butlersnow.com
*Featured in Corporate/Commercial (Mississippi)*

**Practice Areas:** Public finance; economic development incentives; municipal bonds.

**Professional Memberships:** American Bar Association; National Association of Bond Lawyers (Chair, Bond Attorneys' Workshop Panel for Manufacturing Facilities, Enterprise Zone Bonds and GO Zone Bonds); Mississippi Bar (Board of Directors of Young Lawyers Division, Delivery of Legal Services Committee); Mississippi Society of Certified Public Accountants.
**Career:** "Dealmaker of the Year" by American Lawyer (2006); Best Lawyers in America (Public Finance); Mid-South Super Lawyers®, Bonds/Government Finance.
**Personal:** University of Florida, LLM, taxation, 1991; Mississippi College, JD, with distinction, 1989; University of Mississippi, BA, cum laude, 1984.

**FAIR, George R**
Watkins & Eager PLLC, Jackson
601 965 1900
gfair@watkinseager.com
*Featured in Corporate/Commercial (Mississippi)*
**Practice Areas:** Banking, corporate, commercial transactions, public utilities, construction, fidelity and surety, commercial litigation.
**Professional Memberships:** The Mississippi Bar; Mississippi Bar Foundation; Capital Area Bar Association; American Bar Association; American Bar Foundation.
**Career:** Business and trial practice with Watkins & Eager PLLC since 1974; Jackson Young Lawyers (President, 1982); The Mississippi Bar (President, 2009-10); Best Lawyers in America, 1983-2013 (Banking, Corporate); Mid-South Super Lawyers, 2011 - 2013 (Banking, Business Litigation, Business/Corporate).
**Personal:** University of Mississippi (BA, 1971; JD, 1973); Editorial Board, Mississippi Law Journal.

**FORD, Barry W**
Baker, Donelson, Bearman, Caldwell & Berkowitz, PC, Jackson
601 351 8925
bford@bakerdonelson.com
*Featured in Litigation (Mississippi)*
**Practice Areas:** Since joining Baker Donelson in 2000, Judge Ford's practice has been primarily in the areas of product liability, general civil litigation, nursing home litigation and commercial litigation since joining the firm in 2000. He also has tried medical malpractice and labor and employment cases to verdict. He is AV Peer Review Rated by Martindale-Hubbell. Prior to joining the firm, he served three terms as a State Court Trial Judge in the First Circuit Court District of Mississippi.
**Professional Memberships:** Mississippi, Magnolia and Hinds County Bar Associations; Litigation Counsel of America; DRI. ABOTA.
**Career:** Licensed in Mississippi since 1979.

**FOX, Betty Ruth**
Watkins & Eager PLLC, Jackson
601 965 1881
bfox@watkinseager.com
*Featured in Environment (Mississippi)*
**Practice Areas:** Environmental, bankruptcy, administrative.

**Professional Memberships:** ABA – Environmental, Energy and Resources Section; Mississippi Bar – Natural Resources, Energy and Environmental Law Section – Business Law Section; MS Bankruptcy Conference; DRI; Mississippi Manufacturers Association; Mississippi Women Lawyers Association; Air and Waste Management Association.
**Publications:** Author, "Bankruptcy Court Can 'Make It Rain'", January 2013; Co-author, "Turning Trash Into Cash: Brownfield Redevelopment Makes 'Cents'", Winter 2012; Author, "Bankruptcy: Behold or Beware?" December 2010.
**Personal:** Admitted in Mississippi; US District Court Southern District of Mississippi; U. S. District Court Northern District of Mississippi; U. S. Court of Appeals 5th Circuit.

**GALLOWAY, Robert C**
Butler, Snow, O'Mara, Stevens & Cannada, PLLC, Gulfport
228 575 3019
bob.galloway@butlersnow.com
*Featured in Litigation (Mississippi)*
**Practice Areas:** Product liability; commercial litigation; professional liability defense; maritime law.
**Professional Memberships:** American Bar Association; Defense Research Institute; Maritime Law Association of the United States; International Association of Defense Counsel; Mississippi Bar (Litigation Section, Past Chairman); Harrison County Bar Association (Past President).
**Career:** AV-rated, Martindale-Hubbell; American College of Trial Lawyers (Fellow and past State Chair for Mississippi); Maritime Law Association; Mississippi Bar Foundation (Fellow, Past President); American Board of Trial Advocates (Past President, Mississippi Chapter); The Best Lawyers in America (Personal Injury); Mid-South Super Lawyers (Business Litigation).
**Personal:** University of Mississippi, JD, 1967; BA, 1964.

**GOODMAN III, Will**
Watkins & Eager PLLC, Jackson
601 965 1998
wgoodman@watkinseager.com
*Featured in Products Liability (Nationwide), Litigation (Mississippi)*
See under Nationwide for profile.

**GOODMAN JR, William F**
Watkins & Eager PLLC, Jackson
601 965 1900
goodmanjr@watkinseager.com
*Featured in Litigation (Mississippi)*
**Practice Areas:** General civil practice -emphasis in commercial, banking, business litigation, appellate practice.
**Professional Memberships:** American College of Trial Lawyers; American Academy of Appellate Lawyers; American Inns of Court; American Bar Foundation; Mississippi Bar Foundation.
**Career:** Trial and appellate practice since 1953; Best Lawyers in America 1983-2012 (Appellate, Banking, Energy, Natural Resources, Oil and Gas

Law; Bet-the-Company, Commercial, Personal Injury Litigation); Lifetime Achievement Awards: The Mississippi Bar (2009); Mississippi Defense Lawyers Association (2010). University of Mississippi School of Law Alumni Hall of Fame (2010).
**Personal:** Millsaps College (BA, cum laude, 1949); University of Mississippi (LLB, with distinction, 1951).

**GRENFELL, Matthew H**
Butler, Snow, O'Mara, Stevens & Cannada, PLLC, Ridgeland
601 985 4592
matt.grenfell@butlersnow.com
*Featured in Real Estate (Mississippi)*
**Practice Areas:** Real estate law; business planning and operations; commercial lending.
**Professional Memberships:** American Bar Association; Mississippi Bar (Real Property and Business Law sections); Tri County Real Estate Attorneys' Association (former President); Capital Area Bar Association; Leadership Greater Jackson 2010-11; Jackson Young Lawyers (former Speaker's Bureau Co-Chairman).
**Career:** Mid-South Rising Stars (Real Estate); Real estate counsel for developers in Central and North Mississippi; Lender's counsel in connection with $80 million construction and revolving facilities for energy company.
**Personal:** University of Mississippi, BA, magna cum laude, 2002; JD, 2005.

**GUNN, Paul L**
Watkins & Eager PLLC, Jackson
601 965 1900
pgunn@watkinseager.com
*Featured in Real Estate (Mississippi)*
**Practice Areas:** Real estate, commercial finance and lending, including affordable housing and new market tax credit developments, new urban and mixed use developments, condominium, multi-family, retail and commercial projects.
**Professional Memberships:** Mississippi Bar (Real Property Section Past Chairman); American College of Mortgage Attorneys (Fellow); Tri-County Real Estate Association.
**Career:** Admitted to Mississippi Bar in 1983; Best Lawyers in America (Real Estate Law); Mid-South Super Lawyers (Real Estate; Securities and Corporate Finance); Admitted in all Mississippi state and federal courts.
**Personal:** University of Mississippi (BBA, cum laude, 1980; JD, 1983); Phi Delta Phi.

**HARRISON, J Clifford**
Butler, Snow, O'Mara, Stevens & Cannada, PLLC, Ridgeland
601 985 4529
cliff.harrison@butlersnow.com
*Featured in Corporate/Commercial (Mississippi)*
**Practice Areas:** Banking and financial institutions; financial services; consumer credit regulation; commercial lending.
**Professional Memberships:** American Bar Association (Business Law section, Consumer Financial Services Committee, Banking Law Committee); Mississippi Bar (Business Law section); Mississippi Bankers Association (Bank

Attorneys Committee); Capital Area Bar Association.
**Career:** AV-rated, Martindale-Hubbell; The Best Lawyers in America (Banking Law); Fellow, Mississippi Bar Foundation; Mid-South Super Lawyers®, Banking; Mississippi and Tennessee Editor, HouseLaw; former General Counsel for regional bank and bank holding company.
**Personal:** University of Mississippi, JD, 1978.

**HEMBREE, G. Dewey**
McGlinchey Stafford PLLC, Jackson
601 960 8425
ghembree@mcglinchey.com
*Featured in Litigation (Mississippi)*
**Practice Areas:** Commercial and business litigation; consumer financial services; general litigation; commercial transactions
**Professional Memberships:** American and Mississippi Bar Associations; Capital Area Bar Association; Mississippi Defense Lawyers Association.
**Career:** Managing member of the firm's Jackson, Mississippi office. Has more than 25 years of litigation experience focusing on business litigation and consumer finance. Practice also includes general litigation, complex real estate and other business transactions. AV-rated, Martindale-Hubbell.
**Personal:** University of Mississippi, JD (1986); University of Mississippi, BBA, Banking & Finance (1983).

**HENDRIX, Steven M**
Forman Perry Watkins Krutz & Tardy LLP, Jackson
601 960 8603
shendrix@fpwk.com
*Featured in Real Estate (Mississippi)*
**Practice Areas:** Mr Hendrix is exclusively involved in a transactional practice with significant experience in the following areas: real estate acquisitions, development and financings, corporate structuring, and related securities, taxation and environmental issues. He has been extensively involved in representing companies, both public and private, lenders and governmental entities in major real estate investments and developments including international joint ventures, developments utilizing both historical and new market tax credits and public/private partnerships.
**Professional Memberships:** The Mississippi Bar; State Bar of Texas; American Bar Association.
**Career:** Mr Hendrix is the Lead Partner in the firm's Business and Corporate Practice Group and a member of the firm's Executive Committee. Mr Hendrix is recognized by The Best Lawyers In America (corporate compliance, corporate governance, corporate, real estate and tax law), Mid-South Super Lawyers (real estate) and is rated Preeminent AV by Martindale Hubbell. In 2011, Mr Hendrix was elected Mississippi Corporate Compliance Lawyer of the Year by Best Lawyers in America and a Top 50 Mississippi Super Lawyer. Mr Hendrix Co-Chaired the Mississippi Secretary of State's 2008 Business Reform Committee for LLCs and Partnerships.

**Personal:** University of Mississippi (JD, cum laude, 1986; MAccy, with honors, 1984; BAccy, 1983).

### HENEGAN, John C
Butler, Snow, O'Mara, Stevens & Cannada, PLLC, Ridgeland
601 985 4530
john.henegan@butlersnow.com
*Featured in Litigation (Mississippi)*
**Practice Areas:** Antitrust; intellectual property; complex commercial litigation; media defense; telecommunications.
**Professional Memberships:** American Bar Association (Antitrust, Litigation, Patent and Copyright Sections and Communications Law Forum); Federal Bar Association; Federal Circuit Bar Association; Fifth Circuit Bar Association; Media Law Resource Center (Past Chair, Employment Libel and Privacy Committee).
**Career:** AV-rated, Martindale-Hubbell; Fellow, American Academy of Appellate Lawyers; Fellow, Mississippi Bar Foundation; Best Lawyers in America (Appellate, Bet-the-Company, Commercial Litigation and First Amendment Law); Distinguished Service Award (Hinds County Bar); Former Chief of Staff, Office of Governor of State of Mississippi.
**Personal:** University of Mississippi, JD, with honors, 1976.

### HERBERT, Mark D
Jones Walker LLP, Jackson
601 949 4750
mherbert@joneswalker.com
*Featured in Litigation (Mississippi)*
**Practice Areas:** Construction Law, Fidelity and Surety Law, Outdoor Advertising; Chair, Construction Practice Group.
**Professional Memberships:** The Mississippi Bar; American Bar Association, Forum Committee on the Construction Industry; American Arbitration Association, National Panel of Commercial and Construction Arbitrators and Mediators; Associated Builders and Contractors of Mississippi; Associated General Contractors of Mississippi; Surety Association of Mississippi; International Association of Defense Counsel; Outdoor Advertising Association of America, Inc.; Mississippi Bar Foundation, 1995 - 1996, President.
**Career:** Honors: Listed in Chambers USA: America's Leading Business Lawyers, Litigation: Construction; Listed in Leadership in Law, 2010 Class (MBJ) Speaking Engagements: 'Current Issues in Mississippi Construction Lien Law, Mid-South Super Lawyers.
**Publications:** Prejudice to the Compensated Surety as a Defense to Liability; Contractor's State License Bonds, Desk Reference.
**Personal:** Classes/Seminars Taught: IRMI Construction Risk Conference, featured panelist; Mississippi Construction Payment Rights; Construction Contracting for Public Entities in Mississippi; Fifth National Forum on Toxic Mold Litigation; Advanced Construction Law in Mississippi; Mechanics' Lien Law and Strategies in

Mississippi; Fidelity and Surety Trial Practice Program, IADC.

### HISE, Daniel G
Butler, Snow, O'Mara, Stevens & Cannada, PLLC, Ridgeland
601 985 4509
dan.hise@butlersnow.com
*Featured in Corporate/Commercial (Mississippi)*
**Practice Areas:** Gaming law; corporate law.
**Professional Memberships:** International Association of Gaming Attorneys; American Bar Association (Business Law Section); Mississippi Bar (Former Chairman of Business Law and Gaming Law Sections); Capital Area Bar Association.
**Career:** AV-rated, Martindale-Hubbell; Best Lawyers in America (Corporate Law and Gaming Law); Mid-South Super Lawyers (Securities and Corporate Finance); 2010 Client Service All-Star, BTI Consulting Group; member of Business Law Advisory Group and Former Chairman of Trademark Committee for Mississippi Secretary of State.
**Personal:** Mississippi College, JD, with special distinction, 1985; Tulane University, PhD, 1973; University of California, Berkeley, BA, 1965.

### HODGE JR, E Clifton
Baker, Donelson, Bearman, Caldwell & Berkowitz, PC, Jackson
601 968 5575
ech@wisecarter.com
*Featured in Corporate/Commercial (Mississippi)*

### HOUSTON III, Jamie G
Watkins & Eager PLLC, Jackson
601 965 1900
jhouston@watkinseager.com
*Featured in Corporate/Commercial (Mississippi)*
**Practice Areas:** Corporate and entities, commercial finance, business planning, taxation, tax controversy, estate planning, estate administration.
**Professional Memberships:** Mississippi Bar; American Bar Association; Capital Area Bar Association; American Institute of Certified Public Accountants; Mississippi Society of Certified Public Accountants; American College of Trust and Estate Counsel; Mississippi Estate Planning Council.
**Career:** Corporate, commercial, business, taxation, and estate planning practice since 1976; Best Lawyers in America, 1997-2013 (Corporate, Tax, Trusts and Estates); Mid-South Super Lawyers, 2007-2012 (Business/Corporate; Tax; Estate Planning and Probate).
**Personal:** University of Mississippi (BBA, 1974; JD 1976); New York University (Master of Laws, 1978); Certified Public Accountant (1979-present).

### IRBY, Peyton
Jones Walker LLP, Jackson
601 949 4810
pirby@joneswalker.com
*Featured in Labor & Employment (Mississippi)*
**Practice Areas:** Labor and employment compliance, labor and employment litigation, OSHA, labor relations/union negotiations.

**Professional Memberships:** American Bar Association, Labor and Employment Law Section; Federal Bar Association; The Mississippi Bar, Labor and Employment Law Section.
**Career:** Past Employment Positions: National Labor Relations Board, Trial and Supervisory Attorney.
**Publications:** Mississippi Employment Law Letter; The Americans with Disabilities Act: The Employer's Perspective.
**Personal:** Honors: Fellow, College of Labor and Employment Lawyers; Cy Burnett Award for Service to Lodging Industry.

### JACOBS, Donna Brown
Butler, Snow, O'Mara, Stevens & Cannada, PLLC, Ridgeland
601 985 4538
donna.jacobs@butlersnow.com
*Featured in Litigation (Mississippi)*
**Practice Areas:** Appellate litigation; pharmaceutical product liability defense; media defense.
**Professional Memberships:** American Bar Association (Appellate Practice Committee); Defense Research Institute (Appellate Advocacy Committee); Media Law Resource Center; Mississippi Bar; Capital Area Bar Association; Bar Association of 5th Federal Circuit.
**Career:** The Best Lawyers in America (Appellate Law); Mid-South Super Lawyers (Appellate); author of Mississippi Law Section, 50-State Survey of Law of Defamation and Invasion of Privacy and Quarterly Procedural Update of Fifth Circuit Reporter.
**Personal:** University of Mississippi, BPA, summa cum laude, 1985; JD, magna cum laude, 1988.

### JACOBS, Gina
Jones Walker LLP, Jackson
601 949 4705
gjacobs@joneswalker.com
*Featured in Corporate/Commercial (Mississippi)*
**Practice Areas:** Commercial lending and finance, loan workouts and foreclosures, business planning and operations, mergers/acquisitions, business and real estate transactions.
**Professional Memberships:** Mississippi Secretary of State's Business Reform Committee - Corporations Law and UCC Committees; American Bar Association (Business Law Section); The Mississippi Bar (Business Law Section).
**Career:** Admitted: Mississippi; US District Court Northern and Southern Districts of Mississippi; US Court of Appeals 5th Circuit.
**Publications:** Commercial Loan Workouts - Strategies for Troubled Loans (Mississippi Banker's Seminar 2009); Review of a Corporate Opinion Letter and What It Means (Mississippi State Bar Annual Meeting 2007).
**Personal:** Junior League of Jackson.

### JOHNSON III, Charles F
Butler, Snow, O'Mara, Stevens & Cannada, PLLC, Ridgeland
601 985 4528
charles.johnson@butlersnow.com
*Featured in Corporate/Commercial (Mississippi)*
**Practice Areas:** Pharmaceutical, Life Sciences, Medical Device, Biotechnology and Healthcare;

Joint Ventures, Mergers and Acquisitions; Healthcare Operations and Compliance (including Internal and External Investigations); Physician Practice Management; Corporate Law
**Professional Memberships:** American Bar Association (Health Law and Business Law Sections); American Health Lawyers Association; Mississippi Bar (Health Law and Business Law Sections); Capital Area Bar Association
**Career:** AV-rated, Martindale-Hubbell; The Best Lawyers in America®, (Corporate Law, Health Care Law, Mergers and Acquisitions Law).
**Personal:** University of Mississippi, JD, with honors, 1974; BS, 1969.

### JONES, Christy D
Butler, Snow, O'Mara, Stevens & Cannada, PLLC, Ridgeland
601 985 4523
christy.jones@butlersnow.com
*Featured in Litigation (Nationwide), Products Liability (Nationwide), Litigation (Mississippi)*
See under Nationwide for profile.

### JONES, Walker (Bill)
Baker, Donelson, Bearman, Caldwell & Berkowitz, PC, Jackson
601 351 2413
wjones@bakerdonelson.com
*Featured in Litigation (Mississippi)*
**Practice Areas:** Practice concentrated in insurance, commercial and product liability litigation. Extensive experience handling mass tort defense, construction law and chemical/toxic tort litigation.
**Professional Memberships:** American, Mississippi, Texas and Tennessee Bar Associations (Member, Sections on Litigation, Public Contract Law, Tort and Insurance Practice). Member, Trial Attorneys of America, The American Board of Trial Advocates and President of Mississippi Chapter (2005-06), International Association of Defense Counsel, Litigation Counsel of America and Maritime Law Association of the United States.
**Career:** Licensed in Mississippi since 1973, Texas since 1996 and Tennessee since 1997. Listed in Chambers and Best Lawyers in America since 2003.

### KEITH, James A
Adams and Reese LLP, Jackson
601 292 0718
jim.keith@arlaw.com
*Featured in Labor & Employment (Mississippi)*
**Practice Areas:** Partner - Labor and Employment Team Leader, Labor and Employment, Education Law.
**Career:** Jim Keith's areas of practice include employment, education and administrative law. A specialized aspect of his practice involves the representation of educational entities, including school districts, community colleges and universities. He has represented numerous school districts in all areas of education law, including employee matters, student issues, board/administration interaction, and education of students with disabilities.

**Personal:** JD, University of Mississippi School of Law, 1982; BS, Mississippi State University, 1971.

## KRUTZ, Fred
Forman Perry Watkins Krutz & Tardy LLP, Jackson
601 960 8600
fred@fpwk.com
*Featured in Litigation (Mississippi)*

**Practice Areas:** Mr Krutz has many years of experience in defending thousands of mass tort and multiple plaintiff cases in state and federal courts, including asbestos, silica, noise-induced hearing loss, personal injuries from alleged pollution of air and surface waters, and consumer finance cases; He also has extensive experience in defending multi-defendant litigation (MDL) cases, including asbestos, silica, and pedicle screw; He is National Coordinating Counsel for US Steel Corporation for their benzene, silica, asbestos, and coal tar litigation.

**Professional Memberships:** Served on the Mississippi Law Journal, Editorial Board; The Mississippi Bar

**Career:** Founding Partner of Forman Perry Watkins Krutz & Tardy LLP, 1986; Butler, Snow, O'Mara, Stevens & Cannada - Associate (1978-82), Partner (1982-86).

**Publications:** Silicosis: Explaining the Inconsistency Between Declining Public Health Statistics and the Epidemic in Litigation, Chest 128, Suppl. 4:2145, 2005; MEALEY'S LITIGATION REPORT: Silica, Commentary - In The Wake Of Silica MDL 1553, Vol. 4, No. 5 (January 2006); Federal Jurisdiction - Civil Rights Jurisdiction Under 28 USC §1349(3) Not Available When Equitable Monetary Relief, Sought Under 42 USC §1983, Would Stem Directly From Municipal Funds, Miss. LJ, Vol. 47 (1976).

**Personal:** Graduated from University of Mississippi Law School, December 1977 with highest honors; admitted to the bar in 1978; received the Phi Delta Phi Award for the outstanding law school graduate in 1977; Chairman of the Defendants' Steering Committee in the Silica MDL 1553 in Corpus Christi, TX, which litigation ended with an historic order and opinion by Judge Janis Jack as reported in numerous media, including the New York Times, Fortune Magazine, The Wall Street Journal, and Reader's Digest; reviewed and selected by his peers to be listed in 'The Best Lawyers in America', 2007-2013 and Mid-South Super Lawyers, 2006-2013; selected as 2009 "Local Litigation Star" in Benchmark Litigation, The Definitive Guide to America's Leading Litigation Firms and Attorneys; selected as "Best Lawyers" Lawyer of the Year 2013; has spoken at many conferences and seminars all over the country, including AEI-Brookings Institute - Toxic Torts Judicial Symposium, Mealey's Silica & Asbestos Claims Conference, DRI Silica Medicine Seminar, US Chamber Of Commerce - Diagnosing for Dollars: The Engine Driving Mass Torts Litigation; Mealey's Mass Medical Screenings Teleconference - Investigations into Fraudulent Asbestos & Silica Claims. On October 27, 2010, Forman Perry Watkins Krutz & Tardy

was presented with the US Chamber of Commerce Institute for Legal Reform's 2010 Award for Outstanding Organization. In selecting Forman Perry for the honor, the Chamber recognized Forman Perry's ongoing work to expose screening fraud in mass tort cases nationwide. These efforts include work that produced the historic decision by Judge Janis Jack in 2005 dismissing more than 20,000 silica claims based on fraudulent actions by plaintiffs and their attorneys, in which Mr Krutz was the Chairman of the Defendants' Steering Committee. Jan. 2008 started trial in the first silica case in Mississippi (mistrial after three days of trial); Dec. 2008 started trial in benzene case in Marshall, TX (settled after voir dire). Lead trial lawyer in the first silica case tried to verdict in Mississippi (in Port Gibson, Mississippi May 11-21, 2009). The jury returned a verdict for the defendants, which is the first defense verdict in a mass tort case in Claiborne County, Mississippi. This historic victory was reported by numerous media, including The American Lawyer, NPR, The Clarion Ledger, Fox Business.com, Trial.com, HarrisMartin, Androvett Legal Media & Marketing and Claimsjournal.com; Lead counsel in Clark Sand, et al v. Ruby Kelley, (Miss. 2010), in which the Mississippi Supreme Court reversed and rendered the trial court's denial of summary judgment. The Supreme Court ruled that plaintiff lacked standing to file suit on behalf of the decedent who died of lung cancer caused by exposure to silica. For the first time in Mississippi jurisprudence, the Court defined exactly what an "interested party" is under the wrongful death statute; Lead counsel for defendant/appellants in Kinsey v. Pangborn Corp., 78 So. 3d 301 (Miss.2011), who successfully argued before the Harrison County trial court for dismissal based on the failure to file within the statute of limitations and lack of standing of the plaintiff. In a unanimous decision the Supreme Court affirmed the trial court's dismissal. The Kinsey decision further upheld the April 2011 Clark Sand case; Lead counsel for McGraw Hill and its subsidiary Standard and Poor's in litigation filed by the Mississippi Attorney General. This litigation alleges that rating agencies incorrectly rated mortgage backed securities and that the State of Mississippi was harmed by those ratings. The case is still pending in Federal District Court in Mississippi; Lead counsel for defendant/appellants in Empire Abrasive Equipment Corp., et al v. Henry Morgan, Jr., who successfully argued summary judgment on the statute of limitations before the MS Supreme Court in May 2012. Mr Morgan filed his suit seeking damages allegedly related to exposure to silica. Mr Morgan died during the pendency of his suit, but no proper party was substituted for him after death. More than three years after Morgan, Sr.'s death, his son, Morgan, Jr., then filed a wrongful death claim. The Supreme Court reversed and rendered the ruling by the Circuit Court of Adams County, MS stating that neither the savings statute nor any tolling period applied to Morgan, Jr.'s wrongful death suit and therefore it was time-barred; Lead counsel for TIN, a sub-

sidiary of International Paper Company, in connection with a lawsuit filed by the District Attorney for Washington Parish, Louisiana, arising out of an August 2011 incident in which TIN's Bogalusa Paper Mill released weak black liquor into the Pearl River resulting in a significant fish kill. The lawsuit sought to impose civil penalties in excess of $250 million on TIN for the fish kill. TIN requested the case be dismissed on the basis that TIN had settled the civil penalties claim with the Louisiana Department of Wildlife and Fisheries. The trial court refused that request and declared the LDWF-TIN settlement to be void. Forman Perry filed a successful interlocutory appeal of the trial court ruling to the Louisiana First Circuit Court of Appeal. The First Circuit reversed the trial court, and dismissed the District Attorney's lawsuit with prejudice. The District Attorney has appealed the First Circuit judgment to the Louisiana Supreme Court, and Forman Perry has opposed that appeal. The Louisiana Supreme Court should decide that appeal in first half of 2013.

## LANDRUM, Craig
Jones Walker LLP, Jackson
601 949 4973
clandrum@joneswalker.com
*Featured in Corporate/Commercial (Mississippi)*

**Practice Areas:** Business Planning and Operations, Financial Institutions, Mergers and Acquisitions, Securities.

**Professional Memberships:** Mississippi and American Bar Associations; Mississippi Bankers Association, Bank Attorney's Committee.

**Career:** Honors: Mississippi Banking Lawyer of the Year, 2013 and 2009 by Best Lawyers in America; Distinguished Faculty Award, Mississippi School of Banking.

**Publications:** Publications: "An Effective Records Management Program", Commercial Lending Review, 2006; Mississippi Practice Series, Encyclopedia of Mississippi Law, Banking Law Section; Speaking Engagement: Mississippi Bankers Association 2010 CEO Executive Management Conference, "Current Regulatory Examination Issues"; Mississippi School of Banking: Sale of Non-Deposit Investment Products.

**Personal:** Bar Admissions: Mississippi; US District Court Northern District of Mississippi; US District Court Southern District of Mississippi; US Court of Appeals 5th Circuit.

## LAZARUS, Robert
Jones Walker LLP, Jackson
601 949 4930
blazarus@joneswalker.com
*Featured in Corporate/Commercial (Mississippi)*

**Practice Areas:** State and local tax incentives, public finance economic development, corporate finance incentive programs.

**Professional Memberships:** American Bar Association; Mississippi Bar; National Association of Bond Lawyers; Ohio State Bar.

**Career:** Jackson, MS Best Lawyers Public Finance Lawyer of the Year; Regular Fellow and Member of Board of Directors of American College of

Bond Counsel; Member of Board of Directors of Jones Walker LLP.

**Personal:** Boston University School of Law (JD, 1976, cum laude); Dartmouth College (BA, 1973, magna cum laude); Phi Beta Kappa; admitted to practice in Mississippi and Ohio.

## LINDSAY, Timothy W
Ogletree, Deakins, Nash, Smoak & Stewart, Jackson
601 360 8444
timothy.lindsay@ogletreedeakins.com
*Featured in Labor & Employment (Mississippi)*

**Practice Areas:** Labor and employment, litigation.

**Professional Memberships:** American Bar Association (Labor and Employment Section, EEO Committee), Mississippi Bar Association (Labor and Employment Section).

**Career:** Admitted to practice in Mississippi. More than 25 years of litigation experience. Has practiced exclusively in the field of labor and employment law since 1987. Managing Shareholder in Jackson, MS office of Ogletree Deakins.

**Publications:** Has served as faculty member at numerous seminars covering current and developing employment laws. Co-Author: Employment in Gaming: Recent Discrimination Issues, Gaming Law Review (Vol. 8 No. 2)(April 2004).

**Personal:** University of Mississippi (BA, 1981), University of Mississippi (JD, 1984).

## MADDUX, Christopher R
Butler, Snow, O'Mara, Stevens & Cannada, PLLC, Ridgeland
601 985 4502
chris.maddux@butlersnow.com
*Featured in Corporate/Commercial (Mississippi)*

**Practice Areas:** Bankruptcy; Business Reorganizations; Business Litigation.

**Professional Memberships:** American Bankruptcy Institute; Mississippi Bar Association; Tennessee Bar Association; Capital Area Bar Association.

**Career:** The Best Lawyers in America® (Bankruptcy and Creditor Debtor Rights / Insolvency and Reorganization Law); Mid-South Rising Stars® (Bankruptcy & Creditor/Debtor Rights).

**Personal:** Vanderbilt University, BS, 1996; JD, 1999.

## MARTIN, David L
Jones Walker LLP, Jackson
601 949 4901
davidmartin@joneswalker.com
*Featured in Corporate/Commercial (Mississippi)*

**Practice Areas:** David Martin is a special counsel in the firm's Business & Commercial Transactions Practice Group and practices from the firm's Jackson office. He is an experienced banking, securities, and finance lawyer who primarily represents entities in the insurance industry. He has formed private and publicly held insurance entities. His work ranges from significant mergers, acquisitions and reinsurance transactions to routine regulatory matters such as rate, form, and other filings. He has extensive experi-

ence with insurer insolvencies and guaranty associations. He also provides legislative and government relations services. He has been issuer's counsel for asset backed financings, primarily public offerings, that total nearly $2 billion. He also serves as counsel for two well-funded nonprofit corporations that provide services for Mississippi students.
**Career:** US Navy Reserve Officer (1970-1975); Federation of Regulatory Counsel; Listed in The Best Lawyers in America® 2013 (Copyright 2012 by Woodward/White, Inc., Aiken, SC) in the areas of Administrative/Regulatory Law, Banking & Finance Law, Corporate Law, Financial Services Regulation Law, and Insurance Law (listed annually since 2005); Named "Jackson Administrative/Regulatory Law Lawyer of the Year" 2013; AV® Peer Review Rating in Martindale-Hubbell.
**Personal:** University of Virginia School of Law (JD 1976); Millsaps College (BA, 1969).

## MCDANIEL JR, Dan M
Baker, Donelson, Bearman, Caldwell & Berkowitz, PC, Jackson
601 351 2493
DMcDaniel@bakerdonelson.com
*Featured in Corporate/Commercial (Mississippi)*
**Practice Areas:** Shareholder and manager of the firm's Gaming Practice. Represents domestic and international clients before gaming authorities with regard to licenses, registrations, findings of suitability, transfers of ownership, financings, patron disputes, disciplinary proceedings, work permits and other regulatory matters.
**Professional Memberships:** International Association of Gaming Advisors (Board of Trustees and former president); Mississippi Association of Gaming Attorneys (founding member); The Mississippi Bar (Chairman, Gaming Section, 2000-01); Federal Bar Association; American Bar Association (Co-Chair - Section on Gaming Law, 2001).
**Career:** Licensed in Mississippi, 1973.
**Personal:** University of Mississippi, JD, 1973. University of Southern Mississippi, BS, 1971.

## MENDENHALL, William
Baker, Donelson, Bearman, Caldwell & Berkowitz, PC, Jackson
601 969 4647
bmendenhall@bakerdonelson.com
*Featured in Real Estate (Mississippi), Corporate/Commercial (Mississippi)*
**Practice Areas:** Shareholder in the business section concentrating in commercial real estate, corporate practice, economic development, and insurance regulatory matters.
**Professional Memberships:** American, Mississippi and Hinds County Bar Associations. Admitted, 5th Circuit Court of Appeals.
**Career:** Licensed in Mississippi, 1984. Former Chairman, Mississippi Law Institute. Member, Mississippi Secretary of State's Business Law Advisory Group (1993-2009) and Chairman, Corporate Laws Subcommittee (2005-07). President, Business Section of Mississippi Bar (2009-10).

**Personal:** University of Mississippi (JD-1984, cum laude; BBA-1980, magna cum laude). Named in leading US legal publication. Elder, Fondren Presbyterian Church (PCUSA). Member, Haiti Network Coordinating Committee, Living Waters for the World.

## MILAM, Kenneth E
Watkins & Eager PLLC, Jackson
601 965 1900
kemilam@watkinseager.com
*Featured in Labor & Employment (Mississippi)*
**Practice Areas:** Labor and employment; administrative claims before EEOC, NLRB, and Department of Labor; employment agreements; collective bargaining negotiations; maintaining non-union status; management training.
**Professional Memberships:** Mississippi Bar; American College of Labor and Employment Lawyers (Fellow); American Employment Law Council.
**Career:** Labor and employment law, emphasis in defense of employers; Mississippi Economic Council (Chairman, 1987-88); Best Lawyers in America (ADR; Labor and Employment 1989-2012 Best Labor Lawyer, Mississippi, 2011).
**Personal:** University of Mississippi (BA, 1966; JD, 1969); 1st Lt, US Army (Vietnam Service); Harvard University Mediation School (1994).

## MILLER, Dennis
Jones Walker LLP, Jackson
601 949 4776
dmiller@joneswalker.com
*Featured in Energy & Natural Resources (Mississippi)*
**Practice Areas:** Legislative and governmental relations, public utilities.
**Professional Memberships:** Mississippi Forestry Association, Board of Directors; Mississippi Bar, Natural Resources, Energy and Environmental Law Section; The Mississippi Bar, Gaming Law Section; Mississippi Manufacturers Association, Governmental Affairs and Energy Committees.
**Career:** Honors: Attended 2010 US Army War College National Security Seminar.
**Publications:** Lobbying, PACs and Campaign Finance (50 State Handbook) Mississippi Chapter.
**Personal:** Bar Admissions US Supreme Court; US Court of Appeals District of Columbia Circuit; US Court of Appeals 5th Circuit; Mississippi; US District Court Southern District of Mississippi.

## MONTJOY II, R Wilson
Butler, Snow, O'Mara, Stevens & Cannada, PLLC, Ridgeland
601 985 4576
wilson.montjoy@butlersnow.com
*Featured in Energy & Natural Resources (Mississippi)*
**Practice Areas:** Energy law; energy and industrial project development; public utilities; economic development tax incentives; taxation.
**Professional Memberships:** American Bar Association (Board of Governors; House of Delegates; Nominating Committee; Young Lawyers Division,Section on Environment); Institute for Professionals in Taxation; Mississippi Bar (former chair, Alternative Dispute Resolution

Section; Fellow, Young Lawyers Division); Capital Area Bar (Board of Directors).
**Career:** Best Lawyers in America (Energy Law, Natural Resources Law, Oil and Gas Law); American Bar Endowment (Fellow); Who's Who in the World; Who's Who in American Law; Governor Phil Bryant's Policy Transition Team - Energy Committee.
**Personal:** University of Mississippi, JD, 1978.

## MUNFORD, Luther T
Butler, Snow, O'Mara, Stevens & Cannada, PLLC, Ridgeland
601 985 4418
luther.munford@butlersnow.com
*Featured in Litigation (Mississippi)*
**Practice Areas:** Appellate litigation, media law, constitutional law, professional liability, product liability law.
**Professional Memberships:** Mississippi Bar Association; American Bar Association; American Academy of Appellate Lawyers (Past President , Editor, The Appellate Advocate, 2009-13); Mississippi Code of Judicial Conduct Study Committee (Chair, 2009-13)
**Career:** The Best Lawyers in America® - Litigation; "Lawyer of the Year" – First Amendment Law, Best Lawyers, 2012; Mid-South Super Lawyers.
**Personal:** University of Virginia, JD, 1976. Oxford University, BA, 1973. Princeton University, AB, 1971.

## OGLETREE, Powell G
Adams and Reese LLP, Jackson
601 292 0740
gee.ogletree@arlaw.com
*Featured in Real Estate (Mississippi)*
**Practice Areas:** Partner: Real estate, banking, finance, forestry, economic development, environmental, eminent domain.
**Professional Memberships:** ABA Timber Resources Committee, Mississippi Forestry Association, Rankin County Chamber of Commerce, Board of Directors for American Bar Association Section of Environment, Energy and Resources.
**Career:** Real estate, forestry, natural resources, business and trial attorney, with litigation experience including general civil litigation in state, federal district and appellate courts and administrative proceedings with an emphasis in real estate, forestry, environmental, business and employment disputes.
**Personal:** JD, University of Mississippi School of Law, 1980; BS, University of Southern Mississippi, 1977.

## PAINTER, William S
Baker, Donelson, Bearman, Caldwell & Berkowitz, PC, Jackson
601 351 2425
wpainter@bakerdonelson.com
*Featured in Corporate/Commercial (Mississippi)*
**Practice Areas:** Practice concentrated in corporate transactions, tax and healthcare restructuring. Extensive experience in employee benefits and deferred compensation; federal, state and local taxation; securities and trusts and estates.

**Professional Memberships:** Fellow, American College of Trust and Estate Counsel. Fellow, American College of Tax Counsel. Former Chair, Mississippi Secretary of State's Task Force on Business Law Reform. Former Chair, Mississippi Secretary of State's Business Law Advisory Group. Member, American, Mississippi and Hinds County Bar Associations.
**Career:** Licensed in Mississippi since 1974 and US Tax Court since 1975.

## PALMER, JR, James I
Butler, Snow, O'Mara, Stevens & Cannada, PLLC, Oxford
662 513 8008
jimmy.palmer@butlersnow.com
*Featured in Environment (Mississippi)*
**Practice Areas:** Environmental Law; Natural Resources Law; Energy Law; Administrative law
**Professional Memberships:** Environmental Council of the States (ECOS)
**Career:** Registered Professional Engineer, Mississippi Special Assistant Attorney General, Office of the Attorney General of Mississippi, 1980-84; Administrative Assistant and Staff Counsel, Office of the Governor of Mississippi, 1984-87; Executive Director, Office of General Services, Office of the Governor of Mississippi, 1986-87; Executive Director, Mississippi Department of Environmental Quality, 1987-99; Region 4 Regional Administrator, United States Environmental Protection Agency, 2002-09

## PARKER, Myles A
Carroll Warren & Parker PLLC, Jackson
601 592 1010
mparker@cwplaw.com
*Featured in Litigation (Mississippi)*
**Practice Areas:** General civil litigation, product liability litigation, commercial litigation, insurance coverage disputes and litigation, large loss subrogation, municipal annexation litigation, bad faith litigation, oilfield liability litigation and property and casualty loss coverage.
**Professional Memberships:** Federal Bar Association, American Bar Association, The Mississippi Bar, The Texas Bar, Federal Bar of Puerto Rico, Capital Area Bar Association, Bar Association of the Fifth Federal Circuit, International Association of Defense Counsel, The American Association for Justice, Barrister Member, American Inns of Court, Fellow, Litigation Counsel of America, Member, Super Lawyers, Million Dollar Advocates, Member, The Lamar Order, Member, ARIAS-US and American Society of Legal Advocates Top 100 Litigation Lawyers.
**Career:** Member: Carroll Warren & Parker PLLC 2002-present; Partner: Mitchell, McNutt & Sams 1995-2001; associate: Watkins & Eager 1990-95.
**Publications:** A list of publications is available upon request.
**Personal:** Northwestern State University, BS, 1987; University of Mississippi, JD with honors, 1990. Licensed: Mississippi; Texas; US District Court, District of Puerto Rico; US Fifth Circuit; and US Supreme Court.

**PARROTT, Charles N**
Adams and Reese LLP, Jackson
601 292 0782
charles.parrott@arlaw.com
*Featured in Corporate/Commercial (Mississippi)*
**Practice Areas:** Partner: banking and finance;
forestry; agricultural chemicals.
**Professional Memberships:** The Mississippi
Bar; American Bar Association; Hinds County Bar
Association.
**Career:** As a team leader of the Banking and
Finance Team, Parrott has 30 years of experience
representing clients in a variety of matters, includ-
ing: banking law and regulation, commercial law,
corporate law, real estate, insurance, consumer
finance, commercial transactions, commercial
lending and banking expert testimony. He is past
Chairman of the Mississippi Bankers Association
Bank Attorneys' Committee and is a trained
mediator.
**Personal:** JD, University of Mississippi, 1978; BS,
Delta State College, 1974.

**PATTERSON, J Randall**
Baker, Donelson, Bearman, Caldwell &
Berkowitz, PC, Jackson
601 351 2454
rpatterson@bakerdonelson.com
*Featured in Labor & Employment (Mississippi)*
**Practice Areas:** Practice concentrated in labor
and employment law. Represents employers
before the EEOC and other administrative agen-
cies, as well as in state and federal court. Advises
employers on policies and procedures, reductions
in force, wage and hour issues, employee hand-
books and general employment issues.
Experienced in ERISA litigation, antitrust and
white-collar criminal defense.
**Professional Memberships:** Member, Hinds
County, Mississippi, North Carolina State and
American Bar Associations; Defense Research
Institute; Society of Human Resource
Management.
**Career:** Licensed in Mississippi, 1991; North
Carolina, 1992; Tennessee 2007.
**Personal:** Citadel, BA, 1979; Mississippi College
School of Law, JD with special distinction, 1991.

**PERRY, Alan W**
Forman Perry Watkins Krutz & Tardy LLP,
Jackson
601 960 8600
aperry@fpwk.com
*Featured in Litigation (Mississippi)*
**Practice Areas:** Mr Perry is involved in a wide
variety of complex commercial and corporate litigation, including disputes related to environmental matters, trade secrets, antitrust, banking, public
utilities, professional liability of accountants and
lawyers, and the obligations of corporate directors
and officers. He frequently advises corporate
boards of directors on corporate governance matters and potential litigation.
**Professional Memberships:** Fellow, American
College of Trial Lawyers. Former Member,
Standing Committee of Rules and Procedure of
the Judicial Conference of the United States.
Former Member, Board of Visitors, Harvard Law
School.

**Career:** Clerked for Judge Charles Clark, United
States Court of Appeals, Fifth Circuit (1972-73);
Butler, Snow, O'Mara, Stevens & Cannada (1973-
86); Founding Partner of Forman Perry Watkins
Krutz & Tardy, 1986.
**Publications:** 'Partnerships and Tax Shelters:
The Crane Rule Goes Public', 27 'Tax Law Review'
525 (1972); 'The Model Business Corporation Act:
Does the Mississippi Version Lime the Bushes?', 46
Miss. L J 371 (1975) (with E Clifton Hodge).
**Personal:** JD, magna cum laude, Harvard Law
School, 1972 (Fay Diploma, first in class). Editor
and senior editor, Harvard Law Review. BBA
(Accountancy), summa cum laude, University of
Mississippi, 1969 (first in class). Silver Medal for
second highest grade in United States on CPA
Examination. Director of BancorpSouth, Inc and
BancorpSouth Bank; Trustee of Mississippi
Institutions of Higher Learning; Trustee of Robert
M Hearin Foundation and Robert M Hearin
Support Foundation. Listed in The Best Lawyers
in America in five categories: Bet-The-Company
Litigation, Commercial Litigation, Corporate Law,
Litigation-Banking and Finance, and Litigation-
Real Estate; Best Lawyers' 2009 Mississippi Bet-
the-Company Litigator of the Year; Best Lawyers'
2010 Jackson, Mississippi Corporate Lawyer of the
Year; Best Lawyers' 2012 Jackson, Mississippi
Corporate Governance Lawyer of the Year.

**RAULSTON, Keith R**
Jones Walker LLP, Jackson
601 949 4609
kraulston@joneswalker.com
*Featured in Litigation (Mississippi)*
**Practice Areas:** Commercial litigation, insur-
ance litigation, product liability defense, personal
injury defense.
**Professional Memberships:** American Bar
Association, Litigation and Tort & Insurance
Practice Sections; Mississippi Bar; Federal Bar
Association; Mississippi Defense Lawyers
Association; Defense Research Institute; Litigation
Counsel of America.
**Career:** Order of the Coif; Benwood Scholar;
Wald Prize; Morrill Prize; Phi Alpha Delta Award
for Outstanding Scholastic Achievement;
American Jurisprudence Award; Provident Bank
Prize; John R. Saylar Prize; Mississippi Law
Institute (Past Chairman and Editor-in-Chief);
Mississippi Board of Bar Admissions, Character
and Fitness Committee (Past Chairman).
**Publications:** "Judicial Resistance to Arbitration
Waning but Persistent," MDLA Quarterly
(Summer, 2006); Metamorphosis of a Big Case,"
Mississippi Lawyer (June/July 1999).

**RAY, William F**
Watkins & Eager PLLC, Jackson
601 965 1900
wray@watkinseager.com
*Featured in Litigation (Mississippi)*
**Practice Areas:** Litigation - emphasis in commercial litigation, banking/financial services, professional liability defense, consumer/commercial
credit disputes, securities litigation and arbitration, life and disability insurance and ERISA bene-

fits litigation, insurance sales practices and policy
disputes, non-competition/trade secrets litigation.
**Professional Memberships:** Mississippi Bar;
DRI (Chair, Commercial Litigation Section; Chair,
Law Institute); FINRA Board of Arbitrators.
**Career:** General litigation and arbitration prac-
tice since 1986; Best Lawyers 2009-2013
(Commercial Litigation, Litigation
Banking/Finance); Mid-South Super Lawyers
(Business Litigation; Employee Benefits/ERISA;
Banking, Top 50 Mississippi 2010-2012).
**Personal:** University of Mississippi (BA, cum
laude, 1983; JD, cum laude, law review, 1986);
Duke University Mediator Certification Program
(2002).

**REED, William N (Bill)**
Baker, Donelson, Bearman, Caldwell &
Berkowitz, PC, Jackson
601 351 2410
wreed@bakerdonelson.com
*Featured in Litigation (Mississippi)*
**Practice Areas:** Practice concentrated in class
action, insurance coverage, and banking and busi-
ness litigation. Has tried more than 100 commer-
cial and tort cases in federal and state courts in 11
states and has handled appeals in Mississippi and
four federal circuits.
**Professional Memberships:** Fellow:
Mississippi Bar Foundation, Litigation Counsel of
America, American Bar Foundation. Member,
Defense Research Institute, Mississippi Defense
Lawyers Association, Bar Association of the Fifth
Federal Circuit, International Association of
Defense Counsel. Board of Directors, TerraLex.
Faculty member, IADC Trial Academy (2011).
**Career:** Mississippi, 1977. Listed in Best Lawyers
in America since 2001, Mid-South Super Lawyers
since 2006.

**ROBINSON III, E Barney**
Butler, Snow, O'Mara, Stevens & Cannada,
PLLC, Ridgeland
601 985 4525
barney.robinson@butlersnow.com
*Featured in Litigation (Mississippi)*
**Practice Areas:** Financial Services Litigation;
Sales Practices Litigation; Contract
Litigation;General Business Litigation; Director
and Officer Defense; Intellectual Property
Litigation; Unfair Competition and Trade Secret
Litigation
**Professional Memberships:** American Bar
Association (International Law section); Defense
Research Institute; Federalist Society; Mississippi
Bar.
**Career:** The Best Lawyers in America
(Commercial Litigation); Mid-South Super
Lawyers (Business Litigation); "Litigation Star" by
Benchmark Litigation Magazine, Fifth Edition;
Deputy Staff Judge Advocate, Joint Force
Headquarters; Standing Committee on Local Civil
Rules for the US District Court (Northern and
Southern Districts of Mississippi).
**Personal:** University of Mississippi, JD, magna
cum laude, 1991.

**ROSENBLATT, Stephen W**
Butler, Snow, O'Mara, Stevens & Cannada,
PLLC, Ridgeland
601 985 4504
steve.rosenblatt@butlersnow.com
*Featured in Corporate/Commercial (Mississippi)*
**Practice Areas:** Bankruptcy; creditors' rights;
commercial litigation.
**Professional Memberships:** American
Bankruptcy Institute; Association of Insolvency &
Restructuring Advisors; Turnaround Management
Association; Mississippi Bankruptcy Conference
(founding member and past President);
Mississippi Bar; Jackson Young Lawyers(past
President); Charles Clark Inn of Court, 2009-
2011.
**Career:** AV-rated, Martindale-Hubbell; Former
Chair, Butler Snow (1998-2005); Best Lawyers in
America (Bankruptcy and Creditor-Debtor
Rights); Mississippi Bar Foundation (Fellow);
Mid-South Super Lawyers®, Bankruptcy and
Creditor/Debtor Rights (2006-11); Lex Mundi
College of Mediators; Business Bankruptcy
Specialist, American Board of Certification.
**Personal:** University of Mississippi, JD, with
honors, 1975; Vanderbilt University, BA, 1970.

**RUEFF JR, David A**
Baker, Donelson, Bearman, Caldwell &
Berkowitz, PC, Jackson
601 351 2469
drueff@bakerdonelson.com
*Featured in Real Estate (Mississippi)*
**Practice Areas:** Commercial real estate, financ-
ing and leasing. Governmental services relating to
HUD and CDBG grant management including
policy and process design and implementation,
fraud, compliance and management of closings
for disaster relief grant programs.
**Professional Memberships:** American and
Mississippi Bar Associations. Associate Member:
International Council of Shopping Centers,
American Society of Landscape Architects.
Certified Project Management Professional
(PMP).
**Career:** Licensed in Mississippi, Tennessee. Legal
Project Management Officer: Assisted in develop-
ment of firm's LPM system. Special Counsel,
Governor's Commission for Hurricane Katrina
Recovery (2005).
**Personal:** Mississippi College School of Law, JD.
Louisiana State University, MLA. University of
Tennessee, BS.

**SHELDON, Jerry**
Adams and Reese LLP, Jackson
601 292 0728
jerry.sheldon@arlaw.com
*Featured in Energy & Natural Resources (Mississippi)*
**Practice Areas:** Partner: energy and environmental; forestry.
**Professional Memberships:** Mississippi Oil
and Gas Lawyers Association; Mid-Continent Oil
and Gas Association; Mississippi Association of
Petroleum Landmen; American Association of
Petroleum Landmen.
**Career:** He has over 35 years of experience in the
preparation of title opinions for oil and timber
companies and in the representation of clients

before the Mississippi State Oil and Gas Board. He has delivered numerous presentations on real estate and oil and gas law and conducted various continuing legal education seminars.

**Personal:** JD, University of Mississippi School of Law, 1970; BA, Millsaps College, 1967.

## SHEPHERD III, Thomas B
Jones Walker LLP, Jackson
601 949 4711
tshepherd@joneswalker.com
*Featured in Corporate/Commercial (Mississippi)*

**Practice Areas:** Gaming regulatory law, mergers and acquisitions, gaming and resort development.

**Professional Memberships:** International Association of Gaming Advisors (President-Elect); Mississippi Secretary of State Business Law Advisory Group (Chairman); National Conference of Commissioners on Uniform State Laws; Rotary Club of Jackson (President).

**Publications:** Mississippi Corporations: Formation and Operation with Forms; Encyclopedia of Mississippi Law, Mississippi Practice Series; International Casino Law, Institute for the Study of Gambling & Commercial Gaming.

**Personal:** Honors: Jackson, MS Gaming Law Lawyer of the Year; Mississippi 2011 Attorney of the Year, MS Business Journal.

## SMITH III, William C
Watkins & Eager PLLC, Jackson
601 965 1809
wsmith@watkinseager.com
*Featured in Real Estate (Mississippi)*

**Practice Areas:** Commercial and residential real estate including new urbanism development, multi-family development, condominium law, mixed use developments, retail shopping centers, office complexes, real estate finance, complex contracts, zoning, environmental issues.

**Professional Memberships:** Mississippi Bar; Capital Area Bar Association; Tri-County Real Estate Association.

**Career:** Admitted to practice in all Mississippi state and federal courts, US Court of Appeals, Fifth Circuit; advises major regional and national developers regarding financing, development issues, contracts and Public Service Commission issues in both commercial and residential areas; Best Lawyers in America (Land Use, Real Estate, Zoning Law).

**Personal:** University of Mississippi (BA, 1985; JD, 1987).

## STEPHENSON III, Paul H
Watkins & Eager PLLC, Jackson
601 965 1900
pstephenson@watkinseager.com
*Featured in Litigation (Mississippi)*

**Practice Areas:** General civil practice -emphasis in commercial, banking, business litigation (including class actions), appellate practice.

**Professional Memberships:** Mississippi Bar (Ethics Committee); Mississippi Bar Foundation, Fellow; American Bar Association (Litigation Section); Bar Association of the Fifth Federal Circuit.

**Career:** Trial and appellate practice since 1977; Best Lawyers in America (Bet-the-Company Litigation; Commercial Litigation; Oil and Gas Law); Mid-South Super Lawyers (Business Litigation; Class Action/Mass Torts; Civil Litigation Defense); Benchmark Litigation "Local Litigation Star".

**Personal:** University of Mississippi (BBA, with distinction, 1974; JD, with Honors, 1977); Member, Board of Editors, Mississippi Law Journal, 1975-76.

## STEWART, Jefferson
Adams and Reese LLP, Jackson
601 292 0713
jay.stewart@arlaw.com
*Featured in Energy & Natural Resources (Mississippi)*

**Practice Areas:** Partner: Energy and environmental; construction and real estate.

**Professional Memberships:** Mississippi Oil and Gas Lawyers; Mississippi Association of Petroleum Landmen; US Oil and Gas Association.

**Career:** 30 years in all phases of exploration, development, production, transportation and regulation of oil and gas operations in the Gulf Coast region. He has experience rendering title opinions, assisting in curing title defects and litigation over title issues pertaining to oil and gas production. Drafting and lobbying for statutory and regulatory changes in conservation and environmental issues in Mississippi.

**Personal:** JD, Tulane University Law School, 1976; BA, Centenary College, 1969.

## SYKES, Phillip S
Forman Perry Watkins Krutz & Tardy LLP, Jackson
601 969 7840
psykes@fpwk.com
*Featured in Litigation (Mississippi)*

**Practice Areas:** Recognized for broad experience in litigation including professional liability; breach of contract; securities fraud; and products liability. Representative high profile matters include defense of theft of trade secrets litigation in aerospace industry; defense of national law firm for fraud and malpractice allegations related to issuance of an opinion letter; defense of publicly traded company and its CEO from claims by former president of $100 million subsidiary related to his termination for cause; and defense of majority shareholder in lawsuit by former executive related to an incentive compensation agreement. Representative trials and arbitrations include accounting malpractice; derivative action related to formation of bank holding company; and breach of fiduciary duty and fraud related to an initial public offering.

**Professional Memberships:** American Institute of Certified Public Accountants; Mississippi Society of Certified Public Accounts; American Bar Association; Mississippi Bar Association; International Association of Defense Counsel (IADC); Defense Research Institute.

**Career:** KPMG 1990-92; Forman Perry Watkins Krutz & Tardy LLP 1995 - present.

**Personal:** Bachelor of Public Accountancy (Magna Cum Laude), Mississippi State University (1990); Juris Doctor (Magna Cum Laude), University of Mississippi School of Law (1995).

## TARDY III, Thomas W
Forman Perry Watkins Krutz & Tardy LLP, Jackson
601 960 8633
ttardy@fpwk.com
*Featured in Litigation (Mississippi)*

**Practice Areas:** Mr Tardy has more than 30 years of experience in Toxic Tort, Environmental and Products Liability litigation. He has represented dozens of companies sued in asbestos litigation throughout the Southeast, and has served as national coordinating counsel for three of those companies and as regional trial counsel for others. Mr Tardy led the Forman Perry litigation/appellate teams in cases which have been instrumental in changing Mississippi's asbestos landscape. These cases include the seminal decision of the Mississippi Supreme Court in Forman Perry's appeal in Harold's Auto Parts, Inc. v. Mangialardi, 889 So. 2d 493 (Miss. 2004), in which the court held that the prevailing practice of mass joinder of asbestos plaintiffs in Mississippi was improper, that single-plaintiff actions would be required, and that asbestos complaints would have to meet fact-specific pleading standards. Similarly, Mr Tardy led the Forman Perry efforts in Amchem Products, Inc. v. Rogers, 912 So. 2d 853 (Miss. 2005), in which the Mississippi Supreme Court held that out-of-state asbestos plaintiffs with no viable connection to Mississippi in terms of worksites or claims against a resident defendant must be dismissed – thus paving the way for the dismissal of tens of thousands of plaintiffs from Mississippi court dockets. In addition, in Forman Perry's appeal in Gorman-Rupp Co. v. Hall, 908 So. 2d 749 (Miss. 2005), the court made summary judgment a viable option for many asbestos defendants in Mississippi by explicitly adopting the Lohrmann standard and requiring that an asbestos plaintiff come forward with sufficient and concrete evidence of frequency, regularity and proximity of exposure to respirable asbestos. Mr Tardy served as head of the Forman Perry team for the MARDOC MDL litigation which ultimately resulted in the dismissal of all cases against Forman Perry clients. Mr Tardy currently serves as special counsel for General Electric Company in all cases pending in the federal asbestos MDL. Mr Tardy orally argued and participated in the briefing in Faddish v. General Electric Co., 2010 WL 4146108 (E.D. Pa)(10/20/10)(MDL-875), a landmark decision in which US District Judge Eduard Robreno held that the federal contractor defense barred the asbestos claim of a naval serviceman against GE because it had supplied marine turbines to the Navy pursuant to military specifications, the turbines conformed to the specifications for design and warnings, and the Navy itself knew of any hazards from asbestos. Although the federal contractor defense had been used for the removal of state cases to federal court, Faddish is the first reported decision from the asbestos multi-district court to apply the defense on the merits in favor of an equipment manufacturer. Moreover, in Conner v. Alfa Laval, Inc., 2011 WL 3101810 (E.D. Pa. 7/22/11) (MDL-875), Mr Tardy successfully argued for General Electric in the MDL that substantive maritime law, rather than state tort law, applied to the asbestos claims of sailors whose claims arose from the repair of equipment on naval vessels on the high seas or in drydock. In a subsequent landmark decision in the same case, also argued by Mr Tardy, the MDL held that under applicable maritime law, manufacturers of equipment for Naval vessels had no duty to warn of hazards from asbestos insulation later placed on the equipment by shipyards or the Navy. Conner v. Alfa Laval, Inc., 2012 WL 288364 (E.D. Pa. 2/1/12) (MDL-875). The court's recognition of the "bare metal" defense either directly or indirectly impacts scores of similar claims pending in the MDL.

**Professional Memberships:** International Association of Defense Counsel; Defense Research Institute; The Lamar Order of the University of Mississippi Alumni Association; Mississippi Defense Lawyers Association; Graduate, National Institute of Trial Advocacy's advanced training program; Graduate, Court Practice Institute's program of trial advocacy; Barrister, Charles Clark Inns of Court, 1994-1995; Instructor in trial advocacy for the Trial Practice Academy of the Mississippi Defense Lawyers Association, 1985. Mr Tardy is listed in "The Best Lawyers in America" and has been designated a Mid-South Super Lawyer. He is licensed in Mississippi and Texas.

**Career:** February 1, 1995 to present: Forman Perry Watkins Krutz & Tardy, LLP, Jackson, Mississippi, Partner; January 1974 to January 31, 1995: Thomas, Price, Alston, Jones & Davis (1974-92), Alston, Rutherford, Tardy & Van Slyke (1993-Jan. 1995), Partner

**Publications:** 'Liability of Equipment Manufacturers for Products of Another: Is Relief in Sight?' lead author, Silica, Harris Martins Columns, April 2007; 'Effective Use of Coordinated Defense Support and National Coordinating Counsel by the Peripheral Asbestos Defendant' Defense Research Institute, Asbestos Personal Injury Litigation (Miami, FL, November 2-3, 2000) [paper published in connection with seminar presentation]; 'Pre-Emerging Toxic Torts: Birth of a Toxic Tort' Mealey's, Toxic Torts: New Exposures (Amelia Island, FL, February 20-21, 1997) [paper published in connection with seminar presentation]; 'Multi-Defendant Litigation: Consolidated Defense Arrangements from Litigation Counsel's Perspective' American Conference Institute, Insurance Litigation Cost-Management (New York, NY, April 18-19, 1995) [paper published in connection with seminar presentation].

**Personal:** Attended Mississippi State University (BS, Accounting, 1968) and University of Mississippi School of Law (JD, with Distinction, 1973). Military experience as Lt. Inf., US Army 1968-71; Instructor, Officer's Candidate School, Fort Benning, Georgia; and Reconnaissance Platoon Leader, Vietnam. Leisure interests include golf and reading.

**TAYLOR, Zachary**
Jones Walker LLP, Jackson
601 949 4860
ztaylor@joneswalker.com
*Featured in Corporate/Commercial (Mississippi)*
**Practice Areas:** Public finance, economic development, corporate finance, tax credits in Mississippi.
**Professional Memberships:** American Bar Association; The Mississippi Bar;Salvation Army of Mississippi, Advisory Board, Past Chairman; Harvard University Alumni Association, Regional Director; Harvard Club of Mississippi, Schools and Scholarship Committee; Harvard Club of Mississippi, Schools and Scholarship Committee.
**Personal:** Honors and Awards: Listed in The Best Lawyers in America (Corporate Law, Municipal Law, Project Finance Law, Public Finance Law and Structured Finance Law); Mississippi Law Journal.

**THAMES, Lee Davis**
Butler, Snow, O'Mara, Stevens & Cannada, PLLC, Ridgeland
601 985 4517
lee.davis.thames@butlersnow.com
*Featured in Litigation (Mississippi)*
**Practice Areas:** Product liability; drug and medical device; commercial litigation; class actions/mass tort litigation; environmental liability.
**Professional Memberships:** Product Liability Advisory Council; International Association of Defense Counsel; American Bar; Defense Research Institute; Mississippi Bar (Board of Commissioners); Mississippi Defense Lawyers.
**Career:** AV-rated, Martindale-Hubbell; Fellow, American College of Trial Lawyers; Best Lawyers in America (Bet-the-Company Litigation, Commercial Litigation, Personal Injury Litigation, Product Liability Litigation, 2012 Lawyer of the Year, Product Liability Litigation - Defendants; Mid-South Super Lawyers (Class Action/Mass Torts); Who's Who Among International Product Liability Lawyers; American College of Trial Lawyers (Fellow); American Bar Association (Fellow); Mississippi Bar Foundation (Fellow).

**THOMPSON JR, J Carter**
Baker, Donelson, Bearman, Caldwell & Berkowitz, PC, Jackson
601 351 8942
cthompson@bakerdonelson.com
*Featured in Litigation (Mississippi)*
**Practice Areas:** Personal injury defense; drug/medical device; product liability; professional liability defense.
**Professional Memberships:** Product Liability Advisory Council; Lawyers for Civil Justice; Litigation Counsel of America; Defense Research Institute (Program Chair, Drug & Device Steering Committee); Federation of Defense & Corporate Council; The International Who's Who of Product Liability Defence Lawyers 2011; Product Liability Editorial Advisory Board, Law360; American Bar Association (Litigation &Torts, Insurance); Mississippi Bar (General Litigation & Health Law); Mississippi Defense Lawyers Association.

**Career:** AV-rated, Martindale-Hubbell; Best Lawyers in America (Product Liability); Mid-South Super Lawyers (Personal Injury Defense); Lawdragon 3000.
**Personal:** University of Mississippi (JD-1984); Mississippi College (BA-1981)

**THREADGILL, Timothy M**
Butler, Snow, O'Mara, Stevens & Cannada, PLLC, Ridgeland
601 985 4594
tim.threadgill@butlersnow.com
*Featured in Labor & Employment (Mississippi)*
**Practice Areas:** Employment litigation; labor law.
**Professional Memberships:** American Bar Association (Labor and Employment and Litigation sections); American Employment Law Council; Mississippi Bar (Board of Commissioners; former Chairman of Labor and Employment section; former President of Young Lawyers Division); Capital Area Human Resource Association.
**Career:** The Best Lawyers in America (Labor and Employment Law); Fellow, Young Lawyers Division of Mississippi Bar.
**Personal:** University of Mississippi, BBA, 1988; University of Alabama, JD, 1990.

**TOHILL, Jim**
Jones Walker LLP, Jackson
601 949 4790
jtohill@joneswalker.com
*Featured in Real Estate (Mississippi)*
**Practice Areas:** Real estate transactions/financing, commercial law and lending; public/private finance.
**Professional Memberships:** The Mississippi Bar, Real Property Section (Former Chairman); Dixie Land Title Association.
**Career:** Honors: Fellow, American College of Mortgage Attorneys; Fellow, American College of Real Estate Lawyers; Top 50 Mississippi Lawyers in Mid-South Super Lawyers; AV® Peer Review Rating in Martindale-Hubbell; The Best Lawyers in America® 2012 (Copyright 2011 by Woodward/White, Inc., Aiken, SC) Jackson, MS Best Lawyers Real Estate Lawyer of the Year 2012; Fellow, Mississippi Bar Association.
**Personal:** University of Mississippi School of Law (JD, 1974, cum laude); Millsaps College (BA, 1969); Bar Admissions: Mississippi, 1974; US District Court Northern District of Mississippi, 1974; US District Court Southern District of Mississippi, 1974.

**TROTTER, Jeffrey**
Adams and Reese LLP, Jackson
jeff.trotter@arlaw.com
*Featured in Energy & Natural Resources (Mississippi)*
**Practice Areas:** Partner, energy and environmental, forestry, asbestos, commercial litigation, condemnation and eminent domain.
**Professional Memberships:** Mississippi Oil and Gas Lawyers Association, Mississippi Bar Association, Section on Natural Resources, Mississippi Association of Petroleum Landmen, US Oil and Gas Association.

**Career:** Trotter is the Energy and Environmental Practice Team Leader. He regularly advises clients involved in upstream and midstream operations on environmental and regulatory compliance, acquisition/divestiture of assets, landowner and title disputes, title examination and renders drilling and division order title opinions.
**Personal:** JD, University of Mississippi School of Law, 1993; BS, Mississippi State University, 1985.

**TURNER, Keith**
Watkins & Eager PLLC, Jackson
601 965 1958
kturner@watkinseager.com
*Featured in Environment (Mississippi)*
**Practice Areas:** Environmental, economic development, water and sewer, energy.
**Professional Memberships:** American Bar Association; The Mississippi Bar - Natural Resources, Energy and Environmental Law Section; Environmental Law Institute; Geological Society of America; Environmental Law Association; State of Tennessee, Professional Geologist TN2111.
**Publications:** "Co-author chapter in 2nd edition of "Implementing Institutional Controls at Brownfields and Other Contaminated Sites".
**Personal:** Admitted in Mississippi; US District Court Southern District of Mississippi; US District Court Northern District of Mississippi; US Court of Appeals 5th Circuit; Adjunct Professor, Clean Water Act & Hazardous Waste Law - Mississippi College School of Law.

**TWIFORD, Hunter**
McGlinchey Stafford PLLC, Jackson
601 960 3523
htwiford@mcglinchey.com
*Featured in Litigation (Mississippi)*
**Practice Areas:** Business, commercial and consumer financial services litigation; class action defense; antitrust.
**Professional Memberships:** American Board of Trial Advocates; Mississippi Defense Lawyers; Mississippi Bar (past trustee, executive commitee); Mississippi Bar Foundation (fellow, past president); Mississippi Bar Technology Committee (founding member, past chairman, executive committee); Mississippi Board of Bar Admissions (1994-08); William C. Keady Chapter of American Inns of Court (Bencher).
**Career:** Represents businesses, including financial institutions, in class actions, complex lender liability and consumer financial services litigation and antitrust litigation; considered an expert in courtroom and litigation presentation technology and e-discovery; listed in Best Lawyers in America, Commercial Litigation, Litigation – Banking & Finance and Litigation – Municipal, Municipal Law (multiple editions); Mid-South Super Lawyers, Commercial Litigation and Class Actions/Mass Actions (multiple editions) and Top 50 Lawyers in Mississippi (2009); Mississippi Business Journal's "Top 50 Lawyers in Mississippi" (2010).
**Publications:** Numerous scholarly articles, including multiple national publications on Class Action Fairness Act (CAFA) and class actions; co-

founder and former Editor-in-Chief of CAFA Law Blog; multiple publications on ESI and e-discovery.
**Personal:** University of Mississippi, BA (English, Psychology, Sociology) (1971), JD (1972).

**ULMER, Michael**
Watkins & Eager PLLC, Jackson
601 965 1948
mulmer@watkinseager.com
*Featured in Litigation (Mississippi)*
**Practice Areas:** General, tort, business, and product liability litigation.
**Professional Memberships:** Mississippi Bar; Mississippi Bar Foundation; American College of Trial Lawyers (Fellow); American Board of Trial Advocates.
**Career:** Trial and appellate practice since 1976; Best Lawyers in America (Mass Tort, Medical Malpractice, Personal Injury Litigation for more than twenty years; Lawyer of the Year 2011, Mass Tort Litigation and 2013, Personal Ingjury Litigation, Jackson); Mid-South Super Lawyers (Personal Injury Defense: Products, General; Top 50 lawyers in Mississippi); Mississippi Business Journal's Top 50 Leadership in Law Class of 2010.
**Personal:** University of Mississippi (BBA, 1973; JD, with Honors, 1976).

**VANCE, Alison**
Butler, Snow, O'Mara, Stevens & Cannada, PLLC, Ridgeland
601 985 4415
alison.vance@butlersnow.com
*Featured in Labor & Employment (Mississippi)*
**Practice Areas:** Labor and employment litigation; labor and employment compliance counseling.
**Professional Memberships:** American Bar Association (Employment Rights And Responsibilities Subcommittee Co-Chair); Mississippi Bar Association (Labor and Employment Law Section - Executive Committee); Mississippi Defense Lawyers Association.
**Career:** The Best Lawyers in America (Employment Law - Management); Mid-South Rising Stars (Employment & Labor); Graduate, International Association of Defense Counsel (IADC) Trial Academy, Stanford Law School.
**Personal:** University of Mississippi, JD, magna cum laude, 2003; University of Southern Mississippi, BA, with high honors, 1999

**VARNER, Thad W**
Butler, Snow, O'Mara, Stevens & Cannada, PLLC, Ridgeland
601 985 4518
thad.varner@butlersnow.com
*Featured in Corporate/Commercial (Mississippi)*
**Practice Areas:** Municipal bonds; economic development incentives; public finance.
**Professional Memberships:** American Bar Association; National Association of Bond Lawyers; Mississippi Bar; Capital Area Bar Association
**Career:** AV-rated, Martindale-Hubbell; Best Lawyers in America (Public Finance Law); Mid-South Super Lawyers®,

Government/Cities/Municipalities; regularly serves as Bond Counsel, Underwriter's Counsel, Trustee Counsel and other loan counsel for various issuances of debt by governmental entities and private companies, including healthcare organizations, multi-family housing projects, public universities; correctional authorities, secondary schools and municipalities.
**Personal:** University of Mississippi, B Accy, 1988; JD, 1992; Emory University, LLM, 1993.

### WALKER, Jeffrey A
Butler, Snow, O'Mara, Stevens & Cannada, PLLC, Ridgeland
601 985 4558
jeff.walker@butlersnow.com
*Featured in Labor & Employment (Mississippi)*
**Practice Areas:** Labor and Employment Law; Litigation (discrimination claims, FLSA, ERISA, employment-related torts, non-competition matters); Traditional Labor Law, Union Organizing Campaigns, Collective Bargaining, Labor Arbitration, OSHA; Government Investigations.
**Professional Memberships:** Mississippi Bar (Past Chairman of Labor and Employment Law section); Mississippi Defense Lawyers Association; American Bar Association (Labor and Employment and Litigation sections); Defense Research Institute.
**Career:** AV-rated, Martindale-Hubbell; The Best Lawyers in America (Labor and Employment Law); Mid-South Super Lawyers (Employment and Labor); Fellow, College of Labor and Employment Lawyers.
**Personal:** University of Mississippi, JD, 1978; University of Wisconsin-Madison, BS, 1975.

### WALL, Randall
Jones Walker LLP, Jackson
601 949 4760
rwall@joneswalker.com
*Featured in Corporate/Commercial (Mississippi)*
**Practice Areas:** Education law, public finance, economic development.
**Professional Memberships:** American Bar Association; Mississippi Bar; National Association of Bond Lawyers; Mississippi Economic Council; Harvard Club of Mississippi.
**Career:** Speaking Engagements: Numerous presentations to municipal attorneys and public officials regarding municipal law and finance. Recent presentations include: Presentation to municipal officials at the Mid-winter Mississippi Municipal League convention on the subject of Tax Increment Financing and Economic Development; Presentation to Board Attorneys at the Mississippi Association of Supervisors Mid-winter Convention; presentation to first year students at the University of Mississippi Law School on Governmental Law and Economic Development.
**Publications:** Borrowing and Debt Administration Chapter in "The Mississippi Association of Supervisors, County Government in Mississippi," published by Center for Governmental Training & Technology, Mississippi State University Extension Service; Bonds, Borrowing and Debt Administration Chapter in

"Municipal Government in Mississippi," published by Center for Governmental Training & Technology, Mississippi State University Extension Service.
**Personal:** Honors: Mississippi Bar Foundation, Fellow; Jackson, MS, Best Lawyers Municipal Law Lawyer of the Year" 2013 (Copyright 2012 by Woodward/White, Inc., Aiken, SC).

### WARREN, Jim
Carroll Warren & Parker PLLC, Jackson
601 592 1010
jwarren@cwplaw.com
*Featured in Litigation (Mississippi)*
**Practice Areas:** General civil litigation, commerical litigation, insurance coverage litigation, construction defect litigation, large loss subrogation, arbitration and mediation.
**Professional Memberships:** Admitted Mississippi (State and Federal Courts), Florida (State and Federal Courts), United States Virgin Islands (Superior and Federal Court), Puerto Rico (Federal Court), Eastern and Southern Districts of Texas (Federal Courts). Also admitted US Courts of Appeal for the Third, Fifth and Eleventh Circuits and United States Supreme Court. Member, American Bar Association, The Mississippi Bar, The Florida Bar, Bar Association of the Fifth Federal Circuit and the Bar Association of the Virgin Islands. Mississippi Court Annexed Mediator, Fellow, Mississippi Bar Foundation, Member, Unauthorized Practice of Law Committee, USVI, FINRA Arbitrator. Member ARIAS-US and Member, Chartered Institute of Arbitrators.
**Career:** Carroll Warren & Parker PLLC 2002-present; Partner: Mitchell, McNutt &Sams 1997-2001; Partner: Waycaster & Warren 1990-97; Mississippi Attorney General's Office 1988-90; Assistant District Attorney 1987.
**Personal:** University of Southern Mississippi, BS, 1984; University of Mississippi, JD, 1987.

### WATKINS JR, Walter G
Forman Perry Watkins Krutz & Tardy LLP, Jackson
601 960 8600
wwatkins@fpwk.com
*Featured in Litigation (Mississippi)*
**Practice Areas:** 30+ years Toxic Tort; 30+ years environmental regulation and litigation.
**Professional Memberships:** Member, The Mississippi Bar - 1979; Member, USDC of Mississippi (Northern) - 1979; Member, USDC of Mississippi (Southern) - 1979; Member, USDC of Texas (Southern) - 2006; Member, 5th Circuit Court of Appeals - 1979; Member, Mid-South Super Lawyers since 2006; Member, The Best Lawyers in America since 2007; The Best Lawyers in America 2012 Jackson, MS Mass Tort Litigation/Class Actions - Defendants Lawyer of the Year; and Top 50 Mississippi Super Lawyers since 2008.
**Career:** December 1986 to Present Forman Perry Watkins Krutz & Tardy LLP Jackson, Mississippi (Founding Partner); 1979 to December 1986 Butler, Snow, O'Mara, Stevens & Cannada Jackson, Mississippi (Partner 1982-86); Phi Delta

Phi, 1978, Magister; Mississippi Law Journal, 1977-78, research editor, note editor and associate editor; and Phi Delta Phi Graduate of the Year, 1978-79.
**Publications:** "Lawyers Seek Dismissal of Asbestos Lawsuits" National Public Radio July 10, 2006
**Personal:** For over thirty years, Mr Watkins has been one of the leading asbestos defense lawyers in the country having tried numerous cases to verdict in across the country in both state and federal courts. He is national trial counsel and/or National Coordinating Counsel for several companies involved in mass tort cases. He currently serves as Chairman of the Defense Liaison Committee for MDL 875 in Philadelphia, PA. He has also served as lead negotiator for many companies in complex mass tort settlements involving cases across the country. His experience includes head of the litigation team in cases involving asbestos, silica, chemical exposures, and wood preservatives including creosote, dioxins, CCA, and PAHs. He enjoys a national reputation in both litigating and resolving cases involving mass torts.

### WELCH, W Scott
Baker, Donelson, Bearman, Caldwell & Berkowitz, PC, Jackson
601 351 2440
swelch@bakerdonelson.com
*Featured in Litigation (Mississippi)*
**Practice Areas:** Trials and appeals: Business, product liability, insurance coverage, other civil litigation.
**Professional Memberships:** Fellow-American College of Trial Lawyers, Mississippi and American Bar Associations, American Board of Trial Advocates, International Association of Defense Counsel, Litigation Counsel of America, Trial Attorneys of America, US Supreme Court Bar.
**Career:** Past President: American Board of Trial Advocates and The Mississippi Bar; ABA: Board of Governors, State Delegate, House of Delegates. Mississippi Defense Lawyers Lifetime Achievement Award 2012. In 'The Best Lawyers in America' (since 1996), 45 + years trial and appellate experience.
**Personal:** University of Mississippi, LLB; University of the South, BA.

### WILLIAMS JR, M Binford
Watkins & Eager PLLC, Jackson
601 965 1968
bwilliams@watkinseager.com
*Featured in Real Estate (Mississippi)*
**Practice Areas:** Commercial lending; real estate transactions; mergers and acquisitions.
**Professional Memberships:** The Mississippi Bar; National Association of Bond Lawyers.
**Career:** Admitted to Mississippi Bar, 1986; Jackson Young Lawyers (President, 1994); Mississippi Outstanding Young Lawyer (1995); Best Lawyers in America 2007-2013 (Corporate Law, Commercial Transactions / UCC Law, Project Finance Law; Real Estate Law); Mid-South Super Lawyers 2011-2012 (Banking).

**Personal:** University of Mississippi (BBA, summa cum laude, 1982; MBA, magna cum laude, 1983; JD, cum laude, 1986); Member, Board of Editors, Mississippi Law Journal (1985-86); James O. Eastland Scholar.

### WILMESHERR, Edward A
Butler, Snow, O'Mara, Stevens & Cannada, PLLC, Ridgeland
601 985 4512
ed.wilmesherr@butlersnow.com
*Featured in Corporate/Commercial (Mississippi)*
**Practice Areas:** Business planning and operations; banking regulation; bankruptcy and creditors' rights; commercial transactions.
**Professional Memberships:** American Bar Association (Consumer Financial Services Committee, Banking Law Committee, Dispute Resolution Committee); Mississippi Bar (Financial Institutions Subcommittee); Mississippi Bankers Association (Bank Attorneys Committee); Mississippi Bankruptcy Conference (former President).
**Career:** AV-rated, Martindale-Hubbell; Best Lawyers in America, Lawyer of the Year, (Banking and Finance Law); Mid-South Super Lawyers®, Banking; former Assistant General Counsel and Senior V.P. for Deposit Guaranty National Bank; Founder of Mississippi Regulatory Compliance Group (1989) and Mid-South Regulatory Compliance Group (2003); Mississippi Editor for HouseLaw.
**Personal:** University of Mississippi, JD, 1973.

### ZMITROVICH, Gretchen
Baker, Donelson, Bearman, Caldwell & Berkowitz, PC, Jackson
601 351 8954
gzmitrovich@bakerdonelson.com
*Featured in Environment (Mississippi)*
**Practice Areas:** Concentrates practice in environmental, white collar criminal defense, internal and government investigations, and general civil defense. Environmental practice includes experience in permitting and enforcement matters, civil and criminal litigation, advising on environmental liability associated with real estate and corporate transactions, compliance and auditing.
**Professional Memberships:** Member: Mississippi Bar (past-chair of Section on Natural Resources, Energy, and Environmental Law); American Bar (SEER), Mississippi Women Lawyers, Mississippi Defense Lawyers, and Air & Waste Management Associations; DRI.
**Career:** Licensed in Mississippi.
**Personal:** Mississippi College School of Law, JD, 2004, summa cum laude; Mississippi State, BS, biological engineering, 1997, magna cum laude.

# BRUNINI, GRANTHAM, GROWER & HEWES, PLLC

www.brunini.com **tel:** 601 960 8684 **fax:** 601 960 6902

**Chairman:** Granville Tate, Jr
Number of partners: 47  Number of lawyers: 65

**Firm Overview:**
Established over one century ago, Brunini is one of Mississippi's largest and most respected law firms. The firm serves primarily business clients, including a number of *Fortune* 500 companies, a major chemical manufacturer, major energy companies, the nation's largest privately held wireless company, one of Mississippi's largest health insurer and one of the state's largest banks and largest healthcare systems.

**Main Areas of Practice:**

**General & Commercial:**
Brunini's litigation practice includes complex commercial transactions, mass torts, environmental issues, pharmaceutical products, consumer fraud, employment discrimination, products liability, premises liability, fires and explosions, breach of contract, antitrust, securities fraud, business torts, taxation, gaming and white collar crime. The firm has extensive experience in state and federal trial and appellate courts and has served as national counsel as well as lead counsel in some of Mississippi's largest and most complex litigation.
**Contact:** David Kaufman
**Email:** dkaufman@brunini.com

**Healthcare:**
The firm has a comprehensive healthcare practice, representing hospitals, physician groups, nursing homes, and other healthcare providers in malpractice litigation as well as in all related regulatory matters. The firm has broad experience in administrative proceedings and litigation concerning Certificates of Need, Medicaid fraud, nursing home care, fraud and abuse-Stark II, private inurement, the Affordable Care Act and other legal issues facing the healthcare industry.
**Contact:** John E Wade,
**Email:** jwade@brunini.com

**Construction Law & Surety & Fidelity:**
The firm's construction attorneys have a vast range of experience representing owners, contractors, subcontractors and sureties in the construction industry. Specifically, the firm's experience includes drafting and negotiating contract agreements, preparing and presenting construction claims, bid protests, business consultation, project workouts and mediation, arbitration or litigation of claims and disputes which arise in the course of construction projects. Further, its attorneys are experienced in surety bond litigation/claims resolution and fidelity bond claims and coverage issues.
**Contact:** Sam Kelly
**Email:** skelly@brunini.com

**Labor & Employment:**
The firm represents employers' interests both in litigation and in a broad array of state and federal administrative settings, including disputes involving all forms of discrimination and disputes arising under state law involving alleged wrongful discharge and breach of employment contracts and non-competition agreements. The firm also advises employers in the development and enforcement of personnel policies, alternative dispute resolution agreements and a variety of other employment issues.
**Contact:** Steve Carmody
**Email:** scarmody@brunini.com

**Corporate, Banking, Real Estate, Tax & Estates:**
Brunini attorneys are recognized among their peers as leaders in their respective areas of business expertise, including general corporate law, mergers and acquisitions, securities regulation, banking, real estate transactions, insurance regulation, syndication, estate planning and corporate and personal taxation. Additionally, the firm has extensive experience in state and local industrial and economic development financing with state and federal tax incentives.
**Contact:** Walter Weems
**Email:** wweems@brunini.com

**Environmental:**
The firm is acknowledged as a statewide leader in Environmental Law. Its attorneys have broad experience in both environmental litigation and regulatory proceedings and have defended numerous enforcement actions instituted by the United States Department of Justice, Region IV of the Environmental Protection Agency, and the Bureau of Pollution Control. The firm also represents clients in proceedings before the Mississippi Department of Environmental Quality and the Mississippi Environmental Quality Permit Board.
**Contact:** John Milner
**Email:** jmilner@brunini.com
**Contact:** John Brunini
**Email:** jbrunini@brunini.com

**Energy Exploration, Transportation, Storage & Project Development:**
Brunini represents clients in all upstream and midstream operations including drilling title opinions, division order title opinions and title examination for right-of-way acquisition, negotiating and drafting surface use agreements, leases, exploration agreements and satisfying all regulatory requirements for drilling, production operation of gas and liquid storage facilities; and producing properties. The firm represents clients before the State Oil and Gas Board in obtaining regulatory relief and in disputes between operators and landowners, and before federal and state courts concerning title, contracts, drainage, gas balancing, gas processing, well damage, blow-outs, enforcing lessee's rights, oil field contamination and eminent domain proceedings. The firm also represents clients involved in downstream activities, including representation of a major local natural gas distribution company and petroleum marketers.
**Contact:** Watts Ueltschey
**Email:** wueltschey@brunini.com

**Public Utilities & Telecommunications:**
The firm serves as corporate counsel to the nation's largest privately held wireless carrier. It practices extensively before the Mississippi Public Service Commission, representing a number of intrastate pipeline companies and telecommunications, gas, water and sewer companies. The firm has served as counsel in administrative proceedings and litigation regarding rates and service and application for certificates of public convenience and necessity for the construction of electric generation facilities, natural gas transmission and distribution facilities, underground natural gas storage facilities and telecommunications facilities.
**Contact:** James Halford
**Email:** jhalford@brunini.com
**Contact:** Charles McBride
**Email:** cmcbride@brunini.com

# BURR AND FORMAN LLP

www.burr.com  **tel:** 800 GET BURR

**Chairman:** Lee Thuston
Managing Partners: 9  Number of partners: 178  Number of lawyers: 288

## Firm Overview:

Burr & Forman is a full service law firm with a long history of serving clients in Alabama, Florida, Georgia, Mississippi and Tennessee. The firm's forward-thinking approach allows it to provide legal solutions appropriate to the needs of its clients. With nearly 300 attorneys, Burr & Forman offers a wide range of business and litigation services to diverse clients with local, national and international interests.

## Main Areas of Practice:

**Automotive:**
Represents automotive dealerships in claims associated with franchise agreements, breach of contract, sales and acquisitions, non-competes and wrongful termination.

**Banking & Finance:**
Represents lenders of all types in lending and financial transactions for working capital needs, refinancings, specific personal and real property asset acquisitions and development and company acquisitions in the middle and large corporate markets.

**Commercial Litigation:**
Represents financial institutions, businesses and officers and directors in complex commercial disputes and securities litigation.

**Corporate & Tax:**
Represents businesses and not-for-profits of all sizes and in all stages of development in complex business matters, mergers and acquisitions, capital raises and regulatory compliance issues.

**Creditors' Rights & Bankruptcy:**
Represents financial services institutions, asset-based lenders and local, regional and national banks in significant and complex bankruptcy proceedings.

**Construction:**
Represents owners, contractors, suppliers and design professionals in all construction-related transactional matters and in the litigation or dispute resolution of all construction claims.

**Economic Development:**
Leading economic development firm in the Southeast. Projects reflect a diversity of industries and represent over $16 billion of capital investment and over 25,000 new jobs created.

**Environmental:**
Represents industries, developers, financial institutions and individuals in environmental matters related to business strategy, permitting and regulatory compliance, litigation, sustainability, and administrative proceedings.

**Financial Services Litigation:**
Represents banks, mortgage, finance and credit card companies in all types of litigation involving deceptive loan origination, predatory lending, wrongful foreclosure, mortgage fraud and statutory violation claims.

**Health Care:**
Represents all types of health care organizations in a variety of litigation, regulatory, compliance, licensure and corporate law matters.

**Insurance Regulatory:**
Represents all types of businesses and insurance entities in connection with structuring solutions to their business insurance needs and maintaining regulatory compliance.

**Labor & Employment:**
Represents employers of all sizes in matters ranging from drafting policies and handbooks to defending against the entire gamut of employment-related claims.

**Maritime & Transportation:**
Represents clients whose businesses are in, around or near navigable waters with all types of litigation claims, financing activities, contract negotiations, employment matters and other regulatory issues.

**Products Liability:**
Represents clients in all industries with products and premises liability, personal injury, industrial and construction site accidents, pharmaceuticals, medical devices, mass torts and toxic tort cases.

**Real Estate:**
Represents commercial real estate development companies in land planning, entitlement and development, governmental incentives, title matters, acquisition and disposition and performing and distressed assets.

**Securities Litigation:**
Represents broker-dealers and investment bankers in disputes, such as mutual-fund class-actions, derivative contracts trials, government enforcement actions and constitutional challenges to municipal securities rules.

**Technology:**
Represents businesses in protection of, and licensing strategies for, intellectual property, contract negotiation,

## OFFICES

**MISSISSIPPI**
**JACKSON:** The Heritage Building, 401 E Capitol Street, Suite 100, MS 39201
Tel: 601 355 3434  Fax: 601 355 5150

**ALABAMA**
**BIRMINGHAM:** 420 North 20th Street, Suite 3400, AL 35203
Tel: 205 251 3000  Fax: 205 458 5100

**MOBILE:** RSA Tower, 11 North Water Street, Suite 22200, AL 36602
Tel: 251 344 5151  Fax: 251 344 9696

**MONTGOMERY:** RSA Tower, 201 Monroe Street, Suite 1950, AL 36104
Tel: 334 241 7000  Fax: 334 262 0020

**FLORIDA**
**FT. LAUDERDALE:** Las Olas Centre I, 450 East Las Olas Boulevard, Suite 700, FL 33301
Tel: 954 414 6200  Fax: 954 414 6201

**ORLANDO:** 200 South Orange Avenue, Suite 800, FL 32801
Tel: 407 540 6600  Fax: 407 540 6601

**TAMPA:** One Tampa City Center, Suite 3200, FL 33602
Tel: 813 221 2626  Fax: 813 221 7335

**GEORGIA**
**ATLANTA:** 171 17th Street, NW Suite 1100, GA 30363
Tel: 404 815 3000  Fax: 404 817 3244

**TENNESSEE**
**NASHVILLE:** 700 Two American Center, 3102 West End Avenue, TN 37203
Tel: 615 724 3200  Fax: 615 724 3290

growth, investment and acquisition strategies.

## Clients:

American Cast Iron Pipe Company; ADTRAN; American Suzuki Motor Corporation; Assuranceforeningen Gard-gjensidig; Bank of America; Bank of Tampa; Brasfield and Gorrie General Contractors; Brice Building Company; Budgetext; Capital One; Charles Schwab & Co., Inc.; Circle K; Citibank; City of Tampa; Coastal Forest Products; Coca-Cola Enterprises; CVS Caremark; Daniel Realty Company; Dillard's; East Alabama Medical Center; First American; Founders Insurance Company; Gray Construction; HealthSouth Corporation; Laboratory Corporation of America; Mercedes-Benz U.S. International, Inc.; M/I Homes; Millard Maritime; Morgan Keegan & Co.; National Steel Car; Nissan Motors of America, Inc.; Nutech Medical Inc.; Nu Tech Spine, Inc.; ProAssurance; RockTenn Company; Rinnai; Standard Insurance; Southpace Properties; SunTrust Mortgage; Synovus Bank; Tacala; Tenet Healthcare Corporation; Guardian Life; ThyssenKrupp; Time Insurance Company; TriNovus Capital, LLC; UAB Health Services Foundation; United States Steel; Wells Fargo Bank; Wells Fargo Advisors; Whirlpool

BURR ••• FORMAN LLP
*results matter*

# BUTLER, SNOW, O'MARA, STEVENS & CANNADA, PLLC

www.butlersnow.com  **tel:** 601 948 5711  **fax:** 601 985 4500

**Chairman:** Donald Clark, Jr
Number of partners: 145  Number of other lawyers: 106

## Firm Overview:

Butler Snow attorneys are consistently ranked by respected national consultants among the best nationwide in client service – in anticipating needs, in a commitment to help, in providing value and in overall client satisfaction. This client-focused measurement is a driving principle and core value of the firm. With this foundation firmly in place, Butler Snow has developed into a regional firm with national scope, regularly providing legal services to diverse clients from *Fortune* 100 companies to emerging-technology start-ups.

## Main Areas of Practice:

### Litigation:

**Appellate & Written Advocacy:** This federal and state appellate practice handles novel and complex legal issues in all fields of law.

**Commercial Litigation:** Comprised of some of the most experienced trial lawyers in the country, the firm's size and formidable litigation resources attract a significant number of representations in large commercial disputes involving complex issues, but basic contract and business dissolution matters are also a significant part of the practice.

**Product Liability:** Group represents both manufacturers and sellers in product liability litigation in the state and federal courts of the United States and abroad. The group equally works well with the design engineers and the operators in the field. From dioxin to PCBs, HCL, agricultural chemicals and other substances, they have successfully defended toxic exposure cases across the US.

**General Litigation:** This group represents a wide variety of clients in litigated matters in both state and federal court, including personal injury, insurance coverage/bad faith and transportation matters.

**Investigations:** Former US Attorneys and Assistant US Attorneys lead Butler Snow's Criminal and Government Compliance Team to provide counseling and defense to corporate clients and individuals.

**Labor & Employment:** Private and public sector employers are represented by this team in every aspect of the employment relationship. The firm adheres to a philosophy that preventive advice and action are the most efficient means for resolving and preventing workplace disputes.

### Business:

**Business Services:** The firm's business attorneys regularly offer counsel regarding formation, operation and transactions involving corporations and other business entities.

**The Intellectual Property Group:** This group is experienced in technology commercialization, domestic and international licensing and related litigation matters. Clients include small startups to larger technology giants.

**Banking, Real Estate & Financial Services:** This group serves financial services providers throughout Mississippi and across the nation. These attorneys have wide-ranging experience as in-house bank lawyers and with the Comptroller of the Currency. Butler Snow has maintained a substantial and diverse real estate practice for years. The firm's attorneys provide a full range of services to clients, including initial purchases development, financing and leasing through the sale or syndication of such real property.

**Government Relations:** Butler Snow has extensive experience in representing government entities and officials at the local, state and federal levels, and the firm regularly assists private clients in solving problems through the regulatory and legislative process. The team includes four former chiefs of staff for Mississippi governors.

### Environmental:

The Environmental team includes those degreed in engineering, and includes the former administrator for Region IV of the US Environmental Protection Agency. As Mississippi's largest environmental law practice, the attorneys have a proven record addressing environmental issues for businesses and government entities.

### Public Finance & Incentives:

This group offers a comprehensive and diverse public finance practice ranging from all forms of state and municipal bonds and obligations to the full complement of techniques available to finance healthcare, industrial/economic development, exempt facilities, utilities and housing.

### Taxation:

The firm's tax expertise encompasses all aspects of federal, state and local taxation; and the firm's attorneys regularly advise fiduciaries involved in the administration of estates and trusts.

### Industries:

**Energy:** The firm's energy lawyers have experience including pipelines, electric generation, eminent domain, renewable energy projects, gas processing, gas storage and related litigation.

**Pharmaceutical, Medical Device & Healthcare:** This group regularly represents pharmaceutical manufacturers, professionals, providers and businesses in the industry on a national, regional and statewide basis, including physicians and medical practices, hospitals and hospital systems and companies providing products and services. This group is also involved with government compliance, regulatory and industry counseling and defense.

### Clients:

Butler Snow represents a wide range of clients which includes pharmaceutical companies, healthcare providers, manufacturers, insurance companies, government and government-related entities, energy companies, transportation and financial services organizations.

**BUTLER | SNOW**

## OFFICES

### MISSISSIPPI

**RIDGELAND:** 1020 Highland Colony Parkway, Suite 1400, PO Box 6010, MS 39158-6010
Tel: 601 948 5711  Fax: 601 985 4500
Email: info@butlersnow.com

**BAY ST LOUIS:** 833 Highway 90, Suite 1, MS 39520
Tel: 228 467 5426

**GULFPORT:** 1300 25th Avenue, Suite 204, MS 39502
Tel: 228 864 1170  Fax: 228 868 1531

**OXFORD:** 1200 Jefferson Avenue, Suite 205, MS 38655
Tel: 662 513 8000  Fax: 662 513 8001

### ALABAMA

**BIRMINGHAM:** Colonial Plaza, Suite 1125, 2101 6th Avenue North, AL 35203
Tel: 205 297 2200  Fax: 205 297-2201

**MONTGOMERY:** 250 Commerce St., Suite 203, AL 36104
Tel: 334 832 2900  Fax: 334 832-2901

### GEORGIA

**ATLANTA:** Regus Suites, 400 Gallaria Pkwy, Suite 1500, GA 30339
Tel: 678 385 6500  Fax: 678 385 6501

### LOUISIANA

**BATON ROUGE:** City Plaza, 445 North Boulevard, Suite 810, LA 70802
Tel: 225 325 8700  Fax 225 325 8800

**NEW ORLEANS:** 201 St Charles Ave, Suite 3310, LA 70170
Tel: 504 299 7700  Fax: 504 299 7701

### PENNSYLVANIA

**FORT WASHINGTON:** 500 Office Center Drive, Suite 400, PA 19034
Tel: 267 513-1885  Fax: 267 513 1701

**BETHLEHEM:** 1414 Millard, PA 18018
Tel: 610 691 8507

### TENNESSEE

**NASHVILLE:** The Pinnacle at Symphony Place 150 3rd Avenue, Suite 1600, TN 37201
Tel: 615 651 6700  Fax: 615 651 6701

**MEMPHIS:** Crescent Center, 6075 Poplar Avenue, Suite 500, TN 38119
Tel: 901 680 7200  Fax: 901 680 7201

# CARROLL WARREN & PARKER PLLC

www.cwplaw.com **tel:** 601 592 1010 **fax:** 601 592 6060

**Managing Partner:** Jim Warren
**Senior Counsel:** James L Carroll
Number of members: 9
Number of lawyers: 18

## Firm Overview:

CWP was founded in 2002 with a core group of veteran litigators (Jim Carroll, Jim Warren and Myles Parker) who have extensive national and international experience. CWP lawyers hold licenses in Alabama, Florida, Mississippi, New York, Puerto Rico, Texas and the US Virgin Islands. CWP lawyers are currently handling or have handled cases in those jurisdictions as well as in Arkansas, California, Louisiana, Missouri, New Jersey, New York, Oklahoma and Pennsylvania. Outside the US, CWP lawyers are currently involved in or have been involved in cases in Aruba, Barbados, France, Greece, Jamaica, Poland and Trinidad. CWP's legal team includes lawyers proficient in French and Spanish.

## Main Areas of Practice:

Property insurance and its offspring are a dominant aspect of CWP's practice areas. From first party representation of insurers in the initial stages of the claims process to early dispute resolution, mediation, arbitration, litigation and appeal of coverage and large loss subrogation cases, CWP provides a full range of legal services to insurers.

CWP lawyers also represent clients in a wide variety of litigation matters outside the insurance arena, including construction defect, product liability, contract disputes and municipal annexation matters.

## Clients:

CWP represents numerous North American, British, European and Bermuda insurers and reinsurers. CWP provides an extensive range of legal services to these clients in handling complex matters, including the provision of coverage advice and representation in high profile arbitration and litigation proceedings. CWP also represents a host of other clients including governmental entities, corporations and individuals in various matters.

## OFFICES

**MISSISSIPPI**
**JACKSON:** 188 East Capitol Street, Suite 1200, MS 39201
Tel: 601 592 1010   Fax: 601 592 6060

Post Office Box 1005, Jackson, 39215-1005

**FLORIDA**
**MIAMI:** 1111 Brickell Avenue, 11th Floor, FL 33131
Tel: 305 913 8634

**TEXAS**
**HOUSTON:** 5300 Memorial Drive, Suite 960, TX 77007
Tel: 713 863 9029   Fax: 713 583 6531

# FORMAN PERRY WATKINS KRUTZ & TARDY LLP

**www.**fpwkt.com **tel:** 601 960 8600 **fax:** 601 960 8613

**Executive Committee:** Walter G Watkins Jr, Fred Krutz, Thomas W Tardy III, Steven M Hendrix
Number of partners: 52  Number of lawyers: 48
Languages: *English*

### Firm Overview:

Forman Perry Watkins Krutz & Tardy LLP was founded in 1986, in Jackson, Mississippi, as a general litigation firm. The firm now has seven offices and a national reputation for its innovative and creative techniques in defending clients in virtually every type of litigation from simple negligence claims to complex mass tort and commercial litigation. The firm also provides quality representation in other areas including corporate law, commercial lending, bankruptcy, securities, commercial real estate, public utilities, antitrust, and administrative law. Forman Perry has been on the forefront of the development and use of the latest technology to handle all aspects of litigation from discovery through trial. By electronically gathering and maintaining historical case data, discovery information, expert depositions, and medical and technical libraries, the firm has access to vast amounts of information that can provide the difference in winning and losing cases. The firm's goal is to always provide the best possible representation for the lowest possible cost.

### Main Areas of Practice:

**Litigation:**

**Class Actions:** Forman Perry attorneys have extensive experience in class action cases, litigating the issues of class certification, class and merits discovery, negotiating and obtaining approval for class settlements, and appellate practice involving all aspects of class action litigation.

**Commercial Disputes:** Attorneys in the firm are experienced in handling a full range of complex commercial disputes, and understand and appreciate the factually complex business, financing and operational issues at the core of most commercial disputes. Forman Perry has extensive experience representing individuals, partnerships, and publicly traded and privately held corporations before state and federal courts and administrative agencies. Forman Perry regularly represents clients in litigation involving lending and public finance, transportations, telecommunications, real estate, public utilities, securities, technology, manufacturing and distribution, lender liability claims, contract disputes, shareholder disputes, securities fraud, trade regulation, antitrust claims, and debtor-creditor disputes.

**Drugs & Medical Devices:** The firm has been involved in all aspects of drug and medical device litigation, defending a broad array of pharmaceutical claims, and acting as national coordinating counsel.

**Environmental & Toxic Torts:** Forman Perry is actively involved in defending numerous environmental and toxic torts including asbestos, silica, welding rod, lead paint, mold, PVC, PCB and wood preservatives and is also very involved in benzene litigation serving several states as national coordinating counsel and local counsel. Forman Perry's work on behalf of defendants in asbestos litigation on the local and national fronts is unparalleled. The firm represents over 250 asbestos clients and is handling more than 250,000 individual claims nationwide, representing clients in 23 states, with particular emphasis in Mississippi, Texas and Louisiana. Forman Perry lawyers serve as national counsel and national trial counsel to a number of major asbestos defendants. Forman Perry is also extensively involved in silica litigation nationally, representing numerous defendants and acting as national counsel for others. Forman Perry's successes in mass tort have been documented in many publications, including The Wall Street Journal, The New York Times, Fortune and the National Law Journal. Forman Perry's litigation experience also includes defense of claims of alleged environmental contamination from industrial and oilfield operations involving various chemicals, including PCBs, BTEX/TPH, heavy metals, organic solvents, salt water and NORM. Forman Perry also represents clients in litigation arising out of exposure to wood preservative chemicals (creosote, pentachlorophenol and CCA, dioxins and PAHs).

**Insurance:** Forman Perry represents insurance companies in may different cases, including third-party and first-party claims, coverage issues, commercial general liability claims (CGL), property, casualty, automobile, environmental and fleet insurance.

**Products Liability:** From the firm's inception, Forman Perry has enjoyed a close working relationship with manufacturers and insurers in defending products liability cases, successfully defending a full spectrum of products liability cases.

**Professional Negligence:** The firm handles professional negligence claims including accounting, legal and medical malpractice. Several of the firm's litigation attorneys who handle accounting negligence claims are certified public accountants who have practiced in major public accounting firms.

### Business & Corporate Practice:

**General:** Forman Perry's Business and Corporate Practice includes representation of both privately held and publicly traded corporations in a wide variety of industries. The firm regularly provides counsel to banks and financial institutions, institutions of higher learning, REITs, manufacturers and distributors, private foundations, public utilities, municipalities, telecommunications companies and other businesses, working closely with clients to understand and analyze the legal and business issues behind a deal to provide clients with creative, cost-effective strategies and solutions for complex transactions.

**Lending:** The firm regularly represents community, state and national banking institutions in connection with commercial lending activities, including large multi-state financings. Forman Perry also represents insurance companies and other national financing institutions as both lead and local counsel with respect to loans in Mississippi.

**Real Estate:** Forman Perry's Commercial Real Estate Practice is national in scope. The firm regularly represents NYSE-listed REITs and other companies in connection with acquisitions, development, dispositions, joint ventures, and financings. Forman Perry attorneys also have extensive national leasing expertise representing publicly traded companies.

**Transactions/Securities:** Forman Perry has substantial experience representing buyers and sellers in major transactions, from asset and stock transactions to mergers, acquisitions and corporate reorganizations, including both registered and exempt offerings.

**OFFICES**

**MISSISSIPPI**
**JACKSON:** City Centre, Suite 100, 200 South Lamar Street, MS 39201-4099
Tel: 601 960 8600  Fax: 601 960 8613
**JACKSON:** PO Box 22608, MS, 39225-2608

**COLORADO**
**DENVER:** Denver Financial Center, Tower 1, 1775 Sherman Street, Suite 1900, CO 80203-4356
Tel: 303 837 6400  Fax: 303 318 9669

**LOUISIANA**
**NEW ORLEANS:** 701 Poydras Street, Suite 4350, LA 70139-6001
Tel: 504 799 4383  Fax: 504 799 4384

**NEW JERSEY**
**RED BANK:** 328 Newman Springs Road, NJ 07701-5605
Tel: +732 852 4400  Fax: +732 862 4401

**TEXAS**
**DALLAS:** 2001 Bryan Street, Suite 1300, TX 75201-3008
Tel: 214 905 2924  Fax: 214 905 3976
**HOUSTON:** 4900 Woodway Drive, Suite 940, TX 77056-1800
Tel: 713 402 1717  Fax: 713 621 6746

**MICHIGAN**
**LIVONIA:** Powerscourt, 17199 North Laurel Park Drive, Suite 314, MI 48152-7904
Tel: 734 591 0454  Fax: 734 591 2073

# MITCHELL, McNUTT & SAMS, P.A.

www.mitchellmcnutt.com **tel:** 662 842 3871 **fax:** 662 842 8450

**Firm President:** John Hill
Number of Lawyers: 34

## Firm Overview:

As part of one of Mississippi's oldest law firms, the attorneys at Mitchell, McNutt & Sams have established reputations as respected practitioners of commercial law, general litigation, and diversified areas of civil law, serving local, state and national clients. The firm is especially well positioned to serve clients in the southeastern region of the United States, with over 30 lawyers admitted to practice in Mississippi, Tennessee and Alabama, who regularly handle complex and challenging transactions as well as trials and appeals before all state and federal courts and agencies. From Tupelo, Columbus, Corinth, Oxford and Memphis locations, the firm offers clients a wide range of practice groups carefully developed over 100 years in business. The breadth of attorneys' experience and the depth of their professionalism have aided them in forging long-standing client relationships which include city governments, health care facilities, public utilities, railroads, banking institutions, various manufacturing companies and industries, large retail establishments and major corporations as well as locally owned businesses and many insurance companies. At the same time, members of the firm devote substantial time and attention to the special concerns of individuals.

## Main Areas of Practice:

The firm is engaged in a general civil practice with heavy emphasis on corporate representation and on litigation of all types.

- Alternative Dispute Resolution
- General Litigation
- Banking and Financial Institutions
- Health Care
- Bankruptcy and Creditors' Rights
- Insurance
- Business/Commercial Litigation
- Intellectual Property
- Civil Rights and Public Entity Litigation

- Labor, Employment and ERISA
- Communications
- Marketing, Trade and Antitrust
- Complex Litigation
- Municipal, County and Governmental Entities
- Construction
- Product Liability
- Criminal Defense
- Professional Liability
- Environmental and Natural Resources
- Railroad and Transportation
- Estate Planning, Probate and Elder Law
- Real Estate

- Family Law
- Taxation – Individual and Corporate
- General Business, Corporate and Finance
- Utilities
- Workers' Compensation

## Clients:

Mitchell, McNutt & Sams represents a wide range of business organizations such as technology financial institutions, manufacturers, contractors, health care providers, insurance companies, transportation as well as governmental entities, utilities and the needs of individuals.

## OFFICES

**MISSISSIPPI**

**TUPELO:** 105 South Front Street, PO Box 7120, MS 38802
Tel: 662 842 3871  Fax: 662 842 8450

**COLUMBUS:** 215 Fifth St. North, PO Box 1366, MS 39703
Tel: 662 328 2316

**OXFORD:** 1216 Van Buren, PO Box 947, MS 38655
Tel: 662 234 4845

**CORINTH:** 508 Waldron St., PO Box 1200, MS 38835
Tel: 662 286 9931

**MEMPHIS:** 22 North Front St., Suite 1030, TN 38103
Tel: 901 527 2585

# WATKINS & EAGER PLLC

www.watkinseager.com  **tel:** 601 965 1900  **fax:** 601 965 1901

**Managing Member:** M Binford Williams, Jr
**Senior Member:** William F Goodman, Jr
Number of members: 50  Number of other lawyers: 25

**OFFICES**

MISSISSIPPI
**JACKSON:** The Emporium Building, 400 East Capitol
Street, MS 39201
Tel: 601 965 1900  Fax: 601 965 1901

## Firm Overview:

Established in 1895, Watkins & Eager PLLC is a full-service, diversified law firm, specializing in a multitude of practice areas. These areas include an extensive real estate, banking, corporate and business practice, as well as the firm's broad trial and appellate practice.

Watkins & Eager is proud of the academic achievements and honorary qualifications of its lawyers. The firm's lawyers are members of prestigious professional organizations, including the American College of Trial Lawyers, American Academy of Appellate Lawyers, American Board of Trial Advocates, American College of Labor and Employment Lawyers, American College of Mortgage Attorneys, American College of Trust and Estate Counsel, and the Product Liability Advisory Council. The National Law Review featured Watkins & Eager in an article entitled "Small Mississippi Firm Makes Big Name for Itself." The article emphasized some of the major US corporations that the firm represents, including Chevron Corp., Bayer Corp., Pfizer, Inc., and Toyota Motor Sales USA, Inc.

Today, Watkins & Eager has inherited a legacy of excellence and the firm's name has been synonymous with integrity, experience, dedication, responsiveness, critical thinking and creativity. The firm possesses the skills and the commitment to responsibly address complex legal problems and is dedicated to building long-term client relationships.

## Main Areas of Practice:

### Commercial & Business Litigation:
The firm is fully engaged in all aspects of contract and business litigation and arbitration, including a large variety of commercial controversies and business tort disputes, as well as antitrust, lender liability, consumer fraud and securities litigation. Several members of the firm serve as arbitrators and mediators of various business disputes.
**Contact:** Jamie G Houston, III (Business), James J Crongeyer, Jr (Litigation)

### Tort/Mass Tort Litigation:
Firm lawyers defend tort claims of all types. A substantial part of the firm's tort practice is the defense of product liability actions, representing a number of manufacturers of aircraft, automotive products, chemicals, farm implements, firearms, heavy equipment, tires, tools, medical devices, and pharmaceuticals throughout the state and beyond its borders. As defense attorneys, the firm's lawyers assume leadership roles on a local, regional and national basis in mass tort litigation of matters such as pharmaceutical products, chemical exposure, asbestos, and welding. The defense of professional malpractice claims against doctors, dentists, lawyers, architects, engineers and accountants is another significant segment of the firm's tort practice.

### Banking & Finance:
The firm represents various financial institutions both in and out of state, maintaining a regular clientele of the state's leading financial institutions. The firm's banking work includes advice and counsel, transactional work, letters of credit, regulatory guidance, drafting bank forms, litigation and loan workouts.

### Corporate:
The firm's Corporate Practice covers a broad range, including mergers and acquisitions, commercial finance, the formation of and counsel to business entities, securities and capital formation, and the drafting of commercial contracts.

### Tax:
The firm has three lawyers who are experienced tax attorneys, two of whom are also CPAs. In addition to providing tax counsel and advice to businesses, individuals, and foundations, firm members have also represented clients in tax disputes before the IRS, the Mississippi Department of Revenue (formerly State Tax Commission) and local public bodies.

### Wills, Trusts & Estates:
Estate planning, wills, trusts and probate are an integral part of the firm's practice.

### Public Utility Law:
The firm has extensive experience representing utilities before the Public Service Commission, which regulates public utilities in Mississippi.

### Construction Law:
The firm represents owners, architects, engineers, contractors and sureties in construction disputes, project development, and general business activities.

### Bankruptcy:
The firm represents various lenders and other creditors in workouts and in bankruptcy proceedings.

### Labor & Employment:
The firm possesses considerable experience in representation of management in various employer-related transactions and disputes, including day to day employment issues, litigation, collective bargaining and proceedings before the federal and state regulatory bodies.

### Environmental:
The firm's Environmental Practice includes representation of clients in litigation in both federal and state courts, as well as before the Mississippi Department of Environmental Quality, the EPA and other administrative agencies. Representation includes the defense of toxic claims, environmental permitting and compliance matters, and negotiating and drafting of environmental related contract provisions.

### Real Estate:
The firm has a broad Real Estate Practice with extensive depth and expertise. The real estate practice includes representation of local residential and commercial developers, and involves new urbanism, multifamily, commercial developments and tax credit financing in Mississippi and neighboring states. The firm also serves as local counsel for numerous out-of-state lending institutions.

### Insurance:
The firm has considerable experience in insurance matters. Firm members possess experience in handling claims involving fire, property, casualty, workers' compensation, fidelity and surety, officers and directors, errors and omissions insurance, as well as matters regarding life, health and accident insurance.

### Government Entities:
The firm represents a number of governmental bodies on various matters. The firm possesses expertise in tax and economic development incentives, and has been involved in a variety of public/private projects. The firm provides legal services related to the post-Hurricane Katrina Restoration of the Port of Gulfport, Mississippi, a $1.5 billion project, which both former Governors Haley Barbour and William Winter describe as "the most important economic development project in the history of the state."

### Clients:
Watkins & Eager's client base includes banks and financial institutions, manufacturers, oil and gas companies, pharmaceutical companies, commercial real estate developers, healthcare providers, investors, insurers, institutions of higher learning, and government agencies at the municipal, county, state, and federal levels.

## How lawyers are ranked

Every year we carry out thousands of in-depth interviews with clients in order to assess the reputations and expertise of business lawyers worldwide. The qualities we look for (and which determine rankings) include technical legal ability, professional conduct, client service, commercial awareness/astuteness, diligence, commitment, and other qualities most valued by the client. For details of our research team, see p.5.

**Contents:**

# CORPORATE/M&A

### Corporate/M&A: Kansas City & Surrounds
#### Leading Firms

**Band 1**
Husch Blackwell LLP
Polsinelli PC *
Stinson Morrison Hecker LLP

**Band 2**
Bryan Cave LLP
Dentons *
Lathrop & Gage LLP

**Band 3**
Spencer Fane Britt & Browne LLP

## Corporate/M&A

### Armstrong Teasdale LLP

**THE FIRM** This St. Louis-based team has wide experience across business law, corporate finance and investment. It places particular focus upon work in the technology, healthcare and life sciences sectors. Key clients include Centene, Centric Group, Lake Regional Health and Mississippi Lime.

**Sources say:** *"We are extremely satisfied. They have done a great job, the service is great, they are very responsive and the legal opinions very sound."* *"We found them to be consensus builders."*

**KEY INDIVIDUALS** Department head **David Braswell** is commended for his management of the firm's corporate group. Clients say he is *"extremely competent – he holds up well under stress, and is very honest and ethical. We really value him."* Key matters in recent months have included working on a share exchange and merger. **Stephen Jones** is highly regarded by sources, who state: *"He is incredibly decisive. You know he is going to stand behind you and support you."* His recent matters include managing a team on an internally led LBO. **Daniel Godar** focuses on corporate governance, transactions and commercial contracts, with particular expertise in the health and entertainment sectors. Most recently, he has worked on the structuring and negotiation of several high-value coal transactions, as well

### Corporate/M&A: Kansas City & Surrounds
#### Senior Statesmen

**Senior Statesmen: distinguished older practitioners**

| | |
|---|---|
| Fisher Robert | *Dentons* * |
| Marvin John | *Dentons* * |

#### Leading Individuals

**Band 1**

| | |
|---|---|
| Ash James | *Husch Blackwell LLP* |
| Granda John A | *Stinson Morrison Hecker LLP* |
| Van Dyke Thomas W | *Bryan Cave LLP* |

**Band 2**

| | |
|---|---|
| Barnes Robert M | *Bryan Cave LLP* |
| Bluhm Mark A | *Lathrop & Gage LLP* |
| Carman Steven F | *Husch Blackwell LLP* |
| Davison Bruce C | *Dentons* * |
| Evans Craig L | *Stinson Morrison Hecker LLP* |
| Gilson Gary | *Husch Blackwell LLP* |
| Mahood III William W | *Polsinelli PC* |
| Medved Joseph W | *Lathrop & Gage LLP* |
| Monroe C Robert | *Stinson Morrison Hecker LLP* |
| Rist Steven L | *Dentons* * |
| Ross Jr Frank J | *Polsinelli PC* |
| Sweeney Kevin R | *Polsinelli PC* |
| Van Dyke Michael J | *Dentons* * |

**Band 3**

| | |
|---|---|
| Allen James W | *Stinson Morrison Hecker LLP* |
| Bayer Jr Jacob W | *Polsinelli PC* |
| Brockhoff Wallace E | *Lathrop & Gage LLP* |
| Fitzgerald Jr Robert E | *Polsinelli PC* |
| Frazen Laurence M | *Bryan Cave LLP* |
| Frizell Edward E 'Trip' | *Polsinelli PC* |
| Polsinelli James A | *Polsinelli PC* |
| Pryde James P | *Bryan Cave LLP* |
| Reschly Jason | *Husch Blackwell LLP* |
| Westerhaus Victoria R | *Stinson Morrison Hecker LLP* |

*Indicates individual/firm with profile.*

as power plant sales. **Mark Stoneman** is highlighted as a bright up-and-coming attorney. Recently, he led a multi-disciplinary Armstrong team representing Grey Eagle Distributors in its proposed acquisition of Anheuser-Busch wholesaler Illinois Distributing. His other clients include Boehringer Ingelheim Vetmedica.

### Bryan Cave LLP

**THE FIRM** Bryan Cave's St. Louis office houses a strong group of M&A and private equity lawyers, while its clients also benefit from its large network of offices both across the USA and abroad. Among its impressive client roster are Energizer, The Mutual Fund Store and Monsanto. Work is drawn from a wide variety of sectors, with particular activity in the areas of financial services, food and technology. In 2012 it represented Ralcorp Holdings in a $930 million tax-free spin-off to its shareholders of Post Holdings.

**KEY INDIVIDUALS** Highly respected practitioner **Thomas Van Dyke** is described as a smart attorney who works hard and knows how to make a deal. He is praised for his skills in both securities and M&A work. **James Pryde** is known for his particular skills in the areas of venture capital and private equity. In a recent highlight, he advised Cretcher Heartland in its takeover of The Scotland Group. **Don Lents** is the chair of Bryan Cave and is well respected for his deep experience in M&A, securities law and corporate governance. **James Nouss** is considered to be a strong and exceptionally capable attorney by sources. He is known for his corporate finance and transactional expertise, and is appreciated for bringing a business focus to legal matters. Department head **William Seabaugh** is described as an excellent M&A counsel for the larger, more complex transactions. He was involved in a series of high-stakes transactions in 2012, including leading the team on the aforementioned Ralcorp Holdings matter. **Robert Barnes** is praised for his ability to listen well and understand the needs of a clients. He acted for The Mutual Fund Store during its sale of a majority interest to Warburg Pincus. German-speaker **Fred Bartelsmeyer** looks after the firm's interests in Europe from his St. Louis base, as well as representing clients from elsewhere in the USA and

## Corporate/M&A: St. Louis & Surrounds

### Leading Firms

**Band 1**

Bryan Cave LLP

Thompson Coburn LLP

**Band 2**

Armstrong Teasdale LLP

**Band 3**

Greensfelder, Hemker & Gale, P.C.

Husch Blackwell LLP

Lewis, Rice & Fingersh LC *

Polsinelli PC *

### Leading Individuals

**Band 1**

| Lents Don G | Bryan Cave LLP |
| Litz Thomas A | Thompson Coburn LLP |
| Nouss Jr James L | Bryan Cave LLP |
| Seabaugh William F | Bryan Cave LLP |

**Band 2**

| Bartelsmeyer Fred W | Bryan Cave LLP |
| Braswell David W | Armstrong Teasdale LLP |
| Erb Thomas C | Lewis, Rice & Fingersh LC * |
| Jones Stephen C | Armstrong Teasdale LLP |
| LaRose Robert M | Thompson Coburn LLP |
| Lause Michael F | Thompson Coburn LLP |
| Minogue Thomas J | Thompson Coburn LLP |
| O'Connell Mary Anne | Husch Blackwell LLP |
| Wang R. Randall | Bryan Cave LLP |

**Band 3**

| Baumer Steven M | Bryan Cave LLP |
| Chuquimia Ruben K | Polsinelli PC |
| Godar Daniel | Armstrong Teasdale LLP |
| Hoyne Andrew | Polsinelli PC |
| Lehrer Joseph D | Greensfelder, Hemker & Gale, P.C. |
| Porter Jr Joseph T | Polsinelli PC |
| Suelthaus Kenneth H | Polsinelli PC |

**Up-and-coming individuals**

| Stoneman Mark | Armstrong Teasdale LLP |

*\* Indicates individual with profile.*
*Alphabetical order within each band. Band 1 is the highest.*

overseas. He is praised as a highly skilled international M&A counsel and as an excellent strategist. He recently represented Sigma-Aldrich in the $350 million acquisition of Bio Reliance Holdings from Avista Capital. **Randall Wang** is widely praised by clients and peers for his intelligence and technical skills. He recently worked on the Ralcorp matter with Seabaugh. **Steven Baumer** is noted for his excellent understanding of business objectives of a deal. He represented Bunge when it sold a 28% interest in Solae to DuPont for $440 million. **Laurence Frazen** is the firm's Kansas City bankruptcy specialist, and is widely appreciated for his skills in this area. He is also instructed on restructuring and workouts.

## Dentons

**See profile on p.449**

**THE FIRM** Global firm Dentons is noted for offering international law firm expertise at Midwestern rates. It serves corporate clients from offices in both Kansas City and St. Louis on M&A and private equity transactions. After its merger with leading European and Canadian firms Salans and Fraser Milner Casgrain, the firm is now able to offer a wider reach to clients.

**KEY INDIVIDUALS** Senior practitioner **Robert Fisher** (see p.1636) is best known for his M&A capabilities, especially in the private midmarket. He is highly respected among peers, who describe him as *"a very smart guy who has been doing deals forever and has a great reputation."* **John Marvin** (see p.1637) is also a widely respected senior partner at the firm, giving the team the benefit of more than 30 years of practice. He is notably strong for securities regulation work, including IPOs, after-market trading and control compliance, and general corporate law. **Bruce Davison** (see p.1636) is appreciated for his strong technical abilities and expertise in tax matters. He focuses upon M&A and real estate work for limited liability companies, exempt organizations, and trusts and estates. **Steven Rist** (see p.1638) has a strong reputation in the private equity space where he acts for private equity funds on M&A, restructurings, workouts and leveraged recapitalizations. He leads the firm's Kansas City corporate practice. **Michael Van Dyke** (see p.1638) has over 35 years of experience in the corporate practice and is prized for his particular strengths in M&A and business finance. His work has often focused on representing financial institutions, including lenders on financing for startups.

## Greensfelder, Hemker & Gale, P.C.

**THE FIRM** This St. Louis-headquartered firm is active in sales and acquisitions in a variety of industries. In the last year this has included deals in the areas of financial services, hospitality and shipping. In a major highlight, it advised Sequa with regard to its $2.2 billion sale to The Carlyle Group.

**Sources say:** *"We use the firm in St. Louis for a lot of different work. We like them a lot."*

**KEY INDIVIDUALS** Greensfelder's corporate group leader **Joseph Lehrer** is described as having *"a significant presence in our area."* Recently, he acted for HBE Corporation, owners of the Adams Mark Hotel group, in the sale of 25 Adams Mark Hotels to purchasers. He also led the team handling the aforementioned Sequa transaction.

## Husch Blackwell LLP

**THE FIRM** Expanding national firm Husch Blackwell handles a range of substantial M&A and joint venture matters from its offices in Kansas City and St. Louis. The firm recently advised the Sisters of Charity of Leavenworth Health System in its $275 million acquisition of three Exempla hospitals from the Community First Foundation, and also advised American Airlines on the acquisition of a number of high-value aircraft engines. Other clients include Novelis, H&R Block and Anheuser-Busch.

**Sources say:** *"They're the very best value for the money we spend, and have a good continuity of client service."*

**KEY INDIVIDUALS** The *"very successful"* **James Ash** is praised for his skill in M&A and securities work. He recently represented an energy client on an asset purchase agreement for the transfer of a grain business between two companies. Chair of the firm's corporate department **Steven Carman** is praised for his leadership skills on large transactions. *"He always knows what's going on,"* reports one client. **Gary Gilson** led a multidisciplinary Husch team on the $660 million sale of RSM McGladrey Auction by key client H&R Block. He has over 30 years' experience in M&A, and chairs the M&A group for the firm. He is praised for his practical approach. Securities expert **Mary Anne O'Connell** represented CFB Venture Fund and Digi-Star Acquisition Holdings in the $60 million sale of an operating company by a group of private equity firms. She is praised for her well-rounded abilities. *"She has all the tools – she has good judgment, knowledge, is hard-working and a good negotiator,"* sources say. **Jason Reschly** is *"one of the best tax lawyers in town,"* sources report. He handles federal and state tax law work with a particular focus on federal income taxation. He assisted Gary Gilson on the H&R Block matter above.

## Lathrop & Gage LLP

**THE FIRM** As Kansas City's oldest continuously operating law firm, Lathrop & Gage has deep connections with local businesses. Especially active in the midmarket, it has solid experience in the corporate M&A and corporate advisory spheres, with clients spanning a range of industries including mining, entertainment, telecom and finance. It is particularly prized for its transaction structuring and due diligence investigation expertise. Among its recent clients are BSC Holding, BlueScope Steel North America, Grantham University and DST Systems.

**Sources say:** *"We feel exceptionally pleased with their work."* *"They have all the resources that you need."*

**KEY INDIVIDUALS Mark Bluhm** is experienced in a wide variety of business transactions and corporate matters, including strategic alliances, startups and equity investments. **Joseph Medved** is noted for being *"a deal-doer, not a deal-breaker"* who *"brings good Midwestern workmanship and negotiating skills"* to matters. He heads the practice, and specializes in corporate M&A, securities and corporate finance. **Wallace Brockhoff** is equally at home working with public or privately held companies, and has advised on a number of high-profile national and international deals. Clients appreciate him for being *"very knowledgeable, evenhanded and capable of processing multiple things at the same time,"* as well as for his reassuring manner. *"He always makes me feel confident even in challenging situations,"* sources attest.

## Lewis, Rice & Fingersh LC

**See profile on p.1640**

**THE FIRM** Lewis, Rice & Fingersh consults on the full range of M&A, dispositions and LBOs. Its recent highlights include advising SRAM Holdings, Sage Capital and WellPoint on corporate transactions.

**KEY INDIVIDUALS** Described as *"the go-to guy in financial services,"* **Thomas Erb** (see p.1636) is the chairman of the firm and has a good reputation in St. Louis and beyond. He acted for Sage Capital in the sale of 100% of the membership interests of Revenue Cycle Partners to H&R Accounts.

## Polsinelli PC
See profile on p.1641

**THE FIRM** Kansas City-based Polsinelli is growing rapidly, and has taken on a number of additional partners over the past year. It covers a range of corporate M&A and private equity deals out of both Kansas City and St. Louis, and is particularly active in the healthcare and insurance sectors. Key clients include Catholic Health Initiatives, St. Joseph Health Systems, the University of Kansas Hospital Authority and Sprint Nextel.

**KEY INDIVIDUALS** Chair of Polsinelli's corporate finance practice group **William Mahood** is known for his work with Sprint Nextel. He represents his client in governance, financing and other issues, and was most recently involved in advising on almost $3 billion of debt financings. He has also worked on significant fund matters, including forming the third-generation Plaza Beaumont III $60 million fund. **Frank Ross** in Kansas City is one of the key partners responsible for Polsinelli's rapid growth. He is described as *"bigger than life – a real go-getter."* He recently acted for Mariner Holdings in its multimillion-dollar fund matters. Clients describe Kansas City attorney **Kevin Sweeney** as *"very good at problem solving and execution."* An expert on advising life sciences businesses, he also has deep corporate finance expertise. **Jacob Bayer** is vice chair of the firm's corporate M&A group. He is well known for his work on transactions for small to medium-sized companies, especially in the IT and communications sectors. Firm founder **James Polsinelli** remains deeply involved in client matters, and is particularly prized for his high level of experience in M&A, corporate law and business succession planning. Recent clients include a major grocery chain. He also has long-standing client relationships with many startups which have grown up alongside Polsinelli Shughart itself. Colleague **Robert Fitzgerald** is another highly experienced partner in the state. He is frequently instructed on corporate M&A and regulatory matters, as well as real estate work. **Trip Frizell** is noted for being *"extremely customer-focused."* As one source explained, *"he will take the time to understand the issue and*

ensure his customers have the appropriate attorneys working for their best interest." He has a national practice, and advises clients on business acquisitions and dispositions, restructurings and real estate matters. **Andrew Hoyne** specializes in work for technology companies and those in the life sciences sphere, both in the private and public sectors. Clients single out his strong intellect and solid grasp of technical detail as key strengths. *"He is a lawyer's lawyer – very precise,"* notes one commentator. **Joseph Porter** is highly trusted on banking and finance matters, and has been practicing corporate law for more than three decades. *"He is very well known and respected for banking deals,"* says one source. Well-known senior practitioner **Kenneth Suelthaus** is known for being *"very careful, diligent and experienced."* He has recently been involved in a number of complex acquisitions and dispositions. He is based in St. Louis. **Ruben Chuquimia** is well regarded in the market and known for his work on a wide range of transactional, corporate and securities matters. One source described him as *"a very good lawyer who I have the utmost respect for."*

## Spencer Fane Britt & Browne LLP

**THE FIRM** Spencer Fane has a large, well-established team in Kansas City, which offers the full range of corporate services to its clients. The firm has recently recruited a new partner to the corporate group, David Zimmerman, who brings additional expertise in advising private foundations and other tax-exempt organizations.

**KEY INDIVIDUALS** Norman Fretwell is a key contact for corporate and finance matters.

## Stinson Morrison Hecker LLP

**THE FIRM** This strong Kansas City-based firm is particularly well known for its tax and financial services expertise. It serves as outside corporate counsel to many public companies in the Kansas City area, and also has offices in St. Louis and Jefferson City. It recently acted for Tallgrass Energy Partners in its $3.3 billion acquisition of natural gas pipelines, processing and treatment facilities from Kinder Morgan Energy Partners. The firm has also recently been instructed by Layne Christensen, Entertainment Properties Trust, UMB Financial and H&R Block.

**Sources say:** *"They do very professional and high-quality legal work, and are very focused." "They are up to speed on best practices and are responsive to client needs, providing quick turnarounds when required."*

**KEY INDIVIDUALS** Clients describe **John Granda** as *"the dean of the securities Bar within the Midwest."* He also has deep experience advising boards of directors on gover-

nance issues. **Robert Monroe** is widely appreciated for his specialized knowledge and experience in banking matters. Peers describe him as *"very talented – the number-one guy in Kansas City,"* and say: *"There is nobody better on banking in this region, from Chicago to Dallas."* **James Allen** is strong on securities advice and serves as outside general counsel to public and private companies covering a range of industries. **Craig Evans** advises large public companies on both M&A and securities issues. He is praised by many clients, one of whom says: *"He does a very nice job. He delivers really good counsel and advice to the company, and is very much trusted by our board."* **Victoria Westerhaus** represents clients on a wide range of corporate matters. *"She provides excellent client service, sound expertise in securities laws, and commercially practical solutions,"* according to one source.

## Thompson Coburn LLP

**THE FIRM** With 37 corporate attorneys operating out of its St. Louis office, Thompson Coburn has a strong offering in both transactional and corporate governance matters. The group is mostly called upon to advise on negotiated transactions, but also has expertise assisting in hostile takeovers. It has recently recruited four partners from other firms, boosting its offering across tax, banking, securities and bankruptcy.

**Sources say:** *"Their advice is proactive, comprehensive and well thought out."*

**KEY INDIVIDUALS Thomas Litz** is noted for being *"a strong player"* as well as *"an outstanding M&A and securities lawyer."* He recently led a multidisciplinary team acting for Forsyth Capital Investors on its acquisition of Baldwin Technology, and the latter's subsequent delisting from NYSE Amex as a result. He cochairs the firm's corporate and securities practice group with **Robert LaRose**. An experienced practitioner, LaRose is noted for his skills in advising on securities issues during transactions. He was lead partner on the $110 million sale of Federal Signal Technologies, the transportation and electronic tolling unit of Federal Signal Corporation, to 3M. **Michael Lause** is the chair of the corporate department and its public finance and public law practice. He acted as issuer's counsel for the Higher Education Loan Authority of the State of Missouri on a complex asset-backed notes issuance worth $256 million. Firm chairman **Thomas Minogue** represents Peabody Energy on an ongoing basis, and recently advised on its corporation accounts receivable securitization program. Clients highlight the fact that he *"always provides thoughtful business-related solutions."*

# ENVIRONMENT

Commentary about individuals can be found under their firm's paragraph. If the firm has no paragraph (is not ranked) look at Other Notable Practitioners.

## Environment: Kansas City & Surrounds
### Leading Firms

**Band 1**
Lathrop & Gage LLP
Shook, Hardy & Bacon LLP *
Stinson Morrison Hecker LLP

**Band 2**
Spencer Fane Britt & Browne LLP

### Leading Individuals

**Band 1**

| | |
|---|---|
| Anstoetter Mark | *Shook, Hardy & Bacon LLP* |
| Beck William G | *Lathrop & Gage LLP* |
| Erickson David | *Shook, Hardy & Bacon LLP* |
| Hockley Michael D | *Spencer Fane Britt & Browne LLP* |
| Price James | *Spencer Fane Britt & Browne LLP* |
| Satterlee Terry J | *Shook, Hardy & Bacon LLP* |
| Shorr David A | *Lathrop & Gage LLP* |
| Tripp David | *Stinson Morrison Hecker LLP* |

**Band 2**

| | |
|---|---|
| Blanton WC | *Husch Blackwell LLP* |
| Evans Parthenia B | *Stinson Morrison Hecker LLP* |
| Ford Jr William F | *Lathrop & Gage LLP* |
| Grever Thomas | *Shook, Hardy & Bacon LLP* |
| Ryan Thomas A | *Lathrop & Gage LLP* |
| Schiller Baerbel | *Spencer Fane Britt & Browne LLP* |
| Session William T | *The Session Law Firm (ONP)†* |
| Stotts Stacy | *Stinson Morrison Hecker LLP* |
| Sullivan Sarah Toevs | *Stinson Morrison Hecker LLP* |

## Environment: St. Louis & Surrounds
### Leading Firms

**Band 1**
Husch Blackwell LLP
Thompson Coburn LLP

**Band 2**
Armstrong Teasdale LLP
Bryan Cave LLP

### Leading Individuals

**Band 1**

| | |
|---|---|
| Guariglia Dale A | *Bryan Cave LLP* |
| Nassif Joseph G | *Husch Blackwell LLP* |
| Strassner Peter S | *Thompson Coburn LLP* |
| von Stamwitz George | *Armstrong Teasdale LLP* |

**Band 2**

| | |
|---|---|
| Cohen Edward | *Thompson Coburn LLP* |
| Hackmann Frank H | *Dentons (ONP)† *|
| Jeffery Stephen G | *Jeffery Law Group (ONP)†* |
| O'Keefe Julie | *Armstrong Teasdale LLP* |
| Poplawski Steven J. | *Bryan Cave LLP* |
| Wachs Amy L | *Husch Blackwell LLP* |
| Wilkinson Robert F | *Husch Blackwell LLP* |

**Band 3**

| | |
|---|---|
| Ahrens Richard A. | *Lewis, Rice & Fingersh LC (ONP)† *|
| Erker Christopher E | *Bryan Cave LLP* |
| Kellmeyer Joseph M | *Thompson Coburn LLP* |

*\* Indicates firm / individual with profile.*
*Alphabetical order within each band. Band 1 is the highest.*

---

*The editorial is in alphabetical order by firm name.*

## Armstrong Teasdale LLP

**THE FIRM** This St Louis-based group has particular strength in the redevelopment of brownfield land, including managing contaminated areas and providing ongoing advice regarding Superfund sites. The practice continues to advise 42 members of the Missouri Electric Works Site Trust on the management of its Superfund site, including litigation and lease negotiation. Other clients include AmerenUE, the City of St Louis, Fluor Corporation and Kinder Morgan.
**Sources say:** *"Our experience has been absolutely excellent."*
**KEY INDIVIDUALS** Head of the group **George von Stamwitz** is described as *"clever and creative."* He assisted Niagara Development on its acquisition of industrial properties which have been environmentally affected. **Julie O'Keefe** has more than two decades' experience defending companies in both environmental and health and safety actions. She is praised as *"well versed in environmental issues. She knows what the regulations are and how to interface with the agencies."*

## Bryan Cave LLP

**THE FIRM** Bryan Cave has a full-service environmental group which is popular with clients both inside and outside the state. The firm is regularly called upon to advise on litigation, compliance counseling and brownfield land development. It also has expertise in the area of clean technology.
**KEY INDIVIDUALS Dale Guariglia** has a strong reputation in the market, and is appreciated for his efficiency and legal knowledge. Clients praise his ability to blend the law and science together in a practical and useful manner. **Steven Poplawski** heads Bryan Cave's environmental group from the firm's St Louis office. He is sought out for his ability to get to the heart of a matter and take a leadership role if necessary. **Christopher Erker** has been attracting increasing attention over the past few years for his work on transactional and compliance issues for a range of clients.

## Husch Blackwell LLP

**THE FIRM** This firm operates a national environmental practice from its St Louis office, and is also regularly called upon to advise on international issues. The group maintains strong litigation expertise, and routinely offers com-

pliance counseling to its clients, which include Arch Chemicals, Harcos Chemical, Monsanto Company and Olin Corporation.
**Sources say:** *"They have a strong practice in St Louis, handling some high-profile matters."*
**KEY INDIVIDUALS Joseph Nassif** is a *"force to be reckoned with,"* say impressed interviewees, who also point out that *"he has been doing environmental law forever and is a terrific, tenacious advocate."* He is renowned for his skill in handling complex litigation and dispute resolution matters, often involving several parties. Recently, he acted for several national clients, advising them on significant and sensitive enforcement matters. **Amy Wachs** is noted for being *"detail oriented and an excellent communicator."* She is particularly involved with assisting private and public sector clients on regulatory compliance requirements. One happy client said: *"We utilize Amy on just about any significant environmental issue we have. She is so knowledgeable".* **Robert Wilkinson** advises on environmental and health and safety compliance, permitting and enforcement defense, and is especially noted for his expertise in issues relating to air. **WC Blanton** has a reputation as a fine trial lawyer. He recently successfully defended a tannery owner in a number of claims alleging wrongful death, among other matters, as a result of long-term exposure to a chemical used in tannery wastewater treatment.

## Lathrop & Gage LLP

**THE FIRM** This widely respected Kansas City group advises companies across the USA on federal and state environmental laws, with a focus on the adage that prevention is better than cure. Nevertheless, it performs strongly in court when good planning and negotiation fail, recently representing ConocoPhillips in its defense of a $100 million suit brought by the US government. The case concerned the costs associated with the cleanup of a contaminated former defense production plant run by ConocoPhillips
**Sources say:** *"They truly outworked and outmaneuvered our adversaries."*
**KEY INDIVIDUALS** Trial attorney **William Beck** has more than three decades' experience defending corporate clients in the courts on environmental matters, including major toxic tort litigation. He is prized by clients for his ability to foresee the direction a case is heading. One said: *"He's the guy who has been there, done it, and done it well. I have complete confidence in his judgment."* Former director of the Missouri Department of Natural Resources **David Shorr** recently acted for clients in matters involving the Clean Water Act and the Endangered Species Act. Sources describe him as *"an excellent environmental attorney"* with a *"strong regulatory background."* He is partner-in-charge of Lathrop's Jefferson City office, and is licensed to practice in Ohio as well as Missouri. A veteran of numerous multi-million-dollar lawsuits, litigator **William Ford** has wide-

*The editorial is in alphabetical order by firm name.*

ranging experience. He is adept at handling a variety of cases, including those which involve underground storage tanks, government remediation funds, and both hazardous and non-hazardous waste treatment sites. Head of the group, **Thomas Ryan** has particular experience defending chemical exposure toxic tort litigation, often involving personal injury claims. He is *"excellent to work with,"* a *"zealous advocate for his clients,"* say interviewees.

### Shook, Hardy & Bacon LLP
See profile on p.1644

**THE FIRM** Litigation powerhouse Shook Hardy & Bacon is widely lauded for its success in significant environmental and toxic tort actions in both environmental and state courts across the USA. The 55-strong group focuses on getting clients back to business as soon as possible, and is also sought out for transactional and regulatory compliance. Key matters include the Passaic River litigation in New Jersey, where the team acted as common litigation counsel to the 113 third-party defendants involved in challenging the state's attempts to seek damages for alleged pollution in the Passaic River.

**Sources say:** *"I believe that Shook is unsurpassed in its ability to successfully manage complex litigation and other related matters." "I have specifically appreciated their willingness to work with me to help control costs. Also very good at maintaining an appropriate level of communication."*

**KEY INDIVIDUALS** Department head **David Erickson** is described by a client as *"a very experienced, skilled and professional litigation lawyer."* His peers point out that he is *"somebody who would definitely be on my conflict referral list."* His clients include Coca-Cola, who he represented in an environmental and mass tort action regarding the historic treatment of wastewater at the company's plant near Paw Paw. **Terry Satterlee** has continued to represent the St Louis Sewer District in litigation against the EPA, the State of Missouri and the Missouri Coalition for the Environment alleging violations of the Clean Water Act. Sources say: *"The market recognizes her as one of the best lawyers in Kansas City."* **Mark Anstoetter** *"has consistently demonstrated an exceptional understanding of complex environmental and toxic tort matters,"* report interviewees. Clients praise **Thomas Grever** as *"extremely responsive and easy to work with. He has proven to be very practical and efficient in providing advice, and in negotiation."* He acted for International Paper on a Superfund private party cost recovery action pertaining to the remediation of a contaminated lumber and plywood mill.

### Spencer Fane Britt & Browne LLP

**THE FIRM** The team at Spencer Fane is compact but commands an enduring reputation for its full-range expertise of environmental issues, both in and out of the courtroom. The firm has developed a practice of creating tailored strategic plans for businesses which enable them to look to address issues in advance. It offers environmental advice from both St Louis and Kansas City, but has a particular focus on the latter.

**KEY INDIVIDUALS** Practice leader **James Price** is described as *"one of the best lawyers in Kansas City."* He has a broad practice which encompasses regulation and compliance as well as litigation, including insurance coverage and toxic tort issues. According to sources, **Michael Hockley** is able to *"manage a complex situation in a very logical way – that's a key thing."* He is well respected in the market, acting across the litigious, regulatory and enforcement areas while also handling renewable energy work. He is appreciated for his skill in representing clients that operate landfills or which own land which was previously used for this purpose. **Baerbel Schiller** operates out of both the Kansas City and St Louis offices, and has 15 years' previous experience of working in the EPA. Commentators note the value this adds to her practice, describing her as having a *"very interesting background – she is very smart."*

### Stinson Morrison Hecker LLP

**THE FIRM** This group assists clients with compliance, regulatory and transactional matters, including pursuing and defending Superfund actions and challenging environmental permits. It is particularly sought out for its expertise in Clean Air Act and Clean Water Act actions. Recent matters include representing an electrical utility company in connection with litigation filed by the EPA and the DOJ. These two organizations claimed the utility company violated Clean Air Act requirements at four coal-fired power plants in Missouri. Other clients include the City of Hastings, Kansas University and the National Beef Packing Company.

**KEY INDIVIDUALS** **David Tripp** heads the department, and is appreciated by sources for his past experience working at the EPA: *"He's very thoughtful and his past experience is truly valuable."* He was lead attorney representing Harcos Chemicals in a federal and state agency investigation which alleged improper storage and disposal of hazardous waste at company facilities. **Sarah Toevs Sullivan** also previously worked at the EPA. Her skills were recently called upon by a gas and electricity utility which owns former manufactured gas plant sites where there were releases of hazardous substances, and which is taking part in the state voluntary cleanup program. She is assisting the client with its remediation activities after successfully renegotiating the structure of a previous remediation agreement with another company. Clients say **Parthenia Evans** *"has an encyclopedic understanding of water law which is unique in our state. She is terrific."* She assisted a municipal coal-fired electricity utility with three power plants with Clean Air Act issues, including challenging and commenting on state and federal Clean Air Act rulemakings in several areas, in particular with regard to ozone maintenance areas. **Stacy Stotts** led a team acting for The Doe Run Resources Company with regard to allegations of violations of five federal environmental laws across ten of its facilities in Missouri. Clients say that *"she has a good relationship with the EPA, and she's a very good person to work with."*

### Thompson Coburn LLP

**THE FIRM** This firm has a strong track record on complex environmental litigation, offering extensive coverage on matters including criminal and enforcement defense and cost recovery actions. It also advises on noncontentious environmental issues which arise in corporate transactions, and provides a non-legal team of experts which assist clients on expert retention, corporate environment, health and safety policies and compliance audits. Key clients include Agrium, Baldor Electric Company, BNSF Railway Company and Bunge North America.

**Sources say:** *"They are a true-quality firm, and they are very cost effective." "Their strengths are their personnel and knowledge of dealing with the EPA and its regulations."*

**THE FIRM** Cochair of the department **Peter Strassner**, is appreciated by clients and peers alike for his advocacy skills and good sense of strategy. *"He rendered exceptional and excellent legal service, was extremely knowledgeable and cost-effective,"* one interviewee pointed out. Another revealed: *"I'd single him out – he's top tier, very deliberate and thorough, and pleasant to work with."* He took the lead in defending ExxonMobil Coal USA in a Mining Act citizens' suit, which sought to injunct ExxonMobil to excavate a 400 acre coal refuse disposal area at a closed mine. **Edward Cohen** also cochairs the practice, and is a talented litigator. In recent months he has advised on a multiparty case involving a large organic chemical plume which is alleged to have affected a water supply. He acts for clients across the country, and is praised as *"a very capable individual – a great attorney."* **Joseph Kellmeyer** is a veteran of civil and criminal litigation under a range of federal and state environmental laws. Sources describe him as *"a strong lawyer and litigator, who is quick witted and good on his feet,"* as well as being *"extremely responsive to your needs. He gets back to you very promptly and produces significant positive results."* His expertise extends to product liability and personal injury matters.

### Other Notable Practitioners

**Richard Ahrens** (see p.1635) of Lewis, Rice & Fingersh LC is widely considered to be the firm's environmental expert and is particularly prized for his trial abilities. One commentator said that *"he performs at a high level in litigation, and he has a full skill set."* **Frank Hackmann** (see p.1637) of Dentons has a broad environmental practice. One recent highlight includes acting for Lafarge North America in a resolution to an enforcement action after industrial waste overflowed into a tributary of a river from Lafarge's mine reclamation site. Some of his other key clients include Dyno Nobel, HTR Group and THF Realty. **Stephen Jeffery** of Jeffery Law Group is recognized as a leading individual in this practice area. He represents clients across the USA on a broad range of environmental matters. Peers have high regard for **William Session** of The Session Law Firm. He advises clients on the full portfolio of environmental matters, and has notable experience representing clients in multidefendant Superfund matters.

# INTELLECTUAL PROPERTY

## Band 1

## Armstrong Teasdale LLP

**THE FIRM** This leading IP practice fields one of the strongest teams in the state, making it a go-to outfit for IP litigation and the filing, prosecuting and managing of patents. It continues to work with household names such as Cass Information Systems, and has also secured significant wins in the airline industry.
**Sources say:** *"I view them more as team members than outside counsel." "The billing structure is excellent, and they clearly have a philosophy of providing overall value to their clients."*

**KEY INDIVIDUALS** Highly regarded practitioner **Christopher Goff** is active on several of the team's most eye-catching multijurisdictional matters, including a worldwide patent prosecution for a leading consumer products company. He has a strong focus on chemical and biochemical patents work. **Patrick Rasche** leads the firm's IP practice and is praised for his strong patent litigation experience. In a recent highlight, he acted for securities technology client Morpho Detection on its celebrated patent win over Smiths Detection. Sources confirm that experienced name **John Beulick** is a *"very skilled patent prosecutor."* He worked with Patrick Rasche on the aforementioned patent case for Morpho Detection. Clients praise **Michael Munsell**'s technical expertise, and describe him as *"very easy to work with and always willing to help."* His recent patent work for semiconductor producer MEMC Electronic Materials is among several substantial matters that highlight his strengths in engineering and technology. **Richard Schuth** gains market respect for his significant chemical engineering experience combined with his personable, approachable style. Clients *"think highly of him,"* and find him *"attuned to technical areas."* Associate **Lucas Wenthe** has also impressed clients of late. He recently handled the IP aspects of a significant cross-border venture.

## Husch Blackwell LLP

**THE FIRM** This well-resourced team is equipped to handle the full range of IP work, including multimillion-dollar licensing and litigation matters. Clients are drawn from a diverse range of sectors, from outsourcing to engineering. Rawlings Sporting Goods and Saint Louis University have both instructed the team recently. The firm continues to be active on international enforcement work.
**Sources say:** *"A very good firm that does excellent work for us."*
**KEY INDIVIDUALS Alan Nemes** is *"the Yoda of that group; all-knowing,"* according to an enthusiastic client, who also praises the *"horsepower"* he is able to bring to IP matters. He has successfully enforced several trademarks involving bad faith claims against respondents in non-US jurisdictions. **Sam Digirolamo** attracts market praise for his *"deep experience and knowledge,"* allied with his *"strong client counseling skills."* He recently advised Sunbeam Products on the worldwide enforcement of its trademarks.

## Senniger Powers LLP
### See profile on p.1643
**THE FIRM** This St. Louis IP boutique has a formidable reputation in Missouri. It offers clients deep expertise in a wide variety of industries, and is especially active in the areas of biotech, chemical, medical device and technology. Key clients include Covidien, Monsanto, Microsoft and Diebold. Lately, the firm has also experienced an uptick in work defending clients from patent troll actions.

**Sources say:** *"They are a very strong law firm in St. Louis, head and shoulders above the rest." "They have served us exceptionally well with good advice. Their primary goal is to provide overall satisfaction to the client, and they accomplish this."*
**KEY INDIVIDUALS** Head of the firm's litigation department **Robert Evans** (see p.1636) is noted for his experience as a trial lawyer, and is praised for his deft strategic acumen. He has litigated matters all over the USA, and is particularly knowledgeable on IT, e-commerce and electronics matters. Sources say: *"He is outstanding in his efforts to win on behalf of his clients."* **Michael Godar** (see p.1637) commands the deep respect of his peers, and has a quarter of a century's experience in patent prosecution, licensing and enforcement. He specializes in mechanical technology, and also advises clients on trademark matters. A source said: *"Mike Godar is top of our list."* **Kurt James** (see p.1637) heads the firm's mechanical practice group and has over two decades of experience in IP law. He brings his training as a mechanical engineer to bear when prosecuting and enforcing patents on a range of devices. **Mark Vander Tuig** (see p.1638) is an up-and-coming attorney who scores well with clients, and is also attracting attention from peers. He is described as *"a very good strategist, who pays enormous attention to detail and doesn't leave any stone unturned."*

## Shook, Hardy & Bacon LLP
### See profile on p.1644
**THE FIRM** This Kansas City-based firm has an excellent reputation for litigation work, and its IP litigation practice is no exception. The firm has been especially active in defending clients against patent troll litigation. It recently represented DuPont with regard to litigation concerning 11 patents for automated seed sampling, known as 'chipping'. The group also draws praise for its work on patent preparation, risk analysis, trademark, and copyright and licensing matters. It advises big-name clients such as Microsoft, Coca-Cola and Nike.
**Sources say:** *"I have been impressed by Shook's combination of expertise, trial skill and business savvy."*
**KEY INDIVIDUALS** Department head **Trent Webb** is sought out for technology and engineering mandates. He is head of IP litigation for the firm and is deeply appreciated by clients for his litigation skills. A source said: *"He is excellent in his thought processes and litigation management."* **Mike Gross** is described as *"polished and professional,"* and is especially noted for his work on patent prosecution and engineering. Along with Webb he has filed many patent applications over the past year for Sprint Nextel and Nike.

## Band 2

### Bryan Cave LLP

**THE FIRM** This respected team benefits from the firm's strong national network. It is especially active on patent infringement cases, helping clients to obtain a raft of favorable judgments relating to encryption technology, tracking systems and electronic catalogs. It counts Walmart and Neiman Marcus among its enviable client roster.

**Sources say:** *"You want someone who is on your side, and you feel that with these guys."*

**KEY INDIVIDUALS** *"Outstanding lawyer and strategist"* **Edward Hejlek** is *"one of the best"* in the patent prosecution area according to peers, who also describe him as *"a seasoned attorney with a high skill level."* His admission to practice in both Missouri and California facilitates his life sciences and pharmaceutical focus, though his clients span many sectors. **Bennett Clark** has a strong track record in advising groups of defendants, such as successfully defending Disney, Buena Vista Home Entertainment and Key Pix

Productions against allegations of copyright infringement. **David Roodman** is a respected litigator who defends national clients in cases involving high-profile technology infringement allegations.

### Polsinelli PC
See profile on p.1641

**THE FIRM** Polsinelli's Kansas City office houses both its national science and technology group and a strong IP litigation group. The firm's strong science credentials mean it has acted for pharmaceutical, biotech, animal healthcare and life sciences clients. The firm handles patent prosecution, transactional and clearance work, and IP litigation.

**Sources say:** *"I thought they were excellent. They listen to their clients and what they want, and put together a litigation strategy looking to achieve these goals."*

**KEY INDIVIDUALS Keith Grady** is praised for being *"knowledgeable and expert in IP,"* as well as *"a skilled negotiator."* Another source notes that *"he is extremely valuable in getting our points and specific goals across."* He recently

acted for national stock exchange BATS when it was sued for patent infringement in the Eastern District of Texas, alongside other entities. **Patrick Woolley** is known for his biotech work, and is described as *"a very sharp and skilled attorney."* His clients include Sergeant's Pet Care Products. He covers a range of areas, including patent prosecution, trademarks and copyright.

### Thompson Coburn LLP

**THE FIRM** This St. Louis team covers the full range of IP protection work, and has a particular focus on biotechnology and pharmaceutical products. It counts Enterprise Rent-A-Car, Eveready, FURminator and Insituform Technologies among its recent clients.

**KEY INDIVIDUALS Thomas Polcyn** is appreciated for both his patent and trademark capabilities. He also brings an international focus to his work on licensing agreements and settlements related to worldwide IP rights. Sources say: *"He is excellent, sharp and easy to get along with. He knows trademarks very well."*

# LABOR & EMPLOYMENT

Commentary about individuals can be found under their firm's paragraph. If the firm has no paragraph (is not ranked) look at Other Notable Practitioners.

| Labor & Employment: Kansas City & Surrounds Leading Firms |
| --- |
| **Band 1** |
| Husch Blackwell LLP |
| Lathrop & Gage LLP |
| Littler Mendelson, PC * |
| Ogletree, Deakins, Nash, Smoak & Stewart, PC * |
| Seyferth Blumenthal & Harris, LLC |
| **Band 2** |
| Fisher & Phillips LLP * |
| Polsinelli PC * |
| Shook, Hardy & Bacon LLP * |
| Stinson Morrison Hecker LLP |
| **Band 3** |
| Constangy, Brooks & Smith, LLP |
| Spencer Fane Britt & Browne LLP |

*Indicates firm with profile.*
*Alphabetical order within each band. Band 1 is the highest.*

*The edit is in alphabetical order by firm name.*

### Armstrong Teasdale LLP

**THE FIRM** This St. Louis-based team has a strong bench of labor and employment specialists who are adept at defending clients against discrimination lawsuits and wrongful dismissal claims. It has impressed on a series of matters across Illinois, Kansas and Missouri, including winning a recent disability discrimination and retaliation lawsuit under the Missouri Human Rights Act. Additionally, the team is well versed in actions enforcing noncompete and nonsoliciting clauses, as well as confiden-

tiality agreements. Key clients include AmerenUE, Centene, the Metropolitan Sewer District and Mississippi Lime.

**Sources say:** *"Armstrong Teasdale is a strong presence in St. Louis."* *"They have a sound, broad-based practice and a number of strong practitioners."*

**KEY INDIVIDUALS Daniel O'Toole** chairs the firm's litigation department, and is widely respected for his skills both in and out of the courtroom. He has impressive experience in working with the EEOC, the Missouri Human Rights Commission, and the DOL. Sources say: *"He is a client-first lawyer. He always focuses on fighting hardest for his clients' interests instead of litigating for the sake of litigating."* Kansas City-based **John Vering** is praised for his wide knowledge of the employment field as well as his focused approach to his work. He spends an increasing amount of time on mediation, and is also praised for being *"an excellent arbitrator."* **Robert Kaiser** is noted for his success in court as well as for his *"incredible depth of knowledge."* Sources report that *"he is very good at showing you both sides of a conversation, listening, and working through all options."* He is based in St. Louis.

### Bryan Cave LLP

**THE FIRM** Bryan Cave has built up a fine reputation for labor and employment law and litigation. In a recent highlight, it acted for several companies against unfair labor practice charges. It is also noted for its ability to call in resources from other offices, thanks to its shared rapid response client advice team. Top clients include Browning NA, Deffenbaugh Industries, Dickinson Financial and

HCA Midwest Health System. It has specialists based in both St. Louis and Kansas City.

**KEY INDIVIDUALS Dennis Donnelly** is described as one of the deans of the firm's employment group, having amassed more than 45 years' experience in the field. He recently represented Scottrade Center in an arbitration relating to contractual and termination issues arising from a layoff. **Jerry Hunter** is considered to be a formidable opponent in union cases. As a former general counsel of the NLRB, he knows the system inside out. He recently defended Houston Refining against a number of unfair labor practice charges filed by the United Steelworkers International Union. **Charles Jellinek** is another heavy hitter in the St. Louis team. Clients praise his sector knowledge and responsiveness. He recently secured a summary judgment for a client in a major wrongful dismissal case. **Elaine Drodge Koch** runs the firm's global labor and employment team from its Kansas City office. Her strengths lie in assisting clients through employment trials, as well as counseling them on the full gamut of employment issues, from HR strategy to ongoing management. **Daniel O'Keefe** in St. Louis handles a mix of traditional labor counseling and employment litigation, and is especially active in the area of discrimination defense. Sources appreciate his practical approach, his integrity and his experience in this area.

### Constangy, Brooks & Smith, LLP

**THE FIRM** This compact Kansas City boutique has a strong track record in this area, with particular strength in traditional labor law. In a recent success, it defended Waffle House against a statewide class action wage and hour dis-

*The editorial is in alphabetical order by firm name.*

## Labor & Employment: Kansas City & Surrounds

### Leading Individuals

**Star individuals**

| | |
|---|---|
| Martucci William | *Shook, Hardy & Bacon LLP* |

**Band 1**

| | |
|---|---|
| Donnelly Paul | *Stinson Morrison Hecker LLP* |
| Drake Denise K | *Littler Mendelson, PC* * |
| Finucane Brian J | *Fisher & Phillips LLP* * |
| Kilroy W Terrence | *Polsinelli PC* |
| McNamara Rosalee M | *Lathrop & Gage LLP* |
| Phillips John R | *Husch Blackwell LLP* |
| Seyferth Paul D | *Seyferth Blumenthal & Harris, LLC* |

**Band 2**

| | |
|---|---|
| Blumenthal Michael L | *Seyferth Blumenthal & Harris, LLC* |
| Boatright Daniel | *Littler Mendelson, PC* * |
| Byergo Anthony B | *Ogletree, Deakins, Nash, Smoak & Stewart* * |
| Coffey J Randall | *Fisher & Phillips LLP* * |
| Davis Timothy A | *Constangy, Brooks & Smith, LLP* |
| DeVeney Jeannie M | *Littler Mendelson, PC* * |
| Harris Jr Charlie J | *Seyferth Blumenthal & Harris, LLC* |
| Janowitz Robert | *Constangy, Brooks & Smith, LLP* |
| Jones Kimberly | *Seyferth Blumenthal & Harris, LLC* |
| Koch Elaine Drodge | *Bryan Cave LLP* |
| Prophete Donald S | *Ogletree, Deakins, Nash, Smoak & Stewart* * |
| Rowe Jack D | *Lathrop & Gage LLP* |
| Vering III John A | *Armstrong Teasdale LLP* |
| Vogel David C | *Lathrop & Gage LLP* |
| Wing David | *Spencer Fane Britt & Browne LLP* |

**Band 3**

| | |
|---|---|
| Barnett Carol | *Polsinelli PC* |
| Connors Richard L | *Stinson Morrison Hecker LLP* |
| Coverdale Brent | *Seyferth Blumenthal & Harris, LLC* |
| Holland James | *Fisher & Phillips LLP* * |
| Hulla Patrick F | *Ogletree, Deakins, Nash, Smoak & Stewart* * |
| Konopka Patricia A | *Stinson Morrison Hecker LLP* |
| Matula Michael L. | *Ogletree, Deakins, Nash, Smoak & Stewart* * |
| Pautler Paul | *Husch Blackwell LLP* |
| Robbins Jr William S | *Polsinelli PC* |
| Welch Sara | *Stinson Morrison Hecker LLP* |
| Welker Mark D | *Husch Blackwell LLP* |
| Willman Sue K. | *Spencer Fane Britt & Browne LLP* |

**Up-and-coming individuals**

| | |
|---|---|
| Abramov Hope | *Thompson Coburn LLP* |
| Fowler Amy | *Husch Blackwell LLP* |
| McAtee Carrie A | *Shook, Hardy & Bacon LLP* |
| O'Dell Julie | *Seyferth Blumenthal & Harris, LLC* |
| Reisdorff Kerri S. | *Ogletree, Deakins, Nash, Smoak & Stewart* * |

* *Indicates firm / individual with profile.*

† *ONP = Other Notable Practitioner*

pute. Other key clients include Southwest Airlines, HCA, Hallmark, Ferrellgas and InkCycle.

**KEY INDIVIDUALS** The well-known **Robert Janowitz** has been at the forefront of labor law for several decades. He previously served as a regional attorney for the NLRB, and since turning to private practice has focused on litigating cases before the board. He is described as *"an excellent traditional labor practitioner."* **Timothy Davis** is head of the Kansas City office and a key adviser to businesses on

## Labor & Employmentt: St. Louis & Surrounds

### Leading Firms

**Band 1**

| |
|---|
| Armstrong Teasdale LLP |
| Bryan Cave LLP |
| Husch Blackwell LLP |

**Band 2**

| |
|---|
| Greensfelder, Hemker & Gale, P.C. |
| Ogletree, Deakins, Nash, Smoak & Stewart, PC * |
| Thompson Coburn LLP |

### Senior Statesmen

**Senior Statesmen: distinguished older practitioners**

| | |
|---|---|
| Donnelly Dennis C | *Bryan Cave LLP* |

### Leading Individuals

**Band 1**

| | |
|---|---|
| Godiner Clifford A | *Thompson Coburn LLP* |
| Hunter Jerry M | *Bryan Cave LLP* |
| O'Toole Daniel K | *Armstrong Teasdale LLP* |
| Tomaso Robert | *Husch Blackwell LLP* |

**Band 2**

| | |
|---|---|
| Collins Dennis G | *Greensfelder, Hemker & Gale, P.C.* |
| Hiles Bradley | *Husch Blackwell LLP* |
| Jellinek Charles B | *Bryan Cave LLP* |
| Lemley Gregg M | *Ogletree, Deakins, Nash, Smoak & Stewart* * |
| McCarthy Thomas | *McMahon Berger (ONP)* † |
| McLaughlin Kevin T | *Greensfelder, Hemker & Gale, P.C.* |
| O'Keefe Daniel M | *Bryan Cave LLP* |
| Wellford Jr Harry W | *Littler Mendelson, PC* * |

**Band 3**

| | |
|---|---|
| Harrison Rodney A | *Ogletree, Deakins, Nash, Smoak & Stewart* * |
| Kaiser Robert | *Armstrong Teasdale LLP* |

### Up-and-coming individuals

| | |
|---|---|
| Needham Amie E | *Littler Mendelson, PC* * |
| Yates Kimberly | *Littler Mendelson, PC* * |

employee and labor relations work. He has a special focus on policy development and improving systems that guide the employer-employee relationship.

## Fisher & Phillips LLP
### See profile on p.1107

**THE FIRM** The Kansas City branch of this national employment firm attracts a loyal client base. It handles a range of employment litigation, including EEOC and OSHA claims and class actions, and it is also instructed on traditional labor work. In a recent highlight, it successfully defended DST Systems against a substantial age discrimination and retaliation lawsuit.

**Sources say:** *"Their strengths are their knowledge, timeliness and responsiveness."*

**KEY INDIVIDUALS Brian Finucane** (see p.1636) has a justifiably high profile in the market. *"I cannot say enough good things about the advice we have received,"* enthuses one client, another noting that *"he is one of the best employment litigators in Missouri. He has a great presence with the jury."* He led on the aforementioned DST Systems matter.

**Randall Coffey** (see p.1635) recently attained a summary judgment for Kansas City Power & Light before the Missouri State Court on a disability discrimination claim. He is praised for his *"very practical"* approach, as well as for his *"experience both in the courtroom and on complex matters."* **James Holland** (see p.1637) is considered by sources to be *"an excellent trial lawyer."* Clients also appreciate his personable approach and strong negotiation skills. He led on two sensitive employment litigations within the past year.

## Greensfelder, Hemker & Gale, P.C.

**THE FIRM** This team handles a range of employment litigation, and is also highly experienced in traditional labor relations work. Highlights include defending companies in cases relating to the WARN Act and negotiating with unions on collective bargaining agreements. SSM Health Care, Schnuck Markets and Edward Jones are all clients of the firm.

**Sources say:** *"They have a very strong team in St. Louis. They've really done a terrific job, and are an extraordinarily thorough and very experienced group of lawyers."*

**KEY INDIVIDUALS** Senior partner **Dennis Collins** is well known in the St. Louis area, and is particularly strong on traditional labor mandates. *"He is a very experienced lawyer – smart, capable and very thorough,"* reports one source. Group leader **Kevin McLaughlin** is skilled in employment litigation matters, and regularly represents clients in discrimination, noncompete and confidentiality litigation in both federal and state courts. He also advises on labor and union matters.

## Husch Blackwell LLP

**THE FIRM** This full-service firm scores highly thanks to its deep bench and wide-ranging expertise. The group has a forte in defending discrimination litigation and wage and hour class actions, while it also places a strong emphasis on preventive advice. It has an equally strong presence in both Kansas City and St. Louis, as well as notable representation in other centers across Missouri. A sample of its impressive client base includes Commerce Bancshares, Hallmark Cards, Forest Pharmaceuticals and CNA Insurance.

**Sources say:** *"They have strong knowledge of employment law, and strong overall litigation experience."*

**KEY INDIVIDUALS** Litigator **John Phillips** is renowned for his excellence in the employment litigation field. *"He is a superb lawyer, maybe the best in town,"* says one source. He also acts as an arbitrator and mediator in employment disputes. **Robert Tomaso** is a highly respected practitioner who is noted for his smooth handling of employment discrimination cases. Interviewees report: *"He's very congenial and down-to-earth, but at the same time very professional."* **Bradley Hiles** continues to attract significant mandates from clients across the country. His wide-ranging practice covers matters such as labor law, union avoidance strategies, employment discrimination and OSHA defense matters. **Mark Welker** is an expert on employment tax and employee benefits, and chairs the firm's specialist department for these matters. He is described as *"a great guy who is extremely knowledgeable."* **Amy Fowler** continues to

*The editorial is in alphabetical order by firm name.*

impress in the labor and employment market and has represented clients across the country on a range of issues, including harassment, disability and other discrimination cases. Sources say: *"She is highly thought of as a smart, hard worker."* **Paul Pautler** has been newly ranked this year after receiving high praise from both clients and peers. He advises on both traditional labor and employment litigation across the USA and also in the UK, and has recently secured a number of favorable judgments on wage and hour and discrimination cases. One satisfied client describes Pautler as *"a very good counsel, who is very responsive and always provides good, solid advice."*

### Lathrop & Gage LLP

**THE FIRM** Kansas City institution Lathrop & Gage is deeply embedded in the Missouri business environment, boasting a large stable of long-standing clients which it represents both locally and across the country. It has had successes in the courts over the past year in significant wage and hour, discrimination, retaliation and whistleblower cases.

**Sources say:** *"I've been very impressed with them. They are a bit more of a national firm, and so have multiple deals going on, but they are staffed so that they can deal with things quickly."*

**KEY INDIVIDUALS Jack Rowe** is described as a *"trusted counsel"* who *"knows us inside-out and has an encyclopedic memory of things."* His broad practice encompasses acting for employers on discrimination issues, as well as handling traditional labor work. **Rosalee McNamara** is commended for her adept handling of defense work for corporate clients, ranging from discrimination cases to class actions. Clients say: *"She knows our business and she's very sharp and hard-working. We have a lot of confidence in her."* **David Vogel** is appreciated for his skills in both employment litigation and day-to-day counseling. Sources say: *"He is very pragmatic. He has a rare ability to put his businessperson's hat on to present the options and risks clearly."*

### Littler Mendelson, PC
See profile on p.688

**THE FIRM** Global employment boutique Littler Mendelson has been making waves in Missouri since setting up shop in 2006, not least because of its judicious acquisition of top legal talent from across the local area. While remaining relatively compact, this growing group continues to impress on a wide range of matters in both employment law and labor relations, and has been praised particularly on recent wage and hour and discrimination cases.

**Sources say:** *"They are able to communicate complicated legal scenarios and possible outcomes in lay terms."*

**KEY INDIVIDUALS Denise Drake** (see p.1636) is known for her *"fantastic client relations and great litigation skills." "She is very easy to work with, very responsive, and clearly an experienced litigator,"* note sources. She recently acted for LaVie Management Services and Ashton Court, a nursing home, regarding a proposed nationwide wage and hour collective action. **Harry Wellford** (see p.1639) heads up the department from the firm's St. Louis office, and is noted

for being *"professional, effective and smart."* Last year he represented CLJM in the St. Louis County Circuit Court, where he successfully enforced a nonsolicitation clause against a former employee. **Daniel Boatright** (see p.1635) is the managing partner of the Kansas City office, and is noted for being *"very sharp. He really knows his stuff and is very responsive."* Recent matters include defending Securitas Security Services USA against a class action claim by employees in Iowa and Wisconsin. **Jeannie DeVeney** (see p.1636) is appreciated for her down-to-earth approach and ability to inspire trust and confidence during investigations. This is nevertheless partnered with a strong performance on disputes. She is described as *"a tough negotiator and an aggressive litigator."* **Amie Needham** (see p.1638) joined the St. Louis office in July 2012, moving over from rival firm Thompson Coburn. She is known for her skills advising on traditional labor law alongside employment counseling and litigation. She is described as being *"good at the negotiating table"* as well as *"excellent with wage and hour issues."* **Kimberly Yates** (see p.1639) is also based in the St. Louis office, and focuses on labor and employment litigation in federal and state court. She assisted Harry Wellford on the CLJM matter above.

### Ogletree, Deakins, Nash, Smoak & Stewart, PC
See profile on p.1110

**THE FIRM** This well-known employment specialist has a strong presence in Missouri, combined with a formidable national footprint. In the last year it has been especially busy on wage and hour cases and class actions, although the team has capabilities across the full spectrum of work. In St. Louis, Ogletree has also developed client training into a separate business, Ogletree Deakins Learning Solutions, which provides interactive training programs for clients. Major clients include American Water Works Service, Arrow Electronics, Barnes & Noble and Kinder Morgan Energy Partners.

**Sources say:** *"It is an exceptional law firm – effective, with a highly professional, personal level of service."*

**KEY INDIVIDUALS Gregg Lemley** (see p.1637) recently represented a large university in a major sex discrimination and retaliation case. He is appreciated for his intelligence as well as his rational and logical approach. **Anthony Byergo** (see p.1635) is considered to be a quick thinker with good client responsiveness. He recently defended Boehringer Ingelheim Vetmedica against a discrimination claim. Sources say: *"He has been very good in contentious labor matters and at giving us his perspective from his work with other clients."* **Patrick Hulla** (see p.1637) runs the firm's Kansas City group, and is known for his strong litigation skills. Commentators say: *"If you have a significant fight he is good to have in your corner."* **Rodney Harrison** (see p.1637) is noted for being *"very fast, very thorough and very impressive. He gets the result that you need."* In one highlight, he successfully defended GoJet Airlines against a class action by a flight attendant who claimed that her dismissal – which was as a result of her union activities – violated the Railway Labor Act. Kansas City-based **Donald Prophete** (see p.1638) handles class actions, employment

litigation and traditional labor work. Interviewees say: *"He is an absolutely extraordinary relationship partner. He makes us feel we are his only clients."* **Michael Matula** (see p.1637) handles both employment litigation and counseling work. He impresses peers, who describe him as *"one of the hardest-working lawyers in town, who is well liked by defense lawyers and the plaintiff Bar."* **Kerri Reisdorff** (see p.1638) is making a name for herself in protecting companies against labor and employment claims. She is described as *"highly technical, with an ability to communicate our position very well. She is able to be very diplomatic, but can also be very aggressive when necessary."*

### Polsinelli PC
See profile on p.1641

**THE FIRM** This firm represents a wide range of clients, from small privately owned firms to Fortune 500 companies. It advises on the full range of employment matters both in and out of the courtroom, and also places a strong emphasis on preventive advice. Recent highlights include a noncompetition and violation of trade secrets litigation, as well as traditional labor negotiations. The group has a strong geographic spread in the state, with lawyers based in Kansas City, St. Louis, Springfield and St. Joseph.

**Sources say:** *"They have pertinent experience, candor and professionalism."*

**KEY INDIVIDUALS Terrence Kilroy** is renowned for his expertise in the traditional labor sphere. Recent successes include acting as lead negotiator for Budweiser distributor County Beverage in contract negotiations and strike settlement negotiations. Sources say that he is *"extremely knowledgeable about all aspects of traditional labor law,"* as well as *"a very accomplished guy with a good reputation as a litigator."* **William Robbins** is likewise strong on traditional labor matters and employment disputes. He recently successfully negotiated with the Teamsters Union on behalf of client North Kansas City Beverage on new contracts, meeting his client's financial objectives. He is described as *"an absolute professional."* **Carol Barnett** is prized for her deep knowledge of labor law, and is also highly experienced on discrimination, harassment and sexual misconduct employment issues. Sources say: *"Carol is very strong on the labor side and we have confidence in her ability to handle any issues that might confront us."*

### Seyferth Blumenthal & Harris, LLC

**THE FIRM** This Kansas City employment litigation boutique stands out for its high-quality bench of specialists. The firm acts on employment litigation across the country, and its clients include some of the biggest multinational companies. It also defends government officials against discrimination claims.

**Sources say:** *"It's a strong firm." "There are some very good lawyers there. They've done a nice job of working with their clients."*

**KEY INDIVIDUALS** Former prosecutor **Paul Seyferth** is admired for his skills in courtrooms across America, and is described as *"an experienced trial lawyer, and very practical."* He is especially noted for his work on noncompetition and nonsolicitation disputes, trade secrets issues and

*The editorial is in alphabetical order by firm name.*

employment discrimination claims. **Michael Blumenthal** has a broad practice encompassing both traditional labor law and employment law. One client says: "*He achieved outstanding results for us – he is always very strategic. He doesn't mind being aggressive, but he is really polite and civil too.*" **Charlie Harris** is a highly regarded partner in the Kansas City market. He primarily advises on race, sex and age discrimination, as well as sexual harassment matters in the workplace. **Kimberly Jones** is much praised for her trial work, having a string of successful employment litigation matters under her belt. She is also popular with clients for her day-to-day counseling and training work. The "*very smart*" **Brent Coverdale** also displays strong trial skills, and is particularly active on EEOC discrimination cases. He is "*fantastic – a very smart guy,*" sources report. **Julie O'Dell** handles employment litigation in the areas of discrimination allegations, sexual harassment, retaliation and wrongful discharge. One source says: "*She's a very good litigator – practical and tenacious, with a nice manner.*" Others add that "*her instincts are very good. She's a savvy litigator and a wonderful person, too.*"

## Shook, Hardy & Bacon LLP
See profile on p.1644

**THE FIRM** Litigation heavy hitter Shook, Hardy & Bacon is noted for its effective work on class actions, wage and hour disputes, and discrimination cases. Recent matters include acting as lead counsel for Foot Locker in connection with a New York action brought by assistant managers, filed under both state and federal law, successfully reducing a statewide class action by 1,000 employees to a group action by only 25. Other key clients include Cerner, Lowe's Home Improvement, Layne Christensen and NPC International.

**KEY INDIVIDUALS** Star player **William Martucci** operates in a league of his own when it comes to employment law. He is singled out for his deep knowledge, together with his "*tremendous people skills*" and "*very good trial presence.*" He recently acted for Philip Morris in an age discrimination and retaliation case. **Carrie McAtee** is noted for her experience working with government agencies as well as

her success in mediation. She was recently part of the team that helped PlattForm Advertising to resolve a class action by call center employees in the District Court of Kansas. She is described as "*excellent – very efficient, good to work with, and her knowledge of Missouri law is superb.*"

## Spencer Fane Britt & Browne LLP

**THE FIRM** Employment and labor law are both traditional fortes of Spencer Fane Britt & Browne, which draws upon the expertise of an experienced bench of partners. The group represents local and national employers on a range of matters, from human resources advisory to employment litigation.

**Sources say:** "*They have a good depth of attorneys, and are organized and resourceful.*"

**KEY INDIVIDUALS** Highly regarded partner **David Wing** is sought out for his advice on union activity, and also advises on employment disputes, including discrimination claims. He has a particular focus on clients in the medical, construction, financial services and manufacturing sectors. Clients turn to **Sue Willman** for a variety of employment mandates, and she is especially skilled on disability-related matters and the FMLA.

## Stinson Morrison Hecker LLP

**THE FIRM** This Kansas City-based team is strong on both employment litigation and counseling. It has seen its litigation work increase in the area of wage and hour claims, in particular. The firm represents a large number of Chubb Group insureds on a variety of matters, including discrimination and workplace health and safety issues.

**Sources say:** "*They have a corporate practice that lends itself to a strong employment practice.*"

**KEY INDIVIDUALS Paul Donnelly** is highly commended by market sources, who say: "*He is terrific – a very capable guy.*" He leads the firm's work for a variety of Chubb insureds across matters ranging from charges of discrimination to single and multiplaintiff lawsuits. **Patricia Konopka** is an accomplished litigator, who is described as "*a strong attorney with an excellent presence.*" She defended Lincare against multiple lawsuits which alleged discrimi-

nation by the employer. Recently, **Sara Welch** led a team defending a large employer in a nationwide collective action under the FLSA. She also obtained summary judgment in a race discrimination case where the employee alleged discrimination was the reason for her lack of promotion in her job. Sources "*think very highly of her skills in litigation.*" Commentators note that **Richard Connors** stands out as "*knowledgeable across a breadth of issues.*" In the last year, he has advised a number of restaurant chains in relation to training on nationwide immigration I-9 form and E-Verify.

## Thompson Coburn LLP

**THE FIRM** Thompson Coburn is sought out for employment litigation and traditional labor relations by clients across the USA. Recent matters include acting for Bunzl Distribution in the successful defense of a $2.1 million age discrimination case filed by a former employee. The firm has bolstered its offering with the recruitment of experienced partner Hope Abramov.

**KEY INDIVIDUALS** Leading practitioner **Clifford Godiner** has an excellent reputation among clients and peers alike, advising on a range of labor and employment litigation matters. He is described by sources as "*an outstanding attorney*" who is "*brilliant, creative, and has a desire to win for his clients.*" **Hope Abramov** joined the team in July 2012. She acts for employers on labor issues and employment law compliance, including discrimination, wage and hour issues, benefits, health and safety, and workers' compensation. She is described as "*wonderful, smart, very strategic, responsive, and a hard worker.*"

## Other Notable Practitioners

**Thomas McCarthy** of McMahon Berger is a well-respected attorney with deep experience on labor matters. He has been particularly busy lately acting for clients on discrimination cases, including obtaining summary judgment in a case alleging discrimination under the Missouri Human Rights Act. He is described as "*an excellent attorney with good traditional labor skills.*"

# LITIGATION

White-Collar Crime & Government Investigations p.1629

Commentary about individuals can be found under their firm's paragraph. If the firm has no paragraph (is not ranked) look at Other Notable Practitioners.

| Litigation: General Commercial: Kansas City & Surrounds | | |
|---|---|---|
| **Leading Firms** | | |
| **Band 1** | | |
| Polsinelli PC * | | |
| Rouse Hendricks German May PC * | | |
| Shook, Hardy & Bacon LLP * | | |
| **Band 2** | | |
| Berkowitz Oliver Williams Shaw & Eisenbrandt LLP | | |
| Bryan Cave LLP | | |
| Husch Blackwell LLP | | |
| Lathrop & Gage LLP | | |
| Stinson Morrison Hecker LLP | | |
| Wyrsch Hobbs & Mirakian PC * | | |
| **Band 3** | | |
| Baker Sterchi Cowden & Rice LLC | | |
| Dentons * | | |

| Litigation: General Commercial: Kansas City & Surrounds | | |
|---|---|---|
| **Senior Statesmen** | | |
| Senior Statesmen: distinguished older practitioners | | |
| Balloun J Eugene | Shook, Hardy & Bacon LLP | |
| Wolf Jerome | Dentons * | |
| **Leading Individuals** | | |
| **Star individuals** | | |
| Ward R Lawrence | Polsinelli PC | |
| **Band 1** | | |
| Adams Robert | Shook, Hardy & Bacon LLP | |
| Brown Spencer J. | Deacy & Deacy LLP (ONP)[†] | |
| Dalgleish Douglas | Lathrop & Gage LLP | |
| German Charles | Rouse Hendricks German May PC | |
| Griffin James | Husch Blackwell LLP | |
| Kaplan Harvey | Shook, Hardy & Bacon LLP | |
| O'Dear Craig S | Bryan Cave LLP | |
| Rebein Joseph | Shook, Hardy & Bacon LLP | |
| Sampson William | Shook, Hardy & Bacon LLP | |
| **Band 2** | | |
| Aisenbrey John C | Stinson Morrison Hecker LLP | |
| Belzer Irvin V | Bryan Cave LLP | |
| Brandt William Perry | Bryan Cave LLP | |
| Cowden John | Baker Sterchi Cowden & Rice LLC * | |
| Hendricks Randall | Rouse Hendricks German May PC | |
| Jones Jr Russell S | Polsinelli PC | |
| Kokoruda Thomas G | Polsinelli PC | |
| May Kirk | Rouse Hendricks German May PC | |
| Oliver David | Berkowitz Oliver Williams Shaw | |
| Thompson Robert M. | Bryan Cave LLP | |
| Voigts Gene | Shook, Hardy & Bacon LLP | |
| Welsh W Russell | Polsinelli PC | |
| Woods Curtis E | Dentons * | |
| **Band 3** | | |
| Beil William D | Rouse Hendricks German May PC | |
| Boulware R Dan | Polsinelli PC | |
| Dean Cathy J | Polsinelli PC | |
| Kilroy Jr John M | Polsinelli PC | |
| Ruskamp Todd W | Shook, Hardy & Bacon LLP | |
| Schult Thomas P | Berkowitz Oliver Williams Shaw | |
| Seigfreid Jr James T | Baker Sterchi Cowden & Rice LLC * | |
| Tucker Laurence | Armstrong Teasdale LLP | |
| Verschelden Matthew J | Stinson Morrison Hecker LLP | |
| Williams Kurt | Berkowitz Oliver Williams Shaw | |

* Indicates individual with profile.

[†] ONP = Other Notable Practitioner

The edit is in alphabetical order by firm name.

## Armstrong Teasdale LLP

**THE FIRM** This expanding St. Louis group continues to gain a stronger hold on the litigation market as it impresses both clients and peers with its successes in court. The group covers the whole range of litigation matters for companies, but is particularly strong on employment, medical malpractice and white-collar crime mandates. Clients include Ascension Health, BMO Harris Bank, St. Luke's Hospital and UPS.

**Sources say:** "Their strength is in having extremely qualified attorneys that understand the law, are easy to talk with, and can advise on all aspects of the case in a moment's notice." "They're excellent. Very responsive, very knowledgeable – really great experts."

**KEY INDIVIDUALS James Virtel** has "a good reputation," according to commentators, who draw attention to his expertise in the area of commercial and class action litigation. He recently obtained a mandatory injunction in a breach of contract action for a key client. **Clark Cole** is an expert trial attorney who focuses on insurance and commercial litigation. He recently achieved a favorable beforetrial settlement of a common law whistle-blower case in St. Clair County, Illinois. Peers say: "He is a darn good lawyer. I wouldn't hesitate to send work his way." **William Corrigan** is particularly strong on employment and contractual disputes involving issues such as noncompete agreements, trade secrets and breach of fiduciary duty. In a recent breach of noncompete clause matter, he successfully secured a permanent injunction on a former employee on behalf of Midwest Employers Casualty Group and Midwest Employers Casualty Company. Clients are impressed with his subject knowledge, saying of him that

"he is very straightforward and gets the job done well." **Laurence Tucker** "has as fine a reputation as anyone in the state," according to one source, and is especially prized for his work on civil lawsuits. He is the firm's managing partner for the Kansas City and Overland Park offices. Former

US Attorney for the Eastern District of Missouri **James Martin** is highly respected for his white-collar crime expertise, and is described as "thorough, knowledgeable, personable and responsive." His practice also encompasses corporate governance and business litigation. White-collar crime expert **Jeffrey Demerath** has a fine reputation, and is appreciated for his ability to handle the most difficult of cases. Interviewees say: "He's very personable with his clients, communicates well, and they clearly trust him a tremendous amount." Those who know senior partner **Paul Kovacs** call him both wonderful and well regarded. He has over 40 years of courtroom experience, and continues to litigate complex cases.

## Baker Sterchi Cowden & Rice LLC

**THE FIRM** This relatively compact firm is headquartered in Kansas City and noted for its strength acting on tortious matters, including product liability cases which involve domestic and cross-border elements. In addition to Kansas City, Baker Sterchi has offices in St. Louis and Overland Park, Kansas.

**KEY INDIVIDUALS John Cowden** (see p.1636) is acknowledged by sources as "a well-respected attorney in Kansas City who also has an extensive litigation practice." He handles a wide range of cases, including product liability and aviation defense. He has particular expertise in personal injury defense. **James Seigfried** (see p.1638) is known for his work defending complex product liability and toxic tort cases, and is described as "a go-to guy on multidistrict complex litigation." His clients are typically found in the automotive, agricultural, power tool and marine product manufacturing industries.

## Berkowitz Oliver Williams Shaw & Eisenbrandt LLP

**THE FIRM** This litigation boutique has carved a niche for itself in the Kansas City market, providing tailored representation for clients at trials, appeals, arbitrations, and regulatory and administrative proceedings. The group primarily acts for clients in the areas of professional liability, class action defense, tort and general businesses litigation, and features several experienced experts.

**Sources say:** "They are very savvy and very good."

**KEY INDIVIDUALS** Founding member **James Eisenbrandt** is an acknowledged white-collar crime defense attorney. He has experience in public corruption, antitrust and fraud cases, as well as whistle-blower cases across a range of industries. **Jeffrey Morris** advises clients both on commercial litigation and white-collar crime mandates. He has developed particular expertise in a range of cases, including healthcare and mortgage fraud disputes. He is regularly called upon to advise companies on investigations regarding possible white-collar wrongdoing. **David Oliver** is well known in courtrooms across the

*The editorial is in alphabetical order by firm name.*

## Litigation: General Commercial: St. Louis & Surrounds

### Leading Firms

**Band 1**
Armstrong Teasdale LLP
Bryan Cave LLP
Thompson Coburn LLP

**Band 2**
Husch Blackwell LLP
Lewis, Rice & Fingersh LC *

**Band 3**
Greensfelder, Hemker & Gale, P.C.
Kohn, Shands, Elbert, Gianoulakis & Giljum, LLP

**Band 4**
Dowd Bennett LLP
Stinson Morrison Hecker LLP
Williams, Venker, Sanders LLC

### Senior Statesmen

**Senior Statesmen: distinguished older practitioners**

| | |
|---|---|
| Kohn Alan C | Kohn, Shands, Elbert, Gianoulakis & Giljum |
| Kovacs Paul | Armstrong Teasdale LLP |

### Leading Individuals

**Band 1**

| | |
|---|---|
| Ball Dan H | Bryan Cave LLP |
| Gianoulakis John | Kohn, Shands, Elbert, Gianoulakis & Giljum |
| Short Barry A | Lewis, Rice & Fingersh LC * |
| Virtel James J | Armstrong Teasdale LLP |
| Walsh Thomas C | Bryan Cave LLP |

**Band 2**

| | |
|---|---|
| Bennett Jim | Dowd Bennett LLP * |
| Carney Thomas M | Husch Blackwell LLP |
| Cole Clark | Armstrong Teasdale LLP |
| Everson David | Stinson Morrison Hecker LLP |
| Harris David | Greensfelder, Hemker & Gale, P.C. |
| Higgins Stephen | Thompson Coburn LLP |
| Rothschild Andrew | Lewis, Rice & Fingersh LC * |
| Rovak Stephen H | Dentons * |
| Wells W David | Thompson Coburn LLP |

**Band 3**

| | |
|---|---|
| Corrigan Jr William M | Armstrong Teasdale LLP |
| Ebert Jr Robert T | Bryan Cave LLP |
| Hohn Christopher | Thompson Coburn LLP |
| Massey Raymond L | Thompson Coburn LLP |
| Minton Michael B. | Thompson Coburn LLP |
| Moticka John W. | Stinson Morrison Hecker LLP |
| Strauss Bettina | Bryan Cave LLP |
| Venker Paul | Williams, Venker, Sanders LLC |
| Wuller Roman P | Thompson Coburn LLP |

*\* Indicates firm / individual with profile.*

*Alphabetical order within each band. Band 1 is the highest.*

## Litigation: White-Collar Crime & Government Investigations

### Leading Individuals

**Band 1**

| | |
|---|---|
| Aisenbrey John C | Stinson Morrison Hecker LLP |
| Demerath Jeffrey T | Armstrong Teasdale LLP |
| Eisenbrandt James | Berkowitz Oliver Williams Shaw |
| German Charles | Rouse Hendricks German May PC |
| Hobbs James R | Wyrsch Hobbs & Mirakian PC |
| Martin James G | Armstrong Teasdale LLP |
| Morris Jeffrey D. | Berkowitz Oliver Williams Shaw |
| Short Barry A | Lewis, Rice & Fingersh LC * |
| Wyrsch James R | Wyrsch Hobbs & Mirakian PC |

**Band 2**

| | |
|---|---|
| Ankney Gordon L | Thompson Coburn LLP |
| Bradshaw II Jean Paul | Lathrop & Gage LLP |
| Dowd Jr Edward | Dowd Bennett LLP * |
| Higgins Stephen | Thompson Coburn LLP |
| Hill Stephen L | Husch Blackwell LLP |
| Woods Curtis E | Dentons * |

**Band 3**

| | |
|---|---|
| Bennett Jim | Dowd Bennett LLP * |
| McInerney Patrick | Husch Blackwell LLP |
| O'Malley Kevin | Greensfelder, Hemker & Gale, P.C. |

Midwest, and has particular skills in class action work in state and federal multidistrict litigation. He also handles securities and product liability litigation. Observers say: *"He does an excellent job on business litigation cases. He is very well respected in the legal community."* **Thomas Schult** has deep experience acting on product liability litigation in

courts across the USA, and represents a number of companies as their regional defense counsel on such matters. **Kurt Williams** has notable expertise working on commercial litigation and on large class actions.

### Bryan Cave LLP

**THE FIRM** With a large and strong bench in both St. Louis and Kansas City, Bryan Cave is active and respected in the market for its skilled handling of complex litigation. It attracts clients from both inside and outside of Missouri. Clients are particularly impressed by its work on product liability matters, for which it has built up a strong national reputation. The group is also known for producing excellent class action work. Clients include Arvest Bank, BMO Harris Bank, Merck and Wells Fargo Advisors.

**KEY INDIVIDUALS Dan Ball** is noted for his skills in the courtroom, particularly on product liability matters, where he defends his clients' interests passionately. Clients are especially impressed with his superb trial skills. Senior St. Louis partner **Thomas Walsh** enjoys a fine reputation in the market, and covers a range of cases, including employment, antitrust, commercial disputes and constitutional matters. He is especially strong in appeal cases, recently representing Fluor in appealing a large jury verdict. **Robert Ebert** works on both general business litigation and product liability matters. He recently successfully represented a client in a large False Claims Act case. He has a deep understanding of clients' commercial needs as he also serves as a board member of a technology business. **Bettina Strauss** of St. Louis heads up the firm's product liability group and has a national practice. She has particular experience acting for clients in the pharmaceutical, medical device and automotive sectors, and in the past year has represented Ford and Merck. Kansas City-based **Craig O'Dear** is a

highly respected attorney in the sector. He has a particularly sterling reputation on class action matters. He acted as lead trial counsel for the Residential Funding Corporation in an appeal over a judgment which awarded the other party $100 million in damages. The matter was settled for $14.5 million before the trial for the appeal. Kansas City partner **Robert Thompson** is noted for his knowledge, thorough preparation before a trial, and good relationships with his clients. Clients describe him as a personable advocate who is able to understand all parties' perspectives in a matter. **Irvin Belzer** runs the department from the firm's Kansas City office, and is particularly strong on financial services disputes, including mortgage lending and securitized lending, as well as contract disputes in the healthcare, banking, telecom and real estate sectors. **Perry Brandt**, also in Kansas City, is known for his work on class, shareholder derivative and multiplaintiff litigation. He is currently representing a broker-dealer in a case involving claims of bid-rigging in the municipal derivatives markets.

### Dentons

**See profile on p.449**

**THE FIRM** This group of dedicated commercial litigation attorneys is well versed in defending clients against class actions and bet-the-company cases, and has particular expertise acting for the insurance and financial services industries. It is also mandated on IP, antitrust and construction cases, among other matters.

**KEY INDIVIDUALS Stephen Rovak** (see p.1638) operates a varied practice which takes in commercial, product liability, IP and franchise litigation. He is chair of the litigation and arbitration practice in St. Louis, and is also an experienced mediator and arbitrator. Noted for his *"prestige and experience,"* **Jerome Wolf** (see p.1639) is also described as *"well respected by the court."* He specializes in complex civil and commercial litigation. A recent highlight saw him achieving decertification of a putative class of over a thousand plaintiffs. Kansas City attorney **Curtis Woods** (see p.1639) draws particular respect from peers for his white-collar criminal litigation skills. He also handles commercial, antitrust, business tort, IP and fraud cases.

### Dowd Bennett LLP

**THE FIRM** White-collar defense specialist Dowd Bennett has become a respected fixture in the St. Louis landscape since opening in 2006, and has been engaged by some of America's biggest names in business. The group prides itself on not shying away from taking cases to court where necessary, and aggressively pursues clients' interests.

**Sources say:** *"They have a quick response time and communicate effectively. There is a heavy emphasis on extremely good client service."*

**KEY INDIVIDUALS Jim Bennett** (see p.1635) is described as *"brilliant, incredibly hard-working and efficient."* He focuses on multijurisdictional cases both at trial and appellate level, often acting as lead attorney. **Edward Dowd** (see p.1636) specializes in representing clients with complicated civil and criminal federal cases, and has deep experience appearing before the SEC, the DOJ and the EPA, among others. Sources say: *"He was formerly a US*

*The editorial is in alphabetical order by firm name.*

Attorney and has been a well-known commodity in this area."

## Greensfelder, Hemker & Gale, P.C.

**THE FIRM** This St. Louis-based team offers representation in state and federal court, as well as in arbitration proceedings and before regulatory agencies. It has particular expertise in defending medical and legal professionals against professional liability claims. The group works with a range of clients, from large multinationals to small, closely held businesses, such as Shell, BP and Edward Jones. **Sources say:** *"Greensfelder is very strong."*
**KEY INDIVIDUALS David Harris** co-heads the department, and counts BP and Shell among his clients. Recently, he represented BP in a $120 million trial where franchisees alleged BP and its real estate broker NRC had misrepresented the level of sales possible in certain sites where they had taken on gas stations and convenience stores. Former federal prosecutor **Kevin O'Malley** leads the medical negligence, white-collar crime and regulatory compliance practices. He has 35 years of trial experience, including time spent as a federal prosecutor. Sources say he *"gets good results for his clients, and is good in court."*

## Husch Blackwell LLP

**THE FIRM** The firm has a strong offering in both Kansas City and St. Louis and is increasingly visible outside Missouri after growing its offering through a series of judicious mergers. This, along with a respected bench, has helped carve out a successful practice which offers deep expertise in complex business litigation, particularly in class actions, and which often acts as national counsel to large corporations. Clients include Career Education Corporation, Express Scripts, WireCo WorldGroup, the Olin Corporation and AgriBank.
**KEY INDIVIDUALS Thomas Carney** focuses primarily on product liability, toxic torts and environmental litigation. He was recently a key partner in Husch's successful defense of Monsanto on a product liability case in which plaintiffs claimed they developed Hodgkin's lymphoma as a result of PCBs ingested through the food chain. **James Griffin** is prized for his determination to win cases as well as his excellent trial presence. Sources say: *"He is very knowledgeable on the law and very personable. I like the way he reacts and relates to the jurors."* He recently led client WireCo WorldGroup to a $2.1 million win in arbitration in a complex case involving allegations of breach of contract, professional negligence and unpaid invoices. Sources say **Stephen Hill** *"is a very knowledgeable and skilled trial attorney, and has a great practice in the region."* He is increasingly focused on complex investigations and white-collar criminal defense work, and is chair of the firm's government, compliance, investigations and litigation department. Clients benefit from his experience as a former US Attorney. **Patrick McInerney** is regularly called upon to advise on investigations initiated by the SEC. Commentators note that he is a litigator who *"is hard-nosed but cordial at the same time, with wonderful trial skills."*

## Kohn, Shands, Elbert, Gianoulakis & Giljum, LLP

**THE FIRM** This compact St. Louis firm has a fine bench of experienced attorneys who focus primarily on litigation. The group has carved a niche in working alongside bigger firms, and has a particular focus on the areas of employment and education law.
**KEY INDIVIDUALS Alan Kohn** is seen as *"clearly one of the great lawyers"* as well as *"a go-to guy who is very smart."* He advises on a variety of matters, including antitrust, securities, contract and domestic relations disputes, class actions and professional malpractice defense. **John Gianoulakis** is commended for his impressive court presence and effective advocacy. Sources say: *"He is one of the finest I have seen in court – smart, great on his feet, and the judges in town know and respect him."* His prime areas of expertise are general business litigation, legal malpractice defense, and education and employment law matters.

## Lathrop & Gage LLP

**THE FIRM** Clients of Kansas City firm Lathrop & Gage benefit from the practice's deep and long-lasting local connections, as well as its wide-ranging expertise. The group is seen as especially strong in class action, IP and mass tort work, and it is also regularly called on for complex white-collar mandates. A highlight saw the team successfully represent Mediacom in an insurance recovery case. Key clients include Wells Fargo, PetSmart, Bank of America, Synergy and Beldon.
**Sources say:** *"They are very professional and good value for money. You get a first-rate service."*
**KEY INDIVIDUALS Douglas Dalgleish** is described as *"an exceptional litigator who knows how to get to the point, is a quick study, and is very persuasive."* He has 25 years' experience in disputes resolution and is also prized as a personable advocate who is *"very likable – judges and juries like him."* **Jean Paul Bradshaw** specializes in white-collar criminal defense, internal investigations, and healthcare fraud and abuse. He also handles commercial litigation, recently leading on the successful defense of a $3 million nuisance claim against Premium Standard Farms and Smithfield Foods.

## Lewis, Rice & Fingersh LC

See profile on p.1640

**THE FIRM** This firm has a sizable litigation team with widely respected practitioners in both St. Louis and Kansas City, though most of its experts are located in the former. It offers a full range of litigation expertise, and is particularly respected in product liability, class actions and contractual disputes. The group regularly acts for clients in the insurance industry.
**Sources say:** *"We are extremely pleased with the quality. They are extremely professional, competent and thorough."*
**KEY INDIVIDUALS** Senior partner **Barry Short** (see p.1638) is noted for being *"a very strong attorney"* who is seen as particularly good on white-collar crime matters. He is also known for his antitrust, toxic tort, environmental and securities experience, built up over four decades. **Andrew Rothschild** (see p.1638) and has a good reputa-

tion in the market, where he practices in the areas of commercial and toxic tort litigation. He also has experience handling admiralty litigation and professional liability matters.

## Polsinelli PC

See profile on p.1641

**THE FIRM** This well-regarded Kansas City group is often seen litigating high-stakes class actions for the construction, banking, logistics and insurance industries, as well as for government entities. It also has a strong practice in antitrust matters. The practice continues to develop, interviewees noting that its St. Louis arm is growing in both size and stature. Highlights include representing Crago and Texas Digital Systems in TFT-LCD price-fixing litigation, and Brainlab in over 50 personal injury and wrongful death cases. Key clients include Kansas City Power & Light, Kansas City Police Commission, US Bank and Jack Henry.
**Sources say:** *"One of the best firms in Missouri. It is becoming a big player in the defense Bar in St. Louis just like it has been in Kansas City for years. One of the most respected firms."*
**KEY INDIVIDUALS** Highly experienced litigator **Lawrence Ward** has a *"stellar reputation,"* sources enthuse, adding that *"he is one of the kings of the trial Bar in the Kansas City area. He is fantastic."* Others highlight his *"ability to translate the intellectual into the practical."* **Russell Jones** is known for his skills in trying complex litigation, and is currently engaged in a complicated consumer class action. He has a particular emphasis on IP and securities disputes. **Russell Welsh** is commended as a skilled trial lawyer. His areas of expertise center around product liability, business torts, trade secrets and bankruptcy matters. **Thomas Kokoruda** specializes in healthcare-related cases. Recently, he led a team acting for HCA against the Health Care Foundation of Greater Kansas City in a complicated lawsuit which claimed damages of more than $109 million for alleged noncompliance with post-closing covenants in an asset purchase agreement. **Cathy Dean** has three decades of experience in the courtroom, and focuses on complex commercial litigation and antitrust, trade secret and product liability mandates. She supported Thomas Kokoruda in the HCA matter described above. **John Kilroy** has a particular focus on professional liability, financial, fiduciary and antitrust matters. He acts for clients in a range of industries, and is well noted for his work representing those in the legal and accountancy professions. **Dan Boulware** recently acted for Edward T Gavin, the plan administrator of the Crossroads Wireless Liquidating Trust, in a contested bankruptcy case valued at $42 million and involving 66 parties.

## Rouse Hendricks German May PC

See profile on p.1642

**THE FIRM** This nimble litigation boutique has a great reputation in the market and advises clients on a range of issues, from product liability to white-collar crime. Successes include winning $31 million in damages and costs for Kansas City-based multinational Hallmark. The case concerned the misappropriation of trade secrets by investment firm Monitor Clipper, which purchased Recycled Paper Greetings, a rival company to Hallmark, and whose related company, Monitor Company Group, previously worked with Hallmark.

**Sources say:** *"They are a fine firm – very strong."*

**KEY INDIVIDUALS Charles German** is very active in class action litigation and has had a number of successes in this field, sealing his reputation as one of the best litigators in the state. Commentators say: *"He's a bulldog and he has a reputation of being candid but reasonable."* In 2012 he represented the prominent Copaken, White, Blitt, Fingersh, Morgan and Dreiseszun banking families, gaining a ruling which held that Chicago lawyer Shayle Fox had breached a contract. **Randall Hendricks** is noted for his tenacious approach toward getting the best result for clients in complex commercial litigation matters. He acts for a range of clients, including financial institutions and power plants. **Kirk May** is commended for his work representing both plaintiffs and defendants in business litigation, both at trial and appeal. **William Beil** continues to impress in the courtroom, particularly when acting for clients in class actions and in business litigation. According to sources, he is *"very bright and knows the law. He is articulate and a very good trial lawyer."* He recently secured a $4.5 million settlement in a dispute regarding the insurance coverage of collapsed company Go Fig in the US Bankruptcy Court for the Eastern District of Missouri. His client was a former trustee of the collapsed company.

## Shook, Hardy & Bacon LLP
See profile on p.1644

**THE FIRM** This firm's stellar reputation stems from its excellent capabilities in product liability defense, built on its representation of tobacco companies. Its offering remains very strong in this area, and now is equally robust in its work for the pharmaceutical and medical device industries. The team is also skilled in the commercial, IP, labor and employment, and environmental spheres. The practice counts Ford and Coca-Cola among its clients, and continues to act for Philip Morris in a large number of product liability matters. Other representative matters include acting for Bausch & Lomb in defending allegations that its contact lens solution caused a fungal infection of the cornea.

**Sources say:** *"They're very experienced, with good support staff. Good strategic thinkers at all levels."*

**KEY INDIVIDUALS Eugene Balloun** is the vice chair of the firm's general litigation committee. He brings over 40 years of experience in litigation to assist clients. His practice is mainly focused around tort, antitrust and business litigation, as well as appellate matters. **William Sampson** receives top marks for being *"extraordinarily accommodating, well connected, very practical and very smart."* He works on a range of matters, particularly product liability cases. **Robert Adams** is a key partner in the firm's representation of Boston Scientific and Covidien in a mass litigation involving pelvic mesh products. Sources say: *"He is outstanding – one of the best in the state."* **Harvey Kaplan** is described as *"the dean of the pharmaceutical defense Bar"* because of his *"tremendous experience, knowledge and*

*information at his fingertips."* He is currently representing Mylan Pharmaceuticals as national counsel in more than 1,300 product liability cases across several states. **Joseph Rebein**'s practice includes acting for clients on antitrust matters and securities class actions. He is also experienced in mediation and arbitration proceedings. **Gene Voigts** is a senior partner who has been practicing for more than 35 years. He has a varied practice which encompasses both civil and criminal cases. **Todd Ruskamp** is recognized for his skilled handling of complex matters, and is described as *"one of the go-to guys for business-related litigation."* He specializes in advising clients in the telecom and financial services sectors, and also works on bankruptcy and restructuring mandates.

## Stinson Morrison Hecker LLP

**THE FIRM** With a respected roster of attorneys based in St. Louis and Kansas City, Stinson Morrison Hecker is a strong litigation firm which represents clients across the country. Clients often comment on the firm's value-for-money services, as well as its willingness to negotiate alternative fee arrangements. In the past year, it has represented Deloro Stellite in a large number of toxic tort cases across 12 states, as well as the American Samoa Power Authority in pursuing an insurance claim for the losses which it suffered as a result of the earthquakes and tsunamis which hit American Samoa in 2009.

**Sources say:** *"I think they're all experts in their field and I feel comfortable using them." "We're absolutely pleased with the results we got."*

**KEY INDIVIDUALS Matthew Verschelden** is the chair of the firm's appellate practice group and handles a range of cases, including commercial disputes, employment disputes and antitrust litigation. **John Aisenbrey** is appreciated for his deep knowledge of the law, and is sought out for both difficult business litigation and white-collar crime mandates. Sources say: *"His trial skills are excellent. He has a commanding presence, but at same time speaks on the jurors' level and relates to them."* The much-admired **David Everson** is described as *"the dean of the antitrust Bar,"* as well as *"a very conscientious, hard-working and effective trial attorney, who has a big heart."* He focuses on large-scale civil, antitrust and business litigation, while also trying criminal cases pro bono. **John Moticka** has been litigating cases in court for over 25 years, and is praised for his *"invaluable insights."* Sources add: *"Whether he's the lead counsel, co-counsel or just an adviser, he will think about your litigation positioning and strategy in a unique way."* Clients also appreciate his ability to work closely with their in-house teams. In the past year, he represented Playtex Products in decertifying a class in a purported class action litigation.

## Thompson Coburn LLP

**THE FIRM** This large St. Louis team has a strong bench of litigators who are praised for their responsiveness and ability to achieve high-profile wins for their clients. It represented Hosanna-Tabor Evangelical Lutheran Church against a claim by a former employee in the Supreme Court, where the court held that ministerial exception was

a defense in employment discrimination claims. Other key clients for the firm include US Bank, Monsanto, Kawasaki Motors Corp USA and AT&T.

**Sources say:** *"They bring a seemingly boundless enthusiasm and energy to every assignment, along with a dogged determination to seek the very best possible outcome for their client." "Very effective lawyers and also very nice."*

**KEY INDIVIDUALS** Former US Attorney and department head **Stephen Higgins** is described as *"well known and successful,"* and is known for working with his team to provide solid legal research and analysis. He is sought out for commercial litigation work by communications companies in particular, and is also prized for his white-collar criminal defense capabilities. **Gordon Ankney** is also highly respected in the field of white-collar crime defense, and is noted for being *"very helpful and responsive, with great contacts in the area."* He also has particular experience representing clients in environmental and product liability cases, and is chair of the firm's corporate compliance, investigation and defense group. **Raymond Massey** handles a range of cases, including those in the admiralty, maritime, agriculture, manufacturing and transportation sectors. He has particular expertise defending product liability cases. **David Wells** is one of Thompson Coburn's most experienced litigators, with a particular focus on appellate proceedings in both state and federal courts. He is popular with banking and finance clients. **Michael Minton** is described as *"very intelligent, and very good at dealing with clients."* He acts as chair of the firm's tobacco litigation group as well as cochair of the firm's consumer products and electronic discovery groups. **Roman Wuller** has built up a strong reputation on class actions and multidistrict cases, as well as difficult commercial litigation. He is regularly sought out by mining and natural resources clients, as well as those from the automotive and telecom industries. One of the group's younger partners, **Christopher Hohn** is increasingly recognized as a skilled practitioner. He mainly focuses on class actions and business litigation, with clients ranging across the financial services, agriculture and telecom industries. He is noted for being *"very easy to work with and very straightforward."*

## Williams, Venker, Sanders LLC

**THE FIRM** This growing litigation boutique debuts in the rankings this year thanks to a very satisfied roster of clients across a range of industries. The group has a particular focus on medical malpractice defense and product liability claims. It also focuses on providing a cost-effective service. Key clients include Anheuser-Busch InBev, Caterpillar, Saint Louis University and Barnes-Jewish Hospital.

**Sources say:** *"They are great – they are incredibly responsive and have gotten good results. Their rates are reasonable, and we'll keep using them."*

**KEY INDIVIDUALS Paul Venker** is a trial and appellate attorney with broad experience in employment, medical malpractice, product liability and environmental matters. Clients say: *"He's excellent at understanding the business risk and desires, measured against litigation possibilities."*

*The editorial is in alphabetical order by firm name.*

### Wyrsch Hobbs & Mirakian PC
See profile on p.1645

THE FIRM This highly respected Kansas City litigation boutique handles some of the most complicated and sensitive litigation around, and is highly respected in the areas of white-collar criminal defense, complex civil litigation, and business litigation. Clients include US Bank Trust National Association, Coleman American Van Lines, Priests of the Catholic Diocese of Kansas City-St. Joseph and Sinclair Oil. Attorneys at the firm are often brought in to act as co-counsel or support for other firms on complex matters.

Sources say: *"They are tremendous to work with."*

KEY INDIVIDUALS Former Jackson County public defender **James Hobbs** is described by one peer as *"one of the top five criminal defense lawyers in Missouri."* *"He fights hard for his clients and gets great results,"* adds another interviewee. He is particularly skilled in white-collar crime defense, environmental matters and the defense of political corruption prosecutions. **James Wyrsch** is regarded as a highly skilled attorney who has the ability to *"deal with complex legal issues, not nickel and dime-type issues."* Recent matters include representing Belgian company Gosselin Worldwide Moving in a civil suit under the Federal False Claims Act.

### Other Notable Practitioners

**Spencer Brown** of Kansas City firm Deacy & Deacy LLP brings to bear nearly 50 years of experience in legal practice. He has a particular focus on acting for insurance clients. Sources say: *"He is a terrific trial lawyer – spectacular."*

# REAL ESTATE

Commentary about individuals can be found under their firm's paragraph. If the firm has no paragraph (is not ranked) look at Other Notable Practitioners.

| Real Estate: Kansas City & Surrounds |
| --- |
| **Leading Firms** |
| **Band 1** |
| Polsinelli PC * |
| Stinson Morrison Hecker LLP |
| **Band 2** |
| Husch Blackwell LLP |
| Lathrop & Gage LLP |
| Lewis, Rice & Fingersh, L.C. * |
| White Goss Bowers March Schulte & Weisenfels |
| **Band 3** |
| Dentons * |
| * Indicates firm with profile. |
| Alphabetical order within each band. Band 1 is the highest. |

*The edit is in alphabetical order by firm name.*

### Armstrong Teasdale LLP

THE FIRM This large team based predominantly in St. Louis is renowned for its large bench of highly skilled practitioners as well as its capability in the full range of real estate and public finance matters. Its clients include developers based both in the local area and across the USA, as well as corporate, institutional and governmental entities. The group works closely with litigation partners to enhance its offering to clients in matters where disputes arise. Recent highlights include acting as bond counsel for the City of St. Louis in the issuance of $30 million leasehold revenue bonds to finance improvements to Forest Park, as well as representing Boehringer Ingelheim in a $25 million build-to-suit lease for office and warehouse facilities.

Sources say: *"The team is top flight and we have been fortunate to have it."* *"There is no need to look elsewhere – they deliver quality products and wise counsel."*

KEY INDIVIDUALS Department head **Timothy Tryniecki** has particular skill in the energy and transportation sectors, and is noted for *"doing a fine job for his clients."* In 2012 he led a team advising Kelson Energy on its sale of a stake in a power plant. As a former city manager, **James Mello** offers a unique set of skills to his clients. He is the City of Chesterfield's special counsel for development issues, and has assisted with establishing a community improvement district and creating a transport development district for two separate outlet mall projects. Clients say he is *"very confident and well versed. He has incredible knowledge of the law, and is very accessible and understanding of my needs."* Among **Daniel Wofsey**'s key matters in 2012 was acting as lead counsel for the Bank of Washington in a $32 million financing for the acquisition and renovation of Westport Plaza, a 700,000 sq ft mixed-use project. **Robert Klahr** assisted on the aforementioned City of Chesterfield matters. His *"quality of work is second to none,"* clients say, and he also wins praise for his responsiveness: *"He is busy with his active practice but gets back to me in a timely fashion."*

### Bryan Cave LLP

THE FIRM This leading full-service firm has a national reputation for its real estate expertise. It has 31 real estate attorneys in Missouri, though its team is predominantly St. Louis-based. The group represents clients in matters across the country, and is praised for its ability to deal with a demanding workload. It is skilled in all areas of real estate, including transactions, leasing, development, finance and ongoing ownership issues. It also offers a team which focuses on construction. Key clients include Emerson Electric, Regus, Monsanto, Sara Lee Corporation (Hillshire) and Hanesbrands.

KEY INDIVIDUALS **George Murray** counts Monsanto among his clients. He advises the company on the sale and leasing of its real estate across the USA, as well as the acquisition, leasing and development of its properties in O'ahu and Maui, Hawaii. **Linda Martinez** moves up the rankings this year thanks to her growing reputation in the market, as well as her having worked on some interesting and complex real estate matters. She acted for Laurel Partners on a historical renovation and development in downtown St. Louis. Her advice on the matter included a variety of tax credits and financings. **Harold Burroughs** has a strong transactional practice. He is particularly skilled at acting for developers and lenders, in addition to advising on leasing matters. He also represents clients in the areas of finance and securities. **Bruce Lowry** is experienced in the areas of finance, land use, development, acquisitions and leasing. He recently represented Global Brass & Copper regarding the leasing, acquisition and sale of facilities, as well as zoning, real estate tax appeals and related litigation. **John Hoffman** is praised for his methodical and detail-oriented approach. Recent clients include Hanesbrands, for which he handled the sale of a manufacturing plant in North Carolina, as well as several lease agreements. **Stephen Sparks** is well known for his knowledge of public financing, real estate finance and corporate finance. He acted as national bond counsel and counsel on a number of real estate financings across the USA for AIMCO Properties. He is based in Kansas City.

### Dentons
See profile on p.449

THE FIRM This practice is able to draw upon national and international resources beyond those available in its Missouri-based offices. The firm represents a wide range of clients, from investors and lenders to developers and owners. It has a diverse workload, advising on planning and zoning matters, regeneration and tax-efficient structuring.

*The editorial is in alphabetical order by firm name.*

## Real Estate: Kansas City & Surrounds
### Senior Statesmen

Senior Statesmen: distinguished older practitioners

| | |
|---|---|
| Carr William E | *Lewis, Rice & Fingersh, L.C.* * |

### Leading Individuals

**Band 1**

| | |
|---|---|
| Dagenais Don F | *Lathrop & Gage LLP* |
| DiGiovanni Peter | *Lewis, Rice & Fingersh, L.C.* * |
| Fenley David A | *Husch Blackwell LLP* |
| Flanigan Daniel J | *Polsinelli PC* |
| Frantze David | *Stinson Morrison Hecker LLP* |
| Miller Charles F | *Lewis, Rice & Fingersh, L.C.* * |
| Shalton Lonnie J | *Polsinelli PC* |
| White Michael | *White Goss Bowers March Schulte & Weisenfels, A Professional Corporation* |

**Band 2**

| | |
|---|---|
| Blond Irwin E | *Polsinelli PC* |
| LaSala Todd A | *Stinson Morrison Hecker LLP* |
| March Aaron | *White Goss Bowers March Schulte & Weisenfels, A Professional Corporation* |
| Riffel Jerome | *Lathrop & Gage LLP* |
| Shortlidge Neil | *Stinson Morrison Hecker LLP* |
| Snyder John L | *Dentons* * |
| Sparks Stephen S | *Bryan Cave LLP* |

**Band 3**

| | |
|---|---|
| Cruz John E | *Lewis, Rice & Fingersh, L.C.* * |
| Fitzgerald Jr Robert E | *Polsinelli PC* |
| Haines Lisa | *Polsinelli PC* |
| Hauber Catherine | *Stinson Morrison Hecker LLP* |
| Klahr Robert | *Armstrong Teasdale LLP* |
| McMahon Maribeth | *Polsinelli PC* |
| Mitchell Stephen G | *Lathrop & Gage LLP* |
| Simmons F Chase | *Polsinelli PC* |
| Thomson Spencer R | *Thomson Walker, LLC (ONP)[†]* |
| Weisenfels John R | *White Goss Bowers March Schulte* |

### Up-and-coming individuals

| | |
|---|---|
| Crossley John | *Husch Blackwell LLP* |

**KEY INDIVIDUALS Jennifer Marler** (see p.1637) is particularly noted as *"a good finance lawyer,"* although her expertise also extends to development work. She focuses her practice on projects which involve public incentives and large construction loans. She works with both national and regional financial institutions. **John Snyder** (see p.1638) is the managing partner of the firm's Kansas City office, and also heads its real estate team. He handles a range of commercial real estate matters, from financing to leasing, both locally and nationally. He has been increasingly busy in the area of distressed assets and loans.

## Greensfelder, Hemker & Gale, P.C.

**THE FIRM** Greensfelder has a relatively compact but well-regarded team which is centered in St. Louis. It has a broad commercial real estate practice, advising on such matters as purchase and sales, leasing, development, financing and zoning. It is experienced in advising on transactions involving a range of property types, including industrial, multifamily, hospitality and healthcare buildings. Key

## Real Estate: St. Louis & Surrounds
### Leading Firms

**Band 1**

Armstrong Teasdale LLP

Bryan Cave LLP

Husch Blackwell LLP

Thompson Coburn LLP

**Band 2**

Greensfelder, Hemker & Gale, P.C.

Dentons *

### Leading Individuals

**Band 1**

| | |
|---|---|
| Macon Paul M | *Thompson Coburn LLP* |
| Murray George E | *Bryan Cave LLP* |
| Smith Gregory R | *Husch Blackwell LLP* |
| Tryniecki Timothy J | *Armstrong Teasdale LLP* |

**Band 2**

| | |
|---|---|
| Biesterfeld Craig | *Husch Blackwell LLP* |
| Colagiovanni Joseph | *Fulbright & Jaworski LLP (ONP)[†] * |
| Engle Daniel T | *Thompson Coburn LLP* |
| Feder Gary H | *Husch Blackwell LLP* |
| Hetland Janice E | *Polsinelli PC* |
| Marler Jennifer A | *Dentons* * |
| Martinez Linda M. | *Bryan Cave LLP* |
| McNearney John | *Husch Blackwell LLP* |
| Mello James | *Armstrong Teasdale LLP* |
| Misko Charles | *Stinson Morrison Hecker LLP* |
| Stone Steven M | *Stone Leyton & Gershman (ONP)[†]* |
| Story Thomas L | *Greensfelder, Hemker & Gale, P.C.* |
| Wofsey Daniel | *Armstrong Teasdale LLP* |

**Band 3**

| | |
|---|---|
| Burroughs Harold R | *Bryan Cave LLP* |
| Feldman Richard E | *Husch Blackwell LLP* |
| Hoffman John W. | *Bryan Cave LLP* |
| King John P | *Lathrop & Gage LLP* |
| Linenbroker David A | *Husch Blackwell LLP* |
| Lowry Jr Bruce E | *Bryan Cave LLP* |
| Mueller Kathleen T | *Husch Blackwell LLP* |

### Up-and-coming individuals

| | |
|---|---|
| Frankel Amelia | *Thompson Coburn LLP* |
| Minkoff Jared M | *Polsinelli PC* |

* *Indicates firm / individual with profile.*

[†] *ONP = Other Notable Practitioner*

clients include Pace Properties, Schnuck Markets, Edward Jones and SSM Health Care.

**Sources say:** *"They've done a terrific job. Very timely as well as very thorough."*

**KEY INDIVIDUALS** Among **Thomas Story**'s recent highlights was advising on significant deals involving acquiring and turning around troubled retail and residential projects and loan workouts.

## Husch Blackwell LLP

**THE FIRM** This highly respected firm has a strong real estate presence in both St. Louis and Kansas City, in addition to a deep bench of experienced attorneys. It offers a multidisciplinary approach where it can draw upon resources in a range of different disciplines to assist with sophisticated real estate mandates. The group has expertise across the spectrum, with a particular emphasis on advising corporate clients on real estate finance and workouts, developments and public incentives.

**Sources say:** *"Husch has a good team of people." "We run up against them a lot – they are our main competitor."*

**KEY INDIVIDUALS Gregory Smith** is the firm's CEO and managing partner, and is based in St. Louis. One client describes him as his *"go-to guy on TIF"* matters, adding that *"Greg has a regional and national reputation in governmental financing."* **Craig Biesterfeld** has nearly 30 years' experience in this field, with a particular emphasis on acquisition, leasing and development, zoning, and state and government regulation and permitting. **Gary Feder** is noted for being *"a fine lawyer who is good at zoning work as well as real estate purchase and sales."* In addition to these areas of work, he also handles related litigation matters. **John McNearney** predominantly acts for financial institutions across the country as well as in Missouri, advising them on their involvement in large developments and real estate acquisitions. **Richard Feldman** focuses particularly on the disposition of real estate development strategies, portfolio management and in-construction projects. His experience stretches across a wide range of sectors. **David Linenbroker** is appreciated for his expertise stretching across commercial leasing, acquisitions and dispositions, as well as commercial and agricultural financing. Sources say: *"I've seen him on transactions and he knows what needs to be done to get the deal completed."* **Kathleen Mueller** has a respected traditional real estate practice and is able to act across the spectrum involving everything from agricultural issues to transactions relating to schools. She is described as having *"a good, solid reputation and experience"* in this field. **David Fenley** is a well-known figure in Kansas City, where he has been a leading practitioner on commercial developments and PPP matters for more than three decades. He is described as being *"a very, very talented lawyer."* **John Crossley** is also based in Kansas City, and is noted for being *"good to work with and very knowledgeable."* He specializes in advising clients on traditional and renewable energy projects across the country, from financing through to construction and acquisition.

## Lathrop & Gage LLP

**THE FIRM** Lathrop & Gage has a real estate practice across both St. Louis and Kansas City, though it is particularly renowned in the latter, where the firm has its base. The team advises on the full gamut of real estate matters, and has much experience working closely with public bodies. Recent highlights include representing the Catholic Diocese of Kansas City-St. Joseph in a $5 million reissuance of Missouri Health & Educational Facilities bonds for the St. Pius X High School in Kansas City.

**KEY INDIVIDUALS** Department leader **Don Dagenais** handles all aspects of commercial real estate transactions, acting for developers, investors, lenders and property managers. He has worked on residential, retail, industrial and medical projects. Of late, he has been mandated on a residential redevelopment project, as well as refinancing and

*The editorial is in alphabetical order by firm name.*

leasing matters. **Jerome Riffel** runs the firm's public law team, and is experienced in tax increment financing (TIF) developments, urban developments, economic development incentives and special business districts. Recent matters include advising the Union Hill Development group on the large restructuring and refinancing of a development project valued at $3.5 million. **Stephen Mitchell** led on the St. Pius X High School matter described above. He has particular expertise in zoning matters, including historic preservation regulation issues. Mitchell also recently represented the Belger Group in an exercise to refinance its multimillion-dollar loans. **John King** is based in St. Louis, and is counsel of choice for zoning matters in the wider metropolitan area. Commentators say: *"He is a very good zoning lawyer. If you were doing a deal in the suburbs he'd be the first person you'd think of."*

## Lewis, Rice & Fingersh, L.C.
See profile on p.1640

**THE FIRM** The strong roster of attorneys at this firm provide a full-service offering, and they are regularly sought out for advising on leasing mandates involving companies with multiple sites across the USA. In the past year, this group has worked with retail tenants, including restaurant chains, communications businesses, hospitals and mining companies. Its key clients include Fred Weber, SRAM, Covington Realty Partners and CORTEX.
Sources say: *"They are very good lawyers with intellectual clout."*
**KEY INDIVIDUALS** Senior partner **William Carr** (see p.1635) is widely respected, and brings over three decades of experience to the team. He advises clients on a range of real estate matters, representing landlords and tenants, lenders and borrowers, and financial partners across office, industrial, retail, residential and mixed-use projects. **Peter DiGiovanni** (see p.1636) is marked for his expertise in large retail developments, in particular shopping mall developments both inside and outside urban areas. His clients are most often developers, as well as national and regional tenants. **Charles Miller** (see p.1637) is praised for his attention to detail and notable skill in drafting contracts. Sources say: *"He is an excellent attorney. He is very knowledgeable about all matters, including development and economic incentives."* **John Cruz** (see p.1636) specializes in retail and office leasing, and acts for both sides of the negotiating table. Commentators note that Cruz continues to build his real estate expertise, one describing him as *"a go-to guy who you see as lead lawyer on deals all the time."*

## Polsinelli PC
See profile on p.1641

**THE FIRM** This growing team continues to be one of the highest-performing real estate groups in Kansas City, with a strong bench which is particularly prized for its finance work. The firm represents investors, lenders and developers across the full range of real estate matters, including equity and debt financing and workouts, loan enforcements, restructuring and bankruptcy. Clients are based both inside and outside Missouri, and the group has a growing clientele in New York. The group recently acted

for Extell Development on the negotiation of a $700 million construction loan financing with Bank of America. The loan will enable the construction of a 708,000 sq ft, 90-story mixed-use building in the city. Other clients include the City of Kansas City, Ladder Capital, Cerner and OnGoal.
Sources say: *"We see them a lot and they have a lot of work going on."* *"It has developed a great practice and is one of the fastest-growing law firms in the area."*
**KEY INDIVIDUALS Lonnie Shalton** has been a trusted adviser to both national and international real estate developers. He led on the Extell Development matter described above. **Daniel Flanigan** is a *"top-notch lawyer,"* enthuse interviewees. He focuses on helping rescue distressed developments, and led a team representing Extell Development on the workout of a loan on an iconic New York property. **Irwin Blond** specializes in real estate transactions, representing clients with retail, residential, office and manufacturing properties. He is also regularly called upon for his lease negotiation expertise, and has experience negotiating leases on large shopping malls. **Chase Simmons** *"continues to excel,"* and has a growing reputation in the market. He led on the $90 million redevelopment of Woodside Health & Tennis Club, a mixed-use residential, commercial and leisure development in Kansas. **Lisa Haines** advises clients across the spectrum of real estate matters, and is particularly strong on commercial development and financing matters. Recent highlights include working with Lonnie Shalton on the aforementioned Extell Development matter. **Maribeth McMahon** is particularly praised for her skills in real estate finance. She acted as lead attorney advising lender KeyBank National Association Regular in several loans across the USA, totaling over $450 million. Kansas City partner **Robert Fitzgerald** has a mixed practice, advising clients on general corporate matters as well as real estate transactions. He brings more than 35 years' experience to bear. **Janice Hetland** is chair of the Affordable Housing and Tax Credit Finance and Development practice group at the firm, and is based in St. Louis. She is described as *"a fine lawyer"* who *"is very good in her field,"* and is known for her national practice advising on real estate and finance matters. She is engaged for her expertise in federal and state tax structuring, tax credits and other incentives. **Jared Minkoff** is increasingly visible in the market, described by sources as *"very strong and starting to develop an independent practice."* He focuses in particular on multifamily residential and commercial tax credit development.

## Stinson Morrison Hecker LLP

**THE FIRM** This leading firm has a robust real estate offering out of Kansas City, as well as a growing presence in St. Louis. It is best known for its work in the western part of the state, where it has built up a very strong reputation, particularly for its work on high-profile public developments. The firm continues to work with long-standing client Entertainment Properties Trust, for which it has assisted on the acquisition of more than 110 movie theaters over the past year. Other clients include Gavilon

Grain, Ash Grove Cement, Fischer & Frichtel and Angelica Corporation.
Sources say: *"We are definitely pleased with the work. We are getting cost-effective delivery and high-quality work products."*
**KEY INDIVIDUALS** Cochair of the department **David Frantze** is well known for his wide-ranging practice, which includes new developments and redevelopments, lease negotiations, dispositions and financing projects. He is particularly sought out for his knowledge of economic incentives, which has led to a rich vein of PPP mandates. Key matters include advising the largest online US freight shipping provider, Freightquote, on the $44 million development of its new headquarters and office space in Missouri. **Todd LaSala** continues to represent the City of Overland Park as a special real estate and development counsel on its 58-acre Prairiefire museum and shopping center development, a mixed-use project worth around $448 million. **Neil Shortlidge** is *"a really good litigator – he's calm, he answers our questions,"* and is patient, says one client. He mainly acts for public sector clients, capitalizing on his previous experience as a city attorney for three local government entities and staff attorney for the League of Kansas Municipalities. **Catherine Hauber** has a wide-ranging practice, and leads the group in its role as national real estate counsel to Entertainment Properties Trust, an NYSE-listed REIT. She is described as a creative problem solver who *"is very solution-oriented. She understands risk, but also understands that we want to get to the solution."* **Charles Misko** is the managing partner of the firm's St. Louis office and is instructed on a range of matters, including acquisitions, dispositions, developments, leasing and financing. Recently, he acted for the seller in the $12 million sale and financing of a significant development in St. Louis, which included an application for Disabled Area Land Assemblage Tax Credits and renegotiation of existing development agreements and public financing incentives.

## Thompson Coburn LLP

**THE FIRM** A well-respected practice in St. Louis, Thompson Coburn reports a strong year and continues to develop its team. It acts for a range of clients, but has a particular focus on midmarket clients based in the local area. It is especially noted for its strength in financing, as well as its growing focus on tax credit work. Key clients include US Bank, Wells Fargo, PNC Bank and Bunge North America.
Sources say: *"They are a very good real estate group with talented people."*
**KEY INDIVIDUALS Paul Macon** is described as *"a very good technical lawyer,"* and is recognized as one of St. Louis' leading real estate attorneys. A recent highlight was advising a client on all aspects of the construction of a new public facility. Trusted adviser **Daniel Engle** is sought out for his development and leasing expertise. Recently, he represented CityView on the acquisition and redevelopment of five registered historic buildings in downtown St. Louis into a multifamily complex of more than 900 units, valued at $35 million. **Amelia Frankel** is noted for being *"a very meticulous lawyer who gets deals done and is good at finding*

solutions." Frankel leads the firm's tax credit and incentives team, and is increasingly called upon to advise on the federal New Markets Tax Credit Program. In the past year, she assisted the US Treasury in determining which community development entities should be awarded new market credit allocations.

## White Goss Bowers March Schulte & Weisenfels, A Professional Corporation

**THE FIRM** This boutique firm in Kansas City is often the first place clients turn to with land use and zoning mandates, not least because a number of its attorneys previously held public office or worked in local government before joining the practice. The group is particularly skilled at identifying and accessing development incentives, as well as advising on ongoing development issues. It also advises on acquisitions, dispositions and leasings.

**Sources say:** *"We used them for property purchases and leases, and were very impressed."*

**KEY INDIVIDUALS Michael White** is described as *"an excellent land use lawyer"* and *"a deep thinker."* He is highly respected in the market, advising on development, economic incentives, TIF and zoning matters. **Aaron March** focuses on all aspects of public law regarding planning and development. He is noted for his diligence, with one source commenting: *"Nobody is going to outwork Aaron."* He is a former city attorney for Kansas City. **John Weisenfels** has more than three decades' experience working on real estate developments throughout the USA, and also has a strong reputation in financing matters.

### Other Notable Practitioners

Construction and engineering expert **Joseph Colagiovanni** (see p.1636) joined Fulbright & Jaworski LLP from Dentons in 2012. He divides his time between St. Louis and Dubai, and acts for clients in several jurisdictions across the Middle East. He handles both transactional and litigious matters, and in the past year represented an entertainment company in the negotiation and drafting of a contract for the design and construction of a new $20 million entertainment venue in Las Vegas. St. Louis-based **Steven Stone** of Stone Leyton & Gershman handles both corporate real estate and related taxation matters. He has experience of advising on complex financing work, involving PPP and TIF issues. **Spencer Thomson** of Thomson Walker, LLC is best known for his commercial real estate experience, and has a particular focus on the zoning, development and financing of major projects. He set up his practice with another former Husch Blackwell real estate attorney, Kristin Walker, in 2012.

# Leaders' Profiles in Missouri

## AHRENS, Richard A.
Lewis, Rice & Fingersh LC, St Louis
314 444 7719
rahrens@lewisrice.com
*Featured in Environment (St Louis & Surrounds)*
**Practice Areas:** Environmental, Chemical & Toxic Tort, Class Action, Appellate Litigation, Commercial Litigation, Natural Resources and Alternative Energy.
**Professional Memberships:** American Bar Association, Litigation Section and Section on National Resources and Environmental Law; Bar Association of Metropolitan St. Louis.
**Career:** Member, Lewis, Rice & Fingersh, L.C. (1977-present); Law clerk, Hon. Wm. H. Webster, U.S. Circuit Judge (1976-1977); Staff law clerk, U.S. Court of Appeals, Eighth Circuit (1975-1976). Mr Ahrens regularly appears in appellate courts in Missouri and elsewhere, having appeared in the Supreme Court of Missouri, Eighth Circuit Court of Appeals, and Missouri Court of Appeals.

## BENNETT, Jim
Dowd Bennett LLP, St Louis
314 889 7302
jbennett@dowdbennett.com
*Featured in Litigation (St Louis & Surrounds), Litigation (Missouri)*
**Career:** Mr Bennett has a national practice that is focused on cases that are not expected to settle before trial or appeal. Since 2006, he has tried to verdict or judgment numerous cases, seven of which involved more than $20,000,000 in controversy and three of which involved more than $100,000,000. He has been lead trial counsel in cases in Missouri, Illinois, Texas, Massachusetts and Delaware and has been identified as the Best Lawyer in St. Louis, among the top 100 lawyers in Missouri, and is listed in the Best Lawyers in

America. He is a former law clerk to Justice Kennedy and to J.L. Edmondson of the Eleventh Circuit.

## BOATRIGHT, Daniel
Littler Mendelson, PC, Kansas City
816 627-4401
DBoatright@littler.com
*Featured in Labor & Employment (Kansas City & Surrounds)*
**Practice Areas:** Wage and Hour; Hospitality; Class Actions; Discrimination and Harassment.
**Professional Memberships:** Employment Rights and Responsibilities Committee – American Bar Association; Co-chair, Complex Litigation Subcommittee of Employment Rights and Responsibilities Committee – American Bar Association; Global Alliance of Hospitality Attorneys.
**Career:** Counsels employers on compliance and provides management training on anti-harassment and other matters. Before joining Littler, practiced employment law exclusively on behalf of management for 19 years.
**Publications:** "Final Amended FLSA Regulations Make Significant Changes to Tip Credit Processes and Proposed Fluctuating Work Week Rules," April, 2011.
**Personal:** JD, University of Missouri, Kansas City, 1991, With Distinction; BA, Kansas State University, 1986, cum laude.

## BYERGO, Anthony B
Ogletree, Deakins, Nash, Smoak & Stewart, PC, Kansas City
816 471 1301
tony.byergo@ogletreedeakins.com
*Featured in Labor & Employment (Kansas City & Surrounds)*
**Practice Areas:** Union prevention/avoidance, collective bargaining, and other traditional labor

relations matters; employment litigation, including discrimination, harassment, and retaliation.
**Professional Memberships:** ABA Developing Labor Law and NLRB Policy & Practice Committees; Missouri and Illinois Bar.
**Career:** In private practice since 1990 with national firms in Chicago, Boston, and Kansas City. From 2000 to 2004, served in lead legal and labor relations roles for two Fortune 100 companies. Shareholder at Ogletree Deakins since 2005. Chair of firm collective bargaining subgroup.
**Personal:** Northwestern University Law School (JD, cum laude, 1990); Northwestern University Law Review (1988-90); Georgetown University (B.S.F.S., 1987).

## CARR, William E
Lewis, Rice & Fingersh, L.C., Kansas City
816 472 2503
wecarr@lrf-kc.com
*Featured in Real Estate (Kansas City & Surrounds)*
**Practice Areas:** All aspects of commercial real estate, including finance, development, acquisitions and sales, joint ventures and leasing.
**Professional Memberships:** Admitted to practice in Missouri and Kansas (1971). Member, Kansas and Missouri Bar Associations; Member, Kansas City Metropolitan Bar Association (past Chairman, Real Estate Section and Managing Partners Section); Fellow, American College of Real Estate Lawyers (past Chairman, Leasing Committee; Board of Governors 2006-08); Member, Advisory Board, Georgetown University Law School Advanced Commercial Leasing Institute (2001-06).
**Career:** Joined Brown, Koralchik & Fingersh, predecessor to Lewis, Rice & Fingersh in 1973; Chairman, Real Estate Department 1983-96; Managing Member of Kansas City office, 1997 to present; selected Real Estate Lawyer of the Year

2009 for Kansas City, MO by The Best Lawyers in America; recipient of the 2009 Baron of the Boardroom Award from the Kansas City Metropolitan Bar Association in recognition of distinguished service to corporate and business clients.
**Publications:** Co-author, 'The International Practice of Real Estate, 'Probate & Property, September/October 1996, The Magazine of Real Property, Probate and Trust Law Section of the American Bar Association (Recipient of the 1996 Excellence in Writing Award). Author, 'Negotiation of Commercial Leases,' the Commercial Property Lease, 1993 American Bar Association Section of Real Property, Probate and Trust Law. Author, 'Boxed In: The Rise of the Box Store and the Downfall of the Traditional Shopping Center Lease,' American College of Real Estate Lawyers, Spring 2001, Williamsburg, VA, published as part of the ACREL Papers by ALI-ABA.
**Personal:** Born July 20, 1946, JD, University of Chicago Law School, 1971; AB, University of California at Berkeley, 1968. President, Jewish Federation of Greater Kansas City, 2009-2011. Past President, The Temple, Congregation B'nai Jehudah, Overland Park, Kansas.

## COFFEY, J Randall
Fisher & Phillips LLP, Kansas City
816 842 8770
rcoffey@laborlawyers.com
*Featured in Labor & Employment (Kansas City & Surrounds)*
**Career:** Randy Coffey is a Partner in the Kansas City office. He represents employers in state and federal courts throughout the United States. Randy has litigated numerous multi-plaintiff and class-action cases, as well as cases brought by individual plaintiffs. He also provides representation

before state and federal administrative agencies, including the Equal Employment Opportunity Commission, the National Labor Relations Board, and the Occupational Safety and Health Administration. His experience includes traditional labor representation, such as labor contract negotiations, NLRB-supervised representation elections and litigation, and union avoidance. Randy serves as Management Chair of the American Bar Association Equal Employment Opportunity Committee.

### COLAGIOVANNI, Joseph
Fulbright & Jaworski LLP, Houston
314 505 8835
jcolagiovanni@fulbright.com
*Featured in Real Estate (St Louis & Surrounds)*
**Practice Areas:** Construction.
**Career:** Practice focuses on construction, design and development law and public/private partnerships involving infrastructure, domestically and internationally. Colagiovanni handles transactional counseling (encompassing finance, joint ventures, contracts, insurance, labor, licensing, environmental, intellectual property and land use matters) and domestic and international litigation and arbitration with respect to complex development projects, including utility and infrastructure systems; environmental remediation; commercial and residential complexes; industrial and manufacturing plants; hospitals, healthcare and research facilities; sports arenas; convention centers; hotel, casino and resort developments; and renovation and rehabilitation of historic structures.
**Personal:** A.B. Brown University (1979) JD Boston University School of Law (1982).

### COWDEN, John
Baker Sterchi Cowden & Rice LLC, Kansas City
816 471 2121
cowden@bscr-law.com
*Featured in Litigation (Kansas City & Surrounds)*
**Practice Areas:** John Cowden's practice includes the defense of product liability claims, aircraft accidents, commercial disputes, and insurance coverage disputes. He has tried numerous major lawsuits in all of these areas.
**Professional Memberships:** American College of Trial Lawyers (Fellow), American Board of Trial Advocates, International Association of Defense Counsel, Product Liability Advisory Council.
**Career:** Former Assistant Attorney General of Missouri, AV® Preeminent™ Peer Review Rated by Martindale-Hubbell, Best Lawyers® in America, Missouri & Kansas Super Lawyers®, Best of the Bar (KC Bus. Journal), Order of the Barristers (University of Missouri), Dean of the Trial Bar (KCMBA).
**Personal:** University of Missouri (JD), Missouri State University (BA).

### CRUZ, John E
Lewis, Rice & Fingersh, L.C., Kansas City
816 472 2540
jecruz@lrf-kc.com
*Featured in Real Estate (Kansas City & Surrounds)*
**Practice Areas:** John concentrates his practice primarily on retail and office leasing, representing

both landlords and tenants. He was nominated as a 'Rising Star' in 2003 by the Georgetown University Law School Advanced Commercial Leasing Institute and listed in Missouri and Kansas Rising Stars® 2009 and 2010.
**Professional Memberships:** Admitted in Kansas (1999) and Missouri (2000). Member of Kansas Bar Association, Kansas City Metropolitan Bar Association and International Council of Shopping Centers. Planning Committee Member, ICSC Next Generation - Kansas City.
**Personal:** Born March 25, 1971; JD, Washburn University School of Law, 1998; BA, University of Kansas, 1994.

### DAVISON, Bruce C
Dentons, Kansas City
816 460 2514
bruce.davison@dentons.com
*Featured in Corporate/M&A (Kansas City & Surrounds)*
**Practice Areas:** Focuses practice on taxation of mergers and acquisitions, limited liability companies and S corporations, real estate, exempt organizations, and trusts and estates. Counsels private companies on the corporate and tax aspects of leveraged buy-outs, including financing of such transactions. Clients include manufacturing, product distribution and leveraged buy-out firms.
**Career:** Joined Dentons in 1999. Has practiced law in Kansas City for more than 25 years.
**Personal:** Georgetown University Law School, JD; University of Kansas, BA, economics.

### DEVENEY, Jeannie M
Littler Mendelson, PC, Kansas City
816 627 4405
JDeVeney@littler.com
*Featured in Labor & Employment (Kansas City & Surrounds)*
**Practice Areas:** Discrimination and Harassment; Complex Litigation and Jury Trials; Class Actions; Retail; Wage and Hour.
**Professional Memberships:** Labor and Employment Section - Kansas Bar Association; Employment Law Committee - National Retail Federation; Equal Employment Opportunity Committee - American Bar Association; Leadership Overland Park; HRMA of Johnson County.
**Career:** Represents retailers, school districts, public entities, and other employers in all types of employment law issues; has appeared before the Equal Employment Opportunity Commission, the Missouri Commission on Human rights, the Kansas Human Rights Commission, the Kansas City Human Relations Department.
**Personal:** JD, Creighton University, 1995, magna cum laude; BA, University of Kansas, 1992, With Distinction, Phi Beta Kappa.

### DIGIOVANNI, Peter
Lewis, Rice & Fingersh, L.C., Kansas City
816 472 2504
pmdigiovanni@lrf-kc.com
*Featured in Real Estate (Kansas City & Surrounds)*
**Career:** Pete represents developers, tenants and other real estate professionals on a national basis, having handled transactions in over 30 states.

These have included the development, acquisition and sale of all types of commercial properties, including retail, office, industrial and mixed use. He has extensive experience in the negotiation of regional mall department store REA's, and has represented a national theater chain for over 30 years. Pete is a Member of the American College of Real Estate Lawyers, and is a frequent speaker at bar association and real estate trade association functions, including the the International Council of Shopping Centers. Pete also has served as an Adjunct Professor at the University of Kansas School of Law, and continues to teach at the Lewis White School of Real Estate at the Bloch School of Business at the University of Kansas City.
**Personal:** Born June 5, 1948; JD University of Kansas School of Law (Order of the Coif and Law Review) 1976; BA University of Kansas 1971. Joined Brown, Koralchik & Fingersh (predecessor to Lewis, Rice & Fingersh) in 1976.

### DOWD JR, Edward
Dowd Bennett LLP, St Louis
314 889 7301
edowd@dowdbennett.com
*Featured in Litigation (Missouri)*
**Career:** Mr Dowd has handled complex commercial litigation and white collar cases his entire career. He has represented numerous clients before the S.E.C., the Department of Justice, the Environmental Protection Agency and many other federal and state agencies. In 1999-2000, Mr Dowd acted as the Deputy Special Counsel in an investigation of the government relating to the Waco tragedy. Mr Dowd served as United States Attorney for the Eastern District of Missouri and as an Assistant US Attorney. He was a Partner at Dowd & Dowd, P.C. and at Bryan Cave, LLP.

### DRAKE, Denise K
Littler Mendelson, PC, Kansas City
816 627 4406
DDrake@littler.com
*Featured in Labor & Employment (Kansas City & Surrounds)*
**Practice Areas:** Discrimination and Harassment; Complex Litigation and Jury Trials; Training - Compliance, Ethics, Leadership; Wage and Hour.
**Professional Memberships:** Program chair, Employment Rights and Responsibilities Committee, Labor and Employment Section - American Bar Association; Management Advisory Committee, Labor and Employment Section - American Bar Association.
**Career:** Represents management in employment lawsuits, including collective, multi-plaintiff and multi-defendant employment actions, and arbitration and mediation.
**Publications:** "U.S. Supreme Court Ruling Provides Guidance on Monitoring Employee Texts and E-Mails," June, 2010.
**Personal:** Prior to joining Littler, was a human resources manager at an investment company. In law school, served as editor of the Kansas Law Review.

### ERB, Thomas C
Lewis, Rice & Fingersh LC, St Louis
314 444 7600
terb@lewisrice.com
*Featured in Corporate/M&A (St Louis & Surrounds)*
**Practice Areas:** Mergers and acquisitions; securities, banking and financial; corporate.
**Professional Memberships:** American Bar Association; Bar Association of Metropolitan St. Louis; Missouri Bar; Illinois Bar; selected by his peers for inclusion in The Best Lawyers in America® 2007-13; selected for inclusion in Missouri & Kansas Super Lawyers® 2007-12; AV® Preeminent™ Peer Review Rated by Martindale-Hubbell.
**Career:** Firm Chairman, Lewis, Rice & Fingersh, L.C. (2012-present).

### EVANS JR, Robert M
Senniger Powers LLP, St Louis
314 345 7000
revans@senniger.com
*Featured in Intellectual Property (Missouri)*
**Practice Areas:** Litigation.
**Professional Memberships:** Missouri Bar, Illinois Bar, United States Court of Appeals for the Federal Circuit, United States Court of Appeals for the Eighth Circuit, United States District Court for the Eastern District of Missouri, United States Patent and Trademark Office.
**Career:** Mr Evans is the practice group leader for Senniger Powers' Litigation Department and has more than 20 years of experience litigating complex intellectual property disputes in the federal courts. He has worked in nearly every major business center in the United States, including 28 states and the District of Columbia, in the course of all phases of litigation.

### FINUCANE, Brian J
Fisher & Phillips LLP, Kansas City
816 842 8770
bfinucane@laborlawyers.com
*Featured in Labor & Employment (Kansas City & Surrounds)*
**Career:** Brian Finucane is the Managing Partner of the Kansas City office. He provides a broad range of legal services in employment law, from daily client consultation designed to avoid legal problems to defending clients in complex class action litigation. He also represents clients in traditional labor law matters, negotiating contracts and handling NLRB matters, union contract arbitration, and union avoidance efforts. He represents employers across the country in state and federal courts and before the state and federal administrative agencies, including the Equal Employment Opportunity Commission, Department of Labor, National Labor Relations Board and Occupational Safety and Health Administration.

### FISHER, Robert
Dentons, Kansas City
816 460 2606
bob.fisher@dentons.com
*Featured in Corporate/M&A (Kansas City & Surrounds)*

**Practice Areas:** Specializes in corporate and transactional matters, principally M&A. Represents financial and strategic buyers and sellers (including private equity firms) of businesses and product lines, mostly in the private middle market. Assists in industry roll-up efforts and ownership transitions of family businesses. Represents public companies in reorganizations or domestic or foreign expansion by acquisition and strategic dispositions. Has counseled on M&A transactions in South America, Europe and Asia. **Professional Memberships:** ABA; Kansas City Metropolitan Bar Association; Missouri Bar Association; Director, Jordan Industries, Inc. **Personal:** Georgetown University Law School, LLM, Taxation, and JD; University of Notre Dame, BA.

**GODAR, Michael E**
Senniger Powers LLP, St Louis
314 345 7000
mgodar@senniger.com
*Featured in Intellectual Property (Missouri)*
**Practice Areas:** Mechanical Patent Prosecution. **Professional Memberships:** Missouri Bar, United States District Court for the Eastern District of Missouri, United States Court of Appeals for the Federal Circuit, United States Patent and Trademark Office. **Career:** Mr Godar has been actively engaged in the prosecution, licensing and enforcement of US and international patents for more than thirty years. His particular emphasis is in the mechanical arts, including such technologies as combinatorial reactor systems, flow control systems, weighing machines, sports and recreational equipment, cutting and welding apparatus, packaging machines and others.

**HACKMANN, Frank H**
Dentons, St Louis
314 259 5804
frank.hackmann@dentons.com
*Featured in Environment (St Louis & Surrounds)*
**Practice Areas:** Concentrates in environmental law, including developing effective compliance monitoring programs; advising on permits and permit applications; evaluating environmental aspects of business transactions, including acquisitions and divestitures; representing PRP's in Superfund issues; negotiating voluntary site cleanups, development on wetlands and handling related environmental and enforcement matters. Advises on issues related to biofuel facility planning and operations. Also has considerable experience in crisis management and conducting large scale compliance reviews. **Career:** Joined Dentons in 1990. **Personal:** Saint Louis University, JD; University of Illinois, Champaign-Urbana, BSChE. Associate Adjunct Professor, Saint Louis University School of Public Health.

**HARRISON, Rodney A**
Ogletree, Deakins, Nash, Smoak & Stewart, PC, St Louis
314 802 3949
rodney.harrison@ogletreedeakins.com
*Featured in Labor & Employment (St Louis & Surrounds)*
**Practice Areas:** Employment litigation and counseling, wage and hour, including class and collective actions, Railway Labor Act, restrictive covenant and trade secret litigation and advice. **Professional Memberships:** ABA, Labor & Employment Law Section; DRI, Employment Law Committee; HRMA; SHRM. **Career:** Shareholder, Ogletree Deakins, 2008-present. Admitted to practice in Missouri (1993). **Publications:** Mr Harrison has written and spoken extensively on a variety of labor and employment topics. **Personal:** Born in Baltimore, Maryland; JD, Washington University (1993); BA, Tufts University (1990).

**HOLLAND, James**
Fisher & Phillips LLP, Kansas City
816 842 8770
jholland@laborlawyers.com
*Featured in Labor & Employment (Kansas City & Surrounds)*
**Career:** Jim Holland is a partner in the Kansas City office. He devotes a substantial part of his practice to counseling employers about issues arising in the workplace including counseling, disciplining and terminating employees. Jim also has litigated matters in federal and state courts across the country. His experience includes NLRB litigation, union related matters and the design of personnel administration systems and policies. Jim also regularly presents seminars on a variety of labor and employment topics.

**HULLA, Patrick F**
Ogletree, Deakins, Nash, Smoak & Stewart, PC, Kansas City
816 471 1301
patrick.hulla@ogletreedeakins.com
*Featured in Labor & Employment (Kansas City & Surrounds)*
**Practice Areas:** Practice is concentrated in the area of complex employment litigation. Hulla has successfully led, and co-led, the defense of dozens of collective actions for numerous Fortune 100 companies. Hulla has also been lead defense counsel in discrimination class actions, age discrimination collective actions, and wage and hour class actions. **Professional Memberships:** Missouri Bar Association, Kansas Bar Association. **Career:** Co-leads firm's Class Action Group. Managing Shareholder of firm's Kansas City, Missouri office. Member of firm's Management, Diversity, and Litigation Support Steering Committees. Former in-house counsel. **Personal:** Baker University (B.S., 1990), University of Missouri - Kansas City (JD, 1993).

**JAMES, Kurt F**
Senniger Powers LLP, St Louis
314 345 7000
kjames@senniger.com
*Featured in Intellectual Property (Missouri)*
**Practice Areas:** Mechanical Patent Prosecution. **Professional Memberships:** Missouri Bar, United States District Court, Eastern District of Missouri, United States Patent and Trademark Office. **Career:** For over twenty years, Mr James has been actively engaged in the prosecution, licensing and enforcement of patents in the United States and abroad. His particular emphasis is in the mechanical arts, including medical devices, refrigeration, pipe rehabilitation systems, paper handling devices, semiconductor growth and processing equipment, pneumatic tools, electric motors and others. Mr James also serves as the Mechanical Department's practice group leader.

**LEMLEY, Gregg M**
Ogletree, Deakins, Nash, Smoak & Stewart, PC, St Louis
314 802 3941
gregg.lemley@ogletreedeakins.com
*Featured in Labor & Employment (St Louis & Surrounds)*
**Practice Areas:** Employment litigation and counseling, including class and collective action litigation; restrictive covenant litigation. **Professional Memberships:** ABA, Section of Labor and Employment Law. **Career:** Founder and Shareholder, St. Louis office of Ogletree Deakins since 2007. Admitted to practice in Missouri (1995) and Illinois (1996). **Publications:** Mr Lemley has written and spoken extensively on a variety of labor and employment topics. **Personal:** Webster University (BA, Music & Philosophy, with distinction, 1992), Washington University (JD, Order of Coif, 1995).

**MARLER, Jennifer A**
Dentons, St Louis
314 259 5874
jennifer.marler@dentons.com
*Featured in Real Estate (St Louis & Surrounds)*
**Practice Areas:** Managing partner, St. Louis office. Represents lenders on loan transactions, with particular expertise on construction lending and projects that involve public incentives. Represents developers and other users of real estate on complex transactions, frequently involving material public incentives. Leads global transactions team for St. Louis, working closely with firm teams across international platform. **Professional Memberships:** Commercial Real Estate Women (CREW) Network, CoreNet, Smith Institute at the University of Missouri (Advisory Board Member), American College of Mortgage Attorneys. **Personal:** Washington University School of Law, JD; University of Missouri-Columbia, BA, summa cum laude, Phi Beta Kappa.

**MARVIN, John**
Dentons, Kansas City
816 460 2513
john.marvin@dentons.com
*Featured in Corporate/M&A (Kansas City & Surrounds)*
**Practice Areas:** 40+ years' experience in securities and general corporate law. Counsels public company boards, management and securities industry broker-dealers, advisors, fund managers. **Professional Memberships:** Former member, State Board of Law Examiners: Society of Corporate Secretaries and Governance Professionals. **Career:** Joined Dentons as Partner, 1996. Previously Managing Partner at a Kansas City law firm and law school professor of securities regulation and corporate and other business problems. **Personal:** University of Missouri at Kansas City, BBA, JD, with distinction, Omicron Delta Kappa, Honors Society; Law Review editor, National Moot Court Team; New York University, Research Fellow, LLM, honors.

**MATULA, Michael L.**
Ogletree, Deakins, Nash, Smoak & Stewart, PC, Kansas City
816 471 1301
mike.matula@ogletreedeakins.com
*Featured in Labor & Employment (Kansas City & Surrounds)*
**Practice Areas:** Labor and Employment Law, Litigation, E-Discovery. Has represented employers in a variety of employment matters, including discharge and harassment cases, non-competition/trade secrets disputes, FLSA claims; also has experience in commercial, tort, and insurance litigation. **Professional Memberships:** The Missouri Bar, Kansas Bar Association, Adjunct Professor - University of Missouri-Kansas City School of Law, Defense Research Institute. **Career:** Admitted to practice in Kansas and Missouri. **Publications:** Has authored numerous employment law articles; co-authored an ABA treatise on professional responsibility in litigation. **Personal:** Claremont McKenna College (BA, 1993), The University of Kansas School of Law (JD, 1996).

**MILLER, Charles F**
Lewis, Rice & Fingersh, L.C., Kansas City
816 472 2512
cfmiller@lrf-kc.com
*Featured in Real Estate (Kansas City & Surrounds)*
**Practice Areas:** Real estate law, including acquisition, sale, financing, leasing, construction, development, redevelopment, incentives, zoning, other governmental approvals and joint ventures. **Professional Memberships:** American College of Real Estate Lawyers; Missouri Economic Development Finance Association (Board of Directors); NAIOP Association of Commercial Real Estate, past local Board of Directors; Missouri Bar Association, Property Law Committee; Kansas City Metropolitan Bar Association, Real Estate Law Committee (past Chairman); Board of Editors (past), Shopping

Center Legal Update; International Council of Shopping Centers; Greater Kansas City Chamber of Commerce, Kansas City, Missouri Committee; Downtown Council of Kansas City (Executive Committee Member); Downtown Development Group (Chair), and other civic and professional organizations.

**Career:** Joined Brown, Koralchik & Fingersh 1979 (predecessor to Lewis, Rice & Fingersh, LC), Chairman of Real Estate Department, Member of Executive Committee; past Adjunct Professor of Law, UMKC Law School; regular speaker at legal and real estate industry events and seminars, including Are Easements Easy, and Case Study of Missouri and Kansas Development Incentives; selected Real Estate Lawyer of the Year 2010 and Land Use & Zoning Law Lawyer of the Year 2012 for Kansas City, MO by The Best Lawyers in America.

**Publications:** Include Missouri Provides Condemnation Powers and Real Estate Tax Abatement for Developers, 'Shopping Center Legal Update', and Landlord's Duty to Relet When a Tenant Abandons Leased Property, 43 'Missouri Law Review' 359, among others.

**Personal:** JD University of Missouri Law School, 1979; Law Review Board of Editors; AB Political Science, University of Missouri, 1976 (summa cum laude), Phi Beta Kappa.

## NEEDHAM, Amie E
Littler Mendelson, PC, St Louis
314 659 2006
aneedham@littler.com
*Featured in Labor & Employment (St Louis & Surrounds)*

**Practice Areas:** Labor & Employment.
**Professional Memberships:** Member, ABA Labor and Employment Law Section, Practice and Procedure Under the NLRA Committee. Member, Illinois and Missouri Bar Associations.
**Career:** Ms Needham has extensive experience in the field of labor-management relations, exclusively representing management side. She has particular expertise in the negotiation of collective bargaining agreements and in union avoidance. Ms Needham also has significant experience counseling companies on discrimination, leaves of absence, compliance, hirings, terminations and layoffs, up to and through completion of litigation.
**Personal:** JD, New York Law School (2000); BS, Oklahoma State University (1996).

## PROPHETE, Donald S
Ogletree, Deakins, Nash, Smoak & Stewart, PC, Kansas City
816 410 2220
don.prophete@ogletreedeakins.com
*Featured in Labor & Employment (Kansas City & Surrounds)*

**Practice Areas:** Represents management in complex employment litigation matters. Has served as lead trial counsel in all types of employment disputes in federal and state courts and in employment arbitration as well as NLRA arbitration matters.

**Professional Memberships:** The Missouri Bar, Kansas Bar Association, The Pennsylvania Bar Association, American Bar Association (Labor and Employment Section), The National Bar Association.
**Career:** Admitted to practice in Missouri, Pennsylvania, U.S. District Court (Eastern and Western Districts of Missouri), U.S. District Court (Kansas), U.S. Court of Appeals (Third and Eighth Circuits).
**Personal:** Fordham University (BA, 1989), The Boston University School of Law (JD, 1992).

## REISDORFF, Kerri S.
Ogletree, Deakins, Nash, Smoak & Stewart, PC, Kansas City
816 471 1301
kerri.reisdorff@ogletreedeakins.com
*Featured in Labor & Employment (Kansas City & Surrounds)*

**Practice Areas:** Advises, defends employers against claims of discrimination, harassment, retaliation, wrongful termination, as well as FMLA claims, and wage and hour violations before federal and state courts and administrative agencies. Assists clients in proactively addressing workplace issues.
**Professional Memberships:** Missouri Bar, Kansas Bar Association, American Bar Association
**Career:** Admitted to practice in Kansas, Missouri, Nebraska, U.S. Court of Appeals, Eighth and Tenth Circuits.
**Publications:** BNA Books (contributing author) - "How to Take a Case Before the NLRB"; Missouri Bar Association CLE - "Missouri Employment Discrimination, Religious Discrimination".
**Personal:** University of Nebraska (B.S., 1994), University of Nebraska (JD, 1999).

## RIST, Steven L
Dentons, Kansas City
816 460 2645
steven.rist@dentons.com
*Featured in Corporate/M&A (Kansas City & Surrounds)*

**Practice Areas:** Concentrates in areas of private equity and M&A. Represents private equity funds in structuring, negotiating and documenting investments in leveraged buyouts of, and sales of, portfolio companies. Extensive experience representing private equity funds in mergers, acquisitions, leveraged recapitalizations, restructurings and workouts and public and private finance. Assists private equity funds in a range of matters not directly related to the formation and investment activities of funds. Serves as "general counsel" to numerous portfolio companies providing day-to-day legal and business advice to the portfolio companies and their sponsors.
**Personal:** University of Kansas, JD, 1984; University of Iowa, 1981.

## ROTHSCHILD, Andrew
Lewis, Rice & Fingersh LC, St Louis
314 444 7600
arothschild@lewisrice.com
*Featured in Litigation (St Louis & Surrounds)*

**Practice Areas:** Admiralty; alternative dispute resolution; environmental, chemical and toxic tort; insurance; natural resources and alternative energy; professional liability.
**Career:** Member, Lewis, Rice & Fingersh, L.C. (1976-present); Municipal Judge, City of Ladue, Missouri (January 2004-January 2006); Assistant Attorney General, State of Missouri for Attorney General John C. Danforth, Counsel for State Auditor, Department of Transportation, Office of Administration and State Parks and Recreation Division of Department of Natural Resources (1973-1976).

## ROVAK, Stephen H
Dentons, St Louis
314 259 5886
stephen.rovak@dentons.com
*Featured in Litigation (St Louis & Surrounds)*

**Practice Areas:** National head, legacy Dentons General Corporate and Specialty Litigation Group; Chair of firm's St. Louis Litigation Practice. Commercial, construction, franchise, intellectual property, distribution law and medical issues. Alternative dispute resolution expert; former chair, Commercial Advisory committee of the American Arbitration Association's St. Louis Region.
**Professional Memberships:**
**Career:** Joined Dentons 1995. Litigation Division; Office of the Judge Advocate General, The Pentagon (1975-77).
**Personal:** Harvard Law School, JD; George Washington University, Master's in Forensic Sciences; Washington University, AB. Fellow, Forensic Medicine, Walter Reed Medical Center. Fellow, American College of Trial Lawyers. Fellow, International Academy of Trial Lawyers. Colonel, USAFR (Ret).

## SEIGFREID JR, James T
Baker Sterchi Cowden & Rice LLC, Kansas City
816 471 2121
seigfreid@bscr-law.com
*Featured in Litigation (Kansas City & Surrounds)*

**Practice Areas:** Mr Seigfreid has successfully tried products liability cases for Fortune 100 companies for more than 25 years. His practice includes the defense of automotive, agricultural, heavy truck, construction and marine manufacturers. He acts as regional trial counsel throughout the Midwest and coordinating counsel supervising product liability and toxic tort litigation throughout the nation.
**Professional Memberships:** International Association of Defense Counsel, Association of Defense Trial Attorneys, Association for the Advancement of Automotive Medicine, American Boat & Yacht Council, Defense Research Institute.
**Career:** Missouri & Kansas Super Lawyers (2008-2011), Chambers USA – recognized for his work in products litigation and savvy in the courtroom (2008), AV® Preeminent™ Peer Review Rated by Martindale-Hubbell.
**Personal:** Drake University (JD, 1984), Regis College (BA, 1979).

## SHORT, Barry A
Lewis, Rice & Fingersh LC, St Louis
314 444 7600
bshort@lewisrice.com
*Featured in Litigation (St Louis & Surrounds), Litigation (Missouri)*

**Practice Areas:** Antitrust; environmental, chemical and toxic tort; securities; white-collar crime.
**Career:** 1977-2011, Member, Lewis, Rice & Fingersh, L.C.; 2011-Present, Of Counsel, Lewis, Rice & Fingersh, L.C.; 1976-77, United States Attorney, Eastern District of Missouri; 1973-76, Assistant United States Attorney, Eastern District of Missouri; 1971-73, King & Short.

## SNYDER, John L
Dentons, Kansas City
816 460 2668
john.snyder@dentons.com
*Featured in Real Estate (Kansas City & Surrounds)*

**Practice Areas:** Represents developers and companies on complex real estate projects, including development, land use, financing and economic incentives; represents landlords and tenants on lease negotiations; represents banks and loan servicers on loan transactions, workouts, and foreclosures; and represents real estate funds and other buyers of distressed assets and debt.
**Professional Memberships:** Member, Missouri Bar, Kansas Bar and KC Metropolitan Bar Association; KCADC Board, KC Civic Council; Ronald McDonald House; National MS Society.
**Career:** Managing partner - Kansas City office
**Personal:** University of Kansas School of Law, JD, Order of the Coif; Illinois Wesleyan University, BA, magna cum laude.

## VAN DYKE, Michael J
Dentons, Kansas City
816 460 2621
michael.vandyke@dentons.com
*Featured in Corporate/M&A (Kansas City & Surrounds)*

**Practice Areas:** Areas of concentration include mergers and acquisitions, taxable and taxfree spinoffs, venture capital, small business investment companies, corporate finance, securities and secured lending, strategic partnerships and joint ventures, outsourcing, business transition and succession planning, business tax and estate planning, business reorganizations and financial workouts, media and direct marketing, financial services, construction, manufacturing, healthcare, ground transportation, product marketing and distribution and educational and other nonprofit entities.
**Publications:** The Missouri Bar 'Business Organizations' and "Business Transitions" Lawyer's Desk Books 1986 through 2011 chapters on 'Patterns of Sale.'
**Personal:** University of Missouri, LLM, JD; Notre Dame, BA.

## VANDER TUIG, Marc W
Senniger Powers LLP, St Louis
314 345 7000
mvandertuig@senniger.com
*Featured in Intellectual Property (Missouri)*

## WELLFORD JR, Harry W
Littler Mendelson, PC, St Louis
314 432 4797
hwellford@littler.com
*Featured in Labor & Employment (St Louis & Surrounds)*

**Practice Areas:** Labor & Employment: Unfair Competition; Sports; Contingent Work Force; & Financial Services.

**Professional Memberships:** American Bar Association: Labor and Employment Section/Fair Labor Standards; Subcommittee Member (2000-2013); Illinois, Missouri, Metropolitan St. Louis, and Tennessee Bar Associations; Expert witness on Missouri Employment Law for Missouri Bar Plan; Civic: Humane Society of Missouri (Former Board of Director), WORTH Industries Sheltered Workshop (Former President), Attorney for Civil Pictures (Emmy nominated documentary on the St. Louis Arch).

**Publications:** Co-Editor ABA Fair Labor Standards Act Committee's Treatise on SOX/Dodd Frank Acts, 2013.

**Personal:** JD, University of Tennessee, 1981, Order of the Coif; BA, Washington and Lee University, cum laude, 1976.

## WOLF, Jerome
Dentons, Kansas City
816 460 2420
jerome.wolf@dentons.com
*Featured in Litigation (Kansas City & Surrounds)*

**Practice Areas:** Concentrates in civil and commercial litigation. Experience in class actions, energy, environmental, antitrust, intellectual property, franchise litigation, construction litigation, alternative dispute resolution.

**Professional Memberships:** Founding President of the Kansas City Metropolitan Bar Foundation, cofounder of the Federal Court Advocates Section, Kansas City Metropolitan Bar Association, Recipient of the Lifetime Achievement Award, Kansas City Metropolitan Bar Association, past President, Kansas City Metropolitan Bar Association. Founding Managing Partner, legacy Dentons Kansas City office, past Member, Policy and Planning Committee (legacy Dentons's management committee).

**Personal:** Harvard Law School, JD. Yale University, BA magna cum laude, Phi Beta Kappa.

## WOODS, Curtis E
Dentons, Kansas City
816 460 2425
curtis.woods@dentons.com
*Featured in Litigation (Kansas City & Surrounds), Litigation (Missouri)*

**Practice Areas:** Concentrates in business litigation, emphasizing complex civil, commercial, and white collar criminal litigation, with extensive experience in class actions, antitrust, intellectual property, business torts, unfair competition, shareholder, and franchise litigation. Experience representing US and foreign individuals and businesses in federal and state grand jury and other government investigation throughout the country, and handling post-trial motions and appeals.

**Career:** Dentons 1994-present; Spencer Fane Britt & Browne 1976-1994.

**Personal:** Northwestern University, JD, cum laude, Order of the Coif; University of Missouri, BA, cum laude.

## YATES, Kimberly
Littler Mendelson, PC, St Louis
314 659 2005
KYates@littler.com
*Featured in Labor & Employment (St Louis & Surrounds)*

**Practice Areas:** Labor and Employment.

**Career:** Ms Yates focuses her practice on labor and employment litigation, particularly in the areas of wage and hour collective and class action matters, restrictive covenant contracts and non-competes cases, and discrimination and retaliation lawsuits. She provides client counseling concerning risk management and compliance with state and federal employment laws.

**Personal:** J.D., University of Missouri School of Law, 2000; AB, University of Missouri, Columbia, 1992.

# LEWIS, RICE & FINGERSH, LC

www.lewisrice.com

**Managing Partner, St Louis:** Thomas C Erb
**Managing Partner, Kansas City:** William E Carr

### Firm Overview:

The law firm of Lewis, Rice & Fingersh, LC traces its history to the founding of Lewis & Rice in St Louis during 1909 and of Brown, Koralchik & Fingersh in Kansas City during 1948. In August 1989, the two firms merged to form the present organization, having offices in Kansas City, St Louis, Jefferson City, Town & Country and Washington, Missouri; Overland Park, Kansas and Belleville, Illinois. With more than 150 lawyers practicing in all of the major legal specialty areas, Lewis, Rice & Fingersh is not only a leading regional firm but has a broad base of national clients as well, who draw upon its talents in such diverse areas as admiralty, antitrust, corporate, heathcare, intellectual property, labor and employment, litigation, estate planning, tax and real estate.

### Main Areas of Practice:

**Corporate/Business, Tax & Estate Planning:**

The firm's Corporate Practice encompasses many disciplines, including banking, securities, corporate finance, mergers and acquisitions, healthcare, bankruptcy, closely-held businesses, employee benefits and e-commerce. The firm serves the diverse needs of public and private businesses of all sizes and in all industries. The attorneys in the firm's Tax Department handle a variety of federal, state and local matters involving tax planning and tax disputes. The firm's estate planning attorneys advise clients regarding individual tax and estate planning, prenuptial agreements, charitable giving and intrafamily wealth transfers.

**Contacts:**
**St Louis:** John J Riffle, Larry H Weltman
Marian V Mehan
**Kansas City:** Stan C Johnston

**Litigation & Labor:**

The firm's Litigation Department represents clients in all types of commercial disputes, including claims brought under general contract law, business tort law, insurance policies, the Uniform Commercial Code, federal and state securities laws, lender liability and class action representations. The department has extensive experience in complex litigation, which often requires in-depth review and analysis of thousands of documents, and in alternative dispute resolution techniques. The Labor and Employment Group represents management in employment-related litigation in federal and state courts in actions involving Title VII, the ADA, the ADEA, ERISA, the FMLA, the PDA, state anti-discrimination statutes, and various state law theories, such as wrongful discharge claims and non-competition disputes.

**Contacts:**
**St Louis:** Richard B Walsh, Jr
**Kansas City:** Robert W Tormohlen

**Real Estate:**

The firm's Real Estate Practice includes representation of lenders, developers, institutional investors, contractors, architects, investment advisors, mortgage bankers, brokers and tenants. The department has extensive experience in financing, development, acquisition, joint ventures, taxation, leasing, environmental law, zoning, and work-outs, involving complex, large-scale transactions of all kinds and in nearly every state, as well as several foreign countries. A significant number of attorneys within the department have been recognized by inclusion in, for example, the American College of Real Estate Lawyers, and several leading legal publications, as well as being called upon to teach their specialty at area law schools.

**Contacts:**
**St Louis:** Jacob W Reby
**Kansas City:** Charles F Miller

## PRACTICE AREAS

Business
Corporate
Estate Planning
Labor
Litigation
Real Estate
Tax

## OFFICES

### MISSOURI

**ST LOUIS:** 600 Washington Avenue, Suite 2500, St Louis, MO 63101

Tel: 314 444 7600  Fax: 314 241 6056

**KANSAS CITY:** 1010 Walnut, Suite 500, Kansas City, MO 64106

Tel: 816 421 2500  Fax: 816 472 2500
Email: firm@lrf-kc.com

**JEFFERSON CITY:** 221 E Capitol Avenue, Jefferson City, MO 65101

Tel: 573 893 7724

**TOWN & COUNTRY:** 12935 North Outer Forty, Suite 210, Town & Country, MO 63141

Tel: 314 439 5169

**WASHINGTON:** 1200 Jefferson; PO Box 1040, Washington, MO 63090

Tel: 636 239 7747

### ILLINOIS

**BELLEVILLE:** 325 S. High Street, Belleville, IL 62220

Tel: 618 234 8636

### KANSAS

**OVERLAND PARK:** 7007 College Boulevard, Suite 440, Overland Park, KS 66211

Tel: 913 381 8898

# LEWIS RICE
# FINGERSH L.C.

# POLSINELLI PC

**www.**polsinelli.com **tel:** 816 753 1000 **fax:** 816 753 1536

**Chairman:** W Russell Welsh
Number of partners: 352   Number of lawyers: 631

## Firm Overview:

Polsinelli serves corporate, institutional, entrepreneurial, and individual clients worldwide with a commitment to exceeding expectations and providing its clients with what they want most – practical legal guidance, infused with insightful business perspective. Polsinelli attorneys invest in understanding their clients' businesses from all angles, as well as the risks, challenges and issues affecting a given industry. With more than 630 attorneys across 50 practice areas and 16 cities, Polsinelli was named by Inc. magazine as one of the fastest-growing, full-service law firms in America (2012). Polsinelli is a recognized leader in the industries driving its overall growth – including health care, financial services, real estate development and transactions, science and technology, energy, and business litigation.

## Main Areas of Practice:

### Health Care:

The American Health Lawyers Association ranked Polsinelli as the seventh largest health care law firm in the nation in 2012. With 110 attorneys focused on meeting the needs of health care providers across the industry, Polsinelli integrates its services and disciplines to ensure its clients receive practical advice with an eye toward driving growth and avoiding hidden pitfalls. A recent successful collaboration includes guiding a 13-hospital system through its sale to a larger entity, resulting in one of the largest hospital sale transactions in US history.

### Real Estate Development & Transactions:

The firm's full-service real estate transactions, zoning and land use groups are well known for their specialties in economic development incentives (tax increment financing, STAR Bonds, transportation development districts, etc), development, public/private partnerships, like-kind exchanges, construction and design, tax credits and lending. The firm has been lead counsel on some of the largest projects in the nation, including casinos, sports facilities and associated retail and destination entertainment, as well as alternative energy projects and major hotel, condominium and multifamily projects in New York, Chicago and Miami.

### Financial Services:

The firm's national financial services practice encompasses all aspects of debt financing - from secured lending and securitization to loan origination and loan enforcement - providing a 'one-stop shop' for lenders. Polsinelli's attorneys have documented and closed more than 2,030 commercial real estate loans ($20 billion in principal amount) across 50 states and the District of Columbia. The department also has extensive experience in asset-based and other commercial lending, syndicated lending, securitizations and other capital markets transactions. The firm's bankruptcy team represents debtors, creditors' committees, lenders, and other stakeholders.

### Science & Technology:

In an era when science and technology industries are experiencing rapid growth, Polsinelli's multidisciplinary attorneys provide tailored representation to early-stage, emerging, and mature businesses in the areas of intellectual property, technology transfer, licensing, health care, corporate finance, mergers and acquisitions and real estate development. Recent work examples include assisting technology and life sciences companies in utilizing state tax incentives to raise early stage capital, as well as counseling clients through periods of growth that have involved venture capital investments and sales to international private equity funds.

### Energy:

Polsinelli's attorneys offer national experience representing energy companies, utilities, developers, lenders and investors in connection with the acquisition, development, construction, finance and operation of energy projects. Polsinelli's attorneys advise clients across a wide range of legal issues facing their businesses. Recent highlights include the firm's representation of an investor-owned utility in the construction and regulatory approvals of a $2 billion electricity-generating facility, as well as representation of an independent oil producer in a major drilling program involving in excess of 400 wells.

### Business Litigation:

Polsinelli's business litigation attorneys provide companies and professionals with practical legal advice that is founded on a thorough understanding of substantive legal issues, real courtroom experience and sound business judgment. The firm specializes in helping clients make good business decisions based not only on the facts and law, but also on economic evaluation, cost and measured risk. Polsinelli has recently defended a publically-traded hospital in a $450 million lawsuit; obtained a $270 million verdict on behalf of a commercial client; and successfully defended the City of Kansas City in a property tax election dispute.

## OFFICES

**MISSOURI**

**KANSAS CITY:** 700 W. 47th Street, Suite 1000, MO 64112
Tel: 816 753 1000   Fax: 816 753 1536
Email: solutions@polsinelli.com

**KANSAS CITY:** 120 W. 12th Street, MO 64105
Tel: 816 421 3355   Fax: 816 374 0509

**ST. LOUIS:** 100 S. Fourth Street, Suite 1000, MO 63102
Tel: 314 889 8000   Fax: 314 231 1776

**ST. LOUIS:** 7733 Forsyth Boulevard, Suite 750, MO 63105
Tel: 314 889 8000   Fax: 314 727 7166

**JEFFERSON CITY:** 221 Bolivar Street, MO 65101
Tel: 573 636 8135   Fax: 573 636 5226

**SPRINGFIELD:** 901 St. Louis Street, Suite 1200, MO 65806
Tel: 417 869 3353   Fax: 417 869 9943

**ST. JOSEPH:** 3101 Frederick Avenue, MO 64506
Tel: 816 364 2117   Fax: 816 279 3977

**ARIZONA**

**PHOENIX:** One East Washington, Suite 1200, AZ 85004
Tel: 602 650 2000   Fax: 602 264 7033

**CALIFORNIA**

**LOS ANGELES:** 2049 Century Park East, Suite 2300, CA 90067
Tel: 310 556 1801   Fax: 310 556 1802

**COLORADO**

**DENVER:** 1515 Wynkoop Street, Suite 600, CO 80202
Tel: 303 572 9300   Fax: 303 572 7883

**DELAWARE**

**WILMINGTON:** 222 Delaware Avenue, Suite 1101, DE 19801
Tel: 302 252 0920   Fax: 302 252 0921

**DISTRICT OF COLUMBIA**

**WASHINGTON, DC:** 1152 15th Street, N.W., Suite 800, DC 20005
Tel: 202 783 3300   Fax: 202 783 3535

**ILLINOIS**

**CHICAGO:** 161 N. Clark Street, Suite 4200, IL 60601
Tel: 312 819 1900   Fax: 312 819 1910

**EDWARDSVILLE:** 105 W. Vandalia Street, Suite 400, IL 62025
Tel: 618 692 2600   Fax: 618 655 9640

**KANSAS**

**OVERLAND PARK:** 6201 College Boulevard, Suite 500, KS 66211
Tel: 913 451 8788   Fax: 913 451 6205

**TOPEKA:** 555 S. Kansas Avenue, Suite 101, KS 66603
Tel: 785 233 1446   Fax: 785 233 1939

**NEW YORK**

**NEW YORK:** 805 Third Avenue, Suite 2020, NY 10022
Tel: 212 684 0199   Fax: 212 684 0197

**TEXAS**

**DALLAS:** 2501 N. Harwood, Suite 1900, TX 75201
Tel: 214 397 0030   Fax: 214 397 0033

# ROUSE HENDRICKS GERMAN MAY PC

**www.**rhgm.com  **tel:** 816 471 7700 **fax:** 816 471 2221

**Managing Partner:** Committee
Number of partners: 10   Number of lawyers: 16
Languages: *English, Spanish*

## Firm Overview:

Established in 1992, Rouse Hendricks German May prosecutes and defends complex litigation matters throughout the country. The firm has a formidable track record of success in high-stakes trials, arbitrations and appeals and a national reputation for an aggressive yet practical approach. The firm has the flexibility to offer hourly or alternative fee arrangements (including contingency or blended arrangements). The firm was the only one in Kansas City to receive honor as "Law Firm of the Year" in the 2013 Missouri Lawyers Weekly Awards.

## Main Areas of Practice:

### Business Litigation:

- Following a 10-day trial in 2012, the firm obtained a jury verdict for $21.3 million in actual damages and $10 million in punitive damages in favor of Hallmark in a trade secret misappropriation lawsuit against private equity firm Monitor Clipper Partners. The victory followed collection of a 2010 settlement for $12.5 million from affiliated consulting company Monitor Company Group. Hallmark Cards, Inc. v. Monitor Clipper Partners, LLC (United States District Court for the Western District of Missouri)
- At conclusion of six-week arbitration of breach of contract dispute, the firm obtained a $373 million award in favor of the firm's corporate client. Award was confirmed at trial court level, and a total of nearly $384 million was paid (including interest). This is the largest known collected judgment in Missouri history. American Century Investment Management, Inc. v. J.P. Morgan Invest Holdings, LLC (AAA Arbitration, confirmed, Circuit Court of Jackson County, Missouri)
- Represented financial services company and obtained Rule 12(b)(6) dismissal of multi-million dollar claims brought by former executive resulting from stock redemption contract. Kmak v. American Century Companies, Inc. (United States District Court for the Western District of Missouri)
- In 2013, obtained voluntary dismissal of client after taking key depositions of plaintiff Pizza Hut and franchisees in case alleging years-long manipulation of the Chicago Mercantile Exchange. Pizza Hut, Inc. et al. v. Dairy Farmers of America, et al. (Circuit Court of Jackson County, Missouri)
- Currently prosecuting claims for breach of fiduciary duty, fraud, breach of contract, and conspiracy on behalf of Denver-based oil and gas exploration company against former joint venture partner and co-conspirators arising out of acquisition of oil and gas interests. Rocky Mountain Exploration, Inc. v. Tracker Resource Exploration ND, LLC, et al. (District Court for the City and County of Denver, Colorado)
**Contact:** Charles German **Email:** charleyg@rhgm.com
**Contact:** Randall Hendricks **Email:** randyh@rhgm.com

### Antitrust:

- Obtained summary judgment in favor of client in antitrust class action alleging more than $618 million (before trebling) in damages. The court denied summary judgment motions filed by co-defendants (represented by other firms). Southeast Milk Antitrust Litigation (US District Court for Eastern District of Tennessee)
- Obtained court ruling striking plaintiff's antitrust damage claim against non-profit hospital client. Heartland Surgical Specialty Hospital v. Midwest Division, Inc. (US District Court for District of Kansas)
- Currently prosecuting opt-out antitrust action against cartel of polyurethane foam manufacturers. LaCrosse Furniture Company v. Future Foam, Inc. et al. (US District Court for the Northern District of Ohio)
**Contact:** Brandon Boulware **Email:** brandonb@rhgm.com
**Contact:** Daniel Hodes **Email:** danh@rhgm.com

### Securities:

- Represented American Century in complex litigation involving the Investment Act of 1940. Court dismissed plaintiffs' claims that exceeded $700 million after striking plaintiffs' experts and sustaining other motions filed by American Century. Baker et al. v. American Century Investment Management Inc. (US District Court for Western District of Missouri)
- Represented board chairman of public company in securities class action, shareholder derivative suits, and SEC enforcement action. Client settled SEC case for nominal amount, while company's former CEO (represented by another firm) paid more than $1 million to settle SEC case and spent 18 months in prison. In re American Italian Pasta Securities Litigation (US District Court for Western District of Missouri)
- Currently represent Sprint Corporation in securities class action (US District Court of District of Kansas)
**Contact:** Randall Hendricks **Email:** randyh@rhgm.com
**Contact:** Brandon Boulware **Email:** brandonb@rhgm.com

### Products Liability:

- Obtained $452 million jury verdict for KCPL on product liability claims arising out of power plant explosion. After trial court reversed verdict, firm successfully appealed and verdict was reinstated in full. Kansas City Power & Light Co. v. Rockwell Automation, Inc. (Circuit Court of Jackson County, Missouri)
- Serve as national trial counsel for manufacturer of tractor-trailer suspension systems and distributor of exercise equipment.
**Contact:** William Beil **Email:** billb@rhgm.com

### Professional Malpractice:

- After month-long trial, obtained $21.7 million verdict in accounting malpractice action involving accounting firm's acquisition audit for purchase of manufacturing company. Battenfield of Am. Holding Co. et al. v. [Large Accounting Firm] (US District Court for District of Kansas)
- Currently represent multiple law firms and accounting firms in malpractice actions, including defense of one of Missouri's largest law firms in malpractice action claiming a nine-figure amount in damages. (Circuit Court of Jackson County, Missouri)
**Contact:** Phillip Greenfield **Email:** philg@rhgm.com

### White Collar/Internal & Governmental Investigations:

- RHGM attorneys have extensive experience litigating against federal and state regulatory and enforcement agencies, including DOJ, SEC, CFTC, IRS, FDIC, Federal Reserve, SIG-TARP, EPA, FTC, and state attorneys general. The firm also discreetly conducts internal investigations of corporations ahead of, and in some cases during, government investigations.
**Contact:** Charles German **Email:** charleyg@rhgm.com
**Contact:** Brandon Boulware **Email:** brandonb@rhgm.com

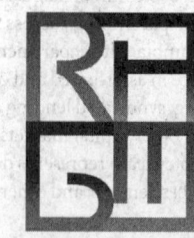

# SENNIGER POWERS LLP

www.senniger.com **tel:** 314 345 7000 **fax:** 314 345 7600

**Managing Partner:** Keith A Rabenberg
Number of partners: 18
Number of lawyers: 35

**OFFICES**

MISSOURI
**ST LOUIS:** 100 N Broadway, 17th Floor, MO 63102
Tel: 314 345 7000  Fax: 314 345 7600

## Firm Overview:

Senniger Powers is the largest firm in Missouri and one of the largest in the Midwest that limits its practice to intellectual property. This focus and the firm's depth of talent place it in a unique position among competitive firms in being able to help clients achieve their patent and trademark goals. The firm has several attorneys with educational and practical expertise in each of the core technology areas – chemical, life sciences, mechanical, and electrical – providing the horsepower to effectively service medium- and large-sized businesses. The diverse technical capabilities of the firm's professionals are hard at work serving clients in a wide array of industries including pharmaceuticals, life sciences, materials, chemicals, biotechnology, mechanical arts, electronics, computer systems and software. The firm has an active litigation practice including eleven full-time intellectual property litigators, and several others in supporting roles. The firm was founded in 1919.

## Main Areas of Practice:

### IP Litigation Practice:

The litigators at Senniger Powers have extensive experience representing clients in federal district court and appellate litigation relating to intellectual property. Litigation matters handled by the firm include patent and trademark infringement, antitrust concerns, breach of contract, copyright infringement, unfair competition, defense of trade secrets and other complex commercial litigation. Senniger Powers also represents clients' interests in government proceedings such as patent interference proceedings before the Board of Patent Appeals and Interferences and trademark and service mark opposition and cancellation proceedings before the Trademark Trial and Appeal Board. The firm's litigators are proficient in handling the demands of high stakes litigation, both from a legal and technological standpoint. For example, e-discovery is managed in-house resulting in substantial cost savings to clients. Senniger Powers has specially trained in-house staff, software and servers that allow its attorneys to process and produce discovery efficiently and without the use of outside vendors.

### Chemical, Life Sciences & Pharmaceuticals:

Senniger Powers maintains one of the leading chemical, life sciences and pharmaceuticals patent practices. The firm's professionals have applied their expertise to innovations ranging from herbicides and alternative fuels to chemical manufacturing process engineering and performance chemicals for electronics manufacturing. Attorneys work in areas related to advanced materials and coatings, biomedical materials, nuclear materials, extractive metallurgical processes, gas and liquid phase catalytic oxidation reactions, preparation of various agrochemicals, sulfuric acid production and lithographic plate chemistry. Long-standing patent work in the chemical industry has helped springboard Senniger Powers to be recognized as one of the leading life sciences/pharmaceuticals patent firms in the United States. Attorneys in the life sciences/pharmaceuticals practice hold degrees in biology, chemistry, chemical engineering and organic chemistry, and they focus on a variety of technologies - from DNA polymerase and bioinformatics to recombinant plant productions and animal pharmaceuticals.

### Mechanical Arts:

The firm provides counsel in a broad range of mechanical areas including machines, articles and process concepts, manufacturing concepts and civil, structural and industrial engineering concepts and techniques. The professionals at Senniger Powers have experience with inventions ranging from household products and vending machines to medical devices, aircraft engines, semiconductor manufacturing equipment, pipe rehabilitation systems, paper handling devices, pneumatic tools, hydraulic systems, plastic product packaging equipment, combinatorial reactor systems, flow control systems, sports and recreational equipment and others.

### Electronics, Computer Systems & Software:

Senniger Powers has a deep understanding of IP legal issues relating to electrical systems, electronics, computer systems, software and related technical fields. This understanding stems from years of working with clients to assess and protect their intellectual property rights involving, for example, web-based services, encryption, digital signatures, metadata handling, medical devices, semiconductors, motors, spectrometers, controller-area-network (CAN) bus systems, light emitting diode (LED) controls, ballasts, superconducting magnets, signal processing and telecommunications. The professionals at Senniger Powers also have substantial expertise counseling clients on IP due diligence, right-to-use investigations, landscape analyses to determine the state-of-the-art, and software licensing.

### Trademark Practice and Copyright Practice:

Senniger Powers' trademark attorneys counsel clients on a variety of topics, including infringement risks, combating infringement and dilution, domain name registration and use of trademarks on the Internet. The firm is especially known for the candid and effective advice it renders regarding the selection of new trademarks. Attorneys at Senniger Powers also offer advice in a variety of copyright-related areas, including qualifying for copyright protection, copyright infringement, fair use, obtaining permission to use a copyrighted work and the use and protection of copyrighted works on the Internet.

### Clients:

Please visit us at www.senniger.com to view a list of representative clients.

# SHOOK, HARDY & BACON LLP

www.shb.com **tel:** 816 474 6550 **fax:** 816 421 5547

**Chairman:** John F Murphy
**Managing Partners:** Michelle Mangrum (Washington, DC), Daniel Molony (Tampa), Doug Robinson (Orange County), James Shepherd (Houston), William Geraghty (Miami), Tammy Webb (San Francisco)
Number of partners & counsel: 259
Number of attorneys: 453

## Firm Overview:

Shook, Hardy & Bacon has long been recognized as one of the premier litigation defense firms in the country. For more than a century, SHB has defended companies in their most substantial national and international products liability, mass tort and complex litigation matters. SHB's success in these areas has captured the attention of many in the industry, including The American Lawyer, which recognized the firm as its Product Liability Litigation Department of the Year in its 2012 and 2008 contests, as well as a finalist in the 2010 edition. The ABA Journal has described SHB as the 'darling of corporate America' and 'the firm many of the world's biggest companies turn to at the first hint of trouble'. For eight consecutive years, Shook, Hardy & Bacon has also been named the Global Product Liability Law Firm of the Year by Who's Who Legal: The International Who's Who of Business Lawyers and named to the IP Law & Business rankings 'Who Protects Innovation in America?' and 'Top Guardian of the IP Nest'.

## Main Areas of Practice:

Shook, Hardy & Bacon is known for its abilities and expertise in litigation – more than 90 percent of its attorneys are litigators and many have advanced degrees in health and sciences fields. The firm has represented leading international companies in a variety of industries, including tobacco, pharmaceutical and medical device, chemical and automotive. In the past three years alone, SHB lawyers have tried more than 35 cases to verdict in state and federal courts, successfully defending clients against claims involving products liability, environmental and toxic tort, patent infringement, labor and employment and other claims against their businesses.
Shook, Hardy & Bacon has represented the industry's leading pharmaceutical manufacturers for nearly 40 years. The firm currently serves or has served as National Counsel in litigations for six of the top 10 pharmaceutical companies, as well as for many other pharmaceutical and medical device manufacturers. The firm has also represented US cigarette manufacturers in product liability litigation continuously since 1957, and currently represents the largest US tobacco company as lead trial counsel in its pending litigation.
Over the past several years, the firm has leveraged its complex products litigation expertise to expand into several other practice areas and advance its mission of 'being the best in the world at providing creative and practical solutions at unsurpassed value'. As a result, the firm has built substantial national practices in intellectual property, environmental and toxic tort litigation, employment litigation, commercial litigation, government enforcement and compliance and public policy. While products liability remains a core strength and a growth area for the firm, practice diversification allows SHB to offer additional services and expertise to its long-standing institutional clients.

## Unbeatable Value:

The American Lawyer reported that Shook, Hardy & Bacon 'approaches potential new clients with an underdog's attitude', calling attention to 'the firm's experience handling litigation as effectively as the New York firm next door, but for less money'. The magazine has been highlighting SHB's use of alternative fee arrangements for several years. The American Lawyer also reported that 'the firm's Kansas City base also allows it to bill at least a quarter less than coastal competitors. Some 29 percent of the firm's work is covered by alternative fee arrangements'.
Law360 reported similarly that SHB has 'stayed on top in the recession, leveraging its Midwestern roots to provide unbeatable value to clients', and the ABA Journal maintains that SHB has 'defended everything from pharmaceuticals and medical devices to automobiles, chemicals, consumer products and foods', adding that, 'part of its appeal, according to clients, are lower rates than those charged by firms of similar size and experience in larger cities'.

## Clients:

Shook, Hardy & Bacon has represented more than half of the current *Fortune* 100 companies. The firm's clients include global industry leaders who demand proven legal strategies. As a result, the firm has developed long-standing relationships with many of its clients. 'There is no short list for national counsel of a major pharmaceutical company that doesn't include Shook', said the former General Counsel of one of the nation's leading pharmaceutical companies in a recent article on SHB. Another client added that Shook attorneys litigate like they're going to trial, but not unnecessarily. 'If a matter does end up going to trial, they'll be in the best possible position to defend it', the SHB client told the ABA Journal.

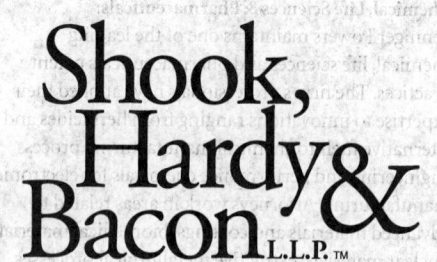

# WYRSCH HOBBS & MIRAKIAN, PC

www.whmlaw.net **tel:** 816 221 0080 **fax:** 816 221 3280

Managing Partners: 1
Number of partners: 8
Number of lawyers: 10
Languages: *English*

## Firm Overview:

The team of legal professionals at Wyrsch Hobbs Mirakian uses a wide depth and breadth of education, skill and legal experience to protect people and businesses both in and out of the courtroom. While we focus primarily on trial work of all kinds, particularly complex civil and criminal litigation, we are also skilled in assisting clients at the negotiating table, in the boardroom and before regulatory agencies. They are not just lawyers—they are problem solvers.

## Main Areas of Practice:

**White-Collar Criminal Defense, Criminal Defense, Complex Civil Litigation, & Business Litigation:**
8 partners and 13 fee earners based in Kansas City, Missouri.

- Represented US Bank Trust National Assoc. in several cases as counsel with Maslon firm regarding third-party claims against a number of defendants for improperly charging mortgagors on second mortgages. Value: at least $92,000,000
- Represented Gosselin Worldwide Moving, in United States, ex rel. Kurt Bunk, et al. v. Birkart Globistics GmbH & Co., et al. and United States, ex rel. Ammons v. The Pasha Group, et al. Trial spanned 3 weeks in Federal Court in Alexandria, VA involving a qui tam suit under the Federal False Claims Act, originally brought by private individuals. The case arose out of a criminal anti-trust prosecution wherein Mr Wyrsch's client, Gosselin, entered conditional plea of guilty, providing a factual basis for one of the allegations against Gosselin in the qui tam matter. Summary judgment for $865,000 on one of the issues was granted. At the trial's conclusion, the jury found for Gosselin on one of the main claims of the government but found liability as to violations of the False Claims Act. However, post-trial, the court dismissed the second claim, eliminated any requirement for Gosselin to pay the $865,000 granted in the summary judgment, and found that the plaintiff was not entitled to penalties. While the potential liability included $270million actual damages plus potential statutory penalties in the hundreds of millions of dollars, the judgment against Gosselin is $5,500.00. The case is pending appeal. Co-counsel in the trial was Kerri Ruttenberg of Jones Day who is currently handling the appeal. The firm currently represents Gosselin in a related FOIA matter.
- Representing Sinclair Oil Company in In re Convenience Xpress, Debtor, and In re Convenience USA, LP, Debtor; Eric Rajala, Chapter 7 Trustee v. M&W Midwest Properties. Bankruptcy adversary proceeding to recover approximately $700,000 in fraudulently converted assets. The firm has acted as regional counsel for Sinclair in a number of matters since 1987.
- Representing Fr Thomas Cronin, Fr John Tulipana and Fr Francis McGlynn (now deceased) in separate matters brought against them alleging millions of dollars. Motions to dismiss have been sustained on seven of eleven counts in the Cronin and Tulipana matters. Fr McGlynn died during the pendency of his case.
- Represented Bishop Robert Finn of the Catholic Diocese of Kansas City-St. Joseph in State of Missouri v. Finn, et al. The defendants were charged in a novel prosecution with failure to report the activities of a priest who had taken improper photographs of young children. This was the first case of a sitting Catholic bishop charged criminally and raised issue of mandatory reporting duties of a bishop and other clergy. After a jury-waived bench trial, Bishop Finn was acquitted on one count and convicted on another count and given a suspended imposition of sentence disposition. Under Missouri law, upon successful completion of probation, there will be no conviction, and the Court case will be a closed record.
- Represented Rodney Anderson in US v. Anderson, et al. Partner/owner of a well-known steak house was alleged to be part of a conspiracy to commit arson and related charges. Much of the government's evidence was through security camera footage. Mr Anderson was found guilty by a jury and is awaiting sentencing that involves mandatory minimum and consecutive statutory sentences.
- Represented Paul Klein and Klein Motors, Inc. In State of Missouri v. Paul Klein and others. Successfully defended Paul Klein in a criminal assault charge brought against him by his brother, a fellow corporate officer. This result led to successfully defending Klein Motors in an employment security matter involving the same facts which led to the removal of Mr Klein's brother as a corporate officer and director.
- Representing David Cline in various matters in state and federal courts around the country. The litigation involves complex legal and factual matters which have migrated to grand jury investigations, primarily in San Diego, California.
- Represented Joseph Whitfield in a Motion to Recall the Mandate in the Missouri Supreme Court. Whitfield was sentenced to death for a murder in the City of St. Louis after the jury deadlocked on punishment. After direct review of Whitfield's conviction, the denial of state post-conviction relief, and the denial of federal habeas corpus relief, the firm brought the Motion to Recall the Mandate based on the US Supreme Court decision in Ring v. Arizona, 536 US 584 (2002), holding that a capital defendant is entitled to jury determination of facts upon which a death sentence is based. Mr Whitfield and other similarly situated death-sentenced convicts were resentenced to life imprisonment.

## Clients:

Gosselin World Wide Moving, GmbH; US Bank Trust National Association; Coleman American Van Lines, Inc.; Bishop Robert Finn, and various priests of the Catholic Diocese of Kansas City-St. Joseph; T.D. Auto Finance, LLC; Sinclair Oil Company; Coinmach Corporation

 **WYRSCH HOBBS MIRAKIAN**

## How lawyers are ranked

Every year we carry out thousands of in-depth interviews with clients in order to assess the reputations and expertise of business lawyers worldwide. The qualities we look for (and which determine rankings) include technical legal ability, professional conduct, client service, commercial awareness/astuteness, diligence, commitment, and other qualities most valued by the client. For details of our research team, see p.5.

**Contents:**

# CORPORATE/M&A

Commentary about individuals can be found under their firm's paragraph. If the firm has no paragraph (is not ranked) look at Other Notable Practitioners.

### Corporate/M&A
### Leading Firms

**Band 1**
Browning, Kaleczyc, Berry & Hoven PC
Crowley Fleck PLLP *
Dorsey & Whitney LLP *
Holland & Hart LLP *

**Band 2**
Boone Karlberg PC
Garlington, Lohn & Robinson, PLLP *

### Leading Individuals

**Star individuals**

| | |
|---|---|
| Manning Jack | Dorsey & Whitney LLP |

**Band 1**

| | |
|---|---|
| Boone Thomas | Boone Karlberg PC |
| Chisholm David | Christian, Samson, Jones (ONP)[†] |
| Chumrau Gary B | Garlington, Lohn & Robinson, PLLP * |
| Hingle Charles | Holland & Hart LLP * |
| Kaleczyc Stanley | Browning, Kaleczyc, Berry & Hoven PC |
| Lamdin III William | Crowley Fleck PLLP * |
| Petersen Larry | Holland & Hart LLP * |

**Band 2**

| | |
|---|---|
| Beatty Kim | Browning, Kaleczyc, Berry & Hoven PC |
| James Doug | Moulton Bellingham PC (ONP)[†] |
| Semmens Daniel | Dorsey & Whitney LLP |
| VanCanagan William K | Datsopoulos, MacDonald & Lind (ONP)[†] |

**Band 3**

| | |
|---|---|
| Loble Jason | Crowley Fleck PLLP * |
| Stensland Dean | Boone Karlberg PC |
| Stonecipher Thomas | Tarlow, Stonecipher & Steele, PLLC (ONP)[†] |
| Taylor Mark | Browning, Kaleczyc, Berry & Hoven PC |

**Up-and-coming individuals**

| | |
|---|---|
| Boyar Brand | Boyar & Kuntz, PLLC (ONP)[†] |

**Associates to watch**

| | |
|---|---|
| Brown Jeremy | Dorsey & Whitney LLP |

\* Indicates individual with profile.
[†] ONP = Other Notable Practitioner.

## Band 1

### Browning, Kaleczyc, Berry & Hoven PC

**THE FIRM** This firm has a long-standing and well-deserved reputation for the high-quality corporate and commercial advice it offers to businesses large and small. M&A, commercial contracts, banking, finance and tax matters are all strong suits. An interesting feature of the team is its depth of experience and expertise in commercial litigation, making it a compelling one-stop shop. Clients include Anheuser-Busch, Benefis Health System and Union Pacific.

**KEY INDIVIDUALS Kim Beatty** advises a variety of clients, including a number of oil and gas concerns, on all manner of corporate and commercial transactions, corporate structure, and regulatory and litigious matters. **Stanley Kaleczyc** is an all-around business lawyer with many years of experience handling business, legislative, litigation and regulatory matters. Sources say he is *"very detail-oriented,"* which is *"very helpful when contracts really need to be to the letter and carefully calibrated,"* and that he *"can figure out how to do pretty much anything."* **Mark Taylor** is praised for his consummate ability at commercial matters and his lobbying skills. One client said he *"makes great recommendations, has a lot of energy and is very well connected in the state."*

### Crowley Fleck PLLP
See profile on p.1656

**THE FIRM** Crowley Fleck, as the largest firm in the state, can muster the resources to handle the most complex and seemingly intractable business problems. Within Montana, the firm has six offices, and a number of outposts in neighboring states. Corporate, securities, capital markets, tax and state law issues are areas of strength, as is its deep understanding of the local oil and gas industry.

**KEY INDIVIDUALS William Lamdin** (see p.1654) has an admirably broad practice which takes in bankruptcy, banking, corporate organization and M&A, for which he is very well thought of statewide. **Jason Loble** (see p.1654) is skilled and practiced in a range of commercial law matters, such as M&A, drafting and negotiating commercial agreements and private securities offerings.

### Dorsey & Whitney LLP
See profile on p.1583

**THE FIRM** Dorsey & Whitney's high-quality corporate and commercial offering in Montana is further bolstered by the talent on hand across the firm's national platform. The lawyers counsel SMEs and local family-owned businesses, regional technology startups, out-of-state investors and a number of oil and gas companies involved in the exploration of the Bakken Formation, one of the nation's largest oil shale patches.

**KEY INDIVIDUALS Jack Manning** manages the Missoula office. A corporate securities and M&A lawyer, he helps SMEs, private and public, with IPOs and other financing matters, aiming to provide them with high-quality and sophisticated advice. **Daniel Semmens** is an expert at public finance law. He is praised above all for his thorough and helpful manner, and his deep understanding of financing models and bond laws in particular. **Jeremy Brown** is an up-and-coming associate. He is experienced across the full range of corporate matters, such as M&A, securities, corporate reorganization and venture capital financing.

### Holland & Hart LLP
See profile on p.727

**THE FIRM** This venerable regional firm's Montana team engages in bankruptcy, corporate organization, M&A and real estate work on behalf of out-of-state and Canadian clients, multinational banks and mining companies, as well as homegrown businesses. As with most large firms in the region, the team manages a good deal of corporate and commercial matters relating to the oil and gas industry.

**KEY INDIVIDUALS Charles Hingle** (see p.1654) excels at all manner of banking, bankruptcy, corporate and commercial legal advice, and is hailed for his broad knowledge and intelligence. **Larry Petersen** (see p.1655), described as *"excellent"* by sources, specializes in banking, commercial, M&A, real estate and above all tax law.

## Band 2

### Boone Karlberg PC

**THE FIRM** This Missoula firm has a strong presence across the principal areas of business law in Montana, and so is no stranger to weighty transactional and corporate engagements. The firm's strength in commercial litigation gives the lawyers added insight into how to solve commercial problems, and its bankruptcy and banking law expertise is consistently cited as a prominent area of excellence. **KEY INDIVIDUALS Thomas Boone** is a seasoned practitioner of all manner of business law matters, including corporate and real estate transactions, banking, tax and succession planning. **Dean Stensland** also has a well-rounded business law practice and many years of experience behind him. As well as M&A and commercial transactions, he is also noted for his knowledge of creditor bankruptcy issues, banking law and commercial litigation.

### Garlington, Lohn & Robinson, PLLP
See profile on p.1657

**THE FIRM** This long-established, leading Missoula firm offers its business clients a full service, and is as adept at advising startup and emerging companies as it is at handling complex problems faced by large regional businesses. M&A, corporate governance and planning, tax-related reorganization and creditors' rights are all areas of notable strength.

**KEY INDIVIDUALS Gary Chumrau** (see p.1653) enjoys a strong reputation across the range of commercial and corporate law. Expert in corporate transactions, banking and real estate law, he counts a number of hospitals and medical organizations among his clients.

### Other Notable Practitioners

**Brand Boyar** of Boyar & Kuntz, PLLC is a fixture in the state for sophisticated transactional work, estate planning, probate and succession planning and tax-exempt organizations. **David Chisholm** of Christian, Samson, Jones & Chisholm, PLLC specializes in banking mergers, for which

he is considered a leader in the state. He also handles M&A, commercial and corporate governance and transactional issues. **Doug James** of Moulton Bellingham PC receives plaudits for his expertise in bankruptcy law, as well as his experience in banking, real estate development and business transactions. **William VanCanagan** of Datsopoulos, MacDonald & Lind, P.C. is described as *"very smart"* and *"hard-working,"* and is well liked for his *"easygoing"* manner. His practice covers the range of business law appropriate for small, medium and regional entities. **Thomas Stonecipher** of Tarlow, Stonecipher & Steele, PLLC is thought of by market insiders as a *"very good real estate and banking lawyer."* Based in Bozeman, he has a comprehensive business law and transactional practice.

# LABOR & EMPLOYMENT

Commentary about individuals can be found under their firm's paragraph. If the firm has no paragraph (is not ranked) look at Other Notable Practitioners.

| Labor & Employment |
| :--- |
| **Leading Firms** |
| **Band 1** |
| Crowley Fleck PLLP * |
| Garlington, Lohn & Robinson, PLLP * |
| **Band 2** |
| Browning, Kaleczyc, Berry & Hoven PC |
| Gough, Shanahan, Johnson & Waterman PLLP * |
| Holland & Hart LLP * |
| Hughes, Kellner, Sullivan & Alke |
| Worden Thane PC |
| **Band 3** |
| Brown Law Firm PC |
| Ugrin, Alexander, Zadick & Higgins, PC |

\* Indicates firm with profile.
*Alphabetical order within each band. Band 1 is the highest.*

## Band 1

### Crowley Fleck PLLP
See profile on p.1656

**THE FIRM** This heavyweight regional firm has a broad network of offices, with teams based in Billings, Helena, Missoula, and adjoining states. Its prolific employment law workload includes defending clients against wrongful discharge and discrimination charges leveled by former employees. On the labor side, the firm represents employers in connection with union grievances and union forma-

tion attempts. Pensions and ERISA matters are further strengths of the practice.

**KEY INDIVIDUALS** Billings-based **Steven Lehman** (see p.1654) specializes in trial work, defending businesses from wrongful dismissal and discrimination charges. He is also a much sought-after adviser on employee relations. **Marcia Davenport** (see p.1653) is a *"very talented litigator"* who takes on a wide variety of civil and commercial suits. A large proportion of her caseload is dedicated to wrongful dismissal and discrimination defense work. **Joe Maynard** (see p.1654) is a highly respected figure renowned for his expertise in workers' compensation cases. **Daniel Johns** (see p.1654) has a great deal of experience in employment disputes centering on compensation, discrimination, sexual harassment and wrongful discharge, as well as NLRB cases.

### Garlington, Lohn & Robinson, PLLP
See profile on p.1657

**THE FIRM** This superb Missoula-based practice is a byword for quality and efficiency in western Montana and beyond. The team acts for a range of employers across the gamut of labor and employment issues, advising on both contentious and noncontentious matters. The firm is noted for the depth of its experience in the medical sector, and for its expertise in workers' compensation law.

**KEY INDIVIDUALS Candace Fetscher** (see p.1654) is much sought-after for her advice and litigation support to employers in the healthcare industries. Peers have high regard for **Charles Hansberry's** (see p.1654) litigation

prowess, which includes impressive expertise in workers' compensation. Sources consider **Bradley Luck** (see p.1654) to be *"an excellent lawyer – very persuasive and reasonable."* He has a renowned practice in alternative dispute resolution. **Kelly Wills** is a respected authority on the law concerning workers' compensation, and represents various insurers and employers.

## Band 2

### Browning, Kaleczyc, Berry & Hoven PC

**THE FIRM** The employment group at this distinguished firm has an excellent reputation for its area expertise, which is called on by major names across a range of sectors. The team offers a comprehensive service, advising clients on wage and hour, benefits, workers' compensation, and Montana Safe Place to Work Act matters. Healthcare-related claims is a growth area for the group, and its clients in this arena include Benefis Health System, Northern Montana Hospital and Marias Medical Center.

**KEY INDIVIDUALS Leo Ward** is a skilled litigator with an excellent record in defending employers and insurers against claims related to workers' compensation and occupational disease. **Oliver Goe** is highly regarded by peers for his employment expertise. His wide-ranging caseload includes a number of wrongful discharge and discrimination claims. **David McLean** has a sterling reputation for his work on various liability and wage and hour cases, as well as claims in the healthcare sector. Clients find him *"very* *helpful, experienced, and a good person to guide us through our litigation strategy."* **Andrew Adamek** is *"very detail-oriented, energetic and dynamic."* He is well known for defending clients in wrongful discharge and discrimination claims, as well as workers' compensation matters.

## Gough, Shanahan, Johnson & Waterman PLLP

### See profile on p.1658

THE FIRM This firm has offices in Helena, Billings and Missoula, and provides a full labor and employment service to clients based in Montana and beyond. On the employment side, it represents clients in discrimination and wrongful discharge litigation, as well as advising on personnel policies. The team's labor law capabilities include advice on wage and hour matters and collective bargaining claims.

KEY INDIVIDUALS Peers commend the wealth of knowledge that **Thomas Hattersley** brings to bear in employment work. He handles a variety of litigation matters, including discrimination and wage and hour cases. **Teri Walter** handles a large volume of wrongful discharge and discrimination claims and safety compliance issues, and also has a renowned labor law practice.

## Holland & Hart LLP
### See profile on p.727

THE FIRM The Billings office of this regional powerhouse handles the full range of employment and labor work. In noncontentious issues, the team advises on employee handbooks, ERISA and compliance with changes in health insurance legislation. It also defends clients in discrimination, wrongful discharge, Montana human rights law and wage and hour actions.

KEY INDIVIDUALS **Elizabeth Nedrow** (see p.1655) offers valuable expertise in ERISA and employee benefits matters. She advises clients on the treatment of these benefits in M&A transactions, and on the adjustment of medical plans to comply with recent legislative developments. **Jeanne Matthews Bender** (see p.1653) is renowned for her experience in this field, and described by peers as a *"reservoir of great employment law knowledge."* **Jason Ritchie** (see p.1655) is a *"very bright"* attorney, who handles a range of labor and employment issues on behalf of employers.

## Hughes, Kellner, Sullivan & Alke

THE FIRM This Helena firm offers a comprehensive labor and employment service to its clients, which include various high-profile corporations and public bodies. Highlights include mandates regarding employee discipline, workplace investigations, contracts and personnel policies. On the contentious side, the team also handles a variety of discrimination, wrongful discharge and wage and hour suits.

KEY INDIVIDUALS **John Sullivan** is a *"very smart guy, with an excellent reputation."* He is a seasoned mediator, and has also litigated numerous discrimination, harassment and wrongful discharge cases. **Amy Christensen** is a litigator and a healthcare law expert, and is often called on by hospitals and medical centers to advocate in wrongful discharge cases.

## Worden Thane PC

THE FIRM Based in Missoula, this team has a broad range of talents in the labor and employment arena. Its labor expertise is widely heralded, and the firm has extensive experience in advising on the negotiation of collective bargaining agreements, and attempts by unions to organize employees. The employment offering extends from counseling on noncontentious pastoral matters to litigation.

KEY INDIVIDUALS **Ronald Bender** has a longstanding reputation in Montana's labor and employment field, and is highly respected for his skills as a trial lawyer.

## Band 3

## Brown Law Firm PC

THE FIRM Operating from offices in Billings and Missoula, this firm assists employers with a range of labor and employment issues. Labor relations, workplace safety and workers' compensation are areas of strength for the team.

KEY INDIVIDUALS The *"very talented"* **Michael Heringer** earns strong praise from interviewees for his skills in disability discrimination and wrongful discharge claims. He is also well known for his expertise across the board in employment law and workers' compensation issues.

## Ugrin, Alexander, Zadick & Higgins, PC

THE FIRM This group is based in Great Falls, and is called on for its extensive knowledge of employment trial proceedings. Its lawyers also have considerable experience in mediation and arbitration cases. The team is well regarded for its work on discrimination, civil rights and Montana Human Rights Act issues.

KEY INDIVIDUALS **Mark Higgins** is a partner in the firm's employment group.

## Other Notable Practitioners

The *"excellent"* **John Crist** of Crist Law Firm, LLC is commended by fellow attorneys for the strength of his employment practice. He is well known for both his defense and plaintiff work, and also for his skills as a mediator. **William Andrew Forsythe** of Moulton Bellingham PC advises companies on the full range of employment law matters, and is a noted defense litigator. **Jean Faure** of Faure Holden PC is *"deeply experienced in employment litigation,"* and is a go-to name for clients seeking advice in Great Falls. **Elizabeth O'Halloran** of Milodragovich, Dale, Steinbrenner & Nygren, P.C. is well known in Missoula and beyond for her skills in employment law. Her client base includes a range of plaintiffs as well as defendants.

# LITIGATION

| Litigation: General Commercial Leading Firms | | |
|---|---|---|
| **Band 1** | | |
| Boone Karlberg PC | | |
| Garlington, Lohn & Robinson, PLLP * | | |
| Moore, Cockrell, Goicoechea & Axelberg, P.C. | | |
| **Band 2** | | |
| Browning, Kaleczyc, Berry & Hoven PC | | |
| Crowley Fleck PLLP * | | |
| Ugrin, Alexander, Zadick & Higgins, PC | | |
| **Band 3** | | |
| Brown Law Firm PC | | |
| Gough, Shanahan, Johnson & Waterman PLLP * | | |
| Hughes, Kellner, Sullivan & Alke | | |
| Moulton Bellingham PC | | |
| Poore, Roth & Robinson, P.C. | | |

\* Indicates firm/individual with profile.
†ONP = Other Notable Practitioner.

| Litigation: General Commercial Leading Individuals | |
|---|---|
| **Band 1** | |
| Cox Randy | Boone Karlberg PC |
| Hoven Daniel | Browning, Kaleczyc, Berry & Hoven PC |
| Matovich Carey E | Matovich & Keller PC (ONP)† |
| McIntosh Ian | Crowley Fleck PLLP * |
| Moore Mikel L | Moore, Cockrell, Goicoechea & Axelberg, P.C. |
| Sheridan Robert E | Garlington, Lohn & Robinson, PLLP * |
| Zadick Gary M | Ugrin, Alexander, Zadick & Higgins, PC |
| **Band 2** | |
| Davis Maxon | Davis, Hatley, Haffeman & Tighe (ONP)† |
| Goicoechea Sean | Moore, Cockrell, Goicoechea & Axelberg, P.C. |
| Gratton Scott | Brown Law Firm PC |
| Hayhurst Matthew B | Boone Karlberg PC |
| James Robert F | Ugrin, Alexander, Zadick & Higgins, PC |
| Kaleczyc Stanley | Browning, Kaleczyc, Berry & Hoven PC |
| Luck Bradley | Garlington, Lohn & Robinson, PLLP * |
| Murphy Gerald | Moulton Bellingham PC |
| Phillips Robert J | Phillips Law Firm PC (ONP)† |
| Stacey Calvin J | Stacey & Funyak (ONP)† |
| Sullivan Robert J | Boone Karlberg PC |
| Taleff Ward E | Taleff Law Offices PC (ONP)† |
| Waterman Ronald F | Gough, Shanahan, Johnson & Waterman |
| **Band 3** | |
| Bender Ronald | Worden Thane PC (ONP)† |
| Daly Lawrence | Garlington, Lohn & Robinson, PLLP * |
| Prinzing Jones Natasha | Boone Karlberg PC |
| Riley Larry | Garlington, Lohn & Robinson, PLLP * |
| Rogers Guy W | Brown Law Firm PC |
| Russell John J | Brown Law Firm PC |
| Stensland Dean | Boone Karlberg PC |
| Sullivan Patrick M | Poore, Roth & Robinson, P.C. |
| **Band 4** | |
| Berg Sara | Browning, Kaleczyc, Berry & Hoven PC |
| DeSoto Kathleen L | Garlington, Lohn & Robinson, PLLP * |
| Lichte Julie | Crowley Fleck PLLP * |
| Rohan Brendon | Poore, Roth & Robinson, P.C. |
| Stearns Scott M | Boone Karlberg PC |
| **Up-and-coming individuals** | |
| Braukmann Michele | Moulton Bellingham PC |
| McLean David | Browning, Kaleczyc, Berry & Hoven PC |

| Litigation: Mainly Plaintiff Leading Individuals | |
|---|---|
| **Band 1** | |
| Beck Monte D | Beck & Amsden, PLLC (ONP)† |
| Bishop L Randall | Bishop and Heenan (ONP)† |
| Blewett III Alexander | Hoyt & Blewett PLLC (ONP)† |
| Culver Triel | Edwards Frickle & Culver (ONP)† |
| Edwards A Clifford | Edwards Frickle & Culver (ONP)† |
| Goetz James | Goetz, Gallik & Baldwin, PC (ONP)† |
| Lewis Tom L | Lewis, Slovak & Kovacich, PC (ONP)† |
| Zadick Gary M | Ugrin, Alexander, Zadick & Higgins, PC |

| Litigation: Mediators Leading individuals | |
|---|---|
| **Band 1** | |
| Axelberg Tracy | Moore, Cockrell, Goicoechea & Axelberg |
| Kellner Stuart | Hughes, Kellner, Sullivan & Alke |
| Lind Dennis | Datsopoulos, MacDonald & Lind (ONP)† |
| Sheridan Robert E | Garlington, Lohn & Robinson, PLLP * |
| Sullivan John | Hughes, Kellner, Sullivan & Alke |
| Taleff Ward E | Taleff Law Offices PC |

## Band 1

### Boone Karlberg PC

**THE FIRM** This leading Missoula firm has an excellent reputation across the state and beyond for its litigation skills and experience. The group is well known for representing the State of Montana and government entities as well as local and regional businesses, including a number of major railroad companies. Commercial disputes are an area of strength, as are product and public liability cases, and legal and medical malpractice suits.

**KEY INDIVIDUALS Randy Cox** is described by sources as a *"veteran defense litigator"* and is highly regarded for his representation of railroad companies. He also undertakes a large number of medical negligence and product liability cases. Market commentators laud **Robert Sullivan** as a talented banking, real estate and general commercial litigator. **Matthew Hayhurst** excels in commercial, insurance, personal injury and product liability cases. **Natasha Prinzing Jones** is *"a very strong lawyer,"* who advises clients across the board on litigation proceedings. Her caseload includes insurance coverage and defense work, and medical and municipal liability actions. **Dean Stensland** is a seasoned litigator whose experience covers a variety of contentious matters, including creditor bankruptcy, banking and construction cases. **Scott Stearns** handles a range of litigation mandates, with an emphasis on insurance, personal injury and railroad defense.

### Garlington, Lohn & Robinson, PLLP

See profile on p.1657

**THE FIRM** This Missoula firm's formidable litigation team engages almost exclusively in defense work, and has more than a dozen litigators practicing across a wide range of legal disciplines and industries in Montana. The practice handles a broad spectrum of litigation encompassing areas such as insurance, medical malpractice, premises and product liability, and transport law.

**Sources say:** *"Top-flight lawyers."*

**KEY INDIVIDUALS Robert Sheridan** (see p.1655) is highly rated for his *"great judgment"* and ability to *"understand the complexities and nuances"* of any given case. His practice is largely concerned with insurance defense, product liability and mediation work. He also acts for various railroads in cases under the Federal Employers Liability Act (FELA). **Bradley Luck's** (see p.1654) focus lies primarily in insurance defense litigation, and he advises clients on a number of bad faith claims. His workload also includes class action defense. **Lawrence Daly** (see p.1653) is a seasoned veteran when it comes to contentious work, in particular commercial, construction and medical malpractice litigation. **Larry Riley** (see p.1655) is a noted authority in medical malpractice litigation, commended by peers for his wealth of experience. **Kathleen DeSoto** (see p.1653) is acclaimed for her skills and experience as a trial lawyer. She has a particularly strong understanding of bad faith claims and appellate matters, and away from the courtroom garners favorable feedback for her written litigious work.

### Moore, Cockrell, Goicoechea & Axelberg, P.C.

**THE FIRM** This leading Kalispell-based firm has consistently demonstrated its versatility and sophistication in representing a range of businesses, institutions and individuals in disputes. Its caseload features matters spanning the spectrum of commercial and civil law, with insurance defense and bankruptcy-related suits being areas of particular strength.

**Sources say:** *"They have excellent people, among the best litigators in the state."*

**KEY INDIVIDUALS Tracy Axelberg** dedicates the vast majority of his practice to mediation and alternative dispute resolution, in which he is described as *"clearly one of the best in the state."* **Mikel Moore** is an *"extremely intelligent litigator."* His fortes include medical and legal malpractice defense. **Sean Goicoechea** is highly respected by market sources, who commend his strong practice in medical negligence proceedings, and the brio with which he takes cases into court.

## Band 2

### Browning, Kaleczyc, Berry & Hoven PC

THE FIRM This firm advises clients from its offices in Bozeman, Helena and Missoula, and has extensive and wide-ranging trial experience. This covers a variety of major disputes, including medical malpractice, product liability and FELA actions, as well as contract claims. The team is prized by clients for its responsiveness and commercial awareness, as well as its litigation prowess.

KEY INDIVIDUALS **Daniel Hoven** is described by commentators as *"exceptionally approachable and thorough,"* and has considerable experience in handling administrative proceedings, sports law and environmental and natural resources litigation. **Stanley Kaleczyc** has valuable expertise in commercial disputes, and is praised as *"client-oriented and responsive."* **Sara Berg** has a prolific litigation practice, and handles all manner of commercial disputes as well as medical malpractice and FELA defense work. Peers describe **David McLean** as a *"bright, hard-working young lawyer who has done extremely well."* His well-rounded practice includes a range of insurance, employment and professional liability defense mandates.

### Crowley Fleck PLLP
See profile on p.1656

THE FIRM This large regional team handles a wide variety of commercial disputes, as well as medical negligence, insurance and professional liability defense work. It also acts on a number of cases in the oil and gas industry, which is a highly active arena in Montana and adjoining states since the discovery of the Bakken formation oil shale patch.

KEY INDIVIDUALS Peers hold **Ian McIntosh** (see p.1655) in high regard, singling him out as *"an outstanding litigator, and a real go-getter."* He is well known for his product liability defense work, alongside his high-volume commercial litigation caseload. Peers are impressed by **Julie Lichte**'s (see p.1654) litigation talents, particularly in the medical malpractice and negligence arena, where her prior experience working as a nurse gives her a unique perspective.

### Ugrin, Alexander, Zadick & Higgins, PC

THE FIRM Based in Great Falls, this firm is above all a litigation specialist, and its lawyers have a wealth of experience in contentious proceedings and trial work. Fortes of the team include bankruptcy suits, insurance cases and product liability defense. The firm is held in high esteem among the business and legal communities of the state for its prolific caseload and high-caliber expertise.

KEY INDIVIDUALS **Gary Zadick** is a *"first-rate lawyer,"* who is considered to be *"excellent on insurance defense"* as well as personal injury and product liability cases. Sources also highlight his enviable trial record. **Robert James** is a highly experienced trial lawyer whose wide-ranging practice takes in commercial litigation, insurance bad faith actions, and employment and appellate law.

## Band 3

### Brown Law Firm PC

THE FIRM This firm counts litigation as a cornerstone of its offering, and advises a broad spectrum of clients from its offices in Billings and Missoula. The team is well known for its expertise in insurance cases, and handles a broad range of personal injury and bad faith actions. Further areas of strength include product liability, medical malpractice and negligence, and disputes relating to the construction and natural resource sectors.

KEY INDIVIDUALS **Scott Gratton** specializes in insurance suits, often involving negligence law, railroad liability, and bad faith claims. His practice spans the whole of the state, leading one peer to describe him as a *"road warrior."* **Guy Rogers** is praised for his intelligence and extensive trial experience. He has an enviably broad practice which focuses on personal injury, bankruptcy and complex commercial litigation. **John Russell** has a practice dedicated mainly to insurance disputes and the defense of medical practitioners against malpractice and negligence claims.

### Gough, Shanahan, Johnson & Waterman PLLP
See profile on p.1658

THE FIRM This firm has offices in Billings, Helena and Missoula, and excels in an impressive variety of commercial and civil disputes. Its handling of personal injury and product liability offerings is highly regarded, and the team is experienced in employment and construction litigation. It can also offer expert guidance in environmental and administrative proceedings.

KEY INDIVIDUALS **Ronald Waterman**'s practice covers disputes relating to commercial contracts, insurance defense, personal injury and toxic torts.

### Hughes, Kellner, Sullivan & Alke

THE FIRM This Helena-based firm undertakes a broad range of contentious matters, with an accent on insurance coverage, construction litigation and the representation of large utilities before the state's Public Services Commission. The team also acts for a number of hospitals in the state, and mandates of late include medical malpractice allegations and commercial leasing disputes.

KEY INDIVIDUALS Sources hold **Stuart Kellner** in high regard as a *"very successful mediator – few can match him."* He oversees a wide variety of commercial, employment and securities cases. **John Sullivan** is well known for his sterling mediation practice, and is described as *"very smart and detail-oriented."*

### Moulton Bellingham PC

THE FIRM Litigators at this Billings firm represent businesses and institutional clients throughout the state and the wider region in a range of commercial and civil actions. Insurance defense and professional liability matters are strong suits for the firm, as is Indian law. Lawyers at Moulton Bellingham represent members and non-members of recognized tribes in state, federal and tribal courts.

KEY INDIVIDUALS **Gerald Murphy** represents clients from Montana and beyond in disputes concerning aviation law, banking, business litigation, insurance defense and product liability. **Michele Braukmann** is singled out by peers as a strong lawyer, and undertakes commercial, employment, insurance and municipal liability disputes.

### Poore, Roth & Robinson, P.C.

THE FIRM This well-established Butte firm represents corporations, institutional clients and municipalities in a wide variety of disputes. Its sector-spanning expertise includes valuable knowledge of construction, gaming and banking cases. The team also advises clients on toxic torts, and professional and product liability.

KEY INDIVIDUALS **Patrick Sullivan** is the firm's senior litigator, and has a wealth of trial and litigation experience. He handles all manner of commercial and civil cases, including construction litigation, product liability, insurance and toxic tort defense actions. **Brendon Rohan** is commended for his developing practice, which covers banking, gaming and toxic torts.

### Other Notable Practitioners

**Monte Beck** of Beck & Amsden, PLLC is a *"first-rate plaintiff lawyer,"* who is lauded by peers for his excellent track record in this arena. **Ronald Bender** of Worden Thane PC enjoys a strong reputation statewide for his handling of contract disputes as well as bankruptcy, banking, insurance coverage and product liability cases. **Randall Bishop** of Bishop and Heenan is widely renowned for his representation of plaintiffs in health, disability and life insurance bad faith claims. **Alexander Blewett** of Hoyt & Blewett PLLC, based in Great Falls, is said to be *"as good a plaintiff lawyer as there is in Montana."* He acts for plaintiffs on a broad spectrum of cases, such as those relating to personal injury, insurance bad faith and fraud. He also handles a number of workplace safety mandates, including proceedings brought under the FELA. Sources describe **Triel Culver** at Edwards Frickle & Culver as *"one of the best plaintiff lawyers in the state."* He represents clients in an array of matters, including insurance bad faith, personal injury, product liability, toxic torts and securities litigation. **Maxon Davis** of Davis, Hatley, Haffeman & Tighe, PC is a *"very strong litigator,"* who impresses sources with his practical approach. His practice covers a variety of fields, among them business litigation, insurance defense, and professional and product liability defense. Edwards Frickle & Culver's **Clifford Edwards** is a leading plaintiff litigator, who is commended for his high-profile successes. He is *"excellent at assimilating the facts and the thrust of a case on short notice,"* said one interviewee. **James Goetz** of Goetz, Gallik & Baldwin, PC is widely considered to be one of the state's finest trial lawyers when it comes to plaintiff work. He is also commended for his expertise in appellate matters. **Tom Lewis** of Lewis, Slovak & Kovacich, PC in Great Falls is regarded by numerous sources as one of Montana's most experienced and talented plaintiff attorneys. He handles cases involving personal injury, toxic and workplace torts, insurance bad faith and environmental claims.

Dennis Lind of Datsopoulos, MacDonald & Lind, P.C. is described as a *"top-flight mediator"* by market sources. His caseload features a broad spectrum of matters, from business disputes to personal injury and medical malpractice suits. Carey Matovich of Matovich & Keller PC in Billings has an enviable reputation for her work as a defense litigator, and acts on cases regarding unfair insurance practices,

personal injury, professional negligence and contract law suits. Robert Phillips of Phillips Law Firm PC is a Missoula-based expert in insurance law, and advises clients on coverage and bad faith actions before state, tribal and federal courts. Calvin Stacey of Stacey & Funyak has an excellent reputation for his litigation prowess, and advises clients on a variety of civil and commercial cases. His caseload includes a number of insurance actions, construction disputes, professional negligence and wrongful death suits. Ward Taleff of Taleff Law Offices PC has many years of experience as a defense litigator, and is now also one of the state's most sought-after mediators. One source said: *"If I have a complex case where I need someone with a firm hand but a nice way with people, I'll take him."*

# NATURAL RESOURCES & ENVIRONMENT

Commentary about individuals can be found under their firm's paragraph. If the firm has no paragraph (is not ranked) look at Other Notable Practitioners.

## Natural Resources & Environment
### Leading Firms

**Band 1**
Browning, Kaleczyc, Berry & Hoven PC
Crowley Fleck PLLP *
Holland & Hart LLP *

**Band 2**
Doney Crowley Payne Bloomquist P.C.
Gough, Shanahan, Johnson & Waterman PLLP *
Poore, Roth & Robinson, P.C.

### Senior Statesmen

Senior Statesmen: distinguished older practitioners

| | |
|---|---|
| Broeder Gary | Crowley Fleck PLLP * |

### Leading Individuals

**Band 1**

| | |
|---|---|
| Alke John L | Hughes, Kellner, Sullivan & Alke (ONP)† |
| Bloomquist John | Doney Crowley Payne Bloomquist P.C. |
| Brown Stephen Ross | Garlington, Lohn & Robinson (ONP)† |
| Cockrell Dale R | Moore, Cockrell, Goicoechea (ONP)† |
| Franz Holly | Franz & Driscoll PLLP (ONP)† |
| Joscelyn Alan L | Gough, Shanahan, Johnson & Waterman |
| Lee Don | Lee Law Office PC (ONP)† |
| Ruffatto Steven P | Crowley Fleck PLLP, * |

**Band 2**

| | |
|---|---|
| Berry Leo | Browning, Kaleczyc, Berry & Hoven PC |
| Crowley Frank | Doney Crowley Payne Bloomquist P.C. |
| Davis John | Poore, Roth & Robinson, P.C. |
| Gray Kyle | Holland & Hart LLP * |
| Laughner Catherine A. | Browning, Kaleczyc, Berry & Hoven PC |
| Lee John R | Crowley Fleck PLLP,* |
| Mangen Jr Christopher | Crowley Fleck PLLP.* |
| Mitchell W Scott | Holland & Hart LLP * |
| Payne Allan | Doney Crowley Payne Bloomquist P.C. |
| Ross John Walker | Brown Law Firm PC (ONP)† |
| Summerville Rebecca L | Datsopoulos, MacDonald & Lind (ONP)† |
| Wade Steven T | Browning, Kaleczyc, Berry & Hoven PC |

**Associates to watch**

| | |
|---|---|
| Tietz W John | Browning, Kaleczyc, Berry & Hoven PC |

\* Indicates firm/individual with profile.
† ONP = Other Notable Practitioner.

## Band 1

### Browning, Kaleczyc, Berry & Hoven PC

THE FIRM This environment and natural resources practice has a firmly established name within Montana, and clients can call on an impressive depth of experience. A truly comprehensive workload includes defending clients against claims made by government and private entities, as well as toxic tort litigation. The team handles various matters connected to the exploitation of the Bakken formation oil shale patch, and cases relating to air, water and biodiversity quality.

KEY INDIVIDUALS Leo Berry is a *"very strong government affairs lawyer,"* prized for his deep understanding of the regulatory regimes governing this arena. Catherine Laughner *"is very bright and shows outstanding judgment,"* according to one highly satisfied client. She is a go-to lawyer for companies defending against allegations of criminal wrongdoing and environmental damage, as well as for permitting and due diligence. Steven Wade is particularly well regarded for his representation of clients in the Montana State Legislature, and has considerable lobbying experience. His workload also includes obtaining permits, compliance advice and litigation defense. John Tietz is well known for his command of water law, and clients can call on his prior experience as an environmental consultant.

### Crowley Fleck PLLP

See profile on p.1656

THE FIRM The team at Crowley Fleck operates from six offices across the state and continues to be one of the first ports of call for clients investing in the Bakken formation. Furthermore, the team is well placed to advise companies drawn to Montana's coal reserves, which are among the largest in the USA. Environmental litigation defense and applications for hard rock mining permits are also areas of strength.

KEY INDIVIDUALS Gary Broeder (see p.1653) is commended for his *"extensive background in fundamental oil and gas law."* He is sought-after for representations before regulatory bodies, and also handles transactional and title examination work. Steven Ruffatto (see p.1655) is a *"very accomplished"* natural resources specialist who advises on various matters pertaining to coal mining and oil and gas

extraction. John Lee (see p.1654) is prized for his knowledge of oil and gas regulation, and focuses largely on corporate transactions and title matters. Christopher Mangen (see p.1654) is a respected authority on title matters across the natural resources industries.

### Holland & Hart LLP

See profile on p.727

THE FIRM This Billings-based team is recognized as one of the top natural resources and environment groups in Montana, and has a particularly strong reputation for its handling of property transactions in the oil and gas space. The team provides a comprehensive service to both established players and newer entrants across the natural resources sector, representing clients in fossil fuels and renewable energy matters.

KEY INDIVIDUALS Scott Mitchell (see p.1655) devotes much of his practice to environmental litigation, acting on a number of Superfund cases. Noncontentious work includes advising clients on environmental regulations and commercial contracts. Kyle Gray (see p.1654) is an accomplished litigator, prized by blue-chip energy companies. One major client describes her as *"terrific – she listens carefully to what you need and produces on time to a very high quality."*

## Band 2

### Doney Crowley Payne Bloomquist P.C.

THE FIRM Operating from offices in Dillon and Helena, this team offers a wide-ranging environment and natural resources service. Its diverse skill set includes CERCLA/Superfund liability issues, mining rights, easements and access questions, and land use and zoning. The team also has impressive expertise in water rights matters.

KEY INDIVIDUALS Frank Crowley is highly respected for his knowledge of water rights and related permitting issues. He has a fine reputation for his advice on environmental regulations, and previous roles include acting as Chief Legal Counsel at the Montana Department of Health and Environmental Sciences. Allan Payne's multifaceted experience in the environmental arena includes working as an environmental consultant, and as Special Assistant

Attorney General in Montana's Superfund program. He is considered a go-to name for regulatory advice and litigation engagements. **John Bloomquist** is a noted authority on water rights law, and acts for agricultural and industrial users of water, from ranchers to large water projects. His time as a Water Master for the state water court makes him a popular choice for such engagements.

### Gough, Shanahan, Johnson & Waterman PLLP

**See profile on p.1658**

**THE FIRM** This firm advises clients from its offices in Billings, Helena and Missoula, and is strong across the board in matters concerning endangered species, state and federal reclamation, air and water quality. The firm is best known in this area for its adroit handling of legal matters regarding natural resources exploitation, particularly mining and timber law.

**KEY INDIVIDUALS** The *"excellent"* **Alan Joscelyn** is widely considered to be one of the best mining law attorneys in the state. He also focuses on water and property rights and their relation to natural resource extraction.

### Poore, Roth & Robinson, P.C.

**THE FIRM** Located in Butte, this firm is well known for its litigation expertise, and receives plaudits for its track record in mining and Superfund work. It is also well regarded for its regulatory compliance advice. Clients value the team's pragmatic outlook and its knowledge of local agencies.

**KEY INDIVIDUALS John Davis** is a highly esteemed specialist in mining law and environmental litigation. Clients describe him as *"fantastic – down to earth and hard-working."*

### Other Notable Practitioners

Helena-based **John Alke** of Hughes, Kellner, Sullivan & Alke is a leading energy and public utility law specialist, and is commended for his authoritative knowledge of the state's energy regulation. **Dale Cockrell** of Moore, Cockrell, Goicoechea & Axelberg, P.C., based in Kalispell, is widely regarded as one of the most experienced mining law practitioners in Montana. Sources describe Helena-based **Holly Franz** of Franz & Driscoll PLLP as *"a superb water lawyer – one of the best."* **Don Lee** of Lee Law Office PC in Shelby is regarded as one of the deans of the state Bar for oil and gas work, handling a range of matters across the state. **Rebecca Summerville** of Datsopoulos, MacDonald & Lind, P.C. is highly respected as a litigator, and handles cases concerning toxic torts, CERCLA and Superfund issues, and environmental risk allocation. Her noncontentious work includes counseling clients on due diligence and mining law. **Stephen Ross Brown** (see p.1653) of Garlington, Lohn & Robinson, PLLP enjoys a statewide reputation for his expertise in environmental remediation and site cleanup, as well as for his knowledge of water law. **John Walker Ross** of Brown Law Firm PC has an impressively broad practice in environment and natural resources law, which encompasses litigation defense as well as noncontentious compliance advice.

# REAL ESTATE

Commentary about individuals can be found under their firm's paragraph. If the firm has no paragraph (is not ranked) look at Other Notable Practitioners.

| Real Estate | | |
| --- | --- | --- |
| **Leading Firms** | | |
| **Band 1** | | |
| Boone Karlberg PC | | |
| Crowley Fleck PLLP * | | |
| Worden Thane PC | | |
| **Band 2** | | |
| Browning, Kaleczyc, Berry & Hoven PC | | |
| Garlington, Lohn & Robinson, PLLP * | | |
| Moulton Bellingham PC | | |

\* *Indicates firm/individual with profile.*
† *ONP = Other Notable Practitioner.*

| Leading Individuals | |
| --- | --- |
| **Band 1** | |
| Boone Thomas | Boone Karlberg PC |
| Dayton Peter S | Worden Thane PC |
| Dockery Michael | Crowley Fleck PLLP * |
| Karell Allan L | Karell Dyre Haney PLLP (ONP)† |
| Stensland Dean | Boone Karlberg PC |
| Wagner William | Garlington, Lohn & Robinson, PLLP * |
| **Band 2** | |
| Cummings Steven | Moore, Cockrell, Goicoechea (ONP)† |
| Hansen Max A | Max A. Hansen & Associates (ONP)† |
| King Martin S | Worden Thane PC |
| Maclay Helena | Maclay Law Firm (ONP)† |
| McCormick Alan | Garlington, Lohn & Robinson, PLLP * |
| Sullivan Robert J | Boone Karlberg PC |
| **Band 3** | |
| Dowdall Colleen | Worden Thane PC |
| Etchart Mark | Browning, Kaleczyc, Berry & Hoven PC |
| Jones John | Moulton Bellingham PC |
| Swartley Christopher | Christopher B. Swartley (ONP)† |
| Swimley Susan | Susan B. Swimley Attorney at Law (ONP)† |
| **Up-and-coming individuals** | |
| Sherman Gina S | Crowley Fleck PLLP * |

## Band 1

### Boone Karlberg PC

**THE FIRM** Based in Missoula, Boone Karlberg is well known for the quality and range of its real estate practice. A diverse transactional workload includes deals involving ranch, residential, commercial, industrial and leisure properties. The team is also deeply experienced in private and commercial financing, title litigation, bankruptcy and foreclosure matters.

**KEY INDIVIDUALS Thomas Boone** is a seasoned real estate practitioner with extensive experience in commercial and residential transactions. His expertise in trusts and estates also makes him much sought-after for succession matters involving ranch property. **Dean Stensland** is a highly esteemed commercial and business lawyer, with noted expertise in bank foreclosures, property transactions and construction issues. **Robert Sullivan** is commended for his comprehensive real estate law practice, which includes various transactional, regulatory and litigious engagements.

### Crowley Fleck PLLP

**See profile on p.1656**

**THE FIRM** This team is a dominant force throughout the region, with five offices in Montana and a further four in adjoining states. The firm is lauded for its impressive track record in representing banks and other commercial lenders. Further areas of strength include agricultural, commercial, and residential matters.

**KEY INDIVIDUALS Michael Dockery** (see p.1653) is a dedicated real estate specialist. Alongside sales and leasing transactions, he is skilled in developing, financing, foreclosure, planning and zoning matters. **Gina Sherman** (see p.1655) continues to build her reputation in the real estate arena, and devotes much of her time to real estate development, transactions and financings.

### Worden Thane PC

**THE FIRM** This Missoula firm maintains its impressive reputation across the spectrum of real estate matters, and is well regarded for its lawyers' transactional, banking and land use expertise. Other strong suits include the restructuring and reorganization of real estate assets and associated debts, as well as matters involving real estate finance and foreclosures.

**KEY INDIVIDUALS Peter Dayton** has an enviably broad practice with regard to property law, which takes in sales, commercial leasing, litigation and access and easement issues. **Martin King** engages in banking, litigious and transactional work within the purview of real estate, including litigation relating to easement and land use. **Colleen Dowdall** is a noted expert in regulatory issues affecting land use and development, such as public and private access.

## Band 2

### Browning, Kaleczyc, Berry & Hoven PC

**THE FIRM** This firm continues to impress market commentators with its high-caliber expertise. Its workload covers the gamut of real estate matters, including purchases, sales, commercial leasing, subdivisions and large develop-

ment projects. The firm has a deep reservoir of expertise in matters regarding public lands and railroads. Clients include Benefis Hospital, ConocoPhillips and Union Pacific.
**KEY INDIVIDUALS Mark Etchart** has a wide-ranging practice that includes litigation, large ranch transactions and public lands matters.

## Garlington, Lohn & Robinson, PLLP
**See profile on p.1657**
**THE FIRM** This firm advises clients throughout the state from its Missoula base, on the full range of transactional and contentious real estate matters. Its areas of expertise include condominium and collective developments, easements, land use and zoning.
**KEY INDIVIDUALS William Wagner** (see p.1655) is a well-known figure in the real estate arena, and is much sought-after for his advice on major development projects.
**Alan McCormick** (see p.1655) advises government and private sector clients on a range of land use, zoning and

development matters, and has a very strong command of permitting requirements. He is also a seasoned litigator, and his experience includes a variety of land use-related law suits.

## Moulton Bellingham PC
**THE FIRM** Located in Billings, Moulton Bellingham has a broad and sophisticated real estate, land use and construction practice. An array of public and private sector clients call on the team for their legal requirements. Its many strengths include engagements regarding large commercial development centers.
**KEY INDIVIDUALS John Jones** is an accomplished all-around business lawyer who regularly counsels clients on all manner of real estate law transactions and procedures.

## Other Notable Practitioners

**Allan Karell** of Karell Dyre Haney PLLP has a statewide practice counseling on foreclosures, real estate financing and transactions concerned with agricultural and commercial property. **Steven Cummings** of Moore, Cockrell, Goicoechea & Axelberg, P.C. handles all manner of transactions and legal services within the purview of real estate law from the firm's offices in Kalispell. **Max Hansen** of Max A. Hansen & Associates, P.C. in Dillon offers guidance on a broad range of real estate sales and exchanges. **Helena Maclay** of Maclay Law Firm, based in Missoula, is a statewide authority on transactions involving agricultural property, with a particular emphasis on ranches and conservation land. **Christopher Swartley** of Christopher B. Swartley, PLLC works on large real estate developments, often acting on behalf of banks and financial institutions. **Susan Swimley** of Susan B. Swimley Attorney at Law advises private, business and municipal clients on real estate and land use matters.

# Leaders' Profiles in Montana

**BENDER, Jeanne Matthews**
Holland & Hart LLP, Billings
406 252 2166
jbender@hollandhart.com
*Featured in Labor & Employment (Montana)*
**Practice Areas:** Of Counsel to Holland & Hart LLP, practicing in commercial, employment, and natural resources litigation.
**Professional Memberships:** Member: American Bar Association Foundation; Montana Bar Association; American Bar Association; and the Montana Defense Trial Lawyers Association.
**Career:** Admitted to the Montana (1985) and Colorado (1988) Bars, the United States District Court and the Ninth Circuit Court of Appeals.
**Publications:** Editor, Montana Employment Law Letter. Included in leading American publication's list of top employment lawyers, 2007 to present. Super.
**Personal:** Received a JD (1985) and a BA (1965) from the University of Montana.

**BROEDER, Gary**
Crowley Fleck PLLP, Billings
406 252 3441
gbroeder@crowleyfleck.com
*Featured in Natural Resources (Montana)*
**Practice Areas:** Oil and gas law, primarily in title examination and property acquisitions and divestitures.
**Professional Memberships:** State Bar of Montana and American Bar Association.
**Career:** JD from University of Montana. Admitted to practice in Montana in 1974. Retired as a partner from Crowley Fleck PLLP in 2011. Currently of counsel with Crowley Fleck PLLP working part time on a limited number of oil and gas matters.
**Personal:** Born June 25, 1946. Now spends most days simply enjoying time with spouse and family

and participating in outdoor activities such as hiking, skiing, fishing, and hunting.

**BROWN, Stephen Ross**
Garlington, Lohn & Robinson, PLLP, Missoula
srbrown@garlington.com
*Featured in Natural Resources (Montana)*
**Practice Areas:** Environmental, natural resources and energy law, with particular emphasis on project permitting, regulatory compliance, natural resource transactions and defense of enforcement actions. He also assists clients including landowners, lenders, private utilities and energy companies, recreational resorts, and state and local government on matters involving water rights, oil and gas interests, wind energy, water and air quality, and hazardous waste matters.
**Professional Memberships:** American College of Environmental Lawyers.
**Career:** Best Lawyers in America (Environmental Law).
**Personal:** JD, Northwestern School of Law of Lewis and Clark College, cum laude (1989); BS Geology, Whitworth College (1983).

**CHUMRAU, Gary B**
Garlington, Lohn & Robinson, PLLP, Missoula
gbchumrau@garlington.com
*Featured in Corporate/M&A (Montana)*
**Practice Areas:** Gary's practice has historically been focused in the area of commercial law and transactions. Although he still practices banking law, secured transactions and real estate, his primary focus has become hospital and health care law. He has been involved in numerous joint venture arrangements between tax exempt health care entities and private physicians.
**Career:** AV-rated, Martindale Hubbell; Best Lawyers in America (Corporate Law, Health Care

Law, Mergers and Acquisitions Law); Super Lawyers (Business/Corporate, Health Care, Real Estate).
**Personal:** JD, University of Montana (1977); BA, Stanford University (1973).

**DALY, Lawrence**
Garlington, Lohn & Robinson, PLLP, Missoula
lfdaly@garlington.com
*Featured in Litigation (Montana)*
**Practice Areas:** Larry has practiced primarily in the litigation field, focusing on medical malpractice defense, contract, construction and commercial litigation and product liability. Larry has extensive civil trial and appellate experience in both state and federal courts.
**Career:** AV-rated, Martindale Hubbell; Best Lawyers in America (Commercial Litigation, Personal Injury Litigation); Super Lawyers (Business Litigation, Civil Litigation Defense, Health Care).
**Personal:** JD, University of Montana with honors (1968), BS in Engineering, Seattle University.

**DAVENPORT, Marcia**
Crowley Fleck PLLP, Helena
406 449 4165
mdavenport@crowleyfleck.com
*Featured in Labor & Employment (Montana)*
**Practice Areas:** Investigates complaints of harassment, discrimination, retaliation, wage claims and constructive and wrongful discharge. Provides training on Montana employment law, and day-to-day employment advice, to employers. Defends harassment, discrimination, retaliation, wage claims, and constructive and wrongful discharge claims.
**Professional Memberships:** Montana Defense Trial Lawyers Association, DRI, and Litigation Counsel of America (by invitation).

**Career:** Partner, Crowley Fleck PLLP. Joined firm in 1998. Previously, private practice with another local law firm from 1989-1998. US District Court, Ninth Circuit Court of Appeals, Montana Supreme Court, U.S. Supreme Court.
**Personal:** Born September 4, 1961. JD, University of Missoula with honors (1989).

**DESOTO, Kathleen L**
Garlington, Lohn & Robinson, PLLP, Missoula
406 523 2500
kldesoto@garlington.com
*Featured in Litigation (Montana)*
**Practice Areas:** Defense of insurance unfair claims practices act cases, school liability defense, and federal criminal defense.
**Personal:** JD, University of Montana with highest honors (1999); BA in English Literature, Santa Clara University (1989).

**DOCKERY, Michael**
Crowley Fleck PLLP, Billings
406 252 3441
mdockery@crowleyfleck.com
*Featured in Real Estate (Montana)*
**Practice Areas:** Commercial and Real Estate Law, including sale and lease transactions, secured financing, real estate development, title insurance law and municipal finance.
**Professional Memberships:** State Bar of Montana, American Bar Association, American College of Real Estate Lawyers, National Association of Bond Lawyers, Montana Land Title Association and American Land Title Association.
**Career:** BA from Montana State University; JD from the University of Montana School of Law. Admitted to practice in 1983. Joined Crowley, Haughey, Hanson, Toole & Dietrich (now Crowley Fleck PLLP) in June 1983.

**Personal:** Born May 13, 1955, Lewistown, Montana. Enjoys golf and reading.

## FETSCHER, Candace
Garlington, Lohn & Robinson, PLLP, Missoula
ccfetscher@Garlington.com
*Featured in Labor & Employment (Montana)*
**Practice Areas:** Health care, including medical malpractice defense, and employment law.
**Career:** AV-rated, Martindale Hubbell; Best Lawyers in America (Health Care Law, Labor and Employment Law); Super Lawyers (Employment and Labor, Alternative Dispute Resolution)
**Personal:** University of Montana School of Law, Missoula, Montana JD - 1975 Law Review: Montana Law Review, Note Editor, 1975 University of Montana, Missoula, Montana BA (Magna Cum Laude) - 1968 Honors: With High Honors.

## GRAY, Kyle
Holland & Hart LLP, Billings
406 252 2166
kgray@hollandhart.com
*Featured in Natural Resources (Montana)*
**Practice Areas:** Complex civil litigation and appellate advocacy, with an emphasis on environmental litigation.
**Professional Memberships:** ABA Environment, Energy and Resources Section; Montana Bar Association, Women's Law Section; Wyoming Bar Association; ACLU of Montana Litigation Committee.
**Career:** Practicing since 1986 with Holland & Hart; Clerkship with Chief US District Court Judge Clarence Brimmer, 1984 – 1986.
**Publications:** Co-author of CERCLA chapter in Environmental Regulation (Second Edition, American Law of Mining, 2003).
**Personal:** University of Michigan School of Law (JD 1984, cum laude); Michigan State University (BA 1981, summa cum laude).

## HANSBERRY, Charles
Garlington, Lohn & Robinson, PLLP, Missoula
406 523 2500
cehansberry@Garlington.com
*Featured in Labor & Employment (Montana)*
**Practice Areas:** Commercial, environmental and employment litigation. Chuck has litigated matters on a wide range of issues – from pollution to breach of construction contracts – under a varied set of laws – from the Federal Clean Air Act to the Montana Wrongful Discharge Act – in a multitude of forums – from federal court to state agency hearings.
**Career:** 2005 to Present: Garlington, Lohn & Robinson, PLLP; 1997 to 2005: Holland and Hart, LLP
**Personal:** JD, University of Montana with honors (1997); MS in Environmental Studies, University of Montana (1997); BA, Wake Forest University (1991).

## HINGLE, Charles
Holland & Hart LLP, Billings
406 896 4606
chingle@hollandhart.com
*Featured in Corporate/M&A (Montana)*
**Practice Areas:** Practice focuses on banking, business bankruptcy and creditors' rights with extensive experience in lending and real estate transactions and commercial litigation. Mr Hingle is a Business Bankruptcy Specialist by the American Board of Certification (1993 - Present).
**Professional Memberships:** State Bar of Montana; Wyoming State Bar.
**Career:** Admitted to the Montana, Wyoming and Louisiana (inactive) State Bars.
**Publications:** Authored Montana Chapter of "Commercial Lending Law" published by the American Bar Association; Authored the "Law of Guaranties: a Jurisdiction-by-Jurisdiction Guide to U.S. and Canadian Law".
**Personal:** JD Louisiana State University (1976) and BA Tulane University (1972).

## JOHNS, Daniel
Crowley Fleck PLLP, Kalispell
406 752 6644
djohns@crowleyfleck.com
*Featured in Labor & Employment (Montana)*
**Practice Areas:** Represents and counsels employers in employment law issues, including traditional labor law (eg NLRA and all matters related to labor unions); drafting and reviewing employment agreements, covenants not to compete, confidentiality agreements, and personnel policies; defending claims arising out of the employment relationship (eg unlawful discrimination, sexual harassment, wrongful termination, wage and hour claims, etc.); and advises clients on the ADA, ADEA, FMLA, and other state and federal employment laws and regulations.
**Career:** Admitted to practice Indiana 1973, Montana 1979.
**Personal:** St. Olaf College, BA 1968 Indiana University, JD and MBA 1973.

## LAMDIN III, William
Crowley Fleck PLLP, Billings
406 252 3441
blamdin@crowleyfleck.com
*Featured in Corporate/M&A (Montana)*
**Practice Areas:** Commercial and Real Estate Lending, mergers and acquisitions, federal and state bank regulatory matters, director and officer liability, workouts and foreclosures, creditor's rights in bankruptcy, and financing transactions with Native American Tribes and Tribal business entities. Represents banks throughout the Rocky Mountain region.
**Professional Memberships:** Yellowstone Area and Montana Bar Associations.
**Career:** AV Preeminent, Martindale-Hubbell, Best Lawyers in America (Lawyer of the year, banking law); Chambers USA, Leading Business Lawyers (corporate/M&A law); Mountain States Super Lawyers (banking law).
**Personal:** Rocky Mountain College, summa cum laude, 1979; UM Law, with high honors, 1983.

## LEE, John R
Crowley Fleck PLLP, Billings
406 252 3441
jlee@crowleyfleck.com
*Featured in Natural Resources (Montana)*
**Practice Areas:** Energy, Environment, and Natural Resources, his practice is concentrated on all aspects of oil and gas law.
**Professional Memberships:** Faculty of the Rocky Mountain Mineral Law Foundation Federal Oil and Gas Leasing Short Course, teaching the subject areas of unitization, communitization and operations.
**Career:** BSBA University of North Dakota 1981, JD University of North Dakota Law 1989 where he earned Juris Doctorate and was Order of the Coif. He joined Crowley Fleck in 1989 and currently is a Partner.

## LEHMAN, Steven
Crowley Fleck PLLP, Billings
406 252 3441
slehman@crowleyfleck.com
*Featured in Labor & Employment (Montana)*
**Practice Areas:** Civil litigation with concentration in employment litigation in the areas of discrimination and wrongful discharge. Active in advising employers on union organizing attempts & employee relations, including, how to avoid wrongful discharge & discrimination claims.
**Professional Memberships:** American Bar Association, Montana Bar Association, Defense Research Institute, Inc., Best Lawyers Lawyer of the Year (Labor & Employment), AV Rating Martindale-Hubbell, Super Lawyers, Chambers Leading Lawyers.
**Career:** 1978 JD University of Wisconsin Law School; Joined Firm 1978; Partner 1983.
**Personal:** Born on June 8, 1950; Attended University of Wisconsin, Madison Undergraduate, Economics degree in 1972; Lives in Billings, Montana.

## LICHTE, Julie
Crowley Fleck PLLP, Bozeman
jlichte@crowleyfleck.com
*Featured in Litigation (Montana)*
**Practice Areas:** Includes representation of healthcare providers in professional negligence matters, licensure complaints, and employment matters. Represents employers in wrongful termination matters; advises healthcare providers on issues as peer review, risk management, and quality assurance.
**Professional Memberships:** Montana State Bar Association, American Bar Association, Defense Research Institute, Litigation Counsel of America (by invitation).
**Career:** Licensed in Illinois and Montana. Former partner of Quinn, Johnston, Henderson & Pretorius Peoria, Illinois. Currently, Partner with Crowley Fleck, PLLP.
**Personal:** Attended St. Francis Medical Center School of Nursing, Bradley University (BS, MBA) and University of Washington School of Law. Lives in Livingston, Montana.

## LOBLE, Jason
Crowley Fleck PLLP, Helena
406 449 4165
jloble@crowleyfleck.com
*Featured in Corporate/M&A (Montana)*
**Practice Areas:** Focuses on mergers and acquisitions, private securities offerings, and business governance matters. Clients include entrepreneurs, hospitals, physician groups, technology companies, investors and a diverse group of new and established businesses across Montana.
**Career:** Admitted in WA 1996 (inactive) and Montana 2002. Prior to joining Crowley Fleck in 2002, Jason practiced with Preston, Gates & Ellis (now K&L Gates) and Davis Wright Tremaine in Seattle, WA.
**Personal:** Born 1968, Helena, Montana. BA, University of Montana, 1991; MA, Purdue University, 1993; JD, University of Montana, 1996. Co-Editor in Chief, 'Montana Law Review', 1996.

## LUCK, Bradley
Garlington, Lohn & Robinson, PLLP, Missoula
406 523 2595
bjluck@garlington.com
*Featured in Labor & Employment (Montana), Litigation (Montana)*
**Practice Areas:** Insurance related litigation specializing in bad faith, personal injury, professional negligence and workers' compensation law.
**Career:** AV-rated, Martindale Hubbell; Best Lawyers in America (Insurance Law, Legal Malpractice Law, Personal Injury Litigation, Workers' Compensation Law); Super Lawyers (Personal Injury Defense, Professional Liability, Workers' Compensation).
**Personal:** University of Montana School of Law, Missoula, Montana JD - 1977 Honors: With Honors University of Montana, Missoula, Montana BA (Cum Laude) - 1974 United States Naval Academy, Annapolis, Maryland.

## MANGEN JR, Christopher
Crowley Fleck PLLP, Billings
406 252 3441
cmangen@crowleyfleck.com
*Featured in Natural Resources (Montana)*
**Practice Areas:** Energy, Enviroment, and Natural Resources, emphasizing on oil, gas, and water law.
**Professional Memberships:** Faculty of the Rocky Mountain Mineral Law Foundation Short Course on Federal Oil and Gas Leasing and has served as the faculty chairman for the course. He has also lectured on various topics in the Natural Resources and Real Estate areas.
**Career:** B.A. Montana State University 1976, JD University of Montana School of Law 1980. He joined Crowley Fleck in 1980 and currently works as lead counsel for Natural Resource Litigated matters.

## MAYNARD JR, Joe
Crowley Fleck PLLP, Billings
406 252 3441
jmaynard@crowleyfleck.com
*Featured in Labor & Employment (Montana)*

**Practice Areas:** Primarily defense of workers' compensation claims. Defended multimillion dollar claims against the officers of Touch America and Montana Power in connection with the collapse of both companies. Extensive experience in estate litigation, utility-based person injury defense, and medical malpractice defense.

**Professional Memberships:** American Bar Association, Montana Defense Trail Lawyers, DRI, Workers' Compensation Rules Committee, Montana State Bar Association.

**Career:** AV Preeminent, Best Lawyers in America, Mountain States Super Lawyers, Chambers USA, and Benchmark

**Personal:** Montana State University 1983 with honors; University of Montana Law School 1987 with high honors.

## MCCORMICK, Alan
Garlington, Lohn & Robinson, PLLP, Missoula
406 523 2500
afmccormick@garlington.com
*Featured in Real Estate (Montana)*

**Practice Areas:** Land use, zoning, real estate and local government law with a particular emphasis on development permitting and related transactions.

**Career:** AV-rated, Martindale Hubbell; Best Lawyers in America (Land Use & Zoning).

**Personal:** University of Montana School of Law, Missoula, Montana Honors: With High Honors Virginia Polytechnic Institute and State University, Blacksburg, Virginia Master of Urban and Regional Planning - May, 1993 Virginia Polytechnic Institute and State University BS - 1991 Major: Horticulture.

## MCINTOSH, Ian
Crowley Fleck PLLP, Bozeman
406 556 1430
imcintosh@crowleylaw.com
*Featured in Litigation (Montana)*

**Practice Areas:** Litigation including products liability, insurance bad faith, commercial litigation, and personal injury.

**Professional Memberships:** Certified Public Accountanat (Inactive).

**Career:** Admitted MT 1998. AV rated Martindale-Hubbell.

**Personal:** Born 1970; JD University of Montana, with Honors, 1998. Member, Association of Ski Defense Attorneys.

## MITCHELL, W Scott
Holland & Hart LLP, Billings
406 252 2166
smitchell@hollandhart.com
*Featured in Natural Resources (Montana)*

**Practice Areas:** Partner practicing in commercial, natural resources, oil and gas, employment, and products liability litigation.

**Professional Memberships:** Member: ABA, Litigation and Natural Resources Sections; Montana Bar Association; Montana Defense Trial Lawyers Association; Yellowstone County Bar Association; University of Montana School of Law Clinical Board of Visitors.

**Career:** Admitted to the Montana Bar (1992), the United States District Court for the District of Montana, and Ninth Circuit Court of Appeals.

**Personal:** University of Montana School of Law (JD 1992); Montana State University (BS Agricultural Engineering 1983).

## NEDROW, Elizabeth A
Holland & Hart LLP, Billings
406 896 4635
enedrow@hollandhart.com
*Featured in Labor & Employment (Montana)*

**Practice Areas:** Advises employers on aspects of employee benefits including pension, welfare, and executive compensation & 409A plans, ERISA, Employee Stock Ownership Plan Transactions, Mergers and Acquisitions, Healthcare Reform and Equity Compensation.

**Professional Memberships:** ABA; Montana Bar Association; Past President Western Pension and Benefits Conference, Montana Chapter; National Center for Employee Ownership (Member); ESOP Association (Member).

**Career:** Partner; Past chair of the firm's Benefits Law Group; Member of the firm's Management Committee.

**Publications:** Advisory Board of Editors, Benefits & Compensation Law Alert, 2009 - present.

**Personal:** JD, University of Pennsylvania (1995); BA, Harvard University (1990).

## PETERSEN, Larry
Holland & Hart LLP, Billings
406 896 4622
lpetersen@hollandhart.com
*Featured in Corporate/M&A (Montana)*

**Practice Areas:** Mr Petersen's practice focuses on tax, estate planning, real estate, natural resources, mergers, and acquisitions. He has extensive experience with probates; formation of LLC's, partnerships and corporations; coal leasing, acquisitions, and entity formations; purchase and sale of oil and gas and entity formation; and healthcare.

**Professional Memberships:** American Bar Association, Montana Bar Association, Yellowstone County Bar Association, ACTEC.

**Career:** Admitted to Montana Bar (1967).

**Personal:** Received a JD from University of Montana (1967), a BS in Economics from the Wharton School at the University of Pennsylvania (1964), and an LLM from New York University (Taxation, 1970).

## RILEY, Larry
Garlington, Lohn & Robinson, PLLP, Missoula
406 523 2500
leriley@garlington.com
*Featured in Litigation (Montana)*

**Practice Areas:** Larry practices as a trial lawyer with a special emphasis on medical legal matters. Larry has tried numerous jury trials throughout the state of Montana in both state and federal court.

**Professional Memberships:** American Board of Trial Advocates; American College of Trial Lawyers (fellow).

**Career:** AV-rated, Martindale Hubbell; Best Lawyers in America (Medical Malpractice Law, Personal Injury Litigation); Super Lawyers (Personal Injury Defense, Medical Malpractice, Health Care).

**Personal:** JD, University of Montana (1966); BS In Political Science, University of Montana (1963).

## RITCHIE, Jason S
Holland & Hart LLP, Billings
406 896 4611
jritchie@hollandhart.com
*Featured in Labor & Employment (Montana)*

**Practice Areas:** Mr Ritchie represents and advises clients in several areas, including claims of wrongful discharge, harassment, discrimination, breach of employment contract, response to state and federal investigations and claims arising under the Americans with Disabilities Act, Montana Human Rights Act, Family and Medical Leave Act, and the National Rehabilitation Act.

**Professional Memberships:** Member of the American, Montana, and Yellowstone County Bar Associations.

**Career:** Mr Ritchie represents clients in Montana State and Federal courts, Montana Human Rights Commission, Montana Supreme Court and Ninth Circuit Court of Appeals.

**Personal:** JD, University of Montana School of Law (2004); BA, Carroll College (2001).

## RUFFATTO, Steven P
Crowley Fleck PLLP, Billings
406 252 3441
sruffatto@crowleyfleck.com
*Featured in Natural Resources (Montana)*

**Practice Areas:** Acquisition, development, financing and divestiture of mineral extraction, transportation, generation and processing facilities.

**Professional Memberships:** Rocky Mountain Mineral Law Foundation (Trustee, Board); Mining, Petroleum and Bar Associations; Mountain States Legal Foundation; American College of Real Estate Lawyers.

**Career:** AV Preeminent, Martindale-Hubbell; Best Lawyers (Lawyer of the Year); Super Lawyers; Chambers Leading Lawyers; International Who's

Who, Mining Lawyers; Top Rated Lawyer, Energy, Environmental & Natural Resources; American Lawyer/Corporate Counsel Magazine; Firm's Excutive Committee.

**Publications:** Works on mineral interests and development, mine reclamation, environmental law, and federal oil and gas law.

**Personal:** UM Law, distinction, 1976; MSU Engineering, honors, 1971.

## SHERIDAN, Robert E
Garlington, Lohn & Robinson, PLLP, Missoula
resheridan@garlington.com
*Featured in Litigation (Montana)*

**Practice Areas:** Bob's practice has focused on defense litigation with primary emphasis in the areas of railroad (FELA) law, products liability, governmental liability, premises liability and vehicular liability. He also has extensive experience in defending workers' compensation claims. In addition to his civil trial experience he has handled numerous appellate matters in both the state and federal appellate systems.

**Career:** AV-rated, Marindale Hubbell; Best Lawyers in America (Railroad Law); Super Lawyers (Civil Litigation Defense, General Litigation, Alternative Dispute Resolution).

**Personal:** JD, University of Montana (1967); BS in Finance, University of Notre Dame (1964).

## SHERMAN, Gina S
Crowley Fleck PLLP, Bozeman
gsherman@crowleyfleck.com
*Featured in Real Estate (Montana)*

**Practice Areas:** Real Estate development and transactions in Montana.

**Career:** Admitted MT 1987. AV rated Martindale-Hubble.

**Personal:** Born 1969, BS Montana State University, JD University of Montana.

## WAGNER, William
Garlington, Lohn & Robinson, PLLP, Missoula
406 523 2500
wtwagner@garlington.com
*Featured in Real Estate (Montana)*

**Practice Areas:** Bill's practice is primarily in the areas of real estate, business, probate, limited domestic relations, related areas of litigation and mediation.

**Career:** AV-rated, Martindale Hubbell; Best Lawyers in America (Real Estate Law); Super Lawyers (Real Estate, General Litigation, Business Litigation).

**Personal:** JD, University of Montana (1974); BS in Accounting, Gonzaga University (1971).

# CROWLEY FLECK PLLP

www.crowleyfleck.com **tel:** 406 252 3441 **fax:** 406 259 4159

**Managing Partner:** Neil G Westesen
Number of partners: 75
Number of other attorneys: 133

**Firm Overview:**

Crowley Fleck PLLP is a multi-service regional firm that handles a wide variety of legal matters for clients. The firm has over 130 lawyers licensed not only in Montana, North Dakota and Wyoming, but also in several surrounding states including South Dakota, Idaho, Minnesota, Nebraska and Iowa. Currently, Crowley Fleck PLLP has offices in Billings, Bozeman, Butte, Helena, Kalispell and Missoula, Montana, Bismarck and Williston, North Dakota, and Casper and Sheridan Wyoming.

The firm represents an impressive and wide range of clients, including national and international corporations. The firm has a commitment to provide the highest quality legal services and has built upon a strong tradition of legal expertise and high ethical standards.

**Main Areas of Practice:**

**Corporate/Banking & Finance:**

The firm handles antitrust, bond offerings, public finance, public utilities, banking, business organizations, corporate, securities, financing transactions, intellectual property, employee benefits, mergers and acquisitions, non-profit corporations, creditors' rights, real estate, agricultural, regulatory and immigration.

**Intellectual Property:**

The IP Practice Group advises clients on a wide range of matters including patents, copyrights, trademarks, trade secrets, unfair competition, license agreements, non-disclosure agreements and franchise concerns.

**Labor & Employment Practice:**

The firm represents management in all areas of employment law especially employee relations, wrongful discharge and discrimination claims.

**Litigation:**

The firm covers all aspects of litigation through its seven offices. The Litigation Practice Group handles a wide variety of matters for commercial clients including administrative law, arbitration, condemnation, intellectual property, mediation, insurance defense, personal injury, malpractice, products liability, worker's compensation, commercial litigation, construction law, employment, foreclosures and bankruptcy.

**Energy, Environment & Natural Resources:**

The firm's Natural Resources Practice Group is one of the largest in Montana and North Dakota, specializing in coal, conservation commission hearings, public land issues, regulatory matters, title examinations, utilities, oil and gas, mining, water, energy transmission, environmental compliance and permitting and Indian law.

**Real Estate:**

The firm focuses mainly on commercial and agricultural transactions including subdivision, development, finance and bankruptcy proceedings, commonly representing creditors.

**Tax & Estate Planning:**

The firm has extensive experience in advising commercial and individual clients in complex probate and estate planning matters.

**Clients:**

Allstate Insurance Co.; Arch Coal Inc.; The Bank of Baker; Big Sky Economic Development Authority; Billings Clinic; Blue Cross and Blue Shield of Montana; Chartis Insurance; Chicago Title Insurance Co.; Chubb Group of Insurance Cos.; City of Billings; CNA Insurance; Conoco Inc.; Crawford & Co.; CTA; Decker Coal Co.; The Doctor's Co.; Enerplus; Farmers Alliance Mutual Insurance Company; Farmers Insurance Group; Fidelity National Title Insurance Co.; Fireman's Fund Insurance Co.; First American Title Insurance Co.; First Interstate Bank; Ford Motor Company; General Motors Acceptance Corp.; Great American Insurance Co.; Hartford Insurance Group; Headington Oil; Hess Corporation; Kemper Insurance Co.; Liberty Mutual Insurance Co.; Marathon Oil Company; MDU Resources Group, Inc.; Metropolitan Life Insurance Co.; Montana State Compensation Insurance Fund; Natural Gas Processing Company; New York Life Insurance Co.; Noranda Minerals Corp.; Northwestern Energy; Old Republic Insurance Co.; Petro-Hunt LLC; Sinclair Oil Corp.; SM Energy Company; St. Paul Insurance Cos.; Stockman Bank; Streeter Brothers Realty Corp.; The Travelers; Turner Enterprises, Inc.; UMC Petroleum Corp.; Utah Medical Insurance Association; Western Litigation Inc.; Whiting Oil & Gas Corporation; Yellowstone Banks; Zurich American Insurance Group.

**PRACTICE AREAS**

Corporate/Banking Finance
Intellectual Property
Labor & Employment
Litigation
Energy, Environment & Natural Resources
Real Estate
Tax & Estate Planning

**OFFICES**

MONTANA

**BILLINGS:** 500 Transwestern Plaza II, 490 North 31st Street, MT 59101-1288
Tel: 406 252 3441  Fax: 406 259 4159
Email: crowley@crowleyfleck.com

**BOZEMAN:** 45 Discovery Drive, MT 59718-6957
Tel: 406 556 1430  Fax: 406 556 1433

**BUTTE:** Thornton Building, 65 East Broadway, Suite 503, MT 59701
Tel: 406 533 6892  Fax: 406 533 6830

**HELENA:** 900 N. Last Chance Gluch, MT 59601
Tel: 406 449 4165  Fax: 406 449 5149

**KALISPELL:** 1667 Whitefish Stage Road, MT 59901
Tel: 406 752 6644  Fax: 406 752 5108

**MISSOULA:** 305 South 4th East, Suite 100, MT 59801-2701
Tel: 406 523 3600  Fax: 406 523 3636

NORTH DAKOTA

**BISMARCK:** 400 East Broadway, Suite 600, ND 58501
Tel: 701 223 6585  Fax: 701 222 4853

**WILLISTON:** 1331 9th Ave NW 58801
Tel: 701 572 2200  Fax: 701 572 7072

WYOMING

**CASPER:** 152 North Durbin Street, Suite 220, WY 82601
Tel: 307 265 2279  Fax: 307 265 2307

**SHERIDAN:** 101 West Brundage Street, WY 82801
Tel: 307 673 3000  Fax: 307 672 1732

# GARLINGTON, LOHN & ROBINSON

**www.**garlington.com  **tel:** 406 523 2500  **fax:** 406 523 2595

**Managing Partner:** Brian J Smith
Number of partners: 23  Number of other lawyers: 12

**OFFICES**

MONTANA

**MISSOULA:** 350 Ryman Street, MT 59802
Tel: 406 523 2500  Fax: 406 523 2595

## Firm Overview:
The law firm of Garlington, Lohn & Robinson, PLLP, has roots that go back to the founding of Missoula more that 130 years ago. Today, the firm has grown into one of the largest law firms in the state and the region. In addition to their strong client base in Montana, theyfrequently act as local counsel for out-of-state clients.

## Main Areas of Practice:

### Arbitration & Mediation:
Mediations, primarily in the form of settlement conferences, are an integral part of Montana litigation practice because federal and state district courts require mediation prior to setting a date for the trial. Several attorneys in the firm have developed extensive experience serving as mediators/settlement masters both in litigation and in informal, pre-litigation situations. These confidential proceedings are governed by statute and court rules, offer an alternate form of dispute resolution and allow for an independent evaluation of a case by experienced counsel.
**Contact:** Bill Wagner

### Business & Tax:
GLR's Business and Tax Practice Group provides a variety of services for a diverse client base that ranges from individuals to start-up ventures to large multi-national corporations operating across the entire spectrum of industries and services. The firm's representation of business entities includes sole proprietors, partnerships, limited liability companies, limited liability partnerships, corporations, and tax-exempt organizations.
**Contact:** Gary Chumrau

### Healthcare & Medical Malpractice Defense:
GLR has a long tradition of advising and successfully representing healthcare providers in all aspects of healthcare law throughout the state and region. The firm's transactional attorneys also advise healthcare providers in all aspects of the business side of healthcare, including joint ventures, mergers, business entity formation and organization. The firm's medical malpractice defense practice is one of the strongest and busiest in the region and its attorneys regularly advise physicians, hospitals and other health care providers on all areas of compliance with state and federal laws.
**Contact:** Gary Chumrau (healthcare), Peter Stokstad (medical malpractice)

### Insurance:
GLR attorneys provide counsel to large and small regional and national insurance companies, agencies, and adjusters on a wide range of insurance issues. The firm specializes in matters related to insurance defense, coverage opinions, the duty to defend and indemnify, underinsured and uninsured motorist coverage issues, advancement of payments, stacking of coverage, Unfair Trade Practices Act claims, bad faith, subrogation, indemnity, contribution, and State Fund and Workers Compensation.
**Contact:** Brad Luck

### Intellectual Property:
The IP Group handles litigation, licensing and registrations primarily for trademark and copyright issues. The firm has also worked as trial counsel on patent cases, working with licensed patent attorneys. The firm frequently serves as primary or local counsel in federal court actions to protect or defend the intellectual property rights of businesses anywhere in the state of Montana.
**Contact:** Bob Lukes

### Labor & Employment:
GLR's Employment Practice Group is the largest in the firm, and is among the most dynamic employment law contingents in Western Montana. Practice fields cover all labor issues and forums (i.e. transaction, arbitration, mediation, and litigation) including employee contract negotiation and drafting; collective bargaining agreements; employment handbook review and creation; discrimination claims, including claims of sexual harassment, disability, and FMLA; wrongful discharge defense; and ERISA and COBRA claims, among others.
**Contact:** Candace Fetscher

### Litigation:
The firm helps its clients avoid litigation, where possible, by providing advice and counsel founded upon a tradition of experience and sound judgment. When litigation cannot, or should not, be avoided, the firm is ready to provide courtroom representation to its clients before all federal, state and administrative forums in Montana. The litigators work with clients to plan and prepare for litigation in advance, in order to protect the client's long-term needs and interests.
**Contact:** Brian Smith

### Real Estate, Land Use & Environmental:
Attorneys in GLR's Real Estate, Land Use and Environmental Practice Area provide a wide range of transactional, regulatory and litigation services in all aspects of land use, environmental, commercial, ranching and residential real estate law. Real estate services range from routine purchase and sale matters to complex negotiations, easement disputes, financings and large-scale development projects. The firm's land use and environmental services include general counsel on legal requirements for land development and representation before local, state and federal regulatory agencies, boards, councils and commissions.
**Contact:** Steve Brown

### Transportation:
GLR Transportation Law Department provides representation to motor carriers, brokers, logistics providers, railroads and all other transportation related entities. With over 15 years of experience in representing transportation companies, the firm is experienced in all issues relating to the transportation business, including licensing, insurance, compliance and other regulatory issues, accident litigation, leasing and contracts, brokerage matters and cargo claims litigation.
**Contact:** Brian Smith

### Trusts, Estates, & Probate:
GLR's Trusts and Estates Practice Group provides a variety of services for individuals and private industry, handling legal matters involving tax-sensitive estate planning, estate administration, trust administration, and charitable gift planning and providing advice for charitable organizations and related planning and litigation matters.
**Contact:** Kristina McMullin

### Clients:
GLR represents the diverse legal needs of a broad range of large and small Montana businesses, as well as numerous national corporations, healthcare institutions, insurance companies, and governments.

# GOUGH, SHANAHAN, JOHNSON & WATERMAN PLLP

www.gsjw.com  **tel:** 406 442 8560  **fax:** 406 442 8783

**Managing Partners:** Thomas E Hattersley, III, Teri A Walter, Dana L Hupp
Number of partners: 14
Number of other lawyers: 3

## Firm Overview:

Established in 1879, Gough, Shanahan, Johnson and Waterman, PLLP, is the oldest, and one of the leading law firms in Montana. In addition to the general practice of law, the firm's practice emphasizes natural resources and environmental law, insurance defense and insurance coverage law, commercial litigation, employment counseling and litigation, administrative law, banking law and regulation, governmental relations, estate and property law energy, transportation, products liability and construction litigation. The firm has well established specialty practices in employment, mining, water quality, tribal law, water rights, endangered species, public school districts, patents, state and local taxation. Headquartered in Montana's capital city with satellite offices in Billings, Bozeman and Missoula, the firm is expert in the workings of the state and federal government at all levels. GSJW is the Montana member firm of the State Capital Group.

## Main Areas of Practice:

### Commercial Litigation:

The firm's litigation practice covers state and federal courts including appellate advocacy, especially before the Supreme Court of Montana. The ability to provide effective representation at all phases of litigation assures the client's rights are fully protected, before, during and following a trial. The firm also works using mediation and other forms of alternative dispute resolution to resolve matters expeditiously for clients.
**Contact:** Ronald F Waterman
**Email:** rfw@gsjw.com

### Employment:

The firm represents employers of all sizes, including regular representation of large employers headquartered outside of Montana. With offices in Helena, Billings and Missoula. The firm's statewide employment practice serves the needs of a diversified clientele including technology, services, telecommunications, manufacturers, mining, energy and oil and gas, as well as agricultural, timber and construction industries.
**Contact:** Thomas E Hattersley, III
**Email:** teh@gsjw.com
**Contact:** Teri A Walter
**Email:** taw@gsjw.com

### Environmental:

The firm's environmental law expertise is applied on behalf of its clients on a daily basis across the spectrum of legal matters, including transactions, regulatory and permitting issues and litigation. The firm has deep expertise in surface and ground water quality matters, including the federal Clean Water Act and the Montana Water Quality Acts, and deals regularly with solid hazardous waste issues, facility citing laws, pesticide regulation and environmental regulation specific to areas such as forest products, coal bed natural gas, mining, manufacturing and real estate transactions.
**Contact:** Alan L Joscelyn
**Email:** alj@gsjw.com
**Contact:** Dana L Hupp
**Email:** dlh@gsjw.com

### Government Relations/Regulatory:

The firm has extensive experience in natural resources, public utility regulation, taxation and legislative representation and places an emphasis on cost-effective problem-solving. As a longstanding and respected member of the Montana community, the firm is particularly well-suited to represent diverse corporate clients before Montana local or state government.
**Contact:** Peter G Scott
**Email:** pgs@gsjw.com

### Natural Resources:

The firm's practice encompasses all areas of natural resources law, with an emphasis on mining, coal bed methane, water law, water quality and NEPA issues. The firm represents local, national and international clients on air, surface and ground water (both quality and quantity), and waste issues arising from development, operation and reclamation of natural resource projects. The firm represents clients in all local, state and federal contexts, including regulatory agencies, contested case hearings, district and appellate courts, including the Montana Supreme Court, the US Supreme Court, the Ninth Circuit Court of Appeals and the Federal Circuit Court of Appeals. The firm's Natural Resource Team takes a comprehensive approach to addressing its client's legal, political and public relations needs.
**Contact:** Alan L Joscelyn
**Email:** alj@gsjw.com

### Real Estate/Banking/Finance:

The firm's commercial lawyers regularly assist in-state and out-of-state clients in real estate purchases and development and with lending transactions. The firm's Banking and Lending Practice assists both state and federally regulated financial institutions with all aspects of lending transaction, loan workouts, collection and foreclosure litigation and creditor bankruptcy matters. The firm also assists new and existing financial institutions with regulatory issues including new charters, compliance and acquisitions and mergers in Montana.
**Contact:** Jock O Anderson
**Email:** joa@gsjw.com

### Intellectual Property:

The firm represents entrepreneurs and corporate clients in the establishment, development, maintenance and protection of their intellectual property rights. This area of practice includes copyright, patent and trademark law. The firm has licensed representation before the US Patent and Trademark Office, as well as state and federal courts. It keeps a registry of its clients' trademark and patent registrations, to monitor continued maintenance. In addition to those areas, the firm handles trade secret, trade name and unfair trade practice matters.
**Contact:** William L MacBride Jr
**Email:** wlm@gsjw.com

## PRACTICE AREAS

Banking & Finance
Commercial Litigation
Employment
Environmental
Government Relations
Insurance Defense
Intellectual Property
Natural Resources
Real Estate
Regulatory

## OFFICES

MONTANA
**BILLINGS:** 2722 3rd Avenue N., Suite 400, MT 59101
Tel: 406 248 3214  Fax: 406 245 0627

**BOZEMAN:** 682 Ferguson, Suite 4, Bozeman, MT 59718
Tel: 406 585 3295  Fax: 406 585 3321

**HELENA:** 33 South Last Chance Gulch, PO Box 1715,
MT 59624
Tel: 406 442 8560  Fax: 406 442 8783

**MISSOULA:** 280 E. Front Street, Suite B, MT 59802
Tel: 406 728 2770  Fax: 406 728 2778

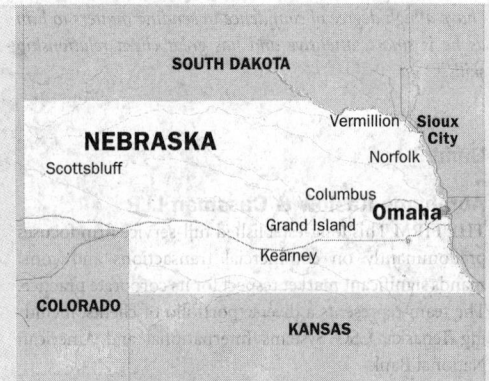

SOUTH DAKOTA

**NEBRASKA**

Scottsbluff

Vermillion **Sioux City**

Norfolk

Columbus

**Omaha**

Grand Island

Kearney

**COLORADO**

**KANSAS**

## How lawyers are ranked

Every year we carry out thousands of in-depth interviews with clients in order to assess the reputations and expertise of business lawyers worldwide. The qualities we look for (and which determine rankings) include technical legal ability, professional conduct, client service, commercial awareness/astuteness, diligence, commitment, and other qualities most valued by the client. For details of our research team, see p.5.

# CORPORATE/COMMERCIAL

Commentary about individuals can be found under their firm's paragraph. If the firm has no paragraph (is not ranked) look at Other Notable Practitioners.

### Corporate/Commercial
### Leading Firms

**Band 1**
Baird Holm LLP
Cline, Williams, Wright, Johnson & Oldfather LLP
Koley Jessen P.C.
Kutak Rock LLP *
McGrath North Mullin & Kratz PC

**Band 2**
Fraser Stryker PC LLO
Husch Blackwell LLP
McGill, Gotsdiner, Workman & Lepp PC LLO *

**Band 3**
Abrahams Kaslow & Cassman LLP
Woods & Aitken LLP

* Indicates firm / individual with profile.
†ONP = Other Notable Practitioner.

## Band 1

### Baird Holm LLP

**THE FIRM** This first-rate, full-service firm is home to some of the most well-regarded corporate and finance lawyers in Nebraska. Its 16-partner team is frequently sought after by a broad base of clients such as financial institutions, technology firms, healthcare providers, real estate developers and manufacturers. It has recently been active representing banks in various transactions. For example, the team recently acted for Northwest Bank on its acquisition of a branch of Liberty Bank. Other key clients include Blue Cross Blue Shield, Bridges Investment Management and Woodmen of the World Life Insurance Society.
**Sources say:** *"They are an extremely valuable resource that I could not function without and I would use them again in a heartbeat."*
**KEY INDIVIDUALS** Market-leading practitioner **Steven Turner** chairs the firm's financial transactions department and is particularly well regarded for his wealth of experience handling bankruptcy, workouts and financing trans-

### Leading Individuals

**Band 1**

| | |
|---|---|
| Dixon Joyce A | Kutak Rock LLP * |
| Freeman Robert | Fraser Stryker PC LLO |
| Hefflinger David L | McGrath North Mullin & Kratz PC |
| Kaslow Howard | Abrahams Kaslow & Cassman LLP |
| Turner Steven C | Baird Holm LLP |
| Wells Roger W | McGrath North Mullin & Kratz PC |
| Zeilinger John S | Baird Holm LLP |

**Band 2**

| | |
|---|---|
| Dixon Dale | Kutak Rock LLP * |
| Gardels David E | Husch Blackwell LLP |
| Gehring Stephen | Cline, Williams, Wright, Johnson |
| Gotsdiner Gary M | McGill, Gotsdiner, Workman & Lepp PC LLO * |
| Herdzina John W | Abrahams Kaslow & Cassman LLP |
| Hupp Michael M | Koley Jessen P.C. |
| McGaughey Shaun | Koley Jessen P.C. |

**Band 3**

| | |
|---|---|
| Handlos Bryan G | Kutak Rock LLP * |
| Malicki Thomas J | Abrahams Kaslow & Cassman LLP |
| Merritt William Lee | Woods & Aitken LLP |
| Miles John C. | Cline, Williams, Wright, Johnson |
| Parsonage Ronald K. | Parsonage Vandenack Williams LLC (ONP)† |
| Pirruccello Jeffrey | McGrath North Mullin & Kratz PC |
| Putnam Richard E | Baird Holm LLP |
| Slattery Alan D | Rembolt Ludtke LLP (ONP)† |

**Up-and-coming individuals**

| | |
|---|---|
| Penne Jeffrey S. | McGrath North Mullin & Kratz PC |

actions. **John Zeilinger** is another respected figure in the market who earns widespread recognition for his expertise in banking matters. He recently acted for American State Bank of Pierre in its sale to Leacko Bank Holding. **Richard Putnam** is the firm's managing partner and clients appreciate that *"his communication skills are extremely good, especially in dealing with the other party in transactions."*

### Cline, Williams, Wright, Johnson & Oldfather LLP

**THE FIRM** This long-standing market player is a go-to firm for corporate and commercial matters, particularly in Lincoln. It earns plaudits not only for its high quality of work but also the excellent client service it provides. Its team has a broad range of expertise including M&A, joint ventures, financing, restructuring and reorganization, formation of entities and business succession planning. The team is also especially experienced in advising clients on securities law as well as regulatory proceedings.
**Sources say:** *"The most important thing is their responsiveness, which is outstanding – so it's not just quality work but also customer service."*
**KEY INDIVIDUALS Stephen Gehring** is a highly experienced practitioner with a broad practice encompassing M&A, biotechnology licensing, IP and securities work. He is particularly well versed in state and federal securities laws, IPOs and regulatory proceedings. **John Miles** *"is thorough, very knowledgeable and creative – if we bring a problem or something we want to do, he gives us suggestions, is creative in achieving a solution to the issue and knows everything there is to know about,"* according to clients. His practice focuses predominantly on securities work.

### Koley Jessen P.C.

**THE FIRM** This firm remains a strong contender in the market despite the sad loss of leading lawyer Paul Jessen. The team has a strong portfolio of long-standing clients such as Dover Corporation for which it handles numerous transactions. It has also been active representing clients in significant sales and acquisitions of assets, and IPOs and secondary offerings.
**KEY INDIVIDUALS** President of Koley Jessen, **Michael Hupp** also chairs the M&A and securities department. He earns plaudits for his broad range of experience in securities, M&A, corporate law and real estate. **Shaun McGaughey**, another key member of the practice, heads the firm's business group. He offers clients the benefit of his experience in all aspects of business transactions.

## Kutak Rock LLP
See profile on p.1670

**THE FIRM** This firm is a major force in the Nebraska market and is frequently sought for its depth of expertise. It further consolidated its place at the top of the field with the addition of more leading corporate and finance attorneys to its team. Corporate finance, public finance and regulatory laws are key strengths within its broad offering. It also offers clients the benefit of a strong network of offices across numerous states.

**Sources say:** *"A very solid firm – professional, great value for money and we would use them in the future."*

**KEY INDIVIDUALS Joyce Dixon** (see p.1667) is a distinguished attorney who recently joined Kutak Rock from Husch Blackwell and brings with her a wealth of experience in corporate and finance matters. *"She's just an outstanding, first-rate corporate attorney,"* say market observers. Highly regarded practitioner **Dale Dixon** (see p.1667) was also previously at Husch Blackwell, joining the team in 2012. His practice focuses primarily on finance transactions, structured finance and M&A work. Seasoned banking lawyer **Bryan Handlos** (see p.1668) brings to the table extensive experience advising financial service providers, banks and commercial customers on consumer financial services and regulatory matters.

## McGrath North Mullin & Kratz PC

**THE FIRM** This well-established firm enjoys an enviable position in the market due to its outstanding bench of lawyers. Clients particularly appreciate the breadth of experience within the firm as well as its close attention to client service. The team represents a healthy portfolio of clients including The Gavilon Group, Valmont Industries and Louis Dreyfus Commodities. It has recently acted for ConAgra on various transactions, such as the acquisition of National Pretzel Company and Odom's Tennessee Pride Sausage. In addition to a strong transactional practice, this team is especially experienced in advising on corporate and commercial tax matters.

**Sources say:** *"They are a very, very solid firm across the board and relative rates are very competitive."*

**KEY INDIVIDUALS David Hefflinger** is one of the firm's most well-known names and offers clients deep experience advising on corporate, securities and tax matters. He frequently acts as securities counsel in IPOs, and represents clients in mergers and SEC reporting and disclosure. **Roger Wells** is another leading practitioner in the field and is an *"incredibly talented and very sharp transaction attorney; very helpful to us in our various capacities,"* according to clients. He is the current president of the firm. **Jeffrey Pirruccello** is very well regarded in the market for his tax expertise and advises clients on a vast array of matters including local, state and federal taxes, IRS protests and

appeals, and taxation and estate planning. He cochairs the firm's tax practice. **Jeffrey Penne** is a young partner who is quickly establishing an impressive reputation in the market and plays a key role in advising The Gavilon Group on various transactions.

## Band 2

### Fraser Stryker PC LLO

**THE FIRM** This renowned firm maintains a strong foothold in the Nebraska corporate market, regularly attracting significant transactional and regulatory work. It is particularly known for its expertise in corporate tax, disposals and M&A transactions on behalf of an array of local clients in Omaha.

**KEY INDIVIDUALS Robert Freeman** is one of Nebraska's leading corporate attorneys and is frequently sought after for complex transactions.

### Husch Blackwell LLP

**THE FIRM** This acclaimed firm is a key player in the corporate field with a broad offering of expertise including corporate governance, corporate finance, M&A and investment management. It is also widely recognized for its distinguished renewable energy practice, recently advising a bioenergy technology company, Benefuel, on its joint venture and strategic investment in the development and operation of biodiesel facilities. Other key clients include Bank of the West, First Bank of Omaha and Third Planet Wind.

**Sources say:** *"They are good at listening and understanding what kind of deal we want done, and work hard to get it done."*

**KEY INDIVIDUALS David Gardels** is a highly esteemed corporate and finance lawyer and the leading figure of the Omaha corporate practice. He heads the firm's renewable energy practice and is very well recognized for his contribution in this industry.

### McGill, Gotsdiner, Workman & Lepp PC LLO
See profile on p.1671

**THE FIRM** This local firm enjoys a prominent reputation in the market and has been highly active as the Nebraska market continues to flourish. It has recently represented numerous regional banks in various acquisitions, and acted for lenders on private equity deals and commercial loans.

**Sources say:** *"They are a great firm and they've done an excellent job."*

**KEY INDIVIDUALS** Clients say **Gary Gotsdiner** (see p.1668) has *"an outstanding legal mind and is one of the best attorneys in Omaha."* Peers think equally highly of him and

*"have a high degree of confidence in sending matters to him as he is smart, attentive and has great client relationship skills."*

## Band 3

### Abrahams Kaslow & Cassman LLP

**THE FIRM** This long-established full-service firm focuses predominantly on commercial transactions and commands significant market respect for its corporate practice. The team represents a diverse portfolio of clients, including Tenaska, CSG Systems International and American National Bank.

**Sources say:** *"We have a good working relationship with them so we've come to understand each other and they know what we want."*

**KEY INDIVIDUALS** Veteran practitioner and founding partner **Howard Kaslow** *"remains one of the most senior and brilliant attorneys in our community,"* according to sources. He is frequently called upon for his in-depth corporate and finance experience. **John Herdzina** is a very well-respected lawyer with a broad practice encompassing corporate, franchise, energy and administrative law. He counts the likes of Tenaska and First National Bank among his clients. **Thomas Malicki** is a talented practitioner with a strong transactional practice. He is particularly adept at handling energy and power plant transactions as well as estate planning and probate matters.

### Woods & Aitken LLP

**THE FIRM** This Omaha-based boutique is widely recognized for its specialty in construction law. The team is well equipped to advise on the corporate and commercial aspects of construction projects ranging from drafting and negotiating contracts to disputes and settlement proposals.
**KEY INDIVIDUALS Lee Merritt** is the leading figure of the firm's transaction and business planning group. His practice focuses on M&A, corporate transactions, banking and financial institution planning.

### Other Notable Practitioners

**Ronald Parsonage** is a founding partner of Parsonage Vandenack Williams LLC. With over four decades of practice in Omaha, he is a very well-known figure in the market and brings an impressive breadth of experience to the table. **Alan Slattery** of Rembolt Ludtke LLP is a seasoned practitioner based in Lincoln and has a broad practice which includes corporate transactions, IP, franchising, real estate and estate planning.

# HEALTHCARE

Commentary about individuals can be found under their firm's paragraph. If the firm has no paragraph (is not ranked) look at Other Notable Practitioners.

### Healthcare
### Leading Firms

**Band 1**
Baird Holm LLP

**Band 2**
Kutak Rock LLP *
Stinson Morrison Hecker LLP

**Band 3**
Cline, Williams, Wright, Johnson & Oldfather LLP
Koley Jessen P.C.

### Leading Individuals

**Band 1**

| | |
|---|---|
| Clarke Alex M | Baird Holm LLP |
| Cohen Robert | Kutak Rock LLP * |
| Holdenried John R | Baird Holm LLP |
| Shuler Karen M | Koley Jessen P.C. |
| Zieg Patricia A | Stinson Morrison Hecker LLP |

**Band 2**

| | |
|---|---|
| Ahlers Vickie Brady | Baird Holm LLP |
| Bowman Carl | Stinson Morrison Hecker LLP |
| Jensen Jill Gossin | Cline, Williams, Wright, Johnson |
| Knutson Julie | Baird Holm LLP |
| Person Barbara E | Baird Holm LLP |
| Phillips Christopher | Kutak Rock LLP * |

**Band 3**

| | |
|---|---|
| Hahn Howard F | Kutak Rock LLP * |
| Quinlan James | Fraser Stryker PC LLO (ONP)† |

\* Indicates firm / individual with profile.

†ONP = Other Notable Practitioner.

## Band 1

### Baird Holm LLP

**THE FIRM** Baird Holm is widely considered one of the finest full-service firms in Nebraska, and offers a tremendous bench of healthcare experts. It is known for its long-established relationships with key healthcare clients such as Nebraska Methodist Health System and Hospital, Box Butte General Hospital and Great Plains Regional Medical Center. Recent highlights include advising Iowa Primary Care Association on the organization and development of an Accountable Care Organization involving numerous health centers in Nebraska.

**Sources say:** *"They have expertise and legal capabilities in the various areas that meet our needs, and provide very competent service."*

**KEY INDIVIDUALS Alex Clarke** is one of the most well-recognized healthcare experts in Nebraska, and market sources note that *"he is one of the best speakers in terms of healthcare and really knows the business."* He specializes in transactional, regulatory and corporate compliance matters. Market-leading practitioner **John Holdenried** heads the firm's healthcare practice and *"is very competent and*

*eager to serve, and gives good, sound advice,"* according to clients. He led the team representing the Iowa Primary Care Association. **Vickie Brady Ahlers** has a broad healthcare practice encompassing transactional, regulatory and compliance matters, and is widely recognized as an expert in Health Insurance Portability and Accountability Act (HIPAA). She has acted for various clients on HIPAA complaints filed with the Office of Civil Rights (OCR) and investigations by the OCR for data breach. **Julie Knutson** is an esteemed lawyer with a strong healthcare background. She focuses on advising healthcare facilities and physician practices on a broad range of operational and healthcare compliance issues. **Barbara Person** is best known for her regulatory healthcare practice and frequently advises hospitals on regional health systems affiliations, management agreements, asset transfers and reorganizations.

## Band 2

### Kutak Rock LLP
**See profile on p.1670**

**THE FIRM** One of the full-service powerhouses in Nebraska, this firm makes the most of its resources and network of offices to offer an impressive national healthcare practice. Hospital acquisitions across the country have kept the team particularly busy. Most notably, the group acted for Alegent Health on its acquisition of a teaching hospital, including its physician practice and medical school affiliate.

**Sources say:** *"The firm is very responsive and efficient cost-wise."*

**KEY INDIVIDUALS Robert Cohen** (see p.1667) is one of the most well-known names in the healthcare industry and focuses predominantly on healthcare transactions. He has a national practice and represents major clients including Alegent Health and Virtua Health in their various mergers and acquisitions. **Christopher Phillips** (see p.1668) has an esteemed healthcare regulatory practice and regularly advises clients on a vast array of matters, such as physician contracting, healthcare compliance, practice acquisitions and physician contracting. **Howard Hahn** (see p.1668) is an experienced practitioner who played a key role in the formation of one of the first Accountable Care Organizations in the country for two competing health systems. He currently represents the largest hospital and academic medical center in Nebraska.

### Stinson Morrison Hecker LLP

**THE FIRM** This local firm maintains a strong position in the market thanks to its dedicated team of experienced healthcare lawyers. Clients are full of praise, commending the team's excellent understanding of the industry, as well as its responsiveness and attention to their needs. It has recently advised hospital clients on the implementation of

new Joint Commission Medical Staff standards, HIPAA and Health Information Technology for Economic and Clinical Health Act (HITECH) provisions. The team has also recently defended numerous professionals in various investigations by regulatory agencies.

**KEY INDIVIDUALS Patricia Zieg** is one of Nebraska's leading healthcare specialists and is *"always very knowledgeable about health law issues,"* according to market sources. She chairs the healthcare practice and has deep experience advising on transactional, regulatory and compliance matters. **Carl Bowman** is especially well regarded for his understanding of the healthcare industry, having previously served as the CFO of a large regional medical center. *"He is very responsive and easy to work with,"* said one client, adding: *"He helps to educate me on legal issues I might not be aware of."*

## Band 3

### Cline, Williams, Wright, Johnson & Oldfather LLP

**THE FIRM** This Lincoln-based firm has significant experience in the healthcare sector, advising on a wide spectrum of matters faced by the industry. It represents a diverse portfolio of healthcare clients, ranging from large to small physician centers, and tax-exempt healthcare entities and hospitals, to individual physicians, nurses and long-term care facilities. It also offers expertise in employment benefits and compensation in relation to healthcare providers.

**KEY INDIVIDUALS** Clients say **Jill Jensen** *"is very well versed in HIPAA issues, and has always been very helpful."* She has extensive experience representing physician centers, care entities and nonprofit healthcare clients in a wide range of issues, including policy development, transactions and employment contracts.

### Koley Jessen P.C.

**THE FIRM** This compact healthcare practice is well known for representing physician groups and individual physicians. The team has extensive experience in advising clients on a wide range of matters, including regulatory compliance, tax compliance and day-to-day issues facing healthcare businesses.

**KEY INDIVIDUALS** Head of the healthcare practice, **Karen Shuler** is a distinguished practitioner who is widely recognized for representing individual physicians and physician groups.

### Other Notable Practitioners

**James Quinlan** of Fraser Stryker PC LLO is a seasoned practitioner known for representing a range of hospitals and care facilities, as well as individual healthcare professionals.

# LABOR & EMPLOYMENT

Commentary about individuals can be found under their firm's paragraph. If the firm has no paragraph (is not ranked) look at Other Notable Practitioners.

### Labor & Employment
### Leading Firms

**Band 1**
Baird Holm LLP
Fraser Stryker PC LLO
Jackson Lewis LLP *

**Band 2**
Cline, Williams, Wright, Johnson & Oldfather LLP
Harding & Shultz PC
McGrath North Mullin & Kratz PC

### Senior Statesmen

Senior Statesmen: distinguished older practitioners
Miller Roger      McGrath North Mullin & Kratz PC

### Leading Individuals

**Band 1**

| | |
|---|---|
| Barrett Patrick J | Fraser Stryker PC LLO |
| Bogue Stevenson | McGrath North Mullin & Kratz PC |
| Fahleson Mark A | Rembolt Ludtke LLP (ONP)† |
| Hedican Chris R | Baird Holm LLP |
| Loudon Timothy D | Jackson Lewis LLP * |
| Rossiter Robert | Fraser Stryker PC LLO |
| Stevenson Randy RJ | Baird Holm LLP |

**Band 2**

| | |
|---|---|
| Harding William A | Harding & Shultz PC |
| Moore Scott S | Baird Holm LLP |
| Pigsley Jerry L | Harding & Shultz PC |
| Schorr Mark M | Erickson & Sederstrom PC (ONP)† |

**Band 3**

| | |
|---|---|
| Berens Kelvin C | Jackson Lewis LLP * |
| Breuning Jonathan R. | Baird Holm LLP |
| Buntain David | Cline, Williams, Wright, Johnson |
| Dreesen Joseph S | Jackson Lewis LLP * |
| Hewitt John | Cline, Williams, Wright, Johnson |
| Hoyme Christopher | Jackson Lewis LLP * |

**Up-and-coming individuals**

| | |
|---|---|
| Baumert Michaelle L | Husch Blackwell LLP (ONP)† |

### Labor & Employment: ERISA
### Leading Individuals

**Band 1**

| | |
|---|---|
| Clatterbuck Gary N | Baird Holm LLP |
| Limbeck Randal | Jackson Lewis LLP * |
| Mueller Michael | Cline, Williams, Wright, Johnson |
| Schembari John E | Kutak Rock LLP (ONP)† * |

*Indicates firm / individual with profile.
†ONP = Other Notable Practitioner.

## Band 1

### Baird Holm LLP

**THE FIRM** This Nebraska heavyweight has one of the deepest and most well-respected benches of labor and employment lawyers in the state. Recently the team has handled an increasing amount of public sector labor and employment matters, and has represented the City of Omaha. In addition to a strong traditional labor law offering, it is particularly adept at handling ERISA matters and employment litigation. Notably, the team successfully obtained a summary judgment dismissing claims of over $500,000 against Union Pacific Railroad in allegations of wrongful termination of employment.
**Sources say:** *"They are very in tune with the real world and can work with us on the impacts in real-world situations."*
**KEY INDIVIDUALS Gary Clatterbuck** heads the employee benefits and ERISA practice and is one of the most well-recognized practitioners in this sector. Clients say he is *"very skilled, always up to speed and very good at brainstorming solutions for difficult or complex situations."* **Chris Hedican** is one of Nebraska's leading employment litigation experts and heads that group within the firm. He led the team that successfully represented Union Pacific Railroad. **Randy Stevenson** chairs the labor, employment and employee benefits department and is one of the firm's most well-known names. Clients appreciate that he is *"very skilled and very good at helping us think through problems and come up with solutions."* *"Outstanding employment law expert"* **Scott Moore** continues to impress clients with his extensive experience. He is *"someone that I would recommend who is very up to date on laws and regulations,"* said one client. **Jonathan Breuning** recently rejoined the team after several years acting as general counsel at a national technology company based in Omaha. *"He is probably the best legal writer of all the attorneys I know and is very skilled at coming up with good solutions to difficult or complex issues,"* says one interviewee.

### Fraser Stryker PC LLO

**THE FIRM** This market-leading labor and employment team has been kept busy with a considerable volume of public sector employment law instructions of late. It represents Omaha's main utilities companies, including Omaha Public Power District and the Metropolitan Utilities District, and acted for the latter before the Commission of Industrial Relations on a high-value wage case and on collective bargaining negotiations. The team is also well equipped to handle matters ranging from day-to-day employment issues to employment litigation and traditional labor law.
**Sources say:** *"They give us exceptionally well-researched and documented opinions, and are very timely in getting back to us and great people to work with."*
**KEY INDIVIDUALS Patrick Barrett** has a wealth of experience in practicing labor and employment law and has established an outstanding reputation in the field. His practice covers a vast array of matters, from general employment issues and traditional labor law to employment litigation and contract negotiations. **Robert Rossiter** is another market-leading figure within this firm's labor and employment practice and is noted for his wide-ranging employment and traditional labor expertise. Clients note that he is *"very responsive and very technically competent in this space."*

### Jackson Lewis LLP
**See profile on p.1982**
**THE FIRM** This national labor and employment specialist undoubtedly has one of the strongest teams in Nebraska, and represents clients such as ConAgra Foods, Nucor, Jack Links Beef Jerky and First National of Nebraska. The Omaha-based team consists of eight partners with experience advising on a host of matters including traditional labor law, ERISA, employment benefits, executive compensation, class actions and employment litigation.
**Sources say:** *"Their knowledge of legal and regulatory matters is very good and their technical expertise is high. They are very responsive and successful in representing us and giving advice because of their understanding of our organization."*
**KEY INDIVIDUALS** *"Outstanding attorney"* **Randal Limbeck** (see p.1668) is one of Nebraska's finest experts for ERISA, executive compensation and employee benefits matters. Clients frequently turn to him for his *"technical expertise, responsiveness and knowledge."* **Timothy Loudon** (see p.1668) is a distinguished labor and employment specialist who is noted for his breadth of expertise. He earns plaudits from peers and clients for his *"great background of knowledge."* **Kelvin Berens** (see p.1667) is the managing partner of the firm's Omaha office and has a wealth of knowledge in traditional labor law, as well as extensive experience handling class actions and advising on workplace safety. **Christopher Hoyme** (see p.1668) has a well-established practice with a focus on employment litigation, defending employers before state and federal courts across the country. **Joseph Dreesen** (see p.1667) is a seasoned practitioner with extensive experience in the field. He has a broad practice encompassing employment issues, traditional labor law, collective bargaining agreements, wage and hour and OSHA matters.

## Band 2

### Cline, Williams, Wright, Johnson & Oldfather LLP

**THE FIRM** This full-service firm is a significant market player that offers clients support in employment matters. It acts exclusively for employers, representing management across all areas of employment law, including employment litigation. Its employee benefits practice also continues to be increasingly active.
**Sources say:** *"I have found their work to be of superior quality, thorough and timely. I believe the annual employment law legal update they offer to public and private employers is exceptional and well received."*

KEY INDIVIDUALS **Michael Mueller** is the firm's expert on employee benefits, and clients find him to be *"helpful in identifying issues that we have not seen or weren't aware of."* **David Buntain** heads the labor and employment practice and offers a broad range of expertise in labor and employment, healthcare and litigation, among other areas. *"I appreciate the energy and enthusiasm he brings. He is very reliable and has done an excellent job,"* says a client. **John Hewitt** has a well-established practice focused on advising employers on all aspects of labor and employment. He handles work involving the negotiation of labor agreements.

## Harding & Shultz PC

THE FIRM This Lincoln-based firm has established a strong reputation for its expertise in employment law. Its compact team of highly experienced lawyers is frequently sought by public sector clients for the full range of employment issues.

KEY INDIVIDUALS Co-founding partner **William Harding** has more than 40 years' experience representing clients in labor and employment matters, and has established a strong following. **Jerry Pigsley** is a well-respected practitioner with extensive experience in advising employers on a wide range of matters. He is particularly active advising public sector clients.

## McGrath North Mullin & Kratz PC

THE FIRM This labor and employment practice maintains a healthy presence in Nebraska, attracting a strong portfolio of clients including Physicians Mutual Insurance, Werner Enterprises and Omaha Airport Authority. The six-lawyer team has extensive market experience and is especially well positioned to advise on traditional labor law, union work and proceedings before the NLRB. It has also been particularly busy advising public sector clients.

Sources say: *"We've always been very happy and always found them knowledgeable, responsible and responsive."*

KEY INDIVIDUALS **Stevenson Bogue** heads this labor and employment practice, and earns tremendous praise from peers and clients. *"He's very intelligent, quick-witted and fun to work with, and we trust him completely,"* says a source. With nearly 40 years in this field, **Roger Miller** is a highly experienced lawyer. Clients appreciate the deep subject expertise he brings to the table.

## Other Notable Practitioners

**Mark Fahleson** is the driving force of Rembolt Ludtke LLP's labor and employment practice. *"Mark is a no-nonsense, straightforward adviser whose advice and counsel was extremely accurate. He understands the courts and judges, and his work and management of the matter was extremely efficient,"* said one interviewee. **John Schembari** (see p.1669) of Kutak Rock LLP is *"one of the best I've had the pleasure of working with – he's amazingly smart, has good experience and understands the industry. He is really one of a kind,"* says a client. Schembari chairs the corporate finance group and is best known for his employee benefits practice. **Mark Schorr** of Erickson & Sederstrom PC acts almost exclusively for employers, advising them on regulatory compliance issues, employment litigation and traditional labor matters. **Michaelle Baumert** is a younger partner at Husch Blackwell LLP who continues to impress clients. She is described as *"incredibly responsive and good at being direct and giving directions that are so helpful."*

# LITIGATION

Insurance p.1664; Intellectual Property p.1664; Mediators p.1664

Commentary about individuals can be found under their firm's paragraph. If the firm has no paragraph (is not ranked) look at Other Notable Practitioners.

| Litigation: General Commercial Leading Firms |
| --- |
| **Band 1** |
| Baird Holm LLP |
| Cline, Williams, Wright, Johnson & Oldfather LLP |
| Fraser Stryker PC LLO |
| Kutak Rock LLP * |
| McGrath North Mullin & Kratz PC |
| **Band 2** |
| Erickson & Sederstrom, PC |
| Husch Blackwell LLP |

*Indicates firm with profile.*
*Alphabetical order within each band. Band 1 is the highest.*

*The edit is in alphabetical order by firm name.*

## Baird Holm LLP

THE FIRM This full-service firm commands healthy market respect thanks to its deep bench of highly experienced litigators. Clients appreciate the firm's strength across the board and the seamless interaction between its various practices. Recent highlights include the team successfully defending Bank of the West in a class action counterclaim arising out of an initial foreclosure action. It also successfully obtained a summary judgment for Unum Life Insurance Company of America as defendant in a $2 million claim for disability benefits.

Sources say: *"Baird Holm is an excellent firm and provides good solid legal services without huge fees attached."*

KEY INDIVIDUALS **Jill Robb Ackerman** chairs Baird Holm's litigation practice and is widely recognized as a first-rate IP litigation expert. Clients say she is *"very level-headed, very good at listening, good at ramping up when we need to and able to understand the bigger picture."* **Kirk Blecha** is one of the most well-known names in the litigation field and is described by clients as a *"trial attorney who is very creative, very good at what he does and has always had a good relationship with us in resolving complex situations."* He led the team representing Bank of the West in the class action defense. **William Dittrick** offers clients a wealth of commercial litigation experience. He has also handled significant product liability and class action cases. **Steven Davidson** is a well-respected litigator who peers *"hold in high regard"* and look to as a first port of call in a referral. He has a broad practice which covers commercial, healthcare, insurance and employment disputes. He leads the insurance litigation practice. Clients are full of praise for **Thomas Johnson** and say: *"He is very seasoned and careful in pulling your case together, uses associates to the right extent, and stays involved. He is also thorough in his case development but also strong in assessing a case and providing counsel on chances of success, and doesn't oversell the idea of going to trial."*

## Cassem Tierney Adams Gotch & Douglas

THE FIRM This traditional firm prides itself on providing the highest quality of service and its responsiveness to clients' needs. It is widely recognized for its insurance defense work, and more particularly, insurance coverage disputes. The team also offers strong arbitration and mediation capabilities.

KEY INDIVIDUALS **John Douglas** is of counsel at the firm and a seasoned and extremely well-respected insurance litigator. He is a *"phenomenal lawyer and a dean of insurance,"* according to market observers. *"Excellent attorney"* **Michael Kinney**, another important member of the team, has an esteemed insurance litigation practice and is also increasingly active in the region as a mediator. **Charles Gotch** is a veteran in the insurance litigation field and is still called upon for his extensive market experience.

## Cline, Williams, Wright, Johnson & Oldfather LLP

THE FIRM This distinguished firm maintains its market-leading position and is regularly instructed on some of Nebraska's most complex cases. It earns plaudits from clients, who appreciate the team's dedication to client service as well as its depth of trial experience. In addition to a very strong commercial litigation offering, it is also well equipped to handle mediation and arbitration proceedings.

## Litigation: General Commercial
### Senior Statesmen

Senior Statesmen: distinguished older practitioners

| | |
|---|---|
| Mark Wayne J | Fraser Stryker PC LLO |
| Meusey Joseph K | Fraser Stryker PC LLO |

### Leading Individuals

**Band 1**

| | |
|---|---|
| Bausch James M | Cline, Williams, Wright, Johnson |
| Blecha Kirk S | Baird Holm LLP |
| Coyle Michael F | Fraser Stryker PC LLO |
| Culhane Thomas | Erickson & Sederstrom, PC |
| Dahlk Thomas | Kutak Rock LLP * |
| Dittrick William G | Baird Holm LLP |
| Domina David A | Domina Law plc LLO (ONP)† |
| Fitzgerald James | McGrath North Mullin & Kratz PC |
| McLeay Bartholomew L | Kutak Rock LLP * |

**Band 2**

| | |
|---|---|
| Bausch Trenten P | Cline, Williams, Wright, Johnson |
| Davidson Steven D | Baird Holm LLP |
| Hargens William F | McGrath North Mullin & Kratz PC |
| Jones Joseph E | Fraser Stryker PC LLO |
| Slovek Robert M | Kutak Rock LLP * |

**Band 3**

| | |
|---|---|
| Bargen David J. A. | Rembolt Ludtke LLP (ONP)† |
| Barry Andre | Cline, Williams, Wright, Johnson |
| Bothe Robert | McGrath North Mullin & Kratz PC |
| Degan Michael | Husch Blackwell LLP |
| Johnson Thomas E | Baird Holm LLP |
| Powers James G | McGrath North Mullin & Kratz PC |
| Warin Edward G | Kutak Rock LLP * |

## Litigation: Insurance
### Leading Firms

**Band 1**

Cassem Tierney Adams Gotch & Douglas

Fraser Stryker PC LLO

Lamson, Dugan & Murray, LLP

**Band 2**

McGrath North Mullin & Kratz PC

Sources say: *"Their standards of practice are excellent and their responsiveness is very client-oriented. It is just a very good group to work with."*
**KEY INDIVIDUALS** The *"tenacious"* **James Bausch** heads the firm's litigation practice and is described by sources as a *"senior litigator with enormous experience and excellent judgment."* **Mark Christensen** is an esteemed litigator who is best known for his medical malpractice defense expertise. He has also established a strong reputation in the market for his mediation work. *"Fantastic litigator"* **Trenten Bausch** has a broad commercial practice with an emphasis on commercial, IP, trademark, franchising and energy-related disputes. **Andre Barry** joins the rankings this year following widespread market recognition of his contribution to the team's success. *"Andy is extraordinarily thorough, extremely intelligent, has courage, is very articulate, an excellent litigation writer and litigation savvy,"* say sources.

## Litigation: Insurance
### Senior Statesmen

Senior Statesmen: distinguished older practitioners

| | |
|---|---|
| Gotch Charles F | Cassem Tierney Adams Gotch & Douglas |

### Leading Individuals

**Band 1**

| | |
|---|---|
| Coyle Michael F | Fraser Stryker PC LLO |
| Douglas John R | Cassem Tierney Adams Gotch & Douglas |
| Lamson William | Lamson, Dugan & Murray, LLP |
| Mullin Jr Robert D | McGrath North Mullin & Kratz PC |

**Band 2**

| | |
|---|---|
| Christensen Mark A | Cline, Williams, Wright, Johnson |
| Johnson Thomas E | Baird Holm LLP |
| Johnson William | Lamson, Dugan & Murray, LLP |
| Jones Joseph E | Fraser Stryker PC LLO |
| Kinney Michael F | Cassem Tierney Adams Gotch & Douglas |
| Laughlin Mark C | Fraser Stryker PC LLO |

**Up-and-coming individuals**

| | |
|---|---|
| Mullin David C. | Fraser Stryker PC LLO |

## Litigation: Intellectual Property
### Leading Individuals

**Band 1**

| | |
|---|---|
| Ackerman Jill Robb | Baird Holm LLP |
| Passarelli John P | Kutak Rock LLP * |

## Litigation: Mediators
### Leading Individuals

**Band 1**

| | |
|---|---|
| Brownrigg John | Erickson & Sederstrom, PC |
| Christensen Mark A | Cline, Williams, Wright, Johnson |
| Keating Con M | Keating, O'Gara, Nedved, Peter (ONP)† |
| Kinney Michael F | Cassem Tierney Adams Gotch & Douglas |
| Mullin Michael G | Kutak Rock LLP * |

* Indicates firm / individual with profile.

† ONP = Other Notable Practitioner.

## Erickson & Sederstrom, PC

**THE FIRM** This local firm continues to make significant headway in the Nebraska litigation market and is home to a compact and efficient team of litigators. It represents a diverse portfolio of clients on cases ranging from personal injury and product liability claims to complex commercial cases.

**KEY INDIVIDUALS** **Thomas Culhane** is a senior partner of the firm and has established an outstanding reputation in the litigation field. *"He's a good lawyer who gets to the bottom of things and the clients feel very comfortable with him,"* according to sources. **John Brownrigg** is one of the most in-demand mediators in Nebraska, thanks to his extensive litigation experience. He is particularly adept in product liability, commercial, construction, insurance, personal injury and real estate litigation.

## Fraser Stryker PC LLO

**THE FIRM** The litigation group at this full-service firm is one of the strongest in Nebraska and nurtures a wealth of talent in commercial and insurance litigation. The team is involved in a significant number of complex commercial cases including product liability, class action defense and IP disputes. In addition, insurance litigation has been a core strength within the practice and continues to be a key area of activity. The team has also been kept busy with an increasing number of disputes arising from the railroad industry.

**Sources say:** *"Their knowledge, especially on business law, is probably as good as we have in this region. An established and well-respected firm and there really isn't much that they can't deal with."*

**KEY INDIVIDUALS** **Michael Coyle** is a leading name in Nebraska's litigation field and the leading figure of the firm's practice. In addition to a strong commercial and insurance defense practice, he has a significant plaintiff practice and brings unsurpassed experience trying cases before juries. **Joseph Jones** is an experienced generalist litigator who is well positioned to represent clients on a vast array of cases including commercial, class action, insurance defense and commercial defense. **Mark Laughlin** is well recognized for his strong insurance litigation practice, and more particularly for his extensive class action experience. He has also been appointed by Nebraska's Attorney General in four education funding cases to represent the Governor and state officials. **David Mullin** is a younger partner who is quickly making a name for himself in the insurance field. He is taking the lead on an increasing amount of insurance defense work. *"He's a real up-and-coming lawyer who's done well,"* say market observers. Veteran litigator **Wayne Mark** is occasionally called upon to provide the benefit of his in-depth litigation experience. **Joseph Meusey** is another senior figure who is of counsel to the firm and on hand to provide important industry insight.

## Husch Blackwell LLP

**THE FIRM** This firm remains a strong contender in the market, offering wide-ranging litigation capabilities and extensive trial experience within the practice. Its team consists of ten lawyers based in Omaha and Lincoln and is strongly supported by a broad network of offices. The team has also been increasingly active handling IP cases in the region. Key clients include Union Pacific, Roberts Dairy and The Nebraska Medical Center.

**KEY INDIVIDUALS** **Michael Degan** is a talented litigator with wide-ranging trial experience including commercial, insurance and product liability litigation.

## Kutak Rock LLP

See profile on p.1670

**THE FIRM** This prominent firm complements its strength across various practice areas with a distinguished litigation and mediation practice. It also benefits from being able to draw upon experience and knowledge from its 16-office national network. The team has recently achieved positive results for its clients in high-value disputes, and its mediators have also been highly active, mediating a vast array of civil, commercial and business disputes.

**Sources say:** *"They're a solid firm we work with extensively – their resources have been exceptional."*

**KEY INDIVIDUALS Bartholomew McLeay** (see p.1668) chairs the firm's litigation group and is the driving force behind its prominence in this field. He has recently been at the forefront of some of the team's most significant trial successes. **Thomas Dahlk** (see p.1667) recently joined the firm from Husch Blackwell. He is a leading figure in the litigation arena and is highly experienced in handling complex corporate and commercial cases. He has recently represented a group of investment representatives in a securities suit before the Federal Court in Delaware. **Michael Mullin** (see p.1668) is one of the mediators most sought in the state and who handles a wide variety of civil cases including class actions, Federal Employers Liability Act disputes, medical malpractice and commercial disputes. **John Passarelli** (see p.1668) is one of the leading IP litigation experts in Nebraska and brings to the table extensive Bench and jury trial experience. Clients truly appreciate his work and describe him as an *"excellent resource."* **Robert Slovek** (see p.1669) is a talented trial attorney with a broad practice encompassing corporate and commercial, healthcare, professional negligence, product liability and personal injury cases. **Edward Warin** (see p.1669) is an experienced litigator with a practice that focuses predominantly on government regulatory proceedings and general corporate litigation.

## Lamson, Dugan & Murray, LLP

**THE FIRM** This local firm is a popular choice for insurance defense litigation. The team handles a considerable volume of insurance coverage defense work as well as professional negligence cases, both legal and medical, obtaining numerous notable defendant verdicts in sophisticated cases in both areas.

Sources say: *"We've been very pleased with the work they have done for us."*

**KEY INDIVIDUALS** Founding partner **William Lamson** is held in the highest regard by clients, who praise his deep expertise in handling sophisticated litigation. His broad practice incorporates insurance and reinsurance disputes, as well as environmental and professional negligence claims. **William Johnson** focuses his practice on a range of commercial disputes including breach of contract, product liability defense and professional negligence cases.

## McGrath North Mullin & Kratz PC

**THE FIRM** This well-established firm is home to one of the most celebrated teams of litigators in Nebraska. Its excellent track record of cases and outstanding client service have attracted an impressive portfolio of clients including ConAgra Foods, First National Bank of Omaha, Motorist Insurance Group and Valmont Industries. Notable work includes successfully obtaining summary judgment for ConAgra in claims brought by an engineering firm arising out of an explosion which resulted in a number of deaths and injuries. The team is also very well positioned to handle insurance defense work and has been very active in that sector.

Sources say: *"They're just a phenomenal group of lawyers, the best I've ever encountered – a really strong and talented bunch."* *"We like them and continue to use them because they are very responsive to our needs and value us as a client."*

**KEY INDIVIDUALS James Fitzgerald** is one of Nebraska's leading litigators and is famed for handling some of the firm's largest and most complex corporate and commercial cases. He recently successfully defended senior executives in a derivative action claiming damages of over $20 million. **Robert Mullin** earns widespread recognition for his outstanding insurance defense work. He is frequently sought by insurance carriers and self-insured corporations, as well as injured claimants. He co-heads the insurance litigation practice. **William Hargens** continues to impress clients, who praise his *"very prompt attention to our needs and his ability to deal with high-pressure situations and yet remain very calm; his ability to analyze issues from both legal and practical perspectives has given us a great deal of value."* **James Powers** co-heads the litigation department. Clients are full of praise and say: *"He's our go-to guy – outstanding, he has really good business acumen and is responsive to what we need."* Clients say **Robert Bothe** is *"an outstanding performer, big-picture thinker and tremendous resource"* and particularly appreciate that *"he's very highly experienced, tenacious in a good way and has the ability to deal with situations from a practical standpoint."*

### Other Notable Practitioners

**David Domina** of Domina Law pc llo *"gets remarkable results for his clients,"* according to commentators. He has a broad litigation practice which takes in the full range of business and commercial disputes. **Con Keating** of Keating, O'Gara, Nedved & Peter, P.C., L.L.O. enters the rankings this year having been identified by market sources as a leading mediator in Nebraska. He has particular expertise in personal injury and product liability disputes. New entry **David Bargen** of Rembolt Ludtke LLP is described as *"outstanding"* by his clients, who particularly praise his writing and counseling skills.

# REAL ESTATE

Commentary about individuals can be found under their firm's paragraph. If the firm has no paragraph (is not ranked) look at Other Notable Practitioners.

## Band 1

### Baird Holm LLP

**THE FIRM** This well-established firm has a market-leading position in real estate thanks to its outstanding team of highly experienced and talented lawyers. It offers strong transactional expertise, recently acting for LBD Properties on the $4.45 million sale of the Briar Hills Apartment Complex. It also worked closely with the firm's banking and tax experts to represent Educare of Winnebago with respect to its new markets tax credit investment in early childhood development in the Winnebago Indian Reservation.

Sources say: *"We have a great relationship with them and it is great to be able to go to a firm that you trust."*

**KEY INDIVIDUALS Scott Dye** is a leading figure in Nebraska's real estate sector and the market is united in praising his wealth of experience in real estate transactions, zoning and public bidding and contracting. **Jon Blumenthal** is a highly rated practitioner who is best recognized for his real estate lending expertise. Clients say: *"He's really good at making sure the right people are on the case and very conscientious of making sure the service is great."* **David Levy** heads the firm's real estate practice and focuses primarily on zoning and land use matters, as well as environmental issues. He is also heavily involved in wind energy generation projects. **Lawrence Kritenbrink** has significant experience in real estate financing and is regularly sought by project owners, investors, lenders and contractors. Younger partner **Jude Beller** is rapidly making a name for himself in the market and specializes in the financing aspects of commercial real estate transactions.

## Fullenkamp, Doyle & Jobeun

**THE FIRM** This traditional firm maintains a prominent position in the Nebraska market and earns widespread recognition for its strength in zoning, land use and planning matters. Its highly experienced team of lawyers is praised by clients for its strong expertise in obtaining government permits and development projects. It is also well equipped to advise on the financing aspects of real estate transactions and development.

**KEY INDIVIDUALS** Founding partner **John Fullenkamp** is one of the most well-known names in the field and offers extensive experience in real estate transactions, zoning and land use matters. *"He is very skilled, very experienced, and knows his way around permits and development matters and how to get something done at the city hall,"* according to clients. Co-founder **Larry Jobeun** is another market-leading figure who is best recognized for his zoning and land use expertise. He is *"as good as anyone in town when it comes to zoning and division matters,"* according to sources.

## Kutak Rock LLP
See profile on p.1670

**THE FIRM** This full-service firm is home to a leading group of real estate lawyers with a broad range of expertise, including commercial transactions, bank financing, franchise lending, healthcare real estate and military housing. It has a strong client base of local and national industry leaders, who also benefit from the firm's strong network of offices in the region.

**Sources say:** *"We like to use them because they are extremely responsive and really well versed in this area of the law."*

**KEY INDIVIDUALS Michael Curry** (see p.1667) is managing partner of the Omaha office and chairs the corporate group. He has a broad practice with an emphasis on real estate lending and financing, and regularly advises on the development of financing programs. **Richard Rosenblatt** (see p.1668) is a well-regarded lawyer with a strong portfolio of clients, including major developers and banks. He is particularly experienced in advising on retail development and leasing. **Brent Burmood** (see p.1667) has a strong national practice and focuses primarily on representing lenders in franchising deals. He also has extensive experience in advising retailers on development and transactional matters. **Walter Griffiths** (see p.1668) is a senior figure within the practice and has a wealth of experience in the financing and development of military housing and lodging privatization matters.

## Pansing Hogan Ernst & Bachman LLP

**THE FIRM** This first-class real estate practice is well recognized for its strong real estate financing and development capabilities. The team frequently advises both developers and lenders on a wide range of matters, including commercial and residential project developments. It also offers extensive experience in zoning and land use, and works closely with local governments.

**KEY INDIVIDUALS Dennis Hogan** is a highly esteemed zoning and development expert who continues to earn widespread recognition from the market for his in-depth experience in this space. **John Bachman** is a well-established lawyer with a broad practice encompassing real estate development, zoning, construction and financing. **James Buser** is praised for his strong real estate lending practice and is frequently sought by major banks in Nebraska.

### Band 2

## Fraser Stryker PC LLO

**THE FIRM** This firm has a strong position in the market thanks to its team of talented and dedicated practitioners. The team provides comprehensive real estate coverage, including strong expertise in renewable energy projects such as wind farms. Its strong client base consists of owners, developers and lenders in both the private and public sector. It has recently been involved in numerous public-private development projects in Nebraska.

**KEY INDIVIDUALS Robert Rieke** is a leading name in the real estate market and the driving force of the firm's practice. He focuses primarily on real estate transactions in the private and public sectors, and regularly represents lenders, owners and developers.

## Husch Blackwell LLP

**THE FIRM** Husch Blackwell is a distinguished full-service firm that offers strong real estate capabilities from its Nebraska practice. It is particularly well recognized for its expertise in major redevelopment projects involving tax-increment financing. For example, the team has recently acted for East Campus Realty on a $250 million mixed-use development project. Other notable clients include Jasper Stone Partners, Colliers International and Curt Hofer Construction.

**Sources say:** *"Really responsive, easy to work with and very knowledgeable."*

**KEY INDIVIDUALS John Katelman** leads the firm's Nebraska real estate practice and is best known for his expertise in redevelopment projects. Peers and clients are full of praise, saying: *"He has a very good reputation in town, is very knowledgeable, presents things in a way that is easy to understand and is very easy to work with."*

## McGrath North Mullin & Kratz PC

**THE FIRM** The compact team at this established full-service firm continues to provide clients with a wide range of expertise. It is well equipped to handle construction and development projects, commercial transactions, real estate finance and leasing matters. Notable highlights include advising TransCanada Keystone Pipeline XL on a pipeline construction project. Its strong client base also includes Blue Cross Blue Shield of Nebraska, Omaha Airport Authority and Darling International.

**KEY INDIVIDUALS Lee Hamann** heads the firm's real estate group and earns widespread respect for his contribution to this field. He is particularly experienced in handling real estate transactions, including leasing, sale and purchase, and construction issues. *"He's very good and really helpful on real estate matters,"* say clients. **Robert Dailey** is respected in the market for his experience in handling hotel and condominium development projects, as well as a wide range of commercial real estate transactions. Sources note that *"he displays a very high degree of knowledge of the legal principles involved."*

### Band 3

## Croker, Huck, Kasher, DeWitt, Anderson & Gonderinger, L.L.C.

**THE FIRM** This firm has a well-respected real estate group that undertakes a significant volume of work. The team is particularly sought for its strong financing expertise. It has been active representing numerous banks in the financing and refinancing of major properties and foreclosures, as well as a considerable amount of Section 1031 exchange work. Clients also benefit from its zoning and land use experience.

**Sources say:** *"They do an excellent job – they are very thorough, always follow through with what they say they will take care of, provide good advice and help us make decisions."*
**KEY INDIVIDUALS** Founding partner **Robert Huck** is a highly esteemed practitioner who is particularly noted for his wealth of experience in zoning and land use matters. **Richard Anderson** is *"very detail oriented, very smart and very bright,"* according to market commentators. He specializes in the financing of real estate transactions and also handles a considerable amount of zoning work.

### Koley Jessen P.C.

**THE FIRM** Koley Jessen joins the rankings this year following widespread recognition of its contribution to the field. The team is best known for its transactional experience, representing clients in real estate leasing, sales, purchases and financing. It is also well equipped to negotiate and draft construction and development contracts.
**KEY INDIVIDUALS Max Burbach** debuts in the table this year following widespread praise from his peers. He chairs the firm's real estate practice and focuses primarily on financing matters relating to the acquisition and construction of development projects.

### Other Notable Practitioners

Lincoln-based attorney **Thomas Huston** of Cline, Williams, Wright, Johnson & Oldfather LLP has a broad practice covering real estate financing, affordable housing development and zoning and planning work, including subdivision and governmental permitting. **Michael Matejka** of Woods & Aitken LLP is a highly respected real estate lawyer, with extensive experience in the Nebraska market. He has handled a wide range of real estate development, tax planning and leasing matters.

# Leaders' Profiles in Nebraska

### BERENS, Kelvin C
Jackson Lewis LLP, Omaha
402 391 1991
BerensK@jacksonlewis.com
*Featured in Labor & Employment (Nebraska)*
**Practice Areas:** Labor, including preventive practices, workplace safety compliance, executive terminations; drug testing; counseling on behalf of management, including discrimination, harassment, retaliation, ADA, FMLA, wage-hour issues, contract negotiations, severance agreements, non-competition agreements, and other employment contracts union avoidance, labor arbitration.
**Professional Memberships:** American Bar Association, Nebraska State Bar Association, Omaha Bar Association.
**Career:** "AV" top rating by the Martindale-Hubbell Law Directory; 1979 – 2009 Managing Partner of Berens & Tate, P.C.
**Personal:** University of Nebraska-Lincoln (BA 1972) with distinction; Duke University (JD 1975).

### BURMOOD, Brent C
Kutak Rock LLP, Omaha
402 346 6000
Brent.Burmood@KutakRock.com
*Featured in Real Estate (Nebraska)*
**Practice Areas:** Partner, real estate/bankruptcy group. Focuses his practice in transactions serving a broad range of client needs, including secured lending, real estate financing, real estate development, sales and acquisitions, sale/leasebacks and commercial leasing. Clients include financial institutions, retailers, real estate investors and insurance companies. Experience includes representing leading lenders in the franchise industry in connection with their real estate and equipment secured financings and large national retailers with respect to the acquisition and development of their retail sites.
**Career:** Education: BA, University of Nebraska-Lincoln (1994); JD, magna cum laude, University of Illinois College of Law (1997).

### COHEN, Robert
Kutak Rock LLP, Omaha
402 346 6000
robert.cohen@kutakrock.com
*Featured in Healthcare (Nebraska)*
**Practice Areas:** Senior partner in firm's health care practice group. Serves as engagement partner for many of the firm's largest health care clients. Practice focuses on health care acquisitions and physician-hospital alignment strategies. He regularly advises hospitals and physician practices on the transactional and regulatory aspects of integration structures, including joint venture, clinical co-management, employment and professional services agreements. He has been lead transaction counsel on multiple acquisitions, mergers, divestitures and joint ventures involving hospitals and health systems, large physician practices, imaging and surgery center providers and other health care entities.
**Career:** Education: JD, University of Chicago Law School (1980).

### CURRY, Michael
Kutak Rock LLP, Omaha
402 346 6000
Michael.Curry@KutakRock.com
*Featured in Real Estate (Nebraska)*
**Practice Areas:** Managing Partner of Omaha office, Chairman of Omaha office's Corporate Department and Member of the firm's Executive Committee. Devotes his practice to various real estate matters and real estate finance. Represents real estate owners and developers, financial institutions, real estate investment trusts, publicly held companies and investment funds and developers in real estate acquisitions and dispositions, commercial lending and structured real estate finance transactions throughout the country.
**Career:** Education: BA (1974) and JD (1978), University of Virginia.

### DAHLK, Thomas
Kutak Rock LLP, Omaha
402 346 6000
thomas.dahlk@kutakrock.com
*Featured in Litigation (Nebraska)*
**Practice Areas:** Experienced trial lawyer who has obtained verdicts for clients in federal and state court. Has provided litigation strategy and multi-jurisdiction litigation management for clients in the banking, mutual fund and securities industries. Cases range from "bet-the-company" civil cases involving complex legal theories to obtaining an acquittal in a criminal case. Has obtained dismissal of RICO claims on behalf of defendants and has represented shareholder groups in derivative actions based upon civil RICO, as well as plaintiffs and defendants in accounting, legal, SEC enforcement actions and financial advisor malpractice cases.
**Career:** Education: JD, magna cum laude (1977), Creighton University.

### DIXON, Dale
Kutak Rock LLP, Omaha
402 346 6000
dale.dixon@kutakrock.com
*Featured in Corporate/Commercial (Nebraska)*
**Practice Areas:** Concentrating his practice in structured finance and finance transactions, Mr Dixon represents issuers in connection with term and variable funding securitizations in excess of $5 billion and involving a variety of asset classes. Regularly represents borrowers in secured and unsecured commercial lending transactions and represents public and private companies with mergers, acquisitions and divestitures. Also represents banks and other financial institutions in regulatory matters, where he has obtained favorable exemptive orders, no-action letters and interpretive advice from the SEC, OCC and other state and federal banking regulators.
**Career:** Education: BSBA (1992) and JD (1994), Creighton University.

### DIXON, Joyce A
Kutak Rock LLP, Omaha
402 346 6000
joyce.dixon@kutakrock.com
*Featured in Corporate/Commercial (Nebraska)*
**Practice Areas:** Guides corporate and financial institution clients in unique, complex transactions. Concentrates practice in asset securitization, commercial loans, cross-border finance, agricultural lending and Chapter 11 exit and debtor-in-possession financing. Also assists financial institution clients with regulatory compliance matters and creation and implementation of new products. Has pioneered development of credit card securitization structures and has served as outside senior legal advisor on corporate issues for numerous companies. Has also acted as financial and regulatory counsel for de novo charters, acquisitions, sales and mergers of financial institutions.
**Career:** Education: JD, summa cum laude, Creighton University (1975); editor-in-chief, Creighton Law Review.

### DREESEN, Joseph S
Jackson Lewis LLP, Omaha
402 391 1991
DreesenJ@jacksonlewis.com
*Featured in Labor & Employment (Nebraska)*
**Practice Areas:** Labor, including negotiations, preventive practices; Workplace Safety Compliance; Non-Competes and Protection Against Unfair Competition; Wage and Hour Compliance.
**Professional Memberships:** Member of American Bar Association and the following State Associations: Iowa, Nebraska, Omaha, Minnesota and South Dakota.
**Career:** AV" top rating by Martindale-Hubbell; 1983-2009 Partner, Berens & Tate, P.C.
**Publications:** "Is Employment-At-Will Alive and Well in Nebraska?", Creighton Law Review 21.2 (January 1987).

**Personal:** Certified by the Minnesota State Bar Association as a Labor and Employment Law Specialist. University of Nebraska-Lincoln (BA) with distinction; University of Minnesota (JD) Cum Laude.

### GOTSDINER, Gary M
McGill, Gotsdiner, Workman & Lepp PC LLO, Omaha
402 492 9200
GaryGotsdiner@mgwl.com
*Featured in Corporate/Commercial (Nebraska)*

**Practice Areas:** Works with closely held companies in a broad range of corporate matters, particularly mergers, acquisitions, reorganizations, real estate, finance, leasing and similar transactions.

**Professional Memberships:** Admitted to practice in Nebraska (1978). Omaha, Nebraska State and American Bar Associations.

**Career:** Joined McGill, Gotsdiner, Workman & Lepp, P.C., L.L.O. in 1978 and became a Partner in 1982. Currently Senior Partner and Chairman of the Board. Martindale® AV Pre-eminent® Peer Review™ Rating; Listed in The Best Lawyers® of America in the practice area of Corporate Law 2007-13, Mergers and Acquisitions 2011-13. Great Plains Super Lawyers®, Mergers & Acquisitions, Business/Corporate, 2009, 2011.

**Personal:** Born 3 March 1953 in Omaha, Nebraska. JD (with distinction) Nebraska University of Law, 1978. BA in Business Administration (with honors) Denver University, 1975.

### GRIFFITHS, Walter L
Kutak Rock LLP, Omaha
402 346 6000
Walter.Griffiths@KutakRock.com
*Featured in Real Estate (Nebraska)*

**Practice Areas:** Senior partner in the real estate group in the Omaha office. Practice includes real estate lending, real estate acquisition and disposition, sale-leaseback transactions, affordable housing tax credit transactions, real estate development and military housing and lodging privatization. Experience includes structuring and closing sale-leaseback (credit tenant loan) transactions, military housing and lodging privatization transactions and credit-enhanced financing transactions, as well as advising clients in commercial, real estate and construction lending transactions.

**Career:** Education: BA, Kearney State College (1968); JD, magna cum laude, Creighton University School of Law (1977).

### HAHN, Howard F
Kutak Rock LLP, Omaha
402 346 6000
Howard.Hahn@KutakRock.com
*Featured in Healthcare (Nebraska)*

**Practice Areas:** Partner, healthcare practice group. Concentrates in healthcare, tax-exempt organizations and seniors housing. Participated in the formation of over 45 tax-exempt, bond-financed independent living facilities. General counsel to the largest hospital in the state. Was counsel with respect to the formation of two partially physician owned hospitals, both specialty

and general. Formed one of the first ACOs in the country. Counsel in connection with formation of comprehensive cancer center.

**Career:** Education: BS, Wharton School, University of Pennsylvania (1967); JD, with distinction, University of Nebraska College of Law (1970); LLM, New York University (1973).

### HANDLOS, Bryan G
Kutak Rock LLP, Omaha
402 346 6000
bryan.handlos@kutakrock.com
*Featured in Corporate/Commercial (Nebraska)*

**Practice Areas:** Partner, financial services group. Has extensive experience in bank regulatory matters including consumer compliance, credit, debit and stored-value cards, retail and online banking, negotiable instruments (traditional and image-based), cash management and treasury products, preemption and exporting, permissible activities, transactions with affiliates, privacy, wholesale and retail electronic fund transfers, payment system risks and regulatory enforcement. Also significant experience in specialized contracting areas, including banking technology, sponsorship arrangements, affinity and co-branding, account acquisitions, corporate and consumer product terms and new products.

**Career:** Education: BA, summa cum laude, Creighton University (1981); JD, magna cum laude, Creighton University School of Law (1984).

### HOYME, Christopher
Jackson Lewis LLP, Omaha
402 827 4232
HoymeC@jacksonlewis.com
*Featured in Labor & Employment (Nebraska)*

**Practice Areas:** Employment litigation, employment advice and counseling for employers, including preventive practices. Practice before federal, state courts.

**Professional Memberships:** Nebraska Bar Association (Labor/Employment Law Section), South Dakota Bar Association (Labor/Employment Section), Iowa Bar Association (Labor/Employment Section), Mississippi Bar Association, Defense Research Institute (Employment Law Committee), Super Lawyers, Corporate Counsel Edition, Great Plains Super Lawyers, AV rated Martindale Hubbell.

**Career:** Jackson Lewis (Partner) 2009-Present; Berens & Tate (Partner), 1989-2009; Watkins, Ludlam & Stennis (Associate) 1984-89.

**Publications:** Frequently published on employment law topics.

**Personal:** University of Mississippi, JD, with honors, 1984; St. Olaf College, BA, with honors, 1981; Married, 4 children.

### LIMBECK, Randal
Jackson Lewis LLP, Omaha
402 827 4266
LimbeckR@jacksonlewis.com
*Featured in Labor & Employment (Nebraska)*

**Practice Areas:** Employee Benefits, Executive Compensation: design and drafting employee benefit plans, executive compensation programs, and ESOPs; representing clients in dealings with IRS and Department of Labor.

**Professional Memberships:** Nebraska State Bar Association; Nebraska Society of CPAs; Nebraska Society of CPAs Foundation (President)

**Career:** 1975-1980 Deloitte and Touche, 1980-2009 McGrath North. "AV" rated by Martindale-Hubbell. Over ten years listing in The Best Lawyers in America. Certified Public Accountant (inactive)-Nebraska. Listed in Great Plains Super Lawyers.

**Publications:** Annual Employee Benefits Update for the Nebraska Society of CPAs.

**Personal:** BSBA, cum laude, Creighton University-1976, JD, cum laude, Creighton University -1978.

### LOUDON, Timothy D
Jackson Lewis LLP, Omaha
402 827 4267
LoudonT@jacksonlewis.com
*Featured in Labor & Employment (Nebraska)*

**Practice Areas:** Labor and employment law advice and counseling.

**Professional Memberships:** American, Nebraska, Omaha Bar Associations.

**Career:** Jackson Lewis 2009-Present; Berens & Tate 1987-2009; Tate & Alden 1985-87.

**Publications:** "Military Leave (USERRA) with a Glance at the Family Military Leave Act of Nebraska" The Nebraska Lawyer (November 2007); Nebraska "How to" Practice Manual 2 (June 1998); "The Civil Rights Act of 1991: What Does it Mean and What Is Its Likely Impact?" Nebraska Law Review 71.1 (July 1992).

**Personal:** University of Nebraska, JD, BA; Best Lawyers in America, Great Plains Super Lawyers, Omaha's Top Lawyers, "AV" rated by Martindale Hubbell.

### MCLEAY, Bartholomew L
Kutak Rock LLP, Omaha
402 346 6000
bart.mcleay@kutakrock.com
*Featured in Litigation (Nebraska)*

**Practice Areas:** Partner who leads Litigation Group for Omaha headquarters and several affiliated offices. Has broad trial experience in commercial litigation, including intellectual property disputes, breach of contract, business torts, water rights, class actions and other complex litigation. Also has experience in the fields of energy, telecommunications, construction, agribusiness, reinsurance and real estate. Has served as lead trial counsel in various lengthy jury and bench trials in federal and state courts and arbitrations, winning several multimillion-dollar cases for firm clients.

**Career:** Education: BSBA, with distinction, University of Arizona (1981); JD, University of Virginia School of Law (1984).

### MULLIN, Michael G
Kutak Rock LLP, Omaha
402 346 6000
Michael.Mullin@kutakrock.com
*Featured in Litigation (Nebraska)*

**Practice Areas:** Partner, Commercial Litigation Group, and head of firm's ADR Group. Having completed more than 50 jury trials, has been recognized by membership in ABOTA, IADC and LCA. Practice is now concentrated on mediation,

and he conducts over 250 mediations per year as the neutral. Is the only Nebraska attorney inducted into the International Academy of Mediators and American College of Civil Trial Mediators. Mediates cases on a national basis through his firm's 16 offices across the US.

**Career:** Education: BA, University of Notre Dame (1977); JD, Creighton University School of Law (1980).

### PASSARELLI, John P
Kutak Rock LLP, Omaha
402 346 6000
John.Passarelli@KutakRock.com
*Featured in Litigation (Nebraska)*

**Practice Areas:** Partner, intellectual property group. Focuses on intellectual property matters, including patents, trademarks, trade secrets and copyrights and related areas of antitrust and franchising. Advises clients in litigation and transactions. Counsels management on issues regarding sophisticated portfolios of IP/IT assets and the use, licensing, protection and litigation relating to such assets. Has acted as lead trial counsel in over 75 complex commercial lawsuits in these practice areas, and often speaks at seminars and publishes articles in intellectual property journals.

**Career:** Education: BSBA, magna cum laude, Creighton University (1977); JD, magna cum laude, Creighton University School of Law (1979).

### PHILLIPS, Christopher
Kutak Rock LLP, Omaha
402 346 6000
chris.phillips@kutakrock.com
*Featured in Healthcare (Nebraska)*

**Practice Areas:** Partner, health care group. Practice encompasses a broad range of health care areas, with particular emphasis on hospital/physician relations, including practice acquisitions, physician compensation models, structuring and restructuring of joint ventures, and clinical co-management arrangements; and legal and regulatory compliance matters, including federal tax-exempt status, Medicare Anti-Kickback and Stark Law issues. Has presented on the Stark Law at national and regional conferences and teleconferences and appears in the HFMA video "Effective Physician Recruitment within the Letter of the Law."

**Career:** Education: AB, Brown University (1976); JD, summa cum laude, Creighton University School of Law (1987).

### ROSENBLATT, Richard
Kutak Rock LLP, Omaha
402 346 6000
Richard.rosenblatt@kutakrock.com
*Featured in Real Estate (Nebraska)*

**Practice Areas:** Partner, real estate department. Represents big-box and outlet retailers and developers, national and state banks and other clients with respect to the acquisition, disposition, development, leasing and financing of commercial real property, with emphasis in complicated, large-scale retail and mixed-use development projects. Special emphasis on complex office and ground leasing. Regularly represents clients before planning commissions, city councils and other governmental bodies. Seconded in–house on–site by multiple clients to cover internal counsel absences and leaves.

**Career:** Education: BA, Indiana University (1990); JD, University of Nebraska College of Law (1993).

---

### SCHEMBARI, John E
Kutak Rock LLP, Omaha
402 346 6000
John.Schembari@KutakRock.com
*Featured in Labor & Employment (Nebraska)*

**Practice Areas:** Partner and Chair of Corporate, Technology and Employee Benefits and Executive Compensation Practice Groups. Concentrates his practice in ERISA, tax and employee benefits law. Works with qualified and nonqualified retirement plans, employee stock ownership plans, insured and self-funded health plans, fiduciary best practices, executive, equity and incentive compensation programs for public and private employers, ERISA litigation, health care reform, and governmental, church and Taft-Hartley plans. Frequent lecturer and author on Employee Benefits and Executive Compensation topics.

**Career:** Education: BS, magna cum laude, Marquette University (1989); JD, magna cum laude, Boston University School of Law (1992).

---

### SLOVEK, Robert M
Kutak Rock LLP, Omaha
402 346 6000
robert.slovek@kutakrock.com
*Featured in Litigation (Nebraska)*

**Practice Areas:** Partner, Litigation Department. Concentrates in complex litigation, including mass claims (toxic torts, pharmaceutical products, food contaminants), healthcare, insurance-related disputes, professional negligence, products liability, personal injury and contract disputes. Lead counsel in numerous bench and jury trials. Substantial experience defending insured professionals against malpractice claims.

**Career:** Education: BA, Creighton University (1980); JD, Creighton University Law School (1984); Law Review Editorial Staff.

**Publications:** Co-Author, Appellate Practice and Procedure and Nebraska section of 'The State of the Art Defense in Product Liability Cases: A Fifty State Survey,' published by the American Bar Association Section of Litigation in 1995 and 2003.

---

### WARIN, Edward G
Kutak Rock LLP, Omaha
402 346 6000
Edward.Warin@KutakRock.com
*Featured in Litigation (Nebraska)*

**Practice Areas:** Partner, Litigation. Former United States Attorney for District of Nebraska. Practice focuses on all aspects of government regulatory representation, including parallel proceedings, corporate internal investigations, federal grand jury investigations, criminal and administrative proceedings involving antitrust, environmental, financial institutions, food safety, fraud, health care, securities and tax law violations. Represents litigants in Federal and state court and administrative proceedings in complex business litigation, commercial disputes and class-action cases. Continues to represent financial institutions, broker-dealers and individuals in Federal and state proceedings involving banking and securities law issues.

**Career:** Education: BS, Creighton University (1969); JD, Georgetown University Law Center (1973).

# KUTAK ROCK LLP

www.kutakrock.com **tel:** 402 346 6000 **fax:** 402 346 1148

**Chairman:** David A Jacobson
Number of partners: 287  Number of other lawyers: 170

## Firm Overview:

Kutak Rock LLP is a firm of over 450 lawyers with 16 offices across the United States. Founded in 1965, the firm serves local, regional and national clients in a practice that spans a broad range of complementary disciplines. The firm's excellent reputation is based on its commitment to exceptional client service at economical rates.

## Main Areas of Practice:

### Bankruptcy & Creditors' Rights:
The firm represents creditors, committees of creditors and equity security holders, indenture trustees and business debtors in all aspects of reorganization, liquidation and workout proceedings. The firm also renders bankruptcy opinions regarding nonconsolidation, true sale and other issues integral to corporate and public finance transactions.

### Corporate:
Corporate lawyers represent clients in mergers and acquisitions, public and private offerings of debt and equity securities, leveraged buyouts, reorganizations, research and development ventures and corporate governance matters.

### Energy:
The firm represents utilities, independent power producers, lenders, developers and investors with respect to the development, financing and operation of utility scale and distributed generation power systems. The practice group has extensive experience with both traditional and renewable energy projects, including expertise with prepaid natural gas financings, biofuel facilities, manufacturing plants and solar and wind transactions.

### Federal Privatization/Military Housing:
The firm has an active practice representing federal agencies, lenders and developers in connection with the privatization of federal infrastructure such as utilities, office buildings and housing developments, among other types of assets. The firm maintains an active practice working with numerous communities and states in matters relating to military base realignment and reuse and the acquisition of federal property.

### Finance:
The firm's finance and commercial practice lawyers have extensive experience structuring and documenting finance transactions involving various assets. The firm works with issuers, investment bankers and credit enhancers to develop unique and innovative asset-backed financings.

### Healthcare:
The firm represents major healthcare systems, individual hospitals and related organizations, physician practice and other physician based entities, ambulatory care facilities, long-term care facilities, insurance companies and managed care organizations throughout the country.

### Insurance:
The firm's service to insurance industry clients extends from general corporate matters to administrative actions before state insurance regulatory authorities; capital market transactions; claim supervision; coverage analysis; defense of insured professionals in litigation; liquidations; reinsurance matters; and suretyship and fidelity matters.

### Intellectual Property & Information Technology:
Lawyers counsel clients on complex intellectual property and information technology matters and litigation attendant to the protection of intellectual property, including patent infringement and trademark litigation and the enforcement of intellectual property rights.

### Labor & Employment/Employee Benefits Law:
Employment lawyers represent corporate clients in a wide range of employment and labor issues on both day to day advisory matters and in state and federal administrative and judicial proceedings. The firm also offers expertise in all aspects of employee benefits law.

### Litigation:
Litigators represent *Fortune* 100 corporations, insurance companies, investment banking firms, multinational financial corporations and various other types of businesses. Areas of concentration include products liability, employment, insurance, intellectual property, technology law, securities litigation and arbitration, white-collar crime, construction law, antitrust and environmental.

### Public Finance:
The firm represents state and local governmental bodies, investment bankers and municipal bond credit and liquidity providers in a national public finance practice. Industry rankings show that for more than 25 years the firm has annually placed among the most active bond counsel and underwriter's counsel firms in the nation.

### Real Estate:
Real estate lawyers represent national, regional and local clients in all aspects of the acquisition, development, construction, management and disposition of real estate assets. Clients include banks, financial institutions, credit enhancers, mortgage conduits, publicly owned real estate funds and real estate investment trusts.

### Tax:
The Tax Department supports the firm's public and corporate finance practices. The firm is nationally recognized for its municipal finance and real estate investment trust tax expertise. The firm's tax lawyers work closely with other departments of the firm in the development of new concepts and in the monitoring of compliance with federal, state and local tax law.

### Tax Credits:
Members of the practice group represent financial institutions, investors, syndicators, state housing agencies and other parties in transactions involving the low-income housing tax credit, historic rehabilitation tax credit, new markets tax credit and energy tax credit programs.

# MCGILL, GOTSDINER, WORKMAN & LEPP, P.C., L.L.O.

www.mgwl.com **tel:** 402 492 9200 **fax:** 402 492 9222

**Chairman:** Gary M Gotsdiner
**Managing Partners:** R Thomas Workman
Number of partners: 11
Number of lawyers: 16
Languages: *English*

## Firm Overview:

McGill, Gotsdiner, Workman & Lepp, P.C., L.L.O. has been serving Midwestern and national commercial enterprises and individual clients in a broad range of civil practice areas since 1975, with particular emphasis on business clientele primarily in Nebraska and Iowa. The firm represents clients in a broad range of industries, including financial services, manufacturing, nonprofit, agribusiness, real estate, healthcare, construction and insurance.

## Main Areas of Practice:

### Banking & Finance:
The firm assists banks, depositors, lenders and borrowers with financial transactions and with state and Federal banking statutes and regulations, including acquisition of loan portfolios and financial institutions, administrative and regulatory matters, litigation, loan transactions, UCC matters and forms and agreements.
**Key Clients:** Great Western Bank; American National Bank **Contact:** Steven J Woolley; Gary M Gotsdiner

### Bankruptcy & Creditor Rights:
The firm represents banks, manufacturers, lessors, creditor committees, lenders, secured and unsecured creditors and bankruptcy trustees in both transactional and litigation services in Bankruptcy Court, as well as state and federal courts.
**Key Clients:** Cornhusker Bank
**Contact:** James P Sam King

### Corporate & Business:
For over 35 years, the firm has guided businesses from inception forward, including formation and reorganization, day-to-day advice on risk management, transactions, intellectual property, securities, litigation and mediation, mergers and acquisitions, liquidations and recapitalizations, divisions and divestitures and tax planning.
**Key Clients:** Behlen Mfg. Co.
**Contact:** Gary M Gotsdiner

### Employee Benefits/ERISA:
The firm works with employers, trustees and fiduciaries in all aspects of employee benefits.
**Key Clients:** Lozier Corporation
**Contact:** Mark A Pieper

### Environmental:
The firm's environmental law practice is designed to support businesses with federal, state and local compliance and with environmental reviews for real estate and other business transactions.
**Key Clients:** Tenaska, Inc.
**Contact:** Nancy A Roberts

### Health Care:
The firm's health care practice encompasses elder law, assisted living, certification and licensure, false claims issues, health law, Medicare and Medicaid, nursing homes, OSHA, purchase and sale of health care facilities, regulatory compliance and surveys.
**Key Clients:** Vetter Health Services, Inc.; American Healthcare Association **Contact:** Robert L Lepp

### Labor & Employment:
The firm's labor and employment attorneys represent management in all forums including federal & state courts, administrative agencies (EEOC, NLRB, Nebraska EOC, DOL) and routinely advise employers in risk prevention, day-to-day management decisions and policies and procedures including affirmative action, ADA, collective bargaining, discrimination and drug testing, employment contracts, policies and practices, COBRA, contract and tort matters, litigation, military rights, OSHA, older workers, harassment, Title VII, wage and hour disputes and wrongful termination allegations.
**Key Clients:** Mutual of Omaha
**Contact:** Mary L Hewitt, Robert L Lepp

### Litigation:
The firm provides day-to-day advice on claim and risk management and mitigation of potential damages as well as commercial and civil litigation services in federal and state courts and administrative litigation in tribunals nationwide.
**Key Clients:** Seldin Company
**Contact:** Robert L Lepp

### Mergers, Acquisitions & Divestitures:
The firm is actively involved in representing buyers, sellers and private equity groups in business realignments through mergers, acquisitions and divestitures, including structural and tax planning, due diligence, documentation, funding and closing, in a broad range of industries such as manufacturing, distribution, banking, financial advisory services, insurance, health care and professional services.
**Key Clients:** American National Bank; Behlen Mfg. Co.
**Contact:** Gary M Gotsdiner

### Nonprofit & Tax Exempt:
The firm has many years' experience working with the special legal needs of nonprofit and tax exempt organizations, including formation, operation and tax-exemption.
**Key Clients:** Bethesda Foundation
**Contact:** R Thomas Workman

### Real Estate:
The firm's real estate attorneys work with individuals, developers, owners, property managers, tenants, financial institutions and investors covering a broad scope of real property and related commercial and personal transactions, including acquisitions, brokerage commission disputes, clean-up reimbursements, construction contract issues, contract and lease negotiations, debt restructurings, environmental remediation, foreclosures, lender liability lawsuits, like-kind exchange financing, loan workouts, financing including non-traditional sources, mortgage financing, property-management issues, real and personal property tax exemption, sale -leaseback financing, title-insurance matters and zoning issues.
**Key Clients:** NewStreet Properties, L.L.C; PepperJax Development Company
**Contact:** Gary M Gotsdiner, Keith A Green

### Wills, Trusts, Estate Planning & Probate:
The firm's estate planning and related practices serve a range of income levels and provide advice on advance directives, estate administration and tax planning/returns, guardianships/conservatorships, insurance trusts, lifetime gifting programs, marital agreements, powers of attorney, private foundations/charitable trusts, probate, wills, trusts, succession planning using corporate recapitalizations, buy-sell agreements, family limited partnerships and ownership transfer restrictions.
**Contact:** R Thomas Workman, Mary L Hewitt

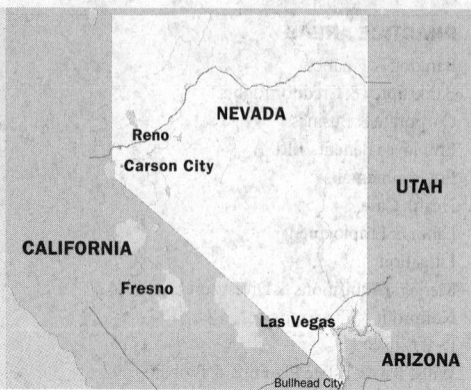

## How lawyers are ranked

Every year we carry out thousands of in-depth interviews with clients in order to assess the reputations and expertise of business lawyers worldwide. The qualities we look for (and which determine rankings) include technical legal ability, professional conduct, client service, commercial awareness/astuteness, diligence, commitment, and other qualities most valued by the client. For details of our research team, see p.5.

## CORPORATE/COMMERCIAL

Commentary about individuals can be found under their firm's paragraph. If the firm has no paragraph (is not ranked) look at Other Notable Practitioners.

### Corporate/Commercial
### Leading Firms

**Band 1**
Brownstein Hyatt Farber Schreck, LLP *
Holland & Hart LLP *
Lionel Sawyer & Collins

**Band 2**
Greenberg Traurig, LLP *
Woodburn and Wedge

### Leading Individuals

**Band 1**

| | |
|---|---|
| Bonner Michael J | Greenberg Traurig, LLP * |
| Fowler John | Woodburn and Wedge |
| Garcia David A | Holland & Hart LLP * |
| Kim Robert C | Ballard Spahr LLP (ONP)† * |
| Schulhofer Ellen L | Brownstein Hyatt Farber Schreck, LLP |
| Zucker Jeffrey | Lionel Sawyer & Collins |

**Band 2**

| | |
|---|---|
| Gabriel Andrew S | McDonald Carano Wilson LLP (ONP)† |
| Klegerman Neal A | Emmel & Klegerman, PC (ONP)† |
| Sklar Alan C | Sklar Williams PLLC (ONP)† |
| Woloson Kenneth | Cotton, Driggs, Walch, Holley (ONP)† * |

**Band 3**

| | |
|---|---|
| Barnard Gregg | Woodburn and Wedge |
| Battcher Fritz R | Holland & Hart LLP * |
| Brewer John N | Greenberg Traurig, LLP * |
| Etem Craig E | Lionel Sawyer & Collins |
| Levine David | Harrell Levine (ONP)† |

\* Indicates firm / individual with profile.
† ONP = Other Notable Practitioner.

### Band 1

#### Brownstein Hyatt Farber Schreck, LLP
See profile on p.725

**THE FIRM** Brownstein Hyatt remains involved in the largest and most complex corporate M&A transactions in the state and continues to be recognized by peers as a genuine market leader. The firm's lawyers recently acted as transaction counsel on General Dynamics' $360 million takeover of Nevada-listed company Force Protection. The team regularly acts as Nevada counsel on large M&A deals involving Nevada-incorporated companies, and additionally has a strong gaming-focused corporate practice that services a number of prominent clients including Station Casinos and Caesars Entertainment.

**KEY INDIVIDUALS** Managing partner **Ellen Schulhofer** is viewed by sources as the firm's *"big gun on the corporate side."* She is recognized by peers for her ability to structure deals and her knowledge of corporate governance and fiduciary issues. She recently advised Tenet Healthcare's board on fiduciary duties and its response to an attempted takeover. *"She is pragmatic in approaching problems and getting to solutions so that the deal can go on,"* say commentators.

#### Holland & Hart LLP
See profile on p.727

**THE FIRM** This firm has bases throughout Nevada with offices in Carson City, Reno and Las Vegas, and represents clients in corporate, M&A and finance deals. The firm recently negotiated a $70 million line of credit for Western Funding, which included negotiating loan documents and modifying the organization's capital structure to accommodate the loan requirements. Other major clients include Harbor Structured Finance, Renown Health and Sierra Nevada Corporation.

**Sources say:** *"It is high-quality legal work and the attorneys are very quick and very responsive to our needs. If we call them up and give them short deadlines they are very good at keeping to them. The whole service level is very good."*

**KEY INDIVIDUALS** Reno partner **David Garcia** (see p.1681) is known in the marketplace for his expertise in M&A deals, corporate structuring and securities offerings. He acted as lead counsel for a mining company on its sale of a Mexican subsidiary. Sources describe him as *"responsive, knowledgeable and good to work with."* **Fritz Battcher** (see p.1681) is well versed in many aspects of the commercial legal sector and sources say he is *"easy to work with, responsive, knowledgeable and always able to tap into the other resources of the firm where appropriate."*

#### Lionel Sawyer & Collins

**THE FIRM** This traditional Nevada powerhouse has a thriving practice that advises clients on all aspects of commercial law. The group benefits from the firm's top-ranked gaming practice and offers a corporate service to many of Nevada's gaming firms. Additionally, the firm's attorneys regularly advise companies on state business laws. The team has represented Las Vegas Sands, the owner of the Palazzo and Venetian resorts in Las Vegas.

**KEY INDIVIDUALS** **Jeffrey Zucker** is highly regarded in the legal community for his top-level real estate and business law practices. He recently counseled Dutch company Consipio Holdings in a battle over the control of Private Media Group. Sources describe him as *"incredibly knowledgeable, very detail-oriented and able to pull perspective from his many years of practice."* **Craig Etem** is respected by peers for his practice which focuses on lending transactions and the law governing business and corporate organizations. He has acted as lead lawyer on the firm's longstanding relationship with casino and resort group Las Vegas Sands.

### Band 2

#### Greenberg Traurig, LLP
See profile on p.1024

**THE FIRM** This firm's well-regarded commercial practice draws strength from its established presence in the gaming sector and its sophisticated corporate securities expertise. The firm's lawyers have been leading a multistate team in Monarch Casino & Resort's $76 million purchase of Riviera Black Hawk Casino in Colorado. Other key clients include Full House Resorts, Gaming Partners International and the Grand Canyon Skywalk Development.

**KEY INDIVIDUALS Michael Bonner** (see p.1681) is described by sources as an *"outstanding commercial transactional securities lawyer."* He heads the firm's corporate team and is recognized for his significant securities expertise. Sources say he is *"a very measured guy, not very excitable, very knowledgeable on law and practical and easy to work with."* Commentators praise **John Brewer's** (see p.1681) *"broad financial securities base"* and say that he is *"very attuned to corporate governance and financing."*

## Woodburn and Wedge

**THE FIRM** This well-regarded Reno practice assists clients with a full range of commercial matters including M&A transactions, business structure and Nevada corporate law. It acts for clients including Sierra Pacific Resources, Centex and Tenet Healthcare.

# ENVIRONMENT

Commentary about individuals can be found under their firm's paragraph. If the firm has no paragraph (is not ranked) look at Other Notable Practitioners.

**KEY INDIVIDUALS John Fowler** elicits approval and respect from across the Nevada Bar. He is recognized for his intimate knowledge of the state's legal system. According to commentators, he is *"a walking encyclopedia of Nevada corporate law."* **Gregg Barnard** is noted by sources for his significant local counsel practice and his strong suit in director duties and corporate governance.

## Other Notable Practitioners

**Robert Kim** (see p.1682) of Ballard Spahr LLP is praised by market sources for his knowledge of securities and *"his innate ability to understand transactions."* He has advised Bank of Nevada on a series of transactional finance matters including loan documentation, workouts and enforcement. *"He is willing to put the work in and he has got the analytical ability to dig into transactions,"* according to commentators. **Andrew Gabriel** of McDonald Carano Wilson LLP splits his practice between commercial real estate and Nevada business law, and regularly advises on corporate governance, M&A transactions and the sale of stocks and shares. He is well regarded by market sources, who particularly

note his ability to engineer creative and innovative solutions to problems. **Neal Klegerman** of Emmel & Klegerman, PC Advises businesses and public corporations on matters including M&A transactions, securities law and financing. His expertise is well respected and his previous experience with a large Eastern law firm is noted; one respondent said: *"He has contacts and perspectives you can't really get locally."* **Alan Sklar** of Sklar Williams PLLC focuses on corporate, commercial, real estate, securities and healthcare law and serves as head of the firm's transactional practice. Sources regard him as *"a talented guy who is not afraid to be aggressive in deals and when negotiating."* **Kenneth Woloson** (see p.1683) of Cotton, Driggs, Walch, Holley, Woloson & Thompson is noted by peers for his thriving business law practice, which deals with matters including entity formation, leasing, acquisition and financing transactions. Sources say that he is an *"excellent lawyer,"* and *"one of the busiest guys in town."* **David Levine** of Harrell Levine focuses on M&A transactions, equity and debt financings, corporate structuring and governance and transactional securities work. He is seen by sources as a *"very smart guy and very easy to work with."*

### Environment
### Leading Firms

**Band 1**
Parsons Behle & Latimer PC *

**Band 2**
Lionel Sawyer & Collins

**Band 3**
McDonald Carano Wilson LLP
Woodburn and Wedge

### Leading Individuals

**Band 1**
| | | |
|---|---|---|
| Bullen Linda M | Lionel Sawyer & Collins | |
| de Lipkau Ross E | Parsons Behle & Latimer PC * | |
| DePaoli Gordon | Woodburn and Wedge | |
| Walch Greg | Cotton, Driggs, Walch, Holley (ONP)† * | |

**Band 2**
| | |
|---|---|
| Butler Jim B | Parsons Behle & Latimer PC * |
| Harrison Sylvia | McDonald Carano Wilson LLP |

**Associates to watch**
| | |
|---|---|
| Zimmerman John | Parsons Behle & Latimer PC * |

* Indicates firm / individual with profile.
†ONP = Other Notable Practitioner.

## Band 1

### Parsons Behle & Latimer PC
See profile on p.2480
**THE FIRM** Parsons Behle & Latimer is known to be the premier environmental law firm in Nevada. Its lawyers are

especially familiar with the mining industry and possess a deep understanding of state and federal environmental law. Recent highlights include assisting Goldcorp with water rights appeals and management, as well as various land matters. Other key clients include General Moly, Round Mountain Gold and Potash America.

**Sources say:** *"They are extremely responsive, extremely knowledgeable on air and water issues, and absolutely client-friendly – they will put the client first over anything else."*

**KEY INDIVIDUALS Ross de Lipkau** (see p.1681) is a specialist in water law and much of his practice involves obtaining governmental permits and licenses for water projects and sales. He recently assisted Barrick Gold with issues surrounding water rights in the area of Bald Mountain. *"He is seasoned, really knows his stuff and has a fabulous, absolutely unbeatable temperament,"* according to commentators. **Jim Butler** (see p.1681) regularly acts for mining companies on environmental matters and has particular expertise in NEPA-related issues. Recent work includes handling NEPA permitting for Echo Bay Exploration's Buckhorn Mountain Exploration project. Sources say he has a *"thorough understanding of the issues at hand and is extremely professional and personable."* **John Zimmerman** (see p.1683) is an expert in Nevada water law and regularly assists with obtaining government water rights permits for projects and handling water sales. He recently assisted Kennecott Nevada Copper Company with the management of its water rights. Interviewees praise his comprehensive understanding of the field and add that he is *"very responsive and efficient."*

## Band 2

### Lionel Sawyer & Collins

**THE FIRM** This firm's environment practice has a particular focus on assisting energy companies with environmental and regulatory issues. Recent highlights include counseling First Solar on the environmental and land use issues surrounding the creation of its 400 MW Silver State solar power project. Other clients include Duke Energy, Boulder City and K Road Solar.

**KEY INDIVIDUALS Linda Bullen** is an expert in federal and state regulations surrounding air, water, waste, renewable energy and NEPA matters. She recently advised Duke Energy on environmental and federal land use issues concerning a wind energy project. *"She is great to work with, very knowledgeable, responsive and attentive, and provides good analysis,"* say sources.

## Band 3

### McDonald Carano Wilson LLP

**THE FIRM** This firm's environmental practice focuses on dealing with permitting and compliance for clients including mining companies and manufacturers.

**KEY INDIVIDUALS Sylvia Harrison** heads the firm's practice in this area. She is adept at handling a wide range of environmental issues, including water and land use, energy and mining and minerals law.

## Woodburn and Wedge

**THE FIRM** This firm acts for clients on the spectrum of environmental law issues, including mining, water and geothermal law. It has a particularly strong involvement in the mining industry and acts for clients including Amax Gold, Glamis Gold and Placer Dome US.

**KEY INDIVIDUALS Gordon DePaoli** is a water lawyer with many years of experience practicing in Nevada. He has acted as counsel to the Walker River Irrigation District.

## Other Notable Practitioners

**Greg Walch** (see p.1683) of Cotton, Driggs, Walch, Holley, Woloson & Thompson has particular expertise in water law, mining and land use. He has direct water engineering experience, having previously trained as an agricultural engineer and worked on water supplies for commercial clients. Sources say he is *"very knowledgeable, very pleasant to deal with and a very good advocate for his clients."*

# GAMING & LICENSING

Commentary about individuals can be found under their firm's paragraph. If the firm has no paragraph (is not ranked) look at Other Notable Practitioners.

### Gaming & Licensing
### Leading Firms

**Band 1**
Brownstein Hyatt Farber Schreck, LLP *
Lionel Sawyer & Collins

**Band 2**
Lewis and Roca LLP

**Band 3**
Gordon Silver
McDonald Carano Wilson LLP

### Leading Individuals

**Star individuals**

| | | |
|---|---|---|
| Faiss Robert D | *Lionel Sawyer & Collins* |
| Schreck Frank A | *Brownstein Hyatt Farber Schreck, LLP* |

**Band 1**

| | |
|---|---|
| Arrajj David R | *Brownstein Hyatt Farber Schreck, LLP* |
| Cabot Anthony N | *Lewis and Roca LLP* |
| Clayton Mark | *Lionel Sawyer & Collins* |
| Hicks Alvin J | *McDonald Carano Wilson LLP* |
| Silver Jeffrey | *Gordon Silver* * |

**Band 2**

| | |
|---|---|
| Alonso Michael G | *Lewis and Roca LLP* |
| Bible Paul | *Lewis and Roca LLP* |
| Bonner Michael J | *Greenberg Traurig, LLP (ONP)[†] *
| Curran William P | *Ballard Spahr LLP (ONP)[†] *
| Giordano P Gregory | *Lewis and Roca LLP* |
| McGuinness Sean M | *Lewis and Roca LLP* |
| Reaser Dan R | *Lionel Sawyer & Collins* |
| Scherer Scott | *Holland & Hart LLP (ONP)[†] *
| Whittemore Ellen | *Lionel Sawyer & Collins* |

**Up-and-coming individuals**

| | |
|---|---|
| Roberts Jennifer | *Lionel Sawyer & Collins* |

[*] *Indicates firm / individual with profile.*
[†] *ONP = Other Notable Practitioner.*

## Band 1

### Brownstein Hyatt Farber Schreck, LLP
See profile on p.725

**THE FIRM** This leading gaming team provides in-depth knowledge of the Nevada licensing environment and a keen sense of the issues at play in the gaming world to domestic and international clients. The firm has been at the forefront of the increasing interest in Nevada shown by international gaming firms, which has included acquiring a nonrestrictive license for British bookmaker William Hill in its purchase of three Nevada sports betting companies. Other clients include gaming luminaries such as Caesars Entertainment, Greenspun Gaming and Tropicana Entertainment.

**Sources say:** *"The firm is very well respected and considered one of the top gaming firms in Nevada."*

**KEY INDIVIDUALS Frank Schreck** is seen by sources as one of the patriarchs of the Nevada gaming sector and is universally respected throughout the state. He specializes in dealing with licensing and regulatory issues for gaming companies. Interviewees note his vast experience, his strong relationships with key players in the sector, and the cutting-edge work he has undertaken with gaming regulatory authorities and Wall Street. One source said: *"He is probably among the best-known gaming lawyers in Nevada, if not the USA."* **David Arrajj** recently advised Deutsche Bank Trust Company Americas on the gaming regulatory, licensing and compliance issues connected with its $200 million loan facility provided to Affinity Gaming. Clients are particularly appreciative of his dependability. One impressed client describes him as *"an incredibly effective lawyer. He understands both the regulatory and business perspectives, as he has had really good experience on both ends."*

### Lionel Sawyer & Collins

**THE FIRM** This firm has long been considered a leader locally, statewide and internationally when it comes to gaming licensing and regulatory matters. It has been heavily involved in representing internet gaming companies entering the state in anticipation of potential federal gaming legislation. Additionally, lawyers from the firm have advised national governments on creating gaming control systems and have consulted with high-ranking government officials on gaming regulatory issues. The firm is involved in technological innovations in the sector, and represented Caesars Entertainment in a successful application for one of the first licenses for in-state internet poker.

**Sources say:** *"The firm has a very strong gaming practice. It is well resourced and its lawyers have lots of historical perspective."*

**KEY INDIVIDUALS Robert Faiss** *"is revered by everyone"* and is considered by sources to be *"one of the senior members of the gaming Bar."* He recently advised Asian Coast Development and the government of Vietnam on the creation of a $4.2 billion gaming resort, and the related transactional and gaming control issues. Sources highlight **Mark Clayton** as someone who *"represents a stable, measured kind of analysis and evaluation."* He represented Gibraltar-registered online gaming company 888 Holdings in an investigation into its suitability by the Nevada Gaming Commission prior to a joint venture with Caesars Entertainment. Sources describe **Dan Reaser** as a *"top-notch gaming lawyer who is a good litigator as well."* He secured approval from the Nevada State Gaming Control Board and Nevada Gaming Commission for International Game Technology's $1.825 billion credit facility extension and its investment in Las Vegas Gaming. Former deputy attorney general for the Gaming Division **Ellen Whittemore** is noted by sources for her background, which *"allows her to grasp the nuances of the Nevada gaming laws."* She has acted for MGM Resorts International on diverse matters, including its application for gaming licenses for the Aria Resort and Casino in the Las Vegas CityCenter development. **Jennifer Roberts** is known to be particularly adept at dealing with local government regulation and licensing issues.

## Band 2

### Lewis and Roca LLP

**THE FIRM** This Southwestern powerhouse has offices in Reno and Las Vegas, and is increasingly praised by peers for its impressive growth in the Nevada gaming sector. It has a particular focus on advising clients on licensing and regulatory matters, internet and interactive gaming and social gaming and sweepstakes. The practice has an international element and assists clients in a diverse range of jurisdictions, including Sri Lanka, Russia, Taiwan and Vietnam.

**Sources say:** *"This is a firm with a practice that is expanding and progressing."*

**KEY INDIVIDUALS Anthony Cabot**'s stellar reputation stems from his position as one of the first lawyers in the state to recognize the potential of online gaming. Sources describe him as *"the leading guy on net gaming in the state, maybe the leading guy in the country."* He has a strong international aspect to his practice and also works with gaming companies to develop and launch new games and gaming devices. **Paul Bible** is based in Reno and is a former head of the Nevada Gaming Commission. He is praised for his vast experience and his intellect; one interviewee described him as *"an incredibly bright guy."* **Michael Alonso** is highly regarded by his peers, one of whom described him as a *"really talented gaming lawyer."* He recently joined the firm's Reno office and is seen by the market as a strong addition to the team. Sources recognize him for his lobbying expertise, describing him as *"a very smart and even-keeled guy, and very pragmatic and conscientious."* **Gregory Giordano** is recognized by market sources for his long experience in the Nevada gaming sphere, and for his particular expertise in the corporate aspects of gaming law. Peers praise his knowledge of Nevada gaming law. **Sean McGuinness** is based in the firm's Reno office and is well regarded by sources. He is recognized for his breadth of experience, which encompasses the gaming sector with a particular niche in bankruptcies related to gaming matters.

## Band 3

### Gordon Silver

**THE FIRM** This gaming practice focuses on acquiring and retaining licenses from the Nevada Gaming Commission for clients. Additionally, Gordon Silver's status as one of the top bankruptcy firms in Southern Nevada has led to a

great deal of bankruptcy-related gaming work following the recent economic downturn.

**KEY INDIVIDUALS Jeffrey Silver** (see p.1683) heads the firm's gaming practice and is viewed by peers as an *"experienced and capable attorney,"* particularly his regulatory and administrative law acumen. According to sources, he *"knows the law, has a good manner which gives you confidence in him and has the respect of the gaming control agencies."*

### McDonald Carano Wilson LLP

**THE FIRM** This well-regarded Nevada firm has offices in Reno and Las Vegas, and a strong focus on the administrative and licensing aspects of gaming law. It is able to draw on seasoned former regulators with strong links to local and state government. The firm's lawyers regularly appear before the State Gaming Control Board, the Nevada Gaming Commission and other local government agencies, and are able to capitalize on their experience within these agencies to expedite the licensing process.

**KEY INDIVIDUALS Alvin Hicks** has a *"stellar reputation"* among the state's legal fraternity and is particularly well recognized for his strong Reno gaming practice. Sources describe him as a *"wonderful lawyer,"* who *"is smart, possesses good contacts, presents well and is very articulate."*

## Other Notable Practitioners

Sources describe **Michael Bonner** (see p.1681) of Greenberg Traurig, LLP as a *"very skilled attorney who works to a large extent in the corporate area."* He heads the firm's gaming practice and largely focuses on the corporate aspects of the gaming world. He was lead partner in Monarch Casino & Resort's purchase of Riviera Black Hawk Casino for $76 million, where he advised on the deal's corporate and gaming regulatory aspects. Ballard Spahr LLP's **William Curran** (see p.1681) has vast experience with local and state-wide government and regulatory bodies. His practice is focused on administrative and regulatory law, and includes a strong gaming aspect. Sources say he *"has a very easygoing manner and long-lasting experience, and is very patient and allows a matter to be fully studied before he moves forward."* **Scott Scherer** (see p.1682) of Holland & Hart LLP is based in Carson City and represents clients in gaming issues throughout the state. Sources identify his experience in the Nevada Gaming Control Board as a considerable advantage. One stated: *"He is a very good lawyer and because of his years on the Control Board he is well rounded and recognizes its ins and outs."* Scherer acts for gaming firms including Golden Route Operations and Brandywine Bookmaking.

# LABOR & EMPLOYMENT

Commentary about individuals can be found under their firm's paragraph. If the firm has no paragraph (is not ranked) look at Other Notable Practitioners.

| Labor & Employment | | |
| --- | --- | --- |
| **Leading Firms** | | |
| **Band 1** | | |
| Kamer Zucker Abbott | | |
| **Band 2** | | |
| Jackson Lewis LLP * | | |
| Littler Mendelson, PC * | | |
| **Band 3** | | |
| Fisher & Phillips LLP * | | |
| Lionel Sawyer & Collins | | |

## Band 1

### Kamer Zucker Abbott

**THE FIRM** This specialist labor and employment firm earns high praise for the skill and knowledge of its lawyers. The team focuses on representing employers and recently obtained the dismissal of a $30 million sexual harassment suit brought again Zappos.com. Other clients include Wynn Las Vegas, Las Vegas Clark County Library District and Cirque du Soleil.

**Sources say:** *"The firm has a very easy-to-work-with attitude and it is calming when you know you are in the midst of something crazy to have somebody helping you through it."*

**KEY INDIVIDUALS Gregory Kamer** regularly represents employers in the full range of labor and employment law issues, including litigation, negotiations, mediations and arbitrations. *"Gregory is charismatic and so knowledgeable*

*that he consistently prevails in whatever area of employment law he may be pursuing,"* say commentators. Managing partner **Scott Abbott** is involved in all aspects of labor and employment law. He regularly defends employers in cases before state and federal courts relating to charges such as discrimination. Sources describe him as *"unflappable, with the quintessential calm and cool head that overcomes any obstacle."* **Carol Zucker** regularly defends organizations facing litigation from employees, and devotes a large part of her practice to educating companies on employment and labor issues. Sources praise her skills in the courtroom: *"She is likable in terms of how she presents to jurors and she has a good reputation with the judges in Las Vegas, both in state and federal courts."* Associate **Bryan Cohen** is involved in all areas of labor and employment law, from negotiation to litigation. He has particular experience in representing gaming companies and casinos. Clients are impressed with his logical approach and knowledge of their businesses.

## Band 2

### Jackson Lewis LLP
See profile on p.1982

**THE FIRM** Jackson Lewis's five-partner Las Vegas team specializes in representing management in labor and employment disputes. The practice has experience in a variety of matters, including wrongful termination suits, class actions, wage and hour disputes and discrimination cases. The firm

| Labor & Employment | | |
| --- | --- | --- |
| **Leading Individuals** | | |
| **Band 1** | | |
| Hicks Patrick H | Littler Mendelson, PC * | |
| Kamer Gregory | Kamer Zucker Abbott | |
| Moss Gary | Jackson Lewis LLP * | |
| Ricciardi Mark J | Fisher & Phillips LLP * | |
| Youchah Elayna J | Jackson Lewis LLP * | |
| **Band 2** | | |
| Abbott Scott M | Kamer Zucker Abbott | |
| Smith Gregory | Lionel Sawyer & Collins | |
| Zucker Carol | Kamer Zucker Abbott | |
| **Band 3** | | |
| Mahoney Scott M | Fisher & Phillips LLP * | |
| Martin Tony | Ogletree, Deakins, Nash, Smoak (ONP) † | |
| Thalacker Laura | Lionel Sawyer & Collins | |
| **Up-and-coming individuals** | | |
| Westbrook Deborah | Littler Mendelson, PC * | |
| **Associates to watch** | | |
| Cohen Bryan J. | Kamer Zucker Abbott | |

| Labor & Employment: ERISA | | |
| --- | --- | --- |
| **Leading Individuals** | | |
| **Band 1** | | |
| Brignone Andrew S | Brownstein Hyatt Farber Schreck (ONP) † | |

\* Indicates firm / individual with profile.

† ONP = Other Notable Practitioner.

acts for clients such as Caesars Entertainment, Pepsi Bottling Group and MGM Resorts International.

**Sources say:** *"They are specialists in employment law, and the attorneys don't have the high billing rate and 'we are all going to wear fancy clothes' attitude. Instead, they focus on providing useful, pragmatic advice."*

**KEY INDIVIDUALS** Experienced labor and employment attorney **Gary Moss** (see p.1682) is particularly noted by sources for his ability and creativity in union contract negotiations. According to interviewees, *"the way he articulates an argument, you would think he is reading from a script because the words just roll off his tongue."* Las Vegas managing partner **Elayna Youchah** (see p.1683) has a fine reputation for her work in Southern Nevada, where sources recognize her ability to take a strategic view of issues and to deliver practical, cost-conscious advice. *"She has a combination of personality, client skills and experience that is simply unmatched,"* say sources.

### Littler Mendelson, PC
See profile on p.688

**THE FIRM** This employment specialist has offices in Las Vegas and Reno and undertakes work across the labor and employment spectrum, including union negotiations, employee benefits, wage and hour issues and defense of class actions. The firm recently acted for Treasure Island Spa on age discrimination and wrongful termination suits. Other major clients include Caesars Entertainment, Flamingo Las Vegas and Proxair.

**Sources say:** *"When representing us the team has the ability to marshal all of the possible issues that might come up and respond to them forcefully."*

**KEY INDIVIDUALS Patrick Hicks** (see p.1681) is respected throughout the Las Vegas legal community. He earns particular praise for his *"overall ability to practice law in such a way that you come away thinking that you are his only client."* Special counsel **Deborah Westbrook** (see p.1683) handles a wide variety of employment law issues, including employment litigation, arbitration and wrongful termination cases. *"Her research skills are tremendous,"* say sources. *"She just has a tremendous ability to find information on any question that comes up."*

### Band 3

### Fisher & Phillips LLP
See profile on p.1107

**THE FIRM** This firm represents public and private sector companies in employment and labor litigation, arbitration and negotiation throughout Southern Nevada. The firm's attorneys have acted for a range of clients, including Caesars Entertainment, Planet Hollywood and the City of Las Vegas.

**Sources say:** *"The team performed well and were a good partner to our company".*

**KEY INDIVIDUALS Mark Ricciardi** (see p.1682) has an excellent reputation as a labor lawyer and is particularly noted for his ability as an advocate and for his speed of thought in the courtroom. *"What is most impressive is his understanding and confidence in how the law can work for employers,"* say commentators. **Scott Mahoney** (see p.1682) is known to be a *"very smart and capable lawyer."* His practice takes in discrimination, harassment and wrongful termination cases in addition to advising employers on their employment policies and procedures.

### Lionel Sawyer & Collins

**THE FIRM** This labor and employment practice focuses on defending employers in traditional employment matters, and on acting for employers on labor matters such as collective bargaining and contract negotiations. The team has represented clients from a range of sectors, including Too Stars, J&R Flooring and Boyd Gaming.

**KEY INDIVIDUALS Gregory Smith** is well established in the Nevada labor and employment law fraternity. He is regularly involved in age, race and disability claims before the Nevada Equal Employment Opportunity Commission and the Equal Rights Commission. **Laura Thalacker** has a reputation as an *"energetic and motivated lawyer"* and is particularly noted for her work relating to workplace social media law. Sources see her as a good performer who is *"very responsive and proactive."*

### Other Notable Practitioners

**Tony Martin** (see p.1682) of Ogletree, Deakins, Nash, Smoak & Stewart has experience in a wide variety of labor and employment matters, including union negotiations and defending class actions brought on grounds of discrimination based on nation of origin, age or sex. **Andrew Brignone** of Brownstein Hyatt Farber Schreck, LLP is acknowledged by sources as the preeminent lawyer in Nevada in the fields of employee benefits and ERISA law. He has been particularly involved with healthcare clients on issues related to recent healthcare legislation. Sources say: *"If you were asked to name the top ERISA specialist, his name would come up."*

# LITIGATION

Commentary about individuals can be found under their firm's paragraph. If the firm has no paragraph (is not ranked) look at Other Notable Practitioners.

## Litigation: General Commercial
### Leading Firms

**Band 1**
Campbell & Williams
Kemp, Jones & Coulthard, LLP
McDonald Carano Wilson LLP

**Band 2**
Brownstein Hyatt Farber Schreck, LLP *
Holland & Hart LLP *
Lewis and Roca LLP
Lionel Sawyer & Collins
Pisanelli Bice PLLC

**Band 3**
Bailey Kennedy *
Greenberg Traurig, LLP *
Jolley Urga Wirth Woodbury & Standish
Morris Peterson
Parsons Behle & Latimer PC *
Santoro Whitmire

*\* Indicates firm / individual with profile.*
*† ONP = Other Notable Practitioner.*

## Litigation: Construction
### Senior Statesmen

**Senior Statesmen: distinguished older practitioners**

| | | |
|---|---|---|
| Haney Dennis R | Cotton, Driggs, Walch, Holley (ONP)† | * |

### Leading Individuals

**Band 1**

| | |
|---|---|
| Mead Leon F | Snell & Wilmer LLP (ONP)† |
| Ogilvy George | McDonald Carano Wilson LLP |
| Spangler Georlen | Kolesar & Leatham Chtd (ONP)† |
| Touton Todd M | Lionel Sawyer & Collins |

### Band 1

### Campbell & Williams

**THE FIRM** This boutique litigation practice is widely respected and enjoys a stellar reputation in the field for its sophisticated work at the very top of the business litigation market. It has represented household names such as CNN, The Wall Street Journal and Toshiba among a broad clientele which includes gaming organizations, professional athletes, entertainers and politicians.

**Sources say:** *"The lawyers are very talented, not afraid of a fight and not afraid of taking on extraordinarily high-profile matters."*

**KEY INDIVIDUALS Donald Campbell** is regularly involved in high-level litigation and has a reputation as an imposing and effective practitioner. *"He represents his clients well, is well known and cuts a wide swath; he is an aggressive litigator but good at what he does,"* say sources. **Colby Williams** is seen as a solid lawyer by commentators, one of whom referred to him as a *"very good guy and very pleasant to work with."*

### Kemp, Jones & Coulthard, LLP

**THE FIRM** This Las Vegas-based litigation group is renowned for its excellent commercial practice and regularly defends and prosecutes on behalf of high-profile businesses throughout Nevada. This is combined with a successful consumer practice noted by sources for its expertise in large class action cases in mass disaster or personal injury situations, including a notable case against a drugs company for its role in the infection of a number of patients with hepatitis C.

**Sources say:** *"It is a unique firm – it straddles the fence and does high-end plaintiff work but also commercial defense work and does a good job of blending the two."*

**KEY INDIVIDUALS Randall Jones** enjoys a fine reputation throughout the state for his civil litigation skills. One source said that he is *"very eloquent and has the ability to put together persuasive and cogent arguments,"* and that to see him in court is to see *"someone at the top of his game."* **Will Kemp** is particularly well known for work on high-profile mass action suits on the side of the plaintiff. He won damages of $667 million in a series of cases against the drug company Teva on behalf of patients who contracted hepatitis C during routine colonoscopy procedures. Sources say: *"He is really a very good strategist – he plans long-term and doesn't miss an issue at all."*

### McDonald Carano Wilson LLP

**THE FIRM** This firm has offices in Las Vegas and Reno and fields a well-respected team of litigators which is known throughout the state. The group acts on both a prosecution and defense capacity and is able to litigate in sectors including construction, insurance, employment, tax and real estate. Its lawyers regularly appear before federal and state courts, and various state and federal administrative agencies, and are also adept at dealing with alternative dispute resolution.

**KEY INDIVIDUALS George Ogilvy** is the managing partner in the firm's Las Vegas office and has a successful practice that encompasses construction law and litigation. *"He has great confidence and great assurance and is well respect-*

ed by judges," say commentators. **Pat Lundvall** is well respected by the legal community and the courts and is seen as particularly skilled in handling litigation arising from complex business disputes. Sources describe her as a *"formidable opponent,"* and one added that she is *"detail-oriented, smart, presents herself forcibly and is someone whose word you can rely on without hesitation."* **Andrew Gordon** focuses on complex commercial litigation in fields including business, real estate and construction, as well as undertaking alternative dispute resolution. *"He is incredibly intelligent, he doesn't stretch an argument further than he should, and in the courtroom he appears aggressive and respectful at the same time,"* according to sources.

## Band 2

### Brownstein Hyatt Farber Schreck, LLP
See profile on p.725

**THE FIRM** This firm has a substantial reputation in complex commercial litigation and regularly acts for public institutions and private clients from fields such as real estate, energy, leisure and transport. The firm's attorneys recently counseled Clark County and McCarran Airport in defense of claims made by several helicopter operators that the airport was improperly retaining passenger facility fees, achieving outright case dismissal.

**KEY INDIVIDUALS Kirk Lenhard** is head of the firm's litigation team and is respected by clients and peers alike, one of whom praised him for his *"clarity of thought and timeliness."* He regularly acts for clients such as Wynn Resorts, Shufflemaster and Republic Services. *"He is a very able advocate for his client,"* say commentators. *"His style is respectful, he is not one to beat his chest and pound the table, it's more that he tells it like it is, and makes the court want to rule in his favor."*

### Holland & Hart LLP
See profile on p.727

**THE FIRM** This firm has offices in Carson City, Las Vegas and Reno and is home to a team of experienced business and construction litigators. Attorneys from the firm recently represented Wells Fargo in suing on a promissory note; the borrowers and guarantors brought a host of counterclaims which the court dismissed and awarded the bank an $8 million settlement.

**Sources say:** *"It is an excellent firm and there are a lot of excellent lawyers over there."*

**KEY INDIVIDUALS** Sources particularly praise **Stephen Peek** (see p.1682) for his in-court ability: *"He is excellent in the courtroom, he has a good rapport with the judge and is a perfect gentlemen but at the same time he is zealously representing his client."*

### Lewis and Roca LLP

**THE FIRM** This firm is based in offices in Reno and Las Vegas and undertakes commercial litigation in sectors across the business spectrum, from banking to construction. Recent highlights for the firm include successfully litigating against a bank that had taken part in a failed con-

struction project, and involvement in the maelstrom of litigation surrounding the $8.5 billion MGM Resorts CityCenter project.

**KEY INDIVIDUALS Von Heinz** is a well-respected commercial litigator, recognized for his expertise in complex civil litigation and his experience at appellate and trial levels. He has represented a number of Indian tribes accused of fraud by the FTC in relation to check-cashing services run from tribal reservations. Sources say: *"He is a brilliant strategist and his written work is superior to anything you will find in Nevada."* **Thomas Ryan** is described by sources as an *"excellent commercial litigator."* He is known for his experience in class actions and is particularly adept at dealing with cases involving product liability issues.

### Lionel Sawyer & Collins

**THE FIRM** This Nevada stalwart is active on a wide range of litigation matters including business disputes, insurance litigation and lender liability. Prominent recent matters the firm's attorneys have handled include advising light-heavyweight boxer Beibut Shumenov on a dispute with a former promoter that was settled to his advantage. The firm's diverse range of clients includes KLAS Channel 8 News Now, Delta Harbor and First American Bank.

**Sources say:** *"It is not a firm that is going to hit you in the face during litigation, but one which will beat you down in the long run with the facts."*

**KEY INDIVIDUALS** Sources describe **Todd Touton** as *"a very fine lawyer"* and note his skills in the courtroom where he is *"good and very effective."* His practice takes in a wide variety of commercial disputes with particular focus on construction, breach of contract and fraud claims. **Paul Hejmanowski** is *"well respected and carries the firm's banner with great pride."* According to commentators, *"he is a serious, no-nonsense guy, he does what he says he is going to do and is a good leader, kind of like a quarterback."*

### Pisanelli Bice PLLC

**THE FIRM** This boutique litigation practice is a relative newcomer to the Nevada legal market, but continues to make its presence felt, attracting significant clients and recruiting shrewdly. The firm has a good reputation among gaming and leisure clients, in addition to handling litigation related to corporate governance, construction and defamation.

**Sources say:** *"For its size the firm gets more than its fair share of big cases and it is definitely a firm on the rise."*

**KEY INDIVIDUALS** Founding partner **James Pisanelli** litigates in a variety of fields including construction, commercial litigation and healthcare law. According to interviewees, *"Jim is a great orator. Great on his feet, very thorough and well prepared, and he does a great job."* **Todd Bice** is well known in Nevada for his imposing style of courtroom advocacy. He litigates in a range of matters including gaming disputes, corporate governance, professional negligence and contract and fraud cases.

## Band 3

### Bailey Kennedy
See profile on p.1684

**THE FIRM** Bailey Kennedy's litigators operate in diverse sectors including real estate, gaming, tourism and the public sector. Its lawyers regularly undertake complex litigation, often resulting in trials in federal and appellate courts.

**Sources say:** "*It is a very competent and thorough firm and you have got to be on your game if their lawyers are involved. Their work is of a high quality, a good written product and a good firm.*"

**KEY INDIVIDUALS Dennis Kennedy** is particularly noted for his strong practice in professional responsibility and legal malpractice cases. "*He is a superb lawyer who takes cases that are meaningful. If it is a large case you would think of Dennis Kennedy,*" say commentators. **John Bailey** focuses in particular on commercial and corporate disputes, gaming litigation and healthcare law. Sources describe him as "*exceptional in court, with an exceptionally smooth presence.*"

### Greenberg Traurig, LLP
See profile on p.1024

**THE FIRM** This large litigation team handles commercial litigation for big-name clients in sectors such as construction, real estate, employment and banking. The firm acts for a diverse range of organizations including Manitowac, Grand Canyon Skywalk, Teva and Base Entertainment.

**Sources say:** "*I have worked with many law firms and lawyers and I am beyond impressed by the responsiveness and attentiveness of the firm and its partners.*"

**KEY INDIVIDUALS Mark Ferrario's** (see p.1681) commercial litigation practice encompasses disputes in real estate, with lenders and borrowers, in the gaming and entertainment industry, with a particular niche in live entertainment tax cases. According to interviewees, "*he is very good in court and zealous on behalf of his clients.*" Seasoned attorney **Thomas Kummer** (see p.1682) is regularly involved in high-level complex commercial litigation. He recently advised boxer Floyd Mayweather on the breach

of contract case he brought against promoters Top Rank relating to revenues for pay-per-view events. Sources describe him as a "*good, solid and capable business litigator.*"

### Jolley Urga Wirth Woodbury & Standish

**THE FIRM** This longstanding Las Vegas law firm has a litigation focus which takes in areas such as construction, real estate, bankruptcy, banking and finance and traditional commercial litigation.

**Sources say:** "*The firm is strong in the the areas of trusts and estates, where its attorneys litigate a fair amount of cases.*"

**KEY INDIVIDUALS** Interviewees say that **William Urga** "*is such a gentleman, he is truly invested in doing the right thing.*" He focuses on real estate and business litigation and is "*very conscientious in his approach.*"

### Morris Peterson

**THE FIRM** This specialist litigation firm represents clients involved in disputes in a wide variety of fields including construction, employment, finance and pharmaceuticals. The team has recently acted on behalf of a series of major clients including Microsoft, Johnson & Johnson, Las Vegas Sands and Harrah's.

**Sources say:** "*They fight like hell and they throw everything they have into a case.*"

**KEY INDIVIDUALS** Sources say that **Steve Morris** is "*such a wonderful lawyer – bright, analytical, confident, highly respected and thoroughly prepared.*" His broad litigation practice takes in real estate, insurance, construction, commercial contracts, corporate restructuring and class actions. He is deeply respected across the state for having "*probably represented all of the highest-end clients in Las Vegas and then some.*"

### Parsons Behle & Latimer PC
See profile on p.2480

**THE FIRM** This firm has a presence in Reno and Las Vegas and handles litigation surrounding bankruptcy, environmental and natural law, business and commercial law and, notably, the mining and energy sectors. The firm's attorneys were recently involved in litigation on behalf of mining company General Moly related to environmental law

and water rights. Other clients of the firm include Couer Rochester, Barrick Goldstrike Mines and Sierra Chemical.

**KEY INDIVIDUALS** Michael Kealy is a key contact for the firm's litigation practice.

### Santoro Whitmire

**THE FIRM** This new boutique firm is home to some well-known litigators with an established reputation in the state. Its attorneys have experience in all aspects of commercial litigation, including business and real estate disputes, and including cases in state and federal courts.

**Sources say:** "*Things will run well in a case with them. They will be reasonable, understand issues and proceed appropriately, but they will also be tough and aggressive and pursue their case with absolute precision.*"

**KEY INDIVIDUALS Nicholas Santoro** is an experienced litigator who has handled trials in contract, business, real estate and professional liability disputes. Sources describe him as "*a very fine attorney and he is a gentleman – cordial and a good advocate.*"

### Other Notable Practitioners

**Dennis Haney** (see p.1681) of Cotton, Driggs, Walch, Holley, Woloson & Thompson has a great deal of experience in the Nevada construction litigation field and is particularly recognized for his work surrounding mechanics' liens. **Leon Mead** of Snell & Wilmer LLP is recognized by commentators as "*one of the authorities in mechanics' lien litigation in the state.*" Numerous sources praise his outstanding knowledge of all issues concerning construction disputes. **Georlen Spangler** of Kolesar & Leatham Chtd is a "*construction litigation lawyer who knows that area inside out,*" according to sources. **Kent Robison** of Robison, Belaustegui, Sharp & Low is based in Reno and is lauded as a "*very able and well-regarded civil litigator.*" He is particularly recognized for his work in the area of lawyers' professional responsibility cases. **Stan Parry** (see p.1682) of Ballard Spahr LLP is "*just an excellent litigator*" who is well regarded throughout Las Vegas and well connected in the community.

# REAL ESTATE

Commentary about individuals can be found under their firm's paragraph. If the firm has no paragraph (is not ranked) look at Other Notable Practitioners.

## Real Estate
### Leading Firms

**Band 1**
Fennemore Craig
Kaempfer Crowell Renshaw Gronauer & Fiorentino
Lionel Sawyer & Collins

**Band 2**
Holland & Hart LLP *
McDonald Carano Wilson LLP
Rice Reuther Sullivan & Carroll, LLP
Snell & Wilmer LLP *

**Band 3**
Ballard Spahr LLP *
Brownstein Hyatt Farber Schreck, LLP *
Goold Patterson Ales & Day
Greenberg Traurig, LLP *

### Senior Statesmen

Senior Statesmen: distinguished older practitioners
Jones Leslie Terry | Brownstein Hyatt Farber Schreck, LLP

### Leading Individuals

**Band 1**
| Buckley Michael E | Fennemore Craig |
| Dennison Karen D | Holland & Hart LLP * |
| Rice Stephen M | Rice Reuther Sullivan & Carroll, LLP |
| Zucker Jeffrey | Lionel Sawyer & Collins |

**Band 2**
| Curtis Patricia | Snell & Wilmer LLP |
| Frankovich John | McDonald Carano Wilson LLP |
| Gabriel Andrew S | McDonald Carano Wilson LLP |
| Goold Barry | Goold Patterson Ales & Day |
| Mace Jim | Greenberg Traurig, LLP * |
| Patterson Jeffrey | Goold Patterson Ales & Day |
| Sharp DeArmond | Robison, Belaustegui, Sharp & Low (ONP)† |
| Watson Matt | Lionel Sawyer & Collins |
| Yoken Stephen | Snell & Wilmer LLP |

**Band 3**
| Davis Jr William C | Fennemore Craig |
| Drury Mary J | Marquis Aurbach Coffing (ONP)† |
| Goldstein Mark | Lionel Sawyer & Collins |
| Goodheart Jodi R | Fennemore Craig |
| Howard R Craig | Holland & Hart LLP * |
| Novacek Stephen V | Holland & Hart LLP * |
| Otto Angela Turriciano | Brownstein Hyatt Farber Schreck, LLP |
| Vermeys Gregg | Greenberg Traurig, LLP * |

**Up-and-coming individuals**
| Shavinsky Mandy | Snell & Wilmer LLP |

## Band 1

### Fennemore Craig

**THE FIRM** Fennemore Craig recently absorbed the well-regarded Jones Vargas team to provide considerable visibility in the state thanks to its offices in Reno and Las Vegas.

## Real Estate: Zoning/Land Use
### Leading Individuals

**Band 1**
| Fiorentino Mark H | Kaempfer Crowell Renshaw Gronauer |
| Kaempfer Christopher L | Kaempfer Crowell Renshaw Gronauer |

**Band 2**
| Curran William P | Ballard Spahr LLP * |
| Gronauer Bob | Kaempfer Crowell Renshaw Gronauer |
| Larsen Paul E | Lionel Sawyer & Collins |

**Up-and-coming individuals**
| Lazovich Jennifer | Kaempfer Crowell Renshaw Gronauer |

\* Indicates firm / individual with profile.
†ONP = Other Notable Practitioner.

Its lawyers are known for their regular appearances in large commercial real estate deals and for their deep knowledge of Nevada real estate law.

**KEY INDIVIDUALS Michael Buckley** is widely respected for his longstanding presence in the field and his tremendous market understanding. Sources recognize his expertise, with one saying: *"He is the go-to resource in Nevada and if I have a question I will run it by him."* **William Davis** is well respected by peers for his Reno-based commercial real estate practice. **Jodi Goodheart** is particularly visible in real estate development and is noted by sources for her ability to cut through complicated government regulations for her clients. Sources describe her as *"tough but knowledgeable,"* and note that *"she has a core of steel and she definitely fights for her clients."*

### Kaempfer Crowell Renshaw Gronauer & Fiorentino

**THE FIRM** This firm owes its fine reputation to the prominence of its land use and zoning practice, which is based in offices in Carson City, Reno and Las Vegas. Its lawyers regularly represent real estate developers appearing before local government entities in matters related to land use and zoning, and have gained permits and licenses for some of the largest real estate developments in the state.

Sources say: *"This is the go-to firm for land use in Nevada."*
**KEY INDIVIDUALS Mark Fiorentino** regularly appears before local and state government bodies to petition on zoning and land use matters. According to commentators, *"he is very focused and knowledgeable. He is very businesslike – he knows his goal and he is going to get it."* Senior partner **Christopher Kaempfer** is lauded for his deep experience and knowledge of the field. *"He is the guru – if you want something done for land use in Clark County you call him. He has the relationships and the touch; he is the key,"* say interviewees. Managing partner **Bob Gronauer** has represented clients throughout the state and is considered by sources to be a personable attorney who is nevertheless *"strong and aggressive."* **Jennifer Lazovich** appears before local government bodies to deal with land use and zoning issues for casinos, real estate developers and educational

institutions, among other clients. She has a reputation as a deal-maker, with sources noting that *"she is good at paving the road to get things through."* She is also known as *"a conciliator who is good at finding solutions that benefit both sides where it doesn't have to come down to a winner and a loser."*

### Lionel Sawyer & Collins

**THE FIRM** This firm's well-respected business law department maintains a significant capacity for handling real estate law matters for clients including banks, gaming companies and real estate developers. The team recently advised the Molasky Group on the financing and construction of a series of FBI facilities across the country. Other clients include Scott Canepa, BGM Red Rock and First American.

**Sources say:** *"They are very professional and have always provided a quality service."*
**KEY INDIVIDUALS Jeffrey Zucker** heads the firm's business law department and splits his practice between corporate and real estate law. His particular real estate expertise lies on the financing side of deals, and much of his current practice revolves around representing lenders. Sources praise his extensive knowledge of the law and say that he *"brings a lot to the table and is very pleasant to work with."* **Matt Watson** is well respected by peers and is considered a rising star of the Las Vegas real estate bar. He recently represented BGM Red Rock in the buyout of co-tenants of a shopping center. Sources say: *"He helps make the deals happen and doesn't mess them up with legal mumbo jumbo."* **Paul Larsen** is primarily recognized for his work in the land use and zoning sphere, where he regularly advises clients on dealing with government regulation and often appears before local government bodies to argue his clients' cases. Sources praise his consensual approach and say *"he is very respectful and easy to work with."* **Mark Goldstein** is primarily acknowledged for his work on the financing side of real estate transactions. *"He has a great reputation as far as legal knowledge and experience go,"* say commentators.

## Band 2

### Holland & Hart LLP
**See profile on p.727**

**THE FIRM** This practice fields attorneys with skills and experience across the board in real estate, and is known for representing lenders and borrowers in all aspects of sales and development work. Recent highlights for the firm include advising a bank on title and loan modification issues related to a real estate development. Clients include financial institutions, mining companies, energy companies and pension plans.

**KEY INDIVIDUALS Karen Dennison** (see p.1681) is seen as one of the leading real estate lawyers in the state. Sources praise her deep knowledge of the field and describe her as *"smart and hard-working, with very good analytical abilities."* **Stephen Novacek** (see p.1682) is based primarily in Reno and focuses on real estate finance and development for buyers, sellers, developers, landlords, tenants and title companies, among other clients. *"He is very down-to-earth. A lot of attorneys don't understand title law and put a load of junk in: he is not one of them,"* say impressed sources. Reno partner **Craig Howard** (see p.1682) advises clients on issues arising from real estate sales, financing and development.

## McDonald Carano Wilson LLP

**THE FIRM** This firm runs a statewide land use and real estate practice from its offices in Reno and Las Vegas. Its attorneys are equipped to deal with a wide range of matters, and represent lenders and borrowers in issues such as financing transactions, loan foreclosures and workouts, structured financing, lease disputes and zoning.

**KEY INDIVIDUALS John Frankovich** is the firm's managing partner and is based in Reno. His real estate practice covers sales, acquisitions and financings, among other areas. **Andrew Gabriel** is noted by sources for his reputation in transactional real estate work in southern Nevada. Matters he has handled include negotiating real estate transactions, real estate financings, restructuring and loan workouts, foreclosures, and representing landlords and tenants in negotiations.

## Rice Reuther Sullivan & Carroll, LLP

**THE FIRM** This boutique firm operates in the areas of business law and real estate law, and is able to handle a wide variety of transactional real estate matters. The firm's attorneys have the expertise and experience to represent any party in a transaction, and regularly handle a range of real estate matters, including acquisitions, dispositions, developments, financings, foreclosures, restructuring and loan workouts.

**Sources say:** *"It's always a pleasure to deal with them."*

**KEY INDIVIDUALS Stephen Rice** is well respected among peers and clients alike for his knowledge and experience of the field and his ability to cut through extraneous issues and focus on the matter at hand. According to sources, *"he has a very disarming style which helps him get deals done."*

## Snell & Wilmer LLP

See profile on p.517

**THE FIRM** This firm is praised by clients for its lawyers' knowledge of Nevada real estate law and the strong emphasis it places on client service and responsiveness. The real estate practice focuses on three main areas: distressed loan work, real estate development and secured lending. The firm regularly acts for banks, mortgage companies, commercial finance groups, asset management companies and real estate development companies.

**Sources say:** *"They are very easy to deal with – they're effective and efficient, and use their clients' time and money well. They are experts in the field and their breadth and scope of knowledge is excellent."*

**KEY INDIVIDUALS Patricia Curtis** is well respected by her peers and is particularly noted for her work representing lenders. *"She knows her stuff and is a go-to person,"* say interviewees. **Stephen Yoken** advises clients on issues such as foreclosures, real estate finance, loan restructuring and real estate acquisitions and disposals. Sources particularly note his presence in real estate financing work and describe him as *"a pleasure to work with and very amiable."* **Mandy Shavinsky** focuses on real estate transactions, real estate development, loan workouts and commercial finance. *"She is very effective – she is creative in deal-making and resolving apparently insurmountable obstacles between parties,"* say sources.

## Band 3

### Ballard Spahr LLP
See profile on p.2234

**THE FIRM** Ballard Spahr is known for its transactional real estate practice, but it is the firm's land use and zoning practice upon which its reputation is built. The land use team is closely related to the firm's governmental relations practice and its lawyers regularly appear before local government bodies on behalf of clients. The firm recently advised Elite Media on issues related to large 'supergraphics' signs mounted on buildings and their legality. Other key clients include Miracle Mile Shops, Bank of America and the Bank of Nevada.

**KEY INDIVIDUALS William Curran** (see p.1681) is the key figure in the firm's zoning and land use practice. He recently advised Miracle Mile Shops at Planet Hollywood Resort & Casino on land use and permitting issues. Sources say he is *"smart, good at what he does, very personable, approachable and respectful."*

### Brownstein Hyatt Farber Schreck, LLP
See profile on p.725

**THE FIRM** This firm's Nevada real estate group is closely related to its successful gaming practice and consequently much of its work involves real estate relating to the Las Vegas gambling industry. Recent highlights for the practice include acting as Nevada counsel on Station Casinos' bankruptcy restructuring, which involved a number of loans secured by real estate. Other clients include Barden Companies, Tropicana Entertainment, Caesars Entertainment and Wynn Resorts.

**Sources say:** *"There are some terrific lawyers over there and you see them when it involves a gaming aspect."*

**KEY INDIVIDUALS** Nevada practice leader **Angela Turriciano Otto** regularly handles the real estate aspects of gaming transactions. She recently acted as real estate counsel for Barden Nevada Gaming on its $18 million sale of Fitzgeralds Hotel & Casino in Las Vegas. Sources describe

her as *"a fine young lawyer who is going places."* **Leslie Jones** is a senior counsel at the firm and has long been respected for his knowledge of Nevada real estate law.

## Goold Patterson Ales & Day

**THE FIRM** This Las Vegas-based boutique specializes in real estate and has a particularly strong reputation in development work. Additional expertise offered by the firm includes the ability to advise on real estate financing, construction contracts, lease negotiation and commercial creditor representation.

**KEY INDIVIDUALS Barry Goold** is an experienced real estate attorney who focuses on commercial real estate sales, real estate financing and commercial leasing. *"He is very knowledgeable and it is always good to work with people like him who know what they are doing,"* say interviewees. **Jeffrey Patterson** splits his practice between commercial transactions and commercial real estate. He also represents creditors and landlords in bankruptcy cases.

## Greenberg Traurig, LLP
See profile on p.1024

**THE FIRM** Greenberg's real estate practice has a strong suit in representing developers and has been involved in some of the biggest developments in Las Vegas. It recently advised Forest City Enterprises on the Civic Center Project, which involved the redevelopment of three city blocks in downtown Las Vegas. Other major clients include Newland Real Estate Group, MGM Resorts International, Penn National Gaming and Lamar Companies.

**Sources say:** *"The attorneys have very exact specialties and are extremely knowledgeable in their practice areas."*

**KEY INDIVIDUALS Jim Mace** (see p.1682) is widely respected for his vast experience in real estate development, and additionally handles matters such as real estate financing, transactional work and regulatory compliance and zoning issues. *"He is very experienced, very knowledgeable and an excellent drafter,"* say sources. **Gregg Vermeys** (see p.1683) focuses on transactional real estate and regularly represents buyers and lenders in real estate deals. Additional areas of his practice include real estate financing, leasing, development and sales. He recently counseled Newland Real Estate Group in its acquisition of blocks of property in Las Vegas for a proposed condominium development. Sources praise his *"ability to identify a problem and to get involved and work with all parties to resolve the issues."*

## Other Notable Practitioners

**DeArmond Sharp** of Robison, Belaustegui, Sharp & Low is well regarded for his transactional real estate practice, based in Reno. Sources say *"he is a smart guy and very well connected in Reno."* **Mary Drury** heads the transactional real estate department at Marquis Aurbach Coffing. She regularly handles work such as acquisitions, disposals, sale of land, construction agreements and real estate financing.

# Leaders' Profiles in Nevada

**BATTCHER, Fritz R**
Holland & Hart LLP, Reno
775 327 3033
fbattcher@hollandhart.com
*Featured in Corporate/Commercial (Nevada)*
**Practice Areas:** Mr Battcher chairs Holland & Hart's emerging growth practice group and focuses on mergers and acquisitions, venture financing, public and private securities offerings and other corporate matters.
**Professional Memberships:** Member, State Bars of Nevada and Illinois, Washoe County and American Bar Associations.
**Career:** Began his law career as a clerk for Chief Judge Howard D McKibben of the US District Court, District of Nevada, and was a shareholder at Hale Lane before joining Holland & Hart.
**Personal:** JD - DePaul University School of Law (Order of the Coif) 1998; BA - University of Southern California 1994.

**BONNER, Michael J**
Greenberg Traurig, LLP, Las Vegas
702 599 8030
BonnerM@gtlaw.com
*Featured in Corporate/Commercial (Nevada),*
*Gaming & Licensing (Nevada)*
**Practice Areas:** Managing Shareholder, Las Vegas. Corporate/securities; gaming; mergers/acquisitions.
**Professional Memberships:** Former Chairman, Corporations Sub-Committee, Business Law Committee , Member, Executive Committee, Gaming Law Section, State Bar of Nevada; former Chairman and current Member, Board of Trustees, Las Vegas Metro Chamber of Commerce; Board of Trustees/Executive Committee, Las Vegas Global Economic Alliance; Member; International Association of Gaming Advisors; YPO and WPO.
**Career:** Selected: Super Lawyers, 2007-12; Best Lawyers in America® in 2008-13; Chambers USA Guide, 2002-13. Rated, AV® Preeminent™ 5.0 out of 5.
**Personal:** JD, University of California, Los Angeles, 1981; BS, high distinction, University of Nevada, Las Vegas, 1978.

**BREWER, John N**
Greenberg Traurig, LLP, Las Vegas
702 599 8032
BrewerJN@gtlaw.com
*Featured in Corporate/Commercial (Nevada)*
**Professional Memberships:** Member: American Bar Association; Nevada State Bar; Clark County Bar Associations; ABA Small Business Committee, ABA Opinion Law sub-committee. General counsel to Nevada Ballet Theatre, Inc. (Chair, Personnel Committee, Executive Board Member, Member of Strategic Planning and Finance Committees).
**Career:** Rated, AV® Preeminent™ 5.0 out of 5. Listed: Best Lawyers in America®, 2008-13; Chambers USA Guide, 2008-13; Nevada Super Lawyers magazine, 2009-12.

**Personal:** JD, Northwestern School of Law at Lewis and Clark College, 1984; BS University of Minnesota, 1979.

**BUTLER, Jim B**
Parsons Behle & Latimer PC, Reno
801 532 1234
JButler@parsonsbehle.com
*Featured in Environment (Nevada), Energy & Natural*
*Resources (Utah)*
**Practice Areas:** Natural resources and environmental law, including public land law, NEPA, Endangered Species Act, mining and mineral processing, mine permitting and appeals, environmental permitting and compliance, due diligence for mining property transactions, environmental citizens' suits, CERCLA, RCRA, hazardous and solid waste.
**Professional Memberships:** State Bar of Nevada, Utah State Bar Association, American Bar Association, Board of Trustees of Rocky Mountain Mineral Law Foundation.
**Career:** Shareholder.
**Personal:** JD, University of Utah, Order of the Coif. BA, University of Utah, magna cum laude.

**CURRAN, William P**
Ballard Spahr LLP, Las Vegas
702 387 3084
curranb@ballardspahr.com
*Featured in Gaming & Licensing (Nevada), Real*
*Estate (Nevada)*
**Practice Areas:** Bill Curran is Managing Partner of the Las Vegas office. He practices in administrative and government law, particularly in the areas of real estate, land use, and gaming. He serves on a number of compliance committees for gaming companies and resort hotels.
**Professional Memberships:** American Bar Association Board of Governors, 2006-2009 State Bar of Nevada President, (1988-1989).
**Career:** Chairman, Nevada Gaming Commission (1991-1999) Chairman, International Association of Gaming Regulators (1993-1994) Admissions: California Nevada US Supreme Court.
**Personal:** University of California, Berkeley, School of Law (JD 1972) University of Minnesota (BA 1969).

**DE LIPKAU, Ross E**
Parsons Behle & Latimer PC, Reno
775 323 1601
Rdelipkau@parsonsbehle.com
*Featured in Environment (Nevada)*
**Practice Areas:** Water law, including governmental permitting and licensing of water projects, due diligence analysis of water rights, and water rights opinion letters. Hearings before Nevada State Engineer and judicial matters in state/federal courts.
**Professional Memberships:** Nevada State Bar. Trustee, Rocky Mountain Mineral Law Foundation.
**Career:** Shareholder. Was partner of Nevada firm Marshall Hill Cassas & de Lipkau. Served as Deputy Attorney General to Nevada State

Engineer. Recognized in Best Lawyers of America, Natural Resources.
**Personal:** BS, Mechanical Engineering, United States Merchant Marine Academy, Kings Point, New York. JD, McGeorge School of Law.

**DENNISON, Karen D**
Holland & Hart LLP, Reno
775 327 3075
kdennison@hollandhart.com
*Featured in Real Estate (Nevada)*
**Practice Areas:** Virtually all aspects of real estate law including acquisition, development, leasing, sale and financing, focusing on master planned communities and resort development, including time shares.
**Professional Memberships:** Vice-Chair, Real Property Section of the State Bar of Nevada, American College of Real Estate Lawyers, State Chair of the American College of Mortgage Attorneys, the American Resort Development Association State Legislative Committee, State Bar of Nevada and State Bar of California.
**Career:** Partner in the law firm of Holland & Hart.
**Publications:** 'Advanced Principles of Title Insurance'; 'Foreclosure in Lean Times'.
**Personal:** JD, University of San Francisco Law School (1971).

**FERRARIO, Mark E**
Greenberg Traurig, LLP, Las Vegas
702 792 3773
FerrarioM@gtlaw.com
*Featured in Litigation (Nevada)*
**Practice Areas:** Litigation; commercial litigation; construction litigation; election litigation; civil rights defense.
**Professional Memberships:** Board of Directors, Nevada Federal Credit Union for over 15 years; Board of Trustees, Safe Nest. Member: ABA; State Bar of Nevada; Clark County Bar Association. Former member, State Bar of Nevada Professionalism committee.
**Career:** Listed, Chambers USA Guide, 2007-13. Rated, AV® Preeminent™ 5.0 out of 5.
**Publications:** Co-Author, 'Keeping it Real: Connecting with the Jury in a Digital Age', Communiqué, October 2011.
**Personal:** JD, University of California at Los Angeles, School of Law, 1981; BS, Accounting, University of Nevada, Las Vegas, 1978.

**GARCIA, David A**
Holland & Hart LLP, Reno
775 327 3021
dgarcia@hollandhart.com
*Featured in Corporate/Commercial (Nevada)*
**Practice Areas:** Mr Garcia practices corporate and securities law with extensive experience in venture capital financing, mergers and acquisitions, and securities offerings. He has counseled companies in their corporate affairs and securities law compliance; additionally structuring corporate partnering transactions and technology

development, distribution and licensing arrangements.
**Professional Memberships:** Member, American Bar Association and State Bars of California and Nevada.
**Career:** Practiced with Wilson Sonsini Goodrich and Rosati, Venture Law Group, and Hale Lane prior to its combination with Holland & Hart in 2008.
**Personal:** JD - Harvard Law School (cum laude) 1992; AB - Stanford University 1989.

**HANEY, Dennis R**
Cotton, Driggs, Walch, Holley, Woloson & Thompson, Las Vegas
775 851 8700
Dhaney@nevadafirm.com
*Featured in Litigation (Nevada)*
**Practice Areas:** Expertise in the legal field includes contractor licensing and other licensing matters, contract preparation for major hotels and casinos, public works owners, contractors and design professionals. Background and work experience includes real estate acquisitions, construction of buildings and fixed works for both owners and contractors. Mr Haney has assisted owners, contractors, design professionals and trade contractors with various project disputes including lien claims, bond claims, delay, disruption and impact issues. He is an arbitrator actively involved in dispute resolution primarily relating to construction and real estate matters.
**Professional Memberships:** State Bars of Nevada and California, American Bar Association
**Career:** JD, 1967. Joined Cotton, Driggs, Walch et al. in 2008.
**Publications:** Authored Nevada Construction Law and Mechanics' Lien Law.
**Personal:** Born 1943. Attended University of Nevada, Reno and University of Utah College of Law. Lives in Lake Tahoe, Nevada.

**HICKS, Patrick H**
Littler Mendelson, PC, Las Vegas
702 862 7700
phicks@littler.com
*Featured in Labor & Employment (Nevada)*
**Practice Areas:** Discrimination and Harassment Competition and Trade Secret Law Training - Compliance, Ethics, Leadership Alternative Dispute Resolution Hospitality.
**Career:** A highly-experienced employment law litigator and trial attorney in Nevada, Patrick H. Hicks has successfully defended scores of jury trials and has handled numerous arbitrations and mediations. He regularly appears in all state and federal courts in Nevada and represents clients before the Equal Employment Opportunity Commission, the Nevada Equal Rights Commission and various other states' administrative agencies. He has obtained defense verdicts in jury trials involving race discrimination, age discrimination, national origin and disability discrimination, and single and multi-plaintiff sexual harassment cases.

## HOWARD, R Craig
Holland & Hart LLP, Reno
775 327 3025
choward@hollandhart.com
*Featured in Real Estate (Nevada)*

**Practice Areas:** Mr Howard concentrates his practice on real property and water law including residential, commercial and industrial real estate development; master planned communities; real property sales/purchases, and financing transactions; water projects and water issues including large water rights transfers and water rights acquisitions/sales; infrastructure issues in real property development and general real property matters.
**Professional Memberships:** State Bar of Nevada (Executive Committee Member, Real Property Law Section Chair, Natural Resources Subcommittee); Builders Association of Northern Nevada; Nevada Water Resource Association
**Personal:** JD - University of Denver (With Honors) 1970. BA - University of Nevada, Reno 1967.

## KIM, Robert C
Ballard Spahr LLP, Las Vegas
702 868 7512
kimr@ballardspahr.com
*Featured in Corporate/Commercial (Nevada)*

**Practice Areas:** Robert C Kim is the administrative partner of the Las Vegas office. Mr Kim practices in the areas of corporate law, mergers and acquisitions, securities and gaming matters, and he is a member of Ballard Spahr's Korea initiative. He has represented clients in business entity formation and operation, corporate governance matters, public offerings, private placements, licensing, and energy-related agreements. He has experience in renewable energy, public finance, public-private partnerships, and distressed real estate.
**Professional Memberships:** State Bar of Nevada.
**Career:** Admissions: California Nevada.
**Personal:** University of Southern California, Gould School of Law (JD 1996) and Marshall School of Business (MBA 1996) Cornell University (BA 1992).

## KUMMER, Thomas F
Greenberg Traurig, LLP, Las Vegas
702 938 6866
KummerT@gtlaw.com
*Featured in Litigation (Nevada)*

**Practice Areas:** Litigation; construction litigation; business and commercial litigation; complex litigation; professional responsibility; mediation/arbitration.
**Professional Memberships:** Member: Clark County Bar Association; American Bar Association; Nevada Supreme Court Bench Bar Committee; Board of Trustees and legal counsel, HELP of Southern Nevada; Board of Directors, Las Vegas Country Club; Former Nevada Supreme Court Settlement Conference Judge.
**Career:** Rated, AV® Preeminent™ 5.0 out of 5. Listed: Chambers USA Guide, 2003, 2007-13; Best Lawyers, 2006-13; Mountain States Super Lawyers,

2007-12; Corporate Counsel Edition of Super Lawyers, April 2008.
**Personal:** JD, Saint Louis University, 1968; BSC, Saint Louis University, 1965.

## MACE, Jim
Greenberg Traurig, LLP, Las Vegas
702 599 8067
MaceJ@gtlaw.com
*Featured in Real Estate (Nevada)*

**Practice Areas:** Real estate; acquisition development, real estate financing; structure and regulatory compliance of mixed use, condominium, retail and resort hotel projects; corporate, business law.
**Professional Memberships:** Member: State Bar of Nevada; Clark County Bar Association; Florida Bar; New York State Bar. Board Member, Child Focus, Inc.
**Career:** Listed: Best Lawyers in America, 2003-13; Chambers USA Guide, 2002-13; Mountain States Super Lawyers, 2005-12. Rated, AV® Preeminent™ 5.0 out of 5.
**Personal:** Served, 82nd Military Police Company, 82nd Airborne Division, US Army. JD, cum laude, Syracuse University College of Law, 1983; BA, State University of New York at Buffalo, 1981.

## MAHONEY, Scott M
Fisher & Phillips LLP, Las Vegas
702 252 3131
smahoney@laborlawyers.com
*Featured in Labor & Employment (Nevada)*

**Career:** Scott Mahoney is a partner in the Las Vegas office. He is an experienced trial lawyer who defends harassment, discrimination, retaliation, wrongful termination and other cases. He also advises employers regarding employee handbooks, policies and procedures, terminations, employment contracts and responses to administrative agency complaints, with special emphasis in the hospitality and gaming industries. Prior to joining the firm, Scott was Vice-President and Counsel for Park Place Entertainment Corporation, which operated hotel and gaming properties throughout the world.

## MARTIN, Tony
Ogletree, Deakins, Nash, Smoak & Stewart, PC, Las Vegas
702 369 6800
tony.martin@ogletreedeakins.com
*Featured in Labor & Employment (Nevada)*

**Practice Areas:** Practice encompasses two primary components: 1) representation of management in traditional labor matters including R-Cases, ULP charges, labor arbitrations, union avoidance, collective bargaining agreements; 2) defense of employers in claims including, but not limited to, suits brought pursuant to Title VII, ADA, FLSA, FMLA, ADEA, state law claims and administrative charges.
**Professional Memberships:** Georgia, Nevada State Bar Associations.
**Career:** Admitted to practice in Georgia, Nevada, U.S. Court of Appeals, Ninth Circuit.
**Personal:** Managing Shareholder of Firm's Las Vegas office. Cornell University (BSILR, 1993),

Georgia State University (MPA, 1999), Georgia State University (JD 2000)

## MOSS, Gary
Jackson Lewis LLP, Las Vegas
702 921 2460
MossG@jacksonlewis.com
*Featured in Labor & Employment (Nevada)*

**Practice Areas:** Labor and employment.
**Professional Memberships:** Admitted in California, Nevada and Iowa.
**Career:** Has represented clients in all areas of labor and employment law including collective bargaining negotiations, strikes, arbitrations, union organizing campaigns, cases before federal and state courts and administrative agencies regarding labor and employment law issues, advice relating to sales, mergers, acquisitions, shutdowns and bankruptcies.
**Publications:** Authored numerous articles for various professional treatises, periodicals and journals.
**Personal:** JD, University of Iowa (1969); BA, University of Illinois (1966).

## NOVACEK, Stephen V
Holland & Hart LLP, Reno
775 327 3020
snovacek@hollandhart.com
*Featured in Real Estate (Nevada)*

**Practice Areas:** Mr Novacek has 38 years of practice in the area of real estate law. He has focused his work on real estate financing, which has included residential and commercial construction and permanent loan transactions. Additionally, he has extensive experience in commercial asset-based lending transactions and commercial real estate loan workouts and foreclosures.
**Professional Memberships:** Member: Nevada, Washoe County, Clark County, and American Bar Associations.
**Career:** He joined Hale Lane (now Holland & Hart) in 1974 and has been a shareholder since 1980.
**Personal:** BS (Finance) from the University of Nevada and JD from Willamette University College of Law.

## PARRY, Stanley W
Ballard Spahr LLP, Las Vegas
702 387 3083
parrys@ballardspahr.com
*Featured in Litigation (Nevada)*

**Practice Areas:** Stanley W Parry concentrates on commercial litigation. His practice encompasses real estate, regulatory matters, eminent domain, construction, insurance, white-collar criminal defense, and business entity member disputes. For the past 30 years, Mr Parry has been a trial attorney. He was a successful prosecutor for the Clark County District Attorney and the US Department of Justice.
**Professional Memberships:** American Bar Association.
**Career:** Southern Utah University, National Advisory Board Comenius University, Bratislava, Slovakia, Visiting Professor, 2010 Admissions: Nevada.

**Publications:** "Extraordinary Remedies," Nevada Civil Practice Manual.
**Personal:** Brigham Young University, J Reuben Clark Law School (JD 1977) Southern Utah University (BS 1974, with highest honors).

## PEEK, J Stephen
Holland & Hart LLP, Las Vegas
702 222 2544
speek@hollandhart.com
*Featured in Litigation (Nevada)*

**Practice Areas:** A premier Nevada trial lawyer, Mr Peek practices commercial and business litigation for diverse clients within the gaming and financial industries. He has brought clarity to complex cases and delivered favorable outcomes to his clients for more than 40 years. Mr Peek guides public and private companies alike through the entanglements of high-profile lawsuits, and he has helped clients favorably resolve matters ranging from shareholder derivative suits to wrongful termination claims.
**Professional Memberships:** Member: Nevada, Clark County, and American Bar Associations.
**Personal:** JD - Georgetown University Law School (1972); BA - University of Nevada (1968).

## RICCIARDI, Mark J
Fisher & Phillips LLP, Las Vegas
702 252 3131
mricciardi@laborlawyers.com
*Featured in Labor & Employment (Nevada)*

**Career:** Mark Ricciardi is the Managing Partner of the Las Vegas office. He represents hotels, casinos, government agencies and other employers in labor and employment matters and is one of the leading authorities in Nevada on wage-hour law. Ricciardi has successfully tried jury and bench trials in wrongful termination, retaliation, sexual harassment, discrimination, and wage-hour claims. He has also litigated unfair labor practice charges and union election objections before the National Labor Relations Board. Mark has conducted supervisory training in the areas of discrimination and harassment awareness, union avoidance, and employment law compliance.

## SCHERER, Scott
Holland & Hart LLP, Carson City
775 684 6011
sscherer@hollandhart.com
*Featured in Gaming & Licensing (Nevada)*

**Practice Areas:** Mr Scherer practices primarily in the area of regulatory and administrative law with special emphasis on gaming matters. He was previously General Counsel and Chief of Staff to Governor Kenny C Guinn and a Member of the State Gaming Control Board. While with the Board, he also served as Chair of the International Association of Gaming Regulators. Prior to that time, he worked for International Game Technology, handling legal and business development issues.
**Professional Memberships:** Executive Committee, Gaming Law Section, State Bar of Nevada.
**Personal:** JD - University of Washington 1984; AB - The Johns Hopkins University 1981.

### SILVER, Jeffrey
Gordon Silver, Las Vegas
702 796 5555
jsilver@gordonsilver.com
*Featured in Gaming & Licensing (Nevada), Gaming & Licensing (Nationwide)*

**Practice Areas:** Gaming & Regulatory Compliance, Internet Gaming, Liquor Licensing & Hospitality, Privileged Licensing, and Government Relations.

**Professional Memberships:** International Association of Gaming Advisors, Counsellor; Las Vegas Events, Board Member; Las Vegas FBI Citizens Academy Alumni Association, Secretary and Director; National Museum of Organized Crime and Law Enforcement, Board Member.

**Career:** Jeffrey Silver is a shareholder and is the chairman of Gordon Silver's Administrative, Gaming & Government Affairs Department. He has been involved in every aspect of gaming, liquor licensing and regulatory law, as well as planning and zoning matters and transportation law. Mr Silver has testified before the Nevada Legislature and US Congressional sub-committees on gaming law issues and has consulted on gaming regulatory matters in several jurisdictions. He served as a former Clark County Chief Deputy District Attorney, and was the resident Las Vegas Member of the Nevada State Gaming Control Board during the state's tumultuous period of developing regulatory oversight. He has also held numerous executive positions at resort hotels in Las Vegas. Mr Silver was named a "Lawyer of the Year" designee in the 2012 and 2013 editions of Best Lawyers in America. He is regularly listed in Mountain States Super Lawyers and Nevada Super Lawyers. Mr Silver is also listed in Woodward & White's "Best Lawyers in America." Additionally, Mr Silver holds the highest "AV®" classification issued by Martindale-Hubbell®.

**Publications:** Author, "Gaming Law," ABA The Compleat Lawyer, 1997.

### VERMEYS, Gregg
Greenberg Traurig, LLP, Las Vegas
702 792 3773
VermeysG@gtlaw.com
*Featured in Real Estate (Nevada)*

**Practice Areas:** Real Estate; Land Development.
**Professional Memberships:** Member: State Bar of Nevada; Clark County Bar Association; University of Southern California Alumni Association.
**Career:** Selected, Chambers USA Guide, 2011-13; Best Lawyers in America, 2013; Mountain States Super Lawyers, 2011-12; Legal 500 US, 2010; One of the Top 100 attorneys in Nevada in the 2009 Legal Elite edition by Nevada Business Magazine, September 2009. Team Member, Winning Team, 2010 Chambers and Partners USA Award for Excellence in Real Estate; Law360 'Real Estate Practice Group of the Year', 2011-12.
**Personal:** JD, University of San Diego, 1992; BA, University of Southern California, 1988.

### WALCH, Greg
Cotton, Driggs, Walch, Holley, Woloson & Thompson, Las Vegas
702 791 0308
GWalch@NevadaFirm.com
*Featured in Environment (Nevada)*

**Practice Areas:** Now Of Counsel to the firm, Mr Walch continues his involvement in the firm's Natural Resource Group, which focuses on water, environmental, eminent domain, and administrative and commercial litigation matters, and assists clients in all aspects of water and natural resource development.
**Professional Memberships:** State Bar of Nevada; American Bar Association.
**Career:** Co-founded the firm in 1996 and was appointed General Counsel to the Southern Nevada Water Authority and Las Vegas Valley Water District in May 2012.
**Personal:** BS Agricultural Engineering, Iowa State University, 1985, and JD, Lewis & Clark Northwestern School of Law, 1992.

### WESTBROOK, Deborah
Littler Mendelson, PC, Las Vegas
702 862 7735
dwestbrook@littler.com
*Featured in Labor & Employment (Nevada)*

**Practice Areas:** Appellate Practice; Discrimination and Harassment; Hospitality; Leaves of Absence and Disability Accommodation; Policies, Procedures and Handbooks.
**Professional Memberships:** Washington State Bar Association; Labor and Employment Section - State Bar of Nevada.
**Career:** Has appeared before the Nevada Supreme Court, the Equal Employment Opportunity Commission, and the Nevada Equal Rights Commission; Before joining Littler, clerked for the Honorable Eric T Washington on the District of Columbia Court of Appeals.
**Publications:** "Ninth Circuit Issues Its First Ruling Setting Forth the Elements for Sarbanes-Oxley Whistleblower Claims," September 3, 2009.
**Personal:** JD, University of Washington School of Law, 2002, With Honors; BS, University of Washington, 1998; Order of the Coif.

### WOLOSON, Kenneth
Cotton, Driggs, Walch, Holley, Woloson & Thompson, Las Vegas
702 791 0308
Kwoloson@nevadafirm.com
*Featured in Corporate/Commercial (Nevada)*

**Practice Areas:** Corporate, Business, Real Property, Estate Planning, and Wills and Trust. An "AV" rated attorney with 33 years of legal experience as both general and local counsel for numerous gaming and non-gaming clients in connection with acquisitions, sales, leasing and financing transactions, mergers and exchanges, stock and asset purchases.
**Professional Memberships:** Nevada State Bar Business Law Section Executive Committee; Southern Nevada Estate Planning Council; American Bar Association, Taxation, Corporation, Banking and Business Law Sections.
**Career:** University of Nevada Las Vegas; Columbia University, JD, 1980; University of San Diego, Masters in Taxation. Joined CDW in 2008.
**Personal:** Long-time resident of Nevada. Married and actively engaged in raising two energetic children. Interests include music and playing keyboards and singing in a rock 'n roll band.

### YOUCHAH, Elayna J
Jackson Lewis LLP, Las Vegas
702 921 2460
YouchahE@jacksonlewis.com
*Featured in Labor & Employment (Nevada)*

**Practice Areas:** Employment Litigation and Counseling.
**Professional Memberships:** Bar Associations: Nevada ; California ; New York; Washington, DC; US Supreme Court; Neutrals Panel American Arbitration Association.
**Career:** Bar admissions: California 1994; Nevada 1995; Washington, DC 2002; NY 2003; Jackson Lewis Equity Partner 2009.
**Personal:** University of Southern California, JD, 1993, Order of the Coif; Law Clerk, Honorable Lawrence R Leavitt, United State Magistrate Judge, 1993-1994; University of Washington, MSW, 1983; University of Michigan, BA Graduation with Distinction; Clark County Children's Pro Bono Award, 2004. AV Preeminent Rated by Martindale-Hubbell. Listed: Chambers USA, Best Lawyers in America, Mountain States Super Lawyers.

### ZIMMERMAN, John
Parsons Behle & Latimer PC, Salt Lake City
775 323 1601
jzimmerman@parsonsbehle.com
*Featured in Environment (Nevada)*

**Practice Areas:** Water and mining law, including diligence, transactions, permitting, and administrative appeals and litigation related to water, mining and agricultural projects. Experience structuring and negotiating acquisitions; performing title review; and assisting with legal review, acquisition and maintenance of water, mineral, surface and access rights.
**Professional Memberships:** American Bar Association; Nevada State Bar; Washoe County Bar; Nevada Lawyer Editorial Board.
**Career:** Shareholder, Environmental, Energy & Natural Resources department.
**Personal:** JD, University of Nevada, Las Vegas, 2005. MS, 2002; BS, 2000, University of Nevada, Reno.

# BAILEY KENNEDY

www.baileykennedy.com **tel:** 702 562 8820 **fax:** 702 562 8821

**Managing Partner:** John R. Bailey
**Senior Partner:** Dennis L. Kennedy
Number of partners: 4 (with Joshua M. Dickey and Sarah E. Harmon)
Number of lawyers: 10

## PRACTICE AREAS

Commercial Litigation
Appellate Practice
Healthcare Law
Professional Responsibility
Administrative Law

## OFFICES

NEVADA

**LAS VEGAS:** Bailey Kennedy, 8984 Spanish Ridge Avenue,
Nevada 89148-1302
Tel: 702 562 8820  Fax: 702 562 8821

## Firm Overview:

Bailey Kennedy was founded in 2001 by John R. Bailey. Its team of professionals represents, among others, top healthcare facilities, publicly traded corporations, gaming companies, financial institutions, travel and tourism leaders, public utilities, local governmental entities, real estate developers, entertainment concerns and entrepreneurs.

The firm is known as one of the top litigation firms in Nevada and has been named among the state's "Best Places To Work" by the Las Vegas Business Press, Vegas Inc magazine and Nevada Business magazine. In 2010 and 2011, the firm was included in Inc. 5000's annual list of America's fastest growing private companies.

Bailey Kennedy is led by managing shareholder John R. Bailey and partners Dennis L. Kennedy, Joshua M. Dickey and Sarah E. Harmon. Bailey and Kennedy were previously shareholders in Nevada's largest law firm, Lionel Sawyer & Collins, before Bailey left to form his own practice.

Bailey is one of Nevada's most renowned health care litigators and has been practicing law in Las Vegas for almost 30 years. He has been named a "Super Lawyer" every year since 2007 as well as a "Nevada Super Lawyer" in both 2007 and 2008.

Bailey is a past member and two-time past chairman of the Nevada State Athletic Commission. He has served as Vice Chairman and a member of the Moral Character and Fitness Committee of the Nevada State Bar for 15 years and is a former General Counsel for the State Republican Party. He has been recommended to the President of the United States for a Judgeship on the U.S. Court of Appeals for the Ninth Circuit by Senator Harry Reid.

Bailey is a well-known community leader in Nevada. He currently serves on the board of directors for SHFL entertainment, director and executive committee member for the Public Education Foundation, and chairman of the governing board for the Andre Agassi College Preparatory Academy.

Bailey Kennedy shareholder Dennis L. Kennedy's practice focuses on business and professional liability litigation. He has been listed with a "1" ranking in the Chambers USA category of Litigation: General/Commercial in Nevada since 2003. He has also been named one of the Top 75 "Mountain States Super Lawyers" every year since 2007 and a "Nevada Super Lawyer" every year since 2007.

One of Nevada's most renowned litigators, Kennedy has for the past 14 consecutive years been named one of the Best Lawyers In America for Bet-The-Company litigation, commercial litigation and healthcare law.

Kennedy has been practicing law in Nevada for 38 years and has represented many of the country's leading drug, food, health care, insurance, tobacco, hotel-casino, and other companies in both the enforcement and defense of their rights. He is a former adjunct professor of law at UNLV's Boyd School of Law and currently the co-editor of the Nevada Civil Practice Manual -- the definitive authority on Nevada civil practice and procedure.

Mr. Kennedy is active in the community and serves as Chairman of the Board of Trustees of Nathan Adelson Hospice in Las Vegas.

Joshua M. Dickey is a shareholder in the firm and was chosen by Super Lawyers as a "Mountain States Super Lawyer" every year since 2010, a "Mountain States Rising Star" in 2009 and a "Nevada Rising Star" in 2008.

Dickey's legal practice focuses on complex civil litigation, including disputes in such areas as commercial law, corporate law, business torts, and constitutional law. He is a member of the Southern Nevada Disciplinary Board of the State Bar of Nevada and is on the editorial staff of the Nevada Civil Practice Manual.

In 2011, Bailey Kennedy promoted Sarah E. Harmon to partner. Harmon has been a member of the firm since 2006 and practices in the area of complex civil litigation, including disputes in such areas as class actions, product defects, tobacco litigation, business torts, and commercial and corporate law.

## Main Areas of Practice:

Bailey Kennedy primarily practices in general commercial litigation, appellate work, healthcare law, professional responsibility and administrative law.

**Key Clients:** Bailey Kennedy's representation includes work for clients such as:
- William T. Walters
- MGM/City Center
- HCA Healthcare
- Dignity Health
- Universal Health Services, Inc.

- RJ Reynolds Tobacco
- Phillip Morris Tobacco (Altria)
- Humana Inc.
- Nevada Power Co. (NV Energy)
- City of Henderson, Nevada

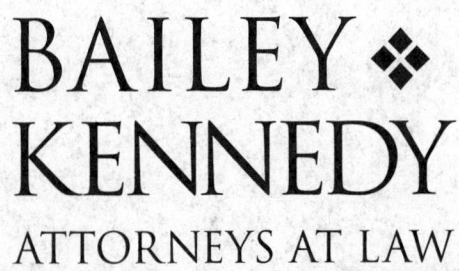

BAILEY ❖
KENNEDY
ATTORNEYS AT LAW

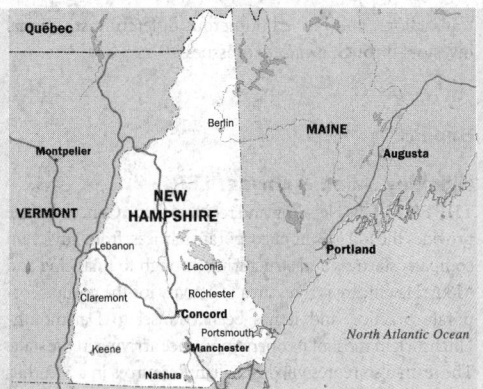

## How lawyers are ranked

Every year we carry out thousands of in-depth interviews with clients in order to assess the reputations and expertise of business lawyers worldwide. The qualities we look for (and which determine rankings) include technical legal ability, professional conduct, client service, commercial awareness/astuteness, diligence, commitment, and other qualities most valued by the client. For details of our research team, see p.5.

# CORPORATE/COMMERCIAL

Commentary about individuals can be found under their firm's paragraph. If the firm has no paragraph (is not ranked) look at Other Notable Practitioners.

### Corporate/Commercial
### Leading Firms

**Band 1**

Cook, Little, Rosenblatt & Manson PLLC

McLane, Graf, Raulerson & Middleton Professional *

Sheehan Phinney Bass + Green PA *

**Band 2**

Devine, Millimet & Branch, P.A.

Nixon Peabody LLP *

**Band 3**

Hinckley, Allen & Snyder LLP

Rath, Young and Pignatelli PC

\* Indicates firm with profile.

† ONP = Other Notable Practitioner.

### Corporate/Commercial
### Leading Individuals

**Band 1**

| | |
|---|---|
| Burger Peter | Orr & Reno PA (ONP)† |
| Cohen Steven | Devine, Millimet & Branch, P.A. |
| Cook James G | Cook, Little, Rosenblatt & Manson PLLC |
| Hood James | Nixon Peabody LLP * |
| Little Jr Curtis W | Cook, Little, Rosenblatt & Manson PLLC |
| Manson Thomas P | Cook, Little, Rosenblatt & Manson PLLC |
| Pueschel Scott E | Pierce Atwood LLP (ONP)† * |
| Reische Alan L | Sheehan Phinney Bass + Green PA * |
| Samuels Richard A | McLane, Graf, Raulerson & Middleton * |

**Band 2**

| | |
|---|---|
| Drooff Michael J | Sheehan Phinney Bass + Green PA * |
| Ellison Scott W | Cook, Little, Rosenblatt & Manson PLLC |
| McCue Mark S | Hinckley, Allen & Snyder LLP |
| Taub Philip B | Nixon Peabody LLP * |

**Band 3**

| | |
|---|---|
| Beals John P | Nixon Peabody LLP * |
| Benson Matthew H | Cook, Little, Rosenblatt & Manson PLLC |
| Burke Steven M | McLane, Graf, Raulerson & Middleton * |
| DiBrigida Joseph A | Sheehan Phinney Bass + Green PA * |
| Fries David K | Cleveland, Waters and Bass PA (ONP)† |
| Norris Daniel J | McLane, Graf, Raulerson & Middleton * |
| Sklar Daniel W | Nixon Peabody LLP * |

**Up-and-coming individuals**

| | |
|---|---|
| Martin Angela B | Devine, Millimet & Branch, P.A. |

### Corporate/Commercial: Bankruptcy
### Leading Individuals

**Band 1**

| | |
|---|---|
| Foster Joseph A | McLane, Graf, Raulerson & Middleton * |
| Sklar Daniel W | Nixon Peabody LLP * |
| Sullivan John M | Preti Flaherty Beliveau & Pachios (ONP)† * |

### Corporate/Commercial: Finance
### Leading Individuals

**Band 1**

| | |
|---|---|
| Barnes David H | Devine, Millimet & Branch, P.A. |
| Di Croce Camille Holton | Devine, Millimet & Branch, P.A. |

**Band 2**

| | |
|---|---|
| Tucker William C | Wadleigh, Starr & Peters PLLC (ONP)† * |

### Corporate/Commercial: Tax
### Leading Individuals

**Band 1**

| | |
|---|---|
| Ardinger William F J | Rath, Young and Pignatelli PC |
| Beach Peter T | Sheehan Phinney Bass + Green PA * |
| Burke Steven M | McLane, Graf, Raulerson & Middleton * |
| Cohen Steven | Devine, Millimet & Branch, P.A. |

**Band 2**

| | |
|---|---|
| Hughes John E | McLane, Graf, Raulerson & Middleton * |
| Sparkman Jon B | Devine, Millimet & Branch, P.A. |
| Zorn William V A | McLane, Graf, Raulerson & Middleton * |

## Band 1

### Cook, Little, Rosenblatt & Manson PLLC

**THE FIRM** This business boutique has an outstanding reputation in the local market for representing clients on a wide range of corporate matters. The talented team has experience handling small to midlevel M&A transactions, company startups and joint ventures. Sources particularly commend its visibility in New Hampshire's burgeoning technology sector.

**Sources say:** *"There is no doubting this firm has excellent lawyers. This is a business boutique offering specialized advice."*

**KEY INDIVIDUALS James Cook** commands significant respect as one of New Hampshire's leading corporate practitioners. He has more than 30 years' experience and is described as *"the heart and soul of the practice."* He is particularly visible in the transactional arena. **Curtis Little** is a founding partner of the firm and a leading figure of the corporate team. His practice is focused on representing banks and financial institutions on matters ranging from securities to financing. Fellow name partner **Thomas**

**Manson** plays a leading role within the firm. Over the years he has advised on many of the state's most important corporate transactions, including a number of large loans and financings. **Scott Ellison** is a well-regarded corporate lawyer who advises business clients on M&A, financings and company structuring. His practice is boosted by previous experience working for the US Department of Commerce. **Matthew Benson** is described by sources as a *"key member of the team."* He is a go-to partner for compa-

ny startups, and particularly is active in the healthcare industry.

### McLane, Graf, Raulerson & Middleton Professional Association

See profile on p.1700

**THE FIRM** McLane has a long-standing position as one of New Hampshire's leading firms for advice on corporate matters. The group is frequently highlighted for the depth of its practice, with lawyers on hand to advise clients on matters ranging from company startups and acquisitions by private equity firms to related tax and IP matters. Recent highlights include handling several facets of the $600 million merger of a software company on behalf of the management, and working on the construction and financing of a solar generation project.

**Sources say:** *"This firm has always been a very strong competitor in the market."*

**KEY INDIVIDUALS Steven Burke** (see p.1694) heads the firm's tax department and advises clients on tax implications of their transactions, as well as transfer pricing structures and tax audits. **Joseph Foster** (see p.1695) chairs the firm's bankruptcy practice and is acclaimed by sources as *"one of the best bankruptcy lawyers in the state."* **Richard Samuels** (see p.1697) is a highly polished corporate and securities lawyer who has previously chaired the firm's corporate department. Commentators single him out as an *"experienced and savvy lawyer worthy of recognition."* **John Hughes** (see p.1695) and **William Zorn** (see p.1699) are experienced specialists in trusts and estate planning whose crossover knowledge of tax adds further depth to the team's corporate lineup. **Daniel Norris** (see p.1696) is the current chair of the firm's corporate department. His practice is focused on M&A and securities transactions, as well as advising on the development of projects in the region.

### Sheehan Phinney Bass + Green PA
See profile on p.1701

**THE FIRM** This firm receives a sizable market share of corporate activity in New Hampshire and has a strong reputation for housing a large number of experienced business lawyers. Recent activity has been focused on a series of mid-market M&A, financing and securities transactions. The team is comfortable working across borders, and recently worked alongside Canadian powerhouse Fasken Martineau as it represented N-Able Technologies International as issuers in an equity investment by Accel-KKR.

**Sources say:** *"A very strong practice that is up there with the best."*

**KEY INDIVIDUALS Peter Beach** (see p.1694) is one of the state's leading tax practitioners and provides clients with important support in the tax implications of their commercial activities. *"He's great for tax,"* competitors admit. **Alan Reische** (see p.1697) is a senior corporate and transactional attorney of many years' standing in the market. *"He's been around for a long time and is definitely at the top,"* state peers. **Michael Drooff** (see p.1695) brings his New York experience to bear when advising the firm's clients on M&A and financing transactions. He has recently been involved in business financings and joint ventures in the healthcare sector. **Joseph DiBrigida** (see p.1694) is president and managing director of the firm. He has built up a reputation as a trusted adviser to business clients.

### Band 2

### Devine, Millimet & Branch, P.A.

**THE FIRM** This full-service corporate firm offers a wide range of corporate services to a client base made up of small and medium-sized businesses, and has particular experience working with leading financial institutions such as RBS Citizens Bank and Bank of America. The firm recently launched a small business initiative whereby it offered startup companies free advice in their formation and successfully registered more than 100 new entities, subsequently gaining many of these new companies as permanent clients.

**Sources say:** *"Each attorney we have worked with at this firm has provided prompt, proactive and knowledgeable service. We would refer others to them without hesitation."*

**KEY INDIVIDUALS David Barnes** is a specialist debt counsel, having advised issuers on more than $400 million worth of bond financings in the public, private and municipal bond markets. **Steven Cohen** is one of New Hampshire's most trusted corporate advisers, acclaimed by sources as an *"experienced and smart attorney who excels at solving problems."* His tax expertise is also valued by clients: *"He is extremely knowledgeable in tax surrounding complex corporate issues."* **Camille Holton Di Croce** chairs the firm's finance group. She is a popular adviser with local and national financial institutions on matters related to credit enhancements and bond purchases. **Jon Sparkman** heads the corporate team and is particularly noted for his tax knowledge. Clients applaud his teamwork skills and laud him as a *"respectful and smart attorney who knows what's required to achieve the desired outcome."* **Angela Martin** is a young partner who wins enthusiastic client admiration: *"She's quickly becoming an important resource for all our corporate legal issues."* She launched the firm's small business initiative.

### Nixon Peabody LLP
See profile on p.1526

**THE FIRM** This national firm has established a firm foothold in the New Hampshire legal market, leveraging its US-wide expertise to handle many local transactions through its Manchester office. While the group is adept at handling most corporate matters, it stands out for its activity in the transactional arena and has recently worked with a number of private equity firms in the purchase of local companies.

**Sources say:** *"This firm gets results. They provide very important guidance to our company and we feel fortunate to have their advice."*

**KEY INDIVIDUALS James Hood** (see p.1695) has a broad corporate practice and leads on many of the firm's most critical transactions. Sources herald his international knowledge, dedication and experience. **Daniel Sklar** (see p.1698) adds an extra dimension to the lineup with his bankruptcy knowledge. *"He's very efficient and particularly strong at sorting out purchases of distressed assets,"* say clients. **Philip Taub** (see p.1698) splits his time between the firm's Boston and Manchester offices. He has a stellar reputation for transactional work in the region and heads the firm's private equity practice. Clients commend his *"common sense, practicality and understanding of business."* **John Beals** (see p.1484) is a solid transactional lawyer held in particularly high regard for his work in private equity

transactions, and has led numerous different institutional investors through a variety of issues.

### Band 3

### Hinckley, Allen & Snyder LLP

**THE FIRM** This New England regional firm's Concord office provides the full gamut of corporate services, from advice on company startups and structuring through to financing and M&A. Healthcare is a key area of activity for the group's corporate practice, and it has been counsel to Dartmouth-Hitchcock in most of its operations since arriving in the state. The team also represented Brazilian Resources in a $15 million financing for a property purchase in Brazil.

**Sources say:** *"A strong corporate practice which can draw on wider resources when necessary."*

**KEY INDIVIDUALS Mark McCue** is the leading light of the practice and is especially valued by the group's healthcare clients. He is also well respected within the New Hampshire legal community, with peers remarking: *"He's the clear leader of that practice, a very good lawyer indeed."*

### Rath, Young and Pignatelli PC

**THE FIRM** Market sources highlight this firm as a key player in the state for lobbying, government relations and public policy expertise. The firm also provides general business advice to clients, with commentators highlighting the strength of the tax group in particular.

**Sources say:** *"This firm is a strong political player and packs a punch in tax."*

**KEY INDIVIDUALS William Ardinger** is consistently identified for his strengths in the area of tax and for the successes he has achieved before the authorities throughout his career. *"He's very well connected and an incredibly smart guy,"* sources confirm.

### Other Notable Practitioners

**Peter Burger** of Orr & Reno PA is a seasoned corporate practitioner with broad experience with transactions in the real estate and hospitality sectors. *"He's clearly top tier,"* sources confirm. **John Sullivan** (see p.1698) is a director at Preti Flaherty Beliveau & Pachios, LLP where he handles a wide range of corporate matters. He is particularly regarded in the market for his experience in Chapter 11 reorganizations. **William Tucker** (see p.1698) of Wadleigh, Starr & Peters PLLC is a senior figure of the New Hampshire legal market, and is esteemed for his knowledge of real estate financing matters. **David Fries** of Cleveland, Waters and Bass PA has a broad corporate practice, encompassing M&A, financing and business structuring. *"A highly capable attorney,"* say sources. **Scott Pueschel** (see p.1697) of Pierce Atwood LLP wins rave reviews from clients: *"He's responsive, meets deadlines and budget expectations, and always produces quality work."* Peers are equally forthcoming in their praise: *"A top-quality business lawyer."*

# ENVIRONMENT

Commentary about individuals can be found under their firm's paragraph. If the firm has no paragraph (is not ranked) look at Other Notable Practitioners.

| Environment | |
|---|---|
| **Leading Firms** | |
| **Band 1** | |
| McLane, Graf, Raulerson & Middleton * | |
| Sheehan Phinney Bass + Green PA * | |
| **Band 2** | |
| Devine, Millimet & Branch, P.A. | |
| Rath, Young and Pignatelli PC | |

| Leading Individuals | |
|---|---|
| **Band 1** | |
| Cheney Robert P | Sheehan Phinney Bass + Green PA * |
| Dwyer John V | Winer & Bennett LLP (ONP) † |
| Needleman Barry | McLane, Graf, Raulerson & Middleton * |
| Peltonen John E | Sheehan Phinney Bass + Green PA * |
| Smith Gregory H | McLane, Graf, Raulerson & Middleton * |
| Young Sherilyn Burnett | Rath, Young and Pignatelli PC |
| **Band 2** | |
| Bisbee Dana | Devine, Millimet & Branch, P.A. |
| Kinder E Tupper | Nelson Kinder + Mosseau, PC (ONP) † |
| Quinn Michael J | McLane, Graf, Raulerson & Middleton * |
| **Band 3** | |
| Beeson Peter G | Devine, Millimet & Branch, P.A. |
| Lucic Robert R | Sheehan Phinney Bass + Green PA * |
| Rouvalis Mark | McLane, Graf, Raulerson & Middleton * |

\* Indicates firm / individual with profile.
†ONP = Other Notable Practitioner.

## Band 1

### McLane, Graf, Raulerson & Middleton Professional Association
See profile on p.1700

**THE FIRM** This firm is widely acknowledged as one of the leading environment practices in New Hampshire, with a team well drilled in the technical aspects of the law and noted for its ability to lead high-profile litigations. The group handles a wide variety of issues, covering hazardous waste, clean air and water issues, and Superfund litigations on behalf of both companies and communities. **KEY INDIVIDUALS Barry Needleman** (see p.1696) is one of the firm's standout lawyers for environmental mat-

ters. He has experience handling a wide range of issues on behalf of his clients but is particularly notable for his experience in gas plant liabilities. *"He's carved out quite a reputation in that field,"* sources state. **Gregory Smith** (see p.1698) chairs the firm's environmental practice. He has represented the residents of the Town of Newbury in an ongoing conservation case for more than two decades, and also represents companies on regulatory and permitting issues. *"He has his hand in a lot of matters and is one of the mainstays of the practice,"* peers confirm. **Michael Quinn** (see p.1697) is an esteemed practitioner in all areas of environmental disputes. In an ongoing case, he has represented EnergyNorth Natural Gas in a multimillion-dollar hazardous waste case brought by the New Hampshire Department of Environmental Services. **Mark Rouvalis** (see p.1697) has ample experience in the area of Superfund litigation and continues to represent a number of the firm's clients in this regard.

### Sheehan Phinney Bass + Green PA
See profile on p.1701

**THE FIRM** This firm is home to a comprehensive environment practice that is regularly called upon in administrative, regulatory and contentious matters by clients in industries ranging from government entities to the energy sector. Of late it has been particularly active in private costs recovery actions and issues related to the CWA. The team is also engaged on matters outside of New Hampshire, and successfully represented its client IMC Eastern in a case brought by the State of New York. **KEY INDIVIDUALS Robert Cheney** (see p.1694) has a wealth of experience related to regulatory environment matters. He is commended as a lawyer with *"a broad environmental practice."* **John Peltonen** (see p.1697) leads many of the firm's most high-profile cases, and is counsel to the City of Dover in a large dispute against the New Hampshire Department of Environmental Services. *"He's a top-notch lawyer, and very skilled in hazardous waste and Superfund work,"* competitors confirm. **Robert Lucic** (see p.1696) is an experienced lawyer who has made a name for himself in environmental circles for his work in Superfund litigation, and represented IMC Eastern in the case mentioned above.

## Band 2

### Devine, Millimet & Branch, P.A.
**THE FIRM** This firm provides its clients, both municipal and corporate, with important support on environmental issues related to permitting, development and land use. The experienced team also advises on hazardous waste enforcement and criminal litigation, and has recently worked on a number of water quality cases. **KEY INDIVIDUALS Peter Beeson** is a highly experienced litigator who has worked on a number of contentious environmental cases in the state. **Dana Bisbee** brings with him significant experience from his time working at the assistant and acting commissioner of the New Hampshire Department of Environmental Services. *"He has a lot of experience in environmental cases,"* sources say.

### Rath, Young and Pignatelli PC
**THE FIRM** This firm is well known for its robust renewable energy practice and is consequently equipped to offer broad advice to clients on environmental issues arising in that arena. Among the areas the group advises on is the redevelopment of contaminated properties, water usage and shoreline structuring. **KEY INDIVIDUALS Sherilyn Burnett Young** heads the environmental practice and is esteemed for her work in the area. She is an expert in environmental compliance and land use matters and is lauded by peers as a *"very capable attorney."*

## Other Notable Practitioners

**John Dwyer** of Winer & Bennett LLP is highly regarded for his work in the area of environmental litigation, particularly in hazardous waste and Superfund cases. *"He has a wonderful reputation; he's right up there in the top league,"* market commentators say. **Tupper Kinder** of Nelson Kinder + Mosseau, PC is another esteemed litigator with extensive experience with regulatory issues related to environmental law. *"An outstanding attorney – active and capable,"* peers say.

# LABOR & EMPLOYMENT

Commentary about individuals can be found under their firm's paragraph. If the firm has no paragraph (is not ranked) look at Other Notable Practitioners.

## Labor & Employment
### Leading Firms

**Band 1**
McLane, Graf, Raulerson & Middleton *
Sheehan Phinney Bass + Green PA *

**Band 2**
Bernstein Shur *
Devine, Millimet & Branch, P.A.
Jackson Lewis LLP *

**Band 3**
Cook, Little, Rosenblatt & Manson PLLC
Sulloway & Hollis PLLC

### Leading Individuals

**Band 1**

| | | |
|---|---|---|
| Broth Mark T | Drummond Woodsum (ONP)[†] |
| Ford Debra Weiss | Jackson Lewis LLP * |
| Johnson Linda S | McLane, Graf, Raulerson & Middleton * |
| Reidy James P | Sheehan Phinney Bass + Green PA * |

**Band 2**

| | |
|---|---|
| Chatfield Andrea G | Cook, Little, Rosenblatt & Manson PLLC |
| Closson Thomas M | Jackson Lewis LLP * |
| Kaplan Edward | Sulloway & Hollis PLLC |
| Moeckel Jennifer Shea | Cook, Little, Rosenblatt & Manson PLLC |
| Wieland Diana | Sheehan Phinney Bass + Green PA * |

**Band 3**

| | |
|---|---|
| Bailey Elizabeth A. | Sheehan Phinney Bass + Green PA * |
| McGrath David W | Sheehan Phinney Bass + Green PA * |
| Parent Jennifer L | McLane, Graf, Raulerson & Middleton * |
| Poole Jeanine L | Sulloway & Hollis PLLC |
| Rice Emily Gray | Bernstein Shur |
| Schwarz Dan P | Jackson Lewis LLP * |
| Shilling Cameron G | McLane, Graf, Raulerson & Middleton * |
| Shumaker III Edward (Terry) | Bernstein Shur |
| Stevens Charla B | McLane, Graf, Raulerson & Middleton * |
| Van Oot Martha | Jackson Lewis LLP * |
| Winer Steven L | Orr & Reno PA (ONP)[†] |

**Associates to watch**

| | |
|---|---|
| Aframe Karen | Bernstein Shur |

## Labor & Employment:
### Employee Benefits & Compensation
### Leading Individuals

**Band 1**

| | |
|---|---|
| Cleveland Alan P | Sheehan Phinney Bass + Green PA * |
| Kershaw Jr. Newton H | Devine, Millimet & Branch, P.A. |
| Rich Jr John E | McLane, Graf, Raulerson & Middleton * |

\* Indicates firm / individual with profile.
[†]ONP = Other Notable Practitioner.

## Band 1

### McLane, Graf, Raulerson & Middleton Professional Association
See profile on p.1700
**THE FIRM** This premier New Hampshire firm offers a stellar labor and employment service which is consistent with its across-the-board business strengths. The group handles day-to-day employment issues encompassing immigration advice, contractual matters and seminars for employers. The team also handles litigation cases on behalf of companies in cases of harassment and other lawsuits. **Sources say:** *"A fine group of lawyers."* **KEY INDIVIDUALS** As cochair of the firm's education and litigation practices, **Linda Johnson** (see p.1695) provides a wealth of experience in labor and employment issues related to the education sector. **John Rich** (see p.1697) is director of the tax department and provides the team with important crossover knowledge in employee benefits and welfare and compensation. **Jennifer Parent** (see p.1696) chairs the firm's employment law practice. She is particularly regarded for her prolific activity defending employers in cases of harassment, discrimination, and employee misconduct and dismissals. *"There's no question she knows this area of law,"* peers remark. **Cameron Shilling** (see p.1698) is another esteemed commercial litigator in the group who has been engaged in a substantial number of employment mandates over the course of his career, and is notable for his expertise in trade secrets. **Charla Stevens** (see p.1698) has a broad employment practice across a variety of sectors, and has worked in litigious matters as well as advising on labor audits and personnel policies.

### Sheehan Phinney Bass + Green PA
See profile on p.1701
**THE FIRM** This local powerhouse is home to a market-leading labor and employment team, which represents clients such as Walmart, Cobham Surveillance and several important public institutions. The group is equipped to handle all aspects of the law, from resolving sensitive employee issues to labor audits and collective bargaining agreements. The team has also handled a number of race, sex and disability discrimination suits. **Sources say:** *"This is a top-tier employment department with senior attorneys experienced in all aspects of the law."* **KEY INDIVIDUALS James Reidy** (see p.1697) is highly valued by clients for his track record in dealing with thorny employer/employee disputes inside or outside the courtroom. Sources single him out as a *"well-balanced, dedicated and senior labor and employment lawyer."* **Diana Wieland** (see p.1699) is of counsel at the firm, and has more than 25 years' experience representing management in labor and employment matters. She is highlighted for her counseling and training expertise. **Elizabeth Bailey**

(see p.1694) commands much respect in the market for her work in the prevention and defense of employment disputes. She has represented public and private sector clients before all levels of local regulation. **David McGrath** (see p.1696) is respected as an astute commercial litigator who has handled a large number of employment-related disputes concerning discrimination and predatory hiring cases. **Alan Cleveland** (see p.1694) is of counsel at the firm, and is the group's resident expert in ERISA and pension matters.

## Band 2

### Bernstein Shur
See profile on p.1406
**THE FIRM** This firm has a distinguished reputation in the market for a labor and employment practice which stands out for its day-to-day advisory service in labor relations and general employment policies. The team's offering has also broadened in recent times with the hire of an extra attorney in the litigation side to handle contentious issues. The group continues to represent the New Hampshire Electric Cooperative in an ongoing collective bargaining agreement, and other labor advice. **Sources say:** *"We have created a really fruitful relationship with this team. Their advice is clear, the responsiveness is incredible and the turnaround time on queries is exceptional."* **KEY INDIVIDUALS Terry Shumaker** is a highly experienced labor lawyer, known for his effectiveness as a mediator and arbitrator. Clients are effusive in their praise: *"I can't speak highly enough of him; he is pragmatic, educative and fair-minded."* **Karen Aframe** now heads the labor and employment practice. She wins staunch client admiration: *"Her performance is consistently strong; she is thoughtful, patient and always takes the time to understand our issues before proposing well thought-out recommendations."* **Emily Gray Rice** recently joined from Orr & Reno and bolsters the team with her strong track record in labor and employment litigation.

### Devine, Millimet & Branch, P.A.
**THE FIRM** This firm has a robust management-side labor and employment practice which offers a wide complement of services in the area. The group advises its clients on compliance and counseling matters, and handles traditional labor issues such as collective bargaining. The team has also been engaged in a number of litigation and arbitration cases related to sexual harassment, discrimination and dismissals. **Sources say:** *"An experienced group that provides a fine service."* **KEY INDIVIDUALS Newton Kershaw** works with clients on the structuring of pensions, profit sharing and retire-

ment plans, as well as dealing with any issues that should arise from employee benefit schemes.

### Jackson Lewis LLP
See profile on p.1982

**THE FIRM** The Portsmouth office of this national labor and employment giant has become a key port of call for companies operating in New Hampshire since its inception in 2008. With a client roster including the likes of Zurich and Sig Saeur, the group is adept at handling the employment demands of big business, and is highlighted for its robust defense of company management in labor issues and litigations brought by employees.

**Sources say:** "This is an excellent litigation shop. The lawyers truly represent the employer's interests and are responsive, supportive and easy to work with."

**KEY INDIVIDUALS Debra Weiss Ford** (see p.1695) is managing partner of the Portsmouth office and a firm client favorite: "A wonderful labor and employment lawyer. Her response rate is perfect – no matter what time of the day or night, she will have responded within five minutes." **Thomas Closson** (see p.1694) is a highly regarded lawyer who successfully represented the Hollis School Board in a public sector labor case at the New Hampshire Supreme Court. **Dan Schwarz** (see p.1698) has enjoyed recent success defending his clients in longrunning disputes in dis-

ability discrimination and other workplace disputes. **Martha Van Oot** (see p.1698) joined from Orr & Reno in mid-2012 and will add considerable depth to the firm's bench in employment litigation.

### Band 3

### Cook, Little, Rosenblatt & Manson PLLC

**THE FIRM** This local stalwart has a compact but solid labor and employment advisory service. The group offers its corporate clients day-to-day advice on risk management, compliance personnel policies and other issues. The team is also on hand to represent clients should any significant dispute arise.

**KEY INDIVIDUALS Andrea Chatfield** and **Jennifer Shea Moeckel** are the firm's resident experts in this practice area, and between them provide significant expertise in workplace investigations and training, payroll compliance and discrimination issues. "Both of them are very well regarded, and particularly shine in counseling and compliance," commentators say.

### Sulloway & Hollis PLLC

**THE FIRM** This firm provides a comprehensive labor and employment service that is particularly regarded for its

experience handling union issues in the education sector. The team is also qualified to advise on the development of employee policies such as ERISA and employee handbooks, and handles a range of employment litigations.

**KEY INDIVIDUALS Edward Kaplan** commands significant market respect for his experience in all aspects of this practice area, particularly in the education space. One source comments that "he would be my go-to guy for advice in this area – he's a highly regarded trial lawyer and does a great job on collective bargaining." **Jeanine Poole** leads the firm's labor and employment practice. For more than 20 years she has supported the firm's clients in every aspect of their employment-related decisions and policies.

### Other Notable Practitioners

**Steven Winer** of Orr & Reno PA is a highly experienced employment lawyer who, over the course of his career, has advised companies on matters ranging from HR policies and contractual matters to employee terminations and lawsuits. **Mark Broth** recently left Devine, Millimet & Branch to join Drummond Woodsum. He has built an outstanding presence in this field, achieved over nearly three decades of practice. "He's highly experienced and really knows his stuff," comment peers.

# LITIGATION GENERAL COMMERCIAL

Commentary about individuals can be found under their firm's paragraph. If the firm has no paragraph (is not ranked) look at Other Notable Practitioners.

| Litigation: General Commercial |
| --- |
| **Leading Firms** |
| **Band 1** |
| McLane, Graf, Raulerson & Middleton Professional * |
| Nixon Peabody LLP * |
| Sheehan Phinney Bass + Green PA * |
| **Band 2** |
| Devine, Millimet & Branch, P.A. |
| Hinckley, Allen & Snyder LLP |
| Sulloway & Hollis PLLC |
| **Band 3** |
| Bernstein Shur * |
| Cook, Little, Rosenblatt & Manson PLLC |
| Nelson Kinder + Mosseau, PC |
| Orr & Reno PA |
| Upton and Hatfield LLP |

\* Indicates firm with profile.
Alphabetical order within each band. Band 1 is the highest.

### Band 1

### McLane, Graf, Raulerson & Middleton Professional Association
See profile on p.1700

**THE FIRM** This is one of New Hampshire's strongest firms and has a deep bench of litigators capable of representing clients in a wide range of matters. The group has litigated in cases related to insurance recovery, trademark infringement, unfair competition and hazardous waste. In recent highlights, it helped Dell settle during the discovery process in a patent action brought by Media Digital, and it continues to represent Irving Oil in one of the largest environmental cases in the state's history.

**Sources say:** "We've worked with lots of attorneys and they are definitely at the top."

**KEY INDIVIDUALS Cochair Bruce Felmly** (see p.1695) is widely regarded as one of the state's leading litigators. With almost four decades' experience, he is frequently called upon to lead some of the most high-profile cases in New Hampshire. Peers describe him as "a highly accomplished lawyer with plentiful experience and expertise." **Wilbur Glahn** (see p.1695) is cochair of the firm's business litigation group and has practiced at McLane for more than 30

years. Acclaimed as a "top-notch" litigator, his activity in the past year has seen him litigate in class action, constitutional litigation and breach of contract cases. **Thomas Donovan** (see p.1694) focuses mostly on areas that tie in with intellectual property law. He is a highly regarded litigator concerning trademarks, patents and copyright infringement. **David Wolowitz** (see p.1699) is a highly experienced litigator who particularly stands out in the market for his defense of educational institutions. He has had an active year in this regard, acting for schools on claims brought by former pupils. Although firm president **Jack Middleton** (see p.1696) is no longer on the front line of its daily activity, he is still on hand to provide clients with the benefit of his half-century of experience.

### Nixon Peabody LLP
See profile on p.1526

**THE FIRM** The Manchester office of this national firm has a wealth of talent in the litigation department and is among the biggest hitters in the state for this work. As well as honing a reputation as a go-to group for class actions, it acts for a comprehensive client base spanning multiple industries. Peers recognize the breadth and depth of talent within this strong and highly active team, and acknowledge it to be one of the preeminent litigation teams in New Hampshire.

**Sources say:** *"A very talented group of people."*

**KEY INDIVIDUALS Scott O'Connell** (see p.1696) is highlighted as *"a very good lawyer who is very interested in his clients."* He has an outstanding reputation for representing financial institutions in cases in front of both federal and state courts, as well as regulatory bodies. He acted as lead counsel for a large group of healthcare providers and policyholders in a successful class action with up to $110 million at stake. **Kevin Fitzgerald** (see p.1695) also acted on that case, and is recognized by peers as *"a very*

*strong player"* in the field. **Gordon MacDonald** (see p.1696) is lauded as a *"tremendous writer and tremendous thinker,"* as well as *"a very good lawyer and very able advocate."* He represents clients of all stripes, including nonprofit groups, public organizations and private companies. **David Vicinanzo** (see p.1698) is said to be *"one of the go-to guys in white-collar crime."* His practice ranges beyond this sphere alone, however, and he has recently successfully represented the New Hampshire legislature in redistricting litigation.

### Sheehan Phinney Bass + Green PA
See profile on p.1701

**THE FIRM** Working from the firm's Manchester, Concord and Hanover offices, this team has a stellar track record in representing small businesses across New Hampshire. It does not exclusively deal with smaller clients, however, and was recently engaged by a regional Fortune 500 company on a breach of contract suit. The group is consistently spoken of in the highest terms by clients satisfied with its cohesive team approach to litigation and its ability to produce successful outcomes in their cases.

**Sources say:** *"They managed the case with exceptional competence and kept me completely in the loop and involved in key decisions along the way. I could not have been more pleased with their efforts or the ultimate outcome."*

**KEY INDIVIDUALS James Shirley** (see p.1698) is seen as a *"wonderful lawyer"* by peers brimming with respect for his practice. He brings more than 30 years' experience to bear on a great range of corporate disputes. Impressed sources say **Michael Harvell** (see p.1695) is *"very good at what he does."* He has extensive experience in intellectual property and income tax litigation, as well as in stockholder and partnership disputes. **Christopher Cole** (see p.1694) is well received by clients, who describe him as *"intelligent, personable, client-friendly and exceptionally competent."* He recently successfully defended Black Bear Micro-Roastery in a trademark dispute with Starbucks. The experienced **Peter Cowan** (see p.1694) has honed his practice over many years in the field. He has a strong history of advising on employment disputes, though his practice extends to more general business litigation.

### Band 2

### Devine, Millimet & Branch, P.A.

**THE FIRM** This team has a rich history of involvement in complex and significant litigation, and is among the oldest practices in the state. Peers show every respect for this highly capable group, which offers support in regard to almost any contentious matter. It recently successfully represented the City of Laconia in a case regarding damages from use of lead paint.

**Sources say:** *"Everything that they have worked on for our organization has had a positive outcome. From a client perspective, I think the culture of Devine Millimet is perfect for our organization."*

**KEY INDIVIDUALS Daniel Will** is *"very cerebral, with excellent writing and analytical skills,"* say admiring peers.

He recently represented Motorola and one of its employees in a partnership dispute, achieving successful judgments on all counts. As chair of the firm's healthcare and litigation practices, **Elaine Michaud** has extensive experience in disputes within the sector. She is representing six individuals in a class action against New Hampshire officials for failure to provide sufficient resources to prevent the institutionalization of individuals with mental illness. **George Moore** has experience in litigation within a variety of spheres. As well as more general commercial litigation, he has handled cases involving securities, professional liability and intellectual property rights. **Ovide Lamontagne** specializes in representing nonprofit organizations, as well as healthcare clients. He speaks fluent French.

### Hinckley, Allen & Snyder LLP

**THE FIRM** Market observers contend that Hinckley Allen's healthcare litigation department is an impressive contender for work of that nature. It also represents other nonprofit groups, including educational institutions and government groups, and maintains a robust practice serving commercial clients. It covers the full range of contentious matters from its Concord office.

**KEY INDIVIDUALS Michael Connolly** is described by clients as *"an outstanding lawyer"* and *"one of the best in the region."* His practice has a particular leaning towards the defense of white-collar criminal matters, and he is frequently seen in high-value business litigation.

### Sulloway & Hollis PLLC

**THE FIRM** This team offers expertise in a wide range of dispute resolution, and is particularly highly regarded within the market for its handling of medical malpractice cases. It is engaged by clients for diverse matters, and is involved in matters relating to school law, professional liability, construction disputes, and a variety of commercial and domestic areas.

**KEY INDIVIDUALS Michael Lehman** is a highly experienced attorney who receives high praise for his expertise in healthcare matters. Commentators say he is *"as good as you get in medical malpractice matters"* and *"very good at healthcare. It's very specialized, and he's one of only a handful of people who do it well."* **Edward Kaplan** is seen as the team's *"premier commercial litigator."* Peers recommend his practice, and laud him as being *"very accomplished and serious."* He is particularly active in employment matters.

### Band 3

### Bernstein Shur
See profile on p.1406

**THE FIRM** Bernstein Shur's team is often seen in employment litigation from its Manchester office. The firm is based in Maine and is making real strides in the New Hampshire market. The group covers the full range of contentious commercial matters for a diverse client base. It is a growing practice that has demonstrated a desire to expand its presence in the area through the lateral hires of highly regarded attorneys.

**KEY INDIVIDUALS Emily Gray Rice** is a recent arrival from Orr & Reno and is universally acclaimed as *"a very strong litigator."* An experienced and well-established figure in the New Hampshire courts, she has represented clients from a variety of fields, including insurers, easement holders and employers. **Andru Volinsky** is admired for his tenacity, and is seen as a *"bulldog"* who *"does a very good job for his clients."* He is predominantly active in commercial litigation, including unfair trade practices disputes and matters involving white-collar crime.

## Cook, Little, Rosenblatt & Manson PLLC

**THE FIRM** This Manchester-based team is building a growing reputation, and is recognized by peers for its heightened visibility in the market. A versatile group, it is able to represent clients in a wide range of matters, including patent and intellectual property disputes, contract issues and contentious technology issues.

**KEY INDIVIDUALS** Founding partner **Arnold Rosenblatt** continues to be regarded as a market-leading figure. Peers praise him as a *"stellar"* attorney and applaud his skill as a strategist. *"A first-tier lawyer who belongs at the top,"* he is highly respected throughout the wider market.

## Nelson Kinder + Mosseau, PC

**THE FIRM** This is the team of choice for clients from various sectors, including financial institutions, retail chains and construction organizations. It prides itself on its client-friendly approach and endeavors to offers its services with minimal disruption to clients' businesses. It covers a wide range of cases, including lender liability issues, bankruptcy and intellectual property disputes.

**KEY INDIVIDUALS** As head of the firm's medical malpractice team, **Peter Mosseau** has cultivated an exceptional reputation for his trial work. *"A terrific lawyer,"* peers believe that he is *"plainly top notch and would be a credit to anywhere he worked."*

## Orr & Reno PA

**THE FIRM** This compact team is composed of experienced litigators who are also able to offer expertise in negotiations and alternative dispute resolution procedures. Serving a wide range of clients from its Concord base, the team is involved in cases of great variety, including media and First Amendment matters, civil rights cases and appellate work, as well as general commercial cases.

**KEY INDIVIDUALS William Chapman** has almost 40 years of litigation experience in New Hampshire. The primary focus of his work has been cases involving media law, though he has also undertaken significant work regarding charitable tax exemptions.

## Upton and Hatfield LLP

**THE FIRM** This New Hampshire firm covers all issues that may lead to major commercial litigation. It handles disputes arising from contracts, business formation and dissolution, and management issues. It also offers mediation and dispute resolution services, and has represented clients in both state and federal courts.

**Sources say:** *"The best lawyers for plaintiff employers law in the state. They are the toughest adversaries I face."*

**KEY INDIVIDUALS Russell Hilliard** is *"extremely well known and respected"* for his litigation capabilities. Peers believe that he is *"top-notch. A superb commercial litigator with great personal abilities."* He is among the most renowned and acclaimed litigators in the state.

## Other Notable Practitioners

**Andrew Serell** of Rath, Young and Pignatelli PC is an impressive figure in the market, commanding the respect of commentators. His comprehensive practice includes experience in cases relating to insurance, land use, family law and education. **James Wheat** (see p.1699) of Wadleigh, Starr & Peters PLLC is said to *"know everything about insurance."* With nearly four decades of experience in the field, he has handled cases of all varieties, though he currently focuses on complicated commercial matters. **Jamie Hage** of Hage Hodes PA is well liked by clients, who believe that he is *"really good"* and state that they *"couldn't recommend him more highly."* He has more than 30 years of experience in civil and commercial litigation. **Thomas Pappas** of Primmer Piper Eggleston & Cramer PC has been practicing for almost 30 years in DC and New Hampshire. Peers are unanimous in their support for his work and believe his arrival will be a boon to the firm. **William Saturley** (see p.1697) of Preti Flaherty Beliveau & Pachios, LLP is something of an intellectual leader in the field, and has authored multiple publications. His work focuses on employment and intellectual property litigation, as well as commercial matters. **Charles Bauer** of Gallagher, Callahan and Gartrell, PC is a trial lawyer who is also a regarded as *"a very effective mediator."* His practice is focused chiefly on employment litigation, civil rights issues and private matters. At the same firm, **Michael Callahan** has formidable experience in handling cases in New Hampshire, and has been involved in some of the state's most high-profile and valuable cases in recent history. **Mary Elizabeth Tenn** of Tenn & Tenn PA represents both commercial and individual clients. Alongside her prominence in personal injury matters, she is also a fêted business litigator and has undertaken many complex cases for large clients. **James Tenn** of Tenn & Tenn PA is *"ubiquitous in the community"* in the eyes of peers. He is especially active in family law issues, though he is also noted by the market for his capability in commercial litigation.

# REAL ESTATE

Commentary about individuals can be found under their firm's paragraph. If the firm has no paragraph (is not ranked) look at Other Notable Practitioners.

## Real Estate
### Leading Firms

**Band 1**

McLane, Graf, Raulerson & Middleton *

Sheehan Phinney Bass + Green PA *

**Band 2**

Devine, Millimet & Branch, P.A.

Donahue, Tucker & Ciandella

Nixon Peabody LLP *

Wadleigh, Starr & Peters PLLC *

**Band 3**

D'Amante Couser Pellerin & Associates, P.A.

Sulloway & Hollis PLLC

Upton and Hatfield LLP

### Senior Statesmen

**Senior Statesmen: distinguished older practitioners**

| | |
|---|---|
| Rotch Peter B | McLane, Graf, Raulerson & Middleton * |

### Leading Individuals

**Band 1**

| | |
|---|---|
| Imse Peter | Sulloway & Hollis PLLC |
| Manchester Susan A | Sheehan Phinney Bass + Green PA * |
| Tucker William C | Wadleigh, Starr & Peters PLLC * |

**Band 2**

| | |
|---|---|
| Connell Linda C | McLane, Graf, Raulerson & Middleton * |
| Lazos Nicholas J | Stebbins Lazos & Van Der Beken (ONP)† |
| Leeming Simon C | Preti Flaherty Beliveau & Pachios (ONP)† * |
| McGinley Karen S | Devine, Millimet & Branch, P.A. |
| Poulos Denise A | Donahue, Tucker & Ciandella |
| Raymond James F | Upton and Hatfield LLP |
| Sokul Jr John H | Hinckley, Allen & Snyder LLP (ONP)† |
| Sullivan Kathleen | Wadleigh, Starr & Peters PLLC * |
| Viscarello Kenneth A | Sheehan Phinney Bass + Green PA * |
| Westgate J Bradford | Winer & Bennett LLP (ONP)† |

**Band 3**

| | |
|---|---|
| Cleary Charles F | Wadleigh, Starr & Peters PLLC * |
| Davis Beth | Hamblett & Kerrigan, P.A. (ONP)† |
| Keefe Jo | Cook, Little, Rosenblatt & Manson (ONP)† |
| Kerouac James D | Nixon Peabody LLP * |
| Nylund Jessica A | McLane, Graf, Raulerson & Middleton * |
| Pellerin Bryan | D'Amante Couser Pellerin & Associates, P.A. |
| Robinson Denis O | Pierce Atwood LLP (ONP)† * |
| Tucker Charles F | Donahue, Tucker & Ciandella |

\* Indicates firm / individual with profile.

†ONP = Other Notable Practitioner.

## Real Estate: Land Use
### Leading Individuals

**Band 1**

| | |
|---|---|
| D'Amante Raymond | D'Amante Couser Pellerin & Associates, P.A. |
| Manchester Susan A | Sheehan Phinney Bass + Green PA * |
| Tucker William C | Wadleigh, Starr & Peters PLLC * |
| Uchida Richard Y | Hinckley, Allen & Snyder LLP (ONP)† |

**Band 2**

| | |
|---|---|
| Duprey Susan V | Devine, Millimet & Branch, P.A. |
| Hildreth Thomas W | McLane, Graf, Raulerson & Middleton * |
| Sullivan Kathleen | Wadleigh, Starr & Peters PLLC * |

## Band 1

### McLane, Graf, Raulerson & Middleton Professional Association
See profile on p.1700

**THE FIRM** The breadth of this firm's real estate practice is widely noted around the region. The team has lately been called upon to act on distressed real estate matters, including foreclosures, loan workouts and bankruptcy-related acquisitions. The group also acts as local counsel to numerous national clients, including retailers, on their New Hampshire real estate issues. It also advises local developers on purchases and related financing needs.

**KEY INDIVIDUALS Linda Connell** (see p.1694) is widely renowned for her intelligence and experience in this sector. She recently advised numerous clients, including an electricity utility and a telecoms provider, on licensing issues in the state. **Thomas Hildreth** (see p.1695) has a respected land use and permitting practice. He is well known for his work with telecoms companies, and recently worked with Connell on the aforementioned permitting and licensing work for a telecoms provider. **Jessica Nylund** (see p.1696) has had a particularly active year, and is noted as one of the strongest young attorneys in the state. She recently advised a New Hampshire-based developer on strengthening its real estate portfolio. **Peter Rotch** (see p.1697) continues to be one of the most respected real estate attorneys in the state, with sources describing him as "a star" and "very respected and experienced."

### Sheehan Phinney Bass + Green PA
See profile on p.1701

**THE FIRM** This firm continues its reputation for excellence in the real estate space, offering clients an impressive breadth of services. Recent highlights include acting as buyer's counsel in the purchase and redevelopment of Balsams Resort. The team also advised Summit Land Development on numerous matters, including acquisitions, financing and leasing.

**Sources say:** "Strong lawyers who work well with clients."

**KEY INDIVIDUALS Susan Manchester** (see p.1696) is one of the most active real estate practitioners in the state and has developed an enviable client base over her years of service. She recently led on the work for Summit Land Development, showcasing her breadth of expertise. **Kenneth Viscarello** (see p.1699) receives plaudits from across the market and is known as "a deal-maker and a proactive person." He has recently been noted for his tax credit financing expertise and represented Great Bridge Properties on a low-income housing development.

## Band 2

### Devine, Millimet & Branch, P.A.

**THE FIRM** Devine, Millimet & Branch is especially well known for its strong transactional practice and often advises on local and cross-border deals. The firm acts on leasing, zoning, land use, acquisitions and development of commercial, residential and mixed-use projects across the state. A recent undertaking involved advising two mobile telecoms providers on planning and zoning issues related to the construction of cellular towers.

**Sources say:** "Extremely knowledgeable, prompt in responding and proactive in advising clients."

**KEY INDIVIDUALS Susan Duprey** is one of the most well-known land use lawyers in the state. Her impressive reputation earns her many faithful clients, who seek her out for expert advice. **Karen McGinley** is "a strong lawyer who can be counted on to represent her client well." She recently worked on the aforementioned cellular tower planning and zoning matter.

### Donahue, Tucker & Ciandella

**THE FIRM** This firm is a top choice for municipalities around the state, and is well known for its strong zoning and land use work. The firm has offices in Portsmouth, Exeter and Meredith, providing good geographical coverage for local clients.

**KEY INDIVIDUALS** Lender-focused **Denise Poulos** has a great reputation among local banks, and is often seen acting for them on finance deals. Sources says she does "a great job untangling very complex deals." **Charles Tucker** "has an excellent reputation in land use, representing municipalities and businesses," according to peers.

### Nixon Peabody LLP
See profile on p.1526

**THE FIRM** This team is able to leverage off the firm's strong regional and nationwide relationships in advising leading clients on their real estate needs in New Hampshire. The group's work covers finance, leasing, sales and purchases.

**KEY INDIVIDUALS James Kerouac** (see p.1696) has a diverse client base and is well known for his strong transactional practice. He also advises on zoning and permitting issues.

## Wadleigh, Starr & Peters PLLC
See profile on p.1702

**THE FIRM** This full-service Manchester firm is noted for its real estate practice, and has a solid foothold among local developer clientele. The group focuses on the transactional side, advising on buying, selling and associated finance work.

**KEY INDIVIDUALS** *"Excellent soup-to-nuts lawyer"* **William Tucker** (see p.1698) is one of the preeminent names in the New Hampshire real estate Bar. Commentators note his *"wealth of experience in permitting and finance transactions."* Another of the firm's frequently mentioned names is **Kathleen Sullivan** (see p.1698), who is *"very active locally on land use and representing developers."* She is noted for her strong relationships with key players around the state. **Charles Cleary** (see p.1694) is known for his transactional real estate work. Sources label him *"a good lawyer."*

## Band 3

## D'Amante Couser Pellerin & Associates, P.A.

**THE FIRM** This group offers clients comprehensive advice on construction, zoning, land use and real estate transactions. The team is well placed to advise on residential, commercial, industrial and mixed-use projects, and is one of the biggest names in Concord and its surrounding areas for such work.

**KEY INDIVIDUALS** Peers note **Raymond D'Amante**'s *"knowledge of the nuts and bolts of construction, as well as his knowledge of financing and land use."* His is a well-known name in the area, and he attracts many of Concord's most active players in real estate. **Bryan Pellerin** is called *"the real deal"* for his impressive, broad real estate practice. He has a strong transactional focus and has

advised on several multimillion-dollar acquisitions for his regional clientele.

## Sulloway & Hollis PLLC

**THE FIRM** This group acts for municipalities, developers and banks on the full range of their needs in the real estate space. The firm is particularly well known for its work on behalf of nonprofit organizations and that talent extends to the real estate practice, which is a leading choice for such clients.

**KEY INDIVIDUALS** The *"excellent"* **Peter Imse** is one of the state's most experienced practitioners. He has a broad client base and is praised for his *"good reputation in permitting and real estate financing."*

## Upton and Hatfield LLP

**THE FIRM** This firm is one of the best for advice to New Hampshire's various municipalities and it enjoys a leading reputation in that arena. The group is widely recognized for its strong handle on zoning and land use, but it also gets called upon to advise on a range of other real estate matters.

**KEY INDIVIDUALS** Managing partner **James Raymond** has an excellent reputation among leading lenders in the region. He has been an active name in the market for many years and is widely respected by peers and clients.

## Other Notable Practitioners

**Nicholas Lazos** of Stebbins Lazos & Van Der Beken is the first name on many clients' lips for high-end real estate work. He has attracted a loyal following around the region and is praised as a *"very good lawyer."* The *"very knowledgeable"* **Simon Leeming** (see p.1696) of Preti Flaherty Beliveau & Pachios, LLP has a broad real estate practice that draws praise from all corners. Leeming has a strong presence with nonprofit clients and also handles a significant amount of sustainable energy projects. A strong real estate generalist, **Bradford Westgate** of Winer & Bennett LLP is *"very highly regarded; you bump into him first in any transaction with a Nashua connection,"* according to sources. He is equally strong on transactional and land use matters, and often acts for developers and lenders on a wide range of work. **Jo Keefe** of Cook, Little, Rosenblatt & Manson PLLC is a Manchester-based practitioner who focuses on transactions. She represents borrowers and lenders in an array of commercial real estate matters. **Denis Robinson** (see p.1697) of Pierce Atwood LLP is a firm favorite of local, regional and national clients, thanks to his strong handle on transactional and leasing matters. Clients describe him as *"effective and collaborative,"* and praise his ability to *"help sort through thorny issues."* **Beth Davis** of Hamblett & Kerrigan, P.A. is another impressively experienced and well-known name in the New Hampshire real estate market. Nashua-based Davis is noted for both dirt law and finance. **Richard Uchida** of Hinckley, Allen & Snyder LLP offers a practice that covers transactional, advisory and disputes work for regional clients. Commentators are quick to praise his particular expertise in zoning law. Sources note that **John Sokul**, also of Hinckley, Allen & Snyder LLP, *"does an excellent job"* on a wide variety of real estate matters. Sokul, who is based in Concord, is recommended for transactional real estate work.

## Leaders' Profiles in New Hampshire

**BAILEY, Elizabeth A.**
Sheehan Phinney Bass + Green PA,
Manchester
603 627 8241
ebailey@sheehan.com
*Featured in Labor & Employment (New Hampshire)*
**Practice Areas:** Labor, employment and
employee benefits, alternative dispute resolution,
business litigation.
**Professional Memberships:** New Hampshire
Bar Association, Labor and Employment Practice
Section of the New Hampshire Bar Association,
New Hampshire Women's Bar Association, Smith
College Alumnae Association, New Hampshire
Municipal Management Association, Society for
Human Resource Management and Lex Mundi
Labor and Employment Practice Group. Admitted
to practice in New Hampshire, the Court of
Appeals for the First Circuit and the United States
Supreme Court.
**Career:** Represents Management. Extensive expe-
rience before state and federal agencies and
courts.
**Personal:** JD, Suffolk University Law School; BA,
cum laude, Smith College.

**BEACH, Peter T**
Sheehan Phinney Bass + Green PA,
Manchester
603 627 8185
pbeach@sheehan.com
*Featured in Corporate/Commercial (New Hampshire)*
**Practice Areas:** Taxation (federal, state and
international) of corporate and partnership mat-
ters with emphasis on structuring mergers, acqui-
sitions, divestitures and reorganizations; partner-
ship and joint venture formation and restructur-
ing; tax-exempt organizations; tax controversies.
**Professional Memberships:** Admitted in New
Hampshire, California and the District of
Columbia.
**Career:** Former Partner with Ernst & Young,
associate with Miller & Chevalier, Washington,
DC. Assisted private and public companies with
tax planning and controversy matters since 1984.
Best Lawyers in America, New England Super
Lawyers.
**Personal:** BA, summa cum laude, Maharishi
University of Management; JD, magna cum laude,
Cornell Law School (Managing Editor, Cornell
Law Review).

**BEALS, John P**
Nixon Peabody LLP, Manchester
603 628 4056
jbeals@nixonpeabody.com
*Featured in Private Equity (Massachusetts),
Corporate/Commercial (New Hampshire)*
See under Massachusetts for profile.

**BURKE, Steven M**
McLane, Graf, Raulerson & Middleton
Professional Association, Manchester
603 628 1454
steve.burke@mclane.com
*Featured in Corporate/Commercial (New Hampshire)*

**Practice Areas:** Corporate Business Law *
Education and Independent Schools *
Employment and Labor Law * Small Business Law
* Taxation Law
**Professional Memberships:** New Hampshire
& Massachusetts Bars, New Hampshire Society of
CPAs, AICPA, American College of Tax Counsel.
**Career:** Shareholder, Director, Tax Department
Chair; Past President-NHSCPA; Past President-
Tax Section NH Bar; Past President-NH Employee
Benefits Council; Adjunct Professor-Pierce Law
School. Listed in Woodward's 'Best Lawyers in
America'. Board Chair, The Derryfield School.
**Personal:** BA, Bates College, 1981; MBA,
University of Massachusetts – Lowell, 1984; JD
Pierce Law School, 1987; LLM in Taxation, Boston
University School of Law, 1990.

**CHENEY, Robert P**
Sheehan Phinney Bass + Green PA, Concord
603 223 2020
rcheney@sheehan.com
*Featured in Environment (New Hampshire)*
**Practice Areas:** Environmental and energy law,
lobbying, export compliance, special counsel to
Pease International Tradeport and Port of NH.
**Professional Memberships:** Admitted to NH
federal and state bars; member American Bar
Association.
**Career:** Served in the New Hampshire Attorney
General's Office - Chief of the Environmental
Bureau from 1984-88 and Associate Attorney
General from 1988-92. Recognized as one of top
eight environmental lawyers in New Hampshire
and by Best Lawyers in America. Speaks German.
Member, American College of Environmental
Lawyers; Board of Directors, Japan-America
Society of New Hampshire.
**Personal:** BS, Cornell University; JD, University
of San Diego School of Law.

**CLEARY, Charles F**
Wadleigh, Starr & Peters PLLC, Manchester
603 206-7207
ccleary@wadleighlaw.com
*Featured in Real Estate (New Hampshire)*
**Practice Areas:** Real Estate, Land Use,
Corporate Law.
**Professional Memberships:** New Hampshire
Bar Association.
**Career:** Joined firm in 1990.
**Personal:** Colby College (BA 1986); Boston
University (JD 1990). Mr Cleary is the President
of William Lawrence Camp, Inc., a nonprofit
summer camp located in Center Tuftonboro, New
Hampshire.

**CLEVELAND, Alan P**
Sheehan Phinney Bass + Green PA,
Manchester
603 627 8149
acleveland@sheehan.com
*Featured in Labor & Employment (New Hampshire)*
**Practice Areas:** Labor and employment law,
Retirement Plans and ERISA.

**Professional Memberships:** New Hampshire
and Massachusetts Bar Associations, New
Hampshire Bar Foundation, American College of
Employee Benefits Counsel, National Association
of Public Pension Attorneys, International Society
of Certified Employee Benefit Specialists, Boston
Security Analysts Society, Center for Business
Ethics at Bentley College, National Association of
Corporate Directors, International Corporate
Governance Network, Council of Institutional
Investors, Pension Rights Center.
**Career:** Practice Chair of Retirement Plans and
ERISA Group. Recognized in Best Lawyers in
America.
**Personal:** JD, Harvard Law School; BA,
University of New Hampshire.

**CLOSSON, Thomas M**
Jackson Lewis LLP, Portsmouth
603 559 2729
Thomas.Closson@jacksonlewis.com
*Featured in Labor & Employment (New Hampshire)*
**Practice Areas:** Labor and employment.
**Professional Memberships:** New Hampshire
Bar Association.
**Career:** Jackson Lewis LLP (Partner – May 2010
to present) Flygare, Schwarz & Closson, PLLC
(Founder/Partner – July 1998 – May 2010).
**Personal:** 1990 – University of New Hampshire,
BA, summa cum laude. 1993 – Harvard Law
School, JD.

**COLE, Christopher**
Sheehan Phinney Bass + Green PA,
Manchester
603 627 8223
ccole@sheehan.com
*Featured in Litigation (New Hampshire)*
**Practice Areas:** Employment and business liti-
gation, including trade secret and non-competi-
tion matters, intellectual property, trademarks and
patents, breach of fiduciary duty and corporate
governance.
**Professional Memberships:** Admitted, New
Hampshire and New York. Member, New York,
New Hampshire and American Bar Associations,
US Court of Appeals (First and Second Circuits),
US District Court (Southern District of New York
and District of New Hampshire).
**Career:** Best Lawyers in America, New England
Super Lawyers.
**Personal:** BA, Phi Beta Kappa, University of New
Hampshire; JD, Syracuse University College of
Law. Law Clerk, Honorable Richard J.
Cardamone, US Court of Appeals for Second
Circuit 1988-89.

**CONNELL, Linda C**
McLane, Graf, Raulerson & Middleton
Professional Association, Manchester
603 625 6464
linda.connell@mclane.com
*Featured in Real Estate (New Hampshire)*
**Practice Areas:** Banking Law * Corporate
Business Law * Energy, Utilities and

Telecommunications * Land Use and
Development Law * Real Estate Law
**Professional Memberships:** Member of both
the New Hampshire Bar Association and
American Bar Association; Best Lawyers in
America, Land Use & Zoning Law; Best Lawyers
in America, 2004-2010, Real Estate Law.
**Career:** Admitted to work in New Hampshire;
Greater Manchester Chamber of Commerce
Downtown Committee; Member and Past
President of the Board of Directors of the Plan
New Hampshire Foundation.
**Personal:** JD, University of Connecticut, 1977
and BS, East Carolina University, 1974.

**COWAN, Peter S**
Sheehan Phinney Bass + Green PA,
Manchester
603 627 8193
pcowan@sheehan.com
*Featured in Litigation (New Hampshire)*
**Practice Areas:** Business litigation, including
trade secret, non-competition and confidentiality
cases, consumer protection act, misrepresentation,
breach of contract, breach of fiduciary duty and
shareholder disputes. Represents owners and con-
tractors in construction contract disputes.
**Professional Memberships:** Admitted in New
Hampshire state and federal courts, before the
First Circuit Court of Appeals. Member of New
Hampshire and American Bar Associations
(ABA),and the ABA's Forum on the Construction
Industry.
**Career:** Recognized in New England Super
Lawyers and Best Lawyers in America.
**Personal:** BA, cum laude, Dartmouth College;
JD, Boston College.

**DIBRIGIDA, Joseph A**
Sheehan Phinney Bass + Green PA,
Manchester
603 627 8158
jdibrigida@sheehan.com
*Featured in Corporate/Commercial (New Hampshire)*
**Practice Areas:** Communications and broad-
casting, private companies, mergers and acquisi-
tions, business formation and succession plan-
ning, corporate law and governance, entertain-
ment, media and publishing.
**Professional Memberships:** Admitted in New
Hampshire. Member of the Manchester and New
Hampshire Bar Associations.
**Career:** Selected as one of state's "Forty Under
40" in 2002 by the New Hampshire Union Leader.
Recognized in Best Lawyers in America and New
England Super Lawyers. Graduate of Leadership
New Hampshire.
**Personal:** BA, Dartmouth College; JD, Boston
College Law School.

**DONOVAN, Thomas J**
McLane, Graf, Raulerson & Middleton
Professional Association, Manchester
603 628 1337
tom.donovan@mclane.com
*Featured in Litigation (New Hampshire)*

**Practice Areas:** * Intellectual Property Litigation * Computer Software Ownership, Licensing Litigation * Web Site and E-Mail Misuse (cyber privacy and cyber smears) * Trade Secret and Non-Competition Disputes * Commercial Litigation * Court litigation consistent with regulation of electric telecommunication and water industries
**Professional Memberships:** Admitted to New Hampshire state and federal courts, as well as federal courts in Massachusetts, Indiana and Colorado, as well as the First and Federal Circuits. Former Chair of New Hampshire Bar Association Business Litigation Section. Commercial arbitrator, American Arbitration Association.
**Career:** Shareholder/Director, 1985.
**Personal:** Harvard College, BA magna cum laude 1975; University of Pennsylvania Law School, JD 1978.

**DROOFF, Michael J**
Sheehan Phinney Bass + Green PA, Manchester
603 627 8167
mdrooff@sheehan.com
*Featured in Corporate/Commercial (New Hampshire)*
**Practice Areas:** Venture capital finance, syndicated private placements, public offerings, privately negotiated mergers and acquisitions, public company reporting and compliance, private equity fund formation, equity incentive plan design and implementation.
**Professional Memberships:** Admitted in New Hampshire and New York, and a Member of the New Hampshire and the American Bar Associations.
**Career:** Chair of Public Finance Group. Prior to SPB+G, practiced with a major New York City law firm.
**Publications:** Author: Raising Capital for the Emerging Business; Contributor: Selling the Private Business.
**Personal:** BA, cum laude, Dartmouth College; JD, University of Chicago. Working knowledge of Spanish.

**FELMLY, Bruce W**
McLane, Graf, Raulerson & Middleton Professional Association, Manchester
603 628 1448
bruce.felmly@mclane.com
*Featured in Litigation (New Hampshire)*
**Practice Areas:** Arbitration and Mediation; Business Litigation; Employment and Labor Law; Personal Injury Litigation.
**Professional Memberships:** American College of Trial Lawyers (Member/Board of Regents), American and New Hampshire Association of Justice, American Law Institute, and a Fellow of the American and New Hampshire Bar Foundations. New Hampshire Bar Association and U.S. District Court for Vermont.
**Career:** Shareholder/Director,1979. President of the New Hampshire Bar Association (1995-96). Woodward's 'Best Lawyers In America'. Chair of the long range planning committee for the New Hampshire justice system (2004-05).

**Personal:** JD, Cornell Law School, 1972. BA, University of Rhode Island, 1969.

**FITZGERALD, Kevin M**
Nixon Peabody LLP, Manchester
603 628 4016
kfitzgerald@nixonpeabody.com
*Featured in Litigation (New Hampshire)*
**Practice Areas:** Kevin M Fitzgerald is a member of the litigation department and Managing Partner in Nixon Peabody LLP's Manchester, New Hampshire office. He is immediate past Chairman of the Policy Committee, the firm's principal governance board. Mr Fitzgerald practices nationally in the area of complicated business disputes. He has successfully prosecuted and defended, as lead counsel, multimillion-dollar litigation involving receiverships, financial transactions, mergers and acquisitions, corporate fiduciary duty, directors and officers liability, securities enforcement and insurance coverage. Most recently, he was lead counsel in a complex litigation winning a $110m judgment for a class of 6000+ healthcare providers.

**FORD, Debra Weiss**
Jackson Lewis LLP, Portsmouth
603 559 2700
FordD@jacksonlewis.com
*Featured in Labor & Employment (New Hampshire)*
**Practice Areas:** Labor and employment; employment litigation, counseling and training.
**Professional Memberships:** New Hampshire, Massachusetts, Maine Bar Associations, American Bar Association, U.S. Supreme Court.
**Career:** Managing partner, Portsmouth, NH.
**Publications:** Author New Hampshire Workplace Privacy.
**Personal:** Temple University Law School, JD; Drew University, BA. Fellow College of Labor and Employment Lawyers. Management Lawyer of the Year 2012: Best Lawyers in America. New Hampshire's Best Labor and Employment Lawyer: Business NH Magazine. Top NH Lawyers Labor and Employment: New Hampshire Magazine. Top 50 Women Lawyers, Top 100 lawyers in New England: New England Super Lawyers . Rated AV by Martindale-Hubbell.

**FOSTER, Joseph A**
McLane, Graf, Raulerson & Middleton Professional Association, Manchester
603 628 1175
joe.foster@mclane.com
*Featured in Corporate/Commercial (New Hampshire)*
**Practice Areas:** Commercial Finance; Corporate Business Law; Financial Services * Government Relations * Lobbying Services * Real Estate Law.
**Professional Memberships:** American Bankruptcy Institute; New Hampshire Bar Association.
**Career:** Joined firm in 1984; Shareholder and Director; former state senator. Chair of Bankruptcy Practice Group.
**Personal:** Tufts University (BA Magna Cum Laude 1981); George Washington University (JD 1984); Member: Board of Directors, Greater Nashua Chamber Of Commerce. Recognized in

'Best Lawyers In America' in Bankruptcy and Creditor-Debtor Rights Law.

**GLAHN III, Wilbur A**
McLane, Graf, Raulerson & Middleton Professional Association, Manchester
603 6281469
bill.glahn@mclane.com
*Featured in Litigation (New Hampshire)*
**Practice Areas:** Business Litigation * Employment and Labor Law * General Civil Litigation * Securities Law * Appellate
**Professional Memberships:** New Hampshire and American Bar Associations, New Hampshire; Fellow, American College of Trial Lawyers.
**Career:** New Hampshire (1976) and Massachusetts (1972); First Circuit Court of Appeals (1976); US Supreme Court (1978). Former Assistant Attorney General and Head of Civil Division of the Office of the Attorney General (New Hampshire).
**Personal:** Trinity College, BA 1969 (Phi Beta Kappa); University of Chicago Law School, JD 1972. Recognized in 'Best Lawyers In America'.

**HARVELL, Michael C**
Sheehan Phinney Bass + Green PA, Manchester
603 627 8133
mharvell@sheehan.com
*Featured in Litigation (New Hampshire)*
**Practice Areas:** Stockholder and partnership disputes; state and federal tax, intellectual property, and probate litigation.
**Professional Memberships:** Admitted to practice in New Hampshire and United States Supreme Court. Member of New Hampshire Bar Association.
**Career:** US Navy (nuclear submarines) 1968-72. Recognized in Best Lawyers in America, New England Super Lawyers. Fellow, American College of Trial Lawyers.
**Personal:** BA, Yale University; JD, cum laude, Boston University. Former chair, Board of Trustees, Portsmouth Music Hall; former Chair, Strawbery Banke Museum; former Chair, NH Preservation Alliance; Director of the Portsmouth Chamber of Commerce; former Trustee, NH Society for the Protection of NH Forests.

**HILDRETH, Thomas W**
McLane, Graf, Raulerson & Middleton Professional Association, Manchester
603 628 1177
tom.hildreth@mclane.com
*Featured in Real Estate (New Hampshire)*
**Practice Areas:** Corporate Business Law * Education and Independent Schools * Employment and Labor Law * Energy, Utilities and Telecommunications * Immigration Law * International Trade * Land Use and Development Law * Real Estate Law * Small Business Law
**Professional Memberships:** Admitted in NH, ME and MA. Member of American and New Hampshire Bar Associations, American Immigration Lawyers Association, and Listed in Woodward's Best Lawyers of America.
**Career:** Corporate Director, Shareholder since 1996. Chair of Telecommunications Law Practice

Group. Founder of Immigration Law Practice Group.
**Personal:** BA, Bates College, 1983; JD, Suffolk University Law School, 1987.

**HOOD, James**
Nixon Peabody LLP, Manchester
603 628 4051
jchood@nixonpeabody.com
*Featured in Corporate/Commercial (New Hampshire)*
**Practice Areas:** James concentrates his practice in corporate governance, restructuring, acquisitions, mergers, debt and equity financing, shareholder dispute resolution, joint venture formation and distribution arrangements, limited liability company formation, and strategic partnerships. He acts as general counsel to both US and European based medium-to-large, privately owned companies in the hospitality, theater and entertainment sectors, as well as soft drink and liquor production and distribution companies headquartered here and abroad.
**Professional Memberships:** Mr Hood is a member of the New Hampshire and American bar associations.
**Personal:** Georgetown University Law Center, JD; University of New Hampshire, BA.(Phi Beta Kappa).

**HUGHES, John E**
McLane, Graf, Raulerson & Middleton Professional Association, Manchester
603 628 1347
john.hughes@mclane.com
*Featured in Corporate/Commercial (New Hampshire)*
**Practice Areas:** Estate Planning and Trust and Estate Administration; Pension/Profit Sharing/Employee Benefits Law; Small Business Law; Taxation Law.
**Professional Memberships:** Union Leader's New Hampshire's '40 Under 40'; Selected by peers for inclusion in The Best Lawyers in America, in the area of tax and trusts and estates.
**Career:** John is admitted in New Hampshire, Massachusetts and Washington, D.C.
**Personal:** LLM, Boston University School of Law; JD, with Honors, Catholic University, Columbus School of Law and B.A., Saint Anselm College.

**JOHNSON, Linda S**
McLane, Graf, Raulerson & Middleton Professional Association, Manchester
603 628 1267
linda.johnson@mclane.com
*Featured in Labor & Employment (New Hampshire)*
**Practice Areas:** Arbitration and Mediation * Education and Independent Schools * Employment and Labor Law * General Civil Litigation * Lobbying Services
**Professional Memberships:** Past President, Manchester Area Human Resources Association; Member, National Society for Human Resource Management; Employment Law Sections of New Hampshire and American Bar; Human Resource Committee, NH Business and Industry Association.
**Career:** Recipient of the 2002 Marilla Ricker Award (NH Women's Bar); 2002 New Hampshire

Civil Liberties Union Award; 2006 Outstanding Women in Business; and 2006 Hollman Equality Award. Listed in 'Best Lawyers in America'. Co-chair of the Litigation Department and Education Law Group.

**Personal:** JD, Boston University, 1984.

---

**KEROUAC, James D**
Nixon Peabody LLP, Manchester
603 628 4096
jkerouac@nixonpeabody.com
*Featured in Real Estate (New Hampshire)*

**Practice Areas:** Jim Kerouac concentrates his practice on the transactional aspects of real estate and commercial lending. His practice includes the purchase and sale of real estate, commercial leasing, financing of real estate, and asset based lending. Jim represents clients in many industries, including resort operators and developers, owners and developers of market rate and low-income housing projects, retail developers, institutional owners of real estate, lenders and special servicers, and hospitals. Jim also represents clients before local, state, and federal regulators in regulatory and permitting proceedings.

**Personal:** Boston University School of Law, JD; University of New Hampshire, BA and BS.

---

**LEEMING, Simon C**
Preti Flaherty Beliveau & Pachios, LLP, Concord
603 410 1500
sleeming@preti.com
*Featured in Real Estate (New Hampshire)*

**Practice Areas:** Banking law; corporate law; real estate; business law; land use and permitting; mergers and acquisitions; international law; estate planning.

**Professional Memberships:** Admitted to practice in New Hampshire, Massachusetts and Maine, and as a barrister and solicitor in New Zealand. Member of New Hampshire Bar Association, Maine Bar Association, Wellington District Law Society (NZ), New Zealand Law Society.

**Career:** Formerly a principal of Leeming Law, PLLC in Concord, NH. Appointed as New Zealand Honorary Consul to New England (2001).

**Personal:** Born, New Zealand, October 19, 1953. Suffolk University, JD, 1980, University College, Cardiff, Wales, 1973-74; Boston University, BA, 1976.

---

**LUCIC, Robert R**
Sheehan Phinney Bass + Green PA, Manchester
603 627 8188
rlucic@sheehan.com
*Featured in Environment (New Hampshire)*

**Practice Areas:** Commercial litigation experience including administrative agency proceedings, arbitrations, jury trials and appellate practice involving both multi-national corporations and small businesses, antitrust compliance issues, environmental litigation and arbitration, patent, trademark, trade secret disputes, stockholder and partnership disputes, and investor disputes.

**Professional Memberships:** Admitted to practice in New Hampshire, New York and

Massachusetts as well as in the First Circuit, Second Circuit and Federal Circuit Courts of Appeal. Member of the New Hampshire Bar Association.

**Career:** Named a Best Lawyer in America for Commercial Litigation and a Super Lawyer for Environmental Litigation.

**Personal:** BA, Dartmouth College; JD, University of Chicago.

---

**MACDONALD, Gordon J**
Nixon Peabody LLP, Manchester
603 628 4068
gmacdonald@nixonpeabody.com
*Featured in Litigation (New Hampshire)*

**Practice Areas:** Gordon MacDonald's practice focuses on representing clients in business-related disputes and litigation. His practice includes matters involving trade secret, non-competition and other restrictive covenant claims, fiduciary duty and corporate governance disputes, contract and intellectual property claims, internal investigations, as well as other complex commercial and financial matters. His clients include private and publicly traded companies, financial institutions, non-profit organizations, religious institutions, as well as professionals and individuals.

**Personal:** Cornell Law School, JD. Dartmouth College, AB.

---

**MANCHESTER, Susan A**
Sheehan Phinney Bass + Green PA, Manchester
603 627 8245
smanchester@sheehan.com
*Featured in Real Estate (New Hampshire)*

**Practice Areas:** Commercial real estate, lending and leasing, condominium law, construction law, land use.

**Professional Memberships:** New Hampshire Bar Association.

**Career:** Real Estate and Lending Group Chair. America's Leading Business Lawyers; Best Lawyers in America; New England Super Lawyers, Continental/Presidential Who's Who; Member, American College of Real Estate Lawyers.

**Personal:** BA, magna cum laude, Brown University; JD, Boston University. Heritage United Way, former clerk, Trustees; Stewardship, CE Superindendant; Board Member and Secretary, NH Association of Blind; Manchester Rotary Club; NH Bar Foundation Board Member; member, Amherst Land Trust. Heritage United Way Volunteer of Year; YWCA Susan B Anthony Award.

---

**MCGRATH, David W**
Sheehan Phinney Bass + Green PA, Manchester
603 627 8255
dmcgrath@sheehan.com
*Featured in Labor & Employment (New Hampshire)*

**Practice Areas:** Chair of firm's Litigation Department. Practice focuses on commercial and employment litigation, alternative dispute resolution. Includes trade secret, non-competition, predatory hiring, fiduciary duty, discrimination and wage and hour cases.

**Professional Memberships:** Admitted to practice in New Hampshire, before the United States District Court, District of New Hampshire, and before the First Circuit Court of Appeals. Member of the New Hampshire Bar Association (Ethics Committee).

**Career:** Recognized in New England Super Lawyers and Best Lawyers in America.

**Publications:** Please go to www.sheehan.com

**Personal:** JD, Cornell University Law School; BA, Framingham State College.

---

**MIDDLETON, Jack B**
McLane, Graf, Raulerson & Middleton Professional Association, Manchester
603 628 1446
jack.middleton@mclane.com
*Featured in Litigation (New Hampshire)*

**Practice Areas:** Arbitration and Mediation; Business litigation; Personal injury litigation.

**Professional Memberships:** Certified Civil Trial Specialist; Former Secretary, member, Board of Governors, American Bar Association (ABA); member, ABA House of Delegates; Fellow, American College of Trial Lawyers; former president, New Hampshire and New England Bar Associations, the National Conference of Bar Foundations and National Conference of Bar Presidents; former Chairman, New Hampshire Bar Foundation.

**Career:** Shareholder and Director (1962). New Hampshire District Court Judge (1964-87). New Hampshire Business Leader of the Year, 2002. Named 'New Hampshire's Lawyers' Lawyer'. Listed in 'Best Lawyers In America'.

**Personal:** JD, Boston University, 1956.

---

**NEEDLEMAN, Barry**
McLane, Graf, Raulerson & Middleton Professional Association, Concord
603 230 4407
barry.needleman@mclane.com
*Featured in Environment (New Hampshire)*

**Practice Areas:** Environmental litigation; Environmental Compliance Counseling; Energy, Utilities and Telecommunications; Land Use and Development Law; Manufacturing.

**Professional Memberships:** Admitted to New Hampshire state and federal courts. Pro hac vice admissions in Connecticut and South Carolina federal courts, and New York State courts. Former chair of New Hampshire Bar Association Environmental and Natural Resources Section.

**Career:** Shareholder and director since 2000; former Chair of Management Committee; Listed in Woodward's Best Lawyers in America.

**Personal:** BA, Clark University, 1987; JD, cum laude Lewis & Clark College, Northwestern School of Law, 1992; LLM (Environmental) with highest honors, George Washington University, National Law Center, 1993.

---

**NORRIS, Daniel J**
McLane, Graf, Raulerson & Middleton Professional Association, Manchester
603 628 1408
daniel.norris@mclane.com
*Featured in Corporate/Commercial (New Hampshire)*

**Practice Areas:** Corporate Business Law; Energy, Utilities and Telecommunications; Land Use and Development Law; Professional Sesrvices; Securities Law; Small Business Law; Technology.

**Professional Memberships:** Admitted in NH and MA; American Bar Association, Business Law Section.

**Career:** Law clerk, New Hampshire Superior Court; Intern, Civil Bureau of the New Hampshire Attorney General's Office. Graduate of Leadership New Hampshire.

**Personal:** BA, Purdue University, 1992 (with Distinction) Phi Beta Kappa; JD, Northeastern University School of Law, 1995.

---

**NYLUND, Jessica A**
McLane, Graf, Raulerson & Middleton Professional Association, Manchester
603 628 1292
jessica.nylund@mclane.com
*Featured in Real Estate (New Hampshire)*

**Practice Areas:** Corporate Business Law; Land Use and Development Law; Real Estate Law.

**Professional Memberships:** New Hampshire Bar Association; New Hampshire Women's Bar Association; past Board and Program Director.

**Career:** Admitted in New Hampshire and Massachusetts.

**Personal:** JD, George Washington University Law School, with Honors, 2000. BA, Dartmouth College, 1994.

---

**O'CONNELL, Scott**
Nixon Peabody LLP, Manchester
617 345 1150
soconnell@nixonpeabody.com
*Featured in Litigation (New Hampshire)*

**Practice Areas:** Scott O'Connell is Deputy Chair of the Litigation Department. His practice focuses on class action and aggregate litigation. He is currently representing financial services companies, health care providers and energy companies and traders and manufactures in federal and state court litigation around the country. He has extensive experience defending financial institutions as well as their officers and directors in class actions concerning lender liability, breach of contract, breach of fiduciary duty, breach of good faith, unfair and deceptive trade practices, fraud, misrepresentation, fair debt collection practices, and civil RICO.

---

**PARENT, Jennifer L**
McLane, Graf, Raulerson & Middleton Professional Association, Manchester
603 628 1360
jennifer.parent@mclane.com
*Featured in Labor & Employment (New Hampshire)*

**Practice Areas:** Arbitration and Medication; Business/Commercial Litigation; Employment Litigation; Land Use Litigation.

**Professional Memberships:** New Hampshire, Massachusetts and Federal courts and First Circuit. Board of Governor for New Hampshire Bar Association. Former President of New Hampshire Women's Bar Association. Named as one of New Hampshire Union Leader's 'Forty Under 40' Business Leaders(2007).

**Career:** Shareholder/Director, 2003. Robert E Kirby Award (2003), presented by New Hampshire Bar Foundation. Suffolk University Law School, Daniel J Fern Award for highest cumulative average (1995).
**Personal:** Suffolk University Law School, JD, 1995; Boston College, BA, cum laude 1992; St. Paul's School Advanced Studies Program, summer 1987.

**PELTONEN, John E**
Sheehan Phinney Bass + Green PA, Manchester
603 627 8291
jpeltonen@sheehan.com
*Featured in Environment (New Hampshire)*
**Practice Areas:** Environmental and energy matters, brownfields redevelopment, alternative dispute resolution.
**Professional Memberships:** Member of the New Hampshire and American Bar Associations. Admitted to practice in New Hampshire.
**Career:** Practiced law since 1967, including representation of business and municipal clients on a wide range of environmental and commercial matters. Practice is focused on environmental compliance, permitting, the defense of environmental enforcement matters, the development of remedial alternatives, the redevelopment of contaminated properties and litigation. Recognized in New England Super Lawyers and Best Lawyers in America.
**Personal:** BA, Dartmouth College; MA, Political Science, University of Arkansas; JD, Boston College Law School.

**PUESCHEL, Scott E**
Pierce Atwood LLP, Portsmouth
603 373 2019
spueschel@pierceatwood.com
*Featured in Corporate/Commercial (New Hampshire)*
**Practice Areas:** Business and tax, securities, mergers and acquisitions, venture capital.
**Professional Memberships:** Adjunct Professor at University of New Hampshire Law School in Concord, NH.
**Career:** Scott's practice focuses on emerging companies, early and late stage venture capital transactions, mergers and acquisitions, and public and private offerings of securities. Scott has acted as counsel to buyers and sellers, issuers, investors and underwriters in numerous private equity financings, public offerings, mergers, acquisitions and divestitures.
**Personal:** Boston College Law School, JD, magna cum laude. Georgetown University's School of Foreign Service, BS in Foreign Service, magna cum laude.

**QUINN, Michael J**
McLane, Graf, Raulerson & Middleton Professional Association, Portsmouth
603 334 6925
mike.quinn@mclane.com
*Featured in Environment (New Hampshire)*
**Practice Areas:** Energy, Utilities and Telecommunications * Environmental Law * Government Relations * Insurance

**Professional Memberships:** Admitted to practice before New Hampshire state and federal courts, and the First and Circuit Court of Appeals. Former Chairman of New Hampshire Bar Association Environmental and Natural Resources Law Section.
**Career:** Shareholder and Director since 1997.
**Publications:** Co-Author New Hampshire Environmental Law Handbook (Government Institutes, Inc.); Flood Damage Insurance Coverage: New Hampshire Law Provides a Powerful Tool for Policyholders, New Hampshire Business Review.
**Personal:** St. Lawrence University, 1983; University of Maine School of Law, 1988.

**REIDY, James P**
Sheehan Phinney Bass + Green PA, Manchester
603 627 8217
jreidy@sheehan.com
*Featured in Labor & Employment (New Hampshire)*
**Practice Areas:** Employment law, labor relations and management training.
**Professional Memberships:** Society for Human Resource Management, Manchester Area Human Resources Association, ABA and Lex Mundi Labor and Employment, New Hampshire State Council. Admitted in New Hampshire and Massachusetts.
**Career:** Chair of Labor and Employment Group. Represents management. Extensive experience before state and federal agencies on employment issues. Best Lawyers in America; Best Lawyers in NH; NE Super Lawyers; Corporate Citizen of the Year, BIA Above and Beyond and GSHRC HR Hero.
**Publications:** Please see www.sheehan.com.
**Personal:** JD, cum laude, New England School of Law; MPA, Northeastern University; BA, Assumption College.

**REISCHE, Alan L**
Sheehan Phinney Bass + Green PA, Manchester
603 627 8225
areische@sheehan.com
*Featured in Corporate/Commercial (New Hampshire)*
**Practice Areas:** Corporate finance, mergers and acquisitions, succession planning, international joint ventures.
**Professional Memberships:** Admitted, New Hampshire and American Bar Associations. Member, American Bar Association (Business, International Law).
**Career:** Clients range from family-owned companies to those with diverse shareholder ownership. Recognized in Best Lawyers in America, New England Super Lawyers.
**Personal:** Harvard College (BA); University Pennsylvania Law School (LLB); Boston University Law School (LLM, tax). Director, NH International Trade Association; Governor's Advisory Committee on Capital Formation; Vice-Chairman, NH Workforce Opportunity Council; Venture for Growth Committee, NH Community Loan Fund; Director, New Hampshire Center for

Non-Profits; Chair, Governor Lynch Finance Committee.

**RICH JR, John E**
McLane, Graf, Raulerson & Middleton Professional Association, Manchester
603 628 1438
john.rich@mclane.com
*Featured in Labor & Employment (New Hampshire)*
**Practice Areas:** Corporate Business Law; Education and Independent Schools; Employment and Labor Law; Estate Planning and Trust and Estate Administration; Financial Services; Health Care Law; Pension/Profit Sharing/Employee Benefits Law; Taxation Law.
**Professional Memberships:** Shareholder and Director; Concentration on ERISA, COBRA, HIPAA and complex federal laws applicable to employee benefit plans.
**Career:** Admitted to New Hampshire and Connecticut. Woodward and White's Best Lawyers; Superlawyers.
**Publications:** Recession Realities of Benefit Plans (2009); New Hampshire Legislature Legalizes Same Sex Marriage: How Should Employers Prepare?
**Personal:** JD, Boston University; BA Dartmouth College.

**ROBINSON, Denis O**
Pierce Atwood LLP, Portland
603 373 2003
drobinson@pierceatwood.com
*Featured in Real Estate (New Hampshire)*
**Practice Areas:** Denis counsels clients in all aspects of commercial transfer, leasing, financing and development of real estate. Represents a variety of commercial entities, including owners and developers of health care, resort, residential subdivision, industrial, and retail properties. Prior in-house experience includes closing and securitizing credit tenant lease loans with $1B+ Wall Street lender.
**Professional Memberships:** N.H. Bar Association: Real Estate Section; Title Standards Review Committee; Manchester Bar Association.
**Personal:** BS in Industrial Management from Carnegie Mellon University, University Honors (1988); JD from University of New Hampshire School of Law (1993).

**ROTCH, Peter B**
McLane, Graf, Raulerson & Middleton Professional Association, Manchester
603 628 1305
peter.rotch@mclane.com
*Featured in Real Estate (New Hampshire)*
**Practice Areas:** Commercial Finance * Corporate Business Law * Land Use and Development Law * Real Estate Law
**Professional Memberships:** Fellow of the American College of Real Estate Lawyers, New Hampshire and American Bar Associations.
**Career:** Admitted in New Hampshire, 1966; shareholder and Partner, 1974. Listed in Woodward's 'Best Lawyers In America'.
**Personal:** Dartmouth College, 1963, AB; University of Chicago Law School, 1966, JD.

**ROUVALIS, Mark**
McLane, Graf, Raulerson & Middleton Professional Association, Manchester
603 628 1329
mark.rouvalis@mclane.com
*Featured in Environment (New Hampshire)*
**Practice Areas:** Arbitration and Mediation * Environmental Litigation * Government Relations * Insurance * Commercial Litigation * Construction Litigation * Corporate / Partnership Disputes
**Professional Memberships:** New Hampshire Bar Association; Massachusetts Bar Association; American Bar Association.
**Career:** Shareholder/Director, 1997; Chair, Delivery of Legal Services Committee, New Hampshire Bar Association; New Hampshire Bar Finance Committee, Member; BV Peer Review Rated, Martindale-Hubbell.
**Personal:** JD with honors - Boston College Law School, 1988; BA - Brown University, 1983.

**SAMUELS, Richard A**
McLane, Graf, Raulerson & Middleton Professional Association, Manchester
603 628 1470
richard.samuels@mclane.com
*Featured in Corporate/Commercial (New Hampshire)*
**Practice Areas:** Mergers and Acquisitions * Securities Law * Corporate Business Law * Small Business Law * Energy, Utilities and Telecommunications * Banking Law
**Professional Memberships:** In 2013, Dick has been elected to serve as the firm's Managing Director for the next three years. Board of Directors and Chair of the Fiscal Policy Committee of the Business & Industry Association of New Hampshire. Dick has served as the New Hampshire liaison to the American Bar Associations Business Law Section's Committee on State Regulation of Securities.
**Career:** Admitted in MA and NH.
**Personal:** BA, Union College, 1974; MA, Duke University, 1976; JD, Cornell University, 1980.

**SATURLEY, William C**
Preti Flaherty Beliveau & Pachios, LLP, Concord
603 410 1557
wsaturley@preti.com
*Featured in Litigation (New Hampshire)*
**Practice Areas:** Commercial, trade secret, and intellectual property litigation; professional liability and discipline matters.
**Professional Memberships:** AV Peer Review Rated (Martindale-Hubbell); Chambers USA; Benchmark Litigation; Best Lawyers in America; Fellow, NH Bar Foundation; Fellow, American Bar Foundation.
**Publications:** New Hampshire Bar Journal: Jurisdiction.com: Personal Jurisdiction in Cyberspace (1997); Lawyers & Insolvent Clients (2009); The Ethical Dilemma of Disclosure and Confidentiality in Trade Secrets (2012); The Minefield of Threats in Litigation (2012). Other: numerous articles for Massachusetts Law Weekly and New Hampshire Bar News.

**Personal:** Dartmouth College (AB, 1977, magna cum laude); Harvard Law School (JD, 1980, cum laude).

## SCHWARZ, Dan P
Jackson Lewis LLP, Portsmouth
603 559 2730
Daniel.Schwarz@jacksonlewis.com
*Featured in Labor & Employment (New Hampshire)*

**Practice Areas:** Private and public sector labor and employment law, including grievance arbitration, wage and hour, wrongful termination, anti-discrimination/retaliation, covenants against competition and breach of confidentiality.Court-appointed mediator for both the New Hampshire Superior Court system and the Federal District Court of New Hampshire.

**Professional Memberships:** New Hampshire, Maine and American Bar Associations; Defense Research Institute.

**Career:** Sheehan, Phinney, Bass + Green, Manchester, NH 1985-1998, Partner 1991-1998 Flygare, Schwarz & Closson, Exeter, NH Partner 1998-May 2010. AV-Rated, Martindale Hubbell. Recognized in 2013 Best Lawyers in America.

**Personal:** BA Northwestern University-1979; JD Boston University Law School-1985.

## SHILLING, Cameron G
McLane, Graf, Raulerson & Middleton Professional Association, Manchester
603 628 1351
cameron.shilling@mclane.com
*Featured in Labor & Employment (New Hampshire)*

**Practice Areas:** Business Litigation; Employment and Labor Law; Privacy and Data Security.

**Professional Memberships:** President, Employment Law Section of NH Bar; Co-Chair, ABA Committee on Trade Secret and Non-competition Litigation; Legislative Chair, Seacoast Human Resources Association; Executive Board of Daniel Webster Inn of Court. Massachusetts Bar Association.

**Publications:** Electronic Discovery: Litigation Crashes into the Digital Age, ABA Labor Lawyer (2007); Inevitable Disclosure Doctrine - A Necessary and Precise Tool for Trade Secret Law, ABA 'Best Of' Periodicals (2005).

**Personal:** Cornell Law School, JD 1995. B.A., Lewis & Clark College, 1992.

## SHIRLEY, James Q
Sheehan Phinney Bass + Green PA, Manchester
603 627 8142
jshirley@sheehan.com
*Featured in Litigation (New Hampshire)*

**Practice Areas:** Over 35 years experience trying cases in state and federal courts in New Hampshire and neighboring jurisdictions. Commercial litigation, focusing on professional negligence, product liability, toxic torts, real estate and insurance coverage.

**Professional Memberships:** Member of New Hampshire, California and American Bar Associations; Dartmouth Lawyers Association; American Board of Trial Advocates; American College of Trial Lawyers; and International Society

of Barristers. Admitted to practice in New Hampshire and California.

**Career:** Recognized in New England Super Lawyers and Best Lawyers in America.

**Personal:** BA, Dartmouth College, MA, San Francisco State University, JD, University of San Francisco School of Law.

## SKLAR, Daniel W
Nixon Peabody LLP, Manchester
603 628 4008
dsklar@nixonpeabody.com
*Featured in Corporate/Commercial (New Hampshire)*

**Practice Areas:** Concentrates on lending transactions, loan workouts and liquidations, bankruptcy reorganizations, and lender liability. He has extensive experience in the area of corporate law and commercial transactions. He has represented debtors, trustees, secured creditors, committees, stockholders, lessors, and senior executives in large Chapter 11 cases around the country, and has been involved in a number of international insolvencies.

**Career:** Daniel lectures for both bar associations and private continuing education groups. He is an adjunct professor of law at the UNH Law School, where he teaches bankruptcy and reorganization.

**Personal:** Boston University, LLM; Boston College, JD; University of Pennsylvania, BA.

## SMITH, Gregory H
McLane, Graf, Raulerson & Middleton Professional Association, Concord
603 230 4401
greg.smith@mclane.com
*Featured in Environment (New Hampshire)*

**Practice Areas:** Business Litigation; Energy, Utilities and Telecommunications; Environmental Law; Government Relations; Land Use and Development Law; Lobbying Services.

**Professional Memberships:** New Hampshire Bar Association; New Hampshire Association for Justice; Board of Directors of The New England Council; Woodward's 'Best Lawyers In America'; Terralex Representative (1997-Present).

**Career:** Attorney General for the State of New Hampshire (1980-84); Editor/Co-Author, 'NH Environmental Handbook'; Chairman, NH Environmental Comparative Risk Project; Legal Counsel, NH Senate (1992-93). New Hampshire, US District Court for New Hampshire and United States Supreme Court.

**Personal:** BA, University of New Hampshire 1969; JD University of Maine, 1973.

## STEVENS, Charla B
McLane, Graf, Raulerson & Middleton Professional Association, Manchester
603 628 1363
charla.stevens@mclane.com
*Featured in Labor & Employment (New Hampshire)*

**Practice Areas:** Business Litigation; Education and Independent Schools; Employment and Labor Law; Health Care Law.

**Professional Memberships:** Admitted in New Hampshire and Massachusetts.

**Publications:** Independent Contractor or Employee? Proper Classification of Workers is Critical.

**Personal:** Trained mediator; JD, cum laude, Boston College Law School.

## SULLIVAN, John M
Preti Flaherty Beliveau & Pachios, LLP, Concord
603 410 1550
jsullivan@preti.com
*Featured in Corporate/Commercial (New Hampshire)*

**Practice Areas:** Extensive experience in mergers and acquisitions, corporate reorganizations, real estate, and general corporate matters.

**Professional Memberships:** Admitted to practice in New Hampshire (1981); United States District Court, District of New Hampshire (1981); Massachusetts (2001); United States District Court, District of Massachusetts (2005); Maine (2007); and United States District Court, District of Maine (2007).

**Career:** Sulloway Hollis & Soden, Concord, N.H., 1981-2002; Management Committee; Managing Partner 1999-2000; Joined Preti Flaherty 2002; Director - N.H. Office. Member, Preti Flaherty Management Committee. Awards: Martindale-Hubbell A-V Rating; Listed in Best Lawyers in America and Super Lawyers; N.H. Bar Association President's Award for Outstanding Pro Bono Service 1994.

**Publications:** Comment, 'Your Papers, Please' - Is An Identification Requirement Constitutional?, 37 Washington & Lee Law Review 253 (1990); Author and Panelist several Continuing Legal Education Programs on Bankruptcy Law.

**Personal:** Born 12 August 1956; JD, Washington & Lee University, 1981; BA (cum laude), Bowdoin College, 1978; St. Paul's School, Concord, N.H., 1974.

## SULLIVAN, Kathleen
Wadleigh, Starr & Peters PLLC, Manchester
603 206 7272
ksullivan@wadleighlaw.com
*Featured in Real Estate (New Hampshire)*

**Practice Areas:** Real Estate, Zoning and Planning, Commercial and Residential Development, Election Law.

**Professional Memberships:** New Hampshire Bar Association.

**Career:** Joined firm in 1981.

**Personal:** Holy Cross (BA Cum Laude 1976); Cornell University (JD 1981). Ms. Sullivan is listed with "Best Lawyers in America" for land use and zoning, and real estate law, and has been named as one of NH's top lawyers by NH Magazine. Ms. Sullivan is well known throughout NH for her involvement in electoral politics, serving as chairwoman of the NH Democratic Party for eight years.She currently is the Democratic National Committeewoman for New Hampshire.

## TAUB, Philip B
Nixon Peabody LLP, Manchester
603 628 4038
ptaub@nixonpeabody.com
*Featured in Corporate/Commercial (New Hampshire)*

**Practice Areas:** Philip Taub is the former Chair of Nixon Peabody's Business and Finance Department and currently leads the firm's nationally recognized Private Equity Group. He focuses

his practice on corporate transactional work, including mergers, acquisitions, leveraged buy-outs, joint ventures, start-ups, shareholder disputes and venture capital financing. Mr Taub acts as corporate counsel to publicly and privately held businesses in the US and abroad.

**Personal:** George Washington University, JD; Boston University, BS.

## TUCKER, William C
Wadleigh, Starr & Peters PLLC, Manchester
603 206 7200
btucker@wadleighlaw.com
*Featured in Corporate/Commercial (New Hampshire), Real Estate (New Hampshire)*

**Practice Areas:** Real Estate, Finance and Corporate Law.

**Professional Memberships:** Manchester Bar Association, New Hampshire Bar Association, American Bar Association.

**Career:** Joined firm in 1969.

**Personal:** Yale University (BA 1966); Harvard Law School (JD 1969). In addition to being recognized in Chambers USA, Mr Tucker is rated AV by Martindale-Hubbell and listed with "Best Lawyers in America" in the areas of land use and zoning, and real estate law since its inception in 1983.

## VAN OOT, Martha
Jackson Lewis LLP, Portsmouth
603 559 2735
Martha.VanOot@jacksonlewis.com
*Featured in Labor & Employment (New Hampshire)*

**Practice Areas:** Labor and employment; employment litigation, counseling and training.

**Professional Memberships:** New Hampshire, Vermont and Massachusetts Bar Associations, ABA, the American Law Institute, and American College of Trial Attorneys.

**Career:** Extensive trial experience in state and federal court with an emphasis on employment litigation, defending against discrimination, wage and hour and wrongful termination claims, and enforcing non-compete agreements. Mediator for the federal district court and NH Commission for Human Rights.

**Personal:** Northeastern School of Law, JD. Middlebury College, BA. Active in nonprofit organizations including the NH Endowment for Health, Granite United Way, and the Norris Cotton Cancer Center.

## VICINANZO, David
Nixon Peabody LLP, Boston
617 345 1177
dvicinanzo@nixonpeabody.com
*Featured in Litigation (New Hampshire)*

**Practice Areas:** Practices primarily in the area of government investigations and the representation of organizations and individuals in complex civil and criminal matters.

**Professional Memberships:** Admitted to practice in New York and New Hampshire; the United States Courts of Appeals (First, Second, and District of Columbia circuits); numerous federal district courts.

**Career:** He served as a federal prosecutor in Washington, DC, and New England for 13 years; was as an advisor to the US attorney general, and

a chief prosecutor in the campaign finance investigation of the 1996 presidential election.
**Personal:** Fordham University, JD; Harvard University, BA, with Honors.

## VISCARELLO, Kenneth A
Sheehan Phinney Bass + Green PA, Manchester
603 668 0300
kviscarello@sheehan.com
*Featured in Real Estate (New Hampshire)*
**Practice Areas:** Affordable housing development, commercial real estate, construction law, commercial lending, corporate law.
**Professional Memberships:** Admitted to practice in the State of New Hampshire and the Commonwealth of Massachusetts.
**Career:** Chair of Affordable Housing Group, practiced law since 1986, he has extensive experience representing owners in affordable housing development utilizing Low Income Housing Tax Credits and other state and federal resources. He also practices in the areas of commercial real estate development, construction law, commercial lending and corporate law. Recognized in Best Lawyers in America and New England Super Lawyers.
**Personal:** AB, Boston College; JD, cum laude, Boston College.

## WHEAT, James C
Wadleigh, Starr & Peters PLLC, Manchester
603 206 7241
jwheat@wadleighlaw.com
*Featured in Litigation (New Hampshire)*
**Practice Areas:** Litigation.
**Professional Memberships:** New Hampshire Bar Association.
**Career:** Joined firm in 1972.
**Personal:** University of Massachusetts (BA 1968); Boston University (JD 1971). In addition to being recognized by Chambers USA, Mr Wheat has been included in the Best Lawyers in America for its Commercial Litigation rankings and is listed in Superlawyers for Business Litigation, Professional Liability Defense and Construction Litigation, and has won the NH Bar Association's President's Award for Service to the Profession. Mr Wheat is a Fellow of the American College of Trial Lawyers.

## WIELAND, Diana
Sheehan Phinney Bass + Green PA, Manchester
603 627 8236
dwieland@sheehan.com
*Featured in Labor & Employment (New Hampshire)*
**Practice Areas:** Labor relations and employment law representing management.
**Professional Memberships:** Member of the New Hampshire Bar Association.

**Career:** Extensive experience before various federal and states agencies, including US Equal Employment Opportunity Commission and US Department of Labor, New Hampshire Department of Labor, New Hampshire and Missouri Commissions for Human Rights. Extensive experience in counseling employers in human resource and labor issues and providing training in those areas to management. Recognized in Best Lawyers in America.
**Publications:** Please go to www.sheehan.com
**Personal:** BA, cum laude, Stephens College; JD, Washington University School of Law.

## WOLOWITZ, David
McLane, Graf, Raulerson & Middleton Professional Association, Portsmouth
603 436 2818
david.wolowitz@mclane.com
*Featured in Litigation (New Hampshire)*
**Practice Areas:** Business Litigation * Education and Independent Schools * Employment and Labor Law.
**Professional Memberships:** Admitted to practice before the state and federal courts in New Hampshire and Massachusetts. Member of the New Hampshire, Massachusetts, and American Bar Associations.
**Career:** Shareholder and Director since 1991; Guest faculty Harvard Law School, Trial Advocacy Workshop (1984 to present). Listed in

Woodward's 'Best Lawyers In America' in multiple categories.
**Personal:** Washington University, 1968, AB; Harvard University, 1971, MA; University of Michigan, 1975, JD.

## ZORN, William V A
McLane, Graf, Raulerson & Middleton Professional Association, Manchester
603 628 1340
bill.zorn@mclane.com
*Featured in Corporate/Commercial (New Hampshire)*
**Practice Areas:** Asset Protection and Wealth Preservation * Corporate Business Law * Estate Planning and Trust and Estate Administration * Health Care Law * International Trade * Small Business Law * Taxation Law
**Professional Memberships:** NH Bar Association (former Tax Section Chair; Corporate Section Member); MA Bar Association; ABA (Tax Section); ACTEC (Asset Protection Committee).
**Career:** Admitted in NH, MA and US Tax Court.
**Personal:** AB, Dartmouth College, 1975; JD, Boston University, 1978; LLM, Taxation, Boston University, 1983. McLane Partner since 1986. Recognized in 'The Best Lawyers In America' in Tax and Employee Benefits law.

# MCLANE GRAF RAULERSON & MIDDLETON, PA

www.mclane.com **tel:** 603 625 6464 **fax:** 603 625 5650

**2012 Managing Director:** Joseph A Foster
**2013 Managing Director:** Richard A Samuels
**Senior Partner:** Jack B Middleton

Number of partners: 42
Number of other lawyers: 50

**OFFICES**

**NEW HAMPSHIRE**
**MANCHESTER:** City Hall Plaza, 900 Elm Street, NH 03101
Tel: 603 625 6464  Fax: 603 625 5650

**CONCORD:** 11 South Main Street, Suite 500, NH 03301
Tel: 603 226 0400  Fax: 603 230 4448

**PORTSMOUTH:** 100 Market Street, Suite 301, NH 03801
Tel: 603 436 2818  Fax: 603 436 5672

**MASSACHUSETTS**
**WOBURN:** 300 TradeCenter, Suite 7000, MA 01801
Tel: 781 904 2700  Fax: 781 904 2701

## Firm Overview:

With more than 90 attorneys, the McLane Law Firm advises a variety of domestic and international clients with their legal needs. McLane attorneys are licensed in all New England states (including 45 attorneys in MA) as well as 14 additional states. The firm's TradeCenter office in Woburn has played a critical role in the firm's growth. Originally opened in 2008, the office has grown to include 15 attorneys with an emphasis on business, tax, employment, real estate and intellectual property law as well as trust and estate matters. Clients have been complimentary of the depth and experience that the firm brings to the metro-Boston area including its New Hampshire fee structure. McLane attorneys are recognized by their peers for knowledge and exceptional client service.

The firm is a member of Terralex and attorneys are annually recognized by Woodward & White's Best Lawyers and Super Lawyers. Additionally McLane counts among its attorneys - Regents and Fellows of the American College of Trial Lawyers, Real Estate Lawyers, Environmental Lawyers, Tax Counsel and Trust and Estate Counsel.

## Main Areas of Practice:

### Corporate:

The firm's Corporate Department advises clients on merger and acquisition transactions and securities matters, including public and private offerings of equity securities, as well as entity formation, governance, commercial matters and all aspects of corporate finance. The department has industry focus areas in the energy, healthcare, manufacturing, technology and financial services industries. Representative transactions for publicly and privately held clients range from $10 million to $1 billion.
**Contact:** Daniel J Norris

### Environmental:

The Environmental Practice covers administrative law and litigation under all the major federal environmental laws and their state program analogues. The firm's lawyers have extensive experience in Superfund and state hazardous waste cases, Clean Air Act, Clean Water Act, Wetlands, TSCA, EPCRA, NEPA, energy facility siting, and natural resource law, in both permitting and enforcement cases. The firm has handled cases throughout New England, New York, Georgia, South Carolina, and California.
**Contact:** Gregory H Smith

### Commercial Litigation:

Commercial litigation is a major focus of the firm's work. It received top New Hampshire honors in this practice area in Chambers USA from the first edition to the present. McLane trial lawyers appear extensively in state and federal courts, and increasingly in jurisdictions beyond New England. The firm's experience in insurance recovery and contribution actions on behalf of utilities for environmental claims has attracted national interest and recently brought that team of attorneys litigation in New York, South Carolina, and Connecticut. McLane attorneys also handle a wide range of contract disputes, intellectual property claims, unfair competition and antitrust cases, and corporate governance claims.
**Contact:** Bruce W Felmly, Linda S Johnson

### Energy & Utility Law:

The firm represents gas, telephone, and water utilities; competitive energy suppliers; small power producers and other wholesale electric generators; wireless communications companies; utility holding companies; municipalities and industrial and commercial customers of electric utilities. Recent work includes restructuring of the electric and gas industries, electric and water municipalization litigation, gas, electric and water rate proceedings and numerous financings.
**Contact:** Steven V Camerino

### Employment:

Representation includes defending and prosecuting claims, workplace audits, managerial and workforce training programs, development of personnel policies and practices, and consultation and advice on the challenges employers face every day, including internal employee complaints, responding to government investigations, or resolving disability, compensation, benefits, misconduct and termination issues.
**Contact:** Jennifer L Parent

### Real Estate:

The firm's Real Estate Practice advises clients throughout New England on general commercial and construction financing, land use matters, leasing, and other aspects of real estate and business ownership. The firm recently obtained all permits for an electric generating station producing competitive-cost power. Representation included the acquisition of all real estate, easements for the transmission lines and all environmental and regulatory work for the new 16-mile, interstate gas transmission pipeline.
**Contact:** Linda C Connell

### Tax:

The firm's Tax Department, represents individuals, and businesses, buyers and sellers, in a variety of tax-related transactions, planning and issues. McLane's tax lawyers represent clients in every phase of contact with the IRS and state revenue agencies, including audit, collection, appeals, abatement requests, and dispute resolution. When necessary, litigators experienced in tax matters assist in any matters that require litigation.
**Contact:** Steven M Burke

### Intellectual Property:

The firm's Intellectual Property Practice represents clients on a wide range of US and international intellectual property matters. In litigated matters, the group has helped large software companies, such as Microsoft Corporation, protect their copyright ownership in software against piracy and counterfeiting. The Intellectual Property Group handles all aspects of intellectual property protection, including patent, trademark, copyright, trade secret, licensing and e-commerce law.
**Contact:** Mark A Wright

### Family Law:

The firm's Domestic Law Group handles all aspects of family law, including the preparation and execution of prenuptial agreements, adoptions, legal separations, divorce and annulments. Some members are trained Collaborative Law Practitioners and trained Marital Mediators.
**Contact:** David DePuy, Jeanmarie Papelian

### Trusts & Estates:

The group consists of attorneys who are experienced in trust and estate planning, Medicaid planning, business entity selection and formation, commercial litigation, bankruptcy and family law matters. The firm has combined these areas of law because asset protection strategies and solutions vary greatly depending on each client's personal and business circumstances, as well as the nature of the assets to be protected.
**Contact:** William VA Zorn

McLane, Graf,
Raulerson & Middleton
Professional Association

# SHEEHAN PHINNEY BASS + GREEN PA

**www.**sheehan.com **tel:** 603 668 0300 **fax:** 603 627 8121

**Managing Partner:** Joseph A DiBrigida
Number of partners: 46  Number of other lawyers: 15

### Firm Overview:

Established in 1937, Sheehan Phinney Bass + Green PA is one of the premier business law firms in Northern New England. The firm has grown to over 60 attorneys with four offices throughout New Hampshire and Boston, Massachusetts while representing local, national and international businesses. Since opening the Boston office in 2002, the firm has experienced significant growth in the Massachusetts market in part by offering a New Hampshire fee structure. Sheehan Phinney is known for professional excellence, practical counsel and commitment to both its clients and the communities it serves, and for providing innovative approaches and practical solutions to client issues. The firm's attorneys continue to be recognized by Woodward/White's *Best Lawyers, Super Lawyers* and many are ranked in the top tier of *Chambers USA*. In the 2013 edition of *Best Lawyers*, the firm ranked first in New Hampshire in the areas of Bankruptcy & Creditor-Debtor Rights, Bet-the-Company Litigation, Commercial Litigation, Corporate Law, Employee Benefits, Healthcare, Insurance, Labor, Litigation & Controversy, Tax and Mediation. In 2010, the firm was chosen as *Business NH Magazine*'s "Business of the Decade" based on business success, contributions and leadership within the legal profession, community and state during the past 10 years.

Through its affiliate, the Sheehan Phinney Capitol Group, the firm provides government relations and lobbying services. Sheehan Phinney is the exclusive member firm for New Hampshire of Lex Mundi, the world's leading association of premier independent law firms.

### Main Areas of Practice:

**Corporate:**
The firm has extensive experience in mergers and acquisitions, corporate finance, healthcare, real estate, employment law, tax, intellectual property, patents and trademarks. Areas of practice also include public and private securities, bankruptcy and insolvency, business formation, education, environmental and energy, governmental affairs, import/export control and trust and estate planning.
**Contact:** Alan L Reische

**Banking & Finance:**
In addition to frequent representation of borrowers and lenders in routine and complex commercial transactions, the firm also represents clients in public finance transactions including New Hampshire's largest issuer of tax-exempt bonds, as well as borrowers, underwriters and corporate trustees.
**Contact:** Michael J Drooff

**Environmental & Energy Practice:**
This group, recognized as one of the best in New England, counsels clients on regulatory compliance, permitting, cleanup and re-development issues. Group members provide representation before state and federal environmental and energy agencies, as well as state and federal courts.
**Contact:** John E Peltonen

**Intellectual Property & Technology:**
Group members work with clients to evaluate, protect and enforce their intellectual property and technology rights, while helping them create an effective intellectual property portfolio with respect to licensing, financing, and merger or acquisition transactions. Services include patents, trademarks, copyrights, ecommerce, trade secrets, export and import assistance, litigation and licensing.
**Contact:** Peter A Nieves

**Healthcare:**
This group represents hospitals, nursing homes and other healthcare facilities, including physician and professional practice groups, sole practitioners, medical partnerships, professional corporations and limited liability entities. Group members advise healthcare clients on all aspects of their businesses, including regulatory compliance, contract issues, patient care issues, financing and securities transactions, real estate acquisitions and development, facilities construction, tax planning and general corporate matters.
**Contact:** Katherine M Hanna

**International:**
This group offers a full range of services to clients engaged in international commerce. The group focuses on helping clients maximize the benefits of participating in the global marketplace, while avoiding the pitfalls of international trade.
**Contact:** Robert P Cheeney

**Labor & Employment:**
A recognized leader in this area of the law, this group regularly assists clients with a wide variety of compliance issues under federal and state labor and employment laws. Members handle a wide variety of disputes before government agencies, arbitration panels and state/federal courts. This group serves as panel counsel to several major EPLI carriers.
**Contact:** James P Reidy

**Litigation:**
The firm's business litigators routinely represent clients in both state and federal courts, before administrative agencies and in arbitration and mediation settings. Group members regularly represent clients with matters involving shareholder and partnership disputes, intellectual property rights, trade secrets, non-competition/non-solicitation covenants, predatory hiring, employment claims/disputes, securities, construction, consumer protection, class action defense, environmental issues, insurance coverage and state and federal tax cases.
**Contact:** David W McGrath

**Real Estate:**
The firm works with clients in all areas of commercial real estate financing and construction matters, advising and representing developers, lenders and users of commercial properties such as office buildings, shopping centers, condominiums, affordable housing projects, corporate headquarters and airports.
**Contact:** Susan A Manchester

SHEEHAN PHINNEY BASS + GREEN
PROFESSIONAL ASSOCIATION
*the business law firm*

# WADLEIGH, STARR & PETERS, PLLC

**www.**wadleighlaw.com **tel:** 603 669 4140 **fax:** 603 669 6018

**Managing Member:** Donald J Perrault
Number of Attorneys: 27

**OFFICES**

NEW HAMPSHIRE
**MANCHESTER:** 95 Market Street, NH 03101
Tel: 603 669 4140   Fax: 603 669 6018

## Firm Overview:

Founded in 1899, Wadleigh, Starr & Peters, P.L.L.C. provides highly responsive legal services to local and national clients. Working closely with clients from a wide cross section of the private and public sectors, Wadleigh's approach is to help clients achieve their objectives with practical, results-oriented representation. The firm prides itself in combining quality, large firm representation with common sense strategies, always putting the needs of the client first.

Wadleigh has a tradition of public service dating back to one of the founders, George Bingham, who served as both Justice of the New Hampshire Supreme Court and a Judge of the United States Circuit Court of Appeals between 1913 and 1934. Other members of the firm have served with distinction as Judges in the New Hampshire court system, Attorneys General of the state of New Hampshire and members of the United States Congress.

The firm's practice encompasses a full range of legal services, including corporate and transactional, litigation, real estate, labor and employment, education, municipal, professional malpractice defense, insurance, administrative, family, estate planning and probate law. The firm is a member of the American Law Firm Association (ALFA), an international organization whose member firms are chosen by peer evaluation and provide a broad spectrum of services to the business community.

## Main Areas of Practice:

### Real Estate:

With a top-tier real estate practice, Wadleigh handles a variety of matters, focusing on commercial development such as shopping malls, office buildings, hospitality and recreational uses ranging from hotels to ski areas, and institutional facilities in the area of health care and education, as well as large scale residential subdivisions and condominium projects. Wadleigh has been involved in some of the largest real estate projects in the state, representing developers, lenders, commercial tenants and purchasers. The firm's attorneys have significant experience in finance, development, sales and acquisition, state and local land use permitting, environmental, leasing and workout transactions. It also handles property management, brokerage and consulting contracts and related matters.

### Litigation:

Widely respected throughout New Hampshire for its litigation practice in both state and federal courts, Wadleigh's representation includes product liability, medical and other professional malpractice defense, insurance defense, constitutional law, real estate, construction, contracts disputes and employment law. Medical institutions and professionals, law firms and other professionals, such as architects, engineers and accountants, regularly hire Wadleigh, either directly or through insurance carriers, to defend them against claims for professional liability. Wadleigh's trial lawyers have served as lead counsel in many of the largest and most complex construction and commercial claims litigated in the state and have provided representation

for many of the nation's major manufacturers. Wadleigh also represents school districts in education litigation such as special education, expulsions, bullying complaints and personnel matters.

### Corporate:

Wadleigh's corporate attorneys advise the firm's clients on day to day corporate and business considerations, including formation and capitalization of partnerships, corporations, profit and not for profit, and limited liability companies.

### Labor & Employment:

Wadleigh works with employers in all areas of labor and employment law, including policy development, risk management, litigation, and labor relations and collective bargaining.

### Clients:

Wadleigh's clients range from individuals, start-up ventures and closely held firms to publicly traded domestic and international corporations. The clients represented by the firm's insurance litigation group include CIGNA, CNA, Liberty Mutual, Peerless, St. Paul/Travelers, as well as numerous title insurance companies.

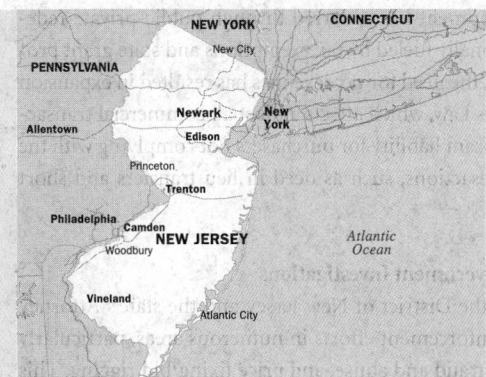

## How lawyers are ranked

Every year we carry out thousands of in-depth interviews with clients in order to assess the reputations and expertise of business lawyers worldwide. The qualities we look for (and which determine rankings) include technical legal ability, professional conduct, client service, commercial awareness/astuteness, diligence, commitment, and other qualities most valued by the client. For details of our research team, see p.5.

## Contents:

# NEW JERSEY: An introduction
## Contributed by Gibbons P.C.

### Business & Commercial Litigation

New Jersey state courts have adopted a four-track case management system that aligns each case with an appropriate discovery period and degree of case management depending on its complexity. "Complex commercial" cases proceed under "Track IV" and are case-managed by a single judge handling all pretrial matters. Many counties also have designated Track IV judges. Additionally, New Jersey courts have a separate Chancery Division, which handles disputes where some form of equitable relief is sought and in which matters are case-managed by a single judge. New Jersey's federal courts engage in active case management primarily through its magistrate judges and frequently employ early dispute-resolution efforts, resulting in one of the shortest median-time-to-resolution intervals among the federal district courts.

### Corporate

The New Jersey business environment continues to improve as the state becomes more business friendly. Companies are increasingly involved in all types of corporate transactions, mergers and acquisitions, capital raising, commercial financings, restructurings and various other transactions in and around New Jersey. For example, there has recently been an uptick in inbound foreign investment, and area companies are more readily obtaining growth capital and higher business sale multiples.

### Environmental

Numerous contaminated sites in New Jersey, including "mega-sites", implicate both state and federal environmental laws, such as the lower Passaic River and Berry's Creek. Although some are far along in the remediation process, responsible parties are still pursuing cost recovery litigation to recover an equitable share of remediation costs from other responsible parties. The state recently enacted a significant change to its site remediation program, essentially privatizing the remediation of contaminated sites through the Licensed Site Remediation Professional (LSRP) program, under which remediations are overseen by licensed consultants hired and paid by the remediating party, rather than by state regulators.

### Healthcare

New Jersey is experiencing major shifts in hospital ownership. Mergers and acquisitions involve nonprofit hospitals, for-profit hospitals, and for-profit conversions. Reshuffled provider alliances and new provider entrants have increased innovative partnerships and business models, as competitors jockey for advantage in the rapidly changing marketplace. Accountable care organization (ACO) formation is establishing higher levels of clinical integration. Attention has turned to the acquisition and financing of sophisticated information systems in support of clinical integration activities. Hospital acquisition of specialty physician practices mirrors a national trend, as hospitals seek clinical integration and as specialists seek relief from the burdens and uncertainties of running their own private practices.

### Insurance

Individuals and businesses in New Jersey are focused on the availability of insurance coverage for losses suffered as a result of Superstorm Sandy. Many of the coverage issues now confronting policyholders and insurers have not been litigated in analogous circumstances within the tri-state area, so there is a dearth of case law to guide the parties and the courts. Moreover, policyholders will be filing claims against their insurance broker for not obtaining the coverage necessary to protect against significant damages and losses.

### Intellectual Property

The patent docket of the US District Court for the District of New Jersey is one of the nation's heaviest, particularly since its 2009 adoption of local patent rules that expedite and streamline patent litigation and include special provisions for handling Hatch-Waxman Act cases more efficiently than many jurisdictions, a key issue for New Jersey's large pharmaceutical industry. In 2011, the district court was selected as one of only 14 nationwide participating in the Patent Pilot Program. New Jersey's state courts are similarly well regarded by litigants involved in disputes relating to proprietary information and trade secrets. The 2012 New Jersey Trade Secrets Act is expected to increase trade secrets litigation, since it contains unique provisions specifically designed to protect the subject trade secrets throughout the litigation process.

## Labor & Employment

Most employment litigation in New Jersey is brought under the New Jersey Law Against Discrimination (NJLAD), which is more pro-plaintiff than federal law, and more expansive than most federal and state statutes. With fee shifting, no caps, more protected categories, and no requirement to exhaust administrative remedies, employers find themselves at a distinct disadvantage. Additionally, because most cases are litigated in state court with its own unique rules and practices, and where summary judgment is often difficult to obtain, many employers are moving toward the use of mandatory arbitration agreements.

## Products Liability

New Jersey has a long history of serving as the headquarters for major pharmaceutical, life science, and medical device companies and also includes among its ranks many Fortune 500 manufacturing and chemical companies. With an activist Supreme Court and four full-time mass tort judges in the Superior Court, New Jersey is a leader in the area of product liability law and home to a robust, nationally recognized products liability Bar.

## Real Estate

New Jersey is a highly desirable real estate market due to its dense, affluent, educated population, with high barriers to entry in many areas and blight in others. Much recent development has occurred through public-private redevelopment projects, additionally fueled by tax exemptions and state grant programs. As with many states, the need for tax revenues has resulted in expansion of the New Jersey Bulk Sales Law, which affects almost all commercial transactions and can lead to significant liability for purchasers not complying with the law and impede some transactions, such as deed in lieu transfers and short sales.

## White-Collar Criminal/Government Investigations

Both the US Attorney for the District of New Jersey and the state's Attorney General have stepped up enforcement efforts in numerous areas, particularly insider trading, healthcare fraud and abuse, and price fixing/bid rigging. This has augmented, rather than replaced, both parties' decades-long emphasis on political corruption; these enforcement efforts are expected to increase in the wake of Hurricane Sandy. New Jersey also vigorously regulates professionals, both criminally and through licensing proceedings brought by watchdog groups and professional boards administered by the state. The investigative force of the independent State Commission on Investigation adds another layer of law enforcement, rendering New Jersey a particularly challenging environment for business and a particularly fertile one for creative prosecutorial efforts.

# BANKRUPTCY/RESTRUCTURING

Commentary about individuals can be found under their firm's paragraph. If the firm has no paragraph (is not ranked) look at Other Notable Practitioners.

## Band 1

### Cole, Schotz, Meisel, Forman & Leonard PA
See profile on p.1752

THE FIRM This practice is universally recognized as a leader within New Jersey and is backed by the firm's presence further afield in such states as Delaware and New York. With deep bench strength and experience across the full spectrum of bankruptcy issues, the team represents debtor and creditor committees in a range of actions, including litigation. The group's client roster includes a number of leading companies such as Hewlett-Packard and Highland Capital.
Sources say: *"Amazingly available." "They have represented me in a variety of instances relating to bankruptcy proceedings and have always done a great job." "A fantastic presence in all areas – I can't say enough about how good they are."*
KEY INDIVIDUALS **Michael Sirota** (see p.1748) is described by those within the marketplace as *"the top of the Bar in New Jersey."* He is cochair of the group and was lead partner representing YA Global Investments in appealing against the dismissal of summary judgment motions before the US Bankruptcy Court for the District of New Jersey. **Gerald Gline** (see p.1736) continues to represent clients across the full spectrum of bankruptcy law. **Stuart Komrower** (see p.1740) moves up a band within the rankings thanks to ringing endorsements from sources in the marketplace. Komrower is seen as *"an integral part of the practice"* by one interviewee and *"a great bankruptcy litigator"* by another. **Warren Usatine** (see p.1749) debuts in the rankings having received high praise in relation to his Chapter 11 work. Described as *"a seasoned practitioner,"* he was co-lead partner to the debtors in the Wave2Wave Communications bankruptcy. **Felice Yudkin** (see p.1750) is building a good reputation thanks to her assistance in several high-value bankruptcy matters in recent months. **David Bass** (see p.1731) joins the rankings on the back of some very favorable client commentary. Sources laud the *"extraordinary performance from an extremely attentive and unbelievably accessible attorney."*

### Lowenstein Sandler LLP
See profile on p.1757

THE FIRM Lowenstein Sandler's bankruptcy practice group is active in representing both creditors' committees and debtors, advising each on Chapter 11 proceedings and all forms of bankruptcy-related litigation. The firm is currently acting as debtors' counsel to the Coach America Holding Chapter 11 filing, and it is also representing the committee of unsecured creditors in connection with the bankruptcy of Global Aviation. Commentators concur that the firm deserves its place within Band 1 of the rankings.
Sources say: *"The firm is well managed, accessible and responsive to client needs." "Very skilled and qualified; available all the time."*
KEY INDIVIDUALS Departmental vice chair **Sharon Levine** (see p.1741) is praised by commentators as *"exceptionally bright – a New York attorney at a New Jersey price point."* She has recently been invited by the American Bankruptcy Institute Commission to advise on Chapter 11 reform. **Kenneth Rosen** (see p.1746) ascends to Band 1 of the rankings as a result of exemplary comments from sources. He is praised as a *"good negotiator and very skilled at getting good results."* **Bruce Buechler** (see p.1732) *"keeps a level head and does a great job,"* according to souces. He is commended across the board for his demeanor and ability to *"juggle all the balls without dropping them."* **Michael Etkin** (see p.1735) is described by commentators as *"very plugged-in"* and *"instrumental in providing tactical advice."* He is particularly active in complex Chapter 11 filings and reorganizations. **John Sherwood** (see p.1747) is applauded by clients as an *"excellent litigator and very professional – a lawyer's lawyer."*

| Bankruptcy/Restructuring Leading Firms | | |
|---|---|---|
| **Band 1** | | |
| Cole, Schotz, Meisel, Forman & Leonard PA * | | |
| Lowenstein Sandler LLP * | | |
| **Band 2** | | |
| Drinker Biddle & Reath LLP * | | |
| Gibbons P.C. * | | |
| McCarter & English, LLP * | | |
| Riker Danzig Scherer Hyland & Perretti LLP * | | |
| Sills Cummis & Gross P.C. * | | |
| **Band 3** | | |
| Archer & Greiner, A Professional Corporation * | | |
| Dilworth Paxson LLP | | |
| Fox Rothschild LLP * | | |
| **Band 4** | | |
| Porzio, Bromberg & Newman PC | | |
| Rabinowitz, Lubetkin & Tully, LLC | | |
| Wilentz, Goldman & Spitzer, P.A. * | | |
| Wilson, Elser, Moskowitz, Edelman & Dicker LLP * | | |

## Band 2

### Drinker Biddle & Reath LLP
See profile on p.2238

THE FIRM This practice group has extensive experience in representing all parties to bankruptcy proceedings. It has recently been particularly active in representing unsecured creditors as members of creditors' committees. The firm is currently acting for the Advanta Trust in this capacity in a matter valued at over $150 million. Other current clients include Citi and TMX Corp.

Sources say: "*Extremely efficient and reasonable – they did not miss a beat.*"

KEY INDIVIDUALS **Robert Malone** (see p.1741) was lead counsel on the Advanta Trust matter and has been applauded by market sources as an "*extraordinarily gifted lawyer who will tell you the answer to your question before you ask it.*" **Frank Velocci** (see p.1749) earns praise for his accessibility, responsiveness and skill as a negotiator.

### Gibbons P.C.
See profile on p.1754

THE FIRM Gibbons's bankruptcy practice group runs the gamut of debtor and creditor representations, and it recently welcomed a new partner to its already significant bench. Notable highlights include representing a trustee of the DBSI Private Actions Trust in litigating against a broker-run Ponzi scheme, as well as acting for United Gilsonite Laboratories in a Chapter 11 procedure. Other current clients include Google and Sharp.

Sources say: "*Professional, with excellent relationships with other firms and the courts.*"

KEY INDIVIDUALS **Karen Giannelli** is chair of the department and lead counsel on the DBSI matter. Greatly respected by clients and peers alike, she is described as "*a technical specialist*" and "*one of the best attorneys in the state.*" **Frank Vecchione** is regarded by many commentators as the dean of New Jersey bankruptcy law. He is

| Bankruptcy/Restructuring Senior Statesmen | | | | |
|---|---|---|---|---|
| **Senior Statesmen:** distinguished older practitioners | | | | |
| Vecchione Frank J | *Gibbons P.C.* | | Zackin Jack M | *Sills Cummis & Gross P.C.* * |

| Leading Individuals | | | | | |
|---|---|---|---|---|---|
| **Band 1** | | | **Band 3** | | |
| Giannelli Karen A | *Gibbons P.C.* | | Becker Ben | *Becker Meisel (ONP)*[†] | |
| Levine Sharon L | *Lowenstein Sandler LLP* * | | Conlan Mark | *Gibbons P.C.* | |
| Lubertazzi Jr Joseph | *McCarter & English, LLP* * | | Etkin Michael S | *Lowenstein Sandler LLP* * | |
| O'Grady Dennis | *Riker Danzig Scherer Hyland & Perretti LLP* | | Kelley Anne Marie P | *Dilworth Paxson LLP* | |
| Packman Stephen M | *Archer & Greiner* * | | Komrower Stuart | *Cole, Schotz, Meisel, Forman & Leonard* * | |
| Rosen Kenneth A | *Lowenstein Sandler LLP* * | | Papalia Vincent | *Saiber LLC (ONP)*[†] | |
| Sirota Michael | *Cole, Schotz, Meisel, Forman & Leonard* * | | Testa Jeffrey | *McCarter & English, LLP* * | |
| Stanziale Charles | *McCarter & English, LLP* * | | **Band 4** | | |
| **Band 2** | | | Bass David | *Cole, Schotz, Meisel, Forman & Leonard* * | |
| Buechler Bruce | *Lowenstein Sandler LLP* * | | Brody Alan | *Greenberg Traurig, LLP (ONP)*[†] * | |
| Gline Gerald | *Cole, Schotz, Meisel, Forman & Leonard* * | | Crapo David | *Gibbons P.C.* * | |
| Greenhalgh Walter J | *Duane Morris LLP (ONP)*[†] | | Flores Daniel F | *Wilson, Elser, Moskowitz, Edelman* * | |
| Kimmelman Simon | *Sills Cummis & Gross P.C.* * | | Freedman Scott | *Dilworth Paxson LLP* | |
| Malone Robert | *Drinker Biddle & Reath LLP* * | | Lubetkin Jay | *Rabinowitz, Lubetkin & Tully, LLC* * | |
| Martin Jr Warren J | *Porzio, Bromberg & Newman PC* | | Patella Raymond | *Fox Rothschild LLP* * | |
| Meth Richard | *Fox Rothschild LLP* * | | Perkins Eric | *McElroy, Deutsch, Mulvaney (ONP)*[†] | |
| Nies Robert | *Wolff & Samson PC (ONP)*[†] | | Sherwood John K | *Lowenstein Sandler LLP* * | |
| Rabinowitz Jonathan | *Rabinowitz, Lubetkin & Tully, LLC* * | | Usatine Warren A. | *Cole, Schotz, Meisel, Forman & Leonard* * | |
| Schwartz Joseph L | *Riker Danzig Scherer Hyland & Perretti LLP* | | Velocci Frank | *Drinker Biddle & Reath LLP* * | |
| Sherman Andrew H | *Sills Cummis & Gross P.C.* * | | **Associates to watch** | | |
| Zuber Scott A | *Wilson, Elser, Moskowitz, Edelman* * | | Leney Douglas | *Archer & Greiner* * | |
| | | | Yudkin Felice | *Cole, Schotz, Meisel, Forman & Leonard* * | |

\* *Indicates individual with profile.*

[†] *ONP = Other Notable Practitioner.*

described as "*gentlemanly, wise and professional.*" **David Crapo** (see p.1733) earns accolade for his business understanding. "*His advice is very practical and he really understands the commercial aspects of a matter,*" sources state. **Mark Conlan** is commended by clients as a "*workhorse and a straight shooter who does not litigate for the sake of it.*"

### McCarter & English, LLP
See profile on p.1759

THE FIRM Although this Newark-based bankruptcy practice group is well equipped to handle all varieties of bankruptcy matters, it has of late been especially active representing debtors, Chapter 11 and 7 trustees and secured and unsecured creditors. The firm recently served as counsel to the liquidating trustee in the $2 billion Solomon Dwek Chapter 11 bankruptcy.

Sources say: "*They are very responsive and met all of our demands.*"

KEY INDIVIDUALS **Charles Stanziale** (see p.1748) continues to play an active role within McCarter's bankruptcy practice and is described by sources as a senior figure who commands respect. He is also praised for his "*excellent knowledge of the law and his keen business sense.*" Sources describe **Jeffrey Testa** (see p.1749) as "*a very experienced bankruptcy practitioner*" who has earned his good reputation. **Joseph Lubertazzi** (see p.1741) leads the firm's representation of Aramark on asset recovery and bankruptcy

matters. He is described by market commentators as simply "*a great lawyer.*"

### Riker Danzig Scherer Hyland & Perretti LLP
See profile on p.1761

THE FIRM This group is particularly adept in representing creditors to bankruptcy proceedings including banks, financial institutions and companies. The team is also active in the healthcare field, where it counts Dr Reddy's Laboratories and the Provident Bank among its roster of clients. Recent work highlights include representing Wells Fargo as secured lender in the TexStyle Chapter 11 reorganization.

Sources say: "*Very well managed and professional. They represent the highest standards of any New Jersey firm I have worked with.*"

KEY INDIVIDUALS **Dennis O'Grady** is held in the greatest regard by market sources, who report that "*if you are filing for bankruptcy protection in the Third Circuit, you can't do better than Dennis O'Grady.*" **Joseph Schwartz** is lauded by clients as "*probably the best-prepared attorney that I have ever seen. He really does his homework.*" Recent work highlights include closing the purchase of the assets of R&S Strauss and Strauss Discount Auto for client Somerset Tire Service.

## Sills Cummis & Gross P.C.
See profile on p.1762

THE FIRM Sills Cummis's bankruptcy practice group has experience across the full breadth of bankruptcy-related matters, though it is particularly adept at representing creditors. The firm has also continued to expand its reach into the healthcare arena, including recently representing creditors in the sale of millions of dollars worth of assets released from two failing hospitals.

Sources say: *"These guys have been the most professional firm I have seen in New Jersey. They really hold their own against big-city lawyers."*

KEY INDIVIDUALS Andrew Sherman (see p.1747) is viewed as the future of the practice by market sources. He is described as a *"very fine lawyer who does a terrific job for his clients."* A skilled litigator and Chapter 11 reorganization specialist, Simon Kimmelman (see p.1739) is praised for his *"total mastery of the bankruptcy code."* Jack Zackin (see p.1750) is held in the highest regard by market sources. As a vastly experienced practitioner and as *"the face of Sills Cummis,"* there is a broad consensus that he has earned his senior statesman ranking.

## Band 3

### Archer & Greiner, A Professional Corporation
See profile on p.1751

THE FIRM The team is known for its experience in representing the full range of clients across a number of industry sectors in Chapter 7, 11 and 15 proceedings. The firm has also of late been expanding its cross-border work in Western Europe, Asia and South America. Archer & Greiner's bankruptcy practice group also draws on the firm's presence in Delaware, New York and Philadelphia.

KEY INDIVIDUALS Stephen Packman (see p.1744) has recently been representing the trustee in the Universal Marketing Chapter 7 filing, one of the largest such cases in the region. He is described by market sources as *"proactive and always on top of the issues."* Douglas Leney (see p.1740) is described by sources as *"a very bright guy and a pleasure to work with."*

### Dilworth Paxson LLP

THE FIRM This group is widely renowned for its high-quality work across the full range of bankruptcy-related matters. Noted for being holistic in its approach, the firm is able to offer its services at competitive, cost-effective rates. The addition of three partners in the last twelve months bears testament to the volume of work the team is undertaking.

Sources say: *"The firm has always exceeded my expectations."*

KEY INDIVIDUALS Scott Freedman stands out for having assisted on a number of high-value bankruptcy-related

matters. Anne Marie Kelley is applauded by market sources as *"an expert in her field who knows the law and how to apply it so that our best interests are taken care of."*

### Fox Rothschild LLP
See profile on p.2242

THE FIRM This team is acknowledged as having significant clients within the real estate, pharmaceutical and biotechnology fields. With a presence on the West Coast as well as the South West of the country, the team prides itself on its geographical coverage. Recent work highlights include representing the unsecured creditors' committee for Fontainebleau Las Vegas in attempts to recoup bank debts and contractor claims.

Sources say: *"Excellent work, prompt responses and always someone available to talk to."*

KEY INDIVIDUALS Richard Meth (see p.1742) centers his practice on creditors' rights, workouts, reorganizations and insolvency-related matters. Market sources report: *"He is very well known in the industry"* and that *"he values his professional relationships – he communicates well with clients."* Raymond Patella (see p.1744) has a national practice that spans the full gamut of bankruptcy and related litigation matters.

## Band 4

### Porzio, Bromberg & Newman PC

THE FIRM This Morristown-based bankruptcy practice group is particularly active within the healthcare industry, where it represents both debtors and committees of creditors. The firm has also been involved with Madoff-related litigation at an international level. Current clients include Capital One Bank and Hertz.

KEY INDIVIDUALS Warren Martin is regarded as *"a well-known expert"* on bankruptcy law. He represented Christ Hospital in Jersey City over restructuring $160 million of debt down to $60 million.

### Rabinowitz, Lubetkin & Tully, LLC

THE FIRM This Livingston-based group focuses on representing both creditors and debtors in workouts and federal bankruptcy remedies, as well as litigation. Founded in 2007, the firm is active both nationwide and internationally. Recently the team has been retained by Chartworld Shipping to defend against claims filed by the Chapter 7 trustee of Eastwind Maritime.

Sources say: *"They are very responsive and thorough. They cover all the angles and come up with excellent strategies."*

KEY INDIVIDUALS Jonathan Rabinowitz (see p.1745) specializes in creditors' rights and is praised by market sources as *"extremely smart and thorough – he explains everything very well and makes sure I understand."* Jay Lubetkin (see p.1741) is the managing partner of the firm

and a Chapter 7 panel trustee. He is currently acting as Chapter 7 trustee to Martin Cadillac in Bergen County, New Jersey.

### Wilentz, Goldman & Spitzer, P.A.
See profile on p.1763

THE FIRM Wilentz, Goldman & Spitzer's compact creditors' rights and bankruptcy practice group actively represents clients in both New Jersey and further afield in New York, Pennsylvania and Delaware. The team comes particularly recommended for its work in Chapter 11 reorganizations and Chapter 7 liquidations as well as loan restructurings. Current clients include JPMorgan Chase and The Provident Bank.

Sources say: *"Extremely responsive. I know what to expect from them and it has always been a positive relationship."*

KEY INDIVIDUALS David Stein chairs the practice.

### Wilson, Elser, Moskowitz, Edelman & Dicker LLP
See profile on p.2017

THE FIRM This practice group offers extensive experience across the full range of bankruptcy matters. The team continues to consolidate its position within the wider marketplace thanks to the hire of several practitioners from Day Pitney.

KEY INDIVIDUALS Scott Zuber (see p.1750) is applauded by sources in the New Jersey area as a *"very capable attorney."* Daniel Flores (see p.1735) is regarded highly by peers and clients alike for his experience both in private practice and in-house.

## Other Notable Practitioners

Walter Greenhalgh of Duane Morris LLP is experienced across the full spectrum of bankruptcy law and is lauded by peers as *"a passionate advocate with an excellent knowledge of bankruptcy and commercial litigation."* Ben Becker of Becker Meisel is a stalwart of the New Jersey bankruptcy market. He receives praise as an *"amazing attorney,"* specializing in midmarket cases. Vincent Papalia chairs the bankruptcy practice group at Saiber LLC and is described by sources as *"very bright and a pleasure to deal with."* Robert Nies of Wolff & Samson PC has over 25 years' experience representing clients across the full spectrum of bankruptcy-related matters. Alan Brody (see p.1732) of Greenberg Traurig, LLP recently represented Stant Parent Corporation in negotiating a debtor-in-possession financing, sale of assets and restructuring of the company's businesses. Eric Perkins of McElroy, Deutsch, Mulvaney & Carpenter, LLP is held in high regard by market sources for his ability to *"look at things from a business perspective."*

# CORPORATE/M&A

Commentary about individuals can be found under their firm's paragraph.  If the firm has no paragraph (is not ranked) look at Other Notable Practitioners.

| Corporate/M&A | |
| --- | --- |
| **Leading Firms** | |
| **Band 1** | |
| Day Pitney LLP * | |
| Dentons * | |
| Lowenstein Sandler LLP * | |
| **Band 2** | |
| Gibbons P.C. * | |
| McCarter & English, LLP * | |
| Morgan, Lewis & Bockius LLP * | |
| Riker Danzig Scherer Hyland & Perretti LLP * | |
| Sills Cummis & Gross P.C. * | |
| **Band 3** | |
| DLA Piper LLP (US) * | |
| Giordano Halleran & Ciesla PC | |
| Greenbaum, Rowe, Smith & Davis LLP * | |
| Reed Smith LLP | |
| Wilentz, Goldman & Spitzer, P.A. * | |
| Wolff & Samson PC | |
| **Band 4** | |
| Greenberg Traurig, LLP * | |

## Band 1

### Day Pitney LLP
See profile on p.1753

**THE FIRM** Located in Parsippany, the substantial M&A group at Day Pitney provides support on a full range of corporate matters, including tax and banking regulations. In 2012 the group won a number of significant mandates to act on complex midmarket transactions, and clients continue to benefit from its experience handling cross-border transactions. In a recent highlight, it represented Valley National Bancorp in its $222 million acquisition of State Bancorp. Its other active clients include Xerox, Nephros and Fuel System Solutions.
**Sources say:** *"I have found their work to be incredible."*
**KEY INDIVIDUALS** Practice head **Ronald Janis** (see p.1738) is widely regarded as one of the deans of the New Jersey corporate market. He is praised as *"extremely useful and someone who always comes up with a solution. His support is invaluable."* He was lead counsel representing Valley National Bancorp. **Warren Casey** (see p.1733) earns accolades for his extensive knowledge and his responsiveness. Market sources describe an attorney who *"quickly understands the issues and answers all questions."* Described as *"very capable and conscientious,"* **Michael Rave** (see p.1745) is acknowledged by many for both his technical expertise and accessibility to clients. He was lead counsel representing the Connecticut Bank & Trust in its $37 million bank acquisition. **Michael Dunne** (see p.1735) represents clients across a wide range of industries, and his practice is bent toward transactions with significant elements of IT and IP. Well equipped to deal with extremely complex transactions, he is described as *"a deep thinker."* **Scott Goodman** (see p.1736)

debuts on the rankings having received particular praise for his in-depth knowledge of SEC regulations. Clients also cite Goodman's responsiveness.

### Dentons
See profile on p.449

**THE FIRM** The New Jersey transactional group at this international firm is particularly notable for the breadth of its practice, acting for a range of investors, lenders and companies of all sizes. The success of its emerging companies practice can in part be attributed to the group's deep expertise in technology, pharmaceuticals and life sciences. In a recent highlight, the group represented broadband solutions company Nistica in its sale to Japanese fiber-optics supplier Fujikura.
**Sources say:** *"I have a great respect for the firm in terms of response time and accessibility. They are very practical and have a strong understanding of the business realities that underlie the issue."*
**KEY INDIVIDUALS Victor Boyajian** (see p.1732) is lauded by peers and clients alike as a *"clear practice leader within the investment community."* Head of the firm's venture technology practice, he was lead counsel representing Canaan Partners in its $12 million investment in rental home services provider Onefinestay. **Jeffrey Baumel** (see p.1731) receives praise from market sources for his *"vast experience,"* which provides him with a *"really strategic focus."* Baumel, who heads the firm's health and life sciences group, recently advised ADMA Biologics on a $17.5 million private placement and reverse merger with R&R Acquisition VI. Managing partner of the firm's Short Hills office, **John Cleary** (see p.1733) is highly regarded for his ability to work well *"under stressful situations."* His highlights include a $30 million Series D financing for Circulite. With a focus on negotiation and structuring of technology transactions, **James Jasaitis** (see p.1738) was lead counsel representing Sungevity in a $22 million venture capital investment. Sources say Jasaitis is *"very connected in the marketplace."* **David Papier** (see p.1744) focuses his practice on venture capital and investment banking. He recently represented DoubleVerify in a $33 million Series C financing.

### Lowenstein Sandler LLP
See profile on p.1757

**THE FIRM** This corporate powerhouse is seen by clients and peers alike as one of the most preeminent M&A firms in the state. The group houses a prolific and highly acclaimed technology and venture capital practice, and also proves popular with investment management clients, investment banks and issuers. In a recent highlight, the firm represented tech company Buddy Media in its sale to Salesforce.com. Other clients include Tower International, Indorama Ventures and Cerberus Capital Management.

| Corporate/M&A | | |
| --- | --- | --- |
| **Band 1** | | |
| Aiello John | Giordano Halleran & Ciesla PC | |
| Boyajian Victor | Dentons * | |
| Cohen Steven | Morgan, Lewis & Bockius LLP * | |
| Ehrenberg Peter H | Lowenstein Sandler LLP * | |
| Gilbert Andrew P | DLA Piper LLP (US) * | |
| Janis Ronald H | Day Pitney LLP * | |
| Sunberg Randall B | Morgan, Lewis & Bockius LLP * | |
| Zimmerman Edward M | Lowenstein Sandler LLP * | |
| **Band 2** | | |
| Casey Warren J | Day Pitney LLP * | |
| Davis Alan E | Greenbaum, Rowe, Smith & Davis LLP | |
| Felton W Raymond | Greenbaum, Rowe, Smith & Davis LLP | |
| Frenier Diane M | Reed Smith LLP | |
| Gross Steven E | Sills Cummis & Gross P.C. * | |
| Kailes Howard | McCarter & English, LLP * | |
| Kamen Steven R | Sills Cummis & Gross P.C. * | |
| Pergola Anthony O | Lowenstein Sandler LLP * | |
| Rave Michael T | Day Pitney LLP * | |
| Rosenberg Ira A | Sills Cummis & Gross P.C. * | |
| Stamelman Andrew J | Riker Danzig Scherer Hyland & Perretti LLP | |
| Wovsaniker Alan | Lowenstein Sandler LLP * | |
| **Band 3** | | |
| Baumel Jeffrey | Dentons * | |
| Broderick David F | McCarter & English, LLP * | |
| Cleary II John L | Dentons * | |
| Colella Paul | Giordano Halleran & Ciesla PC | |
| Connolly William G | Riker Danzig Scherer Hyland & Perretti LLP | |
| Crane R Max | Sills Cummis & Gross P.C. * | |
| Detrizio Charles | Riker Danzig Scherer Hyland & Perretti LLP | |
| Dunne Michael J | Day Pitney LLP * | |
| Forlenza Philip D | Giordano Halleran & Ciesla PC | |
| Harris Brett | Wilentz, Goldman & Spitzer, P.A. | |
| Jasaitis James E | Dentons * | |
| Marino James J | Dechert LLP (ONP) † * | |
| Minion Robert G | Lowenstein Sandler LLP * | |
| Papier David J | Dentons * | |
| Shur Paul H | Blank Rome LLP (ONP) † * | |
| Thek Raymond P | Lowenstein Sandler LLP * | |
| **Band 4** | | |
| Cannone Frank T | Gibbons P.C. * | |
| Glazer David G | Morgan, Lewis & Bockius LLP * | |
| Goodman Scott Warren | Day Pitney LLP * | |
| Heeb Lisa | McCarter & English, LLP * | |
| Laracy Ward | McCarter & English, LLP * | |
| Segota Denis | Morgan, Lewis & Bockius LLP * | |
| Smith Laurence | Wolff & Samson PC | |
| Tucker H. Glenn | Greenberg Dauber Epstein & Tucker (ONP) † | |
| Yan Betty | Reed Smith LLP | |

\* Indicates firm / individual with profile.
† ONP = 'Other Notable Practitioner.'

Sources say: *"Excellent in their drafting and always ready, willing and able to do anything. Brilliant lawyers who know how to do everything."*

**KEY INDIVIDUALS** Practice chair **Peter Ehrenberg** (see p.1735) remains one of the most prominent names within New Jersey corporate law. Sources hail him as a *"deep thinker"* and a *"top-of-the-line attorney,"* with one impressed interviewee describing Ehrenberg as *"an extraordinary litigator and one of the hardest-working lawyers I have ever worked with."* **Edward Zimmerman** (see p.1750) is chair of the firm's technology group and was lead partner in the Buddy Media sale. A well-known and respected rainmaker, he is described as *"working hard to make sure clients get the service they need."* Heavily involved in the Buddy Media sale and vice chair of the firm's tech group, **Anthony Pergola** (see p.1744) is regarded as *"a master draftsman, remarkably responsive and fun to work with."* **Alan Wovsaniker** (see p.1750) is regarded by those in the marketplace to be building a *"great reputation in the state."* He is also noted for his abundant knowledge of SEC regulations. Technology vice chair **Raymond Thek** (see p.1749) is praised by market sources as *"a master at structuring deals and one of the best negotiators I have ever met."* Thek splits his time between the firm's Roseland and New York offices, and his recent highlights include representing online fashion retailer Moda Operandi in a $36 million investment deal with Condé Nast and others. Investment management group chair **Robert Minion** (see p.1742) has been lead attorney in respect to the firm's advice to clients such as Cerberus Capital Management and Marathon Asset Management. He is noted for his skills in advising on ongoing business development.

## Band 2

### Gibbons P.C.
See profile on p.1754

**THE FIRM** Gibbons's Newark-based M&A practice continues to grow. The group comprises 19 highly active partners who cater to a range of midmarket corporates, financial sponsors and government bodies on a host of transactional activities. Clients also benefit from the firm's international strengths, with particular expertise concerning Western Europe, Australia and Japan. Its client roster features JPMorgan Securities and Bayer HealthCare Pharmaceuticals, and in a recent highlight the firm advised the County of Monmouth on its $97 million general obligation bond issuance.

Sources say: *"They are outstanding. The knowledge displayed in each of the practice areas was phenomenal. I was always made to feel like I was the priority."*

**KEY INDIVIDUALS** Corporate department chair **Frank Cannone** (see p.1732) debuts in the rankings this year on the back of strong market praise. Interviewees say Cannone is *"extremely responsive"* and further highlight his sage business counsel.

### McCarter & English, LLP
See profile on p.1759

**THE FIRM** This corporate group has been involved in some particularly high-value transactions in the past year, such as representing Verisk Analytics in its $700 million refinancing deal. Other recent representations, such as Hayward Industries' acquisition of a majority stake in Clevaquip, showcase the team's ability to act for multinationals active across several continents. New client wins for the group include Alliant Technologies and United Overseas Bank in Singapore.

Sources say: *"They know their stuff."* *"Their support and expertise are wonderful."*

**KEY INDIVIDUALS** **Howard Kailes**'s (see p.1738) practice focuses on M&A and financing for public and private entities. He is described by market sources as *"highly intuitive about how to structure deals."* **David Broderick** (see p.1732) is co-head of the firm's small business investment practice and has significant expertise in Chinese cross-border deals. He is praised as one of *"the best venture capital lawyers"* in the state. The service provided by **Lisa Heeb** (see p.1737) is described as *"consistently exceptional and responsive."* She was lead counsel representing Verisk Analytics in its $348 million acquisition by MediConnect Global. **Ward Laracy** (see p.1740) debuts in the rankings this year, and sources say he is *"fantastic with tax issues."* He played a pivotal role in structuring the Hayward Industries transactions.

### Morgan, Lewis & Bockius LLP
See profile on p.2246

**THE FIRM** This international giant's Princeton-based transactional group is particularly active in technology, life sciences and private equity deals. With the ability to call on the combined expertise of over 130 business and finance partners firmwide, the New Jersey practice group has acted on a number of highly significant mandates in 2012. One such transaction was representing Danish pharmaceutical company Lundbeck in a development and commercialization deal with a potential value running into billions of dollars.

Sources say: *"They are very responsive, understand our business objectives and are flexible enough to initiate alternative fee arrangements."*

**KEY INDIVIDUALS** **Randall Sunberg** (see p.1749) is vice chair of the firm's global life sciences practice group and is particularly active in the biotech and large pharmaceutical industry sectors. Market sources praise his ability to *"understand how the business functions and what agreements have to say to make them work."* **Steven Cohen** (see p.1733) receives plaudits for his *"understanding of the dynamics of small companies"* as well as *"how to balance cost and expenditure."* He was lead counsel representing Ascend Performance Materials in its $550 million Term Loan B financing deal. **Denis Segota** (see p.1747) joins this year's rankings on the back of strong market praise. He is *"an excellent negotiator with expert knowledge of all aspects of the pharmaceutical and biotech industry,"* says one source. **David Glazer** (see p.1736) makes his first appearance in the rankings, having been described as *"a good drafter and*

adviser and a very good problem solver."* His highlights include advising LifeNet on its acquisition of Northwest Tissue Services to form a new wholly-owned subsidiary.

### Riker Danzig Scherer Hyland & Perretti LLP
See profile on p.1761

**THE FIRM** Riker Danzig's New Jersey corporate team comprises nine partners and 15 associates. The group possesses extensive experience across a wide variety of industry sectors including pharmaceuticals, healthcare, telecoms and energy. With a strong commitment to understanding their clients' businesses, the group focuses on midmarket deals and has international expertise in the Russian market.

Sources say: *"Their work is excellent."*

**KEY INDIVIDUALS** Department head **Andrew Stamelman** receives praise as *"one of the brightest attorneys I have ever worked with. He analyzes risks and understands how to structure a deal accordingly."* His depth of corporate knowledge also attracts positive commentary. **William Connolly** earns praise from clients for his *"excellent communication skills when negotiating and advising, so that all the relevant parties understand."* His practice focuses squarely on small and medium-sized companies. **Charles Detrizio** recently represented Northern Lights Power in its $6 million sale of a holding company. He is described as *"practical business attorney – a great drafter with great attention to detail."*

### Sills Cummis & Gross P.C.
See profile on p.1762

**THE FIRM** This Newark-based corporate team has considerable experience across the full spectrum of public and private corporate matters. The firm represents clients in a variety of industries, including pharmaceuticals, life sciences, technology and the financial services. Over the years the group has developed something of a specialty in acting for foreign companies trading in the USA.

Sources say: *"They are very responsive and accessible, and I get a quick response when I need one."*

**KEY INDIVIDUALS** Chairman **Steven Gross** (see p.1736) has over 30 years' experience handling complex corporate transactions. Market sources describe him as a *"very smart guy and a very good global strategist."* Sources describe **Steven Kamen** (see p.1738) as solution-oriented, able to present a solution *"before the problem even becomes apparent."* He is also praised for his attention to detail and his responsiveness. Department co-head **Ira Rosenberg** (see p.1746) is particularly active within the life sciences space. He has remained busy acting on a number of significant transactions in recent months. **Max Crane** (see p.1733) is held in high regard by market sources. They describe him as *"an entrepreneur at heart who understands all the aspects of a business as well as being gifted legally."*

## Band 3

### DLA Piper LLP (US)
See profile on p.1971

**THE FIRM** The compact New Jersey M&A team at DLA Piper is particularly active within the life sciences and technology industry sectors. The five-lawyer team supports transactions for companies of all sizes and is equipped to act on a broad range of related tax and restructuring issues as well. Its clients include Archive Systems, Ports America and ViroPharma.

**Sources say:** *"They have been terrific. They offer a nice mix of practical advice while ensuring we get what we need."*

**KEY INDIVIDUALS Andrew Gilbert** (see p.1736) earns accolades as a *"great lawyer but also a guy with invaluable business savvy."* Recent work highlights include representing ViroPharma in its $165 million acquisition of DuoCort Pharma.

### Giordano Halleran & Ciesla PC

**THE FIRM** This tight-knit corporate department is well known in the New Jersey market for its work on midmarket transactions across a wide variety of industries. Its client roster features a range of public and private companies, partnerships and individual entrepreneurs.

**Sources say:** *"They give a high level of personal touch with very skilled attorneys who are knowledgeable in corporate law."*

**KEY INDIVIDUALS** Department head **John Aiello** is seen by market commentators as one of the leading practitioners with New Jersey corporate law. He is described simply as a *"remarkable lawyer."* **Paul Colella** splits his practice between advising on compliance issues and in relation to raising capital in public and private markets. **Philip Forlenza** is a *"24/7 guy; he is always available,"* say sources. He focuses his practice on financing, restructuring and securities.

### Greenbaum, Rowe, Smith & Davis LLP
See profile on p.1755

**THE FIRM** This Woodbridge-based corporate group has a core of eight attorneys with extensive experience in all corporate matters. The group is able to represent clients across a host of industry sectors on matters ranging from routine to high-profile projects. The firm also has extensive expertise in IP and real estate. Clients have praised the group's responsiveness.

**Sources say:** *"They are able to provide for all our legal needs and their response time is amazing."*

**KEY INDIVIDUALS** Described as an *"excellent attorney,"* **Alan Davis** is the former chair of the group and focuses his practice on representing small to medium-sized clients. Corporate practice group chair **Raymond Felton** is highly regarded within the New Jersey marketplace. Sources cite his ability to *"understand the realities of business and get things done in an efficient and timely manner."*

### Reed Smith LLP

**THE FIRM** Reed Smith's Princeton-based corporate group is best known for its transactional work within the life sciences industry. The group is experienced in representing companies at each stage of the business life cycle, and counts among its clients global players such as GlaxoSmithKline and Eli Lilly alongside development-stage companies like Ascenta Therapeutics. The group also proves popular with foreign companies seeking counsel on inbound transactions.

**Sources say:** *"With Reed Smith I know that I'm going to get excellent service quickly."*

**KEY INDIVIDUALS** Department head **Diane Frenier** is widely regarded as *"an extremely competent life sciences attorney."* Recently, she acted as lead counsel representing Dr Reddy's Labs in a co-development deal with MerckSerno. The *"very bright"* **Betty Yan** joins this year's rankings. One enthusiastic source said: *"She knows our business and understands the important things we are looking for in a transaction."*

### Wilentz, Goldman & Spitzer, P.A.
See profile on p.1763

**THE FIRM** The well-rounded team at Wilentz, Goldman & Spitzer has developed a strong focus on the technology sector. Its transactional group caters to software developers, online businesses and outsourcing firms on the full spectrum of corporate matters. Its clients include the New Jersey Turnpike Authority, AtlantiCare and the Arnold P Gold Foundation.

**Sources say:** *"A top-notch firm with a bullpen filled with great players."*

**KEY INDIVIDUALS** *"Results-focused"* **Brett Harris** was lead counsel representing the New Jersey Turnpike Authority on a recent multistate public procurement exercise valued at approximately $100 million within the state. Sources say Harris is adept at *"identifying the risk factors"* and *"coming up with solutions and alternatives that can work."*

### Wolff & Samson PC

**THE FIRM** Wolff & Samson in West Orange is a corporate group possessed of considerable experience across a range of industry sectors, including the financial services, real estate and manufacturing. The firm is well known in the New Jersey corporate market for its skill in representing clients on small to medium-sized deals. Nimble staffing and partners who are willing to roll their sleeves up enable the firm to compete vigorously in terms of billing. Foster Wheeler and Bayshore Recycling count among the firm's clients.

**KEY INDIVIDUALS** Department co-head **Laurence Smith** enters the rankings this year, having been particularly active within the healthcare arena. He has a broad corporate practice and is a member of the firm's corporate travel group.

## Band 4

### Greenberg Traurig, LLP
See profile on p.1024

**THE FIRM** This Florham Park corporate group has experience across the full gamut of M&A and corporate matters. Its ability to draw on the wider support of Greenberg Traurig offices domestically as well as internationally is an additional bonus.

**Sources say:** *"Their New Jersey practice group is excellent, as is the level of deal they get."*

**KEY INDIVIDUALS** Robert Wexler is a key contact.

### Other Notable Practitioners

**James Marino** (see p.1741) of Dechert LLP is managing partner of the firm's Princeton's office as well as chair of its corporate and securities life science group. He is known within the New Jersey market for an acute understanding of the business realities underpinning corporate transactions. **Paul Shur** (see p.1748) of Blank Rome LLP is held in high regard by market sources for his breath of knowledge and experience in financing transactions. **Glenn Tucker** of Greenberg Dauber Epstein & Tucker is chair of the corporate department at the firm's Newark office. With over 30 years' experience, he is a prominent name within the New Jersey corporate market.

# EMPLOYEE BENEFITS & EXECUTIVE COMPENSATION

Commentary about individuals can be found under their firm's paragraph. If the firm has no paragraph (is not ranked) look at Other Notable Practitioners.

### Employee Benefits & Executive Compensation
#### Leading Firms

**Band 1**
Day Pitney LLP *
McCarter & English, LLP *

**Band 2**
Epstein Becker & Green PC *
Lowenstein Sandler LLP *

#### Leading Individuals

| **Band 1** | |
| --- | --- |
| Daniele Mark A | *McCarter & English, LLP* * |
| Disler Joan A | *Epstein Becker & Green PC* * |
| Graw Andrew E | *Lowenstein Sandler LLP* * |
| Lawler Kathy A | *Day Pitney LLP* * |
| Mercer Joy | *Joy M Mercer PC (ONP)[†]* |
| Witman Leonard J | *Witman Stadtmauer, PA (ONP)[†]* |

| **Band 2** | |
| --- | --- |
| Brescher John B | *McCarter & English, LLP* * |
| Doyle David P | *Day Pitney LLP* * |

\* Indicates firm / individual with profile.
[†] ONP = Other Notable Practitioner.

## Band 1

### Day Pitney LLP
See profile on p.1753
**THE FIRM** This stalwart of the New Jersey employee benefits and executive compensation arena is experienced across the full spectrum of benefit matters. The firm is renowned for its work with Fortune 500 and well-known multinational companies, and routinely represents publicly traded companies across a range of industry sectors. An illustrious client list includes The New York Times Company, Volvo and Agfa.
**Sources say:** "*They are outstanding. They make themselves available to us all the time, and we are very pleased with the quality of their work.*"
**KEY INDIVIDUALS Kathy Lawler** (see p.1740) is a highly experienced market-leading attorney whose practice encompasses the full spectrum benefit matters. One inter-

viewee attests that "*she knows her stuff, and we trust her implicitly.*" **David Doyle** (see p.1734) is lauded by one client as an "*expert on regulations, and very helpful in organizing our plans in terms of the tax implications.*" He handles a comprehensive range of matters, including benefits issues arising from mergers and acquisitions, and qualified and non-qualified pension plans.

### McCarter & English, LLP
See profile on p.1759
**THE FIRM** The tax, employee benefits and private clients group at the firm is experienced across the full range of employee benefit matters. Its robust team counsels clients on the design, interpretation and administration of retirement, welfare and executive compensation plans, and is noted for its handling of tax or ERISA issues that may arise. Recently the group acted as special ERISA counsel to the committee of retirees of Nortel Networks in relation to the termination of benefit plans.
**Sources say:** "*We found the firm very thorough in their analysis of relevant legislation, and very helpful in looking for alternative ways to overcome difficulties.*"
**KEY INDIVIDUALS Mark Daniele** (see p.1734) heads up the team. He was lead counsel in the matter for Nortel Networks described above. Sources remark that "*he is fantastic. He is a great asset in helping us navigate around pension issues.*" **John Brescher** (see p.1732) recently acted for the Institute of Electrical and Electronics Engineers in connection with the amendment of its retirement plans. Sources laud his "*technical knowledge, as well as his ability to relate to clients and communicate difficult concepts to them in a simple way.*"

## Band 2

### Epstein Becker & Green PC
See profile on p.1972
**THE FIRM** Epstein's full-service employee benefits New Jersey practice group offers experience across retirement plans, health and welfare, executive compensation, multiemployer plans, and fiduciary training. The firm can count

Oppenheimer Funds, BlackRock and News America among an impressive roster of clients.
**Sources say:** "*Outstanding. Excellent responsiveness, and availability has never been an issue.*"
**KEY INDIVIDUALS Joan Disler** (see p.1734) is chair of the firm's national employee benefits steering committee, and a fixture of the New Jersey employee benefits sphere. "*I think she does a fantastic job of ensuring that we stay on top of the required changes and ensures that we make good choices in fixing any issue,*" says one impressed source.

### Lowenstein Sandler LLP
See profile on p.1757
**THE FIRM** This firm's employee benefits and executive compensation group regularly advises in matters stemming from mergers, acquisitions and bankruptcies. The team recently represented Pall Corporation with respect to the creation of new executive compensation plans. Other clients include Telcordia Technologies and Cerberus Capital.
**Sources say:** "*I am very impressed with their work. They offer high-quality legal work, and are very responsive and easy to work with.*"
**KEY INDIVIDUALS Andrew Graw** (see p.1736) is held in high regard by peers and clients alike. He is chair of the firm's employee benefits and executive compensation group, and is praised by clients as "*a very practical lawyer who will tell us what he thinks we should do, but also offer us alternatives.*"

### Other Notable Practitioners

Sole practitioner **Joy Mercer** earns praise for her knowledge base and diligence in employee benefits and ERISA matters. "*She is able to communicate well to laypeople and she is a good counsel,*" sources say. **Leonard Witman** of Witman Stadtmauer, PA is renowned for his knowledge of ERISA matters and tax issues stemming from compensation and benefits plans. "*I have a tremendous amount of respect for him. He is a great lawyer and a terrific sounding board,*" reports one interviewee.

# ENVIRONMENT

Commentary about individuals can be found under their firm's paragraph. If the firm has no paragraph (is not ranked) look at Other Notable Practitioners.

## Environment
### Leading Firms

**Band 1**

Archer & Greiner, A Professional Corporation *

Drinker Biddle & Reath LLP *

K&L Gates *

Lowenstein Sandler LLP *

McCarter & English, LLP *

Riker Danzig Scherer Hyland & Perretti LLP *

Wolff & Samson PC

**Band 2**

Fox Rothschild LLP *

Gibbons P.C.

Giordano Halleran & Ciesla PC

Greenbaum, Rowe, Smith & Davis LLP *

Norris McLaughlin & Marcus, PA

**Band 3**

Day Pitney LLP *

Porzio, Bromberg & Newman PC

Saul Ewing LLP *

Sokol, Behot & Fiorenzo

\* Indicates firm / individual with profile.

† ONP = Other Notable Practitioner.

### Leading Individuals

**Band 1**

| | |
|---|---|
| Bromberg Lisa | Porzio, Bromberg & Newman PC |
| Farer David B | Greenbaum, Rowe, Smith & Davis LLP |
| Gross Michael J | Giordano Halleran & Ciesla PC |
| Harris Glenn A | Ballard Spahr LLP (ONP)† * |
| Hluchan Richard M | Hyland Levin (ONP)† |
| Hogan Edward A | Norris McLaughlin & Marcus, PA * |
| Hyatt, Jr William H | K&L Gates * |
| Krumholz Dennis J | Riker Danzig Scherer Hyland & Perretti LLP |
| Kurzweil Lanny S | McCarter & English, LLP * |
| Picco Steven J | Saul Ewing LLP |
| Ricci Richard F | Lowenstein Sandler LLP * |
| Rodburg Michael L | Lowenstein Sandler LLP * |
| Toft Dennis M | Wolff & Samson PC |
| Warren William L | Drinker Biddle & Reath LLP * |
| Yoskin Neil | Sokol, Behot & Fiorenzo |

**Band 2**

| | |
|---|---|
| Conway Richard | Schenck, Price, Smith & King, LLP (ONP)† |
| DeStefano Louis | Buchanan Ingersoll & Rooney PC (ONP)† * |
| Diamond Lawrence W | Duane Morris LLP (ONP)† |
| Donovan Martha N | Norris McLaughlin & Marcus, PA * |
| Dore Michael | Lowenstein Sandler LLP * |
| Ericsson Richard J | Cole, Schotz, Meisel, Forman (ONP)† * |
| Freilich Irvin M | Gibbons P.C. |
| Gengel Gary P | Latham & Watkins LLP (ONP)† |
| Gibson Christopher R | Archer & Greiner * |
| Gottlieb Ira | McCarter & English, LLP * |
| Hatfield William S | Gibbons P.C. * |
| Judge Marty | Flaster Greenberg PC (ONP)† |
| Lynott Keith E | McCarter & English, LLP * |
| Mack Kenneth H | Fox Rothschild LLP * |
| McKinney Jr John A | Wolff & Samson PC |
| Monaghan Sean | Drinker Biddle & Reath LLP * |
| Montag Brian S | K&L Gates * |
| Pollock Jeffrey M | Fox Rothschild LLP * |
| Robins Andrew B | Sills Cummis & Gross P.C. (ONP)† * |
| Rollo Marc A | Archer & Greiner * |

| | |
|---|---|
| Schneider David P | Bressler Amery & Ross (ONP)† |
| Schneider Paul H | Giordano Halleran & Ciesla PC |
| Stewart James | Lowenstein Sandler LLP * |
| Waeger Ann M | Greenbaum, Rowe, Smith & Davis LLP |

**Band 3**

| | |
|---|---|
| Bennett Herbert B. | Sokol, Behot & Fiorenzo |
| Bruno Kevin | Blank Rome LLP (ONP)† * |
| Cappola Jeffrey | Wilentz, Goldman & Spitzer, P.A. (ONP)† |
| Donovan Colleen R | Day Pitney LLP * |
| Dritsas Paul C | McCarter & English, LLP * |
| Greenberg Marilynn R | Riker Danzig Scherer Hyland & Perretti LLP |
| Karp Susan C. | Cole, Schotz, Meisel, Forman (ONP)† * |
| Klock John H | Gibbons P.C. |
| Lehman Robert T | Archer & Greiner * |
| Lewin Ross A | Drinker Biddle & Reath LLP * |
| McAuliffe Christopher | Morgan, Lewis & Bockius LLP (ONP)† |
| McGahren John | Patton Boggs LLP (ONP)† |
| Mills Lori | Drinker Biddle & Reath LLP * |
| Minuskin Heidi S | Coughlin Duffy LLP (ONP)† |
| Moulthrop Samuel P | Riker Danzig Scherer Hyland & Perretti LLP |
| Peticolas Susanne | Gibbons P.C. |
| Policastro Marc | Giordano Halleran & Ciesla PC |
| Reitano Anthony | Herold Law, P.A. (ONP)† |
| Roth David A | Greenbaum, Rowe, Smith & Davis LLP |
| Sadat Ellen Radow | Drinker Biddle & Reath LLP * |
| Senior Steven T | Riker Danzig Scherer Hyland & Perretti LLP |
| Spiesman Thomas | Porzio, Bromberg & Newman PC |
| Spinello John F | K&L Gates * |
| Wagenbach Jeffrey B | Riker Danzig Scherer Hyland & Perretti LLP |
| Ward Catherine M. | Stradley Ronon Stevens & Young (ONP)† |

**Up-and-coming individuals**

| | |
|---|---|
| Buongiorno Diana | Wolff & Samson PC |
| Otero Camille | Gibbons P.C. * |
| Sinclair Stacey | Archer & Greiner * |

**Associates to watch**

| | |
|---|---|
| Richmond-LaLonde Alexa | Riker Danzig Scherer Hyland & Perretti |

## Band 1

### Archer & Greiner, A Professional Corporation
See profile on p.1751

**THE FIRM** This Haddonfield-based team is renowned as one of the leading environmental litigation groups in the state. The firm is engaged by numerous clients in relation to multiplaintiff personal damage litigation, advising a range of international names from the petrochemical industry. Its areas of expertise also include permitting, site remediation, Superfund disputes and air and water pollution. In one highlight, the group successfully defended a major client in one of the first cases arising under the New Jersey Spill Act Contribution Amendment.

**Sources say:** *"They are excellent – my model of a great firm."*
**KEY INDIVIDUALS Marc Rollo** (see p.1746) is described by market sources as a *"very seasoned environmental attorney, who is very responsive and client-focused."* He also attracts plaudits for his strategic skills, and is *"very good at knowing what is coming round the corner."* Department co-head and president of the firm **Christopher Gibson** (see p.1736) is a *"fantastic attorney,"* who is valued for his expertise in complex litigation. The highly reputed **Robert Lehman** (see p.1740) is lauded by peers for his strong courtroom performance. Clients describe **Stacey Sinclair** (see p.1748) as *"excellent – she delivers high-quality consistent work and is highly valued."*

### Drinker Biddle & Reath LLP
See profile on p.2238

**THE FIRM** This high-caliber practice covers the full gamut of environmental law, and is highly active in air and solid waste enforcement matters. The firm has impressive expertise in advising large manufacturing and solid waste companies on site remediation and regulatory compliance. In addition, it continues to be a driving force in the Lower Passaic River Superfund litigation, defending affiliated companies in the largest Superfund site in the state's history. An impressive client roster includes the Chrysler Group and Republic Services/Allied Waste Industries.

**Sources say:** *"Drinker Biddle & Reath has given us uniformly professional service in all areas that we have engaged them."*

**KEY INDIVIDUALS William Warren** (see p.1749) is described by market sources as *"one of the deans of environmental law practice in New Jersey."* He is currently representing two clients in relation to the ongoing Passaic River litigation. **Sean Monaghan** (see p.1743) is *"a great attorney,"* described as *"well versed and easy to work with."* His practice covers litigation and regulatory compliance issues as well as transactional matters. **Ross Lewin** (see p.1741) handles a range of litigation and regulatory counseling, and is well known for his experience in the solid waste industry. He represented Republic Services in a $100 million contract bid dispute. **Lori Mills** (see p.1742) is praised as a *"very conscientious and thoughtful lawyer,"* who represents clients at several Superfund sites across the state and nationwide. Clients describe **Ellen Radow Sadat** (see p.1747) as a *"very knowledgeable and very practical"* counselor, with valuable regulatory knowledge.

## K&L Gates
See profile on p.2245

THE FIRM The environmental team at this international giant offers expert advice across the spectrum of compliance and litigation issues. Its diverse client base covers a wide range of industries, and the firm represents local and national names in the mining, cement and fragrance industries. It also works with various business associations in the state, counseling both the New Jersey Asphalt Pavement Association and the Chemical Council of New Jersey. The group has considerable experience in matters arising from the CAA, as well as Superfund matters, and acts as coordinating counsel to the Lower Passaic River Study Area Cooperating Parties Group (CPG).

Sources say: *"The firm has been terrific – the whole group really contributes and is extremely responsive to our needs." "Excellent judgment and incisive counseling."*

KEY INDIVIDUALS Sources hold **William Hyatt** (see p.1738) in high regard, describing him as *"extremely knowledgeable, bright and easygoing."* The well-regarded **Brian Montag** (see p.1743) handles various compliance and litigation matters, as well as both state and federal permitting. Clients laud him as *"excellent – he has a keen mind, and is an effective communicator."* **John Spinello** (see p.1748) has significant expertise in compliance counseling, and is renowned for his work in New Jersey and across the country.

## Lowenstein Sandler LLP
See profile on p.1757

THE FIRM Lowenstein Sandler's environmental practice is lauded for its impressive depth of resources and high-quality work product. Its extensive experience covers the full range of environmental matters, and the group's caseload includes hazardous waste litigation and Superfund remediation as well as the defense of toxic tort cases. In standout work, the firm defended the Marmon Group in 21 toxic tort cases filed on behalf of more than 1,000 individual plaintiffs in Illinois. Other clients include Sanofi, Aramark and the Global Landfill PRP Group.

Sources say: *"They are one of the top firms in New Jersey and they have plenty of resources."*

KEY INDIVIDUALS **Michael Rodburg** (see p.1746) combines in-depth knowledge of environmental law with a valuable understanding of chemical engineering. Clients have a high regard for his experience in pollution issues, describing him as *"seasoned veteran of the Bar in one of the most densely polluted areas of the world."* Practice chair **Richard Ricci** (see p.1745) is praised by market sources for his ability to resolve conflicts, and to offer clarity of insight when it comes to complex issues. **James Stewart** (see p.1748) has considerable expertise in the renewable energy sector, and acted for Sanofi on the negotiation of a solar power purchase agreement. **Michael Dore** (see p.1734) defends a variety of corporate clients in toxic tort allegations, and represented Unidynamics in an environmental discharge class action.

## McCarter & English, LLP
See profile on p.1759

THE FIRM This leading team has strengthened its bench with the addition of an experienced energy practitioner, further boosting its capabilities in the renewable energy arena. The group's broader skill set includes extensive expertise in legacy site remediation and land transfer issues. In highlights, the practice served as lead counsel to Becton, Dickinson & Company in the Berry's Creek Study Area Superfund site remediation investigation. The firm's diverse client roster also features KDC Solar, Buzzi Unicem USA and United Nuclear Corporation.

Sources say: *"Excellent firm – the lawyers are practical and very responsive."*

KEY INDIVIDUALS **Lanny Kurzweil** (see p.1740) distinguishes himself in the field of environmental litigation and receives praise from sources for his creativity and foresight. One satisfied client asserted: *"If I had an environmental issue I would not go to anyone else."* Former EPA lawyer **Ira Gottlieb** (see p.1736) is head of the environmental and energy practice group at the firm. He has significant insurance experience, and sources comment that he *"performs flawlessly and comes up with brilliant strategy."* **Keith Lynott** (see p.1741) has a wide-ranging workload, counseling clients on regulatory compliance and transactional matters. The *"very smart, very practical"* **Paul Dritsas** (see p.1735) debuts in the rankings having received a variety of plaudits from clients. He is *"incredibly knowledgeable, and his advice always considers the broader picture and strategy."*

## Riker Danzig Scherer Hyland & Perretti LLP
See profile on p.1761

THE FIRM Riker Danzig's Morristown-based team has a broad base of experience covering the full spectrum of environmental matters. Clients can call on the talents of experts in transactional work, litigation, site remediation and land use. The firm acts on behalf of financial services providers and real estate developers, as well as advising major names in the defense and petrochemical industries. The group represented G&S Motor Equipment in a $65 million site remediation dispute regarding a former transformer rebuilding factory. Other major clients include AIG and Berry Plastics.

Sources say: *"Their strengths are their knowledge, expertise, depth of personnel and unique ability to find good solutions to difficult issues."*

KEY INDIVIDUALS **Dennis Krumholz** is a highly experienced specialist, who of late has represented a big-ticket defense client in a New Jersey Spill Act suit. **Samuel Moulthrop** is a former Assistant District Attorney for New Jersey and a skilled litigator, who acts for a group of clients involved in the Lower Passaic River litigation. Clients are enthusiastic in their praise of **Steven Senior**, who is *"great at focusing on the essential issues, and a very good detail man."* **Jeffrey Wagenbach** represented G&S Motor Equipment in the abovementioned remediation litigation. **Marilynn Greenberg** is a highly valued member of the team, who*"in addition to her extensive knowledge, experience and expert legal advice, is an excellent team administra-

tor and leader."* Praised by clients as *"very able,"* **Alexa Richmond-LaLonde** is deemed a future star.

## Wolff & Samson PC

THE FIRM This firm is renowned for its wealth of experience in regulatory compliance and transactional matters, and offers formidable strength in environmental litigation. The team is often engaged by large manufacturing and utilities companies, and also counts high-profile real estate developers among its client base. The team recently acted for the Public Service Enterprise Group (PSEG) in obtaining approvals for major transmission upgrade projects valued at hundreds of millions of dollars.

KEY INDIVIDUALS Co-head of the department **Dennis Toft** is lead partner in the PSEG matter and is recognized by clients and peers alike as one of the top transactional attorneys in the state. He is described as a *"bright guy, and a terrific attorney."* **John McKinney** is a *"top-flight environmental attorney who is very easy to work with."* He earns accolades for his decades of high-quality work in environmental matters, and is valued by clients for his efficiency. **Diana Buongiorno** is lauded by peers for continuing to build her practice, and represents clients in a variety of complex high-value environmental litigation.

## Band 2

## Fox Rothschild LLP
See profile on p.2242

THE FIRM This full-service firm has a sterling reputation for its environmental litigation practice, and is also widely praised for its work in site remediation. The team often acts for large chemical, biochemical and cosmetic companies, and has distinguished itself in environmental matters with an insurance or bankruptcy component. The firm represented Compaction Systems in an extremely complex case before the New Jersey Federal Court in relation to remedial costs sought at the Combe Fill South Superfund site.

Sources say: *"Outstanding representation – in every department they have a team of specialists who work together to solve problems."*

KEY INDIVIDUALS Practice cochair **Kenneth Mack** (see p.1741) is *"practical and hard-working – a great litigator who brings those skills to the environmental field."* Standout matters include a case relating to the Passaic River litigation. **Jeffrey Pollock** (see p.1745) combines his extensive environmental expertise with impressive strength in insurance coverage matters. Sources characterize him as *"resourceful and intelligent, with determination and a great breadth of knowledge."*

## Gibbons P.C.
See profile on p.1754

THE FIRM Gibbons's New Jersey team has welcomed three new partners, as well as gaining a fourth through internal promotion. William Hatfield and Camille Otero add further depth to the firm's impressive litigation capabilities, while David Freeman brings considerable expertise in the development of contaminated property. The firm's workload features a variety of high-value contentious cases, including complex multiparty sediment site issues. In standout matters, the team represented Honeywell in connection with the Berry's Creek sediment megasite case. Other major clients include Hoffmann-La Roche, Shell and Tiffany & Co.

**Sources say:** "*The firm's representation went beyond the simple legal matter – our attorney counseled us on the financial and business decisions involved.*"

**KEY INDIVIDUALS** The "*smart and practical*" **Irvin Freilich** is the environmental team leader at the firm. He represented Novartis in connection with the the Rolling Knolls Landfill case. Clients have high praise for **John Klock**, who is "*a wonderful guy, with an incredible background in complex environmental remediation projects.*" **Susanne Peticolas** is a "*very bright attorney, who is very well versed in environmental law.*" She is also commended for her negotiation skills. **Camille Otero** (see p.1744) is well regarded by peers for her strength in environmental and toxic tort litigation. **William Hatfield** (see p.1737) is one of the leading partners advising various clients of the firm on the headline-grabbing Newark Bay Complex sediment case. The matter has a potential value of hundreds of millions of dollars.

### Giordano Halleran & Ciesla PC

**THE FIRM** Giordano's Red Bank-based environmental practice group has carved out a niche for itself in the representation of some of the state's largest trade associations, including the New Jersey Builders Association and the National Brownfield Association. In addition, the group is experienced in advising developers of industrial and manufacturing facilities, as well as telecom companies. The team acted for Toll Brothers in obtaining environmental and land use approvals from the New Jersey Department of Environmental Protection for a proposed development valued at more than $100 million.

**Sources say:** "*They have been absolutely incredible – very knowledgeable and responsive, exceptional attorneys.*"

**KEY INDIVIDUALS** Practice head **Michael Gross** is held in high regard by clients, who consider him "*top of the line in terms of environmental law in New Jersey – very well respected, thorough, knowledgeable and never misses a thing.*" **Paul Schneider** is cochair of the litigation practice at the firm. He focuses his environmental practice on matters pertaining to land use, site remediation and regulatory compliance, and is an "*excellent and knowledgeable*" adviser. **Marc Policastro** is frequently called on for representation in complex site remediation matters, as well as for compliance advice.

### Greenbaum, Rowe, Smith & Davis LLP
See profile on p.1755

**THE FIRM** This group offers valuable experience across the full range of environmental issues at both state and federal level. The team is well equipped to assist clients with their environmental needs, whether these entail advice on legacy remediation obligations, negotiations with government bodies or representation in complex liti-

gation. The firm continues to act for L'Oréal on the acquisition and development of facilities in central New Jersey, and also advises the New Jersey Natural Gas Company on a variety of environmental and land use issues. Other major clients include Wells Fargo and Tyco International.

**Sources say:** "*They are very practical and hands-on, incredibly responsive and efficient.*"

**KEY INDIVIDUALS David Farer** is head of the environment practice. He is an "*excellent practitioner,*" commended for his well-rounded regulatory knowledge and his "*great attention to detail.*" Clients appreciate **David Roth's** commitment to client service, describing him as a "*practical guy, who listens to his clients, and is very responsive.*" **Ann Waeger** is an "*excellent attorney,*" who focuses on environmental insurance and transactional matters.

### Norris McLaughlin & Marcus, PA

**THE FIRM** This multitalented environmental group continues to attract a variety of high-profile contentious work, as well as advising clients on regulatory issues. The team is also well known for its expertise in Superfund site issues. In one standout litigation mandate, the team defended MIG-Alberici in a long-running $271 million action regarding the transportation of contaminated concrete. Further highlights include work for Georgia-Pacific and Cardolite.

**Sources say:** "*Always responsive, they bring a sound understanding of New Jersey's regulations and they perform excellently.*"

**KEY INDIVIDUALS Edward Hogan** (see p.1737) is considered to be one of the leading members of the Bar when it comes to site remediation, and is generally "*very knowledgeable about the environmental regulations in New Jersey.*" Practice cochair **Martha Donovan** (see p.1734) is praised as a formidable advocate for her clients, as well as receiving plaudits for her intelligence, responsiveness and focus on detail.

## Band 3

### Day Pitney LLP
See profile on p.1753

**THE FIRM** After experiencing some departures in 2012, this team has bolstered its capabilities with the addition of a new partner and two associates. The group is highly skilled in compliance counseling and transactional work, and also advises on a variety of litigation cases. Its diverse client roster spans a wide range of sectors, and features Coca-Cola, BASF and ExxonMobil. The group represented a number of Fortune 100 clients in connection with a highly complex sediment site investigation, and the resulting multiparty litigation.

**Sources say:** "*Strong on client service and substantive knowledge.*"

**KEY INDIVIDUALS** Head of the environmental practice **Colleen Donovan** (see p.1734) is regarded by market sources as a "*very bright, capable and hard-working attorney.*"

### Porzio, Bromberg & Newman PC

**THE FIRM** This full-service Morristown-based group has a strong background in regulatory counseling as well as site remediation and transactional work. The team is praised for its dedication to service, and attracts a diverse array of clients ranging from startups to Fortune 500 companies. It represented Buckeye Partners in the acquisition of a large former Chevron site in New Jersey. Additional clients include Crestron Electronics and Hertz.

**Sources say:** "*Excellent service, and excellent subject matter expertise.*"

**KEY INDIVIDUALS** Practice co-head **Lisa Bromberg** was lead partner acting for Buckeye Partners in the abovementioned acquisition. Clients report that she is "*extremely focused on the issues – the New Jersey law in this area has changed a lot and she knows all the new laws intimately.*" **Thomas Spiesman** receives high praise from market sources, who assert that he is "*extremely skilled and responsive, and takes customer service to a new level.*"

### Saul Ewing LLP
See profile on p.2249

**THE FIRM** This firm is highly respected by peers for the strength of its environmental practice in New Jersey. The team offers considerable experience in bringing large-scale development projects to completion, and is well versed in land use, transactions and litigation. Its skills are called on by a number of major trade associations, as well as petrochemical, aviation and real estate companies.

**Sources say:** "*They have great expertise in environmental law in New Jersey, and provide prompt and practical advice.*"

**KEY INDIVIDUALS Steven Picco** divides his time between regulatory counseling, project development and litigation. A seasoned veteran, he is lauded by clients for his "*great expertise in environmental law in New Jersey, and his prompt and practical advice.*"

### Sokol, Behot & Fiorenzo

**THE FIRM** The firm's Princeton-based practice is particularly active within the site remediation, environmental counseling and litigation arena, although it is more than equipped to deal with any environmental issue that may arise. The group most commonly represents municipal government, financial institutions and property owners.

**KEY INDIVIDUALS Neil Yoskin** is regarded as "*one of the leading land use guys in the state,*" and is lauded for his knowledge of water-related environmental issues. His broad-based experience includes waterfront development, wetlands and groundwater pollution. **Herbert Bennett** is also a former staff attorney with the New Jersey Department of Environmental Protection, and divides his practice between site remediation, pollution issues and insurance coverage matters.

### Other Notable Practitioners

**Glenn Harris** (see p.1737) of Ballard Spahr LLP is an "*outstanding lawyer and a great litigator,*" described by clients as "*particularly adept at taking a large volume of facts and boiling them down.*" **Louis DeStefano** (see p.1734) of

Buchanan Ingersoll & Rooney PC is highly regarded as a stalwart of the market, and has represented clients in various aspects of brownfield redevelopment and environmental compliance. He also advises on Superfund issues, and in the opinion of one source he *"knows Superfunds better than anybody."* **David Schneider** of Bressler Amery & Ross is a former New Jersey Deputy Attorney General with more than 25 years of experience in the environmental arena. Sources describe him as *"smart and practical, and a great attorney."* **Kevin Bruno** (see p.1732) is the chair of Blank Rome LLP's environmental practice, and defends clients in cases brought by government agencies in relation to CERCLA, RCRA, TSCA and CWA. **Richard Ericsson** (see p.1735) of Cole, Schotz, Meisel, Forman & Leonard PA heads the environmental team, and is an *"excellent lawyer"* who receives a range of plaudits for his practicality and strategic abilities. **Heidi Minuskin** of Coughlin Duffy LLP regularly advises companies on the business implications of environmental regulations, and is commended for her impressive level of insight. **Lawrence Diamond** at Duane Morris LLP has over 30 years of experience in defending clients in both state and federal enforcement proceedings. Clients are enthusiastic in their feedback, describing him as

*persuasive in his arguments and approach, with strong problem-solving capabilities – he consistently gets good results."* *"Tenacious advocate"* **Marty Judge** of Flaster Greenberg PC is admired by peers and clients alike for his broad-ranging talents. He *"has an incredible attention to detail, and knows the issues inside and out – you will never catch him sleeping."* Highlights include defending Reichhold in connection with third-party claims in the Passaic River litigation. Hyland Levin's **Richard Hluchan** has over 35 years of experience in counseling clients on compliance with environmental regulations. A seasoned litigator, he is praised for his skills in land use work, including coastal planning issues. **Gary Gengel** chairs the environmental team at Latham & Watkins LLP's Newark office, and his diverse workload includes regulatory advice and toxic tort litigation. **Andrew Robins** (see p.1746) of Sills Cummis & Gross P.C. is well known for his expertise in transactional work and site remediation issues, and is commended for his *"good grasp of the issues."* The *"very knowledgeable and responsive"* **Anthony Reitano** of Herold Law, P.A. debuts in the ranking after receiving strong feedback from market sources for his regulatory prowess. **Richard Conway** of Schenck, Price, Smith & King, LLP is cochair of

the environmental practice at the firm and has over 30 years of experience in advising clients on the business impact of environmental law. **John McGahren** of Patton Boggs LLP is the managing partner of the firm's New Jersey office, and is a seasoned veteran in environmental litigation and compliance. **Catherine Ward** of Stradley Ronon Stevens & Young LLP focuses her practice on regulatory and contractual environmental matters, counseling clients on brownfield redevelopment and remediation issues. **Christopher McAuliffe** of Morgan, Lewis & Bockius LLP is a *"fine lawyer, tenacious and with an eye for detail."* He acted for ConocoPhillips in acquiring approvals under the Industrial Site Recovery Act for the relocation of one of its petroleum refineries. Clients have high praise for **Jeffrey Cappola** of Wilentz, Goldman & Spitzer, P.A. who is *"fantastic – he has a tremendous depth of knowledge in the environmental world, and goes above and beyond."* **Susan Karp** (see p.1739) of Cole, Schotz, Meisel, Forman & Leonard PA makes her first appearance in the rankings after receiving excellent feedback from clients. One source asserted: *"I have never seen anyone so prepared and who knew the issues so thoroughly – she keeps digging and understands everything until she gets to the bottom of the matter."*

# HEALTHCARE

Commentary about individuals can be found under their firm's paragraph. If the firm has no paragraph (is not ranked) look at Other Notable Practitioners.

| Healthcare |
| --- |
| **Leading Firms** |
| **Band 1** |
| Brach Eichler L.L.C. |
| Giordano Halleran & Ciesla PC |
| McElroy, Deutsch, Mulvaney & Carpenter, LLP * |
| Sills Cummis & Gross P.C. * |
| **Band 2** |
| Drinker Biddle & Reath LLP * |
| Fox Rothschild LLP * |
| Garfunkel Wild P.C. |
| McCarter & English, LLP * |
| Norris McLaughlin & Marcus, PA |
| Wilentz, Goldman & Spitzer, P.A. * |
| **Band 3** |
| Gibbons P.C. * |
| Reed Smith LLP |
| Wolff & Samson PC |

\* Indicates firm with profile.
Alphabetical order within each band. Band 1 is the highest.

## Band 1

### Brach Eichler L.L.C.

**THE FIRM** This firm has one of the most prominent healthcare practices in the state, and has particular expertise in transactional and regulatory matters. The team has recently been heavily involved in counseling clients in relation to Affordable Care Act compliance. As well as regularly representing physicians and healthcare providers, the

firm also represents a number of local healthcare associations.
**Sources say:** *"It is a leading physician firm."*
**KEY INDIVIDUALS Todd Brower** focuses his practice on corporate transactions and regulatory compliance. He regularly represents hospital clients and medical staff. **John Fanburg** is head of the firm's healthcare practice group. His practice is primarily concerned with the representation of physicians in transactional and regulatory matters. **Joseph Gorrell** earns recognition thanks to his deep experience and expertise in transactional and litigation work within the healthcare arena. **Mark Manigan** has a healthy reputation in the field, thanks to his impressive work on behalf of doctors and ambulatory services.

### Giordano Halleran & Ciesla PC

**THE FIRM** This compact practice is known and respected for its deep experience across the full range of healthcare issues at both state and federal level. The group has recently handled a number of contract issues on behalf of medical practitioners and organizations, as well as dealing with high-value antitrust matters as they relate to the healthcare industry. Key clients include Underwood Memorial Hospital, The Valley Hospital and JFK Medical Center.
**Sources say:** *"They have been representing hospitals for decades and have been very successful. Highly competent and well regarded."*
**KEY INDIVIDUALS Frank Ciesla** is head of the healthcare group at the firm and is held in high regard by his peers. *"He is universally recognized as a high-quality healthcare attorney,"* say sources. **Elizabeth Christian** focuses her

practice on counseling clients on their compliance with federal healthcare regulations as well as transactional matters. **Sharlene Hunt** is well regarded within the New Jersey healthcare Bar for the counsel she provides to both institutional healthcare providers and individual practitioners.

### McElroy, Deutsch, Mulvaney & Carpenter, LLP
See profile on p.1760

**THE FIRM** This established healthcare group is involved in the full range of healthcare matters at both state and federal level, handling regulatory compliance issues and with particular strength in healthcare dispute work. The firm is held in high regard among peers thanks to its strength and depth of expertise in the field. Clients include local hospitals and physician groups.
**Sources say:** *"A deep bench of some of the finest practitioners in the state".*
**KEY INDIVIDUALS Andrew McBride** (see p.1742) is held in high regard by market commentators as *"very capable and a good guy."* *"Excellent lawyer"* **James Robertson** (see p.1745) concentrates his practice on transactional and compliance matters within the healthcare practice area. **Michael Kalison** (see p.1738) earns praise from interviewees as *"a superb healthcare lawyer."* He has a broad expertise in healthcare law issues.

### Sills Cummis & Gross P.C.
See profile on p.1762

**THE FIRM** This firm offers its healthcare clients a full-service practice, with related expertise in regulatory compliance, government investigations, real estate and dispute resolution. The team also has experience in handling transactional work on behalf of its clients, which include healthcare providers and individual healthcare professionals. Clients are quick to praise the firm for its high levels of performance and responsiveness to their needs.

**Sources say:** *"They have been outstanding. They handle everything with a high degree of professionalism, are very prompt and efficient and work independently when needed."* **KEY INDIVIDUALS** Department chair **Gary Herschman** (see p.1737) is described by commentators as *"a very good strategic thinker who really sees the big picture and provides good advice so that the client knows the legal issues."* **Anjana Patel** (see p.1744) *"has a tremendous understanding of the regulatory issues and is very good at explaining the details of a transaction so that businesspeople can understand them,"* say sources. **Jack Wenik** (see p.1749) debuts in the ranking having been applauded by market sources for his *"tremendously detailed knowledge of the regulatory issues and his practical approach to matters."*

## Band 2

### Drinker Biddle & Reath LLP
See profile on p.2238

**THE FIRM** The compact New Jersey practice at this national firm is able to call on its vast network to provide local healthcare clients with a truly broad legal service. The key focus of the team is on transactional healthcare work, but it also houses deep expertise in regulatory and dispute resolution work. Key clients include Springpoint Senior Living, Princeton Healthcare System and Meridian Health System.

**Sources say:** *"The firm provides prompt and effective legal services in various areas of the law."*

**KEY INDIVIDUALS** *"Excellent attorney"* **George Kendall** (see p.1739) is vice chair of the healthcare practice. He has recently been involved in a range of transactional, contractual and regulatory issues on behalf of clients.

### Fox Rothschild LLP
See profile on p.2242

**THE FIRM** With three offices in New Jersey, this national firm enjoys a strong standing within the state. The practice represents both large institutional healthcare providers and individual physicians, as well as pharmaceutical and insurance companies, providing expertise across the full gamut of healthcare issues.

**Sources say:** *"A really strong healthcare group with a deep bench and some vastly experienced lawyers."*

**KEY INDIVIDUALS Elizabeth Litten** (see p.1741) *"understands health policy at state and federal level"* and *"has the ability to connect the dots at a strategic and then practical level,"* according to impressed sources. **Jonathan Weiner** (see p.1749) routinely acts on behalf of hospitals and long-term care nursing homes in a variety of healthcare law matters.

### Garfunkel Wild P.C.

**THE FIRM** This firm counsels a range of healthcare industry clients on a range of issues including regulatory compliance and transactional work, particularly on behalf of hospitals. Clients are quick to praise the team's expertise in the managed care sector, while peers recognize the depth within the group.

**KEY INDIVIDUALS** Experienced practitioner **Jeffrey Brown** represents healthcare providers across the full variety of issues.

### McCarter & English, LLP
See profile on p.1759

**THE FIRM** This 21-partner practice earns recognition for its deep experience and expertise in transactional healthcare matters, particularly in M&A and financing deals. Recent highlights include acting for the former Warren Hospital in its merge into the regional St Luke's Health System. Other key clients include Trinitas Regional Medical Center, Springpoint Senior Living and CentraState Healthcare System.

**Sources say:** *"We were entirely happy with the team. They were stellar – they explained everything to me and it was a huge help."*

**KEY INDIVIDUALS Scott Kobler** (see p.1740) is head of the healthcare practice group at the firm. Sources describe him as a *"an expert in bond financing in the nonprofit world."*

### Norris McLaughlin & Marcus, PA

**THE FIRM** This diverse practice covers a range of matters in the healthcare field and is particularly active in the transactional and regulatory space. The team has been particularly active in representing healthcare providers in a range of M&A transactions, and also represents clients in physician contracting issues.

**KEY INDIVIDUALS** *"Exceptional lawyer"* **Anthony Manger** is held in high regard by market sources for the quality of his transactional work within the healthcare arena. **Ira Novak** focuses his healthcare practice on the representation of hospitals and professional medical practices in M&A and regulatory matters.

### Wilentz, Goldman & Spitzer, P.A.
See profile on p.1763

**THE FIRM** This practice has extensive experience across the healthcare sector, with particular activity in transactional issues. Recent highlights include the representation of Rutgers in its merger with the University of Medicine and Dentistry of New Jersey. The team has also been involved in a series of healthcare provider sales.

**Sources say:** *"There is exceptionally good communication between the attorneys at the firm."*

**KEY INDIVIDUALS Michael Schaff** is head of the healthcare department at the firm. *"He is a top-notch healthcare attorney, very skilled in his interactions with hospitals and healthcare professionals,"* say sources.

## Band 3

### Gibbons P.C.
See profile on p.1754

**THE FIRM** This team focuses on transactional and regulatory healthcare work, as well as housing expertise in healthcare fraud and abuse among other areas. The broad nature of the practice is exemplified by its recent work on behalf of medical technology company Stryker in drafting a series of agreements, and for Barnabas Health and Saint Barnabas Medical Center in a number of real estate and land use issues.

**KEY INDIVIDUALS** *"Very good attorney"* **Bruce Levy** focuses his practice on the defense of healthcare providers from allegations of fraud and abuse.

### Reed Smith LLP

**THE FIRM** This international giant's Princeton healthcare practice is able to call on a vast network of healthcare experts across the wider firm in order to provide a high level of service to its clients. The group's broad expertise enables it to represent a variety of clients including healthcare providers, pharmaceutical companies and medical device manufacturers.

**Sources say:** *"An excellent firm."*

**KEY INDIVIDUALS Murray Klein** splits his time between the firm's Princeton and San Francisco locations. His practice focuses on provider reimbursement.

## Wolff & Samson PC

**THE FIRM** This firm joins the rankings following extensive praise from its clients, who laud the team's deep

expertise and ability to respond effectively to their needs. The group acts for a host of organizations within the sector including hospitals and other providers, medical device manufacturers and insurance companies.

**Sources say:** *"They are excellent. They respond quickly and are always very timely in coming back with answers to questions."*

**KEY INDIVIDUALS** David Hyman is a key contact for the healthcare practice.

## Other Notable Practitioners

**Daniel Frier** of Frier Levitt represents all manner of healthcare providers across the full gamut of healthcare-related legal matters. **Maryann Kicenuik** of Windels Marx Lane & Mittendorf, LLP focuses her practice on the representation of hospitals and other healthcare providers in connection with financing arrangements.

# INTELLECTUAL PROPERTY

Commentary about individuals can be found under their firm's paragraph. If the firm has no paragraph (is not ranked) look at Other Notable Practitioners.

| Intellectual Property Leading Firms | |
|---|---|
| **Band 1** | |
| Lerner David Littenberg Krumholz & Mentlik, LLP * | |
| **Band 2** | |
| Gibbons P.C. * | |
| Greenberg Traurig, LLP * | |
| Lowenstein Sandler LLP * | |
| McCarter & English, LLP * | |
| **Band 3** | |
| Dentons * | |
| Wolff & Samson PC | |
| **Band 4** | |
| Giordano Halleran & Ciesla PC | |
| Riker Danzig Scherer Hyland & Perretti LLP * | |

## Band 1

### Lerner David Littenberg Krumholz & Mentlik, LLP
See profile on p.1756

**THE FIRM** Lerner David is regarded by clients and competitors alike as the premier IP firm in the state. The firm can call on the combined knowledge and expertise of 80 attorneys to cover the full range of IP law. The team acts for a number of international clients with respect to their US patent, trademark and copyright concerns and has recently handled notable patent infringement cases and advised on multi-patent strategies.

**Sources say:** *"They absolutely sit above the rest."*

**KEY INDIVIDUALS Stephen Roth** (see p.1746) is promoted to the top tier of the table thanks to effusive praise from sources. An expert IP litigator who impresses with his strategic mindset, his advice is seen by sources as *"on the money."* **Joseph Littenberg** (see p.1741), a founding partner of the firm, specializes in patent licensing and litigation. Invaluable to clients is his ability to negotiate research agreements at an international level. **Shawn Foley** (see p.1735) practices primarily within the biotechnology field. He brings prior experience of working for the USPTO. According to sources, **Charles Kennedy** (see p.1739) is *"a*

*very versatile, bright and hard-working"* attorney. He offers expertise in a wide variety of IP matters, including trademarks, copyright and patent litigation. *"A worthy adversary,"* **William Mentlik** (see p.1742) combines his role as the managing partner of the firm with a role as a technology patent litigator. He has recently been involved in extensive litigation stemming from Hatch-Waxman cases. **Bruce Sales** (see p.1747) is experienced in all aspects of copyright, trademarks and patent protection. He is known for his hard-working attitude and ability to respond quickly to urgent matters, as well as his skill in *"balancing business and legal considerations."*

## Band 2

### Gibbons P.C.
See profile on p.1754

**THE FIRM** As well as handling trademarks, copyright and Hatch-Waxman litigation, this team is involved in transactional issues such as IP due diligence and patent management. It represents some of the biggest names in the technology industry including GE and Google, and includes among its ranks a number of former in-house patent lawyers. The team also represents General Cigar Company on brand protection issues.

**Sources say:** *"They have the skill and capabilities. They allow me to contribute and they have a good understanding of the commercial realities."*

**KEY INDIVIDUALS** Practice chair **David De Lorenzi** is an *"all-around fantastic patent attorney."* He represented Hoffmann-La Roche in a patent interference matter involving the Japanese Cancer Foundation. **Sheila McShane** has a strong track record in Hatch-Waxman litigation. She has been lead partner in such matters for well-known multinational companies including Pfizer and Procter & Gamble.

### Greenberg Traurig, LLP
See profile on p.1024

**THE FIRM** The group divides its time between trademarks, licensing, patent prosecution and litigation. It has

| Intellectual Property Leading Individuals | | |
|---|---|---|
| **Band 1** | | |
| Littenberg Joseph S | Lerner David Littenberg Krumholz * | |
| Mentlik William L | Lerner David Littenberg Krumholz * | |
| Roth Stephen F | Lerner David Littenberg Krumholz * | |
| Sales Bruce | Lerner David Littenberg Krumholz * | |
| **Band 2** | | |
| Anderson Kurt E | Giordano Halleran & Ciesla PC | |
| Bock Joel N | Dentons * | |
| Christie Scott | McCarter & English, LLP * | |
| De Lorenzi David E | Gibbons P.C. | |
| Hildebrand Mary J | Lowenstein Sandler LLP * | |
| Kennedy Charles P | Lerner David Littenberg Krumholz * | |
| Lizza Charles M | Saul Ewing LLP (ONP)† | |
| Politano Frank L | K&L Gates (ONP)† * | |
| Schindler Barry J | Greenberg Traurig, LLP * | |
| Schoenberg Robert J | Riker Danzig Scherer Hyland & Perretti LLP | |
| Weinick Jeffrey | Wolff & Samson PC | |
| **Band 3** | | |
| Foley Shawn P | Lerner David Littenberg Krumholz * | |
| Friscia Michael R | McCarter & English, LLP * | |
| Kesslen Mark | Lowenstein Sandler LLP * | |
| Lubit Beverly W | Greenberg Traurig, LLP | |
| McShane Sheila | Gibbons P.C. | |
| Nussbaum Peter | Wolff & Samson PC | |
| Paradiso Robert | Lowenstein Sandler LLP * | |
| Samay Christian | Dentons * | |
| Selitto, Jr Ralph W | Greenberg Traurig, LLP * | |
| Shepherd Robert G | Porzio, Bromberg & Newman PC (ONP)† | |
| Smith Robert W. | McCarter & English, LLP * | |
| **Associates to watch** | | |
| Ignacio Vanessa | Lowenstein Sandler LLP * | |
| Short Jonathan | McCarter & English, LLP * | |
| Skrocki Melissa | Giordano Halleran & Ciesla PC | |

\* Indicates firm / individual with profile.
† ONP = Other Notable Practitioner.

enjoyed a period of recent growth, drawing on the resources that come with being part of a sizable international firm. It has also been building its cross-border patent prosecution portfolio, where standout clients include Alcoa.

**Sources say:** *"It's clear that they care about the work. It's a real partnership."*

**KEY INDIVIDUALS** Sources applaud **Beverly Lubit** for her unique combination of scientific, business and legal skills. As an impressively well-qualified practitioner *"she has exceptional knowledge and judgment in all three areas."* **Barry Schindler** (see p.1747) jointly oversees the firm's patent prosecution practice. In the past year he has successfully prosecuted numerous patent applications for Israeli IP law firm Reinhold Cohn & Partners. **Ralph Selitto** (see p.1747) represents major domestic and foreign companies on a range of IP matters, including patentability investigations, technology licensing and trademark applications.

## Lowenstein Sandler LLP
See profile on p.1757

**THE FIRM** Lowenstein Sandler is widely recognized for its sophistication in representing companies requiring advice on critically important IP concerns. Its work includes counseling a global healthcare corporation in managing 5,000 trademark assets in over 100 jurisdictions. It also has an impressive track record advising on prosecuting, managing and litigating patents. Active clients including JPMorgan Chase, Johnson & Johnson and Google.

**Sources say:** *"They are always up to date with current issues, and are flexible and available whenever we need them."*

**KEY INDIVIDUALS Mark Kesslen** (see p.1739) chairs the group and is described as a *"fantastic attorney; very knowledgeable and responsive."* He advised Knewton over an agreement to bring online educational products to market. **Robert Paradiso** (see p.1744) is deemed a *"fantastic strategist"* and brings a *"calming presence,"* sources say. He delivers advice on patent prosecution, patent protection and licensing agreements. According to sources, the *"detail-oriented"* **Mary Hildebrand** (see p.1737) is *"responsive, reliable and intelligent."* She specializes in advising technology firms, where highlights include representing CIT Group in renegotiating a licensing agreement central to the company's operations. Trademark specialist **Vanessa Ignacio** (see p.1738) *"delivers everything that she promises,"* sources report. She works particularly closely with clients in the pharmaceutical and healthcare industries.

## McCarter & English, LLP
See profile on p.1759

**THE FIRM** This team is known primarily for its work on patent prosecutions in the technology and life sciences spheres, though it also offers expertise across IP litigation, trademark and copyright protection. It brings significant recent experience of trying Hatch-Waxman cases on behalf of top names such as AstraZeneca, Warner Chilcott and Novartis. Further clients include Princeton University and Excelsior Medical.

**Sources say:** *"Very responsive from partner level down."* *"Knowledgeable and available at all hours."*

**KEY INDIVIDUALS Scott Christie** (see p.1733) is described by sources as *"an expert on e-commerce"* and *"a 24/7 guy."* He recently represented Novartis in its challenge to a patent term adjustment granted by the USPTO. Described by sources as a *"go-to guy"* in patents, **Michael Friscia** (see p.1735) recently defended ASICS against patent infringement claims brought by Akeva. Sources say that **Robert Smith** (see p.1748) is *"a great technician"* who achieves successful results for clients. He continues to assist Hain Celestial Group in managing the company's global trademarks portfolio. **Jonathan Short** (see p.1748) is described by sources as *"a star of the future."* He assisted Hayworth Industries in defending and litigating allegations of patent infringement against Pentair Water Pools & Spa.

## Band 3

### Dentons
See profile on p.449

**THE FIRM** This group, backed by the resources of a global law firm, takes a holistic approach to IP and is active in trademark, copyright, patent prosecution, licensing and portfolio management concerns. Recent work highlights include representing Columbia University on a number of matters relating to biotech and robotics patents.

**Sources say:** *"They were more than professional. They make themselves available all the time."*

**KEY INDIVIDUALS Joel Bock** (see p.1732) leads the group and is particularly well respected for his technical prowess. According to sources, he *"comes up with practical solutions,"* is *"attentive to our needs"* and is *"very smart."* His experience covers a wide breadth of issues, from transactional IP concerns to patent prosecutions and litigation. *"Client-focused"* IP litigator **Christian Samay** (see p.1747) is praised by sources for his *"excellent advocacy skills"* and his powers of analysis.

### Wolff & Samson PC

**THE FIRM** While active across the board in intellectual property, this team is particularly active in licensing and infringement proceedings. It has also attracted an impressive volume of work relating to the management of trademarks, assisting clients in enforcing their rights both in the USA and overseas. Key highlights include assisting AT&T in applying for and prosecuting patents.

**Sources say:** *"They are excellent; extremely careful and thorough. We rely on that care and thoroughness and will continue to use them going forward."*

**KEY INDIVIDUALS** Described by sources as an *"outstanding"* practitioner, **Jeffrey Weinick** co-leads the team. He represents Alcatel-Lucent in patent prosecutions. **Peter Nussbaum** is praised by clients for his ability to *"organize the approach and make it as simple as possible."* He is regularly called on to handle copyright and trademark disputes.

## Band 4

### Giordano Halleran & Ciesla PC

**THE FIRM** This group enters the rankings on the back of much praise from sources, its commitment to client responsiveness standing out as a particular source of strength. Members of the team are particularly active within internet, e-commerce, privacy and licensing concerns. Highlights include advising logistics software company Log-Net on litigation proceedings brought by DHL.

**Sources say:** *"They are very responsive and have always given us good service."*

**KEY INDIVIDUALS** Sources praise **Kurt Anderson** for his ability to look at issues from a variety of angles and the ease with which he can explain trademark issues. *"He is a real pro and knows how to explain complex issues in simple terms,"* sources report, adding that *"his insight makes us feel so much more confident."* **Melissa Skrocki** is singled out as being *"technically sound and very analytical."* She focuses on technology concerns.

### Riker Danzig Scherer Hyland & Perretti LLP
See profile on p.1761

**THE FIRM** This group is highlighted for its work in managing trademark and licensing agreements, as well as for representing major pharmaceutical and software companies in patent, trademark and copyright litigation. Highlights include co-counseling The Tetris Company and Tetris Holding in copyright infringement and unfair competition litigation. The team counts IBM, Johnson & Johnson and Berkeley among its roster of clients.

**Sources say:** *"Their performance has been exceptional."*

**KEY INDIVIDUALS Robert Schoenberg** is praised by sources for bringing *"a great feel for fashioning an argument and putting forward productive strategies."* He represented IBM in defending a software copyright infringement action.

### Other Notable Practitioners

**Frank Politano** (see p.1745) of K&L Gates is held in high regard by sources from around the market. A stalwart of the IP community, he also assists clients in filing trademark applications and negotiating licensing agreements overseas. **Robert Shepherd** of Porzio, Bromberg & Newman PC is particularly well known for his work in trademark litigation. **Charles Lizza** of Saul Ewing LLP is commended by sources for his *"attention to detail"* and ability to *"understand how judges think."* He has a strong following among pharmaceutical companies, his clients including the likes of Procter & Gamble, Merck and GlaxoSmithKline.

## LABOR & EMPLOYMENT

Commentary about individuals can be found under their firm's paragraph. If the firm has no paragraph (is not ranked) look at Other Notable Practitioners.

### Labor & Employment
### Leading Firms

**Band 1**
Day Pitney LLP *
McElroy, Deutsch, Mulvaney & Carpenter, LLP *
Ogletree, Deakins, Nash, Smoak & Stewart, PC *

**Band 2**
Drinker Biddle & Reath LLP *
Epstein Becker & Green PC *
Fox Rothschild LLP *
Gibbons P.C. *
Jackson Lewis LLP *
Morgan, Lewis & Bockius LLP *
Nukk-Freeman & Cerra
Proskauer Rose LLP *

**Band 3**
Ballard Spahr LLP *
Carmagnola & Ritardi LLC
Genova, Burns & Giantomasi
K&L Gates *
Littler Mendelson, PC *
Lowenstein Sandler LLP *
Lum, Drasco & Positan, LLC *

**Band 4**
Greenberg Traurig, LLP *
Pepper Hamilton LLP *
Riker Danzig Scherer Hyland & Perretti LLP *
Sills Cummis & Gross P.C. *
Wolff & Samson PC

\* Indicates firm / individual with profile.
† ONP = Other Notable Practitioner.

### Senior Statesmen

**Senior Statesmen: distinguished older practitioners**

| | | |
|---|---|---|
| Jacob Cynthia M | Fisher & Phillips LLP (ONP)† * | |

### Leading Individuals

**Star individuals**

| | |
|---|---|
| Dee Francis X | McElroy, Deutsch, Mulvaney & Carpenter * |

**Band 1**

| | |
|---|---|
| Alito Rosemary | K&L Gates * |
| Amalfe Christine A | Gibbons P.C. |
| Brady Patrick G | Epstein Becker & Green PC |
| Carmagnola Domenick | Carmagnola & Ritardi LLC |
| Genova Angelo | Genova, Burns & Giantomasi |
| Parliman Gregory C | Day Pitney LLP * |
| Peirano John J | McElroy, Deutsch, Mulvaney & Carpenter * |
| Positan Wayne J | Lum, Drasco & Positan, LLC * |
| Ridley John | Drinker Biddle & Reath LLP * |
| Rosenblatt Richard G | Morgan, Lewis & Bockius LLP * |
| Suflas Steven W | Ballard Spahr LLP * |

**Band 2**

| | |
|---|---|
| Avallone Vincent N | K&L Gates * |
| Bennett John K | Jackson Lewis LLP * |
| Cerra Suzanne | Nukk-Freeman & Cerra * |
| Cino Vincent | Jackson Lewis LLP * |
| Diana Mark | Ogletree, Deakins, Nash, Smoak & Stewart * |
| Furey Michael K | Riker Danzig Scherer Hyland & Perretti LLP |
| Garland David W | Epstein Becker & Green PC * |
| Goldstein Marvin M | Proskauer Rose LLP |
| Goodman Stanley | Fox Rothschild LLP * |
| Hughes Peter O | Ogletree, Deakins, Nash, Smoak & Stewart * |
| Iannaccone Carmine A | Epstein Becker & Green PC * |
| Johnson Rene M | Morgan, Lewis & Bockius LLP * |
| Johnson Lario Wendy | Greenberg Traurig, LLP * |
| Keyser Denise M | Ballard Spahr LLP * |
| McCarthy Patrick J | Day Pitney LLP * |
| Ploscowe Stephen A | Fox Rothschild LLP * |

| | |
|---|---|
| Stanton Patrick M | Ogletree, Deakins, Nash, Smoak & Stewart * |
| Riordan J Michael | McElroy, Deutsch, Mulvaney & Carpenter * |
| Sandak Lawrence R | Proskauer Rose LLP |
| Smith Patricia A | Ballard Spahr LLP * |
| Wells Catherine | Wolff & Samson PC |
| Wissert David M | Lowenstein Sandler LLP * |

**Band 3**

| | |
|---|---|
| Anderson Lynne Anne | Drinker Biddle & Reath LLP * |
| Barry John P | Proskauer Rose LLP |
| Becker Jay | Giordano Halleran & Ciesla PC (ONP)† |
| Bird Kelly Ann | Gibbons P.C. |
| DeBlasio Joseph | Giordano Halleran & Ciesla PC (ONP)† |
| DelDuca Matthew V | Pepper Hamilton LLP * |
| English Holly | Nukk-Freeman & Cerra * |
| Feher Kristine | Greenberg Traurig, LLP * |
| Greenbaum William | Lowenstein Sandler LLP * |
| Kelly Theresa A | Day Pitney LLP * |
| Meklinsky Ian D | Fox Rothschild LLP * |
| Nardone Susan L | Gibbons P.C. |
| Nukk-Freeman Katherin | Nukk-Freeman & Cerra * |
| Ritardi Steven F | Carmagnola & Ritardi LLC |
| Rome Robin | Nukk-Freeman & Cerra * |
| Rosen David I | Sills Cummis & Gross P.C. * |
| Schey Richard W | Jackson Lewis LLP |
| Smith Glenn | Littler Mendelson, PC |

**Up-and-coming individuals**

| | |
|---|---|
| Castaldo Paula | McElroy, Deutsch, Mulvaney & Carpenter |
| Dorsi Carla | Gibbons P.C. * |
| Kierkut Galit | Sills Cummis & Gross P.C. * |
| Komoroski-Wiwi Amy | Lowenstein Sandler LLP * |
| O'Rourke Wood Margaret | Wolff & Samson PC |

## Band 1

### Day Pitney LLP
See profile on p.1753

**THE FIRM** This firm continues to operate at the forefront of the New Jersey labor and employment market. The team has a significant footprint in union negotiations and notable experience in a full range of employment matters both in single plaintiff and class actions. The group recently represented telecom giant Verizon in its replacement of a collective bargaining agreement for its 45,000 unionized employees. The firm also counts AT&T, Novartis Pharmaceuticals Corporation and UPS on its current client roster.
**Sources say:** *"They have been very efficient. Their experience is top notch and they are very accessible and responsive."*
**KEY INDIVIDUALS Gregory Parliman** (see p.1744) is held in exceptionally high regard by clients and peers alike. He is retained by such high-end clients as AT&T and Pfizer, while sources describe him as *"one of the best attorneys I have ever worked with"* and note that *"if you need an attorney who can give a pragmatic answer to a very complex question then Gregory is your man."* **Patrick McCarthy** (see

p.1742) focuses his practice on traditional labor matters, negotiating on behalf of employers in collective bargaining arrangements and union relations. Sources say: *"He is a great negotiator and arbitrator."* **Theresa Kelly** (see p.1739) is particularly active in counseling companies in relation to their statutory employment obligations. She is praised for her skill in presenting *"a 360-degree analysis and for her knowledge of new developments in the business sector."*

### McElroy, Deutsch, Mulvaney & Carpenter, LLP
See profile on p.1760

**THE FIRM** This Morristown-based practice group is highly experienced across the full range of labor and employment matters. The group is considered a market leader for the provision of compliance counseling, the negotiation of collective bargaining arrangements, and complex arbitration or litigation. The firm is particularly active within the financial services, pharmaceutical and technology industry

sectors and counts Johnson & Johnson and Merck & Co among its roster of current clients.
**Sources say:** *"It is the kind of firm that pays close attention to the client's needs. We trust them implicitly."*
**KEY INDIVIDUALS** Department co-head **Francis Dee** (see p.1734) is considered to be one of the leading lights of the New Jersey employment Bar. Sources describe him as *"an excellent attorney"* who is *"at the top of the profession."* He recently acted for Ethicon in defense of a whistle-blower and age discrimination case brought by a former executive. Market sources applaud **John Peirano** (see p.1744) as *"a superstar attorney in front of a jury."* He handles a broad range of employment litigation and has an acknowledged excellence in traditional labor matters. **Michael Riordan** (see p.1745) receives warm praise from market observers. One interviewee reports: *"He has a quick mastery of the facts, knows the law, keeps up to date with the changes and is really on top of the big picture."* **Paula Castaldo** debuts in

the rankings, having been lauded as *"a brilliant technical lawyer. She is very smart and she writes beautifully."*

## Ogletree, Deakins, Nash, Smoak & Stewart, PC
See profile on p.1110

**THE FIRM** The Ogletree labor and employment group focuses its practice on representing employers and management across the full spectrum of employment-related matters. With a deep bench, encompassing ten partners and nine associates, the firm is well placed to excel in this space. Clients include BASF and First Energy.

**Sources say:** *"Very smart, very efficient and excellent customer service."*

**KEY INDIVIDUALS Mark Diana** (see p.1734) receives particular praise for his representation of management clients in the public and private sectors. Sources describe him as *"a great lawyer and very smart."* **Peter Hughes** (see p.1738) is an experienced litigator in all matters pertaining to labor and employment. His practice also includes client counseling. **Patrick Stanton** (see p.1748) is considered a figurehead of the firm's New Jersey practice. He has long been recognized as a leader in labor and employment matters.

## Band 2

## Drinker Biddle & Reath LLP
See profile on p.2238

**THE FIRM** This full-service firm is renowned in the New Jersey labor and employment marketplace for its defense work in class action and whistle-blower cases. The team has particularly close ties with the pharmaceutical and healthcare sectors, and is also experienced in handling matters for industrial manufacturers, retailers and public institutions. The team recently successfully defended Toshiba in a gender discrimination putative class action suit valued at $100 million.

**Sources say:** *"They were eloquent and responsive to a tee. Everyone has been extremely helpful."*

**KEY INDIVIDUALS John Ridley** (see p.1745) was lead counsel in the Toshiba matter, and is held in high regard by clients and peers alike. *"He is a seasoned litigator and has been doing employment law for so long that he is a real asset,"* comments one client. **Lynne Anne Anderson** (see p.1731) is well reputed for her handling of employment law issues in the life sciences industry sector. She is praised for her ability to *"remain calm amid the nastiness of litigation."*

## Epstein Becker & Green PC
See profile on p.1972

**THE FIRM** This firm represents management clients in a full spectrum of employment matters. The team is closely associated with clients in the life sciences, financial services, healthcare and hospitality sectors. The group has recently represented Home Depot USA in a nationwide collective action seeking overtime payment. Other clients include PepsiCo and Quest Diagnostics.

**Sources say:** *"Their performance has been outstanding. They have a wide range of expertise and availability has never been an issue."*

**KEY INDIVIDUALS Patrick Brady** was lead counsel in the Home Depot matter and is well regarded within the market. One source describes him simply as *"an excellent attorney."* **Carmine Iannaccone** (see p.1738) is described as the *"ideal business person's lawyer; he really transcends the lawyer in him and is able to tell you exactly what is needed."* **David Garland** (see p.1736) has over 20 years' experience in the New Jersey labor and employment arena. Sources say: *"He fully understands the business realities and gives practical advice."*

## Fox Rothschild LLP
See profile on p.2242

**THE FIRM** This group focuses its practice on representing mid-sized companies across the full gamut of labor and employment matters. On the employment side, the firm is noted for its handling of class actions, discrimination claims, and for its attendant expertise in pension and benefits litigation. The team also excels in traditional labor work, representing management clients in union negotiations and collective bargaining matters.

**Sources say:** *"I have found them to be terrific."*

**KEY INDIVIDUALS Stephen Ploscowe** (see p.1744) is praised by clients and peers in equal measure. *"His responsiveness is unmatched and his advice is always on point and 100% reliable,"* sources say. Head of department **Stanley Goodman** (see p.1736) is praised by sources who note that *"one of his strengths is that he anticipates our needs before we even know them."* Areas of excellence include labor negotiations, discrimination claims and wrongful termination. **Ian Meklinsky** (see p.1742) debuts in the rankings having been praised for his ability *"to take a complex issue and boil it down, and make practical arguments."* He represents management in a wide range of labor and employment matters.

## Gibbons P.C.
See profile on p.1754

**THE FIRM** This firm's employment and labor law practice is largely weighted towards employment law, but is also noted for its handling of traditional labor matters. The group has been particularly active in its representation of pharmaceutical and financial services companies in discrimination and wage and hour matters. Current clients include Manhattan Physicians Laboratories and JPMorgan Chase.

**Sources say:** *"They go above and beyond on responsiveness and accessibility and when they do something it is done right first time."*

**KEY INDIVIDUALS Christine Amalfe** is chair of the department at the firm. Market sources praise her as *"a brilliant legal mind,"* and remark that *"she gets to the heart of the matter and can zero in on how to attack the problem."* Market sources praise **Kelly Ann Bird** for her ability to *"understand the realities of running a business and taking those realities into account in her advice."* She focuses her practice on employer training, compliance counseling and

litigation. **Susan Nardone** is described by sources as *"very strong in dealing with internal investigations as well as litigation."* She is an experienced employment litigator, with strong experience before state and federal court and the Equal Employment Opportunity Commission (EEOC). **Carla Dorsi** (see p.1734) debuts in the rankings having received strong feedback from the market. She provides employment litigation and counseling to management clients.

## Jackson Lewis LLP
See profile on p.1982

**THE FIRM** Jackson Lewis is particularly active in employment litigation and counseling, representing multinational companies such as Merck & Co and Alcatel-Lucent in matters such as wrongful termination, discrimination and harassment cases. Recently, the firm successfully defended Pfizer from a claim by a former high-ranking company attorney for a year's severance pay in addition to the two years already provided. The arbitrator rendered a judgment in favor of Pfizer.

**Sources say:** *"If we need something done it is only a phone call away... these guys are on it straight away."*

**KEY INDIVIDUALS John Bennett** (see p.1731) is described by those within the New Jersey marketplace as *"a subject matter expert"* who *"can quickly asses the case and understand the issues that arise."* He handles employment litigation in both state and federal court, and is experienced in labor matters before the NLRB. National director of litigation **Vincent Cino** (see p.1733) is hailed by market sources as *"an excellent attorney and litigator."* He was lead counsel on the Pfizer matter outlined above. **Richard Schey** *"is very thoughtful and pragmatic and his advice and counsel is excellent,"* sources say. He concentrates his practice on traditional labor law.

## Morgan, Lewis & Bockius LLP
See profile on p.2246

**THE FIRM** Morgan Lewis offers a full-service labor and employment practice in New Jersey. It is particularly active in financial services, pharmaceuticals and public utilities industries and is noted for its experience in complex litigation, including defending wage and hour class and collective actions. Clients include Amazon.com, American Express and Morgan Stanley.

**Sources say:** *"They are very good at coming up with a forward-thinking plan and developing a sound litigation strategy."*

**KEY INDIVIDUALS Richard Rosenblatt** (see p.1746) has been particularly active defending wage and class actions in the US District Court. Sources report *"a lot of respect for him."* Interviewees attest that head of department **Rene Johnson** (see p.1738) is *"fantastic"* and able to *"immediately come up with different angles that enable us to solve a case."* She is a respected employment litigator.

## Nukk-Freeman & Cerra

**THE FIRM** This boutique firm is experienced across the full range of employment law. The team is noted for its provision of employment counseling and training, its defense of employers in state and federal litigation, and its handling of workplace investigations. The firm also offers attendant expertise in executive compensation and employee benefits.

Sources say: "*They are extremely sensitive to client needs. They are very smart group of attorneys with excellent analytical and writing skills.*"

KEY INDIVIDUALS Suzanne Cerra (see p.1733) is managing partner at the firm, and has been particularly active in employment litigation and serving as a third party investigator. Sources say: "*She is excellent and great at investigations.*" Holly English (see p.1735) is described as "*a very solid litigator*" by market sources. She also provides employment law training to employers and human resource professionals. Katherin Nukk-Freeman (see p.1743) is held in high regard by market sources. She is a seasoned litigator and negotiator whose "*preparation allows her to anticipate what the other side will claim.*" Robin Rome (see p.1746) focuses her practice on defending employers and management in all employment law matters, from wrongful termination to discrimination and harassment.

## Proskauer Rose LLP
See profile on p.2001

THE FIRM Proskauer's Newark-based labor and employment team focuses its practice on representing major companies within the financial services, entertainment and real estate industries. Current clients include JPMorgan Chase and Bed Bath & Beyond. Recently, the firm was successful in its defense of Metropolitan Life Insurance Company in a FINRA arbitration alleging wrongful termination in which the claimant sought $15 million.

Sources say: "*Excellent in terms of responsiveness and accessibility. They are willing to explain and to simplify and they coordinate very well.*"

KEY INDIVIDUALS Head of the Newark office Lawrence Sandak is a stalwart of the New Jersey employment arena. "*His oration and presence in front of the judge and jury are formidable and highly effective,*" sources say. John Barry debuts in the ranking having received vociferous praise from clients. Sources say: "*He has an excellent knowledge of what approach to take and is extremely responsive.*" Marvin Goldstein's practice includes counseling employers in labor relations matters and defending companies in discrimination class actions.

## Band 3

## Ballard Spahr LLP
See profile on p.2234

THE FIRM This nationally renowned firm has a solid reputation for its representation of employers in union negotiations. A successful year has seen the group become the first outside counsel to be appointed chief spokesperson for DuPont during union negotiations. The group also counts the American Red Cross and the State of New Jersey among its roster of current clients.

Sources say: "*They are an excellent firm. They give you good work for a good price. The response time is always excellent.*"

KEY INDIVIDUALS "*Intellectual powerhouse*" Steven Suflas (see p.1748) is applauded by interviewees for his ability to "*analyze complex issues and come up with equally sophisticated solutions, and see them through to success.*" He took the lead in the DuPont negotiations described above. Denise Keyser (see p.1739) is a veteran of over 30 years of complex labor negotiations. Sources describe her as "*very knowledgeable and confident.*" Patricia Smith (see p.1748) focuses her practice on employment law and related litigation. Market sources praise her as "*extremely professional and confident, with an approachable style that works very well in arbitration.*"

## Carmagnola & Ritardi LLC

THE FIRM This highly regarded boutique firm is focused on the defense of employers and management at both state and federal level. The group has an excellent track record in litigating EEOC and wage and hour cases as well as labor relations matters before the NLRB. The firm represents clients across a wide range of industry sectors.

KEY INDIVIDUALS The "*excellent*" Domenick Carmagnola is widely regarded as one of the leading practitioners in the state. He focuses his practice on counseling private and public companies across all labor and employment-related matters. Steven Ritardi is well respected for his expertise litigating matters before the NLRB, EEOC and the New Jersey Department of Labor.

## Genova, Burns & Giantomasi

THE FIRM This firm's full-service labor and employment practice group is particularly active within the ambit of traditional labor relations. The Newark-based team is also experienced in representing employers in all aspects of employment litigation, from wrongful termination through wage and hour and discrimination matters. The group is experienced in acting for companies in the public and private sectors.

KEY INDIVIDUALS Angelo Genova is a stalwart of labor and employment law in New Jersey. Sources describe him as "*a superb attorney*" and "*one of the big hitters in the state.*"

## K&L Gates
See profile on p.2245

THE FIRM The K&L Gates labor and employment team has recorded some impressive victories of late. The group is renowned in the New Jersey market for its tenacious style of litigation, notably brought to bear in the firm's successful defense of the Port Authority of New York and New Jersey in an equal pay action brought by the EEOC. Other current clients include Microsoft and Celanese.

Sources say: "*I think that they go above and beyond. They are extremely responsive and very willing to accommodate.*"

KEY INDIVIDUALS Rosemary Alito (see p.1731) was lead counsel in the Port Authority matter referred to above, and is praised by market sources as a "*very knowledgeable and strategic*" attorney. Vincent Avallone (see p.1731) earns accolades for the "*thorough, proactive and strategic manner in which he approaches matters.*" He anchors the

firm's relationship with Celanese, providing employment counseling and litigation defense.

## Littler Mendelson, PC
See profile on p.688

THE FIRM Littler Mendelson's full-service labor and employment group is recognized for its handling of contentious and noncontentious employment matters. Recent work highlights include achieving the summary judgment dismissal of a disability discrimination allegation brought by a long-term employee of AT&T. The team also acts for clients such as Coca-Cola and Brooks Brothers.

Sources say: "*We have had an excellent relationship. The service has been good and they have gotten results.*"

KEY INDIVIDUAL Glenn Smith is praised by sources for the "*practical business experience*" that he brings to the table. He is experienced in representing clients before a range of bodies, including the NLRB and EEOC.

## Lowenstein Sandler LLP
See profile on p.1757

THE FIRM Lowenstein Sandler's Roseland-based employment group handles employer training, compliance counseling and litigation. It represents clients from across a range of industry sectors, but has particularly close ties to the pharmaceutical and corporate industries. Clients include Bristol-Myers Squibb and Regeneron Pharmaceuticals.

Sources say: "*The advice is not only something that I can rely on from a legal perspective, it also offers business strategy.*"

KEY INDIVIDUALS William Greenbaum (see p.1736) handles a broad range of employment law matters, including workplace investigations, severance agreements and EEOC matters. "*His strength is that he is very knowledgeable in the law and very thorough,*" sources say. David Wissert (see p.1750) is a seasoned litigator, and receives plaudits from clients for his "*practical and pragmatic approach*" and his "*creative problem solving.*" Amy Komoroski-Wiwi (see p.1740) handles matters including restrictive covenant agreements, severance agreements and human resources training. "*She is very good and conscientious,*" relates one interviewee.

## Lum, Drasco & Positan, LLC
See profile on p.1758

THE FIRM The labor and employment group at this firm primarily focuses on employer defense litigation, regularly handling discrimination, whistle-blowing, and wage and hour disputes. The group recently represented Welco in its successful negotiation of new collective bargaining agreements.

Sources say: "*Outstanding in terms of accessibility and responsiveness. They are very good at keeping us informed and handling unique issues with blue-sky thinking.*"

KEY INDIVIDUALS Wayne Positan (see p.1745) is chair of the labor and employment group at the firm, and is regarded by market observers as one of the leading lights of New Jersey labor and employment law. "*He is very practical and has very good business judgment,*" according to sources.

## Band 4

### Greenberg Traurig, LLP
See profile on p.1024

**THE FIRM** This firm is recognized for its defense of employers in single or multiplaintiff litigation at state or federal level, routinely handling matters such as wage and hour and noncompete cases. The group has extensive experience within the pharmaceutical, life sciences and education sectors. Clients include Lockheed Martin and Princeton University.

**Sources say:** "*They have a good depth of substantive expertise and they are very flexible and responsive.*"

**KEY INDIVIDUALS Kristine Feher** (see p.1735) has adapted to life at the firm quickly following her departure from Day Pitney. Sources describe her as "*a great litigator*" who is "*very bright and capable.*" **Wendy Johnson Lario** (see p.1738) is chair of the New Jersey labor and employment practice group. She receives praise from market sources as "*a fantastic attorney; very responsive and strategic.*"

### Pepper Hamilton LLP
See profile on p.2248

**THE FIRM** This firm debuts in the ranking in recognition of its excellent work in complex employment litigation, including EEOC class action matters. The group also has considerable experience in traditional labor matters, ranging from collective bargaining through arbitration and issues stemming from corporate reorganizations. The group can count First Choice Bank, Princeton HealthCare System and NRG Energy among its roster of current clients.

**Sources say:** "*They have been excellent at discussing strategies and keeping us abreast of the possible positions to take. Their professionalism is amazing.*"

**KEY INDIVIDUALS Matthew DelDuca** (see p.1734) chairs the labor and employment practice group. Sources say: "*He is a very effective litigator and has great insights into the issues of a case.*"

### Riker Danzig Scherer Hyland & Perretti LLP
See profile on p.1761

**THE FIRM** This Morristown-based team is predominantly focused on employment litigation. Of late, the group has successfully represented IBM in two instances of alleged discrimination. Other clients include Johnson & Johnson and United American Insurance Group.

**Sources say:** "*Responsiveness is excellent. We need quick answers and that is what they provide.*"

**KEY INDIVIDUALS Michael Furey** is co-head of the practice group at the firm and a seasoned employment litigator. He was lead counsel for IBM in the matters described above.

### Sills Cummis & Gross P.C.
See profile on p.1762

**THE FIRM** This firm offers a full-service labor and employment team. Areas of expertise include employment litigation, strategic counseling, employee handbooks and human resources training. Recent contentious matters include the representation of employers in discrimination and restrictive covenant matters.

**Sources say:** "*Very responsive, excellent at communicating and, more importantly, extremely competent.*"

**KEY INDIVIDUALS David Rosen** (see p.1746) debuts in the rankings, having received particular praise for his skill as a "*persuasive negotiator*" who is "*very articulate and eloquent.*" **Galit Kierkut** (see p.1739) is well versed in all employment litigation and counseling matters, and is adept at carrying out employment due diligence in connection with transactions.

### Wolff & Samson PC

**THE FIRM** This firm is focused on the defense of management clients in employment matters ranging from discrimination and harassment to wage and hour and whistle-blower cases. Clients include Bank of America and Vigo Industries.

**KEY INDIVIDUALS Catherine Wells** handles a range of employment litigation including harassment and discrimination matters. She elicits praise from market sources, who describe her as a "*good combination of a great litigator and a strategic thinker.*" **Margaret O'Rourke Wood** "*is very strong in depositions, and knows how to assess the documentation and figure out the best course of action,*" relates one impressed client.

### Other Notable Practitioners

**Cynthia Jacob** (see p.1738) of Fisher & Phillips LLP focuses her practice on employment litigation including discrimination and wrongful termination cases. She is highly regarded by peers and clients alike. **Joseph DeBlasio** of Giordano Halleran & Ciesla PC has 20 years' experience litigating employment law matters. "*His knowledge cannot be surpassed. He keeps up to date with everything,*" sources say. **Jay Becker**, also at Giordano Halleran & Ciesla PC, divides his practice between counseling companies on labor relations and litigating employment law matters. He is cochair of the labor and employment practice group at the firm's Red Bank location.

# LITIGATION

Insurance p.1723; Products Liability p.1723; White-Collar Crime & Government Investigations p.1723

Commentary about individuals can be found under their firm's paragraph. If the firm has no paragraph (is not ranked) look at Other Notable Practitioners.

## Litigation: General Commercial

### Leading Firms

**Band 1**
Gibbons P.C. *
Lowenstein Sandler LLP *
McCarter & English, LLP *
Sills Cummis & Gross P.C. *

**Band 2**
Cole, Schotz, Meisel, Forman & Leonard PA *
Day Pitney LLP *
Drinker Biddle & Reath LLP *
Riker Danzig Scherer Hyland & Perretti LLP *
Wolff & Samson PC

**Band 3**
Dechert LLP *
Greenbaum, Rowe, Smith & Davis LLP *
Greenberg Traurig, LLP *
Herrick, Feinstein LLP
Latham & Watkins LLP *
McElroy, Deutsch, Mulvaney & Carpenter, LLP *
Morgan, Lewis & Bockius LLP *
Saiber LLC
Wilentz, Goldman & Spitzer, P.A. *

\* Indicates firm / individual with profile.
†ONP = Other Notable Practitioner.

*The edit is in alphabetical order by firm name.*

## Anderson Kill & Olick, P.C.
See profile on p.1954

**THE FIRM** This group's expertise spans the full gamut of insurance recovery, and the team represents policyholders in a variety of disputes with insurance providers. After the arrival of Robert Chesler in late 2012, the practice now offers the expertise of six partners, and can also call on the knowledge of 63 specialists nationwide. Clients include major real estate trusts and pharmaceutical companies, as well as clients from the food and beverage sector, who engage the firm's services in contamination and recall issues.
**Sources say:** *"The firm has an extensive insurance litigation practice which continues to provide high-caliber work."*
**KEY INDIVIDUALS Robert Chesler** (see p.1733) joined the firm in fall 2012, bringing with him a wide range of experience that includes environmental, construction and asbestos cases. One client commented: *"I can't say enough good things about his knowledge, intellect and style – there is no one in the industry I would prefer to have on my side."* **Steven Pudell** (see p.1745) focuses on insurance recovery cases, representing clients from the pharmaceutical, chemical and real estate sectors.

## Senior Statesmen

**Senior Statesmen: distinguished older practitioners**

| | | |
|---|---|---|
| Gibbons John | Gibbons P.C. | |
| O'Shaughnessy William J | McCarter & English, LLP * | |
| Rowe Paul A | Greenbaum, Rowe, Smith & Davis LLP | |

### Leading Individuals

**Band 1**

| | |
|---|---|
| Campion Thomas | Drinker Biddle & Reath LLP *. |
| Drasco Dennis J | Lum, Drasco & Positan, LLC (ONP)†, * |
| Eakeley Esq Douglas S | Lowenstein Sandler LLP * |
| Griffinger Michael R | Gibbons P.C. |
| Kraus Alan E | Latham & Watkins LLP |
| Orloff Laurence B | Orloff, Lowenbach, Stifelman (ONP)† |
| Sellinger Philip R | Greenberg Traurig, LLP * |

**Band 2**

| | |
|---|---|
| Buckley Joseph L | Sills Cummis & Gross P.C. * |
| Clark Glenn A | Riker Danzig Scherer Hyland & Perretti LLP |
| Curtin Thomas | Graham Curtin (ONP)† |
| Greenbaum Jeffrey J | Sills Cummis & Gross P.C. * |
| Harris David L | Lowenstein Sandler LLP * |
| LaFiura Dennis R | Day Pitney LLP * |
| LaSala Joseph P | McElroy, Deutsch, Mulvaney & Carpenter * |
| Liloia Gerald A | Riker Danzig Scherer Hyland & Perretti LLP |
| Maderer William F | Saiber LLC |
| Marchetta Anthony J | Day Pitney LLP * |
| Meisel Michael S | Cole, Schotz, Meisel, Forman & Leonard *. |
| Orlofsky Stephen | Blank Rome LLP (ONP)†, * |
| Rolnick Lawrence M | Lowenstein Sandler LLP * |

**Band 3**

| | |
|---|---|
| Andretta Gage | Wolff & Samson PC |
| Beckelman Steven | McCarter & English, LLP * |
| Beran Richard | McCarter & English, LLP * |
| Bunn Andrew O | DLA Piper LLP (US) (ONP)†, * |
| Calmann Arnold B | Saiber LLC |
| Cocoziello J. Barry | Podvey, Meanor, Catenacci, Hildner (ONP)†, * |
| Feinberg Robert J | Giordano Halleran & Ciesla PC (ONP)† |

| | |
|---|---|
| Goldstein Arthur S | Wolff & Samson PC |
| Greenberg William S | McCarter & English, LLP |
| Haworth Gregory R | Duane Morris LLP (ONP)† |
| Kearney Dennis T | Day Pitney LLP * |
| Kearney John B | Ballard Spahr LLP * |
| Klein Steven R | Cole, Schotz, Meisel, Forman & Leonard * |
| Kotler David | Dechert LLP * |
| Leyva Leo V | Cole, Schotz, Meisel, Forman & Leonard * |
| MacPherson Robert J | Gibbons P.C. |
| McDonald Michael R | Gibbons P.C. |
| McLean David J | Latham & Watkins LLP |
| McMahon Brian J | Gibbons P.C. |
| Molloy Brian J | Wilentz, Goldman & Spitzer, P.A. |
| Mulvaney James M | McElroy, Deutsch, Mulvaney & Carpenter * |
| Naar Alan S | Greenbaum, Rowe, Smith & Davis LLP |
| North John D | Greenbaum, Rowe, Smith & Davis LLP |
| Pollock Jeffrey M | Fox Rothschild LLP (ONP)†, * |
| Rooney Gavin J | Lowenstein Sandler LLP * |
| Rosenberg Ezra D | Dechert LLP * |
| Sperling Joy Harmon | Day Pitney LLP * |
| Stein Michael | Pashman Stein (ONP)†, * |
| Sullivan Diane P | Weil, Gotshal & Manges LLP (ONP)†, * |
| Tross Scott | Herrick, Feinstein LLP |
| Van Deventer Kenneth M | Riker Danzig Scherer Hyland & Perretti |
| Wallach William D | McCarter & English, LLP * |
| Wild Jeffrey J | Lowenstein Sandler LLP * |

**Up-and-coming individuals**

| | |
|---|---|
| Bearce Nicole Denise | Lowenstein Sandler LLP * |
| Kistler David | Blank Rome LLP (ONP)†, * |

## Arseneault, Whipple, Fassett & Azzarello, LLP

**THE FIRM** The specialists at this boutique litigation firm have an enviable combined experience in white-collar crime defense. The team is renowned for the quality of its work in multidefendant criminal actions and public corruption matters, and has been increasingly active in the medical field of late. Clients can call on expert guidance throughout each stage of criminal investigations, as well as in litigation at state and federal level.
**KEY INDIVIDUALS** Sources regard **Jack Arseneault** as a *"superb lawyer."* His broad-based practice covers securities and antitrust disputes, mail fraud and environmental litigation. **John Whipple** has 25 years of experience across a wide variety of contentious matters, including securities fraud and political corruption cases. He is highly respected by peers, who consider him *"a very good and tenacious attorney."*

## Ballard Spahr LLP
See profile on p.2234

**THE FIRM** This practice has garnered considerable acclaim for the quality of its work in the product liability arena. The group focuses on the defense of consumer product class actions on behalf of a variety of manufacturing and pharmaceutical companies. Highlights include work for US subsidiaries of several international names, and the team represented Kia Motors America in a class action over alleged brake defects. DuPont, Miele USA and Subaru are among the other names in its client roster.
**Sources say:** *"The attorneys possess invaluable trial advocacy skills and industry knowledge."*
**KEY INDIVIDUALS Neal Walters** (see p.1749) is the head of the practice's product liability and mass tort group, and was the lead partner on the abovementioned Kia Motors America matter. His litigation prowess is extolled by a variety of clients, who value the fact that *"he is responsive and*

*The editorial is in alphabetical order by firm name.*

## Litigation: Insurance
### Leading Firms

**Band 1**

Drinker Biddle & Reath LLP *
Lowenstein Sandler LLP *
McCarter & English, LLP *
Riker Danzig Scherer Hyland & Perretti LLP *

**Band 2**

Anderson Kill & Olick, P.C. *
Clyde & Co US LLP *
Coughlin Duffy LLP
McElroy, Deutsch, Mulvaney & Carpenter, LLP *

### Leading Individuals

**Band 1**

| | | |
|---|---|---|
| Altieri James M | Drinker Biddle & Reath LLP * |
| Bennett Lynda | Lowenstein Sandler LLP * |
| Chesler Robert D | Anderson Kill & Olick, P.C. * |
| Kelly Shawn L | Riker Danzig Scherer Hyland & Perretti LLP |
| Pastor Sherilyn | McCarter & English, LLP * |
| Quinn Thomas | Wilson, Elser, Moskowitz, Edelman (ONP) † |
| Rothschild Gita F | McCarter & English, LLP * |
| Wolff Kevin | Coughlin Duffy LLP |

**Band 2**

| | |
|---|---|
| Cohen Michael | Saiber LLC |
| Coughlin Kevin | Coughlin Duffy LLP |
| Gottlieb Ira | McCarter & English, LLP * |
| Gugig Michael | Saul Ewing LLP (ONP) † |
| Marone Michael | McElroy, Deutsch, Mulvaney & Carpenter * |
| McNally Daren S | Clyde & Co |
| O'Donnell Brian | Riker Danzig Scherer Hyland & Perretti LLP |
| Pollock Jeffrey M | Fox Rothschild LLP * |
| Priestley Robert | Clyde & Co US LLP |
| Pudell Steven J | Anderson Kill & Olick, P.C. * |
| Rothschild Kenneth A | Golden, Rothschild, Spagnola, Lundell (ONP) † |
| Sellinger Philip R | Greenberg Traurig, LLP * |

**Band 3**

| | |
|---|---|
| Horowitz Gregory | McCarter & English, LLP * |
| Osias Brian J | McCarter & English, LLP * |
| Sheridan Mark D | Patton Boggs LLP (ONP) † |

## Litigation: Product Liability
### Leading Firms

**Band 1**

Dechert LLP *
McCarter & English, LLP *

**Band 2**

Drinker Biddle & Reath LLP *
Gibbons P.C. *
Porzio, Bromberg & Newman PC
Sills Cummis & Gross P.C. *

**Band 3**

Ballard Spahr LLP *
Day Pitney LLP *

### Leading Individuals

**Band 1**

| | |
|---|---|
| Kott David R | McCarter & English, LLP * |
| Rose Beth S | Sills Cummis & Gross P.C. * |
| Rosenberg Ezra D | Dechert LLP * |
| Sullivan Diane P | Weil, Gotshal & Manges LLP * |

**Band 2**

| | |
|---|---|
| Campion Thomas | Drinker Biddle & Reath LLP * |
| Catullo Kim M | Gibbons P.C. |
| Cooner David | McCarter & English, LLP * |
| Haglund Benjamin E | Day Pitney LLP * |
| Levine Ronald J | Herrick, Feinstein LLP |
| Rothschild Gita F | McCarter & English, LLP * |
| Sharko Susan M | Drinker Biddle & Reath LLP * |
| Tyrrell James E | Patton Boggs LLP (ONP) † |
| Walters Neal | Ballard Spahr LLP * |

**KEY INDIVIDUALS Daren McNally** receives considerable acclaim from market sources, who describe him as *"very knowledgeable and very experienced."* He is also *"an exceptional oral advocate."* **Robert Priestley** is a seasoned trial attorney who has represented clients in insurance disputes in New Jersey, California and Florida. Sources agree that *"he is vastly experienced in the insurance practice area."*

### Cole, Schotz, Meisel, Forman & Leonard PA
See profile on p.1752

**THE FIRM** This Hackensack-based group is renowned for the quality of its work in commercial litigation, and acts for clients in connection with real estate, construction and securities disputes. Its diverse caseload has recently included work for major clients in a number of headline-grabbing cases. In one such matter, the firm is defending Highland Capital Management in an ongoing $470 million action filed by the Bass and Boeddekker families over its retention of a recovered loan. Other clients include The Home Depot and the New Jersey Sports and Exposition Authority.

**KEY INDIVIDUALS** Department cochair **Michael Meisel** (see p.1742) is called on by a variety of clients for assistance with complex business and construction disputes. He is commended for his formidable trial performance, and also has extensive experience serving as an arbitrator and mediator. **Steven Klein** (see p.1740) is a seasoned veteran of complex commercial litigation in state, federal and appel-

## Litigation: White-Collar Crime & Government Investigations
### Leading Firms

**Band 1**

Lowenstein Sandler LLP *
Walder, Hayden & Brogan P.A.

**Band 2**

Arseneault, Whipple, Fassett & Azzarello, LLP *
Gibbons P.C. *
Krovatin Klingeman LLC

**Band 3**

Critchley, Kinum & Vazquez, LLC
Day Pitney LLP *
McCarter & English, LLP *
Sills Cummis & Gross P.C. *

### Leading Individuals

**Band 1**

| | |
|---|---|
| Arseneault Jack | Arseneault, Whipple, Fassett & Azzarello |
| Ashley Thomas | Law Office of Thomas R Ashley (ONP) † |
| Critchley, Sr. Michael | Critchley, Kinum & Vazquez, LLC |
| Dauber Edward J | Greenberg Dauber Epstein & Tucker (ONP) † |
| Hayden Joseph | Walder, Hayden & Brogan P.A. |
| Himmel Michael B | Lowenstein Sandler LLP * |
| Horn Lawrence S | Sills Cummis & Gross P.C. * |
| Krovatin Gerald | Krovatin Klingeman LLC |
| Lustberg Lawrence S | Gibbons P.C. |
| Nittoly Paul G | Drinker Biddle & Reath LLP * |
| Walder Justin | Walder, Hayden & Brogan P.A. |
| Whipple John | Arseneault, Whipple, Fassett & Azzarello |

**Band 2**

| | |
|---|---|
| Kipnees Robert J | Lowenstein Sandler LLP * |
| Klingeman Henry | Krovatin Klingeman LLC |
| Marino Kevin H | Marino, Tortorella & Boyle PC (ONP) † |
| Mintz Robert A | McCarter & English, LLP * |
| Moulthrop Samuel P | Riker Danzig Scherer Hyland & Perretti LLP |
| O'Connor Aidan | Pashman Stein (ONP) † |
| Olinsky Mark S | Sills Cummis & Gross P.C. * |
| O'Reilly John J | Day Pitney LLP * |
| Poplar Carl | Carl D Poplar, P.A., Attorneys at Law (ONP) † |
| Timpone Walter F | McElroy, Deutsch, Mulvaney & Carpenter * |
| Zegas Alan | Law Offices of Alan L. Zegas (ONP) † |

*\* Indicates firm / individual with profile.*
*† ONP = Other Notable Practitioner.*

*takes a practical approach in resolving issues."* Highlights of **John Kearney**'s (see p.1739) practice include representing Jim Beam Brands and Beam Global Spirits & Wine in an action brought by a nationwide class claiming consumer fraud and breach of warranty.

### Clyde & Co US LLP
See profile on p.440

**THE FIRM** The New Jersey office of this international firm is highly skilled in insurance matters, and can call on the broader expertise of the firm's global network. With significant experience in litigation at both state and federal level, the group acts for some of the world's largest insurance companies in matters ranging from general liability insurance coverage to professional liability and mass tort. The team is well positioned to advise clients on trials and arbitrations both in the USA and abroad.

late courts. He successfully represented Mr Barjinder Singh Brar and his company in an action to reassert Mr Brar's control over a nonprofit corporation following his removal for alleged misconduct. **Leo Leyva** (see p.1741) was lead partner in the aforementioned Highland Capital matter. Practicing in both New Jersey and New York, he is most active in real estate litigation and complex commercial cases.

### Coughlin Duffy LLP

**THE FIRM** This full-service firm is renowned for the strength of its insurance litigation practice. Acting on behalf of insurers and reinsurers, the group has earned a reputation for excellence in complex coverage matters, reg-

*The editorial is in alphabetical order by firm name.*

ulatory advice and coordinating mass tort actions. Its wide-ranging experience in the insurance arena includes advising on environmental, professional and employment liabilities, as well as bad faith claims.

**Sources say:** *"They are very well versed, and very outspoken on behalf of their clients."*

**KEY INDIVIDUALS** One of the founding partners of the firm, **Kevin Wolff** is at the forefront of insurance and reinsurance practice in the state. He represents insurance companies in complex general liability, environmental and employment matters, and is described by peers as *"extremely knowledgeable, with a very high profile."* **Kevin Coughlin** focuses his practice on the representation of insurance companies in coverage disputes both in the USA and Europe, as well as counseling them on the full spectrum of regulatory issues.

## Critchley, Kinum & Vazquez, LLC

**THE FIRM** The white-collar crime group at this litigation boutique is praised by market sources for the level of sophistication it shows in its representation of clients. The team is highly experienced in representing individuals and institutions in mail and wire fraud, antitrust issues and political corruption matters. The firm is also well versed in professional misconduct and malpractice matters.

**KEY INDIVIDUALS** **Michael Critchley** has 30 years of litigation experience at both state and federal level. He focuses his white-collar crime practice on defending individuals and institutions from allegations of trust violations and tax fraud.

## Day Pitney LLP
See profile on p.1753

**THE FIRM** This regional powerhouse remains an active presence across the board in New Jersey litigation. The firm can offer an impressive depth of trial experience in a range of commercial issues, as well as in white-collar crime defense and product liability litigation. The group is well equipped to represent clients from all industry sectors, and its services are frequently engaged by major names involved in high-stakes disputes. Current clients include Deutsche Bank Trust Company Americas, GlaxoSmithKline and UPS.

**Sources say:** *"Very thorough, great communication and excellent legal expertise."*

**KEY INDIVIDUALS** **John O'Reilly** (see p.1743) focuses his practice on the defense of corporations and individuals in white-collar crime cases. A former Warren County prosecutor, sources describe him as *"a really talented lawyer, and a fantastic litigator."* **Benjamin Haglund** (see p.1737) is co-head of the product liability group, and has played a leading role in some of the firm's most high-profile matters. He is *"a strong attorney,"* who is known for his skills in environmental litigation. Among his practice highlights, **Dennis LaFiura** (see p.1740) advised the Avis Budget Group on two class actions alleging breach of contract and consumer fraud. Sources regard him as *"a very good lawyer with an excellent reputation."* **Anthony Marchetta** (see p.1741) continues to impress with his work on complex commercial disputes. A seasoned civil trial practitioner, he

has appeared on numerous occasions before state and federal courts. **Dennis Kearney** (see p.1739) has a wide-ranging client base which includes a number of major financial services institutions. Chair of the consumer finance and creditor rights group, **Joy Harmon Sperling** (see p.1748) is a highly respected member of the commercial litigation team.

## Dechert LLP
See profile on p.1969

**THE FIRM** The Princeton office of this international giant is active across a diverse range of practice areas, and is highly praised for the strength of its commercial and product liability litigation groups. Highlights of the team's caseload include a number of high-stakes consumer class actions, as well as white-collar crime cases and IP litigation. Its client base features some of the world's best-known brands and several Fortune 500 companies, including major pharmaceutical and financial services names. In standout matters, the group continued to represent Oppenheimer Acquisition Corporation and Oppenheimer Funds in various actions arising from the clients' ownership of hedge funds that had invested billions with Bernard Madoff.

**Sources say:** *"The firm's attorneys are smart, responsive, sensitive to business needs and creative problem solvers."*

**KEY INDIVIDUALS** **Ezra Rosenberg** (see p.1746) divides his practice between complex commercial and product liability litigation. Sources describe him as a go-to name for big-ticket cases: *"He is the real deal and a superb attorney – the bigger it gets the better."* **David Kotler** (see p.1740) debuts in the rankings after receiving excellent feedback for his commercial litigation work. Clients enthuse that he is *"very smart, and his written work is top-notch – I can feel confident that his work will be great and he will represent our company well."*

## Drinker Biddle & Reath LLP
See profile on p.2238

**THE FIRM** Drinker Biddle's New Jersey litigation group has distinguished itself through high-quality work that spans the full breadth of the commercial arena. The firm is well known for its stellar services, whether acting for leading enterprises on bet-the-company mass tort proceedings, or defending individuals and corporations from allegations of securities fraud or antitrust violations. In product liability matters, the team continued to act as national coordinating counsel for Johnson & Johnson in connection with its Levaquin product, in proceedings which comprise nearly 1,700 cases in the New Jersey state mass tort program.

**Sources say:** *"Responsive and collegial."*

**KEY INDIVIDUALS** A prominent member of the commercial litigation and white-collar defense group, **Paul Nittoly** (see p.1743) is singled out for praise as *"definitely a top-tier guy – very personable, detail-oriented and strategic, and very well respected by the authorities."* **Thomas Campion** (see p.1732) divides his time between general commercial and product liability litigation. A seasoned trial lawyer, he often defends pharmaceutical companies in

product liability and consumer fraud matters. Sources report: *"He is a very smart attorney with a quiet excellence."* **Susan Sharko** (see p.1747) represents Johnson & Johnson in the abovementioned Levaquin disputes. She has valuable experience in product liability, and sources describe her as *"a brilliant strategist and manager of large-scale litigation."* **James Altieri** (see p.1731) is chair of the insurance coverage practice, and regularly represents clients from the insurance and financial services sector in courts throughout the country.

## Gibbons P.C.
See profile on p.1754

**THE FIRM** This regional giant has a reputation for fielding excellent attorneys, and attracts some of the most high-profile cases in the state. In big-ticket work, the team represented the New Jersey Sports and Exposition Authority in numerous litigation matters relating to its sports and entertainment properties. Other standout matters include fraud and bankruptcy proceedings and product liability class actions. JPMorgan Securities, Chubb Group and Brother International are counted among the firm's impressive clients.

**Sources say:** *"We love the firm for their knowledge and their responsiveness. They are also very efficient and very economical."*

**KEY INDIVIDUALS** **Lawrence Lustberg** has a wealth of experience in criminal defense and appellate litigation before state and federal courts. He is chair of the criminal defense practice group at the firm, and sources describe him as *"a great guy and a very gifted attorney."* **Michael Griffinger** is described by sources as *"at the top of his practice."* He successfully defended the City of Newark in a suit brought by Avis Budget Group, and Hertz over a tax on automobile rentals in certain industrial zones in the city, which results in around $8.1 million a year in city revenues. **Kim Catullo** has acquired a exemplary reputation within the product liability arena. Practice highlights include acting for Stryker and Howmedica Osteonic in personal injury and product liability matters. **Robert MacPherson** focuses his practice on commercial and construction litigation, and represents civil contractor EE Cruz in connection with several infrastructure projects. **Michael McDonald** advised Skinder-Strauss Associates on a suit brought by a New York City law firm regarding an alleged unsolicited facsimile advertisement. Chair of the business and commercial litigation group **Brian McMahon** focuses his practice on antitrust and trade regulations and securities litigation. He is a seasoned veteran of jury and nonjury trial at state and federal level. Former Chief Judge of the Third Circuit Court of Appeals, **John Gibbons** is regarded by sources as one of the deans of the New Jersey commercial litigation Bar. With a career spanning 50 years, he offers an invaluable depth of knowledge in dispute proceedings.

## Greenbaum, Rowe, Smith & Davis LLP
See profile on p.1755

**THE FIRM** This full-service group has a strong presence in New Jersey commercial litigation, and fields a team of 34 partners. The group represents a diverse range of clients, from individual entrepreneurs through to multinational corporations, and acts across the full gamut of commercial litigation. Among its practice highlights, the team represented Crescent Heights of America in a construction defect case brought by a condominium association, valued at more than $19 million. Additional clients include Wells Fargo and the New Jersey Association of Realtors.

**KEY INDIVIDUALS Alan Naar** is vice chair of the department and active across the full range of civil litigation matters, from corporate and partnership disputes to antitrust and land use litigation. Sources characterize him as *"extremely knowledgeable and confident."* The *"very knowledgeable"* **John North** is praised as *"an extremely good trial lawyer. He cross-examines without notes and yet has it all at his fingertips."* **Paul Rowe** is chairman of the firm's litigation department. A seasoned practitioner, market sources praise him as *"one of the finest trial lawyers in New Jersey. He has a great knowledge of the law and has tried many cases."*

### Greenberg Traurig, LLP
See profile on p.1024

**THE FIRM** This international giant's Florham Park-based practice offers experience spanning a wide variety of contentious proceedings. The 12-partner group can also call on the combined expertise of over 600 litigators throughout the USA and Europe. The firm is highly active in class actions and high-stakes litigation for a number of financial services and technology clients. It recently defended Verizon Communications and Verizon Wireless in a breach of contract dispute with damages valued at $10 billion.

**KEY INDIVIDUALS Philip Sellinger** (see p.1747) is both the managing shareholder of the firm's New Jersey practice, and the chair of the firm's class action practice. He was lead partner on the aforementioned Verizon matter, and is described by those within the market as a *"great attorney and an excellent litigator."*

### Herrick, Feinstein LLP

**THE FIRM** Highly active prominent in class actions, construction disputes and real estate cases, Herrick's Newark commercial litigation group is also commended for its strength in securities work. Clients have high praise for the firm's strategic capabilities and its commitment to customer service. In standout matters, the team successfully defended Bridgestone in a series of class actions regarding a new tire design. The firm also counts major technology, banking and consumer product names among its client roster.

**Sources say:** *"They are very responsive, provide high-quality work and always get good results."*

**KEY INDIVIDUALS** Group co-head **Ronald Levine** has extensive experience representing clients in consumer class actions, and attracts stellar feedback from sources across the market. Impressed clients report that *"he is very responsive, can quickly analyze any situation and provides business-oriented, practical advice quickly. He is also an excellent litigator."* **Scott Tross** debuts in the ranking in recognition of excellent work in real estate and securities litigation.

Sources describe him as an *"expert in creditor and real estate matters who is very sharp on analysis, knows what the issues are and is succinct with regards to how to resolve a problem."*

### Krovatin Klingeman LLC

**THE FIRM** This Newark-based litigation boutique is well equipped to handle any variety of state or federal white-collar crime litigation. Its services are often engaged in multifaceted disputes, and the team offers valuable knowledge of a wide range of regulatory investigations. It advises lawyers, accountants and doctors in connection with allegations of professional misconduct and abuse, and also acts for corporate institutions and their shareholders.

**KEY INDIVIDUALS** A former prosecutor at the District Attorney's office, **Henry Klingeman** is a seasoned veteran in all forms of criminal defense in both state and federal court. Sources describe him as a *"good trial lawyer and well respected in the state."* **Gerald Krovatin** focuses his practice on the defense of individuals and institutions in all aspects of white-collar crime proceedings.

### Latham & Watkins LLP
See profile on p.446

**THE FIRM** This excellent Newark-based litigation group is comprised of 13 attorneys, who can also call on the combined expertise of litigation experts spread over three continents. Latham's skills in complex commercial and environmental litigation attract high-caliber clients, which seek out its expertise for state and federal cases. Notable work includes acting for ConocoPhillips in a complex negligence action in New Hampshire with damages estimated at $850 million.

**KEY INDIVIDUALS Alan Kraus** is lead partner in the aforementioned ConocoPhillips matter and splits his time between New Jersey and New York. With a focus on environmental and consumer class actions, he has represented clients in over 50 matters before courts and arbitrators. Managing partner of the firm's New Jersey group, **David McLean** is fêted for his work in complex commercial litigation. High-stake mandates include representing the Eaton Corporation in a sex discrimination class action valued at $100 million.

### Lowenstein Sandler LLP
See profile on p.1757

**THE FIRM** Lowenstein Sandler's full-service litigation group offers extensive experience in advising major corporations on high-stakes disputes. The team's outstanding expertise in commercial litigation and white-collar crime defense attracts a wide range of clients, including names from the pharmaceuticals, consumer goods and educational sectors. The group is also well known for its skills in insurance proceedings, and has represented Wyndham Worldwide, Lehigh Cement and Georgia-Pacific in related cases. Highlights include successfully representing KPMG in the New Jersey Supreme Court, securing the overturn of a $40 million jury verdict against the firm's client.

**Sources say:** *"They are clear market leaders in the state."*

**KEY INDIVIDUALS Michael Himmel** (see p.1737) is chair of the litigation practice and the white-collar crime defense group at the firm. Sources consider him to be *"a fantastic guy – he is a litigator and a deal-maker, and is very pragmatic."* **Robert Kipnees's** (see p.1739) white-collar crime practice covers criminal antitrust and tax cases, as well as securities and insurance fraud. He represents both individual clients and companies across a wide variety of industry sectors. **Lynda Bennett** (see p.1731) is regarded as a *"brilliant attorney – she explains the issues clearly and comes up with excellent strategies."* She is head of the insurance litigation group at the firm, and represents Lehigh Cement in a number of insurance coverage matters. **Douglas Eakeley** (see p.1735) is a *"terrific lawyer,"* valued by clients for his *"excellent ability to develop and present arguments."* Of late, he has represented Merck in a class action suit worth hundreds of millions of dollars. **David Harris** (see p.1737) is chair of the commercial and business litigation group at the firm. He is commended for his *"excellent business judgment,"* and his *"phenomenal memory, which gives him an advantage in any discussion or arguments."* **Lawrence Rolnick** (see p.1746) chairs the firm's securities litigation and enforcement practice group, and is also active within capital markets litigation and investment management. He typically represents investment funds and municipal pension funds. **Jeffrey Wild** (see p.1749) offers expert guidance in securities litigation, and is cochair of the firm's capital markets litigation and fiduciary counseling and litigation groups. **Gavin Rooney** (see p.1746) debuts in the rankings after receiving enthusiastic praise from clients, who describe him as *"very smart and a great advocate, with great strategic sense."* He is also valued for his understanding of clients' business needs. Cochair of the appellate practice group at the firm, **Nicole Denise Bearce** (see p.1731) is a forceful litigator who represents clients in commercial and fiduciary cases.

### McCarter & English, LLP
See profile on p.1759

**THE FIRM** This regional heavyweight has a multifaceted litigation department which attracts rave reviews from sources across the market. Of late, the group excelled in its representation of Consolidated Rail against Texas Eastern Pipeline, achieving a favorable ruling for its client with national precedential value. In the product liability arena, the team defended Goodyear in a class action suit regarding an allegedly defective product, with a potential multi-million-dollar exposure. Additional clients include the New York Giants and Black & Decker.

**Sources say:** *"Responsive lawyers at the top of their game."* *"Superb performance – they are efficient, strategic and commercially minded, and get great results."*

**KEY INDIVIDUALS** Former Assistant US Attorney **Robert Mintz** (see p.1742) is chair of the government investigations and white-collar criminal defense group. He attracts a range of plaudits, and is commended for his *"great substantive legal knowledge and wealth of experience – he is very well respected everywhere."* **David Kott** (see p.1740) is an *"amazing lawyer and an excellent strategic thinker,"* who represented Ryobi Technologies in a suit

*The editorial is in alphabetical order by firm name.*

regarding allegations of a defective table saw design. **David Cooner** (see p.1733) is *"very attuned to providing quality legal services in a cost-effective manner."* He has acted on behalf of Ashland and Hercules on product defect and asbestos matters. **Gita Rothschild's** (see p.1747) varied practice includes insurance coverage disputes and product liability actions. With 36 years of experience spanning a wide range of sectors, she has impressive market standing and is regarded by clients as *"a phenomenal lawyer – there is no one better at the settlement table."* **Sherilyn Pastor** (see p.1744) is the head of the insurance group, and is described as *"a top-notch attorney and a great strategic thinker."* **Ira Gottlieb** (see p.1736) represents policyholders in insurance coverage disputes, and has valuable expertise in environmental matters. Clients report that *"he performs flawlessly and comes up with brilliantly strategic positions."* Head of the business and financial services litigation group at the firm, **Richard Beran** (see p.1731) is lauded for his *"excellent analysis, demeanor and strategy."* Market sources consider **Steven Beckelman** (see p.1731) to be a *"very strategic and intelligent"* adviser who can quickly get to the heart of issues. **William Greenberg** is a former assistant counsel to the governor of New Jersey, and has 45 years of litigation experience at both state and federal level. **William Wallach** (see p.1749) is lead partner in the aforementioned Consolidated Rail case. He handles a variety of shareholder disputes and matters arising out of the UCC. The eminently experienced **William O'Shaughnessy** (see p.1743) is renowned for his *"deep understanding of the New Jersey Bar."* Sources describe **Gregory Horowitz** (see p.1737) as *"an excellent negotiator with an imposing personal presence, who is able to defuse controversial situations."* **Brian Osias** (see p.1743) has distinguished himself in his representation of policyholders in complex insurance coverage disputes. One satisfied client asserted: *"He is a rising star and a great strategic thinker."*

## McElroy, Deutsch, Mulvaney & Carpenter, LLP
See profile on p.1760

**THE FIRM** This regional firm has a strong footprint in New Jersey, with offices based in Morristown, Newark and Ridgewood. The litigation team is experienced across the full spectrum of disputes, and is held in particularly high regard for the quality of its commercial and insurance coverage work. Its caseload features complex contract disputes, insurance coverage cases and construction claims, and the New Jersey team can call on the combined knowledge of 300 attorneys spread over ten states.

**KEY INDIVIDUALS** Seasoned trial attorney **Walter Timpone** (see p.1749) was formerly Chief of Special Prosecution at the US Attorneys Office. He focuses his practice on white-collar crime defense and is well known for his internal investigations work. **Michael Marone** (see p.1742) has a highly active insurance coverage practice, including a number of employment insurance issues, and represents a range of carriers. **Joseph LaSala** (see p.1740) is held in high regard by market sources for the breadth and depth of his experience in complex commercial litigation. **James Mulvaney** (see p.1743) is described as *"a very solid*

*lawyer who is knowledgeable in the substantive law."* He represents clients in complex commercial matters, including construction disputes.

## Morgan, Lewis & Bockius LLP
See profile on p.2246

**THE FIRM** This practice is called on by a wide variety of clients for representation in complex commercial litigation. Its client roster features names from the pharmaceutical, manufacturing and energy sectors, and the team defended Pathfinder Energy Services in an alleged contamination matter in the Western District of New York. Additional clients include Mincing Trading and Ascend Performance Materials.

**Sources say:** *"They have a great reputation in the practice area, and the professionalism and quality of research were very good."*

**KEY INDIVIDUALS** Christopher Loeber is a key contact for the practice.

## Porzio, Bromberg & Newman PC

**THE FIRM** This practice maintains its reputation for high-caliber work in product liability. The group handles environmental and medical exposure matters as well as large consumer class actions, acting for a range of clients including major pharmaceutical and chemical manufacturing companies. Among its standout matters are several disputes handled on behalf of DuPont, including complaints filed by hundreds of homeowners situated near a plant site in Pompton Lakes. It receives excellent feedback for the level of client service on offer, and the team is praised for its responsiveness and pragmatism.

**Sources say:** *"Attentive, focused and practical."*

**KEY INDIVIDUALS** Department head Steven Benenson is the key contact for the practice.

## Riker Danzig Scherer Hyland & Perretti LLP
See profile on p.1761

**THE FIRM** This Morristown-based litigation group is active across the spectrum of dispute resolution, and is renowned for the strength of its work on commercial and insurance disputes. The team acts for an array of large pharmaceutical companies, as well as representing high-profile insurance names based both nationally and internationally. These include the Harleysville Insurance Companies and Zurich. The team also acted for Riverstone Claims Management on behalf of TIG Insurance, in an action brought by IMO Industries claiming nearly $350 million in asbestos claims coverage and damages.

**Sources say:** *"We have been especially impressed with the firm's ability to bring speed and energy to matters without sacrificing thoroughness and diligence."*

**KEY INDIVIDUALS Shawn Kelly** is *"a very good attorney and an excellent judge of character,"* who represents Riverstone Claims Management in the abovementioned asbestos-related case. Managing partner **Glenn Clark** is a seasoned practitioner in the commercial litigation arena, with 30 years of experience in complex disputes before state and federal courts. **Gerald Liloia** is head of the firm's litigation department and handles a wide-ranging case-

load. Of late he has been increasingly active in securities cases and lender liability claims. **Samuel Moulthrop** divides his time between environmental litigation and white-collar crime defense, advising on a range of insurance coverage and securities fraud cases. Cochair of the insurance and reinsurance group **Brian O'Donnell** recently acted for Mitsui Sumitomo Insurance Company of America in a claim by Gibson Guitar for losses arising from the 2010 Nashville floods. Clients assert that *"he is very organized, exhaustive in his analysis and always up to speed on the work that needs to be done."* **Kenneth Van Deventer** has a diverse breadth of practice, advising clients from the financial services and communications industries on a wide range of matters.

## Saiber LLC

**THE FIRM** This broad-based practice handles a variety of commercial litigation mandates from its offices in Florham Park and Newark. Its client roster spans an array of industries, including real estate, banking and construction. The team's broad range of experience covers labor disputes, environmental claims and securities arbitration, as well as mass tort litigation.

**KEY INDIVIDUALS Michael Cohen** is a seasoned insurance dispute litigator, described as *"an excellent advocate, and very knowledgeable."* Managing member of the firm **William Maderer** is *"an excellent attorney"* who focuses his practice on business disputes and employment litigation. Former Deputy Attorney General **Arnold Calmann** has 38 years of experience litigating a variety of matters in state and federal court. His commercial practice includes franchise and sales and distribution matters.

## Sills Cummis & Gross P.C.
See profile on p.1762

**THE FIRM** This regional stalwart offers significant expertise across the breadth of litigation matters. Its wide-ranging skill set includes sought-after expertise in product liability disputes, which is called on by high-profile names in the pharmaceutical industry. Other highlights of the practice's civil caseload include big-ticket construction arbitration, antitrust litigation and breach of contract disputes. On the criminal side, the team is well known for its expertise in handling cases brought by the tax authorities. Its client base features a variety of Fortune 500 and multinational companies, including a number of global financial services providers.

**Sources say:** *"Besides its high-quality trial and litigation advocacy, the firm's strongest point is its ability to adapt to the specific need of the client."*

**KEY INDIVIDUALS Lawrence Horn** (see p.1737) receives glowing praise for his talents in litigation, and is dubbed *"a first-rate white-collar crime attorney."* He is also renowned for his talents in tax litigation, and one source describes him as *"one of the best tax defense attorneys in New Jersey – if you have a federal tax issue then he is your guy."* **Beth Rose** (see p.1746) is the head of the product liability practice at the firm. She is regularly engaged by pharmaceutical companies in high-stakes litigation, and is valued by clients for being *"very efficient, and very proactive in staying up to* date." **Joseph Buckley** (see p.1732) has acted on behalf of several major banks and financial institutions in lender liability litigation. Sources praise him as *"extremely knowledgeable, with extensive litigation and trial advocacy skills."* **Jeffrey Greenbaum** (see p.1736) is chair of the class action group at the firm, and a seasoned trial lawyer. He has appeared in state and federal court in an array of commercial matters, representing individuals and corporations in disputes regarding professional liability, breach of contract and antitrust issues. A former federal prosecutor at the US Attorneys Office, **Mark Olinsky** (see p.1743) has 30 years of experience in both civil and criminal litigation. His white-collar crime practice includes defending clients from allegations of securities and consumer fraud as well as insider trading.

### Walder, Hayden & Brogan P.A.

**THE FIRM** The attorneys at Walder Hayden are seasoned veterans in white-collar crime defense, and are entrusted with some of the most high-profile and sensitive cases in the state. The team's impressive experience includes advising a range of individuals and institutions facing investigations and litigation at state and federal level. Among its diverse areas of expertise, clients can call on the group's knowledge of official misconduct, securities fraud and RICO offenses.

**Sources say:** *"They are great attorneys, the real deal – they leave no stone unturned."*

**KEY INDIVIDUALS** Former Deputy Attorney General **Justin Walder** is deemed to be *"one of the deans of the Bar,"* and has a wealth of courtroom experience. The highly respected **Joseph Hayden** is also a former Deputy Attorney General, and divides his time between New York and New Jersey. He is well known for his work on complex cases.

### Wilentz, Goldman & Spitzer, P.A.
See profile on p.1763

**THE FIRM** With significant expertise across the full gamut of commercial litigation, the firm is well known for its work in antitrust, trade secret and restrictive covenant litigation. The group is regularly engaged to litigate in both state and federal courts, and has extensive trial experience. Market sources praise the group's work on behalf of plaintiffs.

**KEY INDIVIDUALS** **Brian Molloy** is the firm's managing partner, whose broad-ranging litigation experience includes antitrust and false advertising matters.

### Wolff & Samson PC

**THE FIRM** Wolff & Samson's West Orange-based practice focuses on securities and environmental litigation as well as contractual disputes. The team acts for a range of major corporate clients and their shareholders, including various companies in the healthcare sector, and is also experienced in representing government bodies such as the New Jersey Turnpike Authority. Standout matters include real estate, estate and partnership disputes.

**KEY INDIVIDUALS** **Gage Andretta** has 30 years of experience litigating across a range of matters, including real estate, condemnation and land use. **Arthur Goldstein** is known as a formidable litigator, and has considerable experience in banking and estate cases.

### Other Notable Practitioners

Peers have a high regard for **Thomas Ashley** at the Law Office of Thomas R Ashley, Esq. He is described as *"brilliant – he has an incredible presence, is quick on his feet and relates well to juries."* **Andrew Bunn** (see p.1732) of DLA Piper LLP (US) has a varied caseload, handling a range of trial work, alternative dispute resolution and investigations for clients, including major financial services institutions. **Barry Cocoziello** (see p.1733) is co-managing partner at Podvey, Meanor, Catenacci, Hildner, Cocoziello & Chattman, P.C., and handles a range of commercial, construction and real estate litigation. One of the founding members of Graham Curtin, **Thomas Curtin** is renowned for the quality of his commercial litigation work. His practice also includes alternative dispute resolution and IP. **Edward Dauber** is a white-collar expert at Greenberg Dauber Epstein & Tucker. A former Assistant Attorney General for New Jersey, he is well known for his work on sophisticated cases. **Dennis Drasco** (see p.1734) of Lum, Drasco & Positan, LLC is a vastly experienced trial attorney with a practice encompassing commercial, construction and condemnation litigation. Sources report that *"he is highly regarded within the state and national Bar."* **Robert Feinberg** of Giordano Halleran & Ciesla PC represents a diverse client base in all manner of commercial disputes, and advised Commerce Plaza on a complex dispute with its tenant. **Michael Gugig** of Saul Ewing LLP regularly represents insurance companies in coverage disputes at both state and federal level. **Gregory Haworth** of Duane Morris LLP has represented clients before a number of state and federal courts. He concentrates his practice on commercial litigation and bankruptcy matters. **David Kistler** (see p.1739) of Blank Rome LLP is building a reputation as a go-to commercial attorney within the state. *"He has great strategic skills and is a very hard worker,"* say sources. **Kevin Marino** of Marino, Tortorella & Boyle PC is *"a fantastic attorney,"* who is highly valued by clients for his expertise in white-collar defense. **Aidan O'Connor** (see p.1743) of Pashman Stein, has an excellent reputation within New Jersey's white-collar crime Bar, and offers valuable expertise in securities fraud and internal investigations. *"He draws upon his experience as a federal prosecutor to provide insights helpful to private clients,"* say sources. **Laurence Orloff** of Orloff, Lowenbach, Stifelman & Siegel is widely held to be at the top of the New Jersey commercial litigation Bar. *"He is a very intense litigator and goes to the mat for his clients – everyone respects him,"* sources say. **Stephen Orlofsky** (see p.1743) is head of the appellate group at Blank Rome LLP, and maintains a thriving commercial litigation practice. A former District of New Jersey magistrate judge, *"he has seen everything one possibly can in terms of litigation and gives great advice."* The *"very versatile"* **Jeffrey Pollock** (see p.1745) of Fox Rothschild LLP is known as a formidable advocate for his clients, and advises on a range of commercial and insurance coverage matters. Sources praise him as *"intelligent, responsive and resourceful, with a great breadth of knowledge."* White-collar specialist **Carl Poplar** of Carl D Poplar, P.A., Attorneys at Law is *"an excellent attorney – very tenacious, diligent and a great trial lawyer."* Sources also note that *"he is extremely well respected by the judiciary and very well known throughout the state."* **Thomas Quinn** (see p.1745) of Wilson, Elser, Moskowitz, Edelman & Dicker LLP attracts praise from peers, who describe him as a *"very smart attorney."* He has 30 years of experience representing insurance companies in coverage disputes. **Kenneth Rothschild** of Golden, Rothschild, Spagnola, Lundell, Boylan & Garubo P.C. is a *"high-quality attorney"* with over 30 years of experience in representing clients in insurance coverage disputes. **Mark Sheridan** of Patton Boggs LLP represents clients in state and federal courts in a broad range of insurance coverage litigation. *"He is a very practical trial lawyer and a great leader, and his accessibility is amazing,"* say clients. **Michael Stein** (see p.1748) of Pashman Stein is praised by sources for the high quality of both his written work and his performance at trial. Cofounder of the firm and chair of the litigation practice, he is an extremely experienced commercial litigator. **Diane Sullivan** (see p.414) of Weil, Gotshal & Manges LLP is described by one market source as *"one of the best trial attorneys I have ever seen."* She divides her time between New York and New Jersey and focuses her practice on commercial and product liability litigation. **James Tyrrell** of Patton Boggs LLP is described by sources as *"a brilliant lawyer, very articulate, very well prepared and very good at presenting arguments."* He divides his time between the firm's New Jersey and New York offices, and chairs the firm's toxic tort and product liability practice group. A former chair of the criminal law section of the New Jersey Bar, **Alan Zegas** of the Law Offices of Alan L. Zegas is described by sources as *"a terrific trial lawyer, and very knowledgeable."*

# REAL ESTATE

Commentary about individuals can be found under their firm's paragraph. If the firm has no paragraph (is not ranked) look at Other Notable Practitioners.

## Real Estate
### Leading Firms

**Band 1**

Cole, Schotz, Meisel, Forman & Leonard PA *

Drinker Biddle & Reath LLP *

Greenbaum, Rowe, Smith & Davis LLP *

McCarter & English, LLP *

Sills Cummis & Gross P.C. *

**Band 2**

Day Pitney LLP *

Gibbons P.C. *

Giordano Halleran & Ciesla PC

Hyland Levin

Wilentz, Goldman & Spitzer, P.A. *

**Band 3**

Ballard Spahr LLP *

Brach Eichler L.L.C.

Hill Wallack LLP

Lowenstein Sandler LLP *

Riker Danzig Scherer Hyland & Perretti LLP *

## Band 1

### Cole, Schotz, Meisel, Forman & Leonard PA
See profile on p.1752

**THE FIRM** An impressive amount of market praise propels this firm to the highest rank in the New Jersey real estate arena. The group handles a wide range of matters including development and leasing, acquisitions, financing and debt restructuring. It continues to act on behalf of impressive clients such as Toys R Us and Savanna Real Estate Fund. Sources consistently praise the outstanding level of client service that the group displays in its work. **Sources say:** *"They have been excellent. They are very timely and efficient, and they are very experienced in leasing and transactional matters and great at customer service."* **KEY INDIVIDUALS Richard Abramson** (see p.1731) has recently handled a number of acquisitions and financing transactions on behalf of real estate investment funds. *"He can view a matter from a business perspective and not just a legal one,"* sources state.

### Drinker Biddle & Reath LLP
See profile on p.2238

**THE FIRM** Drinker Biddle & Reath has an outstanding reputation in the full spectrum of real estate matters. The firm continues to handle high-value acquisitions, dispositions and leasing on behalf of realtors, investors and institutional companies, while its zoning and land use group is considered a go-to shop for the securing of approvals and negotiation with government agencies. The real estate team's enviable track record is illustrated by its continuing representation of a number of real estate investment companies, including Matrix Realty and The Hampshire Companies.

## Real Estate
### Senior Statesmen

**Senior Statesmen: distinguished older practitioners**

Radzely Edward S — Giordano Halleran & Ciesla PC

### Leading Individuals

**Band 1**

| Abramson Richard W | Cole, Schotz, Meisel, Forman & Leonard * |
| Bershad Russell B | Gibbons P.C. |
| Dollinger Martin E | Greenbaum, Rowe, Smith & Davis LLP |
| Dowd Martin F | McCarter & English, LLP * |
| Gordon David S | Wilentz, Goldman & Spitzer, P.A. |
| Hammer Alan R | Brach Eichler L.L.C. |
| Newman Jeffrey Hugh | Sills Cummis & Gross P.C. * |
| Rothpletz Jr Michael E | Drinker Biddle & Reath LLP * |

**Band 2**

| Babineau Anne S | Wilentz, Goldman & Spitzer, P.A. |
| Black Margaret F | Sills Cummis & Gross P.C. * |
| Butler Edward | McCarter & English, LLP * |
| Casey Barbara A | Ballard Spahr LLP * |
| Coakley Kevin | Connell Foley LLP (ONP)† |
| Donovan Colleen R | Day Pitney LLP * |
| Fleissig Steven D | Greenberg Traurig, LLP (ONP)† * |
| Kahn Richard R | Winne Banta Hetherington Basralian (ONP)† |
| Klausner Robert A | Fox Rothschild LLP (ONP)† * |
| Li Christine F | Greenbaum, Rowe, Smith & Davis LLP |
| Moore Deirdre E | Fox Rothschild LLP (ONP)† * |
| Racioppi Jr Nicholas | Riker Danzig Scherer Hyland & Perretti LLP |
| Shapiro Mark D | Hyland Levin |

**Band 3**

| Denitzio Jr Thomas J | Greenbaum, Rowe, Smith & Davis LLP |
| Goldstein Richard J | Hangley Aronchick Segal Pudlin (ONP)† * |
| Hunter Edward | Lowenstein Sandler LLP * |
| Markowitz Philip | Sills Cummis & Gross P.C. * |
| Popowitz Allen J | Brach Eichler L.L.C. |

**Up-and-coming individuals**

| Rider Christopher M | Fox Rothschild LLP (ONP)† * |

**Sources say:** *"The quality of their work is exceptional. They are always willing to do everything it takes to get the job done."* **KEY INDIVIDUALS** The *"meticulous"* and *"efficient"* **Glenn Pantel** (see p.1744) is considered an authority on zoning and land use law. Sources report that *"he always makes you feel that your concerns are his concerns and he is also a very good creative thinker."* Sources praise real estate practice group chair **Michael Rothpletz** (see p.1747) for his extraordinary focus: *"He never loses sight of the end goal, does not get side tracked by ego and is very bright and an excellent negotiator."* Rothpletz has handled much of the firm's work for Matrix Realty and The Hampshire Companies.

## Real Estate: Zoning/Land Use
### Senior Statesmen

**Senior Statesmen: distinguished older practitioners**

Hall Thomas Jay — Sills Cummis & Gross P.C. *

### Leading Individuals

**Band 1**

| Bisgaier Carl S | Bisgaier Hoff LLC (ONP)† |
| Fersko Jack | Greenbaum, Rowe, Smith & Davis LLP |
| Gonchar Meryl A G | Greenbaum, Rowe, Smith & Davis LLP |
| Hluchan Richard M | Hyland Levin |
| Pantel Glenn S | Drinker Biddle & Reath LLP * |

**Band 2**

| Barcan Stephen E | Wilentz, Goldman & Spitzer, P.A. |
| Carroll Thomas F | Hill Wallack LLP |
| Eisdorfer Stephen M | Hill Wallack LLP |
| Giunco Jr John A | Giordano Halleran & Ciesla PC |
| Goldsmith Robert S | Greenbaum, Rowe, Smith & Davis LLP |
| Meiser Kenneth E | Hill Wallack LLP |
| Moore Kevin J | Sills Cummis & Gross P.C. * |
| Waeger Ann M | Greenbaum, Rowe, Smith & Davis LLP |
| Wolfson Douglas K | Schwartz, Simon, Edelstein & Celso (ONP)† |

**Up-and-coming individuals**

| DeSimone Vincent | Law Office of Vincent M. DeSimone (ONP)† |

\* Indicates firm / individual with profile.

†ONP = Other Notable Practitioner.

### Greenbaum, Rowe, Smith & Davis LLP
See profile on p.1755

**THE FIRM** This heavyweight real estate team has enjoyed yet another outstanding year. The group is noted for its significant expertise in acquisitions, sales and leases across commercial, retail and residential property. In addition, the team also has extensive experience in zoning and land use matters, regularly obtaining approvals and negotiating agreements with state and municipal entities. The group is currently acting on behalf of Avidan Management in the sale of a nine-property portfolio. Other current clients include Wells Fargo, KPMG and Montclair State University.

**KEY INDIVIDUALS Martin Dollinger** recently represented Wilson Entities in the $6.3 million refinancing of a portfolio of properties. He focuses his practice on transactional work in relation to industrial and retail property. Sources applaud **Jack Fersko**, noting that *"his negotiating style is very thoughtful and he has an excellent command of the technical aspects of the law."* He recently assisted Avidan Management in the negotiation and closing of a nine-property portfolio sale. Cochair of the real estate group **Meryl Gonchar** is described by sources as a *"terrific lawyer."* She concentrates her practice on land use and zoning matters. **Robert Goldsmith** is chair of the firm's redevelopment practice group. He recently played a key role in the $8 million sale of One BMW Plaza in Montvale, New Jersey. He is held in high regard by commentators for his expertise in the real estate space. **Christine Li** is chair of the planned real estate practice group and a recognized expert in the field of condominium development. Market sources applaud her as *"an excellent condominium lawyer."* **Ann Waeger** focuses her real estate practice on transactional matters. Sources praise her as *"very well prepared and professional."* **Thomas Denitzio** is cochair of the real estate department at the firm and has notable experience in all manner of real estate transactions, including mortgaging, leasing, sales and acquisitions.

### McCarter & English, LLP
See profile on p.1759

**THE FIRM** This robust 22-lawyer real estate group is renowned for the quality of its office leasing practice and its representation of lenders in real estate financing transactions. Clients are drawn from a diverse range of industry sectors in the state, and include such well-known entities as the New York Football Giants, Wells Fargo and Capital One. The team recently acted for Prudential Financial in connection with the site acquisition and land use approvals for its corporate headquarters.

**Sources say:** *"Prompt turnaround and very competent attorneys who are a pleasure to interact with."*

**KEY INDIVIDUALS Martin Dowd** (see p.1734) is a seasoned real estate practitioner and has played a lead role in much of the firm's aforementioned work for Prudential Financial. Sources label him *"a tremendous attorney."* **Edward Butler** (see p.1732) acts on behalf of a range of clients in connection with all aspects of commercial real estate transactions. Sources note that he is *"well versed on all matters"* in this arena.

### Sills Cummis & Gross P.C.
See profile on p.1762

**THE FIRM** This impressive real estate team handles the full range of matters including financing, sale and purchases, and land use and zoning. The group routinely handles retail, office, industrial and warehouse leasing, and is noted for its work with condominiums. Clients include major retailers and financial institutions.

**Sources say:** *"Their performance for us has been outstanding. They are very responsive and are always accessible."*

**KEY INDIVIDUALS Jeffrey Hugh Newman** (see p.1743) is chair of the real estate group and has significant experience in all matters relating to real estate law. *"He exhibits great leadership and strategy, and puts the right team together to solve a problem,"* say sources. He is especially renowned for his expertise in retail leasing. *"Fine attorney"* **Margaret Black** (see p.1731) focuses her real estate practice on commercial transactions, including acquisitions, dispositions and leasing. She advises a wide range of clients in this space. **Kevin Moore** (see p.1743) is described by sources as *"one of the most experienced land use attorneys around."* He is *"a great attorney and a quick study,"* according to one interviewee. **Philip Markowitz** (see p.1742) is frequently called upon by national retailers and developers to assist in the acquisition, disposition and financing of large-scale shopping centers throughout the country. Former policy and planning adviser to the Office of the

Governor of the State of New Jersey **Thomas Jay Hall** (see p.1737) is well versed in all aspects of land use and development, and is highly regarded by peers and clients alike.

## Band 2

### Day Pitney LLP
See profile on p.1753

**THE FIRM** Day Pitney's real estate practice group acts on behalf of a multitude of investors and developers on a range of acquisitions and sales. In addition, the firm's land use and zoning group has overseen a number of approvals on behalf of developer clients. The group has recently acted for AT&T Wireless in a number of land use development applications throughout New Jersey.

**Sources say:** *"They have great bench strength and do a very good job representing their clients."*

**KEY INDIVIDUALS Colleen Donovan** (see p.1734) is head of the commercial real estate and development group at the firm. She is an experienced brownfields development practitioner who sources regard as *"a very solid attorney."*

### Gibbons P.C.
See profile on p.1754

**THE FIRM** This Newark-based real estate practice group regularly acts on behalf of large developers and major corporations across a range of real estate matters. The group has been involved in assisting Honeywell International with the redevelopment of 100 acres of brownfield land in partnership with the City of Jersey City. Other clients include McDonald's, Hoffman – La Roche and JPMorgan Chase.

**Sources say:** *"They are excellent. They are very responsive and very thorough and they care deeply about their work."*

**KEY INDIVIDUALS Russell Bershad** recently represented Bayer Healthcare Pharmaceuticals in the consolidation of its offices into one campus. Sources describe him as a *"tremendous lawyer, amazingly gifted and knowledgeable."*

### Giordano Halleran & Ciesla PC

**THE FIRM** The real estate practice group at this firm's Red Bank office represents residential and commercial developers in every stage of the development process. In the past year the team assisted national home builders Hovnanian Enterprises in the creation of a $125 million land banking arrangement between the builders and GSO Capital Partners. The team has also acted on behalf of Quick Chek Corporation in connection with land acquisitions and leasing matters in both New York and New Jersey.

**Sources say:** *"They are very efficient and I feel I get great value for money."*

**KEY INDIVIDUALS John Giunco** is chair of the land use and development department at the firm. In May 2012 he successfully gained site plan approval for the development of a solar field in Franklin Township, New Jersey. **Edward Radzely** offers extensive experience across a broad range of real estate matters. Whether negotiating lease agreements or representing clients before county or state agencies, peers agree *"he is a great attorney."*

## Hyland Levin

**THE FIRM** This firm represents a multitude of clients in the purchase, sale and leasing of all types of property. The team also acts on behalf of clients in obtaining land use approvals from both state and federal agencies. Clients regard the group highly for the efficiency it exhibits in achieving results.

**Sources say:** *"I would certainly recommend them as high caliber professionals."*

**KEY INDIVIDUALS Richard Hluchan** is considered a leading authority on land use and zoning matters. Sources describe him as *"highly qualified and effective at getting results."* **Mark Shapiro** is renowned for his work in connection with the acquisition, sale and financing of multifamily apartment complexes. *"I only have positive things to say about him. He has great business acumen and is very experienced in all aspects of real estate,"* relates one interviewee.

### Wilentz, Goldman & Spitzer, P.A.
See profile on p.1763

**THE FIRM** This firm typically represents larger companies and regional developers in major transactions. The group has a wealth of experience across a wide range of dispositions, acquisitions and leasing, and prides itself on a cradle to grave approach to matters.

**Sources say:** *"They have extremely talented individuals and their real estate practice is well known in New Jersey."*

**KEY INDIVIDUALS David Gordon** focuses his practice on the disposition and leasing of commercial property. Sources describe him as a *"tremendous attorney"* and someone who *"knows his stuff very well, is steeped in real estate knowledge and is very good on the leasing side."* **Anne Babineau** is a redevelopment specialist who peers agree is *"one of the leading redevelopment attorneys in the state."* **Stephen Barcan** is recognized for his expertise in land use law. He routinely assists in obtaining development approvals and in performing development-related due diligence investigations.

## Band 3

### Ballard Spahr LLP
See profile on p.2234

**THE FIRM** The three-partner practice group at this firm's Cherry Hill location has been particularly active in assisting clients in redevelopment work following the devastation wrought by Hurricane Sandy, while the team's staple work areas include development and redevelopment, financing, construction and housing matters. The group counts the Camden Redevelopment Agency and Eastern Pacific Development among its current client roster.

**Sources say:** *"They are very good and have good bench strength."*

**KEY INDIVIDUALS Barbara Casey** (see p.1732) is *"a very thorough and competent attorney,"* sources say. Recently, she assisted The Carlyle Group in connection with a series of matters relating to The Grand, a distressed condominium project in Diamond Beach, New Jersey.

## Brach Eichler L.L.C.

**THE FIRM** The real estate practice group at this firm's Roseland office routinely acts on behalf of investment funds and realty companies in large investment transactions within the multifamily housing realm. The team recently assisted the Rockpoint Group in the $470 million purchase of 5,500 multifamily units in Maryland.

**Sources say:** *"They have a great ability to solve problems and to close deals."*

**KEY INDIVIDUALS** Peers and clients assert that **Alan Hammer** is one of the finest real estate attorneys in the state of New Jersey. They describe a *"wonderfully creative problem solver"* who has a *"wealth of knowledge."* He focuses his practice on large investment transactions in the retail and residential arena. **Allen Popowitz** is head of the real estate practice group at the firm. Sources describe him as *"a very skilled attorney"* and note that *"he gets the job done very well and is extremely hard-working."* Recently, he acted on behalf of the Kushner Companies in the buyout of existing joint venture partners on 14 multifamily properties.

## Hill Wallack LLP

**THE FIRM** This respected firm is particularly noted for its expertise in land use and zoning matters. The team is experienced in obtaining planning approvals, representing clients in negotiations with state agencies or advising clients in connection with New Jersey's complex regulatory zoning framework. The group represents both private and public sector clients across the full range of land use matters.

**Sources say:** *"They are a very good and well-known real estate firm."*

**KEY INDIVIDUALS Thomas Carroll** is a *"top-notch attorney,"* say sources. He focuses his practice on land use and zoning matters and related litigation. **Stephen Eisdorfer** is highly regarded for his work in the affordable housing sphere. He represents both private and public

entities in all land use and zoning matters. **Kenneth Meiser** enjoys a strong reputation within the New Jersey land use community. He is well versed in all matters relating to redevelopment and the issuance of approvals.

## Lowenstein Sandler LLP

See profile on p.1757

**THE FIRM** This team is highly regarded for its transactional work in relation to all manner of commercial real estate matters. The real estate practice group regularly handles acquisitions and dispositions, leasing, financing and development matters. Clients include real estate investment funds and financial institutions.

**Sources say:** *"I have received great advocacy and advice. They have done a great job at prioritizing the issues and are very cost efficient."*

**KEY INDIVIDUALS Edward Hunter** (see p.1738) is chair of the real estate practice group at the firm. He handles all matters pertaining to commercial real estate.

## Riker Danzig Scherer Hyland & Perretti LLP

See profile on p.1761

**THE FIRM** This 15-strong real estate practice group handles a full range of real estate and land use matters. The group recently acted for Bed Bath & Beyond in relation to a number of retail leasings and acquisitions across the USA. Other representative clients include Bank of America, The Great Atlantic & Pacific Tea Company and The Heller Group.

**Sources say:** *"They are very well versed on the business realities, make sure all the timings are correct and do a great job of coordinating between the counsels of the various parties."*

**KEY INDIVIDUALS Nicholas Racioppi** has played a leading role in much of the firm's work for Bed Bath & Beyond. Sources report: *"His general legal knowledge is great. He is a transactional lawyer who concentrates on achieving the completion of the transaction."*

## Other Notable Practitioners

**Carl Bisgaier** of Bisgaier Hoff LLC is noted for his land use work in the affordable housing space. *"He is a leading practitioner in the area and a genuinely good guy,"* say sources. **Kevin Coakley** of Connell Foley LLP is highly experienced in development and redevelopment projects throughout the state, and is a skilled real estate litigator. **Steven Fleissig** (see p.1735) of Greenberg Traurig, LLP recently represented Treetop Development in the purchase of four properties in New York City. Sources describe him as *"a great attorney."* **Richard Kahn** of Winne Banta Hetherington Basralian & Kahn, P.C. is described by market sources as *"a capable and enthusiastic lawyer."* He handles residential and commercial real estate matters. Land use expert and noted litigator **Douglas Wolfson** of Schwartz, Simon, Edelstein & Celso LLC is hailed by sources as *"hard-working and very smart."* **Richard Goldstein** (see p.1736) of Hangley Aronchick Segal Pudlin & Schiller is noted for his representation of shopping mall owners in a plethora of real estate matters. **Vincent DeSimone** of the Law Office of Vincent M. DeSimone, LLC is gaining a reputation for quality work in the New Jersey land use and zoning arena. **Robert Klausner** (see p.1739) recently joined Fox Rothschild LLP from Day Pitney. He *"is amazingly responsive, willing to do whatever it takes to get the job done and has a great big-picture perspective,"* sources assert. Klausner has been joined at Fox Rothschild by **Deirdre Moore** (see p.1743), who has also made the move from Day Pitney. She focuses her practice on the representation of clients in corporate, commercial and residential developments. Market sources applaud her as an *"extremely talented transactional real estate lawyer."* **Christopher Rider** (see p.1745) is the third member of the team to join Fox Rothschild LLP from Day Pitney. He *"is very responsive, bright and very accommodating,"* say sources.

# Leaders' Profiles in New Jersey

## ABRAMSON, Richard W
Cole, Schotz, Meisel, Forman & Leonard PA, Hackensack
201 525 6218
rabramson@coleschotz.com
*Featured in Real Estate (New Jersey)*
**Practice Areas:** Co-chairman of the firm's Real Estate Department. Practice is national in scope and encompasses a broad range of transactions, with particular emphasis on acquisitions, dispositions, development and commercial leasing. Practice includes counseling developers, real estate equity and opportunity funds, real estate investment trusts, investors, owners and tenants in all aspects of commercial real estate transactions, including the acquisition, disposition, leasing, management, financing and construction of commercial, retail, industrial and residential properties; mezzanine financings; joint ventures; and acquisition and disposition of distressed debt.
**Personal:** University of Miami School of Law, JD, 1984.

## ALITO, Rosemary
K&L Gates, Newark
973 848 4022
rosemary.alito@klgates.com
*Featured in Labor & Employment (New Jersey)*
**Practice Areas:** A co-chair of the firm's Labor, Employment and Workplace Safety practice, Ms Alito represents management in employment law and employee benefit law issues. She defends employers in litigation including employment discrimination, wage and hour, whistleblowing, harassment and employee benefit plan terminations, and provides counsel on workplace issues, policies and compliance. An experienced litigator in trials and appeals in both state and federal courts, she has served as lead counsel in the successful defense of class actions under ERISA, the ADEA, the FLSA and the LMRA, and in trials of class actions challenging termination of retiree medical benefits.

## ALTIERI, James M
Drinker Biddle & Reath LLP, Florham Park
973 549 7060
james.altieri@dbr.com
*Featured in Litigation (New Jersey)*
**Practice Areas:** Managing Partner of the firm. Chair of national insurance coverage practice. Concentrates on complex commercial litigation representing clients in the financial services, insurance, pharmaceutical, entertainment, consumer products and related industries. Extensive trial experience in NY and NJ state and federal courts.
**Professional Memberships:** American and New Jersey State Bar Associations; Association of the Federal Bar; Bar of the City of New York. Admitted in NY, NJ and AZ.
**Career:** Joined firm in 1985 after practicing at Simpson Thacher & Bartlett, New York.
**Personal:** Fordham University School of Law, JD 1975; University of Maryland, BS 1971, magna cum laude.

## ANDERSON, Lynne Anne
Drinker Biddle & Reath LLP, Florham Park
973 549 7140
lynne.anderson@dbr.com
*Featured in Labor & Employment (New Jersey)*
**Practice Areas:** Lynne handles a wide range of employment and restrictive covenant litigation, including jury/bench trials and arbitrations. Whether providing strategic counseling on business restructuring, handling whistleblower investigations, or conducting compliance audits/training, she approaches each situation with an understanding of the company's business needs and culture, and offers practical guidance. Clients trust her implicitly to counsel them through the ever-growing maze of employment laws and to defend them tenaciously in the event of litigation.
**Professional Memberships:** American Employment Law Council, Fellow-Litigation Counsel of America, Past President - NJ Women Lawyers Association.
**Career:** 2009 NJWLA Women's Initiative & Leaders In Law Award.

## AVALLONE, Vincent N
K&L Gates, Newark
973 848 4027
vincent.avallone@klgates.com
*Featured in Labor & Employment (New Jersey)*
**Practice Areas:** Mr Avallone represents employers throughout the country in labor and employment law litigation and arbitration matters, including employment discrimination, harassment, whistle-blowing, family and medical leave, wage and hour matters, employment contract disputes, enforcement of confidentiality and non-compete agreements, and claims under ERISA relating to employee and retiree benefits. He also counsels management on the full spectrum of workplace policies and practices, conducts in-house training programs, drafts agreements, advises clients on internal investigations, reductions in force, and compliance matters, and defends employers in administrative agency actions, including before the EEOC and the NLRB.

## BASS, David
Cole, Schotz, Meisel, Forman & Leonard PA, Hackensack
*Featured in Bankruptcy/Restructuring (New Jersey)*
**Practice Areas:** Member of the firm's Bankruptcy & Corporate Restructuring Department. Concentrates his practice in bankruptcy and restructuring, insolvency and creditors' rights, and related litigation. He has represented a broad spectrum of clients in bankruptcy, complex commercial litigation and loan workouts. Mr Bass has also represented trustees and official committees in bankruptcy cases throughout the United States. He is experienced in all aspects of reorganization and liquidation matters, and has considerable expertise in litigating disputes arising under the Uniform Commercial Code, as well as other business and commercial litigation.
**Personal:** New York Law School, JD, 1994.

## BAUMEL, Jeffrey
Dentons, Short Hills
973 912 7189
jeffrey.baumel@dentons.com
*Featured in Corporate/M&A (New Jersey)*
**Practice Areas:** Head of legacy Dentons's Health and Life Sciences sector team. Provides representation to a broad range of companies in connection with financing, M&A and corporate transactions, primarily in the life sciences, biotechnology and technology industries. Has substantial experience representing issuers, underwriters and placement agents in connection with public offerings and private placements of equity and debt securities. Experience also includes counseling private and public Boards of Directors in connection with corporate governance, compensation and securities law compliance issues.
**Personal:** Cornell Law School, JD; University of Rochester, BA.

## BEARCE, Nicole Denise
Lowenstein Sandler LLP, Roseland
646 414 6801
nbearce@lowenstein.com
*Featured in Litigation (New Jersey)*
**Practice Areas:** Nicole Denise Bearce is a dynamic and hard-driving litigator at both the trial and appellate levels, concentrating her practice in complex business litigation. Nicole is experienced in matters involving mass torts, consumer fraud allegations, fiduciary duty disputes, shareholder suits, oppression claims, and commercial litigation. She co-chairs the firm's Appellate Practice and co-leads the Task Force on Electronic Discovery and Information Governance.
www.lowenstein.com/nbearce

## BECKELMAN, Steven
McCarter & English, LLP, Newark
973 639 2055
sbeckelman@mccarter.com
*Featured in Litigation (New Jersey)*
**Career:** Mr Beckelman regularly represents financial institutions and other corporations in major commercial disputes. He has also served as counsel for corporate defendants and individual directors in class-action and derivative litigation. Mr Beckelman has both defended and prosecuted a variety of securities cases, including 10b5 litigation. For full bio:
http://www.mccarter.com/Steven-A-Beckelman/

## BENNETT, John K
Jackson Lewis LLP, Morristown
973 538 6890
BennettJ@jacksonlewis.com
*Featured in Labor & Employment (New Jersey)*
**Practice Areas:** Employment litigation including trials, employment arbitration hearings, traditional labor matters; advice to employers regarding all aspects of labor and employment law.
**Professional Memberships:** ABA and NJ State Bar Assn; DRI.
**Career:** Law Clerk, Justice Robert L. Clifford, Supreme Court of NJ, 1980-81; Associate and

Partner, Carpenter, Bennett & Morrissey, 1981-98; Partner and Chair, Employment Law Practice, Connell Foley LLP, 1998-2010.
**Publications:** New Jersey Federal Civil Procedure, Ch. 26, Special Considerations in Labor and Employment Cases (NJLJ Books); various articles.
**Personal:** Lafayette College, BA 1977; Seton Hall University Law School, JD 1980; New York University, LLM Labor Law, 1989.

## BENNETT, Lynda
Lowenstein Sandler LLP, Roseland
973 597 6338
lbennett@lowenstein.com
*Featured in Litigation (New Jersey)*
**Practice Areas:** Lynda A Bennett, Chair of Lowenstein Sandler's Insurance Coverage practice, has more than 19 years of experience in complex commercial litigation, primarily fighting for corporate policyholder rights in insurance coverage disputes. She has recovered hundreds of millions of dollars for clients in environmental, asbestos, construction defect, mass tort, product liability, D&O and professional liability cases. She also counsels clients with respect to contractual insurance requirements, new insurance products, innovative risk management tools, and assessment of their insurance programs.
www.lowenstein.com/lbennett

## BERAN, Richard
McCarter & English, LLP, Newark
973 639 7965
rberan@mccarter.com
*Featured in Litigation (New Jersey)*
**Career:** Mr Beran practices in the area of business law with an emphasis in financial products litigation. He conducts corporate internal and financial fraud investigations. He has represented financial institutions ranging from mutual savings and loan associations to stock savings banks and their boards of directors in trials and appeals; child care providers and religious organizations in lawsuits and investigations involving sexual tort claims nationwide; and broker-dealers, investment advisors and insurance producers before the SEC, FINRA, the Bureau of Securities, and the Department of Banking and Insurance. For full bio: http://www.mccarter.com/Richard-A-Beran/

## BLACK, Margaret F
Sills Cummis & Gross P.C., Newark
973 643 5715
mblack@sillscummis.com
*Featured in Real Estate (New Jersey)*
**Practice Areas:** Margaret F Black is the Deputy Chair - Administration of the firm's Real Estate Department. Her real estate practice covers the gamut of commercial transactions, from acquisitions and sales to leasings and financings. Those transactions, which often involve properties nationwide, relate primarily to shopping centers, office and industrial buildings, and other types of commercial properties.

**Professional Memberships:** Member, International Council of Shopping Centers; Vice Chair, Board of Trustees, New Jersey Lawyers Assistance Program.
**Personal:** Rutgers University School of Law, JD, 1976; Rutgers University, Douglass College, BA, with honors, Phi Beta Kappa, 1973.

### BOCK, Joel N
Dentons, Short Hills
973 912 7174
joel.bock@dentons.com
*Featured in Intellectual Property (New Jersey)*
**Practice Areas:** Represents emerging growth and Fortune 500 companies, universities and federal labs on IP issues, structuring and negotiating transactions involving IP assets, IP diligence, asset assessment and valuation, patent portfolio prosecution, management and evaluation. Litigates complex patent infringement suits relating to electronics, semiconductors, software and telecommunications systems, sensors, mechanical systems, medical devices and pharmaceuticals. Advises on business and IP strategy, landscape and competitive analyses, patentability and freedom to operate analyses, litigation strategy, post-grant, derivation, reexamination and reissue strategy, M&A and Open Source issues.
**Personal:** New York University School of Law, JD; St. John's University, MBA; Pratt Institute, BSEE.

### BOYAJIAN, Victor
Dentons, Short Hills
973 912 7171
victor.boyajian@dentons.com
*Featured in Corporate/M&A (New Jersey)*
**Practice Areas:** Head of legacy Dentons's Venture Technology practice and Technology, Media and Telecommunications sector team. Represents emerging growth and Fortune 500 companies in a broad array of venture capital, securities and strategic transactions, as well as universities, federal labs and corporations in their efforts to commercialize technology. Counsels senior executives of venture-backed and publicly-traded emerging growth companies and venture firm principals. Advises on business strategy, finance, mergers and acquisitions, executive compensation, board governance, intellectual property and litigation strategy.
**Professional Memberships:** New York Venture Capital Association Churchill Club.
**Personal:** University of Pennsylvania School of Law, JD; University of Rochester, BA.

### BRESCHER, John B
McCarter & English, LLP, Newark
973 639 2012
jbrescher@mccarter.com
*Featured in Employee Benefits & Executive Compensation (New Jersey)*
**Career:** Mr Brescher maintains a practice in tax, estate planning, employee benefits, ERISA, and related tax and labor law matters. This includes the design and administration of benefit plans, such as pension, profit sharing, cash or deferred, and employee stock ownership plans; welfare plans such as health, life disability and flexible

benefit plans; and deferred compensation plans such as qualified and nonqualified stock options, supplemental executive retirement plans as well as funding mechanisms such as rabbi trusts and annuities for taxable and tax-exempt entities. For full bio: http://www.mccarter.com/John-B-Brescher-Jr/

### BRODERICK, David F
McCarter & English, LLP, Newark
973 639 2031
dbroderick@mccarter.com
*Featured in Corporate/M&A (New Jersey)*
**Career:** Mr Broderick practices in the areas of corporate and securities law, including mergers and acquisitions, venture capital and strategic investments, private securities offerings, and joint ventures. He is particularly skilled in venture capital and private equity investment transactions. His involvement with the SBIC program dates back to 1993 when he successfully represented a client in obtaining one of the first participating securities licenses issued by the Small Business Administration. As a result of that experience, he has represented numerous SBIC licensees in connection with their fund formation, SBIC licensing, fund-raising and regulatory compliance. For full bio: http://www.mccarter.com/David-F-Broderick/

### BRODY, Alan
Greenberg Traurig, LLP, Florham Park
973 443 3543
BrodyA@gtlaw.com
*Featured in Bankruptcy/Restructuring (New Jersey)*
**Practice Areas:** Business reorganization and financial restructuring; bankruptcy litigation; securities fraud enforcement actions; receiverships and state insolvency proceedings.
**Professional Memberships:** Member: American Bankruptcy Institute; Turnaround Management Association; New Jersey State Bar Association, Bankruptcy Law Section; New York State Bar Association, Committee on Bankruptcy Litigation.
**Career:** Member, Winning Team, U.S. News - Best Lawyers 'Law Firm of the Year' in Bankruptcy & Creditor Debtor Rights/Insolvency & Reorganization Law and Litigation – Bankruptcy, 2013; Listed, Chambers USA Guide, 2012-13.
**Personal:** JD, cum laude, New York Law School, 1991 (Editor, New York Law School Law Review); BS, Accounting, University of Delaware, 1988.

### BRUNO, Kevin
Blank Rome LLP, Princeton
609 750 2994
KBruno@BlankRome.com
*Featured in Environment (New Jersey)*
**Practice Areas:** Kevin Bruno has 25 years of experience in complex commercial litigation, concentrating his practice in environmental, mass tort, products and insurance recovery litigation. He is Co-Chair of the firm's Environmental Practice Group. His experience encompasses every major federal environmental program and includes the representation of clients in some of the largest mass tort, CERCLA and natural resource damages cases. He represents clients in

civil and criminal proceedings, as well as internal audits and investigations. He also represents companies in their pursuit of insurance for most first and third party liability losses, including environmental. For more information:
www.BlankRome.com/KBruno

### BUCKLEY, Joseph L
Sills Cummis & Gross P.C., Newark
973 643 5394
jbuckley@sillscummis.com
*Featured in Litigation (New Jersey)*
**Practice Areas:** Joseph L Buckley, member of the Firm's Management and Executive Committees and Litigation Department Chair, has 30+ years of first chair trial experience in a wide variety of complex cases in federal and state courts in New Jersey and New York.
**Professional Memberships:** American Bar Association; New Jersey State Bar Association; Association of the Bar of the City of New York; Association of the Federal Bar of New Jersey; Federal Bar Council; New York State Bar Association.
**Career:** Certified Civil Trial Attorney.
**Personal:** The University of Chicago Law School, JD, 1978; Rutgers College, BA, with high honors, 1975.

### BUECHLER, Bruce
Lowenstein Sandler LLP, Roseland
973 597 2308
bbuechler@lowenstein.com
*Featured in Bankruptcy/Restructuring (New Jersey)*
**Practice Areas:** Bruce Buechler focuses his practice on bankruptcy law, debtor-creditor law and bankruptcy litigation. He represents business entities such as debtors and creditors committees in Chapter 11 reorganizations, out-of-court workouts and other financial reorganizations. He proactively engages with clients to achieve solutions consistent with their business objectives. He regularly litigates commercial disputes in both federal and state bankruptcy court and provides business consulting in this area. Bruce was lead counsel for the creditors' committee in the Borders bankruptcy.
www.lowenstein.com/bbuechler

### BUNN, Andrew O
DLA Piper LLP (US), Florham Park
973 520 2562
andrew.bunn@dlapiper.com
*Featured in Litigation (New Jersey)*
**Practice Areas:** Litigation.
**Career:** He represents companies in court, arbitration and regulatory proceedings, in cases including individual and class-action claims on such issues as consumer complaints, business disputes, contract and policy interpretations, benefit entitlements, sales practices, ERISA, securities, financial instruments, telecommunications, managed care and regulatory disputes. Among his clients are some of the country's largest life and health insurance companies, telecommunications providers and manufacturers. He has tried numerous jury and non-jury cases to verdict, and he has extensive appellate experience.

**Personal:** JD, Rutgers, The State University of New Jersey School of Law, Newark; BA, Kenyon College.

### BUTLER, Edward
McCarter & English, LLP, Newark
973 639 6938
ebutler@mccarter.com
*Featured in Real Estate (New Jersey)*
**Career:** Mr Butler has been closing commercial real estate transactions and handling foreclosures for more than twenty-two years. His practice focuses on all aspects of commercial real estate, including leasing transactions, loan closings, and the purchase and sale of real estate of all types. He has recently represented a national big-box retailer in connection with leases and acquisitions, a large energy company acquiring land rights, lenders making multimillion-dollar loans secured by mortgages on office buildings and shopping centers, and a REIT in a large leasing transaction. For full bio: http://www.mccarter.com/Edward-J-Butler-Jr/

### CAMPION, Thomas
Drinker Biddle & Reath LLP, Florham Park
973 549 7300
Thomas.Campion@dbr.com
*Featured in Products Liability (Nationwide), Litigation (New Jersey)*
**Practice Areas:** Partner, Co-Head of Professional Liability Claims Practice and Senior Member of Products Liability Practice. Focuses on civil litigation, including professional liability, products liability, business litigation and employment law.
**Professional Memberships:** Admissions: New Jersey and New York. Fellow, American College of Trial Lawyers, American Bar Foundation and the International Academy of Trial Lawyers; past Chairman of the New Jersey Supreme Court Board of Trial Attorney Certification.
**Career:** Joined Drinker Biddle in 1999.
**Publications:** Numerous.
**Personal:** LLB, Cornell Law School, 1961; AB, Fordham University, 1957.

### CANNONE, Frank T
Gibbons P.C., Newark
973 596 4621
fcannone@gibbonslaw.com
*Featured in Corporate/M&A (New Jersey)*
**Practice Areas:** Corporate law; securities; mergers and acquisitions; private equity.
**Career:** Frank T Cannone is the Chair of the Corporate Department at Gibbons P.C. He has extensive experience representing clients in connection with mergers and acquisitions, public and private capital raising, private equity investments, private fund formation, public private partnerships (PPP), governmental corporate restructurings, alternative energy finance, venture capital transactions, cross border transactions, and distressed situations and opportunities.

### CASEY, Barbara A
Ballard Spahr LLP, Cherry Hill
856 761 3430
caseyb@ballardspahr.com
*Featured in Real Estate (New Jersey)*

**Practice Areas:** Barbara A Casey is a partner in the Real Estate Department and Practice Leader of the Real Estate Development Group. Her practice is concentrated in the areas of real property acquisition, development, sales and leasing, commercial lending, and condominium development and registration.
**Professional Memberships:** New Jersey State Bar Association New Jersey Builders' Association Urban Land Institute.
**Career:** Admissions: New Jersey Pennsylvania.
**Publications:** Distressed Condominium Projects: Fractional Interest Sales Might Save the Day, New Jersey Law Journal, 22 June 2009.
**Personal:** Rutgers, The State University of New Jersey School of Law-Camden (JD 1985, high honors) University of Cincinnati (BA 1981, magna cum laude).

### CASEY, Warren J
Day Pitney LLP, Parsippany
973 966 8025
wcasey@daypitney.com
*Featured in Corporate/M&A (New Jersey)*
**Career:** Mr Casey serves as outside general corporate and securities counsel to a variety of publicly held and privately held companies, including retail, manufacturing, technology, asset management, hospitality, semiconductor technology and document and data services companies. Mr Casey is the leader of the firm's Public Companies practice group. Representative clients include: The Talbots Inc., International Flavors & Fragrances, Joseph Abboud, Dress Barn, The Phoenix Companies, Inc., Agfa Film, Wyndham Worldwide Corporation, Virtus Investment Partners, Rudolph Technologies, Innovation Data Processing, Liberty Science Center, The Seeing Eye and The Geraldine R. Dodge Foundation.

### CERRA, Suzanne
Nukk-Freeman & Cerra, Short Hills
973 564 9100
scerra@nfclegal.com
*Featured in Labor & Employment (New Jersey)*

### CHESLER, Robert D
Anderson Kill & Olick, P.C., Newark
973 642 5864
rchesler@andersonkill.com
*Featured in Litigation (New Jersey)*
**Practice Areas:** Robert D Chesler represents policyholders in a broad variety of coverage claims against their insurance companies and advises companies with respect to their insurance programs. A pioneer in the birth of modern insurance law in the early 1980s, he is a leader in such new areas of insurance coverage as cyber-insurance, D&O, IP, privacy and "green" insurance. He has served as the attorney of record in more than 30 reported insurance decisions, representing clients including General Electric, Ingersoll-Rand, Westinghouse, Schering, BOC, Chrysler, and Unilever, as well as many small businesses including gas stations and dry cleaners. Mr. Chesler teaches insurance law at Rutgers Law School and often writes, speaks and chairs seminars on a broad range of insurance recovery top-

ics, including food contamination insurance issues.
**Publications:** Mr Chesler is co-author of the seminal article "Patterns of Judicial Interpretation of Insurance Coverage for Hazardous Waste Site Liability," 18 Rutgers L.J. 9 (1986), which has been cited by numerous courts, including seven state supreme courts and the Second Circuit; co-author of "Insurance Coverage for Intellectual Property and Cyber Insurance Claims" (Thomson West); and is former co-editor in chief of the Environmental Claims Journal.

### CHRISTIE, Scott
McCarter & English, LLP, Newark
973 848 5388
schristie@mccarter.com
*Featured in Intellectual Property (New Jersey)*
**Career:** Mr Christie is a trial lawyer who actively litigates intellectual property, information technology and data privacy cases as well as white-collar criminal cases. He regularly litigates patent, trademark, trade dress and copyright infringement cases; trademark counterfeiting, trademark dilution, unfair competition and deceptive commercial advertising matters; violations of the Digital Millennium Copyright Act; and claims involving misappropriation of trade secrets. He assists clients with registration, valuation, licensing, assignment, sale and other transactional issues pertaining to patents, trademarks, copyrights and trade secrets. He pursues arbitration and litigation against cybersquatters, typosquatters and other online infringers. For full bio: http://www.mccarter.com/Scott-S-Christie/

### CINO, Vincent
Jackson Lewis LLP, Morristown
973 538 6890
CinoV@jacksonlewis.com
*Featured in Labor & Employment (New Jersey)*
**Practice Areas:** Employment Litigation and counseling on behalf of management.
**Career:** Chief of Litigation, Office of Essex County Counsel, 1987-1990. Assistant Prosecutor, Union County, NJ. 2013 Elected Firm Chairman, Jackson Lewis. Former National Director of Litigation and Counsel to the Firm. AAA-certified Arbitrator and Mediator.
**Publications:** "Boost for Bosses: Court Compels Arbitration," New Jersey Law Journal: "One-Sided Fee Shifting in LAD, CEPA Harms the Legal System," New Jersey Law Journal.
**Personal:** New Jersey Super Lawyer; Rutgers Law School, 1979; Rutgers University Graduate School, 1974, M.A.; former Master of Arthur T. Vanderbilt Inn of Court; AV rating by Martindale-Hubbell.

### CLEARY II, John L
Dentons, Short Hills
973 912 7173
john.cleary@dentons.com
*Featured in Corporate/M&A (New Jersey)*
**Practice Areas:** Represents public and private companies encompassing mergers and acquisitions, venture capital, securities transactions, as well as joint ventures, strategic alliances and general corporate representation. Advises privately-held venture capital funds on organizational

structure, issuance of securities and the acquisition of portfolio companies. Mr. Cleary's practice has a strong emphasis on medical device and life sciences companies, strategic planning and positioning for M&A opportunities.
**Career:** Joined Dentons in 2004.
**Personal:** New York University School of Law, LLM, Taxation; Catholic University of America Columbus School of Law, JD; Seton Hall University W.P. Stillman School of Business, BS and BA.

### COCOZIELLO, J. Barry
Podvey, Meanor, Catenacci, Hildner, Cocoziello & Chattman, P.C., Newark
BCocoziello@podvey.com
*Featured in Litigation (New Jersey)*
**Practice Areas:** Complex and Commercial Litigation; Professional Liability, Accountability and Relationships; White Collar Crime, Civil Fraud & Insurance Fraud; Construction Litigation; Personal Injury; Insurance Coverage Claims and Subrogation; Estate Litigation; Real Estate and Real Estate Litigation.
**Career:** Barry Cocoziello is the co-managing director of Podvey Meanor and an experienced civil and criminal litigator with extensive trial and appellate experience. Barry received his undergraduate degree from Washington College, his law degree from Rutgers-Newark, and served as a Law Clerk to the Honorable Robert Muir, Superior Court of New Jersey. He has been designated by the New Jersey Supreme Court as a Certified Civil Trial Attorney. From 2004 through the present, he has been designated as a "Super Lawyer" in the area of business litigation in the New Jersey Monthly and New York Monthly magazines. Barry is also one of less than a hundred lawyers in New Jersey designated in Chambers USA America's Leading Lawyers For Business as a "Leading Individual" in the area of general commercial litigation. Barry has served as an adjunct professor at Rutgers Law School – Newark teaching Pretrial Civil Practice and served as a Master in the Vanderbilt Inns of Court. He has also, through his participation in the American Bar Association, served as a panelist and speaker at the Litigation Section forums. He has a wide range of experience in trial practice, including complex commercial litigation, fraud and RICO law, construction litigation, employment litigation and disciplinary proceedings before professional boards.

### COHEN, Steven
Morgan, Lewis & Bockius LLP, Princeton
606 919 6604
scohen@morganlewis.com
*Featured in Corporate/M&A (New Jersey)*
**Practice Areas:** Steve M Cohen is a partner in, and co-manager of, Morgan Lewis's global Emerging Business and Technology Practice. Mr Cohen's practice focuses on advising emerging growth companies and private equity investors throughout the mid-Atlantic region. He represents companies and investors in venture capital financings; issuers in IPOs and secondary public offerings, acquisitions, divestitures and mergers, joint ventures, and international strategic partner-

ships; and has provides general corporate and securities advice to publicly held corporations and limited partnerships. Mr Cohen assists life sciences, information technology, clean technology, consumer products, chemical and applied materials, and other companies in implementing growth strategies.

### COONER, David
McCarter & English, LLP, Newark
973 639 6971
dcooner@mccarter.com
*Featured in Litigation (New Jersey)*
**Career:** Mr Cooner's practice focuses on representing medical product manufacturers; pharmaceutical and chemical companies; and other manufacturers in product liability, consumer fraud and class-action cases. He handles product liability cases throughout the nation, serving as regional and national counsel for several companies. Mr Cooner also regularly speaks on topics of relevance to the product manufacturers and has authored several publications that discuss legal issues in pharmaceutical, medical device and other product liability cases, including most recently articles concerning scientific evidence, punitive damages and the defense of consumer class actions. For full bio: http://www.mccarter.com/David-J-Cooner/

### CRANE, R Max
Sills Cummis & Gross P.C., Newark
973 643 5055
mcrane@sillscummis.com
*Featured in Corporate/M&A (New Jersey)*
**Practice Areas:** R Max Crane, Managing Partner of the firm, counsels private and public companies and their executives on most aspects of law and business including corporate finance, mergers and acquisitions, securities and crisis management.
**Professional Memberships:** Member, Board of Trustees, Montclair Art Museum; Member, Board of Trustees, Students 2 Science, Inc.; New Jersey State Liaison, Business Law Section of American Bar Association, Corporate Laws Committee; Member, New Jersey State Bar Association.
**Career:** The Best Lawyers in America since 2010; New Jersey Super Lawyers since 2005.
**Personal:** Rutgers University, JD, with honors, 1979; University of Pennsylvania, BA, cum laude, 1973.

### CRAPO, David
Gibbons P.C., Newark
973 596 4523
dcrapo@gibbonslaw.com
*Featured in Bankruptcy/Restructuring (New Jersey)*
**Practice Areas:** Bankruptcy; debtor/creditor law; healthcare, commercial law; equipment leasing
**Career:** Mr Crapo represents debtors, secured lenders, trade creditors, landlords, governmental entities, equipment lessors, non-debtor licensees of intellectual property, bidders at bankruptcy sales, and trustees and other fiduciaries. He negotiates and prepares financing transaction documents and plans of reorganization in bankruptcy cases. He also analyzes commercial, corporate, and

municipal bond transactions to minimize bankruptcy and insolvency-related risks. Mr Crapo earned an LLM in Health Law and Policy and represents a range of healthcare industry stakeholders regarding various healthcare issues.

## DANIELE, Mark A
McCarter & English, LLP, Newark
973 639 2090
mdaniele@mccarter.com
*Featured in Employee Benefits & Executive Compensation (New Jersey)*
**Career:** Mr Daniele focuses on advising clients with respect to the design, interpretation and regulatory compliance of pension, 401(k), 403(b), ESOPs, health, severance, retiree medical (and VEBAs), section 125 cafeteria and nonqualified executive compensation plans. He counsels on tax and ERISA issues regarding pension and welfare benefit plans in connection with domestic and international acquisitions, dispositions and mergers. Mr Daniele advises boards of directors and plan committees on plan governance and ERISA fiduciary obligations. He advises bankruptcy trustees on employee benefits issues. For full bio: http://www.mccarter.com/Mark-A-Daniele/

## DEE, Francis X
McElroy, Deutsch, Mulvaney & Carpenter, LLP, Morristown
973 425 8708
fdee@mdmc-law.com
*Featured in Labor & Employment (New Jersey)*
**Practice Areas:** Mr Dee represents corporations in cases alleging wrongful discharge, discrimination, sexual harassment, breach of express and implied contract, and related claims of defamation, negligence, tortious interference, and false imprisonment.
**Professional Memberships:** Mr Dee is admitted to the bars of the states of New York and New Jersey. He is a fellow of the American College of Trial Lawyers. Mr Dee is also fellow of the International Academy of Trial Lawyers, the College of Labor and Employment Lawyers, and the American Bar Foundation.
**Personal:** New York University School of Law (LLM); Catholic University of America (JD); Manhattan College (BA).

## DELDUCA, Matthew V
Pepper Hamilton LLP, Princeton
609 951 4187
delducam@pepperlaw.com
*Featured in Labor & Employment (New Jersey)*
**Practice Areas:** Partner; Chair, Labor and Employment Practice Group. Represents employers in state and federal labor and employment litigation involving claims of discrimination, wrongful discharge and defamation. Also represents employers in litigation to protect confidential information and trade secrets and to enforce restrictive covenants.
**Professional Memberships:** Member, Federal Practice and Procedure Section, Labor and Employment Section, and Pro Bono Committee of New Jersey State Bar Association; Member, Federal Bar Association of New Jersey.

Personal: BA 1983 Ursinus College; JD, cum laude, 1986 Rutgers University School of Law - Camden.

## DESTEFANO, Louis
Buchanan Ingersoll & Rooney PC, Princeton
973 424 5601
louis.destefano@bipc.com
*Featured in Environment (New Jersey)*
**Career:** Louis is a Shareholder in the firm's Energy Section and Co-chair of the firm's Environmental Practice Group. He represents clients in commercial matters and environmental counseling and litigation. In addition to his general litigation practice, Louis has represented clients in many aspects of environmental compliance and litigation including cases involving sediment remediation and natural resource damages. Additionally, he has particular depth in the petrochemical and automotive industries and has acted as common counsel in several multi-party superfund matters. He earned his JD (cum laude) from Seton Hall University and was in the top 1 percent of his class.

## DIANA, Mark
Ogletree, Deakins, Nash, Smoak & Stewart, PC, Morristown
973 656 1600
mark.diana@ogletreedeakins.com
*Featured in Labor & Employment (New Jersey)*
**Practice Areas:** Labor and employment law, restrictive covenants, litigation.
**Professional Memberships:** American Bar Association (Labor and Employment Section); New Jersey State Bar Association (Executive Board Member, Labor and Employment Law Section).
**Career:** Admitted to practice in New Jersey, U.S. District Court (District of New Jersey), U.S. Court of Appeals (First and Third Circuits); Managing Shareholder Morristown Office.
**Publications:** Production Editor of The Suffolk Law Review; Lectures and writes frequently on labor and employment law issues.
**Personal:** University of Delaware (BS, 1985), Suffolk Law School (JD, cum laude, 1988).

## DISLER, Joan A
Epstein Becker & Green PC, Newark
973 639 8298
jdisler@ebglaw.com
*Featured in Employee Benefits & Executive Compensation (New Jersey)*
**Practice Areas:** Chair of the firm's national Employee Benefits Practice Steering Committee. Ms Disler focuses on pension and welfare plans under ERISA and the Internal Revenue Code. She counsels clients on mergers and acquisitions, qualified and non-qualified plans, deferred compensation and executive bonus plans, plan and trust documents, administrative services agreements, and plan terminations and reversions.
**Professional Memberships:** IRS Northeastern Pension Liaison Group, New Jersey State Bar Association, Worldwide Employee Benefits Network
**Personal:** LLM, New York University Law School, in Taxation, 1980; JD, Rutgers School of

Law, 1976; BA, Douglass College of Rutgers University, 1973.

## DONOVAN, Martha N
Norris McLaughlin & Marcus, PA, Bridgewater
908 252 4240
mndonovan@nmmlaw.com
*Featured in Environment (New Jersey)*
**Practice Areas:** Environmental, Litigation.
**Professional Memberships:** New Jersey State Bar Association, Environmental Law Section; American Bar Association.
**Career:** Devotes practice to environmental law and complex litigation with an emphasis on the defense of environmental property damage and toxic tort claims and related insurance coverage matters. Counsels clients on a variety of environmental issues, including ISRA compliance, lender liability, and underground storage tank laws. Litigated matters relating to generation, storage, discharge or release of hazardous substances, including representation under 'CERCLA' and 'Superfund'. Aids in the resolution of matters involving air emissions, waste water discharges, noise pollution, and responses to spill events.

## DONOVAN ESQ, Colleen R
Day Pitney LLP, Parsippany
973 966 8135
cdonovan@daypitney.com
*Featured in Environment (New Jersey), Real Estate (New Jersey)*
**Career:** Ms Donovan, Commercial Real Estate and Development Transactions practice chair, practices in the areas of financial services, environmental, and real estate law. Ms Donovan represents lending institutions in all types of real estate financings. She has experience advising lenders in the work-out and restructuring of loans and represents clients on the sale, acquisition, and leasing of real estate, and related financing of commercial and industrial properties. Ms Donovan advises lenders with respect to compliance obligations under New Jersey's Industrial Site Recovery Act, underground storage tank regulations, and other laws regulating the use and disposition of real estate in N.J.

## DORE, Michael
Lowenstein Sandler LLP, Roseland
973 597 2344
mdore@lowenstein.com
*Featured in Environment (New Jersey)*
**Practice Areas:** Michael Dore has more than 25 years of experience representing corporate clients in complex toxic tort and environmental litigation, and counseling. His experience handling industrial accidents, fires, explosions and other critical incidents has also helped him gain special understanding of catastrophe response and crisis management. As former counsel for BOC Group, Inc., Michael was responsible for the Fortune 500 company's environmental affairs. He is also the author of Thomson/West's five-volume Law of Toxic Torts. www.lowenstein.com/mdore

## DORSI, Carla
Gibbons P.C., Newark
973 596 4673
CDorsi@gibbonslaw.com
*Featured in Labor & Employment (New Jersey)*
**Practice Areas:** Employment litigation and counseling.
**Career:** Ms Dorsi, a Director in the firm's Employment & Labor Law Department, litigates in various legal forums on behalf of employers sued for discrimination, harassment, retaliation, wage and hour violations and breach of contract. Her experience includes single- and multi-plaintiff lawsuits as well as collective actions. Ms Dorsi also counsels employers on a wide range of issues, including family and medical leaves, disability accommodation, wage and hour compliance and performance management. She also partners with management to draft and revise workplace policies and handbooks and provides training on various employment issues.

## DOWD, Martin F
McCarter & English, LLP, Newark
973 639 2013
mdowd@mccarter.com
*Featured in Real Estate (New Jersey)*
**Career:** Mr Dowd's practice comprises all aspects of real estate law, with a particular focus on the areas of the acquisition and disposition of commercial real estate and commercial leasing transactions. Mr Dowd represents both landlords and tenants in preparing and negotiating office, industrial and retail leases for properties throughout the United States. He represents institutional investors, national developers and corporate users in the structuring and implementation of complex real estate transactions, development of major real estate projects, and acquisition and disposition of real estate investments and portfolios. For full bio: http://www.mccarter.com/Martin-F-Dowd/

## DOYLE, David P
Day Pitney LLP, Parsippany
973 966 8136
ddoyle@daypitney.com
*Featured in Employee Benefits & Executive Compensation (New Jersey)*
**Career:** Mr Doyle counsels clients with respect to all aspects of employee benefits and executive compensation matters, including merger and acquisition issues, qualified and nonqualified pension plans, stock bonus and profit-sharing plans, employment and separation agreements, employee stock-ownership plans, employee welfare-benefit plans, golden parachutes, incentive and nonqualified stock option plans, employee stock-purchase plans and other forms of equity-based compensation, cafeteria plans, and rabbi trusts. He counsels clients regarding the ERISA and tax implications of employee benefit plan investments in various partnership and fund vehicles.

## DRASCO, Dennis J
Lum, Drasco & Positan, LLC, Roseland
973 228 6770
ddrasco@lumlaw.com
*Featured in Litigation (New Jersey)*

**Practice Areas:** 39 years experience state/federal litigation NJ/NY. Business litigation; condemnation; construction; professional liability; appellate; arbitration/mediation.
**Professional Memberships:** Admitted: NJ, NY; ABA HOD; Chair ABA Section of Litigation (2004-05); Chair ABA Comm on American Jury (2006-9); Pres-Assn of Fed Bar of NJ (2008-9); Fellow: American College of Trial Lawyers; IATL; Civil Trial Achievement Award, ECBA;Best Lawyers In America, NJ Superlawyers "Top 10".
**Career:** Lum, Drasco & Positan LLC; Chair, Litigation Group.
**Publications:** 'How To Get From The War Room To The Court Room: The Basics For Civil Trial Preparation'; 'Construction Contracts' NJ Lawyer
**Personal:** BA, Pol Sci, Fordham; JD, Rutgers-Newark.

**DRITSAS, Paul C**
McCarter & English, LLP, Newark
973 639 2063
pdritsas@mccarter.com
*Featured in Environment (New Jersey)*
**Career:** Mr Dritsas practices in the area of environmental law and counsels clients regarding the investigation, remediation and redevelopment of contaminated properties, real estate and corporate transactions, and regulatory and permit compliance. His represents major companies, REITs and financial institutions in transactional due diligence (including Phase I and Phase II site assessments); identification and evaluation of environmental contingent liabilities; and preparation and negotiation of purchase and sale agreements, including environmental indemnification agreements. He also has significant experience handling environmental due diligence investigations and negotiations with respect to facilities both in the United States and internationally. For full bio: http://www.mccarter.com/Paul-C-Dritsas/

**DUNNE, Michael J**
Day Pitney LLP, Parsippany
973 966 8138
mdunne@daypitney.com
*Featured in Corporate/M&A (New Jersey)*
**Career:** Mr Dunne practices in general corporate law, with a focus on information technology and intellectual property. He represents owners and users of technology and intellectual property assets in the computer technology, manufacturing, health care, and financial services industries with respect to corporate and regulatory matters, mergers and acquisitions, strategic alliances, and information technology. His experience includes acquisitions by and of technology companies, enterprise-wide licensing arrangements, outsourcing, technology joint ventures, and advising businesses on structures to protect and enhance the value of intellectual property assets.

**EAKELEY ESQ, Douglas S**
Lowenstein Sandler LLP, Roseland
973 597 2348
deakeley@lowenstein.com
*Featured in Litigation (New Jersey)*

**Practice Areas:** Douglas S Eakeley chairs Lowenstein's Class Action & Derivative Litigation practice group and co-chairs the Appellate and Antitrust & Trade Regulation practice groups. He is an experienced trial and appellate lawyer, specializing in complex commercial litigation, including securities fraud, antitrust, consumer fraud, class actions, products liability and derivative litigation. A former Rhodes Scholar and First Assistant Attorney General of New Jersey, he served as Chairman of the Board of Directors of the Legal Services Corporation (1993-2003) and is the Alan V. Lowenstein Professor of Corporate and Business Law at Rutgers School of Law – Newark. www.lowenstein.com/deakeley

**EHRENBERG, Peter H**
Lowenstein Sandler LLP, Roseland
212 204 8697
pehrenberg@lowenstein.com
*Featured in Corporate/M&A (New Jersey)*
**Practice Areas:** Peter H Ehrenberg chairs Lowenstein's Corporate Department. He assists companies in various stages of capital formation and business development and counsels on exit strategies. He represents issuers and investment firms in private and public offerings of debt and equity securities, and acquirers and sellers of businesses. He counsels on complex M&A transactions, recapitalizations, employee benefits, and secured and unsecured borrowings. He advises public company Boards and Board committees on compliance and public reporting responsibilities, including duties under Sarbanes-Oxley and Dodd-Frank Acts and other corporate governance reforms. www.lowenstein.com/pehrenberg

**ENGLISH, Holly**
Nukk-Freeman & Cerra, Short Hills
973.564.9100
henglish@nfclegal.com
*Featured in Labor & Employment (New Jersey)*

**ERICSSON, Richard J**
Cole, Schotz, Meisel, Forman & Leonard PA, Hackensack
201 525 6346
rericsson@coleschotz.com
*Featured in Environment (New Jersey)*
**Practice Areas:** Chair of the firm's Environmental Department. Extensive experience in impact of environmental laws on business and real estate transactions including brownfield redevelopment, regulatory compliance, oversight of environmental cleanups, permits and funding, environmental insurance, responses to governmental enforcement actions. Counsels lenders on environmental issues related to loan transactions, workout and foreclosure issues, lender liability and practical aspects of addressing contaminated real estate. Counsels borrowers seeking loans secured by environmentally troubled properties.
**Personal:** Vermont Law School, 1981

**ETKIN, Michael S**
Lowenstein Sandler LLP, Roseland
973 597 2312
metkin@lowenstein.com
*Featured in Bankruptcy/Restructuring (New Jersey)*
**Practice Areas:** Michael S Etkin is a senior partner in Lowenstein Sandler's Bankruptcy, Financial Reorganization and Creditors' Rights Department and Complex Business Litigation Group, representing creditors, investors, creditors' committees and debtors in a variety of complex bankruptcies and bankruptcy-related litigation. A recognized leader in the representation of investors and class action claimants in bankruptcy proceedings, he's lectured on the rights of class action claimants in a Chapter 11 context. He also represents major energy companies in Chapter 11 proceedings involving their counterparties, and has spoken before financial institutions and credit associations about industry-related bankruptcy issues. www.lowenstein.com/metkin

**FEHER, Kristine**
Greenberg Traurig, LLP, Florham Park
973 443 3273
FeherK@gtlaw.com
*Featured in Labor & Employment (New Jersey)*
**Practice Areas:** Labor and employment; employment litigation; business immigration and compliance.
**Professional Memberships:** Member: Morris County Bar Association; American Immigration Lawyers Association; New Jersey Women Lawyers Association.
**Career:** Team Member, Law360 'Employment Practice Group of the Year', 2011. Chambers USA Guide, 2011-13; Super Lawyers magazine - Rising Stars, 2006-09; Benchmark: Litigation, the Definitive Guide to America's Leading Litigation Firms and Attorneys, 2009. Rated, AV® Preeminent™ 5.0 out of 5.
**Personal:** JD, University of Pennsylvania Law School, 1995; BA, Tufts University, 1992; Phillips Academy at Andover, 1988.

**FLEISSIG, Steven D**
Greenberg Traurig, LLP, Florham Park
973 443 3281
FleissigS@gtlaw.com
*Featured in Real Estate (New Jersey)*
**Practice Areas:** Real estate; sales and purchases; leasing; asset-based financing; restructuring; workouts; mortgage foreclosure; UCC issues; section 1031 tax deferred exchanges.
**Professional Memberships:** Past President and Board Member, Association of Commercial Finance Attorneys; fellow, American College of Commercial Finance Lawyers; fellow, American College of Mortgage Attorneys.
**Career:** Selected: The Best Lawyers in America, 2007-13; Super Lawyers magazine, 2006-12; Chambers USA Guide, 2011-13. Profiled, 'Multi-Pointed Stars,' New Jersey & Company, November/December 2010. Rated, AV® Preeminent™ 5.0 out of 5.
**Personal:** JD, Georgetown University Law Center, 1976; BA, cum laude, State University of New York at Buffalo.

**FLORES, Daniel F**
Wilson, Elser, Moskowitz, Edelman & Dicker LLP, Florham Park
973 735 5769
daniel.flores@wilsonelser.com
*Featured in Bankruptcy/Restructuring (New Jersey)*
**Practice Areas:** Daniel Flores is chair of Wilson Elser's Financial Services practice. He focuses on creditors' rights, including loan work-out and restructuring, commercial litigation and bankruptcy matters. He is experienced in all aspects of state and federal court litigation, including defensive litigation, actions to enforce promissory notes and guarantees, mortgage foreclosure proceedings and replevin actions. He also represents clients in Chapter 11 bankruptcy proceedings, including matters related to use of cash collateral, asset sales, stay relief motions, assumption or rejection of executory contracts and unexpired leases, and plan confirmation.
**Personal:** JD, Rutgers School of Law (Law Review); BA, Rutgers College.

**FOLEY, Shawn P**
Lerner David Littenberg Krumholz & Mentlik, LLP, Westfield
908 518 6346
sfoley@ldlkm.com
*Featured in Intellectual Property (New Jersey)*
**Practice Areas:** Expert in creating global patent estates, conducting due diligence review and opinions, with emphasis on commercial products in biotechnology, pharmaceutical, and various chemical fields including personal care products. Highly experienced in US Patent and European practices including reexamination, oppositions, and special programs including alternatives to appeal and accelerated examination. Advises clients with diverse legal interests including not-for-profits, start-ups, and mid-and major corporations.
**Professional Memberships:** US Patent and Trademark Office; Federal Circuit Bar Association; AIPLA; New Jersey and North Carolina Bars.
**Career:** Lerner David Littenberg Krumholz & Mentlik, LLP.
**Personal:** JD, George Mason University Law School; BA, Biochemistry, University of Pennsylvania.

**FRISCIA, Michael R**
McCarter & English, LLP, Newark
973 848 8308
mfriscia@mccarter.com
*Featured in Intellectual Property (New Jersey)*
**Career:** Mr Friscia is a registered patent attorney and has been practicing patent and trademark law for over 20 years. He handles the preparation and prosecution of substantial patent portfolios for his clients in the mechanical and electrical fields, including computer systems, business methods, medical devices and other technologies. Mr Friscia regularly assists clients with contentious matters and has successfully represented clients in patent and trademark litigation in many federal courts. He has also represented clients in a large number of inter partes proceedings before the Trademark Trial and Appeal Board. For full bio: http://www.mccarter.com/Michael-R-Friscia/

## GARLAND, David W
Epstein Becker & Green PC, Newark
212 351 4708
DGarland@ebglaw.com
*Featured in Labor & Employment (New Jersey)*
**Practice Areas:** Chair of the firm's Labor and Employment Practice Steering Committee. Mr. Garland defends clients in employment discrimination, wrongful discharge, and other employment-related litigation, including cases involving allegations of sexual harassment, FMLA, whistle-blowing, wage and hour, public policy, tort claims, and restrictive covenants.
**Professional Memberships:** Academy of New Jersey Management Attorneys, American Bar Association, American Employment Law Council, Litigation Counsel of America, National Finance Industry, New Jersey State Bar Association, New York State Bar Association.
**Personal:** JD, George Washington University Law School, 1985; BA, College of William and Mary, 1980.

## GIBSON, Christopher R
Archer & Greiner, A Professional Corporation, Haddonfield
856 354 3077
cgibson@archerlaw.com
*Featured in Environment (New Jersey)*
**Practice Areas:** Christopher Gibson is President of Archer & Greiner and Chair of the Firm's Litigation Department, and both the Environmental Law and Eminent Domain practice groups. He has forged a reputation as one of New Jersey's preeminent litigators, particularly in the areas of environmental and eminent domain law. Mr Gibson acts as local, regional and national counsel to many nationally known corporations. He has successfully tried several cases involving hundreds of millions of dollars on behalf of large companies. He also represents numerous major governmental agencies in New Jersey and Pennsylvania.

## GILBERT, Andrew P
DLA Piper LLP (US), Florham Park
973 520 2553
andrew.gilbert@dlapiper.com
*Featured in Corporate/M&A (New Jersey)*
**Practice Areas:** Corporate, Securities, M&A.
**Career:** He represents public and private companies primarily in the technology, life sciences and healthcare industries as well as investment firms that serve these sectors. He is highly experienced in securities law compliance and corporate governance matters. He counseled numerous entrepreneurs and emerging growth companies in planning profitable liquidity strategies. He regularly serves as outside general counsel for private and public companies at various stages of development.
**Personal:** JD, Rutgers University School of Law; BA, Colgate University.

## GLAZER, David G
Morgan, Lewis & Bockius LLP, Princeton
609 919 6624
david.glazer@morganlewis.com
*Featured in Corporate/M&A (New Jersey)*

**Practice Areas:** David G Glazer is a partner in Morgan Lewis's Business and Finance Practice. Mr Glazer's practice focuses on advising and representing life sciences, healthcare, medical devices, and technology companies. Mr Glazer regularly serves as outside counsel to these companies and counsels them in a variety of different transactions as well as strategic advice. His practice includes negotiation and structuring of licensing and other complex collaborations, corporate partnering arrangements, strategic alliances, mergers and acquisitions, manufacturing, supply and distribution arrangements, co-promotions and joint ventures, ranging from early-stage research collaborations to global alliances to develop and commercialize products and technologies.

## GLINE, Gerald
Cole, Schotz, Meisel, Forman & Leonard PA, Hackensack
201 525 6240
ggline@coleschotz.com
*Featured in Bankruptcy/Restructuring (New Jersey)*
**Practice Areas:** Member of Bankruptcy & Corporate Restructuring department. Represents public and privately-held corporate debtors, trustees, secured and unsecured creditors, and creditor committees in all phases of insolvency practice. Represented Beth Israel Hospital Association of Passaic as debtor-in-possession in its Chapter 11 case, the Bond Insurer, the largest secured and unsecured creditor in the Bayonne Medical Center Chapter 11 case and United Healthcare Systems, Inc. as the debtor-in-possession in one of the largest health care Chapter 11 cases in the history of New Jersey.
**Personal:** Rutgers University School of Law - Newark, JD, with honors, 1977.

## GOLDSTEIN, Richard J
Hangley Aronchick Segal Pudlin & Schiller, Cherry Hill
856 616 2172
rgoldstein@hangley.com
*Featured in Real Estate (New Jersey)*
**Practice Areas:** Broad based commercial real estate practice which includes acquisition and transfer of real property, commercial leasing, and commercial development. Mr Goldstein's practice also features zoning and land use.
**Professional Memberships:** Member of Pennsylvania and New Jersey bars, American Bar Association, Pennsylvania Bar Association, Philadelphia Bar Association, New Jersey Bar Association and Camden County Bar Association.
**Career:** Shareholder, Hangley Aronchick Segal Pudlin & Schiller, 1995-Present; Shareholder and Associate, Cohen, Shapiro, Polisher, Shiekman and Cohen, 1978-1995; associate, Eilberg, Corson, Getson & Tuteur 1977-78. Temple University School of Law, JD, 1977; Temple University, BA, 1974.

## GOODMAN, Scott Warren
Day Pitney LLP, Parsippany
973 966 8226
sgoodman@daypitney.com
*Featured in Corporate/M&A (New Jersey)*

**Career:** Mr Goodman counsels publicly and privately held companies on corporate, transactional and securities law matters. His focus is mergers and acquisitions, including stock and asset acquisitions and dispositions, corporate reorganizations, public offerings, private placements, venture capital transactions and compliance with public reporting responsibilities, including duties under the Sarbanes-Oxley Act. Scott has worked on initial public offerings and other offerings registered with the Securities and Exchange Commission, as well as private offerings exempt from registration. His transactional and counseling practice covers a wide array of industries, including manufacturing, energy, banking and various service industries.

## GOODMAN, Stanley
Fox Rothschild LLP, Roseland
973 994 7520
sgoodman@foxrothschild.com
*Featured in Labor & Employment (New Jersey)*
**Practice Areas:** Represents management clients in labor relations, employment discrimination and wrongful termination. Handles complex labor relations transactions and litigation matters involving whistle-blowers, race/age discrimination and breach of contract before administrative agencies and state and federal courts.
**Professional Memberships:** Member: Executive Committee, NJ State Bar Association Labor and Employment Law Section.
**Career:** Office Managing Partner, firm's Roseland, NJ office. Co-Chair, Labor & Employment Group. Advises employers nationwide in various industries, frequently lectures on employment/labor topics. Rated AV® Preeminent™ Martindale-Hubbell.
**Publications:** Co-author, New Jersey Employment Law, published by West Publishing Company.
**Personal:** JD, New York University, 1977; BA, Columbia College, 1974.

## GOTTLIEB, Ira
McCarter & English, LLP, Newark
973 639 7984
igottlieb@mccarter.com
*Featured in Environment (New Jersey), Litigation (New Jersey)*
**Career:** Mr Gottlieb is the Firm's Environment and Energy Practice Group Leader. He effectively assists clients with practical solutions to complex problems by relying on a wealth of experience gathered from litigating and trying a variety of cases and from his time as an Assistant Regional Counsel with the EPA. Mr Gottlieb is presently handling diverse matters involving large surface water sites, an oil platform accident in the North Sea, D&O litigation involving foreign currency trading, and an intellectual property and antitrust case concerning flash memory products. For full bio: http://www.mccarter.com/Ira-M-Gottlieb/

## GRAW, Andrew E
Lowenstein Sandler LLP, Roseland
973 597 2588
agraw@lowenstein.com
*Featured in Employee Benefits & Executive Compensation (New Jersey)*

**Practice Areas:** Andrew E Graw chairs the firm's Employee Benefits and Executive Compensation Group. He has 30 years of experience in executive compensation, employee benefits, employment and labor law. Andy advises clients on all aspects of employee benefit and executive compensation matters, including "Section 409A" compliance, fiduciary responsibilities, equity compensation arrangements, reporting and disclosure obligations, employment agreements, sophisticated pension fund investments, corporate governance and securities disclosure rules, Health Reform, ERISA litigation and benefit claim disputes, and the implications of downsizings, acquisitions and divestitures on compensation and benefits. www.lowenstein.com/agraw

## GREENBAUM, Jeffrey J
Sills Cummis & Gross P.C., Newark
973 643 5430
jgreenbaum@sillscummis.com
*Featured in Litigation (New Jersey)*
**Practice Areas:** Jeffrey J Greenbaum, Chair of the firm's Class Action Defense Practice Group, is an active litigator specializing in complex business litigation and defending class action litigation. He has handled cases of national prominence.
**Professional Memberships:** He is a leader in the ABA Section of Litigation (Former Officer, Member of Section's Executive Committee and Governing Council; former Chair, Class Actions & Derivative Suits Committee); Association of the Federal Bar of New Jersey (former President); Fellow, LCA.
**Personal:** Certified Civil Trial Attorney; former Assistant US Attorney; University of Michigan, JD, cum laude, 1972; University of Pennsylvania, Wharton School, BS, 1969.

## GREENBAUM, William
Lowenstein Sandler LLP, Roseland
973 422 6766
wgreenbaum@lowenstein.com
*Featured in Labor & Employment (New Jersey)*
**Practice Areas:** William I Greenbaum practices employment law, focusing on the practical resolution of sensitive and difficult workplace problems. He has more than 25 years of experience in the life sciences and pharmaceutical industry handling all employment matters, including employee leave issues, internal investigations, employee discipline and discharge, the protection of proprietary and confidential information, and employment policies and practices. Bill's extensive experience also includes counseling clients on the full range of discrimination, harassment, retaliation, whistle-blowing, and contractual and statutory issues and claims that frequently arise in the workplace. www.lowenstein.com/wgreenbaum

## GROSS, Steven E
Sills Cummis & Gross P.C., Newark
973 643 5080
sgross@sillscummis.com
*Featured in Corporate/M&A (New Jersey)*
**Practice Areas:** Steven E Gross is the Chairman of the firm. His corporate and securities practice is international in scope. He counsels companies

and senior executives on M&A transactions, financial restructurings and fund raisings, and advises boards of directors and senior executives on fiduciary duties, corporate compliance and government regulatory matters. His banking practice involves representing institutional creditors and corporate borrowers in lending transactions, workouts and creditors' rights matters.
**Professional Memberships:** Non-Profit Board Memberships: Director - New Jersey Performing Arts Center; Trustee - The Healthcare Foundation of New Jersey.
**Career:** Listed in The Best Lawyers in America since 1993; and Chambers USA and New Jersey Super Lawyers since their inception.
**Personal:** Harvard University Law School, JD, 1962; 50th Reunion Vice Chairman, Gift and Fund Raising Committee, Harvard Law School; Baruch College - City College of New York, BBA, 1959; Stuyvesant High School (NYC), 1956.

### HAGLUND, Benjamin E
Day Pitney LLP, Parsippany
973 966 8155
bhaglund@daypitney.com
*Featured in Litigation (New Jersey)*
**Career:** Mr Haglund practices in the areas of products liability disputes, shareholder/investor suits, and commercial disputes. Mr Haglund's experience includes jury trials, bench trials, arbitration hearings, and mediation in complex matters, as well as evaluation and planning of short- and long-term litigation strategy at the state, regional, and national levels. Mr Haglund leads joint litigation defense groups in New Jersey and New York and also serves as lead medical counsel and liaison counsel.

### HALL, Thomas Jay
Sills Cummis & Gross P.C., Newark
973 643 5738
thall@sillscummis.com
*Featured in Real Estate (New Jersey)*
**Practice Areas:** Thomas Jay Hall, Senior Counsel to the firm's Real Estate Department, counsels clients on a variety of land use and environmental issues, including representation before planning boards and boards of adjustment seeking approval of planned unit developments, subdivisions, site plans and variances; and for applications for permits before the Department of Environmental Protection. He has also appeared in administrative, trial and appellate courts.
**Personal:** Rutgers University Law School, JD, 1983; Rutgers University Graduate School, PhD, Political Science, 1975; Rutgers University Graduate School, Eagleton Institute of Politics, MA, Political Science, 1966; The University of Arizona, BA, Government, 1964.

### HARRIS, David L
Lowenstein Sandler LLP, Roseland
973 597 2378
dharris@lowenstein.com
*Featured in Litigation (New Jersey)*
**Practice Areas:** David L Harris is first and foremost a trial lawyer with the unique capacity to quickly synthesize complex issues and present them to a jury in a clear, precise and convincing

manner. He is at his finest when the factual issues are technically obtuse, the legal issues are complex and the stakes are high. David has been lauded as one of the top 10 litigators in New Jersey, and he is known for his trial, appellate and arbitration skills in complex business litigation spanning multiple jurisdictions, including intellectual property, antitrust and trade secrets litigation. www.lowenstein.com/dharris

### HARRIS, Glenn A
Ballard Spahr LLP, Cherry Hill
856 761 3440
harrisg@ballardspahr.com
*Featured in Environment (New Jersey)*
**Practice Areas:** Glenn A Harris is a partner in the Environmental Group. He focuses on environmental litigation and has served as common counsel, shared counsel, or liaison counsel on significant Superfund matters, representing groups and individual companies. He has mediated hundreds of environmental and commercial disputes. He also handles insurance litigation coverage matters and is a former adjunct professor of insurance at Rutgers School of Law—Camden.
**Professional Memberships:** American Bar Association New Jersey State Bar Association.
**Career:** Admissions: New Jersey Pennsylvania.
**Publications:** Contributor, chapter on "Contaminated Sites Cost Recovery under CERCLA" in Environmental Litigation: Law and Strategy.

### HATFIELD, William S
Gibbons P.C., Newark
973 596 4511
WHatfield@gibbonslaw.com
*Featured in Environment (New Jersey)*
**Practice Areas:** Environmental litigation and counseling.
**Career:** Mr Hatfield, a Director in the firm's Real Property & Environmental Department, has extensive litigation experience involving CERCLA, RCRA, CWA, underground storage tanks, toxic torts, and the New Jersey Spill and Landfill Closure Acts. He counsels clients on matters regarding environmental investigations and cleanup matters; ISRA applicability and compliance; natural resource damages; permitting and enforcement issues specific to the USEPA, NJDEP, NYSDEC, and other state environmental agencies and EHA audits. He earned his JD (cum laude) and MSL (summa cum laude) in Environmental Law from Vermont Law School and BA from Brown University.

### HEEB, Lisa
McCarter & English, LLP, Newark
973 848 5356
lheeb@mccarter.com
*Featured in Corporate/M&A (New Jersey)*
**Career:** Ms Heeb is a partner in the firm's Corporate, Securities and Financial Institutions Group and represents clients in mergers and acquisitions, private equity and venture capital transactions, and general corporate legal matters. With a concentration in mergers and acquisitions, she has extensive experience in representing both private and public entities in acquisitions and

sales of companies, asset acquisitions and dispositions, and joint ventures in a variety of industries. Ms Heeb currently serves as a member of the firm's Professional Personnel Committee. For full bio: http://www.mccarter.com/Lisa-A-Heeb/

### HERSCHMAN, Gary W
Sills Cummis & Gross P.C., Newark
973 643 5783
gherschman@sillscummis.com
*Featured in Healthcare (New Jersey)*
**Practice Areas:** Gary W Herschman, Chair of the Health Care Practice Group, represents hospitals, healthcare systems, long-term care facilities, home health companies, ASCs, labs, ambulance companies, private equity funds, and other healthcare facilities and businesses. He handles strategic transactions, joint ventures, mergers, acquisitions, affiliations, physician alignment strategies, major contracts, federal and state regulatory compliance issues, government investigations and healthcare litigation.
**Professional Memberships:** Vice Chair, AHLA's Fraud & Abuse Practice Group. Involved in several other health industry and bar associations.
**Publications:** Frequently presents seminars nationally and locally. Authors articles on cutting-edge healthcare law and industry issues in national and local publications.

### HILDEBRAND, Mary J
Lowenstein Sandler LLP, Roseland
973 597 6308
mhildebrand@lowenstein.com
*Featured in Intellectual Property (New Jersey)*
**Practice Areas:** Mary J Hildebrand, partner in the Tech Group and Chair of the Privacy Practice, concentrates on technology and intellectual property transactions including tech transfers and licensing, outsourcing, collaboration, strategic alliance and joint development agreements; open source issues; online and e-commerce businesses; and due diligence evaluations of intellectual property and data privacy issues in M&A and venture capital transactions. She has broad counseling experience in data privacy/security issues, online advertising and marketing practices and privacy compliance. www.lowenstein.com/mhildebrand

### HIMMEL, Michael B
Lowenstein Sandler LLP, Roseland
646 414 6904
mhimmel@lowenstein.com
*Featured in Litigation (New Jersey)*
**Practice Areas:** Michael B Himmel chairs Lowenstein Sandler's Litigation Department and White Collar Criminal Defense Group. A former Assistant US Attorney (D-NJ), his national criminal defense practice includes defending individuals and corporations (public and private) under investigation and/or at trial for matters concerning securities fraud, tax fraud, antitrust, FCPA, environmental crimes, and political corruption. He is also known for his complex business litigation work, which has resulted in several billion dollar victories. www.lowenstein.com/mhimmel

### HOGAN, Edward A
Norris McLaughlin & Marcus, PA, Bridgewater
908 722 0700
eahogan@nmmlaw.com
*Featured in Environment (New Jersey)*
**Practice Areas:** Environment.
**Professional Memberships:** New Jersey State Bar Association, Environmental Law Section, Past Chair; Commerce and Industry Association of New Jersey, Past General Counsel; New Jersey Business and Industry Association, Environmental Quality Committee, Past Chair.
**Career:** Forefront of site remediation issues in New Jersey. Represents and counsels developers, redevelopers, manufacturers, commercial entities, and highly-regulated service businesses in all aspects of environmental law and litigation. Develops integrated strategies for responding to governmental mandates, pursuing cost recovery actions, and facilitating purchase, sale and redevelopment of contaminated properties.

### HORN, Lawrence S
Sills Cummis & Gross P.C., Newark
973 643 5484
lhorn@sillscummis.com
*Featured in Litigation (New Jersey)*
**Practice Areas:** Lawrence S Horn, Chair of the firm's Business Crimes and Tax Litigation Practice Groups, is a certified criminal trial attorney. He defends individuals and companies who are the targets of federal white collar criminal investigations, with a special emphasis on criminal tax cases. He was an AUSA for the District of New Jersey where he specialized in tax fraud prosecutions.
**Professional Memberships:** American College of Tax Counsel; New York Council of Defense Lawyers; Federal Bar Council (NY); National Association of Criminal Defense Lawyers; American Bar Association, Section on Taxation, Committee on Civil and Criminal Tax Penalties.

### HOROWITZ, Gregory
McCarter & English, LLP, Newark
973 639 7933
ghorowitz@mccarter.com
*Featured in Litigation (New Jersey)*
**Career:** Over the past twenty years, Mr Horowitz has successfully litigated, arbitrated and counseled corporate clients and helped recover hundreds of millions of dollars in connection with various coverage disputes around the globe involving additional insured, advertising injury, asbestos, bad-faith, breast implants, business interruption, construction, environmental, intellectual property, and product liability and warranty claims as well as complex finite and captive reinsurance disputes. Mr Horowitz also serves as counsel to various entities involved in domestic and international insurance intermediary disputes and has successfully represented a variety of commercial clients in connection with other complex litigation matters. For full bio:
http://www.mccarter.com/Gregory-H-Horowitz/

**HUGHES, Peter O**
Ogletree, Deakins, Nash, Smoak & Stewart, PC, Morristown
973 630 2301
peter.hughes@ogletreedeakins.com
*Featured in Labor & Employment (New Jersey)*
**Practice Areas:** Labor and employment law; litigation; Sarbanes-Oxley; class action; trade secret.
**Professional Memberships:** ABA; NJSBA; Turnaround Management Association.
**Career:** Shareholder since 1995. Admitted to practice in New Jersey, U.S. District Court (District of New Jersey, Northern District of Texas, Western District of Michigan, District of Colorado), U.S. Court of Appeals (First, Second, Third, Fourth, and District of Columbia Circuits).
**Publications:** "Beyond the FMLA: Medical Leave As Reasonable Accommodation," ACCA Docket 20, no. 3 (March 2002); Contributing author, New Jersey Labor and Employment Law (NJICLE).
**Personal:** Franklin & Marshall College (BA, 1984), Seton Hall University School of Law (JD, 1987).

**HUNTER, Edward**
Lowenstein Sandler LLP, Roseland
973 597 2590
ehunter@lowenstein.com
*Featured in Real Estate (New Jersey)*
**Practice Areas:** Ted Hunter chairs Lowenstein's Real Estate Group. Based in New York and New Jersey but with a national practice, Ted has extensive experience in all areas of commercial real estate. Ted was lead attorney on a deal named Project Finance's "2009 North American Real Estate Deal of the Year" and lead attorney on a deal named REBNY's 2010 "Most Creative Retail Deal of the Year." Under Ted's direction, Lowenstein's Real Estate Group is currently working on a portfolio hotel privatization transaction involving 18,000 rooms across the US and the transfer of approximately 700 service stations in seven states. www.lowenstein.com/ehunter

**HYATT, JR, William H**
K&L Gates, Newark
973 848 4045
william.hyatt@klgates.com
*Featured in Environment (New Jersey)*
**Practice Areas:** Concentrating in environmental law and related litigation, Mr Hyatt has extensive experience in Superfund matters. He has frequently acted as common or shared counsel representing parties before the EPA and counterpart agencies, and in cost recovery and contribution litigation. He has taken leadership roles on behalf of private parties at many of the most significant Superfund sites, including four of the top six sites listed on the NPL. He has negotiated landmark settlements with EPA and the Department of Justice.

**IANNACCONE, Carmine A**
Epstein Becker & Green PC, Newark
973 639 8271
ciannaccone@ebglaw.com
*Featured in Labor & Employment (New Jersey)*

**Practice Areas:** Member of Firm, Labor and Employment Practice; Vice-Chairman of the firm's Board of Directors. Mr Iannaccone focuses on labor relations, employment litigation, counseling, and trial practice. He has extensive jury trial experience representing employers in state and federal courts, before the NLRB, and other administrative agencies and arbitration panels. He counsels clients on employment discrimination, Title VII, wrongful termination, sexual harassment, negotiating collective bargaining agreements, employment agreements, and managing unionized and non-unionized workforces.
**Professional Memberships:** American Arbitration Association, American Bar Association, New Jersey Bar Association.
**Personal:** JD, Tulane University School of Law, 1977; BA, Villanova University, 1973.

**IGNACIO, Vanessa**
Lowenstein Sandler LLP, Roseland
973 422 6426
vignacio@lowenstein.com
*Featured in Intellectual Property (New Jersey)*
**Practice Areas:** Vanessa Ignacio focuses her practice on domestic and international trademark counseling, clearance, prosecution and enforcement. She strategically manages all aspects of maintaining clients' global trademark and copyright portfolios. Vanessa is skilled at carefully crafting trademark applications to avoid the issues that can invite agency refusals. Even when refusals occur, she enjoys a stellar track record of overcoming them with responses that address objections, securing valuable trademark registrations for her clients. Vanessa has extensive expertise handling domain name and Internet issues. She represents clients across a spectrum of industries, with highest concentration in technology, pharmaceuticals and consumer goods. www.lowenstein.com/vignacio

**JACOB, Cynthia M**
Fisher & Phillips LLP, Murray Hill
908 516 1050
cjacob@laborlawyers.com
*Featured in Labor & Employment (New Jersey)*
**Career:** Cynthia Jacob is Senior Counsel in the New Jersey office. She has extensive trial experience, in both bench and jury trials. She concentrates on arbitrating and litigating employment-related cases, including wrongful termination, race, sex and age discrimination, and other civil rights litigation. A past President of the New Jersey State Bar Association (the second elected woman officer in the Association's 100-year history), Jacob received a JD from Yale Law School.

**JANIS, Ronald H**
Day Pitney LLP, Parsippany
973 966 8263
rjanis@daypitney.com
*Featured in Corporate/M&A (New Jersey)*
**Career:** Mr Janis is a partner in the Corporate and Business Law department of the firm, and chair of the Mergers, Acquisitions and Joint Ventures practice group. Mr Janis is actively involved in counseling a variety of clients on acquisitions, federal securities law compliance, financial institutions regulatory matters (banks, broker-dealers, and insurance agents), and corporate governance (Sarbanes-Oxley, as well as NYSE, AMEX, and NASDAQ). He has served as counsel to targets, acquirers, and investment banks in a variety of public company mergers, as well as private company acquisitions.

**JASAITIS, James E**
Dentons, Short Hills
973 912 7175
james.jasaitis@dentons.com
*Featured in Corporate/M&A (New Jersey)*
**Practice Areas:** Represents public and private companies encompassing mergers and acquisitions, venture capital, commercial loan transactions and securities transactions, as well as joint ventures, strategic alliances and general corporate representation. Counsels companies regarding corporate control and governance issues, as well as executive and director compensation matters. Represents venture capital funds, angel networks and high net worth individuals in connection with their private company investment transactions.
**Personal:** George Washington University, JD; University of Virginia, BA.

**JOHNSON, Rene M**
Morgan, Lewis & Bockius LLP, Princeton
609 919 6607
rjohnson@morganlewis.com
*Featured in Labor & Employment (New Jersey)*
**Practice Areas:** Rene M Johnson is a partner in Morgan Lewis's Labor and Employment Practice and is head of the practice in Princeton. Rene has extensive experience representing employers in the financial services and pharmaceutical industries. Rene has handled jury trials, bench trials, and AAA and FINRA arbitrations in both New York and New Jersey. She also counsels clients regularly on FMLA, ADA, and leave issues, as well as layoffs, restructurings, and reorganizations.
**Personal:** Attended University of Michigan Law School, 1993, JD; Cornell University, 1990, BA.

**JOHNSON LARIO, Wendy**
Greenberg Traurig, LLP, Florham Park
973 360 3274
LarioW@gtlaw.com
*Featured in Labor & Employment (New Jersey)*
**Practice Areas:** Chair, New Jersey Labor, Employment Practice.
**Professional Memberships:** NJWLA: (President, 2011-12; Past President, Nominations Chair, 2012-13). Trustee, Association of the Federal Bar of the State of New Jersey. Board of Visitors, Seton Hall University School of Law.
**Career:** Recognized: NJBIZ Best 50 Women in Business, 2012; Super Lawyers: 2005-09, 2011-13, (Corporate Counsel edition, 2010); Chambers USA, 2011-13; Professional Lawyer of the Year, NJ Commission on Professionalism in the Law, 2010. AV® Preeminent™ 5.0 out of 5. Member, Law360 'Employment Practice Group of the Year', 2011.
**Personal:** JD, Seton Hall University School of Law, 1992; BA, Duke University, 1986.

**KAILES, Howard**
McCarter & English, LLP, Newark
973 848 5350
hkailes@mccarter.com
*Featured in Corporate/M&A (New Jersey)*
**Career:** Mr Kailes has advised public and privately held principals in a variety of transactions, extending to industrial, consumer products, financial services, technology and life sciences enterprises. Recent representative transactions include the divestitures of the largest independent US beauty products distributor, leading aerospace defense contractors, a regional bank holding company, an international industrial filtration division, and a medical device provider and multiple acquisitions, including leveraged buyouts of human tissue banks, swimming pool equipment manufacturers and construction firms. Mr Kailes has acted as counsel in the creation of a number of domestic and offshore fund structures. For full bio: http://www.mccarter.com/Howard-Kailes/

**KALISON, Michael J**
McElroy, Deutsch, Mulvaney & Carpenter, LLP, Morristown
973 348 5493
mkalison@mdmc-law.com
*Featured in Healthcare (New Jersey)*
**Practice Areas:** Mr Kalison concentrates his practice in health and hospital law, healthcare reimbursement, finance and administrative law. His current focus is aligning provider incentives, including the Medicare Physician-Hospital Collaboration Demonstration involving hospitals in New Jersey and New York.
**Professional Memberships:** Mr Kalison is admitted to practice in New Jersey and is a member of the American Health Lawyers Association.
**Publications:** Mr Kalison has published many articles and has been a frequent lecturer on financial and corporate issues affecting hospitals.
**Personal:** University of Pennsylvania (JD); University of Pennsylvania (BS).

**KAMEN, Steven R**
Sills Cummis & Gross P.C., Newark
973 643 5072
skamen@sillscummis.com
*Featured in Corporate/M&A (New Jersey)*
**Practice Areas:** Steven R Kamen, Co-Chair of the firm's Corporate Practice Group, provides corporate counseling to public and private companies, including the structuring and negotiating of complex acquisitions, debt and equity financings, joint ventures/collaborations and various other commercial transactions in a wide variety of industries and business sectors.
**Career:** Prior to joining the firm, he was Senior Vice President and General Counsel to a New York City-based internet company, and later, Senior Vice President and General Counsel to a New York City-based private equity firm.
**Personal:** Columbia Law School, JD, 1990; University of Michigan, AB, 1985.

## KARP, Susan C.
Cole, Schotz, Meisel, Forman & Leonard PA, Hackensack
201 525 6348
skarp@coleschotz.com
*Featured in Environment (New Jersey)*
**Practice Areas:** Focuses on a broad array of environmental matters, including brownfield redevelopment, contaminated site remediation, ISRA compliance and cost recovery. Assists clients in evaluating remedial options and associated cleanup costs involved with environmental compliance. Provides due diligence counseling in evaluating environmental conditions and liabilities related to the acquisition and disposition of industrial and commercial real properties. Counsels clients on available avenues of environmental cost recovery, including general liability insurance. Pursued numerous Redevelopment Agreements with the New Jersey Economic Development Authority and cleanup grants through the New Jersey Department of Environmental Protection.
**Personal:** Seton Hall University School of Law, 1994.

## KEARNEY, Dennis T
Day Pitney LLP, Parsippany
973 966 8039
dkearney@daypitney.com
*Featured in Litigation (New Jersey)*
**Career:** Mr Kearney represents corporations, nonprofit organizations, and financial institutions in all facets of complex civil and criminal litigation. He has successfully defended St. Mary's Abbey/Delbarton against allegations of improper zoning, a nationwide manufacturer against alleged environmental crimes, and Wachovia Bank before a jury against allegations that the bank breached a fiduciary duty. Mr Kearney tried the first bank valuation case under New Jersey's new standards of review, and prosecuted to verdict two federal trademark infringement cases. In the healthcare arena, he acts as a civil prosecutor. Mr Kearney was formerly an assistant prosecutor with the Essex County prosecutor's office.

## KEARNEY, John B
Ballard Spahr LLP, Cherry Hill
856 761 3482
kearneyj@ballardspahr.com
*Featured in Litigation (New Jersey)*
**Practice Areas:** Mr Kearney focuses his practice on complex civil cases with an emphasis on commercial, product liability, toxic tort, and environmental litigation. He has extensive experience in alternative dispute resolution, including arbitration and mediation.
**Professional Memberships:** American Bar Association, New Jersey State Bar Association, Camden County Bar Association, Association of the Federal Bar of NJ.
**Career:** Admissions: New Jersey, Pennsylvania, U.S. District Court for the District of New Jersey and Eastern District of Pennsylvania, U.S. Court of Appeals for the Third Circuit, U.S. Supreme Court.

**Personal:** University of Pennsylvania Law School (JD), The College of the Holy Cross (BA).

## KELLY, Theresa A
Day Pitney LLP, Parsippany
973 966 8168
tkelly@daypitney.com
*Featured in Labor & Employment (New Jersey)*
**Career:** Ms Kelly practices in the area of employment litigation, including defense of employment discrimination actions, wrongful discharge suits, whistleblower actions, and employee benefits litigation. She represents employers in federal and state courts, as well as before the EEOC and the New Jersey Division on Civil Rights. Her practice also includes counseling and training on a broad spectrum of employment matters, including workforce reductions, employee discipline and discharge matters, family and medical leave, employee handbooks, employment policies, disability issues, sexual harassment issues, negotiation and preparation of employment and separation agreements, and compliance with federal and state labor and employment laws.

## KENDALL, George H
Drinker Biddle & Reath LLP, Florham Park
973 549 7070
George.Kendall@dbr.com
*Featured in Healthcare (New Jersey)*
**Practice Areas:** Partner and Vice-Chair of the firm's Health Care Practice Group. George H Kendall has represented hospitals and health systems, home health agencies, physician groups, and pharmaceutical, medical device and medical equipment companies for over 25 years. His areas of experience include mergers, acquisitions, divestitures and restructurings, hospital-physician alignment, governance and compliance, joint ventures, managed care, reimbursement, and medical staff matters. George has advised numerous clients in connection with governmental and internal investigations involving fraud and abuse, EMTALA, licensure and other matters.
**Personal:** Villanova University School of Law, JD (cum laude); Franklin & Marshall College, AB.

## KENNEDY, Charles P
Lerner David Littenberg Krumholz & Mentlik, LLP, Westfield
908 518 6307
ckennedy@ldlkm.com
*Featured in Intellectual Property (New Jersey)*
**Practice Areas:** Complex intellectual property litigation, including patents, trademarks and copyrights. Hands-on involvement in all phases of disputes, trials and appeals to US circuit courts.
**Professional Memberships:** New Jersey and New York Bars; New Jersey Intellectual Property Law Association; Federal Circuit Bar Association; Master and former Co-Chair of John C. Lifland American Inn of Court.
**Career:** Partner at Lerner David Littenberg Krumholz & Mentlik, LLP. Only attorney named Best Lawyers in America 2012 "Lawyer of the Year" for Litigation-Intellectual Property in New Jersey. Author and lecturer on aspects of litigation and damage recoveries.

**Publications:** Intellectual Property Chapter in New Jersey Federal Civil Procedure.
**Personal:** JD, University of Virginia Law School; BA, Economics, College of William and Mary.

## KESSLEN, Mark
Lowenstein Sandler LLP, Roseland
646 414 6793
mkesslen@lowenstein.com
*Featured in Intellectual Property (New Jersey)*
**Practice Areas:** Mark P Kesslen, Chair of the Intellectual Property Group, counsels technology-based businesses on IP strategy on issues ranging from litigation assessment to patent scope, open source, trademarks, privacy and ownership risks to venture-backed companies in digital and social media, software, big data, medical devices, cleantech and fin-tech; research and development entities, universities and major financial service companies. Prior to joining Lowenstein, Mark ran JPMorgan Chase's Technology, Sourcing & Intellectual Property Practice Group for the Legal Department worldwide.
www.lowenstein.com/mkesslen

## KEYSER, Denise M
Ballard Spahr LLP, Cherry Hill
856 761 3442
keyserd@ballardspahr.com
*Featured in Labor & Employment (New Jersey)*
**Practice Areas:** For more than 25 years, Denise M Keyser has represented national and locally based businesses in all types of labor and employment matters, including collective bargaining, arbitrations, OSHA, ERISA, wage and hour, employment-at-will, wrongful discharge, discrimination, management training, and affirmative action.
**Professional Memberships:** American Bar Association New Jersey State Bar Association.
**Career:** New Jersey Pennsylvania.
**Publications:** Contributing author, "New Jersey Workplace Law," the ICLE/New Jersey State Bar Association compendium of New Jersey employment law.
**Personal:** University of Pennsylvania Law School (JD 1983) State University of New York at Stony Brook (BA 1980, with high honors).

## KIERKUT, Galit
Sills Cummis & Gross P.C., Newark
973 643 5896
gkierkut@sillscummis.com
*Featured in Labor & Employment (New Jersey)*
**Practice Areas:** Galit Kierkut concentrates her practice on employment and restrictive covenant litigation and counseling. She conducts human resources audits and performs management and employee training in all areas. She also drafts employee handbooks, social media and arbitration policies and employment contracts.
**Professional Memberships:** President Elect, New Jersey Women Lawyers Association; Executive Committee Member, Labor and Employment Section, New Jersey State Bar Association; National Association of Women Lawyers.
**Career:** 2011 Professional Lawyer of the Year Award.

**Personal:** University of Pennsylvania Law School, JD, cum laude, 1995; University of Pennsylvania, BA, 1991.

## KIMMELMAN, Simon
Sills Cummis & Gross P.C., Princeton
609 227 4680
skimmelman@sillscummis.com
*Featured in Bankruptcy/Restructuring (New Jersey)*
**Practice Areas:** Simon Kimmelman is Co-Managing Partner of the firm's Princeton Office and Princeton Chair of the firm's Creditors' Rights/Bankruptcy Reorganization Practice Group. His practice is focused on bankruptcy, creditors' rights, secured transactions and general corporate matters. He primarily represents secured creditors, lessors, trustees and other parties in interest in a wide variety of bankruptcy and restructuring matters with particular emphasis on work-outs and Chapter 11 proceedings.
**Professional Memberships:** Fellow, American College of Bankruptcy; American Bar Association; New Jersey State Bar Association; Mercer County Bar Association.
**Personal:** Vanderbilt University Law School, JD, 1978; University of Pennsylvania, BA, 1975.

## KIPNEES, Robert J
Lowenstein Sandler LLP, Roseland
973 597 6220
rkipnees@lowenstein.com
*Featured in Litigation (New Jersey)*
**Practice Areas:** Robert J Kipnees' practice focuses on complex white collar cases, including securities fraud, tax fraud, antitrust and environmental crimes and political corruption cases. He has significant trial experience in both prosecution and defense work and handles complex civil securities fraud cases, criminal and civil RICO cases, class actions, complex civil fraud and antitrust cases, and civil tax matters. www.lowenstein.com/rkipnees

## KISTLER, David
Blank Rome LLP, Princeton
609 750 2643
Kistler@BlankRome.com
*Featured in Litigation (New Jersey)*
**Practice Areas:** David Kistler, a partner in Blank Rome's Commercial Litigation practice group, focuses his practice on class action defense, business torts, contract disputes and appellate litigation. David also provides counsel in litigation involving intellectual property and corporate governance disputes. For more information, see: www.BlankRome.com/Kistler

## KLAUSNER, Robert A
Fox Rothschild LLP, Roseland
973 994 7575
rklausner@foxrothschild.com
*Featured in Real Estate (New Jersey)*
**Practice Areas:** 20+ years of legal/business experience in real estate industry; handles leasing, acquisitions, dispositions, joint venture structuring, financing, build-to-suit development.
**Professional Memberships:** American, New Jersey, New York State bar associations
**Career:** Represented clients in leasing 15 million+ square feet of office, industrial, retail space;

purchase/sale of $4 billion+ of office, industrial, retail properties; borrowing /lending of $2 billion+ of office, industrial and retail properties. Clients include winners of four out of last 10 NAIOP Deal of the Year.
**Personal:** LLM, Tax, New York University School of Law; JD, George Washington University Law School; BA, Emory University, 1982.

### KLEIN, Steven R
Cole, Schotz, Meisel, Forman & Leonard PA, Hackensack
201 489 3000
sklein@coleschotz.com
*Featured in Litigation (New Jersey)*
**Practice Areas:** Co-Chair of the Litigation Department. Extensive civil litigation practice that emphasizes complex commercial and corporate litigation in the state and federal trial and appellate courts. Focuses in the areas of chancery and real estate litigation for private and public companies and in significant arbitration matters. Has been appointed by the courts in major shareholder and partnership disputes and corporate and partnership dissolutions to serve as special fiscal agent, special officer, provisional director, and custodial and/or liquidating receiver.
**Personal:** Duke University School of Law, JD, 1981.

### KOBLER, Scott A
McCarter & English, LLP, Newark
973 639 2019
skobler@mccarter.com
*Featured in Healthcare (New Jersey)*
**Career:** Over 30 years, Mr Kobler has established a substantial, comprehensive practice as both capital and general business counsel to scores of nonprofit and for-profit healthcare, educational, and civic and social service organizations as well as counsel to commercial and investment banks. He brings into his practice the perspective of being a board leader on several of New Jersey's most prominent nonprofit boards. For full bio: http://www.mccarter.com/Scott-A-Kobler/

### KOMOROSKI-WIWI, Amy
Lowenstein Sandler LLP, Roseland
awiwi@owenstein.com
973 597 2336
*Featured in Labor & Employment (New Jersey)*
**Practice Areas:** Amy Komoroski Wiwi focuses her practice on employment counseling, drafting and litigation. She represents management in a wide range of litigation under federal and state laws, primarily involving claims of discrimination, wrongful termination and sexual harassment. She also handles contract disputes concerning noncompetition and confidentiality agreements, and drafts and negotiates executive employment and consulting agreements, restrictive covenant agreements, and separation and release agreements. She also counsels employers on hiring, disciplining and terminating employees; family and medical leaves; disability leaves and accommodations; compliance with antidiscrimination and antiretaliation laws; and reductions in workforce.
www.lowenstein.com/awiwi

### KOMROWER, Stuart
Cole, Schotz, Meisel, Forman & Leonard PA, Hackensack
201 525 6331
skomrower@coleschotz.com
*Featured in Bankruptcy/Restructuring (New Jersey)*
**Practice Areas:** Concentrates his practice in bankruptcy, debtor-creditor issues and insolvency-related commercial litigation. Represents debtors, creditors, trustees, creditors' committees and litigants before the state, federal and bankruptcy courts. Concentration in secured asset recoveries, debtor-in possession financing, Section 363 sales and dispositions under Article 9 of the Uniform Commercial Code. Represented the Official Committee of Unsecured Creditors in the successful Chapter 11 case of First Interregional Advisors Corp., one of the largest cases filed in the District of New Jersey.
**Personal:** Seton Hall University School of Law, JD, 1984.

### KOTLER, David
Dechert LLP, Princeton
609 955 3226
david.kotler@dechert.com
*Featured in Litigation (New Jersey)*
**Practice Areas:** Mr Kotler represents clients in a wide range of complex corporate and commercial litigation matters involving the financial markets, with a particular focus on investment advisers, hedge funds, and other financial services firms both within and outside the mutual fund industry.
**Professional Memberships:** Member, New Jersey and New York Bars; admitted to practice before the US Supreme Court and numerous federal courts; member, International Association of Defense Counsel
**Personal:** Cornell University Industrial and Labor Relations School (BA, 1990); New York University School of Law (JD, 1993; staff editor, Annual Survey of American Law).

### KOTT, David R
McCarter & English, LLP, Newark
973 639 2056
dkott@mccarter.com
*Featured in Litigation (New Jersey)*
**Career:** Mr Kott is a trial lawyer with extensive jury trial experience, having tried over fifty civil jury trials to verdict. Mr Kott has acted as lead counsel in multiple class-action lawsuits and has consulted with manufacturers and carriers on the trial of products liability cases. Mr. Kott has been certified by the New Jersey Supreme Court as a Certified Trial Attorney. Mr. Kott is a Fellow of the American College of Trial Lawyers. For full bio: http://www.mccarter.com/David-R-Kott/

### KURZWEIL, Lanny S
McCarter & English, LLP, Newark
973 639 2044
lkurzweil@mccarter.com
*Featured in Environment (New Jersey)*
**Career:** Mr Kurzweil represents oil, chemical, financial services and manufacturing companies and real estate developers in environmental matters, while continuing to counsel a range of

domestic and foreign companies on general commercial and product liability matters. An experienced trial attorney in federal and state courts, Mr Kurzweil handles cost recovery actions in environmental cases involving landfills, groundwater, soil contamination and underground storage tanks and advises clients on natural resource damages issues. Mr. Kurzweil regularly works with clients to navigate complex regulatory matters and assists them with environmental issues arising in transactions. For full bio: http://www.mccarter.com/Lanny-S-Kurzweil/

### LAFIURA, Dennis R
Day Pitney LLP, Parsippany
973 966 8068
dlafiura@daypitney.com
*Featured in Franchising (Nationwide), Litigation (New Jersey)*
**Career:** Dennis LaFiura practices in the following distinct areas of litigation: franchising, with particular emphasis in matters involving motor vehicles, hotels, rental cars, and consumer products and services; officer and director liability; securities litigation; professional liability; consumer litigation; and general equity matters. He regularly represents companies in arbitrations, mediations, and other alternative dispute resolution proceedings. He clerked for The Honorable George H. Barlow, chief judge, United States District Court for the District of New Jersey.

### LARACY, Ward
McCarter & English, LLP, Newark
973 848 5352
wlaracy@mccarter.com
*Featured in Corporate/M&A (New Jersey)*
**Career:** Mr Laracy practices in the areas of corporate and individual federal and state taxation, emphasizing in tax issues arising in corporate mergers and acquisitions, trust and estate administration, probate law, estate planning and antitrust. He advises clients such as foreign and US corporations and partnerships, investment funds and venture capital funds, entrepreneurs, and funds established by foreign investors in the US. His practice in the trusts and estates area includes assisting domestic and foreign clients with estate planning matters, including providing advice on the application of federal income taxes, estate taxes and state inheritance taxes. For full bio: http://www.mccarter.com/Ward-C-Laracy/

### LASALA, Joseph P
McElroy, Deutsch, Mulvaney & Carpenter, LLP, Morristown
973 425 8749
jlasala@mdmc-law.com
*Featured in Litigation (New Jersey)*
**Practice Areas:** Mr LaSala has experience in product liability actions, multi-party toxic tort litigation, asbestos litigation, commercial litigation, environmental coverage matters, securities cases, and patent cases.
**Professional Memberships:** Mr LaSala is admitted to practice in New Jersey and New York. He is a fellow of the American College of Trial Lawyers. He was a master of the Essex Inns of Court, Arthur T Vanderbilt Chapter, from 1988-

92 and has been a master and co-coordinator of the Seton Hall Law Alumni Inn of Court since its inception.
**Personal:** Seton Hall Law School (JD, 1972); St Peter's College (BS, 1969).

### LAWLER, Kathy A
Day Pitney LLP, Parsippany
973 966 8172
klawler@daypitney.com
*Featured in Employee Benefits & Executive Compensation (New Jersey)*
**Career:** Ms Lawler is a member of the Day Pitney's Executive Board. Her practice involves the design, submission, implementation, merger, termination, and interpretation of qualified pension plans, as well as advice regarding fiduciary issues in connection with ERISA plans. She designs non-qualified plans such as excess benefit plans, SERPs, deferred compensation arrangements, and rabbi trusts to fund such plans. Ms Lawler advises clients on benefits issues in corporate transactions and outsourcing arrangements; on the tax and ERISA implications of issues related to welfare benefit plan design, amendment, and termination; and on Medicare Part D issues, PPACA, COBRA, and HIPAA.

### LEHMAN, Robert T
Archer & Greiner, A Professional Corporation, Haddonfield
856 354 3070
rlehman@archerlaw.com
*Featured in Environment (New Jersey)*
**Practice Areas:** Robert T Lehman concentrates his practice on complex environmental litigation, handling cases in jurisdictions throughout the United States and in the Caribbean. Mr Lehman has tried several cases on the leading edge of shaping the law under the New Jersey Spill Compensation and Control Act. Examples include his successful defense of one of the first cases under the Spill Act Contribution Amendment, and successfully trying the first two full arbitration proceedings under the act, involving complex hydrogeologic, chemical and utility cost analysis. He has obtained defense verdicts in multi-plaintiff, ground contamination and intrusion cases.

### LENEY, Douglas
Archer & Greiner, A Professional Corporation, Haddonfield
856 616 2608
dleney@archerlaw.com
*Featured in Bankruptcy/Restructuring (New Jersey)*
**Practice Areas:** Douglas Leney concentrates his practice in bankruptcy, corporate restructuring, and debtor/creditor rights. He has experience representing debtors, trustees, creditors' committees, unsecured creditors, and secured creditors in Chapter 11 reorganization and liquidation cases, Chapter 7 and 13 cases, and related adversary proceedings. Mr Leney's practice also includes representing debtors, creditors, and liquidating trustees in bankruptcy cases arising under Chapter 15 of the Bankruptcy Code. He also represents parties in non-bankruptcy state and federal court matters, ranging from commercial workouts and foreclosures to cases brought in federal District Court

under the Perishable Agricultural Commodities Act (PACA) and similar statutory regimes.

### LEVINE, Sharon L
Lowenstein Sandler LLP, Roseland
973 597 2374
slevine@lowenstein.com
*Featured in Bankruptcy/Restructuring (New Jersey)*
**Practice Areas:** Sharon L Levine is a partner in Lowenstein's Bankruptcy, Financial Reorganization & Creditors' Rights Department. Her bankruptcy practice includes representation of purchasers, debtors, creditors' committees, unsecured creditors, individual creditors, senior, junior and unsecured debt holders, sponsors, equity holders, boards and board members. Sharon spends substantial time in bankruptcy court trying contested and litigated matters, including as special bankruptcy trial counsel on complex pension, benefit or labor issues. She frequently provides bankruptcy advice on "out of court" corporate reorganizations, corporate and structured finance matters, and acquiring assets out of bankruptcy or in circumstances where one party may be insolvent.
www.lowenstein.com/slevine

### LEWIN, Ross A
Drinker Biddle & Reath LLP, Princeton
609 716 6614
Ross.Lewin@dbr.com
*Featured in Environment (New Jersey)*
**Practice Areas:** Partner, Environment and Energy and Commercial Litigation Groups. Focuses on environmental litigation, including cost recovery actions, natural resources damages lawsuits, toxic exposure claims and environmental issues arising out of business transactions.
**Professional Memberships:** Admitted in New Jersey. Member, Board of Directors of Legal Services of New Jersey.
**Career:** Served as deputy chief counsel to Governors Thomas Kean and James Florio. Served as a deputy attorney general and assistant section chief in the environmental protection section, where he was in charge of hazardous and solid waste matters.
**Personal:** JD, Yale Law School, 1982. BA, Trinity College, Phi Beta Kappa,1977.

### LEYVA, Leo V
Cole, Schotz, Meisel, Forman & Leonard PA, Hackensack
201 525 6294
lleyva@coleschotz.com
*Featured in Litigation (New Jersey)*
**Practice Areas:** Co- Chair of the Firm Litigation Department. His practice includes complex commercial litigation, corporate reorganization, and construction and real estate services. Represents clients in real estate litigation, corporate dissolution and shareholder oppression actions, contract claims, construction performance and payment disputes and director and officer liability matters. Represents private equity and real estate opportunity funds in connection with various real estate matters including the acquisition of distressed properties and debt, foreclosures

and bankruptcy related workouts and restructuring.
**Personal:** Rutgers University School of Law-Newark, JD, 1988; Rutgers Law Review, Editor.

### LITTEN, Elizabeth
Fox Rothschild LLP, Lawrenceville
609 895 3320
elitten@foxrothschild.com
*Featured in Healthcare (New Jersey)*
**Practice Areas:** 20+ years in the health care industry, counseling health care facilities, practitioners and health plans on regulatory and legislative issues, and structuring innovative health care payment and delivery models.
**Professional Memberships:** Board of Directors, The Evergreens, a nonprofit Continuing Care Retirement Community; Editor, Garden State FOCUS; Board of Advisors, CareKinesis, Inc.
**Career:** Co-chair, Government Relations Practice. Member, Health Care Reform Working Group. Registered NJ lobbyist working with NJ agencies dealing with health care provider/payer issues. Author of NJ health care legislation.
**Publications:** Fox Rothschild HIPAA, HITECH & HIT Blog (http://hipaahealthlaw.foxrothschild.com/).

### LITTENBERG, Joseph S
Lerner David Littenberg Krumholz & Mentlik, LLP, Westfield
908 518 6303
jlittenberg@ldlkm.com
*Featured in Intellectual Property (New Jersey)*
**Practice Areas:** Specializes in IP licensing, litigation and business development. Helps clients understand and employ patent assets as a revenue source. Advises on and achieves beneficial and early resolution of patent litigation and licensing disputes. Obtaining of commercially significant patents.
**Professional Memberships:** US Patent and Trademark Office; International Association for Protection of Industrial Property; Licensing Executives' Society; Member of the Bars of New York and New Jersey.
**Career:** Listed in "The Best Lawyers of America" (Woodward/White) for over 20 consecutive years; founding Partner-Lerner David Littenberg Krumholz & Mentlik, LLP.
**Personal:** JD, Seton Hall University Law School; BS, Industrial Engineering, Rutgers University.

### LUBERTAZZI JR, Joseph
McCarter & English, LLP, Newark
973 639 2082
JLubertazzi@McCarter.com
*Featured in Bankruptcy/Restructuring (New Jersey)*
**Career:** Mr Lubertazzi's practice focuses on creditor rights and distressed debt. He is skilled in handling commercial litigation and in representing financial institutions, secured creditors, special servicers, lessors and indenture trustees in real and personal property foreclosures, bankruptcy, healthcare insolvencies, telecommunications insolvencies and out-of-court loan workouts. In Bankruptcy Court, he has provided representation to trustees, creditors' committees, secured creditors, unsecured creditors, indenture trustees and

plan proponents in all aspects of negotiation and litigation. Mr Lubertazzi gained his workout/foreclosure experience from representing plaintiff mortgagees and defendant mortgagors in uncontested and contested foreclosures aggregating millions of dollars. For full bio: http://www.mccarter.com/Joseph-Lubertazzi/

### LUBETKIN, Jay
Rabinowitz, Lubetkin & Tully, LLC, Livingston
973 597 9100
jlubetkin@rltlawfirm.com
*Featured in Bankruptcy/Restructuring (New Jersey)*
**Practice Areas:** Jay Lubetkin represents all parties in interest in chapter 11 and chapter 7 bankruptcy cases, including corporate, partnership, and individual debtors; chapter 11 trustees; secured creditors; official committees; competing plan proponents; landlords; liquidators; and equity interest holders.
**Career:** He is a chapter 11 trustee by appointment from the U.S. Trustee's Office and chapter 7 panel trustee for the District of New Jersey, Region 3, Newark Vicinage, where he has administered over 7,500 bankruptcy cases. He also maintains substantial real estate, commercial litigation, and transactional practices.
**Personal:** Mr Lubetkin is a graduate of Emory University School of Law and the University of Pennsylvania.

### LYNOTT, Keith E
McCarter & English, LLP, Newark
973 639 7940
klynott@mccarter.com
*Featured in Environment (New Jersey)*
**Career:** In addition to representing clients in connection with environmental litigation, environmental insurance coverage and regulatory matters, Mr Lynott has represented major corporations and financial institutions in business transactions involving audits, due diligence, preparation and negotiation of acquisition and financing agreements, and compliance with federal and state environmental laws and regulations as they relate to transactions, including the New Jersey Industrial Site Recovery Act (ISRA). Mr Lynott has extensive experience in counseling clients with respect to permitting and regulatory compliance and is an experienced negotiator with federal and state environmental regulators. For full bio: http://www.mccarter.com/Keith-E-Lynott/

### MACK, Kenneth H
Fox Rothschild LLP, Lawrenceville
609 895 6631
kmack@foxrothschild.com
*Featured in Environment (New Jersey)*
**Practice Areas:** Practices in areas of complex environmental, commercial and toxic tort litigation; and environmental aspects of transactions.
**Professional Memberships:** Fellow, American College of Environmental Lawyers, American Bar Association (ABA) - Former Chair, Superfund and Natural Resource Damages Litigation Committee of SEER; NJ Bar Association - Former Chair, Environmental Law Section; ABA - Environment, Energy and Resources Section.

**Career:** Martindale-Hubbell 'AV Preeminent' rated; Included in list of International Who's Who of Business Lawyers, 'The Best Lawyers in America' and NJ 'Super Lawyers' - Environmental Law.
**Personal:** New York University School of Law, 1971; Rutgers University, 1968.

### MALONE, Robert
Drinker Biddle & Reath LLP, Florham Park
973 549 7080
Robert.Malone@dbr.com
*Featured in Bankruptcy/Restructuring (New Jersey)*
**Practice Areas:** Partner, Vice-Chair Corporate Restructuring Practice Group. Focuses on bankruptcy and insolvency law with emphasis upon sophisticated corporate reorganizations and out-of-court restructurings. Bob has headed engagements in such notable bankruptcy cases as St. Mary's Hospital; Meadowcraft, Inc; HomeBanc; Accredited Home Lenders; Advanta Corp.; Resorts International; Mutual Benefit Overseas; Grand Union; Nortel Systems; A&P Supermarkets; and Eastman Kodak.
**Professional Memberships:** Member, NJ Bar, US District Courts, NJ, SDNY and EDNY, Court of Appeals, 3d Circuit. American Bankruptcy Institute.
**Personal:** Catholic University of America, BA; Seton Hall Law School, JD. Clerkship: Hon. William H. Gindin, US Bankruptcy Court, District of NJ.

### MARCHETTA, Anthony J
Day Pitney LLP, Parsippany
973 966 8032
amarchetta@daypitney.com
*Featured in Litigation (New Jersey)*
**Career:** A Certified Civil Trial Attorney of the State of New Jersey, Mr. Marchetta practices exclusively in the area of civil trial law, including complex commercial, securities, product liability and negligence litigation, patent, trademark, insurance, and environmental. Mr Marchetta was a lead trial counsel for W.R. Grace and GAF Corporation in their asbestos litigation and served as national coordinating counsel for a number of major corporations in product liability and negligence litigation. He has handled numerous class actions and securities litigations, and tried cases in state and federal courts around the country, handling all appellate work connected with such trials.

### MARINO, James J
Dechert LLP, Princeton
609 955 3230
james.marino@dechert.com
*Featured in Corporate/M&A (New Jersey)*
**Practice Areas:** Mr Marino represents public and privately held life sciences companies, including biotechnology, medical device, healthcare, and pharmaceuticals, in the full range of corporate, transactional and finance matters.
**Professional Memberships:** Member, New Jersey Bar; admitted to practice before the U.S. District Court for the District of New Jersey.

**Career:** Co-founder of BIONJ, a New Jersey-based trade association of biotechnology companies.

**Personal:** Rutgers University (BA, 1972, magna cum laude; MBA, 1976); Rutgers University School of Law Newark (JD, 1979, member (1977-79), project editor (1978-79), Rutgers Law Review).

## MARKOWITZ, Philip
Sills Cummis & Gross P.C., Newark
973 643 4778
pmarkowitz@sillscummis.com
*Featured in Real Estate (New Jersey)*

**Practice Areas:** Philip Markowitz, a Member of the firm's Real Estate Department, represents purchasers, developers and sellers, with respect to many asset types. Specifically, he has experience with transactions involving grocery-anchored shopping centers, hotels and industrial property, whether a single-asset deal, a portfolio transaction or by joint venture. In addition, he has a national retail-leasing practice, with ground leases, and associated development agreements, being a large subset of such practice. He also works on New York-based office leasing, and branch-bank leases throughout the United States.

**Personal:** BA, Rutgers College, 1993; JD, Harvard Law School, 1997.

## MARONE, Michael
McElroy, Deutsch, Mulvaney & Carpenter, LLP, Morristown
973 425 8722
mmarone@mdmc-law.com
*Featured in Litigation (New Jersey)*

**Practice Areas:** Mr Marone's areas of practice include a variety of complex litigation areas including insurance defense and coverage, products liability, employment practices, professional liability, commercial, construction, multi-party toxic tort, and environmental litigation.

**Professional Memberships:** Mr Marone is admitted to practice in New Jersey and New York. He is a fellow of the American College of Trial Lawyers, a member of the American Board of Trial Advocates, and is a Certified Civil Trial Attorney. Mr Marone is the Immediate Past President of the Trial Attorneys of New Jersey.

**Personal:** Seton Hall Law School (JD); University of Delaware (BA).

## MCBRIDE III, Andrew F
McElroy, Deutsch, Mulvaney & Carpenter, LLP, Morristown
973 348 5304
amcbride@mdmc-law.com
*Featured in Healthcare (New Jersey)*

**Practice Areas:** Mr McBride concentrates his practice in corporate healthcare law, antitrust, managed care, healthcare litigation and alternate dispute resolution. Mr McBride also has extensive experience in general health care law matters, including clinically integrated healthcare provider organizations, mergers and acquisitions, professional staff and health care antitrust matters.

**Professional Memberships:** Mr McBride is admitted to the bars of the States of New York and New Jersey. Mr McBride is also a member of the

American Bar Association, and the American Health Lawyers Association.

**Personal:** Columbia University School of Law (JD); Columbia University (MS); Providence College (AB cum laude).

## MCCARTHY ESQ, Patrick J
Day Pitney LLP, Parsippany
973 966 8117
pmccarthy@daypitney.com
*Featured in Labor & Employment (New Jersey)*

**Career:** Mr McCarthy assists employers in complying with federal and state labor regulations governing union and nonunion-represented work forces and with their relations with labor unions, including negotiating and administering collective bargaining agreements. He has represented management in some 450 grievance and interest arbitrations. He appears before state and federal departments of labor on all workplace matters, and has successfully obtained injunctions and has litigated unfair labor practice cases before the National Labor Relations Board. Mr McCarthy provides strategic advice to employers on workforce planning and dispositions in connection with all types of business change.

## MEISEL, Michael S
Cole, Schotz, Meisel, Forman & Leonard PA, Hackensack
201 525 6222
mmeisel@coleschotz.com
*Featured in Litigation (New Jersey)*

**Practice Areas:** Co-Chairman of the firm's Litigation Department. Practice includes shareholder disputes, directors & officers liability and corporate/insurance reorganization. Tries many arbitration cases, mediated disputes, serves as special master, mediator and arbitrator. Recent matters include; Mutual Benefit Life Ins. Co.; Mandlebaum, Salsburg v. General Ins. Company of America; Printing Mart v. Sharp Electronics; Kazmer-Standish Consultants, Inc. v. Schoeffel Instruments Corp.; Dunkin Donuts Incorporated v. Double D., LLC; Land N Sea v. United Retail Group.

**Personal:** George Washington University Law School, JD.

## MEKLINSKY, Ian D
Fox Rothschild LLP, Philadelphia
609 895 6756
imeklinsky@foxrothschild.com
*Featured in Labor & Employment (New Jersey)*

**Practice Areas:** Represents employers in union/non-union contexts.

**Professional Memberships:** Executive Committee, Labor & Employment Section, New Jersey State Bar Association; Camden County, Mercer County, Pennsylvania and Philadelphia Bar Associations; Academy of New Jersey Management Attorneys; Board of Member: Luther Rice Society, George Washington University; The Joshua Kahan Fund; Jewish Senior Housing & Healthcare Services of Southern New Jersey.

**Career:** Bencher/Former Executive Director Southern New Jersey, Sidney Reitman Employment Law American Inn of Court; Past

Chair, Employment Law Group, Lexwork North America.

**Personal:** JD, George Washington University School of Law; BA, magna cum laude, George Washington University School of Business.

## MENTLIK, William L
Lerner David Littenberg Krumholz & Mentlik, LLP, Westfield
908 518 6305
wmentlik@ldlkm.com
*Featured in Intellectual Property (New Jersey)*

**Practice Areas:** Complex patent litigation (trial and appellate) in all fields of technology (including pharmaceuticals and medical devices); argued and/or briefed over 30 appeals in the Federal Circuit involving all facets of intellectual property law.

**Professional Memberships:** Lawyers Advisory Committee of the US District Court, District of New Jersey; New York and New Jersey Bars; New Jersey Intellectual Property Law Association; John C. Lifland, American Inn of Court.

**Career:** Managing Partner of Lerner David Littenberg Krumholz & Mentlik, LLP; listed in "The Best Lawyers of America" (Woodward/White) for 20 consecutive years; named by "Best Lawyers in America 2012" "Lawyer of the Year" for Patent Litigation-Intellectual Property in New Jersey; listed in "IAM Patent 1000" (Intellectual Asset Management), as one of "The World's Leading Patent Practitioners" for 2012; listed in 2012 "Guide to World's Leading Patent Law Practitioners," (Legal Media Group); Patent Examiner, USPTO 1969-1973; trial attorney, U.S. Dept. of Justice, Antitrust Division 1973-1975.

**Personal:** JD (Order of the Coif), George Washington University National Law Center, BS Chemical Engineering, University of Pennsylvania.

## METH, Richard
Fox Rothschild LLP, Roseland
973 994 7515
rmeth@foxrothschild.com
*Featured in Bankruptcy/Restructuring (New Jersey)*

**Practice Areas:** Creditors' rights, workouts, reorganizations, insolvency-related issues. Clients: major corporations, lenders, Chapter 11 committees. Court – appointed mediator.

**Professional Memberships:** American Bankruptcy Institute: member, Board of Directors; member, National Ethics Task Force; former VP, Publications; Ethics Committee Co-Chair (2001-08); ABA Business Bankruptcy Committee: Co-Chair, Abuses of Bankruptcy Process Subcommittee and Liaison to ABI. ADL: National Associate Commissioner (2000-present); former Chair, NJ Region (1996-99). Bankruptcy Court (D.N.J.), Local Bankruptcy Rules Revision Committee.

**Career:** Martindale-Hubbell 'AV' rated; 'Super Lawyers' New Jersey, 2005-2009/2011-2012; Best Lawyers in America (2010-13).

**Personal:** JD, Georgetown University Law Center, 1975; BA, magna cum laude, Tufts University, 1972.

## MILLS, Lori
Drinker Biddle & Reath LLP, Princeton
609 716 6632
Lori.Mills@dbr.com
*Featured in Environment (New Jersey)*

**Practice Areas:** Partner, Environment and Energy Practice Group. Practice is marked by versatility – integrating a strong litigation practice with the roles of compliance counselor and transactional lawyer to help clients manage environmental risk. Experienced in site remediation; NRD; purchase/sale of contaminated properties; settlement and allocation strategies; and cost recovery litigation.

**Professional Memberships:** Member, American, New Jersey and Pennsylvania Bar Associations.

**Career:** Following law school, served as law clerk to the Hon. Paul A. Lowengrub, Superior Court of New Jersey, Chancery Division.

**Personal:** JD with honors, Rutgers University School of Law, 1988; BA, magna cum laude, Temple University, 1985.

## MINION, Robert G
Lowenstein Sandler LLP, Roseland
646 414 6930
rminion@lowenstein.com
*Featured in Corporate/M&A (New Jersey)*

**Practice Areas:** Robert G Minion is Chairman of Lowenstein Sandler's Investment Management Group. An authority in securities law, investment partnerships, mergers and acquisitions and related corporate transactions, he represents clients throughout the United States and internationally in a wide variety of investment fund, capital formation and corporate finance transactions, and high profile SEC regulatory and compliance matters. He has completed hundreds of fund organizations, mergers and acquisitions, and corporate finance transactions, many of which have multi-billion dollar transaction values. Robert is nationally recognized as a leading practitioner in the investment management community. www.lowenstein.com/rminion

## MINTZ, Robert A
McCarter & English, LLP, Newark
973 639 7916
rmintz@mccarter.com
*Featured in Litigation (New Jersey)*

**Career:** Mr Mintz is a nationally recognized authority on white-collar criminal defense and corporate fraud issues. He served four years as Assistant Counsel to Governor Thomas H. Kean and almost nine years as an Assistant US Attorney and Deputy Chief of the Organized Crime Strike Force Division for the District of New Jersey. Mr Mintz has successfully represented individuals and Fortune 100 corporations in a number of high-profile matters. He practices in the areas of complex commercial litigation, governmental and regulatory investigations, securities litigation, civil RICO, Foreign Corrupt Practices Act, healthcare, and public strategy. For full bio: http://www.mccarter.com/Robert-A-Mintz/

**MONAGHAN, Sean**
Drinker Biddle & Reath LLP, Florham Park
973 549 7230
sean.monaghan@dbr.com
*Featured in Environment (New Jersey)*
**Practice Areas:** Partner, Environment and
Energy Practice Group. Concentrates in environ-
mental law, including transactions, site remediation,
regulatory compliance and litigation.
**Professional Memberships:** Admitted in New
Jersey. Member: American Bar Association; New
Jersey State Bar Association, Environmental and
Business Law Sections; Chair, ISRA and
Environmental Issues Committee of Business Law
Section; National Brownfields Association;
Regional Plan Association; and Master, Justice
Pollock Environmental American Inn of Court.
**Career:** Joined Drinker Biddle in 1989.
**Publications:** Author, New Jersey Chapter of the
Treatise "Brownfields," published by the American
Bar Association.
**Personal:** JD, Seton Hall University School of
Law, 1983; BA, University of Pennsylvania, 1979.

**MONTAG, Brian S**
K&L Gates, Newark
973 848 4044
brian.montag@klgates.com
*Featured in Environment (New Jersey)*
**Practice Areas:** Focusing his practice on
Federal and State environmental permitting, compliance and litigation matters, including enforcement and administrative proceedings, Mr Montag
has extensive experience representing clients in
matters before numerous state environmental
agencies, as well as the United States
Environmental Protection Agency. He has served
in leadership roles and as lead counsel in landmark regulatory and litigation matters, including
settlements involving Superfund, environmental
justice, air, water, and solid and hazardous waste
matters. His practice spans all environmental
media, as well as products liability and toxic tort
litigation.

**MOORE, Deirdre E**
Fox Rothschild LLP, Roseland
973 994 7574
dmoore@foxrothschild.com
*Featured in Real Estate (New Jersey)*
**Practice Areas:** Works with commercial/resi-
dential developers/investors on acquisition, sale,
leasing, management, financing of commercial,
retail, mixed-use development, redevelopment,
industrial, golf course projects.
**Professional Memberships:** New Jersey State
Bar Association (New Jersey Real Property and
Probate Section, Board of Consulters); NJ
Chapter, ICREW; CREW National Network,
Morris Habitat for Humanity Development
Leadership Council
**Career:** New Jersey Super Lawyers in real estate
(2006-12); "Top 50 female New Jersey Super
Lawyers," (2009 and 2012); The Best Lawyers in
America in Real Estate Law (2007-13).
**Personal:** JD, Rutgers University School of Law –
Newark; BS, magna cum laude, Montclair State
University.

**MOORE, Kevin J**
Sills Cummis & Gross P.C., Princeton
609 227 4620
kmoore@sillscummis.com
*Featured in Real Estate (New Jersey)*
**Practice Areas:** Kevin Moore, Member of the
firm's Real Estate Department, focuses on solar
energy, redevelopment, land use, land use litiga-
tion and commercial real estate law.
**Professional Memberships:** Legislative
Committee, New Jersey Chapter of the National
Association of Industrial and Office Properties;
New Jersey State Bar Association.
**Career:** Fellow, American College of Real Estate
Lawyers; 2010 Industry Service Award and 2007
President's Award, New Jersey Chapter of the
National Association of Industrial and Office
Properties.
**Personal:** New York University, School of Law,
JD, 1981; Drew University, BA, summa cum laude,
1978.

**MULVANEY, James M**
McElroy, Deutsch, Mulvaney & Carpenter,
LLP, Morristown
973 425 8712
jmulvaney@mdmc-law.com
*Featured in Litigation (New Jersey)*
**Practice Areas:** Mr Mulvaney has diverse litigation experience in a variety of areas of the law. He
is uniquely qualified in the areas of construction
litigation and surety and fidelity bonding. He has
also provided numerous insurance company
clients with coverage counseling in a wide range
of areas, including claim analysis and litigation.
**Professional Memberships:** Mr Mulvaney is
admitted to practice in New Jersey, New York and
Pennsylvania. He has served as Chairman of the
Fidelity and Surety Committee of the New Jersey
State Bar Association.
**Personal:** Seton Hall Law School (JD); Seton
Hall University (BA).

**NEWMAN, Jeffrey Hugh**
Sills Cummis & Gross P.C., Newark
973 643 5788
jnewman@sillscummis.com
*Featured in Real Estate (New Jersey)*
**Practice Areas:** Jeffrey Hugh Newman, Real
Estate Department Chair, has practiced real estate
law for 25+ years focusing on the shopping center
industry, with an emphasis on retail tenants,
shopping center landlords and developers. He has
developed a national reputation representing
institutional clients throughout the US due to his
numerous writings and speaking engagements
nationwide. He is an experienced litigation strategist.
**Career:** Member, firm's management and executive committees.
**Publications:** Mastering the Art and Skill of
Negotiation: A Guide to Negotiation, and The
Leadership Matrix, Aspen Publishers, 2012.
**Personal:** New York University (LLM, 1977; JD,
1969; BA, Phi Beta Kappa, 1966).

**NITTOLY, Paul G**
Drinker Biddle & Reath LLP, Florham Park
973 549 7180
paul.nittoly@dbr.com
*Featured in Litigation (New Jersey)*
**Practice Areas:** Partner, commercial litigation
and white-collar defense and corporate investiga-
tions Groups. New Jersey Supreme Court certified
civil and criminal trial attorney.
**Professional Memberships:** Fellow, American
College of Trial Lawyers; American Board of Trial
Advocates; former chair Subcommittee,
Environmental Crimes, ABA Section of Litigation;
Past President, Trial Attorneys of NJ; Board,
Association of Federal Bar of NJ.
**Career:** Former assistant prosecutor, Essex
County, NJ.
**Publications:** Two chapters, Readings in White-
Collar Crime, Meckler (1991); 'Environmental
Criminal Cases: The Dawn of a New Era', Seton
Hall Law Review, Vol. 21:4.
**Personal:** JD, New York Law School, 1973; AB,
Rutgers College, 1970.

**NUKK-FREEMAN, Katherin**
Nukk-Freeman & Cerra, Short Hills
973 564 9100
knukk@nfclegal.com
*Featured in Labor & Employment (New Jersey)*

**O'CONNOR, Aidan**
Pashman Stein, Hackensack
201 270 4940
aoconnor@pashmanstein.com
*Featured in Litigation (New Jersey)*
**Practice Areas:** Aidan O'Connor has tried
approximately 20 federal jury trials and has extensive experience in negotiating successful resolutions to difficult cases in both civil and criminal
contexts. He was a former Assistant United States
Attorney in the District of New Jersey for 18 years,
serving in the Criminal Division, the Organized
Crime Strike Force and as the Chief of the Violent
Crimes Unit. Mr O'Connor has represented
clients in federal and state criminal cases and
appeals involving allegations of mortgage, bank,
securities, tax, insurance and health care fraud,
racketeering, bid-rigging, labor and political corruption as well as narcotics, violent crime and sexual abuse.

**OLINSKY, Mark S**
Sills Cummis & Gross P.C., Newark
973 643 5402
molinsky@sillscummis.com
*Featured in Litigation (New Jersey)*
**Practice Areas:** Mark S Olinsky, a Member of
Sills Cummis & Gross and Co-Chair of its
Healthcare Government Investigations Practice
Group, is a first-chair trial lawyer with 30 years of
complex litigation experience in industries such as
healthcare and real estate. His practice encom-
passes sophisticated business disputes and busi-
ness crimes defense (including pharma/healthcare
executives and companies).
**Career:** Served as a federal prosecutor under
Samuel Alito, US Attorney for New Jersey; Listed
in The Best Lawyers in America and New Jersey
Super Lawyers.

**Personal:** Harvard Law School, JD, cum laude,
1981; Yale University, BA, summa cum laude, Phi
Beta Kappa, 1978.

**O'REILLY, John J**
Day Pitney LLP, Parsippany
973 966 8043
joreilly@daypitney.com
*Featured in Litigation (New Jersey)*
**Career:** Mr O'Reilly is a certified criminal trial
attorney in New Jersey practicing in the areas of
commercial litigation and white collar criminal
defense. In addition to representing corporate
clients in a wide range of litigation, he represents
corporations and individuals who may be targets,
victims or witnesses in criminal matters involving
the securities, the environment, wire and mail
fraud, OSHA, RICO, embezzlement, identity theft,
and questioned documents in both federal and
state jurisdictions. Mr O'Reilly served as
Prosecutor of Warren County from 1992-98.

**ORLOFSKY, Stephen**
Blank Rome LLP, Princeton
609 750 2646
Orlofsky@BlankRome.com
*Featured in Litigation (New Jersey)*
**Practice Areas:** Stephen Orlofsky leads Blank
Rome's Appellate practice and serves as
Administrative Partner of the Princeton, New
Jersey office. Mr Orlofsky is a former United
States District Judge for the District of New Jersey
and United States Magistrate Judge for the District
of New Jersey. Mr Orlofsky concentrates his prac-
tice in complex litigation and alternative dispute
resolution. He counsels clients throughout the
U.S. in federal and state civil and criminal courts,
both at the appellate and trial level. He has experience litigating, arbitrating, mediating, and serving
as a special master in a wide variety of matters.
More information:
www.BlankRome.com/Orlofsky

**O'SHAUGHNESSY, William J**
McCarter & English, LLP, Newark
973 639 2094
woshaughnessy@mccarter.com
*Featured in Litigation (New Jersey)*
**Career:** Mr O'Shaughnessy is a trial lawyer, concentrating on complex litigation of all kinds,
including antitrust, intellectual property, class-
action defense, unfair competition and contract
disputes. He regularly appears at the trial and
appellate levels of the federal and state courts,
both in and out of New Jersey, and has been chief
counsel in domestic and international arbitrations. He currently handles, or has handled, a
wide variety of antitrust cases in New Jersey and
elsewhere that involve price-fixing, group boycott,
monopolization, resale price maintenance and
price discrimination claims. For full bio:
http://www.mccarter.com/William-J-
OShaughnessy/

**OSIAS, Brian J**
McCarter & English, LLP, Newark
973 639 6956
bosias@mccarter.com
*Featured in Litigation (New Jersey)*

**Career:** Mr Osias represents policyholders in complex, high-stakes insurance coverage litigation in federal and state courts. Matters involve a broad variety of coverage claims, including construction, D&O, asbestos, silica, environmental, first-party property, employment and professional liability. He also analyzes insurance policies and programs and advises policyholder clients regarding the scope of their existing coverage. For full bio: http://www.mccarter.com/Brian-J-Osias/

### OTERO, Camille
Gibbons P.C., Newark
973 596 4509
COtero@gibbonslaw.com
*Featured in Environment (New Jersey)*

**Practice Areas:** Environmental litigation and environmental counseling.

**Career:** Ms Otero, a Director in the firm's Real Property & Environmental Department, has extensive litigation experience involving CERCLA, RCRA, underground storage tanks, toxic torts, and the New Jersey Spill and Landfill Closure Acts. She counsels clients on matters regarding remediation activities and compliance, environmental due diligence, ISRA applicability and compliance, enforcement issues specific to the USEPA, NJDEP, NYSDEC, and other state environmental agencies, petroleum franchise law, and corporate and real estate transactions. Ms Otero earned her JD from Rutgers University School of Law and her BS from Bloomfield College.

### PACKMAN, Stephen M
Archer & Greiner, A Professional Corporation, Haddonfield
856 354 3078
spackman@archerlaw.com
*Featured in Bankruptcy/Restructuring (New Jersey)*

**Practice Areas:** Stephen M Packman chairs the firm's Bankruptcy Practice Group and serves as co-Chair of the International Law Group. His experience includes representing hundreds of companies, committees, trustees, lenders, creditors and other parties, in reorganizations and liquidations (both in and outside of bankruptcy), and in connection with other debtor and creditor matters (foreclosures, litigation and workouts), regionally, throughout the US, and internationally. Steve has considerable experience in cross-border matters including Chapter 15 bankruptcy proceedings. Steve is certified in business bankruptcy law by the American Board of Certification and is a Fellow of INSOL, the international association of restructuring professionals.

### PANTEL, Glenn S
Drinker Biddle & Reath LLP, Florham Park
973 549 7020
Glenn.Pantel@dbr.com
*Featured in Real Estate (New Jersey)*

**Practice Areas:** Partner, Real Estate Practice. Experienced in land development, commercial real estate transactions, and regulatory matters, including wetlands issues, ISRA compliance, waterfront development, and local zoning and planning approvals. Represents major developers and corporate users in large-scale development plans and acquisitions.

**Professional Memberships:** Admitted in New Jersey (1978), Pennsylvania (1978), Florida (1980), the US District Court for the District of New Jersey and US Court of Appeals for the Third Circuit. Member, New Jersey, Pennsylvania and Florida Bar Associations.

**Career:** Joined Drinker Biddle in 1979.

**Personal:** JD, University of Pennsylvania Law School, 1978; BA, Johns Hopkins University, 1975.

### PAPIER, David J
Dentons, Short Hills
973 912 7172
david.papier@dentons.com
*Featured in Corporate/M&A (New Jersey)*

**Practice Areas:** Chair of the New Jersey State Bar Association Venture Capital and Emerging Growth Technology Company Committee, Mr. Papier counsels public and private companies, venture capital funds and investment banking firms in a broad array of transactions, including public and private debt and equity offerings, mergers and acquisitions and going private transactions. Has extensive experience in financing transactions for borrowers and lenders and advises senior executives of tech and life sciences companies in securities offerings, strategic alliances, board governance and executive compensation.

**Personal:** Fordham University School of Law, JD; Yeshiva University, BA (magna cum laude).

### PARADISO, Robert
Lowenstein Sandler LLP, Roseland
973 597 2404
rparadiso@lowenstein.com
*Featured in Intellectual Property (New Jersey)*

**Practice Areas:** Robert is the Chair of the Life Sciences Patent Group at Lowenstein Sandler and has significant experience in virtually all aspects of intellectual property, including patent prosecution, noninfringement, patentability, litigation, freedom to operate and technology transfer. He regularly advises clients on product acquisition and divestiture, joint ventures and alliances, technology licensing, outsourcing, and other technology-related transactions. Over the course of his career, he has counseled clients on the discovery, design and protection of many successful therapeutic and diagnostic products with important commercial and humanitarian benefits. Robert is an Adjunct Professor at Rutgers University and Seton Hall Law Schools.
www.lowenstein.com/rparadiso

### PARLIMAN, Gregory C
Day Pitney LLP, Parsippany
973 966 8015
gparliman@daypitney.com
*Featured in Labor & Employment (New Jersey)*

**Career:** Mr Parliman's substantial employment litigation and trial experience includes defense of wrongful discharge suits, whistleblower actions, EEO discrimination litigation, ERISA litigation, and arbitration involving claims for benefits under severance plans and change in control agreements, actions involving employee pirating and covenants not to compete, as well as labor litigation involving actions to enjoin strikes, strike violence, and illegal picketing. Mr Parliman's prac-

tice involves employment counseling, including employee discipline and discharge, negotiation and preparation of employment agreements and separation agreements, and counseling and training on matters relating to the Americans with Disabilities Act, family and medical leave, and sexual harassment.

### PASTOR, Sherilyn
McCarter & English, LLP, Newark
973 639 2070
spastor@mccarter.com
*Featured in Litigation (New Jersey)*

**Career:** Ms Pastor is Practice Leader of the Insurance Coverage Group. She has secured millions of dollars in insurance for corporate policyholders. Ms Pastor litigates coverage matters throughout the country. She provides policyholders with advice that includes assessing their potential risks and insurance programs and analyzing insurance products. Ms Pastor is Policyholder Chair of the ABA section of Litigation's Insurance Coverage Litigation Committee. She is a member of the New Jersey Supreme Court's Professional Responsibility Rules Committee and serves on the Firm's Executive Committee. She regularly speaks and writes on trial, insurance and ethics matters. For full bio: http://www.mccarter.com/Sherilyn-Pastor/

### PATEL, Anjana D
Sills Cummis & Gross P.C., Newark
973 643 5097
apatel@sillscummis.com
*Featured in Healthcare (New Jersey)*

**Practice Areas:** Anjana Patel's healthcare practice includes representing a diverse group of healthcare providers, including hospitals, long-term care providers, ambulatory surgery centers, private equity funds, physicians and other healthcare businesses. She handles a variety of complex business transactions, including establishing accountable care organizations and other strategic affiliations as part of health care reform, mergers and acquisitions and joint ventures. She also provides guidance and compliance strategies with respect to fraud and abuse, self-referral and tax-exemption law issues.

**Professional Memberships:** American Bar Association; New Jersey State Bar Association, Health and Hospital Law Section; American Health Lawyers Association; The Governance Institute (Faculty).

### PATELLA, Raymond
Fox Rothschild LLP, Atlantic City
609 572 2254
rpatella@foxrothschild.com
*Featured in Bankruptcy/Restructuring (New Jersey)*

**Practice Areas:** National practice in bankruptcy, corporate restructurings, business finance and related litigation matters. Represents individual creditors, asset purchasers, creditors' committees, debtors, banks, funds, utilities, trustees, etc.

**Professional Memberships:** Member, Philadelphia Chapter, Turnaround Management Association, former board member (2006-12). Former Co-Chair, Education Committee for

Eastern District of Pennsylvania Bankruptcy Conference.

**Career:** Frequent lecturer/author on bankruptcy issues; speaker at annual convention for National Association of Credit Managers.

**Publications:** Author: 'Representing Small Businesses in Bankruptcy,' Aspatore Books.

**Personal:** JD, summa cum laude, New York Law School, 1996; BS, Rutgers, the State University of New Jersey at New Brunswick, 1993.

### PEIRANO, John J
McElroy, Deutsch, Mulvaney & Carpenter, LLP, Morristown
973 425 8711
jpeirano@mdmc-law.com
*Featured in Labor & Employment (New Jersey)*

**Practice Areas:** Mr Peirano represents management in employment and labor matters including traditional labor practice. He is an experienced negotiator, both as principal spokesperson and as Counsel to principal negotiators.

**Professional Memberships:** Mr Peirano is a member of the New Jersey State and American Bar Associations, including their Labor and Employment Law Sections, a fellow of the College of Labor and Employment Lawyers, member of the National Association of College and University Attorneys, and a master of the bench for the Sidney Reitman American Inn of Court.

**Personal:** Seton Hall Law School (JD, 1977); Mount St Mary's College (BS, 1967).

### PERGOLA, Anthony O
Lowenstein Sandler LLP, New York
212 204 8689
apergola@lowenstein.com
*Featured in Corporate/M&A (New Jersey)*

**Practice Areas:** Anthony O Pergola is Vice Chair and Co-Founder of Lowenstein Sandler's Tech Group. He represents clients that create, finance and bring to market new technologies in the digital media, adtech, cloud computing, IT/software, communications, fintech, pharma, and life sciences/biotech industries, among others. An active angel investor, Anthony is a founding board member of AngelVineVC, a network of angel investors and venture funds, and co-founder of GrapeArborVC, an angel investing group. www.lowenstein.com/apergola

### PLOSCOWE, Stephen A
Fox Rothschild LLP, Roseland
973 994 7500
sploscowe@foxrothschild.com
*Featured in Labor & Employment (New Jersey)*

**Practice Areas:** Represents management before National Labor Relations Board, state/federal discrimination agencies, union negotiations, arbitrations and in formulating strategies regarding plant relocation, consolidations, mergers and acquisitions. Represents numerous manufacturing, service and distribution companies; hospitals; nursing homes; and not-for-profit organizations. Serves as labor counsel to Cornell University, Princeton University, and New Jersey Symphony Orchestra.

**Career:** Martindale-Hubbell 'AV' rated; Judge William B Groat Award (Cornell University, School of Industrial & Labor Relations); Included in 'Best Lawyers in America' - Labor & Employment Law (25 years); 'Super Lawyers' - New Jersey Monthly Magazine/Law & Politics Magazine (2006-11).

**POLITANO, Frank L**
K&L Gates, Newark
973 848 4150
frank.politano@klgates.com
*Featured in Intellectual Property (New Jersey)*
**Practice Areas:** Frank Politano has more than 35 years of global trademark, copyright, and brand licensing experience, counseling clients on a variety of unfair competition, infringement, dilution, affirmative and defensive litigation, entertainment law, and other intellectual property matters. He has advised numerous companies involved in merger and acquisition transactions and represented them in federal and state court litigation relating to their intellectual property rights. Prior to joining K&L Gates, he was in-house trademark and copyright counsel at AT&T where he was responsible for its global trademark and copyright portfolio.

**POLLOCK, Jeffrey M**
Fox Rothschild LLP, Lawrenceville
609 896 7660
jmpollock@foxrothschild.com
*Featured in Environment (New Jersey), Litigation (New Jersey)*
**Practice Areas:** Complex litigation, environmental law, and policyholder representation.
**Professional Memberships:** Elected to American Law Institute; NJ and NY State Bar Associations; Defense Research Institute; Risk Insurance Management Society, NJ and NY; American Bar Association, Litigation and Special Programs Chair.
**Career:** Certified Civil Trial Attorney by NJ Supreme Court. Frequent speaker and prolific author on complex litigation, policyholder representation and environmental issues. Editor, Environmental Liability, Enforcement and Penalties Reporter.
**Personal:** Martindale-Hubbell 'AV' rated; Included in list of 'Best Lawyers in America,' Environmental Law (since 2006) and in 'Super Lawyers,' NJ Monthly Magazine and Law & Politics Magazine (2007-11).

**POSITAN, Wayne J**
Lum, Drasco & Positan, LLC, Roseland
973 228 6730
wpositan@lumlaw.com
*Featured in Labor & Employment (New Jersey)*
**Practice Areas:** 38 yrs experience state/federal labor/employment/litigation (mgmt/defts); non-compete matters; chancery/business; appellate.
**Professional Memberships:** Admitted: NJ/NY; NJ State Delegate-ABA HOD; ABA Bd Govs (2006-9), X-Comm; ABA Ctr Prof Resp: Council; Chair-ABA Comm MJP; Chair-Jt Comm Ethics & Professionalism-ABA CPR/SOC; Pres-NJSBA (2006-7); ABA Sec of Litigation: Mng Dir, Council; Chair-NJSBA Labor & Emp Sec; Fellow: College Labor & Emp Lawyers; IATL,LCA; ECBA Prof Achievement Award; "Best Lawyers"; 'Top 10 NJ Superlawyers'.

**Career:** Lum, Drasco & Positan LLC.
**Publications:** Editor-in-Chief, "NJ Labor and Employment Law" (NJICLE).
**Personal:** Boston U: BA Govt, magna cum laude; NYU: JD; BU CAS Collegium of Distinguished Alumni.

**PUDELL, Steven J**
Anderson Kill & Olick, P.C., Newark
973 642 5877
spudell@andersonkill.com
*Featured in Litigation (New Jersey)*
**Practice Areas:** Steven J Pudell has represented food industry companies, multi-national chemical manufacturers, pharmaceutical companies and real estate developers in insurance recovery matters, including environmental, product liability and business income recoveries. In recent client matters, Mr Pudell represented over 75 Taco Bell Franchisees – encompassing over 1000 locations – in litigation with respect to insurance coverage for the 2006 E Coli break out. Mr Pudell also helped secure a favorable confidential insurance settlement for a manufacturer in a coverage battle over losses arising from $6 million in tainted baby formula. He has been called upon to counsel large corporations with respect to securing insurance recovery that would enable settlement of large securities or consumer class action lawsuits. He has also been retained to represent companies regarding losses sustained in Superstorm Sandy. He currently serves as the co-chair of the ADR/Settlement Subcommittee of the American Bar Association, Litigation Committee and is on the NJ Supreme Court Committee for Civil Jury charges.
**Publications:** Mr. Pudell frequently lectures and writes on insurance recovery matters, including those affecting the food industry.

**QUINN, Thomas**
Wilson, Elser, Moskowitz, Edelman & Dicker LLP, Florham Park
973 735 6036
thomas.quinn@wilsonelser.com
*Featured in Litigation (New Jersey)*
**Practice Areas:** Thomas Quinn has a 30-year commercial civil litigation practice focused on insurance coverage and professional liability defense. He represents insurance companies and reinsurers in coverage disputes and rendering coverage opinions. He also represents lawyers, accountants, insurance brokers and other professionals in malpractice and ethics cases. In addition, he has a general commercial litigation practice handling ERISA and environmental matters, including class actions.
**Professional Memberships:** A New Jersey Certified Civil Trial Attorney, he will become the president of the Essex County Bar Association in April 2013.
**Personal:** JD Seton Hall University School of Law (cum laude); BA Georgetown University.

**RABINOWITZ, Jonathan**
Rabinowitz, Lubetkin & Tully, LLC, Livingston
973 597 9100
jrabinowitz@rltlawfirm.com
*Featured in Bankruptcy/Restructuring (New Jersey)*

**Practice Areas:** Jonathan Rabinowitz concentrates his practice in business insolvencies in all types of industries, including manufacturing and retail, with a special concentration in real estate reorganizations. He also has extensive experience in all aspects of healthcare restructuring, including hospitals, group medical practices, and nursing homes.
**Career:** He represented the State of New Jersey in various healthcare matters, including the NJ HIP bankruptcy, and also served as acting counsel to the New York State Higher Education Services Corporation. Mr Rabinowitz is an adjunct professor at Rutgers University School of Law in Newark, where he teaches Bankruptcy, Business Associations, and the Uniform Commercial Code.

**RAVE, Michael T**
Day Pitney LLP, Parsippany
973 966 8123
mrave@daypitney.com
*Featured in Corporate/M&A (New Jersey)*
**Career:** Michael T Rave counsels business entities on corporate and securities law issues including mergers and acquisitions and public and private capital raising. Mr Rave advises public companies on federal securities law compliance and corporate governance. He also advises financial institutions on state and federal regulatory issues. Mr Rave was the law clerk to The Honorable Edward M. Coleman, Superior Court of New Jersey, Somerset County, during the 1995-1996 term.

**RICCI, Richard F**
Lowenstein Sandler LLP, Roseland
973 597 2462
rricci@lowenstein.com
*Featured in Environment (New Jersey)*
**Practice Areas:** Richard F Ricci is Chair of the firm's Environmental Law and Litigation Group. He works on a broad range of matters, including Superfund and toxic tort litigation, injunctive and penalty proceedings, construction, environmental, insurance coverage and commercial litigation. He serves as common counsel to a number of companies that are investigating and remediating waste disposal sites.Rich has successfully litigated environmental matters in New York, Pennsylvania, Illinois, Missouri, and Arkansas, as well as New Jersey. www.lowenstein.com/rricci

**RIDER, Christopher M**
Fox Rothschild LLP, Roseland
973 994 7576
crider@foxrothschild.com
*Featured in Real Estate (New Jersey)*
**Practice Areas:** Represents a range of clients, including owners, developers, real estate funds, and financial institutions. Extensive experience in acquisitions and sales, commercial mortgage, mezzanine and construction financings, debt restructurings, joint ventures, development and construction projects and commercial leasing. Regularly advises clients with respect to realty transfer tax issues and the restructuring of real property holdings.
**Professional Memberships:** American Bar Association; New Jersey Chapter of NAIOP.

**Career:** Certified Public Accountant (license inactive) at Coopers & Lybrand LLP prior to practice of law.
**Personal:** JD, with high honors, Rutgers University School of Law – Newark; BS, with high honors, Rutgers College.

**RIDLEY, John**
Drinker Biddle & Reath LLP, Florham Park
973 549 7030
John.Ridley@dbr.com
*Featured in Labor & Employment (New Jersey)*
**Practice Areas:** Partner, Labor and Employment Practice. Practice focuses on labor and employment law, litigation, and employment and labor disputes.
**Professional Memberships:** Admitted in New Jersey. Member, Essex County, New Jersey State and American Bar Associations, the Equal Employment Opportunity Committee of the American Bar Association's Section on Labor and Employment Law. Appointments: Executive Committee of the Labor and Employment Section of the New Jersey State Bar Association; past Board Member of the Trial Attorneys of New Jersey.
**Career:** Joined Drinker Biddle in 2002.
**Personal:** JD, University of Virginia, 1968; AB, St Peter's College, 1965.

**RIORDAN, J Michael**
McElroy, Deutsch, Mulvaney & Carpenter, LLP, Morristown
973 425 8676
jmriordan@mdmc-law.com
*Featured in Labor & Employment (New Jersey)*
**Practice Areas:** Mr Riordan has experience representing Fortune 500 and other clients in employment law and commercial matters. His work in the financial services industry includes securities litigation and arbitration as well as corporate investigations.
**Professional Memberships:** Mr Riordan is admitted to practice in New Jersey, New York, and Pennsylvania. He is a member of the Federal Mediation Program, District of New Jersey, Panel of Arbitrators, American Arbitration Association, Supreme Court Committee on Character and Fitness, and also served previously as Chair of the New Jersey District X Ethics Committee.
**Personal:** Villanova University School of Law (JD); Princeton University (AB).

**ROBERTSON, James A.**
McElroy, Deutsch, Mulvaney & Carpenter, LLP, Morristown
973 348 5307
jrobertson@mdmc-law.com
*Featured in Healthcare (New Jersey)*
**Practice Areas:** Mr Robertson practice is concentrated on health and hospital law, Medicare and Medicaid reimbursement matters, complex commercial and corporate litigation, corporate compliance matters, mergers and acquisitions, and health care regulatory matters.
**Professional Memberships:** Mr Robertson is admitted to practice in New Jersey and Pennsylvania. He is a member of the American Health Lawyers Association, the Health and

Hospital Law Section of the New Jersey Bar Association, and serves on the Publications Committee of the New Jersey Chapter of the Healthcare Financial Management Association.
**Personal:** Villanova University School of Law (JD); Rutgers University, Cook College (BS)

## ROBINS, Andrew B
Sills Cummis & Gross P.C., Newark
973 643 5277
arobins@sillscummis.com
*Featured in Environment (New Jersey)*
**Practice Areas:** Andrew B Robins counsels clients on regulatory compliance, cost recovery litigation, redevelopment, brownfields, transaction negotiation and risk analysis.
**Professional Memberships:** NJ-NAIOP; National Association of Home Builders, American Bar Association; New Jersey State Bar Association; National Brownfield Association; New Jersey Builders Association; Shore Builders Association of Central NJ; several NJDEP Stakeholder Groups.
**Career:** New Jersey Builders Association Redevelopment and Brownfields Committee Chairman's Award; The Best Lawyers in America since 2011; NJ-NAIOP Regulatory Committee Presidents' Award; Inducted into the New Jersey Builders Association's Associates Hall of Fame.
**Personal:** Rutgers University School of Law, JD, 1986; University of Pennsylvania, BA, 1982.

## RODBURG, Michael L
Lowenstein Sandler LLP, Roseland
973 597 2466
mrodburg@lowenstein.com
*Featured in Environment (New Jersey)*
**Practice Areas:** Michael L Rodburg is a partner in Lowenstein Sandler's Environmental Law & Litigation Group. He has more than 35 years of experience in complex litigation and has practiced exclusively in environmental law since 1973. Michael represents business and industry in connection with significant business transactions, civil litigation and administrative agency proceedings arising out of a wide variety of environmental issues. His extensive areas of expertise include: hazardous substances litigation, mass tort defense, acquisition counseling, and climate change initiatives. www.lowenstein.com/mrodburg

## ROLLO, Marc A
Archer & Greiner, A Professional Corporation, Haddonfield
856 354 3061
mrollo@archerlaw.com
*Featured in Environment (New Jersey)*
**Practice Areas:** Marc Rollo is Chair of the firm's Petroleum Industry Practice Group. He concentrates his practice in the area of environmental litigation in both state and federal courts, with a specific emphasis on natural resource damage, cost recovery, underground storage tank and MTBE product liability litigation. He has significant experience in class action and complex litigation involving allegations of, among others, personal injury, property damage and stigma, and cleanup reimbursement and contribution. He also counsels petrochemical companies on numerous

state agency regulatory matters involving environmental remediation and compliance issues.
**Professional Memberships:**

## ROLNICK, Lawrence M
Lowenstein Sandler LLP, Roseland
973 597 2468
lrolnick@lowenstein.com
*Featured in Litigation (New Jersey)*
**Practice Areas:** Lawrence M Rolnick is Chair of Lowenstein Sandler's Securities Litigation & Enforcement Group. He represents institutional investors, hedge funds, private equity firms and investment managers in securities litigation, bondholder litigation, credit facility enforcement and appraisal rights actions. He counsels plaintiffs and defendants and has represented institutional investor clients in plaintiff-side securities litigations and appraisal rights actions, private equity portfolio companies in complex commercial cases, public companies in defense of class actions, and directors and officers in defense of alleged breach of fiduciary duty claims. www.lowenstein.com/lrolnick

## ROME, Robin
Nukk-Freeman & Cerra, Short Hills
973 564 9100
rrome@nfclegal.com
*Featured in Labor & Employment (New Jersey)*

## ROONEY, Gavin J
Lowenstein Sandler LLP, Roseland
973 597 2472
grooney@lowenstein.com
*Featured in Litigation (New Jersey)*
**Practice Areas:** Gavin Rooney focuses his practice on the defense of class actions, mass torts, and other kinds of high-stakes, aggregate litigation. He represents large corporate and institutional clients in securities, shareholder derivative, consumer fraud, and RICO claims in venues across the US. His ability to understand massive, complex claims and explain those issues simply and directly to an audience (whether judge or jury), while remaining the client's central point of contact, is the key to his winning formula. www.lowenstein.com/grooney

## ROSE, Beth S
Sills Cummis & Gross P.C., Newark
973 643 5877
brose@sillscummis.com
*Featured in Litigation (New Jersey)*
**Practice Areas:** Beth S Rose, Chair of the firm's Product Liability Practice Group and Co-Chair of the Litigation Practice Group, is nationally known for her defense of pharmaceutical and medical device companies in complex product liability and mass tort litigation.
**Career:** Law360's "10 Most Admired Product Liability Lawyers in 2010"; The Best Lawyers in America since 2005; NJ Super Lawyers since 2005; Named one of the "Top 50 NJ Female Super Lawyers" (2007, 2009-2012); "Forty under Forty" NJ Law Journal (2002); NJ Bar (1987); NY Bar (1989).

**Personal:** Wesleyan University, BA, with honors, 1984; Georgetown University Law Center, JD, 1987.

## ROSEN, David I
Sills Cummis & Gross P.C., Newark
973 643 5558
drosen@sillscummis.com
*Featured in Labor & Employment (New Jersey)*
**Practice Areas:** David I Rosen has represented management clients on all labor and employment law matters since 1977. His practice extends to employment litigation (discrimination, whistleblower, restrictive covenant, & wrongful discharge), day-to-day counseling, in-house training, NLRB proceedings, collective bargaining and labor arbitrations, appellate advocacy, union pre-election campaign development, wage & hour, employment and separation agreements, policy development.
**Professional Memberships:** Fellow, The College of Labor and Employment Lawyers; Treasurer, Academy of NJ Management Attorneys; Member, Executive Committee, NJ Bar Labor & Employment Law Section.
**Personal:** JD, Case Western Reserve University School of Law, 1977; BA, Tufts University, magna cum laude, 1974.

## ROSEN, Kenneth A
Lowenstein Sandler LLP, Roseland
973 597 2548
krosen@lowenstein.com
*Featured in Bankruptcy/Restructuring (New Jersey)*
**Practice Areas:** Kenneth A Rosen is Chair of Lowenstein Sandler's Bankruptcy, Financial Reorganization & Creditors' Rights Group. He has extensive experience helping companies develop viable solutions to financial crises, including Chapter 11 reorganization, out-of-court workouts, financial reorganization, and litigation, Ken is a regular contributor to NY metro area real estate publications, and has written extensively about bankruptcy in real estate and general business press. www.lowenstein.com/krosen

## ROSENBERG, Ezra D
Dechert LLP, Princeton
609 955 3222
ezra.rosenberg@dechert.com
*Featured in Products Liability (Nationwide), Litigation (New Jersey)*
**Practice Areas:** Mr Rosenberg represents corporations in many industries in consumer fraud, mass torts, and product liability class action suits and other complex commercial litigation at the trial and appellate levels. He served several terms on the firm's policy committee and as a deputy chair of the firm.
**Professional Memberships:** Member, New Jersey and District of Columbia Bars; admitted to practice before the US Supreme Court and numerous federal courts; recipient, American Jewish Committee Judge Learned Hand Award.
**Personal:** University of Pennsylvania (BA, 1971, cum laude); New York University School of Law (JD, 1974, cum laude, Order of the Coif).

## ROSENBERG, Ira A
Sills Cummis & Gross P.C., Newark
973 643 5082
irosenberg@sillscummis.com
*Featured in Corporate/M&A (New Jersey)*
**Practice Areas:** Ira A Rosenberg is Co-Chair of the firm's Corporate Practice Group and Chair of the firm's Life Sciences Practice Group. He regularly represents private and public companies in connection with mergers and acquisitions, financings, joint ventures and private placements. He has extensive experience relating to corporate spinoffs, corporate collaborations, product and technology licensing, development and distribution arrangements, and strategic alliances.
**Career:** The Best Lawyers in America since 1995; New Jersey Super Lawyers since its inception in 2005.
**Personal:** New York University School of Law, JD, 1978; Boston University, BS, cum laude, 1975.

## ROSENBLATT, Richard G
Morgan, Lewis & Bockius LLP, Princeton
609 919 6609
rrosenblatt@morganlewis.com
*Featured in Labor & Employment (New Jersey)*
**Practice Areas:** Richard G Rosenblatt is a partner in Morgan Lewis's Labor and Employment Practice resident in Princeton and Philadelphia. Rich represents employers nationwide in state and federal courts and agencies. In addition to an extensive counseling practice defending against all forms of discrimination and retaliation claims, Rich has extensive experience as lead counsel handling wage and hour and ERISA class actions, and trade secret and non-compete litigation. Rich is a certified Legal Process Manager and serves as Business Operations Partner for labor and employment law.
**Personal:** Attended Cornell Law School, 1990, JD; Duke University, 1987, AB.

## ROTH, Stephen F
Lerner David Littenberg Krumholz & Mentlik, LLP, Westfield
908 518 6362
sroth@ldlkm.com
*Featured in Intellectual Property (New Jersey)*
**Practice Areas:** Specializes in IP litigation. Serves as lead counsel on jury and bench trials. Trains litigation associates within the firm. Frequently lectures and teaches IP law. Successfully resolves disputes in a swift and efficient manner. Highly professional and admired by peers. Honored with the 2013 Lawyer of the Year for Patent Litigation in the Newark Metropolitan region.
**Professional Memberships:** Member of New Jersey and Pennsylvania Bars; American Intellectual Property Law Association; Director of the John C. Lifland American Inn of Court.
**Career:** Mr Roth is a Partner at Lerner David Littenberg Krumholz & Mentlik, LLP.
**Personal:** JD, Rutgers University; MA, Psychology, New York University, BS, Biology, Washington University.

## ROTHPLETZ JR, Michael E
Drinker Biddle & Reath LLP, Florham Park
973 549 7284
Michael.Rothpletz@dbr.com
*Featured in Real Estate (New Jersey)*
**Practice Areas:** Partner and Chair, Real Estate Group. Experienced in a variety of real estate areas, including purchases, sales, leasing, financing, joint ventures, construction, development approvals and land preservation.
**Professional Memberships:** Member of the American College of Real Estate Lawyers. Admitted to practice in New Jersey and Pennsylvania.
**Publications:** Co-author, Conveyance of Commercial Real Estate Chapter, 'Commercial Real Estate Transactions in New Jersey', published by New Jersey Institute of Continuing Legal Education (2003 and 2nd Ed, 2006, and 3rd Ed, 2009).
**Personal:** JD with high honors, Rutgers University School of Law (Newark), 1993; BA, University of Pennsylvania, 1987.

## ROTHSCHILD, Gita F
McCarter & English, LLP, Newark
973 639 7969
grothschild@mccarter.com
*Featured in Litigation (New Jersey)*
**Career:** Ms Rothschild practices in areas of complex litigation, including insurance coverage, class actions, defense of employers, products liability and toxic torts, commercial contracts, and business torts. Ms Rothschild has defended companies against a wide variety of claims involving products liability and commercial issues. She currently defends research-based pharmaceutical companies in litigation involving employment matters and prescription and over-the-counter medicines. She has been representing corporate policyholders for more than 30 years, litigating and resolving coverage disputes involving products liability; environmental impairment; directors' and officers' liability; errors and omissions; and fidelity claims, principally for Fortune 500 companies. For full bio:
http://www.mccarter.com/Gita-F-Rothschild/

## SADAT, Ellen Radow
Drinker Biddle & Reath LLP, Princeton
609 716 6611
Ellen.Sadat@dbr.com
*Featured in Environment (New Jersey)*
**Practice Areas:** Partner, Environmental Group. Focuses on air, hazardous substance and water regulation permitting and enforcement at both the New Jersey and federal levels, including self-reporting, auditing and internal investigations.
**Professional Memberships:** Admitted, New Jersey and Pennsylvania. Serves on NJDEP's Air Industrial Advisory Group; Member, Environmental and Natural Resources Sections of American and New Jersey Bar Associations.
**Career:** Previously served as an attorney in the EPA Region 2 Air and Superfund Branches and held various positions at the New Jersey Department of Environmental Protection.

**Personal:** JD, Temple University School of Law, 1978. BA, Rider University, 1975.

## SALES, Bruce
Lerner David Littenberg Krumholz & Mentlik, LLP, Westfield
908 518 6311
bsales@ldlkm.com
*Featured in Intellectual Property (New Jersey)*
**Practice Areas:** Domestic and international IP issues relating to trademarks, patents, copyrights, monetization, litigation, licensing, acquisition and exploitation. Developing and implementing worldwide strategic planning for intellectual property assets. Clients range from major multinational corporations to start-up corporations.
**Professional Memberships:** US Patent and Trademark Office; Member of New Jersey, California, and DC Bars; Inn of Transactional Counsel; Association Internationale por la Protection de la Propriete Intellectualle.
**Career:** Mr Sales is a Partner at the firm and is the Managing Partner of the firm's office in Guangzhou, China.
**Personal:** JD, Hofstra University Law School; MS, Microbiology, BS, Biochemistry, Rutgers University.

## SAMAY, Christian
Dentons, Short Hills
973 912 7180
christian.samay@dentons.com
*Featured in Intellectual Property (New Jersey)*
**Practice Areas:** Christian E Samay is a partner at Dentons. He is an experienced civil trial lawyer litigating intellectual property and commercial disputes in federal and state courts across the United States. He has particular expertise in trade secrets and patent litigation and matters for emergent injunctive relief. His courtroom experience spans a broad range of industries, including consumer products, life sciences, energy, aviation, fashion and apparel, food and beverage, sports, and technology. He also maintains a transactional and IP/IT counseling practice.
**Personal:** Seton Hall University School of Law, JD; Bucknell University, BA.

## SCHINDLER, Barry J
Greenberg Traurig, LLP, Florham Park
973 360 7944
SchindlerB@gtlaw.com
*Featured in Intellectual Property (New Jersey)*
**Practice Areas:** Co-Chair, Global Patent Prosecution Practice. Intellectual property and technology; media and telecommunications; litigation; globalization and commercialization.
**Professional Memberships:** Member: American Institute of Chemical Engineers; Institute of Food Technologists; American Society of Agricultural Engineers; American Intellectual Property Law Association.
**Career:** Selected: Chambers USA Guide, 2008-13; 'The IAM Patent 1000', Prosecution in New York & New Jersey, IAM Magazine, 2012; Legal 500 US, 2008-10.
**Publications:** Co-author: 'Using U.S. Patent Reform to Drive Corporate Policy', New Jersey Law Journal, September 26, 2011.

**Personal:** JD, University of Houston Law Center; BS, Cornell University.

## SEGOTA, Denis
Morgan, Lewis & Bockius LLP, Princeton
609 919 6622
dsegota@morganlewis.com
*Featured in Corporate/M&A (New Jersey)*
**Practice Areas:** Denis Segota is a partner in Morgan Lewis's Business and Finance Practice, resident in the Princeton office. Mr Segota has an extensive background in transactions including mergers and acquisitions, strategic alliances and private financing transactions, representing financial institutions and companies in venture capital and private equity financing. Mr Segota devotes substantial time in the life sciences area, representing pharmaceutical and biotechnology companies in product acquisitions and divestitures, complex joint ventures, strategic alliances, licensing, and other partnering arrangements promoting the research, development, and commercialization of new products.
**Personal:** Rutgers University School of Law, JD; Rutgers College, BS, Cum Laude.

## SELITTO, JR, Ralph W
Greenberg Traurig, LLP, Florham Park
973 443 3550
SelittoR@gtlaw.com
*Featured in Intellectual Property (New Jersey)*
**Practice Areas:** Co-Chair, New York Metro Intellectual Property Practice. Patent prosecution (domestic/foreign); trademark prosecution (domestic/foreign); copyright registration; litigation (patents/trademarks/copyrights); licensing; due diligence investigations; infringement/validity investigations; mechanical arts; electrical arts; metallurgy.
**Career:** Moldflow Corp. v. Simcon, Inc., 296 F.Supp.2d 34 (D. Mass. 2003).
**Publications:** Co-author, 'Life In The Fast Lane Of The Patent Prosecution Highway', Law360, November 23, 2011; Co-author, 'Extra-Territorial Reach Shortened: Case Makes Suing Foreign Entity for Indirect Patent Infringement Outside U.S. More Difficult,' New Jersey Law Journal, April 2007.
**Personal:** JD, The Catholic University of America, Columbus School of Law, 1974; BE, Stevens Institute of Technology, 1971.

## SELLINGER, Philip R
Greenberg Traurig, LLP, Florham Park
973 360 7910
SellingerP@gtlaw.com
*Featured in Litigation (New Jersey)*
**Practice Areas:** Co-Chair, Global Litigation Practice. Co-Managing Shareholder, New Jersey Office. Handles trials, class actions, and complex litigation.
**Professional Memberships:** Founding Chair, Class Action Committee, New Jersey State Bar Association. Board Member, Atlantic Legal Foundation. Former Chair and current member, Lawyers Advisory Committee, New Jersey Federal Judiciary.
**Career:** Former federal clerk and Assistant United states Attorney. Learned Hand Award,

American Jewish Committee. Distinguished Legal Services Award, Corporate Legal Times. Selected: Best Lawyers in America, 2005-12; Chambers USA Guide, 2007-13; Super Lawyers magazine, 2006-12. (Among others.)
**Personal:** JD, New York University School of Law; BA, summa cum laude, University of Massachusetts-Amherst.

## SHARKO, Susan M
Drinker Biddle & Reath LLP, Florham Park
973 549 7350
susan.sharko@dbr.com
*Featured in Litigation (New Jersey)*
**Practice Areas:** Partner. Concentrates practice on civil litigation and trial work with a focus on pharmaceutical defense work. Serves as national, regional, science and local counsel, as well as court-appointed lead liaison and lead counsel in pharmaceutical products liability litigation, tries cases and has successfully argued Daubert and class action motions in pharmaceutical litigation.
**Professional Memberships:** Member: New Jersey Bar Association; Member: International Association of Defense Counsel; Fellow: American Bar Foundation; Member: Product Liability Advisory Council; Member: American Law Institute.
**Career:** Joined Drinker Biddle in 1980.
**Personal:** JD, New York University School of Law, 1979; BA, Lehigh University, 1976.

## SHERMAN, Andrew H
Sills Cummis & Gross P.C., Newark
973 643 6982
asherman@sillscummis.com
*Featured in Bankruptcy/Restructuring (New Jersey)*
**Practice Areas:** Andrew H Sherman, Co-Chair of the firm's Creditors' Rights/Bankruptcy Reorganization Practice, represents clients in complex business reorganizations, debt restructurings, commercial litigation and insolvency matters nationally. He has represented parties in restructurings in industries such as health care, real estate, gaming, transportation, retail and manufacturing. Clients include official and ad hoc creditors' committees, lenders, court-appointed fiduciaries, debtors and investors that focus on distressed situations and insolvency proceedings.
**Professional Memberships:** American Bankruptcy Institute; American Bar Association; New York State Bar Association; Essex County Bar Association.
**Personal:** Yeshiva University, Benjamin N. Cardozo School of Law, JD, 1991; Cornell University, AB, 1988.

## SHERWOOD, John K
Lowenstein Sandler LLP, Roseland
973 597 2538
jsherwood@lowenstein.com
*Featured in Bankruptcy/Restructuring (New Jersey)*
**Practice Areas:** Jack Sherwood focuses his practice on bankruptcy and debtor-creditor matters, including related litigation and counseling corporate management in insolvency situations. He debtors; creditor committees; secured creditors; landlords; stockholders; trustees; directors; officers; employees and other parties in bankrupt-

cy cases and non-bankruptcy business reorganizations. He also represents parties in debtor-creditor litigation matters such as fraudulent conveyances, preferences, director and officer liability, contract disputes and similar matters. www.lowenstein.com/jsherwood

## SHORT, Jonathan
McCarter & English, LLP, Newark
973 848 5394
jshort@mccarter.com
*Featured in Intellectual Property (New Jersey)*
**Career:** Mr Short practices intellectual property law, representing clients in disputes and transactions relating to patent, trademark, trade dress, copyright and trade secrets, as well as unfair trade/business practices, cyberlaw and data privacy issues. He is dedicated to providing business-minded solutions to corporate clients (from start-ups to international market leaders), including litigation avoidance and prelitigation counseling. Mr Short has extensive experience with litigation and transactional counseling relating to computer technology, including flash memory products, and he has additional patent litigation experience relating to variable-speed pool pumps, athletic footwear technology and other consumer products. For full bio:
http://www.mccarter.com/Jonathan-Short/

## SHUR, Paul H
Blank Rome LLP, Princeton
609 750 7708
PShur@BlankRome.com
*Featured in Corporate/M&A (New Jersey)*
**Practice Areas:** Paul Shur has more than 30 years of experience in commercial transactions, financial transactions, loan workouts and restructures. Mr Shur has handled numerous matters in the following areas: sales and lease transactions; secured transactions; asset based financing; real estate financing; real estate title defense and litigation; creditors' rights litigation; and commercial and corporate finance. For more information: www.BlankRome.com/PShur

## SINCLAIR, Stacey
Archer & Greiner, A Professional Corporation, Haddonfield
856 795 2121
ssinclair@archerlaw.com
*Featured in Environment (New Jersey)*
**Practice Areas:** Stacey Sinclair concentrates her practice in complex litigation, including mass tort and product liability matters with a focus on environmental issues facing the petroleum industry. She represents large petrochemical companies and provides guidance on issues ranging from soil and groundwater contamination and natural resources damages to contaminant exposure and cost recovery. In addition to her litigation focus, Stacey provides advice regarding environmental cleanup, regulatory compliance, property transfer and state fund reimbursements. Stacey has considerable experience in guiding clients through electronic discovery in federal and state courts and has been instrumental in development of the firm's Litigation Technology Team.

## SIROTA, Michael
Cole, Schotz, Meisel, Forman & Leonard PA, Hackensack
201 525 6262
msirota@coleschotz.com
*Featured in Bankruptcy/Restructuring (New Jersey)*
**Practice Areas:** Co-Managing Shareholder of the firm and Co-Chair of the firm's Bankruptcy & Corporate Restructuring Department, concentrates in all facets of restructurings, insolvency law and complex bankruptcy and commercial litigation. Represents clients in a myriad of industries including casino and gaming, healthcare, real estate, manufacturing, distribution, finance and transportation. Represents publicly and privately held debtors, trustees, secured and unsecured creditors, equity holders, indenture trustees, venture capitalists, private equity/hedge funds and parties with substantial interests in distressed situations and insolvency proceedings throughout the country.
**Personal:** Syracuse University College of Law, JD, cum laude, 1986.

## SMITH, Patricia A
Ballard Spahr LLP, Cherry Hill
856 873 5521
smithpa@ballardspahr.com
*Featured in Labor & Employment (New Jersey)*
**Practice Areas:** Patricia A Smith represents management in all areas of employment and labor law and litigation. She has significant jury trial experience in state and federal courts. Ms Smith has an active ERISA litigation practice, including ERISA class action and multi-employer pension plan matters, and counsels employers on avoiding and resolving employment-related problems.
**Professional Memberships:** American Bar Association New Jersey Bar Association.
**Career:** New Jersey Pennsylvania.
**Personal:** Rutgers, The State University of New Jersey School of Law-Camden (JD 1981) Rowan University (BA 1973).

## SMITH, Robert W.
McCarter & English, LLP, Newark
973 639 2061
rsmith@mccarter.com
*Featured in Intellectual Property (New Jersey)*
**Career:** Mr Smith focuses on trademark and copyright registration matters; trademark opposition proceedings in the US Patent and Trademark Office; and trademark, trade secret, unfair competition and copyright infringement litigation. He regularly counsels clients in licensing and franchising matters and concerning due diligence and other intellectual property issues arising in the course of corporate acquisition/divestiture and financing transactions. For full bio:
http://www.mccarter.com/Robert-W-Smith/

## SPERLING, Joy Harmon
Day Pitney LLP, Parsippany
973 966 8217
jsperling@daypitney.com
*Featured in Litigation (New Jersey)*
**Career:** Joy Harmon Sperling is chair of Day Pitney's Creditors' Rights and Real Estate Litigation practice group. Her practice involves representing consumer lending institutions, such as mortgage lenders, as well as investors and servicers, in connection with the defense of claims by borrowers in individual and class-action claims. Her practice includes the defense and prosecution of mortgage fraud claims, and the litigation of cases involving federal and state lending regulations and common law causes of action relating to the origination and enforcement of residential and commercial mortgage loans. Ms Sperling also represents banking institutions in commercial collection and foreclosure matters.

## SPINELLO, John F
K&L Gates, Newark
973 848 4061
john.spinello@klgates.com
*Featured in Environment (New Jersey)*
**Practice Areas:** Mr Spinello's practice focuses on regulatory counseling and environmental litigation for clients in the energy, maritime, cement, glass, iron, chemical, mining and highway construction industries. In addition to having represented clients in a wide range of Clean Air Act matters at the state and federal level, he has also defended clients in civil and administrative enforcement actions by state and federal agencies, as well as citizen suits. He was previously an Associate General Counsel for the United States Environmental Protection Agency, and Assistant Counsel to the Governor of New Jersey.

## STANTON, Patrick M
Ogletree, Deakins, Nash, Smoak & Stewart, PC, Morristown
973 630 2300
patrick.stanton@ogletreedeakins.com
*Featured in Labor & Employment (New Jersey)*
**Practice Areas:** Labor and employment.
**Professional Memberships:** Chair, Academy of New Jersey Management Attorneys (2010 -); New Jersey State Bar Association (Chair, Labor and Employment Law Section 2003-05); Fellow, College of Labor and Employment Lawyers (1998-).
**Career:** Admitted: New Jersey, New York, Ohio (inactive), U.S. Supreme Court, U.S. District Courts (D.N.J.; S.D.N.Y.; E.D.N.Y.; S.D.OH.), U.S. Court of Appeals (Third and D.C. Circuits).
**Publications:** "New Jersey Employment Laws and Regulations: A Practical Guide For Employers" (1993).
**Personal:** St. Joseph's (Pa.) University (B.S., 1969), University of Virginia School of Law (J.D., 1972), Fairleigh Dickinson University (Executive M.B.A. Program, 1984).

## STANZIALE, Charles
McCarter & English, LLP, Newark
973 639 7908
cstanziale@mccarter.com
*Featured in Bankruptcy/Restructuring (New Jersey)*
**Career:** Mr Stanziale's concentration for over 45 years has been in the area of financial restructuring, insolvency and creditors' rights. He has represented debtors, trustees, creditors' committees, banks and other secured parties. He was appointed a Chapter 11 and Chapter 7 Trustee by the Department of Justice, Office of the U.S. Trustee, and a Liquidating Trustee and Assignee in cases for numerous industries. Representative matters include Trump Entertainment Resorts; Tower Air, Inc.; Solomon Dwek; Integrated Packaging, Inc.; Evergreen Energy, Inc. (Colorado); Golden Guernsey Dairy, LLC (Wisconsin); Conex International LLC (Texas); and Big Island Carbon LLC (Hawaii). For full bio:
http://www.mccarter.com/Charles-A-Stanziale/

## STEIN, Michael
Pashman Stein, Hackensack
201 270 4906
mstein@pashmanstein.com
*Featured in Litigation (New Jersey)*
**Practice Areas:** Michael Stein, co-founder and head of the firm's litigation practice, specializes in complex commercial litigation, chancery litigation, legal ethics and appellate advocacy. He has substantial trial and appellate experience in both state and federal courts. He also serves as an advisor to the firm's corporate clients on such matters as partnership and shareholder agreements, intellectual property rights, construction disputes, intellectual property disputes, trust and estates litigation, consumer fraud, class actions, lender liability issues, land use requirements, contracts, restrictive covenants and chancery law.

## STEWART, James
Lowenstein Sandler LLP, Roseland
973 597 2522
jstewart@lowenstein.com
*Featured in Environment (New Jersey)*
**Practice Areas:** James Stewart has extensive experience in environmental issues and complex litigation, with an emphasis on environmental litigation and class-action toxic torts. He also focuses on renewable energy issues, particularly solar energy projects, and has counseled project developers and solar power purchasers on contracting and financing issues and environmental attributes such as SRECs. He also handles environmental compliance issues and the impact of environmental liabilities on mergers and acquisitions and complex issues including the sale of RCRA-permitted facilities, the sale of grossly contaminated property, and the environmental aspects of transactions involving facilities in numerous states. www.lowenstein.com/jstewart

## SUFLAS, Steven W
Ballard Spahr LLP, Cherry Hill
856 761 3466
suflas@ballardspahr.com
*Featured in Labor & Employment (New Jersey)*
**Practice Areas:** Steven W Suflas is managing partner of the New Jersey office. He represents management in all phases of labor and employment matters, including collective bargaining and traditional labor law issues, employment litigation and trials, appearances before courts and administrative agencies, ERISA, and wage and hour law.
**Professional Memberships:** New Jersey State Bar Association, Trustee New Jersey Supreme Court -Advisory Committee on Professional Ethics, Member The National Employment Law Institute, National Advisory Board.

**Career:** Admissions: New Jersey Pennsylvania.
**Publications:** Employment Litigation in New Jersey, LexisNexis.
**Personal:** University of North Carolina School of Law (JD 1976) Davidson College (BA 1973).

### SULLIVAN, Diane P
Weil, Gotshal & Manges LLP, Princeton
212 310 8897
diane.sullivan@weil.com
*Featured in Products Liability (Nationwide), Litigation (New Jersey)*
See under Nationwide for profile.

### SUNBERG, Randall B
Morgan, Lewis & Bockius LLP, Princeton
609 919 6606
rsunberg@morganlewis.com
*Featured in Corporate/M&A (New Jersey)*
**Practice Areas:** Randall B Sunberg is a partner with Morgan Lewis, vice chair of the firm's Life Sciences Interdisciplinary Group, co-chair of the firm's Life Sciences Transactions Practice, and Managing Partner of the Princeton office. His clients range from early-stage biotechnology start-ups to global pharmaceutical companies, as well as medical device, diagnostics, and other technology companies. He also advises private equity, venture capital, and investment banking firms focused on the life sciences industry. Mr Sunberg's experience includes negotiating and structuring complex collaborations, mergers and acquisitions, divestitures, joint ventures, corporate partnering, licensing and royalty monetization transactions.

### TESTA, Jeffrey
McCarter & English, LLP, Newark
973 639 7939
jtesta@mccarter.com
*Featured in Bankruptcy/Restructuring (New Jersey)*
**Career:** Mr Testa represents Chapters 11 and 7 bankruptcy trustees in cases across the nation as well as creditors' committees, lenders, purchasers of distressed real estate, receivers and assignees. He prosecutes and defends fraudulent conveyance, preference, Ponzi actions and claim disputes. He represents those involved in business litigation, construction and white-collar disputes in state and federal courts. Recent engagements include debtor's counsel to Trump Entertainment Hotel & Casino Resorts Inc. in its Chapter 11 bankruptcy filings and the Chapter 11 Trustee of Solomon Dwek, who defrauded investors in a Ponzi scheme that has garnered national headlines. For full bio: http://www.mccarter.com/Jeffrey-T-Testa/

### THEK, Raymond P
Lowenstein Sandler LLP, Roseland
646 414 6795
rthek@lowenstein.com
*Featured in Corporate/M&A (New Jersey)*
**Practice Areas:** Ray Thek's passion for innovation guides his practice as a deal lawyer focusing on financings and exits for companies whose core assets are intellectual property. He helps companies and investors at all stages identify, finance and monetize technologies, processes, products and brands, working closely with the creative entrepreneurs behind the ideas. On the buy side, he helps

established companies target and acquire fits for their strategic objectives. An angel investor himself, Ray is co-founder of First Growth Venture Network and GrapeArborVC, and is on the Executive Committee of AngelVineVC. www.lowenstein.com/rthek

### TIMPONE, Walter F
McElroy, Deutsch, Mulvaney & Carpenter, LLP, Morristown
973 425 8701
wtimpone@mdmc-law.com
*Featured in Litigation (New Jersey)*
**Practice Areas:** Mr Timpone's areas of practice include white-collar criminal work, corporate internal investigations, health care compliance and defense, labor law for labor unions and complex civil litigation. Mr Timpone represents health care industry organizations, companies, institutions, and individuals.
**Professional Memberships:** Mr Timpone is admitted to practice in New Jersey and New York. He presently serves as a Commissioner on the New Jersey Election Law Enforcement Commission. In addition, Mr Timpone acts as an Associate General Executive Board Attorney for the LIUNA Union.
**Personal:** Seton Hall Law School (JD); St. Francis College (BA).

### USATINE, Warren A.
Cole, Schotz, Meisel, Forman & Leonard PA, Hackensack
201 525 6233
wusatine@coleschotz.com
*Featured in Bankruptcy/Restructuring (New Jersey)*
**Practice Areas:** Focuses on all aspects of litigation and insolvency matters in the state and federal courts. Experience in chancery and commercial litigation matters, as well as representation of Chapter 11 debtors and creditors in bankruptcy courts. Representations include: lead counsel for the official committee of unsecured creditors in the chapter 11 proceedings of Kara Homes, Inc.; Tarragon Corporation,and twenty-four of its affiliates in their chapter 11 proceedings; and Zayat Stables, LLC, in its chapter 11 proceeding in the District of New Jersey.
**Personal:** University of Pennsylvania Law School, JD, 1995.

### VELOCCI, Frank
Drinker Biddle & Reath LLP, Florham Park
973 549 7078
Frank.Velocci@dbr.com
*Featured in Bankruptcy/Restructuring (New Jersey)*
**Practice Areas:** Partner in the Corporate Restructuring Practice and Commercial Litigation Groups. Frank represents debtors, trustees, committees and secured creditors in complex Chapter 11 cases. He recently assisted St. Mary's Hospital to confirm the first standalone reorganization for a New Jersey hospital in more than a decade. His experience also includes litigation and arbitration in the areas of real estate, telecommunications, health care, prerogative writs and legal malpractice.

**Professional Memberships:** Member of the New Jersey and New York Bar Associations and American Bankruptcy Institute
**Personal:** Montclair State University, BA, 1996 ; Seton Hall University School of Law, JD, 1999.

### WALLACH, William D
McCarter & English, LLP, Newark
973 639 7918
wwallach@mccarter.com
*Featured in Litigation (New Jersey)*
**Career:** Mr Wallach focuses his commercial law practice on the following areas: situations arising under Articles 2, 3, 4 and 9 of the Uniform Commercial Code; disputes in the context of closely held companies; and commercial breach of contract disputes. Mr Wallach has extensive experience both in litigating these types of matters and achieving their resolution outside the courtroom. For full bio: http://www.mccarter.com/William-D-Wallach/

### WALTERS, Neal
Ballard Spahr LLP, Cherry Hill
856 761 3438
waltersn@ballardspahr.com
*Featured in Products Liability (Nationwide), Litigation (New Jersey)*
**Practice Areas:** Neal Walters is a partner in the Litigation Department and Practice Leader of the Product Liability/Mass Tort Group. He defends/coordinates product liability/consumer claims through trial in jurisdictions nationwide. He defends class certification proceedings and has successfully challenged class proceedings in various settings, including striking the pleadings, developing/challenging experts, extensive CAFA analysis, and coordination of MDL/competing actions. He counsels companies on regulatory/liability issues arising in the sale/marketing of products.
**Professional Memberships:** Defense Research Institute.
**Career:** New Jersey Pennsylvania U.S. Court of Appeals (Third Circuit).
**Personal:** Rutgers University, The State University of New Jersey School of Law-Newark (JD) Rutgers College (BA).

### WARREN, William L
Drinker Biddle & Reath LLP, Princeton
609 716 6603
william.warren@dbr.com
*Featured in Environment (New Jersey)*
**Practice Areas:** Partner, Environment and Energy Practice Group. Experienced in virtually every aspect of environmental law, including: negotiation with federal and state environmental agencies and cost recovery, toxic tort and other environmental litigation, and counseling with respect to federal and state remedial requirements, New Jersey Industrial Site Recovery Act, and environmental issues arising out of the purchase or sale of real estate, businesses or companies.
**Professional Memberships:** New Jersey, New York and American Bar Associations and American College of Environmental Lawyers.
**Career:** Joined Drinker Biddle in 1995.

**Personal:** JD, New York University School of Law, 1973; BA, Colgate University, 1969.

### WEINER, Jonathan D
Fox Rothschild LLP, Lawrenceville
609 895 3324
jweiner@foxrothschild.com
*Featured in Healthcare (New Jersey)*
**Practice Areas:** Represents NJ health care providers including hospitals, comprehensive rehabilitation hospitals, long-term care nursing homes, assisted living facilities and medical day care programs.
**Professional Memberships:** Member: American Health Lawyers Association, American Academy of Hospital Attorneys and Supreme Court of NJ Civil Practice Committee.
**Career:** General counsel to Health Care Association of NJ since 1976 (largest state interest group of proprietary and not-for-profit health care institutions). Martindale-Hubbell 'AV' rated.
**Publications:** Presents seminars to attorneys throughout the US regarding the representation of nursing facilities.
**Personal:** JD, Temple University School of Law, 1969; AB, Hamilton College, 1966.

### WENIK, Jack
Sills Cummis & Gross P.C., Newark
973 643 5268
jwenik@sillscummis.com
*Featured in Healthcare (New Jersey)*
**Practice Areas:** Jack Wenik, Co-Chair - Sills Cummis & Gross Health Care Government Investigations Practice Group, has extensive federal and state trial experience, both civil and criminal. He represents a wide array of corporations and individuals in complex civil litigation and grand jury investigations. He has particular expertise representing major health care institutions and physicians in federal and state government investigations and other proceedings.
**Professional Memberships:** Involved in several health industry and bar associations.
**Personal:** JD, Yale University, School of Law, 1985 (Editor, Yale Law Journal); BA, State University of New York, Albany, summa cum laude, Phi Beta Kappa, 1982.

### WILD, Jeffrey J
Lowenstein Sandler LLP, Roseland
973 597 2554
jwild@lowenstein.com
*Featured in Litigation (New Jersey)*
**Practice Areas:** Jeffrey J Wild is Co-Chair of the firm's Capital Markets Litigation and Fiduciary Counseling & Litigation groups. With more than 25 years of experience in complex, high-stakes financial litigation and arbitration, he is the "go to" litigator for numerous high-profile clients. Jeff's practice includes capital markets litigation (including claims relating to Wall Street transactions), securities litigation, contract/fraud litigation, trust-and-estate litigation, and other financial/commercial litigation.
www.lowenstein.com/jwild

## WISSERT, David M
Lowenstein Sandler LLP, Roseland
646 414 6912
dwissert@lowenstein.com
*Featured in Labor & Employment (New Jersey)*
**Practice Areas:** David M Wissert has more than 15 years of experience representing employers. He is Chair of Lowenstein Sandler's Employment Group and Deputy General Counsel to the firm. He has significant trial experience defending employers in harassment, discrimination and other employment-related claims and has conducted and overseen sensitive and complex internal investigations of employment complaints. He also counsels clients regularly on all matters affecting the workplace and assists employers in meeting their obligations under federal employment statutes and their state law counterparts. www.lowenstein.com/dwissert

## WOVSANIKER, Alan
Lowenstein Sandler LLP, Roseland
973 597 2564
awovsaniker@lowenstein.com
*Featured in Corporate/M&A (New Jersey)*
**Practice Areas:** Alan Wovsaniker is a partner in the firm's Corporate Department and Securities and Specialty Finance groups. He has more than 35 years of experience in a wide range of matters involving mergers and acquisitions, securities regulation, corporate finance, financial restructurings in and out of bankruptcy, and business divorce.

He counsels clients on the funding and structuring of business organizations and the buying and selling of businesses, and represents issuers in connection with public securities offerings, private equity investments, equity-based compensation plans, and periodic reporting requirements. www.lowenstein.com/awovsaniker

## YUDKIN, Felice
Cole, Schotz, Meisel, Forman & Leonard PA, Hackensack
201 525 6261
fyudkin@coleschotz.com
*Featured in Bankruptcy/Restructuring (New Jersey)*
**Practice Areas:** Areas of practice include complex Chapter 11 reorganizations, workouts, creditors' rights, avoidance actions and other bankruptcy related litigation. She represents Chapter 11 debtors, unsecured creditors' committees, secured and unsecured creditors, commercial landlords and other parties-in-interest in all facets of bankruptcy cases.
**Personal:** Fordham University School of Law, JD, 2005.

## ZACKIN, Jack M
Sills Cummis & Gross P.C., Newark
973 643 6975
jzackin@sillscummis.com
*Featured in Bankruptcy/Restructuring (New Jersey)*
**Practice Areas:** Jack M Zackin, Co-Chair of the firm's Creditors' Rights/ Bankruptcy

Reorganization Practice Group, represents debtors, trustees, secured lenders and acquirers of assets in major Chapter 11 cases and out-of-court work-outs.
**Professional Memberships:** Fellow, American College of Bankruptcy; Past Chair, Bankruptcy Section of the New Jersey State Bar Association.
**Personal:** University of Virginia, JD, 1974; University of Virginia, BA, with high honors, 1971.

## ZIMMERMAN, Edward M
Lowenstein Sandler LLP, Roseland
212 204 8696
ezimmerman@lowenstein.com
*Featured in Corporate/M&A (New Jersey)*
**Practice Areas:** Edward M Zimmerman founded and chairs Lowenstein Sandler's Tech Group. Ed represents tech companies and funds in venture, growth and M&A, including the sale of Buddy Media to Salesforce. Fund clients include Sequoia, Accel, Insight, NEA, IVP and First Round Capital. Ed founded and Chairs www.FirstGrowthVN.com, a NY-based consortium of venture funds, angels and tech executives mentoring high-potential start-up tech companies. An Adjunct Professor of Venture Capital at Columbia Business School, Ed actively angel invests through www.GrapeArborVC.com, an investment vehicle he co-leads. Ed also founded and co-chairs www.AngelVineVC.com, a network of angels, VCs and tech companies. He has repeat-

edly appeared on TV, radio (including his own wine-related show), and in the press on issues important to technology companies and their investors. Ed has a recurring slot on "The Accelerators" page of The Wall Street Journal, where he's published more than two dozen posts about tech ventures. www.lowenstein.com/ezimmerman

## ZUBER, Scott A
Wilson, Elser, Moskowitz, Edelman & Dicker LLP, Florham Park
973 735 5776
scott.zuber@wilsonelser.com
*Featured in Bankruptcy/Restructuring (New Jersey)*
**Practice Areas:** Scott Zuber is a member of Wilson Elser's national Financial Services practice. He handles all facets of bankruptcy practice/creditors' rights and related commercial litigation, including post-petition financing and cash collateral matters; plan negotiation and confirmation issues; asset sales; representation of, and participation on, creditors' committees; federal appellate practice; trading in claims; avoidance action litigation; pre-bankruptcy workouts; commercial collections; and negotiating and drafting commercial loan documents, including those related to asset-based transactions.
**Professional Memberships:** He is a member of the ABA and the NJ State Bar Association.
**Personal:** JD, Rutgers School of Law; BA Rutgers College.

# ARCHER & GREINER

www.archerlaw.com **tel:** 856 795 2121 **fax:** 856 795 0574

**Managing Partners:** James H Carll, Christopher R Gibson
Number of partners: 126
Number of lawyers: 209

## Firm Overview:

Archer & Greiner is a full service, regional law firm with a reputation for providing the highest quality, result-driven legal services to corporate and individual clients. One of the largest law firms in the Delaware Valley and among the five largest in New Jersey, Archer & Greiner serves businesses and individuals throughout the region and in an increasing number of other states and jurisdictions. With a network of regional offices, the firm has more than 200 lawyers practicing in all major legal disciplines.

The firm's principal office is located in Haddonfield, New Jersey, a suburb of Philadelphia. Additional offices are located in Philadelphia, Pennsylvania, Princeton, Hackensack, Flemington, and Shrewsbury, New Jersey, Wilmington and Georgetown, Delaware and New York City. To obtain more information about Archer & Greiner and its attorneys please visit the firm website, contact any of the offices or send an e-mail to: marketing@archerlaw.com

## Main Areas of Practice:

### Corporate:
The Corporate Department provides advice on general corporate representation and contract negotiation, mergers and acquisitions, the formation and structuring of business entities and joint ventures, securities law representation, and debt and equity financings of both a private and public nature.

### Bankruptcy:
The Bankruptcy Group provides guidance and counsel to business, institutional and individual clients in reorganizing and resolving both their own financial affairs and difficulties as well as dealing with those of their clients and customers.

### Environmental:
The environmental law attorneys handle all facets of environmental practice from litigating major cases to counseling clients on permitting, ISRA, air and water pollution, wetlands, solid and hazardous wastes, contract documentation and litigation involving the remediation of environmental sites, compliance counseling, industrial pretreatment, lender liability, oversight of environmental assessments in land sales, and land use/environmental approvals.

### Intellectual Property:
The Intellectual Property Practice includes the full range of patent, trademark, copyright, trade secret, and computer and internet law experience in the areas of litigation, licensing and transfer, registration and counseling.

### Labor & Employment:
The labor and employment law attorneys represent management and defendants in employment litigation; discrimination litigation; non-competition disputes; and traditional labor law, including drafting and negotiating collective bargaining agreements, rendering advice concerning strike planning. They also counsel non-union employers facing union boycotts, organizational campaigns and other union activity.

### Land Use:
The Land Use and Environmental Permitting and Compliance Group regularly obtains permits, approvals and certifications from local planning and zoning boards, county boards, special regional agencies, and State and Federal agencies concerning every aspect of land use, land development and regulatory compliance.

### Litigation:
The firm's Litigation Department is its largest, with over 90 lawyers and several formal practice groups, covering labor and employment, environmental litigation, personal injury litigation, bankruptcy and creditors' rights, and commercial litigation. Litigation department attorneys are also members of interdepartmental practice groups in computer and high technology law, education law, environmental law, estates law, healthcare law, intellectual property, and media and communications law.

### Real Estate:
Archer & Greiner's real estate attorneys handle matters involving every facet of the sale, leasing, development, financing and acquisition of real property. They regularly handle complex multi-state sales, acquisitions and financings, as well as simple real estate transactions.

### Estates & Trusts:
The Estates and Trusts Department provides estate, business continuity, charitable giving and elder care planning, estate and trust administration and litigation services, as well as tax services to individuals, professionals and institutions.

## OFFICES

**NEW JERSEY**

**HADDONFIELD:** One Centennial Square, 33 East Euclid Avenue, NJ 08033
Tel: 856 795 2121   Fax: 856 795 0574

**FLEMINGTON:** Plaza One, 1 State Route 12, Suite 201, NJ 08822
Tel: 908 788 9700   Fax: 908 788 7854

**HACKENSACK:** Court Plaza South, West Wing, 21 Main Street, Suite 353, NJ 07601-7095
Tel: 201 342 6000   Fax: 201 342 6611

**PRINCETON:** 700 Alexander Park, Suite 102, NJ 08540
Tel: 609 580 3700   Fax: 609 580 0051

**SHREWSBURY:** 830 Broad Street, Suite B
Tel: 732 741 9993   Fax: 732 741 9944

**DELAWARE**

**WILMINGTON:** 300 Delaware Avenue, Suite 1370, DE 19801
Tel: 302 777 4350   Fax: 302 777 4352

**GEORGETOWN:** 9 East Market Street, PO Box 977, DE 19947
Tel: 302 858 5151   Fax: 302 858 5161

**NEW YORK**

**NEW YORK:** 2 Penn Plaza, Suite 1500, NY 10121
Tel: 212 292 4988   Fax: 212 629 4568

**PENNSYLVANIA**

**PHILADELPHIA:** One Liberty Place, Thirty-Second Floor, 1650 Market Street, PA 19103
Tel: 215 963 3300   Fax: 215 963 9999

**Archer&Greiner** P.C.
ATTORNEYS AT LAW

# COLE, SCHOTZ, MEISEL, FORMAN & LEONARD, P.A.

www.coleschotz.com **tel:** 201 489 3000 **fax:** 201 489 1536

**Managing Partners:** Michael D Sirota and Samuel Weiner
Number of partners: 82
Number of lawyers: 114

## Firm Overview:

Cole Schotz serves clients throughout the United States with offices in New York, New Jersey, Delaware, Maryland and Texas. The firm represents hundreds of closely-held businesses and individuals as well as Fortune 500 companies.

Founded in 1928, the firm has grown to 114 attorneys who work in eight primary areas of practice: Litigation; Real Estate; Bankruptcy and Corporate Restructuring; Tax, Trusts and Estates; Corporate, Finance and Business Transactions; Employment; Environmental; and Construction Services.

## Main Areas of Practice:

### Litigation:

With unparalleled experience litigating hundreds of trials in state and federal courts, the group is recognized as the region's "bet the company" litigation team throughout New Jersey, New York, Delaware and Maryland. In addition, the firm is frequently called upon to arbitrate and mediate as alternatives to litigation.

### Real Estate:

The group is among the largest real estate practice groups in New Jersey, with additional offices in New York City and Baltimore. The scope of the practice includes the acquisition, sale, asset management, risk and business opportunity analysis, development, redevelopment, financing, leasing, subleasing, syndication and environmental concerns of commercial (including retail, office and hotel), industrial, warehouse and multi-family residential properties.

### Bankruptcy & Corporate Restructuring:

A national platform team with veteran attorneys based in Delaware, Maryland, New Jersey, New York and Texas, who have vast experience in complex corporate restructurings, state and federal insolvency proceedings and high stakes bankruptcy litigation. Clients include debtors, creditors' and other statutory committees, institutional creditors, asset purchasers, indenture trustees, bond insurers, venture capitalists, secured parties, lessors and contract parties, equity holders, directors, and court-appointed fiduciaries.

### Tax, Trusts & Estates:

Counsels individuals and businesses in a wide range of tax and estate planning strategies. Clients include owners of family businesses where succession planning and asset protection are linked, and individuals of substantial means who wish to take advantage of sophisticated tax planning techniques to retain and build their wealth for future generations.

### Corporate, Finance & Business Transactions:

The group leverages their extensive legal knowledge and business and tax backgrounds to provide practical advice to clients regarding all business matters, from simple governance issues to complex corporate transactions. Clients vary in size from public corporations to closely held and family owned businesses and sole proprietorships. They also span a wide range of industry and market sectors, including, finance, venture capital, private equity, manufacturing, distribution, professional services, technology, pharmaceutical, health care, insurance and surety.

### Employment:

Provide preventive counseling to both large and small employers on a wide range of compliance issues and evolving statutory requirements, including those related to wrongful discharge, discrimination, sexual and other forms of harassment, family and medical leaves of absence, disability and substance abuse.

### Environmental:

Vast experience guiding companies who buy, sell and conduct business on commercial or industrial property through a wide range of environmental matters by leveraging knowledge of the state and federal laws regulating environmental site assessment, remediation and cleanup, as well as the development of contaminated or environmentally sensitive properties. In addition the team works with clients whose business activities directly impact the environment, including gasoline service stations, automotive dealerships, dry cleaners, composting and recycling facilities and transfer stations.

### Construction Services:

Provides sophisticated and cost-effective legal services to clients involved in major construction projects in New Jersey, New York and around the country. Drawing on the knowledge and skills of colleagues from the Real Estate, Litigation, Bankruptcy and Environmental departments, the team represents owner-developers, including REITs, real estate and private equity funds, national retail chains, *Fortune* 500 companies, residential developers, health care providers and automobile dealers, as well as general contractors, construction managers, trade contractors, paving and road contractors, sewer contractors, utility contractors, material suppliers, design professionals and bonding companies.

### Intellectual Property:

Counsels clients in acquiring and protecting the trademarks, copyrights, patents and trade secrets that can be a business's most valuable assets and in avoiding and defending against infringement charges that can create roadblocks to doing business. As advisors to local, national and international businesses, the group's broad experience ranges from traditional brick-and-mortar enterprises to the digital world, including software and the Internet.

### White Collar & Investigations:

Represents individuals and corporations, both U.S. and international, in grand jury proceedings, quasi-criminal investigations, administrative enforcement proceedings, criminal trials and internal investigations.

# DAY PITNEY LLP

**www.**daypitney.com **tel:** 973 966 6300 **fax:** 973 966 1015

**Managing Partner:** Stanley A Twardy, Jr
Number of partners: 134
Number of attorneys: 319

## Firm Overview:

Day Pitney is a leading full-service regional US law firm with a more than 100-year reputation for superior client service and high-value legal representation. With more than 300 attorneys in nine offices throughout the Northeast, the firm is well-positioned to provide regional, national and international clients results-based representation and forward-thinking solutions to complex litigation, transactions and regulatory matters.

## Main Areas of Practice:

### Litigation:
The firm's highly skilled and experienced litigators are frequently called upon to handle difficult and important cases. Day Pitney's established reputation as trial lawyers strengthens its ability to resolve disputed matters using alternative dispute resolution, including mediation and arbitration. Day Pitney has worked on almost every type of litigation, including antitrust and unfair competition, contract disputes, construction and infrastructure projects, consumer finance, creditors' rights, white-collar, franchises and distributorships, insurance and reinsurance, product liability and other torts.
**Contacts:** Benjamin E Haglund, James H Rotondo

### Corporate:
Day Pitney's corporate lawyers serve as securities and corporate counsel to NYSE-, NASDAQ- and AMEX-listed companies across a wide variety of industries including energy, banking, defense, communications, manufacturing and technology. The firm's practice advises on corporate governance, regulatory compliance, securities law, state corporate law, tax and benefits issues and offers a strong transactional practice in the areas of capital markets, joint ventures and mergers and acquisitions. With the recent shift in market valuation, Day Pitney's Distressed Asset practice group counsels investors, sellers and others who seek to capitalize on the recent instability in the capital markets.
**Contact:** R Scott Beach

### Energy & Utilities:
Day Pitney's energy and utility clients benefit from more than 50 years of comprehensive advice and representation to some of the sector's largest national and international developers, contractors, utilities and institutional investors. The firm's lawyers represent clients before local, state and federal regulatory agencies, including the Federal Energy Regulatory Commission, the Environmental Protection Agency and the Nuclear Regulatory Commission in the areas of regulatory reform and industry structure.
**Contact:** David T Doot

### Financial Services:
Day Pitney's financial services lawyers assist a wide range of banks, financial services companies and corporations in creatively structuring transactions that achieve their business and legal objectives. Day Pitney's Financial Services group advises on a variety of issues including bank lending, project finance, structured finance, lease finance, real estate finance, private placements, municipal finance, bankruptcy, creditors' rights and workouts and restructurings.
**Contact:** Richard J Wasserman

### Individual Clients:
Day Pitney provides the full range of services needed by individuals and their families with respect to estate and tax planning, business succession planning, administration of decedents' estates, administration of trusts, guardianships, conservatorships and other matters relating to incapacity, divorce law and probate litigation.
**Contact:** Gregory A Hayes

### Intellectual Property:
Day Pitney's Intellectual Property group has broad technical experience in computer science, media and communications, antitrust, and science and engineering, and offers clients counseling and litigation services, including patent and trademark prosecution, litigation and transactions. Day Pitney has coordinated worldwide legal proceedings as part of a client's overall patent strategy.
**Contact:** Elizabeth A Alquist

### Labor, Employment & Benefits:
Day Pitney lawyers devise preventative and cost-effective solutions regarding personnel policies, internal audits, the Americans with Disabilities Act and ever-evolving federal and state laws regulating the workplace. When a client's best strategy calls for vigorous litigation in matters such as employer/employee disputes, including discrimination cases, labor disputes, disputes between employers and government enforcement agencies and ERISA contract disputes, Day Pitney is able to assist.
**Contact:** Daniel L Schwartz

### Real Estate, Environmental & Land Use:
The firm has broad environmental, land use and real estate capabilities, representing lenders, developers, owners and prospective purchasers of real estate projects of all kinds. Areas of practice include redevelopment—targeting, analyzing and resolving transactional and environmental hurdles—and representing clients at the trial and appellate levels in state and federal courts as well as in arbitration proceedings and other forms of alternative dispute resolution. Day Pitney's team also provides environmental regulatory advice and has counseled clients on "green" projects and LEED-certified buildings.
**Contact:** Dennis M Reznick

### Clients:
The firm's clients range from *Fortune* 500 corporations and large and medium-sized companies in the public and private sectors, to start-ups, non-profits, educational institutions and individuals. Industry experience includes, among others, chemical, energy, financial services, franchise, insurance, life sciences, manufacturing, non-profit, pharmaceutical, real estate, retail and telecommunications.

# GIBBONS P.C.

**www.**gibbonslaw.com **tel:** 973 596 4500 **fax:** 973 596 0545

**Chairman & Managing Director:** Patrick C Dunican Jr
Number of directors: 116  Number of other lawyers: 114

## Firm Overview:

With 230 attorneys, Gibbons is a leading law firm in New Jersey, New York, Philadelphia and Delaware, ranked among the nation's top 200 by *American Lawyer*. Gibbons is one of only 20 law firms nationwide to be named to the *National Law Journal's* inaugural 'Midsize Hot List,' which recognized firms with fewer than 300 lawyers that found innovative ways to position themselves in the recent market, demonstrating creativity and success in recruiting and retaining top talent, developing practice areas and managing operations. A 2009 winner of the prestigious Catalyst Award, a pre-eminent corporate honor recognizing excellence in the advancement of women in the workplace, Gibbons is ranked by *Working Mother* magazine as one of the top 50 firms nationwide for working women and by *Minority Law Journal* as a top 50 firm for diversity.

## Main Areas of Practice:

**Business & Commercial Litigation:**
Handling sophisticated and complex commercial litigation, including securities class actions, insurance coverage disputes, regulatory and administrative law, Lanham Act and unfair competition, restrictive covenants and all manner of contractual disputes. Active E-Discovery Task Force helping companies to prevent document retention and electronic discovery problems, and to solve such problems that do arise.
**Contact:** Brian J McMahon

**Corporate:**
Advising leading area and global corporations and other businesses and financial institutions on the full range of corporate law matters, including mergers, acquisitions, divestitures, restructurings, joint ventures, licensing, corporate finance, commercial lending, capital raising, regulatory compliance, corporate governance, tax and specialized business transactions requiring novel solutions, as well as serving as outside general counsel.
**Contact:** Frank T Cannone

**Criminal Defense:**
Investigating and defending against allegations of business, accounting, securities, bank, insurance, tax, healthcare and government contract fraud. Department attorneys have been involved in many high profile investigations and prosecutions of alleged political corruption and business crime, particularly in the pharmaceutical and communications industries.
**Contact:** Lawrence S Lustberg

**Employment & Labor Law:**
Representing employers in federal and state court, in litigation involving discrimination, harassment, retaliation, wage and hour, employment contract, restrictive covenant, wrongful discharge, employee benefits and ERISA claims. Providing the full range of preventive and compliance counseling and training with an emphasis on discipline and discharge, harassment, disability-related leaves and accommodations, workforce restructurings, restrictive covenants and executive compensation, as well as workplace investigations and audits of employment practices. In the labor arena, addressing union organizational drives, election campaigns and related union activities; labor audits; labor contract negotiations and administration, grievances and labor arbitrations; unfair labor practice charges; plant relocations and closings; successorship and double-breasting problems; and pension liability issues.
**Contact:** Christine A Amalfe

**Financial Restructuring & Creditors' Rights:**
Representing creditors, debtors, and various fiduciaries in all aspects of complex business insolvency issues and proceedings, including federal bankruptcy proceedings; state court litigation involving receiverships, attachments, replevins and foreclosures; out-of-court 'workouts' and related debtor and creditor relations counseling to resolve insolvency issues; and disputes outside of formal proceedings.
**Contact:** Karen A Giannelli

**Government Affairs:**
Counseling entities in the public, private and nonprofit sectors on state and federal government relations issues, including legislative lobbying, regulatory counseling, and interaction with state agencies.
**Contact:** David A Filippelli

**Intellectual Property:**
Providing a full range of patent, trademark, copyright, unfair competition, e-commerce, trade secret and computer and internet law experience in the areas of litigation, strategic licensing and transactional work, patent prosecution, trademark and copyright registrations, corporate due diligence, intellectual property audits, and general intellectual property counseling.
**Contact:** David E De Lorenzi

**Products Liability:**
Representing product manufacturers in a variety of industries. Defending pharmaceutical and medical/surgical device manufacturers, as well as diagnostic laboratories, in complex matters involving issues such as purported adverse effects; design, warnings, and/or manufacturing defects; and results of laboratory analyses. Defending industrial equipment, automotive, and consumer product manufacturers in a wide variety of claims relating to products liability issues.
**Contact:** Kim M Catullo

**Real Property & Environmental:**
Providing real estate and environmental counseling and litigation services for all types of properties. Extensive real property practice handling sales, purchases and development of properties, including office buildings, industrial and flex buildings, retail centers, apartment buildings and hotels. Environmental practice providing assistance with a variety of clients' litigation, regulatory, and transactional needs.
**Contact:** Russell B Bershad, Douglas J Janacek

**International Work:**
Serving as a bridge between different business and legal systems and possessing cultural and commercial fluency in support of US clients and their transactions throughout Europe, Asia and Latin America, with a particular focus on Germany. Providing similar services to international clients seeking to make acquisitions, strategic alliances, joint ventures, or investments in the US. Gibbons is also a member of the Geneva Group International, a network of independent professional service firms offering a full range of legal, accounting, and other services worldwide.

## OFFICES

**NEW JERSEY**
**NEWARK:** One Gateway Center, NJ 07102
Tel: 973 596 4500  Fax: 973 596 0545
Email: firm@gibbonslaw.com

**TRENTON:** 50 West State Street, Suite 1104, NJ 08608
Tel: 609 394 5300  Fax: 609 394 5301

**DELAWARE**
**WILMINGTON:** 1000 N. West Street, Suite 1200, DE 19801
Tel: 302 295 4875  Fax: 302 295 4876

**NEW YORK**
**NEW YORK:** One Pennsylvania Plaza, 37th Floor, NY 10119
Tel: 212 613 2000  Fax: 212 290 2018

**PENNSYLVANIA**
**PHILADELPHIA:** 1700 Two Logan Square, PA 19103
Tel: 215 665 0400  Fax: 215 636 0366

# GREENBAUM, ROWE, SMITH & DAVIS LLP

www.greenbaumlaw.com **tel:** 732 549 5600 **fax:** 732 549 1881

**Chairman:** Paul A Rowe
**Managing Partners:** W Raymond Felton, Mark H Sobel
Number of partners: 60  Number of total lawyers: 97
Languages: *English*

## Firm Overview:

Founded in 1914, the firm has distinguished itself as a market leader by serving a broad range of local, regional and national clients doing business in New Jersey and surrounding areas. The firm earns the trust and loyalty of clients by providing sophisticated, creative and cost-effective representation delivered through collaborative teamwork, proactive legal strategies, attention to detail and relationship-oriented service. Attorneys practice in five departments – litigation, corporate, real estate, environmental and tax, trusts and estates, which are augmented by interdisciplinary practice groups focused on niche areas. This integrated service profile meets the needs of entrepreneurial ventures, mid-sized businesses and large corporate and multinational entities alike.

## Main Areas of Practice:

### Litigation:
34 partners
The department is among the most highly regarded in the state, offering both the big firm resources to handle 'bet the company' litigation where cost is not an issue, and the efficiency to take on more routine matters where cost is a key element of the overall result. Matters include commercial and business litigation, product liability, real estate, eminent domain, environmental, insurance, banking and creditors' rights, bankruptcy and reorganization, employment, construction, white-collar defense, corporate compliance, professional negligence, intellectual property and family law. The firm's philosophy is rooted in the belief that each case is unique and requires evaluation of the client's specific goals and expectations. While some cases are best resolved through negotiation, others must be litigated to conclusion. Recognizing the difference combines both legal analysis and consideration of the client's business objectives, personal circumstances and budgetary constraints.
**Contact:** Paul A Rowe, Chair  **Tel:** 732 549 5600
**Email:** PRowe@greenbaumlaw.com
**Contact:** Alan S Naar, Vice Chair  **Tel:** 732 476 2530
**Email:** ANaar@greenbaumlaw.com

### Corporate:
5 partners
The firm represents large businesses as well as smaller entrepreneurial firms who lack in-house counsel. Regardless of client size, the firm keeps tabs on the bottom line by maintaining a consistent focus on quality, responsiveness and efficiency. The department handles both routine matters and high profile projects including mergers and acquisitions, financing transactions and securities offerings, and is highly skilled in all areas of business law. Attorneys also draw upon the knowledge of colleagues practicing in areas including employment, real estate, white-collar defense, securities, environmental, tax and litigation. With nearly a century-long history in New Jersey, the firm is well placed to deal with the business, legal and government communities at all levels.
**Contact:** W Raymond Felton, Chair  **Tel:** 732 476 2670
**Email:** RFelton@greenbaumlaw.com

### Environmental:
3 partners
This department was established in 2012 to enhance the firm's existing environmental practice. Clients are counseled on the full spectrum of environmental laws and regulations and their impact on real estate, business and lending transactions and operations in New Jersey and beyond. Real estate developers, property and business owners and operators, manufacturers, REITS, landlords, tenants, lenders, trustees and individuals are among those who turn to the firm with environmental issues. Matters include the management of environmental risk and transactional dilemmas in brownfield cleanups and redevelopment of contaminated properties; compliance with federal Superfund law and state analogs; waste generation and disposal issues; air, water and wetlands issues and permits; transaction-triggered environmental laws; financing options for contaminated property redevelopment; environmental cleanup cost recovery; disclosure obligations; penalty and enforcement proceedings; due diligence and contractual allocation of environmental risks in transactions; institutional and engineering controls; environmental insurance; sustainable development initiatives.
**Contact:** David B Farer, Chair  **Tel:** 732-476-2476
**Email:** DFarer@greenbaumlaw.com

### Real Estate:
15 partners
The firm represents public and private sector clients with interests in residential, industrial, retail, office and mixed use commercial properties, including regional and national developers, property and land owners, REITS, investors, landlords, tenants, contractors and municipalities. Attorneys counsel clients on all aspects of real estate law: acquisitions and sales; contracts and leasing; development and redevelopment including brownfields and contaminated projects; land use and zoning issues; permitting and approvals; affordable housing issues; sustainable and green development including solar projects; eminent domain; community associations; planned real estate; condominium formation; distressed real estate; real estate brokerage law; restructuring and workouts.
**Contact:** Thomas J Denitzio, Jr, Co-Chair **Tel:** 732 476 2610
**Email:** TDenitzio@greenbaumlaw.com
**Contact:** Meryl AG Gonchar, Co-Chair **Tel:** 732 476 2690
**Email:** MGonchar@greenbaumlaw.com

### Tax, Trusts & Estates:
4 partners
The department provides a full spectrum of basic and sophisticated services related to business and personal tax issues, estate planning and estate administration. Representation encompasses wealth preservation and accumulation strategies; asset protection planning; tax minimization; federal and state tax controversies; succession planning; elder law issues; employee benefits; executive compensation; estate litigation; and non-profit/tax exempt issues. Clients include individuals, business owners, corporate executives and directors, and nonprofit and tax exempt entities.
**Contact:** Michael A Backer, Chair **Tel:** 732 476 2450
**Email:** MBacker@greenbaumlaw.com

## PRACTICE AREAS

Alternative Dispute Resolution
Alternative Energy & Sustainable Development
Banking, Business Financing & Creditors' Rights
Bankruptcy & Reorganization
Community Association Law
Condemnation & Eminent Domain
Construction
Distressed Real Estate
Employee Benefits
Employment
Family Law
Healthcare
Insurance
Land Use
Planned Real Estate
Product Liability
Real Estate Brokerage
Redevelopment
Technology
White Collar Defense & Corporate & International Human Rights Compliance

## OFFICES

NEW JERSEY
**WOODBRIDGE:** 99 Wood Avenue South, NJ 07095
Tel: 732 549 5600  Fax: 732 549 1881
**ROSELAND:** 75 Livingston Avenue, NJ 07068

## LERNER DAVID LITTENBERG KRUMHOLZ & MENTLIK, LLP

**www.**ldlkm.com  **tel:** 908 654 5000  **fax:** 908 654 7866

**Managing Partner:** William L Mentlik
Number of partners: 32
Number of other lawyers: 38

### Firm Overview:

Lerner David has focused exclusively on intellectual property (IP) law since 1969. Seventy lawyers apply the firm's extensive expertise across the spectrum of IP matters. Lerner David attorneys hold scientific or technical undergraduate degrees, and many have post-graduate degrees, as well as significant commercial experience in various technology sectors. The firm's approach extends well beyond the traditional, task-oriented attorney-client relationship: Lerner David regards IP asset growth and protection as an integral part of every client's business goals and strategies. The highly developed business sense of its attorneys allows them to provide sound, practical advice that helps companies make intelligent decisions about the benefits and potential risks associated with intellectual property. Lerner David brings understanding and direction to complex IP matters, particularly when working as part of a team that includes the client and its advisors in corporate, tax, regulatory and other areas.

### Main Areas of Practice:

All aspects of intellectual property law including patent, trademark, unfair competition and copyright litigation, risk assessment and due diligence for new products and in mergers & acquisitions, licensing, freedom to operate opinions, portfolio management, procurement and strategic planning.

### Clients:

Lerner David's client base includes the leading corporations of the world in such diverse industries as medical devices, software, electrical and computer products, pharmaceuticals, aviation, telecommunications, footwear and apparel, biotechnology, consumer products, chemicals, business methods, retail, food and beverages, toys, marketing and advertising.

### International Work:

Lerner David develops and protects intellectual property assets throughout the world by representing US corporations in foreign jurisdictions and foreign corporations in the United States, notably from the firm's office in Guangzhou, China, and also with its many preferred associate attorneys in Europe and elsewhere. Through this extensive experience, the firm has become exceptionally adept at converting the varied protections afforded by different jurisdictions into valuable, synergistic corporate IP strategies – allowing effective representation no matter what a client's business interests and opportunities may be. As a result, Lerner David's clients have been able to maximize the value of their IP assets through successful licensing and litigation on virtually every continent. Lerner David is the first American intellectual property law firm located in the Pearl River Delta – the most economically dynamic region of China. Licensed by the Chinese Ministry of Justice, Lerner David's fully-staffed Guangzhou office focuses on counseling Chinese companies and law firms on intellectual property matters in the United States, and US companies on intellectual property matters in China. Whether from China or the US, Lerner David offers the same level of concern, expertise and commitment to all its clients.

### PRACTICE AREAS

Intellectual Property

### OFFICES

NEW JERSEY

**WESTFIELD:** 600 South Avenue West, NJ 07090-1497
Tel: 908 654 5000   Fax: 908 654 7866
Email: info@ldlkm.com

### INTERNATIONAL OFFICES

The firm also has an office in Guangzhou, Guangdong, China.

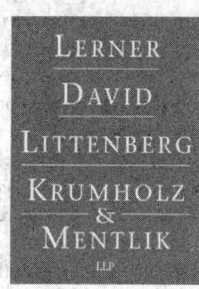

# LOWENSTEIN SANDLER LLP

www.lowenstein.com **tel:** 973 597 2500 **fax:** 973 597 2400

**Managing Partner:** Gary M Wingens
Number of partners: 115  Number of other lawyers: 157

**Firm Overview:**

Lowenstein Sandler is a leading provider of transactional, litigation, and bankruptcy and creditors' rights legal services to many of the country's top companies and funds. Close to 300 lawyers in New York, New Jersey and California offices immerse themselves in clients' industries in order to deeply understand their businesses. The firm is characterized by its passion for clients' success, its commitment to its people, and its pro bono and public interest work in the communities that it serves.

## Main Areas of Practice:

### Corporate:

Lowenstein Sandler has extensive experience in corporate counseling and transactional work, as well as business reorganizations. The Corporate Department provides a full range of services to clients in connection with the organization and structuring of business entities; initial public offerings and subsequent offerings; general business counseling; mergers and acquisitions; financing transactions; and investment management and derivatives. Lowenstein Sandler also provides a full range of tax and employee benefits/executive compensation services to the business community, as well as tax and estate planning for individuals.

### Litigation:

The firm's Litigation Department represents clients in all stages of litigation (both trial and appellate) in both state and federal courts, as well as before administrative and governmental agencies. Lowenstein Sandler has developed several prominent, nationally recognized niche practices in areas such as complex litigation, environmental litigation and toxic tort defense, insurance coverage litigation, capital markets and securities litigation, and white-collar defense.

### Bankruptcy, Financial Reorganization & Creditors' Rights:

Lowenstein Sandler's Bankruptcy Department has extensive experience representing debtors, trustees, secured and unsecured creditors, and investors in high-profile Chapter 11 reorganizations, out-of-court workouts, financial restructurings, and litigation. The group also frequently provides bankruptcy advice on corporate and structured finance matters, and on the acquisition of assets out of bankruptcy.

### Employment:

Lowenstein Sandler's Employment Practice works with clients ranging from dynamic start-ups to multinational corporations, developing employee relations strategies that address clients' challenges and leverage their opportunities, while helping management comply with the growing array of employment laws that regulate the workplace. The firm's attorneys focus on preventing claims and on pursuing litigation strategies that enhance the ability of clients to manage their employees in an effective manner that strengthens their organizations and promotes productivity.

### Environmental:

Lowenstein Sandler's Environmental Law and Litigation Practice assists clients with virtually every type of lawsuit involving environmental matters in federal and state courts throughout the country. The firm counsels clients on a variety of matters including compliance and auditing; acquisitions and divestitures; site remediation; natural resource damages; toxic tort cases; occupational health and safety; and insurance coverage.

### Insurance:

Lowenstein Sandler is one of a handful of nationally known firms that pioneered the development of insurance coverage litigation. Lowenstein Sandler attorneys have litigated coverage cases in more than 20 states, appeared for the policyholder in more than 30 reported decisions, and have collected more than $500 million in settlements and judgments. Lawyers in the practice advise and litigate in insurance matters involving Directors & Officers coverage, professional liability, employment practices liability, construction defect liability, cyber liability, consumer product liability, fiduciary liability, broker liability and first party property losses.

### Real Estate:

Lowenstein Sandler's national Real Estate Practice covers transactions and disputes involving investments in all types of commercial real estate. Developers and landlords, leading financial institutions (including investment advisers, private equity firms, and commercial and investment banking institutions), Fortune 100 companies, national and regional retailers, and closely held businesses all turn to Lowenstein Sandler's Real Estate Practice for legal counsel on a wide range of sophisticated transactions involving real properties located throughout the United States.

### Technology, IP & Venture Capital:

The Tech Group at Lowenstein Sandler counsels technology-driven businesses and their investors at all stages of growth and has earned a reputation for excellence in venture capital and other financing transactions. The group has closed hundreds of private company financing transactions including, angel rounds, complex venture financings, bridge fundings and IPOs. Members of the Tech Group include intellectual property attorneys, and registered patent lawyers and practitioners who counsel clients on matters pertaining to intellectual property, technology and privacy law.

### Trusts & Estates:

Lowenstein Sandler's Trusts and Estates Practice helps clients preserve and pass on their families' wealth, while minimizing taxes and assisting fiduciaries in fulfilling their duties. The group's attorneys are skilled in fiduciary litigation, business counseling, and domestic and international business tax planning, all of which enhance both its planning and administration practices.

### White-Collar Defense:

Lowenstein Sandler's White-Collar Defense Group has decades of experience defending corporate and individual clients in state and federal prosecutions, as well as conducting internal investigations for private and public corporations. The group regularly defends clients in all phases of criminal proceedings, including grand jury investigations, trials and appeals.

# Lowenstein Sandler

**OFFICES**

NEW JERSEY
**ROSELAND:** 65 Livingston Avenue, NJ 07068
Tel: 973 597 2500   Fax: 973 597 2400

CALIFORNIA
**PALO ALTO:** 390 Lytton Avenue, CA 94301
Tel: 650 433 5800   Fax: 650 328 2799

NEW YORK
**NEW YORK:** 1251 Avenue of the Americas, NY 10020
Tel: 212 262 6700   Fax: 212 262 7402

# LUM, DRASCO & POSITAN LLC

**www.lumlaw.com tel:** 973 403 9000 **fax:** 973 403 9021

**Managing Director:** Wayne J Positan
**Senior Members:** Dennis J Drasco, Wayne J Positan, Paul A Sandars, III
Number of members: 11  Number of lawyers: 25
Languages: *English, Spanish*

**Firm Overview:**

The firm, which traces its roots back to 1870, represents a wide range of clients in litigation, labor and employment law, and business law throughout the State of New Jersey. It has a reputation for excellence and involvement in the legal community, and has been recognized as a LexisNexis Martindale-Hubbell 2013 Top Ranked Law Firm, and by ALM as a 2013 Go-To Law Firm at the Top 500 Companies. Sixteen of its lawyers are currently recognized as NJ Superlawyers or Rising Stars.

**Main Areas of Practice:**

**Litigation:**
4 partners; 11 fee earners
- Currently defending several class actions in New Jersey Federal Court against a manufacturer of red light cameras
- Representing a majority shareholder of a large urban mall in a dispute with a minority shareholder in Chancery court
- Representing a software designer in New Jersey Federal Court for breach of contract and professional negligence
- Representing a large chemical company threatened with eminent domain
- Defending a large urban county in litigation to compel development of a medical use at the site of a former hospital

**Key Clients:** Redflex Traffic Systems, Inc.; Mednax Services, Inc.; Efstathios Valiotis; GEO Specialties; County of Essex; Comax Manufacturing Corp.
**Contact:** Dennis J Drasco **Tel:** 973 228 6770
**Email:** ddrasco@lumlaw.com
**Contact:** Paul A Sandars, III **Tel:** 973 228 6767
**Email:** psandars@lumlaw.com
**Contact:** Kevin J O'Connor **Tel:** 973 228 6760
**Email:** koconnor@lumlaw.com
**Contact:** Gina M Sorge **Tel:** 973 228 6758
**Email:** gsorge@lumlaw.com

**Labor & Employment:**
3 partners; 7 fee earners
- Represented United States Mineral Products d/b/a/ Isolatek in non-compete NJ Chancery litigation, AAA arbitration and federal court confirmation of judgment of appx. 800g on counterclaim against former President/COO
- Representing medical group in USDCNJ in a qui tam action under False Claims Act by former hospital employees involving Medicare claims and payments
- Conducting labor negotiations on behalf of Dry Ice Corp, GTS Welco Gas Technologies, and Welco Acetylene Corp in Northeast with Teamsters

- Obtained jury verdict of no cause of action on disability discrimination case under NJ Law Against Discrimination; Pacelli v. Passaic County, Superior Court of NJ, Passaic County
- Represent clients in state court Chancery Division and federal court in cases re: minority shareholder rights, employment agreements, non-compete matters, internal disputes among shareholders, partners, officers, employees, other entities in food ops, medical practices, service industry, joint ventures and post-acquisition disputes

**Key Clients:** Marotta Controls Inc.; Dry Ice Corp.; GTS Welco Gas Technologies; Passaic County; UMDNJ; State of NJ
**Contact:** Wayne J Positan **Tel:** 973 228 6730
**Email:** wpositan@lumlaw.com
**Contact:** Christina Silva **Tel:** 973 228 6763
**Email:** csilva@lumlaw.com
**Contact:** Daniel M Santarsiero **Tel:** 973 228 6780
**Email:** dsantarsiero@lumlaw.com

**Corporate/Commercial:**
2 partners; 7 fee earners
- Represented Seller in stock sale of manufacturing company to multi-national corporation
- Represented Buyer of chain of self-storage facilities in tri-state area
- Represented Seller of shopping center
- Represented Software company in corporate restructuring and shareholder agreements

**Key Clients:** Marotta Controls, Inc.; Clorox Company; CG USA Inc.; Coilhose Pneumatics
**Contact:** Steven J Eisenstein **Tel:** 973 228 6815
**Email:** seisenstein@lumlaw.com
**Contact:** Kevin F Murphy **Tel:** 973 228 6777
**Email:** kmurphy@lumlaw.com

**Construction:**
3 partners; 7 fee earners
- Representing a general contractor on a New Jersey Turnpike paving project for contract balances, extras and delay damages
- Successfully represented condominium association in

fraud action versus manufacturer of synthetic stucco
- Currently representing condominium association in transition litigation against sponsor/developer, including claims for building envelope water penetration
- Representing a Community College in litigation involving the construction of a parking garage with a claim by a general contractor for extra work

**Key Clients:** Port Liberte Condominium Association I; Hudson Tea Buildings Condominium Association, Inc.; Essex County College; Lucas Construction Co.
**Contact:** Dennis J Drasco **Tel:** 973 228 6770
**Email:** ddrasco@lumlaw.com
**Contact:** Paul A Sandars, III **Tel:** 973 228 6767
**Email:** psandars@lumlaw.com
**Contact:** Bernadette H Condon **Tel:** 973 228 6741
**Email:** bcondon@lumlaw.com

**Environment:**
2 partners; 2 fee earners
- Represented Owner of contaminated real estate in federal court litigation against Fortune 100 Corporation to successfully shift liability for remediation
- Oversight of remediation of environmental contamination following sale of real property
- Representing corporation in lawsuit against insurance companies for defense and indemnity
- Represented company in defense of liability for Superfund site

**Key Clients:** Marotta Controls, Inc.; Clorox Company; Paulsboro Acquisition Corp.; Coilhose Pneumatics
**Contact:** Steven J Eisenstein **Tel:** 973 228 6815
**Email:** seisenstein@lumlaw.com
**Contact:** Dennis J Drasco **Tel:** 973 228 6770
**Email:** ddrasco@lumlaw.com

# MCCARTER & ENGLISH, LLP

**WWW.**mccarter.com

**Chairman:** Michael P Kelly
**Managing Partner:** Stephen M Vajtay, Jr
Number of partners in US offices: 197   Number of other lawyers in US offices: 205

**Firm Overview:**

McCarter & English, LLP is a firm of more than 400 lawyers with offices in Boston, Hartford, Stamford, New York, Newark, Philadelphia and Wilmington. In continuous business for more than 160 years, the firm is among the oldest and largest law firms in America. McCarter represents *Fortune* 500 and mid-cap companies, including many of the country's leading financial, industrial and commercial enterprises, in a full range of legal services.

**Main Areas of Practice:**

**Bankruptcy & Restructuring:**
Well-versed in commercial law, including contracts, commercial transactions, creditor committee issues, fraud, foreclosure, shareholder disputes, lender liability, collection, corporate and bankruptcy aspects of commercial entities, and all facets of debtor-creditor relations, including appointment as trustee in bankruptcy matters.

**Business Litigation:**
Litigates matters such as unfair competition, patent infringement, fraud and commercial torts. Seeks non-litigation methods to resolve client matters such as contractual disputes, regulatory audits and government agency inquiries.

**Construction:**
Counsels clients in the private, public and non-profit sectors. The lawyers handle contract drafting, negotiation and administration; litigation, mediation and ADR; bid protests; construction insurance procurement and coverage disputes and business advisory services at the national and international level.

**Corporate:**
General and special counsel to public and private companies. The work includes M&A, public and private offerings of securities, going-private transactions, leveraged buyouts, SEC compliance and SBICs. The group acts as principal counsel to lenders and borrowers in public and private financings, and as counsel in corporate finance matters involving venture capital and SBICs.

**Employee Benefits:**
Handles plan qualification rules under the Internal Revenue Code, plan administration and related ERISA fiduciary issues and executive compensation. The group designs employee pension and welfare benefit plans, including tax qualified pension, profit-sharing, 401(k), ESOP and non-qualified deferred compensation plans; health, life, disability, severance, fringe benefit and cafeteria plans; and VEBAs.

**Environmental Law:**
Represents clients in all aspects of environmental law,

such as permit applications and enforcement proceedings relating to hazardous and solid waste regulations, as well as air and water pollution control regulations.

**Financial Services Litigation:**
Represents financial services providers in internal investigations, litigation and arbitration. Clients include chartered banks; investment houses; hedge funds; private equity firms; financial advisers; broker-dealers; life, health and disability insurers; third-party administrators and plan fiduciaries. The group handles white-collar criminal defense in both criminal and parallel proceedings.

**Intellectual Property:**
With 100 intellectual property lawyers and professionals, 25 with PhDs, members have graduate degrees in relevant science and engineering fields. Clients include prominent names in biotechnology, pharmaceutical, high-tech and life sciences fields for whom the firm is building and managing complex patent portfolios to protect blockbuster drugs and critical technologies.

**Insurance Coverage:**
Handles claims under all commercial lines of coverage, around the country and abroad. For 25+ years, the group has counseled policyholders by assessing their potential risks, considering new insurance products and analyzing their existing insurance programs.

**Labor & Employment:**
Represents employers in litigation ranging from single plaintiff cases to class actions. Lawyers also appear before administrative agencies in cases relating to discrimination, sexual harassment, wrongful discharge, unfair labor practices and breach of contract.

**Private Clients:**
Advises individuals on strategies to minimize income, estate, gift and generation skipping tax exposure. The group's estate, retirement, charitable gift and business planning experience enables clients to achieve their personal and financial goals.

**Product Liability:**
Represents manufacturers and sellers of pharmaceuticals, medical devices, industrial and

consumer products. The group tries to verdict numerous cases each year and handles products liability appeals in appellate courts. The firm is counsel of record in more than 120 reported products liability decisions and regularly plays a lead role litigating mass tort, class action and multi-district litigation issues.

**Public Finance:**
Handles transactions such as general, moral and special obligation bonds; bond and tax anticipation notes; certificates of participation; variable and fixed-rate obligations; demand bonds; pooled bonds; stripped municipal securities; credit-enhanced obligations and current and advanced refundings.

**Real Estate:**
Represents owners, lenders, banks, life insurance companies, investors and developers in connection with the acquisition, sale, financing, leasing and development of real estate. The group also handles land use planning, zoning and tax abatement/appeal matters, including appearances before administrative and judicial bodies.

**Tax:**
Work includes tax controversies, multistate tax advice regarding business operations and acquisitions, business tax planning and real estate tax appeals. The group also assists clients in maximizing tax credit opportunities ranging from research and development incentives to low-income housing tax credits.

**International Work:**
The firm represents US and foreign entities in international purchase and sale, export control compliance, distribution, licensing and joint venture agreements; M&A transactions; intellectual property patents, trademarks and trade secrets; litigation and foreign-based arbitrations; architectural, finance, leasing and indenture trustee agreements. Work is focused particularly in China, India, Europe and Latin America.

**OFFICES**

**NEW JERSEY**
**NEWARK:** Tel: 973 622 4444  Fax: 973 624 7070

**CONNECTICUT**
**HARTFORD:** Tel: 860 275 6700  Fax: 860 724 3397
**STAMFORD:** Tel: 203 399 5900  Fax: 203 399 5800

**DELAWARE**
**WILMINGTON:** Tel: 302 984 6300  Fax: 302 984 6399

**MASSACHUSETTS**
**BOSTON:** Tel: 617 449 6500  Fax: 617 607 9200

**NEW YORK**
**NEW YORK:** Tel: 212 609 6800 Fax: 212 609 6921

**PENNSYLVANIA**
**PHILADELPHIA:** Tel: 215 979 3800 Fax: 215 979 3899

McCARTER & ENGLISH
ATTORNEYS AT LAW

# McELROY, DEUTSCH, MULVANEY & CARPENTER, LLP

**www.**mdmc-law.com **tel:** 973 993 8100 **fax:** 973 425 0161

**Chief Financial & Operating Officer:** John A Dunlea
**Managing Partner:** Edward B Deutsch, Esq
Number of partners: 113  Number of lawyers: 305
Languages: *Chinese, English, Filipino, French, Hebrew, Romanian, Spanish and Italian.*

## Firm Overview:

Established in 1983, McElroy, Deutsch, Mulvaney & Carpenter, LLP (MDM&C) is a diverse practice with lawyers who place the client first. MDM&C has more than 300 lawyers in ten offices in seven states, and offers a full range of legal services including municipal and local government, litigation, labor and employment, bankruptcy and restructuring, healthcare, real estate, insurance, environmental, fidelity and surety, construction, corporate transactions, white-collar crime and corporate compliance. MDM&C's philosophy provides clients with the critical edge they need to achieve their legal and business objectives. Clients who seek the assistance of MDM&C will discover lawyers dedicated to providing superior service and personal attention to clients' needs. The firm has developed a national reputation and regional expertise without abandoning the focus on efficiency and client satisfaction that is oftentimes the hallmark of the best small firms.

## Main Areas of Practice:

### Litigation:

MDM&C's Litigation Practice includes both trial and appellate work in the following areas: commercial disputes and business torts, insurance defense, insurance coverage, environmental, fidelity and surety, product liability and toxic tort, malpractice, errors and omissions, directors and officers, construction, private and public contract disputes, healthcare, workers' compensation, labor and employment, trade regulation, antitrust, intellectual property, franchise, real estate, banking, pension, probate, and white-collar criminal defense. Although the firm is pleased to be recognized nationally for its efforts in complex litigation, it is also equipped to handle smaller litigated matters with equal efficiency and zeal.
**Contact:** Edward B Deutsch

### Labor & Employment:

MDM&C is the preeminent labor and employment firm in New Jersey and experienced in all aspects of labor and employment law. Attorneys at the firm have handled labor and employment matters on behalf of public entities in state and federal courts as well as before the New Jersey Public Employment Relations Commission, New Jersey Merit System Board, New Jersey Division on Civil Rights, Equal Employment Opportunity Commission, National Labor Relations Board, and Division of Wage and Hour.
**Contact:** Francis X Dee

### Insurance:

Attorneys in MDM&C's Litigation and Insurance Services Group have represented clients in all facets of insurance law. The firm's expertise includes managing all manner of claims, from single-policy, single-claimant matters to multi-billion dollar, multi-jurisdictional coverage disputes involving many scores of parties. MDM&C litigators are highly experienced in the defense of insureds and self-insureds in cases involving high exposure claims in the following areas: construction defects; mass torts; personal injury; premises liability; product liability; and professional liability. In the context of insurance coverage litigation, the attorneys have been national or regional counsel for several of the world's largest carriers in nearly every type of coverage dispute.
**Contact:** Michael J Marone, John T Coyne

### Fidelity & Surety:

The firm has developed a national reputation in construction law and litigation. The heart of this practice remains the resolution of construction claims, but it also involves a wide array of related issues such as bidding disputes, arbitrations, mediations, regulatory matters, contract negotiation and formulation, liens, environmental problems, construction defect and accident litigation, as well as surety bonding questions in both the public and private sectors. In addition to representing elite heavy construction contractors, the firm enjoys similar recognition and is equally experienced in the field of surety bond claims and litigation.
**Contact:** James M Mulvaney, Wendy Kennedy Venoit

### Corporate:

The firm's corporate lawyers counsel its business clients in all the traditional areas of corporate practice. The firm's business clients cover the entire spectrum of industry, ranging from entrepreneurial start-up businesses to large publicly-held and privately-held companies and banks. The firm regularly provides strategic advice and practical solutions on the planning, organization, recapitalization, and restructuring of new or existing businesses, guiding its clients through the applicable legal landscape, assuring compliance with laws and regulations, and assuming responsibility for managing all issues in connection with the undertaking – all with the aim of best meeting clients' business objectives.
**Contact:** Joseph P LaSala

### Bankruptcy/Restructuring:

The attorneys in MDM&C's Bankruptcy and Corporate Restructuring Group are experienced in advising and representing the full spectrum of parties affected by insolvency, bankruptcy and financially troubled businesses. With experience spanning numerous industries and areas of practice, MDM&C offers a depth of knowledge and resources to address the impact of financial distress.
**Contact:** Gary D Bressler, Barry D Kleban, Eric R Perkins

### Healthcare:

MDM&C's Healthcare Law Practice carries a statewide and national reputation in the healthcare field. The practice is comprehensive and ranges from counseling clients on the day-to-day issues that arise in their practices to representing large healthcare systems and business corporations in complex corporate, transactional, and litigation matters.
**Contact:** James A Robertson

## OFFICES

### NEW JERSEY

**MORRISTOWN:** 1300 Mount Kemble Avenue, PO Box 2075, NJ 07962-2075
Tel: 973 993 8100  Fax: 973 425 0161
Email: info@mdmc-law.com

**NEWARK:** Three Gateway Center, 100 Mulberry Street, NJ 07102-4079
Tel: 973 622 7711  Fax: 973 622 5314

**RIDGEWOOD:** 40 West Ridgewood Avenue, NJ 07450
Tel: 201 445 6722  Fax: 201 445 5376

### COLORADO

**GREENWOOD VILLAGE:** 5600 South Quebec Street, Suite C100, CO 80111
Tel: 303 293 8800  Fax: 303 839 0036

### CONNECTICUT

**HARTFORD:** One State Street, 14th Floor, CT 06103-3102
Tel: 860 522 5175  Fax: 860 522 2796

**SOUTHPORT:** 30 Jelliff Lane, CT 06890
Tel: 203 319 4000  Fax: 203 259 0251

### DELAWARE

**WILMINGTON:** 300 Delaware Avenue, Suite 770, DE 19801
Tel: 302 300 4515  Fax: 302 654 4031

### MASSACHUSETTS

**BOSTON:** One Financial Center, 15th Floor, MA 02111
Tel: 617 748 5500  Fax: 617 748 5555

### NEW YORK

**NEW YORK:** 88 Pine Street, 24th Floor, NY 10005
Tel: 212 483 9490  Fax: 212 483 9129

### PENNSYLVANIA

**PHILADELPHIA:** 1617 JFK Boulevard, Suite 1500, PA 19103-1815
Tel: 215 557 2900  Fax: 215 557 2990

# RIKER DANZIG SCHERER HYLAND & PERRETTI LLP

**www.**riker.com **tel:** 973 538 0800 **fax:** 973 538 1984

**Managing Partner:** Glenn A Clark
Number of partners: 58
Number of other attorneys: 95

## Firm Overview:

Riker Danzig Scherer Hyland and Perretti LLP is proud to have served the business community for over 125 years. Riker Danzig has earned a national reputation as the firm to go to in New Jersey for practical, innovative and cost-effective legal solutions. The reputation of the firm and its lawyers provides inherent credibility in the capital markets, courts and government hallways.

## Main Areas of Practice:

### Litigation:
Riker Danzig's seasoned trial and appellate attorneys, numbering over 100 strong, have earned the firm a national reputation as zealous courtroom advocates. The group litigates complex civil cases, and is a leader in banking, securities arbitrations, fraud claims and class actions, insurance, reinsurance (national and international), product liability, construction and intellectual property litigation. Its litigators appear regularly in federal and state courts, as well as before federal, state and administrative agencies.
**Contact:** Gerald A Liloia

### Real Estate:
Riker Danzig has handled some of the largest workouts and foreclosures in New Jersey, and is an industry leader in land use issues and real estate transactions. Its Real Estate Practice includes all aspects of real estate law, transactions and litigation, including substantial property acquisitions, complex sales and exchanges, sale-leasebacks and build-to-suits, commercial, retail and industrial leasing, joint-venture projects, zoning and planning, mortgage lending and financing, construction contracts, title litigation and real property tax appeals.
**Contact:** Nicholas Racioppi, Jr

### Employment:
The employment law attorneys at Riker Danzig counsel clients on the full range of issues, including employee relations, wage and hour and contract issues. They also defend management in federal and state courts in New Jersey and elsewhere on all employment-related claims, including discrimination, wrongful termination, whistleblower, restrictive covenants, unfair competition and employee fidelity bonds. They also conduct internal investigations.
**Contact:** Michael K Furey

### Corporate:
A diverse client base seeks counsel and solutions from Riker Danzig's corporate attorneys, from start-up entrepreneurial enterprises to *Fortune* 500 companies. The group counsels clients on the full spectrum of corporate matters, including mergers, acquisitions and divestitures, joint ventures, corporate finance, technology licensing, international transactions, tax and regulatory matters, and logistics and distribution, as well as the issues unique to non-profit and tax-exempt corporations.
**Contact:** Andrew J Stamelman

### Environmental:
In a state noted for its strict and pace-setting environmental legislation, Riker Danzig's Environmental Group is among the largest and most diverse practices of its kind. The firm's experienced environmental lawyers have in-depth knowledge of federal, state and local law. They handle litigation, regulatory, permitting and counseling, and real estate development matters addressing all environmental areas, including hazardous substances, air, water and noise pollution, and solid waste.
**Contact:** Dennis J Krumholz

### Insurance:
Riker Danzig's Insurance and Reinsurance Group has provided unparalleled representation to the insurance industry for over 30 years. The firm represents its clients in a variety of insurance matters, including insurance coverage, reinsurance, bad faith litigation, insurance defense, insolvencies, intermediary and agency disputes and legislative and regulatory matters.
**Contact:** Shawn L Kelly

### Bankruptcy:
Riker Danzig is unique among prominent New Jersey law firms for experience and expertise in bankruptcy litigation, corporate reorganization, real estate restructurings, non-bankruptcy insolvency proceedings and also for its practice on a national platform. The firm has earned a nationwide reputation for its representation of debtors, secured creditors, landlords, equipment lessors, indenture trustees, bondholders, private equity groups, creditors' committees, trustees, as well as third party plan proponents (i.e. takeovers) in all aspects of litigation under the Bankruptcy Code.
**Contact:** Dennis J O'Grady

## OFFICES

**NEW JERSEY**
**MORRISTOWN:** Headquarters Plaza, One Speedwell Avenue, NJ 07962-1981
Tel: 973 538 0800   Fax: 973 538 1984
Email: info@riker.com

**TRENTON:** 50 West State Street, Suite 1010, NJ 08608-1220
Tel: 609 396 2121   Fax: 609 396 4578

**NEW YORK**
**NEW YORK:** 500 Fifth Avenue, NY 10110
Tel: 212 302 6574   Fax: 212 302 6628

## INTERNATIONAL OFFICES
The firm also has an office in London, UK.

## Clients:
Bank of America; Carrier Clinic; CIGNA Corp.; Crum & Forster Corp.; Ecko.Complex, L.L.C.; Global Reinsurance Corporation of America; Gold Medal Products; Harleysville Insurance Co.; IBM; Johnson & Johnson; JPMorgan Chase; Lakeland Bank; LG Electronics; Lucent Technologies, Inc.; McNeil Pharmaceuticals; Mersen USA; Mitsui Sumitomo Insurance; New Jersey Bankers Association; New York Community Bank; NVE Bank; Prudential Insurance Company of America; R.J. Reynolds Tobacco Co.; TD Bank; The Provident Bank; UBS; Wakefern Food Corp.

## International Work:
Riker Danzig's London office reflects an expansion of the firm's international practice in insurance, reinsurance, banking and commercial litigation. In addition, Riker Danzig's Corporate Group has developed a significant in-bound cross-border practice, advising overseas clients on the corporate and tax issues faced when setting up US offices, making acquisitions, assuming debt, selling assets or engaging in other transactions in the United States.

# SILLS CUMMIS & GROSS P.C.

www.sillscummis.com **tel:** 973 643 7000 **fax:** 973 643 6500

**Chairman:** Steven E Gross
**Managing Partner:** R Max Crane
Number of partners: 61   Number of other lawyers: 87

## Firm Overview:

Sills Cummis & Gross P.C., a full-service corporate law firm, represents national and international clients. The firm's work is diversified among industries such as pharmaceutical and medical device, banking and finance, healthcare, life sciences, retail and commercial real estate, manufacturing and technology. The firm is an Am Law 200 firm and has been selected as a '2013 Go-To Law Firm ® for the Top 500 Companies'.

## Main Areas of Practice:

### Banking & Finance:

The firm represents international and national banks, commercial finance companies, debt and equity funds, and private lenders, with financings across the spectrum of public and private debt transactions. The firm also represents the financial services industry in a wide array of legal disputes and litigation matters in state and federal courts.

### Bankruptcy:

The group is experienced in all aspects of bankruptcy, reorganization and creditors' rights matters, including complex litigation cases, representing debtors, official and unofficial committees, secured and unsecured creditors, trustees and other parties in interest in out-of-court restructurings and in Chapter 11 reorganization cases. The group also structures "pre-negotiated" plans of reorganization to expedite the Chapter 11 process and is experienced in representing creditors in Uniform Commercial Code lien enforcement issues in state and federal courts.

### Complex Litigation/Class Action Defense:

The firm has a broad spectrum of litigation expertise reflecting the diversity of its clients. The firm's litigators regularly assist companies in cases involving commercial transactions, banking, healthcare, intellectual property, technology, construction, real estate, insurance, administrative law, antitrust, directors' and officers' liability, employment, unfair competition, securities, tax and business crimes.

### Construction Law:

The firm represents clients at various stages of construction projects, including project delivery systems, contracts/project documentation/risk allocation, claims avoidance, delay/defect claims, financial structuring and restructuring, trial advocacy and surety claims/defense.

### Corporate Internal Investigations & Business Crimes:

The group designs and implements corporate compliance programs, conducts internal investigations, provides legal counseling to executives and corporate boards and defends those who are subjects of criminal investigations. The group includes several former prosecutors.

### Corporate/M&A/Securities:

The firm has one of the largest corporate practices in New Jersey regularly advising both public and private companies. The firm's attorneys regularly handle US and cross-border M&A matters; corporate, securities and regulatory compliance issues; and joint ventures. They also create and implement corporate governance and compliance programs.

### Employment & Labor:

The group provides the highest level of employment counseling, training and management side litigation. The group routinely defends clients in federal, state and appellate courts and before the Equal Employment Opportunity Commission, and all federal and state administrative agencies. It also provides assistance with compliance and investigations, and traditional labor law representation.

### Healthcare:

The firm provides a full range of legal services to the healthcare industry, including transactions and corporate law, regulatory and compliance, government and internal investigations, finance, employment and labor law, litigation, real estate and antitrust. Clients include health systems, hospitals, nursing homes, long-term care facilities, ambulatory surgery centers, home health companies, investment funds, imaging centers, medical groups, ambulance companies, specialty care networks, management companies and other health care businesses.

### Intellectual Property:

The group's services range from prosecution for emerging companies, to "high-stakes" litigation on behalf of multinational corporations. The attorneys specialize in patents, trademarks, copyrights, trade secrets and internet law in litigation, licensing and transfer, analysis and counseling.

### Life Sciences:

The group handles a wide range of matters, including licensing arrangements, strategic alliances and collaborations, joint ventures, manufacturing, supply and distribution agreements, intellectual property, research and development, mergers and acquisitions, litigation, public and private financing, technology transfers, national and international corporate counseling, governance and compliance, employment law, real estate, regulatory and tax.

### Pharmaceutical/Medical Device:

The group's transactional attorneys provide strategic legal advice on mergers, acquisitions and divestitures; capital raising; manufacturing and distribution; and licensing, collaboration and technology transfer issues. The group's litigators act as national and local counsel in mass tort, major class action, and related product liability, warranty and infringement litigation; patent prosecution; business disputes; internal investigations and regulatory compliance matters.

### Product Liability:

The firm has earned a reputation as a "go-to" firm for defending complex product liability cases and mass tort litigation, successfully representing pharmaceutical, medical device, consumer product, industrial equipment and chemical companies as national, regional and New Jersey counsel in "bet the company" litigation. The product liability and mass tort lawyers are known for their legal, scientific, technical, trial and settlement expertise.

### Real Estate:

The group provides a full range of legal and related services to participants in all areas of the real estate industry, focusing on investment, vertical and horizontal acquisition and disposition; condominiumizations; retail, office, industrial and warehouse leasing; and mixed- and single-use development/redevelopment and construction. Expertise is also provided in the areas of government relations, zoning and land use; and conventional and capital markets financing (including securitized and mezzanine financings).

## OFFICES

**NEW JERSEY**
**NEWARK:** The Legal Center, One Riverfront Plaza, NJ 07102
Tel: 973 643 7000   Fax: 973 643 6500
Email: sillsmail@sillscummis.com

**PRINCETON:** 650 College Road East, NJ 08540
Tel: 609 227 4600   Fax: 609 227 4646

**NEW YORK**
**NEW YORK:** 30 Rockefeller Plaza, NY 10112
Tel: 212 643 7000   Fax: 212 643 6500

# WILENTZ, GOLDMAN & SPITZER, PA

www.wilentz.com  **tel:** 732 636 8000  **fax:** 732 855 6117

**Chairman:** Frederic K Becker
**Managing Partner:** Brian J Molloy
Number of partners: 73
Number of other lawyers: 51

## Firm Overview:

Founded in 1919, Wilentz, Goldman & Spitzer is a full service law firm that has earned a stellar reputation as a formidable advocate and astute advisor. Presidents, senators, governors and mayors have relied upon firm lawyers for nearly a century. With four offices located in New Jersey, New York and Pennsylvania, firm lawyers provide legal acumen and a commitment to make a difference for the businesses and individuals it serves.

## Main Areas of Practice:

### Business/Corporate Law:
Team lawyers advise clients on the planning, organizing and restructuring of new or existing businesses, and assist in documenting the relationship between, and among, the business entity and its owners.

### Business/Commercial Litigation:
The team has a nationwide reputation for handling complex litigation. The firm's approach to commercial litigation is always to protect the client's overall business interests.

### Creditors' Rights & Bankruptcy:
Team lawyers are experienced in all aspects of bankruptcy law and creditors' rights, commercial foreclosures and asset recovery. The team represents a myriad of interested parties in distressed financial situations and works collaboratively with clients and firm practice groups to enable clients to identify and find viable solutions for financially troubled businesses, individuals and their creditors.

### Environmental:
Team lawyers have substantial experience in regulatory permitting, regulatory compliance and policy matters involved in development and redevelopment projects.

### Family Law:
The team has extensive experience handling complex and sophisticated financial aspects of divorce, such as identifying, valuing and distributing assets and liabilities subject to equitable distribution, and in divorce mediation and arbitration.

### Financial Services:
The team represents both lenders and borrowers with specific areas of experience including: corporate finance, secured lending, asset based lending, lease finance, healthcare finance, international finance, leveraged buyout finance, mezzanine finance, commercial real estate finance, debt restructuring, loan participations, and syndications.

### Employment Law:
The team is experienced in a wide range of employment negotiation, mediation, arbitration, trial litigation and appellate litigation.

### Healthcare:
The provision of health services has become ever more affected by regulation. The team has been active in helping clients operate in this changing environment, advising on the formation and structure of entities and joint ventures, involving corporations, partnerships and limited liability companies. The team also handles all aspects of sales, purchases, mergers and acquisitions of healthcare entities, and related licensure issues.

### Land Use:
The team is focused on all phases of land use approvals at all governmental levels and related regulatory matters, as well as litigation and appeals involving the approval and permitting process. Team attorneys represent clients on a wide range of matters including site plans, variances, subdivisions, developer agreements, access permits, rezoning applications, master plan changes and related litigation.

### Public Finance:
For many years, the team has been involved in the issuance of opinions for tax-exempt municipal obligations. Team members have participated in both competitively bid and negotiated transactions, and while their primary experience is as bond counsel to public entity bond issuers, they have also served as underwriter's counsel, trustee's counsel and company counsel on numerous financings.

### Public Utilities & Renewable Energy:
Representing clients in the energy, telecommunication, water and utility industries requires a thorough understanding of the history and objectives of regulation in the current environment. The team provides advice to clients requiring innovative solutions to their energy needs.

### Real Estate:
The team has extensive collective experience providing integrated multidisciplinary legal solutions for property investment, development, management, and on finance transactions. Team members are adept at strategic counseling, coordination of permitting and enhancement of business opportunities for projects of all sizes, through knowledge and application of the law and effective relationships with many of the regulating agencies. The team has extensive experience in handling large, complex projects and transactions that entail legal, political and economic obstacles.

### Redevelopment:
Team lawyers offer the benefits of extensive state-wide experience on redevelopment projects. The team has represented public and private clients engaged in revitalization of urban and suburban communities and has the ability to deliver timely and effective service on projects ranging from a single apartment building to multi-acre, mixed-use developments.

### Tax, Trusts & Estate Planning:
Team lawyers focus on estate planning and administration; family business succession; tax planning; wills; trusts; private foundations; pension and retirement plans; and elder law.

WILENTZ, GOLDMAN & SPITZER P.A.
*Commitment to Make a Difference™*

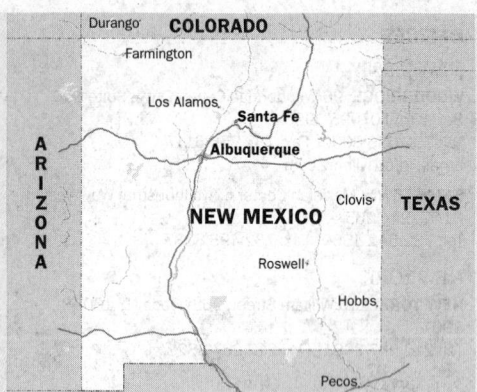

## How lawyers are ranked

Every year we carry out thousands of in-depth interviews with clients in order to assess the reputations and expertise of business lawyers worldwide. The qualities we look for (and which determine rankings) include technical legal ability, professional conduct, client service, commercial awareness/astuteness, diligence, commitment, and other qualities most valued by the client. For details of our research team, see p.5.

## CORPORATE/COMMERCIAL

Commentary about individuals can be found under their firm's paragraph. If the firm has no paragraph (is not ranked) look at Other Notable Practitioners.

### Corporate/Commercial
**Leading Firms**

**Band 1**
Brownstein Hyatt Farber Schreck, LLP *
Modrall, Sperling, Roehl, Harris & Sisk, PA
Rodey, Dickason, Sloan, Akin & Robb, PA *
Sutin, Thayer & Browne

**Band 2**
Lewis and Roca LLP

#### Senior Statesmen

**Senior Statesmen:** distinguished older partners

| | |
|---|---|
| Heyman Robert | *Sutin, Thayer & Browne* |

#### Leading Individuals

**Band 1**

| | |
|---|---|
| Bendicksen III Perry E | *Brownstein Hyatt Farber Schreck, LLP* |
| Brown Duane | *Modrall, Sperling, Roehl, Harris & Sisk, PA* |
| Buchholtz David P | *Brownstein Hyatt Farber Schreck, LLP* |

**Band 2**

| | |
|---|---|
| Hall Alan | *Rodey, Dickason, Sloan, Akin & Robb, PA* * |
| Monnheimer Donald B | *Rodey, Dickason, Sloan, Akin & Robb, PA* * |
| Muirhead Chris | *Modrall, Sperling, Roehl, Harris & Sisk, PA* |
| Paisley Bonnie J | *Brownstein Hyatt Farber Schreck, LLP* |
| Parker James | *Modrall, Sperling, Roehl, Harris & Sisk, PA* |
| Rosenblum Jay | *Sutin, Thayer & Browne* |
| Schuler Alison | *Schuler.Daly (ONP)†* |
| Sweeney Jill K | *Brownstein Hyatt Farber Schreck, LLP* |

**Band 3**

| | |
|---|---|
| Browne Anne P | *Sutin, Thayer & Browne* |
| Franklin Peter | *Modrall, Sperling, Roehl, Harris & Sisk, PA* |
| Horwitz Justin A | *Rodey, Dickason, Sloan, Akin & Robb, PA* * |
| Jontz Dennis | *Lewis and Roca LLP* |

**Up-and-coming individuals**

| | |
|---|---|
| King Rachel | *Sutin, Thayer & Browne* |

\* Indicates firm / individual with profile.
†ONP = Other Notable Practitioner.

### Corporate/Commercial: Tax
**Leading Individuals**

**Band 1**

| | |
|---|---|
| Kelly Henry | *Sutin, Thayer & Browne* |
| Parker James | *Modrall, Sperling, Roehl, Harris & Sisk, PA* |
| Sprouls Tracy | *Rodey, Dickason, Sloan, Akin & Robb, PA* * |
| Van Valen Timothy | *Brownstein Hyatt Farber Schreck, LLP* |

### Band 1

#### Brownstein Hyatt Farber Schreck, LLP
See profile on p.725

**THE FIRM** This active and highly regarded practice handles a range of M&A, tax and public finance work, including the issuance of bonds. The firm frequently advises state agencies and the Albuquerque city authorities, and is also prominent in private sector transactions, acting for clients such as Mexican cement and materials company Grupo Cementos de Chihuahua. The team recently represented New Mexico Mutual Casualty Company in a closely scrutinized stock acquisition of third party insurance adjustment firm Keenan & Associates.

**Sources say:** "*Far and away the best law firm in New Mexico for corporate transactions.*"

**KEY INDIVIDUALS** Practice head **David Buchholtz** is valued for his ability to "*communicate complex financial matters in a way the unfamiliar can understand.*" He recently acted for the New Mexico State Board of Finance on the public sales of general obligation and severance tax bonds. **Perry Bendicksen** is noted for "*the speed, energy and efficiency of his work, his sound business judgment and his encyclopedic knowledge of the law.*" He specializes in M&A and matters involving private equity and venture capital funds. Bendicksen was a key figure in the firm's work for the New Mexico Mutual Casualty Company. **Timothy Van Valen** attracts enthusiastic client praise, not only for his responsiveness and exceptional technical knowledge, but also for his "*pragmatism and local practice expertise.*" He is widely regarded as a leading authority in New Mexico on corpo-

rate taxation matters. **Bonnie Paisley** is best known for her bond counsel work and recently advised the City of Albuquerque on the public sale and private placement of general obligation bonds. Clients value her "*clear, concise documentation,*" and that she "*keeps the long term as a primary focus.*" **Jill Sweeney** specializes in government finance law, with recent clients including the New Mexico Finance Authority, the New Mexico State Board of Finance and a number of public improvement and tax increment districts.

#### Modrall, Sperling, Roehl, Harris & Sisk, PA

**THE FIRM** This large team has extensive experience in the public finance sphere, representing New Mexico state, county and municipal authorities, medical facilities and educational establishments. Another key area of specialization is the development of renewable energy projects, and particularly taxation issues concerning such enterprises. Recent highlights include advising Element Power US on a $140 million industrial revenue bond financing for a solar energy farm in Luna County.

**KEY INDIVIDUALS Duane Brown** is a public finance specialist, praised for "*taking a leadership role in driving the details of issuing or refunding bonds and coordinating all aspects of the transaction with the various players concerned.*" He played a leading role in the aforementioned Element Power matter. **James Parker** is especially highly regarded in the taxation sphere, where his expertise is frequently called upon for the most complicated and sensitive matters. **Chris Muirhead** is widely respected for his expertise in the public finance space. Clients testify to his "*complete understanding of public financing rules and regulations, including those unique to New Mexico.*" He recently acted as lead partner in the firm's role as bond issuer's counsel to the New Mexico Hospital Equipment Loan Council on a $71.745 million transaction. **Peter Franklin** brings previous experience as general counsel to the New Mexico Department of Finance and Administration. His public finance practice covers a range of work, including bond transactions, and advice on compliance with federal tax and securities regulations.

## Rodey, Dickason, Sloan, Akin & Robb, PA
See profile on p.1775

**THE FIRM** This firm fields one of the largest corporate and commercial teams in the state, providing counsel on matters ranging from business formation through transactional and governance issues to exit strategies. Key areas of strength include advising on the issuance of securities and the structuring of stock option plans, tax planning and public finance. In one recent highlight, the firm advised Tres Amigas on the first phase of its $1.5 billion Merchant Transmission Facility Project.

**KEY INDIVIDUALS Tracy Sprouls** (see p.1774) is widely respected for his mastery of state and federal tax issues, including negotiations with the IRS. He recently played a significant role advising R-Qubed Energy on the first phase of the development of its $87 million biodigester project. **Alan Hall** (see p.1773) receives enthusiastic client praise for his "*extremely detail-oriented*" approach and ability to "*make a local transaction fit into an overall corporate program.*" He handles a range of M&A, securities, municipal and industrial revenue bonds, and other development incentives. **Donald Monnheimer** (see p.1774) heads the practice and has particular expertise in matters involving industrial revenue and municipal bonds, and securities. He recently acted for the New Mexico Spaceport Authority on the development of the world's first commercial spaceport in Sierra County. **Justin Horwitz** (see p.1773) frequently advises on bonds relating to development initiatives. He notably acted for Western Albuquerque Land Holdings on the creation of the Lower Petroglyphs Public Improvement District, including a levy bond transaction.

## Sutin, Thayer & Browne

**THE FIRM** Sutin, Thayer & Browne combines broad practice area coverage with an impressive depth of experience, acting for both public and private sector clients. It is noted for its adroit handling of public finance matters, as well as a range of other corporate and tax-related issues for prestigious clients, including leading oil and gas and construction companies. The firm's key clients include Yates Petroleum, the New Mexico Finance Authority and Memorial Medical Center.

**Sources say:** "*The firm is excellent, and offers a wide range of specialized expertise.*" "*Their professionalism and client service are the best I have seen in a firm. They always call you back and keep you informed of the status of the engagement.*"

**KEY INDIVIDUALS Robert Heyman** remains an authority in the public finance and banking sectors, where he represents both local and out-of-state financial institutions as well as state entities. He frequently provides bond counsel to the New Mexico Finance Authority. **Henry Kelly** is noted for his specialist tax expertise, which includes advising on the taxation aspects of M&A, tax-free reorganizations, and matters concerning S corporations and partnerships. His key clients include Yates Petroleum. **Jay Rosenblum** is active across the corporate field, and regularly advises on M&A matters in the automobile, construction and restaurant sectors. He is also noted for his expertise in entity formation, governance and shareholder disputes. **Anne Browne** is acclaimed for her "*extremely high degree of professionalism and knowledge.*" She advises both borrowers and lenders on major financial transactions, and is also active in advising clients on business formation and governance matters. **Rachel King** is praised as "*an excellent and versatile attorney who is usually able to respond immediately to issues or questions arising on almost any topic,*" with one source describing her as "*a future leader in the public finance sphere.*" King acts for the New Mexico Renewable Energy Transmission Authority, as well as a number of educational institutions.

### Band 2

### Lewis and Roca LLP

**THE FIRM** This large regional firm offers clients access to expertise in New Mexico and across the Southwest. The practice handles a broad range of work, including M&A, securities, public finance and intellectual property matters. **KEY INDIVIDUALS** Albuquerque-based partner **Dennis Jontz**'s key areas of expertise include M&A, business formation planning and intellectual property.

### Other Notable Practitioners

**Alison Schuler** of Schuler.Daly is a widely respected attorney, best known for her work for new or smaller companies. Her key areas of expertise include entity formation, corporate governance issues and securities transactions.

# ENVIRONMENT, NATURAL RESOURCES & REGULATED INDUSTRIES

Water Law p.1766

Commentary about individuals can be found under their firm's paragraph. If the firm has no paragraph (is not ranked) look at Other Notable Practitioners.

| Environment, Natural Resources & Regulated Industries | |
| --- | --- |
| **Leading Firms** | |
| **Band 1** | |
| Hinkle Hensley Shanor & Martin LLP | |
| Holland & Hart LLP * | |
| Modrall, Sperling, Roehl, Harris & Sisk, PA | |
| Montgomery & Andrews, PA | |
| **Band 2** | |
| Rodey, Dickason, Sloan, Akin & Robb, PA * | |

\* Indicates firm / individual with profile.
†ONP = Other Notable Practitioner.

| Leading Individuals | | |
| --- | --- | --- |
| **Star individuals** | | |
| Carr William F | Holland & Hart LLP * | |
| **Band 1** | | |
| Ausherman Larry P | Modrall, Sperling, Roehl, Harris & Sisk, PA | |
| Butzier Stuart | Modrall, Sperling, Roehl, Harris & Sisk, PA | |
| Campbell Michael | Campbell Trial Law, LLC (ONP)† | |
| Cooney John R | Modrall, Sperling, Roehl, Harris & Sisk, PA | |
| Hensley Jr Harold | Hinkle Hensley Shanor & Martin LLP | |
| Nibert Gregory J | Hinkle Hensley Shanor & Martin LLP | |
| Rose Louis W | Montgomery & Andrews, PA | |
| Scott William C | Modrall, Sperling, Roehl, Harris & Sisk, PA | |
| Stern III Walter E | Modrall, Sperling, Roehl, Harris & Sisk, PA |
| **Band 2** | |
| Adams Mark K | Rodey, Dickason, Sloan, Akin & Robb, PA * |
| Hall Scott | Montgomery & Andrews, PA |
| Kendrick Edmund H | Montgomery & Andrews, PA |
| Moellenberg Dalva | Gallagher & Kennedy PA (ONP)† |
| **Band 3** | |
| Cloutier Andrew J | Hinkle Hensley Shanor & Martin LLP |
| Feldewert Michael | Holland & Hart LLP * |
| **Associates to watch** | |
| Rankin Adam G. | Holland & Hart LLP * |

## Band 1

### Hinkle Hensley Shanor & Martin LLP

**THE FIRM** This firm's Roswell and Santa Fe offices are highly regarded for their capacity to handle natural resources law, especially where it relates to the oil and gas industries. Its attorneys are able to advise clients across the full range of matters in this sector, including title examination work, financing transactions, and interactions with administrative and regulatory authorities. Sources also note the firm's strengths in advising on mining-related matters, water rights law and issues of environmental compliance.

**Sources say:** "*The preeminent law firm for oil and gas.*"

**KEY INDIVIDUALS Harold Hensley** is one of the most highly regarded litigators in the natural resources space and he regularly handles complex matters involving the oil and gas industry. He is active in the district courts of both New Mexico and Texas, and the New Mexico Supreme Court, and is also admitted to practice before a number of federal tribunals, including the Supreme Court.

**Star individuals**

| | |
|---|---|
| Draper John B | Montgomery & Andrews, PA |

**Band 1**

| | |
|---|---|
| Adams Mark K | Rodey, Dickason, Sloan, Akin & Robb, PA * |
| Henrie Michelle | MHenrie (ONP)† |
| O'Brien Maria | Modrall, Sperling, Roehl, Harris & Sisk, PA |
| Stein Jay | Stein & Brockmann PA (ONP)† |

**Band 2**

| | |
|---|---|
| Nixon Sunny J | Rodey, Dickason, Sloan, Akin & Robb, PA * |
| Sims Steven O | Brownstein Hyatt Farber Schreck (ONP)† |
| Utton John W. | Sheehan & Sheehan, PA (ONP)† |

*\* Indicates individual with profile.*
*Alphabetical order within each band. Band 1 is the highest.*

**Gregory Nibert** acts almost exclusively on oil and gas matters. He handles a comprehensive range of issues within this field, including title examination, financial and contractual arrangements, and acquisitions and divestitures. **Andrew Cloutier** specializes in complex litigation and administrative proceedings for clients in the oil and gas industries. He has extensive experience of dealing with agencies such as New Mexico's Oil Conservation Division and Department of Taxation and Revenue, as well as the federal Minerals Management Service.

## Holland & Hart LLP
See profile on p.727

**THE FIRM** The Santa Fe office of this major Mountain West firm receives comprehensive praise from clients for the excellence of its oil and gas practice and its combination of a broad regional reach with in-depth local knowledge and connections. Sources also credit the team with particular proficiency in assisting natural resources businesses on waste management and environmental issues and in representing them before regulatory authorities. One significant recent mandate was the practice's selection to act as adviser to the New Mexico Oil and Gas Association (NMOGA) in the formulation of new regulations governing the hydraulic fracturing of oil and gas wells, horizontal drilling operations, and waste disposal. Other notable clients include Chevron and OXY USA.
**Sources say:** "*A top-notch law firm with excellent attorneys.*"
**KEY INDIVIDUALS William Carr** (see p.1773), who acted as lead partner advising the NMOGA, continues to be regarded by several sources as "*the preeminent oil and gas attorney in the state.*" Sources highlight his "*tremendous breadth of knowledge,*" as well as the fact that he "*understands the dynamics and politics of the different regulatory bodies and knows all the individuals.*" **Michael Feldewert** (see p.1773) is an oil and gas law specialist who "*provides great legal advice and has excellent contacts at the state agencies.*" He is also noted for preparing his clients thoroughly for the most difficult hearings. Clients note that leading associate **Adam Rankin** (see p.1774) is "*very responsive and provides a good service,*" while various sources agree that he "*shows great promise.*" He focuses on administrative and

regulatory matters, and his work for oil and gas clients is particularly highly regarded.

## Modrall, Sperling, Roehl, Harris & Sisk, PA

**THE FIRM** This firm operates out of offices in Albuquerque and Santa Fe and represents clients in New Mexico and across the region. It represents a range of natural resources developers, including companies involved in the mining of coal and uranium, while it is also recognized for its expertise in the spheres of water rights, utilities and renewable energy. The team recently acted for the London-based Anglo-Pacific Group with regard to its financing of uranium developer Laramide Resources. It also represented BHP Billiton subsidiary San Juan Coal in a dispute with Tucson Electric Power.
**Sources say:** "*Big enough to cover the full range of issues that come up in transactions – they make the coordination of legal advice easier and more efficient.*"
**KEY INDIVIDUALS Larry Ausherman** acts across a broad range of energy, natural resources and environmental issues and recently acted for Rio Grande Resources in proceedings concerning the renewal of permits for the Mount Taylor uranium mine. Sources note his strong local knowledge, with one satisfied client stating that "*he did a great job analyzing the environmental issues and going beyond the information we gave because he knows the specific situation in New Mexico so well.*" Department head **Stuart Butzier** specializes in mining and energy matters and is acclaimed for his ability to "*remain calm and collected and give sound counsel in an environment where things can get very frustrating.*" His recent clients include Freeport McMoRan Copper & Gold and the environmental consulting firm Souder Miller & Associates. **John Cooney** is widely acclaimed for his vast experience in the field of natural resources law, including the handling of contractual, title and royalty disputes. He acted as lead partner in the San Juan Coal matter. **Maria O'Brien** has a high level of visibility in water-related matters, including the purchase or leasing of water rights, permitting and quality issues, and litigation. **William Scott** is widely considered to be "*a valued adviser on environmental issues in New Mexico.*" He is experienced in representing clients before city and county zoning and land use authorities, as well as state and federal agencies such as the Environmental Improvement Board, Water Quality Control Commission and EPA. **Walter Stern** is singled out by clients for his management capabilities and for "*marshaling all the right resources, synthesizing his advice correctly and providing it in a user-friendly format.*" He played a key role in the Anglo-Pacific Group matter and also acted as lead partner advising Resource Capital Partners on an investment in a uranium mining enterprise.

## Montgomery & Andrews, PA

**THE FIRM** This practice is active across the board on energy, resources and environmental matters, with a particular focus upon the environmental space and on water-related issues. It regularly assists New Mexico-based businesses in compliance with environmental regulations across a range of matters, including M&A, brownfield

developments and site remediation. It also acts for both public and private entities in the sale and lease of water rights, the resolution of interstate water disputes and the litigation of water disputes from state to Supreme Court level.
**Sources say:** "*First-rate in water and environmental matters.*"
**KEY INDIVIDUALS John Draper** is widely regarded as "*preeminent in water matters.*" He has represented clients in numerous Supreme Court proceedings, and is noted for his expertise across a range of water rights matters, including interstate matters and stream system adjudications. **Louis Rose** advises on environmental compliance and litigation at state and federal level and he has considerable expertise in state environmental law and regulations. He receives specific praise for his understanding of environmental issues concerning the mining sector. **Scott Hall** is experienced in the handling of all legal issues affecting the oil and gas industry, including title examination, contractual dispute litigation and right-of-way questions. He acts predominantly for oil and gas producers, whom he regularly represents before the New Mexico Oil Conservation Division and the Oil Conservation Commission. **Edmund Kendrick** maintains a broad environmental practice which includes advice on regulatory compliance concerning air, water, waste, and oil and gas. He frequently acts for New Mexico municipalities in their interactions with the EPA.

## Band 2

### Rodey, Dickason, Sloan, Akin & Robb, PA
See profile on p.1775

**THE FIRM** This firm provides a full suite of transactional, regulatory and litigation services in the natural resources and environmental sphere. The team operates out of offices in Albuquerque and Santa Fe, but it has a nationwide reach and has recently handled matters involving Australian, British and Canadian investment. It possesses notable expertise in mining matters and recently represented New Mexico Copper in connection with the reopening of operations at its Copper Flat mine and mill. In another key mandate it advised Peabody Energy on land and water issues affecting its New Mexico coal mines.
**KEY INDIVIDUALS** Practice head **Mark Adams** (see p.1773) is noted for his vast experience in environmental matters, and clients highlight his "*excellent responsiveness and turnaround time.*" He is held in high regard for his handling of water law matters, which forms part of a broad practice encompassing mining rights and issues concerning the oil and gas sector. **Sunny Nixon** (see p.1774) is a respected specialist in environmental issues and is particularly noted for her work in administrative proceedings concerning utilities and water rights before the New Mexico Public Regulation Commission and State Engineer. She recently acted as lead partner advising Peabody Energy.

## Other Notable Practitioners

**Michael Campbell** of Campbell Trial Law, LLC is a sole practitioner who is highly regarded for his handling of oil and gas disputes, including royalty controversies, antitrust claims and surface use disputes. **Michelle Henrie** is a sole practitioner at MHenrie. She specializes in advising clients on development projects, in particular aspects concerning water law. **Jay Stein** of Stein & Brockmann PA focuses exclusively upon water law matters, including administra-

tive, district court and appellate proceedings at both state and federal level. He is active in interstate water disputes and has represented clients in the Southwest and beyond, including Kansas, Nebraska, Wyoming and also Mexico. **Steven Sims** of Brownstein Hyatt Farber Schreck, LLP concentrates on transactional, administrative and litigation matters in the water law sphere. Sources note his considerable public and private sector experience, with one satisfied client describing him as *"a leading expert on water law and litigation in a number of jurisdictions across the USA."*

**John Utton** of Sheehan & Sheehan, PA is a water law specialist who acts for both public and private sector clients in New Mexico. He is best known for his work in water planning issues and in matters of water rights litigation, including stream system adjudications, at both state and federal level. **Dalva Moellenberg** of Gallagher & Kennedy PA is a leading figure in the mining and environmental spheres. One client reports that he *"understands mining and engineering better than any other attorney I know."*

# LABOR & EMPLOYMENT

Commentary about individuals can be found under their firm's paragraph. If the firm has no paragraph (is not ranked) look at Other Notable Practitioners.

### Labor & Employment
#### Leading Firms

**Band 1**
Rodey, Dickason, Sloan, Akin & Robb, PA *

**Band 2**
Conklin, Woodcock & Ziegler, P.C.
Modrall, Sperling, Roehl, Harris & Sisk, PA

**Band 3**
Jackson Lewis LLP *
Moody & Warner PC
Tinnin Law Firm

#### Leading Individuals

**Band 1**

| | | |
|---|---|---|
| Conklin | Robert | Conklin, Woodcock & Ziegler, P.C. |
| Gordon | Scott D | Rodey, Dickason, Sloan, Akin & Robb, PA * |
| Stahl | Thomas L | Rodey, Dickason, Sloan, Akin & Robb, PA * |

**Band 2**

| | | |
|---|---|---|
| Jarrett | Danny W | Jackson Lewis LLP * |
| McFall | George | Modrall, Sperling, Roehl, Harris & Sisk, PA |
| Moody | Christopher M | Moody & Warner PC |
| Parrish | Theresa W | Rodey, Dickason, Sloan, Akin & Robb, PA * |
| Stephenson | Barbara G | Sheehan & Sheehan, PA (ONP)[†] |
| Warner | Whitney | Moody & Warner PC |
| Woodcock | Jacqueline | Conklin, Woodcock & Ziegler, P.C. |
| Ziegler | John K | Conklin, Woodcock & Ziegler, P.C. |

**Band 3**

| | | |
|---|---|---|
| Cook | James L | Law Office of James L Cook PC (ONP)[†] |
| Howell | Trent | Sawtell Wirth & Biedscheid PC (ONP)[†] |
| Kotovsky | Stanley | Tinnin Law Firm |
| Lamont | Charlotte | Littler Mendelson P.C. (ONP)[†] * |
| Tinnin Jr | Robert P | Tinnin Law Firm |
| Vigil | Charles J | Rodey, Dickason, Sloan, Akin & Robb, PA * |

## Band 1

### Rodey, Dickason, Sloan, Akin & Robb, PA
See profile on p.1775

**THE FIRM** This firm possesses one of the largest and most specialized labor and employment practices in New Mexico, acting for a range of employers at the local, regional and national levels. It houses lawyers with expertise in all

### Labor & Employment: Employee Benefits & Compensation
#### Leading Individuals

**Band 1**

| | | |
|---|---|---|
| Neerken | Julie P | Rodey, Dickason, Sloan, Akin & Robb, PA * |
| Panter | Danielle | Hurley Toevs Styles Hamblin & Panter (ONP)[†] |
| Parker | James | Modrall, Sperling, Roehl, Harris & Sisk, PA |

\* Indicates firm / individual with profile.
[†]ONP = Other Notable Practitioner.

key aspects of employment law, including advocacy before state and federal courts and regulatory bodies, nonadversarial issues and preventive training, and employee benefits planning. The team recently acted successfully for the Los Alamos National Laboratory in securing the dismissal of a $500,000 wrongful discharge suit brought by a former employee. In the traditional labor law sphere, acting for the City of Albuquerque, it was instrumental in persuading the New Mexico Supreme Court to overturn a ruling by the state's Court of Appeals which had favored the city's labor union.

**Sources say:** *"They have always been a superb firm to work with. They are prompt and supportive."*

**KEY INDIVIDUALS Scott Gordon** (see p.1773) enjoys an excellent reputation in the employment sphere, and he is particularly noted for his civil litigation skills. He acted as lead partner in the Los Alamos National Laboratory matter and also played a significant role advising Sandia during the successful defense of a former employee's claim of age and race discrimination, plus retaliation. **Julie Neerken** (see p.1774) is an acknowledged expert in employee benefit and ERISA matters and a popular choice for peer referrals. **Thomas Stahl** (see p.1774) heads the practice and specializes in the defense of employers in state and federal court litigation and alternative dispute resolution proceedings. He *"inspires a lot of confidence"* in his clients, providing advice which is *"surgically precise, to the point and reasonable."* He was the lead partner in the City of Albuquerque matter, and he has also successfully represented Smith's Food & Drug Centers in a series of labor law disputes. **Theresa Parrish** (see p.1774) specializes in the litigation, mediation and arbitration of employment law

disputes. Clients characterize her as a *"tough but fair"* practitioner, particularly noted for her excellent communication skills, sensitivity to client needs and readiness *"to go the extra mile in any situation."* **Charles Vigil** (see p.1774) is an *"upstanding, reliable and very good lawyer"* who is handling an increasing number of employment litigation matters. One impressed commentator describes him as *"a seasoned negotiator with excellent judgment and a gift for boiling issues down to their essentials."*

## Band 2

### Conklin, Woodcock & Ziegler, P.C.

**THE FIRM** This practice is noted for its capacity to provide cost-effective solutions to employment disputes, either through litigation or by alternative means of dispute resolution. The team is praised by clients for its wide range of skills and exceptional levels of motivation, thoroughness and reliability. Recent work highlights include acting for Presbyterian Healthcare Services in a contract action with a potential exposure in excess of $4 million, in which the firm's attorneys helped secure a successful resolution at a far lower level. In other work highlights, the group has represented the City of Albuquerque in a number of labor law arbitrations and recently acted for PNM Resources in the successful resolution of a race discrimination suit.

**Sources say:** *"All of the lawyers are experts in their areas of expertise and easy to work with; a professional, highly functioning team."*

**KEY INDIVIDUALS** Clients state that **Robert Conklin** is *"especially strong in familiarizing himself with our business"* and in accurately weighing up the relative pros and cons of crucial decisions. He acted as lead partner in the Presbyterian Healthcare matter. **Jacqueline Woodcock** also attracts client praise for her understanding of the businesses she represents. She acts extensively, at state and federal level, on sensitive matters of employee discipline and termination, and also cases involving allegations of harassment or discrimination. **John Ziegler** is described by one commentator as a *"prompt, attentive attorney who researches thoroughly, explains things clearly, and has a good under-*

*standing of the way our organization works."* He was the lead partner in the PNM Resources case in Texas and he also recently obtained the dismissal of a $250,000 race discrimination claim brought against a client operating a McDonald's franchise.

## Modrall, Sperling, Roehl, Harris & Sisk, PA

**THE FIRM** This firm covers the full range of employment law-related litigation and also advises clients on the transactional and litigation aspects of employee benefits and ERISA. Key areas of expertise include matters involving the Navajo Nation and the representation of educational authorities, while the firm has handled an increasing volume of labor law work for natural resources clients. The team recently acted successfully for Freeport-McMoRan Chino Mines in a national origin discrimination suit heard by the US District Court and it has also advised Albuquerque Public Schools in a number of matters.
**Sources say:** *"The firm has consistently provided excellent counsel and achieved good results."*
**KEY INDIVIDUALS James Parker** is a *"very fine lawyer,"* widely acknowledged as one of New Mexico's leading employee benefits attorneys. He has over 40 years' experience in this area, notably in the healthcare sector. Team leader **George McFall** is a seasoned civil litigator and labor law specialist who acted as lead partner in the Freeport-McMoRan Chino matter. He is widely praised by clients who variously comment on his constructive and communicative demeanor, his *"thoughtful approach and down-to-earth advice,"* and his ability to provide *"honest analysis of the respective strengths of opposing legal positions."*

## Band 3

### Jackson Lewis LLP
See profile on p.1982
**THE FIRM** The Albuquerque office of this workplace law boutique acts exclusively for management and is able to tap into a nationwide network of expertise in handling employment and traditional labor law issues. The team's specializations include the representation of Native American employers and of companies doing business on tribal land, while it is also highly experienced in the management of minimum wage, discriminatory issues and grievance arbitrations. Key clients include Kit Carson Electric Cooperative, Gallup McKinley County Schools and HB Management.
**KEY INDIVIDUALS** Practice head **Danny Jarrett** (see p.1773) is acclaimed as an *"excellent lawyer"* who is particularly recommended for his labor law expertise, which includes the negotiation of collective bargaining agreements and representation before the NLRB.

## Moody & Warner PC

**THE FIRM** This practice acts for both employers and employees in workplace-related disputes and is particularly well known for its representation of labor unions. The team handles litigation at state and federal level, as well as appearing before the EEOC and NLRB, while several lawyers are noted for their expertise in handling arbitrations and mediations. The firm is highly regarded for its management of class actions brought by plaintiffs on the grounds of wage and hour violations or of sexual or racial discrimination.
**KEY INDIVIDUALS Whitney Warner** is best known for her representation of plaintiffs in unfair labor practice proceedings before state and federal courts and regulatory bodies, but she is also experienced in acting for employers. She has considerable expertise in a range of employment matters including discrimination, EEOC charges and wrongful termination. **Christopher Moody** acts for both employers and employees, and he attracts strong praise for his depth of experience and tenacious approach to matters. He is well renowned for his skill in handling class actions, while he also advises managers on collective bargaining strategy, representation proceedings and grievance arbitrations. Sources also note his particular expertise in arbitration and mediation.

## Tinnin Law Firm

**THE FIRM** This firm acts primarily for employers in the public and private sectors, advising them on matters of employment litigation, relations with unions and the preventive management of discrimination and disciplinary issues. Its attorneys are experienced in handling litigation in the state and federal courts, advising on proceedings before the NLRB, and assisting clients in arbitrations and mediations.
**KEY INDIVIDUALS Stanley Kotovsky** is an experienced litigator with particular expertise in representing corporate and public sector clients in matters concerning discrimination, breach of contract and retaliation. He enjoys an *"excellent, solid reputation"* for his work in New Mexico and the wider Southwest. **Robert Tinnin** earns praise as a highly capable attorney with a *"wealth of experience"* who *"really knows labor law."* He regularly represents clients in NLRB proceedings, as well as matters concerning collective bargaining and discrimination. Sources also note his particular expertise in guiding clients through mediations.

## Other Notable Practitioners

Sources recommend **Danielle Panter** of Hurley Toevs Styles Hamblin & Panter PA for her handling of complex employee benefit plans and ERISA issues. **Barbara Stephenson** of Sheehan & Sheehan, PA acts exclusively for employers at both a local and national level, defending them against a broad range of charges. Commentators characterize her as *"great at keeping clients out of trouble,"* citing her as *"a go-to person for an independent, outside attorney."* **James Cook** of the Law Office of James L Cook PC is known for his keen understanding of business practicalities when advising on employment and labor law issues. **Trent Howell** of Sawtell Wirth & Biedscheid PC handles employment law matters primarily for defendants, as well as some plaintiffs. He is particularly well regarded for the excellence of his work on ERISA-related issues. **Charlotte Lamont** (see p.1774) is Littler Mendelson P.C.'s chief New Mexico-based representative on employment matters. She advises employers across a wide range of industries on discrimination, wrongful discharge and related matters. Clients identify her as a *"very good negotiator,"* particularly on contractual issues, while peers recommend her as an attorney who's *"great to work with"* and a strong option for client referrals.

# LITIGATION

Commentary about individuals can be found under their firm's paragraph. If the firm has no paragraph (is not ranked) look at Other Notable Practitioners.

## Litigation: General Commercial

### Leading Firms

**Band 1**

Modrall, Sperling, Roehl, Harris & Sisk, PA

Rodey, Dickason, Sloan, Akin & Robb, PA *

**Band 2**

Atkinson, Thal, & Baker P.C.

Keleher & McLeod, PA

Peifer, Hanson & Mullins PA

Sutin, Thayer & Browne

**Band 3**

Freedman Boyd Hollander Goldberg Ives & Duncan P.A.

Hinkle Hensley Shanor & Martin LLP

Holland & Hart LLP *

### Senior Statesmen

**Senior Statesmen: distinguished older partners**

| | |
|---|---|
| Bardacke Paul | Sutin, Thayer & Browne |
| Hall Bruce | Rodey, Dickason, Sloan, Akin & Robb, PA * |
| Harrigan Kenneth | Modrall, Sperling, Roehl, Harris & Sisk, PA |

### Leading Individuals

**Band 1**

| | |
|---|---|
| Baker Douglas | Atkinson, Thal, & Baker P.C. |
| Peifer Charles | Peifer, Hanson & Mullins PA |
| Shanor Stuart D | Hinkle Hensley Shanor & Martin LLP |

**Band 2**

| | |
|---|---|
| Atkinson Clifford K. | Atkinson, Thal, & Baker P.C. |
| Berge Bradford | Holland & Hart LLP * |
| Franse Nelson | Rodey, Dickason, Sloan, Akin & Robb, PA * |
| Gallegos J. E. | Gallegos Law Firm PC (ONP)† |
| Goldberg Joseph | Freedman Boyd Hollander Goldberg Ives |
| Reid Spencer | Keleher & McLeod, PA |
| Schultz Andrew G | Rodey, Dickason, Sloan, Akin (ONP)† * |
| Stelzner Luis | Stelzner, Winter, Warburton, Flores, Sanchez |

**Band 3**

| | |
|---|---|
| Anderson Jennifer | Modrall, Sperling, Roehl, Harris & Sisk, PA |
| Bohnhoff Henry M | Rodey, Dickason, Sloan, Akin & Robb, PA * |
| Campbell Michael | Campbell Trial Law, LLC (ONP)† |
| Gottlieb Gail | Sutin, Thayer & Browne |
| Thal John | Atkinson, Thal, & Baker P.C. |

**Up-and-coming individuals**

| | |
|---|---|
| Allison Benjamin | Sutin, Thayer & Browne |
| Thomas Benjamin E. | Sutin, Thayer & Browne |

## Band 1

### Modrall, Sperling, Roehl, Harris & Sisk, PA

**THE FIRM** Modrall Sperling houses a substantial team of experienced litigators with expertise covering the oil and gas and healthcare sectors, as well as specific skills in handling product liability, personal injury and insurance-related cases. The team was recently successful in greatly reducing the volume of claims being made against Janssen

## Litigation: Medical Malpractice & Insurance Defense

### Leading Individuals

**Band 1**

| | |
|---|---|
| Allen Ben M | Allen, Shepherd, Lewis, Syra (ONP)† |
| Lasater Jr W Robert | Rodey, Dickason, Sloan, Akin & Robb, PA * |

**Band 2**

| | |
|---|---|
| Beitler Rick | Rodey, Dickason, Sloan, Akin & Robb, PA * |
| Franse Nelson | Rodey, Dickason, Sloan, Akin & Robb, PA * |
| Pharris Charles A | Keleher & McLeod, PA |

\* Indicates firm / individual with profile.

†ONP = Other Notable Practitioner.

Pharmaceutica concerning alleged misrepresentation of the effects of the drug Risperdal. It also acted for the New Mexico Gas Company on defending a putative class action concerning an emergency curtailment of service which affected 28,000 customers.

**Sources say:** "*They are pretty extraordinary and ready to serve in a very wide range of areas: the go-to firm in this region.*"

**KEY INDIVIDUALS Kenneth Harrigan** is an exceptionally experienced attorney specializing in business and tort litigation, with notable strengths in product liability and insurance-related work. Department head **Jennifer Anderson** litigates across an extensive range of issues, including employment, healthcare and product liability cases. Clients and peers characterize her as an attorney who is "*at the top of her game, working at a high level of efficiency and effectiveness.*"

### Rodey, Dickason, Sloan, Akin & Robb, PA
See profile on p.1775

**THE FIRM** This large team is widely acclaimed by clients for its handling of a range of litigation at state and federal level, as well as pursuing mediation and arbitration alternatives and creative settlements. Key areas of expertise include medical malpractice litigation, product liability defense and contract disputes. The firm represents Ardent Health Services and Presbyterian Healthcare Services, as well as several motor manufacturers, including Ford, Hyundai and Toyota.

**Sources say:** "*A top-notch defense firm.*" "*Excellent litigators and very good healthcare expertise.*"

**KEY INDIVIDUALS Robert Lasater** (see p.1774) maintains his reputation as one of the preeminent medical malpractice lawyers in the state. He regularly acts for physicians, hospitals and other healthcare providers on professional and managed care liability claims. **Rick Beitler** (see p.1773) also acts predominantly in the healthcare space and is well regarded for his skillful, thoughtful approach to matters. He handles litigation at state and federal level, as well as representing clients before the New Mexico Medical Review Commission. Sources also note his skills as a medi-

ator in the medical malpractice sphere. **Nelson Franse** (see p.1773) heads the professional liability group at the firm. He attracts extensive praise for his "*local knowledge and considerable trial experience,*" while one source describes him as "*an excellent litigator who's particularly good on his feet.*" He recently acted as lead partner defending Ardent Health Services in two cases of alleged malpractice. **Andrew Schultz** (see p.1774) specializes in complex and commercial litigation in state and federal courts, with a particular interest in class action and civil rights cases. Recent highlights include representing Vanderbilt Capital Advisors in a class action concerning investments made by the New Mexico Educational Retirement Board, and acting for a number of leading financial institutions and internet travel companies. **Henry Bohnhoff** (see p.1773) handles a broad range of commercial and real estate litigation. In one notable recent mandate he successfully represented a group of Republican voters with regard to the redrawing of New Mexico's voting district boundaries. **Bruce Hall** (see p.1773) continues to be seen as one of the best and most experienced trial lawyers in the state. His expertise spans a wide range of disciplines, including commercial, employment and environmental law.

## Band 2

### Atkinson, Thal, & Baker P.C.

**THE FIRM** This dedicated litigation practice is small but highly visible in the market and its attorneys are capable of handling litigation, arbitration and mediation for a diverse range of clients. The firm has particular specialties in the energy, construction and transport sectors, acting regularly for New Mexico's various railroad operators and advising clients in the aviation industry on commercial litigation, personal injury and wrongful death cases.

**KEY INDIVIDUALS Douglas Baker** attracts high praise from sources, and is considered by many to be a first port of call for peer referrals. He is noted for his work in insurance coverage disputes and product liability matters. **Clifford Atkinson** is renowned as a tough, determined and especially hard-working litigator. He is well known for his handling of energy and natural resources work, as well as railroad-related litigation. **John Thal** also has considerable experience in the sphere of railroad litigation, as well as strong capabilities in energy, natural resources and environmental law.

### Keleher & McLeod, PA

**THE FIRM** This firm houses a substantial team of litigators capable of handling disputes across the full range of commercial and civil law disciplines. Key areas of expertise include complex litigation, insurance defense and the representation of financial institutions.

KEY INDIVIDUALS **Charles Pharris** is a highly recommended practitioner in the medical malpractice space, and also has expertise in personal injury and product liability issues. Sources note his considerable experience of mediation and arbitration. **Spencer Reid** is a tough, respected litigator who acts chiefly in the commercial sphere, with specialist expertise in matters involving antitrust and banking law.

## Peifer, Hanson & Mullins PA

**THE FIRM** This Albuquerque firm focuses exclusively on litigation, representing both corporate and individual clients in matters concerning antitrust and insurance coverage, as well as the real estate and oil and gas sectors. The group handles trial litigation at both state and federal level, and is also accomplished in representing clients in appellate hearings.

**Sources say:** "*A premier litigation boutique.*"

KEY INDIVIDUALS **Charles Peifer** is widely acclaimed for his litigation expertise, which encompasses employment, tort and product liability matters.

## Sutin, Thayer & Browne

**THE FIRM** Sutin, Thayer & Browne maintains one of the largest commercial litigation practices in the state. It has traditional strengths in securing the enforcement of creditors' rights on behalf of banks and other lenders, and in the representation of clients in the construction industry; it has also represented a number of clients in the healthcare sector. Recent highlights have included successful representing Wells Fargo against alleged violations of the automatic bankruptcy stay, and acting for Fine Point Group on the appeal of a tribal gaming license revocation by the Pojoaque Gaming Commission.

**Sources say:** "*Their depth is impressive and their professionalism and client service are the best I have seen in any firm.*"

KEY INDIVIDUALS **Paul Bardacke** is highly experienced in the general commercial, environmental and Indian law spheres, and earns widespread praise for his alternative dispute resolution capabilities. Sources describe him as the "*preeminent mediator in the state*" and "*a seasoned litigator with a thriving mediation practice.*" **Gail Gottlieb** is best known for her expert representation of creditors and other interested parties in bankruptcy proceedings, including

complex Chapter 7 and 11 issues. She is also highly experienced in handling foreclosure and receivership matters for financial institutions and agricultural lenders. **Benjamin Allison** specializes in intellectual property matters affecting clients in the arts and heritage sector. He advises the Conan Doyle Estate on the US trademark and copyright protection of Sherlock Holmes. One client praises his combination of "*quiet intelligence, calming demeanor and old-fashioned American can-do,*" adding: "*He has our best interests at heart and is always ready to bring in the right expertise just where it's needed.*" **Benjamin Thomas** is most active in the commercial foreclosure and creditors' rights spheres. He is praised as being "*very intelligent and extremely disciplined, and he makes sure things don't slip through the cracks.*" One peer describes him as "*a rising star on the commercial litigation scene to whom I'd refer clients without hesitation.*"

# Band 3

## Freedman Boyd Hollander Goldberg Ives & Duncan P.A.

**THE FIRM** This litigation boutique has a solid reputation for the quality of its civil rights and mass tort work, and also houses a strong commercial litigation capacity. The team of six partners and one of counsel handles an extensive range of trial and appellate matters, from the municipal level right up to the Supreme Court.

KEY INDIVIDUALS **Joseph Goldberg** has extensive litigation experience in complex commercial matters, including antitrust issues and class actions.

## Hinkle Hensley Shanor & Martin LLP

**THE FIRM** This firm operates in both New Mexico and Texas, and is particularly well known for its representation of clients in the oil and gas industries. The large litigation team is well equipped to tackle disputes over title, contractual arrangements and day-to-day operations, and also deals with environmental issues and personal injury claims. The firm's wider commercial litigation practice is also highly regarded, with other key areas of expertise including medical malpractice and product liability matters.

**Sources say:** "*Outstanding: a first-class firm.*"

KEY INDIVIDUALS **Stuart Shanor** is a commercial litigator with specializations in the product liability and employment spheres. He is also noted for his capacity to handle mediations and arbitrations.

## Holland & Hart LLP
See profile on p.727

**THE FIRM** This firm has a strong general commercial litigation practice, with a particular focus on matters arising in the oil, gas and mining industries. The team has recently been engaged in the ongoing representation of BP America with regard to a complex property trespass matter, and for Energen Resources in a high-stakes dispute with the Office of Natural Resources Revenue over federal natural gas royalties.

KEY INDIVIDUALS **Bradford Berge** (see p.1773) is acclaimed by both peers and clients as "*a very fine lawyer*" for commercial litigation. He has been a key member of the team acting for both BP America and Energen Resources, and is also adept in the handling of environmental disputes and class actions.

## Other Notable Practitioners

**Ben Allen** of Allen, Shepherd, Lewis, Syra & Chapman P.A. is widely acclaimed for his handling of medical malpractice cases, which forms part of his broader insurance defense practice. **J. E. Gallegos** of Gallegos Law Firm PC is a respected litigator, best known for his expertise in handling natural resources, energy and water law issues. **Luis Stelzner** of Stelzner, Winter, Warburton, Flores, Sanchez & Dawes, P.A. is recommended by peers as a "*very tenacious, very smart guy*" with a particular aptitude for complex cases and mediations. His workload covers redistricting matters, personal injury and mass tort. **Michael Campbell** of Campbell Trial Law, LLC has considerable experience of litigation in New Mexico's state and federal courts, and is recommended for his specialized knowledge of oil and gas and environmental litigation, as well as antitrust matters.

# NATIVE AMERICAN LAW

Commentary about individuals can be found under their firm's paragraph. If the firm has no paragraph (is not ranked) look at Other Notable Practitioners.

| Native American Law | |
|---|---|
| **Leading Firms** | |
| **Band 1** | |
| Modrall, Sperling, Roehl, Harris & Sisk, PA | |
| Nordhaus Law Firm LLP | |
| **Band 2** | |
| Holland & Hart LLP * | |
| Sutin, Thayer & Browne | |

| Leading Individuals | |
|---|---|
| **Star individuals** | |
| Slade Lynn H | Modrall, Sperling, Roehl, Harris & Sisk, PA |
| **Band 1** | |
| Bladh Wayne | Nordhaus Law Firm LLP |
| Frye Paul | Frye Law Firm, P.C. (ONP)† |
| Stern III Walter E | Modrall, Sperling, Roehl, Harris & Sisk, PA |
| **Band 2** | |
| Rey-Bear Dan | Nordhaus Law Firm LLP |
| Scott William C | Modrall, Sperling, Roehl, Harris & Sisk, PA |
| Sheridan Mark F | Holland & Hart LLP * |
| West Christina S | Sutin, Thayer & Browne |

\* Indicates firm / individual with profile.
† ONP = Other Notable Practitioner.

## Band 1

### Modrall, Sperling, Roehl, Harris & Sisk, PA

**THE FIRM** This firm acts primarily for nontribal entities doing business in Indian country and receives high marks from commentators for the high quality of its attorneys and for their ability to cement durable relationships with their clients. Its full-service offering includes coverage of finance, taxation, and labor and employment issues, while it is especially lauded for its work in energy and natural resources project development and litigation. The team recently acted for a number of pipeline companies with regard to the negotiation of rights-of-way across lands belonging to the Jicarilla Apache and Navajo Nations in northwest New Mexico and Arizona.
**Sources say:** "*One of the strongest regional Indian law practices I've seen; it's spectacular.*"
**KEY INDIVIDUALS** Practice head **Lynn Slade** heads the practice and draws strong praise for his depth of knowl-

edge, excellent relations with tribal governments, tight focus on his clients' long-term interests and outstanding courtroom advocacy. He recently assisted a number of national investment service providers in the establishment of agreements with tribes governing the management of gaming proceeds on behalf of certain types of beneficiary. **Walter Stern** is described as "*a stellar fellow,*" valued for the way in which he uses his "*knowledge of day-to-day dealings with tribes and good perspective on previous deals*" to inform his advice. He has particularly strong expertise in matters concerning natural resources, energy and the environment. **William Scott** is recognized for his keen understanding of the interaction between Indian law and environmental law, especially where matters of air and water regulation are concerned. He played a significant role in the practice's successful representation of three clients in a dispute over the rights-of-way for pipelines and utility transmission lines across Navajo allotments in northwest New Mexico.

### Nordhaus Law Firm LLP

**THE FIRM** This boutique acts exclusively for tribal clients and maintains, in addition to its premises in Albuquerque and Santa Fe, an office in DC which allows it to represent them at the national level. It offers a comprehensive range of services and is particularly noted in New Mexico for its strength in matters involving gaming, taxation and water rights settlements. It regularly lobbies the New Mexico legislature on behalf of its clients and is also known for its constructive relationship with such state agencies as the Taxation and Revenue Department.
**Sources say:** "*The premier firm for tribes.*"
**KEY INDIVIDUALS Wayne Bladh** is managing partner of the Santa Fe office and an attorney with nearly 40 years' experience in Indian law. An accomplished litigator and legal strategist, he focuses on lobbying and government liaison issues at state level and also possesses strong expertise on matters concerning taxation and natural resources. Albuquerque partner **Dan Rey-Bear** specializes in litigation concerning issues of tribal jurisdiction, federal trust duty and taxation, as well as the handling of fee land and trust land acquisition transactions. The high quality and intelligence of his work at the appellate level attracts special comment.

## Band 2

### Holland & Hart LLP
See profile on p.727
**THE FIRM** This respected practice is able to draw upon the substantial resources of 14 offices across the Mountain West and a 15th in DC. The Santa Fe office handles a broad range of issues for its tribal and nontribal clientele, including litigation, government relations and general business law, as well as fielding a particular strength in the natural resources space. Key areas of expertise include matters including coal, natural gas and water rights.
**KEY INDIVIDUALS Mark Sheridan** (see p.1774) has over 30 years' legal experience and is best known for his keen litigation and alternative dispute resolution skills. He has practiced extensively in matters involving water rights and the exploitation of oil and gas resources on Indian land.

### Sutin, Thayer & Browne

**THE FIRM** This team acts both for tribes and for organizations doing business with them, combining an in-depth understanding of traditional Indian law with an ability to handle complex business and political issues. A number of the attorneys are licensed to practice in tribal as well as state and federal courts, while others specialize in providing commercial lending and financing advice to tribal entities and to banks involved in Indian country investment. The practice also acts as general counsel to a number of tribally owned corporations, providing counsel on such matters as contractual disputes and employment issues.
**KEY INDIVIDUALS Christina West** is a "*very well-regarded lawyer*" who is "*always professional and enjoyable to work with.*" Her practice focuses on the economic development of tribal entities, to which she brings noted skills in complex commercial litigation and extensive experience in employment and financing matters.

### Other Notable Practitioners

**Paul Frye** of Frye Law Firm, P.C. in Albuquerque is a "*very well-respected*" and "*very, very good*" practitioner who acts for both tribal and nontribal clients. He has a longstanding association with the Navajo Nation.

# REAL ESTATE

Commentary about individuals can be found under their firm's paragraph. If the firm has no paragraph (is not ranked) look at Other Notable Practitioners.

## Real Estate
### Leading Firms

**Band 1**
Modrall, Sperling, Roehl, Harris & Sisk, PA
Myers Oliver & Price
Rodey, Dickason, Sloan, Akin & Robb, PA *

**Band 2**
Hurley Toevs Styles Hamblin & Panter PA

**Band 3**
Campbell & Wells, P.A.

### Senior Statesmen

**Senior Statesmen: distinguished older partners**

| | |
|---|---|
| Ek Dale | Modrall, Sperling, Roehl, Harris & Sisk, PA |
| Hurley Patrick | Hurley Toevs Styles Hamblin & Panter PA |
| Keleher William B. | Keleher & McLeod, PA (ONP)† |
| Price Charles | Myers Oliver & Price |

### Leading Individuals

**Band 1**

| | |
|---|---|
| Goldberg Catherine T | Rodey, Dickason, Sloan, Akin & Robb, PA * |
| Meister Margaret L | Modrall, Sperling, Roehl, Harris & Sisk, PA |
| Myers John A | Myers Oliver & Price |
| Salazar John P | Rodey, Dickason, Sloan, Akin & Robb, PA * |
| Schifani Ruth M | Modrall, Sperling, Roehl, Harris & Sisk, PA |
| Wells Lawrence | Campbell & Wells, P.A. |

**Band 2**

| | |
|---|---|
| Castle Bruce | Bruce Castle (ONP)† |
| Patterson John | Scheuer Yost & Patterson PC (ONP)† |
| Styles Mark | Hurley Toevs Styles Hamblin & Panter PA |

**Band 3**

| | |
|---|---|
| Ahern Janice M | Rubin Katz Ahern Herdman (ONP)† |

**Up-and-coming individuals**

| | |
|---|---|
| Moore Jean C. | Sutin, Thayer & Browne (ONP)† |

\* Indicates firm / individual with profile.

†ONP = Other Notable Practitioner.

## Band 1

### Modrall, Sperling, Roehl, Harris & Sisk, PA

**THE FIRM** This team offers clients a one-stop shop for all real estate-related matters, grounded in close integration between the real estate team and the work of other practice groups, as well as an intimate understanding of the New Mexico business community. The firm covers a range of transactional and regulatory compliance issues, and has noted specialist expertise in advising on the development of renewable energy projects, as well as in negotiating real estate transactions with Native American tribes and pueblos. The group recently acted for Element Power subsidiary Macho Springs Solar with regard to the development of a photovoltaic project in Luna County.

**Sources say:** "The Modrall firm compares favorably with other law firms – it is one of the premier law firms in New Mexico."

**KEY INDIVIDUALS Ruth Schifani** specializes in the negotiation, structuring and documentation of real estate transactions of all kinds. Clients pay enthusiastic tribute to "her practical, no-nonsense application of her legal knowledge" and describe her as "phenomenal to work with." She was one of the lead partners in the Macho Springs Solar matter. **Margaret Meister** heads the department and acts on a wide range of matters, with particularly noteworthy strengths in matters involving renewable energy or Native American law aspects. Clients value her high reputation and good connections in the business community and report that "she brings a thoughtful, measured approach to all issues, carefully presenting both the pros and the cons." She recently acted for Haverland Carter Lifestyle Group Property Holdings in its acquisition of land in Rio Rancho for the purposes of constructing a retirement community. **Dale Ek** has worked in the real estate sphere for over 40 years and is renowned for his representation of regional real estate developers, ranchers and farmers, and financial institutions.

### Myers Oliver & Price

**THE FIRM** This Albuquerque boutique acts predominantly in the real estate space, handling transactional, litigation, and zoning and land use issues. Clients and peers note the firm's adept handling of substantial developments in the Albuquerque metropolitan area, as well as agricultural real estate transactions such as farm and ranch sales. **Sources say:** "We use them for things where good relationships are more important."

**KEY INDIVIDUALS John Myers** is praised as an excellent attorney whose chief strengths lie in the fields of land use, zoning and real estate development. He also possesses over 30 years' experience in the financing, leasing and sale or purchase of commercial real estate. Of counsel **Charles Price** is noted for his "wide variety of experience" and for being "really great to work with." His practice is largely focused on real estate development matters, of which he covers a comprehensive range, including acquisition, planning, financing and sales.

### Rodey, Dickason, Sloan, Akin & Robb, PA
See profile on p.1775

**THE FIRM** This practice tackles all aspects of real estate projects, from site selection, through financing and development, to completion, sale and, where necessary, litigation. It is a favored choice of national companies with New Mexico interests, and it deals with zoning and land use issues up to federal level. Clients pay warm tribute to the team's exhaustive knowledge of the New Mexico real estate and wider business scene and to its thorough, responsive service. The firm recently advised the Simon Property

Group on negotiations concerning its development interests in Albuquerque's Uptown district. Other significant recent clients include Peabody Energy, Pegasus Global and Chubb Group.

**Sources say:** "A high-quality, business-practical and efficient legal product: their ability to integrate seamlessly with our business needs is terrific."

**KEY INDIVIDUALS Catherine Goldberg** (see p.1773) is an "amazing, very careful lawyer" who commands considerable respect for her knowledge of the New Mexico market. She acts for both buyers and sellers in real estate transactions, with particular expertise in financing, subdivision and zoning matters. She was active in the firm's recent representation of the Simon Property Group. **John Salazar's** (see p.1774) many sterling qualities include "his depth of knowledge on all legal matters and personal input on political and economic issues in New Mexico." Clients also value his "attentiveness to our needs and business goals" and ability to "act as a good ambassador for us in the community." Salazar was the lead partner in the Simon Property matter, and he also advised the University of New Mexico in a successful appeal against a decision by the City of Albuquerque Environmental Planning Commission.

## Band 2

### Hurley Toevs Styles Hamblin & Panter PA

**THE FIRM** This small Albuquerque firm focuses closely on commercial real estate matters and is widely respected for its bench strength in this practice area. It handles all forms of real estate transaction in New Mexico, from initial financing and acquisition, through development, to leasing and sale. The firm is a popular choice for individual clients and small businesses, while it also has extensive experience in the handling of complex matters.

**KEY INDIVIDUALS Mark Styles** is described as "a good listener who's good to work with and good at figuring out how to make things work." He is also noted for his encyclopedic knowledge, responsiveness and excellent communication skills. **Patrick Hurley** has been in real estate practice for over 40 years and remains an active and highly respected attorney. He is particularly noted for his expertise in financing transactions and in development and leasing matters.

## Band 3

### Campbell & Wells, P.A.

**THE FIRM** This small but well-respected Albuquerque outfit focuses chiefly on assisting clients in the purchase, leasing or sale of real estate assets and advising on land use issues affecting new developments. The team also handles litigation arising out of defaults or disputes between landlords and tenants.

**KEY INDIVIDUALS Lawrence Wells** enjoys a strong reputation for thoroughness and reliability. He is noted for his particular expertise in land use matters and major refinancings.

## Other Notable Practitioners

**William Keleher** of Keleher & McLeod, PA is a veteran and highly respected practitioner with over 50 years' experience in the Albuquerque legal scene. His mastery of both real estate and wider business law enables him to handle especially complex matters which transcend practice area boundaries. Sole practitioner **Bruce Castle** is an "*all-around excellent lawyer,*" respected by his peers for his comprehensive range of commercial real estate skills. He is specifically praised for his close attention to detail and technical expertise. **John Patterson** of Scheuer Yost & Patterson PC enjoys an excellent reputation in the New Mexico market. He is best known for his handling of matters concerning condominiums and is also active on issues involving homeowner associations and boundary disputes. **Janice Ahern** of Rubin Katz Ahern Herdman & MacGillivray, P.A. is also a respected condominium law specialist, having been one of the coauthors of the New Mexico Condominium Act as well as other real estate-related state laws. She regularly represents real estate developers, banks, title insurance companies and underwriters. **Jean Moore** of Sutin, Thayer & Browne is an experienced and well-respected attorney whom peers regard as an increasingly impressive performer in real estate matters. Clients see her as a "*very bright lawyer who's been around the block and keeps on top of things.*" Moore has expertise across a broad range of real estate matters, including both commercial and residential transactions, and zoning and land use issues. She is especially well known for her representation of New Mexico universities and colleges.

# Leaders' Profiles in New Mexico

**ADAMS, Mark K**
Rodey, Dickason, Sloan, Akin & Robb, PA,
Santa Fe
505 954 3903
madams@rodey.com
*Featured in Environment (New Mexico)*
**Practice Areas:** Natural resources, water,
renewable energy and corporate law.

**BEITLER, Rick**
Rodey, Dickason, Sloan, Akin & Robb, PA,
Albuquerque
505 768 7260
rbeitler@rodey.com
*Featured in Litigation (New Mexico)*
**Practice Areas:** Health law and litigation with
an emphasis on medical malpractice defense.

**BERGE, Bradford**
Holland & Hart LLP, Santa Fe
505 954 7284
bberge@hollandhart.com
*Featured in Litigation (New Mexico)*
**Practice Areas:** Mr Berge represents operators,
mining companies, and integrated energy companies in disputes relating to surface use, subsurface
rights, contamination claims, royalty and contract.
He also represents clients from various industries
in commercial disputes, personal injury and
wrongful death claims, and insurance and insur-
ance coverage.
**Professional Memberships:** American and
Colorado Bar Associations, New Mexico State Bar,
American Board of Trial Advocates.
**Career:** Certified civil trial specialist by the
National Board of Trial Advocacy and the Board
of Legal Specialization of the New Mexico State
Bar.
**Personal:** JD - University of Denver 1978. BA -
Pomona College, Colorado College 1975.

**BOHNHOFF, Henry M**
Rodey, Dickason, Sloan, Akin & Robb, PA,
Albuquerque
505 768 7237
hbohnhoff@rodey.com
*Featured in Litigation (New Mexico)*
**Practice Areas:** Complex and commercial litigation including business and real estate litigation,
title, boundary, development and access disputes.

**CARR, William F**
Holland & Hart LLP, Santa Fe
505 954 7285
wcarr@hollandhart.com
*Featured in Environment (New Mexico)*
**Practice Areas:** Mr Carr concentrates his prac-
tice on regulatory matters, lobbying and litigation,
with a focus on issues before the New Mexico Oil
Conservation Division/Commission.
**Professional Memberships:** State Bar of New
Mexico, First Judicial District and American Bar
Associations, Rocky Mountain Mineral Law
Foundation.
**Career:** Certified as natural resources law, oil and
gas specialist by the New Mexico State Bar;
Adjunct Professor of Law, University of New

Mexico, School of Law; Member, Governor's
Energy Policy Advisory Board, 1991-94; Co-
Chairman, Regulatory Practices Committee, New
Mexico Oil and Gas Association, 2000-present.
**Personal:** Earned JD and BA from the University
of New Mexico.

**FELDEWERT, Michael**
Holland & Hart LLP, Santa Fe
505 988 4421
MFeldewert@hollandhart.com
*Featured in Environment (New Mexico)*
**Practice Areas:** Mr Feldewert is a certified spe-
cialist in natural resources and oil and gas law by
the Board of Legal Specialization of the New
Mexico State Bar. He advises clients on oil and gas
regulatory matters, tax issues, and litigation. He
represents clients before the New Mexico Oil
Conservation Division/Commission, New Mexico
Taxation and Revenue Department, and New
Mexico state and federal courts.
**Professional Memberships:** State Bar of New
Mexico, First Judicial District and American Bar
Associations, New Mexico Oil and Gas
Association, Rocky Mountain Mineral Law
Foundation.
**Personal:** Washington University in St. Louis
(JD,1990); Benedictine College (BA,1986).

**FRANSE, Nelson**
Rodey, Dickason, Sloan, Akin & Robb, PA,
Albuquerque
505 768 7259
nfranse@rodey.com
*Featured in Litigation (New Mexico)*
**Practice Areas:** Professional malpractice
defense, medical malpractice defense, product liability, personal injury defense, entertainment and
sports law.

**GOLDBERG, Catherine T**
Rodey, Dickason, Sloan, Akin & Robb, PA,
Albuquerque
505 768 7318
cgoldberg@rodey.com
*Featured in Real Estate (New Mexico)*
**Practice Areas:** Real estate, financings, banking,
foreclosures, commercial law, leases, contracts,
corporate law, complex purchase and sale, financing, leasing, landlord-tenant, liquor license matters.

**GORDON, Scott D**
Rodey, Dickason, Sloan, Akin & Robb, PA,
Albuquerque
505 768 7264
sgordon@rodey.com
*Featured in Labor & Employment (New Mexico)*
**Practice Areas:** Representation of employers in
discrimination, wrongful termination, breach of
contract and personal injury claims, trainning
managers and teaching seminars on a variety of
employment-related topics including avoidance of
wrongful discharge and discrimination litigation.

**HALL, Alan**
Rodey, Dickason, Sloan, Akin & Robb, PA,
Albuquerque
505 768 7203
ahall@rodey.com
*Featured in Corporate/Commercial (New Mexico)*
**Practice Areas:** Municipal bonds, industrial
revenue bonds and other economic development
incentives, securities, mergers and acquisitions,
and general corporate work.

**HALL, Bruce**
Rodey, Dickason, Sloan, Akin & Robb, PA,
Albuquerque
505 768 7249
bhall@rodey.com
*Featured in Litigation (New Mexico)*
**Practice Areas:** Complex litigation and appeals
in many areas (products liability, commercial,
employment, environmental and professional liability); experienced in jury and non-jury cases at
all levels of state and federal courts in New
Mexico, lead appellate counsel in a number of
cases which established the parameters of medical
malpractice and products liability law in New
Mexico; presented oral argument in the United
States Supreme Court.

**HORWITZ, Justin A**
Rodey, Dickason, Sloan, Akin & Robb, PA,
Albuquerque
505 768 7317
jhorwitz@rodey.com
*Featured in Corporate/Commercial (New Mexico)*
**Practice Areas:** Economic development initiatives, including industrial revenue bonds, public
improvement district and tax increment development district bonds, and local economic development transactions, as well as state and federal
securities law, corporate governance, and business
transactions.

**JARRETT, Danny W**
Jackson Lewis LLP, Albuquerque
505 878 0515
JarrettD@jacksonlewis.com
*Featured in Labor & Employment (New Mexico)*
**Practice Areas:** Board Certified Specialist:
Labor and Employment Law. Southwest Super
Lawyer. Practices before federal/state/tribal courts,
NLRB, EEOC, DOL.
**Professional Memberships:** New Mexico Bar;
Santa Clara Pueblo; Associated Builders and
Contractors; Association of Commerce and
Industry.
**Career:** Joined as partner, 2008; Noeding &
Jarrett,P.C., 2001; Commissioner, N.M. Board of
Bar Commissioners. AV-rated, Martindale.
**Publications:** NLRB Asserts Jurisdiction in
Indian Country, Casino Lawyer (2005), State Bar
of New Mexico, Indian Law Section Newsletter
(2007); Final USERRA Regulations Issued by
DOL, New Mexico Business Journal (2006);
USERRA Compels Employer Regard for Military
Service, New Mexico Business Journal (2005);
Proposed Legislation Would Hurt Employers,
Workers, Albuquerque Journal (2008).

**Personal:** University of New Mexico, JD, 1996 /
BS, 1989.

**LAMONT, Charlotte**
Littler Mendelson P.C., Albuquerque
505 244 3117
clamont@littler.com
*Featured in Labor & Employment (New Mexico)*
**Practice Areas:** Discrimination and harass-
ment; hiring, performance management and ter-
mination; appellate practice; wage and hour; poli-
cies, procedures and handbooks.
**Professional Memberships:** State Bar of New
Mexico; Albuquerque Bar Association; American
Bar Association; Greater Albuquerque Chamber of
Commerce; Society for Human Resource
Management.
**Career:** Certified by the New Mexico Board of
Specialization in employment and labor law.
Works with clients in manufacturing, banking,
retail, professional services, healthcare and gaming.
**Publications:** "New Mexico Charge of
Discrimination Form Creates Trap for the
Unwary," February 27, 2012.
**Personal:** JD, College of William and Mary,
1988; BBA, Virginia Commonwealth University,
1982; BA, The University of Virginia, 1981, With
Distinction.

**LASATER JR, W Robert**
Rodey, Dickason, Sloan, Akin & Robb, PA,
Albuquerque
505 768 7287
rlasater@rodey.com
*Featured in Litigation (New Mexico)*
**Practice Areas:** Representation of tertiary and
rural hospitals, physicians, skilled and long-term
care facilities, and other health care providers in
the area of health law and litigation, including litigating professional and managed care liability
claims and a wide variety of other health care
issues, advising clients in such areas as bioethics,
products liability, risk management and credentialing.

**MONNHEIMER, Donald B**
Rodey, Dickason, Sloan, Akin & Robb, PA,
Albuquerque
505 766 7556
dmonnheimer@rodey.com
*Featured in Corporate/Commercial (New Mexico)*
**Practice Areas:** Industrial revenue bonds, public improvement district bonds and tax increment
for development bonds, Local Economic
Development Act, governmental bonds, securities,
renewable energy projects, corporate law, mergers
and acquisitions, real estate law and transactions,
New Mexico constitutional debt issues, organization of business entities.

**NEERKEN, Julie P**
Rodey, Dickason, Sloan, Akin & Robb, PA,
Albuquerque
505 766 7557
jneerken@rodey.com
*Featured in Labor & Employment (New Mexico)*
**Practice Areas:** Employee benefits law.

**NIXON, Sunny J**
Rodey, Dickason, Sloan, Akin & Robb, PA,
Albuquerque
505 954 3917
snixon@rodey.com
*Featured in Environment (New Mexico)*
**Practice Areas:** Commercial utility, natural
resources, water and environmental law, including
litigation, administrative proceedings and transactional work; administrative law, including utility
proceedings and water rights cases.

**PARRISH, Theresa W**
Rodey, Dickason, Sloan, Akin & Robb, PA,
Albuquerque
505 768 7202
tparrish@rodey.com
*Featured in Labor & Employment (New Mexico)*
**Practice Areas:** Employment law and litigation,
complex and high risk litigation, commercial litigation, personal injury litigation including catastrophic injuries.

**RANKIN, Adam G.**
Holland & Hart LLP, Santa Fe
505 954 7294
agrankin@hollandhart.com
*Featured in Environment (New Mexico)*
**Practice Areas:** Mr Rankin's practice focuses
on regulatory matters and litigation involving
energy development and natural resource issues,
including water law.
**Professional Memberships:** State Bar of New
Mexico, First Judicial District and American Bar
Associations, Rocky Mountain Mineral Law
Foundation.

**Career:** Co-Editor Natural Resources Journal;
Natural Resources Law Certificate; Utton Natural
Resources Law Award; Clerk to Justice Edward L.
Chávez, New Mexico Supreme Court.
**Publications:** Geologic Sequestration of CO2 :
How EPA's Proposal Falls Short, Natural
Resources Journal, Vol. 49, Nos. 3/4.
**Personal:** JD University of New Mexico (Order
of the Coif); MA, MS Columbia University, BA
Amherst College.

**SALAZAR, John P**
Rodey, Dickason, Sloan, Akin & Robb, PA,
Albuquerque
505 768 7220
jsalazar@rodey.com
*Featured in Real Estate (New Mexico)*
**Practice Areas:** Real estate law, including transactional work (sale, purchase, and lease of vacant
and developed properties), land use and development law, including comprehensive plan, area
plan and sector plan amendments, annexation,
zoning, site plan approval, utility extension, storm
drainage and access considerations, and traffic, air
quality, and environmental studies, municipal and
administrative law, eminent domain litigation.

**SCHULTZ, Andrew G**
Rodey, Dickason, Sloan, Akin & Robb, PA,
Albuquerque
505 768 7205
aschultz@rodey.com
*Featured in Litigation (New Mexico)*
**Practice Areas:** Complex and commercial litigation including class action and civil rights litigation, as well as other complex procedural and
appellate work.

**SHERIDAN, Mark F**
Holland & Hart LLP, Santa Fe
505 954 3671
msheridan@hollandhart.com
*Featured in Native American Law (Nationwide),
Native American Law (New Mexico)*
**Practice Areas:** Complex civil matters in federal and state trial and appellate courts, particularly
business and natural resources litigation, including antitrust, contracts, securities, business tort,
real property, land use, oil and gas, and water
rights. Mr Sheridan's significant Indian law matters include Indian water rights, tribal royalties on
reservation oil and gas production, tribal taxation
and environmental regulation, Indian gaming
transactions, Indian rights-of-way, and tribal
court jurisdiction.
**Professional Memberships:** State Bar of New
Mexico; American Bar Association.
**Personal:** London School of Economics and
Political Science (LLM 1975); University of Illinois
(JD 1974); Benedictine College (AB 1970, magna
cum laude).

**SPROULS, Tracy**
Rodey, Dickason, Sloan, Akin & Robb, PA,
Albuquerque
505 768 7355
tsprouls@rodey.com
*Featured in Corporate/Commercial (New Mexico)*
**Practice Areas:** Entity formation, corporate
law, state and federal tax planning, state and federal tax controversies and estate planning.

**STAHL, Thomas L**
Rodey, Dickason, Sloan, Akin & Robb, PA,
Albuquerque
505 768 7240
tstahl@rodey.com
*Featured in Labor & Employment (New Mexico)*
**Practice Areas:** Representation of employers in
a wide range of employment actions, including
claims of age, race, religion, sex and disability discrimination, sexual harassment, retaliatory discharge, breach of contract and defamation, providing employer counseling and training on the
legal aspects of human resource issues.

**VIGIL, Charles J**
Rodey, Dickason, Sloan, Akin & Robb, PA,
Albuquerque
505 768 7377
cvigil@rodey.com
*Featured in Labor & Employment (New Mexico)*
**Practice Areas:** Labor and employment law,
commercial litigation, products liability and professional liability.

# RODEY, DICKASON, SLOAN, AKIN & ROBB, P.A.

www.rodey.com **tel:** 505 765 5900 **fax:** 505 768 7395

**Managing Partner:** Charles J Vigil

Number of partners: 49  Number of associates: 18  Of Counsel: 5

## Firm Overview:

Rodey, Dickason, Sloan, Akin & Robb, P.A. has been serving regional and national clients since 1883. With 70+ lawyers and full-service offices in Albuquerque and Santa Fe, the firm maintains a strong presence throughout the state of New Mexico. The firm has a reputation for delivering innovative, efficient and economical solutions for a full-range of business and litigation matters.

**OFFICES**

NEW MEXICO

**ALBUQUERQUE:** 201 3rd Street, NW, Suite 2200, 87102
Tel: 505 765 5900   Fax: 505 768 7395
Email: cvigil@rodey.com

**SANTA FE:** 315 Paseo de Peralta, 87501-2034
Tel: 505 954 3900   Fax: 505 954 3942
Email: mmowery@rodey.com

## Main Areas of Practice:

### Complex & Commercial Litigation:

National law firms and in-house counsel utilize the firm's litigators when they need the most experienced counsel for the most difficult cases. The firm is nationally recognized as the pre-eminent New Mexico class action defense firm and defends clients in putative class actions involving antitrust, consumer fraud, defective drugs and medical devices, employment discrimination law, modal premium insurance, casualty insurance, automobile defects, unfair pricing practices and Constitutional law.

**Key Clients:** Albertsons, Inc., Daimler Chrysler Corporation, Dow Chemical Company, Ford Motor Company, Lovelace Health Plan, Microsoft Corporation, Los Alamos National Laboratory

**Contact:** Andrew G Schultz  **Tel:** 505 768 7205

**Email:** aschultz@rodey.com

### Health Law:

The firm is a leader in defending medical malpractice and other types of healthcare litigation in New Mexico. It has defended hundreds of cases, including cases involving multiple plaintiffs and complex issues of causation and damages. The firm has considerable expertise in litigation involving healthcare clients including antitrust, products liability, commercial disputes, employment and civil rights claims.

**Key Clients:** Ardent Health Services, Presbyterian Healthcare Services

**Contact:** Ellen T Skrak  **Tel:** 505 768 7232

**Email:** eskrak@rodey.com

### Labor & Employment Law:

The full-service labor and employment law practice represents local, regional and national employers in cases involving federal and state laws affecting the employer-employee relationship. The group represents employers in all courts and before a broad spectrum of administrative bodies. The group advises clients in non-adversarial aspects of labor relations including employment terminations, early retirement plans, preparation of employee manuals, affirmative action plans, grievance procedures, the ADA and preventive counseling.

**Key Clients:** Albertson's, LLC, Central New Mexico Community College, Los Alamos National Laboratory, Northrop Grumman, Sandia National Laboratories,

Smith's Food and Drug Centers, Western Refining

**Contact:** Jeffrey L Lowry  **Tel:** 505 766 7541

**Email:** jlowry@rodey.com

### Banking, Financing & Commercial Lending:

This group represents lenders, borrowers, locally owned businesses and *Fortune* 500 companies. Its expertise and experience includes negotiating and documenting complex transactions, workouts and loan acquisitions; representing clients in foreclosures and commercial litigation; and working with financial institutions in regulatory and business matters.

**Key Clients:** Bank of America, Bank of the West, Wells Fargo

**Contact:** Catherine T Goldberg  **Tel:** 505 768 7318

**Email:** cgoldberg@rodey.com

### Bonds & Securities:

The Bonds and Securities practice has extensive experience in the issuance of tax-exempt governmental obligations, including general obligation bonds and tax-backed revenue bonds, project revenue bonds and special assessment district, public improvement district, and tax increment for development district bonds payable from special levies. It has substantial experience preparing disclosure documents and assisting clients with transactions structured to qualify for exemptions from registration under federal securities laws and regulations, including the Regulation D; with respect to non-issuer resale transactions, including Rules 144 and 144A; and general experience with New Mexico and other state securities laws.

**Key Clients:** Tres Amigas, Intrepid Potash, Fort Washington Capital Partners, Leprino Foods Company, Life BioScience, Louisiana Energy Services

**Contact:** Donald L Monnheimer  **Tel:** 505 766 7556

**Email:** dmonnheimer@rodey.com

### Employee Benefits:

The Employee Benefits group counsels clients regarding ERISA, providing advice on taxation of benefits, deduction of contributions, and qualification of plans and drafting and negotiating qualified and non-qualified retirement and executive compensation agreements. It provides advice regarding operation of retirement and benefit plans, including domestic relation orders, and ERISA litigation. It advises clients on executive compensation and severance arrangements and designs

welfare benefits, including cafeteria plans and counsels on the impact of health care reform.

**Key Clients:** Asian Technology, Bio Pappel International, Eye Associates of New Mexico

**Contact:** Julie P Neerken  **Tel:** 505 766 7557

**Email:** jneerken@rodey.com

### Environment & Natural Resources, Water & Utilities:

This practice group provides transactional, regulatory and litigation assistance to clients with properties and operations in New Mexico. It represents clients in the coal, copper, industrial minerals, oil, gas, potash, precious metals, uranium, water, water utility, and electric generation, transmission and distribution businesses in virtually every aspect.

**Key Clients:** Citigroup Financial Products, Citizens for Economic Growth & Environmental Protection, Intrepid Potash, Joule Unlimited, Neutron Energy, St. Cloud Mining, Tri-State Generation and Transmission Cooperative

**Contact:** Mark K Adams  **Tel:** 505 954 3903

**Email:** madams@rodey.com

### Real Estate:

The real estate practice assists clients in planning, acquisition, sale, development, construction, leasing and financing of projects including residential and commercial development and financing, hotel and resort properties, shopping centers, office buildings, ranches, mixed use projects and commercial and residential development.

**Key Clients:** Central New Mexico Community College, Coast Range Investments, Diamond Tail Estates, General Growth Properties, New Mexico Development Partners, University of New Mexico

**Contact:** John P Salazar  **Tel:** 505 768 7220

**Email:** jsalazar@rodey.com

### Taxation: Federal, State & Local:

The tax practice helps clients with tax controversies, at administrative levels and in litigation. Its transactional tax practice represents clients in all aspects of tax and business planning including planning and negotiating acquisitions, restructurings, and dispositions, both taxable and tax free.

**Contact:** R Tracy Sprouls  **Tel:** 505 768 7355

**Email:** tsprouls@rodey.com

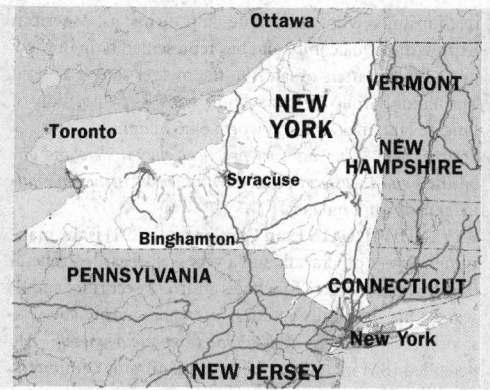

## How lawyers are ranked

Every year we carry out thousands of in-depth interviews with clients in order to assess the reputations and expertise of business lawyers worldwide. The qualities we look for (and which determine rankings) include technical legal ability, professional conduct, client service, commercial awareness/astuteness, diligence, commitment, and other qualities most valued by the client. For details of our research team, see p.5.

# ANTITRUST

Commentary about individuals can be found under their firm's paragraph. If the firm has no paragraph (is not ranked) look at Other Notable Practitioners.

| Antitrust |
| --- |
| **Leading Firms** |
| **Band 1** |
| Davis Polk & Wardwell LLP * |
| Simpson Thacher & Bartlett LLP * |
| Skadden, Arps, Slate, Meagher & Flom LLP & Affiliates * |
| **Band 2** |
| Cravath, Swaine & Moore LLP * |
| Sullivan & Cromwell LLP * |
| Wachtell, Lipton, Rosen & Katz * |
| **Band 3** |
| Axinn, Veltrop & Harkrider LLP * |
| Boies, Schiller & Flexner LLP * |
| Paul, Weiss, Rifkind, Wharton & Garrison LLP * |
| Wilson Sonsini Goodrich & Rosati * |
| **Band 4** |
| Cahill Gordon & Reindel LLP * |
| Debevoise & Plimpton LLP * |
| Gibson, Dunn & Crutcher LLP * |
| Shearman & Sterling LLP * |
| White & Case LLP * |
| Willkie Farr & Gallagher LLP * |
| Winston & Strawn LLP * |

*\* Indicates firm with profile.*
*Alphabetical order within each band. Band 1 is the highest.*

## Band 1

### Davis Polk & Wardwell LLP
See profile on p.442

**THE FIRM** The team at Davis Polk prides itself on its ability to undertake the full panoply of antitrust work and its deep bench reflects this variety of expertise. Sources are quick to point to the firm's connections and reputation within the federal agencies. Among its recent work is its continuing multifaceted representations on behalf of Comcast, including in a class action relating to the bundling of cable television channels.

Sources say: "*They have a whole slew of great attorneys who work seamlessly with us. We know we'll get the best from them.*"
**KEY INDIVIDUALS Ronan Harty** (see p.1901) is "*ridiculously smart and knowledgeable about antitrust*" according to sources, who also praise him for his "*practical guidance.*" Recently he has advised CNOOC in connection with its acquisition of Nexen, a deal worth $15.1 billion. In contrast to Harty, **Arthur Golden**'s (see p.1897) practice mostly takes in litigation work and he brings over 40 years' experience to the practice group. Sources point out his "*wonderful reputation*" in the areas of antitrust, corporate governance and M&A. The "*fantastic*" and "*really smart*" **Arthur Burke** (see p.626) is quickly coming to prominence as a highly talented litigator who also possesses excellent counseling skills. He has a raft of major clients including Comcast, Bank of America and TE Connectivity, whom he advised in relation its EUR1.55 billion acquisition of SAS. Sources "*think the world*" of the "*excellent*" **Joel Cohen** (see p.1885). In the antitrust arena he recently represented AstraZeneca in defense of a class action case initiated by health insurers.

### Simpson Thacher & Bartlett LLP
See profile on p.2006

**THE FIRM** Market observers heap praise on this firm's ability in antitrust litigation and merger clearance. Its transactional work is particularly highly regarded, having lately worked on various ten-figure deals such as Varian Semiconductor's $4.9 billion sale to Applied Materials. On the litigation side, it represented JPMorgan Chase in the LIBOR class action antitrust litigation.
Sources say: "*They have a lot of first-rate academic lawyers.*"
**KEY INDIVIDUALS** Sources name **Kevin Arquit** (see p.1874) "*one of the great antitrust lawyers in the country*" and revere his "*unmatched strategic ability.*" Recently he secured victory in the New York Court of Appeals on behalf of Equitas in a case concerning reinsurance. **Joseph Tringali** (see p.1947) is a litigator with a very good reputation among his peers for his antitrust work. Of late he represented Viacom in the successful affirmation of an earlier dismissal in a suit concerning the packaging of cable and satellite television channels. **Aimee Goldstein** (see p.1897) is an "*excellent*" and "*very well thought-of*" attorney who is recognized by peers for her antitrust work in relation to M&A.

### Skadden, Arps, Slate, Meagher & Flom LLP & Affiliates
See profile on p.2008

**THE FIRM** Skadden is another outstanding firm for antitrust in New York, garnering praise for the broad reach of its practice and its strength across the board. Peers consistently rate it as one of the top firms in the area, with a particular emphasis on the transactional and government investigation aspects of the practice. Its recent representations include achieving a settlement for HarperCollins Publishers in a DOJ investigation into e-book publishers.
Sources say: "*I was extremely impressed by the unparalleled level of quality control – they had superb people top to bottom.*"
**KEY INDIVIDUALS Clifford Aronson** (see p.1874) wins outstanding praise from observers, who note that he has had a "*fantastic year.*" This has included the aforementioned representation for HarperCollins, in addition to advising Express Scripts in relation to its $29.1 billion acquisition of Medco Health Solutions. He is mostly known for his transactional work, although he is also an active antitrust litigator. **Shepard Goldfein** (see p.322) is a "*great litigator*" with an "*encyclopedic knowledge of the*

**Senior Statesmen: distinguished older practitioners**

| Scher Irving | Greenberg Traurig, LLP (ONP)[†] * |

**Band 1**

| | | | | |
|---|---|---|---|---|
| Aronson Clifford H | Skadden, Arps, Slate, Meagher & Flom * | | Albert Lauren S | Axinn, Veltrop & Harkrider LLP * |
| Arquit Kevin J | Simpson Thacher & Bartlett LLP * | | Boast Molly S | WilmerHale (ONP)[†] * |
| Gotts Ilene Knable | Wachtell, Lipton, Rosen & Katz * | | Goldstein Aimee H | Simpson Thacher & Bartlett LLP * |
| Harty Ronan | Davis Polk & Wardwell LLP * | | Guryan Peter | Fried, Frank, Harris, Shriver (ONP)[†] * |
| Jacobson Jonathan | Wilson Sonsini Goodrich & Rosati | | Herfort John | Gibson, Dunn & Crutcher LLP * |

**Band 2**

| | | | | |
|---|---|---|---|---|
| Axinn Stephen | Axinn, Veltrop & Harkrider LLP * | | Katz Elai | Cahill Gordon & Reindel LLP * |
| Boies David | Boies, Schiller & Flexner LLP | | Keyte James | Skadden, Arps, Slate, Meagher & Flom * |
| Byowitz Michael H | Wachtell, Lipton, Rosen & Katz * | | Kubek Gary W | Debevoise & Plimpton LLP |
| Chesler Evan R | Cravath, Swaine & Moore LLP * | | Martin Scott | Greenberg Traurig, LLP (ONP)[†] * |
| Collins Wayne Dale | Shearman & Sterling LLP | | McGrath Thomas | Linklaters (ONP)[†] |
| Fastow Jay N | Dickstein Shapiro LLP (ONP)[†] * | | Schmidt Jeffrey | Linklaters (ONP)[†] |
| Flexner Donald L | Boies, Schiller & Flexner LLP | | Sorkin Laurence T | Cahill Gordon & Reindel LLP * |
| Golden Arthur F | Davis Polk & Wardwell LLP * | | Taffet Richard S | Bingham McCutchen LLP (ONP)[†] * |
| Goldfein Shepard | Skadden, Arps, Slate, Meagher & Flom * | | Urowsky Richard J | Sullivan & Cromwell LLP * |
| Harkrider John D | Axinn, Veltrop & Harkrider LLP * | | Varney Christine | Cravath, Swaine & Moore LLP * |
| Kessler Jeffrey L | Winston & Strawn LLP * | | Victor A Paul | Winston & Strawn LLP * |
| Quinn Yvonne S | Sullivan & Cromwell LLP * | | | |
| Steuer Richard M | Mayer Brown LLP (ONP)[†] | | **Band 5** | |
| Weiner Michael L | Dechert LLP (ONP)[†] * | | Biggio Charles E | Wilson Sonsini Goodrich & Rosati |

**Band 3**

| | | | | |
|---|---|---|---|---|
| Angland Joseph | White & Case LLP * | | Donovan Richard E | Kelley Drye & Warren LLP (ONP)[†] |
| Burke Arthur J | Davis Polk & Wardwell LLP * | | Dunlop Lisl J | Shearman & Sterling LLP |
| Cohen Joel M | Davis Polk & Wardwell LLP * | | Farren Patricia | Cahill Gordon & Reindel LLP * |
| Holley Steven L | Sullivan & Cromwell LLP * | | Finch Andrew | Paul, Weiss, Rifkind, Wharton & Garrison * |
| Jaffe Helene D | Proskauer Rose LLP (ONP)[†] | | Ladner Mark P | Morrison & Foerster LLP (ONP)[†] * |
| Johnston Elaine | Allen & Overy LLP (ONP)[†] | | Litwin Ethan | Hughes Hubbard & Reed LLP (ONP)[†] * |
| Larson Joseph D | Wachtell, Lipton, Rosen & Katz * | | Mahoney Stacey Anne | Bingham McCutchen LLP (ONP)[†] * |
| Morgenstern Saul P | Kaye Scholer LLP (ONP)[†] * | | Milne Robert A | White & Case LLP * |
| Neill David S | Wachtell, Lipton, Rosen & Katz * | | Mitnick Joel | Sidley Austin LLP (ONP)[†] * |
| Prince Kenneth S | Shearman & Sterling LLP | | O'Kelly Eamon | Arent Fox LLP (ONP)[†] * |
| Rooney William H | Willkie Farr & Gallagher LLP * | | Orr Dennis P | Morrison & Foerster LLP (ONP)[†] * |
| Schaeffer Fiona A | Jones Day (ONP)[†] * | | Powell Wesley | Willkie Farr & Gallagher LLP * |
| Silverman Moses | Paul, Weiss, Rifkind, Wharton & Garrison * | | Robins Harry T | Morgan, Lewis & Bockius LLP (ONP)[†] * |
| Sullivan Peter | Gibson, Dunn & Crutcher LLP * | | Schneider Bruce H | Stroock & Stroock & Lavan LLP (ONP)[†] |
| Synnott Aidan | Paul, Weiss, Rifkind, Wharton & Garrison * | | Serota James I | Greenberg Traurig, LLP (ONP)[†] * |
| Tringali Joseph | Simpson Thacher & Bartlett LLP * | | Stoll Neal R | Skadden, Arps, Slate, Meagher & Flom * |
| | | | Tween Douglas | Baker & McKenzie (ONP)[†] * |

**Band 4**

| | | | | |
|---|---|---|---|---|
| Abuhoff Daniel M | Debevoise & Plimpton LLP | | **Up-and-coming individuals** | |
| | | | Antoine Olivier | Crowell & Moring LLP (ONP)[†] * |
| | | | Buffier Beau W | Shearman & Sterling LLP |
| | | | Hemlock Adam C. | Weil, Gotshal & Manges LLP (ONP)[†] * |
| | | | Stock Eric J | Hogan Lovells US LLP (ONP)[†] |

antitrust world" according to commentators. A pure litigator, he has acted for clients in antitrust disputes in a variety of criminal and civil cases. **James Keyte** (see p.1908) is noted for his *"cerebral approach to antitrust"* and his client-friendly manner, which he utilizes across an array of litigation and transactional work. He recently represented SanDisk in two matters, successfully defending the firm in antitrust suits brought by Kingston Technologies and PNY Technologies. **Neal Stoll** (see p.1945) is a seasoned antitrust practitioner who sources note for his depth of knowledge. He particularly focuses on government investigations and antitrust matters concerning M&A.

## Band 2

### Cravath, Swaine & Moore LLP
See profile on p.1966

**THE FIRM** This team has a broad-spectrum antitrust practice, with experience in class action litigation, Sherman Act cases and transactions. It has long-standing relationships with such blue-chip firms as American Express and Qualcomm and has represented both of these in multiple matters of late. On the merger side, it advised The Linde Group in connection with its acquisition of Lincare Holdings in a deal worth $4.6 billion.

**Sources say:** *"They are very practical, they understand our business and I was very pleased with the consistency in quality of their work product."*

**KEY INDIVIDUALS Evan Chesler** (see p.294) is the managing partner of Cravath and a very well-regarded general litigator whose practice includes antitrust, securities and IP work. One peer calls Chesler *a terrific, terrific lawyer – someone I'd turn to if I couldn't represent myself."* He defended IBM in a suit concerning mainframe computers. **Christine Varney** (see p.1948) chairs the antitrust practice and is described by sources as an *"extremely sophisticated"* lawyer. Practicing on the transactional side, she has acted for Grupo Modelo in connection with its proposed acquisition by Anheuser-Busch.

### Sullivan & Cromwell LLP
See profile on p.2011

**THE FIRM** The Sullivan & Cromwell antitrust group has an exceptional reputation for work relating to the financial services industry, both in transactional and litigation matters. In this area it has represented Barclays in the LIBOR investigation. Beyond financial services, the firm has also undertaken significant work in the technology sector, including for Microsoft, which it successfully defended in a multibillion-dollar suit brought by Novell.

**Sources say:** *"They're pretty flawless in their advice and execution and are able to tailor advice to the client well."*

**KEY INDIVIDUALS** The *"terrific"* **Yvonne Quinn** (see p.1929) is known as an outstanding transactional lawyer, with sources describing her as *"extremely thoughtful with a very deep knowledge of the financial services industry."* She acted for the Bank of Montreal in the acquisition of Marshall & Ilsley, a deal worth $4.1 billion. Commentators call **Steven Holley** (see p.1904) an *"outstanding," "full-service"* antitrust lawyer who is able to give *"sound, practical advice."* He is a longstanding representative for Microsoft, acting for it lately in the case against Novell. **Richard Urowsky** (see p.1948) has a varied practice, with antitrust expertise being joined by tax and securities work. Sources call him a *"very smart, very good lawyer."* Lately he has acted for Pharmasset in its $11 billion acquisition by Gilead Sciences.

### Wachtell, Lipton, Rosen & Katz
See profile on p.2012

**THE FIRM** This group has a fine reputation for transactional antitrust work. The quality of its work product relating to M&A is considered outstanding and the group has a cohort of exceptional deal lawyers. Among its recent clients is Motorola Mobility, which it represented in its $12.5 billion sale to Google. The team also acted for United Technologies in its $18.4 billion acquisition of Goodrich.

**Sources say:** *"In terms of deals, Wachtell is as good as it gets. It is a well-oiled machine delivering consistent quality."*

KEY INDIVIDUALS **Ilene Knable Gotts** (see p.1898) is a *"fabulous lawyer"* with *"fantastic knowledge,"* according to sources. She practices exclusively in the M&A antitrust area and recently represented PPG in the merger of Chlor-Alkali with Georgia Gulf. Commentators variously describe **Michael Byowitz** (see p.1882) as a *"phenomenal"* and *"fantastic antitrust lawyer."* Another experienced merger specialist, he was the lead lawyer for the firm in the United Technologies deal mentioned above. **Joseph Larson** (see p.1911) is highly regarded by peers as an *"outstanding"* and *"extremely effective"* transactional antitrust attorney. He recently represented McGraw-Hill in a joint venture involving CME Group Index Services. **David Neill** (see p.1922) is seen by sources as one of the leading financial services antitrust lawyers around. He has an accomplished practice involving numerous representations before government agencies.

## Band 3

### Axinn, Veltrop & Harkrider LLP
See profile on p.1956

THE FIRM This compact group is well regarded for its expertise in the crossover between antitrust and IP matters, whether it be in litigation, deals or investigations. It recently represented Google in multiple matters, including in its much-heralded $12.5 billion acquisition of Motorola Mobility and also in an FTC investigation concerning the use of patents.
Sources say: *"They are relatively small but extremely responsive and have a very high caliber of lawyers across the board."*
KEY INDIVIDUALS **John Harkrider** (see p.1901) is a *"really terrific lawyer"* who is a *"very smart, excellent writer."* In addition to taking the lead in the firm's representations for Google, Harkrider has also acted as lead antitrust counsel to XL Health in its $2 billion sale to UnitedHealth Group. **Stephen Axinn** (see p.1875) is described as *"a real intellectual"* who is *"very much a force"* as a litigator. Among his clients is Zuffa, which he represented in an FTC investigation into its acquisition of Strikeforce. The *"excellent"* **Lauren Albert** (see p.1872) undertakes a variety of complex commercial litigation with an emphasis on antitrust and IP.

### Boies, Schiller & Flexner LLP
See profile on p.1958

THE FIRM Litigation specialist Boies, Schiller & Flexner is a capable antitrust firm, whose big-name litigators are renowned for their skill and experience in the area. Practicing both on the plaintiff and defense side, it is particularly well regarded for its class action practice.
KEY INDIVIDUALS **David Boies** is *"the litigation crisis guy"* according to sources. He is held in the highest regard by peers for his *"exceptional advocacy"* in antitrust disputes. **Donald Flexner** also garners *"high respect"* from commentators for being a *"very tough antitrust litigator"* and for his outstanding knowledge in the area. He is the firm's managing partner.

### Paul, Weiss, Rifkind, Wharton & Garrison LLP
See profile on p.1997

THE FIRM This team focuses largely on antitrust litigation and cartel matters, with considerable expertise in those areas. Its strong bench has a good mix of youth and experience and is frequently seen by peers in a range of antitrust cases. Recent representations include for MasterCard in the credit card interchange fee litigation and Deutsche Bank in the LIBOR price-fixing consolidated class action case.
Sources say: *"It is a litigation powerhouse."*
KEY INDIVIDUALS **Moses Silverman** (see p.1942) is a *"huge force"* and a *"superb litigator"* whose ambit covers antitrust, securities and general commercial litigation. He acted as lead counsel for Deutsche Bank in the LIBOR class action case. The *"impressive"* **Aidan Synnott** (see p.1946) is described by one source as a *"high-class antitrust expert"* noted for his responsiveness and strategic decision-making. He leads the firm's representation on a number of recent cases, including for Pfizer in a patent antitrust case. **Andrew Finch** (see p.1892) is recognized by peers as a strong young partner who has *"good command of the subject."* He has been part of the firm's representation for UBS in a DOJ investigation concerning alleged bid rigging.

### Wilson Sonsini Goodrich & Rosati
See profile on p.700

THE FIRM Wilson Sonsini's New York antitrust practice is gaining traction as a strong presence in the market. The firm concentrates largely on antitrust litigation and investigations, but is also recognized for its handling of merger-related work. Among its blue-chip clients is Google, which it represents in several matters including an FTC investigation relating to the search and advertising aspects of its business.
Sources say: *"I really love their work. They are fantastic, responsive and easy to work with."*
KEY INDIVIDUALS **Jonathan Jacobson** is a *"brilliant antitrust lawyer"* who combines *"insightful and practical advice"* with *"great litigation skills,"* say sources. He is heavily involved in the firm's representation of Google. **Charles Biggio** practices in antitrust and trade regulation matters. Recently he has provided advice to Micron in relation to the $2.5 billion acquisition of Elpida Memory.

## Band 4

### Cahill Gordon & Reindel LLP
See profile on p.1960

THE FIRM The majority of this group's practice is in civil and criminal antitrust litigation and counseling, with particular expertise in financial services and media-related antitrust. It has recently represented Credit Suisse in the LIBOR investigation and related class actions, and has advised AIG on its antitrust compliance policy.
Sources say: *"They are quite knowledgeable and their analytical skills are strong."*
KEY INDIVIDUALS **Elai Katz** (see p.1908) is described by sources as *"a really smart guy who is dedicated to antitrust."* Lately he has represented Ascend Health in its $500 million

acquisition by Universal Health Services. **Laurence Sorkin** (see p.1943) is considered an *"excellent"* and *"respected"* antitrust practitioner by impressed sources. He recently represented Akzo Nobel in various matters related to the vitamins industry. **Patricia Farren** (see p.1891) is a *"terrific antitrust litigator,"* say sources. She was part of a team that represented The New York Times, CNBC and Move, Inc. in an alleged price-fixing case.

### Debevoise & Plimpton LLP
See profile on p.1968

THE FIRM This firm covers a range of antitrust work including matters relating to M&A and civil antitrust litigation. It recently represented The Rank Group in a series of substantial acquisitions across a variety of manufacturing industries. It also acted for International Paper in its $4.3 billion acquisition of Temple-Inland.
KEY INDIVIDUALS Antitrust practitioner **Daniel Abuhoff** is known by peers as a skilled litigator. He represented both The Rank Group and International Paper in the matters mentioned above. **Gary Kubek** is seen by clients as a knowledgeable and responsive lawyer. He acted for Schneider in its $2 billion acquisition of software company Telvent.

### Gibson, Dunn & Crutcher LLP
See profile on p.682

THE FIRM This firm's New York practice supplements its nationally renowned cartel expertise with an active litigation and M&A presence. Among its major recent matters are representing Schlumberger in two major transactions and acting for UBS in the LIBOR class action cases.
Sources say: *"They are very thorough and very smart, while being good at analyzing the situation and developing plans to address the issues."*
KEY INDIVIDUALS **Peter Sullivan** (see p.1945) does a *"fabulous job"* according to sources. He has a varied antitrust practice, covering criminal and civil antitrust litigation as well as transactional work. In addition to representing UBS, he has also acted for MonoSol in its sale to Kuraray. Antitrust and complex commercial litigator **John Herfort** (see p.1902) is described by commentators as a *"tremendous lawyer"* who takes a *"very smart and common-sense"* approach to antitrust work. He recently defended CareCore in an antitrust suit brought by Eastside Medical Radiology.

### Shearman & Sterling LLP
See profile on p.2005

THE FIRM This group is involved in a variety of significant antitrust work including civil and criminal litigation and transactional work. It has strong international capabilities, with multiple partners qualified to practice in the EU. Lately it has represented NASDAQ OMX in a contested bid for NYSE Euronext. Other clients include Viacom and Citi.
KEY INDIVIDUALS **Wayne Dale Collins** is known as a *"superb"* and *"formidable"* antitrust lawyer who focuses his practice mainly on transactional defense. He recently advised Citibank in relation to the sale of EMI's music publishing arm. **Kenneth Prince** is well regarded by sources for his experience and skill across the antitrust

field. Recently he has acted for Cargolux in multiple actions alleging price fixing among air cargo companies. Counsel **Lisl Dunlop** receives plaudits and recognition from peers as a talented antitrust specialist who is *"very articulate and intelligent."* She was part of the firm's representation for Barclays Bank in the highly publicized card interchange fee litigation. **Beau Buffier** co-heads the firm's global antitrust practice and is praised for his effectiveness in front of the regulators. He recently acted for BASF in its $1.02 billion acquisition of Becker Underwood.

## White & Case LLP
See profile on p.451

THE FIRM The White & Case team is well regarded for the strength of its antitrust practice, notably with respect to its work in the pharmaceutical and electronics sectors. It has represented Novartis in a number of major matters and also acted for Pfizer in cases concerning the drugs Lipitor and Effexor.

KEY INDIVIDUALS The *"fabulous"* and *"pragmatic"* **Joseph Angland** (see p.1873) was part of the team that represented Novartis in a class action concerning the use of the drug Diovan. **Robert Milne** (see p.1920) is noted by commentators for his *"amazing work ethic"* and *"very polished"* style. He acted for Saudi Aramco in defense of a class action case brought by private plaintiffs against several OPEC members claiming trillions of US dollars.

## Willkie Farr & Gallagher LLP
See profile on p.2016

THE FIRM This group prides itself on the breadth of its antitrust practice, with the ability to undertake cases across the board. It continues to represent MasterCard in a number of matters including in the card interchange fee litigation, as well as acting for Marsh & McLennan in an insurance brokerage suit.

Sources say: *"They are very professional, responsive and thorough and we know we can rely on their judgment."*

KEY INDIVIDUALS The *"excellent"* **William Rooney** (see p.1932) is praised by commentators for his antitrust deal-work, and is also an active litigator. He recently defended Mueller Industries in a class action concerning alleged anticompetitive practices in the sale of copper tubing. **Wesley Powell** (see p.1928) recently represented Silver Lake Technology Management in a putative class action concerning the LBO market. Sources *"rank him highly"* and credit his litigation prowess.

## Winston & Strawn LLP
See profile on p.1267

THE FIRM The Winston & Strawn antitrust group received a substantial boost with the addition of ten partners from Dewey & LeBoeuf . The team has particular strength in cartel defense matters and sports-related antitrust. Members of the practice group have recently represented such clients as Uralkali in litigation concerning potash price fixing.

KEY INDIVIDUALS *"Terrific trial lawyer"* **Jeffrey Kessler** (see p.346) is an antitrust lawyer with a focus on the sports industry. Sources report that *"his mind works at breakneck*

*speed, comprehending and breaking down issues in a way few can."* He acted for the NBA Players Association in the antitrust issues arising from the NBA lockout. **Paul Victor** (see p.1948) is well regarded for his cartel defense practice, with a particular emphasis on the representation of Japanese clients. Lately he has acted for NTN Corporation in defense of a putative class action alleging rigging of bids for industrial bearings.

## Other Notable Practitioners

Sources praise **Olivier Antoine** (see p.1874) of Crowell & Moring LLP for being "tremendously hard-working and diligent" and note he is "pragmatic and hands-on." He primarily focuses on transactions. **Molly Boast** (see p.1879) of WilmerHale is described by sources as a "bona fide antitrust heavy hitter." She was part of a team that acted for International Paper in its acquisition of Temple Inland. Sources call **Richard Donovan** of Kelley Drye & Warren LLP a "bright and articulate" antitrust attorney who "knows his way around the DOJ." He co-heads the firm's antitrust practice group and also undertakes white-collar and other general litigation work. **Peter Guryan** (see p.1900) of Fried, Frank, Harris, Shriver & Jacobson LLP is "very strong" in the area and is noted for his counseling skill and knowledge of the regulatory agencies. The "impressive and experienced" **Jay Fastow** (see p.1891) of Dickstein Shapiro LLP is "as smart as it gets," report commentators. Recent representations include defending Saudi Arabian Airlines in a class action case concerning the alleged price fixing of air cargo services. **Adam Hemlock** (see p.1902) of Weil, Gotshal & Manges LLP practices in general commercial litigation and antitrust, and has particular experience of representing Asian clients in US antitrust matters. Sources note his strong client-facing skills and his "business-oriented legal advice."**Helene Jaffe** of Proskauer Rose LLP joined the firm from Weil Gotshal in January 2012 and now heads up its antitrust offering. In addition to antitrust, she also practices in unfair trading and trademark work. **Elaine Johnston** of Allen & Overy LLP heads up the firm's antitrust practice group. She primarily practices as a transactional antitrust lawyer, although she also undertakes litigation. **Mark Ladner** (see p.351) of Morrison & Foerster LLP handles financial services-related antitrust work. He has acted for Bank of America in the card interchange fee litigation. **Ethan Litwin** (see p.1914) of Hughes Hubbard & Reed LLP is a noted antitrust litigator. Sources describe him as a "very strong antitrust lawyer" who "knows his stuff."**Scott Martin** (see p.1917) of Greenberg Traurig, LLP wins plaudits as a fast-rising junior partner who is "excellent in his analysis." He recently defended CTIA - The Wireless Association in a putative class action concerning alleged antitrust violations in relation to text messaging. At Bingham McCutchen LLP, **Stacey Anne Mahoney** (see p.1916) has an "excellent antitrust litigation practice" according to commentators. She practices across litigation, M&A and antitrust counseling. At Linklaters, **Thomas McGrath** is a "very tenacious advocate" who is "extremely bright and well prepared." McGrath has advised on a number of major recent deals, including Deutsche Börse's combination with NYSE

Euronext and Glencore's proposed acquisition of Xstrata. **Joel Mitnick** (see p.1920) of Sidley Austin LLP has a practice focusing on antitrust and securities. Lately he acted for MacMillan in a case brought against it and other e-book publishing companies. **Saul Morgenstern** (see p.1921) of Kaye Scholer LLP is particularly known for his expertise in the pharmaceutical and publishing industries. He receives credit from sources for his "excellent legal expertise and pragmatic counseling style." **Eamon O'Kelly** (see p.1925) of Arent Fox LLP gains plaudits for his "sharp" and "impressive" practice. His recent representations include defending Munich Re in a class action case concerning alleged insurance bid rigging. **Dennis Orr** (see p.1925) of Morrison & Foerster LLP is another attorney at the firm with a broad-based practice which includes antitrust. He continues to defend Cadbury in litigation alleging the price fixing of chocolate. **Harry Robins** (see p.1931) of Morgan, Lewis & Bockius LLP is an "excellent strategist" whose intellect and client management skills are praised by clients. He has worked on a number of major recent deals including for Autonomy in its $10.2 billion sale to Hewlett-Packard. **James Serota** (see p.1940) of Greenberg Traurig is a litigator with substantial antitrust experience. He represented Northeast Pharmaceutical Group in the vitamin C antitrust litigation. **Fiona Schaeffer** (see p.1936) of Jones Day is described by commentators as "terrific" and a "strong player." She has expertise in healthcare and energy antitrust and recently represented Sanofi in the sale of part of its business to Valeant Pharmaceuticals. The "terrific" **Irving Scher** (see p.1937), at Greenberg Traurig, is described by commentators as "still being on top of his game" and lately acted for Lorillard Tobacco in defense of a class action alleging price fixing by cigarette manufacturers. **Jeffrey Schmidt** of Linklaters recently advised Actavis Group on its $4.25 billion disposal to Watson Pharmaceutical. **Bruce Schneider** of Stroock & Stroock & Lavan LLP is recognized by sources as a "bright and quick" antitrust lawyer and as a strong orator. He recently represented Fujifilm in defense of a monopolization claim brought by an independent party. "Great lawyer" **Richard Steuer** of Mayer Brown LLP handles antitrust litigation and transactional work. He also undertakes work in IP and franchising. **Eric Stock** of Hogan Lovells US LLP practices in complex commercial litigation with a strong emphasis on antitrust. He acted for Home City Ice in antitrust litigation concerning packaged ice. **Richard Taffet** (see p.1946) of Bingham McCutchen LLP is known for his expertise in matters at the intersection between antitrust and IP law. He recently represented Sharp in the TFT-LCD antitrust litigation. **Douglas Tween** (see p.1948) of Baker & McKenzie is a white-collar criminal lawyer with a significant practice in cartel matters. According to one source, "he is terrific - he has lots of experience and is very levelheaded." **Michael Weiner** (see p.1950) of Dechert LLP is cited by sources as "an outstanding lawyer" who "really understands the antitrust law and is very easy to work with." His work encompasses deals and antitrust litigation, and lately he has acted for Travelport in major antitrust litigation against American Airlines.

# BANKRUPTCY/RESTRUCTURING

Commentary about individuals can be found under their firm's paragraph. If the firm has no paragraph (is not ranked) look at Other Notable Practitioners.

## Bankruptcy/Restructuring
## Leading Firms

**Band 1**
Akin Gump Strauss Hauer & Feld LLP *
Davis Polk & Wardwell LLP *
Kirkland & Ellis LLP *
Kramer Levin Naftalis & Frankel LLP *
Milbank, Tweed, Hadley & McCloy LLP *
Paul, Weiss, Rifkind, Wharton & Garrison LLP *
Skadden, Arps, Slate, Meagher & Flom LLP & Affiliates *
Weil, Gotshal & Manges LLP *

**Band 2**
Cleary Gottlieb Steen & Hamilton LLP *
Jones Day *
Wachtell, Lipton, Rosen & Katz *
Willkie Farr & Gallagher LLP *

**Band 3**
Brown Rudnick LLP *
Cadwalader, Wickersham & Taft LLP *
Kasowitz, Benson, Torres & Friedman LLP *
Latham & Watkins LLP *
Morrison & Foerster LLP *
Quinn Emanuel Urquhart & Sullivan, LLP
Simpson Thacher & Bartlett LLP *
White & Case LLP *

**Band 4**
Bingham McCutchen LLP *
Chadbourne & Parke LLP *
Proskauer Rose LLP *
Ropes & Gray LLP *
Schulte Roth & Zabel LLP *
Stroock & Stroock & Lavan LLP *

**Band 5**
Debevoise & Plimpton LLP *
Dechert LLP *
Fried, Frank, Harris, Shriver & Jacobson LLP *
Kelley Drye & Warren LLP *
Luskin, Stern & Eisler LLP
Mayer Brown LLP *
Shearman & Sterling LLP *
Sullivan & Cromwell LLP *

* Indicates firm with profile.
Alphabetical order within each band. Band 1 is the highest.

## Band 1

### Akin Gump Strauss Hauer & Feld LLP
See profile on p.904

**THE FIRM** Akin Gump continues to foster its reputation as one of the preeminent creditors' committee practices in the country. The group has added to a catalogue of high-profile representations this year, most recently being appointed to represent the unsecured creditors' committee

in the Chapter 11 bankruptcy of Overseas Shipholding, one of the largest oil tanker companies in the world. Akin also represents the unsecured creditors' committee in the bankruptcy of aircraft manufacturer Hawker Beechcraft. The team is not limited to creditor-side representations, however, and has acted as debtors' counsel for the likes of TerreStar Networks, Pinnacle Airlines and Inner City Media.

**Sources say:** *"They get it, and understand what it is to deal with creditors and hedge funds. They know how to get things done." "The Akin team has carved out an interesting and very effective role in the market."*

**KEY INDIVIDUALS** The *"effective"* **Daniel Golden** (see p.322) is a *"top-tier, go-to person in the creditors committee world today,"* say sources. He is regularly singled out for his efficient management of the firm's resources in achieving results for his clients. He is currently leading the unsecured creditors' committee in the high-value Overseas Shipholding bankruptcy. Golden appears in that matter alongside Akin's financial restructuring practice head **Fred Hodara** (see p.335). Hodara is a constructive negotiator who is praised by commentators as *"a tough and aggressive deal-maker."* **Ira Dizengoff** (see p.305) is highlighted by clients as *"very effective with big-picture strategy,"* and for being *"extremely good at finding ways to navigate through the legal complexities to structure negotiated solutions."* He recently represented the unsecured creditors' committee in the $4 billion Chapter 11 proceedings of Dynegy Holdings. **Michael Stamer** (see p.1944) garners praise for his balanced approach to negotiations, with interviewees noting that he is *"calm but sharp elbowed when necessary,"* before adding that *"we really like having him on our side – he is our go-to choice for bankruptcy counsel."* The *"absolutely unflappable"* **Lisa Beckerman** (see p.1877) is experienced in both debtor and creditor-side representations. She recently acted for the debtor in the Pinnacle Airlines bankruptcy, as well for the ad hoc lender group in the bankruptcy of Houghton Mifflin Harcourt Publishing. Clients are pleased that *"she is very upfront and direct; you want someone who'll fight for you, and she really does."* **David Botter** (see p.1880) is playing a prominent role in acting for the Official Committee of Unsecured Creditors of Hawker Beechcraft in relation to its $2.5 billion Chapter 11 bankruptcy. He receives recognition from commentators for his evenhanded approach and his ability to find pragmatic solutions.

### Davis Polk & Wardwell LLP
See profile on p.442

**THE FIRM** Davis Polk's large team of all-around corporate insolvency experts has established itself as one of the front runners in the industry. It is traditionally considered a formidable creditor-side practice, concentrating on the intersection between insolvency, M&A and capital markets. Highlights include its ongoing representation of Citibank in the $950 million DIP financing for Eastman Kodak. Davis Polk is, however, also adept across the bank-

ruptcy spectrum, including in representing debtors. The firm also recently represented the joint administrators of Lehman Brothers International (Europe) in relation to the litigation and settlement of $38 billion in claims between it and Lehman Brothers Inc. The team is also playing a prominent role for several major financial institutions in connection to the implementation of the Dodd-Frank Act.

**Sources say:** *"Excellent lawyers, negotiators and business people. They have a firm grasp of the specific nuances of Chapter 11, but can also act as good counselors on making informed business decisions." "They are very skilled in litigation, and it has impressed me that they display immense calm under pressure."*

**KEY INDIVIDUALS** Department co-head **Donald Bernstein** (see p.282) continues to garner a tremendous amount of respect for his experience and strategic foresight. He has been instrumental in Davis Polk's ongoing advice to a number of major financial institutions in connection to the implementation of the Dodd-Frank Act. Bernstein has also been heavily involved as lead counsel to Citibank in the aforementioned Kodak DIP financing, alongside fellow co-head **Marshall Huebner** (see p.337). Huebner is described by sources as *"an excellent negotiator with a strong reputation in court. In face-to-face meetings he is not only strong from a legal standpoint, he has the ability and reputation for being effective in getting to a solution."* He is currently lead counsel to Patriot Coal and Pinnacle Airlines in their respective Chapter 11 bankruptcies. **Damian Schaible** (see p.1937) appears alongside Huebner in Davis Polk's representations of both Pinnacle Airlines and Patriot Coal. He continues to foster acclaim as one of the brightest prospects in the industry. Clients praise his *"unique ability to blend his expertise with traditional legal and commercial negotiating skills. He has picked up on rather esoteric business issues quickly, and was able to offer good advice on solutions."* **Brian Resnick** (see p.1930) has a strong following among Davis Polk's financial institution clients. He operates across the spectrum of corporate insolvency matters, with particular expertise in DIP and exit financings, 363 sales, bankruptcy litigation, and monoline insurance restructurings. He plays a key role in advising Citigroup as lead arranger of Eastman Kodak's DIP facility.

### Kirkland & Ellis LLP
See profile on p.1254

**THE FIRM** Kirkland & Ellis is internationally renowned as one of the deepest and most successful restructuring groups in the country. The team offers a comprehensive array of experts covering every aspect of distressed and restructuring situation, nationally and internationally. Kirkland is particularly recognized for large-scale debtor-side representations, with roles in a number of the nation's most significant bankruptcies in recent years. Highlights include advising prominent aircraft manufacturer Hawker Beechcraft, as well as Global Aviation Holdings, in their

## Bankruptcy/Restructuring

### Senior Statesmen

**Senior Statesmen: distinguished older practitioners**

| | | |
|---|---|---|
| Cronin Denis | Vinson & Elkins LLP (ONP)† * | |
| Jerome John | Sullivan & Cromwell LLP * | |
| Milmoe J Gregory | Skadden, Arps, Slate, Meagher & Flom * | |

### Leading Individuals

**Star individuals**

| | |
|---|---|
| Miller Harvey R | Weil, Gotshal & Manges LLP * |

**Band 1**

| | |
|---|---|
| Baker D J (Jan) | Latham & Watkins LLP * |
| Ball Corinne | Jones Day * |
| Bernstein Donald S | Davis Polk & Wardwell LLP * |
| Bienenstock Martin J | Proskauer Rose LLP |
| Cieri Richard M | Kirkland & Ellis LLP * |
| Dunne Dennis | Milbank, Tweed, Hadley & McCloy LLP * |
| Goffman Jay M | Skadden, Arps, Slate, Meagher & Flom * |
| Golden Daniel H | Akin Gump Strauss Hauer & Feld LLP * |
| Goldstein Marcia | Weil, Gotshal & Manges LLP * |
| Huebner Marshall S | Davis Polk & Wardwell LLP * |
| Karotkin Stephen | Weil, Gotshal & Manges LLP * |
| Kirpalani Susheel | Quinn Emanuel Urquhart & Sullivan, LLP |
| Kornberg Alan W | Paul, Weiss, Rifkind, Wharton & Garrison * |
| Mayer Thomas Moers | Kramer Levin Naftalis & Frankel LLP * |
| Novikoff Harold S | Wachtell, Lipton, Rosen & Katz * |
| Sprayregen James HM | Kirkland & Ellis LLP * |

**Band 2**

| | |
|---|---|
| Abrams Marc | Willkie Farr & Gallagher LLP * |
| Basta Paul M | Kirkland & Ellis LLP * |
| Bromley James L | Cleary Gottlieb Steen & Hamilton LLP * |
| Charles Scott K | Wachtell, Lipton, Rosen & Katz * |
| Davis George A | Cadwalader, Wickersham & Taft LLP * |
| Dizengoff Ira S | Akin Gump Strauss Hauer & Feld LLP * |
| Eckstein Kenneth H | Kramer Levin Naftalis & Frankel LLP * |
| Feldman Matthew A | Willkie Farr & Gallagher LLP * |
| Fife Lori R | Weil, Gotshal & Manges LLP * |
| Friedman David M | Kasowitz, Benson, Torres & Friedman LLP * |
| Hansen Kristopher M | Stroock & Stroock & Lavan LLP |
| Harris Adam C | Schulte Roth & Zabel LLP * |
| Henes Jonathan S | Kirkland & Ellis LLP * |
| Hodara Fred S | Akin Gump Strauss Hauer & Feld LLP * |
| Holtzer Gary T | Weil, Gotshal & Manges LLP * |
| Lauria Thomas E | White & Case LLP * |
| Leake Paul | Jones Day * |
| Levin Richard | Cravath, Swaine & Moore LLP (ONP)† * |
| Pantaleo Peter V | Simpson Thacher & Bartlett LLP * |
| Rapisardi John J | Cadwalader, Wickersham & Taft LLP * |
| Rosenberg Andrew N | Paul, Weiss, Rifkind, Wharton & Garrison * |
| Schonholtz Margot | Willkie Farr & Gallagher LLP * |
| Stamer Michael S | Akin Gump Strauss Hauer & Feld LLP * |
| Stark Robert | Brown Rudnick LLP |
| Uzzi Gerard | Milbank, Tweed, Hadley & McCloy LLP * |
| Weisfelner Edward | Brown Rudnick LLP |
| Ziman Kenneth S | Skadden, Arps, Slate, Meagher & Flom * |

**Band 3**

| | |
|---|---|
| Bane Mark | Ropes & Gray LLP |
| Barr Matthew S | Milbank, Tweed, Hadley & McCloy LLP * |
| Bartner Douglas | Shearman & Sterling LLP * |
| Beckerman Lisa G | Akin Gump Strauss Hauer & Feld LLP * |
| Brilliant Allan S | Dechert LLP * |
| Carr James | Kelley Drye & Warren LLP |
| Coleman Ken | Allen & Overy LLP (ONP)† |
| Cook Michael L | Schulte Roth & Zabel LLP * |
| Despins Luc A | Paul Hastings LLP (ONP)† |
| Dietderich Andrew G | Sullivan & Cromwell LLP * |
| Flaschen Evan D | Bracewell & Giuliani LLP (ONP)† * |
| Flics Martin | Linklaters (ONP)† |
| Garrity James | Morgan, Lewis & Bockius LLP (ONP)† * |
| Giddens James W | Hughes Hubbard & Reed LLP (ONP)† * |
| Gross Steven R | Debevoise & Plimpton LLP |
| Hahn Richard | Debevoise & Plimpton LLP |
| Ivester Eric | Skadden, Arps, Slate, Meagher & Flom * |
| Kieselstein Marc | Kirkland & Ellis LLP * |
| Lennox Heather | Jones Day * |
| Luskin Michael | Luskin, Stern & Eisler LLP |
| Marcus Jacqueline | Weil, Gotshal & Manges LLP * |
| Mason Richard G | Wachtell, Lipton, Rosen & Katz * |
| Miller Brett | Morrison & Foerster LLP * |
| Mindlin Philip | Wachtell, Lipton, Rosen & Katz * |
| Palmer Deryck A | Pillsbury Winthrop Shaw Pittman (ONP)† |
| Reilly Michael J | Bingham McCutchen LLP * |
| Reisman Steven J | Curtis, Mallet-Prevost, Colt & Mosle (ONP)† * |
| Rosner David S | Kasowitz, Benson, Torres & Friedman LLP * |
| Sabin Jeffrey S | Bingham McCutchen LLP * |
| Sage Michael | Dechert LLP * |
| Scheler Brad Eric | Fried, Frank, Harris, Shriver & Jacobson * |
| Schweitzer Lisa M | Cleary Gottlieb Steen & Hamilton LLP * |
| Seider Mitchell A | Latham & Watkins LLP * |
| Seife Howard | Chadbourne & Parke LLP * |
| Shimshak Stephen J | Paul, Weiss, Rifkind, Wharton & Garrison * |
| Smolinsky Joseph H | Weil, Gotshal & Manges LLP * |
| Stern Richard | Luskin, Stern & Eisler LLP |
| Togut Albert | Togut Segal & Segal LLP (ONP)† |
| Trust Brian | Mayer Brown LLP |
| Zirinsky Bruce R | Greenberg Traurig, LLP (ONP)† * |

**Band 4**

| | |
|---|---|
| Anker Philip D | WilmerHale (ONP)† * |
| Beltzer Howard S | Mayer Brown LLP |
| Botter David H | Akin Gump Strauss Hauer & Feld LLP * |
| Califano Thomas | DLA Piper LLP (US) * |
| Cornish Kelley A | Paul, Weiss, Rifkind, Wharton & Garrison * |

| | |
|---|---|
| Feinstein Robert J | Pachulski Stang Ziehl & Jones (ONP)† |
| Feldman David | Gibson, Dunn & Crutcher LLP (ONP)† * |
| Fuhrman Steven M | Simpson Thacher & Bartlett LLP * |
| Goldman Andrew N | WilmerHale (ONP)† * |
| Halperin Alan D | Halperin Battaglia Raicht LLP (ONP)† |
| Harner Paul E | Latham & Watkins LLP * |
| Hazan Scott L | Otterbourg, Steindler, Houston & Rosen (ONP)† |
| Hermann Brian S | Paul, Weiss, Rifkind, Wharton & Garrison * |
| Hillman David M | Schulte Roth & Zabel LLP * |
| Hirschfield Marc E | Baker & Hostetler LLP (ONP)† |
| Ivanick Peter | Hogan Lovells US LLP (ONP)† |
| Kaplan Gary L | Fried, Frank, Harris, Shriver & Jacobson * |
| Kruger Lewis | Stroock & Stroock & Lavan LLP |
| Lee Gary | Morrison & Foerster LLP * |
| LeMay David M. | Chadbourne & Parke LLP |
| Levitin Joel H | Cahill Gordon & Reindel LLP (ONP)† * |
| Liscio Mark F | Kaye Scholer LLP (ONP)† * |
| Longmire John C | Willkie Farr & Gallagher LLP * |
| Mitchell Nancy A | Greenberg Traurig, LLP (ONP)† * |
| Nashelsky Larren M | Morrison & Foerster LLP * |
| O'Neal Sean | Cleary Gottlieb Steen & Hamilton LLP * |
| Parkins Lenard | Haynes and Boone, LLP (ONP)† |
| Princi Anthony | Morrison & Foerster LLP * |
| Raval Abhilash | Milbank, Tweed, Hadley & McCloy LLP * |
| Rogoff Adam | Kramer Levin Naftalis & Frankel LLP * |
| Saferstein Jeffrey D | Paul, Weiss, Rifkind, Wharton & Garrison * |
| Sassower Edward O | Kirkland & Ellis LLP * |
| Schaible Damian S. | Davis Polk & Wardwell LLP * |
| Shalhoub Paul V | Willkie Farr & Gallagher LLP * |
| Somerstein Mark R. | Ropes & Gray LLP |
| Steinberg Arthur | King & Spalding LLP (ONP)† * |
| Strickland Rachel C | Willkie Farr & Gallagher LLP * |
| Sussberg Joshua A | Kirkland & Ellis LLP * |
| To My Chi | Debevoise & Plimpton LLP |
| Williams Matthew J | Gibson, Dunn & Crutcher LLP (ONP)† * |
| Wilson Eric | Kelley Drye & Warren LLP |
| Wofford Keith H | Ropes & Gray LLP |

**Up-and-coming individuals**

| | |
|---|---|
| Abelson Philip | Proskauer Rose LLP |
| Finestone Ben | Quinn Emanuel Urquhart & Sullivan, LLP |
| Fleck Evan | Milbank, Tweed, Hadley & McCloy LLP * |
| Kiplok Christopher | Hughes Hubbard & Reed LLP (ONP)† * |
| Mannal Douglas | Kramer Levin Naftalis & Frankel LLP * |
| Marinuzzi Lorenzo | Morrison & Foerster LLP * |
| Minias Joseph G. | Willkie Farr & Gallagher LLP * |
| Resnick Brian | Davis Polk & Wardwell LLP * |
| Torkin Michael H | Sullivan & Cromwell LLP * |

* Indicates individual with profile.

Alphabetical order within each band. Band 1 is the highest. †ONP = Other Notable Practitioner.

respective Chapter 11 bankruptcies. The team has also advised on high-value out-of-court restructurings for Barneys New York and luxury resort developer Kerzner International.

**Sources say:** *"They worked around our time and our hours, but at the same time they were always available to us. They were very good at understanding our business and the sensitivity of the industry – that got us through the bankruptcy a lot quicker." "There is a depth of experience; the team provides a wide range of expertise, and has seen and done just about everything."*

**KEY INDIVIDUALS** The *"spectacular"* **Richard Cieri** (see p.295) is described as a *"real rainmaker"* by interviewees, many of whom recognize that *"he has been around along time and has great market recognition."* His recent highlights include representing Hawker Beechcraft in its aforementioned Chapter 11 bankruptcy proceedings. He is also representing Ally Financial and Ally Bank during the large-scale bankruptcy of its wholly owned mortgage subsidiary, Residential Capital (ResCap). **James Sprayregen** (see p.411) is among the most respected bankruptcy attorneys in the country, with interviewees describing him as *"tireless and very creative. He is very good in complicated and difficult situations – he just knows how to work the process on the legal side and, more importantly, the deal side of it. He balances those dynamics well."* Sprayregen splits his time between the firm's Chicago and New York offices. **Paul Basta** (see p.280) receives praise as a *"very effective lawyer who is practical in his approach,"* and is described as *"incredible when it comes to court and credibility with the judges."* He has played leading roles in a number of the firm's most significant bankruptcy matters, having recently advised both Barneys New York and Kerzner International on high-value out-of-court restructurings. Commentators describe **Jonathan Henes** (see p.1902) as one of the *"next generation of leaders"* in the industry. He continues to build his prominent profile, recently representing Global Aviation Holdings in connection with its $495 million Chapter 11 bankruptcy. Interviewees describe him as *"very active, with a strong presence."* Clients give **Marc Kieselstein** (see p.1909) *"the highest marks"* for his superb and personable approach, with many commenting on his excellent responsiveness and ability to *"add clarity and humor to what can be a dreadful experience."* His recent highlights include advising women's fashion retailer United Retail Group in relation to its Chapter 11 restructuring. **Edward Sassower** (see p.400) continues to build on his reputation as a *"professional, business savvy deal-maker." "He has shown a good soft touch to clients,"* report interviewees, *"and has a good relationship with all the other professionals as well, which transcends the adversarial aspect of the case."* Sassower operates across the spectrum of bankruptcy-related issues. The *"extremely smart, capable and responsive"* **Joshua Sussberg** (see p.1945) played an integral role in the out-of-court restructurings of Barneys New York and Kerzner International. He advises clients on all types of bankruptcy issues.

## Kramer Levin Naftalis & Frankel LLP
See profile on p.1987

**THE FIRM** This corporate restructuring and bankruptcy group moves into the top tier for the first time on the back of a stellar year. Kramer Levin's diverse team boasts experience in all manner of restructuring issues, with particular expertise in creditor-side representations, where it has acted for committees in many of the year's most significant bankruptcies. Its recent highlights include advising the unsecured creditors' committee in ResCap's high-profile $15 billion Chapter 11 bankruptcy proceedings. Additional engagements include representing the unsecured creditors' committees in the high-stakes bankruptcies of Patriot Coal, Hostess Brands and AES Eastern Energy.

**Sources say:** *"They have lawyers who are exceptional and top in their fields; highly experienced and very intelligent. They are outstanding at thinking of creative solutions when you are in a particularly difficult situation."*

**KEY INDIVIDUALS** Group cochair **Thomas Moers Mayer** (see p.363) garners acclaim for providing *"thorough, detailed and excellent analysis."* He has been instrumental to some of the firm's greatest successes, and is leading for the creditors' committee in the bankruptcies of Hostess Brands and Patriot Coal, as well as advising an ad hoc group of holders in the Eastman Kodak Chapter 11 proceedings. He is described as *"among the most intellectual of all bankruptcy lawyers; extremely knowledgeable on the law and how things will play out."* Mayer cochairs the practice alongside **Kenneth Eckstein** (see p.308). Eckstein is currently acting for the unsecured creditors' committee in the ResCap bankruptcy and is also adept at handling company-side matters, with his representation of St Vincent's Catholic Medical Centers being a prime example. Clients note that *"he has an outstanding reputation and an excellent presence in court; he can establish an excellent rapport with the judges."* **Adam Rogoff** (see p.1932) is experienced across the full spectrum of bankruptcy work and possesses expertise in a range of industries, including healthcare, manufacturing, aviation and automotive. He is presently playing a prominent role in the bankruptcy of Patriot Coal, on which Kramer Levin acts for the unsecured creditors' committee. The *"very aggressive, intelligent and creative"* **Douglas Mannal** (see p.1916) enters the rankings as someone who is *"among the top junior partners in the Bar."* Recent work includes his representation of the unsecured creditors' committee in the Chapter 11 bankruptcy of ResCap.

## Milbank, Tweed, Hadley & McCloy LLP
See profile on p.448

**THE FIRM** Milbank continues to be involved in many of the country's most significant bankruptcy matters. While most famed for its bondholder- and creditor-side representations, the group has also built a formidable practice representing debtors, bolstering its already-prominent reputation for handling bankruptcy issues on all fronts. Recent years have seen the team win a number of significant creditor-side engagements, including representing the Official Committee of Unsecured Creditors in the $6.7 billion Eastman Kodak Chapter 11 bankruptcy. The group is

also acting for the Official Committee of Unsecured Creditors of real estate company Arcapita, which has $2.55 billion in liabilities, as well as representing an ad hoc creditor group of secured noteholders in the $15 billion bankruptcy of ResCap. Company-side highlights include representing startup telecoms company LightSquared during its reorganization.

**Sources say:** *"The sheer volume of incredible talent that Milbank has brought to its representation has been very impressive." "Very balanced guys, not chest-thumpers or grenade-throwers – they are problem solvers. They understand issues very quickly and give you the firepower to go back as a business person and make a decision. Very commercially articulate and capable strategists."*

**KEY INDIVIDUALS** Group cochair and *"fearless leader"* **Dennis Dunne** (see p.307) is praised as *"very knowledgeable and insightful, and, because his demeanor is balanced, it allows him to control the table."* Sources go on to remark that *"he is hands-on with his work and is at the core of finding solutions to bankruptcy issues. He is commercially minded and gives the practical business perspective."* He is an expert in a number of areas of bankruptcy, and is currently advising the Official Committee of Unsecured Creditors in the Eastman Kodak Chapter 11 proceedings. **Gerard Uzzi** (see p.1948) is a recent addition to the Milbank team from White & Case. He continues to garner praise for his efficient, strategic approach, with one commentator stating that he is *"the single best deal-maker in the bankruptcy Bar – he is able to bring together various parties and reach consensus in highly contentious situations."* Recent highlights for Uzzi include representing major ad hoc creditor groups in the Chapter 11 bankruptcies of ResCap and American Airlines. **Matthew Barr** (see p.1876) is admired for his commercial acumen, with one source noting: *"He is among the most practical lawyers I've dealt with. He has a good idea of what our end goals are and doesn't get hung up in the weeds."* He has experience in a wide range of bankruptcy situations, ranging from distressed asset acquisitions to debtor representations, with a prominent example being his current advice to telecoms business LightSquared during its Chapter 11 bankruptcy. **Abhilash Raval** (see p.1930) has had a successful year playing prominent roles representing the Official Committee of Unsecured Creditors in both the ResCap and Arcapita Chapter 11 bankruptcies. He continues to receive admiration for his even-keeled and forward-thinking approach. New entrant **Evan Fleck** (see p.1893) has been earmarked by commentators as someone who *"is going to become a major player as he ages."* Other sources note that *"he is very balanced; he knows how to put his foot down, but not in a way that is divisive. He is very articulate, able to communicate issues succinctly and then come up with a solution."*

## Paul, Weiss, Rifkind, Wharton & Garrison LLP
See profile on p.1997

**THE FIRM** This team combines bench strength, diverse expertise and client focus with formidable firm-wide resources to produce one of the top bankruptcy and corporate reorganization offerings in the country. The group has continued its successful track record with a wide range of high-profile representations. On the company side, it acted for Houghton Mifflin Harcourt Publishing in relation to its prepackaged Chapter 11 bankruptcy plan, which eliminated around $3.1 billion of debt. Other highlights include its representation of Silver Point Capital as pre and post-petition agent for the lenders to Hostess Brands, as well as its ongoing engagement for the ad hoc committee of bondholders of Dynegy Holdings.

**Sources say:** *"They have a very talented bench, as well as talent the next level down. Creative and great to work with, they are smart, responsive and not afraid to give you a tough answer." "I find the entirety of that practice impressive and extremely good. They drive us strongly towards consensual solutions."*

**KEY INDIVIDUALS Alan Kornberg** (see p.349) is chair of the bankruptcy and corporate reorganization department and a member of the firm's management committee. He is described by sources as one of the *"top creditor-side lawyers in the country – he is immensely practical, commercial, intelligent and hard-working."* Interviewees also say that *"he has a nice gentle style to him"* and *"is a very pleasant person to build a relationship with."* **Andrew Rosenberg** (see p.394) is *"somebody who is always a pleasure to work with or opposite,"* say interviewees, who add: *"He is one of the finest bondholder/creditor attorneys I've ever worked with."* Clients add that *"he understood the position the company was in and he played a really good role in-between groups of creditors."* His recent highlights include acting for the ad hoc committee of bondholders in the Dynegy Chapter 11 bankruptcy. **Stephen Shimshak** (see p.1941) operates across the spectrum of bankruptcy-related issues, and comes highly praised for his expertise in bankruptcy litigation. He is lauded by clients for his ability to *"bring practical insight to the table."* **Kelley Cornish** (see p.1886) is a member of the firm's management committee and acts for a full range of parties in bankruptcy-related situations. She is praised as a *"creative, smart and hard-working"* attorney. The *"super smart and effective"* **Jeffrey Saferstein** (see p.1935) has *"demonstrated excellence in boiling down complex issues and creating solutions,"* according to market sources. He is presently a key player in advising Houghton Mifflin Harcourt Publishing in its $3.1 billion prepackaged Chapter 11 bankruptcy proceedings. **Brian Hermann** (see p.1902) is currently advising energy company Bicent Holdings and its affiliates in relation to their prepackaged Chapter 11 bankruptcy. Interviewees are impressed by his commercial approach, noting that he is *"very constructive in getting deals done."*

## Skadden, Arps, Slate, Meagher & Flom LLP & Affiliates
See profile on p.2008

**THE FIRM** Skadden's top corporate restructuring group remains a powerhouse for all types of bankruptcy work, particularly for large-scale company-side work. The team has adapted to a shifting market in recent years and is adept in acting for various interests, leveraging admirably from the firm's stellar corporate and M&A offerings. This allows Skadden to step in to advise clients at an early stage, either on an out-of-court basis or through the prepackaged bankruptcy process that was pioneered by the firm. The group's recent highlights include the representation Danish shipping company TORM in relation to its multi-billion-dollar out-of-court restructuring. The team also provided advice to Barclays Bank in a $1.45 billion DIP credit facility for ResCap during its Chapter 11 proceedings. Skadden also continues to represent the unsecured creditors' committee in the American Airlines bankruptcy.

**Sources say:** *"Skadden has been very smart and helpful in getting the right result in an extremely complex multijurisdictional case." "They did an outstanding job for us. They worked constructively and didn't get in the way of a deal."*

**KEY INDIVIDUALS** Skadden's global head of corporate restructuring is **Jay Goffman** (see p.322). Sources praise him as *"exceptionally creative and innovative; he really thinks outside box and can tackle interesting new problems unconstrained."* He is currently advising TORM in its aforementioned restructuring, and is also acting for the unsecured creditors' committee in the American Airlines bankruptcy. Deputy practice group leader **Kenneth Ziman** (see p.431) *"is very insightful and an excellent technician,"* remark sources. One client says: *"He is very commercial and practical, and has helped us work through complex issues and helped all parties get to a result."* He has played integral roles in Skadden's representation of Barclays Bank in connection with a $1.45 billion DIP credit facility for ResCap. **Eric Ivester** (see p.1906) represents a diverse range of clients from various sectors, and is regularly noted for his even temperament and adaptable intellect. Recent highlights include his continued representation of online travel business Travelport in relation to its $3.8 billion cross-border restructuring. **Gregory Milmoe** (see p.369) is *"one of the fathers of the modern industry of restructuring,"* according to market sources, who add that *"his depth of knowledge is fantastic and unusual. He has a great, calming demeanor in pressured situations."*

## Weil, Gotshal & Manges LLP
See profile on p.2015

**THE FIRM** This global powerhouse is continually recognized for the roles it has played on behalf of debtors in a major proportion of the most significant bankruptcy filings in history. Its enviable bench strength and experience enables the team to act quickly and effectively in any distressed financial situation, no matter the size or industry. Weil's emphasis on large-scale debtor filings has continued in recent years, with the team advising the likes of AMR, AES Eastern Energy, Lehman Brothers, Washington Mutual and MF Global UK in relation to their respective multibillion-dollar restructurings.

**Sources say:** *"The Weil team offers a great breadth of experience. It is very responsive, commercial, hard-working, and they have a very strong bench." "They clearly have a lot of resources and experienced partners who are known and respected by judges."*

**KEY INDIVIDUALS** Practice group founder **Harvey Miller** (see p.369) is described by sources as *"the dean of bankruptcy lawyers; he is a big-picture guy with extensive experience."* He is a preeminent figure in the international bankruptcy landscape, one who remains *"very client-conscious, unbelievably knowledgeable, and who has the respect of the everyone at the Bar."* **Marcia Goldstein** (see p.323) heads up Weil's business finance and restructuring group. Widely admired and respected, she has built her name as a practitioner who is *"insightful, with a strong knowledge base, and gives very practical advice."* She played a leading role for MF Global UK in relation to MF Global's well-publicized Chapter 11 proceedings. Goldstein is not solely focused on debtor representations, however, and recently advised Citibank and Barclays in relation to a $500 million DIP credit facility in the Patriot Coal Chapter 11 bankruptcy. **Stephen Karotkin** (see p.343) is currently leading Weil's representation of AMR, the parent company of American Airlines, during its large-scale Chapter 11 bankruptcy proceedings. He is regularly lauded for his creative problem solving, with one source noting: *"He is a very quick study who gets up to speed on our business and helps us to understand complex bankruptcy issues."* **Lori Fife** (see p.312) is praised by interviewees as *"very hard-working, thoughtful and helpful in working through difficult problems. She is responsive and has a broad remit of expertise – she's involved in everything."* Fife has over 28 years of bankruptcy experience and is a member of the firm's management committee. **Gary Holtzer** (see p.1904) moves up in the rankings on the back of a successful year in which happy clients continue to praise his knowledge and work ethic. He advises across the full spectrum of bankruptcy situations, regularly representing debtors, creditors and lenders. Sources also note his creative and client-focused approach. **Jacqueline Marcus** (see p.1916) is described by interviewees as *"extremely helpful, practical and very involved."* She is broadly experienced and has advised both creditors and debtors in various restructurings, both in and out of court. The *"exceptionally talented"* **Joseph Smolinsky** (see p.1942) is *"a delight to work with,"* according to market sources, who add that he *"is extremely responsive, smart and practical. He has a strong bedside manner, is equally adept at both creditor and debtor matters, and he really is a compliment to that practice."* He is lead counsel for AES Eastern Energy during its $1 billion Chapter 11 bankruptcy.

## Band 2

## Cleary Gottlieb Steen & Hamilton LLP
See profile on p.1963

**THE FIRM** This group leverages admirably from the firm's internationally recognized banking and finance practice, and continues to be involved in many high-value bankruptcy and restructuring matters in the USA and around the world. This is a major differentiator for a practice which is experienced at the highest level across a comprehensive range of bankruptcy situations. In recent highlights, the group assisted Overseas Shipholding Group in filing for Chapter 11 protection in one of the largest bankruptcy cases of the past year. Other highlights have included representing Fintech Advisory, the largest creditor of Mexican glassmaker Vitro SAB de CV, in Vitro's complex

Mexican restructuring, as well as in related Chapter 15 proceedings in the USA.

Sources say: *"A strong group with a good breadth of expertise. They deal well with complex bankruptcy matters. They also have breadth within the transactions and litigation groups, which makes them strong on cross-border stuff."*

KEY INDIVIDUALS **James Bromley** (see p.288) is head of Cleary's global restructuring and insolvency practice. He is an acclaimed expert in international restructurings, described by interviewees as a *"very good, practical lawyer with a calm demeanor."* He is lead counsel for the second largest publicly traded oil tanker company in the world, Overseas Shipholding Group, during its high-profile Chapter 11 bankruptcy proceedings. **Lisa Schweitzer** (see p.1939) is *"hard-working and extremely bright,"* according to sources, many also praising her unerring dedication to finding the right solutions for her clients. She continues to advise Nortel Networks as its lead restructuring counsel. **Sean O'Neal** (see p.1925) is currently advising Wilmington Trust as special counsel to the indenture trustee in the ResCap bankruptcy. He is also representing several major international and domestic financial institutions in relation to their required compliance with the Dodd-Frank Act. Interviewees describe O'Neal as a *"phenomenal bankruptcy lawyer who is intelligent, commercial and practical."*

## Jones Day
See profile on p.919

THE FIRM Jones Day's business restructuring and reorganization team is renowned for undertaking influential roles in some of the largest restructurings in the USA in the past few years. The group's diverse network of experts around the country enables it to excel in any debtor or creditor representation. Its recent highlights include the team's ongoing representation of Hostess Brands in one of the most high-profile Chapter 11 bankruptcies of 2012. Hostess and its affiliated debtors owe more than $800 million in secured debt. Jones Day also acted for AFA Foods during its recently filed Chapter 11 proceedings.

Sources say: *"They not only have an excellent knowledge of bankruptcy law but a good understanding of the business. Adding to that an ability to be practical and incisive on key and difficult legal points enabled the client to get to a good result."*

KEY INDIVIDUALS Department cochair **Corinne Ball** (see p.277) is currently leading for the debtors in the Hostess Brands Chapter 11 bankruptcy. Market sources are unanimous in their praise: *"She is all business, and extremely intelligent. She can see things faster than most I've ever seen – she's that good."* Clients also praise her as *"very confident, responsive, bright, and very effective."* The *"terrific"* **Paul Leake** (see p.353) cochairs the business restructuring and reorganization group alongside Ball. He is admired by interviewees as someone who is *"practical and a pleasure to deal with"* during contentious situations. **Heather Lennox** (see p.2104) is described by sources as an *"an impeccable attorney,"* who is *"very articulate and good at dealing with multiple group entities."* Other commentators are quick to note that they have *"never seen anyone so well prepared for court and with such a grasp of the minute details. Her abili-*

*ty to size up a situation quickly and figure out what's going to be a problem is really impressive."*

## Wachtell, Lipton, Rosen & Katz
See profile on p.2012

THE FIRM This restructuring and finance group receives tremendous respect from peers as one of the intellectually preeminent teams in the industry. Wachtell primarily represents major financial institutions, hedge funds and private equity clients in major bankruptcies. It acts for clients such as JPMorgan Chase and Bank of America in bankruptcy-related cases which have recently included MF Global, Hawker Beechcraft and Arcapita Bank. The team has recently been involved in a number of high-profile pre and post-petition litigation matters, an area where the firm is building substantial expertise.

Sources say: *"A really excellent quality firm."*

KEY INDIVIDUALS **Harold Novikoff** (see p.378) is the chair of Wachtell's restructuring and finance department. *"A great bankruptcy mind,"* Novikoff receives praise across the board, with one sources noting: *"If Congress needed an opinion, he's the guy you'd get to do it."* He is ever-present in many of the firm's most high-profile engagements, and, with over 30 years in the industry, he is experienced in most facets of bankruptcy cases. **Scott Charles** (see p.293) is experienced in navigating bankruptcies, restructurings, and distressed mergers and acquisitions, all of which he has actively handled since 1984. He counts various institutional lenders, creditors' committees and distressed securities investors as high-profile clients. **Richard Mason** (see p.362) is an expert in hotel, retail and resort-related bankruptcies. He is active in conducting both in-court and out-of-court restructurings. He receives recognition from sources for his mastery of courtroom battles and difficult negotiations. Of counsel **Philip Mindlin** (see p.1920) is widely acknowledged for his intellectual prowess, as well as for his even-handed demeanor during negotiations. His recent work has predominantly involved distressed mergers and acquisitions.

## Willkie Farr & Gallagher LLP
See profile on p.2016

THE FIRM This business reorganization and restructuring practice group has one of the most respected names in the industry. Traditionally a major player in company-side matters, the team has also fast developed a reputation for its expert handling of lender-side representations. Recent highlights include acting for RG Steel in connection with its $1 billion Chapter 11 bankruptcy proceedings. The team has also advised Broadview Networks and KV Pharmaceutical in their respective bankruptcy cases.

Sources say: *"Willkie's partners and associates are very business savvy and focus on getting the best business result for their client. They also have the ability to quickly marshal the expertise of others in the firm and tackle any of the complexities that arise in a bankruptcy."*

KEY INDIVIDUALS Business reorganization and restructuring group cochair **Marc Abrams** (see p.271) is *"one of the premier bankruptcy lawyers out here – he really knows how to get things done,"* according to sources. He is regular-

ly recommended for his expertise in navigating large companies through bankruptcy, and is equally adept at advising creditors. **Matthew Feldman** (see p.1891) cochairs the practice alongside Abrams. Feldman is vastly experienced in all manner of bankruptcy-related situations, and acts for a range of parties. He is highly regarded as an attorney who always has an eye on his clients' best interests. He leads the firm's representations of RG Steel and KV Pharmaceutical in each of their high-profile Chapter 11 bankruptcies. **Margot Schonholtz** (see p.1938) is highly respected for her expertise in representing creditor and lender clients. She is a *"tremendous lawyer,"* say sources: *"Practical and assertive, with a good sense of humor. She is very responsive, too – she explains what is important, and has a wealth of bankruptcy experience."* She recently advised Bank of America in relation to the high-profile bankruptcy cases of MF Global and Patriot Coal. **John Longmire** (see p.1915) is *"a great communicator, who has a very good business sense and is also very responsive,"* remark interviewees. They add: *"Not only can he keep track of all of the various items that need to be accomplished to navigate through bankruptcy, but he can prioritize them in the proper manner and explain them to business folks in a way that non-lawyers understand."* The *"tremendous"* **Rachel Strickland** (see p.1945) is hailed as *"a zealous advocate for her clients,"* and is highlighted in particular for her superb in-court skills. She has wide-ranging bankruptcy experience and is representing Broadview Networks in connection with its recent Chapter 11 filing. **Paul Shalhoub** (see p.1940) has a vast array of experience spanning debtor, creditor, lender and finance issues. *"He is really good with the technical side of things,"* say sources. He recently played a prominent role in the Chapter 11 bankruptcy filing of KV Pharmaceutical. The *"responsive and commercial"* **Joseph Minias** (see p.1920) enters the rankings as an up-and-comer who *"has an ability to view things as a whole, and understands what drives a business as well as how to apply the law to what each situation requires."*

## Band 3

### Brown Rudnick LLP
See profile on p.437

THE FIRM Brown Rudnick is famed for its passionate representation of its clients' interests. The group is recognized as a leading choice for creditor and lender clients in hard-fought bankruptcy litigation, particularly for hedge funds and other high-yield investors. Recent highlights include its role on behalf of the Official Committee of Unsecured Creditors of former powerhouse law firm Dewey & LeBoeuf. The team is also currently representing an ad hoc consortium of senior unsecured noteholders in the $3 billion Chapter 11 bankruptcy of Patriot Coal.

Sources say: *"Hard-hitting equity committee guys." "They like to look at situations where you need creative solutions to get where you want be."*

KEY INDIVIDUALS **Edward Weisfelner** is head of Brown Rudnick's bankruptcy and corporate restructuring practice. He is renowned for his lender-side representations, and is currently lead counsel for the Official Committee of Unsecured Creditors in the $450 million bankruptcy of Dewey & LeBoeuf. Commentators note that Weisfelner *"writes brilliantly and is excellent if you're in a difficult position."* **Robert Stark** *"spends a lot of time understanding the client's company itself,"* say interviewees, who add that *"he is really good at finding creative solutions."* His recent highlights include leading an ad hoc consortium of senior unsecured noteholders in the aforementioned bankruptcy proceedings of Patriot Coal.

## Cadwalader, Wickersham & Taft LLP
See profile on p.438

THE FIRM Cadwalader's New York-based financial restructuring department benefits greatly from the firm's vast network of resources, providing a formidable offering for any party dealing with bankruptcy issues. The team has become a powerhouse in various niches, including the automotive, real estate, energy and insurance sectors. The group has acted for major creditor groups in several energy-related restructurings, including Dynegy, AES Eastern and EME Homer City Generation. It is also representing MBIA Insurance in connection with over $2 billion in claims against ResCap.

Sources say: *"They are detail-oriented and practice in maintaining legal and business perspectives. They focus on practical solutions."*

KEY INDIVIDUALS **George Davis** (see p.1887) is cochair of the department. Sources describe him as *"a real leader in the bankruptcy space. We get nothing but the best advice from him, and are comfortable handing him key matters."* He is an expert in energy-related bankruptcies, and represents creditor groups in the Dynegy, AES Eastern and EME Homer City Generation bankruptcies. Clients note that he *"is very even-tempered, never inflames a situation unnecessarily, and brings a measured, thoughtful approach."* Fellow practice group cochair **John Rapisardi** (see p.1929) is highly regarded for his commercially minded approach. He is vastly experienced, and possesses particular expertise in the application of the Chinese Bankruptcy Code.

## Kasowitz, Benson, Torres & Friedman LLP
See profile on p.1983

THE FIRM This creditors' rights and bankruptcy team is widely acknowledged for its expertise in representing creditors, lenders and investors in high-stakes bankruptcy litigation. Kasowitz is regularly singled out as a firm that zealously and creatively pursues its clients' best interests. It is currently acting for the Federal Housing Finance Agency in the ResCap Chapter 11 proceedings, as well as for the Official Committee of Former Partners in the bankruptcy proceedings of Dewey & LeBoeuf.

Sources say: *"They are a strong advocate and great at what they do."* *"They are diligent, they are creative, and I think they represent good value."*

KEY INDIVIDUALS **David Friedman** (see p.317) cochairs Kasowitz's creditors' rights and bankruptcy group. He is admired for his ability to marry the need to obtain practical business solutions with the need to aggressively pursue litigation. His recent highlights include acting

for the Official Committee of Former Partners in Dewey & LeBoeuf's Chapter 11 bankruptcy. **David Rosner** (see p.1933) remains a highly regarded bankruptcy practitioner who, according to interviewees, brings a creative and effective approach to negotiations and in-court arguments. He continues to act as lead on several of the group's major engagements.

## Latham & Watkins LLP
See profile on p.446

THE FIRM This firm's nine-partner New York restructuring, insolvency and workouts team is recognized nationally for the quality of its work. The team is traditionally singled out for representing secured and unsecured lenders, however it is equally adept at advising creditors, debtors and distressed asset acquirers. Recent highlights include representing US Airways in relation to the well-publicized American Airlines bankruptcy proceedings. On the company side, Latham advised shipping and container business Eagle Bulk Shipping in connection with a $1.2 billion out-of-court restructuring.

Sources say: *"A very good firm which has some very good partners there."*

KEY INDIVIDUALS Global practice group cochair **Jan Baker** (see p.277) *"is a terrific attorney and a great man,"* according to commentators. Described as *"one of the senior-most attorneys in the industry,"* he is praised for his constructive and pragmatic approach to matters. He is one of the leading experts for advising companies in distressed situations. Fellow cochair **Mitchell Seider** (see p.1939) is immensely experienced in all facets of bankruptcy representation. He is described by interviewees as *"really good at negotiating and guiding towards solutions."* He recently advised Jefferies in relation to its funding of the exit of Satelites Mexicanos from prepackaged bankruptcy in Mexico. Seider is also lauded as an expert in Latin American bankruptcies. **Paul Harner** (see p.1901) receives acclaim for his prominent role in the representation of Eagle Bulk Shipping in its aforementioned restructuring, as well as for advising US Airways in connection with the American Airlines bankruptcy.

## Morrison & Foerster LLP
See profile on p.1990

THE FIRM This group has continued to make great strides in the bankruptcy and restructuring industry with a steady flow of extremely high-profile engagements. Its broad range of expertise includes debtor, creditor and lender-side matters. On the debtor side, it is currently advising Residential Capital and the Chapter 11 trustee of MF Global in relation to each of their high-profile bankruptcies. On the creditor side, the team advised the unsecured creditors' committees in connection with the PMI and Pinnacle Airlines Chapter 11 proceedings.

Sources say: *"They're very commercial and aggressive, with a very good understanding of the market around them. They take into account all aspects of the situation."*

KEY INDIVIDUALS **Brett Miller** (see p.369) has gained considerable prominence of late from his ongoing representation of Louis Freeh, Chapter 11 trustee in the MF

Global bankruptcy. He is described as a *"professional, smart, deal-oriented lawyer."* Miller is particularly highlighted for his expertise in the aviation sector, and is currently advising the unsecured creditors' committee in the bankruptcy of Pinnacle Airlines. **Larren Nashelsky** (see p.1922) was recently appointed global chair of Morrison & Foerster. Prior to being elected, Nachelsky led the firm's representation of ResCap in its $15 billion bankruptcy case. **Gary Lee** (see p.1912) is cochair of the bankruptcy and restructuring group. He is currently lead counsel to ResCap during its Chapter 11 bankruptcy, and has quickly made a name for himself in the industry. Interviewees praise him as *"very smart, direct and to the point. He doesn't break glass and he makes sure he maximizes his time – there is no guesswork in what he thinks or says."* **Anthony Princi** (see p.1929) is acclaimed for his *"excellent communication and understanding of the commercial and economic impacts of various legal outcomes."* While maintaining a broad range of expertise, he is especially noted for his knowledge of representing creditors' committees in insurance company restructurings. **Lorenzo Marinuzzi** (see p.1917) takes the spotlight with a number of prominent roles in some of the most significant bankruptcies this past year. Interviewees are *"incredibly impressed with his ability to convey positions to the judge."*

## Quinn Emanuel Urquhart & Sullivan, LLP

THE FIRM Quinn Emanuel has established itself as a market-leading presence for contentious bankruptcy-related situations. This is due in part to the firm's effective combination of its preeminent commercial litigation practice and the extensive expertise within the bankruptcy and restructuring team itself. The group has acted for creditors, lenders, investors and committee groups in many of the most significant bankruptcies of the past year, including Vertrue, Lehman Brothers, Jefferson County, Alabama, NewPage and Trident Microsystems.

Sources say: *"They did a great job of getting up to speed on complex bankruptcy and business issues in a short period of time."* *"The firm has an unparalleled track record, having achieved unexpected victories in seemingly hopeless situations."*

KEY INDIVIDUALS Bankruptcy department head **Susheel Kirpalani** took the spotlight with his high-profile appointment as examiner in the Dynegy Holdings bankruptcy. He garners praise from all quarters, with sources citing his *"incredible skill at piercing through legal issues quickly and coming up with perspective. He is a tremendous courtroom advocate."* *"Consensus-builder"* **Ben Finestone** *"has a deft grasp of legal nuance along with a business person's commercial instinct,"* according to sources. Others point to his *"unique capacity to distill issues quickly to their core in a way that really enables us to make thoughtful, informed, strategic decisions."*

## Simpson Thacher & Bartlett LLP
See profile on p.2006

THE FIRM Simpson Thacher's five-partner New York bankruptcy team is a mainstay of the industry, regularly representing senior lenders in major bankruptcies. This is partly due to an enviable platform provided by the firm's capital markets and M&A practices. The team counts JPMorgan, Deutsche Bank, Blackstone Group, Barclays Capital and Centerbridge Partners as prominent clients. Recent highlights include advising JPMorgan as agent for two syndicates claiming a total of $1.4 billion in the MF Global bankruptcy. It is also representing JPMorgan in relation to the Chapter 9 bankruptcy of Jefferson County, Alabama.

**KEY INDIVIDUALS Peter Pantaleo** (see p.381) is the head of Simpson Thacher's bankruptcy group, and sources say that he *"does a fantastic job"* in representing his lender clients. He recently advised JPMorgan in relation to the aforementioned MF Global bankruptcy. **Steven Fuhrman** (see p.1895) maintains an active practice acting on behalf of lenders and financial institutions. He has been engaged in a number of out-of-court restructurings of late, as well as fostering an increasing workload involving Chapter 9 bankruptcies.

## White & Case LLP
See profile on p.451

**THE FIRM** This financial restructuring and insolvency practice is renowned for its vigorous pursuit of creative solutions for its stable of major bondholder, lender and investor clients. The team is also well placed to take advantage of the firm's global resources, and is often involved in cross-border bankruptcies. Recent highlights include representing a committee of secured lenders in connection with the out-of-court restructuring of TORM.

**Sources say:** *"They have managed to have a thorough understanding of the law, our restrictions and position better than other firms. Their negotiation skills are exemplary."*

**KEY INDIVIDUALS** The *"dynamic"* **Thomas Lauria** (see p.352) is the global financial restructuring and insolvency practice head. He boasts extensive experience in all facets of bankruptcy representations, from debtors to distressed investors. He is lead counsel in the majority of White & Case's significant engagements in recent years, and has been integral to the firm's rising prominence in the bankruptcy field.

---

### Band 4

## Bingham McCutchen LLP
See profile on p.1515

**THE FIRM** Bingham McCutchen's well-regarded financial restructuring team in New York benefits from the firm's extensive worldwide presence. The team is heavily involved in international restructurings and cross-border Chapter 15 matters, and is able to connect easily with local experts around the world. Bingham is focused primarily on creditor-side representations, and boasts institutional relationships with many leading financial powerhouses.

**Sources say:** *"They look for a business outcome that works for their clients, sometimes at the expense of their bills. These guys were all about the client, which is rare. The focus is on getting a great result time and time again."*

**KEY INDIVIDUALS** Practice cochair **Michael Reilly** (see p.391) is described by interviewees as *"a pillar of the bankruptcy Bar; internationally known and respected."* A practitioner of immense experience, Reilly holds particular expertise in cross-border restructurings. Clients note that *"he is always in control, very calm, and steady-handed."* **Jeffrey Sabin** (see p.398) cochairs the group alongside Reilly. He is adept at representing clients across the bankruptcy spectrum. In recent years he has played significant roles in advising financial heavyweight clients on the implications of the Dodd-Frank reforms. *"He's very deal savvy,"* say sources, *"and knows the outer-most money that his client can get and goes after it. He has business sense and incredible persistence."*

## Chadbourne & Parke LLP
See profile on p.1962

**THE FIRM** This full-service bankruptcy and financial restructuring group has been involved in many significant bankruptcies in recent years. The team is particularly skilled in advising on Chapter 15 filings, and also regularly advises major senior lenders and Chapter 11 creditors' committees. Recent highlights include representing court-appointed examiner Arthur Gonzalez in the ResCap bankruptcy. It is also currently advising the overseas liquidators in relation to respective Chapter 15 filings by Greek company Hellas Telecommunications and the Australian business ABC Learning Centres.

**Sources say:** *"Highly competent, very responsive, and user-friendly." "A good complement of different types of lawyers who work together well."*

**KEY INDIVIDUALS** Practice group chair **Howard Seife** (see p.1939) is described as *"an excellent strategist and relationship manager with an established presence. He is calm and deliberate, and doesn't come to snap judgments."* Seife is a cross-border restructuring expert, and also boasts considerable experience in creditor representations. **David LeMay** *"knows the Bankruptcy Code inside and out,"* according to commentators. He is experienced across the bankruptcy spectrum, with clients noting that he has *"consistently demonstrated a good courtroom presence, and is very thoughtful and intellectually powerful."*

## Proskauer Rose LLP
See profile on p.2001

**THE FIRM** Proskauer Rose's bankruptcy and restructuring team has greatly benefited from the recent addition of the preeminent Martin Bienenstock and his team of restructuring experts from Dewey & LeBoeuf. The arrivals have added to an already respected bankruptcy and restructuring group that is now well placed for success, with a slew of ongoing high-value representations and a prominent employment practice serving to enhance future prospects.

**Sources say:** *"A full-service shop with a deep knowledge base as well as a breadth of partners and senior associates available to provide excellent advice."*

**KEY INDIVIDUALS** Newly-appointed group chair **Martin Bienenstock** is regarded as one of the foremost bankruptcy experts in the industry. Sources note that *"he is*

top drawer; a wonderful person and deep strategist. His work is thorough, detailed and clever."* He continues to lead high profile engagements in relation to the bankruptcies of NewPage, MF Global and Capmark Financial. **Philip Abelson** is highlighted by commentators as *"a good quarterback, who communicates well with the client and different creditor counsels. He does a great job keeping everyone focused on a successful emergence."* He is a well-rounded practitioner who advises on a range of areas.

## Ropes & Gray LLP
See profile on p.1528

**THE FIRM** This dynamic five-partner bankruptcy and business restructuring team works on large-scale bankruptcies, often in tandem with the firm's highly regarded Boston and London offices. The team primarily represents creditor and lender clients, with particular expertise within the energy sector. Recent highlights include advising an ad hoc group of security holders in the high-profile Chapter 11 bankruptcy of ResCap.

**KEY INDIVIDUALS Mark Bane** leads the team and is highly respected for his bankruptcy expertise. He predominantly advises distressed debt and equity investors, hedge funds and bondholder groups. **Mark Somerstein** is a *"well-respected and high-quality practitioner"* recommended for his business-oriented approach. His recent highlights include representing indenture trustee Wilmington Trust in relation to $3.5 billion in the Dynegy Holdings bankruptcy. **Keith Wofford** recently acted as lead counsel to an ad hoc group of security holders in the ResCap Chapter 11 bankruptcy. He is praised by commentators for his dedication to his clients, with one source noting that he is a *"key player in our market, and a very talented lawyer."*

## Schulte Roth & Zabel LLP
See profile on p.2003

**THE FIRM** This high-quality business restructuring team is firmly entrenched as a formidable player in representing private investment, private equity and hedge fund clients. Prominent regular clients include Cerberus, Duff & Phelps, Anchorage and Owl Creek. The firm also stables excellent corporate and tax departments, which clients have noted are helpful when it comes to structuring bankruptcy solutions and distressed M&A transactions.

**Sources say:** *"A strategic team that pays attention to detail. They are good listeners, client-centric, innovative and creative. They have a deep bench of excellent associates and other partners."*

**KEY INDIVIDUALS** Department head **Adam Harris** (see p.1901) *"is an extremely respected senior bankruptcy partner,"* say sources, and *"is good at negotiating a deal. He is a strategic thinker who knows when to finalize a transaction and get a resolution."* **Michael Cook** (see p.1886) is an immensely experienced practitioner who garners tremendous respect. He has a strong client base which includes major lenders, creditors and acquirers, such as Cerberus and Duff & Phelps. **David Hillman** (see p.1903) is described by interviewees as an *"excellent litigator and strategist who is brilliant in DIP financings."* He continues to display immense talent, clients noting that he *"works* *very hard as a hungry bankruptcy attorney who is not afraid to mix it up with the other side. He is very good at negotiating."*

## Stroock & Stroock & Lavan LLP
See profile on p.2010

THE FIRM Stroock's financial restructuring group comes highly recommended for representing large finance houses, bondholders and creditors' committees. The team's recent highlights include representing a minority group of security holders in relation to the Chapter 11 bankruptcy of AES Eastern Energy, and also advising an ad hoc group of first-lien lenders and DIP financing lenders in the bankruptcy proceedings of AMF Bowling Worldwide.

**Sources say:** *"They have a strong overall practice with a culture of getting transactions done. Solutions-oriented and incredibly creative."*

**KEY INDIVIDUALS** *"Practical deal-maker"* **Kristopher Hansen** is the practice group cochair. He is described by interviewees as *"knowledgeable on all aspects of bankruptcy law. He is able to bring to bear his business acumen and thought process. He looks at the big picture and is a visionary."* The tremendously experienced **Lewis Kruger** is recognized as *"fiercely bright – he understands the issues and is very creative in his suggested solutions, all the time never imposing his own personal agenda on the client."*

## Band 5

## Debevoise & Plimpton LLP
See profile on p.1968

THE FIRM Debevoise & Plimpton's business restructuring and workouts group represents a full range of clients, including debtors, creditors and equity groups in distressed asset acquisitions. It also boasts particular expertise in the airline and insurance industries, continuing to advise American Airlines as special aircraft financing counsel in the AMR bankruptcy.

**Sources say:** *"The Debevoise team is always extremely well prepared, and they think about every detail. They are very responsive, creative, and give well thought-out responses to difficult questions."*

**KEY INDIVIDUALS Steven Gross** is *"always a great source of knowledge, and brings a level of experience and calmness to any situation,"* say sources. He recently led the team representing water treatment company Culligan in connection with a multinational $700 million restructuring. Group cochair **Richard Hahn** *"is extremely knowledgeable, and has an upstanding demeanor in negotiations,"* according to sources, who also note that *"he is a very measured and objective lawyer."* He has experienced a successful year, and recently led on behalf of American Airlines as special aircraft financing counsel. The *"unflappable"* **My Chi To** possesses an *"impressive set of credentials and experiences,"* say interviewees, adding that *"she serves clients extremely well."* She is currently playing a leading role for Oriental Trading in its Chapter 11 bankruptcy proceedings.

## Dechert LLP
See profile on p.1969

THE FIRM This solid business restructuring and reorganization group maintains its excellent reputation as a significant player in this market. The team boasts experience across the bankruptcy spectrum, with particular renown attached to its expertise in representing bondholders, creditors and parties involved in distressed M&A. Recent highlights include advising the Government of Singapore Investment Corporation in connection with its $1.5 billion bid to purchase the assets of MSR Resorts.

**Sources say:** *"They are very experienced, certainly know their way around, and know all the various players. They are also very aggressive, good about following up on points and at representing client demands."*

**KEY INDIVIDUALS** The business restructuring and reorganization group is cochaired by **Allan Brilliant** (see p.1880) and **Michael Sage** (see p.1935). Brilliant is recognized as being *"generous and effective – he gets things done and gives clients a reasonable bill."* The *"calm and reasoned"* Sage, meanwhile, is a well-rounded practitioner with broad-ranging bankruptcy expertise. He is an *"extremely practical lawyer and nice to deal with, too,"* say interviewees.

## Fried, Frank, Harris, Shriver & Jacobson LLP
See profile on p.1975

THE FIRM Fried Frank's bankruptcy and restructuring offering spans the full spectrum of bankruptcy representations, from financially troubled companies to bondholders and lenders. The team also comes recommended for its excellent cross-border expertise. Recent highlights include advising GS Capital Partners in relation to $2 billion of debt claimed in the Chapter 11 bankruptcy of aircraft business Hawker Beechcraft.

**Sources say:** *"We hire them because they are a full-service firm with a deep bench, and can give a full range of advice."*

**KEY INDIVIDUALS Brad Eric Scheler** (see p.1937) is the chair of Fried Frank's bankruptcy and restructuring department. He leads a large proportion of the team's big-ticket matters, and is praised for being *"really good at bringing about consensus. He's a very smooth guy who knows how to calm a room down – very effective in breaking through conflict and getting people to the table."* **Gary Kaplan** (see p.1907) is a *"practical business person"* who knows how to bring a matter to its conclusion. He represents a range of clients from various industries, and is recognized for his expertise in contentious negotiations and litigation. He is lead counsel for GS Capital Partners in the aforementioned Hawker Beechcraft bankruptcy.

## Kelley Drye & Warren LLP
See profile on p.1985

THE FIRM Kelley Drye's excellent restructuring team is renowned for its creditor, bondholder, indenture trustee and committee work, with a stable of prominent creditor clients seeking it out in many high-profile bankruptcies. The team stands out in particular for its niche expertise in the retail, commercial real estate, energy and maritime sectors. In recent highlights the firm represented the US Bank

National Association as indenture trustee in the Chapter 11 bankruptcy of ResCap.

**Sources say:** *"They can quickly get to the relevant matters and influence good outcomes for the constituents that they represent. They get the deal done in an efficient and justifiable manner."*

**KEY INDIVIDUALS** Practice chair **James Carr** is an expert in representing creditor clients, particular when it pertains to the retail, commercial real estate and energy sectors. He is *"very impressive both in knowledge and results,"* say sources, who add that *"he knows the major players in the field and has been able to obtain great results."* He is lead counsel for the indenture trustee in the ResCap bankruptcy. **Eric Wilson** also played a key role in the firm's work involving ResCap. He also represented the Official Committee of Unsecured Creditors of Women's Apparel in connection with its $100 million Chapter 11 bankruptcy.

## Luskin, Stern & Eisler LLP

THE FIRM Luskin, Stern & Eisler was reformed in 2012 following its founding partners' departure from Hughes Hubbard & Reed. The firm has seamlessly picked up where it left off, carrying with it an excellent reputation for advising financial institutions in a full range of bankruptcy and restructuring-related representations. Key clients include Société Générale, Citibank, Bank of America and BNP Paribas.

**Sources say:** *"They are excellent negotiators and litigators who are skilled at legal representation in any direction a case takes.*

**KEY INDIVIDUALS Michael Luskin** comes highly recommended for his litigation and negotiation skills. *"He is particularly adept at cutting through issues quickly, particularly when others in the room are posturing and creating a fog around their own agendas,"* according to interviewees. **Richard Stern** recently took the spotlight with his role as court-appointed fee examiner in the Eastman Kodak bankruptcy. *"Richard is excellent at bringing people to consensus and getting deals done,"* say interviewees, who add that *"among Mr Stern's many strengths is his ability to resolve complex legal issues with practical and creative business solutions."*

## Mayer Brown LLP
See profile on p.1257

THE FIRM The restructuring, bankruptcy and insolvency practitioners at Mayer Brown are especially commended as experts in representing creditors in complex bankruptcies. The team is traditionally known for its focus on acting for institutional lenders, distressed investors and committees, with prominent clients including Bank of America, Deutsche Bank, Barclays Bank and the Bank of New York Mellon. However, the group is also increasingly involved in representing debtors, particularly in relation to cross-border issues.

**Sources say:** *"At all levels of the firm the depth of knowledge is superior, and the service unfailingly professional and efficient. The firm has experience across a multitude of industries and diverse legal disciplines for comprehensive advice."*

**KEY INDIVIDUALS Brian Trust** is global co-head of the firm's restructuring, bankruptcy and insolvency practice. He specializes in advising large institutional creditors. Trust *"has a wealth of restructuring experience,"* say sources, *"and has a superior ability to thoroughly analyze complex issues from both the legal and the business sides."* The *"extremely responsive, user-friendly and goal-oriented"* **Howard Beltzer** is highlighted for his breadth of expertise in both debtor and creditor-side representations. He garners acclaim for his *"tremendous bedside manner that puts his clients very much at ease."*

## Shearman & Sterling LLP
See profile on p.2005

**THE FIRM** The bankruptcy and reorganization practice at Shearman & Sterling remains a highly respected name in the industry. The firm itself is a global presence, and the bankruptcy team is able to leverage off of Shearman's venerable M&A practice. The group offers a full service, encompassing company and creditor-side work. Its recent highlights include advising Citigroup Global Markets in connection with $500 million in DIP financing for Houghton Mifflin Harcourt during its well-publicized bankruptcy proceedings.

**KEY INDIVIDUALS** Senior partner **Douglas Bartner** (see p.1876) is described by sources as *"one of the most practical bankruptcy lawyers out there."* He is experienced across the bankruptcy spectrum and regularly advises debtors, creditors and investors in distressed assets.

## Sullivan & Cromwell LLP
See profile on p.2011

**THE FIRM** Sullivan & Cromwell's increasingly prominent restructuring and bankruptcy group took the spotlight this year with its role as lead debtors' counsel for Eastman Kodak. Supported by an enviable corporate platform, the team has shown itself to be more than capable of handling large-scale and complex restructuring matters, ranging from company-side Chapter 11 representations to advising investors on distressed asset acquisitions.

**Sources say:** *"They have good depth of knowledge and experience. They tend to adopt a team approach to staffing, which gives you the benefit of a group of excellent lawyers focusing on your issues."*

**KEY INDIVIDUALS Andrew Dietderich** (see p.305) is founder and head of Sullivan & Cromwell's restructuring and bankruptcy practice. He was lead counsel to Kodak during its Chapter 11 bankruptcy, and is equally adept at handling contentious and transactional situations, with interviewees praising his intelligent approach to deal-making. Special counsel **Michael Torkin** (see p.1947) plays a significant role in many of the group's most notable cases. One client said: *"He is one of the smartest attorneys I've ever worked with. Not only does he give you an answer very quickly, it is always right. He was incredibly incisive and very impressive."* **John Jerome** (see p.1906) is a highly experienced bankruptcy attorney, having practiced in the industry for over 40 years. He has firsthand experience in a number of the sector's groundbreaking bankruptcies, and

played a key role in the development of the Bankruptcy Code.

## Other Notable Practitioners

**Philip Anker** (see p.1873) cochairs the bankruptcy and financial restructuring practice at WilmerHale. He represents a range of clients, and receives praise for his expertise in conducting bankruptcy litigation. He recently defended Tribune in relation to several fraudulent transfer actions arising out of its high-profile bankruptcy. **Thomas Califano** (see p.1882) of DLA Piper LLP (US) "is an aggressive and fierce advocate for his clients," according to interviewees. He has a diverse range of expertise, with a particular focus on the healthcare sector. Clients are "extremely impressed at his ability to control a room and get an outcome." **Ken Coleman** leads Allen & Overy LLP's US financial restructuring and insolvency department. In line with the firm's renown for international reach, he is widely renowned for his expertise in cross-border insolvency matters. Interviewees note that he is "very practical and business-attuned - he knows what we need to do to get things done." "Tremendous strategist" **Denis Cronin** (see p.1887) of Vinson & Elkins LLP has over 35 years of experience in the bankruptcy and restructuring industry. He holds a tremendous amount of respect among both his clients and fellow bankruptcy professionals. Chair of Paul Hastings LLP's global restructuring practice **Luc Despins** specializes in representing creditors and committees. He has acted as lead counsel to committees in a number of high-profile and large-scale bankruptcies in recent years. Sources give high praise to his aggressive litigation style and excellent client-handling skills. **Robert Feinstein** founded the New York office of boutique Californian bankruptcy firm Pachulski Stang Ziehl & Jones LLP. He is praised as "very bright and practical - he understands how to get a deal done and uses leverage to negotiate favorably. He can be very tough, but understands when to move in to settle." The "fantastic" **David Feldman** (see p.1891) is cochair of Gibson, Dunn & Crutcher's business restructuring and reorganization practice. He is an expert in representing lenders and creditors in complex bankruptcies, as well as in advising investors in relation to distressed asset acquisitions. **Evan Flaschen** (see p.1893) "is very creative, and is able to pull deals together when you really feel like all hope is lost," according to interviewees. He is head of the financial restructuring group at Bracewell & Giuliani LLP, and primarily represents creditors, lenders and investors. **Martin Flics** of Linklaters mirrors his firm's reputation for global capabilities and, as such, is an expert in international and cross-border restructurings. He is described as "very practical, knowledgeable and responsive," by clients, who add that "he has an excellent bedside manner about him as well." **James Garrity** (see p.1895) of Morgan, Lewis & Bockius LLP specializes in representing creditors, lenders, trustees and examiners. He regularly represents large financial institutions such as JPMorgan Chase, Wells Fargo and The Bank of New York. The "tremendously insightful" **James Giddens** (see p.1896) of Hughes Hubbard & Reed LLP has garnered acclaim for his role as trustee in two of

the biggest bankruptcies ever filed, Lehman Brothers and MF Global. Interviewees note that "first and foremost, he has deep understanding of the financial services industry. The other thing is that he is unflappable - in a huge case with lots of adversaries and politics, he puts one foot in front of the other and unwinds these complex negotiations." **Andrew Goldman** (see p.1897) cochairs the bankruptcy and financial restructuring practice at WilmerHale. He is a bankruptcy litigation specialist who advises a wide range of debtors, committees, DIP lenders and acquirers of distressed assets. **Alan Halperin** is a founding partner of boutique bankruptcy practice Halperin Battaglia Raicht LLP. He is a hugely experienced attorney with expertise in representing all manner of parties in bankruptcy cases. His recent highlights include acting as lead counsel to Word World, an Emmy Award-winning children's television show producer, during its recent bankruptcy. **Scott Hazan** of Otterbourg, Steindler, Houston & Rosen, PC is renowned for his expertise in the retail sector. He is vastly experienced and can advise a full range of clients in distressed situations, from companies to creditors. **Marc Hirschfield** (see p.1903) of Baker & Hostetler LLP is a well-rounded practitioner with experience across a full range of bankruptcy-related cases. Sources say: "He is a consummate professional and is extremely well versed in the Bankruptcy Code. He is an extraordinarily fair, clear-headed and attentive individual." Peter Ivanick has joined Hogan Lovells US LLP following the dissolution of Dewey & LeBoeuf. He advises clients on all aspects of bankruptcy, with particular expertise in the insurance sector, and has acted in many of the country's biggest insurance insolvencies in recent years. **Christopher Kiplock** (see p.1909) of Hughes Hubbard & Reed LLP has been working alongside James Giddens in the bankruptcies of MF Global and Lehman Brothers. Interviewees are quick to note that "he brings energy, youth and vitality to the process," and also describe him as "tireless, incredibly responsive and very smart." **Richard Levin** (see p.355) is chair of Cravath, Swaine & Moore's restructuring practice. As one of the primary authors of the Bankruptcy Code, Levin is eminently respected and was recently appointed as chair of the National Bankruptcy Conference. Interviewees note that "having someone with his gravitas helps during discussions and negotiations." **Joel Levitin** (see p.1913) of Cahill Gordon & Reindel LLP is recommended for his "strategic thinking and his ability to analyze a situation and explain it to the board in concise and clear terms." He represents companies, creditors and investors on a full range of bankruptcy issues. **Mark Liscio** (see p.1914) of Kaye Scholer LLP specializes in representing creditors and lenders in complex restructurings, with a large amount of his recent work involving distressed structured credit transactions. Sources note that he "is not only very strong on legal skills, but his business skills make him a critical partner in complex and long-lived restructuring situations." **Nancy Mitchell** (see p.1920) is New York practice group chair at Greenberg Traurig, LLP. She is praised by sources as "very bright and a great leader." She is a broadly experienced practitioner who represents debtors, creditors and bondholders. **Deryck Palmer** of Pillsbury Winthrop Shaw

Pittman LLP boasts extensive experience representing both debtor and creditor-side clients in complex Chapter 11 bankruptcies and out-of-court restructurings. He regularly receives recommendations for his litigation skills. **Lenard Parkins** of Haynes and Boone, LLP is a vastly experienced bankruptcy practitioner who advises clients that range from debtors to distressed asset investors. He specializes in a number of industries, including the aviation, real estate, energy and telecoms sectors. **Steven Reisman** (see p.1930) cochairs the restructuring and insolvency group at Curtis, Mallet-Prevost, Colt & Mosle LLP. He operates across the bankruptcy spectrum, having carved a particular niche for conflicts counsel representations.

Commentators note that Reisman "has a very good reputation as someone who gets deals completed. He is someone who is creative in working towards completing transactions, and uses out-of-the-box thinking." "Towering intellect" **Arthur Steinberg** (see p.1944) is a senior financial restructuring partner at King & Spalding LLP. Sources describe him as "extremely smart and sensitive to the realities and dynamics of bankruptcy practice in New York." He is currently representing the newly formed General Motors in relation to contested matters arising out of the original GM bankruptcy case. **Albert Togut** has developed a strong niche in representing distressed companies as conflicts counsel. He is a founding partner of corporate

bankruptcy boutique Togut Segal & Segal LLP. "Star in the making" **Matthew Williams** (see p.1951) is a partner at Gibson, Dunn & Crutcher LLP. He is praised by creditor and bondholder clients as a "fantastic young partner who gets the issues, is great at working with hedge funds, and understands the way we think about the world." **Bruce Zirinsky** (see p.431) of Greenberg Traurig, LLP is cochair of the firm's global business reorganization and financial restructuring practice. He is a highly respected player in the industry and predominantly advises on creditor-side matters. Sources describe him as a "very talented and tenacious advocate for his clients."

# CONSTRUCTION

Commentary about individuals can be found under their firm's paragraph. If the firm has no paragraph (is not ranked) look at Other Notable Practitioners.

| Construction |
| --- |
| **Leading Firms** |
| **Band 1** |
| Peckar & Abramson, P.C. * |
| **Band 2** |
| Duane Morris LLP * |
| Mazur Carp & Rubin PC |
| Zetlin & De Chiara LLP |
| **Band 3** |
| Goetz Fitzpatrick LLP * |
| Holland & Knight LLP * |
| McCarter & English, LLP * |
| Schnader Harrison Segal & Lewis LLP |
| **Band 4** |
| Tarter Krinsky & Drogin LLP |
| Welby Brady & Greenblatt LLP |

*Indicates firm with profile.*
*Alphabetical order within each band. Band 1 is the highest.*

## Band 1

### Peckar & Abramson, P.C.
**See profile on p.1998**
**THE FIRM** This construction powerhouse remains at the forefront of industry developments, frequently acting for leading general contractors and construction managers on high-profile matters. It demonstrates particular skill in large projects, such as sports arenas, bridges, airports and government buildings. The team also offers its expertise to projects located outside of the USA, in places such as the Middle East, India and China.
**Sources say:** *"A dedicated and client-driven firm that provides prompt and excellent advice."*
**KEY INDIVIDUALS Robert Peckar** (see p.1926) is widely recognized as an industry leader, with sources listing *"per-*

sonality, responsiveness, client empathy and subject matter knowledge" among his key attributes. He is also described as *"the master at driving any case to a creative solution."* Sources praise the *"very personable"* **Steven Charney** (see p.1883) for his ability to *"provide excellent advice on difficult situations."* He focuses on representing some of the country's largest contractors. **Gregory Chertoff** (see p.1884) is *"a great all-around lawyer who can help navigate a case to the best possible outcome."* His key area of focus is the successful resolution of complex construction disputes, through various mediums. Sources commend **Bruce Meller** (see p.1919) as being *"forthright, honest and aggressive in his approach."* He mainly acts on behalf of contractors and has advised on numerous types of projects, including museums, hospitals, high-rise buildings and bridges. **Howard Rosen** (see p.1932) regularly acts for developers and construction companies on substantial transactional projects and disputes.

## Band 2

### Duane Morris LLP
**See profile on p.2239**
**THE FIRM** This experienced construction group advises clients from all areas of the industry on the full spectrum of issues, including bid protests, delay claims and contract defaults and terminations. In a representative highlight of the past year, the team has been acting as counsel to a high-end Manhattan condominium developer.
**Sources say:** *"They're very responsive, very professional, very thorough."* *"They have a real depth of experience and a very deep understanding of the construction business."*
**KEY INDIVIDUALS Arthur Silverman** is *"one of the deans of the New York construction Bar"* and is extremely experienced in the area, with sources describing him as a

*"big-picture person."* He has been advising a developer client on the high-profile conversion of landmark buildings into residential condominiums. **Frederick Cohen** is well known in the New York market, and recently represented Madison Equities in connection with the contracts for a 150,000 sq ft hotel and residential development in Soho. Interviewees appreciate that **Richard Dyer** is *"very responsive and very clear with everything."* Lately, he has been part of the team representing a client in a $300 million dispute with the Port Authority, relating to the 9/11 Memorial. **Ken Lazaruk** offers particular expertise on transactional matters. He acts as construction counsel for a number of clients active on major projects, such as Columbia University and Related Management, the owners of the Time Warner Center. Sources hold the *"exceptionally capable"* **Allen Ross** in high regard. In the past year he has been involved in a major piece of litigation for a large developer client.

### Mazur Carp & Rubin PC
**THE FIRM** This highly regarded boutique offers experience across the full range of construction matters, but has seen an increased focus on litigation over the past year. The group regularly represents a broad range of clients, including subcontractors, contractors, developers and owners, in matters including dispute resolution, project counseling and insurance litigation.
**Sources say:** *"We were very impressed with the knowledge and advice that we received from the firm and would highly recommend it."* *"They are truly experts in the construction field."*
**KEY INDIVIDUALS Gary Rubin** is involved in a number of arbitrations and mediations for clients, and also recently handled the renegotiation of a multibillion-dollar project for a public authority. Interviewees describe him as *"level-headed and very professional."* **Sayward Mazur** is well

## Construction

### Senior Statesmen

**Senior Statesmen:** distinguished older practitioners

| | |
|---|---|
| Goetz Peter | Goetz Fitzpatrick LLP |
| Montgomery David | David E. Montgomery ADR Services (ONP)[†] |
| Ross Allen J | Duane Morris LLP |
| Rubin Robert A | McCarter & English, LLP * |

### Leading Individuals

**Band 1**

| | |
|---|---|
| Mazur Sayward | Mazur Carp & Rubin PC |
| Peckar Robert S | Peckar & Abramson, P.C. * |
| Rohn Frederick | Holland & Knight LLP * |
| Schulman Ira M | Pepper Hamilton LLP (ONP)[†] * |
| Zetlin Michael S | Zetlin & De Chiara LLP |

**Band 2**

| | |
|---|---|
| Augustine Mary Jane | McCarter & English, LLP * |
| Charney Steven M | Peckar & Abramson, P.C. * |
| De Chiara Michael K | Zetlin & De Chiara LLP |
| St Marie Scott D | Schnader Harrison Segal & Lewis LLP |

**Band 3**

| | |
|---|---|
| Abraham Aaron N | Goulston & Storrs (ONP)[†] |
| Biser Sarah | McCarter & English, LLP * |
| Cohen Frederick | Duane Morris LLP |
| Eiseman Neal M | Goetz Fitzpatrick LLP |
| Fodor Susanna S | Jones Day (ONP)[†] * |
| Pfeffer David J | Tarter Krinsky & Drogin LLP |
| Rosen Howard M | Peckar & Abramson, P.C. * |
| Silverman Arthur C | Duane Morris LLP |
| Westermann David | Westermann Sheehy Keenan (ONP)[†] |

**Band 4**

| | |
|---|---|
| Block Ken | Tannenbaum Helpern Syracuse (ONP)[†] |
| Chertoff Gregory H | Peckar & Abramson, P.C. * |
| Dyer Richard P. | Duane Morris LLP |
| Finegan Thomas S | Goetz Fitzpatrick LLP |
| Frankel Jamie | Arent Fox LLP (ONP)[†] * |
| Grubin John | Wasserman, Grubin & Rogers (ONP)[†] |
| Hecht Theodore L. | Schnader Harrison Segal & Lewis LLP |
| Lazaruk Ken | Duane Morris LLP |
| Meller Bruce | Peckar & Abramson, P.C. * |
| Patterson Carol J | Zetlin & De Chiara LLP |
| Rubin Gary L. | Mazur Carp & Rubin PC |
| Welby Thomas H | Welby Brady & Greenblatt LLP |

\* Indicates firm / individual with profile.
[†]ONP = Other Notable Practitioner.

known and widely recognized as an *"outstanding lawyer in both litigation and arbitration."* Peers highlight his *"keen sense of what's important and what's not,"* and would readily refer matters to him in the case of a conflict. Mazur recently succeeded in a major arbitration, achieving a $12 million award for his client.

### Zetlin & De Chiara LLP

**THE FIRM** This preeminent construction boutique is respected for its expertise in acting for engineers, architects and other design professionals. The group offers broad experience and skill in handling matters at all stages of the construction and design process, including contract nego-

tiation, risk management and, if required, litigation or alternative dispute resolution.
**Sources say:** *"They inspire confidence in litigation."*
**KEY INDIVIDUALS Michael Zetlin** is praised as *"a very sophisticated problem solver"* and *"as good as it gets"* when it comes to construction specialists. He regularly advises clients on construction contracts, risk management and general business issues, as well as handling multimillion-dollar litigation. **Carol Patterson** regularly handles design and construction matters relating to museums, hospitals, and residential and office buildings for leading national and international clients. Sources describe her as *"a wonderful lawyer"* who is *"great to work with."* The *"extremely confident"* **Michael De Chiara** is a *"very strong advocate for his clients,"* according to interviewees. He offers a wealth of experience across all facets of law relating to the construction and design industry, and frequently acts for developers, engineers, owners and contractors, among other clients.

### Band 3

### Goetz Fitzpatrick LLP
See profile on p.1977

**THE FIRM** Goetz Fitzpatrick's group of construction specialists frequently acts for design professionals, contractors, and public and private owners, among others. The team has particular expertise in the area of construction disputes, and the attorneys are experienced in handling all types of alternative dispute resolution, as well as litigation related to bid protests, injunctions and malpractice issues.
**Sources say:** *"An extremely well-focused and professional team."*
**KEY INDIVIDUALS Thomas Finegan** is praised for his *"general level of excellence,"* and sources add that *"he's a delight to deal with and he never seems to lose his sense of humor."* He has a wealth of experience across the breadth of construction matters. The *"very intelligent"* **Neal Eiseman** is *"a breath of fresh air,"* according to interviewees, who appreciate that he *"puts aside the minor issues and focuses on the major issues."* He regularly handles commercial litigation matters for corporate clients. The highly regarded **Peter Goetz** is well known for his trial abilities, and also offers experience in construction transactions, landlord-tenant law and real estate matters.

### Holland & Knight LLP
See profile on p.1028

**THE FIRM** This firm's New York construction practice regularly handles both transactional and litigation matters, for contractors, owners and construction managers. A recent highlight saw the group acting for a New York State public authority on a $200 million infrastructure improvement project. The impressive client list also includes Gotham Construction, The Metropolitan Museum of Art and En-Tech.
**KEY INDIVIDUALS** Sources describe **Frederick Rohn** (see p.1932) as an *"amazing lawyer,"* and particularly appreciate his *"good practical mentality."* He recently repre-

sented the Metropolitan Transportation Authority in design and construction dispute matters relating to the East Side Access project.

### McCarter & English, LLP
See profile on p.1759

**THE FIRM** The construction group at McCarter & English comprises transactional and litigation experts who represent developers, contractors and owners, among others, in a wide range of matters. In the past year, the team represented Michael Van Valkenburgh Associates in connection with the $200 million construction of a 90-acre waterfront park in Tulsa. Other key clients include Technion, Consorcio Gavilan and KDC Solar.
**Sources say:** *"They care about the client and are always available for consultation no matter the day or time."*
**KEY INDIVIDUALS** The *"excellent"* **Mary Jane Augustine** (see p.1875) is admired for her ability to *"resolve disputes before they become disputes."* She recently advised MetLife Stadium on the design and construction documents for the new $1.2 billion New Meadowlands Stadium. **Sarah Biser** (see p.1879) wins praise for her decision-making capability and planning ability and *"knowledge of the industry."* Her highlights of the past year include acting for Technion on the $2 billion development of the new applied science research facility on Roosevelt Island, in a joint venture with Cornell University. The *"truly outstanding"* **Robert Rubin** (see p.1934) has been involved in representing Consorcio Gavilan in an international dispute related to a $48.8 million breach of an engineering, procurement and construction (EPC) contract. He is widely respected for his strength in mediation.

### Schnader Harrison Segal & Lewis LLP

**THE FIRM** This firm's construction practice focuses on handling major litigation and connected forms of dispute resolution for key industry clients. Highlights include representing a joint venture client in multistate litigation relating to the construction of power transmission lines. The team's enviable client list also includes Balfour Beatty, Chubb Group and M.J. Electric.
**KEY INDIVIDUALS** Interviewees recognize **Theodore Hecht** as an *"excellent construction attorney."* In a recent work highlight, he represented Power Line Constructors in a misappropriation of trade secrets case, successfully obtaining a preliminary injunction and $406,800 in sanctions. **Scott St Marie** wins praise for his *"big-picture thinking while keeping attention to the details."* Sources also admire his *"ability to integrate himself with the team such that he is not just outside legal counsel, but an extension of our construction team."* St Marie is an expert in surety litigation and recently represented Chubb Group in defending claims related to slurry wall construction.

### Band 4

### Tarter Krinsky & Drogin LLP
**THE FIRM** The full-service construction group at this firm specializes in handling a broad range of construction-

related transactional and dispute resolution issues for developers and institutional owners. Recently, the team acted on behalf of Nomura Securities/Nomura Holdings with regards to the design and construction of its new US headquarters, encompassing 900,000 sq ft at New York's Worldwide Plaza. The firm also acts for Cayuga Capital Management, JT Toll Development and Testwell Laboratories.

**Sources say:** *"The firm truly delivers top-tier legal services at fair and competitive billing rates."*

**KEY INDIVIDUALS** Interviewees are full of praise for construction chair **David Pfeffer**, describing him as *"a great communicator who is responsive, has our interests at heart and gives his all for our matters."* Sources also admire that he is *"professional, courteous, and patient from beginning to end."*

## Welby Brady & Greenblatt LLP

**THE FIRM** This full-service Westchester-based construction group serves a broad client base of subcontractors, developers, engineers and owners, among others. The group has substantial experience representing clients in a number of construction and real estate-related matters,

including mediations, trials, arbitration proceedings and appeals.

**KEY INDIVIDUALS Thomas Welby** offers a wealth of experience in all areas of construction law, with a particular focus on mechanic's liens, construction disputes and contract claims. He is highly regarded by sources.

## Other Notable Practitioners

Sources admire the *"very impressive and extremely smart"* **Aaron Abraham** of Goulston & Storrs because *"he sees the big picture, he's very practical and he has the business sense – he knows what to care about in a deal."* *"Well-respected"* **Susanna Fodor** (see p.1893) of Jones Day is an experienced construction and real estate attorney. She concentrates on advising a varied client base, including investment banks, developers and governmental entities, on the full range of construction matters, from risk analysis to major project financing. The *"outstanding"* **Jamie Frankel** (see p.1894) of Arent Fox LLP is praised for his *"very caring"* approach, and for the *"great level of personal attention"* that he delivers. In the past year, he has been part of the team representing the City of New York in ongoing litiga-

tion stemming from the 7 World Trade Center collapse. The *"very talented"* **John Grubin** of Wasserman, Grubin & Rogers LLP is highly respected in the market. His practice encompasses litigation, arbitration and other forms of dispute resolution related to construction and real estate. **Ken Block** of Tannenbaum Helpern Syracuse & Hirschtritt is a very well-known practitioner, who offers significant expertise in both construction and real estate. His experience includes the representation of developers, lenders, tenants and construction professionals in litigation and transactional matters. Interviewees appreciate that **Ira Schulman** (see p.1938) of Pepper Hamilton LLP is *"practical with a lot of commonsense."* He has substantial experience across the full spectrum of construction law matters, but is especially noted for his expertise in contract negotiations and dispute resolution. **David Westermann** of Westermann Sheehy Keenan Samaan & Aydelott, LLP is renowned for his litigation expertise. His practice encompasses surety and construction disputes, as well as transactional matters. Sole practitioner **David Montgomery** is highly recommended for his skill as an arbitrator and mediator of construction disputes.

# CORPORATE/M&A

Highly Regarded p.1794;

Commentary about individuals can be found under their firm's paragraph. If the firm has no paragraph (is not ranked) look at Other Notable Practitioners.

### Corporate/M&A: The Elite
### Leading Firms

**Band 1**
Cravath, Swaine & Moore LLP *
Davis Polk & Wardwell LLP *
Simpson Thacher & Bartlett LLP *
Skadden, Arps, Slate, Meagher & Flom LLP & Affiliates *
Sullivan & Cromwell LLP *
Wachtell, Lipton, Rosen & Katz *

**Band 2**
Cleary Gottlieb Steen & Hamilton LLP *
Debevoise & Plimpton LLP *
Weil, Gotshal & Manges LLP *

**Band 3**
Kirkland & Ellis LLP *
Latham & Watkins LLP *
Paul, Weiss, Rifkind, Wharton & Garrison LLP *
Shearman & Sterling LLP *

**Band 4**
Fried, Frank, Harris, Shriver & Jacobson LLP *
Willkie Farr & Gallagher LLP *

**Band 5**
Gibson, Dunn & Crutcher LLP *
Jones Day *

* Indicates firm with profile.
Alphabetical order within each band. Band 1 is the highest.

## Band 1
## Corporate/M&A: The Elite

### Cravath, Swaine & Moore LLP
See profile on p.1966

**THE FIRM** Cravath's powerful corporate practice has M&A experience in nearly every industry sector. The market continues to view the team as one of New York's best, which is also evident from the volume and quality of high-end work it undertakes. Recent highlights include representing DreamWorks in a joint venture with China Media Capital and others to form Oriental DreamWorks, and advising Grupo Modelo on its $20.1 billion buyout by Anheuser-Busch InBev. The enviable client roster also includes IBM, Unilever and Qualcomm.

**Sources say:** *"They're not going to get the wool pulled over their eyes by the other side."* *"Superb legal and commercial knowledge."*

**KEY INDIVIDUALS Richard Hall** (see p.1900) is seen as one of the most esteemed practitioners in the state. He divides his time between New York and the firm's London office, and recently advised the Linde Group on its $4.6 billion acquisition of Lincare Holdings. **Scott Barshay** (see p.1876) is an impressive performer who clients say is *"brilliant."* His recent highlights include advising Barnes & Noble on a $300 million investment from Microsoft into its digital reading subsidiary, NOOK Media. Interviewees say **Faiza Saeed** (see p.1935) is *"a superstar."* She recently represented Pentair in its $10 billion combination with Tyco's Flow Control business. **Robert Townsend** (see

p.1947) represented Olin Corporation in acquiring bleach manufacturer K.A. Steel Chemicals for $328 million. He also recently closed the $19.7 billion acquisition of Synthes for Johnson & Johnson. Clients say **Philip Gelston** (see p.1896) *"is very pragmatic and will give you a straight answer right away."* His clients include Mondelez International (formerly Kraft Foods), which he recently represented in the creation of a North American grocery entity and a global snacks business. Sources say **George Schoen** (see p.1937) can be counted on to provide *"terrific"* advice and client service. He acted alongside Townsend on the K.A. Steel acquisition for Olin, and also represented IBM in its acquisition of TealeafTechnology and the $850 million sale of its retail point-of-sale solutions arm to Toshiba. **Mark Greene** (see p.1899) recently advised the Linde Group on its $4.6 billion acquisition of Linacre Holdings, and represented Unilever in the $267 million sale of its frozen meals division to ConAgra Foods.

### Davis Polk & Wardwell LLP
See profile on p.442

**THE FIRM** Sources consistently praise this firm's high-quality advice on some of the most complex and substantial transactions in the state. Highlights from the past year include representing Aetna in its $7.3 billion acquisition of Coventry Health Care, and advising Chinese conglomerate Dalian Wanda on its $2.6 billion acquisition of AMC Entertainment. Other top-drawer clients include AstraZeneca, CNOOC and Comcast.

## Corporate/M&A

### Senior Statesmen

**Senior Statesmen:** distinguished older practitioners

| | | |
|---|---|---|
| Beattie Richard I | Simpson Thacher & Bartlett LLP * | |
| Cogut Charles 'Casey' | Simpson Thacher & Bartlett LLP * | |
| Fleischer Jr Arthur | Fried, Frank, Harris, Shriver & Jacobson * | |
| Lipton Martin | Wachtell, Lipton, Rosen & Katz * | |
| Nusbaum Jack H | Willkie Farr & Gallagher LLP * | |

### Leading Individuals

**Star individuals**

| | |
|---|---|
| Cohen H Rodgin | Sullivan & Cromwell LLP * |

**Band 1**

| | |
|---|---|
| Aquila Francis J | Sullivan & Cromwell LLP * |
| Atkins Peter Allan | Skadden, Arps, Slate, Meagher & Flom * |
| Barshay Scott A | Cravath, Swaine & Moore LLP * |
| Bason Jr George R | Davis Polk & Wardwell LLP * |
| Block Dennis J | Greenberg Traurig, LLP * |
| Emmerich Adam O | Wachtell, Lipton, Rosen & Katz * |
| Fox David | Kirkland & Ellis LLP * |
| Frumkin Joseph B | Sullivan & Cromwell LLP * |
| Hall Richard | Cravath, Swaine & Moore LLP * |
| Herlihy Edward D | Wachtell, Lipton, Rosen & Katz * |
| Katz David A | Wachtell, Lipton, Rosen & Katz * |
| Kling Lou R | Skadden, Arps, Slate, Meagher & Flom * |
| Lewkow Victor I | Cleary Gottlieb Steen & Hamilton LLP * |
| Morphy James C | Sullivan & Cromwell LLP * |
| Profusek Robert A | Jones Day * |
| Rosen Jeffrey J | Debevoise & Plimpton LLP |
| Saeed Faiza J | Cravath, Swaine & Moore LLP * |
| Schnell Paul | Skadden, Arps, Slate, Meagher & Flom * |

**Band 2**

| | |
|---|---|
| Aiello Michael | Weil, Gotshal & Manges LLP * |
| Brownstein Andrew R | Wachtell, Lipton, Rosen & Katz * |
| Caplan David L | Davis Polk & Wardwell LLP * |
| Ellin Howard L | Skadden, Arps, Slate, Meagher & Flom * |
| Horowitz Gary I | Simpson Thacher & Bartlett LLP * |
| Neff Daniel A | Wachtell, Lipton, Rosen & Katz * |
| Nugent Eileen T | Skadden, Arps, Slate, Meagher & Flom * |
| Pierce Morton A | White & Case LLP * |
| Reiss John | White & Case LLP * |
| Schumer Robert B | Paul, Weiss, Rifkind, Wharton & Garrison * |
| Shim Paul J | Cleary Gottlieb Steen & Hamilton LLP * |
| Shube Eric | Allen & Overy LLP |
| Townsend III Robert I | Cravath, Swaine & Moore LLP * |

**Band 3**

| | |
|---|---|
| Alvino Tim | McDermott Will & Emery LLP * |
| Arcano Stephen F | Skadden, Arps, Slate, Meagher & Flom * |
| Aslani-Far Adel | Latham & Watkins LLP * |
| Bird Paul S | Debevoise & Plimpton LLP |
| Boston David | Willkie Farr & Gallagher LLP * |
| Cerabino Thomas M | Willkie Farr & Gallagher LLP * |
| Chatzinoff Howard | Weil, Gotshal & Manges LLP * |
| Fraidin Stephen | Kirkland & Ellis LLP * |
| Friedman Dennis J | Gibson, Dunn & Crutcher LLP * |
| Goldberg Louis L | Davis Polk & Wardwell LLP * |
| Kennedy Thomas H | Skadden, Arps, Slate, Meagher & Flom * |
| Kotran Stephen M | Sullivan & Cromwell LLP * |

| | |
|---|---|
| Lyons Peter D | Shearman & Sterling LLP * |
| Meyerson Lee | Simpson Thacher & Bartlett LLP * |
| Mills Phillip R | Davis Polk & Wardwell LLP * |
| Myerson Toby S | Paul, Weiss, Rifkind, Wharton & Garrison * |
| Nussbaum Andrew J | Wachtell, Lipton, Rosen & Katz * |
| O'Brien Clare | Shearman & Sterling LLP * |
| Ponce Mario | Simpson Thacher & Bartlett LLP * |
| Richter Philip | Fried, Frank, Harris, Shriver & Jacobson * |
| Roberts Thomas A | Weil, Gotshal & Manges LLP * |
| Ryan Michael L | Cleary Gottlieb Steen & Hamilton LLP * |
| Seidman Steven | Willkie Farr & Gallagher LLP * |
| Shine David N | Fried, Frank, Harris, Shriver & Jacobson * |
| Smith Scott | Covington & Burling LLP * |
| Spatt Robert E | Simpson Thacher & Bartlett LLP * |
| Sternberg Daniel S | Cleary Gottlieb Steen & Hamilton LLP * |
| Thierfelder Mark E | Dechert LLP * |
| Wolf Daniel E | Kirkland & Ellis LLP * |

**Band 4**

| | |
|---|---|
| Annex Alan I | Greenberg Traurig, LLP * |
| Austin Christopher E | Cleary Gottlieb Steen & Hamilton LLP * |
| Becker Barbara | Gibson, Dunn & Crutcher LLP * |
| Cochran Eric L | Skadden, Arps, Slate, Meagher & Flom * |
| Coco Joseph A | Skadden, Arps, Slate, Meagher & Flom * |
| Dawson R Alec | Morgan, Lewis & Bockius LLP * |
| Eitel Mitchell S | Sullivan & Cromwell LLP * |
| Gelston Philip A | Cravath, Swaine & Moore LLP * |
| Greenberg Joel I | Kaye Scholer LLP * |
| Khadavi Steven | Dorsey & Whitney LLP |
| Klingsberg Ethan A | Cleary Gottlieb Steen & Hamilton LLP * |
| Lefkowitz Ken | Hughes Hubbard & Reed LLP * |
| Marzulli Jr John A | Shearman & Sterling LLP * |
| Rosenblum Steven A | Wachtell, Lipton, Rosen & Katz * |
| Samuelson Charles A | Hughes Hubbard & Reed LLP * |
| Schaefer David S | Loeb & Loeb LLP (ONP)[†] * |
| Schwartzbaum David M | Greenberg Traurig, LLP * |
| Weinberg J D | Covington & Burling LLP * |

**Band 5**

| | |
|---|---|
| Abbott James E | Seward & Kissel LLP * |
| Adams Bert | Sutherland Asbill & Brennan LLP |
| Beinecke Candace Krugman | Hughes Hubbard & Reed LLP * |
| Bevilacqua Louis J | Cadwalader, Wickersham & Taft LLP * |
| Bick John | Davis Polk & Wardwell LLP * |
| Casey George | Shearman & Sterling LLP |
| Cerasani Denise | White & Case LLP * |
| Cherney Emanuel S | Kaye Scholer LLP * |
| Cohen David | Vinson & Elkins LLP * |
| Curbow William | Simpson Thacher & Bartlett LLP * |
| Davis Robert P | Cleary Gottlieb Steen & Hamilton LLP * |

| | |
|---|---|
| Dufner Jr Daniel G | White & Case LLP |
| Engros Jr Charles E | Morgan, Lewis & Bockius LLP * |
| Fuchs Nancy E | Kaye Scholer LLP * |
| Gietz Raymond | Weil, Gotshal & Manges LLP * |
| Gilligan Michael | Allen & Overy LLP |
| Ginsberg Paul D | Paul, Weiss, Rifkind, Wharton & Garrison * |
| Goldberg Steven H | Baker & Hostetler LLP * |
| Green Frederick S | Weil, Gotshal & Manges LLP * |
| Greene Mark I | Cravath, Swaine & Moore LLP * |
| Herman Howard R. | Moses & Singer LLP (ONP)[†] |
| Kelly James | Pillsbury Winthrop Shaw Pittman LLP |
| Knapp Tobias | Jenner & Block LLP * |
| Koeppel John | Nixon Peabody LLP * |
| Lubowitz Michael | Weil, Gotshal & Manges LLP * |
| McGarry Martha E | Skadden, Arps, Slate, Meagher & Flom * |
| Modlin James | Hughes Hubbard & Reed LLP * |
| Moran Patricia | Skadden, Arps, Slate, Meagher & Flom * |
| Norwitz Trevor | Wachtell, Lipton, Rosen & Katz * |
| Nussbaum Martin | Dechert LLP * |
| Nussbaum Mitchell S | Loeb & Loeb LLP (ONP)[†] * |
| Papa Ronald | Proskauer Rose LLP |
| Prounis Othon A | Ropes & Gray LLP |
| Regner William D | Debevoise & Plimpton LLP |
| Ruegger Philip T | Simpson Thacher & Bartlett LLP * |
| Sauermilch Thomas | McDermott Will & Emery LLP * |
| Schoen George F | Cravath, Swaine & Moore LLP * |
| Shapiro David | Wachtell, Lipton, Rosen & Katz * |
| Shoemate Steven R | Gibson, Dunn & Crutcher LLP * |
| Sorkin John E | Fried, Frank, Harris, Shriver & Jacobson * |
| Spilko Howard T | Kramer Levin Naftalis & Frankel LLP * |
| Wechsler Ernest | Kramer Levin Naftalis & Frankel LLP * |
| Weidhaas Andrew J | Goodwin Procter LLP * |
| Weingarten Marc | Schulte Roth & Zabel LLP * |
| Wittlin Craig | Harter, Secrest & Emery LLP (ONP)[†] * |
| Wojciechowski Mark S | Allen & Overy LLP |

**Up-and-coming individuals**

| | |
|---|---|
| Franchini John D. | Milbank, Tweed, Hadley & McCloy LLP * |
| Greenberg Leo M. | Kirkland & Ellis LLP * |
| Herman Matthew | Freshfields Bruckhaus Deringer US LLP * |
| Jebejian Sarkis | Kirkland & Ellis LLP * |
| Makinen Marita A | Lowenstein Sandler LLP (ONP)[†] * |
| Marell Jeffrey D | Paul, Weiss, Rifkind, Wharton & Garrison * |
| O'Reilly Benet | Cleary Gottlieb Steen & Hamilton LLP * |
| Sibbett Benjamin | Clifford Chance US LLP * |
| Sorabella William B | Kirkland & Ellis LLP * |
| Turteltaub Adam M | Willkie Farr & Gallagher LLP * |
| Williams Marc O | Davis Polk & Wardwell LLP * |
| Winokur Derek | Dechert LLP * |

* Indicates individual with profile.
[†]ONP = Other Notable Practitioner.

**Band 1**

Dechert LLP *

Morgan, Lewis & Bockius LLP *

Schulte Roth & Zabel LLP *

Sidley Austin LLP *

White & Case LLP *

**Band 2**

Allen & Overy LLP *

Covington & Burling LLP *

Greenberg Traurig, LLP *

Hughes Hubbard & Reed LLP *

Milbank, Tweed, Hadley & McCloy LLP *

Proskauer Rose LLP *

Ropes & Gray LLP *

**Band 3**

Akin Gump Strauss Hauer & Feld LLP *

Baker Botts LLP *

Cadwalader, Wickersham & Taft LLP *

Clifford Chance US LLP *

Goodwin Procter LLP *

Hogan Lovells US LLP *

Kaye Scholer LLP *

Kramer Levin Naftalis & Frankel LLP *

McDermott Will & Emery LLP *

Morrison & Foerster LLP *

Paul Hastings LLP *

Vinson & Elkins LLP *

**Band 4**

Baker & Hostetler LLP *

Bracewell & Giuliani LLP *

DLA Piper LLP (US) *

Dorsey & Whitney LLP *

Freshfields Bruckhaus Deringer US LLP *

Jenner & Block LLP *

Pillsbury Winthrop Shaw Pittman LLP *

WilmerHale *

**Band 5**

Arnold & Porter LLP *

Ellenoff Grossman & Schole LLP

Nixon Peabody LLP *

Seward & Kissel LLP *

Sutherland Asbill & Brennan LLP

*\* Indicates firm with profile.*

*Alphabetical order within each band. Band 1 is the highest.*

**Sources say:** *"DPW fosters a collaborative environment that enables each lawyer to leverage the functional expertise of a broad array of colleagues. I have found their work product to be consistently excellent." "Davis Polk is exceptional – as sophisticated as it gets."*

**KEY INDIVIDUALS** Global M&A co-head **David Caplan** (see p.1882) has had a remarkably busy year. In addition to representing Aetna in its acquisition of Coventry, he represented Campbell Soup in its $1.55 billion acquisition of Bolthouse Farms, advised the New York Mets on the sale of minority interests in the team, and acted for Comcast on the $3.6 billion purchase by Verizon Wireless of 122 AWS spectrum licenses owned by Comcast joint venture entity SpectrumCo. Sources are *"struck by his creativity and constructiveness."* Fellow global co-head **George Bason** (see p.279) receives plaudits for his pragmatism when brokering a deal. He has an impressive pedigree in cross-border deals, and in 2012 acted for Japanese life insurer Dai-ichi Life on the acquisition of a 15-20% stake in the company by Janus Capital, and for Chinese oil and gas exploration company CNOOC on its $15.1 billion bid to acquire Canadian energy giant Nexen. Clients laud **Louis Goldberg** (see p.1897) as both a technician and a master strategist. Sources say he *"has proved himself capable of navigating a variety of highly difficult circumstances."* He recently advised CVS Caremark on the $250 million sale of its TheraCom business. Clients say **Phillip Mills**'s (see p.1919) *"business and strategic acumen, depth of knowledge and negotiation skills have been invaluable."* He is also praised for his client-handling skill and ability to interact with other lawyers, as well as his *"grasp of every detail."* He advised Dalian Wanda on its acquisition of AMC Entertainment, and represented Cigna in its $3.8 billion HealthSpring acquisition. Clients are also quick to praise **John Bick** (see p.1878), with one source describing him as *"one of the most creative, deal-oriented guys I've ever worked with."* *"Smart, diligent and constructive,"* **Marc Williams** (see p.1951) is noted as a rising star. He has advised Roche on a number of transactions, including its unsolicited proposal to acquire Illumina for $6.7 billion, its $230 million acquisition of Anadys Pharmaceuticals, and the sale of assets in the RNA therapy space to nanotechnology firm Arrowhead Research.

## Simpson Thacher & Bartlett LLP
See profile on p.2006

**THE FIRM** This pre-eminent New York corporate group includes 36 partners committed to M&A. The firm's transactional dominance is further complemented by strengths in capital markets, banking and funds work. Its list of clients features many household names as well as some of the domestic and international markets' largest strategic acquirers and private entity sponsors, including Microsoft, L-3 Communications, AIG, The Blackstone Group and TPG. The team recently acted for Cogeco Cable on its proposed $1.36 billion acquisition of Atlantic Broadband.

**Sources say:** *"We chose Simpson Thacher because we have full confidence in them to work on a high-profile deal." "Almost every time at the plate they hit the ball out of the park."*

**KEY INDIVIDUALS** Firm chairman **Richard Beattie** (see p.280) is a senior figure in the New York Bar, and over a distinguished career has handled some of the largest M&A deals in the city. He is routinely called upon for his advice on governance issues, corporate offers and crisis situations. Clients enjoy working with **Casey Cogut** (see p.296) because he *"brings a lifetime of experience"* and *"he's good at relationships with both sides of the transaction; he understands how to reach out and find alternative ways of communicating."* Commentators say **Gary Horowitz** (see p.336) is an *"indefatigable"* deal lawyer with a *"commercially reasonable"* outlook. Horowitz has been representing Cogeco Cable in its $1.36 billion acquisition of Atlantic Broadband. **Mario Ponce** (see p.1928) is praised for his client-friendly approach. He and Cogut advised Eaton on its $11.8 billion acquisition of Cooper Industries. **Robert Spatt** (see p.1944) recently advised Weight Watchers International on a modified Dutch auction tender offer and a $780 million acquisition of common stock from Artal Holdings. Department head **Lee Meyerson** (see p.368) recently advised TD Bank Group on the potential acquisition of Target's US credit card portfolio, valued at $5.9 billion. **William Curbow** (see p.1887) has been identified by sources as *"an extremely practical and bright attorney"* whose calm demeanor is *"very helpful in group dynamics and with all parties concerned."* **Philip Ruegger** (see p.1934) chairs the firm's executive committee, and advises on a diverse array of corporate transactional matters.

## Skadden, Arps, Slate, Meagher & Flom LLP & Affiliates
See profile on p.2008

**THE FIRM** This Manhattan corporate team frequently handles domestic and cross-border transactions of significant size and complexity. It is praised by clients for the personalization of its service, and for the strength it is able to draw from the wider global firm. Its standout deals for 2012 included representing Anheuser-Busch InBev in its $20.1 billion acquisition of Grupo Modelo, and acting for Pfizer on the $11.9 billion divestiture of its pediatric nutrition business unit. The team also counseled Amylin Pharmaceuticals on its $7 billion acquisition by Bristol-Myers Squibb. Other major clients include Gilead Sciences, Amerigroup, News Corporation and Disney.

**Sources say:** *"They have always exceeded our expectations and have enormous strength and breadth." "The culture of the firm is amazing. Nothing is too much trouble – incredible service."*

**KEY INDIVIDUALS** Market observers praise **Peter Atkins**'s (see p.1875) intelligent and flexible negotiating. He recently supported Martin Marietta Materials in its $4.7 billion proposed business combination with gravel producer Vulcan Materials. The *"terrific"* **Lou Kling** (see p.1909) recently advised News Corporation on the separation of its publishing and entertainment arms, and represented Express Scripts in its $29.1 billion acquisition of Medco Health Solutions. The *"very high-powered"* **Howard Ellin** (see p.1890) rises in this year's rankings. *"A phenomenal tactical M&A lawyer"* who *"has the whole toolkit,"* Ellin made headlines around the world when he led an inter-office Skadden team advising Disney on its $4.05 billion acquisition of Lucasfilm. **Eileen Nugent** (see p.378) represented Cephalon in defending an unsolicited $5.7 billion takeover bid instigated by Valeant Pharmaceuticals International, and later in its acquisition by Teva Pharmaceutical Industries for $6.8 billion. She also represented Amylin Pharmaceutical in its acquisition by Bristol-Myers Squibb, as part of a deal structured to allow BMS to co-run the company with AstraZeneca. **Paul Schnell** (see p.1937) attracts ample praise for his *"excellent judgment"* and creativity. His highlights include a deal for

Pfizer involving an $11.9 billion divestiture of its business to Nestlé. He was also a key part of the team advising Anheuser-Busch InBev on its $20.1 billion Grupo Modelo takeover. New York M&A head **Stephen Arcano** (see p.1874) is *"a very practical and insightful person"* who *"keeps things moving along in a very helpful way."* He represented Gilead Sciences in its bespoke $11 billion deal to acquire Pharmasset. *"Smart and strategic"* **Thomas Kennedy** (see p.1908) is noted for his highly cerebral approach, which makes him an excellent fit for particularly technical deals. He recently assisted GTCR with acquiring Fundtech, an Israeli payment systems software provider. **Eric Cochran** (see p.1884) worked with Atkins to advise Martin Marietta Materials on its bid for Vulcan Materials. He continues to be highly regarded by peers in the New York legal community. Sources highlight **Joseph Coco**'s (see p.296) team management skills, saying he *"can seamlessly orchestrate all the interdisciplines within Skadden."* **Martha McGarry**'s (see p.1918) recent work includes assisting American Express with its agreement with Lianlian Group to roll out its Serve digital payments platform in China. **Patricia Moran** (see p.1920) is *"a fantastic lawyer"* who *"gives her clients great advice and service."* She recently advised Japanese company Marubeni on its $3.6 billion acquisition of Gavilon Group, and on its agreement to assume $2 billion of the company's debt. The firm recently mourned the passing of **Morris Kramer** (see p.1911).

## Sullivan & Cromwell LLP
See profile on p.2011

**THE FIRM** Sullivan & Cromwell's prowess in domestic and cross-border M&A is widely acknowledged, and it has been involved in some of the most dazzlingly complex deals handled in the country. The firm is trusted by banks to execute their own M&A, and is routinely called upon to advise on financial adviser duties. Major transactions include handling Anheuser-Busch InBev's $20.1 billion acquisition of Grupo Modelo, and Justice Holdings' combination with Burger King. Other stellar clients include Amgen, AT&T, Ontario Teachers and Goldman Sachs.
**Sources say:** *"Probably the best at finding creative solutions in the banking world."* *"They are able to guide clients through the complex requirements of the US takeover regime and associated securities law requirements while at the same time remaining focused on the strategic and material issues."*
**KEY INDIVIDUALS** Clients are full of praise for senior chairman **Rodgin Cohen** (see p.297), who is widely regarded as one of the most accomplished figures in the New York M&A arena. One interviewee said: *"I am always amazed how quickly Rodgin Cohen returns calls. He provides an answer in ten minutes that would take any other lawyer two to three hours."* Cohen's recent highlights include acting for Mitsubishi subsidiary UnionBanCal on its $1.5 billion acquisition of Pacific Capital Bancorp. Practice cohead **Francis Aquila** (see p.1874) recently represented Anheuser-Busch InBev in its $20.1 billion acquisition of Grupo Modelo, and in the $1.85 billion sale of a 50% interest in Crown Imports to Constellation Brands. Sources say **Joseph Frumkin** (see p.317) *"is at the forefront of market*

*practice in M&A, from Delaware courts to how boards are thinking about transactions."* He also receives emphatic praise for his client service. He recently advised the special committee of the board of directors of Southern Union Company on its acquisition by ETE. Clients say **James Morphy** (see p.1921) *"is particularly compelling when it comes to explaining the significance of legal issues to the senior businesspeople within a client organization."* Morphy provided counsel to Medco Health Solutions on its $29.1 billion merger with Express Scripts. **Stephen Kotran**'s (see p.1910) talents were recently put to use in representing Wells Fargo in its acquisition of BNP Paribas's North American energy lending unit. **Mitchell Eitel** (see p.309) also receives praise from interviewees. His recent highlights include advising Regions Financial on the sale of Morgan Keegan to Raymond James Financial, valued at $1.18 billion.

## Wachtell, Lipton, Rosen & Katz
See profile on p.2012

**THE FIRM** This M&A-focused team is seen as one of the leaders in unsolicited takeovers and hostile bids, and from its sole office in New York attracts domestic and cross-border mandates which are the envy of many an international player. Interviewees say they benefit from the firm's deep immersion in M&A, and that Wachtell brings an assertive edge to negotiations. It is regularly sought out by blue-chip clients and banks for 'bet the ranch' deals, and attracted headlines when it was chosen by El Paso to advise on its $38 billion acquisition by Kinder Morgan.
**Sources say:** *"You can ask the most esoteric question related to M&A and they've seen it, done it and documented it."* *"Wachtell brings a fearsome reputation on aggressive hostile deals. You want them on your side."*
**KEY INDIVIDUALS** Sources hail **Adam Emmerich** (see p.1890) as a *"phenomenal"* lawyer with *"tremendous understanding of issues of law"* and the ability to find creative solutions. *"His service level is exceptional,"* say clients. He recently advised Deutsche Telekom on T-Mobile's $30 billion combination with MetroPCS. **Edward Herlihy** (see p.334) recently advised the transaction committee of the Jefferies board of directors on its $2.6 billion merger with Leucadia. He also counseled Vulcan Materials on the successful defense of an unsolicited $4.7 billion tender offer for its outstanding common shares led by Martin Marietta. **David Katz** (see p.1908) recently advised the board of directors of Chesapeake Energy on a number of matters, including the sale of most of its midstream assets to Access Midstream Partners for $2.16 billion, and the sale of midstream assets and some Permian Basin properties to Chevron, Shell and others for $6.9 billion. **Andrew Brownstein** (see p.1881) cochairs the firm's corporate group and is deeply experienced in a series of high-value M&A deals and corporate governance matters. **Daniel Neff** (see p.1922) is an attorney with *"judgment and experience,"* say sources. He acted for Alibaba on reacquiring $7.8 billion of its stock from Yahoo!, and on the restructuring of its Aliplay subsidiary in conjunction with Yahoo! and Softbank. **Steven Rosenblum** (see p.1933) also earns significant praise. He is *"highly commercial"* and both *"focus-*

*es on the significant issues in a transaction, and recognizes those that are less significant."* **Andrew Nussbaum** (see p.1924) represented Ancestry.com in its buyout by a Permira-led investment group for $1.6 billion. **David Shapiro** (see p.1940) is an *"excellent lawyer"* who provides prompt, succinct advice to his clients, say sources. He advised AOL on the sale of most of its patent portfolio to Microsoft at auction for $1.1 billion, and on defending against Starboard's proxy contest. He also worked on Jefferies' $2.6 billion merger with Leucadia. **Trevor Norwitz** (see p.1924) recently acted for McGraw-Hill on the spinning out of McGraw-Hill Markets and McGraw Hill Education, and the $2.5 billion sale of its education business to Apollo. Founding partner **Martin Lipton** (see p.1914) is an immensely experienced attorney whose name commands deep respect in the M&A world. He worked with Shapiro to advise AOL on its patent sale to Microsoft and its successful defense from Starboard's proxy contest. Commentators say Lipton remains a major asset and *"a fabulous resource."*

## Band 2
## Corporate/M&A: The Elite

## Cleary Gottlieb Steen & Hamilton LLP
See profile on p.1963

**THE FIRM** This acclaimed New York M&A team is enormously experienced in technology and life sciences M&A, and acts on a wide array of high-end transactions, many of which have an international flavor. Its M&A clients also benefit from the firm's powerful domestic capital markets practice and the support of its many international offices in Europe, Asia and South America. The group recently acted for Google on its $12.5 billion acquisition of Motorola Mobility, Google's largest acquisition to date.
**Sources say:** *"They had strong background in our industry and were able to offer excellent service."*
**KEY INDIVIDUALS** Sources characterize **Victor Lewkow** (see p.1914) as *"an incredible resource."* He is praised as *"calm and balanced,"* accessible and *"highly experienced, particularly in hostile public offering situations."* He recently represented GlaxoSmithKline in the negotiation of a $3.6 billion merger agreement with Human Genome Sciences following an earlier hostile bid and tender offer. Market commentators say **Paul Shim** (see p.405) has *"a calm manner"* and is *"very smart."* He advised TPG on a deal alongside Leonard Green & Partners to acquire Savers in a $1.7 billion recapitalization. He also advised TPG's Primedia subsidiary on acquiring Rent.com from eBay for $145 million. **Michael Ryan** (see p.397) has a lauded financial and corporate advisory practice, and is particularly strong in work for private equity clients. **Daniel Sternberg**'s (see p.1944) recent highlights include advising Alkermes on its $1 billion combination with Elan Drug Technologies. **Ethan Klingsberg** (see p.1909) *"is a brilliant business lawyer who gives very solid advice for companies that are dealing with very complex corporate governance issues,"* clients say. He recently advised Agilent Technologies in its $2.2 billion acquisition of Danish can-*

cer diagnostics company Dako. **Christopher Austin** (see p.1875) recently counseled Asahi Kasei on its $2.21 billion acquisition of critical care device manufacturer ZOLL Medical. **Robert Davis** (see p.1887) recently advised Biomet on its $280 million acquisition of DePuy Orthopaedics from Johnson & Johnson, and counseled Bausch + Lomb on its $500 million acquisition of eye care business Ista Pharmaceuticals. **Benet O'Reilly** (see p.1925) joins the rankings having had a busy year and earned high market praise as a *"very cool, professional, efficient and organized"* attorney. He acted alongside Klingsberg on Agilent's deal to acquire Dako, and alongside Lewkow on GSK's merger with Human Genome Sciences. He also led the team advising GlaxoSmithKline on its $213 million investment in Theravence.

## Debevoise & Plimpton LLP
See profile on p.1968

**THE FIRM** The team at Debevoise & Plimpton maintains its high standing following another year of top-drawer transactions and wide market commendation. With over 30 partners dedicated to M&A, the group capably handles large-scale deals for the likes of Amazon.com, The Carlyle Group and AIG. It advised Warner Music Group-owned Access Industries, as part of a consortium of acquirers, on its acquisition of $7.5 billion oil and gas exploration assets from El Paso. Verizon also sought Debevoise's counsel on its $3.6 billion acquisition of AWS spectrum licenses from SpectrumCo.

**Sources say:** *"A fine first team and a deep bench." "Their ability to win points is valuable to me."*

**KEY INDIVIDUALS Jeffrey Rosen** chairs the corporate department and is *"very knowledgeable, insightful and experienced with public company transactions,"* according to interviewees. Recent transactions include representing LA asset manager the TCW Group in its sale to The Carlyle Group. **Paul Bird** cochairs the firm's corporate and M&A departments. His recent transactions include handling The Carlyle Group's $3.3 billion acquisition of Getty Images. **William Regner** chairs the M&A group. Clients say he *"has a keen understanding of the dynamics of public company deals,"* and *"superb negotiating and drafting"* skills. He recently led a team acting on Verizon Wireless's $3.6 billion acquisition of AWS spectrum licenses from SpectrumCo.

## Weil, Gotshal & Manges LLP
See profile on p.2015

**THE FIRM** This team continues to act on some of the state's biggest mandates, and has an especially secure footing in the areas of energy, healthcare and technology. Interviewees appreciate the strength it can draw from the firm's vast and well-connected international network. The team recently represented Kinder Morgan in a series of transactions, including its $38 billion acquisition of El Paso and subsequent $7.15 billion sale of El Paso's exploration and production unit to a consortium of acquirers. AMC, GE and Centerbridge Partners also feature in the firm's enviable roster of strategic acquirer and private equity fund clients.

**Sources say:** *"What I really like about Weil is they are seamless. They really operate as a team."*

**KEY INDIVIDUALS Michael Aiello** (see p.1872) receives high praise from clients, who report that he *"has good business as well as legal judgment, which really helps to move the deal over the finish line."* Other sources add that he is *"highly intelligent,"* and appreciate his *"incredibly hands-on advice"* and ability to quickly martial a team. He recently represented Linacre Holdings in its $4.6 billion acquisition by Linde. **Howard Chatzinoff** (see p.1884) remains *"level-headed"* in difficult deal situations, observers say, and attracts major blue-chip clients through his keen sense of commerciality. He represented GE in its $535 million acquisition of a 15% stake in China XD Electric as part of an international partnership agreement. **Thomas Roberts** (see p.1931) has a *"very calm personality"* and is *"highly proactive,"* say interviewees. He recently represented Kinder Morgan in the $38 billion acquisition of El Paso. **Frederick Green's** (see p.1899) highlights include representing the Port Authority of New York and New Jersey in a restructuring and development transaction with a $500 million capital commitment. **Raymond Gietz** (see p.1896) recently led on GE's $300 million investment in Brazilian industrial conglomerate The EBX Group. **Michael Lubowitz** (see p.1915) is an esteemed practitioner whose recent highlights include representing Centerbridge Partners in its $1.1 billion take-private of P.F. Chang's China Bistro.

## Band 3
## Corporate/M&A: The Elite

## Kirkland & Ellis LLP
See profile on p.1254

**THE FIRM** This M&A group acts on the full range of corporate and transactional matters for strategic buyers and private equity groups, and has established a reputation for working on unsolicited bids and hostile takeovers. The team advises Bristol-Myers Squibb, Burger King Worldwide and Avis Budget Group, among others. Recent highlights include handling NRG's $4.1 billion acquisition of GenOn Energy.

**Sources say:** *"They have the talent to assist companies in all aspects of business and legal strategies." "It's a terrific firm to work with."*

**KEY INDIVIDUALS** Department head **David Fox** (see p.1893) is widely praised for his expertise in public company M&A. Commentators say he is a *"no-nonsense"* lawyer who *"helps clients get their transaction done in an expeditious way."* He recently led on Bristol-Myers Squibb's $7 billion acquisition of Amylin Pharmaceuticals, and on its $3.4 billion agreement to collaborate post-closing with AstraZeneca on developing Amylin. Sources commend **Daniel Wolf** (see p.1952) for providing *"comprehensive, unembellished and strong tactical negotiating advice."* Others add he has *"an encyclopedic mind as it relates to the law,"* and is *"utterly tireless."* He recently led a team representing Tronox in its $3.4 billion acquisition of industrial sands operations from Exxaro Resources. **Stephen Fraidin**

(see p.1894) is particularly commended for his expertise in board governance and his *"unique ability to articulate and manage difficult, complex issues and problems."* He recently advised the special committee to the board of directors of Expedia on Expedia's announced spin-off of TripAdvisor. Rising star **Leo Greenberg** (see p.1899) is held in high regard by market sources. Clients praise him as *"commercial, extremely hard-working and extremely relationship-focused."* Also up-and-coming is **William Sorabella** (see p.1943), whom clients have described as *"extremely creative, highly commercial and very much willing to step outside the box."* He recently acted for Solutia alongside Fox on its $4.7 billion acquisition by Eastman Chemical Company. **Sarkis Jebejian** (see p.1906) recently joined the firm from Cravath. Clients say he is a *"commercially astute, responsive"* lawyer who *"can put together a high-quality legal team on very short notice to handle any project."* He recently represented BAE Systems in the sale of Safariland to a Kanders & Company-affiliated acquisition vehicle.

## Latham & Watkins LLP
See profile on p.446

**THE FIRM** The 15-partner team at Latham & Watkins advises some of the county's largest acquirers and financial advisers on M&A and corporate matters across a diverse range of industries; key clients include Eli Lilly, Disney, JPMorgan, GE Capital and Credit Suisse. Particular industry specialties include technology, media and entertainment, energy and healthcare. The firm recently represented Roche's nominated directors to the board of Illumina in its unsolicited $6.7 billion cash tender offer for Illumina's outstanding publicly-held shares.

**Sources say:** *"They are true experts in understanding and negotiating legal terms and conditions of M&A deals."*

**KEY INDIVIDUALS** *"Responsive and commercial,"* **Adel Aslani-Far** (see p.1874) leads the team. Sources say he is *"solution-oriented"* and *"thoughtful in the advice that he gives."* He led the team that advised Roche's nominated directors.

## Paul, Weiss, Rifkind, Wharton & Garrison LLP
See profile on p.1997

**THE FIRM** This team continues to be recognized as a major player on the New York M&A scene, a position supported by its recent activity on significant transactions with industry-wide ramifications. The firm is also particularly experienced in proxy contests and contested transactions. Noteworthy clients include Time Warner Cable, Citi and Ericsson. In a recent highlight, the group acted for Apollo Global Management on its $7.15 billion deal to co-acquire El Paso's power and energy business arm.

**Sources say:** *"The Paul Weiss team distinguishes itself by its quality of service and commitment to us." "They have the depth we need."*

**KEY INDIVIDUALS Robert Schumer** (see p.1938) chairs the firm's corporate practice and is praised by clients as *"incredibly hands-on," "super smart"* and *"highly tactical."* His recent highlights include advising Time Warner Cable on its $3 billion acquisition of Insight Communications, and acting for Nexen on its $15.1 billion acquisition by CNOOC. M&A co-head **Toby Myerson** (see p.1921) *"is a talented, responsive and insightful lawyer,"* and clients appreciate the extra insight he is able to provide through his experience as a former banker. He recently represented Sumitomo in its $340 million acquisition of Standard Steel. The *"very thoughtful, experienced"* **Paul Ginsberg** (see p.1896) is *"a reassuring, steady presence at the negotiating table,"* say clients. In recent months he has worked alongside Schumer on Interline Brands' $1 billion sale to affiliates of GS Capital and P2 Capital, and on talent agency William Morris Endeavor's agreement to partner with Silver Lake. Clients say **Jeffrey Marell** (see p.1917) *"understands the art of negotiation – where to make compromises as well as where to push back."* He led a team that represented Great Wolf Resorts in its acquisition by Apollo affiliates for $798 million, following a bidding war.

## Shearman & Sterling LLP
See profile on p.2005

**THE FIRM** Interviewees praise the cohesive cross-border capability of this corporate group. The team is widely acknowledged for its excellent financial services M&A practice, which advises major international players such as Citi, Bank of America Merrill Lynch and Deutsche Bank. It also serves major corporates such as Danone, Thomson Reuters and Dow Chemical. It recently represented long-time client Anglo American in a $2.8 billion partnership agreement with Codelco relating to its Chilean copper interests.

**Sources say:** *"We value the breath of international experience that Shearman can bring to our business."*

**KEY INDIVIDUALS Peter Lyons** (see p.1915) is widely recognized for his *"wealth of experience"* in M&A. He is known as a strong player to work with on more complex and sophisticated deals. **John Marzulli** (see p.1917) continues to be a respected player in the corporate arena. His practice focuses on international transactions and corporate finance. **Clare O'Brien** (see p.1924) is praised as *"intelligent"* and *"user-friendly."* She recently represented Mubadala Development Company in its $2 billion investment in EBX Group. Clients enthuse about **George Casey**'s (see p.1883) outstanding dedication and performance, saying: *"He's as sharp on day four of all day negotiations as on day one."* Casey is particularly singled out for his cross-border M&A expertise and has advised on major deals in Africa, Asia and Europe.

## Band 4
## Corporate/M&A: The Elite

## Fried, Frank, Harris, Shriver & Jacobson LLP
See profile on p.1975

**THE FIRM** This team is routinely selected to handle sophisticated transactions for public and private companies, financial institutions and private equity clients. In 2012, it represented SPX in a $1.15 billion sale of its automotive service solutions arm to Robert Bosch. It also represented Toreador Resources in its merger with ZaZa

Energy, forming a combined company with a market cap of $294 million.

**Sources say:** *"You don't have to worry about the job getting done – you know that it will."*

**KEY INDIVIDUALS Philip Richter**'s (see p.1931) recent transaction highlights include representing supermarket retailer Controladora Comercial Mexicana in its $760.4 million deal to sell a 50% interest in its Costco de Mexico joint venture to Costco Wholesale. M&A group cochair **David Shine** (see p.1941) *"can cut through a lot of noise to focus on issues of significance,"* clients say. He recently advised Thomson Reuters on its $625 million acquisition of FX Alliance. Highlights for **John Sorkin** (see p.1943) include playing an advisory role to Deutsche Bank as financial adviser to TransUnion on its sale to Goldman Sachs Capital Partners and Advent International. He also represented Goldman Sachs as financial adviser to HealthSpring on its $3.8 billion acquisition by Cigna. **Arthur Fleischer** (see p.1893) represented SmartBalance in its $125 million acquisition of Udi's Healthy Foods, and acted for Toreador Resources on its merger with ZaZa Energy.

## Willkie Farr & Gallagher LLP
See profile on p.2016

**THE FIRM** Willkie Farr & Gallagher's 41-partner New York M&A group remains an excellent fit for technical transactions and governance matters, and is especially popular with REITs, asset managers and clients in the communications and insurance industries. The group works effectively with the firm's restructuring department on distressed transactions and acquisitions emerging from reorganization proceedings. Highlights include acting for insurer Allied World Assurance on its $8.5 billion merger with Transatlantic Holdings.

**Sources say:** *"What differentiates Willkie for me is really the personalization and the way they make us feel like we're one of their premier clients."* *"They are very good at working out issues through calm, reasoned discussion."*

**KEY INDIVIDUALS Jack Nusbaum** (see p.1924) is *"extraordinary,"* say sources. He is sought out by boards of directors of public companies for his counsel on M&A and governance issues. M&A cochair **David Boston** (see p.1880) is a *"superlative lawyer,"* according to market sources. Clients are full of praise, with one saying: *"He's highly effective in negotiations and getting our views, as well as in helping us understand the other side, which helps pull parties together."* Boston represented Telcordia Technologies in its $1.15 billion sale to Ericsson. Sources say **Thomas Cerabino** (see p.1883) is *"a terrific lawyer with great judgment."* He recently represented the founder of AlixPartners in the company's recapitalization, with CVC Capital Partners taking a majority stake in the business. **Steven Seidman** (see p.1939) recently represented Ventas in acquiring a medical facilities REIT, Cogdell Spencer, for $770 million. He also acted for Allied World Assurance Company Holdings on an $8.5 billion merger with Transatlantic Holdings. Seidman cochairs the firm's M&A, corporate and financial services groups. The *"incredibly diligent"* **Adam Turteltaub** (see p.1948) is another up-and-comer who attracts market praise, with one client charac-

terizing him as a *"dedicated, thorough technician."* Turteltaub recently represented the chairman and CCO of Kenneth Cole Productions in his $245 going-private acquisition of the company.

## Band 5
## Corporate/M&A: The Elite

## Gibson, Dunn & Crutcher LLP
See profile on p.682

**THE FIRM** The 19 partners in Gibson, Dunn & Crutcher's New York M&A team act on a broad spectrum of transactions for public and private companies and their financial advisers, on some of the biggest transactions in the state. The team recently acted for Tenet Healthcare on defending a $7.95 billion unsolicited acquisition bid from Community Health Systems.

**KEY INDIVIDUALS** Sources say M&A practice leader **Dennis Friedman** (see p.1894) has *"good judgment"* and *"serves his clients well."* He recently acted for Hewlett-Packard on its $11.3 billion acquisition of Autonomy Corporation. **Barbara Becker** (see p.1877) is *"delightful to work with"* and *"keeps the trains moving on financing,"* according to clients. She was instrumental in a $16 billion project for Kraft to create a tax-free spin-off of its North American grocery business. **Steven Shoemate** (see p.406) is lauded as *"a very savvy lawyer and highly commercial – having him on your side is incredibly productive."* He recently advised GE's wholly-owned bank affiliate, GE Capital Financial, on acquiring MetLife's retail deposit business for $7.5 billion.

## Jones Day
See profile on p.919

**THE FIRM** Jones Day enters the Elite rankings in New York on the back of wide market praise for its handling of top-drawer domestic and cross-border transactional work. The group recently advised Goodrich on its $18.4 billion merger with United Technologies. It also represented Procter & Gamble in divesting its Pringles snack business to Kellogg for $2.7 billion, and in a $1 billion joint venture agreement with Teva Pharmaceutical Industries relating to over-the-counter medicines.

**Sources say:** *"The most important thing about this team is that they all think very commercially. They have the experience and wisdom to know what is important to us and what's not."*

**KEY INDIVIDUALS** Firmwide M&A practice head **Robert Profusek** (see p.1929) is recommended by clients for bet-the-company matters. He led the teams on the aforementioned Goodrich and Procter & Gamble deals.

## Band 1
## Corporate/M&A: Highly Regarded

## Dechert LLP
See profile on p.1969

**THE FIRM** This excellent M&A practice draws considerable strength from the firm's vast international network, and from its particularly deep bench in private equity, financial services and life sciences matters. Its clients include Bregal Partners, Griffon Corporation and One Equity Partners. The group recently represented Inhibitex in its $2.5 billion acquisition by Bristol-Myers Squibb.

**Sources say:** *"Dechert always impresses with their strong legal advice and pragmatic approach. They are amiable, affable and available, making them a pleasure to work with."*

**KEY INDIVIDUALS** In the words of one client, department head **Mark Thierfelder** (see p.1947) is *"a fantastic leader, with practical legal advice and strong business sense."* He recently advised DSI Renal, a Centre Partners Management company, on its $690 million sale to DaVita. **Martin Nussbaum** (see p.1924) has a fine reputation in the M&A market, and in the past year has provided counsel to the parent company of Monster.com on strategic matters relating to the future of the business. **Derek Winokur** (see p.1951) is *"responsive, quick, balanced and easy to deal with,"* say clients. Interviewees particularly highlight his skill in weighing up business and legal risks. He recently represented One Equity Partners in its proposed $1.1 billion buyout of clinical documentation services firm M*Modal.

## Morgan, Lewis & Bockius LLP
See profile on p.2246

**THE FIRM** This superior M&A group is part of the firm's large business and finance practice. It has particular expertise in energy, media and maritime transactions, and also acts for financial sponsors and leading banks. Its impressive client roster features Apollo, Ares, Pearson, Reed Elsevier and Morgan Stanley. Recent highlights include acting for Maersk on the sale of its equipment services subsidiary, Direct Chassislink, to Littlejohn & Co.

**KEY INDIVIDUALS** Clients are effusive in their praise for **Alec Dawson** (see p.1888), saying: *"In the chess game of these deals, he's thinking out ahead a few moves. He's excellent tactically and strategically."* He recently represented Jefferies in its $348 million acquisition of Prudential Bache. Managing partner **Charles Engros** (see p.1890) is a *"terrific lawyer,"* according to sources. He acted for Pearson on its $294 million acquisition of Chinese EFL education company Global Education, as part of the continued development of its English language teaching business.

## Schulte Roth & Zabel LLP
See profile on p.2003

**THE FIRM** This 15-partner business transactions group handles significant M&A, primarily for private equity funds, asset managers and other portfolio owners. It works closely with related departments within the firm to deliver results for clients on financings, restructurings and distressed deals. Highlights include representing Cerberus in its acquisition of a 53% stake in AT&T's Yellow Pages business, in a $950 million transaction.

**KEY INDIVIDUALS** **Marc Weingarten** (see p.1950) is noted by sources for his *"excellent client skills"* and *"calm, cool and collected demeanor."* He advised retail group Charmed Shoppes on its $890 million acquisition by Ascena Retail.

## Sidley Austin LLP
See profile on p.1264

**THE FIRM** Sidley Austin's eight-partner New York M&A and private equity group acts on the full range of private and public M&A, as well as unsolicited takeover proposals and defense work. It attracts work from clients such as BNP Paribas, AIG, Morgan Stanley and the Government of Singapore's sovereign wealth fund, the GIC. Highlights include representing Cerveceria Nacional Dominicana in its $1.248 billion sale to Ambev, and acting for Compass on its acquisitions of various tech companies.

**KEY INDIVIDUALS** Scott Freeman heads the department.

## White & Case LLP
See profile on p.451

**THE FIRM** White & Case's New York M&A group advises the likes of Sony, Disney and the Hess Corporation, among other major organizations. It is routinely sought to handle technical cross-border transactions for public and private companies, and acts for private equity funds across a vast range of industries. In a recent highlight, it acted for ICBC on a first-of-its-kind, $140 million acquisition of an 80% stake in a US retail bank, The Bank of East Asia.

**Sources say:** *"A truly global platform."*

**KEY INDIVIDUALS** Clients describe **Morton Pierce** (see p.1927) as a *"knowledgeable, thorough and insightful lawyer."* Interviewees further highlight the pragmatic outlook he brings to bear on sophisticated transactions. *"He always supplements his legal perspectives with a consideration of the business matters and issues we are hoping to address and resolve,"* said one interviewee. **John Reiss** (see p.1930) *"provides a remarkable level of leadership in tense situations,"* and has *"great intuition for deal dynamics."* He acted for ICBC on its US bank acquisition, and also advised Canadian distribution utility Fortis on its $1.5 billion acquisition of CH Energy. New arrival **Denise Cerasani** (see p.1883) *"is extremely experienced, very pragmatic and commercial,"* as well as *"always responsive and well prepared,"* according to sources. She has particularly noteworthy experience advising banks on fairness opinions and elements of financial advisory disclosure. After a four-year tenure as head of M&A at Linklaters, **Daniel Dufner** rejoined White & Case early in 2013. He is recognized by peers as a solid M&A lawyer in the city, and caters to an impressive array of clients. Highlights from his past year include representing WellPoint in two substantial acquisitions.

## Band 2
### Corporate/M&A: Highly Regarded

## Allen & Overy LLP
See profile on p.433

**THE FIRM** This five-partner New York M&A team counts major names such as Shell, Thomson Reuters, Novartis, GlaxoSmithKline and GE among its clients. The firm proves particularly attractive to major international players seeking to acquire or do business with US companies, such as German multinational SAP, which it advised on its $3.4 billion acquisition of SuccessFactors. Increasingly, however-

er, the group is being mandated to act on significant domestic deals, such as its recent representation of GE Capital in a commercial agreement with CIFC.

**Sources say:** *"They have a broad global reach, and so whenever there are pieces that are outside of the US I know I have my one go-to person here who can leverage relationships across the globe."*

**KEY INDIVIDUALS** Clients say US M&A leader **Eric Shube** provides commercially practicable advice, and describe him as *"extraordinarily knowledgeable,"* *"insightful"* and *"highly creative."* He advised GE Capital on its strategic transaction with CIFC. **Michael Gilligan** *"keeps his eye focused on what's important,"* say clients. He recently advised Dell on a deal to acquire CIT Vendor Finance's Dell-related assets, plus sales and servicing functions in Europe. **Mark Wojciechowski** is highly experienced in M&A, as well as leveraged and acquisition finance. He continues to advise major banks, as well as long-term client Balfour Beatty, on a range of corporate matters.

## Covington & Burling LLP
See profile on p.441

**THE FIRM** This strong M&A team acts for some of the market's biggest players on a range of high-caliber transactions, in part because of the recognized strength of its sophisticated regulatory and regulated industry practices. The group has a stellar list of active clients, including Microsoft, Johnson & Johnson, Procter & Gamble, Disney, AstraZeneca and UBS. Its New York team recently advised Thomson Reuters on the $1.25 billion sale of its healthcare arm to a Veritas Capital affiliate.

**Sources say:** *"The Covington team is very responsive and incredibly diligent on all matters."*

**KEY INDIVIDUALS** **Scott Smith** (see p.1942) is a *"smart, thoughtful"* lawyer, according to commentators. He recently advised SandRidge Energy on its $1.275 billion acquisition of Dynamic Offshore Resources. Clients say **J D Weinberg** (see p.1950) is *"always extremely helpful when we need the creative thinking and judgment that only a seasoned partner can provide."* He led on Thomson Reuters' aforementioned divestiture of its healthcare business.

## Greenberg Traurig, LLP
See profile on p.1024

**THE FIRM** Greenberg Traurig in New York maintains a strong M&A presence. Highlights from the past year include representing Black Entertainment Television founder Robert Johnson in his acquisitions of Image Entertainment and Acorn for $160 million to form RLJ Entertainment, and advising DPL on its $4.7 billion sale to AES. Among financial advisers, it receives mandates from Barclays, Deutsche Bank and Bank of America Merrill Lynch, and was recently selected by Morgan Stanley to be its counsel on Grupo Modelo's $20.1 billion acquisition by Anheuser-Busch InBev.

**Sources say:** *"They're extremely responsive and do extensive research on any topics that come up, as well as how we practice, within our industry."*

**KEY INDIVIDUALS** **Dennis Block** (see p.1879) has a considerable reputation in corporate legal circles, with one source saying he is *"a legend in M&A."* A strong personality in the transactional world, Block represents a *"fantastic asset for Greenberg,"* say commentators. He recently advised DPL on its sale to AES. Clients say global M&A cochair **David Schwartzbaum** (see p.1939) is a *"very bright guy"* and *"one of a handful who really know how banks do business."* He recently represented interclick in its $270 million acquisition by Yahoo!, and advised Morgan Stanley in its capacity as financial adviser to Grupo Modelo. The *"terrific"* **Alan Annex** (see p.1874) *"understands the interplay"* between business needs and legal risk, according to clients. He recently co-led an inter-office Greenberg team advising LSE-listed acquisition vehicle Justice Holdings on its $5 billion acquisition of Burger King Worldwide Holdings, which was structured as a merger to allow Burger King to return to the NYSE.

## Hughes Hubbard & Reed LLP
See profile on p.1981

**THE FIRM** This M&A group handles the full range of transactional needs for public and private companies, particularly those in the life sciences, media and financial services sectors. The group's active clients include big names such as Viacom, Sony Music and the US Treasury Department. It continues to receive a significant amount of work from Ernst & Young in its capacity as joint administrator of Nortel's insolvent European, Middle East and African entity.

**Sources say:** *"Highly intelligent and personable advisers who are easy to access and fully committed to their clients' goals."*

**KEY INDIVIDUALS** M&A and corporate group cochair **Ken Lefkowitz** (see p.1912) is a popular figure in the New York M&A market. According to market sources, *"he is smart, super practical and down to earth. I can see why he does well with clients. His informal style inspires confidence, which he backs up with intelligent and savvy deal skills."* The *"pragmatic, business-friendly"* **Charles Samuelson** (see p.1936) earns praise from clients, with one reporting: *"He is very efficient and he doesn't beat around the bush. He gets it done."* He recently represented Wafra in its $1 billion investment in Triple Point Capital. Firm chair **Candace Beinecke** (see p.1877) is an influential figure in the New York legal scene. She maintains a busy practice advising many of the firm's significant clients on governance issues. Sources find M&A cochair **James Modlin** (see p.1920) to be *"straightforward, knowledgeable and easy to work with."*

## Milbank, Tweed, Hadley & McCloy LLP
See profile on p.448

**THE FIRM** Milbank's transactional team excels across a range of corporate matters, and is particularly well known for its work on distressed deals as well as energy and aircraft leasing transactions. Standout highlights include acting for ITOCHU as part of a consortium with KKR and others on the $7.2 billion acquisition of Samson Investment. The team also advised Catalyst Health on its $4.75 billion merger with SXC Health Solutions.

**Sources say:** *"Their ability to provide us depth across the firm – in terms of the talent we've been able to get – is great."*

**KEY INDIVIDUALS John Franchini** (see p.1894) is *"highly client-oriented,"* and is highlighted by sources for his pragmatism and skill in negotiations. He advised Strategic Value Partners on its sale of Liberty Electric to an affiliate of Energy Capital Partners.

## Proskauer Rose LLP
See profile on p.2001

**THE FIRM** This strong 30-partner M&A team acts on domestic and cross-border deals for top-drawer clients such as Ares, Accor and Bed Bath & Beyond. It is particularly active for clients in the chemical and industrial industries, and for an enviable range of retailers and financial services firms. Highlights include advising Neuberger Berman on its $1.5 billion buyout of Lehman Brothers' remaining stake in the company.

**Sources say:** *"We trust them because they have the ability to stay three steps ahead and get results in an efficient manner."*

**KEY INDIVIDUALS Ronald Papa** is *"highly responsive"* and *"excellent technically."* One client highlighted his skill in *"getting our chemistry to the point where he can know our position implicitly."* Papa recently advised French chemicals group Arkema on the sale of its tin stabilizer business to PMC.

## Ropes & Gray LLP
See profile on p.1528

**THE FIRM** This East Coast favorite's New York corporate team has healthy expertise in securities, M&A and private equity deals. Over the past year it has remained active on both buy and sell-side transactions for WCAS, and advised State Street on its $550 million acquisition of Goldman Sachs' hedge fund administration business. Other key clients include Bain Capital, Dunkin' Brands and Health Enterprise Partners.

**KEY INDIVIDUALS Othon Prounis**'s work of late has included advising WCAS on a number of transactions. His practice emphasizes LBOs and work in the healthcare and technology sectors.

## Band 3
## Corporate/M&A: Highly Regarded

## Akin Gump Strauss Hauer & Feld LLP
See profile on p.904

**THE FIRM** Akin Gump's strength in M&A is evident in its high-quality work for serial acquirers, distressed companies and hedge funds. The firm continues to benefit from its role in the formation of several hedge fund-sponsored offshore reinsurance firms, in the form of ongoing mandates for strategic and transactional support. Its clients include Cerberus, Citi Global Markets and Lukoil. The team recently represented glass container manufacturer Anchor in its $880 million sale to Luxembourg-based Ardagh Group.

**KEY INDIVIDUALS Kerry Berchem** heads the department.

## Baker Botts LLP
See profile on p.2427

**THE FIRM** This nine-partner corporate team benefits greatly from the firm's strong position in the energy sector, and also handles impressive transactions in the media, technology, telecoms and real estate sectors. Its active clients include Mediacom, QVC and Ascent Capital. It recently advised Liberty on its $10 billion plans to spin-off all its assets not affiliated with the Starz entertainment brand into a new subsidiary, Liberty Media, with the intention of renaming its parent company 'Starz'.

**KEY INDIVIDUALS Bob Murray** is a key contact for the practice.

## Cadwalader, Wickersham & Taft LLP
See profile on p.438

**THE FIRM** Cadwalader's impressive M&A group ably handles a broad array of transactions for clients such as Elan Corporation, AngioDynamics, Nektar Therapeutics and new client wins Tower Watson & Co and Marsh & McLennan Companies. Its recent mandates include representing the chairman and CEO of Quest Software in relation to its $2.17 billion buyout by Insight Venture Partners. One particular area of expertise for the group is corporate takeover defense and preparedness.

**KEY INDIVIDUALS** The M&A practice at Cadwalader is led by **Louis Bevilacqua** (see p.1878). As practice chair, he has worked hard at developing the team in recent months, and is also known more widely in the market for his commerciality and business skills.

## Clifford Chance US LLP
See profile on p.439

**THE FIRM** This 16-partner group handles numerous high-caliber, cross-border transactions, drawing in part on the firm's impressive global network. The M&A group advised Hearst on its $1 billion acquisition of several magazine properties owned by Hachette. The team also collaborated with the firm's Sydney office to advise Irish aircraft lessor FLY Leasing on the acquisition of 49 Boeing and Airbus aircrafts.

**Sources say:** *"Consistently high quality."*

**KEY INDIVIDUALS** Sources say rising star **Benjamin Sibbett** (see p.1941) is *"gifted in terms of simplifying complex topics."* He is also praised as a *"thoughtful and hard negotiator"* who *"can deliver a stern message without offending the other side."*

## Goodwin Procter LLP
See profile on p.1522

**THE FIRM** Goodwin Procter's corporate team has benefited from the arrival of seven corporate attorneys from Dewey & LeBoeuf. It represents a mix of investment funds, corporates and venture growth companies, and has a particularly strong reputation in cleantech, life sciences, healthcare and digital technologies. Its new intake of partners brings clients such as Insight Venture Partners to a roster which includes Ampio Pharmaceuticals, Great Hill Partners and Lycera.

KEY INDIVIDUALS **Andrew Weidhaas** (see p.1949) currently divides his time between New York and Silicon Valley. He acted for Behrman Capital on the sale of its interests in five portfolio companies from Behrman funds.

## Hogan Lovells US LLP

THE FIRM This 16-partner M&A group acts for major organizations such as News Corporation, Hulu, HarperCollins and UnitedHealth. It recently represented ExxonMobil in the $3.9 billion sale of its Japanese oil refinery subsidiary ExxonMobil Yugen Kaisha to TonenGeneral Sekiyu. It also advised News Corporation on its agreement to acquire ESPN's 50% stake in ESPN STAR Sports, making it a wholly-owned News Corporation subsidiary.

KEY INDIVIDUALS Michael Silver heads the team in New York.

## Kaye Scholer LLP
See profile on p.1984

THE FIRM Kaye Scholer advises numerous domestic companies and private equity funds on a broad range of complex deals in the middle and upper middle-markets. Its M&A group also receives frequent mandates from Canadian and European companies seeking counsel on inbound M&A. One area of focus for the team is the transactional representation of companies with substantial IP assets. Clients appreciate the team's high levels of service as well as its advice on corporate governance and matters of future business strategy.

Sources say: *"The team works very well together, and is highly responsive and a pleasure to work with."*

KEY INDIVIDUALS **Joel Greenberg** (see p.1899) is a *"great resource,"* who impresses with his comprehensive knowledge of M&A. He cochairs the firm's Canada group, and recently advised Toronto-based Onex and its affiliates on an $871 million investment in doors and windows manufacturer JELD-WEN Holdings. The *"excellent"* **Nancy Fuchs** (see p.1895) is known among sources as a *"very strong negotiator."* She recently advised Pon North America on its acquisition of the Hiller Group and subsidiaries. She is also routinely sought after to advise on corporate matters in aerospace and defense. Interviewees describe corporate department cochair **Emanuel Cherney** (see p.1884) as a *"creative, flexible, responsive"* attorney whose negotiating style is *"nuanced and subtle."* He is also noted for his *"excellent business judgment."* He recently represented Sundance Holdings Group and its equity holders in its sale to Brentwood Associates.

## Kramer Levin Naftalis & Frankel LLP
See profile on p.1987

THE FIRM This firm handles a wide range of strategic, distressed and private equity-led M&A deals, and is praised for its efficiency and commerciality throughout the transactional process. In a recent highlight, the group advised Fundtech on its $700 million all-stock merger with S1, a provider of software for the financial services industry. It also represented Answers.com in its acquisition by AFCV Holdings.

Sources say: *"The team is extremely efficient and worked seamlessly together with my team to get deals done." "As an inhouse lawyer I am charged with being more commercial than legal. Kramer Levin helps us translate legal advice into a business discussion right away."*

KEY INDIVIDUALS Clients say **Howard Spilko** (see p.1944) *"has great skills and is highly practical,"* as well as *"entrepreneurial."* He recently represented AIG in its $35 million sale of two insurance companies. According to commentators, **Ernest Wechsler** (see p.1949) *"is extremely commercial and knows how to get a transaction done without getting into a legal fight of the kind that tends to bog down attorneys. He knows how to protect you in a commercial sense."* He recently advised BlackRock on the sale of chemical company Wellman.

## McDermott Will & Emery LLP
See profile on p.1258

THE FIRM The team at McDermott Will & Emery remains a solid choice for transactions in the healthcare and life sciences sectors, and is increasingly popular with clients active in energy, metals and mining. Its recent highlights include advising Singapore-listed Olam International on joint ventures with US commodity merchandiser Lansing Trade Group and with cocoa supplier Blommer Chocolate. Other clients include Standard General, Morgan Stanley, Thompson Creek Metals and E.ON.

Sources say: *"They work with you to find practical solutions."*

KEY INDIVIDUALS **Tim Alvino** (see p.1873) has a healthy reputation in the New York market, and is noted for advising Irving Oil on strategic M&A possibilities. Impressed sources say **Thomas Sauermilch** (see p.1936) *"brings a lot of experience, practicality and business sense to the table,"* and *"fosters a partnering relationship."*

## Morrison & Foerster LLP
See profile on p.1990

THE FIRM The New York office of this preeminent West Coast firm houses a six-partner M&A team with expertise in life sciences and technology, as well as apparel and financial services. As a consequence of the firm's strong Asian offering, the group continues to receive mandates from top-drawer Far East clients such as Terumo and Toshiba. Important domestic clients include DaVita and Qatalyst Partners. Recent highlights include advising CNOOC's financial advisers BMO Nesbitt Burns on the company's $19.4 billion deal to acquire Nexen.

KEY INDIVIDUALS Global M&A head Spencer Klein works from the firm's New York office.

## Paul Hastings LLP
See profile on p.1996

THE FIRM Paul Hastings advises clients ranging from promising startup companies through to more established players on matters of corporate governance and M&A. In particular, it is noted for its representation of financial services and investment management clients in both domestic and cross-border deals. Highlights from the past

year include acting for cable and broadband provider Suddenlink on its $6.6 billion purchase by BC Partners, CPPIB and a CEO-led management team. Other clients include Citibank and Equinox.

Sources say: *"They really took the time to understand the business." "They've been very responsive to our needs at all times."*

KEY INDIVIDUALS Tom Kruger is a key practice contact in New York.

## Vinson & Elkins LLP
See profile on p.2459

THE FIRM The New York office of this dominant player in the energy sector fields a corporate team that handles domestic and cross-border M&A for private equity funds, acquirers and targets. Big-name clients include The Carlyle Group, White Deer Energy and Warburg Pincus. It recently advised TPG Capital on its role as part of a consortium acquiring $1.25 billion preferred assets in a subsidiary of Chesapeake Energy.

Sources say: *"They offer practical advice and solutions, rather than over-lawyered advice, and they deliver on their commitments."*

KEY INDIVIDUALS Energy M&A specialist **David Cohen** (see p.297) is *"top-notch,"* according to interviewees, who add that he is *"creative with solutions on structuring"* and *"very client-focused."* Recent mandates include advising Pioneer Natural Resources on its acquisition of Carmeuse Holdings' US industrial sands business.

## Band 4
## Corporate/M&A: Highly Regarded

## Baker & Hostetler LLP
See profile on p.2119

THE FIRM The New York business transactions group at this Midwest stalwart is experienced in handling deals for technology, media and financial services clients. It is a favorite for cross-border deals and has considerable expertise in acting for German companies on inbound transactions, and for US entities on outbound Indian transactions. Highlights from the past year include acting for French 3D design company Dassault Systèmes' US subsidiary on its $10 million acquisition of Enginuity.

Sources say: *"High-quality, responsive and extremely client-oriented." "They are very well prepared to handle matters of importance and complexity, and pay equal attention to smaller matters and inquiries as well."*

KEY INDIVIDUALS Sources appreciate **Steven Goldberg**'s (see p.1897) *"great business sense,"* and praise him as a *"master legal technician"* who produces *"careful and tightly written work."* He has recently advised a number of large US entities on investment opportunities and asset purchases in India.

## Bracewell & Giuliani LLP
See profile on p.2429

THE FIRM This five-partner team caters to the full range of public and private companies, including venture growth startups, private equity sponsors and hedge funds. The team is particularly adept in transactions with a strong reorganizational element. Recent work includes advising USAA Real Estate on its purchase of a 49% equity interest in Square Mile Capital Management.

**Sources say:** *"They are really responsive, always available and highly creative."*

**KEY INDIVIDUALS** Robb Tretter heads the department.

### DLA Piper LLP (US)
See profile on p.1971

**THE FIRM** This team acts on a considerable range of high-end M&A, and benefits from a strong global platform with offices in virtually every major financial center and emerging market. It was one of a select panel of firms to advise Pfizer on the $11.9 billion sale of its nutrition business to Nestlé. Other highlights include acting on Atlanta Spirit's $170 million sale of the Atlanta Thrashers hockey team to True North.

**Sources say:** *"They are focused on delivering a successful outcome."*

**KEY INDIVIDUALS** Jonathan Klein heads the practice in New York.

### Dorsey & Whitney LLP
See profile on p.1583

**THE FIRM** This New York team handles transactions for major domestic and international clients, as well as venture growth companies. It draws on support from offices across the USA, including the firm's home base in Minneapolis. Its clients include the North American Soccer League, Canon USA and Banco de la Nacion Argentina. Team highlights include representing IntegraMed America in its $169.5 million sale to Sagard Capital Partners.

**Sources say:** *"Dorsey is a large firm but it feels much smaller, more personable and much easier to deal with."*

**KEY INDIVIDUALS** Clients say department co-leader and New York office head **Steven Khadavi** is extraordinarily responsive, and report that he *"focuses on solutions not problems."* He recently represented Chinese company Xuzhou Construction Machine Group in acquiring a controlling interest in German manufacturer Schwing.

### Freshfields Bruckhaus Deringer US LLP
See profile on p.443

**THE FIRM** This compact M&A team attracts significant mandates from such major clients as Rolls-Royce, Swiss Re, ArcLight and Japan Tobacco. It is a popular choice among European and Asian entities for inbound US transactions, due in part to Freshfields's stellar reputation around the world. It also advises on significant domestic deals, such as acting for Tyco's financial adviser on Pentair's $7.7 billion acquisition of the company's flow control division.

**Sources say:** *"The great thing is that you have someone who really gets under the skin of the deal, asks good questions and is utterly reliable in a meeting or in drafting."*

**KEY INDIVIDUALS** *"Excellent all-around,"* **Matthew Herman** (see p.1902) has an ascendant profile in the New York M&A world. Sources say he provides *"clever solutions to difficult problems."*

### Jenner & Block LLP
See profile on p.1252

**THE FIRM** This tight-knit M&A group has abundant domestic and international transactional expertise. It has a solid base of life sciences and technology clients, as well as a strong presence in energy and manufacturing. Related highlights include representing PowerFuels in its $381 million merger with Heckmann.

**KEY INDIVIDUALS Tobias Knapp** (see p.1910) recently represented Duff & Phelps in acquiring a stake in WR Managed Accounts as part of a strategic partnership deal.

### Pillsbury Winthrop Shaw Pittman LLP
See profile on p.2000

**THE FIRM** This firm's 13-partner New York group frequently works closely with transactional teams in other Pillsbury offices to deliver efficient results. In 2012 it represented Bonded Services in four acquisitions in the UK and the USA. It also advised XO Holdings on its take-private acquisition by ACF Industries.

**KEY INDIVIDUALS** The *"responsive and reliable"* **James Kelly** is identified by sources as someone who *"possesses great creative and innovative instincts in structuring and drafting deals."*

### WilmerHale
See profile on p.930

**THE FIRM** Life sciences and technology are two hallmark strengths of this respected East Coast practice. In a recent highlight, the firm represented Bristol-Myers Squibb in the restructuring of its alliance with Sanofi across multiple jurisdictions. Its other clients include CitiBank, Isis and Constellation Pharmaceuticals.

**KEY INDIVIDUALS** Andrew Nagel is chair for M&A.

### Band 5
### Corporate/M&A: Highly Regarded

### Arnold & Porter LLP
See profile on p.906

**THE FIRM** Arnold & Porter's New York office handles a significant range of transactional matters for financial institutions and investment fund clients. The group also benefits from the firm's significant links to clients in Latin America, such as Banco do Brasil. Its recent highlights include representing State Bancorp in its $222 million sale to Valley National Bancorp. Other notable clients include Aurora Bank and York Capital.

**Sources say:** *"I would describe them as very talented, creative and easy to work with."*

**KEY INDIVIDUALS** Robert Azarow is a key contact here.

### Ellenoff Grossman & Schole LLP

**THE FIRM** This boutique houses a large corporate and securities team that continues to attract fine mandates. Given the firm's deep expertise in special purpose acquisition company (SPAC) IPOs, it is sought out for its counsel on deals involving SPACs. In a recent highlight of this nature, the firm advised the special committee of Image

Entertainment on its combination with Acorn Media Group to create RLJ Entertainment, following RLJ Acquisition's purchase of both companies.

**KEY INDIVIDUALS** Douglas Ellenoff heads the firm's corporate and securities practices.

### Nixon Peabody LLP
See profile on p.1526

**THE FIRM** Nixon Peabody's M&A group handles the gamut of transactions in the middle and lower middle-markets for a number of significant companies. It is particularly active in life sciences, consumer products, manufacturing, energy and technology, with several of its transactions involving significant cross-border elements of late.

**Sources say:** *"They have the ability to spot issues really comprehensively and deal with whatever matter we're working on. They give us good, strong guidance, and alert us to other tangents without getting bogged down in them."*

**KEY INDIVIDUALS John Koeppel** (see p.348) chairs the firm's private equity and investment funds practice. Clients say he offers *"good practical advice about how to get a deal done,"* and is adept at *"weighing business risks."*

### Seward & Kissel LLP
See profile on p.2004

**THE FIRM** Seward & Kissel offers talent in midmarket M&A, as demonstrated by its many deals for investment management clients. Benefiting from the firm's impressive shipping finance practice, the New York corporate group also attracts impressive mandates in the world of shipping, including one from OceanFreights relating to its $239 million acquisition by DryShips.

**Sources say:** *"The fact they are proactive or quickly reactive is of huge benefit to us."*

**KEY INDIVIDUALS James Abbot** (see p.1871) co-heads the firm's M&A practice. Sources say he *"brings a wealth of experience to the table"* and *"has a great grasp of commercial issues spanning a variety of industry segments."* He recently advised Parfums de Coeur on its sale to Yellow Wood Partners.

### Sutherland Asbill & Brennan LLP

**THE FIRM** This corporate group is a popular choice for transactions in the insurance space, as well as in other regulated industries such as financial services. The group counts Swiss Re and Hartford Life Insurance among its clients. Interviewees praise the team for its nimble execution of mid-to-large size deals, and commend its willingness to adopt cost-effective fee structures, sometimes in conjunction with the firm's offices in DC and Atlanta.

**KEY INDIVIDUALS Bert Adams** is praised by sources for his impressive ability to understand all aspects of a transaction. He recently represented Freepoint Commodities in acquiring J.P. Morgan Metals and Concentrates.

### Other Notable Practitioners

Rochester-based **Craig Wittlin** (see p.1952) of Harter, Secrest & Emery LLP is well respected among sources. He recently advised Health Management Associates on a $875 million senior notes exchange. Loeb & Loeb LLP corporate department chair and New York managing partner **David Schaefer** (see p.1936) has *"tremendous tenacity,"* according to sources, who add: *"He's got the courage of his convictions and good judgment."* **Mitchell Nussbaum** (see p.1924) is chair of Loeb & Loeb's capital markets and Asia practices.

His recent highlights include representing Harbin Electric in a $768 million buyout by its CEO, Abax Global Capital and Abax affiliates. Lowenstein Sandler PC's M&A chair **Marita Makinen** (see p.1916) is described as *"extremely knowledgeable,"* and is praised for her *"unbelievable attention to detail."* She led a team acting for Buddy Media on its

sale to salesforce.com, one of 2012's major tech deals. **Howard Herman** is co-head of the M&A department at Moses & Singer LLP. *"A gem"* in the M&A world, he *"writes well"* and *"understands the issues,"* according to sources.

# EMPLOYEE BENEFITS & EXECUTIVE COMPENSATION

Commentary about individuals can be found under their firm's paragraph. If the firm has no paragraph (is not ranked) look at Other Notable Practitioners.

## Employee Benefits & Executive Compensation
### Leading Firms

**Band 1**
Cleary Gottlieb Steen & Hamilton LLP *
Davis Polk & Wardwell LLP *
Simpson Thacher & Bartlett LLP *
Skadden, Arps, Slate, Meagher & Flom LLP & Affiliates *
Sullivan & Cromwell LLP *

**Band 2**
Debevoise & Plimpton LLP *
Proskauer Rose LLP *
Wachtell, Lipton, Rosen & Katz *

**Band 3**
Fried, Frank, Harris, Shriver & Jacobson LLP *
Paul, Weiss, Rifkind, Wharton & Garrison LLP *
Pillsbury Winthrop Shaw Pittman LLP *
Shearman & Sterling LLP *

**Band 4**
Cadwalader, Wickersham & Taft LLP *
Cravath, Swaine & Moore LLP *
Latham & Watkins LLP *
Morgan, Lewis & Bockius LLP *
Seyfarth Shaw LLP *
Weil, Gotshal & Manges LLP *

\* Indicates firm / individual with profile.
† ONP = Other Notable Practitioner.

## Senior Statesmen

**Senior Statesmen: distinguished older practitioners**

| | | | |
|---|---|---|---|
| Schwartz Max J | Sullivan & Cromwell LLP * | Susko A Richard (Brick) | Cleary Gottlieb Steen & Hamilton LLP * |

### Leading Individuals

**Star individuals**

| | | | |
|---|---|---|---|
| Serota Susan P | Pillsbury Winthrop Shaw Pittman LLP | Rabitz Steven | Stroock & Stroock & Lavan LLP (ONP)† |
| Sirkin Michael | Proskauer Rose LLP | Raskin Kenneth A | King & Spalding LLP (ONP)† * |
| | | Rothstein Gary S | Morgan, Lewis & Bockius LLP * |

**Band 1**

| | | | |
|---|---|---|---|
| Cagney Lawrence K | Debevoise & Plimpton LLP | | |
| Carleen Donald P | Fried, Frank, Harris, Shriver & Jacobson * | **Band 3** | |
| FitzGerald Edmond | Davis Polk & Wardwell LLP * | Albert Rory | Proskauer Rose LLP |
| Fleder Robert C | Paul, Weiss, Rifkind, Wharton & Garrison * | Bernstein Andrew | Mintz Levin Cohn Ferris Glovsky (ONP)† * |
| Grala Bronislaw E | Cadwalader, Wickersham & Taft LLP * | Conway Jennifer S | Cravath, Swaine & Moore LLP * |
| Kohn Arthur H | Cleary Gottlieb Steen & Hamilton LLP * | Goldstein Jeremy | Wachtell, Lipton, Rosen & Katz * |
| Olshan Regina | Skadden, Arps, Slate, Meagher & Flom * | Hunt Peter J | Pillsbury Winthrop Shaw Pittman LLP * |
| Pianko Howard | Seyfarth Shaw LLP * | Lewis Jon | Debevoise & Plimpton LLP |
| Rappaport Linda E | Shearman & Sterling LLP | Morgenbesser Henry | Allen & Overy LLP (ONP)† |
| Robbins Brian D | Simpson Thacher & Bartlett LLP * | Rattner Andrea S. | Proskauer Rose LLP |
| Segal Michael J | Wachtell, Lipton, Rosen & Katz * | Raymond Robert J | Cleary Gottlieb Steen & Hamilton LLP * |
| Trevino Marc R | Sullivan & Cromwell LLP * | Rothenberg Laraine S | Fried, Frank, Harris, Shriver & Jacobson |
| | | Wahlquist Andrea K | Simpson Thacher & Bartlett LLP * |
| **Band 2** | | Wessel Paul J | Weil, Gotshal & Manges LLP * |
| Cannon III John J | Shearman & Sterling LLP | Williamson Bradd L | Latham & Watkins LLP * |
| Cohen David | Schulte Roth & Zabel LLP (ONP)† * | Witdorchic Lawrence | Paul, Weiss, Rifkind, Wharton & Garrison * |
| Friestedt Matthew M | Sullivan & Cromwell LLP * | | |
| Gaines Andrew L | Paul, Weiss, Rifkind, Wharton & Garrison * | **Band 4** | |
| Leff Neil M | Skadden, Arps, Slate, Meagher & Flom * | Albano Michael J | Cleary Gottlieb Steen & Hamilton LLP * |
| McLoughlin Jean | Davis Polk & Wardwell LLP * | Brickner Jed | Latham & Watkins LLP * |
| O'Brien Jeannemarie | Wachtell, Lipton, Rosen & Katz * | Frazier James | Cadwalader, Wickersham & Taft LLP * |
| Oringer Andrew L | Dechert LLP (ONP)† * | Grogan Gregory | Simpson Thacher & Bartlett LLP * |
| Price Scott D | Kirkland & Ellis LLP (ONP)† * | Hilfers Eric W. | Cravath, Swaine & Moore LLP * |
| | | Ross Jeffrey | Fried, Frank, Harris, Shriver & Jacobson * |
| | | Rubin Amy M | Weil, Gotshal & Manges LLP * |

## Band 1

### Cleary Gottlieb Steen & Hamilton LLP
See profile on p.1963

**THE FIRM** Cleary Gottlieb is widely acknowledged as a standout firm in employee benefits and compensation in New York. The group focuses on transactional work, with notable expertise in M&A and private equity compensation matters. Recent work includes representing The Home Depot in its acquisition of Redbeacon, and acting for Primedia on its acquisition of Rent.com from eBay. In addition to its deal-based practice, the group advises on ERISA fiduciary matters, and is viewed as a go-to choice in this area for banking giants such as BNP Paribas, JPMorgan and Credit Suisse.
**Sources say:** *"A very high-quality firm and practice."*
**KEY INDIVIDUALS** One of the most experienced practitioners in this field, **Brick Susko** (see p.415) advises large financial groups on the regulatory aspects of executive compensation and on ERISA fiduciary matters. *"He is a terrific professional,"* clients comment. **Arthur Kohn** (see

p.348) is hugely experienced in the full spectrum of benefits and compensation work, and has acted for a number of large national companies, including McDonald's and Bank of America, on issues relating to compensation disclosure. Sources say: *"He is truly phenomenal."* **Robert Raymond** (see p.1930) specializes in counseling private equity clients on executive compensation. He recently advised TPG Capital on its internal compensation structure. Described as *"one to watch,"* **Michael Albano** (see p.1872) has a growing reputation in the New York benefits and compensation world. He advises on a diverse range of issues and often represents large multinational clients, including Google and Coca-Cola.

### Davis Polk & Wardwell LLP
See profile on p.442

**THE FIRM** Davis Polk is renowned for the strength and depth of its executive compensation and employee benefits practice. The group focuses on transactional work, acting for an impressive list of clients including Heinz, PwC and the NYSE. Its experience covers M&A, LBOs and bankruptcy work, and recent highlights saw the firm guide Patriot Coal through its Chapter 11 reorganization and related DIP financing. The team also advises hedge funds and private equity groups on ERISA fiduciary matters.
**Sources say:** *"In what they specialize in, you can't get any-one better. They are great with M&A transactions, with contracts, and in advising on complicated investment issues."*
**KEY INDIVIDUALS** **Edmond FitzGerald** (see p.313) is a *"very talented tax lawyer who provides excellent advice on a*

variety of compensation and benefit matters." He recently represented Campbell Soup in its $1.55 billion acquisition of Bolthouse Farms. Sources agree: "He is a top practitioner in this area." **Jean McLoughlin** (see p.1918) is praised by clients as a "tireless worker and creative problem solver who is unflappable and has a good business sense." She specializes in the creation and application of management equity arrangements and executive compensation agreements, and recently acted for Spanish banking group BBVA on the sale of its Puerto Rican-based operations.

### Simpson Thacher & Bartlett LLP
See profile on p.2006

THE FIRM Simpson Thacher is a dominant firm in this area, and its highly regarded team stands out for its focus on private equity transactions. It has substantial experience in public financing transactions and regularly advises on the implementation of pension plan investments in private equity funds. The firm also has a thriving transactional practice, advising public companies on the full spectrum of benefits and compensation matters. Recent work highlights include representing Blackstone in its $2 billion acquisition of Vivint.

Sources say: "I rate them very highly – they are outstanding advocates for their clients."

KEY INDIVIDUALS Department head **Brian Robbins** (see p.1931) is acclaimed for his knowledge and experience in dealing with Title I and Title IV of ERISA, particularly in relation to M&A. He also advises on ERISA fiduciary matters and prohibited transactions. Recent work highlights include representing private equity group Apax Partners in its $1.1 billion acquisition of Garda World Security. **Gregory Grogan** (see p.1900) represents private equity groups in the full range of employee benefits and executive compensation matters. He also has an active practice advising on CEO succession planning, and recently acted as counsel to Gannett as it sought to appoint a new CEO. **Andrea Wahlquist** (see p.1949) focuses on LBOs and M&A, and recently advised Sealy on its acquisition by Tempur-Pedic. Her transactional expertise includes offering advice on executive compensation relating to IPOs and bankruptcy.

### Skadden, Arps, Slate, Meagher & Flom LLP & Affiliates
See profile on p.2008

THE FIRM Skadden specializes in complex executive compensation arrangements and employee benefits matters arising from M&A. The team handles senior executive employment contracts and severance agreements, and is well regarded for its work on deferred compensation and golden parachutes. It is also well known for its expertise in executive compensation under the Troubled Asset Relief Program (TARP). Recent highlights include advising Marubeni on its $5.6 billion acquisition of Gavilon Group.

Sources say: "Excellent and highly responsive. Available 24/7." "They know our business very well and consider our practical needs."

KEY INDIVIDUALS **Regina Olshan** (see p.1925) is "considered to be the leading authority on 409(a) in the USA,"

and regularly advises boards, compensation committees and senior executives on matters in this area. Recent work highlights saw her act for Express Scripts on its $29.1 billion acquisition of Medco Health Solutions. According to clients, **Neil Leff** (see p.1912) "knows his stuff inside and out." He advises on employee benefits and executive compensation issues relating to M&A transactions, and recently represented Amylin Pharmaceuticals in connection with its $7 billion acquisition by pharmaceutical giant Bristol-Myers Squibb.

### Sullivan & Cromwell LLP
See profile on p.2011

THE FIRM This well-known New York firm has a vibrant employee benefits and executive compensation practice that is renowned for its expertise in transactional matters. The team covers areas relating to post-transaction structural matters, business administration, and tax and disclosure. It also advises on the impact of increased regulation on compensation. Representative highlights include working with ING on the benefits and compensation implications of its sale of ING Direct Canada to Scotiabank.

KEY INDIVIDUALS The eminent **Max Schwartz** (see p.402) is held in high regard as "an expert technician" in this field. He focuses on tax and securities matters relating to the compensation of senior executives and issues surrounding governance, advising the likes of Facebook and gaming giant Activision Blizzard. **Marc Trevino** (see p.1947) is "very business focused – he is smart, able to handle big-picture stuff, but also willing to dive into the details." He handles a wide range of issues, including those relating to M&A, corporate governance and regulatory law, and recently advised AIG on the sale of AIG common stock by the US Treasury. **Matthew Friestedt** (see p.1895) is a rising star on the New York executive compensation scene. He advises on everything from employment agreements to issues surrounding severance, and recently advised Skype on executive compensation matters. His expertise extends beyond transactional work to everyday advice relating to governance and disclosure.

## Band 2

### Debevoise & Plimpton LLP
See profile on p.1968

THE FIRM This highly regarded group works with both public and private companies on employee benefits and executive compensation. The firm has significant experience relating to transactions as well as ongoing business issues, including proxy statement disclosure, corporate governance and enforcement. Recent work includes advising The Carlyle Group on its $3.3 billion acquisition of Getty Images from the Hellman & Friedman private equity group.

KEY INDIVIDUALS **Lawrence Cagney** chairs the group, focusing on the creation of compensation plans for senior executives. He acts for individuals, boards and compensation committees, as well as for both public and private companies. He recently advised the board of Martha

Stewart Living Omnimedia on a new employment agreement with the group's founder and namesake. **Jon Lewis** advises on executive compensation with a focus on management equity agreements. He recently advised Clayton, Dubilier & Rice on its acquisition of David's Bridal.

### Proskauer Rose LLP
See profile on p.2001

THE FIRM This group advises Fortune 500 companies on a wide range of transactional matters, including large cross-border M&A deals. Notably, the firm acts for NYSE Euronext on international employment, benefits and compensation issues. It also advises corporate boards, management employees and committees on executive compensation, benefits plans and related issues. Key clients include Reed Elsevier, the Metropolitan Museum of Art and Yahoo!'s compensation committee.

Sources say: "They leave no stone unturned – they provide a very thorough legal analysis."

KEY INDIVIDUALS Star individual **Michael Sirkin** cochairs the firm's benefits and compensation department, and is acclaimed for his expertise in advising on employment and compensation agreements for senior executives. In highlights, he represented the Yahoo! compensation committee in the hiring of its new CEO. "Mike is a wonderful attorney – I would trust him with my life," said one interviewee. **Rory Albert** is recognized for his specialization in benefits plan and fund work. In the past year he has acted as general counsel to a range of entertainment industry-based health and welfare, retirement and 401(k) funds, such as the Writers Guild Industry Health Fund and the Broadway League Staff Retirement Plan. **Andrea Rattner** is praised for her "wonderful broad knowledge" of compensation and employee plans, with a focus on tax and securities, corporate governance and ERISA fiduciary issues. She recently advised Solera Capital on the benefits and compensation implications relating to the IPO of one of its portfolio companies.

### Wachtell, Lipton, Rosen & Katz
See profile on p.2012

THE FIRM This prominent firm is best known for its deal-driven employee benefits and executive compensation practice. The group regularly advises on compensation arrangements in relation to large M&A deals, as well as on management succession, board composition and other related issues.

KEY INDIVIDUALS **Michael Segal** (see p.1939) is a "terrific lawyer" with substantial experience advising on the benefits and compensation aspects of M&A and joint ventures. **Jeannemarie O'Brien** (see p.1924) works closely with the firm's M&A department on the benefits and compensation implications of transactions. She regularly represents financial services sector clients, advising on corporate governance and regulatory compliance. "She is a first-rate lawyer," according to one source. The impressive **Jeremy Goldstein** (see p.1897) is well regarded by peers and clients alike. His practice focuses on corporate transactions, and he is the chair of the M&A subcommittee of the executive compensation committee of the American Bar Association.

## Band 3

### Fried, Frank, Harris, Shriver & Jacobson LLP
See profile on p.1975
THE FIRM This well-regarded group has a broad practice and is active across the employee benefit and executive compensation spectrum. The firm advises individuals, compensation committees and company boards on a wide range of issues, including employment agreements, deferred compensation, and retirement and welfare plans. It also advises on corporate transactions, and recently represented Permira in its $1.6 billion acquisition of Ancestry.com.
Sources say: "Their performance is excellent – they have the right approach, they're very quick, and they know the market well."
KEY INDIVIDUALS Donald Carleen (see p.1882) is renowned for his knowledge of benefits and compensation matters. One peer commented: "You won't have an experience with him where you don't learn something." In recent highlights, Carleen advised GS Capital Partners on its acquisition of a stake in Interline Brands. Of counsel Laraine Rothenberg advises on corporate governance and executive compensation. She regularly works with executives, boards and compensation committees on employment agreements, equity benefit plans, and tax and security matters. Jeffrey Ross (see p.1933) is widely regarded as a growing force in the New York employee benefits and executive compensation arena, described as a "rising star" by senior practitioners. One interviewee said: "When he talks, people listen." Ross advises private investment funds on ERISA matters, and recently advised Onex on its acquisition of SGS international in a deal involving an equity investment by the management of both companies.

### Paul, Weiss, Rifkind, Wharton & Garrison LLP
See profile on p.1997
THE FIRM This well-known firm has a dynamic employee benefits and executive compensation practice that focuses on high-level M&A. It recently represented Apollo Global Management as part of a consortium in the $7.15 billion acquisition of the energy and power arm of El Paso. The group also advises on tax, securities and corporate fiduciary issues relating to deferred compensation and equity-based plans, as well as on legal issues arising under ERISA.
KEY INDIVIDUALS Department head Robert Fleder (see p.1893) stands out on the benefits side, where his experience includes advising on benefit plans in relation to major transactions. Representative work highlights include advising Time Warner Cable on its $3 billion acquisition of Insight Communications, including in relation to golden parachutes and retention arrangements for senior executives. Andrew Gaines (see p.1895) has a broad practice representing clients ranging from public companies to private equity groups and investment funds in various types of transactions. "He is always responsive and comes up with practical solutions," say sources. Lawrence Witdorchic (see p.1951) advises public and private groups on M&A, IPOs and takeover transactions. Recent highlights include representing Grupo Salinas in its cross-border acquisition of Advance America.

### Pillsbury Winthrop Shaw Pittman LLP
See profile on p.2000
THE FIRM The firm is noted for its expertise in plan design and implementation, ERISA compliance and related litigation. It also advises on regulatory law, including the requirements for executive compensation under Dodd-Frank and the Affordable Care Act. In a recent highlight, the team advised Amphenol on the administration of its new restricted stock plan for directors.
KEY INDIVIDUALS Clients praise Susan Serota as being "accessible and responsive," while peers call her "a leader in her field." She specializes in advising on ERISA fiduciary issues and cross-border compensation and benefits matters. Peter Hunt (see p.1905) is a "very solid ERISA lawyer" who, clients say, makes challenging parts of their jobs easier. He has a great deal of experience advising on ERISA compliance as counsel to both companies and investment groups.

### Shearman & Sterling LLP
See profile on p.2005
THE FIRM This group handles a range of benefits and compensation matters, including compensation package design and implementation. The team works closely with the firm's tax and corporate departments, and regularly advises on transactions as well as on ERISA compliance. It recently advised Citi on its divesture of EMI, and represented Donald Layton in connection with his employment agreement following his appointment as CEO of Freddie Mac.
Sources say: "They point out the next five things I need to do. They are very proactive – they delve into plans and make sure we are well covered."
KEY INDIVIDUALS Linda Rappaport is "at the top of the field," say interviewees. She has a wealth of experience in the formation and administration of executive compensation plans, including retirement, welfare and equity-based plans. She advised Citi on the compensation and benefits issues relating to its aforementioned sale of EMI Records to Vivendi. Practice group leader John Cannon has "excellent judgment and insight," and is an "excellent negotiator," clients say. He is recognized for his experience advising on compensation and corporate governance, and recently advised Fujifilm Holdings on these and other matters relating to its purchase of SonoSite.

## Band 4

### Cadwalader, Wickersham & Taft LLP
See profile on p.438
THE FIRM Cadwalader is celebrated for its expert knowledge of the ERISA fiduciary world, and for its pension plan investment work. The group also has a budding M&A practice, and handles compensation and benefits matters relating to a wide range of corporate transactions. Recent highlights include representing a new bond agency with respect to its inclusion as an agency approved by the Employee Benefits Security Administration to determine the eligibility of securities for purchase by ERISA plans.
Sources say: "They are fantastic – I've come to expect stellar things, and I only get stellar things."
KEY INDIVIDUALS The hugely experienced Broni Grala (see p.325) is praised for his ability to apply his extensive knowledge to practical situations. An ERISA specialist, he is widely regarded as a go-to person for this type of work, and is considered "one of the greatest" in this area. One peer enthused: "He is at the top level of the profession – we all value him tremendously." James Frazier (see p.1894) advises clients on prohibited transactions under ERISA as well as on ERISA fiduciary issues. Well regarded by both peers and clients, he has been hailed as creative and responsive, with impressive turnaround times.

### Cravath, Swaine & Moore LLP
See profile on p.1966
THE FIRM This firm is highlighted for its M&A-focused benefits and compensation practice. The team advises on the legal implications of transactions, and on the creation of new plans and compensation arrangements. It advised Johnson & Johnson on its $19.7 billion acquisition of Synthes. As well as its deal-based practice, the firm also assists clients with ongoing tax, securities and ERISA issues in connection with the day-to-day operation of their compensation and benefit plans.
Sources say: "They are always knowledgeable and responsive, and have good legal sense and good commercial sense." "Every time we are blown away by how good they are."
KEY INDIVIDUALS Jennifer Conway (see p.1886) "knows her area inside and out," say interviewees. She focuses on transactions, with notable experience in compensation and benefits issues related to M&A and IPO deals. Eric Hilfers (see p.1903) heads the firm's executive compensation and employee benefits practice. His wide-ranging expertise covers M&A, as well as the appointment and severance of senior executives, and employment and compensation arrangements. He recently advised Barnes & Noble on a strategic partnership with Microsoft. Sources comment: "He is a joy to work with."

### Latham & Watkins LLP
See profile on p.446
THE FIRM This firm's robust employee benefits and executive compensation department often works with private equity clients on both transactions and day-to-day issues. The team in New York recently represented Odyssey Investment Partners in its acquisition of a number of port-

folio companies, including in respect to deferred compensation and golden parachute issues.

**Sources say:** *"They are very knowledgeable, you get a good work product, they're responsive, and they're just enjoyable to work with. All in all it's a very good relationship."*

**KEY INDIVIDUALS Bradd Williamson** (see p.1951) regularly advises on incentive-based compensation for both public and private groups. He also has a lively deal-based practice, and recently advised English football club Manchester United on employee-related matters in connection with its IPO on the NYSE. An expert on ERISA compliance, **Jed Brickner** (see p.1880) often advises investment funds on how to configure investments to adhere to ERISA fiduciary rules.

## Morgan, Lewis & Bockius LLP
See profile on p.2246

**THE FIRM** This national firm offers day-to-day advice on benefits and compensation issues, and advises companies on M&A, public offerings, spin-offs and other corporate transactions. Other areas of expertise include Title IV of ERISA and ESOPs. Recent work highlights include advising the management of AmWINS Group on its $1.3 billion recapitalization with New Mountain Capital.

**KEY INDIVIDUALS Gary Rothstein** (see p.1933) has *"excellent client service and commercial awareness."* He has substantial expertise in representing senior management groups in LBOs, and also has a thriving practice dealing with nontransactional compensation work. One source enthused: *"Gary is an exceptional employment attorney. I would recommend him and his firm very highly."*

## Seyfarth Shaw LLP
See profile on p.1262

**THE FIRM** New to the rankings, this group focuses on the creation and administration of retirement and health and welfare plans. The team handles the full range of day-to-day employee benefits issues, and is entrusted by a number of large New York law firms to manage their plans. The group is also highly experienced in plan governance, and continues to handle work of this nature for the US-based arm of shipping and logistics heavyweight OOCL.

**Sources say:** *"We were given excellent advice very quickly."*

**KEY INDIVIDUALS** Peers and clients alike praise **Howard Pianko** (see p.1927) for his judgment and experience in this area. He is noted for his expertise in ERISA governance, pension investments and executive compensation, and recently acted for Wolseley Group Services on the expansion of its executive share scheme.

## Weil, Gotshal & Manges LLP
See profile on p.2015

**THE FIRM** This benefits and compensation practice group is recognized for its work on large transactions. Working closely with other departments at the firm, the team handles both US and cross-border matters in areas such as M&A, bankruptcy and private equity. Recent highlights saw the team represent Lincare Holdings in its cross-border acquisition by Linde of Germany.

**KEY INDIVIDUALS** Department head **Paul Wessel** (see p.1950) focuses on transactional work for private equity groups and public companies. He also advises on pensions and benefits in the context of restructuring and bankruptcy. **Amy Rubin** (see p.1934) is well known for her work on M&A deals involving private equity groups. She recently advised Golf Town Canada on its $97.2 million purchase of Golfsmith International Holdings.

## Other Notable Practitioners

**David Cohen** (see p.1885) of Schulte Roth & Zabel LLP advises on benefits and compensation issues affecting hedge funds and private equity groups, and is viewed by peers as *"a leader in terms of investment."* He also advises on ERISA and qualified plans. **Andrew Oringer** (see p.380) of Dechert LLP is renowned for his expertise in the ERISA arena, and for his knowledge of benefits issues involving retirement, health and welfare plans. **Scott Price** (see p.1929) of Kirkland & Ellis LLP *"goes to great lengths to provide superb legal advice,"* clients say. He has a broad practice, with substantial expertise in the creation of employment and incentive plans. Recent work includes advising Bristol-Myers Squibb on its acquisitions of Amylin and Inhibitex. **Steven Rabitz** of Stroock & Stroock & Lavan LLP is recognized for his focus on ERISA fiduciary issues. He is sought after by large financial institutions for his advice in this area, and acts for the likes of Credit Suisse and JPMorgan. *"He is a great lawyer – very smart and very thoughtful,"* say sources. **Kenneth Raskin** (see p.1930) is the chair of the benefits and compensation practice at King & Spalding LLP, where he concentrates on the creation and administration of benefits plans, including retirement and welfare plans. He recently advised Roark Capital Group on benefit plan issues in relation to the financing of a large transaction. **Henry Morgenbesser** of Allen & Overy LLP is well regarded for his expertise in transactional matters. He recently represented Australian company Computershare in its $550 million acquisition of The Bank of New York Mellon's Shareowner Services Business. **Andrew Bernstein** (see p.1878) of Mintz Levin Cohn Ferris Glovsky and Popeo PC covers a wide range of compensation work, and regularly represents CEOs in LBOs and other transactions.

# ENERGY & NATURAL RESOURCES

Commentary about individuals can be found under their firm's paragraph. If the firm has no paragraph (is not ranked) look at Other Notable Practitioners.

## Energy: State Regulatory & Wholesale Electric Market

### Leading Firms

**Band 1**

Cullen and Dykman LLP

Nixon Peabody LLP *

**Band 2**

Couch White, LLP

Greenberg Traurig, LLP *

Hiscock & Barclay LLP *

Read and Laniado

### Senior Statesmen

Senior Statesmen: distinguished older practitioners

| | |
|---|---|
| Gioia Paul L | Law Offices Of Paul L Gioia (ONP)[†] |

### Leading Individuals

**Band 1**

| | |
|---|---|
| Dax John | The Dax Law Firm, PC (ONP)[†] |
| FitzGerald Brian T | Cullen and Dykman LLP |
| Loughney Robert | Couch White, LLP |
| Widger Stanley | Nixon Peabody LLP * |

**Band 2**

| | |
|---|---|
| Cogen Richard M | Nixon Peabody LLP * |
| Helmer Maureen | Hiscock & Barclay LLP * |
| Johnson David | Read and Laniado |
| Laniado Sam | Read and Laniado |
| Mager Michael | Couch White, LLP |
| Pond George M | Hiscock & Barclay LLP * |
| Saia Doreen U | Greenberg Traurig, LLP * |
| Singer Leonard | Couch White, LLP |

**Band 3**

| | |
|---|---|
| Flynn William | Harris Beach LLP (ONP)[†] |

* Indicates firm / individual with profile,
Alphabetical order within each band. Band 1 is the highest.

## Band 1

### Cullen and Dykman LLP

**THE FIRM** This firm recently acquired a market-leading New York team from Dewey & LeBoeuf, affording it the capacity to handle the full range of energy issues including rate cases, financings and siting matters. The team also deals with New York State Public Service Commission (PSC) proceedings. Clients include a series of utilities such as GDF SUEZ, Rochester Gas & Electric, and New York State Electric & Gas.

**KEY INDIVIDUALS Brian FitzGerald** is held in high regard as a well-connected practitioner in the sector. He has recently been working to obtain, on behalf of GDF SUEZ, regulatory approvals for its purchase of the outstanding shares of International Power.

### Nixon Peabody LLP

See profile on p.1526

**THE FIRM** The team here is equipped to handle a wide range of work on behalf of its energy and utility clients, including M&A approval, regulatory compliance, rate cases and financing. It is a frequent presence before the PSC and other regulatory bodies, up to and including the FERC. Clients include Niagara Power Coalition, Corning Natural Gas and Puerto Rico Electric Power Authority.

**Sources say:** "A strong group and a quality shop."

**KEY INDIVIDUALS Stanley Widger** (see p.1951) is an "outstanding lawyer and a great guy," according to sources. An expert in the full range of regulatory concerns, he continues to advise the likes of T Rowe Price Associates and Niagara Power Coalition on matters ranging from merger clearance to rate changes. **Richard Cogen** (see p.1885) is noted for his expertise in project development and permitting matters, with sources labeling him "a very good lawyer; very deliberate and methodical."

## Band 2

### Couch White, LLP

**THE FIRM** The team here has an excellent reputation in the energy field, providing counsel to clients involved in generation, delivery and consumption on a wide variety of regulatory, policy and other concerns. Among its most active practices is advising developers on the siting and permitting implications of new infrastructure projects, such as power plants and transmission facilities.

**Sources say:** "A very strong across-the-board practice."

**KEY INDIVIDUALS Robert Loughney** specializes in representing clients in proceedings before regulatory bodies such as the PSC and FERC. He is also experienced in negotiating operating contracts and supply agreements. Also seen frequently at the PSC and FERC is **Michael Mager**. He focuses on representing large energy consumers in rate cases, regulatory proceedings and contract negotiations. **Leonard Singer** is noted for his expertise in siting and permitting. He does a lot of the firm's work relating to the construction of power plants and transmission lines.

### Greenberg Traurig, LLP

See profile on p.1024

**THE FIRM** The team at Greenberg Traurig has a focus on IPPs and the wholesale electric market, representing clients such as GenOn and US Power Generating. Among other things, it is regularly sought out by clients to handle matters relating to the New York Independent System Operator's Services Tariff.

**KEY INDIVIDUALS Doreen Saia** (see p.1935) is noted for her representation of merchant generators, with sources describing her as "very knowledgeable." She has been representing clients such as Entergy Nuclear Power Marketing,

US Power Generating, TransCanada Ravenswood and NRG in various negotiations and proceedings.

### Hiscock & Barclay LLP

See profile on p.1980

**THE FIRM** This team joins the rankings following extensive client endorsement. The group is recognized for its active practice before the PSC and other state agencies, representing generators, distributors and developers in a range of regulatory matters. Among its clients are National Grid, Cable Telecommunications Association of New York and Transmission Developers (TDI).

**Sources say:** "Very solid, pragmatic and businesslike." "Their services are exemplary."

**KEY INDIVIDUALS** Clients "can not say enough good things about" **George Pond** (see p.1928), who is hailed for his "unbelievable grasp of the issues and associated law." He has recently been representing TDI in relation to a high-voltage direct current transmission project from the Canadian border to New York City. **Maureen Helmer** (see p.1902) is "an excellent lawyer and practitioner," according to sources, who identify her strengths as being "very smart, responsive" and having "a great deal of knowledge and key contacts." She has represented TransCanada in relation to generation service issues before the PSC.

### Read and Laniado

**THE FIRM** Read and Laniado focuses on representing clients before state and federal energy agencies in relation to ratemaking, siting and various other regulatory matters. It is experienced before the PSC and New York Independent System Operator (NYISO), and also brings matters before the FERC. It has a strong client base among wholesale electric generators.

**KEY INDIVIDUALS Sam Laniado** has deep experience in advising on power plant and transmission line siting, as well as ratemaking issues. **David Johnson** has a well-established reputation before the PSC, NYISO, and state and federal courts, as well as taking cases all the way to the FERC. His clients include owners and operators, trade associations and power marketers.

## Other Notable Practitioners

The respected **John Dax** of The Dax Law Firm, PC counsels utility and energy industry clients, including developers, owners and large consumers, on a wide range of regulatory and commercial concerns. **William Flynn** of Harris Beach LLP has a broad practice that spans regulation and legislation relating to gas, electricity, water and telecoms. Senior practitioner **Paul Gioia** of the Law Offices Of Paul L Gioia continues to practice in the areas of energy and utility regulation. He is praised for his deep experience and key relationships.

# ENVIRONMENT

Mainly Transactional p.1808

Commentary about individuals can be found under their firm's paragraph. If the firm has no paragraph (is not ranked) look at Other Notable Practitioners.

## Environment
### Leading Firms

**Band 1**

Bryan Cave LLP

Nixon Peabody LLP *

Sive Paget & Riesel PC *

**Band 2**

Phillips Lytle LLP *

Whiteman Osterman & Hanna LLP

Young, Sommer, Ward, Ritzenberg, Baker & Moore LLC

**Band 3**

Bond, Schoeneck & King, PLLC

Carter Ledyard & Milburn LLP *

Hodgson Russ LLP

## Band 1
## Environment

### Bryan Cave LLP

**THE FIRM** This five-partner environment group is well regarded in the New York market and offers services across the full range of environmental issues, including litigation, transactions and counseling, for government agencies, financial institutions and businesses. The team acts for Empire State Development on the $4.9 billion development of Atlantic Yards in Brooklyn. Clients include Terex, New York University and Och-Ziff Real Estate.
**KEY INDIVIDUALS Kevin Healy** is praised for his superb expertise in the field and for his excellent strategic sense. Recently, he represented New York University with regards to the proposed construction of a 2.5 million sq ft mixed-use development in Manhattan. **Roberta Gordon** is popular among interviewees, many of whom praise her detail oriented approach and her abilities as a negotiator. She has continued to advise McAllister Towing and Transportation Company on all the environmental issues relating to its coastal operations. **Philip Karmel** has been representing Moynihan Station Development in the proposed development of a new train station in Manhattan. Sources praise him as an excellent attorney and litigator.

### Nixon Peabody LLP

See profile on p.1526

**THE FIRM** This full-service environmental group handles matters including Superfund cases, toxic tort actions and regulatory compliance issues for clients in a diverse range of industries. The team has acted for Citi on occupational health and safety matters. It also represents Goldman Sachs, Centerline Capital Group and RXR Realty.
**Sources say:** *"They're excellent; very thorough and supportive." "They are very prepared in all their dealings and leave no stone unturned in their preparation."*

**KEY INDIVIDUALS John Greenthal** (see p.1899) has particular expertise in the area of Superfund and brownfield issues. He wins praise from sources, who find that *"he's diligent and he knows environmental law inside and out."* Interviewees highlight that the *"superb"* **Jean McCreary** (see p.1918) is *"a pleasure to work with,"* and particularly appreciate that she is *"very detail oriented and thorough."* She has recently been busy working on a number of complex Superfund matters. **Scott Turner** (see p.1948) concentrates his practice on the regulation and permitting of electric generators. According to market commentators, he *"is very knowledgeable, brings in a lot of applicable experience, and has good relationships with the agencies."* The *"incredibly commercial and helpful"* **Jesse Hiney** (see p.1903) *"instills confidence"* in client sources. He advises Goldman Sachs' affordable housing lending and investment group on environmental risk and compliance.

### Sive Paget & Riesel PC

See profile on p.2007

**THE FIRM** This boutique firm has been a key player in the New York environmental market for over 50 years and is well regarded for its expertise in environmental litigation and brownfield issues. The team has a fine reputation for work on important infrastructure projects, and a major focus of the past year has been representing the New York State Thruway Authority on the $5 billion Tappan Zee Bridge. It also represents American Sugar Refining and The Port Authority of New York and New Jersey.
**Sources say:** *"An excellent law firm."*
**KEY INDIVIDUALS Mark Chertok** *"knows what's around the corner before he goes around it,"* according to sources, who agree that *"he's very good at what he does."* He recently acted for the Port Authority of New York and New Jersey on two major bridge projects. **Michael Bogin** offers expertise on waterfront projects and continues to be involved in the $60 million development of Admirals Row for Brooklyn Navy Yard Development. He is described as *"a great guy."* The *"talented and knowledgeable"* **David Paget** is well known in the industry. He has been leading the team on the huge Tappan Zee Bridge project. **Daniel Riesel** is widely regarded as a dean of environmental law. Sources say *"he's a delight to work with. He works hard to find practical solutions."* Interviewees describe **Jeffrey Gracer** as *"an excellent transactional lawyer."* He is expert cross-border matters, and has recently been representing the US subsidiary of a global company in connection with its involvement in the Passaic River Superfund site.

## Senior Statesmen

**Senior Statesmen:** distinguished older practitioners

| | |
|---|---|
| Kafin Robert | Proskauer Rose LLP (ONP)[†] |
| Kass Stephen | Carter Ledyard & Milburn LLP |
| Paget David | Sive Paget & Riesel PC |
| Riesel Daniel | Sive Paget & Riesel PC |

## Leading Individuals

**Band 1**

| | |
|---|---|
| Chertok Mark | Sive Paget & Riesel PC |
| Healy J Kevin | Bryan Cave LLP |
| Ruzow Daniel | Whiteman Osterman & Hanna LLP |
| Sommer Dean | Young, Sommer, Ward, Ritzenberg, Baker |

**Band 2**

| | |
|---|---|
| Bernstein Kevin M | Bond, Schoeneck & King, PLLC * |
| Freeman David | Gibbons P.C. (ONP)[†] * |
| Gracer Jeffrey B | Sive Paget & Riesel PC |
| Greenthal John | Nixon Peabody LLP * |
| Karmel Philip E | Bryan Cave LLP |
| Leland Richard G | Fried, Frank, Harris, Shriver & Jacobson * |
| McCreary Jean H | Nixon Peabody LLP * |
| Turner Scott M | Nixon Peabody LLP * |
| Warren Charles S | Kramer Levin Naftalis & Frankel LLP (ONP)[†] * |

**Band 3**

| | |
|---|---|
| Alessi Robert | DLA Piper LLP (US) (ONP)[†] * |
| Fazio Christine A | Carter Ledyard & Milburn LLP |
| Fein Scott N | Whiteman Osterman & Hanna LLP |
| Flynn David P | Phillips Lytle LLP * |
| Graham Morgan G | Phillips Lytle LLP * |
| Kogut Barry R | Bond, Schoeneck & King, PLLC * |
| Robb Kathy | Hunton & Williams LLP (ONP)[†] * |
| Robbins Virginia C | Bond, Schoeneck & King, PLLC * |
| Rothenberg Eric | O'Melveny & Myers LLP |
| Simmons Doreen A | Hancock Estabrook LLP (ONP)[†] |
| Stever Donald W | K&L Gates (ONP)[†] * |
| Suchman E Gail | Stroock & Stroock & Lavan LLP (ONP)[†] |

**Band 4**

| | |
|---|---|
| Bogin Michael S | Sive Paget & Riesel PC |
| Gordon Stephen L | Beveridge & Diamond PC (ONP)[†] * |
| Hogan Kevin M | Phillips Lytle LLP * |
| Pardo James A | McDermott Will & Emery LLP (ONP)[†] * |
| Rosenberg Mark F | Sullivan & Cromwell LLP * |
| Sacripanti Peter | McDermott Will & Emery LLP (ONP)[†] * |
| Young Kevin | Young, Sommer, Ward, Ritzenberg, Baker |

**Up-and-coming individuals**

| | |
|---|---|
| Hiney Jesse | Nixon Peabody LLP * |
| Pratt Jason | Shearman & Sterling LLP |

**Associates to watch**

| | |
|---|---|
| Folb Kerri | Kramer Levin Naftalis & Frankel (ONP)[†] * |

* Indicates firm / individual with profile.

[†] ONP = Other Notable Practitioner.

## Band 2
## Environment

### Phillips Lytle LLP
See profile on p.1999

**THE FIRM** Phillips Lytle's environmental group offers expertise on regulatory matters as well as litigation, regularly handling brownfield redevelopments, renewable energy projects and enforcement proceedings for a diverse client base. The team represent CBS in a number of environmental issues, including negotiating a consent decree at a West Virginia Superfund site. Other clients include VanDeMark Chemical, Reichhold and AT&T Mobility.
**Sources say:** *"They're very easy to work with, they're nice people and they're good at what they do." "They think like business lawyers, looking for a positive solution."*
**KEY INDIVIDUALS Kevin Hogan** (see p.1904) is *"technically excellent,"* according to sources, who particularly highlight that he *"knows exactly how to get to the heart of the matter and doesn't beat around the bush."* He recently brought a federal court action on behalf of AT&T Wireless, successfully overturning a denied zoning variance. The *"very affable"* **David Flynn** (see p.1893) *"has a great sense of business, and knows when it is important to give on wording and issues to get a deal done."* He has been representing URS in several complicated compliance and regulatory issues. According to one interviewee, **Morgan Graham** (see p.1899) is *"one of the most business-oriented lawyers I could hope for – he's a problem solver and a tremendous guy to work with."* Graham is an expert in permitting matters, handling a number of those for key client DuPont.

### Whiteman Osterman & Hanna LLP

**THE FIRM** This well-known upstate firm fields experts in areas such as emissions, corporate compliance, and solid and hazardous waste. Including many former government agency officials, the 12-partner environmental team regularly acts for Fortune 500 companies in the pharmaceuticals, manufacturing and chemicals sectors.
**Sources say:** *"A great firm."*
**KEY INDIVIDUALS** According to interviewees, **Daniel Ruzow** is *"very strong and very capable."* He focuses his practice on matters related to environmental compliance, permitting and litigation. The *"very practical-minded"* **Scott Fein** concentrates on handling regulatory compliance, enforcement matters and internal investigations for public agencies and corporations.

### Young, Sommer, Ward, Ritzenberg, Baker & Moore LLC

**THE FIRM** This top-notch boutique firm offers clients decades of experience dealing with a wide spectrum of environmental issues, such as air quality, waste management, brownfields redevelopment and mining. In the alternative energy sphere, the group is a leader in the development of New York policy, and represents key players.
**Sources say:** *"They're a specialty firm and really top notch at what they do."*
**KEY INDIVIDUALS** The *"absolutely brilliant"* **Dean Sommer** is well known in the New York market, and sources highlight that *"he has a very good sense of what's at issue."* His area of particular expertise is litigation involving hazardous waste, petroleum, hazardous substances and solid waste that has been released into the atmosphere. **Kevin Young** is experienced in all facets of land use and environmental regulations, and has frequently been involved in brownfield and Superfund site litigation.

## Band 3
## Environment

### Bond, Schoeneck & King, PLLC

**THE FIRM** This upstate firm is highly recommended for its depth and breadth of expertise in a variety of environmental and energy matters, including hazardous waste, water quality, solid waste and wetlands. It has in-depth knowledge of environmental laws on a local, state and federal level, and frequently provides compliance and regulatory advice to a client base that includes commercial entities, municipalities and individuals.
**Sources say:** *"They're very good. I highly recommend them."*
**KEY INDIVIDUALS Kevin Bernstein** (see p.1878) is recognized for his work in the solid waste area. His significant experience includes obtaining the required permits and approvals for power generation, wind energy and gas storage projects. **Virginia Robbins** (see p.1931) chairs the environmental and energy group, and offers particular expertise in issues covered by the 1990 Clean Air Act Amendments. She also provides regulatory and compliance counseling in matters relating to waste management and water and air pollution. Sources enjoy working with **Barry Kogut** (see p.1910), noting that he *"instills a great level of confidence."* He has a broad range of experience in environmental matters, particularly in the area of regulatory compliance and enforcement matters, which he handles at both the state and federal level.

### Carter Ledyard & Milburn LLP
See profile on p.1961

**THE FIRM** This firm's environmental group works cohesively with the firm's other practice groups, such as real estate and tax, to provide a seamless service for clients, which include both public and private entities. The group has a broad depth of experience, regularly handling compliance, licensing, litigation and environmental diligence matters.
**KEY INDIVIDUALS Christine Fazio** cochairs the environmental practice and is *"excellent in clean air,"* according to sources. Her practice also incorporates brownfields redevelopment, maritime matters and energy law. The *"wonderful"* **Stephen Kass** also cochairs the practice. He is well respected in the industry, and offers expertise across a range of environmental issues, including transactions, permitting and litigation.

### Hodgson Russ LLP

**THE FIRM** This group regularly acts for a broad mix of clients, including municipalities, energy developers, corporations and financing entities. It provides expertise across a range of environment-related issues, and has particular experience advising on the full life cycle of renewable energy projects. Key clients include IDEX, Tonawanda Coke, Tops Markets and Baillie Lumber.
**Sources say:** *"We trust the advice and expertise of Hodgson Russ. It is a firm of integrity and legal acumen."*
**KEY INDIVIDUALS** Rick Kennedy is the practice contact.

## Band 1
## Mainly Transactional

### Cravath, Swaine & Moore LLP
See profile on p.1966

THE FIRM This firm's environmental group is recognized for its expertise in transactions and has a broad range of experience acting for clients in industries such as manufacturing, alternative energy, pharmaceuticals and petroleum. Recently, the team advised Grupo Modelo on the environmental issues related to Anheuser-Busch InBev's $20.1 billion acquisition of the remaining stake in the company. It also acts for IBM, Goldman Sachs and Unilever.

Sources say: *"One of the best firms in the whole world."*

KEY INDIVIDUALS Interviewees appreciate that **Matthew Morreale** (see p.1921) *"gets a great result for his client, and does it in a way that is very effective and genial."* Morreale is a partner in the firm's corporate department, and recently advised Nalco Holding on the environmental aspects of its $8.1 billion merger with Ecolab. **Annmarie Terraciano** (see p.1946) advises on all environmental issues relating to financings, securities offerings and other transactions. She recently advised Ashland on the $3.2 billion acquisition of International Specialty Products, and sources praise her *"business-oriented way of work."*

### Davis Polk & Wardwell LLP
See profile on p.442

THE FIRM This high-quality practice works hard to provide innovative solutions for its clients, and is renowned for its expertise in capital markets, project finance and M&A transactions. The group represented Morgan Stanley and Citi in connection with their role as lead arrangers of a $6.75 billion unsecured facility for power management company Eaton. Other key clients include Murphy Oil, Metalmark Capital and PPL.

Sources say: *"They're very organized and everyone at the firm communicates well with each other."* *"They're excellent."*

KEY INDIVIDUALS The *"wonderful"* **Loyti Cheng** (see p.1884) receives praise from sources, who comment that *"she's great at understanding the risk from both a theoretical and a business perspective."* Cheng recently acted for Taylor Wimpey on the $955 million sale to TMM Holdings of its Canadian and US business. Interviewees state that **Betty Moy Huber** (see p.1905) is *"as good as it gets"* when it comes to environmental transactions, and particularly admire that she is *"incredibly knowledgeable, diligent, responsive and effective."* She has been advising Crestview Partners on $7.3 billion of oil and gas investments. **Hayden Baker** (see p.1875) offers significant expertise in capital markets and M&A transactions. Sources *"truly trust his recommendations"* and highlight him as *"a very bright individual who remains very much informed on industry trends."*

### Simpson Thacher & Bartlett LLP
See profile on p.2006

THE FIRM This sophisticated practice regularly advises the firm's private equity clients on the environmental aspects of transactions, and has extensive experience in the areas of electrical power generation, oil and gas pipelines,

refining, and alternative energy sources. The group recently acted for Eaton on its $11.8 billion acquisition of Cooper Industries. Other key clients include Blackstone, JPMorgan Chase and Centerbridge Partners.

Sources say: *"They do excellent work."*

KEY INDIVIDUALS Sources praise the *"super-effective"* **Adeeb Fadil** (see p.1891) as being *"good at thinking on the fly and constructing concise, clear language."* He represented the underwriters in relation to a $1 billion debt offering by Halliburton. Interviewees agree that **Michael Isby** (see p.1906) has *"enormous experience"* in the area. He recently acted for First Reserve on its acquisition of a 1 GW generation portfolio.

## Band 2
## Mainly Transactional

### Debevoise & Plimpton LLP
See profile on p.1968

THE FIRM The team at Debevoise & Plimpton offers vital support to the firm's corporate group, advising on all the environmental aspects of financings, M&A transactions and securities offerings. In one recent highlight, it represented International Paper in connection with its $4.3 billion acquisition of Texas-based manufacturer Temple-Inland. Other notable clients include Diamond Castle Holdings, Kelso & Company, and Clayton, Dubilier & Rice.

Sources say: *"A fine firm."*

KEY INDIVIDUALS **Stuart Hammer** wins praise: *"He's great to work with, very quick and very responsive."* He was recently part of a team acting for Reynolds Group and Rank Group on more than $15 billion of transactions, including the $6 billion acquisition of Pactiv.

### Sullivan & Cromwell LLP
See profile on p.2011

THE FIRM This high-quality practice has capabilities in all aspects of environmental law, but is especially recognized for its expertise in handling transactional matters for substantial mining, petroleum and chemicals sector clients. One highlight of late saw the group act for biotechnology company Amgen on its acquisition of KAI Pharmaceuticals. The firm also represents Eastman Kodak, BHP Billiton and Bucyrus International.

Sources say: *"An excellent firm."*

KEY INDIVIDUALS **Matthew Brennan** (see p.1880) is widely regarded as *"a fantastic lawyer,"* with sources especially commending his *"combination of substantive skill and deal savvy."* He recently advised United Rentals on its $4.2 billion acquisition of RSC Holdings. **Mark Rosenberg** (see p.1933) offers particular expertise in the area of environmental insurance issues, and has been representing a client involved in personal injury litigation relating to the World Trade Center. Commentators describe him as *"very solid, with many years of experience."*

## Band 3
## Mainly Transactional

### Allen & Overy LLP
See profile on p.433

THE FIRM Allen & Overy's environmental group operates on a truly international level, and is most widely recognized for handling deal-related indemnity disputes and major transactional-related issues. A recent highlight saw the team represent SAP in connection with its purchase of NYSE-listed cloud computing company SuccessFactors for $3.4 billion. Other key clients include Jabil Circuit, Adisseo France SAS and AllianceBernstein.

Sources say: *"Excellent for environmental compliance."*

KEY INDIVIDUALS Head of the firm's environmental law group, **Kenneth Rivlin** is a *"very effective lawyer and negotiator,"* according to sources, who particularly highlight his *"energetic"* and *"proactive"* approach. He is the key contact for major client GE, and helps to manage its transactions on a worldwide scale. The *"extremely knowledgeable"* **Felise Cooper** offers expertise on the law related to product safety and supply chains. She regularly advises clients on the environmental aspects of major transactions.

### Fried, Frank, Harris, Shriver & Jacobson LLP
See profile on p.1975

THE FIRM The environment group at Fried Frank offers expertise in a broad variety of matters, including environmental litigation, project development and land use. It also has an active practice handling the environmental aspects of bankruptcy proceedings and corporate transactions. Recently, it advised SPX on the $1.15 billion disposal of its automotive service business to Robert Bosch.

Sources say: *"They have a talented environmental group."*

KEY INDIVIDUALS **Richard Leland** (see p.1913) is described as *"a really excellent transactional lawyer."* He is an experienced real estate attorney, who specializes in land use and development. **Richard Schwartz** (see p.1938) heads the environmental group and is highly recommended for his skill in sureties. His broad practice also covers bankruptcies, M&A transactions, and private equity.

### O'Melveny & Myers LLP
See profile on p.693

THE FIRM This firm's environmental practice provides deep experience across the spectrum of environmental matters, including litigation and transactions, as well as governmental and regulatory affairs. The team regularly advises clients like Apollo Management, Edison Mission Energy and ExxonMobil. A recent highlight saw the group represent Chromalax in relation to the sale of portfolio company Heat Holding to Sentinel Capital Partners.

Sources say: *"They're very responsive and very knowledgeable, and they get us good results."*

KEY INDIVIDUALS Environmental department head **Eric Rothenberg** is popular among interviewees, who admire his *"enormous depth of knowledge,"* and highlight that he *"knows Superfund work well."*

## Shearman & Sterling LLP
See profile on p.2005

**THE FIRM** The environmental group at this international firm is highly recommended for its work advising corporate clients on transactional issues. It also provides counseling on carbon emissions and carbon trading. The group recently advised Ardagh Group on the environmental aspects of its $881 million purchase of Anchor Glass Container from Wayzata Investment Partners. Other clients include Deere & Company, Dow Chemical and the United States Department of Energy.
**Sources say:** *"They have a great national practice."*
**KEY INDIVIDUALS** The *"excellent"* **Jason Pratt** offers a wealth of expertise, counseling individuals, financial institutions and companies on the impact of environmental regulations and laws on commercial transactions. Department head **Jeffrey Salinger** is praised by sources, who appreciate that he *"has clear vision and good judgment."* He recently represented BE Aerospace in its $400 million acquisition of UFC Aerospace.

## White & Case LLP
See profile on p.451

**THE FIRM** The environmental group at White & Case makes use of the firm's global platform in order to advise international clients on cross-border matters. It represents clients in a range of industries, including mining, pharmaceuticals, electronics and aviation. The group provides a range of environmental services, including transactional due diligence, compliance and regulatory advice.
**Sources say:** *"A very fine firm."*
**KEY INDIVIDUALS** The *"very strong"* **Paul Milmed** (see p.1920) focuses on representing lenders and principals, providing advice on the environmental aspects of financial and corporate transactions, on a national and international level. Interviewees enjoy working with **Richard Horsch** (see p.1905), and describe him as *"a feisty, vibrant guy."* He

offers a wealth of experience representing clients in toxic tort litigation, as well as Superfund cost recovery actions.

## Other Notable Practitioners

**Stephen Gordon** (see p.1898) of Beveridge & Diamond PC is noted for his work on power plants, and recently advised Bayonne Energy Center on the permitting required for construction of a submarine electric transmission system between New York and New Jersey. Former EPA regional administrator **Charles Warren** (see p.1949) is chair of the environmental group at Kramer Levin Naftalis & Frankel LLP. He advises clients on issues arising under many key statutes, including the Clean Water, Clean Air and Toxic Substances Control Acts. Formerly of Latham & Watkins, **Matthew Ahrens** (see p.1872) is now at Milbank, Tweed, Hadley & McCloy LLP and acts for clients on a variety of environmental issues. He has notable experience in resolving matters related to M&A and corporate restructurings. Sources like **Robert Alessi** (see p.1872) of DLA Piper LLP (US), who they describe as *"outstanding – shrewd, politically astute, a great thinker in terms of strategy, and easy to work with."* Formerly of Dewey & LeBouef, Alessi now heads the environmental group at DLA. Recently, he has been representing Central New York Oil and Gas Company in litigation relating to the MARC I Hub Line Project. **Kathy Robb** (see p.1931) of Hunton & Williams LLP is noted for her skill and prominence in water law. She represents investors, water districts and developers in contentious, transactional and advisory matters. **Doreen Simmons** of Hancock Estabrook LLP is *"highly responsive, proactive, engaged and dedicated to achieving results."* She is an expert in environmental permitting, and also has substantial experience in Marcellus Shale oil and gas. **Donald Stever** (see p.1944) of K&L Gates is recognized as *"a very strong practitioner"* in the New York market. He is a skilled litigator who offers expertise in complex regulatory matters. **Kerri Folb** (see p.1893) of Kramer Levin

Naftalis & Frankel LLP is celebrated for her *"thoughtful analysis, responsiveness, and ability to help quantify and assess risks."* The *"terrific"* **Maureen Crough** (see p.1887) of Sidley Austin LLP is described by interviewees as *"a very strong environmental attorney; she's very innovative, and also very creative in evaluating issues and helping to find solutions."* **Gail Suchman** of Stroock & Stroock & Lavan LLP has more than 25 years of experience in the field. Her broad practice covers environmental litigation, compliance, permitting and transactional due diligence. The *"very intelligent"* **Jeffrey Smith** (see p.1942) of Crowell & Moring LLP earns effusive praise from interviewees: *"He's very strategic, he understands all the moving parts in a transaction, and how the environmental issues and risks need to be integrated into the transaction."* **David Freeman** (see p.1894) of Gibbons P.C. focuses on handling environmental due diligence and toxic exposure litigation. He is also experienced in representing the sellers, developers and buyers of brownfields sites. **Gail Port** heads the environmental group at Proskauer Rose LLP. Clients appreciate that she *"is efficient and understands our business needs."* **Robert Kafin**, also of Proskauer Rose LLP, is *"very well known and very respected"* in the industry. He spends much of his time advising nonprofit environmental organizations. Interviewees praise **Gregory Battista** (see p.1876) of Cahill Gordon & Reindel LLP, noting he is *"a very thoughtful and very effective guy."* Formerly a partner at Cravath, he joined Cahill in 2012 after working in-house at LRN. **James Pardo** (see p.1926) of McDermott Will & Emery LLP is described as *"a very strong writer, detail oriented but also strategic, and able to see the big picture."* Sources highlight that *"his advice is always cogent, practical and useful."* Interviewees highlight that the *"very experienced"* **Peter Sacripanti** (see p.1935), also of McDermott Will & Emery LLP, is *"very much focused on getting the best result"* for his client. He has extensive experience representing large corporations in mass tort, class action and product liability litigation.

# HEALTHCARE

Healthcare p.1811

Commentary about individuals can be found under their firm's paragraph. If the firm has no paragraph (is not ranked) look at Other Notable Practitioners.

## Band 1

## Epstein Becker & Green PC
See profile on p.1972

**THE FIRM** Epstein's preeminent healthcare and life sciences practice is noted for its depth in a wide range of matters, including regulatory compliance, contracting, joint ventures and litigation. The group wins particular acclaim for its work involving healthcare providers and payors, as well as major names in the life sciences arena. Its enviable client list includes Millennium Pharmaceuticals, Daiichi Sankyo, Montefiore Medical Center and Triple S Management.
**Sources say:** *"The firm has been around for a long time and has a very solid healthcare practice."*
**KEY INDIVIDUALS** Firm cofounder **Jeffrey Becker** is highlighted by sources for being *"very creative and ridicu-*

*lously smart."* He is known for his broad-ranging practice encompassing transactional and regulatory work, and for taking leading roles on behalf of the some of the group's most significant clients, including the Mount Sinai Medical Center and Gold Health Strategies. **Wendy Goldstein** (see p.1898) chairs the firm's pharmaceutical industry health regulatory practice group. As such, she is renowned for her expertise in pharmaceutical and life science issues. One peer said: *"She is a superstar in the pharmaceutical area and I would love to have her at my firm, she is that good."*

## Manatt Phelps & Phillips LLP
See profile on p.690

**THE FIRM** Manatt Phelps takes a leading position in the rankings this year due to tremendous market recognition of its expertise in healthcare IT and reform work on behalf

of clients such as Montefiore Medical Center, Health Plus and Memorial Sloan-Kettering Cancer Center. The group is also credited for the unique advantage offered by its dedicated Manatt Health Solutions team, a department combining a range of policy, operational, regulatory and strategic counsel for clients.
**Sources say:** *"The practice is very active in healthcare IT matters around the country." "It is very in touch with the latest healthcare issues and has an incredible depth of expertise."*
**KEY INDIVIDUALS William Bernstein** chairs the firm's healthcare practice group. He is especially recommended for his expertise in healthcare reform issues, and *"has been a player in healthcare law for many years."* Sources go on to praise him as *"highly professional, articulate, accessible and personable."* The immensely experienced **Robert Belfort** has in-depth expertise in transactional healthcare and regulatory compliance matters, covering the areas of fraud

## Healthcare

### Leading Firms

**Band 1**
Epstein Becker & Green PC *
Manatt Phelps & Phillips LLP *
Proskauer Rose LLP *
Ropes & Gray LLP *

**Band 2**
Arent Fox LLP *
Greenberg Traurig, LLP *
Mintz Levin Cohn Ferris Glovsky and Popeo PC *
Nixon Peabody LLP *

**Band 3**
Cadwalader, Wickersham & Taft LLP *
Garfunkel Wild P.C.
Hodgson Russ LLP
Hogan Lovells US LLP
Katten Muchin Rosenman LLP *

and abuse, HIPAA and privacy, and managed care work. Sources describe him as *"extremely knowledgeable, encyclopedic, very careful at detailed work and a really good attorney."* **James Lytle** (see p.1916) is lauded in particular as *"a very good regulatory healthcare attorney."* He heads the firm's Albany office as well as its New York state legislative lobbying and regulatory practice group. The up-and-coming **Melinda Dutton** plays a lead role in the Manatt Health Solutions team. She has a solid healthcare practice advising clients on general business, regulatory and policy issues. Sources say she is *"fabulous to work with, very responsive, and has an incredible depth of expertise."* Similarly highlighted as a future star of the sector, **Helen Pfister** (see p.1927) also counsels her clients on a range of regulatory, policy and general business matters.

### Proskauer Rose LLP
See profile on p.2001

**THE FIRM** Proskauer's outstanding healthcare practice has all-encompassing expertise and depth, and includes reimbursement, fraud and abuse, transactions and financing, and regulatory and compliance work. Clients include AthenaHealth, Ascension Health Care Network and Catholic Health Services of Long Island. In recent highlights, the group represented Richmond University Medical Center in the establishment of a clinical affiliation with Mount Sinai Medical Center, and in the discontinuation of its joint venture in the Heart Institute.
**Sources say:** *"The practice has an exceptionally deep understanding of healthcare law in New York."*
**KEY INDIVIDUALS Edward Kornreich** wins tremendous client acclaim, with many describing him as a *"very responsive"* attorney and *"a seasoned practitioner with a top-notch healthcare practice."* His recent work includes representing Beth Israel Medical Center in an investigation by the US Attorney for the Southern District of New York. **Richard Zall** chairs the firm's healthcare group, and maintains an excellent practice covering a range of regulatory and transactional issues. He is *"extremely easy to work with,"* say sources; *"exceptionally bright, very well connected, resourceful and generally a great guy."*

### Ropes & Gray LLP
See profile on p.1528

**THE FIRM** This firm's exceptional New York team is highlighted for its deep bench and versatility in the healthcare arena. The group has a strong and longstanding line in representing major healthcare providers, community hospitals and academic medical centers, as well as pharmaceutical, medical device and biotech companies. Its recent highlights include assisting North Shore Long Island Jewish Health System in numerous healthcare concerns, including in relation to DOJ investigations and transactional issues.
**Sources say:** *"They master a broad scope of knowledge and are completely accessible."*
**KEY INDIVIDUALS** Sources are immensely impressed by the leading **Stephen Warnke**: *"He is absolutely the best! He's terrific, very precise and exact, and clear – he leaves no stone unturned."* His wide-ranging practice is particularly commended in the areas of regulatory compliance, healthcare reform, and Medicare and Medicaid reimbursement.

## Band 2

### Arent Fox LLP
See profile on p.905

**THE FIRM** Arent Fox's New York-based healthcare group forms an integral part of the firm's increasingly recognized national practice. Its sizable team undertakes all manner of regulatory, compliance, investigation, transactional and litigious assignments on behalf of a broad and enviable list of clients, including Maxim Healthcare Services, Fundamental Long Term Care and the Visiting Nurse Association of Long Island.
**Sources say:** *"I'm impressed with the team's responsiveness, reliability, accessibility, professionalism and quality of work product."*
**KEY INDIVIDUALS** The tremendously experienced **Connie Raffa** (see p.1929) is the founding member of the firm's healthcare group in New York. Interviewees describe her as *"very adept at understanding the scope of the problem, and designing and revising strategies to address issues."* She wins accolades across a number of areas, including Medicare and hospice and palliative care. The *"very talented"* **Michael Blass** (see p.1879) has a solid practice handling general business transactions, corporate matters and regulatory issues in the healthcare space. He is a go-to adviser for many of the firm's most significant healthcare clients, including Maxim Healthcare Services, who he advises on a range of corporate, finance and regulatory matters. **Rachel Hold-Weiss** (see p.1904) enters the rankings this year on the back of excellent support of her status as a future star of the sector. According to sources, she is *"very smart and knows how the system works."*

### Greenberg Traurig, LLP
See profile on p.1024

**THE FIRM** Greenberg Traurig's superb healthcare practice group counsels clients across a range of transactional and regulatory issues, and brings a particular advantage to the table in the form of its government affairs and legislative

### Senior Statesmen

**Senior Statesmen:** distinguished older practitioners

| | |
|---|---|
| Nadel Peter F | *Katten Muchin Rosenman LLP* |

### Leading Individuals

**Band 1**

| | |
|---|---|
| Becker Jeffrey H | *Epstein Becker & Green PC* |
| Bernstein William S | *Manatt Phelps & Phillips LLP* |
| Iselin Harold N | *Greenberg Traurig, LLP* * |
| Kornreich Edward S | *Proskauer Rose LLP* |
| Millock Peter J | *Nixon Peabody LLP* * |
| Schneider Jeffrey G | *Hogan Lovells US LLP* |
| Warnke Stephen A | *Ropes & Gray LLP* |
| Wild Robert Andrew | *Garfunkel Wild P.C.* |
| Zall Richard J | *Proskauer Rose LLP* |

**Band 2**

| | |
|---|---|
| Belfort Robert D | *Manatt Phelps & Phillips LLP* |
| Fabian James | *Nixon Peabody LLP* * |
| Goldstein Wendy C | *Epstein Becker & Green PC* * |
| Ivill David S | *McDermott Will & Emery LLP (ONP)† * |
| Platton Brian J. | *Mintz Levin Cohn Ferris Glovsky* * |
| Raffa Connie A | *Arent Fox LLP* * |
| Robfogel Susan S | *Nixon Peabody LLP* * |
| Roth Andrew B | *Mintz Levin Cohn Ferris Glovsky* * |
| Serbaroli Francis J | *Greenberg Traurig, LLP* * |
| Weissman Ellen V. | *Hodgson Russ LLP* |
| Willey Joseph | *Katten Muchin Rosenman LLP* |

**Band 3**

| | |
|---|---|
| Blass Michael S | *Arent Fox LLP* * |
| Greene Robert M | *Phillips Lytle LLP (ONP)† * |
| Luband Charles | *Dentons (ONP)† * |
| Lytle James W | *Manatt Phelps & Phillips LLP* * |
| Masucci Michele | *Nixon Peabody LLP* * |
| McGovern Brian | *Cadwalader, Wickersham & Taft LLP* * |
| Mourning Paul W. | *Cadwalader, Wickersham & Taft LLP* * |
| Ruggiero Jeffrey | *Arnold & Porter LLP (ONP)† * |
| Schnell Paul | *Skadden, Arps, Slate, Meagher (ONP)† * |

**Band 4**

| | |
|---|---|
| Hodes Joel | *Whiteman Osterman & Hanna (ONP)†* |
| Iseman Robert H | *Iseman Cunningham Riester (ONP)†* |
| Thrope Jeff | *Foley & Lardner LLP (ONP)†* |

**Up-and-coming individuals**

| | |
|---|---|
| Dutton Melinda J. | *Manatt Phelps & Phillips LLP* |
| Egan Peter | *Nixon Peabody LLP* * |
| Hills Bethany J. | *Hodgson Russ LLP* |
| Hold-Weiss Rachel | *Arent Fox LLP* * |
| Pfister Helen R | *Manatt Phelps & Phillips LLP* * |

\* *Indicates firm / individual with profile.*
† *ONP = Other Notable Practitioner.*

lobbying strength. In recent highlights, the group provided regulatory advice to Amerigroup on its purchase of Health Plus, one of the largest Medicaid managed care companies in New York. Other major clients include MVP HealthCare, UnitedHealthcare, Affinity Health Plan and Jewish Home Lifecare.
**Sources say:** *"The team does a lot of work in the New York healthcare market, and offers its clients a complete package, including counseling, advice and litigation."*

**KEY INDIVIDUALS** The *"collaborative and results-oriented"* **Harold Iselin** (see p.1906) is managing partner of the firm's Albany office. A preeminent practitioner in the healthcare arena and a former DOJ trial attorney, he wins particular acclaim for his expertise in healthcare plans and reimbursement, and undertakes a range of governmental affairs and regulatory issues, among other matters. The tremendously experienced **Francis Serbaroli** (see p.1939) has a respected and broad-ranging healthcare practice. His highlights include recently representing EmblemHealth in a significant contract negotiation with ExpressScripts in relation to the outsourcing of prescriptions for the former's members.

## Mintz Levin Cohn Ferris Glovsky and Popeo PC
See profile on p.1523

**THE FIRM** Mintz Levin's increasingly recognized New York healthcare group forms a key part of the firm's superb East Coast practice. The team is praised for its depth across a range of transactional and regulatory matters, including litigation and healthcare IT issues. Particular areas of expertise also include cross-border assignments and physician residency programs. Key clients include HealthpointCapital, Fidelis Care New York, the Wartburg Adult Care Community and North Shore-Long Island Jewish Health System.

**Sources say:** *"The practice has very good people with a deep knowledge of the New York healthcare environment, as well as with deep expertise in M&A work."*

**KEY INDIVIDUALS** **Brian Platton** (see p.1928) is lauded as *"knowledgeable, thorough, thoughtful"* and *"highly collaborative."* Clients praise not just his in-depth healthcare expertise but also his capabilities in M&A work. Backed by more than 30 years' experience in the field, **Andrew Roth** (see p.1933) has all-encompassing healthcare expertise. Clients appreciate that *"he is always available"* for them, and *"provides great-quality work."*

## Nixon Peabody LLP
See profile on p.1526

**THE FIRM** Nixon Peabody maintains a sterling, deep and broad-based healthcare practice group in New York. The team handles all manner of corporate, regulatory, reimbursement, medical staff and compliance issues, among other types of matter. Its clientele includes a range of healthcare providers, integrated delivery systems, pharmaceutical companies and physicians groups.

**Sources say:** *"The team has excellent communication skills, knowledge, adaptability to client needs and great contacts in peer institutions."*

**KEY INDIVIDUALS** **Peter Millock** (see p.1919) is considered a go-to attorney in regulatory and policy issues in the healthcare space. He is tremendously experienced in the field, and has in the past served as general counsel at the New York State Department of Health. The *"very talented"* **Susan Robfogel** (see p.393), chair of the firm's life sciences practice group, occupies a strong niche in handling complex labor and employment matters involving the healthcare and life science sectors. **James Fabian** (see p.1891) is *"very purposeful, logical and a good strategist,"* say sources.

Backed by more than 30 years of experience, he has a strong practice acting on behalf of healthcare providers, academic medical centers and teaching hospitals, among others. **Michele Masucci** (see p.1917) leads the firm's health services practice group. She is an expert in acting for healthcare providers, particularly in relation to reform legislation, regulatory issues and M&A-related compliance matters. Sources also highlight her excellence with physician issues. A new entry in this year's rankings, **Peter Egan** (see p.1890) comes highly recommended as a future star of the sector. *"He is an excellent attorney,"* say sources; *"well versed in all aspects of healthcare law, state and federal regulations, business law and contract negotiation."*

## Band 3

### Cadwalader, Wickersham & Taft LLP
See profile on p.438

**THE FIRM** Cadwalader's established New York team offers a broad array of healthcare advice, and is particularly highlighted for its in-depth expertise in issues relating to long-term care. As such, it is considered a go-to group for the likes of Leading Age Care, who the team regularly advises across a range of regulatory, policy, tax and corporate issues, among other types of matter. Other notable representations include its enviable role as general corporate counsel to CenterLight Health System.

**Sources say:** *"The team is formed by consummate professionals who are a pleasure to deal with."*

**KEY INDIVIDUALS** **Brian McGovern** (see p.1918) is highly active in enforcement and regulatory issues, and is highlighted in particular for his expertise in compliance issues relating to long-term care. He recently represented Brownsville Multi-Service Family Health Center in issues concerning an audit and administrative hearing relating to alleged Medicaid overpayments. **Paul Mourning** (see p.1921) continues to garner acclaim for his corporate governance and transactional expertise, particularly on behalf of nonprofit organizations and long-term care providers. He has played a lead role in the group's activities on behalf of CenterLight.

### Garfunkel Wild P.C.

**THE FIRM** This highly respected and longstanding healthcare boutique firm is noted for its representation of a major proportion of the state's most significant healthcare providers. The group undertakes a full array of issues for its clients, ranging from regulatory counsel to corporate transactions.

**Sources say:** *"An enormous breadth of practice."*

**KEY INDIVIDUALS** Firm founder and chairman **Robert Wild** is renowned for his all-encompassing expertise in representing hospitals in New York state. One peer notes: *"He is fantastic! I have the highest respect for him!"*

### Hodgson Russ LLP

**THE FIRM** Hodgson Russ is known for the breadth of the excellent work it undertakes on behalf of healthcare clients, including healthcare and long-term care providers,

academic medial centers, hospitals and pharmaceutical companies. In recent highlights, the group represented Kaleida Health, in an appeal against two Medicaid reimbursement-related issues.

**Sources say:** *"The practice offers responsiveness and a great depth of resources."*

**KEY INDIVIDUALS** **Ellen Weissman** leads the firm's healthcare practice group, and was recently appointed chair of the Health Law Section of the New York State Bar Association. As such, she is an esteemed figure in the sector, particularly in relation to regulatory and reimbursement issues, with many describing her as *"very bright and very persistent"* as well as *"extremely personable."* The up-and-coming **Bethany Hills** has a practice covering a wide range of healthcare reimbursement and regulatory compliance issues.

### Hogan Lovells US LLP

**THE FIRM** Hogan Lovells is able to provide in-depth and wide-ranging healthcare advice thanks to the firm's extensive reach and resources. The team in New York represents all manner of healthcare, medical device and pharmaceutical entities. Key clients include the State University of New York, Jefferson Regional Medical Center and the American Board of Neurological Surgery.

**Sources say:** *"The practice has deep expertise in a variety of complex healthcare matters."*

**KEY INDIVIDUALS** The preeminent **Jeffrey Schneider** is *"an absolute pleasure to work with,"* say clients; *"he is extremely responsive and knowledgeable."* Peers also praise him as one of the most talented healthcare attorneys in the state across a range of transactional and regulatory matters.

### Katten Muchin Rosenman LLP
See profile on p.1253

**THE FIRM** Katten Muchin's small but highly effective New York healthcare team handles an array of regulatory, transactional and reimbursement matters, and is highlighted in particular for its excellence in litigation assignments. Its clients include the New York City Health & Hospitals Corporation, Greater New York Hospital Association and Catholic Health Services of Long Island.

**Sources say:** *"The group is very knowledgeable."*

**KEY INDIVIDUALS** Of counsel **Peter Nadel** is a highly respected and experienced authority in the sector. He focuses on healthcare matters, undertaking litigation, transactional and regulatory work on behalf of healthcare providers. With more than 30 years of experience in the healthcare sector, **Joseph Willey** comes recommended as an excellent choice for Medicare and Medicaid reimbursement work. One client mentioned that *"he is a good litigator, and also a very pleasant person to deal with."*

## Other Notable Practitioners

**David Ivill** (see p.1906) is partner-in-charge of the New York healthcare practice group at McDermott Will & Emery LLP. He takes the lead in a significant proportion of the firm's healthcare matters, and is a regular adviser to clients like TeamHealth. The *"very smart"* **Robert Iseman** of Iseman Cunningham Riester & Hyde LLP is an immensely experienced healthcare attorney, with more than 35 years of experience in the sector. He has a broad-ranging practice acting on behalf of insurers and healthcare providers. **Charles Luband** (see p.1915) joined the healthcare group at Dentons from Ropes & Gray in January 2012. He is best known for his Medicaid reimbursement expertise. His recent highlights include representing the University of North Carolina Health Care System in relation to Medicaid supplemental payment issues. **Joel Hodes** is a founding partner of Whiteman Osterman & Hanna LLP. With a strong and wide-ranging healthcare practice, he enters this year's rankings on the back of tremendous client praise. *"He is thoughtful and considerate in all issues, a good listener and assesses things well,"* say sources. **Jeffrey Ruggiero** (see p.1934) is a partner in the firm's FDA and healthcare practice group of Arnold & Porter LLP. He continues to receive acclaim as an *"effective and direct communicator, a good strategic thinker, and a good resource in helping to resolve issues and develop effective solutions."* **Paul Schnell** (see p.1937) of Skadden, Arps, Slate, Meagher & Flom LLP & Affiliates has a broad-based transactional practice encompassing corporate, M&A, private equity and healthcare matters. He is renowned as *"a great transactional lawyer who does really big deals."* **Robert Greene** (see p.1899) of Phillips Lytle LLP is known for his tremendous experience across a wide variety of healthcare law matters, including corporate governance, regulatory and reimbursement issues. **Jeff Thrope** of Foley & Lardner LLP is highlighted by sources as a *"very smart regulatory guy"* and an expert in range of healthcare issues on behalf of providers. His key clients include Medisys Health Network and Nassau Health Care.

# IMMIGRATION

Commentary about individuals can be found under their firm's paragraph. If the firm has no paragraph (is not ranked) look at Other Notable Practitioners.

| Immigration |
| :--- |
| **Leading Firms** |
| **Band 1** |
| Fragomen, Del Rey, Bernsen & Loewy, LLP * |
| Kramer Levin Naftalis & Frankel LLP * |
| **Band 2** |
| Cyrus D Mehta & Associates PLLC |
| Proskauer Rose LLP * |
| Satterlee Stephens Burke & Burke LLP |
| **Band 3** |
| Barst Mukamal & Kleiner LLP |
| Gibney, Anthony & Flaherty LLP |
| Harter, Secrest & Emery LLP * |
| Laura Devine Attorneys LLC |
| Miller Mayer LLP |
| Wormser, Kiely, Galef & Jacobs LLP |
| * Indicates firm with profile. |
| *Alphabetical order within each band. Band 1 is the highest.* |

## Band 1

### Fragomen, Del Rey, Bernsen & Loewy, LLP
See profile on p.1974

**THE FIRM** This highly esteemed international immigration boutique is perfectly structured to handle the immigration requirements of entities of all sizes. The team handles inbound and outbound immigration matters, and frequently provides assistance to clients looking to develop their own immigration policies. The firm's global footprint ensures that it is able to provide a seamless service to the highest-profile multinational companies.
**Sources say:** *"Being a large international law firm provides it with a lot of resources, connections and leverage for all of its clients."*
**KEY INDIVIDUALS Michael Patrick** *"stands out"* as an immigration practitioner with a wealth of experience. He has particular expertise in helping clients to develop immigration policies, I-9 compliance and corporate restructuring immigration due diligence. **Austin Fragomen** is *"one of the deans"* of immigration law and a founding partner of

the firm. He continues to be highly respected in the field and involved in the immigration law community.

### Kramer Levin Naftalis & Frankel LLP
See profile on p.1987

**THE FIRM** This firm's business immigration group continues to garner an excellent reputation in the field. The group handles a variety of immigration matters including immigrant and nonimmigrant visas, permanent residency cases, compliance and the immigration-related elements of corporate transactions. An impressive client roster includes Santander, HBO and Louis Vuitton.
**Sources say:** *"A very, very fine firm."*
**KEY INDIVIDUALS Theodore Ruthizer** (see p.1934) *"really knows his stuff"* according to sources. He is a long-standing and well-respected practitioner in the field, and an expert in business immigration matters. **Mark Koestler** (see p.1910) is described as *"a very bright guy"* by market observers. He advises individuals and organizations from a wide range of industry sectors, including banking, advertising, entertainment, luxury goods, e-commerce and insurance. **Matthew Dunn** (see p.1889) continues to impress commentators. He assists a variety of clients and has particularly strong expertise in healthcare, hospitality, banking and advertising.

## Band 2

### Cyrus D Mehta & Associates PLLC
**THE FIRM** The attorneys at this boutique immigration and nationality firm provide services across a broad spectrum of business and family-related immigration matters, including labor certifications, citizenship, removal defense and related litigation. The firm's clients range from individuals to Fortune 500 companies, and come from a variety of sectors, including IT, education, finance and professional services.

**Sources say:** *"An excellent firm. They are experts in the field and are of the highest integrity. They deliver results that are both accurate and timely, and are a pleasure to deal with."*
**KEY INDIVIDUALS Cyrus Mehta** is described by commentators as *"a genius"* and *"one of the premier experts in this field,"* who *"gives personal attention and is available and willing at all times."* He has experience in many areas, including business, employment and family-related immigration, naturalization and asylum. Clients appreciate **Cora-Ann Pestaina** for being *"easy to deal with"* and note that she *"distinguishes herself with thorough expertise in immigration matters."* She focuses her practice on business immigration.

### Proskauer Rose LLP
See profile on p.2001

**THE FIRM** The Proskauer Rose immigration and nationality group provides a full range of business immigration services to clients, including the hiring and transfer of personnel, compliance, investment and corporate immigration policy. The firm acts as sole US immigration counsel to clients of the caliber of The New York Times Company and Willis North America.
**KEY INDIVIDUALS David Grunblatt** is a *"very smart, careful and thoughtful immigration lawyer,"* observers note. He has experience in a complete set of immigration matters, and has particular expertise in advising clients on I-9 compliance and the immigration ramifications of corporate transactions.

### Satterlee Stephens Burke & Burke LLP
**THE FIRM** The immigration and nationality group at this firm continues to maintain its solid reputation in New York state. The team advises both US and international companies with their visa, citizenship and compliance matters. The firm's clients are drawn from a range of industry sectors, including manufacturing, fashion and design, and entertainment.
**KEY INDIVIDUALS Ted Chiappari** focuses on business immigration and is noted for his expertise in the tax impli-

## Immigration
### Leading Individuals

#### Band 1
| | |
|---|---|
| Grunblatt David | Proskauer Rose LLP |
| Mehta Cyrus D | Cyrus D Mehta & Associates PLLC |
| Patrick Michael D | Fragomen, Del Rey, Bernsen & Loewy, LLP |
| Ruthizer Theodore | Kramer Levin Naftalis & Frankel LLP * |
| Yale-Loehr Stephen W | Miller Mayer LLP |

#### Band 2
| | |
|---|---|
| Axelrad Alexis S | Barst Mukamal & Kleiner LLP |
| Catillaz Margaret A | Harter, Secrest & Emery LLP |
| Chiappari Ted | Satterlee Stephens Burke & Burke LLP |
| David Cheryl | The Law Office of Cheryl R. David (ONP)† |
| Fragomen Jr Austin T | Fragomen, Del Rey, Bernsen & Loewy, LLP |
| Koestler Mark D | Kramer Levin Naftalis & Frankel LLP * |
| Maltby Stephen J O | Gibney, Anthony & Flaherty LLP * |
| Morell Avram E | Pryor Cashman LLP (ONP)† |
| Moseley Thomas | The Law Offices of Thomas Moseley (ONP)† |
| Notkin Deborah | Barst Mukamal & Kleiner LLP |
| Seltzer Suzanne | Klasko Rulon Stock & Seltzer (ONP)† |

#### Band 3
| | |
|---|---|
| Berger Frances C. | Masliah & Soloway, PC (ONP)† |
| Carpentier Joan-Elisse | McDermott Will & Emery LLP (ONP)† * |
| D'Avolio Lisa | Skadden, Arps, Slate, Meagher (ONP)† * |
| Dunn Matthew S | Kramer Levin Naftalis & Frankel LLP * |
| Groban Jr Robert S | Epstein Becker & Green PC (ONP)† * |
| Kleiner Philip J | Barst Mukamal & Kleiner LLP |
| Levine Roxanne | Tarter Krinsky & Drogin LLP (ONP)† |
| Masliah Noemi | Masliah & Soloway, PC (ONP)† |
| Novak Frank A | Harter, Secrest & Emery LLP |
| Reich William Z | Serotte, Reich & Wilson LLP (ONP)† |
| Tonello Anastasia | Laura Devine Attorneys LLC |
| Wolfson Donald | Wormser, Kiely, Galef & Jacobs LLP |

#### Up-and-coming individuals
| | |
|---|---|
| Kalmykov Kate | Greenberg Traurig, LLP (ONP)† * |
| Koerner Andrew | Tarter Krinsky & Drogin LLP (ONP)† |

#### Associates to watch
| | |
|---|---|
| Koski Ceridwen | Laura Devine Attorneys LLC |
| Pestaina Cora-Ann V. | Cyrus D Mehta & Associates PLLC |

* Indicates individual with profile.
† ONP = Other Notable Practitioner.

cations of personnel transfers. Sources note that he is *"well regarded"* and *"recognized in the field."*

## Band 3

### Barst Mukamal & Kleiner LLP
**THE FIRM** This boutique firm provides a full range of immigration law services such as labor certification, visas, residency, enforcement and EB-5 investment. The team's expertise is sought by clients from a variety of industries, including entertainment, retail and manufacturing.
**Sources say:** *"Excellent."* *"An old-time immigration boutique firm."*
**KEY INDIVIDUALS Deborah Notkin** is a *"very bright woman who writes extensively and insightfully,"* say sources. She is particularly well known for her work on PERM mat-

ters. **Alexis Axelrad** is known as *"one of the stalwarts in the New York immigration Bar."* She practices in both business and family-related immigration law. **Philip Kleiner** focuses his practice on corporate immigration matters. He advises his clients on hiring foreign workers and planning corporate immigration policies.

### Gibney, Anthony & Flaherty LLP
**THE FIRM** This firm's respected immigration practice continues to represent many different clients from entrepreneurs and new startups to multinational companies. The team focuses primarily on employment-based immigration law and employer compliance, and has a growing presence in the e-commerce arena.
**KEY INDIVIDUALS** The *"excellent"* **Stephen Maltby** (see p.1916) heads the firm's immigration practice group. He concentrates on assisting clients to develop corporate immigration strategies, and advising employers on compliance matters.

### Harter, Secrest & Emery LLP
**See profile on p.1979**
**THE FIRM** Clients continue to be impressed by the business immigration services provided by this Rochester-based firm. Recent successes include the achievement of a landmark decision in the Second Circuit Court of Appeals in relation to foreign professionals obtaining licenses. The firm's clients include Talisman Energy, Carestream Health and Kodak.
**Sources say:** *"We consider them true partners."*
**KEY INDIVIDUALS Margaret Catillaz** is an established practitioner who clients say *"has an ability to distill information in a very user-friendly way."* She is recommended for her sound advice on the transfer of foreign nationals for work or studies, employer compliance and the immigration consequences of corporate transactions. The *"fantastic"* **Frank Novak** is appreciated by clients for being *"very responsive."* He has notable experience in the representation of clients in the healthcare, education and biotechnology industries.

### Laura Devine Attorneys LLC
**THE FIRM** Laura Devine Attorneys is highly regarded among peers and clients alike. The firm practices in both US and UK immigration and nationality law. Recent highlights include a number of impressive extraordinary ability cases in business and in the arts. Clients include high net worth individuals, entrepreneurs and multinational corporate entities.
**Sources say:** *"Extremely professional and absolute experts in their field."*
**KEY INDIVIDUALS** Clients value managing partner **Anastasia Tonello**'s creative approach and her commercial awareness, with one interviewee noting that she is *"very quick to attend to our matters."* She is dual-qualified in the USA and the UK, and is frequently called upon to provide advice on outbound and global immigration matters. **Ceridwen Koski** is admired for her responsiveness and for her *"complete professionalism, and her calm and accurate manner."* Koski advises individuals, investors, startup com-

panies and corporations in compliance matters and immigrant and nonimmigrant visa needs.

### Miller Mayer LLP
**THE FIRM** This Ithaca-based firm offers a full array of immigration services to individuals, students, investors, small businesses and large corporations. The team has earned an excellent reputation for investor category visas, and for representing clients in the healthcare and education sectors.
**KEY INDIVIDUALS Stephen Yale-Loehr** is *"one of the deans on the EB-5 investor visa program and a leading practitioner in that area,"* according to one impressed interviewee. His formidable academic credentials augment a respected advisory practice.

### Wormser, Kiely, Galef & Jacobs LLP
**THE FIRM** This well-established immigration practice group offers a wide variety of services to individuals and corporate clients, including citizenship and family-based immigration. The team offers advice to clients from a plethora of industry sectors, including media, financial services and manufacturing.
**KEY INDIVIDUALS Donald Wolfson** is a *"smart fellow"* and *"a prestigious lawyer"* according to commentators. Wolfson is a former trial attorney, and currently heads the firm's immigration group.

### Other Notable Practitioners

The *"wonderful"* **Suzanne Seltzer** of Klasko Rulon Stock & Seltzer is well known for her representation of clients in the healthcare sector and academia. She has particular expertise in dealing with complex national waiver and extraordinary ability visa issues. **Frances Berger** of Masliah & Soloway, PC is very well respected in the immigration law community. She focuses on employment-based work but her expertise extends to family-based immigration and naturalization matters. **Joan-Elisse Carpentier** (see p.1882) of McDermott Will & Emery LLP is *"absolutely fabulous; creative, reliable and approachable"* according to sources. She handles immigrant, nonimmigrant and nationality matters for corporate clients in an assortment of industries, including finance, banking, entertainment and pharmaceuticals. **Robert Groban** (see p.1900) of Epstein Becker & Green PC has a wealth of experience in assisting corporate clients in their recruitment of foreign nationals. He is also noted for the quality of his compliance counseling and for his advice on the immigration implications of corporate transactions. **Kate Kalmykov** (see p.1907) of Greenberg Traurig, LLP is appreciated by clients for being *"very detailed, extremely responsive, very thorough and extremely attentive."* She focuses on business immigration and is prominent in the field of EB-5 investor categories. She has recently worked with New Jersey Liberty Regional Center and Extell New York Regional Center. The *"fantastic"* **Cheryl David** of The Law Office of Cheryl R. David is well regarded in the field for her prowess in the area of detention, enforcement and removals. Additionally, she practices in business immigration law matters.

Thomas Moseley of The Law Offices of Thomas Moseley is "*probably the brightest immigration lawyer on the planet,*" according to one observer. His advice and assistance is highly sought after, especially in the areas of removal defense and federal court immigration litigation. Sources describe **Lisa D'Avolio** (see p.1887) of Skadden, Arps, Slate, Meagher & Flom LLP & Affiliates as "*dedicated, very knowledgeable and terrific in every way.*" She manages business immigration matters for clients from all industry sectors. **William Reich** of Serotte, Reich & Wilson LLP is an expert on border practices and on the transfer of personnel under NAFTA. Reich is frequently consulted about challenging cases. **Roxanne Levine** of Tarter Krinsky & Drogin LLP "*is exceptional,*" say sources, who add that "*she handles cases with meticulous detail.*" Levine handles all manner of employment and family-based immigration matters for individuals and corporations. A new entrant this year, **Andrew Koerner** of Tarter Krinsky & Drogin LLP is considered to be "*very on the ball, thorough, open-minded and creative.*" He is recommended for his representation of individuals and companies in an all-encompassing array of employment and family-based immigration matters and nationality issues. **Noemi Masliah** of Masliah & Soloway, PC is active in the immigration law community and has a strong reputation in the field. She focuses her practice on employment-based immigration work. **Avram Morell** of Pryor Cashman LLP is "*wonderful,*" according to sources. He assists clients with a range of matters, including their immigrant and nonimmigrant visa needs.

# INSURANCE

Dispute Resolution: Policyholder p.1816;   Transactional & Regulatory p.1816

Commentary about individuals can be found under their firm's paragraph.  If the firm has no paragraph (is not ranked) look at Other Notable Practitioners.

| Insurance: Dispute Resolution: Insurer Leading Firms |
| --- |
| **Band 1** |
| Cahill Gordon & Reindel LLP * |
| Simpson Thacher & Bartlett LLP * |
| **Band 2** |
| Chaffetz Lindsey LLP |
| Dentons * |
| Stroock & Stroock & Lavan LLP * |
| Wollmuth Maher & Deutsch LLP * |
| **Band 3** |
| Clyde & Co US LLP * |
| Debevoise & Plimpton LLP * |
| Hogan Lovells US LLP |
| Mound Cotton Wollan & Greengrass * |
| Sullivan & Cromwell LLP * |
| **Band 4** |
| Edwards Wildman Palmer * |
| Grais & Ellsworth LLP |
| Quinn Emanuel Urquhart & Sullivan, LLP |
| Skadden, Arps, Slate, Meagher & Flom LLP & Affiliates * |
| *Indicates firm with profile.* |

## Anderson Kill & Olick, P.C.
See profile on p.1954

**THE FIRM** Anderson Kill has a longstanding reputation for successfully representing policyholders in sophisticated coverage matters. The team has a broad range of expertise spanning from toxic torts to professional liability claims. Recent highlights include involvement in multidistrict litigation arising from the Deepwater Horizon oil spill, and acting for DSW in a dispute with AIG surrounding computer fraud coverage.

**Sources say:** "*They have the significant ability to think about insurance coverage issues, with a deep bench of people who do this day in and day out.*"

**KEY INDIVIDUALS** Leading partner **Robert Horkovich** (see p.336) "*has a strong 'client-first' attitude*" and is held in high esteem by peers. He represented the State of California in the Stringfellow Acid Pits cleanup matter, a 14-year environmental coverage dispute between the state and its insurance companies. **William Passannante** (see p.382) is a "*go-to attorney for high-dollar insurance coverage litigation,*" and "*knows the industry inside-out.*" His caseload encompasses D&O and asbestos liability issues. Sources describe **Finley Harckham** (see p.1901) as "*a tenacious litigator and a real gentleman.*" He is an expert in business interruption and first-party property coverage disputes.

## Cahill Gordon & Reindel LLP
See profile on p.1960

**THE FIRM** This firm is acclaimed for its active and preeminent presence in the insurance industry. Its reputation is connected to its involvement in high-end litigation related to both direct insurance and reinsurance. Recent highlights include acting for Chartis in two disputes involving a series of issues, including breach of contract and allegations of fraud. Other prominent insurance company clients include Lexington, National Union Fire Insurance and AIG.

**KEY INDIVIDUALS** Peers "*have great respect*" for **Edward Krugman** (see p.350), who is "*at the top of the game.*" He is an acknowledged practitioner in reinsurance and general insurance coverage matters. **Thorn Rosenthal** (see p.1933) is active in big-ticket coverage cases and complex multijurisdictional reinsurance disputes. He attracts praise for his ability to achieve good results, and sources say that he is "*a pleasure to deal with.*"

## Chaffetz Lindsey LLP

**THE FIRM** This firm has an exceptional reputation in the reinsurance space, and is also prominent in the direct insurance field. Its five partners and ten associates earn client praise for their hands-on and open-minded approach to issues. The group recently achieved a settlement on behalf of Lexington Insurance in one of the nation's largest asbestos disputes. Other significant insurance clients include AIG, Chugg, Travelers and Zurich.

**Sources say:** "*One of their strengths is their courage in approaching difficult cases.*"

**KEY INDIVIDUALS** Founding partner **Peter Chaffetz** (see p.293) is a driving force in reinsurance matters. He is "*very bright and experienced, and provides very sound practical advice.*" Sources assert that "*he is able to develop theories and arguments in respect of a matter that the majority of people in a room may not even have come close to thinking of.*" Associate **Karen Baswell** (see p.1876) has a growing reputation in the market, and is active in general insurance and reinsurance matters.

## Clifford Chance US LLP
See profile on p.439

**THE FIRM** This firm maintains a healthy presence in New York's insurance transactional and regulatory space. The team recently advised General Motors Asset Management on the restructuring of its pension plans, worth $25 billion in assets. Other major clients include JPMorgan, Citi, Swiss Re and Deutsche Bank.

**KEY INDIVIDUALS** A popular choice among clients, **Paul Meyer** (see p.1919) "*knows a lot of the players, so is not just giving legal advice but also legal advice in a business context.*" Sources are impressed by his "*intelligence, insight and calm demeanor.*"

## Clyde & Co US LLP
See profile on p.440

**THE FIRM** Clyde & Co's growing insurance litigation team offers services in both the insurance and reinsurance fields. It has established itself as a solid New York presence, becoming a popular choice for insurance companies looking for skilled and experienced litigators. The attorneys at this firm offer a full range of insurance services, dealing with issues ranging from complex Bermuda Form matters to domestic professional liability.

**KEY INDIVIDUALS** Sources recognize **Michael Knoerzer** as an "*excellent lawyer*" and a highly skilled adviser in the reinsurance space. Experienced litigator **Paul Koepff** is applauded for "*his intellect and knowledge of the law.*" He represents insurers in complex appellate matters involving a wide array of coverage cases.

## Insurance: Dispute Resolution: Insurer

### Senior Statesmen

**Senior Statesmen: distinguished older practitioners**

| | |
|---|---|
| Newman Thomas R | Duane Morris LLP (ONP)[†] |

### Leading Individuals

**Band 1**

| | |
|---|---|
| Krugman Edward P | Cahill Gordon & Reindel LLP * |
| Nonna John M | Patton Boggs LLP (ONP)[†] |
| Ostrager Barry R | Simpson Thacher & Bartlett LLP * |
| Vyskocil Mary Kay | Simpson Thacher & Bartlett LLP * |

**Band 2**

| | |
|---|---|
| Amer Andrew S | Simpson Thacher & Bartlett LLP * |
| Ashinoff Reid | Dentons * |
| Barr Michael H | Dentons * |
| Byrne Jane | Quinn Emanuel Urquhart & Sullivan, LLP |
| Chaffetz Peter | Chaffetz Lindsey LLP * |
| Grais David J | Grais & Ellsworth LLP |
| Knoerzer Michael A | Clyde & Co US LLP |
| Koepff Paul | Clyde & Co US LLP |
| Maher William | Wollmuth Maher & Deutsch LLP * |
| Rosenthal Thorn | Cahill Gordon & Reindel LLP * |
| Schiffer Larry P | Patton Boggs LLP (ONP)[†] |
| Schwartz Steven | Locke Lord LLP (ONP)[†] * |

**Band 3**

| | |
|---|---|
| Abrams Marc | Wollmuth Maher & Deutsch LLP * |
| Carlinsky Michael | Quinn Emanuel Urquhart & Sullivan, LLP |
| Cohen Harry P | Crowell & Moring LLP (ONP)[†] * |
| Cotton Stuart | Mound Cotton Wollan & Greengrass |
| Ellsworth Kathryn | Grais & Ellsworth LLP |
| Goodman Robert D | Debevoise & Plimpton LLP |
| Greengrass Lawrence S | Mound Cotton Wollan & Greengrass * |
| Jacobson Michele L | Stroock & Stroock & Lavan LLP |
| Lewin Robert | Stroock & Stroock & Lavan LLP |
| McCormack Aidan | DLA Piper LLP (US) (ONP)[†] * |
| Murphy Michael | DLA Piper LLP (US) (ONP)[†] * |
| Reynolds Timothy G | Skadden, Arps, Slate, Meagher & Flom * |
| Rosenberg Mark F | Sullivan & Cromwell LLP * |
| Schallert Edwin | Debevoise & Plimpton LLP |
| Schiavoni Tancred | O'Melveny & Myers LLP (ONP)[†] |
| Silva David A | Mound Cotton Wollan & Greengrass * |
| Silverberg Philip C | Mound Cotton Wollan & Greengrass * |
| Sottile James | Zuckerman Spaeder LLP (ONP)[†] |
| Vitkowsky Vincent J | Edwards Wildman Palmer * |
| Walsh Kevin | Locke Lord LLP (ONP)[†] * |

**Up-and-coming individuals**

| | |
|---|---|
| Monaco Francis | Hogan Lovells US LLP |
| Zola Jared | Dickstein Shapiro LLP * |

**Associates to watch**

| | |
|---|---|
| Baswell Karen | Chaffetz Lindsey LLP * |

*Indicates firm / individual with profile.*

[†]*ONP = Other Notable Practitioner.*

### Debevoise & Plimpton LLP

See profile on p.1968

**THE FIRM** As well as remaining a driving force in the insurance transactional and regulatory space, Debevoise also has a solid presence in dispute resolution on behalf of insurers. Clients praise the high level of service and atten-

---

## Insurance: Dispute Resolution: Policyholder

### Leading Firms

**Band 1**

Kasowitz, Benson, Torres & Friedman LLP *

**Band 2**

Anderson Kill & Olick, P.C. *

Proskauer Rose LLP *

Reed Smith LLP

**Band 3**

Dickstein Shapiro LLP *

Jones Day *

Morgan, Lewis & Bockius LLP *

Willkie Farr & Gallagher LLP *

### Leading Individuals

**Band 1**

| | |
|---|---|
| Cohen Robin L | Kasowitz, Benson, Torres & Friedman LLP * |
| Horkovich Robert M | Anderson Kill & Olick, P.C. * |

**Band 2**

| | |
|---|---|
| Gross John | Proskauer Rose LLP |
| Passannante William G | Anderson Kill & Olick, P.C. * |
| Schafler Seth B | Proskauer Rose LLP |

**Band 3**

| | |
|---|---|
| Auslander Mitchell J | Willkie Farr & Gallagher LLP * |
| Breene Paul Evan | Reed Smith LLP |
| Harckham Finley | Anderson Kill & Olick, P.C. * |
| Joyce Edward M | Jones Day * |
| Kramer Ann | Reed Smith LLP |
| Luttinger Jr David A | Morgan, Lewis & Bockius LLP * |

**Up-and-coming individuals**

| | |
|---|---|
| McKenna Keith | Kasowitz, Benson, Torres & Friedman LLP * |

tion they receive from its attorneys. The team's client list contains major names like AXA, Goldman Sachs, Manulife, Prudential and John Hancock Life Insurance. Recent highlights include counseling Goldman Sachs Reinsurance Group in its acquisition of the Bermuda-based reinsurance operations of Ariel Holdings.

**Sources say:** *"Their work is stellar and their lawyers – from senior ones to associates – are all extremely intelligent, very smart tactically and excellent analytically."*

**KEY INDIVIDUALS** Peers and clients alike enjoy working with **Nicholas Potter**, who is said to be *"a good lawyer and a nice guy."* His work concentrates on life insurance and related M&A. He led the aforementioned Goldman Sachs transaction. Corporate partner **Thomas Kelly** assists insurers in capital markets and M&A transactions. He is described by one source as *"a strong, thoughtful and well-rounded insurance-focused transactional lawyer."* **Edwin Schallert** is known as a go-to lawyer for complex life insurance issues. He has recently represented Prudential and Manulife in multiple matters arising out of the aftermath of the global financial crisis. Experienced litigator **Robert Goodman** recently acted for Travelers on the asbestos-related bankruptcy of Pittsburgh Corning. He has also dealt with mortgage insurance policy and captive insurance matters for JPMorgan Chase. **Wolcott Dunham** is considered *"the dean of the New York insurance Bar."* He remains one of the most influential names in the insurance

---

## Insurance: Transactional & Regulatory

### Leading Firms

**Band 1**

Debevoise & Plimpton LLP *

Willkie Farr & Gallagher LLP *

**Band 2**

Sidley Austin LLP *

Skadden, Arps, Slate, Meagher & Flom LLP & Affiliates *

Sullivan & Cromwell LLP *

**Band 3**

Clifford Chance US LLP *

Edwards Wildman Palmer *

Mayer Brown LLP *

Simpson Thacher & Bartlett LLP *

Stroock & Stroock & Lavan LLP *

### Senior Statesmen

**Senior Statesmen: distinguished older practitioners**

| | |
|---|---|
| Dunham Jr Wolcott B | Debevoise & Plimpton LLP |
| Gabay Donald | Stroock & Stroock & Lavan LLP |

### Leading Individuals

**Band 1**

| | |
|---|---|
| Dye Alexander M | Willkie Farr & Gallagher LLP * |
| Liebmann Jeff S | Sidley Austin LLP * |
| Potter Nicholas F | Debevoise & Plimpton LLP |
| Rowen Andrew S | Sullivan & Cromwell LLP * |
| Sullivan Robert J | Skadden, Arps, Slate, Meagher & Flom * |

**Band 2**

| | |
|---|---|
| Freedman Jonathan L | Sidley Austin LLP * |
| Groll Michael | Willkie Farr & Gallagher LLP * |
| Kelly Thomas M | Debevoise & Plimpton LLP |
| Meyer Paul | Clifford Chance US LLP * |
| Schwolsky John | Willkie Farr & Gallagher LLP * |

**Band 3**

| | |
|---|---|
| Alberts David | Mayer Brown LLP |
| Campbell Leah | Willkie Farr & Gallagher LLP * |
| Dwyer James R | Sutherland Asbill & Brennan LLP (ONP)[†] |
| Henderson Jr Donald B | Willkie Farr & Gallagher LLP * |
| Herzeca Lois F | Gibson, Dunn & Crutcher LLP (ONP)[†] * |
| Horowitz Gary I | Simpson Thacher & Bartlett LLP * |
| Kotran Stephen M | Sullivan & Cromwell LLP * |
| Latza William | Stroock & Stroock & Lavan LLP |
| Madigan Michael | Sidley Austin LLP * |
| Nadell Bernhardt | Stroock & Stroock & Lavan LLP |
| Nicenko Vladimir | Willkie Farr & Gallagher LLP * |
| Pearson Nick | Edwards Wildman Palmer * |
| Pierce Kenneth R | Mayer Brown LLP |
| Shoss Cynthia R | Sutherland Asbill & Brennan LLP (ONP)[†] |

### Dentons

See profile on p.449

**THE FIRM** Commentators praise this firm for its strength in the insurance dispute resolution space. It is particularly known for serving the insurance sector, with a focus on representing primarily life insurers and property and casualty carriers. Significant clients include Genworth

Mortgage Insurance and Transamerica Life Insurance Company.

**Sources say:** *"Strong litigators and good, results-oriented strategists."*

**KEY INDIVIDUALS** Clients laud **Reid Ashinoff** (see p.274) as an *"experienced, knowledgeable and pragmatic"* lawyer. Over the past year, he has been active in matters involving securities fraud, class actions and misappropriation of trade secrets. **Michael Barr** (see p.278) cochairs the firm's global insurance team and is experienced in litigating cases pertaining to the financial crisis and environmental tort issues. He recently acted for Royal Indemnity against Commercial Money Center in relation to a fraudulent inducement of surety bonds.M&A world.

## Dickstein Shapiro LLP
See profile on p.911

**THE FIRM** This team is experienced in a wide range of insurance coverage areas on behalf of policyholders, including political risk and cyber security risk. The group is noted for its expertise in matters pertaining to the entertainment and sports industries. Recent highlights include securing more than $1.8 billion in settlements on behalf of IMO Industries in a lawsuit against Transamerica, its former parent company, and over 50 carriers.

**Sources say:** *"They are very knowledgeable in the insurance coverage area – their litigation skills are superior."*

**KEY INDIVIDUALS Jared Zola** (see p.1953) is recognized by clients as a *"very accomplished"* attorney committed to representing corporate policyholders. His clients include IMO Industries, 3G Capital and Gruppo, Levey & Co.

## Edwards Wildman Palmer
See profile on p.1520

**THE FIRM** This firm houses a go-to regulatory team and a solid dispute resolution group. It is active in sophisticated transactional arrangements, including insurance-linked securities and the formation of captives. Recent highlights include assisting SCOR UK with underwriting guidelines, and providing regulatory analysis on behalf of Aspen Specialty Insurance Company.

**Sources say:** *"They give us pragmatic advice, telling us how we can do what we need to do instead of just telling us what we need to do."*

**KEY INDIVIDUALS Nick Pearson** (see p.1926) is endorsed by commentators as *"a fine lawyer"* who is *"very strong on the regulatory side."* He played a central role in the formation of Thomson Reuters's captive insurance company, the first captive in the State of Connecticut. **Vincent Vitkowsky** (see p.1948) is known in the market as a dispute resolution practitioner with robust experience in reinsurance arbitrations. He is also recognized for his expertise on cyber security and risks.

## Grais & Ellsworth LLP

**THE FIRM** Litigation firm Grais & Ellsworth is recognized in the insurance space for its focus on structured finance matters. The group represents investors across the whole range of structured finance securities, ranging from mortgage-backed to trust-preferred ones.

**KEY INDIVIDUALS David Grais** is held in high esteem by peers, who identify him as a *"very fine lawyer."* He focuses on hotly disputed MBS matters. Formerly at Dewey & LeBoeuf, **Kathryn Ellsworth** is singled out by commentators as a *"very talented"* attorney.

## Hogan Lovells US LLP

**THE FIRM** This well-established global firm has a strong focus on reinsurance, with particular expertise in the London market. Key clients include Argonaut Insurance, AXA, Berkshire Hathaway Group and Transport Insurance Company, all of which it has represented in high-profile disputes. The team recently represented Argonaut Insurance in an action against the Insurance Company of the State of Pennsylvania seeking to recover under a facultative reinsurance contract.

**Sources say:** *"They have a really smart way of doing business that makes the client feel it is more of a partnership. That is why I keep on going back to them."*

**KEY INDIVIDUALS** New entry **Francis Monaco** recently joined Hogan Lovells from Dewey & LeBoeuf. He is highly recommended by clients, who find him to be *"very knowledgeable, diligent and very respectful."* He is known in the market for life reinsurance financing work as part of a broad insurance practice.

## Jones Day
See profile on p.919

**THE FIRM** Policyholder litigation remains a key part of this firm's strong national practice. The group is able to handle the full range of disputes, but is especially known in the market for its expertise in D&O-related matters. The team has recently been involved in finalizing a large settlement on behalf of Energy Solutions with its D&O insurers, in connection with a securities class action and derivative lawsuits.

**KEY INDIVIDUALS Edward Joyce** (see p.1907) is held in high esteem by peers, who view him as a key player on the policyholder insurance side. He recently represented Michaels Stores in liability coverage disputes relating to PIN pad hacking.

## Kasowitz, Benson, Torres & Friedman LLP
See profile on p.1983

**THE FIRM** This impressive firm continues to develop its name in the insurance policyholder arena and has come to be recognized by commentators as a major player. While the team has suffered following the tragic loss of leading partner Randy Paar, it has maintained its solid reputation in the market. In a recent highlight, it represented Visa in a dispute surrounding professional liability coverage. Other key clients include Syracuse University, Philips Electronics North America and RealPage.

**Sources say:** *"They are clearly experts in their field – they know the players and the law. They are very dedicated to the work and are very responsive to client demands."*

**KEY INDIVIDUALS Robin Cohen** (see p.297) attracts praise from peers and clients alike, with sources stating that she has the ability to *"adopt a broad and high-level perspective to really take things in,"* allowing her to devise strategies tailored to the situations in hand. She led the team representing Visa in connection with professional liability coverage issues. Rising star **Keith McKenna** (see p.1918) earns plaudits from market commentators for being *"great at court depositions and at putting the arguments together in a compelling fashion."*

## Mayer Brown LLP
See profile on p.1257

**THE FIRM** This firm continues to stand out for its local, national and global insurance work. The New York team has a healthy reputation in insurance-linked securities, and covers all insurance transactional aspects relevant to the corporate world, from M&A to tax matters. It has recently dealt with two high-profile catastrophe bond transactions for Embarcadero Re and Everglades Re, in relation to earthquake and hurricane damage, respectively.

**Sources say:** *"They understand the business framework very well. This makes them quite a unique player."*

**KEY INDIVIDUALS David Alberts** is credited with knowing how to navigate his clients through corporate transactional and regulatory insurance processes, and is *"very much at home in this complex area."* *"Very intelligent and very knowledgeable,"* **Kenneth Pierce** is highly recommended for his business awareness, which derives from his professional experience both in investment banking and in law.

## Morgan, Lewis & Bockius LLP
See profile on p.2246

**THE FIRM** This corporate policyholder insurance group continues to handle a number of toxic tort and property damage coverage matters. The New York office is known for its attorneys' expertise in representing clients from a variety of industries, including financial institutions, large multinationals, manufacturers and retailers. It recently acted for Goulds Pumps on seeking more than $700 million in coverage for asbestos-related product liability losses.

**KEY INDIVIDUALS David Luttinger** (see p.1915) is recognized for his expertise in environmental and asbestos insurance coverage disputes. He recently represented ITT Corporation in a major asbestos coverage trial.

## Mound Cotton Wollan & Greengrass
See profile on p.1992

**THE FIRM** This insurer team is noted by commentators as a longstanding player in the New York market thanks to its experience and broad range of insurance coverage services. Clients are quick to highlight its deep subject matter expertise and attentiveness to their business needs.

**KEY INDIVIDUALS Stuart Cotton** has a broad practice, covering matters ranging from property damage to business interruption claims. **Lawrence Greengrass** (see p.1899) is a respected insurance and reinsurance litigator, concentrating on financial insurance issues. He also has vast experience in handling reinsurance arbitrations. **Philip Silverberg** (see p.1942) is well regarded as an expert in insurance and reinsurance matters. He has recently been very active in the captive insurance space. Deeply experienced practitioner **David Silva** (see p.1941) is held in high regard by market sources for his expertise in complex reinsurance arbitrations.

## Proskauer Rose LLP
See profile on p.2001

THE FIRM Sources identify this established policyholder group as a strong player in the most sophisticated and high-end coverage litigation across a range of industries. This was recently displayed by its representation of Union Carbide in $2 billion coverage litigation in New York against more than 30 insurance companies for asbestos-related claims. Clients particularly praise the firm for its deep technical expertise and commercial approach.

**Sources say:** *"They are knowledgeable, efficient and pragmatic."*

**KEY INDIVIDUALS** Peers recognize **John Gross** as a leading practitioner with deep expertise in acting for policyholders in the financial services industry. *"Fine lawyer"* **Seth Schafler** is an expert in coverage litigation, particularly professional liability and fiduciary liability matters.

## Quinn Emanuel Urquhart & Sullivan, LLP

THE FIRM This 14-partner team is a new addition to the insurance rankings this year. Sources praise its advocacy skills and recognize the group's solid presence in MBS matters. The team acts on behalf of Chartis, Allstate and Berkshire Hathaway, among other prominent clients.

**Sources say:** *"A firm of exceptional talent – they understand the issues very well, they write well and they argue well."*

**KEY INDIVIDUALS** *"Superb insurance attorney"* **Jane Byrne** is a favorite among clients, who highlight that she *"understands the technical inner workings of insurance and reinsurance."* **Michael Carlinsky** is held in high esteem by peers, who consider him to be *"one of the top trial lawyers in the country."* He recently acted for AIG and its subsidiaries in a large putative class action.

## Reed Smith LLP

THE FIRM Clients praise this practice for its expertise in policyholder issues, and for the trial ability of its lead insurance partners. The group concentrates on commercial insurance coverage issues, particularly D&O and E&O liability claims. Recent highlights include representing Forest Labs in a D&O coverage claim that settled for $65 million. The team also acted for 1765 First Associates in a matter involving the collapse of a tower crane in Midtown Manhattan.

**Sources say:** *"They are well recognized in their field of expertise, and put out a very good product."*

**KEY INDIVIDUALS Paul Evan Breene** is highly regarded in the market for his knowledge of all aspects of policyholder insurance recovery. He recently settled a property insurance dispute connected to the collapse of a building for A&C Investment Group. Experienced partner **Ann Kramer** is active in the D&O, product liability and toxic tort insurance areas. She has particular expertise in working with clients within the pharmaceutical industry.

## Sidley Austin LLP
See profile on p.1264

THE FIRM This established firm has a standout reputation for insurance transactional and regulatory work. The team has an active practice in M&A, life insurance, insurance-linked securities, private equity funds and annuities. Recent highlights include assisting Apollo Unit on a $1.8 billion deal to acquire the US operations of major British insurer Aviva. Other key industry clients include MetLife and Swiss Re.

**Sources say:** *"The key factors that we enjoy in dealing with them are their authority and their judgment. Their judgment is excellent because of their very deep experience."*

**KEY INDIVIDUALS Jeff Liebmann** (see p.356) is an expert in life insurance transactions, and is considered by peers to be one of the strongest insurance insolvency practitioners in town. He recently represented Goldman Sachs Group in connection with a longevity reinsurance transaction to provide coverage for pension liability of Prudential Financial's subsidiaries. **Jonathan Freedman** (see p.316) concentrates on insurance insolvency, regulatory and life insurance work. He is held in fine regard by market commentators. **Michael Madigan**'s (see p.1916) experience in insurance-linked securities *"makes him the authority on structuring issues."* He has particularly strong expertise in catastrophe bonds.

## Simpson Thacher & Bartlett LLP
See profile on p.2006

THE FIRM Clients are effusive in their praise for this New York stalwart, thanks to its deep expertise in the insurance and reinsurance sphere. The firm has a stellar reputation for contentious work, and regularly acts for major players including Travelers, Swiss Re and Berkshire Hathaway. The team's success in the past year is exemplified by a summary judgment victory for Travelers in an asbestos case with an award of more than $420 million. The transactional and regulatory group is dedicated to M&A transactions, regularly representing issuers and their underwriters.

**Sources say:** *"Their willingness to actually litigate as opposed to just file papers makes them stand above the others."*

**KEY INDIVIDUALS** *"Household name"* **Barry Ostrager** (see p.381) continues to be known as one of the strongest practitioners in the sector. He recently acted for the Fidelity title insurance companies in a series of antitrust class actions. *"Outstanding lawyer"* **Mary Kay Vyskocil** (see p.422) earns widespread praise from market commentators. She is active in reinsurance litigation and arbitrations, both in the USA and abroad. Client favorite **Andrew Amer** (see p.1873) is praised for being *"hands-on, accessible and experienced; he is a talented trial and arbitration attorney, with excellent writing skills."* He handles insurance disputes as part of a broad commercial litigation practice. Transactional partner **Gary Horowitz** (see p.336) recently led the firm's representation of CNO Financial Group in its $1 billion recapitalization. He also regularly acts for major financial institutions such as Barclays Capital, Wells Fargo Securities and Goldman Sachs.

## Skadden, Arps, Slate, Meagher & Flom LLP & Affiliates
See profile on p.2008

THE FIRM This group has a healthy reputation in insurance transactional and regulatory work, and attracts particular praise for its experience in handling M&A deals. Skadden's client portfolio includes General Reinsurance, HealthSpring and Manulife Financial. The team's expertise in sophisticated deals is exemplified by its representation of Amerigroup in connection with its $4.9 billion acquisition by WellPoint. The insurance practice also offers strength in coverage disputes on behalf of the industry.

**Sources say:** *"Their client communication was exemplary, and their preparedness and counsel clearly made a difference in the transaction outcome for the better."*

**KEY INDIVIDUALS** According to sources, transactional leader **Robert Sullivan** (see p.414) *"is knowledgeable, practical and unflappable in difficult situations. He never loses focus of the business objective and works creatively to get both sides where they want to go."* He has recently worked on a number of high-value deals for Massachusetts Mutual Life Insurance, Jackson National Life Insurance and SCOR SE. Litigator **Timothy Reynolds** (see p.1931) is noted by peers for his *"good strategic sense."* He recently acted for the Port Authority of New York and New Jersey, concluding nine years of litigation to secure insurance recovery for property damage and lost revenues connected to 9/11.

## Stroock & Stroock & Lavan LLP
See profile on p.2010

THE FIRM This practice stands out in the New York insurance market on both the dispute resolution and the transactional and regulatory fronts. The full-service nature of the firm means clients benefit from expertise in matters ranging from high-exposure reinsurance disputes to complex corporate transactions. The team recently represented Arch Insurance in a dispute against a number of entities relating to allegations of unauthorized workers' compensation. Other noteworthy clients include Goldman Sachs, Crédit Agricole, Liberty Mutual Insurance and Bank of America Merrill Lynch.

**Sources say:** *"They really understand insurance and reinsurance, and are creative and very diligent in what they do."*

**KEY INDIVIDUALS** Litigator **Michele Jacobson** is highly rated by peers, who identify her as a target for referrals. She has a solid reputation for her work in reinsurance disputes. Experienced and respected insurance litigator **Robert Lewin** has recently been involved in representing the Insurance Corporation of New York in litigation to recover losses due under a reinsurance treaty. Clients are *"extremely satisfied"* with **Bernhardt Nadell**'s representation. According to commentators, he is a *"good deal-maker who is very savvy and able to negotiate complex insurance transactions."* Experienced partner **William Latza** has a wide practice focusing on corporate insurance transactions. He has advised large insurance businesses on devising restructuring plans of late. Senior practitioner and *"great guy"* **Donald Gabay** is deeply respected by peers as a longstanding authority in insurance transactional and regulatory work.

## Sullivan & Cromwell LLP
See profile on p.2011

**THE FIRM** Sullivan & Cromwell earns strong market endorsement in the dispute resolution and transactional and regulatory arenas. It is heavily involved in bankruptcy-related coverage issues, and also handles asbestos and environmental disputes. On the transactional side, the group assists clients in secured major M&A transactions, with highlights including acting for Swiss Re on the proposed $900 million sale of a portion of its Admin Re division to Jackson National.

**Sources say:** *"Very high-caliber people – intelligent and hard-working, commercially and legally shrewd."*

**KEY INDIVIDUALS** Market commentators consider the *"bright and commercial"* **Andrew Rowen** (see p.1933) to be an influential practitioner in the insurance transactional space. Sources also highlight his deep securities expertise. Clients praise **Stephen Kotran** (see p.1910) for his insurance M&A work. He is admired by commentators for being *"strong, brilliant and hard-working."* Litigator **Mark Rosenberg** (see p.1933) recently represented BAT Industries in connection with a complex environmental insurance dispute arising out of PCB contamination in the Fox River in Wisconsin.

## Willkie Farr & Gallagher LLP
See profile on p.2016

**THE FIRM** This firm's transactional practice has shot to prominence following its recent intake of a series of leading practitioners from Dewey & LeBoeuf. The team has deep experience in a range of high-value deals, and recent highlights include representing Aviva in a $400 million hybrid securities offering. On the dispute side, the firm regularly represents insurance brokers and intermediaries. It recently acted for Marsh & McLennan on a $50 million fiduciary duty claim.

**Sources say:** *"They combine in-depth knowledge of the industry with top-notch transactional skills and experience, sensitivity to cost and an emphasis on delivering excellent client service."*

**KEY INDIVIDUALS** The *"very talented"* **Alexander Dye** (see p.307) is a prominent figure in the insurance transactional space. He recently acted for Tower Group on its approximately $75 million investment in Canopius Group and its merger with one of its subsidiaries. Clients describe **John Schwolsky** (see p.1939) as a *"strong transactional lawyer focused on the insurance industry, who is very responsive and client centered."* He focuses on sophisticated insurance M&A and capital markets work transactions. **Michael**

Groll (see p.326) recently closed a public offering of $160 million of preference shares on behalf of Aspen Insurance Holdings. He is lauded by clients for being deeply committed to their needs. **Donald Henderson** (see p.333) has a healthy reputation in insurance transactions. He recently played a key role for Assurant on the formation of its catastrophe bond shelf program. **Vladimir Nicenko's** (see p.1923) litigation practice focuses on capital markets. With a steadily growing reputation, he is considered *"brilliant and hard-working"* among clients. Peers also praise his impressive handling of complicated transactions. Regulatory attorney **Leah Campbell** (see p.1882) is well respected among peers. She is considered a leader in her area of practice and a key member of the firm's insurance team. **Mitchell Auslander** (see p.1875) leads the insurance dispute resolution group and is applauded for his strength as a litigator. He regularly handles big-ticket matters for Marsh & McLennan, and recently represented Cameron International in a dispute connected to the Deepwater Horizon oil spill.

## Wollmuth Maher & Deutsch LLP
See profile on p.2018

**THE FIRM** This firm stands out for its high-end and sophisticated commercial insurance and reinsurance work, and is frequently active on complicated arbitration proceedings. It also has recognized expertise in the London market. Clients include Chartis, Hanover Insurance and Zurich.

**Sources say:** *"Their strongest point is undoubtedly their attention to detail, especially on arbitration matters. They had specific challenges to overcome in understanding the peculiarities of the London insurance market and I was very impressed with how quickly they grasped the issues."*

**KEY INDIVIDUALS William Maher** (see p.1916) heads the firm's insurance and reinsurance group. One client was *"very impressed with his presentations, his manner and the way in which he can present clients' issues and challenge opposing counsel."* Clients have nothing but praise for **Marc Abrams** (see p.1871), whose *"attention to detail is second to none – he is a pleasure to work with."*

## Other Notable Practitioners

**John Nonna** of Patton Boggs LLP was formerly at Dewey & LeBoeuf and is an active player in the reinsurance space. Sources describe him as a *"first-class lawyer"* who *"has very strong connections and is able to convey complicated ideas."* **Larry Schiffer**, also of Patton Boggs LLP, is acknowledged

as an *"excellent"* reinsurance attorney. He recently acted for General Re Life in an ERISA benefit plan action for long-term disability benefits. **Tancred Schiavoni** of O'Melveny & Myers LLP has a reputation for *"being creative"* and *"tireless in his efforts."* He is an experienced insurance litigator with core expertise in bankruptcy and environmental cases. **Steven Schwartz** (see p.403) of Locke Lord LLP is a recognized name in the reinsurance field, and is praised as a *"very competent and very solid lawyer."* The *"very highly regarded"* **Kevin Walsh** (see p.1949), also of Locke Lord LLP, has a strong presence in the insurance and reinsurance space. Sources admire his *"enormous amount of experience domestically,"* and recognize *"his excellent reputation in the market."* He recently assisted Hannover Re in a multimillion-dollar reinsurance dispute. **Harry Cohen** (see p.1885) of Crowell & Moring LLP has longstanding experience in representing insurance and reinsurance companies. He has played a key role in major arbitrations and prominent commercial disputes. The highly rated **Aidan McCormack** (see p.1918) of DLA Piper LLP (US) acts on issues ranging from fraud to D&O liability. He is admired by sources for being *"gifted with a capacity to offer simple and straightforward solutions to apparently unsolvable problems, which makes him invaluable when handling complex cases."* DLA Piper LLP's global head of insurance and reinsurance **Michael Murphy** (see p.1921) has recently represented Brazil's largest reinsurer, IRB Brazil Re, in a series of international reinsurance arbitrations. Clients praise his *"very rare ability to effectively communicate complicated facts and arguments."* Clients praise insurance litigator **James Sottile** of Zuckerman Spaeder LLP as an *"outstanding"* and *"very practical"* attorney, who *"focuses on the right issues."* Esteemed practitioner **Thomas Newman** of Duane Morris LLP is an experienced attorney who practices in insurance and reinsurance law, in particular appearing in appellate matters. He is also known in the market for his work as an arbitrator. **Cynthia Shoss** of Sutherland Asbill & Brennan LLP is praised by commentators for her leading regulatory expertise. She is heavily involved in major insurance industry demutualizations and mergers. **James Dwyer**, also of Sutherland Asbill & Brennan LLP, concentrates his practice on M&A transactions. He regularly handles high-value deals on behalf of major insurance industry players. Sources describe acclaimed attorney **Lois Herzeca** (see p.1903) of Gibson, Dunn & Crutcher LLP as *"intelligent, articulate, knowledgeable, thorough and timely."* She has recently been involved in major transactional work on behalf of property and casualty reinsurer Transatlantic Holdings.

# INTELLECTUAL PROPERTY

Trade Mark & Copyright p.1821

Commentary about individuals can be found under their firm's paragraph. If the firm has no paragraph (is not ranked) look at Other Notable Practitioners.

## Intellectual Property: Patent
### Leading Firms

**Band 1**
Fitzpatrick, Cella, Harper & Scinto *
Kirkland & Ellis LLP *

**Band 2**
Quinn Emanuel Urquhart & Sullivan, LLP
Ropes & Gray LLP *
WilmerHale *

**Band 3**
Cadwalader, Wickersham & Taft LLP *
Cravath, Swaine & Moore LLP *
Fish & Richardson PC
Gibson, Dunn & Crutcher LLP *
Goodwin Procter LLP *
Jones Day *
Kaye Scholer LLP *
Kenyon & Kenyon LLP
Patterson Belknap Webb & Tyler LLP *
Paul Hastings LLP *
Paul, Weiss, Rifkind, Wharton & Garrison LLP *
Skadden, Arps, Slate, Meagher & Flom LLP & Affiliates *

**Band 4**
Baker Botts LLP *
King & Spalding LLP *
Milbank, Tweed, Hadley & McCloy LLP *
Orrick, Herrington & Sutcliffe LLP *
Sidley Austin LLP *
Weil, Gotshal & Manges LLP *
White & Case LLP *
Willkie Farr & Gallagher LLP *
Winston & Strawn LLP *

\* Indicates firm / individual with profile.
† ONP = Other Notable Practitioner.

## Intellectual Property: Patent
### Senior Statesmen

**Senior Statesmen:** distinguished older practitioners

| | | | |
|---|---|---|---|
| Baechtold Robert L | Fitzpatrick, Cella, Harper & Scinto * | Sobel Gerald | Kaye Scholer LLP * |

### Leading Individuals

| | | | |
|---|---|---|---|
| **Band 1** | | Bresnick Sandra A | Quinn Emanuel Urquhart & Sullivan, LLP |
| Ben-Ami Leora | Kirkland & Ellis LLP * | Brooks Roger G | Cravath, Swaine & Moore LLP * |
| Chesler Evan R | Cravath, Swaine & Moore LLP * | Chalsen Christopher | Milbank, Tweed, Hadley & McCloy LLP * |
| Desmarais John M | Desmarais LLP (ONP) † | Cherny Steven C | Kirkland & Ellis LLP * |
| Diskant Gregory L | Patterson Belknap Webb & Tyler LLP * | Conde Dominick A | Fitzpatrick, Cella, Harper & Scinto * |
| Groombridge Nicholas | Paul, Weiss, Rifkind, Wharton & Garrison * | Dabney James W | Fried, Frank, Harris, Shriver (ONP) † † |
| Jenner Jesse J | Ropes & Gray LLP | DiMatteo John M | Willkie Farr & Gallagher LLP * |
| | | Elkin Michael | Winston & Strawn LLP * |
| **Band 2** | | Flattmann Gerald J | Paul Hastings LLP * |
| Armenio Peter J | Quinn Emanuel Urquhart & Sullivan, LLP | Francescani David | Fish & Richardson PC |
| Arovas Gregory S | Kirkland & Ellis LLP * | Friedman Marc S | Dentons (ONP) † * |
| Coruzzi Laura A | Jones Day * | Gupta Paul R | DLA Piper LLP (US) (ONP) † |
| DeLucia Richard L | Kenyon & Kenyon LLP | Haley Jr James F | Ropes & Gray LLP |
| DeVito Daniel A | Skadden, Arps, Slate, Meagher & Flom * | Hashmall David M | Goodwin Procter LLP * |
| Drivas Dimitrios | White & Case LLP * | Hershkowitz Benjamin | Gibson, Dunn & Crutcher LLP * |
| Filardi Edward V | Skadden, Arps, Slate, Meagher & Flom * | Holland Elizabeth | Kenyon & Kenyon LLP |
| Gunther Jr Robert J | WilmerHale * | Hsing Benjamin | Kaye Scholer LLP * |
| Hughes Christopher | Cadwalader, Wickersham & Taft LLP * | Lee Steven J | Kenyon & Kenyon LLP |
| Hummel Keith R | Cravath, Swaine & Moore LLP * | Lennon Michael | Kenyon & Kenyon LLP |
| Krevitt Josh | Gibson, Dunn & Crutcher LLP * | Lewis Jeffrey I D | Patterson Belknap Webb & Tyler LLP * |
| O'Malley Jr Joseph M | Paul Hastings LLP | Radulescu David | Quinn Emanuel Urquhart & Sullivan, LLP |
| Sweeney John F | Locke Lord LLP (ONP) † * | Scheinfeld Robert C | Baker Botts LLP * |
| Wexler Bruce | Paul Hastings LLP | Solander William | Fitzpatrick, Cella, Harper & Scinto * |
| | | Taylor Errol B | Milbank, Tweed, Hadley & McCloy LLP * |
| **Band 3** | | Thomasch Daniel J | Gibson, Dunn & Crutcher LLP * |
| Abate Mark J | Goodwin Procter LLP * | Weiswasser Elizabeth S | Weil, Gotshal & Manges LLP * |
| Badke Bradford J | Ropes & Gray LLP | Wintringham Drew | DLA Piper LLP (US) (ONP) † * |
| Bassett David | WilmerHale * | | |
| Beck Thomas H | Sidley Austin LLP * | | |

## Arnold & Porter LLP
See profile on p.906

**THE FIRM** Arnold & Porter's New York IP practice concentrates mainly on the registration, management, enforcement and protection of well-known brands in consumer goods, fashion, luxury goods and retail. In addition to trademark work, the team also excels in anticounterfeiting, design and trade dress protection. Clients include Bulgari, Gucci America and Pernod Ricard.

**KEY INDIVIDUALS Louis Ederer** (see p.1889) heads the firm's New York IP practice and is a *"top-notch litigator."* Clients in the luxury goods and beverage sectors swear by his *"superb and specific"* knowledge of the law and their industry.

## Baker & McKenzie
See profile on p.435

**THE FIRM** Baker & McKenzie's New York IP group focuses mainly on transactions, in which copyrighted material and trademarks are the core assets, as well as brand management and protection programs. Key areas of the team's expertise include e-commerce and internet business, media and software-related issues.

**Sources say:** *"They're an integral part of our overall transactional team."*

**KEY INDIVIDUALS Pamela Church** is head of department and concentrates on copyright law in particular, although she also advises on data protection and privacy matters. Interviewees say she is *"very forward-looking, responsive"* and *"picks up on things that others don't."* **Lisa Rosaya** is an internet and branding expert who operates at the forefront of the law and policies governing domain names. One impressed client said: *"She understands what we need from our advisers in terms of responsiveness and working within our processes."*

## Baker Botts LLP
See profile on p.2427

**THE FIRM** This national firm's New York office has a truly comprehensive practice, embracing commercial advice, transactional, litigious and prosecution work involving the full array of IP rights. Bolstered by a number of lateral hires in recent years, the team's coverage in terms of technical expertise and industry knowledge continues to impress clients such as Columbia University, Genentech and Samsung Electronics.

**Sources say:** *"They've seen it all. I can pick up the phone and get an answer straight away."*

**KEY INDIVIDUALS Robert Scheinfeld** (see p.1937) chairs the IP department in New York and internationally. He is a renowned authority on patent law, and litigates hi-tech cases, particularly those with a focus on computer science and mathematics.

## Cadwalader, Wickersham & Taft LLP
See profile on p.438

**THE FIRM** Cadwalader offers its clients a comprehensive IP service, and is particularly well known for the strength of its work in patent prosecution, portfolio management, USPTO opposition proceedings and patent litigation. The team has the education and experience necessary to handle matters involving consumer electronics, telecoms, medical devices, biotechnology, semiconductors and pharmaceuticals at home and in overseas jurisdictions.

**KEY INDIVIDUALS Christopher Hughes** (see p.1905) is appreciated by clients for the depth of his experience and his knowledge of the *"ins and outs of patent law in the USA and beyond."* He focuses primarily on prosecution, strategic advice and litigation support.

## Cowan, Liebowitz & Latman
**THE FIRM** IP law is a central constituent of this firm's business, and its work in copyright, trademark and internet-related matters is held in particularly high regard. Its copyright practice covers new media and online rights, as well as more traditional areas such as broadcasting, music and publishing. Its trademark arm also looks after brands belonging to market leaders in a wide range of industries.

**KEY INDIVIDUALS Richard Dannay** is a much-vaunted copyright and trademarks specialist, with a number of sources citing him as being one of the city's premier copyright lawyers. He has a very large client following in the publishing industry. **Christopher Jensen** is described by one legal source as a *"top-flight"* litigator. He takes on disputes centering on copyright and trademark infringement claims, as well as licensing agreements, trade secrets and patents.

## Cravath, Swaine & Moore LLP
See profile on p.1966

**THE FIRM** Cravath has an all-around IP capability, and its patent litigation offering comes in for special praise. Its

attorneys represent both defendants and plaintiffs in infringement claims, as well as in related antitrust and breach of license actions. The firm recently scored a final victory on behalf of Bristol-Myers Squibb and Sanofi in a long-running patent dispute with Apotex regarding anti-clotting agent Plavix.

**Sources say:** *"Very impressed with the level of focus that they can maintain."*

**KEY INDIVIDUALS Evan Chesler** (see p.294) is the firm's chairman. He has a distinguished litigation and trial practice, much of which is devoted to IP disputes. He played an instrumental role in the aforementioned victory on behalf

of Bristol-Myers Squibb and Sanofi. **Keith Hummel** (see p.1905) is praised by clients as an *"outstanding patent litigator."* He also oversees clients' global litigation strategies and has recently been deeply involved in a round of medical device-related patent disputes dubbed the 'Stent Wars'. **Roger Brooks** (see p.1881) is a highly talented, all-around IP litigator, whose recent cases have involved digital and satellite technology, software copyrights, technology licensing, trade secrets and antitrust issues.

## Davis & Gilbert LLP
**THE FIRM** This venerable, single-office firm's IP and branding offering includes strong transactional, copyright and trademark filing, registration, portfolio management and litigation expertise. The team represents a host of prominent brand and copyright-reliant businesses, such as American Express, Iman Cosmetics, Princeton University and Sony.

**KEY INDIVIDUALS Jeffrey Katz** (see p.1908) is an expert in trademark law, and focuses on filing, registration and transactions, including licensing agreements. One client said: *"He provides good, succinct advice, which is always communicated in a way that is easily understood."*

## Davis Wright Tremaine LLP
See profile on p.2544

**THE FIRM** This firm's New York IP presence is highly regarded for the quality of its representations in matters concerning copyrights, trademark prosecution and litigation, and trade secrets. The firm has a longstanding and loyal client following in the broadcasting, media and publishing sectors, and also among world-famous apparel and consumer brands who look to DWT for its robust anti-counterfeiting and trademark enforcement work.

**Sources say:** *"They have a great sense of where the market is and where it's going."*

**KEY INDIVIDUALS Marcia Paul** is universally acclaimed by sources as one of the leading copyright, advertising and trademark attorneys in the city. Her clients include household name apparel, media and broadcasting companies, and much of her work is highly complex and multijuris-dictional in character. **Edward Davis** is *"very smart, very thorough, and has a good sense of humor,"* according to interviewees. He counsels clients such as Amazon.com, Bloomberg LP, Martha Stewart Living Omnimedia and The Onion on registration, transactional and litigious IP matters.

## Debevoise & Plimpton LLP
See profile on p.1968

**THE FIRM** This firm's New York-based IP offering extends to the full range of IP rights and legal scenarios, from prosecution through transactional and due diligence work to litigation, although it is in the domain of copyright, trademarks and trade secrets that it is most celebrated. Within that domain, high-profile and business-critical litigation is a major forte of the team, although this should not detract from its excellent reputation for noncontentious work.

**Sources say:** *"A sophisticated, high-value and well-balanced practice."*

KEY INDIVIDUALS **David Bernstein** commands *"tremendous respect"* as a litigator among clients and across his profession. He has experience in cases involving anti-counterfeiting, copyright, contested domain names, false advertising, and trademark, trade secret and trade dress infringement. **Bruce Keller** is a *"terrific trial lawyer and knows his area very well,"* according to one market-leading client. Head of the IP litigation practice at the firm, his work straddles IP and entertainment law, and typically consists of matters regarding copyrights, false advertising, rights of publicity and trademarks.

## Dorsey & Whitney LLP
### See profile on p.1583
THE FIRM The IP team at Dorsey handles matters involving patents, copyright and trademarks and other rights, although its reputation is especially high with regard to nonutility rights. This offering is bolstered by its lawyers' relatively rare combination of copyright and trademark expertise and experience at litigating and trying disputes. Clients include Atari Interactive, Boston Beer and Procter & Gamble.

KEY INDIVIDUALS **Sandra Edelman** heads up Dorsey's worldwide trademarks group. She acts for world-famous brands across a range of industries, and has a particularly strong background in pharmaceuticals branding and its relationship with FDA regulations. **Bruce Ewing** leads the firm's New York trial group, and is a seasoned copyright and trademarks litigator. He has recently represented globally recognized brands in the leisure, luxury goods, pharmaceuticals and online entertainment sectors.

## Fish & Richardson PC
THE FIRM The New York office of this nationally recognized leader in IP law is certainly representative of the firm in terms of the talent of its attorneys and the sophistication of the work it undertakes. Areas of strength include Hatch-Waxman Act patent litigation, including acting for branded companies against generic pharmaceutical companies, and its thriving patent prosecution practice.

Sources say: *"Very accommodating in helping us to move things along, and in understanding some of the more complicated patent issues."*

KEY INDIVIDUALS **David Francescani** is managing principal of the New York office. His mainstay is patent litigation in the areas of computer software, electronics, optics and semiconductors.

## Fitzpatrick, Cella, Harper & Scinto
### See profile on p.1973
THE FIRM This IP boutique continues to ride high on the strength of its world-class work and superior attorneys, and remains one of the most sought-after destinations for leading pharmaceutical manufacturers seeking to defend their products or else expand their businesses further. Current clients in this sector include AstraZeneca, Merck and Novartis. Aside from life sciences and pharmaceuticals, the team has also longstanding relationships with giants in the consumer electronics sector, such as Canon and IBM.

Sources say: *"An incredible stable of lawyers."*

KEY INDIVIDUALS **Dominick Conde** (see p.1886), according to one source, *"completely stands out in terms of raw intelligence, lawyering skills and putting together the perfect case."* He is frequently deployed to fight some of the most challenging briefs going, particularly in the biotechnology, life sciences and pharmaceuticals spheres. **William Solander** (see p.1943) enjoys a *"fantastic reputation"* for his depth of experience in and skillful handling of patent cases, often overseeing the global litigation strategy of a client with respect to the contested product. He is a noted authority on the law regarding biotechnology and life sciences patents and Hatch-Waxman Act litigation. **Robert Baechtold** (see p.276) is described as *"the dean of pharmaceutical patent litigation"* and *"an unquestionable superstar."* Now in an of counsel role, he is of supreme importance to longstanding clients as an adviser on litigation and expansion strategy.

## Fross Zelnick Lehrman & Zissu PC
### See profile on p.1976
THE FIRM This august IP boutique is one of the best and largest firms dedicated to the procurement, handling and enforcement of nonutility rights, including copyright, trademarks, design patents and internet-related matters. The firm's work is international in outlook, and some of the world's best-known brands trust the attorneys to look after their interests in foreign jurisdictions. Clients include Gap, Honeywell and Tiffany & Co.

Sources say: *"They do a great job of recruiting and maintaining diverse talent."*

KEY INDIVIDUALS **Roger Zissu** has long been known as one of the most distinguished practitioners in the fields of copyright, trademarks and unfair competition, particularly with regard to entertainment and the arts. He continues to fight cases and is also someone *"you'd want as the éminence grise"* in matters of global brand strategy. **Susan Upton Douglass** focuses predominantly on copyright filing and counseling, as well as trademark portfolio management, filing, searching, litigation and internet-related licensing agreements. **James Weinberger** is prized by big-name brands for his deep knowledge and extensive experience of copyright, trade dress and trademark matters both international and domestic. His work is primarily contentious and extends across a wide range of industry sectors. **Richard Lehv** specializes largely in adversarial situations, including copyright, false advertising, trademark and unfair competition cases before the courts, as well as cancellation and opposition actions before the Trademark Trial and Appeal Board.

## Gibson, Dunn & Crutcher LLP
### See profile on p.682
THE FIRM In terms of caseload and the value of these actions, Gibson Dunn & Crutcher is one of the largest IP practices in the city, and its rapid and sustained growth is a testament to the dynamism and quality of its attorneys. Companies engaged in business-critical litigations, including a number of players in the 'smartphone wars', look to

the team to initiate sometimes dramatic reversals of fortune in the courtroom.

Sources say: *"They know the field very well. Excellent trial lawyers."*

KEY INDIVIDUALS **Josh Krevitt** (see p.1911) manages the IP group nationally, and he wins special acclaim for his ability to organize and manage cases, as well as for his superb lead in trial situations. Clients describe him as *"extremely smart"* and *"an excellent trial lawyer."* **Daniel Thomasch** (see p.1947) cochairs the firm's life sciences group. He is an accomplished patent litigator who is highlighted for his capabilities in handling interrelated cases involving multiple patents and jurisdictions. **Benjamin Hershkowitz's** (see p.1902) primary focus is patent litigation, with a strong emphasis on cases involving computer electronics and telecoms technology. Sources remark on his intellect and diligence.

## Goodwin Procter LLP
### See profile on p.1522
THE FIRM Goodwin Procter is one of the leading firms in the city for Hatch-Waxman Act patent litigation on behalf of generic pharmaceuticals manufacturers. This doesn't detract from the team's excellent reputation for handling cases concerning electronics, software, computer science and data systems for financial institutions before the courts and the ITC. Clients include Hewlett-Packard, IBM and Merrill Lynch.

Sources say: *"An exceptional IP litigation practice."*

KEY INDIVIDUALS **Mark Abate** (see p.1871) is a consummate IP litigator, well known for his work before the ITC as well as before district and federal courts across the land. He specializes in cases involving software, computer technology and financial services tools. Clients laud his *"sharp insights into how to win patent cases"* and his *"exceptional client service."* **David Hashmall** (see p.1901) leads the firm's litigation group, and spearheads the generic pharmaceuticals patent litigation practice. Key clients say he is *"quick on his feet"* and has a *"very nice way about him"* in court.

## Jones Day
### See profile on p.919
THE FIRM Jones Day's New York office houses one of the firm's largest IP hubs in the USA, and globally, for that matter. All aspects of IP law are covered here, including patent prosecution, IP-heavy corporate transactions, and tech transfer and license agreements. The firm's patent litigation capabilities are particularly strong, with its life sciences work coming in for special acclaim. Clients include Dainippon Sumitomo Pharma, Genentech and DIRECTV.

Sources say: *"A significant force to be reckoned with."*

KEY INDIVIDUALS **Dr Laura Coruzzi** (see p.1886) heads up the firm's life sciences practice group. Clients place great trust in her judgment and strategic sense, while peers point to her *"encyclopedic knowledge on biotechnology patent issues."*

## Kaye Scholer LLP
See profile on p.1984

**THE FIRM** Kaye Scholer remains a powerhouse of elite-standard IP litigation, especially with regard to patent disputes of great complexity. The firm has a well-deserved reputation for its work in defense of the interests of some of the world's most eminent manufacturers of branded pharmaceuticals, as well as its representations of clients in the adjacent spheres of biotechnology and medical devices. **Sources say:** *"Kaye Scholer excels in pharmaceutical patent litigation, especially ANDA litigation on behalf of innovators."* **KEY INDIVIDUALS** Senior in-house lawyers working for giants of the branded pharmaceuticals industry sing the praises of patent litigator **Benjamin Hsing** (see p.1905). One stated: *"His preparation was outstanding, and this really came across at the trial."* Special counsel **Gerald Sobel** (see p.410) is a *"towering figure"* in the field of patent litigation. He is especially renowned for his ability to effectively judge strategic direction in the management of crucial life sciences patent cases.

## Kenyon & Kenyon LLP

**THE FIRM** This venerable firm is dedicated to the practice of IP law, and it shows. Its elite phalanx of lawyers maintain superb expertise, experience and authority in all conceivable disciplines and procedures in the IP sphere. Patent prosecution and Hatch-Waxman Act patent litigation are famously areas of strength for the team. Key clients include Barnes & Noble, Teva and Volkswagen. **Sources say:** *"They are just spectacularly good lawyers who have a strong knack for cutting straight to the chase."* **KEY INDIVIDUALS Richard DeLucia** is a seasoned patent litigator and courtroom advocate, whose easy manner and meticulous professionalism inspire confidence in his clients, many of whom are leading generic pharmaceuticals manufacturers. **Steven Lee** cochairs the firm's chemicals and life sciences group. He advises on all aspects of the prosecution, management and enforcement of biotechnology, chemicals and pharmaceuticals. **Michael Lennon** chairs the firm's European-focused practice. He undertakes a mix of IP litigation and transactional work, such as technology transfers and copyright, patent and trademark agreements. Sources are uniformly impressed by **Elizabeth Holland**'s assured handling of even the most complex pharmaceuticals patent cases. In a recent high-profile matter, she served as lead counsel for Teva in a case involving Copaxone – its flagship drug – and won a significant victory.

## Kilpatrick Townsend & Stockton LLP
See profile on p.1109

**THE FIRM** Kilpatrick is firmly established among the elite providers of legal services regarding copyrights, trademarks and trade secrets. The attorneys oversee the full cycle of rights, including initial name searches, registrations, portfolio management, litigation and challenge infringements. Clients include American Eagle Outfitters, Chippendales and Pearson Education.

**Sources say:** *"They set the gold standard in IP registration and protection."* **KEY INDIVIDUALS Joe Petersen** is rapidly gaining an enviable reputation as a *"terrific copyright lawyer."* He has a strong practice in the protection and enforcement of trademarks, and has niche expertise in disputes concerning royalty structures for the public performance of musical works.

## King & Spalding LLP
See profile on p.445

**THE FIRM** The team at King & Spalding's New York office specializes in patent litigation, although this is not to the exclusion of other disciplines falling within the banner of IP, and the group maintains a deep bench of specialists in the other IP disciplines. The team frequently tries high-value cases for the likes of Alcatel-Lucent, Google, Hoffmann-La Roche and Merck. **Sources say:** *"The King & Spalding team was very charismatic, relating to us not only on a professional level but on a personal one as well."* **KEY INDIVIDUALS** Robert Perry is managing partner of the firm's New York office.

## Kirkland & Ellis LLP
See profile on p.1254

**THE FIRM** Kirkland & Ellis continues to go from strength to strength as a top destination for leading companies looking for representation across the spectrum of IP law. Its patent litigation offering, already one of the best with regards to hi-tech and electronics, has bolstered its pharmaceuticals and medical devices expertise in recent years. The New York office is also home to one of the city's leading copyright, trademark and branding practices. **Sources say:** *"From a strategy perspective, they are one of the most creative firms."* **KEY INDIVIDUALS Leora Ben-Ami** (see p.282) is considered one of the best-known pharmaceutical patent litigators in the country, and the firm continues to count its blessings for having welcomed her into its ranks. Sources praise her *"excellent"* strategic thinking and her practical, plain-speaking approach. **Dale Cendali** (see p.1883) chairs the firm's copyright, trademark, internet and advertising practice group. As one of the most celebrated lawyers in this field in the country, she is something of a talismanic figure for the firm, and has an enviable client roster which includes Fox Entertainment Group, JK Rowling and Disney. **Gregory Arovas** (see p.1874) is, according to sources, a *"superb lawyer"* and a *"go-to"* for in-house counsel at some of the world's best-known technology companies. He has argued sophisticated patent cases before district and federal courts, and the ITC in DC. **Steven Cherny** (see p.1884) is an IP litigator other lawyers would *"recommend in a heartbeat,"* and is valued by clients for being *"very effective at quickly grasping issues and boiling down what they mean to the case, their implications on long-term strategy as well as short-term goals."* **Claudia Ray** (see p.1930) is a copyright, internet law, trademark and unfair competition specialist with a particular emphasis on the

consumer products, financial services, hi-tech, and media and entertainment sectors.

## Milbank, Tweed, Hadley & McCloy LLP
See profile on p.448

**THE FIRM** This compact but highly effective team offers a full IP service, including patent applications prosecution, transactional work and litigation in all rights. The group also assists with the restructuring of IP assets on behalf of creditors in cases of bankruptcy. Key sectors of expertise include financial services, media, pharmaceuticals, technology, and communications and wireless. **KEY INDIVIDUALS Errol Taylor** (see p.1946) leads Milbank's biotechnology and pharmaceuticals patent litigation practice, with a specialization in generic drug approval matters and Hatch-Waxman Act cases. **Christopher Chalsen** (see p.1883) heads up the IP department. He is an accomplished trial lawyer, and has won cases in district, appellate and ITC proceedings. A speaker of Japanese, he has extensive experience representing technology companies from throughout the Far East.

## Orrick, Herrington & Sutcliffe LLP
See profile on p.1994

**THE FIRM** Orrick's IP practice in New York is geared mainly toward patent litigation, although the team does also turn its hand to patent prosecution and strategic counseling for key clients. Its principal areas of expertise include patents relating to the financial service industry, hi-tech and consumer electronics. Clients include Apple, Facebook, Microsoft and NVIDIA. **KEY INDIVIDUALS** Alex Chachkes is a key contact.

## Patterson Belknap Webb & Tyler LLP
See profile on p.1995

**THE FIRM** This New York City firm has a well-balanced IP department and is a leader in the law concerning patents and nonutility rights, such as copyright, trademarks and trade secrets. On the patent side, its main areas of focus are medical devices and pharmaceuticals. Central to the firm's ethos is its emphasis on the importance of trying cases in court, or at least being prepared to take matters to trial if need be. Regarding nonutility rights, trademark enforcement and anticounterfeiting measures are particular strengths of the team. **KEY INDIVIDUALS Gregory Diskant** (see p.1888) is a senior patent litigator, and one of the most effective resources the firm has to offer. He has an *"understated"* manner but also a *"definite edge to him in the courtroom,"* and he *"knows how to use his smarts to get the result needed,"* according to sources. **Robert LoBue** (see p.1915) handles copyright and trademark disputes, typically acting on the proprietary side, often for clients in media and entertainment. Much of his work focuses on the protection of financial data and published content. He heads the copyrights and trademarks practice. **Jeffrey Lewis** (see p.1914) is a seasoned patent litigator whose recent highlights include representing Endo Pharmaceuticals, the manufacturer of the drug frovatriptan, which is prescribed to treat migraines, in an action against Mylan Pharmaceuticals.

The latter is seeking FDA approval for the generic version of the drug. The *"pleasant"* yet *"tenacious"* Geoffrey Potter (see p.1928) is one of the firm's most distinguished experts on trademark enforcement and anticounterfeiting. He recently led a team in a bid to prevent the importation and distribution of counterfeit versions of client LifeScan's OneTouch Ultra blood glucose test strips.

## Paul Hastings LLP
See profile on p.1996

**THE FIRM** This firm's growing New York IP practice has a sterling record in litigation and in court. Its life sciences and pharmaceuticals practice is already well established, while the group continues to further expand its hi-tech and electronics caseload. The firm is also recognized for the quality of its work in copyright and trademark law.
**KEY INDIVIDUALS Joseph O'Malley** is lauded for his *"great experience and capacity to give answers very quickly and smoothly."* He cochairs the IP practice, and is particularly renowned for his work in life sciences and pharmaceuticals cases. **Victoria Cundiff** heads the firm's trade secrets practice, and so her work occupies a strong position in IP and employment law. She is a seasoned litigator and highly experienced in the crafting of restrictive covenant and IP ownership agreements applied to many jurisdictions. **Gerald Flattmann** is a patent litigation specialist who takes on a range of biotechnology, life science and pharmaceutical issues. In addition to disputes, he also counsels on commercial and transactional IP matters. Sources say *"there is no denying* **Robert Sherman** *has a great practice in the area"* of copyright, false advertising, trademark and unfair competition law. He heads the firm's comprehensive trademark practice. Interviewees are especially impressed by **Bruce Wexler**'s talents as a patent litigator in the life sciences sector. One such source praised him as *"a very fine lawyer; extremely smart, with encyclopedic knowledge of patent law."*

## Paul, Weiss, Rifkind, Wharton & Garrison LLP
See profile on p.1997

**THE FIRM** This firm is a go-to for global leaders in IP-reliant industries facing particularly challenging issues. Litigation is far and away the group's main focus, and it excels with regards to patent, copyright, trademark and trade secrets disputes. Life sciences and electronics are the mainstay for the patent arm, while its nonutility side is celebrated for its work in the entertainment industry.
**KEY INDIVIDUALS Nicholas Groombridge** (see p.1900) is widely considered to be one of the finest biotechnology and life sciences litigators in New York and further afield. *"He is an incredibly good trial attorney,"* say sources, *"who takes the time to master every detail of a case and dominates the courtroom with his knowledge of both the law and the facts."*

## Proskauer Rose LLP
See profile on p.2001

**THE FIRM** Proskauer Rose enters the rankings this year on the back of praise for its strength in copyright and trademark work for stellar names in the worlds of consumer products, music, publishing and sport. The New York group's patent litigation offering also continues to grow and impress market sources. Clients include Colgate-Palmolive, Lady Gaga, Major League Baseball and Reed Elsevier.
**KEY INDIVIDUALS** Brendan O'Rourke is co-head of the firm's litigation group and its false advertising and trademark practice.

## Quinn Emanuel Urquhart & Sullivan, LLP

**THE FIRM** Already thought of as one of the powerhouses of patent litigation in New York, sources consider Quinn Emanuel to still be very much on the ascendant, in terms of its ability to attract the best lawyers and its capability to take the toughest high-value cases to trial. A number of lateral hires have seen the firm acquire ever more expertise and clients in pharmaceuticals, and the group remains very strong with regard to electronics cases.
**Sources say:** *"They work really hard for their clients."*
**KEY INDIVIDUALS Peter Armenio** is praised for his artful advocacy in the courtroom and his uncanny feel for jury psychology. One source said: *"I have had nothing but success with Peter – he is money in the bank."* He cochairs the firm's global life sciences practice. **Sandra Bresnick** is praised for the breadth of her knowledge and her talents as a trial lawyer. She concentrates mainly on patent infringement and product liability actions, particularly within the life sciences, medical device and pharmaceuticals spheres. **David Radulescu** is much sought after by companies for which success in a patent action against a rival is of the most critical importance to its strategy. He has extensive experience of trying multipatent cases in many jurisdictions, typically where electrical engineering technologies are at issue. **Robert Raskopf** is a widely respected trial lawyer in the fields of copyright, design patent, advertising, trade dress, trademarks and trade secrets. Many of his clients are prime movers in the media, entertainment and sports worlds.

## Ropes & Gray LLP
See profile on p.1528

**THE FIRM** Ropes & Gray's IP practice is divided into three groups – patent litigation, noncontentious and transactional patent work, and copyrights, trademarks and other nonutility rights. The patent capability is an even spread between mechanical engineering and hi-tech electronics on the one hand, and biotechnology, medical devices and pharmaceuticals on the other. Clients include Bayer HealthCare, Google, Pfizer and SAMSUNG.
**Sources say:** *"Excellent work – they always come up with a highly polished product."*
**KEY INDIVIDUALS Jesse Jenner** is a venerable first-chair trial lawyer steeped in multipatent, multijurisdictional litigation, and so is someone *"you want on your side,"* according to sources. Much of his time has recently been devoted to leading a team on behalf of Motorola Mobility in a high-profile dispute with Microsoft. **James Haley** has a distinguished practice centered around patent preparation, prosecution, portfolio management and enforcement. He

has prepared and prosecuted patents amounting to billions of dollars in value for clients in the biotechnology, chemical and pharmaceutical industries. **Bradford Badke** is *"intelligent, calm, client focused"* and *"an articulate orator"* in trial situations, according to one client. He recently helped engineer resounding victories for clients Becton Dickinson and Nova Biomedical in a hard-fought patent challenge mounted by life sciences giants Abbott Laboratories and Therasense.

## Sidley Austin LLP
See profile on p.1264

**THE FIRM** Sidley Austin's New York-based IP team undertakes sophisticated and high-stakes patent litigation, with a focus on life sciences, biotechnology, pharmaceuticals and medical dressings, although the group also handles disputes concerning cutting-edge electronics and circuitry as well. Key client names include ConvaTec, LSI, Merck and Johnson & Johnson.
**KEY INDIVIDUALS Thomas Beck** (see p.1877) chairs the New York IP department, and mainly focuses on biotechnology and pharmaceutical patent litigation. He recently acted for ConvaTec in a case mounted by Wake Forest University regarding the rights to a negative pressure wound treatment.

## Skadden, Arps, Slate, Meagher & Flom LLP & Affiliates
See profile on p.2008

**THE FIRM** Skadden has an excellent name in New York and around the world for its litigation-focused IP practice. The team here litigates and tries cases centering on copyrights, false advertising, internet issues and domain names, patents, trademarks and trade secrets. Sectors of which the team has particularly extensive experience include the energy, financial services, healthcare, publishing, media and entertainment industries.
**Sources say:** *"They truly take the client's interests to heart."*
**KEY INDIVIDUALS Daniel DeVito** (see p.1888) is a patent litigator who has tried cases before district and appellate courts as well as the ITC. He takes on matters concerning computer software, digital technology, semiconductors and even aircraft engines. **Edward Filardi** (see p.1892) combines a *"vibrant and energetic"* manner with the wise, strategic-minded counsel that comes with many years of experience trying IP cases of the greatest complexity. He litigates patent and trade secrets cases, as well as related antitrust and unfair competition disputes. Key clients appreciate **Bruce Goldner**'s (see p.1897) services for the *"great combination of practical and legal advice"* they receive. He is co-head of the firm's IP and technology practice group, and advises on transactions and license agreements involving a range of IP rights.

## Weil, Gotshal & Manges LLP
See profile on p.2015

**THE FIRM** The IP offering at Weil Gotshal's head office in New York is truly comprehensive, with its patent litigation capability, and increasingly, its handling of copyright and trademark matters being of widespread renown. This hard-hitting team combines deep technical understanding with extensive experience of fighting cases in the high-end life sciences and electronics arenas. Clients include Apple, Oxford University Press, SAMSUNG and Sanofi.

**KEY INDIVIDUALS Bruce Rich** (see p.1931), a copyright, trademark and antitrust specialist, supervises the firm's non-patent practice and chairs its overall IP department. Market sources remark on his prowess as a litigator, with one impressed source saying: *"He is one of the finest lawyers I've ever encountered."* **Benjamin Marks** (see p.1917) handles copyright and trademark cases, and has a number of blue-chip clients operating in the media, entertainment and financial services industries. He recently upheld client McGraw-Hill's summary judgment win and the injunction in an action brought against the International Securities Exchange's unlicensed use of the S&P 500 on appeal. **Elizabeth Weiswasser** (see p.1950) continues to impress with her superb work as a patent litigator concentrating on biologics and pharmaceuticals.

### White & Case LLP
See profile on p.451

**THE FIRM** This global powerhouse's IP team in New York covers matters concerning copyright, trademarks and patents. Its prowess in the realm of pharmaceuticals patent litigation comes in for special mention by market sources, although this should not overshadow the significance of its representations in hi-tech electronics. Clients include Google, Novartis and Pfizer.

**KEY INDIVIDUALS Dimitrios Drivas** (see p.1889) heads the firm's global IP practice group. He is highlighted in particular for his expertise in patent litigation, strategic advice, licensing and technology transfer agreements.

### Willkie Farr & Gallagher LLP
See profile on p.2016

**THE FIRM** This firm's New York-based IP team has a well-developed life sciences offering providing litigation services, transactional support and regulatory advice to market leaders in biotechnology, medical devices and pharmaceuticals. Computing, data transmission, software and financial services patents are also areas of strength for the practice.

**KEY INDIVIDUALS John DiMatteo** (see p.1888) chairs the firm's IP practice and is a trial lawyer with an excellent track record in district and federal courts. He recently led Bloomberg to victory in a case brought by Swatch.

### WilmerHale
See profile on p.930

**THE FIRM** WilmerHale is consistently lauded for the dynamism and talent of its IP team, which features leading attorneys steeped in the laws governing patents, copyright and trademarks. Its patent capabilities, with particular

regard to life sciences, come in for special praise. The team has tried and overseen cases held in all the USA's patent litigation hotspots, the ITC, and courts in IP-leading economies such as the UK and Germany. Clients include Abbott Laboratories, Columbia University and Novartis.

**Sources say:** *"A rockstar of a firm. Firing on all cylinders."*

**KEY INDIVIDUALS Robert Gunther** (see p.1900) comes in for superb praise from all sources, with one client saying he is an *"outstanding lawyer, a real pleasure to work with"* and has *"one of the best courtroom styles of any lawyer."* He tries cases across the board of patent litigation, from consumer electronics through petrochemicals to pharmaceuticals. **David Bassett** (see p.1876) litigates and tries cases from start to finish, with a strong emphasis on disputes involving biotechnological patents for market-leading clients such as Cephalon and Procter & Gamble.

### Winston & Strawn LLP
See profile on p.1267

**THE FIRM** Winston & Strawn's New York IP practice enters this year's rankings on the strength of its impressive trial capabilities, particularly with regards to patent litigation. Complex, cutting-edge hi-tech and Hatch-Waxman cases are key strengths for the team. Clients include AOL, Yahoo! and Voxx International.

**Sources say:** *"They spent a good deal of time getting to understand our product, and their willingness to put in that effort was key to the successful outcome."*

**KEY INDIVIDUALS Michael Elkin** (see p.1890) manages the New York office, and is a well-respected patent litigator with a nationally acclaimed practice representing digital media and entertainment companies in high-profile, business-critical cases.

### Other Notable Practitioners

**John Desmarais** of Desmarais LLP leads a trial practice geared toward the representation of defendants as well as plaintiffs in high-value patent actions of the highest complexity. He is variously described as *"outstanding"* and *"in a class of his own."* One source describes **Drew Wintringham** (see p.1951) of DLA Piper LLP (US) as *"an excellent patent litigator with one of the quickest technical minds I've ever encountered."* He has experience in handling cases on behalf of clients in the automotive, e-commerce, medical device and software industries. **Paul Fakler** (see p.1891) of Arent Fox LLP is well known as a copyright law specialist, although he also advises clients on trademark matters. He undertakes litigation and advisory work, often on behalf of clients in the media, entertainment and internet spheres. **James Dabney** (see p.1887) of Fried, Frank, Harris, Shriver & Jacobson LLP leads the firm's IP and technology practice group. He is highly experienced at jury and nonjury trials, arbitrations and proceedings

before the USPTO. **Mark Mutterperl** (see p.1921) of Fulbright & Jaworski LLP is an expert in the enforcement and protection of trademarks and copyright, and in similar measures such as anticounterfeiting, false advertising and unfair competition procedures. **John Sweeney** (see p.1946) of Locke Lord LLP chairs the firm's IP department and has decades of experience litigating patent, antitrust, trade dress, trademark and trade secrets cases. He has particularly deep understanding of matters involving mathematics and computer science. **Robert Penchina** (see p.1927) of Levine Sullivan Koch & Schulz LLP is praised as *"incredibly responsive and knowledgeable."* He leads the firm's New York IP practice, and concentrates on litigation and advisory work for clients in areas such as broadcasting, publishing and sports. **Bridget Short** of Lathrop & Gage LLP undertakes complex and often multiclaim disputes involving copyright, trade dress and trademark infringement, false advertising and unfair competition, as well as advising clients on the exploitation and management of US and overseas trademark portfolios. **Monica Richman** (see p.1931) of Dentons is *"particularly adept in dealing with a complex matter and making it understandable to the client,"* according to sources. She is a copyright and trademarks specialist, and heads the firm's fashion, cosmetics and apparel practice. **Marc Friedman** (see p.1894), also of Dentons, is a highly esteemed expert on patent law. He has practice undertaking both complex litigation and the creation and implementation of companies' IP and patent portfolio strategies. **Paul Garrity** of Sheppard, Mullin, Richter & Hampton LLP is valued by clients for his creativity and his ability to *"come up with a solution or angle to a problem not evident at first."* He handles patent, trademark and unfair competition cases. **Steven Pokotilow** of Stroock & Stroock & Lavan LLP chairs the firm's IP practice group. He specializes in IP litigation and the treatment of IP assets in licensing agreements, technology transfer and corporate M&A. **William Hansen** of Lathrop & Gage LLP is a prominent trial attorney who has extensive experience of representing global blue-chip companies in copyright, false advertising, patent and trademark infringement disputes. **William Golden** of Kelley Drye & Warren LLP works in the copyright, trademarks and branding arenas, often representing luxury goods distributors and manufacturers. He recently acted for Bacardi USA in a successful case against Pernod USA regarding the Havana Club trademark. **Andrea Calvaruso**, also of Kelley Drye & Warren LLP, handles prosecution clearance and licensing as well as litigation involving copyright, internet domain names, and trademarks on behalf of well-known brands such as Gucci and Polo Ralph Lauren. **Paul Gupta** recently joined DLA Piper LLP (US) from Orrick, Herrington & Sutcliffe. Gupta litigates and tries cases involving hi-tech electronic, software and internet-related patents.

# LABOR & EMPLOYMENT

Commentary about individuals can be found under their firm's paragraph. If the firm has no paragraph (is not ranked) look at Other Notable Practitioners.

## Labor & Employment
### Leading Firms

**Band 1**
Proskauer Rose LLP *

**Band 2**
Jones Day *
Morgan, Lewis & Bockius LLP *
Paul Hastings LLP *
Weil, Gotshal & Manges LLP *

**Band 3**
Orrick, Herrington & Sutcliffe LLP *
Seyfarth Shaw LLP *
Sullivan & Cromwell LLP *

**Band 4**
Bond, Schoeneck & King, PLLC
Davis & Gilbert LLP
Epstein Becker & Green PC *
Jackson Lewis LLP *
Outten & Golden LLP †

\* Indicates firm / individual with profile.
†ONP = Other Notable Practitioner.

## Senior Statesmen
**Senior Statesmen: distinguished older practitioners**

| | | |
|---|---|---|
| Bernstein Michael I | Bond, Schoeneck & King, PLLC * | |

## Leading Individuals

**Band 1**

| | |
|---|---|
| Curley Michael | Curley, Hessinger & Johnsrud LLP (ONP)† |
| Delikat Michael | Orrick, Herrington & Sutcliffe LLP * |
| Fasman Zachary D | Paul Hastings LLP * |
| Goldsmith Willis J | Jones Day * |
| Klein Jeffrey | Weil, Gotshal & Manges LLP * |
| Plevan Bettina | Proskauer Rose LLP * |
| Rogers Jr Theodore O | Sullivan & Cromwell LLP * |
| Salvatore Paul | Proskauer Rose LLP * |
| Shea Patrick W | Paul Hastings LLP * |
| Waks Jay W | Kaye Scholer LLP (ONP)† * |

**Band 2**

| | |
|---|---|
| DiLorenzo Louis P | Bond, Schoeneck & King, PLLC * |
| Friedman Gary D | Weil, Gotshal & Manges LLP * |
| Ganz Howard | Proskauer Rose LLP * |
| Kohn Jeffrey | O'Melveny & Myers LLP (ONP)† |
| Leblang Kevin B | Kramer Levin Naftalis & Frankel (ONP)† * |
| McKenna Kathleen | Proskauer Rose LLP * |
| Schaffran Andrew | Morgan, Lewis & Bockius LLP * |
| Shaulson Samuel S | Morgan, Lewis & Bockius LLP * |

**Band 3**

| | |
|---|---|
| Babson Marshall B | Seyfarth Shaw LLP * |
| Bassen Ned | Hughes Hubbard & Reed LLP (ONP)† * |
| Baumgarten Joseph | Proskauer Rose LLP * |
| Braid Frederick | Holland & Knight LLP (ONP)† * |
| Cerasia II Ed | Ogletree, Deakins, Nash, Smoak (ONP)† * |
| Collins Erika C | Paul Hastings LLP * |
| Davis Robert P | Mayer Brown LLP (ONP)† |
| Green Ronald M | Epstein Becker & Green PC * |

| | |
|---|---|
| Lampe Matthew W | Jones Day * |
| Plum Bernard | Proskauer Rose LLP * |
| Rosenberg Jill L | Orrick, Herrington & Sutcliffe LLP * |
| Sonnenberg Stephen | Paul Hastings LLP * |
| Starr Michael | Holland & Knight LLP (ONP)† * |
| Turnbull Kenneth J | Morgan, Lewis & Bockius LLP * |

**Band 4**

| | |
|---|---|
| Almon Lorie | Seyfarth Shaw LLP * |
| Berkowitz Philip M | Littler Mendelson, PC (ONP)† |
| Bloom Allan S. | Paul Hastings LLP * |
| Bloom Elise M | Proskauer Rose LLP * |
| Chase Terri L | Jones Day * |
| Collins Patrick | McCarter & English, LLP (ONP)† * |
| Dinkoff Allan | Weil, Gotshal & Manges LLP * |
| Dowling Donald C | White & Case LLP (ONP)† * |
| Goldberg Jerrold F | Greenberg Traurig, LLP (ONP)† * |
| Hoey Barbara | Littler Mendelson, PC (ONP)† |
| Rubin Howard | Davis & Gilbert LLP * |
| Sack Laura | Vedder Price PC (ONP)† * |
| Schwartz David E | Skadden, Arps, Slate, Meagher (ONP)† * |
| Sulds Jonathan L | Greenberg Traurig, LLP (ONP)† * |
| Wallach Eric J | Kasowitz, Benson, Torres & Friedman (ONP)† * |

**Up-and-coming individuals**

| | |
|---|---|
| Brochin Gregg | Davis & Gilbert LLP * |
| Cortes Jessica | Davis & Gilbert LLP * |
| Del Rey-Cone Christie | Curley, Hessinger & Johnsrud LLP (ONP)† |
| Hamid Jyotin | Debevoise & Plimpton LLP (ONP)† |
| Traub Amy | Baker & Hostetler LLP (ONP)† * |

## Band 1

### Proskauer Rose LLP
See profile on p.2001

**THE FIRM** Proskauer Rose continues to be recognized as New York's leading labor and employment team. The group is routinely relied upon by a host of blue-chip clients in relation to a full range of matters, including labor relations, class action and single plaintiff discrimination litigation, and the labor and employment implications of mergers and acquisitions. The team's exceptional reputation is reflected in its continuing representation of major national sports leagues, including the NFL, NBA and MLB. Other clients include NYSE Euronext and NBC Universal.
**Sources say:** *"They are the crème de la crème. When it comes to a new area of law or something unique or difficult they are a fabulous place to go."*
**KEY INDIVIDUALS Bettina Plevan** co-heads both the international labor and employment group and the class action group. She is widely considered to be one of the leading employment litigators in the state, and counts leading law firms and financial institutions among her clients. Sources attest that she *"has a way of seeing the strategic end of a long journey before many others do."* Market observers laud the expertise of **Paul Salvatore** with respect to collective bargaining and litigation and arbitration arising from employment disputes and labor relations. Interviewees note his *"bright, knowledgeable, direct"* style, and point to his possession of *"the one skill most lack – the ability to negotiate a situation."* Clients include Ralph Lauren. **Elise Bloom** recently achieved a highly favorable settlement for Hanesbrands in relation to a race discrimination suit after successfully achieving summary judgment

with respect to harassment and retaliation allegations. She specializes in the representation of employers in individual and class actions. **Howard Ganz** is a labor and employment specialist, as well as a recognized authority on sports law. He anchors much of the firm's work for the NBA, which he has represented in collective bargaining negotiations and litigation brought by the National Basketball Players Association. **Kathleen McKenna** recently defended Whole Foods Market in relation to a lawsuit alleging a series of employment law violations. Clients confirm that she is *"personable but fierce,"* with one interviewee remarking that *"I would trust her in every way possible to do what's in the best interests of the company."* **Joseph Baumgarten** is praised for his *"deep knowledge and pragmatic advice."* Recent matters include representing a leading financial institution in relation to a case alleging gender discrimination. **Bernard Plum** is co-head of the firm's labor management relations group. He serves clients which include The New York Times and the NBA. Admiring sources relate that *"he has no affectations and no pretensions – he distills things very well."*

## Band 2

### Jones Day
See profile on p.919

**THE FIRM** This firm has a fine reputation in the defense of class and collective actions, discrimination litigation and labor relations before the NLRB. Recent matters include the representation of the New York Philharmonic in its collective bargaining negotiations with the American Federation of Musicians. Other clients include Verizon Communications and Electrolux North America.
**KEY INDIVIDUALS Willis Goldsmith** (see p.1897) is an acknowledged leader in the field of collective bargaining and labor relations. He led the team in the aforementioned work for the New York Philharmonic. He is experienced before state, federal and appellate courts. **Matthew Lampe** (see p.1911) represents management clients in class action and other employment-related litigation. He recently defended Service Corporation International in relation to a putative nationwide class action involving claims for unpaid wages. **Terri Chase** (see p.1884) is noted for her

abilities in discrimination, harassment and retaliation litigation. Recent cases include the successful representation of Estee Lauder in an employment discrimination suit.

## Morgan, Lewis & Bockius LLP
See profile on p.2246

**THE FIRM** This firm offers its formidable labor and employment expertise to leading corporate entities, and is particularly noted for its close ties to New York's financial services sector. The team handles FLSA class and collective actions for clients such as UBS, Deutsche Bank and Morgan Stanley. Recent matters include the defense of two nationwide wage and hour class and collective actions on behalf of a leading financial institution.

**Sources say:** *"They are our go-to firm. The key, really, is responsiveness, flexibility and business-focused advice."*

**KEY INDIVIDUALS Andrew Schaffran** (see p.1936) co-heads the firm's financial services employment law team, and is widely admired for his handling of complex employment litigation. One satisfied client relates: *"I thought he did an amazing job. Employment cases have both legal and psychological aspects. He dealt not just with legal issues but emotional ones too."* **Samuel Shaulson** (see p.1940) is described by sources as *"a very fine lawyer,"* with one interviewee noting that *"if we need a clear-cut opinion that explains what the law is succinctly, we go to Sam."* Recent highlights include the representation of a financial institution embroiled in a putative action alleging the failure to pay overtime. Shaulson's work led to the court granting a motion to compel arbitration. **Kenneth Turnbull** (see p.1948) represents employers in a full range of employment disputes, including discrimination, restrictive covenants and trade secrets. Sources reveal that *"he works well with both clients and decision makers in the courts."*

## Paul Hastings LLP
See profile on p.1996

**THE FIRM** The Paul Hastings labor and employment group continues to be recognized for its sophisticated representation of employers in all types of employment litigation. The team has impressed observers with its handling of labor contract renegotiations pursuant to the Chapter 11 reorganization of client American Airlines, while it has also won notable court victories for clients in the telecoms and financial services industries.

**Sources say:** *"A deep bench with a lot of good lawyers."*

**KEY INDIVIDUALS** The highly respected **Zachary Fasman** is national cochair of the firm's employment discrimination practice. He handles the full range of employment litigation and labor relations matters for a high-profile roster of clients. **Patrick Shea** is widely considered to be among the leading employment litigators in New York. He garners strong praise from the market, with sources referring to his *"great passion, personal skills and knowledge,"* and noting that he is *"a great trial lawyer."* **Allan Bloom** recently defended a leading investment bank in relation to a wage and hour class action. He cochairs the firm's New York employment law practice. **Erika Collins** is noted by market observers for her international employment law

expertise. She advises blue-chip corporate clients in relation to cross-border employment matters, including restrictive covenants and document retention. **Stephen Sonnenberg** defends employers with respect to the full range of employment litigation, and is particularly noted by market sources for his expertise in disability law. According to one interviewee, he *"brings a calm and perception about people to the table, and he understands the practicalities of the workplace."*

## Weil, Gotshal & Manges LLP
See profile on p.2015

**THE FIRM** This firm's employment litigation practice group routinely handles complex high-stakes disputes for an impressive client base. The team is particularly noted for its handling of class and collective actions, while it continues to counsel clients in relation to matters arising from M&A, bankruptcy and workforce reduction. Recent matters include representing Alliant Insurance Services with respect to three lawsuits involving trade secrets and restrictive covenants. Other clients include United Health Group and Bank of America Merrill Lynch.

**Sources say:** *"Very, very smart people. They seamlessly pull together as a group."*

**KEY INDIVIDUALS Jeffrey Klein** (see p.1909) is head of the employment litigation group and led the team in the aforementioned matter for Alliant Insurances Services. Sources pay tribute to his *"ability, knowledge base and 'board-ready' analytics."* **Gary Friedman** (see p.1894) is praised for his *"strong strategic sense."* He recently defended Elite Model Management in a restrictive covenants and trade secrets litigation. The experienced **Allan Dinkoff** (see p.1888) recently acted for Merrill Lynch in a high-profile race discrimination case.

## Band 3

## Orrick, Herrington & Sutcliffe LLP
See profile on p.1994

**THE FIRM** The Orrick labor and employment team is recognized for its handling of a wide range of employment litigation matters, including trade secrets litigation, discrimination cases, and wage and hour class action defense. Recent matters include achieving a summary judgment dismissing a class action claim concerning overtime on behalf of Roche Pharmaceuticals. Other clients include Facebook and Credit Suisse.

**KEY INDIVIDUALS** The *"very talented"* **Michael Delikat** (see p.1888) is chair of the labor and employment team and a leading figure in the state's employment bar. He recently achieved a landmark ruling by the New York Supreme Court on behalf of law firm Holland & Knight in relation to a discrimination case. **Jill Rosenberg** (see p.1932) advises clients in relation to the full range of employment law matters. Recent highlights include defending Bank of America in a Sarbanes-Oxley whistle-blower suit.

## Seyfarth Shaw LLP
See profile on p.1262

**THE FIRM** This firm provides a deep level of labor and employment expertise to a roster of blue-chip clients. The team is particularly noted for its handling of class action employment litigation, in which it has scored considerable success in cases for clients such as Konica Minolta Nationwide and Family Dollar Stores. Other clients include 24 Hour Fitness, AIG and BNP Paribas.

**Sources say:** *"Excellent employment attorneys. They have a vast amount of practical experience and are excellent writers."*

**KEY INDIVIDUALS Marshall Babson** (see p.1875) represents management clients with respect to labor relations and litigation. He recently represented luxury department store owner Neiman Marcus in a class action waiver case. **Lorie Almon** (see p.1872) is a class action employment litigator who draws warm praise from market observers. Sources relate that she is *"excellent at stepping back and seeing the bigger picture as well as drawing on her experience to address the current situation."*

## Sullivan & Cromwell LLP
See profile on p.2011

**THE FIRM** Sullivan & Cromwell advises clients in a range of sectors in relation to the full spectrum of employment law matters, including discrimination litigation, trade secret claims, restrictive covenant cases and workforce restructuring. Recent matters include acting as lead counsel to Eastman Kodak in relation to all labor and employment matters stemming from its Chapter 11 reorganization.

**KEY INDIVIDUALS** The *"venerable"* **Theodore Rogers** (see p.1932) heads the firm's labor and employment group, and is a highly respected figure in the state employment bar. Sources describe him as *"a terrific lawyer"* and *"very inspiring."*

## Band 4

## Bond, Schoeneck & King, PLLC

**THE FIRM** This firm advises management clients in relation to a full spectrum of employment litigation. The team routinely handles class and collective actions, and is noted for its provision of compliance counseling and collective bargaining negotiations. Clients are drawn from a range of sectors including manufacturing, healthcare and financial services.

**Sources say:** *"Very cost-effective and great to work with."*

**KEY INDIVIDUALS** The vastly experienced **Louis DiLorenzo** (see p.1888) represents clients in all aspects of labor and employment law. He is particularly noted for his expertise in NLRB proceedings and collective bargaining. **Michael Bernstein** (see p.1878) handles all areas of labor and employment law on behalf of profit and nonprofit clients.

## Davis & Gilbert LLP

**THE FIRM** While this firm is perhaps best known for its work in the advertising space, the team attracts clients from numerous industries for its services in labor and employment. The firm's recent work includes employment policies, wage and hour disputes, and training and compliance. Its client list includes Turner Construction, Fortress Investment Group and Ogilvy & Mather.

**Sources say:** *"They're excellent – extremely responsive. Very good at giving practical advice. Deadline focused."*

**KEY INDIVIDUALS Howard Rubin** (see p.1934) is praised by interviewees for his *"deep knowledge, personal attention, pragmatism and subject matter expertise."* He recently acted for Pershing LLC and The Bank of New York Mellon in a Sarbanes-Oxley whistle-blower case. **Gregg Brochin** (see p.1880) is an emerging talent in employment law matters. He represents management clients in service sector companies, and clients are quick to praise his responsiveness and availability. **Jessica Cortes** (see p.1886) is highly rated for her hands-on approach with clients, and has been especially active in guiding them through internal training programs.

## Epstein Becker & Green PC
See profile on p.1972

**THE FIRM** This firm continues to be recognized for its representation of management clients with respect to all facets of labor and employment litigation and compliance counseling. Clients include Zurich Financial Services Group, OppenheimerFunds and Sumitomo Corporation.

**Sources say:** *"The team is top notch – they've always done well for us."*

**KEY INDIVIDUALS Ronald Green** is cofounder of the firm and founder of the national labor and employment practice. He receives strong praise from market observers, who note that he is *"a master negotiator, strategist and litigator."*

## Jackson Lewis LLP
See profile on p.1982

**THE FIRM** This national labor and employment boutique provides a solid offering from its four offices in New York State. Notable successes include the successful representation of key client IBM in a case alleging claims under the Equal Pay Act. The firm has also represented Nassau County in a series of disputes with public employee unions.

**Sources say:** *"Absolutely positive impression. They're extremely responsive."*

**KEY INDIVIDUALS** New York City managing partner Kevin Lauri is a key contact.

## Outten & Golden LLP

**THE FIRM** This team is widely noted as the leading name for plaintiffs' work in the state. The group specializes in employment litigation and is singled out by numerous defendant-side peers as their toughest opponent in the market.

**Sources say:** *"In terms of plaintiffs' side, Outten would be at the top. No other firm is anywhere near as prominent." "They tend to seek out ground-breaking issues, and have succeeded in the employment litigation space at creating a high-level shop."*

**KEY INDIVIDUALS** Name partner Wayne Outten is a key contact.

## Other Notable Practitioners

**Ned Bassen** (see p.1876) of Hughes Hubbard & Reed LLP recently advised the trustee for the liquidation of MF Global in relation to WARN Act proceedings in the US Bankruptcy Court. Sources describe him as *"bright, charismatic and very tough when he needs to be."* **Philip Berkowitz** cochairs the international employment law practice group at Littler Mendelson, PC and is recognized for his acumen concerning cross-border employment law matters. According to one source: *"I have been equally pleased and impressed by the breadth of Phil's knowledge, and by his ability to be practical."* **Frederick Braid** (see p.1880) heads the New York labor and employment practice group at Holland & Knight LLP. He is particularly noted for his expertise with respect to labor relations, collective bargaining and union organizing. **Edward Cerasia** (see p.1883) of Ogletree, Deakins, Nash, Smoak & Stewart, PC is an experienced trial lawyer with a focus on employment, wage and hour, and benefits litigation. Recent matters include defending WPIX in an age discrimination case brought by its former news director. Clients praise *"excellent writer"* and labor disputes expert **Patrick Collins** (see p.1886) of McCarter & English, LLP for being *"very available, personable and bright. He related very well to witnesses, and also handled the other side very well."*

**Michael Curley** is managing partner and founder member of Curley, Hessinger & Johnsrud LLP. He handles all aspects of labor and employment law, and is praised by interviewees, who state that he *"instills confidence"* and *"is the best labor lawyer I have ever worked with."* **Robert Davis** of Mayer Brown LLP provides *"really invaluable"* guidance in relation to contentious employment matters, say sources. His clients include AXA Equitable Life Insurance Company and Quicken Loans. **Christie Del Rey-Cone**, also at Curley, Hessinger & Johnsrud LLP, is emerging as a fine talent in litigious labor and employment matters. Areas of excellence include matters pertaining to harassment, discrimination and wage and hour cases. **Donald Dowling** (see p.1889) of White & Case LLP has *"significant knowledge of international labor and employment law,"* say sources, who also praise his commitment to client service.

Clients include Western Union, which he advises on cross-border employment issues. **Jerrold Goldberg** (see p.1897) of Greenberg Traurig, LLP is highly rated by clients for his responsiveness and astute handling of a wide range of labor and employment litigation matters. **Jyotin Hamid** of Debevoise & Plimpton LLP is lauded by sources as *"fantastically responsive, tremendously able and client focused."* He recently represented a former CMO in a case concerning noncompete and non-solicit covenants. Littler Mendelson, PC's **Barbara Hoey** is commended for her *"astounding grasp of the law."* She concentrates her practice on single plaintiff and class action employment law litigation. **Jeffrey Kohn** heads the New York labor and employment practice at O'Melveny & Myers LLP. He recently represented CEVA Freight in a putative wage and hour class action alleging that the drivers of the carrier are employees rather than independent contractors. **Kevin Leblang** (see p.1912) heads the employment law department at Kramer Levin Naftalis & Frankel LLP. He counsels employers on employment law disputes and advisory matters. **Laura Sack** (see p.1935) of Vedder Price PC recently successfully represented The Weather Channel in a race and sex discrimination case in the Second Circuit Court of Appeals. She chairs the firm's New York labor and employment practice group, and focuses her practice exclusively on the representation of management clients.

**David Schwartz** (see p.1938) of Skadden, Arps, Slate, Meagher & Flom LLP & Affiliates is *"a brilliant lawyer"* with an ability to *"assemble and manage a team, create a strategy and negotiate,"* say sources. Recent matters include advising Express Scripts on the employment aspects of its acquisition of Medco Health Solutions. At Holland & Knight LLP, **Michael Starr** (see p.1944) is an employment litigator who is experienced before state and federal court. He recently defended InnerWorkings in a noncompete lawsuit, culminating in an advantageous settlement for his client. The *"very efficient, knowledgeable and responsive"* **Amy Traub** (see p.1947) recently joined Baker & Hostetler LLP from Epstein Becker & Green. Traub continues to be recognized as one of the next generation of market leading employment lawyers. **Jonathan Sulds** (see p.1945) heads the New York labor and employment team at Greenberg Traurig, LLP. He represents management in a full range of matters, and is particularly noted for his expertise in labor relations and collective bargaining. Sources pay tribute to the *"tenacious"* **Jay Waks** (see p.1949) of Kaye Scholer LLP, with one describing his *"complete knowledge of the kind of issues that anyone would face."* Areas of focus include internal investigations and employee relations. Employment chair **Eric Wallach** (see p.1949) of Kasowitz, Benson, Torres & Friedman LLP is enthusiastically praised by several clients. One impressed source says: *"He is creative in terms of coming up with arguments and is also technically very good. The papers he writes are just very, very good. He's aggressive in a nice way with whoever we're involved with."*

# LATIN AMERICAN INVESTMENT

Commentary about individuals can be found under their firm's paragraph. If the firm has no paragraph (is not ranked) look at Other Notable Practitioners.

## Latin American Investment
## Leading Firms

### Band 1
Cleary Gottlieb Steen & Hamilton LLP *

### Band 2
Davis Polk & Wardwell LLP *
Milbank, Tweed, Hadley & McCloy LLP *
Shearman & Sterling LLP *
Simpson Thacher & Bartlett LLP *
Skadden, Arps, Slate, Meagher & Flom LLP & Affiliates *
Sullivan & Cromwell LLP *

### Band 3
Allen & Overy LLP *
Chadbourne & Parke LLP *
Clifford Chance US LLP †
Latham & Watkins LLP *
Mayer Brown LLP *
White & Case LLP *

### Band 4
Debevoise & Plimpton LLP *
Linklaters *
Paul Hastings LLP *
Proskauer Rose LLP *
Sidley Austin LLP *

*Indicates firm / individual with profile.*
†*ONP = Other Notable Practitioner.*

## Band 1

### Cleary Gottlieb Steen & Hamilton LLP
See profile on p.1963
**THE FIRM** Cleary continues its transactional dominance in Latin America, with an impressive roster of institutional corporate clients. Its large Latin America team is principally based in New York, though it also makes use of its offices in São Paulo and Buenos Aires. The team is regularly present on many of the region's most significant deals. It advised General Mills on the acquisition of Brazilian food company Yoki Alimentos – a deal estimated at BRL1.75 billion, and part of which involved the company also taking on Yoki's approximately BRL200 million in debt. On the securities side, the team recently advised leading Mexican telecom operator América Móvil on multiple debt offerings, including the EUR1 billion issue of senior notes. It has also undertaken mandates for the likes of PEMEX, Banco Davivienda and Empresa Brasileira de Telecomunicações (EMBRATEL).
**Sources say:** *"The undisputed leader." "Capable, professional and service-oriented lawyers."*
**KEY INDIVIDUALS Richard Cooper** (see p.1886) has an excellent reputation, particularly for complex restructuring and refinancing work. He was one of the lead advisers to the steering committee of bank creditors – including BNP Paribas and RBS – on the refinancing of CEMEX's approximately $7 billion of debt. Sources agree that securities expert **Nicolas Grabar** (see p.1898) is *"the full package: always on top of everything, knowledgeable, and an easy guy to deal with."* **Francesca Odell** (see p.1925) recently worked alongside Grabar advising Petrobras and its subsidiaries on several multimillion-dollar global notes offerings. **Jeffrey Lewis** (see p.1914) is noted for his M&A expertise, with recent highlights including advising Brazilian mining giant Vale on the $407 million disposition of its Colombian assets. Fluent in Spanish and Portuguese, **Carmen Amalia Corrales** (see p.1886) is well known as an expert on securities matters and sovereign debt restructuring. Clients describe her as *"very bright and business-minded."* **Jorge Juantorena** (see p.1907) advises on a range of finance, securities and M&A issues. He recently counseled the initial purchasers on Alpek's $782.1 million debut global equity offering. Senior counsel **Wanda Olson** (see p.1925) is described by sources as *"super-knowledgeable and super-efficient."*

## Band 2

### Davis Polk & Wardwell LLP
See profile on p.442
**THE FIRM** This firm maintains a strong showing in Latin American transactions. The New York-based team regularly works in conjunction with its colleagues in São Paulo, and is noted for its high level of activity in the securities space. It was recently lead counsel to Santander Mexico during its IPO, valued in the region of $4.2 billion, which involved the issue of both common stock and American Depositary Shares. Other notable highlights include counseling a consortium of international banks – among them, HSBC and Santander Mexico – regarding the increase of the limit of its revolving credit facility to Grupo Bimbo.
**Sources say:** *"Its strengths are the quality and performance of its lawyers, together with their commitment and availability."*
**KEY INDIVIDUALS Manuel Garciadiaz** (see p.1895) is widely regarded as one of the leading capital markets attorneys focused on Latin America. His recent highlights include advising Mexichem on an equity offering valued at $1 billion, and on the debt side on a Rule 144A note offering with an aggregate value of $1.15 billion. **John Amorosi** (see p.1873) focuses on public and private M&A. He is regularly instructed by the EBX Group, recently acting for EBX subsidiary MPX on an BRL850 million joint venture with E.ON. **James Florack**'s (see p.314) clients include many of the world's leading financial institutions, several of which frequently instruct him on deals in Latin America. Peers agree he is *"a quality lawyer."*

## Senior Statesmen

Senior Statesmen: distinguished older practitioners

| | | |
|---|---|---|
| Quale Jr Andrew C | Sidley Austin LLP * | |

## Leading Individuals

### Band 1
| | | |
|---|---|---|
| Cooper Richard J | Cleary Gottlieb Steen & Hamilton LLP * |
| Fitzgerald Michael L | Paul Hastings LLP |
| Galvis Sergio J | Sullivan & Cromwell LLP * |
| Grabar Nicolas | Cleary Gottlieb Steen & Hamilton LLP * |
| Schnell Paul | Skadden, Arps, Slate, Meagher & Flom * |
| Stolper Antonia E | Shearman & Sterling LLP |

### Band 2
| | |
|---|---|
| Albarracín Carlos | Milbank, Tweed, Hadley & McCloy LLP * |
| Bartfeld Daniel D | Milbank, Tweed, Hadley & McCloy LLP * |
| Darrow Peter V | DLA Piper LLP (US) (ONP) † * |
| Garciadiaz Manuel | Davis Polk & Wardwell LLP * |
| Kartheiser Robert | Allen & Overy LLP |
| Mottesi Marcelo A | Milbank, Tweed, Hadley & McCloy LLP * |
| Odell Francesca | Cleary Gottlieb Steen & Hamilton LLP * |
| Reiter Glenn M | Simpson Thacher & Bartlett LLP * |
| Urda Kassis Cynthia | Shearman & Sterling LLP |
| Williams David L | Simpson Thacher & Bartlett LLP * |

### Band 3
| | |
|---|---|
| Corrales Carmen Amalia | Cleary Gottlieb Steen & Hamilton LLP * |
| Del Pino Antonio | Latham & Watkins LLP * |
| Fleischmann Stuart K | Shearman & Sterling LLP |
| Grant Denise M | Shearman & Sterling LLP |
| Juantorena Jorge U | Cleary Gottlieb Steen & Hamilton LLP * |
| Lewis Jeffrey S | Cleary Gottlieb Steen & Hamilton LLP * |
| Mann Christopher L | Sullivan & Cromwell LLP * |
| McLaughlin Cathleen | Allen & Overy LLP |
| Miller Allen | Chadbourne & Parke LLP * |
| Navia Talbert I | Chadbourne & Parke LLP * |
| Olson Wanda J | Cleary Gottlieb Steen & Hamilton LLP * |
| Tan Gregory | Shearman & Sterling LLP |

### Band 4
| | |
|---|---|
| Alexander Troy | White & Case LLP * |
| Amorosi John | Davis Polk & Wardwell LLP * |
| Arca Emil | Hogan Lovells US LLP (ONP) † |
| Cohen Evan | Clifford Chance US LLP * |
| Duffee David K | Mayer Brown LLP * |
| Florack James A | Davis Polk & Wardwell LLP * |
| Gillespie Michael J | Debevoise & Plimpton LLP |
| Gooding Gregory | Debevoise & Plimpton LLP |
| Grikscheit Alyssa A | Sidley Austin LLP * |
| Kelley Kevin | Gibson, Dunn & Crutcher LLP (ONP) † * |
| Kleinman Howard | Dechert LLP (ONP) † * |
| Kraiem Rubén | Covington & Burling LLP (ONP) † * |
| Lozano Paola | Skadden, Arps, Slate, Meagher & Flom * |
| Martinez Carlos E | Proskauer Rose LLP |
| Mattei Ivan E | Debevoise & Plimpton LLP |
| Méndez-Peñate Carlos | Akerman Senterfitt (ONP) † |

## Milbank, Tweed, Hadley & McCloy LLP
See profile on p.448

**THE FIRM** Milbank is widely considered the leading firm for project finance in Latin America, and is increasingly strong in the capital markets arena. It has a large team comprising many seasoned regional experts, many of whom are based in New York. The team recently advised a consortium of international lenders on the $378 million financing for the construction of a gas pipeline in Mexico's Chihuahua state. In another lender-side highlight, the firm advised on the $547 million loan for the construction of a deepwater drilling rig, intended for leasing to PEMEX. **Sources say:** *"Deep knowledge of the region and a great deal of experience."*

**KEY INDIVIDUALS** Project finance specialist **Daniel Bartfeld** (see p.1876) is praised by sources for his *"hands-on"* approach, in addition to his high level of experience in Latin America. He frequently represents lenders, including, of late, the Export-Import Bank of Korea, Bank of Tokyo-Mitsubishi UFJ and Crédit Agricole. All-around transactional lawyer **Carlos Albarracín** (see p.1872) joined the firm from Chadbourne & Parke in 2012. Sources highlight his depth of experience in the Colombian and Argentine markets. **Marcelo Mottesi** (see p.1921) heads the firm's global securities group, and recently guided Corporación Azucarera del Perú through a $325 million high-yield offering.

## Shearman & Sterling LLP
See profile on p.2005

**THE FIRM** Sources applaud this practice for its strength in project finance and development, where it has a strong track record acting both for sponsors and developers. A highlight of special note is its advice to Vancouver-based Quadra FNX Mining on its joint venture with Sumitomo Metal Mining for the development of the Sierra Gorda mine in Chile. In another major highlight, the team acted for Grupo de Inversiones Suramericana (Grupo Sura) on the $3.6 billion acquisition of selected Latin American assets of ING; the firm also advised Grupo Sura on the financing for the deal. Shearman also has considerable depth of resources for Latin American capital markets deals. In this practice area it has recently advised issuers such as Inversiones La Construcción, COFIDE and Intercorp Retail, and is well regarded by numerous underwriters. **Sources say:** *"Great expertise and highly qualified lawyers."* *"Very experienced in the region."*

**KEY INDIVIDUALS** Multiple sources commend practice head **Antonia Stolper** as one of the leading capital markets attorneys focused on Latin America. One interviewee comments: *"I regard her as essential for getting a deal done safely."* **Cynthia Urda Kassis** focuses on project finance and development. She continues to advise Goldcorp on ongoing issues associated with its controversial El Morro gold and copper mine in Chile. **Stuart Fleischmann** has three decades' legal experience, focused primarily on capital markets and regulatory finance issues. According to clients, *"Stuart stands out as a very knowledgeable and hands-on partner; I always ask for him to be involved on my deals."*

**Denise Grant** recently represented IFC on a $349 million loan to utilities provider Empresas Públicas de Medellín, to fund improvements to the water and electricity distribution networks in Colombia's Medellín region. **Gregory Tan** is another *"key member of the projects team."* He is advising the Central American Bank for Economic Integration (CABEI) on the $1.2 billion financing for a 220 MW hydroelectric project in Nicaragua.

## Simpson Thacher & Bartlett LLP
See profile on p.2006

**THE FIRM** This highly experienced team is singled out for its excellent relationships with Latin American corporates and locally based counsel. The group has had notable success in finance, capital markets and M&A matters of late, with New York-based practitioners regularly working alongside the firm's team in São Paulo. On the M&A side, it is currently acting for Mercantil Colpatria and two minority stakeholders of Colombian pension fund Colfondos on the sale of a controlling interest in Colfondos to Scotiabank. The team's capital markets highlights include counseling Citi, HSBC and JPMorgan as the initial purchasers in Banco de Bogotá's debut debt offering. **Sources say:** *"Very reliable and always available when you need them."* *"One of the main strengths is the quality of the associates – all of them do remarkably well for their seniority, which makes the firm itself very efficient."*

**KEY INDIVIDUALS** Fluent Spanish speaker **David Williams** (see p.1951) heads the Latin American practice. He is revered for his many years' experience in finance, securities and M&A transactions throughout the region, and is regarded as *"an excellent lawyer"* by clients and fellow practitioners alike. **Glenn Reiter** (see p.391) became of counsel in January 2013, having previously been a partner for close to 30 years. One client observes: *"When it comes to an area with no clear answers, we often turn to Glenn, due to his long tenure and experience."*

## Skadden, Arps, Slate, Meagher & Flom LLP & Affiliates
See profile on p.2008

**THE FIRM** This Latin America group upholds Skadden's reputation as a premier transactional firm. The team is regularly involved in some of the highest-value M&A deals in the region, the majority of which are staffed by individuals from its New York office. It acted for Brazilian conglomerate Cosan on its $1.8 billion purchase of a controlling stake in Companhia de Gás de São Paulo from the BG Group. In finance, the team advised Colombia's Cementos Argos on a $200 million financing for its acquisition of selected US assets of Lafarge, a $760 million transaction on which the group also advised. **Sources say:** *"Unparalleled interpersonal skills, coupled with a deep technical understanding."* *"It is frequently creative in offering alternatives that'll work for both sides."*

**KEY INDIVIDUALS** Practice head **Paul Schnell** (see p.1937) continues to inspire great admiration among the legal profession. He takes a lead role on many of the team's highlight M&A transactions, including Anheuser-Busch InBev's $20.1 billion buyout of its fellow Grupo Modelo

stakeholders. Sources affirm that **Paola Lozano** (see p.1915) *"is one of the leading lawyers in the region"* and note that she *"combines her deep knowledge of US deal-making with an unrivaled understanding of Latin America."*

## Sullivan & Cromwell LLP
See profile on p.2011

**THE FIRM** Interviewees continue to rate this practice highly for the depth of its expertise in M&A and project finance. The team is also commended for the longevity of many of its client relationships. Sullivan & Cromwell was one of several firms advising Anheuser-Busch InBev on its Grupo Modelo acquisition, and also acted for Ally Financial on its $865 million sale of its Mexican subsidiary to the ACE Group. Other highlights include advising First Bauxite on all matters concerning its refractory grade bauxite project in Guyana. **Sources say:** *"Very thorough and detail-oriented."* *"A combination of LatAm expertise, strong transactional experience and a practical approach."*

**KEY INDIVIDUALS** Latin America practice head **Sergio Galvis** (see p.1895) has more than 25 years' transactional experience, and is widely considered one of the leading US attorneys for deals related to Latin America. He was one of the lead partners advising Chile's LAN Airlines on its combination with Brazilian carrier TAM. **Christopher Mann** (see p.361) is also regarded highly in the market. According to one client, *"when the stakes are high and negotiations become sensitive, I can't think of a better lawyer to have on your side. He commands the respect of everyone in the room."*

## Band 3

## Allen & Overy LLP
See profile on p.433

**THE FIRM** This compact practice is particularly focused on project finance, but also maintains a regular flow of capital markets deals. It is currently counseling HSBC, Bancolombia and Export Development Canada as lead arrangers to a 512 MW power project in Peru, the financing for which is valued at $700 million. The same practice group is also active in the Caribbean. **Sources say:** *"We appreciate the personal approach they have to deals."*

**KEY INDIVIDUALS** **Robert Kartheiser** heads the New York project finance group, and is fluent in both Spanish and Portuguese. He has advised lenders on a broad spectrum of major Latin American projects in the course of his career. **Cathleen McLaughlin** has particular expertise in debt securities, having recently guided Peruvian bottler Corporación Lindley through its issuance of Regulation S bonds, valued at $320 million.

## Chadbourne & Parke LLP
See profile on p.1962

**THE FIRM** Chadbourne's Latin America group remains one of the broadest practices in the market, with its New York hub able to call on support from the firm's offices in São Paulo, Mexico City and, for insurance matters,

London. It is particularly active on behalf of private equity funds and clients in the energy sector.

**Sources say:** "*The strengths of the team are its knowledge of public sector deals, commitment to service, responsiveness, and practical, pro-business advice.*"

**KEY INDIVIDUALS Allen Miller** (see p.1919) co-heads the Latin America practice. "*He is by far the most responsive attorney we have ever encountered,*" said one impressed interviewee. Fellow co-head **Talbert Navia**'s (see p.1922) principal expertise is in the private equity space. Clients appreciate "*his effort to keep things simple and practical, as well as his receptiveness to the customer's focus and desires.*"

## Clifford Chance US LLP
See profile on p.439

**THE FIRM** This firm has one of the dominant international practices in São Paulo, and its New York office offers excellent support to that branch. The team is particularly notable for its finance work. Recent highlights include advising TAM on its merger with LAN, and counseling the Inter-American Development Bank on the restructuring of a $488 million loan to Brazil's Delba Drilling for the construction of an ultra-deepwater drilling platform.

**Sources say:** "*They'll tell you in the first meeting what you need to watch out for.*"

**KEY INDIVIDUALS Evan Cohen**'s (see p.1885) recent work includes advising Abengoa on a $200 million credit line from the Inter-American Development Bank, for the development of infrastructure and energy projects throughout Latin America.

## Latham & Watkins LLP
See profile on p.446

**THE FIRM** New York is the key office for this firm's Latin America group. The team often represents players in the private equity space, including The Carlyle Group, Linzor Capital Partners and Odyssey Investment Partners, regarding their Latin American buyouts. Project finance and securities issuances are other areas of expertise.

**Sources say:** "*Partners and associates are very talented and proactive.*"

**KEY INDIVIDUALS** Practice cochair **Antonio Del Pino** (see p.1888) advises clients on a range of M&A, financing and restructuring issues. He recently advised Quiñenco on its $320 million acquisition of various Chilean assets from Organización Terpel.

## Mayer Brown LLP
See profile on p.1257

**THE FIRM** Mayer Brown's Latin America practice incorporates practitioners based in New York, Chicago, Houston and Washington, DC. It continues to attract significant praise from peers and clients for its broad practice. The New York team recently advised Santander Investment Securities and Sovereign Bank on their provision of a $97.5 million credit facility to Telefónica Chile.

**Sources say:** "*Very knowledgeable and professional.*"

**KEY INDIVIDUALS** Peers continue to rate **David Duffee** highly, with one noting that "*he is a very, very good techni-*

*cal lawyer, and also user-friendly – he won't let his ego get in the way of a deal.*"

## White & Case LLP
See profile on p.451

**THE FIRM** While White & Case handles much of its Latin American work out of Miami and São Paulo, its New York presence remains an important component of its practice. This is particularly apparent in the project finance arena. The New York office led the firm's advice to the lead arrangers on the $1.1 billion financing for the OSX-2 FPSO vessel, chartered to OGX Petróleo e Gás. On the M&A side, a team comprising lawyers in New York and Mexico City advised Sherwin-Williams on its acquisition of Consorcio Comex, for approximately $2.4 billion.

**Sources say:** "*Responsive and highly qualified practitioners.*"

**KEY INDIVIDUALS** Sources describe project finance partner **Troy Alexander** (see p.272) as "*excellent to work with.*" He recently acted as co-lead counsel to the initial purchasers on project bond issuances by two Mexican wind farm projects, which had a combined principal value of $298 million.

## Band 4

## Debevoise & Plimpton LLP
See profile on p.1968

**THE FIRM** This firm's institutional strength in private equity matters carries over into its work in Latin America, while the firm is also active in a select number of high-value M&A and capital markets matters. It recently advised regular client Globo Comunicação e Participações, of Brazil, on a $300 million offering of senior notes, and on the partial sale of SKY Brasil to DIRECTV. The team also advised Ambev on its indirect acquisition of Cervecería Nacional Dominicana.

**Sources say:** "*An excellent firm.*"

**KEY INDIVIDUALS** Corporate partners **Michael Gillespie** and **Gregory Gooding** frequently represent the firm's established Latin American clients in high-value M&A transactions. Project finance and infrastructure group chair **Ivan Mattei** has particularly notable experience in toll road transactions in Chile, Mexico and Puerto Rico.

## Linklaters
See profile on p.447

**THE FIRM** Linklaters remains active in the Latin America market. The practice continues to grow, having added a number of new partners over the past few years. Its highlights include advising Schahin Engenharia on the senior secured project financing for the construction of the deepwater drillship 'Cerrado' and chartering of the vessel to Petrobras. Banco Itaú, Bancolombia and Ecopetrol also feature on the firm's list of clients.

**Sources say:** "*We get partner attention on deals.*"

**KEY INDIVIDUALS** Conrado Tenaglia and Michael Bassett are the main contacts in New York.

## Paul Hastings LLP
See profile on p.1996

**THE FIRM** Paul Hastings entered the Latin American scene in 2012, following the lateral hire of a team of lawyers from Dewey & LeBoeuf. The team is especially strong in the securities space, with a particular emphasis on the Mexico market. It has advised on a number of major deals of late, including acting for the initial purchasers and dealer manager on Grupo Kuo's $325 million offering of high-yield bonds.

**KEY INDIVIDUALS** There is broad agreement among peers that **Michael Fitzgerald** is "*the top man for anything in Mexico,*" and that "*he's an excellent lawyer with a strong reputation, and very well known in the field.*"

## Proskauer Rose LLP
See profile on p.2001

**THE FIRM** While this firm is increasingly acclaimed for the strength of its São Paulo office, New York remains an important hub for its Latin America practice, especially in M&A. Among its recent work in that space, it advised Colombian financial institution Banco GNB Sudameris on the acquisition of HSBC's assets in four Latin American countries, including Colombia. It continues to expand its Latin American client base, recently adding Brasbunker Participações and Colombian cable manufacturer Procables.

**Sources say:** "*A bilingual team that is culturally savvy, which can be crucial for certain transactions.*"

**KEY INDIVIDUALS** Practice head **Carlos Martinez** advises on finance, M&A and securities matters across the region. His recent work includes advising Cervecería Costa Rica on its $388 million acquisition of North American Breweries Holdings.

## Sidley Austin LLP
See profile on p.1264

**THE FIRM** This firm is particularly active on matters in the Dominican Republic, acting for several of the country's leading corporates. It advised Banco Multiple Leon on a potential investment by multiple European investment funds, and also acts as counsel to Cervecería Nacional Dominicana on several ongoing matters. Its clients elsewhere in the region include Colombia's Asesorias e Inversiones, which it advised recently on US regulatory issues.

**KEY INDIVIDUALS Alyssa Grikscheit** (see p.1900) is described by sources as "*an excellent negotiator*" and "*very business-oriented.*" She recently advised Banco BBM on the foundation of its BBM Brazil Equity Fund for overseas investors. Senior counsel **Andrew Quale** (see p.1929) continues to advise Cervecería Nacional Dominicana and its parent company E. Leon Jimenes on the $1.1 billion partial sale of CND to an affiliate of Ambev.

## Other Notable Practitioners

Peers rate **Emil Arca** of Hogan Lovells US LLP very highly for his expertise in structured finance and securitization. In the words of one source, "*he pays a lot of attention to get-*

ting things right." **Kevin Kelley** (see p.1908) cochairs the Latin American practice at Gibson, Dunn & Crutcher LLP, where a major part of his practice involves advising Brazilian entities on their New York securities issuances. He is highly respected by peers, one of whom observed that "*he is easy to work with at the same time as being a good lawyer.*" Sources recommend **Howard Kleinman** (see p.1909) of Dechert LLP as a partner who "*is always avail-*

*able and responds very promptly to any inquiries or requests.*" **Rubén Kraiem** (see p.349) heads the Latin America corporate practice at Covington & Burling LLP. Peers acknowledge his depth of experience in the Mexican market. This expertise recently led to his counseling Grupo Financiero Banorte on its acquisition of Afore Bancomer, a deal valued at $1.6 billion. **Carlos Méndez-Peñate** cochairs the Latin America & Caribbean practice at Akerman Senterfitt.

He has over 35 years' experience in corporate law, and is particularly noted for his expertise in relation to Cuba. **Peter Darrow** (see p.1887) of DLA Piper LLP (US) recently advised the lenders backing Central America's largest hydroelectric plant, including RBC Merchant Bank, on the restructuring, recapitalization and refinancing of a $180 million project financing facility. He is also highly experienced in securities matters.

# LITIGATION

General Commercial: The Elite p.1833; General Commercial p.1833; Securities p.1834; Securities Mainly Plaintiff p.1835; White-Collar Crime & Government Investigations p.1835: Securities: Institutional Plaintiffs p.1836

Commentary about individuals can be found under their firm's paragraph. If the firm has no paragraph (is not ranked) look at Other Notable Practitioners.

## Litigation: General Commercial: Highly Regarded Leading Firms

**Band 1**
Allen & Overy LLP *
Kaye Scholer LLP *
O'Melveny & Myers LLP *

**Band 2**
Arnold & Porter LLP *
Cooley LLP
Friedman Kaplan Seiler & Adelman LLP
Greenberg Traurig, LLP *
Mayer Brown LLP *
Morrison & Foerster LLP *
Paul Hastings LLP *

**Band 3**
Freshfields Bruckhaus Deringer US LLP *
Hogan Lovells US LLP
Richards Kibbe & Orbe LLP *

### Akin Gump Strauss Hauer & Feld LLP
See profile on p.904

**THE FIRM** Akin Gump is increasingly gaining prominence in the white-collar crime and government investigations arena for its ability to represent individual and institutional clients in a range of matters. The highly experienced team offers particular expertise in representing investment funds in regulatory and enforcement proceedings while drawing on significant international strength and presence. Examples of its recent work include representing US hedge fund Greenlight Capital and its president, David Einhorn, in a high-profile investigation conducted by the UK Financial Services Authority.

**Sources say:** "*They are extremely easy to deal with, understand the issues extraordinarily well and work hard to serve their clients' interests.*"

**KEY INDIVIDUALS** Securities enforcement and litigation practice head **James Benjamin** (see p.1878) is highly recommended as a "*very good strategist who fights hard for his client.*" Sources particularly highlight his practical approach to complex matters, with one impressed client stating: "*He takes time to understand the business reality of*

## Litigation: General Commercial: The Elite Leading Firms

**Band 1**
Cleary Gottlieb Steen & Hamilton LLP *
Cravath, Swaine & Moore LLP *
Davis Polk & Wardwell LLP *
Paul, Weiss, Rifkind, Wharton & Garrison LLP *
Simpson Thacher & Bartlett LLP *
Skadden, Arps, Slate, Meagher & Flom LLP & Affiliates *
Sullivan & Cromwell LLP *
Wachtell, Lipton, Rosen & Katz *

**Band 2**
Boies, Schiller & Flexner LLP *
Debevoise & Plimpton LLP *
Fried, Frank, Harris, Shriver & Jacobson LLP *
Gibson, Dunn & Crutcher LLP *
Kirkland & Ellis LLP *
Quinn Emanuel Urquhart & Sullivan, LLP
Weil, Gotshal & Manges LLP *

**Band 3**
Cahill Gordon & Reindel LLP *
Kasowitz, Benson, Torres & Friedman LLP *
Kramer Levin Naftalis & Frankel LLP *
Latham & Watkins LLP *
Milbank, Tweed, Hadley & McCloy LLP *

**Band 4**
Cadwalader, Wickersham & Taft LLP *
Jones Day *
Proskauer Rose LLP *
Shearman & Sterling LLP *
White & Case LLP *
Willkie Farr & Gallagher LLP *
WilmerHale *

what we are trying to do and comes up with a creative solution." **Robert Hotz** (see p.1905) leads the firm's New York litigation section, and is a former prosecutor in the US Attorney's Office for the Southern District of New York. He is noted for his command of both civil and criminal litigation, and is considered "*very pleasant to deal with, with a manner that regulators and co-counsel appreciate.*" **Michael**

**Asaro** (see p.1874) is "*an experienced and skillful advocate*" who "*has a real ability to articulate what information he thinks is material and why.*" His experience includes representing clients in investigations and litigation related to a wide range of regulatory matters.

### Allen & Overy LLP
See profile on p.433

**THE FIRM** The respected litigation team in Allen & Overy's New York office is gaining an increasingly impressive foothold in both the criminal investigation arena and the general commercial space. Its noteworthy client base benefits from its cross-border capabilities and international presence; key names include RBS, Deutsche Bank and JPMorgan Chase. The team's ongoing representation of former Lehman Brothers chairman Richard Fuld shows its noted ability to handle high-profile government and civil proceedings. The team's trial expertise was also recently demonstrated by its defense of PCCP in the New York Supreme Court.

**Sources say:** "*They were very attentive and thorough; they thought through the issues very well and reasoned them out. It was all in all a very good experience.*"

**KEY INDIVIDUALS Patricia Hynes** is tremendously experienced in commercial litigation, and is praised by clients as someone who "*covers all the bases and knows the courthouse in and out.*" She recently played a key role in successfully defending JPMorgan Chase against claims relating to the Madoff Ponzi scheme. **Pamela Chepiga** is a highly regarded senior partner at the firm, and is noted for her expertise in both general commercial litigation and white-collar criminal investigations. Sources particularly highlight her "*very good and very creative*" approach, and praise her as a "*forceful and zealous advocate.*" She continues to represent former Goldman Sachs vice president Fabrice Tourre in defending against SEC charges. **Michael Feldberg**'s expertise covers both criminal investigation matters and complex commercial disputes. He is commended for his "*extraordinary judgment and excellent manner with people.*" He recently defended UK-based Victor Dahdaleh against charges brought by both the UK Serious Fraud Office and the DOJ. **David Esseks** draws on

## Litigation: General Commercial
### Senior Statesmen

**Senior Statesmen:** distinguished older practitioners

| | | | |
|---|---|---|---|
| Lerner Jonathan J | Skadden, Arps, Slate, Meagher & Flom * | Wachtell Herbert M | Wachtell, Lipton, Rosen & Katz * |
| Nussbaum Bernard W | Wachtell, Lipton, Rosen & Katz * | | |

### Leading Individuals

**Star individuals**

| | |
|---|---|
| Boies David | Boies, Schiller & Flexner LLP |
| Wells Jr Theodore V | Paul, Weiss, Rifkind, Wharton & Garrison * |

**Band 1**

| | |
|---|---|
| Chesler Evan R | Cravath, Swaine & Moore LLP * |
| Giuffra Jr Robert J | Sullivan & Cromwell LLP * |
| Joseph Gregory P | Gregory P Joseph Law Offices LLC (ONP) † |
| Ostrager Barry R | Simpson Thacher & Bartlett LLP * |
| Quinn James W | Weil, Gotshal & Manges LLP * |
| Roth Eric M | Wachtell, Lipton, Rosen & Katz * |

**Band 2**

| | |
|---|---|
| Baron Robert | Cravath, Swaine & Moore LLP * |
| Berke Barry H | Kramer Levin Naftalis & Frankel LLP * |
| Butwin Bradley | O'Melveny & Myers LLP * |
| Fagen Leslie Gordon | Paul, Weiss, Rifkind, Wharton & Garrison * |
| Flumenbaum Martin | Paul, Weiss, Rifkind, Wharton & Garrison * |
| Gilman Charles A | Cahill Gordon & Reindel LLP * |
| Ichel David W | Simpson Thacher & Bartlett LLP * |
| Kasowitz Marc E | Kasowitz, Benson, Torres & Friedman LLP * |
| Kavaler Thomas J | Cahill Gordon & Reindel LLP * |
| Kiernan John S | Debevoise & Plimpton LLP |
| Levine Alan | Cooley LLP |
| Mastro Randy | Gibson, Dunn & Crutcher LLP * |
| Naftalis Gary P | Kramer Levin Naftalis & Frankel LLP * |
| Snyder Orin | Gibson, Dunn & Crutcher LLP * |

**Band 3**

| | |
|---|---|
| Barenholtz Celia | Cooley LLP |
| Bodian Robert | Mintz Levin Cohn Ferris Glovsky (ONP) † * |
| Brandt James E | Latham & Watkins LLP * |
| Calamari Peter E | Quinn Emanuel Urquhart & Sullivan, LLP |
| Carlinsky Michael | Quinn Emanuel Urquhart & Sullivan, LLP |
| Chepiga Pamela | Allen & Overy LLP |
| Dunne Carey R | Davis Polk & Wardwell LLP * |
| Edlin Richard A | Greenberg Traurig, LLP * |
| Fader Bruce E | Proskauer Rose LLP |
| Feldberg Michael | Allen & Overy LLP |
| Fetterman Daniel J | Kasowitz, Benson, Torres & Friedman LLP * |
| Flaum Douglas H | Fried, Frank, Harris, Shriver & Jacobson * |
| Frackman Andrew | O'Melveny & Myers LLP |
| Friedman Lawrence B | Cleary Gottlieb Steen & Hamilton LLP * |
| Glazer Dennis | Davis Polk & Wardwell LLP * |
| Hynes Patricia | Allen & Overy LLP |
| Karp Brad S | Paul, Weiss, Rifkind, Wharton & Garrison * |

| | |
|---|---|
| Klapper Richard | Sullivan & Cromwell LLP * |
| Lefkowitz Jay | Kirkland & Ellis LLP * |
| Mansfield Alan | Greenberg Traurig, LLP * |
| Marks Aaron H. | Kasowitz, Benson, Torres & Friedman LLP * |
| McGuinness William G | Fried, Frank, Harris, Shriver & Jacobson * |
| Miller Michael | Steptoe & Johnson LLP (ONP) † |
| Moloney Thomas J | Cleary Gottlieb Steen & Hamilton LLP * |
| Orr Dennis P | Morrison & Foerster LLP * |
| Polkes Jonathan | Weil, Gotshal & Manges LLP * |
| Rubinstein Aaron | Kaye Scholer LLP * |
| Ruskin Bradley I | Proskauer Rose LLP |
| Seiler Eric | Friedman Kaplan Seiler & Adelman LLP |
| Shuster Michael S | Holwell Shuster & Goldberg LLP (ONP) † |
| Solomon Louis M | Cadwalader, Wickersham & Taft LLP * |
| Werder Jr Richard I | Quinn Emanuel Urquhart & Sullivan, LLP |
| Wolinsky Marc | Wachtell, Lipton, Rosen & Katz * |

**Band 4**

| | |
|---|---|
| Addison Linda L | Fulbright & Jaworski LLP (ONP) † * |
| Archer Judith A | Fulbright & Jaworski LLP (ONP) † * |
| Beller Daniel J | Paul, Weiss, Rifkind, Wharton & Garrison * |
| Boyle Edward | Venable LLP (ONP) † * |
| Cunha Mark | Simpson Thacher & Bartlett LLP * |
| Cyr Joe | Hogan Lovells US LLP |
| Fishbein Stephen | Shearman & Sterling LLP * |
| Gelfand David | Milbank, Tweed, Hadley & McCloy LLP * |
| Goldstein Stephanie J | Fried, Frank, Harris, Shriver & Jacobson * |
| Gruenglas Michael H | Skadden, Arps, Slate, Meagher & Flom * |
| Haas Erik | Patterson Belknap Webb & Tyler LLP * |
| Januszewski David | Cahill Gordon & Reindel LLP * |
| Katz Jerome C | Ropes & Gray LLP (ONP) † |
| Kurtz Glenn M | White & Case LLP * |
| Kurzweil Harvey | Winston & Strawn LLP (ONP) † * |
| Lender David | Weil, Gotshal & Manges LLP * |
| McCormack Thomas | Chadbourne & Parke LLP (ONP) † * |
| Monaghan Maura | Debevoise & Plimpton LLP |
| Platt Charles C | WilmerHale * |
| Pratt William | Kirkland & Ellis LLP * |
| Saltzstein Susan L | Skadden, Arps, Slate, Meagher & Flom * |
| Sher Barry G | Paul Hastings LLP |
| Weiner Gregg L | Fried, Frank, Harris, Shriver & Jacobson * |
| Wolowitz Steven | Mayer Brown LLP |

**Up-and-coming individuals**

| | |
|---|---|
| Hennes David | Fried, Frank, Harris, Shriver & Jacobson * |

\* Indicates firm / individual with profile.

† ONP = Other Notable Practitioner.

his experience as an Assistant US Attorney for the Southern District of New York when representing both individuals and institutions in multifaceted investigations and litigation. He is held in high esteem for his *"measured, calm and thoughtful approach."* He recently worked alongside Feldberg on the Dahdaleh matter.

### Arnold & Porter LLP
See profile on p.906

**THE FIRM** Arnold & Porter's impressive litigation group has significant strength in New York. Its broad client base benefits from the group's ability to cover a wide range of civil and white-collar criminal disputes. The firm also earns praise for its dedicated approach to client service, and its notable commercial awareness. Its recent work includes representing Western Digital in its attempt to contest an arbitration award issued against it. Other key clients include JPMorgan Chase and BP.

**Sources say:** *"They are really good at practical advice. They have a really good understanding of our business that allows them to think strategically not just about legal issues but the commercial side too."*

**KEY INDIVIDUALS** A former Assistant US Attorney for the Southern District of New York, **Marcus Asner** (see p.1875) is a highly regarded new entry to the rankings. He is praised by sources as *"a very good trial practitioner"* and *"a skilled negotiator."*

### Baker & Hostetler LLP
See profile on p.2119

**THE FIRM** Baker Hostetler houses an expanding team of litigators that covers a range of white-collar criminal, securities and commercial matters. Sources particularly highlight the group's responsiveness and the experience of its strong bench of former government practitioners. The firm's high-profile role as counsel to the Securities Investor Protection Act trustee for the liquidation of Bernard Madoff Investment Securities continues to attract praise in the market. Its client base also includes MasterCard and Deutsche Bank.

**Sources say:** *"I want quick and thoughtful advice that is grounded in sound knowledge and experience – I get that when I call them."*

**KEY INDIVIDUALS George Stamboulidis** (see p.1944) is a new entry in the table and is commended for his expertise in white-collar criminal litigation. Sources praise his experience as a former member of the DOJ, and comment that he is *"very effective in court."* He is considered *"the complete package."* White-collar defense and corporate investigations group cochair **John Carney** (see p.1882) remains highly regarded for his ability to represent individuals and corporate entities in substantial regulatory matters and litigation. He was selected by the SEC to act as the receiver of Michael Kenwood Capital Management in a matter worth more than $500 million.

### Bernstein Litowitz Berger & Grossmann LLP
See profile on p.1957

**THE FIRM** Bernstein Litowitz maintains its preeminent presence in the securities plaintiff arena. It has an impressive track record and expertise in acting for clients on prosecuting some of the largest private and class actions in recent times. An indicative example was the group's role in reaching the proposed $2.43 billion settlement of claims brought against Bank of America in relation to its acquisition of Merrill Lynch.

**KEY INDIVIDUALS Max Berger** (see p.1878) is consistently viewed as a leader in the securities plaintiff world. He is recommended by sources as a *"dean of the Bar,"* and continues to work on some of the most high-profile actions in this space. His highlights include the recovery of $315 million from MBS issuer Merrill Lynch. **Salvatore Graziano** (see p.1899) is another of the firm's impressive

## Litigation: Securities
### Leading Firms

**Band 1**
Cravath, Swaine & Moore LLP *
Paul, Weiss, Rifkind, Wharton & Garrison LLP *
Simpson Thacher & Bartlett LLP *
Skadden, Arps, Slate, Meagher & Flom LLP & Affiliates *
Sullivan & Cromwell LLP *
Wachtell, Lipton, Rosen & Katz *

**Band 2**
Cleary Gottlieb Steen & Hamilton LLP *
Davis Polk & Wardwell LLP *
Debevoise & Plimpton LLP *
Gibson, Dunn & Crutcher LLP *
Milbank, Tweed, Hadley & McCloy LLP *
Weil, Gotshal & Manges LLP *
Willkie Farr & Gallagher LLP *
WilmerHale

**Band 3**
Bingham McCutchen LLP *
Cadwalader, Wickersham & Taft LLP *
Shearman & Sterling LLP *
Sidley Austin LLP *

**Band 4**
Cahill Gordon & Reindel LLP *
Fried, Frank, Harris, Shriver & Jacobson LLP *
Hughes Hubbard & Reed LLP *
Latham & Watkins LLP *
O'Melveny & Myers LLP *

## Litigation: Securities
### Senior Statesmen

**Senior Statesmen: distinguished older practitioners**

| | | | | |
|---|---|---|---|---|
| DiBlasi Gandolfo V | Sullivan & Cromwell LLP * | | Lerner Jonathan J | Skadden, Arps, Slate, Meagher & Flom * |

### Leading individuals

**Star individuals**

| | |
|---|---|
| Karp Brad S | Paul, Weiss, Rifkind, Wharton & Garrison * |
| Kasner Jay B | Skadden, Arps, Slate, Meagher & Flom * |

**Band 1**

| | |
|---|---|
| Angiolillo Bruce | Simpson Thacher & Bartlett LLP * |
| Benedict James | Milbank, Tweed, Hadley & McCloy LLP * |
| Clary Richard W | Cravath, Swaine & Moore LLP * |
| Giuffra Jr Robert J | Sullivan & Cromwell LLP * |
| Kirsch Mark | Gibson, Dunn & Crutcher LLP * |
| Kramer Daniel J | Paul, Weiss, Rifkind, Wharton & Garrison * |
| Lowenthal Mitchell | Cleary Gottlieb Steen & Hamilton LLP * |
| Mirvis Theodore N | Wachtell, Lipton, Rosen & Katz * |
| Portnoy Lawrence | Davis Polk & Wardwell LLP * |
| Young Michael | Willkie Farr & Gallagher LLP * |

**Band 2**

| | |
|---|---|
| Allerhand Joseph S | Weil, Gotshal & Manges LLP * |
| Auspitz Jack | Morrison & Foerster LLP * |
| Baron Robert | Cravath, Swaine & Moore LLP * |
| Curnin Paul C | Simpson Thacher & Bartlett LLP * |
| Edelman Scott | Milbank, Tweed, Hadley & McCloy LLP * |
| Hakki Adam S | Shearman & Sterling LLP |
| Hoff Jonathan M | Cadwalader, Wickersham & Taft LLP * |
| Holland Mark | Goodwin Procter LLP (ONP)† * |
| Hunter Jr Fraser L | WilmerHale * |
| Maguire William R | Hughes Hubbard & Reed LLP * |
| Markel Gregory A | Cadwalader, Wickersham & Taft LLP * |
| Musoff Scott | Skadden, Arps, Slate, Meagher & Flom * |
| Pietrzak Robert | Sidley Austin LLP * |
| Polkes Jonathan | Weil, Gotshal & Manges LLP * |
| Rosen Richard | Paul, Weiss, Rifkind, Wharton & Garrison * |
| Ruthberg Miles | Latham & Watkins LLP * |
| Shane Penny | Sullivan & Cromwell LLP * |
| Smith Jeffrey Q | Bingham McCutchen LLP * |
| Washer Herbert S | Cahill Gordon & Reindel LLP * |
| Youngwood Jonathan K | Simpson Thacher & Bartlett LLP * |

**Band 3**

| | |
|---|---|
| Baskin Stuart | Shearman & Sterling LLP |
| Bendinger Gary F | Sidley Austin LLP * |
| Goldstein Sandra C | Cravath, Swaine & Moore LLP * |
| Kazanoff Peter E | Simpson Thacher & Bartlett LLP * |
| Murphy Sean M | Milbank, Tweed, Hadley & McCloy LLP * |
| Rosenberg Jonathan | O'Melveny & Myers LLP * |
| Rouhandeh James | Davis Polk & Wardwell LLP * |
| Saltzstein Susan L | Skadden, Arps, Slate, Meagher & Flom * |
| Sama Vincent A | Kaye Scholer LLP * |
| Vizcarrondo Jr Paul | Wachtell, Lipton, Rosen & Katz * |
| Zweifach Lawrence J. | Gibson, Dunn & Crutcher LLP * |

**Band 4**

| | |
|---|---|
| Butwin Bradley | O'Melveny & Myers LLP * |
| De Simone Joseph | Mayer Brown LLP |
| Eckas Scott E | Bingham McCutchen LLP * |
| Fishman Marshall | Freshfields Bruckhaus Deringer LLP * |
| Flaum Douglas H | Fried, Frank, Harris, Shriver & Jacobson * |
| Frackman Andrew | O'Melveny & Myers LLP |
| Halper Jason M | Cadwalader, Wickersham & Taft LLP * |
| Hawkins Howard | Cadwalader, Wickersham & Taft LLP * |
| Klapper Richard | Sullivan & Cromwell LLP * |
| Liman Lewis J | Cleary Gottlieb Steen & Hamilton LLP * |
| Martin Richard | Orrick, Herrington & Sutcliffe LLP (ONP)† * |
| Onorato David J | Freshfields Bruckhaus Deringer US LLP * |
| Rashkover Barry | Sidley Austin LLP * |
| Rice Thomas C | Simpson Thacher & Bartlett LLP * |
| Serino, Jr Joseph | Kirkland & Ellis LLP * |
| Shapiro Stuart | Shapiro Forman Allen & Sava LLP (ONP)† |
| Slifkin Daniel | Cravath, Swaine & Moore LLP * |
| Tambe Jayant | Jones Day * |
| Thau Clifford | Vinson & Elkins LLP (ONP)† * |
| Yanez Antonio | Willkie Farr & Gallagher LLP * |

**Up-and-coming individuals**

| | |
|---|---|
| Neuwirth John | Weil, Gotshal & Manges LLP * |
| Ryan Antony | Cravath, Swaine & Moore LLP * |

*\* Indicates firm / individual with profile.*
*†ONP = Other Notable Practitioner.*

litigators. He earns particular praise for his ability to *"speak the language of defense practitioners"* when representing plaintiffs in high-value cases. **Steven Singer** (see p.1942) enters the rankings on the back of strong support from market commentators. He played a key role in the Bank of America litigation referred to above, and also recently recovered $150 million from Satyam Computer Services.

## Bingham McCutchen LLP
See profile on p.1515

**THE FIRM** Bingham McCutchen is commended for its securities litigation and regulatory expertise, and its New York-based practitioners form a key part of this nationwide strength. The team's noted experience in representing financial institutions is reflected in its impressive client roster, which includes Wells Fargo, MBIA Insurance and Deutsche Bank. The team recently represented Credit Suisse Securities in defending claims of around $2 billion related to the National Century Financial Enterprises ABS litigation.

**Sources say:** *"They understand the approach we need to take and have been efficient with how they deploy their partners and junior staff. They get to the issue quickly, understand it and don't spent too much time on it."*

**KEY INDIVIDUALS Jeffrey Smith** (see p.409) is held in extremely high regard for his *"very keen awareness of financial product issues"* and his ability to act as a *"senior and trusted adviser."* He represents Morgan Stanley Capital Holdings in defending claims brought by the Central

Mortgage Company in a case concerning the role of mortgage servicing entities in litigation arising from the credit crisis. **Scott Eckas** (see p.1889) has extensive experience in the securities litigation market. He is particularly noted for his ability to represent financial institutions in matters requiring a deep understanding of complex products, and has recently been involved in a precedent-setting case involving CDO transactions.

## Boies, Schiller & Flexner LLP
See profile on p.1958

**THE FIRM** There is little in today's litigation arena that this highly skilled group is not able to handle. Its leading practitioners are experienced trial lawyers with success across a broad spectrum of industries, and who are regu-

larly involved in some of the most significant cases. Commentators particularly highlight the group's versatility in representing institutional plaintiffs in securities litigation, and its experience in defending securities cases.

**Sources say:** *"It has one of the most active trial practices and is really good at it."*

**KEY INDIVIDUALS David Boies** is consistently lauded by sources as *"the best civil litigator in the country,"* and stands out for his ability to *"make the impossible understandable."* Those who have witnessed his work consider him to be *"brilliant in the courtroom,"* and confirm his reputation as a star litigator both in New York and across the country.

## Brune & Richard LLP
See profile on p.1959

**THE FIRM** Brune & Richard is steadily gaining prominence as a highly respected boutique with proven experience litigating across a range of matters. Its white-collar criminal defense practice is complemented by significant regulatory and civil litigation expertise, and its client base includes companies such as Laurus Capital Management as well as individuals.

**Sources say:** "The firm has great depth and skill in civil and criminal litigation." "They provide an excellent work product, and they are effective courtroom advocates as well."

**KEY INDIVIDUALS** "Phenomenal lawyer" **Susan Brune** (see p.1881) is "highly respected in the white-collar criminal defense field." She is also praised for her experience in commercial litigation, and brings "a combination of creativity, rigor and superb strategic sense to her analysis of a case." **Nina Beattie** (see p.1877) is a new entry in the rankings, and is considered an "exceptionally talented" attorney by market sources. Her practice covers both civil and white-collar criminal litigation.

## Cadwalader, Wickersham & Taft LLP
See profile on p.438

**THE FIRM** This team is highly regarded for its ability to handle a wide range of securities and general commercial litigation. Its broader expertise across multiple practice areas is also particularly noted, with clients highlighting its cohesive approach to dealing with complex matters. The impressive client portfolio includes MBIA Insurance, Omnicare and Credit Suisse. The team's recent work includes successfully representing defendants Credit Suisse Securities and Column Financial in a case in which the

plaintiffs claimed the defendants broke a verbal agreement regarding a mezzanine loan.

**Sources say:** "They are very client-friendly and always attentive. They look out for our best interests and we have a real partnership with them." "In the midst of battle, the team is fierce, inexhaustible and always ready, while at the same time keeping the sense of humor that is so essential to team success."

**KEY INDIVIDUALS Gregory Markel** (see p.361) is highly praised for his deep experience in securities litigation. His recent work includes representing BP Argentina Exploration in a case brought against Bridas regarding a share purchase agreement. He is a "very wise and practical counselor, in addition to being a strong litigator," say sources. **Jonathan Hoff** (see p.1904) is an "excellent securities litiga-

tor" who is able to "handle big-picture cases while finding time to really get into the weeds of a matter," say sources. His recent work includes continuing to act for MBIA Insurance on bringing claims against Residential Funding Company (RFC) relating to insurance provided for residential mortgage securitizations. This matter is further complicated by bankruptcy proceedings involving RFC. **Jason Halper** (see p.1900) continues to earn plaudits for his securities litigation expertise and experience. Sources praise his tactical approach, and note that he "translates strategies into workable and efficient litigation game plans." He recently obtained the dismissal of a $60 million claim brought by BayernLB against Aladdin Capital Management. **Louis Solomon** (see p.1943) is recognized for his commercial litigation practice and trial strength. He offers experience in a range of complex civil disputes on a national and international level. His recent clients include AriZona Iced Tea and Mead Johnson. **Howard Hawkins** (see p.1902) enters the rankings having earned significant praise from clients. He is "extremely well regarded" for representing financial institutions in a range of disputes involving securities and bankruptcy litigation. He is particularly good at "distilling things down and taking a pragmatic approach," say clients.

## Cahill Gordon & Reindel LLP
See profile on p.1960

**THE FIRM** Cahill Gordon is highly regarded for its experience across a wide range of criminal, commercial and securities litigation. It is particularly praised for its ability to handle a broad spread of matters for clients, and for its creative and pragmatic approach to disputes. The team's recent caseload includes representing McGraw-Hill and subsidiary Standard & Poor's Financial Services in nationwide litigation relating to the ratings given to various securities products.

**Sources say:** "They provide excellent client service. They are always aware of the issues and are entrenched in the solutions."

**KEY INDIVIDUALS Thomas Kavaler** (see p.1908) is held in high regard for his commercial litigation expertise. One source described him as "a brilliant cross-examiner, with one of the smartest analytical minds I have ever come across." Kavaler has handled a range of commercial and securities-related matters for Option One Mortgage and HSBC, among others, of late. Sources praise **Charles Gilman** (see p.1896) for his significant commercial litigation capabilities, and particularly highlight his impressive advocacy skills and experience as "a strategic thinker." He recently represented New Eagle Holdings in a dispute concerning a transaction agreement entered into with Natexis. **David**

## Litigation: White-Collar Crime & Government Investigations

### Senior Statesmen

**Senior Statesmen:** distinguished older practitioners

| | | |
|---|---|---|
| Abramowitz Elkan | Morvillo Abramowitz Grand Iason & Anello * | |
| Stillman Charles | Stillman & Friedman, P.C. (ONP)† | |
| Wing John R | Lankler Siffert & Wohl LLP * | |

### Leading Individuals

**Star individuals**

| | |
|---|---|
| Levander Andrew J | Dechert LLP * |
| Naftalis Gary P | Kramer Levin Naftalis & Frankel LLP * |
| Pedowitz Lawrence B | Wachtell, Lipton, Rosen & Katz * |
| Pomerantz Mark F | Paul, Weiss, Rifkind, Wharton & Garrison * |
| Wells Jr Theodore V | Paul, Weiss, Rifkind, Wharton & Garrison * |
| White Mary Jo | Debevoise & Plimpton LLP |

**Band 1**

| | |
|---|---|
| Benjamin, Jr James J | Akin Gump Strauss Hauer & Feld LLP * |
| Berke Barry H | Kramer Levin Naftalis & Frankel LLP * |
| Bohrer Barry A | Schulte Roth & Zabel LLP (ONP)† |
| Carroll John K | Skadden, Arps, Slate, Meagher & Flom * |
| Chavkin Peter | Mintz Levin Cohn Ferris Glovsky (ONP)† * |
| Kelley David N | Cahill Gordon & Reindel LLP * |
| Richards III Lee S | Richards Kibbe & Orbe LLP |
| Seymour Karen Patton | Sullivan & Cromwell LLP * |
| Seymour Samuel W | Sullivan & Cromwell LLP * |
| Shechtman Paul | Zuckerman Spaeder LLP (ONP)† |
| Strassberg Richard M | Goodwin Procter LLP (ONP)† * |
| Wohl Frank | Lankler Siffert & Wohl LLP * |
| Zornow David M | Skadden, Arps, Slate, Meagher & Flom * |

**Band 2**

| | |
|---|---|
| Barr Evan | Steptoe & Johnson LLP (ONP)† |
| Brodsky David E | Cleary Gottlieb Steen & Hamilton LLP * |
| Brune Susan | Brune & Richard LLP * |
| Byrne Lawrence | Pepper Hamilton LLP (ONP)† * |
| Ceresney Andrew J | Debevoise & Plimpton LLP |
| Chepiga Pamela | Allen & Overy LLP |
| Cleary Robert J | Proskauer Rose LLP |
| Curnin Paul C | Simpson Thacher & Bartlett LLP * |
| Dassin Lev | Cleary Gottlieb Steen & Hamilton LLP * |
| Dunne Carey R | Davis Polk & Wardwell LLP * |
| Edelman Scott | Milbank, Tweed, Hadley & McCloy LLP * |
| Fetterman Daniel J | Kasowitz, Benson, Torres & Friedman LLP * |
| Fishbein Matthew E | Debevoise & Plimpton LLP |
| Heiss Howard E | O'Melveny & Myers LLP |
| Hirshman Michele | Paul, Weiss, Rifkind, Wharton & Garrison * |

| | |
|---|---|
| Johnson William | Fried, Frank, Harris, Shriver & Jacobson * |
| Kim Michael S | Kobre & Kim LLP * |
| Kobre Steven G | Kobre & Kim LLP * |
| Krakaur Keith D | Skadden, Arps, Slate, Meagher & Flom * |
| Liman Lewis J | Cleary Gottlieb Steen & Hamilton LLP * |
| Loewenson Jr Carl H | Morrison & Foerster LLP * |
| Marcu Aaron R | Freshfields Bruckhaus Deringer US LLP * |
| Muller Scott | Davis Polk & Wardwell LLP * |
| Owens Richard D | Latham & Watkins LLP * |
| Park Tai H | Park & Jensen LLP (ONP)† |
| Peikin Steven R | Sullivan & Cromwell LLP * |
| Petrillo Guy | Petrillo Klein & Boxer LLP (ONP)† |
| Romano Benito | Freshfields Bruckhaus Deringer US LLP * |
| Savarese John F. | Wachtell, Lipton, Rosen & Katz * |
| Schwartz William J | Cooley LLP |
| Siffert John S | Lankler Siffert & Wohl LLP * |
| Spears David | Spears & Imes LLP |
| Stein Mark | Simpson Thacher & Bartlett LLP * |
| Vinegrad Alan | Covington & Burling LLP * |
| Yannett Bruce E | Debevoise & Plimpton LLP |

**Band 3**

| | |
|---|---|
| Albert Richard | Morvillo Abramowitz Grand Iason & Anello * |
| Anders David B | Wachtell, Lipton, Rosen & Katz * |
| Anello Robert J | Morvillo Abramowitz Grand Iason & Anello * |
| Asner Marcus | Arnold & Porter LLP * |
| Bach Jonathan | Cooley LLP |
| Beamon Martine | Davis Polk & Wardwell LLP * |
| Beattie Nina | Brune & Richard LLP * |
| Breen Kenneth M | Paul Hastings LLP |
| Carney John J | Baker & Hostetler LLP * |
| Clark Christopher J | Latham & Watkins LLP * |
| Cohen Mark S | Cohen & Gresser LLP * |
| Cohen Steven M. | Zuckerman Spaeder LLP (ONP)† |
| Cooney Jr John P | McKool Smith (ONP)† * |
| Esseks David | Allen & Overy LLP |
| Feldberg Michael | Allen & Overy LLP |
| Finzi Roberto | Paul, Weiss, Rifkind, Wharton & Garrison * |

| | |
|---|---|
| Fishbein Stephen | Shearman & Sterling LLP * |
| Genser Andrew M | Kirkland & Ellis LLP * |
| Goldstein Howard W | Fried, Frank, Harris, Shriver & Jacobson * |
| Hafetz Fred | Hafetz Necheles & Rocco (ONP)† |
| Hecker Sean | Debevoise & Plimpton LLP |
| Hotz, Jr. Robert H. | Akin Gump Strauss Hauer & Feld LLP * |
| Iason Lawrence | Morvillo Abramowitz Grand Iason & Anello * |
| Imes Linda | Spears & Imes LLP |
| Jaffe Bloom Suzanne | Winston & Strawn LLP (ONP)† * |
| Johnson Boyd | WilmerHale * |
| Jossen Robert J | Dechert LLP * |
| Koff Douglas I | Paul Hastings LLP |
| Lawrence Carmen J | Fried, Frank, Harris, Shriver & Jacobson * |
| Levine Josh | Simpson Thacher & Bartlett LLP * |
| Little Edward JM | Hughes Hubbard & Reed LLP * |
| Pitofsky David | Goodwin Procter LLP (ONP)† * |
| Polkes Jonathan | Weil, Gotshal & Manges LLP * |
| Rashkover Barry | Sidley Austin LLP * |
| Rogoff Michael A. | Kaye Scholer LLP * |
| Schachter Michael | Willkie Farr & Gallagher LLP * |
| Siegel Adam | Freshfields Bruckhaus Deringer US LLP * |
| Snell Dietrich | Proskauer Rose LLP |
| Sorkin Ira Lee | Lowenstein Sandler LLP (ONP)† * |
| Stamboulidis George A. | Baker & Hostetler LLP * |
| Temkin Jeremy | Morvillo Abramowitz Grand Iason & Anello * |
| Weinberg Richard D. | Morvillo Abramowitz Grand Iason & Anello * |
| Weinstein Marc A. | Hughes Hubbard & Reed LLP * |

**Up-and-coming individuals**

| | |
|---|---|
| Abernethy Jonathan S. | Cohen & Gresser LLP * |
| Asaro Michael | Akin Gump Strauss Hauer & Feld LLP * |
| Bansal Anirudh | Cahill Gordon & Reindel LLP * |
| Bourtin Nicolas | Sullivan & Cromwell LLP * |
| Glaser Steven | Skadden, Arps, Slate, Meagher & Flom * |
| Kwan-Gett Mei Lin | Willkie Farr & Gallagher LLP * |
| Ruzumna Daniel | Patterson Belknap Webb & Tyler LLP * |
| Zelenko Daniel | Crowell & Moring LLP (ONP)† * |

**Kelley** (see p.1908) is highly respected as a leading white-collar criminal defense practitioner, and is recognized by sources for his ability to *"get to the crux of the issue."* He has a *"huge amount of experience due to his abilities as a former prosecutor,"* and is *"very strong in defending clients,"* say interviewees. **David Januszewski** (see p.1906) handles a range of commercial litigation matters, and is also noted for his experience in securities disputes. Clients appreciate that he is *"efficient, pragmatic and responsive – he is a true business partner guiding clients to the best legal result."* Commentators are quick to praise **Herbert Washer** (see p.1949) for his *"tremendous knowledge, communication skills and genuine interest in helping his clients."* The breadth of his securities litigation expertise is particularly highlighted, as is his *"extremely commercial approach."* **Anirudh Bansal** (see p.1876) is a new addition to the rankings, and

is recognized for his *"amazing breadth of experience"* in white-collar criminal defense work. He also undertakes commercial and securities litigation.

### Cleary Gottlieb Steen & Hamilton LLP
See profile on p.1963

**THE FIRM** Cleary houses an impressive bench of renowned litigators whose ability to handle the most complex disputes keeps the firm at the top of the list for high-profile clients. Its notable experience in matters involving financial institutions continues to see it involved in key commercial and securities disputes on both a national and international scale. The team is also highly regarded for its expertise in the white-collar criminal defense arena, and is bolstered by its significant complement of former government practitioners. It currently represents a range of finan-

cial heavyweights in securities actions triggered by the collapse of Lehman Brothers, including Caja Madrid, Bank of America and HSBC. Other recent highlights include successfully acting for underwriters including Merrill Lynch and Citigroup Global Markets in a securities class action. **Sources say:** *"They have a very broad base of expertise, and real depth that extends globally."* *"They offer outstanding strategic and expert litigation advice."*

**KEY INDIVIDUALS Thomas Moloney** (see p.1920) is an experienced and respected litigator, whose expertise covers a range of securities, commercial and bankruptcy matters. His work includes the high-profile representation of HSBC in matters relating to the Madoff Ponzi scheme. **Lawrence Friedman** (see p.1894) is held in high regard for his commercial litigation practice, and is described as *"masterful in court"* and *"great with strategy; practical and tactical."* He is experienced in handling disputes on a global scale, and his client base includes Crédit Lyonnais and People's United Bank. The *"highly efficient"* **Mitchell Lowenthal** (see p.359) is an esteemed securities litigator who handles complex and high-value civil disputes for clients such as Bank of America. He is particularly noted for his ability to *"synthesize a large amount of information very quickly and get clients the best response to everything."* **David Brodsky** (see p.1881) is praised for the depth of his experience in white-collar criminal defense matters. He is also respected for his ability to handle securities investigations and enforcement matters. He consistently demonstrates a sterling ability to work with both individuals and institutions in high-profile investigations. **Lewis Liman** (see p.1914) is highly regarded for his white-collar criminal expertise, and is also recognized for his experience in securities litigation. He is *"effective, well known and formidable,"* and is highlighted for his *"ability to really dig in on complicated factual issues."* **Lev Dassin** (see p.1887) continues to impress commentators with his extensive experience as a *"seasoned white-collar practitioner,"* and is particularly highlighted for his trial skills. His *"incredibly good judgment and rapport with clients"* see him retained on a raft of complex matters for clients.

### Cohen & Gresser LLP
See profile on p.1964

**THE FIRM** Cohen & Gresser enters the rankings having earned significant praise for its boutique litigation practice. It houses a team of highly experienced white-collar criminal practitioners, and is also able to handle commercial and securities litigation. The group has seen significant growth of late, and offers clients the added benefit of a presence in South Korea as well as New York. Key clients include LG Electronics, Bank of America Merrill Lynch and Southwest Airlines.
**Sources say:** *"They focus intensely on litigation and have a lot of experience in our field."*
**KEY INDIVIDUALS** As a former Assistant US Attorney, **Jonathan Abernethy** (see p.1871) is a *"very talented attorney with a strong background in securities and criminal laws,"* say sources. He offers particular expertise in matters related to the Foreign Corrupt Practices Act (FCPA), and is praised as *"thorough, responsive and very knowledgeable."* **Mark Cohen** (see p.1885) is lauded for his expertise in white-collar criminal defense, and is recognized as *"a very talented courtroom lawyer who is very savvy about commercial issues."* He is a former Assistant US Attorney for the Eastern District of New York.

### Cooley LLP

**THE FIRM** Cooley is highly regarded for its extensive litigation capabilities and notable trial expertise. It offers an impressively diverse practice, with attorneys handling a range of white-collar criminal investigations and complex commercial disputes. This diversity is equally represented in its client base, which includes Facebook, Credit Suisse and Hypo Real Estate. The team's representation of individuals is also highlighted, and is exemplified by its recent defense of Joseph Collins, a former partner at law firm

Mayer Brown, in a high-profile case related to the disintegration of commodities broker REFCO.
**KEY INDIVIDUALS Alan Levine** is praised for his experience in litigating a wide range of commercial and criminal disputes on behalf of institutions and individuals. Sources highlight his great presence in the market, and his creative approach to handling cases. **Celia Barenholtz** is characterized as a highly effective advocate whose practice encompasses both civil and criminal litigation. Her recent work includes representing HSBC Business Credit in an antitrust action brought in the District of Delaware. **William Schwartz** is highly recommended for the experience and expertise he brings to matters, and for his strong strategic and tactical sense. He is particularly recommended as a white-collar criminal defense attorney, and is highly experienced in trying cases. **Jonathan Bach** handles an impressive range of disputes for clients, and is particularly noted for his white-collar criminal expertise. Sources are quick to praise his strong presence in the courtroom. He has acted for several high-profile individuals and organizations of late.

### Covington & Burling LLP
See profile on p.441

**THE FIRM** This respected team is recognized for its extensive expertise in a broad range of regulatory and white-collar criminal defense matters. Its experience in handling matters related to the FCPA is particularly highlighted, as is its strong bench of regulatory attorneys. The practice also undertakes securities litigation, and recently represented Del Monte in numerous shareholder class action lawsuits triggered by a $5.3 billion merger.
**Sources say:** *"It is their prior experience as well as their substantive knowledge that keeps me working with them." "I give full marks to their professional judgment, work habits and ability to understand complex matters."*
**KEY INDIVIDUALS** The *"extremely impressive"* **Alan Vinegrad** (see p.1948) is respected for his creative approach to white-collar criminal matters, and *"inspires a lot of confidence and is very experienced."* He represents both individuals and companies in regulatory and criminal matters, and also handles civil litigation.

### Cravath, Swaine & Moore LLP
See profile on p.1966

**THE FIRM** Cravath has an illustrious reputation in the New York litigation arena, and remains at the forefront of the most complex disputes. It houses some of the premier names in securities and commercial litigation, and as such remains a top choice for an impressive portfolio of clients. The group prides itself on its ability to handle a diverse spread of matters, and is praised for its notable commercial awareness and trial expertise. Its recent work includes acting as national coordinating counsel for JPMorgan Chase on the entirety of its RMBS litigation; the team also plays the same role for Credit Suisse. Other clients include Deloitte & Touche, NCR, Chemed and Vivendi.
**Sources say:** *"I have never seen such a concerted and talented effort consistently, day in and day out. They really are a collaborative organization, and their client service is superb.*

*When you stand back and look at organizations, and put together your list of who you would go to if the world came to an end, it's Cravath."*
**KEY INDIVIDUALS** The *"extremely impressive"* **Richard Clary** (see p.295) is widely recognized as a leading securities litigator, whose extensive expertise in the arena sees him working on the most complex and high-profile cases. In addition to praising his advocacy skills, sources note that *"he sits side by side with you as a trusted adviser, and understands the context of the dispute."* His recent work includes coordinating the representation of Credit Suisse in all disputes arising from its RMBS transactions. Head of litigation **Sandra Goldstein** (see p.1898) is a *"very tough litigator who is extremely client-friendly,"* say sources. She remains highly regarded for the breadth of her expertise, and handles a wide range of securities and commercial disputes. Her recent work includes representing Xerox in securities class action litigation relating to its restructuring. **Robert Baron** (see p.278) is highly praised for his ability to handle both securities and commercial litigation, and offers impressive experience in complex disputes. He recently successfully represented Qualcomm in several shareholder suits triggered by the company's acquisition of Atheros Communications. The renowned **Evan Chesler** (see p.294) is characterized as being *"absolutely extraordinary,"* and epitomizes the firm's dedication to providing broad-based, leading litigation expertise. He is noted as a *"very effective and skilled advocate,"* and works with an impressive range of clients, including Novartis, Morgan Stanley and Merck. **Daniel Slifkin** (see p.1942) is a *"terrific"* new addition to the rankings, highly praised for his securities litigation expertise. Sources note that *"he has the demeanor that gives you confidence when dealing with problems,"* and praise his ability to *"cut right through to the issue."* **Antony Ryan** (see p.397) is recognized as an *"extremely smart and capable"* securities litigator, and is increasingly gaining prominence for his expertise in the accounting sphere. He represents PwC in a range of securities-related disputes.

### Davis Polk & Wardwell LLP
See profile on p.442

**THE FIRM** Davis Polk is highly acclaimed for its leading litigation practice in New York. Its expertise covers all aspects of complex commercial, securities and white-collar criminal litigation, and its highly experienced practitioners are praised for their ability to handle an impressively broad spread of matters. The team offers particular strength to clients with multijurisdictional disputes, due to its impressive global footprint. Its ability to work on complex litigation arising from the financial crisis remains an impressive feature, as demonstrated by its representation of Morgan Stanley in matters arising from its write-down of $9.4 billion related to subprime-related trading. Other clients include BHP Billiton, Morgan Stanley and MF Global.
**Sources say:** *"They are stellar as a firm and they know exactly how to treat a client. One of their standout strengths is their commercial awareness – in terms of strategy and tactics, they are among the best and they have all the right tools in place."*

**KEY INDIVIDUALS** Litigation practice chair **Carey Dunne** (see p.1889) is a *"very distinguished"* attorney whose experience encompasses a range of white-collar criminal defense and commercial litigation. He represented JPMorgan Chase in its $88.3 million settlement with the Office of Foreign Assets Control (OFAC) arising from allegations of undertaking transactions with countries included in sanctions programs. **Dennis Glazer** (see p.1896) remains *"a very highly regarded lawyer"* in the commercial litigation sphere, given his *"very smart and practical"* approach to complex disputes. He is particularly experienced in litigation arising from M&A, and has an impressive client base. **Lawrence Portnoy** (see p.1928) is held in high esteem as a *"go-to guy for securities-related litigation,"* and is praised as an *"incredibly bright and effective lawyer."* He recently represented Credit Suisse in the successful dismissal of a large and long-running securities fraud class action. **Scott Muller** (see p.372) offers superb expertise in white-collar criminal defense matters, and is praised as a *"true strategic thinker."* His recent work includes representing Intesa Sanpaolo in a multifaceted investigation brought by several US government entities regarding allegations of sanctions violations. **Martine Beamon** (see p.1877) is noted for her experience in a broad range of white-collar criminal defense matters, and is held in high regard for the expertise she brings to working with both institutions and individuals. **James Rouhandeh** (see p.1933) heads the firm's litigation practice, and is praised for his *"very creative, thoughtful and intelligent"* approach to securities litigation. He recently led the representation of the Facebook IPO underwriters in securities fraud claims brought by shareholders.

## Debevoise & Plimpton LLP
### See profile on p.1968
**THE FIRM** This leading group is highly commended for its ability to handle high-value litigation and arbitration for a notable roster of clients. It is renowned for its expertise in white-collar criminal investigations, and its skill set encompasses all areas of securities and commercial litigation. Sources particularly highlight the group's dedication to client service, and the deep bench of experts available in a wide range of practice areas. Its recent highlights include representing the Federal Reserve Bank of New York in defending a suit brought by AIG shareholder Starr International. Other clients include Shell, Deloitte and the NFL. Shortly before going to press Mary Jo White, one of the luminaries of the white-collar criminal defense and securities enforcement spaces, was confirmed by the senate as the chair of the SEC.
**Sources say:** *"I have been very pleased with their quality of work, strong commercial acumen and pragmatism."* *"They put so much emphasis on client service that when I call and ask for something, they will work day and night until it is done. Responsiveness has been ingrained into their psyche."*
**KEY INDIVIDUALS Bruce Yannett** is a *"well-respected expert in the FCPA field,"* praised for his ability to *"clearly translate the depth of his expertise and experience into workable and pragmatic advice that takes into account client operations and commercial concerns."* His practice covers a range of matters within the white-collar criminal defense arena. The *"fantastic"* **Andrew Ceresney** maintains a highly regarded practice in the securities enforcement and white-collar criminal defense space. His recent work includes representing JPMorgan Chase in investigations conducted by various agencies into the acquisition and securitization of mortgages. **Sean Hecker** is *"extremely knowledgeable and very practical,"* say sources, and is *"really intelligent and strategic"* in his handling of white-collar criminal matters. **Mary Jo White** is praised as a *"spectacular white-collar defense lawyer,"* and as someone who *"really has the whole package and a well-rounded perspective."* Her *"extraordinary"* expertise is enhanced by her *"stellar record of achievement on the ground outside of the firm,"* and extends to both regulatory and white-collar criminal defense work, and commercial litigation. Her recent work includes representing former Bank of America CEO and chairman Ken Lewis in complex and multifaceted litigation stemming from the Merrill Lynch acquisition. **John Kiernan** is highly valued for his impressive breadth of litigation expertise, and handles complex commercial disputes for a range of national and international clients. Sources particularly praise his *"incredibly well-prepared"* approach to trial, and highlight his *"excellent oral advocacy."* **Maura Monaghan** is a new entry to the rankings, and is praised for her commercial litigation practice. She is considered a *"really good strategist,"* whose *"very high-level analytical skills"* merit particular acclaim. Her expertise also extends to product liability disputes. **Matthew Fishbein** is praised for his *"great wealth of experience"* in white-collar criminal defense work. He is *"a fierce defender who is very passionate about what he does, and is a very strong advocate,"* say sources.

## Dechert LLP
### See profile on p.1969
**THE FIRM** Dechert maintains its impressive white-collar criminal defense offering, and is increasingly recognized for its expertise in the securities litigation arena. It houses a noteworthy group of former government practitioners whose experience in a raft of regulatory and enforcement matters is complemented by extensive trial capabilities. Its litigators are also able to handle a range of complex commercial disputes. The team's recent work includes representing ten independent directors of Lehman Brothers in multiple lawsuits and investigations arising out of the company's collapse. Other clients include UBS and Deutsche Bank.
**Sources say:** *"They are very responsive and efficient. The quality of the work product is always excellent, without exception."* *"They have expertise in various areas and so if one person doesn't have the subject knowledge, there will always be someone else who does."*
**KEY INDIVIDUALS** *"Very dedicated and creative,"* **Andrew Levander** (see p.1913) is acclaimed as a leading white-collar and securities litigator, and a *"terrific oral advocate."* Sources also comment that he is *"among the best litigators currently practicing."* His recent work includes representing former MF Global CEO Jon Corzine in matters arising from the company's bankruptcy. **Robert Jossen**

(see p.1907) is noted for his *"very knowledgeable, calm and reassuring"* approach. He focuses on white-collar criminal and securities litigation, and is highly experienced in representing individuals and institutions in high-profile matters.

## Freshfields Bruckhaus Deringer US LLP
### See profile on p.443
**THE FIRM** Freshfields's New York-based litigation group is increasingly highly regarded for the quality and experience of its litigators. It offers respected expertise in white-collar criminal defense matters, and handles a broad range of commercial litigation. It is also increasingly recognized for its experience in the securities arena. Sources particularly highlight the team's ability to handle multijurisdictional disputes in a streamlined and effective way. Its recent work includes representing Citi in a complex dispute involving claims of fraud and breach of contract. Other clients include Tiffany & Co, BP and RBS.
**Sources say:** *"The coordination among the experts was seamless. Meetings were extremely well organized, efficient and highly effective."* *"They were very client-friendly and responsive, and the quality of the legal work was very high."*
**KEY INDIVIDUALS** The *"extremely experienced and energetic"* **Aaron Marcu** (see p.1916) is held in high regard by market sources for his white-collar criminal defense practice. His experience also extends to securities enforcement matters and litigation. Sources highlight his *"strategic thinking and ability to understand the business."* **Benito Romano** (see p.1932) wins acclaim for his impressive white-collar defense practice. Sources describe him as *"extremely experienced and incredibly down to earth,"* and praise his *"excellent client service skills."* He is also noted for his ability to *"think strategy through and come up with solutions."* The *"very strategic"* **David Onorato** (see p.1925) focuses on securities litigation. His recent work includes representing Bank of America Merrill Lynch in multijurisdictional litigation with the Italian region of Lazio, relating to interest rate swaps and currency sales. He is further praised as *"extremely smart, creative and hard-working."* **Marshall Fishman** (see p.1892) has an excellent reputation for his securities litigation expertise, and offers additional experience in commercial disputes. His recent work includes defending Citi against claims brought by a bank which had purchased more than $200 million in CDOs. As one impressed source said, *"his expertise and business judgment are particularly impressive."* **Adam Siegel** (see p.1941) enters the rankings on the back of praise for his broad-based expertise in government investigations. His experience spans a wide range of matters, including investigations concerning FCPA violations and insider trading. He also handles civil litigation on behalf of domestic and international clients.

## Fried, Frank, Harris, Shriver & Jacobson LLP
### See profile on p.1975
**THE FIRM** This highly regarded practice maintains an acclaimed presence in the litigation arena. Its widespread experience sees it handle a broad range of cases, illustrating the group's strength in commercial, securities and

white-collar criminal work. It adopts a holistic approach to tackling disputes, and houses a significant bench of regulatory and transactional attorneys alongside its litigators. Recent highlights include representing the former president of Lehman Brothers, Joe Gregory, in multiple lawsuits and investigations. The group also represented Merck in class actions triggered by the acquisition of Inspire Pharmaceuticals.

**Sources say:** *"We get instant service and attention, and their work product is top-notch. They really understand and add value to our business."*

**KEY INDIVIDUALS William McGuinness** (see p.1918) is highly regarded for his litigation expertise, and offers extensive experience in handling commercial and securities disputes. Sources praise his *"stellar reputation and excellent presence,"* and note that *"he has a commanding presence in the courtroom and excellent oral advocacy."* Market commentators applaud **William Johnson**'s (see p.1906) impressive experience in the white-collar defense and investigations sphere. He is *"extremely responsive"* when working with clients. His recent work includes representing employees of ICP Investment Management in an SEC investigation into CDOs. **Douglas Flaum** (see p.1893) handles general commercial and securities litigation with equal aplomb, and is particularly praised for his advocacy skills. His expertise also extends into criminal investigations and enforcement proceedings. He recently successfully represented Wells Fargo, Wachovia and former Wachovia employees in two high-profile securities class actions and several other related cases. The *"very experienced"* **Howard Goldstein** (see p.1897) is held in high regard for his white-collar criminal defense expertise. His practice also includes a range of securities enforcement matters, and he works with a wide range of corporations, labor unions and individuals. **Carmen Lawrence** (see p.352) offers a wealth of experience in securities enforcement and white-collar defense, particularly in relation to matters involving the SEC, having formerly served as one of its regional directors. She recently represented David Lerner Associates in an enforcement action brought by FINRA. **Stephanie Goldstein** (see p.1898) impresses clients with her *"very proactive"* approach to a wide range of commercial and securities disputes. Her practice also includes a notable focus on corporate governance matters. A new entry in this year's rankings, **Gregg Weiner** (see p.1950) is recognized for his extensive commercial litigation practice. *"He has a superior ability to simplify the complex issues and translate them,"* say sources, and has *"good oral advocacy"* and an *"impressive command of the law and the facts."* The firm also houses the *"fantastic"* **David Hennes** (see p.1902), who is praised for his ability to handle a wide range of corporate, securities and white-collar criminal litigation. He is particularly commended for his responsiveness and client service.

## Friedman Kaplan Seiler & Adelman LLP

**THE FIRM** Friedman Kaplan is highly respected for its dedicated approach to complex litigation. Its breadth of expertise sees it represent clients from a wide range of industries, and its boutique approach is a notable draw for

sources. The team offers substantial trial experience, and its expertise spans a wide range of commercial, securities and employment disputes, among other matters.

**KEY INDIVIDUALS** *"Fantastic litigator"* **Eric Seiler** is recommended for his *"very smart and perceptive"* approach. His practice covers a wide range of disputes, including securities, and commercial and insurance litigation.

## Gibson, Dunn & Crutcher LLP
See profile on p.682

**THE FIRM** This impressive team continues to draw acclaim for its extensive litigation expertise. It has an excellent command of commercial and securities litigation, and houses an impressive white-collar criminal defense and investigations practice. Sources underline the benefits of the firm's impressive international network, noting that the team is able to comfortably handle complex, multijurisdictional disputes. Its bench of experienced trial lawyers also attracts particular praise. It recently represented a significant group of clients in a class action relating to liability for underwriting more than $600 million securities for MF Global. Key clients include Goldman Sachs, Citigroup Global Capital Markets and Deutsche Bank Securities.

**Sources say:** *"They are not only sensational lawyers but are also very responsive. When you deal with them, you really feel like they jump in and try to understand the commercial context of matters."* *"They brought to the table a very clear strategy and a plan to execute it – their work product was incredibly well put together."*

**KEY INDIVIDUALS Randy Mastro** (see p.1917) is held in high regard for his extensive commercial litigation practice. He is particularly praised for his dedicated approach to matters, with one client stating that he is *"a superb litigator who really has a gift for seeing the deep structure of a problem and cutting away all the complications."* **Orin Snyder** (see p.1942) is recommended for his excellent command of complex litigation. His expertise covers an impressive range of disputes, and he is especially recommended for his work in media and entertainment litigation. His recent work includes successfully representing VOOM HD Holdings in a major case against EchoStar. Sources are also quick to praise his *"exemplary trial skills."* **Mark Kirsch** (see p.1909) is an experienced litigator with expertise in a range of securities, financial and commercial disputes. He is praised as being *"very good at strategy and very responsive to client needs."* His recent highlights include representing UBS in a class action filed after the arrest of London-based rogue trader Kweku Adoboli. The *"extremely experienced"* **Lawrence Zweifach** (see p.1953) earns praise for his *"very smart and creative"* securities litigation practice. He offers expertise in both civil and criminal disputes, to a wide range of clients.

## Grant & Eisenhofer PA
See profile on p.780

**THE FIRM** This firm remains a leading choice for its expertise in securities litigation. It is applauded for its ability to represent plaintiffs in large and complex class actions across a range of industries, and has an impressive success

rate in terms of recoveries. The firm also offers a deep bench of experienced litigators with notable trial expertise. **KEY INDIVIDUALS Stuart Grant** (see p.771) and **Jay Eisenhofer** (see p.770) are held in high esteem for their in-depth experience of securities litigation. They represent clients in the most complex and high-profile disputes, and are praised for their *"smart and formidable"* approach. They both also offer expertise in Delaware corporate law.

## Greenberg Traurig, LLP
See profile on p.1024

**THE FIRM** Greenberg Traurig's New York-based litigators are respected for their ability to handle complex commercial disputes. The firm's extensive presence across the USA and other jurisdictions is a notable strength, as is its experienced group of trial lawyers. The team continues to work with key client Lorillard Tobacco on a number of significant cases. Key clients also include Par Pharmaceuticals, Getty Petroleum Marketing and Hearst Communications. **KEY INDIVIDUALS Richard Edlin** (see p.1889) is highly praised for his *"full panoply of experience"* as a commercial litigator. He has notable experience of trying cases, and handles matters across a broad range of industries. **Alan Mansfield** (see p.1916) is an experienced litigator, whose practice spans both civil and criminal disputes. His recent work includes representing Verizon Communications and Verizon Services in defending a case brought regarding the West Virginia Human Rights Act. He chairs the firm's litigation practice in New York.

## Hogan Lovells US LLP

**THE FIRM** Hogan Lovells is increasingly recognized for its excellence in the New York litigation market. Clients are quick to praise its dedicated approach to service and its ability to offer expertise across a range of sectors. The team handles complex commercial litigation and has significant international capabilities. A significant amount of its recent work has involved financial institutions and disputes arising from the automotive industry. Clients include Barclays, Kia Motors and Dow Jones.

**Sources say:** *"We go back to them because they have a broad and diverse practice. They have excellent lawyers and rank very highly when you look at the level of expertise and sophistication across the whole firm."*

**KEY INDIVIDUALS Joe Cyr** is highly experienced in the commercial litigation arena. In addition to his arbitration skills, he is particularly noted for his expertise in international disputes.

## Hughes Hubbard & Reed LLP
See profile on p.1981

**THE FIRM** Hughes Hubbard's sterling team is particularly praised for its expertise in securities litigation. Its practice also maintains a strong focus on white-collar criminal defense and investigations work, and its notable trial lawyers are equally adept at handling commercial disputes. Recent highlights include representing Ernst & Young Cayman in a class action.

**Sources say:** *"They are creative, strategic in their thinking and very responsive, and have a very high level of advocacy."*

**KEY INDIVIDUALS William Maguire** (see p.360) is an *"outstanding litigator"* who takes a *"very experienced and sophisticated"* approach to securities litigation. Sources particularly highlight his oral advocacy skills, and state that *"he is somebody who can take a fairly complex matter and synthesize it into something more manageable."* **Edward Little** (see p.1914) is *"an extremely focused, experienced and effective trial lawyer,"* say sources. He chairs the firm's white-collar group and is experienced in representing a range of clients in investigations and lawsuits. His recent work includes representing the manager of two Bear Stearns hedge funds, Ralph Cioffi, in SEC enforcement proceedings. **Marc Weinstein** (see p.1950) is a *"practical and strategic"* attorney with experience in representing individuals and institutions in a range of regulatory and enforcement matters. His recent work includes representing Eugene Burger, a former trader at Moore Capital Management, in actions related to alleged manipulation of certain commodities markets.

## Jones Day
See profile on p.919

**THE FIRM** Jones Day draws praise for its impressive litigation practice spanning the USA and further afield. It has a significant bench of experienced trial lawyers who are adept at handling a range of complex commercial disputes and securities litigation. The group's client base is demonstrative of its broad expertise, and includes Chevron, Goldman Sachs and Bombardier.
**Sources say:** *"It is an excellent firm and has a great litigation practice."*
**KEY INDIVIDUALS Jayant Tambe** (see p.1946) enters the rankings backed by extensive praise for his securities litigation practice. He is a *"tremendously valuable litigator"* who is considered *"a sort of miracle in the derivatives field due to his deep understanding of all aspects of it."*

## Kasowitz, Benson, Torres & Friedman LLP
See profile on p.1983

**THE FIRM** This highly skilled firm is a strong contender for many clients in the commercial litigation space, and also offers significant expertise in white-collar criminal defense and investigations. Its dedicated approach to litigation is a noted strength, and sees it increasingly retained to handle plaintiff-side securities litigation on behalf of institutions. Its practice also extends to defending individuals and companies in securities disputes. Recent work includes representing the Federal Housing Finance Agency in bringing actions against several major financial institutions related to RMBS sold to Freddie Mac and Fannie Mae.
**Sources say:** *"They are amazing to watch work – besides being very creative, they are wonderful on their feet and wonderful at client service, at responsiveness and in their ability to deal with huge amounts of material."*
**KEY INDIVIDUALS Aaron Marks** (see p.1917) is an *"excellent tactician"* with a *"very effective and well-prepared"* approach to complex cases. He focuses on commercial litigation, and is an experienced trial lawyer. **Marc Kasowitz** (see p.1907) remains a highly regarded figure in

the New York market, and attracts extensive praise for his creative approach to litigation and his ability to *"get right to the heart of the issue."* He is considered a *"very smart and strategic guy,"* whose trial skills garner him particular praise. **Daniel Fetterman** (see p.1892) is held in high esteem for his extensive experience in white-collar criminal defense and commercial litigation. Sources note that he *"understands in every matter how all the parts fit together,"* and consider him to be a *"very strategic and experienced"* trial attorney.

## Kaye Scholer LLP
See profile on p.1984

**THE FIRM** Kaye Scholer's solid litigation group has expertise in civil and criminal disputes, and handles a range of high-profile matters. Its attorneys offer expertise across a broad range of practice areas, and are particularly noted for their strength in matters arising from the financial services and life sciences fields. Recent highlights include representing Archer Capital Fund in three cases related to mortgage foreclosures, demonstrating the team's trial and appellate strength. The group's increasing expertise in securities litigation has seen it retained by clients such as Brookfield Homes and UBS.
**Sources say:** *"They provide a first-rate service, they are always available and they work extremely well together. They also have a good knowledge of – and sensitivity to – commercial, business and financial issues."*
**KEY INDIVIDUALS Aaron Rubinstein** (see p.1934) is commended for his extensive commercial and securities litigation expertise. Clients are impressed by his significant litigation experience, and highlight his *"intelligent, thoughtful and tenacious"* approach to advocacy. His recent work includes representing Bank of America in high-value litigation related to the bankruptcy of American Home Mortgage. **Vincent Sama** (see p.1935) chairs the firm's securities and derivative litigation practice group. He is also noted for his experience in handling commercial disputes. Sources are quick to praise his *"extremely intelligent and very practical"* approach, and comment that *"he has great analytical skills and is a good advocate in the courtroom."* **Michael Rogoff** (see p.1932) is a new entry to the table, and is praised for his expertise in white-collar litigation and investigation matters. He is characterized as a *"very powerful and effective advocate"* who *"exercises nuanced judgment"* when representing clients. He recently represented Novartis in a qui tam action brought under the False Claims Act.

## Kirkland & Ellis LLP
See profile on p.1254

**THE FIRM** There is no doubt that Kirkland has a leading nationwide litigation practice, and its New York office is another example of this strength. Its attorneys are highly skilled at trial and appellate levels, and offer an impressive breadth of expertise across a wide range of commercial dispute types. The team also focuses on white-collar criminal defense and securities litigation, while maintaining strength in numerous other areas, including product liabil-

ity and environmental disputes. Key clients include UBS Financial Services, CIGNA and Facebook.
**Sources say:** *"They are extremely consistent, deliver a high-quality work product and are very easy to work with. Their advice isn't just thoughtful but practical too."*
**KEY INDIVIDUALS William Pratt** (see p.1928) is an extremely experienced commercial litigator, and is highly praised for his trial expertise. His recent work includes successfully representing Verizon in a jury trial relating to environmental tort claims. *"He has very creative arguments,"* said one impressed source, *"and is able to respond to any questions that are put to him as he has instant access to the facts of the law – he has a gift!"* **Jay Lefkowitz** (see p.1912) is held in high regard by commentators for his impressive trial and appellate expertise, and is considered a *"master strategist and tactician."* Clients particularly value his dedicated commitment to cases and the experience he brings as a *"brilliant Supreme Court advocate."* **Andrew Genser** (see p.1896) is a noted white-collar criminal defense litigator, and is held in high regard for his dedication to client service. His recent work has seen him represent companies and individuals in significant investigations and litigation. Sources commend **Joseph Serino** (see p.1940) as a *"great trial lawyer"* who *"has a command of every aspect of a case."* He is particularly noted for his experience in the securities litigation space, and has represented a wide range of financial services clients.

## Kobre & Kim LLP
See profile on p.1986

**THE FIRM** Kobre & Kim continues to impress with its dedicated approach to litigation, and is gaining an increasingly prominent foothold in the market. It is particularly noted for its experience in white-collar criminal defense and investigations, and also offers expertise in civil disputes. The firm's ability to handle matters with international aspects is also highlighted, with its offices in the British Virgin Islands, Hong Kong and London providing additional strength. Recent work includes representing UK-based Alexander Hunter and Thomas Hunter in their response to an SEC enforcement action. The team also represented a Korean senior executive, Kyoungwon Pyo, in negotiations with the DOJ after indictment by the agency's antitrust division.
**Sources say:** *"They give very practical and useful advice, and are extremely thorough in their approach to a case."*
**KEY INDIVIDUALS Michael Kim** (see p.1909) has *"truly outstanding expertise"* in the white-collar criminal investigation arena, and is also increasingly recognized for his civil work. His recent highlights include representing former MF Global broker Joseph Welsh in numerous actions relating to a CFTC investigation into alleged manipulation of certain commodities markets. The *"energetic and knowledgeable"* **Steven Kobre** (see p.1910) stands out for his experience in a range of white-collar investigation and civil litigation matters. His trial abilities are particularly highlighted, and he is praised for his *"very practical"* approach to complex cases.

## Kramer Levin Naftalis & Frankel LLP
See profile on p.1987

**THE FIRM** Kramer Levin has a prominent litigation practice, and houses a stellar team of trial lawyers. Its strength in the white-collar criminal defense and government investigations space is a key draw for clients, and it also gains praise for its ability to handle commercial and securities litigation. The team's recent work includes successfully representing SiriusXM Radio in a breach of contract action brought against it by One Twelve. It also continues to represent Bear Stearns in multiple investigations and lawsuits stemming from the financial crisis.

**Sources say:** *"They are really strong in litigation – they have good courtroom skills, and they have them in spades." "They give you the gold standard of advice, so you feel that you have gone to the best."*

**KEY INDIVIDUALS** *"World-renowned"* **Gary Naftalis** (see p.1921) maintains his place as a preeminent litigator in this market, particularly in relation to white-collar criminal defense work. He is repeatedly retained for complex and high-value disputes, and earns praise for his trial prowess. His recent work includes the high-profile representation of former McKinsey managing director Rajat Gupta in an SEC enforcement action and criminal prosecution. **Barry Berke** (see p.282) is a *"uniquely talented trial lawyer,"* and is highly praised for his ability to handle white-collar criminal defense and complex civil litigation. He is *"one of the most creative and resourceful lawyers"* in the market, say sources. His recent work includes representing a former portfolio manager at Moore Capital Management, Christopher Pia, in a CFTC investigation.

## Labaton Sucharow LLP
See profile on p.1988

**THE FIRM** Labaton Sucharow is held to be one of the leading firms in the plaintiff securities litigation space, and is respected by peers and clients for its exceptional experience in the most complex of cases. Its litigators have an impressive track record in obtaining large-scale settlements for a wide range of clients. In recent highlights, the group acted for Michigan Retirement Systems on securing a $275 million settlement with Bear Stearns.

**Sources say:** *"The firm as a whole really knows how to put everything together and leaves no stone unturned." "They have an impressive grasp of increasingly complex financial markets."*

**KEY INDIVIDUALS** **Lawrence Sucharow** (see p.1945) is a *"wonderful lawyer, a deeply thoughtful strategist, and a man whose word you can cash at any financial institution,"* according to sources. He is a key figure in plaintiff-side securities litigation. **Thomas Dubbs** (see p.1889) has extensive experience in representing institutional investors in securities litigation. His recent work includes acting for Ohio Public Employees Retirement System, State Teachers Retirement System of Ohio and Ohio Police & Fire Pension Fund in a case brought against AIG, obtaining a $725 million settlement with the organization.

## Lankler Siffert & Wohl LLP
See profile on p.1989

**THE FIRM** Lankler Siffert is highly regarded for its dedicated approach to litigation. It is particularly noted for its experience in representing institutions and individuals in a range of white-collar criminal and regulatory matters. The firm has an impressive group of expert trial lawyers.

**Sources say:** *"They are great and have been great for a very long time – they are one of the mainstays of the New York white-collar practice."*

**KEY INDIVIDUALS** **John Siffert** (see p.1941) is highly regarded for his white-collar criminal defense and investigation expertise. He is characterized as a *"classic counselor, who is also a superb trial lawyer."* Market commentators are quick to praise **Frank Wohl's** (see p.1952) extensive white-collar criminal expertise, and consider him an *"extremely talented"* member of the Bar. He is recognized as a *"go-to person"* for a wide range of civil, criminal and regulatory matters. Highly experienced practitioner **John Wing** (see p.1951) focuses his highly respected practice on criminal matters. He is considered a *"fantastic lawyer"* and maintains an active role in some of the most high-profile cases and investigations.

## Latham & Watkins LLP
See profile on p.446

**THE FIRM** This firm's experienced litigators are well versed in complex commercial disputes, white-collar criminal defense and securities litigation. Sources are quick to highlight the team's ability to handle the most high-value and complex cases across a broad range of practice areas. Its New York-based team can also draw on an extensive national and international network of litigators, providing an additional draw for clients. Recent highlights include representing an affiliate of Cartesian Capital Group in a dispute regarding a $45 million loan facility. The practice's recent securities-related highlights include representing Ernst & Young in a class action sparked by the collapse of IndyMac Bank. Other clients include Deutsche Bank, KPMG and Atlantic TeleNetworks.

**Sources say:** *"They have an excellent quality of work and client service. They definitely understand our business and how to try a case." "They have got some of the best lawyers I have ever worked with."*

**KEY INDIVIDUALS** **Richard Owens** (see p.1925) is an *"incredibly good strategist,"* whose *"tremendous knowledge and ability to think on his feet"* make him a popular choice among clients. He is recognized for his regulatory and white-collar criminal defense expertise, and also increasingly handles securities litigation. His recent work includes representing Deutsche Bank in investigations relating to its RMBS work. **James Brandt** (see p.1880) is a *"seasoned litigator"* and a *"great negotiator,"* who is praised for his *"experience and grasp of issues,"* and his *"very pragmatic, calm approach to addressing them."* He centers his practice on complex commercial litigation. **Miles Ruthberg** (see p.397) attracts significant praise for his securities litigation expertise, and is characterized by sources as a *"superb trial lawyer."* His recent work includes defending Ernst & Young against claims relating to its role as an auditor of Lehman

Brothers. The *"extremely talented and very creative"* **Christopher Clark** (see p.1884) is recognized as an excellent addition to Latham's white-collar criminal defense and government investigation practice. He is praised for his commercial awareness, with one source stating that he *"is able to fit legal advice to clients' needs."*

## Linklaters
See profile on p.447

**THE FIRM** This internationally renowned firm's New York-based group maintains a solid presence in the litigation arena. Its practice spans the full range of white-collar criminal defense matters, and it also has broad-based strength in commercial litigation. The team has been involved in some of the key recent investigations in the financial services space, and is noted for its ability to handle disputes on a wider global scale. Its impressive client roster includes Air France, Barclays Bank, KPMG and BAE Systems.

**Sources say:** *"We have been impressed with the breadth of knowledge and services the firm provides."*

**KEY INDIVIDUALS** Joseph Armao is head of US litigation.

## Mayer Brown LLP
See profile on p.1257

**THE FIRM** Mayer Brown is renowned for the experience its litigators bring to a wide range of complex disputes. It is particularly noted for its ability to handle high-value commercial disputes, and for its securities litigation expertise. It recently represented Morgan Stanley Capital Services in two significant cases brought against several monoline insurers. It also advises Ally Financial on a range of nationwide RMBS-related cases. The firm's notable global footprint is also a particular draw for clients.

**Sources say:** *"They have first-rate lawyers with expertise across a broad range of areas."*

**KEY INDIVIDUALS** **Joseph De Simone** enters the rankings on the back of praise for his securities litigation practice and his experience in handling a range of regulatory and investigative matters. He plays a key role in acting for AIG on some of its most complex securities disputes. **Steven Wolowitz** draws on extensive experience in representing financial institutions in a range of commercial and securities disputes. His recent work includes acting for Bank of America in a case concerning the actions of an alleged rogue trader.

## Milbank, Tweed, Hadley & McCloy LLP
See profile on p.448

**THE FIRM** The growing litigation group at this highly respected firm is commended for its ability to handle complex disputes for an impressive roster of clients. Its experienced trial lawyers cover a wide array of commercial disputes and securities litigation, and have particular expertise in bankruptcy-related cases and matters involving FINRA. The team's cross-border capabilities are illustrated by its recent work representing Vitro SAB Asset in a restructuring matter. The team also represented Citi in a case involving investment vehicles created by Abdullah and Ghazi Abbar.

**Sources say:** *"They are very client-friendly and have really good thoughts on how to approach issues without running around in circles. Their approach is very effective and creative."*

**KEY INDIVIDUALS David Gelfand** (see p.1895) is a *"great strategist,"* praised for his superb trial capabilities. He concentrates mainly on commercial litigation, and has particular experience in representing financial institutions in complex disputes. **James Benedict** (see p.1877) is a leading securities litigator and is consistently praised for his extensive experience in the field. His expertise in acting for mutual funds is particularly highlighted, and he is also noted for his ability to handle a broad range of litigation stemming from the financial crisis. **Sean Murphy** (see p.1921) is a *"very knowledgeable"* member of the team, and focuses on a wide range of securities litigation. He is characterized by one source as a *"strategic and very skilled presenter of information."* **Scott Edelman**'s (see p.308) expertise spans both civil and criminal litigation. He offers expertise across commercial, securities and white-collar criminal litigation. Sources note that he is *"very good at identifying what will save the day,"* and state that they *"value both his legal and business judgment."*

## Morrison & Foerster LLP
See profile on p.1990

**THE FIRM** The New York-based contingent of this impressive firm offers substantial litigation capabilities both in the USA and on an international scale. Sources highlight the exceptional depth of its litigation bench, highlighting the quality of its practitioners, from associates to partners. The team handles a broad range of commercial litigation, and is also noted for its securities and white-collar criminal defense expertise. It works with high-profile clients such as Cadbury, Ernst & Young, Nikon and Novartis.

**Sources say:** *"It is an excellent firm to work with and has very capable attorneys. They are very customer service-oriented."*

**KEY INDIVIDUALS** The *"excellent"* **Jack Auspitz** (see p.1875) is highly commended for his securities litigation expertise. *"He knows the field inside out and has great presence,"* say sources. He has particular expertise in representing non US-based clients in securities disputes, such as Astellas Pharma and Qiao Xing Universal Telephone. **Carl Loewenson** (see p.1915)is acclaimed for his *"very experienced and calm"* approach to handling white-collar criminal defense litigation and investigations. He represents individuals and institutions in a range of matters, and has acted as receiver in three enforcement actions brought by the SEC. Market commentators highlight **Dennis Orr**'s (see p.1925) notable experience as a trial lawyer. He focuses on commercial litigation, and his client base reflects the impressive breadth of his practice.

## Morvillo Abramowitz Grand Iason & Anello P.C
See profile on p.1991

**THE FIRM** Morvillo Abramowitz remains a preeminent choice for clients seeking a dedicated litigation boutique with expert trial lawyers and former government attorneys. The firm has extensive capabilities across the civil and criminal spheres, and is particularly noted for its expertise in all stages of white-collar criminal investigations and trials. The team also handles a range of enforcement proceedings conducted by bodies such as the CFTC and the SEC, on behalf of individuals and institutions. Recent highlights include acting for Steven Davis, the former chairman of Dewey & LeBoeuf, on responding to investigations conducted into the firm's demise.

**Sources say:** *"They have the combination of great lawyers and terrific experience, which makes them an easy choice for clients." "They are exceptional; they have flawless legal acumen, and no detail goes unnoticed."*

**KEY INDIVIDUALS Lawrence Iason** (see p.1905) *"has a wealth of experience in SEC matters,"* and is also praised as an expert white-collar criminal defense attorney. Sources consider him a *"great strategist"* and note his extensive trial capabilities. **Elkan Abramowitz** (see p.1871) draws praise for his impressive white-collar criminal defense work, and is able to handle both criminal and civil matters. Sources commend his *"unusually good way of emotionally connecting to people,"* and state that his ability to communicate makes him *"very effective and persuasive."* **Jeremy Temkin** (see p.1946) is a *"terrific white-collar lawyer and a criminal tax specialist,"* sources say. One adds: *"He is a very smart and tenacious litigator who is great in terms of strategy and giving his all for the client."* **Robert Anello** (see p.1873) has expertise in a broad range of investigations, criminal matters and civil litigation. He is a highly impressive trial lawyer, and is experienced in representing both institutions and individuals. A new entry in this year's rankings, **Richard Albert** (see p.1872) is praised for his experience in white-collar criminal litigation. He also focuses on civil disputes and investigations, and is a *"great trial lawyer"* who is an *"extremely effective advocate for his client."* **Richard Weinberg** (see p.1950) is another new entry to this table, and is considered *"superb, very practical and a quick study."* He is commended for his experience in acting for clients in investigations conducted by a range of regulatory agencies, and on enforcement matters. He is considered *"incredibly thorough,"* and *"represents his clients incredibly well."*

## O'Melveny & Myers LLP
See profile on p.693

**THE FIRM** Market commentators highlight the impressive breadth of this firm's litigation practice, in terms of both its geographic reach and its expertise. Its attorneys are highly regarded for their trial experience and for their sterling expertise across commercial and securities litigation. The group works with some of the giants of the financial services arena, and recently acted for Credit Suisse on defending suits relating to the Madoff Ponzi scheme.

**Sources say:** *"They are very good litigators who are smart, very commercial, creative and strategic. They are very good at thinking through what the end game is and how we will get there."*

**KEY INDIVIDUALS** The *"very thoughtful and creative"* **Bradley Butwin** (see p.1882) is well versed in all aspects of commercial and securities litigation. He is highly praised for his *"client-focused and very receptive"* approach. He recently acted for Bank of America in litigation relating to its acquisition of Countrywide. Sources highlight **Andrew Frackman**'s impressively diverse litigation practice, and classify him as an *"extremely good lawyer who really can try cases."* His expertise spans a wide range of commercial and securities disputes, and he is particularly noted for his experience in antitrust matters. **Jonathan Rosenberg** is increasingly recognized for his expertise in securities litigation, as well as in white-collar matters. He recently represented UBS in a significant appeal related to previously dismissed accusations of currency transactions linked to terrorists. Commentators highlight **Howard Heiss** as a skilled trial lawyer who brings a *"very client-focused"* approach to white-collar criminal defense representations. He is noted for his *"tremendous experience and very sound, practical advice."*

## Patterson Belknap Webb & Tyler LLP
See profile on p.1995

**THE FIRM** Patterson Belknap is rapidly gaining in prominence in the New York litigation market, and is highly regarded for its experience in representing clients across a wide range of areas. It is particularly highlighted for its recent high-profile work in representing monoline insurers in plaintiff-side RMBS litigation against financial institutions. The team is also increasingly recognized for its expertise in white-collar criminal defense matters.

**Sources say:** *"They are very agile in terms of being able to assemble the proper team to look at an issue or problem from a number of different perspectives in order to arrive at the right result." "The caliber of people at both partner and associate level is exceptional."*

**KEY INDIVIDUALS Daniel Ruzumna** (see p.1934) heads the firm's white-collar criminal defense group and earns praise for his ability to handle both criminal and civil disputes. His recent highlights include acting for the Alavi Foundation and 650 Fifth Avenue Company on a civil forfeiture started by the DOJ, as well as related criminal investigations. **Erik Haas** (see p.1900) enters the rankings having earned strong praise for his *"good courtroom manner and terrific client service."* He is *"effective across the board"* in a range of securities and commercial litigation. His recent work includes representing the Johnson & Johnson Board of Directors in a shareholder derivative case.

## Paul Hastings LLP
See profile on p.1996

**THE FIRM** The New York-based litigators at this respected international firm maintain a solid presence in the market, in both commercial disputes and regulatory investigations. Its expertise in business litigation is particularly noted, and it retains an impressive success rate when representing clients as diverse as UBS and Invensys. The group's ability to handle multijurisdictional cases was demonstrated by its recent representation of Korean Airlines in a class action concerning allegations of price-fixing in the air cargo market.

**Sources say:** *"They are very insightful, and really have a good knack for creating strong relationships and trust."*

**KEY INDIVIDUALS Barry Sher** is a highly experienced trial lawyer with expertise covering a range of commercial disputes. His recent highlights include successfully representing UBS in a case concerning a complex credit default swap. **Douglas Koff** demonstrates *"total dedication and commitment,"* say interviewees, and *"has a gift in being able to develop relationships and work well with people."* His practice is centered on white-collar criminal litigation and investigations. Clients hold **Kenneth Breen** in high esteem, praising his *"ability to look across the full spectrum"* of white-collar criminal matters. *"He is very focused, incredibly direct and also really strategic,"* impressed sources continue. He recently represented Schottenfeld Group in responding to claims of insider trading.

## Paul, Weiss, Rifkind, Wharton & Garrison LLP
### See profile on p.1997

**THE FIRM** This long-standing and preeminent litigation heavyweight continues to impress sources with its extensive trial practice. It fields a leading group of litigators whose combined experience extends across the full range of commercial, securities and criminal matters. Sources consistently highlight the depth of the firm's bench, and praise its ability to represent leading financial institutions in the most high-value cases. The team also works with clients from a broad range of other sectors, and increasingly from the pharmaceutical arena. Recent highlights include successfully representing Citi in the Second Circuit Court of Appeals in a case brought by Banca Carige and Terra Securities. It also represented Bank of America in a high-profile case arising from its merger with Merrill Lynch.

**Sources say:** *"They have world-class expertise for any area of litigation or regulatory exposure."* *"They were exemplary in every respect. Their reputation as a gold standard law firm is well deserved."*

**KEY INDIVIDUALS** *"Superstar"* **Theodore Wells** (see p.424)is hailed as *"the finest white-collar trial lawyer in the country,"* and is praised for his ability to *"connect with people in an amazing way."* He offers all-encompassing experience in criminal and commercial litigation. **Mark Pomerantz** (see p.1928) *"lives up to his stellar reputation,"* say sources, and is further described as a *"dean of the white-collar Bar in New York."* He is also recognized as a nationwide trial lawyer, and is highly experienced in representing both individuals and corporations. **Martin Flumenbaum** (see p.1893) is highly recommended in the commercial litigation space, as well as in securities-related disputes and white-collar criminal defense. He is praised for his *"excellent strategic judgment"* and *"imminently practical"* approach. **Leslie Fagen** (see p.1891) focuses predominantly on commercial litigation, and is a highly regarded trial

lawyer who is *"spectacular in the courtroom."* His recent highlights include representing Liz Claiborne in a securities class action relating to the company's work with Macy's. **Daniel Beller**'s (see p.1877) respected litigation practice covers a wide range of disputes. The breadth of his expertise is particularly noted, as is his experience as a trial lawyer. Sources consider him to be *"very creative and a brilliant writer"* who is able to *"handle adroitly the most complex and crucial of matters."* Firm chair **Brad Karp** (see p.343) maintains his preeminent position as a leading litigator, and earns significant praise for his expertise and experience. Sources note that *"he has a stellar reputation in securities litigation,"* as well as in complex commercial, regulatory and white-collar criminal matters. He is also praised as being *"absolutely excellent and beyond compare in terms of his client service."* **Daniel Kramer** (see p.350) is a leading securities litigator whose expertise covers the full breadth of disputes within this arena for high-profile clients such as Bank of America and AIG. He is highlighted for his *"incredibly smart, no-nonsense approach."* **Richard Rosen** (see p.394) is an experienced securities litigator and represents clients across the country. He is considered *"very smart and detail-oriented"* by commentators. His recent work includes successfully defending Morgan Stanley against claims relating to its MBS exposure. **Michele Hirshman** (see p.1903) continues to earn praise for her excellence in white-collar criminal defense work. She is considered *"a real force and a tremendous litigator."* **Roberto Finzi** (see p.1892) is an *"excellent white-collar lawyer and litigator,"* say sources, and is experienced in representing institutions and individuals in a range of investigations and enforcement matters.

## Proskauer Rose LLP
### See profile on p.2001

**THE FIRM** Proskauer Rose is praised for its dedication to litigation, and remains a key player in the New York market. Its impressive commercial litigation expertise is complemented by its ability to handle a range of white-collar criminal defense matters. The group is also increasingly highlighted for its securities litigation practice. Its recent work demonstrates a diverse practice, with attorneys representing clients in antitrust, healthcare and sports-related disputes, among other types. Its client base includes Deutsche Bank, NYSE Euronext and Zurich.

**Sources say:** *"They have first-rate client service and responsiveness, and enormous resources and experience."*

**KEY INDIVIDUALS Robert Cleary** is highly praised for his experience in white-collar criminal litigation, and for his expertise as a trial lawyer. He has the ability to *"move seamlessly between criminal and civil matters,"* say sources, *"and tremendous experience and intuition."* His recent work includes successfully representing former Marsh executive William Gilman. **Bruce Fader** is a highly experienced, *"knowledgeable and practical"* litigator. He is noted for his expertise in a wide range of commercial litigation and arbitration. **Bradley Ruskin** has superb strength in commercial litigation and trials, and notable expertise in disputes relating to sports law. His recent work highlights include representing the Office of the Commissioner of

Major League Baseball in matters arising from the Los Angeles Dodgers bankruptcy litigation. *"Talented litigator"* **Dietrich Snell** is a new entry to the rankings. He has significant experience in white-collar criminal defense, having served as New York Attorney General and an Assistant US Attorney. He recently represented Columbia Utilities in an investigation into its marketing strategies.

## Quinn Emanuel Urquhart & Sullivan, LLP

**THE FIRM** Quinn Emanuel offers leading nationwide litigation capabilities and a preeminent bench of experienced trial attorneys, and its New York-based group is no exception to this. Its broad-based practice sees it handle the full range of civil disputes, and it earns particular praise for its expertise in litigation involving financial institutions. The team's experience in securities litigation enables it to act for these institutions on both defense and plaintiff-side matters, and it has played a key role in RMBS-related disputes. It also has a growing presence in the white-collar criminal arena. In recent highlights, the group represented the Federal Housing Finance Agency in attempts to regain significant losses made by Freddie Mac and Fannie Mae during the recent financial crisis.

**Sources say:** *"They have a very intelligent and creative approach to problem solving."* *"They have incredible breadth and a lot of energy."*

**KEY INDIVIDUALS Peter Calamari** is highly regarded for his commercial litigation expertise, and is increasingly recognized for his ability to handle securities-related disputes. He is praised for his *"excellent instincts and great courtroom presence."* He regularly leads on some of the firm's most significant representations. Market commentators continue to highlight **Michael Carlinsky** as an excellent and *"tough litigator"* whose deep trial capabilities see him act for clients in high-value commercial and securities-related cases. **Richard Werder** is a *"superb advocate"* offering extensive experience across a range of commercial and securities litigation matters. He is highlighted as being *"absolutely tireless, incredibly responsive and very creative."*

## Richards Kibbe & Orbe LLP
### See profile on p.2002

**THE FIRM** This group remains a prominent player in the litigation arena, and is acclaimed for its expertise in the financial services sector. Its attorneys are well versed in white-collar criminal defense and regulatory investigations, and also handle complex commercial and securities litigation matters. Recent highlights include representing the CFO of MF Global Holdings in a number of matters stemming from the company's bankruptcy. It also acted for Financial Guaranty Insurance Company in five separate cases filed across several different states.

**Sources say:** *"What makes them excellent is that they are extraordinarily knowledgeable about the areas they work in. They are very wise and seasoned, and are classic trusted advisers who are also very user-friendly."*

**KEY INDIVIDUALS** The *"superb"* **Lee Richards** is widely considered a leading member of the white-collar criminal defense Bar. He also offers extensive experience in handling regulatory and enforcement matters within the securities litigation space. He recently represented Wachovia in defending class actions concerning allegations of price-fixing.

## Robbins Geller Rudman & Dowd LLP
See profile on p.696

THE FIRM Robbins Geller has a superb focus on securities litigation on behalf of plaintiffs, and an impressive track record in recoveries obtained. It is staffed by a notable bench of former government practitioners, and has extensive experience in taking cases to trial.

KEY INDIVIDUALS **Samuel Rudman** (see p.1934) is considered *"a household name"* in the plaintiff-side securities litigation arena, and is noted for his expertise. He regularly undertakes large-scale class actions for clients, and also has additional experience as a former attorney for the SEC.

## Shearman & Sterling LLP
See profile on p.2005

THE FIRM Sources are quick to highlight Shearman's highly regarded litigation capabilities and its expertise across a wide range of sectors. It is particularly noted for its experience in securities and commercial litigation, and is also gaining prominence in the white-collar criminal arena. Clients praise the benefits of the cohesive team approach, and its deep understanding of the financial services space. The group continues to play a key role for clients such as Countrywide. Its recent highlights include successfully representing Viacom in a dispute with YouTube.

Sources say: *"They provide good, pragmatic advice and do an excellent job. Their lawyers were commercial, thoughtful and understanding of my position as the client."*

KEY INDIVIDUALS **Stuart Baskin** has a respected securities litigation practice, and also offers experience in white-collar criminal defense and regulatory work. His recent highlights include successfully representing Ford in a securities class action. **Adam Hakki** is held in high esteem for his expertise in securities litigation, and heads the firm's global litigation group. He is praised as a *"very smart and practical lawyer, who is on top of all of the cutting-edge issues in the field."* His experience also extends to white-collar criminal defense. He recently represented Galleon Management in its recent insider trading case. **Stephen Fishbein** (see p.1892) stands out as a *"good trial lawyer with strong analytical skills."* He acts for clients in a range of commercial disputes and white-collar criminal defense matters. He recently represented former Diamondback Capital Management portfolio manager Todd Newman in a DOJ prosecution.

## Sidley Austin LLP
See profile on p.1264

THE FIRM Sidley Austin's respected and expanding group of litigators in New York is noted for its strength in securities and commercial litigation. Its attorneys are experienced trial lawyers, and have played a key role in cases across a broad spread of sectors. The broad-based securities practice is complemented by a strong regulatory and enforcement group. In recent highlights, the team repre-

sented The Norinchukin Bank in class actions regarding claims of manipulation of the LIBOR rate.

Sources say: *"A top-notch firm that delivers a top-notch product."*

KEY INDIVIDUALS **Robert Pietrzak** (see p.1927) is an expert in securities litigation, and is praised by sources for his impressive client roster and extensive experience in the field. He recently defended Principal Financial Group against claims regarding management fees. **Barry Rashkover** (see p.1929) is highly regarded for his notable experience in securities enforcement matters, and also undertakes significant white-collar criminal defense and civil litigation. **Gary Bendinger** (see p.1877) continues to impress sources with his broad litigation practice, which covers both commercial and securities disputes, as well as regulatory matters. He is praised as being *"amazing in trial."*

## Simpson Thacher & Bartlett LLP
See profile on p.2006

THE FIRM Simpson Thacher fields a highly regarded litigation group, which maintains its leading position in the market through its extensive trial expertise and depth of experience. Its commercial and securities litigation capabilities see it retained by high-profile clients such as JPMorgan Chase, Deutsche Bank and The Blackstone Group. The team is also increasingly recognized for its ability to handle a range of white-collar criminal defense and regulatory investigations, with a particular focus on antitrust, FCPA and insider trading-related matters. Its impressive track record is illustrated by a recent recovery of $146 million for Merrill Lynch Capital Services.

Sources say: *"Their ability to get up to speed very quickly impresses me, as do their creative ideas on complex issues."*

KEY INDIVIDUALS **Barry Ostrager** (see p.381) is considered *"a spectacular lawyer"* with significant experience across a range of commercial, insurance and antitrust disputes. He is additionally praised as a leading trial lawyer, and his recent work includes representing The Travelers Companies in numerous complex cases. Market commentators confirm **Bruce Angiolillo**'s (see p.273) leading position in the rankings, and characterize him as a *"very dedicated litigator with great judgment."* He centers his practice on securities litigation, and also offers expertise in commercial disputes. He recently defended Blackstone in two class actions regarding the purchase of shares in Kosmos Energy. **David Ichel** (see p.1905) is highly regarded by sources for his tenacious and dedicated approach to litigation. His extensive experience has seen him act in a wide range of commercial cases for clients, and he also offers additional expertise in product liability-related matters. **Jonathan Youngwood** (see p.1952) upholds his impressive strength in securities litigation, and is described by one source as *"very hard-working, client-driven, not afraid to take on any challenges and able to think outside the box."* He represents private equity firms and financial institutions in a range of matters, and has particular expertise in disputes involving auction rate securities. **Peter Kazanoff** (see p.1908) is an *"outstanding young litigator"* who focuses on securities-related matters. His expertise in disputes involv-

ing M&A is particularly highlighted, as is his *"good business sense."* **Mark Stein** (see p.1944) is praised as a *"very experienced, good and practical"* white-collar criminal attorney. He is highly regarded for his expertise in representing individuals and institutions in a range of investigations and trials. His recent work includes representing a healthcare entity in a criminal investigation conducted by the DOJ into antitrust concerns. **Paul Curnin** (see p.300) is esteemed by sources for his ability to handle a wide range of civil and criminal matters, and has extensive expertise in securities and white-collar criminal defense matters. He cochairs the firm's litigation department and is praised for his *"excellent, knowledgeable and very sensible"* approach to work. **Josh Levine** (see p.1913) is praised for his *"incredibly calm and very thoughtful"* approach to white-collar criminal litigation, and is rapidly gaining prominence in the market. He is highly experienced in the regulatory investigation and enforcement space. He recently represented a Europe-based hedge fund in an investigation conducted by the CFTC. **Mark Cunha** (see p.1887) is recognized as a *"very talented"* litigator, and is highly experienced as a trial lawyer. He offers particular expertise in a wide range of commercial litigation, and has recently represented individuals connected with Fairfield Greenwich Group in matters stemming from the Madoff Ponzi scheme. **Thomas Rice** (see p.1931) cochairs the firm's litigation group, and is highly regarded for his expertise in securities and commercial litigation. Sources comment that he *"is extremely knowledgeable about the law, has vast experience and is extremely responsive."*

## Skadden, Arps, Slate, Meagher & Flom LLP & Affiliates
See profile on p.2008

THE FIRM Skadden's highly impressive litigation group has a market-leading reputation in New York, and is praised for its preeminent capabilities across the full range of securities, commercial and white-collar criminal defense matters. It is renowned for its strength in handling high-profile work involving financial institutions, and also offers experience in representing clients across a broad range of other sectors. Its deep and expansive bench of trial lawyers is a noted draw for clients, as is its significant global presence. Recent highlights include representing the underwriting syndicate of Deutsche Bank Securities in obtaining the dismissal of a class action regarding RMBS exposure.

Sources say: *"They have deep subject matter expertise and experience, and are extremely responsive and client-focused."*

KEY INDIVIDUALS **Jay Kasner** (see p.1907) is widely recognized as a *"superstar"* in the securities litigation space, and *"lives up to his reputation in every way."* He is an experienced trial litigator who is *"a pleasure to work with and deeply committed to his clients and to getting the best results."* His recent work includes acting for UBS on defending a suit brought by the Federal Housing Finance Agency. *"Tremendous litigator"* **Scott Musoff** (see p.373) has notable experience in securities litigation, and additional expertise in commercial disputes. He is highlighted for his *"extremely responsive and very creative"* approach to complex cases. His recent highlights include representing Fortis Securities and Fortis Bank. The *"superb"* **Jonathan Lerner** (see p.355) is praised for his *"charming and vigorous approach"* to commercial and securities litigation. His extensive experience sees him acting for clients in significant and complex cases. **Michael Gruenglas** (see p.1900) is an experienced commercial litigator, whose expertise also encompasses securities-related matters. His highlights include the recent representation of SanDisk in a Bench trial concerning an acquisition made several years ago. **John Carroll** (see p.1883) has a *"stellar reputation"* in the white-collar criminal defense space, and is seen as a leading choice for his expertise in a wide range of investigations and litigation. He recently represented the president of Harbinger Capital Partners, Omar Asali, in responding to an SEC Wells Notice. **Susan Saltzstein** (see p.1935) continues to gain recognition for her *"good, practical approach"* to both commercial and securities litigation. She plays a key role in some of the firm's most significant matters, including in its recent defense of UniCredit against $60 billion claims made by the trustee for the liquidation of Bernard Madoff Investment Securities. The *"excellent"* **David Zornow** (see p.1953) is considered a leader in the white-collar criminal space, and is highly praised for his experience and expertise. There is *"nobody more three-dimensional than he is,"* said one impressed source; *"he understands every facet of the area."* Zornow's recent highlights include representing PokerStars in obtaining a settlement with the DOJ following an investigation into suspected fraud. **Keith Krakaur** (see p.1910) is respected as *"one of the most prominent white-collar practitioners"* at the firm, and draws on extensive experience as a former federal prosecutor. He has particular expertise in representing non-US based financial institutions in investigations conducted on a worldwide scale. **Steven Glaser** (see p.1896) is increasingly recognized for his white-collar criminal defense and government enforcement expertise. He is praised for his ability to *"figure out how to get to the nub of a problem quickly."* Sources go on to note that he is *"always more than willing to talk through strategy and weigh the pros and cons of different approaches."*

## Spears & Imes LLP
See profile on p.2009

**THE FIRM** Spear & Imes is held in high esteem for its extensive securities enforcement and white-collar criminal defense capabilities. Its boutique approach enables an effective focus on litigation, and as such its attorneys are highlighted for their notable trial experience. The team's recent work includes representing BayernLB in bringing an action against Aladdin Capital Management in a case concerning losses made in a CDO investment. The firm's client roster also includes UBS and Spring Mountain Capital.
**KEY INDIVIDUALS David Spears** is highly recommended for his experience in a wide range of white-collar criminal defense and enforcement matters. His practice also involves civil disputes. He is *"very focused and targeted; someone who thinks about things strategically,"* sources say. **Linda Imes** maintains a respected practice in the white-collar criminal defense space, and is also noted for her

expertise in civil litigation. Her recent work includes representing a senior HSBC executive in an investigation into the potential risk of money launderers targeting worldwide banks.

## Sullivan & Cromwell LLP
See profile on p.2011

**THE FIRM** There is a strong consensus among commentators that Sullivan & Cromwell remains a leading force in the New York litigation space. The group represents clients from a broad range of industries, but is most recommended for its expertise in disputes involving financial institutions. Its highly regarded team of litigators offers leading experience in the full spread of disputes, including commercial, securities and white-collar criminal defense matters. Major clients include Standard Chartered Bank, Goldman Sachs and BP. In recent work, the team continues to represent key financial institutions in a case brought against MBIA, regarding the restructuring of MBIA Insurance.
**Sources say:** *"An outstanding firm – they are very practical and creative, and know how to get things done efficiently."*
**KEY INDIVIDUALS** *"Brilliant advocate"* **Robert Giuffra** (see p.321) is highly valued for his *"deep and vast experience."* He is considered *"one of the preeminent lawyers"* in the civil and regulatory space, and handles securities and commercial litigation with equal aplomb. The tremendously experienced **Gandolfo DiBlasi** (see p.304) is highly praised as *"one of the best securities lawyers in the country,"* and remains one of the sector's leading authorities in the sector. He offers extensive experience in investigations and litigation, and is particularly noted for his expertise in disputes arising from the financial services industry. Market commentators are quick to praise **Penny Shane**'s (see p.1940) strength in securities litigation. She has significant experience in acting for clients in disputes involving financial institutions; her expertise also includes commercial disputes and First Amendment-related matters. **Samuel Seymour** (see p.1940) is considered *"a leading figure of the white-collar Bar,"* and centers his practice on a range of criminal defense and regulatory matters. His recent work includes acting for HSBC in investigations conducted by a range of government agencies into money laundering and compliance with sanctions policy. The *"terrific"* **Karen Patton Seymour** (see p.1940) continues to attract widespread acclaim for her leading litigation practice. She is an expert in white-collar criminal defense and regulatory investments, and also offers experience in handling civil litigation. She recently represented Goldman Sachs in an SEC enforcement proceeding, and in a DOJ investigation. **Steven Peikin** (see p.1927) is praised for his *"excellent"* practice as a white-collar criminal attorney. He is considered a *"good negotiator"* by sources, and also offers impressive trial experience. His recent work includes acting for SAC Capital employee Jon Horvath on civil and criminal charges of insider trading. **Richard Klapper** (see p.1909) is increasingly recognized for his commercial and securities litigation capabilities, and is highlighted as a *"quick and forceful advocate for his clients."* He has recently secured several victories for Goldman Sachs, including in putative

shareholder derivative lawsuits. **Nicolas Bourtin** (see p.1880) is respected for his growing white-collar criminal defense practice acting on behalf of both individuals and institutions. He also offers experience in enforcement proceedings, investigations and civil litigation.

## Wachtell, Lipton, Rosen & Katz
See profile on p.2012

**THE FIRM** Wachtell retains its widely acclaimed position as a first-rate litigation practice. It is respected for its ability to handle the most high-value disputes for clients, whether in the commercial, securities or white-collar criminal arenas. It is praised for its cross-border expertise, and has a highly experienced team of trial lawyers undertaking all aspects of disputes for clients. Sources highlight the group's particular expertise in litigation arising from M&A. In recent highlights, the team represented Vulcan Materials in the attempted hostile takeover bid made by Martin Marietta.
**Sources say:** *"A great law firm, with really smart people."*
**KEY INDIVIDUALS Theodore Mirvis** (see p.370) is considered *"a leading light in securities litigation,"* and a *"really savvy and intelligent lawyer."* His experience includes working with clients on high-profile matters involving M&A, corporate defense and corporate governance-related disputes. Sources highlight **Eric Roth** (see p.1933) for his *"very intelligent approach"* to disputes. He is particularly noted for his expertise in commercial litigation, and is praised as a *"thoughtful and highly analytical"* practitioner. **Bernard Nussbaum** (see p.378) has extensive experience across a wide range of disputes. He centers his practice on securities and corporate litigation, and is praised for his long-standing reputation in the market. **Herbert Wachtell** (see p.422) is *"very well respected and a great lawyer."* He is a leading figure in the commercial litigation space. His practice is enhanced by his extensive experience as a trial lawyer, and he continues to handle complex disputes for clients. There is no shortage of praise for the *"incredibly talented"* **Lawrence Pedowitz** (see p.1926). He is highlighted as an *"extraordinarily well-known white-collar criminal attorney,"* and is commended by sources as a *"phenomenal lawyer, and a legend"* in the field. His extensive expertise sees him work with a wide range of clients in regulatory proceedings, investigations and civil litigation, among other matters. **John Savarese** (see p.1936) has a *"very established reputation in the white-collar criminal Bar."* He draws on extensive experience in representing clients in regulatory enforcement matters, securities litigation and investigations. He recently represented JPMorgan Securities in an SEC investigation concerning a large synthetic CDO. Commentators praise **Paul Vizcarrondo** (see p.421) as a *"top-quality litigator who has great knowledge of the securities laws."* His practice extends across a range of securities and commercial litigation, and he also handles white-collar criminal defense work for clients. **David Anders** (see p.1873) is increasingly recognized as a prominent white-collar criminal litigator with strength in civil litigation. He is praised as a *"terrific litigator – a force who is well deserving of ranking."* **Marc Wolinsky** (see p.1952) handles a broad range of litigation matters, and is highly

praised for his expertise as a trial lawyer. He is particularly noted for his experience in commercial disputes, and also undertakes insurance and securities matters.

## Weil, Gotshal & Manges LLP
See profile on p.2015

**THE FIRM** Weil Gotshal maintains an impressive litigation practice, and is highly respected for its ability to handle complex disputes on a global scale. It offers extensive commercial litigation expertise, and is also noted for its dedicated securities litigation practice. The team has additional experience across a range of regulatory and government investigation matters. Its recent caseload includes representing GE in a jury trial against Mitsubishi Heavy Industries regarding patents in the wind turbine market. Other key clients include DMX, the NFL Players Association and Ralph Lauren.

**Sources say:** *"They have all of the know-how and horsepower needed, but they also have a pragmatic and reasoned approach and are results-oriented."*

**KEY INDIVIDUALS Jonathan Polkes** (see p.386) *"really knows his way around a courtroom,"* say sources. His practice covers a broad spread of commercial, securities and white-collar criminal matters. He is praised for his *"pragmatic, smart and sensible"* approach, and is highly experienced in both litigation and investigations. The *"world-class"* **James Quinn** (see p.388) is renowned as *"a real trial lawyer,"* and as a *"very experienced and knowledgeable"* litigator in a wide range of disputes. He is highly regarded for his expertise in sports law, and maintains an active caseload in that area. His recent highlights include successfully representing ESPN and other defendants in a $130 million case against DISH Network. Sources applaud **Joseph Allerhand** (see p.273) as a *"well-known securities litigator"* who displays *"great judgment in terms of strategizing."* His recent work includes representing Kinder Morgan in a shareholder dispute stemming from its $37 billion acquisition of El Paso. Litigation practice group chair **David Lender** (see p.1913) is recognized as a highly experienced commercial litigator. He is *"extremely organized, extremely thorough and a good strategist,"* say interviewees. He led in the aforementioned case for GE. **John Neuwirth** (see p.1923) is increasingly recognized for his expertise in securities litigation, and is praised for his *"good courtroom presence and business sense."* He recently successfully defended Providence Equity Partners against a putative shareholder class action relating to its acquisition of Blackboard.

## White & Case LLP
See profile on p.451

**THE FIRM** White & Case houses a well-established litigation group whose notable commercial dispute capabilities extend across a wide range of sectors and jurisdictions. It also handles securities litigation, and offers clients notable strength in finance-related disputes, bolstered by the firm's presence in many key financial hubs across the globe. The team handles matters for a range of high-profile clients, including Pitney Bowes, Experian and Saudi Aramco.

**KEY INDIVIDUALS Glenn Kurtz** (see p.1911) is a highly experienced commercial litigator, and is considered

*"smart, hard-working and effective"* in his advocacy. He heads the firm's global commercial litigation group, and has significant expertise in trying cases. His recent workload includes defending Royal Ahold and US Foodservice in large multidistrict litigation involving claims of breach of contract and RICO violations.

## Willkie Farr & Gallagher LLP
See profile on p.2016

**THE FIRM** Willkie Farr's highly experienced litigation team is composed of a deep bench of attorneys with expertise covering complex securities disputes, and commercial and regulatory matters, among other issues. Its practice includes a strong focus on financial reporting matters in particular. The group is praised by interviewees for its practical and responsive approach. The group has worked with an impressive portfolio of clients, including Morgan Stanley, Facebook and AIG. Recent highlights include successfully representing Marsh & McLennan in a breach of fiduciary duty claim brought against it by Emerson Electric.

**Sources say:** *"They have tremendous and broad-ranging experience, and have handled a large number of high-profile cases. They are solution-oriented and are driven to get the best result for their client."*

**KEY INDIVIDUALS Michael Young** (see p.1952) is *"clearly a first-tier securities litigator,"* and is highly experienced in handling disputes and enforcement matters for a wide range of clients. He chairs the practice group and has a particular focus on cases involving accounting firms. He is currently representing AIG Risk Management in a range of investigations and litigation. One source stated: *"You couldn't envision a more client-focused lawyer."* **Antonio Yanez** (see p.1952) is noted for his securities litigation practice, and offers expertise in a range of M&A litigation and financial reporting matters. His recent highlights include representing C&D Technologies in defending class actions concerning a proposed merger. **Mei Lin Kwan-Gett** (see p.1911) co-heads the firm's white-collar criminal defense group, and is praised for her *"experience and tremendous connections,"* having served as an Assistant US Attorney for the Southern District of New York. She has expertise in representing both individuals and institutions in a range of regulatory and criminal matters. Fellow practice group cochair **Michael Schachter** (see p.1936) enters the rankings this year. He is highlighted in particular for his expertise in matters involving insider trading, and for his experience as a former Assistant US Attorney. One source comments: *"He is very responsive, and has the ability to provide you with legal analysis that has a practical and real-world overlay."*

## WilmerHale
See profile on p.930

**THE FIRM** This firm is renowned for its depth of expertise in a wide range of litigation matters. Its strong securities and white-collar criminal defense capabilities are complemented by a leading regulatory and enforcement practice, and the team also handles a range of complex commercial disputes. Its highly regarded New York-based trial

lawyers also benefit from the noted capabilities of the firm's experts in Washington, DC. The group's recent highlights include representing Diamondback Capital Management in investigations conducted by the SEC and the US Attorney's Office for the Southern District of New York into matters relating to insider trading. Other key clients include Bank of America, State Street Bank & Trust, and Credit Suisse Securities.

**Sources say:** *"From top to bottom they are very experienced, and have incredibly smart people with very good judgment."*

**KEY INDIVIDUALS Charles Platt** (see p.1927) is an experienced commercial litigator, whose practice also encompasses securities-related disputes. He offers particular expertise in defending insurance companies and financial institutions in class actions. *"Very client-friendly"* securities litigation practitioner **Fraser Hunter** (see p.1905) offers expertise across a range of enforcement matters and commercial disputes. His recent work includes acting for an offshore CDO on defending claims brought by AIG Financial Products. **Boyd Johnson** (see p.1906) enters the rankings following 13 years with the US Attorney's Office for the Southern District of New York. He is praised for his *"very responsive and practical"* approach to investigations and white-collar criminal work. He offers extensive trial experience, and has represented individuals and institutions in civil and criminal matters.

## Other Notable Practitioners

Experienced trial lawyer **Linda Addison** (see p.1871) leads Fulbright & Jaworski LLP's New York office, and is an expert in all manner of commercial and securities litigation. She recently represented GE Energy in a whistleblower case involving the Dodd-Frank Act. Also at Fulbright & Jaworski LLP, **Judith Archer** (see p.1874) is respected for her solid commercial litigation expertise. She is experienced in trying cases at both trial and appellate levels, and also undertakes securities litigation and IP-related disputes, among other types of matter. **Evan Barr** of Steptoe & Johnson LLP is increasingly recognized for his impressive white-collar criminal defense practice. He is highly praised for his skills as a *"good trial lawyer,"* and is described as *"attentive, thoughtful and experienced."* He recently represented the assistant treasurer at MF Global, Edith O'Brien, in multiple investigations conducted into the company's demise. **Stanley Bernstein** of Bernstein Liebhard LLP is praised as a *"very effective"* advocate, and centers his practice on plaintiff-side securities litigation. He recently represented the Public Employees Retirement Association of New Mexico in bringing $100 million claims against Clearlend Securities. **Robert Bodian** (see p.1879) heads Mintz Levin Cohn Ferris Glovsky and Popeo PC's New York litigation practice, and is noted for his experience across a wide range of commercial disputes. He is commended for his *"excellent analytical skills,"* and offers impressive commercial awareness in his practice. **Barry Bohrer** (see p.1879) recently joined Schulte Roth & Zabel LLP from Morvillo Abramowitz. He is praised as *"a fabulous white-collar defense lawyer"* who is *"one of the best in New York."* He brings *"lots of wisdom and experience"* to the firm, and is highly regarded for his trial expertise when handling both civil and criminal cases. **Edward Boyle** (see p.1880) chairs the New York commercial litigation group at Venable LLP. He is *"very responsive to client needs,"* and *"handles litigation matters extraordinarily well."* His recent work includes defending Morgan Stanley against a case brought by a hedge fund. **Lawrence Byrne** (see p.1882) of Pepper Hamilton LLP is *"one of the finest examples of the transition from government to private practice,"* and focuses on white-collar criminal defense and regulatory matters. His practice also encompasses civil litigation, and he works with a wide range of clients. He is praised for his ability to *"distill complex issues into very ordinary and simple concepts."* He recently arrived from Linklaters.

**Peter Chavkin** (see p.1884) chairs the white-collar criminal defense group at Mintz Levin Cohn Ferris Glovsky and Popeo PC. His *"outstanding interpersonal skills"* and *"extraordinary ability to communicate his thoughts"* see him retained by clients on their most complex matters. One of many impressed clients said: *"He lived up to my expectations in a million ways."* At Zuckerman Spaeder LLP, **Steven Cohen** is a new entry to the rankings. He represents individuals and companies in a range of criminal and civil matters, and is praised for his *"ability to think about the 360-degree ramifications of civil law, criminal law and regulatory law."* *"Seasoned litigator"* **John Cooney** (see p.1886) of McKool Smith is praised for his *"smart, thoughtful and very practical"* approach to white-collar criminal and civil litigation. His recent work has included representing individuals in an investigation into potential OFAC infringements. **Sanford Dumain** of Milberg LLP is a highly experienced member of the securities Bar, and has a nationwide presence in plaintiff-side litigation. He recently led in the representation of three shareholders in bringing putative class actions against the Oppenheimer Rochester Funds Group. **Fred Hafetz** of Hafetz Necheles & Rocco is *"one of the very well-respected white-collar practitioners in New York,"* and is noted as a *"tireless trial lawyer."* He is highly experienced in representing both individuals and institutions in a range of complex matters. At Goodwin Procter LLP, **Mark Holland** (see p.335) is praised for his wealth of experience in securities litigation. Sources are quick to highlight his excellent client service skills, and praise his expertise in working with financial institutions on complex matters. He recently represented Bank of America/Countrywide in defending suits brought by several monoline insurers. **Suzanne Jaffe Bloom** (see p.1906) of Winston & Strawn LLP is a respected white-collar criminal practitioner at Winston & Strawn

LLP. Her practice includes a strong focus on representing clients involved in healthcare fraud-related matters, at both the investigation and litigation stage. One source comments: *"She has greatly impressed me with her experience, knowledge and advice."* The *"extremely highly regarded"* **Gregory Joseph** of Gregory P Joseph Law Offices LLC is a *"phenomenal thinker"* who is able to *"really crystallize the most complicated issues"* in his advocacy. He has expertise across a range of commercial litigation. **Jerome Katz** of Ropes & Gray LLP is commended for his impressive analysis and advocacy skills, and is a noted commercial litigator. He recently represented Casita in a case brought against MapleWood concerning claims of breach of fiduciary duty. **Harvey Kurzweil** (see p.1911) of Winston & Strawn LLP is highly regarded by sources as a *"true trial lawyer"* whose commercial litigation practice sees him handle a broad array of disputes for clients. Sources praise his *"decades of experience; his words carry a tremendous weight."* Renowned white-collar criminal litigator **Ira Lee Sorkin** (see p.1943) of Lowenstein Sandler LLP wins acclaim for his extensive experience in representing individuals and entities. He is praised as a *"seasoned decision-maker and strategist,"* and offers clients additional expertise gained through having served in a range of senior government positions.

*"Very knowledgeable and extremely responsive,"* **Richard Martin** (see p.1917) of Orrick, Herrington & Sutcliffe LLP enters the rankings having earned extensive praise for his securities litigation practice. He offers particular strength in multijurisdictional disputes, and has a noted depth of experience in cases involving Italian law. Experienced trial lawyer **Thomas McCormack** (see p.1918) of Chadbourne & Parke LLP is well versed in a wide range of commercial and securities litigation matters. He represents a number of directors and officers of HQ Sustainable Maritime Industries in relation to both an SEC investigation and a class action litigation. At Steptoe & Johnson LLP, *"brilliant communicator and remarkable strategist"* **Michael Miller** is a highly regarded litigator described by one source as *"an exceptionally able trial lawyer, who handles both white-collar and commercial litigation with great skill, persistence and success."* His highlights include representing Otkritie Bank in its attempt to regain more than $160 million of funds lost due to fraudulent activities by former employees. **Tai Park** is an experienced white-collar criminal practitioner based at Park & Jensen LLP. Sources highlight him as a *"phenomenal and very efficient attorney"* who is able to *"be compassionate and really understand the key issues"* in a case. **Guy Petrillo** of Petrillo Klein & Boxer LLP *"is excep-*

*tionally smart and has fabulous judgment,"* according to sources. He is held in high regard for his experience in both criminal and civil matters, and continues to represent clients in a wide range of white-collar criminal investigations and regulatory enforcement proceedings. Goodwin Procter LLP partner **David Pitofsky** (see p.1927) is praised as a *"fantastic"* and highly experienced white-collar criminal defense practitioner. His recent work includes representing the Gulf Coast Claims Facility in matters related to the Deepwater Horizon incident. **Stuart Shapiro** of Shapiro Forman Allen & Sava LLP is a highly regarded securities litigator. He is praised by sources as an *"extremely smart"* and *"formidable adversary."* The *"extraordinary"* **Paul Shechtman** of Zuckerman Spaeder LLP is a highly experienced white-collar criminal litigator, praised for his trial and appellate expertise. *"He is one of the finest lawyers I have ever worked with,"* said one source, and also draws praise for his *"great creativity."* **Michael Shuster** is a founding member of Holwell Shuster & Goldberg LLP. He impresses commentators with his broad-based commercial litigation practice, and is considered an *"extraordinarily sound litigator."* Clients go on to praise his *"exceptional awareness of commercial considerations,"* and describe him as *"a tireless advocate who works with great energy and vigor."*

**Charles Stillman** of Stillman & Friedman, P.C. is deemed a leading expert in the white-collar criminal arena. He has extensive experience in representing entities and individuals in a broad spread of investigations. He also undertakes civil litigation. **Richard Strassberg** (see p.1945) of Goodwin Procter LLP is renowned as *"one of the best white-collar criminal defense lawyers"* in the market. He has a highly impressive track record in trying cases, and is *"outstanding on his feet,"* note observers. His recent work includes representing Swiss bank Wegelin & Co in connection with criminal investigations in tax matters. **Clifford Thau** (see p.1947) is an experienced commercial and securities litigator at Vinson & Elkins LLP. His recent highlights include representing Applied Energetics in a dispute with NewOak Capital Markets. He is praised for his *"exceptional ability to think through every angle of a conversation, through to the end result."* **Daniel Zelenko** (see p.1953) of Crowell & Moring LLP is acclaimed for his dedicated white-collar criminal defense practice, and has a noted focus on antitrust and securities-related matters. Sources praise him as being *"very even-keeled and analytical, and a very effective advocate who sees the whole picture."*

# MEDIA & ENTERTAINMENT CORPORATE

Commentary about individuals can be found under their firm's paragraph. If the firm has no paragraph (is not ranked) look at Other Notable Practitioners.

## Media & Entertainment: Corporate
### Leading Firms

**Band 1**
Cravath, Swaine & Moore LLP *
Debevoise & Plimpton LLP *
Paul, Weiss, Rifkind, Wharton & Garrison LLP *

**Band 2**
Davis Polk & Wardwell LLP *
Hogan Lovells US LLP
Skadden, Arps, Slate, Meagher & Flom LLP & Affiliates *
Weil, Gotshal & Manges LLP *

**Band 3**
Baker Botts LLP *
Hughes Hubbard & Reed LLP *
Morgan, Lewis & Bockius LLP *

### Leading Individuals

**Band 1**

| | |
|---|---|
| Gillespie Michael J | Debevoise & Plimpton LLP |
| Saeed Faiza J | Cravath, Swaine & Moore LLP * |
| Schumer Robert B | Paul, Weiss, Rifkind, Wharton & Garrison * |
| Weinstein Mark | Hogan Lovells US LLP |

**Band 2**

| | |
|---|---|
| Bohm Richard D | Debevoise & Plimpton LLP |
| Chatzinoff Howard | Weil, Gotshal & Manges LLP * |
| Engros Jr Charles E | Morgan, Lewis & Bockius LLP * |
| Kling Lou R | Skadden, Arps, Slate, Meagher & Flom * |
| Schwab James H | Paul, Weiss, Rifkind, Wharton & Garrison * |

**Band 3**

| | |
|---|---|
| Pierce Morton A | White & Case LLP (ONP)† * |
| Weiss Lisa | Dentons (ONP)† * |

**Up-and-coming individuals**

| | |
|---|---|
| Schnapp Daniel E | Hughes Hubbard & Reed LLP * |

*\* Indicates firm / individual with profile.*
*Alphabetical order within each band. Band 1 is the highest.*

## Band 1

### Cravath, Swaine & Moore LLP
See profile on p.1966

**THE FIRM** The firm maintains its historically dominant position within the corporate media space. The team has been active working across a whole range of areas from M&A and capital markets to banking and finance, on a national and cross-border level. The group continues to be engaged in some of the biggest and most pioneering deals in this arena, including its recent work for Dreamworks Animation regarding the formation of a joint venture entertainment company in China.
**Sources say:** *"They get work from a variety of industries and have done significant transactions."*
**KEY INDIVIDUALS Faiza Saeed** (see p.1935) is an excellent corporate and M&A lawyer with a particular media industry focus. She is currently leading the team on the Chinese joint venture deal with Dreamworks above, as well as working with Time Warner and Viacom.

### Debevoise & Plimpton LLP
See profile on p.1968

**THE FIRM** The media and telecommunications practice at this firm regularly manages both national and international corporate transactions. With a team of over 35 lawyers dedicated to this space, it is involved in radio, newspapers, cable television and online media. It works with a whole host of big media clients such as NBCUniversal, News Corporation, Amazon.com and the Associated Press. It recently advised Living Social on its acquisition of South Korean website Ticket Monster.
**Sources say:** *"They are as good as you can get – extremely responsive, experienced, knowledgeable and thoughtful."*
**KEY INDIVIDUALS Michael Gillespie** is cochair of the media and telecommunications group and a respected and experienced practitioner within the space. He has been leading the team acting for NBCUniversal in relation to its joint venture with Comcast worth $37.5 billion. Sources consider him *"very impressive."* **Richard Bohm** is praised by sources for his deep understanding of the media industry and his ability to balance the legal and business priorities of his clients when confronted with a problem. *"He is great and very thoughtful. He is what you want in a corporate lawyer. He has excellent legal skills and knowledge coupled with a pragmatic sense of how to get things done."*

### Paul, Weiss, Rifkind, Wharton & Garrison LLP
See profile on p.1997

**THE FIRM** This long-standing corporate powerhouse continues to represent clients from all corners of the media space, such as theater, film, music and book publishing. The team undertakes M&A work, joint ventures and capital markets, and advises on bankruptcy and restructuring issues. Its enviable client roster includes the likes of Time Warner, Discovery and Sony Music. A recent highlight is the team's work for Barclays Capital regarding the securitization of the Miramax film library.
**Sources say:** *"High-quality work, extremely responsive, quality lawyers and thoughtful advice."*
**KEY INDIVIDUALS Robert Schumer** (see p.1938) is *"a well-known and respected practitioner, with a lot of experience and great skill in crafting a deal."* This year he acted for long-standing client Time Warner Cable in its $3 billion acquisition of Insight Communications. **James Schwab** (see p.1938) has broad experience in M&A and corporate finance transactions. He heads the media and entertainment department at the firm and has acted on numerous media entity acquisitions. He represented the restaurant and entertainment reviewer Zagat Survey in its acquisition by Google.

## Band 2

### Davis Polk & Wardwell LLP
See profile on p.442

**THE FIRM** The media and entertainment practice at Davis Polk receives praise for its strength across multiple disciplines and areas, advising clients on M&A, capital markets, credit, antitrust and tax. The team has been increasingly present on some of the most significant domestic and cross-border deals in this space. It recently assisted NBCUniversal on its purchase of a 50% share in MSNBC Digital Network from Microsoft. Other notable clients include Comcast, Technicolor and the New York Mets.
**Sources say:** *"A blue-chip firm – one of the top in New York!"*
**KEY INDIVIDUALS** David Caplan is a key contact at the firm.

### Hogan Lovells US LLP

**THE FIRM** The New York office of this global firm continue to represent some of the biggest names in the media and entertainment industry. Clients include News Corporation, HarperCollins Publishers and Hulu. It has been busy this year on a variety of high-profile acquisitions and joint ventures including News Corporation's purchase of a 50% stake in ESPN Star Sports.
**KEY INDIVIDUALS Mark Weinstein** remains a well-respected and leading tax specialist who brings his expertise to media and entertainment corporate deals. He recently acted as special tax counsel to MGM Studios in relation to the sale of its interest in Latin American television network CineCanal.

### Skadden, Arps, Slate, Meagher & Flom LLP & Affiliates
See profile on p.2008

**THE FIRM** This firm is renowned for its first-rate M&A practice. The team provides counsel to corporations and individuals within the media space on the full spectrum of corporate transactions from financing and restructuring to M&A and tax. In addition to transactions, the media and entertainment group is able to advise media clients on litigation and regulatory matters. The team represented Summit Entertainment in its recent high-profile acquisition by Lionsgate.
**Sources say:** *"They are terrific at what they do: pragmatic, proactive and creative."*
**KEY INDIVIDUALS Lou Kling** (see p.1909) is lauded by peers as *"a fantastic M&A lawyer"* who has *"done a lot of significant transactions in the media space."* He continues to have his primary focus in the news industry, acting for significant client News Corporation.

## Weil, Gotshal & Manges LLP
See profile on p.2015

**THE FIRM** Part of the overall corporate department, Weil's media and entertainment practice has expertise in private equity, M&A, capital markets, finance and IP matters. The team has been active this year on a multitude of prominent M&A deals within a range of media industries, including HIT Entertainment's multimillion-dollar acquisition by Mattel, and with theater chain AMC Entertainment, on its sale to Chinese conglomerate Dalian Wanda Group.

**Sources say:** "A great firm to work with. I have seen Weil from both sides of the table and have been impressed by them. They are very respectful."

**KEY INDIVIDUALS Howard Chatzinoff** (see p.1884) attracts consistent praise from peers and clients alike. One source noted: "He is trusted and very strong – he really is a pro. He is very levelheaded, keeps a firm spine when he needs to but at the same time tries to reach an agreement with both sides."

## Band 3

## Baker Botts LLP
See profile on p.2427

**THE FIRM** The team at Baker Botts has a considerable history within the media and entertainment industry. It represents a broad array of clients across telecommunications and broadcasting. The group continues to advise long-standing client Liberty Media, as well as Ascent Capital Group, OpenTV and Mediacom Communications.

**KEY INDIVIDUALS** Robert Murray is a key contact for corporate media and entertainment work.

## Hughes Hubbard & Reed LLP
See profile on p.1981

**THE FIRM** Hughes Hubbard has been noted for its new media and technology expertise. This 20-strong team assists some of the media industry's most prominent traditional and digital entities. The group acted for Sony Music Entertainment in its recent project to combine independent digital music distributors The Orchard and IODA.

**Sources say:** "They are experts in this space."

**KEY INDIVIDUALS Daniel Schnapp** (see p.1937) heads the new media, entertainment and technology practice at the firm. He is noted by clients as "thoughtful, responsive and clearly knowledgeable on the subject matter." He assisted News Corporation this year in its investment in digital media brand Roku.

## Morgan, Lewis & Bockius LLP
See profile on p.2246

**THE FIRM** The New York office's 25-strong media and entertainment team provides a one-stop shop for the needs of its corporate clients. The team advises on M&A and finance, in addition to litigation, employment and IP. The team was recently retained by Pearson in its purchase of Connections Education.

**Sources say:** "Fantastic! They are extremely knowledgeable, not just on the financing aspects, but the media business as well."

**KEY INDIVIDUALS Charles Engros** (see p.1890) continues to focus on M&A transactions within the media and entertainment space. He is commended by clients for his client care and deep understanding of the media industry. "He is extremely knowledgeable, focused and client-centric. He understands media and law, and the intersection of the two."

## Other Notable Practitioners

**Morton Pierce** (see p.1927) of White & Case LLP has over three decades of M&A experience under his belt. He continues to represent some of the biggest investors and corporate entities in the media and entertainment arena. **Lisa Weiss** (see p.1950) of Dentons has been active working with a range of the media industry's most illustrious clients, including EMI Group, MeetMe and Sony. One client enthuses: "She is a consummate professional who clearly has my interests at heart. She is incredibly bright, with a tremendous capacity for retaining every aspect of a complex deal. She goes the extra mile."

---

## MEDIA & ENTERTAINMENT FILM, MUSIC, TELEVISION & THEATER

Theatre p.1850

Commentary about individuals can be found under their firm's paragraph. If the firm has no paragraph (is not ranked) look at Other Notable Practitioners.

| Media & Entertainment: Film, Music, Television & Theater | |
|---|---|
| **Leading Firms** | |
| **Band 1** | |
| Frankfurt Kurnit Klein & Selz | |
| Franklin, Weinrib, Rudell & Vassallo, PC | |
| Loeb & Loeb LLP * | |
| **Band 2** | |
| Levine Plotkin & Menin | |
| Pryor Cashman LLP | |
| **Band 3** | |
| Greenberg Traurig, LLP * | |
| Grubman, Indursky & Shire, PC | |
| Schreck Rose Dapello Adams & Hurwitz LLP | |

| Media & Entertainment: Film & Television | | |
|---|---|---|
| **Leading Individuals** | | |
| **Band 1** | | |
| Chamlin | Marc | Loeb & Loeb LLP * |
| Googe Jr | Charles H | Paul, Weiss, Rifkind, Wharton (ONP)[†] * |
| Heller | Richard B | Frankfurt Kurnit Klein & Selz * |
| Hofstetter | Richard | Frankfurt Kurnit Klein & Selz * |
| Rudell | Michael | Franklin, Weinrib, Rudell & Vassallo, PC |
| Sheanshang | George L | Law Offices of George Sheanshang (ONP)[†] |
| **Band 2** | | |
| Arar | Roger M | Loeb & Loeb LLP * |
| Shire | Lawrence | Grubman, Indursky & Shire, PC |
| Sloss | John | Sloss Eckhouse LawCo LLP (ONP)[†] |
| Weinrib | Kenneth | Franklin, Weinrib, Rudell & Vassallo, PC |
| **Band 3** | | |
| Janowitz | James | Pryor Cashman LLP |
| Johnston | James L | Davis & Gilbert LLP (ONP)[†] * |
| **Associates to watch** | | |
| Pisacane | Maggie | Frankfurt Kurnit Klein & Selz * |

| Media & Entertainment: Music | | |
|---|---|---|
| **Leading Individuals** | | |
| **Band 1** | | |
| Gordon | Nicholas | Franklin, Weinrib, Rudell & Vassallo, PC |
| Jacobson | Marc | Marc Jacobson, P.C. (ONP)[†] * |
| Sukin | Michael | Sukin Law Group (ONP)[†] |
| **Band 2** | | |
| Anderson | Kenneth B | Sheppard, Mullin, Richter & Hampton (ONP)[†] |
| Grubman | Allen | Grubman, Indursky & Shire, PC |
| Kress | Alan H | Law Offices of Alan Kress (ONP)[†] * |
| Schindler | Paul D | Greenberg Traurig, LLP * |
| Siegel | Howard | Pryor Cashman LLP |
| Tavel | Andrew G | Tavel & Associates, PC (ONP)[†] |

\* Indicates firm / individual with profile.

[†]ONP = Other Notable Practitioner.

## Band 1

## Frankfurt Kurnit Klein & Selz

**THE FIRM** The entertainment group at this firm has a deep bench of talent and is highly regarded for its first-class work within the television and film industries, and for its big-picture thinking. It advises clients on the full spectrum of media issues, including publishing, music, theater, fashion and talent work. The team has been further strengthened with some new additions, and is currently expanding into the 'interactive entertainment' market. Clients include the Tribeca Film Festival and Tribune Entertainment.

**Sources say:** "They care about their clients, and they have smart legal minds. They have a thorough understanding of television production, they know how to deal with deadlines and they work hard for you."

**KEY INDIVIDUALS Richard Heller** (see p.1902) has expertise in a broad spectrum of matters, but is particularly well known for his work in the film and television industries. He impresses clients with his business acumen and deep understanding of the media arena. "*He is a big-picture thinker and wants to build the business rather than just processing contracts. He is clear-thinking, logical, thorough and proactive.*" **Mark Merriman** (see p.1919) has a strong theater and book publishing practice. Having previously worked in the theater, he can offer a unique insight into the industry. **Maggie Pisacane** (see p.1927) is a "*terrific, diligent and forward-thinking*" member of the entertainment team. She has impressed clients with her industry knowledge, intellect and client service. **Richard Hofstetter** (see p.1904) is lauded by peers and clients alike for his work in film and television. "*He is knowledgeable, practical and wise, and has always provided sound advice.*"

## Franklin, Weinrib, Rudell & Vassallo, PC

**THE FIRM** This boutique entertainment firm continues to represent clients from all corners of the industry, from traditional television, film, music and theater to more innovative new media. It is commended for its breadth and depth of industry knowledge.
**Sources say:** "*High quality!*"
**KEY INDIVIDUALS Elliot Brown** maintains his reputation as a preeminent media attorney, with a focus on and expertise in theater matters. **Nicholas Gordon** has a strong music-focused practice. He assists clients with music publishing, recording rights, producing and agency matters. **Michael Rudell** is a well-respected and leading attorney. Peers consider him "*a tough negotiator,*" "*the dean of the Bar*" and "*one of the best TV lawyers*" within the industry. He is particularly adept at publishing law. **Kenneth Weinrib** is held in high esteem by peers for his all-around knowledge and experience of the entertainment sector. He acts for individuals and companies in motion pictures, television, theater and book publishing.

## Loeb & Loeb LLP
See profile on p.689
**THE FIRM** The New York office of this national powerhouse adopts a multidisciplinary approach to clients' media and entertainment issues. It continues to demonstrate particular strength in the television, film and theater

industries, and is exalted by clients for its cohesive and interdisciplinary team approach and client service. Its enviable list of clients includes BBC America, Amazon Studios, Sharpe Entertainment and Glenn Close. It recently advised Netflix on original programming deals.
**Sources say:** "*They are really great. They work as such a seamless team. They are very responsive, pragmatic and positive. Although they are lawyers, they have business minds.*"
**KEY INDIVIDUALS Marc Chamlin** (see p.1883) is an extremely talented media attorney, who has become a luminary in the areas of film and television. He has represented a medley of big television networks and production companies of late, in production and licensing transactions. Clients regard him as a "*superstar,*" with one source noting: "*He is prompt, intelligent, shrewd and informed, and keeps good solid relationships.*" **Seth Gelblum** (see p.1895) practice is mostly theater-focused, but he also deals with matters in documentary film business. He represents some of the biggest names on Broadway, including 'The Lion King' director Julie Taymor and Dodger Productions, which produces 'Jersey Boys'. **Roger Arar** (see p.1874) has impressed sources with his experience and "*vast industry knowledge.*" While he is a versatile attorney, Arar continues to be particularly active in licensing and development deals regarding scripted and unscripted television series.

## Band 2

## Levine Plotkin & Menin
**THE FIRM** This New York-based entertainment boutique handles matters across the gamut of media industries. The team has particular expertise in television, theater, film, music, dance and fashion. Clients include actors, directors, producers, artists and fashion designers.
**KEY INDIVIDUALS Loren Plotkin** is one of the leading names in the theater industry, with a strong and well-respected practice. He is noted in particular for his work with producers.

## Pryor Cashman LLP
**THE FIRM** This firm's entertainment, media and communications department has particular strength within the film, television and music industries. Although smaller than some of its competitors, the team handles impressive transactional and litigation work for clients within this space. The group represents EMI Music Publishing, Def Jam Records and Kanye West.
**Sources say:** "*They are very practical and effective. They are very creative when finding practical solutions to quite complex problems, and they have good commercial awareness.*"
**KEY INDIVIDUALS Howard Siegel** is an esteemed entertainment lawyer with over 30 years of experience. His practice has a music industry focus, and he acts for some of the most acclaimed artists, producers and managers in the business. **James Janowitz** is "*smart and well reasoned,*" and exudes gravitas. He heads the entertainment team and is noted for his film finance and production work, and is also an acclaimed litigator.

## Band 3

## Greenberg Traurig, LLP
See profile on p.1024
**THE FIRM** Greenberg Traurig remains heavily focused on the music industry and is well known and respected for its work in this space. It continues to expand its merchandising and brand-focused work, dealing with a variety of these matters for many of the world's most famous musicians.
**KEY INDIVIDUALS Paul Schindler** (see p.1937) is chair of the media and entertainment department at the firm. He has a broad practice dealing with clients from all sectors of the media world, and continues to expand into merchandising and new media.

## Grubman, Indursky & Shire, PC
**THE FIRM** This practice is able to offer clients a full range of advice on film, television and theater, and continues to attract particular praise for its work in the music industry. The team specializes in copyright and other IP, licensing and new media.
**Sources say:** "*They have been fantastic – available, articulate, caring, knowledgeable and reasonable.*"
**KEY INDIVIDUALS** With over three decades of experience, **Allen Grubman** is a prominent entertainment lawyer, well known for his work with the biggest names in the music business. **Lawrence Shire** has a broad range of expertise across the media spectrum. He remains the go-to guy at the firm for television and film matters.

## Schreck Rose Dapello Adams & Hurwitz LLP
**THE FIRM** This strong niche practice specializes in the film, television and theater industries, and is highly commended for its work in these areas. The firm advises a varied cross-section of talent, including directors, writers and theater producers.
**KEY INDIVIDUALS Nancy Rose** has made a name for herself with her work in the theater industry. She has built a strong practice representing some of the most prominent authors and producers in theater.

## Other Notable Practitioners

**Marc Jacobson** (see p.1906) of Marc Jacobson, P.C. impresses clients with his versatility and in-depth specialized industry knowledge. He runs a virtual law firm and continues to focus on the film and television industries. "*You cannot do better than Marc – he is fast, tenacious, detail-oriented, proactive, responsive and sensitive to the needs of the clients.*" He recently represented Qtrax in pan-European licensing negotiations. **Charles Googe** (see p.1898) of Paul, Weiss, Rifkind, Wharton & Garrison LLP has impressed clients with his conscientious client care and levelheadedness. One source states: "*He's spectacular! He is one of the top people in the field – one of the best lawyers around. I couldn't rate him higher.*" Recent highlights include representing Warner Music Group in its $3.3 billion sale to Access Industries. **Scott Lazarus** of Lazarus & Harris LLP is a "*fantastic*" and "*dedicated*" media lawyer.

He maintains a theater-focused practice and is noted for his work with top producers. Sole practitioner **George Sheanshang** is well known for his work on independent film matters. He remains an esteemed and respected practitioner, regarded by sources as *"fantastic."* **Michael Sukin** of Sukin Law Group is a leading light in the music industry, with one source commenting: *"No one knows more about the music publishing business than he does – he is fantastic."* **Kenneth Anderson** of Sheppard, Mullin, Richter & Hampton LLP focuses on music matters. He represents clients across the board in the music space, including the Beastie Boys, Ben Folds and the National Music Publishers

Association. **Graham Coleman** remains the go-to theater practitioner at Davis Wright Tremaine LLP, although his practice does extend to other entertainment industries. He has been busy acting as production counsel for Broadway Stage Productions, and representing Scott Sanders Theatrical Productions. *"He has high standards and he reaches them. He is smart, practical and responsive,"* say interviewees. **John Sloss** of Sloss Eckhouse LawCo LLP maintains his reputation as an independent film specialist. He represent a broad array of clients in film production and financing matters. **Andrew Tavel** of Tavel & Associates, PC is an experienced entertainment and sports attorney,

and is well known for his work in the music industry. **James Johnston** (see p.1907) of Davis & Gilbert LLP is lauded by clients for being *"beyond fabulous – he has one of the most stupendous and bright legal minds. He is unbelievably responsive and has an in-depth knowledge of the business."* He has been particularly active in new media and technology deals. **Alan Kress** (see p.1911) of Law Offices of Alan Kress is an experienced and *"effective"* media lawyer. He advises clients from the full spectrum of entertainment industries.

# MEDIA & ENTERTAINMENT LITIGATION

Commentary about individuals can be found under their firm's paragraph. If the firm has no paragraph (is not ranked) look at Other Notable Practitioners.

| Media & Entertainment: Entertainment Litigation Leading Firms | |
|---|---|
| **Band 1** | |
| Debevoise & Plimpton LLP * | |
| Gibson, Dunn & Crutcher LLP * | |
| Loeb & Loeb LLP * | |
| Weil, Gotshal & Manges LLP * | |
| **Band 2** | |
| Kirkland & Ellis LLP * | |
| Patterson Belknap Webb & Tyler LLP * | |
| Proskauer Rose LLP * | |
| Quinn Emanuel Urquhart & Sullivan, LLP | |
| **Band 3** | |
| Cowan, Liebowitz & Latman | |
| Paul, Weiss, Rifkind, Wharton & Garrison LLP * | |

| Media & Entertainment: Copyright & Contract Disputes Leading Individuals | |
|---|---|
| **Band 1** | |
| Cendali Dale | Kirkland & Ellis LLP * |
| Dannay Richard | Cowan, Liebowitz & Latman |
| Keller Bruce P | Debevoise & Plimpton LLP |
| Rich R Bruce | Weil, Gotshal & Manges LLP * |
| Snyder Orin | Gibson, Dunn & Crutcher LLP * |
| **Band 2** | |
| Bart Andrew | Jenner & Block LLP (ONP)† * |
| Cohen Jay | Paul, Weiss, Rifkind, Wharton & Garrison * |
| McNamara Elizabeth A | Davis Wright Tremaine LLP |
| Ortner Charles B | Proskauer Rose LLP |
| Paul Marcia B | Davis Wright Tremaine LLP |
| Ramos Carey R | Quinn Emanuel Urquhart & Sullivan, LLP |
| Sims Charles | Proskauer Rose LLP |
| Slotnick Barry I | Loeb & Loeb LLP * |
| Zavin Jonathan | Loeb & Loeb LLP * |
| **Band 3** | |
| Crawshaw-Sparks Sandra | Proskauer Rose LLP |
| Elkin Michael | Winston & Strawn LLP (ONP)† * |
| Raskopf Robert | Quinn Emanuel Urquhart & Sullivan, LLP |
| Shapiro Saul B | Patterson Belknap Webb & Tyler LLP * |
| Singer Randi W | Weil, Gotshal & Manges LLP * |
| Stevens Jane | Mitchell Silberberg & Knupp LLP (ONP)† |
| Wogan Maura | Frankfurt Kurnit Klein & Selz (ONP)† * |
| **Up-and-coming individuals** | |
| Baum David R | Dentons (ONP)† * |

| Media & Entertainment: First Amendment Litigation Leading Individuals | |
|---|---|
| **Star individuals** | |
| Abrams Floyd | Cahill Gordon & Reindel LLP * |
| **Band 1** | |
| Kovner Victor A | Davis Wright Tremaine LLP |
| McNamara Elizabeth A | Davis Wright Tremaine LLP |
| Schulz David A | Levine Sullivan Koch & Schulz LLP * |
| **Band 2** | |
| Bolger Katherine M | Levine Sullivan Koch & Schulz LLP * |
| Buckley Susan | Cahill Gordon & Reindel LLP * |
| Ringel Dean | Cahill Gordon & Reindel LLP * |

| Media & Entertainment: Media Litigation Leading Firms |
|---|
| **Band 1** |
| Cahill Gordon & Reindel LLP * |
| Davis Wright Tremaine LLP * |
| Levine Sullivan Koch & Schulz LLP * |

*\* Indicates firm / individual with profile.*
*Alphabetical order within each band. Band 1 is the highest.*

## Band 1
## Entertainment Litigation

### Debevoise & Plimpton LLP
See profile on p.1968
**THE FIRM** Debevoise has built an outstanding reputation as a heavyweight in copyright litigation. The group regularly advises important motion picture studios, television broadcasters, record companies and talent on high-profile disputes. It has recently worked on various copyright infringement and right of publicity claims. Clients include Disney, NBCUniversal and CBS.

**KEY INDIVIDUALS Bruce Keller** is commended for his vast experience handling copyright infringement and right of publicity disputes for a wide selection of entertainment organizations. He is currently acting for the NFL on a right of publicity case brought by former NFL players.

### Gibson, Dunn & Crutcher LLP
See profile on p.682
**THE FIRM** This firm has gone from strength to strength in media and entertainment litigation. With a bicoastal reach, the team deals with IP, class action, regulatory and commercial disputes. The firm represents a medley of big media clients, including NBCUniversal and Cablevision.

Sources say: *"Absolutely top-notch. The Gibson Dunn team has a unique ability to function effectively in any forum. The team is creative in identifying ways to put forward the client's affirmative case."*

**KEY INDIVIDUALS Orin Snyder** (see p.1942) is an esteemed copyright and contract litigator who represents heavyweight media organizations in large commercial contract disputes. One source noted: *"He is one of the brightest attorneys I have ever worked with. He has the ability to understand a complex business situation in a short amount of time, and has a great understanding of the industry."*

### Loeb & Loeb LLP
See profile on p.689
**THE FIRM** With a deep bench of talent and litigation firepower, this firm continues to build its reputation within the media space. It offers clients a team of litigators with a broad range of expertise in different areas. It represents prominent clients from the film, television, music and publishing industries, in IP, privacy, publicity and competition matters. The team recently acted for Sony/ATV Publishing in a music copyright ownership dispute.

Sources say: *"They are very thorough and considerate."*
**KEY INDIVIDUALS** *"Tremendous litigator"* **Jonathan Zavin** (see p.1953) is renowned for his expertise in copyright matters, and recognized for his representation of major motion picture studios and television networks. He is currently defending DreamWorks Animation against a copyright infringement claim. **Barry Slotnick** (see p.1942) is *"articulate, positive, realistic, extremely patient and avail-*

*able, and has good industry knowledge.*" He heads the entertainment and media practice at the firm, and has been busy of late with impressive clients David Guetta, Sony and the National Music Publishers Association.

### Weil, Gotshal & Manges LLP
See profile on p.2015

**THE FIRM** This litigation powerhouse maintains its position at the cutting edge of media issues. The team is active on a broad range of matters, including copyright, trademark, misappropriation and First Amendment. It continues to act for an enviable list of top media clients, such as HarperCollins Publishers, Oxford University Press and DMX Music. It is currently assisting StubHub and parent company eBay in a number of commercial litigation matters concerning e-commerce issues.

**Sources say:** "*Weil maintains a virtual monopoly when it comes to representation of sophisticated music user clients in rate-setting matters. They have been responsible for so many positive legal precedents in this arena.*"

**KEY INDIVIDUALS** Head of department **Bruce Rich** (see p.1931) has built a solid reputation as a "*brilliant*" litigator. He impresses clients with his sharp intellect, great writing and team-leading skills. His practice focuses on copyright, trademark and music licensing. **Randi Singer** (see p.1942) continues to handle a broad array of entertainment issues, including trademark, copyright, false advertising, privacy and First Amendment. Sources commend her "*sensitivity to clients*" and her skill in "*modulating her style to fit the court she is in.*"

## Band 2
## Entertainment Litigation

### Kirkland & Ellis LLP
See profile on p.1254

**THE FIRM** This international firm houses a formidable litigation team noted for its trial experience. The team is known for its outstanding expertise in copyright, trademark, patent and advertising disputes. It advises some of the entertainment industry's leading individuals and corporations, including JK Rowling, the Associated Press and Fox Entertainment, the latter of which it is currently defending in a copyright infringement claim.

**Sources say:** "*A first-rate firm with a great trial litigation and patent practice.*"

**KEY INDIVIDUALS Dale Cendali** (see p.1883) is a formidable litigator, considered one of the best in her field. She has been litigating some of the most prominent IP cases for various media giants, and is currently leading the team in the aforementioned copyright lawsuit for Fox.

### Patterson Belknap Webb & Tyler LLP
See profile on p.1995

**THE FIRM** The media and entertainment department at Patterson Belknap continues to field a strong team of litigators with a depth of experience in this space. The team has been active in a broad array of areas, including copyright infringement, regulatory and right of publicity. The

group recently acted for McGraw-Hill in important corporate espionage litigation regarding data security.

**KEY INDIVIDUALS Saul Shapiro** (see p.1940) leads the team in the corporate espionage case for McGraw-Hill. He is head of the firm's media and entertainment practice, and focuses on contract and general commercial litigation within the media arena.

### Proskauer Rose LLP
See profile on p.2001

**THE FIRM** This highly regarded media team litigates on the whole spectrum of entertainment matters, such as contracts, defamation, First Amendment and IP. It offers both transactional and litigation advice to an impressive roster of clients, including Lady Gaga, Sony Music and Warner Music. The group recently represented the English FA Premier League in its copyright infringement case against YouTube.

**KEY INDIVIDUALS Charles Ortner** cochairs the media and entertainment group and has an emphasis on copyright infringement, class actions and contract disputes in the music industry. His A-list clients include Lady Gaga and Madonna. **Charles Sims** is considered a "*wonderful*" copyright and First Amendment litigator. He is currently leading the team in the above case for the Premier League. **Sandra Crawshaw-Sparks** maintains a vibrant practice representing some of the biggest talents in music.

### Quinn Emanuel Urquhart & Sullivan, LLP

**THE FIRM** This dynamic firm is highly regarded for its litigation capabilities and trial experience. It handles a broad range of issues for studios, networks, production companies and talent. It recently defended YouTube and parent company Google against a lawsuit brought by Viacom.

**Sources say:** "*They are terrific!*"

**KEY INDIVIDUALS Carey Ramos** has a broad practice with a focus on the media and entertainment industry. He assists high-profile clients from the music, film, theater and digital industries. **Robert Raskopf** handles the gamut of media and entertainment issues, from IP and privacy to First Amendment and advertising. According to one source, "*he is exactly the kind of litigator we love – aggressive but thoughtful. I would recommend him utterly and without reservation.*"

## Band 3
## Entertainment Litigation

### Cowan, Liebowitz & Latman

**THE FIRM** This boutique IP and litigation firm is highly recommended for its copyright and trademark expertise. The team represents a whole host of media entities, from publishing, music, broadcasting and other entertainment industries.

**Sources say:** "*They are copyright experts.*"

**KEY INDIVIDUALS Richard Dannay** is a highly respected media and entertainment litigator with extensive court experience. Peers describe him as an "*excellent*" and "*brilliant*" copyright attorney.

### Paul, Weiss, Rifkind, Wharton & Garrison LLP
See profile on p.1997

**THE FIRM** This litigation powerhouse handles a significant amount of media and entertainment work. The team represents an array of top clients, from record labels and film studios to film financing vehicles and playwrights. It is currently acting for MTV Networks in a lawsuit concerning copyright and trademark infringement claims.

**KEY INDIVIDUALS Jay Cohen** (see p.1885) heads the department and is highly rated by peers. He regularly represents some of the most dominant media entities in copyright and licensing disputes. He is currently acting for the American Society of Composers, Authors & Publishers on various licensing negotiations.

## Band 1
## Media Litigation

### Cahill Gordon & Reindel LLP
See profile on p.1960

**THE FIRM** The formidable media litigation department at this firm impresses clients with its breadth of experience and expertise. It continues to gain renown for its cutting-edge First Amendment work. The team is currently representing Time Warner Cable in a First Amendment appeal against the FCC.

**Sources say:** "*They work well with in-house as well as business clients. They have great commercial awareness and are sensitive to the business needs of the client.*"

**KEY INDIVIDUALS Floyd Abrams** (see p.271) remains one of the most esteemed First Amendment litigators in the country. He has appeared before various appellate courts, including the Supreme Court, on a variety of First Amendment matters. "*He is extraordinarily knowledgeable and down to earth, and commands respect in the field from lawyers and judges. We look to him if there is an important First Amendment matter.*" **Susan Buckley** (see p.1881) has a strong media litigation practice, with a focus on First Amendment issues, and is commended by peers for her expertise in this area. She remains busy acting for a number of prominent news organizations, including ABC and CBS, on their challenge of state efforts to restrict exit polling reporting activities on election day. **Dean Ringel** (see p.1931) advises an array of top media clients on a broad range of issues, including defamation, rights of publicity and privacy, copyright and trademarks.

### Davis Wright Tremaine LLP
See profile on p.2544

**THE FIRM** This top-class firm is well equipped to handle the full spectrum of media litigation matters, but continues to be best known for its outstanding First Amendment work. The team acts for prominent media clients including Viacom, MTV and Paramount, and recently defended TripAdvisor against a libel claim.

**Sources say:** "*Very practical, very smart, focused and responsive.*"

**KEY INDIVIDUALS Victor Kovner** remains a notable heavyweight in this area, with a glowing reputation for his

First Amendment work. He has been busy of late providing a wide variety of media entities with pre-publication and pre-broadcast reviews. He is described as *"a wonderful litigator."* **Elizabeth McNamara** has a varied practice in this field, covering libel, privacy, copyright and trademark disputes. Her broad client base includes publishers, radio broadcasters, cable companies and motion picture producers. Sources regard her as *"excellent"* and of *"the highest caliber."* **Marcia Paul** has been busy representing high-profile media entities in intellectual property disputes. She is the lead partner defending MTV and Viacom in a trademark infringement case.

### Levine Sullivan Koch & Schulz LLP
See profile on p.921

**THE FIRM** This niche entertainment firm maintains its dominance in First Amendment and IP matters, focusing on libel, rights of access and news gathering disputes. With new addition Kate Bolger, the team looks likely to strengthen its grip on this area even further. The team continues to work on the significant Guantánamo access litigation case. **Sources say:** *"At the top of this space."*
**KEY INDIVIDUALS David Schulz** (see p.402) has a highly respected First Amendment practice, and is often involved in some of the most critical and high-profile cases. He is currently involved in the Guantánamo litigation. New addition **Kate Bolger** (see p.1879) brings a wealth of experience and *"high energy"* to the media and entertainment team. She continues to specialize in First Amendment law, defending news and entertainment organizations.

### Other Notable Practitioners

**Michael Elkin** (see p.1890) of Winston & Strawn LLP is a noted litigator with years of experience to draw upon. He continues to concentrate on IP disputes. **Andrew Bart** (see p.1876) of Jenner & Block LLP goes from strength to strength in the media arena. He is well known for his work with motion picture and music industry clients, and is commended by peers for his involvement in *"cutting-edge industry cases."* **Jane Stevens** of Mitchell Silberberg & Knupp LLP has over 30 years of experience litigating a wide range of disputes. She receives particular praise for her copyright work. **David Baum** (see p.1877) of Dentons is a talented young partner singled out for his promise in the media space. One client states: *"He is brilliant, direct and you feel taken care of. He is an expert at copyright matters and has a very good understanding of the industry."* **Maura Wogan** (see p.1952) of Frankfurt Kurnit Klein & Selz continues to receive praise for her media litigation work. She is well known for her work within the publishing industry.

# REAL ESTATE

Commentary about individuals can be found under their firm's paragraph.  If the firm has no paragraph (is not ranked) look at Other Notable Practitioners.

| Real Estate: Mainly Corporate & Finance Leading Firms |
| --- |
| **Band 1** |
| Cleary Gottlieb Steen & Hamilton LLP * |
| Simpson Thacher & Bartlett LLP * |
| Skadden, Arps, Slate, Meagher & Flom LLP & Affiliates * |
| Sullivan & Cromwell LLP * |
| **Band 2** |
| Cadwalader, Wickersham & Taft LLP * |
| Kaye Scholer LLP * |
| Paul, Weiss, Rifkind, Wharton & Garrison LLP * |
| Proskauer Rose LLP * |
| **Band 3** |
| Allen & Overy LLP * |
| Debevoise & Plimpton LLP * |
| Dechert LLP * |
| DLA Piper LLP (US) * |
| Gibson, Dunn & Crutcher LLP * |
| Latham & Watkins LLP * |
| Schulte Roth & Zabel LLP * |
| Shearman & Sterling LLP * |
| Weil, Gotshal & Manges LLP * |
| Willkie Farr & Gallagher LLP * |
| **Band 4** |
| Bingham McCutchen LLP * |
| Fried, Frank, Harris, Shriver & Jacobson LLP * |
| Haynes and Boone, LLP * |
| Kirkland & Ellis LLP * |
| Sidley Austin LLP * |
| Stroock & Stroock & Lavan LLP * |

*Indicates firm with profile.*
*Alphabetical order within each band. Band 1 is the highest.*

*The editorial is in alphabetical order by firm name.*

### Allen & Overy LLP
See profile on p.433

**THE FIRM** The real estate group at this international firm is particularly finance-focused, and comes highly recommended for its expertise in complex debt and equity transactions. In standout matters, the team advised Lone Star Real Estate Funds on its $4.5 billion acquisition of Anglo Irish Bank's nonperforming loan portfolio. An impressive client list also includes AG Insurance, Krung Thai Bank and SL Green.
**Sources say:** *"Top-notch and very professional."*
**KEY INDIVIDUALS** Sources value the way that department head **Kevin O'Shea** *"cuts through all the red tape and works very hard for his clients to get a good solution."* He is also praised because he *"has the foresight to see trends and capitalize on them."* He was the lead partner on the above-mentioned Lone Star matter. **Erwin Dweck** represented AllianceBernstein in its joint venture acquisition of two Upper West Side multifamily apartment buildings. An interviewee placed particular value in his ability to *"be really creative in structure to ensure we get what we need in deals."*

### Arent Fox LLP
See profile on p.905

**THE FIRM** This wide-ranging practice offers expertise across the full spectrum of real estate work, and has been particularly busy of late dealing with substantial leasing matters and workouts. The group also advised Fannie Mae on the refinancing and restructuring of a $450 million loan for Parkmerced. Other notable clients include BBC America, PepsiCo and Acadia Realty Trust.

**Sources say:** *"They were really terrific – a very practical and diligent approach, and they got right to the issues."*
**KEY INDIVIDUALS Jacqueline Weiss** (see p.1950) receives a range of plaudits from clients, who value her as *"a deal-maker"* who is *"smart, fast and accessible."* She has recently handled a number of portfolio management and leasing matters for fashion brands Lacoste USA and Diesel USA.

### Bingham McCutchen LLP
See profile on p.1515

**THE FIRM** The finance-focused group at Bingham is well known for its strength in handling complex loan originations and distressed loan workouts for major financial institutions. Notable matters include acting for Gotham Construction on the closing of a $520 million bond financing for the construction of a large Manhattan residential complex. Key clients also include M&T Bank, Wells Fargo and Citibank.
**Sources say:** *"They're excellent."*
**KEY INDIVIDUALS** The *"absolutely top-notch"* **Richard Fries** (see p.317) is regarded by sources as *"one of the premier real estate litigators in the city."* He advised M&T Bank on the origination of loans to leading developers worth many billions of dollars. Interviewees are keen to praise his *"excellent demeanor,"* and also comment that *"his depth of expertise and intelligence are just wonderful."* Interviewees highlight that **Scott Stern** (see p.1944) is *"always reliable and available when needed."* Practice highlights include advising Silverpeak Real Estate Partners on the ongoing restructuring of distressed development projects, loans and joint venture interests.

*The editorial is in alphabetical order by firm name.*

## Real Estate

### Senior Statesmen

**Senior Statesmen: distinguished older practitioners**

| | |
|---|---|
| Boxer Leonard | Stroock & Stroock & Lavan LLP |
| Edelman Martin L | Paul Hastings LLP |
| Needell Benjamin F | Skadden, Arps, Slate, Meagher & Flom * |

### Leading Individuals

**Star individuals**

| | |
|---|---|
| Mechanic Jonathan L | Fried, Frank, Harris, Shriver & Jacobson * |

**Band 1**

| | |
|---|---|
| Ivanhoe Robert J | Greenberg Traurig, LLP * |
| Mermelstein Joshua | Fried, Frank, Harris, Shriver & Jacobson * |
| Neveloff Jay A | Kramer Levin Naftalis & Frankel LLP * |
| Simkin Steven | Paul, Weiss, Rifkind, Wharton & Garrison * |
| Smith Chris M | Shearman & Sterling LLP |
| Sorin Robert J | Fried, Frank, Harris, Shriver & Jacobson * |

**Band 2**

| | |
|---|---|
| Kane Meredith J | Paul, Weiss, Rifkind, Wharton & Garrison * |
| Klein Steven D | Willkie Farr & Gallagher LLP * |
| Lance Andrew A | Gibson, Dunn & Crutcher LLP * |
| Lenobel Jeffrey A | Schulte Roth & Zabel LLP * |
| Mass Stuart | Haynes and Boone, LLP |
| Pinover Eugene | Willkie Farr & Gallagher LLP * |
| Polevoy Martin D | DLA Piper LLP (US) * |
| Rabinowitz Stephen L | Greenberg Traurig, LLP * |
| Schwartz Wallace L | Kasowitz, Benson, Torres & Friedman (ONP)[†] * |
| Sernau Ronald D | Proskauer Rose LLP |
| Stein Joshua | Joshua Stein PLLC (ONP)[†] |
| Uram Gerald R | Davis & Gilbert LLP * |
| Wertheimer Robert J | Paul Hastings LLP |

**Band 3**

| | |
|---|---|
| Bressman Robert I | Willkie Farr & Gallagher LLP * |
| Feuerstein Eric M | Gibson, Dunn & Crutcher LLP * |
| Freidus Harris B | Paul, Weiss, Rifkind, Wharton & Garrison * |
| Herz Andrew L | Patterson Belknap Webb & Tyler LLP * |
| Irwin Peter J | Debevoise & Plimpton LLP |
| Kleinman Gary S | Greenberg Traurig, LLP * |
| Landau Eric R | Paul Hastings LLP |
| Levy Andrew H | DLA Piper LLP (US) * |
| Miller Peter A | Greenberg Traurig, LLP * |

| | |
|---|---|
| Moskowitz Steven | Stroock & Stroock & Lavan LLP |
| Olsen Peter C | Paul Hastings LLP |
| Pattiz Keith | McDermott Will & Emery LLP (ONP)[†] * |
| Sanseverino Raymond A | Loeb & Loeb LLP (ONP)[†] * |
| Schwartz Carl F | Hunton & Williams LLP (ONP)[†] * |
| Weil Alan S | Sidley Austin LLP * |

**Band 4**

| | |
|---|---|
| Fisch Peter E | Paul, Weiss, Rifkind, Wharton & Garrison * |
| Fodor Susanna S | Jones Day (ONP)[†] * |
| Godman James | Kramer Levin Naftalis & Frankel LLP * |
| Hisiger James I | Latham & Watkins LLP * |
| Korda Peter | Seyfarth Shaw LLP (ONP)[†] * |
| Leitman Bailey Adam | Adam Leitman Bailey, PC (ONP)[†] * |
| Miner Martin P | Holland & Knight LLP (ONP)[†] * |
| Moerdler Jeffrey | Mintz Levin Cohn Ferris Glovsky (ONP)[†] * |
| Rock Neil L | Skadden, Arps, Slate, Meagher & Flom * |
| Ross Samuel | Olshan Frome Wolosky LLP (ONP)[†] * |
| Safron Robert M | Patterson Belknap Webb & Tyler LLP * |
| Saft Stuart M | Holland & Knight LLP (ONP)[†] * |
| Scanna Karen | Stroock & Stroock & Lavan LLP |
| Silver Ross Z | Fried, Frank, Harris, Shriver & Jacobson * |
| Silvera Harry R | Fried, Frank, Harris, Shriver & Jacobson * |
| Sold Kenneth W | Loeb & Loeb LLP (ONP)[†] * |
| Stachenfeld Bruce | Duval & Stachenfeld LLP |
| Weiss Jacqueline A. | Arent Fox LLP * |
| Wohl Russell G. | Skadden, Arps, Slate, Meagher & Flom * |

**Up-and-coming individuals**

| | |
|---|---|
| Blacklow Kimberly B | Cleary Gottlieb Steen & Hamilton LLP * |
| Eliopoulos Elias | McDermott Will & Emery LLP (ONP)[†] * |
| Shapiro Noah D | Haynes and Boone, LLP |

**Associates to watch**

| | |
|---|---|
| Beim Aaron | Haynes and Boone, LLP |

## Real Estate: Corporate

### Leading Individuals

**Band 1**

| | |
|---|---|
| Panovka Robin | Wachtell, Lipton, Rosen & Katz (ONP)[†] * |
| Pinover Eugene | Willkie Farr & Gallagher LLP * |
| Ressa Gregory J | Simpson Thacher & Bartlett LLP * |
| Shenker Joseph C | Sullivan & Cromwell LLP * |

**Band 2**

| | |
|---|---|
| Bond W Michael | Weil, Gotshal & Manges LLP * |
| Colletta Anthony J | Sullivan & Cromwell LLP * |
| Horowitz Steven G | Cleary Gottlieb Steen & Hamilton LLP * |
| Lichtenfeld Steven L | Proskauer Rose LLP |
| Rosen J Philip | Weil, Gotshal & Manges LLP * |

**Band 3**

| | |
|---|---|
| Berger Scott A | Kirkland & Ellis LLP * |
| Diamond Brian | Stroock & Stroock & Lavan LLP |
| Djaha David | Ropes & Gray LLP (ONP)[†] * |
| Kobak Scott M | Simpson Thacher & Bartlett LLP * |
| Levin Mesard Nicole | Debevoise & Plimpton LLP |
| Luskin Martin | Blank Rome LLP (ONP)[†] * |
| Price Christopher B | Goodwin Procter LLP (ONP)[†] * |
| Schechter Jonathan A | Kirkland & Ellis LLP * |
| Wilner Steven L | Cleary Gottlieb Steen & Hamilton LLP * |
| Wise Julian | Schulte Roth & Zabel LLP * |

**Up-and-coming individuals**

| | |
|---|---|
| Dweck Erwin | Allen & Overy LLP |
| Mehrara Sasan | Simpson Thacher & Bartlett LLP * |
| Morgan Jennifer M | Kirkland & Ellis LLP * |

*\* Indicates individual with profile.*
*[†]ONP = Other Notable Practitioner.*

## Bryan Cave LLP

**THE FIRM** The 11-partner team at Bryan Cave offers expertise across the full spectrum of real estate matters, including a sophisticated land use practice. Of late, the team has been busy representing private equity fund Och-Ziff Real Estate in numerous real estate investments. The firm also acts for NorthStar Realty Finance, Vico Capital and Dune Real Estate Partners.
**KEY INDIVIDUALS Robert Davis** heads up the firm's land use practice. He regularly handles litigation, administrative proceedings and permitting matters for a varied client base, including lenders and developers.

## Cadwalader, Wickersham & Taft LLP
### See profile on p.438

**THE FIRM** This strong, finance-focused group is well known for its representation of prominent financial institutions, and especially for its work in securitization and loan origination. It recently advised JPMorgan, Citi and Deutsche Bank on the financing for The Blackstone Group's acquisition of Accor's Motel 6 chain. Other key clients include UBS, Westbrook Partners and Macquarie Bank.
**Sources say:** *"The lawyers are levelheaded and responsive – a great firm."*
**KEY INDIVIDUALS Fredric Altschuler** (see p.273) is an *"excellent attorney,"* who wins effusive praise for his *"perfect combination of zealous advocacy on behalf of his client, while at the same time being pro-business and solution-oriented."* He advised UBS as placement agent on the $580 million refinancing of the Fontainebleau Miami Beach Hotel. The highly regarded **William McInerney** (see p.365) acted on behalf of JPMorgan Chase in connection with a $400 million mezzanine and mortgage loan for New York's HSBC

Tower. Firm chairman **Christopher White** (see p.1951) has substantial expertise in a variety of debt origination matters, and acts for several major institutional investors based in the USA and overseas.

## Cleary Gottlieb Steen & Hamilton LLP
### See profile on p.1963

**THE FIRM** This sophisticated practice focuses on handling complex corporate and finance-related matters for a high-end client base. The team offers particular experience in securitization, leasing and capital markets, and regularly lends this expertise to some of the most prestigious projects in the USA. One highlight saw the group acting on behalf of Goldman Sachs, providing advice on the origination and securitization of a $1.4 billion mortgage loan secured by Hawaii's Ala Moana Center.
**Sources say:** *"Their client service is outstanding." "The response time is immediate and they know how to get deals done and protect the client."*
**KEY INDIVIDUALS** The *"incredibly intelligent"* **Michael Weinberger** (see p.1950) is praised by sources for being able to *"synthesize the key risks for businesspeople, and guide their decision making."* He advised Goldman Sachs on a $135 million loan advanced for the acquisition of 222 Broadway. **Steven Wilner** (see p.1951) is a *"businessman's lawyer"* who *"puts the legal issues in the appropriate context"* according to interviewees. Standout matters include advising Genting Group affiliates on the development and financing of a proposed $500 million Massachusetts resort casino. Sources appreciate that **Steven Horowitz** (see

*The editorial is in alphabetical order by firm name.*

## Real Estate: Finance
### Senior Statesmen

**Senior Statesmen:** distinguished older practitioners

| | |
|---|---|
| Fass Peter M | *Proskauer Rose LLP* |

### Leading Individuals

**Band 1**

| | |
|---|---|
| Altschuler Fredric L | *Cadwalader, Wickersham & Taft LLP* * |
| Forte Joseph Philip | *DLA Piper LLP (US)* * |
| Fries Richard S | *Bingham McCutchen LLP* * |
| Horowitz Steven G | *Cleary Gottlieb Steen & Hamilton LLP* * |
| Uris Harvey R | *Skadden, Arps, Slate, Meagher & Flom* * |
| Weinberger Michael | *Cleary Gottlieb Steen & Hamilton LLP* * |

**Band 2**

| | |
|---|---|
| Adler Arthur S | *Sullivan & Cromwell LLP* * |
| Bernstein Warren J | *Kaye Scholer LLP* * |
| Campbell William | *Stroock & Stroock & Lavan LLP* |
| Ciabarra Laura G | *Dechert LLP* * |
| Gliatta Stephen | *Kaye Scholer LLP* * |
| McInerney William P | *Cadwalader, Wickersham & Taft LLP* * |
| Montgomery Malcolm K | *Shearman & Sterling LLP* |
| O'Shea Kevin | *Allen & Overy LLP* |

**Band 3**

| | |
|---|---|
| Edelstein Mark S | *Morrison & Foerster LLP (ONP)[†]* |
| Hisiger James I | *Latham & Watkins LLP* * |
| Jones Richard D | *Dechert LLP* * |
| Koen Robert | *Mayer Brown LLP (ONP)[†]* |
| Steiner Jeffrey B | *DLA Piper LLP (US)* * |
| Stern Scott L | *Bingham McCutchen LLP* * |
| Weinberger David J | *Proskauer Rose LLP* |
| White W Christopher | *Cadwalader, Wickersham & Taft LLP* * |

**Up-and-coming individuals**

| | |
|---|---|
| Levy Evan R | *Skadden, Arps, Slate, Meagher & Flom* * |

## Real Estate: Zoning/Land Use
### Leading Individuals

**Band 1**

| | |
|---|---|
| Lefkowitz Stephen A | *Fried, Frank, Harris, Shriver & Jacobson* * |
| Selver Paul D | *Kramer Levin Naftalis & Frankel LLP* * |

**Band 2**

| | |
|---|---|
| Davis Robert S | *Bryan Cave LLP* |
| Goldman Howard | *GoldmanHarris LLC (ONP)[†]* |
| Korbey Mitchell | *Herrick, Feinstein LLP* |
| Masyr Jesse | *Wachtel & Masyr LLP (ONP)[†]* |
| Meyers Melanie | *Fried, Frank, Harris, Shriver & Jacobson* * |
| Moskowitz Ross F | *Stroock & Stroock & Lavan LLP* |

## Real Estate: Mainly Dirt
### Leading Firms

**Band 1**

Fried, Frank, Harris, Shriver & Jacobson LLP *
Greenberg Traurig, LLP *

**Band 2**

Kramer Levin Naftalis & Frankel LLP *
Paul Hastings LLP *
Paul, Weiss, Rifkind, Wharton & Garrison LLP *
Proskauer Rose LLP *
Skadden, Arps, Slate, Meagher & Flom LLP & Affiliates *
Stroock & Stroock & Lavan LLP *

**Band 3**

Davis & Gilbert LLP
DLA Piper LLP (US) *
Willkie Farr & Gallagher LLP *

**Band 4**

Arent Fox LLP *
Bryan Cave LLP
Duval & Stachenfeld LLP
Herrick, Feinstein LLP
Patterson Belknap Webb & Tyler LLP *

* Indicates firm / individual with profile.
[†]ONP = Other Notable Practitioner.

p.337) is *"a lawyer's lawyer and is very well grounded."* He advised Genting Organization on a proposed $4 billion investment for a major exhibition and convention center development at Aqueduct Racetrack in Queens. **Kimberly Blacklow** (see p.1879) advised multiple CMBS 2.0 lenders on the origination of repo facilities totaling more than $500 million. Sources highlight that she is *"a very savvy attorney, highly proficient in the workout of complex structured real estate transactions, and also a very skilled negotiator."*

### Davis & Gilbert LLP
**THE FIRM** This group offers experience across the full spectrum of real estate matters, and is well known for its prolific leasing practice. The team is regularly involved in representing landlords, owners and lessees in some of the City's most substantial office, commercial and retail leases. Highlights include flagship store lease negotiations for major fashion clients.
**Sources say:** *"They're a terrific firm."* *"Very conscientious, smart and good at what they do."*
**KEY INDIVIDUALS** Chair of the practice **Gerald Uram** (see p.1948) is celebrated as *"an excellent leasing lawyer"* by sources, who also note that *"he's a terrifically nice guy and very responsive."* His clients include Lehman Brothers Holdings, which has sought his advice on a variety of leasing transactions in New York and across the country.

### Debevoise & Plimpton LLP
See profile on p.1968
**THE FIRM** This real estate practice is known for its expertise in corporate and finance matters, and also offers experience on the dirt side, regularly representing clients in acquisitions, dispositions and leasings. One highlight was the team's representation of the Westfield Group in the $1.15 billion sale of seven US shopping centers to a consortium led by Starwood Group. Other notable clients include Beacon Capital Partners, Tishman Speyer and Rockefeller Group.
**Sources say:** *"They work extremely hard and always in a timely manner."*
**KEY INDIVIDUALS Peter Irwin** chairs the real estate group, and has a strong reputation in the market. He represented a fund advised by JPMorgan Investment Management in connection with the joint venture acquisi-

tion and financing of New York's 200 Fifth Avenue, the former International Toy Center building. **Nicole Levin Mesard** is a hit with clients, who assert that *"she is extremely savvy on the give and take of negotiation, and how to argue our points and advance our interests."* In practice highlights, she advised Westfield Group on a $1.225 billion investment in the World Trade Center retail development site.

### Dechert LLP
See profile on p.1969
**THE FIRM** This well-regarded team is particularly recommended for its skills in finance work, and offers high-caliber expertise in securitization and structured finance issues. Noteworthy mandates include representing a foreign government's investment arm in connection with its $1 billion financing of Las Vegas' Hard Rock Hotel and Casino. Other key clients include Morgan Stanley, Berkadia Commercial Mortgage and Credit Suisse.
**Sources say:** *"The firm does a good job of leveraging its attorneys to make a transaction efficient."*
**KEY INDIVIDUALS** The *"very smart"* **Laura Ciabarra** (see p.1884) is well respected in the industry, and sources recommend her for highly structured transactions. She has represented the mezzanine lenders in the restructuring of a wide range of Blackstone financings, including the workout of the $1 billion Carr America financing. Interviewees highlight that **Richard Jones** (see p.1907) *"has great insight into how to balance the legal and business issues, so that clients get the right result."* Of late, he has advised Macquarie Bank on the acquisition of mortgage assets from Société Générale worth nearly $600 million.

### DLA Piper LLP (US)
See profile on p.1971
**THE FIRM** The real estate group at this international firm can draw on decades of experience handling complex matters on both the dirt and the corporate and finance side. Its deep bench and impressive pool of resources mean the team can take on a raft of substantial projects. One highlight was the representation of Bank of China's New York branch in the $275 million refinancing of Rego Park II, a 610,000 sq ft shopping center.
**Sources say:** *"A top-notch firm."*
**KEY INDIVIDUALS Joseph Philip Forte** (see p.1893) recently joined the team from Alston & Bird. He is hailed as *"a legend"* who is *"at the top of his game."* The arrival of Forte adds considerable strength to the firm's real estate finance offering. **Martin Polevoy** (see p.1928) is the head of the New York real estate group, and recently represented Kroonenberg Groep in the $100 million conversion of 404 Park Avenue South from an office building to a luxury condominium. **Andrew Levy** (see p.1913) has a broad practice which includes advising clients on joint ventures, restructurings, REITs and debt and equity transactions. Head of the corporate and finance practice **Jeffrey Steiner** (see p.1944) regularly acts as adviser to prominent investors and financial institutions based in London and in New York.

*The editorial is in alphabetical order by firm name.*

## Duval & Stachenfeld LLP

THE FIRM This distinguished real estate group focuses on handling sophisticated transactional matters, with particular expertise in mezzanine financings, preferred equity and distressed real estate. Notable clients include Deutsche Bank, Credit Suisse, Ralph Lauren and Phoenix Realty Group.

KEY INDIVIDUALS The *"terrific"* Bruce Stachenfeld is the firm's managing partner. He offers a wealth of experience in guiding clients through workouts, bankruptcies and insolvencies.

## Fried, Frank, Harris, Shriver & Jacobson LLP
See profile on p.1975

THE FIRM This powerhouse of the New York market is well regarded for its expertise across the whole spectrum of transactions, including leasings, restructurings and financings. The team works closely with the firm's other departments, such as litigation, bankruptcy and tax, in order to provide a seamless service, and also has notable land use and zoning capabilities. Key clients include Related Retail, Tishman Speyer and Centerbridge Partners.

Sources say: *"The firm is one of the best and brightest in terms of speed, accuracy, efficiency and just getting the job done."*

KEY INDIVIDUALS Department chairman Jonathan Mechanic (see p.1918) attracts an array of plaudits from sources across the market, and is widely regarded as *"a legend"* in the real estate field. He regularly represents REITs, developers, lenders and investors in transactions involving commercial real estate. Clients note that *"he is very skillful in terms of making big deals happen – he makes a big difference in the New York City real estate landscape."* The *"fabulous"* Stephen Lefkowitz (see p.1912) is hailed as a *"go-to zoning lawyer"* by interviewees. He advises a range of companies on the structuring of development projects, and major financing transactions with the City and State of New York. Joshua Mermelstein (see p.367) offers extensive experience advising clients on joint ventures, developments, acquisitions and financings. He is popular among sources, who describe him as *"a really super lawyer,"* as well as *"very smart, and very savvy."* Robert Sorin (see p.1943) is noted for his advice to clients on leasing, developments, joint ventures and various financings across the commercial property spectrum. Sources highlight that *"he's a fantastic negotiator."* The *"very thoughtful"* Melanie Meyers (see p.1919) concentrates her practice on zoning, land use, public approvals and environmental review matters. Ross Silver (see p.1941) possesses a wealth of experience in matters relating to office buildings, hotels, residential properties and shopping centers. He regularly advises high-profile clients including MetLife and Highgate Hotels. The *"extraordinarily competent"* Harry Silvera (see p.1941) is praised for his *"good commercial instincts."* He represents both borrowers and lenders in construction, commercial mortgage and mezzanine financing.

## Gibson, Dunn & Crutcher LLP
See profile on p.682

THE FIRM This team is recognized for its strength in representing REITs, private equity funds and developers across a broad range of real estate matters, and is commended for its high-quality client service. Of particular note, the team recently advised Tishman Speyer on the $1.5 billion acquisition of an Australian REIT. The firm also acts for Rockpoint Group, German American Capital and Alexandria Real Estate Equities.

Sources say: *"They're very knowledgeable, smart and incredibly hard-working people. They know the area very well, and are good at introducing you to new business possibilities."*

KEY INDIVIDUALS Sources are full of praise for the *"extremely knowledgeable"* Andrew Lance (see p.1911), stating that *"he just knows everything and everyone in the industry, and has a very calming demeanor about him that people on both sides like to work with."* He handles a lot of work for German American Capital, and his expertise includes complex debt restructuring and equity interests in developed ventures. Eric Feuerstein (see p.1892) is described by interviewees as *"a very hard and diligent worker, who brings a lot of accuracy and attention to the work."* He represented RXR Realty in its $920 million acquisition of New York's Starrett-Lehigh building.

## Greenberg Traurig, LLP
See profile on p.1024

THE FIRM This preeminent firm is recognized for its expertise in all areas of real estate law, and regularly handles diverse matters such as joint ventures, restructurings, commercial leasing, and acquisitions and dispositions. In one highlight, the team represented public REIT UDR in its $630 million purchase of a five-property portfolio on Manhattan's Upper West Side. Other key clients include SL Green, Glenwood Management and Square Mile Capital.

Sources say: *"One of the strongest firms in NYC matters."* *"They look at real estate like the client wants to look at real estate, and take a business approach to a transaction."*

KEY INDIVIDUALS The *"very impressive"* Robert Ivanhoe (see p.339) *"leads a phenomenal team"* at the firm. He is well regarded in the New York market, and sources highlight that he is *"very thoughtful and bright."* Gary Kleinman (see p.1909) offers experience across a wide array of real estate issues, and wins praise from clients, who assert that *"he's wonderful – he's always available, he's always looking out for us and sending us new ideas."* Peter Miller (see p.1919) recently advised Ironstate Development on the acquisition of two plots of land bordering New York Bay, to be developed into a new mixed-use site. Interviewees report that *"he does an excellent job for his client."* Stephen Rabinowitz (see p.1929) wins praise for being *"extraordinary on difficult transactions."* Notable work includes acting for SL Green on the $135 million acquisition of 304 Park Avenue South.

## Haynes and Boone, LLP
See profile on p.444

THE FIRM This real estate group enters the rankings in recognition of its burgeoning presence in the New York market, following a number of lateral hires over recent years. The team is particularly noted for its expertise in leasing, and recently advised Brookfield Office Properties on the lease of 1.2 million sq ft at Manhattan's One New York Plaza to Morgan Stanley. The firm also acts for Fisher Brothers, SL Green Realty and L&L Holding.

Sources say: *"They are very responsive, hard-working, thoughtful and have good business sense."*

KEY INDIVIDUALS Stuart Mass is described as *"very knowledgeable, very bright, very thorough and detailed."* He offers a wealth of experience in the ground leasing of high-end buildings in New York and New Jersey.

Noah Shapiro represented SL Green Realty in connection with Random House's lease at New York's 1745 Broadway. Interviewees assert that he *"has a good sense of what the market is,"* and also note that he is *"very knowledgeable, very smart and very careful in his language."* Aaron Beim wins praise from interviewees who describe him as *"an excellent lawyer – highly intelligent and with a grasp of the issues way beyond his years."*

## Herrick, Feinstein LLP

THE FIRM This firm bolstered its New York real estate expertise with the addition of a nine-strong team from Stark & Stark in autumn 2012. These new hires bring substantial expertise in a range of areas including condominium and cooperative matters. In practice highlights, the team represented the Republic of Turkey in connection with the construction of a new consulate. Other key clients include Sherwood Equities, Toll Brothers and The Port Authority of New York & New Jersey.

Sources say: *"Excellent – very up to date and very well rounded."*

KEY INDIVIDUALS Clients are impressed by Mitchell Korbey, reporting that he is *"knowledgeable and gives great advice."* He has also served in various roles at New York City departments, giving him valuable insight into city workings.

## Kaye Scholer LLP
See profile on p.1984

THE FIRM The group at Kaye Scholer is widely recognized for its strength in the CMBS area, and frequently represents portfolio lenders in construction and syndicated term financings. Recent highlights include representing Jefferies LoanCore in the provision of $160 million of preferred equity financing for New York's Park Avenue Seagram Building. Other key clients include Greenfield Partners, Deutsche Bank Securities and AWH Partners.

Sources say: *"We have never before encountered a firm that has so consistently outperformed the expectations of both their own client and the counterparty."* *"The lawyers have proven to be invaluable counsel on real estate transactions."*

KEY INDIVIDUALS Warren Bernstein (see p.1878) is praised for his *"superb people skills"* along with his ability *"to anticipate issues in transactions and defuse them before*

*The editorial is in alphabetical order by firm name.*

they become material obstacles." He recently advised a European bank with regards to its $125 million financing for the acquisition of a large California hotel. The *"very pragmatic"* **Stephen Gliatta** (see p.1896) is commended for his *"technical mastery of commercial real estate finance and all of its facets."* In standout matters, he represented Deutsche Bank Securities in the $80 million financing of a Chicago Ridge mall.

### Kirkland & Ellis LLP
See profile on p.1254

**THE FIRM** This firm's real estate practice offers particular experience in advising major real estate private equity funds, and guides clients through joint ventures, financing transactions and debt restructuring. The team recently acted for Starwood Capital on the formation of a joint venture and the subsequent acquisition of seven shopping malls from Westfield Group. An impressive client list also includes Kerzner International Holdings, Archstone and Lubert-Adler Partners.

**Sources say:** *"They are respectful of their client's time and they're well organized. It's a pleasure to work with the Kirkland people." "Very creative and very available."*

**KEY INDIVIDUALS Scott Berger** (see p.1878) is a very highly regarded figure in the real estate market, with vast experience in private equity issues. His multifaceted practice includes advising international as well as domestic interests on transactions, financings and joint ventures. Interviewees appreciate the way **Jonathan Schechter** (see p.1937) can *"draw on a wealth of prior transactional experience,"* and also highlight that he is *"very responsive and diligent."* He advised Starwood Capital on the formation of a joint venture for the purpose of developing a New York eco-friendly hotel and condominium community. The *"very commercial"* **Jennifer Morgan** (see p.1920) is *"very calm, doesn't overreact to things and is always looking for constructive solutions."* She focuses her practice on real estate private equity, and recently advised Kerzner International on the restructuring of $3 billion of debt.

### Kramer Levin Naftalis & Frankel LLP
See profile on p.1987

**THE FIRM** This firm's real estate department is renowned for its breadth of expertise in both litigation and transactional matters, and regularly acts for investors, owners, developers and bankers. Its excellent zoning and land use practice is also recognized as one of the best in the city. A recent highlight saw the team acting on behalf of New York Life on its $360 million purchase of an office building. The firm also represents Toll Brothers, Rockrose Development and Forest City Ratner.

**Sources say:** *"Responsive and creative." "They are extremely bright, business-savvy and they blend tremendous business awareness with exceptional legal judgment."*

**KEY INDIVIDUALS Jay Neveloff** (see p.1923) is celebrated among sources, who report that *"his judgment is outstanding, as is his understanding of business aspects, and he has great talent in structuring and negotiating transactions."* He represents a number of leading companies with regards to their real estate matters. The *"very experienced"* **Paul**

**Selver** (see p.1939) is a recognized land use expert who *"really knows his business."* Recently, he advised Extell Development on obtaining land use approvals for the 3 million sq ft Riverside Center. Interviewees find that *"he's very thoughtful, pragmatic and is a problem solver."* Commentators admire **Jay Godman**'s (see p.1896) *"depth of experience"* in real estate matters, and comment that he has *"a really good understanding from a business perspective of the details involved, as well as from a legal perspective."*

### Latham & Watkins LLP
See profile on p.446

**THE FIRM** This real estate group is a key player in the capital markets space, and also regularly handles real estate transactions on a local or international basis. The team recently represented the Yucaipa Companies in connection with the $240 million acquisition of UK-based Soho House, a private members' club with locations across Europe and the USA. An enviable client list also includes The Carlyle Group, Goldman Sachs and Starwood Capital.

**Sources say:** *"They have a lot of experience in business transactions so they can help us and know when to push the agenda."*

**KEY INDIVIDUALS James Hisiger** (see p.1903) is commended for his *"ton of experience in the space,"* and is also valued as *"a very good negotiator."* He represented Barclays in the sale of interests in US and Caribbean real estate with a combined worth of $300 million.

### Patterson Belknap Webb & Tyler LLP
See profile on p.1995

**THE FIRM** This group is particularly well known for handling top-notch leasing matters on behalf of both landlords and tenants. In one standout deal, the group represented WTC Tower 1 in connection with a lessee's decision to rent a further three office floors at the site, in addition to an already-leased 1 million sq ft. The firm also acts for Morrison & Foerster, Mount Sinai Medical Center and the Durst Organization.

**Sources say:** *"A terrific firm."*

**KEY INDIVIDUALS** The *"terrific"* **Andrew Herz** (see p.1903) has *"developed a great reputation for himself"* in the New York market, and contemporaries state that they would refer leasing matters to him *"without a shadow of a doubt."* He represented a single-purpose entity controlled by AEW Capital Management in connection with the $50 million lease of four floors of 250 Park Avenue to Pernod Ricard. **Robert Safron** (see p.1935) offers more than 40 years of experience in the area of commercial real estate. He recently advised a party owned and controlled by Durst Organization on a new lease of 360,000 sq ft at 114 West 47th Street.

### Paul Hastings LLP
See profile on p.1996

**THE FIRM** The real estate practice at this international firm is known for representing big-ticket financial institutions, developers, opportunity funds and pension funds. In notable mandates, the group acted for Morgan Stanley on the $189 million financing of 50 Beale Street in San Francisco, California. An enviable client list also includes

William Macklowe, Millennium Partners and Tan-Eu Capital.

**Sources say:** *"They're really tremendous – the response is immediate." "They're excellent business attorneys, and there isn't a deal structure they haven't dealt with."*

**KEY INDIVIDUALS Robert Wertheimer** is *"extraordinarily knowledgeable not just in real estate, but in most areas of law,"* according to interviewees. In a recent highlight, he advised a joint venture on the $425 million refinancing of Illinois's Woodfield Mall shopping center. **Peter Olsen** was involved in advising William Macklowe on the $264 million disposition of majority interests in two Manhattan office buildings. Sources describe him as *"terrific – a practical lawyer, who sees the bigger picture."* The *"highly experienced"* **Eric Landau** is lauded for his expertise in land use and zoning matters. His various roles within the real estate field include acting as outside general counsel to Millennium Partners. The *"fabulous"* **Martin Edelman** wins praise from sources, who note that *"he's just extraordinarily strategic, and extraordinarily smart."*

### Paul, Weiss, Rifkind, Wharton & Garrison LLP
See profile on p.1997

**THE FIRM** This five-partner department offers a breadth of experience in real estate matters, acting for a diverse client base comprising government agencies, investors, developers and REITs among others. The group is recognized for its strength in dirt matters, as well as in corporate and finance issues. In practice highlights, the team assisted Time Warner with its negotiations to acquire over 4 million sq ft of New York office space.

**Sources say:** *"Outstanding – it doesn't seem as though you can come up with a problem so difficult that they can't find a solution."*

**KEY INDIVIDUALS** Department head **Steven Simkin** (see p.1942) is described as *"enormously skilled and experienced"* by interviewees, who also highlight that he is *"able to see solutions from many different sides, and always has client interests as primary."* He represented New York Proton Management in connection with the proposed development of the city's first proton center for the treatment of cancer patients. **Harris Freidus** (see p.1894) advised CIM Group on the acquisition of premier development site 432 Park Avenue. Commentators describe him as *"a terrific lawyer."* Sources find **Peter Fisch** (see p.1892) *"a pleasure to deal with."* He represented joint venture Rock Ohio Caesars in connection with a $275 million senior secured credit facility and a $380 million notes offering. The *"absolutely fabulous"* **Meredith Kane** (see p.1907) is *"state of the art in her field"* according to interviewees. She advised New York City Economic Development Corporation on the $2 billion development of an applied sciences and engineering graduate campus. Sources particularly highlight her *"deep understanding of transactional matters with a focus on tax issues."*

### Proskauer Rose LLP
See profile on p.2001

**THE FIRM** The practice at Proskauer Rose offers expertise across the whole gamut of real estate issues, on both the

*The editorial is in alphabetical order by firm name.*

dirt side and in corporate and finance matters. The team regularly handles complex projects for REITs, developers and institutional lenders, and of late has represented Vornado Realty Trust in a number of high-profile leasing transactions in New York and Chicago. Other key clients include CBRE, Hermes of Paris and UBS Securities.

**Sources say:** *"A deep bench of superior attorneys."*

**KEY INDIVIDUALS Steven Lichtenfeld** is highlighted by commentators as an *"expert on all matters related to real estate finance and capital markets."* He advised American Realty Capital Trust on its initial listing on NASDAQ. **Ronald Sernau** represented Extell Development in connection with the development of Nordstrom's new Manhattan flagship store. Sources note that he is *"efficient, smart and really knows his leasing area."* **David Weinberger** is *"very detail-oriented, and extremely knowledgeable about the lender's viewpoint on loans."* In notable highlights, he advised the owners of Harbor Group International on the acquisition, sale and financing of various properties, including the $270 million sale of Four New York Plaza. Interviewees hail **Peter Fass** as *"the 'Godfather' of the modern REIT."* Work highlights include providing ongoing advice to American Realty Capital and Realty Capital Securities in connection with REIT public offerings worth a total of more than $14 billion.

## Schulte Roth & Zabel LLP
See profile on p.2003

**THE FIRM** This group is recognized for its expertise in representing private equity funds, and also has vast experience in structuring complex finance deals for both borrowers and lenders. A recent work highlight saw the team advise The Praedium Group on the $500 million acquisition, financing and disposition of 16 properties across multiple states. Other notable clients include GE Asset Management, Blackstone Real Estate Advisors and the Museum of Modern Art.

**Sources say:** *"There's a lot of personal attention there; there's a real thoroughness and a real practicality."*

**KEY INDIVIDUALS Jeffrey Lenobel** (see p.1913) is praised as a *"gifted lawyer with a first-rate mind,"* and sources are particularly impressed by his *"vast experience and knowledge."* He heads the group and represented the Museum of Modern Art in matters relating to its acquisition of the American Folk Art Museum building. **Julian Wise** (see p.1951) offers a wealth of expertise across the real estate spectrum, and is highly commended for his *"extensive lending experience."* He is described by interviewees as *"very practical, very thoughtful and very thorough."*

## Shearman & Sterling LLP
See profile on p.2005

**THE FIRM** This four-partner practice is highly regarded for its skills in real estate finance. The group has recently been involved in a number of headquarter leasings for leading institutions, and highlights include representing Viacom International in the 15-year lease renewal and expansion of its 1515 Broadway headquarters, valued at more than $1 billion. The firm also represents Solow Realty & Development, Shorenstein Properties and Wafra Partners.

**Sources say:** *"The work is very strong, they're always thoughtful and timely, and the turnaround is very quick."*

**KEY INDIVIDUALS** The *"incredibly intelligent"* **Chris Smith** heads up the department and is *"a pleasure to work with,"* according to sources. He acted for IntercontinentalExchange with regards to the lease of three floors of the Park Avenue Plaza building, to be used for its New York headquarters. **Malcolm Montgomery** handles a range of cross-border and domestic real estate finance and investment matters. Interviewees regard him as *"a phenomenal force"* in the market.

## Sidley Austin LLP
See profile on p.1264

**THE FIRM** The diverse practice group at Sidley handles a wide array of complex and often high-profile transactions. One highlight saw the group represent Drawbridge Special Opportunities Fund with regards to a $355 million construction loan origination and syndication, for two Boston office building developments. Key clients also include MetLife Real Estate, Starwood Property Trust and Forest City Enterprises.

**KEY INDIVIDUALS** The *"superb"* **Alan Weil** (see p.424) is *"very calm, very thoughtful and very focused on getting deals done,"* according to sources, who also describe him as *"a wonderful person to work with."* He has been representing Agricultural Bank of China, in connection with its first US bank operation, negotiating the lease for 277 Park Avenue.

## Simpson Thacher & Bartlett LLP
See profile on p.2006

**THE FIRM** This leading real estate practice is widely recognized for its skills in handling sophisticated matters for leading private equity houses and funds, and has advised The Blackstone Group on a range of transactions. The team also represented affiliates of The Blackstone Group in their acquisition of an 82-office property portfolio from Duke Realty for more than $1 billion. In other highlights, the firm acted for Barclays on the $2.9 billion sale to Lehman Brothers of Barclays' and Bank of America's interest in Archstone.

**Sources say:** *"A premier real estate equity firm." "It's a great real estate group."*

**KEY INDIVIDUALS** Practice leader **Gregory Ressa** (see p.392) leads the firm's work for The Blackstone Group, and is lauded by sources as *"one of the best private equity guys"* in the market. He advised Blackstone Real Estate Partners VII on the proposed $1.9 billion acquisition of Accor's US economy hotels division. **Scott Kobak** (see p.1910) is recognized by interviewees as *"a very practical lawyer,"* who is *"very good on all aspects of real estate."* He leads the firm's relationship with major private equity player The Carlyle Group. The *"superb"* **Sasan Mehrara** (see p.1919) concentrates his practice on handling joint ventures, financings and real estate acquisitions and dispositions on behalf of private equity firms. In particular, he has handled a lot of work for The Blackstone Group.

## Skadden, Arps, Slate, Meagher & Flom LLP & Affiliates
See profile on p.2008

**THE FIRM** This group receives high praise from market sources, who confirm its position as a market leader. The team regularly handles complex transactions for a diverse client base, and is commended for its experience in corporate, finance and dirt matters. In one standout deal, the team advised Centro Properties on its AUD16 billion Australian debt restructuring, via a debt-for-equity exchange. Its enviable client roster also includes Sungate Properties, Genesis HealthCare and FelCor Lodging Trust.

**Sources say:** *"They are top-tier. I love dealing with them." "They do everything really well."*

**KEY INDIVIDUALS** Practice head **Harvey Uris** (see p.420) is *"a smart lawyer who doesn't miss anything,"* and who is lauded for his strong problem-solving skills. He offers a wealth of expertise in all finance-related issues, and recently led the team on the abovementioned Centro Properties matter. **Neil Rock** (see p.393) has worked on a number of healthcare-related matters. He also represented Gaylord Entertainment in its conversion into a REIT, which involved the sale of the Gaylord brand to Marriott International for $210 million. The *"fantastic"* **Benjamin Needell** (see p.1922) recently represented Silverstein Properties in a $364 million joint venture with Dune Real Estate and Four Seasons Hotels & Resorts (Canada), to develop a new Four Seasons Hotel at Disney World Resort, Orlando. Interviewees assert that *"he's a brilliant negotiator."* **Evan Levy** (see p.1914) wins praise from sources who value the fact that *"his manner and the way he articulates issues are really helpful to us."* Formerly of Patterson Belknap, **Russell Wohl** (see p.1952) joined the real estate group at Skadden in September 2012. He is an expert in commercial leasing matters, especially new construction and complicated condominium leasing.

## Stroock & Stroock & Lavan LLP
See profile on p.2010

**THE FIRM** This group is widely recognized as a go-to practice in New York, and sources comment on its particular strength in the area of condominiums. The team frequently handles projects encompassing the whole spectrum of real estate issues, from workouts to joint ventures and acquisitions. Highlights include advising a pension fund on a joint venture acquisition of 15 acres outside of Washington, DC for the development of a large mixed-use site. Key clients include Silverstein Properties, AIG and JPMorgan Asset Management.

**Sources say:** *"They're extremely smart, organized and have a deep bench."*

**KEY INDIVIDUALS William Campbell** is a *"very smart individual,"* who has been busy advising a fund on the complex acquisition of a distressed senior mortgage loan. **Ross Moskowitz** is a *"really great"* adviser, whose practice highlights include representing a joint venture client involved in a mixed-use development valued at $1 billion. **Brian Diamond** is *"a true businessman's attorney"* who is praised by interviewees as *"extraordinarily skilled at negotiating."* Of late, he has represented a real estate fund in relation to the multistate disposition of 12 senior housing facilities for over $500 million. **Steven Moskowitz** represented a pension fund client in the acquisition of a portfolio made up of 50 Texas properties for more than $500 million. Interviewees highlight that he *"takes charge, and makes sure the client's needs are met."* Clients speak very highly of **Karen Scanna**, who acted for Silverstein Properties on the proposed development of three towers on the World Trade Center site. The well-regarded **Leonard Boxer** is described as *"a brilliant legal mind who really understands the way New York City works."* He offers a wealth of experience across both residential and commercial real estate issues, and sources enthuse: *"He does great things for the real estate community."*

## Sullivan & Cromwell LLP
See profile on p.2011

**THE FIRM** The team at Sullivan & Cromwell offers a seamless multidisciplinary service to clients involved in complex, high-value matters, with particular expertise in joint ventures, financings, restructurings, and acquisitions and dispositions. One significant achievement was the group's representation of Frank McCourt, advising him on the record-breaking sale of the Los Angeles Dodgers and the Dodgers Stadium for $2.15 billion. The firm also acts for Vornado Capital Partners, General Growth Properties and Bank of America.
**Sources say:** *"Great lawyers, great firm."*
**KEY INDIVIDUALS Joseph Shenker** (see p.1941) is described as *"one of the most highly respected real estate practitioners"* in New York, and sources agree he is *"a very talented, very smart guy."* Joseph acts as a personal adviser to numerous influential clients, and represented General Growth Properties in the $270 million acquisition of 11 Sears 'anchor pads' in malls across multiple states. **Arthur Adler** (see p.271) offers a broad range of experience spanning all areas of real estate, with a particular focus on the finance side. He advised Vornado Capital Partners on the $132 million acquisition of a Miami Beach retail property, as well as its synchronous mortgage loan from Bank of America. The *"unbelievably smart"* **Anthony Colletta** (see p.298) handles loan workouts, private equity fund formations and transactional matters for an impressive client base. Interviewees particularly appreciate his *"good business judgment."*

## Weil, Gotshal & Manges LLP
See profile on p.2015

**THE FIRM** This corporate-focused practice is highly regarded for its expertise in debt restructuring, having worked on some of the most complex and high-profile workouts of recent years. The team continues to represent Lehman Brothers Holdings, and advised on its $3 billion purchase of the remaining 53% stake in Archstone. Other notable clients include General Growth Properties, Fortress Investment and Brookfield Asset Management.
**Sources say:** *"Weil has excellent service, responsiveness and completion of engagements."*
**KEY INDIVIDUALS** The *"phenomenal"* **Michael Bond** (see p.1879) is described by sources as *"the calming, knowl-*

*edgeable and creative presence in the room."* He handled the Archstone matter for Lehman Brothers, and also advised Lehman on the $820 million sale of a stake in LCOR to the California State Teachers' Retirement System (CalSTRS). **Philip Rosen** (see p.1932) represented Brookfield Asset Management in its $400 million joint venture with Hillwood Development to acquire and develop US industrial properties. Interviewees report that he is *"very smart, understands the arguments, and is very articulate."*

## Willkie Farr & Gallagher LLP
See profile on p.2016

**THE FIRM** This real estate group is highly recommended for its expertise in complex restructurings, which it handles for a diverse client base of investors, developers, hedge funds and sponsors. In one standout deal, the team represented prominent healthcare REIT Ventas in its $770 million acquisition of Cogdell Spencer, including 72 medical office buildings. The firm also acts for Morgan Stanley, Colony Capital and Citi.
**Sources say:** *"They are very capable, responsive and hardworking."*
**KEY INDIVIDUALS Steven Klein** (see p.1909) is cochair of the real estate group, and his experience covers the gamut of transactions. Practice highlights include advising on a number of loan restructurings for a real estate fund. Sources assert that he is *"very thorough, very experienced and has very good judgment."* Fellow practice co-chair **Eugene Pinover** (see p.385) is *"an excellent lawyer,"* whose can offer expert guidance on securitizations and offerings and advises REITs, investors and underwriters. He also represented Sunrise Senior Living in real estate aspects of its acquisition by Health Care REIT. **Robert Bressman** (see p.1880) concentrates on complex development and equity matters, as well as sophisticated leasing and financing matters.

## Other Notable Practitioners

New entry **David Djaha** (see p.1889) of Ropes & Gray LLP joins the rankings following impressive feedback from the market. According to his clients, he is *"extremely knowledgeable and his depth of real estate experience is very useful."* **Mark Edelstein** of Morrison & Foerster LLP is described by interviewees as *"thoughtful, smart and responsive,"* and is also praised as *"very creative in problem solving."* He represented JPMorgan Chase in the restructuring and enforcement of a $580 million loan for a planned community project in Nevada. Interviewees are impressed by **Elias Eliopoulos** (see p.1890) of McDermott Will & Emery LLP, describing him as *"very smart, friendly, knowledgeable and quick,"* as well as *"in sync with the needs and desires of his clients."* **Susanna Fodor** (see p.1893) of Jones Day is described as *"extraordinary in construction lending."* Sources cite her *"tremendous experience"* coupled with her ability to understand the client's point of view as her key strengths. **Howard Goldman** of GoldmanHarris LLC is an expert in land use and city planning, who offers more than 35 years of experience in the industry. **Robert Koen** of Mayer Brown LLP wins praise from sources for his *"attention to detail – he makes sure that he leaves no stone unturned, and he fights*

*very hard."* He represented HFZ Capital in multiple transactions totaling $600 million. **Peter Korda** (see p.1910) is cochair of the structured and real estate finance group at Seyfarth Shaw LLP. He offers experience in all types of real estate lending, and has recently been advising clients on their distressed loan matters, including enforcement actions, sales and workouts. Real estate litigation expert **Adam Leitman Bailey** (see p.1912) of Adam Leitman Bailey, PC *"puts in a tremendous amount of time and a tremendous amount of effort,"* according to sources. Interviewees also value the fact that *"you feel like you have a zealous advocate out there working for you, and you never worry about things when they are in his hands."* **Martin Luskin** (see p.1915) heads up the real estate group at Blank Rome LLP. He focuses on handling LBOs and mergers for a varied client base. **Jesse Masyr** of Wachtel & Masyr LLP comes recommended as one of the city's *"go-to zoning and land use lawyers."* His vast range of expertise in the area includes commercial, industrial and residential development. **Martin Miner** (see p.1920) is co-head of the practice at Holland & Knight LLP; he wins praise for his *"great technical ability and experience."* He represented Carey Added Value in the $120 million restructuring of its US operations. The *"fantastic"* **Jeffrey Moerdler** (see p.1920) of Mintz Levin Cohn Ferris Glovsky and Popeo PC is described by sources as being *"right on the cutting edge"* in terms of his work. Practice highlights include advising the Metropolitan Council on Jewish Poverty on the $75 million acquisition of 15 acres of land on Staten Island for the development of a senior housing facility.

**Robin Panovka** (see p.1925) is co-head of Wachtell, Lipton, Rosen & Katz's real estate and REIT M&A group. He offers particular expertise in fund formations, complex private equity transactions and REIT matters. Sources look to **Keith Pattiz** (see p.1926) of McDermott Will & Emery LLP as *"a voice of reason,"* and laud him for being *"strategic, clever, methodical and purposeful in negotiations."* He advised King & Grove on its $33 million acquisition of Brooklyn's Hotel Williamsburg. The *"very intelligent"* **Christopher Price** (see p.1929) of Goodwin Procter LLP is praised by interviewees for his *"great business mind and keen sense of how to get a deal done."* Recently, he advised Silverpeak Real Estate Partners on the sale of office portfolio interests for $1.3 billion. **Samuel Ross** (see p.1933) of Olshan Frome Wolosky LLP is described as *"knowledgeable, thoughtful and thorough."* He represents clients in the purchase and sale of apartment buildings, retail space, hotels and large office buildings. Former Dewey & LeBoeuf partner **Stuart Saft** (see p.1935) recently joined the team at Holland & Knight LLP as a co-head of the practice. He is recommended by sources as a *"go-to guy on condominiums,"* and his recent experience includes representing Marriott International in the $381 million purchase of Manhattan's Essex House Hotel. **Raymond Sanseverino** (see p.1936) of Loeb & Loeb LLP is dubbed *"a superstar"* by sources, who also note that he is *"extremely knowledgeable about commercial leasing, and a very good advocate for his client's position."* Recently, he advised Coty on a lease for 120,000 sq ft of expansion space at the Empire State Building. **Carl Schwartz** (see p.1938) is head of the real estate group at Hunton & Williams LLP, and interviewees report that *"he is a superior negotiator, combining legal acumen with excellent business counsel."* Recently he advised World-Wide Holdings on the development of a whole city block for more than $550 million. **Wallace Schwartz** (see p.1938) of Kasowitz, Benson, Torres & Friedman LLP *"is a very calm and effective negotiator"* according to sources,

who also highlight that *"very little comes up that he hasn't previously had experience with, which makes him a very effective adviser."* He is experienced in all facets of real estate, from leasing to capital markets. **Kenneth Sold** (see p.1943) of Loeb & Loeb LLP is praised for his *"superior communication skills"* as well as for being *"responsive and knowledgeable."* He represented Trinity Real Estate in a

lease for 77,000 sq ft at One Hudson Square to Getty Images. The *"absolutely fantastic"* **Joshua Stein** of Joshua Stein PLLC is popular among interviewees, who say he acts as *"both a teacher and a lawyer,"* and that he *"is incredibly knowledgeable in every area of real estate."*

# TAX

Commentary about individuals can be found under their firm's paragraph. If the firm has no paragraph (is not ranked) look at Other Notable Practitioners.

## Tax
### Leading Firms

**Band 1**

Cleary Gottlieb Steen & Hamilton LLP *
Cravath, Swaine & Moore LLP *
Davis Polk & Wardwell LLP *
Skadden, Arps, Slate, Meagher & Flom LLP & Affiliates *
Sullivan & Cromwell LLP *
Wachtell, Lipton, Rosen & Katz *

**Band 2**

Debevoise & Plimpton LLP *
Kirkland & Ellis LLP *
Paul, Weiss, Rifkind, Wharton & Garrison LLP *
Simpson Thacher & Bartlett LLP *
Weil, Gotshal & Manges LLP *

**Band 3**

Cadwalader, Wickersham & Taft LLP *
Fried, Frank, Harris, Shriver & Jacobson LLP *
Latham & Watkins LLP *
McDermott Will & Emery LLP *
Milbank, Tweed, Hadley & McCloy LLP *
Shearman & Sterling LLP *
Sidley Austin LLP *
Willkie Farr & Gallagher LLP *

**Band 4**

Clifford Chance LLP *
Kramer Levin Naftalis & Frankel LLP *
Mayer Brown LLP *
Morrison & Foerster LLP *
Roberts & Holland LLP
Schulte Roth & Zabel LLP *
White & Case LLP *

*Indicates firm with profile.*
*Alphabetical order within each band. Band 1 is the highest.*

## Band 1

### Cleary Gottlieb Steen & Hamilton LLP
See profile on p.1963

**THE FIRM** This outstanding firm commands a great deal of respect from market sources. It attracts particular approbation for its capability in tax matters relating to capital markets and financial products, and advises on a range of tax issues in the field of M&A, recapitalizations, structured finance, reorganizations, and legislative and regulatory matters. Further strength resides in the firm's capacity to advise international and financial clients engaged in controversy and IRS audits and appeals, and in a tax bench

that offers a commercial, proactive, professional and excellent value for money service. Key clients include Goldman Sachs, Warburg Pincus and Google, the latter of which recently sought the firm's counsel in a matter concerning the tax aspects of its multibillion-dollar acquisition of Motorola Mobility.
**Sources say:** *"Always professional and proactive in their analysis and services. They always seem to be one step ahead of the process."* *"Absolutely world-class. A top-notch firm with some of the smartest lawyers in the city."*
**KEY INDIVIDUALS** The income tax practice of **Erika Nijenhuis** (see p.1923) is characterized by an emphasis on international tax planning and financial products, including advising foreign and domestic clients on inbound and outbound business activities, capital markets transactions and financial production formulation. She is *"very good, very thoughtful, and knows tax law very well,"* say sources. Her distinguished clients include Credit Suisse. **James Peaslee's** (see p.1926) practice comprises a variety of US tax matters. He has particular expertise in structured finance and financial products, and has represented an array of financial organizations engaged in IRS-audit disputes. Peers regard him as *"a star: one of the best tax lawyers in the country and a brilliant fellow."* **Leslie Samuels** (see p.1936) is well known for the expertise he brings to matters relating to domestic and international taxation, including the direct investment in the USA by foreign entities, M&A and the development of new financial products. He recently brought his considerable attributes to bear on a matter concerning SABMiller's multibillion-dollar acquisition of Foster's Group. **James Duncan** (see p.1889) specializes in the tax aspects of major joint ventures and restructurings, M&A, securities transactions, financial products, and tax planning for multinationals and financial services organizations. He recently represented Alpha Natural Resources in its multibillion-dollar merger with Massey Energy, and is regarded as an excellent lawyer who has *"very good business sense, and is very creative and very practical."* The deeply knowledgeable **Yaron Reich** (see p.1930) is renowned for his expertise in the tax issues relating to bankruptcy and insolvency, financing, real estate and M&A matters. He recently advised Conversus Capital regarding the sale of its portfolio of co-investments and private equity fund interests. **Jason Factor** (see p.1891) has a burgeoning reputation for handling tax matters in the field of joint ventures, partnerships, private equity and hedge funds, financings and M&A transactions. He is *"very fluent, very deal-savvy and very practical,"* say sources. M&A, reorganizations, spin-offs and private equi-

ty investments comprise a considerable portion of **Kristofer Hess's** (see p.1903) tax practice. He also handles structured finance transactions, often on an international basis, and has been involved in handling work for a number of leading investment banks. **William McRae** (see p.1918) impresses peers with his thoughtful and analytical approach to a range of matters in the field of federal income tax. He has particular expertise in M&A, financial products and general corporate transactions, and, in common with his colleague Kristofer Hess, has also been involved in handling work for a number of leading investment banks.

### Cravath, Swaine & Moore LLP
See profile on p.1966

**THE FIRM** The tax group at this extremely impressive firm is recognized as a powerful force in the formulation of tax-efficient structures for major transactions and in the negotiating and structuring of spin-offs, private equity acquisitions and financings, securities offerings and M&A matters. Much of this work is carried out on a cross-border and international basis, with a combination of responsiveness and diligence that has attracted an array of distinguished clients, such as Barnes & Noble, DreamWorks Animation and Johnson & Johnson. In recent highlights, the team represented BAE Systems in relation to the sale of the California-based manufacturer Safariland.
**Sources say:** *"A top-tier firm which provides top-tier advice and good value for money."* *"The firm attracts a high quality of talent, offers excellent quality of service, is very professional and extremely sophisticated. One of the best."*
**KEY INDIVIDUALS Stephen Gordon** (see p.1898) heads the firm's tax group. His practice incorporates a host of major transaction types, including handling the tax aspects involved in joint ventures, restructurings, M&A transactions and spin-offs. His clients include JPMorgan Chase and Time Warner. He is recognized for his professional aptitude, which one interviewee describes as *"far above that of any other tax professional I've ever dealt with."* **Andrew Needham's** (see p.1922) practice is also marked by significant transactional expertise encompassing joint venture formation, spin-offs and M&A. In addition to a number of investment banking firms, his distinguished roster of clients features Johnson & Johnson, Weyerhaeuser and IBM. Interviewees describe him as *"very approachable, and very highly regarded in the tax community."* **Michael Schler's** (see p.1937) impressive practice covers a variety of matters in the field of corporate tax, international transactions, M&A and corporate finance. His

## Tax
### Leading Individuals

**Band 1**

| | | |
|---|---|---|
| **Blessing** Peter H | Shearman & Sterling LLP | |
| **Goldring** Stuart J | Weil, Gotshal & Manges LLP * | |
| **Gordon** Stephen L | Cravath, Swaine & Moore LLP * | |
| **Hariton** David P | Sullivan & Cromwell LLP * | |
| **Heitner** Kenneth H | Weil, Gotshal & Manges LLP * | |
| **Needham** Andrew W | Cravath, Swaine & Moore LLP * | |
| **Nijenhuis** Erika W | Cleary Gottlieb Steen & Hamilton LLP * | |
| **Peaslee** James M | Cleary Gottlieb Steen & Hamilton LLP * | |
| **Rosen** Matthew A | Skadden, Arps, Slate, Meagher & Flom * | |
| **Samuels** Leslie B | Cleary Gottlieb Steen & Hamilton LLP * | |
| **Schler** Michael L | Cravath, Swaine & Moore LLP * | |
| **Schwartz** Jodi J | Wachtell, Lipton, Rosen & Katz * | |
| **Shachar** Avishai | Davis Polk & Wardwell LLP * | |
| **Todrys** Steven C | Simpson Thacher & Bartlett LLP * | |

**Band 2**

| | |
|---|---|
| **Blanchard** Kimberly S | Weil, Gotshal & Manges LLP * |
| **Braiterman** Andrew H | Hughes Hubbard & Reed LLP (ONP) † |
| **Cassanos** Robert | Fried, Frank, Harris, Shriver & Jacobson |
| **Cohen** Benjamin J | Cahill Gordon & Reindel LLP (ONP) † |
| **Creamer Jr** Ronald E | Sullivan & Cromwell LLP * |
| **Dimon** Samuel | Davis Polk & Wardwell LLP * |
| **Duncan** James | Cleary Gottlieb Steen & Hamilton LLP * |
| **Faber** Peter L | McDermott Will & Emery LLP * |
| **Friedman** Gary M | Debevoise & Plimpton LLP |
| **Furci** Peter | Debevoise & Plimpton LLP |
| **Gallagher** Patrick C | Kirkland & Ellis LLP * |
| **Gonzalez** Edward E | Skadden, Arps, Slate, Meagher & Flom * |
| **Hart** John | Simpson Thacher & Bartlett LLP * |
| **Kayle** Bruce E | Milbank, Tweed, Hadley & McCloy LLP * |
| **Leblang** Stuart E | Akin Gump Strauss Hauer & Feld (ONP) † |
| **Lee** Carolyn Joy | Jones Day (ONP) † * |
| **Mason** Andrew S | Sullivan & Cromwell LLP * |
| **Miller** David S | Cadwalader, Wickersham & Taft LLP * |
| **Paul** Deborah L | Wachtell, Lipton, Rosen & Katz * |
| **Reich** Yaron Z | Cleary Gottlieb Steen & Hamilton LLP * |
| **Reinhold** Richard L | Willkie Farr & Gallagher LLP * |
| **Rosen** Burt | Debevoise & Plimpton LLP |
| **Schnabel** David H | Debevoise & Plimpton LLP |
| **Sicular** David R | Paul, Weiss, Rifkind, Wharton & Garrison * |
| **Sit** Po | Davis Polk & Wardwell LLP * |
| **Solomon** Andrew P | Sullivan & Cromwell LLP * |
| **Warnke** Gordon E | Linklaters (ONP) † |
| **Wollman** Diana L | Sullivan & Cromwell LLP * |

**Band 3**

| | |
|---|---|
| **Barr** Neil J | Davis Polk & Wardwell LLP * |
| **Bronstein** Richard J | Paul, Weiss, Rifkind, Wharton & Garrison * |
| **Factor** Jason R | Cleary Gottlieb Steen & Hamilton LLP * |
| **Farr** Lucy W | Davis Polk & Wardwell LLP * |
| **Ferrell** Kathleen | Davis Polk & Wardwell LLP * |
| **Finkelstein** Stuart M | Skadden, Arps, Slate, Meagher & Flom * |
| **Holmes** Joshua | Wachtell, Lipton, Rosen & Katz * |
| **Karig** Adele M | Debevoise & Plimpton LLP |
| **Leavy** Richard A. | Sidley Austin LLP * |
| **Lee-Lim** Jiyeon | Latham & Watkins LLP * |
| **Lopo** Diana M | Skadden, Arps, Slate, Meagher & Flom * |
| **Mandel** Gary B | Simpson Thacher & Bartlett LLP * |
| **Mayo** David W | Paul, Weiss, Rifkind, Wharton & Garrison * |
| **Mehlman** Nancy | Simpson Thacher & Bartlett LLP * |
| **Mollerus** Michael | Davis Polk & Wardwell LLP * |
| **Nirenberg** David Z | Ashurst (ONP) † |
| **Raab** David S | Latham & Watkins LLP * |
| **Rievman** David | Skadden, Arps, Slate, Meagher & Flom * |
| **Rosen** Arthur R | McDermott Will & Emery LLP * |
| **Samuels** Jeffrey B | Paul, Weiss, Rifkind, Wharton & Garrison * |
| **Scarborough** Robert | Freshfields Bruckhaus Deringer US (ONP) † * |
| **Scharfstein** Joel | Fried, Frank, Harris, Shriver & Jacobson * |
| **Shapiro** David I | Fried, Frank, Harris, Shriver & Jacobson * |
| **Shulman** Dean S | Skadden, Arps, Slate, Meagher & Flom * |
| **Swartz** Linda Z | Cadwalader, Wickersham & Taft LLP * |
| **Tanenbaum** Edward | Alston & Bird LLP (ONP) † * |
| **Walker** Andrew R | Milbank, Tweed, Hadley & McCloy LLP * |
| **Wallace** W Kirk | Skadden, Arps, Slate, Meagher & Flom * |
| **Wolf** Lary S | Roberts & Holland LLP |

**Band 4**

| | |
|---|---|
| **Andersen** Richard | WilmerHale (ONP) † * |
| **Angelilli** Lauren | Cravath, Swaine & Moore LLP * |
| **Ballan** Harry | Davis Polk & Wardwell LLP * |
| **Barzilai** Laura M | Sidley Austin LLP * |
| **Benedict** Philippe | Schulte Roth & Zabel LLP * |
| **Berg** Andrew | Debevoise & Plimpton LLP |
| **Brown** James | Willkie Farr & Gallagher LLP * |
| **Bunning** David W. | Greenberg Traurig, LLP (ONP) † * |
| **Carden** Donald | Clifford Chance US LLP * |
| **Catalano** Richard | Clifford Chance US LLP * |
| **Cavanagh** William G | Chadbourne & Parke LLP (ONP) † * |
| **Clemens** Steven E | Kirkland & Ellis LLP * |
| **Cohen** Edmund S | Winston & Strawn LLP (ONP) † * |
| **Connors** Peter J | Orrick, Herrington & Sutcliffe LLP (ONP) † |
| **Creed** John J | Simpson Thacher & Bartlett LLP * |
| **Dantzler Jr** J William | White & Case LLP * |
| **Farber** Michael | Davis Polk & Wardwell LLP * |

| | |
|---|---|
| **Fields** Craig | Morrison & Foerster LLP * |
| **Frankel** Paul H | Morrison & Foerster LLP * |
| **Gartner** Gary J | Kaye Scholer LLP (ONP) † * |
| **Geller** Marcy | Simpson Thacher & Bartlett LLP * |
| **Giegerich** Thomas | McDermott Will & Emery LLP * |
| **Heinberg** Jack | Allen & Overy LLP (ONP) † |
| **Herzog** Barry | Kramer Levin Naftalis & Frankel LLP * |
| **Hess** Kristofer | Cleary Gottlieb Steen & Hamilton LLP * |
| **Hollender** Victor | Skadden, Arps, Slate, Meagher & Flom * |
| **Holo** Robert | Simpson Thacher & Bartlett LLP * |
| **Jones** Maria | Kramer Levin Naftalis & Frankel LLP * |
| **Kaplan** Barbara T | Greenberg Traurig, LLP (ONP) † * |
| **Kopp** Steven | Ashurst (ONP) † * |
| **Kreitman** Robert M | Sidley Austin LLP * |
| **Mahmoudov** Vadim | Debevoise & Plimpton LLP |
| **Matays** Steven J. | Skadden, Arps, Slate, Meagher & Flom * |
| **McFadyen** Douglas R | Shearman & Sterling LLP |
| **McGinley** Elizabeth L | Bracewell & Giuliani LLP (ONP) † * |
| **McRae** William | Cleary Gottlieb Steen & Hamilton LLP * |
| **Milkes** Jay | Ropes & Gray LLP (ONP) † |
| **Miller** Michael J | Roberts & Holland LLP |
| **Peters** Christopher | Willkie Farr & Gallagher LLP * |
| **Phillips** Greer L | Kirkland & Ellis LLP * |
| **Pollack** Martin D | Weil, Gotshal & Manges LLP * |
| **Ponikvar** Dale L | Milbank, Tweed, Hadley & McCloy LLP * |
| **Rosen** Seth | Debevoise & Plimpton LLP |
| **Schoenbrun** Gary | Dickstein Shapiro LLP (ONP) † * |
| **Schuur** Peter F G | Debevoise & Plimpton LLP |
| **Sontag** Scott M | Weil, Gotshal & Manges LLP * |
| **Staffaroni** Robert J | Debevoise & Plimpton LLP |
| **Teitelbaum** Marc | Dentons (ONP) † * |
| **Thurston** Sally A | Skadden, Arps, Slate, Meagher & Flom * |
| **Trinklein** Jeffrey M | Gibson, Dunn & Crutcher LLP (ONP) † * |
| **Twerski** Shlomo C | Schulte Roth & Zabel LLP * |
| **Uffner** Jeffrey | Stroock & Stroock & Lavan LLP (ONP) † |
| **Zuckerbrot** Kenneth | Greenberg Traurig, LLP (ONP) † |

### Up-and-coming individuals

| | |
|---|---|
| **Bazar** Jason S. | Mayer Brown LLP |
| **Gelber** Avrohom | Clifford Chance US LLP * |
| **Jacobson** Hillel | Willkie Farr & Gallagher LLP * |
| **Light** Russell S. | Kirkland & Ellis LLP * |
| **Simonetti** Marc | Sutherland Asbill & Brennan LLP (ONP) † |
| **Stange** Eiko | Wachtell, Lipton, Rosen & Katz * |
| **Teti II** J Leonard (Len) | Cravath, Swaine & Moore LLP * |
| **Wagman** Philip | Clifford Chance US LLP * |

* Indicates individual with profile.
† ONP = Other Notable Practitioner.

clients include the Linde Group and Goldman Sachs, and he is regarded by one client as *"one of the top corporate tax lawyers in the USA: 100% accurate in his advice, pleasant and congenial in his rapport and a thought leader in the US tax profession."* **Lauren Angelilli** (see p.1873) represents clients engaged in private ruling matters before the IRS, and advises on the structuring of domestic and cross-border joint ventures, fund formation, restructurings, M&A

and spin-offs. Her clients include DreamWorks Animation, Starbucks and Time Warner. Peers speak favorably of the professional and personal attributes of **Leonard Teti** (see p.1946), who continues to develop his reputation for the quality of advice he is able to offer on bank financings, private equity transactions, intricate M&A and spin-offs.

## Davis Polk & Wardwell LLP
See profile on p.442

**THE FIRM** The superb depth of this firm's tax bench enables it to assist clients with a range of matters, including those relating to financial products, derivatives, corporate structures, sophisticated transactions and controversy matters. It is perhaps most admired for its innovative activities in the field of investment funds, bankruptcy and

M&A, and has attracted a number of major clients in this area. Among these are the pharmaceutical company AstraZeneca, GS Capital Partners and CIGNA, the latter of which it recently advised on the multibillion-dollar acquisition of HealthSpring, a provider of Medicare Advantage care plans.

Sources say: *"Davis Polk & Wardwell is an outstanding service provider with extremely talented attorneys: intelligent, responsive and commercial."*

KEY INDIVIDUALS **Michael Mollerus** (see p.1920) advises private equity fund and corporate clients on the tax aspects of substantial transactions, focusing in particular on spin-offs, structured financings and M&A. His clients include Becton Dickinson, Cobalt International Energy and the pharmaceutical company Shire, which he recently advised in a matter concerning its multimillion-dollar acquisition of FerroKin BioSciences. **Samuel Dimon** (see p.1888) brings a combination of practicality and intellectual agility to a range of advisory work in the field of federal income tax. He handles significant matters relating to tax audits, reorganizations, M&A, hedge fund organizations and financial product development, and recently advised the US Treasury in relation to its offering of $5.8 billion of AIG common stock. **Po Sit**'s (see p.1942) impressive practice incorporates partnerships, derivative products and M&A. He is particularly experienced in representing financial institutions engaged in matters relating to derivatives and financial products, and has established a distinguished portfolio of clients that includes Barclays, Credit Suisse and Morgan Stanley. **Neil Barr** (see p.1876) is highlighted for the acuity of the advice he offers in the field of federal income tax. He handles domestic and cross-border spin-offs, dispositions and M&A transactions, and also advises on a range of tax controversy matters. His clients include Comcast, AstraZeneca and JPMorgan. International and domestic transactions feature prominent in **Michael Farber**'s (see p.1891) practice. He offers advice to financial institutions and investment banks on securities offerings, joint ventures and M&A transactions, among other matters. His clients include JPMorgan, Bank of America and Deutsche Bank. **Lucy Farr** (see p.1891) is regarded as *"a very fine lawyer."* She attracts this recognition for a practice that focuses on international and domestic tax planning for financial institutions, corporate finance, and derivatives and structured finance. She also works on the formulation and implementation of sophisticated financial products, and was recently involved in a multibillion-dollar matter for Morgan Stanley concerning a substantial number of structured price offerings. Spin-offs and M&A constitute a major part of **Kathleen Ferrell**'s (see p.1891) transactional practice, in which she advises both corporate and private equity fund clients. Her impressive clients include GS Capital Partners and CIGNA, the latter of which she recently advised on its acquisition of the Medicare provider HealthSpring. **Harry Ballan** (see p.1875) lends further strength to his firm's domestic and cross-border transactional practice. He handles spin-offs, securities offerings, M&A and tax planning, and has also acquired a wealth of experience in tax litigation. His clients include Aetna, Citi and Campbell's. Head

of department **Avishai Shachar** (see p.1940) has forged a stellar reputation for the quality of advice he offers clients such as CIGNA, Citi and Comcast in relation to financial products, M&A and spin-offs. Interviewees describe him as *"very creative and terrific at assessing risk,"* and *"very capable, extremely bright, thoughtful and thorough."*

## Skadden, Arps, Slate, Meagher & Flom LLP & Affiliates
See profile on p.2008

THE FIRM This excellent tax group offers outstanding breadth of expertise. Its capabilities span the entire gamut of domestic, cross-border and international transactions. Strong connections with the government sector and the IRS mean that it is particularly well equipped to undertake complex tax controversies and litigation. It has represented a range of distinguished organizations on appeal and at trial. Recent case highlights include advising Express Scripts concerning the multibillion-dollar acquisition of Medco Health Solutions.

Sources say: *"They are terrific: hard-working, creative and responsive."*

KEY INDIVIDUALS **Matthew Rosen** (see p.1932) is co-head of his firm's tax group. His practice focuses on the tax issues associated with domestic and cross-border restructurings, M&A, joint ventures and the formulation of financial instruments. He recently advised Yahoo! in a high-value matter relating to the sale of a portion of its stake in the Alibaba Group. He is regarded by peers as a *"leading light in M&A."* **David Rievman** (see p.1931) is also an expert in complex transactions. He handles major divestitures, spin-offs, joint ventures, financings, restructurings and cross-border M&A. His clients include Summit Entertainment and DuPont, the latter of which he recently represented in its acquisition of the food manufacturer Danisco. **Edward Gonzalez**'s (see p.1898) respected practice encompasses restructurings, private equity, M&A, finance, cross-border transactions and controversy. His recent case highlights include acting for Cementos Argos' acquisition of a Lafarge-owned US cement business. Peers praise him as *"careful, thoughtful, quick to understand and very practical."* **Stuart Finkelstein** (see p.1892) heads the firm's tax group. His expertise covers spin-offs, joint ventures, bankruptcies and M&A transactions, and his clients include Bank United and Jackson Hewitt Tax Service. He recently advised Hughes Telematics on its acquisition by Verizon. The astute and practical **Diana Lopo** (see p.1915) is well known for her broad-ranging tax practice involving complex corporate and partnership transactions. She is particularly well versed in international and cross-border transactions. **Dean Shulman** (see p.1941) is admired for his judicious and able handling of a variety of domestic and international transactions, including buyouts, fund formations, divestitures, spin-offs and M&A. He also has considerable experience in the field of real estate transactions. His recent highlights include advising the Alaska Communications Systems Group on a high-value joint venture with General Communication. **Kirk Wallace** (see p.1949) has established a fine reputation for the work involving investment fund offerings, M&A and interna-

tional financings. He is also known for representing issuers and underwriters involved in international and domestic financial products, REITs and IPOs. His key clients include Chase Bank USA and Domino's Pizza. **Victor Hollender**'s (see p.1904) practice comprises international and domestic M&A, spin-offs, financings, divestitures, and taxation issues relating to sovereign entities. He also advises on joint ventures and the development of financial products, and is admired by clients for his expertise and the quality of his judgment. **Steven Matays** (see p.1917) also handles a variety of international and domestic tax matters, with particular expertise in debt and equity offerings, joint ventures, corporate and partnership restructurings, divestitures and M&A. He recently assisted BNP Paribas in the sale of its lending business to Wells Fargo. **Sally Thurston** (see p.1947) undertakes a range of tax matters, including issues arising from the repatriation of offshore funds, and cross-border investment structures and transactions. She is also active in the field of restructurings, divestitures, joint ventures and M&A, and recently advised Marubeni in connection with its multibillion-dollar acquisition of the Gavilon Group.

## Sullivan & Cromwell LLP
See profile on p.2011

THE FIRM The distinguished tax group is renowned for its expertise in the resolution of significant tax controversies, and in the field of international tax planning. Its impressive roster of clients comprises both individuals and corporations, and features such names as LAN Airlines, AIG and Barclays. The team also undertakes a significant amount of multijurisdictional tax concerns. It acted in one of the largest healthcare deals in recent years, representing Medco Health Solutions in its multibillion-dollar merger with Express Scripts.

KEY INDIVIDUALS **David Hariton** (see p.1901) is an expert in the US tax aspects of cross-border investments, financial instruments and transactions, and in using this expertise to advise a variety of clients in connection with controversies at audit and appeal levels. His recent highlights include his role in the remarketing of $2.5 billion of subordinated notes for Goldman Sachs. **Ronald Creamer** (see p.1886) heads the firm's tax group. He has a distinguished M&A practice and is especially active in cross-border transactions. He also advises on IRS reviews of tax-efficient capital markets strategies and financing techniques. He is a *"very impressive figure,"* remark sources, *"with a tremendous amount of technical knowledge, and is excellent in the field of corporate partnerships."* The thoughtful and talented **Andrew Mason** (see p.1917) has an established practice comprising a range of state and federal tax matters. He is particularly adept at handling work in the field of joint ventures, M&A transactions, IRS issues and real estate. His impressive roster of clients includes Justice Holdings and AT&T. **Andrew Solomon** (see p.1943) brings his assured manner to bear on a variety of matters in the field of tax planning and dispute resolution, including divestitures, cross-border transactions, joint ventures and IRS matters. He recently took a lead role in a transaction concerning Silver Lake Partners' sale of Skype to Microsoft.

Diana Wollman (see p.1952) is an expert in corporate, bank and federal tax matters. Clients seek her assistance across a range of complex international tax issues, compliance, controversies and audits.

## Wachtell, Lipton, Rosen & Katz
See profile on p.2012

**THE FIRM** This preeminent group is highly regarded for its handling, on behalf of large multinationals, of a host of complex transactions. It is particularly adept at addressing the sophisticated international and domestic issues relating to M&A, restructurings and reorganizations, financings, joint ventures and spin-offs, among other things. The firm's tax group is also able to conduct novel real estate transactions, and bring the talents of its creative attorneys to bear upon the development of innovative financial products.

**Sources say:** *"They are fantastically good." "They would be in my top five."*

**KEY INDIVIDUALS Joshua Holmes** (see p.1904) is an expert in cross-border and domestic corporate transactions, including in spin-offs, financial instruments, joint ventures and M&A transactions. He is *"a fine attorney,"* say sources; *"very intellectual, practical and possessed of an impeccable work ethic."* **Deborah Paul** (see p.1926) also handles domestic and cross-border corporate transactions. Peers note her intellectual rigor, and praise her for handling joint ventures, spin-offs and M&A in staunch pursuit of her clients' interests. *"If I negotiate against her,"* states one interviewee, *"I have to be on my toes."* **Jodi Schwartz** (see p.1938) is regarded as *"a top-rate tax deal lawyer: very smart, and very savvy."* She has tremendous experience in domestic and cross-border transactions in a range of industries, including in the tax issues arising from financial instruments, M&A, joint ventures and spin-offs. **Eiko Stange** (see p.1944) lends further strength to his firm's capacity in the field of cross-border and domestic transactions, including dispositions, M&A, financing transactions and joint ventures. He is described as an individual who *"is smart and practical: a lawyer that can get the project done."*

## Band 2

## Debevoise & Plimpton LLP
See profile on p.1968

**THE FIRM** This firm's highly capable and professional tax group serves clients from a diverse range of industries, including energy, insurance, communications and media, international trade, real estate and investment. Its capabilities cover all types of complex M&A, joint ventures, financings, bankruptcies and restructurings. The group is also highlighted for its expertise in hedge fund formation issues. Its distinguished clients include American Airlines and AIG. In recent highlights, the team represented Access Industries in connection with its multibillion-dollar acquisition of the production and exploration assets of El Paso.

**Sources say:** *"They are great. They really are a leader in large fund formation work, and they have terrific tax expertise that is very proactive and very effective."*

**KEY INDIVIDUALS Gary Friedman** is a highly respected expert in multijurisdictional M&A, and the domestic and international tax issues arising therein. *"He has a very good mind, and he thinks problems through very well, and quickly,"* states one impressed peer. *"If I were hiring a tax lawyer, he would be near the top of my list."* **Peter Furci** has an established practice that incorporates private investment funds, debt and equities securities, joint ventures and cross-border M&A. He is well respected for his knowledge and ability to solve problems, and is regarded as *"an expert and pragmatic lawyer."* **Burt Rosen** chairs the firm's tax department. His practice comprises M&A and complex financing transactions, and he is praised for his wisdom and the ability to tackle the most obscure of tax implications. His recent highlights include handling the multibillion-dollar acquisition of SRA International by Providence Equity Partners. Private fund formation, M&A and acquisition financing make up a major part of **David Schnabel's** practice. He recently represented Access Industries in connection with its high-value acquisition of El Paso assets, and is regarded as *"absolutely outstanding: levelheaded and extremely intelligent."* **Andrew Berg's** broad transactional practice includes spin-offs, private equity and real estate, joint ventures, debt restructurings and M&A. His clients include the Rockefeller Group, Broadway Partners and Goldman Sachs. **Adele Karig** brings *"a really good marriage of technical expertise and very good commercial sense"* to her engagements. She is an expert in a range of buyout, private equity and venture capital issues. **Vadim Mahmoudov's** practice encompasses bankruptcies and restructurings, private equity fund formation, and domestic and cross-border M&A. He was recently involved in the restructuring of financing and purchase arrangements for American Airlines, and is admired by peers for the quality of his intellect. **Seth Rosen** handles a variety of tax issues arising from the activities of insurance companies, including insurance company M&A, reinsurance and annuity products, insurance development, and financings and restructurings. *"He is a very fine tax lawyer and a very good person,"* states a peer; *"he's very astute, has a very good technical understanding of a transaction, and brings good business judgment as well as good tax judgment."* **Peter Schuur's** practice includes undertaking the structuring of international transactions. He handles partnership transactions, dispositions, acquisitions, and financings and restructurings. He is admired for his command of US and international tax law, and is regarded as *"a fabulous tax lawyer who is very proactive and has terrific insight."* **Robert Staffaroni** has an excellent and broad-ranging practice incorporating financial products, leasing, equipment finance and securities. He recently took a leading role, alongside Vadim Mahmoudov, in the restructuring of financing and purchase agreements for American Airlines.

## Kirkland & Ellis LLP
See profile on p.1254

**THE FIRM** Kirkland & Ellis's admirable tax group offers in-depth expertise in a range of sophisticated transactions, including domestic and international M&A, bankruptcies, restructurings, fund formation, buyouts, financings and

executive compensation arrangements. It also represents clients engaged in disputes with state and foreign tax authorities, and with the IRS. Its clients include Burger King, 3G Capital Management and Apax Partners. The team recently represented ABB in connection with the multibillion-dollar acquisition of Thomas & Betts.

**Sources say:** *"A very experienced team that is able to handle European tax, US tax and wider international tax jurisdictions. They have a very commercial approach."*

**KEY INDIVIDUALS Patrick Gallagher** (see p.1895) is widely respected for his handling of cross-border acquisitions and divestitures, restructurings, public offerings and fund formation. Much of this work is undertaken on behalf of private equity clients. His recent highlights include representing WideOpenWest (now known as WOW!) in its high-value acquisition of Knology. *"I have a very positive impression of him,"* states one interviewee. **Steven Clemens** (see p.1884) is admired by peers for his assured and accomplished manner. He is an expert in the fields of domestic and cross-border M&A, private equity and investment fund formation, and securities. His distinguished clients include TowerBrook Capital Partners and ABB. **Greer Phillips** (see p.1927) handles a range of sophisticated domestic and cross-border transactions, including spin-offs, joint ventures, workouts and bankruptcies, and M&A. He recently led on behalf of Burger King in its high-value partial sale to the shareholders of Justice Holdings. The talented **Russell Light** (see p.1914) is admired by clients for bringing a creative approach to complex transactions, including in private equity investments, M&A and buyouts. Clients describe him as *"a very personable guy who is very front-footed in terms of tackling quite complex issues, and very commercial."*

## Paul, Weiss, Rifkind, Wharton & Garrison LLP
See profile on p.1997

**THE FIRM** This firm's accomplished tax group offers a broad-based practice covering all manner of high-value transactions. Its creative and judicious attorneys are particularly adept at developing and implementing tax strategies for the handling of cross-border M&A transactions, buyouts, multinational investments and venture capital funds, divestitures, securities offerings and REITs. Its enviable client roster includes Time Warner Cable and Citi. It also recently represented Apollo Global Management in its complex merger with Stone Tower Capital.

**Sources say:** *"They have incredible depth across the board and the most talented lawyers imaginable. They have creativity, attention to detail, and the ability to solve difficult problems and to look at things from a wide angle while drilling down to specifics."*

**KEY INDIVIDUALS Richard Bronstein** (see p.1881) co-heads the firm's tax group. He advises a variety of financial institutions on matters relating to capital markets, international M&A and fund formation, and is experienced in handling federal and state controversies. His clients include Oaktree Capital Management and Virtu Financial. *"Brilliant tax lawyer"* **David Sicular** (see p.1941) has an established practice undertaking investment funds, financial products, restructurings and M&A matters. He recently represented the Warner Music Group in its sale to Access Industries. He is *very imaginative and a pleasure to work with,* say sources. **David Mayo** (see p.1917) is an expert in M&A, corporate and partnership taxation, and restructurings. He is regarded as *a very able, knowledgeable tax lawyer,* and recently brought these attributes to bear on KPS Capital Partners' acquisition of American & Efird. **Jeffrey Samuels** (see p.1935) co-heads the firm's tax department. He handles domestic and international transactions, including joint ventures, REIT formation, and public and private M&A deals. Clients value his *great ability to simplify complex tax points in a way that makes clients comfortable,* while peers are particularly impressed by his *calm and rational demeanor.*

## Simpson Thacher & Bartlett LLP
See profile on p.2006

**THE FIRM** This accomplished tax group comes highly recommended for its representations of leading private equity and hedge funds, multinational corporations, tax-exempt entities, and investment and commercial banks. It offers particular strength in the structuring of real estate investments, financial instrument development, cross-border financings, investment fund formation and M&A matters. Its clients include Hellman & Friedman, The Carlyle Group and Accenture.

**Sources say:** *I can think of no way in which the firm might improve its service. It is strong in every area, under every circumstance.*

**KEY INDIVIDUALS Steven Todrys** (see p.1947) heads the firm's tax department. He has an outstanding practice in area of federal income tax, including in restructurings, joint ventures, real estate and M&A. *He is just amazing,* states one interviewee; *he is very practical, extremely well rounded, and he knows everything about everything.* The *very experienced* **John Hart**'s (see p.1901) diverse practice incorporates investment fund formation, publicly traded partnerships, REITs, M&A, and workouts and restructurings. He recently handled a matter relating to the formation of a private equity real estate fund for AllianceBernstein. **Gary Mandel** (see p.1916) is an expert in federal income tax, and advises financial institutions and private equity fund clients across all manner of corporate M&A, spin-off, restructuring and joint venture issues. His clients include Microsoft and Vestar Capital Partners. Peers describe him as an individual *who knows how to get a deal closed* in the face of *seemingly intractable tax issues.* **Marcy Geller** (see p.1895) also handles a range of work in the field of federal income tax. Within this area, she undertakes matters relating to international joint ventures, real estate funds, financial instruments and M&A. She recently represented JLL Partners in connection with its acquisition of American Dental Partners. **John Creed** (see p.1887) is experienced in advising on financing transactions, securitizations, hedge funds, private equity funds, partnerships, joint ventures, M&A and tax-free spin-offs. His clients include The Carlyle Group and Evercore Partners, and he is particularly well regarded for his ability to *make tax understandable to the layperson.* **Robert Holo**

(see p.1904) brings further strength to his firm's federal income tax capacity. Capital markets, financing transactions, corporate M&A and joint ventures all feature heavily in his practice. His clients include TSG Consumer Partners, First Reserve and Nielsen. **Nancy Mehlman** (see p.1918) is *a fine lawyer who is very personable, and very good at representing her clients,* say sources. She is commended in particular for her expertise with real estate transactions, joint ventures, partnerships and M&A. Her recent highlights include representing a consortium led by KKR in the multibillion-dollar acquisition of Samson Investment.

## Weil, Gotshal & Manges LLP
See profile on p.2015

**THE FIRM** This 17-partner team has acquired a strong reputation for its handling of major tax matters generated by an array of cross-border and domestic transactions. Traditionally known for its proficiency in the area of bankruptcies, it is increasingly active in private equity deals, and also demonstrates considerable capabilities in restructurings and capitalizations, capital markets, real estate and M&A. Its clients include GE, Thomas H Lee Partners and Lehman Brothers, which it recently advised in its multibillion-dollar purchase of a stake in Archstone.

**KEY INDIVIDUALS Kimberly Blanchard** (see p.1879) is regarded as *extremely smart and responsive.* She advises multinational, foreign and domestic clients engaged in fund formation, real estate and partnerships, and also handles corporate M&A, joint ventures and restructurings. Her recent highlights include advising GE in its multimillion-dollar investment in the EBX Group. **Kenneth Heitner** (see p.1902) cochairs Weil's global tax practice. He undertakes tax issues relating to real estate, joint ventures, spin-offs, M&A, executive compensation and benefits. He recently advised GE in the multibillion-dollar sale of its real estate lending unit to EverBank Financial. Fellow practice group cochair **Martin Pollack** (see p.1928) is recognized for his superb federal income tax practice encompassing private equity matters, M&A, leasings and bankruptcy issues. He recently acted on behalf of Thomas H Lee Partners in its multibillion-dollar acquisition of a substantial stake in US party goods retailer Party City. **Scott Sontag** (see p.1943) is also a cochair of his firm's global tax practice. His practice features a range of international and domestic matters involving real estate, M&A and the formation of REITs. His clients include General Growth Properties and Lehman Brothers. **Stuart Goldring** (see p.1897) commands considerable respect for his excellent federal income tax practice focusing on the representation of distressed companies. His recent highlights include representing AMR in its multibillion-dollar Chapter 11 bankruptcy proceedings.

## Band 3

## Cadwalader, Wickersham & Taft LLP
See profile on p.438

**THE FIRM** This tax group handles a range of matters relating to banking and finance, fund formation, bankruptcy and restructurings, capital markets and M&A. Within these areas it is especially adept in financial products, debt and equity offerings, the structuring of tax-efficient and tax-free M&A, and debtor and credit representations. Its clients include Pfizer, JPMorgan and Procter & Gamble.

**KEY INDIVIDUALS David Miller** (see p.1919) specializes in international and domestic M&A, hedge funds and private equity funds, bankruptcies, financial instruments and cross-border lending transactions. He is admired for the intelligent and nuanced approach he brings to his work. **Linda Swartz** (see p.1945) is chair of the firm's tax department. She has an excellent practice undertaking the planning of foreign tax strategies, international M&A, joint ventures, restructurings and spin-offs.

## Fried, Frank, Harris, Shriver & Jacobson LLP
See profile on p.1975

**THE FIRM** This group's international tax practice covers most significant types of corporate transaction. It is particularly active in the field of spin-offs, joint ventures, M&A and dispositions, and also handles bankruptcy and restructuring matters. Additional areas of expertise include tax issues arising from financings, and those related to asset management. Its clients include Thomson Reuters, Merrill Lynch and Goldman Sachs, the latter of which it recently represented in its high-value agreement to acquire Interline Brands.

**Sources say:** *They advise us on transactions, and the advice they offer is diligent, business-oriented and flawless.*

**KEY INDIVIDUALS Robert Cassanos** (see p.1883) heads the firm's tax department. His practice encompasses cross-border taxation issues, joint ventures, REITs and M&A matters. His clients include Lee Equity Partners and GS Capital Partners. *He is very creative, always finds solutions, and has a very deep knowledge of tax law,* state interviewees. **David Shapiro**'s (see p.1940) practice covers most aspects of corporate tax. He is particularly proficient in the areas of asset management and M&A, and in acting on behalf of mezzanine and private equity funds engaged in dispositions and acquisitions. *We use him for our most complicated funds,* states a client. *He is very careful and he can translate tax language into business parlance very effectively.* **Joel Scharfstein** (see p.1937) also practices in the area of corporate tax. He is especially well regarded for his handling of partnership transactions, and has additional expertise in acquisitions, divestitures and restructurings. He recently represented Thomson Reuters in its agreement to acquire FX Alliance.

## Latham & Watkins LLP
See profile on p.446

**THE FIRM** Latham's tax group continues to offer international and domestic clients a strong service in complex transactional assignments. Notable areas of expertise include cross-border M&A, financing, joint ventures and fund formation, among other types of matters. Its clients include Apollo Global Management and Barclays, to name a few. Its highlights include representing The Blackstone Group in its multibillion-dollar equity investment in the Sabine Pass Liquefaction Project.

**Sources say:** "*Latham displays a good working understanding of the law and does a nice job of understanding that the facts are not always perfect and that oftentimes common sense must be applied. In these instances their track record shows good judgment and wise counsel. They have been very professional and responsive to our needs.*"

**KEY INDIVIDUALS Jiyeon Lee-Lim**'s (see p.1912) practice focuses on international and corporate tax matters affecting both US and multinational financial institutions. She is praised for her practical approach and the elegance of the solutions she finds to complex issues. Her key clients include Barclays, Deutsche Bank and Crédit Agricole. **David Raab** (see p.1929) is an expert in corporate and partnership taxation. "*On all the complicated issues, I know I will get the right answer and a good result,*" states one interviewee. "*He is a fantastic tax lawyer; he covers the gamut of matters in a way that is totally expert.*"

## McDermott Will & Emery LLP
See profile on p.1258

**THE FIRM** Clients seeking sophisticated and novel tax structuring advice will find considerable strength in this firm's tax group. Working for financial institutions, large-scale companies and a variety of other sizable organizations, it handles an array of state and local tax (SALT), and international and US federal tax issues. It is particularly adept at managing M&A, joint ventures and financings, and at offering representation in SALT and federal controversy matters. Among its many notable clients are Goldman Sachs, Barclays, American Express, and American Airlines.

**Sources say:** "*I have high regard for everything they do.*" "*They have a very deep understanding, a deep knowledge of municipal derivatives and structured deals, and they provide a lot of good market knowledge.*"

**KEY INDIVIDUALS Peter Faber** (see p.1891) is highly respected for his SALT expertise. Within this area, he specializes in controversy and tax planning, representing numerous clients at the appellate and audit levels, and advising on the SALT implications of corporate transactions. His clients include Morgan Stanley and Goldman Sachs. **Arthur Rosen** (see p.1932) lends further strength to his firm's SALT practice. His handling of planning and litigation matters for individuals, corporations and partnerships wins particular acclaim. **Thomas Giegerich** (see p.1896) heads the firm's tax department. He is an expert in offering transactional tax advice and corporate tax planning. He also handles federal tax controversy matters.

## Milbank, Tweed, Hadley & McCloy LLP
See profile on p.448

**THE FIRM** This firm's tax group attracts recognition for its development and implementation of financial products, and for its superb expertise in bankruptcy and restructuring issues, and increasingly in controversy issues. Its clients include Citi, Goldman Sachs, Credit Suisse and Sharp, Japan's largest manufacturer of solar panels.

**KEY INDIVIDUALS Bruce Kayle** (see p.1908) chairs the firm's tax group. He is an expert in the tax issues involved in restructurings, M&A, domestic and foreign securities offerings, and financial products. Peers praise him as "*very practical, thoughtful and easy to work with.*" **Andrew Walker** (see p.1949) is well regarded for his handling of a range of tax issues, including in securities offerings, derivatives and financial products, restructurings, financings and M&A. He is particularly proficient in assisting international investors in their inbound investments. **Dale Ponikvar**'s (see p.1928) practice incorporates outsourcing, restructuring and M&A transactions. He has represented the creditors' committee in a number of significant bankruptcies, and has advised on private equity investments for the likes of Cerberus Capital Management and Goldman Sachs.

## Shearman & Sterling LLP
See profile on p.2005

**THE FIRM** This firm maintains a dynamic presence in the field of cross-border and international transactions. The team comes highly recommended for undertaking a range of M&A, spin-off, joint venture and bankruptcy tax issues, among other things. It acts for an array of clients, including Barclays, Citi and Ford. Recent highlights include representing SunGard Data Systems in its $1.775 billion sale of its higher education businesses to affiliates of Hellman & Friedman.

**KEY INDIVIDUALS Peter Blessing** has established an exceptionally strong practice encompassing REITs and investment funds, restructurings, spin-offs and M&A matters. He also handles tax controversy, and is regarded by peers as "*a truly outstanding lawyer.*" **Douglas McFadyen**'s corporate tax practice includes cross-border and international tax planning. His clients include the Victorian Funds Management Corporation, Dow Chemical and Merrill Lynch.

## Sidley Austin LLP
See profile on p.1264

**THE FIRM** This firm's admirable eight-partner tax group attracts recognition for its growing presence in this practice area. Its broad federal tax practice incorporates tax matters relating to structured finance, M&A, capital markets, securities and investment funds, while its state and local tax activities cover property taxes, telecommunications, banking and state income tax. The team is also noted for its solid tax controversy expertise. Its distinguished clients include JPMorgan Chase, Goldman Sachs and Bank of America.

**Sources say:** "*They are fantastic. They take the time to understand issues and make a sensible, logical solution.*"

"*They offer understanding and simplicity: practical solutions that bring economic value at a reasonable cost.*"

**KEY INDIVIDUALS Laura Barzilai** (see p.1876) co-heads the firm's tax group. She has considerable federal income tax experience, including in restructurings and cross-border M&A transactions, and in state and federal controversies. She is "*very nice to deal with: smart and practical and able to negotiate a deal that is fair,*" say sources. Fellow practice group co-head **Robert Kreitman** (see p.1911) specializes in finance, credit derivatives and securitization. He is praised for his ability to carry out innovative transactions. His recent highlights include representing ANZ, Commonwealth Bank of Australia, National Australia Bank and Westpac Banking in the establishment of global covered bond programs. **Richard Leavy** (see p.1912) is praised for the quality of his state and local tax practice. Within this area he handles litigation, controversy and planning. "*He is very creative and smart, and has seen and done a lot,*" states a peer; "*that experience serves him well in terms of serving his clients.*"

## Willkie Farr & Gallagher LLP
See profile on p.2016

**THE FIRM** Willkie's tax team continues to offer a strong service across a range of taxation issues, including REIT, joint venture, M&A and fund formation matters. It also advises creditors and debtors in restructuring transactions, and handles controversies with state and local tax authorities and the IRS. Its impressive list of clients includes Insight Venture Partners, Zurich and Warburg Pincus.

**Sources say:** "*It is an excellent firm. They have a lot of experience in M&A, represent a lot of hedge funds and private equity funds, and have competitive billing rates. I would recommend them: when we run into conflicts we refer clients here.*"

**KEY INDIVIDUALS James Brown** (see p.1881) is an expert in complex tax issues relating to investment fund transactions. He brings to this work a "*very sophisticated understanding*" of tax law. He is further praised for his knowledge and responsiveness. **Hillel Jacobson**'s (see p.1906) practice encompasses a range of federal income tax matters., including advising foreign and domestic clients on bankruptcy and reorganizations, M&A and partnerships. He was recently involved in representing Jay Alix in the negotiation of an amended partnership agreement for AlixPartners. **Christopher Peters** (see p.1927) is regarded as a talented and accomplished practitioner who is a pleasure to work with. His clients include Platinum, Insight Venture Partners and Level 3 Communications. Head of department **Richard Reinhold** (see p.1930) is praised by clients for the ease with which he is able to combine "*expertise with practicality and the ability to explain issues in a noncomplex manner.*" He is an expert in a host of international and domestic business tax matters.

## Band 4

### Clifford Chance LLP
See profile on p.439

**THE FIRM** This seven-partner tax group continues to attract recognition for the work it undertakes involving investment funds, corporate tax and securities, and especially for its strength in REIT-related issues. The group's access to talent and resources in an impressive network of non-US offices means that it is particularly well equipped to handle work involving foreign jurisdictions. Recent highlights include advising Citi on the restructuring of high-value loans made during the course of its buyout of EMI.

**Sources say:** *"A solid, full-service firm with experience, knowledge and judgment."*

**KEY INDIVIDUALS Donald Carden** (see p.1882) practices in the area of state and federal income taxation, focusing on tax matters arising from structured finance transactions, and corporate and partnership taxation. He recently played a key part in the representation of North Star Reality Finance in connection with its acquisition of the equity interests and management rights of CapLease. **Richard Catalano** (see p.292) undertakes corporate tax planning, partnership, and the taxation of investment funds and REITs. He is *"very good at identifying risks and issues, making recommendations, and is extremely smart and a great source of advice,"* say sources. Joint ventures, spin-offs, restructurings, and cross-border and domestic M&A all feature in **Philip Wagman**'s (see p.1949) superb tax practice. His clients include Citi, Mitsubishi and the Milestone Aviation Group. Peers laud him as *"a careful, thoughtful tax lawyer."* The *"very practical and solution-oriented"* **Avrohom Gelber** (see p.1895) is an expert in the tax issues involved in capital markets transactions and cross-border finance. He recently advised Ajegroup in connection with a sophisticated and international bond placement.

### Kramer Levin Naftalis & Frankel LLP
See profile on p.1987

**THE FIRM** This firm's tax group maintains an excellent planning and advisory practice involving state, local, federal and international tax matters. It is particularly well known for its handling of partnerships and joint ventures for clients in the hedge fund, private equity and entertainment industries. It also handles restructurings; gift, income and estate taxation for individuals; international and domestic M&A; and executive compensation and employee benefits. It recently represented HiTouch Services in its acquisition and subsequent restructuring of MyOffice Products.

**Sources say:** *"It is an excellent outfit."*

**KEY INDIVIDUALS Barry Herzog**'s (see p.1903) practice encompasses almost every aspect of federal income tax. He is an especially seasoned handler of partnerships, real estate transactions, public and private M&A, bankruptcies, and financial products. He is described as *"commercial, and quick to understand the tax implications of investments."* **Maria Jones** (see p.1907) plays a lead role in the firm's state

and local tax practice. She represents a number of high net worth individuals in connection with questions of income allocation and residency, and has litigated on behalf of clients such as Bank of Tokyo-Mitsubishi UFJ and UniCredit in relation to international banking facilities.

### Mayer Brown LLP
See profile on p.1257

**THE FIRM** Almost every aspect of partnership, individual and corporate taxation is covered by the tax group at Mayer Brown. In each of these areas it is able to offer strong representation in state and local tax issues, cross-border transactions and litigation, and has particular proficiency in restructurings, planning, M&A and audits. It also represents clients engaged in transfer pricing concerns. Recent case highlights include representing Kenner & Company in its multimillion-dollar acquisition of Dynacast.

**Sources say:** *"They combine client advocacy with integrity and are always there to be of assistance. What impresses me most about the firm is that they are very team-oriented and have this effervescent desire to collaborate to obtain the best result."*

**KEY INDIVIDUALS Jason Bazar** receives praise for his sophisticated transactional practice. He advises banking and corporate clients on tax issues arising from corporate and financing transactions, and has forged a reputation for being *"very good at complicated transactions, very good at navigating them, and able to keep a relationship on good and friendly terms."*

### Morrison & Foerster LLP
See profile on p.1990

**THE FIRM** The tax group here has a burgeoning reputation for its federal tax and state and local tax practice. In the former area it advises clients on dispositions, M&A, reorganizations, joint ventures, restructurings and financings, among other matters. Its impressive clients include BNP Paribas and the Bank of Montreal. The group also recently represented Merrill Lynch in a matter relating to the development of notes connected to the Investable Volatility Index.

**Sources say:** *"There is always someone available to address any problems or issues that might arise. The firm has always been very responsive."*

**KEY INDIVIDUALS Craig Fields** (see p.1892) is admired for his capabilities in state tax litigation and planning. Clients praise his ability to *"balance what the state is trying to do and what the taxpayer is trying to accomplish,"* and regard him as a *"very effective litigator: highly competent, and very good at articulating his points."* **Paul Frankel** (see p.315) practices in the area of federal tax controversy and state and local tax. Sources laud him as *"a nationally renowned state tax attorney and litigator."*

### Roberts & Holland LLP

**THE FIRM** This firm's highly respected tax team is able to handle an array of matters covering state and local tax, cross-border, controversy, real estate and corporate tax issues, among other things. It represents clients from a

variety of industries, including transportation, power generation and manufacturing. Its roster of clients also includes a number of public charities, and it frequently advises on tax-free reorganizations.

**Sources say:** *"A terrific boutique tax firm."*

**KEY INDIVIDUALS Lary Wolf** is commended for his expertise in real estate, REIT and partnership tax issues, as well as tax controversy work. His clients include both US and non-US organizations. The *"terrific"* **Michael Miller** is regarded as a rising player in the tax issues surrounding the structuring of inbound US investments.

### Schulte Roth & Zabel LLP
See profile on p.2003

**THE FIRM** The tax group is increasingly recognized for the services it offers to a range of clients in the financial services industry. It is especially proficient in the area of private equity, hedge, and investment funds, and is able to handle a range of transactions, including M&A and reorganizations. Its recent highlights include representing ABS Investment Management in Evercore Partners' $45 million purchase of a noncontrolling stake in the company.

**Sources say:** *"We have had a very rewarding and gratifying relationship. The firm is responsive, smart, very thoughtful in its responses and very creative."*

**KEY INDIVIDUALS Philippe Benedict** (see p.1877) is an expert in a whole host of international transactions, including real estate, finance, investment funds and M&A. He is regarded as practical and personable, and is praised for understanding *"the necessity of making decisions."* **Shlomo Twerski**'s (see p.1948) practice shows strength in the field of private equity partnerships, real estate and corporate transactions, and onshore and offshore investment funds. *"An excellent communicator,"* sources admire the breadth of his expertise, with one client stating: *"He seems to have the answer to everything, and does a very good job of calmly explaining complex issues to non-tax lawyers and nonlawyers."*

### White & Case LLP
See profile on p.451

**THE FIRM** This firm's 11-partner tax group is experienced in representing major corporations, financial institutions, investment funds and sovereign wealth funds. It advises clients in a range of asset and project financings, M&A, joint ventures, restructurings and bankruptcies, transfer pricing and IPOs. The team's clients include Fougera Pharmaceuticals, the Starwood Capital Group and Deutsche Bank.

**KEY INDIVIDUALS William Dantzler** (see p.1887) heads the firm's tax practice. He is praised for the practical and thoughtful approach he brings to a range of work, including tax controversy and M&A. He recently represented Fougera Pharmaceuticals in its $1.525 billion sale to Sandoz.

## Other Notable Practitioners

**Richard Andersen** (see p.1873) of WilmerHale is widely respected for his expertise in the tax issues relating to cross-border M&A, securities, joint ventures and financings, among other things. **Andrew Braiterman** (see p.1880) chairs the tax practice at Hughes Hubbard & Reed LLP. He has an excellent practice covering M&A, financial products, joint ventures, and corporate finance, and is described by peers as *"a very smart and thoughtful practitioner, and very knowledgeable."* His clients include Continental Airlines and Sony Music Entertainment. **David Bunning** (see p.1881) of Greenberg Traurig, LLP has an established practice covering appeals, audits, administrative proceedings, litigation and controversy at federal, state and local levels. **William Cavanagh** (see p.1883) of Chadbourne & Parke LLP has a diverse tax practice encompassing state and local tax and IRS disputes, as well as transactional matters. His clients include Access Industries, GLG Partners and Toms King Holdings. **Benjamin Cohen** (see p.1885) of Cahill Gordon & Reindel LLP is admired for his combination of authority and experience in a variety of tax planning matters, including those relating to US and non-US financial products, joint ventures financings, M&A, and cross-border transactions. His clients include JPMorgan, GE and AIG.

**Edmund Cohen** (see p.1885) of Winston & Strawn LLP is praised for the charismatic and engaged manner in which he handles tax planning for investment funds, high net worth multinationals and international corporations. He also handles derivatives transactions, tax-advantaged financings, and the structuring of investments in US real estate by non-US organizations. **Peter Connors** of Orrick, Herrington & Sutcliffe LLP is admired by peers for the strength of his activity in the field of cross-border transactions. He also represents clients before the US Tax Court, and handles corporate reorganizations, financial transactions and private equity investments. **Gary Gartner** (see p.1895) chairs the tax group at Kaye Scholer LLP. His expertise covers the structuring of financing plans, securities, cross-border acquisitions, joint ventures and divestitures. His clients include KERN Partners and Potash Corporation of Saskatchewan. **Jack Heinberg** heads the tax group at Allen & Overy LLP, and is admired by clients for the creative and thoughtful advice he offers in cross-

border financing and securities, derivatives and financial instruments, and international and domestic tax planning. He recently advised Barclays Capital in a matter concerning the application of catastrophe-linked securities. **Carolyn Joy Lee** (see p.1912) of Jones Day has an excellent reputation for state and local tax issues, as well as for a wide range of transactional and controversy matters. Sources describe her as a *"pleasure to deal with."* **Barbara Kaplan** (see p.342) chairs the New York tax practice at Greenberg Traurig, LLP, and represents individuals, foreign corporations and partnerships in state and local tax and federal tax controversy, litigation and examinations. *"She is an expert attorney in the field of international and domestic tax,"* states a peer; *"I have an enormous amount of respect for her talents and expertise."* **Steven Kopp** (see p.1910) of Ashurst is an expert in tax issues relating to structured finance transactions, among other types of transaction. He is also highlighted for his knowledge of CLO and offshore transactions.

**Stuart Leblang** (see p.1912) co-heads the tax department at Akin Gump Strauss Hauer & Feld LLP. He has an established reputation for undertaking tax issues across multiple jurisdictions, including corporate and financial tax advice, and foreign and domestic business transactions. **Elizabeth McGinley** (see p.1918) is head of the tax practice at Bracewell & Giuliani LLP. She is experienced in partnership tax, corporate tax, and in tax matters generated by energy investments. Her clients include ConocoPhillips and Chesapeake Energy. **Jay Milkes** of Ropes & Gray LLP is praised for his *"highly professional and accessible"* approach to tax matters. He recently advised UK company AnaCap Financial Partners in connection with its multi-million-dollar acquisition of a European trust services business. **David Nirenberg** (see p.1923) of Ashurst is an expert across a range of tax matters, particularly in relation to derivative products, investment funds and structured finance. **Robert Scarborough** (see p.1936) of Freshfields Bruckhaus Deringer US LLP undertakes sophisticated corporate and financial transactions. He has assisted private investment funds engaged in matters relating to multi-jurisdictional corporate acquisitions, and has advised

domestic financial institutions on tax accounting matters. **Gary Schoenbrun** (see p.1938) of Dickstein Shapiro LLP represents private and public companies in taxable and tax-exempt M&A transactions, and investment funds in regulatory, taxation and compensation issues. Interviewees describe his *"great knowledge of the law"* and say he *"is a very good negotiator."* **Marc Simonetti** of Sutherland Asbill & Brennan LLP is renowned as a rising star in the state and local tax arena. **Edward Tanenbaum** (see p.1946) cochairs the tax group at Alston & Bird LLP. He is well regarded by peers for his international tax practice, in which he represents high net worth individuals and foreign multinational corporations engaged in cross-border investments and business transactions. **Marc Teitelbaum** (see p.1946) chairs the tax department at Dentons. His practice encompasses the handling of international joint ventures, debt and equity financings, investment strategies and M&A transactions. He is also experienced in the formation of hedge funds and private equity funds. **Jeffrey Trinklein** (see p.1947) of Gibson, Dunn & Crutcher LLP is *"particularly good at getting to a holistic point of view on corporate tax issues,"* and is praised for his user-friendly service. He is especially adept at advising domestic clients engaged in international activity, and in advising non-US clients on US investments.

**Jeffrey Uffner** heads the tax group at Stroock & Stroock & Lavan LLP. He is admired for the client-friendly service he offers across a range of commercial and transactional tax matters. He is *"very client-centric and very knowledgeable,"* remark sources. **Gordon Warnke** heads the tax practice at Linklaters. His federal income tax practice encompasses domestic and international divestitures, restructurings and M&A. His recent highlights include advising WellPoint on its multibillion-dollar acquisition of Amerigroup. **Kenneth Zuckerbrot** (see p.1953) of Greenberg Traurig, LLP undertakes a range of debt restructuring and bankruptcies, and the handling of real estate and tax matters for private and public corporations. He recently assisted Global Tower Partners in implementing several tax-efficient structures for a range of international projects.

# TECHNOLOGY & OUTSOURCING

Commentary about individuals can be found under their firm's paragraph. If the firm has no paragraph (is not ranked) look at Other Notable Practitioners.

## Technology & Outsourcing
### Leading Firms

**Band 1**
Morrison & Foerster LLP *

**Band 2**
Pillsbury Winthrop Shaw Pittman LLP *
Skadden, Arps, Slate, Meagher & Flom LLP & Affiliates *
Weil, Gotshal & Manges LLP *

**Band 3**
Baker & McKenzie *
Loeb & Loeb LLP *
Proskauer Rose LLP *
Venable LLP *

**Band 4**
Bierce & Kenerson, P.C.
Gibson, Dunn & Crutcher LLP *
Greenberg Traurig, LLP *
Kaye Scholer LLP *
Morgan, Lewis & Bockius LLP *
Simpson Thacher & Bartlett LLP *
White & Case LLP *
Willkie Farr & Gallagher LLP *

## Senior Statesmen

**Senior Statesmen: distinguished older practitioners**

| | | |
|---|---|---|
| Millstein Julian S | Moses & Singer LLP (ONP)[†] | |

### Leading Individuals

**Band 1**

| | |
|---|---|
| Delaney John | Morrison & Foerster LLP * |
| Finkel Robert | WilmerHale (ONP)[†] * |
| Hansen Edward J | Baker & McKenzie * |
| Howard Nigel L | Covington & Burling LLP (ONP)[†] * |
| Levi Stuart D | Skadden, Arps, Slate, Meagher & Flom * |
| Tanenbaum William A | Kaye Scholer LLP * |

**Band 2**

| | |
|---|---|
| Adler Kenneth A | Loeb & Loeb LLP * |
| Epstein Michael | Weil, Gotshal & Manges LLP * |
| Hanson Vivian L | Morrison & Foerster LLP * |
| Konvisser Joshua B | Pillsbury Winthrop Shaw Pittman LLP * |
| Lesser Lori E | Simpson Thacher & Bartlett LLP * |
| Nordahl Stephen D | Gibson, Dunn & Crutcher LLP * |
| Osterman Jeffrey D | Weil, Gotshal & Manges LLP * |
| Raysman Richard | Holland & Knight LLP (ONP)[†] * |
| Russell William | Venable LLP * |
| Sandhu Charan J | Weil, Gotshal & Manges LLP * |
| Stern Akiba | Loeb & Loeb LLP * |

**Band 3**

| | |
|---|---|
| Aciman Carole | Carole Aciman PLLC (ONP)[†] |
| Bierce William B | Bierce & Kenerson, P.C. * |
| Bortstein Lawrence | Bortstein Legal Group (ONP)[†] * |
| Brown Peter | Peter Brown & Associates (ONP)[†] * |
| Caplan Gordon | Willkie Farr & Gallagher LLP * |
| Glazer Daniel C | Fried, Frank, Harris, Shriver (ONP)[†] * |
| Mathews Kristen | Proskauer Rose LLP |
| Nelson James E | Venable LLP * |
| Neuberger Jeffrey | Proskauer Rose LLP |
| Nishawala Vipul N | Pillsbury Winthrop Shaw Pittman LLP * |
| Scherzer Dov H | Moses & Singer LLP (ONP)[†] |
| Semerdjian Steve A | Loeb & Loeb LLP * |
| Sutin Alan N. | Greenberg Traurig, LLP * |

**Up-and-coming individuals**

| | |
|---|---|
| Petretti Vito | Morgan, Lewis & Bockius LLP * |
| Pichler Rufus | Morrison & Foerster LLP * |

**Associates to watch**

| | |
|---|---|
| Angel Daniel | Gibson, Dunn & Crutcher LLP * |

\* Indicates firm / individual with profile.
[†] ONP = Other Notable Practitioner.

## Band 1

### Morrison & Foerster LLP
See profile on p.1990

**THE FIRM** Morrison & Foerster maintains its position at the top of the rankings. Its technology transactions and global sourcing group is recognized for the breadth of expertise it offers. Market commentators note the legal and commercial acumen displayed by members of the practice in a range of transactions, such as outsourcing, acquisitions, licensing and life sciences. Clients benefit from the group's ability to harness the firm's international presence for cross-border deals. Lawyers from the group continue to be retained by Warner Music Group, Moody's Investors Service and Intel, the latter of which the team recently advised on IP issues relating to a series of strategic transactions.

**Sources say:** *"It is a top-quality firm and brings a great depth of knowledge and skill." "Their client service is unparalleled."*

**KEY INDIVIDUALS Vivian Hanson** (see p.330) *"is super bright, multilingual and a tough negotiator without seeming so, and has great depth in numerous commercial areas as well as all aspects of IT transactions."* She is well known for her skill in the field of large-scale outsourcing, particularly matters with an international element. She is also commended for her knowledge and understanding of the Japanese market. Recent work highlights include representing Toshiba in an $850 million buyout of IBM's retail services division. Interviewees draw attention to **John Delaney**'s (see p.1888) established reputation in the field, noting an impressive strength of practice. He is best known for the caliber of his work in the technology and outsourc-

ing sector, but also advises on matters involving privacy and data security. His highlights include representing a multinational consumer goods company in privacy and data security matters spanning more than 90 countries. Rising star **Rufus Pichler** (see p.1927) *"knows his stuff really well,"* say sources; *"in terms of being able to solve problems, he is very practical and quick, and understands all arguments."* Pichler is recognized for his prowess in matters concerning patent portfolios, software and licensing. He

recently acted for Hitachi on the sale of its hard disk drive and data storage business.

## Band 2

### Pillsbury Winthrop Shaw Pittman LLP
See profile on p.2000

**THE FIRM** This established firm is singled out for the high quality of its work. The global sourcing practice wins praise for its focus on the business needs of clients and for the skillful legal counsel provided by the team, with interviewees commenting on the impressive standard at which practitioners operate. The practice is equipped to handle a wide range of transactions, including ITO, BPO, cloud computing and facilities management. Clients are drawn predominantly from the pharmaceutical, financial, retail, technology and healthcare industries, and include CAQH and Barclays Capital.

**Sources say:** *"They have an advanced, sophisticated and commercially informed practice with a deep bench and outstanding forms, precedents and protocols."*

**KEY INDIVIDUALS Joshua Konvisser** (see p.1910) is held in high esteem as *"a talented lawyer with excellent business acumen."* Sources appreciate his ability to understand their business models and consider him to be *"fully integrated in client business operations."* He recently advised Dun & Bradstreet on a complex outsourcing matter. The highly respected **Vipul Nishawala** (see p.1923) is commended for the strength of his outsourcing practice and is also notable for his strength across a range of technology transactions. He has advised clients on numerous strategic outsourcing arrangements, licensing agreements and technology-related disputes.

### Skadden, Arps, Slate, Meagher & Flom LLP & Affiliates
See profile on p.2008

**THE FIRM** Skadden continues to be recognized for the stellar business-focused advice provided by its New York outsourcing team. Sources highlight its ability to draw on the firm's wider resources to handle multifaceted deals. The lawyers regularly guide companies through the outsourcing cycle with a much-valued alacrity that makes them indispensable to clients. The practice's recent highlights include representing McGraw-Hill in a series of outsourcing agreements.

**Sources say:** *"They are strong across the board and very efficient."*

**KEY INDIVIDUALS** Market commentators are effusive in their praise of practice head **Stuart Levi**'s (see p.1913) ability to marshal the firm's resources to best meet the business needs of clients. Clients hold him in high regard for his willingness to take a hands-on approach to navigating risks. Sources note that he is *"indefatigable with regards to analyzing and thinking through the issues."* The last year has seen him work extensively with Citi.

## Weil, Gotshal & Manges LLP
See profile on p.2015

**THE FIRM** Weil maintains its reputation as a leader in the field of licensing and technology. Members of the technology and IP transactions group are regularly retained to act on behalf of high-profile entities such as Estée Lauder, Sanofi and Verizon. The practice is well known for its expertise in matters connected to patent litigation and involving the licensing and acquisition of IP assets. Clients hail from a range of industries, including financial services, pharmaceutical, software and energy.

**Sources say:** *"They do terrific work with a number of the partners being thought leaders. They approach issues intelligently."*

**KEY INDIVIDUALS** Clients praise the *"smart and dedicated"* **Charan Sandhu** (see p.1936), commending her strength as a negotiator and her commercial awareness. She focuses on substantial technology transactions, including outsourcing, licensing agreements and strategic alliances. She recently represented GE in its acquisition of a 15% stake in China XD Electric. **Jeffrey Osterman** (see p.1925) continues to earn respect as an established practitioner. The caliber of his practice is illustrated by his work on substantial global transactions such as Centerbridge Partners's $1.1 billion take-private of a restaurant chain spanning the USA, Central America and the Middle East. He has built up a wealth of expertise in handling licensing, outsourcing and technology transfer transactions. Department head **Michael Epstein** (see p.1890) is singled out as being *"easy to work with, client-focused and commercially oriented."* He is well known for his experience in the IP sphere, and is highly skilled in handling related acquisitions, licensing agreements and outsourcing transactions. Over the past year he has represented Sanofi in the numerous technology and IP matters related to its investment in Warp Drive Bio.

## Band 3

## Baker & McKenzie
See profile on p.435

**THE FIRM** Clients value this firm's global platform, and praise the team's excellent market awareness and professional approach, which allows transactions to be structured in a business-oriented manner. The practice focuses on business-critical transactions that involve complex outsourcing arrangements and substantial strategic agreements. High-profile clients include Estée Lauder and Universal Music Group.

**Sources say:** *"Due to the volume of business they conduct and the quality of their people, they have a huge advantage in terms of domain expertise."*

**KEY INDIVIDUALS** *"Recognized industry authority"* **Edward Hansen** (see p.1900) is singled out for his vast experience in major sourcing initiatives and his significant business acumen. Interviewees applaud his impressive negotiating style, with one relating that *"he is highly competent and effective, and is respected by everyone involved in the deal."* Sources remark that Handen is *"fabulous at*

understanding how to construct complex outsourcing agreements that move beyond heavy-handed risk shifting to mutual gain and win-win."*

## Loeb & Loeb LLP
See profile on p.689

**THE FIRM** Loeb & Loeb maintains a strong reputation in the field of technology and outsourcing. The team is noted for its breadth and depth of experience, encompassing all issues relating to IT and outsourcing. Clients are drawn from a host of industries, such as retail, finance and telecoms. Lawyers are particularly noted for the expertise they have developed in cloud computing.

**Sources say:** *"The partners give you their full attention. They really will go the extra mile and they are very good at staying in budget."*

**KEY INDIVIDUALS** Market commentators draw attention to **Steve Semerdjian's** (see p.1939) detail-oriented approach, with one client suggesting that *"he really made it his business to get to know our business – he can see where all the answers lie."* Semerdjian focuses on outsourcing arrangements and licensing and development agreements. **Akiba Stern** (see p.412) is held in high esteem by clients for his skills as a negotiator, with one interviewee commenting that *"the fact that he understands outsourcing extremely well means that he knows what to focus on and what not to labor."* He acts for a host of industry-leading clients, including Citi and IMG, and has counseled major corporations on the full spectrum of technology-related transactions and outsourcing deals. Practice head **Kenneth Adler** (see p.1872) is described as having *"an encyclopedic knowledge of the industry – if you are doing something he has seen it."* He also wins plaudits for his appreciation of a client's need for an integrated and seamlessly delivered service. His recent clients include Comcast and Harvard Pilgrim Healthcare.

## Proskauer Rose LLP
See profile on p.2001

**THE FIRM** This firm's technology, media and telecommunications practice is held in high regard for its consistently high-quality work. A range of industry leaders look to the practice for its broad expertise in handling issues surrounding new media and technology companies, and also those that wish to acquire or dispose of technology or related services. Key clients include Time Warner Cable and American Express. The group also advised the US Golf Association on the development of Apple and Android mobile applications.

**Sources say:** *"Excellent. They are very responsive and provide superb client service. They are fully versed in commercial issues."*

**KEY INDIVIDUALS** Practice co-head **Jeffrey Neuberger** is valued by clients for his familiarity with industry practices, and they note that he is *"especially adept at finding solutions to difficult problems."* He is well known for the extent of his expertise in the use of social media and emerging technologies, and also offers a wealth of experience in the strategic application of online resources. Recent months have seen him guide Brooklyn Health Information Exchange through the creation of a statewide medical

records system. Privacy and data security specialist **Kristen Mathews** wins praise for her *"incredible intellect, brilliant mind and work ethics."* She focuses on technology, media and communications-based transactions involving privacy and data security compliance issues or breach response incidents. She has an outstanding ability to *"quickly assess the situation and fact scenario we have presented her with,"* says one impressed client.

## Venable LLP
See profile on p.927

**THE FIRM** Venable's technology transactions and outsourcing team continues to receive acclaim for its high-quality service on both the vendor and customer side of transactions. The practice is well known for its experience across a range of technology-related transactions, including licensing, outsourcing, M&A and IP management. The team regularly represents clients from a variety of industries, but is best known for its work in healthcare and life sciences. It attracts work from both early stage companies and established corporations such as GE Healthcare and Cover-All Technologies.

**Sources say:** *"They provide excellent client services and support."*

**KEY INDIVIDUALS** Practice cochair **William Russell** (see p.1934) maintains an enviable reputation, with sources praising his *"outstanding expertise, judgment and responsiveness."* He concentrates on licensing, outsourcing, and supply and distribution-focused transactions. Recent highlights include acting for GE Healthcare on negotiating a number of strategic alliance, development and distribution agreements. Fellow cochair **James Nelson** (see p.1923) is held in high regard by market commentators, with one interviewee noting that *"he knows our business, our concerns and what issues are important to us."* Nelson is best known for the strength of his outsourcing practice, and also offers expertise in the licensing, acquisition and disposition of IP assets. He has recently represented Jones Lang LaSalle in a range of facilities management, project management and lease administration outsourcings.

## Band 4

## Bierce & Kenerson, P.C.

**THE FIRM** This boutique firm is singled out for its ability to offer experienced counsel on matters outside the USA. Clients benefit from the group's deep knowledge of international jurisdictions, with specific capabilities in Europe and Asia. The group regularly guides industry leaders through a range of IT, licensing, outsourcing and strategic alliance transactions.

**Sources say:** *"As a small firm their client service has been well suited for my needs, with strong responsiveness and flexibility."*

**KEY INDIVIDUALS** Department head **William Bierce** (see p.1878) remains a respected figure, and is particularly notable for his international expertise. Clients appreciate his ability to combine a business-oriented approach with impressive legal acumen. Interviewees note: *"He is very* *knowledgeable and really knows what the important points are."*

### Gibson, Dunn & Crutcher LLP
See profile on p.682

**THE FIRM** Gibson, Dunn & Crutcher's strategic sourcing and technology transactions group continues to win plaudits for its excellent client service. Lawyers are experienced in a broad range of transactions, including strategic alliances, shared services structuring and renegotiations. The practice attracts global clients from a multitude of industries, and is regularly called upon to guide companies such as Shazam and Grundfos through complex business-critical matters.

**Sources say:** *"I would not hesitate to recommend them or work with them again; strength, capability, client service and commercial awareness are all great strengths of this practice."*
**KEY INDIVIDUALS** Interviewees remark that **Stephen Nordahl** (see p.377) is *"extremely well versed in his subject matter, but understands the needs of clients to reach closure in a timely manner without undue risk, and that all client situations are different."* He focuses on global transactions, either structuring complex agreements or helping to resolve related disputes. Recent highlights include representing Credit Suisse Asset Management in a series of outsourcing transactions. Interviewees *"really can't say enough positive things"* about senior associate **Daniel Angel** (see p.1873), who is building a strong reputation for his skill in handling both outsourcing and technology transactions. His recent clients include GE Capital Financial and Johnson & Johnson, the latter of which he advised on the $450 million outsourcing of its international desktop support and service desk.

### Greenberg Traurig, LLP
See profile on p.1024

**THE FIRM** Greenberg Traurig remains a respected member of the technology community and is recognized for the breadth of its practice. The team regularly acts on behalf of clients from a variety of industries, advising on the full spectrum of technology and outsourcing transactions. Lawyers offer deep expertise in areas ranging from licensing and systems acquisitions to online ventures and strategic alliances. High-profile clients include Calvin Klein and Godiva Chocolatier.

**KEY INDIVIDUALS Alan Sutin** (see p.1945) leads the firm's global IP and technology practice and the New York technology, media and telecommunications practice. Interviewees regard him as a highly experienced adviser with an extensive knowledge base. He is best known for his skill in handling work with a strong IP flavor.

### Kaye Scholer LLP
See profile on p.1984

**THE FIRM** Kaye Scholer's intellectual property and outsourcing group is noted for its strength in IP, and valued for its expertise in handling issues related to emerging technologies such as big data and the combination of analytics and social media. Lawyers regularly advise high-profile entities on the full spectrum of outsourcing, IT and privacy and data protection issues that arise throughout the business life cycle. Clients include Novartis Pharmaceuticals and Morgan Stanley.

**Sources say:** *"Kaye Scholer has consistently brilliant lawyers throughout the firm."*
**KEY INDIVIDUALS** Practice chair **William Tanenbaum** (see p.1946) is *"at a stage in his career where no issue is unfamiliar, too complex or intimidating to take on."* Sources praise his ability to bring *"wide and diverse perspectives to any situation as a result of his mastery of related disciplines such as patent, IP, corporate and energy."* He focuses on guiding clients through the combination of new IT models with existing infrastructures.

### Morgan, Lewis & Bockius LLP
See profile on p.2246

**THE FIRM** The outsourcing and technology transactions team here remains highly regarded by the industry. The practice is known for its expert handling of matters involving new technologies such as cloud computing and data analytics. Lawyers have experience of working with a range of industries, including life sciences, retail, hospitality and financial services. The team's illustrious clientele includes Colgate-Palmolive and HSBC.

**Sources say:** *"We have been so happy with the work – sometimes I forget they are outside counsel!"*
**KEY INDIVIDUALS** Rising star **Vito Petretti** (see p.1927) focuses on domestic and international outsourcing agreements, and advises on technology-related matters. The last year has seen him represent a number of industry leaders.

### Simpson Thacher & Bartlett LLP
See profile on p.2006

**THE FIRM** Simpson Thacher's IP transactions group is recognized for its strength in handling the IP issues that stem from deals originating in the capital markets, bankruptcy and M&A sectors. Its broad expertise includes technology, patents and data privacy. Lawyers regularly represent a wide cross section of clients, such as leading private equity firms and entertainment companies. Key clients include Blackstone and Microsoft.

**Sources say:** *"I thought everybody there was really intelligent and proactive in their thinking – a step ahead."*
**KEY INDIVIDUALS** Those who work with **Lori Lesser** (see p.1913) are effusive in their praise, with one interviewee noting that *"she is so knowledgeable about technology law and technology itself – she understands the development that makes good business possible."* Lesser has significant experience in M&A, restructuring, outsourcing and litigation. She recently acted for Lightyear Capital on a $335 million acquisition.

### White & Case LLP
See profile on p.451

**THE FIRM** White & Case remains highly regarded as an international player in the technology and outsourcing sector, with clients benefiting from the team's integration with overseas offices. The sourcing and technology practice represents a range of industry leaders, such as financial institutions, telecom companies and global household names. Members of the team offer expert advice on a range of strategic sourcing matters, and are also well versed in technology-related transactions including licensing, joint ventures and service agreements.

**KEY INDIVIDUALS** Adam Chernichaw is a key contact for the New York office.

### Willkie Farr & Gallagher LLP
See profile on p.2016

**THE FIRM** This firm's technology and outsourcing group wins plaudits for its client-centric approach. An integrated approach allows lawyers to call on the firm's wider expertise to benefit clients. The group has the capability to advise throughout the life cycle of a company, and has notably advised on a large number of strategic alliances and joint ventures over the course of the past year. Clients are drawn from a range of industries and include GFI Software and Mount Sinai School of Medicine.

**KEY INDIVIDUALS Gordon Caplan** (see p.1882) remains a much-trusted adviser to a host of high-profile clients, with one interviewee noting: *"I don't do anything from a legal perspective without his involvement."* Caplan heads the practice and recently advised Insight Venture Partners on the taking private of database applications provider Quest Software.

## Other Notable Practitioners

Special counsel **Julian Millstein** of Moses & Singer LLP remains an elder statesman of the legal community, with sources drawing attention to his remarkable experience. He is known for his expertise in both transactional and litigious matters. **Nigel Howard** (see p.337) of Covington & Burling LLP is a *"tremendous attorney"* singled out for his detail-oriented approach. Commentators note his admirable commercial awareness, which achieves business-focused results. He specializes in complex transactions such as strategic alliances, licensing and outsourcing. Clients range from emerging entities to international corporations, in numerous industries. He continues to represent American Airlines. **Carole Aciman** of Carole Aciman PLLC focuses on cross-border technology, IP and media-related matters. She is highly experienced in handling strategic alliance, technology transfer and outsourcing transactions. Clients benefit from her expert understanding of European legal issues, with a particular focus on France. **Robert Finkel** (see p.313) of WilmerHale is respected as an established figure with a wealth of experience across the board. He is held in high esteem by peers and clients alike, who commend his understanding of a range of industries and how to tailor transactions to their individual needs. His practice is well known for the high caliber of work it attracts. **Lawrence Bortstein** (see p.1879) of Bortstein Legal Group wins praise for perspective that allows him to recognize the business needs of clients. Sources are impressed by his responsiveness and efficiency, relating that he is *"a real get-it-done kind of guy."* He is best known for his work with clients from the financial sector. Interviewees appreciate that **Richard Raysman** (see p.1930) of Holland & Knight LLP really learns their business. An established figure in the legal community, he has "*extensive experience and knowledge about complex information technology-related transactions.*" His practice focuses on technology and IP outsourcing and licensing matters. **Dov Scherzer** of Moses & Singer LLP is "*an absolute expert in the area of technology and outsourcing.*" Interviewees state: "*Dov has an outstanding combination of business and legal acumen, which is why he remains our company's go-to lawyer on so many matters.*" Scherzer is also valued for his experience as both a transactional lawyer

and a litigator. He practices on both a domestic and international level, advising on the full spectrum of technology and outsourcing matters. **Peter Brown** (see p.1881) recently left Baker & Hostetler to set up Peter Brown & Associates and remains active in the field of IT-related litigation and transactions. He also acts as a mediator and arbitrator in technology and IP-related alternative dispute resolution. Clients recognize that "*his breadth of knowledge on issues of technology law and the practical application of that law have been very helpful to the operation of our business.*"

"*Consummate professional*" **Daniel Glazer** (see p.1896) of Fried, Frank, Harris, Shriver & Jacobson LLP handles a wide range of IT and IP transactions. Sources remark that he "*synthesizes considerations from a number of legal areas to provide well-tailored legal advice that addresses applicable business considerations.*" He is also commended for the depth and breadth of his knowledge: "*He will point out aspects you hadn't thought of or considered.*"

# Leaders' Profiles in New York

**ABATE, Mark J**
Goodwin Procter LLP, New York
212 459 7031
mabate@goodwinprocter.com
*Featured in Intellectual Property (New York)*
**Practice Areas:** Mr Abate concentrates his practice on trials and appeals of patent infringement cases. He has expertise in electronics, computers and computer software, financial systems, chemical compositions and processes, and medical devices. He has tried cases to their successful conclusions in US district courts and the US International Trade Commission and has handled appeals before the US Court of Appeals for the Federal Circuit. He also counsels clients on a wide range of intellectual property matters.
**Personal:** JD, George Washington University Law School, 1988 (high honors, Order of the Coif); BS, Rutgers University, 1984 (highest honors, Tau Beta Pi).

**ABBOTT, James E**
Seward & Kissel LLP, New York
212 574 1226
abbott@sewkis.com
*Featured in Corporate/M&A (New York)*
**Practice Areas:** Business Transactions, M&A, Private Equity.
**Professional Memberships:** New York State Bar Association (International Law and Practice Section, Committee on Foreign Investments in the US).
**Career:** Co-Head of Business Transactions Group. Represents public and private companies, private investment funds, investment management firms, financial institutions, business owners and managers in connection with a variety of business transactions, financings and general corporate matters. Representative transactions: mergers and acquisitions, private equity, debt and venture capital transactions, seed capital arrangements, joint ventures, and strategic alliances.
**Personal:** Colgate University, BA (magna cum laude, Phi Beta Kappa); New York University School of Law, JD 1984.

**ABERNETHY, Jonathan S.**
Cohen & Gresser LLP, New York
212 707 1322
Jabernethy@CohenGresser.com
*Featured in Litigation (New York)*
**Practice Areas:** Mr Abernethy represents clients in white collar criminal and regulatory investigations, internal investigations, and complex commercial litigation. He is a recognized authority on the Foreign Corrupt Practices Act (FCPA) and regularly advises global companies on FCPA matters. Additionally, he represents companies and individuals in sensitive investigations and prosecutions involving securities fraud, wire and mail fraud, antitrust, commodities fraud, and other white collar matters. He has extensive experience with various U.S. Attorney's Offices, the Department of Justice, the SEC, the CFTC, and the Manhattan D.A.'s Office.
**Professional Memberships:** Member of the American Bar Association (Criminal Justice Section); the New York State Bar Association (Committee on White Collar Criminal Litigation); the Association of the Bar of the City of New York; and the Federal Bar Council.
**Career:** Prior to joining Cohen & Gresser, Mr Abernethy served as an Assistant U.S. Attorney in the Southern District of New York, where he was a lead prosecutor on FCPA, money laundering, and financial fraud cases; practiced at Fulbright & Jaworski L.L.P.; and served as a Law Clerk to the Honorable Ronald L. Buckwalter of the U.S. District Court for the Eastern District of Pennsylvania.
**Publications:** Mr Abernethy is a frequent lecturer and has written articles for the New York Law Journal, the ABA Securities Litigation Journal, and other publications.
**Personal:** Mr Abernethy is a graduate of Columbia Law School, where he was a Harlan Fiske Stone Scholar and Editor-in-Chief of the Columbia Human Rights Law Review. Mr Abernethy received his undergraduate degree with highest honors from Stanford University.

**ABRAMOWITZ, Elkan**
Morvillo Abramowitz Grand Iason & Anello P.C, New York
212 880 9500
eabramowitz@maglaw.com
*Featured in Litigation (New York)*
**Practice Areas:** Elkan Abramowitz is a leading white collar criminal defense lawyer experienced in handling civil and criminal matters in state and federal court for individual and corporate clients. He has built his career as a trial lawyer representing prestigious clients fallen into high stakes personal and professional crises both in and outside the courtroom. Named a leading lawyer by Chambers USA: America's Leading Lawyers in the area of Litigation: White Collar Crime & Government Investigations every year since Chambers' 2003 launch in the United States, he has been described as "an unquestioned dean of the field … with a potent combination of experience, intelligence and composure."
**Professional Memberships:** Fellow of the American College of Trial Lawyers and a former director of the New York Council of Defense Lawyers.
**Career:** Former Chief of the Criminal Division for the U.S. Attorney's office for the Southern District of New York.
**Publications:** Co-author of "Corporate Sentencing: A Current Perspective" (New York State Bar Association, 1991) and of the "White-Collar Crime" column in the New York Law Journal.
**Personal:** New York University School of Law (LLB, Pomeroy Scholar and an editor of the Law Review), Brown University (A.B.).

**ABRAMS, Floyd**
Cahill Gordon & Reindel LLP, New York
212 701 3000
fabrams@cahill.com
*Featured in First Amendment Litigation (Nationwide), Media & Entertainment (New York)*
See under Nationwide for profile.

**ABRAMS, Marc**
Wollmuth Maher & Deutsch LLP, New York
212 382 3300
mabrams@wmd-law.com
*Featured in Insurance (New York)*

**Practice Areas:** Marc Abrams concentrates his practice in commercial litigation and arbitration with extensive experience in the areas of insurance and reinsurance dispute resolution. Over the course of his career, Marc has litigated and arbitrated a wide range of disputes affecting the insurance and reinsurance industry including matters involving coverage, rescission, allocation, aggregation, notice, follow the fortunes, security, payment of interest, set-offs, employment practices liability, insolvency, claims handling practices, underwriting intent, and consolidation, among other issues. These disputes have provided Marc with broad experience in a diverse range of business classes and insurance and reinsurance vehicles and products.
**Publications:** Mr Abrams has co-authored and edited several published articles on insurance and reinsurance issues and has spoken at conferences on reinsurance issues.
**Personal:** Northwestern University, BA cum laude, 1994; University of Virginia School of Law, JD, 1998.

**ABRAMS, Marc**
Willkie Farr & Gallagher LLP, New York
212 728 8200
mabrams@willkie.com
*Featured in Bankruptcy/Restructuring (Nationwide), Bankruptcy/Restructuring (New York)*
See under Nationwide for profile.

**ADDISON, Linda L**
Fulbright & Jaworski LLP, New York
212 318 3456
laddison@fulbright.com
*Featured in Litigation (New York)*
**Practice Areas:** Complex commercial litigation.
**Professional Memberships:** American Board of Trial Advocates; American Law Institute; Life Fellow:American Bar Foundation; Texas Bar Foundation; Houston Bar Foundation.
**Career:** Partner-in-Charge of the New York office and serves on the firm's Executive Committee. Honored by the American Bar Association with Margaret Brent Women Lawyers of Achievement Award; named as one of the "50 Most Influential Women Lawyers in America" and one of the "100 Most Influential Lawyers in America." Has tried over 50 cases as lead counsel.

**Personal:** JD, University of Texas School of Law (1976); BA, cum laude, University of Texas (1973)

### ADLER, Arthur S
Sullivan & Cromwell LLP, New York
212 558 3960
adlera@sullcrom.com

*Featured in Real Estate (Nationwide), Capital Markets (Nationwide), Real Estate (New York)*
See under Nationwide for profile.

### ADLER, Kenneth A
Loeb & Loeb LLP, New York
212 407 4284
kadler@loeb.com

*Featured in Outsourcing (Nationwide), Technology (New York)*
**Practice Areas:** Concentrates on complex global/domestic outsourcing transactions. His practice includes drafting/negotiating all types of business process and information technology outsourcing arrangements. Significant experience in the creation of, and strategies relating to, multi-sourced environments, and renegotiation/termination of existing outsourcing agreements. Advises on all facets of technology transactions/sourcing, including e-commerce, emerging technologies, telecommunications and computer law, and IP, privacy and data security.
**Career:** Joined Loeb as Partner in 2008. Technology/Outsourcing Practice Group Chair.
**Personal:** George Washington University Law School (JD, 1986); Union College (BS in Computer Science, cum laude, 1983).

### AHRENS, Matthew
Milbank, Tweed, Hadley & McCloy LLP, New York
212 530 5882
mahrens@milbank.com

*Featured in Environment (New York)*
**Practice Areas:** Mr Ahrens is of counsel in the firm's Corporate Group and is in charge of the Environmental Practice Area. He advises clients on a wide range of environmental matters, with an emphasis on identifying, evaluating and resolving environmental issues and liability associated with financing, project development, mergers, acquisitions, real estate development, securities offerings and corporate restructuring. He has vast experience throughout a wide variety of domestic and international industries, especially the renewable energy, power, oil and gas and mining sectors.

### AIELLO, Michael
Weil, Gotshal & Manges LLP, New York
212 310 8552
michael.aiello@weil.com

*Featured in Corporate/M&A (New York)*
**Practice Areas:** Michael J. Aiello is Chairman of the Corporate Department, Co-head of the New York Private Equity and Mergers & Acquisitions Department and a member of the firm's Management Committee. Mr Aiello regularly advises acquirors, targets, boards, special committees and investment banks in complex domestic and international negotiated and unsolicited merger and acquisition transactions across the most active sectors. His clients include: AIG, Cedar Fair, Goldman Sachs, Merrill Lynch I Bank

of America, Ontario Teachers', The Reader's Digest, Sanofi, Thomas H. Lee and Willis Group Holdings.
**Personal:** New York University (BA, 1991); Widener University (JD, 1994).

### ALBANO, Michael J
Cleary Gottlieb Steen & Hamilton LLP, New York
212 225 2438
malbano@cgsh.com

*Featured in Employee Benefits & Executive Compensation (New York)*
**Practice Areas:** Executive compensation, including taxation, design and negotiation of agreements and arrangements; corporate governance and disclosure; pension investment and ERISA fiduciary matters; compensation and benefits aspects of mergers and acquisitions; private equity compensation; and employment law and related matters.
**Professional Memberships:** Member of the Bar of New York.
**Career:** Joined firm, 2001; became Partner, 2010. JD, magna cum laude, Georgetown University Law Center (2001); BA, magna cum laude, Duke University (1998).

### ALBARRACÍN, Carlos
Milbank, Tweed, Hadley & McCloy LLP, New York
212 530 5116
calbarracin@milbank.com

*Featured in Latin American Investment (New York)*
**Practice Areas:** Mr Albarracín is a partner in the Global Securities Group and a member of the Latin America Group. He advises domestic and international clients in a broad range of matters involving Latin America, including debt and equity offerings, bank and project financings, debt restructuring, and cross-border mergers and acquisitions, with a focus on the oil and gas, power, mining and transportation sectors.

### ALBERT, Lauren S
Axinn, Veltrop & Harkrider LLP, New York
212 728 2230
lsa@avhlaw.com

*Featured in Antitrust (New York)*
**Practice Areas:** Antitrust and intellectual property litigation, as well as general commercial litigation; antitrust merger reviews, government investigations, and counseling.
**Professional Memberships:** Chair, Association of the Bar of the City of New York's Antitrust Committee; Founder and Chair, New York Women Antitrust Lawyers Group; Member, ABA Antitrust Section.
**Career:** Litigations include representing: Fossil, Inc. and Macy's in a trademark/patent infringement litigation; Group Health Inc. in successfully defeating the City of New York's request for a Temporary Restraining Order enjoining its merger with Health Insurance Plan of New York; Actavis Pharmaceuticals in a litigation brought under the Lanham Act by Johnson & Johnson, the manufacturer of Neosporin, challenging the packaging of the private label triple antibiotic ointment Actavis makes for major retail chains. Recent

mergers include representing Bemis Company in its acquisition of the flexible wrapping assets from Rio Tinto Americas, BellSouth in its merger with AT&T, GameStop Corp. in its acquisition of Electronics Boutique, MovieGallery in its acquisition of Hollywood Video, and BellSouth and Cingular in their acquisition of AT&T Wireless.
**Publications:** Smart Pill: When Private Labels Need a Closer Look, IP Law & Business, June 2009; Rethinking Second Requests, The Deal, September 26, 2005, Antitrust Law; Co-Editor, Handbook on the Antitrust Aspects of Standards Setting, American Bar Association, Antitrust Section 2004; Non-Reportable Smaller Deals May Present Greater Risks, Costs Than Big-Ticket Deals That Must Be Reported to FTC, DOJ, 18 BNA Corp. Couns. Wkly. 280, 2003; U.S. Supreme Court Again Clarifies the Power of Arbitrators, 229 N.Y.L.J. 4, 2003.
**Personal:** Ms Albert graduated magna cum laude from Brown University with a BS in 1985 and received her JD with Honors in 1988 from George Washington University, National Law Center, where she was a member of the Law Review.

### ALBERT, Richard
Morvillo Abramowitz Grand Iason & Anello P.C., New York
212 880 9560
ralbert@maglaw.com

*Featured in Litigation (New York)*
**Practice Areas:** Richard F Albert represents clients in white collar criminal and regulatory matters, and in civil litigation. His cases have included a wide range of allegations of securities fraud, including claims of market manipulation, insider trading, and accounting violations, as well as alleged Foreign Corrupt Practices Act violations, healthcare fraud, money laundering, antitrust violations, tax fraud and obstruction of justice. He has conducted internal investigations and represented public companies, banks, brokerage firms, hedge funds, and their officers and employees in complex civil litigation and arbitration.
**Professional Memberships:** Member of the New York Council of Defense Lawyers, the New York City Bar Association (Committee on Criminal Advocacy, 2000-03), the Federal Bar Council (Program Committee, 2009-present; Committee on Second Circuit Courts, 2003-09), and the American Bar Association (Criminal Justice and Litigation Section). Member of the Criminal Justice Act Panel for the Southern District of New York where he represents indigent defendants.
**Career:** Served as Assistant US Attorney for the Southern District of New York.
**Publications:** Co-author of the "White Collar Crime" column for the New York Law Journal. Contributor to The Insider Blog at forbes.com/sites/insider.
**Personal:** Harvard Law School (JD, cum laude), University of Pennsylvania – Wharton (BS, summa cum laude).

### ALESSI, Robert
DLA Piper LLP (US), New York
212 335 4866
robert.alessi@dlapiper.com

*Featured in Environment (New York)*
**Practice Areas:** Environment
**Career:** He represents Fortune 500 companies, governmental entities and cultural institutions and often appears on behalf of clients in federal and state trial and appellate courts and in administrative tribunals where he has successfully tried and argued numerous matters. He has led major project developments before federal, state and local agencies, either reaching negotiated outcomes with stakeholders or defending project objectives in contested proceedings.
**Personal:** JD, Albany Law School, cum laude; BS, Albany College of Pharmacy and Health Sciences.

### ALEXANDER, Troy
White & Case LLP, New York
212 819 8532
talexander@whitecase.com

*Featured in Latin American Investment (New York), Projects (Nationwide)*
See under Nationwide for profile.

### ALLERHAND, Joseph S
Weil, Gotshal & Manges LLP, New York
212 310 8725
joseph.allerhand@weil.com

*Featured in Securities (Nationwide), Litigation (New York)*
See under Nationwide for profile.

### ALMON, Lorie
Seyfarth Shaw LLP, New York
212 218 5517
lalmon@seyfarth.com

*Featured in Labor & Employment (New York)*
**Practice Areas:** Focus on class action and complex litigation, with an emphasis on complex, collective and class employment litigation. Extensive trial experience before juries, judges and FINRA panels. Recognized by The American Lawyer, NACD and the National Law Journal as one of the country's top attorneys.
**Career:** Seyfarth Shaw (1998-present), Co-Managing Partner, NY Office, Member, L&E Leadership Team; NYC Law Department (1994-1998), Assistant Corporation Counsel.
**Publications:** Board of Editors, Wage & Hour Collective and Class Litigation (ALM).
**Personal:** JD 1994, University of Virginia School of Law; BA 1991, University of Vermont; Chair, Advisory Board, Jumpstart for Young Children.

### ALTSCHULER, Fredric L
Cadwalader, Wickersham & Taft LLP, New York
212 504 6525
fredric.altschuler@cwt.com

*Featured in Real Estate (Nationwide), Real Estate (New York)*
See under Nationwide for profile.

### ALVINO, Tim
McDermott Will & Emery LLP, New York
212 547 5409
talvino@mwe.com

*Featured in Corporate/M&A (New York)*

**Practice Areas:** Lead counsel in numerous domestic and cross-border mergers, acquisitions, divestitures and joint ventures. Also advises on other corporate matters, including capital markets activities and corporate governance. Has represented clients in a wide range of industry sectors including avionics, energy, manufacturing, media, retail, staffing, and software.
**Professional Memberships:** ABA; New York State Bar; Association of the Bar of the City of New York; advisor and past president of the Columbia Law School Association and member of Columbia Law School's Board of Visitors.
**Personal:** Columbia Law School (JD, Harlan Fiske Stone Scholar); Columbia College (BA, Cum Laude, Phi Beta Kappa).

## AMER, Andrew S
Simpson Thacher & Bartlett LLP, New York
212 455 2953
aamer@stblaw.com
*Featured in Insurance (New York)*
**Practice Areas:** Litigation Partner representing clients in a broad range of commercial litigation, with emphasis on reinsurance and insurance-related coverage disputes and matters involving science or technology. Has served in the role of National Coordinating Counsel for various insurers with respect to insurance and reinsurance issues. Has represented insurers in direct insurance coverage actions involving asbestos, pollution, radiation and other mass tort claims, and has represented both ceding insurers and reinsurers in a number of significant reinsurance coverage arbitrations and lawsuits, including over twenty arbitrations that have gone to award.
**Personal:** BSE, Cornell University (1983); JD, University of Pennsylvania (1986).

## AMOROSI, John
Davis Polk & Wardwell LLP, New York
212 450 4000
john.amorosi@davispolk.com
*Featured in Latin American Investment (New York)*
**Practice Areas:** Member of Davis Polk's Corporate Department (mergers and acquisitions). He handles all manner of M&A transactions on behalf of strategic and private equity clients, both internationally and domestically. Clients include Morgan Stanley, Cosan, Ameriprise, EBX, GS Capital Partners, Corsair and General Atlantic. Some of the recent transactions on which he has worked include the $12bn Cosan/Shell JV, the $2.4bn investments in EBX by Mubadala and GECC, GSCP's and Advent's $3bn acquisition of TransUnion and Morgan Stanley's sale of its retail asset management business and its aircraft leasing business and its Japanese investment banking joint venture with MUFG.

## ANDERS, David B
Wachtell, Lipton, Rosen & Katz, New York
212 403 1307
DBanders@wlrk.com
*Featured in Litigation (New York)*
**Practice Areas:** Practice focuses on the representation of Fortune 500 corporations, major financial institutions, law firms, and corporate officers and directors in connection with the

defense of regulatory, white-collar criminal and complex civil litigation matters. He also regularly advises clients in connection with internal investigations and corporate governance and compliance reviews.
**Professional Memberships:** Has served on several committees of the Association of the Bar of the City of New York, including the White Collar Criminal Law Committee (Secretary), Criminal Advocacy Committee, and Criminal Law Committee. Also serves as a board member for The Fund for Modern Courts and as an Officer of the Board of Directors of the Fordham Law School Alumni Association. He is a member of American Bar Association and the Federal Bar Council. Currently serves on the New York State White Collar Task Force, which is charged with examining New York's s white-collar crime laws with the goal of recommending legislative and executive changes.
**Career:** Joined Wachtell, Lipton, Rosen & Katz in 2006 and became a partner on January 1, 2008. Served as an assistant United States attorney for the Southern District of New York from September 1998 until January 2006 where he investigated and prosecuted a wide variety of securities, commodities, and other investment fraud schemes, money laundering, immigration, racketeering, and associated violent crime. Tried 13 felony cases to verdict, and briefed and argued numerous appeals before the United States Court of Appeals for the Second Circuit. Was involved in several significant prosecutions during that time, including the investigation and prosecution of the fraud at WorldCom. Served as Law Clerk to the Honorable Denny Chin, United States District Judge, Southern District of New York (1995-96) and was an associate adjunct professor at Fordham University School of Law from 1997 through 2006.
**Publications:** Is a frequent speaker to bar associations and professional organizations on issues relating to white collar criminal and regulatory matters and internal investigations, including the American Bar Association, Federal Bar Council and Practicing Law Institute. Has published numerous articles on these topics.
**Personal:** Graduated from Dartmouth College with an AB in Government in 1991 and graduated from Fordham University School of Law in 1994, where he served as an associate editor of the law review.

## ANDERSEN, Richard
WilmerHale, New York
212 295 6827
richard.andersen@wilmerhale.com
*Featured in Tax (New York)*
**Practice Areas:** Mr Andersen advises clients on the legal and tax aspects of international investments and business transactions. He represents clients in domestic and international corporate reorganizations, acquisitions and divestitures, and joint ventures and fund formation matters, and regularly counsels clients with regard to general corporate, partnership and financial matters.
**Professional Memberships:** International Fiscal Association; American Bar Association;

International Bar Association; New York State Bar Association; Advisory Boards for "Journal of International Taxation" and "Tax Management."
**Personal:** LLM, New York University, 1987; JD, 1981, BA, 1978, Columbia University.

## ANELLO, Robert J
Morvillo Abramowitz Grand Iason & Anello P.C, New York
212 856 9600
ranello@magislaw.com
*Featured in Litigation (New York)*
**Practice Areas:** Robert J. Anello has litigated in the federal and state courts for more than thirty years. He focuses his practice on white collar criminal defense, complex civil litigation, internal investigations and reviews, and appeals. His white collar practice involves representing defendants charged with a wide range of business crimes, regulatory and tax violations, and civil frauds. His clients include individuals and public and private companies such as financial institutions, Fortune500 companies, defense contractors, and law firms. In addition to his trial and appellate work, he specializes in pretrial representation, internal investigations, and representation of professionals before ethics and licensing boards. He has acted as independent, outside counsel to Deloitte & Touche LLP and Morgan Stanley in connection with SEC Look-Back Programs and reviews of the firms' internal compliance programs.
**Professional Memberships:** President of the Federal Bar Council; Fellow of the American College of Trial Lawyers, the American Bar Foundation and the New York State Bar Foundation.
**Publications:** Co-author of "White Collar Crime" column for the New York Law Journal. Contributor to The Insider Blog at forbes.com/sites/insider
**Personal:** Syracuse University (JD, magna cum laude, Order of the Coif, Notes and Comments Editor, Syracuse Law Review), SUNY - Albany, BA.

## ANGEL, Daniel
Gibson, Dunn & Crutcher LLP, New York
212 351 2329
DAngel@gibsondunn.com
*Featured in Technology (New York)*
**Practice Areas:** Focuses on outsourcing transactions, intellectual property licensing, commercial technology transactions and IP and IT issues in connection with mergers, acquisitions and financing transactions. Has worked with a broad variety of clients ranging from market leaders to start-ups in a wide range of industries including financial services, private equity funds, life sciences and specialty chemicals, insurance, energy and telecommunications.
**Career:** Represented client on technology related transactions since 2003. Served as a judicial extern for Judge Zainey at the U.S. District Court for the Easter District of Louisiana.
**Personal:** B.ChE in Chemical Engineering, Villanova University, 1995; JD, Tulane University, 2003.

## ANGELILLI, Lauren
Cravath, Swaine & Moore LLP, New York
212 474 1016
langelilli@cravath.com
*Featured in Tax (New York)*
**Practice Areas:** Lauren Angelilli is a partner in Cravath's Tax Department. Her practice focuses on advising clients on the tax and structuring aspects of mergers and acquisitions, spin-offs, restructurings, corporate joint ventures and fund formations, both domestically and cross-border. Ms Angelilli also works with clients on securities offerings and other financing transactions and regularly represents clients in front of the IRS on private ruling matters.
**Personal:** Harvard Law School (JD, cum laude, 2000); The Wharton School, University of Pennsylvania (BS, 1996). For more information: http://www.cravath.com/langelilli

## ANGIOLILLO, Bruce
Simpson Thacher & Bartlett LLP, New York
212 455 3735
bangiolillo@stblaw.com
*Featured in Securities (Nationwide), Litigation (New York)*
See under Nationwide for profile.

## ANGLAND, Joseph
White & Case LLP, New York
212 819 7916
jangland@whitecase.com
*Featured in Antitrust (New York)*
**Career:** Joseph Angland is a member of White & Case's Global Antitrust/Competition Group. He has represented clients in a variety of industries, including most significantly the automobile, pharmaceutical, financial services and semiconductor industries. He has litigated jury and non-jury cases before federal and state courts and has handled administrative matters before the Federal Trade Commission. At the request of the Department of Justice and the Federal Trade Commission, he has served as an advisor to the International Competition Network, the organization of the world's antitrust enforcement agencies. To view a comprehensive biography, please visit www.whitecase.com/jangland.

## ANKER, Philip D
WilmerHale, New York
212 230 8890
philip.anker@wilmerhale.com
*Featured in Bankruptcy/Restructuring (New York)*
**Practice Areas:** Mr Anker is Vice Chair of WilmerHale's Bankruptcy and Financial Restructuring Group and a member of the Transactional and Litigation Departments. He has played a leading role in insolvency-related litigation matters, both at trial and on appeal, and has represented debtors, trustees, post-confirmation trusts, creditors' committees, secured creditors, unsecured creditors, equity holders, investors and purchasers of companies and assets in Chapter 11 cases.
**Professional Memberships:** Member, American Bankruptcy Institute.
**Career:** JD, George Washington University Law School, Editor-in-Chief, George Washington Law

Review; BA, University of Pennsylvania; Law Clerk, Hon. Paul H. Roney, US Court of Appeals, Eleventh Circuit.

## ANNEX, Alan I
Greenberg Traurig, LLP, New York
212 801 9323
AnnexA@gtlaw.com
*Featured in Corporate/M&A (New York)*

**Practice Areas:** Co-Chair, New York Corporate & Securities. Mergers/acquisitions; public/private debt, equity offerings; Securities Exchange Act reporting/compliance obligations; SPAC's, other alternative public offerings.
**Professional Memberships:** Board of Directors, JCC of Midwestchester; Board of Advisors, NYU Cochlear Implant Center.
**Career:** Selected: Winning Deal Team - M&A Deal of the Year (over $2.5B), Cross-Border Deal of the Year (over $500M) and Consumer and Retail Products (over $500M), M&A Advisor Awards 2012; Winning Deal Team - Consumer and Retail Products, International M&A Awards, 2012; Chambers USA, 2008-13.
**Personal:** JD, cum laude, New York Law School; BS, cum laude, State University of New York-Albany.

## ANTOINE, Olivier
Crowell & Moring LLP, New York
212 803 4022
oantoine@crowell.com
*Featured in Antitrust (New York)*

**Practice Areas:** Counsel with Crowell & Moring's Antitrust Group. His practice involves antitrust counseling on a broad range of competition and antitrust law matters in the United States and abroad, with particular focus on mergers, acquisitions, and joint ventures, as well as U.S. and international monopolization issues. He has extensive experience representing corporate clients in difficult merger and antitrust investigations before the Federal Trade Commission, the Department of Justice, the European Commission, and other foreign antitrust agencies. In addition, his practice includes civil and criminal antitrust enforcement matters, private antitrust litigation, and compliance and audit counseling.

## AQUILA, Francis J
Sullivan & Cromwell LLP, New York
212 558 4048
aquilaf@sullcrom.com
*Featured in Corporate/M&A (New York)*

**Career:** Partner since 1992. Co-heads General Practice Group, with responsibility for 450+ lawyers in 12 offices worldwide. Negotiated and unsolicited M&A; complex cross-border transactions; global joint ventures; private equity transactions; and corporate governance matters. Advises Amgen, Anheuser-Busch InBev, Avon, Diageo, International Consolidated Airlines Group (IAG) and United Rentals. Recognitions: Chambers Global (Band 1), American Lawyer's "Dealmaker of the Year," the Atlas Award's "Global M&A Lawyer of the Year," National Association of Corporate Directors' (NACD) "Directorship 100,"

the Burton Award for Legal Achievement (2005 and 2010) and the ABA's "Legal Rebel."
**Personal:** Brooklyn Law School (JD, 1983); Columbia University (AB, 1979).

## ARAR, Roger M
Loeb & Loeb LLP, New York
212 407 4906
rarar@loeb.com
*Featured in Media & Entertainment (New York)*

**Practice Areas:** Concentrates on motion picture and television finance, production, distribution and talent. Principal clients include television networks, motion picture and television production and distribution companies and producers, actors, writers, directors and investors.
**Professional Memberships:** New York Media/Entertainment Roundtable; UCLA Entertainment Symposium Advisory Committee (also former Co-Chair); ABA - Entertainment ADR Committee.
**Career:** Partner since 1990.
**Publications:** Author, 'A Rational Approach to Trademark Parody' (unpublished).
**Personal:** Columbia University Law School (JD, 1982, Harlan Fiske Stone Scholar, articles editor - Columbia Law Review); Yale University (BA, magna cum laude, 1977).

## ARCANO, Stephen F
Skadden, Arps, Slate, Meagher & Flom LLP & Affiliates, New York
212 735 3542
stephen.arcano@skadden.com
*Featured in Corporate/M&A (New York)*

**Practice Areas:** Practice leader of the firm's New York Mergers and Acquisitions Group. Concentrates primarily in mergers and acquisitions, and other corporate and securities laws matters. Represents companies and boards in broad range of corporate matters. Has represented acquirors, sellers and targets, committees of directors, and investment banking firms in a variety of high profile transactions; including public and private merger and acquisition transactions, cross-border transactions, and leveraged buyout transactions.
**Career:** JD, Georgetown University Law Center, 1988 (magna cum laude; Order of the Coif; The Tax Lawyer); BSFS, Georgetown University School of Foreign Service, 1984.

## ARCHER, Judith A
Fulbright & Jaworski LLP, New York
212 318 3342
jarcher@fulbright.com
*Featured in Litigation (New York)*

**Practice Areas:** Litigation, arbitration
**Professional Memberships:** Federal Bar Council, Member, Committee on the Second Circuit; Association of the Bar of the City of New York, Committee on Women in the Profession; American Bar Association.
**Career:** Judith has diverse experience, having worked as both outside and in-house counsel on a wide variety of cases in state and federal courts across the U.S. at the trial and appellate level, as well as arbitrations and regulatory proceedings. She specializes in complex commercial matters,

including contract disputes, telecommunications, financial services and entertainment.
**Personal:** JD, Fordham Law School (1988); BA, cum laude, Fordham University (1985)

## ARONSON, Clifford H
Skadden, Arps, Slate, Meagher & Flom LLP & Affiliates, New York
212 735 2644
Clifford.Aronson@skadden.com
*Featured in Antitrust (New York)*

**Practice Areas:** Represents clients in antitrust matters relating to mergers and acquisitions. Has experience advising clients on other types of antitrust matters, including litigation and investigations, and representing them before federal and state courts, antitrust agencies, and before grand juries.
**Professional Memberships:** Previous Vice-Chair, Mergers & Acquisitions Committee of the Antitrust Section of the American Bar Association.
**Career:** JD, Georgetown University Law Center, 1980; BS, Wharton School, University of Pennsylvania, 1977 (cum laude).
**Publications:** Co-editor, "Mergers and Acquisitions - Understanding the Antitrust Laws," American Bar Association.

## AROVAS, Gregory S
Kirkland & Ellis LLP, New York
212 446 4766
greg.arovas@kirkland.com
*Featured in International Trade (Nationwide), Intellectual Property (New York)*

**Practice Areas:** Greg Arovas' practice focuses on patent, trade secret, unfair competition and related litigation in the state and federal courts as well as the International Trade Commission. His experience includes representing clients ranging from Fortune 100 companies to smaller rapidly growing technology companies in disputes involving integrated circuits, wireless communications, telecommunications equipment, microprocessors, personal computers, optics, industrial control systems, semiconductor processing technology, aerospace equipment, software, medical products and financial products.
**Personal:** University of Michigan, BS, magna cum laude, 1989; University of Michigan Law School, JD, cum laude, 1992.

## ARQUIT, Kevin J
Simpson Thacher & Bartlett LLP, New York
212 455 7680
karquit@stblaw.com
*Featured in Antitrust (New York)*

**Practice Areas:** Head of Firm's Antitrust Group. Has represented companies in high profile antitrust litigation and before government competition regulatory authorities. Representations include Office Depot in announced merger with OfficeMax, Priceline in the Online Travel Antitrust Class Action litigation and Virgin Media in joint venture with Delta Air Lines. Advised Sirius Satellite Radio in merger with XM radio and DoubleClick in its acquisition by Google.

**Career:** Prior to private practice, he was General Counsel of the FTC and then Director of its Bureau of Competition.
**Personal:** BA, cum laude, St. Lawrence University (1975); JD, cum laude, Cornell Law School (1978).

## ASARO, Michael
Akin Gump Strauss Hauer & Feld LLP, New York
212 872 8100
masaro@akingump.com
*Featured in Litigation (New York)*

**Practice Areas:** Michael A. Asaro focuses on U.S. Securities and Exchange Commission (SEC) investigations, white-collar criminal defense, corporate internal investigations and commercial litigation. Mr Asaro has extensive litigation and investigatory experience involving matters arising under the federal securities laws, including insider trading, market manipulation, accounting irregularities, Foreign Corrupt Practices Act (FCPA) violations, and broker-dealer and investment advisor regulation.
**Career:** Served for five years as a federal prosecutor and four years as an enforcement attorney at the SEC.
**Personal:** JD, magna cum laude, Brooklyn Law School, editor-in-chief, Brooklyn Journal of International Law. BS, Boston University.

## ASHINOFF, Reid
Dentons, New York
212 768 6730
reid.ashinoff@dentons.com
*Featured in Insurance (Nationwide), Insurance (New York)*

See under Nationwide for profile.

## ASLANI-FAR, Adel
Latham & Watkins LLP, New York
212 906 1770
adel.aslanifar@lw.com
*Featured in Corporate/M&A (New York)*

**Practice Areas:** Global Co-Chair of Mergers and Acquisitions Group. Practice focuses on mergers, tender and exchange offers, stock and asset acquisitions, strategic investments, recapitalizations and joint ventures. Substantial experience in negotiated and hostile public M&A transactions and in a broad range of private M&A transactions representing large multinational companies and private equity firms. Advises numerous special committees of boards of directors and regularly counsels clients on corporate governance and takeover defense.
**Professional Memberships:** Committee on Mergers, Acquisitions and Corporate Control Contests of the Association of the Bar of the City of New York.
**Personal:** AB, Columbia University; JD, Georgetown University.

## ASNER, Marcus
Arnold & Porter LLP, New York
212 715 1789
Marcus.Asner@aporter.com
*Featured in Litigation (New York)*

**Practice Areas:** Marcus Asner is an experienced trial lawyer in Arnold & Porter's New York office, where he handles a wide variety of white collar criminal and civil litigation matters. Mr Asner served as an AUSA in the SDNY for nine years, where he was Chief of the Major Crimes unit for two years. Mr Asner's white collar practice includes matters involving alleged violations of the FCPA, and cases involving alleged insider trading, healthcare fraud, cyber crime, data breaches, tax fraud, public corruption, and environmental crime. His civil practice includes complex commercial and expedited litigation matters.

**ATKINS, Peter Allan**
Skadden, Arps, Slate, Meagher & Flom LLP & Affiliates, New York
212 735 3700
Peter.Atkins@skadden.com
*Featured in Corporate/M&A (New York)*
**Practice Areas:** Senior partner specializing in Skadden's M&A and corporate governance practices. Extensive experience representing acquirors, targets, boards of directors, special committees and investment banks in full range of M&A transactions, including mergers, acquisitions, takeovers, LBOs and JVs. Extensive experience also corporate governance arena, including counseling regarding directors' duties and responsibilities, responding to activists, and internal investigations, often in high-visibility situations. Broad industry experience, including airline, building materials, defense, energy, financial institutions, healthcare, information technology, insurance, media and telecommunications, retail and utilities. Member of firm's senior management.
**Career:** LLB, Harvard University, 1968; AB, Brooklyn College, 1965.

**AUGUSTINE, Mary Jane**
McCarter & English, LLP, New York
212 609 6831
maugustine@mccarter.com
*Featured in Construction (New York)*
**Career:** Ms Augustine is a construction transactional lawyer who has provided legal representation for more than 37 years to various participants in the construction industry, including owners, developers, contractors, construction managers and design professionals. Her practice currently focuses on the development of project delivery strategies and the preparation and negotiation of design, construction and related contracts for complex domestic and international construction projects. Ms Augustine is a U.S. Green Building Council LEED Accredited Professional (LEED AP) and is knowledgeable about Green Building requirements, practices and procedures. For full bio: http://www.mccarter.com/Mary-Jane-Augustine/

**AUSLANDER, Mitchell J**
Willkie Farr & Gallagher LLP, New York
212 728 8201
mauslander@williki.com
*Featured in Insurance (New York)*
**Practice Areas:** Co-Chair, Litigation Department; Chair, Insurance and Reinsurance Practice Group. Specializes in commercial litigation with emphasis on insurance and reinsurance matters worldwide and government investiga-

tions. Practice includes litigation, litigation avoidance, and coverage counseling for natural and man-made losses. Representative matters: lead counsel in federal multi-district litigation arising out of government investigations of insurance industry; lead insurance counsel for key defendant in Deepwater Horizon litigation; defense of insurance brokers in scores of major coverage disputes; D+O and E+O insurance counseling for major securities, insider trading and bankruptcy matters.
**Publications:** "Litigation Avoidance and Prevention" chapter in acclaimed NY Commercial Litigation Treatise.
**Personal:** JD (with honors), Rutgers University School of Law, 1980; Editor, Law Review. BA, cum laude, New York University, 1977. See: http://www.willkie.com/MitchellAuslander

**AUSPITZ, Jack**
Morrison & Foerster LLP, New York
212 468 8046
jauspitz@mofo.com
*Featured in Litigation (New York)*
**Practice Areas:** More than thirty years of experience in commercial litigation, with an emphasis on securities, banking, and other complex civil litigation. Has litigated numerous private and class action securities and banking cases. Represents China-based companies in US litigation. Court-appointed Special Counsel and Special Escrow Agent in various SEC cases.
**Career:** Admitted to practice in New York.
**Personal:** AB, Columbia University, 1964, c.l.; JD, Harvard Law School, 1968, m.c.l.; Law Clerk, Honorable Irving Kaufman, US Court of Appeals, Second Circuit.

**AUSTIN, Christopher E**
Cleary Gottlieb Steen & Hamilton LLP, New York
212 225 2434
caustin@cgsh.com
*Featured in Private Equity (Nationwide), Corporate/M&A (New York)*
**Practice Areas:** Practice focuses on public and private M&A transactions; corporate governance matters. Represented Asahi Kasei (Zoll Medical); Sony (Sony Ericsson); Coca-Cola (Great Plains); Hewlett-Packard (3PAR, 3Com, EDS); JPMorgan Chase (RBS-Sempra acquisition); Goldman Sachs (Dwight, Fremont, Popular, Litton); ING (sale of U.S. broker-dealers); 3M (Cogent, pharma divestitures); Hellman & Friedman (Neuberger Berman, Grosvenor, Artisan Partners, Mondrian, Gartmore); OMX (Nasdaq merger); Bank of America (MBNA); Capital One (North Fork, Hibernia).
**Professional Memberships:** New York Bar.
**Career:** Joined firm, 1983; became Partner, 1992. Hong Kong office, 1993-1998. JD, New York University School of Law (1983); BA, summa cum laude, Tulane University (1980).

**AXINN, Stephen**
Axinn, Veltrop & Harkrider LLP, New York
212 728 2222
sma@avhlaw.com
*Featured in Antitrust (New York)*

**Practice Areas:** Antitrust and trade regulation, complex litigation.
**Professional Memberships:** American Bar Association, Antitrust Section, 1980-83; Chair, Committee on Section 7 of the Clayton Act; member, Council 1983-84; New York State Bar Association, Antitrust Section, 1982-85; Chair, Practicing Law Institute, 1991; Co-Chair, White-Collar Crime and Advisor to the U.S. Sentencing Commission.
**Career:** Stephen M Axinn is the firm's senior partner. Over the course of his career spanning almost 50 years, he has represented many of this country's leading corporate and individual clients in a wide variety of precedent-setting cases in trial and appellate courts throughout the nation. He also has counseled clients as to the antitrust aspects of many of the most significant merger and acquisition transactions in the past thirty years. Mr Axinn is also an experienced antitrust criminal defense attorney. He recently served as lead counsel to Bemis Company in connection with its acquisition of the assets of Rio Tinto's Alcan Packaging Food Americas' division. He successfully defended the insurance company, GHI in a court challenge to its merger with HIP. In 2009, he was lead counsel to Ball Corp. in its acquisition of certain Anheuser Busch Inbev aluminum can manufacturing assets. Other clients have included McKesson Corp., Zuffa Enterprises, Hollywood Media, Harcourt General and the Stanley Works. Earlier, Mr Axinn also represented MasterCard's International's Board of Directors in connection with the antitrust aspects of the design of the initial public offering of MasterCard securities. In 2006, Mr Axinn represented BellSouth in the merger with AT&T. In 2005, he successfully represented GameStop in its acquisition of Electronics Boutique and Movie Gallery in its acquisition of Hollywood Video.
**Personal:** Mr Axinn has taught at NYU and Columbia Law Schools.

**BABSON, Marshall B**
Seyfarth Shaw LLP, New York
212 218 5559
mbabson@seyfarth.com
*Featured in Labor & Employment (New York)*
**Practice Areas:** Labor law specialty representing corporations and private equity firms in all aspects of labor relations, including litigation and counseling, NLRB, EEOC, wage/hour, collective bargaining, the labor implications of the acquisition of businesses and employee use of social media. Testified before Congress and Dunlop Commission regarding status of US labor laws. Authored numerous articles on labor law.
**Professional Memberships:** Member, Practice and Procedure Committee, ABA Labor Law Section; Board of Directors, National Chamber Litigation Center and NCLC's Labor Law Advisory Committee; Advisory Board, Institute of Law and Economics, University of Pennsylvania; Advisory Board, NYU Labor and Employment Law Center.

**BAECHTOLD, Robert L**
Fitzpatrick, Cella, Harper & Scinto, New York
212 218 2213
rbaechtold@fchs.com
*Featured in Life Sciences (Nationwide), Intellectual Property (New York)*
See under Nationwide for profile.

**BAKER, D J (Jan)**
Latham & Watkins LLP, New York
212 906 1293
dj.baker@lw.com
*Featured in Bankruptcy/Restructuring (Nationwide), Bankruptcy/Restructuring (New York)*
See under Nationwide for profile.

**BAKER, Hayden**
Davis Polk & Wardwell LLP, New York
212 450 4000
hayden.baker@davispolk.com
*Featured in Environment (New York)*
**Practice Areas:** Counsel in Davis Polk's Environmental Group. He represents companies, private equity firms and financial institutions in connection with the environmental aspects of mergers and acquisitions, securities offerings, financing transactions, bankruptcies and real estate investments. He assists clients in evaluating environmental liabilities, understanding emerging environmental requirements and negotiating transaction structures, indemnities and cost-sharing arrangements to allocate or mitigate environmental risks. He regularly advises on environmental issues affecting oil and gas, mining, energy, chemicals and other environmentally sensitive businesses.

**BALL, Corinne**
Jones Day, New York
212 326 7844
cball@jonesday.com
*Featured in Bankruptcy/Restructuring (Nationwide), Bankruptcy/Restructuring (New York)*
See under Nationwide for profile.

**BALLAN, Harry**
Davis Polk & Wardwell LLP, New York
212 450 4827
harry.ballan@davispolk.com
*Featured in Tax (New York)*
**Practice Areas:** Partner in Davis Polk's Tax Department. Mr Ballan has advised on the tax aspects of domestic and cross-border mergers, acquisitions, spinoffs and securities offerings, as well as cross-border tax planning for such clients as Aetna, Artio, Bertelsmann, Campbell Soup, Julius Baer, Morgan Stanley. His private equity and hedge fund clients have included Citigroup, Corsair, Credit Suisse, Francisco Partners, Highbridge, Lindsay Goldberg, Metalmark, Old Lane, TPG-Axon, Welsh Carson. Mr Ballan has extensive experience in resolving transfer pricing disputes and other tax controversies for multinational firms in the pharmaceutical and technology industries.

**BANSAL, Anirudh**
Cahill Gordon & Reindel LLP, New York
212 701 3207
abansal@cahill.com
*Featured in Litigation (New York)*

**Practice Areas:** Advises financial institutions and multinational companies, boards, committees, and directors and officers in internal investigations and criminal and regulatory enforcement and matters, including investigations by the Department of Justice and U.S. Attorney's Offices, the SEC, the Department of the Treasury and State Attorneys General.

**Career:** Prior to joining Cahill, Anirudh served as an Assistant United States Attorney for the Southern District of New York, where he was Co-Chief of the Complex Frauds Unit, and a member of the Securities and Commodities Fraud Task Force.

**Publications:** Princeton University, AB, 1990. New York University School of Law, JD, 1993

### BARON, Robert
Cravath, Swaine & Moore LLP, New York
212 474 1422
rbaron@cravath.com
*Featured in Securities (Nationwide), Litigation (New York)*
See under Nationwide for profile.

### BARR, Matthew S
Milbank, Tweed, Hadley & McCloy LLP, New York
212 530 5194
mbarr@milbank.com
*Featured in Bankruptcy/Restructuring (Nationwide), Bankruptcy/Restructuring (New York)*
**Practice Areas:** Mr Barr is a partner in the Financial Restructuring Group. He has extensive experience in representing debtors and creditors in chapter 11 reorganization cases and out-of-court restructurings in the US and internationally. He also represents acquirers and sellers of assets of chapter 11 debtors and financially distressed companies; hedge funds and other financial institutions acquiring controlling positions in financially distressed companies, in and out of court; and negotiating debtor in possession financing and exiting financing facilities. His engagements span an array of industries, including retail, telecommunication, chemical, pharmaceutical, textile, energy, automotive, apparel, manufacturing, pharmaceutical, project finance and shipping.

### BARR, Michael H
Dentons, New York
212 768 6788
michael.barr@dentons.com
*Featured in Insurance (Nationwide), Insurance (New York)*
See under Nationwide for profile.

### BARR, Neil J
Davis Polk & Wardwell LLP, New York
212 450 4000
neil.barr@davispolk.com
*Featured in Tax (New York)*
**Practice Areas:** Mr Barr is a member of Davis Polk's Tax Department, who frequently advises clients on federal income tax matters, including domestic and cross-border mergers, acquisitions and dispositions, spinoffs and splitoffs. He frequently advises with respect to group structuring, including as to the application of the consolidated return regulations. In addition, he has advised

clients in connection with various tax controversy matters.

### BARSHAY, Scott A
Cravath, Swaine & Moore LLP, New York
212 474 1009
sbarshay@cravath.com
*Featured in Corporate/M&A (New York)*
**Practice Areas:** Scott Barshay serves as the Head of Cravath's Corporate Department. Mr Barshay's practice focuses on advising public companies, boards of directors and special committees in connection with mergers and acquisitions and other significant corporate matters, including consensual and hostile transactions, leveraged buy-outs, takeover defense, proxy contests and hedge fund activism. He also regularly counsels corporations and their directors on corporate governance and fiduciary duty matters.
**Personal:** Columbia Law School (JD, 1991; Harlan Fiske Stone Scholar); Colgate University (BA, magna cum laude, 1988; Phi Beta Kappa). For more information:
http://www.cravath.com/sbarshay

### BART, Andrew
Jenner & Block LLP, New York
212 891 1645
abart@jenner.com
*Featured in Media & Entertainment (New York)*
**Career:** Andrew H. Bart is an experienced commercial litigator and is Co-Chair of the Content, Media & Entertainment Practice. Clients in the entertainment industry, particularly recording companies, film studios and music publishers, seek his counsel on intellectual property issues and contractual disputes. His cases have resulted in precedent-setting decisions in copyright law, the law of privacy and publicity, and artist-label relations. Mr Bart has successfully handled bench and jury trials in both state and federal courts and arbitrations, argued numerous appeals and conducted complex and multi-party mediations and settlement negotiations.

### BARTFELD, Daniel D
Milbank, Tweed, Hadley & McCloy LLP, New York
212 530 5185
dbartfeld@milbank.com
*Featured in Latin American Investment (New York), Projects (Nationwide)*
**Practice Areas:** Mr Bartfeld is a partner in the Project Finance Group. His practice focuses primarily on the representation of financial institutions, developers and multi-national companies in a wide range of oil/gas, petrochemical, power, renewable energy, mining and other infrastructure-related projects in the U.S. and Latin America. Mr Bartfeld has particular expertise in multi-sourced financings (including those through official credit agencies), as well as representation of Asian-based investors focusing on development and M&A activities in the U.S. and Latin America.

### BARTNER, Douglas
Shearman & Sterling LLP, New York
212 848 8190
dbartner@shearman.com
*Featured in Bankruptcy/Restructuring (New York)*
**Professional Memberships:** Committee on Commercial Bankruptcy, New York County Lawyers' Association; INSOL International; American Bankruptcy Institute.
**Career:** Mr Bartner is a partner in Shearman & Sterling LLP's Bankruptcy & Reorganization Group. He regularly represents debtors and creditors and acquirors of assets in chapter 11 bankruptcies and out-of-court restructurings. Recently Mr Bartner has represented Media General in its sale of newspaper assets to and financing agreements with Berkshire Hathaway, Celpa in its chapter 15 proceeding, Provo Craft in its out-of-court recapitalization, Cinram in its out-of-court recapitalization and in its subsequent chapter 15 proceeding, and Nomura in the Lehman chapter 11 proceeding.

### BARZILAI, Laura M
Sidley Austin LLP, New York
212 839 6739
lbarzilai@sidley.com
*Featured in Tax (New York)*
**Practice Areas:** Partner in Sidley's New York office and co-head of the firm's Tax practice. Laura focuses on federal income tax matters, advising clients in domestic and cross-border mergers and acquisitions, and other major corporate transactions. In addition, she advises clients in connection with offerings and investments in insurance-linked securities and related investment vehicles. She also represents clients in federal and state tax controversies, including at all stages of the administrative process.
**Personal:** New York University School of Law (LLM, 1991) University of Virginia School of Law (JD, 1986) Wellesley College (BA, 1981).

### BASON JR, George R
Davis Polk & Wardwell LLP, New York
212 450 4340
george.bason@davispolk.com
*Featured in Private Equity (Nationwide), Financial Services Regulation (Nationwide), Corporate/M&A (New York)*
See under Nationwide for profile.

### BASSEN, Ned
Hughes Hubbard & Reed LLP, New York
212 837 6090
bassen@hugheshubbard.com
*Featured in Labor & Employment (New York)*
**Practice Areas:** Partner and Chair, Labor and Employment Law Department: all aspects of labor and employment law, including non-competes, unlawful competition and defamation claims. Complex and government contract litigation
**Professional Memberships:** Fellow, The College of Labor and Employment Lawyers; ABA Labor Law Section, Committee on Development of the Law Under the National Labor Relations Act; International Bar Association, Employment and Industrial Relations Law Committee.

**Personal:** 2011 Burton Award For Legal Achievement, Distinguished Writing In Law; Cornell Law School, Law Review, Note and Comment Editor, JD, 1973; Cornell University, BS, 1970.

### BASSETT, David
WilmerHale, New York
212 230 8858
david.bassett@wilmerhale.com
*Featured in Intellectual Property (New York)*
**Practice Areas:** Former chair of WilmerHale's IP Litigation Practice. Practice concentrates on IP litigation, particularly biotechnology and pharmaceutical patent disputes. Represents clients in variety of other business disputes, including breach of contract, Lanham Act and internet-related claims. Covers all facets of litigation, including discovery, settlement, alternative dispute resolution, trials and appeals.
**Professional Memberships:** American and Massachusetts Bar Associations; Co-Chair, Intellectual Property Litigation Committee of the Boston Bar Association.
**Career:** Admitted to New York Bar, Massachusetts Bar and Indiana Bar. Joined firm in 1989.
**Personal:** Harvard Law School (JD, cum laude); Indiana University (BA, with Honors and Distinction National Merit Scholarship).

### BASTA, Paul M
Kirkland & Ellis LLP, New York
212 446 4750
paul.basta@kirkland.com
*Featured in Bankruptcy/Restructuring (Nationwide), Bankruptcy/Restructuring (New York)*
See under Nationwide for profile.

### BASWELL, Karen
Chaffetz Lindsey LLP, New York
212 257 6967
karen.baswell@chaffetzlindsey.com
*Featured in Insurance (New York)*
**Practice Areas:** Commercial litigation and insurance/reinsurance dispute resolution.
**Career:** Karen Baswell joined Chaffetz Lindsey when it was founded in May 2009. Previously, she was an Associate with Clifford Chance in New York. Karen has broad experience with disputes involving the insurance and reinsurance sectors, including disputes involving the follow the fortunes and allocation issues.
**Personal:** BS and BA, University of Richmond (2000); JD, summa cum laude, Hofstra University (2007).

### BATTISTA, Gregory J.
Cahill Gordon & Reindel LLP, New York
212 701 3662
gbattista@cahill.com
*Featured in Environment (New York)*
**Practice Areas:** Has over 25 years of experience handling environmental law matters, including corporate transactions, remediation and enforcement. Provides advice in a variety of areas including: environmental, health and safety compliance and litigation matters, site investigation and clean-up, SEC disclosure, sustainability strategy and reporting, climate change regulation, OSHA mat-

ters, auditing, supply chain risk, real estate development projects, and due diligence with respect to financing, M&A and other corporate matters.
**Personal:** Boston College, BA, 1980. Rider University, MBA, 1983. Seton Hall University School of Law, JD, 1986.

### BAUM, David R
Dentons, New York
212 768 6925
david.baum@dentons.com
*Featured in Media & Entertainment (New York)*
**Practice Areas:** David Baum is a partner in legacy Dentons's Litigation practice, with a broad background in complex commercial, media, entertainment, intellectual property, art law, sports, finance, bankruptcy and insurance disputes. He has substantial first chair trial experience, and litigates in federal and state courts, on both the trial and appellate levels, across the country.
**Career:** New York University School of Law, JD; College of Arts and Sciences, Cornell University, BA

### BEAMON, Martine
Davis Polk & Wardwell LLP, New York
212 450 4000
martine.beamon@dpw.com
*Featured in Litigation (New York)*
**Practice Areas:** Partner in Davis Polk's Litigation Department. She concentrates in white collar criminal defense, securities enforcement and other regulatory actions, as well as complex commercial litigation. Her matters have included grand jury and regulatory investigations and class action litigation, representing both companies and individuals in connection with allegations of securities fraud, pharmaceutical marketing violations, foreign corrupt practices, and insider trading, among other areas. She has participated in a number of confidential internal investigations on behalf of clients facing potential criminal and regulatory exposure and has advised corporate boards of directors and subcommittees on matters of corporate governance and compliance.

### BEATTIE, Nina
Brune & Richard LLP, New York
212 668 1900
nbeattie@bruneandrichard.com
*Featured in Litigation (New York)*
**Practice Areas:** Practice areas include white collar criminal and regulatory defense, federal securities and commercial litigation, and government investigations. Matters have included allegations of securities and bank fraud, insider trading, accounting fraud, Foreign Corrupt Practices Act violations, health care and other government contract fraud, antitrust violations, and money laundering.
**Professional Memberships:** Board member of the City Bar Justice Center and the Fund for Modern Courts; former Board Member of the New York Council of Defense Lawyers; Panel Chair of Departmental Disciplinary Committee appointed by the Appellate Division, First Judicial Department of New York; member of the NYC Bar Association Committee on White Collar Law

and the NYS Bar Association Committee on White Collar Criminal Litigation.
**Career:** From 1996 to 1997, law clerk to the Honorable Kimba M. Wood in the United States District Court for the Southern District of New York. From 1998-1999, attorney for Capital Defender Office in New York City.
**Personal:** Yale Law School, JD, 1996, recipient of the C. LaRue Munson Prize for Excellence; President of Yale Law Women; Dartmouth College, A.B., 1989, graduated magna cum laude and Phi Beta Kappa, recipient of the Salvador Allende Gossens Memorial Prize.

### BEATTIE, Richard I
Simpson Thacher & Bartlett LLP, New York
212 455 2635
rbeattie@stblaw.com
*Featured in Private Equity (Nationwide),*
*Corporate/M&A (New York)*
See under Nationwide for profile.

### BECK, Thomas H
Sidley Austin LLP, New York
212 839 5940
tbeck@sidley.com
*Featured in Intellectual Property (New York)*
**Practice Areas:** Partner and head of Sidley's New York IP Group. Recently won a jury trial for Sunovion against generic company Mylan on the asthma drug Xopenex, including lost profits and willful infringement. Currently lead counsel for Noven on the transdermal patch Daytrana, and for ConvaTec against Wake Forest on negative pressure wound treatments. Also lead for LSI against Thinking Machines on router and RAID storage technology.
**Professional Memberships:** NY Intellectual Property Law Association; AIPLA; ABA; Federal Circuit Bar Association; numerous Federal District Courts.
**Personal:** Harvard Law School, JD, 1979; North Dakota State University, BS, 1975. Admission: New York.

### BECKER, Barbara
Gibson, Dunn & Crutcher LLP, New York
212 351 4062
bbecker@gibsondunn.com
*Featured in Corporate/M&A (New York)*
**Practice Areas:** Advises public companies, boards of directors and special committees on M&A, corporate governance, strategic matters and hedge fund activism. Noteworthy representations include Kraft Foods in connection with its $19 billion acquisition of Cadbury and the spin-off of its North American grocery business; Northrop Grumman in the $6 billion spin-off of its ship-building business to Northrop's stockholders; and Tenet Health Systems in defense against a $7.95 billion hostile takeover attempt by Community Health Systems.
**Career:** M&A Practice Co-chair, Executive Committee Member, New York Office Hiring Partner, Firmwide Diversity Committee Chair.
**Personal:** JD, New York University School of Law.

### BECKERMAN, Lisa G
Akin Gump Strauss Hauer & Feld LLP, New York
212 872 8012
lbeckerman@akingump.com
*Featured in Bankruptcy/Restructuring (New York)*
**Practice Areas:** Lisa Beckerman is a Partner in the Financial Restructuring Group, focusing on corporate insolvency. She has represented official and unofficial unsecured creditors' committees and bondholder committees, debtors, unofficial committees of secured noteholders and acquirers of distressed businesses and assets. Recent matters include WCI Communities, Inc., Panolam Holdings Co., Idearc, Inc., Houghton Mifflin Harcourt Publishing Company, Delta Air Lines, Kaiser Aluminum Corporation, ATA Holdings, Inc., Weirton Steel Corporation, Hawaiian Airlines, National Steel Corporation, Florsheim Shoe and LTV Steel Corporation.
**Personal:** BA, University of Chicago (1984); MBA, University of Texas (1986); JD, Boston University (1989).

### BEINECKE, Candace Krugman
Hughes Hubbard & Reed LLP, New York
212 837 6040
beinecke@hugheshubbard.com
*Featured in Corporate/M&A (New York)*
**Practice Areas:** Corporate transactions, governance and internal investigations.
**Professional Memberships:** Vice Chair, Partnership for New York City; Board of Advisors, Yale Law School Center for the Study of Corporate Law; Member, Women's Forum.
**Career:** Chair, Hughes Hubbard & Reed LLP since 1999; Chair, First Eagle Funds; Director, ALSTOM, Vornado Realty Trust, Rockefeller Financial Services, Inc.; Trustee, The Metropolitan Museum of Art, The Wallace Foundation.
**Personal:** Named among: "100 Most Influential Women in NYC Business" and "50 Most Powerful Women in NY" by Crain's; "50 Most Influential Women Lawyers in America" by The National Law Journal; "Outstanding Women of the Bar" by the New York County Lawyers' Association; "Women of Power and Influence" by the NYC Chapter of The National Organization for Women.

### BELLER, Daniel J
Paul, Weiss, Rifkind, Wharton & Garrison LLP, New York
212 373 3312
dbeller@paulweiss.com
*Featured in Litigation (New York)*
**Practice Areas:** Senior Partner in the Litigation Department. Extensive experience handling complex civil and criminal matters, including antitrust, securities, real estate and general commercial litigation, government enforcement matters, internal corporate investigations and compliance, and white-collar criminal defense. Representative engagements include obtaining preliminary injunction and successful settlement in major real estate partnership dispute; upholding at trial and on appeal a major paper company acquisition against novel government antitrust challenge; successful defense of an action for securities fraud and breach of fiduciary duty before

Florida jury. Fellow of the American College of Trial Lawyers; former Chief of the Major Crimes Unit in the United States Attorney's Office for the Southern District of New York.

### BEN-AMI, Leora
Kirkland & Ellis LLP, New York
212 446 5943
leora.benami@kirkland.com
*Featured in Life Sciences (Nationwide), Intellectual Property (New York)*
See under Nationwide for profile.

### BENDINGER, Gary F
Sidley Austin LLP, New York
212 839 5387
gbendinger@sidley.com
*Featured in Litigation (New York)*
**Practice Areas:** Partner Gary Bendinger has devoted more than 35 years to complex commercial litigation. He has substantial experience as lead counsel in numerous antitrust, securities and complex commercial litigation matters in numerous jurisdictions across the nation. Those cases have involved billions of dollars in damage claims. Additionally, Mr Bendinger has substantial trial experience and has been brought in as lead trial counsel in many of those matters.
**Personal:** University of San Francisco School of Law, JD, 1975, cum laude; Hastings College, BS, 1972, cum laude; United States Air Force Acad, BS, 1969.

### BENEDICT, James
Milbank, Tweed, Hadley & McCloy LLP, New York
212 530 5696
jbenedict@milbank.com
*Featured in Securities (Nationwide), Litigation (New York)*
**Practice Areas:** Mr Benedict is head of the Securities Litigation Practice Group and Chair of the Litigation & Arbitration Group. He focuses in complex commercial litigation, with emphasis on multiparty class and derivative suits in state and federal courts throughout the nation. In his more than 35 years of practice, Mr Benedict has handled a wide variety of trial and appellate civil litigation involving securities, antitrust and other issues for some of the largest and best known corporations in America, including Citigroup, Inc., MasterCard International Incorporated, Merrill Lynch & Co., Inc., Prudential Financial and The Coca-Cola Company.

### BENEDICT, Philippe
Schulte Roth & Zabel LLP, New York
212 756 2124
philippe.benedict@srz.com
*Featured in Tax (New York)*
**Practice Areas:** Practice focuses on the tax aspects of investment funds, mergers and acquisitions, international transactions, real estate transactions and financial instruments. Has been involved in many transactions involving sales or spin-offs of investment fund managers.
**Career:** SRZ Partner since 2000.
**Publications:** Writes in area of expertise; frequent speaker at prominent industry events.

**Personal:** New York University School of Law, LLM in taxation and JD, recipient of a Gruss Fellowship, served on the staff of the Journal of International Law and Politics; Adelphi University, BS, summa cum laude.

## BENJAMIN, JR, James J
Akin Gump Strauss Hauer & Feld LLP, New York
212 872 8091
jbenjamin@akingump.com
*Featured in Litigation (New York)*
**Practice Areas:** Represents clients in a wide variety of government and regulatory investigations and litigation, including insider trading, improper accounting and disclosure, market manipulation, commodities regulation and foreign corrupt practices cases.
**Career:** Federal prosecutor, U.S. Attorney's Office, Southern District of New York; law clerk, U.S. Supreme Court, Justices Lewis F. Powell Jr. and John Paul Stevens; law clerk, Honorable J. Frederick Motz, District of Maryland.
**Personal:** AB, magna cum laude, Phi Beta Kappa, Dartmouth College (1987); JD, University of Virginia School of Law, research and projects editor, Virginia Law Review, Order of the Coif (1990).

## BERGER, Max W
Bernstein Litowitz Berger & Grossmann LLP, New York
212 554 1400
mwb@blbglaw.com
*Featured in Securities (Nationwide), Litigation (New York)*
**Practice Areas:** Complex litigation; securities fraud litigation; subprime-related litigation; derivative actions; class actions; accounting malpractice; directors' and officers' liability; employment discrimination; civil rights.
**Professional Memberships:** Member, Dean's Council, Columbia Law School; Member, Board of Trustees, Baruch College; Member, Advisory Board, Columbia Law School Center on Corporate Governance; NYS, NYC and American Bar Associations; former Chairman, Commercial Litigation Section of the American Association for Justice (formerly the Association of Trial Lawyers of America).
**Career:** Representing numerous public and private institutional investors, he has served as Lead Counsel in many of largest and most significant securities cases in history, including WorldCom ($6.15 billion), Cendant ($3.3 billion), Bank of America/Merrill Lynch ($2.425 billion), Nortel ($1.3 billion), and McKesson ($1.04 billion). Honored for outstanding contribution to public interest by Trial Lawyers For Public Justice as 1997 'Trial Lawyer of the Year' Finalist for work as Lead Counsel in precedent-setting discrimination case Roberts, et. al. v. Texaco, on behalf of Texaco's African-American employees. Consistently recognized as a top lawyer in field: featured as a 'leading litigator' by the Legal 500; a 'litigation star' by Benchmark (Euromoney/Institutional Investor); named one of '10 Legal Superstars' in the US by Securities Law360; one of the '500 Leading Lawyers in America' and '100 Securities Litigators

You Need to Know', by Lawdragon; and named a top commercial litigator by U.S. News/Best Lawyers.
**Publications:** Has written and lectured extensively on securities fraud, shareholder rights and corporate governance trends.
**Personal:** Baruch College, 1968; Columbia University Law School, 1971; 2006 Distinguished Alumnus, Baruch College. 2011 Medal of Excellence Recipient, Columbia Law School. "Idealist of the Year" Award, City Year New York, 2005.

## BERGER, Scott A
Kirkland & Ellis LLP, New York
212 446 6464
scott.berger@kirkland.com
*Featured in Real Estate (New York)*
**Practice Areas:** Scott Berger is a partner in the firm's Real Estate Practice Group. Scott focuses on the private equity aspects of domestic and international real estate and real estate related transactions. He regularly advises sponsors, owners, developers and equity investors on matters such as joint ventures, investment funds, club arrangements, capital markets transactions, dispositions, acquisitions, financings and development. Scott is regularly involved in cross border transactions and matters involving non-US parties.
**Personal:** JD with honors, Hofstra University School of Law; BS, University of Connecticut, Honors Scholar.

## BERKE, Barry H
Kramer Levin Naftalis & Frankel LLP, New York
212 715 7560
bberke@kramerlevin.com
*Featured in Litigation (Nationwide), Litigation (New York)*
See under Nationwide for profile.

## BERNSTEIN, Andrew
Mintz Levin Cohn Ferris Glovsky and Popeo PC, New York
212 692 6742
ajbernstein@mintz.com
*Featured in Employee Benefits & Executive Compensation (New York)*
**Practice Areas:** Andrew has extensive experience handling executive compensation issues in mergers and acquisitions, venture capital investments, and private equity financings. He represents CEOs of publicly and privately held companies and management teams in connection with leveraged buyouts by private equity sponsors, and in negotiations with compensation committees and boards. He represents companies in litigating federal and state labor, employment discrimination, trade secret, compensation, and restrictive covenant claims.
**Professional Memberships:** Member, Bar Association of the City of New York; Management Attorneys Conference.
**Publications:** Deal Points: The Management Team, Bloomberg.
**Personal:** AB, with honors, University of Michigan. JD, Fordham Law.

## BERNSTEIN, Donald S
Davis Polk & Wardwell LLP, New York
212 450 4000
donald.bernstein@davispolk.com
*Featured in Bankruptcy/Restructuring (Nationwide), Bankruptcy/Restructuring (New York)*
See under Nationwide for profile.

## BERNSTEIN, Kevin M
Bond, Schoeneck & King, PLLC, Syracuse
315 218 8329
kbernstein@bsk.com
*Featured in Environment (New York)*
**Practice Areas:** Practice includes permitting, regulatory compliance, and litigation in matters relating to energy (including power, transmission, oil and gas), stormwater and wastewater discharge, landfills, petroleum contamination, wetlands, hazardous substance and petroleum bulk storage tanks, SEQRA, toxic torts, defending criminal investigations, and zoning and land use. Representation also includes defending claims asserted by agencies for cleanup costs, penalties, and other enforcement matters brought under Superfund statutes, Navigation Law, and the Clean Water Act.
**Personal:** State University of New York College at Brockport (BS, 1982); Vermont Law School (JD, 1985).

## BERNSTEIN, Michael I
Bond, Schoeneck & King, PLLC, New York
646 253 2310
mbernstein@bsk.com
*Featured in Labor & Employment (New York)*
**Practice Areas:** Mr Bernstein's peers have recognized him as among the 'Top 100 New York Super Lawyers' and Best Lawyers in America. He has chaired the Labor and Employment Law Section, New York State Bar Association, the Labor Committee, New York City Bar Association, and the Federal Labor Standards Legislation Committee, American Bar Association; was appointed to Task Forces of the Governor and Lieutenant Governor of New York; and was elected Fellow of the College of Labor and Employment Lawyers and of the New York Bar Foundation.
**Personal:** University of Michigan (BA, Economics, 1959); Columbia University Law School (1962).

## BERNSTEIN, Warren J
Kaye Scholer LLP, New York
212 836 8073
warren.bernstein@kayescholer.com
*Featured in Real Estate (New York)*
**Practice Areas:** Warren J. Bernstein, Co-Chair of the Real Estate Department, handles a broad range of financing, acquisition and investment transactions throughout the US. He represents international and domestic financial institutions in direct and syndicated lending transactions, including construction and permanent financing for a broad range of real estate assets. He advises clients in the acquisition and sale of real property and equity interests and has extensive experience in dealing with distressed real estate and loan situations, including loan sales and restructurings that

are addressed on a consensual basis as well as through state, federal and bankruptcy court proceedings.

## BEVILACQUA, Louis J
Cadwalader, Wickersham & Taft LLP, New York
212 504 6057
louis.bevilacqua@cwt.com
*Featured in Corporate/M&A (New York)*
**Practice Areas:** Co-Chair, Corporate Department. Concentrates in corporate transactions, securities law, mergers and acquisitions. Represents clients in tender offers, mergers, leveraged buyouts, proxy contests, joint ventures, and public and private offerings of debt and equity securities. Significant experience in complex international transactions. Advises public and private companies regarding contractual negotiation, financial structuring, corporate governance, other general legal matters. Special counsel to Independent Directors Committees in international mergers and going-private transactions. Frequently lectures on domestic and international corporate and securities law.
**Professional Memberships:** New York County Lawyers Association and American Bar Association.
**Personal:** JD, Fordham University School of Law; MBA, New York University; BA, Holy Cross College.

## BICK, John
Davis Polk & Wardwell LLP, New York
212 450 4000
john.bick@dpw.com
*Featured in Corporate/M&A (New York)*
**Practice Areas:** Head of Davis Polk's Corporate Department. Member of Davis Polk's Management Committee. Mr Bick advises clients in mergers and acquisitions, private equity transactions, joint ventures, partnerships, takeover defenses and corporate governance issues. He also represents clients in general corporate and securities law matters. Mr Bick has worked extensively in the area of private equity, representing Morgan Stanley Private Equity, Metalmark Capital Partners and Tailwind Capital Partners.

## BIERCE, William B
Bierce & Kenerson, P.C., New York
212 840 0080
wbierce@biercekenerson.com
*Featured in Technology (New York)*
**Practice Areas:** Award-winning global business and technology transaction attorney. Advises on corporate, international business, outsourcing, technology transactions, trade and investment. Focuses on strategic business alliances and technology-enabled business operations. Serves domestic and foreign clients. Fluent: English, French.
**Professional Memberships:** Global Sourcing Council (Board of Directors); American Foreign Law Association (former Vice President); Information Technology Law Association; New York City Bar Association (past Chairman, Foreign and Comparative Law Committee); American Bar Association.

**Career:** Founded Bierce & Kenerson, P.C. 1990. **Publications:** Publisher, Outsourcing Law and Business Journal ™; 80+ published articles; Editor-in-Chief, www.outsourcing-law.com. **Personal:** NYU School of Law (JD); Law Faculty, University of Grenoble, France (with honors) and Yale University.

## BISER, Sarah
McCarter & English, LLP, New York
212 609 6859
sbiser@mccarter.com
*Featured in Construction (New York)*

**Career:** Ms Biser is a leader in construction law, focusing on domestic and foreign clients in large construction projects and related litigation. Her job experience in the field and expertise in the courtroom has contributed to the successful representation of owners, contractors, developers, architects and engineers, both in the United States and abroad, in projects including fossil fuel and hydroelectric power plants, manufacturing facilities, telecommunications, solar installations, healthcare facilities, financial institutions, schools, and hospitality companies in all stages of the construction process, including contract drafting, contract negotiating and contract administration and, where necessary, dispute resolution. For full bio: http://www.mccarter.com/Sarah-B-Biser/

## BLACKLOW, Kimberly B
Cleary Gottlieb Steen & Hamilton LLP, New York
212 225 2018
kblacklow@cgsh.com
*Featured in Real Estate (New York)*

**Practice Areas:** Wide range of real estate and other asset-based finance transactions, structured finance and capital markets in the U.S. and abroad, with significant real estate acquisition and joint venture experience including advising clients on loan acquisitions and participations and transactions involving distressed assets. Regularly represents issuers and underwriters in both public and private securities offerings, including commercial mortgage-backed securities and collateralized debt obligations. **Professional Memberships:** Member of the Bar in New York. **Career:** Joined firm, 1994; became partner, 2003; partner, Tokyo office (1999-2000). JD, Columbia University School of Law (1994); BS, Harvard-Radcliffe (1988).

## BLANCHARD, Kimberly S
Weil, Gotshal & Manges LLP, New York
212 310 8799
kim.blanchard@weil.com
*Featured in Tax (New York)*

**Practice Areas:** Kimberly Blanchard's practice encompasses a variety of international transactions involving mergers and acquisitions, private equity investments and joint ventures. She has lectured and published extensively on topics ranging from international tax planning for US businesses to the special tax issues facing foreign persons, pension plans and other exempt investors who invest in US private equity partnerships and in US real estate. Ms Blanchard is the former Chair of

the Tax Section of the New York State Bar Association. **Personal:** Dartmouth College (BA, 1976); University of Wisconsin (MS, 1978); New York University School of Law (JD, 1981).

## BLASS, Michael S
Arent Fox LLP, New York
212 484 3902
michael.blass@arentfox.com
*Featured in Healthcare (New York)*

**Practice Areas:** Michael Blass is the Managing Partner of the New York City office of Arent Fox, where he concentrates on corporate transactions and regulatory matters involving health care providers. In addition to structuring and implementing healthcare transactions, Michael and his group conduct all healthcare regulatory, corporate, and legal due diligence, and coordinate change of ownership ("CHOW") procedures for state licensure, certificate of need, and Medicare and Medicaid certifications. He handles transactions for a broad variety of health care providers, including long-term care companies, hospital operators, dialysis providers, and home health companies. His transactions frequently involve national health care companies, requiring coordination of numerous state and federal regulatory authorities. Apart from acquisitions, Michael routinely assists health care clients with financings, joint ventures, facility leases, management contracts, and operations transfers. **Personal:** Fordham University School of Law, JD; Georgetown University, AB.

## BLOCK, Dennis J
Greenberg Traurig, LLP, New York
212 801 2222
BlockD@gtlaw.com
*Featured in Corporate/M&A (New York)*

**Practice Areas:** Concentrates in mergers and acquisitions and corporate transactions, corporate governance, and securities law. Handles M&A transactions on behalf of acquirers and targets, proxy contests, joint ventures, self-tender offers, spin-offs and other corporate restructurings. Highly visible transactions include DPL's acquisition by AES, Pfizer's acquisition of King Pharmaceuticals, Pfizer's acquisition of Wyeth, Bear Stearns Companies Inc. acquisition by JPMorgan Chase, Pfizer's sale of its consumer healthcare business to Johnson & Johnson, Pfizer's sale of its Capsugel business to KKR, Republic Bancorp Inc.'s merger with Citizens Banking Corp., and Procter & Gamble's acquisition of Gillette. Represents Boards of Directors and Board Committees involved in corporate transactions, and public companies, investment and commercial banks, hedge funds and entrepreneurs in connection with transactional work and issues of public interest and debate. **Career:** Former Branch Chief of Enforcement, New York Regional Office, SEC. **Publications:** 'The Business Judgment Rule: Fiduciary Duties of Corporate Directors', 5th edition (co-author). 'The Corporate Counselor's Deskbook (co-editor). Numerous articles on M&A, Corporate and Securities Law, Fiduciary

Duties of Directors and Special Committees; Internal Investigations and the Attorney-Client Privilege.

## BOAST, Molly S
WilmerHale, New York
212 230 8887
molly.boast@wilmerhale.com
*Featured in Antitrust (New York)*

**Practice Areas:** More than 30 years of experience in both senior federal government positions and private practice. Practice focuses on high-profile antitrust regulatory and litigation matters. **Professional Memberships:** Served on governing bodies of the litigation and antitrust sections of the American Bar Association and New York State Bar Association. First woman to chair the federal courts committees of both the Federal Bar Council and the New York City Bar Association. **Career:** Deputy Assistant Attorney General of the Antitrust Division of the US Department of Justice (2009-2011); Deputy Director/Director of the Bureau of Competition at the Federal Trade Commission (1999-2001).

## BODIAN, Robert
Mintz Levin Cohn Ferris Glovsky and Popeo PC, New York
212 692 6726
RBodian@mintz.com
*Featured in Litigation (New York)*

**Practice Areas:** Bob is the Managing Parnter of Mintz Levin. He is nationally recognized as a leading trial attorney, and represents major corporations and their senior executives. His practice focuses on employment and commercial disputes, private equity, financial services, insurance, securities, real estate, and banking litigation. **Professional Memberships:** The Association of the Bar of the City of New York; New York State Bar Association; American Bar Association; Litigation Section of the New York County Bar Association. **Career:** Bob successfully has tried through verdict numerous jury and non-jury trials in the federal and state courts. He is admitted to practice in New York and before the U.S. Court of Appeals and the U.S. District Courts, Southern and Eastern Districts of New York. **Personal:** BS in accounting, summa cum laude, from the State University of New York at Binghamton; JD from Stanford Law School.

## BOHRER, Barry A
Schulte Roth & Zabel LLP, New York
212 756 2380
barry.bohrer@srz.com
*Featured in Litigation (New York)*

**Practice Areas:** Handles white-collar criminal and complex civil matters in federal and state courts, including high-profile and complex cases, jury trials, regulatory actions, investigations. Has won appeals at all levels of federal and state court systems throughout the nation. **Professional Memberships:** Fellow, American College of Trial Lawyers; Former President, NY Council of Defense Lawyers; Chair of Executive Committee, Fund for Modern Courts and

Committee for Modern Courts; Board of Directors, Legal Aid Society. **Publications:** Co-author, "White-Collar Crime" column, New York Law Journal; Board of Editors, White Collar Crime Reporter. **Personal:** Duke University, BA; New York University School of Law, JD.

## BOLGER, Katherine M
Levine Sullivan Koch & Schulz LLP, New York
212 850 6123
kbolger@lskslaw.com
*Featured in Media & Entertainment (New York)*

**Practice Areas:** Represent and counsel media clients in defamation, invasion of privacy, First Amendment, copyright, and trademark matters. Extensive experience performing pre-publication review for newspapers, magazines, and books. **Professional Memberships:** Co-Chair, ABA First Amendment and Media Litigation Committee; Chair, ABA Women in Communications Law; past-Chair, Media Law Resource Center, Entertainment Law Committee. **Career:** Previously partner at Hogan Lovells. **Publications:** "A Comparative French and U.S. Law Approach to Scènes à Faire and Other Non-Protectable Elements in Copyright Law." Propriétés Intellectuelles. **Personal:** JD, University of Chicago, 1998; BA, University of Virginia, 1994.

## BOND, W Michael
Weil, Gotshal & Manges LLP, New York
212 310 8035
michael.bond@weil.com
*Featured in Real Estate (New York)*

**Practice Areas:** Michael Bond co-heads the Real Estate Practice. He has a diverse practice including general corporate matters, distressed debt, mortgage-backed securitizations, commercial lending, company and asset portfolio acquisitions, private equity transactions and real estate transactions (including acquisitions, development, financing and leasing of large commercial real estate projects.) He also has substantial experience representing capital sources and various providers of products or services in forming joint ventures and strategic alliances to pursue new businesses. He advises clients in restructurings and the acquisition and disposition of distressed debt. **Personal:** University of South Carolina (BS, 1977); University of Virginia (JD, 1980).

## BORTSTEIN, Lawrence
Bortstein Legal Group, New York
646 240 4872
lbortstein@blegalgroup.com
*Featured in Technology (New York)*

**Practice Areas:** Technology, market data, outsourcing, procurement/sourcing, vendor management, data centers. **Professional Memberships:** New York State Bar, Association of the Bar of the City of New York, Former Member, SIFMA Technology & Regulation Committee, Former Co-Chair, SIFMA Technology & Regulation Committee Working Group on Open Source Software, Former Member, SIFMA Technology & Regulation Committee Subcommittee on Outsourcing and

Subcommittee on Market Data, Former Member, Information Technology Committee, Association of the Bar of the City of New York City.
**Career:** Bortstein Legal Group, Founding Partner, 2008 - present, Lehman Brothers, Global Head of Technology Law, 2005 - 2008, American Express, Senior Technology Counsel, 2000 - 2005, Willkie Farr & Gallagher, Attorney, 1994 - 2000.
**Personal:** State University of New York at Albany, BA, Brooklyn Law School, JD.

### BOSTON, David
Willkie Farr & Gallagher LLP, New York
212 728 8625
dboston@willkie.com
*Featured in Corporate/M&A (New York)*
**Practice Areas:** Partner in Corporate and Financial Services Department. Co-Chair of the Mergers and Acquisitions Practice Group. Provides general corporate advice to both public and private companies and concentrates on mergers and acquisitions, public offerings and Rule 144A offerings of debt and equity securities, and private equity investments.
**Personal:** JD, Stone Scholar, Columbia University School of Law, 1991. BA, with distinction, Stanford University, 1988. See: http://www.willkie.com/DavidBoston

### BOTTER, David H
Akin Gump Strauss Hauer & Feld LLP, New York
212 872 1055
dbotter@akingump.com
*Featured in Bankruptcy/Restructuring (New York)*
**Practice Areas:** Focuses on corporate restructurings, with an emphasis on creditors' committees and bondholder committees in large, complex cases both out of court and in Chapter 11. Represents bondholders, noteholders, institutional investors, hedge funds and other interested parties. Also has represented debtors in possession, post-petition lenders and acquirers of distressed assets.
**Career:** Outstanding Young Restructuring Lawyer, Turnarounds & Workouts (2004).
**Personal:** BA, Syracuse University (1986); JD, cum laude, Boston University School of Law, Paul J. Liacos Distinguished Scholar, G. Joseph Tauro Scholar (1989).

### BOURTIN, Nicolas
Sullivan & Cromwell LLP, New York
212 558 3920
Bourtinn@sullcrom.com
*Featured in Litigation (New York)*
**Professional Memberships:** NYCBA; Federalist Society (member, Steering Committee); Federal Bar Council; Eastern District Association.
**Career:** Partner since 2008. Represents individuals, corporations and financial institutions in a broad variety of matters involving white-collar crime and internal investigations, class action defense, and complex civil litigation. Has a particular expertise in defending against cross-border criminal and regulatory investigations involving antitrust, the FCPA, OFAC and trade sanctions, money laundering, and accounting and other types of fraud.

**Personal:** Columbia Law School (JD, 1996); University of Notre Dame (BA, 1993).

### BOYLE, Edward
Venable LLP, New York
212 808 5675
epboyle@Venable.com
*Featured in Litigation (New York)*
**Practice Areas:** Commercial Litigation, Class Action Defense, Litigation
**Career:** Mr Boyle chairs Venable's New York Commercial Litigation Group and Venable's Class Action Defense Group. He represents clients in financial services, hospitality, consumer products, advertising, sports and entertainment, and non-profit sectors. His practice focuses on federal and state litigation involving complex transactions, and defending consumer and securities class actions. He serves as a court-appointed mediator on the SDNY panel.
**Personal:** Clerk, Honorable Joseph M McLaughlin, U.S. Court of Appeals for the Second Circuit, 1993-95, JD, Vanderbilt University Law School; Editor-in-Chief, Vanderbilt Law Review, 1992-93, BA, Duke University, 1989.

### BRAID, Frederick
Holland & Knight LLP, New York
212 513 3200
fred.braid@hklaw.com
*Featured in Labor & Employment (New York)*
**Practice Areas:** Partner in the firm's Litigation Section and leader of its New York Labor and Employment team. He has represented employers in the private sector for over 40 years on matters including counseling and litigation concerning union organizing activity; collective bargaining and contract administration; grievance and interest arbitration; acquisitions, closures, relocations, restructuring and bankruptcy; occupational safety and health; employment discrimination and affirmative action compliance; whistle-blowing; employment at will, employment agreements, restrictive covenants, trade secret confidentiality; employment benefits; personnel practices and employment policies. He represents employers of all sizes across all industries, as well as employer associations.

### BRAITERMAN, Andrew H
Hughes Hubbard & Reed LLP, New York
212 837 6315
braiterm@hugheshubbard.com
*Featured in Tax (New York)*
**Practice Areas:** Taxation, with an emphasis on domestic and international mergers and acquisitions and joint ventures, equipment leasing, and financing transactions.
**Professional Memberships:** New York State Bar Association Tax Section, co-chair of Committee on Consolidated Returns, former co-chair, Committee on Foreign Activities of U.S. Taxpayers; City Bar Association New York, former chair, Committee on Taxation of Business Entities; International Fiscal Association, New York Chapter Steering Committee; Fellow, American College of Tax Counsel.
**Career:** Chair, Tax Department, Hughes Hubbard & Reed LLP, Partner since 1989.

**Personal:** Harvard College, BA, magna cum laude, 1977; Harvard Law School, JD, magna cum laude, 1980.

### BRANDT, James E
Latham & Watkins LLP, New York
212 906 1278
james.brandt@lw.com
*Featured in Litigation (New York)*
**Practice Areas:** Litigation: Complex Commercial, Securities, Insolvency & Workout Litigation, M&A.
**Professional Memberships:** Member of the Boards of the Columbia College Alumni Association and of NYLAG.
**Career:** Mr Brandt, Managing Partner of Latham's New York office, focuses on sophisticated financial litigation, including securities and M&A; insolvency litigation, including bankruptcy court litigation; and complex commercial matters. An experienced trial attorney who practices in the state and federal courts, Mr Brandt has also handled numerous cross border matters. Mr Brandt speaks and writes regularly on topics in his expertise.
**Personal:** JD, University of Michigan Law School; AB, Columbia University

### BRENNAN, Matthew J
Sullivan & Cromwell LLP, New York
212 558 4724
brennanm@sullcrom.com
*Featured in Environment (New York)*
**Professional Memberships:** ABA; NJBA; ABCNY.
**Career:** Special counsel since 1998. Advises on environmental issues in commercial transactions for the firm's corporate, M&A, project finance, real estate, securities and corporate finance groups. Evaluates environmental issues for clients that include Amgen, AT&T, BP, Goldman Sachs, Philips, Mitsui, Vornado and Rhône Capital, structures transactions to minimize risk, and negotiates environmental terms in commercial transactions. Over 20 years' experience providing environmental advice to a diverse clientele, including corporations, lenders and governments.
**Publications:** Writes/speaks on environmental issues.
**Personal:** University of Pennsylvania Law School (JD, 1986); State University of New York at New Paltz (BA, 1979).

### BRESSMAN, Robert I
Willkie Farr & Gallagher LLP, New York
212 728 8236
rbressman@willkie.com
*Featured in Real Estate (New York)*
**Practice Areas:** Partner, Real Estate Department, specializing in complex real estate financing and leasing transactions, and major development and equity deals. Recent transactions include representation of AXA/Morgan Stanley as owner of class A office building in NYC in the leasing of 950,000 square feet of office space to UBS; Paramount Real Estate Group in refinancing of $750,000,000 of debt secured by Class A office building in New York City and San Francisco, representation of Morgan Stanley as landlord in leas-

ing of over 1 million square feet of Class A office space in New York City and advising Boston Properties in New York City on acquisition of newly constructed, 350,000 square foot, Class A office building in New York City from affiliates of Harry Macklowe.
**Personal:** JD, Rutgers University School of Law, 1980. BA, cum laude, Columbia University, 1976. See: http://www.willkie.com/RobertBressman

### BRICKNER, Jed
Latham & Watkins LLP, New York
212 906 1200
Jed.Brickner@lw.com
*Featured in Employee Benefits & Executive Compensation*
**Practice Areas:** Advising on all employee benefits aspects of M&A transactions (including Secs. 280G and 409A); Plan assets investment:, with expertise in structuring investment funds to comply with ERISA plan asset rules (including VCOC's); Representing lenders in structuring their arrangements to avoid benefits-related liabilities; and public and private company employee benefits, advising Compensation Committees and senior executives regarding commencement and termination of employment arrangements, equity and cash compensation programs, and issues with the IRS, DOL and PBGC.
**Career:** Admitted 1980 (CA) and 1993(NY). Served as Employee Benefits Chair and Tax Co-Chair in NY Office. Frequent author and lecturer.

### BRILLIANT, Allan S
Dechert LLP, New York
212 698 3600
allan.brilliant@dechert.com
*Featured in Bankruptcy/Restructuring (New York)*
**Practice Areas:** Mr Brilliant, co-chair of the firm's business restructuring and reorganization practice, represents bank groups, unsecured creditors' and bondholder committees, acquirers, and debtors in large-scale restructurings and reorganizations and in non-judicial workouts. His bankruptcy experience includes fraudulent transfer and preference litigation.
**Professional Memberships:** Member, New York and Illinois Bars; admitted to practice before the U.S. Supreme Court and numerous federal courts.
**Personal:** The Wharton School, University of Pennsylvania, (BS, 1982, cum laude); Northwestern University School of Law (JD, 1986, with honors, Order of the Coif).

### BROCHIN, Gregg
Davis & Gilbert LLP, New York
212 468 4950
gbrochin@dglaw.com
*Featured in Labor & Employment (New York)*
**Practice Areas:** Labor and employment.
**Career:** Mr Brochin counsels management on employment issues including compliance with federal, state and local discrimination, wage and hour, leave and other employment laws, hiring, termination, employment policies and handbooks, and restrictive covenants in various service-sector industries including advertising, public relations, media, hospitality and financial services.

Mr Brochin has substantial experience negotiating and drafting various contracts including employment, separation, and restrictive covenant agreements. He represents employers in claims relating to employment contracts, discrimination, harassment, fiduciary duty, and wage payment laws in court as well as before federal, state and local administrative agencies.

### BRODSKY, David E
Cleary Gottlieb Steen & Hamilton LLP, New York
212 225 2910
dbrodsky@cgsh.com
*Featured in Litigation (New York)*
**Practice Areas:** Securities enforcement, white-collar criminal defense, internal investigations. Represents corporations and individuals in investigations involving alleged insider trading, accounting and securities fraud, foreign corrupt payments, bid rigging, obstruction of justice.
**Professional Memberships:** NY Council of Defense Lawyers; Board of Directors (2002-04), Membership Committee (2011-present). The Association of the Bar of The City of NY; Committee on White Collar Criminal Law (2010-present); Committee on Professional and Judicial Ethics (2003-06).
**Career:** Joined firm (1991); partner (1994). U.S. Attorney's Office, Southern District of NY (1984-91); Chief Appellate Attorney (1990-91).
**Personal:** JD, Yale Law School (1983); BA, summa cum laude, Rutgers College (1980).

### BROMLEY, James L
Cleary Gottlieb Steen & Hamilton LLP, New York
212 225 2264
jbromley@cgsh.com
*Featured in Bankruptcy/Restructuring (Nationwide), Bankruptcy/Restructuring (New York)*
See under Nationwide for profile.

### BRONSTEIN, Richard J
Paul, Weiss, Rifkind, Wharton & Garrison LLP, New York
212 373 3744
rbronstein@paulweiss.com
*Featured in Tax (New York)*
**Practice Areas:** Co-chair of Tax Department. Nationally-recognized tax advisor who focuses primarily on representation of private investment funds and their portfolio companies. He has had extensive experience with the representation of private investment funds (including private equity, distressed debt and hedge fund clients) in domestic and international mergers and acquisitions transactions, fund formation and capital markets matters. Has planned and executed numerous secured financing transactions, and he regularly handles federal and New York tax audit and tax controversy matters. Member of the Tax Section of the New York State Bar Association

### BROOKS, Roger G
Cravath, Swaine & Moore LLP, New York
212 474 1072.
rgbrooks@cravath.com
*Featured in Intellectual Property (New York)*

**Practice Areas:** A wide range of courtroom litigation for technologically intensive companies, including disputes concerning patents, licensing, trade secrets and technology-related antitrust claims. Expert in licensing and competition law issues relating to standardized technologies and so-called "FRAND" licensing.
**Career:** Partner since 1999. Clerkship: Hon John D Butzner, Jr (US Court of Appeals, Fourth Circuit).
**Publications:** Contributing author in intellectual property law.
**Personal:** University of Virginia (JD, 1987; Law Review Articles Editor); University of Virginia (MA, History, 1987); Regent College Seminary (MDiv, 1995); Princeton University (AB, 1984).

### BROWN, James
Willkie Farr & Gallagher LLP, New York
212 728 8287
jbrown@willkie.com
*Featured in Tax (New York)*
**Practice Areas:** Specializes in tax aspects of complex investment fund transactions. Regularly advises sponsors of investment funds on tax structuring and operational issues relating to these funds, including taxation of registered and unregistered investment funds (eg, private equity funds, debt funds, hedge funds, commodities funds and regulated investment companies or mutual funds). Advises on acquisitions, mergers, recapitalizations, joint ventures and other types of transactions involving funds, their portfolio investments and their sponsors.
**Personal:** JD, Harvard Law School, 1991. BA, University of Texas at Austin, 1988. See: http://www.willkie.com/JamesBrown

### BROWN, Peter
Baker & Hostetler LLP, New York
212 589 4660
pbrown@bakerlaw.com
*Featured in Technology (New York)*
**Career:** Leader of BakerHostetler's national Technology Law team, Peter Brown maintains an active information technology practice including intellectual property and technology litigation and all types of IT transactions. Mr Brown has been the lead counsel in litigated matters involving computer software, electronic components, outsourcing, financial services, software development disputes, breach of contract claims, trade secrets, patents, trademarks and copyrights. These cases have been litigated in federal and state courts in jurisdictions across the county. He has negotiated all types of agreements used by computer and web-based companies. Mr Brown also has broad experience in ADR as an advocate, arbitrator and mediator.

### BROWNSTEIN, Andrew R
Wachtell, Lipton, Rosen & Katz, New York
212 403 1233
arbrownstein@wlrk.com
*Featured in Corporate/M&A (New York)*
**Practice Areas:** Specialises in mergers and acquisitions and corporate governance matters; has been engaged in many high profile matters that include cross-border transactions, leveraged

buyouts, complex restructuring deals, proxy fights and takeovers. Significant representations include: Walgreen Co. in its acquisition of a 45% stake in Alliance Boots GmbH and option to acquire the remainder, with an aggregate value of $27 billion, and its previous acquisitions of Duane Reade and Option Care; ConocoPhillips in its $33 billion spin-off of its downstream businesses as Phillips 66 and in its $35.6 billion acquisition of Burlington Resources, as well as Phillips Petroleum in its $35 billion combination with Conoco and numerous other transactions; Forest Laboratories in successive proxy contests with Carl Icahn; Genzyme in its sale to Sanofi-Aventis; Novartis in its $49.7 billion multistep acquisition of Alcon, as well as in its $8.2 billion acquisition of Hexal AG and Eon Labs and its $5.1 billion acquisition of Chiron; Schering-Plough in its $41 billion combination with Merck and its $14 billion acquisition of Organon; and BEA Systems in responding to an activist campaign by Carl Icahn and in its merger with Oracle.
**Professional Memberships:** Has been an adjunct professor of securities law at Rutgers University Law School; serves on the executive planning committee and is past chairman of the Ray Garrett Jr Corporate and Securities Law Institute at Northwestern University School of Law.
**Career:** Partner at Wachtell, Lipton, Rosen & Katz since 1985. Co-Chair of the firm's Corporate Department. Clerked for the Honorable Leonard Garth of the US Court of Appeals for the Third Circuit.
**Publications:** Frequent author and lecturer on corporate-related subjects.
**Personal:** Graduated summa cum laude from the University of Pennsylvania in 1975 (BA, English; BS, Economics), from the Wharton School of the University of Pennsylvania in 1976 (MBA) and with honors from Harvard Law School in 1979 (JD), where he was articles editor of the Harvard Law Review. He is active in numerous civic and charitable organisations, and is past president of the Board of Trustees of the Trinity School in New York City, a member of the Board of Overseers of the Annenberg Center at the University of Pennsylvania, a member of the Board of Directors of the New York City Public Art Fund and of the F·E·G·S Health and Human Services System.

### BRUNE, Susan
Brune & Richard LLP, New York
212 668 1900
sbrune@bruneandrichard.com
*Featured in Litigation (New York)*
**Practice Areas:** White-collar criminal defense and commercial litigation, including cases involving allegations of securities fraud, accounting fraud, insider trading, healthcare and other government contract fraud, tax-related fraud, money laundering, antitrust violations, Foreign Corrupt Practices Act violations and bank fraud. Practices in federal and state court, and before the SEC, FINRA and other enforcement agencies.
**Career:** Admitted to practice in New York. From 1988 to 1990, served as law clerk to the Honorable

Whitman Knapp in the U.S. District Court for the Southern District of New York (S.D.N.Y.) From 1990 to 1997, served as an Assistant U.S. Attorney in the S.D.N.Y, prosecuting fraud, public corruption, embezzlement and healthcare fraud cases. Most recently, obtained the acquittal of a Bear Stearns hedge fund manager in a federal jury trial and the dismissal of a civil suit against a hedge fund manager related to short selling. Awarded Honorable S. Thurgood Marshall Award for Outstanding Practitioner by the New York State Association of Criminal Defense Lawyers.
**Personal:** JD, Harvard Law School, 1988; MA, Columbia University, 1985; BA, Honors College of the University of Michigan, 1983.

### BUCKLEY, Susan
Cahill Gordon & Reindel LLP, New York
212 701 3862
sbuckley@cahill.com
*Featured in Media & Entertainment (New York)*
**Practice Areas:** Represents journalists and media entities in cases concerning press access issues, reporter's privilege, prior restraint doctrine and interplay between national security interests and rights of the press. Defense counsel in defamation and privacy cases, copyright matters and litigation challenging governmental efforts to restrict newsgathering including state efforts to restrict exit polling by media. Extensive experience in litigation challenging the constitutionality of campaign finance restrictions on First Amendment grounds.
**Professional Memberships:** Governing Board Member, ABA's Forum on Communications Law. Master, Federal Bar Council Inn of Court.
**Personal:** Mount Holyoke College, BA, 1973. Fordham University School of Law, JD, 1977.

### BUNNING, David W.
Greenberg Traurig, LLP, New York
212 801 9318
BunningD@gtlaw.com
*Featured in Tax (New York)*
**Practice Areas:** Tax.
**Professional Memberships:** Member: American Bar Association, Tax Section; New York State Bar Association, Tax Section, and its committees on New York State taxes and New York City taxes; California State Bar Association, Tax Section; among others.
**Career:** Listed: The Legal 500 United States, 2011-12; Super Lawyers magazine, New York Super Lawyers, 2007-12; Chambers USA Guide, 2013.
**Personal:** LLM, Taxation, New York University School of Law, 1997; JD, University of the Pacific, McGeorge School of Law, 1982 (Order of the Coif; American Jurisprudence Award for Constitutional Law); BA, cum laude, Economics, Claremont McKenna College, 1979.

### BURKE, Arthur J
Davis Polk & Wardwell LLP, Menlo Park
212 450 4352
arthur.burke@davispolk.com
*Featured in Antitrust (New York), Antitrust (California)*
See under California for profile.

**BUTWIN, Bradley**
O'Melveny & Myers LLP, New York
212 408 2424
bbutwin@omm.com
*Featured in Litigation (New York)*
**Practice Areas:** Brad Butwin is the Chair of
O'Melveny & Myers LLP and former Chair of the
Litigation Department. Brad is a trial lawyer
whose practice encompasses a broad spectrum of
complex commercial matters, including securities
litigation. He is a go-to litigator for major financial firms and his recent work includes handling
subprime, auction-rate securities, and Bernard
Madoff-related matters. Brad is a member of the
board of advisors of The American Society of
Legal Writers, as well as the New York City Bar
Association's Committee on Financial Reporting
and Task Force on New Lawyers in a Changing
Profession.

**BYOWITZ, Michael H**
Wachtell, Lipton, Rosen & Katz, New York
212 403 1268
mhbyowitz@wlrk.com
*Featured in Antitrust (New York)*
**Practice Areas:** Practice focuses on antitrust
law and policy, and principally advising multinational corporations on major domestic and international mergers, acquisitions, joint ventures and
corporate takeovers. Represents clients at the
Department of Justice, the Federal Trade
Commission, and State Attorneys General in the
United States and also consults on investigations
by antitrust authorities in the European Union,
the United Kingdom, Argentina, Australia, Brazil,
Canada, China, Colombia, Mexico, Venezuela and
many other countries. Major matters in which he
has served as antitrust counsel include for United
Technologies in its acquisition of Goodrich,
Novartis in its acquisition of Alcon, Maytag in its
acquisition by Whirlpool, and many others.
**Professional Memberships:** New York State
co-chair of the fellows of the American Bar
Foundation (and received the ABA Fellows
Outstanding State Co-chair Award in February
2012). Represented the American Bar
Association's Section of International Law in the
ABA House of Delegates from 2006 to 2012 (and
was a member of House of Delegates Committee
on Issues of Significance to the Legal Profession).
Served as chair of the ABA International Law
Section in 2005-2006, is former chair of three of
the Section's Divisions (including Business
Regulation and Public International Law), and is
also former chair of the Section's International
Antitrust Law Committee, and present co-chair of
its International Pro Bono Committee. Received
the Section's Lifetime Achievement Award in
August 2011. Member of the Executive
Committee of the New York City Bar and chaired
the City Bar's subcommittee that evaluated Elena
Kagan's qualifications to serve on the U.S.
Supreme Court. Served as chair of the City Bar's
Council on International Affairs (2006-2009) and
as chair of its Antitrust & Trade Regulation
Committee (1998-2001). Honorary lifetime mem-
ber of AIJA (the International Association of
Young Lawyers).

**Career:** Partner at Wachtell, Lipton, Rosen &
Katz, where he has practiced antitrust law for 28
years. Served as senior trial attorney and trial
attorney with the Department of Justice's
Antitrust Division from 1979-83.
**Publications:** Contributor to many legal publications and a frequent speaker on antitrust law
and compliance in the U.S. and abroad.
Consistently ranked among leading antitrust specialists in peer review rankings (e.g., Global
Competition Review, Who's Who Legal, Super
Lawyers, and Chambers).
**Personal:** Graduated from Columbia University
in 1973 (AB) and from New York University
School of Law in 1976 (JD), where he was awarded the Order of the Coif and served as an editor of
the Law Review. Admitted to the bar in New York
(1983) and Washington, DC (1976).

**BYRNE, Lawrence**
Pepper Hamilton LLP, New York
212 808 2701
byrnel@pepperlaw.com
*Featured in Litigation (New York)*
**Practice Areas:** Partner. Handles complex
white-collar criminal, government regulatory and
civil litigation matters. Has experience in antitrust,
securities, class action defense, commercial, bankruptcy, and First Amendment and media litigation. Extensive experience representing clients
involved in all types of government and internal
investigations, and related trial and appellate matters.
**Personal:** JD 1984 New York University School
of Law; BA, magna cum laude, 1981 Hofstra
University.

**CALIFANO, Thomas**
DLA Piper LLP (US), New York
212 335 4990
thomas.califano@dlapiper.com
*Featured in Bankruptcy/Restructuring (New York)*
**Practice Areas:** Bankruptcy/Restructuring.
**Career:** He has a broad-ranging practice in all
aspects of insolvency matters, including out-of-
court workouts and chapter 11 reorganizations
and liquidations. He represents distressed companies, creditors' committees, lending institutions,
private equity funds, purchasers of distressed debt
and other secured and unsecured creditors. His
particular emphasis is on company and buyer side
representation.
**Personal:** JD, St. John's University; BA, St. John's
University.

**CAMPBELL, Leah**
Willkie Farr & Gallagher LLP, New York
212 728 8217
lcampbell@willkie.com
*Featured in Insurance (New York)*
**Practice Areas:** Ms Campbell represents US
and international clients in a wide range of insurance and reinsurance regulatory matters. She
advises clients on the insurance regulatory aspects
of, and obtains insurance regulatory approvals for,
insurance industry mergers and acquisitions, significant reinsurance transactions, affiliate arrangements and the transfer and sale of insurance and
reinsurance businesses. Ms Campbell's insurance

law expertise includes legal investment issues,
insurance product regulation, insurance broker
matters and non admitted insurance and surplus
lines operations. She regularly provides clients
strategic advice on emerging insurance regulatory
issues. Recent matters include representing WRM
America in its acquisition of Fidelity National
Financial's flood insurance business.
**Personal:** JD, Hofstra University School of Law,
1982. BA, cum laude, with high honors, New York
University 1979. See:
http://www.willkie.com/LeahCampbell

**CAPLAN, David L**
Davis Polk & Wardwell LLP, New York
212 450 4000
david.caplan@davispolk.com
*Featured in Corporate/M&A (New York)*
**Practice Areas:** Global co-head of Davis Polk's
M&A Department. Advises corporate and invest-
ment banking clients in mergers and acquisitions,
joint ventures, corporate governance issues and
related matters. Has regularly represented a num-
ber of clients, including Aetna, Campbell Soup,
Canadian National Railway, Comcast, Limited
Brands, NBCUniversal, Ralph Lauren,
PricewaterhouseCoopers and Sterling Equities/the
New York Mets, in a range of transactions, gover-
nance issues and other matters.

**CAPLAN, Gordon**
Willkie Farr & Gallagher LLP, New York
212 728 8266
gcaplan@willkie.com
*Featured in Private Equity (Nationwide), Technology
(New York)*
**Practice Areas:** Partner in Corporate and
Financial Services Department; Chair of Private
Equity Practice; Member of Executive Committee.
Specialises in private equity, leveraged buy-outs,
mergers and acquisitions, recapitalisations and
venture capital. Represents equity sponsors, public
and private companies in corporate matters, private equity financings, securities offerings, mergers and acquisitions, technology transfer agreements, joint ventures and licensing. Responsible
for structuring and negotiation of significant
technology licensing, procurement and outsourcing transactions for major telecommunications
and technology companies.
**Personal:** JD, Fordham Law School, (Editor,
Fordham Law Review), 1991. BA, Cornell
University College of Arts and Sciences, 1988. See:
http://www.willkie.com/GordonCaplan

**CARDEN, Donald**
Clifford Chance US LLP, New York
212 878 4928
donald.carden@cliffordchance.com
*Featured in Tax (New York)*
**Practice Areas:** Focuses on all areas of Federal
and New York State income taxation, with a particular expertise in structured finance, including
CBO/CLO transactions, asset-backed and mortgage securitization, insurance, capital markets and
real estate capital markets transactions.
**Career:** Partner at Clifford Chance since 2000.
Georgetown University, BA, 1983; Georgetown

University Law Center, JD, magna cum laude,
1986. Elected to the Order of the Coif.

**CARLEEN, Donald P**
Fried, Frank, Harris, Shriver & Jacobson LLP,
New York
212 859 8202
Donald.Carleen@FriedFrank.com
*Featured in Employee Benefits & Executive
Compensation (New York)*
**Practice Areas:** Chair of executive compensation and employee benefits practice. Advises corporations, boards of directors, compensation
committees and senior executives on all aspects of
executive compensation and employee benefits,
including ERISA and tax, employment and securities law matters. Advises in complex M&A, leveraged buyouts, private equity, hedge fund, bankruptcy and restructuring transactions. Specializes
in structuring and negotiation of executive
employment, severance and equity participation
arrangements in M&A transactions.
**Career:** Joined in 1983; became partner in 1987.
**Personal:** JD, summa cum laude, Brooklyn Law
School (1983); BA, St. Johns School of Risk
Management (formerly The College of Insurance)
(1977).

**CARNEY, John J**
Baker & Hostetler LLP, New York
212 589 4255
jcarney@bakerlaw.com
*Featured in Litigation (New York)*
**Career:** A seasoned advocate in the courtroom
and boardroom, Mr Carney utilizes his background as Securities Fraud Chief, Assistant U.S.
Attorney, Securities and Exchange Commission
Senior Counsel and practicing CPA in representing public corporations, officers, directors,
employees, regulated entities and others in SEC
and criminal law enforcement investigations and
related civil litigation. Because of his "hands on"
experience in government investigations, finance
and accounting, Mr Carney frequently serves in
an advisory role to help avoid securities and FCPA
violations by domestic and international companies. Mr Carney also serves as a SEC Receiver over
multiple international hedge funds and investment advisory firms.

**CARPENTIER, Joan-Elisse**
McDermott Will & Emery LLP, New York
212 547 5544
jcarpentier@mwe.com
*Featured in Immigration (New York)*
**Practice Areas:** Practices all areas of immigration and nationality law affecting corporations
and other businesses in a wide range of industries.
Represents artists, entertainers, authors and others
in the arts in their immigration matters. Works on
behalf of United States citizens and foreign
nationals to obtain visas for other countries.
Represents clients with respect to immigration
compliance issues, including government audits.
**Professional Memberships:** Member,
Massachusetts, New York and California Bars;
member of American Immigration Lawyers
Association.

**Personal:** Boston University School of Law (JD); St. Lawrence University (BA, cum laude).

## CARROLL, John K
Skadden, Arps, Slate, Meagher & Flom LLP & Affiliates, New York
212 735 2280
john.carroll@skadden.com
*Featured in Litigation (New York)*
**Practice Areas:** Represents institutional and individual clients in criminal, regulatory and complex civil disputes. Has extensive experience representing clients in domestic and multinational criminal and regulatory investigations relating to alleged financial fraud, corrupt payments and other matters. Regularly counsels financial institutions and their senior officers in matters involving the Department of Justice, the Securities and Exchange Commission and state attorneys general and has tried numerous criminal and commercial cases.
**Career:** Assistant U.S. Attorney (S.D.N.Y.) 1983-1992; Chief, Securities and Commodities Fraud Task Force 1991-92, Partner at Clifford Chance 1992-2008. Joined Skadden in 2008.

## CASEY, George
Shearman & Sterling LLP, New York
212 848 8787
gcasey@shearman.com
*Featured in Corporate/M&A (New York)*
**Career:** George Casey is co-head of Shearman & Sterling's Global M&A Group. He has extensive experience in U.S. domestic and cross-border M&A transactions, venture capital financings, strategic investments and joint venture transactions, representing some of the largest multinational corporations, such as Anglo American, ArcelorMittal, Dow Chemical, Liberty Global, Thomson Reuters and others. From 2002 through 2005, Mr Casey was based in the firm's London office. Mr Casey is also a Lecturer in Law in M&A at the University of Pennsylvania Law School and presented guest lectures at l'École de Droit de la Sorbonne - Université Paris I.

## CASSANOS, Robert
Fried, Frank, Harris, Shriver & Jacobson LLP, New York
212 859 8278
Robert.Cassanos@FriedFrank.com
*Featured in Tax (New York)*
**Practice Areas:** Tax partner, chair of the New York tax department. Has extensive experience in all aspects of cross-border taxation and provides counsel on various transactions including public and private M&A, leveraged buyouts, cross-border acquisitions, financings, joint ventures, fund formations (hedge funds, private equity funds and hybrid funds), infrastructure funds, real estate and REITs. Author of "Single Taxation of Publicly Traded Entities", 99 Tax Notes 1663, June 16, 2003; and "An Alternative Approach to the Offshore Lender's Dilemma", Tax Notes, January 5, 2009.
**Career:** Joined in 1981; became partner in 1988.
**Personal:** JD, Rutgers University (1981); AB, Cornell University (1974).

## CATALANO, Richard
Clifford Chance US LLP, New York
212 878 8421
richard.catalano@cliffordchance.com
*Featured in Capital Markets (Nationwide), Tax (New York)*
See under Nationwide for profile.

## CAVANAGH, William G
Chadbourne & Parke LLP, New York
212 408 5388
wcavanagh@chadbourne.com
*Featured in Tax (New York)*
**Practice Areas:** Bill Cavanagh is Chair of Chadbourne's tax practice group. He has a broad-based corporate, partnership and international tax practice and advises U.S. and multinational clients in structuring, negotiating and implementing significant domestic and cross-border mergers and acquisitions, spin-offs, project finance transactions, securities offerings and private equity deals. He has also represented clients in numerous tax controversy disputes with the Internal Revenue Service and with various state and local tax authorities.
**Personal:** Syracuse University, BA, 1972; George Washington University Law School, JD, 1975; New York University School of Law, LLM, 1979.

## CENDALI, Dale
Kirkland & Ellis LLP, New York
212 446 4846
dale.cendali@kirkland.com
*Featured in Intellectual Property (New York), Media & Entertainment (New York)*
**Practice Areas:** Dale Cendali heads Kirkland's Copyright, Trademark and Internet Practice and is a nationally recognized leader in IP litigation, handling numerous high-profile cases involving such things as the Obama "Hope" poster, Harry Potter, the Spider-Man musical, Disney T-shirts, Tetris, MySpace, X-Men, Lionel Trains, Colgate "Total", Bratz dolls, iTunes, Martha Graham's dances, and sophisticated software and technology. She argued before the U.S. Supreme Court in Dastar v Twentieth Century Fox and represented Victoria's Secret in the Supreme Court. Dale won the Harry Potter Lexicon trial for JK Rowling and Warner Bros. She is an adjunct professor at Harvard Law School.

## CERABINO, Thomas M
Willkie Farr & Gallagher LLP, New York
212 728 8208
tcerabino@willkie.com
*Featured in Corporate/M&A (New York)*
**Practice Areas:** Partner of Willkie Farr & Gallagher in New York and Co-Chairman of the Firm; Member, Executive Committee. Specializes in mergers and acquisitions, joint ventures, and general corporate and securities matters. Lead corporate lawyer in number of high-profile transactions on behalf of firm's clients. Represented various public and private companies, private equity funds, and investment banking firms in wide range of domestic and cross border transactions, including business combinations, divestitures, leveraged buyouts, public and private offerings of securities, and change-of-control matters. Advised

boards of directors and board committees on variety of governance and other issues.
**Personal:** JD, St. John's University School of Law, (notes and comments editor, St. John's Law Review), 1981. BSFS, Georgetown University, 1978. See:
http://www.willkie.com/ThomasCerabino

## CERASANI, Denise
White & Case LLP, New York
212 819 8400
dcerasani@whitecase.com
*Featured in Corporate/M&A (New York)*
**Career:** Denise A. Cerasani is a partner in the Mergers & Acquisitions Group, practicing principally in the areas of securities, mergers and acquisitions (M&A), and corporate finance. Ms Cerasani has counseled and represented firm clients in a variety of industries and has developed a niche practice devoted to the Firm's investment banking clients. To view a comprehensive biography, please visit www.whitecase.com/dcerasani.

## CERASIA II, Ed
Ogletree, Deakins, Nash, Smoak & Stewart, PC, New York
212 492 2502
edward.cerasia@ogletreedeakins.com
*Featured in Labor & Employment (New York)*
**Practice Areas:** Mr Cerasia represents clients in employment, wage and hour, and employee benefits matters in the financial services, insurance, pharmaceutical, healthcare, transportation, media and retail industries. He is an experienced trial attorney who has successfully handled jury and bench trials involving claims of sexual, racial, age and disability harassment; race, age, disability and gender discrimination; retaliation; constructive discharge; and entitlement to employee benefits.
**Professional Memberships:** American Bar Association, Section of Labor and Employment Law
**Personal:** JD, University of Bridgeport School of Law, Valedictorian, summa cum laude, 1991; BS, Syracuse University, 1987.

## CHAFFETZ, Peter
Chaffetz Lindsey LLP, New York
212 257 6961
Peter.Chaffetz@chaffetzlindsey.com
*Featured in Insurance (Nationwide), Insurance (New York)*
See under Nationwide for profile.

## CHALSEN, Christopher
Milbank, Tweed, Hadley & McCloy LLP, New York
212 530 5380
cchalsen@milbank.com
*Featured in Intellectual Property (New York)*
**Practice Areas:** Mr Chalsen is head of the Intellectual Property Group. He specializes in intellectual property law, including patent and trademark licensing, litigation and prosecution. His practice concentrates in electrical and computer-related technologies, semi-conductors, telecommunications and mechanical and medical products. His experience includes judge and jury trials, appeals to the Court of Appeals for the Federal Circuit, representation of clients before

agencies such as the United States Customs Service and International Trade Commission, arbitrations (including AAA and ICC) and all phases of patent, trademark and copyright prosecution practice in the United States Patent and Trademark Office and the Copyright Office.

## CHAMLIN, Marc
Loeb & Loeb LLP, New York
212 407 4855
mchamlin@loeb.com
*Featured in Media & Entertainment (New York)*
**Practice Areas:** Represents cable networks, production companies, internet content companies, producers, actors, directors, series/screenplay writers, book authors, newscasters and advertising/promotion/public relations agencies. Transactional work includes reality and scripted television series development, production and distribution; advertiser-financed television series and television motion picture production; animation and live action television production and distribution; documentary and feature film production; merchandising and licensing; book publishing agreements; television commercials production; product endorsements; sports tour, event sponsorship and athlete service contracts; executive employment contracts.
**Career:** Partner since 1988. Television Practice Group Chair.
**Personal:** NYU Law School (JD, 1980); Princeton University (AB, 1977, magna cum laude).

## CHARLES, Scott K
Wachtell, Lipton, Rosen & Katz, New York
212 403 1202
skcharles@wlrk.com
*Featured in Bankruptcy/Restructuring (Nationwide), Bankruptcy/Restructuring (New York)*
See under Nationwide for profile.

## CHARNEY, Steven M
Peckar & Abramson, P.C., New York
212 382 0909
scharney@pecklaw.com
*Featured in Construction (New York)*
**Practice Areas:** Mr Charney is a counselor and litigator for some of the Nation's most prominent members of the construction industry. His leadership role includes counseling Ground Zero contractors following the 9/11 terrorist attacks.
**Professional Memberships:** Fellow, American College of Construction Lawyers; AGC. Admitted to practice law in NY and NJ.
**Career:** Chairman of Peckar & Abramson and is based out of the NY office. Masters in Construction Management and experience as Contractor.
**Publications:** Drafted first standard "Green" building agreement, developed first guidelines addressing mold in construction; GC to the BTEA of NY.
**Personal:** For more information, please visit: www.pecklaw.com

**CHASE, Terri L**
Jones Day, New York
212 326 8386
tlchase@jonesday.com
*Featured in Labor & Employment (New York)*
**Practice Areas:** Terri has experience handling employment litigation matters, including defending against employment discrimination, harassment and retaliation claims, FLSA and state wage and hour actions, breach of employment contract and noncompete agreement claims, defamation and employment torts, and employee benefits claims. She represents clients through litigation and arbitration, and argues appeals, summary judgment motions, and preliminary injunction motions. Terri counsels employers on wage and hour compliance, Dodd-Frank and Sarbanes-Oxley whistleblower rules, the FMLA, reductions in force, restrictive covenants, employment and severance agreements, managing union workforces, and personnel policies and procedures. She advises on employment issues that arise in transactional contexts.

**CHATZINOFF, Howard**
Weil, Gotshal & Manges LLP, New York
212 310 8340
howard.chatzinoff@weil.com
*Featured in Media & Entertainment (New York), Corporate/M&A (New York)*
**Practice Areas:** Howard Chatzinoff is Co-head of Weil's M&A Practice. He has a diverse corporate practice, emphasizing public and private M&A transactions and spin-offs. He has advised NBC and parent General Electric in GE's $18.1 billion sale of its remaining 49 percent stake in NBCUniversal and related real estate to Comcast; CBS in its development of CBS Sports Radio; and GE in its acquisition of a minority stake in China XD Electric. Other clients include: Elizabeth Arden, Cablevision and Guggenheim Partners.
**Professional Memberships:** Princeton University (BS.E, 1974); University of Virginia (JD, 1977).
**Personal:** PENCIL.

**CHAVKIN, Peter**
Mintz Levin Cohn Ferris Glovsky and Popeo PC, New York
212 692 6231
PChavkin@Mintz.com
*Featured in Litigation (New York)*
**Practice Areas:** Peter's practice focuses on white-collar criminal defense for individuals and institutions, complex civil litigation, regulatory, enforcement and compliance matters. He has represented individuals in some of the most significant financial, political and antiquity related legal, regulatory and congressional investigations, including Ruth Madoff and a major institution at the center of the financial crisis. He's tried nearly 20 cases to verdict, argued over a dozen appeals, but also has persuaded the government to drop indictments against his clients several times.
**Career:** Law clerk to Federal District Judge; Special Assistant to Assistant Attorney General, Civil Division; U.S. Department of Justice; Assistant U.S. Attorney (criminal).

**Personal:** BA, Princeton University's Woodrow Wilson School; JD, Harvard Law School.

**CHENG, Loyti**
Davis Polk & Wardwell LLP, New York
212 450 4000
loyti.cheng@davispolk.com
*Featured in Environment (New York)*
**Practice Areas:** Counsel in Davis Polk's Corporate Department. As a Co-Head of the Environmental Group, concentrates in providing advice on environmental, including climate change, and toxic tort matters to domestic and international companies and financial institutions involved in a variety of transactions, such as mergers and acquisitions, real estate investments, securities offerings and bank lending transactions. Assists clients in thoroughly understanding potential environmental liabilities and on allocating or disclosing those liabilities in the context of the transaction. Has experience with environmental issues arising in various types of industries, including oil and gas and power generation.

**CHERNEY, Emanuel S**
Kaye Scholer LLP, New York
212 836 7061
emanuel.cherney@kayescholer.com
*Featured in Corporate/M&A (New York)*
**Practice Areas:** Emanuel Cherney, Co-Chair of Kaye Scholer's Corporate Department and a member of the firm's Executive Committee, regularly represents private equity firms and other buyers and sellers of public and private companies, represents issuers in securities offerings and advises boards of directors and independent committees concerning corporate governance and other matters. Some of his regular clients include American Securities, Arlington Capital, ACI Capital, Compass International, Caisse de dépôt et placement du Québec (including its investment arm Ivanhoe Cambridge), Ingleside Investors and Fremont Group.

**CHERNY, Steven C**
Kirkland & Ellis LLP, New York
212 446 4965
steven.cherny@kirkland.com
*Featured in Intellectual Property (New York)*
**Practice Areas:** Steve Cherny is a partner in Kirkland & Ellis LLP's New York office. Steve's practice focuses on patent litigation before the Federal Courts and the United States International Trade Commission. He is lead counsel in numerous high profile patent cases spanning technologies including telecommunications, medical devices, electronics, pharmaceuticals, financial and business methods and consumer products. His clients include Cisco, C.R. Bard, Convergex, IBM, Motorola, Netgear, Oracle, Sony, Tellabs and Thomson.

**CHERTOFF, Gregory H**
Peckar & Abramson, P.C., New York
212 382 0909
gchertoff@pecklaw.com
*Featured in Construction (New York)*
**Practice Areas:** Mr Chertoff focuses his practice on construction law, regularly counseling general contractors, construction managers, EPC con-

tractors and owners on contract negotiations, risk management and disputes. His practice emphasizes resolving complex construction disputes through negotiation, mediation, and where necessary arbitration and litigation, on projects in NY, nationwide and internationally.
**Professional Memberships:** Past Secretary of the Construction Law Committee of the New York City Bar Association.
**Career:** Co-Managing Partner of the New York office.
**Publications:** Lecturer on NY Mechanic's Lien Law and Construction Risk Management to lawyers and construction industry professionals.
**Personal:** For more information, please visit: www.pecklaw.com.

**CHESLER, Evan R**
Cravath, Swaine & Moore LLP, New York
212 474 1243
echesler@cravath.com
*Featured in Antitrust (New York), Life Sciences (Nationwide), Litigation (Nationwide), Intellectual Property (New York), Litigation (New York)*
See under Nationwide for profile.

**CIABARRA, Laura G**
Dechert LLP, Hartford
860 524 3926
laura.ciabarra@dechert.com
*Featured in Real Estate (New York)*
**Practice Areas:** Ms Ciabarra focuses her practice on subordinate lending with an emphasis on mezzanine finance, B-notes and participation interests, and complex intercreditor and co-lender agreements. She represents major real estate funds, banks, and other financial institutions in large-scale transactions involving complicated mezzanine and subordinate debt structures. She also represents large private real estate funds with respect to development and acquisition joint ventures in the U.S. and Latin America.
**Professional Memberships:** Member, Connecticut and New York Bars.
**Personal:** Yale University (BA, 1989; JD, 1992); Completed graduate studies at both the University of Cambridge and the London School of Economics.

**CIERI, Richard M**
Kirkland & Ellis LLP, New York
212 446 4770
richard.cieri@kirkland.com
*Featured in Bankruptcy/Restructuring (Nationwide), Bankruptcy/Restructuring (New York)*
See under Nationwide for profile.

**CLARK, Christopher J**
Latham & Watkins LLP, New York
212 906 1350
Christopher.clark2@lw.com
*Featured in Litigation (New York)*
**Practice Areas:** White Collar Defense and Government Investigations.
**Career:** Mr Clark's practice focuses on securities law, foreign and domestic anti-corruption law. Represents public companies, alternative investment entities such as hedge funds, and individuals in criminal and civil investigations involving state and federal law enforcement authorities. Has rep-

resented hedge fund clients in precedent setting matters involving Section 5 of the Securities Act, Rule 105 of Regulation M and the rules regarding insider trading; currently represents Mark Cuban in SEC v Mark Cuban.
**Personal:** JD, Columbia University School of Law, cum laude; BA, Univ. of California, Berkeley, Phi Beta Kappa.

**CLARY, Richard W**
Cravath, Swaine & Moore LLP, New York
212 474 1227
rclary@cravath.com
*Featured in Litigation (Nationwide), Securities (Nationwide), Litigation (New York)*
See under Nationwide for profile.

**CLEMENS, Steven E**
Kirkland & Ellis LLP, New York
212 446 4787
steven.clemens@kirkland.com
*Featured in Tax (New York)*
**Practice Areas:** Steven Clemens focuses his practice primarily on tax matters that arise from complex mergers and acquisitions, both domestic and cross-border. He represents both strategic and financial clients. Mr Clemens has significant experience in the tax aspects of financial restructurings, both in and out of bankruptcy. He also advises clients on the formation of investment funds, such as private equity funds, and has represented both fund sponsors and significant investors in newly formed investment funds.
**Personal:** Harvard Law School, JD, magna cum laude, 1994; Eastern University, BA, magna cum laude, 1991.

**COCHRAN, Eric L**
Skadden, Arps, Slate, Meagher & Flom LLP & Affiliates, New York
212 735 2596
Eric.Cochran@skadden.com
*Featured in Corporate/M&A (New York)*
**Practice Areas:** Concentrates in mergers and acquisitions, securities law and general corporate law. Has advised clients on a wide variety of friendly and hostile transactions. Recent transactions have included negotiated acquisitions and divestitures, hostile defenses, proxy fights, restructurings (including Chapter 11 proceedings), leveraged buyouts, private equity investments, minority buyouts and unsolicited offers. Also has advised clients on corporate governance matters.
**Career:** JD, New York University School of Law, 1986; MS, New York University, 1984; BA, Williams College, 1982.

**COCO, Joseph A**
Skadden, Arps, Slate, Meagher & Flom LLP & Affiliates, New York
212 735 3050
Joseph.Coco@skadden.com
*Featured in Private Equity (Nationwide), Corporate/M&A (New York)*
See under Nationwide for profile.

**COGEN, Richard M**
Nixon Peabody LLP, Albany
518 427 2665
rcogen@nixonpeabody.com
*Featured in Energy & Natural Resources (New York)*

**Practice Areas:** Development, financing, siting and permitting of electric generation and transmission facilities and other industrial and infrastructure facilities, throughout the US, including fossil fuel, wind, solar, solid waste, biomass, and nuclear generating facilities.
**Professional Memberships:** Admitted to practice: New York and Northern and Western Districts of New York. American Bar Association; NY State Bar Association; Air and Waste Management Association; American Wind Energy Association; American Council on Renewable Energy.
**Career:** Partner and Past Chair of Energy and Environmental Practice Group, Nixon Peabody.
**Personal:** JD, Cornell Law School. BA, University of Rochester.

## COGUT, Charles 'Casey'
Simpson Thacher & Bartlett LLP, New York
212 455 2550
ccogut@stblaw.com
*Featured in Private Equity (Nationwide),*
*Corporate/M&A (New York)*
See under Nationwide for profile.

## COHEN, Benjamin J
Cahill Gordon & Reindel LLP, New York
212 701 3853
bcohen@cahill.com
*Featured in Tax (New York)*
**Practice Areas:** Specializes in tax planning, with emphasis on structuring of mergers and acquisitions, joint ventures, financings, international transactions and financial products. Served in the office of the Chief Counsel of the IRS and in the Office of Tax Legislative Counsel of the U.S. Treasury Department, working on legislative and regulatory matters, including those relating to corporate reorganizations and spin-offs.
**Professional Memberships:** Member emeritus, Tax Forum, NY Bar Association (Tax section), Association of the Bar of the City and State of NY, and MA Bar Association.
**Personal:** Brown University, AB, 1970, magna cum laude. Yale Law School, JD, 1974.

## COHEN, David
Schulte Roth & Zabel LLP, New York
212 756 2141
david.cohen@srz.com
*Featured in Employee Benefits & Executive*
*Compensation (New York)*
**Practice Areas:** Fiduciary responsibility, The Employee Retirement Income Security Act of 1974 (ERISA) and qualified plans.
**Professional Memberships:** American Bar Association.
**Career:** His experience includes the private sector (as vice president and assistant general counsel of a major investment firm) and government service (with the Department of Labor Employee Benefits Security Administration's Divisions of Regulatory Coordination and Exemptions).
**Publications:** He speaks and writes widely on ERISA and benefit fund-related issues.
**Personal:** The George Washington University Law School, JD; Columbia University, BA.

## COHEN, David
Vinson & Elkins LLP, New York
dcohen@velaw.com
*Featured in Energy & Natural Resources*
*(Nationwide), Corporate/M&A (New York)*
See under Nationwide for profile.

## COHEN, Edmund S
Winston & Strawn LLP, New York
212 294 2634
ecohen@winston.com
*Featured in Tax (New York)*
**Practice Areas:** Tax and international high net worth.
**Career:** Mr Cohen provides tax advice to some of the world's leading financial services and industrial companies. His extensive experience in various tax matters includes tax planning for international corporate businesses; tax advantaged financings and derivative transactions; tax planning for investment funds; tax planning for high net worth multinational families; structuring foreign investment in U.S. real estate; and foreign tax credit optimization. He joined Winston & Strawn in 2005 after serving as chairman of Coudert Brothers' tax practice for nearly 20 years.

## COHEN, Evan
Clifford Chance US LLP, New York
212 878 8518
evan.cohen@cliffordchance.com
*Featured in Latin American Investment (New York)*
**Practice Areas:** Evan Cohen is the Americas Region Managing Partner. Mr Cohen has over twenty years of experience representing clients in the areas of acquisition and leveraged finance, project financing, syndicated lending and restructurings. His clients include commercial and investment banks, borrowers, institutional investors and project sponsors. Mr Cohen's extensive experience spans multiple jurisdictions including the Americas, the UK, Europe and Asia. He spent eight years in Asia leading the US Banking practice.
**Career:** Wharton School of Finance at the University of Pennsylvania, BS, 1984; University of Pennsylvania Law School, JD, 1987. Admitted in New York.

## COHEN, H Rodgin
Sullivan & Cromwell LLP, New York
212 558 4000
cohenhr@sullcrom.com
*Featured in Financial Services Regulation*
*(Nationwide), Corporate/M&A (New York)*
See under Nationwide for profile.

## COHEN, Harry P
Crowell & Moring LLP, New York
212 803 4044
hcohen@crowell.com
*Featured in Insurance (New York)*
**Practice Areas:** Partner in the Crowell & Moring's Insurance/Reinsurance Group. Represented insurance/reinsurance companies, brokers, agents and others in negotiations/mediations/arbitrations and litigations in matters involving issues that relate to the reinsurance relationship and issues arising under the Federal Arbitration Act. Including workers' compensation

reinsurance, pre-need/final expense life insurance, finite reinsurance/fronting arrangements, spirals/arbitrage, agency/brokerage disputes/captive insurance/reinsurance arrangements, environmental reinsurance allocations, extracontractual obligations, IBNR recoverability, punitive damages, recovery of declaratory judgment expenses, direct and reinsurance pooling arrangements. Handles direct insurance defense cases, coverage disputes, and disputes between insurance companies and agents in the property and casualty, life, and accident and health.

## COHEN, Jay
Paul, Weiss, Rifkind, Wharton & Garrison LLP, New York
212 373 3163
jaycohen@paulweiss.com
*Featured in Media & Entertainment (New York)*
**Practice Areas:** Co-Chair of Litigation Department. Nationally recognized trial lawyer and corporate counselor, with comprehensive expertise in media, antitrust, securities, intellectual property and general complex commercial disputes and large and complex class action cases. Represents various sectors of music industry in precedent-setting matters, including mechanical rights and rights of public performance. Helped to secure compensation for songwriters and music publishers for reproduction and distribution of their musical works by record companies and digital music companies. Often plays key role in structuring and negotiation of high-stakes corporate transactions and conducting internal investigations on behalf of public companies and their boards.

## COHEN, Joel M
Davis Polk & Wardwell LLP, New York
212 450 4000
joel.cohen@davispolk.com
*Featured in Antitrust (New York)*
**Practice Areas:** Represents clients in a variety of antitrust and general civil litigation and arbitration matters, including cartel investigations and related civil litigation. Also represents clients in merger investigations, joint ventures, and/or antitrust counseling and litigation. Has advised numerous clients regarding licensing and distribution strategies and the permissible uses of intellectual property, and has represented clients in patent and antitrust ligiation concerning the alleged misuse of patents. Representations also include civil litigation, international arbitration and governmental investigations in the areas of M&A, securities law enforcement, false advertising, False Credit Reporting Act, commercial contracts and others.

## COHEN, Mark S
Cohen & Gresser LLP, New York
212 957 7601
mcohen@cohengresser.com
*Featured in Litigation (New York)*
**Practice Areas:** Mr Cohen is a co-founder of Cohen & Gresser LLP and the head of the firm's Litigation & Arbitration and White Collar Defense, Regulatory Enforcement and Internal Investigations practice groups. Mr Cohen main-

tains an active trial practice of both civil and criminal cases and has tried approximately 20 cases to verdict. He has also appeared numerous times before the United States Court of Appeals for the Second Circuit. His litigation practice includes complex commercial litigation, shareholder, securities, and derivatives litigation, corporate control and M&A litigation, and antitrust litigation. He also represents companies, financial institutions, and individual clients in white collar criminal cases, federal and state regulatory proceedings, proceedings before self-regulatory organizations, and corporate internal investigations. Mr Cohen has served as counsel in some of the most important white collar investigations of the past few years.
**Professional Memberships:** Member of the Association of the Bar of the City of New York; Securities Industry and Financial Markets Association (Compliance and Legal Division); the Federal Bar Council; UJA-Federation of New York (Lawyers Division, Criminal Law Group); and the American Bar Association (Section on Litigation). Co-Chair of the American Bar Association's Securities Subcommittee of the Committee on Commercial and Business Litigation. Former board member of the New York Council of Defense Lawyers.
**Career:** Prior to co-founding Cohen & Gresser, Mr Cohen practiced with Fried, Frank, Harris, Shriver & Jacobson and served as an Assistant United States Attorney for the Eastern District of New York.
**Personal:** Mr Cohen is a magna cum laude graduate of the University of Michigan Law School, where he was a Note Editor of the Law Review.

## COHEN, Robin L
Kasowitz, Benson, Torres & Friedman LLP, New York
212 506 1770
rcohen@kasowitz.com
*Featured in Insurance (Nationwide), Insurance (New York)*
See under Nationwide for profile.

## COLLETTA, Anthony J
Sullivan & Cromwell LLP, New York
212 558 4608
collettaa@sullcrom.com
*Featured in Real Estate (Nationwide), Capital Markets (Nationwide), Real Estate (New York)*
See under Nationwide for profile.

## COLLINS, Patrick
McCarter & English, LLP, New York
*Featured in Labor & Employment (New York)*
**Career:** Mr Collins has over 20 years' experience representing employers in all aspects of labor and employment law. He has successfully litigated single- and multi-plaintiff cases involving contracts, restrictive covenants, discrimination, and wage and hour claims. He has had marked success at the appellate level in both federal and state courts. Mr Collins regularly represents and defends employers in labor arbitrations and in matters before the NLRB, federal and state departments of labor, and human rights agencies. He is coauthor of the Employer's Guide to Union Organizing

Campaigns (2012 Edition), the preeminent treatise on the subject. For full bio: http://www.mccarter.com/Patrick-M-Collins/

### CONDE, Dominick A
Fitzpatrick, Cella, Harper & Scinto, New York
212 218 2204
dconde@fchs.com
*Featured in Intellectual Property (New York)*
**Practice Areas:** Dominick A Conde is Chair of the firm's Pharmaceuticals Practice Group and is active in all aspects of Fitzpatrick, Cella, Harper & Scinto's patent practice, focusing particularly on large-scale litigation matters related to chemistry, pharmaceuticals and pharmaceutical devices and diagnostics. Specific technologies that Mr Conde has worked with include chemotherapy agents, anti-viral agents, expectorants, anti-bacterial agents, anti-histamines, anti-hypertension agents, filtration devices, writing instruments and fire fighting apparatus. Clients Mr Conde has represented include Bristol-Myers Squibb, Daiichi Sankyo, Eli Lily & Co., Entegris, Merck & Co., Reckitt-Benckiser, Reliable Sprinkler Company, Sanofi, Sunovion, and Warner Chilcott, primarily as lead trial counsel. Mr Conde was selected by Managing Intellectual Property Magazine in June 2012 as one of the Top Life Sciences Litigators in the U.S. Mr Conde also has been listed as a Top New York City IP Litigator in the 2006-2010 & 2012 issues of Super Lawyers; a leading lawyer in LMG Life Sciences 2012 and a top intellectual property law practitioner in the 2012 edition of Best Lawyers. Mr Conde was recognized in Chambers USA 2011 for his outstanding work in the patent category, "his expertise in pharma work is phenomenal" and in 2012 as being "level headed and very service oriented."
**Professional Memberships:** American Bar Association; New York Bar Association; Federal Circuit Bar Association; New York Intellectual Property Law Association.
**Career:** Mr Conde formerly served as the firm's Managing Partner and is currently on the firm's Management Committee.
**Publications:** Extending the 30-Month FDA Stay in an ANDA Litigation, Fitzpatrick Case Update, July 9, 2009; Navigating the Challenges of ANDA Disputes, Law 360, July 28, 2009.
**Personal:** JD, Franklin Pierce Law Center, BS, Mechanical Engineering, Rensselaer, Polytechnic Institute. Married with two children.

### CONWAY, Jennifer S
Cravath, Swaine & Moore LLP, New York
212 474 1316
jconway@cravath.com
*Featured in Employee Benefits & Executive Compensation (New York)*
**Practice Areas:** Jennifer S. Conway is a partner in Cravath's Executive Compensation and Benefits Department. Her practice focuses on executive compensation and employee benefit matters, principally in connection with mergers and acquisitions, initial public offerings and other business transactions. Ms Conway also regularly counsels public and private companies on the design, implementation and disclosure of equity and cash

incentive compensation and retention programs and the negotiation of executive employment and separation agreements.
**Personal:** Columbia Law School (JD, 2001; James Kent Scholar; Managing Editor, Journal of Transnational Law); Georgetown University (BSFS, cum laude, 1996). For more information: http://www.cravath.com/jconway

### COOK, Michael L
Schulte Roth & Zabel LLP, New York
212 756 2150
michael.cook@srz.com
*Featured in Bankruptcy/Restructuring (New York)*
**Practice Areas:** Corporate restructuring, workouts and creditors' rights litigation, including mediation and arbitration.
**Professional Memberships:** American College of Bankruptcy (President, 2012-; Fellow and Director, 1997-; Chair, Board of Regents, 2010-2012); New York Bankruptcy Assistance Project (Chair, Steering Committee, 2005-2008); Lawyers Alliance for New York (Chair, 1999-2001).
**Career:** SRZ Partner since 2000; Skadden, Arps, Slate, Meagher & Flom, Partner and Practice Leader, Corporate Restructuring Group, 1980-2000; Weil, Gotshal & Manges Partner, 1975-80, associate, 1970-75.
**Publications:** Lectures and writes extensively. Editor, Bankruptcy Litigation Manual (2012-13 rev. ed.).
**Personal:** Columbia University, AB; New York University School of Law, JD.

### COONEY JR, John P
McKool Smith, New York
212 402 9400
jcooney@mckoolsmith.com
*Featured in Litigation (New York)*
**Practice Areas:** White-collar defense.
**Professional Memberships:** Fellow, American College of Trial Lawyers; Federal Bar Council; Chairman, Bar and Bench Liaison Committee; New York Council of Criminal Defense Lawyers; Wong Sung Society; Supreme Court Historical Society, New York Chair, 1999.
**Career:** Mr Cooney represents clients in a wide range of white-collar matters, including allegations involving securities fraud, insider trading, mail and wire fraud, tax, antitrust, FCPA, and FDA violations, government contracting, OFAC, and accounting irregularities. He is consistently recognized by leading legal directories, including Chambers USA and Best Lawyers.
**Personal:** Duke University School of Law (JD, 1969); Indiana University (BS, 1966).

### COOPER, Richard J
Cleary Gottlieb Steen & Hamilton LLP, New York
212 225 2276
rcooper@cgsh.com
*Featured in Latin American Investment (New York)*
**Practice Areas:** Restructurings, M&A, finance. Restructuring transactions: Axtel, Cap Cana, San Antonio Oil and Gas, Sanluis, IUSA, Su Casita, CEMEX, Fibria, Gruma, Controladora Comercial Mexicana, Grupo Cementos de Chihuahua, Independencia, Iusacell, Transportadora de Gas

del Norte, Metrogas, Vitro. M&A clients: Ashmore Investments, Fintech, Acon Investments, Carlyle Riverstone, Fortress Investments, Marathon Asset Management, Pampa Holdings, Sempra Energy, TPG. Leverage finance clients: Goldman Sachs, Deutsche Bank, Pampa Holdings, Petrobras, UBS; Government of Puerto Rico with enactment of its Public Private Partnership law.
**Career:** Columbia Law School (1986), Parker School of Foreign and Comparative Law, London School of Economics (1983), Duke University (1982).

### CORNISH, Kelley A
Paul, Weiss, Rifkind, Wharton & Garrison LLP, New York
212 373 3493
kcornish@paulweiss.com
*Featured in Bankruptcy/Restructuring (New York)*
**Practice Areas:** Partner in the Bankruptcy and Corporate Reorganization Department, Ms Cornish represents the full range of participants in bankruptcy cases and corporate restructurings, most notably debtors, strategic stakeholders and acquirers of distressed assets. Ms Cornish has substantial experience in bankruptcy-related litigation, including contested plan confirmation, fraudulent transfers, preferences and equitable subordination. She has served as debtor's counsel to large public and private companies including AbitibiBowater Inc., The Warnaco Group, The Penn Traffic Company and London Fog Industries, and has represented key stakeholders and committees in matters such as Southern Air, Howrey LLP, Winn Dixie and NorthWestern Corporation.

### CORRALES, Carmen Amalia
Cleary Gottlieb Steen & Hamilton LLP, New York
212 225 2982
ccorrales@cgsh.com
*Featured in Latin American Investment (New York)*
**Practice Areas:** Capital markets, including sovereign transactions. Represented Argentina in the largest sovereign debt restructurings in history, the Province of Buenos Aires and the Dominican Republic in their debt restructurings and financings (as well as other sovereign entities and banks). Worked on infrastructure and project financings. Participated in debt and equity corporate offerings in international markets, including registered offerings for LAN airlines and BanColombia and numerous 144A offerings.
**Professional Memberships:** Member of the Bar in New York and New Jersey.
**Career:** Joined firm, 1990; became partner, 1998. JD, Harvard Law School (1989), BA, University of Pennsylvania (1986).

### CORTES, Jessica
Davis & Gilbert LLP, New York
212 468 4808
jcortes@dglaw.com
*Featured in Labor & Employment (New York)*
**Practice Areas:** Labor and employment.
**Career:** Jessica Golden Cortes regularly counsels and litigates in all aspects of employment law. Ms Cortes investigates discrimination and whistle-

blower complaints and advises clients on hiring, terminations, reductions in force, restrictive covenants, wage and hour issues, federal and state family and medical leave laws, employment policies, handbooks, and employment and separation agreements. She also regularly defends clients in federal and state courts, arbitrations, mediations, and before the EEOC and various state agencies in the areas of discrimination, harassment and retaliation, and breach of contract actions relating to post-employment obligations and for cause terminations.

### CORUZZI, Laura A
Jones Day, New York
212 326 8383
lacoruzzi@jonesday.com
*Featured in Intellectual Property (New York)*
**Practice Areas:** Dr. Coruzzi has represented biotechnology and pharmaceutical clients for nearly 30 years, practicing all aspects of patent laws related to life sciences — molecular biology, virology, vaccines, therapeutic antibodies, biologic and small molecule therapeutics for oncology and genetic disorders, drug delivery and diagnostics. She counsels clients on strategic planning of patent portfolios, prosecution, interferences, oppositions, due diligence, opinions and licensing. Her practice includes patent litigation and appeals before PTAB, the Federal Circuit — and, most recently, defending the constitutionality and validity of Myriad's BRCA "gene" patents challenged by the ACLU, which is now before the US Supreme Court.

### CREAMER JR, Ronald E
Sullivan & Cromwell LLP, New York
212 558 4665
creamerr@sullcrom.com
*Featured in Tax (New York)*
**Career:** Partner since 2000. Head of Tax Group, leads Group's M&A practice and has extensive experience with cross-border transactions and distressed acquisitions and dispositions. Regularly advises on execution and IRS review of tax-efficient corporate financing techniques and capital markets strategies. Also counsels investment banking and other clients in the taxation of derivatives trading strategies and financial instrument design. Clients include leading financial institutions, consumer products companies, healthcare and biotechnology corporations and mining and energy concerns.
**Personal:** Yale Law School (JD, 1991); Yale School of Organization and Management (MPPM, 1991); Princeton University (AB, 1987).

### CREED, John J
Simpson Thacher & Bartlett LLP, New York
212 455 3485
jcreed@stblaw.com
*Featured in Tax (New York)*
**Practice Areas:** Tax Partner concentrating on private investment and hedge fund formation; publicly traded partnerships; capital markets; and M&A. Fund experience includes, private equity, hedge, infrastructure, credit opportunity and other asset categories for leading sponsors, including Blackstone, Carlyle, KKR, First Reserve,

Corsair and Citigroup. Represented Carlyle in connection with its IPO, Silver Lake in connection with its proposed acquisition of Dell Inc., Office Depot in connection with its proposed merger with Office Max, and L3 in connection with its spin-off of Engility.
**Personal:** Trinity College Dublin (BA, Law, with Honors, 1985); New York University School of Law (LLM, Taxation, 1988).

## CRONIN, Denis
Vinson & Elkins LLP, New York
212 237 0080
dcronin@velaw.com
*Featured in Bankruptcy/Restructuring (New York)*
**Practice Areas:** Restructuring and reorganization.
**Career:** An accomplished lawyer with 38 years of experience, Denis is Of Counsel in V&E's New York office and former Co-Chair of the firm's Restructuring and Reorganization Practice Group. Denis' principal areas of focus are corporate restructurings, workouts, chapter 11 reorganizations, mergers and acquisitions, general corporate and commercial law, and mediation. He has also been appointed by bankruptcy courts and litigants as a mediator in large commercial disputes.
**Personal:** Denis received his AB from Colgate University and his JD from Fordham University School of Law (Board of Editors, Fordham Law Review).

## CROUGH, Maureen
Sidley Austin LLP, New York
212 839 7323
mcrough@sidley.com
*Featured in Environment (New York)*
**Practice Areas:** Counsel in Sidley's New York office, practicing in the Environmental Group. She represents domestic and non-US purchasers, sellers, lenders, landlords and tenants in the environmental aspects of a broad range of financial transactions. She has been involved in numerous aspects of environmental due diligence, evaluation of environmental insurance for use in transactions, negotiation of environmental provisions in acquisition and loan agreements, resolution of environmental matters in bankruptcy and environmental counseling pertaining to financial transactions.
**Personal:** The University of Michigan Law School, JD, 1986, cum laude; Princeton University, AB, 1983, magna cum laude. Admissions: Illinois, New York.

## CUNHA, Mark
Simpson Thacher & Bartlett LLP, New York
212 455 3475
mcunha@stblaw.com
*Featured in Litigation (New York)*
**Practice Areas:** Partner specializing in complex commercial litigation including securities, antitrust, class action, internal investigations, mass tort, products liability, attorney liability, fraud, estate and contract disputes. Representations include Fairfield Greenwich (Madoff litigation), JPMorgan Securities (analyst litigation), Princeton University (Robertson litigation), Heineken, BAT.

Industries (attorney general tobacco litigation), M-real (antitrust) and Enel S.p.A. (takeover).
**Professional Memberships:** Past Chair, Legal Services NYC; Past Chair, Executive Committee, NYC Bar Association; Chevalier de l'Order des Palms Academique.
**Career:** White House Intern, 1979; joined firm, 1980; Partner since 1989.
**Personal:** BA, magna cum laude, Phi Beta Kappa, Cornell University (1977); JD, Stanford Law School (1980).

## CURBOW, William
Simpson Thacher & Bartlett LLP, New York
212 455 3160
wcurbow@stblaw.com
*Featured in Corporate/M&A (New York)*
**Practice Areas:** Merger and acquisitions Partner. Has represented First Reserve Partners, L-3 Communications, Vodafone Group and others. Transactions include the First Reserve acquisitions of TPC Group and Ameriforge, its investments in PBF Energy and Glencore International and its sale of Acteon Group; representing L-3 in the spin-off of Engility; representing Vodafone in connection with its investment in Verizon Wireless; and Genesee & Wyoming in its acquisition of RailAmerica.
**Career:** Joined Firm, 1989; Partner, 1996.
**Personal:** BA, summa cum laude, University of Connecticut (1984); JD, Harvard Law School (1987).

## CURNIN, Paul C
Simpson Thacher & Bartlett LLP, New York
212 455 2519
pcurnin@stblaw.com
*Featured in Securities (Nationwide), Litigation (New York)*
See under Nationwide for profile.

## D'AVOLIO, Lisa
Skadden, Arps, Slate, Meagher & Flom LLP & Affiliates, New York
212 735 2916
Lisa.DAvolio@skadden.com
*Featured in Immigration (New York)*
**Practice Areas:** Advises clients on a broad range of employment-related matters. Represents employers before federal and state courts, administrative agencies and arbitration panels. Litigation experience includes defense of discrimination, wrongful termination, breach of contract and fraud claims, as well as Sarbanes-Oxley whistleblower complaints. Represents clients in cases involving wage and hour violations, the enforcement of contracts and restrictive covenants. Provides immigration-related advice and assistance, as well as counsel in connection with disciplinary and termination issues and adoption of workplace policies and procedures.
**Personal:** JD, University of Michigan Law School, 1996; BA, University of Michigan, 1991.

## DABNEY, James W
Fried, Frank, Harris, Shriver & Jacobson LLP, New York
212 859 8966
James.Dabney@FriedFrank.com
*Featured in Intellectual Property (New York)*

**Practice Areas:** Litigation partner and intellectual property practice group leader. Experienced in trial and appellate litigation of patent, trademark, copyright, and related causes. Adjunct Professor of Law, Cornell Law School.Member, American Law Institute. Was partner at Pennie & Edmonds LLP from 1989-2003.
**Career:** Joined as partner in 2004.
**Personal:** JD, magna cum laude, Cornell Law School (1979), Order of the Coif and on the Board of Editors of Cornell Law Review; AB, magna cum laude, Harvard College (1976); The Hotchkiss School (1972).

## DANTZLER JR, J William
White & Case LLP, New York
212 819 8543
jdantzler@whitecase.com
*Featured in Tax (New York)*
**Career:** J. William Dantzler, Jr. heads the Americas White & Case Tax Practice. He has a domestic and international corporate tax practice, with emphasis on M&A and tax controversies. His M&A experience includes tax-free transactions where White & Case provided the enabling tax opinion or structuring. Some transactions have required unique structural solutions to accommodate the needs of sellers or to position the acquiring company for future tax savings. He also serves as principal outside tax counsel to several US public companies and advises non-US companies that are forming or recapitalizing US subsidiaries and branches. To view his biography, visit www.white-case.com/jdantzler.

## DARROW, Peter V
DLA Piper LLP (US), New York
212 335 4720
peter.darrow@dlapiper.com
*Featured in Latin American Investment (New York)*
**Practice Areas:** Finance
**Career:** He is a highly experienced finance and securities lawyer who focuses on capital markets financing, acquisition and leveraged financing, structured financing, project and infrastructure financing, debt restructuring and liability management transactions, particularly in Latin America and other emerging markets.
**Personal:** JD, University of Michigan Law School (Member, Michigan Law Review); B.Phil., Trinity College, Oxford University; BA, Columbia University

## DASSIN, Lev
Cleary Gottlieb Steen & Hamilton LLP, New York
212 225 2790
ldassin@cgsh.com
*Featured in Litigation (New York)*
**Practice Areas:** Complex commercial litigation, including white-collar criminal defense, regulatory enforcement and internal investigations.
**Professional Memberships:** New York Bar; US Supreme Court, Second Circuit Court of Appeals, US District Courts (Southern and Eastern Districts of New York).
**Career:** Joined firm in 2009 as a partner. US Attorney's Office, Southern District of NY (Acting US Attorney, 2008-2009; Deputy US Attorney,

2008; Chief of the Criminal Division, 2005-2007; Assistant US Attorney, 1992-1998). Law, Clerk, US District Court, Southern District of NY.
**Personal:** JD, NYU School of Law (1990); BA, magna cum laude, Cornell University (1987).

## DAVIS, George A
Cadwalader, Wickersham & Taft LLP, New York
212 504 6797
george.davis@cwt.com
*Featured in Bankruptcy/Restructuring (Nationwide), Bankruptcy/Restructuring (New York)*
**Practice Areas:** Co-Chair, Financial Restructuring Department. Represents debtors, secured lenders, agents, unsecured creditor groups and investors in complex corporate reorganizations, debt restructurings, and distressed M&A across an array of industries , including chemical, real estate, gaming, financial, retail, telecommunications, energy, airline, steel and manufacturing. Leading role in some of the most significant and innovative recent restructurings involving: AES Eastern, Twin River Casinos, Caribbean Petroleum, Centro Properties, Dynegy, EME Homer City, LyondellBasell and Millennium Custodial Trust.
**Professional Memberships:** Committee on Bankruptcy and Corporate Reorganizations, Association of the Bar of the City of NY; American Bankruptcy Institute; Turnaround Management Association.
**Career:** Adjunct professor at Georgetown University Law Center, teaching bankruptcy and creditors' rights.
**Publications:** Contributing author, Cadwalader Restructuring Review (www.restructuringreview.com).
**Personal:** JD, Hofstra University School of Law (with distinction); BS, SUNY Binghamton (magna cum laude).

## DAVIS, Robert P
Cleary Gottlieb Steen & Hamilton LLP, New York
212 225 2670
rdavis@cgsh.com
*Featured in Corporate/M&A (New York)*
**Practice Areas:** Mergers, acquisitions, divestitures, joint ventures, acquisition finance, international securities offerings, corporate restructurings and other financial transactions, with particular focus on the healthcare, telecommunications, airline industries. Represented Warburg Pincus (Bausch & Lomb; CFHC Holdings, Rural/ Metro); Warburg Pincus/Vestar Capital Partners (Triton Container International Limited); Barclays (Lehman Brothers); American Tower; Cascade Investment; Blackstone/Goldman Sachs/KKR/TPG (Biomet); TPG/Warburg Pincus (Neiman Marcus); T-Mobile USA (SunCom Wireless); Ricoh (IBM Printing Systems Division).
**Professional Memberships:** Member of the Bar in New York.
**Career:** Joined firm, 1978; partner, 1986. Hong Kong: 1993-1995. JD, magna cum laude, Cornell Law School (1978); BA, cum laude, Yale University (1975).

**DAWSON, R Alec**
Morgan, Lewis & Bockius LLP, New York
212 309 7092
adawson@morganlewis.com
*Featured in Private Equity (Nationwide), Corporate/M&A (New York)*
**Practice Areas:** R. Alec Dawson is a Partner in Morgan Lewis's Business and Finance Practice and serves as co-chair of the Firm's private equity practice. His practice focuses on US and cross-border transactional matters, including structuring and negotiating M&A and joint venture transactions for strategic and financial acquirers. He provides advice to public companies in the US involved in various transactional matters, including counseling boards and special committees in connection with interested party transactions. Mr Dawson has a focus on representing financial services companies involved in acquisitions, divestitures and joint ventures, including broker dealers, investment managers and hedge funds.

**DEL PINO, Antonio**
Latham & Watkins LLP, New York
212 906 1200
antonio.delpino@lw.com
*Featured in Latin American Investment (New York)*
**Practice Areas:** Global Chair of firm's Latin America Practice and a leading practitioner for Latin American transactions. Focuses on cross-border acquisitions, private equity, and different types of financings. Has recently worked on a number of significant multi-national acquisitions and joint ventures in Latin America and has extensive experience in energy and infrastructure financings. Has represented more than half a dozen governments in their privatisation programmes.
**Professional Memberships:** Appointed to the U.S. State Department's Advisory Committee on International Economic Policy and sits on the Board of the Council of the Americas.

**DELANEY, John**
Morrison & Foerster LLP, New York
212 468 8040
jdelaney@mofo.com
*Featured in Outsourcing (Nationwide), Technology (New York)*
**Practice Areas:** Focuses on technology, outsourcing and IP matters. Counsels clients on a broad range of copyright, trademark and patent-related transactions. Founder and leader of the firm's Social Media practice, and editor of Socially Aware, a blog and newsletter devoted to social media law.
**Professional Memberships:** Chair, PLI Annual Social Media Conference; Co-Chair, PLI Annual Outsourcing Conference; Board Member, Volunteer Lawyers for the Arts; Board Member, iMentor.
**Career:** Former Co-Chair of the firm's Technology Group. Recognized as one of the 'Lawyers for the New Economy' by American Lawyer. On Crain's New York Business 'Technology 100' list.

**DELIKAT, Michael**
Orrick, Herrington & Sutcliffe LLP, New York
212 506 5230
mdelikat@orrick.com
*Featured in Labor & Employment (New York)*
**Practice Areas:** Mike Delikat, Orrick's Global Employment Law practice chair, represents multinational clients in all facets of employment law, including internal investigations involving alleged corporate wrongdoing; wage-and-hour and discrimination class actions brought by private plaintiffs and governmental agencies and trade secret misappropriation cases. Mike has an active bench and jury trial, arbitration and appellate practice and is known for handling high-exposure cases. He has established a leading practice representing major corporations and board of director committees in the investigation and defense of Sarbanes-Oxley, Dodd-Frank and other whistle-blower claims and is the author of the first treatise published on this subject.

**DEVITO, Daniel A**
Skadden, Arps, Slate, Meagher & Flom LLP & Affiliates, New York
212 735 3210
daniel.devito@skadden.com
*Featured in Intellectual Property (New York)*
**Practice Areas:** Daniel A DeVito has considerable experience litigating intellectual property cases, including complex high technology patent cases, at both the trial and appellate level. He also has extensive experience in proceedings before the International Trade Commission. Mr DeVito has a significant focus on financial and business method patents, and has litigated matters involving digital electronics, computer software, online technologies, intelligent information systems, advanced telecommunications systems, semiconductor design, fiber optic transmission systems, cellular network systems, mobile telephone application programs, complex wavelength division multiplexing technology, and aircraft engines.
**Career:** JD, St John's University, 1987; BSEE, Manhattan College, 1982.

**DIBLASI, Gandolfo V**
Sullivan & Cromwell LLP, New York
212 558 3836
diblasig@sullcrom.com
*Featured in Securities (Nationwide), Litigation (New York)*
See under Nationwide for profile.

**DIETDERICH, Andrew G**
Sullivan & Cromwell LLP, New York
212 558 3830
dietdericha@sullcrom.com
*Featured in Bankruptcy/Restructuring (Nationwide), Bankruptcy/Restructuring (New York)*
See under Nationwide for profile.

**DILORENZO, Louis P**
Bond, Schoeneck & King, PLLC, New York
646 253 2315
ldilorenzo@bsk.com
*Featured in Labor & Employment (New York)*
**Practice Areas:** Represents management in labor and employment law matters. Chair of the firm's Labor, Employment Law, Employee Benefits Group; Fellow, College of Labor & Employment Lawyers and Litigation Council of America; Member of the Federation of Defense and Corporate Counsel; Best Lawyers in America and Super Lawyers, Top 10 in Upstate New York; Syracuse University Adjunct Professor; several published articles and books; named "Great Negotiator" by Corporate Legal Times. Named to Top 10 Labor Lawyer by Human Resources Executive Magazine. General Counsel to Agway, Inc. (2002-04).
**Personal:** Syracuse University (BA, 1973); University of Buffalo Law School (JD, 1976); SPHR.

**DIMATTEO, John M**
Willkie Farr & Gallagher LLP, New York
212 728 8299
jdimatteo@willkie.com
*Featured in Intellectual Property (New York)*
**Practice Areas:** Chair, Intellectual Property Department; Partner, Litigation Department. Patent litigation, complex patent prosecution, trademarks, trade secrets, copyrights, and IP licensing. Represents technology leaders in jury and non-jury cases in federal courts across United States, and in other patent forums, including ITC and U.S. Court of Appeals for Federal Circuit.
**Professional Memberships:** Member of American Chemical Society; Institute of Electrical and Electronics Engineers
**Personal:** MA (Biology), Columbia University (in progress). LLM, Trial Advocacy, Temple University School of Law, 2001. MSCS (Computer Science), Polytechnic University of New York, 2000. JD, St. John's University School of Law, 1988. BSE, (Engineering), Polytechnic Institute of New York in 1984.
See:http://www.willkie.com/JohnDiMatteo

**DIMON, Samuel**
Davis Polk & Wardwell LLP, New York
212 450 4000
samuel.dimon@davispolk.com
*Featured in Tax (New York)*
**Practice Areas:** Member of Davis Polk's Tax Department. Advises clients on federal income tax matters in a variety of contexts, domestic and international, including financial product development and use of derivatives, bankruptcy reorganizations, workouts, tax audits, tax planning for financial institutions, hedge fund organisation and investments, securities offerings, mergers and acquisitions and joint ventures.

**DINKOFF, Allan**
Weil, Gotshal & Manges LLP, New York
212 310 6771
allan.dinkoff@weil.com
*Featured in Labor & Employment (New York)*
**Practice Areas:** Allan Dinkoff has more than 30 years of experience handling employment and complex commercial litigation matters. Before joining Weil, he served as Managing Director at Merrill Lynch, where he led the Employment Law Group and advised executive management and the board on global employment matters. He has extensive experience coordinating employment issues arising in crisis management situations and cross-border contexts, negotiating executive compensation and separation arrangements, managing employment discrimination class actions and FSLA matters, and litigating restrictive covenant matters and high-profile individual discrimination claims.
**Personal:** Drew University (BA, cum laude, 1977); Hofstra University Law (JD, with distinction, 1980).

**DISKANT, Gregory L**
Patterson Belknap Webb & Tyler LLP, New York
212 336 2710
gldiskant@pbwt.com
*Featured in Intellectual Property (New York)*
**Practice Areas:** Gregory Diskant is a senior litigation Partner at Patterson Belknap, where he served as Chair of the firm from 1997-2007. As part of his active trial practice, Mr Diskant regularly tries cases in federal and state courts and before arbitration panels, focusing on complex commercial, securities and intellectual property litigation. He has secured billions of dollars in judgments and settlements for his clients, with multiple verdicts greater than $100 million. In jury trials around the country, Mr Diskant has successfully represented both plaintiffs and defendants. Two of his jury victories for plaintiffs were cited as major plaintiff's verdicts of the year; two of his jury wins for defendants were cited as major defendant's verdicts of the year. In February 2010, he obtained a settlement in a series of patent cases of $1.7 billion, the largest patent settlement ever. In April 2011, he obtained a multi-billion dollar settlement resolving distribution rights to a pharmaceutical. Most recently, in May 2012, he obtained a defendant's jury verdict defeating a $500 million patent infringement claim involving the market's leading contact lenses.
**Professional Memberships:** Fellow, American College of Trial Lawyers.
**Career:** Prior to joining Patterson Belknap, Mr Diskant served as Assistant United States Attorney, Southern District of New York (1976-80), and served as Chief Appellate Attorney in 1980. He also served as a law clerk to the Hon. Thurgood Marshall, Supreme Court of the United States and the Hon J Skelly Wright, U.S. Court of Appeals for the District of Columbia Circuit.
**Personal:** Columbia Law School (JD 1974), James Kent Scholar, Harlan Fiske Stone Scholar, Editor-in-Chief, Columbia Law Review; Princeton University (AB, Chemistry, 1970).

**DIZENGOFF, Ira S**
Akin Gump Strauss Hauer & Feld LLP, New York
212 872 1096
idizengoff@akingump.com
*Featured in Bankruptcy/Restructuring (Nationwide), Bankruptcy/Restructuring (New York)*
See under Nationwide for profile.

**DJAHA, David**
Ropes & Gray LLP, New York
212 841 0489
David.Djaha@ropesgray.com
*Featured in Real Estate (New York)*

**Practice Areas:** As head of the firm's Real Estate Practice Group, David focuses his practice on complex core and distressed acquisitions and dispositions as well as asset- and mortgage-backed finance. He has extensive experience advising investment banks, private equity funds, domestic and international developers and investors on transactions where real estate is their core strategy. David advises clients on matters involving capital markets, asset-based, mezzanine finance, warehouse and construction lending, real estate private equity, and joint ventures.
**Career:** New York Bar.
**Personal:** JD, Dean's List, Brooklyn Law School (1988); BA, cum laude, State University of New York at Buffalo (1985).

### DOWLING, Donald C
White & Case LLP, New York
212 819 8665
ddowling@whitecase.com
*Featured in Labor & Employment (New York)*
**Career:** Donald C. Dowling, Jr concentrates his practice on outbound international employment law, which is cross-border human resources law issues for multinational employers. Multinationals globalizing their business operations increasingly need to align certain aspects of employment law compliance across borders. Working daily with White & Case's global team of employment lawyers, and also with employment lawyers in emerging markets worldwide, Mr Dowling advises multinational headquarters on cross-border solutions to specific international employment law compliance challenges. To view a comprehensive biography, please visit www.whitecase.com/ddowling.

### DRIVAS, Dimitrios
White & Case LLP, New York
212 819 8286
ddrivas@whitecase.com
*Featured in Intellectual Property (New York)*
**Career:** Mr Drivas is the Chair of the Firm's Global Intellectual Property Practice Group. His practice is in patent litigation and counseling and technology transfer. Mr Drivas is a registered US patent attorney and represents clients in patent and technology related disputes in the Patent Office, courts and before arbitration panels. In addition to his litigation practice, Mr Drivas advises clients on the acquisition and licensing of intellectual property rights, joint development agreements and strategic alliances. To view a comprehensive biography, please visit www.whitecase.com/ddrivas.

### DUBBS, Thomas
Labaton Sucharow LLP, New York
212 907 0871
tdubbs@labaton.com
*Featured in Securities (Nationwide), Litigation (New York)*
**Practice Areas:** Securities Litigation.
**Professional Memberships:** Thomas Dubbs, a recognized leader in the field of securities litigation, focuses his practice on the representation of institutional investors in securities cases. He has served as lead or co-lead counsel in some of the

most important federal securities class actions in recent years, including those against AIG, Goldman Sachs, the Bear Stearns Companies, Broadcom and Facebook. Mr Dubbs has played an integral role in securing significant settlements in high-profile cases including: In re American International Group, Inc. Securities Litigation (settlements totaling more than $1 billion pending final court approval); In re HealthSouth Securities Litigation ($671 million settlement); Eastwood Enterprises LLC v. Farha et al. (Wellcare) (over $200 million settlement); In re Broadcom Corp. Securities Litigation ($160.5 million settlement and an additional $13 million with Broadcom's auditor, Ernst & Young); In re St. Paul Travelers Securities Litigation ($144.5 million settlement); and In re Vesta Insurance Group, Inc. Securities Litigation ($79 million settlement). He has argued before the United States Supreme Court and in federal and state appellate courts. Mr Dubbs is a prolific writer and a frequent speaker on the subject of securities litigation. Prior to joining Labaton Sucharow, Mr Dubbs was Senior Vice President and Senior Litigation Counsel for Kidder, Peabody & Co. Incorporated.

### DUNCAN, James
Cleary Gottlieb Steen & Hamilton LLP, New York
212 225 2140
jduncan@cgsh.com
*Featured in Tax (New York)*
**Practice Areas:** U.S. and international tax law. Domestic and cross-border acquisitions; private equity transactions; restructurings and joint ventures; structural planning for multinational businesses; tax issues affecting financial services companies; derivatives and financial products.
**Professional Memberships:** New York Bar; International Fiscal Association.
**Career:** Joined firm, 1979; became Partner, 1987. London office, 1992-2008. LLM, New York University Law School (1984); JD, magna cum laude, Harvard Law School (1979); BA, cum laude, Yale University (1975).

### DUNN, Matthew S
Kramer Levin Naftalis & Frankel LLP, New York
212 715 9408
mdunn@kramerlevin.com
*Featured in Immigration (New York)*
**Practice Areas:** Matthew Dunn's Immigration Law Practice focuses on representing Fortune 100 companies, especially in the areas of banking, healthcare, hospitality, and advertising, as well as companies of all sizes facing an I-9 audit by Immigration and Customs Enforcement. He is Co-Chair of the NY State Bar Association's Immigration and Nationality Law Committee and a past Chair of the American Immigration Lawyers Association's NY Chapter. Mr Dunn appears on CNN, NBC, FOX and Channel 9 UPN and is quoted regularly in New York dailies. He is listed in The Best Lawyers in America, Chambers USA - America's Leading Lawyers for Business, The International Who's Who of Corporate

Immigration Lawyers for 2010-present, and New York Super Lawyers 2007-2012.
**Personal:** Received a JD Degree from Brooklyn Law School in 1993 and a BS Degree from Cornell University in 1990.

### DUNNE, Carey R
Davis Polk & Wardwell LLP, New York
212 450 4000
carey.dunne@davispolk.com
*Featured in Litigation (New York)*
**Practice Areas:** Chair of Davis Polk's Litigation Department and member of the firm's three-person Management Committee. Represents clients in a wide variety of criminal, civil and regulatory matters, including grand jury inquiries, internal investigations, enforcement actions by state and federal agencies, and complex commercial disputes. Most of the cases that he handles involve 'parallel proceedings': competing actions and investigations that must be defended simultaneously in multiple forums. Recent clients have included Intesa Sanpaolo Bank, Consolidated Edison, Hyundai Heavy Industries, Philip Morris International and Hyosung Corporation. President of the New York City Bar Association, 2012-2014.

### DUNNE, Dennis
Milbank, Tweed, Hadley & McCloy LLP, New York
212 530 5770
ddunne@milbank.com
*Featured in Bankruptcy/Restructuring (Nationwide), Bankruptcy/Restructuring (New York)*
See under Nationwide for profile.

### DYE, Alexander M
Willkie Farr & Gallagher LLP, New York
212 728 8642
adye@willkie.com
*Featured in Insurance (Nationwide), Insurance (New York)*
See under Nationwide for profile.

### ECKAS, Scott E
Bingham McCutchen LLP, New York
212 705 7743
scott.eckas@bingham.com
*Featured in Litigation (New York)*
**Practice Areas:** Securities and commercial litigator with extensive experience in matters involving complex debt transactions and bankruptcy-related issues. Uses financial knowledge and capabilities to address the risk management and dispute resolution needs of financial services and insurance firms. High-profile work includes representing senior investors in some of the first suits filed in distressed CDO cases, one of the first securities class action filings involving mortgage-backed securities and the defense of a financial institution in a precedent-setting public nuisance litigation.
**Personal:** Yale Law School, JD, 1989; University of Colorado at Boulder, BA, magna cum laude, 1986.

### ECKSTEIN, Kenneth H
Kramer Levin Naftalis & Frankel LLP, New York
212 715 9229
keckstein@kramerlevin.com
*Featured in Bankruptcy/Restructuring (Nationwide), Bankruptcy/Restructuring (New York)*
See under Nationwide for profile.

### EDELMAN, Scott
Milbank, Tweed, Hadley & McCloy LLP, New York
212 530 5149
sedelman@milbank.com
*Featured in Securities (Nationwide), Litigation (New York)*
See under Nationwide for profile.

### EDERER, Louis S
Arnold & Porter LLP, New York
212 715 1102
Louis.Ederer@aporter.com
*Featured in Intellectual Property (New York)*
**Practice Areas:** Louis Ederer focuses on intellectual property law, covering the areas of trademark, patent, and copyright litigation, prosecution, and counseling. He has particular experience in brand protection and enforcement, including anticounterfeiting matters, for prominent luxury goods and apparel companies. During his nearly 30 years of practice, he has been involved in precedent-setting cases expanding protection for trade dress and design marks, and the law governing recoveries of damages and profits in counterfeiting cases. Mr Ederer has extensive experience in sports and entertainment law, having negotiated agreements with entertainers and professional athletes, venue leases, sponsorships, management/operation agreements, and franchise agreements.

### EDLIN, Richard A
Greenberg Traurig, LLP, New York
212 801 6528
EdlinR@gtlaw.com
*Featured in Litigation (New York)*
**Practice Areas:** Chair, Regional Operations. Chair, New York Litigation Practice. Corporate and securities; securitization; venture capital; securities litigation; regulatory investigations.
**Professional Memberships:** Trustee, Carnegie Council on Ethics in International Affairs; Member, The Economic Club of New York; Board of Governors, Hackensack University Medical Center; Board of Trustees, New Jersey Seeds; Member, Judiciary Committee of the Federation Internationale du Sport Universitaire; Member, International Bar Association.
**Career:** Listed: Best Lawyers in America, 2005-13; Super Lawyers, 2006-12; Who's Who in American Law. Rated, AV® Preeminent™ 5.0 out of 5.
**Personal:** JD, Columbia University School of Law; BA, magna cum laude, Tufts University.

### EGAN, Peter
Nixon Peabody LLP, New York
516 832 7633
pegan@nixonpeabody.com
*Featured in Healthcare (New York)*

**Practice Areas:** Peter Egan's practice includes mergers and acquisitions and other complex business transactions, as well as regulatory and tax analysis for health care clients. He has extensive experience in capital raising, advising clients with respect to fraud and abuse laws, and regulatory issues such as the corporate practice of medicine. Peter's practice includes work on behalf of for-profit health care companies, medical centers, and nonprofit providers. He has considerable experience implementing and restructuring relationships between clients and their employed/affiliated physicians. Peter regularly advises hospitals on a broad spectrum of health care matters.

### EISENHOFER, Jay W
Grant & Eisenhofer PA, Wilmington
302 622 7050
jeisenhofer@gelaw.com
*Featured in Securities (Nationwide), Chancery (Delaware), Litigation (New York)*
See under Delaware for profile.

### EITEL, Mitchell S
Sullivan & Cromwell LLP, New York
212 558 4960
eitelm@sullcrom.com
*Featured in Financial Services Regulation (Nationwide), Corporate/M&A (New York)*
See under Nationwide for profile.

### ELIOPOULOS, Elias
McDermott Will & Emery LLP, New York
212 547 5412
eeliopoulos@mwe.com
*Featured in Real Estate (New York)*
**Practice Areas:** Based in the firm's New York Office. As a member of the Corporate Department and the Firm's Real Estate Practice Group, his primary focus is commercial real estate matters, including sales and acquisitions, financing and the structuring of partnerships for the purchase and operation of real estate assets.
**Personal:** Georgetown University Law Center, JD, (magna cum laude), 1994, Brown University, BA, 1989.

### ELKIN, Michael
Winston & Strawn LLP, New York
212 294 6729
melkin@winston.com
*Featured in Intellectual Property (New York), Media & Entertainment (New York)*
**Practice Areas:** Michael Elkin heads Winston's New York office and chairs the Copyright, Entertainment & Digital Media practice. He is widely recognized for litigating cutting-edge digital copyright issues. He recently was named a 2013 Law360 IP MVP. Mr Elkin has successfully handled a number of "bet the industry" cases that now define the contours of intellectual property law involving emerging technologies. He has represented traditional content owners and distributors, high technology companies, and ISPs in precedent setting disputes on complex intellectual property liability issues.
**Professional Memberships:** Copyright Society of the United States of America.
**Personal:** French-American Chamber of Commerce.

### ELLIN, Howard L
Skadden, Arps, Slate, Meagher & Flom LLP & Affiliates, New York
212 735 2438
howard.ellin@skadden.com
*Featured in Corporate/M&A (New York)*
**Practice Areas:** Howard L. Ellin is a global co-head of Skadden's Corporate Transactions and Mergers and Acquisitions practices. His practice involves a wide variety of transactions, including public and private company mergers and acquisitions, cross-border transactions, private equity and leveraged buyouts, corporate restructurings and financings, and general corporate advice. Mr Ellin also serves as Skadden's global hiring partner.
**Professional Memberships:** Member, Board of Trustees, Carnegie-Mellon University; Chairman, Compensation Committee, Carnegie-Mellon Board of Trustees; Member, Board of Trustees, The NALP Foundation .
**Career:** JD, Harvard Law School, 1988; BS, Carnegie-Mellon University, 1985.

### EMMERICH, Adam O
Wachtell, Lipton, Rosen & Katz, New York
212 403 1234
aoemmerich@wlrk.com
*Featured in Capital Markets (Nationwide), Corporate/M&A (New York)*
**Practice Areas:** Mergers and acquisitions and securities law matters. Practice includes a broad and varied representation of public and private corporations and other entities in a variety of industries throughout the United States and globally, in connection with mergers and acquisitions, divestitures, spin-offs, joint ventures, and financing transactions. Also has extensive expertise and experience in takeover defence and corporate governance issues. Among the many transactions in which he has taken a leading role are representing: Deutsche Telekom and T-Mobile USA in the agreed combination of T-Mobile and MetroPCS Communications at a $30 billion enterprise valuation; América Móvil, S.A.B. de C.V. in its acquisition of 21% of Telekom Austria AG; GlaxoSmithKline in its unsolicited offer and acquisition of Human Genome Sciences for US$3.6 billion; Sunrise Senior Living in connection with its sale to Health Care REIT, in transactions involving total investment by Health Care REIT of $4.3 billion; Deutsche Telekom in its agreed US$39 billion sale of T-Mobile to AT&T; AMB Property Corporation in its US$15 billion merger with ProLogis, to create a REIT with combined assets owned and under management of US$46 billion; Google in its participation in the Nortel patent auction; Grupo Prisa in its US$1.5 billion transaction with Liberty Acquisition Holdings Corp.; the board of directors of Wyeth in its US$68 billion acquisition by Pfizer; Simon Property Group in connection with its offer to acquire General Growth Properties for US$31 billion; Swarth Investments in the sale of its controlling interest in GVT (Holding) SA, Brazil to Vivendi in a transaction valuing GVT at US$4.2 billion; Alcoa in the US$14 billion investment in Rio Tinto by Chinalco and Alcoa; the US$4.7 bil-

lion acquisition of Constellation Energy by MidAmerican Energy; Iscar in its US$5 billion acquisition by Berkshire Hathaway, and Iscar in its US$1 billion acquisition of Tungaloy of Japan; Acciona in its 43.7 billion acquisition with Enel of Endesa and in relation to EON's prior proposed transaction; Tishman-Speyer and Lehman Brothers in their US$22.2 billion acquisition of Archstone-Smith; Vornado Realty Trust, Starwood Capital and Walton Street in their US$39 billion bid to acquire Equity Office Properties Trust; Man Group's acquisition of Refco' s regulated futures business through Refco' s bankruptcy proceeding; Taubman Centers', Dana Corporation' s and Circuit City's successful defences of hostile takeover attempts by Simon Property Group, ArvinMeritor and Highfields Capital, respectively; the acquisition by Wal-Mart of an interest in Seiyu in Japan and in transactions in Brazil, China, Puerto Rico and the UK; MacAndrews & Forbes in its recapitalisation of Revlon; Cable & Wireless in its exit from its US activities; the successful US $6 billion unsolicited offer by Public Storage for Shurgard; the Mills in its US $7.8 billion sale to a partnership of Simon Property Group and Farallon; the acquisition by Morgan Stanley and Onex of Town & Country; Lend Lease in the sale of its US businesses; MetLife in a variety of transactions; the acquisition by Raytheon of the defence business of Hughes Electronics from General Motors, and Raytheon's acquisition of Texas Instruments defence business and sale of its Amana appliance unit; the Cisneros family of Venezuela in transactions with Coca-Cola and Bell South; Seagram/Universal's acquisition of Viacom's interest in USA Network; and MCA's sale to Matsushita.
**Professional Memberships:** Co-Chair of the International Institute for the Study of Cross-Border Investment and M&A (a joint venture between the Guanghua School of Management at Peking University, the Pollack Center for Law and Business at New York University, and Judge Business School at the University of Cambridge); co-chair of the Advisory Board of New York University's REIT Center for the Study of Public Real Estate Companies and co-chair of the NYU Real Estate Institute's Annual Symposium on REITs since its inception; member of the Corporate Academic Bridge Group of the NYU Center for Law and Business; frequent contributor to the Harvard Law School Forum on Corporate Governance and Financial Regulation; member of the board of the American Friends of the Israel Museum and the Ramaz School; president of the Friends of the Israel Antiquities Authority and of the Friends of Rambam Medical Center; previously a member of the board of the Lawyers Alliance for New York, the Visiting Committee of the University of Chicago Law School and co-chair of the School's capital campaign, and co-chair of the Young Lawyers Division of the UJA-Federation in New York.
**Career:** Joined Wachtell, Lipton, Rosen & Katz in 1986 and named partner in 1991. BA, Swarthmore College and JD with honors, University of Chicago. Topics and comments editor of the

University of Chicago Law Review; Order of the Coif; Olin Fellow in law and economics. Law clerk to Hon. Abner J. Mikva, United States Court of Appeals for the District of Columbia Circuit. A frequent speaker at bar and professional conferences on topics relating to mergers and acquisitions, including at MIT's Sloan Convocation and on India's CNBC-TV18.
**Personal:** Born 15 December 1960. Married with three children.

### ENGROS JR, Charles E
Morgan, Lewis & Bockius LLP, New York
212 309 6880
cengros@morganlewis.com
*Featured in Media & Entertainment (New York), Corporate/M&A (New York)*
**Practice Areas:** Charles Engros focuses his practice on mergers and acquisitions and a range of other US domestic and international transactions, particularly in the media and information industries. He works with a large number of major domestic and non-US media companies as well as specialist investment banks and funds in that industry. He is also the managing partner of Morgan Lewis responsible for its international practice, the leader of the firm's business & finance practice globally and the managing partner of its New York office.
**Personal:** Harvard Law School, 1978, JD; Princeton University, 1975, BA

### EPSTEIN, Michael
Weil, Gotshal & Manges LLP, New York
212 310 8432
michael.epstein@weil.com
*Featured in Technology (New York)*
**Practice Areas:** Michael Epstein, Head of Weil's Technology & IP Transactions Practice, is a recognized expert in intellectual property and technology law. His practice involves transactions, litigation and counseling in all areas of IP and technology. His transactional work includes intellectual property acquisitions, technology transfer and licensing arrangements, outsourcing, joint ventures and other targeted alliances. His litigation experience includes misappropriation of trade secrets, breach of non-compete agreements, trademark infringement and false advertising. He is the author of 'Epstein on Intellectual Property' and co-editor of "Drafting License Agreements."
**Personal:** Lehigh University (BA, 1975); New York University School of Law (JD, 1979).

### FABER, Peter L
McDermott Will & Emery LLP, New York
212 547 5585
pfaber@mwe.com
*Featured in Tax (Nationwide), Tax (New York)*
**Practice Areas:** Focuses on corporate and business tax planning and controversy work at the federal, state and local levels. Advises corporations (both publicly and privately held), partnerships, and individuals on a wide variety of transactions, including mergers, acquisitions, and spin-offs. Extensive experience advising US and foreign corporations on state and local tax aspects of structuring US operations. Has litigated state tax issues around the country.

**Professional Memberships:** Chaired American Bar Association Section of Taxation.
**Personal:** Harvard Law School (LLB, cum laude); Swarthmore College (AB, high honors).

**FABIAN, James**
Nixon Peabody LLP, New York
212 940 3071
jfabian@nixonpeabody.com
*Featured in Healthcare (New York)*

**Practice Areas:** Practice includes the representation of academic medical centers, teaching hospitals, medical schools and hospital systems. Experience includes the handling of legal matters in structuring of physician/hospital relationships, faculty practice plans, hospital governance, affiliation arrangements, acquisitions, managed care, fraud and abuse, Medicare and Medicaid, professional and general liability insurance, medical staff membership, residency training programs, and interactions with regulatory agencies and accrediting bodies.
**Professional Memberships:** Member, American Health Lawyers Association.
**Career:** Partner since 1998; former Chair: Health Services Practice Group at Nixon Peabody 1998-2008.
**Personal:** Education: Oberlin College, BA; St John's University School of Law, JD.

**FACTOR, Jason R**
Cleary Gottlieb Steen & Hamilton LLP, New York
212 225 2694
jfactor@cgsh.com
*Featured in Tax (New York)*

**Practice Areas:** Tax matters, particularly formation of investment funds and other partnerships, acquisitions and divestitures, workouts and bankruptcy, partnership tax, and compensation of partners and employees.
**Professional Memberships:** Member of the Bar in New York.
**Career:** Joined firm, 1997; became partner, 2005. JD, magna cum laude, valedictorian, University of Michigan Law School (1995); BA, magna cum laude with highest honors in History, Phi Beta Kappa, Harvard College (1992).

**FADIL, Adeeb R**
Simpson Thacher & Bartlett LLP, New York
212 455 7070
afadil@stblaw.com
*Featured in Environment (New York)*

**Practice Areas:** Senior Counsel, Corporate Department, focusing on environmental matters. Advises clients about a wide range of environmental issues (including risk identification, diligence and allocation) in acquisitions, divestitures, loans, securities offerings, project financings, bankruptcies and restructurings. Industries include chemical, paper, steel, pharmaceuticals, and other manufacturing; electrical power generation and transmission, petroleum exploration, refining and distribution; mining; transportation; communications; food raising and processing; and real estate development. Also advises on environmental management, compliance, and dispute resolution.

**Career:** Joined the firm 1989; became Counsel 1994; Senior Counsel 2007.
**Personal:** BA, with highest distinction, University of Virginia (1980); JD, Yale Law School (1984).

**FAGEN, Leslie Gordon**
Paul, Weiss, Rifkind, Wharton & Garrison LLP, New York
212 373 3231
lfagen@paulweiss.com
*Featured in Litigation (New York)*

**Practice Areas:** Senior Partner in Litigation Department; Member of Management Committee. Extensive experience handling complex civil litigation matters for plaintiffs and defendants across legal disciplines. Strong record of wins and favorable settlements at trial and appellate levels in federal and state courts and in alternative dispute resolution proceedings. Representations include Citigroup, JPMorgan Chase, Bank of New York Mellon, Wachovia Corporation, Viacom, Paramount, CBS, AIG, Polo Ralph Lauren, Kohlberg & Co., Harbinger Capital and Calvin Klein, Inc. Director, Lawyers Committee for Civil Rights Under Law and a Trustee of The Kohlberg Foundation. Adjunct Lecturer at Columbia Law and Adjunct Professor at Brooklyn Law. American College of Trial Lawyers Fellow.

**FAKLER, Paul**
Arent Fox LLP, New York
212 457 5445
paul.fakler@arentfox.com
*Featured in Intellectual Property (New York)*

**Practice Areas:** Paul M Fakler is a partner at Arent Fox. His practice focuses on litigation and counseling in the fields of copyright, trademark, entertainment and computer/Internet law. He assists clients across a broad range of industries, including the music, motion picture, publishing, software development and Internet industries, and has litigated numerous cutting-edge cases involving digital music and the intersection of copyright and the Internet. Paul represents digital music services in royalty rate-setting litigation and also assists recording artists and other authors with respect to recapturing ownership of their copyrights pursuant to the transfer termination provisions of the Copyright Act.

**FARBER, Michael**
Davis Polk & Wardwell LLP, New York
212 450 4000
michael.farber@davispolk.com
*Featured in Tax (New York)*

**Practice Areas:** Member of Davis Polk's Tax Department. Has advised clients on a variety of domestic and international transactions. Regularly advises banks, investment banks and other financial institutions, including JPMorgan Chase, Goldman Sachs, UBS, Barclays, Deutsche Bank and Ally Bank, in connection with their financial instruments, derivatives and capital markets activities. Co-Chair of the Committee on Financial Instruments of the New York State Bar Association Tax Section.

**FARR, Lucy W**
Davis Polk & Wardwell LLP, New York
212 450 4000
lucy.farr@davispolk.com
*Featured in Tax (New York)*

**Practice Areas:** Member of Davis Polk's Tax Department. She concentrates in the taxation of corporate finance, derivatives and structured finance and on domestic and international tax planning for financial institutions. She has advised financial institutions and issuers in the development and execution of complex public and private financial products designed to achieve capital raising, hedging or other objectives. She has also done significant work representing investment funds and insurance companies.

**FARREN, Patricia**
Cahill Gordon & Reindel LLP, New York
pfarren@cahill.com
*Featured in Antitrust (New York)*

**Practice Areas:** Seasoned litigator of jury trials, bench trials, appeals, motion practice, discovery and alternate dispute resolution in complex antitrust cases. Senior advisor to multinational companies and trade associations with respect to antitrust compliance, merger analysis, trade association oversight, vertical integration, franchise law issues. Represents clients in governmental investigations and related proceedings.
**Personal:** Panel Chair for the Departmental Disciplinary Committee of the Appellate Division of the New York Supreme Court, First Department; Member, Executive Committee, Counsel of the NYCLA chapter of the American Inns of Court; JD, Fordham University School of Law; AB, Emmanuel College.

**FASTOW, Jay N**
Dickstein Shapiro LLP, New York
212 277 6767
fastowj@dicksteinshapiro.com
*Featured in Antitrust (New York)*

**Practice Areas:** Jay Fastow is co-leader of Dickstein Shapiro's Antitrust & Financial Services Practice. He has tried antitrust and financial services cases as well as a recent international arbitration in the pharmaceutical industry, and has argued appeals in numerous federal and state courts.
**Publications:** Mr Fastow is a member of the advisory board of BNA's Antitrust and Trade Regulation Report and a former adjunct lecturer in consumer finance law.
**Personal:** Brandeis University (BA, 1974); Yale Law School (JD, 1977).

**FELDMAN, David**
Gibson, Dunn & Crutcher LLP, New York
212 351 2366
dfeldman@gibsondunn.com
*Featured in Bankruptcy/Restructuring (New York)*

**Practice Areas:** Co-Chair, Business Restructuring and Reorganization Group. Twenty years' experience representing distressed investors, lenders, debtors, bondholders and creditor committees in bankruptcy cases, out-of-court restructurings, and distressed asset and debt transactions. Represented CCI (fka LDH Energy) in connection

with acquisition of Dynegy Roseton facility, Garrison Investments in connection with their chapter 11 acquisition of Church Street Health Management, Credit Suisse as First Lien Agent in connection with restructuring of Wastequip Inc., Luxor Capital in their chapter 11 acquisition of William Lyon Homes, and Law Debtenture as Indenture Trustee for the subordinated notes of AMBAC in connection with successful chapter 11.

**FELDMAN, Matthew A**
Willkie Farr & Gallagher LLP, New York
212 728 8651
mfeldman@wilkie.com
*Featured in Bankruptcy/Restructuring (Nationwide), Bankruptcy/Restructuring (New York)*

**Practice Areas:** Co-Chair, Business Reorganization and Restructuring Department; Member, firm's Executive Committee, Chair of the firm's Business Committee. Clients include debtors, creditors, investors, lenders, governmental agencies, and committees. Significantly involved in numerous complex chapter 11 cases and non-judicial restructurings, both US and cross-border. Former Chief Legal Advisor to Treasury Department's Task Force on Auto Industry, which helped develop groundbreaking legal proceedings to restructure and recapitalize General Motors Corporation and Chrysler under a compressed timeline set by President Obama. Recent accolades include Financial Times' "U.S. Innovative Lawyer of the Year 2010" and The American Lawyer's "Dealmaker of the Year." Is generally considered by clients to be among the best in the field in developing innovative solutions to complex, multi-dimensional problems.
**Personal:** JD, New York University School of Law, 1988. BA, (magna cum laude), Tufts University, 1985. See: http://www.willkie.com/Matthew_Feldman

**FERRELL, Kathleen**
Davis Polk & Wardwell LLP, New York
212 450 4000
kathleen.ferrell@davispolk.com
*Featured in Tax (New York)*

**Practice Areas:** Member of Davis Polk's Tax Department. Advises on domestic and cross-border mergers and acquisitions, spinoffs and restructurings, including recapitalizations and acquisitions of financial institutions. She also advises clients on joint ventures, bankruptcy restructurings, and tax legislative and administrative matters. She is a frequent speaker on M&A tax topics and an active member of the Executive Committee of the New York State Bar Association. She served in the Treasury Department's Office of Tax Policy from 1987 to 1990, in the Office of Tax Legislative Counsel and as the Special Assistant to the Assistant Secretary of Tax Policy.

**FETTERMAN, Daniel J**
Kasowitz, Benson, Torres & Friedman LLP, New York
212 506 1934
dfetterman@kasowitz.com
*Featured in Litigation (New York)*

**Practice Areas:** Former federal prosecutor and trial lawyer focusing on complex commercial litigation and white-collar criminal defense. Represents companies and individuals in high-stakes commercial litigation, grand jury investigations and enforcement proceedings.

**Career:** Assistant U.S. Attorney, Criminal Division (SDNY), recipient of Justice Department Director's Award for Superior Performance. Law clerk, Honorable Ellsworth A. Van Graafeiland, U.S. Court of Appeals for the Second Circuit.

**Publications:** Co-editor and co-author of first and second editions of white collar treatise, "Defending Corporations and Individuals in Government Investigations," West.

**Personal:** Washington & Lee University School of Law (JD, magna cum laude, Order of the Coif, 1987).

### FEUERSTEIN, Eric M
Gibson, Dunn & Crutcher LLP, New York
212 351 2323
efeuerstein@gibsondunn.com
*Featured in Real Estate (New York)*

**Practice Areas:** Mr Feuerstein's practice concentrates on acquisitions, joint ventures, and financings with recent extensive experience in restructuring securitized mortgage and mezzanine loans and sales and purchases of mortgage and mezzanine debt, distressed assets and interests in real estate companies.

**Personal:** JD, Benjamin Cardozo School of Law, 1995. BA, Cornell University, 1991, cum laude.

### FIELDS, Craig
Morrison & Foerster LLP, New York
212 468 8193
cfields@mofo.com
*Featured in Tax (New York)*

**Practice Areas:** Co-chair, firmwide Tax Department. Chair, firmwide State + Local Tax Group. His practice focuses on litigation and planning relating to state and local tax matters. He has been involved in controversies regarding state and local tax issues before the administrative and judicial systems of jurisdictions throughout the United States as well as having resolved hundreds of non-public record cases around the country. He has provided advice regarding the potential tax consequences of complex restructurings involving the corporation income (franchise) taxes, the sales and use taxes, and miscellaneous taxes of many jurisdictions.

**Career:** Recommended by Chambers USA 2012, Legal 500 US 2011-12. Named to State Tax Notes' 2011 "Top 10 Tax Lawyers" list.

**Publications:** His articles have appeared in numerous publications, including Tax Management's Multistate Tax Report, State Tax Notes, Research Institute of America's State and Local Taxes Weekly, the COSTState Tax Report, the Journal of State Taxation, the Journal of Multistate Taxation and Incentives, the Journal of New York Taxation, Interstate Tax Report, and the American Bar Association's The State & Local Tax Lawyer. He is a contributing author to "Doing Business in the United States: New York," a handbook in the Practical Law Company's "PLC Cross-border" series.

### FIFE, Lori R
Weil, Gotshal & Manges LLP, New York
212 310 8318
lori.fife@weil.com
*Featured in Bankruptcy/Restructuring (Nationwide), Bankruptcy/Restructuring (New York)*
See under Nationwide for profile.

### FILARDI, Edward V
Skadden, Arps, Slate, Meagher & Flom LLP & Affiliates, New York
212 735 3060
edward.filardi@skadden.com
*Featured in Intellectual Property (New York)*

**Practice Areas:** Heads Skadden's Patent Litigation practice; handles patent, trade secret, unfair competition and antitrust-related matters, specifically litigation and dispute resolution. Registered US patent attorney with jury trial and appellate experience; litigates patent and trademark cases for plaintiffs and defendants. Lead trial counsel in matters involving technologies, including lasers, biologics, medical devices, pharmaceuticals, telecommunications, and mechanics in federal and state courts, and before the International Trade Commission. Has been a AAA and WIPO arbitrator and a court-appointed neutral evaluator in intellectual property rights infringement matters.

**Career:** JD, New York Law School, 1968 (articles editor, Law Review); BS, Iona College, 1965.

### FINCH, Andrew
Paul, Weiss, Rifkind, Wharton & Garrison LLP, New York
212 373 3460
afinch@paulweiss.com
*Featured in Antitrust (New York)*

**Practice Areas:** Partner in the Litigation Department with extensive litigation experience, including trial and appellate matters, and civil and criminal government investigations. Finch focuses on Antitrust and previously served as Counsel to the Assistant Attorney General at the Antitrust Division of the US Department of Justice. Since joining Paul, Weiss, he has represented clients in investigations and civil litigation involving a wide range of antitrust issues, including alleged price fixing, market allocation, and monopolization. He also regularly counsels clients on the antitrust implications of business practices such as exclusive dealing, interlocking directorates, joint ventures, price discrimination, and resale price maintenance.

### FINKEL, Robert
WilmerHale, New York
212 295 6555
robert.finkel@wilmerhale.com
*Featured in Outsourcing (Nationwide), Technology (New York)*
See under Nationwide for profile.

### FINKELSTEIN, Stuart M
Skadden, Arps, Slate, Meagher & Flom LLP & Affiliates, New York
212 735 2841
Stuart.Finkelstein@skadden.com
*Featured in Tax (New York)*

**Practice Areas:** Head of Skadden's NY Tax Group. Represents clients, many in the financial services industry, on a wide range of tax matters, with emphasis on mergers, acquisitions and divestitures, including spin-offs, debt and equity offerings and joint ventures. Also devotes a significant amount of time to advising troubled companies, both in and out of bankruptcy.

**Professional Memberships:** Admitted in New York and Illinois.

**Career:** JD, The University of Michigan Law School, 1985 (cum laude); BBA, The University of Michigan School of Business Administration, 1982 (with distinction).

**Publications:** Has spoken nationwide and published several articles on corporate tax planning matters.

### FINZI, Roberto
Paul, Weiss, Rifkind, Wharton & Garrison LLP, New York
212 373 3311
rfinzi@paulweiss.com
*Featured in Litigation (New York)*

**Practice Areas:** Former federal prosecutor; partner, Litigation Department. Focuses on white collar criminal matters, regulatory enforcement proceedings, and internal investigations. Since his return from government service in 2006, has represented individuals and organizations in many recent law enforcement initiatives, including prosecutions and investigations involving stock options backdating, violations of the Foreign Corrupt Practices Act, insider trading, accounting fraud, health care fraud and criminal anti-trust issues. Practice includes representing clients in all aspects of government inquiries, from the investigation stage through trial, and regular counseling of public companies and general counsels on all areas of criminal and regulatory enforcement proceedings.

### FISCH, Peter E
Paul, Weiss, Rifkind, Wharton & Garrison LLP, New York
212 373 3424
pfisch@paulweiss.com
*Featured in Real Estate (New York)*

**Practice Areas:** Partner in the Real Estate Department. Regularly represents developers, entrepreneurial investors, institutional investors, lenders and other parties in all aspects of transactional real estate, including acquisitions and dispositions, joint ventures, conventional and securitized financings, workouts, sale-leasebacks and management contracts, involving a balance of office, retail, hotel, multifamily and industrial properties, as well as development rights and commercial condominium regimes. Recognized as a leading Real Estate lawyer by Legal 500. Contributor to the Real Estate Finance Journal and the National Law Journal.Co-authors a regular column on transactional real estate law for the New York Law Journal.

### FISHBEIN, Stephen
Shearman & Sterling LLP, New York
212 848 4424
sfishbein@shearman.com
*Featured in Litigation (New York)*

**Practice Areas:** Criminal defense, internal investigations, antitrust, and commercial litigation. Specialization in trials and arbitrations of criminal and complex commercial matters.

**Professional Memberships:** American College of Trial Lawyers. New York State Commercial Division Advisory Committee.

**Career:** Clerked for Hon. Jon O. Newman, United States Court of Appeals Second Circuit, 1987-1988. Assistant U.S. Attorney, Southern District of New York 1988-1993. Joined Shearman & Sterling in 1993.

**Personal:** Born 1961. Attended Dartmouth College (1983) and Yale Law School (1987). Lives in New York City with wife, Jennifer Baker a professor of English at New York University, and their three children.

### FISHMAN, Marshall
Freshfields Bruckhaus Deringer LLP, Washington, DC
202 777 4500
marshall.fishman@freshfields.com
*Featured in Litigation (New York)*

**Practice Areas:** Marshall, a leader in Freshfields' US securities and commercial litigation practice, is widely regarded as a preeminent securities and commercial litigator. For over 30 years, global financial institutions have relied on Marshall for their complex multi-jurisdictional securities and commercial litigation matters. Marshall has successfully tried numerous cases in courts and in arbitrations throughout the country, and regularly handles class actions involving securities offerings and derivatives products. Marshall is also a leading appellate advocate and clients frequently turn to Marshall for his appellate practice. He also regularly counsels clients in FINRA arbitrations and regulatory proceedings.

### FITZGERALD, Edmond
Davis Polk & Wardwell LLP, New York
212 450 4000
edmond.fitzgerald@davispolk.com
*Featured in Employee Benefits & Executive Compensation (Nationwide), Employee Benefits & Executive Compensation (New York)*
See under Nationwide for profile.

### FLASCHEN, Evan D
Bracewell & Giuliani LLP, Hartford
860 256 8537
evan.flaschen@bgllp.com
*Featured in Bankruptcy/Restructuring (Nationwide), Bankruptcy/Restructuring (New York)*

**Practice Areas:** Head of the firm's financial restructuring practice. His practice includes representation of many of the world's largest institutional investors, private investment funds, Wall Street desks, fund managers, leveraged finance participants and financial services companies in out-of-court restructurings, in-court proceedings and distressed M&A transactions, both domestically and internationally. He has represented note-

holder and bondholder groups, first and second lien lender groups, official creditors' committees or bank agents and syndicates in numerous high profile U.S. and international restructurings.
**Career:** Adjunct Professor, University of Connecticut School of Law.
**Personal:** JD, University of Connecticut School of Law, 1982; BA, Wesleyan University, 1979.

### FLAUM, Douglas H
Fried, Frank, Harris, Shriver & Jacobson LLP, New York
212 859 8259
Douglas.Flaum@FriedFrank.com
*Featured in Litigation (New York)*
**Practice Areas:** Vice Chair of Global Litigation Department. Represents clients in complex financial and business litigations, including securities cases under the 1933 and 1934 Acts; business tort, contract matters; antitrust disputes; issues of corporate governance, alleged breaches of fiduciary duties; contests for corporate control, special committee representations; real estate matters. Clients include ACA Financial Guaranty; AspenRe; Brookfield Properties; CA, Inc.; Chelsea Piers; CIT, Inc.; Costco Wholesale; Goldman Sachs & Co.; Malaysia Airlines; Merck, Inc.; Wells Fargo, Inc.
**Career:** Joined in 1986; became partner in 1993.
**Personal:** JD, Rutgers School of Law (1986); BA, Tufts University (1982).

### FLECK, Evan
Milbank, Tweed, Hadley & McCloy LLP, New York
212 530 5567
efleck@milbank.com
*Featured in Bankruptcy/Restructuring (New York)*
**Practice Areas:** Mr Fleck is a partner and a member of the Financial Restructuring Group. He has worked on a wide range of corporate restructurings and bankruptcies, representing debtors and creditors, including ad hoc groups and official committees, lenders and other parties in in-court and out-of-court restructurings. He has advised creditors in other distressed situations, and has focused on the insolvency aspects of derivative and structured financing transactions.

### FLEDER, Robert C
Paul, Weiss, Rifkind, Wharton & Garrison LLP, New York
212 373 3107
rfleder@paulweiss.com
*Featured in Employee Benefits & Executive Compensation (Nationwide), Employee Benefits & Executive Compensation (New York)*
**Practice Areas:** Chair, Employee Benefits and Executive Compensation Group. Extensive, sophisticated experience in legal, accounting, actuarial and human resource issues connected with implementation and operation of employee benefit plans and executive compensation arrangements. Has addressed issues that arise in connection with the assumption of (or failure to assume) benefit plans and other employee obligations in M&A transactions. Involved in defending and settling ERISA fiduciary claims involving private plaintiffs and the Department of Labor. Has

advised on ERISA fiduciary matters for investment funds and plan fiduciaries. Has provided support in corporate bankruptcies dealing with PBGC and multiemployer pension plan withdrawal liability.

### FLEISCHER JR, Arthur
Fried, Frank, Harris, Shriver & Jacobson LLP, New York
212 859 8120
Arthur.Fleischer@FriedFrank.com
*Featured in Corporate/M&A (New York)*
**Practice Areas:** Senior corporate of counsel. Practice encompasses negotiated and contested transactions for both acquirers and targets. Advises special committees formed to review buy-out proposals and corporate restructurings, and boards of directors on corporate governance. Has led the Firm's M&A practice for over 40 years.
**Career:** Joined in 1958; became partner in 1967. Co-author, Takeover Defense, a seminal treatise on hostile transactions and mergers and acquisitions; co-author, Board Games. Executive Assistant to Chairman of the US Securities and Exchange Commission (1961-1964).
**Personal:** LLB, Yale Law School (1958), Editor, Yale Law Journal, Order of the Coif; BA, Yale University (1953).

### FLORACK, James A
Davis Polk & Wardwell LLP, New York
212 450 4000
james.florack@davispolk.com
*Featured in Latin American Investment (New York), Banking & Finance (Nationwide)*
See under Nationwide for profile.

### FLUMENBAUM, Martin
Paul, Weiss, Rifkind, Wharton & Garrison LLP, New York
212 373 3191
mflumenbaum@paulweiss.com
*Featured in Litigation (New York)*
**Practice Areas:** Senior partner and former chair of the Litigation Department. Focuses practice on all aspects of commercial litigation, including securities enforcement proceedings, corporate internal investigations, private securities litigation and arbitration. Regularly advises U.S. and international clients on a broad range of litigation issues, with an emphasis on securities, mergers and acquisitions, commercial litigation, intellectual property, antitrust and white-collar criminal matters. Extensive experience representing board committees, institutions and individuals in connection with investigations, litigation and SEC enforcement proceedings. Recognized by Chambers USA and The Best Lawyers in America as one of the country's leading lawyers in Bet the Company Litigation, Commercial Litigation, White Collar Litigation and Securities Regulation/Enforcement. Fellow of the American College of Trial Lawyers.

### FLYNN, David P
Phillips Lytle LLP, Buffalo
716 847 5473
dflynn@phillipslytle.com
*Featured in Environment (New York)*

**Practice Areas:** Mr Flynn's practice is concentrated in the area's of environmental law and energy. With respect to environmental law, Mr Flynn concentrates on brownfield redevelopment, regulatory compliance and remediation of contaminated sediments. He was involved in the first successful conversion of a former industrial brownfield into a modern manufacturing facility in New York State. In addition, Mr Flynn advises clients on business development issues and the regulation of energy before state and federal authorities. He also advises clients on the development and siting of renewable energy projects and licensing of hydropower projects, and Marcellus formation natural gas opportunities.
**Professional Memberships:** American Bar Association, Section of Science and Technology, Section of Natural Resources, Energy and Environmental Law, Vice Chair-Brownfields, Site Remediation Committee and Energy Infrastructure and Siting Section, Vice-Chair 2009-10; New York State Bar Association, Environmental Law Section; Bar Association of Erie County; American Council on Renewable Energy (ACORE), Leadership Council; The National Brownfield Association, National Board of Directors and Chair, New York Chapter.
**Career:** Joined firm in 1987 and has been a Partner since 1997.
**Publications:** He has written and spoken extensively on environmental, energy and nanotechnology topics.
**Personal:** State University of New York at Buffalo School of Law, JD, cum laude, 1987 and State University of New York at Buffalo, BA, 1983.

### FODOR, Susanna S
Jones Day, New York
212 326 3476
ssfodor@jonesday.com
*Featured in Construction (New York), Real Estate (New York)*
**Practice Areas:** Experience in all aspects of real property transactions, including portfolio acquisitions/dispositions, development, restructurings, sale/leasebacks, public private partnerships, construction and financing of commercial, healthcare, infrastructure hospitality, industrial, energy, sports and other projects. Recognized globally both, as a leading real estate and a leading construction lawyer.
**Professional Memberships:** American College of Real Estate Lawyers; American College of Construction Lawyers; Real Estate Board of NY; American Arbitration Association's Large Complex Neutral Case Panel; Co-Chair of NY State Bar Association's Construction Law Committee.
**Publications:** Writes and lectures for the Practising Law Institute, American Arbitration Association, Cornet, NY State Bar Association and NYU.

### FOLB, Kerri
Kramer Levin Naftalis & Frankel LLP, New York
212 715 9208
kfolb@kramerlevin.com
*Featured in Environment (New York)*
**Practice Areas:** Ms Folb's practice concentrates in matters arising under federal, state and local environmental laws and regulations. Ms Folb litigates claims relating to the adequacy of environmental reviews under the New York State Environmental Quality Review Act and New York City's implementing regulations, as well as claims arising under state and federal hazardous substances laws and claims relating to land use laws and regulations. Ms Folb reviews and negotiates environmental agreements in connection with corporate and real estate transactions, and conducts environmental due diligence. Ms Folb also advises clients as to environmental impact review requirements, permitting and reporting obligations.

### FORTE, Joseph Philip
DLA Piper LLP (US), New York
212 335 4806
joseph.forte@dlapiper.com
*Featured in Real Estate (New York)*
**Practice Areas:** Real Estate: Finance
**Career:** He focuses on real estate finance with an emphasis on origination, structuring, workout and enforcement of commercial mortgage loans for portfolios, syndication and securitization. His experience includes permanent, bridge and construction mortgage lending; mezzanine finance; pari-passu and subordinate debt; co-lending and participation arrangements; loan sales and purchases; loan workouts, foreclosures and restructurings; and environmental risk management for lenders. He advises lenders and investors on mortgage banking, licensing, usury, federal preemption and investment authority as well as secondary mortgage and capital markets issues.
**Personal:** JD, St. John's University School of Law; BA, St. Francis College.

### FOX, David
Kirkland & Ellis LLP, New York
212 446 4994
david.fox@kirkland.com
*Featured in Corporate/M&A (New York)*
**Practice Areas:** David Fox is a partner in Kirkland's New York office and a member of Kirkland's Worldwide Executive Management Committee. He advises leading companies on multifaceted transactions, including many of the highest-profile deals of the last decade. He counsels senior management on crisis situations and governance matters and is recognized as a leading lawyer by many publications. He has represented clients including Avis Budget, Aztar Corp., BHP Billiton, Bristol-Myers Squibb, Clearwire, Duff & Phelps, Landmark Communications, Solutia, Sun Pharma, Reliance Industries, Teva Pharmaceutical, Travelport and Wyndham Worldwide.
**Career:** Hebrew University, Jerusalem (LLB, 1982; valedictorian, Law Review editorial board).

## FRAIDIN, Stephen
Kirkland & Ellis LLP, New York
212 446 4840
stephen.fraidin@kirkland.com
*Featured in Corporate/M&A (New York)*

**Practice Areas:** Mr Fraidin's practice focuses on the representation of major companies and investment groups, acquisitions, proxy contests and the representation of special committees and boards of directors regarding corporate governance and other matters. He recently represented 3G Capital in its agreement, along with Berkshire Hathaway, to buy HJ Heinz for $28 billion. Other clients include Community Health Systems, Raytheon Co, Pershing Square Capital, NRG Corp, PHH Corp. and Burger King.
**Personal:** Tufts University (BA, 1961); Yale University (LLB, 1964).

## FRANCHINI, John D.
Milbank, Tweed, Hadley & McCloy LLP, New York
212 530 5491
JFranchini@milbank.com
*Featured in Corporate/M&A (New York)*

**Practice Areas:** Mr Franchini is a partner and a member of the firm's Corporate, Private Equity, Power and Energy and Latin American Practice Groups. He has experience representing corporations, private equity sponsors, hedge funds and their portfolio companies in investment, acquisition, restructuring, disposition and fund-of-fund transactions. He also has significant transactional experience involving power generation (conventional and renewable) and transmission assets, as well as other energy and infrastructure projects.

## FRANKEL, Jamie
Arent Fox LLP, New York
212 457 5409
james.frankel@arentfox.com
*Featured in Construction (New York)*

**Practice Areas:** Jamie is the chairman of the Construction Group with a focus on front-end project structuring, transactional documentation, contentious dispute resolution, M&A structuring and business advisory services to the owner, architect, engineering, and construction communities on a domestic and international platform. Jamie was selected to counsel the first SPAC transaction within the A/E/C community and he and his team act as SEC counsel within that community. He was recognized by the Financial Times in 2012 for his "Innovation" within the legal community: a Mission – Ready Capital Improvement Solution created to finance, design and build facilities for nonprofit institutions.

## FRANKEL, Paul H
Morrison & Foerster LLP, New York
212 468 8000
pfrankel@mofo.com
*Featured in Tax (Nationwide), Tax (New York)*
See under Nationwide for profile.

## FRAZIER, James
Cadwalader, Wickersham & Taft LLP, New York
212 504 6963
james.frazier@cwt.com
*Featured in Employee Benefits & Executive Compensation (New York)*

**Practice Areas:** Concentrates in ERISA and employee benefits. Advises clients with respect to application of ERISA's fiduciary standards and prohibited transaction provisions to activities in transactional and regulatory matters. Routinely advises financial services firms with respect to structuring of investment vehicles and other investment products (including complex structured products and derivatives) offered to employee benefit plans and entities deemed to hold the assets of such plans and advises financial services firms in connection with the provision of services (e.g., investment management and brokerage services) to such plans or entities. Advises clients regarding issues that arise under ERISA and the Internal Revenue Code in the context of corporate transactions. Regularly represents clients before U.S. Department of Labor's Employee Benefits Security Administration.
**Personal:** JD, University of Arkansas School of Law (cum laude); LLM Taxation, Certificate Employee Benefits Law; LLM, Labor Law, Georgetown University Law Center (with distinction); BA, University of North Carolina.

## FREEDMAN, Jonathan L
Sidley Austin LLP, New York
212 839 6782
jfreedman@sidley.com
*Featured in Insurance (Nationwide), Insurance (New York)*
See under Nationwide for profile.

## FREEMAN, David
Gibbons P.C., New York
212 613 2079
DFreeman@gibbonslaw.com
*Featured in Environment (New York)*

**Practice Areas:** Environmental transactions, litigation and counseling.
**Career:** Mr Freeman, a Director in the Real Property & Environmental Department, represents buyers, sellers, and developers of contaminated properties and brownfields; parties engaged in hazardous waste cleanups and litigation; and clients with environmental due diligence, sustainability, climate change, and green buildings issues. He serves as President of the New York City Brownfield Partnership, Co-Chair of the New York State Bar Association Environmental Law Section's Hazardous Waste/Site Remediation Committee and Brownfield Task Force; and Vice Chair of the New York League of Conservation Voters Education Fund.

## FREIDUS, Harris B
Paul, Weiss, Rifkind, Wharton & Garrison LLP, New York
212 373 3064
hfreidus@paulweiss.com
*Featured in Real Estate (New York)*

**Practice Areas:** Partner in the Real Estate Department. Advises public and private companies, developers, entrepreneurial and institutional investors and lenders in all areas of commercial real estate, including developments, financings, joint ventures, sales and acquisitions, construction, leasing and restructurings. His expertise covers all real estate asset classes, with special expertise in gaming, hospitality and health care. Major transactions include gaming resort developments and financings in the United States, Macau and Singapore and many New York City acquisitions, joint ventures, developments and financings. Representative clients include Las Vegas Sands Corp.; CIM Group; Fortress; HCP Inc.; Fontainebleau Miami; and Douglaston Development/Levine Builders.

## FRIEDMAN, David M
Kasowitz, Benson, Torres & Friedman LLP, New York
212 506 1740
dfriedman@kasowitz.com
*Featured in Bankruptcy/Restructuring (Nationwide), Bankruptcy/Restructuring (New York)*
See under Nationwide for profile.

## FRIEDMAN, Dennis J
Gibson, Dunn & Crutcher LLP, New York
212 351 3900
dfriedman@gibsondunn.com
*Featured in Corporate/M&A (New York)*

**Practice Areas:** Widely recognized corporate lawyer with over 40 years in the mergers and acquisitions and corporate governance areas.
**Career:** In addition to a 35-year legal career. Mr Friedman was an investment banker at several major Wall Street firms where he was a senior M&A banker and also the head of a merchant banking group.
**Personal:** JD, Georgetown University Law Center, 1969, Articles Editor of the 'Georgetown Law Journal'. BS, Economics, University of Pennsylvania, Wharton School of Finance, 1966.

## FRIEDMAN, Gary D
Weil, Gotshal & Manges LLP, New York
212 310 8963
gary.friedman@weil.com
*Featured in Labor & Employment (New York)*

**Practice Areas:** Gary Friedman, long recognized as one of the leading employment lawyers in the US, focuses on all aspects of high-stakes, nationwide employment litigation, including complex class, collective, and mass actions, and restrictive covenant/trade secret cases. He has tried and argued cases and appeals in federal and state courts, and in numerous arbitral forums. His expertise includes: defending employers in employment discrimination and wage-and-hour class actions; prosecuting and defending restrictive covenant/trade secrets cases on behalf of employers; and advising corporate clients, and their boards, regarding complex and sensitive employment matters, including internal investigations, workplace consolidations, and e-discovery issues.
**Personal:** Duke University (BA, magna cum laude); Georgetown University Law Center (JD;

Law Review – The Tax Lawyer; Dean's List; American Jurisprudence Award).

## FRIEDMAN, Lawrence B
Cleary Gottlieb Steen & Hamilton LLP, New York
212 225 2840
lfriedman@cgsh.com
*Featured in Litigation (New York)*

**Practice Areas:** Focuses on international and domestic commercial litigation and arbitration, including in international banking, mergers and acquisitions, joint ventures, and license and distribution agreements, and intellectual property infringement and misappropriation disputes.
**Professional Memberships:** Member of the New York Bar; Inaugural chair, International Commercial Dispute Resolution Committee of the Association of the Bar of the City of New York.
**Career:** Joined firm, 1983; became Partner, 1991. JD, cum laude, Harvard Law School (1982); BS, summa cum laude, Georgetown University School of Foreign Service (1979). Law clerk to Hon. Charles P. Sifton, U.S. District Court, Eastern District of New York (1982-83).

## FRIEDMAN, Marc S
Dentons, New York
212 768 6767
marc.friedman@dentons.com
*Featured in Intellectual Property (New York)*

**Practice Areas:** Intellectual Property and Technology, and Litigation and Arbitration. Over 40 years of experience representing technology and other companies in intellectual property, technology and other business disputes.
**Professional Memberships:** International Technology Law Association (past-president) District of New Jersey Ad Hoc Patent Rules Committee
**Career:** Law Clerk to the Honorable Leonard I. Garth, US Court of Appeals for the Third Circuit.
**Publications:** A Vendor's Guide to Computer Contracting (Prentice-Hall) and more than 100 articles.
**Personal:** The George Washington University Law School, 1971 with honors, JD(Editor of Law Review and Trustee Scholar); The Johns Hopkins University, 1968

## FRIES, Richard S
Bingham McCutchen LLP, New York
212 705 7312
richard.fries@bingham.com
*Featured in Real Estate (Nationwide), Real Estate (New York)*
See under Nationwide for profile.

## FRIESTEDT, Matthew M
Sullivan & Cromwell LLP, New York
212 558 3370
friestedtm@sullcrom.com
*Featured in Employee Benefits & Executive Compensation (New York)*

**Practice Areas:** Experienced in handling all matters involving compensation of senior executives, including employment, bonus, change in control, equity compensation and severance arrangements. Extensive expertise in compensation matters arising in mergers, acquisitions, divestitures and leveraged buyouts. Also, regularly advises on governance, disclosure, compliance matters.

**Career:** Recent representations: Intercontinental Exchange merger with NYSE Euronext; ING sale of ING Direct to Capital One and acquisition of Aetna, Amgen acquisitions of BioVex and Micromet and Cablevision in acquisition of Brennan Communications.

**Personal:** New York University School of Law (LLM, 1997); Vanderbilt University School of Law (JD, 1996); University of the Pacific (BS, 1993).

## FRUMKIN, Joseph B

Sullivan & Cromwell LLP, New York
212 558 4101
frumkinj@sullcrom.com

*Featured in Energy & Natural Resources (Nationwide), Corporate/M&A (New York)*

See under Nationwide for profile.

## FUCHS, Nancy E

Kaye Scholer LLP, New York
212 836 8565
nancy.fuchs@kayescholer.com

*Featured in Corporate/M&A (New York)*

**Practice Areas:** Nancy Fuchs represents US and foreign corporate, strategic, private equity, financial and venture capital clients in acquisitions, divestitures, investments and joint venture transactions. She has extensive experience representing foreign companies in acquisition and investment transactions in the US, including those involving national security issues and Exon-Florio reviews before the Committee on Foreign Investment in the US (CFIUS). She serves as US general counsel for a flow control and material handling equipment services and distribution company and as a board member of its US holding company. She also has experience in acquisitions and restructuring of financially distressed companies.

## FUHRMAN, Steven M

Simpson Thacher & Bartlett LLP, New York
212 455 2000
sfuhrman@stblaw.com

*Featured in Bankruptcy/Restructuring (New York)*

**Practice Areas:** Bankruptcy Partner advising clients in connection with Chapter 11 cases, the largest ever filed Chapter 9 case, out-of-court restructurings, DIP and exit financings, acquisitions of distressed assets and companies, and the structuring of corporate and credit transactions. For more than 25 years, his focus has been the representation of agent banks, steering committees and lenders in the restructuring of large syndicated credit facilities extended to borrowers in a wide variety of businesses and industries.

**Career:** Joined the firm in January, 1987.

**Personal:** BA, summa cum laude, Tufts University (1982); JD, with honors, New York University School of Law (1985).

## GAINES, Andrew L

Paul, Weiss, Rifkind, Wharton & Garrison LLP, New York
212 373 3339
againes@paulweiss.com

*Featured in Employee Benefits & Executive Compensation (New York)*

**Practice Areas:** Mr Gaines is a partner in Paul, Weiss's executive compensation and benefits practice. He advises employers on all aspects of executive compensation and employee benefit plans and their treatment in corporate transactions and in bankruptcy. He also regularly assists investment fund sponsors on ERISA issues associated with the formation of private investment funds and the structuring of underlying investments. Additionally, he counsels employers and executives in the negotiation of employment and severance agreements and private equity clients in structuring complex equity compensation arrangements for management employees.

**Personal:** Hobart College (BA); Benjamin N Cardozo School of Law (JD).

## GALLAGHER, Patrick C

Kirkland & Ellis LLP, New York
212 446 4998
patrick.gallagher@kirkland.com

*Featured in Tax (New York)*

**Practice Areas:** Patrick Gallagher handles structuring and tax aspects of complex domestic and cross-border transactions, including acquisitions and divestitures, fund formation, financings and restructurings, for private equity and other clients.

**Professional Memberships:** New York State Bar Association, Tax Section: Chair (2007), Executive Committee (since 1993); American Bar Association, Tax Section.

**Career:** Partner at Kirkland since 1991.

**Personal:** Harvard Law School, JD, 1985; University of Chicago, MA, 1977; Pomona College, BA, 1974.

## GALVIS, Sergio J

Sullivan & Cromwell LLP, New York
212 558 4740
galviss@sullcrom.com

*Featured in Latin American Investment (New York), Projects (Nationwide)*

**Career:** Partner since 1991. M&A, JVs, projects, securities, private equity, restructuring. Head, Latin America/Spain practices; Global Recruiting. Representations: Bancolombia's pending HSBC (Panama) acquisition; Ally Financial dispositions; BBVA Latin American pensions sales; UnitedHealth/Amil; LAN-TAM combination; Sierra Gorda project in Chile.

**Publications:** Partner since 1991. M&A, JVs, projects, securities, private equity, restructuring. Head, Latin America/Spain practices; Global Recruiting. Representations: Bancolombia's pending HSBC (Panama) acquisition; Ally Financial dispositions; BBVA Latin American pensions sales; UnitedHealth/Amil; LAN-TAM combination; Sierra Gorda project in Chile.

**Personal:** Harvard Law (JD, 1983); William and Mary (BA, 1980). Clerk, Hon. Lawrence Pierce, US Second Circuit. Languages: Spanish, Portuguese.

## GARCIADIAZ, Manuel

Davis Polk & Wardwell LLP, New York
21 450 4000
manuel.garciadiaz@davispolk.com

*Featured in Latin American Investment (New York)*

**Practice Areas:** Partner in Davis Polk's Corporate Department. Regularly advises US and non-US corporations and leading investment banks on a broad range of capital markets transactions (including initial public offerings, follow-on offerings, spin-offs, investment grade and high-yield debt offerings, exchange offers and other securities underwriting), mergers and acquisitions transactions, structured and project financings and debt restructurings, primarily in Latin America. Has represented BofA Merrill Lynch, Credit Suisse, Itau BBA, JPMorgan, Morgan Stanley and other corporate clients in international corporate finance transactions.

## GARRITY, James

Morgan, Lewis & Bockius LLP, New York
212 309 6220
jgarrity@morganlewis.com

*Featured in Bankruptcy/Restructuring (New York)*

**Practice Areas:** James L. Garrity, Jr. is a partner in the Business and Finance practice at Morgan Lewis & Bockius LLP, resident in its New York office where he leads the firm's bankruptcy and restructuring practice. His practice includes representing debtors, creditors and court-appointed fiduciaries in Chapter 11 and cross-border cases. He previously served as a judge in the U.S. Bankruptcy Court for the Southern District of New York and as an Assistant U.S. Attorney in the Southern District of New York.

## GARTNER, Gary J

Kaye Scholer LLP, New York
212 836 8358
gary.gartner@kayescholer.com

*Featured in Tax (New York)*

**Practice Areas:** Gary Gartner is a member of the Executive Committee, Chair of the Tax Department and Co-Chair of the Canada Group at Kaye Scholer. He counsels clients on US and foreign tax consequences of transactions, restructurings and securities offerings. Gary helps clients navigate complex cross-border issues related to acquisitions, divestitures, joint ventures and financing transactions, and provides ongoing strategic and global tax planning advice to a range of US and overseas clients. He has written and lectured extensively on international tax topics and previously served as the head of the international tax division at a major accounting firm.

## GELBER, Avrohom

Clifford Chance US LLP, New York
212 878 3108
avrohom.gelber@cliffordchance.com

*Featured in Tax (New York)*

**Practice Areas:** Focuses on the US tax aspects of capital markets and finance transactions. Has advised both issuers and underwriters in connection with the formation and offerings of mutual and other fund issuers. Also provides tax and structuring advice for a wide variety of international financial and business transactions, includ-

ing corporate acquisitions and restructurings, and derivative financial instruments.

**Career:** Columbia University, JD, 1996, Harlan Fiske Stone Scholar; Yeshiva University, BA and MS, summa cum laude, 1991.

## GELBLUM, Seth D

Loeb & Loeb LLP, New York
212 407 4931
sgelblum@loeb.com

*Featured in Media & Entertainment (New York)*

**Practice Areas:** Represents producers, theatre owners, motion picture studios, directors, playwrights, composers, performers, music publishers, designers, investors, not-for-profit theatres and licensing agencies for Broadway/Off-Broadway, touring and foreign live stage productions. In feature film, documentary film and television, represents directors, writers and producers. Provides contractual, IP and financing/securities services in all of foregoing areas.

**Professional Memberships:** Chairman of the Board - New Dramatists.

**Career:** Partner at Loeb since 1998. Theatre Chair.

**Publications:** Lecturer at Columbia Law School, Yale University School of Drama, Commercial Theatre Institute.

**Personal:** Georgetown University Law Center (JD, 1982); Wesleyan University (BA, 1975).

## GELFAND, David

Milbank, Tweed, Hadley & McCloy LLP, New York
212 530 5520
DGelfand@milbank.com

*Featured in Litigation (New York)*

**Practice Areas:** Mr Gelfand is a partner and a member of the Litigation & Arbitration Group since 1996. He served from 2001 through 2009 as the Practice Group Leader for the group. Mr Gelfand's practice is highly diversified, with a concentration in complex civil and corporate litigation. He regularly represents financial institutions and corporations in class actions, securities and bankruptcy litigation cases. He has tried jury and non-jury trials in state and federal courts throughout the country and has extensive experience representing clients in fiduciary and estate litigation.

## GELLER, Marcy

Simpson Thacher & Bartlett LLP, New York
212 455 3543
mgeller@stblaw.com

*Featured in Tax (New York)*

**Practice Areas:** Tax Partner concentrating on financial products and derivatives, mergers and acquisitions, and the formation of and acquisitions by investment funds (including private equity and real estate opportunity funds). Advises on tax matters for, among others, the Firm's private equity clients and investment banking clients.

**Professional Memberships:** Member of Executive Committee of NYSBA Tax Section.

**Personal:** University of Pennsylvania (BS, magna cum laude, 1994); New York University School of Law (JD, magna cum laude, 1997; LLM 2000).

## GELSTON, Philip A
Cravath, Swaine & Moore LLP, New York
212 474 1548
pgelston@cravath.com
*Featured in Corporate/M&A (New York)*

**Practice Areas:** Philip A. Gelston is a partner in Cravath's Corporate Department and serves as the Chair of its Mergers and Acquisitions practice. He has extensive experience in mergers and acquisitions, joint ventures and general corporate counseling. Mr Gelston's practice encompasses complicated negotiated transactions, hostile transactions (both offense and defense), cross-border transactions and advising boards and senior executives. **Personal:** Harvard Law School (JD, magna cum laude, 1977; Sears Prize; Supreme Court Note Editor, Law Review); Harvard College (AB, cum laude, 1974; Phi Beta Kappa). For more information: http://www.cravath.com/pgelston

## GENSER, Andrew M
Kirkland & Ellis LLP, New York
212 446 4809
andrew.genser@kirkland.com
*Featured in Litigation (New York)*

**Practice Areas:** Andrew is a partner in Kirkland's New York office in the white-collar defense and litigation practice groups. A former federal prosecutor, he defends corporations, financial institutions, hedge funds and individual clients in a broad array of government investigations and prosecutions, including tax fraud, healthcare fraud, FCPA violations, insider trading, accounting fraud and other securities law violations, environmental crimes, money-laundering, and unfair and deceptive trade practices. He conducts internal investigations and advises corporations on a variety of governance and compliance issues. **Personal:** Harvard Law School, JD, cum laude, 1994; Cornell University, BA, summa cum laude, Phi Beta Kappa, 1991.

## GIDDENS, James W
Hughes Hubbard & Reed LLP, New York
212 837 6810
kiplok@hugheshubbard.com
*Featured in Bankruptcy/Restructuring (Nationwide); Bankruptcy/Restructuring (New York)*

**Practice Areas:** Trustee for the liquidation of MF Global, Inc. Trustee for the liquidation of Lehman Brothers, Inc. Created the Corporate Reorganization Group of Hughes Hubbard & Reed LLP. Served as Trustee for various SIPC broker-dealer liquidations. Served as SEC Restitution Fund Administrator for A.R. Baron & Co., Inc. Emphasis on acquisitions and sales of financially distressed entities and representation of major creditor constituencies. Various articles and lecturer on insolvency matters. SPIC Modernization Task Force, 2012. **Professional Memberships:** American Bankruptcy Institute, American Bar Association, Association of the Bar of City of New York, International Bar Association and INSOL. **Career:** Chair, Corporate Reorganization Group, Hughes Hubbard & Reed LLP. Partner since 1974.

**Personal:** Dartmouth College, BA; Yale Law School, LLB; Board of Overseers, Hopkins Center (Dartmouth College); National Advisory Council for Austin Riggs Hospital, Board of Trustees, Williamstown Theater Festival.

## GIEGERICH, Thomas
McDermott Will & Emery LLP, New York
212 547 5335
tgiegerich@mwe.com
*Featured in Tax (New York)*

**Practice Areas:** Member of firm's tax department, head of tax in New York office; advises domestic and international clients on wide range of corporate tax planning and transactional matters, including taxable and tax-free mergers, acquisitions and divestitures, corporate restructurings, and cross-border joint ventures. **Professional Memberships:** New York and United States Tax Court; member, Tax Section American Bar Association, Tax Section New York State Bar Association. **Personal:** Duke University School of Law, JD (with distinction, Order of the Coif), 1980; New York University School of Law, LLM, 1986; Fordham University, BA (summa cum laude in cursu honorum, Phi Beta Kappa), 1977.

## GIETZ, Raymond
Weil, Gotshal & Manges LLP, New York
212 310 8702
raymond.gietz@weil.com
*Featured in Corporate/M&A (New York)*

**Practice Areas:** Mr Gietz regularly represents buyers, sellers, boards of directors, committees of independent directors and financial advisors in connection with complex mergers and acquisitions transactions, including public and private companies, LBOs, asset sales and joint ventures. He also regularly advises boards of directors and committees on defense, corporate governance and other matters. His representations involve a range of industries, including healthcare, financial services, steel and defense. Current clients include Eli Lilly, General Electric, Gentiva Health Services, AK Steel, GECC, Franklin Resources and Magellan Health Services. **Personal:** Columbia College (BA, 1978); Columbia University School of Law (JD, 1981).

## GILMAN, Charles A
Cahill Gordon & Reindel LLP, New York
212 701 3403
cgilman@cahill.com
*Featured in Litigation (New York)*

**Practice Areas:** National trial and appellate practice and extensive experience leading complex MDL, often involving parallel federal and state class actions and governmental investigations. Managed committee investigations concerning corporate fraud and mismanagement, insider trading, foreign payments and accounting restatements. In 2007-08, counseled investment banks concerning over $200 billion in troubled credit transactions. **Professional Memberships:** Court-Appointed Mediation Panels of U.S. District Courts for the Southern and Eastern Districts of New York.

Commercial Panel Arbitrator of American Arbitration Association. **Personal:** Co-Administrative Partner. Wharton School of the University of Pennsylvania, BS, 1971, with honors; University of Virginia School of Law, JD, 1974.

## GINSBERG, Paul D
Paul, Weiss, Rifkind, Wharton & Garrison LLP, New York
212 373 3131
pginsberg@paulweiss.com
*Featured in Corporate/M&A (New York)*

**Practice Areas:** Partner, Corporate Department, and co-head of the firm's Global Mergers and Acquisitions Group. Focuses practice on mergers and acquisitions, private equity investments and corporate finance. Recognized as a leading lawyer in Legal 500 for mergers, acquisitions and buyouts (mega-deals $5b+) and private equity and in Best Lawyers in America for mergers & acquisitions and corporate law. Named by The American Lawyer as a "Dealmaker of the Year" for advising Triarc Companies, Inc. in its acquisition of Wendy's International, Inc. and a "Dealmaker of the Week" for advising General Atlantic LLC in its acquisition of First Republic Bank.

## GIUFFRA JR, Robert J
Sullivan & Cromwell LLP, New York
212 558 3121
giuffrar@sullcrom.com
*Featured in Securities (Nationwide), Litigation (New York)*

See under Nationwide for profile.

## GLASER, Steven
Skadden, Arps, Slate, Meagher & Flom LLP & Affiliates, New York
212 735 2465
steven.glaser@skadden.com
*Featured in Litigation (New York)*

**Practice Areas:** Mr Glaser represents corporations, officers, directors and employees in a wide variety of criminal and civil enforcement matters. He has extensive trial and appellate experience, and has handled complex white collar matters in both federal and state courts, and in connection with investigations by the DOJ, SEC, and various state attorneys general's and district attorneys' offices. He handles matters including securities and commodities fraud, FCPA violations, price-fixing, health care fraud and money laundering offenses. **Career:** JD, Harvard Law School, 1995 (cum laude); BA, Cornell University, 1992 (cum laude, Phi Beta Kappa).

## GLAZER, Daniel C
Fried, Frank, Harris, Shriver & Jacobson LLP, New York
212 859 8674
daniel.glazer@friedfrank.com
*Featured in Technology (New York)*

**Practice Areas:** Corporate partner, co-head of Firm's technology transactions practice. Focuses on complex domestic and cross-border IP/IT transactions, including licensing, outsourcing, and technology services arrangements. Advises on IP, technology and commercial issues for clients

ranging from technology start-ups (particularly in New York and the UK) to Fortune 50 corporations. Also handles IP/IT aspects of mergers and acquisitions, joint ventures, and other complex corporate transactions. **Career:** Joined as partner in 2012; Senior Editor of The Trademark Reporter and Member of Intellectual Property Magazine's advisory board. **Personal:** JD, Harvard Law School (1998); AB, summa cum laude, Dartmouth College (1995).

## GLAZER, Dennis
Davis Polk & Wardwell LLP, New York
212 450 4900
dennis.glazer@davispolk.com
*Featured in Litigation (New York)*

**Practice Areas:** Member of Davis Polk's Litigation Department. Represents clients in securities litigation, major commercial matters, mergers and acquisitions and related litigation. Mr Glazer litigates cases throughout the country relating to significant commercial disputes and merger and acquisition transactions (both friendly and hostile). Also spends a significant amount of time advising boards of directors and special committees and representing clients in regulatory matters brought by the SEC, NASD, NYSE and other regulatory agencies. Representative clients in publicly disclosed matters have included J.P. Morgan, CVS, WellCare Health Plans, Paul Hastings, Westar Energy, ImClone Systems and E*Trade.

## GLIATTA, Stephen
Kaye Scholer LLP, New York
212 836 8618
steve.gliatta@kayescholer.com
*Featured in Real Estate (New York)*

**Practice Areas:** Stephen Gliatta, Co-Chair of both the Executive Committee and the firm's Real Estate Department, represents banks, investment banks and other institutional lenders in the origination of first mortgage debt, mezzanine loans and preferred equity investments. Steve also represents senior lenders, mezzanine lenders, servicers and special servicers in the workout and restructuring of large commercial real estate loans with respect to all commercial property types. In addition, he regularly represents opportunity funds in the purchase of whole loans, B-notes and loan participation interests and in joint ventures with operating partners in the acquisition and financing of real estate projects.

## GODMAN, James
Kramer Levin Naftalis & Frankel LLP, New York
212 715 9466
jgodman@kramerlevin.com
*Featured in Real Estate (New York)*

**Practice Areas:** Mr Godman's practice focuses primarily on real estate financings, development, joint ventures, sales and acquisitions, and leasing transactions. He represents real estate lenders, developers, investors, sellers, purchasers, borrowers, landlords and tenants. Mr Godman has been recognized by Best Lawyers, New York Super Lawyers, and Legal 500 U.S.

**GOFFMAN, Jay M**
Skadden, Arps, Slate, Meagher & Flom LLP
& Affiliates, New York
212 735 2120
Jay.Goffman@skadden.com
*Featured in Bankruptcy/Restructuring (Nationwide),*
*Bankruptcy/Restructuring (New York)*
See under Nationwide for profile.

**GOLDBERG, Jerrold F**
Greenberg Traurig, LLP, New York
212 801 9209
GoldbergJ@gtlaw.com
*Featured in Labor & Employment (New York)*
**Practice Areas:** Labor and employment - management; real estate operations; hospitality; ADA, Accessibility, Building and Life Safety Codes; retail; sports facilities and entertainment venues.
**Career:** Selected: Best Lawyers in America, 2012-13; Legal Elite - Real Estate, AVENUE magazine, April 2011; Super Lawyers magazine, 2006-07, 2011-12; a Law360 2011 Employment Practice Group of the Year. Rated, AV® Preeminent™ 5.0 out of 5.
**Personal:** JD, New York University School of Law, 1979; BS, School of Industrial and Labor Relations, Cornell University, 1976.

**GOLDBERG, Louis L**
Davis Polk & Wardwell LLP, New York
212 450 4000
louis.goldberg@davispolk.com
*Featured in Corporate/M&A (New York)*
**Practice Areas:** Member of Davis Polk's Corporate Department, practicing in the Mergers and Acquisitions Group. Practice focuses on public and private mergers and acquisitions, private equity transactions, corporate crisis situations, board and corporate governance advice, joint ventures, spinoffs, and restructurings and recapitalisations.

**GOLDBERG, Steven H**
Baker & Hostetler LLP, New York
212 589 4219
sgoldberg@bakerlaw.com
*Featured in Corporate/M&A (New York)*
**Career:** Co-Chair of BakerHostetler's nationwide Transactions team, Steven H Goldberg practices in M&A, private equity, joint ventures and strategic investments. Steven routinely represents publicly traded and privately held companies on transactional matters, representing U.S. and non- U.S. companies in their global M&A matters. His representations include matters in the U.S., EU, Canada and Asia (including India). He is also experienced in corporate governance and securities matters and equity and debt restructurings. Steven was recognized by Legal500 as among the top 10 lawyers in mid-market transactions and his work was named the 2012 Media Deal of the Year by M&A Advisor.

**GOLDEN, Arthur F**
Davis Polk & Wardwell LLP, New York
212 450 4000
arthur.golden@davispolk.com
*Featured in Antitrust (New York)*
**Practice Areas:** Partner and a Member of the Management Committee for nine years. Leads the firm's practice in competition and antitrust matters, including domestic and international mergers and acquisitions, counselling and litigation. Regularly represents large multinational companies in negotiated and contested acquisition-related transactions, governance matters, civil and criminal antitrust matters and litigation. Lead Counsel for Roche in its current hostile tender offer for Illumina and acquisition of Genentech and in its contested takeover of Ventana, Gillette in its acquisition by Procter & Gamble and Comcast in its acquisition of AT&T Broadband. One of the two lead negotiators for the US tobacco industry in the effort to resolve, through legislation and settlements, the legal issues facing that industry. Represented Freeport in the criminal investigation of the copper concentrate industry and Hoffmann-LaRoche in the vitamin cartel litigation and was counsel of record for the defense group in the Supreme Court. Is currently a Director and member of the Executive Committee of Emerson Electric, a Trustee of Rensselaer and has been on the board of several other NYSE companies.

**GOLDEN, Daniel H**
Akin Gump Strauss Hauer & Feld LLP, New York
212 872 8010
dgolden@akingump.com
*Featured in Bankruptcy/Restructuring (Nationwide),*
*Bankruptcy/Restructuring (New York)*
See under Nationwide for profile.

**GOLDFEIN, Shepard**
Skadden, Arps, Slate, Meagher & Flom LLP
& Affiliates, New York
212 735 3610
Shepard.Goldfein@skadden.com
*Featured in Antitrust (New York), Sports Law*
*(Nationwide)*
See under Nationwide for profile.

**GOLDMAN, Andrew N**
WilmerHale, New York
212 230 8836
andrew.goldman@wilmerhale.com
*Featured in Bankruptcy/Restructuring (New York)*
**Practice Areas:** Mr Goldman is vice chair of WilmerHale's Bankruptcy and Financial Restructuring Practice. His practice is broad and includes representation of large public company debtors, creditors' committees, DIP lenders, acquirers and individual institutional creditors, in both out-of-court workouts and formal restructuring processes (both domestic and of the cross-border type).
**Professional Memberships:** 2010 and 2011 Editorial Advisory Board for Bankruptcy Law360; Member of the Brooklyn Law School Zaretsky Roundtable; Guest lecturer at Brooklyn Law School.
**Personal:** JD, Brooklyn Law School, 1992; BS, The Wharton School of Business at the University of Pennsylvania, 1989.

**GOLDNER, Bruce J**
Skadden, Arps, Slate, Meagher & Flom LLP
& Affiliates, New York
212 735 2972
bruce.goldner@skadden.com
*Featured in Intellectual Property (New York)*
**Practice Areas:** Bruce Goldner is co-head of Skadden's Intellectual Property and Technology Group. His principal areas of concentration include transactions, licensing and counseling involving brands, content, technology, social media, software, and persona rights, and pharmaceutical, biotechnology and medical device products. He also oversees Skadden's U.S. and international trademark clearance and prosecution practice.
**Career:** JD, University of Michigan Law School, 1992 (cum laude; articles editor, Michigan Law Review); BA, Amherst College, 1987 (summa cum laude; Phi Beta Kappa).

**GOLDRING, Stuart J**
Weil, Gotshal & Manges LLP, New York
212 310 8312
stuart.goldring@weil.com
*Featured in Tax (New York)*
**Practice Areas:** Stuart Goldring is a nationally recognized authority on federal income tax matters involving financially troubled companies. He has extensive experience advising debtors, creditors, potential acquirers, and investors in troubled companies. Mr Goldring also regularly advises on the structuring of acquisitions, dispositions, and other transactions involving corporations and multi-corporate groups. He co-authored the treatise Tax Planning for Troubled Corporations (2013 ed. CCH) and is an adjunct professor at NYU School of Law.
**Personal:** University of Michigan (BBA, 1979); University of Michigan Law School (JD, 1982); New York University School of Law (LLM, 1983).

**GOLDSMITH, Willis J**
Jones Day, New York
212 326 3649
wgoldsmith@jonesday.com
*Featured in Labor & Employment (New York)*
**Practice Areas:** Headed the firm's Labor and Employment Practice from 1991 through mid-2006 and the firm's New York Office from 2008 through 2012. Represents management in all phases of labor and employment law. Identified as one of the top labor and employment lawyers in the US in a large number of publications and surveys.
**Professional Memberships:** Fellow of the College of Labor and Employment Lawyers. Adviser, American Law Institute (Restatement Third, Employment Law). Advisory Board NYU School of Law Center for Labor and Employment Law. Admitted, New York and District of Columbia.
**Career:** Partner since 1983.

**GOLDSTEIN, Aimee H**
Simpson Thacher & Bartlett LLP, New York
212 455 7681
agoldstein@stblaw.com
*Featured in Antitrust (New York)*

**Practice Areas:** Antitrust litigation, complex transactions and investigations. Representations: HCA in a class action regarding nurse wage suppression; CSL in class action alleging collusion in plasma products; CoStar's proposed acquisition of LoopNet; Tyco/ADT's acquisition of Broadview Security; HCA's sale of Palmyra to Georgia Hospital Authority and acquisitions of Heart Hospital of Austin and Texsan Heart; Tops Markets/Penn Traffic supermarkets; Covidien/Triad Isotopes; Sirius/XM; Smithfield's sale of Beef Group to JBS Swift and acquisition of Premium Standard Farms; PanAmSat/Intelsat; Adidas/Reebok; Abbott's acquisition of divested assets from Guidant/ Boston Scientific.
**Personal:** BA, summa cum laude, Emory University (1988); JD, Harvard Law School (1991).

**GOLDSTEIN, Howard W**
Fried, Frank, Harris, Shriver & Jacobson LLP, New York
212 859 8502
Howard.Goldstein@FriedFrank.com
*Featured in Litigation (New York)*
**Practice Areas:** Litigation partner. Focuses on white-collar criminal defense, internal investigations, RICO and fraud-related civil litigations. Represents individuals, corporations and labor unions in criminal and civil RICO proceedings and lawsuits throughout the US. Has handled criminal and civil securities investigations, litigations, criminal customs, tax fraud and antitrust matters.
**Career:** Joined as partner in 1990; Assistant US Attorney in the Southern District of New York (1976-1980).
**Personal:** JD, New York University School of Law (1973), graduated first in class, member, Law Review, Order of the Coif, Arthur Garfield Hays Civil Liberties Fellow; BA, Northwestern University (1970), with distinction, Phi Beta Kappa.

**GOLDSTEIN, Jeremy**
Wachtell, Lipton, Rosen & Katz, New York
212 403 1305
JLGoldstein@wlrk.com
*Featured in Employee Benefits & Executive*
*Compensation (New York)*
**Practice Areas:** Advises companies on complex issues involving executive compensation and corporate governance with a particular emphasis on such issues as they arise in the context of transformative corporate events and sensitive situations.
**Professional Memberships:** Chair of the Mergers and Acquisition Subcommittee of the Executive Compensation Committee of the American Bar Association Business Section and member of the New York State Bar Association. Also a member of the Professional Advisory Board of the NYU Journal of Law and Business, the New Leadership Council of Make-A-Wish Foundation® of Metro New York and a member of the Board of Directors of Fountain House, a charity dedicated to the recovery of men and women with mental illness.

**Career:** Joined Wachtell, Lipton, Rosen & Katz in 2000 and has been a partner since 2008. Mr Goldstein has been involved in many of the largest corporate transactions of the past decade, including the pending acquisition of NYSE by Intercontinental Exchange, the acquisition of Goodrich by United Technologies; Duke Energy/Progress Energy; Sanofi-Aventis/Genzyme; Merck/Schering Plough Corporation; The Dow Chemical Company/Rohm and Haas Company; Goldman Sachs et al./Kinder Morgan, Inc.; Verizon Wireless/ALLTEL Corporation; Goldman Sachs and TPG/ALLTEL Corporation; NYSE Group Inc./Euronext; Bank of America Corporation/MBNA Corporation; SBC Communications Inc./AT&T Corp.; Chevron Texaco Corporation/Unocal Corporation; Kmart Holding Corporation/Sears, Roebuck and Co.; Sanofi-Synthelabo SA/Aventis SA; Cingular Wireless Corporation/AT&T Wireless Services, Inc.; J.P. Morgan Chase & Co./Bank One Corporation; Bank of America Corporation/FleetBoston Financial Corp.; South African Breweries plc/Miller Brewing Company; and Phillips Petroleum Company/Conoco Inc.
**Publications:** Writes and speaks frequently on corporate governance and executive compensation issues; listed as a leading executive compensation lawyer in The Legal 500.
**Personal:** Holds a JD from New York University School of Law, an MA from the University of Chicago and a BA cum laude and with Distinction in All Subjects from Cornell University.

## GOLDSTEIN, Marcia
Weil, Gotshal & Manges LLP, New York
212 310 8214
marcia.goldstein@weil.com
*Featured in Bankruptcy/Restructuring (Nationwide),*
*Bankruptcy/Restructuring (New York)*
See under Nationwide for profile.

## GOLDSTEIN, Sandra C
Cravath, Swaine & Moore LLP, New York
212 474 1075
sgoldstein@cravath.com
*Featured in Litigation (New York)*
**Practice Areas:** Broad litigation practice with a particular focus on securities, mergers and acquisitions and commercial disputes. Recent successes include her victory for Barnes & Noble in a landmark poison pill trial in Delaware Chancery Court and affirmance in the Delaware Supreme Court. Other clients have included Xerox, IBM, J.Crew (Special Committee), NCR, Nalco, Morgan Stanley, The Williams Companies, HCA, Novartis, Occidental Petroleum, Noven Pharmaceuticals, Time Warner, Lucent Technologies and Tyco.
**Career:** Head of Litigation (2010-present); Litigation Managing Partner (2005-2010); partner since 1994.
**Personal:** New York University Law School (JD, 1987); Barnard College (BA, summa cum laude, 1984).

## GOLDSTEIN, Stephanie J
Fried, Frank, Harris, Shriver & Jacobson LLP, New York
212 859 8254
Stephanie.Goldstein@FriedFrank.com
*Featured in Litigation (New York)*
**Practice Areas:** Litigation partner. Focuses on commercial, securities and corporate governance matters. Regularly practices in trial and appellate courts throughout the country, as well as in arbitration proceedings.
**Career:** Joined in 1992 and became partner in 2000. Co-author of a chapter on mergers & acquisitions in the treatise Business and Commercial Litigation in Federal Courts.
**Personal:** JD, summa cum laude, Benjamin N. Cardozo School of Law, Yeshiva University (1992), editor, Law Review; BA, magna cum laude, Brandeis University (1989).

## GOLDSTEIN, Wendy C
Epstein Becker & Green PC, New York
212 351 3737
wgoldstein@ebglaw.com
*Featured in Healthcare (New York)*
**Practice Areas:** Chair of the firm's national Health Care and Life Sciences Practice Steering Committee; Member of the firm's Board of Directors. Ms Goldstein represents pharmaceutical manufacturers, biotechnology companies, and managed care organizations. She provides health regulatory counsel, including fraud and abuse, FDCA, PDMA, third-party coverage and reimbursement, Medicaid Drug Rebate and other government pricing programs, and corporate compliance.
**Professional Memberships:** American Bar Association, American Health Lawyers Association, New York State Bar Association, Women in Health Management
**Personal:** JD, University of Houston Law Center, 1995; M.P.H, University of Texas Health Science Center, 1995; BA, University of Michigan, Honors College, 1992.

## GONZALEZ, Edward E
Skadden, Arps, Slate, Meagher & Flom LLP & Affiliates, New York
212 735 3160
Edward.Gonzalez@skadden.com
*Featured in Tax (New York)*
**Practice Areas:** Handles tax aspects of a variety of transactions, including mergers and acquisitions, US and non-US financial instruments, leveraged buyouts, private equity investments, cross-border financial transactions, debt restructurings, asset-based financings, derivatives and tax controversies. Has advised investment banks, corporations, and investment partnerships in structuring of acquisitions, financings and refinancings. Has helped develop financial products such as tracking stock, 100 year debt, trust preferred securities, and financial institution regulatory capital products. Has worked with real estate investment trusts, including development of the first timber REIT.
**Career:** JD, Columbia University, 1979; AB, Princeton University, 1976 (summa cum laude; Phi Beta Kappa).

## GOOGE JR, Charles H
Paul, Weiss, Rifkind, Wharton & Garrison LLP, New York
212 373 3345
cgooge@paulweiss.com
*Featured in Media & Entertainment (New York)*
**Practice Areas:** Chair of firm's Entertainment Department and Head of Corporate Department's Intellectual Property Group. Represents individuals and companies involved in all aspects of entertainment industry, including film, television, publishing, music, new media and live stage. Film experience covers clients in independent film world and producers, writers, directors and film editors working with major Hollywood studios. Represents record labels, several popular recording artists, stage producers, institutional theaters, authors, composer/lyricists, directors, choreographers and designers. Key player in several notable transactions in publishing industry. Focuses on all aspects of intellectual property, including copyright, trademark, patent, trade secret and internet law.

## GORDON, Stephen L
Cravath, Swaine & Moore LLP, New York
212 474 1704
gordon@cravath.com
*Featured in Tax (New York)*
**Practice Areas:** Stephen L. Gordon is a partner at Cravath and serves as the Head of the Tax Department. His practice focuses on advising clients on the tax aspects of mergers and acquisitions and other major transactions, including spin-offs, international restructurings and corporate joint ventures. He also works with clients on issues related to corporate finance and domestic and international taxation.
**Personal:** Harvard Law School (JD, cum laude, 1981; Editor, Harvard Law Review); Cornell University (AB, cum laude, 1978). For more information: http://www.cravath.com/gordon

## GORDON, Stephen L
Beveridge & Diamond PC, New York
212 702 5410
sgordon@bdlaw.com
*Featured in Environment (New York)*
**Practice Areas:** Provides legal services to local government, energy, real estate development, natural resource, manufacturing and waste management companies in all aspects of environment and land use law. Mr Gordon has been involved in all aspects of environmental and land use law and has lectured extensively before professional organizations concerning environmental law and litigation. Previously served as a Deputy Attorney General in the State of New Jersey, representing the New Jersey Department of Environmental Protection. Also served as Enforcement Counsel, Deputy Commissioner, and First Deputy Commissioner of the New York State Department of Environmental Conservation.

## GOTTS, Ilene Knable
Wachtell, Lipton, Rosen & Katz, New York
212 403 1247
ikgotts@wlrk.com
*Featured in Antitrust (New York)*

**Practice Areas:** Specialises in antitrust matters, particularly relating to mergers and acquisitions. Recent transactions in which Mrs Gotts advised include ConAgra/Ralcorp, Aetna/Coventry, Georgia Gulf/PPG, International Paper/Temple-Inland, CenturyTel/Savvis, CenturyTel/Qwest, Simon Properties/Prime Outlets, Publicis/Rosetta, and Google/Nortel.
**Professional Memberships:** Has long been an active participant in the Section of Antitrust Law of the American Bar Association, including having served as the section chair, international officer and the chair of the Mergers and Acquisitions Committee; currently a member of the American Law Institute. Served as the president of the Washington Council of Lawyers in 1995, as the chair of the Antitrust and Trade Regulation Section of the Federal Bar Association from 1995-97 and as chair of the New York State Bar Association's Antitrust Section in 2005-06.
**Career:** Partner at Wachtell, Lipton, Rosen & Katz. Previously worked as a staff attorney in the Bureau of Competition of the Federal Trade Commission in conduct and merger investigations, and in the Federal Trade Commission Bureau of Consumer Protection.
**Publications:** Frequent lecturer on antitrust topics; authored over 150 published articles on antitrust-related topics; editor of the ABA 'Merger Review Process Handbook', LBR 'Private Competition Enforcement Review, and LBR 'Merger Control Review"; serves on the advisory boards of 'Antitrust & Trade Regulation Report', 'Antitrust Counselor', 'Antitrust Report', and 'Competition Law International'.
**Personal:** Graduated magna cum laude from the University of Maryland (BA), where she was elected to membership in Phi Beta Kappa; and cum laude from Georgetown University Law Center in 1984 (JD). Member of Board of Legal Advisors of Legal Momentum and Counsel's Council of Lincoln Center.

## GRABAR, Nicolas
Cleary Gottlieb Steen & Hamilton LLP, New York
212 225 2414
ngrabar@cgsh.com
*Featured in Latin American Investment (New York),*
*Capital Markets (Nationwide)*
**Practice Areas:** International capital markets, securities regulation and representation of large reporting companies. Extensive experience in international financings in public and private markets, US securities law applicable to foreign issuers, and regulation of financial reporting. Specializes in telecommunication and natural resource sectors, and advises on acquisitions and restructuring.
**Professional Memberships:** Tribar Opinion Committee; ABA Federal Securities Law Subcommittee; former Chair, ABCNY Financial Reporting Committee.
**Career:** Joined firm, 1984; became partner, 1991. JD, cum laude, Harvard Law School (1982); BA, magna cum laude, Harvard College (1978).

**Publications:** Co-author, U.S. Regulation of International Securities and Derivatives Markets (Wolters Kluwer, 10th edition 2011).

### GRAHAM, Morgan G
Phillips Lytle LLP, Buffalo
716 847 7070
mgraham@phillipslytle.com
*Featured in Environment (New York)*

**Practice Areas:** Mr Graham concentrates his practice in environmental law; energy and land use, including telecommunications. With a knowledge of all major Federal and New York environmental laws, he counsels on environmental compliance, regulations, litigation, natural resources, renewable energy, greenhouse gas emissions, and environmental due diligence with respect to real property use, redevelopment and other commercial transactions. Mr Graham also focuses on brownfield redevelopment and related project development, Great Lakes Basin regulations, as well as defense of government civil and criminal enforcement of environmental laws.
**Professional Memberships:** American Bar Association, Section on Natural Resources, Energy and Environmental Law; New York State Bar Association, Environmental Law Section; Bar Association of Erie County, Environmental Law Committee; Buffalo and Erie County Historical Society; University at Buffalo Law School, Dean's Advisory Council, Member.
**Career:** Joined firm in 1984 and has been a Partner since 1991. Served as firm's Managing Partner from 2001-07.
**Publications:** Authored white paper titled "Energy Companies, Investors and Lenders Take Notice - New York Takes the Lead on Climate Change Disclosures."
**Personal:** Indiana School of Law, Bloomington, JD, 1984 and University of North Carolina at Chapel Hill, BA, 1979.

### GRALA, Bronislaw E
Cadwalader, Wickersham & Taft LLP, New York
212 504 6466
bronislaw.grala@cwt.com
*Featured in Employee Benefits & Executive Compensation (Nationwide), Employee Benefits & Executive Compensation (New York)*
See under Nationwide for profile.

### GRANT, Stuart M
Grant & Eisenhofer PA, Wilmington
302 622 7070
sgrant@gelaw.com
*Featured in Securities (Nationwide), Chancery (Delaware), Litigation (New York)*
See under Delaware for profile.

### GRAZIANO, Salvatore J
Bernstein Litowitz Berger & Grossmann LLP, New York
212 554 1538
sgraziano@blbglaw.com
*Featured in Securities (Nationwide), Litigation (New York)*

**Practice Areas:** Complex litigation; securities fraud litigation; subprime-related litigation; shareholder litigation.

**Professional Memberships:** President, The National Association of Shareholder and Consumer Attorneys; Member, NYC Bar Association (Financial Reporting Committee; Securities Regulation Committee).
**Career:** A member of the firm's management committee, he served as Lead Counsel in many successful securities class actions, including Raytheon (over $460 million); Refco (over $400 million); MIcroStrategy (over $150 million); Bristol-Myers Squibb ($125 million); and New Century (nearly $125 million). Former Assistant District Attorney - Manhattan. He is ranked a New York "Future Star" - Benchmark Litigation; one of only a handful of "Key Individuals" nationally in Plaintiff Securities Litigation - Chambers USA; recommended nationally in Plaintiff Securities Litigation - Legal 500 USA; one of the "500 Leading Lawyers in America" nationally - Lawdragon; and as a "Leading Lawyer" nationally in Class Action Litigation - U.S. News/Best Lawyers.
**Publications:** Has written and lectured on securities fraud litigation and shareholder rights.
**Personal:** New York University, College of Arts & Science, 1988; New York University School of Law, 1991.

### GREEN, Frederick S
Weil, Gotshal & Manges LLP, New York
212 310 8524
frederick.green@weil.com
*Featured in Corporate/M&A (New York)*

**Practice Areas:** Mr Green is Co-chair of Weil's Transactions Practice (M&A, PE, Infrastructure Investment). His practice focuses on business combination transactions, including public and private mergers, acquisitions, leveraged buyouts, P3 and other infrastructure investment transactions, joint ventures, restructurings, spin-offs, proxy contests, and counseling boards of directors on complex governance matters and fiduciary duties. He also advises leading investment banking firms on M&A matters. Mr Green's clients include: General Motors; Port Authority of NY/NJ; DIRECTV; GDF Suez; Macquarie; Verizon; IFM; ALFA Group; Legg Mason; Citigroup; Evercore; and Goldman Sachs.
**Personal:** University of Pennsylvania, Wharton School (BS, 1976); Fordham University (JD, 1979).

### GREENBERG, Joel I
Kaye Scholer LLP, New York
212 836 8201
joel.greenberg@kayescholer.com
*Featured in Corporate/M&A (New York)*

**Practice Areas:** Joel Greenberg is the Senior Corporate Partner of the firm, as well as Co-Chair of the Canada group. He concentrates in domestic and cross-border mergers and acquisitions of public and private companies, representation of financial sponsors, joint ventures, and securities offerings. He also advises on a wide variety of corporate governance and corporate matters (including representation of special committees), as well as transactional matters.

**Professional Memberships:** Past Chair, Committee on Mergers & Acquisitions of the ABA Section of Business Law; Member, ABA Section of Business Law (Member of Section Council and Editorial Board of The Business Lawyer).

### GREENBERG, Leo M.
Kirkland & Ellis LLP, New York
212 446 4799
leo.greenberg@kirkland.com
*Featured in Corporate/M&A (New York)*

**Practice Areas:** Leo Greenberg serves as counsel to large and middle market buyout funds and their portfolio companies in a variety of domestic and cross-border transactions, including public and private acquisitions, divestitures, growth capital investments, joint ventures, equity financings, corporate restructurings and workouts. Representative industries include technology, media, healthcare, consumer products, manufacturing, financial services, logistics/transportation services, oil and gas services and retail.
**Personal:** Fordham University School of Law, JD, 2005 magna cum laude, Order of the Coif, Fordham Law Review, Dean's List 2002-05; University of Pennsylvania, M.S.Ed., Secondary Education, 1997; University of Pennsylvania, BA, Biology, 1996 Dean's List 1995-96.

### GREENE, Mark I
Cravath, Swaine & Moore LLP, New York
212 474 1150
mgreene@cravath.com
*Featured in Corporate/M&A (New York)*

**Practice Areas:** Mark I. Greene is a partner in Cravath's Corporate Department and serves as the Leader of its International Practice and Chair of the Firm's Business Development Group. His practice focuses on mergers and acquisitions, corporate governance and securities matters, including advising on cross-border transactions, private equity deals, complex restructuring transactions, proxy fights, takeover defense and global securities offerings. Mr Greene counts among his diverse client base Unilever, KPN, Novartis, Akzo Nobel, Saint-Gobain, Schneider Electric, Linde, Amdocs, Mylan, Stanley Black & Decker and Perry Capital.
**Personal:** University of Pennsylvania (JD, 1993); Cornell University (BA, 1989). For more information: http://www.cravath.com/mgreene

### GREENE, Robert M
Phillips Lytle LLP, Buffalo
716 847 7038
rgreene@phillipslytle.com
*Featured in Healthcare (New York)*

**Practice Areas:** Mr Greene's practice is concentrated in the fields of health law and related not-for-profit corporate law. With respect to health law, Mr Greene advises health systems, hospitals, nursing homes, continuing care communities, home care agencies, physicians, and other health care providers with respect to licensure, Medicare and Medicaid, medical staff issues, reimbursement, medical records and related issues of security and privacy, corporate compliance as well as incorporation, tax exemption, formation of health systems, governance, hospital foundations, the management and use of endowment funds.

**Professional Memberships:** American Health Lawyers Association, Health Care Compliance Association, College of Law Practice Management of which he served as President 1996-1999, the Catholic Health Association, the New York State and Erie County Bar Associations.
**Career:** Joined the firm in 1971, has been a Partner since 1976, served as Managing Partner 1982-1995 and Chief Executive Officer 1982-2003.
**Publications:** Author, "Managing Partner 101: A Primer on Firm Leadership," published by the American Bar Association and re-published by the American Institute of Certified Public Accountants. Author, "Making Partner: A Guide for Law Firm Associates," published by the American Bar Association. Editor,"The Quality Pursuit: Assuring Standards in the Practice of Law," published by the American Bar Association. Mr Greene also edited and wrote articles as well as lectured extensively on law firm management and leadership.
**Personal:** New York University LLM (1971); University of Notre Dame School of Law, JD (1969); Canisius College, AB, magna cum laude (1966). Mr Greene was selected as 2012 Lawyer of the Year for Health Care Law by The Best Lawyers in America®.

### GREENGRASS, Lawrence S
Mound Cotton Wollan & Greengrass, New York
212 804 4237
lgreengrass@moundcotton.com
*Featured in Insurance (New York)*

**Practice Areas:** Insurance, reinsurance, litigation and arbitrations; property, casualty, life, accident and health insurance and reinsurance; brokers' errors and omissions; asbestos-related claims; ERISA; RICO; insolvency; toxic torts; financial reinsurance.
**Career:** Has over 35 years of experience. His current areas of concentration include, allocation of asbestos, environmental and 9/11 WTC claims, disputes under life, accident and health reinsurance contracts, reinsurance spirals, and other related complex subjects. He has conducted over 250 reinsurance arbitrations and has litigated state and federal courts throughout the US. He speaks annually at insurance industry events.
**Publications:** Best's Review, Insurance Advocate, The United States Reinsurance Report, ReActions, International Insurance Monitor, Chapter, Arbitration of Reinsurance Cases (Co-Author), Prosecuting and Defending Insurance Claims (John Wiley & Sons), 1989.
**Personal:** New York University School of Law (JD 1976), City College of the City of New York (BA 1973).

### GREENTHAL, John
Nixon Peabody LLP, Albany
518 427 2650
jgreenthal@nixonpeabody.com
*Featured in Environment (New York)*

**Practice Areas:** Environmental enforcement defense, judicial/administrative proceedings, and Federal Superfund and Brownfield matters. Advice on, and negotiation with, Federal governmental authorities on issues involving remediation requirements, non-compliance, and all areas of proposed regulatory activity.

**Professional Memberships:** Admitted to practice in NY. NY State Bar Association (former Chair, Environmental Law Section); NY League of Conservation Voters (Board Member); Schenectady County Environmental Advisory Council (Member).

**Career:** 1976-1987: NY State Department of Environmental Conservation's Director of Division of Environmental Enforcement; Compliance Counsel; Regional Attorney. Chair, 11-State Northeast Hazardous Waste Project.

**Personal:** Harvard University, JD; Amherst College, BA, cum laude.

### GRIKSCHEIT, Alyssa A
Sidley Austin LLP, New York
212 839 8509
agrikscheit@sidley.com
*Featured in Latin American Investment (New York)*

**Practice Areas:** Alyssa Grikscheit, a partner in Sidley's New York office, has a diverse corporate practice that currently emphasizes complex transactions and alternative investment funds. Her experience includes private equity and hedge funds, mergers and acquisitions, strategic alliances and restructurings. Ms Grikscheit is fluent in Spanish and French and has extensive experience in international transactions, particularly those involving Latin America and other emerging markets such as China and India.

**Personal:** The University of Michigan Law School (JD, 1994, cum laude); College of Europe, Bruges (Diploma, 1991); Harvard University (AB, 1990, magna cum laude). Admission: New York.

### GROBAN JR, Robert S
Epstein Becker & Green PC, New York
212 351 4689
rgroban@ebglaw.com
*Featured in Immigration (New York)*

**Practice Areas:** Chair of the firm's national Immigration Law Group. Mr Groban counsels employers on how to employ foreign nationals, assisting them in developing appropriate risk management policies, and representing them in worksite enforcement and other immigration-related civil or criminal litigation. Mr Groban represents many major multinational and domestic organizations in various industries: financial services, health care and life sciences, specialty fashion, hospitality, and technology.

**Professional Memberships:** American Immigration Lawyers Association, Federal Bar Council.

**Personal:** JD, New York University Law School, 1973; BA, Williams College, 1970.

### GROGAN, Gregory
Simpson Thacher & Bartlett LLP, New York
212 455 2477
ggrogan@stblaw.com
*Featured in Employee Benefits & Executive Compensation (New York)*

**Practice Areas:** Practice includes executive compensation and employee benefits in connection with corporate transactions, with a particular focus on private equity and leveraged buyout transactions. Advises public and private company boards and compensation committees with regard to CEO succession matters (Wachovia, WaMu, Hilton, Gannett). Significant engagements include more than 30 acquisition and divestiture transactions for Blackstone (Hilton, SeaWorld, Equity Office, Motel 6) and multiple transactions for AIG, AOL, Carlyle, CBRE, Centerbridge, PPL, Teleflex and Tyco. Experienced in PBGC negotiations.

**Career:** Joined Firm, 2000; Partner 2007.

**Personal:** BA, California State University, Northridge, 1995; JD, Georgetown University Law Center, 1998.

### GROLL, Michael
Willkie Farr & Gallagher LLP, New York
212 728 8616
mgroll@willkie.com
*Featured in Insurance (Nationwide), Insurance (New York)*
See under Nationwide for profile.

### GROOMBRIDGE, Nicholas
Paul, Weiss, Rifkind, Wharton & Garrison LLP, New York
212 373 3212
ngroombridge@paulweiss.com
*Featured in Intellectual Property (New York)*

**Practice Areas:** Partner, Litigation Department. Has been lead counsel in numerous patent cases and has extensive trial experience (both bench and jury). Has successfully argued many cases in the Court of Appeals for the Federal Circuit. In the pharmaceuticals and biotechnology area, has handled numerous matters involving biologics, diagnostics, drugs, delivery systems and research tools. Patent litigation experience also includes medical devices, software, consumer electronics, specialty chemicals, automotive parts, financial services and alternative energy. Secretary, Federal Circuit Bar Association. Adjunct professor, teaching patent litigation at Columbia Law School and biotechnology patent law at NYU School of Law.

### GRUENGLAS, Michael H
Skadden, Arps, Slate, Meagher & Flom LLP & Affiliates, New York
212 735 3567
Michael.Gruenglas@skadden.com
*Featured in Litigation (New York)*

**Practice Areas:** Represents corporations and individuals in complex litigation involving a wide range of corporate, commercial and securities matters. Practices in federal and state courts, and in arbitration proceedings. Has represented a broad spectrum of clients, as plaintiffs and defendants, in cases involving claims for breach of contract, fraud, breach of fiduciary duty, tortious interference, antitrust issues and violations of civil RICO. Has represented a number of publicly traded corporations in some of the most significant securities class actions in recent years.

**Career:** JD, New York University School of Law, 1990; BS, City University of New York, Brooklyn College, 1983.

### GUNTHER JR, Robert J
WilmerHale, New York
212 230 8830
robert.gunther@wilmerhale.com
*Featured in Intellectual Property (New York)*

**Practice Areas:** Mr Gunther represents technology and pharmaceutical clients in intellectual property litigation at both the trial and appellate level. He has litigated patent and other IP cases before numerous federal district courts and arbitration tribunals, and has argued appeals before the US Court of Appeals for the Federal Circuit and litigated patent disputes before the US ITC.

**Professional Memberships:** Member of American Intellectual Property Law Association.

**Career:** Mr Gunther is former vice chair of the Global Litigation Department of Latham & Watkins.

### GURYAN, Peter
Fried, Frank, Harris, Shriver & Jacobson LLP, New York
212 859 8477
Peter.Guryan@FriedFrank.com
*Featured in Antitrust (New York)*

**Practice Areas:** Antitrust partner. Focuses on antitrust counseling, government review of mergers and acquisitions, criminal investigations, and litigation. Represents major corporations within various industries in merger and civil non-merger investigations before the DOJ, the FTC and state antitrust authorities. Representative clients: Merck, Tradeweb, Imerys, APP Pharmaceuticals, Hawker Beechcraft, Thomson Reuters, MRC Global, Houghton International, Compression Polymers, Goldman Sachs, New Mountain, AEA Investors, Permira Advisors, Onex, Luxfer.

**Career:** Joined in 2001. Trial attorney, Antitrust Division, Department of Justice, Telecommunications Task Force (1998-2001).

**Personal:** JD, Cornell Law School (1996), cum laude, editor, Cornell Law Review; BA, Cornell University (1992).

### HAAS, Erik
Patterson Belknap Webb & Tyler LLP, New York
212 336 2117
ehaas@pbwt.com
*Featured in Litigation (New York)*

**Practice Areas:** Erik Haas is a member of the firm's litigation department and Co-Chair of the firm's Mortgage and Credit Crisis Team, concentrating his practice in complex commercial litigation. In addition to a wide range of general commercial disputes, the substantive areas of his practice include (i) complex securities and securitizations, (ii) pricing and reimbursement fraud and False Claims Act matters, (iii) shareholder class actions, (iv) antitrust, (v) products liability, and (vi) intellectual property litigation, including false advertising, patents and trademarks.

**Professional Memberships:** American Bar Association; New York State Bar Association; Association of the Bar of the City of New York

**Career:** Before attending law school, Mr Haas spent three years with Arthur Andersen & Company, where he focused on structured finance and securitization transactions, and secured his CPA license.

**Personal:** New York University School of Law (JD 1993), American Jurisprudence Awards; The State University of New York (BA 1987), magna cum laude.

### HALL, Richard
Cravath, Swaine & Moore LLP, New York
212 474 1293
rhall@cravath.com
*Featured in Corporate/M&A (New York)*

**Practice Areas:** Richard Hall is a partner in Cravath's Corporate Department. His practice focuses on mergers and acquisitions and corporate governance advice. Mr Hall is Cravath's Head of the Mergers and Acquisitions practice for EMEA. His clients have included Archer-Daniels-Midland Company, Banco Santander, Barrick Gold Corporation, ConocoPhillips, Hochtief AG, Royal Dutch Shell, Time Warner Inc., The Linde Group, Weyerhaeuser Company, The Williams Companies, Inc. and Xstrata plc.

**Personal:** Harvard University (LLM, 1988); University of Melbourne (LLB, with Honors, 1986; BComm, with Honors, 1984). For more information: http://www.cravath.com/rhall

### HALPER, Jason M
Cadwalader, Wickersham & Taft LLP, New York
212 504 6112
jason.halper@cwt.com
*Featured in Litigation (New York)*

**Practice Areas:** Represents domestic and foreign clients in complex business disputes and arbitrations in federal and state courts throughout the country. Clients include public and private companies, underwriters, lenders, professional firms, corporate directors and individuals in a variety of industries. Experience in securities, derivative, ERISA and RICO class actions; SEC and stock exchange investigations and arbitrations; breach of fiduciary duty claims, insider trading or other misconduct by corporate directors; substantial contract disputes; bankruptcy-related proceedings; and litigation arising from M&A and transactions involving changes or contests for corporate control in Delaware Chancery Court and elsewhere.

**Professional Memberships:** Trial Bar, U.S. DC for the Northern District of Illinois; Editorial Board, ABA, Energy Litigation Committee; and member, ABA, Securities, Class Action, and Business Litigation Committees.

**Personal:** Law Clerk, Hon. David Edelstein, U.S. DC for the Southern District of NY; JD, Fordham University School of Law (cum laude); BA, Wharton School, University of Pennsylvania.

### HANSEN, Edward J
Baker & McKenzie, New York
212 626 4508
Ed.Hansen@bakermckenzie.com
*Featured in Outsourcing (Nationwide), Technology (New York)*

**Practice Areas:** Outsourcing (ITO, BPO); Transformational Technology Transactions; ADM; Web-enabled solutions (cloud, etc). Works with

clients on sourcing and re-sourcing multi-country, multi-tower transactions with emphasis on long term projects that have a transformative impact on the client organization.
**Professional Memberships:** ABA; SIM; SIG; North American Advisory Board of Shared Services and Outsourcing Network (SSON); Information Week Innovator and Influencer's List.
**Career:** Admitted in New Jersey (1990) and New York (1991).
**Publications:** Frequent writer and speaker about global sourcing and IT issues.
**Personal:** NYU (BA in Economics), St. John University (JD); Instrument Rated Private Pilot.

### HANSON, Vivian L
Morrison & Foerster LLP, New York
212 506 7393
vhanson@mofo.com
*Featured in Outsourcing (Nationwide), Technology (New York)*
See under Nationwide for profile.

### HARCKHAM, Finley
Anderson Kill & Olick, P.C., New York
212 278 1543
fharckham@andersonkill.com
*Featured in Insurance (New York)*
**Practice Areas:** Finley Harckham represents and advises corporate policyholders in insurance coverage matters. He has successfully litigated, arbitrated and settled hundreds of complex coverage claims. His areas of particular expertise include property loss, business interruption, construction, directors and officers liability, professional liability and general liability claims. He also has extensive experience in the field of international arbitration. His arbitration clients include government contractors, consumer products companies and manufacturers which Anderson Kill has represented in a wide range of disputes involving, among other things, insurance claims, service contracts, the purchase and sale of components, raw materials and products, and licensing agreements. He has successfully prosecuted and defended arbitrations in European countries and the United States under the London Arbitration Act, and the AAA, ICC and UNCITRAL arbitration rules.
**Publications:** Mr Harckham has written numerous articles on insurance coverage topics for publications such as CPCU Journal, The John Liner Review, Risk Management Magazine, The National Law Journal, and New York Law Journal. He is also co-author of the book, Legal Issues in Risk Management: A Policyholder's Guide, published by Aspen Publishers, and authored a chapter on "Insurance For Business Disruptions and Other First-Party Claims" for the multi-volume treatise, Successful Partnering Between Inside and Outside Counsel (Thompson Reuters West 2011). Mr Harckham is often quoted in the Wall Street Journal, Business Insurance and other publications for his recognized experience in insurance coverage matters.

### HARITON, David P
Sullivan & Cromwell LLP, New York
212 558 4248
haritond@sullcrom.com
*Featured in Tax (New York)*
**Professional Memberships:** Co-Chairman, Subcommittee on Hybrid Debt Instruments, ABA; Executive Committee member and former chairman, Tax Section, NYSBA; Tax Forum; Tax Club.
**Career:** Partner since 1994. Focuses on US federal income taxation of financial instruments/transactions and on cross-border investment. Represents securities industry in Washington, DC and has advised the government in these matters.
**Publications:** Has published more than 60 articles and reports on the taxation of financial instruments and transactions. Frequent speaker at PLI, NYU Institute on Federal Income Taxation, and on government panels.
**Personal:** Stanford Law School (JD, 1985; Order of the Coif); Stanford University (BA, 1981).

### HARKRIDER, John D
Axinn, Veltrop & Harkrider LLP, New York
212 728 2210
jdh@avhlaw.com
*Featured in Antitrust (New York)*
**Practice Areas:** Co-Chair of Antitrust Practice.
**Professional Memberships:** American Bar Association, Editorial Board of Antitrust from 2007 to present and was the Vice-Chair Economics Committee of Antitrust Section, 2003-06; New York State Bar Association; New York City Bar Association.
**Career:** John Harkrider co-chairs the firm's Antitrust Practice. His practice concentrates on mergers, litigation and counseling. In the merger context, he advised Google in its US$12.5 billion acquisition of Motorola Mobility as well as its US$700 million acquisition of ITA, SunGard in its US$1.6 billion sale of SunGard Higher Education to Datatel, XLHealth in its US$2.2 billion sale to United Health, Thermo Fisher Scientific in its US$2.1 billion acquisition of Dionex, Bemis in its US$1.2 billion acquisition of the Food Americas' assets of Alcan, Ball in its US$577 million acquisition of the MCC assets from Anheuser-Busch InBev, Cingular in its US$41 billion acquisition of AT&T, BellSouth in its US$67 billion acquisition by AT&T, Omnicare in its hostile takeover of both Pharmerica and NeighborCare, and Harcourt General with respect to its US$4.5 billion sale to Reed Elsevier and Thompson. In litigation, Mr Harkrider represented both Tyson and George's with respect to Tyson's sale of assets to George's in the Western District of Virginia, Omnicare with respect to its Section One conspiracy claims against United Health in both the Northern District of Illinois and the Seventh Circuit, SunGard in the District of Columbia against a challenge by the Department of Justice to enjoin its acquisition of Comdisco, Harcourt General in defense of monopolization claims against APTS in the Ninth Circuit, United Technologies Corporation in connection with Walker Process and Handgards claims in the Northern District of Illinois and the District of Maryland, and IBP in opposition class certification in the Middle

District of Alabama. In counseling, he has advised MasterCard's Board of Directors with respect to their IPO as well as the Board of Directors of a major European air cargo company with respect to possible criminal liability. In addition, Mr Harkrider represented the US Department of Justice in its investigation and suit to enjoin WorldCom's US$120 billion attempted acquisition of Sprint. Mr Harkrider delivered remarks at the prestigious Milton Handler Annual Antitrust Review sponsored by the Association of the Bar of the City of New York and has published extensively on antitrust.
**Personal:** University of Michigan, PhD program (did not complete dissertation), University of California, Hastings College of the Law, San Francisco, California, 1991 JD cum laude. Honors: Order of the Coif; Thurston Society, 1991. University of Michigan, Ann Arbor, Michigan, 1988 BA Honors: Highest Honors.

### HARNER, Paul E
Latham & Watkins LLP, New York
212 906 1234
paul.harner@lw.com
*Featured in Bankruptcy/Restructuring (New York)*
**Practice Areas:** Practice focuses on corporate bankruptcy, restructuring and other matters involving financially distressed entities. Represents debtors, committees and other parties in interest; has played leading roles in various major national and international corporate restructurings. Extensive experience representing private equity investors, bank groups, institutional investors, secured lenders and other parties in bankruptcy cases, out-of-court workouts and related litigation. Represents multiple clients in distressed mergers, acquisitions and other corporate transactions.
**Career:** Qualified since 1990. Fellow of the American College of Bankruptcy and member of the American Bankruptcy Institute, the American Bar Association and the New York and Illinois State Bar Associations.

### HARRIS, Adam C
Schulte Roth & Zabel LLP, New York
212 756 2253
adam.harris@srz.com
*Featured in Bankruptcy/Restructuring (Nationwide), Bankruptcy/Restructuring (New York)*
**Practice Areas:** Chapter 11 cases and out-of-court workouts and restructurings. Principally represents investment funds and financial institutions (traditional and non-traditional lenders and investors) in connection with loans to, and investments in, distressed companies. These representations have involved acquisitions of distressed companies, restructurings of existing debt (including debt-for-equity swaps) and new extensions of credit, including debtor-in-possession and exit financing facilities. Has also represented debtors in Chapter 11 cases and out-of-court restructurings.
**Professional Memberships:** NYC Bar Association.
**Career:** SRZ Executive Committee.

**Personal:** Georgetown University Law Center, JD, magna cum laude; Emory University, BA.

### HART, John
Simpson Thacher & Bartlett LLP, New York
212 455 2830
jhart@stblaw.com
*Featured in Tax (New York)*
**Practice Areas:** Tax partner concentrating on private funds; REITs and real estate; publicly traded partnerships; and asset manager M&A. Experience forming real estate, private equity, infrastructure, debt and other fund types for leading sponsors, including Blackstone, CVC, EQT, Hellman & Friedman and Macquarie. Advised on formation of BREP VII and EQT Infrastructure II; acquisitions of Motel 6; US retail portfolio of Centro; and Apple REIT 6 (pending); Oaktree IPO.
**Professional Memberships:** Member, past chair, Private Investment Fund Tax Forum; member, past president, NYC Tax Club.
**Personal:** Harvard Law School (JD, cum laude, 1979); University of Michigan (AB, High Distinction, 1976).

### HARTY, Ronan
Davis Polk & Wardwell LLP, New York
212 450 4000
ronan.harty@davispolk.com
*Featured in Antitrust (New York)*
**Practice Areas:** Partner in Davis Polk & Wardwell's Litigation Department, provides general antitrust counseling to US and non-US companies and represents clients in enforcement agency investigations, domestic and cross-border acquisitions and joint ventures, and litigations. Recent matters include representation of parties in antitrust lawsuits and before the US federal antitrust enforcement agencies in a variety of transactions, including mergers, joint ventures and other matters in the telecommunications, electronics, paper, agricultural biotechnology, chemicals, pharmaceutical, publishing and banking industries.

### HASHMALL, David M
Goodwin Procter LLP, New York
212 459 7430
dhashmall@goodwinprocter.com
*Featured in Intellectual Property (New York)*
**Practice Areas:** Mr Hashmall has extensive experience in complex commercial disputes at both the trial and appellate levels. His practice encompasses patent and intellectual property litigation, as well as business litigations and arbitrations involving securities fraud, breach of contract, shareholder and partnership disputes, defense of issuers and their officers and directors in class and derivative claims, and RICO claims. He has prosecuted and defended numerous applications for preliminary and permanent injunctive relief in matters involving the theft of trade secrets and enforcement of restrictive covenants.
**Personal:** JD, New York University School of Law, 1977; BA, The Johns Hopkins University, 1972.

## HAWKINS, Howard
Cadwalader, Wickersham & Taft LLP, New York
212 504 6422
howard.hawkins@cwt.com
*Featured in Litigation (New York)*
**Practice Areas:** Represents major financial institutions in securities, financial, and bankruptcy litigation arising out of structured products and derivatives, including CDOs, CDS, CMBS, and RMBS, proprietary sales and trading, lending, broker-dealer and advisory services. Experienced trial lawyer, has acted as a lead trial counsel and on appeal in federal and state courts throughout the U.S. Broad experience advising clients in litigation in Europe, the Middle East, Asia, the Caribbean, and South America, and has handled cases and investigations in the U.S. for non- U.S. international companies and individuals.
**Professional Memberships:** Member, Maryland and New York bars; admitted to practice in federal trial and appellate courts throughout the U.S.; member, Federal Bar Council; International Member, U.K. Law Society; solicitor in England.
**Personal:** JD, Fordham Law School; AB, Harvard College (cum laude).

## HEITNER, Kenneth H
Weil, Gotshal & Manges LLP, New York
212 310 8288
kenneth.heitner@weil.com
*Featured in Tax (New York)*
**Practice Areas:** Kenneth Heitner is a Co-head of Weil's global Tax Practice. He regularly acts on the full range of tax issues affecting corporations transacting their business in the US and abroad as well as on numerous tax-efficient structures for cross-border transactions. Mr Heitner is an adjunct professor at NYU School of Law.
**Professional Memberships:** Member, New York State Bar Association, Tax Section; Member, American Bar Association; Member, Bar Association of the City of New York; Member, Tax Club.
**Personal:** Rutgers University (BA, 1969); New York University School of Law (JD, 1973; LLM, 1977).

## HELLER, Richard B
Frankfurt Kurnit Klein & Selz, New York
212 826 5533
rheller@fkks.com
*Featured in Media & Entertainment (New York)*
**Practice Areas:** Co-chair of the firm's Entertainment Group. Practice focuses on motion pictures and television, new media, publishing, celebrity branding and intellectual property. Clients include onscreen talent, writers, producers, directors, production companies and distributors in the motion picture and television fields. Handles independent film clients from acquisition of rights through financing, production and exploitation of projects. Actively counsels prominent best-selling authors, doctors, journalists, designers and other celebrity clients, as well as global brands, in managing their valuable intellectual property rights and implementing fully coor-

dinated strategies for exploiting motion picture, television, print, audio, electronic new media, merchandising/licensing and other rights. Represents numerous foreign companies, charitable organizations and individuals doing business in the US. Former Adjunct Faculty Member, New York University School of Law. Listed in Best Lawyers in America and among the country's leading copyright lawyers by The Legal 500. Named a New York-area 'Super Lawyer' in the field of entertainment and sports.
**Professional Memberships:** Member, Legal Affairs Committee, Magazine Publishers of America; the New York City Bar Association's Committee on Entertainment and Sports Law; American Bar Association's Section on Patent, Trademark and Copyright Law; American Bar Association's Forum Committee on the Entertainment and Sports Industries.

## HELMER, Maureen
Hiscock & Barclay LLP, Albany
518 429 4220
mhelmer@hblaw.com
*Featured in Energy & Natural Resources (New York)*
**Practice Areas:** Represents energy, cable and telecommunications clients before regulators in policy, transactional and enforcement cases. Advises investors regarding regulatory trends affecting business risks and opportunities. Consults on ethics and security issues.
**Professional Memberships:** Director, Plug Power Inc.; Board, Women in Communications and Energy; Board, Center for Economic Growth; Board , Center for Internet Security; member of New York Bar Association and Energy Bar Association.
**Career:** Former General Counsel and Chair of the New York Public Service Commission during the transition to competition in electricity and telecommunications.
**Personal:** BS in Economics, SUNY Albany, 1979; JD SUNY Buffalo, 1982.

## HEMLOCK, Adam C.
Weil, Gotshal & Manges LLP, New York
*Featured in Antitrust (New York)*
**Practice Areas:** Adam Hemlock represents clients in a variety of antitrust and commercial litigation matters, specializing in international cartel investigations. He represents clients in US criminal cartel investigations, as well as follow-on class actions and coordination of international government investigations. He also regularly represents clients with respect to the intersection of antitrust and intellectual property, including standard setting, patent pooling and other technology licensing, technology joint ventures, and copyright issues.
**Professional Memberships:** Vice Chair, Intellectual Property Committee, ABA Antitrust Section. Member, Executive Committee, NY State Bar Association Antitrust Section.

## HENDERSON JR, Donald B
Willkie Farr & Gallagher LLP, New York
212 728 8262
dhenderson@willkie.com
*Featured in Insurance (Nationwide), Insurance (New York)*
See under Nationwide for profile.

## HENES, Jonathan S
Kirkland & Ellis LLP, New York
212 446 4927
jonathan.henes@kirkland.com
*Featured in Bankruptcy/Restructuring (Nationwide), Bankruptcy/Restructuring (New York)*
**Practice Areas:** Jonathan Henes is a partner in Kirkland's Restructuring Group. Mr Henes represents debtors in Chapter 11 cases, including Tronox Inc., Solutia Inc., ION Media, Citadel Broadcasting, Masonite Corporation and Wellman Corporation. He also advises private equity funds and hedge funds in Chapter 11 cases and acquisitions.
**Personal:** Benjamin N. Cardozo Law School, JD, 1996; Union College, BA, 1991.

## HENNES, David
Fried, Frank, Harris, Shriver & Jacobson LLP, New York
212 859 8355
david.hennes@friedfrank.com
*Featured in Litigation (New York)*
**Practice Areas:** Litigation partner. Has litigated a broad array of corporate disputes, with an emphasis on complex corporate litigation, securities cases, corporate-control disputes and enforcement litigation. Frequently handles complicated federal securities class actions and state law derivative actions, and advises boards on their responses to these litigations. Represents buyers, sellers and financial advisors in merger litigation.
**Career:** Joined in 1996; became partner in 2003.
**Personal:** JD, cum laude, University of Pennsylvania Law School (1995), senior editor, Law Review, co-chairman, Moot Court Board; BA University of Michigan (1991) with high distinction.

## HERFORT, John
Gibson, Dunn & Crutcher LLP, New York
212 351 3832
jherfort@gibsondunn.com
*Featured in Antitrust (New York)*
**Practice Areas:** Focuses on antitrust trials, investigations, counseling and complex commercial litigation. Significant practice in merger investigations, treble damage cases, and criminal investigations. Representative clients include Schlumberger Limited, CareCore National, Investcorp, Aetna, Unilever, Northrop Grumman, CCC Holdings, Random House, Title Insurance Rating Bureaus.
**Career:** Clerked for U.S. Circuit Judge J. Skelly Wright, U.S. Court of Appeals for the District of Columbia Circuit. Served as assistant to U.S. Attorney General Elliot Richardson. Reporter, Boston Globe, 1968-69.
**Personal:** BA Harvard College, magna cum laude, 1968;JD, cum laude, Harvard Law School,

1972; Supreme Court Note and Note Editor for Harvard Law Review.

## HERLIHY, Edward D
Wachtell, Lipton, Rosen & Katz, New York
212 403 1207
edherlihy@wlrk.com
*Featured in Financial Services Regulation (Nationwide), Corporate/M&A (New York)*
See under Nationwide for profile.

## HERMAN, Matthew
Freshfields Bruckhaus Deringer US LLP, New York
212 277 4037
matthew.herman@freshfields.com
*Featured in Corporate/M&A (New York)*
**Practice Areas:** Matthew Herman is the head of Freshfields Bruckhaus Deringer's US corporate practice, based in the New York office. Matthew's practice focuses on international transactions, advising corporations and financial sponsors in connection with mergers and acquisitions, leveraged buyouts, joint ventures and capital raising transactions. Matthew also counsels financial advisors in public mergers and acquisitions, and provides advice to companies on their day-to-day legal and business issues, including corporate governance and compliance matters.

## HERMANN, Brian S
Paul, Weiss, Rifkind, Wharton & Garrison LLP, New York
212 373 3545
bhermann@paulweiss.com
*Featured in Bankruptcy/Restructuring (New York)*
**Practice Areas:** Partner, Bankruptcy and Corporate Reorganization Department, and member of the Firm's Media & Entertainment Practice. Focuses on restructuring and bankruptcy matters for borrowers and lenders. Extensive experience representing clients in complex out-of-court restructurings and chapter 11 cases nationwide and across a variety of industries. Also represents clients in complex litigation arising out of chapter 11. Company-side representations include Bicent Power, Fontainebleau Hotel, Progressive Moulded, Foamex, Cone Mills and Penn Traffic. On the creditor side, official committees, secured lenders, bondholder groups and significant investors in, among others, bankruptcies of Hostess Brands, Tronox, Simmons Bedding, Spectrum Brands and Nortek.

## HERSHKOWITZ, Benjamin
Gibson, Dunn & Crutcher LLP, New York
212 351 2410
bhershkowitz@gibsondunn.com
*Featured in Intellectual Property (New York)*
**Practice Areas:** Partner in litigation and corporate departments. Extensive experience as lead counsel in complex patent and other intellectual property litigation. Additional focus on patent licensing and counseling on intellectual property matters arising in corporate transactions. Represents companies from start-ups to leading technology companies in a wide range of technologies including telecommunications, consumer electronics, computer hardware, financial instru-

ments, software, internet, ecommerce, semiconductor and industrial equipment.

**Career:** Frequent author and speaker. Served as Editor-in-Chief of Patent Strategy & Management. Active in NYIPLA and Hon. William C. Conner Inn of Court.

**Personal:** JD, NYU, 1993. BSEE, highest honors, Rutgers University, 1990.

### HERZ, Andrew L
Patterson Belknap Webb & Tyler LLP, New York
212 336 2910
alherz@pbwt.com
*Featured in Real Estate (New York)*

**Practice Areas:** Andy Herz is a member of the American College of Real Estate Lawyers and is a recognized authority and frequent lecturer in the areas of commercial office leasing, mortgage financing and workouts. His clients include major real estate owners and developers, commercial banks, investment banking firms, technology providers, hospitals, professional service companies, charitable institutions and other law firms.

**Professional Memberships:** Andy has held leadership positions in numerous professional organizations, having served as chair of the Leasing Committee of the American College of Real Estate Lawyers; co-chair of the Office Leasing Committee and the Real Estate Asset Management Committee of the American Bar Association; and chair of the New York State Bar Association's Commercial Leasing Committee. Andy has also been an adjunct professor at Vanderbilt Law School. He has participated in seminars on workouts, commercial leasing, loan restructurings and mortgage financing for numerous industry groups, including the New York University Real Estate Institute, the Real Estate Board of New York, the Practising Law Institute, the New York Law Journal, The National Association of Corporate Real Estate Executives and the Harvard Business School Real Estate Club. Andy served as a contributing editor to the New York Bar Association's text, Commercial Leasing, published in 2010, and chaired New York State Bar Association panels entitled "Commercial Leases – Troubled Landlords, Troubled Tenants" and "Commercial Leasing in a Distressed Market – The Rules Have Changed." He has also been designated as a Fellow of the American Bar Foundation and is a member of the New York City Committee of the Regional Plan Association.

**Career:** Earlier in his career, Andy was the General Counsel of the New York State Mortgage Loan Enforcement and Administration Corporation, the workout arm of New York's Urban Development Corporation, which handled its defaulted 1.2 billion dollar mortgage portfolio.

**Personal:** JD, 1971, Columbia Law School, Harlan Fiske Stone Scholar; Articles Editor, Columbia Journal of Law and Social Problems; BA, 1968, Columbia College, Columbia University. Andy is Treasurer and a board member of Planned Parenthood of New York City, Inc.

### HERZECA, Lois F
Gibson, Dunn & Crutcher LLP, New York
212 351 2688
lherzeca@gibsondunn.com
*Featured in Insurance (New York)*

**Practice Areas:** Corporate practice including M&A, capital markets, and joint ventures. Specialty in insurance transactional matters and fashion and retail industries. Representations include Transatlantic Holdings in its terminated merger agreement with Allied World, hostile defense against Validus, and merger with Alleghany Corporation valued at $3.4 billion; CommScope, Inc. in its $3.9 billion sale to The Carlyle Group; and Brian Atwood in the sale of his business to The Jones Group.

**Professional Memberships:** Director – Women in Need.

**Publications:** Authored over 30 articles for legal and financial publications. Frequent speaker at industry conferences.

**Personal:** JD, cum laude, Boston University School of Law.

### HERZOG, Barry
Kramer Levin Naftalis & Frankel LLP, New York
212 715 9130
bherzog@kramerlevin.com
*Featured in Tax (New York)*

**Practice Areas:** Mr Herzog focuses his practice on all aspects of federal income taxation. He has extensive experience in the tax implications of public and private mergers and acquisitions, bankruptcy restructurings, debt and equity offerings and other forms of financing, partnerships, real estate transactions, executive compensation, financial products, securitization transactions and other areas of federal income tax law.

### HESS, Kristofer
Cleary Gottlieb Steen & Hamilton LLP, New York
212 225 2638
khess@cgsh.com
*Featured in Tax (New York)*

**Practice Areas:** Tax matters, including tax aspects of mergers and acquisitions, joint ventures, spinoffs, reorganizations, private equity investments, financial products, and capital markets transactions.

**Professional Memberships:** Member of the Bars in New York, the District of Columbia, Wisconsin and the U.S. Court of Appeals for the Fifth Circuit.

**Career:** Joined firm, 1998; became Partner, 2006. University of Chicago Law School (JD, Law Review, With Honors), 1997; University of Wisconsin (BA, With Academic Distinction), 1992; Fulbright Scholar, Universität zu Köln and Rheinische Friedrich-Wilhelms-Universität, 1993-94.

**Publications:** Articles on net operating loss trading orders in bankrupcies.

### HILFERS, Eric W.
Cravath, Swaine & Moore LLP, New York
212 474 1352
ehilfers@cravath.com
*Featured in Employee Benefits & Executive Compensation (New York)*

**Practice Areas:** Eric W. Hilfers is a partner and head of Cravath's Executive Compensation and Benefits (ECB) Department. His practice focuses on ECB matters principally in connection with M&A and other business transactions. These representations include the hiring (and termination) of chief executives and other officers; the design and implementation of compensation programs; the crafting of public disclosures regarding executive pay; and the management of the many legal and regulatory concerns generated by compensation practices, including securities law, tax, ERISA and financial accounting.

**Personal:** University of Chicago (JD, with Honors, 1998); Princeton University (AB, 1995). For more information: http://www.cravath.com/ehilfers

### HILLMAN, David M
Schulte Roth & Zabel LLP, New York
212 756 2174
david.hillman@srz.com
*Featured in Bankruptcy/Restructuring (New York)*

**Practice Areas:** Corporate restructuring and creditors' rights litigation, with emphasis on representation of secured and unsecured creditors and other parties in Chapter 11 bankruptcy cases. Significant experience litigating issues involving solvency, valuation, plan confirmation, financing and cash collateral disputes, contested 363 sales, fraudulent transfers, preferences, equitable subordination, recharacterization, substantive consolidation, breach of fiduciary duty and similar disputes.

**Professional Memberships:** American Bankruptcy Institute; NYC Bankruptcy Assistance Project, Steering Committee Member.

**Personal:** Albany Law School, JD, cum laude; State University of New York, Oneonta, BA, cum laude.

### HINEY, Jesse
Nixon Peabody LLP, Jericho
516 832 7624
jhiney@nixonpeabody.com
*Featured in Environment (New York)*

**Practice Areas:** Jesse is versed in transactional and regulatory facets of environmental law. His experience includes environmental diligence for complex real estate transactions, environmental cleanups, brownfield redevelopment, permitting, compliance and enforcement issues, SEQRA and OSHA-related matters. Jesse has completed the LEED Green Associate certification.

**Professional Memberships:** Admitted New York, New Jersey.

**Publications:** Contributor: Environmental Claims Journal, Environmental Aspects of Real Estate and Commercial Transactions, and Environmental Law & Regulation in New York. Speaker: Fordham University School of Law,

Stony Brook University, and The Business Council of New York State.

**Personal:** New York Law School, JD, cum laude; Alfred University, BA.

### HIRSCHFIELD, Marc E
Baker & Hostetler LLP, New York
212 589 4610
mhirschfield@bakerlaw.com
*Featured in Bankruptcy/Restructuring (New York)*

**Career:** Marc Hirschfield is experienced in insolvency and reorganization matters, regularly representing debtors, creditors' committees, debtor-in-possession lenders, secured and unsecured creditors and acquirers of assets in both out-of-court workouts and bankruptcy cases. He is experienced in cross-border insolvency cases, having been involved in cases in various countries such as Bermuda, the British Virgin Islands, Canada and Australia. Marc is a court certified mediator and has been appointed to the Mediation Panels for the United States Bankruptcy Courts for the Southern and Eastern Districts of New York and the District of Delaware. He is a member of the American Bankruptcy Institute.

### HIRSHMAN, Michele
Paul, Weiss, Rifkind, Wharton & Garrison LLP, New York
212 373 3747
mhirshman@paulweiss.com
*Featured in Litigation (New York)*

**Practice Areas:** Partner, Litigation Department. Focuses on white collar defense, regulatory enforcement matters, internal investigations. Represents public and privately held companies and individuals before Department of Justice, state attorneys general and other law enforcement and regulatory authorities. Has advised financial institutions, pharmaceutical manufacturers, insurers, marketing companies and political organizations in federal and state criminal and civil investigations. Formerly first deputy attorney general for the State of New York and a prosecutor in the U.S. Attorney's Office for the Southern District of New York, where she was deputy chief appellate attorney and chief of the General Crimes and Public Corruption Units.

### HISIGER, James I
Latham & Watkins LLP, New York
212 906 1200
james.hisiger@lw.com
*Featured in Real Estate (New York)*

**Practice Areas:** Real Estate and Real Estate Finance

**Career:** Mr Hisiger is experienced in a wide variety of real estate development and real estate finance matters including securitized financings, syndications and participations and loan restructurings, sale-leasebacks and OpCo/PropCo structures, with respect to various asset classes, the formation and negotiation of complex joint ventures (mergers and acquisitions, passive equity and management roles), limited partnerships and LLCs, development, major acquisitions, dispositions and exchanges, option agreements, ground and commercial leases. He has a subspecialty in the Gaming and Hospitality industry.

**Personal:** Qualified since 1980. Chair of the Global Real Estate Practice.

## HODARA, Fred S
Akin Gump Strauss Hauer & Feld LLP, New York
212 872 8040
fhodara@akingump.com
*Featured in Bankruptcy/Restructuring (Nationwide), Bankruptcy/Restructuring (New York)*
See under Nationwide for profile.

## HOFF, Jonathan M
Cadwalader, Wickersham & Taft LLP, New York
212 504 6474
jonathan.hoff@cwt.com
*Featured in Litigation (New York)*
**Practice Areas:** Represents public companies and financial institutions in corporate and securities litigation, including shareholder class action and derivative suits, M&A transactions, accounting- and finance-related litigations, corporate- and securities-related government and internal investigations, as well as public and private companies in connection with complex business disputes. Represented major financial institutions in the defense of securities class actions involving billions in potential damages and in connection with various litigations and disputes involving sub-prime mortgages, commercial and residential real estate securitizations, CDOs, derivatives and other structured products; a major pharmaceutical company in the defense of a multi-billion dollar securities class action; the directors of a major financial institution in connection with a shareholder derivative action (and related SEC investigation) and the Audit Committee concerning an internal investigation; and a major private company in connection with numerous business and commercial litigations.
**Personal:** JD, University of California, Los Angeles; BS, University of California, Berkeley.

## HOFSTETTER, Richard
Frankfurt Kurnit Klein & Selz, New York
212 826 5537
rhofstetter@fkks.com
*Featured in Media & Entertainment (New York)*
**Practice Areas:** Co-chair of firm's Entertainment Group. Particular emphasis in all forms of television development, production, distribution, and ancillary platforms, including licensing, merchandising, and advertiser-supported and branded entertainment. Represents performers, producers, writers, and production companies for scripted and dramatic programs, and for news and reality-based programming. Represents distribution companies and television networks in programming/distribution for network, syndication, cable, public television, children's programming, international production/distribution, advertising sponsorships, and format sales. Counsels international producers in licensing formats, producing and distributing their programming in the US. Former Adjunct Faculty Member, New York University. Listed in Best Lawyers in America. Named a New York-area

'Super Lawyer' in the field of entertainment and sports.
**Professional Memberships:** Voting Member, Academy of Television Arts and Sciences; International Television Academy; BAFTA; Board of Advisors, New York Television Festival; Member, American Bar Association's Patent, Trademark and Copyright Law; American Bar Association's Entertainment and Sports Industries Forum Committee.

## HOGAN, Kevin M
Phillips Lytle LLP, Buffalo
716 847 8331
khogan@phillipslytle.com
*Featured in Environment (New York)*
**Practice Areas:** Mr Hogan concentrates his practice in the area of environmental law, including prosecution and defense of CERCLA and petroleum spill cost recovery actions in state and federal courts, counseling industrial clients on environmental regulatory compliance at both the state and federal levels, assisting a variety of clients with environmental due diligence with respect to real property acquisitions, use, and divestitures, and counseling banking clients with environmental concerns that arise with commercial and lending transactions.
**Professional Memberships:** American Bar Association, Litigation Section, Natural Resources Section and Energy and Environmental Law Section; New York State Bar Association, Environmental Law Section; Bar Association of Erie County, Environmental Law Committee; Federal Practice and Procedure Committee; Defense Research Institute; Western New York Trial Lawyers Association and International Association of Defense Counsel.
**Career:** Joined firm in 1992 and has been a Partner since 2000. Mr Hogan currently is the firm's Environment and Energy Practice Team Leader and previously served as it's Trial Department Administrator. Judicial Clerkship Hon. Richard C Cardamone; U.S. Court of Appeals, Second Circuit, 1991-92.
**Publications:** He has written extensively on environmental topics.
**Personal:** Vermont Law School, JD summa cum laude, 1991 and University of Connecticut, BS Mechanical and Metallurgical Engineering, 1983.

## HOLD-WEISS, Rachel
Arent Fox LLP, New York
212 484 3999
rachel.hold-weiss@arentfox.com
*Featured in Healthcare (New York)*
**Practice Areas:** Rachel Hold-Weiss' clients include hospices, home health agencies, durable medical equipment providers, long term care providers and physician practices. Rachel advises clients in fraud and abuse matters, federal and state audits and investigations, compliance audits, development and implementation of compliance programs, survey and reimbursement issues and healthcare privacy and security matters. Rachel serves on the Regulatory Committee of NHPCO, and is an active speaker on hospice, home health and compliance topics at national and local con-

ferences. Rachel is a nationally certified physician assistant registered to practice in New York, who previously practiced in hospital and outpatient settings.

## HOLLAND, Mark
Goodwin Procter LLP, New York
212 459 7152
mholland@goodwinprocter.com
*Featured in Securities (Nationwide), Litigation (New York)*
See under Nationwide for profile.

## HOLLENDER, Victor
Skadden, Arps, Slate, Meagher & Flom LLP & Affiliates, New York
212 735 2825
victor.hollender@skadden.com
*Featured in Tax (New York)*
**Practice Areas:** Victor Hollender advises on a wide range of domestic and international tax matters, including mergers and acquisitions, divestitures, cross-border financings, spin-offs, initial public offerings and taxation of sovereign entities. Mr Hollender has extensive experience advising on and structuring a wide variety of financial products, hybrid capital and derivatives transactions, as well as transactions involving the formation and operation of partnerships and joint ventures.
**Career:** JD, The University of Chicago Law School, (honors); BA, The University of Chicago, (honors; Phi Beta Kappa).

## HOLLEY, Steven L
Sullivan & Cromwell LLP, New York
212 558 4737
holleys@sullcrom.com
*Featured in Antitrust (New York)*
**Practice Areas:** Antitrust counseling and litigation; patent and securities litigation; complex commercial disputes. Extensive experience counseling clients on competition issues, including prospective merger reviews and other investigations by US and European regulators. Has handled state and federal cases and is experienced with various forms of ADR. Has represented Microsoft since 1992 in wide range of antitrust matters in US and abroad. Other clients include Chrysler, Diageo, Eastman Kodak, Gildan, Sea Star Line and United Rentals.
**Professional Memberships:** ABA; ABCNY; NYSBA.
**Career:** Partner since 1991. Law clerk, Hon. José Cabranes.
**Personal:** NYU School of Law (JD, 1983); Indiana University (BA, 1980).

## HOLMES, Joshua
Wachtell, Lipton, Rosen & Katz, New York
212 403 1306
JMHolmes@wlrk.com
*Featured in Tax (New York)*
**Practice Areas:** Focuses on the tax aspects of corporate transactions, including mergers and acquisitions, joint ventures, spin-offs and financial instruments. Has been the principal tax lawyer on numerous domestic and cross border transactions in a wide range of industries.

**Professional Memberships:** Active member of the Executive Committee of the Tax Section of the New York State Bar Association. Member of the Tax Section of the American Bar Association, also is a member of the New York Committee of Realty Trust Tax Lawyers.
**Career:** Joined the Tax Department of Wachtell, Lipton, Rosen & Katz as an associate in 1999 and was elected partner in 2007.
**Personal:** Received a BA from the University of Pennsylvania in 1993, an MA in Economics from Stanford University in 1996, a JD from Stanford Law School in 1999 and an LLM in Taxation from New York University School of Law in 2004.

## HOLO, Robert
Simpson Thacher & Bartlett LLP, New York
212 455 2514
rholo@stblaw.com
*Featured in Tax (New York)*
**Practice Areas:** Tax Partner concentrating on federal income tax matters, with an emphasis on corporate mergers and acquisitions, cross-border and international tax matters, joint ventures, and capital markets and financing transactions. Advises on tax matters for, among others, the Firm's corporate clients, bank clients, private equity clients and international clients.
**Career:** Joined the Firm in 1997; became Partner in 2001. Former clerk on the United States Ninth Circuit Court of Appeals.
**Personal:** BA, University of California, Santa Cruz (1987); JD, University of California, Los Angeles (1991).

## HOLTZER, Gary T
Weil, Gotshal & Manges LLP, New York
212 310 8463
gary.holtzer@weil.com
*Featured in Bankruptcy/Restructuring (Nationwide), Bankruptcy/Restructuring (New York)*
**Practice Areas:** Domestic and international restructurings, crisis management, corporate governance, financings and acquisitions involving distressed situations. Lead role in company side restructurings includes General Growth, LodgeNet, Financial Guaranty Insurance Company, Centro Properties, Highland Hospitality, Nortek, Pilgrim's Pride, Panolam, TI Auto, Vertis Holdings, Syncora, Silicon Graphics, and Parmalat. Represented investors, lenders and purchasers in financings and acquisitions involving troubled companies, including Aquilex, Ener1, Penton Media, Circuit City, Sea Containers, Calpine, Montgomery Ward, Kmart, Comdisco, Conseco Finance, and Clark Retail. Adjunct Professor, Cardozo School of Law; Fellow of the American College of Bankruptcy.
**Personal:** Cornell University; Benjamin N. Cardozo School of Law.

## HORKOVICH, Robert M
Anderson Kill & Olick, P.C., New York
212 278-1322
rhorkovich@andersonkill.com
*Featured in Insurance (Nationwide), Insurance (New York)*
See under Nationwide for profile.

**HOROWITZ, Gary I**
Simpson Thacher & Bartlett LLP, New York
212 455 7113
ghorowitz@stblaw.com
*Featured in Private Equity (Nationwide),*
*Corporate/M&A (New York), Insurance (New York)*
See under Nationwide for profile.

**HOROWITZ, Steven G**
Cleary Gottlieb Steen & Hamilton LLP, New York
212 225 2580
shorowitz@cgsh.com
*Featured in Real Estate (Nationwide), Real Estate (New York)*
See under Nationwide for profile.

**HORSCH, Richard**
White & Case LLP, New York
212 819 8866
rhorsch@whitecase.com
*Featured in Environment (New York)*
**Career:** Mr Horsch represents clients in environmental and toxic tort litigation and advises on all aspects of environmental law. He also represents clients in cost recovery actions under CERCLA and other environmental statutes. Mr Horsch also provides advice on environmental issues in domestic and international mergers and acquisitions, including those involving the chemical, lead-acid battery, mining, petroleum storage and distribution, oil refining, pulp and paper, and oil exploration, production and development industries; he also regularly advises on environmental issues in project financings, domestically and internationally. Mr Horsch also counsels clients on compliance with environmental laws. To view his biography, visit www.whitecase.com/rhorsch.

**HOTZ, JR., Robert H.**
Akin Gump Strauss Hauer & Feld LLP, New York
212 872 1028
rhotz@akingump.com
*Featured in Litigation (New York)*
**Practice Areas:** Mr Hotz is co-head of the firm's New York litigation section and represents individuals and corporations in white collar matters and related civil litigation.
**Career:** Served for five years as a prosecutor in the U.S. Attorney's Office for the Southern District of New York and was a member of the Securities and Commodities Fraud Task Force. Co-lead prosecutor in the successful insider trading prosecutions arising out of the leak of the U.S. Treasury Department's decision to suspend issuance of the 30-year bond.
**Personal:** JD, Georgetown University Law Center, cum laude, 1992. BA, Georgetown University, cum laude, 1989.

**HOWARD, Nigel L**
Covington & Burling LLP, New York
212 841 1020
nhoward@cov.com
*Featured in Outsourcing (Nationwide), Technology (New York)*
See under Nationwide for profile.

**HSING, Benjamin**
Kaye Scholer LLP, New York
212 836 8735
benjamin.hsing@kayescholer.com
*Featured in Intellectual Property (New York)*
**Practice Areas:** Benjamin Hsing, a Partner in Kaye Scholer's Intellectual Property Department, focuses his practice on litigation and trials before the US district courts and the US International Trade Commission, and appeals to the US Court of Appeals for the Federal Circuit. He has litigated patent cases on behalf of major pharmaceutical and technology companies. In addition to his litigation and appellate practice, Ben counsels US and international clients regarding US intellectual property law by providing them with infringement, validity, enforceability and clearance opinions, and by advising them in licensing and antitrust matters.

**HUBER, Betty Moy**
Davis Polk & Wardwell LLP, New York
212 450 4764
betty.huber@davispolk.com
*Featured in Environment (New York)*
**Practice Areas:** Co-head of Davis Polk's Environmental Group and Counsel in the firm's Corporate Department. Represents companies, boards, financial institutions, private equity groups and others on a wide range of environmental, health and safety matters, including liability analysis, corporate governance matters and, in the context of transactions, structuring, diligence, disclosure, protective devices and risk allocation in complex mergers and acquisitions and other forms of investments, securities offerings, bank financings and bankruptcies and restructurings.

**HUEBNER, Marshall S**
Davis Polk & Wardwell LLP, New York
212 450 4099
marshall.huebner@davispolk.com
*Featured in Bankruptcy/Restructuring (Nationwide), Bankruptcy/Restructuring (New York)*
See under Nationwide for profile.

**HUGHES, Christopher**
Cadwalader, Wickersham & Taft LLP, New York
212 504 6891
christopher.hughes@cwt.com
*Featured in Intellectual Property (New York)*
**Practice Areas:** Head, Intellectual Property Group. Experience in complex patent trials and litigation (District Courts, ITC and arbitrations); trade secret and trademark litigation (Federal Circuit Appeals); licensing; and IP counseling and diligence. Experience coordinating patent infringement trials and hearings throughout U.S. and Europe (preliminary relief, cross-border injunctions, and nullity, cancellation, and opposition proceedings). Representative engagements: IBM (patent litigations in DC and ITC); Medinol Ltd. (US and International patent infringement actions for cardiovascular stent technologies); Priceline.com ("Priceline Patent"); Qualcomm (DC); and AT&T (DC). Special Master, U.S. District Court for the District of Rhode Island in Arendi U.S.A., Inc. v Microsoft Corporation.

Other clients: Eastman Kodak, Heidelberger Druckmaschinen, Lucent Technologies, Osteonics, Robert Bosch, Symbol Technologies and Stryker.
**Professional Memberships:** Professional organizations including Board of Directors, New York Intellectual Property Law Association; Fellow, American Bar Foundation.
**Personal:** JD, New York University School of Law; BS, New York University School of Engineering and Science.

**HUMMEL, Keith R**
Cravath, Swaine & Moore LLP, New York
212 474 1772
khummel@cravath.com
*Featured in Intellectual Property (New York)*
**Practice Areas:** Extensive experience litigating and trying complex intellectual property disputes for plaintiffs and defendants. Handles cases for clients in diverse fields, including telecommunications, medical devices, computer hardware/software, food additives, luxury flooring products, pharmaceuticals and biotechnology. Frequently advises clients on national and worldwide intellectual property strategy.
**Career:** Partner since 1998.
**Personal:** Georgetown University Law Center (JD, magna cum laude, 1990; Senior Notes and Comments Editor of the Georgetown Law Journal; Order of the Coif); University of Notre Dame (BA, 1987); Board of Visitors, Georgetown University Law Center.

**HUNT, Peter J**
Pillsbury Winthrop Shaw Pittman LLP, New York
212 858 1139
peter.hunt@pillsburylaw.com
*Featured in Employee Benefits & Executive Compensation (New York)*
**Practice Areas:** Mr Hunt advises employers, financial institutions and investment funds on fiduciary and compliance issues under ERISA, the Internal Revenue Code and securities laws. He regularly advises on the employee benefits and executive compensation aspects of corporate acquisitions and dispositions. Recent experience also includes designing and drafting equity-based compensation plans, deferred compensation plans, and complex employer pension and profit-sharing plans.
**Professional Memberships:** American College of Employee Benefits Counsel; American Bar Association; New York State and New York City Bar Associations.
**Personal:** JD, New York University, 1984; BS, University of Virginia, 1978.

**HUNTER JR, Fraser L**
WilmerHale, New York
212 230 8882
fraser.hunter@wilmerhale.com
*Featured in Litigation (New York)*
**Practice Areas:** Member of both the Securities and Litigation Departments. Has represented individuals, accountants, broker-dealers, investment banks, hedge funds and other financial institutions in broad range of complex litigation, regulatory and enforcement matters. Experience in

securities enforcement, white collar crime, internal investigations and complex commercial and class action litigation.
**Professional Memberships:** Member, American Bar Association, Federal Bar Council and the Association of the Bar of the City of New York, where he has served on the Committee on International Human Rights, the Committee on Securities Regulation and the Securities Litigation Committee.
**Personal:** JD, Columbia Law School; BA, Brown University.

**IASON, Lawrence**
Morvillo Abramowitz Grand Iason & Anello P.C., New York
212 856 9600
liason@magislaw.com
*Featured in Litigation (New York)*
**Practice Areas:** Lawrence Iason represents financial institutions, major corporations and their senior corporate officers, and prominent individuals in a wide variety of high-profile and complex white collar cases. He has successfully represented clients in investigations by the Securities and Exchange Commission, the Department of Justice, and the Financial Industry Regulatory Authority. An experienced trial attorney, he has successfully represented clients at all stages of criminal and civil trials, in arbitrations and on appeal. He also counsels corporate boards in connection with corporate governance and accounting issues.
**Professional Memberships:** Fellow of the American College of Trial Lawyers.
**Career:** Appointed by the District Attorneys Association of the State of New York to the New York State White Collar Crime Task Force that is charged with examining New York's anti-fraud and anti-corruption laws. Former head of the New York office of the Securities and Exchange Commission. Served as an Assistant Special Prosecutor in the Watergate Special Prosecution Force and as Assistant U.S. Attorney for the Southern District of New York.
**Personal:** New York University School of Law (JD cum laude, member of the Order of the Coif and an editor of the Law Review).

**ICHEL, David W**
Simpson Thacher & Bartlett LLP, New York
212 455 2000
dichel@stblaw.com
*Featured in Products Liability (Nationwide), Litigation (New York)*
**Practice Areas:** Partner specializing in complex commercial litigation and counseling, including for Vivendi, Ducati, Heineken, Toys "R" Us, JPMorgan Chase, among others. Active in matters of commercial fraud and contract, product liability and mass tort, securities litigation, insurance coverage/insolvency, distributor termination, antitrust, defamation, advertising/labeling.
**Professional Memberships:** Chair, Duke Law School Board of Visitors (2009-present); American Law Institute.

**Career:** Joined Simpson Thacher, 1978; Partner since 1985. Teaches Complex Litigation at Duke Law School.
**Personal:** BA, summa cum laude, Duke University (1975); JD, Duke University School of Law (1978). Bar Admissions NY, NJ, DC, U.S. Supreme Court and numerous federal Circuit courts.

### ISBY, Michael
Simpson Thacher & Bartlett LLP, New York
212 455 3915
misby@stblaw.com
*Featured in Environment (New York)*
**Practice Areas:** Senior Counsel and member of the Firm's Corporate Department. He practices in the firm's Environmental Practice Group concentrating on the environmental aspects of mergers and acquisitions, securities offerings, and lendings. Practice also includes environmental law compliance counseling.
**Career:** Law Clerk to Hon. David Edelstein, United States District Judge, SDNY (1986-88). Joined the firm in 1988.
**Personal:** BA, summa cum laude, Phi Beta Kappa, Queens College (1983); JD, Fordham University School of Law (1986); associate editor, Fordham Law Review.

### ISELIN, Harold N
Greenberg Traurig, LLP, Albany
518 689 1415
IselinH@gtlaw.com
*Featured in Healthcare (New York), Healthcare (Nationwide)*
**Practice Areas:** Managing Shareholder-Albany Office. Co-Chair, Global Insurance Regulatory and Transactions Practice. Governmental affairs, Health and FDA Business.
**Professional Memberships:** Member: New York State Bar Association; District of Columbia Bar Association; American Health Lawyers Association; NYS Archives Partnership Trust; Capital Repertory Theater.
**Career:** Listed: Best Lawyers in America, 2009-13; Super Lawyers magazine, 2007-12; Hudson Valley Magazine, 2007. Rated, AV® Preeminent™ 5.0 out of 5. US Department of Justice, 1984-86; former Assistant Counsel to Governor of New York.
**Personal:** JD, Columbia University School of Law; BA, magna cum laude, Wesleyan University, Phi Beta Kappa.

### IVANHOE, Robert J
Greenberg Traurig, LLP, New York
212 801 9333
IvanhoeR@gtlaw.com
*Featured in Real Estate (Nationwide), Real Estate (New York)*
See under Nationwide for profile.

### IVESTER, Eric
Skadden, Arps, Slate, Meagher & Flom LLP & Affiliates, New York
212 735 3111
Eric.Ivester@skadden.com
*Featured in Bankruptcy/Restructuring (New York)*
**Practice Areas:** Represents clients including borrowers, creditors, investors, sellers, purchasers

and other parties in all stages of complex restructuring transactions, such as in-court and out-of-court reorganizations, debt restructurings, acquisitions and divestitures. Recent representations include Travelport Holdings in its out-of-court restructuring; Ipsen Pharma S.A. in the sale of its hemophilia products to Baxter and Cangene, DISH Network Corporation in its $1.4 billion acquisition of 100 percent of the equity of DBSD North America, Inc.; and MF Global Holdings, Ltd. in its Chapter 11 filing.
**Career:** JD, University of Oklahoma, 1985 (highest honors; Order of the Coif); BA, University of Oklahoma, 1982.

### IVILL, David S
McDermott Will & Emery LLP, New York
212 547 5698
divill@mwe.com
*Featured in Healthcare (New York)*
**Practice Areas:** Partner-in-charge of the health industry advisory practice in New York. Extensive experience in statutory and regulatory issues affecting the provision of health care services, particularly with respect to New York State; practice includes counseling with respect to operational and management issues, fraud and abuse, Medicaid Managed Care, compliance programs, as well as reimbursement matters, corporate practice of medicine issues and not-for-profit/tax-exempt matters.
**Professional Memberships:** American Health Lawyers Association; Bar of the City of New York.
**Personal:** New York University School of Law, JD; Pennsylvania College of Podiatric Medicine, DPM; Westminster College, BS (cum laude).

### JACOBSON, Hillel
Willkie Farr & Gallagher LLP, New York
212 728 8655
hjacobson@willkie.com
*Featured in Tax (New York)*
**Practice Areas:** Specializes in federal income tax matters and advises US and non-US clients on partnership tax matters, mergers and acquisitions, international tax matters, bankruptcy reorganizations, matters relating to private equity funds, hedge funds and their investors, and private foundation tax matters.
**Personal:** JD, Columbia University, 1999. AB, Beth Medrash Govoha, 1991. For more information: http://www.willkie.com/HillelJacobson

### JACOBSON, Marc
Marc Jacobson, P.C., New York
212 245 8955
marc@marcjacobson.com
*Featured in Media & Entertainment (New York)*
**Practice Areas:** Marc is a top music lawyer and is especially well regarded for his work in international licensing of publishing rights for digital providers. Marc has a strong reputation for his work in the film business, including financing structures, production work and distribution agreements.
**Professional Memberships:** Founding Chairman, NYS Bar Association Section on Entertainment, Arts & Sports Law; Member, Executive Committee, International Association of

Entertainment Lawyers; Member, Board of Directors, Long Island Film and Television Foundation; Member: Independent Feature Project, The Copyright Society of the USA, Association of Independent Music Publishers. Formerly Chairman, The Internet Alliance; Member, Board of Directors, Direct Marketing Association.
**Career:** Marc's decades of experience at the intersection of traditional content and the internet is unique. His film & music background goes back to his childhood. He is a frequent panelist at Internet, music, and film conferences around the world. He is admitted to practice in NY, CA and FL.
**Personal:** JD, NYU School of Law; BA, magna cum laude, SUNY at Buffalo.

### JAFFE BLOOM, Suzanne
Winston & Strawn LLP, New York
sbloom@winston.com
*Featured in Litigation (New York)*
**Practice Areas:** Suzanne Jaffe Bloom represents companies, board committees and individuals in white-collar criminal and regulatory matters, internal investigations, and related proceedings, including those involving alleged health care fraud, commercial fraud, official corruption, securities fraud, bribery, obstruction of justice, accounting fraud and tax fraud. She also represents clients in connection with qui tam/whistleblower litigation, complex commercial litigation and the development and implementation of compliance programs.
**Career:** Former federal prosecutor: US Attorney's Office, Southern District of New York; US Attorney's Office, Eastern District of New York (Deputy Chief of the Long Island Criminal Division).
**Personal:** Harvard Law School, JD'88 cum laude

### JANUSZEWSKI, David
Cahill Gordon & Reindel LLP, New York
212 701 3352
djanuszewski@cahill.com
*Featured in Litigation (New York)*
**Practice Areas:** Serves as lead counsel in complex litigation challenges including securities, insurance, employment, bankruptcy and environmental issues. Leads internal investigations arising from alleged violations of banking, insurance, securities and other laws and regulations, as well as allegations of accounting irregularities. Has defended corporations and individuals in investigations by the Securities and Exchange Commission, Department of Justice and other federal and state agencies.
**Personal:** Yale University, BA, 1985, summa cum laude, Harvard Law School, JD, 1988, cum laude.

### JEBEJIAN, Sarkis
Kirkland & Ellis LLP, New York
212 446 5944
sarkis.jebejian@kirkland.com
*Featured in Corporate/M&A (New York)*
**Practice Areas:** Sarkis Jebejian focuses his practice primarily on mergers and acquisitions, both domestic and cross border. He also provides governance and other general corporate counseling to

clients and their boards of directors, including Dodd Frank Act compliance. He has advised clients including Northrop Grumman, PSEG, Genpact, NextEra Energy, BAE Systems, British American Tobacco plc and the independent directors of General Motors.
**Career:** Sarkis was formerly a partner at Cravath, Swaine & Moore LLP.
**Personal:** Columbia Law School (JD, 1994; Harlan Fiske Stone Scholar); Columbia College (BA, 1991).

### JEROME, John
Sullivan & Cromwell LLP, New York
212 558 3696
jeromej@sullcrom.com
*Featured in Bankruptcy/Restructuring (New York)*
**Professional Memberships:** Official mediator, U.S. Bankruptcy Court, Southern District of New York; Member, Disciplinary Committee, NYS Supreme Court-Appellate Division, First Department; American Bankruptcy Institute, American Bar Association, International Insolvency Institute, the New York City Bar Association, and National Bankruptcy Conference.
**Career:** Of Counsel, July 2011. Actively involved in development of 1978 Bankruptcy Code. Over 25 years as lead outside counsel for The Chase Manhattan Bank on financial restructuring/bankruptcy issues. Previously, partner at Saul Ewing LLP, partner and head of restructuring/bankruptcy practice, Milbank, Tweed, Hadley & McCloy LLP.
**Personal:** St. John's University Law School (JD, 1961); St. John's University (BBA, 1958)

### JOHNSON, Boyd
WilmerHale, New York
212 230 8862
boyd.johnson@wilmerhale.com
*Featured in Litigation (New York)*
**Practice Areas:** Represents corporations and executives in criminal and civil investigations conducted by a variety of government regulators, including the DOJ, SEC, NY Attorney General's Office and the UK's FSA, and advises businesses on crisis response and media relations. Experience includes insider trading, financial fraud investigations, FCPA and public corruption probes, antitrust inquiries, anti-money laundering issues, FCA and FIRREA actions, and cybersecurity matters.
**Career:** At the Southern District of New York, served as the Deputy US Attorney; Chief of the Public Corruption Unit; and Chief of the International Narcotics Trafficking Unit.

### JOHNSON, William
Fried, Frank, Harris, Shriver & Jacobson LLP, New York
212 859 8765
William.Johnson@FriedFrank.com
*Featured in Litigation (New York)*
**Practice Areas:** Head, White Collar Criminal Defense Practice. Co-head, White Collar Criminal Defense and Securities Enforcement Practice Group. Co-head, Internal Investigations and Monitoring practice. Represents clients in white

collar criminal and regulatory matters involving DOJ, SEC, and other agencies. Conducts internal investigations and advises on anti-corruption matters.
**Career:** Former Chief, Securities and Commodities Fraud Task Force, USAO, SDNY. Prosecuted former WorldCom CEO Bernard Ebbers and CFO Scott Sullivan. Former SEC attorney. Currently Independent Monitor for Virgin Islands Police Department.
**Personal:** JD, American University, Washington College of Law (1991); BA, cum laude, Ohio Wesleyan University (1988).

### JOHNSTON, James L
Davis & Gilbert LLP, New York
212 468 4867
jjohnston@dglaw.com
*Featured in Media & Entertainment (New York)*
**Practice Areas:** Media and entertainment: film and television.
**Career:** Mr Johnston represents global media companies, producers, agencies and advertisers in connection with the development, production and distribution of television programs, motion pictures, digital and other audiovisual content. His practice focuses on alternative means of financing and distributing content across multiple platforms. In addition, he negotiates a full range of agreements including content library acquisition, live event programming, sponsorship and other cross-promotions agreements. Mr Johnston also advises clients on SAG, AFTRA and other union issues facing content producers. He is recognized by The Legal 500 U.S. for advertising and marketing law.

### JONES, Maria
Kramer Levin Naftalis & Frankel LLP, New York
212 715 9256
mjones@kramerlevin.com
*Featured in Tax (New York)*
**Practice Areas:** A leading practitioner in the field of state and local tax matters, Ms Jones heads Kramer Levin's tax practice, concentrating on state and local tax planning and controversies for corporations and individuals. Prior to private practice, Ms Jones served as a Commissioner of the New York State Tax Appeals Tribunal as one of the first three Commissioners to adjudicate taxpayer disputes and as Deputy Commissioner for Legal Affairs for the New York City Department of Finance, advising the Commissioner on legal and policy issues.

### JONES, Richard D
Dechert LLP, New York
212 698 3844
richard.jones@dechert.com
*Featured in Real Estate (New York), Real Estate (Pennsylvania)*
**Practice Areas:** Mr Jones, co-chair of Dechert's finance and real estate group, focuses his practice on capital markets and mortgage finance.
**Professional Memberships:** Member, Connecticut, New York and Pennsylvania Bars; former president, CRE Finance Council; co-founder, Commercial Real Estate Institute; mem-

ber and past governor, American College of Real Estate Lawyers; member, Executive Committee, Commercial Mortgage Board of Governors of the Mortgage Bankers Association of America.
**Personal:** Washington and Lee University (BA, 1975, magna cum laude); University of Virginia School of Law (JD, 1978); Boston University School of Law (LLM, 1981).

### JOSSEN, Robert J
Dechert LLP, New York
212 698 3639
robert.jossen@dechert.com
*Featured in Litigation (New York)*
**Practice Areas:** Mr Jossen is chair of the firm's litigation department and focuses his practice on commercial litigation, securities, and white collar criminal defense. He has devoted a significant portion of his career to legal ethics and has lectured extensively on the subject.
**Professional Memberships:** Member, New York Bar; fellow, American College of Trial Lawyers; instructor, National Institute for Trial Advocacy.
**Career:** Chief Appellate Attorney, U.S. Attorney's Office, Southern District of New York
**Personal:** Cornell University (BS, 1969); Columbia Law School (JD, 1972, notes and comments editor, Columbia Law Review).

### JOYCE, Edward M
Jones Day, New York
212 326 3834
emjoyce@jonesday.com
*Featured in Insurance (New York)*
**Practice Areas:** Extensive experience in insurance coverage litigation resulting in several landmark court decisions. Ed has secured more than $800 million in verdicts/settlements. Ed represents policyholders in various industries including food/beverage, industrial, textile, retail, real estate/construction, media/entertainment, pharmaceuticals, healthcare, telecommunications, energy, financial services, and municipalities. Ed's experience includes professional liability, directors/officers liability, property/business interruption, employee dishonesty, data/equipment damage, unfair competition, construction, intellectual property, advertising injury, business torts, products liability, employment liability, and environmental liability. Ed has been recognized in Legal 500 and Best Lawyers in America. Ed speaks at industry functions and at the Risk and Insurance Management Society's Annual Conference.

### JUANTORENA, Jorge U
Cleary Gottlieb Steen & Hamilton LLP, New York
212 225 2758
jjuantorena@cgsh.com
*Featured in Latin American Investment (New York)*
**Practice Areas:** Cross-border capital markets transactions and mergers and acquisitions, with a concentration in Latin America. Extensive experience representing foreign SEC reporting companies in corporate governance matters.
**Professional Memberships:** Member of the Bars in New York and California.

### Career:
**Career:** Joined firm, 1992; became partner, 2000. JD, cum laude, New York University School of Law (1991); BA, Cornell University (1988).

### KALMYKOV, Kate
Greenberg Traurig, LLP, Florham Park
973 443 3276
KalmykovK@gtlaw.com
*Featured in Immigration (New York)*
**Practice Areas:** Business Immigration & Compliance.
**Professional Memberships:** Chair, Immigration Committee, Section of Administrative Law, American Bar Association, 2011-13.
**Career:** Listed: New Jersey Law Journal, 'New Leaders of the Bar', 2012; Super Lawyers magazine, New York Super Lawyers, 'Rising Star', 2012; Outstanding Subcommittee Chair, American Bar Association, Litigation Section, Immigration Litigation Committee, 2010-11; Education Committee Co-Chair of the Year/Conference Committee Co-Chair, American Immigration Lawyers Association (AILA), Washington D.C. chapter, 2007.
**Personal:** MA, International Affairs, American University, 2005; JD, American University Washington College of Law, 2005; BA, magna cum laude, International Studies, American University, 2002.

### KANE, Meredith J
Paul, Weiss, Rifkind, Wharton & Garrison LLP, New York
212 373 3065
mjkane@paulweiss.com
*Featured in Real Estate (New York)*
**Practice Areas:** Partner, Real Estate Department. Represents developers, equity investors, institutional and entrepreneurial owners and government agencies in all aspects of real estate development, finance, acquisitions and sales, equity joint ventures, restructuring, leasing, securitization and public/private joint venture projects. Named one of Top 50 Women in Real Estate and one of 25 Current Leaders in the Industry by Real Estate Weekly; Best in Real Estate by Euromoney Americas Women in Business, Top 10 Women in Real Estate Development by Grid Magazine. Mayoral and gubernatorial appointee to several New York City and State boards and commissions.

### KAPLAN, Barbara T
Greenberg Traurig, LLP, New York
212 801 9250
KaplanB@gtlaw.com
*Featured in Tax (Nationwide), Tax (New York)*
See under Nationwide for profile.

### KAPLAN, Gary L
Fried, Frank, Harris, Shriver & Jacobson LLP, New York
212 859 8812
Gary.Kaplan@FriedFrank.com
*Featured in Bankruptcy/Restructuring (New York)*
**Practice Areas:** Bankruptcy and restructuring partner. Has extensive domestic, international and cross-border experience in representing debtors and official and unofficial creditors' and equity

committees in chapter 11 cases, out-of-court restructurings as well as in foreign proceedings. He also represents significant creditors, lenders and third-party purchasers in connection with chapter 11 cases and out-of-court restructuring situations. Regularly appears in bankruptcy courts throughout the United States on a wide range of issues.
**Career:** Joined in 1998; became partner in 2005. Contributing author to "Collier on Bankruptcy."
**Personal:** JD, with honors, Rutgers School of Law (1997); BA, University of Maryland (1994).

### KAROTKIN, Stephen
Weil, Gotshal & Manges LLP, New York
212 310 8350
stephen.karotkin@weil.com
*Featured in Bankruptcy/Restructuring (Nationwide), Bankruptcy/Restructuring (New York)*
See under Nationwide for profile.

### KARP, Brad S
Paul, Weiss, Rifkind, Wharton & Garrison LLP, New York
212 373 3316
bkarp@paulweiss.com
*Featured in Financial Services Regulation (Nationwide), Securities (Nationwide), Litigation (New York)*
See under Nationwide for profile.

### KASNER, Jay B
Skadden, Arps, Slate, Meagher & Flom LLP & Affiliates, New York
212 735 2628
Jay.Kasner@skadden.com
*Featured in Securities (Nationwide), Litigation (New York)*
**Practice Areas:** Heads Skadden's Securities Litigation Practice. Experienced in federal and state court litigation, including securities, corporate and takeover litigation and general commercial matters. Defends public companies and their directors/officers in actions arising under federal and state securities and corporate laws. Handles litigation arising from corporate control contests. Received "Business Trial Lawyer Award" for Excellence from Chambers USA 2008.
**Professional Memberships:** Co-Chair, Practising Law Institute Securities Litigation Conference (1996-2004).
**Career:** JD, Boston University, 1980 (cum laude; Editor, Boston University Law Review; Author, 'Minimizing Minimization: Scott v United States', Boston University Law Review); BA, Union College, 1977 (magna cum laude).

### KASOWITZ, Marc E
Kasowitz, Benson, Torres & Friedman LLP, New York
212 506 1710
mkasowitz@kasowitz.com
*Featured in Litigation (New York)*
**Practice Areas:** Marc Kasowitz is widely regarded as one of the nation's preeminent business litigators and trial lawyers. He has extensive experience in all areas of complex commercial litigation, including antitrust, securities, mass tort and real estate. He has also conducted numerous internal corporate investigations.

**Career:** Featured by The American Lawyer as a "Litigator in the Spotlight," "Heavy Hitter" and in the cover story "Fast Rise To The Top," recognized in Chambers USA ("creative and aggressive litigator," "a dynamic presence"), Benchmark Litigation ("superb advocate"), Legal 500 ("superb track record as a trial lawyer") and Lawdragon 500 ("cream of the crop").

## KATZ, David A
Wachtell, Lipton, Rosen & Katz, New York
212 403 1309
dakatz@wlrk.com
*Featured in Corporate/M&A (New York)*
**Practice Areas:** Specialises in mergers and acquisitions, corporate governance and complex securities transactions; has been involved in many major domestic and international mergers and acquisitions, and has been involved in many major corporate transactions and in a number of complex public and private offerings and corporate restructurings. In addition to representing a companies making public and private company acquisitions and engaging in negotiated merger transactions, has represented of companies in launching and defending against hostile takeovers and proxy contests as well as special committees of boards of directors in conflict or interested-party transactions. Counsels boards of directors and board committees on corporate governance matters and crisis management.
**Professional Memberships:** Member of the American Bar Association (Section on Business Law); member of the Committee on Mergers and Acquisitions subcommittee for Acquisitions of Public Companies; co-chair of the Committee on Mergers and Acquisitions Task Force on the Dictionary of M&A Terms; member of the Federal Securities Laws Committee, the New York State Bar Association (Section on Business Law), the Association of the Bar of the City of New York and National Association of Corporate Directors and the Society of Corporate Secretaries and Governance Professionals.
**Career:** Partner at Wachtell, Lipton, Rosen & Katz since 1996. Senior professional fellow at New York University Center for Law and Business, adjunct professor at Vanderbilt University Law School and an adjunct professor at New York University School of Law. Formerly was adjunct professor at the Owens Graduate School of Management at Vanderbilt University. In 2004, was chosen by 'The American Lawyer' as one of the 45 highest performing members of the private bar under the age of 45; in 2005 and 2012 he was selected by 'The American Lawyer' as a Dealmaker of the Year; in 2007. 2009 and 2012, he was named by 'Directorship' in its ranking of the 100 most influential players in corporate governance and, in 2009, 2010, 2011 and 2012, he was named Who's Who Legal's Mergers and Acquisitions Lawyer of the Year. Also member of the Board of Directors of The Partnership at Drugfree.org and of the Advisory Board at the John L. Weinberg Center for Corporate Governance at the University of Delaware.
**Publications:** Has written extensively and lectures frequently on mergers and acquisitions, cor-

porate governance and securities regulation matters. Writes a bi-monthly column on Corporate Governance for the 'New York Law Journal'.
**Personal:** Graduated from Brandeis University and from New York University School of Law.

## KATZ, Elai
Cahill Gordon & Reindel LLP, New York
212 701 3039
ekatz@cahill.com
*Featured in Antitrust (New York)*
**Practice Areas:** Elai's practice focuses on a wide range of antitrust matters, including M&A, counseling, litigation, and investigations. He has guided many transactions through merger reviews and has a strong record obtaining quick and positive resolutions early in the regulatory process. He has advised clients on joint ventures, distribution arrangements, pricing policies, and trade associations. Elai also represents clients in complex class actions alleging price fixing and monopolization, including the representation of defendants in Nicsand v. 3M (6th Cir.) and IPO Fee Antitrust Litigation (2d Cir.), among others.
**Personal:** Yale University, BA, 1992, Columbia Law School, JD, 1996.

## KATZ, Jeffrey
Davis & Gilbert LLP, New York
212 468 4823
jkatz@dglaw.com
*Featured in Intellectual Property (New York)*
**Practice Areas:** Intellectual Property; Trade Mark & Copyright.
**Career:** Jeffrey Katz's practice involves representing companies, institutions and individuals in connection with trademark and copyright matters. Mr Katz has extensive experience in the areas of domestic and international trademark clearance, registration, maintenance, policing and enforcement, and license agreements. He regularly counsels clients on issues relating to selection of marks, searching, registration, policing, enforcement proceedings (administrative and judicial), diligence in corporate transactions, and use and protection of trademarks in advertising and marketing communications, in digital communications and on the Internet. Mr Katz is also heavily involved with domain name protection and enforcement proceedings.

## KAVALER, Thomas J
Cahill Gordon & Reindel LLP, New York
212 701 3406
tkavaler@cahill.com
*Featured in Litigation (New York)*
**Practice Areas:** Litigates high-visibility matters in virtually every major field, including financial services, entertainment, energy, telecommunications, publishing, professional services, insurance, food and agriculture, healthcare and heavy manufacturing. His practice is as varied as his clientele, with a long track record of victories in commercial litigation, securities, class actions, insurance, intellectual property, antitrust, employment, tax, corporate governance, product liability, contracts and criminal law matters.
**Career:** Member, firm's Executive Committee. Fellow, International Academy of Trial Lawyers.

**Personal:** CCNY, BA, 1969. Fordham University School of Law, JD, 1972, Editor-in-Chief, Fordham Law Review. New York University, LLM, Trade Regulation, 1975.

## KAYLE, Bruce E
Milbank, Tweed, Hadley & McCloy LLP, New York
212 530 5956
BKayle@milbank.com
*Featured in Tax (New York)*
**Practice Areas:** Complex corporate transactions, derivative products and specialized financing techniques, including financial products, structured transactions, mergers and acquisitions, tax controversy, financial restructurings and US and foreign securities offerings.
**Professional Memberships:** President Emeritus The Tax Club. Member of The Tax Forum, The Board of Directors MFY Legal Services, Board of Directors Legal Services for Bronx, New York, Advisory Board of Low-Income Taxpayer Clinic Legal Aid Society.
**Career:** Practice Group Leader, Tax.
**Personal:** JD, Harvard Law School. BSE & BA, University of Pennsylvania.

## KAZANOFF, Peter E
Simpson Thacher & Bartlett LLP, New York
212 455 3525
PKazanoff@stblaw.com
*Featured in Litigation (New York)*
**Practice Areas:** Litigation Partner focusing on securities and M&A. M&A experience includes: KKR's acquisitions of Del Monte, TXU, HCA, Dollar General and Laureate; Blackstone's acquisitions of Polymer and Prime Hospitality; Apax's acquisition of Kinetic Concepts; and numerous strategic transactions such as Eaton/Cooper, Sealy/Tempur-Pedic, Xerox/ACS, Schwab/optionsXpress, DIRECTV/Liberty Entertainment, Wyeth/Pfizer, and Mars/Wrigley. Counsel for Fairfield Greenwich in matters arising out of investments made with Bernard Madoff.
**Career:** Joined the firm in 1997; Partner since 2006. Editor of Securities Law Alert.
**Personal:** The University of Chicago Law School (JD, cum laude, 1997); Bowdoin College (AB, magna cum laude, 1992).

## KELLEY, David N
Cahill Gordon & Reindel LLP, New York
212 701 3050
dkelley@cahill.com
*Featured in Litigation (New York)*
**Practice Areas:** Senior advisor to public companies, boards of directors, audit committees, and officers and directors in significant matters involving business crime and investigations by federal and state government prosecutors and regulators such as the Securities and Exchange Commission, Department of Justice, Office of the Comptroller of the Currency, and State Attorneys General. Representations include federal securities and commercial litigation as well as Grand Jury investigations, prosecutions and Congressional inquiries.
**Personal:** Prior to joining Cahill, served 17 years in the U.S. Attorney's Office for the Southern

District of New York. The College of William and Mary, AB, 1981, New York Law School, JD, 1986.

## KELLEY, Kevin
Gibson, Dunn & Crutcher LLP, New York
212 351 4022
kkelley@gibsondunn.com
*Featured in Latin American Investment (New York)*
**Practice Areas:** Co-Chair of the Latin American Practice Group. He has been active in Latin American, particularly Brazilian, capital markets and acquisition work since the early 1990s. His practice encompasses a broad range of capital markets transactions involving non-U.S. issuers (corporate and sovereign) engaging in U.S. public or private securities offerings and exchange and tender offers. He represents issuers and underwriters in public and 144A offerings of debt and equity securities, compliance with U.S. securities laws and NYSE and NASDAQ listings by foreign issuers.
**Personal:** JD, University of Pennsylvania, Articles Editor of the Law Review.

## KENNEDY, Thomas H
Skadden, Arps, Slate, Meagher & Flom LLP & Affiliates, New York
212 735 2526
Thomas.Kennedy@skadden.com
*Featured in Corporate/M&A (New York)*
**Practice Areas:** Focuses on mergers, acquisitions and other transactions with an emphasis on the telecommunications and technology industries. He is also the firm's global head of Knowledge Strategy. He has experience in many bankruptcies, hostile transactions, leveraged buyouts, proxy fights and other governance matters.
**Career:** JD, Georgetown University Law Center, 1981; BA, University of Virginia, 1978.

## KESSLER, Jeffrey L
Winston & Strawn LLP, New York
212 294 4698
jkessler@winston.com
*Featured in Antitrust (New York), Sports Law (Nationwide)*
See under Nationwide for profile.

## KEYTE, James
Skadden, Arps, Slate, Meagher & Flom LLP & Affiliates, New York
212 735 2583
james.keyte@skadden.com
*Featured in Antitrust (New York)*
**Practice Areas:** Handles a variety of antitrust litigation, transactional and advisory matters across industries. Represented Anheuser-Busch InBev, American Airlines Unsecured Creditors Committee, Martin Marietta, SanDisk, Pfizer, Express Scripts, Digital Globe, New York Presbyterian Hospital, Coca-Cola, MacAndrews and 3taps. Played a significant role in sports-related litigations, including for the NHL, NFL and NBA.
**Professional Memberships:** Chair of the Trade, Sports and Professional Associations Committee of the ABA.
**Career:** JD, Loyola Law School, 1986 (Law Review); BA, Harvard University, 1981 (cum laude).

**Publications:** Served as senior editor of the Antitrust Law Journal and Antitrust Magazine. Published over 20 articles on antitrust subjects.

### KIESELSTEIN, Marc
Kirkland & Ellis LLP, San Francisco
212 446 4665
marc.kieselstein@kirkland.com
*Featured in Bankruptcy/Restructuring (Nationwide), Bankruptcy/Restructuring (New York)*

**Practice Areas:** Marc Kieselstein has extensive experience in complex corporate restructurings, representing debtors and creditors in all aspects of insolvency practice, including Chapter 11 reorganizations, out-of-court workouts, sale of financially distressed companies, distressed debt transactions and Section 363 asset sales and purchases. His recent representations include serving as lead counsel for Nebraska Book Company, South Bay Expressway, United Retail Group, Lear Corporation, Tropicana Resorts and Visteon Corporation.
**Personal:** University of Chicago Law School, JD, 1988; City University of New York, Queens College, BA, magna cum laude, 1985.

### KIM, Michael S
Kobre & Kim LLP, New York
212 488 1201
michael.kim@kobrekim.com
*Featured in Litigation (New York)*

**Practice Areas:** Michael S Kim, a co-founder of the firm, focuses his practice on high-stakes international financial disputes and criminal investigations. He has served as lead counsel in numerous international investigations in South America, Europe and Asia on behalf of Special or Audit Committees of Boards of Directors of public companies. Mr Kim also has extensive experience advising private clients in addressing investigations or prosecutions by law enforcement authorities, with special emphasis on FCPA, antitrust, tax and accounting fraud, and securities/commodity futures laws. He has served as an expert witness on international criminal law in legal proceedings in the United Kingdom and Switzerland, and lectures regularly on various specialized topics in this area. Mr Kim is also a well-known advocate in international judgment enforcement/cross-border insolvency and financial services disputes. He has served as lead counsel in numerous cross-border disputes involving US $100 million+ relating to structured products, hedge funds, joint ventures, bankruptcy/debtor-creditor laws, and international asset tracing.
**Career:** Prior to establishing Kobre & Kim, he served as an Assistant US Attorney in the Criminal Division of the US Attorney's Office for the Southern District of New York (DOJ-SEC-CFTC Securities & Commodities Fraud Task Force). While serving as an Assistant US Attorney, Mr Kim focused on white-collar criminal cases, many of which involved international asset tracing and forfeiture. Earlier in his legal career, Mr Kim practiced at Davis Polk & Wardwell LLP in New York.
**Personal:** Mr Kim received a BA from Harvard College and a JD from Harvard Law School,

where he served as an Executive Editor of the Harvard Law Review. Prior to becoming a lawyer, Mr Kim served as a US Army infantry officer (airborne) and rifle platoon leader.

### KIPLOK, Christopher
Hughes Hubbard & Reed LLP, New York
212 837 6810
kiplok@hugheshubbard.com
*Featured in Bankruptcy/Restructuring (New York)*

**Practice Areas:** Judicial and out-of-court insolvency and financial litigation, with a particular expertise in the liquidation of brokerage firms. Chief of Staff in the Lehman Brothers Inc. and MF Global Inc. liquidations. Routinely briefs congressional committees, domestic and foreign regulators, and self regulatory organizations. Regular lecturer on topics including "too big to fail" insolvencies, cross-border bankruptcies, and complex financial litigation.
**Professional Memberships:** American Bankruptcy Institute; INSOL.
**Career:** Partner, Corporate Reorganization Group, Hughes Hubbard & Reed LLP.
**Personal:** Georgetown University, School of Foreign Service, BSFS New York University School of Law, JD Director, Greenwich House Inc., Director Barrow Street Nursery School.

### KIRSCH, Mark
Gibson, Dunn & Crutcher LLP, New York
212 351 2662
mkirsch@gibsondunn.com
*Featured in Securities (Nationwide), Litigation (New York)*

**Practice Areas:** Co-Chair of Gibson Dunn's Litigation Practice Group. Focuses on securities litigation, white-collar defense, commercial litigation and antitrust litigation. Extensive experience in defending clients in large-scale, complex class actions. Also regularly advises on internal investigations, federal and state criminal investigations and proceedings, and regulatory investigations and proceedings.
**Career:** Partner at Gibson Dunn & Crutcher; former partner and Global Head of Litigation at Clifford Chance; former Assistant U.S. Attorney; former law clerk to John M. Walker, Jr.
**Personal:** Cornell University, AB, With Distinction in All Subjects. Yale Law School, JD, Law & Policy Review.

### KLAPPER, Richard
Sullivan & Cromwell LLP, New York
212 558 3555
klapperr@sullcrom.com
*Featured in Litigation (New York)*

**Professional Memberships:** ABA; American Law Institute; FBC; NYCBA; NYSBA.
**Career:** Partner since 1987. Managing Partner, Litigation Group, 1999-2004. Wide-ranging practice covering civil litigation, including antitrust, securities, corporate governance and intellectual property disputes, as well as regulatory and white-collar investigations. Also has significant experience in cases involving complex antitrust, financial and intellectual property issues that require extensive use of experts and presentation of complex technical concepts to courts and juries.

Clients have included AIG, Bank of New York, Bankers Trust, Goldman Sachs and Microsoft.
**Personal:** Yale Law School (JD, 1979); Yale University (MA, 1979); Hamilton College, (AB, 1975).

### KLEIN, Jeffrey
Weil, Gotshal & Manges LLP, New York
212 310 8790
jeffrey.klein@weil.com
*Featured in Labor & Employment (New York)*

**Practice Areas:** Jeffrey Klein chairs Weil's global Labor and Employment Practice and has been consistently recognized as one of the nation's top management attorneys. Employers across many industries, such as Avon Products, MasterCard, UnitedHealthcare, and Jumeirah Hotels, look to him to handle their most difficult and important employment matters, including class actions (discrimination, ERISA and wage-and-hour cases), restrictive covenants/trade secrets disputes, terminations and workforce restructurings, investigations, and counseling. He also has an active sports law, licensing and endorsement practice.
**Personal:** Fellow, College of Labor and Employment Lawyers; Amherst College (BA, magna cum laude, 1978); Columbia University Law School (JD, 1981).

### KLEIN, Steven D
Willkie Farr & Gallagher LLP, New York
212 728 8221
sklein@willkie.com
*Featured in Real Estate (New York)*

**Practice Areas:** Co-Chair of Real Estate Department. Specializes in REIT offerings, REIT mergers, joint ventures, formation of investment funds, acquisitions and dispositions, financings, restructurings, and leasing transactions. Represents clients in all types of real estate transactions, and in drafting and negotiating related agreements, including REIT and securitized financing agreements, construction, permanent and mezzanine loan agreements, loan restructuring agreements, partnership and limited liability company agreements, private placement memoranda, property management agreements, construction and development agreements, contracts of sale, retail and office leases, and regional shopping centre agreements.
**Personal:** JD, Rutgers University, 1986. BA, Queens College, 1983. See: http://www.willkie.com/StevenKlein

### KLEINMAN, Gary S
Greenberg Traurig, LLP, New York
212 801 6486
KleinmanG@gtlaw.com
*Featured in Real Estate (New York)*

**Practice Areas:** Real Estate: acquisitions and dispositions; loan and real property portfolio transactions; partnerships and joint ventures; mortgage and mezzanine financing; preferred equity investments; debt restructuring and workouts.
**Professional Memberships:** Member, American Bar Association.
**Career:** Listed: Best Lawyers in America, 2009-13; Super Lawyers magazine, 2009-12; Chambers

USA Guide, 2010-13. Rated, AV® Preeminent™ 5.0 out of 5.
**Personal:** JD, University of Pennsylvania Law School, 1982; BSBA, magna cum laude, Georgetown University, 1979.

### KLEINMAN, Howard
Dechert LLP, New York
212 698 3567
howard.kleinman@dechert.com
*Featured in Latin American Investment (New York)*

**Practice Areas:** Mr Kleinman focuses on capital markets and financial transactions, representing domestic and foreign issuers, underwriters, and others in equity and debt offerings. Fluent in Spanish, he has significant experience in Latin America.
**Professional Memberships:** Member, New York and New Jersey Bars; member, American Bar Association's International Law Section; member, Association of the Bar of the City of New York
**Personal:** Columbia University (BA,1984, with honors); London School of Economics and Political Science (MA, 1986); New York University School of Law (JD, 1988, Boudin Fellowship, articles editor, The Journal of International Law and Politics).

### KLING, Lou R
Skadden, Arps, Slate, Meagher & Flom LLP & Affiliates, New York
212 735 2770
Lou.Kling@skadden.com
*Featured in Media & Entertainment (New York), Corporate/M&A (New York)*

**Practice Areas:** Has extensive experience in mergers and acquisitions of public and private companies, subsidiaries and divisions, including negotiated and contested acquisitions, leveraged buyouts and recapitalizations. Represents borrowers and issuers in a broad spectrum of financing transactions. Serves on firm's Policy Committee, its top governing committee. Currently co-chairman of the firm's Opinion Committee, and chairman of the Financial Oversight Audit Committee.
**Career:** JD, New York University, 1977 (Order of the Coif; Law Review); MA, Mathematics, University of Illinois, 1974; BA, New York University, 1973 (magna cum laude; Phi Beta Kappa). Co-Author, 'Negotiated Acquisitions', a treatise.

### KLINGSBERG, Ethan A
Cleary Gottlieb Steen & Hamilton LLP, New York
212 225 2588
eklingsberg@cgsh.com
*Featured in Corporate/M&A (New York)*

**Practice Areas:** M&A, public company board, corporate and securities matters. Recent clients: Google, Goldman Sachs, Stanley Black & Decker, Alpha Natural Resources, Home Depot, Family Dollar, Kindred Healthcare, Interpublic, Agilent, Timken, Higher One, Enzon Pharmaceuticals, Syntel, Stora Enso. Notable representations: Home Depot (BlackLocus, Redbeacon, Hughes Supply); Stanley (Niscayah; sale of Hardware/Home Improvement); Google (Motorola, Wildfire, AdMob, ITA; divestiture of Motorola Home);

Alpha (Massey, Foundation); Family Dollar (defense against Trian); special committee of Interactive Data Corp (2010's largest LBO).
**Professional Memberships:** New York Bar.
**Career:** Joined firm (1994); Partner (2001); JD, Yale (1989); BA, magna cum laude, U. Pennsylvania (1985).

### KNAPP, Tobias
Jenner & Block LLP, New York
212 891 1655
tknapp@jenner.com
*Featured in Corporate/M&A (New York)*
**Career:** Tobias L. Knapp is Co-Chair of the Private Equity/Investment Funds Practice and a member of the Mergers & Acquisitions and Securities Practices. Mr Knapp represents clients in mergers, acquisitions and divestitures, including cross-border acquisitions; joint ventures; private equity; and securities transactions and advises corporations and boards on matters of corporate governance, fiduciary duties and federal securities law. He has led transactions in a range of industries, including automotive, clean energy, defense and aerospace, media, technology, financial services and investment management. Mr Knapp is proficient in Russian and has experience in Russia and other CIS countries and the European Union.

### KOBAK, Scott M
Simpson Thacher & Bartlett LLP, New York
212 455 7210
skobak@stblaw.com
*Featured in Real Estate (New York)*
**Practice Areas:** Real Estate Partner representing real estate opportunity funds and other investors in complex domestic and international real estate transactions, real estate company acquisitions and developments, joint ventures and financings. Transactions include Blackstone's sale of a $6.5 billion portfolio relating to the Equity Office transaction, Carlyle Realty's acquisition, financing and development of the Riverside South Project, 650 Madison, 666 Fifth Avenue and several condominium projects and primary counsel for Morgan Stanley and KKR's real estate business.
**Career:** Joined firm 1993; became Partner in 2000.
**Personal:** BS, Binghamton University (1989); JD, magna cum laude, Boston University Law School (1992).

### KOBRE, Steven G
Kobre & Kim LLP, New York
212 488 1202; 852 2127 3280
steven.kobre@kobrekim.com
*Featured in Litigation (New York)*
**Practice Areas:** Steven G Kobre, a co-founder of the firm, is an experienced trial lawyer and investigator who practices in the area of government and regulatory investigations. He is often retained by multinational companies and executives in the US, Asia, and Europe, who are involved in investigations regarding securities fraud, FCPA violations, and accounting fraud, among others. Mr Kobre regularly represents and advises executives in connection with investigations by the US government, including the US

Department of Justice and the US Securities and Exchange Commission. Mr Kobre also has an active civil practice focusing on high-value disputes among commercial entities, Fortune 500 companies, and other large institutions, one of which involves more than US $100 million in controversy.
**Career:** Prior to establishing Kobre & Kim, Mr Kobre served as an Assistant US Attorney in the Criminal Division of the US Attorney's Office for the Southern District of New York (Securities & Commodities Fraud Task Force) as well as an Assistant District Attorney in the New York County District Attorney's Office. After law school, Mr Kobre clerked for the Honorable Lowell A. Reed, Jr. of the US District Court for the Eastern District of Pennsylvania.
**Personal:** Mr Kobre received a BA from the University of Pennsylvania and a JD from The George Washington University Law School, where he served as Senior Notes Editor of the George Washington Law Review.

### KOEPPEL, John
Nixon Peabody LLP, New York
716 853 8137
jkoeppel@nixonpeabody.com
*Featured in Investment Funds (Nationwide), Corporate/M&A (New York)*
See under Nationwide for profile.

### KOESTLER, Mark D
Kramer Levin Naftalis & Frankel LLP, New York
212 715 9385
mkoestler@kramerlevin.com
*Featured in Immigration (Nationwide), Immigration (New York)*
**Practice Areas:** Mr Koestler has developed a national reputation in handling immigration law matters in the areas of advertising, finance, theater and film (including representing numerous Tony and Academy Award winners), and has authored a number of articles in the field. He is a past Chair of the American Immigration Lawyers Association's NY Chapter, and has lectured on a number of different business immigration topics at regional and national conferences of the American Immigration Lawyers Association. Mr Koestler is listed in The Best Lawyers in America, Chambers Global, New York Super Lawyers, The International Who's Who of Corporate Immigration Lawyers.

### KOGUT, Barry R
Bond, Schoeneck & King, PLLC, Syracuse
315 218 8181
bkogut@bsk.com
*Featured in Environment (New York)*
**Practice Areas:** Mr Kogut has a varied environmental practice, including Federal/State regulatory compliance and enforcement matters, brownfields development, remediation of sites impacted by petroleum and hazardous wastes/substances, and environmental issues that arise in real property and business matters. Of particular note, Mr Kogut has been involved with college/university clients on a range of environment law-related issues. He was Chair of the Environmental Law

Section of the New York State Bar Association from June 1, 2010 to May 31, 2011.
**Professional Memberships:**
**Personal:** Syracuse University (BA, summa cum laude, 1974); University of Virginia (JD, 1977).

### KOHN, Arthur H
Cleary Gottlieb Steen & Hamilton LLP, New York
212 225 2920
akohn@cgsh.com
*Featured in Employee Benefits & Executive Compensation (Nationwide), Employee Benefits & Executive Compensation (New York)*
See under Nationwide for profile.

### KONVISSER, Joshua B
Pillsbury Winthrop Shaw Pittman LLP, New York
212 858 1027
joshua.konvisser@pillsburylaw.com
*Featured in Outsourcing (Nationwide), Technology (New York)*
**Practice Areas:** Mr Konvisser represents clients in complex sourcing, technology and commercial transactions including information technology and business process outsourcing; technology transfers and distribution agreements; software licensing, marketing and development agreements, and SAAS and other cloud computing agreements. His multidisciplinary practice includes advising both suppliers and customers of technology and sourcing services on leading-edge issues such as disputes and "workouts" relating to troubled IT transactions. He has lectured on technology and law at Columbia University.
**Career:** Admitted: NY, MA and DC.
**Personal:** JD, Harvard Law School, 1997, magna cum laude; MS, University of Texas, 1994; BAS, University of Pennsylvania, 1992.

### KOPP, Steven
Ashurst, New York
212 205 7070
steven.kopp@ashurst.com
*Featured in Tax (New York)*
**Practice Areas:** Steven Kopp is a Tax partner in the New York Securities and Derivatives group. His tax practice covers structured finance transactions with an emphasis on fixed income and equity derivatives, options on managed accounts, DRD transactions, contingent debt, REMICs, CLOs (including synthetics), loan agreements, and offshore transactions (including PFICs and CFCs). He has written extensively, and regularly advises, on FATCA-related issues.
**Personal:** Steve is a graduate of the Wharton School of the University of Pennsylvania (BSE magna cum laude) and New York University School of Law (JD and LLM Taxation).

### KORDA, Peter
Seyfarth Shaw LLP, New York
212 218 5260
pkorda@seyfarth.com
*Featured in Real Estate (New York)*
**Practice Areas:** Co-chair, Structured and Real Estate Finance Practice Group.
**Career:** Peter Korda's practice concentrates on representing members of the lending community

on real estate finance matters, including loan originations and workouts. He has extensive experience in real estate projects across the US, including handling multi-tier, multi-state, fee, leasehold and syndicated financings of multi-family, cooperative/condominium, shopping center, office building, hotel and industrial projects.
**Publications:** Mr Korda has written and spoken on various real estate topics, including most recently, moderating a CREFC seminar on "Loan Origination in the 2.0 World"
**Personal:** JD, New York University; AB, magna cum laude, Brown University.

### KORNBERG, Alan W
Paul, Weiss, Rifkind, Wharton & Garrison LLP, New York
212 373 3209
akornberg@paulweiss.com
*Featured in Bankruptcy/Restructuring (Nationwide), Bankruptcy/Restructuring (New York)*
See under Nationwide for profile.

### KOTRAN, Stephen M
Sullivan & Cromwell LLP, New York
212 558 4963
kotrans@sullcrom.com
*Featured in Corporate/M&A (New York), Insurance (New York)*
**Practice Areas:** M&A, insurance, private equity, healthcare and life sciences. Clients include: Acosta, AIG, Bank of America, Barclays, Cytec Industries, Eastman Kodak, Evercore Partners, Goldman Sachs, ING, Ipsen, Prudential Financial, Swiss Reinsurance and Wells Fargo.
**Professional Memberships:** American Bar Association Business Law Section's Mergers & Acquisitions Committee (Co-Chair of Financial Advisor Task Force) and Committee on Federal Regulation of Securities.
**Career:** Partner since 1999. Law clerk, Honorable Edward R. Becker, US Court of Appeals Third Circuit, 1990-1991.
**Personal:** University of Virginia Law (JD, 1990); Harvard (BA, 1985).

### KRAIEM, Rubén
Covington & Burling LLP, New York
212 841 1002
rkraiem@cov.com
*Featured in Climate Change (Nationwide), Latin American Investment (New York)*
See under Nationwide for profile.

### KRAKAUR, Keith D
Skadden, Arps, Slate, Meagher & Flom LLP & Affiliates, New York
212 735 2809
Keith.Krakaur@skadden.com
*Featured in Litigation (New York)*
**Practice Areas:** A senior partner in the firm's White Collar and Government Enforcement Practice. A former federal prosecutor with over 25 years of trial and appellate experience. Represents corporations and their directors and officers in domestic and cross-border criminal and regulatory investigations. Advises boards of directors and management of public companies in connection with compliance and internal control issues relating to government investigations, and assists

boards and audit committees in conducting internal investigations.
**Career:** JD, NYU School of Law, 1984 (Executive Editor, Law Review); BA, Wesleyan University, 1981. Law clerk, Judge Irving Goldberg, Fifth Circuit Court of Appeals (1984-85).

**KRAMER, Daniel J**
Paul, Weiss, Rifkind, Wharton & Garrison LLP, New York
212 373 3020
dkramer@paulweiss.com
*Featured in Securities (Nationwide), Litigation (New York)*
See under Nationwide for profile.

**KRAMER, Morris J**
Skadden, Arps, Slate, Meagher & Flom LLP & Affiliates, New York
212 735 2700
Morris.Kramer@skadden.com
*Featured in Corporate/M&A (New York)*
**Practice Areas:** Practice includes friendly and hostile transactions and has involved many of the largest and most publicised deals. Counsels bidders, targets and their financial advisors in non-negotiated acquisition situations. Extensive experience in strategic and negotiation issues involving public and private company mergers, acquisitions and dispositions. Advises shareholders, boards of directors and managements in leveraged and management buyouts, proxy fights and other corporate control transactions. Represents parties from around the globe in transactions into and from North America, as well as cross-border intra-European deals.
**Career:** LLB, Harvard University, 1966; AB, Dartmouth College, 1963.

**KREITMAN, Robert M**
Sidley Austin LLP, New York
212 839 8637
rkreitman@sidley.com
*Featured in Tax (New York)*
**Practice Areas:** Partner in Sidley's New York office and a coordinator of the firm's Tax practice. He focuses on structured finance, securitization, financial products and credit derivatives. Mr Kreitman's principal areas of experience include residential and commercial mortgage-backed securitization, asset-backed securitization (including credit card, auto loan, auto lease, consumer loan, consumer lease and student loan securitizations) and structured finance including the structuring of debt repackagings, catastrophe bonds, insurance-linked securities, distressed asset funds, credit-default swaps and synthetic securitizations.
**Publications:** Mr Kreitman is a co-author of the Little, Brown and Company book on mortgage-backed securities.

**KRESS, Alan H**
Law Offices of Alan Kress, New York
212 944 6622
ahkress@kresslaw.com
*Featured in Media & Entertainment (New York)*
**Practice Areas:** Entertainment law specializing in music/music publishing, film/TV/video, talent/touring, theater and intellectual property/copyright matters. Particular expertise in

copyright reversions and terminations, licensing, international transactions and complex music clearance issues.
**Professional Memberships:** Copyright Society of the US; NYC Bar Assoc.
**Career:** Mr Kress was Vice President of Legal/Business Affairs for RCA Records/BMG Music, BMG International, Warner Home Video, several music publishers and has over 30 years' experience.
**Publications:** Editor of the two music and music publishing volumes of the Matthew Bender/LexisNexis 10 volume treatise entitled "Entertainment Industry Contracts".
**Personal:** NYU Law School (LLM); George Washington Law School (JD with Honors); New York University (BA).

**KREVITT, Josh**
Gibson, Dunn & Crutcher LLP, New York
212 351 2490
JKrevitt@gibsondunn.com
*Featured in Intellectual Property (New York)*
**Practice Areas:** Co-Chair of the Intellectual Property Practice and widely acknowledged to be one of the top patent trial lawyers in the country. He has successfully litigated complex, high-stakes patent cases in courts throughout the country and in the International Trade Commission, and has repeatedly secured complete defense jury verdicts in significant trials. He serves as lead trial counsel for many of the leading technology companies in the world in some of their most important and challenging patent cases, including Apple, AT&T, T-Mobile, Novo Nordisk, Sharp, RealNetworks, Viacom, Cablevision, and Amazon.com.
**Personal:** JD, Boston University, 1992; BA, Columbia University, 1989.

**KRUGMAN, Edward P**
Cahill Gordon & Reindel LLP, New York
212 701 3506
ekrugman@cahill.com
*Featured in Insurance (Nationwide), Insurance (New York)*
See under Nationwide for profile.

**KURTZ, Glenn M**
White & Case LLP, New York
212 819 8252
gkurtz@whitecase.com
*Featured in Litigation (New York)*
**Career:** Glenn Kurtz is the Head of Commercial Litigation at White & Case. He is an experienced trial and appellate lawyer, who handles complex cases, primarily class action, multi-jurisdiction and bankruptcy litigations throughout the US. He focuses on commercial cases, often arising out of debt and equity investments and other sophisticated agreements and instruments. Glenn represents a myriad of high-profile clients, including a founder of the Fairfield Greenwich Group in a multibillion dollar, multi-district putative class action and Royal Ahold in connection with one of the largest multi-district class action securities fraud/ERISA cases ever filed. To view his biography, visit www.whitecase.com/gkurtz.

**KURZWEIL, Harvey**
Winston & Strawn LLP, New York
*Featured in Litigation (New York)*
**Practice Areas:** Has acted as lead trial counsel in major litigations for many years, in cases involving exposure in the hundreds of millions to billions of dollars. Lead counsel in areas as diverse as antitrust, intellectual property, insurance coverage, securities, contested works of art, defamation, ERISA, and consumer class actions.
**Professional Memberships:** International Academy of Trial Lawyers, American Bar Foundation, Federal Bar Council, New York State Bar Association, Columbia Law School: Board of Visitors (2000-present) and Menninger Foundation: Board of Trustees (1997-present).
**Personal:** A.B., Columbia College, 1966. JD, Columbia University School of Law, 1969.

**KWAN-GETT, Mei Lin**
Willkie Farr & Gallagher LLP, New York
212 728 8503
mkwangett@willkie.com
*Featured in Litigation (New York)*
**Practice Areas:** Partner in Litigation Department and co-head of firm's White Collar Criminal Defense Practice Group. Specializes in white collar criminal defense, regulatory enforcement matters, internal investigations, and complex commercial litigation. Has lectured on securities fraud, federal criminal prosecution, trial practice, "bet the company" litigation and ethics. Has also taught white collar criminal law as an Adjunct Professor of Law at Fordham Law School.
**Personal:** JD, Yale Law School, 1992. AB, Harvard University, 1989. See: http://www.willkie.com/Mei_LinKwan_Gett

**LADNER, Mark P**
Morrison & Foerster LLP, New York
212 468 8035
mladner@mofo.com
*Featured in Antitrust (New York), Financial Services Regulation (Nationwide)*
See under Nationwide for profile.

**LAMPE, Matthew W**
Jones Day, New York
212 326 8338
mwlampe@jonesday.com
*Featured in Labor & Employment (New York)*
**Practice Areas:** Employment class action and other complex litigation, with particularly broad experience in FLSA, ERISA, Title VII, and ADEA cases. He has litigated numerous class and collective actions to successful conclusions for employers across the country. He has extensive experience leading the defense of clients facing class actions in multiple jurisdictions. He also advises management on wage and hour compliance, work force restructuring, and litigation avoidance. He lectures widely on class action topics.
**Personal:** Cornell University (JD magna cum laude 1989; Order of the Coif); Kenyon College (BA magna cum laude 1986; Phi Beta Kappa).

**LANCE, Andrew A**
Gibson, Dunn & Crutcher LLP, New York
212 351 3871
ALance@gibsondunn.com
*Featured in Real Estate (New York)*
**Practice Areas:** Co-leads global hotel /resort practice. Extensive experience in acquiring and financing trophy office and retail properties, and partial interests in owners including private REITs; origination and workout of complex debt structures and equity joint ventures, mixed-use developments, including public-private and ground leased development projects. Represents leading real estate private equity funds, major banking institutions, REITs, public and privately held developers and office, retail and hotel property owners, global hotel operators, buyers of mortgage and mezzanine debt portfolios, and not-for-profits.
**Career:** Member, American College of Real Estate Lawyers. Fellow, American College of Mortgage Attorneys.
**Personal:** JD, Yale University, 1983.

**LARSON, Joseph D**
Wachtell, Lipton, Rosen & Katz, New York
212 403 1360
JDLarson@wlrk.com
*Featured in Antitrust (New York)*
**Practice Areas:** Focuses on antitrust advice in mergers and acquisitions.
**Professional Memberships:** American Bar Association. Former chairman of the Antitrust Committee of the New York City Bar Association.
**Career:** Elected partner at Wachtell, Lipton, Rosen & Katz in 2002 as a member of the Antitrust Department. Provides critical assessment and counsel to merger and acquisition clients with respect to United States antitrust matters and is also familiar with European, South American, Canadian and Asian antitrust standards. Regularly counsels corporations through a wide range of matters, covering pre-merger filings through antitrust challenges, and represents clients before the Department of Justice Antitrust Division, the Federal Trade Commission, the Federal Reserve Board, the Federal Energy Regulatory Commission, and the Department of Defense. His expertise spans diverse industries, including electric and gas utilities, software, Internet, consumer products, defense, petroleum, and banking.
**Personal:** Graduated from St. Johns College (BA, 1990) and magna cum laude from Harvard Law School (JD, 1994).

**LAURIA, Thomas E**
White & Case LLP, Miami
305 995 5282
tlauria@whitecase.com
*Featured in Bankruptcy/Restructuring (Nationwide), Bankruptcy/Restructuring (Florida), Bankruptcy/Restructuring (New York)*
See under Nationwide for profile.

## LAWRENCE, Carmen J
Fried, Frank, Harris, Shriver & Jacobson LLP, New York
212 859 8411
Carmen.Lawrence@FriedFrank.com
*Featured in Securities (Nationwide), Litigation (New York)*
See under Nationwide for profile.

## LEAKE, Paul
Jones Day, New York
212 326 3482
pdleake@jonesday.com
*Featured in Bankruptcy/Restructuring (Nationwide), Bankruptcy/Restructuring (New York)*
See under Nationwide for profile.

## LEAVY, Richard A.
Sidley Austin LLP, New York
212 839 5562
rleavy@sidley.com
*Featured in Tax (New York)*
**Practice Areas:** Partner in Sidley's New York office, practicing in the Tax group. His practice includes all areas of state and local taxation, with a concentration on transactional planning, escheat counseling and litigation, and extensive experience managing and resolving tax controversies.
**Career:** Before joining Sidley in 2010, Mr Leavy was a partner at another prominent international law firm. Previously served as the judicial intern to The Honorable Leonard I. Garth, U.S. Court of Appeals for the Third Circuit.
**Personal:** New York University School of Law, LLM, 1997; Rutgers University School of Law - Newark, JD, 1996; Rutgers University, BA, 1992.

## LEBLANG, Kevin B
Kramer Levin Naftalis & Frankel LLP, New York
212 715 9306
kleblang@kramerlevin.com
*Featured in Labor & Employment (New York)*
**Practice Areas:** Kevin B Leblang heads Kramer Levin's Employment Law Department and concentrates on representing management on employment litigation and advisory matters. He counsels employers on matters ranging from the adoption and application of employee relations policies to the evaluation and minimization of litigation risks of employment decisions. He also represents management clients in litigations before federal and state courts, administrative agencies, and arbitrators. Mr Leblang has extensive experience litigating claims alleging all forms of discrimination, breach of contract and the myriad of tort claims arising out of the employment relationship. He also has extensive experience in employee non-competition law.

## LEBLANG, Stuart E
Akin Gump Strauss Hauer & Feld LLP, New York
212 872 1017
sleblang@akingump.com
*Featured in Tax (New York)*
**Practice Areas:** Co-head, tax practice. His practice includes planning and negotiation of domestic and international business transactions, corporate and financial tax counseling, and representa-

tion of clients on tax legislative and policy issues before the U.S. Congress, the U.S. Department of Treasury and other federal agencies. He also focuses on various investment fund related matters.
**Career:** Associate international tax counsel, U.S. Department of Treasury.
**Personal:** BA, Cornell University (1987); JD, Columbia Law School, James Kent Scholar, Harlan Fiske Stone Scholar, coordinator of the Columbia Moot Court Program (1990).

## LEE, Carolyn Joy
Jones Day, New York
212 326 3966
cjlee@jonesday.com
*Featured in Tax (New York)*
**Practice Areas:** State corporate tax, sales tax, personal income tax, transaction taxes and constitutional issues; Federal, state and local audits and controversies; Federal taxation of real estate transactions, partnerships, S corporations, environmental expenditures, valuations.
**Professional Memberships:** American Bar Association; New York State Bar Association; Association of the Bar of the City of New York; ABA.
**Publications:** Speaks and writes frequently on Federal and state tax topics. Recent examples include 'State Taxation of Partnerships and LLCs and Their Owners'; 'State and Local Tax Issues in Mergers and Acquisitions'; 'Effective Hedge Fund Tax Practices: State and Local Considerations'.

## LEE, Gary
Morrison & Foerster LLP, New York
212 468 8042
glee@mofo.com
*Featured in Bankruptcy/Restructuring (New York)*
**Practice Areas:** Mr Lee is Chair of the Business Restructuring & Insolvency Group and Co-chair of the Finance Department at Morrison & Foerster. He advises clients on domestic and international restructuring and insolvency matters in the U.S., U.K., and Europe. He has been heavily involved in the implementation of foreign liquidations and schemes of arrangement in the U.S. and issues arising under Chapter 15 of the Bankruptcy Code. Mr Lee is currently a fellow of the American Bar Association and Co-chair of the Transnational Bankruptcy Committee of International Insolvency Institute.
**Personal:** LLB, Manchester University, 1988.

## LEE-LIM, Jiyeon
Latham & Watkins LLP, New York
212 906 1298
jiyeon.lee-lim@lw.com
*Featured in Tax (New York)*
**Practice Areas:** Practice covers a wide variety of tax issues in both domestic and international context. In recent years, Ms Lee-Lim have represented numerous domestic and foreign corporations and investment banks in connection with debt and equity offerings, bank financings, derivative transactions, and securitizations and other structured finance transactions. She also frequently advises multinational corporations in restructuring and cross-border tax matters.

**Career:** Qualified since 1987. Member of the Executive Committee of Taxation of the New York State Bar Association since 2002 and a co-chair on Securitizations and Structured Finance of the Tax Section.

## LEFF, Neil M
Skadden, Arps, Slate, Meagher & Flom LLP & Affiliates, New York
212 735 3269
neil.leff@skadden.com
*Featured in Employee Benefits & Executive Compensation (New York)*
**Practice Areas:** Emphasis on executive compensation, particularly mergers and acquisitions, public offerings, bankruptcy reorganizations and other corporate transactions, including tax planning with respect to golden parachute payments, limitations on deductibility of executive compensation, rules relating to deferred compensation, compliance with Section 16 of the Securities Exchange Act of 1934 and other securities laws applicable to executive compensation.
**Career:** JD, New York University, 1980 (Member, Annual Survey of American Law); BA, Brooklyn College of the City University of New York, 1977.

## LEFKOWITZ, Jay
Kirkland & Ellis LLP, New York
212 446 4970
jay.lefkowitz@kirkland.com
*Featured in Litigation (New York)*
**Practice Areas:** A Senior Litigation Partner and Member of Kirkland's Worldwide Management Committee, Jay argued the landmark Pliva v. Mensing before the US Supreme Court, which held 5-4 that federal law preempts failure-to-warn claims against generic drug companies. Jay has served as trial and appellate counsel in securities, shareholder derivative, antitrust, breach of contract, class action and white collar cases. He conducts internal investigations for public company audit committees and represents investment banks, hedge funds, airlines, and pharmaceutical and telecommunications companies. He served as senior White House advisor to both Presidents Bush and as US Special Envoy on Human Rights in North Korea. Columbia Law School Faculty.
**Personal:** Columbia College, AB, 1984; Columbia Law School, JD, 1987.

## LEFKOWITZ, Ken
Hughes Hubbard & Reed LLP, New York
212 837 6557
lefkowit@hugheshubbard.com
*Featured in Corporate/M&A (New York)*
**Practice Areas:** Concentrates on mergers and acquisitions, joint ventures, public and private financings, corporate governance, proxy contests, venture capital and private equity.
**Career:** Deputy Chair of Hughes Hubbard & Reed and Co-Chair of the firm's Corporate Department. Member of firm's Executive Committee. Partner, New York since 1993.
**Personal:** Born February 4, 1958. Tufts University BA 1980 (summa cum laude, Phi Beta Kappa); Cornell Law School JD (cum laude) 1983.

## LEFKOWITZ, Stephen A
Fried, Frank, Harris, Shriver & Jacobson LLP, New York
212 859 8780
Stephen.Lefkowitz@FriedFrank.com
*Featured in Real Estate (New York)*
**Practice Areas:** Real estate partner. Practice focuses on real estate development; emphasis on land use, zoning and large-scale, complex projects involving public/private development and financing arrangements; tax/other municipal incentives. Projects include: Yankee Stadium, Barclays Center, Time Warner Center, Hudson Yards, Cornell's NYC Tech Campus, 9/11 Memorial and Museum, Moynihan Station, Hudson Square Rezoning, Major League Soccer Stadium.
**Career:** Joined as partner in 2003. Associate Professor, Columbia Law School, 1976–1982.
**Personal:** LLB, magna cum laude, Harvard Law School (1962), member, Harvard Law Review; BA, summa cum laude, Yale College (1959), Phi Beta Kappa.

## LEITMAN BAILEY, Adam
Adam Leitman Bailey, PC, New York
212 825 0365
alb@alblawfirm.com
*Featured in Real Estate (New York)*
**Practice Areas:** Experienced in all aspects of real property law, Bailey has participated in many of the most important real estate cases in the new millennium including cases involving: 1) securing the largest condominium settlement in New York history, 2) making new appellate law for newly constructed condominium buildings, 3) using a federal statute to prevail in a landmark victories for contract vendees 4) setting new rules for commercial real estate joint venture agreements, 5) expanding the limits of landlord/tenant non-primary residence law, 6) a case of first impression interpreting the limited liability company law, and 7) an interpretation of the recording statute making a new property law. Bailey has successfully defended a number of the largest title companies in the nation, as well as prevailed in numerous trials and settlements involving commercial and residential building owners and tenants, real estate developers, real estate brokerages and cooperative and condominium boards. Bailey litigates mortgage and property-related cases for many of the nation's largest real estate companies and lenders, such as JP Morgan JP Morgan Chase & Company, Merrill Lynch, Bank of America, Deutsche Bank, Wells Fargo, HSBC, GMAC Mortgage and US Bank. Bailey's lease drafting skills received national attention when BlumbergExcelsior, the nation's leading form distributor responsible for over 70 percent of the residential leases signed in the United States, tapped Bailey to draft a new set of New York City, State and national residential and office leases for purchase nationwide. BlumbergExcelsior's principal remarked that Bailey's lease drafting abilities were "remarkable." While almost all New York property owners utilize his leases for residential purposes, his commercial leasing ideas are commonly a part of the entire national commercial leasing scene and have been

included in "The Insider's Best Commercial Lease Clauses" published by the Vendome Group.

**Career:** By pursuing a program of uniting many of the best real estate attorneys of our generation, Adam Leitman Bailey's eponymous firm has become one of New York's most prominent real estate law firms. By solely practicing real estate law and only taking on projects and cases where we believe we are among the very best in the field, Adam Leitman Bailey, P.C. has achieved ground-breaking results in the courtroom, in the board room, at the closing table, in the lobbies of legislative bodies, and in every other venue where talented legal advocacy is key to its clients' interests. Adam Leitman Bailey, P.C. is one of very few law firms with under 30 attorneys to achieve an AV Martindale-Hubbell rating, repeated Super Lawyers and Chambers rankings, and selection into the Bar Registry of Preeminent Lawyers. Actively at the helm of the 25-attorney law firm he started from scratch, Real Estate Weekly noted that "Adam Leitman Bailey has made a name for himself with his success winning cases in the courtroom." That same newspaper called Mr Bailey "famous" for his "condominium, foreclosure and landlord-tenant representation," while the New York Real Estate Journal declared Mr Bailey to be "one of New York's best real estate attorneys." The New York Times praised his "novel" strategy in one case and remarked that in another "Bailey fought on... grinding through excruciating detail and obscure Perry Mason moments." The Wall Street Journal quoted a prominent New York attorney calling a win in a prominent case a "game changer" affecting real estate nationwide and in another case he scored the "largest condominium settlement" in New York history. Another publication noted that "Adam Leitman Bailey is to real estate law what the iPod is to Apple." The Commercial Observer ranked one victory as one of the "15 Most Fascinating New York Real Estate Cases of the 21st Century." Dateline NBC referred to Mr Bailey as "aggressive, tenacious and smart" in asking Mr Bailey to share his negotiating secrets on its nationally syndicated television program. His success as cooperative and condominium general counsel earned Mr Bailey recognition in "Who's Who in Real Estate" by Habitat Magazine. In 2011, Mr Bailey took on the role of author to guide first-time home buyers through the purchase process. John Wiley and Sons published Finding the Uncommon Deal: A Top New York Lawyer Explains How to Buy a Home for the Lowest Possible Price which became a number 1 New York Times bestseller.

**LELAND, Richard G**
Fried, Frank, Harris, Shriver & Jacobson LLP, New York
212 859 8978
Richard.Leland@FriedFrank.com
*Featured in Environment (New York)*
**Practice Areas:** Real estate partner. Specializes in the environmental aspects of real estate development and land use. Counsels clients, including real estate developers, non-profit organizations and public authorities, on a variety of environ-

mental matters: environmental impact, regulatory and transactional counseling, and litigation of land use and environmental matters. Special Professor of Law, Hofstra University School of Law and New York Law School. Adjunct Professor of Real Estate Development at Columbia University's Graduate School of Architecture, and Planning and Preservation.
**Career:** Joined as partner in 2007.
**Personal:** JD, with distinction, Hofstra University School of Law (1974); BS, Cornell University (1971).

**LENDER, David**
Weil, Gotshal & Manges LLP, New York
212 310 8153
david.lender@weil.com
*Featured in Litigation (New York)*
**Practice Areas:** David Lender, Head of Weil's global, 400-attorney Litigation Department, has nearly 20 years of experience litigating complex disputes, with an emphasis on consumer fraud, patent, antitrust, and contract cases. Recent victories include a $170 million jury verdict for GE regarding wind turbine patents; numerous wins for StubHub in consumer class actions regarding ticket sales practices; and a favorable settlement for Exxon in class actions alleging disparities in the energy content of gasoline. He is a recognized expert on e-discovery and co-authored the treatise, Electronic Discovery: Law and Practice.
**Personal:** Duke University (BA); Duke University School of Law (JD).

**LENNOX, Heather**
Jones Day, New York
212 326 3837
hlennox@jonesday.com
*Featured in Bankruptcy/Restructuring (Nationwide), Bankruptcy/Restructuring (New York), Bankruptcy/Restructuring (Ohio)*
See under Ohio for profile.

**LENOBEL, Jeffrey A**
Schulte Roth & Zabel LLP, New York
212 756 2444
jeffrey.lenobel@srz.com
*Featured in Real Estate (New York)*
**Practice Areas:** Chair, Real Estate Group. Development, finance, sales, acquisitions, joint venture and other co-ownership arrangements, commercial mortgage-backed securitizations.
**Professional Memberships:** American College of Real Estate Lawyers; American, NY State and NYC Bar Associations; Mortgage Bankers Association; Commercial Real Estate Finance Council; Editorial Board - Distressed Asset Investor; Executive Committee - National Realty Club.
**Career:** SRZ Partner since 1997; Member, Executive Committee and Operating Committees.
**Personal:** Cumberland School of Law, JD, cum laude, Executive Editor, Cumberland Law Review; Gettysburg College, BA.

**LERNER, Jonathan J**
Skadden, Arps, Slate, Meagher & Flom LLP & Affiliates, New York
212 735 2550
jlerner@skadden.com
*Featured in Securities (Nationwide), Litigation (New York)*
See under Nationwide for profile.

**LESSER, Lori E**
Simpson Thacher & Bartlett LLP, New York
212 455 3393
llesser@stblaw.com
*Featured in Technology (New York)*
**Practice Areas:** Intellectual Property and Litigation Partner. Heads the firm's East Coast IP transactional practice. Advises on all aspects of intellectual property and technology law, including complex corporate transactions, licensing, counseling and litigation, in fields including media and entertainment, computer software and technology, financial information, consumer products, pharmaceuticals and biotechnology, Internet and e-commerce services, fashion design and non-profits. Served as lead IP lawyer in hundreds of public and private transactions.
**Career:** Partner since 2003.
**Personal:** AB, magna cum laude and Phi Beta Kappa, Harvard University (1988); JD, cum laude, Harvard Law School (1993).

**LEVANDER, Andrew J**
Dechert LLP, New York
212 698 3683
andrew.levander@dechert.com
*Featured in Litigation (Nationwide), Securities (Nationwide), Litigation (New York)*
**Practice Areas:** Mr Levander, chair of the firm's policy committee and partner in the white collar and securities litigation group, has represented many high-profile clients in securities fraud litigation and government and criminal investigations. He also has extensive arbitration and international litigation experience.
**Professional Memberships:** Member, New York and District of Columbia Bars.
**Career:** Assistant to Solicitor General; Assistant U.S. Attorney, Southern District of New York (Securities and Commodities Fraud Unit).
**Personal:** Tufts University (BA, 1973, summa cum laude); Columbia University Law School (JD, 1977).

**LEVI, Stuart D**
Skadden, Arps, Slate, Meagher & Flom LLP & Affiliates, New York
212 735 2750
Stuart.Levi@skadden.com
*Featured in Outsourcing (Nationwide), Technology (New York)*
**Practice Areas:** Co-head of Skadden's Intellectual Property and Technology Group. His practice includes outsourcing transactions, technology and intellectual property licensing, technology transfers, strategic alliances and joint ventures. He also counsels clients on a variety of issues, including privacy issues, website and technology policies, intellectual property matters and legislative compliance. His background in com-

puter science and the information technology industry allows Mr Levi to understand the technology and business drivers underlying agreements and transactions in this area.
**Career:** JD, Harvard Law School, 1986 (cum laude); BA, Computer Science and Political Science, Columbia University, Columbia College, 1983 (magna cum laude).

**LEVIN, Richard**
Cravath, Swaine & Moore LLP, New York
212 474 1978
rlevin@cravath.com
*Featured in Bankruptcy/Restructuring (Nationwide), Bankruptcy/Restructuring (New York)*
See under Nationwide for profile.

**LEVINE, Josh**
Simpson Thacher & Bartlett LLP, New York
212 455 7694
jlevine@stblaw.com
*Featured in Litigation (New York)*
**Practice Areas:** Litigation Partner representing companies and individuals in criminal and regulatory matters, including investigations involving alleged insider trading, accounting and other securities fraud, foreign corrupt payments, criminal antitrust violations, and commodities fraud. Also handles internal investigations on behalf of companies and boards of directors.
**Career:** Partner, 2009. Assistant United States Attorney, SDNY (1999-2007); Law Clerk, Judge Shira A. Scheindlin, US District Court, SDNY (1995-96); Special Assistant, Senator Daniel Patrick Moynihan (1991-92).
**Personal:** JD, University of Michigan Law School, Order of the Coif (1995); AB, with Distinction, Cornell University (1991).

**LEVITIN, Joel H**
Cahill Gordon & Reindel LLP, New York
212 701 3770
jlevitin@cahill.com
*Featured in Bankruptcy/Restructuring (New York)*
**Practice Areas:** As a partner in Cahill's business restructuring and bankruptcy group, Joel advises troubled or distressed companies, acquirers of such companies, and trustees, boards of directors, creditors, bondholders, committees, and equity sponsors in restructuring and reorganization matters, in and out of court. Recently, he was lead counsel to Orleans Homebuilders, and SP Newsprint, and he was special counsel to Trico Marine Services in their Chapter 11 cases.
**Personal:** Duke University, AB, magna cum laude, 1984. University of Chicago Law School, JD, with honors, 1987. Clerked for Norma L. Shapiro, U.S. District Judge in the Eastern District of Pennsylvania, 1987-88.

**LEVY, Andrew H**
DLA Piper LLP (US), New York
212 335 4544
andrew.levy@dlapiper.com
*Featured in Real Estate (New York)*
**Practice Areas:** Real estate.
**Professional Memberships:** American College of Real Estate Lawyers.
**Career:** He represents privately held and capital markets industry clients, in virtually every proper-

ty class, in acquisitions and dispositions, development, private equity and debt transactions, limited partnerships, limited liability companies, joint ventures and real estate refinancing, restructurings, bankruptcies, foreclosures and the establishment and re-arranging of complex capital structures. Actively involved in inbound and outbound cross-border transactions and represents a diverse number of institutional and stand-alone real estate opportunity funds, as well as sponsors, operators and developers.

**Personal:** JD and BA, Harvard Law School (cum laude).

### LEVY, Evan R
Skadden, Arps, Slate, Meagher & Flom LLP & Affiliates, New York
212 735 3889
evan.levy@skadden.com
*Featured in Real Estate (New York)*

**Practice Areas:** Mr Levy's practice emphasizes real estate financings, private equity funds, development projects, workouts and restructurings and securities offerings. He has broad experience representing both borrowers and lenders in capital markets and bank syndicate loans. Representations include major financial institutions as well as some of the largest national and international real estate companies. He also counsels on financings, acquisitions and sales by individual property owners and developers.

**Career:** JD, Albany Law School of Union University, 1995 (magna cum laude; Note & Comment Editor, Albany Law Review); M.BA, Union College, 1995; BA, University at Albany, 1991 (magna cum laude).

### LEWIS, Jeffrey I D
Patterson Belknap Webb & Tyler LLP, New York
212 336 2549
jidlewis@pbwt.com
*Featured in Intellectual Property (New York)*

**Practice Areas:** Jeffrey Lewis, a chemical engineer, is a Partner of the firm and a registered patent attorney concentrating his practice in patent litigation. He has represented both patentees and accused infringers in all aspects of patent litigation. Mr Lewis has represented chemical and pharmaceutical companies, including the pharmaceutical innovator in numerous Abbreviated New Drug Application (ANDA) patent litigations and also has represented companies in many other technology areas. He also regularly counsels clients on intellectual property matters, including providing formal opinions, and represents them in transactions. Mr Lewis is also a frequent author and lecturer on patent and patent litigation issues.

**Professional Memberships:** American Intellectual Property Association (AIPLA), President and Fellow; Association Internationale pour la Protection de la Propriété Intellectuelle – United States, President; New York Intellectual Property Association (NYIPLA), Legal Oversight and Amicus Committee; Advisory Board of 'IP Litigator' magazine; Hon. William Connor Inn of Court.

**Career:** Mr Lewis is an Adjunct Professor of Law at Benjamin N. Cardozo School of Law, where he teaches a seminar on Biotechnology and Pharmaceutical Patent Law primarily for LLM and third year students.

**Personal:** Benjamin N Cardozo School of Law (JD 1986), cum laude; Alexander Judicial Fellow (Judge Bennett: Federal Circuit); Eleanor Roosevelt Award; University of Connecticut (BSE, 1983), Chemical Engineering.

### LEWIS, Jeffrey S
Cleary Gottlieb Steen & Hamilton LLP, New York
212 225 2510
jlewis@cgsh.com
*Featured in Latin American Investment (New York), Projects (Nationwide)*

**Practice Areas:** International financing and business transactions. Advises private and public sector clients in connection with M&A, private equity investments, joint ventures and privatization transactions. Also has extensive experience in project financings, including financings for the development of power, ethanol, petrochemical, toll roads, oil refining, steel and mining projects.

**Professional Memberships:** Member of the Bar in New York.

**Career:** Joined firm, 1987; became Partner, 1995. Columbia University School of Law (JD) 1986; Williams College (BA) 1983.

### LEWKOW, Victor I
Cleary Gottlieb Steen & Hamilton LLP, New York
212 225 2370
vlewkow@cgsh.com
*Featured in Corporate/M&A (New York)*

**Practice Areas:** Domestic and international mergers and acquisitions; corporate governance. Represented: GlaxoSmithKline (Human Genome Sciences, Sirtris, Corixa, CNS), Google (Motorola Mobility), Alpha Natural Resources (Massey Energy), Oriental Financial Group (BBVA Puerto Rico), Conversus Capital (HarbourVest), BHP Billiton (PotashCorp bid), Barclays (Lehman US), XL (redomestication), TPG (Armstrong investment), SABMiller (Coors JV), Medtronic (Kyphon), Hartford Financial (Allianz's equity investment), LS Cable (Superior Essex), BBVA (Compass Bancshares), Euronext (NYSE merger), Capital One (North Fork, Hibernia), PeopleSoft (defense and sale to Oracle).

**Professional Memberships:** Tulane Corporate Law Institute.

**Personal:** JD, magna cum laude, University of Pennsylvania Law School (1973); BA, SUNY Binghamton (1970).

### LIEBMANN, Jeff S
Sidley Austin LLP, New York
212 839 6775
jliebmann@sidley.com
*Featured in Insurance (Nationwide), Insurance (New York)*

See under Nationwide for profile.

### LIGHT, Russell S.
Kirkland & Ellis LLP, New York
212 446 6470
russell.light@kirkland.com
*Featured in Tax (New York)*

**Practice Areas:** Russell Light focuses on the tax aspects of mergers, acquisitions, buyouts and private equity investing. He also assists with tax planning for public and closely held entities, complex cross-border investments, real estate investments and debt restructurings and bankruptcy transactions.

**Publications:** Authored several articles. Co-author of "Mergers, Acquisitions, and Buyouts" by Martin Ginsburg, Jack Levin and Donald Rocap. Special editor of "Structuring Venture Capital, Private Equity, and Entrepreneurial Transactions," by Jack Levin and Donald Rocap.

**Personal:** University of Chicago, JD, High Honors, 2001; Massachusetts Institute of Technology, M.Eng. and BS, Computer Science and Engineering, BS, Mathematics, 1998.

### LIMAN, Lewis J
Cleary Gottlieb Steen & Hamilton LLP, New York
212 225 2550
lliman@cgsh.com
*Featured in Litigation (New York)*

**Practice Areas:** Securities, corporate, and commercial litigation, including class action lawsuits and governmental investigations.

**Professional Memberships:** Federal Bar Council; NY Council of Defense Lawyers; Director, Legal Aid Society; Association of the Bar of the City of New York.

**Personal:** Assistant US Attorney, Southern District of New York, (Deputy Chief Appellate Attorney) (1994-99). Law Clerk, US District Court, Southern District of New York (1987-88) and US Supreme Court (1989-90). JD, Yale Law School (1987), MSc, Economics with distinction, London School of Economics (1984), AB, Harvard University (1983).

### LIPTON, Martin
Wachtell, Lipton, Rosen & Katz, New York
212 403 1200
mlipton@wlrk.com
*Featured in Corporate/M&A (New York)*

**Practice Areas:** Specialises in corporate law, corporate governance and mergers and acquisitions.

**Professional Memberships:** Chairman of The Board of Trustees of New York University, a trustee of the New York University School of Law (Chairman 1988-98), an emeritus member of the Council of the American Law Institute, and a director of the Institute of Judicial Administration. Served as counsel to the New York Stock Exchange Committee on Market Structure, Governance and Ownership (1999-2000), as counsel to, and member of, its Committee on Corporate Accountability and Listing Standards [Corporate Governance] (2002) and as chairman of its Legal Advisory Committee (2002-04). Member of the Executive Committee

of the Partnership for New York City and served as its co-chair (2004-06).

**Career:** Founding partner of Wachtell, Lipton, Rosen & Katz, who specialises in advising major corporations on mergers and acquisitions and matters affecting corporate policy and strategy and has written and lectured extensively on these subjects.

**Personal:** Mr Lipton has a BS in Economics from the Wharton School of the University of Pennsylvania and an LLB from the New York University School of Law. Member of The American Academy of Arts & Sciences and Chevalier de la Legion d'Honneur.

### LISCIO, Mark F
Kaye Scholer LLP, New York
212 836 7550
mark.liscio@kayescholer.com
*Featured in Bankruptcy/Restructuring (New York)*

**Practice Areas:** Mark Liscio is Co-Chair of the Bankruptcy & Restructuring Department at Kaye Scholer. For over 25 years, Mark has represented major financial institutions, ad hoc committees, syndicate agents, buy side investors and private equity firms in complex debt restructurings and insolvency proceedings in a broad range of matters. He has recently negotiated and structured several debt for equity conversions on behalf of lender groups, which have been implemented through pre-packaged plans of reorganization. He is presently active in restructurings involving distressed structured credits across a number of asset classes, including aircraft, student loans and commercial real estate.

### LITTLE, Edward JM
Hughes Hubbard & Reed LLP, New York
212 837 6400
little@hugheshubbard.com
*Featured in Litigation (New York)*

**Practice Areas:** Chair, White Collar Group; Co-Chair, Securities Litigation Group. Specializes in defense and trial of white-collar criminal cases charging securities fraud, FCPA violations, improper pharmaceutical marketing, government fraud, political corruption, tax violations, money laundering and related regulatory proceedings, civil litigation and internal investigations.

**Professional Memberships:** Best Lawyers in America in White Collar Defense (2007-2011); SuperLawyers in White Collar Defense, Securities Litigation & Business Litigation (2006-2011).

**Career:** Partner, Hughes Hubbard (2003-present); Managing Partner of NY Office, Zuckerman Spaeder (1993-2003); Partner, Kavanagh Maloney (1989-1993); Assistant United States Attorney (Deputy Chief, Criminal Division), S.D.N.Y. (1982-89); Associate, White & Case (1974-1982).

**Personal:** Boston College Law School JD (1974) (Presidential Scholar; Executive Editor, Law Review); Boston College AB, Classics, magna cum laude (1970).

### LITWIN, Ethan
Hughes Hubbard & Reed LLP, New York
212 837.6540
litwin@hugheshubbard.com
*Featured in Antitrust (New York)*

**Practice Areas:** Antitrust and Competition Law
**Professional Memberships:** New York State Bar; Solicitor of England and Wales
**Career:** Ethan Litwin, Co-Chair of Hughes Hubbard's antitrust group, has extensive experience defending companies and individuals in international cartel investigations and associated class action litigations. In the transactional setting, he has successfully guided companies through the international merger control process in more than 35 jurisdictions. He assists clients in all phases of the transaction, from the drafting of acquisition agreements through compliance with Second Requests in the U.S. and Phase II investigations in Europe.
**Personal:** Georgetown University Law Center, JD; Duke University, BA

**LOBUE, Robert P**
Patterson Belknap Webb & Tyler LLP, New York
212 336 2596
rplobue@pbwt.com
*Featured in Intellectual Property (New York)*
**Practice Areas:** Robert LoBue, Patterson Belknap's Managing Partner, has been a litigator with the firm for more than 25 years. His practice includes both a first-seat role in many of the firm's most significant complex business disputes as well as his long-time focus on intellectual property and First Amendment litigation and counseling. His clients include some of the world's leading media and information services organizations. Mr LoBue is co-author of the Media Law Resource Center's 50-State Survey of Media Privacy and Related Law and of articles on media issues and federal procedure. He has also served as the firm's General Counsel and Chair of its Professional Responsibility Committee, and has served on bar association ethics committees. He is the recipient of the Thurgood Marshall Award conferred by the Association of the Bar of the City of New York for his pro bono service in a death penalty case, and has filed amicus briefs in the US Supreme Court on behalf of retired federal judges and human rights organizations in several landmark cases relating to the 'War of Terror'. He has also filed an amicus brief on behalf of the American Bar Association in the US Supreme Court in a case testing the limits of the Alien Tort Statute.
**Career:** Prior to joining Patterson Belknap, Mr LoBue served as law clerk to the Hon David N Edelstein, US District Court for the Southern District of New York.
**Personal:** University of Pennsylvania Law School (JD 1978); Reeve Award (trusts); Burkan Award (copyright); Order of the Coif; articles editor, University of Pennsylvania Law Review; Brown University (AB 1975), Honors in English Literature, Phi Beta Kappa.

**LOEWENSON JR, Carl H**
Morrison & Foerster LLP, New York
212 468 8000
cloewenson@mofo.com
*Featured in Litigation (New York)*
**Practice Areas:** Focuses on white-collar criminal defense, including regulatory matters, involv-

ing alleged insider trading, accounting fraud, and other securities fraud, foreign corrupt practices, tax evasion, false claims against the government, money laundering, price-fixing, healthcare fraud, and obstruction of justice. Court-appointed receiver in three separate SEC enforcement actions. Led numerous internal investigations for multinational companies.
**Career:** Admitted to practice in New York. From 1985 to 1990, served as an Assistant U.S. Attorney in S.D.N.Y. Currently Co-Chair of the firm's Securities Litigation, Enforcement, and White-Collar Criminal Defense Group.
**Personal:** BA, Princeton University, 1979; JD, Yale Law School, 1983.

**LONGMIRE, John C**
Willkie Farr & Gallagher LLP, New York
212 728 8574
jlongmire@willkie.com
*Featured in Bankruptcy/Restructuring (New York)*
**Practice Areas:** Specializes in bankruptcy and restructuring, acquisitions of distressed companies, and related matters. Involved in numerous complex transactions in the retail, entertainment, automotive, waste management, electronics, telecommunications, airline, medical services and other industries. Matters include restructuring of Barnesy New York and EnviroSolutions, Inc., which received M&A Advisor's Turnaround Award for Excellence; and complex restructurings in the financial services, resort and transportation industries.
**Personal:** JD, summa cum laude, St. John's University School of Law, 1995. Notes and Comments Editor, St. John's Law Review. BS, cum laude, New York University, 1987. See: http://www.willkie.com/JohnLongmire

**LOPO, Diana M**
Skadden, Arps, Slate, Meagher & Flom LLP & Affiliates, New York
212 735 3475
Diana.Lopo@skadden.com
*Featured in Tax (New York)*
**Practice Areas:** Diana M Lopo maintains an active practice in the full range of tax issues associated with corporate and partnership transactions, including public and private mergers and acquisitions, financings, restructurings and joint ventures, with a particular emphasis on international transactions. She regularly advises private equity and hedge funds regarding the tax aspects of their structuring and operations. In addition, Ms Lopo counsels several large family investment offices with regard to a wide range of tax and other issues.
**Career:** LLM, Tax, New York University School of Law, 1982; JD, University of Michigan, 1981; BS, University of Miami, 1978.

**LOWENTHAL, Mitchell**
Cleary Gottlieb Steen & Hamilton LLP, New York
212 225 2760
mlowenthal@cgsh.com
*Featured in Securities (Nationwide), Litigation (New York)*
See under Nationwide for profile.

**LOZANO, Paola**
Skadden, Arps, Slate, Meagher & Flom LLP & Affiliates, New York
212 735 2545
paola.lozano@skadden.com
*Featured in Latin American Investment (New York)*
**Practice Areas:** Represents a variety of clients in mergers, acquisitions, dispositions, private equity transactions and other matters, with emphasis on cross-border and international transactions. Clients include MetLife, Grupo México, Capital International, BHP Billiton, Marubeni Corporation, Grupo Bimbo, Southern Copper Corporation, Empresas Publicas de Medellin, Cementos Argos, and the Ontario Teachers' Pension Plan, as well as Citigroup, Credit Suisse and other investment banks. Previously, she practiced in Colombia, handling numerous landmark M&A and finance transactions.
**Career:** JD, Universidad de los Andes, Bogotá, Colombia; Masters, International Commercial Law, Universidad de los Andes; LLM, Banking and Corporate Finance, Fordham University School of Law.

**LUBAND, Charles**
Dentons, New York
212 768 6942
charles.luband@dentons.com
*Featured in Healthcare (New York)*
**Practice Areas:** Advises on range of Medicare and Medicaid issues and regulatory and strategic issues. Expert on disproportionate share hospital payments, graduate medical education payments, upper payment limits, Medicaid financing, 340B drug pricing program.
**Professional Memberships:** Massachusetts Bar (1996); New York Bar (1997); District of Columbia Bar (1997); US Supreme Court (2002); American Health Lawyers Association.
**Career:** Ropes & Gray (2008-2012); Powell Goldstein (1997-2008); Law Clerk, Hon. Herbert P. Wilkins, Massachusetts Supreme Judicial Court (1996-97).
**Publications:** 'Medicaid Financing,' 2009 Medicare and Medicaid Reimbursement Update.
**Personal:** Harvard Law School (JD, 1996); Kennedy School of Government (MPP, 1996); Brown University (BA, 1990).

**LUBOWITZ, Michael**
Weil, Gotshal & Manges LLP, New York
212 310 8566
michael.lubowitz@weil.com
*Featured in Corporate/M&A (New York)*
**Practice Areas:** Mr Lubowitz is Co-head of Weil's New York Private Equity and M&A Department. He represents public and private companies in a broad range of transactions, including leveraged buyouts, friendly and hostile acquisitions, strategic investments, proxy contests, spin-offs, director governance advice and in-and out-of-court restructurings. Clients include DIRECTV, Macquarie, C.R. Bard, CBS, Verizon, American Securities, and Centerbridge Partners, among others.
**Personal:** Brandeis University (BA); American University (WCL, JD).

**LUSKIN, Martin**
Blank Rome LLP, New York
212 885 5311
MLuskin@blankrome.com
*Featured in Real Estate (New York)*
**Practice Areas:** Martin Luskin chairs the Real Estate and Financial Services Department. He counsels clients in complex commercial real estate transactions, including mergers and leveraged buy-outs. He represents clients, including real estate investment trusts, real estate advisors, financial institutions, developers, and universities, with respect to acquisitions and privatizations of publicly traded REITs; sales and acquisitions of premier office buildings, shopping centers, and apartment complexes around the country; joint ventures, partnerships, and limited liability companies; commercial leases for retail, office, and warehouse space; and financings of multi-state portfolio transactions, including those involving securitized mortgages, loan syndications and mezzanine debt. www.BlankRome.com/MLuskin

**LUTTINGER JR, David A**
Morgan, Lewis & Bockius LLP, New York
212 309 6177
dluttinger@morganlewis.com
*Featured in Insurance (New York)*
**Practice Areas:** Focuses on representing and advising clients involved in litigation, arbitration, and mediation concerning insurance coverage and commercial disputes. Also handles fidelity and crime policies, title insurance policies, mortgage insurance policies, worldwide transportation policies, and representation and warranty policies. Advises corporate insureds on matters in connection with the procurement of insurance by auditing insurance assets, structuring commercial and captive insurance programs, identifying potential legal issues, and advising in the negotiations for more favorable policies terms.
**Professional Memberships:** American Bar Association, NYSBA and RIMS.
**Career:** Former Assistant District Attorney, Trial Division: New York County District Attorney's Office.

**LYONS, Peter D**
Shearman & Sterling LLP, New York
212 848 7666
plyons@shearman.com
*Featured in Corporate/M&A (New York)*
**Career:** Peter Lyons is a partner in the firm's Mergers and Acquisitions Practice Group. He has extensive experience in acquisitions and sales of public and private companies, asset acquisition, disposition transactions, and joint ventures in a number of different industries, including financial services, healthcare, biotechnology, telecommunications and transportation. Regularly, he represents the mergers and acquisitions group of the firm's investment banking clients, and provides general securities law advice. Mr Lyons joined the firm in 1980 and became a partner in 1989.

**LYTLE, James W**
Manatt Phelps & Phillips LLP, Albany
518 431 6704
jlytle@manatt.com
*Featured in Healthcare (New York)*
**Practice Areas:** Lytle oversees Manatt's New York State legislative and regulatory practice. He represents a broad array of clients in heavily regulated industries before the Legislature, executive branch and courts, both within New York State and beyond. Lytle's work includes issues relating to insurance regulation, biomedical research, services and programs for persons with disabilities, procurement and government contracting, human services, the regulation of the professions, and educational issues.
**Career:** Harvard Law School, JD, 1978. Princeton University, AB, 1974.

**MADIGAN, Michael**
Sidley Austin LLP, New York
212 839 5944
mmadigan@sidley.com
*Featured in Insurance (New York)*
**Practice Areas:** Partner in Sidley's Insurance practice in New York. He advises principally on insurance securitizations, such as catastrophe bond transactions, having represented either issuers or their financial advisors in more than one hundred such transactions since 1997. Mr Madigan also has extensive experience in the use of other innovative risk transfer products, including derivative products, as a means of transferring insurance risk to the capital markets.
**Personal:** Harvard Law School, LLM, 1986; University of Stockholm Law School, LLB, 1983. Admission: New York.

**MAGUIRE, William R**
Hughes Hubbard & Reed LLP, New York
212 837 6000
maguire@hugheshubbard.com
*Featured in Securities (Nationwide), Litigation (New York)*
See under Nationwide for profile.

**MAHER, William**
Wollmuth Maher & Deutsch LLP, New York
212 382 3300
wmaher@wmd-law.com
*Featured in Insurance (New York)*
**Practice Areas:** William A Maher is a Founding Member of Wollmuth Maher & Deutsch LLP, is Head of the firm's Litigation Department and its Insurance and Reinsurance Dispute Resolution Practice. Mr Maher has broad experience in arbitration and litigation proceedings arising from commercial contracts, corporate transactions and reinsurance/insurance disputes. He has tried numerous arbitrations and litigations to award or decision, and has represented clients in disputes involving very significant amounts in controversy.
**Professional Memberships:** Member, Council on Judicial Administration, Association of the Bar of the City of New York, 2001-04; Firm Representative, ARIAS-US, 2003-present; Member, Publications Committee, Association of Insurance and Reinsurance Run-Off Companies, 2006-11; Member, New York State Appellate

Division, First Department, Disciplinary Committee, 2009-present.
**Personal:** The College of William & Mary, BA, 1982; The University of Virginia School of Law, JD, 1985; Managing Editor, The Virginia Law Review, 1984-85; Member, Order of the Coif; law clerk to Hon Milton Pollack (US District Judge SDNY), 1985-86.

**MAHONEY, Stacey Anne**
Bingham McCutchen LLP, New York
212 705 7273
stacey.mahoney@bingham.com
*Featured in Antitrust (New York)*
**Practice Areas:** Focuses on antitrust litigation and counseling. Defends private antitrust litigants in federal and state courts throughout the US. Counseling practice focuses on distribution and pricing issues, antitrust investigations, and competitor collaborations. Engages in merger analysis and advocacy before the Department of Justice, the Federal Trade Commission and abroad, providing Hart-Scott-Rodino reporting counseling, handling second requests, and conducting and overseeing domestic and international advocacy strategies before the agencies.
**Publications:** Frequently writes, speaks and guest lectures at universities regarding antitrust issues.
**Personal:** Fordham University School of Law, Juris Doctor, 1994; University of Michigan, Artis Baccalaureate, 1991.

**MAKINEN, Marita A**
Lowenstein Sandler LLP, New York
646 414 6950
mmakinen@lowenstein.com
*Featured in Corporate/M&A (New York)*
**Practice Areas:** Marita Makinen, Chair of Lowenstein's M&A practice, advises public and growth-stage private companies in the areas of mergers and acquisitions, finance, governance and securities law requirements. Marita regularly represents public and venture-backed companies in strategic acquisitions and divestitures and in exit and change of control transactions. Focusing on the technology and consumer industries, Marita has experience in transactions involving complex capital structures, talent retention needs and intellectual property assets. Marita is also active in advising public companies on SEC reporting issues and in structuring joint ventures, spin-offs and distressed company transactions.
http://www.lowenstein.com/mmakinen

**MALTBY, Stephen J O**
Gibney, Anthony & Flaherty LLP, New York
212 705 9838
sjomaltby@gibney.com
*Featured in Immigration (New York)*
**Practice Areas:** Immigration.
**Professional Memberships:** New York State Bar Association; American Immigration Lawyers Association; Pace University School of Law, adjunct professor of law; British American Chamber of Commerce Foundation Inc., Chairman; British American Business Inc., Board of Directors.

**Career:** Partner, Gibney, Anthony & Flaherty, LLP, 1978-Present.
**Publications:** "Immigration Law" - American British Trade & Investment; "US Immigration: The United States continues its debate to define a 21st century immigration policy" - American British Trade & Investment; United States Chapter - Corporate Immigration Review; "Immigration Reform" - American British Business; "Representing an Employer in a Form I-9 Audit: Are You Ready?" New York City Bar CLE; Inside the Minds: New Developments in Immigration Enforcement and Compliance "Trends in Worksite Enforcement Laws and Employer Compliance Best Practices"; "US Immigration: a New Era of Protectionism and Enforcement" - American British Business; "The Challenges of Change" - American British Business; "US Immigration Update" - American British Business
**Personal:** JD, University of Virginia, 1978; BA, Magdalen College, Oxford, UK, 1975.

**MANDEL, Gary B**
Simpson Thacher & Bartlett LLP, New York
212 455 7963
gmandel@stblaw.com
*Featured in Tax (New York)*
**Practice Areas:** Tax Partner concentrating on mergers and acquisitions, joint ventures, restructurings and spin-offs. Advises on matters for, among others, the Firm's private equity fund clients.
**Professional Memberships:** Member of the Executive Committee of the NYSBA Tax Section.
**Career:** Joined the Firm in 1997; became Partner in 2003. Former clerk on the United States Tax Court. Certified public accountant.
**Personal:** BS, Brooklyn College (1985); MBA, Pace University (1990); JD, cum laude, Saint John's School of Law (1994); LLM, with distinction, Georgetown University School of Law (1996). Adjunct Professor at New York Law School; Adjunct Professor at Columbia University Law School.

**MANN, Christopher L**
Sullivan & Cromwell LLP, New York
212 558 4625
mannc@sullcrom.com
*Featured in Latin American Investment (New York), Projects (Nationwide)*
See under Nationwide for profile.

**MANNAL, Douglas**
Kramer Levin Naftalis & Frankel LLP, New York
212 715 9313
dmannal@kramerlevin.com
*Featured in Bankruptcy/Restructuring (New York)*
**Practice Areas:** Mr Mannal represents ad hoc creditor groups, bank agents, creditors' committees and other parties in all aspects of bankruptcy cases, out-of-court restructurings, debtor-in-possession financings, acquisitions, rights offerings and other distressed situations. He also advises hedge funds and financial institutions regarding investments in distressed companies with complex corporate and capital structures. Recent significant representations include Residential Capital

(creditors' committee), General Maritime Corporation (debtor) and Orchard Brands Corporation (DIP lender and second lien agent). Mr Mannal has been recognized by Law360, New York Super Lawyers and Turnarounds & Workouts.

**MANSFIELD, Alan**
Greenberg Traurig, LLP, New York
212 801 9277
MansfieldA@gtlaw.com
*Featured in Litigation (New York)*
**Practice Areas:** Co-Chair, Global Litigation Practice. Financial Institutions.
**Professional Memberships:** Commissioner, New York State Commission on Judicial Nomination, 1996-Present; Member, Independent Judicial Screening Panel; Member, Board of Directors, MFY Legal Services, Inc., 1997-Present; Trustee, Lexington School for the Deaf/Center for the Deaf, 1987-Present; Fellow, The New York Bar Foundation. Member: National Center for State Courts, American Bar Foundation.
**Career:** Listed: Best Lawyers in America, 2005-13; Super Lawyers, 2006-12; Chambers USA, 2009-13. Rated, AV® Preeminent™ 5.0 out of 5.
**Publications:** Frequent speaker and author regarding trial practice.
**Personal:** JD, Duke University School of Law; AB, magna cum laude, Brown University.

**MARCU, Aaron R**
Freshfields Bruckhaus Deringer US LLP, New York
212 277 4000
aaron.marcu@freshfields.com
*Featured in Litigation (New York)*
**Practice Areas:** Aaron heads Freshfields' global financial institutions litigation group. His practice focuses on the defense of white collar criminal and SEC enforcement investigations and related civil litigation. He conducts internal investigations and advises boards and board committees on sensitive matters. Financial institutions and other corporate clients rely on Aaron for his experience handling complex investigations and litigation involving allegations of financial accounting and securities fraud, insider trading, corruption, cartel and other anti-competitive activity.
**Career:** Aaron is a former Assistant US Attorney in the SDNY, and also served as Chief Appellate Attorney, Chief of Major Crimes and Associate US Attorney.

**MARCUS, Jacqueline**
Weil, Gotshal & Manges LLP, New York
212 310 8130
jacqueline.marcus@weil.com
*Featured in Bankruptcy/Restructuring (New York)*
**Practice Areas:** Practice encompasses business finance and restructurings, securitizations and secured transactions. Was one of the lead attorneys representing Extended Stay Inc. and its affiliates in their completed chapter 11 cases. She is also on the team representing Lehman Brothers Holdings Inc. and its affiliates in its bankruptcy proceedings. Creditor practice includes representation of creditors in the chapter 11 cases of Black Diamond Mining Company, Tropicana

Entertainment, Epic Resorts, and Food Barn Stores, as well as in many out-of-court restructurings. She works closely with members of Weil's Structured Finance Practice.
**Personal:** University of Pennsylvania (BA); New York University (JD).

### MARELL, Jeffrey D
Paul, Weiss, Rifkind, Wharton & Garrison LLP, New York
212 373 3105
jmarell@paulweiss.com
*Featured in Corporate/M&A (New York)*
**Practice Areas:** Corporate partner; co-head of firm's North American Mergers and Acquisitions Practice; member, Private Equity Group. Extensive experience representing strategic, private equity and hedge fund clients in full spectrum of public and private merger and acquisition transactions, including negotiated and contested acquisitions and divestitures, minority investments and carve-out transactions. Public company experience also includes numerous proxy contests and special committee assignments. Recent representations include Spectrum Brands in its $1.4 billion acquisition of a division of Stanley Black & Decker, Marcato Capital in a proxy fight with Lear Corporation; Meritage Group in the acquisition of second largest Miller-Coors beer distributor.

### MARINUZZI, Lorenzo
Morrison & Foerster LLP, New York
212 468 8045
lmarinuzzi@mofo.com
*Featured in Bankruptcy/Restructuring (New York)*
**Practice Areas:** Mr Marinuzzi is a partner in the Business Restructuring & Insolvency Group of Morrison & Foerster. Mr Marinuzzi represents debtors, creditors, and creditors' committees in bankruptcy cases, workouts, and litigation in domestic and cross border matters. His cases have spanned a number of industries, including airline and cargo transportation, mortgage origination and servicing, retail, banking and finance, energy, telecommunications, and oil and gas.
**Personal:** BA, Fordham University, 1993; JD, Fordham University School of Law, 1996.

### MARKEL, Gregory A
Cadwalader, Wickersham & Taft LLP, New York
212 504 6112
greg.markel@cwt.com
*Featured in Securities (Nationwide), Litigation (New York)*
See under Nationwide for profile.

### MARKS, Aaron H.
Kasowitz, Benson, Torres & Friedman LLP, New York
212 506 1721
amarks@kasowitz.com
*Featured in Litigation (New York)*
**Practice Areas:** Aaron Marks's practice focuses on complex commercial litigation, including disputes concerning structured finance and derivatives, lender liability, securities, corporate governance, mass tort and intellectual property. He has extensive first chair trial experience, and is currently representing clients in a variety of disputes

relating to the credit market crisis, including disputes over mortgage-backed securities, CDOs, acquisition financings, and defaulted swaps.
**Career:** Recognized as one of 50 of the nation's most accomplished litigators under age 45 ("The Fab Fifty") by The American Lawyer, he is also recommended in Legal 500 and Benchmark Litigation.

### MARKS, Benjamin E.
Weil, Gotshal & Manges LLP, New York
212 310 8029
benjamin.marks@weil.com
*Featured in Intellectual Property (New York)*
**Practice Areas:** Benjamin Marks focuses on IP litigation, with an emphasis on copyright, trademark, misappropriation, unfair competition, and First Amendment disputes. He has handled a wide variety of matters for clients such as The McGraw-Hill Companies, S&P Dow Jones Indices, Thomson Reuters, The Walt Disney Company, the Association of American Publishers, DMX and Bertelsmann. He frequently represents music users such as television stations, television networks, and web site operators in connection with the acquisition of, and litigation over, rights to perform musical compositions.
**Personal:** University of Pennsylvania (BA, 1993, magna cum laude); New York University School of Law (JD, 1997).

### MARTIN, Richard
Orrick, Herrington & Sutcliffe LLP, New York
212 506 5135
rmartin@orrick.com
*Featured in Litigation (New York)*
**Career:** Richard A. Martin, a partner in Orrick's New York office, is a member of the Securities Litigation and Regulatory Enforcement Group. His practice focuses on accountants' liability, securities and commercial litigation, as well as arbitration and international and domestic white-collar criminal law. Mr Martin has been involved in litigation in the state and federal courts of the United States and in Europe for 30 years. His practice has concentrated on international and domestic litigation and arbitration involving securities, accounting and financial services and corporate governance. He also regularly provides advice and assistance in international criminal and civil law matters.

### MARTIN, Scott
Greenberg Traurig, LLP, New York
212 801 2231
MartinSc@gtlaw.com
*Featured in Antitrust (New York)*
**Practice Areas:** Antitrust litigation; class action litigation.
**Professional Memberships:** Executive Committee, Antitrust Section, New York State Bar Association; American Bar Association, Section of Antitrust (Editorial Board, Antitrust Law Developments; Member, Civil Redress Task Force). Member, Law360 Competition Editorial Board, inaugural year and current.
**Career:** Selected: Chambers USA, 2006-13; Euromoney's Guide to the World's Leading Competition & Antitrust Lawyers, 2012; Who's

Who in American Law; Best Lawyers in America, 2012-13; New York Super Lawyers, 2006-12; International Who's Who of Competition Lawyers and Economists 2013; International Who's Who of Business Lawyers, 2013.
**Personal:** JD, Stanford Law School, 1990; AB, Stanford University, 1987.

### MARZULLI JR, John A
Shearman & Sterling LLP, New York
212 848 8590
jmarzulli@shearman.com
*Featured in Corporate/M&A (New York)*
**Practice Areas:** Mr Marzulli focuses on international corporate finance, emphasis on cross-border M&A, defensive assignments, privately negotiated acquisitions and divestitures of stock and assets, joint ventures and related corporate governance matters.
**Professional Memberships:** Member, ABA, Business Law Section; Member, Association of the Bar of the City of NY; Member, Committee on Mergers, Acquisitions and Proxy Contests, Chair, 2008–2011; Member, Committee on Securities Regulations, 2002–2005.
**Career:** Joined the firm in 1980 following a federal district court clerkship; became partner in 1988.
**Personal:** New York University School of Law, JD, 1978, Order of the Coif, Middlebury College, BA, 1975, Phi Beta Kappa.

### MASON, Andrew S
Sullivan & Cromwell LLP, New York
212 558 3759
masona@sullcrom.com
*Featured in Tax (New York)*
**Professional Memberships:** ABA; ABCNY (former Chair, Committee on Taxation of Partnerships and Pass-Through Entities); NYSBA.
**Career:** Partner since 1989. Tax advice on wide range of matters, including M&A, real estate, project finance, leveraged lease, joint ventures and international transactions. Counsels clients regarding adjustments proposed by the IRS. and also has experience handling New York state tax controversies. Mr Mason has successfully worked on matters in the New York conciliation process and has appeared before the New York Tax Tribunal.
**Personal:** Yale Law School (JD, 1981); Yale University (BA, 1978).

### MASON, Richard G
Wachtell, Lipton, Rosen & Katz, New York
212 403 1252
rgmason@wlrk.com
*Featured in Bankruptcy/Restructuring (Nationwide), Bankruptcy/Restructuring (New York)*
See under Nationwide for profile.

### MASTRO, Randy
Gibson, Dunn & Crutcher LLP, New York
212 351 3825
rmastro@gibsondunn.com
*Featured in Litigation (New York)*
**Practice Areas:** Co-Chair of Litigation Practice and Crisis Management Groups. Prominent litigator who handles complex civil cases, securities litigation and white collar criminal matters. Tried

dozens of cases in private practice and as a federal prosecutor in the Southern District of New York and has argued more than 90 appeals in federal and state appellate courts.
**Career:** Among his many high profile matters, Mastro is currently representing Chevron in seeking to prevent enforcement of an $18 billion Ecuadorian judgment.
**Personal:** JD, University of Pennsylvania, 1981, Moot Court Champion, Board of Overseers. BA, Yale University, 1978, cum laude.

### MASUCCI, Michele
Nixon Peabody LLP, New York
516 832 7573
mmasucci@nixonpeabody.com
*Featured in Healthcare (New York)*
**Practice Areas:** Practice Group Leader for the Health Services Group and represents for-profit health care providers with particular experience in transactional matters, including joint ventures with not-for-profit providers. Michele represents specialty pharmacies, dialysis companies, retail based clinics, medi-spas, imaging companies, ambulatory surgery companies, private equity firms and large physician practices. She regularly advises on fraud and abuse and Stark issues, Accountable Care Organizations, health reform and corporate compliance. Michele has lectured extensively on transactional and managed care issues and HIPAA compliance matters.
**Personal:** University of Virginia School of Law, JD; Brown University, BA.

### MATAYS, Steven J.
Skadden, Arps, Slate, Meagher & Flom LLP & Affiliates, New York
212 735 2372
steven.matays@skadden.com
*Featured in Tax (New York)*
**Practice Areas:** Steven J. Matays represents clients on a wide range of domestic and international tax matters, with particular emphasis on mergers and acquisitions, spin-offs and other divestitures, debt and equity offerings, corporate and partnership restructurings and joint ventures. He also advises on the tax aspects of structuring financial instruments and executive compensation.
**Career:** JD, Harvard Law School, 2000 (cum laude); AB, Princeton University, 1997 (summa cum laude, Phi Beta Kappa).

### MAYER, Thomas Moers
Kramer Levin Naftalis & Frankel LLP, New York
212 715 9169
tmayer@kramerlevin.com
*Featured in Bankruptcy/Restructuring (Nationwide), Bankruptcy/Restructuring (New York)*
See under Nationwide for profile.

### MAYO, David W
Paul, Weiss, Rifkind, Wharton & Garrison LLP, New York
212 373 3324
dmayo@paulweiss.com
*Featured in Tax (New York)*
**Practice Areas:** Partner in the Tax Department. Focuses his practice on corporate and partnership

taxation, taxable and tax-free mergers and acquisitions, restructurings and cross-border transactions. David was a member of the Executive Committee of the Tax Section of the New York State Bar Association from 2001 to 2013 and is a past President of the New York City Tax Club.

## MCCORMACK, Aidan
DLA Piper LLP (US), New York
212 335 4750
aidan.mccormack@dlapiper.com
*Featured in Insurance (New York)*
**Practice Areas:** Insurance Litigation
**Professional Memberships:** ARIAS-U.S.; Professional Liability Underwriting Society; Federation of Defense & Corporate Counsel.
**Career:** He concentrates on insurance and reinsurance issues and serves as regional and national counsel for a wide range of companies. His practice includes litigation, appellate work, arbitration and alternative dispute resolution. He has acted as international and national lead counsel for many clients and has handled numerous high-exposure matters.
**Personal:** JD, Marquette University Law School; BA, Creighton University.

## MCCORMACK, Thomas
Chadbourne & Parke LLP, New York
212 408 5182
tmccormack@chadbourne.com
*Featured in Litigation (New York)*
**Practice Areas:** Tom McCormack is a trial lawyer with over 25 years of experience handling complex commercial, securities and class action litigations. During his career, he has tried a wide range of cases, including multi-billion dollar energy supply contracts, bank loans, joint venture agreements, corporate governance and securities claims, drug development projects and many others. His clients include a number of Fortune 500 companies, as well as officers and directors of various publicly traded companies.
**Personal:** Stanford University, BA, 1978; Cornell Law School, JD, 1982; admitted in New York and numerous federal Circuit Courts of Appeals and districts courts.

## MCCREARY, Jean H
Nixon Peabody LLP, Rochester
585 263 1611
jmccreary@nixonpeabody.com
*Featured in Environment (New York)*
**Practice Areas:** US/international transactional due diligence; hazardous waste site investigation and remediation; brownfields redevelopment, cleanup, tax credits; Superfund litigation and common counsel; civil and administrative enforcement defense; environmental health and safety regulatory compliance assessment; management system design and implementation; vapor intrusion; alternative dispute resolution; product labeling/content; permitting and land use.
**Professional Memberships:** Admitted New York; Florida.
**Career:** Former National Practice Group Chair, Energy and Environment (2001-09); Certified Professional Environmental Auditor (BEAC); past

President, The Auditing Roundtable; past TAG Group Leader (ISO 14010).
**Personal:** University of Florida (JD); University of Rochester (BA); two-time Athena Award Nominee; pro bono service awards.

## MCGARRY, Martha E
Skadden, Arps, Slate, Meagher & Flom LLP & Affiliates, New York
212 735 2780
martha.mcgarry@skadden.com
*Featured in Corporate/M&A (New York)*
**Practice Areas:** Corporate Securities Partner with extensive experience in U.S. and international M&A, joint ventures and other strategic collaborations, private equity and corporate governance matters. Named Chambers USA Women in Law Awards 2012 "Corporate/M&A Lawyer of the Year." Representative clients include The Coca-Cola Company, American Express, The Hershey Company, Wal-Mart, Thompson Reuters, CIT Group, The Clorox Company and Harrah's Entertainment. Ms McGarry has substantial experience in consumer products, finance, telecommunications, gaming and lodging, real estate, pharmaceutical and biotechnology. Chair of Skadden's global Client Development Committee and member of the Policy Committee.
**Career:** JD, Fordham University, 1977; BA, Middlebury College, 1973.

## MCGINLEY, Elizabeth L
Bracewell & Giuliani LLP, New York
212 508 6173
elizabeth.mcginley@bgllp.com
*Featured in Tax (New York)*
**Practice Areas:** Heads the firm's tax practice. Represents funds and institutional investors in connection with acquisitions, recapitalizations and joint ventures, with emphasis on distressed situations and bankruptcy. Has broad background in corporate tax, partnership tax and tax issues relating to energy investments. Has represented major public corporations, private investors and real estate developers. Structures and negotiates tax-free reorganizations on behalf of targets and acquirers, advises corporate clients on tax-free separation transactions and negotiates complex partnership transactions.
**Personal:** LLM, Taxation, New York University School of Law, 1999; JD, New York University School of Law, 1996; BS, Lehigh University, 1990.

## MCGOVERN, Brian
Cadwalader, Wickersham & Taft LLP, New York
212 504 6117
brian.mcgovern@cwt.com
*Featured in Healthcare (New York)*
**Practice Areas:** Focuses on legal issues that confront the healthcare provider community, including counsel and advocacy on reimbursement issues; government audits and investigations, including Medicare fiscal intermediary audits and New York State Office of Medicaid Inspector General and Attorney General Medicaid Fraud Control Unit inquiries; regulatory compliance; rate appeals, certificate of need applications, property tax exemption applications and appeals,

and other submissions to administrative and regulatory agencies; patient-care survey deficiency citations; and administrative hearings and litigation in State and Federal courts. Clients include nursing homes, home care agencies, hospices, hospitals, continuing care retirement communities, and pediatric facilities.
**Career:** Former Assistant Attorney General for New York State.
**Personal:** JD, Georgetown University Law Center; BA, Queens College/CUNY.

## MCGUINNESS, William G
Fried, Frank, Harris, Shriver & Jacobson LLP, New York
212 859 8026
William.McGuinness@FriedFrank.com
*Featured in Litigation (New York)*
**Practice Areas:** Litigation partner, chair of the litigation department. Fellow, American College of Trial Lawyers. Handles a broad range of complex commercial litigation, including cases involving securities, mergers and acquisitions and intellectual property. Practice focuses on the brokerage, securities and financial services industries. Also active in the M&A field. Regularly represents issuers and underwriters in shareholder federal securities litigation.
**Career:** Joined in 1979; became partner in 1986.
**Personal:** JD, Columbia Law School (1979); BA, Columbia University (1975).

## MCINERNEY, William P
Cadwalader, Wickersham & Taft LLP, New York
212 504 6118
william.mcinerney@cwt.com
*Featured in Real Estate (Nationwide), Real Estate (New York)*
See under Nationwide for profile.

## MCKENNA, Keith
Kasowitz, Benson, Torres & Friedman LLP, New York
*Featured in Insurance (New York)*
**Practice Areas:** Keith has a diverse commercial litigation background focusing on insurance coverage litigation and counseling for corporate policyholders. He represents large corporate policyholders in federal and state court actions around the country, seeking damages, declaratory judgments, and other relief against prominent American and European insurers. Keith has represented large corporate clients in a variety of contexts, including contract disputes, products liability claims, alter-ego and veil-piercing claims, securities and shareholder claims, patent infringement, and employment discrimination.
**Publications:** Co-Author, "Government Investigations: Are You Covered?," Corporate Board Member; Co-Author, "Coverage for Defense Costs in Consumer Fraud Actions," New York Law Journal.

## MCLOUGHLIN, Jean
Davis Polk & Wardwell LLP, New York
212 450 4000
jean.mcloughlin@davispolk.com
*Featured in Employee Benefits & Executive Compensation (New York)*

**Practice Areas:** Partner in Davis Polk's Corporate Department, concentrating in executive compensation and employee benefits matters. She regularly advises corporate and financial clients on the implementation of management equity programs, the negotiation of executive employment arrangements, and the securities and tax implications of such arrangements.

## MCRAE, William
Cleary Gottlieb Steen & Hamilton LLP, New York
212 225 2188
wmcrae@cgsh.com
*Featured in Tax (New York)*
**Practice Areas:** U.S. tax matters concerning international and domestic M&A (including insolvency workouts and private equity transactions), financial products, international tax planning, and capital markets transactions. Clients include Citigroup and Goldman Sachs. Advised Nortel and Truvo on tax aspects of their bankruptcies, including settlement of $3 billion tax claim.
**Professional Memberships:** Executive Committee Member of NYSBA Tax Section.
**Career:** Joined firm, 1996; became Partner, 2005. LLM, New York University; JD, cum laude, Harvard Law School (1996); BA, magna cum laude, Williams College (1991).
**Publications:** Regularly speaks on tax matters at conferences; published several articles on the taxation of financial products.

## MECHANIC, Jonathan L
Fried, Frank, Harris, Shriver & Jacobson LLP, New York
212 859 8222
Jonathan.Mechanic@FriedFrank.com
*Featured in Real Estate (Nationwide), Real Estate (New York)*
**Practice Areas:** Partner; chair, real estate department. Counsels developers, investors, REITs, lenders in commercial real estate transactions, including acquisition, disposition and development of office, retail, hotel, mixed-use properties; all aspects of financings; joint ventures, restructurings. Represents landlords and tenants in commercial and ground leasing transactions. Clients include Conde Nast; Fortress; Jack Resnick & Sons; RFR Holding; SL Green Realty; Tishman Hotel & Realty; Tishman Speyer; UBS.
**Career:** Joined as partner, 1987. Lecturer, Harvard Law School (2006, 2009-2012). Executive Committee Member-REBNY.
**Personal:** JD, New York University (1977), member, Law Review, Order of the Coif; BA, magna cum laude, Brandeis University (1974).

## MEHLMAN, Nancy
Simpson Thacher & Bartlett LLP, New York
212 455 2328
nmehlman@stblaw.com
*Featured in Tax (New York)*
**Practice Areas:** Tax Partner concentrating on fund formation, mergers and acquisitions, real estate transactions, partnerships, joint ventures and related financing transactions in the credit and capital markets. Advises on tax matters for,

among others, Blackstone, KKR, Carlyle Real Estate and Morgan Stanley.
**Personal:** BA, Williams College (1991); JD, cum laude, New York University School of Law (1999); LLM, New York University School of Law (2002).

### MEHRARA, Sasan
Simpson Thacher & Bartlett LLP, New York
212 455 2783
smehrara@stblaw.com
*Featured in Real Estate (New York)*
**Practice Areas:** Partner in the Real Estate Department. Represents private equity funds, investors, REITs and private companies in a variety of commercial real estate transactions including, acquisitions, dispositions, joint ventures, restructuring, real estate mergers and acquisitions and financings. Representative clients include The Blackstone Group, Centerbridge Partners, The Carlyle Group, Hilton Worldwide, La Quinta Hotels, Extended Stay Hotels, Equity Office Properties and IndCor.
**Career:** Joined firm in 2000; became Partner in 2007.
**Personal:** BA, cum laude, with distinction in History, University of Pennsylvania; JD with honors, The George Washington University Law School; Production Editor - The George Washington University Law Review.

### MELLER, Bruce
Peckar & Abramson, P.C., New York
212 382 0909
bmeller@pecklaw.com
*Featured in Construction (New York)*
**Practice Areas:** Mr Meller has more than 30 years of experience in construction law. He has represented contractors on a wide array of construction projects, including high rise buildings, shopping malls, waste and water treatment plants, hospitals, garages, institutional buildings and laboratories, as well as civil and infrastructure projects.
**Professional Memberships:** Fellow of Litigation Counsel of America. Admitted to practice law in New York and New Jersey.
**Career:** Partner in the New Jersey office.
**Publications:** Lecturer on the intricacies of construction law and author of articles relating to construction issues.
**Personal:** For more information, please visit: www.pecklaw.com

### MERMELSTEIN, Joshua
Fried, Frank, Harris, Shriver & Jacobson LLP, New York
212 859 8137
Joshua.Mermelstein@FriedFrank.com
*Featured in Real Estate (Nationwide), Real Estate (New York)*
See under Nationwide for profile.

### MERRIMAN, Mark
Frankfurt Kurnit Klein & Selz, New York
212 826 5596
mmerriman@fkks.com
*Featured in Media & Entertainment (New York)*
**Practice Areas:** Partner in the Entertainment Group. Focuses on theatre, book publishing and reality television. Represents playwrights, book-

writers, composers, lyricists, dramaturgs, underlying rights holders, estates, music publishers, general managers, investors, co-producers, executive producers, directors, associate directors, resident directors, and other creative team personnel in the live stage industry. Also represents authors of fiction and non-fiction, illustrators, and underlying rights owners in their agreements with publishers, agents and collaborators; and reality television production companies, talent, and content providers.

### MEYER, Paul
Clifford Chance US LLP, New York
212 878 8176
paul.meyer@cliffordchance.com
*Featured in Insurance (Nationwide), Insurance (New York)*
**Practice Areas:** Has over 30 years experience in insurance industry mergers, acquisitions, reorganizations, joint ventures, financings, product development and regulatory matters. Experience includes the first merger of large mutual life insurance companies in the US, the largest US leveraged buyout of a reinsurance company, several life insurance company demutualizations, and the then largest sale of a block of variable life insurance business.
**Career:** Partner at Clifford Chance since 1986. Coe College, BA, summa cum laude. Harvard Law School, JD, cum laude. Harvard Business School, MBA.

### MEYERS, Melanie
Fried, Frank, Harris, Shriver & Jacobson LLP, New York
212 859 8785
Melanie.Meyers@FriedFrank.com
*Featured in Real Estate (New York)*
**Practice Areas:** Real estate partner. Practice focuses on real estate development, specializing in land use, environmental, zoning, public approvals and private/public partnerships. Clients include The Georgetown Company, The Related Companies, Forest City Ratner Companies, Columbia University, Jamestown Properties, Hospital for Special Surgery, Verizon Communications, Rudin Management Company, Inc., Cornell University and Alchemy Properties.
**Career:** Joined as partner in 2003. Prior to joining, General Counsel to the Department of City Planning of New York City.
**Personal:** JD, Columbia Law School (1987), Harlan Fiske Stone Scholar, editor, Columbia Law Review; BS, Massachusetts Institute of Technology (1982).

### MEYERSON, Lee
Simpson Thacher & Bartlett LLP, New York
212 455 2000
lmeyerson@stblaw.com
*Featured in Financial Services Regulation (Nationwide), Corporate/M&A (New York)*
See under Nationwide for profile.

### MILLER, Allen
Chadbourne & Parke LLP, New York
212 408 5454
amiller@chadbourne.com
*Featured in Latin American Investment (New York)*

**Practice Areas:** Head of Chadbourne's Corporate Department. Advises public and private companies and their Boards of Directors on a broad spectrum of matters, including mergers, acquisitions, divestitures, corporate governance issues, securities law matters, restructurings, joint ventures, leveraged buyouts, private placements, public offerings and privatizations. A significant part of Mr Miller's practice consists of cross-border work, particularly in Latin America. Mr Miller lectures frequently throughout the U.S. and Latin America and he publishes regularly.
**Professional Memberships:** American Bar Association (Section on Corporation, Banking and Business Law); International Bar Association.
**Personal:** Cornell Law School, JD, 1979; Notes Editor, International Law Journal.

### MILLER, Brett
Morrison & Foerster LLP, New York
212 468 8051
bmiller@mofo.com
*Featured in Bankruptcy/Restructuring (Nationwide), Bankruptcy/Restructuring (New York)*
See under Nationwide for profile.

### MILLER, David S
Cadwalader, Wickersham & Taft LLP, New York
212 504 6318
david.miller@cwt.com
*Featured in Tax (New York)*
**Practice Areas:** Concentrates on matters relating to the taxation of financial instruments and derivatives, cross-border lending transactions and other financings, international and domestic mergers and acquisitions, multinational corporate groups and partnerships, bankruptcy and workouts, high net worth individuals and families, and public charities and private foundations.
**Professional Memberships:** Former Chair, New York State Bar Association, Tax Section; Tax Forum.
**Publications:** Frequent speaker at conferences and universities. Author of numerous articles for legal publications.
**Personal:** JD, Columbia Law School (Notes and Comments Editor, Columbia Law Review); LLM, New York University School of Law; BA, University of Pennsylvania (summa cum laude); Clerk, Honorable Mary M Schroeder of the Ninth Circuit Court of Appeals (1989-90); Named as "Lawyer Who Leads by Example" by the New York Law Journal for representing more than 200 charities pro bono; Recipient, Burton Award for Legal Achievement (recognizing exceptional legal writing).

### MILLER, Harvey R
Weil, Gotshal & Manges LLP, New York
212 310 8500
harvey.miller@weil.com
*Featured in Bankruptcy/Restructuring (Nationwide), Bankruptcy/Restructuring (New York)*
See under Nationwide for profile.

### MILLER, Peter A
Greenberg Traurig, LLP, New York
212 801 2263
MillerPA@gtlaw.com
*Featured in Real Estate (New York)*
**Practice Areas:** Real estate; acquisition development and financing; joint ventures; complex financial and partnership arrangements; real estate finance.
**Professional Memberships:** Member: New York State Bar Association; Executive Committee, Lawyers Division of UJA-Federation of New York; board of overseers, Jewish Theological Seminary's Rabbinical School. Board Member, Olami Masorti; Board Member, Masorti Foundation for Conservative Judaism in Israel.
**Career:** Listed, The Best Lawyers in America, 2011-13. Team Member, a Law360 'Real Estate Practice Group of the Year', 2011-12.
**Personal:** JD, New York University School of Law, 1984; BS, The Wharton School, University of Pennsylvania, 1980.

### MILLOCK, Peter J
Nixon Peabody LLP, Albany
518 427 2651
pmillock@nixonpeabody.com
*Featured in Healthcare (New York), Healthcare (Nationwide)*
**Practice Areas:** Peter Millock focuses his practice on affiliations and networks of physicians, hospitals and other health and mental health providers, and regulatory and enforcement matters before state agencies.
**Professional Memberships:** Admitted to practice in New York; Member, New York City Bar Association; Member, New York State Bar Association (former Chair, Health Law Section).
**Career:** From 1980-1995 served as General Counsel, New York State Department of Health. He was chief legal advisor to the Commissioner of Health and provided advice to state policy makers on all health-related matters.
**Personal:** Harvard Law School, JD; Harvard College, BA.

### MILLS, Phillip R
Davis Polk & Wardwell LLP, New York
212 450 4000
phillip.mills@davispolk.com
*Featured in Corporate/M&A (New York)*
**Practice Areas:** Member of Davis Polk's Mergers and Acquisitions Group. Advises on US and cross-border strategic transactions. Advised on Mitsubishi Leasing's acquisition of Jackson Square Aviation; Wanda's acquisition of AMC; Cigna's acquisition of HealthSpring; PartnerRe's acquisition of ParisRe; Emerson Electric's acquisition of Chloride and Avocent; MCI's acquisition by Verizon; Kingdom of Sweden's sale of Vin & Sprit; AIG's consortium acquisition of Kinder Morgan; Citigroup's consortium acquisition of Guangdong Development Bank; FirstGroup's acquisition of Laidlaw; Alliance Capital Management's acquisition of Sanford Bernstein; Keebler Foods' acquisition by Kellogg; and various transactions for Comcast, Roche, ImClone, EQT, Quadrangle, JPMorgan and Deutsche Bank.

**MILMED, Paul K**
White & Case LLP, New York
212 819 8751
pmilmed@whitecase.com
*Featured in Environment (New York)*
**Career:** Mr Milmed concentrates on environmental transactional law, representing principals and lenders in connection with the environmental aspects of domestic and international corporate and financial transactions, including M&A, divestitures, public securities offerings, private equity investments, bankruptcies and restructurings, real estate and project finance transactions. His practice involves virtually every industry and a wide range of non-US jurisdictions. Mr Milmed also represents industrial corporations in environmental liability and regulatory matters, including Superfund disputes. Mr Milmed has been named to the panel of mediators selected by the US District Court for the Southern District of NY. To view his biography, visit www.whitecase.com/pmilmed.

**MILMOE, J Gregory**
Skadden, Arps, Slate, Meagher & Flom LLP & Affiliates, New York
212 735 3770
Gregory.Milmoe@skadden.com
*Featured in Bankruptcy/Restructuring (Nationwide), Bankruptcy/Restructuring (New York)*
See under Nationwide for profile.

**MILNE, Robert A**
White & Case LLP, New York
212 819 8924
rmilne@whitecase.com
*Featured in Antitrust (New York)*
**Career:** Robert Milne's principal areas of practice are complex litigation and counseling in the areas of antitrust (civil and criminal) and trade regulation. Mr Milne has litigated jury and non-jury cases before federal and state courts throughout the US, including matters before the US Federal Trade Commission and other state and federal government agencies. He has also handled complex arbitration matters. Prior to joining private practice, Mr Milne served as a trial attorney with the Antitrust Division of the US Department of Justice, involving civil and criminal investigations and trials in jurisdictions nationwide. To view his biography, visit www.whitecase.com/rmilne.

**MINDLIN, Philip**
Wachtell, Lipton, Rosen & Katz, New York
212 403 1217
pmindlin@wlrk.com
*Featured in Bankruptcy/Restructuring (New York)*
**Practice Areas:** Practice focuses on restructuring and international transactions.
**Career:** Of Counsel at Wachtell, Lipton, Rosen & Katz, where he was a partner from 1991 to 2010. Represents buyers, sellers, owners, investors, lenders and borrowers in complex transactions involving balance sheet issues and in cross-border acquisitions. Relevant experience includes representation of key parties in transactions involving Groupe Casino, Knight Capital, UBS Pactual, Burger King do Brasil, NorTel, Pliant Corporation, Aleris International, Bear Stearns, Fannie Mae and

Freddie Mac, Refco Group, Lehman Brothers, Cable and Wireless plc, and Olympia & York.
**Personal:** Graduated from the University of Pennsylvania (BA) and magna cum laude from Fordham University (JD), where he was a member of the Fordham Law Review and was a recipient of the Stillman Memorial Prize, the Chapin Prize and the Constitutional Law Medal.

**MINER, Martin P**
Holland & Knight LLP, New York
212 513 3450
martin.miner@hklaw.com
*Featured in Real Estate (New York)*
**Practice Areas:** Martin "Marty" Miner focuses his practice on commercial real estate. Mr Miner has been involved with substantially all aspects of commercial real estate including acquisitions and dispositions, financing, leasing and joint venture deal structuring. He has handled several billion dollars each of acquisitions and dispositions of real property, financings and leasing transactions. He previously served as an Adjunct Professor at Columbia Business School where he taught a course in real estate transactions.

**MINIAS, Joseph G.**
Willkie Farr & Gallagher LLP, New York
212 728 8202
jminias@willkie.com
*Featured in Bankruptcy/Restructuring (New York)*
**Practice Areas:** Focuses on the representation of hedge funds, commercial banks, and other sophisticated investors. He has broad experience in all types of restructurings, both in and out-of-court, as well as transactions involving the purchase and sale of securities and claims of entities involved in financial restructurings, chapter 11 cases, SIPA proceedings, and receiverships. Also represents ad hoc groups, official creditors' committees, litigation trusts, and serves as special litigation counsel for companies in financial distress.
**Personal:** JD, Emory University School of Law, 2002, Editor-In-Chief, Emory Bankruptcy Developments Journal. BA, University at Albany, 1997. Law Clerk to the Honorable Allan L. Gropper of the United States Bankruptcy Court for the Southern District of New York (2002-2004). See: http://www.willkie.com/JosephMinias

**MIRVIS, Theodore N**
Wachtell, Lipton, Rosen & Katz, New York
212 403 1204
tnmirvis@wlrk.com
*Featured in Securities (Nationwide), Litigation (New York)*
See under Nationwide for profile.

**MITCHELL, Nancy A**
Greenberg Traurig, LLP, New York
212 801 3085
MitchellN@gtlaw.com
*Featured in Bankruptcy/Restructuring (New York)*
**Practice Areas:** New York Co-Managing Shareholder; Operating Shareholder, Business Reorganization & Financial Restructuring Practice. Public finance; corporate/lending; financial institutions; private equity.
**Career:** Listed: Best Lawyers in America, 2007-13; Super Lawyers magazine, 2006-12; Leading

Lawyers Network, 2007-13; Chambers USA Guide, 2005-08, 2011-13.
**Publications:** Co-author: 'Dispelling 10 Misconceptions About Bankruptcy', The Corporate Counselor, February 2013; 'Market Test Required for Plans Giving Equity to Insiders', GT Alert, February 2013; 'Lock Up Your Creditors - Court Gives Broad Protection to Binding Plan Support Agreements', GT Alert, February 2013.
**Personal:** JD, cum laude, University of Michigan Law School, 1987; BA, Indiana University Bloomington, 1984.

**MITNICK, Joel**
Sidley Austin LLP, New York
212 839 5871
jmitnick@sidley.com
*Featured in Antitrust (New York)*
**Practice Areas:** Partner in Sidley's New York office, a global coordinator of the firm's Antitrust and Competition practice, and a coordinator of Sidley's electronic discovery program. Practice focuses on antitrust and securities matters on behalf of financial market, service industry and industrial clients. Represents corporate clients in individual and class action lawsuits arising under the Sherman, Clayton and Robinson-Patman Acts as well as in investigations commenced by federal and state antitrust authorities. Counsels clients on antitrust aspects of mergers and acquisitions, joint ventures and distribution arrangements. Securities practice clients include major international investment banks, broker-dealers, hedge funds, large corporate issuers.

**MODLIN, James**
Hughes Hubbard & Reed LLP, New York
212 837 6817
modlin@hugheshubbard.com
*Featured in Corporate/M&A (New York)*
**Practice Areas:** Corporate, specializing in mergers and acquisitions, joint ventures and other business combinations.
**Career:** Partner and Member of the Executive Committee; admitted in New York.
**Personal:** Cornell University, AB, 1982; Columbia University School of Law, JD, 1985.

**MOERDLER, Jeffrey**
Mintz Levin Cohn Ferris Glovsky and Popeo PC, Boston
212 692 6700
JAMoerdler@mintz.com
*Featured in Real Estate (New York)*
**Practice Areas:** Jeff is a general commercial real estate attorney handling development, acquisitions, sales, leasing and borrowing for all property types. His specialty practice includes technology, telecom and energy related to real estate including representing landlords, tenants and communications service providers in the leasing, purchase, sale and financing of data centers, radio and television broadcast antennas, distributed antenna systems, rooftop antennas, fiber optic transactions, and wiring buildings.
**Professional Memberships:** Member, Executive Committee, Real Property Section, NYSBA. Member, American College of Real Estate Lawyers.

**Career:** Commissioner, Port Authority of NY and NJ.
**Personal:** BA, Columbia University; JD, New York University.

**MOLLERUS, Michael**
Davis Polk & Wardwell LLP, New York
212 450 4000
michael.mollerus@davispolk.com
*Featured in Tax (New York)*
**Practice Areas:** Member of Davis Polk's Tax Department. His practice centers on advice to corporate and private equity fund clients on mergers, acquisitions, spinoffs and other major transactions, including structured financings.

**MOLONEY, Thomas J**
Cleary Gottlieb Steen & Hamilton LLP, New York
212 225 2460
tmoloney@cgsh.com
*Featured in Litigation (New York)*
**Practice Areas:** Big case and complex dispute resolution, including securities, M&A, derivatives, bankruptcy, commercial litigation. Recent clients: Goldman Sachs, HSBC, Citigroup, major financial institutions in Lehman and Madoff-related cases, Dow Chemical.
**Professional Memberships:** New York Bar, U.S. Supreme Court, U.S. Court of Appeals (Second and Fourth Circuits), U.S. District Courts (Southern, Eastern, Northern Districts of NY).
**Career:** Joined firm, 1976; became Partner, 1984. New York University School of Law (JD, Law Review, cum laude, Order of the Coif), 1976; Columbia College (A.B.), 1973; Mayoral Appointee to Workforce Improvement Board; Chairman, Business Advisory Counsel for New York City Public High School.

**MORAN, Patricia**
Skadden, Arps, Slate, Meagher & Flom LLP & Affiliates, New York
212 735 3130
patricia.moran@skadden.com
*Featured in Corporate/M&A (New York)*
**Practice Areas:** Advises clients on the full spectrum of strategic transactions, including mergers and acquisitions, private equity, restructuring, corporate finance and general corporate law matters. Experience includes acquisitions, dispositions and mergers of companies, subsidiaries and divisions – public and private, domestic and international – in both strategic and financial sponsor transactions. Frequently advises non-US clients on US acquisitions and investments. Advises both management and boards on corporate governance and fiduciary duties.
**Career:** JD, Villanova University School of Law (Case and Comment Editor, Villanova Law Review); BS, University of Scranton (magna cum laude; Alpha Sigma Nu, national Jesuit honor society).

**MORGAN, Jennifer M**
Kirkland & Ellis LLP, New York
212 446 4691
jennifer.morgan@kirkland.com
*Featured in Real Estate (New York)*

**Practice Areas:** Jennifer Morgan is a partner in the New York office of Kirkland & Ellis. Jennifer concentrates her practice in real estate private equity, advising fund sponsors and pension funds and other institutional investors in connection with structuring and negotiating fund formations and joint ventures, including private REITS and other structured investments. She also regularly represents real estate private equity clients in connection with asset and entity-level acquisitions and joint ventures, dispositions and financings. **Personal:** Emory University Law School, JD, 1995; University of Virginia, BA, 1991.

### MORGENSTERN, Saul P
Kaye Scholer LLP, New York
212 836 7210
saul.morgenstern@kayescholer.com
*Featured in Antitrust (New York)*
**Practice Areas:** Saul Morgenstern, Co-Head of the firm's Antitrust practice, litigates complex disputes, class actions and multi-jurisdictional cases before US federal and state courts, international arbitral tribunals, and the Federal Trade Commission. He also advises companies with respect to government investigations of mergers, acquisitions, joint ventures, trade associations, distribution and pricing programs and other aspects of competitor and customer relations. Mr Morgenstern has represented clients across a range of industries, including the chemical, computer hardware and software, energy, entertainment, insurance, financial, leisure, luxury consumer goods, pharmaceutical, publishing, real estate, telecommunications, transportation and toy industries.

### MORPHY, James C
Sullivan & Cromwell LLP, New York
212 558 4000
morphyj@sullcrom.com
*Featured in Corporate/M&A (New York)*
**Professional Memberships:** Co-Chairman, Tulane Corporate Institute; Advisory Director, Harvard Law Program on Corporate Governance; ABA Corporate Laws Committee and Task Force on Proxy Access.
**Career:** Partner since 1986. Management Committee since 2007. Head, M&A Practice 1995-2007. Represents clients in friendly/hostile acquisitions. Recent representations: Medco merger with Express Scripts; BHP Billiton acquisition of Petrohawk Energy; Barrick Gold acquisition of Equinox Minerals; AirTran merger with Southwest Airlines; BP on various corporate matters; PepsiAmericas' Transaction Committee in acquisition by PepsiCo; InBev acquisition of Anheuser-Busch; Microsoft bid for Yahoo!; Hershey Foods on various transactions.
**Personal:** Harvard Law (JD, 1979); Harvard (BA, 1976).

### MORREALE, Matthew
Cravath, Swaine & Moore LLP, New York
212 474 1534
mmorreale@cravath.com
*Featured in Environment (New York)*
**Practice Areas:** Matthew Morreale is a partner in Cravath's Corporate Department and is in charge of its environmental practice. Mr Morreale advises the Firm's clients on environmental matters relating to mergers and acquisitions, securities offerings, financings and other business transactions. He also provides counseling on environmental compliance matters; environmental and toxic tort litigation; environmental indemnification disputes; and environmental aspects of periodic reporting obligations under securities laws. **Personal:** Columbia Law School (JD, 1997; Harlan Fiske Stone Scholar; Senior Editor for Articles and Notes, Journal of Environmental Law); University of Pennsylvania (MS, 1994; BAS, BA, 1990). For more information: http://www.cravath.com/mmorreale

### MOTTESI, Marcelo A
Milbank, Tweed, Hadley & McCloy LLP, New York
212 530 5602
mmottesi@milbank.com
*Featured in Latin American Investment (New York)*
**Practice Areas:** Mr Mottesi is a partner and is head of the firm's Global Securities Group and a member of Milbank's Latin America Practice Group. His practice centers on capital markets, finance and corporate matters. His clients include US and foreign banks and underwriting firms, as well as domestic and foreign companies. He has extensive experience across a broad range of industries, including energy, telecommunications, financial services, forestry/agriculture, technology, manufacturing, real estate, entertainment and retail. Mr Mottesi speaks fluent Spanish.

### MOURNING, Paul W.
Cadwalader, Wickersham & Taft LLP, New York
212 504 6216
paul.mourning@cwt.com
*Featured in Healthcare (New York)*
**Practice Areas:** Focuses on representing health care and not-for-profit organizations. Represents tax-exempt entities, including religious organizations, foundations, educational institutions, museums, hospitals and other health care institutions, social service agencies, and trade associations. Significant experience in the establishment, financing, restructuring, and transfer of control of health care and other non-profit organizations, in the disposition of assets of such entities, and in structuring joint ventures among them. **Personal:** JD, University of Virginia School of Law (Editor-in-Chief, The Virginia Journal of International Law); AB, Dartmouth College (magna cum laude, Phi Beta Kappa).

### MULLER, Scott
Davis Polk & Wardwell LLP, New York
212 450 4359
scott.muller@davispolk.com
*Featured in International Trade (Nationwide), Litigation (New York)*
See under Nationwide for profile.

### MURPHY, Michael
DLA Piper LLP (US), New York
212 335 4755
michael.p.murphy@dlapiper.com
*Featured in Insurance (New York)*

**Practice Areas:** Insurance
**Career:** He is the global head of the firm's Insurance and Reinsurance Sector practice. He represents financial services industry clients in a wide range of business litigation with particular emphasis on reinsurance and insurance-related litigation and arbitration. He serves as international counsel for insurers and reinsurers in disputes throughout North America, South America, the United Kingdom, Europe, Australia, Asia, Bermuda and elsewhere around the world. **Personal:** JD, State University of New York at Buffalo School of Law; BA, Canisius College

### MURPHY, Sean M
Milbank, Tweed, Hadley & McCloy LLP, New York
212 530 5688
smurphy@milbank.com
*Featured in Litigation (New York)*
**Practice Areas:** Mr Murphy is a partner in the Litigation & Arbitration Group. His practice focuses on complex securities matters. He has defended dozens of companies and financial institutions in multi-jurisdictional class action and derivative litigation under state and federal securities laws, including claims under the Securities Act of 1933, the Securities Exchange Act of 1934 and the Investment Company Act of 1940. Mr Murphy has extensive experience representing investment advisers in class and derivative litigation involving management fees, revenue sharing, conflicts of interest, prospectus disclosure, distribution and trading, portfolio mismanagement, Rule 12b-1, board oversight and fiduciary duty litigation.

### MUSOFF, Scott
Skadden, Arps, Slate, Meagher & Flom LLP & Affiliates, New York
212 735 7852
Scott.Musoff@skadden.com
*Featured in Securities (Nationwide), Litigation (New York)*
See under Nationwide for profile.

### MUTTERPERL, Mark
Fulbright & Jaworski LLP, New York
212 318 3183
mmutterperl@fulbright.com
*Featured in Intellectual Property (New York)*
**Practice Areas:** Intellectual property and technology.
**Career:** A brand protection partner in the Intellectual Property and Technology Department of Fulbright & Jaworski's New York office, Mark focuses on trademark matters, especially the enforcement of trademark rights against trademark infringement, dilution and counterfeiting. Mark also focuses on copyrights, advertising and unfair competition. A former senior attorney with the U.S. Department of Justice and Special Assistant U.S. Attorney, Mark has litigated cases throughout the U.S. including dozens of cases in the U.S. courts of appeals. **Personal:** JD, Georgetown University Law Center (1974); BA, cum laude, Political Science, Boston University (1971).

### MYERSON, Toby S
Paul, Weiss, Rifkind, Wharton & Garrison LLP, New York
212 373 3033
tmyerson@paulweiss.com
*Featured in Corporate/M&A (New York)*
**Practice Areas:** Partner, Corporate Department, and co-head, Global Mergers and Acquisitions Group. Practices in the areas of mergers and acquisitions of public and private companies, leveraged buyouts, corporate governance and advice to boards of directors. In 1989-90, served as a Managing Director of investment bank Wasserstein Perella & Co. Clients include Citigroup Inc., Chubb Corporation, Resolute Forest Products, Reckitt Benckiser Group plc and NEC Corporation; and investment banks Morgan Stanley, Nomura Securities, Lazard Frères, Perella Weinberg Partners, Rothschilds, and others. For more than 30 years, Toby has advised corporations, financial institutions and investment banks on some of the most high profile merger and acquisition transactions of the day.

### NAFTALIS, Gary P
Kramer Levin Naftalis & Frankel LLP, New York
212 715 9253
gnaftalis@kramerlevin.com
*Featured in Litigation (Nationwide), Litigation (New York)*
**Practice Areas:** One of the nation's leading trial lawyers, Co-Chair of Kramer Levin Naftalis and Frankel LLP and Head of the firm's Litigation Practice. He was recently named as one of the 100 most influential lawyers in America by The National Law Journal and received the 2011 Chambers USA Award for Excellence in White Collar Crime and Government Investigations. For some 40 years, he has represented individuals and corporations in all phases of complex bet-the-company civil, criminal and regulatory matters including those involving allegations of insider trading, market manipulation, accounting irregularities, stock option backdating and other financial fraud. Mr Naftalis has also served as counsel to audit and special committees of a number of major public companies in connection with regulatory issues.
**Professional Memberships:** He is a Fellow of the American College of Trial Lawyers and a member of the Trial Attorney Advisory Board of the Litigation Section of the American Bar Association. He has also served as a director of the Legal Aid Society.
**Career:** During his 40 year career, he has successfully represented numerous securities industry clients, including Salomon Brothers in the investigation of US Treasury auction bidding practices, Kidder, Peabody in the Wall Street insider trading probe, Canary Capital Partners in the mutual fund market timing inquiries, and CIBC in the Enron investigation. He successfully defended Michael Eisner, the CEO of The Walt Disney Company, in the shareholders derivative lawsuit relating to the hiring and termination of Michael Ovitz. After a 37 day trial in the Delaware Chancery Court, Mr Eisner and the other Disney

Directors prevailed on all counts. The Disney case was chosen as one of the top defense wins of 2005 by The National Law Journal. Mr Naftalis won dismissal of all charges brought by then Attorney General Eliot Spitzer against Kenneth Langone, former Chair of the New York Stock Exchange Compensation Committee, relating to the compensation of NYSE Chairman Richard Grasso. Mr Naftalis successfully represented the City of New York in the inquiry relating to the fire at the Deutsche Bank building. No charges were brought against the City, any of its agencies or its officials. He is counsel for significant figures and entities in the current inquiries and related civil litigation concerning corporate accounting irregularities including the recent successful representation of the Chairman and Founder of Global Crossing. He represented the CFOs of Affiliated Computer Services, Cendant and Bristol-Myers Squibb, the CEO of Refco, a director and senior officer of Tyco in securities class action and ERISA litigation, the former CEO of Arthur Andersen in the Enron civil litigation and the former CEO of WorldCom in securities class action litigation. He also represents United Rentals in various securities litigations and regulatory matters. He formerly served as an Assistant US Attorney in the Southern District of New York, holding the title of Deputy Chief of the Criminal Division. He also served as special counsel to the U.S. Senate Subcommittee investigating abuses in the nursing home industry. He has been a member of the faculty at Columbia and Harvard Law Schools. Mr Naftalis recently successfully won summary judgment for Sirius XM Radio dismissing a breach of contract action by Howard Stern seeking $330 million in damages. The Court found that the "clear, unambiguous language" of the contract defeated Stern's claim. Mr Naftalis currently represents Rajat Gupta, former managing director worldwide of McKinsey, against charges relating to the Galleon Group. Mr Naftalis also currently represents the former president and chief operating office of MF Global in government inquiries and related civil litigation.

**Publications:** He is the author or co-author of numerous books and articles including the leading work on the grand jury system: The Grand Jury: An Institution on Trial (with Judge Marvin E Frankel) and Sentencing: Helping Judges Do Their Jobs (also with Judge Frankel).

**Personal:** Received his AB degree from Rutgers University, his MA from Brown University, and his LLB from Columbia Law School. He was awarded the Benemerenti Medal by Pope Benedict XVI, the Robert M Morgenthau Award for the Legal Profession by the Police Athletic League, the George A Katz Torch of Learning Award by The American Friends of the Hebrew University, the Law & Society Award by the New York Lawyers for the Public Interest, the Robert F Wagner, Jr Award by the Citizens Union of the City of New York, and the Norman S. Ostrow Award by the New York Council of Defense Lawyers.

## NASHELSKY, Larren M
Morrison & Foerster LLP, New York
212 506 7365
lnashelsky@mofo.com
*Featured in Bankruptcy/Restructuring (New York)*

**Practice Areas:** Mr Nashelsky is Chair and Chief Executive Partner of Morrison & Foerster. Previously, he was Co-chair of the Business Restructuring & Insolvency Group and the firmwide Managing Partner. Mr Nashelsky focuses his practice on domestic and international restructurings, including chapter 11 cases, workouts, restructurings, secured financings, and distressed acquisitions and investments. Mr Nashelsky has represented all major constituencies in restructurings, across a variety of industries, including real estate, financial services, telecommunications, gaming, transportation, chemical, energy, satellite, and natural resources.

**Personal:** BS, University at Albany; JD, 1988, Hofstra University School of Law, 1991.

## NAVIA, Talbert I
Chadbourne & Parke LLP, New York
212 408 5316
tnavia@chadbourne.com
*Featured in Latin American Investment (New York)*

**Practice Areas:** Talbert Navia is head of the private funds group and co-head of the Latin America practice. In 1998, Mr Navia became a Founding Partner of a private equity firm focusing on investments in the U.S. and Latin America. His experience includes private equity, mergers and acquisitions, capital markets, financings, joint ventures and corporate restructurings in the U.S., Latin America and Spain.

**Publications:** Mr Navia has lectured and written on private equity and securities offerings in Latin America and U.S. investment in Latin America.

**Personal:** Harvard Law School, JD, Editor, Harvard International Law Journal, 1980.

## NEEDELL, Benjamin F
Skadden, Arps, Slate, Meagher & Flom LLP & Affiliates, New York
212 735 2600
Benjamin.Needell@skadden.com
*Featured in Real Estate (New York)*

**Practice Areas:** Practice emphasizes purchase and sale transactions, financings, securitized real estate loans, real estate development, partnership law, real estate investment trusts, syndications, major headquarters leases, hotel operation, development and financing, and matters relating to pension fund investments in real estate.

**Professional Memberships:** Member, Board of Directors, Rock and Roll Hall of Fame (1986-present); Wenner Media, Inc. (1978-present); Stratton Mountain School (1980-present); New York Restoration Project (2002-present), chairman (2002-present); Westchester Land Trust (2001-present).

**Career:** LLB, St John's University, 1966 (Editorial Board, St John's Law Review); BA, Rutgers University, 1963.

## NEEDHAM, Andrew W
Cravath, Swaine & Moore LLP, New York
212 474 1440
aneedham@cravath.com
*Featured in Tax (New York)*

**Practice Areas:** Andrew W. Needham is a partner in Cravath's Tax Department. His practice concentrates on tax advisory work in the private equity and hedge fund sectors, mergers and acquisitions, joint venture formation, spin-offs and general tax planning for the preservation of net operating losses and other tax attributes. Mr Needham's clients have included IBM, Johnson & Johnson and Weyerhaeuser, as well as numerous investment banking firms.

**Personal:** The Wharton School, University of Pennsylvania (MBA, 1992); Georgetown University Law Center (LLM, 1990; JD, 1986); University of Arizona (BA, 1982). For more information: http://www.cravath.com/aneedham

## NEFF, Daniel A
Wachtell, Lipton, Rosen & Katz, New York
212 403 1218
daneff@wlrk.com
*Featured in Corporate/M&A (New York)*

**Practice Areas:** Specialises in mergers and acquisitions. During his more than 30 years of practice has been extensively involved in negotiated as well as hostile acquisitions, and has represented bidders and targets, public and private companies, private equity firms and special committees of directors. Represented companies in divestitures, cross-border transactions and proxy contests and has counselled managements and boards of directors concerning acquisition matters, conflict transactions and other significant issues. Lectures frequently on topics relating to his professional interests, was featured in American Lawyer's Dealmaker of the Year's articles in 2001 and 2012 and is listed in the 'Lawdragon 500' Leading Lawyers of America and Best Lawyers in America. Among other matters, represented Airgas in successfully defending against a $5.8 billion hostile takeover bid by Air Products and Chemicals; Rohm and Haas in its $18 billion sale to Dow Chemical; Unocal Corporation in its acquisition by Chevron Corporation for $19 billion and its acquisition of Pure Resources; El Paso in its $38 billion sale to Kinder Morgan; Berry Petroleum in its pending $4.3 billion sale to Linn Energy; Chicago Bridge & Iron in its $3 billion acquisition of The Shaw Group; Cooper Industries in its $11.8 billion combination with Eaton Corporation; Alibaba Group in its $7.8 billion repurchase of stock from Yahoo!; Kellogg Company in its acquisition of Keebler Foods Company and its $2.7 cash acquisition of Procter & Gamble's Pringles business; Temple-Inland in its $3.7 billion sale to International Paper; Mirant Corporation in its $3.1 billion merger with RRI Energy, Inc. to create GenOn Energy; Smith International in its $11 billion merger with Schlumberger; Centex Corporation in its $3.1 billion merger with Pulte Homes; BEA Systems in its $8.5 billion merger with Oracle; the private equity buyers in the acquisitions of Aramark Corporation, Kinder Morgan, Inc and Harrah's

Entertainment Inc; Knight-Ridder, Inc in its merger with the McClatchy Company; Goldman Sachs Capital Partners and Apollo Advisors LP in their acquisition of Nalco Chemical Company; Western Wireless Corporation in its merger with ALLTEL Corporation; VoiceStream Wireless Corporation in its merger with Deutsche Telekom AG; Litton Industries Inc in its merger with Northrop Grumman Corporation; Orion Power Holdings Inc in its sale to Reliant Resources, Inc; Mirage Resorts Incorporated in its merger with MGM Grand Inc; Vivendi Universal SA in its acquisitions of United States Filter Corporation and Cendant Software Corporation; Transamerica Corporation in its merger with Aegon NV and its acquisition of Whirlpool Financial Corporation; Newmont Mining Corporation in its acquisitions of Franco-Nevada Mining Corporation Limited, Normandy Mining Limited and Santa Fe Pacific Gold Corporation. Also represented Western Atlas Inc in its merger with Baker Hughes Incorporated, and Vons Companies in its merger with Safeway Inc; and represented special board committees of Wausau Insurance, Hayes Wheels International and Enron Oil & Gas Company (now EOG Resources Inc).

**Professional Memberships:** Member of the Law Review at Columbia University School of Law.

**Career:** Partner at Wachtell, Lipton, Rosen & Katz since 1984. Serves as co-chairman of the firm's Executive Committee.

**Personal:** Graduated magna cum laude from Brown University and from the Columbia University School of Law.

## NEILL, David S
Wachtell, Lipton, Rosen & Katz, New York
212 403 1263
dsneill@wlrk.com
*Featured in Antitrust (New York)*

**Practice Areas:** Practice focuses on antitrust, focusing principally on corporate mergers and acquisitions. Has represented clients from a broad range of industries before the United States Department of Justice, the Federal Trade Commission and the Federal Reserve Board. Has represented the buyer or seller in connection with most of the largest financial institution mergers in U.S. history.

**Professional Memberships:** New York State and American (Section on Antitrust); Bar Associations, Fellow of the American Bar Foundation.

**Career:** Partner at Wachtell, Lipton, Rosen & Katz.

**Publications:** Co-author: Antitrust Standards for Bank Holding Company Mergers and Acquisitions, Bank and Corporate Governance Law Reporter, Vol VIII, Nos 4 & 5, p 812 (June/July 1992); Justice's Review of Bank Acquisitions Continues to Reflect Uncertainty, Banking Policy Report, Vol 11, No 23, p 3 (7 December 1992); FDICIA Taxes Justice Department's Antitrust Analysis of Bank Mergers, Banking Policy Report, Vol 12, No 1, p 1 (4 January 1993); Relevant Product and Geographic Markets in Bank Mergers: A Comparison of the

Methodologies Used by the Justice Department and the Federal Reserve Board, Special Report published by BNA (1994); Bank Merger Impact on Small Business Services Is Changing, Banking Policy Report, Vol 15, No 8 (15 April 1996); Documentary Evidence and Antitrust Merger Enforcement, ALI-ABA's Practice Checklist Manual on Advising Business Clients, p 21 (1997); Proposed 'Streamlining' of Bank Merger Antitrust Review by House Banking Bill May Have Unintended Consequences, BNA's Banking Report, Vol 69, No 2, p 93 (14 July 1997); Antitrust Considerations in Mergers and Acquisitions of Financial Institutions, Bank and Corporate Governance Law Reporter, Vol 19, No 5, p 762 (January 1998); Acquisitions of Non-Bank Operations in Financial Holding Company Mergers, The Review of Banking and Financial Services (March 2004); Filing Obligations of Natural Persons under the Hart-Scott-Rudino Act, The Practical Lawyer, p 11 (June 2005); U.S. Anitrust Agencies Unveil Proposed New Horizontal Merger Guidelines, Bank and Corporate Governance Law Reporter, Vol 44, No 5, p 654 (July 2010); Dodd-Frank Act May Complicate Antitrust Review of Acquisitions, BNA's Banking Report, Vol 95, p 334 (24 August 2010); U.S. Antitrust Agencies Issue Final New Horizontal Merger Guidelines, Bank and Corporate Governance Law Reporter, Vol 45, No 3, p 369 (November 2010); Contributor: Bank Mergers and Acquisitions Handbook, American Bar Association (2006); Author: Lending to Small and Medium-Sized Businesses and the Antitrust Analysis of Bank Mergers, BNA's Banking Report, Vol 60, p 814 (31 May 1993); Fed Antitrust Change Could Boost Thrift Acquisitions by Banks, Banking Policy Report, Vol 12, No 17, p 1 (6 September 1993); Antitrust Divestiture Policies Can Impact Bank Merger Planning, Banking Policy Report, Vol 14, No 23, p 1 (4 December 1995); New Antitrust Policies Add Complexity and Uncertainty to Bank Mergers, Bank and Corporate Governance Law Reporter, Vol 17, No 2, p 196 (October 1996); New Safe Harbor or Not? Fed Clarifies Antitrust Thresholds for Bank Deals, Banking Policy Report, Vol 16, No 13, p 1 (7 July 1997); M&A Review Role for the FTC on Banking Deals: A Flawed Idea, Banking Policy Report, Vol 16, No 18, p 1 (15 September 1997); The ATM Surcharge Debate: Logical Fallacies and Antitrust Reality, BNA's Banking Report, Vol 71, No 5, p 233 (3 August 1998); Antitrust Lessons from Recent Bank Megamergers, Banking Policy Report, Vol 17, No 21, p 1 (2 November 1998); US Antitrust Considerations in Mergers and Acquisitions of Bank Holding Companies, Antitrust Report, p 4 (February 1999); Antitrust Merger Review Will be More Complicated After Financial Modernization, Banking Policy Report, Vol 18, No 17, p 1 (7 September 1999); New Banking Act Complicates Merger Review, International Financial Law Review, p 13 (February 2000); A Guide to the Policies and Procedures Affecting Antitrust Divestitures in Bank Mergers, The Banking Law Journal, Vol 118, No 7, p 603 (July/August 2001); Geographic Market Definition in the Antitrust Analysis of Bank Mergers, The Banking Law Journal, Vol 123, No 4, p 291 (April 2006); Bank merger Review in Troubled Times, NERA's Santa Fe 2009 Antitrust Seminar (9 July 2009).
**Personal:** Graduated from Yale University in 1979 (BA); from Goldman School of Public Policy, University of California, Berkeley in 1983 (MPP); and from Columbia Law School in 1984 (JD).

### NELSON, James E
Venable LLP, New York
212 370 6242
jnelson@Venable.com
*Featured in Technology (New York)*
**Practice Areas:** Sourcing, Corporate, M&A, Technology, Life Sciences, Internet and New Media.
**Professional Memberships:** American Bar Association, International Technology Law Association, and Licensing Executives Society
**Career:** James Nelson focuses on technology-driven companies and users of technology with a practice combining corporate and intellectual property. His clients operate in numerous sectors including healthcare, financial services, real estate, IT, new media and mobile. He also has significant experience in sourcing transactions as well as a host of general corporate matters that include formation, financing, governance, M&A and joint ventures.

### NEUWIRTH, John
Weil, Gotshal & Manges LLP, New York
212 310 8297
john.neuwirth@weil.com
*Featured in Litigation (New York)*
**Practice Areas:** John Neuwirth is a partner in Weil's Securities Litigation Practice and is recognized as one of the leading securities litigators in the US. His practice focuses on the litigation of securities, M&A, derivative, and complex business and corporate matters at the trial and appellate levels in both federal and state courts, and before arbitration panels. He also counsels boards, board committees and senior management on M&A, corporate governance, securities, regulatory and other issues, and advises in connection with governmental and internal investigations, and proxy contests.
**Personal:** Hamilton College (BA, 1992); New York University School of Law (JD, 1996).

### NEVELOFF, Jay A
Kramer Levin Naftalis & Frankel LLP, New York
212 715 9290
jneveloff@kramerlevin.com
*Featured in Real Estate (New York)*
**Practice Areas:** Mr Neveloff represents numerous nationally recognized real estate developers and owners in the development, operation and financing of real estate projects, institutional and other ventures in the acquisition of property (including portfolios of properties), and joint ventures involving a broad variety of assets, as well as major international funds and financial institutions, in commercial lending transactions, loan restructurings and workouts.
**Professional Memberships:** Served for several years as the Vice-Chair of the American Bar Association Committee on Partnerships, Joint Ventures and Other Investment Vehicles. He is an active Member of the American College of Real Estate Lawyers (and member of Board of Governors), American College of Mortgage Attorneys and American Law Institute, and is a Member of the Practicing Law Institute Real Estate Advisory Committee. He also served as the Vice-Chair of the International Health Network Society.
**Career:** Mr Neveloff has represented developers of numerous mixed-use, commercial, retail and residential projects, including 432 Park Avenue (representing CIM with Harry Macklowe), Time Warner Center (a joint development among The Related Companies, Apollo Investments, Time Warner and Mandarin Hotels), Trump Tower and the Trump International Hotel and Tower (the former Gulf + Western Building and a joint venture of General Electric Investment Trust, Donald Trump and The Galbreath Organization), as well as numerous regional and local shopping centers, and other commercial projects throughout the country. Mr Neveloff has represented the owner of Starrett City, the largest federally subsidized housing complex in the United States in a major capital transaction, Starwood Hotels in the sale of major assets, financial institutions in complex portfolio mortgage and mezzanine financings, New York Life Insurance Company in the sale of Manhattan House, a residential complex comprising an entire block on the upper east side of Manhattan, and the owner in the sale of a major hotel and casino in Las Vegas, Nevada. Mr Neveloff regularly assists clients actively involved in numerous hotel transactions including the acquisition of numerous hotels, the development of hotels, and loan restructurings relating to numerous hotels including The Plaza Hotel in New York. He also represents numerous opportunity and hedge funds in the acquisition, sale and joint venturing of projects throughout the United States. Mr Neveloff is also a leading practitioner of innovative hotel condominium projects, including The Plaza Hotel, Trump Soho and the St. Regis in New York City; he successfully obtained a critical SEC no-action letter involving a hotel condominium structure. Recently, Mr Neveloff represented Saint Vincent Catholic Medical Centers in the sale of the former hospital site.
**Personal:** Received a JD Degree from New York University in 1974 and a BA Degree from Brooklyn College in 1971.

### NICENKO, Vladimir
Willkie Farr & Gallagher LLP, New York
212 728 8273
vnicenko@willkie.com
*Featured in Insurance (New York)*
**Practice Areas:** Partner in Willkie's New York office practicing in the Corporate and Financial Services Department. Regularly represents insurance and reinsurance companies, investment banks and other financial institutions in the structuring and offering of equity, debt, surplus and hybrid securities, insurance-linked securities and derivative products. Practice focuses particularly on structured finance solutions for the insurance industry, including "embedded value" and excess reserve financing transactions, catastrophe bonds, longevity reinsurance and other alternative risk transfer transactions.
**Personal:** LLM, magna cum laude, Fordham University School of Law, 1997; LLB, University of Sarajevo, 1994. See: http://www.willkie.com/Vladimir_Nicenko

### NIJENHUIS, Erika W
Cleary Gottlieb Steen & Hamilton LLP, New York
212 225 2980
enijenhuis@cgsh.com
*Featured in Tax (New York)*
**Practice Areas:** US income tax, especially development of novel financial products, capital markets and international tax planning. Clients include Citigroup, Goldman Sachs, Morgan Stanley, Barclays.
**Professional Memberships:** NYSBA Tax Section, Executive Committee Member and Former Chair (2009-2010).
**Career:** Became partner, 1997. LLM in Taxation, NYU (1996). JD, cum laude (1987); BA, summa cum laude (1982), University of Pennsylvania. Included in Best Lawyers in America.
**Publications:** Articles on cross-border repos, straddle rules, wash sales, tax shelter disclosure rules, contingent interest and mandatory convertible bonds, securities futures, off-shore 'trading in securities,' global dealing operations, credit default swaps and other financial instruments.

### NIRENBERG, David Z
Ashurst, New York
212 205 7007
david.nirenberg@ashurst.com
*Featured in Tax (New York)*
**Practice Areas:** David is a Tax partner based in the New York Securities and Derivatives Group. He covers the tax aspects of investment funds, structured finance (including municipal finance and bond issues) and derivative products and has played a significant role in the structuring of a wide variety of innovative financial products in both domestic and cross-border markets. David has written and lectured extensively in the area of financial products. He is the co-author of Federal Income Taxation of Securitization Transactions.
**Personal:** David is a graduate of Columbia Law School (JD), Boston University (MBA) and Cornell University (BS).

### NISHAWALA, Vipul N
Pillsbury Winthrop Shaw Pittman LLP, New York
212 858 1021
vipul.nishawala@pillsburylaw.com
*Featured in Outsourcing (Nationwide), Technology (New York)*
**Practice Areas:** Mr Nishawala structures and negotiates complex technology-driven transactions, including strategic IT, business process, and HR outsourcings; software licensing, mainte-

nance, and development agreements; web-hosting and internet-related arrangements; equipment purchase and leasing transactions; and consulting and nondisclosure agreements. He provides clients with assistance in all stages of these transactions, including gathering requirements; developing RFIs and RFPs; conducting competitive negotiations; and implementing supplier strategies. Mr Nishawala also has substantial experience in handling disputes that often arise in such arrangements.

**Personal:** JD, George Washington University Law School, 1995, Law Review; BA, University of North Carolina, 1992, with distinction, Phi Beta Kappa.

### NORDAHL, Stephen D
Gibson, Dunn & Crutcher LLP, New York
212 351 2442
snordahl@gibsondunn.com
*Featured in Outsourcing (Nationwide), Technology (New York)*
See under Nationwide for profile.

### NORWITZ, Trevor
Wachtell, Lipton, Rosen & Katz, New York
212 403 1333
TSNorwitz@wlrk.com
*Featured in Corporate/M&A (New York)*
**Practice Areas:** Practice focuses on mergers and acquisitions, corporate governance and securities law matters. Has advised a range of public and private entities in a variety of industries in connection with mergers, acquisitions, divestitures, hostile takeover bids and defenses, proxy contests, joint ventures, financing transactions and corporate governance matters.
**Professional Memberships:** Member of the American Law Institute, and the American Bar Association, where he is active on the Corporate Governance Committee. Has also served on the ABA Committee on Corporate Laws and the New York City Bar Association Mergers and Acquisitions Committee. Serves on a number of non-profit boards, including Advancing Human Rights, The University of Cape Town Fund, Friends of Ikamva Labantu and Friends of the Mandela-Rhodes Foundation.
**Career:** Joined Wachtell, Lipton, Rosen & Katz in 1994 and was named partner in 1998. Teaches a course in Mergers and Acquisitions at Columbia University School of Law and was a member of an international advisory group to the South African government on company law reform. Regular speaker and panelist at professional conferences, has chaired and participated in numerous Practising Law Institute programs and contributes regularly to professional publications on topics relating to M&A and corporate governance.
**Personal:** Graduated from the University of Cape Town (B.Bus.Sc. (Law)), Oxford University (BA (Juris), MA) (where he was a Rhodes Scholar) and Columbia University School of Law (LLM).

### NOVIKOFF, Harold S
Wachtell, Lipton, Rosen & Katz, New York
212 403 1249
hsnovikoff@wlrk.com
*Featured in Bankruptcy/Restructuring (Nationwide), Bankruptcy/Restructuring (New York)*
See under Nationwide for profile.

### NUGENT, Eileen T
Skadden, Arps, Slate, Meagher & Flom LLP & Affiliates, New York
212 735 3176
Eileen.Nugent@skadden.com
*Featured in Private Equity (Nationwide), Corporate/M&A (New York)*
See under Nationwide for profile.

### NUSBAUM, Jack H
Willkie Farr & Gallagher LLP, New York
212 728 8060
jnusbaum@willkie.com
*Featured in Corporate/M&A (New York)*
**Practice Areas:** Senior Partner; Member, Executive Committee; Chairman, 1987-2009. Specialises in counseling public and private companies in mergers, acquisitions, and divestitures; corporate governance and fiduciary duties; and internal investigations. Advises boards of directors of public companies on issues of fiduciary duty and corporate governance, particularly in context of change-in-control transactions. Involved in many of most notable U.S. and cross-border transactions, including: historic merger of NAS-DAQ with the American Stock Exchange, leveraged buyout of R.J.R. Nabisco, acquisition of McCaw Cellular Communications by AT&T, acquisition of Magma Copper by Broken Hill Proprietary Limited, and various going-private transactions and restructurings. Headed team responsible for 1998 Cendant Report, the internal investigation of Cendant Corporation on behalf of its Audit Committee, which The New York Times called a definitive case study for accountants in the area of accounting irregularities and fraud. Recent deals: representing J. Crew CEO as part of buying team in $3B acquisition of apparel retailer; Ramius in connection with its combination with, and acquisition of in excess of 70% of Cowen Group; Representing the non management members of the board of Citigroup Inc.
**Personal:** JD, Columbia Law School, 1965. BS, Wharton School of the University of Pennsylvania, 1962. See:
http://www.willkie.com/JackNusbaum

### NUSSBAUM, Andrew J
Wachtell, Lipton, Rosen & Katz, New York
212 403 1269
ajnussbaum@wlrk.com
*Featured in Corporate/M&A (New York)*
**Practice Areas:** Practice involves a wide range of merger and acquisition-related matters, including private equity transactions, cross-border transactions, spinoffs, divestitures, carve-out IPOs, and joint ventures. Also handles related work in public offerings, financings, corporate governance and takeovers, and has completed a number of multibillion dollar cross-border transactions involving mergers between U.S. and European

companies, acquisitions in Latin America, investments in China, a public company transaction in Russia and a major transaction involving one of Australia's largest companies. Has extensive experience with international companies and in the media and entertainment areas.
**Professional Memberships:** Member of the New York State and American Bar Associations. Active in various non-profit organizations, including chairman of the Board of Asphalt Green, a New York City sports and fitness organization promoting wellness, water safety and health for New Yorkers of all ages, a member of the Board of Trustees of Amherst College and a member of the Board of Governors of the Folger Shakespeare Library.
**Career:** Member of the Wachtell, Lipton, Rosen & Katz Corporate Department, joining the firm in 1993 and becoming a partner in 1999. Prior to joining the Firm, served as a law clerk to the Honorable Ruth Bader Ginsburg, then of the U.S. Court of Appeals for the District of Columbia Circuit, and thereafter to Justice Antonin Scalia, United States Supreme Court.
**Personal:** Graduated from Amherst College, summa cum laude (1985), and has a master's degree from Oxford University, where he was a Rhodes Scholar. Attended The University of Chicago Law School, where he received his JD with high honors (1991), was a member of Order of the Coif and served as editor-in-chief of The University of Chicago Law Review.

### NUSSBAUM, Bernard W
Wachtell, Lipton, Rosen & Katz, New York
212 403 1266
bwnussbaum@wlrk.com
*Featured in Litigation (Nationwide), Litigation (New York)*
See under Nationwide for profile.

### NUSSBAUM, Martin
Dechert LLP, New York
212 698 3596
martin.nussbaum@dechert.com
*Featured in Corporate/M&A (New York)*
**Practice Areas:** Mr Nussbaum represents corporate clients, financial institutions, boards of directors, and special committees in mergers and acquisitions, corporate governance and securities matters. He also advises clients on transactions involving changes in control and proxy contests.
**Professional Memberships:** Member, New York Bar; admitted to practice before several federal courts; member, Bar of the City of New York's Committee on Insurance Law; member, New York County Lawyers Association's Committee on Securities and Exchanges
**Personal:** Columbia College (A.B., 1967); Columbia Law School (JD, 1970).

### NUSSBAUM, Mitchell S
Loeb & Loeb LLP, New York
212 407 4159
mnussbaum@loeb.com
*Featured in Corporate/M&A (New York)*
**Practice Areas:** Focuses on corporate/securities law, with emphasis on representation of US/foreign public corporations, banks, private emerging

growth companies in public/private financings, and federal securities law compliance. Represented more than 75 Asian companies that have listed on US exchanges. Responsible for developing a groundbreaking new financing structure called the IPACsm, which features many benefits of the SPAC, but offers increased flexibility on pricing and deal structure, and allows for more rapid transaction cycle.
**Career:** Partner and Capital Markets and Asia Chair.
**Personal:** Syracuse University College of Law, JD; University of Rochester, BA.

### O'BRIEN, Clare
Shearman & Sterling LLP, New York
212 848 8966
cobrien@shearman.com
*Featured in Corporate/M&A (New York)*
**Career:** Clare O'Brien is a partner in the firm's Mergers and Acquisitions Practice Group. She has handled a range of mergers and acquisitions work in various industries, including technology, healthcare, consumer products, manufacturing and agriculture. She represents both public and private companies in a broad variety of transactions, including sales of public and private companies and subsidiaries or divisions of public and private companies, joint ventures, and restructurings, as well as advising on corporate governance matters. Ms O'Brien joined the firm in 1988 and became a partner in 1995.

### O'BRIEN, Jeannemarie
Wachtell, Lipton, Rosen & Katz, New York
212 403 1365
JMOBrien@wlrk.com
*Featured in Employee Benefits & Executive Compensation (New York)*
**Practice Areas:** Practice focuses on the executive compensation and employee benefits aspects of transactions, with a particular emphasis on transactions involving financial services institutions. Has been involved in over $500 billion of mergers and acquisitions transactions over the last decade. Also advises companies and their boards on governance issues and also assists companies and senior executives on executive compensation matters in both the public and private sectors, and has particular expertise regarding the compensation structures at financial institutions and the related regulatory considerations.
**Professional Memberships:** New York State and American Bar Associations.
**Career:** Joined Wachtell, Lipton, Rosen & Katz in 1997 and became a partner in the Executive Compensation and Benefits Department in 2003.
**Publications:** In addition to memos and articles on recent developments in the executive compensation area, each year she is an author of a chapter in 'Financial Institutions M&A', an annual review of current topics written by a small group of partners focused on transactions in the financial sector.

## O'KELLY, Eamon
Arent Fox LLP, New York
212 484 3912
eamon.okelly@arentfox.com
*Featured in Antitrust (New York)*

**Practice Areas:** Mr O' Kelly leads the Antitrust & Competition Law practice for Arent Fox. His principal areas of practice include antitrust, complex commercial litigation, arbitration, and contract disputes. He focuses on the preparation and trial of complex cases, including jury trials, as well as the representation of clients in connection with Department of Justice, Federal Trade Commission, and state attorney general investigations. He is a Member of the Editorial Board of the ABA State Antitrust Practice and Statutes treatise and is also a Member of the Executive Committee of the NY State Bar Association's Antitrust Law Section.

## O'NEAL, Sean
Cleary Gottlieb Steen & Hamilton LLP, New York
212 225 2416
soneal@cgsh.com
*Featured in Bankruptcy/Restructuring (New York)*

**Practice Areas:** Restructuring, bankruptcy and related litigation. Represents debtors, creditors, ad hoc groups, and investors in U.S. and cross-border matters. Recent representations: unsecured bondholders in Residential Capital bankruptcy; SuperMedia Inc. as debtor in prepackaged bankruptcy; Colony Capital in dismissal of JER/Jameson chapter 11 case and subsequent restructuring; Goldman Sachs as competing plan proponent in Lehman Brothers chapter 11; financial institutions in Dodd-Frank resolution planning; Truvo Group and Apex Silver as debtors in pre-negotiated chapter 11 cases.
**Career:** Partner 2009. JD, magna cum laude, Tulane Law Review (Editor in Chief), Order of Coif, Tulane University School of Law (2000).

## O'REILLY, Benet
Cleary Gottlieb Steen & Hamilton LLP, New York
boreilly@cgsh.com
212 225 2746
*Featured in Corporate/M&A (New York)*

**Practice Areas:** Public and private mergers and acquisitions, with significant experience representing corporate and PE clients in a variety of industries, including technology, telecommunications, pharmaceuticals and healthcare. Represented GlaxoSmithKline (Human Genome Sciences, Stiefel Laboratories, Reliant Pharmaceuticals and investments in Theravance); Kindred Healthcare (RehabCare); Stanley Black & Decker (AeroScout); SMSC (Microchip); Hewlett-Packard (3PAR, 3Com, EDS, Opsware); Verisign (Symantec); Coca-Cola (BPW); Lafarge (Eagle); TPG Capital (Creative Artists Agency); PeopleSoft (defense and sale to Oracle).
**Professional Memberships:** New York Bar.
**Career:** Joined firm, 1999; became Partner, 2008. JD, magna cum laude, New York University School of Law (1999); AB, University of Chicago (1995).

## ODELL, Francesca
Cleary Gottlieb Steen & Hamilton LLP, New York
212 225 2530
flodell@cgsh.com
*Featured in Latin American Investment (New York)*

**Practice Areas:** Capital markets and other corporate transactions in Latin America, particularly Brazil. Clients include major international investment banks, large foreign private issuers (including Petrobras and Copa) and numerous private equity funds and investors. Also active in restructuring, project financings and cross-border M&A.
**Professional Memberships:** Member of the Bar of the State of New York.
**Career:** Joined firm in 1996; became Partner in 2005. JD, New York University School of Law; BA, University of Wisconsin - Madison. Fluent in Spanish and Portuguese.

## OLSHAN, Regina
Skadden, Arps, Slate, Meagher & Flom LLP & Affiliates, New York
212 735 3963
regina.olshan@skadden.com
*Featured in Employee Benefits & Executive Compensation (Nationwide), Employee Benefits & Executive Compensation (New York)*

**Practice Areas:** Regina Olshan's practice focuses on executive compensation, employee benefits, mergers and acquisitions and corporate governance matters. She regularly advises major public companies on employee benefit and executive compensation arrangements in the context of mergers and acquisitions, public offerings, bankruptcy reorganizations and other corporate structurings. In addition, Ms Olshan regularly advises private equity clients, their portfolio companies and members of management on compensation matters in connection with private equity and leveraged buyout transactions. She is the author of the Section 409A Handbook.
**Career:** JD, Yale Law School; Fulbright Award, College d'Europe, Brussels, Belgium; BA, Harvard University, (physics).

## OLSON, Wanda J
Cleary Gottlieb Steen & Hamilton LLP, New York
212 225 2730
wolson@cgsh.com
*Featured in Latin American Investment (New York)*

**Practice Areas:** Domestic and international finance, including public offerings and private placements of debt and equity securities, commercial bank lending, sovereign liability management and debt restructuring, and merger and acquisition finance.
**Professional Memberships:** Member of the Bar in New York and New Jersey.
**Career:** Joined firm, 1981; became Partner, 1990. New York University School of Law (JD, cum laude) 1981; Johns Hopkins University (BA with honors) 1978; Member of Phi Beta Kappa and Order of the Coif.
**Publications:** Recent Developments in Latin American Sovereign Debt Restructuring, Latin Lawyer (August 2005).

## ONORATO, David J
Freshfields Bruckhaus Deringer US LLP, New York
212 277 4000
david.onorato@freshfields.com
*Featured in Litigation (New York)*

**Practice Areas:** Clients have been turning to David for banking, securities and other complex matters for over 20 years. David handles domestic and cross-border cases and investigations involving anti-money laundering issues, derivatives, M&A transactions, securities, and general commercial disputes. David handles inquiries by banking and securities regulators, including the SEC, State Attorneys General, and the Office of the Comptroller of the Currency. David also counsels clients in M&A transactions regarding due diligence and regulatory issues. He has extensive experience in risk management. David is the former Global Director of Litigation of Bank of America.

## ORINGER, Andrew L
Dechert LLP, New York
212 698 3571
andrew.oringer@dechert.com
*Featured in Employee Benefits & Executive Compensation (Nationwide), Employee Benefits & Executive Compensation (New York)*
See under Nationwide for profile.

## ORR, Dennis P
Morrison & Foerster LLP, New York
212 468 8161
dorr@mofo.com
*Featured in Antitrust (New York), Litigation (New York)*

**Practice Areas:** Dennis Orr is a trial lawyer specializing in high-stakes complex commercial litigation with an emphasis on securities, antitrust, products liability, environmental, mergers and acquisitions, and insurance litigation. He represents companies from various industries, most notably the pharmaceutical, food/beverage, consumer product, accounting, and securities industries.
**Career:** Mr Orr has tried more than 30 cases in his career, and, though he has principally served as a defense lawyer, he has won more than $200 million in verdicts and awards in various proceedings around the United States.
**Personal:** JD, St John's University (editor of law review), 1978. BA, Boston College, 1975.

## OSTERMAN, Jeffrey D
Weil, Gotshal & Manges LLP, New York
212 310 8155
jeffrey.osterman@weil.com
*Featured in Outsourcing (Nationwide), Technology (New York)*

**Practice Areas:** Jeffrey Osterman concentrates on matters with deep commercial or technical complexity. He has experience with pure patent licensing, technology transfer, outsourcing, pharmaceutical collaboration and technology integration. He has advised Sanofi in the restructuring of its 15-year alliance agreement with Bristol-Myers Squibb; Panasonic in connection with a wide range of matters in the field of electronics; and GE

on the IP aspects of numerous corporate transactions. He has lectured on IP, electronic privacy and e-commerce throughout the US and on US IP and contract law in Japan.
**Personal:** Cornell University (BA, 1992); Harvard Law School (JD, 1995).

## OSTRAGER, Barry R
Simpson Thacher & Bartlett LLP, New York
212 455 2655
bostrager@stblaw.com
*Featured in Insurance (Nationwide), Litigation (Nationwide), Insurance (New York), Litigation (New York)*
See under Nationwide for profile.

## OWENS, Richard D
Latham & Watkins LLP, New York
212 906 1396
richard.owens@lw.com
*Featured in Litigation (New York)*

**Practice Areas:** White Collar Defense and Government Investigations; Securities Litigation and Professional Liability
**Career:** Mr Owens represents corporations and individuals in criminal and regulatory matters, conducts internal investigations and advises on compliance matters. He served as Assistant United States Attorney in the US Attorney's Office for the Southern District of New York, and for four years, as Chief of its Securities and Commodities Fraud Task Force. He supervised many of the nation's highest profile corporate fraud and insider trading prosecutions. Chair of the Litigation Department in New York.
**Personal:** JD, Harvard Law School, BA, University of North Carolina, Chapel Hill

## PANOVKA, Robin
Wachtell, Lipton, Rosen & Katz, New York
212 403 1352
rpanovka@wlrk.com
*Featured in Capital Markets (Nationwide), Real Estate (New York)*

**Practice Areas:** Consistently leads many of the largest M&A, takeover and restructuring transactions in the REIT, real estate, hospitality and gaming sectors; large-scale private equity transactions and fund formations in the U.S., Europe and Asia; and the redevelopment of the World Trade Center. Active in a wide variety of sophisticated cross-border transactions across industries, with particular focus on emerging markets and sovereign wealth funds.
**Professional Memberships:** Founding director of the International Institute for the Study of Cross-Border M&A (XBMA), a joint venture among Peking University, Cambridge and NYU, and has co-chaired its recent symposia in Beijing, Cambridge and New York. Adjunct professor at Columbia Business School and Columbia Law School; co-chair of the Advisory Board of NYU's REIT Center; Serves on the boards of Duke University School of Law, Harlem Educational Activities Fund, and NYU's Real Estate Institute; and fellow of the American College of Real Estate Lawyers and the American Bar Foundation. Also serves on the Cornell University Council.

**Career:** Partner in Wachtell, Lipton, Rosen & Katz's Corporate Department and co-head of its Real Estate and REIT M&A groups. Recognized as one of the leading practitioners in the fields of cross-border M&A, REITs and sophisticated real estate and capital markets transactions.
**Publications:** Frequent speaker and author on topics involving mergers and acquisitions, REITs and commercial real estate. Among other publications, co-author of 'REITs: Mergers and Acquisitions', a leading treatise published by Law Journal Press. Featured as an American Lawyer "Dealmaker" for his M&A work, and in several publications for his leadership in the redevelopment of the World Trade Center and REIT M&A.
**Personal:** Holds degrees from Cornell and Duke. Grew up in South Africa and Israel and lives in Manhattan with his family.

### PANTALEO, Peter V
Simpson Thacher & Bartlett LLP, New York
212 455 2220
ppantaleo@stblaw.com
*Featured in Bankruptcy/Restructuring (Nationwide), Bankruptcy/Restructuring (New York)*
See under Nationwide for profile.

### PARDO, James A
McDermott Will & Emery LLP, New York
212 547 5353
jpardo@mwe.com
*Featured in Environment (New York)*
**Practice Areas:** Focuses his practice on complex litigation, including class actions, product liability and multi-party mass tort cases. Works closely with corporate clients to identify, evaluate and address potential environmental, toxic tort and products liabilities before they occur. Has helped many companies develop and implement environmental/health/safety compliance programs, and has served as lead environmental/toxic tort counsel on dozens of mergers and acquisitions, real property transactions and other corporate financing matters.
**Personal:** Northwestern University School of Law, JD, (cum laude), 1993, University of Michigan, BGS, (with high distinction), 1990.

### PASSANNANTE, William G
Anderson Kill & Olick, P.C., New York
212 278 1328
wpassannante@andersonkill.com
*Featured in Insurance (Nationwide), Insurance (New York)*
See under Nationwide for profile.

### PATTIZ, Keith
McDermott Will & Emery LLP, New York
212 547 5379
kpattiz@mwe.com
*Featured in Real Estate (New York)*
**Practice Areas:** Partner-in-charge of New York office and head of the firm's real estate affinity group. Extensive experience in commercial leasing, financing, sales and acquisitions, hotel transactions and real estate workout matters. Clients have included major residential, office, hotel and shopping center developers, lending institutions, and foreign and US investors.

**Professional Memberships:** Real Estate Board of New York; Association of the Bar of the City of New York; Bar of State of New York.
**Personal:** New York University School of Law, JD, 1977; University of Wisconsin - Madison, BA, 1973.

### PAUL, Deborah L
Wachtell, Lipton, Rosen & Katz, New York
212 403 1300
dlpaul@wlrk.com
*Featured in Tax (New York)*
**Practice Areas:** Practice focuses on the tax aspects of corporate transactions, including mergers and acquisitions, spin-offs, financial instruments, restructurings and joint ventures; has been the principal tax lawyer on numerous domestic and cross-border transactions, including strategic acquisitions and private equity buyouts, in a wide array of industries. Frequent speaker at PLI, ABA, NYSBA, NYU Tax Institute and other conferences.
**Professional Memberships:** Active member of the Executive Committee of the Tax Section of the New York State Bar Association (principal author of 2012 May Company regulations report), principal author of 2010 report on uncertain tax positions and M&A, principal co-author of 2008 Section 336(e) report, principal author of 2008 report on distributions and acquisitions, principal author of 2006 qualified foreign corporation report, principal co-author of 2005 Circular 230 report and principal author of 2004 continuity of proprietary interest reports).
**Career:** Partner at Wachtell, Lipton, Rosen & Katz since 2001. Prior to joining the firm in 1997, was an assistant professor at the Benjamin N Cardozo School of Law (1995-97) and an acting assistant professor at New York University School of Law (1994-95). Clerked for Chancellor William T Allen of the Court of Chancery of the State of Delaware (1989-90).
**Publications:** 'Spin-offs, Leverage and Value Extraction—A Spin by Any Other Name . . .' (forthcoming in TAXES); 'Another Look Through the Worthless Stock Deduction: Section 165(g)(3) as Applied to Foreign Subsidiaries' (forthcoming in Virginia Tax Review); 'Taxable Acquisitions of Private Companies' (with Michael Sabbah) (forthcoming in NYU 71st Institute on Federal Taxation); 'The Taxation of Distressed Debt Investments: Taking Stock' (in The Tax Lawyer, 2012); 'Shedding Tiers Over the Plan Asset Regulations' (in Pension & Benefits Week 2007); 'Bringing Profits Home' (with Richard Gipstein) (in Private Equity Manager 2005); 'The Use of Disregarded Entities and Pass-Throughs in Corporate Transactions' (with Richard Gipstein) (in USC 56th Institute on Federal Taxation 2004); 'Tax-Free M&A Transactions' (with Lewis Steinberg) (in NYU 62nd Institute on Federal Taxation 2004); 'Triple Taxation' (in The Tax Lawyer 2003); 'Contingency and the Debt/Equity Continuum' (with Peter Canellos) (in the Journal of Taxation of Financial Products 2002); 'United Dominion: Implications for Attribute Reduction' (in Tax Notes 2002); 'The Sources of Tax Complexity: How Much Simplicity Can

Fundamental Tax Reform Achieve?' (in the North Carolina Law Review 1997).
**Personal:** Graduated from Harvard University in 1986 (AB), from Harvard Law School in 1989 (JD) and from New York University School of Law in 1994 (LLM in taxation).

### PEARSON, Nick
Edwards Wildman Palmer, New York
212 912 2798
npearson@edwardswildman.com
*Featured in Insurance (New York)*
**Practice Areas:** Represents US and foreign insurers, reinsurers and producers and has served as outside general counsel to admitted and non-admitted insurers. Nick has broad regulatory and transactional experience and has successfully represented cedents and reinsurers before arbitration panels.
**Professional Memberships:** American Bar Association; Assoc. of the Bar of the City of N.Y.; Insurance Federation of NY; Federation of Regulatory Counsel International Association of Insurance Receivers.
**Publications:** Nick is widely published in leading treatises and trade magazines and is a frequent presenter at national and international conferences.
**Personal:** Duke University, BA; Duke University School of Law, JD.

### PEASLEE, James M
Cleary Gottlieb Steen & Hamilton LLP, New York
212 225 2440
jpeaslee@cgsh.com
*Featured in Tax (New York)*
**Practice Areas:** US tax matters, with emphasis on financial products and structured finance.
**Professional Memberships:** Member of the Executive Committee of the New York State Bar Association's Tax Section and Chair of the Tax Section from 1991-92.
**Career:** Joined firm, 1976; became partner, 1984. LLM, New York University School of Law (1979); JD, cum laude, Harvard Law School (1976); MA, BA Economics, magna cum laude, Yale University (1973).
**Publications:** Co-author of "Federal Income Taxation of Securitization Transactions and Related Topics" (Fourth Edition – www.securitizationtax.com) and author of many articles on tax subjects.

### PECKAR, Robert S
Peckar & Abramson, P.C., New York
201 343 3434
rpeckar@pecklaw.com
*Featured in Construction (New York)*
**Practice Areas:** Recognized leader of the Construction Bar for more than three decades. His current focus is the creative and strategic avoidance and solution of complex multi-party construction disputes.
**Professional Memberships:** Fellow, American College of Construction Lawyers, American Bar Association, NY and NJ Bar Associations.
**Career:** General Counsel to NY Building Trades Employers Association, former GC National

Construction Financial Management Association, GC Emeritus NY Building Congress, Former Chairman Legal Committee of Construction Management Association of America.
**Publications:** Author of New Jersey Practice:Construction Law; Editor Getting the Deal Through: Construction.
**Personal:** For more information, please visit our web site at www.pecklaw.com.

### PEDOWITZ, Lawrence B
Wachtell, Lipton, Rosen & Katz, New York
212 403 1231
lbpedowitz@wlrk.com
*Featured in Litigation (New York)*
**Practice Areas:** Practice focuses on complex civil and corporate litigation, and regulatory, white-collar criminal and professional liability matters. Co-heads Wachtell Lipton's white collar and regulatory practice group, and often is involved in internal investigations and corporate governance and compliance reviews. His clients include securities firms, investment banks, defense contractors, pharmaceutical companies, law firms and corporate officers.
**Professional Memberships:** Is co-chair of the Brennan Center at New York University Law School and has chaired several committees of the Association of the Bar of the City of New York, including: the Criminal Law, Federal Legislation and Federal Courts Committees. Is currently Chair of the Bar Association's Council on Criminal Justice. In addition, served as vice chairman and director of the Legal Aid Society, and a co-founder of New York Law Firms for the Homeless, a financial support organization for the New York Coalition for the Homeless.
**Career:** Partner at Wachtell, Lipton, Rosen & Katz for almost 30 years. Prior to joining the firm, had significant experience as law clerk to Second Circuit Court of Appeals Chief Judge Henry J. Friendly (1972-73) and to United States Supreme Court Justice William J. Brennan, Jr. (1973-74). Also served as chief appellate attorney (1976-78) and chief of the Criminal Division (1982-84) in the United States Attorney's Office for the Southern District of New York. Was also appointed by the Federal District Court to serve as monitor of the Mason Tenders Union (1995-2002).
**Publications:** Has lectured for numerous continuing education programs, including programs sponsored by the American Bar Association, New York Law Journal, Practising Law Institute, the Association of the Bar of the City of New York, Federal Bar Council and Securities Industry and Financial Markets Association. Has also taught trial practice at New York University Law School.
**Personal:** Graduated summa cum laude from Union College in 1969 (BA) and from New York University Law School in 1972 (JD), where he graduated first in his class, served as editor-in-chief of the Law Review and was a Root-Tilden Scholar for the Second Circuit.

**PEIKIN, Steven R**
Sullivan & Cromwell LLP, New York
212 558 7228
peikins@sullcrom.com
*Featured in Litigation (New York)*
**Practice Areas:** Deputy Managing Partner of Criminal Defense and Investigations Group. Represents institutions and their senior executives in various criminal and regulatory investigations and proceedings, including those involving alleged securities/commodities fraud, FCPA violations, price fixing, healthcare fraud, and money laundering offenses. Recent clients: Barclays, Goldman Sachs, The New York City Council, Bank of New York Mellon and Vitol.
**Career:** Partner since 2006. Assistant US Attorney, SDNY (1996-2004). Chief, SDNY Securities and Commodities Fraud Task Force (2003-2004). Clerk, Judge J. Edward Lumbard, US Court of Appeals, Second Circuit (1992-1993).
**Personal:** Harvard Law School (JD, 1991); Yale University (BA, 1988).

**PENCHINA, Robert**
Levine Sullivan Koch & Schulz LLP, New York
212 850 6109
rpenchina@lskslaw.com
*Featured in Intellectual Property (New York)*
**Practice Areas:** : Twenty-five years experience handling copyright, trademark, right of publicity and related matters for media and non-media clients. Cases include Dallal v New York Times, Broadvision v General Electric Co., and Naked Cowboy v CBS.
**Career:** Previously a partner in Rogers & Wells; Clifford Chance.
**Personal:** Born 18 May 1956. Graduate of Queens College and New York University School of Law. Note and Comment Editor, NYU Law Review. Former law clerk to Hon. Frank X. Altimari, U.S. Court of Appeals for Second Circuit.

**PETERS, Christopher**
Willkie Farr & Gallagher LLP, New York
212 728 8868
cpeters@willkie.com
*Featured in Tax (New York)*
**Practice Areas:** Advises US and non-US clients on tax aspects of structuring and implementing taxable and tax-free mergers, acquisitions, spin-offs, leveraged buy-outs and joint ventures. Provides tax advice on capital markets transactions and regularly advises private equity funds and their investors on their investments and fund-related matters.
**Personal:** JD, magna cum laude, Harvard Law School,1997. AB, magna cum laude, Phi Beta Kappa, Dartmouth College, 1993. See: http://www.willkie.com/ChristopherPeters

**PETRETTI, Vito**
Morgan, Lewis & Bockius LLP, Philadelphia
215 963 5504
vpetretti@morganlewis.com
*Featured in Technology (New York)*
**Practice Areas:** Vito Petretti is a partner in Morgan Lewis's Global Outsourcing, Technology, and Commercial Transactions Practice. Mr

Petretti's practice focuses on technology and outsourcing matters. Mr Petretti regularly drafts and negotiates an array of domestic and international outsourcing service agreements for a variety of business processes, such as information technology, finance and accounting, human resources, and procurement. He also drafts and negotiates a variety of information technology agreements such as software licensing agreements, hardware purchase/lease agreements, data licensing and subscription agreements, hosting and development agreements, e-commerce agreements, and other technology-related agreements, including system implementation and strategic alliance agreements.

**PFISTER, Helen R**
Manatt Phelps & Phillips LLP, New York
212 830 7277
hpfister@manatt.com
*Featured in Healthcare (New York)*
**Practice Areas:** Pfister's practice focuses on advising healthcare providers and nonprofit organizations on legislative, regulatory and transactional matters. She has extensive experience representing clients before state and federal regulatory agencies, including the New York State Department of Health and the Centers for Medicare and Medicaid Services, and in helping clients navigate the legal and political challenges of Medicare, Medicaid and other public health insurance programs. Her areas of expertise include licensure, reimbursement, fraud and abuse, and other regulatory issues. She also frequently advises clients on acquisitions, joint ventures, corporate governance, corporate finance and related matters.

**PHILLIPS, Greer L**
Kirkland & Ellis LLP, New York
212 446 4955
greer.phillips@kirkland.com
*Featured in Tax (New York)*
**Practice Areas:** Mr Phillips plans and structures the tax aspects of complex domestic and cross-border transactions, including private and public mergers, acquisitions and buyouts, spinoffs and spin-merge transactions, joint ventures, bankruptcy and workout transactions and financial instruments. He has structured a wide variety of domestic and cross-border acquisitions, spinoffs, joint ventures and recapitalizations, involving strategic and financial buyers, for European, Asian and Latin American clients and for United States clients in cross-border or other complex transactions.
**Personal:** Harvard Law School, JD, 1982; Princeton University, AB, 1979.

**PIANKO, Howard**
Seyfarth Shaw LLP, New York
212 218 5518
hpianko@seyfarth.com
*Featured in Employee Benefits & Executive Compensation (New York)*
**Practice Areas:** Employee Benefits and Plan Governance; Executive Compensation and Equity Programs; International Benefit and Compensatory Matters.

**Professional Memberships:** ABA; IBA; IPEBLA; and Practicing Law Institute
**Career:** Advises clients on the broad spectrum of employee benefit matters, domestic and international: compliance; equity compensation plans; senior executive employment and severance agreements; plan investments; fiduciary responsibility and plan governance; ERISA litigation; benefit aspects of mergers, acquisitions and joint ventures; and global equity and incentive plans, cross-border employment and severance agreements and global plan governance policies.
**Personal:** BA, City College of New York; JD and LLM (Taxation), New York University School of Law.

**PICHLER, Rufus**
Morrison & Foerster LLP, New York
212 336 4050
rpichler@mofo.com
*Featured in Technology (New York)*
**Practice Areas:** Rufus Pichler represents clients in commercial transactions involving technology and intellectual property. He advises companies in the wireless, computer and IT, semiconductor, biotechnology, and pharmaceutical industries with respect to in- and out-licenses, cross-licensing arrangements, development, collaboration, manufacturing, supply and distribution agreements, and other transactions. Mr Pichler's practice focuses on complex patent licensing transactions, including patent exhaustion issues, patent sales, acquisitions, and monetization strategies, and intellectual property aspects of M&A transactions, both in the U.S. and abroad. He has specific expertise in international intellectual property and commercial law and is admitted to practice in the U.S. and Germany.

**PIERCE, Morton A**
White & Case LLP, New York
212 819 7900
mpierce@whitecase.com
*Featured in Media & Entertainment (New York), Corporate/M&A (New York)*
**Career:** Morton Pierce is a partner in White & Case's Mergers and Acquisitions Practice Group. Mr Pierce has more than 30 years of M&A experience and has participated in numerous merger and acquisition matters and related financings. He has represented acquirers, targets, investment bankers and investors in numerous acquisitions. To view a comprehensive biography, please visit www.whitecase.com/mpierce.

**PIETRZAK, Robert**
Sidley Austin LLP, New York
212 839 5537
rpietrzak@sidley.com
*Featured in Litigation (New York)*
**Practice Areas:** Co-head of Litigation in Sidley's New York office and global co-head of the firm's Securities Litigation practice. His practice primarily involves the litigation in US courts of civil and governmental disputes for global financial institutions, including the defense of securities class actions and large contract actions. He has been counsel in regulatory proceedings and civil actions involving securities industry practices,

bonds, public offerings, investment companies and antitrust claims. He has represented defendants in some of the largest litigations in the US and has represented major Chinese corporations and institutions.

**PINOVER, Eugene**
Willkie Farr & Gallagher LLP, New York
212 728 8254
epinover@willkie.com
*Featured in Real Estate (Nationwide), Real Estate (New York)*
See under Nationwide for profile.

**PISACANE, Maggie**
Frankfurt Kurnit Klein & Selz, New York
212 705 4834
mpisacane@fkks.com
*Featured in Media & Entertainment (New York)*
**Practice Areas:** Counsel in the firm's Entertainment Group. Advises well-known producers, production companies, and financiers on all aspects of their scripted and unscripted television, film and digital projects, from development through exploitation. Also advises actors, writers and directors in negotiating agreements for film, television and digital productions and other business ventures. Represents entertainment, fashion, culinary, and other lifestyle clients in brand-building ventures across all media. Also served as vice president with Sard Verbinnen & Co., providing strategic corporate, financial, and crisis communications counsel to Fortune 500 corporations and other celebrity clients.

**PITOFSKY, David**
Goodwin Procter LLP, New York
212 813 8972
dpitofsky@goodwinprocter.com
*Featured in Litigation (New York)*
**Practice Areas:** Mr Pitofsky is a member of the firm's White Collar Crime & Government Investigations Practice and its Securities Litigation and SEC Enforcement Practice. He represents individuals and corporations in connection with white collar criminal investigations and prosecutions, regulatory investigations and lawsuits, internal corporate investigations and commercial lawsuits and arbitrations. His expertise encompasses accounting, securities, financial institution, mail and wire, tax and health care fraud; insider trading; antitrust; public corruption; money laundering; and violations of the Sarbanes-Oxley and Foreign Corrupt Practices Acts.
**Personal:** JD, Georgetown University Law Center, 1991 (Graduating Dean's List); BA, University of Michigan, 1987 (high honors).

**PLATT, Charles C**
WilmerHale, New York
212 230 8860
charles.platt@wilmerhale.com
*Featured in Litigation (New York)*
**Practice Areas:** Partner-in-Charge, New York Office; Co-Chair, Business Trial Group. Recognized nationally for defense work in class actions, trials, and other complex matters for large financial services institutions and insurance companies.

**Professional Memberships:** 1992, Special Assistant US Attorney for Banco Nazionale Del Lavoro ('Iraqgate') Investigation by US Department of Justice. Member, Board of Trustees of Saint David's School in New York; Board of Trustees of the Federal Bar Council from Nov 2000-Nov 2006. Admitted to practice in New York state and federal courts, most federal circuit courts, and US Supreme Court.
**Personal:** JD, Brooklyn Law School; BA, University of Virginia.

**PLATTON, Brian J.**
Mintz Levin Cohn Ferris Glovsky and Popeo PC, New York
212 692 6838
BJPlatton@mintz.com
*Featured in Healthcare (New York)*
**Practice Areas:** Brian's practice focuses on transactional healthcare and other business law. He represents managed care companies, insurers, academic medical centers, hospital systems, pharmaceutical manufacturers, investors, venture capital and private equity funds, life sciences companies, and information technology companies. His experience includes mergers and acquisitions, financings, investments, licensing, governance structure and relationships, marketing arrangements, services arrangements, outsourcing, and other contracting.
**Career:** Named 2007 "Outstanding Healthcare Transaction Lawyer" by Nightingale's Healthcare News.
**Personal:** BA, SUNY Brockport; JD, New York Law School.

**POLEVOY, Martin D**
DLA Piper LLP (US), New York
212 335 4610
martin.polevoy@dlapiper.com
*Featured in Real Estate (New York)*
**Practice Areas:** Real estate, acquisition and disposition, land use and development.
**Career:** Chair of the New York real estate practice. He represents well known national and international owners, developers, investors, and financial institutions, as well as European investors, in both debt and equity transactions. He is a frequent participant as program chair and speaker in continuing legal education programs and has written extensively on various aspects of real estate law.
**Personal:** LLB, University of Pennsylvania; AB, Colgate University (cum laude).

**POLKES, Jonathan**
Weil, Gotshal & Manges LLP, New York
212 310 8881
jonathan.polkes@weil.com
*Featured in Securities (Nationwide), Litigation (New York)*
See under Nationwide for profile.

**POLLACK, Martin D**
Weil, Gotshal & Manges LLP, New York
212 310 8461
martin.pollack@weil.com
*Featured in Tax (New York)*
**Practice Areas:** Martin Pollack is a Co-head of Weil's global Tax Practice. He regularly advises

clients on the tax aspects of private equity and M&A transactions, the formation and operation of private equity funds, joint ventures, bankruptcy and insolvency, leasing transactions and technology intensive enterprises. He lectures at tax seminars, chairs an American Bar Association Tax Section subcommittee and is a co-author of a treatise on tax considerations pertaining to partnership buy/sell agreements.
**Personal:** Johns Hopkins University (BA, 1973); Johns Hopkins University (MA, 1973); University of Pennsylvania Law School (JD, 1976); New York University School of Law (LLM, 1979).

**POMERANTZ, Mark F**
Paul, Weiss, Rifkind, Wharton & Garrison LLP, New York
212 373 3010
mpomerantz@paulweiss.com
*Featured in Litigation (Nationwide), Litigation (New York)*
**Practice Areas:** Of counsel in the Litigation Department. Nationally known trial lawyer and senior litigator with extensive public and private experience in white-collar criminal and regulatory matters. Has counseled CEOs in proceedings brought by the Justice Department and Securities Exchange Commission and has represented prominent corporations and individuals with regard to many sensitive and high-profile matters. Has tried cases on behalf of commercial clients and individuals before juries and arbitration panels, and also has substantial appellate experience, arguing dozens of appeals before courts throughout the country. Has significant experience in matters involving the financial services industry.

**PONCE, Mario**
Simpson Thacher & Bartlett LLP, New York
212 455 2000
mponce@stblaw.com
*Featured in Corporate/M&A (New York)*
**Practice Areas:** Partner in the Corporate Department. Focuses on negotiated and hostile merger and acquisition transactions, proxy contests, restructurings, joint ventures, corporate governance and securities laws. Represents both public and private companies in a variety of industries and advises private equity clients. Counsel to boards of directors and special committees concerning corporate governance and other matters. Has significant experience in the energy, industrials, retail and healthcare industries.
**Career:** Joined the firm in 1988; became Partner in 1997.
**Personal:** BA, summa cum laude, Phi Beta Kappa, University of Richmond (1984); JD, with honors, Duke University School of Law (1988).

**POND, George M**
Hiscock & Barclay LLP, Albany
518 429 4232
gpond@hiscockbarclay.com
*Featured in Energy & Natural Resources (New York)*
**Practice Areas:** Representation of clients in energy matters, including siting and interconnection; utility rate and tariff changes; regulatory approvals for purchases or sales of facilities; contracting for sales of energy and renewable energy

attributes; and complying with regulatory requirements applicable to Energy Service Companies ("ESCOs") providing service to retail customers in New York State.
**Professional Memberships:** New York Bar, District of Columbia Bar, Energy Bar Association, New York State Bar Association.
**Personal:** University of Michigan (JD), Magna Cum Laude, Order of the Coif, Associate Editor of the Michigan Law Review; University of Michigan (BA), High Honors, Phi Beta Kappa.

**PONIKVAR, Dale L**
Milbank, Tweed, Hadley & McCloy LLP, New York
212 530 5296
DPonikvar@milbank.com
*Featured in Tax (New York)*
**Practice Areas:** Tax aspects of mergers, acquisitions, cross-border transactions, corporate restructurings, outsourcing transactions. Represented Goldman Sachs, Cerberus, Harbinger and Silverpoint in private equity investments. Creditors Committee Tax lawyer: Lehman, Enron, Refco bankruptcies.
**Professional Memberships:** Vice-Chair Tax Section of Public Utility, Communication & Transportation Committee American Bar Association. Board & Legal Counsel to American Council on Germany & US Chairman of its Business Advisory Committee. Member of Board of Governors of New School for Social Research in NY Graduate Faculty.
**Career:** Senior Corporate Tax Partner
**Personal:** JD, NYU; MA, New School for Social Research; BA, Yale. Fluent: German, French. Conversant: Italian.

**PORTNOY, Lawrence**
Davis Polk & Wardwell LLP, New York
212 450 4000
lawrence.portnoy@davispolk.com
*Featured in Securities (Nationwide), Litigation (New York)*
**Practice Areas:** Member of Davis Polk's Litigation Department. Represents clients in a wide range of securities and commercial matters in federal and state courts and before regulatory agencies. Has also represented clients in NASD, NYSE and American Arbitration Association arbitrations. Has represented investment banks and other financial institutions as well as industrial and manufacturing companies in class action litigations in federal district courts in New York, Massachusetts, New Jersey, Pennsylvania, Connecticut, Texas, California, Florida and the District of Columbia. Has also represented clients in state court matters in New York, Delaware, California and South Carolina and in SEC enforcement matters.

**POTTER, Geoffrey**
Patterson Belknap Webb & Tyler LLP, New York
212 336 2050
gpotter@pbwt.com
*Featured in Intellectual Property (New York)*
**Practice Areas:** Geoffrey Potter is a Partner and Chair of the firm's Anti-Counterfeiting Practice

Team. A highly-experienced trial lawyer, Mr Potter litigates counterfeiting and product diversion cases on behalf of major corporations in diverse industries worldwide. These cases primarily involve counterfeit products with the potential to cause serious injury or death, including counterfeit medical devices, chemicals, pharmaceuticals, nutritional supplements, beverages and other consumer, industrial and electronic products. In addition to this work, Mr Potter litigates cases for and against financial institutions and investment funds, as well as cases concerning accountant liability, defamation, consumer and shareholder class actions, unfair competition, copyright, breach of contract and fraud. He has also conducted numerous securities and employment arbitrations and internal investigations involving Foreign Corrupt Practices Act violations, accounting improprieties and employee malfeasance. Outside of litigation, Mr Potter counsels clients on integrated risk reduction solutions and best practices for avoiding counterfeiting problems. He advises on proactive methods to secure products and packaging against counterfeiters and diverters and on the development of programs to guard and monitor distribution channels.
**Professional Memberships:** New York State Bar Association; American Bar Association, Member, Intellectual Property Division.
**Personal:** JD, 1988, New York University School of Law; BA, 1984, Cornell University.

**POWELL, Wesley**
Willkie Farr & Gallagher LLP, New York
212 728 8264
wpowell@willkie.com
*Featured in Antitrust (New York)*
**Practice Areas:** Partner, Litigation Department and Antitrust and Competition Group. Handles complex civil antitrust and securities litigation, mergers, regulatory inquiries and investigations. Major recent matters: represents private equity firm in Dahl v. Bain Capital; and represents MasterCard in both In re Payment Card Interchange Fee and Merchant Discount Antitrust Litigation and in DOJ investigation of merchant rules.
**Personal:** JD, Duke University School of Law, 1994; member, Duke Journal of Gender Law and Policy and the Duke Law Moot Court Board. BA, magna cum laude, Vanderbilt University, 1991; Phi Beta Kappa. See: http://www.willkie.com/WesleyPowell

**PRATT, William**
Kirkland & Ellis LLP, New York
212 446 4862
william.pratt@kirkland.com
*Featured in Litigation (New York)*
**Practice Areas:** Senior Litigation Partner and Founding Partner of Kirkland's New York office. Member of Kirkland's Firmwide Management Committee from 1996-2011. Fellow of the American College of Trial Lawyers. Lead trial counsel on cases (both individual and class action) in a wide variety of substantive areas, including antitrust, securities, intellectual property, environmental, contract, and tort. Substantial

experience before government regulatory agencies, including the Department of Justice, Federal Trade Commission and Securities & Exchange Commission, as well as various state agencies. More than 30 trials and arbitrations.
**Personal:** Tulane University, BA, 1974. Columbia Law School, JD, 1977.

### PRICE, Christopher B
Goodwin Procter LLP, New York
212 813 8951
cbprice@goodwinprocter.com
*Featured in Real Estate (New York)*
**Practice Areas:** Mr Price serves as chair of the firm's Real Estate Finance Practice. He practices in all areas of real estate investment management and real estate finance law, representing domestic and foreign investors, fund sponsors, institutional investment advisors and investment banks. Mr Price represents institutional investors, real estate investment managers and public and private companies in all of their real estate industry needs, including purchases and sales, financings, recapitalizations, restructurings, debt acquisitions, joint ventures and entity-level investments.
**Personal:** JD, Tulane University, 1985 (magna cum laude, Order of the Coif); BA, Middlebury College, 1982 (cum laude, with honors).

### PRICE, Scott D
Kirkland & Ellis LLP, New York
212 446 4851
scott.price@kirkland.com
*Featured in Employee Benefits & Executive Compensation (New York)*
**Practice Areas:** Scott Price is a tax partner in Kirkland's New York office and heads the Firm's Executive Compensation practice group. Mr Price has extensive experience handling executive compensation, benefits and ERISA matters in complex business transactions, including domestic and international mergers, leveraged buyouts and other acquisitions. In addition, Mr Price has represented numerous high profile executives and management teams in negotiating employment and incentive arrangements.
**Personal:** New Mexico State University, BS, Criminal Justice, 1987; Villanova University School of Law, JD, 1990 (summa cum laude, Order of the Coif, Villanova Law Review, Managing Editor).

### PRINCI, Anthony
Morrison & Foerster LLP, New York
212 468 8030
aprinci@mofo.com
*Featured in Bankruptcy/Restructuring (New York)*
**Practice Areas:** Mr Princi is a partner in the Business Restructuring & Insolvency Group of Morrison & Foerster. Mr Princi's practice is concentrated in debt capital markets and restructuring. He has extensive experience representing corporate debtors and secured and unsecured creditors' committees in cross-border bankruptcy proceedings and out-of-court restructurings. Mr Princi regularly represents "special situations" investors in private debt and equity transactions and has extensive trial experience in securities and commercial litigation.

**Personal:** BS, summa cum laude, Fordham University, 1979; JD, Fordham University School of Law, 1982.

### PROFUSEK, Robert A
Jones Day, New York
212 326 3800
raprofusek@jonesday.com
*Featured in Corporate/M&A (New York)*
**Practice Areas:** Chairs the firm's M&A practice globally, working on dozens of transactions involving a total of more than $100 billion since 2010. He is a frequent speaker regarding corporate takeovers and corporate governance, has authored numerous articles, and has testified before Congress and the SEC about takeover and corporate governance. Recognized globally as a leading M&A lawyer, he has been featured in many publications, including being selected in 2005 as Dealmaker of the Year by The American Lawyer, and is a frequent guest commentator on television and radio. He also is a director of two NYSE-listed companies.

### QUALE JR, Andrew C
Sidley Austin LLP, New York
212 839 7360
aquale@sidley.com
*Featured in Latin American Investment (New York)*
**Practice Areas:** Andrew Quale is senior counsel in Sidley's New York office, focusing on international corporate and financial matters, including cross-border banking and capital markets transactions, project finance, securitizations, mergers and acquisitions, privatizations and restructurings. Advises multinational financial and industrial groups, sovereign governments and state-owned enterprises on transactions and projects involving the US, Latin America, Europe and Asia. Adviser to governments and state-owned enterprises throughout Latin America.
**Personal:** Harvard Law School, LLB, 1966, cum laude; Harvard University, AB, 1963, magna cum laude. Admission: New York.

### QUINN, James W
Weil, Gotshal & Manges LLP, New York
212 310 8385
james.quinn@weil.com
*Featured in Litigation (Nationwide), Sports Law (Nationwide), Litigation (New York)*
See under Nationwide for profile.

### QUINN, Yvonne S
Sullivan & Cromwell LLP, New York
212 558 3736
quinny@sullcrom.com
*Featured in Antitrust (New York)*
**Professional Memberships:** ABA (Antitrust Section); NYSBA (Executive Committee, Antitrust Section); New York City Bar Association (former Chair, Antitrust and Trade Regulation Committee); FBC.
**Career:** Partner since 1984. Co-head, Antitrust Group. Antitrust litigation, merger analysis/review and counseling work as well as general commercial litigation. Clients: consumer products companies, leading commercial banks, equity funds, investment banks, insurance companies, cable television operators, television programming suppli-

ers, newspapers, publishers, sports franchise owners, advertising sales, healthcare, pharmaceutical and chemical companies, accounting standards boards, among many others.
**Personal:** University of Michigan Law School (JD, 1976); University of Michigan (MA, Economics, 1977); University of Illinois (BA, 1973).

### RAAB, David S
Latham & Watkins LLP, New York
212 906 1344
David.Raab@lw.com
*Featured in Tax (New York)*
**Practice Areas:** Global Chair of firm's Tax Department. Practice focuses on corporate and partnership taxation. Also expert in the taxation of real estate investment trusts. Considerable experience representing corporations, private equity funds, investment banks, and other public and privately owned companies with respect to tax matters pertaining to mergers, acquisitions, recapitalizations, divestitures, and joint ventures.
**Career:** Qualified since 1988. Formerly served as Global Co-Chair of the Transactional Tax Practice Group and as chair of the New York Tax Department.

### RABINOWITZ, Stephen L
Greenberg Traurig, LLP, New York
212 801 9295
RabinowitzS@gtlaw.com
*Featured in Real Estate (New York)*
**Practice Areas:** Chair, New York Real Estate Practice. Joint ventures, hospitality, REITs, acquisitions/sales, leasing.
**Professional Memberships:** Board of Directors, Secretary, East Harlem Tutorial Program. Board of Trustees, Lupus Foundation of America.
**Career:** Chambers USA, 2007-13; Who's Who in the East, 34th Edition; Best Lawyers, 2007-13; Super Lawyers, 2006-12. Member, Law360 'Real Estate Practice Group of the Year', 2011-12.
**Publications:** Author: 'Real Estate: An Overview', PLC U.S. Special Report, 2008-09, November 2008; 'Country Q&A: United States,' PLC Cross-border Corporate Real Estate Handbook-United States, 2007-08, November 2007.
**Personal:** JD, cum laude, American University Washington College of Law; BA, cum laude, Brandeis University.

### RAFFA, Connie A
Arent Fox LLP, New York
212 484 3926
connie.raffa@arentfox.com
*Featured in Healthcare (New York)*
**Practice Areas:** Connie Raffa's experience includes regulatory/reimbursement issues, fraud/abuse investigations, audits, medical reviews, compliance, survey/certification, and administrative/Federal litigation. Clients include hospitals, palliative care programs, home health agencies, hospices, and physicians. Connie served 15 years with US HHS - OGC and OIG, and was a prosecutor in the NYC DA's Office. She is a frequent lecturer, author, Board and committees' member of HPCANY and NHPCO. Her work was

featured in the Wall Street Journal. Connie's awards include Arent Pro Bono, Meyer Excelsior, Appleseed's Pillar of Justice, Selinske Founders, HCFA Administrator, OIG Superior Achievement, and others. Recognized in Chambers USA and Legal500.

### RAPISARDI, John J
Cadwalader, Wickersham & Taft LLP, New York
212 504 5585
john.rapisardi@cwt.com
*Featured in Bankruptcy/Restructuring (Nationwide), Bankruptcy/Restructuring (New York)*
**Practice Areas:** Co-Chair, Financial Restructuring Department. Represents debtors, creditors and investors, domestically and internationally, in restructuring matters across a variety of industries, including automotive, casinos, chemical, energy, healthcare, retail, real estate, satellite, sports franchises, textile and telecommunications. Served as lead counsel to the Presidential Task Force on the Auto Industry. Leading role in some of the most significant and innovative recent restructuring matters including Angiotech Pharmaceuticals, Black Gaming, Blockbuster, Brookfield, Contec, Fred Leighton, Inner City Media, Xerium Technologies and US Treasury in General Motors, Chrysler, Delphi, and CIT.
**Publications:** Frequent speaker, lecturer and author. Contributing author, Cadwalader Restructuring Review (www.restructuringreview.com). Co-author, The PRC Enterprise Bankruptcy Law: The People's Work in Progress (Beard Group, Inc., 2008); Bankruptcy columnist, New York Law Journal.
**Personal:** JD, Pace University School of Law; LLM, New York University School of Law; BS, Fordham University

### RASHKOVER, Barry
Sidley Austin LLP, New York
212 839 5850
brashkover@sidley.com
*Featured in Securities (Nationwide), Litigation (New York)*
**Practice Areas:** Partner, a co-global coordinator of Sidley's SEC Enforcement Practice. Focuses on representing companies and individuals in investigations and enforcement cases brought by government agencies and other regulators including the SEC, FINRA, other self-regulatory organizations, and criminal authorities. Frequent speaker and writer on SEC enforcement and related issues. Adjunct professor at Fordham Law School, teaches a course on insider trading and other securities fraud issues. Prior to joining Sidley, he was a senior official in the SEC's Division of Enforcement.
**Personal:** Cornell Law School, JD, 1986, Note Editor, Cornell Law Review; Columbia University, AB, 1983. Admission: New York.

## RASKIN, Kenneth A
King & Spalding LLP, New York
212 556 2162
kraskin@kslaw.com

*Featured in Employee Benefits & Executive Compensation (New York)*

**Practice Areas:** Counsels in creation, structure, communication of tax-qualified retirement plans and welfare benefit plans, assisting clients in maintaining IRS and ERISA compliance. Negotiates the resolution of qualification problems under the IRS' and DOL's compliance resolution programs. Establishes and maintains non-qualified plans of deferred compensation and develops funding mechanisms for these plans such as "rabbi trusts." Advises plan trustees, bank trust departments and other fiduciaries regarding ERISA and its investment requirements, and fiduciary issues and responsibilities. Provides transactional counsel in mergers and acquisitions.
**Personal:** Saint Johns University (JD, 1984); SUNY at Binghamton (MBA, 1978); University of Vermont (BA, 1976).

## RAVAL, Abhilash
Milbank, Tweed, Hadley & McCloy LLP, New York
212 530 5123
araval@milbank.com

*Featured in Bankruptcy/Restructuring (New York)*

**Practice Areas:** Mr Raval is a Partner and a member of the firm's Financial Restructuring Group. He has extensive experience representing debtors, statutory or official committees, creditors and other stakeholders in all aspects of reorganization cases, liquidation cases and out-of-court workouts. Mr Raval also regularly represents private equity funds and hedge funds in all aspects of acquiring control positions in financially distressed companies, whether through a chapter 11 process or otherwise. He covers a broad range of industries and also regularly represents prospective lenders in structuring high risk "rescue financings" and chapter 11 "DIP" and "Exit" financings.

## RAY, Claudia
Kirkland & Ellis LLP, New York
212 446 4948
claudia.ray@kirkland.com

*Featured in Intellectual Property (New York)*

**Practice Areas:** Claudia Ray is an IP Litigation partner in Kirkland's New York office. Her practice focuses on copyright, trademark and Internet-related litigation, arbitration and counseling across a wide range of industries, including consumer products, entertainment and media, fashion and apparel, financial services, and technology. Claudia also advises clients on overall IP protection and brand-building strategies and on IP issues arising out of complex commercial transactions. Representative matters have involved the "Spider-Man" musical, the Obama "Hope" poster, the Harry Potter books and films, Colgate Total toothpaste, and the Burberry plaid. Claudia also frequently writes and speaks on IP-related topics.

## RAYMOND, Robert J
Cleary Gottlieb Steen & Hamilton LLP, New York
212 225 2994
rraymond@cgsh.com

*Featured in Employee Benefits & Executive Compensation (New York)*

**Practice Areas:** Executive compensation and employee benefits matters, including: executive employment agreements; equity and non-equity based compensation; carried interest and co-investment plans, particularly in M&A and private equity; general advice regarding federal and state statutes and regulations governing fiduciary relationships, tax and securities laws, terms and conditions of employment, and corporate governance. Recently advised KKR (KKR China Growth Fund formation), Nortel Networks (negotiations with Pension Benefit Guaranty), TPG (application of the ERISA "Plan Asset" rules), Citigroup, Credit Suisse and Deutsche Bank with carried interest, co-investment and investment fund compensation arrangements.
**Career:** JD, summa cum laude, New York Law School (1994).

## RAYSMAN, Richard
Holland & Knight LLP, New York
212 513 3469
richard.raysman@hklaw.com

*Featured in Outsourcing (Nationwide), Technology (New York)*

**Practice Areas:** Richard Raysman, a partner in Holland & Knight's New York office, concentrates on computer law, outsourcing, complex technology transactions and IP issues. Mr Raysman has negotiated billion dollar outsourcing transactions on behalf of his clients. He has litigated reported cases for New York state and federal courts. Mr Raysman is a graduate of M.I.T. Prior to practicing law, he was a Systems Engineer for IBM Corporation for six years. He is on the Intellectual Property & Technology Advisory Board of the Practical Law Company, and writes a monthly column on Technology Law for the New York Law Journal.

## REICH, Yaron Z
Cleary Gottlieb Steen & Hamilton LLP, New York
212 225 2540
yreich@cgsh.com

*Featured in Tax (New York)*

**Practice Areas:** Taxation including tax aspects of corporate acquisitions, restructurings, financings, partnerships, real estate and international transactions; financial institution taxation; tax controversies. Clients include Credit Agricole, Citigroup, Goldman Sachs, Hellman & Friedman, HSBC, Institute of International Bankers, TPG, Veolia.
**Professional Memberships:** NYSBA Tax Section Executive Committee.
**Career:** Joined firm, 1979; became partner, 1986. LLM in Taxation, New York University School of Law (1984); JD (Kent and Stone Scholar), special issue editor of Columbia Law Review, Columbia University School of Law (1978); BA, summa cum laude, Columbia College (1975).

**Publications:** Mr Reich has published several significant articles on international tax issues.

## REILLY, Michael J
Bingham McCutchen LLP, New York
212 705 7763
michael.reilly@bingham.com

*Featured in Bankruptcy/Restructuring (Nationwide), Bankruptcy/Restructuring (New York)*
See under Nationwide for profile.

## REINHOLD, Richard L
Willkie Farr & Gallagher LLP, New York
212 728 8292
rreinhold@willkie.com

*Featured in Tax (New York)*

**Practice Areas:** Chair, Tax Department. Practice includes domestic and international business tax matters relative to mergers and acquisitions, joint ventures, corporate restructurings, and financing transactions. Representative highlights: advising collective of Tranche C lenders in the $3.25 billion credit bid for, and restructuring of, Delphi Corporation; Farmers Group, in its $1.9 billion acquisition of AIG's Personal Auto Group; Ramius in its business combination with Cowen; Soros Fund Management in the investor consortium acquisition of ConAgra Trade Group from ConAgra Foods.
**Personal:** JD, State University of New York at Buffalo School of Law, 1976. AB, Cornell University, 1973. See:
http://www.willkie.com/RichardReinhold

## REISMAN, Steven J
Curtis, Mallet-Prevost, Colt & Mosle LLP, New York
212 696 6065
sreisman@curtis.com

*Featured in Bankruptcy/Restructuring (New York)*

**Professional Memberships:** Association of the Bar of the City of New York - Bankruptcy and Corporate Reorganization Committee; American Bar Association - Litigation Section and Business Law Section; New York State Bar Association - Bankruptcy Law Committee; Turnaround Management Association; American Bankruptcy Institute; International Bar Association - Insolvency & Creditors' Rights Committee & Vice-Chair, Reorganization and Workouts Committee; Commercial Law League of America.
**Career:** Steven J Reisman, partner and co-chair of the Restructuring and Insolvency group of Curtis, has handled a wide range of domestic and international matters involving bankruptcy, restructuring and creditors' rights and has represented clients in all facets of bankruptcy cases and insolvency issues in business transactions and out-of-court restructurings. Highlights of Mr Reisman's recent representations include Lehman Brothers Holdings, et al. in the largest bankruptcy filing in the U.S.; Residential Capital, LLC; Patriot Coal Corporation; General Maritime Corporation; Sbarro Corporation; Hawker Beechcraft, Inc.; Caribe Media, Inc.; and as conflicts counsel to the Official Committee of Unsecured Creditors to Hostess Brands, Inc., et al. and K-V Discovery Solutions, Inc. Mr Reisman has represented various hedge funds, private equi-

ty firms and distressed debt investors with respect to their investments in companies and in restructuring the indebtedness of companies in insolvency matters. He has also worked on several cross-border insolvency proceedings involving Mexico, Canada, Argentina and other countries.
**Publications:** New York Law Journal (February 10, 2011) - "Taking it Back - Recovering Transfers in Bankruptcy"; New York Law Journal (March 1, 2010) - "Reasonable Insecurity: Strategies for Doing Business with Financially Troubled Counterparties"; "To Be or Not to Be: Whether or Not to Be a Stalking Horse in a Bankruptcy Sale," Turnaround Management (Spring 2004).
**Personal:** JD, with Honors, St. John's University School of Law, 1990 BS, magna cum laude, State University of New York at Oneonta, 1987.

## REISS, John
White & Case LLP, New York
212 819 8247
jreiss@whitecase.com

*Featured in Private Equity (Nationwide), Corporate/M&A (New York)*

**Career:** John M. Reiss is the Global Head of White & Case's Mergers & Acquisitions Practice. He represents parties in mergers and acquisitions, private equity transactions, securities transactions and financings of all types. His clients include numerous corporations and private equity groups. To view a comprehensive biography, please visit www.whitecase.com/jreiss.

## REITER, Glenn M
Simpson Thacher & Bartlett LLP, New York
212 455 3358
greiter@stblaw.com

*Featured in Latin American Investment (New York), Capital Markets (Nationwide)*
See under Nationwide for profile.

## RESNICK, Brian
Davis Polk & Wardwell LLP, New York
212 450 4000
brian.resnick@davispolk.com

*Featured in Bankruptcy/Restructuring (New York)*

**Practice Areas:** Brian Resnick is a partner in Davis Polk's Insolvency and Restructuring Group. He has substantial experience in a broad range of corporate restructurings and bankruptcies, representing debtors, creditors, banks, hedge funds, asset acquirers and other strategic parties in connection with bankruptcies, out-of-court workouts, DIP and exit financings, bankruptcy litigation and Section 363 sales. Recent representations include Lehman Brothers International (Europe), Patriot Coal Corporation, DIP Agent's counsel in Eastman Kodak and Delphi, and significant parties in the bankruptcies of MF Global, American Airlines and Capmark. Publications: Contributing author to "Collier on Bankruptcy". Editorial Board Member of "American Bankruptcy Institute Journal".

## RESSA, Gregory J
Simpson Thacher & Bartlett LLP, New York
212 455 7430
gressa@stblaw.com

*Featured in Leisure & Hospitality (Nationwide), Real Estate (Nationwide), Real Estate (New York)*

See under Nationwide for profile.

## REYNOLDS, Timothy G
Skadden, Arps, Slate, Meagher & Flom LLP
& Affiliates, New York
212 735 2316
Timothy.Reynolds@skadden.com
*Featured in Insurance (New York)*
**Practice Areas:** Concentrates in insurance and reinsurance litigation and arbitration, with extensive experience in Bermuda Form arbitrations on behalf of policyholders. Represents clients in insurance and reinsurance disputes concerning life, property, political risks and products liability. Also counsels corporations and their directors and officers with respect to D&O insurance coverage for a variety of claims, and consults internationally with respect to D&O and property insurance placements.
**Career:** JD, Fordham University School of Law, 1980 (cum laude); BS, Fordham College, 1976 (summa cum laude); law clerk, Hon. William Hughes Mulligan, United States Court of Appeals, 2d Cir.

## RICE, Thomas C
Simpson Thacher & Bartlett LLP, New York
212 455 3040
trice@stblaw.com
*Featured in Litigation (New York)*
**Practice Areas:** Co-head of the Litigation Department and member of Firm's Executive Committee. Represents clients in wide variety of complex litigations. Current representations include RBS, DB and UBS in RMBS litigations and JPMorgan Chase in LIBOR litigations. Prior engagements include lead counsel for JPMorgan Chase in Enron litigations, Barclays, Deutsche, JPMorgan Chase and RBS in Fontainebleau litigation and Merrill Lynch in complex derivative instruments suit where Merrill Lynch won $167 million verdict and judgment.
**Career:** Joined the firm in 1981; Partner since 1989.
**Personal:** St. John's University School of Law (JD, 1981); St. John's University (BA, magna cum laude, 1978)

## RICH, R Bruce
Weil, Gotshal & Manges LLP, New York
212 310 8170
bruce.rich@weil.com
*Featured in Intellectual Property (New York), Media & Entertainment (New York)*
**Practice Areas:** Senior partner at Weil and Head of the firm's top-ranked IP/Media Practice, R. Bruce Rich is a nationally recognized expert in intellectual property law, focusing on legal issues presented by the transmission of content on traditional and new media platforms. Areas of concentration include copyright, music licensing, First Amendment, trademark and antitrust law. He has served as lead trial counsel in significant cases for clients including Random House, Bertelsmann, McGraw-Hill, eBay, Sirius XM Satellite Radio, The Walt Disney Company, ABC, CBS, DMX, and the Association of American Publishers.
**Personal:** Dartmouth College (BA); University of Pennsylvania Law School (JD).

## RICHMAN, Monica B
Dentons, New York
212 768 5367
monica.richman@dentons.com
*Featured in Intellectual Property (New York)*
**Practice Areas:** Monica Richman, a partner at Dentons and chair of legacy Dentons's Fashion, Apparel, and Beauty practice, represents many of the world's biggest names in entertainment, fashion, and financial services. Monica frequently advises on licensing, portfolio management, due diligence, adversarial proceedings, and a wide range of other intellectual property matters. She is a frequent writer and speaker, and has been quoted by The Wall Street Journal and USA Today. Emory University School of Law, JD; The George Washington University, BBA, magna cum laude. Law clerk to Hon. Loren A Smith, former Chief Judge United States Court of Federal Claims.

## RICHTER, Philip
Fried, Frank, Harris, Shriver & Jacobson LLP, New York
212 859 8763
Philip.Richter@FriedFrank.com
*Featured in Corporate/M&A (New York)*
**Practice Areas:** Corporate partner; co-head of M&A practice. Represents clients in M&A transactions involving public and private companies; spin-offs, split-off and other business separation transactions; unsolicited proposals and proxy fights; strategic partnerships and joint ventures and minority investments. Advises on corporate governance issues, defensive strategy, and securities law compliance. Frequently represents investment banks serving in a financial advisory role.
**Career:** Joined in 1994; became partner in 2002.
**Personal:** JD, Columbia Law School (1994), editor, senior editor, Columbia Law Review, James Kent Scholar, Harlan Fiske Stone Scholar, John M. Olin Law and Economics Fellow; BA, magna cum laude, Yeshiva University (1991).

## RIEVMAN, David
Skadden, Arps, Slate, Meagher & Flom LLP
& Affiliates, New York
212 735 3257
david.rievman@skadden.com
*Featured in Tax (New York)*
**Practice Areas:** Mr Rievman is a senior partner in the tax practice of Skadden, Arps and is the Global Head of the firm's Regulatory practices. Mr Rievman advises clients on the tax aspects of complex business transactions, including mergers and acquisitions, spin-offs, joint ventures, equity and debt financings, recapitalizations, restructurings and other business transactions. Mr Rievman's clients include public corporations, closely-held businesses, investment banks, private equity funds, family offices and other sponsor entities.
**Career:** JD, Boston College Law School, 1987 (magna cum laude, Order of the Coif); BA, Case Western Reserve University, 1984 (magna cum laude).

## RINGEL, Dean
Cahill Gordon & Reindel LLP, New York
212 701 3521
dringel@cahill.com
*Featured in Media & Entertainment (New York)*
**Practice Areas:** Represents newspapers, publishers, broadcast and cable networks in libel, privacy, reporter's privilege, trademark and right of publicity matters. Experience in IP, antitrust, business torts and appellate law.
**Professional Memberships:** Past: chair/co-chair, Federal Courts Committee & Antitrust Litigation Committee, Commercial and Federal Litigation Section (NYSBA); Member, Antitrust and Trade Regulation, Communications and Federal Legislation Committees (NYSBA); President, Defense Counsel Section (MLRC).
**Publications:** Co-author, Survey of Second Circuit Libel Law, MLRC 50-State Survey.
**Personal:** Clerkship: Judge Anthony Celebrezze, US Court of Appeals for the Sixth Circuit. Columbia University, BA, 1967, with honors, Phi Beta Kappa. Yale Law School, JD, 1971.

## ROBB, Kathy
Hunton & Williams LLP, New York
212 309 1128
krobb@hunton.com
*Featured in Environment (New York)*
**Practice Areas:** Kathy Robb's practice focuses exclusively on environmental law, including litigation in state and federal district and appellate courts, regulatory and compliance advice, and advice on environmental risks and structuring in complex business transactions. Emphasis is on water issues under the Clean Water Act, the Endangered Species Act, NEPA, water-related CERCLA sites with PCBs and other contamination in sediments, and groundwater. Representative clients include water districts, developers, electric utilities, energy companies, investors, lenders, chemical manufacturers, and paper mills. She is also the founder and Director of the firm's Water Policy Institute, seeking innovative, sustainable solutions to water supply and quality issues.

## ROBBINS, Brian D
Simpson Thacher & Bartlett LLP, New York
212 455 3090
brobbins@stblaw.com
*Featured in Employee Benefits & Executive Compensation (Nationwide), Employee Benefits & Executive Compensation (New York)*
**Practice Areas:** Partner in, and Head of, the Firm's Executive Compensation and Employee Benefits Practice Group. Practice has included participation in complex mergers and acquisitions, securities and commercial banking transactions involving issues arising under Title I and Title IV of ERISA and related provisions of the Internal Revenue Code; the structuring and implementation of management equity arrangements, deferred compensation and other executive compensation, employment and severance programs; advice with respect to tax, accounting and securities law issues related to the implementation of qualified and non-qualified compensation arrangements.
**Personal:** BA, Amherst College (1985); JD, Columbia Law School (1988).

## ROBBINS, Virginia C
Bond, Schoeneck & King, PLLC, Syracuse
315 218 8182
vrobbins@bsk.com
*Featured in Environment (New York)*
**Practice Areas:** Heads Environmental and Energy Practice Group. Manages transactions involving contaminated properties, including under the NYS Brownfield Cleanup Program. She has regulatory experience in air and water quality, waste management, and impact reviews under SEQRA and NEPA. She has expertise in Clean Air Act matters, including allowances for carbon dioxide emissions from electric generating facilities subject to the Regional Greenhouse Gas Initiative, New Source Review, and Acid Rain Programs. Has counseled clients siting power projects under Article X of the Public Service Law.
**Personal:** Rutgers University, BA, 1971; Middlebury College, MA, 1972; Rutgers University School of Law, JD, 1986.

## ROBERTS, Thomas A
Weil, Gotshal & Manges LLP, New York
212 310 8479
thomas.roberts@weil.com
*Featured in Corporate/M&A (New York)*
**Practice Areas:** Thomas A. Roberts is a member of Weil's 16-member Management Committee and former Chairman of the Corporate Department. Mr Roberts is involved in major domestic and cross-border mergers, acquisitions, divestitures, contested takeovers, and private equity. He also regularly advises boards and committees generally, and on strategic matters. Clients consist of major international public and private companies, several of the leading private equity funds, and leading investment banks. Examples include: AMR, General Electric, Kinder Morgan, MGM and Willis. He has twice been named "Deal Maker of The Year" for M&A transactions.
**Personal:** Georgetown University (BA and JD).

## ROBFOGEL, Susan S
Nixon Peabody LLP, New York
212 940 3116
srobfogel@nixonpeabody.com
*Featured in Healthcare (New York), Healthcare (Nationwide)*
See under Nationwide for profile.

## ROBINS, Harry T
Morgan, Lewis & Bockius LLP, New York
212 309 6728
hrobins@morganlewis.com
*Featured in Antitrust (New York)*
**Practice Areas:** Harry Robins represents clients, including a number of prominent private equity firms and Fortune 500 companies from industries such as life sciences, publishing, electronics and chemicals, before the U.S. Federal Trade Commission and the U.S. Department of Justice, as well as international regulatory agencies, in connection with antitrust issues in mergers and acquisitions and joint venture transactions.

Mr Robins also handles litigation and counseling matters, including class action litigation and government investigations.

## ROCK, Neil L
Skadden, Arps, Slate, Meagher & Flom LLP & Affiliates, New York
212 735 3787
Neil.Rock@skadden.com
*Featured in Capital Markets (Nationwide), Real Estate (New York)*
See under Nationwide for profile.

## ROGERS JR, Theodore O
Sullivan & Cromwell LLP, New York
212 55 3588
rogerst@sullcrom.com
*Featured in Labor & Employment (New York)*
**Professional Memberships:** ABA; Fellow, College of Labor/Employment Lawyers; American Law Institute; Executive Committee, Labor and Employment Law Section, NYSBA; Advisory Board Member, NYU Law Center for Labor and Employment Law.
**Career:** Partner since 1987. Head, Labor and Employment Law Group. 2012 "New York City Labor Law-Management Lawyer of the Year" (Best Lawyers in America); one of nation's 100 most powerful management attorneys (Human Resource Executive magazine). Estates litigation practice includes will contests, trust accountings, fiduciary responsibility matters.
**Publications:** Contributing author, BNA's Workplace Harassment Law, West's Employment Litigation in New York.
**Personal:** Harvard Law School (JD, 1979); Harvard University (AB, 1976).

## ROGOFF, Adam
Kramer Levin Naftalis & Frankel LLP, New York
212 715 9285
arogoff@kramerlevin.com
*Featured in Bankruptcy/Restructuring (New York)*
**Practice Areas:** Since 1988, Adam C Rogoff has focused his practice on complex transactional, litigation and advisory work relating to restructuring, Chapter 11 bankruptcy cases, workouts and "pre-packaged" Chapter 11 matters and commercial finance. He has extensive experience representing a broad range of corporate debtors, official and ad hoc creditors' committees, secured creditors (including DIP lenders) and other parties in Chapter 11 restructurings and out-of-court workouts. Mr Rogoff's company-side clients include healthcare providers, including acute-care hospitals; manufacturers, notably in steel, alcohol and metals mining; national retailers; shippers; and service providers, particularly in the airline and hotel industries.

## ROGOFF, Michael A.
Kaye Scholer LLP, New York
212 836 7684
michael.rogoff@kayescholer.com
*Featured in Litigation (New York)*
**Practice Areas:** Michael Rogoff, Co-Chair of Kaye Scholer's Complex Commercial Litigation Department and Chair of the White Collar Litigation and Internal Investigations practice, is

an experienced trial and appellate lawyer whose practice focuses on white collar and civil litigation. He has represented major US and international corporations, as well as corporate directors and individuals, in a wide variety of disputes involving health care, securities, product liability, antitrust, consumer class action, trademark and copyright, trade secrets and breach of contract. Michael is also experienced in conducting internal investigations, as well as representing clients in SEC and grand jury investigations.

## ROHN, Frederick
Holland & Knight LLP, New York
212 513 3200
frederick.rohn@hklaw.com
*Featured in Construction (New York)*
**Practice Areas:** Partner in the firm's Litigation Section, he practices construction law and has represented numerous owners, developers, not-for-profit corporations, construction managers and contractors in drafting and negotiating design, design/build and construction contracts and in dispute resolution, arbitration and litigation. His experience includes private and public projects involving renovations, new building construction and heavy construction including residential, commercial, medical and industrial facilities.

## ROMANO, Benito
Freshfields Bruckhaus Deringer US LLP, New York
212 277 4000
benito.romano@freshfields.com
*Featured in Litigation (New York)*
**Practice Areas:** Benito is a partner in Freshfields' litigation practice group. He focuses on white collar defense, including SEC and other regulatory enforcement, and related complex civil litigation. Benito has significant experience dealing with his client's most complex problems—in the courtroom, the boardroom, before governmental bodies or in private arbitration. He represents public companies, board committees and individual officers in internal, criminal and regulatory investigations, prosecutions and related civil litigations. These include investigations of price fixing in the airline industry by the DOJ; options backdating fraud in the auctions rate market; and the bankruptcy of Lehman Brothers by the SEC.

## ROONEY, William H
Willkie Farr & Gallagher LLP, New York
212 728 8259
wrooney@willkie.com
*Featured in Antitrust (New York)*
**Practice Areas:** Chair, Antitrust Practice. Experience with litigations, mergers, investigations, and counseling in matters under the Sherman Act, Clayton Act, and state antitrust and deceptive trade practice laws. Appears regularly in federal court and before antitrust agencies (DOJ, FTC, State AGs) involving antitrust investigations and substantial acquisitions. Recent representations: Teva's international competition interests in its $5B acquisition of ratiopharm; Mueller's defense of district court dismissal in Sixth Circuit

appeal; and Marsh's insurance brokerage antitrust litigation.
**Personal:** Dip Law, University of Oxford (Magdalen College), 1987. JD, Yale Law School, 1983. BA, summa cum laude, University of Notre Dame, 1980. See: http://www.willkie.com/WilliamRooney

## ROSEN, Arthur R
McDermott Will & Emery LLP, New York
212 547 5596
arosen@mwe.com
*Featured in Tax (New York)*
**Practice Areas:** Practice focuses on state and local tax planning and litigation for businesses. Deeply involved in nationwide corporate income/franchise and sales tax issues that arise in the context of remote commerce.
**Career:** Formerly deputy counsel of New York State Department of Taxation and Finance, as well as counsel to governor's Temporary Sales Tax Commission and tax counsel to New York State Senate Tax Committee; held executive tax management positions at Xerox Corporation and AT&T.
**Personal:** St. John's University School of Law (JD); Rensselaer Polytechnic Institute (MBA); New York University (APC, BA).

## ROSEN, Howard M
Peckar & Abramson, P.C., New York
212 382 0909
hrosen@pecklaw.com
*Featured in Construction (New York)*
**Practice Areas:** Mr Rosen has over 35 years experience representing general contractors, construction managers and owners in various courts and alternative dispute resolution forums.
**Professional Memberships:** Past Chairman of the Construction Law Committee of the NY City Bar Association; and recently on the Board of Directors of the Associated General Contractors (AGC) of New York State. Mr Rosen is on the AAA panel of Construction Arbitrators.
**Career:** Partner in the New York office.
**Publications:** Mr Rosen chaired and taught CLE programs on effective construction mediation and the New York Mechanics' Lien Law.
**Personal:** For more information, please visit: www.pecklaw.com

## ROSEN, J Philip
Weil, Gotshal & Manges LLP, New York
212 310 8604
philip.rosen@weil.com
*Featured in Real Estate (New York)*
**Practice Areas:** J Philip Rosen, Co-head of Weil's Real Estate and Infrastructure Practices and Head of Weil's Hospitality & Gaming Practice, is a leading authority in real estate restructuring, real estate mergers and acquisitions, and complex property debt transactions. He has advised on several restructurings for Brookfield Asset Management, Fortress and CW Capital, chapter 11 cases for General Growth Properties and Extended Stay of America, the sale of the Jumeirah Essex House and the sale of Centro Retail's US portfolio. He is also a leading practitioner advising Middle East players in the US.

## ROSEN, Matthew A
Skadden, Arps, Slate, Meagher & Flom LLP & Affiliates, New York
212 735 2230
Matthew.Rosen@skadden.com
*Featured in Tax (New York)*
**Practice Areas:** Global co-head, Skadden's Tax Group. Represents clients in every aspect of tax work, with particular emphasis on acquisitions, divestitures and restructurings, both domestic and cross-border. Also handles matters involving partnerships of every type, joint ventures and executive compensation. In addition, practice includes the development of financial instruments and structured transactions. Clients include many significant public and private companies, investment banks and investment funds. Regularly highly placed in professional rankings. Frequent lecturer on a broad variety of topics.
**Career:** LLM, New York University, 1979 (Memorial Award for Distinction); JD, Boston University, 1976 (cum laude); BA, Swarthmore College, 1973.

## ROSEN, Richard
Paul, Weiss, Rifkind, Wharton & Garrison LLP, New York
212 373 3305
rrosen@paulweiss.com
*Featured in Securities (Nationwide), Litigation (New York)*
See under Nationwide for profile.

## ROSENBERG, Andrew N
Paul, Weiss, Rifkind, Wharton & Garrison LLP, New York
212 373 3158
arosenberg@paulweiss.com
*Featured in Bankruptcy/Restructuring (Nationwide), Bankruptcy/Restructuring (New York)*
See under Nationwide for profile.

## ROSENBERG, Jill L
Orrick, Herrington & Sutcliffe LLP, New York
212 506 5215
jrosenberg@orrick.com
*Featured in Labor & Employment (New York)*
**Practice Areas:** Jill Rosenberg is a nationally recognized employment litigator and counselor. Ms Rosenberg has significant experience defending and advising employers in discrimination, sexual harassment, whistleblowing, wrongful discharge, affirmative action, wage-and-hour and traditional labor matters. She handles complex individual cases, as well as class actions and systemic government investigations. She represents a broad range of companies, including employers in the securities industry, banks and financial institutions, accounting firms, law firms, and employers in the food service and publishing industries. Ms Rosenberg also has particular expertise in the representation of nonprofit entities, including colleges, universities, hospitals, foundations and cultural institutions.

**ROSENBERG, Mark F**
Sullivan & Cromwell LLP, New York
212 558 3647
rosenbergm@sullcrom.com
*Featured in Environment (New York), Insurance (New York)*
**Professional Memberships:** ABA (former Chair, Toxic and Hazardous Substances and Environmental Law Committee, TIPS); NYSBA (Co-Chair, Environmental Committee, International Section).
**Career:** Partner since 1993; Special Counsel 1990-1992. Coordinator, Environmental, Insurance Groups. Litigation/arbitration/transactional experience in wide variety of insurance, reinsurance, complex/mass tort (including asbestos), environmental, foreign sovereign debt recovery, insolvency, bankruptcy, alter ego, successor liability, fraudulent conveyance and other matters. Has acted as lead/national/international counsel, achieving significant judicial/arbitral victories and settlements.
**Publications:** Author of articles and featured speaker concerning practice areas noted above.
**Personal:** George Washington Law School (JD, 1980); Michigan State University (BA, 1977).

**ROSENBLUM, Steven A**
Wachtell, Lipton, Rosen & Katz, New York
212 403 1221
sarosenblum@wlrk.com
*Featured in Corporate/M&A (New York)*
**Practice Areas:** Practice focuses on mergers and acquisitions, buyouts, takeover defense, shareholder and hedge fund activism, proxy fights, joint ventures, corporate governance and securities law. Mr Rosenblum has extensive experience representing major companies in each of these areas.
**Professional Memberships:** American Law Institute; the ABA Corporate Laws Committee, and the Board of Advisors of the Yale Law School Center for the Study of Corporate Law.
**Career:** Partner at Wachtell, Lipton, Rosen & Katz since 1989 and co-chair of the firm's Corporate Department. Prior to joining the firm in 1983, was a law clerk to the Honorable Joseph L Tauro, United States District Court Judge for the District of Massachusetts. His clients include high profile companies in a wide range of industries, including communications, media, technology, financial, energy, packaging, consumer foods, retail, chemicals and travel. Has also written and participated in panels on a number of topics, including mergers and acquisitions, shareholder and hedge fund activism, corporate disclosure, proxy reform and corporate governance and has served as co-chair of the Annual Federal Securities Institute in Miami since 2005.
**Personal:** Graduated magna cum laude from Harvard College in 1978 (BA) and from Yale Law School in 1982 (JD). While at Harvard, he was elected to Phi Beta Kappa.

**ROSENTHAL, Thorn**
Cahill Gordon & Reindel LLP, New York
212 701 3823
trosenthal@cahill.com
*Featured in Insurance (Nationwide), Insurance (New York)*
**Practice Areas:** Has represented many of the largest US, Bermudian and European insurers and reinsurers over the past 30 years in a range of complex disputes, transactions, and regulatory matters. Many have involved hundreds of millions or billions of dollars. Although Thorn has succeeded in settling the majority of disputes he has handled, he has extensive trial experience in state and federal courts, before both judges and juries, and in arbitration/appraisal proceedings.
**Publications:** Drafted Bermuda market excess general liability policy form and drafted numerous other policy forms and reinsurance treaties.
**Personal:** Vassar College, AB, 1972. University of Chicago, JD, 1975.

**ROSNER, David S**
Kasowitz, Benson, Torres & Friedman LLP, New York
212 506 1726
drosner@kasowitz.com
*Featured in Bankruptcy/Restructuring (Nationwide), Bankruptcy/Restructuring (New York)*
**Practice Areas:** David Rosner represents creditors and bondholder committees, distressed hedge funds, private equity funds, litigation trustees, and security holders at every capital structure level. He had central roles in Tribune, Trico Marine, Le*Nature's, Lehman, Smurfit-Stone, Refco, WorldCom, and others.
**Career:** He practices nationally, successfully litigating insolvency-related decisions at the First, Eleventh Circuit Courts of Appeals and District and Bankruptcy Courts country-wide. Recognized in Chambers USA 2004-2012 ("terrifically capable and effective"), Legal 500, The Best Lawyers in America, "America's Top 100 Restructuring Professionals" (K&A) 2004-2011, New York Super Lawyers 2007-2012, and noted as one of Avenue Magazine's "Legal Elite."

**ROSS, Jeffrey**
Fried, Frank, Harris, Shriver & Jacobson LLP, New York
212 859 8678
Jeffrey.Ross@FriedFrank.com
*Featured in Employee Benefits & Executive Compensation (New York)*
**Practice Areas:** Executive compensation and employee benefits partner. Mr Ross has experience with a wide range of benefits and compensation matters and the numerous federal and state laws that govern the field. In addition to assisting in the design and operation of various tax qualified, non-qualified, and equity based compensation arrangements, he has counseled extensively regarding the ERISA issues relating to the organization and operation of private investment funds.
**Career:** Joined in 2008; became partner in 2009.
**Personal:** JD, New York University School of Law (2001), associate casebook editor, Moot Court Casebook; BA, cum laude, Yale University (1998).

**ROSS, Samuel**
Olshan Frome Wolosky LLP., New York
212 451 2253
sross@olshanlaw.com
*Featured in Real Estate (New York)*
**Practice Areas:** Partner in Real Estate group with over 30 years experience representing prominent real estate owners in transactions across the country. Represents sellers and purchasers of major office buildings, apartment complexes, hotels, and retail establishments. He also represents landlords and tenants in office, retail, restaurant and garage leases, and has negotiated important ground leases on behalf of ground lessors and lessees. He also routinely handles major ground lease rent reset arbitrations.
**Professional Memberships:** The Association of the Bar of the City of New York, New York State Bar Association.

**ROTH, Andrew B**
Mintz Levin Cohn Ferris Glovsky and Popeo PC, New York
212 692 6889
ABRoth@mintz.com
*Featured in Healthcare (New York)*
**Practice Areas:** Health law, not-for-profit corporations, educational institutions. Health industry clients include providers (healthcare systems, hospitals, nursing homes, physicians) and payors (insurance companies, MCOs, HMOs). Active in health industry mergers and acquisitions, joint ventures and affiliations. Regulatory: corporate compliance/corporate governance, fraud and abuse, medical staff, HIPAA and Medicare/Medicaid matters. National practice involving ACGME accreditation of graduate medical education programs in academic medical centers and teaching hospitals and LCME accreditation of medical schools.
**Publications:** Author/co-author of two books and many health-law related textbook chapters and articles.
**Personal:** Hofstra Law School, JD (Law Review); SUNY Stony Brook, BA, cum laude.

**ROTH, Eric M**
Wachtell, Lipton, Rosen & Katz, New York
212 403 1257
EMRoth@wlrk.com
*Featured in Litigation (New York)*
**Practice Areas:** Practice focuses on corporate, securities, insurance, creditors' rights and other complex commercial litigation matters. Has been involved in several landmark cases involving mergers and acquisitions including, among others, defending the legality of the 'poison pill' and the ability of a target board to decline to redeem the pill in the face of an inadequate offer, obtaining specific performance of a merger agreement on behalf of the selling corporation and enjoining a defensive restructuring on behalf of a hostile bidder. Represented the insured in the World Trade Center coverage litigation.
**Professional Memberships:** Member of both the Board of Trustees of the Law Center Foundation and the Dean's Strategic Council at New York University School of Law. Member of

the Cornell University Council, Member of the New York State Bar Association, District of Columbia Bar, the American Bar Association and the Federal Bar Council. Board Member and former Chair of MFY Legal Services, Inc., a leading provider of free civil legal services to the poor and mentally ill in New York City.
**Career:** Partner in the Litigation Department of Wachtell, Lipton, Rosen & Katz since 1984. Law clerk to Hon. Lee P. Gagliardi, US District Court, Southern District of New York (1977-79).
**Personal:** Graduated from Cornell University in 1974 (BA) with distinction in all subjects and from New York University School of Law in 1977 (JD), where he served as a note and comment editor of the law review.

**ROTHSTEIN, Gary S**
Morgan, Lewis & Bockius LLP, New York
212 309 6360
grothstein@morganlewis.com
*Featured in Employee Benefits & Executive Compensation (New York)*
**Practice Areas:** Gary S. Rothstein is a partner in Morgan Lewis's Employee Benefits and Executive Compensation Practice, with more than 25 years' experience. His practice encompasses a broad range of employee benefits matters, with a focus on transactional-based executive compensation, including numerous representations of senior management teams in large buyout transactions.
**Personal:** He is a graduate of New York University School of Law (1989, LLM), George Washington University National Law Center (1984, JD, with honors) and Pennsylvania State University (1981, BS, with distinction). Mr Rothstein is admitted to practice in New York.

**ROUHANDEH, James**
Davis Polk & Wardwell LLP, New York
212 450 4000
james.rouhandeh@davispolk.com
*Featured in Litigation (New York)*
**Practice Areas:** Head of Davis Polk's Litigation Department, representing clients in a variety of civil, criminal and regulatory matters. His practice includes representation of clients in complex civil litigation, including class action securities litigation and shareholder derivative actions, as well as grand jury, SEC and internal investigations. He has represented a variety of clients in the most well-known investigations and litigations in recent years; his matters typically involve parallel civil, criminal and regulatory proceedings.

**ROWEN, Andrew S**
Sullivan & Cromwell LLP, New York
212 558 3896
rowena@sullcrom.com
*Featured in Insurance (Nationwide), Insurance (New York)*
**Professional Memberships:** ABA; NYSBA; ABCNY.
**Career:** Partner since 1987. Coordinator, Insurance Group. Practice includes: acquisitions/divestitures and other change-of-control transactions, including insurance regulatory approvals, antitrust advice; securities

offerings/advice regarding SEC disclosure issues and inquiries; corporate governance; demutualizations; reinsurance; offshore companies; private equity investments in/by insurers; securitization of insurance risks; regulatory matters; and insurers in distressed or rehabilitation. Mr Rowen regularly practices before the New York State Department of Insurance. He frequently participates in various litigation/regulatory investigation assignments involving insurers, including the current MBIA situation.
**Personal:** Harvard Law School (JD, 1979); UC-Berkeley (BA, 1976).

### RUBIN, Amy M
Weil, Gotshal & Manges LLP, New York
212 310 8691
amy.rubin@weil.com
*Featured in Employee Benefits & Executive Compensation (New York)*
**Practice Areas:** Amy Rubin is a partner in Weil's global Tax Practice. Her practice focuses on executive compensation, employee benefits, and ERISA matters. Ms Rubin regularly counsels public and private companies in employee benefits and executive compensation aspects of private equity transactions, strategic mergers and acquisitions, recapitalizations, reorganizations, financing transactions, and ongoing company operations. In addition, she has extensive experience advising clients on the negotiation, design, and implementation of executive employment and separation arrangements, as well as other compensation arrangements and employee benefit plans.
**Personal:** University of Michigan (AB, with honors); St. John's University School of Law (JD, cum laude).

### RUBIN, Howard
Davis & Gilbert LLP, New York
212 468 4822
hrubin@dglaw.com
*Featured in Labor & Employment (New York)*
**Practice Areas:** Labor and employment.
**Career:** Co-Chair of the Labor & Employment and Litigation Practice Groups, Mr Rubin counsels a broad range of employers on all aspects of employment law including employment policies and practices, discrimination, restrictive covenants, fair labor standards and affirmative action plans. He has litigated numerous employment-related cases in court and before FINRA and the AAA. His practice includes the defense of First Amendment, defamation, copyright, trademark, breach of contract and business/corporate related disputes. In addition to representing companies, he counsels senior executives in negotiating employment agreements as well as severance packages. He is recognized in The Best Lawyers in America for employment law and selected as a Super Lawyer by New York Metro Super Lawyers.

### RUBIN, Robert A
McCarter & English, LLP, New York
212 609 6861
rrubin@McCarter.com
*Featured in Construction (New York)*
**Career:** Mr Rubin is well regarded for his experience in construction litigation representing gov-

ernmental and private owners, developers, institutions, sureties, project managers, construction managers, general contractors, members of the design team, and trade contractors. He has extensive experience in the use of mediation, arbitration, dispute review boards and other alternative dispute resolution techniques to resolve construction disputes short of litigation. He has been lead partner in charge of drafting and negotiating contracts for projects and in resolving disputes involving energy plants, pipelines, highways, bridges, mass transit, telecommunications, municipal and governmental agencies, and industrial and high-rise buildings. For full bio: http://www.mccarter.com/Robert-A-Rubin/

### RUBINSTEIN, Aaron
Kaye Scholer LLP, New York
212 836 8412
aaron.rubinstein@kayescholer.com
*Featured in Litigation (New York)*
**Practice Areas:** Aaron Rubinstein is Chair of Kaye Scholer's Financial Services Litigation practice and was previously chair of the Litigation Department for twelve years. He has over 35 years of experience representing defendants and plaintiffs in complex commercial litigations, including securities, commodities, derivatives, lender liability and contract claims. He handles both private suits, including class and shareholder derivative actions, and proceedings before government enforcement agencies. His representations have included public and privately held corporations, directors of such companies, individuals and some of the largest domestic and international financial institutions.

### RUDMAN, Samuel
Robbins Geller Rudman & Dowd LLP, Melville
631 367 7100
srudman@rgrdlaw.com
*Featured in Securities (Nationwide), Litigation (New York)*
**Career:** Samuel H. Rudman is a founding member of the Firm, a member of the Firm's Executive and Management Committees, and manages the Firm's New York office. His practice focuses on recognizing and investigating securities fraud, and initiating securities and shareholder class actions to vindicate shareholder rights and recover shareholder losses. He has recovered hundreds of millions of dollars for shareholders, including $129 million in In re Doral Fin. Corp. Sec. Litig.; $74 million in In re First BanCorp Sec. Litig.; and $65 million in In re Forest Labs., Inc. Sec. Litig.

### RUEGGER, Philip T
Simpson Thacher & Bartlett LLP, New York
212 455 3220
pruegger@stblaw.com
*Featured in Corporate/M&A (New York)*
**Practice Areas:** Former Chairman of the Executive Committee. Advises clients on mergers and acquisitions, leveraged buyouts, corporate governance and general corporate law matters. Has represented principals on a number of significant merger transactions. Advises many of the firm's regular clients.

**Career:** Joined the firm in 1974; became a Partner in 1981. Member of the firm's Executive Committee since 1993; Chairman of the Executive Committee 2004-2013. Recipient of 2013 Legal Aid Society Servant of Justice Award.
**Personal:** Chairman of the Board of Henry Street Settlement House; member of the Board of Natural Resources Defense Council; member of the Board of the Partnership for New York City; University of Virginia School of Law (JD 1974); Dartmouth College (AB, magna cum laude, 1971); Phi Beta Kappa.

### RUGGIERO, Jeffrey
Arnold & Porter LLP, New York
212 715 1089
Jeffrey.Ruggiero@aporter.com
*Featured in Healthcare (New York)*
**Practice Areas:** Jeffrey Ruggiero is a partner in the FDA and healthcare group. His practice includes the representation of healthcare providers in corporate, transactional, regulatory, licensure, and litigation matters. Mr Ruggiero structures and negotiates mergers, acquisitions, dispositions, joint ventures, affiliations, and employment and consulting arrangements. He also advises clients on Federal and State fraud & abuse and regulatory laws and regulations, and the development and implementation of compliance programs. He is a frequent lecturer and authority on Accountable Care Organizations and integrated delivery systems, and is cited regularly in national publications.

### RUSSELL, William
Venable LLP, New York
212 370 6268
wtrussell@Venable.com
*Featured in Technology (New York)*
**Practice Areas:** Outsourcing, Technology Transactions, Healthcare, Corporate, Internet and New Media.
**Career:** William Russell is a corporate attorney who focuses in the areas of outsourcing, technology transactions, healthcare and intellectual property. He has extensive experience representing clients on large-scale IT and BPO outsourcing, software licensing and technology development deals, as well as product distribution, manufacturing and supply arrangements. Bill has developed a niche in the areas of medical devices and facilities management outsourcing. He also counsels clients regarding joint ventures, strategic alliances, M&A and general corporate matters.
**Personal:** JD, Boston College Law School, cum laude.

### RUTHBERG, Miles
Latham & Watkins LLP, New York
212 906 1688
miles.ruthberg@lw.com
*Featured in Securities (Nationwide), Litigation (New York)*
See under Nationwide for profile.

### RUTHIZER, Theodore
Kramer Levin Naftalis & Frankel LLP, New York
212 715 9421
truthizer@kramerlevin.com
*Featured in Immigration (Nationwide), Immigration (New York)*
**Practice Areas:** Ted Ruthizer is recognized as one of the country's leading immigration lawyers. He is a partner and Co-Head of Kramer Levin's Business Immigration Group, as well as a past President of the American Immigration Lawyers Association. Mr Ruthizer is a Lecturer in Law at Columbia Law School, where he teaches immigration law and policy. Mr Ruthizer, a graduate of the Columbia Law School, is a frequent lecturer on business immigration law and has authored many publications.
**Personal:** Received a JD Degree from Columbia Law School in 1972 and a BA Degree with honors from Lafayette College in 1969.

### RUZUMNA, Daniel
Patterson Belknap Webb & Tyler LLP, New York
212 336 2034
druzumna@pbwt.com
*Featured in Litigation (New York)*
**Practice Areas:** Daniel Ruzumna is an experienced trial lawyer whose practice focuses on the areas of white collar criminal defense and related regulatory proceedings, internal investigations, asset forfeiture proceedings, and complex financial litigation. He has represented corporations and individuals in many recent high-profile criminal and regulatory investigations involving alleged violations of the securities laws, antitrust laws, tax laws, and Foreign Corrupt Practices Act. Mr Ruzumna regularly conducts confidential investigations on behalf of clients, including a professional sports league, a university, financial firms, and media and entertainment companies. He has also represented pharmaceutical, media, and telecommunications clients in civil litigation and arbitration, including litigations brought under the False Claims Act. Mr Ruzumna is a frequent commentator on issues of criminal law, investigations, and asset forfeiture.
**Professional Memberships:** Member, New York State Bar Association (Section of Commercial and Federal Litigation, Committee on White Collar Criminal Litigation);
**Career:** After graduation from law school, Mr Ruzumna served as a Law Clerk to the late Hon. Jay C. Waldman, United States District Court for the Eastern District of Pennsylvania, and then worked at a private law firm in Washington, DC. Before joining Patterson Belknap in 2005, Mr Ruzumna spent six years working at the United States Attorney's Office for the Southern District of New York, where he last served as Acting Chief of the Major Crimes Unit.
**Personal:** JD, 1994, University of Michigan School of Law, cum laude, served as an Editor of the Michigan Law Review; BA, 1991, University of Michigan, graduated with high distinction.

**RYAN, Antony**
Cravath, Swaine & Moore LLP, New York
aryan@cravath.com
*Featured in Securities (Nationwide), Litigation (New York)*
See under Nationwide for profile.

**RYAN, Michael L**
Cleary Gottlieb Steen & Hamilton LLP, New York
212 225 2520
mryan@cgsh.com
*Featured in Private Equity (Nationwide), Corporate/M&A (New York)*
See under Nationwide for profile.

**SABIN, Jeffrey S**
Bingham McCutchen LLP, New York
212 705 7747
jeffrey.sabin@bingham.com
*Featured in Bankruptcy/Restructuring (Nationwide), Bankruptcy/Restructuring (New York)*
See under Nationwide for profile.

**SACK, Laura**
Vedder Price PC, New York
212 407 6960
lsack@vedderprice.com
*Featured in Labor & Employment (New York)*
**Practice Areas:** Shareholder and Chair of the New York office Labor and Employment practice group. Represents management exclusively. Litigates employment cases before state and federal courts, represents clients before administrative agencies, designs and conducts employee training programs, conducts workplace investigations, and counsels management on labor and employment law issues. Frequent public speaker on employment law issues.
**Career:** Admitted (NY) 1992
**Publications:** Author of numerous publications, including in American Bar Association's 'Employment Law & Litigation' newsletter and 'New Jersey CPA' magazine. Quoted in 'Business Insurance,' 'Fortune,' 'Best Life' and 'HR Magazine.'
**Personal:** JD, Yale Law School; A.B., Brown University

**SACRIPANTI, Peter**
McDermott Will & Emery LLP, New York
212 547 5583
psacripanti@mwe.com
*Featured in Environment (New York)*
**Practice Areas:** Co-chair of the firm. Member of trial department. Concentrates practice on complex business and environmental disputes, including class action litigation, products liability litigation and multi-party mass tort matters. Particular experience defending major corporations and industry groups.
**Professional Memberships:** Chairman, Executive Committee of President's Council at Fordham University; Columbus Citizens Foundation; New York, District of Columbia and New Jersey bars.
**Career:** Began career as a federal prosecutor with the United States Department of Justice.
**Personal:** Pace University School of Law, JD, 1984; Fordham University, BA (summa cum laude), 1982.

**SAEED, Faiza J**
Cravath, Swaine & Moore LLP, New York
212 474 1454
fsaeed@cravath.com
*Featured in Media & Entertainment (New York), Corporate/M&A (New York)*
**Practice Areas:** Faiza J. Saeed is co-Head of Cravath's Mergers and Acquisitions group. She advises public companies, boards of directors and special committees in connection with mergers and acquisitions, corporate governance and crisis management, including consensual and hostile transactions, leveraged buyouts, strategic investments, takeover defense, proxy contests and hedge fund activism. Her clients have included CSX, DreamWorks Animation, Hasbro, Kraft Foods, Moody's, Morgan Stanley, Starbucks, Time Warner and Viacom.
**Personal:** Harvard Law School (JD, magna cum laude, 1991); University of California at Berkeley (BA, with Highest Distinction, 1987; Phi Beta Kappa). For more information: http://www.cravath.com/fsaeed

**SAFERSTEIN, Jeffrey D**
Paul, Weiss, Rifkind, Wharton & Garrison LLP, New York
212 373 3347
jsaferstein@paulweiss.com
*Featured in Bankruptcy/Restructuring (New York)*
**Practice Areas:** Partner in the firm's Bankruptcy and Corporate Reorganization Department, Mr Saferstein practices exclusively in the areas of corporate restructurings and workouts, bankruptcy and specialized financings. He has been involved in major domestic and international restructurings and bankruptcies, including School Specialty, Inc., Buffets Restaurant Holdings, Inc., Lehman Brothers, Houghton Mifflin Harcourt Publishing Company, AbitibiBowater, Samsonite Corporation, Adelphia Communications and Atkins Nutritionals. He has also been involved in several restructurings of Structured Investment Vehicles and in a workout of one of the monoline insurers. Mr Saferstein has written and lectured on numerous bankruptcy topics.

**SAFRON, Robert M**
Patterson Belknap Webb & Tyler LLP, New York
212 336 2250
rmsafron@pbwt.com
*Featured in Real Estate (New York)*
**Practice Areas:** Bob Safron is a member of the American College of Real Estate Lawyers and has more than 40 years of experience in a broad range of commercial real estate matters and has represented lenders, developers, owners and investors throughout the U.S. and in several foreign countries. He represents prominent U.S. and international developers, owners and investors in all types of real estate holdings, including office and apartment buildings, shopping centers, hotels, resorts, industrial, warehouse and other commercial projects. Mr Safron has also represented many domestic and foreign banks, insurance companies, investment houses and other institutions in a variety of real estate financing and securitization matters and in restructuring troubled real estate loans.
**Professional Memberships:** Member, Association of the Bar of the City of New York (formerly served two terms as a member of its Committee on Real Property Law); New York State Bar Association; American Bar Association; American College of Real Estate Lawyers.
**Personal:** JD, 1969, New York University School of Law, cum laude, Pomeroy Scholar; Member, NYU Law Review; BA, 1966, Brandeis University.

**SAFT, Stuart M**
Holland & Knight LLP, New York
212 513 3308
stuart.saft@hklaw.com
*Featured in Real Estate (New York)*
**Practice Areas:** Stuart Saft is co-chair of the firm's New York Real Estate Practice Group and Global Condominium Development Team. He represents: developers and sponsors in developing, financing, and converting properties to condominium and cooperative ownership; investors in restructuring, acquiring and selling residential, commercial and hospitality properties; and lending institutions in construction, mezzanine and permanent financing. Representative projects include: development of the W Downtown Hotel and Residences, Baccarat Hotel and Residences, the Setai Downtown, Morton Square, Trump Coco Beach, Viceroy Resort in Anguilla, the Atelier and the conversion of the Apthorp, the Sheffield, Manhattan House, 737 Park Avenue and others.

**SAGE, Michael**
Dechert LLP, New York
212 698 3503
michael.sage@dechert.com
*Featured in Bankruptcy/Restructuring (New York)*
**Practice Areas:** Mr Sage, co-chair of the firm's business restructuring and reorganization practice, represents ad hoc committees of bondholders, noteholders, term lenders, official creditors' committees, individual creditors, acquirers, and debtors in bankruptcy proceedings and out-of-court restructurings. He also represents financial institutions that have acquired substantial strategic positions in debt issued by troubled companies.
**Professional Memberships:** Member, New York Bar; admitted to practice multiple federal courts; member, New York State Bar Association; Fellow, American College of Investment Counsel
**Publications:** Member, Board of Contributors, The Bankruptcy Strategist
**Personal:** University of Vermont (BA, 1985); Emory University (JD, 1988, with honors)

**SAIA, Doreen U**
Greenberg Traurig, LLP, Albany
518 689 1430
SaiaD@gtlaw.com
*Featured in Energy & Natural Resources (New York)*
**Practice Areas:** Governmental affairs; global energy and infrastructure; climate change. Wide-ranging energy law practice focusing on the representation of national and international corporations that own and operate electric generating facilities and engage in financial transactions trading electricity products.
**Professional Memberships:** Member: American Bar Association, Federal Energy Bar Association and New York State Bar Association. Past President, Northeast Chapter of the Federal Energy Bar Association.
**Career:** Selected: Best Lawyers in America, 2010-13; Super Lawyers magazine, 2008-12; Chambers USA Guide, 2008-13.
**Personal:** JD, magna cum laude, Washington and Lee University School of Law; BA, Williams College.

**SALTZSTEIN, Susan L**
Skadden, Arps, Slate, Meagher & Flom LLP & Affiliates, New York
212 735 4132
Susan.Saltzstein@skadden.com
*Featured in Litigation (New York)*
**Practice Areas:** Extensive experience representing corporations, financial institutions and individuals in securities, corporate and commercial litigation in federal and state courts; counsels clients involved in complex and precedent-setting litigation and arbitration; leads internal investigations; represents clients before governmental entities including the SEC. Named one of Law360's "Outstanding Women" lawyers.
**Professional Memberships:** Judicial invitation to the Attorney's Advisory Group to the Judicial Improvement Committee (SDNY)(2011). Co-Chair, Litigation Institute for Trial Training (2011). Co-Chair, ABA: Expert Committee, Litigation Section Annual Meeting (2010), Securities Litigation Committee (2007-2009).
**Career:** JD, Columbia University School of Law, 1991; BA, University of Pennsylvania, 1987 (magna cum laude).

**SAMA, Vincent A**
Kaye Scholer LLP, New York
212 836 8765
vincent.sama@kayescholer.com
*Featured in Litigation (New York)*
**Practice Areas:** Vincent Sama, Co-Chair of the Complex Commercial Litigation Department and Chair of the Securities and Derivative Litigation practice, focuses on complex commercial litigation, securities and derivative litigation, investigations, international commercial disputes, and arbitration matters. Vinny's litigation experience includes matters involving finance, accounting, and securities law issues, derivative litigation, insurance and reinsurance, intellectual property, sports, entertainment, joint ventures and long-term contractual relationships, real estate development and finance, and antitrust. He has handled high-profile cases in federal and state courts across the country, as well as arbitrations in numerous forums including the International Chamber of Commerce, JAMS and FINRA.

**SAMUELS, Jeffrey B**
Paul, Weiss, Rifkind, Wharton & Garrison LLP, New York
212 373 3112
jsamuels@paulweiss.com
*Featured in Tax (New York)*

**Practice Areas:** Partner and Co-Chair of Tax Department. Member of firm management. Practice covers broad range of international and domestic transactions, including public and private M&A, organization of investment funds, partnership and joint venture transactions, and structuring of complex real estate transactions including the formation of REITs. Clients include leading entertainment, media and communications companies, major banks, investment banks and other financial institutions, and a number of hedge and private equity funds. Author of the U.S. chapter of Real Estate Investment Trusts: A Global Analysis.

### SAMUELS, Leslie B
Cleary Gottlieb Steen & Hamilton LLP, New York
212 225 2250
lsamuels@cgsh.com
*Featured in Tax (New York)*

**Practice Areas:** International and domestic taxation, including mergers and acquisitions, joint ventures, spin-offs, cross-border investments, sovereign wealth funds, financial products, capital markets activities, tax controversies and investigations.
**Professional Memberships:** NYC Bar Association and NYSBA. Member, Advisory Board of The Hamilton Project and The Tax Policy Center.
**Career:** Joined firm, 1968; partner, 1975. Assistant Secretary for Tax Policy of the US Treasury Department (1993-96). Vice-Chair, Committee of Fiscal Affairs, OECD (1994-96). LLB, magna cum laude, Harvard Law School (1966); BS, Economics, Wharton School of Finance and Commerce, University of Pennsylvania (1963). Fulbright Scholar, London School of Economics and Political Science (1967-68).

### SAMUELSON, Charles A
Hughes Hubbard & Reed LLP, New York
212 837 6454
samuelso@hugheshubbard.com
*Featured in Corporate/M&A (New York)*

**Practice Areas:** Concentrates on mergers and acquisitions, proxy contests and other matters relating to corporate control, joint ventures, public and private financings, corporate governance, venture capital and private equity.
**Career:** Partner at Hughes Hubbard & Reed since 2006.
**Personal:** Williams College, BA, 1990; Cornell Law School, JD, 1996.

### SANDHU, Charan J
Weil, Gotshal & Manges LLP, New York
212 310 8983
charan.sandhu@weil.com
*Featured in Technology (New York)*

**Practice Areas:** Ms Sandhu specializes in structuring, drafting and negotiating international transactions (including in China) ranging from joint ventures and strategic alliances, patent licenses, co-marketing and co-promotion arrangements, IP acquisitions and divestitures (including of large patent portfolios), technology transfer

and outsourcing to settlements of IP litigation. Her practice encompasses a wide range of technologies, including consumer electronics, computer hardware and software, semiconductor devices and manufacturing equipment and processes, biotechnology, pharmaceuticals, medical devices, communications (network and telephony) and the Internet. She is a frequent speaker and author on IP issues.

### SANSEVERINO, Raymond A
Loeb & Loeb LLP, New York
212 407 4008
rsanseverino@loeb.com
*Featured in Real Estate (New York)*

**Practice Areas:** Concentrates on commercial real estate emphasizing leasing and brokerage, and conveyancing transactions. Represents both landlords and tenants in leasing including office and retail space. Also advises sellers and purchasers of all types of real estate and real estate brokers and owners in connection with commission and agency agreements and commission claims. Currently, landlord's counsel at numerous office buildings in NY and NJ.
**Career:** Became Partner at Corbin & Gordon in 1978. Joined Loeb as Partner in 2006. Real Estate Chair.
**Personal:** Fordham University School of Law (JD, cum laude, 1972); Franklin & Marshall College (AB, 1968).

### SASSOWER, Edward O
Kirkland & Ellis LLP, New York
212 446 4733
edward.sassower@kirkland.com
*Featured in Bankruptcy/Restructuring (Nationwide); Bankruptcy/Restructuring (New York)*
See under Nationwide for profile.

### SAUERMILCH, Thomas
McDermott Will & Emery LLP, New York
212 547 5532
tsauermilch@mwe.com
*Featured in Corporate/M&A (New York)*

**Practice Areas:** Practices cross-border M&A. Represents publicly listed companies, large family-owned businesses and portfolio companies of large private equity funds. Experience includes cross-border acquisitions, divestitures and joint ventures in more than 30 countries. Special industry experience includes specialty chemicals, pharmaceutical and life sciences, manufacturing, natural resources/mining, aviation, technology and packaging.
**Personal:** Fordham University School of Law (JD); Fletcher School of Law and Diplomacy (MALD); Indiana University School of Law (LLM); University of Kiel-Germany (Staatsexamen).

### SAVARESE, John F
Wachtell, Lipton, Rosen & Katz, New York
212 403 1235
jfsavarese@wlrk.com
*Featured in Litigation (New York)*

**Practice Areas:** Practice focuses on the representation of Fortune 500 corporations, major financial institutions and senior executives in SEC and other regulatory enforcement proceedings, as

well as white-collar criminal investigations, complex securities litigation, and internal investigations. Extensive experience includes major investigations arising out of the financial crisis, as well as accounting fraud, insider trading, criminal tax and criminal antitrust allegations.
**Professional Memberships:** The Association of the Bar of the City of New York (was named the first chairman of a newly formed Committee on White Collar Criminal Law; Secretary-Treasurer, Criminal Law Committee, 1989-92); American Bar Association. Member of the Dean's Advisory Board at Harvard Law School, as well as chairman of the Board of Trustees of the Vera Institute of Justice in New York and the Lawyers' Committee for Civil Rights Under Law.
**Career:** Joined Wachtell, Lipton, Rosen & Katz in 1988, after working for the United States Attorney's Office for the Southern District of New York where he received the Attorney General's John Marshall Award for Outstanding Legal Achievement, and also served as the chief appellate attorney. Prior to his work with the US Attorney's Office, served as a law clerk to the Honorable Louis H Pollak of the United States District Court for the Eastern District of Pennsylvania and to Justice William J Brennan of the United States Supreme Court. Frequent lecturer and panelist for the American Bar Association, the Practicing Law Institute, the Securities Industry and Financial Markets Association, and Stanford Law School's Director's College program concerning a wide variety of topics, including defending civil and criminal litigation, handling corporate crises and conducting internal investigations. Also teaches a course on white-collar criminal law and procedure at Harvard Law School.
**Personal:** Graduated magna cum laude from Harvard University in 1977 (AB) and cum laude from Harvard Law School in 1981 (JD), where he served as articles editor of the Harvard Law Review.

### SCARBOROUGH, Robert
Freshfields Bruckhaus Deringer US LLP, New York
212 277 4000
robert.scarborough@freshfields.com
*Featured in Tax (New York)*

**Practice Areas:** A partner based in Freshfields Bruckhaus Deringer's New York office, Robert specializes in the taxation of structured finance transactions and other complex financings. He also regularly advises on international tax issues and advises non-US corporations on the US tax treatment of demergers and other corporate transactions. He has served as chair of the New York State Bar Association's Tax Section and as Associate Tax Legislative Counsel at the US Treasury Department.

### SCHACHTER, Michael
Willkie Farr & Gallagher LLP, New York
212 728 8102
mschachter@willkie.com
*Featured in Litigation (New York)*

**Practice Areas:** Mr Schachter is co-head of Willkie's white collar criminal defense practice. He specializes in the representation of companies and their executives in a wide variety of government and regulatory investigations and litigation, including insider trading, improper accounting and disclosure, market manipulation, commodities regulation, health care, price-fixing, and foreign corrupt practices cases. Prior to joining Willkie, Mr Schachter served as an Assistant U.S. Attorney in the Southern District of New York, where he focused on the prosecution of securities fraud and was a member of the Securities and Commodities Fraud Task Force.
**Personal:** JD,DePaul University, 1993. BS, Indiana University, 1990. See: http://www.willkie.com/Michael_Schachter

### SCHAEFER, David S
Loeb & Loeb LLP, New York
212 407 4848
dschaefer@loeb.com
*Featured in Corporate/M&A (New York)*

**Practice Areas:** Represents strategic and financial buyers, sellers and investors; financial advisors; and boards of directors and special committees. Distinguishes his practice through concentration in core industries namely financial services, including investment banks and private investment funds; entertainment and sports; traditional and digital media; information technology and private clients.
**Career:** NY Office Managing Partner Office; Chair, Corporate. Finalist for the Association for Corporate Growth's prestigious Dealmaker of the Year Award in 2012.
**Personal:** NYU School of Law (JD, 1981); Massachusetts Institute of Technology (BS, 1977).

### SCHAEFFER, Fiona A
Jones Day, New York
212 326 8378
fschaeffer@jonesday.com
*Featured in Antitrust (New York)*

**Practice Areas:** A truly international competition lawyer with in-depth experience on both sides of the Atlantic in the court room, defending deals and business practices before the competition agencies and advising clients on all manner of IP, distribution and marketing issues. Her international experience brings added value to clients that need to navigate diverse competition regimes. Recognized as one of the top 40 competition lawyers under 40 globally (2007 GCR survey).
**Professional Memberships:** Chair, NYC Bar, Antitrust and Trade Regulation Committee, Council Member, ABA International Section, Co-Chair, International Committee, ABA Antitrust Section, Executive Committee, NYSBA Antitrust Section.

### SCHAFFRAN, Andrew
Morgan, Lewis & Bockius LLP, New York
212 309 6380
aschaffran@morganlewis.com
*Featured in Labor & Employment (New York)*

**Practice Areas:** Andrew J Schaffran is a partner in Morgan Lewis's Labor and Employment Practice. Drew co-heads the firm's Financial

Services Industry Employment Law Practice, and he regularly counsels and represents securities firms, insurance companies, and other financial services companies in all aspects of employment law, including class and collective actions involving wage and hour and discrimination claims, high-profile whistleblower and defamation claims, and other complex and single-plaintiff employment litigation and FINRA arbitrations; and advice concerning compensation, corporate diversity, and ADR policies and programs and class and collective action waivers.
**Personal:** Attended Georgetown University Law Center, JD; Cornell University, BS.

## SCHAIBLE, Damian S.
Davis Polk & Wardwell LLP, New York
212 450 4000
damian.schaible@davispolk.com
*Featured in Bankruptcy/Restructuring (New York)*
**Practice Areas:** Partner in Davis Polk's Insolvency and Restructuring Group. Has worked on a wide range of corporate restructurings and bankruptcies, representing debtors, creditors, agent banks, lenders, asset purchasers and other strategic parties. Played a leading role representing Delta Air Lines and Frontier Airlines in their Chapter 11 restructurings and played a key role in a number of other recent high-profile restructurings, including those of The Tribune Company, NewPage Corporation, Media News Group and C-BASS. Currently helping to lead Davis Polk's representations of Pinnacle Airlines and Patriot Coal in their chapter 11 cases. Leads the bankruptcy teams in several of Davis Polk's "Living Wills" assignments and regularly represents investors in troubled banking institutions and the institutions themselves in connection with bank recapitalizations. Chair of the Courts Subcommittee of the New York City Bar's Committee on Bankruptcy and Corporate Reorganization and Co-Chair of the American Bankruptcy Institute's Secured Credit Committee.

## SCHARFSTEIN, Joel
Fried, Frank, Harris, Shriver & Jacobson LLP, New York
212 859 8172
Joel.Scharfstein@FriedFrank.com
*Featured in Tax (New York)*
**Practice Areas:** Tax partner. Practice focuses on the tax aspects of corporate acquisitions and divestitures, partnership transactions, investment partnerships and restructurings. Member, Executive Committee of the Tax Section of the New York State Bar Association. Current co-chair of its committee on complexity and administrability and has served as co-chair of its committees on bankruptcy, consolidated returns, partnerships, investment funds, reorganizations and basis and cost recovery.
**Career:** Joined in 1977; became partner in 1984.
**Personal:** JD, University of Michigan Law School (1977); AM, Harvard University (1972); AB, Columbia College (1969).

## SCHECHTER, Jonathan A
Kirkland & Ellis LLP, New York
212 446 6472
jonathan.schechter@kirkland.com
*Featured in Real Estate (New York)*
**Practice Areas:** Jonathan Schechter advises both US and non-US clients with respect to a wide range of domestic and international real estate-related transactions, including distressed real estate debt and equity investments. Mr Schechter has extensive experience representing private equity investors in connection with the formation of joint ventures and acquisitions, dispositions, mergers, financings and development of real estate and real estate-related assets. Mr Schechter also represents limited liability companies, partnerships and corporations on general corporate matters.
**Personal:** The George Washington University Law School, JD; City University of New York, Brooklyn College, BA.

## SCHEINFELD, Robert C
Baker Botts LLP, New York
212 408 2512
robert.scheinfeld@bakerbotts.com
*Featured in Intellectual Property (New York)*
**Practice Areas:** Head of NY office's IP Department and Member of firm's Executive Committee. For 29 years, practiced IP law, lead trial counsel in patent and trade secret misappropriation disputes and lawsuits, resulting in favorable district court and Federal Circuit decisions. Technical expertise is diverse and representations involve a broad range of fields in the high tech industry, including cryptography, electronics, software, telecommunications, smart/contactless cards, electronic commerce, LCDs, flash memory, FOTA.
**Career:** Bimonthly 'New York Law Journal' patent columnist (1995-present). NYIPLA, Board of Directors (2005-07), Patent Law and Practice Committee, Chair (2001-04). NY State Advisory Council (2001-present).

## SCHELER, Brad Eric
Fried, Frank, Harris, Shriver & Jacobson LLP, New York
212 859 8019
Brad.Scheler@FriedFrank.com
*Featured in Bankruptcy/Restructuring (Nationwide), Bankruptcy/Restructuring (New York)*
**Practice Areas:** A senior partner and chair of the bankruptcy and restructuring department. Practice includes in-court and out-of-court restructurings and rehabilitation of financially distressed businesses. Represents corporate debtors, creditors' committees, bondholders' committees, equity holders' committees, trustees, financial institutions as lenders to and investors in financially troubled companies, buyers and sellers of distressed securities and businesses, and parties seeking to invest in and/or acquire the assets of financially troubled companies.
**Career:** Joined in 1981; partner since 1984. Contributing author to "Collier on Bankruptcy."
**Personal:** JD, Hofstra University School of Law (1977), research editor, Law Review; BA, high honors, Lehigh University (1974).

## SCHER, Irving
Greenberg Traurig, LLP, New York
212 801 9321
Scherl@gtlaw.com
*Featured in Antitrust (New York)*
**Practice Areas:** Has represented clients in government and private antitrust litigation involving pricing and non-pricing restraints, monopolisation, boycotts, and price discrimination in such industries as: recorded music, automobile, electronics, books and magazines, airlines, grocery and drug products, and retailing. Adjunct professor of antitrust at NYU Law School, Co-Chair, PLI annual Antitrust Institute (1977-2004). Chair, ABA Antitrust Section (1988-89) and NY Bar Ass'n Antitrust Section (1980-81); Editor/Co-Author, Antitrust Adviser (Thomson Reuters 2013). Author, Living With the Robinson-Patman Act, (BNA 2013).
**Career:** Listed: Chambers USA, 2007, 2011-13; Chambers Global, 2012-13.
**Personal:** Columbia University School of Law, JD, City College of New York, BA.

## SCHINDLER, Paul D
Greenberg Traurig, LLP, New York
212 801 6785
SchindlerP@gtlaw.com
*Featured in Media & Entertainment (New York)*
**Practice Areas:** Senior Chair, New York Media and Entertainment Practice. Paul focuses his practice on music, sports, television and film. Represent recording artists, producers, high profile entertainment executives, actors, celebrities, and corporations in all areas of entertainment law - including contract negotiations, licensing, branding, merchandising, distribution, corporate and joint venture agreements.
**Professional Memberships:** Executive Committee: NARAS/Grammy's Entertainment Law Initiative; Lifebeat; TJ Martell Foundation; Nordoff Robbins; City of Hope. Member, NY State Bar Association.
**Career:** Listed: Variety's Dealmakers Impact Report, 2012; Who's Who in Entertainment; Chambers USA Guide, 2006-13; Best Lawyers in America, 2007-13; Legal 500 US, 2007; Super Lawyers magazine, 2006-12; U.S. News-Best Lawyers 'Law Firm of the Year' in Entertainment Law-Music, 2011-12; Profiled, 'Power Lawyers: Top 100 Outside Counsel', The Hollywood Reporter, 2010.
**Personal:** JD, Brooklyn Law School; BA, Syracuse University.

## SCHLER, Michael L
Cravath, Swaine & Moore LLP, New York
212 474 1588
mschler@cravath.com
*Featured in Tax (New York)*
**Practice Areas:** Michael L. Schler is a partner in the Cravath Tax Department. His practice includes corporate tax, corporate finance (including structured finance and securitizations), mergers and acquisitions and international transactions.
**Personal:** New York University School of Law (LLM in Taxation, 1979); Yale Law School (JD,

1973); Harvard University (BA, magna cum laude, 1970). For more information: http://www.cravath.com/mschler

## SCHNAPP, Daniel E
Hughes Hubbard & Reed LLP, New York
212 837 6258
schnapp@hugheshubbard.com
*Featured in Media & Entertainment (New York)*
**Practice Areas:** Specializes in the provision of strategic counsel and negotiation of complex corporate and commercial transactions involving key legal, policy and business issues arising out of the convergence of technology, entertainment, media, advertising and communications.
**Career:** Partner and Chair of New Media, Entertainment and Technology Practice at Hughes Hubbard & Reed.Selected as one of the Top 50 IP Attorneys under 45 in IP Law and Business Magazine.
**Personal:** Syracuse University College of Law, JD, 1994, cum laude; University of Vermont, BA, 1991.

## SCHNELL, Paul
Skadden, Arps, Slate, Meagher & Flom LLP & Affiliates, New York
212 735 23 22
Paul.Schnell@skadden.com
*Featured in Healthcare (New York), Latin American Investment (New York), Corporate/M&A (New York)*
**Practice Areas:** Represents many of the world's leading companies and financial firms in some of the most significant corporate transactions. Practices in M&A, anti-raid, private equity, governance, finance, restructuring. In the past few years, advised on over 90 announced M&A and financing transactions, including over 25 valued above $1 billion, in US, Latin America, Asia and Europe. Active in numerous industries including telecom, technology, consumer, financial services, industrial. Coordinates Skadden's worldwide healthcare practice group. Chairs leading M&A publication; lectures and writes frequently. Active in firm management, including management committee.
**Career:** JD, New York University School of Law; BA, Amherst College.

## SCHOEN, George F
Cravath, Swaine & Moore LLP, New York
212 474 1740
gschoen@cravath.com
*Featured in Corporate/M&A (New York)*
**Practice Areas:** George F. Schoen is a partner in Cravath's Corporate Department and currently serves as the Firm's Corporate Hiring Partner. His practice focuses primarily on mergers, acquisitions and joint ventures, including hostile and contested transactions. He also regularly counsels corporations and their directors on fiduciary duty and corporate governance matters. Mr Schoen's clients have included IBM, Johnson & Johnson, Credit Suisse, United Airlines, EMBARQ, The Jones Group and Pepsi Bottling Group.
**Personal:** University of Chicago Law School (JD, with Honors, 1998); Cornell University (BA, 1994). For more information: http://www.cravath.com/gschoen

**SCHOENBRUN, Gary**
Dickstein Shapiro LLP, New York
212 277 6586
schoenbrung@dicksteinshapiro.com
*Featured in Tax (New York)*
**Practice Areas:** Dickstein Shapiro Partner Gary Schoenbrun concentrates his practice in the areas of taxation and executive compensation. He regularly advises clients as tax counsel in connection with both taxable and tax-free mergers and acquisitions involving both private and public companies. Furthermore, he advises clients on all aspects of partnership taxation. Mr Schoenbrun also represents numerous investment funds on various matters including taxation, compensation, and regulatory issues.
**Personal:** BA, magna cum laude, from the University of Rochester (1980) and JD, cum laude, from Harvard Law School (1983) and his LLM in Taxation from New York University School of Law (1987).

**SCHONHOLTZ, Margot**
Willkie Farr & Gallagher LLP, New York
212 728 8258
mschonholtz@willkie.com
*Featured in Bankruptcy/Restructuring (Nationwide), Bankruptcy/Restructuring (New York)*
**Practice Areas:** Partner in Business Reorganisation and Restructuring Department. Has more than 33 years of experience representing leading institutional creditors and funds, agents to syndicated lending groups, large lender groups, ad hoc groups, and commercial lenders in bankruptcy proceedings, out-of-court debt restructurings, loan workouts, asset sale transactions, and domestic and cross-border matters. Represents lenders in state and federal court proceedings, including actions for enforcement and foreclosure upon collateral, and lender liability and aiding and abetting fraud litigations. Handles all aspects of bankruptcy and creditors' rights litigation, prepares and negotiates complex corporate documents, and organizes and manages large lender syndicates. Has particular knowledge of structured products, financial services, merchant energy, online marketing, retail, commercial real estate, cable and broadcast, telecommunications, manufacturing, mining, and health care industries. Representative clients include Bank of America, Barclays Bank PLC, and Angelo Gordon.
**Personal:** JD, American University Washington College of Law, 1979. BA, Smith College, 1976. For more information:
http://www.willkie.com/MargotSchonholtz

**SCHULMAN, Ira M**
Pepper Hamilton LLP, New York
212 808 2718
schulmani@pepperlaw.com
*Featured in Construction (New York)*
**Practice Areas:** Partner. Experienced in all aspects of construction law with emphasis on all forms of dispute resolution and contract negotiation. Primarily representing owners - public and private, contractors, subcontractors, sureties and school districts - has tried numerous complex construction disputes in jury and bench trials in

state and federal courts and before arbitration panels. Has participated in many mediations and successfully represented clients with construction contract award issues before various city agencies.
**Professional Memberships:** Co-Chair, Construction Law Committee, Westchester County Bar Association.
**Personal:** JD 1979 Georgetown University Law Center; BA, magna cum laude, 1976 Lehigh University. Phi Beta Kappa.

**SCHULZ, David A**
Levine Sullivan Koch & Schulz LLP, New York
212 850 6103
dschulz@lskslaw.com
*Featured in First Amendment Litigation (Nationwide), Media & Entertainment (New York)*
See under Nationwide for profile.

**SCHUMER, Robert B**
Paul, Weiss, Rifkind, Wharton & Garrison LLP, New York
212 373 3097
rschumer@paulweiss.com
*Featured in Media & Entertainment (New York), Corporate/M&A (New York)*
**Practice Areas:** Chair of Corporate Department and Co-Head of M&A Group. Lead lawyer in the negotiation and structuring of mergers and acquisitions, dispositions, joint ventures and leveraged buyouts. Representative transactions include Warner Music Group in its $3.3 billion sale to Access Industries (for which he was named a 'Dealmaker of the Year' by The American Lawyer; deal also named 2011 "Transaction M&A Deal of the Year" by The Deal); RSC Holdings in its $4.2 billion sale to United Rentals; Time Warner Cable in its $3.5 billion acquisition of Insight Communications and its spinoff from Time Warner Inc.; Agrium's $4 billion hostile bid to acquire CF Industries and its $2.65 billion acquisition of UAP; Time Warner Inc.' s $17.9 billion acquisition of Adelphia Communications Corporation's cable properties, for which he was named a 'Dealmaker of the Year' by The American Lawyer; Farallon Capital Management's acquisition with Simon Property Group of The Mills Corporation for $7.9 billion; Wyndham Hotels' acquisition by Blackstone for $3.24 billion; EnCana Corporation, Canada's largest oil and gas company, in its $2.7 billion successful tender offer for Tom Brown, Inc.; Time Warner's $58 billion bid for AT&T Broadband and $9 billion restructuring of Time Warner Entertainment with Comcast and AT&T; and the consortium led by Edgar Bronfman, Jr. in its $15 billion bid for Vivendi S.A.'s entertainment assets. Represents special committees of boards of directors and leading investment banking firms in mergers and acquisitions context.

**SCHWAB, James H**
Paul, Weiss, Rifkind, Wharton & Garrison LLP, New York
212 373 3174
jschwab@paulweiss.com
*Featured in Media & Entertainment (New York)*
**Practice Areas:** Corporate Partner; broad M&A practice with extensive media and entertainment

experience. Representations include: formation of Important Media on behalf of creators of SouthPark and the Book of Mormon; acquisition of CORE Media, an owner of rights to American Idol and the Elvis Presley brand, by an affiliate of Apollo; advising creative team behind Grand Theft Auto in an agreement with Take-Two; sale of the Zagat survey to Google; formation of the El Rey cable television network focused on the Hispanic community; advising Sony on partnership and financing matters as part of the acquisition of EMI's music publishing business.

**SCHWARTZ, Carl F**
Hunton & Williams LLP, New York
212 309 1070
cschwartz@hunton.com
*Featured in Real Estate (New York)*
**Practice Areas:** Carl Schwartz's practice focuses on representing commercial real estate owners, developers and lenders in local, national and international transactions. He advises prominent owners and developers, including REITs and private equity funds, on their real estate acquisitions, dispositions, developments, financings, workouts, restructurings and joint ventures; is active in representing large institutional lenders in mortgage, mezzanine and construction financings; and has served as counsel in some of the nation's most significant Historic Tax Credit transactions. He also represents owners and tenants in major commercial lease transactions. Carl is chair of the New York Real Estate Group.

**SCHWARTZ, David E**
Skadden, Arps, Slate, Meagher & Flom LLP & Affiliates, New York
212 735 2473
david.schwartz@skadden.com
*Featured in Labor & Employment (New York)*
**Practice Areas:** Mr Schwartz advises clients on a full spectrum of employment-related issues. He regularly represents clients before administrative agencies and courts, and in arbitration proceedings. His litigation experience includes defense of discrimination, breach of contract and fraud claims, including potential class actions. He also represents clients in cases concerning the enforcement of restrictive covenants and breaches of fiduciary duties. Mr Schwartz often advises on non-litigation matters, including severance negotiations and internal investigations, and in connection with complex business transactions.
**Career:** JD, Cornell Law School, 1994 (cum laude); BA, University of Rochester, 1989 (cum laude).

**SCHWARTZ, Jodi J**
Wachtell, Lipton, Rosen & Katz, New York
212 403 1212
jjschwartz@wlrk.com
*Featured in Tax (New York)*
**Practice Areas:** Practice focuses on the tax aspects of corporate transactions, including mergers and acquisitions, joint ventures, spin-offs, restructurings and financial instruments. Has been the principal tax lawyer on numerous domestic and cross-border transactions in a wide range of industries.

**Professional Memberships:** Immediate past chair of the New York State Bar Association Tax Section Executive Committee. Serves on the board of the American Jewish Joint Distribution Committee, the Foundation for Jewish Camp and the Jewish Community Project of Lower Manhattan and on the Board of Overseers of the University of Pennsylvania Law School. Also a member of the American College of Tax Counsel.
**Career:** Partner at Wachtell, Lipton, Rosen & Katz since 1991.
**Personal:** Graduated magna cum laude from the University of Pennsylvania in 1981 (BS, economics), from the University of Pennsylvania (Wharton School) in 1984 (MBA), magna laude from the University of Pennsylvania Law School in 1984 (JD), and from New York University Law School in 1987 (LLM, Taxation).

**SCHWARTZ, Max J**
Sullivan & Cromwell LLP, New York
212 558 3936
schwartzma@sullcrom.com
*Featured in Employee Benefits & Executive Compensation (Nationwide), Employee Benefits & Executive Compensation (New York)*
See under Nationwide for profile.

**SCHWARTZ, Richard M**
Fried, Frank, Harris, Shriver & Jacobson LLP, New York
212 859 8263
Richard.Schwartz@FriedFrank.com
*Featured in Environment (New York)*
**Practice Areas:** Partner, corporate department and head of Firm's environmental practice group. Diversified transactional environmental practice includes M&A, private equity, securities offerings, bankruptcy and real estate. Represents clients in enforcement proceedings throughout the US. Has tried and argued cases in federal district and appellate courts.
**Career:** Joined as partner in 1991. Served in US Attorney's Office for Southern District of New York (1984-1991): Chief, Environmental Protection Unit; Deputy Appellate Chief; and Deputy Chief, Civil Division.
**Personal:** JD, University of Chicago Law School (1977); MA, Clare College, University of Cambridge (1978); Mellon Fellowship (1972-74); BA, magna cum laude, Yale College (1972).

**SCHWARTZ, Steven**
Locke Lord LLP, New York
212 812 8312
sschwartz@lockelord.com
*Featured in Insurance (Nationwide), Insurance (New York)*
See under Nationwide for profile.

**SCHWARTZ, Wallace L**
Kasowitz, Benson, Torres & Friedman LLP, New York
212 506 1845
wschwartz@kasowitz.com
*Featured in Real Estate (New York)*
**Practice Areas:** As head of Kasowitz's Real Estate Group, Wallace focuses on real estate development, acquisitions, leasing, partnerships and joint ventures, capital markets and financings,

gaming and lodging, and workouts and restructurings. This past year, he represented Starwood Capital Group in the acquisition of 1372 Broadway; a New Valley/Witkoff joint venture in the acquisition and development of 701 Seventh Avenue; Boston Properties in major leases at 250 West 55th Street and 601 Lexington Avenue; Penn National Gaming with respect to the proposed hotel and casino project in Springfield, Massachusetts; and DLJ Real Estate Capital Partners, relating to two Aruba resorts.

### SCHWARTZBAUM, David M
Greenberg Traurig, LLP, New York
212 801 6544
SchwartzbaumD@gtlaw.com
*Featured in Corporate/M&A (New York)*
**Practice Areas:** Co-Chair of the firm's Global M&A Steering Committee. Practice focuses on mergers and acquisitions, including the representation of principals and financial advisors in public and private M&A transaction; negotiated and unsolicited transactions; cash and stock-for-stock mergers; tender and exchange offers; cross-border transactions; special committee representations; going-private transactions; takeover defense assignments; corporate governance matters.
**Career:** Selected: Chambers USA Guide, 2010-13; Euromoney's Guide to the World's Leading Mergers and Acquisitions Lawyers, 2011-12; Legal 500 US, 2007-12.
**Personal:** JD, cum laude, Harvard Law School, 1987; MA, Yale University, 1984; BA, summa cum laude, Yale University, 1984, Phi Beta Kappa.

### SCHWEITZER, Lisa M
Cleary Gottlieb Steen & Hamilton LLP, New York
212 225 2629
lschweitzer@cgsh.com
*Featured in Bankruptcy/Restructuring (Nationwide), Bankruptcy/Restructuring (New York)*
**Practice Areas:** SpSpecializes in complex bankruptcy and insolvency matters (including out-of-court restructurings) including representation of debtors, creditors, investors and acquirers. Significant experience with distressed M&A transactions and complex cross-border restructurings including in Europe, Asia and Latin America. Recent notable matters: Nortel's US bankruptcy and asset sales including sale of substantial patent portfolio, representation of Fintech Investments Ltd. in the restructuring of Vitro, Barclays Capital (acquisition of Lehman US broker-dealer, investment bank), representation of various financial institutions in subprime bankruptcies, Adelphia and Refco bankruptcies.
**Career:** New York University School of Law (1996); University of Pennsylvania (1991).

### SCHWOLSKY, John
Willkie Farr & Gallagher LLP, New York
212 728 8232
jschwolsky@willkie.com
*Featured in Insurance (Nationwide), Insurance (New York)*
**Practice Areas:** Expertise in the area of corporate mergers and acquisitions and securities law, specifically public and private securities offerings,

mergers and acquisitions, recapitalizations, and other transactions involving the insurance industry. Represented insurance companies and underwriters of their securities in these transactions. Represented insurers and investment banks in connection with domestic and offshore insurance and reinsurance facilities including catastrophe bonds, embedded value transactions, mortality bonds and other risk-linked securities.
**Personal:** JD, Cornell University, 1985; BA, (magna cum laude) Yale University, 1982. See: http://www.willkie.com/JohnSchwolsky

### SEGAL, Michael J
Wachtell, Lipton, Rosen & Katz, New York
212 403 1000
MJSegal@wlrk.com
*Featured in Employee Benefits & Executive Compensation (Nationwide), Employee Benefits & Executive Compensation (New York)*
**Practice Areas:** Practice focuses on employee benefits and executive compensation aspects of mergers and acquisitions, joint ventures and other public and private business combinations, as well as entering and exiting CEO and other senior level employment positions. Recent representations include McDonalds Corporation, Simon Property Group, the National Basketball Association, Brink's Corporation, Michael Dell in the proposed LBO of Dell Inc., SuperValu Inc in its proposed asset sale and tender offer with affiliates of Cerberus, Walgreen Co. in its acquisition of Alliance Boots, Deutsche Telecom in the proposed combination of T-Mobile and MetroPCS, El Paso Corporation in its merger with Kinder Morgan, Ralcorp in its acquisition by ConAgra, a private equity group in its acquisition of the Philidelphia 76ers, AMB Property Corp. in its acquisition of Prologis, Ventas in its acquisition of National Health Properties, Cardinal Health in its spinoff of CareFusion, Delta Airlines in its merger with Northwest Airlines, Phillips-Van Heusen in its acquisitions of Tommy Hilfiger and Warnaco, Smith International in its merger with Schlumberger, Wyeth in its merger with Pfizer, CenturyLink in its acquisitions of Embarq and Savvis, and Morgan Stanley in its joint venture with Citigroup/Smith Barney.
**Career:** Partner at Wachtell, Lipton, Rosen & Katz since 2007. Previously partner at Paul, Weiss, Rifkind, Wharton & Garrison and Willkie, Farr & Gallagher. Has 30 years experience in representing buyers and sellers of businesses and significant corporations (including Board Compensation Committees) in respect of their executive compensation arrangements, and CEOs and other senior executives in connection with their employment and compensation arrangements; as well as advising financial institutions, hedge funds and other clients in ERISA and other employee benefits matters.
**Personal:** Graduated cum laude from The Ohio State University (BS, Accounting), 1980, and from The Ohio State University College of Law (JD), 1983.

### SEIDER, Mitchell A
Latham & Watkins LLP, New York
212 906 1200
mitchell.seider@lw.com
*Featured in Bankruptcy/Restructuring (Nationwide), Bankruptcy/Restructuring (New York)*
**Practice Areas:** Work focused on representing secured lenders, bond holders, and creditors' committees in Chapter 11 cases and workouts.
**Career:** Qualified since 1987. Global Co-Chair of Latham's Insolvency Practice. Admitted to practice in New York, Texas and multiple federal courts. Former chairman of the Professional Ethics Subcommittee of the ABA's Business Bankruptcy Committee. Adjunct University of Michigan Law School (1996).
**Publications:** Author or co-author of published articles on debtor in possession financing, duties of directors of insolvent companies, and professional ethics.

### SEIDMAN, Steven
Willkie Farr & Gallagher LLP, New York
212 728 8763
sseidman@willkie.com
*Featured in Corporate/M&A (New York)*
**Practice Areas:** Co-Chair of Corporate and Financial Services Department; Co-Chair of Mergers & Acquisitions Practice Group. Specializes in M&A, corporate governance, private equity, public offerings, and general corporate and securities law. Significant matters include representation of Bank of America Merrill Lynch in connection with the sale of Heinz; Ventas, Inc. in acquisition of Cogdell Spencer Inc.; Special Committee of Board of Directors of Taro Pharmaceutical Industries Ltd. in Sun Pharmaceutical Industries Ltd.'s going-private offer; Allied World Assurance Company Holdings, AG in connection with Transatlantic Holdings, Inc.; Cablevision independent directors in spin-off of Madison Square Garden business.
**Personal:** JD, University of Virginia Law School, 1990. BA, Yale University, 1987. See: http://www.willkie.com/StevenSeidman

### SEIFE, Howard
Chadbourne & Parke LLP, New York
212 408 5361
hseife@chadbourne.com
*Featured in Bankruptcy/Restructuring (Nationwide), Bankruptcy/Restructuring (New York)*
**Practice Areas:** Howard Seife, global chair of Chadbourne's Bankruptcy and Financial Restructuring Practice, has had a leading role in some of the largest and most complex Chapter 11s - including Tribune Company, Parmalat, Spiegel, Inc./Eddie Bauer and currently represents former Chief Bankruptcy Judge Arthur Gonzalez in his role as the Examiner in ResCap. He is also a leader in cross-border insolvencies, having commenced numerous Chapter 15s, including most recently for Hellas II.
**Professional Memberships:** INSOL International (Board of Directors); International Insolvency Institute.

**Personal:** JD, cum laude, from Georgetown University Law Center; LLM from the London School of Economics.

### SELVER, Paul D
Kramer Levin Naftalis & Frankel LLP, New York
212 715 9199
pselver@kramerlevin.com
*Featured in Real Estate (New York)*
**Practice Areas:** Practice encompasses all aspects of land use and development law, with a special emphasis on environmental, zoning and historic preservation. Over the past 15 years, he has successfully coordinated the public approval and environmental review process for more than 10,000,000 square feet of office space, more than 10,000 apartments, hundreds of thousands of square feet of retail and entertainment space, thousands of hotel rooms, and numerous institutional buildings.
**Publications:** Co-author, New York Practice Guide: Real Estate, Volume II: Land Use Regulation (1986).
**Personal:** JD Harvard University Law School (1972); BA magna cum laude from Harvard College (1969).

### SEMERDJIAN, Steve A
Loeb & Loeb LLP, New York
212 407 4218
ssemerdjian@loeb.com
*Featured in Technology (New York)*
**Practice Areas:** Concentrates on complex outsourcing and information technology matters. Practice includes drafting and negotiating a wide range of agreements, including domestic and international business process and information technology outsourcing agreements and technology procurement, licensing, and system development contracts, advising clients on general business, IT and IP matters.
**Career:** Joined Loeb as Partner in 2008.
**Personal:** St. John's University School of Law (JD, 1996); University of Chicago (BA, 1991).

### SERBAROLI, Francis J
Greenberg Traurig, LLP, New York
212 801 2212
SerbaroliF@gtlaw.com
*Featured in Healthcare (New York)*
**Practice Areas:** Health care corporate, regulatory and litigation matters; health insurance regulatory matters.
**Career:** Rated, AV® Preeminent™ 5.0 out of 5. Selected: Super Lawyers magazine, 2006-12; Chambers USA, 2005-13; Best Lawyers in America, 2011-13.
**Publications:** Author: Health Law column, New York Law Journal; 'The Corporate Practice of Medicine Prohibition in the Modern Era of Health Care' (BNA) and over 125 articles published in various health, pharmaceutical and insurance publications.
**Personal:** JD, Fordham University School of Law; BA, Fordham University. Public Service: Member (1995-2010), New York State Public Health Council: Vice Chairman; Establishment

Committee; (Chair) Special Committee on Medical Information Confidentiality.

## SERINO, JR, Joseph
Kirkland & Ellis LLP, New York
212 446 4913
joseph.serino@kirkland.com
*Featured in Litigation (New York)*

**Practice Areas:** Joseph Serino, Jr., specializes in financial services, commercial and bankruptcy litigation. With respect to financial services, Mr Serino has represented numerous investment banks, broker-dealers, private equity funds and hedge funds in civil actions, class actions, regulatory actions and arbitrations in a wide array of securities related claims involving both traditional and derivative securities. Mr Serino has appeared on behalf of these entities, and their directors, managers and officers, before numerous state and federal courts, bankruptcy courts, securities regulatory agencies and arbitration tribunals.
**Personal:** University of Pennsylvania Law School, JD, 1988; Hamilton College, BA, 1985.

## SEROTA, James I
Greenberg Traurig, LLP, New York
212 801 2277
SerotaJ@gtlaw.com
*Featured in Antitrust (New York)*

**Practice Areas:** Chair, Global Antitrust Litigation and Competition Practice; Chair, Global Antitrust and Trade Regulation Practice.
**Professional Memberships:** Board member, Law Board, Northwestern University School of Law, 1997-Present.
**Career:** Listed: The Best Lawyers in America, Commercial Litigation, 2012-13; Super Lawyers magazine, New York Super Lawyers, 2006-12; Euromoney's Guide to World's Leading Competition and Antitrust Lawyers, 2008-12. Rated, AV® Preeminent™ 5.0 out of 5.
**Personal:** JD, cum laude, Northwestern University School of Law, 1971 (Senior editor, Northwestern Law Review); BA, Washington University in St. Louis, 1968.

## SEYMOUR, Karen Patton
Sullivan & Cromwell LLP, New York
212 558 3196
seymourk@sullcrom.com
*Featured in Financial Services Regulation (Nationwide), Litigation (New York)*

**Professional Memberships:** ABA; White Collar Crime Committee, NYCBA; FBC.
**Career:** Partner since 2000. Co-Managing Partner of Litigation Group. Represents individuals, corporations and financial institutions in state/federal proceedings regarding securities fraud, money laundering, obstruction of justice, insider trading, FCPA violations, OFAC sanctions, healthcare fraud, criminal antitrust violations. Advises non-US parties regarding US investigations. Jury/bench trials in federal/appeals court. Public service in US Attorney's Office, SDNY: Chief, Criminal Division (2002-2004) overseeing WorldCom, Adelphia, ImClone investigations and leading Martha Stewart/Peter Bacanovic prosecution.

**Personal:** University of London (LLM, 1987); University of Texas Law School (JD, 1986); Southern Methodist University (BS; BA, 1983).

## SEYMOUR, Samuel W
Sullivan & Cromwell LLP, New York
212 558 3156
seymours@sullcrom.com
*Featured in Financial Services Regulation (Nationwide), Litigation (New York)*

**Practice Areas:** Managing Partner, Criminal Defense and Investigations Group. White-collar criminal defense, regulatory enforcement matters, internal investigations. Represents individuals/institutions in high-profile inquiries involving allegations of accounting/securities fraud, foreign bribery, price fixing, trade sanctions violations, money laundering and obstruction of justice. Handles derivative cases, shareholder actions, and complex contract disputes. Clients: Lloyds Bank, ABN AMRO, Bank of New York, Spiegel, Bankers Trust, Statoil and former Arthur Andersen partner in criminal probe of Enron/Andersen.
**Professional Memberships:** ABA; ABCNY (President 2010-12).
**Career:** Partner since 1994. Assistant US Attorney/Deputy Chief Appellate Attorney, SDNY (1988-1991).
**Personal:** Columbia Law (JD, 1982); Dartmouth (AB, 1979).

## SHACHAR, Avishai
Davis Polk & Wardwell LLP, New York
212 450 4000
avishai.shachar@dpw.com
*Featured in Tax (New York)*

**Practice Areas:** Head of Davis Polk's Tax Department. Practices primarily in the areas of mergers and acquisitions, spinoffs and financial products. He designed the unique capital structure of SmithKline Beecham and advised on the spinoffs of YUM! Brands from Pepsi, of Visteon from Ford, of Discover from Morgan Stanley, the splitoff of Abercrombie from The Limited, Texaco's merger with Chevron, Comcast on the sale of QVC, the restructuring of Time Warner Entertainment, acquisitions of cable assets from Adelphia and AT&T and NBC, Exxon's acquisition of XTO as well as Citigroup on a variety of transactions including the MSSB joint venture.

## SHALHOUB, Paul V
Willkie Farr & Gallagher LLP, New York
212 728 8764
pshalhoub@willkie.com
*Featured in Bankruptcy/Restructuring (New York)*

**Practice Areas:** Specializes in bankruptcy and corporate restructuring, acquisitions of distressed companies, debtor in possession financing and related matters. Represents debtors in large, complex chapter 11 cases and out of court restructurings (KV Discovery Solutions; RathGibson; LandAmerica Financial Group; Adelphia, others). Also represents hedge funds and other private equity clients in their capacities as investors, lenders and creditors of distressed entities (Twin Haven Capital Management, Warburg Pincus, Brookfield Asset Management, Leonard Green

Partners, TPG, others). He also represents creditors and other stakeholders, investors, acquirers, lenders and financial advisors in both chapter 11 cases and nonjudicial matters (USAA, Take-Two Interactive, others).
**Personal:** JD, New York University School of Law, 1991. BA, SUNY at Binghamton, 1988. See http://www.willkie.com/PaulShalhoub

## SHANE, Penny
Sullivan & Cromwell LLP, New York
212 558 4000
shanep@sullcrom.com
*Featured in Litigation (New York)*

**Practice Areas:** Focuses on litigation involving financial institutions, including class actions and state/federal governmental investigations stemming from securities issuances, allegedly improper securities trading, and other allegedly fraudulent/unfair practices. Also litigates complex contract disputes, including disputes over technology, patents and licenses, and contract performance. Extensive constitutional litigation experience, including landmark cases involving civil rights.
**Professional Memberships:** ABA; FBC; ABCNY.
**Career:** Partner since 2000. Clerk, Honorable Richard Owen, USDC, 1988-1990.
**Personal:** NYU School of Law (JD, 1988); Barnard College, Columbia University (BA, 1985).

## SHAPIRO, David
Wachtell, Lipton, Rosen & Katz, New York
212 403 1314
DEShapiro@wlrk.com
*Featured in Capital Markets (Nationwide), Corporate/M&A (New York)*

**Practice Areas:** Focuses on mergers and acquisitions and complex securities transactions for financial institutions and other clients. Has been involved in many major corporate merger, acquisition and buyout transactions, strategic defense assignments, hostile bids and proxy contests. Also counsels boards of directors and board committees on corporate governance matters.
**Professional Memberships:** American Bar Association.
**Career:** Partner in the Corporate Department at Wachtell, Lipton, Rosen & Katz.
**Publications:** Writes numerous articles on legal developments; co-author of the firm's annual financial developments outline.
**Personal:** Received a BS from the Wharton School of the University of Pennsylvania in 1990 and completed a JD, summa cum laude, from the University of Pennsylvania Law School in 1999 where he was awarded the Peter McCall Prize for being first in his class. Has been featured in The New York Times' Facebook of Wall Street's Future and was named by The American Lawyer as a Dealmaker of the Year. Member of the board of The Door, a not-for-profit comprehensive youth services agency and provides regular legal services pro bono to University Settlement, a not-for-profit settlement house located in New York City.

## SHAPIRO, David I
Fried, Frank, Harris, Shriver & Jacobson LLP, New York
212 859 8039
David.Shapiro@FriedFrank.com
*Featured in Investment Funds (Nationwide), Tax (New York)*

**Practice Areas:** Tax partner. Specializes in representing private equity and mezzanine funds in acquisitions, dispositions and financings; fund sponsors in fund formations (including fund-of-funds), focusing on equity, mezzanine, senior loans, distressed and real estate; and clients investing in, and co-investing with, private equity funds, hedge funds, etc. Clients include Goldman Sachs; AEA; Fortress; Highbridge Principal Strategies; Sankaty; StepStone; high-net worth families and endowments.
**Career:** Joined in 1992; became partner in 2000.
**Personal:** JD, Columbia Law School (1992), Harlan Fiske Stone Scholar, member, Law Review; AB, magna cum laude, with distinction in all subjects, Cornell University (1989).

## SHAPIRO, Saul B
Patterson Belknap Webb & Tyler LLP, New York
212 336 2163
sbshapiro@pbwt.com
*Featured in Media & Entertainment (New York)*

**Practice Areas:** Saul Shapiro's practice focuses on complex business litigation as well as intellectual property. Mr Shapiro is Chair of the firm's Litigation Department and Co-Chair of the firm's Media and Entertainment Practice. He has won the dismissal of numerous cases on pre-trial motions. He has also been lead Counsel in eight trials, and has been victorious in all four of the jury trials he has taken to verdict. Mr Shapiro is an experienced appellate lawyer. He has also conducted numerous internal investigations and defended clients facing government investigation. In the media and communications area, he has represented many major publicly traded companies, including cable television systems, broadcast and cable television networks, recorded music companies, distributors and creators of financial information and financial products, and internet communications companies.
**Professional Memberships:** Chair, Legal Outreach Advisory Board; Board of Brooklyn Legal Services Corporation A.
**Career:** Mr Shapiro clerked for the Hon Robert L Carter in the Southern District of New York before joining Patterson Belknap.
**Personal:** Yale Law School (JD 1986), served as an editor of the Yale Law Journal; Brown University (BA 1981), magna cum laude.

## SHAULSON, Samuel S
Morgan, Lewis & Bockius LLP, New York
212 309 6718
sshaulson@morganlewis.com
*Featured in Labor & Employment (New York)*

**Practice Areas:** Sam Shaulson is a partner in Morgan Lewis's Employment Law practice, co-chair of the firm's Financial Services Industry Employment Law Practice, and a member of the firm's Advisory Board. He routinely handles com-

plex litigation matters, representing clients in more than 100 class or collective actions, including Title VII, ADA, FLSA, and state wage law cases. He also represents clients in significant appeals and whistleblower matters. He has appeared in both civil and criminal court, as well as before various administrative agencies.
**Personal:** Attended University of Pennsylvania School of Law, JD; Boston University, BSBA.

### SHENKER, Joseph C
Sullivan & Cromwell LLP, New York
212 558 3768
shenkerj@sullcrom.com
*Featured in Capital Markets (Nationwide), Real Estate (New York)*
**Career:** Firm Chairman. Multidisciplinary practice including negotiated mergers and acquisitions (public and private); domestic and cross-border joint ventures; representing private equity investors and family investment offices in the Americas, Europe and Asia; securities offerings; private/public financings; commercial real estate; professional sports representation; and related tax and estate planning. Clients include Apollo Management, Canary Wharf Group, General Growth Properties, Goldman Sachs, Heyman Family, Loews Corp., McCourt (LA Dodgers) Family, NY Giants, NY Jets, San Francisco Giants, Ontario Teachers, Pershing Square Capital, Pritzker Family and Vornado Realty Trust.
**Personal:** Columbia Law School (JD, 1980); City University of New York (BS Accounting, 1977).

### SHIM, Paul J
Cleary Gottlieb Steen & Hamilton LLP, New York
212 225 2930
pshim@cgsh.com
*Featured in Private Equity (Nationwide), Corporate/M&A (New York)*
See under Nationwide for profile.

### SHIMSHAK, Stephen J
Paul, Weiss, Rifkind, Wharton & Garrison LLP, New York
212 373 3133
sshimshak@paulweiss.com
*Featured in Bankruptcy/Restructuring (New York)*
**Practice Areas:** Partner, Bankruptcy and Corporate Reorganization Department. Diverse practice (emphasis on bankruptcy litigation) includes U.S. and foreign insolvency proceedings, restructurings, and workouts involving debtors, creditors (including industry players, banks, and hedge funds), court-appointed liquidators, trustees, asset purchasers and private equity investors. Represented Citigroup in connection with bankruptcy matters pertaining to MF Global, Lehman Brothers, Chicago Tribune, Chrysler, WorldCom and Enron; Rockstar Consortium in connection with its $4.5 billion patent acquisition from Nortel; Ericsson in its $1.13 billion acquisition from Nortel; Major League Baseball in the Texas Rangers chapter 11 case and MacAndrews & Forbes in connection with Federal-Mogul.

### SHINE, David N
Fried, Frank, Harris, Shriver & Jacobson LLP, New York
212 859 8284
David.Shine@friedfrank.com
*Featured in Corporate/M&A (New York)*
**Practice Areas:** Corporate partner. Co-head of the mergers and acquisitions group. Has a diversified transactional corporate practice with extensive experience in mergers and acquisitions (both public company transactions and private company transactions), private equity investments, joint venture transactions, and private equity fund formation. Representative clients include Merck & Co.; Siemens; Thomson Reuters; Vodaphone; and Power Corporation of Canada.
**Career:** Joined in 1986; became partner in 1994.
**Personal:** JD, New York University School of Law (1986), editor, Law Review; BA, Columbia University (1982).

### SHOEMATE, Steven R
Gibson, Dunn & Crutcher LLP, New York
212 351 3879
sshoemate@gibsondunn.com
*Featured in Private Equity (Nationwide), Corporate/M&A (New York)*
See under Nationwide for profile.

### SHULMAN, Dean S
Skadden, Arps, Slate, Meagher & Flom LLP & Affiliates, New York
212 735 2008
dean.shulman@skadden.com
*Featured in Tax (New York)*
**Practice Areas:** Dean Shulman represents clients on a range of domestic and international tax matters, including mergers, acquisitions, divestitures, tax-free spin-offs, leveraged buyouts, IPOs and the formation of funds. Mr Shulman has extensive experience advising on and structuring real estate transactions, including partnership workouts and restructurings, like-kind exchanges as well as transactions involving the formation and operation of partnerships, limited liability companies, joint ventures, real estate investment trusts and real estate funds.
**Career:** LLM, Taxation, New York University School of Law, 1993; JD, New York University School of Law, 1991 (cum laude); AB, Muhlenberg College, 1988 (summa cum laude).

### SIBBETT, Benjamin
Clifford Chance US LLP, New York
212 878 8491
benjamin.sibbett@cliffordchance.com
*Featured in Corporate/M&A (New York)*
**Practice Areas:** Benjamin Sibbett is a partner in the US Corporate practice of Clifford Chance. Mr Sibbett's work encompasses a broad range of cross-border and domestic transactions.
**Career:** Mr Sibbett earned a BA from Brigham Young University in 1996 and a JD from Fordham University School of Law in 1999. He has been with Clifford Chance since 1999.

### SICULAR, David R
Paul, Weiss, Rifkind, Wharton & Garrison LLP, New York
212 373 3082
dsicular@paulweiss.com
*Featured in Tax (New York)*
**Practice Areas:** Tax Partner with broad practice in corporate, partnership and international transactions, including public and private mergers and acquisitions, investment funds, financings, restructurings, financial products and general tax planning. Represents public and private companies in the United States and abroad, private equity and other investment funds, private investors and individual entrepreneurs. Second Vice Chair of the Tax Section of the New York State Bar Association. Member of the Tax Forum and the Private Investment Funds Tax Forum.

### SIEGEL, Adam
Freshfields Bruckhaus Deringer US LLP, New York
212 277 4000
adam.siegel@freshfields.com
*Featured in Litigation (New York)*
**Practice Areas:** Adam is a partner in Freshfields' litigation group, based in New York and co-head of the firm's global investigations practice. Clients in a variety of industries rely on him to conduct internal investigations and to defend them against investigations conducted by the Department of Justice, the Securities and Exchange Commission and the State Attorneys General in matters involving alleged violations of the Foreign Corrupt Practices Act, insider trading, off-label promotion of pharmaceutical products and accounting fraud, often involving multiple countries. He also conducts transactional due diligence and designs compliance programs to help clients mitigate risk.

### SIFFERT, John S
Lankler Siffert & Wohl LLP, New York
212 921 8399 (ext. 229)
jsiffert@lswlaw.com
*Featured in Litigation (New York)*
**Practice Areas:** Criminal defense: investigations, trial, appellate. Civil and regulatory litigation.
**Career:** John S Siffert practices civil and criminal litigation. He is a Special Master for the First Department, on the Board of PLI, Adjunct Professor at NYU Law School, and a Member of the Judicial Conference Advisory Committee on Criminal Rules. He co-authored Sand Modern Federal Jury Instructions and Business Crime. He served as a Regent of the American College of Trial Lawyers, a Member of the Disciplinary Committee, an AUSA in the SDNY, and law clerk to Judge Gurfein. He received the 2009 Second Circuit Inn of Court Professionalism Award.
**Personal:** Columbia Law School, JD; Amherst College, BA, cum laude.

### SILVA, David A
Mound Cotton Wollan & Greengrass, New York
212 804 4241
dsilva@moundcotton.com
*Featured in Insurance (New York)*
**Practice Areas:** Reinsurance and insurance arbitration and litigation involving property, casualty, life, accident and health insurance; commutations; actuarial disputes; RICO; insolvency; regulatory; surplus relief; financial reinsurance, and allocation of environmental losses.
**Career:** Has handled reinsurance arbitrations and insurance litigations for over 20 years. His current areas of concentration include disputes under life, accident and health reinsurance treaties (including workers' compensation carve-out and long term care matters), life reinsurance, and many other complex insurance and reinsurance subjects, including commutationi issues, reserving and actuarial disputes, as well as regulatory advice. He has also represented various off-shore captive reinsurers as well as reinsurance pool writers. He has conducted over 80 reinsurance arbitrations and has litigated and conducted trials in state and federal courts throughout the US Mr Silva has also acted as lead counsel in disputes in the UK and Bermuda. Mr Silva is a frequent speaker at insurance industry events on topics of current interest.
**Publications:** Journal of Insurance Coverage.
**Personal:** New York University (BA 1982), Brooklyn Law School (JD 1985).

### SILVER, Ross Z
Fried, Frank, Harris, Shriver & Jacobson LLP, New York
212 859 8078
Ross.Silver@FriedFrank.com
*Featured in Real Estate (New York)*
**Practice Areas:** Real estate partner. Extensive experience in sales and acquisitions, financings, leasings for landlords and tenants, joint ventures, portfolio transactions and property management relating to all types of properties, including office buildings, hotels, residential and commercial buildings. Clients include Highgate Hotels, Lehman Brothers Holdings, Hiro Real Estate, MetLife, The Feil Organization, Goldman Sachs, Blackstone Group, Ruben Companies, Related Retail Corporation, and Normandy Real Estate Partners.
**Career:** Joined in 1987; became partner in 1997.
**Personal:** JD, cum laude, Order of the Coif, New York University School of Law (1987), Pomeroy Scholar; BA/BS, magna cum laude, University of Pennsylvania (1984).

### SILVERA, Harry R
Fried, Frank, Harris, Shriver & Jacobson LLP, New York
212 859 8173
Harry.Silvera@FriedFrank.com
*Featured in Real Estate (New York)*
**Practice Areas:** Real estate partner. Practice covers a broad range of commercial real estate transactions, including joint ventures, acquisition and disposition of office, hotel and other property classes, commercial mortgage, mezzanine and

construction financing (representing both lenders and borrowers), development of office, residential, hotel and mixed-use projects, and commercial leasing. Clients include RXR Realty, IDB Group, Coach, Macquarie, Brookfield, Centerbridge Partners and Fremont Realty Capital.
**Career:** Joined in 1995; became partner in 2005.
**Personal:** JD, Columbia Law School (1995), James Kent Scholar, Harlan Fiske Stone Scholar; BA, magna cum laude, University of California, Los Angeles (1991), Phi Beta Kappa.

### SILVERBERG, Philip C
Mound Cotton Wollan & Greengrass, New York
psilverberg@moundcotton.com
*Featured in Insurance (New York)*
**Practice Areas:** Both first and third-party insurance coverage and defense as well as reinsurance litigation and arbitrations. Represents insurers and reinsurers as respects coverage and defense involving various types of insurance including energy, builders risk, time element, all-risk, boiler and machinery, professional liability, environmental liability, and financial institution coverages. Has handled trials and appeals involving major corporate entities in state and federal courts in various jurisdictions throughout the United States as well as subrogation and fraud claims. Has served as national coverage counsel for major property/ casualty insurers for losses arising out of 9/11, Katrina, Sandy, and other catastrophes. Also a frequent speaker at insurance industry events on topics of current interest.
**Publications:** The Wall Street Journal (quoted), Mealey's Litigation Report, Best's Review, The Journal of Insurance Coverage.
**Personal:** Montclair State University (BA 1980), Benjamin N Cardozo School of Law (JD 1984).

### SILVERMAN, Moses
Paul, Weiss, Rifkind, Wharton & Garrison LLP, New York
212 373 3355
msilverman@paulweiss.com
*Featured in Antitrust (New York)*
**Practice Areas:** Litigation Partner with significant experience in antitrust litigation, securities litigation, corporate and derivative litigation, commercial litigation, bankruptcy litigation and international and domestic arbitration. Has tried cases involving complex commercial disputes, antitrust law, copyright law and employment issues and has argued appeals involving antitrust, securities, patent, bankruptcy and corporate law. Has defended clients in civil and criminal investigations involving antitrust and securities law; represented clients in international arbitration and litigation in Europe, South America and North America; counseled clients on antitrust matters and negotiated mergers and acquisitions with the FTC and Department of Justice.

### SIMKIN, Steven
Paul, Weiss, Rifkind, Wharton & Garrison LLP, New York
212 373 3073
ssimkin@paulweiss.com
*Featured in Real Estate (New York)*

**Practice Areas:** Chair of Real Estate Department. Maintains an active practice in major financings, acquisitions and development projects, representing both lenders and developers. Has been involved in multi-state mortgage financings, real estate-related litigations and disputes, and complex joint ventures, partnership agreements and ground leases (including rent reset disputes). Has extensive shopping center experience, having been involved in the purchase, sale or financing of several hundred regional malls. Has broad experience in the area of commercial office leasing and significant experience in the formation of real estate funds investing domestically and globally.

### SINGER, Randi W
Weil, Gotshal & Manges LLP, New York
212 310 8152
randi.singer@weil.com
*Featured in Media & Entertainment (New York)*
**Practice Areas:** Randi Singer's practice focuses on intellectual property litigation. She has extensive experience with copyright and Lanham Act false advertising and trademark cases, as well as privacy, social media, unfair competition, and First Amendment issues. She regularly counsels clients on cutting-edge intellectual property issues and successfully represents them in court, in arbitrations and before the National Advertising Division on cases involving a broad spectrum of products and services. Ms Singer has taught trademark law and is a frequent speaker on copyright and advertising issues.
**Personal:** Harvard University (AB, magna cum laude, 1994); Columbia Law School (JD, 1998).

### SINGER, Steven
Bernstein Litowitz Berger & Grossmann LLP, New York
212 554 1413
steven@blbglaw.com
*Featured in Securities (Nationwide), Litigation (New York)*
**Practice Areas:** Complex litigation; accounting malpractice; securities fraud litigation; shareholder litigation; class actions
**Professional Memberships:** Member, New York State Bar and American Bar Association.
**Career:** A member of the firm's management committee, Mr Singer recovered billions of dollars for investors in a number of the most significant and high-profile securities cases in the country, including WorldCom ($6.15 billion), Bank of America/Merrill Lynch ($2.425 billion), Lucent Technologies ($667 million), and Lehman Brothers Equity ($516 million), among others. Nominated as finalist for "Trial Lawyer of the Year" by Trial Lawyers for Public Justice for his prosecution of the class action race discrimination litigation, Roberts v. Texaco. He is ranked by the Legal 500 US Guide as one of the "Leading Lawyers" in the field of plaintiffs' securities litigation - one of only seven attorneys in the nation so recognized; a 'litigation star' by Benchmark (Euromoney/Institutional Investor); and named as a New York Super Lawyer by Super Lawyers.

**Publications:** Has written and lectured on securities fraud litigation and shareholder rights.
**Personal:** Duke University, 1988; Northwestern University School of Law 1991.

### SIT, Po
Davis Polk & Wardwell LLP, New York
212 450 4000
po.sit@davispolk.com
*Featured in Tax (New York)*
**Practice Areas:** Member of Davis Polk's Tax Department. Works principally in the areas of derivative products, partnerships, mergers and acquisitions. Has been representing financial institutions primarily in the areas of financial products and derivatives for years.

### SLIFKIN, Daniel
Cravath, Swaine & Moore LLP, New York
212 474 1438
dslifkin@cravath.com
*Featured in Litigation (New York)*
**Practice Areas:** Extensive litigation and trial experience in federal and state courts nationwide, as well as in domestic and international arbitrations. Substantial expertise in securities and general commercial disputes, as well as class action defense, shareholder derivative, employment, bankruptcy and intellectual property matters. Handles high-profile matters for some of the largest corporations in the world including Alcoa, JPMorgan Chase and Vivendi.
**Career:** Partner since 1998.
**Personal:** Harvard Law School; (JD, 1991; Law Review; Sears Prize); Oxford University (BA, first class honors, 1987; Martin Wronker Prize, Torts); Oxford University (BCL, first class honors, 1988).

### SLOTNICK, Barry I
Loeb & Loeb LLP, New York
212 407 4162
bslotnick@loeb.com
*Featured in Media & Entertainment (New York)*
**Practice Areas:** Concentrates on copyright and trademark infringement cases and matters in entertainment industry addressing the respective rights of owners and users, including cases on rights of privacy and publicity. Represents clients in entertainment, advertising, licensing and merchandising industries in courts nationwide.
**Professional Memberships:** Editorial Board, Journal of the Copyright Society of the USA; Board of Directors - Association of Independent Music Publishers; International Trademark Association; ABA.
**Career:** Partner since 2001. Intellectual Property and Entertainment Litigation Chair. Adjunct Professor, Entertainment Law, Syracuse University College of Law.
**Personal:** Syracuse University College of Law (JD 1972); Queens College (BA 1968).

### SMITH, Jeffrey
Crowell & Moring LLP, New York
212 895 4260
JASmith@crowell.com
*Featured in Climate Change (Nationwide), Environment (New York)*
**Practice Areas:** Partner in Crowell & Moring's Environment, Energy and Resources and

Corporate groups. Focuses practice on financings, underwritings and mergers and acquisitions nationally and internationally in all industries. Day-to-day counseling on environmental management and corporate governance issues, environmental issues of interest to the SEC, shareholder relations involving environmental matters and environmental litigation.
**Publications:** Author of numerous articles on SEC disclosure issues and issues relating to climate change.
**Personal:** University of Pennsylvania (JD, 1981); Harvard University (AB, cum laude, 1974). Board Member, The Urban Assembly, the Adams Street Foundation and Environmental Advocates of New York. Fellow, American Bar Foundation.

### SMITH, Jeffrey Q
Bingham McCutchen LLP, New York
212 705 7566
jq.smith@bingham.com
*Featured in Securities (Nationwide), Litigation (New York)*
See under Nationwide for profile.

### SMITH, Scott
Covington & Burling LLP, New York
212 841 1056
ssmith@cov.com
*Featured in Corporate/M&A (New York)*
**Practice Areas:** Mr Smith is Chair of the firm's Corporate Group and M&A Practice. His practice includes advising companies, investment banks and private equity funds on public and private mergers and acquisitions, hostile takeovers, proxy contests and leveraged buyouts. He has advised on a number of multi-billion dollar transactions. He also advises corporate boards and audit committees on corporate governance, and on general securities law matters.
**Personal:** JD, with high honors, The University of Texas (1980), Member of the Order of the Coif; AB, magna cum laude, Harvard University (1976).

### SMOLINSKY, Joseph H
Weil, Gotshal & Manges LLP, New York
212 310 8767
joseph.smolinsky@weil.com
*Featured in Bankruptcy/Restructuring (New York)*
**Practice Areas:** Mr Smolinsky has nearly 25 years of experience in corporate restructuring advising debtors, creditors and lenders in chapter 11 and out-of-court restructuring cases across a wide range of industries. He has been involved in recent high profile cases representing debtors and secured creditors, including Reader's Digest Association, Patriot Coal, General Motors, AES Eastern Energy, TBS Shipping, Pizzeria Unos, CIT, TOUSA, Refco, New Century Mortgage, Calpine and Mirant. He speaks regularly at conferences and seminars and has authored numerous articles.
**Personal:** SUNY Binghamton (BA, 1985); Brooklyn Law School (JD, 1988).

### SNYDER, Orin
Gibson, Dunn & Crutcher LLP, New York
212 351 2400
OSnyder@gibsondunn.com
*Featured in Litigation (New York), Media & Entertainment (New York)*

**Practice Areas:** Has a national civil and criminal litigation practice, including complex commercial, IP and media litigation, internal corporate investigations and other white-collar matters. Successfully represented such corporate clients as Facebook, NBC Universal, Cablevision, Aetna, Goldman Sachs, Starbucks, Time Warner, and Warner Music Group. Has also handled complex litigation for such well-known individuals as Mark Zuckerberg, Jerry Seinfeld, Edgar Bronfman, Jr. and Bob Dylan.
**Career:** Former name partner, Parcher Hayes & Snyder. Former Assistant US Attorney, Southern District of NY, Securities Fraud and Organized Crime Units, and Chief of the Narcotics Unit.
**Personal:** JD, University of Pennsylvania, 1986, cum laude.

### SOBEL, Gerald
Kaye Scholer LLP, New York
212 836 8515
gerald.sobel@kayescholer.com
*Featured in Life Sciences (Nationwide), Intellectual Property (New York)*
See under Nationwide for profile.

### SOLANDER, William
Fitzpatrick, Cella, Harper & Scinto, New York
212 218 2203
wsolander@fchs.com
*Featured in Intellectual Property (New York)*
**Practice Areas:** William E Solander is active in all areas of the firm's litigation practice and has participated in the litigation of numerous patent disputes, including the coordination of litigation occurring on a worldwide basis. His practice has embraced a wide range of technologies including, most recently, prescription anti-psoriasis medications, protein synthesis, anti-platelet inhibitor drugs, anti-cancer drugs, polymorphs, anti-ulcer drugs, structural composites, new battery technologies, and prescription sleep aids. Mr Solander also counsels clients concerning noninfringement, invalidity and freedom to practice in these and other fields. Some of the companies that he has represented or advised include Bristol-Myers Squibb, Debiopharm, LEO Pharma, Merck, Monsanto, Novartis, Sanofi and Sunovion. He was listed in Legal Media Group Guide to the World's Leading Patent Law Practitioners 2007 and was listed in IAM Life Sciences 250- The World's Leading Life Sciences Patent Litigators 2010. He was also listed in IAM Patent 1000 for 2011 and 2012. He was recognized for his outstanding work in the patent category in Chambers USA 2008-2012 and described as "terrific - he really gets into the case, knows the science, is up to date on the law and works well with witnesses."
**Professional Memberships:** American Intellectual Property Law Association; New York Intellectual Property Law Association.
**Career:** Fitzpatrick, Cella, Harper & Scinto, joined, 1995, Partner, 2003.
**Publications:** "Injunctions for patent infringement after the eBay decision," Intellectual Asset Management, February 2007.
**Personal:** California State Polytechnic University (BS Chemistry); Chicago-Kent College of Law (JD

with honors). Married, 3 children. Enjoys music, travel, cooking and watching his children play sports.

### SOLD, Kenneth W
Loeb & Loeb LLP, New York
212 407 4180
ksold@loeb.com
*Featured in Real Estate (New York)*
**Practice Areas:** Concentrates on commercial real estate law, with emphasis on commercial leasing, acquisitions and sales. Extensive experience representing owners of commercial property in their leasing programs, and has acted as national leasing counsel for financial services firms.
**Professional Memberships:** Member, NY State Bar Association.
**Career:** Became Partner in 1987. Joined Loeb in 2006.
**Personal:** Brooklyn Law School (JD, cum laude, 1981) Second Circuit Review Editor, Brooklyn Law Review (1980-1981); State University of New York at Binghamton (BA, 1978).

### SOLOMON, Andrew P
Sullivan & Cromwell LLP, New York
212 558 3783
solomona@sullcrom.com
*Featured in Tax (New York)*
**Professional Memberships:** ABA; NYSBA (Executive Committee, Tax Section).
**Career:** Partner since 1992. Broad-based practice: tax planning, dispute resolution. Advises on structuring acquisitions, divestitures, spin-offs, taxation of complex financial products. Clients: financial institutions (including insurance companies), private equity/hedge funds, global manufacturing companies, high-technology and natural resources companies. Experienced in domestic/international M&A, debt/equity restructuring; cross-border joint ventures; organization, operation and taking public of insurance companies/insurance securitization vehicles.
**Publications:** Writes/speaks on taxation of financial products/institutions, international taxation. Editorial Board, Journal of Taxation and Regulation of Financial Institutions.
**Personal:** Harvard Law (JD, 1984; Editor, Harvard Law Review); Brown (AB, 1975).

### SOLOMON, Louis M
Cadwalader, Wickersham & Taft LLP, New York
212 504 6600
louis.solomon@cwt.com
*Featured in Litigation (New York)*
**Practice Areas:** Chair, Commercial and International Litigation Group, and Co-Chair, Litigation Department. Tried over 50 complex commercial cases. Served as lead counsel in private and class action cases, government and regulatory proceedings, including: antitrust, corporate/commercial finance; employment; patent and other intellectual property; insurance/reinsurance; international bankruptcy/restructurings; pharmaceutical regulation; securities; and telecommunications. International matters have included cases involving many EU countries, Latin America, Asia, Africa and the Middle East. Regularly repre-

sents leading companies such as Andrx, AriZona Iced Tea, Bouygues S.A., Bristol-Myers Squibb, FIFA, Japan Tobacco, KFC, MOMA, the New York Jets, Overseas Shipholding Group, PepsiCo, U.K.'s Premier Football League, and W.R. Huff Companies.
**Professional Memberships:** Lawyers Committee of the National Center for State Courts (NCSC).
**Publications:** Author, International Litigation: Topics and Trends (e-book) and International Practice blog (www.internationalpractice.org).
**Personal:** JD, Harvard Law School (magna cum laude); BA, Yeshiva University (summa cum laude).

### SONTAG, Scott M
Weil, Gotshal & Manges LLP, New York
212 310 8929
scott.sontag@weil.com
*Featured in Tax (New York)*
**Practice Areas:** Scott Sontag is a Co-head of Weil's global Tax Practice. His practice covers a broad range of international and domestic transactions, such as structuring and negotiating complex merger and acquisition transactions for private equity funds and their portfolio companies, as well as for the firm's publicly held clients. In addition, he advises clients extensively on transactions involving the formation and acquisition of REITs and on real estate acquisitions, dispositions, and restructurings.
**Personal:** University of Michigan (BBA); New York University (JD). Mr Sontag is a Certified Public Accountant.

### SORABELLA, William B
Kirkland & Ellis LLP, New York
212 446 4932
william.sorabella@kirkland.com
*Featured in Corporate/M&A (New York)*
**Practice Areas:** William Sorabella regularly represents strategic acquirers and sellers, target companies, private equity funds and special committees in the purchase, merger and sale of companies, business divisions and assets and in the formation and dissolution of joint ventures. He also regularly advises financial advisors in similar transactions. Recent representative clients include Burger King Worldwide, 3G Capital Partners, Sunoco, Wyndham Worldwide, Solutia and Constellation Energy. He has been recognized as a leading deal-maker by several publications.
**Publications:** Georgetown University Law Center, JD, 2000 cum laude; Bowdoin College, AB, Economics & Government, 1997 summa cum laude, Leonard A. Pierce Memorial Prize.

### SORIN, Robert J
Fried, Frank, Harris, Shriver & Jacobson LLP, New York
212 859 8487
Robert.Sorin@FriedFrank.com
*Featured in Real Estate (New York)*
**Practice Areas:** Real estate partner. Practice covers a broad range of commercial real estate transactions, including the development of office, residential, hotel and mixed-use projects, commercial mortgage and mezzanine financing, con-

struction financing, leasing, the sale and acquisition of office, hotel and retail properties, debt restructurings and joint ventures. Clients include Goldman, Sachs & Co.; Google Inc.; Host Hotels and Resorts, Inc.; IDB Group; Macklowe Properties; Meringoff Properties, Inc.; The Children's Investment Fund Management (UK) LLP; The Moinian Group; and UBS.
**Career:** Joined as partner in 1997.
**Personal:** JD, cum laude, Georgetown University (1982); BA, magna cum laude, Washington University (1979).

### SORKIN, Ira Lee
Lowenstein Sandler LLP, New York
646 414 6830
isorkin@lowenstein.com
*Featured in Litigation (New York)*
**Practice Areas:** Ira Lee ("Ike") Sorkin focuses his practice on white collar criminal defense, SEC enforcement and other regulatory investigations and proceedings, internal investigations, corporate governance, FINRA defense, and criminal and civil litigation. He has represented individuals and entities being investigated and prosecuted for insider trading, market manipulation, Regulation M, Regulation SHO, securities fraud, bribery, stock manipulation, Foreign Corrupt Practices Act, Ponzi schemes, perjury, conspiracy, false filings and obstruction of justice, and accounting fraud. His clients include individuals, hedge funds, public and private corporations, and registered entities such as broker/dealers and audit committees of public corporations.
www.lowenstein.com/isorkin

### SORKIN, John E
Fried, Frank, Harris, Shriver & Jacobson LLP, New York
212 859 8980
John.Sorkin@friedfrank.com
*Featured in Corporate/M&A (New York)*
**Practice Areas:** Corporate partner. Focuses his practice on US and cross-border mergers, acquisitions and leveraged buyouts as well as advisory work related to corporate governance. His experience spans corporate transactions, including public and private mergers and acquisitions, proxy contests, spin-offs, exchange offers and representation of financial advisors in a wide range of corporate transactions. Adjunct Professor of Law, Benjamin N. Cardozo School of Law.
**Career:** Joined as partner in 2007.
**Personal:** JD, with honors, University of Chicago Law School (1994); BA, magna cum laude, Yale University (1990).

### SORKIN, Laurence T
Cahill Gordon & Reindel LLP, New York
212 701 3209
LSorkin@cahill.com
*Featured in Antitrust (New York)*
**Practice Areas:** Extensive experience in antitrust counseling, investigations, and litigation. Advises clients on M&As, joint ventures, IP licensing, and dominant firm conduct. Has represented clients in numerous cartel investigations and follow-on damage actions, as well as broad range of antitrust litigation in federal and state courts.

**Personal:** Visiting lecturer, Yale Law School, and adjunct professor, Fordham Law School. Brown University, BA, 1964, summa cum laude; Yale Law School, LLB 1967; London School of Economics, LLM, 1968, Fulbright Scholar. Advisory board, BNA Antitrust & Trade Regulation Report; board of editors, Lexis/Nexis Antitrust Report. Co-chair, ABA Antitrust Section Civil Redress Task Force.

**SPATT, Robert E**
Simpson Thacher & Bartlett LLP, New York
212 455 2000
rspatt@stblaw.com
*Featured in Corporate/M&A (New York)*
**Practice Areas:** Partner specialising in corporate and governance advice to boards of directors, and M&A for companies, financial advisors, control stockholders, LBO firms and special committees. Recent representations include McKesson acquiring PSS World Medical; Clearwire's Special Committee in its pending sale to Sprint; an Apax Partners-led consortium acquiring Kinetic Concepts; Toshiba Medical Systems acquiring Vital Images; CoStar Group acquiring LoopNet; and the financial advisors for UnitedHealth merging with Amil Participações, United Technologies acquiring Goodrich, and Medco Health Solutions merging with Express Scripts.
**Personal:** Brown University (AB, 1977), University of Michigan Law School (JD, magna cum laude 1980; Order of the Coif).

**SPILKO, Howard T**
Kramer Levin Naftalis & Frankel LLP, New York
212 715 9267
hspilko@kramerlevin.com
*Featured in Corporate/M&A (New York)*
**Practice Areas:** Mr Spilko is a Partner in Kramer Levin's Corporate Department and serves on the firm's Executive Committee. Mr Spilko has a diverse practice focused on mergers and acquisitions, joint ventures and finance transactions. He works with a broad range of clients from well-known multinational companies to private equity firms, hedge funds and entrepreneurial ventures. Mr Spilko regularly speaks and writes about mergers and acquisitions and joint ventures.
**Personal:** He graduated from the University of Pennsylvania Law School, cum laude, in 1992, where he was an editor on the Journal of International Business Law. He has an accounting degree, summa cum laude, from Binghamton University.

**SPRAYREGEN, James HM**
Kirkland & Ellis LLP, Chicago
312 862 2481
james.sprayregen@kirkland.com
*Featured in Bankruptcy/Restructuring (Nationwide), Bankruptcy/Restructuring (Illinois), Bankruptcy/Restructuring (New York)*
See under Nationwide for profile.

**STAMBOULIDIS, George A.**
Baker & Hostetler LLP, New York
212 589 4211
gstamboulidis@bakerlaw.com
*Featured in Litigation (New York)*

**Career:** Co-Chair of BakerHostetler's national White Collar Defense and Corporate Investigations team, George Stamboulidis focuses on white collar and corporate criminal and regulatory matters, internal investigations, monitorships, Dodd-Frank issues, FCPA matters and complex litigation. George counsels and defends individuals, corporations, financial institutions, hedge funds and healthcare professionals in federal, local criminal and regulatory investigations involving allegations of accounting, securities, bank, mortgage, insurance and healthcare fraud, money laundering, tax evasion, insider trading and antitrust violations. Appointed by the DOJ as a federal monitor four times, he currently serves as Ethical Practices Attorney for Local 14-14B of the International Union of Operating Engineers.

**STAMER, Michael S**
Akin Gump Strauss Hauer & Feld LLP, New York
212 872 1025
mstamer@akingump.com
*Featured in Bankruptcy/Restructuring (Nationwide), Bankruptcy/Restructuring (New York)*
**Practice Areas:** Concentrates on debtors' and creditors' rights, corporate restructurings and bankruptcy law. Represents official and unofficial committees of unsecured creditors, debtors, secured creditors, DIP lenders and acquirers of business and assets in large, complex Chapter 11 cases and out-of-court restructurings.
**Professional Memberships:** Bars of New York and New Jersey; US District Courts for the Northern, Southern and Eastern Districts of New York and the District of New Jersey.
**Career:** Law clerk for the Honorable Daniel J Moore, USBC District of New Jersey 1989-90.
**Personal:** BA, University of Vermont (1986); JD, Rutgers School of Law - Newark (1989).

**STANGE, Eiko**
Wachtell, Lipton, Rosen & Katz, New York
212 403 1319
TEStange@wlrk.com
*Featured in Tax (New York)*
**Practice Areas:** Practice focuses on the tax aspects of U.S. and cross-border mergers and acquisitions, spin-offs and other dispositions, leveraged buyouts, joint ventures and financing transactions. Has been the principal tax lawyer on numerous domestic and cross-border transactions in various industries, including telecommunications, technology, pharmaceuticals, banking and financial services, media and entertainment, real estate and retail.
**Professional Memberships:** Member of the Tax Sections of the American Bar Association and the New York State Bar Association.
**Career:** Partner at Wachtell, Lipton, Rosen & Katz since 2006.
**Personal:** Graduated from the University of Hamburg, Germany, in 1993 (JD) and from NYU School of Law in 1995 (LLM in Corporation Law) and 1998 (LLM in Taxation).

**STARR, Michael**
Holland & Knight LLP, New York
212 513 3506
Michael.Starr@hklaw.com
*Featured in Labor & Employment (New York)*
**Practice Areas:** Partner in the Litigation Section and New York Labor and Employment team. A Fellow of the College of Labor and Employment Lawyers, Starr practices in all areas of employment and labor relations law, with an emphasis on litigation before state and federal courts involving both trial and appellate advocacy. He represents management in NLRB and other agency proceedings, as well as in arbitration, mediation, and collective bargaining. He has extensive experience in the media, entertainment and hospitality industries, and is actively engaged in defense of employment discrimination claims, non-competition, trade secret and employee disloyalty litigation, and labor-antitrust matters.

**STEIN, Mark**
Simpson Thacher & Bartlett LLP, New York
212 455 2310
mstein@stblaw.com
*Featured in Litigation (New York)*
**Practice Areas:** Litigation Partner representing companies and individuals in investigations conducted by the US DOJ, US Attorney's Offices around the country, the New York State Attorney General's Office, the SEC, and other federal, state and self-regulatory bodies.
**Professional Memberships:** Fellow of the American College of Trial Lawyers.
**Career:** Assistant US attorney in the SDNY (1989-94), ending tenure as Deputy Chief of the Criminal Division. Served as an assistant in the Office of the Independent Counsel for the Whitewater investigation in 1994.
**Personal:** BA, State University of New York at Albany (1980); JD, University of Michigan (1983).

**STEINBERG, Arthur**
King & Spalding LLP, New York
212 556 2158
asteinberg@kslaw.com
*Featured in Bankruptcy/Restructuring (New York)*
**Practice Areas:** In his 32 years of practice, Mr Steinberg has represented a broad range of clients, including examiners, trustees, corporate monitors, debtors, creditors' committees, secured and unsecured creditors groups/individuals, distressed investors and asset buyers, and parties to bankruptcy related litigation. He also has acted as a Receiver and Investment Company Act Trustee for failed hedge funds and investment advisors.
**Professional Memberships:** New York City Bar Association American Bar Association American Bankruptcy Institute Turnaround Managers Association.
**Personal:** JD, New York University BA Economics, cum laude, Columbia University.

**STEINER, Jeffrey B**
DLA Piper LLP (US), New York
212 335 4580
jeffrey.steiner@dlapiper.com
*Featured in Real Estate (New York)*
**Practice Areas:** Real Estate Finance, Corporate.

**Career:** He is chair of the firm's US Corporate and Finance Practice. He regularly represents Wall Street investment banks and institutional lenders in complex structured finance transactions, including construction, conduit, floating and fixed rate financings, forward loan commitments, mezzanine loans, loan participations, low-income housing tax credit, and mortgage-backed securities transactions.
**Personal:** JD, Fordham University School of Law; BA, McGill University

**STERN, Akiba**
Loeb & Loeb LLP, New York
212 407 4235
astern@loeb.com
*Featured in Outsourcing (Nationwide), Technology (New York)*
See under Nationwide for profile.

**STERN, Scott L**
Bingham McCutchen LLP, New York
212 705 7315
scott.stern@bingham.com
*Featured in Real Estate (New York)*
**Practice Areas:** Represents financial institutions in commercial real estate loans and other types of asset-based lending. Represents lenders and owner-developers in transactions involving office buildings, retail, multifamily apartment complexes, cooperatives, condominiums, shopping centers and land development.
**Personal:** Benjamin N. Cardozo School of Law, JD, 1996; University of Wisconsin, BA, 1993.

**STERNBERG, Daniel S**
Cleary Gottlieb Steen & Hamilton LLP, New York
212 225 2630
dsternberg@cgsh.com
*Featured in Corporate/M&A (New York)*
**Practice Areas:** Domestic and international M&A, cross-border transactions. Corporate governance advice to corporate boards and institutional shareholders, including election contests. Represented Robert Rosenkranz (sale of Delphi Financial), América Móvil (Telmex, Telmex International acquisitions), Alkermes (EDT), Vornado (JC Penney), Crucell (Johnson & Johnson), Special Committee of Interactive Data (Silver Lake/ Warburg Pincus LBO), Hellman & Friedman (Neuberger Berman), Istithmar (Barneys, Cirque du Soleil, Kerzner, Loehmann's).
**Professional Memberships:** Member, Former Chairman, NYC Bar M&A Committee.
**Career:** Senior Counsel since 2012. Partner 1998-2011. Paris office, 1991-1996. JD, Columbia Law School (1979), Kent Scholar, editor - Law Review. BA, cum laude, Yale University (1976).

**STEVER, Donald W**
K&L Gates, New York
212 536 4861
don.stever@klgates.com
*Featured in Environment (New York)*
**Practice Areas:** An environmental lawyer with more than 40 years of civil and criminal environmental litigation and counseling experience and a fellow of the American College of Environmental Lawyers, Mr Stever's practice includes air, water,

solid and hazardous waste, CERCLA, noise, environmental impact assessment, natural resource damages, environmental torts and constitutional environmental litigation, oil spill counseling and litigation, and maritime environmental compliance counseling, primarily for industrial clients. He has also managed environmental due diligence and transactional negotiations for hundreds of M&A, project finance, and capital markets transactions. He authored a leading treatise, "Law of Chemical Regulation and Hazardous Waste."

**STOLL, Neal R**
Skadden, Arps, Slate, Meagher & Flom LLP & Affiliates, New York
212 735 3660
Neal.Stoll@skadden.com
*Featured in Antitrust (New York)*
**Practice Areas:** Represents clients involved in investigations conducted by the staff of the Department of Justice, Antitrust Division; Part 2 investigations conducted by the staffs of the Federal Trade Commission's Bureau of Competition and Bureau of Consumer Protection; Part 3 administrative proceedings and appeals; and federal trial and appellate experience in cases involving monopolization, distribution practices, the Robinson-Patman Act and acquisitions. Counsels clients on antitrust issues regarding mergers and acquisitions, as well as antitrust and consumer protection matters, including compliance programs and proposed business plans.
**Career:** JD, Fordham University, 1973 (Member, Fordham Law Review); BA, Pennsylvania State University, 1970.

**STRASSBERG, Richard M**
Goodwin Procter LLP, New York
212 813 8859
rstrassberg@goodwinprocter.com
*Featured in Litigation (New York)*
**Practice Areas:** Mr Strassberg specializes in white-collar criminal defense, corporate internal investigations, corporate regulatory practice, and complex business and financial litigation. In addition to his work in the white-collar and regulatory arenas, he represents clients in complex civil litigation, including representations involving securities class action defense, minority shareholder rights, ERISA class action defense, healthcare and insurance litigation, and employment issues.
**Career:** Previously, Mr Strassberg was the Chief of the Major Crimes Unit in the United States Attorney's Office for the Southern District of New York.
**Personal:** JD, Harvard Law School, 1988 (cum laude); BS, Cornell University, 1985 (with distinction).

**STRICKLAND, Rachel C**
Willkie Farr & Gallagher LLP, New York
212 728 8544
rstrickland@willkie.com
*Featured in Bankruptcy/Restructuring (New York)*
**Practice Areas:** Represents financially distressed companies, debtors, investors, hedge funds, shareholders, ad hoc groups of bondholders and lenders and other creditors in out-of-court and in-court restructurings; acquisition of

and lending to distressed companies; advising on fiduciary duties, fraudulent transfers, legacy liabilities and secured and commercial transactions; litigating valuation and other plan confirmation disputes. Clients include Fidelity National Financial, EchoStar Corporation, Polaroid International, J.P. Morgan Asset Management, Caspian Capital, and Appaloosa Management. Recognized as outstanding restructuring attorney by national and international publications. Frequent lecturer and author on insolvency matters.
**Personal:** JD, New York University School of Law, 1998. BA, Michigan State University, 1994. See: http://www.willkie.com/RachelStrickland

**SUCHAROW, Lawrence**
Labaton Sucharow LLP, New York
212 907 0860
lsucharow@labaton.com
*Featured in Securities (Nationwide), Litigation (New York)*
**Practice Areas:** Securities litigation.
**Career:** With more than three decades of experience, Lawrence Sucharow is an internationally recognized trial lawyer and a leader of the securities class action bar. As Chairman of the Firm, Mr Sucharow focuses on developing creative and compelling strategies to advance and protect clients' interests. Mr Sucharow has prosecuted hundreds of cases and the Firm has recovered more than $8 billion in groundbreaking securities, antitrust, business transaction, product liability and other class actions. In fact the landmark case, In re Real Estate Associates Limited Partnership Litigation, was the very first securities action successfully tried to a jury verdict following the enactment of the Private Securities Litigation Reform Act. His representative matters include: In re CNL Resorts, Inc. Securities Litigation ($225 million settlement); In re Paine Webber Incorporated Limited Partnerships Litigation ($200 million settlement); In re Prudential Securities Incorporated Limited Partnerships Litigation ($110 million partial settlement); and Shea v. New York Life Insurance Company (over $92 million settlement). Mr Sucharow serves as a trustee of the Federal Bar Council Foundation and serves on the Advocacy Committee of the World Federation of Investors Corporation, a worldwide umbrella organization of national shareholder associations. He is also past President of the National Association of Shareholder and Consumer Attorneys, a membership organization of approximately 100 law firms that practice complex civil litigation.

**SULDS, Jonathan L**
Greenberg Traurig, LLP, New York
212 801 6882
SuldsJ@gtlaw.com
*Featured in Labor & Employment (New York)*
**Practice Areas:** Co-Chair, Global Labor & Employment Practice. Co-Chair, Global Human Capital Solutions Practice. Co-Chair, Global Labor & Employment Litigation Practice. Co-Chair, National ERISA Litigation Practice.
**Career:** Selected: Chambers USA Guide, 2007-13; Super Lawyers magazine, 2009-12; The Best

Lawyers in America, 2012-13. Rated, AV® Preeminent™ 5.0 out of 5. Team Member, Law360 'Employment Practice Group of the Year', 2011.
**Publications:** Author, New York Employment Law; Second Edition (Matthew Bender/LEXIS-NEXIS—4 volume treatise updated annually); Co-Editor, 'GT LE Blog: National Developments in Labor & Employment Law' http://www.gtleblog.com/; Author, 'Trade Secret Protection', Security Management, November, 2011.
**Personal:** JD, cum laude, Harvard Law School; MA, with distinction, Colgate University; BA, magna cum laude, Colgate University.

**SULLIVAN, Peter**
Gibson, Dunn & Crutcher LLP, New York
212 351 5370
psullivan@gibsondunn.com
*Featured in Antitrust (New York)*
**Practice Areas:** Co-Chair – Gibson Dunn's Antitrust Practice; Focuses on all aspects of domestic/international antitrust, including civil, criminal; merger/JVs, counseling, cartel investigations, class actions, compliance, monopoly, unfair competition and consumer matters.
**Professional Memberships:** New York and California Bars; Solicitor, England and Wales; Brussels Bar; ABA and IBA.
**Publications:** Lectures extensively on antitrust and litigation topics; Co-author, Antitrust Laws and Trade Regulation (recognized as authoritative by U.S. Supreme Court; cited in over 100 court decisions); Editor, Antitrust & Trade Regulation Report.
**Personal:** JD, cum laude, Fordham Law School, 1977, Articles Editor, Law Review; BA, Columbia University, 1974.

**SULLIVAN, Robert J**
Skadden, Arps, Slate, Meagher & Flom LLP & Affiliates, New York
212 735 2930
Robert.Sullivan@skadden.com
*Featured in Insurance (Nationwide), Insurance (New York)*
See under Nationwide for profile.

**SUSKO, A Richard (Brick)**
Cleary Gottlieb Steen & Hamilton LLP, New York
212 225 2410
bsusko@cgsh.com
*Featured in Employee Benefits & Executive Compensation (Nationwide), Employee Benefits & Executive Compensation (New York)*
See under Nationwide for profile.

**SUSSBERG, Joshua A**
Kirkland & Ellis LLP, New York
212 446 4829
joshua.sussberg@kirkland.com
*Featured in Bankruptcy/Restructuring (New York)*
**Practice Areas:** Josh represents debtors, creditors, equity holders, investors and private equity funds in all aspects of restructuring distressed companies. Representative clients include AMF Bowling, Edison Mission Energy, Barneys, Neways, Kerzner International, Horizon Lines, Orchard Brands, Keystone Automotive, Atrium

Corporation, TOUSA, Citadel Broadcasting, Josh also has recently represented creditors in restructurings involving Reddy Ice, Aquilex, Broadstripe, Caribbean Petroleum, Natural Products Group, Mervyn's, American Home Mortgage and New Century Financial.
**Personal:** Benjamin N Cardozo School of Law, JD, cum laude, 2003; Syracuse University, S.I. Newhouse School of Public Communications, BS, magna cum laude, 2000.

**SUTHERLAND, Susan J**
Skadden, Arps, Slate, Meagher & Flom LLP & Affiliates, New York
212 735 2388
Susan.Sutherland@skadden.com
*Featured in Insurance (New York)*
**Practice Areas:** Susan J. Sutherland is a partner in Skadden's Financial Institutions Group with more than 30 years of experience. Ms Sutherland focuses on representing U.S. and international insurance and reinsurance companies, investment banks and private equity firms in insurance-related corporate transactions, including capital raising, mergers and acquisitions, reinsurance transactions, restructurings and related matters. Ms Sutherland also provides advice on corporate governance, SEC reporting obligations, regulatory requirements and general corporate matters.
**Career:** JD, New York University School of Law, 1982 (Root-Tilden Scholar; Member, Review of Law and Social Change); BA, Denison University, 1979 (highest honors; Phi Beta Kappa).

**SUTIN, Alan N.**
Greenberg Traurig, LLP, New York
212 801 9286
SutinA@gtlaw.com
*Featured in Technology (New York)*
**Practice Areas:** Chair, Global Intellectual Property & Technology Practice. Chair, Technology, Media & Telecommunications Practice.
**Professional Memberships:** Board Member, International Technology Lawyers Association; Vice Chair, Technology Committee, Inter-Pacific Bar Association; Chair, Internet Gambling Subcommittee of the American Bar Association Subcommittee on Cyberspace's Internet Jurisdiction Project.
**Career:** Named, U.S. News-Best Lawyers 'Law Firm of the Year' in Entertainment Law-Music, 2011-12. Selected: Best Lawyers in America, 2005-13; Super Lawyers magazine, 2006-12. Recognized, IAM Licensing 250: The World's Leading Patent and Technology Licensing Practitioners, Intellectual Asset Management (IAM) Magazine, 2010.
**Personal:** JD, University of Georgia School of Law, 1984; BA, Emory University, 1979.

**SWARTZ, Linda Z**
Cadwalader, Wickersham & Taft LLP, New York
212 504 6062
linda.swartz@cwt.com
*Featured in Tax (New York)*
**Practice Areas:** Chair, Tax Department. Concentrates on global mergers and acquisitions,

bankruptcies and restructurings, spin-offs, joint ventures, and financings. Recent transactions include Vertis Holdings in connection with its $363 million sale to Quad/Graphics; Quest Software, Inc. Chairman Vincent Smith in the $2.4 billion sale of Quest Software to Dell Inc.; Towers Watson & Co. in its acquisition of Extend Health Inc.; Procter & Gamble Co. in its sale of the Pringles Group to Kellogg.

**Professional Memberships:** New York State Bar Association Tax Section (Executive Committee); American Bar Association (Tax Section); New York City Tax Club.

**Publications:** "Global Tax-Free Deals: Mergers, Acquisitions and Spins at Home and Abroad;" "ABCs of Cross-Border Derivatives;" "Partnership Bankruptcies;" "A Layman's Guide to LLC Incentive Compensation;" and "Debt Exchanges."

**Personal:** JD, University of Pennsylvania Law School; BA, Bucknell University (Phi Beta Kappa). Named one of top 29 U.S. tax advisors by the Tax Directors Handbook.

## SWEENEY, John F
Locke Lord LLP, New York
212 415 8625
jsweeney@lockelord.com
*Featured in Intellectual Property (New York)*

**Practice Areas:** Mr Sweeney's litigation experience includes patent, antitrust, trademark and trade dress bench and jury trials and appeals. He has argued many times in the US Court of Appeals for the Federal Circuit.

**Professional Memberships:** ABA; AIPLA; Association of the Bar of the City of New York; New York Intellectual Property Law Association.

**Career:** Partner at Locke Lord since 2009.

**Personal:** Georgetown University Law Center (JD, 1973); Carnegie-Mellon University (BS, Mathematics, 1968). Before entering the legal practice, worked as a mathematician and computer analyst for the US Army Strategy and Tactics Analysis Group.

## SYNNOTT, Aidan
Paul, Weiss, Rifkind, Wharton & Garrison LLP, New York
212 373 3213
asynnott@paulweiss.com
*Featured in Antitrust (New York)*

**Practice Areas:** Partner in Litigation Department. Focuses on antitrust litigation and compliance, intellectual property litigation, securities litigation and complex commercial litigation. Has extensive trial experience in state and federal courts as well as in alternative dispute resolution forums such as the American Arbitration Association. Frequently represents clients in antitrust investigations by governmental agencies of the United States and the European Union. Has published in the areas of antitrust, trade regulation and intellectual property law, and has served as a fellow of the American Bar Foundation and as an associate editor of Antitrust Law Journal.

## TAFFET, Richard S
Bingham McCutchen LLP, New York
212 705 7729
richard.taffet@bingham.com
*Featured in Antitrust (New York)*

**Practice Areas:** Serves as lead counsel in a wide range of intellectual property, antitrust and commercial litigation matters. Represents US and foreign-based clients in numerous industries, including consumer electronics, telecommunications, pharmaceuticals, textiles, chemicals, software development, financial industries and publishing. Counsels clients in connection with protecting IP assets and marketing and distribution. Represents clients before federal agencies, including the Department of Justice, the Federal Trade Commission, the US Trade Representatives Office and the Consumer Products Safety Commission.

**Career:** Frequent speaker and contributor to publications on IP and antitrust issues.

**Personal:** Brooklyn Law School, JD, 1980; Sarah Lawrence College, BA, 1977.

## TAMBE, Jayant
Jones Day, New York
212 236 3604
jtambe@jonesday.com
*Featured in Litigation (New York)*

**Practice Areas:** Jay is co-leader of Jones Day's Financial Institutions Litigation & Regulation Practice and advises clients on litigation concerning securities, derivatives, CDOs and other structured products. He currently leads the Firm's representation, as Special Derivatives Counsel, of Lehman Bros. Holdings, Inc. and its affiliated debtors. Jay led the team that prevailed in the first appeal before ISDA's external review panel (In re Cemex, S.A.B. de C.V.). He has also led numerous trial court and appellate victories in securities, derivatives structured finance matters. (See, e.g., Banco Espirito Santo de Investimento v. Citibank, 2003 WL 23018888 (2d Cir 2003).)

## TANENBAUM, Edward
Alston & Bird LLP, New York
212 210 9425
edward.tanenbaum@alston.com
*Featured in Tax (New York)*

**Practice Areas:** Domestic and cross-border mergers and acquisitions and business transactions, primarily planning and structuring for U.S. investments by foreign multinational corporations and high net worth individuals.

**Professional Memberships:** National Council of the International Fiscal Association; Former Chair, Committee on U.S. Activities of Foreign Taxpayers and Tax Treaties of the Tax Section of the American Bar Association. Director and past president, International Tax Institute; Tax Management U.S. International Advisory Board.

**Career:** Co-Chairs firm's Federal and International Tax Group.

**Personal:** BA, magna cum laude, (1971) Queens College; JD (1974) Fordham University; LLM (Taxation) (1980) New York University.

## TANENBAUM, William A
Kaye Scholer LLP, New York
212 836 7661
william.tanenbaum@kayescholer.com
*Featured in Outsourcing (Nationwide), Technology (New York)*

**Practice Areas:** Chair, Intellectual Property and Technology Transactions Group. Chair, GreenTech and Sustainability Group. "Built one of New York City's most outstanding transactional IT practices," "real-world mindset" and "makes excellent judgment calls." (Chambers USA). Assists clients in updating IT systems and integrating Cloud, Big Data, Mobile and Social Media. Lead counsel in technology-enabled business transactions; outsourcing; strategic IP counseling; IP aspects of corporate transactions; cross-border IP, licensing and technology transactions; Healthcare IT; convergence of mainstream business with sustainability technology. Past President, International Technology Law Association. Currently Vice President, CIO-association Society for Information Management (NY). Brown University and Cornell Law School.

## TAYLOR, Errol B
Milbank, Tweed, Hadley & McCloy LLP, New York
212 530 5545
etaylor@milbank.com
*Featured in Intellectual Property (New York)*

**Practice Areas:** Mr Taylor is the leading partner of the Biopharma Patent Litigation Practice and Chair of the Diversity Committee. He focuses mainly on representing research pharmaceutical, biotechnology and chemical companies in patent litigation and related counseling. Mr Taylor has particular expertise in cases involving generic drug approvals and the Hatch-Waxman Act. He has served as lead trial counsel in numerous multi-party, multinational cases involving some of the world's most prescribed medicines.

## TEITELBAUM, Marc
Dentons, New York
212 768 6749
marc.teitelbaum@dentons.com
*Featured in Tax (New York)*

**Practice Areas:** Heads legacy Dentons's Tax practice. Mr Teitelbaum advises public companies, underwriters and investment funds in various areas, including: acquisition and disposition of domestic and foreign corporations (taxable or tax-free transactions); internal restructurings to achieve tax efficiencies; debt and equity financings, including cross-border financing arrangements and restructurings; and the US tax consequences of foreign operations. Mr Teitelbaum advises multinational manufacturing and service organizations, including investment advisors. He advises on investment strategies in partnership form.

**Professional Memberships:** American College of Tax Counsel, The Tax Club (New York).

**Personal:** New York University School of Law, LLM, (Taxation) and JD; University of Chicago, BA.

## TEMKIN, Jeremy
Morvillo Abramowitz Grand Iason & Anello P.C., New York
212 880 9470
jtemkin@magislaw.com
*Featured in Litigation (New York)*

**Practice Areas:** Jeremy H Temkin represents individuals and corporations in federal white collar criminal investigations with a special emphasis on criminal tax cases. He handles a wide variety of criminal, regulatory and civil matters in state and federal courts and before arbitration panels. His cases have involved allegations of tax fraud and securities fraud (including claims of insider trading and accounting violations), as well as violations of the antitrust laws, the Foreign Corrupt Practices Act ("FCPA") and Office of Foreign Asset Control ("OFAC") regulations.

**Professional Memberships:** Board of Directors of Legal Aid Society and the New York Council of Defense Lawyers and Chair of its Ethics, Rules, and Legislation Committee. Recipient of James Fogelson Leadership Award from the UJA-Federation of New York, Lawyer's Division.

**Publications:** Author "Tax Litigation" column in the New York Law Journal. Contributor to The Insider Blog at forbes.com/sites/insider

**Personal:** University of California at Los Angeles (JD, member of the Order of the Coif and an editor of the Law Review). Haverford College (BA, Phi Beta Kappa). Recipient of Department of Justice Director's Award for Superior Performance as an Assistant U.S. Attorney for the Southern District of New York.

## TERRACIANO, Annmarie M
Cravath, Swaine & Moore LLP, New York
212 474 1366
aterraciano@cravath.com
*Featured in Environment (New York)*

**Practice Areas:** Annmarie M. Terraciano is a senior attorney in Cravath's Corporate Department. Ms Terraciano advises the Firm's clients on environmental matters including those relating to mergers and acquisitions, securities offerings, financings and other business transactions. She also provides counseling on environmental compliance matters, environmental proceedings, environmental indemnification disputes and environmental aspects of periodic reporting obligations under securities laws.

**Personal:** Columbia Law School (JD, 1998; Harlan Fiske Stone Scholar; Articles Editor, Human Rights Law Review); University of Wisconsin - Madison (MS, 1994); Wellesley College (BA, cum laude, 1989). For more information: http://www.cravath.com/aterraciano

## TETI II, J Leonard (Len)
Cravath, Swaine & Moore LLP, New York
212 474 1896
lteti@cravath.com
*Featured in Tax (New York)*

**Practice Areas:** J Leonard Teti II is a partner in Cravath's Tax Department. His practice focuses on advising clients on the tax aspects of complex mergers and acquisitions, spin-offs, private equity

transactions and bank financings. Mr Teti's clients have included Barnes & Noble, Credit Suisse, IBM, Johnson & Johnson, The Jones Group, JPMorgan Chase, Lindsay Goldberg and Time Warner.
**Personal:** University of Virginia (JD, 2005; Order of the Coif; Virgina Law Review; Virginia Tax Review; Edwin S Cohen Tax Prize; Robert E Goldsten Award of Distinction in the Classroom); Princeton University (AB, cum laude, 1999). For more information: http://www.cravath.com/lteti

### THAU, Clifford
Vinson & Elkins LLP, New York
212 237 0012
cthau@velaw.com
*Featured in Litigation (New York)*
**Practice Areas:** Commercial litigation with an emphasis on representing clients principally in the financial, energy, media and in other sectors in lawsuits involving the federal securities laws, including representation of issuers, underwriters, officers and directors, and accounting firms in securities laws class actions; securities and private equity firms and senior management in federal and state regulatory proceedings; and Audit Committees in internal investigations and SEC investigations into allegations of accounting irregularities and insider trading.
**Career:** Partner since 2002; currently serves as a member of the Firm's Management Committee and Managing Partner of the New York office.
**Publications:** Lectured on subjects relating to the federal securities law and written several articles for legal publications.
**Personal:** Columbia Law School, JD, 1981; University of Pennsylvania, BA, 1978; admitted to practice in New York, United States Supreme Court, US Court of Appeals, Second and Fifth Circuits, and US District Court, Southern and Eastern Districts of New York.

### THIERFELDER, Mark E
Dechert LLP, New York
212 698 3804
mark.thierfelder@dechert.com
*Featured in Corporate/M&A (New York)*
**Practice Areas:** Mr Thierfelder concentrates his practice on private equity transactions and domestic and international mergers and acquisitions. He represents leading private equity funds and their portfolio companies in a full range of corporate transactions, including recapitalizations, leveraged financings, restructuring, and reorganizations. He negotiates, structures, and executes corporate transactions on behalf of strategic buyers and sellers, and represents lenders in leveraged financings and restructurings.
**Professional Memberships:** Member, New York Bar; member, New York City Bar Association Corporation Law Committee.
**Personal:** Duke University (BA, 1986); Rutgers University School of Law—Newark (JD, 1992, with honors, Order of the Coif).

### THOMASCH, Daniel J
Gibson, Dunn & Crutcher LLP, New York
212 351 3800
DThomasch@gibsondunn.com
*Featured in Products Liability (Nationwide), Intellectual Property (New York)*
**Practice Areas:** Co-Chair, Life Sciences Group and Product Liability Group. Experienced in handling complex litigation on behalf of major companies in the life sciences sector, with a focus on patent litigation, mass torts, and product liability litigation. His trial practice focuses on complex product liability and patent infringement cases.
**Professional Memberships:** Fellow, American College of Trial Lawyers. Steering Committee Member, Defense Research Institute: Drug and Medical Device Litigation Committee. Member, American Intellectual Property Association.
**Career:** Clerked for U.S. District Court Judge Thomas P. Griesa of the Southern District of New York.
**Personal:** JD, Columbia University School of Law, 1981.

### THURSTON, Sally A
Skadden, Arps, Slate, Meagher & Flom LLP & Affiliates, New York
212 735 4140
Sally.Thurston@skadden.com
*Featured in Tax (New York)*
**Practice Areas:** Advises U.S. and international clients on a wide range of tax matters, including tax aspects of mergers and acquisitions, joint ventures, restructurings, divestitures and spin-offs. Advises multinational clients regarding the U.S. tax aspects of cross-border merger and acquisition transactions, repatriation strategies and tax minimization structures. In the U.S., regularly advises clients on taxable and tax-free acquisitions and divestitures and has significant experience in the partnership taxation area.
**Career:** JD, Harvard Law School, 1986 (cum laude); BS, Chemical Engineering, Cornell University, 1983 (with distinction).

### TODRYS, Steven C
Simpson Thacher & Bartlett LLP, New York
212 455 2000
stodrys@stblaw.com
*Featured in Tax (New York)*
**Practice Areas:** Tax Partner and Head of Firm's Tax Department. Experienced in federal income taxation, with a particular emphasis on corporate mergers and acquisitions, joint ventures, restructurings and real estate matters. Experience includes the acquisition by Sealed Air of Diversey Holdings, the acquisition by TD Bank of Chrysler Financial, the split-off of The Mosaic Company from Cargill and numerous buyout transactions for KKR, Hellman & Friedman, and Silver Lake.
**Career:** Joined firm in 1996; served as Chair of Tax Section of NYS Bar Association(1998).
**Personal:** BA, University of Rochester (1975); JD, with honors, University of Chicago(1978).

### TORKIN, Michael H
Sullivan & Cromwell LLP, New York
212 558 3471
torkinm@sullcrom.com
*Featured in Bankruptcy/Restructuring (New York)*
**Professional Memberships:** American Bankruptcy Institute; Turnaround Management Association.
**Career:** Special Counsel since 2011. Represents clients in complex multijurisdictional Chapter 11 reorganizations and out-of-court corporate and financial restructurings. Advises private equity and hedge funds in connection with distressed M&A and distress-for-control transactions. Advises boards of directors of financially distressed companies. Recent representations: Eastman Kodak in its chapter 11 case and pending global reorganization; PMI, in its chapter 11 reorganization; and Versa Capital, as a stalking horse bidder, in connection with its proposed 363 acquisition of United Retail Group.
**Personal:** Osgoode Hall Law School (JD, 1997); University of Western Ontario, (BA, 1993).

### TOWNSEND III, Robert I
Cravath, Swaine & Moore LLP, New York
212 474 1964
rtownsend@cravath.com
*Featured in Corporate/M&A (New York)*
**Practice Areas:** Robert I. Townsend, III is co-Head of Cravath's Mergers and Acquisitions group. His practice focuses primarily on all types of M&A transactions and general corporate governance matters. Mr Townsend's clients have included Arch Chemicals, Brink's, Brunswick, Cincinnati Bell, Clorox, Cummins, Frontier, Johnson & Johnson, Nestlé, Olin, Quest Diagnostics, Sprint and Stanley Black and Decker.
**Personal:** Harvard Law School (JD, magna cum laude, 1990; Executive Editor, Harvard Law Review); Harvard College (AB, magna cum laude, 1987). For more information: http://www.cravath.com/rtownsend

### TRAUB, Amy
Baker & Hostetler LLP, New York
212 589 4248
atraub@bakerlaw.com
*Featured in Labor & Employment (New York)*
**Career:** An experienced employment advisor and litigator, Amy Traub focuses her practice on the full array of employment law matters in all industries, particularly in the healthcare and retail industries. Her focus includes issues surrounding the recruitment and hiring of employees, background checks, employee discipline and terminations, employee leaves of absence, disability and religious accommodation issues, wage and hour law, layoffs and reductions-in-force, and other facets of the employer-employee relationship. Amy also conducts human resources and wage and hour audits, and she litigates the full panoply of employment-related issues in federal and state court, and before administrative agencies.

### TREVINO, Marc R
Sullivan & Cromwell LLP, New York
212 558 4239
trevinom@sullcrom.com
*Featured in Employee Benefits & Executive Compensation (Nationwide), Employee Benefits & Executive Compensation (New York)*
**Career:** Partner since 2002. Managing Partner, Executive Compensation and Benefits Practice. Advises on variety of transactional matters, succession and related compensation matters, regulatory/compliance issues, and regulatory investigations. Recent representations: Kodak in bankruptcy; AIG in US Treasury's investment and in ALICO and AIA divestitures; Barclays in BGI sale to BlackRock; CIT in prepackaged bankruptcy; Wachovia in Wells Fargo merger; United Rentals in acquisition of RSC.
**Publications:** Co-author, The Public Company Deskbook (2009, PLI). Lectures/writes extensively on compensation and corporate governance matters, including for the ABA, ABCNY, NASPP and PLI.
**Personal:** Yale Law School (JD, 1993); Princeton University (AB, 1990).

### TRINGALI, Joseph
Simpson Thacher & Bartlett LLP, New York
212 455 2000
jtringali@stblaw.com
*Featured in Antitrust (New York)*
**Practice Areas:** Litigation Partner representing clients in antitrust litigation and obtaining clearance for mergers before competition authorities. Clients include Kohlberg Kravis Roberts, Blackstone, Viacom, Express Scripts, Silver Lake in its acquisition of Dell and Wyeth in its acquisition by Pfizer.
**Career:** Joined the firm in 1983; became Partner in 1989.
**Publications:** Antitrust Developments in the Media and Entertainment Industries (2009 Antitrust Review of the Americas); Special Issues Affecting Private Equity in Antitrust (2008 Int'l Comparative Legal Guide to Merger Control).
**Personal:** BA, Wesleyan University (1977); JD, New York University School of Law (1980).

### TRINKLEIN, Jeffrey M
Gibson, Dunn & Crutcher LLP, New York
212 351 2344
jtrinklein@gibsondunn.com
*Featured in Tax (New York)*
**Practice Areas:** Has extensive experience in US and international taxation, with emphasis on advice to foreign clients with investments in US and advice to US clients with foreign operations. Clients include sovereign wealth funds, multinational corporations, high-net worth individuals, private equity funds, hedge funds, and real estate opportunity funds. Areas of practice include advice on structuring investment in domestic and foreign real estate, public and private companies, sports franchises and other investment assets. Has worked in firm's US and European offices (London for four years; Munich for four years).
**Personal:** JD, University of Virginia, 1985; AB, University of Chicago, 1982.

## TURNBULL, Kenneth J
Morgan, Lewis & Bockius LLP, New York
212 309 6055
kturnbull@morganlewis.com
*Featured in Labor & Employment (New York)*
**Practice Areas:** Kenneth Turnbull is a partner in Morgan Lewis's Labor and Employment practice. Ken litigates class actions and individual cases involving a range of issues. He represents clients in cases of discrimination and wrongful discharge, defends against claims for bonus and other compensation before FINRA and other arbitration panels, litigates claims involving restrictive covenants and trade secrets and defends against claims arising out of corporate planning and restructuring. He represents employers before the DOL and in court on SOX and wage and hour issues.
**Personal:** Attended Rutgers University School of Law, JD, With Honors, Order of the Coif; Lehigh University, BS.

## TURNER, Scott M
Nixon Peabody LLP, Rochester
585 263 1612
sturner@nixonpeabody.com
*Featured in Environment (New York)*
**Practice Areas:** Project development and permitting of new electric generating and other energy/industrial facilities throughout the US. Clean Air/Clean Water Act permit, enforcement, rulemaking proceedings regarding power plants, waste-to-energy facilities, and landfills. Citizen suit defense. PSD, NANSR and greenhouse gas issues. Endangered species and wetland issues. Federal/State Superfund. Brownfield development.
**Professional Memberships:** Admitted to practice in NY, DC, US District Court (Western District of NY), US Courts of Appeals (Second, Third, Seventh Circuits). American Society of Mechanical Engineers.
**Career:** Energy and Environment Practice Group Leader.
**Personal:** Washington & Lee University, JD, magna cum laude; Colgate University, BA, with honors.

## TURTELTAUB, Adam M
Willkie Farr & Gallagher LLP, New York
212 728 8129
aturteltaub@willkie.com
*Featured in Corporate/M&A (New York)*
**Practice Areas:** Represents a broad range of US and multi-national clients on both negotiated and unsolicited transactions, including mergers, tender offers, stock and asset acquisitions, dispositions and joint ventures. Regularly represents M&A, private equity and venture capital clients and advises clients on matters relating to corporate governance. Recently advised Kenneth Cole in the going-private transaction of Kenneth Cole Productions, Inc.; AlixPartners LLP founder Jay Alix in CVC Capital Partners' recapitalization of global business advisory firm; and Riverstone Holdings in the leveraged buyout of El Paso Corporation's oil and gas exploration and produc-

tion units. Recent clients include Colony Capital, LLC and Take-Two Interactive Software, Inc.
**Personal:** Personal: JD, New York University School of Law, 1998. BS, University of Vermont, 1994. For more information:
http://www.willkie.com/AdamTurteltaub

## TWEEN, Douglas
Baker & McKenzie, New York
212 626 4355
douglas.tween@bakermckenzie.com
*Featured in Antitrust (New York)*
**Practice Areas:** Chair of Baker & McKenzie's New York Litigation Practice Group and the Firm's Global Cartel Task Force. Represents clients in antitrust and white-collar criminal and regulatory investigations and complex civil litigation and class actions.
**Professional Memberships:** Co-Chair, Cartel and Criminal Practice Committee of ABA Antitrust Section; International Competition Network Non-Governmental Advisor.
**Career:** Baker & McKenzie partner since 2005. Trial Attorney, U.S. Department of Justice Antitrust Division (1990-2005).
**Personal:** JD Northwestern University (cum laude 1989); BA, Columbia University (1984). Law Clerk, Hon. William H Timbers, U.S. Court of Appeals for the Second Circuit. Admitted in New York and Connecticut.

## TWERSKI, Shlomo C
Schulte Roth & Zabel LLP, New York
212 756 2510
shlomo.twerski@srz.com
*Featured in Tax (New York)*
**Practice Areas:** Focuses his practice on the tax aspects of onshore and offshore investment funds, registered investment companies and business development companies, private equity partnerships, real estate and corporate transactions, restructurings and workouts, securitizations, and existing and emerging financial instruments. Regularly speaks at industry conferences and events and recently participated in a series of presentations concerning the impact of the current economic downturn on the alternative investment industry.
**Professional Memberships:** Tax Section of the New York State Bar Association.
**Career:** SRZ Partner since 1993.
**Personal:** Hofstra University School of Law, JD, Articles Editor, Hofstra Law Review.

## URAM, Gerald R
Davis & Gilbert LLP, New York
212 468 4815
guram@dglaw.com
*Featured in Real Estate (New York)*
**Practice Areas:** Real estate.
**Career:** Gerald R Uram is a partner in Davis & Gilbert's Real Estate Practice Group, and was formerly chair of the group for 38 years. Mr Uram concentrates on commercial leasing and serves as counsel to many building owners. He has handled some of New York's largest leasing transactions, including representing SJP Properties in its lease with Proskauer Rose LLP, Major League Baseball in its Fan Cave venue lease, and headquarter leases

including the National Football League and Commerzbank. He is recognized as a leading real estate lawyer by Best Lawyers and New York Metro Super Lawyers (Top 100 from 2008 - 2012).

## URIS, Harvey R
Skadden, Arps, Slate, Meagher & Flom LLP & Affiliates, New York
212 735 2212
Harvey.Uris@skadden.com
*Featured in Real Estate (Nationwide), Real Estate (New York)*
See under Nationwide for profile.

## UROWSKY, Richard J
Sullivan & Cromwell LLP, New York
212 558 3546
urowskyr@sullcrom.com
*Featured in Antitrust (New York)*
**Practice Areas:** Focuses on antitrust, securities and tax litigation, as well as other forms of complex litigation. Has extensive experience in counseling clients on competition issues, including mergers, acquisitions, joint ventures and pricing policy. Advises leading financial institutions and commercial corporations, including Goldman Sachs, Microsoft, National Australia Bank, Computer Associates, Diageo, RR Donnelley, Tenaris and Cullen/Frost Bankers.
**Professional Memberships:** ABA; ABCNY; FBC; NYCLA.
**Career:** Partner since 1980. Law Clerk to Hon. Stanley F. Reed (US Supreme Court, 1972-73).
**Personal:** Yale Law School (JD, 1972); Oxford University (BPhil, 1970); Yale University (BA, 1967).

## UZZI, Gerard
Milbank, Tweed, Hadley & McCloy LLP, New York
212 530 5670
guzzi@milbank.com
*Featured in Bankruptcy/Restructuring (Nationwide), Bankruptcy/Restructuring (New York)*
**Practice Areas:** Mr Uzzi is a partner in the firm's Financial Restructuring Group. He has experience in representing debtors and creditors in chapter 11 cases and out-of-court restructurings in the US. He also has experience in corporate bankruptcy matters and workouts on behalf of distressed companies and other parties in interest. Mr Uzzi has been a driving force in some of the nation's most significant restructurings and bankruptcy representations in recent history, including: Zais VII, Lehman Brothers, Washington Mutual, Charter Communications, Mirant Corporation, and Adelphia Communications.

## VARNEY, Christine
Cravath, Swaine & Moore LLP, New York
212 474 1140
cvarney@cravath.com
*Featured in Antitrust (New York)*
**Practice Areas:** Formulates global antitrust strategy for clients in connection with joint ventures, mergers, acquisitions, dispositions and other business transactions, including advising on business conduct or potential investments to ensure compliance with antitrust laws, securing antitrust regulatory approvals, and handling investigations

into anticompetitive behavior. Clients span diverse industries, including transportation, telecommunications, technology, pharmaceuticals and financial services.
**Career:** Chair of Antitrust practice; partner since 2011. U.S. Assistant Attorney General, Antitrust Division (2009-2011); Commissioner, Federal Trade Commission (1994-1997).
**Personal:** Georgetown University Law Center (JD, 1986); Syracuse University (MPA, 1982); State University of New York at Albany (BA, 1977).

## VICTOR, A Paul
Winston & Strawn LLP, New York
pvictor@winston.com
*Featured in Antitrust (New York)*
**Practice Areas:** Antitrust; Litigation
**Professional Memberships:** ABA, Antitrust Section Leadership
**Career:** Internationally known expert in antitrust law. Involved in many criminal and related civil international cartel cases, representing major corporations and individuals with respect to such products as lysine, nucleotides, carbon fiber, MSG, impact modifiers, air cargo, vitamins, graphite electrodes, compressors, cathode ray tubes, optical disk drives, instrument panel clusters, other auto parts, rechargeable batteries and bearings. Handled multinational transactions and litigated cases in the merger control and Section 1 areas. Frequent speaker, writer and lecturer on antitrust.
**Personal:** BBA, 1960; JD, with distinction, 1963: University of Michigan.

## VINEGRAD, Alan
Covington & Burling LLP, New York
212 841 1000
avinegrad@cov.com
*Featured in Litigation (New York)*
**Practice Areas:** Alan Vinegrad's practice focuses on representing individuals, corporations and corporate board committees in a wide variety of criminal and regulatory enforcement matters, and in complex civil litigation. He has represented numerous clients in connection with investigations and prosecutions by the U.S. Department of Justice, various U.S. Attorney's Offices, the Securities and Exchange Commission, the New York State Attorney General, the Manhattan District Attorney's Office, and other regulators. Mr Vinegrad joined the firm after serving as the United States Attorney for the Eastern District of New York.
**Personal:** Wharton School of Business (1980), NYU School of Law (1984).

## VITKOWSKY, Vincent J
Edwards Wildman Palmer, New York
212 912 2828
vvitkowsky@edwardswildman.com
*Featured in Insurance (New York)*
**Practice Areas:** Vince represents insurance and reinsurance industry clients in significant disputes in all lines of business. He serves as advocate and counselor in litigation, arbitration and mediation concerning reinsurance, high-stakes and complex insurance coverage, regulatory, antitrust, and general commercial matters.

**Professional Memberships:** International Bar Association, Association Internationale de Droit des Assurances; ABA, Chair, International Section; Founding member, International Association of Claim Professionals.

**Publications:** Vince has written dozens of articles on reinsurance, arbitration and international law subjects.

**Personal:** Northwestern University, BA; Cornell University School of Law, JD.

### VIZCARRONDO JR, Paul
Wachtell, Lipton, Rosen & Katz, New York
212 403 1208
pvizcarrondo@wlrk.com
*Featured in Securities (Nationwide), Litigation (New York)*

See under Nationwide for profile.

### VYSKOCIL, Mary Kay
Simpson Thacher & Bartlett LLP, New York
212 455 3093
mvyskocil@stblaw.com
*Featured in Insurance (Nationwide), Insurance (New York)*

See under Nationwide for profile.

### WACHTELL, Herbert M
Wachtell, Lipton, Rosen & Katz, New York
212 403 1216
hmwachtell@wlrk.com
*Featured in Litigation (Nationwide), Litigation (New York)*

See under Nationwide for profile.

### WAGMAN, Philip
Clifford Chance US LLP, New York
212 878 3133
philip.wagman@cliffordchance.com
*Featured in Tax (New York)*

**Practice Areas:** Partner in Clifford Chance's New York office. His practice focuses on the tax aspects of domestic and cross-border mergers, acquisitions, joint ventures, restructurings and financings. He has represented clients in public and private, taxable and tax-free acquisitions and other corporate transactions in a range of industries.

**Career:** Partner at Clifford Chance since 2005. Yale College, BA, 1991; Yale Law School, JD, 1994; New York University Law School, LLM, 2001. Member of the Executive Committee of the New York State Bar Association Tax Section.

### WAHLQUIST, Andrea K
Simpson Thacher & Bartlett LLP, New York
212 455 2622
awahlquist@stblaw.com
*Featured in Employee Benefits & Executive Compensation (New York)*

**Practice Areas:** Executive Compensation and Employee Benefits Partner, emphasizing in representation of acquirers and target companies in leveraged buyout transactions and strategic corporate transactions. Advises private and public companies on compensation and benefits-related issues in IPOs, ongoing company operations (including negotiating executive employment and separation arrangements), and bankruptcy and restructuring transactions. Representative clients

include KKR, Toronto-Dominion Bank and Nielsen Company, among others.

**Career:** Clerk to Hon. Stephen Swift, US Tax Court (1995-1997); In 1997, joined the Firm, becoming a partner in 2008.

**Personal:** BA, University of Virginia (1992); JD, Washington & Lee University School of Law (1995).

### WAKS, Jay W
Kaye Scholer LLP, New York
212 836 8558
jay.waks@kayescholer.com
*Featured in Labor & Employment (New York)*

**Practice Areas:** Jay Waks is Chair of Kaye Scholer's Alternative Dispute Resolution practice and immediate past Chair of its national Employment and Labor Law practice. He is known for his representation of US and international companies in a broad range of employment and labor relations litigations, negotiations and arbitrations, and compliance matters affecting business interests in the US and abroad. His experience includes complex employment rights cases concerning class/collective actions, discrimination, restrictive covenant/forfeiture and internal investigations of employee wrongdoing and retaliation. He is known for his successes litigating high-profile cases and as a leader in arbitration and dispute resolution.

### WALKER, Andrew R
Milbank, Tweed, Hadley & McCloy LLP, New York
212 530 5624
AWalker@milbank.com
*Featured in Tax (New York)*

**Practice Areas:** Focuses on international tax aspects of complex financing transactions, financial products, securities and derivatives, structured finance and securitization. Significant experience in cross-border restructurings, workouts and strategic investments.

**Professional Memberships:** NYSBA: Tax Section Executive Committee, member; Committee on Cross-border Capital Markets, Co-Chair; ABA Tax Section; International Fiscal Association; Tax Forum; Tax Club.

**Career:** Partner in Milbank's Tax Department.

**Publications:** Tax Lawyer, Journal of Corporate Taxation, Derivatives Magazine, Journal of Tax Exempt Organizations, Florida Tax Review.

**Personal:** JD, magna cum laude, Harvard Law School; MA and BA (Hons), University of Cape Town, South Africa.

### WALLACE, W Kirk
Skadden, Arps, Slate, Meagher & Flom LLP & Affiliates, New York
212 735 2933
Kirk.Wallace@skadden.com
*Featured in Tax (New York)*

**Practice Areas:** Practice covers a broad range of federal income tax matters - including international financings, investment fund offerings and M&A transactions - with a particular focus on RICs, financial product development and structured finance transactions. Represents underwriters and issuers regarding a variety of domestic and

international, public and private equity, debt and MLP and equity derivatives and other financial products, as well as asset-backed securitization transactions, REITs, international IPOs, and hedge fund and private-equity structures.

**Career:** LLM, New York University School of Law, 1991; JD, The University of Chicago Law School, 1986 (Law Review Member); BA, Yale University, 1983.

### WALLACH, Eric J
Kasowitz, Benson, Torres & Friedman LLP, New York
*Featured in Labor & Employment (New York)*

**Practice Areas:** Chair of the employment practices group, Eric focuses his practice on complex employment litigation for clients including leading financial services institutions, accounting firms, apparel companies, advertising and marketing firms, and industrial corporations. Specific experience includes actions seeking injunctive relief to protect against theft of trade secrets and misappropriation of confidential information, defense of employment discrimination lawsuits, and defense and prosecution of contract, tort and statutory claims.

**Career:** Recognized in New York's Super Lawyers, The Best Lawyers in America, Human Resource Executive, selected as a '2013 Top Rated Lawyer in Labor & Employment' by American Lawyer Media and Martindale-Hubbell.

### WALSH, Kevin
Locke Lord LLP, New York
212 812 8304
kwalsh@lockelord.com
*Featured in Insurance (New York)*

**Practice Areas:** Represents insurers and reinsurers in arbitrations (ARIAS) and in litigation in United States federal and state courts. Also counsel to insurers/reinsurers on workout, commutation and litigation related issues in acquisitions and run-off transactions and in response to regulatory inquiries from state, federal (SEC) and non-US regulators (FSA). Also represents commercial clients in commercial litigation, including securities, antitrust and commercial disputes.

**Career:** Partner at Locke Lord since 2003.

**Personal:** University of Virginia School of Law (JD); Fordham University (BA, magna cum laude, Phi Beta Kappa).

### WARREN, Charles S
Kramer Levin Naftalis & Frankel LLP, New York
212 715 9387
cwarren@kramerlevin.com
*Featured in Environment (New York)*

**Practice Areas:** Charles S Warren is the chairman of the Environmental Group. A former regional administrator with the US Environmental Protection Agency, Mr Warren has over 30 years experience in environmental law. Mr Warren's practice includes matters under the Clean Air Act, the Clean Water Act, the Toxic Substances Control Act, the Superfund law and other hazardous waste statutes as well as OSHA, environmental auditing, environmental impact review, corporate due diligence, brownfield rede-

velopment, bankruptcy, permitting and enforcement procedures and litigation. Mr Warren currently is a member of the Policy Committee of the New York/New Jersey Harbor Estuary Program.

### WASHER, Herbert S
Cahill Gordon & Reindel LLP, New York
212 701 3435
hwasher@cahill.com
*Featured in Litigation (New York)*

**Practice Areas:** Practice is concentrated on the defense of complex securities, derivative related and commodities matters involving civil, regulatory and criminal proceedings. Herb represents institutions and individuals in federal and state courts, before regulatory bodies and in internal investigations in matters concerning accounting fraud, derivative products, commodities and securities trading, market manipulation, banking and price-fixing.

**Personal:** Indiana University, BS; Boston University School of Law, JD.

### WECHSLER, Ernest
Kramer Levin Naftalis & Frankel LLP, New York
212 715 9211
ewechsler@kramerlevin.com
*Featured in Corporate/M&A (New York)*

**Practice Areas:** Mr Wechsler has a diverse transactional-based practice focusing on domestic and cross-border mergers and acquisitions, corporate restructuring, capital markets transactions, joint ventures and general corporate representations. Mr Wechsler represents a broad range of clients including hedge funds, private equity funds and both private and publicly held operating companies in a range of industries, including high technology, financial services and traditional manufacturing. In addition, Mr Wechsler works extensively with foreign corporations whose shares are traded in the United States.

### WEIDHAAS, Andrew J
Goodwin Procter LLP, New York
212 813 8814
aweidhaas@goodwinprocter.com
*Featured in Corporate/M&A (New York)*

**Practice Areas:** Mr Weidhaas specializes in private equity and venture capital investments, including minority and majority investments, leveraged buyouts and leveraged recapitalizations, going private transactions and private investments in public companies. His experience ranges from the representation of early stage growth companies and buyouts in the micro cap space through later stage LBO's and the representation of Fortune 50 financial institutions in strategic investments, merchant banking activities and private M&A. His industry expertise includes healthcare, defense, technology, real estate and financial services.

**Personal:** JD, Stanford University Law School, 1993 (with distinction); BA, Yale University, 1990 (magna cum laude, with distinction).

**WEIL, Alan S**
Sidley Austin LLP, New York
212 839 5315
aweil@sidley.com
*Featured in Leisure & Hospitality (Nationwide), Real Estate (New York)*
See under Nationwide for profile.

**WEINBERG, J D**
Covington & Burling LLP, New York
212 841 1037
jweinberg@cov.com
*Featured in Corporate/M&A (New York)*
**Practice Areas:** J. D. Weinberg represents buyers, sellers and financial advisors in connection with domestic and cross-border mergers and acquisitions transactions, including acquisitions of public companies, negotiated sales of private companies, subsidiaries and divisions, private equity transactions, leveraged buy-outs and strategic investments. He is a member of the Committee on Mergers, Acquisitions and Proxy Contests of the New York City Bar Association.
**Personal:** JD, cum laude, Order of the Coif, University of Texas School of Law (1990); University of London (1989); BSFS, cum laude, Georgetown University, School of Foreign Service (1987).

**WEINBERG, Richard D.**
Morvillo Abramowitz Grand Iason & Anello P.C, New York
212 880 9485
rweinberg@maglaw.com
*Featured in Litigation (New York)*
**Practice Areas:** Richard Weinberg has substantial expertise and experience in representing individuals and corporations in investigations by the Securities and Exchange Commission, the Financial Industry Regulatory Authority, the United States Department of Justice, and state regulatory agencies, and in conducting corporate internal investigations. He represents clients in highly sensitive and complex civil litigation and regulatory enforcement matters such as those involving allegations of improper trading, misleading or incomplete disclosure, market manipulation and other forms of financial fraud. He also represents individual and corporate clients in parallel investigations conducted by both the Securities and Exchange Commission and the United States Department of Justice.
**Career:** Former Assistant General Counsel and First Vice President of Merrill Lynch. Served as an Assistant Special Prosecutor in the Watergate Special Prosecution Force and as an Assistant US Attorney for the Southern District of New York where he served as Chief Appellate Attorney. Assistant Deputy Commissioner of Investigation, City of New York. Law clerk for the Honorable Harold R. Medina of the U.S. Court of Appeals for the Second Circuit.
**Personal:** Columbia University Law School, JD (Editor, Columbia Law Review), Cornell University, BS.

**WEINBERGER, Michael**
Cleary Gottlieb Steen & Hamilton LLP, New York
212 225 2092
mweinberger@cgsh.com
*Featured in Real Estate (New York)*
**Practice Areas:** Real estate finance and workouts. Recent transactions: $1.4B financing of General Grown Property's Ala Moana Center; $7.4B Extended Stay Hotels restructuring, bankruptcy and refinancing; $500 million financing of Kings Plaza Mall; $1.4B restructuring of Chicago office property portfolio financing; ; $400M multi-state financing of 27 retail malls; origination and restructuring of $1.8B multi-state acquisition financing of 125 hotels; origination and securitization of Rockefeller Center financing.
**Career:** Partner, 2000. Judicial clerk, Hon. Leonard Garth, Third Circuit (1991-92).
**Personal:** JD, magna cum laude, Law Review, Harvard Law School (1991); BA, summa cum laude, Phi Beta Kappa, Yale University (1988).

**WEINER, Gregg L**
Fried, Frank, Harris, Shriver & Jacobson LLP, New York
212 859 8579
Gregg.Weiner@FriedFrank.com
*Featured in Litigation (New York)*
**Practice Areas:** Vice-chair of the Firm's global litigation department and co-head of the real estate litigation practice. Handles a wide range of complex commercial disputes, including matters involving the federal securities laws, partnership disputes, M&A, and commercial insurance claims. Clients include Morgan Stanley, Deutsche Bank, Brookfield Properties, Millennium Hotels, Fortress, Centerbridge Partners.
**Career:** Joined in 1991; became partner in 1999.
**Personal:** JD, Columbia Law School (1991), Harlan Fiske Stone Scholar; BA, University of Michigan (1988), with high distinction, James B. Angell Scholar.

**WEINER, Michael L**
Dechert LLP, New York
212 698 3608
michael.weiner@dechert.com
*Featured in Antitrust (New York)*
**Practice Areas:** Mr Weiner, co-chair of the antitrust/competition group, provides strategic advice, resolves government investigations and litigates on behalf of clients with antitrust issues in a variety of industries, including telecommunications, technology, insurance, real estate brokerage, art auctions, and magnesite. He has significant experience handling price-fixing and other antitrust class actions.
**Professional Memberships:** Member, New York Bar; former Council Member and Officer of the ABA Antitrust Section
**Publications:** Member, editorial board, World Competition Law and Economics Review
**Personal:** University of Pennsylvania (BA, 1976, cum laude); Georgetown University Law Center (JD, 1980, magna cum laude, editor of the Georgetown Law Journal)

**WEINGARTEN, Marc**
Schulte Roth & Zabel LLP, New York
212 756 2280
marc.weingarten@srz.com
*Featured in Corporate/M&A (New York)*
**Practice Areas:** Chair of Business Transactions Group. Practice focuses on mergers and acquisitions, leveraged buy-outs, activist investments, corporate governance, securities law and investment partnerships.
**Professional Memberships:** American Bar Association; New York State Bar Association; New York City Bar Association.
**Personal:** Georgetown University Law Center, JD, Cases and Notes Editor, Georgetown Law Journal; University of Pennsylvania, The Wharton School, BS-Finance. Named "Dealmaker of the Year" by The American Lawyer.

**WEINSTEIN, Marc A.**
Hughes Hubbard & Reed LLP, New York
212 837 6460
weinstei@hugheshubbard.com
*Featured in Litigation (New York)*
**Practice Areas:** Specializes in defense and internal investigations of complex white-collar criminal and regulatory matters involving alleged securities and commodities fraud, FCPA violations, money laundering, forfeiture, health care fraud,and cybercrime, as well as civil litigation of securities and commodities fraud and accounting and other professional malpractice claims.
**Career:** Partner, Hughes Hubbard & Reed LLP (2007-present); Assistant U.S. Attorney Co-Chief Major Crimes Unit,Southern District of New York 1998-2007;Law Clerk, Honorable Mary Johnson Lowe, Southern District of New York 1996-1998; Associate, Hughes Hubbard & Reed LLP 1993-1996.
**Personal:** University of Pennsylvania Law School,JD,1993 Comparative Labor Law Journal;Duke University, BA 1990 cum laude.

**WEISS, Jacqueline A.**
Arent Fox LLP, New York
212 457 5460
jacqueline.weiss@arentfox.com
*Featured in Real Estate (New York)*
**Practice Areas:** Jackie Weiss counsels clients in all aspects of real estate law. She represents property owners and tenants in office, multi-family, retail and industrial transactions throughout the country, including investors, property owners and managers and asset managers in acquisitions, sales, operation management and development transactions. Additionally, she represents investors, and property owners in joint ventures; institutional lenders and borrowers in single property and multistate financing transactions, construction loans, and mezzanine financings; and lenders, investors, secured and unsecured creditors, and creditor groups in debt restructurings. Fordham University, JD; Queens College, City University of New York, BA, magna cum laude.

**WEISS, Lisa**
Dentons, New York
212 768 5362
lisa.weiss@dentons.com
*Featured in Media & Entertainment (New York)*
**Practice Areas:** Mergers and acquisitions, joint ventures, strategic alliances, venture capital transactions and licensing and distribution transactions for media, entertainment and digital media clients. Experience includes transactions in the music, music publishing, film, cable television, games, social networking, advertising, digital marketing and digital distribution sectors.
**Professional Memberships:** Copyright Society of the USA.
**Career:** SVP and General Counsel, Sony Music Entertainment 2001-2005.
**Personal:** Columbia Law School, JD; Yale University, BA.

**WEISWASSER, Elizabeth S**
Weil, Gotshal & Manges LLP, New York
212 310 8022
elizabeth.weiswasser@weil.com
*Featured in Intellectual Property (New York)*
**Practice Areas:** Elizabeth Weiswasser focuses her practice on patent and other intellectual property matters relating to biologic and pharmaceutical technologies. Ms Weiswasser has litigated patent cases in venues across the county and also counsels clients across a broad range of intellectual property issues in the life sciences sector. She regularly handles intellectual property diligence in the context of a broad range of corporate transactions in the life sciences sector.
**Personal:** Law clerk, Judge Lourie, US Court of Appeals Federal Circuit; University of Chicago Law School; Princeton University (graduate); Northwestern University (biochemistry, molecular biology); Adjunct Professor of Law, NYU Law School.

**WELLS JR, Theodore V**
Paul, Weiss, Rifkind, Wharton & Garrison LLP, New York
212 373 3089
twells@paulweiss.com
*Featured in Litigation (Nationwide), Litigation (New York)*
See under Nationwide for profile.

**WESSEL, Paul J**
Weil, Gotshal & Manges LLP, New York
212 310 8720
paul.wessel@weil.com
*Featured in Employee Benefits & Executive Compensation (New York)*
**Practice Areas:** Paul Wessel leads Weil's Executive Compensation and Employee Benefits Practice. He focuses his practice on handling executive compensation and employee benefits matters for corporations, private equity firms, boards of directors, and individual executives in all types of transactions. Mr Wessel regularly counsels clients in connection with executive compensation, employee benefits, and ERISA fiduciary matters. He also represents clients on the compensation and benefits aspects of bankruptcy and restructuring matters.

**Personal:** Cornell University, Industrial & Labor Relations (BS, 1983); State University of NY at Buffalo School of Law (JD, 1987), Editor-in-Chief, Buffalo Law Review.

### WHITE, W Christopher
Cadwalader, Wickersham & Taft LLP, New York
212 504 6633
christopher.white@cwt.com
*Featured in Real Estate (New York)*
**Practice Areas:** Firm Chairman. Concentrates in commercial real estate with emphasis on debt and equity financing. Represents many of the largest US and foreign institutional investors in full spectrum of real estate investment activity. Spearheads firm's representation of investment banks and institutional lenders in public and private securitizations and other secondary market transactions. Handles structured acquisition and financing for commercial properties in Europe and Latin America. Represents institutional investors in joint ventures and other investment vehicles for the acquisition and development of hotels, office buildings, shopping centers. Experienced with hotel and property management agreements, leasing agreements, and structured acquisitions of interests in companies owning and operating hotels, shopping centers, entertainment complexes, office buildings. Experienced in workouts, including restructurings, foreclosures and bankruptcies. Devised procedures for foreclosure by power of sale in NY.
**Personal:** JD, University of Michigan Law School; BA, University of Notre Dame.

### WIDGER, Stanley
Nixon Peabody LLP, New York
585 263 1529
swidger@nixonpeabody.com
*Featured in Energy & Natural Resources (New York)*
**Practice Areas:** Practice concentrates on the energy business: ratemaking and other regulation, mergers and acquisitions, affiliate relationships, procurement, renewable resources, siting and construction. He has appeared in proceedings before the New York Public Service Commission dealing with all of these issues and before the Federal Energy Regulatory Commission and other state and Canadian agencies involving siting and construction of energy facilities, energy imports and exports, and independent power matters. Represented clients in energy related litigation, as well as in settlement negotiations with governmental agencies.
**Personal:** Cornell Law School, JD, Editor-in-Chief, Cornell Law Review; Williams College, BA, Phi Beta Kappa.

### WILLIAMS, David L
Simpson Thacher & Bartlett LLP, New York
212 455 7433
dwilliams@stblaw.com
*Featured in Latin American Investment (New York)*
**Practice Areas:** Corporate Partner advising clients on cross-border corporate finance, M&A and project finance. Concentrates on international financing and business transactions in Latin America where he represents clients in the public

and private sector. Experienced in M&A, initial public offerings, high-yield and investment-grade debt offerings and cross-border banking transactions. Fluent in Spanish.
**Professional Memberships:** American Bar Association, International Law and Practice; Association of the Bar - City of New York, Committee of Inter-American Affairs; Board of Directors, North American-Chilean Chamber of Commerce.
**Career:** Partner since 1991.
**Personal:** BA, Tufts University (1977); JD, Georgetown University School of Law (1982).

### WILLIAMS, Marc O
Davis Polk & Wardwell LLP, New York
212 450 4000
marc.williams@davispolk.com
*Featured in Corporate/M&A (New York)*
**Practice Areas:** Mr Williams is a partner in Davis Polk's Corporate Department. He advises clients on mergers and acquisitions, takeover defenses, private equity transactions, corporate governance and related matters. He has recently worked extensively in hostile situations, representing Roche in its offers for Ventana and Illumina, ConAgra in its offer for Ralcorp and Orient-Express Hotels in its response to an unsolicited offer from a group led by Indian Hotels Company. Mr Williams has also done significant work for Comcast (including its acquisitions of NBCUniversal), Morgan Stanley, Citigroup, Emerson, Banco Santander and VF.

### WILLIAMS, Matthew J
Gibson, Dunn & Crutcher LLP, New York
212 351 2322
mjwilliams@gibsondunn.com
*Featured in Bankruptcy/Restructuring (New York)*
**Practice Areas:** Mr Williams represents creditor groups, official and ad hoc committees, banks, hedge funds and indenture trustees in connection with their investments in and workouts of distressed credits.
**Career:** Clerked, Honorable Francis Conrad, Bankruptcy Court, District of Vermont.
**Personal:** JD, with high honors, Rutgers University.

### WILLIAMSON, Bradd L
Latham & Watkins LLP, New York
212 906 1826
bradd.williamson@lw.com
*Featured in Employee Benefits & Executive Compensation (New York)*
**Practice Areas:** Represents private equity funds and publicly-held corporations in the design and drafting of equity-based and other incentive compensation arrangements. Regularly advises clients with respect to employment agreements, stock-option, restricted stock, deferred compensation and other incentive compensation plans and arrangements and advises clients with respect to tax, securities and corporate law issues that arise in connection with the establishment and administration of such plans.
**Career:** Qualified since 1995. Member of the Employee Benefits Committee of the American

Bar Association Section of Taxation and of the National Association of Stock Plan Professionals.

### WILNER, Steven L
Cleary Gottlieb Steen & Hamilton LLP, New York
212 225 2672
swilner@cgsh.com
*Featured in Real Estate (New York)*
**Practice Areas:** Wide range of domestic and international real estate, financial and corporate matters, with a focus on real estate investment, finance, development, joint ventures and restructurings. Significant practice in hospitality and lodging, including the global development of hotels in the U.S., Europe, Middle East and Asia.
**Professional Memberships:** Member of the Bar in New York.
**Career:** Joined firm, 1988; became partner, 1997; partner, Tokyo office (2001-2005). JD, New York University School of Law (1988); BS, Tufts University (1985).

### WING, John R
Lankler Siffert & Wohl LLP, New York
212 930 1233
rwing@lswlaw.com
*Featured in Litigation (New York)*
**Practice Areas:** Criminal defense: investigations, trial, appellate.
**Career:** John 'Rusty' Wing is a nationally recognized criminal defense lawyer who has been actively engaged in criminal trial and appellate work for more than 25 years. A former chief of the Fraud Unit in the United States Attorney's Office for the Southern District of New York, Mr Wing has represented individuals and corporations in a wide variety of complex criminal matters. He is a Fellow of the American College of Trial Lawyers and past President of the NY Council of Defense Lawyers.
**Personal:** University of Chicago Law School, JD; Yale University, BA.

### WINOKUR, Derek
Dechert LLP, New York
212 698 3860
derek.winokur@dechert.com
*Featured in Corporate/M&A (New York)*
**Practice Areas:** Mr Winokur represents private equity sponsors, strategic buyers and sellers, special committees, majority shareholders, and company management in public and private mergers and acquisitions. He also handles a variety of general corporate matters, including recapitalizations, buybacks, and reforming corporate governance. He has extensive experience advising both corporations and dissident shareholders in corporate control contests, and has represented clients in the technology, telecom, pharmaceuticals, and manufacturing industries.
**Professional Memberships:** Member, New York Bar
**Personal:** Cornell University (BA, 1991); University of Pennsylvania Law School (JD, 1997, magna cum laude; Order of the Coif; articles editor, University of Pennsylvania Law Review)

### WINTRINGHAM, Drew
DLA Piper LLP (US), New York
212 335 4520
drew.wintringham@dlapiper.com
*Featured in Intellectual Property (New York)*
**Practice Areas:** Patent litigation.
**Career:** An experienced IP litigator, he focuses his patent litigation practice on representing clients in the medical device, software, and automotive industries. He has developed an extensive e-commerce practice. He has more than 25 years of experience in managing and trying lawsuits involving sophisticated technological issues. He advises clients in all transactional aspects of intellectual property law.
**Personal:** JD, University of Michigan Law School; BS, Physics, Cornell University (with distinction). He is admitted to practice before the United States Patent and Trademark Office.

### WISE, Julian
Schulte Roth & Zabel LLP, New York
212 756 2135
julian.wise@srz.com
*Featured in Real Estate (New York)*
**Practice Areas:** Practice covers broad range of commercial real estate transactions, including representing lenders, borrowers, private equity funds, developers, investors and others in acquisitions and dispositions of commercial properties, mortgage and mezzanine debt, joint venture and preferred equity agreements, real estate workouts and restructurings and bankruptcies. Clients include major financial and commercial lending institutions; developers and owners of commercial, industrial, retail, office, hotel, resort and large-scale residential and mixed-use properties; and high profile and high net worth individuals.
**Professional Memberships:** American and NYC Bar Associations.
**Career:** SRZ Partner since 2006.
**Personal:** Fordham University School of Law, JD; Emory University, BA.

### WITDORCHIC, Lawrence
Paul, Weiss, Rifkind, Wharton & Garrison LLP, New York
212 373 3237
lwitdorchic@paulweiss.com
*Featured in Employee Benefits & Executive Compensation (New York)*
**Practice Areas:** Partner in the Employee Benefits and Executive Compensation Group. Advises a wide variety of clients in transactional matters, including private equity funds and publicly-held corporations, with respect to the executive compensation and employee benefits features of mergers, takeovers, other acquisitions, dispositions and initial public offerings. Practice includes the structuring and design of equity compensation arrangements, including stock options, stock appreciation rights, restricted stock, phantom stock, performance shares and LLC/partnership interests (including profits interests), and all facets of nonqualified deferred compensation plans and arrangements, including tax and accounting consequences.

**WITTLIN, Craig**
Harter, Secrest & Emery LLP, Rochester
585 231 1260
cwittlin@hselaw.com
*Featured in Corporate/M&A (New York)*

**Practice Areas:** Craig Wittlin represents publicly and privately held clients in merger, acquisition, divestiture, joint venture, securities, and other transactions, as well as counseling on corporate governance matters. He has led HSE's transaction teams on deals ranging in value from under $1 million to more than $3 billion. His recent experience includes representing a NYSE-traded company in its acquisition of seven hospitals in eastern Tennessee for a purchase price of more than $500 million, representing a Fortune 500 company in two merger transactions with public company targets, representing a Nasdaq-traded company in a "going private" transaction, and representing an issuer of more than $2 billion of debt securities under Rule 144A.
**Professional Memberships:** Member of the Board of Directors, Temple B'rith Kodesh; Board Member, YMCA's Camp Gorham; President, Town of Inlet Historical Society; Former Member of Board of Trustees, GEVA Theatre Center; Former Board Member, Cerebral Palsy Association of the Rochester Area.
**Career:** Joined Harter Secrest & Emery LLP in 1992. Admitted to practice in 1993. Partner since 1999. Has served on the HSE Management Committee for 8 of the last 10 years.
**Personal:** Named Mergers and Acquistions Lawyer of the Year in Rochester by U.S. News Best Lawyers in 2013. Listed in The Best Lawyers in America® in the field of Corporate Law and in Super Lawyers® in the fields of Mergers & Acquisitions, Securities and Corporate Finance; Recipient, "Forty Under 40 Award," Rochester Business Journal (2004). Albany Law School of Union University, JD, cum laude, 1992 and Syracuse University, BS, Managerial Law and Public Policy, 1989.

**WOGAN, Maura**
Frankfurt Kurnit Klein & Selz, New York
212 826 5523
mwogan@fkks.com
*Featured in Media & Entertainment (New York)*

**Practice Areas:** Partner in Litigation Group focusing on media law, publishing, copyright, and litigation. She has over 25 years of legal experience in all aspects of intellectual property law, including litigation, counselling, and pre-publication review of intellectual property in all media. She advises clients in the entertainment and publishing industries. Named a New York-area "Super Lawyer" for Intellectual Property Litigation by Law and Politics magazine for six consecutive years.

**WOHL, Frank**
Lankler Siffert & Wohl LLP, New York
212 921 8399
fwohl@lswlaw.com
*Featured in Litigation (New York)*

**Practice Areas:** Criminal defense: investigations, trial, appellate. Civil and regulatory litigation.
**Career:** Frank H. Wohl practices civil and criminal litigation, representing individuals and entities in trials, appeals, arbitrations and investigations. He is a Fellow of the American College of Trial Lawyers and is the President Emeritus of the Federal Bar Council and a member of the First Department Disciplinary Committee of the New York Supreme Court, Appellate Division. From 1998-2002, he served as Chair of the New York City Civilian Complaint Review Board. From 1971-79, he was an Assistant United States Attorney in the Southern District of New York, where he was appointed Deputy Chief of the Criminal Division and, subsequently, Chief of the Civil Division.
**Personal:** University of Chicago Law School, JD; Dartmouth College, BA.

**WOHL, Russell G.**
Skadden, Arps, Slate, Meagher & Flom LLP & Affiliates, New York
212 336 2789
rgwohl@pbwt.com
*Featured in Real Estate (New York)*

**Practice Areas:** Russell Wohl has a wide range of experience in all aspects of transactional real estate, including leasing and subleasing (representing both landlords and tenants), ground leasing, acquisitions and mortgage and other security-based financings. He has significant experience in providing advice to companies and law firms in connection with major office space leasing. Mr Wohl was named a Rising Star by Real Estate Weekly for his work done in the industry.
**Personal:** JD, 1989, St. John's University School of Law; BA, 1986, The State University of New York at Binghamton

**WOLF, Daniel E**
Kirkland & Ellis LLP, New York
212 446 4884
daniel.wolf@kirkland.com
*Featured in Corporate/M&A (New York)*

**Practice Areas:** Daniel focuses on mergers and acquisitions, representing public and private companies and private equity firms in a variety of domestic and international transactions. His transactional experience spans the range of M&A activity, including many significant cross-border and contested transactions. Clients he has represented include Avis Budget, Danaher, Bristol-Myers Squibb, ABB Ltd, BHP Billiton, American General, Cendant, Tronox, Golden Gate Capital, Wyndham Worldwide, Travelport, Janus Capital and Knight Capital.
**Personal:** London School of Economics and Political Science, United Kingdom, LLB, 1995, first class honours.

**WOLINSKY, Marc**
Wachtell, Lipton, Rosen & Katz, New York
212 403 1226
MWolinsky@wlrk.com
*Featured in Litigation (New York)*

**Practice Areas:** Practice includes corporate governance, contracts, insurance, antitrust and securities and bankruptcy litigation. Led the successful defense of the challenge by Air Products to the maintenance of Airgas' "poison pill." Also recently led the representation of Rohm and Haas in compelling Dow Chemical to close on the acquisition of that company, the representation of Tory Burch in litigation with C. Wonder, and the representation of JPMorgan Chase in multi-forum litigation over JPMorgan's acquisition of Bear Stearns. In addition, participated in the successful defense of Delaware Chancery Court litigation between IAC/Interactive and Barry Diller against Liberty Media and John Malone; and was the lead lawyer representing J.C. Flowers, Bank of America and JPMorgan Chase in Delaware Chancery Court litigation with Sallie Mae over whether Sallie Mae had suffered a material adverse change in its business. Following 9/11, was a lead member of the team representing Larry Silverstein in insurance litigation arising out of the destruction of the World Trade Center, and negotiated what has been labeled the largest property insurance settlement in history. Pro bono representations include Joe Steffan, a U.S. Naval Academy Midshipman discharged for acknowledging that he is gay, and Anthony Oddone, a young man wrongly convicted of manslaughter.
**Career:** Has been a partner in the Litigation Department at Wachtell, Lipton, Rosen & Katz since 1987. Clerked for the Honorable Henry J Friendly of the United States Court of Appeals for the Second Circuit from 1980-81. Has argued appeals in the DC Circuit, the New York Court of Appeals and the Appellate Divisions of the New York State Supreme Court. Admitted to practice in the State of New York, the United States District Court for the Southern and Eastern Districts of New York, the United States Courts of Appeals for the Second, Seventh and D.C. Circuits and the United States Supreme Court.
**Personal:** Received his BA with high honors from Swarthmore College in 1977, and his JD with Honors from the University of Chicago Law School. While in law school, was a member of The University of Chicago Law Review and served as a comment and articles editor. Currently serves as a member of the Board of Directors of the Legal Aid Society of New York.

**WOLLMAN, Diana L**
Sullivan & Cromwell LLP, New York
212 558 4055
wollmand@sullcrom.com
*Featured in Tax (New York)*

**Professional Memberships:** NYSBA (Chair, Tax Section); ABA (Tax Section).
**Career:** Partner since 2000. Adjunct Professor, Columbia Law School ("International Taxation" and "Ethical Issues in Tax Practice"); Clerkship, US District Court, SDCA (1991-1992).
**Publications:** Published author on several issues. Frequent speaker: NYSBA, ABA, PLI, IFA, ITI, UCLA Annual M&A Tax Institute, Institute of International Bankers, New York Bankers Association, NYU Tax Planning Institute.
**Personal:** UCLA Law School (JD, 1991); Harvard University (AB, 1986).

**YANEZ, Antonio**
Willkie Farr & Gallagher LLP, New York
212 728-8725
ayanez@willkie.com
*Featured in Litigation (New York)*

**Practice Areas:** Concentrates on securities and mergers and acquisitions litigation. Practice includes representation of issuers, officers, directors, underwriters, accounting firms, and others in securities class actions, M&A cases, SEC proceedings, and other litigation and regulatory matters. Also focuses on internal and independent investigations of financial reporting, accounting, and related issues. Particular experience in matters with international dimension.
**Personal:** JD, Brooklyn Law School, 1996. Editor-In-Chief, Brooklyn Law Review. BA, Vassar College, 1992. See: http://www.willkie.com/AntonioYanez

**YOUNG, Michael**
Willkie Farr & Gallagher LLP, New York
212 728 8280
myoung@willkie.com
*Featured in Securities (Nationwide), Litigation (New York)*

**Practice Areas:** Chair, Securities Litigation and Enforcement Practice Group. Practice concentrates on securities and financial reporting with emphasis in accounting irregularities. Represents companies, audit committees, officers, directors, accounting firms, and investment banks in domestic and international securities class actions, SEC and other governmental proceedings, and special investigations. Experience includes landmark jury verdict for defense in first securities class action tried before jury pursuant to Private Securities Litigation Reform Act of 1995. Recent matters include securities litigation and regulatory proceedings arising out of the subprime crisis, including the representation of AIG risk management, the representation of Bear Stearns' chief accounting officer, and the representation of KPMG.
**Personal:** JD, Duke University School of Law, 1981. Research and Managing Editor, Duke Law Journal. BA, magna cum laude, Allegheny College, 1978; Phi Beta Kappa. See: http://www.willkie.com/MichaelYoung

**YOUNGWOOD, Jonathan K**
Simpson Thacher & Bartlett LLP, New York
212 455 2000
jyoungwood@stblaw.com
*Featured in Securities (Nationwide), Litigation (New York)*

**Practice Areas:** Litigation Partner. Representative cases have included litigation involving The Blackstone Group, EnergySolutions, Enron, Focus Media, Goldman Sachs, HCA, JPMorgan Chase, KKR, Lehman Brothers, MetroPCS, Morgan Stanley, PXRE and UBS.
**Career:** Joined the Firm in 1995; became Partner in 2003. Law clerk to the Honorable Dennis G Jacobs (Second Circuit) 1994-95.
**Personal:** BA, with honors, Brown University (1990); MS, Public Policy, The University of

Chicago (1992); JD, with honors, University of Chicago (1994).

## ZAVIN, Jonathan
Loeb & Loeb LLP, New York
212 407 4161
jzavin@loeb.com
*Featured in Media & Entertainment (New York)*

**Practice Areas:** Concentrates on copyright and trademark litigation and other entertainment and commercial litigation. Advises major motion picture studios, recording and publishing companies, as well as producers in entertainment and new media industries.

**Professional Memberships:** Copyright Society of the USA.

**Career:** Partner at Loeb since 2001.

**Publications:** Has lectured on copyright law at the Copyright Society of the USA, the American Bar Association, Los Angeles Copyright Society and at Columbia University Law School, University of Chicago Law School and Cornell Law School.

**Personal:** Columbia University School of Law (JD, 1973); St John's College (BA, 1968).

## ZELENKO, Daniel
Crowell & Moring LLP, Washington, DC
212 895 4266
dzelenko@crowell.com
*Featured in Litigation (New York)*

**Practice Areas:** Parner in Crowell & Moring's White Collar & Regulatory Enforcement Group. He focuses on securities enforcement investigations, white collar criminal defense, corporate internal investigations, criminal antitrust matters and complex civil litigation.

**Career:** Prior to joining Crowell & Moring in 2008, Dan spent almost nine years in the SEC's Division of Enforcement and as a federal prosecu-

tor with the Department of Justice. Most recently, Dan served as a Branch Chief in the SEC's New York Office, where he was lead counsel and supervised attorneys, accountants and investigators on several high profile investigations and enforcement proceedings.

## ZIMAN, Kenneth S
Skadden, Arps, Slate, Meagher & Flom LLP & Affiliates, New York
212 735 3310
ken.ziman@skadden.com
*Featured in Bankruptcy/Restructuring (Nationwide), Bankruptcy/Restructuring (New York)*

See under Nationwide for profile.

## ZIRINSKY, Bruce R
Greenberg Traurig, LLP, New York
212 801 9222
ZirinskyB@gtlaw.com
*Featured in Bankruptcy/Restructuring (Nationwide), Bankruptcy/Restructuring (New York)*

See under Nationwide for profile.

## ZOLA, Jared
Dickstein Shapiro LLP, New York
212 277 6684
zolaj@dicksteinshapiro.com
*Featured in Insurance (New York)*

**Practice Areas:** Jared Zola is the Northeast Regional Leader of Dickstein Shapiro's Insurance Coverage Group. His practice focuses on representing corporate policyholders in insurance coverage litigation, as well as negotiating settlements with prominent property and casualty insurers. He has dealt with a variety of complex insurance coverage disputes, including professional liability, asbestos, environmental, toxic torts, construction defects, directors and officers, first-party disputes, and bad faith. His work has secured hundreds of

millions of dollars in insurance recoveries for clients.

**Personal:** BA from Clemson University, (1999) and JD from Yeshiva University, Benjamin N. Cardozo School of Law (2003).

## ZORNOW, David M
Skadden, Arps, Slate, Meagher & Flom LLP & Affiliates, New York
212 735 2890
david.zornow@skadden.com
*Featured in Securities (Nationwide), Litigation (New York)*

**Practice Areas:** Global head of Skadden's Litigation/Controversy practices and leads the New York office White Collar Crime Group. Represents corporations and individuals in connection with federal and state grand jury investigations and at trial. Also works on civil enforcement actions, including matters before the SEC, and internal investigations on behalf of corporate boards of directors.

**Career:** Chair, NYC Civilian Complaint Review Board (1994-96); Associate Independent Counsel, Iran/Contra (1987-89); Assistant US Attorney, SDNY (1983-87); law clerk to USDJ Herbert J. Stern, Newark, NJ (1980-82); JD, Yale Law School, 1980; BA, Harvard College, 1976 (summa cum laude; Phi Beta Kappa).

## ZUCKERBROT, Kenneth
Greenberg Traurig, LLP, New York
212 801 6820
ZuckerbrotK@gtlaw.com
*Featured in Tax (New York)*

**Practice Areas:** Chair, Bankruptcy Tax Group. Tax; International Tax.

**Professional Memberships:** Member, American Bar Association, Section of Taxation.

**Career:** Listed: Chambers USA, 2012-13; Super Lawyers, 2006, 2008-12. Rated, AV® Preeminent™ 5.0 out of 5.

**Publications:** Co-author, 'The Stop Tax Haven Abuse Act: Indications of Future Changes In International Tax Landscape.' Practical U.S./International Tax Strategies, Vol. 13, No. 4, February 28, 2009; Co-author, 'So Long GAAP, Hello IFRS (International Financial Reporting System)', Practical U.S. International Tax Strategies, January 2008.

**Personal:** LLM, Taxation, New York University School of Law, 1971; JD, Brooklyn Law School, 1968; BA, Clark University, 1965. Fluent in Spanish.

## ZWEIFACH, Lawrence J.
Gibson, Dunn & Crutcher LLP, New York
212 351 2625
lzweifach@gibsondunn.com
*Featured in Securities (Nationwide), Litigation (New York)*

**Practice Areas:** Mr Zweifach is a Fellow of the Litigation Counsel of America Trial Lawyer Honorary Society. He has tried numerous civil and criminal cases, and he has extensive experience defending parallel civil, regulatory and criminal matters, including: securities and antitrust litigation; SEC, PCAOB and CFTC enforcement investigations and litigation; corporate governance litigation; internal investigations; and white collar criminal investigations and prosecutions. Mr Zweifach represented corporations, investment banks, accounting firms, and officers & directors.

# ANDERSON KILL & OLICK, P.C.

www.andersonkill.com **tel:** 212 278 1000 **fax:** 212 278 1733

**Managing Partner:** Robert M Horkovich
Number of lawyers: 85

## Firm Overview:

Anderson Kill & Olick, P.C. is a full-service corporate law firm that is known for its work in insurance recovery, representing policyholders only in insurance coverage disputes. Anderson Kill's practice areas work closely together, and the firm's unmatched expertise on the insurance recovery front lends an added dimension to the work of its corporate, litigation, bankruptcy and real estate practices. The Wall Street Journal has described Anderson Kill and its insurance coverage practice as combining 'corporate polish with the pugnacity of a plaintiff's firm.'

## Main Areas of Practice:

### Bankruptcy & Restructuring:

Anderson Kill's Bankruptcy and Restructuring Practice represents clients in debt restructurings, bankruptcy cases, creditors' rights matters, bankruptcy litigation and related finance and corporate transactions. The group has earned a solid reputation representing creditors and bondholders in ad hoc and official committees, as part of lending groups and as holders of control positions in restructurings and bankruptcy cases.
**Contact:** Todd E Duffy

### Corporate & Commercial Litigation:

Anderson Kill's corporate and commercial litigation attorneys handle claims on behalf of clients across all industries and business sectors, appearing in trial and appellate courts nationwide in cases involving anti-counterfeiting, antitrust, breach of contract, securities, fraud, the False Claims Act, employment, unfair competition, whistle blower issues, breach of fiduciary duty, waste management, class actions, and white-collar crime.
**Contact:** Larry Kill

### Corporate & Securities:

Anderson Kill's Corporate and Securities Practice counsels domestic and international clients in mergers and acquisitions, divestitures, corporate restructuring, corporate governance and cross-border legal issues. The group's International Business Department represents overseas and multinational corporations in their general business, litigation and cross-border transactional needs, including foreign direct investment, joint ventures, finance and captive insurance companies. Clients are concentrated in industries including private equity, airline, manufacturing, publishing, service, banking, retail, entertainment, software and real estate.
**Contact:** Costa N Kensington

### Corporate Tax:

Anderson Kill's Corporate Tax Practice provides domestic and international tax planning (including employee benefits and ERISA). The practice also offers practical insight and proficient legal advice with regard to captive insurance company compliance and formation and offshore alternatives to risk transfer.
**Contact:** Phillip England

### Employment & Labor Law:

Anderson Kill counsels management in every phase of employment and labor law on a full range of issues affecting the workplace. If litigation ensues, the firm provides cost-effective and results-oriented representation. The firm also represents employers in labor arbitrations, union negotiations and union avoidance.
**Contact:** Bennett Pine

### Estates, Trusts & Tax Services:

Anderson Kill's professionals plan estates, administer trusts and estates, advise clients on personal tax and wealth management issues, and resolve related disputes through negotiation or litigation. The firm's domestic and international clients include highly compensated and moderate to high net worth individuals, owners of successful businesses and families whom the firm has represented for generations.
**Contact:** Dennis Zagroba

### Insurance Recovery:

Anderson Kill has an unparalleled track record recovering billions of dollars in judgments and settlements from insurance companies for policyholders in a broad range of industries. It has successfully pursued high-stakes claims in every type of corporate insurance, including environmental/ asbestos/ toxic tort liability, directors' and officers' liability, products liability, professional liability, intellectual property claims, commercial crime insurance, property losses, business interruption losses and many others. In the process, the Practice has made insurance law in multiple states. Attorneys also represent employers, self-funded plans and plan sponsors in disputes with third-party administrators and insurance companies and advises management in the establishment and operations of captive insurance companies. The firm maintains evidence databanks related to the insurance industry unmatched by any other law firm in the world. For over 40 years, Anderson Kill has declined to defend the insurance industry, establishing its undivided loyalty to the policyholder. Often, the policyholder's defense counsel finds it difficult or impossible to conduct both the defense of the liability claim and resolve the coverage issue with the insurance company. In such cases, Anderson Kill provides discreet, results-oriented insurance 'conflicts counsel' to obtain an insurance recovery without distracting or compromising the defense counsel.
**Contact:** Robert M Horkovich, William G Passannante

### Intellectual Property:

Anderson Kill provides counsel and litigation services to domestic and international clients on a full range of IP issues relating to trademarks, copyrights, trade secrets, patents, and anti-counterfeiting and brand protection services.
**Contact:** Kanishka Agarwala

### Real Estate & Construction:

Anderson Kill provides owners, developers, hospitals, non-profit entities, commercial tenants and investors with land use and development, construction, insurance, purchase and sale, leasing, dispute resolution, and other transactional and legal advisory services for a host of complex real estate and construction projects.
**Contact:** Lawrence J Bartelemucci

### Clients:

Clients include Fortune 1000 companies, large public and private entities, including companies in financial services, hospitality, retail, oil/gas, manufacturing, food and beverage, technology, pharmaceutical and life sciences, utilities, municipalities, religious and not-for-profit organizations, small companies, property owners and individuals.

## OFFICES

**NEW YORK**
**NEW YORK:** 1251 Avenue of the Americas, NY 10020
Tel: 212 278 1000  Fax: 212 278 1733

**CALIFORNIA**
**VENTURA:** 864 East Santa Clara Street, CA 93001
Tel: 805 288 1300  Fax: 805 288 1301

**CONNECTICUT**
**STAMFORD:** 1055 Washington Boulevard, Suite 510, CT 06901
Tel: 203 388 7950  Fax: 203 388 0750

**DISTRICT OF COLUMBIA**
**WASHINGTON:** 1717 Pennsylvania Avenue, NW, Suite 200, DC 20006
Tel: 202 416 6500  Fax: 202 416 6555

**NEW JERSEY**
**NEWARK:** One Gateway Center, Suite 1510, NJ 07102
Tel: 973 642 5858  Fax: 973 621 6361

**PENNSYLVANIA**
**PHILADELPHIA:** 1600 Market Street, Suite 2500, PA 19103
Tel: 267 216 2700  Fax: 215 568 4573

# ARENDT & MEDERNACH

www.arendt.com **tel:** 212 554 3541 **fax:** 212 554 3544

**Management Board:** Guy Harles (Chairman), Claude Niedner, Jean-Marc Ueberecken, Paul Mousel (Chairman of the Council)
Number of partners: 37   Number of lawyers: 290
Languages: *English, French, German and Luxembourgish as well as Arabic, Chinese, Dutch, Italian, Polish, Portuguese, Russian and Spanish*

**Firm Overview:**
Arendt & Medernach is the leading independent business law firm in Luxembourg. The firm's international team of more than 290 legal professionals represents Luxembourg and foreign clients in all areas of Luxembourg business law from offices in Brussels, Dubai, Hong Kong, London, Moscow and New York.

**Main Areas of Practice:**

**Administrative Law, Property & Construction:**
The team advises clients on administrative law, urban planning, environmental issues, real estate transactions, domestic development and construction projects.

**Bank Lending & Structured Finance:**
The team advises on all aspects of domestic and multijurisdictional finance and structured finance transactions. Advice includes the structuring of transactions, drafting and negotiation of the relevant contracts and collateral arrangements as well as the issuing of financial instruments.

**Banking & Financial Services:**
The team advises Luxembourg and international credit institutions and other professionals in the financial services sector (PFS) on regulatory matters, contractual arrangements and on their dealings with clients.

**Capital Markets:**
The team advises corporate, institutional, supranational and sovereign issuers in securities laws and capital markets regulation. They also advise on regulatory compliance including regulatory filings, disclosure obligations and corporate governance issues.

**Corporate Law, Mergers & Acquisitions:**
The team advises clients on all types of domestic and crossborder mergers and acquisitions, complex multijurisdictional corporate restructurings, change of control transactions including tender and exchange offers, going private transactions, acquisitions and disposals of subsidiaries, divisions and assets, joint ventures, strategic alliances, recapitalisations and liquidations.

**Dispute Resolution:**
The team has experience of representing domestic and international clients at every level of the Luxembourg civil and commercial courts, including arbitrations, both in relation to commercial and corporate disputes and in fraud and insurance litigation.

**Employment Law, Pensions & Benefits:**
The team advises clients on restructurings, collective bargaining negotiations, work permits, individual contractual negotiations, dismissal procedures, compensation and benefits schemes, pension schemes and related litigation.

**EU & Competition Law:**
In addition to EU and national competition law including State aid and merger control law, the team advises on European banking and financial law; International and European law of the institutions and EU staff law.

**Insolvency:**
The team advises creditors and other stakeholders in financially troubled entities in relation to insolvency, bankruptcy and forced reorganisation proceedings.

**Insurance & Reinsurance Law:**
The team advises insurance and reinsurance companies as well as insurance intermediaries and banks on all insurance regulatory matters, including license applications, passporting rules, the launching of new insurance products, etc.

**IP, Commercial, Communication & Technology:**
The team advises clients in the IP, commercial, communication and technology sectors on general commercial matters, including e-commerce, and on all aspects of IP, IT and TMT law.

**Investment Funds:**
The team advises clients on the structuring and operation of both UCITS and alternative investment structures as well as service providers for Luxembourg and offshore investment funds. The firm has developed significant experience and expertise in relation to all issues the funds and their service providers may face, always focusing on business-oriented and pragmatic solutions.

**Private Equity / Real Estate Investments:**
The team advises on all aspects relating to the structuring and organisation of private equity and real estate funds, managers or advisers, as well as on the investments and transactions made by such private equity and real estate funds, including in particular the crafting of investor codecision rights, carried interest schemes, debt financing arrangements and capital market-related aspects, and the negotiation of purchase agreements.

**Private Wealth:**
The team advises wealthy families and entrepreneurs on their wealth and estate planning matters. Advice includes the appropriate use of legal structures for their wealth and investments, whether through the use of corporate vehicles and partnerships or through contractual vehicles such as insurance contracts or fiduciary agreements. The team also provides family office services and supports private clients in their philanthropic activities.

**Tax Law:**
The team provides bespoke tax advice to a wide range of domestic and international clientele, covering all fields of taxation. The team has particular experience in the establishment of tax efficient acquisition and finance structures, as well as corporate reorganisations in a variety of sectors, with a special focus on the real estate, private equity and investment funds area.

**OFFICES**

**NEW YORK**
**NEW YORK:** Rockefeller Center, 1270 Avenue of the Americas, Suite 1705, NY 10020
Tel: 212 554 3541  Fax: 212 554 3544
Email: bob.calmes@arendt.com

**LUXEMBOURG**
**LUXEMBOURG:** Head Office: 14, rue Erasme, L-2082
Tel: +352 40 78 78 1  Fax: +352 40 78 04
Email: info@arendt.com

**BELGIUM**
**BRUSSELS:** Rue d'Arlon 92, B-1040
Tel: +32 2 282 00 60  Fax: +32 2 230 82 81
Email: marc.sunnen@arendt.com

**HONG KONG**
**CENTRAL:** Suites 3711-12, 37th Floor, Jardine House, 1 Connaught Place, Central
Tel: +852 2801 5808  Fax: +852 2801 5818
Email: stephane.karolczuk@arendt.com

**UNITED ARAB EMIRATES**
**DUBAI:** Dubai International Financial Centre, Currency House, Level 6, Suite 4, PO Box 482012
Tel: +971 44 34 88 96  Fax: +352 44 20 10 40
Email: bishr.shiblaq@arendt.com

**UNITED KINGDOM**
**LONDON:** 46 Gresham Street, EC2V 7AY
Tel: +44 207 776 2962  Fax: +44 207 776 2979
Email: camille.bourke@arendt.com

**RUSSIA**
**MOSCOW:** 8, Presnenskaya Embankment, Capital City, Moscow Bld. 1, suite 385M, 38th Floor, Moscow 123317
Tel: +7 495 721 38 78
Email: max.kremer@arendt.com

# AXINN, VELTROP & HARKRIDER LLP

www.avhlaw.com **tel:** 212 728 2200 **fax:** 212 728 2201

**Senior Partner:** Stephen M Axinn
**Managing Partner:** James D Veltrop
Number of partners: 19
Number of lawyers: 60

## Firm Overview:

Axinn is a different kind of law firm. It combines the skill, experience and dedication of the world's largest firms with the responsiveness, efficiency and attention to client needs of the best boutiques. Axinn was established in the late 1990s by lawyers from premier Wall Street firms with a common vision, and has been joined by lawyers from the best firms and law schools who share that vision. Axinn is devoted to providing the highest conceivable quality of service in three practice areas: antitrust, intellectual property and high-stakes litigation. Time and again, major companies have turned to Axinn for their biggest deals and cases, often on the eve of trial.

## Main Areas of Practice:

### Antitrust:

As one of the only antitrust boutiques in the US, Axinn is positioned as a "best of breed" solution for complex antitrust matters, including mergers and acquisitions, private class action and other antitrust litigation, criminal cartel investigations and prosecutions and competition issues arising at the intersection of antitrust and intellectual property. In mergers and acquisitions, Axinn is often co-counsel with top corporate law firms that can benefit from the specialized experience Axinn's antitrust group provides. In this way, Axinn has acted as lead antitrust counsel in connection with the required filings and reviews on several of the largest and most complex transactions in Wall Street history as well as many of the major transaction of the last year. Because virtually all Axinn antitrust lawyers have considerable trial and class action experience, Axinn partners are regularly engaged to handle not just private litigations, but also are lead antitrust counsel for mergers that are likely to be heavily investigated and perhaps challenged. In recent years, Axinn's cartel practice has grown and the firm has a strong presence in ongoing DOJ criminal antitrust matters. The Antitrust Group also collaborates with the firm's many patent lawyers to provide trial and counseling representation on matters that involve both antitrust and intellectual property issues.
**Contact:** John DeQ Briggs (Co-Chair)
**Email:** jdb@avhlaw.com
**Contact:** John D Harkrider (Co-Chair)
**Email:** jdh@avhlaw.com

### Intellectual Property:

Axinn has numerous seasoned IP trial lawyers and has become a go-to firm for IP matters of strategic importance. The firm typically has two dozen or more pending patent and trade secret cases, and often tries multiple cases annually. The firm has served as lead trial counsel in some of the most significant recent patent cases, including the defense of a multi-billion dollar jury trial. On numerous occasions, the firm has been asked to take over cases during or after discovery and serve as lead counsel at trial.

Axinn attorneys also offer an exceptional depth of technical experience. Approximately 20 attorneys are registered to practice before the USPTO, and over half hold advanced technical degrees or course work. This training and experience supports Axinn's IP litigation practice as well as an extensive counseling practice. Axinn offers skills and experience in numerous industries and technologies, including chemical, mechanical, electrical and computer science. Axinn lawyers possess particularly extensive experience in the biomedical area, where they have handled countless litigations for life sciences and medical device companies. In addition, the firm has a well-known FDA litigation and counseling practice complementing this area.
**Contact:** Matthew J Becker (Co-Chair)
**Email:** mjb@avhlaw.com
**Contact:** Chad A Landmon (Co-Chair)
**Email:** cal@avhlaw.com

### Litigation:

Axinn litigators try cases and win. Often, Axinn is brought in to try cases that have gone badly and are close to trial. The firm has tried several jury cases for each of the last few years, and has represented clients in successful arbitrations and appeals. One Axinn partner tried three jury cases in three months, winning a directed verdict in each case. Axinn is also one of few firms ever to have tried a class action case through to verdict. Recently, Axinn won the dismissal of a class action complaint in federal court in New Mexico after removing the case from state court. Axinn lawyers have successfully handled consumer and business class actions nationwide in many industries, including: insurance, cell phones, infant formula, auto parts, health care financing, home water devices, and cable television. Axinn lawyers have tried cases in many fields including: breach of contracts, business torts, director and officer fiduciary duties, unfair competition, antitrust, employment discrimination, fraud and intellectual property. Despite its size, Axinn has been sought out to represent substantial companies from across the globe ranging from a major European aircraft manufacturer in an ICC contract arbitration in New York, to an importer of construction toys whose shipments from Asia were being blocked from unloading in California.
**Contact:** Lauren S Albert (Chair)
**Email:** lsa@avhlaw.com

### International Work:

Benefitting from several foreign qualified partners and associates, Axinn has served as global coordinating counsel on a number of large merger and cartel matters and has represented and counseled numerous clients in connection with matters before the European Commission, the General Court and the European Court of Justice, as well as the UK Office of Fair Trading and Competition Commission, and other worldwide competition authorities in a broad range of industries.

AXINN | VELTROP | HARKRIDER | LLP

# BERNSTEIN LITOWITZ BERGER & GROSSMANN LLP

www.blbglaw.com **tel:** 212 554 1400 **fax:** 212 554 1444

**Managing Partner:** Max Berger
Number of partners: 15  Number of lawyers: 34
Languages: *English*

## Firm Overview:

Bernstein Litowitz Berger & Grossmann LLP (BLB&G) is a premier litigation firm representing individual and institutional investor clients. Since its founding in 1983, BLB&G has obtained over $25 billion in recoveries for investors and achieved precedent-setting corporate governance reforms on behalf of its institutional investor clients. Working with its clients, its cases have resulted in sweeping corporate governance reforms, changing deficient business practices and serving as models for public companies going forward. The firm has also prosecuted some of the most significant employment discrimination, civil rights and consumer protection cases on record. Equally important, the firm has advanced novel and beneficial principles by developing important new law in the areas in which it litigates. As a result of its accomplishments, the firm and its attorneys have been the subject of numerous feature articles in major media publications in the United States and abroad. A distinguished group of trial-tested litigators, BLB&G has repeatedly and consistently earned high praise from the courts in which it practices, as well as the respect of the defense firms and insurance carriers it faces in court and across the negotiating table.

## Main Areas of Practice:

### Securities Litigation:

BLB&G is widely recognized as one of the leading law firms worldwide representing institutional investors in complex securities fraud litigation ("the biggest star in the firmament" – Financial Times; "one of the best, bar none" – Euromoney; "consistently achieving the highest returns for investors" – The National Law Journal). Regularly appointed by the courts as lead counsel in US securities class actions, BLB&G has distinguished itself by focusing on the representation of respected institutional investors in meritorious cases. The firm is extremely selective in its prosecutions, only pursuing matters where its clients have significant holdings, and is well known for "consistently bringing high impact cases" (Securities Class Action Services).

The firm's reputation for trial readiness is well established. Unique among its peers, BLB&G has successfully tried several of the largest and most high-profile civil fraud cases in history, and has obtained 5 of the 10 largest securities fraud recoveries on record:

- $6.2 billion recovery for investors in In re WorldCom, Inc. Securities Litigation
- $3.3 billion settlement in In re Cendant Corporation Securities Litigation
- $2.425 billion recovery in In re Bank of America Corp. Securities Litigation, by far the largest shareholder recovery related to the subprime meltdown and credit crisis
- $1.3 billion recovery in In re Nortel Networks Corporation Securities Litigation
- $1.04 billion settlement in In re McKesson HBOC, Inc. Securities Litigation

Additionally, the firm is at the forefront of efforts to recover massive shareholder losses resulting from the global financial collapse. As lead counsel in numerous high-profile litigations arising from the subprime mortgage meltdown, BLB&G has already recovered nearly $5 billion for investors in actions against Wall Street banks and other major financial institutions.

### Corporate Governance & Shareholder Rights:

One of the first law firms to demonstrate that litigation can be an effective tool for stimulating positive change in failing corporate management settings, BLB&G is a well-recognized leader in giving shareholders a voice. The firm litigates cutting-edge fiduciary duty issues in order to maximize shareholder value, protect the shareholder franchise and improve corporate governance practices. BLB&G has also obtained billions of dollars in additional consideration for investors, representing them in merger and acquisition transactions structured to deprive shareholders of fair value and unjustly enrich management. For example:

- BLB&G prosecuted the Pfizer Derivative Litigation, which resulted in a historic $75 million dedicated fund to be used solely to support the activities of an unprecedented Regulatory and Compliance Committee which not only materially enhances the Pfizer board's oversight but potentially sets a new benchmark of good corporate governance for all highly regulated companies
- In the UnitedHealth Derivative Litigation, BLB&G obtained an unprecedented clawback of approximately $920 million of ill-gotten pay from the company's former officers and directors – the largest such recovery in history
- Representing a group of public pension funds challenging a conflict-ridden transaction in In re El Paso Corporation Shareholder Litigation, BLB&G achieved a landmark ruling that rebuked Goldman Sachs for neglecting to acknowledge blatant conflicts of interests when advising their corporate clients, and

recovered $110 million for investors, a settlement believed to be the highest post-merger closing money damage recovery in Delaware history

BLB&G has confronted discriminatory management, sought to make corporate boards effective and independent, expanded accountability to the boardroom, and improved the quality of "due diligence" performed by investment banks, changing "Wall Street" practices for the better.

### Complex Commercial & Corporate Litigation:

BLB&G represents institutions and individuals in a wide range of complex commercial litigation – on a contingency basis – involving allegations of breach of contract, accountants' liability, breach of fiduciary duty, fraud and negligence. The firm litigates cases arising from private placements of debt or equity securities, derivatives and other specialty financial instruments; and prosecutes bankruptcy claims on behalf of creditors and litigation trusts or debtors-in-possession. It also specializes in patent infringement and intellectual property rights matters.

### Asset Protection, Fraud Monitoring & Claims Administration:

BLB&G is the trusted securities fraud monitoring counsel for hundreds of public pension funds and institutional investors worldwide. The firm provides comprehensive analysis of the financial and business media, as well as all securities and shareholder derivative litigation to provide its institutional clients with complete reporting on potential claims that may impact their holdings. Additionally, the firm assists its clients in the administration of securities claims.

### International Work:

The firm represents institutional investors worldwide in numerous commercial matters.

**OFFICES**

CALIFORNIA
**SAN DIEGO:** 12481 High Bluff Drive, Suite 300, CA 92130
Tel: 858 793 0070  Fax: 858 793 0323

ILLINOIS
**CHICAGO:** 875 North Michigan Avenue, Suite 3100, IL 60611
Tel: 312 373 3880  Fax: 312 794 7801

LOUISIANA
**NEW ORLEANS:** 2727 Prytania Street, Suite 14, LA 70130
Tel: 504 899 2339  Fax: 504 899 2342

NEW YORK
**NEW YORK:** 1285 Avenue of the Americas; NY 10019
Tel: 212 554 1400  Fax: 212 554 1444
Email: blbg@blbglaw.com

# BOIES, SCHILLER & FLEXNER LLP

www.bsfllp.com **tel:** 212 446 2300 **fax:** 212 446 2350

**Managing Partners:** David Boies, Jonathan D Schiller, Donald L Flexner
Number of partners: 97 Number of other lawyers: 167

**OFFICES**

NEW YORK

**NEW YORK:**575 Lexington Avenue, 7th Floor, NY 10022
Tel: 212 446 2300 Fax: 212 446 2350

## Firm Overview:

Boies, Schiller & Flexner LLP, based in New York City, has over 260 lawyers practicing in offices strategically located throughout the United States. The firm has tried more than 450 cases before juries and judges in federal and state courts throughout the United States. The firm regularly serves as lead counsel on complex, high profile global matters. Firm Chairman David Boies was lead counsel for the United States in United States v Microsoft, and BSF has been lead counsel in many leading cases including for Oracle in copyright infringement litigation against SAP; Jonathan Schiller for Barclays in bankruptcy litigation stemming from Barclays' acquisition of Lehman Brothers' North American operations; Jonathan Schiller for Barclays in defense of U.S. Libor litigation; for Starr International and Maurice 'Hank' Greenberg, former Chairman and CEO of AIG and CEO of Starr, in multiple matters against AIG and regulatory bodies; for American Express against Visa and Mastercard; for NASCAR in major antitrust suits; for plaintiffs in Hollingsworth v. Perry, the federal challenge to California's same-sex marriage ban; for US Vice President Al Gore in Bush v Gore; and for the plaintiff class in In re Vitamins. The firm has established and enjoys a world-class reputation for its highly successful Litigation Practice. In addition, the firm has a successful Corporate Practice based in New York

## Main Areas of Practice:

Complex commercial trials and litigation, including antitrust, securities, financial products, intellectual property, insurance, and international arbitration are the leading and defining forces of Boies, Schiller & Flexner's practice. The firm is widely recognized as having one of the most selective and entrepreneurial class action practices in the country, representing both plaintiffs and defendants in cases involving a broad range of subject matters. The firm also represents corporate clients and financial institutions in significant merger and acquisition, joint venture, commercial banking, securities, venture capital, and private investment fund transactions, including by defending transactions before state and federal agencies. The Corporate Practice has a proven record in representing clients in significant cross-border transactions.

## International Work:

Boies, Schiller & Flexner partners have participated in arbitral proceedings representing clients before tribunals in Paris, Geneva, London, Zurich, Stockholm and Hong Kong and throughout the United States. The international practice is headed by Managing Partner Jonathan Schiller, who is a member of the Milan Chamber of National and International Arbitration Club of Arbitrators and serves as an advocate and arbitrator in international arbitration. In October 2009, Russia's Federal Customs Service dropped a $22.5 billion RICO suit against BSF client The Bank of New York Mellon in Moscow, without any admission of liability by BONY Mellon, in a deal negotiated with the Russian government; the case was settled for $14 million - less than 1% of claimed damages. Jonathan Schiller led the firm's defense of parallel proceedings in the Netherlands and United States courts arising out of Qwest's co-ownership of the Dutch telecommunications joint venture, KPNQwest. Among other successes, the Third Circuit affirmed a dismissal of a $9 billion fraud claim brought by the bankruptcy trustees of the joint venture, and the Amsterdam Commercial Court dismissed a fraud claim on behalf of a Dutch

shareholders' association. The firm's international Arbitration Practice includes ICC, LCIA, UNCITRAL, ICSID, AAA, NASD and ad hoc arbitration.

## Clients:

Boies, Schiller & Flexner headed up the trial team that secured a $1.3 billion jury verdict in the Northern District of California for client Oracle in copyright infringement litigation against SAP, their largest competitor in the enterprise software industry. This win marks the largest copyright infringement verdict in history by a factor of ten and the largest verdict of any kind in 2010. The US Bankruptcy Court for the Southern District of New York, after a six month trial, ruled in favor of Boies, Schiller & Flexner client Barclays PLC on February 22, 2011 that Barclays' purchase of Lehman's broker dealer unit in September 2008 was done in good faith, and denied the bankrupt bank's request to recover an alleged $11 billion 'windfall'. The firm also secured a multi-billion cash and securities settlement for Barclays in December 2008, and is working closely with Barclays in ongoing litigation and regulatory matters surrounding the interest rate benchmark Libor. In a landmark ruling upholding the constitutional right to marry, the Ninth Circuit US Court of Appeals ruled on February 7, 2012, in favor of the plaintiffs in Perry v. Brown, the historic same-sex marriage civil rights case. The lawsuit arrived in the Ninth Circuit after the plaintiffs achieved a resounding victory in the district court in August 2010; the U.S. Supreme Court will hear and rule on the case in 2013. The firm also achieved a $4.3 billion jury verdict in New York for Maurice 'Hank' Greenberg, former Chairman and CEO of American International Group Inc. and CEO of the C.V. Starr companies in action brought by AIG. The firm additionally settled all remaining claims brought by AIG against Greenberg and Starr International Company, including billions of dollars in damages and the return of multi-million dollar works of art. The firm is currently bringing a $50 billion derivatives suit against the U.S. government on behalf of Starr, asserting the unlawful taking of 80% of AIG's common stock without just

compensation. Working as co- lead counsel, the firm reached a proposed settlement for $50 to $80 million for a class of investors in Fairfield Greenwich Group, the largest Madoff "feeder fund," filed November 6, 2012 in New York federal court. On behalf of a class of direct and indirect purchasers, in May 2012 the firm negotiated a $10.5 million settlement in a price-fixing case brought against Chinese producers of vitamin C, marking the first-ever settlement of U.S. civil antitrust claims by a Chinese company. In July 2005, Kentucky Speedway brought monopolization and conspiracy claims against Boies, Schiller & Flexner clients NASCAR and its affiliate International Speedway Corp., seeking more than $1.2 billion in damages. In a unanimous decision released December 11, 2009, the US Court of Appeals for the Sixth Circuit affirmed summary judgment in favor of Boies, Schiller & Flexner clients NASCAR and International Speedway Corp. (ISC) in Kentucky Speedway's antitrust case. BSF won a complete defense victory, affirmed on appeal in December 2012, in the trial of a nationwide class action brought against American Express regarding its travel insurance programs for cardmembers; the firm is also representing American Express in an antitrust suit brought by the US Department of Justice in October 2010. In addition, BSF is handling the representation of DuPont and Pioneer Hi-bred in litigation against Monsanto alleging monopolization by Monsanto of biotech traits in soybeans and corn seeds. The firm's clients include some of the largest and most sophisticated companies in the world: Altria, American Express, Bank of New York Mellon, Barclays, CBS Corporation, C.V. Starr & Co., Delta Air Lines, Del Monte Fresh Produce Co., DuPont, Ernst & Young, Florida Power & Light, Goldman Sachs, Lloyds of London, Maurice 'Hank' Greenberg, NASCAR, The National Football League, New York Life Insurance Company, Oracle, Pfizer, Philip Morris International, Sony Corporation, Starr International Company, The New York Yankees, Tudor Investment, Yankees Entertainment & Sports Network and Zurich Capital Markets.

# BRUNE & RICHARD

www.bruneandrichard.com **tel:** 212 668 1900 **fax:** 212 668 0315

**PRACTICE AREAS**
Commercial Litigation
White Collar Defense

**OFFICES**
CALIFORNIA
**SAN FRANCISCO:** 235 Montgomery Street, Suite 1130
CA 94104
Tel: 415 563 0600  Fax: 415 563 0613

NEW YORK
**NEW YORK:** One Battery Park Plaza, NY 10004
Tel: 212 668 1900  Fax: 212 668 0315

### Firm Overview:

Founded in 1998, Brune & Richard LLP is a litigation boutique with offices in New York and San Francisco. The firm's practice focuses on commercial and securities litigation, white collar criminal defense, and government investigations and enforcement actions. Brune & Richard's attorneys are dedicated and talented lawyers who bring creativity, commitment, and meticulous preparation to every matter that they undertake. The firm's clients include commercial banks, investment firms, hedge funds, major utilities, insurance companies, broker-dealers, and individuals. Each of them relies on the firm's judgment and experience, whether drafting pre-trial motions, trying a case to a jury, warding off indictment or regulatory charges, or advising on business, strategic, and compliance issues. In the firm's experience, the best way to reach a favorable result is to be fully prepared earlier than its adversaries. Brune & Richard's approach combines forceful advocacy with its knowledge of the underlying substantive issues and law and a thorough understanding of each client's needs and objectives. The firm regularly tries both commercial and white collar matters.

### Main Areas of Practice:

#### Commercial & Securities Litigation:

Brune & Richard LLP has substantial experience representing a wide variety of companies and individuals in commercial and securities litigation matters throughout the country. The firm's highly skilled trial and appellate lawyers regularly handle cases in federal and state courts, administrative and regulatory proceedings, and arbitrations for both U.S. and foreign clients. The firm's cases involve alleged violations of federal and state securities laws, contract disputes, business torts, intellectual property issues, fiduciary duty questions, energy transactions, and class action lawsuits. Brune & Richard has handled a number of matters arising out of the subprime mortgage and lending crisis, and have particular expertise with complex financing transactions.

**Contact:** Hillary Richard
Email: hrichard@bruneandrichard.com

#### White Collar Criminal Defense:

Brune & Richard LLP has a wealth of experience representing companies and individuals in all phases of federal and state white collar criminal proceedings from investigation through trial and appeal. The firm has represented clients in many high profile white collar matters in a number of different industries, including financial services, energy, technology, and healthcare. Brune & Richard's white collar criminal matters have included allegations of securities and bank fraud, insider trading, accounting fraud, Foreign Corrupt Practices Act violations, health care and other

government contract fraud, antitrust violations, tax evasion, and money laundering. The firm handles all stages of white collar criminal cases, including testimony and investigative interviews, presentations in an effort to prevent charges, grand jury practice, pre-trial motion practice, trials, plea negotiations, sentencings, and appeals.

**Contact:** Susan Brune
Email: sbrune@bruneandrichard.com

#### Government Investigations & Enforcement Actions:

Individuals and companies routinely turn to Brune & Richard LLP to represent them in government investigations and regulatory enforcement proceedings. The firm represents clients in investigations, administrative proceedings, and enforcement actions by the Securities and Exchange Commission, the U.S. Department of Justice, FINRA, and other law enforcement agencies. The firm has also defended numerous whistleblower actions. Brune & Richard is firm in the belief that the best results in such matters come about from thorough factual and legal research. The firm's cases have involved alleged violations of federal and state securities laws, financial reporting violations, accounting fraud, Foreign Corrupt Practice Act violations, health care fraud, antitrust violations, improper sales practices, and drug mispricing and marketing. Brune & Richard also assists companies and special litigation committees in conducting internal investigations into alleged wrongdoing.

**Contact:** Susan Brune
Email: sbrune@bruneandrichard.com

### Clients:

The firm's clients include commercial banks, investment firms, hedge funds, private equity funds, other financial institutions, major utilities, technology companies, large law firms, universities and non profit organizations and individuals from those fields.

# CAHILL GORDON & REINDEL LLP

www.cahill.com **tel:** 212 701 3000 **fax:** 212 269 5420

**Chairman:** William M Hartnett
**Co-Administrative Partners:** Charles A Gilman, John A Tripodoro
Number of partners: 68
Number of other lawyers: 240

## Firm Overview:

Based in New York and with offices in London and Washington DC, Cahill Gordon & Reindel has thrived for nearly a century by focusing on the most significant opportunities and complex challenges facing the top financial institutions and multinational companies.

## Main Areas of Practice:

### Transactional:

Cahill represents a broad range of financial institutions and other companies in all types of transactional and advisory work. The firm's corporate lawyers regularly participate in the most significant deals in the marketplace. In addition to the firm's industry-leading capital markets and lending practice, its mergers and acquisitions and restructuring practices, supported by specialists in antitrust, communications, executive compensation, environmental, intellectual property, real estate and tax, provide clients with a full complement of qualifications and experience.

### Litigation:

In the firm's litigation practices, lawyers manage large-scale securities, insurance, antitrust, First Amendment, intellectual property, professional liability, product liability, white collar and corporate governance matters that are often international in scope. Among the firm's litigators are former law clerks at the federal trial and appellate levels, including the Supreme Court of the United States, and lawyers who joined Cahill following distinguished careers in the SEC, DOJ, Department of the Treasury and other federal and state bodies.

Keep abreast of Cahill's recent work at: www.cahill.com/news.

## PRACTICE AREAS

Antitrust & Trade Regulation
Bankruptcy & Restructuring
Communications
Corporate
Corporate Governance & Investigations
Crisis Advisory & Management
Executive Compensation & Employee Benefits
Environmental
First Amendment & Media
Insurance
Intellectual Property
Litigation
Pro Bono
Real Estate
Tax
Trusts & Estates

## OFFICES

NEW YORK
**NEW YORK:** Eighty Pine Street, NY 10005-1702
Tel: 212 701 3000   Fax: 212 269 5420

DISTRICT OF COLUMBIA
**WASHINGTON:** 1990 K Street, NW Suite 950, DC 20006
Tel: 202 862 8900   Fax: 202 862 8958

## INTERNATIONAL OFFICES

The firm also has an office in London, UK.

# CAHILL

# CARTER LEDYARD & MILBURN LLP

**www.clm.com tel:** 212 732 3200 **fax:** 212 732 3232

**Managing Partner:** Judith A Lockhart
Number of partners: 46
Number of other lawyers: 50

**OFFICES**

NEW YORK

**NEW YORK:** Two Wall Street, NY 10005
Tel: 212 732 3200  Fax: 212 732 3232
Email: info@clm.com

**NEW YORK:** 570 Lexington Avenue, 41st Floor, NY 10022
Tel: 212 371 2720  Fax: 212 371 4234

### Firm Overview:

Founded in 1854, Carter Ledyard & Milburn LLP is a full service law firm serving corporations, financial institutions, government agencies and individuals. The Litigation and Arbitration Practice concentrates on commercial, securities, employment, environmental, intellectual property, criminal defense, maritime, insurance defense and reinsurance disputes. The Corporate Practice focuses on securities laws, international mergers and acquisitions, joint ventures, IPOs and other public offerings, private equity, asset management and investment funds, commercial contracts, antitrust, and other government regulation. Other practice areas include trusts and estates, intellectual property, bankruptcy and reorganization, real estate, corporate investigations, employment, tax, employee benefits and tax-exempt organizations.

### Main Areas of Practice:

**Litigation/Arbitration:**
Complex litigations, arbitrations and alternative dispute resolution proceedings to resolve commercial contract, securities, employment, environmental, intellectual property, insurance defense, reinsurance, criminal, first amendment and construction disputes.

**Corporate/M&A/Securities:**
Public and private securities offerings, mergers and acquisitions, joint ventures and strategic alliances, venture capital and private equity investments, bank lending, broker dealer, antitrust, telecommunications and other regulatory compliance and investigations.

**Investment Management:**
Advice on the formation, registration, operation and regulation of broker-dealers, investment advisors, exchange-traded funds, unit investment trusts, hedge funds, private equity funds, mutual funds, and other financial institutions.

**Media & Technology:**
Representing technology-based business in media, ecommerce, telecommunications, software and biotechnology industries based in the US and overseas in financing, mergers and acquisitions, licensing transactions and general representation. The firm has helped more than 50 Israeli technology clients start and develop operations in the US.

**Real Estate:**
Representing property owners, lenders, tenants and government agencies in commercial and residential property sales, leases, financings, and development contracts.

**Intellectual Property:**
Advice on protecting and commercialising technology and intellectual property assets. Filing and prosecuting of patents, trademarks, copyrights and domain names, protection of trade secrets, software and technology licensing and e-commerce contracts. Litigation of patent disputes and administrative proceedings.

**Maritime/Shipping:**
Attachments and arrests, insurance coverage and claims, maritime litigation and arbitration, charter parties, cross-border leasing, regulatory advice, environmental advice, bankruptcy and workouts.

**Personal Representation:**
Representing US and offshore individuals in all aspects of their personal affairs requiring legal counsel, including estate and income tax planning and structuring, will and trust instrument drafting and estate administration, real estate and criminal defense work.

**Bankruptcy/Reorganization:**
Representing creditors, debtors asset acquirers and trustees in Chapter 11 and other bankruptcy cases and in nonbankruptcy workouts and enforcement actions.

**Environmental:**
Environmental regulatory advice, litigation and administrative proceedings, land use planning, environmental impact assessment and disclosure, compliance and environmental audits.

**Employment:**
Counseling concerning employment laws, regulations and claims. Litigation and arbitration of employment termination, discrimination, harassment and employee non-competition, confidentiality and trade secret claims.

**Tax/Employee Benefits:**
Tax planning advice, transaction structuring advice, and IRS representation. Planning, documentation, IRS qualification and regulation of employee benefit and incentive plans, executive compensation plans, stock option plans, and other benefits.

**International Work:**
Recent cross-border transactions include representing Radvision Ltd (Israel) in its $230 million acquisition by Avaya Inc.;  GE SeaCo (Barbados) with its sale to HNA Group Company Limited of China; Global Partners Fund and The Gates Group (Canada) in their sale of Imperial Parking Corporation (Impark) to the Ontario Teachers' Pension Plan Board; Sword Group SE (UK) in the sale of Sword Insurance to Thomas H. Lee Partners; UC Rusal (Russia) in connection with the acquisition of a 35% stake in AluminaPartners of Jamaica from Norsk Hydro Asa; City Index Limited (UK) on the integration of its US and UK foreign exchange dealer operations; Magal Security Systems, Ltd. (Israel) in a $16 million rights offering to its shareholders; Prana Biotechnology Limited (Australia) in filing a $50 million shelf registration statement for its "at-the-market" offering program;  Schuler SMG GmbH & Co. (Germany) and Symrise Inc. (Germany) in general corporate matters; National Bank of Canada (Canada) in the pending increase of its U.S. commercial paper program to US$5 billion; Baytex Energy Corp. (Canada) in establishing its shelf registration for up to CDN$500 million of debt securities; Crescent Point Energy Corp. (Canada) in its offering of CDN$375 million of Common Shares.

### Clients:

Clients include Bank of New York Mellon, JPMorgan Chase, Deutsche Bank, Goldman Sachs, National Bank of Canada, Seaco SRL, SPDR® Gold Trust, U.S. BANK n.a.,City Index Limited, UC Rusal, CooperSurgical, Inc., Trinity Biotech plc, Kaneka Ltd., Empire State Development Corporation, Metropolitan Transportation Authority, Lower Manhattan Development Corporation, Honeywell, Victaulic Company, Corbis, Playtex Products, Sixty S.p.A., First Calgary Petroleums, Circle Line-Sightseeing Yachts, Inc., International Organization for Standardization, B Communications Ltd., the City of New York, Spectra Energy, Collegiate Asset Management Corp, California Franchise Tax Board, Manhangar, Wells Fargo Bank N.A.

# CHADBOURNE & PARKE LLP

www.chadbourne.com  **tel:** 212 408 5100  **fax:** 212 541 5369

**Managing Partner:** Andrew A Giaccia
Number of partners worldwide: 133
Number of other lawyers worldwide: 248

## Firm Overview:

Founded in 1902, Chadbourne & Parke LLP has evolved into an international law firm with 12 offices in key markets around the world. The firm represents corporations, international financial institutions, NGOs and individuals in all of its major practices throughout the US, Western Europe, Turkey, Central and Eastern Europe, Russia, the Middle East and North Africa, China, and Latin America. Chadbourne's structure, as a unitary partnership, facilitates collaboration among all of its offices and lawyers. Almost all of the attorneys in Chadbourne's offices outside the US are nationals of those countries and fully admitted to practice there.

## Main Areas of Practice:

Chadbourne provides clients a diverse portfolio of legal services, including antitrust, banking and finance, bankruptcy and financial restructuring, capital markets, commercial litigation, communications and technology, corporate, corporate finance, US and international tax, emerging markets, employment law and ERISA, energy and renewable energy, environmental, government contract matters, insurance and reinsurance, intellectual property, international arbitration, mergers and acquisitions, oil and gas, private funds, products liability litigation, project finance, real estate, securities, special investigations and litigation, and trusts and estates.

## Energy/Project Finance:

Chadbourne is a franchise name in the energy and project finance markets. The firm has worked on projects in more than 80 countries. More than 80 lawyers work full time in the project finance group. A vast majority of the work of the group in the last few years has been in renewable energy, LNG, oil and gas, and power projects. Forty percent of the group's work last year was outside the United States, especially in the Middle East, Africa and Latin America. Chadbourne has always been especially prominent in emerging markets and works heavily with multilateral lending and export credit agencies. It is also prominent in public-private partnerships for basic infrastructure. The Chadbourne project finance group closed on $20 billion in financings in 2011.

## Corporate:

Chadbourne's corporate practice advises domestic and international clients in connection with all manner of business transactions throughout the world. The firm maintains significant practices in the areas of bankruptcy/restructuring, banking and finance, capital markets, corporate governance, general corporate activities, intellectual property, mergers and acquisitions, private funds and securities compliance. Chadbourne offers clients expertise in every major industry, with particular depth in aerospace and defense, consumer products, energy, insurance/reinsurance, manufacturing, pharmaceuticals, and communications and technology. Chadbourne's intellectual property lawyers provide practical business solutions to IP issues in corporate transactions, licensing, and intellectual property monetization. Partners include specialists in current US and UK anti-corruption legislation.

## US & International Tax:

Chadbourne's tax lawyers have planned, structured and implemented numerous high-profile, tax sensitive US and cross-border M&A and project finance transactions and financings and have been the lead lawyers in many significant tax controversy matters. Clients include major public companies and financial institutions, large private equity and hedge funds, and family-owned and closely-held international businesses.

## Litigation & Dispute Resolution:

Chadbourne's litigation practice has earned a national reputation for excellence in complex high-stakes, high-profile business disputes as well as for white collar defense work. The firm's attorneys have worked extensively in the fields of products liability, commercial litigation, accountants' liability, securities litigation and regulatory enforcement, corporate governance, anti-corruption legislation, special investigations, environmental litigation, trusts and estates, insurance/reinsurance and IP litigation. The products liability group is adept at handling the complex challenges faced by manufacturers of pharmaceuticals, household appliances, distilled spirits, cosmetics and other consumer products in the US and around the world including class actions, mass torts and multi-district litigation. The firm's trial lawyers regularly try and win cases in state and federal courts throughout the US and abroad.

## International Arbitration:

Chadbourne is a world leader representing investors and sovereigns in both commercial and investor-state arbitration. Chadbourne's international arbitration team consists of academically distinguished specialists with varied backgrounds, a range of language skills, and long-standing local and practical experience to help navigate its clients through the complex and unique issues that arise in arbitration before international courts and tribunals worldwide.

## Bankruptcy & Financial Restructuring:

Chadbourne's bankruptcy and financial restructuring group has an impressive record of achieving successful outcomes for its clients in major Chapter 11 cases and corporate restructurings both in the US and abroad. Chadbourne plays leading roles in mega-cases such as Residential Capital (ResCap), Tribune Company, Parmalat, Technical Olympic USA (TOUSA), Refco, Lehman and AbitibiBowater. The firm also represents the world's leading banks, including Citigroup, Credit Suisse, The Royal Bank of Scotland and The Royal Bank of Canada, in restructuring distressed loans. Chadbourne is recognized as the leader in cross-border insolvency proceedings and has filed many of the most significant cases brought under Chapter 15 of the Bankruptcy Code.

## Insurance & Reinsurance:

The insurance and reinsurance group offers an experienced, international and interdisciplinary legal team able to address virtually any legal issue affecting the worldwide insurance and reinsurance industries. The team in disputes, corporate transactions, regulatory matters, and myriad other types of matters in the property/casualty and life/health arenas represents insurers, reinsurers, intermediaries, financial institutions and governmental entities.

# CLEARY GOTTLIEB STEEN & HAMILTON LLP
**www.**clearygottlieb.com **tel:** 212 225 2000 **fax:** 212 225 3999

**Managing Partner:** Mark Leddy
Number of partners worldwide: 198  Number of lawyers worldwide: 1,200

## Firm Overview:

**Recent Firm Awards and Achievements:** Law Firm of the Year by Legal Business (2013); "Go To" Firm (IP, Litigation, Securities, Corporate, International) by Corporate Counsel (2012); Investment Funds Client Service Firm of the Year by Chambers USA (20 12); Competition/ Antitrust Firm of the Year by Chambers Global (2012 & 2013) and Latin America Firm of the Year by Chambers Global (2012); US Law Firm of the Year by Legal Business and IFLR (2011); Best Law Firm and Best Law Firm in Latin America by Latin Finance (2013); Top Five Global Law Firm by Law36O's "Global 20" (2012); Top Three Innovative Law Firm in Financial Time's US Innovative Lawyers Survey (2011); Top Ten Law Firm in Vault's Guide to Top 100 Law Firms (2012); Top 25 US Firm (selected by Directors and General Counsel) in Corporate Board Member's "America's Best Corporate Law Firms Survey" (2012); Most Innovative US Firm in Europe by IFLR (2011); Competition/Antitrust Firm of the Year by Chambers USA, US News & World Report, Best Lawyers and Top Legal (2011); Top Two Elite Firm by Global Competition Review (2011 - 20 13); International Trade and Finance Firm of the Year by US News & World Report - Best Lawyers' Best Law Firms, (2013); South Korea International Firm of the Year by Chambers Asia (2013); Italian Competition! EU Firm of the Year by TopLegal (2012); North America Tax Firm and North America Media & Entertainment Tax Firm of the year by International Tax Review (2011); Best International Counsel in Latin America: Corporate/M&A by Chambers Latin America (2013); Best Legal Advisor in Latin America by Global Finance (2012); M&A Practice Group of the Year and Antitrust Practice Group of the Year by Law36O (2013); Tax Team of the Year by Chambers USA (2011); Americas Debt & Equity-Linked Team of the Year by IFLR (2011); Global Elite firm every year since its inception by Legal Business' "Global 100" (2003-20 12); Top Seven firm worldwide appearing as arbitration counsel in The American Lawyer (2011); Top 30 most active firms worldwide by Global Arbitration Review (2011).

**League Table Results:** Number one Global and U.S. Equity & Equity-Reaed Managers' Counsel in Thomson Reuters, (based on value, 2012); number one EMEA Equity ad Equity-Linked Issuers' Counsel in Bloomberg, (based on volume, deal count, 2012); number two U.S. Straight Debt Issuers' Counsel by Thomson Reuters, (based on value, 2012); number three Global Bond Issuers' Counsel in Bloomberg, (based on deal count, 2012); number three U.S. Corporates Issuers' Counsel in Bloomberg, (based on volume, 2012); number one in Russian M&A in Mergermarket, (based on value, 2012); number two in French M&A in Mergermarket, (based on value, 2012); number two in UK M&A in Mergermarket, (based on value, 2012); number three in Emerging Markets M&A in Thomson Reuters, (based on value, announced, 2012); number four in Middle East & North African M&A by Thomson Reuters, (based on value, completed, 2012); number one firm advising US equity ma'nagers in Bloomberg, (based on value, 2011); number two firm advising global bond issuers in'Blobim"berg, (based on deal count, 2011); number three firm advising global bond managers in Bloomberg, (based on deal count, 2011); number two firm advising US equity-linked managers in Bloomberg (based on value, 2011); number four firm advising US investment grade issuers in Bloomberg, (based on value, 2011); number two firm advising Euromarket high-yield issuers (excluding emerging markets) in Bloomberg (based on value, 2011); number five firm advising Malaysia equity IPO issuers in Bloomberg, (based on value, 2011); number five firm advising EMEA equity & equity-linked issuers in Bloomberg, (based on value, 2011); number one firm in Latin America M&A in Thomson Reuters, (based on value, completed, 2011); number one firm in Mexican M&A in Thomson Reuters, (based on value, completed, 2011); number one firm in Russian M&A in Thomson Reuters, (based on value, completed, 201 1); number two firm in German M&A in Thomson Reuters, (based on value, announced, 20'11);tinumber three firm in Italian M&A in Thomson Reuters, (based on value and deal count, comnpleted, 2011); number two firm in Greater China M&A in Mergermarket, (based on value, announced, 2011); number two firm in global metals and mining M&A in Thomson Reuters, based on value, completed, 2011).

**Deals of the Year:** The firm continues to receive consistent recognition by various influential publications as counsel in Deals of the Year.

## Main Areas of Practice:
Antitrust and competition; Asia; banking and financial institutions; bankruptcy and restructuring; capital markets; corporate governance; derivatives; employee benefits; energy; environmental; intellectual property; international trade; Latin America; leveraged finance; litigation and arbitration; mergers, acquisitions and joint ventures; private clients and charitable organizations; private equity; privatizations; pro bono; project finance and infrastructure; real estate; securities enforcement and white-collar defense; sovereign governments and international institutions; structured finance; and tax.

## International Work:
For more than 60 years, Cleary Gottlieb has been pre-eminent in shaping the globalization of the legal profession. The firm's worldwide practice has a proven track record for innovation and providing work of the

highest quality to meet the domestic and international needs of clients. Cleary Gottlieb's clients include multinational corporations and international financial institutions, sovereign governments and their agencies, as well as domestic corporations and financial institutions in the countries where the firm's offices are located. Although each of the 16 offices has its own practice, Cleary Gottlieb's 'one firm' approach offers clients the ability to access the full resources of all of the firm's offices and lawyers worldwide to the extent their matters so require. Approximately 1,200 lawyers work at Cleary Gottlieb worldwide.

## Offices:
**New York Office Profile:** The New York office handles corporate, securities and structured finance matters; mergers, acquisitions and joint ventures; litigation; banking and financial institutions; bankruptcy and restructuring; representation of sovereign governments

in financial matters; taxation; employee benefits; real estate; and work for individual clients and charitable organizations. Clients range from the top investment banking firms and corporate entities to sovereign governments throughout Latin America and high net worth individuals. The New York office has approximately 500 lawyers.

**Washington Office Profile:** The Washington office focuses on banking and financial institutions regulations; corporate and securities law; environmental, public and administrative law; structured finance; litigation; antitrust and international trade; taxation; and legislative counseling. The office serves as the focal point for the firm's US regulatory practice and, in particular, its counsel on corporate governance issues. Clients range from government loan agencies to *Fortune* 500 corporations. Approximately 100 lawyers work in the Washington office.

**OFFICES**
NEW YORK
**NEW YORK:** One Liberty Plaza, NY 10006
Tel: 212 225 2000  Fax: 212 225 3999

DISTRICT OF COLUMBIA
**WASHINGTON:** 2000 Pennsylvania Avenue, NW, DC 20006
Tel: 202 974 1500  Fax: 202 974 1999

**INTERNATIONAL OFFICES**
EUROPE: Brussels, Cologne, Frankfurt, London, Milan, Moscow, Paris and Rome.
ASIA: Hong Kong, Beijing, Seoul.
LATIN AMERICA: Buenos Aires and São Paulo.
MIDDLE EAST: Abu Dhabi

# COHEN & GRESSER LLP

www.cohengresser.com **tel:** 212 957 7600 **fax:** 212 957 4514

**Managing Partner:** Lawrence T Gresser
Number of partners: 13
Number of lawyers: 51
Languages: *English, Cantonese, Farsi, French, German, Hebrew, Hindi, Korean, Portuguese, Punjabi, Russian, Spanish, Urdu*

### Firm Overview:

Cohen & Gresser is a boutique law firm with offices in New York and Seoul. The firm represents clients in complex litigation and corporate matters, and its clients include Fortune 500 companies and major financial institutions across a broad spectrum of industries throughout the United States, Europe, Asia, and Australia. The firm has litigated and negotiated against some of the largest law firms in the world and has an outstanding record of success in high-stakes and high-profile engagements.

### Main Areas of Practice:

**Litigation & Arbitration:**
Cohen & Gresser handles major cases in federal and state courts, before government agencies, and in a variety of domestic and international arbitration settings under the AAA, LCIA, ICC, FINRA, and UNCITRAL Arbitration Rules. The firm has substantial experience in antitrust and unfair competition, bankruptcy litigation and counseling, class actions, commercial litigation, directors and officers litigation, employment, healthcare litigation, partnership disputes, products liability, real estate litigation, and securities law.
**Contact:** Mark S Cohen **Tel:** 212 957 7601
**Email:** mcohen@cohengresser.com

**Intellectual Property & Licensing:**
Cohen & Gresser represents clients in patent, trademark, copyright, trade secret, and unfair competition matters. The firm's patent litigators are skilled in computer software and hardware, mobile technology, electronics, medical devices, life sciences, mechanical engineering, consumer products, financial transactions, and business methods. Its IP litigators also represent clients in trademark, copyright, trade secret, and unfair competition cases and advise clients on Internet privacy issues and technology law. The firm's IP transactional attorneys represent clients in licensing agreements and agreements to transfer technology, patents, copyrights, trademarks, and other intellectual property assets. They also assist clients in evaluating intellectual property in M&A transactions, and in developing business plans, licensing programs, and intellectual property portfolio strategies.
**Contact:** Karen H Bromberg **Tel:** 212 957 7604
**Email:** kbromberg@cohengresser.com

**White Collar Defense, Regulatory Enforcement & Internal Investigations:**
The firm represents corporations and individuals in federal and state regulatory investigations, proceedings before self-regulatory organizations, corporate internal investigations, and white collar criminal cases. Staffed by highly experienced former federal and state prosecutors and defense counsel, this group has represented clients in most of the major investigations of recent years and has defended institutions and senior executives in proceedings involving the United States Department of Justice, the Securities and Exchange Commission, the New York State Attorney General, the NYSE, the NASD, FINRA, the FSA, and the Federal Reserve.
**Contact:** Mark S Cohen **Tel:** 212 957 7601
**Email:** mcohen@cohengresser.com

**Corporate Law:**
Cohen & Gresser assists clients in a wide range of corporate transactions, including mergers and acquisitions, fund formation, venture capital and private equity financings and transactions, and securities and other regulatory matters. The firm's attorneys have represented early-stage and late-stage privately held companies, public companies, non-profit companies and associations, hedge funds, venture capital and buyout firms, and investment banks. The firm also serves as outside general counsel to a number of privately held companies and regularly counsels clients on executive compensation and employment issues.
**Contact:** Lawrence T Gresser **Tel:** 212 957 7602
**Email:** ltgresser@cohengresser.com

### International Office:

Cohen & Gresser opened its Seoul office in October 2012 after becoming the third US law firm to be approved by the Korean Ministry of Justice to open an office in Korea. The Korean office is headed by S C Sohn and focuses on international arbitration, cross-border litigation, products liability, intellectual property (including patent litigation), and international business transactions (including mergers and acquisitions, private equity, venture capital investments, and joint ventures).

**PRACTICE AREAS**
Litigation & Arbitration
Intellectual Property & Licensing
White Collar Defense, Regulatory Enforcement & Internal Investigations
Corporate Law

**OFFICES**
NEW YORK
**NEW YORK:** 800 Third Avenue, NY 10022
Tel: 212 957 7600   Fax: 212 957 4514
Email: info@cohengresser.com

**INTERNATIONAL OFFICES**
The firm also has an office in Seoul, Korea.

# COHEN & GRESSER LLP

# CONDON & FORSYTH LLP

**www.**condonlaw.com  **tel:** 212 490 9100  **fax:** 212 370 4453

**Managing Partners:** Desmond T Barry, Jr; Christopher R Christensen; Bartholomew J Banino
Number of partners: 16
Number of lawyers: 40
Languages: *English, German, Spanish*

## Firm Overview:

Founded in 1935, Condon & Forsyth has handled a spectrum of issues for airlines, manufacturers and their insurers, including litigation arising from major aircraft accidents, product liability counseling and litigation, regulatory advice and representation, class actions, and commercial transactional matters. The firm has successfully leveraged its extensive experience in the aviation industry, including state and federal liability and damages trial and appellate work, multi-district litigation, and National Transportation Safety Board (NTSB) and Federal Aviation Administration (FAA) investigations, along with its attorneys' technical expertise, to expand its practice to areas beyond aviation.

## Main Areas of Practice:

### Aviation & Aerospace:

The firm has unmatched expertise and experience in the representation of airlines and manufacturers in litigation arising from major accidents. Currently counsel for American Airlines in the property litigation arising from the terrorist attacks of September 11, 2001; Colgan Air for claims arising out of the Flight 3407 accident near Buffalo, New York on February 12, 2009; and Caribbean Airlines for claims arising out of the Flight 523 accident in Georgetown, Guyana on July 30, 2011.

### Product Liability:

The firm's product liability attorneys represent and advise a diverse range of manufacturers in complex tort litigation, including manufacturers of commercial and general aviation aircraft and components, industrial machinery, satellites, power plant, and pharmaceutical products. The firm has advised manufacturers about proposed airworthiness directives and product recalls; revising aircraft operators' manuals, instructions and warnings; drafting service bulletins and service information; and organizing pilot and operator seminars.

### Mass Disaster Emergency Response & Crisis Management:

The firm assists transportation-related companies worldwide to mitigate and manage the investigative, legal and publicity matters resulting from mass disasters and crisis situations. Post-emergency objectives include the rapid resumption of normal and ongoing operations, effective victim/family assistance, protection of legal rights, and protection of the client's reputation.

### Insurance/Reinsurance Coverage Advice & Litigation:

The firm has an international reputation as counsel for insurers and reinsurers. The firm has served various insurance markets for decades, providing legal opinions, drafting policy language and litigating or arbitrating complex insurance and reinsurance coverage matters.

### Class Actions:

The firm has successfully defended air carriers in multiple class actions, including litigation arising out of mass passenger disruptions, ticket and cargo fuel surcharges, taxation disputes and consumer protection regulations. It currently represents three European and two US air carriers in class action proceedings arising from the application of an EU consumer protection regulation, as well as defending airlines in civil litigation arising from cargo fuel surcharges. The firm served as defense counsel for a terminal operating group in a class action litigation arising from tarmac delays at JFK International Airport following a 2010 winter storm.

### Regulatory & Government Affairs:

The firm regularly advises aviation clients on regulatory matters involving the US Departments of Transportation (DOT), Justice and Treasury (including OFAC), and the FAA on issues such as trade sanctions, code sharing, licensing, high density traffic airport slots, and regulatory compliance. The firm regularly represents airlines and pilots in investigations and enforcement proceedings before the NTSB, DOT, FAA and other federal agencies.

### Commercial Transactions & Real Estate:

The firm has considerable experience handling commercial transactions and represents airlines, freight forwarders, charter companies, banks, real estate companies, manufacturers and leasing companies in a variety of transactions, including joint venture agreements, the sale and leaseback of commercial aircraft, charter agreements, consulting agreements, commercial real estate leases, and management agreements.

### Employment:

The firm has advised employers on numerous employment-related issues including wrongful termination and discrimination claims. Attorneys also assist in the drafting and review of employee handbooks, affirmative action plans and personnel policies.

### Social Media:

The firm advises clients on the complex legal, regulatory, and policy issues associated with social media, including the creation, monitoring, and maintenance of corporate social media pages; crisis management and emergency response preparedness; and domestic and foreign privacy and data protection issues.

### Electronic Discovery & Information Governance:

The firm advises clients about the proactive use of information governance policies, the cost effective management of electronic discovery, and the strategic use of technology in responding to litigation, government and regulatory agency investigations.

### Clients:

American Airlines, British Airways, General Electric, United Air Lines, Embraer, Global Aerospace, BAE Systems, ACE, Mitsubishi Heavy Industries, Dassault Falcon, Allianz, Southwest Airlines Pilots' Association (SWAPA), ST Aerospace, China Center, Waste Management, KLM Royal Dutch Airlines, Singapore Airlines, Air New Zealand, AIG, Iberia, Lufthansa, Qantas, LOT Polish Airlines.

CONDON & FORSYTH LLP

# CRAVATH, SWAINE & MOORE LLP

www.cravath.com **tel:** 212 474 1000 **fax:** 212 474 3700

**Presiding Partner:** C Allen Parker
Number of partners worldwide: 87  Number of other lawyers worldwide: 354
Languages: *Arabic, Bengali (India), Bulgarian, Cantonese (Chinese), Czech, Dutch, Farsi (Persian), French, German, Greek, Gujarati (India), Hebrew, Hindi (India), Italian, Japanese, Kannada (India), Korean, Malay, Mandarin (Chinese), Portuguese, Romanian, Russian, Spanish, Ukrainian and Urdu (Pakistan)*

## OFFICES

NEW YORK

**NEW YORK:** Worldwide Plaza, 825 Eighth Avenue,
NY 10019
Tel: 212 474 1000  Fax: 212 474 3700

## INTERNATIONAL OFFICES

The firm also has an office in London.

## Firm Overview:

Cravath, Swaine & Moore LLP is widely recognized as one of the preeminent law firms in the world. Each of its practices is highly regarded, and its lawyers are recognized for their commitment to the representation of clients' interests in the US and throughout the world. Cravath was founded in 1819 and maintains offices in New York and London.

## Main Areas of Practice:

### Corporate:

Clients repeatedly choose Cravath in large and complex matters, particularly with respect to cross-border transactions involving multiple jurisdictions. Cravath's corporate lawyers advise global businesses in a diverse range of merger and acquisition transactions, including divestitures, spin-offs and joint ventures. The firm is active in both making hostile bids and defending against takeover attempts, based on the combined strength and depth of its corporate and litigation departments. Cravath has a highly regarded US and international securities practice, with lawyers representing issuers and investment banks in all types of US and global offerings. The firm's commercial banking lawyers regularly represent major financial institutions and borrowers. Cravath's experience in M&A, securities and commercial banking is a significant advantage for the firm's clients, whose business concerns often involve all of these areas. A highly regarded group of environmental lawyers at Cravath work with the firm's clients on matters related to acquisition and disposition strategies, financings and regulatory compliance with respect to a broad range of environmental issues.

### Tax:

Cravath's tax lawyers play an integral role in structuring and negotiating all types of transactions, including mergers, spin-offs, joint ventures, securities offerings, commercial bank facilities and intricate private equity acquisitions and related financings. The Tax Department designs structures for complex domestic and international transactions and has developed innovative types of acquisitions and financings in the US and international markets. In cooperation with tax advisors in other countries, the firm's tax lawyers work to capture the benefits of differences in the tax law in different regions.

### Executive Compensation & Benefits:

Cravath's ECB Department brings experience and judgment to clients' employee benefits and compensation matters, which are often central concerns in acquisitions, dispositions and other transactions. The firm's ECB lawyers advise companies, boards of directors, compensation committees and members of senior management in a variety of compensation and benefit arrangements as well as legal compliance concerns.

### Litigation:

Cravath is known for the breadth and depth of its litigation experience in such diverse areas of the law as the Alien Tort Claims Act, antitrust, bankruptcy, contracts and commercial disputes, corporate investigations and governance, employment, the Employment Retirement Income Security Act (ERISA), the Foreign Corrupt Practices Act (FCPA), intellectual property (patents, trademarks, trade dress, copyrights, trade secrets), mergers and acquisitions, real estate, the Racketeer Influenced and Corrupt Organizations Act (RICO), securities and tax. Cravath litigators are routinely called upon to represent non-US companies in many of the largest and most complex litigations and domestic and international arbitrations (including ICC, LCIA, AAA and private arbitrations), before administrative agencies and regulatory authorities, and in virtually every other type of proceeding, including internal investigations. Cravath litigators handle work involving contested merger and acquisition transactions, while boards of directors and special committees have relied on the firm's lawyers to guide them through the intricacies of shareholder litigation and government investigations. The firm's antitrust experience encompasses a wide range of industries, from mining to telecommunications. A significant portion of the firm's litigation work relates to contracts and commercial disputes, often in the form of business torts as well as other areas of general business litigation. The firm handles a broad range of complex and challenging matters involving intellectual property across all industries, from computers to biotechnology and pharmaceuticals to recording technology. In the area of securities litigation, Cravath is widely recognized for handling complex and often precedent-setting cases.

### Trusts & Estates:

The firm's trusts and estates lawyers have served as legal counsel, advisors and trustees to several generations of the families that built many of the most important businesses in the world. The firm's insight and sound judgment have earned the respect and confidence of generations of some of the most successful private clients in their trusts and estates matters. Today, the firm continues to represent many leading entrepreneurs, senior executives, and private corporations and partnerships. The firm's lawyers work closely with private clients and their families to realize their estate planning and philanthropic goals by creating and endowing trusts, estates and charitable foundations.

### International Work:

For the past 100 years, Cravath has had an international practice representing US firms abroad and non-US firms, both in the US market and worldwide. Cravath lawyers work on a diverse range of matters and regularly advise corporate and financial institution clients on a variety of capital markets, mergers and acquisitions, general corporate, commercial banking and SEC compliance matters. The firm's lawyers often work closely with leading law firms in Europe and elsewhere, providing advice on complex transactions that require extensive knowledge of and experience in the laws of multiple jurisdictions. The firm also handles both US litigation and international arbitrations for non-US clients.

### Clients:

Along with governments and multinational institutions, the firm's client base includes some of the world's best known companies and financial institutions, including: Alcoa, American Express, Avon, AWB Ltd., BAE Systems, Banco Santander, Barnes & Noble, Citigroup, Credit Suisse, Deloitte & Touche, Delta, Deutsche Bank, DreamWorks Animation, DuPont, European Investment Bank, Goldman Sachs, Hertz, IBM, INEOS, Johnson & Johnson, JPMorgan Chase, Kraft Foods, Lindsay Goldberg, Medinol, Merck, Morgan Stanley, Mylan, Naspers, NCR, Nestlé, Novartis, Permira, PricewaterhouseCoopers, QUALCOMM, Royal Dutch Shell, Sappi, Sprint Nextel, Time Warner, UBS, Unilever, Vivendi and Xerox. Approximately one-quarter of the firm's clients are non-US institutions for which the firm provides a wide variety of corporate, tax and litigation representations.

CRAVATH, SWAINE & MOORE LLP

# CURTIS, MALLET-PREVOST, COLT & MOSLE LLP

**www.**curtis.com **tel:** 212 696 6000 **fax:** 212 697 1559

**Chairman:** George Kahale III
**Managing Partners:** Joseph D Pizzurro and Matias A Vega

**Firm Overview:**
Curtis, Mallet-Prevost, Colt & Mosle LLP is a leading international law firm providing a broad range of legal services to clients around the world. Curtis operates through its 16 offices in the United States, Europe, Latin America, the Middle East and Central Asia. The firm's international orientation has been a hallmark of its practice for nearly two centuries. Curtis attorneys are internationalists with a deep understanding of the cultural as well as business sensitivities associated with conducting business across borders.
Curtis represents clients across industry sectors, including multinational corporations and financial institutions, governments and state-owned companies, money managers, sovereign wealth funds, family-owned businesses, individuals and entrepreneurs.

**Main Areas of Practice:**

**Capital Markets:**
Curtis assists clients through all stages of the capital-raising process, from advice on the most appropriate listing venue through preparation of listing and offering documentation and negotiation of all key contractual documents. The firm counsels issuers, investment banks, private equity funds and strategic shareholders in capital raising in different jurisdictions.

**Energy & Power:**
Curtis offers extensive experience in matters relating to the international petroleum and power industries, most of which has been in the representation of states and national oil companies. The firm's work in this area includes the structuring, negotiation and drafting of the full range of international petroleum contracts, project finance transactions and international litigation and arbitration. Curtis has been involved in some of the world's largest energy transactions.

**Finance:**
Curtis attorneys handle the full complement of debt and equity finance issues, including structured and asset-backed lending, issuances and placements in the public and private securities markets, the bilateral and syndicated bank market, and other institutional capital markets. Curtis has been involved in some of the largest project financings worldwide.

**International Arbitration:**
Curtis is ranked as one of the top law firms in the world for international arbitration. The firm has been retained to handle many of the world's largest and most significant disputes. Curtis attorneys are highly experienced in all aspects of international arbitration involving public and private entities. Curtis is well-known for acting on behalf of states, state-owned entities and international organizations both in disputes and non-contentious matters.

**International Investment:**
Curtis is uniquely positioned to help non-American companies take advantage of the business opportunities presented in the US and other jurisdictions. The firm offers a multidisciplinary group of lawyers with backgrounds in commercial transactions, mergers and acquisitions, import/export, intellectual property and tax to tailor and implement strategies that enable clients to achieve their global business goals.

**International Tax:**
Curtis offers clients sophisticated tax counsel in high-profile transactions and disputes, as well as more traditional deals, for private investors, international funds and public and private companies. Curtis has developed particular expertise in cross-border tax planning.

**International Trade:**
Curtis provides clients, government entities as well as domestic and international companies in an array of industries, with practical solutions to global trade, international investment, market access and export control issues. The firm offers clients the full range of international trade services, including all aspects of the myriad laws governing the cross-border shipment of goods and services. The team has represented both exporters and importers in some of the most significant international trade disputes of the past few decades.

**Investment Management:**
Curtis provides advice on all legal aspects of professional investment management, including the structuring, implementation and ongoing maintenance of investment funds, in particular private equity funds, hedge funds and sovereign wealth funds.

**Litigation:**
Curtis provides counsel in contested matters in state and federal courts, domestic and foreign arbitrations, administrative and appellate forums and corporate internal investigations. The firm represents clients in disputes covering contracts, business torts, securities and intellectual property in a wide array of industries including commodities, pharmaceuticals, competition, environment, insurance, real estate and tax, among others. Curtis also has an active white-collar criminal defense and investigations practice.

**Mergers & Acquisitions & Private Equity:**
Curtis represents private and public companies as well as private equity firms, hedge funds, and governments and state-owned companies in a broad range of mergers and acquisitions and has structured and advised on private equity transactions around the world dealing with numerous regulatory, tax and other issues posed by cross-border transactions. Curtis also counsels clients on joint ventures, strategic alliances, long-term supply contracts, and the full range of other long-term commercial agreements and associations.

**Project Finance & Infrastructure Development:**
Curtis plays a leading role in major project finance transactions in the international petroleum and power industries. This work includes structuring and the development of new forms of transactions; adapting international structures to local legal requirements; development of bidding guidelines; and administration of public bidding processes.

**Real Estate:**
Curtis provides legal advice in connection with virtually every type of real property across the globe, including undeveloped land, office properties, hotels, shopping centers, warehouses, and residential, retail and industrial facilities. The firm's clients include governments, private and sovereign funds, REITs, corporate lenders, and developers of all types, as well as individuals, partnerships and corporate investors.

**Restructuring & Insolvency:**
Curtis has developed a national reputation as the leading law firm in "conflicts counsel" and specials counsel engagements in large and complex Chapter 11 restructurings on both the debtor and creditors' committee sides. Clients encompass debtors, creditors and creditors' committees, lenders and other financial institutions, equity owners and investors, trustees, liquidators and other court-appointed fiduciaries, and governmental agencies.

# DEBEVOISE & PLIMPTON LLP

www.debevoise.com **tel:** 212 909 6000 **fax:** 212 909 6836

**Managing Partner:** Michael W Blair
Number of partners (worldwide): 142  Number of other lawyers (worldwide): 500
Languages: *Aramaic, Bosnian, Bulgarian, Chinese (Cantonese, Mandarin and Shanghainese), Czech, Dutch, English, Farsi, French, German, Greek, Hebrew, Hindi, Hungarian, Icelandic, Italian, Japanese, Korean, Malayalam, Polish, Portuguese, Russian, Slovak, Spanish, Swedish, Ukrainian, Urdu*

## Firm Overview:

Debevoise & Plimpton LLP was founded in 1931 with the goal of offering sophisticated legal services. They maintain this tradition of seeking excellence in a comprehensive, modern practice that spans the Americas, Europe and Asia. The firm's lawyers are responsive, thoughtful, ethical and vigorous advocates with a substantive understanding of their clients' business needs and the many marketplaces in which they compete. Debevoise has leading practices that often have a cross border focus due to the firm's international approach to the practice of law. Debevoise places the highest value on collaboration and interdisciplinary cooperation in order to provide clients with seamless representation across practice areas and across continents. They represent multinational, US and non-US industrial and commercial companies, private equity sponsors, financial institutions including insurance companies, investment companies, banks and broker-dealers, and individuals in a comprehensive range of assignments.

## Main Areas of Practice:

### Corporate:

The firm's Corporate Department's work spans the full range of general corporate, transactional and regulatory representations. Their practice includes mergers and acquisitions, capital markets, leveraged finance, business restructuring and workouts, real estate, project finance, equipment finance, structured finance, asset management, intellectual property and environmental law. They have an exceptionally strong track record advising private equity sponsors and their portfolio companies, as well as clients in the media and telecommunications, banking, insurance and energy industries.

### Litigation:

The firm's Litigation Department handles complex matters in courts in the United States, the United Kingdom, France and elsewhere, as well as before arbitration tribunals, agencies and administrative bodies worldwide. The Department includes the Chair, Mary Jo White, the former U.S. Attorney for the Southern District of New York; John S Kiernan, Co-Chair of the Department; Michael B Mukasey, former United States Attorney General and Chief Judge of the United States District Court for the Southern District of New York; Lord (Peter) Goldsmith QC, PC, the European and Asian Chair of Litigation who served as the UK's Attorney General; 8 former Assistant U.S. Attorneys, including a former Under Secretary of the U.S. Treasury for Enforcement and a former Chief Assistant U.S. Attorney for the Southern and Eastern Districts of New York; and a former Associate Director of the Securities and Exchange Commission's Division of Enforcement. Debevoise is the only law firm to include former Attorneys General of both the U.S. and the UK, as well as a Queen's Counsel.

Areas of concentration include securities litigation, white collar crime, investigations, antitrust, bankruptcy, general commercial litigation, international dispute resolution, insurance industry disputes, intellectual property and media, and products liability.

### Tax & Employee Benefits:

The firm's Tax Department works closely with their corporate lawyers in structuring complex transactions. The department also focuses on tax planning and advice for business entities, high net worth individuals and exempt organizations and includes an active executive compensation and employee benefits practice.

## International Work:

### Asia:

Debevoise's Hong Kong and Shanghai offices, with over 20 lawyers, are active throughout China and the Asia-Pacific region. Their corporate team in Asia handles in cross-border investments, formation and deployment of private equity funds, telecommunications and other joint ventures, US securities offerings, general corporate counseling. The firm's litigation and arbitration team in Asia handles international dispute resolution, litigation, white collar and internal investigations matters. Their lawyers in Asia represent multi-national companies, private equity sponsors and other investment funds in a broad range of strategic and financial investments throughout Asia.

### Europe:

Debevoise's London office has approximately 90 lawyers. Its practice focuses on mergers and acquisitions, capital markets transactions, financings and private equity, as well as general corporate and tax matters. It has a strong international arbitration and litigation team. The firm's Paris office has approximately 25 lawyers. Its practice

includes domestic and cross-border mergers and acquisitions, capital markets transactions, financings and private equity, as well as EU competition law, general corporate and tax matters and international arbitration. The Frankfurt office has more than 10 lawyers. The practice focuses on mergers and acquisitions, corporate governance, capital markets transactions, financings and private equity, as well as general corporate and tax matters. The firm's Moscow office has more than 25 lawyers who focus on capital markets transactions, mergers and acquisitions, natural resource projects, financings, as well as general corporate and tax matters.

### Latin America:

Debevoise has been active in Latin America for nearly 50 years and over the past decade has worked on hundreds of completed transactions in the region, including some of the largest and most challenging projects. The firm is a recognized leader among international law firms active in Latin America. Their recent work in the Latin American private equity/fund formation, project finance, media and financial service sectors, as well as their litigation and arbitration practice in the region, has further solidified the firm's reputation. The firm's client base includes many of the most prominent companies and families in Latin America as well as multinational corporations and private equity funds investing in the region.

# DECHERT LLP

www.dechert.com **tel:** 212 698 3500 **fax:** 212 698 3599

**Chairman:** Andrew J Levander
**Chief Executive Officer:** Daniel O'Donnell
**Managing Partners:** Andrew J Levander, Daniel O'Donnell
Number of partners: 303
Number of lawyers: 897
Languages: *Cantonese, Dutch, English, French, German, Mandarin, Russian, Spanish*

## Firm Overview:

With 26 offices throughout the United States, Europe, Asia and the Middle East, Dechert LLP is an international law firm focused on financial services and asset management, complex litigation and international arbitration, corporate and securities, real estate finance, tax law, labor and employment, intellectual property, life sciences, and business restructuring and reorganization. Founded in 1875 in Philadelphia, the firm has more than 800 lawyers.

## Main Areas of Practice:

### Antitrust/Competition:

Clients rely on Dechert's antitrust/competition lawyers for counsel on merger clearance, private litigation, cartel matters, civil investigations and risk prevention.
**Contact:** George Gordon **Tel:** 215 994 2382
**Contact:** Michael Weiner **Tel:** 212 698 3608

### Bankruptcy, Business Restructuring & Reorganization:

Dechert's bankruptcy, business restructuring and reorganization lawyers are experienced practitioners skilled in all aspects of bankruptcy and restructuring transactions, distressed lending and debt trading, distressed mergers and acquisitions, bankruptcy planning and litigation and all related matters and opportunities.
**Contact:** Allan S Brilliant **Tel:** 212 698 3600
**Contact:** Michael J Sage **Tel:** 212 698 3503

### Corporate:

**Mergers & Acquisitions:** Dechert lawyers represent buyers, sellers and advisers in planning, negotiating and executing public and private mergers and acquisitions around the globe.
**Private Equity:** Firm lawyers advise clients at every phase of the investment lifecycle. Dechert lawyers form funds for private equity sponsors and institutional investors and help raise capital; structure investments for private equity funds; and represent the portfolio companies of its private equity clients in a variety of transactions.
**Corporate Finance & Capital Markets:** Dechert lawyers structure and execute complex, market-leading financial transactions worldwide, including in the United States, Europe, the CIS region, the Middle East and North Africa, Latin America and Asia. The firm's lawyers represent corporate and sovereign issuers, underwriters, financial sponsors, investors and selling shareholders in all types of public and private debt, equity, equity-linked and other securities offerings.
**Leveraged Finance:** Firm lawyers advise borrowers, lenders, issuers, equity investors, sponsors, financial advisors and agents in all layers of capital structure, including senior credit facilities, first lien/second lien financings, subordinated/mezzanine debt, structured equity, workouts/restructurings, recapitalizations and Rule 144A and Regulation S offerings.
**Contact:** Henry Nassau **Tel:** 215 994 2138 or 212 698 5667

### Employee Benefits & Executive Compensation:

Dechert lawyers offer a broad range of services relating to employee benefits, executive compensation and retirement plans, including advice on plan structure, implementation and administration, mergers and acquisitions, fringe benefit arrangements, stock-based incentive plans, health and welfare plans, equity-based compensation and employee retention. Dechert lawyers also address the full range of ERISA, tax, securities, stock exchange, employment law and accounting issues impacting executive compensation and benefits planning.
**Contact:** David F Jones **Tel:** 215 994 2822

### Finance & Real Estate:

Dechert's Finance and Real Estate group is a leading provider of legal services to the real estate, structured finance and securitization markets around the world. The group operates as a geographically transparent practice with the international breadth to handle complex cross-border transactions for investment banks, commercial and mortgage banks, investment advisers, fund managers, insurance companies, servicers, rating agencies, developers, property owners and other institutional clients. Dechert lawyers handle the origination, acquisition, disposition and financing of complex commercial real estate loans as well as the resolution of issues relating to distressed commercial real estate assets, including workout and restructuring transactions, bankruptcies and enforcement proceedings. The firm's lawyers also handle virtually every aspect of capital markets finance, including CMBS, CLOs/CDOs, mezzanine financing, ABS and other structured transactions.

## PRACTICE AREAS

Antitrust/Competition
Bankruptcy, Business Restructuring & Reorganization
Corporate
Employee Benefits & Executive Compensation
Energy
Finance & Real Estate
Financial Services & Investment Management
Healthcare
Intellectual Property
International & Domestic Tax
Life Sciences
Litigation
Regulatory
Private Client
Pro Bono

## OFFICES

### CALIFORNIA

**LOS ANGELES:** US Bank Tower, 633 West 5th Street, 37th Floor, CA 90071-2013
Tel: 213 808 5700  Fax: 213 808 5760
Email: edwin.woodsome@dechert.com
**ORANGE COUNTY:** 2010 Main Street, Suite 500, Irvine, CA 92614
Tel: 949 442 6000  Fax: 949 442 6010
Email: robert.robertson@dechert.com
**SAN FRANCISCO:** One Maritime Plaza, Suite 2300, CA 94111-3513
Tel: 415 262 4500  Fax: 415 262 4555
Email: joseph.heil@dechert.com
**SILICON VALLEY:** 2440 W. El Camino Real, Suite 700, Mountain View, CA 94040-1499
Tel: 650 813 4800  Fax: 650 813 4848
Email: frederick.herold@dechert.com

### CONNECTICUT

**HARTFORD:** 90 State House Square, CT 06103-3702
Tel: 860 524 3999  Fax: 860 524 3930
Email: laura.ciabarra@dechert.com

### DISTRICT OF COLUMBIA

**WASHINGTON, D.C.:** 1775 I Street, NW, DC 20006-2401
Tel: 202 261 3300  Fax: 202 261 3333
Email: paul.friedman@dechert.com

### ILLINOIS

**CHICAGO:** 115 S. LaSalle Street, Suite 2600, IL 60603
Tel: 312 646 5800  Fax: 312 646 5858
Email: david.kistenbroker@dechert.com

### MASSACHUSETTS

**BOSTON:** 200 Clarendon Street, 27th Floor, MA 02116-5021
Tel: 617 728 7100  Fax: 617 426 6567
Email: timothy.blank@dechert.com

### NEW JERSEY

**PRINCETON:** 902 Carnegie Center, Suite 500, NJ 08540-6531
Tel: 609 955 3200  Fax: 609 955 3259
Email: james.marino@dechert.com

**Contact:** Joseph Heil **Tel:** 415 262 4510
**Contact:** Richard Jones **Tel:** 212 698 3844

**Financial Services & Investment Management:**
**Investment Funds:** Dechert lawyers advise financial services firms, asset managers, investment funds and fund boards. The firm's clients range from small start-up and boutique operations to some of the largest asset managers in the world. The team advises on fund formation and management, regulatory and compliance matters, investigations by regulatory authorities, and litigation. Dechert lawyers regularly counsel ETF fund sponsors on the development of new products, as well as advise on related regulatory matters.
**Financial Institutions:** For more than 30 years, Dechert's financial institutions attorneys have advised a broad spectrum of large, regional and community financial services companies and investors on a wide variety of transactional, regulatory, enforcement and litigation matters.
**Commodities & Derivatives:** With experience covering all commodities and asset classes, Dechert advises on the law, regulation and practice of commodities and related cash, derivative and structured transactions and products.
**Contact:** Joseph R Fleming **Tel:** 617 728 7161
**Contact:** Robert W Helm **Tel:** 202 261 3356

**Healthcare:**
Dechert lawyers represent a broad range of clients in the healthcare industry, from healthcare providers and systems, managed care organizations, health maintenance organizations, hospital ambulatory surgery centers, rehabilitation centers, extended and elder care facilities, imaging centers and assisted living facilities to pharmaceutical companies and medical equipment and supply manufacturers.
**Contact:** Susan Hendrickson **Tel:** 215 994 2359

**Intellectual Property:**
**IP Litigation:** Dechert lawyers represent technology and life sciences companies in complex patent, trademark, copyright, trade secret and IP antitrust disputes.
**Transactions:** The firm supports clients' licensing and commercial IP needs and counsels on the management and enforcement of patents, trademarks, copyrights and trade secrets — from handling company-wide IP audits and due-diligence matters to counseling on data privacy and data protection issues.
**Patent Counseling:** Dechert's IP counselors develop patent strategies and asset portfolios, advise on international transactions and advocate before the U.S. Patent and Trademark Office.
**Trademark & Copyright:** Dechert is at the forefront of developments in trademark and copyright law, protecting clients' brands and creative expression around the world.

**Privacy & Data Protection:** Dechert lawyers assist clients in complying with the many, and often inconsistent, rules and regulations established to protect the privacy of customer and employee information, working to minimize the cost and time for compliance.
**Outsourcing & Offshoring:** Dechert lawyers help clients adapt to new economic realities, new regulations post Dodd-Frank, new technology capabilities and globalization.
**Contact:** Ann M Caviani Pease, PhD **Tel:** 650 813 4851
**Contact:** Martin Black **Tel:** 215 994 2664

**International & Domestic Tax:**
Dechert's multidisciplinary international and domestic tax lawyers assist clients in addressing their tax planning needs and resolving tax controversies. Dechert lawyers provide transaction structures that maximize tax benefits and minimize tax liability. With tax lawyers in the United States and Europe, the firm is positioned to counsel clients on effective international tax planning strategies, providing integrated, global tax advice.
**Contact:** Daniel M Dunn **Tel:** 212 698 3857

**Life Sciences:**
Dechert lawyers provide a full range of integrated services to address life sciences companies' needs, including M&A, financing, corporate partnering and licensing, patent counseling and litigation, strategic IP transactions, complex commercial and securities litigation, antitrust, product liability and mass torts, fraud investigations and regulatory compliance matters.
**Contact:** George Gordon **Tel:** 215 994 2382
**Contact:** David Schulman **Tel:** 202 261 3440 or (+44) 207 184 7437

**Litigation:**
**White Collar & Securities Litigation:** Dechert lawyers advise and defend both companies and individuals facing allegations of financial and business misconduct as well as facilitate the discreet handling of enforcement investigations, whether those inquiries originate internally or from a regulatory or governmental entity. Dechert lawyers are experienced in nearly all substantive areas, including accounting irregularities, antitrust, bank and financial fraud, FCPA and UK Bribery Act violations, government contract fraud, insider trading, money laundering, RICO, securities fraud, stock market manipulation and tax fraud.
**Product Liability & Mass Torts:** Dechert's nationally recognized practice handles every aspect of today's complex cases — from strategic planning through trial and appeal — for companies in a variety of industries, including pharmaceutical, medical device and consumer products. As local, regional and national counsel with two-plus decades of trial experience,

Dechert lawyers have successfully defended clients in many of the largest mass torts, class actions and multi-district litigations in the United States. Dechert is also widely recognized for winning significant landmark tobacco and pharmaceutical trials.
**Complex Commercial Litigation:** Dechert lawyers defend companies in complex, multidistrict and class action litigation as well as alternative dispute resolution proceedings across a broad range of industries. Dechert lawyers also represent clients in appellate court cases before state supreme courts, federal courts of appeals and the Supreme Court of the United States.
**Labor & Employment:** Dechert lawyers advise and defend companies and individuals in a wide range of labor and employment matters – from large-scale reductions in force and class action wage and hour and ERISA claims to individual disciplinary issues and training. Dechert has successfully handled matters before state and federal courts and agencies throughout the United States, including the EEOC, NLRB, Department of Labor, OSHA and the Office of Federal Contract Compliance Programs.
**Contact:** Robert J Jossen **Tel:** 212.698.3639

**Private Client:**
Dechert lawyers offer personal estate planning advice and financial and tax planning services to high net worth individuals as well as the corporate and individual trustees, executors, personal representatives and other fiduciaries who serve them.
**Contact:** Amy S Ufberg **Tel:** 215 994 2655

# DLA PIPER

**www**.dlapiper.com **tel:** 212 335 4500 **fax:** 212 335 4501

**Americas Co-Chairmen:** Roger Meltzer, Jay Rains
**Americas Co-Managing Partners:** Stasia Kelly, Michael Poulos
**Chief Operating Officer:** Bob Bratt
Number of partners worldwide: 1,400  Number of lawyers worldwide: 4,200
Languages: *Over 60 languages*

## Firm Overview:

In today's economic environment, the concept of 'doing business' has become increasingly complex. More and more businesses have become global, and even local ones are dependent upon or certainly affected by global forces and trends. DLA Piper gets it. In 2005, DLA Piper became one of the world's largest and most prominent legal service providers through a merger of unprecedented scope. The motivation for doing so was not about size or prestige or putting pins in a map. It was to create a global organization capable of quickly and efficiently serving the most important legal needs of clients wherever they do business; whether it is across multiple jurisdictions or in a single market. Today, DLA Piper has 4,200 lawyers in more than 30 countries throughout the world's established and emerging business centers in the United States, Europe, Asia-Pacific and the Middle East. In Latin America, the firm opened an office in Mexico City and works in cooperation with top Brazilian law firm Campos Mello Advogados, with offices in Rio de Janeiro and São Paulo, and it recently reached an agreement with law firm InterJuris Abogados SC to establish a presence in Caracas, Venezuela, where the firm operates as DLA InterJuris Abogados. But DLA Piper believes such a rich global network is only valuable if it helps to better serve the needs of the client. DLA Piper is able to offer clients the advantage of one outside law firm with the depth and geographic coverage to meet most, if not all, of their legal needs anywhere in the world.

## Main Areas of Practice:

### Corporate:
The globalization of business has increased the complexity of public and private equity and debt offerings, mergers and acquisitions, IPOs, venture capital and private equity investments, and other transactional matters. DLA Piper's Corporate Practice includes 400 lawyers in the US and 1,350 worldwide, who advise clients on capital markets, securities compliance governance, IT, tax, executive compensation and technology issues.

### Finance:
Changes in the global economy have created reverberations in the field of finance, resulting in a new set of rules, a different mindset. The lawyers in the firm's Finance Practice -150 in the US and more than 500 worldwide - are fully prepared to provide clients with up-to-date guidance and representation on all aspects of financial lending and restructuring matters.

### Intellectual Property & Technology:
A company's intellectual property is its lifeblood and safeguarding those assets has become more and more difficult in an expanding global economy. DLA Piper's Intellectual Property and Technology Practice includes nearly 200 lawyers in the US and approximately 400 lawyers worldwide, making it among the largest IP practices in the world.

### Legislative & Regulatory:
Businesses today operate in an increasingly aggressive enforcement environment. DLA Piper's 250-lawyer Government Affairs and Regulatory team counsels clients on federal, state, and local government and regulatory matters, as well as all levels of legislation and policy. Among the group's members are several former high ranking government officials.

### Litigation & Arbitration:
While it is transactional matters that enable companies to grow and thrive, litigation is what keeps clients up at night. And when disputes do arise, many of the world's leading companies turn to us to represent their interests. DLA Piper's Litigation and Arbitration Practice, with more than 500 lawyers in the US and 1,500 worldwide, collaborates with clients and counterparts to identify and execute the most advantageous business-oriented solutions.

### Real Estate:
The cyclical, yet explosive, nature of real estate makes it a field where solid experience and the ability to expeditiously close complex deals are crucial. With nearly 200 lawyers in the US and more than 500 worldwide, DLA Piper's Real Estate Practice is the world's largest and the group handles all aspects of real estate transactions.

### Tax:
Growing global markets have given rise to many complex tax issues that require an in-depth knowledge of local and national tax laws augmented by an international perspective. DLA Piper's global Tax Group – consisting of more than 300 tax lawyers and economists – is experienced in the areas critical to multinational companies.

**OFFICES**

**ARIZONA**
**PHOENIX:** Tel: 480 606 5100

**CALIFORNIA**
**LA JOLLA:** Tel: 858 638 6806
**LOS ANGELES:** Tel: 310 595 3000
**SACRAMENTO:** Tel: 916 930 3200
**SAN DIEGO:** Tel: 619 699 2700
**SAN FRANCISCO:** Tel: 415 836 2500
**SILICON VALLEY:** Tel: 650 833 2000

**DELAWARE**
**WILMINGTON:** Tel: 302 468 5700

**DISTRICT OF COLUMBIA**
**WASHINGTON DC:** Tel: 202 799 4000

**FLORIDA**
**MIAMI:** Tel: 305 423 8500
**TAMPA:** Tel: 813 229 2111

**GEORGIA**
**ATLANTA:** Tel: 404 736 7800

**ILLINOIS**
**CHICAGO:** Tel: 312 368 4000

**MARYLAND**
**BALTIMORE:** Tel: 512 457 7000

**MASSACHUSETTS**
**BOSTON:** Tel: 617 406 6000

**MINNESOTA**
**MINNEAPOLIS:** Tel: 612 524 3000

**NEW JERSEY**
**ATLANTIC CITY:** Tel: 609 449 7000
**FLORHAM PARK:** Tel: 973 520 2550

**NEW YORK**
**ALBANY:** Tel: 518 788 9705
**NEW YORK:** Tel: 212 335 4500

**NORTH CAROLINA**
**RALEIGH:** Tel: 919 786 2000

**PENNSYLVANIA**
**PHILADELPHIA:** Tel: 215 656 3300

**TEXAS**
**AUSTIN:** Tel: 512 457 7000
**DALLAS:** Tel: 214 743 4500
**HOUSTON:** Tel: 713 425 8400

**VIRGINIA**
**RESTON:** Tel: 703 773 4000

**WASHINGTON**
**SEATTLE:** Tel: 206 839 4800

**INTERNATIONAL OFFICES**

**AFRICA:** Accra*, Cairo*, Cape Town*, Dar es Salaam*, Johannesburg*, Lusaka*, Mwanza*, Nairobi*. **ASIA PACIFIC:** Auckland*, Bangkok, Beijing, Brisbane, Canberra, Hong Kong, Melbourne, Perth, Seoul, Shanghai, Sydney, Tokyo, Singapore, Wellington*. **EUROPE:** Amsterdam, Antwerp, Berlin, Birmingham, Bratislava, Brussels, Bucharest, Budapest, Cologne, Edinburgh, Frankfurt, Glasgow, Hamburg, Istanbul, Kyiv, Leeds, Liverpool, London, Madrid, Manchester, Milan, Moscow, Munich, Oslo, Paris, Prague, Rome, Sarajevo*, Sheffield, St. Petersburg, Stockholm*, Tbilisi, Vienna, Warsaw, Zagreb*. **MIDDLE EAST:** Abu Dhabi, Bahrain, Doha, Dubai, Kuwait City, Muscat, Riyadh. **SOUTH/LATIN AMERICA:** Caracas*, Mexico City, Sao Paulo*.
* Denotes associate office

# EPSTEIN BECKER GREEN

**www.**ebglaw.com **tel:** 212 351 4500 **fax:** 212 878 8600

**Chair, Board of Directors:** Douglas A Hastings
**Chief Operating Officer:** Steven Di Fiore
Total number of partners: 125  Total number of lawyers: 300

## Firm Overview:

Epstein Becker & Green, P.C., founded in 1973, is a national law firm with approximately 300 lawyers practicing in 11 offices, in Atlanta, Boston, Chicago, Houston, Indianapolis, Los Angeles, New York, Newark, San Francisco, Stamford and Washington, DC. The firm is uncompromising in its pursuit of legal excellence and client service in its areas of practice: health care and life sciences; labor and employment; litigation; corporate services and employee benefits. EBG was founded to serve the health care industry and has been at the forefront of health care legal developments since 1973. The firm is also proud to be a trusted advisor to clients in the financial services, retail, and hospitality industries, among others, representing entities from startups to Fortune 100 companies. In 2012, the firm was ranked in the top 30 among 650 law firms nationwide for outstanding client service in the BTI Consulting Group's 2013 "Client Service A-Team" report.

## Main Areas of Practice:

### Health Care & Life Sciences:

Since its establishment in 1973, EBG's Health Care and Life Sciences practice has been at the forefront of health care law, taking the lead in understanding, interpreting, and shaping the issues and regulations that affect health care and life sciences institutions. EBG has counseled clients during many legal milestones in health care – from the enactment of health planning through the implementation of the Affordable Care Act. The breadth of experience delivered by the firm – to all players throughout every sector of the health care delivery system – sets them apart. The firm continues to engage in the national discourse on health care, and operate within the sectors' elite network of business leaders and top government officials – positioning the firm's 135 health care and life sciences attorneys to legitimately project the path of health care law. The firm provides health care and life sciences clients with transactional, regulatory, compliance, and litigation counsel as well as strategic and advocacy services – from daily decisions to core "bet-the-ranch" determinations. Additionally, the firm offers advice and counsel throughout all phases of agency approval, and submissions, coding, coverage, and reimbursement support.

### Labor & Employment:

As one of the nation's largest practices dedicated exclusively to the representation of management, EBG's Labor and Employment practice is comprised of nearly 140 attorneys skilled in providing counsel on the most complex labor and employment matters and litigation arising under the federal, state, and local laws that regulate the workplace. The practice has a distinct depth of experience representing clients in the health care and life sciences, hospitality, retail and financial services industries. Clients in these sectors benefit from a national team of attorneys who understand the unique labor and employment challenges within their industry. The

practice has a diverse and longstanding client base – a fact the firm attributes to both the quality of legal services and the solid relationships that it establishes with clients.

### Litigation:

Legally challenging, cutting-edge, and "bet the company" cases and investigations – these are the kind of matters typically tackled by EBG's national Litigation practice. EBG's litigators know the intricacies of modern investigations and litigations and are exceptionally qualified to assist clients, either by defending them if they are sued or by helping them use litigation affirmatively to accomplish their business objectives. This practice has litigated complex cases on behalf of domestic and global midsize and Fortune 500 clients in varied industries, including banking and financial services, construction, environment, government, healthcare and biotechnology, insurance, manufacturing, oil and gas, and real estate.

### Corporate Services:

EBG acts as general counsel to private and public companies engaged in a wide variety of industries and business activities. The firm practice focuses on representing the health care industry in diverse corporate and transactional matters, as well as providing legal services to other key industries, such as hospitality, financial services, retail, technology, and entertainment. The attorneys in this practice integrate the advice of EBG's legal professionals in real estate banking, securities, corporate governance, international law, tax, bankruptcy and creditors' rights, technology and intellectual property, employment law, and litigation to help clients achieve their central business goals.

### Employee Benefits:

For both foreign and domestic clients, including taxable and tax-exempt entities, the practice provides a complete range of services relating to the design, structure, implementation, administration, and termination of all

types of retirement, executive compensation, and welfare benefits plans. The practice also provides counsel to employers who participate in multi-employer pension and welfare plans including developing strategies to minimize statutory withdrawal liability related to pension plans. The full capability of the practice is further enhanced by a national, dedicated litigation team staffed with attorneys who combine a real-world understanding of the technical aspects of ERISA with their extensive trial and appellate court litigation experience.

EPSTEINBECKERGREEN

# FITZPATRICK, CELLA, HARPER & SCINTO

www.fitzpatrickcella.com **tel:** 212 218 2100 **fax:** 212 218 2200

**Chairman:** Nicholas M Cannella
**Managing Partner:** Colleen Tracy
Number of partners: 57  Number of lawyers: 174
Languages: *Chinese, Croatian, French, German, Hebrew, Hindi, Russian, Spanish, Swahili, Telugu, Tamil, Vietnamese*

**Firm Overview:**

At Fitzpatrick, intellectual property is not just a practice area – it is their sole focus. They have about 175 attorneys in New York, California and Washington DC practicing exclusively in all areas of intellectual property law, including patents, trademarks, copyrights, unfair competition and trade secrets. The firm's practice covers the spectrum of intellectual property services, including applying for patent and trademark protection, litigation, appeals, interferences, alternative dispute resolution, licensing, opinions, corporate transactions and due diligence. According to Corporate Counsel magazine, Fitzpatrick filed more patent infringement suits than any other US firm in 2010.

Accolades:

- IP Hot List, The National Law Journal, 2012
- Firm of the Year in Pharmaceutical IP Litigation, Managing Intellectual Property, 2012
- Top 10 Life Sciences Litigators in the US, Managing Intellectual Property, 2012
- Tier 1 Intellectual Property Law Firm, Practical Law Company, 2012

**Main Areas of Practice:**

**Patent Litigation:**

- Prevailed for Genzyme in a bench trial against three generic drug manufacturers in a patent challenge against Genzyme's patent covering the use of the vitamin D analog doxercalciferal to treat secondary hyperparathyroidism in patients on dialysis. Genzyme markets doxercalciferal for such use under the trade name Hectorol®.
- Secured the Federal Circuit's affirmance of a district court's decision that Otsuka Pharmaceutical's patent covering the antipsychotic drug Abilify® is valid and infringed
- Prevailed for AstraZeneca in a bench trial against four generic drug manufacturers in a patent challenge to AstraZeneca's blockbuster antipsychotic drug Seroquel XR®
- Obtained summary judgment of non-obviousness for Merck in a patent infringement dispute with Sandoz over Merck's life-saving antifungal drug product, Cancidas®

**Key Clients:** Amgen, AstraZeneca, Canon Inc., Daiichi Sankyo, Eisai, Entegris, Genzyme, Merck, Novartis, Otsuka, Sanofi-Aventis, UCB Pharma, Warner Chilcott
**Contact:** Scott K Reed
**Tel:** +1 212 218 2227  **Email:** sreed@fchs.com

**Patent Prosecution, Reexaminations & Interferences:**

- Successfully prosecuted patents involving a wide array of technologies including in the electronic, chemical, biotechnology and mechanical arts. Filed over 1,500 patent applications for clients in 2011.
- Prevailed on behalf of Canon in four reexamination proceedings initiated by a third party regarding patents concerning process cartridges and photosensitive drums
- Obtained judgment on behalf of Amgen against Human Genome Sciences and Schering Corp. in an interference involving patent rights to a key receptor in the immune system
- Achieved denial of two reexamination petitions filed by Apotex concerning Sanofi's heart medication Plavix®
- Obtained a judgment of priority on behalf of IBM in its patent interference against Rambus over computers that use point-to-point links to transfer data between a memory controller and buffered memory

**Key Clients:** Amgen, Canon Inc., Honeywell, IBM, Medtronic, Michelin, S.C. Johnson, Sanofi, Sirona Dental
**Contact:** Anthony M Zupcic (Patent Prosecution)
**Tel:** +1 212 218 2240  **Email:** azupcic@fchs.com
**Contact:** John D Murnane (PTO Contested Proceedings)
**Tel:** +1 212 218 2527  **Email:** jmurnane@fchs.com

**Trademark & Copyrights:**

- Prevailed in an arbitration on behalf of G Adventures (formerly G.A.P. Adventures), in a domain name dispute before the National Arbitration Forum
- Prevailed on behalf of Metra Electronics in a trademark infringement suit over imports of automobile stereo installation equipment
- Successfully defended The Prudential Insurance Company of America in a proceeding which sought to prevent Prudential from using the mark BCI
- Counselled a non-profit institute on the requirements under the copyright laws relating to reproduction archives of architectural works on the Internet
- Defended Everest Gaming trademarks involving Everest Poker in connection with Harrah's World Series of Poker tournament
- Negotiated the right of client Pan-American Life Insurance Company to adopt, use and register new trademarks, such as Pan American Benefit Solutions

**Key Clients:** Bear USA, Calvin Klein, Canon Inc., Prudential, PVH Corp.
**Contact:** Timothy J Kelly (Trademarks)
**Tel:** +1 212 218 2262  **Email:** tkelly@fchs.com
**Contact:** Donald J Curry (Copyrights)
**Tel:** +1 212 218 2296  **Email:** dcurry@fchs.com

**Licensing, Transactions & Due Diligence:**

- Counselled Gilead Sciences Inc. with respect to the intellectual property aspects of their $11 billion purchase of Pharmasset Inc., including its nucleotide analog technology for the treatment of Hepatitis C virus
- Counselled Warner Chilcott on all intellectual property aspects of their $1.3 billion acquisition of Proctor & Gamble Pharmaceuticals, including its prescription products ACTONEL®, ASACOL® and ENABLEX®
- Counselled major private equity companies in connection with their acquisitions of Tyco Plastics, Adhesives and Coated Products, GE Advanced Materials and Realogy. Collectively, the transactions totalled approximately $13 billion.
- Counselled Ripplewood Holdings in connection with its investment in Hostess Brands (formerly Interstate Bakeries Corp.), the largest wholesale baker in the United States, and owner of the iconic brands TWINKIES® and WONDER®

**Key Clients:** AMG, Citigroup, Gilead, Honeywell, Sanofi, Tudor Investment Corporation
**Contact:** Robert H Fischer (Licensing & Transactions)
**Tel:** +1 212 218 2254  **Email:** rfischer@fchs.com
**Contact:** Brian V Slater (Due Diligence)
**Tel:** +1 212 218 2292  **Email:** bslater@fchs.com

Fitzpatrick
FITZPATRICK, CELLA, HARPER & SCINTO | We are IP

# FRAGOMEN, DEL REY, BERNSEN & LOEWY, LLP

**www.**fragomen.com **tel:** 212 688 8555 **fax:** 212 480 9930

**Executive Committee Members:** Austin T Fragomen, Jr, (Chairman), Lance Kaplan, Cynthia J Lange, Michael D Patrick, Gwendolyn M Robosson, Mitchell L Wexler
Number of partners (in US offices): 70
Number of other attorneys (in US offices): 180

## Firm Overview :

Fragomen, Del Rey, Bernsen & Loewy, LLP is a leading immigration counseling and services provider in the US, with 15 offices across the country in key business destinations. The firm provides corporate immigration services to clients in all industries across the United States and abroad, with an eye toward ongoing expansion into emerging markets both domestically and worldwide. In 2012 alone, Fragomen expanded its presence into Atlanta, Georgia (US), and opened a third office in China. In January 2013, it broadened its presence in the Americas by opening new offices in Brazil and Mexico, and continued its international expansion by opening an office in Switzerland.

As the largest firm in the United States and the world focused exclusively on immigration legal services, Fragomen has extensive knowledge of best practices and industry trends, which it uses to create progressive and compliant immigration programs for its clients. The vast experience of its more than 1,200 immigration professionals and staff in the US allows Fragomen to customize its comprehensive corporate immigration services, and create teams of professionals dedicated to each client and to specialized immigration functions such as export controls, employment verification, government relations and strategy, and analyzing data on immigration trends. The firm's service delivery models are flexible, and are tailored to meet each client's individual needs.

Fragomen's services include strategic legal analysis, consultancy and case preparation. At the most fundamental level, Fragomen ensures that the appropriate status is obtained on behalf of each client, and that documents issued by government authorities are accurate and correct. It does so with a keen awareness of the need for optimal value, efficiency and cost-effectiveness.

In summary, Fragomen offers the following:

**On-the-Ground Knowledge:** Fragomen's locations give the firm on-the-ground knowledge of current immigration trends across the world. The firm's dominant presence in almost all jurisdictions where it has an office means that it has superior local knowledge. It also has an unparalleled ability to directly and appropriately seek favourable adjudication of immigration matters affecting clients.

**Centralized Management:** Fragomen works with colleagues across the globe to assist clients wherever the need arises. The firm can offer support on almost any immigration need in the US or around the world.

**Expanding Reach:** Fragomen opens new offices to anticipate and proactively meet clients' needs.

**Flexible Service Delivery Models:** The firm's experienced professionals develop service delivery models that balance clients' overarching corporate goals with the nuances of local operations.

**Dedicated Client Service Teams:** Fragomen has structured teams of professionals to meet clients' needs, be they country-based or transaction-based.

**Best-In-Class Professionals:** Fragomen is immigration thought-leaders. It builds strong and experienced teams of professionals to improve clients' satisfaction and is recognised in the independent legal directories (including *Chambers and Partners*) as leaders in immigration law.

**Unparalleled Resources:** The firm has substantial human resources and global immigration knowledge and experience. These are complemented by the firm's innovative technology to offer the best service and value-for-money in the immigration industry.

**Advanced Technology Solutions:** Fragomen has superior case management and reporting tools. This enables case processing efficiencies and management information reporting.

**Unmatched Government Relations Capabilities:** The firm's professionals help shape government laws and policies in the US and across the globe. It has unparalleled but appropriate access to immigration bodies and organisations.

**Immigration Updates:** Fragomen issues alerts and update clients with relevant immigration news. The firm also populates its website and develops video content to keep clients informed of relevant immigration issues. It also offers clients training and host events (on- and off-line) to keep them informed of immigration law and policy.

## OFFICES

**NEW YORK**

**NEW YORK:** 7 Hanover Square, NY 10004
Tel: 212 688 8555  Fax: 212 480 9930
Email: newyorkinfo@fragomen.com

**ARIZONA**
**PHOENIX:** Tel: 602 266 1825  Fax: 602 266 1826

**CALIFORNIA**
**IRVINE:** Tel: 949 261 0209  Fax: 949 261 2821
**LOS ANGELES:** Tel: 310 820 3322  Fax: 310 820 2702
**SAN DIEGO:** Tel: 858 793 1600  Fax: 858 793 1686
**SAN FRANCISCO:** Tel: 415 986 1446  Fax: 415 986 7964
**SANTA CLARA:** Tel: 408 919 0600  Fax: 408 919 0615

**DISTRICT OF COLUMBIA**
**WASHINGTON:** Tel: 202 223 5515  Fax: 202 371 2898

**FLORIDA**
**CORAL GABLES:** Tel: 305 774 5800  Fax: 305 774 6666

**GEORGIA**
**ATLANTA:** Tel: 404 856 5500  Fax: 404 856 5555

**ILLINOIS**
**CHICAGO:** Tel: 312 263 6101  Fax: 312 346 1970

**MASSACHUSETTS**
**BOSTON:** Tel: 617 574 0400  Fax: 617 226 4561

**MICHIGAN**
**TROY:** Tel: 248 649 5404  Fax: 248 649 5121

**NEW JERSEY**
**MATAWAN:** Tel: 732 862 5000  Fax: 732 862 5050

**TEXAS**
**DALLAS:** Tel: 972 233 6646  Fax: 972 233 3134

# FRIED, FRANK, HARRIS, SHRIVER & JACOBSON LLP

www.friedfrank.com **tel:** 212 859 8000 **fax:** 212 859 4000

**Chairperson:** Valerie Ford Jacob
**Senior Operating Partner:** Justin Spendlove
Number of partners worldwide: 144  Number of other lawyers worldwide: 365

**Firm Overview:**
From offices strategically located in the world's principal financial centers, Fried Frank serves as counsel to many of the world's largest companies, financial institutions and investment firms. The firm is adept in its deployment of well-configured, cross-border teams that provide the depth of knowledge, breadth of experience and responsive service that clients require to meet their critical business objectives.

**Main Areas of Practice:**
The firm offers legal counsel on antitrust and competition; bankruptcy and restructuring; corporate matters, including asset management, capital markets, corporate governance, financings, mergers and acquisitions, and private acquisitions and private equity; energy and environment; executive compensation and employee benefits; intellectual property and technology; international trade and investment; litigation, including international arbitration and alternative dispute resolution, commercial litigation, government contracts, and securities and shareholder litigation; real estate; tax; trusts and estates; and white collar criminal defense and securities enforcement and regulation.

**Antitrust and Competition:**
The integrated practice works closely with the firm's corporate, litigation and intellectual property practices. Core areas of expertise include the global regulation of mergers and acquisitions, government and criminal investigations, and risk management and compliance.

**Asset Management:**
The practice is often called upon by financial institutions and private investment funds to advise on hedge funds, private equity funds, funds of funds, infrastructure funds, mezzanine funds and related products.

**Bankruptcy & Restructuring:**
The multidisciplinary practice regularly represents a wide range of clients in both formal bankruptcies and out-of-court restructurings of financially troubled companies. The firm uses its understanding of corporate finance and capital markets to assist clients in realizing maximum value and recovery.

**Capital Markets:**
The practice represents issuers, underwriters, financial sponsors, selling stockholders, initial purchasers and dealer-managers in private and US Securities and Exchange Commission-registered debt and equity securities offerings, and related acquisition finance and private equity transactions.

**Energy & Environment:**
The multidisciplinary group has extensive experience advising clients on transactional, regulatory and compliance and litigation matters.

**Executive Compensation & Employee Benefits:**
The practice offers counsel with respect to the structuring and implementation of a wide range of compensation and benefit plans and programs to privately and publicly held corporations, their boards of directors and compensation committees, executives and other employees.

**Financing:**
The practice stands out for its role in all pieces of the capital structure, working on some of the most sophisticated deals in each sector and playing a key role in developing some of the most innovative financing structures.

**Intellectual Property & Technology:**
The group features a renowned IP Litigation Team and a top-tier technology transactions practice. The group's strength in both contentious and non-contentious IP matters is unique among law firms and offers innovative solutions.

**International Trade and Investment:**
The practice counsels a broad range of clients on international trade controls and other related regulatory matters, including matters involving OFAC, EAR, ITAR, FCPA, UK Bribery Act and anti-boycott requirements.

**Litigation:**
The practice represents global corporations, financial institutions and individuals in their most challenging and complex matters. The diverse practice runs the gamut from agency and grand jury investigations to arbitration proceedings to white collar criminal defense.

**Mergers & Acquisitions:**
The practice has handled some of the largest and most complex US and global deals for more than three decades and is one of few firms that represents the full spectrum of M&A players.

**Private Equity:**
The practice is active in myriad aspects of private equity transactions and regularly provides counsel to prominent fund sponsors and investors on the full range of their investment-related activities, including fund formations, leveraged buyouts, consortium bids, syndications and exit strategies.

**Real Estate:**
The practice encompasses a broad range of transactions, including capital markets and financings, acquisitions and dispositions, joint ventures, construction and development projects, leasing, portfolio transactions and real estate investment trusts.

**Tax:**
The practice encompasses all principal forms of corporate transactions, including mergers, acquisitions and dispositions, hedge fund and private equity fund formations, and the tax issues associated with financings, including borrower, lender and capital markets representations.

**White Collar Criminal Defense & Securities Enforcement:**
The practice guides clients through a wide range of enforcement matters, government investigations and internal investigations. The team regularly defends corporations and individuals under criminal and regulatory investigation.

**OFFICES**

DISTRICT OF COLUMBIA
**WASHINGTON, DC:** 801 17th Street, NW, DC 20006
Tel: 202 639 7000   Fax: 202 639 7003

NEW YORK
**NEW YORK:** One New York Plaza, NY 10004
Tel: 212 859 8000   Fax: 212 859 4000

**INTERNATIONAL OFFICES**
The firm also has offices in Frankfurt, Hong Kong, London, Paris and Shanghai.

FRIED FRANK

# FROSS ZELNICK LEHRMAN & ZISSU, P.C.

www.frosszelnick.com **tel:** 212 813 5900 **fax:** 212 813 5901

Number of partners: 24

**PRACTICE AREAS:**
Trademark
Copyright
Design Patents
Unfair Competition

**OFFICES**
NEW YORK
**NEW YORK:** 866 UN Plaza, At First Avenue & 48th Street,
NY 10017
Tel: 212 813 5900   Fax: 212 813 5901

## Firm Overview:

Fross Zelnick Lehrman & Zissu, P.C. was founded in New York in 1969 by a group of leading international trademark lawyers who shared a commitment to provide premium client service and be the best in their field. They set out to challenge the business model of the larger, well-established firms by providing the highest level of international trademark advice at a reasonable cost. Today, Fross Zelnick is a law firm of nearly 50 attorneys, whose practice areas include domestic and international trademark, copyright, design patent and unfair competition law.

According to surveys of in-house and outside counsel, Fross Zelnick are considered the premier firm in the world in their field, and are probably the largest law firm dealing exclusively with this subject matter. The firm's lawyers are also consistently recognized by numerous publications around the world as experts in the field.

## Main Areas of Practice:

Because the firm offers clients comparable strength in both US and international work (a rarity in their field), and maintain active relationships with leading practitioners around the globe, they are uniquely positioned to help owners of worldwide trademark portfolios establish, maintain, protect and make profitable use of their trademark rights. All of their attorneys are trademark experts, and each is an in-depth specialist in at least one area of trademark and unfair competition law.

### Litigate Intellectual Property Rights:

Fross Zelnick stands alone in the top tier of trademark and copyright litigation firms in the US. Their reputation for successful litigation often leads to settling disputes without court proceedings. When litigation is unavoidable, their litigators know how to fight for clients and win. Internationally, Fross Zelnick has wide experience in foreign and multi-country trademark and copyright litigation and a history of success in recapturing pirated well-known marks.

### Register Trademarks, Copyrights & Design Patents:

Fross Zelnick is consistently among the top filers of US trademark applications. They can register their clients' trademarks, copyrights and design patents. The firm's specialized knowledge in this area means that they know how to get the job done efficiently and obtain rights that will stand up in court.

### Combat Counterfeiting:

The firm is highly experienced in anti-counterfeiting and enforcement matters. Fross Zelnick has developed sophisticated and cost-effective enforcement programs for their clients to prevent the importation, sale and distribution of a wide variety of infringing or counterfeit products including apparel, footwear, cosmetics and luxury goods. Included in these programs is the recordal of relevant intellectual property rights with Customs in the US and internationally.

### Manage Global Portfolios:

The firm is known for providing expert global intellectual property management. Working closely with their select network of foreign counsel, Fross Zelnick protects intellectual property rights in the US and throughout the world. The firm's experience enables them to identify, protect and defend their clients' rights under copyright, trademark, trade dress, design patent, trade secret and related laws.

### Negotiate IP Transactions:

Whether a client is buying or selling an entire business or part of a portfolio, Fross Zelnick can negotiate licenses and related agreements that safeguard their clients' business and legal interests. They conduct due diligence reviews for mergers, acquisitions and other corporate ventures, and record the corporate changes against their clients' IP registrations worldwide once the deal is done.

### Protection of Characters & Celebrities:

For decades Fross Zelnick lawyers have protected famous entertainment characters through sophisticated copyright protection strategies and enforcement against infringers. They have also retrieved numerous infringing or disparaging trademarks and domain names for celebrities and litigated high-profile cases involving the unauthorized use of well-known names and likenesses.

### Conquer the Internet:

Internet law is evolving as rapidly as the medium itself and much of it is rooted in trademark and copyright law. The firm's lawyers litigate Uniform Dispute Resolution proceedings (UDRPs) against cybersquatters, advise on worldwide domain name registration and disputes, monitor the web for infringements, negotiate linking and key word agreements, draft privacy policies, and develop strategies for policing and protecting IP rights on the Internet.

**Contacts:** Ron Lehrman (General), Roger Zissu (US litigation), Lawrence Apolzon (US counselling and prosecution), and Peter Silverman (International counselling, prosecution and litigation).

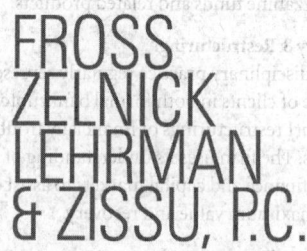

# GOETZ FITZPATRICK LLP

www.goetzfitz.com **tel:** 212 695 8100 **fax:** 212 629 4013

Number of partners: 7  Number of other lawyers: 17

## Firm Overview:

Goetz Fitzpatrick sees itself as partners in its clients' successes and is proud of its long-term client relationships. Since its founding in 1967, the firm has earned a reputation as a powerhouse in the fields of construction, real estate and commercial litigation. It represents all members of the real estate and construction industry. Goetz Fitzpatrick's practice also focuses on business, trusts and estates, intellectual property, technology law, and bankruptcy and reorganization.

## Main Areas of Practice:

### Construction Litigation–Arbitration–Mediation:

The team of construction litigation attorneys serves numerous national and international clients, including some of the best-known names in the construction industry. It is intimately familiar with the nuances of complex legal and regulatory challenges that affect day-to-day operations, and deeply experienced in all forms of construction-related litigation, arbitration and mediation.
Goetz Fitzpatrick regularly represents owners (both public and private), contractors, subcontractors, design professionals, construction lenders, suppliers, sureties, and product manufacturers.
The different matters the firm handles include:
- Termination disputes
- Non-payment disputes, including change order, scope of work, delay and loss of productivity claims
- All forms of alternative dispute resolution, including arbitration, mediation and "mini-trials"
- Construction defect and structural failure litigation
- Administrative appeals on public projects
- Architectural and engineering malpractice
- Bid protests and injunctions
- Presentation and defense of claims to governmental entities

### Construction Contracts & Transactions:

A key factor in successful construction projects is solid, detailed work in the planning and contracting stages. Many problems in the course of and following a project can be avoided through careful and professional preparation of the documents that shape and define the relationships and expectations of the parties to a project. Its attorneys have exceptional experience in supporting clients' contract preparation, contract negotiation and delivery method selection. They assist local, national and international developers and contractors with negotiation and contracting.

### Commercial Litigation:

Goetz Fitzpatrick has an extremely diverse and broad-based litigation practice. Its attorneys also represent local, regional, national, and international clients on a wide range of issues, including business litigation, intellectual property litigation, banking, defamation, and employment discrimination. The firm handles cases from the inception through discovery, trial and appeal. Its litigation practice includes actions in federal and state courts, the appellate levels of each of those courts, and arbitration tribunals. Goetz Fitzpatrick prides itself on its ability to promptly and efficiently respond to emergencies, including provisional remedies, such as injunctive relief, orders of attachment and the appointments of receivers.
The firm's philosophy is to counsel clients to avoid litigation if possible, but to be prepared and aggressive if litigation becomes necessary. Its attorneys are admitted to practice in New York, New Jersey and many federal courts including the United States Supreme Court.

### Real Estate:

The firm's real estate attorneys have the experience, knowledge and ability to react quickly and handle client's real estate needs efficiently and effectively. They attend to the details–seeing the forest without getting lost in the trees. From the simplest of local projects to the most complex multi-jurisdictional transactions, Goetz Fitzpatrick has the experience to visualize, understand and help clients realize their goals.

### Business Law & Transactions:

Goetz Fitzpatrick's attorneys provide a wide range of legal services to established and emerging businesses of all sizes. Some serve as general counsel to many clients, working with them on all of their legal matters. In addition, the firm has served as special counsel in mergers, acquisitions and other specific transactional activities.

### Intellectual Property–Technology–Media:

Intellectual property and technology are the currencies of the Information Age, and the Intellectual Property and Technology group of Goetz Fitzpatrick helps companies protect and increase the value of those assets. It understands where and how technology intersects with law and commands a broad understanding of intellectual property and the technologies to which its concepts apply. The firm's view of the legal treatment of intellectual property is balanced and integrated, keeping in mind that rapidly developing technologies occur amid legal systems steeped in traditions and principles that are often slow to change. Goetz Fitzpatrick's goal is to help its clients prosper in this exciting and promising field by paving their way with timely, resourceful and critical legal advice and service.

### Trusts & Estates:

The firm's trusts and estates lawyers carry on a tradition of quality professional service to individual clients and family foundations. The essence of the trusts and estates practice is helping clients preserve personal wealth and plan for and implement its transfer in a manner that achieves the client's personal objectives, while minimizing related tax and other costs.

### Bankruptcy & Reorganization:

The Business Reorganization and Creditors' Rights Group consists of experienced and innovative attorneys who concentrate on corporate restructuring, loan workouts and other credit transactions, commercial litigation and bankruptcy. Members of the group have historically represented debtors in Chapter 11 cases, secured and unsecured creditors and other parties in interest in business reorganizations and state insolvency proceedings. The firm is continuously active in handling complex workouts both before and during litigation and handling all aspects of bankruptcy practice such as cash collateral agreements, debtor-in-possession lending and implementation of various exit strategies for both secured lenders and corporate debtors.

## PRACTICE AREAS

Construction Litigation-Arbitration Mediation
Construction Contracts & Transactions
Commercial Litigation
Real Estate
Business Law & Transactions
Intellectual Property–Technology–Media
Bankruptcy & Reorganization

## OFFICES

NEW YORK
**NEW YORK:** One Penn Plaza, 44th floor, NY 10119
Tel: 212 695 8100
Email neiseman@goetzfitz.com

**WHITE PLAINS:** One North Broadway, Suite 800, NY 10601
Tel: 914 946 7735

**WOODBURY:** 7600 Jericho Turnpike, Suite 403, NY 11797
Tel: 516 877 9666

NEW JERSEY
**GLEN ROCK:** 55 Harristown Rd., NJ 07452
Tel: 201 612 4444

# HAFETZ NECHELES & ROCCO

www.hnrlawoffices.com **tel:** 212 997 7595 **fax:** 212 997 7646

**OFFICES**

**NEW YORK:** 29th Floor, 500 Fifth Avenue, NY 10110
Tel: 212 997 7595  Fax 212 997 7646
Email: info@hnrlawoffices.com

## Firm Overview:

The firm is a nine lawyer litigation boutique specializing in white collar defense, complex civil litigation, agency enforcement and regulatory proceedings, and internal investigations built around three former prosecutors, including one who headed the Criminal Division in the United States Attorney's Office for the Southern District of New York and another who headed the Criminal Division in the United States Attorney's Office for the Eastern District of New York. One of the partners served as the head of the litigation department of a national firm in New York. Two of the partners are former presidents of the New York Council of Defense Lawyers. Each of the three partners have extensive trial, investigative and appellate experience in complex, often high profile matters. The firm represents professionals and senior executives in a number of industries: Banking, Securities, Insurance, Real Estate, Healthcare, Account Liability, Construction, Maritime, and Pharmaceuticals. Representative matters that the partners have handled include alleged violations of the securities laws, the mail, wire, bank, and securities fraud statutes, antitrust laws, the Foreign Corrupt Practices Act, federal and state tax laws, money laundering statutes, false claims act, bribery statutes, RICO and ERISA.

## Main Areas of Practice:

Fred Hafetz, a former chief of the Criminal Division in the Southern District of New York and a member of the American College of Trial Lawyers, is one of the most respected and experienced trial lawyers in the United States and a dean of the white collar bar in New York. Some of his recent matters include a dismissal after trial for a New York Stock Exchange specialist in a high profile prosecution, a reversal of the conviction of a senior insurance executive for an international insurance company in an accounting fraud conviction and an acquittal after trial of a well-known lawyer in a corruption case.

## Clients:

The firm represents individuals and corporations in a variety of business and regulatory matters.

# HARTER SECREST & EMERY LLP

**www.**hselaw.com **tel:** 585 232 6500 **fax:** 585 232 2152

**Managing Partner:** Michael R McEvoy, Esq.
Number of partners: 66
Number of lawyers: 138
Language: *English*

### Firm Overview:

Based in Upstate New York, with offices in Rochester, Buffalo, Albany and Naples, FL, Harter Secrest & Emery delivers big market legal talent at small market costs. Whether working with a multinational or a one-person start-up company, HSE is dedicated to protecting its clients' interests and helping them gain competitive advantage. HSE is defined by exacting legal standards and a collegial, collaborative and integrated philosophy where clients benefit from access to the right talent for every matter, yielding top quality, cost-effective legal counsel and advocacy.

### Main Areas of Practice:

**Corporate/M&A/Securities:**
19 Partners; 43 fee earners
- The firm served as lead counsel to Norampac in connection with the formation of a joint for the acquisition of a "green", state-of-the-art containerboard manufacturing facility in Niagara Falls, NY
- The firm handled their client Health Management's acquisition of seven hospitals in the Knoxville, Tennessee area for $525 million
- HSE represented Arthur J. Gallagher & Co. and its subsidiary Gallagher Bassett Services, Inc. in an acquisition of the third party administrator business of GAB Robbins North America, Inc.
- HSE was lead transaction counsel for Eastman Kodak Company in the sale of a significant image sensor patent portfolio and related assets

**Key Clients:** Health Management Associates, Eastman Kodak, Paychex, Transcat, Norampac (CA), Arthur J. Gallagher.
**Contact:** Gary L Karl  **Tel:** 585 231 1147
**Email:** gkarl@hselaw.com

**Employee Benefits/Executive Compensation:**
7 Partners; 17 fee earners
HSE provides ongoing advice and counsel to numerous clients with respect to US retirement, health and welfare and executive compensation and benefit matters including:
- American Express Company: Over 38,000 participants in qualified retirement plans
- Health Management Associates, Inc.: Over 40,000 participants
- Ameriprise Financial, Inc.: Over 10,000 participants
- Eastman Kodak Company: Over 50,000 participants
- Arthur J. Gallagher & Co.: Over 17,000 participants

**Key Clients:** American Express, Staples, Viacom, JTEKT, HealthNow and Arthur J. Gallagher.
**Contact:** Paul W Holloway  **Tel:** 585 231 1208
**Email:** pholloway@hselaw.com

**Immigration:**
2 Partners; 8 fee earners
- HSE represented a pharmacist in constitutional challenges to New York State's licensing statutes. The District Court found that New York State violated both the 14th amendment and the Supremacy Clause of the US Constitution and discriminated against pharmacists seeking professional licenses based on their immigration status
- HSE successfully obtained visas for performers of the internationally renowned Garth Fagan Dance Company. Garth Fagan is the Tony-award winning choreographer of The Lion King, in its Broadway and international venues

**Key Clients:** Talisman Energy (CA), Wegmans, Eastman Kodak, Carestream Health, Bausch & Lomb.
**Contact:** Frank A Novak  **Tel:** 585 231 1406
**Email:** fnovak@hselaw.com

**Labor & Employment:**
6 Partners; 14 fee earners
- HSE successfully represented Ithaca Coffee Company, LLC with respect to union organizing
- The firm successfully represented Schlegel Systems, Inc. in connection with an unfair labor practice charge against it by Rochester Regional Joint Board, Workers United, Local 3-T
- HSE assisted a major client with multistate operations in drafting and developing an on-line application process and in client's "going-green" initiative

**Key Clients:** Wegmans, Hobart and William Smith Colleges, Kaleida Health.
**Contact:** Robert C Weissflach  **Tel:** 716 844 3707
**Email:** rweissflach@hselaw.com

**Litigation:**
18 Partners; 41 fee earners
- The New York State Court of Appeals issued a decision in favor of client Buffalo Crushed Stone (BCS) resolving a ten-year dispute between it and the Town of Cheektowaga, NY over the extent of BCS's right to mine its 280-acre quarry located within the Town limits
- Harter Secrest & Emery successfully represented Seneca Niagara Falls Gaming Corporation (SNFGC) in an arbitration against High Concrete Group. The arbitrator awarded SNFGC the full $3.8 million it sought
- The Appellate Division of New York State Supreme Court unanimously affirmed a trial court judgment granted to the New York State Health Facilities Association and its 260 nursing home members striking down a provision of the New York State Public Health Law as unconstitutional

**Key Clients:** Eastman Kodak, Paychex, Bausch & Lomb, Celestica, Corning.
**Contact:** Peter H Abdella  **Tel:** 585 231 1116
**Email:** pabdella@hselaw.com

### PRACTICE AREAS

Bankruptcy & Financial Reorganization
Corporate/M&A
Closely Held Business
Energy
Employee Benefits & Executive Compensation
Government Affairs
Government Investigations
Health Care
Immigration
Intellectual Property
Labor & Employment
Litigation
Not for Profit/Higher Education
Private Equity & Finance
Tax
Trusts & Estates

### OFFICES

**NEW YORK**

**ROCHESTER:** 1600 Bausch & Lomb Place, Rochester, NY 14604
Tel: 585 232 6500  Fax: 585 232 2152
Email: jquinn@hselaw.com

**BUFFALO:** Twelve Fountain Plaza, Suite 400, Buffalo, NY 14202
Tel: 716 853 1616  Fax: 716 853 1616
Email: jhorn@hselaw.com

**ALBANY:** 111 Washington Avenue, Suite 303, Albany, NY 12210
Tel: 518 434 4377 Fax: 518 449 4025
Email: akellogg@hselaw.com

**FLORIDA**

**NAPLES:** 5811 Pelican Bay Boulevard, Suite 600, Naples, FL 34108
Tel: 239 598 2781 Fax: 239 598 2781
Email: bmcavoy@hselaw.com

# HISCOCK & BARCLAY

www.hblaw.com **tel:** 315 425 2700 **fax:** 315 425 2701

**Managing Partner:** John P. Langan
Number of partners: 90  Number of lawyers: 200

## Firm Overview:

Hiscock & Barclay LLP has assembled a team of 200 attorneys across 30 practice areas in eight strategically located offices to provide seamless services to its national and diverse client base, including Fortune 500 companies, medium and small businesses, and individuals. By leveraging its national practices and Northeast regional platform to connect extraordinary legal talent with the needs of its major-market clients, the firm is often able to pass along a highly competitive cost structure. Put simply, Hiscock & Barclay delivers success on a daily basis, and is a market leader in numerous industries and practice areas.

## Main Areas of Practice:

### Energy:

The firm's attorneys combine industry experience and regulatory insight with economic analysis, business understanding and legal know-how to help clients solve and avoid a range of complex regulatory and environmental issues. It is involved at every stage of energy exploration, permitting, generation, transmission and distribution with specific strengths in New York's evolving regulatory environment. That includes the siting and development of interstate pipeline and electric transmission projects, resolving regulatory and environmental issues for power generators and working closely with clients on opportunities for the development of Marcellus and Utica shale deposits.

### Litigation:

The firm actively prosecutes and defends some of the most complex civil litigation cases in the country. It represents large public and private companies and insurers in a myriad of litigation matters. A significant portion of its practice is devoted to general business litigation, including issues involving contracts, intellectual property, securities, corporate governance, ERISA, and white-collar crime, but its practice is by no means limited to those issues, and the firm is well-versed in litigation involving energy and the environment, healthcare, real estate, tax, products liability, insurance coverage and professional liability issues.

### Intellectual Property:

The firm's intellectual property practice is backed by its team of experienced trial lawyers, as well as the academic and industry experience of more than 30 lawyers and specialists. The firm represents clients in obtaining affordable and enforceable patents and trademarks. Its litigation attorneys have years of experience working together to protect their clients in disputes that arise in connection with patents, trademarks, copyrights and trade secrets around the world.

### Project Development & Real Property Tax:

The firm provides coordinated solutions through all stages of a development project, including site selection, project financing, tax mitigation options such as payments in lieu of tax agreements (PILOTS), development incentives and right to build issues. Its attorneys also assist clients in establishing realistic and accurate valuations for their properties and, when necessary, litigate complex tax-reduction cases. The firm is familiar with the equalization process and has ongoing interaction with local and state assessors. Its real property tax practice successfully represents energy and utility clients in jurisdictions across the country.

### Corporate & Tax:

The firm provides legal counseling in areas of strategic planning, operations and evolving business relationships for privately and publically held companies. Its attorneys' experience include a wide variety of business transactions ranging from entity structure/formation, day-to-day operational and existing and evolving financing needs to acquisitions and divestitures, restructuring, succession planning, securities. The firm's knowledge of federal, state and local taxation allows it to customize tax plans that permit its clients to maximize their earnings while minimizing their tax exposure.

### Labor & Employment:

The firm assists private and public employers in all aspects of labor- management relations under the National Labor Relations Act and state labor relations agencies. It advises clients on all matters that affect employment decisions, reviewing proposed personnel actions, including terminations. The firm regularly appears before the EEOC as well as the fair employment practice agencies. It also represents clients before state and federal trial and appellate courts in lawsuits pertaining to various employment matters, from wrongful discharge claims to class action civil rights litigation to enforcement of post-employment non-competition provisions.

### Public Finance:

The firm's attorneys have a comprehensive understanding and extensive experience in all facets of public finance. It has demonstrated its valued combination of skills when serving clients in a wide variety of financings as bond counsel, underwriter's counsel, issuer counsel, letter of credit bank counsel, counsel for profit and not-for-profit conduit borrowers, and trustee's counsel. The firm's attorneys have been instrumental in billions of dollars worth of public revenue bonds, appropriation-backed bonds and general obligation bonds.

### Healthcare:

The firm's attorneys guide a variety of health care institutions, as well as individual providers and medical equipment suppliers on compliance issues, in audits and in litigation. It routinely assists clients in addressing a range of health care compliance and regulatory issues, as well as in government audits and investigations, and, if necessary, litigation. The firm has successfully litigated matters related to Medicare and Medicaid, RICO, consumer fraud and deceptive practices, as well as fraud and abuse and investigation matters, health insurance, licensing and HMO credentialing. The firm guides organizations in developing business strategies, securing financing for projects, and planning and implementing their plans.

### Clients:

AES, Chevron, Combined Systems, Dow Chemical, HEALTHeLINK, Millennium Pipeline, National Grid, PAR Technology, Pharmacists Society of New York, PPC, Reckitt Benckiser, Rite Aid, Rosina Food, Transmission Developers Inc., TransCanada Pipelines, Turner Construction Co., US Energy Development, US Foods, Welch Allyn and Yankee Candle.

HISCOCK & BARCLAY LLP

---

## OFFICES

### NEW YORK

**SYRACUSE:** One Park Place, 300 South State Street, NY 13202
Tel: 315 425 2700  Fax: 315 425 2701

**ALBANY:** 80 State Street, NY 12207
Tel: 518 429 4200  Fax: 518 429 4201

**BUFFALO:** 1100 M&T Center, 3 Fountain Plaza, NY 14203
Tel: 716 566 1300  Fax: 716 566 1301

**NEW YORK:** Suite 600, 1270 Avenue of the Americas, NY 10020
Tel: 212 784 5800  Fax: 212 784 5777

**ROCHESTER:** 2000 HSBC Plaza, 100 Chestnut Street, NY 14604
Tel: 585 295 4400  Fax: 585 295 4401

### MASSACHUSETTS

**BOSTON:** One International Place, 26th Floor, MA 02110
Tel: 617 274 2900  Fax: 617 722 6003

### DISTRICT OF COLUMBIA:

**WASHINGTON DC:** 1325 G Street, NW Suite 500, DC, 20005
Tel: 202 582 0601  Fax: 202 582 0602

Email: info@hblaw.com

## INTERNATIONAL OFFICES

The firm also has an office in Toronto.

# HUGHES HUBBARD & REED LLP

www.hugheshubbard.com

**Chair:** Candace Krugman Beinecke
**Managing Partner:** Theodore V H Mayer

**OFFICES**
New York, Washington, DC, Los Angeles, Miami, Jersey City, Kansas City

**INTERNATIONAL OFFICES**
Paris and Tokyo

**Firm Overview:**

Hughes Hubbard is the number one-ranked firm on The American Lawyer's A-List, which the magazine calls 'the profession's top tier' and the 'best of the all around best' law firms. The firm was founded in 1888 by the renowned jurist and statesman Charles Evans Hughes.

**Main Areas of Practice:**

**Antitrust:**

Hughes Hubbard has a diverse and international Antitrust Practice. The firm counsels clients on all aspects of antitrust law, including cartel-related criminal grand jury investigations, class action litigation, and representing parties before government enforcement agencies (both US and EU) in conduct-related investigations. The firm provides antitrust advice to clients in connection with mergers and acquisitions and day-to-day antitrust counseling on compliance issues, including pricing, distribution, and standard-setting and other IP-related issues.

**Aviation:**

Hughes Hubbard has had a leading Aviation Practice for over 40 years. The firm represents leading airlines, investment banks, leasing companies, hedge funds, and other financial institutions in both domestic and cross-border transactions. The firm has a deep understanding of all manner of aviation finance structures and has been involved in many 'first-in-kind' transactions. The practice covers all aspects of the aviation business, including financings, securities offerings, mergers and acquisitions, workouts and bankruptcies, interairline matters, leasing and litigation.

**Corporate:**

Hughes Hubbard's corporate clients include some of the world's largest domestic and multinational companies. Attorneys in the M&A Practice represent public and private companies in all varieties of stock and asset acquisitions and dispositions, including the full range of public company matters such as hostile takeovers and proxy fights. Attorneys in the M&A Practice also represent special committees of boards of directors in connection with exploration of strategic alternatives and review of going private and related-party transactions. The M&A Practice handles joint ventures and other strategic alliances, including those involving cross-border transactions. Attorneys in the Securities and Capital Markets Practice represent issuers and underwriters in public and private equity and debt offerings, including initial public offerings and equipment financings. The firm also has a strong Banking and Finance Practice which represents numerous financial institutions in syndicated lending, project finance, regulatory matters and derivatives.

**Corporate Reorganization & Bankruptcy:**

This practice is multidisciplinary, with deep and broad experience, including the ongoing liquidations of Lehman Brothers Inc. and MF Global Inc., the largest and eighth largest bankruptcies in history. With over 40 attorneys across five offices, the group represents financial institutions and companies as debtors and creditors in judicial and out-of-court restructurings and related work outs and litigation. The group has particular experience in financial insolvency, cross border restructuring, asset sales, and secured and unsecured creditors' rights.

**International Trade:**

Hughes Hubbard provides comprehensive legal advice to clients on matters involving the entire spectrum of international trade and investment issues faced by governments, multinational corporations, trade associations. The group's practice includes: export controls and economic sanctions, trade remedies, market access, customs counseling, antidumping and countervailing duty proceedings and counseling, WTO and NAFTA dispute avoidance and resolution, investment arbitration, state-to-state arbitration, and anti-corruption and internal investigations.

**Intellectual Property:**

The Intellectual Property Practice advises on patents, trademarks, licenses, copyrights, trade secrets and unfair competition. The group counsels clients on a wide range of IP matters in corporate transactions, licensing programs, product development and clearance programs, litigation and arbitration.

**Litigation:**

Litigation has always been a cornerstone of Hughes Hubbard's practice with the firm's reputation recognized both nationally and internationally by the world's leading legal publications. The firm has the resources and capacity to play virtually any role including: trial, appellate and class action litigators; a dedicated eDiscovery and document management group; and national coordinating experience in many complex cases. The firm has an active general Commercial Litigation Practice. Other major areas include antitrust; appellate; arbitration and ADR; art law; bankruptcy; environmental; financial services and banking; insurance coverage; intellectual property and technology; labor and employment; not-for-profit; product liability and toxic torts; professional liability; securities and white collar crime and corporate compliance.

**Labor & Employment:**

Attorneys are well versed in the full range of employment litigation and issues on behalf of employers including collective bargaining, unfair labor practices, discrimination, harassment, wrongful discharge, wage and hour and noncompetition agreements.

**Real Estate:**

The firm's global Real Estate Practice has clients from a diversity of industries and covers every aspect of real estate and hospitality-related transactions.

**New Media:**

The practice combines the resources and experience of a traditional law firm with an understanding and passion for today's cutting-edge technologies to assist clients in navigating the new realities and challenges arising from this shifting landscape. Attorneys advise clients on matters in the areas of digital media and the Internet, entertainment and technology and information security.

**Tax:**

Attorneys in this area are involved in complex crossborder transactions, including mergers and acquisitions, multinational joint ventures, and financings. The firm's employee benefits attorneys, who are part of the Tax Group, handle all aspects of employee pensions, executive compensation and ERISA work.

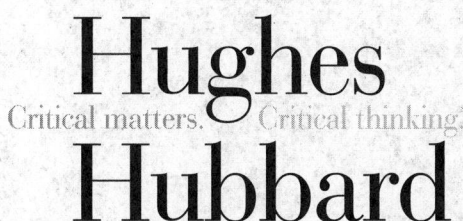

Critical matters. Critical thinking.

# JACKSON LEWIS LLP

www.jacksonlewis.com

**Managing Partner:** Vincent A Cino

### Firm Overview:

Founded in 1958, Jackson Lewis, dedicated to representing management exclusively in workplace law, is one of the fastest growing workplace law firms in the US, with 750 attorneys practicing in 52 locations nationwide. For the 11th consecutive year, Jackson Lewis has been recognized for delivering client service excellence to the world's largest corporations, once again earning a spot on the BTI Client Service A-Team. Jackson Lewis has also been recognized by in-house counsel of *Fortune* 1000 companies after a comprehensive survey, as 'the single highest-ranked firm clients want by their side in employment battles.' In addition, Jackson Lewis is ranked in the First Tier nationally in the category of Labor and Employment Litigation, as well as in both Employment Law and Labor Law on behalf of Management in the US News – Best Lawyers ® 'Best Law Firms,' and is recognized by Chambers and Legal 500. As an 'AmLaw 100' firm, Jackson Lewis has one of the most active employment litigation practices in the United States, with a current caseload of over 6500 litigations and approximately 415 class actions. And finally, Jackson Lewis is a charter member of L & E Global Employers' Counsel Worldwide, an alliance currently of 14 workplace law firms in 14 countries. Additional information about Jackson Lewis can be found at www.jacksonlewis.com.

### Main Areas of Practice:

The firm has a wide-range of specialized practice areas, including: Affirmative Action and OFCCP Planning and Counseling; Disability, Leave and Health Management; Employee Benefits Counseling and Litigation; General Employment Litigation, including Class Actions, Complex Litigation and e-Discovery; Immigration; Labor, including Preventive Practices; Protection Against Unfair Competition; Wage and Hour Compliance; Workplace Safety and Health and Corporate Diversity Counseling. In addition, Jackson Lewis provides advice nationally in other workplace law areas, including: Reductions in Force, WARN Act; Corporate Governance and Internal Investigations; Drug Testing and Substance Abuse Management; International Employment Issues; Management Education, including e-Based Training; Alternative Dispute Resolution; Public Sector Issues; Government Relations; Collegiate and Professional Sports; and Privacy, Social Media and Information Management.

**Affirmative Action & OFCCP Diversity Planning & Counseling:**
Contact: Mickey Silberman

**Class Actions & Complex Litigation:**
Contact: William Anthony

**Corporate Diversity Counseling:**
Contact: Weldon Latham

**Disability, Leave & Health Management:**
Contact: Frank Alvarez

**E-discovery:**
Contact: Brett Anders, Ralph Losey

**Employee Benefits Counseling & Litigation:**
Contact: Michael Jacobster

**General Employment Litigation:**
Contact: Joan Ackerstein

**Immigration:**
Contact: William Manning, Sean Hanagan

**Labor including Preventive Practices:**
Contact: Philip Rosen

**Non-Competes & Protection Against Unfair Competition:**
Contact: A Robert Fischer, Cliff Atlas

**Wage & Hour Compliance:**
Contact: Paul DeCamp

**Workplace Safety & Health:**
Contact: Bradford Hammock

### Clients:

Jackson Lewis represents a wide range of companies in a variety of industries including but not limited to: automotive, banking, construction, education, energy, financial services, government, healthcare, hospitality, insurance, manufacturing, non-profit, pharmaceuticals, real estate, retail and transportation.

**OFFICES**

NEW YORK

**WHITE PLAINS:** One North Broadway, NY, 10601
Tel: 914 328 0404

The firm also has offices in Alabama: Birmingham; Arizona: Phoenix; California: Los Angeles, Orange County, Sacramento, San Diego, San Francisco; Colorado: Denver; Connecticut: Hartford, Stamford; District of Columbia: Washington DC Region; Florida: Jacksonville, Miami, Orlando, Tampa; Georgia: Atlanta; Illinois: Chicago; Indiana, Indianapolis; Louisiana: New Orleans; Maryland, Baltimore; Massachusetts: Boston; Michigan: Detroit, Grand Rapids; Minnesota: Minneapolis; Missouri: St Louis; Nebraska: Omaha; Nevada: Las Vegas; New Hampshire: Portsmouth; New Jersey: Morristown; New Mexico: Albuquerque; New York: Albany, Long Island, New York City, White Plains; North Carolina: Raleigh-Durham; Ohio: Cincinnati, Cleveland; Oregon: Portland; Pennsylvania: Philadelphia, Pittsburgh; Rhode Island: Providence; South Carolina: Greenville; Tennessee: Memphis; Texas: Austin, Dallas, Houston; Virginia: Norfolk, Richmond; Washington: Seattle; Wisconsin: Milwaukee and Puerto Rico: San Juan.

# KASOWITZ, BENSON, TORRES & FRIEDMAN

**www**.kasowitz.com  **tel:** 212 506 1700  **fax:** 212 506 1800

**Managing Partner:** Marc E Kasowitz
Number of partners: 106  Number of other lawyers: 273

## Firm Overview:

Kasowitz, Benson, Torres & Friedman LLP is one of the largest litigation firms in the country. The firm's highly talented lawyers are committed to pursuing creative, aggressive and winning approaches to their clients' most challenging legal matters.

## Main Areas of Practice:

### Litigation:

Kasowitz's litigators represent clients in high-stakes and often precedent-setting lawsuits. The firm's practice encompasses all aspects of litigation, including antitrust, banking, class actions, complex financial products, employment practices, environmental, general corporate and commercial, international arbitration, mass tort and product liability, real estate, securities and white collar criminal defense litigation. The firm uses a decidedly aggressive approach to litigation and strives to achieve the most favorable results for its clients by focusing from the beginning of each case on preparation for trial.

Recent representations: MBIA Inc. in defeat of a lawsuit brought by 19 of the world's largest financial institutions which sought to set aside MBIA's transformation of its structured finance insurance business; Federal Housing Finance Agency, as conservator for Fannie Mae and Freddie Mac, in several actions in federal and state courts against numerous financial institutions concerning misrepresentations regarding pools of mortgage loans that underlie $205 billion of residential mortgage-backed securities; ACA Financial Guaranty Corp. in an action against Goldman Sachs & Co. for fraud and unjust enrichment in connection with a synthetic CDO known as Abacus 2007 AC1; National Australia Bank and its affiliate and the successor to Fortis Bank in actions against OppenheimerFunds and its affiliates concerning defendants' misconduct in purchasing and managing billions of dollars of mortgage-backed securities and CDOs; and Comcast in defending three class actions alleging antitrust violations as a result of 'clustering' in cable markets.

### Creditors' Rights & Bankruptcy:

Kasowitz's Creditors' Rights and Bankruptcy Group represents major parties in the largest bankruptcies and restructurings throughout the country. The firm is a leader in representing investors in securities of distressed companies and in representing debtor companies as well. The firm represents businesses in developing legal strategies for their financial rehabilitation, working closely with the client to achieve an attractive resolution.

Recent representations: Borders Group Inc. in its chapter 11 bankruptcy as well as the representation of creditors, equity committees or indentured trustees in the bankruptcies of Adelphia Communications, Lyondell Chemical Company, Le*Nature's Inc., Tribune Company, Federal Housing Finance Agency and Dewey & LeBoeuf LLP.

### Insurance Recovery:

Kasowitz's Insurance Recovery Group is one of the largest in the nation focused exclusively on policyholder coverage. The firm's attorneys pride themselves on understanding the business needs of their clients and working closely with them to address all of their legal insurance coverage needs, including high-stakes litigation, alternative dispute resolution, policy audits, risk assessments, state insurance regulatory matters and due diligence associated with business transactions. The Insurance Recovery Group's attorneys have recovered more than $2 billion to date for their clients through judgments and settlements.

Recent representations: Clients such as Visa, Syracuse University, Philips Electronics, Tyson Foods, Port Authority of NY & NJ and Pella Windows and Doors have relied on the group for representation.

### Intellectual Property Litigation:

Kasowitz's intellectual property litigators have extensive experience in all aspects of the field, including patent, trademark, trade secret, false advertising, copyright, right of publicity, and related antitrust and unfair competition litigation. The firm's intellectual property lawyers represent clients in disputes concerning computer software and hardware, medical devices, telecommunications, semiconductors, financial services, e-commerce, pharmaceuticals, biotechnology, chemical processes, manufacturing processes, consumer products, and other areas.

Recent representations: A defense verdict for Google and YouTube against Eolas Technologies and the University of California; achieving summary judgment of patent invalidity for Hitachi in infringement claims brought by Magsil and MIT, and for Yahoo! in claims brought by Paid Search Engine Tools.

### Employment Practices & Litigation:

The firm's Employment Practices and Litigation Group represents employers in actions involving claims of race, sex, disability and age discrimination, as well as matters relating to ERISA, wage and hours law, workers' compensation and the Family and Medical Leave Act.

### Transactional Real Estate:

Kasowitz's Transactional Real Estate Group represents, among others, developers, private and institutional investors, opportunity funds, real estate investment trusts (REITs), lenders and servicers, and major corporations in connection with real estate-related matters.

### Clients:

The firm's clients have included: ACA Financial Guaranty Corporation; Adelphia Litigation Recovery Trust; Allied Waste Industries, Inc.; Armstrong World Industries, Inc.; Blackstone Group, LP; Borders Group Inc.; Caxton International LTD; Comcast; EMCORE Corporation; Ernst & Young; Fairfax Financial Corporation; Federal Housing Finance Agency; Federal Deposit Insurance Corporation; Fortress Investment Group; George Weston Bakeries Inc.; Google Inc.; Hilton Worldwide; Hitachi Global Storage Technologies, Inc.; Interstate Bakeries Corp.; Le*Nature's Liquidation Trust; Level 3 Communications; Liggett Group LLC; Lloyds TSB Bank plc; Martha Stewart Living Omnimedia; MBIA Inc.; MEGA Brands, Inc.; Meritor, Inc.; Metropolitan Life Insurance Company; National Australia Bank; New York Jets; News America Corporation; Port Authority of New York and New Jersey; Rabobank International; Source Interlink Companies, Inc; Southern Union Company; Trump Organization; Visa USA, Inc.; Yahoo!; Wenner Media LLC.

## OFFICES

### NEW YORK

**NEW YORK:** 1633 Broadway, NY 10019
Tel: 212 506 1700  Fax: 212 506 1800

### CALIFORNIA

**SAN FRANCISCO:** 101 California Street, Suite 2300, CA 94111
Tel: 415 421 6140  Fax: 415 398 5030

**SILICON VALLEY:** 333 Twin Dolphin Drive, Suite 200, CA 94065
Tel: 650 453 5170  Fax: 650 453 5171

### FLORIDA

**MIAMI:** 1441 Brickell Avenue, Suite 1420, FL 33131
Tel: 305 377 1666  Fax: 305 377 1664

### GEORGIA

**ATLANTA:** 1349 West Peachtree Street, NW, Suite 1500, GA 30309
Tel: 404 260 6080  Fax: 404 260 6081

### TEXAS

**HOUSTON:** 700 Louisiana Street, Suite 2200, TX 77002
Tel: 713 220 8800  Fax: 713 222 0843

# KAYE SCHOLER LLP

www.kayescholer.com **tel:** 212 836 8000 **fax:** 212 836 8689

**Firm Managing Partner:** Michael B Solow
**Executive Committee Co-Chairs:** Michael B Solow, Stephen Gliatta
Number of partners worldwide: 150   Number of lawyers: 460
Languages: *Chinese, English, Farsi, French, German, Greek, Hebrew, Italian, Japanese, Portuguese, Russian, Spanish, Thai, Ukrainian*

## Firm Overview:

Founded in New York in 1917, Kaye Scholer combines the continuity and business acumen of a century-old law firm with a forward-looking, results-driven approach focused around lasting client relationships. With industry strengths in life sciences, financial services, technology, real estate and energy and infrastructure, Kaye Scholer offers strategic guidance and legal services to public and private entities facing litigation, transactional or governance challenges. Kaye Scholer's lawyers regularly advise on matters across multiple legal jurisdictions, including in the US, Canada, UK, EU, China and Japan.

## Main Areas of Practice:

**Bankruptcy & Restructuring:**
- Currently advising the City of Los Angeles and its Department of Airports, as well as a number of owner participants, operating lessors and lenders, on issues related to the American Airlines bankruptcy
- Represented 4Kids Entertainment, Inc. and its affiliates in a successful reorganization plan that allowed the company to sell a popular license, reorganize around its remaining licenses and expand into a new business

**Complex Commercial Litigation:**
- Currently serving as Global Strategic Counsel and National Coordinating Counsel for Pfizer, and its subsidiaries Wyeth and Pharmacia & Upjohn, in more than 10,000 hormone therapy litigation claims
- Advised The Body Shop in a nationwide class action brought by employees seeking overtime wages under the Fair Labor Standards Act

**Corporate:**
- Represented longtime client Novartis and its generics subsidiary Sandoz in the $1.525 billion purchase of Fougera Pharmaceuticals in an all-cash transaction
- Assisted longtime client Onex Corp. in its $2.3 billion acquisition of USI Insurance Services LLC from a private fund managed by Goldman Sachs Group Inc.

**Finance:**
- Represented Bank of America Corp. on nine major transactions, including the two-part sale of the bank's $2.9 billion stake in Archstone to Lehman Brothers
- Advised alternative investment firm Sound Harbor Partners LLC in its recent acquisition of more than $1 billion in collateralized loan obligation contracts from Aladdin Capital Holdings LLC

**Intellectual Property:**
- Helped The Hershey Company obtain a trademark registration for the design configuration of its iconic Hershey's chocolate bar

- Successfully preserved Pfizer's market exclusivity for its blockbuster drug Viagra until 2019 in Pfizer vs. Teva Pharmaceuticals

**National Security, Government Contracts & Regulatory Compliance:**
- Represented MacDonald, Dettwiler & Associates Ltd. in its $1 billion acquisition of Space Systems/Loral, Inc. from Loral Space & Communications Inc.
- Advised France's Safran in its $1.09 billion acquisition of US face-recognition/secured credentialing software maker L-1 Identity Solutions, Inc.

**Real Estate:**
- Advised Bank of America in a $235 million five-year floating rate loan to affiliates of The Blackstone Group LP to finance a portion of the $321 million acquisition of 15 shopping centers from Regency Centers
- Advised Royal Bank of Scotland in a $103 million first mortgage loan secured by 24 properties that was the first Shari'ah-compliant "Top 10 loan" for a CMBS securitization

**Tax & Private Clients:**
- Advising Potash Corporation of Saskatchewan, the world's largest integrated fertilizer manufacture, on ongoing financing and international planning and structuring
- Represented Caisse de dépôt et placement du Québec in its $850 million purchase from ConocoPhillips of a 16.55 percent interest in Colonial Pipeline Company and Colonial Ventures LLC

**Clients:**
Amazon.com, Bank of America, Boston Scientific, Canadian Imperial Bank of Commerce, Exxon-Mobil, Google, Hershey, Novartis, Onex Corporation, Pfizer, Sanofi-aventis, UBS, WestLB.

## PRACTICE AREAS

Antitrust
Appellate
Asset Finance & Leasing
Bankruptcy & Restructuring
Complex Commercial Litigation
Employment & Labor Litigation
Energy & Infrastructure
Financial Services Litigation
Foreign Acquisitions
Government Contracts
Intellectual Property
Intellectual Property & Technology Transactions
Investment Funds
Life Sciences
Media & Entertainment
Mergers & Acquisitions
Patent Litigation
Private Clients
Private Equity
Products Liability
Real Estate
Securities & Derivative Litigation
Securities Transactional
Structured Finance
Syndicated & Leveraged Finance
Tax
Trademark, Copyright & False Advertising
White-Collar Litigation & Internal Investigations

## OFFICES

**NEW YORK**
**NEW YORK:** (Head office) 425 Park Avenue, NY 10022-3598
Tel: 212 836 8000   Fax: 212 836 8689

**CALIFORNIA**
**LOS ANGELES:** 1999 Avenue of the Stars, Suite 1600, CA 90067-6048
Tel: 310 788 1000   Fax: 310 788 1200

**PALO ALTO:** Two Palo Alto Square, 3000 El Camino Real, Suite 400, CA 94306-2112
Tel: 650 319 4500   Fax: 650 319 4700

**DISTRICT OF COLUMBIA**
**WASHINGTON, DC:** The McPherson Building, 901 Fifteenth Street, NW, DC 20005-2327
Tel: 202 682 3500   Fax: 202 682 3580

**FLORIDA**
**WEST PALM BEACH:** Phillips Point, West Tower, Suite 900, 777 South Flagler Drive, FL 33401-6163
Tel: 561 802 3230   Fax: 561 802 3217

**ILLINOIS**
**CHICAGO:** 3 First National Plaza, Suite 4200, 70 West Madison Street, IL 60602-4231
Tel: 312 583 2300   Fax: 312 583 2360

The firm also has offices in London, Frankfurt and Shanghai.

# KELLEY DRYE & WARREN LLP

www.kelleydrye.com **tel:** 212 808 7800 **fax:** 212 808 7897

**Managing Partner:** James J Kirk
Number of partners worldwide: 132
Number of other lawyers and professionals worldwide: 216

**Firm Overview:**
Founded in 1836, Kelley Drye & Warren LLP represents US and international companies across a wide spectrum of practice areas.

**Main Areas of Practice:**

**Advertising Law:**
Counsels on all aspects of advertising, promotions and consumer protection law, representing clients in regulatory matters before the FTC and state attorneys general, and in challenges by competitors or consumers.

**Antitrust:**
Represents clients in trade secrets, unfair competition, product disparagement, false advertising and misrepresentation and consumer protection.

**Bankruptcy & Restructuring:**
Represents trade creditors, creditors' committees and other parties in all aspects of bankruptcy and insolvency.

**Broker-Dealer:**
Counsels and represents full-service broker-dealers, discount brokers, direct access and floor brokerage firms and others.

**Corporate:**
Represents issuers and underwriters in connection with public and private securities offerings; financial institutions in transactions and compliance; and private equity and venture capital firms.

**Employee Benefits & Compensation:**
Advises on a broad spectrum of issues including retirement and welfare programs, executive compensation, and associated legal and tax issues.

**Energy:**
Expertise in conventional issues and at the forefront of issues relating to hydrocarbons as well as wind, solar, biofuels, ethanol, hydropower, nuclear, clean coal, carbon capture and sequestration, and energy/fuel efficiency.

**Entertainment & Media:**
Represents clients in high stakes lawsuits, including talent disputes, idea submission claims, production/distribution/financing disputes and the defense of First Amendment claims.

**Environmental:**
Provides solutions for complex environmental litigation, and administrative and regulatory challenges on Capitol Hill and the Environmental Protection Agency.

**Food & Drug:**
Counsels on the regulatory and legal issues that food and drug companies must navigate to succeed in the U.S. market, including compliance with FDA, USDA and FTC requirements.

**Government Relations & Public Policy:**
Pursues client objectives through multiple strategies, including: issue monitoring and outreach; gathering stakeholders into coalitions; representation before federal agencies; and influencing implementation and enforcement of regulations.

**India:**
Represents US and other clients in their Indian business relationships and Indian businesses operating in the US.

**Information Technology & Outsourcing:**
Negotiates and completes outsourcing arrangements and technology transactions, many spanning multiple jurisdictions worldwide.

**Insurance Recovery:**
Represents policyholders to resolve insurance claims and recover losses relating to all varieties of business insurance policies.

**Intellectual Property:**
Represents clients in a wide range of industries in matters involving patents, trademarks, trade secrets and other assets.

**International Trade:**
Protects domestic manufacturers against unfairly traded goods including: antidumping, countervailing duty, export control and economic sanctions laws.

**Labor & Employment:**
Represents employer-clients before federal, state and local agencies in arbitrations and mediation proceedings.

**Litigation:**
Deep experience in antitrust, class actions, employment, False Claims Act, intellectual property, securities litigation, international arbitration, white collar criminal defense and corporate investigations.

**Privacy & Information Security:**
Counsels on laws governing the collection, use and protection of personal information, and on managing risks and reducing exposure to investigations and litigation.

**Real Estate:**
Represents financial institutions and investors in acquisitions and sales, all varieties of financing, preferred equity investments, fund formation and investments, leasing and sale-leaseback transactions.

**Tax:**
Advises US and international clients in regard to business formation, mergers, equity and debt financing, restructurings and other matters.

**Telecommunications:**
Advises telecommunications companies in the areas of regulatory, compliance and litigation matters; contracts and strategic advice; and corporate and financial transactions at the state, federal and international level.

## OFFICES

**CALIFORNIA**
**LOS ANGELES:** 10100 Santa Monica Blvd, 23rd Floor, CA 90067
Tel: 310 712 6100  Fax: 310 712 6199
Email: awhite@kelleydrye.com

**CONNECTICUT**
**STAMFORD:** 400 Atlantic Street, CT 06901
Tel: 203 324 1400  Fax: 203 327 2669
Email: rchargar@kelleydrye.com

**DISTRICT OF COLUMBIA**
**WASHINGTON, DC:** Washington Harbour, Suite 400, 3050 K Street NW, DC 20007-5108
Tel: 202 342 8400  Fax: 202 342 8451
Email: prosenthal@kelleydrye.com

**ILLINOIS**
**CHICAGO:** 333 West Wacker Drive, 26th Floor, IL 60606
Tel: 312 857 7070  Fax: 312 857 7095
Email: hkelly@kelleydrye.com

**NEW JERSEY**
**PARSIPPANY:** 200 Kimball Drive, NJ 07054
Tel: 973 503 5900  Fax: 973 503 5950
Email: jboyle@kelleydrye.com

**NEW YORK**
**NEW YORK:** 101 Park Avenue, NY 10178-0002
Tel: 212 808 7800  Fax: 212 808 7897
Email: rsteiner@kelleydrye.com

# KOBRE & KIM LLP

www.kobrekim.com **tel:** 212 488 1200 **fax:** 212 488 1220

**Founding Partners:** Steven G Kobre, Michael S Kim
Number of partners: 17
Number of lawyers: 57
Languages: *Afrikaans, Cantonese, Dutch, French, German, Hebrew, Hindi, Italian, Japanese, Korean, Mandarin, Russian, Spanish, Telugu*

**Firm Overview:**

Kobre & Kim LLP devotes 100% of its practice to litigation and arbitration, conducting much of its work as special conflicts counsel in international financial and commercial cases. The firm has a unique business model in that it does not seek ongoing client relationships and instead focuses on discrete special litigation counsel engagements. As such, the firm offers clients a conflict-free team of advocates able to act against virtually any institutional entity. Kobre & Kim LLP is also unusual in that it is one of few litigation boutiques that focus on cross-border disputes, offering US-qualified attorneys working alongside English barristers and solicitors. Many of the firm's cases involve simultaneous proceedings in various US and non-US courts, as well as the offshore jurisdictions (e.g., BVI, Cayman Islands, etc.), and various major international dispute resolution centers in Asia, Europe and the Americas.

**Main Areas of Practice:**

**Financial Products & Services Litigation:**

The firm regularly handles high-stakes litigation and arbitration for major participants in the financial services industry, as both claimants and defendants, involving some of the most complex financial instruments in today's market, including interest rate swaps, credit default swaps, mortgage-backed securities, auction-rate securities and collateralized debt obligations. Several of the firm's lawyers are former federal prosecutors from the SEC-CFTC-DOJ Securities & Commodities Fraud Task Force and former enforcement attorneys from the US Securities and Exchange Commission.

In addition, Kobre & Kim LLP attorneys are able to draw on the firm's analysts, who have detailed knowledge in specific financial product areas such as commodities, securities, derivatives and insurance products.

**Bankruptcy & Debtor-Creditor Disputes:**

Kobre & Kim LLP offers US-qualified attorneys practicing alongside UK-qualified barristers and solicitors experienced in handling insolvency and debt disputes. The firm regularly represents secured and unsecured creditors, debtors, bondholders, and distressed debt investors, in disputes that often require navigating significant competing interests. Operating in multiple jurisdictions in the US, UK, Hong Kong, and offshore jurisdictions, the firm's lawyers are particularly experienced in multi-jurisdictional insolvency disputes.

**International Judgment Enforcement & Offshore Asset Recovery:**

Kobre & Kim LLP is the only firm able to deliver in one package the full spectrum of expertise in global asset recovery matters. The firm's lawyers include several former US Department of Justice and US Securities

and Exchange Commission lawyers with deep experience in international asset investigations and forfeiture, who are co-authors of several books on international asset recovery. The team also includes English solicitors and barristers with a significant track record in litigating in various offshore jurisdictions; in particular, the firm's two English Queen's Counsel have significant experience both attacking and defending offshore structures, including in the context of cross-border insolvency.

**Government Enforcement Defense / Parallel Class & Derivative Actions:**

Kobre & Kim LLP is the only litigation boutique with former US federal prosecutors stationed permanently in Europe and Asia. Led by more than a dozen former government attorneys, the firm's trial attorneys routinely represent institutional and individual clients in some of the highest-profile government investigations into businesses operating in the Americas, Europe and Asia. The firm's government enforcement defense experience, also gives it an edge in handling class or derivative actions brought in the context of criminal or regulatory investigations, with an eye towards avoiding the pitfalls and exploiting the opportunities created by parallel proceedings.

**Investigations & Monitorships:**

The firm has conducted numerous high-profile investigations on behalf of boards or audit committees of some of the largest public and private companies in the world in a variety of industries. The firm is one of the few law firms to have teams of former US prosecutors practicing out of offices in Europe and Asia, as well as the Americas. As a result, the firm has especially valuable experience dealing with varying attorney-client privilege laws, country-specific data protection laws, non-US employment laws, and other special issues that arise in international investigations.

## PRACTICE AREAS

Financial Products & Services Litigation
Bankruptcy & Debtor-Creditor Disputes
International Judgment Enforcement & Offshore Asset Recovery
Government Enforcement Defense
Investigations & Monitorships
Joint Venture & Partnership Disputes
International Arbitrations
Trusts & Estates Litigation
Class & Derivative Actions

## OFFICES

**NEW YORK**
**NEW YORK:** 800 Third Avenue, NY 10022
Tel: 212 488 1200  Fax: 212 488 1220

**DISTRICT OF COLUMBIA**
**WASHINGTON DC:** 1919 M Street, NW, DC 20036
Tel: 202 664 1900  Fax: 202 664 1920

**FLORIDA**
**MIAMI:** 2 South Biscayne Boulevard, 35th Floor, FL 33131
Tel: 305 967 6100  Fax: 305 967 6120

## INTERNATIONAL OFFICES

The firm also has offices in London, Hong Kong, Cayman Islands and British Virgin Islands.

Courts and government agencies also regularly invite the firm to serve as a monitor for institutions facing significant regulatory compliance issues.

**Joint Venture & Partnership Disputes:**

Kobre & Kim LLP's Joint Venture & Partnership Disputes team is retained to handle prominent joint venture and partnership disputes, providing aggressive and independent advocacy even in cases of numerous, overlapping institutional stakeholders' interests. Recent engagements include the real estate, hospitality and gaming, utilities, telecommunications and energy sectors.

**International Arbitrations:**

The firm has experience in a wide range of international and industry forums, including the ICC, HKIAC, SIAC, UNCITRAL, AAA/ICDR, LCIA, DIFC, ICSID, FINRA, ICE, LIFFE, and NFA, among others. Kobre & Kim LLP's team includes practiced arbitrators consisting of Fellows of the Chartered Institute of Arbitrators, the Hong Kong and Singapore Institutes of Arbitrators, a member of the London Court of International Arbitration, and many other arbitration panels.

**Trusts & Estates Litigation:**

Kobre & Kim LLP has advocated in some of the most high-profile trusts disputes acting on behalf of trustees, beneficiaries, and protectors in respect of alleged breaches of trust and fiduciary duty, as well as misappropriate of assets. The firm has handled cross-border trusts and estates litigation in the Americas, Europe, Asia and offshore jurisdictions.

# KRAMER LEVIN NAFTALIS & FRANKEL LLP

www.kramerlevin.com **tel:** 212 715 9100 **fax:** 212 715 8000

**Chairmen:** Gary P Naftalis, Thomas E Constance
**Chairman Emeritus:** Ezra G Levin
**Managing Partner:** Paul S Pearlman
Number of partners: 113   Number of lawyers: 375
Languages: *English, French*

**Firm Overview:**
Kramer Levin Naftalis & Frankel LLP is a premier, full-service law firm with offices in New York, Silicon Valley and Paris. The firm's lawyers are leading practitioners in their respective fields, who understand clients' businesses, demonstrate a strong focus on client service and offer innovative and practical solutions. Kramer Levin represents Global 1000 and emerging growth companies, institutions and individuals, across a broad range of industries.

**OFFICES**

NEW YORK
**NEW YORK:** 1177 Avenue of the Americas, NY 10036
Tel: 212 715 9100

CALIFORNIA
**SILICON VALLEY:** 990 March Road, Menlo Park, CA 94025
Tel: 650 752 1700
The firm also has an office in Paris.

**Main Areas of Practice:**

**Accountants' Liability:**
**Contact:** Arthur H Aufses  **Tel:** 212 715 9234
**Email:** aaufses@kramerlevin.com
**Contact:** Michael J Dell **Tel:** 212 715 9129
**Email:** mdell@kramerlevin.com

**Advertising:**
**Contact:** Harold P Weinberger **Tel:** 212 715 9132
**Email:** hweinberger@kramerlevin.com

**Banking & Finance:**
**Contact:** Kenneth Chin **Tel:** 212 715 9459
**Email:** kchin@kramerlevin.com

**Business Immigration:**
**Contact:** Ted Ruthizer **Tel:** 212 715 9421
**Email:** truthizer@kramerlevin.com
**Contact:** Mark D Koestler **Tel:** 212 715 9385
**Email:** mkoestler@kramerlevin.com

**Capital Markets/Finance:**
**Contact:** Scott S Rosenblum **Tel:** 212 715 9411
**Email:** srosenblum@kramerlevin.com
**Contact:** Thomas D Balliett **Tel:** 212 715 9164
**Email:** tballiett@kramerlevin.com
**Contact:** Richard H Gilden **Tel:** 212 715 9486
**Email:** rgilden@kramerlevin.com

**Corporate:**
**Contact:** Scott S Rosenblum **Tel:** 212 715 9411
**Email:** srosenblum@kramerlevin.com
**Contact:** Thomas D Balliett **Tel:** 212 715 9164
**Email:** tballiett@kramerlevin.com

**Corporate Governance/ Board Committee Representations:**
**Contact:** Kenneth P Kopelman **Tel:** 212 715 9358
**Email:** kkopelman@kramerlevin.com
**Contact:** Thomas E Molner **Tel:** 212  715 9429
**Email:** tmolner@kramerlevin.com

**Corporate Restructuring & Bankruptcy:**
**Contact:** Kenneth H Eckstein **Tel:** 212 715 9229
**Email:** keckstein@kramerlevin.com
**Contact:** Thomas Moers Mayer **Tel:** 212 715 9169
**Email:** tmayer@kramerlevin.com

**Electronic Discovery:**
**Contact:** Norman C Simon **Tel:** 212 715 7816
**Email:** nsimon@kramerlevin.com
**Contact:** Brendan M Schulman **Tel:** 212 715 9247
**Email:** bschulman@kramerlevin.com

**Employee Benefits:**
**Contact:** Christine Lutgens **Tel:** 212 715 9426
**Email:** clutgens@kramerlevin.com

**Employment Law:**
**Contact:** Kevin B Leblang **Tel:** 212 715 9306
**Email:** kleblang@kramerlevin.com

**Environmental:**
**Contact:** Charles S Warren **Tel:** 212 715 9387
**Email:** cwarren@kramerlevin.com

**Financial Services:**
**Contact:** Carl Frischling **Tel:** 212 715 7520
**Email:** cfrischling@kramerlevin.com
**Contact:** Susan J Penry-Williams **Tel:** 212 715 7510
**Email:** spenrywilliams@kramerlevin.com

**Individual Clients:**
**Contact:** John C Novogrod **Tel:** 212 715 9327
**Email:** jnovogrod@kramerlevin.com
**Contact:** Cheryl E Hader **Tel:** 212 715 9245
**Email:** chader@kramerlevin.com

**Intellectual Property:**
**Contact:** Peter A Abruzzese **Tel:** 212 715 7576
**Email:** pabruzzese@kramerlevin.com
**Contact:** Jonathan S Caplan **Tel:** 212 715 9488
**Email:** jcaplan@kramerlevin.com

**Land Use:**
**Contact:** Paul D Selver **Tel:** 212 715 9199
**Email:** pselver@kramerlevin.com
**Contact:** Michael T Sillerman **Tel:** 212 715 7838
**Email:** msillerman@kramerlevin.com

**Litigation:**
**Contact:** Gary P Naftalis **Tel:** 212 715 9253
**Email:** gnaftalis@kramerlevin.com

**Mergers & Acquisitions/Joint Ventures:**
**Contact:** Thomas E Molner **Tel:** 212 715  9429
**Email:** tmolner@kramerlevin.com
**Contact:** Howard T Spilko **Tel:** 212 715  9267
**Email:** hspilko@kramerlevin.com

**Private Equity & Hedge Funds:**
**Contact:** Thomas T Janover **Tel:** 212 715 9186
**Email:** tjanover@kramerlevin.com
**Contact:** Howard T Spilko **Tel:** 212 715 9267
**Email:** hspilko@kramerlevin.com

**Real Estate:**
**Contact:** Michael P Korotkin **Tel:** 212 715 9155
**Email:** mkorotkin@kramerlevin.com
**Contact:** Jay A Neveloff **Tel:** 212 715 9290
**Email:** jneveloff@kramerlevin.com

**Securities & Shareholder Litigation:**
**Contact:** Gary P Naftalis **Tel:** 212 715 9253
**Email:** gnaftalis@kramerlevin.com
**Contact:** Alan R Friedman **Tel:** 212 715 9300
**Email:** afriedman@kramerlevin.com

**Securitization:**
**Contact:** Gilbert Liu **Tel:** 212 715 9460
**Email:** gliu@kramerlevin.com
**Contact:** Laurence Pettit **Tel:** 212 715 9458
**Email:** lpettit@kramerlevin.com
**Contact:** Richard D Rudder **Tel:** 212 715 9470
**Email:** rrudder@kramerlevin.com

**Tax:**
**Contact:** Howard J Rothman **Tel:** 212 715 9242
**Email:** hrothman@kramerlevin.com

**White Collar Defense:**
**Contact:** Gary P Naftalis **Tel:** 212 715 9253
**Email:** gnaftalis@kramerlevin.com
**Contact:** Barry H Berke **Tel:** 212 715 7560
**Email:** bberke@kramerlevin.com

# LABATON SUCHAROW LLP

www.labaton.com **tel:** 212 907 0700 **fax:** 212 818 0477

**Chairman:** Lawrence A Sucharow
Number of partners: 23  Number of lawyers: 70

## Firm Overview:

In its 50 year history, Labaton Sucharow has established a position as comprehensively representing businesses, institutional investors and consumers in complex securities, antitrust and transactional litigation. Whether in the courtroom or the boardroom, Wall Street to Main Street, the more than 70 Labaton Sucharow lawyers are tenacious advocates for their clients, combining superb legal skill with a simple desire to do the right thing. The team is further differentiated by sophisticated financial analysts, e-discovery specialists, investigators and forensic accountants with notable federal and state law enforcement experience. This bench strength ensures that we initiate strong cases and enhance our technical skills with every available resource. The entire team supports the firm's founding principle: 'bring integrity to our work and use our work to bring integrity to the market.'

## Main Areas of Practice:

### Securities Litigation:

In the area of securities fraud, the firm has won precedent-setting decisions and significant monetary recoveries for its clients. In the past year alone, the team secured nearly $1.5 billion in settlements in some of the largest securities class actions in history. The team continues to prosecute actions stemming from the financial crisis, including Goldman Sachs, Morgan Stanley and Fannie Mae. In addition, the firm has established a residential mortgage-backed securities (RMBS) team currently prosecuting more than 50 separate and unique litigations – representing large global institutional investors that invested almost $14 billion in failed investments that were at the heart of the global economic crisis. The firm is also leading the charge in major matters including Facebook, MF Global, Massey Energy and Computer Sciences Corporation.

- In re American International Group Securities Litigation – More than $1 billon total recovery, including a $725 million settlement with AIG
- In re Schering Plough/Enhance Securities Litigation – The $473 million settlement is the largest securities class action settlement ever against a pharmaceutical company, among the all time top 25 securities class action settlements, and ten largest recoveries ever in a securities class action that did not involve a defendant company restating its earnings
- In re Bear Stearns Companies Securities Litigation – $275 million settlement with Bear Stearns/additional $19.9 million settlement with their outside auditor, Deloitte & Touche LLP

**Contact:** Lawrence A Sucharow  **Tel:** 212 907 0860
**Email:** lsucharow@labaton.com

### Antitrust & Competition Litigation:

As commerce grows increasingly more global, the firm is equally active in the antitrust arena on behalf of clients damaged by anti-competitive conduct.

- In re Air Cargo Shipping Services Antitrust Litigation – $490.5 million in partial settlements from a number of international airlines
- In re Aftermarket Automotive Lighting Products Antitrust Litigation – $25.25 million partial settlement with manufacturer of aftermarket autolights

**Contact:** Gregory Asciolla  **Tel:** 212 907 0827
**Email:** gasciolla@labaton.com

### M&A Litigation & Derivative Litigation:

As corporate leaders continue to engage in fraudulent conduct and other mechanisms to unjustly enrich themselves, the firm initiates numerous derivative and M&A-related suits to protect shareholders.

- In re El Paso Corporation Shareholder Litigation – $110 million recovery for shareholders and one of the largest shareholder settlements to come out of the Delaware Court of Chancery. A stipulation in the settlement also prevented Goldman Sachs' $20 million fee for its work on the merger, a condition pursued adamantly by the firm to encourage banks in future deals to take proper steps to reduce conflicts of interest
- In re Barnes & Noble Stockholders Derivative Litigation – $29 million benefit to B&N shareholders

**Contact:** Christine S Azar  **Tel:** 302 573 2530
**Email:** cazar@labaton.com

### Whistleblower Representation Practice:

Lawyers also bring their litigation expertise to the firm's Whistleblower Representation Practice which represents whistleblowers that have original information about violations of the federal securities laws. The practice, chaired by Jordan A Thomas, a 16 year veteran of the US federal government, plays a critical role in exposing otherwise hidden securities fraud and creating the opportunity for necessary corporate reforms. Jordan played a leadership role at the Securities and Exchange Commission (SEC) in the development and finalization of the agency's whistleblower program, which provides significant employment protections and monetary

## PRACTICE AREAS

Securities Litigation
Antitrust & Competition Litigation
Financial Products & Services Litigation
Corporate Governance & Shareholder Rights Litigation
Mergers & Acquisitions Litigation
Derivative Litigation
REITS & Limited Partnerships Litigation
Consumer Litigation
Whistleblower Representation Practice

## OFFICES

NEW YORK

**NEW YORK:** 140 Broadway, New York, NY 10005
Tel: 212 907 0700  Fax: 212 818 0477
Email: info@labaton.com

DELAWARE

**WILMINGTON:** 300 Delaware Avenue, Suite 1225, DE 19801
Tel: 302 573 2540  Fax: 302 573 2529
Email: info@labaton.com

incentives to individuals who provide the SEC with original information about possible violations of the federal securities laws.

**Contact:** Jordan A Thomas  **Tel:** 212 907 0836
**Email:** jthomas@labaton.com

### International Work:

In recent years, as class, group and collective actions for securities fraud have increasingly been filed in jurisdictions around the world, the firm has been at the forefront of a movement to educate investors regarding these new opportunities for recovery outside the US. As one of the first law firms to develop a dedicated International Litigation group, comprised of experienced attorneys, investigators, financial analysts, and data analysts, Labaton Sucharow is uniquely positioned to advise and represent worldwide shareholders in complex investment-related litigation taking place in the EU, US, Asia, Australia, and developing jurisdictions. The team develops a comprehensive view of the potential upsides and risks of participation in each action – resulting in timely advice, encompassing all financial and legal concerns of individual clients. The firm is currently monitoring approximately 30 cases worldwide and are serving as counsel or liaison counsel for clients in cases in Europe, Asia, and Canada. The firm's international client base includes pension funds and their asset managers in the UK, Ireland, Sweden, the Netherlands, Denmark, Norway, Italy, France, and Germany.

# LANKLER SIFFERT & WOHL LLP

www.lswlaw.com **tel:** 212 921 8399 **fax:** 212 764 3701

**OFFICES**

**NEW YORK:** 500 Fifth Avenue, 33rd Floor, 10110
Tel: 212 921 8399 Fax: 212 764 3701

Number of partners: 9
Number of counsel: 4
Number of associates: 14

### Firm Overview:

Lankler Siffert & Wohl LLP concentrates in litigation and dispute resolution. The firm represents individuals and entities in civil, regulatory and whitecollar criminal matters before state and federal courts and grand juries, administrative and regulatory agencies, arbitration panels and professional disciplinary boards. The firm's nine partners have substantial experience in the management of complex litigation in commercial and criminal matters. Six of the nine partners are also former prosecutors, and the partners collectively have tried more than 100 cases. In addition, no attorney is hired by the firm unless he or she possesses superior academic credentials and prior legal experience either through a judicial clerkship, practice at another firm or government service. As a result, Lankler Siffert & Wohl LLP is able to offer superior and cost-effective representation, regardless of whether the matter is simple or complex, and regardless of whether it is in the civil, regulatory or criminal arena.

### Main Areas of Practice

#### Corporate & Securities:

LS&W has defended corporations, underwriters, corporate executives and directors in civil, regulatory and criminal matters arising out of securities offerings, mergers, restructurings and other transactions. LS&W also has pursued securities claims on behalf of institutional investors and other market participants. The firm's practice has caused it to become familiar with a wide variety of primary and derivative financial instruments traded on domestic and foreign exchanges, as well as privately between and among market participants. The firm has also defended accounting professionals, traders, and hedge fund operators, and executives in a variety of tax and securities matters.

#### Banking:

LS&W has defended banks and bankers in civil, regulatory and criminal matters involving claims of fraud, money laundering, RICO violations, violations of Federal banking laws and lender liability. These include matters pending in courts and grand juries, as well as in the offices of banking regulators, including the New York Office of the Federal Reserve, and the Office of Thrift Supervision. The firm also has pursued commercial claims on behalf of banks and their administrators or receivers.

#### Internal Investigations:

LS&W has represented public and private corporations, corporate boards of directors and special committees, non-profit institutions and other entities in conducting internal investigations. These investigations have covered accounting, securities trading, corporate governance, tax, and compliance with various criminal laws, regulatory requirements including OFAC and FCPA and best practices. In addition, LS&W has advised clients on preventive measures and corporate compliance and training programs. LS&W has also represented individuals who are subjects of internal investigations.

#### General Commercial:

LS&W has handled disputes involving a wide variety of commercial transactions, including syndicated bank financings, mergers, acquisitions, reorganizations and squeeze-outs involving public and private corporations, not-for-profit organizations, joint ventures and partnerships. LS&W has also handled disputes involving theatrical ventures, real estate transactions and insurance coverage.

#### Antitrust:

LS&W has defended corporations and corporate executives, both in the United States and abroad, in civil suits alleging violations of the antitrust laws and in criminal prosecutions by the Antitrust Division of the

Department of Justice. The industries have involved US Treasury securities, the auction house business, automotive parts, guaranteed investment contracts/municipal bonds, vitamins, graphite electrodes, industrial equipment and consumer goods.

#### Professional Practice:

LS&W has represented law firms, individual attorneys and accountants in many contexts, including investigations conducted by the SEC and banking regulators, criminal investigations, professional disciplinary matters, civil malpractice suits, sanctions motions and law firm dissolutions.

#### Alternative Dispute Resolution:

LS&W partners have acted as arbitrators, mediators and counsel in both domestic and international arbitrations.

#### International Organisations:

LS&W has represented a major international organization and individuals associated with that organization in matters involving the United States legal system.

# MORRISON & FOERSTER LLP

www.mofo.com **tel:** 212 468 8000 **fax:** 212 468 7900

**Chair of the Firm:** Larren M Nashelsky
**Managing Partners:** Craig D Martin, Eric Piesner, Anna Erickson White
Number of partners worldwide: 365 Number of US partners: 291
Number of other lawyers worldwide: 735 Number of other US lawyers: 579

## Firm Overview:

With more than 1,000 lawyers in 16 offices, Morrison & Foerster is a preeminent global law firm dedicated to delivering business-oriented results to clients across the United States, Europe and Asia. Dynamic technology and life science companies, large financial institutions, leading consumer product companies and other market leaders come to MoFo for knowledge, innovation and business aptitude. MoFo handles some of the world's largest cross-border transactions and resolves major disputes across multiple jurisdictions. The firm has a long-standing commitment to pro bono work and social justice.

## Main Areas of Practice:

### Antitrust & Competition:
The firm's global antitrust lawyers are recognized leaders who resolve complex antitrust cases through dispositive motions, but are capable of taking any case to trial. They draw on a deep well of experience to obtain successful results in criminal investigations and merger reviews.

### Business Restructuring & Insolvency:
MoFo is counsel to debtors, creditors' committees, secured lenders and other participants in the distressed markets in large, complex matters. The firm is a market leader in the restructuring of financial institutions, cross-border insolvencies, distressed real estate, creditors' committee representation, insolvencies involving key intellectual property and hedge fund failures.

### Capital Markets:
The firm is a pioneer in developing synthetic products, hybrid securities, structured products and derivatives. MoFo ranks as one of the leading firms for issuer and underwriter representations for initial public offerings, international offerings, REIT offerings, as well as offerings of debt, hybrid, preferred and structured securities. The firm advises in connection with private placements, PIPEs, IPOs, 144A/Reg S offerings, continuous issuance programs, including MTN, CP and covered bond programs.

### Financial Services:
MoFo has one of the most recognized and most experienced banking and financial services regulatory practices in the United States, with more than five decades of work in the field. The firm represents domestic and foreign banks, credit card and other payment systems companies, savings associations, industrial loan companies and other financial services organisations.

### Finance:
The firm's financial transactions practice provides a wide range of services to both lenders and borrowers, with leading lawyers in finance, investment management, debt trading and infrastructure finance. The firm handles virtually every type of real and personal property secured and unsecured financing transaction.

### Intellectual Property:
MoFo has one of the largest and highest-rated intellectual property practices in the world. The firm provides a full range of services, including counseling, prosecution, litigation, dispute resolution, trade secrets and licensing transactions in patent, trademark and copyright matters.

### Litigation:
The firm's litigators are renowned for their success in high-stakes, complex cases worldwide. MoFo has some of the top trial and appellate lawyers in the United States, as well as leading practitioners in antitrust, securities, white-collar criminal defense, products liability, class action defense, unfair competition, employment, financial services, international arbitration, intellectual property, trade secrets and patents. The firm is noted for its US Supreme Court and appellate practice. MoFo is the only international law firm in Japan with a full-service litigation capacity.

### Mergers & Acquisitions:
Morrison & Foerster has a leading global M&A practice. The depth and breadth of the practice, including a strong focus on cross-border transactions, reflects the dynamic nature of clients, which include Fortune 500 companies, private equity sponsors, investment banks and privately held companies. Lawyers work as an integrated team with colleagues with deep experience in key areas such as IP, antitrust, litigation, tax, labor and benefits, finance and bankruptcy, real estate, environmental law and securities.

### Project Finance & Development:
The firm's project finance lawyers assist clients in all aspects of the development, construction, financing, restructuring and purchase and sale of infrastructure projects around the world with a focus on energy, alternative energy and renewable resources. They also provide political risk insurance counseling.

### Real Estate:
MoFo is a recognized leader across a broad spectrum of real estate activities, including development deals, acquisitions and dispositions, leases, market standard and complex financings and restructurings. Its clients include lenders, developers, equity investors and REITs.

### Tax:
MoFo's tax practice enjoys a global reputation for innovative tax planning and the successful resolution of important tax controversies. The group advises on state and local tax, federal tax, compensation, benefits and ERISA, and trusts, estates and nonprofit organizations.

## PRACTICE AREAS

Antitrust & Competition
Business Restructuring & Insolvency
Capital Markets
Cleantech
Corporate
Employment & Labor
Energy
Financial Services
Financial Transactions
Intellectual Property
Investment Management
Land Use & Environmental
Life Sciences
Litigation, Arbitration, Trials, Appeals & Supreme Court
Mergers & Acquisitions
Privacy & Data Security
Product Liability
Project Finance & Development
Real Estate
Tax
Technology Transactions

## OFFICES

**NEW YORK**
**NEW YORK:** 1290 Avenue of the Americas, NY 10104-0050
Tel: 212 468 8000 Fax: 212 468 7900
Email: info@mofo.com Website: www.mofo.com

**CALIFORNIA**
**SAN FRANCISCO:** 425 Market Street, CA 94105-2482
Tel: 415 268 7000 Fax: 415 268 7522

**DISTRICT OF COLUMBIA**
**WASHINGTON, DC:** 2000 Pennsylvania Avenue, NW, Suite 5500, DC 20006-1888
Tel: 202 887 1500 Fax: 202 887 0763

The firm also has offices in Denver, Los Angeles, Northern Virginia, Palo Alto, Sacramento and San Diego

## INTERNATIONAL OFFICES

The firm has offices in Beijing, Brussels, Hong Kong, London, Shanghai, Singapore and Tokyo.

**MORRISON | FOERSTER**

# MORVILLO ABRAMOWITZ GRAND IASON & ANELLO P.C.

**www.**maglaw.com **tel:** 212 856 9600 **fax:** 212 856 9494

**Senior Partner:** Elkan Abramowitz
Number of partners: 18
Number of lawyers: 42
Languages: *English*

## Firm Overview:

Morvillo Abramowitz has helped institutional and individual clients with complex white collar matters and sophisticated business disputes for nearly 40 years and on a scale that is unique in the US legal market. As a litigation boutique the firm is best known for its unmatched depth of experience in white collar defense, government investigations, securities enforcement, and regulatory matters. An important part of the firm's practice is sophisticated civil litigation for a diverse group of clients – both plaintiffs and defendants.

## Main Areas of Practice:

### White Collar Defense:

Morvillo Abramowitz regularly represents corporate and individual clients in inquiries and investigations by federal authorities, the Department of Justice, state attorneys general, local prosecutors, and in all stages of white collar criminal litigation in federal, state, and local courts.

The firm litigates cases at all levels of the federal and state courts, in arbitration, and before government agencies, regulatory organizations and other tribunals. Notable success has also been achieved in convincing the government not to indict identified grand jury targets, thereby also helping individuals and corporations avoid criminal charges altogether. Where there is an indictment, the firm is often able to obtain favorable pretrial dispositions. Morvillo Abramowitz lawyers understand that every step of a case requires their full attention and effort, and that pretrial preparation and strategy are as important to a successful defense as masterful courtroom representation. Similarly, in civil disputes, the ability and the willingness to try high-stakes cases often helps Morvillo Abramowitz to achieve advantageous settlements without trial.

Institutional clients often retain the firm to conduct sensitive internal investigations aimed at uncovering or resolving allegations of officer, director, trustee, or employee misconduct both in the Untied States and globally. The firm's lawyers are frequently selected to lead court-appointed independent monitorships or are appointed to government-approved positions as corporate integrity counsel as conditions of settling criminal prosecutions or as terms of deferred-prosecution or non-prosecution agreements with Federal and state prosecutors.

Over the past several years, Morvillo Abramowitz has been heavily involved in investigations and litigation relating to insider trading, Foreign Corrupt Practices Act (FCPA) enforcement, options backdating, revenue recognition and accounting restatements, the Madoff scandal, the sale of CDOs and other structured products impacted by the global financial crisis, commodities-related trading, auction rate securities, tax shelters, unreported foreign banking activity, and alleged abuses by market participants at the New York Stock Exchange and other national exchanges. Cases frequently focus on economic crime, as well as complex matters concerning allegations of environmental offenses; customs, insurance, and health care fraud; violations of the False Claims Act and federal and state antitrust laws; and theft of intellectual property, bribery, and political corruption. Morvillo Abramowitz is also well-known for its appellate proficiency and regularly handles complex high-stakes civil and criminal appeals before federal and state courts throughout the nation, often retained to work on appeals for clients who were represented in the lower courts by other law firms.

### Securities Enforcement & Government Investigations:

With substantial expertise in securities litigation and regulatory enforcement proceedings, Morvillo Abramowitz lawyers are frequently called upon to handle most types of government inquiries, investigations, and enforcement actions. The firm regularly represents individuals and companies under investigation or charged in enforcement actions; the issues in these proceedings range from insider trading to options backdating, stock manipulation, and improper sales practices, and from complex accounting questions to misrepresentations and omissions in sales materials.

The firm frequently handles matters for individual and corporate clients in parallel investigations with the Securities and Exchange Commission, the Commodity Futures Trading Commission, the Financial Industry Regulatory Authority (FINRA), the US Department of Justice, state regulatory agencies, Congressional committees, and state law enforcement officials. Many of the firm's lawyers have served as prosecutors and senior government advisors. Morvillo Abramowitz is called upon by financial institutions and their affiliates; securities brokerage firms, investment managers, and traders; hedge funds and hedge fund managers; and public corporations and their officers and directors to provide advice in advance of, or at the early stages of, probes by federal and state regulators. The firm's lawyers have the in-depth knowledge to navigate and guide a client through the scrutiny and the experience to negotiate settlements that achieve favorable results. While well known for its high-profile representations, many of the firm's greatest successes over the years have been for clients who never become known to the public.

### Civil Litigation:

The firm litigates a wide variety of high-profile and complex civil disputes, drawing on its reputation and skills as trial attorneys to achieve the best results for the client regardless of whether the case ultimately goes to trial.

Morvillo Abramowitz represents a wide range of clients, including prominent financial institutions, public and private companies and their officers and directors, accounting firms, insurance companies, smaller organizations such as law firms and partnerships, and individuals, including professional representations on matters often affecting a client's livelihood, reputation, license or right to practice. The firm regularly handles matters in highly specialized areas, including securities laws; antitrust; employment discrimination; copyright, trademark, and trade secret disputes; and RICO, as well as complex commercial disputes involving claims of fraud, breach of contract, breach of fiduciary duty and other business torts, and partnership disputes.

## PRACTICE AREAS

Appellate
Commercial Litigation
Government Investigations
Internal Investigations
Monitorships, Integrity Counsel & Compliance
Professional Representations
Regulatory Enforcement & Securities Litigation
Securities & Financial Services Litigation
White Collar Criminal Defense

## OFFICES

NEW YORK

**NEW YORK:** 565 Fifth Avenue, NY 10017
Tel: 212 856 9600   Fax: 212 856 9494
Email: info@maglaw.com

Morvillo
Abramowitz

Morvillo Abramowitz Grand Iason & Anello PC

# MOUND COTTON WOLLAN & GREENGRASS

**www.**moundcotton.com **tel:** 212 804 4200 **fax:** 212 344 8066

Number of partners: 39
Number of other lawyers: 48

### Firm Overview:

Founded in 1933 and based in New York's financial district, Mound Cotton Wollan & Greengrass is primarily engaged in insurance, reinsurance and commercial litigation and arbitration. The firm also has a growing corporate, securities and commodities practice.

### Main Areas of Practice:

**Insurance & Reinsurance:**

Mound Cotton's focus throughout its 80-year history has been to provide counsel to insurers, reinsurers and other companies in the insurance world on major commercial issues involving contract interpretation, coverage and the various other types of questions that arise in the context of the business of insurance and reinsurance. A major portion of the firm's work has been acting for insurers and reinsurers in complex litigation and arbitration.

Mound Cotton represents reinsureds, reinsurers, intermediaries, pool managers, managing general agencies, underwriters, liquidators, and others with interests in the reinsurance market. Clients are based in the United States, the United Kingdom, Europe, , and other foreign jurisdictions.

The firm is knowledgeable concerning the nature and operations of insurance markets throughout the world, and has considerable experience dealing with insurer and reinsurer insolvencies, as well as specialised classes of business such as environmental, business interruption and other time element, terrorism and war risk, professional indemnity/ errors and omissions, and residual value, efficacy, and performance and other financial guaranty.

### Commercial Litigation:

Mound Cotton's attorneys practice regularly in federal and state courts and before arbitration panels and administrative agencies throughout the United States and the United Kingdom as well as elsewhere abroad. The work includes trials, appeals, hearings, bankruptcy/ creditors' rights proceedings, and mediation/alternative dispute resolution.

### Corporate/Insurance Regulatory:

Mound Cotton is involved in the formation, domestication, and redomestication of insurance and reinsurance companies operating in the property and casualty as well as life, health and accident arenas, for its own clients and as counsel to other law firms. The firm represents individuals and companies in hearings before state insurance and other administrative and regulatory agencies and exchanges. Mound Cotton is also experienced in both the P & C and life arenas in ART transactions, securitization of risk, and other financial vehicles currently utilized by insurers and reinsurers to manage their liabilities/risk portfolios and reserves.

The firm's corporate attorneys are well grounded in statutory and regulatory law and procedure, and thoroughly familiar with the agencies that oversee the activities of insurers, reinsurers, agents, and intermediaries. Their expertise is available to the firm's reinsurance attorneys and is regularly utilized in a wide variety of litigated and arbitrated matters.

### Corporate/Business:

Mound Cotton's work includes counseling clients in corporate matters, both domestic and foreign, such as corporate formation, shareholders' agreements, contract negotiations, employment agreements, distributorships, regulatory and compliance issues, licensing, mergers and acquisitions, managed buyouts, tender offers, restructurings, joint ventures and partnerships, and intellectual property. Clients include telecommunications, computer software, healthcare, venture capital, internet technology, and private investment companies, as well as hedge funds, commodities exchanges and clearing organizations, securities and commodities brokerages, broker/dealers, floor brokers and floor traders, investment advisory firms, commodity pool operators, commodity trading advisors, and labor organizations.

### International Work:

The firm represents insurers, reinsurers, intermediaries, managing agents, pools, and other insurance-related concerns in litigated matters throughout the world, as well as in international arbitrations. Together with local counsel, the firm has acted for clients in the United Kingdom, Bermuda, Canada, Germany, Spain, Italy, Greece, Australia, and Trinidad.

**OFFICES**

NEW YORK

**NEW YORK:** One Battery Park Plaza, NY 10004
Tel: 212 804 4200 Fax: 212 344 8066

**NEW YORK:** 855 Franklin Avenue, Garden City, NY 11530
Tel: 516 417 5700 Fax: 516 741 6831

FLORIDA

**FORT LAUDERDALE:** 101 NE 3rd Avenue, Suite 1500,
FL33301
Tel: 954 467 5800 Fax: 954 467 5880

NEW JERSEY

**NEWARK:** 60 Park Place, NJ 07102
Tel: 973 494 0600 Fax: 973 242 4244

# OLSHAN FROME WOLOSKY LLP

**www.**olshanlaw.com **tel:** 212 451 2300 **fax:** 212 451 2222

**Co-Administrative Partners of the Executive Committee:** Steven R Gursky, Nina Roket
Number of partners: 40   Number of other lawyers: 39

**OFFICES**

NEW YORK

**NEW YORK:** 65 East 55th Street, Park Avenue Tower, NY 10022
Tel: 212 451 2300   Fax: 212 451 2222

## Firm Overview:

Olshan, a law firm based in New York, represents major businesses and entrepreneurs in their most significant transactions, problems and opportunities. Olshan's clients range from public companies, hedge, venture capital, private equity and other investment funds to entrepreneurs and private companies worldwide. Clients choose Olshan for innovative strategies and sophisticated, game-changing advice in corporate, securities law and shareholder activism, complex commercial, corporate and securities litigation, real estate, intellectual property, bankruptcy and creditors' rights, and advertising. Since its founding, Olshan has offered an alternative to the AmLaw 50 law firm business model with responsive, independent and client-focused legal counsel provided by the firm's senior lawyers.

## Main Areas of Practice:

### Corporate/Securities Law:

Olshan's Corporate and Securities Law group provides experienced and creative counsel to public and private issuers, underwriters, venture capital firms and others in a variety of capital-raising transactions. Clients regularly call upon the Corporate and Securities Law group for our expertise in negotiating mergers and acquisitions, credit facilities and other loan transactions, venture capital financings, buyouts and "going private" transactions, navigating contested proxy solicitations, forming, organizing and advising venture capital, hedge fund and private equity partnerships and other matters requiring sophisticated knowledge of the complex federal and state securities and other laws affecting businesses.

### Activist Practice:

Olshan's Activist group is widely recognized as the nation's premier practice in representing activist investors in contested director elections. Lawyers in the Activist group have been involved in seeking Board representation at over 300 public companies. The Activist group counsels clients on a wide variety of activist strategies, from proxy contests, consent solicitations and hostile takeovers to letter-writing campaigns and behind-the-scenes discussions with management and boards of directors.

### Litigation:

The Litigation group represents funds, banks and other investors involving securities fraud allegations, broker-dealer disputes, lending, and contests for corporate control. Additionally, the group includes former prosecutors who maintain a white collar defense and whistleblower practice and general commercial litigators involved in a wide array of business and contract disputes involving software development, sales of businesses, sale of goods, executive raiding, real estate, partnership, restrictive covenants, licensing, trademark and copyright.

### Real Estate Law:

The Real Estate Law attorneys have particular experience serving clients in the areas of major office buildings, including purchases, sales, financings, space leasing and ground leasing of office buildings, hotels and development sites, retail leasing, where we represent major brand retailers in leasing retail space in Manhattan and across the US, and real estate joint ventures. Across the nation and particularly in and around New York, the firm's expertise has garnered it a reputation for having an in-depth knowledge of the industry, providing creativity, diligence and quality service with cost sensitivity.

### Bankruptcy & Financial Restructuring:

The attorneys in the Bankruptcy and Financial Restructuring group represent or have represented creditors, creditors' committees, debtors, trustees, bondholders, secured creditors and lenders, landlords and buyers and sellers of distressed assets and debt or equity positions in out-of-court restructurings as well as in-court insolvency cases. The firm represents litigants in complex litigation, including fraudulent conveyance, director and officer liability, preference and other commercial disputes involving financially distressed businesses.

### Intellectual Property Law:

The Intellectual Property Law group offers expert counsel and litigation capabilities to enable businesses and individuals to establish, protect and exploit their trademarks, copyrights and trade secrets. The trademark practice is particularly extensive. The firm represents clients in contested proceedings before trademark offices domestically and internationally, and initiates litigation worldwide when necessary. Olshan attorneys are highly experienced in obtaining and opposing trademark registrations, enforcing trademarks and defending clients in trademark matters, and in counseling and litigating a wide range of trade secret and unfair competition matters. Firm copyright attorneys offer significant experience in enforcing copyrights and defending against charges of copyright violation.

### Advertising, Marketing & Promotions:

The Advertising, Marketing & Promotions group's attorneys are focused on serving the advertising, Internet, and promotional marketing industries. Whether utilizing the latest in new digital technology to conduct a sweepstakes, incorporating social media into a campaign, or delivering their message through traditional media channels, clients rely on the group for innovative and proactive legal advice that allows them to market effectively. The group's attorneys are nationally recognized by client- and peer-reviewed rating groups for their abilities and effectiveness in the advertising and promotional marketing law practice areas.

### Tax & Personal Planning:

Olshan's Tax & Personal Planning group provides skilled and sophisticated tax and financial planning services to corporations, partnerships/llcs and other business entities, high net worth individuals, families and fiduciaries of complex estates and trusts.

### Employment Practices:

The Employment Practices group assists employers in managing their relationships with employees and independent contractors, including preparation of employment contracts, investigations into allegations of discrimination and harassment, counsel on workplace testing and FCRA compliance, and training on employment law.

### Employee Benefits:

The Employee Benefits group meets the challenges employers face in connection with the compensation of employees and the planning and administration of employee benefits. The Group assists in the design and drafting of all forms of executive compensation plans, arrangements and programs. We have extensive experience in designing and drafting all types of change in control agreements, retention agreements and severance agreements.

### Insurance Coverage Law:

The Insurance Coverage Law group assists insurers and insureds on coverage issues relating to insurance obligations including directors and officers, general liability, commercial property, commercial crime, benefit plans, employment practices, and other forms of insurance.

O L S H A N

# ORRICK HERRINGTON & SUTCLIFFE LLP

www.orrick.com  **tel:** 415 773 5700

**Chairman:** Mitch Zuklie
Number of lawyers worldwide: 1,100   Number of lawyers USA: 760

## Firm Overview:

Orrick is a global law firm with a particular focus on serving companies in the technology, energy and financial sectors. Recognized by Law360 as one of the "Global 20" leading firms, Orrick offers clients a distinctive combination of local insight and consistent global quality across 25 offices. Orrick's lawyers are known for their extraordinary record of wins in high-stakes disputes and for delivering commercially oriented advice on sophisticated transactions. Twice selected by Financial Times as one of the most innovative US law firms, Orrick is recognized for innovation in both client advice and client service. Collaboration-one of the firm's core values-defines the firm's relationships with its clients, among its lawyers and staff, and with its communities.

## Main Areas of Practice:

### Corporate:

- Represented Yammer in its US$1.2 billion acquisition by Microsoft, Instagram in its US$1 billion acquisition by Facebook and Par Pharmaceutical in its US$1.9 billion acquisition by TPG—three of the largest private company acquisitions of 2012
- Represents more than 1,200 emerging companies from Silicon Valley to New York to London to Munich to Beijing at all stages of growth in the cloud computing, gaming, social networking, clean tech, internet and life sciences sectors
- Represented Shutterstock in its NYSE IPO
- Advised Exxaro Resources on the US$3.4 billion combination of its South African and Australian mineral sands operations with the US, Dutch and Australian businesses of Tronox

**Contact:** King Milling
**Email:** kmilling@orrick.com

### Energy & Infrastructure:

- Advising on all of the major transport PPP projects under way in the United States, including the US$1.5 billion financing of the Midtown Tunnel in Virginia; the US$1.1 billion Presidio Parkway project in San Francisco; and the US$935 million I-95 express lanes project in Virginia
- Represented Spanish wind turbine manufacturer Gamesa in a US$888 million wind project
- Advised Recurrent Energy in its sale of four photovoltaic facilities to Google and KKR
- Advised Tennessee Valley Authority on its innovative US$1 billion lease-purchase financing of the John Sevier power plant

**Contact:** Dan Mathews
**Email:** dmathews@orrick.com
**Contact:** Michael Meyers
**Email:** mmeyers@orrick.com

### Finance:

- Ranked No.1 US municipal bond counsel for more than a decade and serves as underwriters' counsel to the most active investment banks in the market; helped the State of California and its agencies to raise more than US$18 billion in 2012, and helped the Port Authority to raise US$3 billion for the redevelopment of New York's World Trade Center site
- Advised the cities of Vallejo and Stockton, California, on their Chapter 9 filings
- Represented Wells Fargo Bank in connection with restructuring the debt of the two largest casino properties in North America: the Foxwoods Resort Casino and the Mohegan Sun
- Represented Barclays Bank Delaware in the establishment of the first new major US credit card master trust in nearly a decade; represented Redwood Trust in all of its pioneering public offerings of private-label MBS since the financial crisis began
- Advised many of the nation's most active real estate investors, including Westbrook Partners, Walton Street Capital, RREEF, Hackman Capital and Colony Capital, in transactions totaling more than US$6 billion in 2012

**Contact:** David Syed
**Email:** dsyed@orrick.com
**Contact:** Howard Altarescu
**Email:** haltarescu@orrick.com

### Intellectual Property:

- Defended Apple in the smartphone battle with S3 Graphics before the ITC—a result that Corporate Counsel selected as the No.1 IP win of the year
- Worked with international law enforcement to help Microsoft dismantle four of the world's largest botnets, introducing new tactics for combating cybercrime
- On behalf of NVIDIA, achieved a successful settlement (including a licensing agreement) with Rambus involving a complex series of patent and antitrust disputes
- Prevailed before the ITC on behalf of Nintendo, defeating a patent infringement claim relating to the Wii system—Financial Times cited this as one of the most innovative client results of 2012
- Secured a victory for Dow AgroSciences in litigation brought by Bayer with respect to genetically modified plant patents
- Representing DISH Network in a copyright infringement battle brought by Fox and other networks relating to DISH's AutoHop DVR feature

**Contact:** Neel Chatterjee
**Email:** nchatterjee@orrick.com
**Contact:** Steve Routh
**Email:** srouth@orrick.com

### Litigation:

- In 2012, American Lawyer named Orrick among the nation's top litigation departments for the second consecutive time and named Josh Rosenkranz, head of Orrick's Supreme Court & Appellate Practice, Litigator of the Year
- Defending Barclays, Credit Suisse, Ally Financial and Nomura in RMBS and related litigation arising from the financial crisis
- Representing Sony in connection with insurance coverage claims arising out of cyber attacks on Sony online entertainment networks
- Resolved trade secrets disputes on behalf of senior executives and their employers, including enabling former HP Chairman and CEO Mark Hurd to join Oracle
- Successfully defended 150+ employment class actions on behalf of clients such as Apple, Electronic Arts, McAfee, Sears, Williams-Sonoma and others
- Obtained a complete acquittal for Gregory Godsey in what is described as the largest foreign bribery prosecution in history—the Africa Sting

**Contact:** Steve Foresta
**Email:** sforesta@orrick.com

# PATTERSON BELKNAP WEBB & TYLER LLP

www.pbwt.com **tel:** 212 336 2000 **fax:** 212 336 2222

**Co-Chairs:** William F Cavanaugh, Jr & Robert P LoBue
**Managing Partner:** Robert P LoBue
Number of partners: 55
Number of lawyers: 202

## Firm Overview:

Founded in 1919, Patterson Belknap is a law firm of more than 200 lawyers committed to providing high quality legal advice and service to clients and to maintaining a congenial and diverse workplace. The firm makes its clients' business issues its own. At the same time, it cares about its attorneys, its staff and the community it is privileged to serve. Patterson Belknap delivers a full range of services across more than 20 practice groups in both litigation and commercial law. The firm's clients are diverse: from pharmaceutical and medical device companies to major media and publishing empires; from consumer products companies to financial institutions; from fine art museums to famous entertainers; from foreign companies seeking to transact business on US stock exchanges to US companies doing business abroad.

## Main Areas of Practice:

### Litigation:

- Representing a *Fortune* 500 media company in a corporate espionage suit arising from a major competitor's allegation that the firm's client employed consultants to illegally access a proprietary database
- Representing several institutional investors with respect to their residential mortgage-backed securities transactions (RMBS) claims. These matters relate to dozens of separate RMBS transactions, including investigation and prosecution of billions of dollars in claims against some of the world's largest financial institutions
- On behalf of a major pharmaceutical company, coordinating the defense of approximately 3,500 product liability claims in state and federal court involving a prescription antibiotic
- Represented the world's leading beverage company in an important case of first impression involving the intersection between FDA labeling rules and advertising law. The Ninth Circuit Court of Appeals ruled in the firm's client's favor.

**Key Clients:** The McGraw-Hill Companies, Inc., Johnson & Johnson, Ambac Assurance Corporation
**Contact:** Saul B Shapiro **Tel:** 212 336 2163
**Email:** sbshapiro@pbwt.com

### Intellectual Property:

- Secured more than $3.6 billion for client, a medical device manufacturer, in a long-running series of litigations relating to coronary stents
- Obtained a substantial settlement for an online investment newsletter, in a copyright case prohibiting competitors from redistributing the firm's client's original content.
- Represented a medical device manufacturer accused of infringing a patent for a type of soft contact lens. Obtained a significant victory from a Florida federal jury.

**Key Clients:** Dow Jones & Company, Inc., Abbott Laboratories, Microsoft Corporation
**Contact:** Robert P LoBue **Tel:** 212 336 2596
**Email:** rplobue@pbwt.com

### White-Collar Defense & Investigations:

- Secured Fourth Circuit affirmance of the dismissal of a False Claims Act complaint alleging off-label marketing by a pharmaceutical manufacturer
- Representing one of Europe's largest banks in connection with the Department of Justice and CFTC's investigation into alleged manipulation of LIBOR
- Representing a senior executive of an international retail chain in an investigation by the Department of Justice and Securities and Exchange Commission of alleged Foreign Corrupt Practices Act violations in Mexico and related derivative and shareholder actions

**Key Clients:** Johnson & Johnson, Siemens, Takeda Pharmaceuticals North America, Inc.
**Contact:** Daniel S Ruzumna **Tel:** 212 336 2034
**Email:** druzumna@pbwt.com

### Commercial:

- Acting as tax counsel for a multinational industrial company manufacturer of machine tools for the aerospace, automotive and alternative energy industries
- Represented the independent directors of a New York City hotel in the sale of the hotel that was a part of a greater transaction worth approximately $570 million
- Advised on an offering of unsponsored Global Depositary Notes, representing $7 billion in aggregate principal amount of Mexican peso denominated notes

**Key Clients:** The Durst Organization Inc., Mount Sinai Medical Center, The Winter Organization
**Contact:** Herman H Raspé **Tel:** 212 336 2301
**Email:** hhraspe@pbwt.com

## PRACTICE AREAS

Alternate Dispute Resolution
Anti-Counterfeiting
Antitrust
Appellate
Art & Museum Law
Biotechnology Practice
Business Reorganization & Creditors' Rights
Complex Commercial Actions
Corporate
Cross-Border Transactions
Employee Benefits & Executive Compensation
Employment Law
False Advertising
False Claims Act & Whistleblower Defense
Insurance Coverage
Intellectual Property Litigation
Intellectual Property Transactions
Law Firm Defense
Litigation
Media & Entertainment
Mergers & Acquisitions
Mortgage & Credit Crisis Team
Private Equity
Products Liability
Real Estate
Securities & Derivatives Litigation
Sports
Tax
Tax-Exempt Organizations
Trusts & Estates
White-Collar Defense & Investigations

## OFFICES

NEW YORK

**NEW YORK:** 1133 Avenue of the Americas, NY 10036
Tel: 212 336 2000  Fax: 212 336 2222

**Patterson Belknap Webb & Tyler** LLP

# PAUL HASTINGS LLP

www.paulhastings.com **tel:** 212 318 6000 **fax:** 212 319 4090

**Chairman:** Seth Zachary
**Managing Partner:** Greg Nitzkowski
Number of partners: 284   Number of lawyers: 900

## Firm Overview:

Founded in 1951, Paul Hastings LLP is a leading global law firm with 20 offices throughout Asia, Europe and the US. Paul Hastings has the global reach and capabilities to provide personalized service wherever the clients' needs take it. Through a collaborative approach, entrepreneurial spirit and firm commitment to client service, the professionals of Paul Hastings deliver innovative solutions to many of the world's top financial institutions and *Fortune 500* companies.

## Accolades:

- The Financial Times ranked Paul Hastings among the top three most innovative lawyer firms in the US Innovative Lawyers 2012 report. The firm won in the categories of Litigation, Intellectual Property and the Business of Law
- The firm ranked second in the American Lawyer's prestigious 2012 A-List, which lists the largest and most prominent law firms based in the United States

## Main Areas of Practice:

### Corporate:

The Paul Hastings Corporate practice is globally recognized in virtually every area of corporate transactions, including mergers and acquisitions, public and private equity and debt financings, formation of investment funds, project finance, securitizations, bankruptcy, corporate restructurings and distressed debt trading, venture capital work, technology licensing, and franchising and distribution arrangements.

### Employment:

The Paul Hastings Labor and Employment practice is recognized as one of the largest in its field, with an outstanding record in defending class actions for large multinational companies. The lawyers counsel clients with respect to all areas of employment law including benefits, discrimination, downsizing, employee mobility, harassment, immigration, traditional labor and wage and hour.

### Litigation:

The firm's Litigation practice provides premier litigation services to clients facing complex legal issues in the US, Europe, South America, the Middle East and Asia. The Litigation practice covers every major practice including securities, subprime litigation, intellectual property, class action and employment litigation, international arbitration, Foreign Corrupt Practices Act and white-collar crime.

### Real Estate:

The Paul Hastings Global Real Estate practice covers all areas of real estate finance, sales and acquisitions, private equity, development, hotels and hospitality, leasing, joint ventures, partnerships and limited liability companies, and bankruptcy and restructuring of real estate portfolios. The practice's environmental, planning, construction and real estate litigation expertise is extensive, as is its experience in debt, equity and hybrid investment.

### Tax:

The firm's Global Tax practice covers mergers and acquisitions, capital market offerings, investment and joint venture structuring, leasing, structured and project finance and financial product planning and structuring. It is internationally known as having one of the preeminent tax practices in telecommunications, real estate, executive compensation and tax-exempt and tax-favored investments.

## OFFICES

### GEORGIA

**ATLANTA:** 1170 Peachtree Street, N.E., Suite 100, GA 30309
Tel: 404 815 2400  Fax: 404 815 2424

### ILLINOIS

**CHICAGO:** 191 N. Wacker Drive, Thirtieth Floor, IL 60606
Tel: 312 499 6000  Fax: 312 499 6100

### CALIFORNIA

**LOS ANGELES:** 515 South Flower Street, Twenty-Fifth Floor, CA 90071
Tel: 213 683 6000  Fax: 213 627 0705

**COSTA MESA:** 695 Town Center Drive, Seventeenth Floor, CA 92626
Tel: 714 668 6200  Fax: 714 979 1921

**PALO ALTO:** 1117 S. California Avenue, CA 94304
Tel: 650 320 1800  Fax: 650 320 1900

**SAN DIEGO:** 4747 Executive Drive, Twelfth Floor, CA 92121
Tel: 858 458 3000  Fax: 858 458 3005

**SAN FRANCISCO:** 55 Second Street, Twenty-Fourth Floor, CA 94105
Tel: 415 856 7000  Fax: 415 856 7100

### NEW YORK

**NEW YORK:** 75 East 55th Street, NY 10022
Tel: 212 318 6000  Fax: 212 319 4090

### TEXAS

**HOUSTON:** Wells Fargo Plaza, 1000 Louisiana Street, Suite 5400, Houston, TX 77002
Tel: 713 860 7300  Fax:  713 353 3100

### DISTRICT OF COLUMBIA

**WASHINGTON DC:** 875 15th Street, N.W., DC 20005
Tel: 202 551 1700  Fax: 202 551 1705

## INTERNATIONAL OFFICES

Europe: Brussels, Frankfurt, London, Milan, Paris
Asia: Beijing, Hong Kong, Seoul, Shanghai, Tokyo

# PAUL, WEISS, RIFKIND, WHARTON & GARRISON LLP

**www.**paulweiss.com **tel:** 212 373 3000 **fax:** 212 757 3990

**Chair of the Firm:** Brad S Karp

**Firm Overview:**

Paul, Weiss, Rifkind, Wharton & Garrison LLP is a firm of more than 700 lawyers who collaborate with clients to help them solve their most challenging legal problems and achieve their business goals. Widely recognized as having leading litigation and corporate capabilities, the firm has developed equally strong practices in the areas of bankruptcy and corporate reorganization, employee benefits and executive compensation, intellectual property, personal representation, real estate and tax law. The firm has an unwavering dedication to representing those in need, and its pro bono efforts continue to benefit individuals and society.

**Main Areas of Practice:**

**Antitrust:**
Paul, Weiss lawyers play an important role in shaping antitrust law in the United States and represent many of the world's largest companies, handling the full range of antitrust matters in the courtroom and before regulators. The team includes former top US Federal Trade Commission and US Department of Justice regulators.

**Bankruptcy & Corporate Reorganization:**
In a challenging business environment, Paul, Weiss has been a critical advisor to companies, creditors and investors responding to rapid market and regulatory change. The bankruptcy practice leverages thorough knowledge of all aspects of bankruptcy law representing lenders and their agents, underwriters, bondholders, and purchasers and sellers of distressed assets.

**Capital Markets & Securities:**
The firm's international capital markets practice represents both issuers and underwriters in a broad range of public and private securities offerings. The group is engaged in helping major private equity firms in acquisition financings, initial public offerings and subsequent financings.

**Employee Benefits & Executive Compensation:**
Paul, Weiss offers experienced lawyers who work on matters including public and private corporate transactions, executive compensation arrangements, investment fund structure and ERISA fiduciary responsibility, and ERISA litigation support.

**Finance:**
Paul, Weiss offers the full range of debt financing expertise, including leveraged finance, structured finance, project finance and derivatives, across an array of industries. The firm's lawyers are adept at representing private equity sponsors and other clients in acquisition financings, portfolio company financings and restructurings of multibillion dollar

companies. The group is regularly at the center of highly innovative intellectual property and whole business securitizations.

**Intellectual Property:**
Paul, Weiss helps clients protect, exploit and enforce intellectual property rights around the world, from licensing brand names and structuring acquisitions with copyright, trademark, patent and e-commerce elements, to handling complex patent and other IP litigation. The firm has long been recognized as one of the world's leading copyright and trademark litigation practices. Its lawyers are well versed in the advanced scientific and technical aspects of patent law and have successfully represented major corporations in scores of complex patent litigations.

**Litigation:**
Paul, Weiss's Litigation Department has been at the center of nearly every major litigation in recent years. The firm's lawyers are sought out for their trial skills in enterprise-threatening suits as well as their sound business counsel and comprehensive strategic advice on managing litigation risk. Paul, Weiss lawyers possess a wide range of experience, both in the private sector and government service, enabling them to respond effectively to the many and ever-changing challenges confronting their clients. As a result, the firm's lawyers handle an array of disputes and representations, including antitrust, bankruptcy, derivatives litigation, employment, environmental, ERISA, benefits and pension litigation, FCPA, financial services, insurance, IP (copyright and trademark litigation), internal investigations and white collar crime, international arbitration, M&A, patent and other scientific litigation, product liability, professional liability, securities litigation and regulatory defense.

**M&A:**
For decades Paul, Weiss M&A lawyers have guided companies, private equity firms, hedge funds, financial advisors and other institutions on some of the most highly publicized M&A transactions of the time. The

firm's lawyers find and implement creative solutions to business and legal problems, creating unique value for their clients.

**Media & Entertainment:**
The firm's Media and Entertainment lawyers handle transactions and settle disputes on behalf of strategic industry participants, financial sponsors and other providers of capital, entrepreneurs, and leading talent on matters that span the spectrum of the media and entertainment industry.

**Personal Representation:**
This group provides services to clients ranging from estate planning and administration and representation of private foundations and public charitable organizations, to litigated surrogate's court cases and the tax issues affecting such matters.

**Private Funds:**
From traditional private equity funds to innovative hedge and hybrid funds, Paul, Weiss has built a stellar reputation advising private funds on strategic transactions, formation and management, seed and strategic investments, and securities law and regulatory compliance.

**Real Estate:**
Paul, Weiss Real Estate lawyers work with some of the most prominent institutions in New York, and around the world, in the development, financing, acquisition and sale of major projects.

**Tax:**
A key part of the firm's transactional team, the Tax lawyers are integral, front-line players in the strategizing and structuring of crucial transactions, often involving billions of dollars.

# PECKAR & ABRAMSON, PC

www.pecklaw.com **tel:** 212 382 0909 **fax:** 212 382 3456

**Chairman:** Steven M Charney
**Vice-Chairman:** Stephen H Reisman
Number of partners: 55   Number of other lawyers: 41
Languages: *English, Spanish*

## Firm Overview:

Peckar & Abramson has been serving the construction industry for 35 years. It has achieved national recognition for its successes in the representation of members of the construction industry, both domestically and internationally. The firm combines its unique problem-solving expertise and litigation/arbitration experience with substantial experience counseling clients in the management of transactional risks inherent in their contracts and the industry. The firm also represents clients through Construlegal™, an alliance of leading construction law firms throughout the Americas working as a team to deliver unique legal and business advice in both local and international construction law matters.

## Main Areas of Practice:

### Construction/Construction Litigation:
45 Partners, 34 Associates
Represent a wide range of construction projects in the public and private sectors with a focus on general contractors and construction managers. The firm has extensive experience on a wide range of projects, including: airports; government buildings; highways; bridges; power generation facilities; railways; tunnels; pipelines; schools; hospitals; sports arenas; manufacturing facilities; hotels and other hospitality-industry projects; residential communities.
**Key Clients:** National and international general contractors, construction managers and other members of the construction industry.
**Contact:** Steven M Charney   **Tel:** 212 382 0909
**Email:** scharney@pecklaw.com

### Corporate:
Represent both public and privately held companies in all matters of corporate law including mergers, acquisitions, public offerings, private placements, venture capital, securities regulation, formation and organization of corporations, partnerships and limited liability companies, joint venture agreements, licensing, corporate governance and general commercial agreements.
**Contact:** Stephen P Katz   **Tel:** 201 343 3434
**Email:** skatz@pecklaw.com

### Corporate Compliance:
Provide advice on internal corporate controls, assistance in constructing and implementing compliance programs, internal investigations of potential ethics violations, and representation of clients in investigations, audits and litigations.
**Contact:** Robert S Peckar   **Tel:** 212 382 0909
**Email:** rpeckar@pecklaw.com

### Government Contracts:
Provide counsel to a wide variety of industries engaged in government contracting, and represent them in connection with an even broader array of contracting issues and disputes.
**Contact:** Patrick J Greene, Jr   **Tel:** 201 343 3434
**Email:** pgreene@pecklaw.com

### Employment:
Handle defense and oversight of Employment Practices Liability and Directors & Officers claims through insurance coverage, and monitors EPLI/D&O claims on behalf of carriers.
**Contact:** Jeffrey M Daitz   **Tel:** 201 343 3434
**Email:** jdaitz@pecklaw.com

### Energy & Defense:
Represent energy and defense firms before federal, state and local courts and agencies in transactions, contracts and disputes.
**Contact:** Ronald H Uscher   **Tel:** 202 293 8815
**Email:** ruscher@pecklaw.com

### Labor Relations:
Counsel private employers, public employers and ERISA entities in all matters of litigation and labor relations management. Provide counseling regarding fair labor practices, union organization campaigns and representation in collective bargaining negotiations.
**Contact:** Gregory R Begg   **Tel:** 201 343 3434
**Email:** gbegg@pecklaw.com

### Public-Private Partnerships:
Regularly counsel clients on complex P3 projects, including civil infrastructure initiatives such as bridges, tunnels, highways, pipelines and railways, and social infrastructure projects such as schools and prisons.
**Contact:** Frank M Rapoport   **Tel:** 212 382 0909
**Email:** frapoport@pecklaw.com

### Real Estate:
Handle every aspect of commercial real estate transactions, including the acquisition, financing, construction financing, leasing and disposition of real property.
**Contact:** Craig D Spector   **Tel:** 201 343 3434
**Email:** cspector@pecklaw.com

### White Collar Criminal Defense:
Extensive experience on both the federal and local levels in criminal trials, the intricacies of the grand jury, and other aspects of the practice of criminal law and issues that arise in the conduct of business.
**Contact:** Thomas J Curran   **Tel:** 212 382 0909
**Email:** tcurran@pecklaw.com

## PRACTICE AREAS

Construction/Construction Litigation
Corporate
Corporate Compliance
Employment
Energy & Defense
Government Contracts
Labor Relations
Public-Private Partnerships
Real Estate
White Collar Criminal Defense

## OFFICES

### CALIFORNIA
**IRVINE:** 20 Pacifica, Suite 260, CA 92618
Tel: 949 608 3100   Fax: 949 608 3103

**LOS ANGELES:** 1875 Century Park East, Suite 550, CA 90067
Tel: 310 228 1075   Fax: 310 228 1076

**SAN FRANCISCO:** Three Embarcadero Center, 8th Floor, CA 94111
Tel: 415 837 1968   Fax: 415 837 1320

### DISTRICT OF COLUMBIA
**WASHINGTON, DC:** Two Lafayette Centre, 1133 21st Street, NW, Suite 500, DC 20036
Tel: 202 293 8815   Fax: 202 293 7994

### FLORIDA
**MIAMI:** One Southeast Third Avenue, Suite 3100, FL 33131
Tel: 305 358 2600   Fax: 305 375 0328

### GEORGIA
**ATLANTA:** 1100 Peachtree Street, Suite 200, GA 30309
Tel: 404 872 4343   Fax: 404 872 4315

### ILLINOIS
**CHICAGO:** 30 North La Salle Street, Suite 4126, IL 60602
Tel: 312 881 6300   Fax: 312 435 2482

### NEW YORK
**NEW YORK:** 41 Madison Avenue, 20th Floor, NY 10010
Tel: 212 382 0909   Fax: 212 382 3456

### NEW JERSEY
**RIVER EDGE:** 70 Grand Avenue, NJ 07661
Tel: 201 343 3434   Fax: 201 343 6306

Peckar & Abramson, P.C.

# PHILLIPS LYTLE LLP

**www.**phillipslytle.com **tel:** 716 847 8400 **fax:** 716 852 6100

**Managing Partner:** David J McNamara
Number of partners: 79   Number of lawyers: 191

## Firm Overview:

Phillips Lytle is a premier law firm, recognized nationally for its legal excellence. Established over 175 years ago, many of the firm's clients have relied for decades on its quality legal services and sound business advice. Its practices include banking and financial services; bankruptcy; corporate; education; employee benefits; energy; environment; health law; intellectual property; international; labor and employment; litigation; real estate and telecommunications.

## Main Areas of Practice:

### Environment:

5 partners; 10 fee-earners

Phillips Lytle is a national leader and has been on the cutting edge of environmental law since the 1960's. The firm has represented hundreds of commercial, manufacturing, technology and industry clients with respect to ever-expanding environmental regulations and their implications on virtually all commercial and corporate transactions. The firm also has one of the leading land use planning and zoning practices in New York State.

- Represents E.I. du Pont de Nemours and Company (DuPont) in Clean Air Act, Clean Water Act, and hazardous waste permitting, enforcement and compliance counseling, including Title V, EPCRA, RCRA, and wetlands matters; related Environmental Protection Agency and New York State DEC administrative permitting and multi-media enforcement matters; and environmental litigation. Partners: Morgan G Graham, Kevin M Hogan.
- Represented CBS Corporation in a CERCLA action in West Virginia. The EPA incurred $25 million in past costs and projected another $20 million in future remedial costs. CBS entered into a multi-party consent decree - one party agreed to perform the remedial work, and CBS and a third party agreed to partially fund that work and reimburse EPA for its past costs. Partners: Morgan G Graham, Kevin M Hogan.
- Represented Sovran Self Storage Inc., in a $175 million acquisition of 21 self-storage facilities in New Jersey and Pennsylvania. The firm handled due diligence of the real property, analysis of pending remediations, negotiation of escrows and indemnities, and the engagement of environmental consultants to complete the remedial work. Also involved was a complex transfer of multi-state solar energy siting agreements. Partners: Kevin M Hogan and David P Flynn.

**Key Clients:** E.I. du Pont de Nemours and Company, Sovran Self Storage Inc., CBS Corporation, Reichhold Inc.

**Contact:** Kevin M Hogan
**Tel:** 716 847 8331  **Email:** khogan@phillipslytle.com

### Energy:

3 Partners; 8 Fee-earners

The firm's Energy Practice offers specific expertise for developers and owners of renewable and other energy projects.

- Represented BQ Energy, developer of a 20 MW wind energy project - the first urban brownfield wind farm in the US. All legal and regulatory approvals were obtained in less than 90 days. Partners: David P Flynn, Adam S Walters.
- Represented a water authority with regard to regulatory considerations and approvals related to treating waste water from Marcellus formation high-volume hydro fracturing wells. Partner: David P Flynn.

**Key Clients:** Apex Wind, BQ Energy, Great Lakes Solar, CG Power Solutions USA.

**Contact:** David P Flynn
**Tel:** 716 847 5473  **Email:** dflynn@phillipslytle.com

### Litigation:

33 partners; 103 fee-earners

The firm's Litigation Practice is recognized nationally, regionally and locally for its outstanding trial and appellate work. Practice areas include: commercial litigation (including financial services, noncompete and employee disloyalty, corporate and shareholder matters, government operations, education, insurance coverage, and class action matters); chemical exposure; products liability; workplace accidents; and labor and employment matters.

**Key clients:** Rich Products Corporation, E.I. du Pont de Nemours and Company, Polytechnic Institute of NYU, Columbus McKinnon, Emerson Electric Co.

**Contact:** Kevin J English
**Tel:** 716 847 5447  **Email:** kenglish@phillipslytle.com

### Banking & Financial Services:

13 partners; 28 fee-earners

The firm has a long established reputation as a premier banking and commercial law firm. Attorneys on this team have worked with over two dozen regional, national and global financial institutions.

- Represented the administrative agent in a 14-bank, $900 million secured loan facility to Moog Inc. Partner: Raymond H Seitz.

**OFFICES**

NEW YORK
**ALBANY:** Omni Plaza, 30 South Pearl Street, 12207
Tel: 518 472 1224  Fax: 518 472 1227

**BUFFALO:** 3400 HSBC Center, 14203
Tel: 716 847 8400  Fax: 716 852 6100

**CHAUTAUQUA:** 201 West Third Street, Suite 205, 14701
Tel: 716 664 3906  Fax: 716 664 4230

**GARDEN CITY:** 1305 Franklin Avenue, Suite 200, 11530
Tel: 516 742 5201  Fax: 516 742 3910

**NEW YORK CITY:** 437 Madison Avenue, 34th Floor, 10022
Tel: 212-759-4888  Fax: 212-308-9079

**ROCHESTER:** 1400 First Federal Plaza, 14614
Tel: 585 238 2000  Fax: 585 232 3141

INTERNATIONAL OFFICES:
The firm also has an office in Canada.

- Represented a public REIT and its affiliates in connection with a $400 million syndicated revolving and term loan facility; a $100 million private note placement used to partially finance the acquisition of self-storage facilities in multiple states; and various securities offerings. Partners: Frederick G Attea, Glenn J Bobeck, David J Murray, Raymond H Seitz.

**Key Clients:** KeyBank N.A., JPMorgan Chase & Co., Citibank, N.A. and Citicorp USA.

**Contact:** Raymond L Ruff
**Tel:** 585 238 2058  **Email:** rruff@phillipslytle.com

### Telecommunications:

6 Partners; 12 fee-earners

The firm represents some of the world's largest telecommunications companies, regional providers, telecommunications entrepreneurs, large and small site owners and managers, as well as lenders and investors across the US. Clients include wireless, wireline and fiber communication carriers, tower owners, internet service providers, developers, property owners, investors and lenders.

The firm's expertise includes: transactional matters, litigation involving claims under the 1996 Telecommunications Act, zoning and land use issues for telecommunications carriers, data centers, tower owners and developers, local and national site leasing work, interconnection and collocation agreements, spectrum leasing, network construction agreements, securing operating authority, dark fiber and managed services agreements, master purchase agreements with original equipment manufacturers, custom network service agreements for enterprise customers, negotiation of municipal franchises and right-of-way agreements and pole attachment agreements.

**Key Clients:** AT&T
**Contact:** Douglas W Dimitroff
**Tel:** 716 847 5408  **Email:** ddimitroff@phillipslytle.com

# PILLSBURY WINTHROP SHAW PITTMAN LLP

www.pillsburylaw.com

**Chair:** James Rishwain Jr
Number of partners worldwide: Approximately 348
Number of other lawyers worldwide: Approximately 355

## Firm Overview:

Pillsbury is a full-service law firm with a keen industry focus on energy and natural resources, financial services, real estate and construction, and technology. Based in the world's major financial, technology and energy centers, Pillsbury counsels clients on global regulatory, litigation and corporate matters. Attorneys at Pillsbury work in multidisciplinary teams that allow the firm to anticipate trends and bring a 360-degree perspective to complex business and legal issues – helping clients to take greater advantage of new opportunities and better mitigate risk. This collaborative work style helps produce the results Pillsbury's clients seek.

## Main Areas of Practice:

### Business:

From entity formation and expansion to project finance, alternative investing to negotiating outsourcing agreements or executive compensation packages, Pillsbury's Business Department advises emerging, middle market and multinational clients on all types of corporate, communications, securities, finance and IP transactions, particularly in the banking, energy, insurance, life sciences, retail, real estate, and technology sectors.

### Litigation:

Pillsbury's Litigation Department boasts more than 200 lawyers throughout the 14 office network. From corporate defense and special investigations to tax controversy, environmental litigation to IP counseling, the firm's litigators have substantial trial experience at the state, federal and appellate level, as well as with the bankruptcy courts. The firm has conducted dispute resolutions before the world's arbitration bodies, and are particularly noted for representing energy, financial services, government contractors, and technology companies in complex litigation matters, restructuring, ERISA and employment-related suits, and patent or trademark disputes.

### Regulatory:

Pillsbury's Regulatory Department offers a wide range of counseling related to compliance, regulatory hearings and investigations and public policy. Among its regulatory areas are aviation, banking and securities compliance, data privacy, energy and environmental, including climate change and sustainability, overnment relations, international trade, liquor and spirits, native american law and political law. The firm regularly negotiates trade agreements under WTO and NAFTA, advise on export and technology transfer controls, and represents clients in trade remedy proceedings before the International Trade Commission and the Court of International Trade, including antidumping, countervailing duty, and safeguard proceedings.

## International Work:

Pillsbury serves a growing international clientele, advising businesses and governments from more than 50 countries on commercial, regulatory and litigation matters at the heart of the global economy. The firm's legal team helps corporations pursue strategic opportunities that span countries and continents, and advise national governments on the unique issues raised by state-sponsored market activity including:

- Acted as lead counsel to the Swiss government in litigation involving attempts by the IRS to obtain thousands of account holders' names from Swiss bank UBS
- Advised government lawyers from Mexico appearing before a three-arbitrator panel at the World Bank in a dispute over trade barriers on high-fructose corn syrup
- Represented Qatar Petroleum in deals and projects including the acquisition of controlling interest in the $2.6 billion Golden Pass terminal and pipeline project, and the South Hook project, which will be the UK's largest integrated LNG terminal
- Represented Emirates Nuclear Energy Company in setting up and negotiating a $20 billion contract for four nuclear units in the United Arab Emirates, the largest turnkey nuclear power contract ever announced
- Represented the Russian Ministry of Economic Development and Trade on legislative reform to encourage venture capital investment in the Russian technology sector
- Assisted Hainan Airlines with its entry into the US market and on corporate, regulatory, commercial, employment, immigration and tax matters
- Advised Asia Alternatives, the largest independent Japanese private equity fund-of-funds, on the $950 million Asia Alternatives Capital Partners II fund. Investors included pension funds, foundations and endowments from North America, Europe and Asia
- Helped Société Générale obtain a favourable reversal at the US Court of Appeals for the Second Circuit in a precedent-setting derivatives decision

## HEAD OFFICES

### NEW YORK
**NEW YORK:** 1540 Broadway, NY 10036
Tel: 212 858 1000 Fax: 212 858 1500

### CALIFORNIA:
**SAN FRANCISO:** 4 Embarcadero Center, Suite 2200, CA 94111
Tel: 415 983 1000 Fax: 415 983 1200

**LOS ANGELES:** 725 South Figueroa Street, Suite 2800, CA 90017
Tel: 213 488 7100 Fax: 213 629 1033

**DISTRICT OF COLUMBIA:** 2300 N. Street, NW, DC 20037
Tel: 202 663 8000 Fax: 202 663 8007

**PALO ALTO:** 2550 Hanover Street, CA 94304
Tel: 650 233 4500 Fax: 650 233 4545

**SACRAMENTO:** 400 Capitol Mall, Suite 1700, CA 95814
Tel: 916 329 4700 Fax: 916 441 3583

**SAN DIEGO:** 12255 El Camino Real, Suite 300, CA 92130
Tel: 619 234 5000 Fax: 858 509 4010

**SAN DIEGO:** 501 West Broadway, Suite 1100, CA 92101
Tel: 619 234 5000 Fax: 619 236 1995

### TENNESSEE
**NASHVILLE (OPERATIONS CENTER):** 333 Commerce Street, TN 37201

### TEXAS
**HOUSTON:** 2 Houston Center, 909 Fannin, Suite 2000, TX 77010
Tel: 713 276 7600 Fax: 713 276 7673

### VIRGINIA
**MCLEAN:** 1650 Tysons Boulevard, VA 22102
Tel: 703 770 7900 Fax: 703 770 7901

## INTERNATIONAL OFFICES
The firm has offices in China, Japan, the United Arab Emirates and the United Kingdom.

- Represented Varig Brazilian Airlines in the first-ever bankruptcy filed under a then-untested Brazilian law in a $2.8 billion restructuring
- Successfully litigated and settled all claims against Petróleos de Venezuela S.A. (PDVSA) and its subsidiary, BITOR, related to a Canadian utility seeking C$2.2 billion in damages
- Represented Marubeni Corporation as a sponsor in the $3.8 billion international project financing of gas pipeline and LNG liquefaction terminal in Pampa Melchorita, Peru
- Advised The Nielsen Company on a $1 billion, 10-year business process outsourcing agreement with India's Tata Consultancy Services (TCS), the largest outsourcing ever to an Indian company

# PROSKAUER ROSE LLP

www.proskauer.com

**Chairman:** Joseph M Leccese
Number of partners: 228

## Firm Overview:

Proskauer is a global firm with more than 700 lawyers. Recognized for matching technical excellence with strong business and industry acumen, Proskauer's lawyers are players in the world's major business and finance hubs and the sectors in which the firm practices. Proskauer's standing in the marketplace puts the firm in the unique position to anticipate its clients' needs and adapt rapidly to changes in the business and legal landscape. Proskauer places a premium on client service and the firm's lawyers continuously seek out new developments and technologies to add value for their clients. The firm's lawyers provide a full range of corporate, litigation, labor and employment, intellectual property, healthcare, personal planning, real estate and tax services to businesses, not-for-profit institutions and individuals.

## Main Areas of Practice:

Proskauer's global network provides top-tier counsel in important areas that include private equity, corporate finance and securities, mergers and acquisitions, capital markets, litigation and dispute resolution, corporate defense and investigations, intellectual property, healthcare, labor and employment, employee benefits and executive compensation, real estate, environmental law, technology, media and communications, privacy and data protection, bankruptcy and restructuring, insurance coverage and recovery, and personal planning. The firm also has significant industry-focused experience across many fields, including financial services, life sciences, sports, media and entertainment, lodging and gaming and technology.

Through a combination of home-grown talent and an extensive lateral hiring program, Proskauer has built top practices in private equity fund formation and transactions (with these practices centered in its Boston, London, Los Angeles, Paris, Hong Kong, Beijing and New York offices), high-stakes litigation and dispute resolution, with a focus on highly complex and cross-border matters, capital markets (particularly high-yield debt and hedge funds), corporate finance (particularly junior capital/mezzanine lending), government investigations and white-collar defense. Proskauer is also distinguished by a leading Latin America practice, which has completed deals for some of the top financial institutions in the region, as well as one of the leading wealth management and personal planning practices in the United States, which advises a number of high-profile, high-net-worth individual and institutional clients.

In addition to being highly skilled practitioners and trusted business counselors, Proskauer's lawyers are civic and philanthropic leaders who have a long-standing commitment to pro bono and community service. Their work on behalf of individuals, families and groups in need spans all of its offices and also includes leadership positions at numerous legal and civic organizations.

## Practice Groups:

Accessibility & Accommodations; Antitrust; Appellate; Broker-Dealer & Investment Management Regulation; Business Solutions, Governance, Restructuring & Bankruptcy; California Labor & Employment Law; Capital Markets; Class/Collective Action; Copyright; Corporate Defense & Investigations; Corporate Governance; Distressed Debt; Dodd-Frank Task Force; E-Discovery; Employee Benefits; Employment Law Counseling & Training; Employment Litigation & Arbitration; Entertainment Industry; Environmental; ERISA Litigation; Executive Compensation; False Advertising & Trademark; Fiduciary Litigation; Finance; Financial Services; French & EU Employment; Government Regulatory Compliance & Relations; Health Care Reform Task Force; Hedge Funds; Immigration & Nationality; Infrastructure; Insurance Recovery & Counseling; International Arbitration; International Labor & Employment; International Practice; Labor-Management Relations; Latin America; Law Firm; Life Sciences; Lodging & Gaming; Mergers & Acquisitions; Multi-Tranche Finance; Non-Compete & Trade Secrets; Not-For-Profit/Exempt Organizations; Patent Law; Privacy & Data Security; Private Equity; Private Equity Real Estate; Private Investment Funds; Private Investment Funds Disputes; Product Liability & Consumer Litigation; Real Estate Capital Markets; Real Estate Finance; Real Estate Litigation; Reductions in Force/Managing Change; Securities Litigation; Sports Law; Strategic Corporate Planning; Technology, Media & Communications; Whistleblowing & Retaliation.

## International Work:

Proskauer's lawyers are active in virtually every major market across the globe. With a strong presence in Europe, Latin America and Asia, the firm's practice includes the representation of clients based and doing business around the world. The firm's Paris and London lawyers serve multinational organizations throughout Europe and focus on corporate transactions, commercial law, labor and employment law, commercial litigation and international arbitration. Proskauer's London lawyers have a strong sector focus within the alternative asset and private investment fund industries, advising managers and investors on all aspects of private equity, venture capital, debt, hedge and other alternative asset classes, as well as mergers and acquisitions. The firm's São Paulo lawyers have played leading roles in a wide range of matters related to Brazil and throughout Latin America, assisting clients in innovative transactions as well as in day to day matters. In the region, the firm has been involved in prominent capital markets, bank financing and private equity deals. Proskauer's Hong Kong and Beijing lawyers represent a diverse range of clients in cross-border transactions and other complex matters including mergers and acquisitions, joint ventures, private equity, investment funds, real estate, capital markets, lodging and gaming, sports and entertainment.

# RICHARDS KIBBE & ORBE LLP

www.rkollp.com

**Managing Partner:** Kenneth E Werner
Number of partners: 36
Number of other lawyers: 39

## Firm Overview:

Richards Kibbe & Orbe LLP (RK&O) is a world leader in financial sector law, business transactions and high-stakes litigation. For more than 20 years, the firm has consistently been at the forefront of emerging legal issues and investment activities, pioneering not only the trading market for distressed debt but also standards and practices that have revolutionized the secondary loan marketplace. The sophistication, intelligence and intensity that have made RK&O a global leader in complex financial transactions and compliance issues have also driven the firm's success in representing institutional clients and individuals confronting government investigations, securities law violations and business disputes.

With a long track record of achieving positive outcomes for clients, RK&O is trusted by the financial and business community to navigate the most difficult legal issues while maintaining a commitment to absolute discretion. Quite simply, no other mid-sized financial and business transaction firm has RK&O's experience, reputation and caliber of clients.

The firm's attorneys are recognized as being among the most qualified legal practitioners in the financial services sector, both in the US and around the globe. Before joining RK&O, firm partners led financial institutions and public companies, or gained years of experience working at the Securities and Exchange Commission (SEC), Department of Justice and other law enforcement agencies. The firm's attorneys have been involved in every aspect of corporate law, civil litigation and government investigations, making them uniquely qualified to navigate the most difficult issues facing the financial industry and business leaders. Worldwide, RK&O has 75 lawyers located in New York, Washington, DC and London.

## Main Areas of Practice:

### Civil Litigation:
Business and commercial disputes; capital markets litigation; creditors' rights and bankruptcy litigation; securities and shareholder suits.

### Corporate & Business Transactions:
Derivatives; distressed debt and claims trading; investment management; joint ventures; lending transactions; mergers and acquisitions; private equity transactions; private fund advisers; securities transactions; tax; venture capital.

### Regulation & Compliance:
Corporate governance; evaluation of regulatory risk; operational advice; private fund advisers; representing lawyers; securities regulation advice and training; trading/ethical policies and compliance.

### Restructuring & Bankruptcy:
Creditors' rights and restructurings; distressed acquisitions; rescue, DIP and exit financing.

### Securities Enforcement, Internal & Government Investigations & Criminal Defense:
Broker-dealer sales practices; corruption, bribery and money laundering; financial and accounting fraud; representing lawyers; securities trading and market manipulation; tax investigations and litigation.

### Clients:
The firm represents some of the world's largest investment banks, financial institutions, public corporations and hedge funds – including eight of the top 10 global investment banks, four of the 10 largest private equity funds, and 31 of the top 100 hedge funds by assets under management. In addition to representing financial institutions and corporate leaders in complex business transactions and disputes, RK&O works on behalf of institutions, executives and corporate board members facing government investigations, white collar litigation and other high-stakes legal issues.

The proof of RK&O's success lies not only in the institutions and individuals it represents, but in the fact that many clients turn to the firm time and time again when facing complex legal situations.

## OFFICES

**NEW YORK**
**NEW YORK:** One World Financial Center, NY 10281-1003
Tel: 212 530 1800   Fax: 212 530 1801

**DISTRICT OF COLUMBIA**
**WASHINGTON DC:** Portrait Building, 701 8th Street NW, DC 20001-3727
Tel: 202 261 2960   Fax: 202 261 2999

## INTERNATIONAL OFFICES

The firm also has an office in London, UK.

# SCHULTE ROTH & ZABEL

www.srz.com  **tel:** 212 756 2000  **fax:** 212 593 5955

**Executive Committee:** Stephanie R Breslow, Adam C Harris, Jeffrey A Lenobel, David Nissenbaum, Martin L Perschetz, Frederic L Ragucci, Ronald E Richman, Paul N Roth, Alan S Waldenberg, Brian F Schare, Richard E Piotrowicz
Number of partners: 87   Number of other lawyers: 265

## Firm Overview:

Founded in 1969, Schulte Roth & Zabel's primary focus is on delivering sophisticated leading-edge business and legal advice to the financial services sector and firms that support that sector, including high-profile institutional, entrepreneurial and individual clients. The firm strives to build and maintain long-term relationships with clients by placing a premium on client service. To address every aspect of a client's business, it is not unusual for attorneys from multiple practice groups to be brought in on a matter.

## Main Areas of Practice:

### Bank Regulatory:

SRZ's bank regulatory attorneys advise a large and diverse group of financial institutions on chartering issues, legal and regulatory compliance, structuring of new businesses and products, and domestic and international transactions, including financings, acquisitions and investments.

### Business Reorganization:

The firm provides counsel and representation to key participants in debt restructurings (workouts and reorganizations), acquisitions of troubled companies, financings (debtor-in-possession and reorganization plans), and bankruptcy litigation (including fraudulent transfer, preference and contract disputes).

### Business Transactions:

SRZ is one of the pre-eminent law firms in the areas of mergers and acquisitions, leveraged buyouts, special opportunity investments, proxy fights, initial public offerings, high-yield debt and PIPEs transactions. Clients include both financial and strategic buyers and sellers involved in domestic and cross-border transactions. The firm often works on large, high-profile transactions and has experience in a wide variety of business sectors, including airlines, automobiles, banking, chemicals, distribution services, financial services, healthcare, investment management, real estate, manufacturing, restaurants and telecommunications.

### Employment & Employee Benefits:

SRZ's employment practice includes ongoing guidance and counsel emphasizing prevention of employment disputes, and if necessary, representation in litigation or arbitration. The firm represents employers in all aspects of labor relations and collective bargaining, and the practice also encompasses every aspect of benefits law and ERISA.

### Environmental:

SRZ attorneys counsel major institutions and *Fortune* 500 companies on a wide range of national and international environmental issues. The firm advises on preventive methods, and has both the technical knowledge and legal experience necessary to provide the best advocacy. The firm represents clients before local, state and federal agencies and courts.

### Finance:

SRZ serves the asset-based lending community in connection with asset-based loans, leveraged acquisitions, financing and restructurings, debtor-in-possession and exit financings, unsecured corporate borrowings, and private placements by investment-grade companies.

### Individual Client Services:

SRZ's individual client services practice is one of the most sophisticated, extensive and diverse of any major law firm. The attorneys represent many of the wealthiest individuals in the country on tax planning, succession planning, charitable giving, will contests and family law matters, including mediation of large divorce matters.

### Intellectual Property, Sourcing & Technology:

SRZ has expertise in all aspects of intellectual property law, including patents, trademarks, copyrights, unfair competition and trade secrets, and information technology licensing, development and outsourcing.

### Investment Management:

SRZ has occupied the fund formation space for over 40 years and has become the go-to firm in this area, providing legal services to nearly half of the world's 100 largest hedge funds. In addition to hedge fund firms, clients include private equity firms, mutual fund complexes and global investment banking and advisory firms.

### Litigation:

More than 75 litigators represent clients in securities litigation and regulatory enforcement, defense of white-collar criminals, anti-money laundering, antitrust, class actions, derivative suits and general commercial litigation and arbitrations.

### Real Estate:

SRZ represents a diverse group of clients in the sale and acquisition of commercial property, securitization of mortgage loans and mezzanine financings, leasing of commercial property, construction and architectural agreements, and all other aspects of the development process and real estate equity funds.

### Regulatory & Compliance:

SRZ offers representation in the areas of regulation, compliance and litigation for investment banks, commercial banks, hedge funds, private equity funds, mutual funds, closed-end funds and business development companies. The firm advises clients on US and UK finance regulations, as well as securities trading issues and bank regulatory issues. It provides compliance reviews, training on compliance issues, and assistance in drafting policies and procedures. SRZ also counsels clients in preparation for examinations by federal and self-regulatory organizations. The group's attorneys have vast experience representing financial services clients in civil and criminal cases and investigations by governmental agencies, including trials and on appeal.

### Structured Products & Derivatives:

SRZ's attorneys structure, negotiate and address trading and regulatory compliance issues regarding over-the-counter (OTC) derivative products. In the structured products area, they have acted as lead counsel in collateralized loan obligations (CLOs) and synthetic collateralized bond obligations (CBOs).

### Tax:

SRZ provides tax planning for mergers, sales and other dispositions, and acquisitions and leveraged buyout arrangements, including analysis of cross-border financing and transfer-pricing issues. The firm's tax attorneys structure sophisticated financing transactions and advise on special tax issues confronting foreign investors making corporate, portfolio securities and real estate investments in the US. Tax advice is also provided to managers of domestic and foreign hedge, private equity and mutual funds.

**OFFICES**

DISTRICT OF COLUMBIA
**WASHINGTON, DC:** 1152 Fifteenth Street NW, Suite 850, DC 20005
Tel: 202 729 7470   Fax: 202 730 4520

NEW YORK
**NEW YORK:** 919 Third Avenue, NY 10022
Tel: 212 756 2000   Fax: 212 593 5955

**INTERNATIONAL OFFICES**

The firm also has an office in London, UK

**Schulte Roth & Zabel LLP**

2003

# SEWARD & KISSEL LLP

www.sewkis.com **tel:** 212 574 1200 **fax:** 212 480 8421

**Executive Committee:** James H Hancock, M William Munno, John E Tavss
Number of partners: 45  Number of other lawyers: 109

**Firm Overview:**

Seward & Kissel LLP, founded in 1890, is a leading US law firm with an international reputation for excellence. The firm, located in New York City and Washington, DC, focuses its practice primarily on corporate and litigation work for clients seeking legal expertise in the financial services, corporate finance and capital markets areas. The firm is particularly well known for its representation of major commercial banks, investment banking firms, investment advisers and related investment funds (including mutual funds and hedge funds), broker-dealers, institutional investors and transportation companies (particularly in the shipping area).

**OFFICES**

NEW YORK

**NEW YORK:** One Battery Park Plaza, NY 10004
Tel: 212 574 1200   Fax: 212 480 8421

DISTRICT OF COLUMBIA

**WASHINGTON, DC:** 901 K Street, NW, DC 20001
Tel: 202 737 8833   Fax: 202 737 5184

**Main Areas of Practice:**

**Investment Management:**
Since 1949, with the establishment of what is considered to be the very first hedge fund, A.W. Jones & Company, Seward & Kissel has been recognized for its work relating to private investment funds, particularly in the 'hedge fund' and alternative investment fund area. Regularly cited as one of the leading legal advisers to the private investment fund industry, Seward & Kissel is recognized for its work in the hedge fund area and for its work representing a wide range of registered investment companies and their advisers.
**Contact:** John E Tavss

**Business Transactions:**
The firm represents clients in connection with: mergers and acquisitions; buyouts, venture capital and private equity; private investments in public equity; private debt transactions; and joint ventures, strategic alliances and seed capital arrangements.
**Contact:** James E Abbott, Craig A Sklar

**Capital Markets & Securities:**
The firm represents issuers and underwriters in US and global offerings of equity and debt securities, including registered initial and secondary public offerings, private placements and Rule 144A and Regulation S offerings.
**Contact:** Gary Wolfe

**Structured Finance & Asset Securitization:**
The firm is recognized as a leader in securitization and structured finance. The firm represents the full range of participants in the structured finance industry in secured and unsecured, asset-based, market value and cash flow transactions, multi-seller commercial paper conduit transactions; commercial lending; subscription finance transactions; CLO transactions; public and private offerings of pass through and pay through securities; project finance; and synthetic and structured derivatives products.
**Contact:** Greg Cioffi, Kalyan ('Kal') Das

**Derivatives:**
The firm advises both dealers and counterparties in structuring, negotiating and documenting over-the-counter and cleared derivative instruments, including hybrid products. The firm advises industry participants concerning regulatory compliance programs, exchange-traded futures and options, and repurchase and securities lending programs.
**Contact:** Craig Hickernell

**Distressed Debt:**
The firm is skilled in the purchase and sale of distressed domestic and foreign loans, sovereign loans and other distressed debt. The firm represents clients in all aspects of the distressed debt practice area including: drafting, reviewing and negotiating trade confirms, assignment and participation agreements and purchase and sale agreements; due diligence reviews; assessing recovery risk; monitoring of bankruptcy proceedings and creditor recoveries; and participating in creditor committees and Chapter 11 reorganizations.
**Contact:** Greg Cioffi, Kalyan ('Kal') Das, John R Ashmead

**Maritime & Aviation Finance:**
The firm represents, financial institutions, lessors, lessees, shipowners, private equity and other investors in connection with a broad range of maritime and shipping matters. The firm advises owners, operators, lessors and financiers of commercial and corporate aircraft in the acquisition, leasing and financing of aviation assets, and the implementation of ownership structures and the procurement of related insurance.
**Contact:** Lawrence Rutkowski, James H Hancock

**Litigation:**
The firm represents banks, broker-dealers, investment managers and other clients in courts, regulatory proceedings, administrative tribunals and arbitrations, focusing on the following areas: securities related litigation; business disputes; government enforcement and internal investigations; employment matters; insurance; maritime; trademark; and bankruptcy and workout matters.
**Contact:** Mark J Hyland, Michael J McNamara

**Bankruptcy & Corporate Reorganization:**
The firm handles bankruptcy, workout and reorganization matters, including court-supervised proceedings and out-of-court restructurings and workouts.
**Contact:** John R Ashmead

**Real Estate:**
The firm advises institutional investors and other real estate owners, operators, developers and lenders in structuring and implementing their real estate portfolios, including investments in office, retail, warehouse, multifamily and hotel facilities and private equity funds.
**Contact:** Mark A Brody

**Tax & Employee Benefits:**
The firm counsels clients on issues including tax, ERISA and employee considerations relevant to structuring complex securities and financing transactions, issues relating to financial products including pooled investment funds and real estate matters.
**Contact:** Ronald P Cima, S John Ryan

**Trusts & Estates:**
The firm assists individuals with tax, estate and charitable planning with the goal of preserving and building wealth for future generations and achieving philanthropic objectives.
**Contact:** Hume R Steyer

**Global Bank & Institutional Finance & Restructuring:**
The firm advises financial institutions in several capacities including as trustees, noteholders, servicers, issuers, and collateral administrators on structured finance transactions. The firm counsels trustees and separate trustees on behalf of investors (including hedge funds) on RMBS repurchase matters. The firm represents both investors and financial institutions in restructuring of complex corporate transactions and bankruptcy matters.
**Contact:** Kalyan ('Kal') Das

**Washington, DC:**
The Washington, DC office focuses on investment management (registered investment companies, investment advisers and other regulated entities) and corporate finance and capital markets practices (securities offerings, retail deposit programs, and maritime finance), as well as providing regulatory representation in connection with those practices. The firm renders advice on regulations that govern banks, investment companies, broker-dealers, transfer agents, clearing agencies and other financial institutions.
**Contact:** Paul T Clark, Paul M Miller

# SHEARMAN & STERLING LLP

**www.**shearman.com **tel:** 212 848 4000 **fax:** 212 848 7179

**Senior Partner:** Creighton Condon
Number of partners worldwide: approx 200   Number of lawyers worldwide: approx 900

## Firm Overview:

Shearman & Sterling LLP distinguishes itself by harnessing the intellectual strength and deep experience of its lawyers across its extensive global footprint. The firm represents many of the world's leading corporations, financial institutions, emerging growth companies, governments and state-owned enterprises. Those clients, in turn, continue to choose Shearman & Sterling for its distinctive ability to leverage the knowledge and judgment of one of the world's largest and most accomplished cross-border legal teams – a team ideally situated to help clients on their complex business transactions. Nearly one half of the firm's attorneys practice outside the United States, and its lawyers are fluent in more than 50 languages. The firm's lawyers practice US, English, French, German, Italian and Hong Kong law. Founded in 1873, Shearman & Sterling is organized as a single, integrated partnership with approximately 900 attorneys in 20 offices located throughout the Americas, Asia, Europe and the Middle East.

## Main Areas of Practice:

### Antitrust/Competition:
The firm's vast experience and presence in key antitrust jurisdictions are integral assets in providing a coordinated strategy in multinational transactions and investigations.

### Bankruptcy & Reorganization:
Shearman & Sterling is one of the leading law firms in the areas of restructurings, recapitalizations and bankruptcies and has been recognized as such for more than a quarter century.

### Capital Markets:
The firm's lawyers advise clients on all types of securities transactions, regulatory compliance, and corporate governance issues, including: public and private securities offerings; structured products and hybrid securities; and securities law.

### Commodities, Futures & Derivatives:
Shearman & Sterling counsels clients in developing, structuring and executing a broad range of complex financings involving derivatives, securitizations, structured products and other sophisticated financing techniques.

### Corporate Governance:
The firm's attorneys advise on a broad range of corporate governance and compliance matters, helping clients achieve business objectives within the framework of best practices for investor protection.

### Executive Compensation & Employee Benefits:
Shearman & Sterling counsels business enterprises, boards and individuals on every aspect of delivering compensation and executive employment from an integrated, multidisciplinary point of view.

### Finance:
The firm's global presence facilitates the largest and most complex dealings in international bank financing, capital markets, acquisition financing, leveraged lending and investment grade financing.

### Financial Institutions Advisory & Financial Regulatory:
Shearman & Sterling provides a full, global service to financial institutions, exchanges, ECNs/MTFs, clearing and settlement providers, fund firms and corporations on the laws and regulations of the world's key financial and commercial centers.

### Intellectual Property:
Shearman & Sterling counsels clients on intellectual property issues arising in all types of corporate and financial transactions and also handles litigation and dispute resolution, global coordination of IP disputes, inter partes proceedings before the United States Patent and Trademark Office, and strategic litigation counseling.

### International Arbitration:
The firm has handled hundreds of arbitrations concerning major businesses and political interests around the world, across virtually all industries and under more than 65 different governing laws.

### Investment Funds:
Shearman & Sterling lawyers are adept at reconciling complex regulatory and tax regimes with the competing requirements of fund managers, their investment strategies and their target investors.

### Litigation:
The firm's litigators are recognized leaders in a wide range of practice areas, including: securities litigation and enforcement; M&A-related litigation; global anti-corruption and FCPA matters; complex commercial disputes; appellate litigation; white-collar criminal defense and investigations; antitrust, arbitration and dispute resolution; banking; bankruptcy; intellectual property; international trade; and tax controversies.

### Mergers & Acquisitions:
Shearman & Sterling is a global leader in large complex M&A transactions, including joint ventures, strategic alliances and minority investments, and in a broad range of industries spanning multiple jurisdictions.

### Private Equity:
Shearman & Sterling has represented private equity funds, portfolio companies, target companies, sovereign wealth funds, and special committees in complex transactions and financings in various jurisdictions.

### Project Development & Finance:
Shearman & Sterling advises project participants and other entities in all manner of project roles and has extensive experience in the full range of financing structures.

### Real Estate:
Shearman & Sterling advises clients on significant real estate transactions in the US, UK, Europe, Middle East and Asia, including financings, acquisitions and dispositions, developments, joint ventures and leasing.

### Sovereign Wealth Funds:
For over 30 years, Shearman & Sterling has been the trusted advisor to many state-owned or controlled investment and development companies around the world.

### Sustainable Development:
This group brings together global experience from across a broad spectrum of renewable resource sectors and has developed market-leading knowledge with respect to carbon markets, alternative energy funds, and domestic and international environmental compliance.

### Tax:
This group provides international strategic tax planning advice and representation on a diverse array of cross-practice matters, including mergers and acquisitions, litigations, financings, restructurings and real estate transactions. The firm also has one of the leading tax controversy practices in the US.

---

## OFFICES

### CALIFORNIA

**PALO ALTO:** Five Palo Alto Square, 6th Floor, 3000 El Camino Real, CA 94306-2155
Tel: 650 838 3600   Fax: 650 838 3699

**SAN FRANCISCO:** Four Embarcadero Center, Suite 3800, CA 94111-5994
Tel: 415 616 1100   Fax: 415 616 1199

### NEW YORK

**NEW YORK:** 599 Lexington Avenue, NY 10022-6069
Tel: 212 828 4000   Fax: 212 848 7179

### DISTRICT OF COLUMBIA

**WASHINGTON:** 801 Pennsylvania Avenue, NW, Suite 900, DC 20004-2634
Tel: 202 508 800   Fax: 202 508 8100

## INTERNATIONAL OFFICES

The firm also has offices in Abu Dhabi, Beijing, Brussels, Düsseldorf, Frankfurt, Hong Kong, London, Milan, Munich, Paris, Rome, São Paulo, Shanghai, Singapore, Tokyo and Toronto.

# SIMPSON THACHER & BARTLETT LLP

**www.**simpsonthacher.com  **tel:** 212 455 2000  **fax:** 212 455 2502

**Chairman, Executive Committee:** William R Dougherty
**Administrative Partners:** Mary Beth Forshaw, Alan M Klein
Number of partners worldwide: 188    Number of other lawyers worldwide: Approx. 650

## Firm Overview:

Simpson Thacher & Bartlett LLP is widely recognised as one of the pre-eminent law firms in the world. The firm devotes to its clients the legal talent and skill of over 850 lawyers with a commitment to hard work, excellence and integrity. The firm advises clients worldwide across a broad spectrum of corporate transactions and litigation matters by offering straightforward, pragmatic advice that recognises the business needs of clients in light of prevailing commercial and legal realities. The firm has played a substantial role in many of the most complex and noteworthy transactions and litigations of the last decade.

## Main Areas of Practice:

### M&A & Private Equity:
- Silver Lake Partners in its announced $24.4 billion acquisition of Dell
- Eaton Corporation in its $13 billion acquisition of Cooper Industries
- Office Depot in its announced merger with OfficeMax
- Spin-off transactions for ARAMARK, Ingersoll-Rand, ITT, L-3 Communications, Sears Holdings and Tyco
- KKR and Alliance Boots in the $6.7 billion acquisition of a 45% equity stake in Alliance Boots by Walgreens
- TD Bank in its $5.9 billion acquisition of Target's US credit card portfolio

**Contact:** Lee A Meyerson **Tel:** 212 455 3675
**Email:** lmeyerson@stblaw.com

### Capital Markets:
- Issuer or underwriters on IPOs for Facebook ($16 billion), Japan Airlines ($8.5 billion), Realogy Holdings ($1.2 billion), Carlyle ($671 million), Dunkin' Brands Group ($455 million) and Chinalco Mining Corp. (HK$3.1 billion)
- Issuer or initial purchasers in 2012 high yield debt offerings for HCA ($4.85 billion), Samson Investment Company ($2.25 billion), First Data ($2.15 billion), Virgin Media ($2 billion) and Air Lease Corporation ($1.45 billion)
- Issuer or underwriters in 2012 debt offerings by Kraft Foods ($6.8 billion), América Móvil (over $6 billion), Oracle ($5 billion), Microsoft ($2.25 billion) and Samsung Electronics ($1 billion)

**Contact:** Arthur D Robinson  **Tel:** 212 455 7086
**Email:** arobinson@stblaw.com

### Banking & Credit:
- Silver Lake in the financing related to its announced $24.4 billion acquisition of Dell
- Eaton Corporation in the $6.75 billion in financing related to its acquisition of Cooper Industries
- Administrative agents in credit facilities for Comcast Corporation ($6.25 billion), eBay ($3 billion), Sprint Nextel ($2.8 billion) and Starwood Hotels & Resorts ($1.75 billion)

**Contact:** Patrick J Ryan **Tel:** 212 455 3463
**Email:** pryan@stblaw.com

### Private Funds:
Acted as sponsor counsel on a number of the largest global private equity fund raisings in 2011 and 2012, including:
- BC European Capital IX
- Blackstone Capital Partners VI
- EQT VI Fund
- Vista Equity Partners Fund IV

**Contact:** Thomas H Bell **Tel:** 212 455 2533
**Email:** tbell@stblaw.com

### Litigation & Arbitration:
- RBS, UBS, Deutsche Bank and other entities including Countrywide Financial in residential mortgage backed litigation and/or investigations
- JPMorgan in connection with LIBOR interest rate manipulation cases and a 2nd Circuit affirmance of dismissal in auction rate securities class actions
- AIG's Board in review and refusal of shareholder demand for a lawsuit against the US Government and the NY Federal Reserve Bank relating to AIG's bailout
- A rare non-enforcement of a $55 million Brazilian ICC international arbitration award against MatlinPatterson
- Favorable settlement during Markman for Human Genome Sciences/Glaxo Group in patent actions for Benlysta®

**Contact:** Paul C Curnin **Tel:** 212 455 2519
**Email:** pcurnin@stblaw.com
**Contact:** Thomas C Rice **Tel:** 212 455 3040
**Email:** trice@stblaw.com

### Antitrust:
- 2nd, 3rd, 5th and 6th Circuit affirmance of antitrust class action dismissals against the Fidelity family of title insurance companies and denial of certiorari by the US Supreme Court
- US antitrust counsel to Virgin Atlantic in its joint venture with Delta Air Lines
- KKR and Blackstone in a purported class action alleging conspiracy among private firms to allocate LBOs among them
- US antitrust clearance for Silver Lake in its announced

acquisition of Dell, Office Depot in its announced merger with OfficeMax, Eaton in its acquisition of Cooper Industries and Sealy in its acquisition by TempurPedic
- Priceline.com in class actions alleging a price-fixing conspiracy for hotel room rates and Viacom in a case brought by Cablevision alleging tying of programming services

**Contact:** Kevin J Arquit **Tel:** 212 455 7680
**Email:** karquit@stblaw.com

### Bankruptcy & Restructuring:
- Senior lenders or agents in the Chapter 11 proceedings or exit financings for Chrysler, Idearc, General Motors, Lee Enterprise, MF Global, MGM Studios, Oriental Trading, Reader's Digest and R.H. Donnelley

**Contact:** Peter V Pantaleo **Tel:** 212 455 2220
**Email:** ppantaleo@stblaw.com

### Energy & Infrastructure:
- Petrohawk in its $15.1 billion sale to BHP Billiton
- KKR and investor group in the $7.2 billion acquisition of Samson Investment Company
- Lenders and initial purchasers in over $2.88 billion in financings for Terra-Gen Power wind power projects
- GeoSouthern Energy in its $1 billion credit facility

**Contact:** David Lieberman **Tel:** 212 455 3545
**Email:** dlieberman@stblaw.com

### Real Estate:
- Blackstone in its $9.4 billion acquisition of the US shopping mall business of Australia's Centro Properties
- The Carlyle Group in connection with transactions for over $1 billion relating to the retail portion of 666 Fifth Avenue in New York City
- Blackstone in the restructuring of $2.9 billion of debt encumbering the La Quinta hotel chain

**Contact:** Gregory J Ressa **Tel:** 212 455 7430
**Email:** gressa@stblaw.com

SIMPSON THACHER & BARTLETT LLP

# SIVE PAGET & RIESEL, P.C.

www.sprlaw.com **tel:** 212 421 2150 **fax:** 212 421 1891

**Founding Partner:** David Sive

Number of principals: 13  Number of other lawyers: 6

**OFFICES**

NEW YORK

**NEW YORK:** 460 Park Avenue, 10th Floor, NY 10022

Tel: 212 421 2150   Fax: 212 421 1891

Email: sprlaw@sprlaw.com

## Firm Overview:

Since its inception in 1962, Sive, Paget & Riesel, P.C. has focused on environmental law and litigation. It has been instrumental in the formulation of many important precedents now comprising the body of environmental law. Today, the firm's extensive experience allows it to bring comprehensive cost-effective solutions to emerging development, business, real estate, and litigation problems that involve almost all aspects of environmental law. **Environmental Law Network:** The firm is a member of the Environmental Law Network, consisting of 18 affiliated environmental law firms throughout the United States.

## Main Areas of Practice:

### General Environmental:

Sive, Paget & Riesel, P.C. solves environmental problems in a broad array of different economic and enforcement situations. Its professional work ranges from advice on future development to the defense of criminal enforcement actions. A significant aspect of the firm's practice involves facilitating financial and real estate transactions, including the performance of due diligence, negotiation of environmental provisions in contractual documents, and obtaining appropriate insurance coverage. The firm is engaged in Superfund and Brownfield remediations, development of commercial, residential and industrial projects, electrical generating facilities, and public infrastructure.

The firm also represents industrial facilities seeking to obtain or renew air, water and hazardous waste permits. The firm provides advice to its institutional clients on their environmental compliance programs, analyzing the company's ability to meet present and ongoing environmental regulations. The firm's Environmental Litigation Practice involves all of the above described aspects of environmental law.

### Development & Land Use:

Large-scale development now faces myriad regulatory hurdles, which range from complex environmental impact studies to the remediation of hazardous waste. Often these issues become enmeshed in political disputes that further obstruct development. The firm evaluates the requirements for development and guides clients through this process by utilizing its knowledge to formulate a time sensitive course of action, assuring that the project successfully emerges from the process in the minimum period of time with a record that will withstand litigation.

**Contact:** David Paget

### Environmental Litigation:

The firm is engaged in extensive environmental litigation, which ranges from cost recovery actions under CERCLA to the defense of toxic tort actions. The firm is often called upon to litigate contract disputes involving environmental liabilities. The firm has been active in litigating decisions made by state and federal regulatory agencies. The firm is also frequently called upon to defend local governments' land use and environmental actions. Usually, the attorney handling the administrative process is the attorney that is fully prepared to litigate any judicial challenge.

**Contact:** Daniel Riesel

### Hazardous & Solid Waste:

The firm's practice involves development and enforcement problems arising from hazardous and solid waste. The firm has developed approaches and techniques to minimize the costs and time involved in the remediation of hazardous substance sites. It has also been active in the reduction, transfer and treatment of solid waste, often representing municipalities as well as private parties.

### General Litigation:

The firm has a robust Civil Litigation Practice and represents clients in matters ranging from employment and real estate litigation to construction disputes. It has also developed a speciality in representing not-for-profit organizations and academic institutions.

### Brownfield Remediation:

**Contact:** Mark Chertok

### Clients:

Sive, Paget & Riesel, P.C. represents a unique range of clients. In addition to a broad array of corporate, development and manufacturing clients, it has and continues to represent government agencies ranging from small townships to state agencies such as the Empire State Development Corporation. It represents domestic and international clients in environmental litigation and in administrative matters involving large-scale development, particularly within the New York Metropolitan area.

### International Work:

Sive, Paget & Riesel, P.C.'s extensive experience in representing the interest of the regulated community allows the firm to represent both domestic and international clients with respect to environmental problems in the United States.

# SKADDEN, ARPS, SLATE, MEAGHER & FLOM LLP & AFFILIATES

www.skadden.com  **tel:** 212 735 3000  **fax:** 212 735 2000

**Executive Partner:** Eric J Friedman
Number of US partners: 331
Number of other US lawyers: Approximately 1,200

## Firm Overview:

Serving clients in every major financial center, Skadden is one of the world's leading law firms, with 23 offices and approximately 1,800 attorneys. The firm's diversified practice enables it to offer solutions to the most challenging legal issues in virtually every area of corporate law, providing the specific legal advice clients need to compete most effectively in a global business environment. With more than 40 distinct areas of practice, the firm's attorneys provide a broad range of legal services across a spectrum of industries.

Skadden represents a wide range of clients including approximately 50 percent of the *Fortune* 250 industrial and service corporations, as well as financial and government entities, start-up companies and nonprofits. For more than 60 years, the firm has advised such entities in many of the most significant corporate and litigation matters worldwide.

## Main Areas of Practice:

### Antitrust/Competition:
Skadden has broad experience counseling clients on antitrust and competition matters in connection with highly complex mergers, acquisitions and joint ventures. The firm's attorneys appear regularly before the US Department of Justice, the Federal Trade Commission and state attorneys general in connection with proposed business combinations. They also obtain clearance from agencies around the globe, including in the EU and China, for highly complex mergers, acquisitions and joint ventures.

### Banking & Finance:
Skadden represents lenders and borrowers on some of the largest and most complex financings and related transactions worldwide. The firm's clients include some of the world's largest commercial banks, investment banks, insurance companies, public and private pension funds, finance companies, investment and merchant banking firms, private investment funds, and other institutional lenders and investors, as well as LBO sponsors, private equity funds, hedge funds, strategic buyers, borrowers and issuers of securities.

### M&A/Corporate:
Skadden is a global leader among law firms involved in mergers and acquisitions and other corporate transactions. The firm's transactional experience and breadth of practice, as well as the geographic reach of its offices, have allowed Skadden to maintain its leadership position, representing a broad array of public and private companies, private equity firms and financial sponsors, investment banks, government entities, and other institutions and individuals in almost every type of M&A situation.

### Corporate Restructuring:
Skadden serves corporations and their principal creditors and investors by providing innovative, practical legal solutions to clients involved in distressed company situations. The firm's goal is to give effective and expedient solutions, which allow clients to minimize costs, enhance value and properly position themselves for the future. Skadden has advised on some of the most widely publicized corporate restructurings and also has a substantial practice in advising clients in nonjudicial restructurings.

### International Arbitration:
With attorneys admitted to practice in more than 30 countries and territories, Skadden has established itself as a leading firm in the area of international arbitration. It has advised clients involved in international arbitrations under all major rules systems and before every major arbitral institution. The firm's international arbitration attorneys, many of whom are bilingual, also serve on international arbitration tribunals and advise clients with respect to foreign arbitral awards.

### Energy/Project Finance:
Skadden represents energy producers, transporters, marketers, distributors and users worldwide. The firm's attorneys provide clients with a full range of legal services — such as corporate, project finance, government regulatory, litigation and legislative services — relating to oil, natural gas, electric power, renewable power and other energy sources.

### Litigation/Controversy:
Skadden's global litigation/controversy practice encompasses a broad range of general commercial litigation, securities litigation, government

enforcement and white collar crime, mass torts, arbitration, trade cases and M&A-related matters. The firm is widely recognized for its experience representing clients in connection with large-scale, bet-the-company matters and other critical litigation issues.

### Real Estate:
Skadden counsels developers, lenders, investment banks, pension funds, real estate investment trusts, US and international investors, and major corporations in transactions involving the purchase, sale, construction, financing, development and management of, as well as investment in, commercial, retail, lodging, industrial and residential projects throughout the US, Europe, South America and Asia.

### Other Areas of Practice:
Environmental law, health care, insurance, intellectual property, international trade, labor and employment and tax.

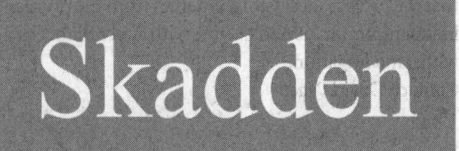

Skadden, Arps, Slate, Meagher & Flom LLP
& Affiliates

# SPEARS & IMES LLP

www.spearsimes.com   **tel:** 212 213 6996   **fax:** 212 213 0849

**OFFICES**

NEW YORK

**NEW YORK:** 51 Madison Avenue, NY 10010
Tel: 212 213 6996   Fax: 212 213 0849

### Firm Overview:

Spears & Imes LLP is a litigation boutique in New York City specializing in white collar criminal defense, securities enforcement defense and complex civil litigation. The firm's lawyers have extensive litigation experience, having tried scores of criminal and civil cases in state and federal courts and having represented clients in numerous hearings, arbitrations and mediations across the country. The firm has also helped many clients avoid charges of any kind and, where charges are filed, achieve favorable resolutions without trial.

Spears & Imes' lawyers have decades of experience defending institutions and individuals against governmental and regulatory authorities, including the U.S. Department of Justice, District Attorney's Offices, state Attorney General's Offices, the Securities and Exchange Commission ("SEC"), and the Financial Industry Regulatory Authority ("FINRA"), through investigation, trial and appeal – often in high-profile matters involving complex legal issues. The firm's lawyers have also represented preeminent domestic and international financial institutions and other entities (both as plaintiffs and defendants) in high-stakes civil lawsuits involving hundreds of millions or billions of dollars. In addition, the firm has expertise in briefing and arguing appeals in civil and criminal cases in federal and state courts and appears regularly in the U.S. Court of Appeals.

At present, Spears & Imes consists of seven male and five female lawyers. The firm employs a richly diverse group of lawyers, legal assistants and staff and is committed to continuing to attract the best talent at all levels to serve clients.

### Main Areas of Practice:

#### White-Collar Criminal Defense:

Partners David Spears, Linda Imes and Joanna Hendon served for a combined 15 years as Assistant U.S. Attorneys in the Criminal Division of the U.S. Attorney's Office for the Southern District of New York, where they were immersed in federal criminal practice. Those same partners have many more years as defense lawyers in private practice. The lawyers at Spears & Imes have defended individuals in all phases of federal and state white collar criminal proceedings, involving a wide array of charges and potential charges based on dozens of different federal and state statutes. The firm's lawyers have also conducted internal investigations for institutional clients. In criminal cases, avoiding indictment is the best possible outcome, and the firm's lawyers specialize in persuading prosecutors not to bring charges. When the firm represents clients who have been indicted, its lawyers' extensive trial experience is brought to bear. In addition, the firm has represented numerous clients in federal sentencing proceedings, and the firm's lawyers have broad experience in the pre-sentencing process, including negotiating plea agreements, communicating effectively with the U.S. Probation Office and preparing persuasive sentencing memoranda.

#### Securities Enforcement:

Spears & Imes has broad experience in defending individuals and institutions in every phase of investigations by and proceedings before the SEC and FINRA (formerly the NYSE and the NASD), including trying cases before these regulators' administrative courts. In addition, early in his career, partner David Spears spent two years as a Trial Attorney and Deputy Chief Trial Attorney in the Enforcement Division of the SEC. From 2006 to 2009, Partner Joanna Hendon worked in-house at Merrill Lynch & Co., where she was responsible for all white collar investigations involving the firm and its employees globally, as well as numerous SEC and FINRA enforcement matters and actions brought by State Attorneys General. While many of the firm's representations in the securities enforcement area have been concluded with no action being taken by the regulator and no public allegations of wrongdoing, the firm's lawyers have also represented clients in trials in U.S. District Courts in cases brought by the SEC, and in administrative hearings before the SEC and before FINRA.

#### Complex Civil Litigation:

Spears & Imes has extensive experience in complex civil litigation. The firm's lawyers have represented institutions and individuals, both as plaintiffs and defendants, in civil cases involving complex financial matters and other issues. The firm has experience in every stage of civil proceedings, including drafting pleadings, motion practice, fact discovery, expert discovery, trial, post-trial briefing and appeal.

#### Appeals:

Spears & Imes has an active and varied appellate practice. Its lawyers have extensive experience briefing and arguing appeals in civil and criminal cases, in federal and state appellate courts, and in government and private practice. Partner Linda Imes served as Deputy Chief of Appeals, Criminal Division, U.S. Attorney's Office for the Southern District of New York. Significant recent appeals include Absolute Activist Value Master Fund Ltd. v. Ficeto, 677 F.3d 60 (2d Cir. 2012) (reversing district court's dismissal of federal securities fraud claim and interpreting Supreme Court's decision in Morrison v. National Australia Bank Ltd., 130 S. Ct. 2869 (2010)), and Bayerische Landesbank, New York Branch v. Aladdin Capital Management LLC, 692 F.3d 42 (2d Cir. 2012) (reversing district court's dismissal of claims against portfolio manager of synthetic CDO).

#### Parallel Proceedings:

Spears & Imes' depth of experience across the foregoing disciplines means that its lawyers are especially qualified to defend institutions and individuals in parallel proceedings, where a criminal investigation, regulatory inquiry and private civil lawsuit progress simultaneously or in quick succession. While many law firms are experienced in dealing with one or two of these multiple practice areas, very few firms have Spears & Imes' knowledge and skill in all three areas.

#### Clients:

Spears & Imes' clients have included individuals from all over the world, as well as sophisticated institutions such as insurance companies, banks, hedge funds, private equity firms, real estate ventures, and other businesses.

**SPEARS & IMES** LLP

# STROOCK & STROOCK & LAVAN LLP

**www.**stroock.com **tel:** 212 806 5400 **fax:** 212 806 6006

**Co-Managing Partners:** Stuart H Coleman, Alan M Klinger

**Firm Overview:**

Stroock & Stroock & Lavan LLP provides transactional and litigation guidance to leading multinational corporations, investment banks and private equity firms in the US and abroad. Stroock's emphasis on client service and innovation has made it one of the nation's leading law firms for over 130 years.

**Main Areas of Practice:**

**Capital Markets/Securities:**
Advises on capital-raising transactions, including IPOs, PIPES, registered directs, private placements and Regulation S/144A transactions. Experience in structured securities, including equity-, credit- and commodity-linked notes and REIT transactions.

**Derivatives, Commodities & Energy:**
Designs vehicles and deal structures to meet specific trading, financial and credit needs; handles counterparty disputes and bankruptcies, trade defaults, margin issues, liquidations and tax, regulatory and compliance issues. Represents sponsors, buyers and sellers in generation and transmission projects, as well as lenders, equity investors and utilities in transactional and regulatory matters.

**Entertainment:**
Represents financiers, studios, networks, production companies and individuals in transactional and litigation matters, including financing, production, licensing transactions and general corporate work.

**Financial Restructuring:**
Represents creditors, investors, purchasers and debtors in bankruptcy proceedings, out-of-court restructurings and strategic and control investments.

**Financial Services Litigation:**
Represents clients in litigation involving every aspect of the financial services business. Significant experience in the defense of consumer class and representative actions brought against financial services companies.

**Government Relations:**
Advises clients on regulatory compliance and approvals, public integrity issues and litigation matters; represents elected officials, unions and private sector clients before governmental agencies.

**Insurance & Reinsurance:**
Provides integrated litigation and transactional advice within insurance and reinsurance arenas, including M&A, reserve financings, embedded value transactions, closed block reinsurance transactions, variable annuity hedging, distressed insurer transactions, derivative use and reinsurance arrangements.

**Intellectual Property:**
Advises clients on obtaining, maintaining, transferring and valuing US and international intellectual property rights, as well as litigating before state and federal courts, the US ITC and the US PTO.

**Investment Management:**
Represents more than 800 mutual funds, closed-end funds, ETFs or business development companies (or their independent board members), with nearly $1 trillion in assets under management (approximately 7% of US investment company assets), as well as investment advisers, industry service providers and unregistered pooled investment vehicles.

**Litigation:**
Handles cases before courts, public agencies, and arbitration tribunals in antitrust, commodities and securities, entertainment, financial services, healthcare, insolvency, insurance and reinsurance, intellectual property, labor, real estate and white-collar crime.

**Personal Client Services:**
Advises on estate planning and related tax work, estate and trust administration and litigation, succession planning for family businesses and charitable giving.

**Real Estate:**
Represents clients in development, acquisitions, dispositions, funds, joint ventures, REITS, financing, restructuring, lending, leasing, infrastructure, land use, cooperatives and condos, greenhouse gas and tax certiorari to real estate and financial services leaders.

## PRACTICE AREAS

Capital Markets/Securities
Commercial Finance
Derivatives & Commodities
Employee Benefits & Executive Compensation
Employment Law
Energy & Project Finance
Entertainment
Environmental Law
Financial Restructuring
Financial Services Litigation
Government Relations
Insurance & Reinsurance
Intellectual Property
Investment Management
Litigation
Mergers, Acquisitions & Joint Ventures
Personal Client Services
Private Equity
Private Funds
Real Estate
Structured Finance
Tax

## OFFICES

**NEW YORK**
**NEW YORK:** 180 Maiden Lane, NY 10038-4982
Tel: 212 806 5400 Fax: 212 806 6006

**CALIFORNIA**
**LOS ANGELES:** 2029 Century Park East, CA 90067-3086
Tel: 310 556 5800 Fax: 310 556 5959

**FLORIDA**
**MIAMI:** 200 South Biscayne Blvd., Suite 3100, FL 33131-5323
Tel: 305 358 9900 Fax: 305 789 9302

**Clients:**

Representative clients include A&P Ad Hoc Committee; American Express; Arrowpoint Capital; Dreyfus Funds; Emblem Health/HIP of Greater New York; Financial Guaranty Insurance Company; FUJIFILM; Goldman Sachs; Hess Corp.; J.P. Morgan Asset Management; Silverstein Properties; Trump Ad Hoc Committee; United Federation of Teachers.

# STROOCK

# SULLIVAN & CROMWELL LLP

www.sullcrom.com  **tel:** 212 558 4000  **fax:** 212 558 3588

**Chairman:** Joseph C Shenker
**Senior Chairman:** H Rodgin Cohen
Number of partners worldwide: 174  Number of other lawyers worldwide: 648

**Firm Overview:**
Sullivan & Cromwell LLP provides the highest quality legal advice and representation to clients worldwide. The firm's record of success and unparalleled client service has set it apart for more than 130 years and made the firm a model for the modern practice of law. Today, S&C is a leader in each of its core practice areas and geographic markets. The firm advises a diverse range of clients on major domestic and cross-border M&A and corporate finance transactions, high-stakes litigation and corporate investigations, and complex regulatory, tax and estate planning matters.

**Main Areas of Practice:**

**Antitrust & EC Competition Law:**
S&C has one of the most diverse practices of any global firm in contentious and uncontentious antitrust and competition law cases. The firm provides clients a co-ordinated approach for securing clearances in the US, the EU and elsewhere for major mergers.

**Capital Markets:**
S&C leads global rankings in both volume and value of offerings and on its ability to structure novel and effective transactions in the representation of issuers, underwriters, selling and controlling shareholders, and other market participants around the world.

**Corporate Governance:**
No law firm has a more thorough understanding of current corporate governance requirements and practices, including the implications and requirements of the Sarbanes-Oxley Act and the related SEC and stock exchange rules.

**Executive Compensation/ERISA:**
S&C advises on a full range of corporate, securities, tax and employment law matters. The firm's lawyers represent many of the largest global companies on employment arrangements, corporate governance, succession matters and incentive compensation plan design, as well as senior executives in negotiations, and play a key role in the firm's international securities and M&A practices.

**Financial Institutions:**
S&C remains the leading global law firm on transactional, regulatory, enforcement and other matters affecting financial institutions. Its expertise extends to clients in the banking, broker-dealer, commodities, futures and derivatives, insurance and investment management sectors. The firm has continued to work with clients on achieving their strategic business objectives despite the challenges of an unpredictable and often difficult global economic climate.

**Healthcare & Life Sciences:**
S&C has played a leading role in the consolidation of the healthcare industry, having advised on eight of the 10 largest pharmaceutical M&A deals to date. The firm represents the largest companies in healthcare and life sciences, as well as smaller biotechnology concerns in strategic acquisitions and capital-raising efforts. S&C has advised clients on the effects of new legislation and regulatory developments.

**Intellectual Property & Technology:**
S&C has extensive experience in handling complex intellectual property disputes, providing advice relating to the successful negotiation and completion of transactions and counseling patent licensing matters. The firm advises clients on the full spectrum of strategic and day-to-day intellectual property related issues associated with the development, acquisition and maintenance of intellectual property portfolios.

**Investment Management:**
S&C combines a traditional investment management and an alternative investment management practice to provide expertise in transactional, structuring, trading, advisory and regulatory matters. The group is at the forefront of assisting clients in the new challenges and opportunities resulting from Dodd-Frank and the changing landscape of the industry.

**Litigation:**
The firm takes a global, multidisciplinary approach to every matter and is regularly chosen as lead counsel in many of the highest profile and most complex matters before courts, arbitration panels and regulators. The strength of its practice is reflected in independent rankings, including #1 rankings by Chambers for general commercial, securities, white-collar crime and government investigations litigation. The firm maintains a strong record of success in its Labor and Employment Practice.

**Mergers & Acquisitions:**
The leading firm in global M&A, S&C mobilizes teams of lawyers worldwide for clients on their largest and most important domestic and cross-border transactions. The firm ranks first by value among law firms over the last 10 years (2003-2012), having acted in approximately $3.96 trillion in announced transactions worldwide.

**Private Equity:**
S&C advises private equity funds, portfolio companies and bidding vehicles on both strategic M&A and other investments and on capital markets and M&A exit strategies in a range of industries worldwide.

**Project Development & Finance:**
S&C is a leader in corporate finance, including project, leveraged and infrastructure finance and has a strong practice in natural resource projects and public-private partnership structures for infrastructure in developed and emerging markets.

**Real Estate:**
S&C combines public/private market expertise and innovative dealmaking skills to assist clients in purchasing, selling, developing and financing real estate companies and assets worldwide, and represents prominent clients in restructuring real estate and other assets to facilitate generational transition and/or resolve disputes.

**Restructuring & Bankruptcy:**
S&C provides clients the creative and commercially effective advice necessary to weather market changes. The group helps clients buy and sell distressed businesses, extend credit with less risk, protect their rights during counterparty bankruptcies, establish best practices for corporate governance insolvency and preserve the value of their businesses while changing capital structures.

**Tax:**
S&C has a global reputation for innovative tax planning, the successful resolution of important tax controversies, as well as providing pivotal tax advice on corporate transactions. S&C plays a significant role in structuring new, tax-advantaged financial instruments and complex M&A transactions, and represents prominent industrial and commercial enterprises in US, French, UK and cross-border tax matters.

## OFFICES

CALIFORNIA
**LOS ANGELES:** 1888 Century Park East, CA 90067-1725
Tel: 310 712 6600  Email: sacksr@sullcrom.com

**PALO ALTO:** 1870 Embarcadero Road, CA 94303-3308
Tel: 650 461 5600  Email: savvaj@sullcrom.com

DISTRICT OF COLUMBIA
**WASHINGTON, DC:** 1701 Pennsylvania Avenue, NW, DC 20006-5805
Tel: 202 956 7500  Email: libowd@sullcrom.com

NEW YORK
**NEW YORK:** 125 Broad Street, NY 10004-2498
Tel: 212 558 4000  Fax: 212 558 3588
Email: shenkerj@sullcrom.com

## INTERNATIONAL OFFICES
The firm also has offices in Beijing, Frankfurt, Hong Kong, London, Melbourne, Paris, Sydney and Tokyo

# WACHTELL, LIPTON, ROSEN & KATZ

**www.wlrk.com  tel:** 212 403 1000  **fax:** 212 403 2000

**Co-Chairmen of the Executive Committee:** Edward D Herlihy, Daniel A Neff
Number of partners worldwide: 81
Number of other lawyers worldwide: 167

### Firm Overview:

Wachtell, Lipton, Rosen & Katz enjoys a global reputation as one of the world's leading business law firms. The firm's vast experience means it regularly handles many of the largest, most complex and demanding transactions in the United States and around the world. Wachtell Lipton also focuses on sensitive investigation and litigation matters and corporate restructurings, and in counseling boards of directors and senior management in the most sensitive situations.

### A Unique Approach:

Wachtell Lipton approaches its clients' legal issues always within the larger framework of the client's strategic, business and financial goals. The firm focuses on matters that require the attention, extensive experience, expertise and reputation of its partners. In order to provide this partner-intensive service, the firm generally does not handle routine matters, it limits the number and type of matters it undertakes and it operates with a ratio of partners to associates far above that of major competitors. Matters undertaken by the firm are at all times afforded the direct personal attention of partners having expertise and sophistication with respect to the issues.

### People:

Wachtell Lipton is consistently ranked as one of the most prestigious and desirable law firms to work for in the United States, enabling the firm to attract the most outstanding and motivated attorneys and law school graduates in the United States and from around the world.

### Achievements:

Wachtell Lipton consistently ranks near the very top of legal advisors by transaction dollar volume, even though it is significantly smaller than all of its major competitors. Over the past ten years, the firm has been the legal advisor on four of the five largest transactions in the United States and four of the ten largest transactions globally, as well as numerous other acquisition and restructuring transactions across many industries and of every description.

### Clients:

Clients include enterprises of virtually every nature in the United States and around the world, including industrial firms, financial institutions, leveraged buyout houses, securities firms, healthcare and pharmaceutical providers, technology companies and media and information systems companies, many of which are Fortune 500 companies and other leading enterprises.

### Advancing the Law:

The firm has repeatedly contributed to major evolutions in corporate law in order to advance the interests of its clients. Among other things, Wachtell Lipton originated the shareholder rights plan or the 'poison pill', structured the first cross-border 'Morris Trust' transaction between SmithKline Beckman and Beecham and has been involved in the transactions giving rise to most of the landmark corporate governance decisions in Delaware, including Household, Revlon, Newmont Mining, Macmillan, Interco, Time Warner, QVC and, most recently, Airgas. The firm also represented the successful defendants in Morrison v. National Australia Bank, the landmark US Supreme Court case that sharply limited the extraterritorial reach of US securities laws.

### Main Areas of Practice:

#### Corporate/M&A:

Wachtell Lipton handles some of the largest and most complex US and international transactions. It advises on a range of corporate matters, including mergers and acquisitions, spin-offs, public offerings, capital raising transactions and innovative financial products. In addition, Wachtell Lipton is recognised as a leading firm for takeover defence, shareholder activism and corporate governance.

Recent major US representations have included:
- Supervalu in its sale of its New Albertson's business and concurrent tender offer of up to 30% of its shares to Cerberus in a transaction valued at $3.3 billion
- Freeport-McMoran Copper and Gold in its $3.4 billion acquisition of McMoran Exploration and its $6.9 billion acquisition of Plains Exploration and Production
- Coventry Healthcare in its pending $7.3 billion sale to Aetna
- Sunoco in its $5.3 billion acquisition by Energy Transfer Partners
- AOL in its auction and subsequent $1.1 billion sale of most of its patent portfolio to Microsoft
- Alleghany Corporation in its $3.4 billion acquisition of Transatlantic Holdings
- El Paso Corporation in its $38 billion sale to Kinder Morgan
- United Technologies Corporation in its $18.4 billion acquisition of Goodrich Corporation
- Motorola Mobility Holdings in its $12.5 billion sale to Google
- Temple-Inland in its $3.7 billion sale to International Paper following a hostile tender offer by International Paper
- The PNC Financial Services Group in its $3.45 billion acquisition of RBC Bank (USA)
- Airgas in successfully defending against a $5.8 billion hostile bid and proxy contest by Air Products and Chemicals
- Duke Energy in its $32 billion merger with Progress Energy

Recent major cross-border or non-US representations have included:
- Deutsche Telekom and T-Mobile USA in the agreed combination of T-Mobile and MetroPCS Communications at a $30 billion enterprise valuation
- Alibaba Group in restructuring its relationship with Yahoo!, including repurchasing $7.8 billion of Yahoo!'s holdings in Alibaba
- Walgreen Co. in its acquisition of a 45% stake in Alliance Boots GmbH and option to acquire the remaining 55% of Alliance Boots, valued at $27 billion
- GlaxoSmithKline plc in its unsolicited offer for, and subsequent $3.6 billion acquisition of, Human Genome Sciences
- América Móvil, S.A.B. de C.V. in its acquisition of 21% of Telekom Austria AG
- Cooper Industries plc in its $11.8 billion combination with Eaton Corporation
- Deutsche Telekom in its $39 billion agreed sale of T-Mobile to AT&T
- Genzyme in its response to an unsolicited takeover and in the subsequent $20 billion negotiated sale to

**PRACTICE AREAS**

Corporate
Litigation
Restructuring & Finance
Executive Compensation & Benefits
Antitrust
Tax
Real Estate M&A

**OFFICES**

NEW YORK
**NEW YORK:** 51 West 52 Street, NY 10019

# WACHTELL, LIPTON, ROSEN & KATZ CONT'D

Sanofi-Aventis
- NYSE Euronext in its pending $8.2 billion acquisition by IntercontinentalExchange, Inc., its $23.4 billion agreed merger with Deutsche Börse and the NYSE in its prior mergers with Euronext, the American Stock Exchange and Archipelago
- Chesapeake Energy in its $2.2 billion sale to CNOOC

Recent spin-off representations have included:
- Covidien plc in its spin-off of its pharmaceuticals business
- Abbott Labs in its separation into two publicly traded companies
- ConocoPhillips in the spin-off of its refining business
- Expedia in the spin-off of TripAdvisor
- Marathon Oil Corporation in the spin-off of its downstream business, renamed Marathon Petroleum Corp.
- Ralcorp in the spin-off of Post Foods
- Sunoco in its initial public offering and subsequent spin-off of SunCoke Energy
- ITT Corporation in its spin-off of the defence and information solutions segment

**Sponsors & Financial Entrepreneurs:**
Wachtell Lipton works closely with leading private equity and hedge fund sponsors. The firm advises sponsors in forming and raising private funds that specialise in a variety of investments, including LBOs, venture capital, distressed debt, loan-to-own, structured financings, financial services platforms and real estate. The firm regularly handles complex M&A and other transactions for sponsors and financial entrepreneurs, such as portfolio investments, corporate acquisitions, PIPEs, sale and IPO exit transactions and financings. The firm advises on reorganisations of sponsors themselves, spinouts and sales of investment managers. In addition, the firm has counselled on significant compliance issues and government investigations involving asset managers.

**Shareholder Activism:**
Wachtell Lipton is a leading defender of companies that are under attack by shareholder activists. The firm has advised numerous public companies in responding to activist shareholders as well as other hedge fund and corporate governance activists.

**Corporate Governance:**
The firm is a thought leader in the area of corporate governance. It has represented the NYSE in connection with the Exchange's listing standards and corporate governance initiatives for listed companies. It has represented a number of major corporations in connection with corporate governance and related matters; it has also advised special committees of boards of directors in connection with corporate

governance investigations and related matters.

**National & International Litigation Practice:**
Wachtell Lipton's litigation practice is consistently at the cutting edge of the leading commercial and corporate litigation battles dominating headlines. Clients are in diverse industries, including finance, insurance, media, high-tech, energy, industrial, consumer, retail and real estate. A tight-knit group of approximately 75 lawyers, they approach each matter with intensity, thoroughness and creativity and build teams appropriate to the circumstances. The firm makes appearances in state and federal courts throughout the country at both trial and appellate levels, as well as in arbitrations and mediations. It also has a leading practice representing companies and individuals in state and federal regulatory and criminal investigations. Many of the firm's litigators served as law clerks in federal or state courts, and several distinguished themselves as assistant United States attorneys or as enforcement attorneys at the SEC.

**Takeover & Merger Litigation:**
The firm is considered one of the leading transaction and takeover litigation firms in the country, having litigated many of the seminal cases establishing US takeover law, including: Moran v. Household Int'l Inc.; Revlon Inc. v. MacAndrews & Forbes Holdings, Inc.; Paramount Communications, Inc. v. Time, Inc.; Paramount Communications, Inc. v. QVC Network, Inc.; and IBP, Inc. v. Tyson Foods. Recent representations have included Airgas in its landmark takeover defence against Air Products, Vulcan Materials in its defence of a bid from Martin Marietta Materials and Lionsgate Entertainment in its closely watched takeover battle. The firm's litigators also advise on a range of corporate governance matters and handle derivative demands and other litigation challenging the actions of boards of directors.

**Complex Commercial & Securities Litigation:**
The firm consistently handles some of the nation's leading commercial disputes covering diverse industries and subject matters.
Recent representations have included:
- National Australia Bank in the landmark Morrison case, in which the United States Supreme Court held that Section 10(b) of the Securities Exchange Act and SEC Rule 10b-5 apply only to purchases and sales of securities in the United States. The decision overturned 40 years of lower-court precedent and eradicated a burgeoning species of securities litigation (so-called "foreign-cubed" and "foreign-squared" class actions) along with billions of dollars in potential liability for foreign securities issuers.

- JPMorgan Chase in the $19 billion litigation brought against it by the trustee for the liquidation of Bernard Madoff's failed firm, in which the firm was able successfully to remove the case from bankruptcy court to federal district court and have the majority of claims dismissed
- Bank of America in negotiating Bank of America's $8.5 billion settlement of claims involving more than 500 trusts for mortgage-backed securities issued by Countrywide and in resolving multibillion-dollar claims arising from the foreclosure crisis with the federal government and 49 state attorneys general
- Philip Morris USA in the multibillion-dollar arbitration that has arisen under the landmark 1998 settlement between the major tobacco companies and 52 states and territories. Wachtell Lipton previously had the lead role structuring and negotiating this more than $200 billion settlement.

**White-Collar & Regulatory Enforcement:**
The firm has a leading white-collar and regulatory enforcement practice. It has represented major financial institutions and multinational corporations, as well as their boards of directors and senior executives, in a broad range of the most complex and typically high-profile white-collar criminal and regulatory enforcement matters, both nationally and internationally. In the past few years alone, firm litigators have handled both US and foreign governmental investigations, focusing on the Foreign Corrupt Practices Act, criminal tax evasion, criminal transfer pricing, the False Claims Act, insider trading, securities fraud, accounting fraud, criminal antitrust and export control violations. In addition, the firm regularly represents boards, audit committees and special committees charged with conducting special investigations in response to whistleblowers or governmental inquiries.

**Pro Bono:**
The firm has an active pro bono litigation practice. Attorneys are encouraged to take on pro bono matters with the full support of the firm and many take advantage of this opportunity. A recent representation was on behalf of the Chief Judge of the State of New York in historic litigation over the state's failure to increase the pay of its judges since 1999. The firm's efforts helped achieve a decision by the state's Court of Appeals holding that, as a matter of state constitutional law, judicial pay cannot be treated as a political matter by the executive and the legislature, but rather must be sufficient to attract well-qualified individuals to serve on the bench.

**Restructuring & Finance:**

# WACHTELL, LIPTON, ROSEN & KATZ CONT'D

Wachtell Lipton has one of the leading restructuring practices in the nation, principally representing banks, hedge funds, private equity funds and other creditors and acquirors in national and multinational bankruptcy cases and out-of-court restructurings. Attorneys in the firm's restructuring practice regularly handle complicated acquisitions or divestitures of businesses in financial distress or bankruptcy, highly-leveraged transactions and other major transactions involving significant debtor/creditor issues. The group's attorneys represented the United States Treasury in connection with the rescues of Fannie Mae and Freddie Mac, including the Treasury's multibillion-dollar investment in the Senior Preferred Stock of the GSEs following the commencement of their conservatorships. Recent restructuring engagements include the representation of major lenders, derivatives counterparties and equity holders in the following chapter 11 cases and out-of-court restructurings: Lehman Brothers, MF Global, Graceway Pharmaceuticals, Hawker Beechcraft, Mach Gem. LLC, Arcapita Bank, Lifecare Holdings, Washington Mutual, Lyondell Chemical, Aleris International, Fairpoint Communications, Hard Rock Hotel, Reddy Ice, Cinram International, Baha Mar, Kerzner, CNL Properties, Thornburg Mortgage, Dreier, Madoff and Terrestar Corporation. In addition, the firm has represented acquirors in the Innkeepers chapter 11 proceeding and potential acquirors in the Blockbuster and NorTel bankruptcy cases, as well as several casino cases. Wachtell Lipton has a market-leading financing practice, with extensive experience in all types of financing transactions, including senior secured facilities, bridge facilities, Rule144A and registered high-yield and investment-grade bond offerings, tender offers, exchange offers and consent solicitations. Many of the firm's financings extend across multiple national borders, and its lawyers are experienced in solving the complex issues that arise in multinational situations and in making sure that cross-border transactions benefit from the latest developments in the financing markets, which often originate in New York. Recent representations have included:

- Abbvie Inc. in its $14.7 billion private offering of senior notes in connection with the separation of Abbvie and Abbott Labs
- United Technologies with obtaining a $15 billion bridge facility to support its acquisition of Goodrich, refinancing two revolving credit facilities, and issuing $10 billion of senior notes and $1 billion of equity units
- Deutsche Telecom/T-Mobile with $20 billion financing in connection with its combination with MetroPCS
- Walgreen Co. with a $3.5 billion bridge financing and subsequent bond take-out in connection with its initial investment for 45% of Alliance Boots
- Kellogg's in connection with obtaining $1 billion bridge financing in connection with its acquisition of Pringles
- PVH with obtaining $4.3 billion of bank and bridge financing commitments to support its acquisition of Warnaco
- Chicago Bridge & Iron in connection with financing commitments of $3.3 billion for its acquisition of Shaw Group

## High-Profile Bankruptcy Litigation:

The firm's specialised litigators handle high-profile litigation matters involving bankruptcy, restructuring and finance issues. Current matters include representing JPMorgan Chase in multibillion-dollar litigations in the Lehman Brothers and Madoff bankruptcy cases, and representing Credit Suisse in multiple lawsuits arising in the Thornburg Mortgage bankruptcy case. Significant prior engagements include key litigation arising in the contexts of the Boston Generating, Innkeepers and National Century Financial Enterprises bankruptcy cases.

## Executive Compensation & Benefits:

Attorneys in the Executive Compensation and Benefits Group work closely with the most senior executives of the firm's clients to address some of the most sensitive issues facing public and private companies, both in deal and non-deal contexts. Executive compensation arrangements often are the foundation of people-based businesses, and management succession, board composition and similar issues are essential to the success of business combinations. The practice continues to evolve as corporate governance standards and executive compensation laws change and expand in response to shareholder activism, pressure from the media and recent unprecedented governmental participation in the management of business enterprises. In this regard, the group has extensive experience in advising institutions receiving assistance from the US government.

## Antitrust:

Wachtell Lipton's Antitrust Practice focuses on mergers and acquisitions and government investigations, including international antitrust and banking antitrust issues. The group analyses transactions to assess potential antitrust issues, develops strategies to address those concerns, and represents clients before the DOJ's Antitrust Division, the FTC, the Board of Governors of the Federal Reserve System, state attorneys general and foreign antitrust enforcement authorities and in litigation challenging transactions on antitrust grounds.

## Tax:

Wachtell Lipton's tax attorneys regularly advise clients on the tax aspects of corporate reorganisations, acquisitions, spin-offs and other dispositions, financings, restructurings and joint ventures. These transactions frequently involve large multinational businesses and raise complex domestic and multinational tax issues. Indeed, tax considerations often determine the form, and occasionally the viability, of contemplated transactions. The group, working together with the corporate and restructuring and finance departments, frequently is called on to participate in the restructuring of existing financial arrangements, including those arising out of private equity and other leveraged transactions. The group is also involved in creating new financial products and in innovative real estate transactions. Members of the group regularly publish and lecture on emerging tax issues and actively participate in the work of tax policy groups, such as the Tax Section of the New York State Bar Association and the International Fiscal Association.

## Real Estate M&A:

Wachtell Lipton's Real Estate Department has a leading practice focused on mergers and acquisitions, private equity, corporate governance, restructurings and joint ventures across the REIT, real estate, hospitality and gaming sectors. The firm consistently plays an active role in major transactions in these sectors, with particular emphasis on large-scale public company M&A and strategic transactions. It has played a leading role in the redevelopment of the World Trade Center and in many of the significant REIT mergers, buyouts and takeovers over the last decade. Representations have included:

- Sunrise Senior Living in its $1.9 billion sale to Health Care REIT
- Simon Property Group in its €1.5 billion acquisition of a stake in Klépierre from BNP Paribas, its $31 billion bid for GGP and its $2.3 billion acquisition of Prime
- The $14 billion merger of equals of ProLogis and AMB that created the largest global industrial REIT with combined assets of $46 billion
- Ventas in its $7.4 billion acquisition of Nationwide Health Properties, Inc., in its $3.1 billion acquisition of Atria's senior housing portfolio and in its $2 billion acquisition of the Sunrise Senior Living REIT
- Chatham Lodging Trust in its bids, partly in a joint venture with Cerberus Capital Management, to acquire 69 hotels for $1.3 billion in Innkeepers USA Trust's bankruptcy auctions
- Silverstein Properties in the redevelopment of the World Trade Center
- Tishman Speyer and Lehman in their $22 billion acquisition of the Archstone apartment REIT

# WEIL, GOTSHAL & MANGES LLP

**www.**weil.com **tel:** 212 310 8000 **fax:** 212 310 8007

**Chairman:** Stephen J Dannhauser **Executive Partner:** Barry M Wolf
Number of partners worldwide: 309 Number of other lawyers worldwide: 938

## Firm Overview:

Weil, Gotshal & Manges LLP is a leader in the marketplace for sophisticated, global legal services. Weil's pioneering 'one firm' approach, including the integration of 21 offices, multiple practice areas, and approximately 1200 attorneys, allows the firm to partner with many of the world's most successful organisations on matters as complex and interconnected as the businesses themselves.

## Main Areas of Practice:

### Business Finance & Restructuring:

Weil has been involved in countless international and US restructurings over the past decade, with representations ranging from top global corporations in mega-restructurings to middle-market debtors. Weil has served as chief debtors' counsel in five of the six largest US bankruptcy filings in history and has represented clients in numerous complicated cross-border insolvency and restructuring matters, including Lehman Bros (the largest US bankruptcy) and the joint special administrators to MF Global UK.

### M&A:

With more than 600 corporate lawyers across the US, Europe, and Asia, Weil is regularly involved in the largest and most complex transactions in the world. The firm regularly ranks among the top ten firms globally for volume of M&A transactions. In 2012, Weil advised on several multi-billion deals including: the sale of AMC to Dalian Wanda; the sale of Lincare to Linde; the Special Committee of the Board of Directors of Shanda Interactive Entertainment in one of the largest going private transactions of a Chinese business listed in the US; and Leucadia's merger with Jefferies Group, among many others.

### Private Equity:

Weil's prominent Private Equity Practice features more than 200 lawyers with expertise in fund formation and buyout transactions, including 60 full time funds lawyers practicing in Asia, Europe, and the US. The firm advised on more than 15 transactions valued at US$1 billion or more in 2012, for many of the largest private equity funds by assets under management, including Advent, Providence, and THL Partners. The firm advises its private equity clients in investments and sales in every part of the world. Weil is among the top five firms globally in Bloomberg's annual ranking of legal advisors in this space.

### Finance:

Weil's leading finance practices include premier global leveraged and acquisition lawyers and highly ranked capital markets and structured finance teams its Asia, Europe, and the US. The firm's lawyers work with leading investment banks and corporate issuers in cross-border debt, equity, high-yield debt, initial public offerings, private placements, secondary offerings, acquisition finance, cash flow and asset based lending, cross-border financing, debtor-in-possession financing, exit financing, restructurings, and investment-grade financing. Weil recently advised Goldman Sachs as lead arranger in the US$3.5 billion bridge facility for Walgreens' US$6.7 billion strategic investment in Alliance Boots, and Goldman Sachs and Merrill Lynch as underwriters in the related $4 billion bond financing.

### Litigation:

Weil's highly ranked, 400-attorney international Litigation Department offers sophisticated, 'one-stop' service and legal advice across all areas of the law, at all phases of the litigation process, and before courts, arbitration tribunals, and regulators in jurisdictions around the globe. In 2012, Weil was lead or co-lead counsel on many high-profile matters, including representation of: the world's second largest entertainment ticketing company in a US$900 million dispute regarding a ticketing agreement; H&H Enterprises Investments in a pending ICSID arbitration arising out of the company's multi-hundred million dollar investment in Egypt; Providence Equity in the 'club deal' LBO litigation - one of the largest class actions in the US; AIG, CBS, and GE, respectively, in high-value securities fraud litigation; GE in a multi-forum dispute with Japan-based Mitsubishi Heavy Industries regarding wind turbine technology; and SEACOR in the mass tort litigation arising out of the 2010 Gulf of Mexico oil spit.

### Tax:

Weil's Tax Practice is integrated with the firm's extensive mergers and acquisitions team, structuring complex, innovative, taxable and tax-free transactions, including joint ventures and spin-offs, and also regularly counsels the firm's clients in the private equity, venture capital, and investment funds marketplace. With lawyers who are well-versed in the tax and employee benefit laws of the US, the UK, France, Germany and Poland, Weil brings a combined experience together to deliver coordinated tax advice in all types of regional and cross-border transactions.

### Executive Compensation & Employee Benefits:

The Executive Compensation and Employee Benefits Practice at Weil advises clients globally in all aspects of compensation and benefits that arise in M&A transactions, and regularly provides advice on senior executive employment arrangements, stock options, restricted stock and other equity compensation, deferred compensation arrangements, golden parachutes, and pension plans. The group also advises Weil's clients on the often complex and interrelated ERISA, tax, securities law, and financial accounting issues that arise in their compensation and benefit programs.

### Pro Bono:

The cornerstone of Weil's award-winning Pro Bono Practice is the firm's ground-breaking pro bono policy, which includes the goal that every lawyer perform 50 hours of pro bono work each year; the expectation that every partner work on a pro bono matter every year; and the requirement that every new attorney take on a pro bono matter within their first two years at the firm. The firm has been recognised by the ABA and Pro Bono Institute for the caliber and volume of its pro bono contributions. The firm's dedication in this area has led to its inclusion with The American Lawyer's "A List" of top firms for both financial success and corporate social responsibility.

## OFFICES

CALIFORNIA
**SILICON VALLEY:** 201 Redwood Shores Parkway, Redwood Shores, CA 94065
Tel: 650 802 3000  Fax: 650 802 3100

DELAWARE
**WILMINGTON:** 1201 N Market Street, Suite 1402, DE 19801
Tel: 302 656 6600  Fax: 302 656 1405

DISTRICT OF COLUMBIA
**WASHINGTON DC:** 1300 Eye Street NW, Suite 900, DC 20005
Tel: 202 682 7000  Fax: 202 857 0940

FLORIDA
**MIAMI:** 1395 Brickell Avenue, Suite 1200, FL 33131
Tel: 305 577 3100  Fax: 305 374 7159

MASSACHUSETTS
**BOSTON:** 100 Federal Street, 34th Floor, MA 02110
Tel: 617 772 8300  Fax: 617 772 8333

NEW JERSEY
**PRINCETON:** 301 Carnegie Center, Suite 303, NJ 08540
Tel: 609 986 1100  Fax: 609 986 1199

RHODE ISLAND
**PROVIDENCE:** 50 Kennedy Plaza, 11th Floor, RI 02903
Tel: 401 278 4700  Fax: 401 278 4701

TEXAS
**DALLAS:** 200 Crescent Court, Suite 300, TX 75201-6950
Tel: 214 746 7700  Fax: 214 746 7777

**HOUSTON:** 700 Louisiana, Suite 1600, TX 77002
Tel: 713 546 5000  Fax: 713 224 9511

## INTERNATIONAL OFFICES

The firm has offices in Beijing, Budapest, Dubai, Frankfurt, Hong Kong, London, Munich, Paris, Prague, Shanghai, and Warsaw.

# WILLKIE FARR & GALLAGHER LLP

**www.**willkie.com **tel:** 212 728 8000 **fax:** 212 728 8111

**Co-Chairmen:** Thomas M Cerabino; Steven J Gartner
Number of partners: 151
Number of lawyers: 385
Languages: *Dutch, English, French, German, Italian*

## Firm Overview:

Established in 1888, Willkie Farr & Gallagher LLP is a full-service international law firm renowned for its expertise in corporate and securities law, litigation, business reorganization and restructuring, real estate and a number of specialized fields including insurance, technology, media and telecommunications, tax, antitrust and competition, government relations, intellectual property, trusts and estates, executive compensation and employee benefits and environmental law. From offices in New York, Washington, Paris, London, Milan, Rome, Frankfurt and Brussels, Willkie provides clients with creativity and skill in structuring and implementing complex transactions and trusted counsel on critical business and legal issues in virtually all areas of business law.

## Main Areas of Practice:

### M&A:

The firm specializes in representing buyers, sellers and investors in LBOs, mergers, acquisitions, tender offers, joint ventures and all related types of transactions in a broad range of industries.

- Represented AboveNet's board of directors in $2.2 billion acquisition of AboveNet, Inc. by Zayo Group LLC
- Advised Aviva plc in $1.8 billion sale of Aviva USA Corporation, its U.S. life and annuities business and related asset management operations, to Athene Holding Ltd.
- Represented Loral Space & Communications Inc. in $1 billion sale of Space Systems/Loral to Canada-based MacDonald, Dettwiler and Associates Ltd.

**Contact:** David K Boston **Tel:** 212 728 8625
**Email:** dboston @willkie.com
**Contact:** Steven A Seidman **Tel:** 212 728 8763
**Email:** sseidman@willkie.com

### Private Equity:

The firm is highly skilled in private equity transactions ranging from complex LBOs that have multi-tiered capital structures to minority investments that address governance and liquidity issues.

- Represented Riverstone Holdings LLC as part of consortium's $7.15 billion LBO of El Paso Corporation's exploration and production units
- Advised AXA Private Equity in sale of majority stake in HSE24 Group to Providence Equity Partners

**Contact:** Gordon Caplan **Tel:** 212 728 8266
**Email:** gcaplan@willkie.com

### Capital Markets:

The firm assists both issuers and underwriters in domestic and international offerings of equity and debt securities and advises clients on all public securities offerings, flotations and financial regulations.

- Represented Teva Pharmaceutical Industries Limited in its $2 billion offering of senior notes
- Advised REIT Ventas, Inc. in $1.13 billion secondary offering
- Represented Ryerson in its offering of $900 million principal amount of senior notes and related tender offers and consent solicitations

**Contact:** Gregory B Astrachan **Tel:** 212 728 8608
**Email:** gastrachan@willkie.com
**Contact:** Peter H Jakes **Tel:** 212 728 8230
**Email:** pjakes@willkie.com

### Complex Litigation:

Willkie is known for its expertise in most major areas of business and corporate litigation, including shareholders' disputes, battle for corporate control, antitrust, compliance and enforcement (FCPA, the U.K. Bribery Act, anti-money laundering, export controls, and trade and financial sanctions) and professional liability actions. It is frequently sought to intervene as counsel or arbitrators in various national and international arbitrations.

- Advised 26 underwriters in multibillion-dollar GE securities litigation
- Represented Facebook in winning dismissal of IPO derivative case in U.S. District Court for Southern District of New York (co-counsel)
- Won dismissal of a $200 million RICO action against Alcatel-Lucent that grew out of an FCPA investigation

**Contact:** Mitchell J Auslander **Tel:** 212 728 8201
**Email:** mauslander@willkie.com
**Contact:** Kevin B Clark **Tel:** +1 202 303 1105
**Email:** kclark@willkie.com

### Antitrust & Competition:

Willkie represents clients in resolving all types of antitrust matters, including national and international merger filings, investigations of alleged cartels, abuses of dominance and other anti-competitive behavior.

- Represented MasterCard in historic settlement in multibillion-dollar class action litigation
- Advised GDF Suez in European antitrust case in which European Union slashed EC antitrust fines by 42 percent

**Contact:** William H Rooney **Tel:** 212 728 8259
**Email:** wrooney@willkie.com

### Business Reorganisation & Restructuring:

The firm regularly assists public and private corporations in internal restructurings and strategic alliances, including in relation to potential insolvency issues. It is regularly involved in judicial stay and bankruptcy proceedings as counsel to debtors and creditors.

- Representing Bank of America as lead counsel in connection with MF Global bankruptcy
- Advised lenders on successful restructuring of Quiznos sandwich chain
- Represented the Teamsters National Freight Industry Negotiating Committee of the International Brotherhood of Teamsters in the out-of-court restructuring of YRC Worldwide, Inc.
- International work included advising Anovo throughout its court-supervised reorganization procedure, including its sale to Butler Capital Partners

**Contact:** Marc Abrams **Tel:** 212 728 8200
**Email:** mabrams@willkie.com
**Contact:** Matthew A Feldman **Tel:** 212 728 8651
**Email:** mfeldman@willkie.com

### Asset Management:

The firm is recognized as preeminent in the asset management area and provides a wide array of legal services to, among other clients, registered and regulated open-end and closed-end funds, hedge funds, private equity funds and other private funds, and their sponsors, advisers, directors, partners, managers, shareholders, clients and service providers.

**Contact:** Barry P Barbash **Tel:** 202 303 1201
**Email:** bbarbash@willkie.com

## PRACTICE AREAS

M&A
Private Equity
Capital Markets
Complex Litigation
Antitrust & Competition
Business Reorganisation & Restructuring
Asset Management

## US OFFICES

**NEW YORK:** 787 Seventh Avenue, NY 10019-6099
Tel:212 728 8000  Fax: 212 728 8111

**WASHINGTON, DC:** 1875 K Street, NW, DC 20006-1238
Tel: 202 303 1000  Fax: 202 303 2000

# WILSON ELSER MOSKOWITZ EDELMAN & DICKER LLP

**www.**wilsonelser.com  **tel:** 212 490 3000  **fax:** 212 490 3038

## Firm Overview:

Wilson Elser helps individuals and organizations transcend challenges and realize goals by offering an optimal balance of legal excellence and bottom-line value. Nearly 800 attorneys strong, the firm serves clients of all sizes, across multiple industries and around the world. Wilson Elser has 24 strategically located offices in the United States, another in London and several European affiliates. This depth and scale has made them one of the nation's most influential law firms, ranked in the Am Law 100 and in the top 50 of the National Law Journal 250.

Since its founding in 1978, Wilson Elser has forged a reputation as a formidable player in insurance coverage and defense. The firm's experience in this tightly regulated, cost-conscious industry has shaped a culture of accomplished professionalism and efficiency that delivers demonstrable value to clients. Today, Wilson Elser provides clients with full-service, first-class legal services, spanning the spectrum of litigation as well as business and financial transactions.

## Main Areas of Practice:

Wilson Elser counsels insurance carriers worldwide on all aspects of high-stakes litigation and coverage analysis. It is recognized globally as a – if not the – leading law firm serving the insurance industry. While best known for its skills in "public facing" lawsuits, the firm also handles smaller, less far-reaching matters with the same degree of rigor and discipline.

Wilson Elser also provides the services of attorneys skilled at addressing the complex legal issues that accompany business and financial transactions. Comprising some of the firm's most prominent and seasoned partners, this team has extensive experience representing clients on a broad range of related matters. Assisted by a cadre of talented associates, they make strategic use of direct lines to other firm practices and resources.

Wilson Elser's practice areas include: Admiralty & Marine, Alternate Dispute Resolution, Appellate, Asbestos, Aviation & Aerospace, Bankruptcy, Class Action Defense, Commercial & Business Litigation, Commercial Contracts & Agreements, Construction, Corporate Governance & Compliance, Crisis Management, Data Security & Cyber Liability, Directors & Officers Liability, e-Discovery, Employment & Labor, Energy, Environmental, Fidelity/Surety, Financial Institutions, Financial Services, General Liability & Casualty, Government Affairs, Government Contacts, Government Investigations, Health Care Law, Hospitality, Intellectual Property, Insurance & Regulatory Compliance, Insurance & Reinsurance Coverage, Insurance & Reinsurance Defense, Insurance & Reinsurance Transactions, Life, Health, Disability & ERISA, Liquor Licensing, Lobby Law Compliance, Municipal/Local Government, Pharmaceuticals & Medical Devices, Product Liability, Professional Liability & Services, Program Management, Real Estate & Development, Risk Analysis & Mitigation, Securities, Senior Trial Group, Toxic Tort and Transportation.

## Litigation:

Wilson Elser is proud of its reputation as one of the largest and most successful litigation firms in the world, due in no small part to the vast experience of its senior litigating partners. Its litigators tailor strategic and cost-effective approaches to each case. By evaluating the strengths and weaknesses of a client's position, they determine the options at each stage of the litigation cycle and adjust their strategy accordingly. The firm's trial attorneys have successfully tried thousands of cases and spared clients the risks and costs of trial in thousands more by obtaining early dismissals or summary judgments. Indeed, opposing counsel's familiarity with the talents and tenacity of these attorneys often leads to early and satisfactory case resolutions.

## Business & Financial Transactions:

Wilson Elser's accomplished representation spans most of the principal business and transactional areas, including mergers and acquisitions, divestitures, commercial contracts and agreements, financings, securities offerings, federal and state reporting and compliance, governance matters, public offerings and private placements.

Whether a case involves routine bankruptcy litigation or more complicated insolvency or corporate reorganizations, the firm's attorneys are committed to providing clients with the highest standard of excellence and consistent, demonstrable value.

## Clients:

Wilson Elser represents a large and diverse base of clients, from entrepreneurial startups to established multinationals. Most are headquartered – or transact business – in the United States. Many are insurance carriers and their insureds, although an increasing number retain the firm for non-insurance purposes, particularly relative to business and financial transactions.

## OFFICES

**CALIFORNIA**
**LOS ANGELES:** Tel: 213 443 5100  Fax: 213 443 5101
**SAN DIEGO:** Tel: 619 321 6200  Fax: 619 321 6201
**SAN FRANCISCO:** Tel: 415 433 0990  Fax: 415 434 1370

**COLORADO**
**DENVER:** Tel: 303 572 5300  Fax: 303 572 5301

**CONNECTICUT**
**STAMFORD:** Tel: 203 388 9100  Fax: 203 388 9101

**DISTRICT OF COLUMBIA**
**WASHINGTON, DC:** Tel: 202 626 7660  Fax: 202 628 3606

**FLORIDA**
**MIAMI:** Tel: 305 374 4400  Fax: 305 579 0261
**ORLANDO:** Tel: 407 423 7287  Fax: 407 648 1376
**WEST PALM BEACH:** Tel: 561 515 4000  Fax: 561 515 4001

**ILLINOIS**
**CHICAGO:** Tel: 312 704 0550  Fax: 312 704 1522

**KENTUCKY**
**LOUISVILLE:** Tel: 502 238 8500  Fax: 502 238 7995

**MARYLAND**
**BALTIMORE:** Tel: 410 539 1800  Fax: 410 962 8758

**MASSACHUSETTS**
**BOSTON:** Tel: 617 422 5300  Fax: 617 423 6917

**NEVADA**
**LAS VEGAS:** Tel: 702 727 1246  Fax: 702 727 1401

**NEW JERSEY**
**FLORHAM PARK:** Tel: 973 624 0800  Fax: 973 624 0808

**NEW YORK**
**ALBANY:** Tel: 518 449 8893  Fax: 518 449 8927 (Fax)
**GARDEN CITY:** Tel: 516 228 8900  Fax: 516 228 0200
**NEW YORK:** Tel: 212 490 3000  Fax: 212 490 3038
**WHITE PLAINS:** Tel: 914 323 7000  Fax: 914 323 7001

**PENNSYLVANIA**
**PHILADELPHIA:** Tel: 215 627 6900  Fax: 215 627 2665

**TEXAS**
**DALLAS:** Tel: 214 698 8000  Fax: 214 698 1101
**HOUSTON:** Tel: 713 353 2000  Fax: 713 785 7780

**VIRGINIA**
**MCLEAN:** Tel: 703-245-9300  Fax: 703-245-9301

**WISCONSIN**
**MILWAUKEE:** Tel: 414 276 8816  Fax: 414 276 8819

## INTERNATIONAL OFFICES
The firm also has an office in London, UK.

# WOLLMUTH MAHER & DEUTSCH LLP

www.wmd-law.com **tel:** 212 382 3300 **fax:** 212 382 0050

**Managing Partners:** David H Wollmuth, William A Maher
Number of attorneys: 35

## Firm Overview:

For over 15 years, Wollmuth Maher & Deutsch LLP has provided sophisticated legal advice in a responsive, efficient and cost-effective manner. Because the firm is based in Manhattan, a significant focus of its practice involves financial services, including representing clients involved in insurance and reinsurance, banking, investment banking, private equity, venture capital and the hedge fund industry.

## Main Areas of Practice:

Commercial litigation and arbitration; corporate, mergers and acquisitions and securities; bankruptcy and reorganization.

## Clients:

Representative clients include American International Group, Inc; Assured Guaranty Corporation; Chartis Insurance Group; Enstar Group of Insurance Companies; Hanover Insurance Group; Lehman Brothers; Holdings Inc.; Mizuho Corporate Bank, Ltd; ORIX Capital Markets LLC; and Western & Southern Financial Group, Inc.

## International Work:

On the dispute resolution side, the firm has represented many international companies and entities, typically on matters pending in US courts or arbitrations. For example, in the last several years, the firm has represented a large multinational insurer against various prominent European reinsurers in a matter venued in the domestic court system and has also represented multinational insurers and reinsurers based in Switzerland and Bermuda in complex litigation disputes venued in various US jurisdictions. The firm also has considerable expertise in reinsurance arbitrations involving international clients headquartered in the UK, France, Switzerland and in other Western European countries. Because these matters are typically confidential, the firm cannot describe them in greater detail, except to say that the firm represents both ceding companies and reinsurers across all lines of business and has successfully handled

numerous disputes involving issues such as contractual interpretation, coverage, late notice, rescission, fraud, allocation, aggregation, follow the fortunes, security, declaratory judgment expenses, loss adjustment expenses, underwriting practices and agency issues. Wollmuth Maher & Deutsch LLP is pleased that its clients in this field range from some of the most prominent insurance and reinsurance companies in the world to start-up entities who have recently entered the market. The firm's attorneys speak at leading industry seminars and conferences and have written articles on contemporary reinsurance and insurance issues. Other recent representative matters include: (i) litigating and obtaining a large settlement for a *Fortune* 500 manufacturer in a dispute arising out of a global supply agreement that also resulted in tortious interference claims against a French competitor of the client; (ii) representing a group of international hedge fund clients arising out of fraud claims against a UK fund manager; (iii) representing a South American company in an ICC arbitration; and (iv) representing various French clients in a litigation arising out of an Enron off-balance sheet partnership.

The firm has been very active in sub-prime mortgage related disputes, principally surrounding reinsurance and financial guarantees of obligations of issuers of sub-prime mortgage-backed securities, but also concerning the rights and obligations of parties to derivatives, CDOs and SIVs tied to the market for such securities. Such representations have had substantial interaction with European and Asian reinsurers and financial institutions entangled in or impacted by such transactions.

On the transactional side, the firm has represented clients in a wide variety of matters including domestic and cross-border acquisitions, joint ventures, public and private securities offerings, venture capital matters, hedge fund formation and representation and corporate governance matters. Examples of recent cross-border transactions include: (i) representing AIG Global Investment Group in connection with its sale of securities in the Mexican IPO and 144A sale of securities of Axtel, SA, a corporation formed under the laws of Mexico; (ii) representing Brasoil Corporation, a Brazilian corporation with US affiliates, in connection with a $100,000,000 financing led by Goldman Sachs; (iii) representing GSO Capital Partners LP in the acquisition of the assets of the thermal processing division of Gibraltar Industries, Inc, comprising 17 heat treatment plants in multiple jurisdictions in the US and Canada; (iv) representing GSO Capital Partners LP in the acquisition of 100% of the common stock of Flex Elektrowerkzeuge GmbH, the premium European power tool manufacturing subsidiary of The Black & Decker Corporation and the subsequent sale of Flex Elektrowerkzeuge GmbH to AXA Private Equity; and (v) representing IPC Systems Holdings, Inc in the acquisition of US and Canadian operations of Positron Public Safety Systems, Inc from Positron Inc. In addition, the firm has represented placement agents and investor groups in private placement transactions involving foreign issuers in a variety of industries, including biotechnology, med-tech, clean-tech, oil and gas, automotive, computer software and hardware, Internet and manufacturing.

**OFFICES**

NEW YORK

**NEW YORK:** 500 Fifth Avenue, NY 10110
Tel: 212 382 3300   Fax: 212 382 0050

NEW JERSEY

**NEWARK:** One Gateway Center, NJ 07102
Tel: 973 733 9200   Fax: 973 733 9292

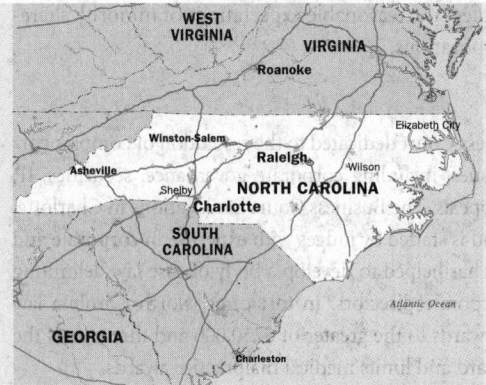

## How lawyers are ranked

Every year we carry out thousands of in-depth interviews with clients in order to assess the reputations and expertise of business lawyers worldwide. The qualities we look for (and which determine rankings) include technical legal ability, professional conduct, client service, commercial awareness/astuteness, diligence, commitment, and other qualities most valued by the client. For details of our research team, see p.5.

## NORTH CAROLINA: An introduction

### Contributed by Smith, Anderson, Blount, Dorsett, Mitchell & Jernigan, LLP

North Carolina is the nation's tenth most populous state. Its diversified economy features a high concentration of knowledge-based industries, including financial services, life sciences and information technology. The state has long enjoyed a business-friendly reputation and perennially ranks at the top of national business location surveys. North Carolina's skilled labor force is supported by an exceptional collection of independent and state institutions of higher education and by the nation's third largest community college system, which offers free customized employee training to eligible employers. The state also offers an affordable cost of living, extensive transportation infrastructure, leading medical and research facilities, and reputation for quality of life.

The Research Triangle region (comprising Raleigh, Durham and Chapel Hill) is one of the country's top centers for biotech companies and a prominent location for IT companies. The area is home to leading research institutions, including Duke University, the University of North Carolina at Chapel Hill, and North Carolina State University; prominent medical research facilities; one of the country's most educated workforces; and a dense network of entrepreneurial associations, ven¬ture capital investors, and private equity firms. The region is home to the world's largest pharmaceuticals services company (Quintiles), the world's largest privately held software company (SAS Institute), the world's largest open source software company (Red Hat) and the US headquarters of one of the world's largest pharma¬ceutical companies (GlaxoSmithKline).

Charlotte is the state's largest city and the nation's second largest financial cen¬ter. The city is home to seven Fortune 500 companies, including Bank of America, Lowe's Companies, Nucor Corporation, and Duke Energy, the nation's largest electric utility. Charlotte also hosted the 2012 Democratic National Convention.

The Piedmont Triad region, consisting of Greensboro, Winston-Salem and High Point, is home to Wake Forest University, numerous manufacturing companies and the world's largest furniture trade show.

North Carolina's coast and mountains are drivers of the state's thriving tourist industry and growing film and television industry. Eastern North Carolina is also home to one of the nation's largest concentrations of military installations. The U.S Army Forces Command, headquarted at Fort Bragg, manages over $30 billion in defense contracts annually.

### Economic Incentives

North Carolina offers a variety of economic incentives to new and expanding businesses. These take the form of tax credits, special rates and exemptions, discretionary grants, and financing assistance.

Income tax credits are available for job creation, investment in real and personal business property, research and development expenditures, as well as more specialized activities such as film production and purchases of renewable energy property. The value of some credits is enhanced for investments or job creation in less developed areas, and special credits are available for use of the state ports at Morehead City and Wilmington. Individuals are entitled to an income tax credit equal to 25% of amounts invested in qualified businesses or $50,000, whichever is less. The state also offers a variety of sales tax exemptions, rate reductions and refunds for certain types of business property purchases.

North Carolina's principal discretionary incentive is its Job Development Investment Grant (JDIG) program. A JDIG award is a series of annual grants to a business locating or expanding in North Carolina. Grant size is based on the amount of state withholding taxes paid with respect to new employees.

The state's One North Carolina Fund provides grants to businesses for equipment, build¬ing renovation and construction of utilities. Awards from the fund are made in conjunction with matching awards by cities or counties. The North Carolina Biotechnology Center also makes grants and loans to life science companies.

North Carolina county financing authorities may issue industrial rev¬enue bonds to assist the financing of qualified manufacturing facilities. The state has also established an Innovation Fund authorized to invest a por¬tion of the state's pension fund in companies with significant operations in North Carolina.

### Labor and Employment

North Carolina is a right-to-work state. It has the nation's lowest unionization rate and imposes significantly fewer workplace restrictions on business than most states. Subject to some public policy and other exceptions, North Carolina is also an at-will employment state. Employee noncompete agreements are generally enforced.

## Business Entity Laws

North Carolina has modern business entity statutes, including a flexible Business Corporation Act and a Limited Liability Company Act that gives maximum effect to the principle of freedom of contract. Cross-entity mergers and conversions are broadly permitted. North Carolina also has two anti¬takeover statutes, the North Carolina Shareholder Protection Act and the North Carolina Control Share Acquisition Act, that offer public companies protections against takeovers. The North Carolina courts have also tradi-

tionally been careful to protect the reasonable expectations of minority shareholders in closely held corporations.

## Business Disputes

North Carolina has a Business Court dedicated to the resolution of complex corporate and commercial issues, including corporate governance, securities, IP, antitrust matters and tax appeals. The Business Court has locations in Charlotte, Greensboro and Raleigh and is staffed by judges with expertise in corporate and commercial law. The court has helped to develop a body of case law delimiting the fiduciary duties of corporate directors. In tort cases, North Carolina law restricts punitive damage awards to the greater of $250,000 and three times the compensatory damages award and limits medical malpractice awards.

# ANTITRUST

Commentary about individuals can be found under their firm's paragraph. If the firm has no paragraph (is not ranked) look at Other Notable Practitioners.

### Antitrust
#### Leading Firms

**Band 1**
Brooks, Pierce, McLendon, Humphrey & Leonard LLP
Ellis & Winters LLP
Robinson, Bradshaw & Hinson PA
Womble Carlyle Sandridge & Rice, LLP *

**Band 2**
Parker Poe Adams & Bernstein LLP

#### Senior Statesmen

**Senior Statesmen:** distinguished older practitioners
Graybeal John F       Parker Poe Adams & Bernstein LLP

#### Leading Individuals

**Band 1**

| | |
|---|---|
| Bowman Everett J | Robinson, Bradshaw & Hinson PA |
| Copenhaver W Andrew | Womble Carlyle Sandridge & Rice, LLP |
| Enns Rodrick J | Enns & Archer LLP (ONP)† |
| Horoschak Mark J | Womble Carlyle Sandridge & Rice, LLP |
| Merritt Mark | Robinson, Bradshaw & Hinson PA |
| Oleynik Jeffrey E | Brooks, Pierce, McLendon, Humphrey |
| Sawchak Matthew W | Ellis & Winters LLP * |
| Van Zant Jennifer K | Brooks, Pierce, McLendon, Humphrey |
| Williams Jim | Brooks, Pierce, McLendon, Humphrey |

\* Indicates firm / individual with profile.
† ONP = Other Notable Practitioner.

## Band 1

### Brooks, Pierce, McLendon, Humphrey & Leonard LLP

**THE FIRM** This North Carolina-based firm boasts an impressive antitrust practice group with particular strength in antitrust litigation. The team's expertise spans a range of sectors, including the healthcare and technology industries, and it advises organizations on compliance issues in state and federal antitrust laws, trade practices and consumer protection laws.
**KEY INDIVIDUALS Jeffrey Oleynik** is a *"very skilled and knowledgeable"* commercial litigator with an excellent reputation and significant experience in handling antitrust matters. The well-regarded **Jennifer Van Zant** is an experienced trial lawyer who has represented clients in a range of antitrust disputes. **Jim Williams** is a highly regarded business litigator with extensive experience in handling complex, antitrust-related matters, particularly on the litigation front, with one source commenting: *"People go to him when there is a really serious business or commercial lawsuit."*

### Ellis & Winters LLP

**THE FIRM** This smaller firm has offices in Greensboro and Raleigh, and enjoys an excellent reputation for its antitrust and trade regulation practice. This group offers expertise in antitrust litigation together with counseling across matters such as alleged price-fixing, monopolization, resale price maintenance and other competition-related matters. Its client roster includes the North Carolina Board of Pharmacy and Guardian Life Insurance.
**Sources say:** *"They've been great on antitrust. The firm puts a premium on client service and makes everything seamless."*
**KEY INDIVIDUALS** The well-regarded **Matthew Sawchak** (see p.2045) continues to head the department and has recently handled numerous matters for CVS, including disputes under state pricing laws. A source reported: *"He is up there with the best I've ever dealt with."*

### Robinson, Bradshaw & Hinson PA

**THE FIRM** Robinson Bradshaw maintains one of the most well-established antitrust practices in North Carolina. The group is particularly recognized for representing clients involved in government investigations and for its expertise in the healthcare industry. The team works in concert with M&A colleagues on merger-related antitrust matters and

represents clients such as CommScope, EnPro and the North Carolina State Bar.
**Sources say:** *"It is difficult to imagine a better performance."*
**KEY INDIVIDUALS Everett Bowman** is department head and focuses his practice on antitrust issues pertaining to the healthcare industry, recently representing Mission Health. A source notes he has a *"combination of mastery over legal issues as well as being really good at recognizing the business and practical side of things."* An experienced litigator, **Mark Merritt** is known for advising clients involved in governmental investigations on antitrust matters. He is *"among the finest antitrust lawyers in North Carolina"* according to one source.

### Womble Carlyle Sandridge & Rice, LLP
See profile on p.2049

**THE FIRM** This firm's antitrust practice is among the finest in the state. The team is known for its strong trial capabilities in both state and federal courts and also offers the gamut of services, covering various aspects of antitrust and trade regulation matters. Their vast expertise allows them to service a range of clients including R.J. Reynolds, Krispy Kreme and Carolinas HealthCare System.
**Sources say:** *"An outstanding law firm with real depth of experience."*
**KEY INDIVIDUALS Andrew Copenhaver** is known for his strength as a leading trial lawyer, focusing his practice on antitrust and trade regulation matters. A source describes him as *"a very experienced litigator who combines common sense with no nonsense."* Department head **Mark Horoschak** is recognized for his expertise in antitrust matters related to the healthcare industry. He recently represented Ardent Health Services and Community Health Systems, and has been praised as being *"extraordinarily good"* by an admiring peer.

## Band 2

### Parker Poe Adams & Bernstein LLP

**THE FIRM** Parker Poe continues to grow its antitrust practice in North Carolina with a strong team of practitioners providing counseling and litigation services. The team routinely acts before the FTC for clients from a range of industries including retail, healthcare and construction, with recent representations including Carolinas AGC.

**Sources say:** *"Very good – their overall confidence, and their ability to get things done on time and deliver what they promise."*

**KEY INDIVIDUALS John Graybeal** commands respect for his extensive experience in handling antitrust and trade regulation matters. He continues to represent clients from the manufacturing and healthcare industries.

## Other Notable Practitioners

The *"very smart and bright"* **Rodrick Enns** of Enns & Archer LLP has significant experience dealing with antitrust-related matters and is particularly well known for his strength as a trial lawyer.

# BANKING & FINANCE

Commentary about individuals can be found under their firm's paragraph. If the firm has no paragraph (is not ranked) look at Other Notable Practitioners.

| Banking & Finance Leading Firms |
| --- |
| **Band 1** |
| Moore & Van Allen, PLLC |
| **Band 2** |
| McGuireWoods LLP * |
| Robinson, Bradshaw & Hinson PA |
| Womble Carlyle Sandridge & Rice, LLP * |
| **Band 3** |
| Mayer Brown LLP * |
| Parker Poe Adams & Bernstein LLP |
| **Band 4** |
| Bradley Arant Boult Cummings LLP * |
| Brooks, Pierce, McLendon, Humphrey & Leonard |
| King & Spalding LLP * |
| Winston & Strawn LLP * |

## Band 1

### Moore & Van Allen, PLLC

**THE FIRM** This firm's banking and finance practice is considered to be one of the finest in the state and the Southeast region. Consisting of a team of over 60 attorneys, the firm offers formidable bench strength. The group's expertise includes asset-based lending, syndicated loans, structured finance and public finance, allowing it to advise clients such as BB&T, Wells Fargo, Bank of America and Stellus Capital Management.

**Sources say:** *"The firm and the group do an excellent job. They provide outstanding advice, are very responsive, very hard-working and very business-oriented."*

**KEY INDIVIDUALS Richard Hazlett** is highly regarded for his securities expertise and has significant experience in lending transactions, M&A and tax-exempt finance. Sources say: *"He has a very strong business sense in addition to extensive local knowledge."* The vastly experienced **James Hovis** focuses his practice on finance and capital markets work. He is described by one source as being an *"experienced and outstanding lawyer."* **Thomas Mitchell** concentrates his practice on representing banks in complex senior finance transactions and has significant experience in dealing with syndicated loans. A satisfied client says: *"He is*

*knowledgeable, responsive and an excellent provider of legal service."*

## Band 2

### McGuireWoods LLP
See profile on p.2519

**THE FIRM** McGuireWoods's well-established banking and finance practice has continued to expand its North Carolina team, so offering further depth and breadth of experience to its clients. The team handles a broad range of transactions, including asset-based lending, and lease, project and real estate finance, and it has particular expertise in syndicated finance.

**Sources say:** *"We have found their advice and assistance in all fields to be outstanding."*

**KEY INDIVIDUALS** The well-respected **Boyd Campbell** is experienced in working with both public and private companies, with expertise in M&A, securities and debt finance.

### Robinson, Bradshaw & Hinson PA

**THE FIRM** This firm has one of the most well-regarded banking and capital markets practices in the state. The group is able to draw on its strong corporate practice, so providing added capacity, and represents both lenders and borrowers in financial transactions. The team's expertise covers public finance, mezzanine financing, senior lending and venture capital, and it acts for an impressive array of clients including Carolinas HealthCare System, Regions Bank and Ares Capital.

**Sources say:** *"Highly professional, highly talented and responsive."*

**KEY INDIVIDUALS** The well-known and respected **Peter Buck** has an outstanding reputation for his corporate law skills combined with his excellent banking and finance and energy law practices. **Edwin Lucas** is the firm's driving force behind its public finance practice and is focused on educational and governmental financings. Recent work includes serving as bond counsel to Mecklenburg County and Guilford County. **Allen Robertson** is well regarded for his banking and public finance work and has recently acted as bond counsel for Duke University Health System. An

| Banking & Finance Senior Statesmen | | |
| --- | --- | --- |
| **Senior Statesmen: distinguished older practitioners** | | |
| Winslow III Edward | | Brooks, Pierce, McLendon, Humphrey |
| **Leading Individuals** | | |
| **Band 1** | | |
| Buck Peter | | Robinson, Bradshaw & Hinson PA |
| Greene Kenneth | | Carruthers & Roth PA (ONP)[†] |
| Hazlett Richard | | Moore & Van Allen, PLLC |
| Hovis James W | | Moore & Van Allen, PLLC |
| Kupec Christopher C | | Bryan Cave LLP (ONP)[†] |
| Leon Christopher E | | Womble Carlyle Sandridge & Rice, LLP |
| Ubell Donald P | | Parker Poe Adams & Bernstein LLP |
| **Band 2** | | |
| Campbell Jr Boyd | | McGuireWoods LLP |
| Fuller III William H | | King & Spalding LLP * |
| Hitselberger Carol A | | Mayer Brown LLP |
| Lucas Edwin F | | Robinson, Bradshaw & Hinson PA |
| McGill Molly | | Winston & Strawn LLP * |
| Oberkfell Keith F | | Mayer Brown LLP |
| Robertson Allen K | | Robinson, Bradshaw & Hinson PA |
| Singer Robert A | | Brooks, Pierce, McLendon, Humphrey |
| **Band 3** | | |
| Camp Jacqueline E | | Womble Carlyle Sandridge & Rice, LLP |
| Lampe Donald C | | Dykema Gossett PLLC (ONP)[†] |
| Lee Charles | | Parker Poe Adams & Bernstein LLP |
| Mitchell Thomas L | | Moore & Van Allen, PLLC |
| Robinson S Graham | | Robinson, Bradshaw & Hinson PA |
| Ryan Timothy R | | Mayer Brown LLP |
| **Band 4** | | |
| Gordon Patricia | | Bradley Arant Boult Cummings LLP |
| **Up-and-coming individuals** | | |
| Amie Tenholder Jolie | | Bradley Arant Boult Cummings LLP |
| Walker Will | | Mayer Brown LLP |
| **Associates to watch** | | |
| Abrao Cybil | | Bradley Arant Boult Cummings LLP |

*Indicates firm / individual with profile.*
[†]*ONP = Other Notable Practitioner.*

admiring source says he is *"responsible, responsive, highly intelligent and takes the initiative to understand client experiences. And "he is one of the smartest attorneys I've ever worked with."* **Graham Robinson** has a diverse practice and is adept in handling commercial lending issues, often acting as counsel for banks and other financial institutions. Recent work includes representing Wells Fargo in the structuring of syndicated credit facilities valued at $325 million.

## Womble Carlyle Sandridge & Rice, LLP
See profile on p.2049

**THE FIRM** This firm's multitalented banking and finance practice is expert in debt offerings, securities, syndicated finance, public finance and asset-based lending. Recent work includes acting as bond counsel for the Board of Governors of The University of North Carolina and the North Carolina Housing Finance Agency. The firm's impressive list of clients also includes BB&T, New York Life and Wells Fargo.

**Sources say:** *"They were familiar with the issues and requirements; moreover, they were familiar with the business aspects in the current market. My go-to law firm in North Carolina."*

**KEY INDIVIDUALS** Head of the capital markets practice group, **Christopher Leon** has significant experience in syndicated financings, securitizations and public and private debt offerings. Sources say: *"He takes a very calm and unflappable approach and is very familiar with market conditions."* **Jacqueline Camp** represents lenders and borrowers in complex financial transactions, with notable experience in syndicated and debt financings. A source said: *"She consistently provides good counsel with respect to legal issues and has the ability to work through issues to resolution."*

## Band 3

## Mayer Brown LLP
See profile on p.1257

**THE FIRM** Mayer Brown retains an excellent banking and finance practice, serving a range of banks, financial institutions and corporate clients. This group is recognized for its expertise in structured finance and complex lending transactions, and recently represented JPMorgan Chase in a $980 million senior secured credit facility. The firm's client portfolio also includes Merrill Lynch, Credit Suisse and Deutsche Bank.

**Sources say:** *"They're excellent to work with. They are responsive and add value to our process."*

**KEY INDIVIDUALS** **Keith Oberkfell** concentrates on securitization and structured finance and has recently represented SunTrust Bank in a $380 million multicurrency revolving credit facility. Head of the finance practice, **Carol Hitselberger** is highly regarded for her deep experience in securitization and structured finance products. Appreciative sources commented: *"She is very smart, very even-tempered, easy to work with and well versed in all types of securitization."* **Timothy Ryan** represents financial institutions, both domestically and internationally, in various

financing transactions. He is noted for his work for Bank of America, which he recently assisted with a $1 billion senior unsecured revolving credit facility. **Will Walker**, who is praised as a *"very good attorney,"* concentrates his practice on representing financial institutions in syndicated loan transactions. His recent notable work includes representing CWCapital in its acquisition from Citibank of the mortgage servicing rights on a $2.6 billion portfolio of mortgage loans.

## Parker Poe Adams & Bernstein LLP

**THE FIRM** This firm's well-established banking and finance practice is highly regarded for its expertise in the public finance arena, acting as bond counsel for various public entities. The group also has a strong loan servicing practice, allowing it to support large banks and financial institutions. The University of North Carolina, the City of Winston-Salem, Wells Fargo and SunTrust Bank are among the firm's client roster.

**Sources say:** *"The skill set of the firm is diverse and helpful. Very professional."*

**KEY INDIVIDUALS** **Donald Ubell** has extensive experience in handling public finance work. He recently acted as counsel for the City of Durham on the issue of $68.3 million municipal bonds. **Charles Lee** focuses on corporate finance, with expertise in middle-market lending and syndicated loan facilities. A source describes him as *"extremely responsive, with an outstanding work ethic and cutting-edge knowledge of commercial loan facilities."*

## Band 4

## Bradley Arant Boult Cummings LLP
See profile on p.476

**THE FIRM** Bradley Arant's banking and finance practice, in concert with its corporate and capital markets teams, is gaining increasing prominence in the Nprth Carolina market. The firm's expertise includes advising on new bank formations, loan financings, financial services litigation and compliance, allowing it to service clients such as HSBC, Ally Financial and GMAC Mortgage, Wells Fargo and Capital One Bank.

**Sources say:** *"Their performance has always been exceptional."*

**KEY INDIVIDUALS** **Patricia Gordon**'s broad practice includes her recognized skills in REITs and construction financings, including home builders and condominium projects. **Jolie Amie Tenholder** acts for a range of financial institutions on lending and corporate transactions including loan financings and workouts of troubled debt. One appreciative source commented: *"She makes me feel comfortable and goes above and beyond to make me understand the issues. Our market changes all the time and she's always up to speed."* **Cybil Abrao** is adept in handling various complex financial transactions, with one source noting that *"she works extremely hard to get a deal done and exceeds everyone's expectations."*

## Brooks, Pierce, McLendon, Humphrey & Leonard

**THE FIRM** This long-established firm has a solid banking practice representing a broad range of clients, from federal and state banks and other financial institutions to title insurance companies and mortgage brokers. Its expertise covers acting as securities counsel and advising on the formation of new banks as well as licensing and regulatory matters.

**KEY INDIVIDUALS** The firm's managing partner, **Edward Winslow** is *"highly regarded in banking and regulatory matters."* His long experience has included representing state and national banks and banking associations, insurers, and other financial services organizations. The highly regarded **Robert Singer** brings a vast range of experience to his clients, including public and private securities, venture capital transactions, private equity placements and corporate law. He serves on the boards of directors of a number of companies and is an in-demand speaker.

## King & Spalding LLP
See profile on p.445

**THE FIRM** King & Spalding has developed a strong reputation in the state for its banking and finance expertise. The firm's national and international presence further boosts its ability to service key financial institutions and corporate clients. The group offers skills across an array of financings such as projects and real estate financings, private placements of debt securities and derivatives, and restructurings. It is known for its middle-market acquisition and leveraged finance expertise and boasts clients such as JPMorgan Chase, Bank of America, Regions Bank and GE Capital.

**Sources say:** *"They're excellent. They understand structures and understand what we're comfortable with in legal terms, and they are always accessible."* *"They do a nice job for us."*

**KEY INDIVIDUALS** **William Fuller** (see p.2041) is lauded as *"a fine attorney."* His practice encompasses debt and acquisition financing, asset-based lending and mezzanine finance, representing lenders, investors and borrowers. He works with clients in industries as diverse as healthcare, aerospace, media and telecom.

## Winston & Strawn LLP
See profile on p.1267

**THE FIRM** This international firm retains a strong corporate lending team in its Charlotte office. The group offers significant expertise in syndicated credit facilities and represents a range of well-known financial institutions and corporates. The team is also known for assisting regional clients on middle-market asset-based and leveraged cash flow lending. Bank of America and Wells Fargo are among the firm's clients.

**KEY INDIVIDUALS** **Molly McGill** (see p.2043) has extensive experience in handling secured lending transactions, including complex deals for financial clients on a national scale. In recent work she represented Bank of America Business Credit in a $200 million syndicated asset-based secured credit facility.

## Other Notable Practitioners

**Kenneth Greene** of Carruthers & Roth PA has a well-regarded bankruptcy and finance practice and is especially experienced in dealing with corporate finance and secure lending transactions. **Christopher Kupec** of Bryan Cave LLP concentrates his practice on middle-market lending transactions with particular expertise in asset-based lending, leveraged loans and mezzanine financings. **Donald Lampe** of Dykema Gossett PLLC is highly regarded for his skilful handling of complex financial transactions together with regulatory matters, frequently acting for loan servicers and creditors. Sources say: *"He is amazing, very sharp, very bright and works really hard."*

# BANKRUPTCY/RESTRUCTURING

Commentary about individuals can be found under their firm's paragraph. If the firm has no paragraph (is not ranked) look at Other Notable Practitioners.

### Bankruptcy/Restructuring
### Leading Firms

**Band 1**

| | |
|---|---|
| K&L Gates * | |
| McGuireWoods LLP * | |
| Moore & Van Allen, PLLC | |
| Parker Poe Adams & Bernstein LLP | |
| Rayburn Cooper & Durham PA | |
| Robinson, Bradshaw & Hinson PA | |

**Band 2**

| | |
|---|---|
| Ellis & Winters LLP | |
| Nexsen Pruet, LLC * | |

### Leading individuals

**Band 1**

| | |
|---|---|
| Booe J Michael | K&L Gates * |
| Cassada Garland S | Robinson, Bradshaw & Hinson PA |
| Darer Brian | Parker Poe Adams & Bernstein LLP |
| Durham Albert F | Rayburn Cooper & Durham PA |
| Eades David L | Moore & Van Allen, PLLC |
| Ford Kiah | Parker Poe Adams & Bernstein LLP |
| Gruendel Stephen E | Moore & Van Allen, PLLC |
| Kahn Ben | Nexsen Pruet, LLC |
| Kluttz Joseph B C | K&L Gates * |
| Myatt Christine | Nexsen Pruet, LLC |
| Northen John A | Northen Blue (ONP)[†] |
| Pope Alan W | Moore & Van Allen, PLLC |
| Porter J William | Parker Poe Adams & Bernstein LLP |
| Pryor Robert H | McGuireWoods LLP |
| Rayburn Jr C Richard | Rayburn Cooper & Durham PA |
| Schilli David | Robinson, Bradshaw & Hinson PA |
| Small John H | Brooks, Pierce, McLendon (ONP)[†] |
| Vaughn Scott | McGuireWoods LLP |
| Walls David S | Moore & Van Allen, PLLC |
| Warren David M | Poyner Spruill LLP (ONP)[†] |

**Band 2**

| | |
|---|---|
| Anderson Jr Charles N | Ellis & Winters LLP * |
| Cox Rob | Bradley Arant Boult Cummings LLP (ONP)[†] |
| Gardner Terri | Nelson Mullins Riley & Scarborough (ONP)[†] * |
| Hogewood Lee | K&L Gates * |
| Sanderson III George F | Ellis & Winters LLP * |

**Up-and-coming individuals**

| | |
|---|---|
| Esser William | Parker Poe Adams & Bernstein LLP |

**Associates to watch**

| | |
|---|---|
| Rayburn Charles (Trey) | Moore & Van Allen, PLLC |

\* Indicates individual with profile.

[†]ONP = Other Notable Practitioner.

## Band 1

### K&L Gates
See profile on p.2245

**THE FIRM** The K&L Gates team continues to offer an outstanding breadth of experience in restructuring and bankruptcy from its Charlotte and Raleigh offices. The group handles restructurings, workouts and increasingly, Chapter 11 reorganizations and liquidations. Working on both the debtor and creditor side, and in combination with its corporate/M&A group, the team can offer comprehensive expertise on the full range of corporate reorganizations, attracting a roster of national and international clients.

**Sources say:** *"Their expertise in bankruptcy law and judicial trends pertaining to bankruptcy and related litigation is superb."*

**KEY INDIVIDUALS** The well-respected **Michael Booe** (see p.2039) is highly appreciated for his restructuring and workout experience. An admiring source noted that he is *"recognized as one of the very best in the state."* **Joseph Kluttz** (see p.2042) handles restructuring work for various clients and has extensive experience in dealing with Chapter 11 proceedings. He is described by a source as a *"super attorney."* **Lee Hogewood** (see p.2041) is hailed as a *"phenomenal bankruptcy attorney."* He concentrates on representing secured creditors in restructurings, foreclosures and complex bankruptcy disputes.

### McGuireWoods LLP
See profile on p.2519

**THE FIRM** McGuireWoods's bankruptcy practice comprises over ten dedicated attorneys, representing secured and unsecured creditors, lenders and trustees in workouts, restructurings, Chapter 11 proceedings and litigation. The firm's national capacity and strong regional presence allow it to deliver its vast expertise to a broad range of clients including key financial institutions.

**Sources say:** *"Excellent. They understand how we do business very well and they structure their practice very well to meet our needs."*

**KEY INDIVIDUALS Robert Pryor** is described as an *"exceptional attorney"* and represents institutional lenders in restructurings, workouts, bankruptcies and litigation. **Scott Vaughn** represents financial institutions in refinancings, restructurings, workouts and bankruptcies. Sources say he is *"very intelligent, thinks on the fly very quickly and has a good business sense to him."*

### Moore & Van Allen, PLLC

**THE FIRM** Moore & Van Allen boasts one of the most well-established bankruptcy practices in the state, with its strong banking and finance abilities giving the group added capacity to cater for its large institutional clients. The team's expertise includes restructuring, bankruptcy and workouts, and it has some seasoned litigators. It serves clients such as Bank of America, Nucor, Wells Fargo and PNC Bank.

**Sources say:** *"They provide solid legal service, and are responsive and practical in their orientation."* *"They are one of the strongest around."*

**KEY INDIVIDUALS** Head of the firm's bankruptcy practice, **David Eades** is very seasoned in bankruptcy and workout matters and has recently represented Bank of America and its affiliate in Chapter 9 proceedings. Sources say he is *"top of the class in bankruptcy."* **Stephen Gruendel** concentrates his practice on representing institutional lenders in workouts and bankruptcy matters pertaining to troubled debtors. A source notes that he is *"incredibly bright and very good at what he does."* The well-regarded **Alan Pope** is recognized for his expertise in counseling institutional clients on bankruptcies and workouts and on structuring intercredit arrangements. **David Walls** is experienced in representing a range of clients in workouts, restructurings and complex bankruptcies. He is described by a source as having *"a significant amount of experience with a wide variety of industries, capital structures and unique circumstances."* The *"incredibly bright"* associate **Trey Rayburn** continues to attract praise, particularly for his workout transactions and corporate bankruptcy practice.

### Parker Poe Adams & Bernstein LLP

**THE FIRM** Parker Poe retains one of the finest bankruptcy practices in the state, with offices in Charlotte and Raleigh. The group predominantly represents lenders in loan workouts, complex disputes and bankruptcy cases with a notable Chapter 11 practice. Clients include banks at the local, regional and national level as well as other large corporate entities. Wells Fargo, SunTrust Bank, Duke Energy and DAK Americas are among the firm's impressive list of clientele.

**Sources say:** *"They have consistently delivered exceptional results."*

**KEY INDIVIDUALS Brian Darer** has vast experience acting on behalf of lenders in workout, foreclosure and bankruptcy matters. Recent work includes representing the official committees of unsecured creditors in a series of

Chapter 11 cases. **Kiah Ford** leads the firm's creditors rights and financial restructuring practice and has extensive experience in representing creditors in bankruptcies, foreclosures and complex disputes. A source describes him as *"a tenacious bankruptcy and litigation practitioner."* **William Porter** represents lenders, with a focus on insolvency law, and is also experienced in Chapter 11 proceedings. An appreciative client reported: *"He has many years of experience, and wisdom that goes beyond his knowledge of the law."* **William Esser** concentrates his practice on litigation, loan workouts, foreclosures, bankruptcies and creditors' rights. He has recently represented Palmetto Bank, Wells Fargo and Rutherford County.

### Rayburn Cooper & Durham PA
**THE FIRM** This Charlotte-based firm is considered to have one of the finest debtor-oriented practices in the state. The team offers expertise in restructurings, workouts and complex bankruptcy disputes. The firm's well-regarded business law and litigation practices combine to offer clients of all sizes the broadest options in protecting corporate assets.
**Sources say:** *"First-rate. Probably the best debtor representation firm in western North Carolina, maybe in all of North Carolina."*
**KEY INDIVIDUALS** Hailed as an *"awesome lawyer,"* **Albert Durham** handles workouts and restructuring as well as bankruptcy cases and is experienced in dealing with Chapter 7 and 11 proceedings. **Richard Rayburn** has a diverse practice and brings his experience as a corporate and trial lawyer to his bankruptcy and restructuring work. One source enthused: *"He is one of the best bankruptcy lawyers I know."*

### Robinson, Bradshaw & Hinson PA
**THE FIRM** Robinson Bradshaw has a 17-strong team serving a diverse client base, but is best known for acting for creditors. The group is noted for its Chapter 11 expertise, in which it represents a wide range of parties including borrowers as well as secured and unsecured lenders. Drawing on its strong corporate practice, it delivers a seamless service to clients including Wells Fargo, Bank of America and EnPro Industries.

**Sources say:** *"We have had lots of success in the matters they have handled for us."*
**KEY INDIVIDUALS Garland Cassada** is sought for his restructuring and bankruptcy expertise and he continues to be a principal adviser to EnPro and Garlock, handling a series of Chapter 11 reorganization cases with a total value of $750 million. **David Schilli** assists lenders in bankruptcies, loan workouts and restructurings. He has recently handled a series of cases involving nonperforming loans, representing F&M Bank, Wells Fargo and Citizens South Bank.

## Band 2

### Ellis & Winters LLP
**THE FIRM** This small North Carolina firm has developed a strong bankruptcy practice with experience in handling foreclosures, restructurings, workouts and complex bankruptcy disputes. The team is also well regarded for its representation of secured creditors in Chapter 11 proceedings. Clients include Bank of America, CVS, SunTrust Bank and Crescent State Bank.
**Sources say:** *"Good lawyers – they're skilled at writing, arguing and presenting their point of view."*
**KEY INDIVIDUALS Charles Anderson** (see p.2039) brings real estate and commercial lending expertise to his bankruptcy practice and has recently represented Bank of America in a Chapter 11 matter. A source noted *"his impressive array of knowledge and ability to combine the transactional and bankruptcy sides"* to be standout qualities. **George Sanderson** (see p.2045) is a skilled commercial litigator with the experience to handle complex bankruptcy cases. Sources say he *"takes a thoughtful approach and gives us good advice."*

### Nexsen Pruet, LLC
See profile on p.2277
**THE FIRM** Headquartered in Columbia, Nexsen Pruet is a substantial Carolinas firm that has established a solid, well-regarded bankruptcy and creditors' rights practice from its Greensboro office. The group's expertise includes bankruptcies, workouts, receiverships and foreclosures, assisting clients such as First Bank, GE Capital Real Estate, Huntington National Bank and Gibraltar Asset Management.
**Sources say:** *"The practitioners all have a breadth of experience in bankruptcy-related matters." "They provide a standout service – we can call lawyers directly, and they give great service."*
**KEY INDIVIDUALS** Acclaimed as a *"great lawyer,"* **Ben Kahn** is an experienced commercial litigator with a well-regarded bankruptcy practice. His expertise includes representing various clients in Chapter 7, 11, 12 and 13 proceedings. Chair of the firm's bankruptcy group, **Christine Myatt** is adept in handling bankruptcies, workouts and restructuring, and has recently represented PNC Bank.

## Other Notable Practitioners

**John Small** of Brooks, Pierce, McLendon, Humphrey & Leonard LLP is a highly regarded bankruptcy attorney with significant experience pertaining to Chapter 7 and 11 proceedings. **Rob Cox** recently joined Bradley Arant Boult Cummings LLP, bringing his experience from McGuireWoods. His practice focuses on restructuring and insolvency, and he assists lenders with commercial workouts and distressed asset acquisitions. **Terri Gardner** (see p.2041) of Nelson Mullins Riley & Scarborough LLP concentrates on lender representation and assists clients with loan workouts, creditors' rights, bankruptcies and corporate reorganizations. Described as a *"great attorney,"* **John Northen** of Northen Blue primarily focuses on debtor representation and his practice centers on financial restructuring work, with extensive experience in handling Chapter 11 proceedings. The highly experienced **David Warren** of Poyner Spruill LLP is adept in representing creditors on bankruptcy, loan workouts, collections and foreclosure issues. He has recently assisted Southern Bank & Trust and New Century Bank, among others.

# CORPORATE/M&A

Commentary about individuals can be found under their firm's paragraph. If the firm has no paragraph (is not ranked) look at Other Notable Practitioners.

## Corporate/M&A
### Leading Firms

**Band 1**
Moore & Van Allen, PLLC
Robinson, Bradshaw & Hinson PA
Smith, Anderson, Blount, Dorsett, Mitchell & Jernigan, LLP *

**Band 2**
K&L Gates *
Womble Carlyle Sandridge & Rice, LLP *

**Band 3**
Brooks, Pierce, McLendon, Humphrey & Leonard LLP
McGuireWoods LLP *
Parker Poe Adams & Bernstein LLP
Smith Moore Leatherwood LLP *
Wyrick Robbins Yates & Ponton LLP

**Band 4**
Alston & Bird LLP *
Hutchison PLLC
Kilpatrick Townsend & Stockton LLP *

## Band 1

### Moore & Van Allen, PLLC

**THE FIRM** Moore & Van Allen's corporate practice group is recognized as one of the finest in North Carolina. With offices in Charlotte and the Research Triangle, the firm is well positioned to serve its corporate clients across the state. A team of 60 attorneys gives the group a deep bench, allowing it to provide an exceptional level of service on various corporate matters, including M&A, commercial contract negotiations, corporate governance and venture capital. Clients include Duke Energy, Nucor, Bank of America and Lowe's.
**Sources say:** "*They make it a point to become knowledgeable about your business, understand your objectives and help achieve your goals.*"
**KEY INDIVIDUALS Mike DeLaney** co-heads the firm's corporate practice and is experienced in handling M&A and joint ventures on a domestic and international scale. "*He has a world of knowledge and is a top-notch guy,*" said one interviewee. The well-regarded **Stephen Hope** focuses on corporate finance and complex M&A transactions. Recent work includes representing Rexam in the $459 million sale of its worldwide consumer plastics business to Albea Group. **Jeremy Godwin** is described as a "*very solid M&A lawyer*" and has had significant experience handling domestic and international M&A transactions for various clients, including Fortune 500 companies.

### Robinson, Bradshaw & Hinson PA

**THE FIRM** Based in Charlotte, this highly regarded firm acts for many key corporate clients within the state's financial center. The group offers unparalleled bench strength in the corporate and M&A spaces, with expertise covering M&A, LBOs, joint ventures, fund formation and securities. Recent work includes representing Fresenius Medical Care in its $385 million acquisition of American Access Care. Other clients include EnPro, Duke Energy and CommScope.
**Sources say:** "*Terrific performance. They do New York-quality work at North Carolina prices.*"
**KEY INDIVIDUALS** A founding partner of the firm, **Russell Robinson** is an experienced corporate attorney with a focus on commercial law, securities and nonprofit organizations. The highly regarded **Peter Buck** previously served as in-house counsel to Duke Energy and is well versed in energy law, in addition to having extensive experience in M&A, corporate law and banking and finance. **Stephen Lynch** focuses his practice on securities transactions and M&A, and has significant experience in private equity investments and public offerings. **Haynes Lea** concentrates his practice on private equity, fund formation and general corporate law. "*He is extraordinary – as knowledgeable as anyone out there about private equity, highly creative and detail-oriented,*" said one interviewee.

### Smith, Anderson, Blount, Dorsett, Mitchell & Jernigan, LLP
See profile on p.2047

**THE FIRM** This well-established firm is situated in Raleigh, placing it in a prime location to serve the economic hub in the Research Triangle Park area. The group counsels a significant number of clients in the technology, healthcare and pharmaceutical industries on the full spectrum of corporate transactional matters, including M&A, joint ventures and securitizations. An impressive client list includes Quintiles, Duke Energy, GlaxoSmithKline and Cree.
**Sources say:** "*They are exceptional – the level of skill and professionalism is outstanding.*"
**KEY INDIVIDUALS John Jernigan** (see p.2041) is experienced in all aspects of M&A, with one admiring source noting: "*He is very experienced, thoughtful, careful and trustworthy in what he does. I'd deem him to be an exceptional lawyer.*" **Gerald Roach** (see p.2044) is adept in M&A, securities, joint ventures and corporate governance matters. **Sources say:** "*He's a lawyer's lawyer, a person of extraordinary integrity and business acumen, and is in a very small circle of the state's top corporate and securities attorneys.*" Experienced corporate lawyer **Byron Kirkland** (see p.2042) is recognized for his venture capital and private equity fund practice. He assists funds and their portfolio companies with acquisitions, investments and fund formations. **Christopher Capel** (see p.2039) counsels companies on corporate, securities and technology law, with a broad practice covering M&A, corporate finance, intellectual property and technology licensing. **Timothy Goettel** (see p.2041) is experienced in handling complex acquisitions, public offerings, financings and corporate governance issues. Recent work includes representing Progress Energy in the issue of

## Corporate/M&A
### Senior Statesmen

**Senior Statesmen: distinguished older practitioners**

| | | |
|---|---|---|
| Dagenhart Larry | | *McGuireWoods LLP* |
| Robinson II Russell M | | *Robinson, Bradshaw & Hinson PA* |

### Leading Individuals

**Band 1**

| | |
|---|---|
| Buck Peter | *Robinson, Bradshaw & Hinson PA* |
| DeLaney III Ernest S (Mike) | *Moore & Van Allen, PLLC* |
| Jernigan John L | *Smith, Anderson, Blount, Dorsett, Mitchell* * |
| Pruden III J Norfleet | *K&L Gates* * |
| Roach Gerald F | *Smith, Anderson, Blount, Dorsett, Mitchell* * |

**Band 2**

| | |
|---|---|
| Campbell Jr Boyd | *McGuireWoods LLP* |
| Hope Stephen D | *Moore & Van Allen, PLLC* |
| Ives III H Bryan | *Alston & Bird LLP* * |
| Kirkland Byron B | *Smith, Anderson, Blount, Dorsett, Mitchell* * |
| Lynch Stephen M | *Robinson, Bradshaw & Hinson PA* |
| Robbins Larry E | *Wyrick Robbins Yates & Ponton LLP* |

**Band 3**

| | |
|---|---|
| Auberry E Kent | *Smith Moore Leatherwood LLP* * |
| Bange Richard | *King & Spalding LLP (ONP)[†] *  * |
| Capel Christopher | *Smith, Anderson, Blount, Dorsett, Mitchell* * |
| Goettel Timothy S | *Smith, Anderson, Blount, Dorsett, Mitchell* * |
| Hutchison Fred D | *Hutchison PLLC* * |
| Johnson III W.H. "Kip" | *Morningstar Law Group (ONP)[†]* |
| Jones Sean M | *K&L Gates* * |
| Kelly Mark | *Alston & Bird LLP* * |
| Lea Haynes | *Robinson, Bradshaw & Hinson PA* |
| Mallard Lynwood | *McGuireWoods LLP* |
| O'Donnell Jr Thomas H | *Dykema Gossett PLLC (ONP)[†]* |
| Reynolds Don | *Wyrick Robbins Yates & Ponton LLP* |
| Smart Skip | *Parker Poe Adams & Bernstein LLP* |
| Watkins Tommy | *Schell Bray Aycock Abel & Livingston (ONP)[†]* |
| Whelpley Jr David B | *McGuireWoods LLP* |

**Band 4**

| | |
|---|---|
| Davidson Mark | *Brooks, Pierce, McLendon, Humphrey* |
| Eaddy Randy | *Kilpatrick Townsend & Stockton LLP* |
| Godwin Jeremy H | *Moore & Van Allen, PLLC* |
| Hay Jeff | *Womble Carlyle Sandridge & Rice, LLP* |
| Joyner III G. William | *Kilpatrick Townsend & Stockton LLP* |
| Kean Warren | *K&L Gates* * |
| Rosenfeld Margaret | *Smith, Anderson, Blount, Dorsett, Mitchell* * |

### Up-and-coming individuals

| | |
|---|---|
| Spencer Aaron | *Williams Mullen (ONP)[†]* |

### Associates to watch

| | |
|---|---|
| Chambers Matthew | *Kilpatrick Townsend & Stockton LLP* |

* Indicates individual with profile.
[†]ONP = Other Notable Practitioner.

senior notes. **Margaret Rosenfeld** (see p.2044) focuses on corporate and securities law with experience in M&A, public offerings and corporate governance. She recently represented Tekelec in a $780 million going-private transaction. A source describes her as having "*standout capabilities, and the ability to bring a lot of information on multiple transactions at various levels to the table and use it effectively.*"

## Band 2

### K&L Gates
See profile on p.2245

**THE FIRM** This firm's corporate group consists of over 35 attorneys spread across its North Carolina offices, offering a deep bench in addition to an international platform. The group is able to provide the full range of corporate services, including M&A, joint ventures and private equity transactions. With offices in Charlotte, Raleigh and Research Triangle Park, the firm's coverage allows it to service diverse clients such as Primo Water and Bank of America. **Sources say:** "*Superb. They're highly responsive and the firm has a very good combination of high-quality service, professionals across the corporate M&A area, and a lot of expertise available because of the size worldwide.*"

**KEY INDIVIDUALS** The highly regarded **Norfleet Pruden** (see p.2044) focuses his practice on M&A, securities and private equity. He is described by a source as "*a wonderful attorney and business adviser.*" **Sean Jones** (see p.2042) concentrates his practice on securities law and has been described as "*somebody who is able to mitigate risk but also has good business intelligence.*" **Warren Kean** (see p.2042) advises unincorporated entities on taxation issues and is adept in M&A, private equity and joint ventures in addition to his expertise in tax law.

### Womble Carlyle Sandridge & Rice, LLP
See profile on p.2049

**THE FIRM** Womble Carlyle retains a team of over 45 attorneys in its corporate and securities practice in North Carolina. In addition to its offices across the state, the firm's regional presence gives it further scope and capacity to assist key corporate clients in M&A, joint ventures and various transactional issues. **Sources say:** "*The firm provides a high degree of value for the cost of its service.*"

**KEY INDIVIDUALS Jeff Hay** represents midmarket, emerging growth and technology companies, in addition to private equity funds and their portfolio companies, in corporate transactional matters. A satisfied client notes: "*Jeff has a high degree of business judgment and is able to take a productive approach to the negotiation process.*"

## Band 3

### Brooks, Pierce, McLendon, Humphrey & Leonard LLP

**THE FIRM** Brooks Pierce retains a solid corporate M&A practice in Greensboro, serving a broad client base. The firm also has a highly regarded media practice, acting for clients such as Time Warner Cable and a range of broadcasters including Hearst Television. It also counts Gateway University Research and Duke Corporate Education among its clients.

**KEY INDIVIDUALS** The experienced **Mark Davidson** is well versed in many areas of corporate law. His broad practice includes taxation, financings, securities, acquisitions and corporate governance.

### McGuireWoods LLP
See profile on p.2519

**THE FIRM** McGuireWoods has over 35 dedicated attorneys spanning its corporate finance and M&A groups in its Charlotte office, giving it the depth to handle a vast amount of corporate transactions. It represents a broad range of corporates and financial institutions, and continues to present a strong securities offering, serving a number of investment groups. **Sources say:** "*I found everybody very responsive; a well-organized group.*"

**KEY INDIVIDUALS** The highly respected **Larry Dagenhart** is an experienced corporate practitioner and has particular expertise in securities law. He currently acts as a board attorney for a number of clients, and also advises on corporate governance matters. The well-regarded **Boyd Campbell** has extensive experience in M&A, securities, corporate governance and corporate finance. **David Whelpley** focuses his practice on M&A, joint ventures, corporate finance and commercial transactions. A source describes him as an "*outstanding individual.*" **Lynwood Mallard** is experienced in M&A, and counsels various clients on domestic and cross-border transactional matters.

### Parker Poe Adams & Bernstein LLP

**THE FIRM** This firm's well-established corporate/M&A team has more than 40 attorneys. It has an emphasis on issues pertaining to midmarket publicly traded companies and also continues to expand its expertise in the private equity space. Recent highlights include acting for Siemens subsidiary Osram Sylvania on its acquisition of Encelium Holdings, which involved cross-border and tax issues. Other clients include Laboratory Corporation of America, Duke Energy and Sunbelt Rentals. **Sources say:** "*Their business experience and negotiation approach have been excellent.*"

**KEY INDIVIDUALS Skip Smart** leads the firm's business law department and is experienced in handling M&A, joint ventures and financings. On his qualities, sources note that "*he is detail-oriented and has a lot of knowledge,*" and "*he gives you his best business judgments.*"

### Smith Moore Leatherwood LLP
See profile on p.2048
**THE FIRM**

This regional firm has a strong corporate M&A presence in North Carolina and is recognized for its broad work in M&A, joint ventures, capital formation and corporate governance. The team works closely with the firm's tax experts

and the healthcare group, handling a range of corporate transactions pertaining to the healthcare industry. Clients include Essilor of America, Cone Health, Great American Insurance Companies and TD Bank. **KEY INDIVIDUALS** Experienced business lawyer **Kent Auberry** (see p.2039) has handled a range of M&A in the past year. His work includes acting as lead counsel on the sale of social media promotions company Big Method to Blitz Digital Studios.

### Wyrick Robbins Yates & Ponton LLP

**THE FIRM** Located in Raleigh, this firm's capital markets and M&A group is well positioned to service both local and international clients. As well as a solid reputation for its M&A expertise, it also handles private equity, corporate governance and securities compliance work. Clients include Credit Suisse, Salix Pharmaceuticals, Hewlett-Packard and Warren Oil. **Sources say:** "*They have been particularly strong in securities compliance and M&A.*"

**KEY INDIVIDUALS Larry Robbins** is an experienced corporate attorney with expertise covering venture capital, corporate finance and M&A. He has recently represented DRI Corporation and Investors Management Corporation. **Don Reynolds** focuses on M&A, securities, venture capital and corporate law. Sources say he "*has the ability to quickly access situations and understand ramifications, and to think outside the box and bring unique solutions to issues as they arise in a timely fashion.*"

## Band 4

### Alston & Bird LLP
See profile on p.1102

**THE FIRM** Alston & Bird retains a 15-strong team in its Charlotte corporate practice and is highly regarded for its private equity expertise. Recent work includes representing The Gores Group in the $380 million acquisition of Elo Touch Solutions from TE Connectivity. Other clients include The Carlyle Group, Pamlico Capital and Ridgemont Capital. **Sources say:** "*Excellent. Very good at what they do.*"

**KEY INDIVIDUALS Bryan Ives** (see p.2041) has a varied practice. In addition to his tax background, he has extensive experience in dealing with M&A, private equity and corporate governance. **Mark Kelly** (see p.2042) leads the firm's private equity practice and handles public offerings, private financings, M&A and general corporate matters. He is described as "*an incredibly experienced private equity adviser who is very familiar with LBOs and public-private transactions.*"

### Hutchison PLLC

**THE FIRM** Based in Raleigh, this firm offers a well-established corporate/M&A practice with experience in sectors ranging from software and social media to pharmaceuticals and biotech. The team's practice experience also covers taxation, venture capital and securities law, servicing clients Geomagic, RTI International and Covis Pharma, among others.

Sources say: *"Very happy with their service. They have strength in the startup field. Dealings with them are very easy and very comforting."*

KEY INDIVIDUALS Fred Hutchison (see p.2041) focuses his practice on venture capital, securities, M&A and corporate law. *"He has high integrity, is very responsive, and has years and years of experience with many companies,"* said one interviewee, adding: *"He makes you feel like he cares about the company."*

## Kilpatrick Townsend & Stockton LLP
See profile on p.1109

THE FIRM This firm retains a broad corporate and M&A practice in North Carolina and is adept in corporate governance, securities, fund formation and investment management compliance issues. Clients include Schaller Equity Partners, BPV Capital Management, Goldsboro Milling and Ultimus Managers Trust.

Sources say: *"They were very skilled in communication and they had specialists available in every critical area of the deal."*

KEY INDIVIDUALS Randy Eaddy enters the rankings this year having been praised as *"a very good adviser – he's one of the best I've ever worked with."* He concentrates his practice on capital formation transactions, M&A, securities and corporate governance. William Joyner has expertise in private equity and venture capital financings, M&A and corporate law. He is described by a source as *"outstanding, knowledgeable and good to work with."* Matthew Chambers focuses on investment management, securities and corporate law. Sources say *"he is very good"* and *"he dug into our business and provided very practical advice."*

## Other Notable Practitioners

Thomas O'Donnell of Dykema Gossett PLLC focuses his practice on corporate finance, securities, M&A and regulatory compliance. Sources say: *"He is client-focused with an* outstanding work ethic and has strong knowledge of this field of law."* Richard Bange (see p.2039) of King & Spalding LLP has significant M&A experience and concentrates on representing private equity and venture capital funds in various transactional matters. He recently assisted Pamlico Capital with the $335 million sale of its portfolio company, TMW Systems. Kip Johnson of Morningstar Law Group has a broad practice, with particular expertise in securities and technology law. He also has experience in handling M&A, private equity and venture capital matters. Tommy Watkins of Schell Bray Aycock Abel & Livingston PLLC is adept in financings, mergers, acquisitions and restructurings. A significant portion of his practice is focused on representing private equity funds in investment-related issues. Aaron Spencer of Williams Mullen handles various commercial and transactional matters, including M&A, joint ventures and private equity. Sources describe him as *"very business-focused, efficient and easy to work with."*

# ENVIRONMENT

Commentary about individuals can be found under their firm's paragraph. If the firm has no paragraph (is not ranked) look at Other Notable Practitioners.

| Environment |
| --- |
| **Leading Firms** |
| **Band 1** |
| Hunton & Williams LLP * |
| **Band 2** |
| Brooks, Pierce, McLendon, Humphrey & Leonard LLP |
| K&L Gates * |
| Kilpatrick Townsend & Stockton LLP * |
| McGuireWoods LLP * |
| Parker Poe Adams & Bernstein LLP |
| Womble Carlyle Sandridge & Rice, LLP * |
| **Band 3** |
| Poyner Spruill LLP |
| Robinson, Bradshaw & Hinson PA |
| Smith Moore Leatherwood LLP * |
| **Band 4** |
| Moore & Van Allen, PLLC |
| Smith, Anderson, Blount, Dorsett, Mitchell & Jernigan, LLP * |
| Williams Mullen |

\* *Indicates firm with profile.*
*Alphabetical order within each band. Band 1 is the highest.*

## Band 1

### Hunton & Williams LLP
See profile on p.2517

THE FIRM Hunton & Williams's environmental practice enjoys an outstanding reputation in the state. The group's strong national presence gives it added capacity to cover the full range of environmental issues including air, chemical and water regulation, brownfields redevelopment and toxic torts. The scope of its expertise allows it to service an array of clients including chemical companies, utility providers, local municipalities and real estate developers. Sources say: *"They're very good, knowledgeable and have the requisite contacts."*

KEY INDIVIDUALS The highly regarded Charles Case (see p.2040) is lauded as *"the dean of environmental law"* and focuses his practice on air and water pollution, energy and power generation, and hazardous products. Craig Bromby (see p.2039) is highly experienced on issues pertaining to water law, including water quality, industrial waste water, stormwater discharge permitting and water resources. Sources say he is *"very thoughtful and very analytical"* and *"his performance has been outstanding."* William Dannelly (see p.2040) is a well-regarded trial lawyer with significant experience in handling matters involving water quality, toxic torts and brownfield sites. He is described by a source as *"a top-notch environmental attorney."* Daniel Uyesato (see p.2046) is praised as *"an excellent lawyer."* His practice focuses on environmental litigation and regulation, with recognized expertise in chemicals and hazardous materials.

## Band 2

### Brooks, Pierce, McLendon, Humphrey & Leonard LLP

THE FIRM This firm presents a well-regarded practice which assists clients with advice on a broad range of environmental matters, including litigation. Its clients include a number of local government agencies and it is particularly active in respect of public water supplies, brownfield redevelopment, hazardous waste and landfill issues. The team is also known for its expertise on the preparation of environmental impact studies and wetland mitigation plans in various high-profile projects in the state. It has a longstanding relationship with Primland Resort, with other clients including City of Greensboro, City of Salisbury, ECOFLO and A&D Environmental.

KEY INDIVIDUALS Practice head George House is an experienced litigator and represents real estate developers, manufacturing and mining companies on environmental matters. He has recently represented PCS Phosphate and Village of Bald Head Island. The *"excellent"* Randall Tinsley has expertise pertaining to water rights and water and sewer utilities. Recent work includes acting as counsel to the Town of Mooresville on the construction and operation of water supply improvements over objections from the lake operator. Robert King is an experienced trial lawyer with a significant focus on environmental law. His expertise includes arbitrations as well as considerable experience before state, federal and appellate courts.

### K&L Gates
See profile on p.2245

THE FIRM K&L Gates's fine practice has been further boosted by its expansion in the Carolinas, combined with the firm's established national presence. It serves an array of clients on environmental issues such as regulatory and permitting matters and litigation. It has been particularly active in respect of brownfield developments, working closely with its highly regarded real estate group.

KEY INDIVIDUALS The *"outstanding"* David Franchina (see p.2040) has a broad practice and concentrates on environmental and regulatory matters, with experience in air and water pollution, hazardous waste and chemical regulation. Stanford Baird (see p.2039) has a focus on environmental litigation and regulatory matters. A source commented of him: "*I have been very impressed with Stanford; he has been extremely helpful when I have run across sites that have any environmental issues.*"

## Kilpatrick Townsend & Stockton LLP
See profile on p.1109

**THE FIRM** Based in the firm's Raleigh office, this group offers a sophisticated blend of skills. The team is adept in environmental regulation, litigation and permitting issues and is known for its work in the air, water and, increasingly, renewable energy spaces. It has recently represented clients ranging from the City of Raleigh and the towns of Caswell Beach and Oak Island, to Krispy Kreme.

**Sources say:** "*Absolutely impressive. The firm has a very good environmental reputation.*"

**KEY INDIVIDUALS** The well-regarded **Steven Levitas** has specific expertise on issues related to water law. One admiring source commented: "*I find him extremely knowledgeable, very articulate, and he has a great personality for achieving compromise and finding common ground. Really skilful.*" **Stephen Berlin** is recognized for his Superfund and RCRA-related work and is adept in environmental litigation and compliance, and handling business transactions which incorporate environmental matters. He is noted as a "*first-rate attorney, a very bright guy and practical-minded.*" **Alan McConnell** is an experienced environmental lawyer, focusing his practice on the regulation of air pollution. One source has said: "*Alan is very practical but also creative, a real expert on the CAA.*" **William Lane** concentrates on environmental litigation and regulatory counseling, with experience in issues pertaining to air quality, water quality, brownfield redevelopment and renewable energy. One satisfied client noted: "*He's our go-to person; he's practical and easygoing.*"

## McGuireWoods LLP
See profile on p.2519

**THE FIRM** This firm boasts a substantial and talented environment team that works closely with its energy and climate change specialists. The teams can dovetail with other departments such as corporate and litigation, offering a full business service. It handles a range of environmental and energy-related issues including water, air, waste and brownfield developments. Drawing on its strong nationwide presence, it serves clients such as Siemens Energy, Ashland, Rockwood Holdings and Waste Management.

**KEY INDIVIDUALS Benne Hutson** is praised as an "*excellent lawyer*" and has experience in various areas of environmental law including hazardous and solid waste, water quality, brownfields and Superfund issues.

## Parker Poe Adams & Bernstein LLP

**THE FIRM** With offices in Charlotte and Raleigh, this firm continues to expand its dedicated environmental practice. The team is well known for its work in renewable energy such as wind, solar and waste-to-energy; highlights include assisting a major renewable energy company with all aspects of an innovative solar energy project. The group equally covers environment-related litigation, compliance and permitting issues, assisting clients such as Stanly County, DAK Americas, Sonic Automotive and AVX Corporation.

**KEY INDIVIDUALS Thomas Griffin** has a broad practice with a specialty in environmental litigation. An admiring source noted: "*He's an excellent lawyer. Very, very good in transactional matters, a very good litigator, very sharp and gives excellent advice.*" The well-regarded **Max Justice** has particularly extensive experience of environment-related regulatory and administrative law, including representing clients in both state and federal courts. **Steven Weber** heads the environmental practice and is a seasoned litigator with significant experience in regulatory compliance matters. One source said: "*He has a very good ability to communicate, take real complex ideas and boil them down to their simplest elements.*"

## Womble Carlyle Sandridge & Rice, LLP
See profile on p.2049

**THE FIRM** This environmental practice is regarded as one of the finest in the state for environmental litigation, recognized for its extensive experience in handling toxic torts. Clients such as Eaton Corporation, Syngenta Crop Protection, Hamilton Beach Brands and Alliance One International also rely on the group's environmental regulation expertise. Recent work includes representing Facebook in obtaining a brownfield agreement for the redevelopment of the site into a new data center, a $900 million investment.

**KEY INDIVIDUALS Bradford De Vore** is an experienced litigator, representing companies in various industries on toxic tort and product liability issues. He led on the Facebook matter and has also recently represented Alliance One International in a class action involving groundwater contamination. **Richard Morton** is in demand for his breadth of experience, particularly as a litigator. He is praised by one admiring commentator for being "*excellent in the compliance and litigation arenas.*"

## Band 3

## Poyner Spruill LLP

**THE FIRM** This Raleigh-based team offers a much sought range of skills. It is especially recognized for its expertise in environmental litigation but also handles a range of transactional matters. Its work includes handling issues around contaminated property and air pollution, and it also assists parties such as buyers, sellers and lenders with environmental matters which arise in real estate transactions. Clients include Neuse River Compliance Association, Town of Apex and Green Recycling.

**Sources say:** "*Very impressive and well regarded. We're very pleased with the firm.*"

**KEY INDIVIDUALS Glenn Dunn** offers tremendous experience to clients, with one source observing: "*He has excellent relationships at both the state and local level, particularly among the regulators, and is well respected in the environmental community.*" **Richard Kane** is recognized for his mastery of the CAA as well as his considerable litigation experience, often representing clients in matters relating to toxic torts. **Keith Johnson** is known for his strong litigation practice and is experienced in handling Superfund matters. One source said: "*He is technically well versed and understands what people on the ground are dealing with. Impressive.*"

## Robinson, Bradshaw & Hinson PA

**THE FIRM** This firm's North Carolina team attracts clients such as GIMCO, CommScope, EnPro and FMC Corporation. It is particularly active in environmental cleanup, waste disposal, water resources and wetlands work. The team also handles any number of environment-related issues that arise from property development.

**KEY INDIVIDUALS William Toole** focuses on environmental litigation and compliance counseling, with specific expertise on issues involving site development, such as wetlands permitting, brownfield sites and Superfund cleanup. Recent work includes representing Landmark Properties in a $20 million brownfield agreement negotiation. **Emily Sherlock** has a strong corporate practice and is experienced in handling environmental compliance matters, with expertise in issues pertaining to Superfund and RCRA.

### Smith Moore Leatherwood LLP
See profile on p.2048

**THE FIRM** This regional firm takes a business-oriented approach to handling environmental issues and is recognized for its Superfund work. The team's expertise covers environmental permitting, litigation, compliance, investigations and, generally, the environment aspects of business transactions. Clients include Nash County, Sandhills Environment, Bank of North Carolina and MNC Holdings.

**Sources say:** "*We were very pleased with them.*"

**KEY INDIVIDUALS Stephen Earp** (see p.2040) is a skilled corporate lawyer who handles complex environmental litigation and regulatory matters. One source said: "*He's fantastic, a great risk assessor, efficient and gives great advice.*" **Ramona O'Bryant** (see p.2043) has a broad administrative law practice which is geared to environmental matters such as permitting and compliance. She has considerable experience in wetland and stream permitting and contamination cases.

### Band 4

### Moore & Van Allen, PLLC

**THE FIRM** This firm's practice group offers expertise in environmental transactions including compliance and litigation. The team works with various industries including chemical, recycling, real estate and manufacturing, with clients such as Nucor, Piedmont Natural Gas and Rexam.

**KEY INDIVIDUALS** Head of department **Peter McGrath** is an experienced litigator who counsels clients on a range of environmental issues, with an emphasis on air and water law. **William White** assists clients on environmental compliance and transactional matters and has significant expertise in handling Superfund issues.

### Smith, Anderson, Blount, Dorsett, Mitchell & Jernigan, LLP
See profile on p.2047

**THE FIRM** This Raleigh-based firm is gaining increased prominence in the environmental space. The team handles a range of transactional matters and has particular strengths in environmental enforcement defense and compliance, together with litigation. It regularly handles site remediation, hazardous waste and permitting matters for a range of clients including Progress Energy Carolinas, Covanta Energy, Earthtec Environmental and S.T. Wooten.

**Sources say:** "*I would have no hesitation referring folks to them. They are solid.*"

**KEY INDIVIDUALS Stephen Parascandola** (see p.2044) is extremely well regarded in the market and is well versed in environmental and land use law, often representing clients on Superfund and RCRA matters.

### Williams Mullen

**THE FIRM** Williams Mullen offers a skilled team with long experience of regulatory, compliance, litigation and permitting issues together with established contacts within both state and federal agencies. The group is practiced in handling air pollution, hazardous waste, wetlands permitting and Superfund cleanup matters, and on behalf of a client recently drafted a response on the EPA's proposed changes to the definition of solid waste. Its clients include KmX Chemical, the City of Oxford and Watts Water Technologies.

**Sources say:** "*The firm is responsive; they know the rules and are able to explain them in an understandable manner.*"

**KEY INDIVIDUALS** Hailed as "*one of the deans of the environmental Bar,*" **Amos Dawson** is a certified mediator in addition to his extensive experience in environmental law. **Sean Sullivan** focuses his practice on compliance counseling and has recently assisted OE Enterprises in obtaining a brownfield agreement to facilitate a redevelopment project.

### Other Notable Practitioners

**William Clarke** of Roberts & Stevens focuses on environmental permitting, compliance, litigation and transactional issues involving contaminated property. He is praised for being "*first-rate*" and "*very good at what he does.*" **Carolyn Jones Van Buren** of Van Buren Law, PLLC is described as an "*excellent attorney*" whose environmental practice covers brownfield, permitting and Superfund issues. Noted as a "*fine practitioner,*" **Frank Sheffield** of Ward and Smith PA is especially knowledgeable about air and water quality, compliance, contaminated property and alternative energy issues.

# INTELLECTUAL PROPERTY

Commentary about individuals can be found under their firm's paragraph. If the firm has no paragraph (is not ranked) look at Other Notable Practitioners.

### Band 1

### Kilpatrick Townsend & Stockton LLP
See profile on p.1109

**THE FIRM** Based in Winston-Salem, this substantial team boasts a well-established and respected patent and trademark practice. In addition to offering patent prosecution and litigation, the team handles a range of copyright and trademark matters. Many of the attorneys are also qualified in engineering, IT and the sciences, adding to the all-around prowess offered to clients such as Amazon.com, AT&T, LabCorp and Alfresco Software.

**Sources say:** "*They have excellent technical skills, are very knowledgeable about the venues and judges, and are very pragmatic about how to get a good result efficiently.*"

**KEY INDIVIDUALS** The highly regarded **Charles Calkins** is known for his expertise in patent law and dealing with IP

transactions. A source commented: "*I have only the highest respect for him and his capabilities.*" Cochair of the firm's patent litigation team, **Steven Gardner** is a well-respected trial lawyer who focuses his practice on patent litigation and counseling. He has recently represented Red Hat and Wells Fargo.

### Moore & Van Allen, PLLC

**THE FIRM** This practice consists of a 32-strong team across its Charlotte and Research Triangle Park offices and offers clients a breadth of experience in contentious, prosecution and transactional patent, trademark and copyright issues. The firm strives for a business-oriented approach and boasts an impressive clientele including Bank of America, Boeing and IBM.

**Sources say:** "*Moore & Van Allen showed that its lawyers can handle even the most complex of cases with lots of moving parts and players in a clear, effective and successful way.*"

**KEY INDIVIDUALS Dickson Lupo** leads the practice group and has a wealth of experience in handling an array of IP issues from litigation to the transactional. Sources describe him as a "*strong advocate*" and "*a premier lawyer at the firm.*"

### Myers Bigel

**THE FIRM** This highly regarded North Carolina boutique offers the full range of IP services, with a marked excellence in its patent law capabilities. The group's technical expertise in biochemical, pharmaceutical, mechanical and technological industries is evidenced by the number of its attorneys holding degrees in engineering and the sciences. The team services a varied client base including Duke

University, Samsung Electronics, Collins & Aikman and Nautilus.
**Sources say:** *"They're excellent." "They approach matters in a very pragmatic way and have a consistent level of quality."*
**KEY INDIVIDUALS** Described as a *"really strong lawyer,"* **Mitchell Bigel** is renowned for his expertise in patent law, with an emphasis on the electronics, communications and software arenas. **James Cannon** focuses on patent prosecution and specializes in mechanical engineering, with extensive experience in manufacturing and components-related fields. An admiring peer notes: *"I only have great respect for him."* The well-regarded **Ken Sibley** is hailed as a *"very good lawyer"* and handles IP matters relating to the biotech and chemical industries.

## Womble Carlyle Sandridge & Rice, LLP
See profile on p.2049
**THE FIRM** Womble Carlyle boasts one of the finest IP practices in North Carolina, with a strong statewide and regional presence. Dedicated teams offer tailored expertise in IP litigation, patent and trademark prosecution and management together with IP transactions. Many of the attorneys also have technical expertise in scientific or engineering fields, allowing the firm to cater to a host of clients which include Remington Arms and Bank of America.
**Sources say:** *"Their IP transactional group is top-notch." "Their patent prosecution has been excellent and cost-effective."*
**KEY INDIVIDUALS Chris Humphrey** is especially known for his mastery of patent prosecution law together with his broad expertise in life science technologies. He is hailed as *"an exceptional patent attorney"* by one source. The experienced **Christopher Bolen** cochairs the firm's IP practice and concentrates on technology licensing, trademarks and copyright as well as IP transactions. A source highlighted that *"accountability, responsiveness, creativity, knowledge of the law and excellent drafting skills are key strengths that he exhibits."*

## Band 2

### Alston & Bird LLP
See profile on p.1102
**THE FIRM** This firm has offices in Charlotte and the Research Triangle and retains a well-established IP practice. A substantial team across the two offices handles a range of services including patent prosecution, IP litigation, counseling and licensing. The firm has recently represented clients such as BB&T, North Carolina State University and Carolinas HealthCare System. It handles the patent prosecution matters for clients including Electrolux both in the USA and abroad.
**Sources say:** *"They are impressive in their ability to provide sound legal counsel with a very high level of quality on any IP-related front."*
**KEY INDIVIDUALS** Co-leader of the patent prosecution group, **Guy Gosnell** (see p.2041) focuses on patent law with a particular expertise in dealing with electronic and computer technology products. **Michael McCoy** (see p.2043) has a diverse practice covering the full range of IP services including trademarks, patents, trade secrets and unfair competition. He has a significant focus on the IT and software industries and has recently represented Navico, handling all of its IP matters. **Murray Spruill** (see p.2045) concentrates on patent law and is particularly recognized for his expertise on issues pertaining to the biotech, biochemical and pharmaceutical industries. A source commented: *"His professionalism and legal acumen are unparalleled."*

### Parker Poe Adams & Bernstein LLP
**THE FIRM** Parker Poe's IP group is noted for its well-established and comprehensive trademarks and patents offering and is also particularly recognized for its transactional expertise, including software licensing. The firm's IP practice is based in Raleigh near the Research Triangle, placing it in a prime location to serve clients including Siemens, Moog Music, Sunbelt Rentals, North Carolina State University and LabCorp.
**Sources say:** *"They did a phenomenal job, it was a tricky situation in terms of legal complexity." "I was absolutely impressed with their performance."*
**KEY INDIVIDUALS Frank Silber** heads the practice group and his expertise spans the software, IT, biotech and healthcare industries. He is praised by a source as being *"one of the best, if not the best, I've ever worked with. Brilliant. Does not miss a thing."* The well-regarded **Arthur DeBaugh** assist clients from various industries with IP infringement and licensing matters. A source noted: *"He has a very good knowledge of USPTO practice and provides good advice and recommendations."* **William Cannon** is building a reputation for his practice in trademarks, copyright and unfair competition. Sources say he is *"excellent – very knowledgeable about trademark law and quick to respond."* **Christopher Thomas** is an experienced trial lawyer and represents clients in disputes in various areas of IP law. Recent work includes representing Ultimate Accents in a case of alleged copyright infringement.

## Band 3

### Williams Mullen
**THE FIRM** Williams Mullen's IP practice is based in Raleigh and continues to grow its presence in North Carolina. The group is well regarded for its IP litigation, licensing and prosecution services, with a particularly strong track record representing technology companies, especially digital media and software companies. The group's clients include QlikTech and Arysta LifeScience.
**Sources say:** *"Their professionalism and expertise in dealing with various issues has been outstanding."*
**KEY INDIVIDUALS Rob Van Arnam** is an experienced IP attorney with a focus on licensing and litigation. A source describes him as *"a very good communicator – the complete package. A strong lawyer."*

## Band 4

### Brooks, Pierce, McLendon, Humphrey & Leonard LLP
**THE FIRM** This firm's IP expertise has a strong emphasis on technology and telecom in all its forms and covers patents, trademarks and copyright protection, together with technology licensing and other transactions. The firm also has a strong bench of trial lawyers and corporate/M&A lawyers who work in concert with the IP team.
**KEY INDIVIDUALS** Raleigh-based Darrell Fruth is a contact.

### Smith Moore Leatherwood LLP
See profile on p.2048
**THE FIRM** Smith Moore Leatherwood has offices across the state and retains a solid IP practice in North Carolina consisting of an 11-strong team. The group offers expert-

ise in patents, trademarks, copyright and trade secrets, enabling it to represent companies in various industries including pharmaceutical, chemical, software and defense. Clients include Kayser Roth and Evonik Stockhausen.

**Sources say:** *"Their technical expertise is impressive and they are responsive and cost-effective."*
**KEY INDIVIDUALS** Phil McCann is the department head.

# LABOR & EMPLOYMENT

Commentary about individuals can be found under their firm's paragraph. If the firm has no paragraph (is not ranked) look at Other Notable Practitioners.

## Labor & Employment
### Leading Firms

**Band 1**
Constangy, Brooks & Smith, LLP
Ogletree, Deakins, Nash, Smoak & Stewart, PC *

**Band 2**
Robinson, Bradshaw & Hinson PA
Smith Moore Leatherwood LLP *

**Band 3**
Brooks, Pierce, McLendon, Humphrey & Leonard LLP
Jackson Lewis LLP *
Kilpatrick Townsend & Stockton LLP *
Parker Poe Adams & Bernstein LLP
Smith, Anderson, Blount, Dorsett, Mitchell & Jernigan, LLP *
Van Hoy Reutlinger Adams & Dunn
Womble Carlyle Sandridge & Rice, LLP *

**Band 4**
Williams Mullen

## Labor & Employment: Immigration
### Leading Individuals

**Band 1**

| | | |
|---|---|---|
| Bradshaw Penni Pearson | Constangy, Brooks & Smith, LLP | |
| Merrills Andrew W | Ogletree, Deakins, Nash, Smoak & Stewart * | |

\* Indicates firm / individual with profile.

†ONP = Other Notable Practitioner.

## Labor & Employment
### Leading Individuals

**Band 1**

| | |
|---|---|
| Carlson Jr Kenneth P | Constangy, Brooks & Smith, LLP |
| Doyle Jr John | Constangy, Brooks & Smith, LLP |
| Farr Thomas A | Ogletree, Deakins, Nash, Smoak & Stewart * |
| Keen C Matthew | Ogletree, Deakins, Nash, Smoak & Stewart * |
| Loftis Jr W Randolph | Constangy, Brooks & Smith, LLP |
| McGinn Daniel | Brooks, Pierce, McLendon, Humphrey |
| Van Hoy Philip M | Van Hoy Reutlinger Adams & Dunn |

**Band 2**

| | |
|---|---|
| Adams Bryan | Van Hoy Reutlinger Adams & Dunn |
| Avram Randall D | Kilpatrick Townsend & Stockton LLP |
| Bell Jr Albert R | Ward and Smith PA (ONP)† |
| Bradshaw Penni Pearson | Constangy, Brooks & Smith, LLP |
| Dunn Stephen | Van Hoy Reutlinger Adams & Dunn |
| Earp Julianna Theall | Smith Moore Leatherwood LLP * |
| Ewalt Gretchen W | Ogletree, Deakins, Nash, Smoak & Stewart * |
| Holland Patricia L | Jackson Lewis LLP * |
| Johnson Charles E | Robinson, Bradshaw & Hinson PA |
| Kenyon Rosemary | Smith, Anderson, Blount, Dorsett, Mitchell * |
| Korando Kimberly J | Smith, Anderson, Blount, Dorsett, Mitchell * |
| Lay Wood W | Winston & Strawn LLP (ONP)† * |
| McAtee Richard S | Jackson Lewis LLP * |
| Oliver George J | Smith Moore Leatherwood LLP * |

| | |
|---|---|
| Rainey Richard L | Womble Carlyle Sandridge & Rice, LLP |
| Weddington Keith M | Parker Poe Adams & Bernstein LLP |
| Wood Stacy K | Parker Poe Adams & Bernstein LLP |

**Band 3**

| | |
|---|---|
| Alexander Mason | Fisher & Phillips LLP (ONP)† * |
| Clark Terry A | Constangy, Brooks & Smith, LLP |
| Crawford Nicole A | Brooks, Pierce, McLendon, Humphrey |
| Crotty Jonathan | Parker Poe Adams & Bernstein LLP |
| Gibbons Susanna | Poyner Spruill LLP (ONP)† |
| Lord Michael C | Williams Mullen |
| Petesch Bruce A | Ogletree, Deakins, Nash, Smoak & Stewart * |
| Shad Kerry | Smith, Anderson, Blount, Dorsett, Mitchell * |
| Spears Jr James B | Ogletree, Deakins, Nash, Smoak & Stewart * |
| Wester John | Robinson, Bradshaw & Hinson PA |
| Wright Jr Julian H | Robinson, Bradshaw & Hinson PA |

**Band 4**

| | |
|---|---|
| Haygood Richard D | Kilpatrick Townsend & Stockton LLP |
| Sar Robert A | Ogletree, Deakins, Nash, Smoak & Stewart * |
| Steen Bruce | McGuireWoods LLP (ONP)† |

**Up-and-coming individuals**

| | |
|---|---|
| Lindsay David | Kilpatrick Townsend & Stockton LLP |
| Ramseur Patti | Smith Moore Leatherwood LLP * |

## Band 1

### Constangy, Brooks & Smith, LLP

**THE FIRM** Regarded as one of the top labor and employment boutiques, this firm is able to draw on its vast number of offices to provide the full spectrum of services to clients across the country. The North Carolina group is recognized for its employment litigation and labor law practices, serving clients such as GE, Wake Forest University and North American Trucks. It has also handled many union campaigns for R. J. Reynolds in the state.
**Sources say:** *"The firm is great – I think they're very knowledgeable but also great at keeping expenses down."*
**KEY INDIVIDUALS Penni Pearson Bradshaw** is a well-regarded employment lawyer and is recognized as a leading expert on immigration law. Seasoned litigator **Kenneth Carlson** acts for companies on various areas of employment law. His practice also covers trade secrets, noncompetition law and the drafting of contracts and agreements. The highly regarded **John Doyle** focuses on representing management clients, acting for employers on labor and employment law issues. **Randolph Loftis** is a skilled trial

lawyer, experienced in defending class action claims, discrimination and harassment cases. **Terry Clark** advises clients on various employer-employee relations issues, and is adept in litigation, counseling, dispute prevention and resolution.

### Ogletree, Deakins, Nash, Smoak & Stewart, PC
**See profile on p.1110**

**THE FIRM** This boutique's national footprint backs up its formidable statewide presence, with offices in Raleigh, Charlotte and Greensboro. This geographical coverage enables the team to serve clients in the state's key business districts seamlessly, with a 39-strong team working in the labor, employment and immigration spaces. The firm's impressive clientele includes Duke University, Deloitte, Honeywell International and The Budd Group.
**Sources say:** *"The best I've ever seen. The results have been wonderful."*
**KEY INDIVIDUALS Matthew Keen** (see p.2042) is a well-regarded litigator with experience in handling wage and hour, discrimination, workplace injuries and ERISA-relat-

ed issues in state and federal courts. Sources say: *"He's wonderful and very responsive."* The highly experienced **Thomas Farr** (see p.2040) focuses on employment litigation, workplace safety and constitutional law. Immigration practice group head **Andrew Merrills** (see p.2043) focuses on employment-based immigration and US and international business visas. **Gretchen Ewalt** (see p.2040) counsels employers on discrimination, harassment, discipline and discharge issues. *"She is just tremendous,"* say clients. *"She has a great sense of the changing dynamic of our organization and gives clear solutions to sticky problems."* Experienced employment lawyer **James Spears** (see p.2045) counsels clients on various employment issues, and handles related litigation in state and federal courts. **Bruce Petesch** (see p.2044) concentrates on traditional labor law and assists employers with contract negotiations, litigation, management training and union-related issues. **Robert Sar** (see p.2045) defends employers in lawsuits relating to trade secret disputes, employment contract violations, wage payment issues and regulatory violations.

## Band 2

### Robinson, Bradshaw & Hinson PA

**THE FIRM** This established labor and employment group is noted for its employment litigation practice, handling claims pertaining to ERISA, FMLA, FLSA and other state and federal statutes. It provides employment counseling and compliance advice to clients such as Charlotte-Mecklenburg Housing Partnership, the City of Charlotte and Wells Fargo.

**KEY INDIVIDUALS** The *"exceptional"* **Charles Johnson** is an experienced employment litigator. He has handled matters before state and federal courts as well as administrative agencies. **Julian Wright** has a broad practice with a focus on employment law. He is adept in employment contractual issues as well as litigating disputes in relation to discrimination, harassment and wrongful termination. Sources note that *"he is an excellent resource to have."* **John Wester** is highly respected as a trial lawyer and has extensive experience in handling discrimination lawsuits.

### Smith Moore Leatherwood LLP
See profile on p.2048

**THE FIRM** This firm's labor and employment practice continues to impress, gaining high praise from clients for its work in employment litigation, labor relations, immigration, employee benefits and workers' compensation. The group is also able to work closely with the firm's life, health and disability practice to assist clients in addressing ERISA-related matters. Clients include US Airways, Moses Cone Hospital, Kindred Healthcare and Vanderbilt Mortgage & Finance.

**Sources say:** *"They are knowledgeable and efficient, and have a very good understanding of the law."*

**KEY INDIVIDUALS** The *"excellent"* **George Oliver** (see p.2043) is an experienced practitioner and counsels employers on all areas of employment law. **Julianna Theall Earp** (see p.2040) is described as a *"terrific lawyer"* and focuses her practice on employment litigation, counseling and training. Department head **Patti Ramseur**'s (see p.2044) practice covers employment litigation, counseling and contracts. An impressed source notes: *"She is unbelievable – an outstanding trial lawyer."*

## Band 3

### Brooks, Pierce, McLendon, Humphrey & Leonard LLP

**THE FIRM** This North Carolina firm handles various areas of labor and employment law, and has a solid reputation for its litigation abilities and familiarity with administrative agencies. The group's areas of expertise include collective bargaining, union avoidance, employment handbooks and policies, and compliance issues.

**KEY INDIVIDUALS** The highly regarded **Daniel McGinn** heads the department and has extensive experience in labor and employment law. **Nicole Crawford** focuses her practice on labor and employment law and is an experi-

enced litigator, defending employers in various kinds of disputes.

### Jackson Lewis LLP
See profile on p.1982

**THE FIRM** This employment boutique is able to draw on its national network of offices to provide full coverage on labor and employment law for clients including local municipalities and corporate entities. The group is able to handle traditional labor work involving unions and collective bargaining, as well as employment litigation, affirmative action plans and updating policy.

**Sources say:** *"They do excellent work and know the law inside and out."*

**KEY INDIVIDUALS** Experienced trial lawyer **Patricia Holland** (see p.2041) has appeared before state and federal courts and often represents employers in discrimination, sexual harassment and wrongful discharge matters. **Richard McAtee** (see p.2043) focuses on employment litigation with an emphasis on discrimination and noncompete cases. He is *"very responsive, intelligent and thorough,"* according to interviewees.

### Kilpatrick Townsend & Stockton LLP
See profile on p.1109

**THE FIRM** This firm handles labor and employment work from its Raleigh and Winston-Salem offices. The team is well regarded for its employment litigation practice, defending employers in discrimination, wage and hour lawsuits and other employment-related disputes. It recently defended Krispy Kreme against an FLSA claim.

**Sources say:** *"We place very high reliance on their knowledge and expertise in contract law and employee litigation."*

**KEY INDIVIDUALS** **Randall Avram** chairs the practice and has extensive experience in the labor and employment arena. *"Randy is an expert in labor relations and all other types of employment law,"* say sources. **Richard Haygood** has a broad labor and employment practice covering organizing campaigns, union avoidance and staff training. His recent clients include Georgia-Pacific and Butterball. **David Lindsay**'s practice includes defending managers in discrimination lawsuits, and counseling employers on union matters, FMLA, FLSA and employee relations issues.

### Parker Poe Adams & Bernstein LLP

**THE FIRM** Parker Poe retains a healthy employment practice with a team of 22 attorneys across its North Carolina offices. The group is highly regarded for its litigation and employee benefits work, serving clients such as Wells Fargo, Laboratory Corporation of America, Time Warner Cable and DAK Americas.

**KEY INDIVIDUALS** *"Very fine employment litigator"* **Keith Weddington** focuses on employment law and represents managers in handling disputes involving employee relations. **Stacy Wood** is known for her expertise in ERISA, discrimination and harassment litigation, and is praised as a *"very talented employment lawyer and a strong advocate for her clients."* **Jonathan Crotty** heads the firm's employment and benefits practice group, and concentrates on

counseling clients on employment regulation and compliance issues.

### Smith, Anderson, Blount, Dorsett, Mitchell & Jernigan, LLP
See profile on p.2047

**THE FIRM** This firm earns high praise from clients for its employment work. The group is noted for its capabilities in employment litigation, EEOC investigations and OSHA-related issues, assisting clients from industries including healthcare, life sciences, manufacturing and insurance. GlaxoSmithKline, Progress Energy, Quintiles and Tekelec are among the firm's clients.

**Sources say:** *"The firm was most helpful in assisting us in laying proper practice foundations upon which we could avoid future problems."*

**KEY INDIVIDUALS** **Kimberly Korando** (see p.2042) heads the labor and employment practice group, and focuses on employment compliance issues. Sources say: *"She is exceedingly professional, practical and thorough."* **Rosemary Kenyon** (see p.2042) is an experienced corporate trial lawyer with a significant labor and employment practice. **Kerry Shad** (see p.2045) concentrates on employment litigation and counseling, and has experience in representing clients in state and federal courts.

### Van Hoy Reutlinger Adams & Dunn

**THE FIRM** This Charlotte-based boutique offers a sophisticated employment practice and is particularly well regarded for its ability to handle discrimination, trade secrets and noncompetition-related disputes. Clients include the Town of Mocksville, Carolinas Center for Medical Excellence, Harper Corporation of America and Park Road Shopping Center.

**KEY INDIVIDUALS** **Philip Van Hoy** is a highly regarded trial lawyer with extensive experience handling complex employment cases in state and federal courts. **Bryan Adams** is known for his expertise in employment-related litigation. *"He is very easy to work with, stays on top of it, keeps us in the loop and has extremely thorough knowledge,"* notes one satisfied client. **Stephen Dunn** is an experienced employment lawyer as well as a certified mediator, focusing on the mediation and arbitration of employment and commercial litigation.

### Womble Carlyle Sandridge & Rice, LLP
See profile on p.2049

**THE FIRM** Womble Carlyle's labor and employment practice is noted for its strengths in employment litigation, representing clients in state and federal courts, and before agencies and arbitration panels. The group also has significant experience in counseling clients on compliance issues. Clients include Carolina Biological Supply, Iredell Memorial Hospital and Charlotte Radiology.

**Sources say:** *"They performed very well. They're responsive, extremely confident, and effective."*

**KEY INDIVIDUALS** **Richard Rainey** is highly regarded for his employment litigation practice, with one interviewee saying: *"He is extremely effective, helpful and always available. Excellent."*

## Band 4

### Williams Mullen

**THE FIRM** This firm is recognized for its strengths in handling traditional labor law issues including union avoidance, collective bargaining and defending employers in claims of unfair labor practices. Drawing on the firm's Virginia offices, the North Carolina group is able to offer greater capacity to serve its varied client base.

**KEY INDIVIDUALS Michael Lord** is an experienced labor and employment lawyer who is known for his employment litigation, advice and counseling practice.

## Other Notable Practitioners

**Mason Alexander** (see p.2039) of Fisher & Phillips LLP is an experienced labor and employment lawyer covering wage and hour law and union avoidance. Sources say: *"He provides excellent employment advice and is a good negotiator."* **Bruce Steen** of McGuireWoods LLP is a highly skilled employment litigator, representing employers in lawsuits involving FLSA, ERISA and other employment-related state and federal statutes. *"Excellent lawyer"* **Albert Bell** of Ward and Smith PA has extensive experience in labor and employment law, focusing on litigation and EEOC matters. **Wood Lay** (see p.2043) of Winston & Strawn LLP is known for his expertise in employment litigation regarding ERISA, noncompetition and trade secret-related issues. He also counsels clients on employment compliance. **Susanna Gibbons** of Poyner Spruill LLP is recognized for her practice in employment compliance and litigation. She has recently represented Golden Corral and Martin Marietta Materials.

# LITIGATION

Healthcare & Medical Malpractice p.2034;  White-Collar Crime & Government Investigations p.2034

Commentary about individuals can be found under their firm's paragraph.  If the firm has no paragraph (is not ranked) look at Other Notable Practitioners.

## Litigation: General Commercial
### Leading Firms

**Band 1**
Brooks, Pierce, McLendon, Humphrey & Leonard LLP
Ellis & Winters LLP
McGuireWoods LLP *
Robinson, Bradshaw & Hinson PA
Womble Carlyle Sandridge & Rice, LLP *

**Band 2**
Moore & Van Allen, PLLC
Parker Poe Adams & Bernstein LLP

**Band 3**
K&L Gates *
Kilpatrick Townsend & Stockton LLP *
Smith Moore Leatherwood LLP *

**Band 4**
Bell, Davis & Pitt, P.A.
Hunton & Williams LLP *
James McElroy & Diehl

## Litigation: First Amendment
### Leading Individuals

**Band 1**

| | |
|---|---|
| Buchan Jr Jonathan E | McGuireWoods LLP |
| Stevens Hugh | Stevens Martin Vaughn & Tadych (ONP)[†] |

* *Indicates firm / individual with profile.*
[†] *ONP = Other Notable Practitioner.*

## Band 1

### Brooks, Pierce, McLendon, Humphrey & Leonard LLP

**THE FIRM** This North Carolina firm is known as a litigation powerhouse that offers a seamless service to clients. The group's formidable bench strength has allowed it to assist with lawsuits ranging from bankruptcy and corporate to environmental and healthcare. A number of its attorneys are also certified mediators, focusing on alternative dispute resolution for development and construction, labor and employment, and civil cases. The firm's clients include Deloitte, Time Warner Cable, Lorillard Tobacco and Norfolk Southern Railway Company.

## Litigation: General Commercial
### Senior Statesmen

**Senior Statesmen: distinguished older practitioners**

| | | |
|---|---|---|
| Hanna III | George V | Moore & Van Allen, PLLC |
| McKeithen | Ward | Robinson, Bradshaw & Hinson PA |

### Leading Individuals

**Band 1**

| | | |
|---|---|---|
| Cooney III | James P | Womble Carlyle Sandridge & Rice, LLP |
| Davis | William K | Bell, Davis & Pitt, P.A. |
| Diehl Jr | William K | James McElroy & Diehl |
| Ellis | Richard W | Ellis & Winters LLP |
| Ey Jr | Douglas W | McGuireWoods LLP |
| Fuller | Robert | Robinson, Bradshaw & Hinson PA |
| Hinson | Edward T | James McElroy & Diehl |
| Merritt | Mark | Robinson, Bradshaw & Hinson PA |
| Wester | John | Robinson, Bradshaw & Hinson PA |
| Williams | Jim | Brooks, Pierce, McLendon, Humphrey |

**Band 2**

| | | |
|---|---|---|
| Arrowood | Catharine Biggs | Parker Poe Adams & Bernstein LLP |
| Barber | Timothy G | King & Spalding LLP (ONP)[†] * |
| Cooley | Jim D | Womble Carlyle Sandridge & Rice, LLP |
| Copenhaver | W Andrew | Womble Carlyle Sandridge & Rice, LLP |
| Cottingham III | T Thomas | Winston & Strawn LLP (ONP)[†] * |
| Davis | Jeffrey J | Sole Practitioner (ONP)[†] |
| Duncan | Alan W | Smith Moore Leatherwood LLP |
| Emory Jr | Frank E | Hunton & Williams LLP * |
| McLoughlin Jr | James P | Moore & Van Allen, PLLC |
| Mehta | Kiran H | K&L Gates * |
| Millen | Pressly M | Womble Carlyle Sandridge & Rice, LLP |
| Oleynik | Jeffrey E | Brooks, Pierce, McLendon, Humphrey |
| Phillips | Jim W | Brooks, Pierce, McLendon, Humphrey |
| Rikard | William L | Parker Poe Adams & Bernstein LLP |
| Sasser | Jonathan D | Ellis & Winters LLP * |

| | | |
|---|---|---|
| Sitton | Larry B | Smith Moore Leatherwood LLP * |
| Taylor | Dan | Kilpatrick Townsend & Stockton LLP |

**Band 3**

| | | |
|---|---|---|
| Charnes | Adam H | Kilpatrick Townsend & Stockton LLP |
| Kenyon | Douglas W | Hunton & Williams LLP * |
| Kutrow | Bradley R | McGuireWoods LLP |
| Marcus | Robert R | Smith Moore Leatherwood LLP * |
| Parsons | Gary S | Troutman Sanders LLP (ONP)[†] |
| Patterson Jr | Carl N | Smith, Anderson, Blount, Dorsett (ONP)[†] * |
| Phillips | Reid L | Brooks, Pierce, McLendon, Humphrey |
| Ruley | Alan M | Bell, Davis & Pitt, P.A. |
| Silver | Hayden J | Womble Carlyle Sandridge & Rice, LLP |
| Wright III | David C | Robinson, Bradshaw & Hinson PA |

**Band 4**

| | | |
|---|---|---|
| Furr | Jeffrey L | King & Spalding LLP (ONP)[†] † |
| Hohnbaum | Cory | King & Spalding LLP (ONP)[†] * |
| Keshian | Richard J | Kilpatrick Townsend & Stockton LLP |
| Long III | Nash E | Winston & Strawn LLP (ONP)[†] * |
| Rom | Fred | Womble Carlyle Sandridge & Rice, LLP |
| Shields | Patricia | Troutman Sanders LLP (ONP)[†] |
| Vaughan | Keith W | Womble Carlyle Sandridge & Rice, LLP |
| Wood Jr | Fred M | Smith Moore Leatherwood LLP * |

**Up-and-coming individuals**

| | | |
|---|---|---|
| Dubis | Melanie Black | Parker Poe Adams & Bernstein LLP |
| Heyl | Jonathan | Smith Moore Leatherwood LLP * |
| McDowell | Valecia M | Moore & Van Allen, PLLC |
| Muckenfuss | Robert A | McGuireWoods LLP |

**Sources say:** *"It was reassuring to have no difficulties in getting prompt and clear answers to our questions in a straightforward, concise manner."*

**KEY INDIVIDUALS Kearns Davis** leads the white-collar criminal defense side of the practice, and is experienced in handling government investigations as well as federal and business litigation. The highly regarded **Jim Williams** focuses on corporate law and business litigation, handling complex disputes in both state and federal court. One source notes: *"He is one of the very best civil litigators in North Carolina, if not the Southeast."* **Jeffrey Oleynik** is a well-reputed trial lawyer with a focus on commercial litigation, bankruptcy and antitrust. In the litigation space, he represents clients in shareholder rights, trade secrets and corporate acquisitions-related suits. **Jim Phillips** concentrates on assisting businesses with a broad range of complex cases involving trade secrets, employment, tax issues and various business torts. **Reid Phillips** is an experienced commercial litigator, representing clients in contracts, securities and IP-related disputes.

## Ellis & Winters LLP

**THE FIRM** Ellis & Winters offers one of the finest litigation practices in the state, with a 28-strong team experienced in handling various complex disputes. The group's depth and breadth of experience has not gone unnoticed by the business community, attracting a roster of high-profile clients which includes Boston Scientific, Sony Mobile Communications and Siemens USA.
**Sources say:** *"Extremely thorough, brilliant lawyers on their staff. I feel I can count on them for anything."*
**KEY INDIVIDUALS** The well-respected **Richard Ellis** has a broad litigation practice with experience representing clients in business, commercial, medical malpractice and product liability disputes. **Leslie Packer** (see p.2044) concentrates on civil litigation, with a focus on product liability and medical malpractice. She is lauded as *"one of the top litigators in the medical malpractice arena."* **Jonathan Sasser** (see p.2045) has extensive experience dealing with complex corporate lawsuits, often representing Fortune 500 companies in high-profile cases.

## McGuireWoods LLP
See profile on p.2519

**THE FIRM** This firm is highly regarded by clients for its strengths in the litigation department, with a deep bench split across three key areas. The firm's complex commercial, business and securities and financial services litigation teams make it a top choice for corporate and banking clients. The group also offers expertise in First Amendment, medical malpractice and white-collar criminal litigation.
**Sources say:** *"McGuireWoods is my go-to firm for litigation matters. Their whole staff is amazing – they just have quality people."*
**KEY INDIVIDUALS Mark Anderson** is an experienced litigator and managing partner of the firm's Raleigh office. According to sources: *"He has great skills in terms of knowledge of trials and processes, is a very hard worker, and is very responsive to clients."* **Ken Bell** is regarded as *"one of the best white-collar lawyers in North Carolina."* He concentrates on government, regulatory and criminal investigations, in addition to representing clients in business-related investigations. The *"fantastic"* **Jonathan Buchan** is an experienced trial lawyer, focusing on business litigation involving media, intellectual property and banking issues. Recent work includes assisting The Charlotte Observer Publishing Company with a defamation suit. Financial services litigation department chair **Douglas Ey** earns praise from clients for being *"enthusiastic about litigation, curious, and passionate about getting to the core of the matter and getting justice."* **Bradley Kutrow** handles complex litigation suits with a focus on securities, product liability and business torts for clients including the Charlotte Pipe and Foundry Company. Sources note that *"he has a really deep, encyclopedic and contemporary knowledge of the law."* **Robert Muckenfuss** concentrates on complex commercial litigation, and also has expertise in motorsports law. Recently, he handled a patent litigation lawsuit on behalf of Newell Rubbermaid.

## Robinson, Bradshaw & Hinson PA

**THE FIRM** This firm is known for its expertise in handling business disputes. It is experienced in complex commercial trials as well as internal and government investigations, making it one of the most highly regarded firms among corporate business clients. Recent work includes representing Family Dollar in a nationwide class action involving claims of discrimination. The group's client portfolio also includes Wells Fargo, Mecklenburg Hospital Authority and Philips.
**Sources say:** *"They focus on providing excellent legal services, which they are known for throughout the country."*
**KEY INDIVIDUALS Robert Fuller** concentrates on business counseling and litigation, with experience in corporate, banking, securities and tax matters. Commentators say: *"He has a brilliant strategic brain, probably the best at strategic thinking in large complex litigation."* **Mark Merritt** focuses on business-related litigation, with expertise in antitrust, securities and class action litigation. Notable work includes representing BB&T in a shareholder derivative action involving auction rate securities sold by a sub-

sidiary. **John Wester** has a broad litigation practice which includes shareholder rights disputes, unfair trade, and federal securities matters. *"He has exceptional intelligence and wit, and is a very strong advocate who is able to operate at all levels of the case,"* say sources. **David Wright** is described by interviewees as a *"very good lawyer,"* focusing on complex commercial, employment and product liability lawsuits. Recent work includes representing Duke Energy and Duke Acquisition Corporation in a class action involving its merger with Progress Energy. **Ward McKeithen** is a highly regarded trial lawyer focusing on civil litigation, with a wealth of experience handling complex cases at both the state and federal level.

## Womble Carlyle Sandridge & Rice, LLP
See profile on p.2049

**THE FIRM** Womble Carlyle has phenomenal strength in the North Carolina litigation arena with its sizable team offering an integrated service to clients. The firm is well reputed for its capabilities in product liability, constitutional torts and complex business disputes. Its varied expertise includes financial services, healthcare, IP and antitrust litigation, allowing it to cater to a range of industries. Clients include Krispy Kreme, Novant Health, Syngenta Crop Protection and GlaxoSmithKline.
**Sources say:** *"They performed very well. The firm is responsive, extremely confident, competent and effective."*
**KEY INDIVIDUALS James Cooney** leads the firm's business litigation practice and focuses on civil and criminal law. He is particularly well regarded for healthcare and white-collar criminal litigation. Sources say: *"He is one of the most confident lawyers. He is responsive, has good judgment, and provides excellent analysis."* **Mark Horoschak** has a broad practice and is recognized as a skilled trial lawyer and renowned for his work in the healthcare antitrust space. **Jim Cooley** is a highly respected litigator with extensive experience in handling complex business disputes. He focuses on representing financial institutions in issues pertaining to the 2008 economic crisis. **Andrew Copenhaver** has extensive trial experience including class actions and federal multidistrict litigation. His practice focuses on matters involving antitrust and trade regulation. **Pressly Millen** is lauded as *"a masterful litigator"* who has handled various class actions, antitrust and complex commercial disputes. **Hayden Silver** concentrates his practice on commercial disputes and intellectual property lawsuits, representing clients in copyright, trademark and patent litigation. Firm chairman **Keith Vaughan** has a wealth of experience in product liability and business-related litigation. **Fred Rom** concentrates on product liability litigation, and is adept in handling matters involving toxic torts, construction and pharmaceuticals. One source notes: *"I think he has an amazing ability to amass large amounts of information and give a concise analysis of it. He is incredibly calm."*

## Band 2

### Moore & Van Allen, PLLC

THE FIRM Moore & Van Allen is recognized for its ability to serve corporate and financial clients in the litigation space, with key strengths in financial services and commercial litigation as well as alternative dispute resolution. The group also continues to expand its cross-border expertise, handling disputes in Asia, Europe and South America in addition to its US operations, making it a stellar choice for multinational companies. Clients include Bank of America, Lowe's, Coca-Cola Bottling and Morgan Stanley. Sources say: "*We are very impressed with the firm. They're always keeping an eye on the detail and work well as a team.*" KEY INDIVIDUALS The highly regarded **James McLoughlin** has a broad litigation practice including securities, ERISA, class action, criminal defense and complex business litigation. Sources say: "*He has a wealth of knowledge and tremendous expertise in a number of areas.*" **George Hanna** is a widely experienced litigator with expertise in disputes pertaining to business and construction law. **Valecia McDowell** is described as a "*highly talented and skilful*" commercial litigator with a focus on complex disputes. Recent work includes representing WR Starkey Mortgage in a mortgage fraud investigation carried out by the DOJ.

### Parker Poe Adams & Bernstein LLP

THE FIRM This firm continues to impress, with over 60 attorneys in its litigation group focusing on complex business litigation matters. Working closely with its regulatory department, the team is able to offer further capacity in the areas of employment and environmental litigation. The firm serves an impressive list of clients, including Ernst & Young, Wells Fargo, Duke Energy and Lyon Aviation. Sources say: "*The attorneys who were involved in the matter and their support staff were superbly professional, helpful and knowledgeable.*" KEY INDIVIDUALS **Harvey Cosper** is highly experienced in the medical malpractice space and represents hospitals, medical professionals and pharmaceutical companies in high-profile professional negligence lawsuits. **Richard Glaser** is an experienced trial lawyer, and concentrates his practice on white-collar criminal defense and internal investigations. **Catharine Biggs Arrowood** is a well-regarded litigator and, in addition to handling complex lawsuits, a significant part of her practice focuses on alternative dispute resolution, arbitrating for various businesses. **William Rikard** is praised as "*an excellent trial lawyer,*" and concentrates on complex civil litigation involving antitrust, business torts, product liability and intellectual property. **Melanie Black Dubis** focuses her practice on commercial litigation, representing clients in unfair trade practices, trade secrets, securities and intellectual property-related lawsuits. A source describes her as "*incredibly articulate and a fantastic litigator.*"

## Band 3

### K&L Gates
See profile on p.2245

THE FIRM This firm is known for its well-established litigation practice, with an international reach and strong national presence often resulting in the group handling large corporate disputes. The team is noted for its litigation abilities in the banking and finance, corporate and utilities spaces.

KEY INDIVIDUALS **Kiran Mehta** (see p.2043) focuses his practice on corporate litigation with expertise in securities, utilities and construction litigation. One source notes that he is "*very good. I'm very impressed by how thoughtful and thorough he has been in representing his clients.*"

### Kilpatrick Townsend & Stockton LLP
See profile on p.1109

THE FIRM This firm gains high praise from its clients, and has a deep bench of trial lawyers handling complex business litigation. The group has expertise in various areas and continues to offer strength in the intellectual property arena, making it a go-to firm for businesses with trademark, copyright and trade secrets-related disputes. Recent work includes representing R.J. Reynolds Tobacco in an ERISA class action and trademark lawsuit.

KEY INDIVIDUALS **Dan Taylor** is an experienced trial lawyer, representing clients in matters involving securities, business torts, contracts and intellectual property. Recent work includes acting on behalf of Lowe's Companies in a series of suits involving patent infringement and trade secrets. **Adam Charnes** is recognized for his appellate and complex commercial litigation work, and has recently represented Krispy Kreme in a breach of agreement lawsuit. Sources say: "*He's skilled, responsive and very talented.*" **Richard Keshian** focuses on product liability and business litigation, recently representing Volvo in a class action involving alleged defective engines. Commentators note that "*he has a lot of experience, is practical, and has terrific presence.*"

### Smith Moore Leatherwood LLP
See profile on p.2048

THE FIRM This regional firm presents an impressive team of litigators and is able to draw on its various offices to provide a breadth of service. The group is particularly well regarded for its work involving commercial, intellectual property, appellate and product liability disputes, serving clients such as GE, Steris, US Airways and Aramark.

KEY INDIVIDUALS **Alan Duncan** is recognized as "*a phenomenal trial lawyer*" and is experienced in handling intellectual property, antitrust and business disputes. **Robert Marcus** (see p.2043) concentrates his practice on complex commercial and appellate litigation, and has recently represented the City of St. Petersburg, Florida in a lawsuit involving a complicated securities transaction with Wachovia Bank. **Fred Wood** (see p.2046) chairs the firm's business litigation team, and handles cases involving unfair business practices, trade secrets, business torts and breach of contract. **Larry Sitton** (see p.2045) is an experienced

commercial litigator with a track record in successfully representing banks and large corporations in complex disputes and class actions. **Jonathan Heyl** (see p.2041) is known for his civil litigation practice and has a focus on commercial-related issues, with experience in handling financial services, legal malpractice and antitrust litigation.

## Band 4

### Bell, Davis & Pitt, P.A.

THE FIRM This North Carolina firm is adept at representing both plaintiffs and defendants in various complex business litigation cases. With offices in Winston-Salem and Charlotte, the firm is well-placed to serve clients in the state's economic centers. Areas of expertise includes stockholder disputes, fraud, intellectual property, business torts and unfair trade practices, allowing it to meet the needs of various corporate clients.

KEY INDIVIDUALS **William Davis** is a highly regarded trial lawyer focusing on complex business and commercial litigation. Sources consider him to be "*one of the absolute best*" in the state. The "*excellent*" **Alan Ruley** is an experienced trial lawyer who concentrates his practice on civil and appellate litigation.

### Hunton & Williams LLP
See profile on p.2517

THE FIRM Hunton & Williams retains a strong litigation practice, with particular focus on representing clients in the banking and financial industries in large commercial disputes. The group is adept at dealing with fraud, contract and trade secrets lawsuits on behalf of clients.

KEY INDIVIDUALS **Frank Emory** (see p.2040) is described as a "*very good lawyer,*" and focuses his practice on complex commercial litigation, representing clients in the financial services industries and other corporate entities. **Douglas Kenyon** (see p.2042) has a broad practice with expertise in intellectual property-related issues and litigation.

### James McElroy & Diehl

THE FIRM This Charlotte firm has a well-regarded litigation practice, representing plaintiffs and defendants in complex business and civil disputes. The group's expertise covers a range of matters involving injury, construction, product liability and professional negligence.

KEY INDIVIDUALS **William Diehl** is described as "*a very good and effective lawyer,*" and is a highly experienced litigator in the areas of civil, family and criminal law. **Edward Hinson** is a respected civil and criminal lawyer, frequently representing clients including medical, legal and business professionals.

### Smith Andesson

THE FIRM This firm is well known for advising on a broad range of commercial litigation, including breach of contract, employment and insurance disputes. The team's recent highlights include representing Progress Energy in numerous state and federal class action shareholder suits regarding the company's proposed merger with Duke Energy.

**Sources say:** "They give us the finest teams, are responsive and staff accordingly. Very thoughtful and pragmatic."

**KEY INDIVIDUALS** Carl Patterson is vastly experienced in handling complex commercial litigation. Recent work includes representing the North Carolina Department of State Treasurer in a dispute concerning investments in a real estate investment fund.

## Other Notable Practitioners

**Joseph Cheshire** of Cheshire Parker Schneider Bryan & Vitale is regarded as one of the finest attorneys in the state for white-collar crime lawsuits, and has dealt with numerous high-profile and complex cases. Sole practitioner **Jeffrey Davis** is an experienced trial lawyer with a focus on alternative dispute resolution. He mediates cases in commercial, construction and securities disputes. **Timothy Barber** (see p.2039) of King & Spalding LLP is recognized as "an excellent trial lawyer," and concentrates on intellectual property litigation. Interviewees note: "He has deep experience with IP litigation, is creative in trying to seek solutions, and has been an effective advocate for us." **Cory Hohnbaum** (see p.2041) of King & Spalding LLP focuses on financial services litigation, complex contract disputes and business torts, recently representing Wells Fargo in a $1 billion breach of contract lawsuit. Sources say: "His ability to come up with strategies was excellent. He is an extremely accomplished trial attorney." **Jeffrey Furr** (see p.2041) of King & Spalding LLP has a broad litigation practice with a national scope, trying cases in various jurisdictions. Recent work includes counseling R.J. Reynolds Tobacco in a product liability action. **Wade Smith** of Tharrington Smith LLP is highly regarded for his work involving criminal law, and is one of the state's most experienced practitioners in the white-collar crime space. **Hugh Stevens** of Stevens Martin Vaughn & Tadych, PLLC focuses his practice on First Amendment and media law, and is a highly regarded trial lawyer. **Dan McLamb** of Yates, McLamb & Weyher LLP practices in the areas of product liability, medical malpractice and civil litigation, and is hailed by sources as "one of the finest litigators that North Carolina has ever produced." **Thomas Cottingham** (see p.2040) of Winston & Strawn LLP focuses on business-related litigation, with an emphasis on the financial and environmental spaces. His clients include Wells Fargo and Allegheny Energy. Praised as a "very good litigator," **Nash Long** (see p.2043) of Winston & Strawn LLP has a broad litigation practice centering on complex disputes, and represents clients including BNP Paribas Suisse and Duke Energy. **Mark Calloway** (see p.2039) of Alston & Bird LLP is well regarded for white-collar criminal defense work. His practice also covers healthcare, antitrust and internal corporate investigations. **Gary Parsons** leads the Troutman Sanders LLP litigation team in Raleigh and handles civil and commercial disputes. Sources praise his trial and advisory skills. **Patricia Shields** of Troutman Sanders LLP focuses on civil litigation and administrative law. She is described by sources as a well-prepared, hard working trial lawyer. **Lee Whitman** of Wyrick Robbins Yates & Ponton LLP is an accomplished commercial litigator particularly recognized for his expertise in the healthcare arena. **Carl Patterson** (see p.2044) is the managing partner of Smith, Anderson, Blount, Dorsett, Mitchell & Jernigan, LLP, and is vastly experienced in handling complex commercial litigation. Recent work includes representing the North Carolina Department of State Treasurer in a dispute concerning investments in a real estate investment fund.

# REAL ESTATE

Commentary about individuals can be found under their firm's paragraph. If the firm has no paragraph (is not ranked) look at Other Notable Practitioners.

*The editorial is in alphabetical order by firm name.*

## Cadwalader, Wickersham & Taft LLP
See profile on p.438

**THE FIRM** This international firm's Charlotte practice is well-placed to offer expertise to key institutional clients. The firm is highly regarded for its knowledge of real estate capital markets and financing, and frequently represents clients such as Wells Fargo, Morgan Stanley Mortgage Capital Holdings and JPMorgan in high-value deals.

**Sources say:** "The firm is very good from a legal and business perspective." **KEY INDIVIDUALS James Carroll** is a well-regarded real estate lawyer focusing on finance and securitization. "He clearly knows the law, but he also knows the big picture, knowing how to get the deal done," said one interviewee.

## Ellis & Winters LLP

**THE FIRM** This North Carolina firm offers a sophisticated real estate practice focusing on real estate development and financings. The group is adept in handling land use, acquisitions and leasing in addition to drawing on the expertise of its transactional attorneys to execute various lending transactions including construction loans, and complex syndicated and revolving credit facilities. Clients include North Carolina Railroad, Dominion Properties and Research Triangle Foundation of North Carolina.

**KEY INDIVIDUALS Charles Anderson** (see p.2039) has a broad practice and brings his expertise in commercial lending to real estate transactions. Sources say he "is very good and very diligent, always follows up and gives sound advice." **Michael Winters** (see p.2046) focuses his practice on commercial and residential real estate development. According to one source, "Mike is a tremendous real estate attorney – he is highly experienced and reasonable, and his documentation is very comprehensive and clearly written. In addition to his legal work, I greatly value his business acumen."

## K&L Gates
See profile on p.2245

**THE FIRM** This firm has long been recognized as a leader in the North Carolina real estate arena, with notable bench strength and a broad range of expertise to service clients' transactional needs at every level. The group offers a sophisticated practice handling real estate development, leasing, financings and land use issues, with marked excellence in commercial real estate loans and acquisitions. With offices in Raleigh, Charlotte and Research Triangle Park, its presence throughout the state makes its a top choice for institutional lenders and developers.

**Sources say:** "Their performance has always been unparalleled."

**KEY INDIVIDUALS** The highly regarded **Walter Fisher** (see p.2040) focuses on the development, leasing, sale and acquisition of commercial real estate. An admiring source says: "He is exceptional – thorough, creative, diligent and appropriately communicative." **Brian Evans** (see p.2040) centers his practice on real estate development, handling matters involving mixed-use and retail developments as well as foreclosure issues. **Maynard Tipps** (see p.2046) is an experienced real estate attorney focusing on complex commercial real estate transactions. He represents developers, landlords and investors in issues involving development, acquisitions and finance.

## Katten Muchin Rosenman LLP
See profile on p.1253

**THE FIRM** This international firm's Charlotte office is highly regarded among commercial real estate lenders. The team has a particular focus on capital markets transactions but is also able to utilize the firm's commercial finance, tax and corporate practices in addition to its network of offices across the state to offer added capacity, making it a standout choice for corporate clients.

**Sources say:** "I have found Katten to be highly efficient and valuable. Also, the work is performed by attorneys with considerable experience who have the time to support follow-up questions and issues."

**KEY INDIVIDUALS Hayden Harrell** focuses on real estate banking and finance, and is adept in mezzanine, syndicated and construction financing. Sources describe him as "very good, smart, reasonable and prepared." **Daniel Huffenus** heads the Charlotte real estate practice and has a national commercial real estate finance practice. He often represents capital markets lenders in commercial mortgage loan transactions. **Frank Arado** handles real estate financing, particularly in the restructuring of debt and the acquisition of loans secured by real estate assets.

*The editorial is in alphabetical order by firm name.*

## Real Estate
### Leading Firms

**Band 1**
K&L Gates *
Moore & Van Allen, PLLC
Robinson, Bradshaw & Hinson PA
Womble Carlyle Sandridge & Rice, LLP *

**Band 2**
Parker Poe Adams & Bernstein LLP
Smith, Anderson, Blount, Dorsett, Mitchell & Jernigan, LLP *

**Band 3**
Ellis & Winters LLP
Manning Fulton & Skinner PA
McGuireWoods LLP *
Nexsen Pruet, LLC *
Poyner Spruill LLP
Smith Moore Leatherwood LLP *
Williams Mullen

## Real Estate
### Leading Individuals

**Band 1**
| Adams Alfred G | Womble Carlyle Sandridge & Rice, LLP |
| Fisher Jr Walter D | K&L Gates * |
| Oliver Jr Samuel | Manning Fulton & Skinner PA |
| Torstrick Brent | Robinson, Bradshaw & Hinson PA |

**Band 2**
| Bagbey Francis C | Smith, Anderson, Blount, Dorsett, Mitchell * |
| Benson Jeffrey A | Kilpatrick Townsend & Stockton (ONP)[†] |
| Donadio Donald A | Womble Carlyle Sandridge & Rice, LLP |
| Evans Brian P | K&L Gates * |
| Glenney Jeffrey W | Moore & Van Allen, PLLC |
| Joyner Gary | Kilpatrick Townsend & Stockton LLP (ONP)[†] |
| Mann Barry D | Manning Fulton & Skinner PA |
| Mason C Steven | Smith, Anderson, Blount, Dorsett, Mitchell * |
| Milgrom Jr Brent M | Parker Poe Adams & Bernstein LLP |
| Oates J Christopher | Moore & Van Allen, PLLC |
| Simmons Robert W | McGuireWoods LLP |
| Sink Robert C | Robinson, Bradshaw & Hinson PA |
| Winters Michael G | Ellis & Winters LLP * |

**Band 3**
| Byrd Brian | Smith Moore Leatherwood LLP * |
| Dorton David R | Williams Mullen |
| Gates Thomas | Robinson, Bradshaw & Hinson PA |
| Loeb Christopher | Robinson, Bradshaw & Hinson PA |
| Matthews Jr William | Womble Carlyle Sandridge & Rice, LLP |
| Ratteree Jane | Robinson, Bradshaw & Hinson PA |
| Smith Jr Skottowe W | Moore & Van Allen, PLLC |
| Tipps Maynard E | K&L Gates * |

## Real Estate: Finance
### Leading Firms

**Band 1**
Katten Muchin Rosenman LLP *

**Band 2**
Cadwalader, Wickersham & Taft LLP *
Moore & Van Allen, PLLC

**Band 3**
Mayer Brown LLP *
Womble Carlyle Sandridge & Rice, LLP *

### Leading Individuals

**Band 1**
| Anderson Jr Charles N | Ellis & Winters LLP * |
| Harrell J Hayden | Katten Muchin Rosenman LLP |
| Huffenus Daniel S | Katten Muchin Rosenman LLP |

**Band 2**
| Carroll James P | Cadwalader, Wickersham & Taft LLP |

**Up-and-coming individuals**
| Arado Frank E | Katten Muchin Rosenman LLP |

## Real Estate: Zoning/Land Use
### Leading Individuals

**Band 1**
| Brian Jr William J | Morningstar Law Group (ONP)[†] |
| Currin Robin Tatum | Currin & Currin Attorneys at Law (ONP)[†] |
| Melvin Jr Charles E | Smith Moore Leatherwood LLP * |
| Reaves Lacy H | Smith, Anderson, Blount, Dorsett, Mitchell * |
| Worth Jr Thomas C | Thomas C Worth Jr (ONP)[†] |

*Indicates firm / individual with profile.*

[†]ONP = Other Notable Practitioner.

## Manning Fulton & Skinner PA

**THE FIRM** This Raleigh firm is noted for its solid commercial real estate practice, representing lenders, developers and real estate brokers. The group is known for its ability to handle various transactional issues, including leasing, financing and acquisitions, and works closely with the firm's tax, corporate and bankruptcy attorneys to offer a seamless client service.

**KEY INDIVIDUALS** The highly regarded **Samuel Oliver** leads the firm's real estate practice and focuses on commercial real estate acquisitions and finance. **Barry Mann** has a broad real estate practice concentrating on representing commercial real estate developers and investors in the development of commercial properties.

## Mayer Brown LLP
See profile on p.1257

**THE FIRM** This global firm's North Carolina real estate team is based in Charlotte, and is known for its expertise in real estate transactional and financing matters. The group has recently handled a series of impressive transactions for Bank of America, including representing the bank in a $3.1 billion refinancing for MGM Resorts International.

**KEY INDIVIDUALS** David Saye is a key contact for the practice.

## McGuireWoods LLP
See profile on p.2519

**THE FIRM** This firm is adept at handling land use, development and finance issues. The group is recognized for its work in the sale and acquisition of commercial real estate, as well as commercial loan transactions. Clients include Time Warner Cable and the Columbus Nova Real Estate Acquisition Group.

**Sources say:** *"The firm is top-notch and we have been extremely happy with their service over the years."*

**KEY INDIVIDUALS Robert Simmons** focuses on commercial real estate and lending transactions. *"He is extremely detailed and knowledgeable, and has been an invaluable asset to our company,"* said one interviewee.

## Moore & Van Allen, PLLC

**THE FIRM** This firm continues to go from strength to strength in the real estate space, and has a 28-strong team based in North Carolina. Working closely with its large corporate practice, the real estate team's bench strength enables it to handle the needs of the firm's corporate clients in addition to serving its own clientele in commercial acquisitions, development, financing and leasing transactions. Recent work includes representing Nexans High Voltage USA in the acquisition and permitting of an industrial park property to be used for a cable manufacturing facility.

**Sources say:** *"Moore & Van Allen has an outstanding real estate practice."* *"They are very good value and they make it a point to become knowledgeable about our business, understand our business objectives and help us achieve our goals."*

**KEY INDIVIDUALS** The well-regarded **Jeffrey Glenney** focuses on handling complex real estate transactions, representing lenders, developers and investors. **Christopher Oates** co-leads the commercial real estate group and has expertise in real estate land use law. He is described as *"excellent, smart and reasonable – all of the stuff you want in a lawyer."* **Skottowe Smith** concentrates his practice on real estate development and recently represented Childress Klein Properties in a 210-acre mixed-use development project.

## Nexsen Pruet, LLC
See profile on p.2277

**THE FIRM** Nexsen Pruet maintains a strong presence across the region, with offices in Greensboro, Raleigh and Charlotte in addition to its formidable South Carolina presence. The group is adept in all areas of real estate transactions, including acquisitions, land use and zoning, financing and development.

**KEY INDIVIDUALS** Jay DeVaney is a key contact for the North Carolina practice.

## Parker Poe Adams & Bernstein LLP

**THE FIRM** This team is particularly well regarded for handling commercial real estate leasing, acquisition and financing transactions, and is able to draw on the firm's tax and construction expertise to add value to its client service. Representative work includes acting for Johnson C. Smith University on its lease of approximately 110,000 sq ft of space for a mixed-use development.

**Sources say:** *"They have a great knowledge and experience base, and are very easy to work with."*

**KEY INDIVIDUALS Brent Milgrom** focuses on commercial real estate development and financing transactions. Sources describe him as *"an excellent attorney with great attention to detail."*

*The editorial is in alphabetical order by firm name.*

## Poyner Spruill LLP

**THE FIRM** This firm is noted for its expertise in issues relating to real estate development projects and commercial real estate transactions, including financing, leasing and acquisitions. Clients include Duke University, Stock Building Supply and Green Recycling.

**KEY INDIVIDUALS** Keith Johnson heads the real estate department.

## Robinson, Bradshaw & Hinson PA

**THE FIRM** Robinson Bradshaw retains one of the most highly regarded real estate groups in the state. The team has immense talent in the real estate development arena, representing developers, investors and lenders across the Southeast region. The group has recently handled a series of noteworthy deals for Crescent Resources; other clients include Regions Bank, CommScope and Pavilion Development Company.

**KEY INDIVIDUALS** **Brent Torstrick** focuses on real estate development and lending. Sources say: *"His knowledge of the process and the right way to do things is what makes him great."* **Robert Sink** is highly experienced in handling the development, financing and sale of commercial real estate. **Thomas Gates** concentrates his practice on the acquisition, leasing, financing and disposal of commercial real estate projects. According to sources, he is *"extremely bright, knowledgeable and inventive."* Lauded as *"an outstanding lawyer,"* **Christopher Loeb** brings expertise in land use and environmental law to his commercial real estate practice. **Jane Ratteree** heads the real estate department and focuses on commercial real estate with an emphasis on lending, leasing and foreclosures.

## Smith Moore Leatherwood LLP
See profile on p.2048

**THE FIRM** This firm is known for its expertise in the land use and financing spaces, particularly pertaining to condominium and retail developments. Clients include Northwoods Investors, Geo Group and Archer Daniels Midland.

**Sources say:** *"I need the firm's expertise in commercial real estate law and environmental law. Its level of professionalism and knowledge in these fields is outstanding."*

**KEY INDIVIDUALS** The highly regarded **Charles Melvin** (see p.2043) has extensive experience in commercial and industrial transactions relating to real estate, and is well known for his zoning practice. **Brian Byrd** (see p.2039) focuses on commercial real estate development and financing. According to commentators, *"his attention to detail and his knowledge of the law are impeccable."*

## Smith, Anderson, Blount, Dorsett, Mitchell & Jernigan, LLP
See profile on p.2047

**THE FIRM** This reputable Raleigh firm is known for its strong corporate practice, and paired with a solid real estate offering it is able to service clients' commercial real estate needs effortlessly. The group is known for its expertise in real estate financing as well as land use and zoning, catering to many financial lenders and developers. Clients include Martin Marietta Materials, Crescent Resources and York Properties.

**KEY INDIVIDUALS** **Lacy Reaves** (see p.2044) is an experienced commercial real estate lawyer who focuses on land use and zoning matters. Sources view him as *"probably the best in land use."* The well-regarded **Francis Bagbey** (see p.2039) has a wealth of real estate experience and handles the full scope of transactional matters, including the financing, leasing, buying and selling of real property. **Steven Mason**'s (see p.2043) broad practice includes corporate law and lending transactions, in addition to commercial real estate. Sources say: *"He has great experience and gives good advice."*

## Williams Mullen

**THE FIRM** Williams Mullen is particularly recognized for its ability to handle transactional real estate issues, specifically leasing. The group is also noted for its land use and litigation capabilities, which allow it to represent various institutional lenders as well as real estate developers.

**KEY INDIVIDUALS** **David Dorton** has extensive experience in dealing with commercial real estate acquisitions, financing, leasing and development.

## Womble Carlyle Sandridge & Rice, LLP
See profile on p.2049

**THE FIRM** Womble Carlyle remains a front runner in the real estate arena, with a deep bench of 38 attorneys serving the North Carolina business community. The group is noted for its strong real estate finance and transactional practices, dealing with development, construction, leasing and financing for various lenders and developers. Clients include KSL Capital, McKibbon Hotel Group and Piedmont Triad Research Park.

**Sources say:** *"They have some of the brightest lawyers and do exceptional work."*

**KEY INDIVIDUALS** Highly regarded real estate attorney **Alfred Adams** is experienced in handling commercial, retail and industrial development projects. Sources say: *"He is an excellent attorney and his practice is extraordinary."* **William Matthews** has extensive experience in commercial real estate and lending. A satisfied client notes: *"We have peace of mind that with him our interests will be rigorously protected."* **Donald Donadio** is described as an *"excellent attorney"* and has a well-regarded public finance and economic development practice in addition to commercial real estate expertise.

## Other Notable Practitioners

**Robin Currin** of Currin & Currin Attorneys at Law is well regarded for her experience in real estate land use and zoning matters. **William Brian** of Morningstar Law Group is described as *"an extraordinary talent."* He focuses his practice on real estate land use and zoning as well as municipal law. **Jeffrey Benson** leads the North Carolina real estate and development team at Kilpatrick Townsend & Stockton LLP and focuses on the zoning and land use, leasing and finance of commercial real estate. Sources praise his deep experience and attention to detail. **Gary Joyner** of Kilpatrick Townsend & Stockton LLP concentrates on commercial real estate and lending, and has expertise in mixed-use, residential and retail developments. *"He is very astute in helping us to structure our transactions and partnerships,"* said one client, adding: *"He is also very insightful in helping us examine the risk involved with each transaction."* **Thomas Worth** is a sole practitioner based out of Raleigh who concentrates his practice on land use and zoning issues.

# Leaders' Profiles in North Carolina

## ALEXANDER, Mason
Fisher & Phillips LLP, Charlotte
704 334 4565
malexander@laborlawyers.com
*Featured in Labor & Employment (North Carolina)*
**Career:** Mason Alexander is the Managing Partner of the Charlotte office. He practices in all areas of labor and employment law, including union avoidance, ERISA and discrimination claims, FMLA, and wage and hour claims. Mason counsels clients on matters such as employee terminations, plant closures, and exit incentive programs. He works with clients concerned about the possibility of union organizing activity to develop proactive employee relations plans. He is certified as a specialist in employment and labor law by the Supreme Court of South Carolina.

## ANDERSON JR, Charles N
Ellis & Winters LLP, Cary
919 865 7011
chuck.anderson@elliswinters.com
*Featured in Bankruptcy/Restructuring (North Carolina), Real Estate (North Carolina)*
**Practice Areas:** •Extensive experience in commercial real estate with emphasis on dispositions and acquisitions, and real estate finance, including construction and permanent financing. •Extensive experience in creditors' rights, including bankruptcy, loan workouts, restructure transactions, forbearance agreements and recovery of real estate collateral by foreclosure.
**Professional Memberships:** •Admitted to practice in North Carolina in 1986 •Member - North Carolina Bar Association and American Bar Association •Past Board Member and General Counsel – Greater Raleigh Chamber of Commerce •Listed in Best Lawyers of America, Chambers and Partners, Business North Carolina, North Carolina's Legal Elite, and North Carolina Super Lawyers.
**Career:** •2000Founding Partner of Ellis & Winters LLP •1986-2000Smith Helms Mulliss & Moore LLP.
**Personal:** •1986 JD, University of North Carolina at Chapel Hill School of Law (High Honors) •1984-1985 Member, North Carolina Law Review •1978BA, North Carolina State University (With Honors).

## AUBERRY, E Kent
Smith Moore Leatherwood LLP, Greensboro
336 378 5284
kent.auberry@smithmoorelaw.com
*Featured in Corporate/M&A (North Carolina)*
**Practice Areas:** Kent Auberry has over 25 years experience in general business representation. He handles a broad spectrum of business needs, from mergers and acquisitions to intellectual property matters. He also assists clients with federal and state securities law compliance and capital formation. He regularly counsels clients on advertising issues, sales and distribution arrangements, premerger clearance filings and other trade regulation matters. Mr Auberry's experience includes representing buyers and sellers in a broad range of

industries, including technology, banking/finance, retail, manufacturing and healthcare.

## BAGBEY, Francis C
Smith, Anderson, Blount, Dorsett, Mitchell & Jernigan, LLP, Raleigh
919 821 6622
fbagbey@smithlaw.com
*Featured in Real Estate (North Carolina)*
**Practice Areas:** Commercial real estate.
**Professional Memberships:** Member, North Carolina Bar Association; Member, Wake County Bar Association; Past President, Wake County Real Property Lawyers Association. Admitted to practice in North Carolina. Previously admitted to practice in New Jersey.
**Career:** Joined Smith Anderson in 1983. Practiced with McCarter & English, Newark, New Jersey, 1980-1983. Listed in The Best Lawyers in America, Business North Carolina Magazine's Legal Elite, and North Carolina Super Lawyers (Real Estate); Martindale-Hubbell AV Rated.
**Personal:** JD Marshall-Wythe School of Law, College of William & Mary, 1980, Professional articles editor of The William & Mary Law Review; AB Princeton University, 1975.

## BAIRD, Stanford D
K&L Gates, Raleigh
919 743 7334
stanford.baird@klgates.com
*Featured in Environment (North Carolina)*
**Practice Areas:** Stanford D Baird focuses his practice on environmental matters, including litigation and controversy matters, and environmental aspects of real estate and business transactions. He routinely negotiates with state and federal environmental agencies on behalf of private parties, handles administrative appeals and enforcement matters, and oversees environmental due diligence and clean up activities. Stanford's practice encompasses environmental issues related to development of contaminated properties, sensitive coastal and wetlands areas, sustainable development and green building, and all aspects of development permitting.

## BANGE, Richard
King & Spalding LLP, Charlotte
704 503 2554
rbange@kslaw.com
*Featured in Corporate/M&A (North Carolina)*
**Practice Areas:** Represents private equity sponsors and venture capital funds in evaluating, structuring and negotiating investment and exit transactions, including leveraged buyouts, growth equity investments, mergers, stock and asset acquisitions and sales, mezzanine investments and recapitalizations. Also has extensive experience representing private equity sponsors in obtaining senior secured and high yield financing for leveraged acquisitions and recapitalizations, including through cash-flow and asset-based senior secured credit facilities and the issuance of high yield bonds.

**Personal:** JD, University of Virginia BA, University of Virginia.

## BARBER, Timothy G
King & Spalding LLP, Charlotte
704 503 2600
tbarber@kslaw.com
*Featured in Litigation (North Carolina)*
**Practice Areas:** A broad-based business litigation practice, with an emphasis on class action and patent infringement litigation.
**Professional Memberships:** Fellow, American College of Trial Lawyers; North Carolina Bar Association and American Bar Association, Litigation Sections. Admitted to practice before the US Supreme Court; US District Courts for the Eastern, Middle and Western Districts of North Carolina; US Court of Appeals for the Federal Circuit; US Court of Appeals for the Fourth Circuit.
**Career:** JD, 1985, Wake Forest University School of Law, (cum laude), Editor-in-Chief, Wake Forest Law Review; BA, 1977, Kenyon College.

## BOOE, J Michael
K&L Gates, Charlotte
704 331 7556
mike.booe@klgates.com
*Featured in Bankruptcy/Restructuring (North Carolina)*
**Practice Areas:** Partner Michael Booe's practice focuses primarily on bilateral and syndicated leveraged lending and commercial real estate financing transactions, both in the structuring and documenting of new transactions and in the restructure, workout, and recovery of non-performing credit facilities. He has extensive Chapter 11 bankruptcy experience, representing primarily secured lenders and equipment lessors in bankruptcy courts around the country. He is a fellow in the American College of Bankruptcy and is certified as a Bankruptcy Specialist by the North Carolina State Bar Board of Legal Specialization.

## BROMBY, Craig A
Hunton & Williams LLP, Raleigh
919 899 3032
cbromby@hunton.com
*Featured in Environment (North Carolina)*
**Practice Areas:** Craig Bromby's practice focuses on environmental and administrative law, with emphasis on surface water and groundwater quality, water law, real property development, redevelopment issues, including wetlands and stormwater regulation, environmental permitting, water resources, land use, and brownfields. Experienced in administrative litigation, negotiating with state and federal regulatory agencies, and providing compliance and regulatory advice. Representative clients include real property developers, manufacturers, utilities, and agricultural interests. Recognized among the NC Legal Elite, Super Lawyers, and Best Lawyers in America.
**Professional Memberships:** Admitted in NC and Florida; Member Environmental Law

Sections of NC Bar Association, Florida Bar, and ABA.

## BYRD, Brian
Smith Moore Leatherwood LLP, Greensboro
336 378 5429
brian.byrd@smithmoorelaw.com
*Featured in Real Estate (North Carolina)*
**Practice Areas:** Brian Byrd practices primarily in the real estate development and finance area, representing developers of office, retail, industrial and residential projects. He assists clients with the acquisition of raw and improved real estate and the various stages of development such as preparation of restrictive covenants for planned commercial, mixed-use and residential developments, condominium formations and conversions, financing of real estate projects and the leasing and sale of such developments. Mr Byrd also regularly represents institutional lenders in connection with commercial mortgage loans, workouts and collateral dispositions.

## CALLOWAY, Mark T
Alston & Bird LLP, Charlotte
704 444 1089
mark.calloway@alston.com
*Featured in Litigation (North Carolina)*
**Practice Areas:** White collar criminal defense, with an emphasis on health care and antitrust, internal corporate investigations, and compliance program auditing.
**Career:** Immediate past leader, firm's Government Investigations & Compliance Group. Served as the United States Attorney for the Western District of North Carolina from 1994 to 2001, as Chair of the Attorney General's Advisory Committee of United States Attorneys, as Director of the Executive Office for United States Attorneys at the DOJ, and as Co-chair of the Attorney General's White Collar Crime Council.
**Personal:** Campbell University (JD, 1983); North Carolina State University (BS, 1980).

## CAPEL, Christopher
Smith, Anderson, Blount, Dorsett, Mitchell & Jernigan, LLP, Raleigh
919 821 6759
ccapel@smithlaw.com
*Featured in Corporate/M&A (North Carolina)*
**Practice Areas:** Has extensive experience in domestic and international mergers and acquisitions; intellectual property and technology licensing and transfer; strategic alliances, collaborations, and joint ventures; private equity and venture capital financings and other funding and investment transactions; securities offerings and public company reporting and compliance; corporate governance; and other general corporate and business law matters.
**Professional Memberships:** Admitted to North Carolina Bar (1985) and New York Bar (1987). Member of Board of Directors, North Carolina Biosciences Organization (NCBio). Member of American Bar Association, North Carolina Bar Association, New York Bar

Association. Chair, Business Law Section of North Carolina Bar Association. Listed in The Best Lawyers in America (named top M&A lawyer in Research Triangle market 2010), Chambers USA, Business North Carolina Legal Elite, and North Carolina Super Lawyers.

**Career:** 1990: Joined Smith Anderson. 1986-90: White & Case, L.L.P., New York, New York. 1985-86: Federal Judicial Law Clerk to Sam J. Ervin, III, United States Court of Appeals, Fourth Circuit. 1979-82: Wachovia Bank, Commercial Loan Officer.

**Personal:** JD (with honors), University of North Carolina School of Law, 1985; BA, University of North Carolina at Chapel Hill, 1979. Member, National Eagle Scout Association.

### CASE, Charles D
Hunton & Williams LLP, Raleigh
919 899 3045
ccase@hunton.com
*Featured in Environment (North Carolina)*

**Practice Areas:** Charles Case's practice focuses on US environmental, health, safety, and administrative law issues, including water and air quality, water rights and natural resources, chemicals and product regulation, toxic and hazardous materials and wastes, brownfields, and contaminated sites remediation.

**Professional Memberships:** Chaired Environmental and Administrative Sections of the North Carolina Bar Association. Member Carolina Air Pollution Control Association; ABA Sections on Environmental, Administrative and Public Utility law.

**Career:** Campbell Law School Adjunct Professor of Environmental Law, also Agricultural and Food Law and Policy.

**Publications:** Co-author, North Carolina Chapter, ABA Brownfields text. Co-author, Administrative Law Chapter, NC Bar Ass. Deskbook.

### COTTINGHAM III, T Thomas
Winston & Strawn LLP, Charlotte
704 350 7745
tcottingham@winston.com
*Featured in Litigation (North Carolina)*

**Practice Areas:** Mr Cottingham is Managing Partner of Winston & Strawn's Charlotte office. His practice focuses on litigation representing national and multinational corporations in jury trials, class actions, and alternative dispute resolutions in cases involving environmental, financial institutions, energy, securities, and commercial contract disputes. He is licensed in the states of North Carolina and Alabama. He has been admitted pro hac vice in almost half the other states, and he has tried more than 100 cases.

**Personal:** AB, Davidson College 1969; United States Army 1969-1972; JD cum laude Cornell University Law School 1976.

### DANNELLY, William D
Hunton & Williams LLP, Raleigh
919 899 3025
wdannelly@hunton.com
*Featured in Environment (North Carolina)*

**Practice Areas:** Mr Dannelly's practice focuses on environmental litigation and other adversarial proceedings, including those involving toxic torts, Superfund, RCRA, water quality, and related matters. Mr Dannelly also has extensive experience with transactions involving complex environmental issues, including compliance and regulatory affairs.

**Publications:** Introduction to the Use of Scientific and Medical Evidence in Toxic Tort Litigation, chapter of 'Toxic Tort Litigation', published by ABA's Section on Environment, Energy, and Resources, 2007. Contributing author, 'Toxic Tort and Hazardous Substance Litigation', published by Michie Butterworth, 1995.

**Personal:** BS, MIT 1973; JD, UNC-CH 1977.

### EARP, Julianna Theall
Smith Moore Leatherwood LLP, Greensboro
336 378 5256
julie.earp@smithmoorelaw.com
*Featured in Labor & Employment (North Carolina)*

**Practice Areas:** Julie Theall Earp concentrates her practice in employment litigation, counseling, and training. A partner with more than 20 years of experience, she regularly litigates employment matters in both federal and state courts, as well as before the EEOC and the state and federal Departments of Labor. Trained as a mediator, as well as a litigator, Ms Earp explores and utilizes alternative forms of dispute resolution when possible in employment matters. Ms Earp is a frequent speaker and trainer to employers and management groups and currently serves on the firm's Diversity Committee.

### EARP, Stephen W
Smith Moore Leatherwood LLP, Greensboro
336 378 5314
steve.earp@smithmoorelaw.com
*Featured in Environment (North Carolina)*

**Practice Areas:** Mr Earp maintains a broad environmental practice that ranges from advising companies regarding acquisitions and contracts to handling complex land use and environmental disputes. He also has a national environmental regulatory practice that includes assisting clients involved in CERCLA sites; air, water and waste permitting; brownfields redevelopment; private cost recovery and contribution actions; multi-party remedial actions; compliance; and enforcement matters. Mr Earp is particularly active in matters involving the metal, plastic and electronics recycling industries.

### EMORY JR, Frank E
Hunton & Williams LLP, Charlotte
704 378 4708
femory@hunton.com
*Featured in Litigation (North Carolina)*

**Practice Areas:** Co-head of the firm's litigation, intellectual property, competition and labor group, Mr Emory's practice focuses on complex commercial litigation. With more than 25 years in practice, Mr Emory has tried more than 60 cases in state and federal courts and before arbitration panels and administrative agencies. He has extensive experience in the financial services industry, handling numerous cases involving structured

finance products and related intellectual property issues, and he has represented several large financial institutions.

**Professional Memberships:** Fellow, Litigation Counsel of America; Fellow, American Bar Foundation; American Bar Association, Section of Litigation (Co-Chair, Trial Evidence Committee 2005-2006); American Law Institute; Permanent Member, Fourth Circuit Judicial Conference; Certified Instructor, National Institute of Trial Advocacy; Mecklenburg Bar (President, 2002-03); North Carolina Bar.

**Personal:** Member, Board of Trustees and Executive Committee, Duke University; Past Chair (2012), Charlotte Chamber of Commerce; Best Lawyers in America, Commercial Litigation (2008-2013); North Carolina Super Lawyers (2009-2013); Recipient, Citizen Lawyer, North Carolina Bar Association (2010); Recipient, Diversity in Business Award sponsored by Charlotte Business Journal (2006). Profiled in the Charlotte Observer's Crossing the Barrier series (2008).

### EVANS, Brian P
K&L Gates, Charlotte
704 331 7479
brian.evans@klgates.com
*Featured in Real Estate (North Carolina)*

**Practice Areas:** Brian P. Evans concentrates his practice on mixed-use and other planned developments, planning and development of single-family subdivisions, and shopping center developments. He has substantial experience in condominium and planned community structure and documentation, including use of common ownership interest community "master" documentation and air rights structures in commercial and mixed-use projects. He also has substantial experience in the acquisition, management, and disposition of distressed real estate.

### EWALT, Gretchen W
Ogletree, Deakins, Nash, Smoak & Stewart, PC, Raleigh
919 789 3173
gretchen.ewalt@ogletreedeakins.com
*Featured in Labor & Employment (North Carolina)*

**Practice Areas:** Represents management in employment law matters, including defense of suits filed in state and federal court, and administrative claims filed with federal and state agencies; provides advice on employment issues (including RIF planning/implementation) and the development of policies and procedures; prepares affirmative action plans and represents employers during audits by the Office of Federal Contract Compliance Programs.

**Professional Memberships:** North Carolina Bar Association (Labor and Employment Law Section), North Carolina State Bar, Society of Human Resource Managers.

**Career:** Admitted to practice in North Carolina.

**Personal:** Virginia Commonwealth University (BA, cum laude, 1985), University of Virginia (JD, 1988).

### FARR, Thomas A
Ogletree, Deakins, Nash, Smoak & Stewart, PC, Raleigh
919 789 3174
thomas.farr@ogletreedeakins.com
*Featured in Labor & Employment (North Carolina)*

**Practice Areas:** Employment, OSHA, Constitutional and Election Law.

**Professional Memberships:** American and North Carolina Bar Associations, Fourth Circuit Judicial Conference, Campbell University (Adj. Professor, 1990-1995).

**Career:** Admitted in North Carolina, Virginia and Georgia. Named in The Best Lawyers in America, 2002-2013 editions of Business North Carolina's Legal Elite and Super Lawyer 2007-2013. Nominated by President George W. Bush in 2006 to be a federal district judge for the Eastern District of North Carolina. (ABA rating of "unanimous well qualified").

**Personal:** Hillsdale College (BLS, summa cum laude, 1976), Emory University (JD, 1979), Georgetown University (LLM, Labor Law, 1983).

### FISHER JR, Walter D
K&L Gates, Charlotte
704 331 7544
walter.fisher@klgates.com
*Featured in Real Estate (North Carolina)*

**Practice Areas:** Walter Fisher, a partner and practice area leader in the real estate practice group, focuses on the acquisition, sale, development, financing, and leasing of commercial real estate and the representation of lenders, borrowers, and investors in financial restructuring and workout transactions. A member of the North Carolina Bar Association Real Property Section, the American Bar Association Real Property & Probate Section, and the Urban Land Institute, he is an LEED-Accredited Professional and has experience negotiating and preparing office leases for space in urban and suburban markets, negotiating and preparing complex retail leases, and representing developers of mixed-use projects.

### FRANCHINA, David A
K&L Gates, Charlotte
704 331 7543
dave.franchina@klgates.com
*Featured in Environment (North Carolina)*

**Practice Areas:** David Franchina, a practice group coordinator in K&L Gates' environment, land & natural resources practice, focuses his practice on environmental matters. With experience in a variety of substantive areas, including brownfields redevelopment, solid and hazardous waste, water quality (including streams, wetlands, and floodplains), air quality, and environmental remediation, he's completed extensive regulatory work with federal, state, and local regulators and is actively involved in administrative and judicial litigation matters. His practice provides support on environmental issues throughout the firm, where he works with the litigation, mergers and acquisitions, finance, real estate, and land use and zoning practices.

## FULLER III, William H
King & Spalding LLP, Charlotte
704 503 2589
bfuller@kslaw.com
*Featured in Banking & Finance (North Carolina)*
**Practice Areas:** Experienced in both leveraged and investment-grade financings in the healthcare, industrial growth, media, telecommunications and aerospace and defense sectors. Mr Fuller has been involved in numerous acquisition financings involving senior secured and subordinated debt. He also represents corporations in connection with their financing needs and has significant experience in the work-out and negotiation of troubled credits.
**Personal:** University of Virginia (JD); University of North Carolina at Chapel Hill (BA Political Science, honors, 1989).

## FURR, Jeffrey L
King & Spalding LLP, Charlotte
704 503 2632
jfurr@kslaw.com
*Featured in Litigation (North Carolina)*
**Practice Areas:** Mr Furr has served as national coordinating counsel in nationwide product liability litigation and has a national trial practice. He has tried cases in diverse jurisdictions including North Carolina, West Virginia, Mississippi, Missouri, Indiana, Florida and California. Mr Furr represents product manufacturers in class actions, mass consolidated proceedings and individual personal injury actions. He has extensive expertise on the full range of legal, factual and scientific issues involved in such litigation.
**Personal:** JD, cum laude, Wake Forest University BS, cum laude, West Virginia University.

## GARDNER, Terri
Nelson Mullins Riley & Scarborough LLP, Raleigh
919 329 3882
terri.gardner@nelsonmullins.com
*Featured in Bankruptcy/Restructuring (North Carolina)*
**Professional Memberships:** American Bar Association; North Carolina Bar Association; North Carolina State Bar (Certified as a Business Bankruptcy Specialist); American Bankruptcy Institute; American Board of Certification(Certified Business Bankruptcy Specialist).
**Career:** Wake Forest University School of Law, JD 1981; Clerk, Rufus W Reynolds, US Bankruptcy Judge, 1981-83; Partner, Smith Debnam, 1983-2001; Partner, Poyner & Spruill, LLP, 2002-07; Partner, Nelson Mullins Riley & Scarborough, LLP 2008 to present.
**Publications:** Frequent speaker at regional and national seminars and contributes to many bankruptcy publications.
**Personal:** Honors: North Carolina "Super Lawyer" (2007-2013) and "Top 50 Women Lawyers" (2007-2012), Best Lawyers in America (2013).

## GOETTEL, Timothy S
Smith, Anderson, Blount, Dorsett, Mitchell & Jernigan, LLP, Raleigh
919 821 6751
tgoettel@smithlaw.com
*Featured in Corporate/M&A (North Carolina)*
**Practice Areas:** Mr Goettel's practice focuses on mergers and acquisitions, corporate governance, and securities law matters. He has substantial experience in public and private acquisition, disposition, and recapitalization transactions across several different industries. He has also advised issuers with respect to securities offerings, ranging from venture capital transactions to public offerings for seasoned issuers.
**Professional Memberships:** Member, North Carolina and American Bar Associations.
**Career:** Joined Smith, Anderson in 2011. Honors include listing in the Best Lawyers in America and BTI Consulting's Client Service All Star Team.
**Personal:** JD University of Virginia, 1987; BA, Magna Cum Laude, Duke University (1983).

## GOSNELL, Guy R.
Alston & Bird LLP, Charlotte
704 444 1029
guy.gosnell@alston.com
*Featured in Intellectual Property (North Carolina)*
**Practice Areas:** Drafting and prosecution of patent applications involving electrical, computer and software technology. Secured patent protection for cutting edge telecommunications technology, including patent protection directed to the handset, to network components and topology, to signaling protocols, and to end user applications. Regularly counsels clients on issues relating to infringement, validity and enforceability of patents, and licensing of IP rights. Experience managing extensive worldwide patent portfolios of research and development-oriented companies.
**Career:** Chair, firm's IP Patents – Electrical & Computer Science Group. Former member, firm's Partners' Committee.
**Personal:** St. Louis University (JD, 1992); University of Missouri (BSEE, BSCoE, 1988).

## HEYL, Jonathan
Smith Moore Leatherwood LLP, Greensboro
jon.heyl@smithmoorelaw.com
*Featured in Litigation (North Carolina)*
**Practice Areas:** Jon Heyl has a civil litigation practice, with a focus on commercial matters. He has participated in the representation of a number of large banking, professional, insurance, and corporate clients in state and federal court in North Carolina and other jurisdictions. His practice has included a range of matters involving legal malpractice, commercial disputes, fiduciary litigation, administrative hearings relating to motor vehicle franchising disputes, financial services litigation, and large-scale antitrust litigation. His experience also includes tort litigation, in which he has served as first-chair trial counsel in cases tried to jury verdicts.

## HOGEWOOD, Lee
K&L Gates, Raleigh
919 743 7306
lee.hogewood@klgates.com
*Featured in Bankruptcy/Restructuring (North Carolina)*
**Practice Areas:** Lee Hogewood litigates for creditors, committees, investors, and developers, pursuing and defending claims in all North Carolina state and federal courts, including bankruptcy court. Mr Hogewood regularly advises clients regarding the resolution of financial disputes through consensual out of court restructurings. Additionally, Mr Hogewood represents purchasers of assets from financially distressed companies, particularly through the Section 363 bankruptcy sale process.

## HOHNBAUM, Cory
King & Spalding LLP, Charlotte
704 503 2561
chohnbaum@kslaw.com
*Featured in Litigation (North Carolina)*
**Practice Areas:** Practice focuses on securities and other financial services litigation, and cases involving complex contract disputes, business torts and shareholder litigation. He regularly represents securities firms and their representatives in civil litigation and arbitrations.
**Professional Memberships:** Mecklenburg County Bar Association, Volunteer Lawyers Program Committee, Chair 2000-2002; Legal Services of Southern Piedmont, Inc., President; Securities Industry and Financial Markets Association, Compliance and Legal Division, Member.
**Personal:** JD, Vanderbilt University BA, cum laude, Westminster College.

## HOLLAND, Patricia L
Jackson Lewis LLP, Raleigh
919 424 8608
Patricia.Holland@jacksonlewis.com
*Featured in Labor & Employment (North Carolina)*
**Practice Areas:** Employment litigation and counseling for management; mediates employment disputes.
**Professional Memberships:** Chambers USA (Leading Employment Lawyer); American Board of Trial Advocates; NCDRC Certified Mediator; Best Lawyers in America (Labor & Employment Law, Alternative Dispute Resolution); North Carolina Business Legal Elite Hall of Fame - Employment Law; NC Super Lawyers (voted one of top 100 attorneys and top 50 female attorneys in NC).
**Career:** Joined Jackson Lewis as Partner in 2010; N.C. Litigation Manager. Assistant U.S. Attorney (1979-1982); Cranfill Sumner & Hartzog LLP (1982 – 2010).
**Personal:** Wake Forest University, JD (Law Review); Wittenberg University, BA, cum laude.

## HUTCHISON, Fred D
Hutchison PLLC, Raleigh
919 829 4300
fhutchison@hutchlaw.com
*Featured in Corporate/M&A (North Carolina)*
**Practice Areas:** Corporate, Venture Capital, Mergers & Acquisitions, Securities.
**Professional Memberships:** Founding President, Council for Entrepreneurial Development; Member, LawExchange International; Director, Past Chairman of the Board of Directors, First Flight Venture Center; Director, Past Chairman of the Board of Directors, NC IDEA.
**Career:** Founded Hutchison PLLC in 1996. Recipient of the Order of the Long Leaf Pine (2006); Business Leader Magazine's Entrebizneur of the Year (2007); listings in Business North Carolina's Legal Elite, North Carolina Super Lawyers and Best Lawyers in America.
**Personal:** JD, University of Virginia (1975); BS, Business Administration, University of North Carolina at Chapel Hill (1971).

## IVES III, H Bryan
Alston & Bird LLP, Charlotte
704 444 1002
bryan.ives@alston.com
*Featured in Corporate/M&A (North Carolina)*
**Practice Areas:** Mergers and acquisitions, private equity, taxation and corporate governance, public and private debt and equity financing, securities regulation and venture capital. Clients in telecommunications, internet, engineering and construction and private equity funds industries.
**Professional Memberships:** American College of Tax Counsel.
**Career:** Co-chair of the firm's Corporate Transactions & Securities Group. Led investigation and analysis of Enron's accounting for its numerous structured finance and special purpose entity transactions on behalf of the Enron bankruptcy Examiner.
**Personal:** BA (1977), JD (1980) - The University of North Carolina at Chapel Hill.

## JERNIGAN, John L
Smith, Anderson, Blount, Dorsett, Mitchell & Jernigan, LLP, Raleigh
919 821 6611
jjernigan@smithlaw.com
*Featured in Corporate/M&A (North Carolina)*
**Practice Areas:** Maintains an active practice including corporate governance, mergers and acquisitions, banking, and corporate law. He represents businesses in complex commercial transactions, and has over 35 years experience structuring, negotiating, and closing mergers and acquisitions involving public companies and large privately-owned companies. He has advised public company boards on special committees, audit committees and corporate governance, and regularly advises companies and their boards and officers on general corporate and business law matters.
**Professional Memberships:** Admitted to North Carolina Bar (1967). Past President of the North Carolina Bar Association. Served as a Member of the Board of Governors of the North Carolina Bar Association from 1989-92, and two terms as Chair of the North Carolina Bar Association's Business Law Section. Member of the American, North Carolina, and Wake County

Bar Associations. Member of the American Judicature Society, American College of Mortgage Attorneys, and American Counsel Association. Fellow of the American Bar Foundation.
**Career:** Chairman of Smith, Anderson, Blount, Dorsett, Mitchell & Jernigan, LLP; Managing Partner from 2001 through 2009. One of four North Carolina lawyers listed in The International Who's Who of Corporate Governance Lawyers and one of two North Carolina lawyers listed in The International Who's Who of Business Lawyers; listed in The Best Lawyers in America in the areas of banking, corporate, mergers and acquisitions, and securities law; included in North Carolina Super Lawyers as an honoree, top 100 lawyers list, and listed in the areas of business/corporate and mergers and acquisitions; listed in Business North Carolina's Legal Elite.
**Personal:** JD, University of North Carolina, 1967; AB, Davidson College, 1964. Past Trustee of Choate Rosemary Hall. Member, Board of Directors, Wells Fargo, North Carolina Triangle East Region. Member, Leadership Council, Wake Education Partnership. Listed in the Triangle Business Journal's "The Triangle's Most Influential Business Leaders."

## JONES, Sean M
K&L Gates, Charlotte
704 331 7406
sean.jones@klgates.com
*Featured in Corporate/M&A (North Carolina)*
**Practice Areas:** Sean M Jones focuses his practice on securities, mergers and acquisitions, and corporate law. He represents a broad range of public and private companies in a variety of securities, merger and acquisition, and general corporate matters. Mr Jones regularly advises clients on corporate governance matters and also represents private equity investors in connection with their formation and investment in portfolio companies.

## KEAN, Warren
K&L Gates, Charlotte
704 331 7413
warren.kean@klgates.com
*Featured in Corporate/M&A (North Carolina)*
**Practice Areas:** Partner Warren Kean focuses his practice on matters relating to limited liability companies, partnerships, and other unincorporated entities and the taxation of those entities. His practice emphasizes venture capital and private equity financings, strategic alliances, and joint ventures. Additionally, Mr Kean is involved with mergers and acquisitions, organizing and advising real estate ventures, advising emerging and other closely-held businesses, and corporate finance.

## KEEN, C Matthew
Ogletree, Deakins, Nash, Smoak & Stewart, PC, Raleigh
919 789 3162
matt.keen@ogletreedeakins.com
*Featured in Labor & Employment (North Carolina)*
**Practice Areas:** Labor and employment. Represents employers in state and federal court in employment discrimination, wage and hour, and ERISA litigation. Advises companies on a national basis on employment law compliance.

**Professional Memberships:** American Bar Association, North Carolina Bar Association (Labor and Employment Law Section, Litigation Section), and American Employment Law Council. Selected by Best Lawyers in America, Legal Elite and Super Lawyers for employment law.
**Career:** Practiced with Ogletree Deakins since 1987; Partner since 1994.
**Publications:** North Carolina Employers' Desk Manual (editor).
**Personal:** North Carolina State University (BS, 1983), University of North Carolina at Chapel Hill (JD, 1987).

## KELLY, Mark
Alston & Bird LLP, Charlotte
704 444 1075
mark.kelly@alston.com
*Featured in Corporate/M&A (North Carolina)*
**Practice Areas:** Private Equity, Mergers and Acquisitions and General Corporate Matters.
**Career:** Mark leads the A&B's private equity practice and has represented private equity firms and their portfolio companies in numerous equity and debt financings, leverage buyouts and exit transactions.
**Personal:** BA, cum laude, Hampden-Sydney College (1983); JD, Washington & Lee University (1986).

## KENYON, Douglas W
Hunton & Williams LLP, Raleigh
919 899 3076
dkenyon@hunton.com
*Featured in Litigation (North Carolina)*
**Practice Areas:** Doug is a litigator with more than 30 years experience. His diverse practice includes antitrust, trademarks, copyrights, unfair competition, counterfeiting, trade secrets protection, publishing, technology licensing, corporate compliance, corporate investigations, and Foreign Corrupt Practices Act representation. He has achieved successful results for clients in venues throughout the world, including the US Supreme Court, Courts of Appeal and District Courts, US Trademark Trial and Appeal Board, European Commission, Office of Harmonization in the Internal Market and World Intellectual Property Organization.
**Professional Memberships:** Intellectual Property Commission of International Chamber of Commerce, AIPLA, American Law Institute, and ABA.

## KENYON, Rosemary
Smith, Anderson, Blount, Dorsett, Mitchell & Jernigan, LLP, Raleigh
919 821 6629
rkenyon@smithlaw.com
*Featured in Labor & Employment (North Carolina)*
**Practice Areas:** Represents management in all aspects of employment law in multiple industries on a full range of complex issues including high risk employment actions, board investigations, government investigations, mergers and acquisitions, employment agreements, severance plans and agreements, policy development, litigation and dispute resolution. Represents senior execu-

tives and officers in connection with their individual employment agreements.
**Professional Memberships:** North Carolina Bar Association: past Member, Board of Governors; past Chair of the Strategic Planning & Emerging Trends committee, the Women in the Profession Committee and the Dispute Resolution Section. Member, American Bar Association and Wake County Bar Association, and Fellow, American Bar Association Foundation. Admitted to practice in North Carolina (1986), Virginia (1980), and Michigan (1979).
**Career:** Partner: Smith, Anderson, Blount, Dorsett, Mitchell & Jernigan, LLP (since 2001). Chair Pro Bono Committee and past member Policy and Planning Committee. Formerly Deputy General Counsel of Carolina Power & Light Company (now Duke Energy). Honors include: Women of Justice Award (Business Practitioner), North Carolina Lawyers Weekly (2012), North Carolina Super Lawyers (Employment and Labor) and Business North Carolina's Legal Elite (Employment).
**Personal:** JD, University of Notre Dame (1979); BA, magna cum laude, Saint Mary's College, Notre Dame, IN (1976). Chair of the Board, Habitat for Humanity of Wake County (2011 to present)(Board member since 2005).

## KIRKLAND, Byron B
Smith, Anderson, Blount, Dorsett, Mitchell & Jernigan, LLP, Raleigh
919 821 6682
bkirkland@smithlaw.com
*Featured in Corporate/M&A (North Carolina)*
**Practice Areas:** Smith Anderson Private Equity Team Leader. Practices in the areas of securities law, corporate law, private equity, venture capital, mergers and acquisitions, and technology law. Extensive experience in public offerings, private equity and venture capital transactions, and mergers and acquisitions for public and private companies.
**Professional Memberships:** Admitted to practice in North Carolina (1987). Member of the American Bar Association, Section of Business Law, North Carolina Bar Association, Wake County Bar Association and American Counsel Association; Member of the Board of Directors of the North Carolina Technology Association; Fellow of the American Bar Foundation; past Chair of the North Carolina Bar Association Young Lawyers Division and Securities Regulation Committee; past Business Law Fellow of the American Bar Association Business Law Section.
**Career:** Smith, Anderson, Blount, Dorsett, Mitchell & Jernigan, L.L.P., 1987-present. Chair, Compensation Committee; Member, Policy and Planning Committee. Honors include listing in The Best Lawyers in America in the areas of Corporate Law, Mergers and Acquisitions, Securities Law, and Venture Capital; included in North Carolina Super Lawyers since inception; Named 2013 Lawyer of the Year in Mergers and Acquisitions for Raleigh by The Best Lawyers in America; Named 2011 Lawyer of the Year in Securities/Capital Markets Law for Raleigh by The

Best Lawyers in America; Listed in Business North Carolina Magazine Legal Elite for Business Law.
**Personal:** Member, University of North Carolina at Chapel Hill Board of Visitors 2011-present; JD (with honors), University of North Carolina at Chapel Hill, 1987; MBA, University of North Carolina at Chapel Hill, 1987; BA, University of North Carolina at Chapel Hill, 1983.

## KLUTTZ, Joseph B C
K&L Gates, Charlotte
704 331 7485
joe.kluttz@klgates.com
*Featured in Bankruptcy/Restructuring (North Carolina)*
**Practice Areas:** Partner Joseph Kluttz focuses his practice on the structuring and restructuring of large financial transactions to avoid and manage insolvency risk. He has extensive experience with Chapter 11 bankruptcies. He has served as counsel for major national banks as agent and participant in a number of syndicated and bilateral credit transactions in need of restructuring, represented private equity investors in restructuring of subordinated debt, preferred stock, and other forms of mezzanine investments, and represented major contractors in a number of subcontractor bankruptcies and restructurings.

## KORANDO, Kimberly J
Smith, Anderson, Blount, Dorsett, Mitchell & Jernigan, LLP, Raleigh
919 821 6671
kkorando@smithlaw.com
*Featured in Labor & Employment (North Carolina)*
**Practice Areas:** Heads Employment, Labor and Human Resources Practice Group. Represents leading employers and government contractors in matters of financial, reputational and operational significance in a wide variety of industries including utilities, pharmaceuticals, biotechnology, hospitals and healthcare, automotive, semiconductor, paper/cellulose/furniture manufacturers, insurance, banking, retail, hospitality, food/beverage distribution, and law firms. Has extensive experience assisting companies based outside the US and North Carolina with establishing workforces in the US and compliance with US and state law and maintaining a union-free workplace; conducting internal harassment and employee misconduct investigations; representing employers in federal and state compliance audits and investigations involving class or systemic allegations; and defending employers in state and federal civil actions, including multiplaintiff and class actions.
**Professional Memberships:** Admitted to practice in North Carolina (1986); US Court of Appeals, Fourth Circuit (1989); US Supreme Court (1991). ABA EEO Committee. American Employment Law Council.
**Career:** Partner since 1993. Listed Best Lawyers in America; North Carolina SuperLawyers; North Carolina Legal Elite; Fellow, American Bar Foundation.
**Publications:** Board of Editors, Employment Discrimination Law, (5th ed.BNA). Author, Model Employee Policies & Forms for North Carolina Employers (NC Chamber 2007). Author, Inside

the Minds: Complying with Employment Regulations, Surviving the Reshaping of America's Workplaces (Aspatore 2010).
**Personal:** JD (with honors), University of Oklahoma, 1986; BS, in Psychology, University of Oklahoma, 1980.

## LAY, Wood W
Winston & Strawn LLP, Charlotte
704 350 7796
wlay@winston.com
*Featured in Labor & Employment (North Carolina)*
**Practice Areas:** Woody Lay's practice focuses on representing and advising companies in complex litigation, non-compete/unfair competition disputes, and matters involving the full range of labor and employment law issues. Mr Lay has significant experience litigating class action and multi-plaintiff ERISA cases and collective/class action wage and hour cases.
**Professional Memberships:** Licensed to practice in North Carolina and Virginia.
**Career:** Extensive experience managing litigation dockets for large, multi-state corporations and litigating cases in federal and state courts throughout the United States. Extensive experience with both labor and private agency arbitrations. Practiced with Hunton & Williams in its Richmond, VA (1992-98) and Charlotte, NC (1998-2010) offices before moving to Winston & Strawn's Charlotte office in April 2010.
**Personal:** University of Virginia (BA, 1988); Washington & Lee University School of Law (JD, 1991), Order of the Coif, Editor-in-Chief, Washington and Lee Law Review; Law Clerk, Hon. Walter E Hoffman, United States District Court, Eastern District of Virginia, 1991-92.

## LONG III, Nash E
Winston & Strawn LLP, Charlotte
704 350 7733
nlong@winston.com
*Featured in Litigation (North Carolina)*
**Practice Areas:** Nash Long focuses his practice on complex litigation including arbitrations, jury trials, bench trials, and class actions related to environmental, business torts, commercial contract, intellectual property, consumer law, and product liability disputes. He served as lead trial counsel for several utility companies in the defense of enforcement actions under the Clean Air Act. He has represented clients, including financial institutions, contractors, energy companies, and manufacturers, in class actions, patent infringement matters, and contract disputes.
**Professional Memberships:** Law 360 "Rising Star"; Best Lawyers in America; Litigation Counsel of America.
**Personal:** JD, magna cum laude (1997), Harvard Law School.

## MARCUS, Robert R
Smith Moore Leatherwood LLP, Greensboro
336 378 5365
rob.marcus@smithmoorelaw.com
*Featured in Litigation (North Carolina)*
**Practice Areas:** Rob Marcus focuses on complex commercial and appellate litigation. He has represented numerous corporations and financial

institutions in high profile and complex litigation matters throughout the state and federal courts. He is also well-versed in alternative dispute resolution, including arbitration. Mr Marcus writes and speaks on the subjects of securities litigation, class actions, appellate practice, and other aspects of litigation, and currently serves as Chairman of the firm's Management Committee.

## MASON, C Steven
Smith, Anderson, Blount, Dorsett, Mitchell & Jernigan, LLP, Raleigh
919 821 6642
smason@smithlaw.com
*Featured in Real Estate (North Carolina)*
**Practice Areas:** Practices in the areas of commercial real estate, lending transactions, and corporate law.
**Professional Memberships:** Admitted to practice in North Carolina (1981). Member of Wake County Bar Association, North Carolina Bar Association and American Bar Association.
**Career:** Joined Smith, Anderson, Blount, Dorsett, Mitchell & Jernigan, L.L.P., 1999. Practiced at Moore & Van Allen P.L.L.C., 1981-99. Honors include listing in Business North Carolina's Legal Elite, voted top in the category of Real Estate in 2008, North Carolina Super Lawyers and Best Lawyers in America. Fellow American College of Mortgage Attorneys.
**Personal:** JD, University of Virginia, 1981; BA, with highest honors, University of North Carolina, 1978.

## MCATEE, Richard S
Jackson Lewis LLP, Raleigh
919 424 8601
McAteeR@jacksonlewis.com
*Featured in Labor & Employment (North Carolina)*
**Practice Areas:** Employment Litigation, including non-compete litigation. Employment Law Advice, including ADA/FMLA issues. Labor Law, including negotiations, arbitrations and NLRB actions. Management Training. Admitted to all North Carolina and Pennsylvania courts and US Supreme Court.
**Professional Memberships:** ABA, NCBA, SHRM.
**Career:** Entire career with Jackson Lewis — currently Managing Partner of Raleigh office.
**Publications:** Law Review Articles.
**Personal:** Passionate about his family, including his wife, son, and daughter, all of whom are active in church, golf and soccer. Duquesne University JD, 1st in Class, 1995. Cornell University ILR, Dean's List, 1991.

## MCCOY, Michael D
Alston & Bird LLP, Charlotte
704 444 1011
mike.mccoy@alston.com
*Featured in Intellectual Property (North Carolina)*
**Practice Areas:** Responsible for all aspects of intellectual property—patents, trademarks, copyrights, unfair competition and trade secrets—practices primarily in electronics and information technology fields, including software and business method patents. His work includes enforcing patent rights, defending against actions brought

by others, conducting investigations for pre-litigation risk assessment and patent clearances (non-infringement and invalidity), licensing and evaluating portfolios, and securing domestic and foreign patent protection. Certified Licensing Professional.
**Career:** Pioneered an interactive patent mapping tool for portfolio assessment and strategic planning. Past coordinator, firm's Intellectual Property Groups.
**Personal:** Chicago-Kent College of Law (JD, 1975); University of Illinois (BSEE, 1972).

## MCGILL, Molly
Winston & Strawn LLP, Charlotte
704 350 7767
mmcgill@winston.com
*Featured in Banking & Finance (North Carolina)*
**Practice Areas:** Molly McGill is a Partner in Winston's New York and Charlotte offices and focuses her practice in asset-based lending and leveraged finance. She routinely represents top-tier bank clients in complex syndicated financings involving a variety of domestic and foreign asset classes and transactional structures. Ms McGill has been ranked in Chambers USA and named in The Best Lawyers in America®. She was honored in 2008 as part of an exclusive group of 145 attorneys nationwide named as "BTI Client Service All-Stars" for "the absolute best client service" representing Fortune 1000 companies.

## MEHTA, Kiran H
K&L Gates, Charlotte
704 331 7437
kiran.mehta@klgates.com
*Featured in Litigation (North Carolina)*
**Practice Areas:** Kiran H Mehta focuses his practice on complex business litigation and has handled a wide variety of complex and multi-party litigation matters, including corporate and commercial disputes, particularly disputes related to securities regulation, private equity investments and corporate governance; energy and utilities litigation; construction litigation; real estate and land use litigation; ERISA litigation; product liability, toxic tort, pharmaceutical, and mass tort litigation; and environmental litigation. Mr Mehta also has extensive experience representing major investor-owned public utilities in matters before regulatory commissions, particularly with respect to the financial aspects (rate of return and capital structure) of utility rate proceedings.

## MELVIN JR, Charles E
Smith Moore Leatherwood LLP, Greensboro
336 378 5204
charlie.melvin@smithmoorelaw.com
*Featured in Real Estate (North Carolina)*
**Practice Areas:** Charlie Melvin practices principally in the real property area of business, commercial and industrial transactions. He also regularly counsels clients concerning acquisitions and sales, zoning, finance and development, and advises a number of international companies on matters of general corporate and real estate law.

## MERRILLS, Andrew W
Ogletree, Deakins, Nash, Smoak & Stewart, PC, Raleigh
919 789 3134
andrew.merrills@ogletreedeakins.com
*Featured in Labor & Employment (North Carolina)*
**Practice Areas:** Global Business Immigration, working with multi-national companies to obtain temporary and permanent work visas both in the US and throughout the world, setting up appropriate employee hiring and permanent residence process strategies, advising companies on employee documentation requirements.
**Professional Memberships:** American Immigration Lawyers Association, North Carolina Bar Association, Wake County Bar Association.
**Career:** Admitted to practice in North Carolina in 1991.
**Publications:** Frequent lecturer on business immigration law topics before trade associations, industry groups and professional organizations. Authored numerous immigration newsletters and articles.
**Personal:** Duke University (BA, 1988), Walter F George School of Law, Mercer University (JD, 1991).

## O'BRYANT, Ramona Cunningham
Smith Moore Leatherwood LLP, Greensboro
336 378 5237
mona.obryant@smithmoorelaw.com
*Featured in Environment (North Carolina)*
**Practice Areas:** Mona O'Bryant practices in administrative law, focused primarily on environmental matters and regulation of tobacco products and alcoholic beverages at federal, state and local levels. Her Environmental Counseling Practice includes environmental compliance, planning and permitting, administrative proceedings, auditing, and business and real estate transactions. Ms O'Bryant also advises clients in tobacco product and alcoholic beverage industries on compliance, excise tax and business issues that arise under federal statutes and the regulation of the Alcohol and Tobacco Tax and Trade Bureau (TTB), as well as state laws and regulations applicable to the manufacture, distribution and sale of these products.

## OLIVER, George J
Smith Moore Leatherwood LLP, Raleigh
919 755 8710
jerry.oliver@smithmoorelaw.com
*Featured in Labor & Employment (North Carolina)*
**Practice Areas:** Jerry Oliver has been practicing labor and employment law for more than twenty years. Mr Oliver is engaged in counseling and representing employers in all aspects of employment law, including federal and state EEOC laws, FMLA and ADA matters, wage and hour issues, personnel practices, wrongful discharge, and safety matters under OSHA. His practice has a heavy emphasis on proactive counseling to assist employers in avoiding litigation and solving labor related problems. He has extensive management side experience in labor law matters including counter unions campaigns, corporate campaigns,

collective bargaining, unfair labor practice litigation, strikes, arbitration and mediation.

## PACKER, Leslie
Ellis & Winters LLP, Cary
919 865 7009
leslie.packer@elliswinters.com
*Featured in Litigation (North Carolina)*

**Practice Areas:** •Class action •Complex commercial and business •Construction •Intellectual property and trade secrets •Internal investigations •Mass torts •Medical malpractice defense •Pharmaceutical and medical device •Products liability •Tort and insurance •Unfair trade practices.

**Professional Memberships:** •American College of Trial Lawyers •North Carolina Association of Defense Attorneys, President, 2006-07 •Federation of Defense and Corporate Counsel, Drug, Device and Biotechnology Section Chair, 2006-07, Corporate Counsel Committee Co-Chair 2012-2013, Board of Directors, 2012-2013 •National Foundation for Judicial Excellence Board member, Program Chair, 2013 Symposium •Defense Research Institute •Tort Issues Task Force, North Carolina Bar Association, 2009-10 •North Carolina Bar Association, Member.

**Career:** •2000 Founding Partner of Ellis & Winters LLP •1986-2000 Smith Helms Mulliss & Moore LLP.

**Personal:** •JD, UNIVERSITY OF NORTH CAROLINA SCHOOL OF LAW, CHAPEL HILL, NORTH CAROLINA, 1986 •Honors: High Honors; Order of the Coif •Law Review: North Carolina Law Review, Research Editor, 1985-1986 •AB, BROWN UNIVERSITY, PROVIDENCE, RHODE ISLAND, 1982 •Honors: magna cum laude; Honors in Anthropology, Phi Beta Kappa.

## PARASCANDOLA, Stephen T
Smith, Anderson, Blount, Dorsett, Mitchell & Jernigan, LLP, Raleigh
919 821 6775
sparascandola@smithlaw.com
*Featured in Environment (North Carolina)*

**Practice Areas:** Chairs Environmental, Health & Safety Practice Group. Practice involves all aspects of environmental, OSHA and land use law, including compliance counseling, permitting and enforcement defense. Regularly counsels clients on risk management, particularly with respect to mergers and acquisitions, due diligence and contract issues, insurance matters, investigations and audits, and public company environmental disclosures. Has extensive experience representing clients before regulatory agencies, in administrative appeals, and judicial proceedings.

**Professional Memberships:** American Bar Association; New York Bar Association; The Florida Bar; North Carolina Bar Association.

**Career:** Associate, Cullen and Dykman LLP (New York City) (1988-1991); Assistant Attorney General, North Carolina Department of Justice (Environmental Protection Division) (1992-1995).

**Publications:** Co-Author, "North Carolina Construction Law Deskbook," Environmental Law Chapter; Co-Author, "What to Do During a Worker Safety Inspection"; Author, "North

Carolina Legal Guide," Environmental Law Chapter.

**Personal:** JD Stetson University (Law Review) 1988; BA Eckerd College 1984.

## PATTERSON JR, Carl N
Smith, Anderson, Blount, Dorsett, Mitchell & Jernigan, LLP, Raleigh
919 821 6647
cpatterson@smithlaw.com
*Featured in Litigation (North Carolina)*

**Practice Areas:** With over 35 years of complex commercial litigation experience, his practice includes contract disputes and commercial litigation, risk management counsel, corporate, and securities litigation. His practice includes representing diverse organizations and individuals, including financial institutions; issuers and purchasers of securities; officers; directors; lenders; professional advisers; and buyers and sellers of both businesses and of goods and services. He led Smith Anderson's Commercial Litigation Practice Group for 25 years.

**Professional Memberships:** Admitted to practice in North Carolina (1976). Member of the Wake County Bar Association, North Carolina Bar Association, Litigation, Business Law and Law Practice Management Sections, American Bar Association, and the American Judicature Society. Past Chair of the Young Lawyers Division of the North Carolina Bar Association. Fellow, Litigation Counsel of America. Member, Fourth Circuit Judicial Conference.

**Career:** Managing Partner of Smith, Anderson, Blount, Dorsett, Mitchell & Jernigan, LLP. Joined Smith Anderson, 1976; became partner, 1981. Member firm Senior Management Team including Policy, Planning and Compensation committees. Honors include listing Business North Carolina Legal Elite, North Carolina Super Lawyers, Best Lawyers in America. Recognized as very well regarded in 2008 premier edition of Benchmark Litigation-The Definitive Guide to America's Leading Lawyers.

**Personal:** JD (with honors), University of North Carolina, 1976; BA, Davidson College, 1973.

## PETESCH, Bruce A
Ogletree, Deakins, Nash, Smoak & Stewart, PC, Raleigh
919 789 3178
bruce.petesch@ogletreedeakins.com
*Featured in Labor & Employment (North Carolina)*

**Practice Areas:** Labor and employment law, representing companies in labor relations issues, including complex contract negotiations, representation elections, merger and acquisition due diligence, arbitration cases and litigation before the National Labor Relations Board.

**Professional Memberships:** American Bar Association, NC Bar, SC Bar, Illinois Bar, Transportation Lawyers Association, North American Transportation Employee Relations Association.

**Career:** Recognized in the Best Lawyers of America 2012, North Carolina Super Lawyers for Labor and Employment Law. Admitted to practice in North Carolina, Illinois, South Carolina, US

Court of Appeals (Fourth and Fifth Circuits), US Supreme Court.

**Personal:** Ripon College (AB, 1966), DePaul University (JD, 1969).

## PRUDEN III, J Norfleet
K&L Gates, Charlotte
704 331 7442
norfleet.pruden@klgates.com
*Featured in Corporate/M&A (North Carolina)*

**Practice Areas:** Partner Norfleet Pruden has broad and extensive experience in many areas of business law, and in recent years has focused his practice on mergers and acquisitions, securities, private equity and general corporate representation. He also serves as special counsel to independent committees, individual directors and minority shareholders in connection with corporate change-in-control transactions and internal investigations.

## RAMSEUR, Patti
Smith Moore Leatherwood LLP, Greensboro
*Featured in Labor & Employment (North Carolina)*

**Practice Areas:** Patti Ramseur is the leader of the firm's labor and employment practice, and is a member of the civil litigation group, counseling employers and litigating when necessary. Patti represents employers for claims under Title VII, ADA, ADEA, FMLA, FLSA, REDA, Sarbanes Oxley Act, and Workers' Compensation Act in federal and state courts. She has experience with cases involving claims of sexual harassment, intentional/negligent infliction of emotional distress, wrongful discharge, wage and hour disputes, unemployment compensation, contractual disputes, covenants not to compete, and trade secrets misappropriation. She also handles cases involving claims of medical malpractice, torts, and contractual disputes.

## REAVES, Lacy H
Smith, Anderson, Blount, Dorsett, Mitchell & Jernigan, LLP, Raleigh
919 821 6704
lreaves@smithlaw.com
*Featured in Real Estate (North Carolina)*

**Practice Areas:** Land Use and Zoning; Commercial real estate.

**Professional Memberships:** Admitted to all North Carolina State and Federal Courts, the United States Tax Court, the United State Court of Appeals for the Fourth Circuit and the United States Supreme Court. Bar Admissions and Memberships include the North Carolina State Bar and the North Carolina Bar Association.

**Career:** Joined Smith Anderson in 2008. Partner, Kennedy, Covington, Lobdell & Hickman, L.L.P. (now K&L Gates L.L.P.), 1995-2008; Poyner & Spruill, L.L.P. 1972-95. Founding chair of the Zoning, Planning and Land Use Section of the North Carolina Bar Association. Featured speaker or moderator for the North Carolina Bar Association, the North Carolina Association of Defense Lawyers, the International Council of Shopping Centers, the American Society of Civil Engineers, the Urban Land Institute, and the Triangle Community Coalition. Selected, Business North Carolina, Legal Elite, 2007-13. Selected,

North Carolina Super Lawyers, Land Use/Zoning, 2007-13. Selected Woodward/White, Inc's The Best Lawyers in America, 2007-13. Martindale-Hubbell AV Rated.

**Personal:** JD with honors, Order of the Coif, North Carolina Law Review, University of North Carolina 1972; AB Economics and Political Science, University of North Carolina 1969.

## ROACH, Gerald F
Smith, Anderson, Blount, Dorsett, Mitchell & Jernigan, LLP, Raleigh
919 821 6668
groach@smithlaw.com
*Featured in Corporate/M&A (North Carolina)*

**Practice Areas:** Gerald Roach focuses his practice on complex corporate transactions including public offerings, domestic and international mergers and acquisitions, joint ventures, corporate governance, private financings, technology law and advising board of directors and special committees. He has served as lead counsel to publicly-traded and privately held companies with North Carolina, US and international interests.

**Professional Memberships:** Admitted to North Carolina Bar (1982). Member, American Bar Association, North Carolina Bar Association (past chair of the Business Law section), Wake County Bar Association, and American Counsel Association. Fellow, American Bar Foundation. Member, Board of Directors, North Carolina Biotechnology Center.

**Career:** Joined Smith Anderson in 1982. Leader of the firm's corporate and securities groups; chair, Policy and Planning Committee; and member, Compensation Committee. Honors include: Legal Elite Hall of Fame, Top Business Lawyer in North Carolina for 2009 by Business North Carolina magazine; The Best Lawyers in America, Best Lawyers in America for Corporate Law (designated as top Corporate lawyer - 2013, top Mergers and Acquisitions lawyer - 2012, top Securities lawyer - 2010, and top Corporate lawyer - 2009 in Triangle market); named 2010 BTI Client Service All Star for US; International Who's Who of Mergers & Acquisitions (only North Carolina lawyer listed); International Who's Who of Business Lawyers (one of two North Carolina lawyers listed); International Who's Who of Corporate Governance Lawyers (one of four North Carolina lawyers listed); named one of "Ten to Watch: Attorneys that have an impact on North Carolina business" by a leading North Carolina business publication; and listed North Carolina Super Lawyers (2006-12), including Top 100 lawyers list.

**Personal:** Board of Trustees, Wake Forest University (2010-Present); Board of Directors, Wake Forest University Health Sciences Inc. (2011-Present); Wake Forest University School of Law (JD, cum laude – 1982); Wake Forest University (BA, cum laude – 1980).

## ROSENFELD, Margaret
Smith, Anderson, Blount, Dorsett, Mitchell & Jernigan, LLP, Raleigh
mrosenfeld@smithlaw.com
*Featured in Corporate/M&A (North Carolina)*

**Practice Areas:** Ms Rosenfeld has corporate and securities law experience both within the United States and internationally and leads the Smith Anderson International Law practice. Her practice includes public company reporting, corporate governance, public offerings and private placements of securities, private equity investments, corporate investigations (internal and government), mergers and acquisitions, and intellectual property protection and licensing as well as general corporation representation.
**Professional Memberships:** •Association for Corporate Growth, Triangle Chapter: President, Board Member •Society of Corporate Secretaries and Governance Professionals, Inc. •American Bar Association •North Carolina Bar Association •Wake County/Tenth Judicial District Bar Association •New York Bar Association; Former Southeast Representative of the New York Bar Association's Committee on Securities Regulation.
**Career:** Before joining Smith Anderson in 2001, Ms Rosenfeld practiced corporate, finance and securities law with Freshfields Bruckhaus Deringer in London, the United Kingdom and Frankfurt, Germany and with Paul, Weiss, Rifkind, Wharton & Garrison in Tokyo, Japan. Honors include: The Best Lawyers in America (Banking & Finance Law, Corporate Law, Securities/Capital Markets Law); Business Leader Magazine's 2012 Top 50 Entrepreneur Award; Triangle Business Journal's 2008 Women in Business Award; Triangle Business Journal's 2006 "40 Under 40" Leadership Award.
**Personal:** •Education: George Washington University, JD, Order of the Coif, 1997 (Senior Projects Editor, The George Washington University Law Review); Rutgers University, BA, Phi Beta Kappa,1992; Konstanz Universität, Konstanz, Germany, Junior Year Abroad 1991; Hiroo School, Tokyo, Japan, Certificate in Japanese Studies 1998 •Speaks and reads German at an intermediate level and has a basic knowledge of spoken Japanese •United Arts Council of Raleigh and Wake County: Board Member.

### SANDERSON III, George F
Ellis & Winters LLP, Cary
919 865 7093
george.sanderson@elliswinters.com
*Featured in Bankruptcy/Restructuring (North Carolina)*
**Practice Areas:** •Antitrust and trade regulation •Appellate •Bankruptcy •Complex commercial and business litigation •Creditors' rights •Securities
**Professional Memberships:** •American Bankruptcy Institute •American Bar Association, Business Law Section •North Carolina Bar Association, Antitrust and Complex Business Disputes Section, Section Chair •North Carolina Bar Association, Bankruptcy Section, Section Council.
**Career:** •Associate, Boies, Schiller & Flexner, 2001-2004 •Associate, Paul, Weiss, Rifkind, Wharton & Garrison, 2000-2001 •Law Clerk, United States Bankruptcy Court for the Eastern District of Virginia, Hon. Stephen C. St. John, 1999-2000.

**Publications:** •Editor, North Carolina Chapter, State Antitrust Practice and Statutes, ABA, 4th ed. And 5th ed. (forthcoming).
**Personal:** •JD, NEW YORK UNIVERSITY SCHOOL OF LAW, NEW YORK, NEW YORK, 1999 •Honors: Semi-finalist, Marden Moot Court Competition, 1999 •Law Journal: New York University Journal of Legislation and Public Policy, Executive Editor, 1998-1999 •AB, GEORGETOWN UNIVERSITY, WASHINGTON, DC, 1995 •Honors: magna cum laude; Phi Beta Kappa; Departmental Honors; John Carroll Scholar.

### SAR, Robert A
Ogletree, Deakins, Nash, Smoak & Stewart, PC, Raleigh
919 787 9700
bob.sar@ogletreedeakins.com
*Featured in Labor & Employment (North Carolina)*
**Practice Areas:** Significant trial/arbitration experience involving labor and employment, including discrimination, harassment, retaliation, wage/hour, class/collective actions, non-competes, trade secrets, whistle-blowers and business litigation. Investigations/compliance/counseling focused on government investigations, executive employment, general HR. Traditional labor practice.
**Professional Memberships:** American Bar Association, North Carolina Bar Association, Best Lawyers in America, Legal Elite, Super Lawyers for employment defense litigation. Chairman of The Conference Table, Board of Visitors of Campbell Law School, Board of Food Bank for Central and Eastern North Carolina.
**Career:** Joined Ogletree Deakins in 1998; Partner since 2005.
**Personal:** Wake Forest University (BS, 1990), Campbell University (JD, 1995).

### SASSER, Jonathan D
Ellis & Winters LLP, Cary
919 865 7002
jon.sasser@elliswinters.com
*Featured in Litigation (North Carolina)*
**Practice Areas:** •Antitrust and trade regulation •Appellate •Complex commercial and business •Constitutional and civil rights litigation •Criminal law and business crimes defense •Environmental, mold and toxic tort •First Amendment, media and communications •Intellectual property and trade secrets •Securities •Unfair trade practices.
**Professional Memberships:** •Tour de Cure (American Diabetes Association), Co-Chair, 2008 •North Carolina School of Science & Math Foundation, Chair, 2003-2004 •North Carolina Bar Association, Constitutional Law Section, Chair, 2002-2003 •United States District Court for the Eastern District of North Carolina, Member, Civil Rules Subcommittee.
**Career:** •Moore & Van Allen, PLLC, 1986-2003 •Paul, Weiss, Rifkind, Wharton & Garrison, 1982-1986.
**Personal:** •JD, UNIVERSITY OF NORTH CAROLINA SCHOOL OF LAW, CHAPEL HILL, NORTH CAROLINA, 1981 •Honors: With

Honors, John M. Morehead Fellow in Law •Law Review: North Carolina Law Review, 1980-1981 •BA, UNIVERSITY OF NORTH CAROLINA, CHAPEL HILL, NORTH CAROLINA, 1978 •Honors: With Honors, Presidential Scholar, Phi Beta Kappa, John M. Morehead Scholar, National Merit Scholar.

### SAWCHAK, Matthew W
Ellis & Winters LLP, Cary
919 865 7004
matt.sawchak@elliswinters.com
*Featured in Antitrust (North Carolina)*
**Practice Areas:** •Antitrust and trade regulation •Appellate •Complex commercial and business.
**Professional Memberships:** •North Carolina Bar Association, Past Chair of Antitrust and Trade Regulation Section and Appellate Rules Committee •American Bar Association •Member of Antitrust Section Leadership •Member of the editorial board for State Antitrust Practice and Statutes (4th ed.) •Chief editor for State Antitrust Enforcement Handbook (2d ed.) •North Carolina Business Court, Rules Advisory Committee.
**Career:** •Clerkship, Justice Clarence Thomas, United States Court of Appeals for the District of Columbia Circuit.
**Publications:** •Defining Unfairness in "Unfair Trade Practices," 90 N.C. L. Rev. 2033 (2012) (with Kip D. Nelson) •Sections on state antitrust law and procedure in ABA Antitrust Section, Antitrust Law Developments (6th ed. 2007). •United States Federal Trade Commission: Organization, Jurisdiction, and Procedure, 89 J. German Pat. B. 288 (1998) (with Christoph Ann) (published in German) •The Department of Defense's Role in Free-World Export Licensing Under the Export Administration Act, 1988 Duke L.J. 785.
**Personal:** •LLM AND JD, DUKE UNIVERSITY SCHOOL OF LAW, DURHAM, NORTH CAROLINA, 1989 •Honors: With Honors; Order of the Coif; Faculty Award •Law Journal: Duke Law Journal, Editor-in-Chief, 1988-1989 •AB, HARVARD UNIVERSITY, CAMBRIDGE, MASSACHUSETTS, 1984 •Honors: cum laude; National Merit Scholarship.

### SHAD, Kerry
Smith, Anderson, Blount, Dorsett, Mitchell & Jernigan, LLP, Raleigh
919 821 6672
kshad@smithlaw.com
*Featured in Labor & Employment (North Carolina)*
**Practice Areas:** Represents employers in connection with all aspects of employment-related litigation and counseling in multiple industries including pharmaceutical, financial, technology, biotech, insurance and hospital/health care. Has extensive experience representing companies in individual, class and collective action discrimination and wage and hour claims at the agency level and in state and federal court; serving as "in house" employment litigation counsel for large company managing litigation in jurisdictions across the country; conducting internal harassment and employee misconduct investigations; and advising companies on a variety of employment-related risk management issues.

**Professional Memberships:** Admitted to practice in North Carolina (1991); US Court of Appeals, Fourth Circuit (1994); Supreme Court of the United States (2005).
**Career:** Partner since 1999; listed Best Lawyers in America and North Carolina Super Lawyers; Member of Smith Anderson's management team including co-chair of the Diversity Committee and member of the Compensation and Recruiting Committees.
**Publications:** Contributor, Chapter 11, "Sexual Orientation and Gender Identity," Employment Discrimination Law (4th Edition 2007, BNA).
**Personal:** JD (with honors), University of North Carolina at Chapel Hill, 1991; BS, in Psychology, Florida State University, 1985.

### SITTON, Larry B
Smith Moore Leatherwood LLP, Charlotte
704 384 2600
larry.sitton@smithmoorelaw.com
*Featured in Litigation (North Carolina)*
**Practice Areas:** Larry Sitton has represented a number of banks, insurance companies, and large corporations in significant complex commercial litigation, including insurance coverage, securities fraud and antitrust violations. He has defended numerous class actions in both state and federal courts involving various commercial disputes and consumer fraud actions. He has been recognized as one of the leading anti-trust and "bet the company" litigators in North Carolina.

### SPEARS JR, James B
Ogletree, Deakins, Nash, Smoak & Stewart, PC, Charlotte
704 342 2588
jim.spears@ogletreedeakins.com
*Featured in Labor & Employment (North Carolina)*
**Practice Areas:** Labor and Employment Litigation; Employment and Labor Law Specialization, SC.
**Professional Memberships:** NC and SC Bar Associations; National Retail Federation Committee on Employment Law, Chair, E.E.O. Subcommittee.
**Career:** Twice argued before the US Supreme Court, including the landmark decision in Gilmer v. Interstate/Johnson Lane Corp., 500 US 20 (1991), enforcing employee arbitration agreements. Listed in The Best Lawyers in America for more than 10 years, Super Lawyers, and The International Who's Who of Business Lawyers.
**Publications:** Lectures and writes for regional and national programs on employment law and litigation matters.
**Personal:** Wake Forest University (BS, 1970), (JD, 1973).

### SPRUILL, W. Murray
Alston & Bird LLP, Durham
919 862 2202
murray.spruill@alston.com
*Featured in Intellectual Property (North Carolina)*
**Practice Areas:** Dr Spruill combines his scientific background with legal expertise to provide high quality patent-related legal services. Scientific expertise includes genetics, cellular and molecular biology, biochemistry, immunology, pharmaceuti-

cals and small molecule therapeutics. He provides legal services relating to all areas of patent law, including patent drafting and prosecution, general patent counseling and strategic planning, patentability, freedom-to-operate opinions, validity and non-infringement opinions and licensing. **Career:** Leader, firm's Biotechnology, Chemical and Pharmaceutical Patents Group; co-leader, firm's Life Sciences Task Force.
**Personal:** The George Washington University (JD, 1992); North Carolina State University (PhD, 1981); East Carolina University (BS, 1976).

---

**TIPPS, Maynard E**
K&L Gates, Charlotte
704 331 7473
maynard.tipps@klgates.com
*Featured in Real Estate (North Carolina)*
**Practice Areas:** Maynard E Tipps has over 39 years of experience representing real estate developers, investors, managers, and landlords in complex commercial real estate transactions involving development, finance, leasing, mining rights, acquisition, and disposition of real estate. His public/private partnership ventures have included the acquisition and build-out of large mixed-use developments, shopping centers, a major office and distribution center, and the rollup of a multi-state apartment portfolio, resulting in a publicly-held REIT.

---

**UYESATO, Daniel E**
Hunton & Williams LLP, Raleigh
919 899 3086
duyesato@hunton.com
*Featured in Environment (North Carolina)*
**Practice Areas:** Mr Uyesato's practice involves US and international regulatory matters, focusing on chemical and other product regulation and environment health and safety issues, especially those related to investigation and remediation of contaminated properties. Mr Uyesato also has extensive experience with US and international business transactions with substantial chemicals and environmental issues.
**Publications:** Contributor, The EU REACH Regulation: Law and Practice (Oxford University Press, forthcoming); Key issues in reform of the Toxic Substances Control Act of 1976, Trends, Vol. 41, No. 4 March/April 2010.
**Personal:** JD, Stanford Law School; BA, University of Kansas.

---

**WINTERS, Michael G**
Ellis & Winters LLP, Cary
919 865 7008
mike.winters@elliswinters.com
*Featured in Real Estate (North Carolina)*
**Practice Areas:** •Extensive experience in commercial real estate with emphasis on asset sales and acquisition; commercial leasing; residential and commercial development, including mixed-use development; development financing, including construction and permanent financing; railroad related real estate issues; and land use matters.
**Professional Memberships:** •Admitted to practice in North Carolina in 1969 •Member - North Carolina Bar Association •Past Board Member and two-time Chair - Cary, North Carolina, Chamber of Commerce •Board Member - Shepherd's Theological Seminary •Listed in Best Lawyers of America, Chambers and Partners, Business North Carolina, North Carolina's Legal Elite, and North Carolina Super Lawyers.
**Career:** •2000 Founding Partner of Ellis & Winters LLP •1984-2000 Smith Helms Mulliss & Moore LLP •1979-1984 Toms, Beebe & Winters •1978-79 Reynolds & Howard.
**Personal:** •1978JD, University of North Carolina at Chapel Hill School of Law •1975BS, University of North Carolina at Chapel Hill (Morehead Scholar).

---

**WOOD JR, Fred M**
Smith Moore Leatherwood LLP, Charlotte
704 384 2646
fred.wood@smithmoorelaw.com
*Featured in Litigation (North Carolina)*
**Practice Areas:** Fred Wood is a Member of the firm's Litigation Group. He represents companies in a variety of matters, including cases involving unfair business practices and methods of competition, the North Carolina Trade Secrets Protection Act, business torts, class actions, product liability and breach of contract. He has also represented companies and individuals in shareholder disputes and oppression claims by minority shareholders. Mr Wood also represents companies in complex arbitrations and before the North Carolina Business Court, and in both State and federal courts.

# SMITH, ANDERSON, BLOUNT, DORSETT, MITCHELL & JERNIGAN, LLP

www.smithlaw.com **tel:** 919 821 1220 **fax:** 919 821 6800

**Chairman:** John L Jernigan
**Managing Partner:** Carl N Patterson, Jr
Number of partners: 80  Number of other lawyers: 42

**OFFICES:**

NORTH CAROLINA
**RALEIGH:** Wells Fargo Capitol Center, Suite 2300,
NC 27601
Tel: 919 821 1220  Fax: 919 821 6800

## Firm Overview:

Since the firm's founding in 1912, it has grown to be the largest law firm in Raleigh and the Research Triangle region of North Carolina, and one of the largest in the state. The firm provides a full range of legal services and is dedicated to the principles of professionalism, excellence and service to its clients and the community. The firm has a broad business practice representing large and medium size public and private companies in sectors that include financial services, pharmaceuticals, energy, healthcare, manufacturing, technology, service and retail and government. The firm represents clients in litigation at every level of the judicial system, including the state and federal trial and appellate courts. It also appears regularly before state and federal agencies and in other forums to advance the interests of its clients and is experienced in all forms of alternative dispute resolution.

## Main Areas of Practice:

### Corporate, Securities, Mergers & Acquisitions:

The firm has one of the state's leading Public Company Practices as measured by number and size of transactions and public company clients. The firm provides a broad range of general corporate, mergers and acquisitions, corporate finance, securities, joint venture, venture capital, private equity, employee benefits, intellectual property and technology advice to clients ranging from established public companies, including some of the state's largest investor-owned utilities, to venture capital backed start-ups and venture funds, many involving life sciences and technology fields. The firm also regularly advises Boards of Directors or committees, including special committees.
**Contact:** Gerald F Roach

### Commercial Transactions:

The firm has been a leader in assisting North Carolina businesses and individuals with commercial transactions, including bank and other private finance, access to capital markets, mergers and acquisitions, environmental compliance, commercial real estate, land use and zoning, construction and bankruptcy. The firm has significant experience in secured and unsecured bank lending, joint ventures, venture and mezzanine investments, leveraged buyouts and acquisition financing, mergers and acquisitions, derivatives, workouts and reorganizations, conduit financing, securitizations and other asset-based financings, divestitures, licensing, and franchising. The firm has an extensive Tax Practice providing planning and advice, as well as representation of clients in tax controversies.
**Contact:** John L Jernigan

### Commercial Litigation:

The firm's Commercial Litigation Practice Group has substantial trial experience, and is adept at handling complex, document-intensive cases. The firm offers expertise in all forms of alternative dispute resolution. Some members of the Commercial Litigation Practice Group are certified mediators or arbitrators. The Group includes members of the American College of Trial Lawyers, the International Society of Barristers, the International Association of Defense Counsel, the American Board of Trial Advocates, the American Judicature Society and the Judicial Conference of the Fourth Circuit Court of Appeals. The firm has extensive experience in counseling and representing clients in banking litigation, disputes between buyers and sellers of goods and services, commercial real estate disputes, insurance matters and class action and derivative shareholder litigation.
**Contact:** Carl N Patterson Jr

### General Litigation:

The firm's Products Liability Group regularly represents large manufacturers in the automotive, chemical and other industries providing services ranging from risk management advice to litigation defense. The firm's Medical Malpractice Practice Group defends physicians, hospitals and other healthcare providers with a philosophy that combines an aggressive and efficient approach to litigation with an in-depth understanding of relevant medical issues.
**Contact:** Samuel G Thompson

### Employment, Labor & Human Resources:

The firm's Employment, Labor & Human Resources Practice has extensive experience serving as general outside Employment Counsel to emerging, growth and mature companies based in North Carolina and subsidiaries of national and international companies doing business in North Carolina. The firm's lawyers have extensive experience with complex and challenging employment issues and litigation, including FLSA/state wage and hour compliance and class litigation; systemic discrimination risk management and litigation; workplace harassment, training and investigation; workforce restructuring merger and acquisition integration; non-competition agreements; executive employment and severance agreements; human resources audits; affirmative action plans and OFCCP audits; policies and procedures development; drug and alcohol testing; workplace violence; and flexible staffing matters.
**Contact:** Kimberly J Korando

### Regulatory - Government Relations, Healthcare, Public Utilities:

The firm has a long history of working on behalf of its business clients with local, state and federal government and represents a broad array of clients before the North Carolina General Assembly. The firm's Healthcare Practice provides business and regulatory counsel to a wide variety of healthcare clients across the Southeast, from physicians and physician organizations to other providers to informatics companies and e-health entities. Services include antitrust, certificate of need, covenants not to compete, employment agreements, HIPAA and other privacy laws, fraud and abuse, medical staff issues, Medicare compliance, mergers and acquisitions/joint ventures, negotiations with insurers, physician organizations, accountable care organizations and hospital/physician affiliations. The firm regularly represents clients engaged in the energy and telecommunications industries, including some of the state's largest public utilities. Services include negotiation with and litigation before state regulatory agencies and representation of clients before the North Carolina General Assembly.
**Contact:** Julian D Bobbitt, Jr

### International Work:

The firm represents a growing number of international companies with business interests in its market, including companies based in the United Kingdom, Europe, the Pacific Rim and South America, as well as numerous companies located in the United States with foreign subsidiaries or interests.

### Clients:

The firm's clients include some of the largest financial institutions, insurance companies, public utilities, retailers, manufacturing, pharmaceutical, and biotechnology companies in its region and the nation, as well as emerging growth and technology companies. The firm also represents smaller businesses and individuals.

# SMITH MOORE LEATHERWOOD LLP

www.smithmoorelaw.com **tel:** 336 378 5200 **fax:** 336 378 5400

**Managing Partner:** Robert R Marcus
Number of partners: 109
Number of other lawyers: 86

## Firm Overview:

Clients of Smith Moore Leatherwood trust that they are receiving creative, cost effective legal services that align with their goals. With seven offices and more than 190 attorneys across North Carolina, South Carolina and Georgia, the firm's core practice areas are focused on Litigation, Labor and Employment, Corporate law, Health Care and Commercial Real Estate.

## Main Areas of Practice:

### Commercial Litigation:

This Group's experience includes commercial and business torts, product liability, health care, construction, financial services, antitrust and trade litigation, class actions, toxic tort, catastrophic injury, insurance, intellectual property, professional liability and licensing, land use development and sports. Many of the firm's litigators are fellows of the American College of Trial Lawyers.

### Appellate:

Members of the firm's Appellate Team are respected as advocates and negotiators in state and federal courts, as well as in mediation and arbitration proceedings.

### Life, Health, Disability & ERISA:

This Team enjoys a national reputation for excellence, having defended claims brought under ERISA, RICO, and the ADA, class actions, discriminatory underwriting claims, allegations of agent misconduct, and breach of contract claims for the recovery of life, accidental death, disability and health insurance benefits.

### Transportation:

The firm has an established Transportation Industry Practice that handles trucking and aviation accident investigations and litigation, business issues, cargo claims and regulatory compliance.

### Labor & Employment:

The Labor and Employment Group represents management with emphasis on employment litigation, labor relations, human resources counseling and training, employee benefits, immigration, workers' compensation and OSHA.

### Corporate:

This Group represents businesses, individuals, banks, venture capital firms and other financial institutions in a variety of transactions, including formation of business entities, business acquisitions, dispositions and reorganizations (from traditional stock and asset sales to mergers, leveraged buyouts and going-private and going-public transactions), and in raising debt and equity capital. Their experience includes assisting with privately held start-up corporations and limited liability companies, joint ventures and strategic alliances, mature private and public corporations and tax exempt entities.

### Banking & Finance:

This Team has significant experience arranging and negotiating secured and unsecured financing and leveraged leasing transactions, collection and enforcement of loan and security instruments. They are also deeply experienced in creditor claims in regulations, compliance, innovative financing arrangements involving public and private sectors and in matters involving government bond financing and other forms of public finance, along with economic development incentives.

### Tax:

The firm's Tax Team assists with federal, state and local tax matters. They counsel closely held and publicly traded businesses, individuals, families, non-profit organizations, foundations and charities on income tax, sales tax, estate and gift tax issues. The Team also handles business tax planning, tax controversies, transactions, mergers and acquisitions, estate planning and exempt organizations.

### Intellectual Property:

This team assesses inventions, handles patent applications, appeals, oppositions, patent counseling on validity issues, and worldwide docketing and portfolio management. It helps clients select and protect trademarks and service marks; protect trade secrets and sensitive commercial information; maximize copyright protection both in the United States and internationally; and structure commercial transactions to allocate risks and responsibilities for the development, protection, licensing, and distribution of cutting-edge technologies.

### Healthcare:

The Health Care Group is one of the largest in the Southeast. The Group currently represents hospitals, hospital systems, long-term care facilities, and physician groups across the country. The Health Care Group focuses on acquisitions, network development, joint ventures, tax-exempt legal issues, corporate compliance, bioethical issues, financial and business transactions, fraud and abuse, HIPAA and privacy issues, managed care, management counseling, medical staff matters, provider defense litigation, Certificate of Need and licensure, regulatory compliance and risk management.

### Commercial Real Estate:

The Commercial Real Estate Group represents lenders, sellers, purchasers, and both national and local financial institutions in the development, financing, sale, purchase and lease of commercial, industrial and residential properties. It also helps clients with contract negotiation, arrangements for financing, leasing, management and sale of commercial and industrial properties. Title examination and certification, subdivision regulations and compliance with federal, state and local regulations are handled as well.

### Land Use and Zoning:

This Team assists with rezonings, variances and building permits; wetlands, surface water, environmental, and OSHA compliance; restrictive growth ordinances and moratoria; and land use litigation.

### International Work:

The firm handles international business transactions, including cross-border business entity structures, asset transfers, economic and local tax incentive planning, immigration, intellectual property, customs, tax considerations, commercial agreements and disputes, and compliance with the Foreign Corrupt Practices Act.

## OFFICES

**NORTH CAROLINA**

**CHARLOTTE:** 525 North Tryon Street, Suite 1400, NC 28202
Tel: 704 384 2600  Fax: 704 384 2800

**GREENSBORO:** 300 N. Greene Street, Suite 1400, NC 27401
Tel: 336 378 5200  Fax: 336 378 5400

**RALEIGH:** 434 Fayetteville Street, Suite 2800, NC 27601
Tel: 919 755 8700  Fax: 919 755 8800

**WILMINGTON:** 300 N. 3rd Street, Suite 301, NC 28401
Tel: 910 815 7100  Fax: 910 815 7200

**SOUTH CAROLINA**

**CHARLESTON:** 25 Calhoun Street, Sutie 250, SC 29401
Tel: 843 300 6700  Fax: 843 300 6700

**GREENVILLE:** 300 East McBee Avenue, Suite 500, SC 29601
Tel: 864 242 6440  Fax: 864 240 2474

**GEORGIA**

**ATLANTA:** Atlantic Center Plaza, 1180 W. Peachtree St. NW, Suite 2300, GA 30309
Tel: 404 962 1000  Fax: 404 962 1200

# WOMBLE CARLYLE SANDRIDGE & RICE LLP

**www.**wcsr.com  **tel:** 336 721 3660  **fax:** 336 721 3660

**Managing Partner:** Keith W Vaughan
Number of partners: 288  Number of lawyers: 540+

**Firm Overview:**
Womble Carlyle Sandridge & Rice, LLP is a full-service business law firm serving regional, national and international clients in sectors that include financial services, technology, life sciences, health care, government, transportation, energy and manufacturing.

**Main Areas of Practice:**

**Complex Litigation:**
204 attorneys, including 91 partners
National litigation practice offers deep bench strength in complex commercial, mass tort product liability, trade secrets, intellectual property, securities and white collar defense matters, and full suite of litigation support services through Case Management Facility, BullDox and FirmLogic teams.
- Secured complete defense verdict for R. J. Reynolds Tobacco Company in landmark health care cost recovery case brought by 37 hospitals in Missouri state court
- Represented German and US manufacturers in claim against US distributor in international arbitration in Frankfurt and won award collected in US under New York Convention
- Acted as lead counsel in connection with regulatory and governmental investigations into Duke Energy Corp
- Represented owners and operators of hazardous waste facility in class actions, and dozens of personal injury, property damage and economic loss claims that arose out of explosion and fire at facility

**Contact:** Keith A Clinard  **Tel:** 336 721 3631
**Email:** kclinard@wcsr.com
**Contact:** James P Cooney, III  **Tel:** 704 331 4980
**Email:** jcooney@wcsr.com

**Capital Markets:**
34 attorneys, including 25 partners
Womble Carlyle's Finance, Capital Markets and Financial Institutions practices represent domestic and foreign financial institutions, investors, borrowers, issuers, governmental entities and other providers and servicers of debt capital and financial services. Womble Carlyle represents clients on tax credit and regulatory compliance issues, negotiating and structuring incentives, and public finance matters.
Womble Carlyle has handled multistate, multilender and multicurrency secured and unsecured financing transactions, public finance projects, third-party credit arrangements, real estate finance, convertible debt, subordinated debt and mezzanine financings, tax-advantaged financings, off-balance sheet financings, letters of credit, structured finance, asset-based financings and public/private debt offerings.

**Contact:** Christopher E Leon  **Tel:** 336 721 3518
**Email:** cleon@wcsr.com

**Corporate & Securities:**
55 attorneys, including 34 partners
Practice includes mergers and acquisitions, private equity and venture capital, securities offerings and securities regulation, fiduciary obligations and rights of directors and officers, company formation and syndication and business contract negotiations.
- Represented Transcend Services, Inc. in its sale to Nuance Communications, Inc. for approximately $300 million
- Represented Endochoice, Inc. in its merger with Peer Medical, Inc. and related investment of $43 million in Series A Preferred Membership Units by Sequoia Capital and other investors to fund projected growth of combined company
- Represented NCR Corporation in acquisition of Radiant Systems, Inc. in amount of $1.2 billion

**Contact:** Jeffrey C Howland  **Tel:** 336 721 3516
**Email:** jhowland@wcsr.com

**Intellectual Property:**
93 attorneys and agents, including 51 partners
Practice includes all aspects of domestic and foreign intellectual property law, including patent, trademark and copyright procurement, counseling and litigation, trade secrets, IP licensing, technology transfer, IP monetization, and data security/privacy. Bench strength includes:
- IP Protection and Commercialization Strategy, IP Due Diligence and Consulting
- Patent Portfolio Management: Software / Electrical; Chemical / Pharmaceutical / Biotechnology; and Mechanical Arts
- Patent Reexamination and Interference
- Brand Strategy and Trademark Protection and Registration
- Promotions and Marketing Arrangements and Regulatory Compliance
- Complex IP Licensing and Technology Transactions

**Contact:** James F Vaughan  **Tel:** 404 962 7528
**Email:** jfvaughan@wcsr.com
**Contact:** M Christopher Bolen  **Tel:** 919 484 2391
**Email:** cbolen@wcsr.com

## PRACTICE AREAS
Admiralty & Maritime
Antitrust, Regulatory & Government Affairs
Bankruptcy & Creditor's Rights
Business Litigation
Capital Markets
Construction
Corporate & Securities
Employee Benefits
Environmental, Energy & Toxic Tort
Health Care
Intellectual Property
Labor & Employment
Product Liability Litigation
Real Estate
Tax, Trusts & Estates

## OFFICES
NORTH CAROLINA

**WINSTON-SALEM (HQ):** One West Fourth Street, NC 27101
Tel: 336 721 3600  Fax: 336 721 3660

**CHARLOTTE:** Tel: 704 331 4900  Fax: 704 331 4955

**GREENSBORO:** Tel: 336 574 8030  Fax: 336 574 4520

**RALEIGH:** Tel: 919 755-2100  Fax: 919 755 2150

**RESEARCH TRIANGLE PARK:** Tel: 919 484 2300
Fax: 919 484 2340

Other office locations: Atlanta; Charleston, Columbia and Greenville, South Carolina; Silicon Valley, California; Tysons Corner, Virginia; Washington, DC; Baltimore, Maryland; Wilmington, Delaware.

**Real Estate:**
48 attorneys, including 25 partners
Represent corporate end-users, developers, builders and lending institutions in the financing, acquisition, entitlement, development, leasing, and disposition of their real property assets, including:
- Land Assemblages and Mixed-use Developments
- Major Office Buildings and Office Parks
- Shopping Malls / Centers, Hotels and Resorts
- Health Care Facilities
- Condominiums and Multifamily Housing Projects

**Contact:** Kenneth W Logwood  **Tel:** 202 857 4410
**Email:** klogwood@wcsr.com

**International Work:**
Practice includes advising on business acquisitions and ventures, intellectual property, sales and distribution arrangements and dispute resolution involving international arbitration, mediation and litigation. Through Lex Mundi, world's largest association of independent law firms, Womble Carlyle is equipped to provide solutions anywhere in the world.

*Any result the lawyer or law firm may have achieved on behalf of clients in other matters does not necessarily indicate similar results can be obtained for other clients.*

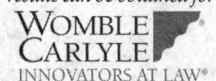

SASKATCHEWAN MANITOBA

Williston Minot

Grand Forks

**NORTH DAKOTA**

Dickinson

**Bismarck** Jamestown

SOUTH DAKOTA

Watertown

## How lawyers are ranked

Every year we carry out thousands of in-depth interviews with clients in order to assess the reputations and expertise of business lawyers worldwide. The qualities we look for (and which determine rankings) include technical legal ability, professional conduct, client service, commercial awareness/astuteness, diligence, commitment, and other qualities most valued by the client. For details of our research team, see p.5.

# BANKRUPTCY/RESTRUCTURING

Commentary about individuals can be found under their firm's paragraph. If the firm has no paragraph (is not ranked) look at Other Notable Practitioners.

**Bankruptcy/Restructuring**

**Leading Firms**

**Band 1**
Anderson, Bottrell, Sanden & Thompson
Olson & Burns PC
Serkland Law Firm, PC
Vogel Law Firm
Zimney Foster PC

**Leading Individuals**

**Star individuals**

| Olson Richard | Olson & Burns PC |
|---|---|

**Band 1**

| Bottrell Lowell | Anderson, Bottrell, Sanden & Thompson |
|---|---|
| Brakke Jon | Vogel Law Firm |
| Foster John S | Zimney Foster PC |
| Johnson David L | McNair, Larson & Carlson Ltd (ONP)† |
| Minch Roger J | Serkland Law Firm, PC |

**Band 2**

| Gust Michael | Anderson, Bottrell, Sanden & Thompson |
|---|---|
| Kennedy Tracy | Zimney Foster PC |

†ONP = Other Notable Practitioner
Alphabetical order within each band. Band 1 is the highest.

## Band 1

### Anderson, Bottrell, Sanden & Thompson

**THE FIRM** This highly respected Fargo-based firm maintains a sterling position in the bankruptcy and restructuring field, and represents all manner of creditors, debtors and trustees.

**KEY INDIVIDUALS Lowell Bottrell** *"does an excellent job"* across a range of creditor and debtor representations. **Michael Gust** has a broad-ranging general practice, but earns most praise for his creditor and debtor assignments.

### Olson & Burns PC

**THE FIRM** With offices in Kenmare and Minot, Olson & Burns is best known for its representation of financial institutions in the region. The group is therefore considered an excellent first choice for lender-side assignments in distressed situations.

**KEY INDIVIDUALS Richard Olson** *"has an excellent reputation"* as one of the state's best experts in defending creditors' rights.

### Serkland Law Firm, PC

**THE FIRM** Serkland Law Firm maintains a prominent presence in North Dakota's bankruptcy and restructuring field. It handles all types of bankruptcy representation, and is particularly lauded for its roles on behalf of creditors and lenders. The group has been especially active in contentious bankruptcy proceedings of late.

**KEY INDIVIDUALS Roger Minch** wins superb praise from clients: *"He is very bright, very knowledgeable and very responsive to our needs,"* said one impressed interviewee. Like his team, Minch has been highly active in litigation, and is also commended for his creditors' rights expertise.

### Vogel Law Firm

**THE FIRM** Vogel earns a tremendous amount of praise for its expertise across an array of creditor and debtor representations, and particularly for the sheer number of experts available to clients. With teams operating out of Bismarck and Fargo, it handles complex bankruptcy, financial restructuring and liquidations.

**Sources say:** *"Vogel has far and away the most depth of any firm in North Dakota."*

**KEY INDIVIDUALS Jon Brakke** has a superb transactional and litigious practice, and is particularly recommended for his expertise in handling creditor and debtors matters, loans, and issues involving the agricultural sector.

**Sources say:** *"He is tenacious and goes all-out for his clients; he gets tremendous results."*

### Zimney Foster PC

**THE FIRM** This Grand Forks-based firm handles all manner of bankruptcy, restructuring, workout and liquidation matters, but is best known for its excellent handling of creditors' rights defense.

**KEY INDIVIDUALS John Foster's** all-compassing commercial practice is especially lauded in the bankruptcy field, and he is highly recommended as one of the *"best in the state"* for a range of creditor and debtor representations. **Tracy Kennedy** has a broad-ranging commercial and business law practice, as well as a sterling track record in representing creditors and debtors.

## Other Notable Practitioners

**David Johnson** of McNair, Larson & Carlson Ltd is highly recommended for his tremendous experience in the field, particularly in relation to the representation of Chapter 7 trustees and debtors.

# CORPORATE/COMMERCIAL

Commentary about individuals can be found under their firm's paragraph. If the firm has no paragraph (is not ranked) look at Other Notable Practitioners.

## Corporate/Commercial
### Leading Firms

**Band 1**
Fredrikson & Byron PA *
Vogel Law Firm
Zimney Foster PC

**Band 2**
Anderson, Bottrell, Sanden & Thompson
Conmy Feste Ltd
Nilles Law Firm
Olson & Burns PC
Tschider & Smith

### Leading Individuals

**Star individuals**

| Foster John S | Zimney Foster PC |
|---|---|

**Band 1**

| Bottrell Lowell | Anderson, Bottrell, Sanden & Thompson |
|---|---|
| Johnson Steven | Vogel Law Firm |
| Olson Richard | Olson & Burns PC |
| Selbo Gregory B | Nilles Law Firm |
| Smith Sean | Tschider & Smith |
| Strinden Jon E | Fredrikson & Byron PA |
| Thomas Michael | Conmy Feste Ltd |

**Band 2**

| Christensen Douglas | Pearson, Christensen & Clapp, (ONP)[†] |
|---|---|
| Flaten Allen J | Zimney Foster PC |
| Foss Marilyn | Sole Practitioner (ONP)[†] |
| Kennedy Tracy | Zimney Foster PC |
| McNeally Nola | Fredrikson & Byron PA |
| Schlossman William | Vogel Law Firm |
| Turman Joseph A | Turman & Lang Ltd (ONP)[†] |

\* Indicates firm / individual with profile.
[†]ONP = Other Notable Practitioner

## Band 1

### Fredrikson & Byron PA
**See profile on p.1584**

**THE FIRM** This firm is increasingly recognized for its corporate capabilities, and complements its Fargo-based team with a strong presence in Minnesota. Its practice covers all aspects of corporate and commercial matters, and works with clients from a range of sectors. Recent work includes handling a debt offering for BlackRidge Financial in order to increase funding for a company within the financial services arena. The team also worked with Leading Edge Angel Fund and Hi-Nergy Angel Fund on a variety of matters related to their investment opportunities.
**KEY INDIVIDUALS Jon Strinden** is highly regarded by clients as someone who *"provides excellent work for us in a number of commercial areas."* He offers leading expertise in M&A, and is highly experienced in angel fund formation. He mainly focuses on handling matters for privately held companies. **Nola McNeally** was recently promoted to partner, and focuses on a range of M&A, real estate and ven-

ture capital matters. She is commended by sources for her committed approach to service, with one client stating: *"She exhausts all resources necessary to help her clients make the best decisions possible for their business."*

### Vogel Law Firm

**THE FIRM** Vogel Law Firm maintains its reputation as a preeminent firm in North Dakota, and works with an impressive range of businesses in the area. Its highly experienced attorneys handle the full range of corporate and commercial matters, including debt restructuring, capital formation and real estate transactions. The team can also draw on support from the firm's lawyers in Minnesota.
**Sources say:** *"Its lawyers cover the full spectrum of legal services with a great deal of expertise and experience."*
**KEY INDIVIDUALS Steven Johnson** is highly respected by commentators for his expertise in an impressive range of commercial and corporate matters. He handles transactions, shareholder disputes and media law-related matters, and is praised for his *"smart and practical"* approach. **William Schlossman** is praised for his *"deep understanding of cooperative law, and expertise in complex transactions and contracts."* He is highly experienced in the transactional real estate space, and also handles a range of business organization and M&A work.

### Zimney Foster PC

**THE FIRM** This highly regarded firm continues to expand its already sizable strength in the corporate and commercial space, housing an impressive bench of lawyers in its Grand Forks office. Sources highlight its expertise in banking and bankruptcy matters, and its practitioners also offer significant experience in handling contract creation, M&A and corporate structuring.
**KEY INDIVIDUALS John Foster** can draw on extensive experience as a corporate/commercial attorney, and his notable expertise sees him recognized as a leading figure in this market. He also focuses on bankruptcy-related matters and business litigation. **Allen Flaten** is a new entry to the table, and handles a wide range of matters in his corporate/commercial practice. He has a focus on employment and bankruptcy law matters, and commercial litigation. **Tracy Kennedy** is praised for her experience in matters related to commercial transactions and litigation. She also handles a range of bankruptcy-related issues for clients.

## Band 2

### Anderson, Bottrell, Sanden & Thompson

**THE FIRM** The experienced practitioners at this respected firm maintain their strength in a wide range of corporate and commercial matters. The firm operates out of Fargo while attracting clients from a broader market, regularly acting for Minnesota-based businesses and Canadian companies. The broad-based practice covers all aspects of

commercial transactions, debt structuring and business organization.
**KEY INDIVIDUALS** Commentators are quick to praise **Lowell Bottrell** for his expertise in a broad range of bankruptcy and corporate matters. He is a highly respected member of the commercial Bar, and also offers experience in agricultural law and patent licensing and infringement in the plant seed arena.

### Conmy Feste Ltd

**THE FIRM** Conmy Feste is recognized for its longstanding experience in the corporate and commercial arena. Its highly regarded attorneys can draw on expertise in all manner of M&A to act for clients across a number a sectors in their key transactions.
**KEY INDIVIDUALS Michael Thomas** is commended for his *"great and diverse practice,"* and is an experienced M&A attorney. His clients also benefit from his expertise in estate planning, loan agreements and business formation.

### Nilles Law Firm

**THE FIRM** Nilles Law Firm operates out of Fargo and Williston, and extends its practice to Montana, Minnesota and South Dakota. The practice spans all areas of commercial and corporate matters, offering expertise in all aspects of business organization, transactions and contracts.
**KEY INDIVIDUALS Gregory Selbo** focuses on a range of business organization matters and transactions. He is also highly experienced in handling real estate and estate planning matters for clients. He is considered a leading practitioner in North Dakota, with one source noting: *"I have a great amount of respect for him, and for his abilities."*

### Olson & Burns PC

**THE FIRM** The experienced practitioners at this firm are noted for their expertise in working with financial institutions across a broad range of commercial matters. They continue to play a leading role in a raft of transactions on behalf of these clients, and also offer significant experience in more general business and estate planning matters. The firm's strength in energy-related work also remains a key selling point for clients.
**Sources say:** *"Their pedigree is great – they have always had successes and a high level of knowledge."*
**KEY INDIVIDUALS Richard Olson** is a highly regarded expert in the corporate and commercial field, and offers particular expertise in handling a wide range of matters for banks and other financial entities. He is praised as *"a great strategist who excels in drawing upon his great knowledge and interpretation, and weaving this into a nice solution."*

### Tschider & Smith

**THE FIRM** This Bismarck-based team handles a broad range of corporate and commercial matters for clients. Its attorneys are respected for their expertise in bankruptcy, estate planning and corporate transactions, among other areas of focus.

**KEY INDIVIDUALS Sean Smith** is respected for his experience in a wide range of corporate matters. He is also noted for his expertise in the real estate arena.

## Other Notable Practitioners

**Douglas Christensen** of Pearson, Christensen & Clapp, PLLP offers clients significant experience in an impressive range of commercial matters, handling litigation, succession planning, and matters related to business organization and tax with equal aplomb. Bismarck-based sole practitioner **Marilyn Foss** is highly experienced in handling

commercial and corporate matters for clients, and is particularly noted for her banking expertise. **Joseph Turman** of Turman & Lang Ltd offers expertise in estate planning, real estate and banking law-related matters, among others. His practice includes a focus on construction and commercial litigation, and he works with clients such as US Bank of Fargo and Harwood State Bank.

# LABOR & EMPLOYMENT

Commentary about individuals can be found under their firm's paragraph. If the firm has no paragraph (is not ranked) look at Other Notable Practitioners.

| Labor & Employment |  |
| --- | --- |
| **Leading Firms** | |
| **Band 1** | |
| Dorsey & Whitney LLP * | |
| Vogel Law Firm | |
| Zuger Kirmis & Smith | |
| **Band 2** | |
| Anderson, Bottrell, Sanden & Thompson | |
| Fredrikson & Byron PA * | |

| **Leading Individuals** | |
| --- | --- |
| **Star individuals** | |
| Herman Sarah Andrews | *Dorsey & Whitney LLP* |
| **Band 1** | |
| Albrecht Kristy L | *Fredrikson & Byron PA* |
| Edison-Smith Lisa | *Vogel Law Firm* |
| Thiem Rebecca | *Zuger Kirmis & Smith* |
| **Band 2** | |
| Donarski Michelle | *Anderson, Bottrell, Sanden & Thompson* |
| Thomas Benjamin | *Wold Johnson PC (ONP)†* |
| Ward Patrick | *Zuger Kirmis & Smith* |

\* *Indicates firm / individual with profile.*
†*ONP = Other Notable Practitioner*

## Band 1

### Dorsey & Whitney LLP
See profile on p.1583

**THE FIRM** This firm continues to be recognized as one of the leading labor and employment shops in North Dakota. The team is particularly noted for its handling of OFCCP and wage and hour matters, and is recognized for its litigation and arbitration expertise. An impressive client roster is drawn from a range of industry sectors, including energy, healthcare and financial services.

Sources say: *"We trust them and know that they have our best interests in mind at all times."*
**KEY INDIVIDUALS Sarah Andrews Herman** heads up the firm's Fargo office, and has an exceptional reputation as a labor and employment litigator. Market observers note that her *"depth of experience and practice is clearly such that she should be top of the rankings,"* while clients report that she is *"open, honest and willing to do whatever we need to ensure our ends are met."*

### Vogel Law Firm
**THE FIRM** This indigenous North Dakota firm offers a comprehensive coverage of the state, and is recognized for its consistently strong showing in the labor and employment sphere. The team has an impressive track record in discrimination cases and other areas of employment litigation, and also provides expertise in compliance counseling and labor union disputes.

Sources say: *"Vogel has far and away the most depth of any firm in North Dakota."*
**KEY INDIVIDUALS Lisa Edison-Smith** has a comprehensive practice encompassing all facets of labor and employment law, including race and age discrimination, and wage and hour disputes. Sources attest that *"her knowledge of employment law is unsurpassed."*

### Zuger Kirmis & Smith
**THE FIRM** This firm continues to be recognized as one of the state's leaders for labor and employment law disputes. The team represents employers in the full range of matters, including sexual harassment cases, wage and hour disputes, and OSHA complaints. The group is also recommended for its compliance and training services to employers.

**KEY INDIVIDUALS Rebecca Thiem** is a *"good practitioner and litigator,"* say sources. She has a broad litigation practice with a focus on employment law disputes. **Patrick**

**Ward** is an experienced arbitrator and mediator, with expertise in labor and employment law matters. He is also an experienced trial lawyer at both state and federal level.

## Band 2

### Anderson, Bottrell, Sanden & Thompson
**THE FIRM** This firm is well placed to handle a wide range of labor and employment matters, including human resources counseling, ERISA matters, labor union disputes and discrimination litigation. The firm also offers employee benefits counseling to its clients.

**KEY INDIVIDUALS Michelle Donarski** is praised by market observers for her handling of labor and employment law and union arbitrations. She has particular expertise in EEOC matters.

### Fredrikson & Byron PA
See profile on p.1584

**THE FIRM** Fredrikson & Byron represents management clients in all aspects of employment law. The team is particularly noted for its excellence in human resources training and compliance counseling, and also offers noted expertise in discrimination litigation. Clients include MBI Energy Services, Discovery Benefits and TMI Hospitality.

**KEY INDIVIDUALS Kristy Albrecht** is recognized for her handling of a range of matters, including employment discrimination claims, workers' compensation claims and wrongful termination claims.

## Other Notable Practitioners

**Benjamin Thomas** of Wold Johnson PC is an experienced litigator with a focus on employment law disputes. Sources describe him as *"a balanced thinker"* and *"a good attorney."*

# LITIGATION

Commentary about individuals can be found under their firm's paragraph. If the firm has no paragraph (is not ranked) look at Other Notable Practitioners.

## Litigation: General Commercial
### Leading Firms

**Band 1**
Nilles Law Firm
Serkland Law Firm, PC
Vogel Law Firm
Zuger Kirmis & Smith

**Band 2**
Crowley Fleck PLLP *
Fredrikson & Byron PA *
Maring Williams Law Office PC

**Band 3**
Camrud, Maddock, Olson & Larson, Ltd.
McGee Hankla Backes & Dobrovolny P.C.
Pearce & Durick
Smith Bakke Porsborg & Schweigert

## Litigation: Energy & Natural Resources
### Leading Individuals

**Band 1**

| | | |
|---|---|---|
| Bender | Lawrence | Fredrikson & Byron PA |
| Morrison | John | Crowley Fleck PLLP * |
| Reierson | Kent | Crowley Fleck PLLP * |

## Band 1

### Nilles Law Firm

**THE FIRM** This firm has a long history in North Dakota, and its ten-strong litigation department is widely acknowledged as one of the strongest in the state. The team regularly appears before federal and state courts in connection with commercial litigation, banking and finance, and insolvency-related cases. Other areas of expertise include environmental litigation, insurance defense and alternative dispute resolution.

**KEY INDIVIDUALS** The highly regarded **Mark Hanson** earns praise for his broad-based commercial litigation practice, which includes significant trial and appellate experience. Sources highlight his expertise in contract disputes, and he also advises on insurance litigation and railroad law. Senior partner **Stephen Plambeck** specializes in product liability, professional liability, construction and insurance litigation, as well as general commercial matters. *"His overall knowledge of the law is extremely impressive,"* say sources. **William Harrie** is recommended for his focus on insurance defense work, and regularly advises on insurance coverage disputes, as well as tort and personal injury matters and third-party liability claims.

### Serkland Law Firm, PC

**THE FIRM** This Fargo-based firm operates a high-level litigation practice, with a focus on bankruptcy and restructuring as well as insurance litigation and personal injury law. The team also represents both plaintiffs and defen-

## Litigation: General Commercial
### Senior Statesmen

**Senior Statesmen: distinguished older partners**

| | | |
|---|---|---|
| Durick | Patrick | Pearce & Durick |
| Kapsner | John | Vogel Law Firm |
| Marcil | Jack G | Serkland Law Firm, PC |

### Leading Individuals

**Star individuals**

| | | |
|---|---|---|
| McLean | Ronald | Serkland Law Firm, PC |

**Band 1**

| | | |
|---|---|---|
| Bakke | Randall J | Smith Bakke Porsborg & Schweigert |
| Dunn | Daniel J | Maring Williams Law Office PC |
| Haggart | Todd | Vogel Law Firm |
| Hanson | Mark R | Nilles Law Firm |
| Hill | James S | Zuger Kirmis & Smith |
| Kirmis | Lyle W | Zuger Kirmis & Smith |
| Maring | David | Maring Williams Law Office PC |
| McGee II | Richard H | McGee Hankla Backes & Dobrovolny P.C. |
| Plambeck | Stephen | Nilles Law Firm |
| Storslee | Steven | Storslee Law Firm (ONP)[†] |
| Thiem | Rebecca | Zuger Kirmis & Smith |
| Zimmerman | Todd E | Fredrikson & Byron PA |

**Band 2**

| | | |
|---|---|---|
| Boschee | Larry | Pearce & Durick |
| Brust | Kim | Conmy Feste Ltd (ONP)[†] |
| Herman | Sarah Andrews | Dorsey & Whitney LLP (ONP)[†] |
| Porsborg | Scott | Smith Bakke Porsborg & Schweigert |

**Band 3**

| | | |
|---|---|---|
| Beehler | Brad | Morley Law Firm Ltd (ONP)[†] |
| Harrie | William | Nilles Law Firm |
| Lillehaug | Duane A. | Maring Williams Law Office PC |
| Norgard | Tami | Vogel Law Firm |
| Vendsel | Jason R | McGee Hankla Backes & Dobrovolny P.C. |
| Vogel | Mart Daniel | Vogel Law Firm |
| Weir Jr. | Pat | Vogel Law Firm |
| Wetch Jr | Joseph A | Serkland Law Firm, PC |
| Williams | Michael | Maring Williams Law Office PC |

**Up-and-coming individuals**

| | | |
|---|---|---|
| Pelham | Zachary | Pearce & Durick |

dants in national class action cases relating to a wide range of matters, including employment, securities fraud, mass torts and environmental torts, among others.

**KEY INDIVIDUALS Jack Marcil** is *"a very skilled litigator"* with *"a world of experience,"* according to interviewees. Formerly the assistant Attorney General for the State of North Dakota, he is now best known for his work in arbitration and mediation. Star individual **Ronald McLean** is *"the go-to guy in the state"* for insurance defense and business litigation. Additionally, his experience encompasses oil and gas disputes, class actions, product liability and employment law. **Joseph Wetch** has a strong track record

## Litigation: Medical Malpractice Defense
### Senior Statesmen

**Senior Statesmen: distinguished older partners**

| | | |
|---|---|---|
| Maddock | Patrick J | Camrud, Maddock, Olson & Larson, Ltd. |

### Leading Individuals

**Band 1**

| | | |
|---|---|---|
| Lord | Angela | Vogel Law Firm |
| Schreiner | Lance D | Zuger Kirmis & Smith |
| Waller | Michael | Crowley Fleck PLLP * |

**Band 2**

| | | |
|---|---|---|
| Hanson | Randall S | Camrud, Maddock, Olson & Larson, Ltd. |
| Udland | Robert J | Vogel Law Firm |

\* Indicates firm / individual with profile.
[†] ONP = Other Notable Practitioner

in advising on negligence and personal injury matters. He also handles oil and gas cases.

### Vogel Law Firm

**THE FIRM** This leading law firm is a strong regional player in litigation. With offices in Fargo, Bismarck and Williston, it is well positioned to advise on cases across the state and further afield. Its clients range from family-owned businesses to multinational corporations, utilities, and oil and gas exploration companies. Recent work includes a range of real estate-related disputes, as well as oilfield and truck accident litigation.

**KEY INDIVIDUALS John Kapsner** is a *"seasoned veteran"* of the North Dakota litigation Bar. He maintains an active practice, and is well known for his long experience of commercial litigation and healthcare law. **Todd Haggart** is an experienced trial lawyer with significant expertise in business dispute resolution, oil and gas litigation and insurance law. He also advises on arbitration and has served as a neutral mediator in construction cases. **Angela Lord** *"is one of the best litigators in the state,"* sources enthuse. She focuses on healthcare and medical malpractice litigation, and market commentators agree she is *"a very skilled practitioner in this field."* **Robert Udland** is recognized for his work on employment and healthcare cases, including medical malpractice defense. He advises on both trial and regulatory matters. *"Solid practitioner"* **Tami Norgard** is rated for her involvement in energy-related cases, including oil and gas and water litigation. **Mart Daniel Vogel** is a *"big-time player"* with a broad practice covering energy, insurance, transportation and product liability litigation. **Pat Weir** is highly regarded for his plaintiff-side wrongful death and personal injury practice. *"He is a very skilled litigator,"* say sources.

### Zuger Kirmis & Smith

**THE FIRM** Though best known for its insurance defense practice, this top litigation firm advises on a wide range of cases, and has comprehensive expertise in areas including bankruptcy, labor and employment, Indian law and tribal jurisdiction. Of late, the team has experienced an uptick in both professional malpractice defense work and oil and gas-related litigation.

**KEY INDIVIDUALS** The experienced **James Hill** is highly recommended for his expertise in legal and medical malpractice litigation. He also handles insurance defense and civil litigation. **Lyle Kirmis** advises on commercial and construction litigation and non-medical malpractice claims. He has also been increasingly active on oil and gas cases. **Lance Schreiner** is well known for his vibrant health law litigation practice, and is widely acknowledged as a leader in this area. **Rebecca Thiem** has a strong presence in the business litigation arena. Sources say: *"Her strong suit is her ability to identify significant issues in the case. She is very well prepared and organized in directing efforts towards those specific issues."*

## Band 2

### Crowley Fleck PLLP
See profile on p.1656

**THE FIRM** Interviewees are quick to highlight this firm's strength in oil and gas litigation in North Dakota. The firm also handles a large market share of construction disputes and medical malpractice cases, and has additional expertise in such areas as professional and product liability, class actions, employment, and title law and litigation. Sources say: *"A very savvy and strong firm."*

**KEY INDIVIDUALS John Morrison** (see p.2055) is recognized by peers for his work on behalf of oil companies. He advises on both litigation and regulatory matters, appearing before such bodies as the North Dakota Industrial Commission and the Bureau of Land Management. **Kent Reierson** (see p.2055) advises on oil and gas litigation and municipal law. *"He is very good at this type of work,"* say sources. **Michael Waller** (see p.2055) is best known for his civil litigation practice. He specializes in medical and dental malpractice claims, and has additional expertise in other matters affecting the healthcare industry.

### Fredrikson & Byron PA
See profile on p.1584

**THE FIRM** This team continues to solidify its presence on the North Dakota litigation scene. The scope of its work is diverse, and the firm's experience encompasses class action claims, alternative dispute resolution, and construction and transportation litigation, in addition to a range of general business matters. Recent highlights include successfully defending Cavendish Farms against a $1 million claim alleging breach of contract and antitrust violations. Sources say: *"A very solid office."*

**KEY INDIVIDUALS Lawrence Bender** is *"one of the highest performers of the whole firm,"* according to interviewees. As the head of the firm's Bismarck office, he focuses prima-

rily on oil and gas-related work. **Todd Zimmerman** *"is the consummate business litigator. He is intelligent, has great analytical skills and understands his clients' business needs."* One source enthused: *"He is a soft-spoken but effective advocate. He is very organized and professional with counsel and in court."*

### Maring Williams Law Office PC

**THE FIRM** This four-strong team specializes in personal injury law, with a focus on plaintiff-side representation. Its expertise covers motor vehicle accidents, farm and construction accidents, and dangerous buildings, as well as wrongful death, commercial litigation and general insurance litigation.

**KEY INDIVIDUALS Daniel Dunn** is a *"highly professional and methodical lawyer,"* say sources. He represents claimants in product liability, business and personal injury lawsuits. **David Maring** is one of the firm's resident specialists in wrongful death, and market commentators agree that he is *"one of the leaders in this market – he is a fantastic litigator."* **Duane Lillehaug** has a longstanding presence in the field of personal injury and insurance coverage litigation. He also advises on employment law. **Michael Williams** specializes in cases involving the rights of people with disabilities. *"I think the world of him,"* said one peer.

## Band 3

### Camrud, Maddock, Olson & Larson, Ltd.

**THE FIRM** Based in Grand Folks, this team undertakes a wide range of litigation defense work, from banking law and commercial cases to personal injury, professional negligence and criminal law matters. The firm also advises on alternative dispute resolution, with a focus on mediation.

**KEY INDIVIDUALS Patrick Maddock** is well regarded for his contributions to the field of legal and medical malpractice defense. He also advises on personal injury, product liability and other tort litigation. **Randall Hanson**'s broad experience encompasses medical malpractice, insurance coverage and pharmaceutical litigation, as well as appellate law.

### McGee Hankla Backes & Dobrovolny P.C.

**THE FIRM** This well-established full-service firm is home to a well-respected litigation department, which advises on all manner of dispute resolution. Located in Minot, the team handles farm accident claims, wrongful death and personal injury litigation, as well as construction and commercial cases, subrogation and insurance defense.

**KEY INDIVIDUALS Richard McGee** is a *"seasoned veteran"* in the litigation arena. His practice covers tort litigation, medical malpractice and product liability litigation. **Jason Vendsel** is recognized for his increasing visibility on the North Dakota litigation scene. He is singled out for his expertise in oil and gas litigation, with one source praising him as *"one of the best in the state."*

### Pearce & Durick

**THE FIRM** This Bismarck-based group concentrates on complex civil litigation. It acts for a range of clients, from private individuals to Fortune 500 companies. The team is best known for its expertise in product liability litigation, oil and gas dispute resolution, and insurance defense.

**KEY INDIVIDUALS** The experienced **Patrick Durick** has a long history advising on product liability litigation in North Dakota and throughout the North and Southwestern USA. Of late, his practice has also expanded to include mineral ownership disputes. Hard-working **Larry Boschee** has a strong profile in energy and natural resources litigation. His practice also covers product liability defense and general business matters. **Zachary Pelham** is an up-and-coming partner at the firm, whose expertise includes product liability litigation, insurance defense and employment law.

### Smith Bakke Porsborg & Schweigert

**THE FIRM** This firm is best known for its personal injury law practice and for its involvement in both defense and plaintiff-side work. Other areas of service include bankruptcy, real estate and general business litigation, as well as government and municipal liability.

**KEY INDIVIDUALS** Civil trial specialist **Randall Bakke** *"has had some great successes,"* say interviewees. He advises on wrongful death, fire and property damage, employment and commercial litigation, among other areas of expertise. *"He is effective and does a good job for his clients,"* say sources. The talented **Scott Porsborg** is *"very well organized and professional"* in his work for defendants. He specializes in civil rights litigation and governmental liability.

### Other Notable Practitioners

**Steven Storslee** of Storslee Law Firm is widely acknowledged as a leader in the area of insurance defense. His practice also covers product liability and property damage subrogation. Rising through the ranks, **Kim Brust** of Conmy Feste Ltd wins praise for his personal injury practice. Sources say: *"He is well respected in the North Dakota community – he is a very solid litigator and advocate for clients."* **Sarah Andrews Herman** of Dorsey & Whitney LLP has a strong profile for her employment litigation practice, with additional expertise in areas such as transportation law, product liability and contentious healthcare matters. One client enthused: *"Working with Sarah gives us a sense of security – she is open, honest and willing to do whatever we need to ensure our needs are met."* **Brad Beehler** of Morley Law Firm Ltd has a rising profile for litigation in North Dakota. His areas of expertise include municipal defense, product and premises liability litigation, and construction law.

# REAL ESTATE

Commentary about individuals can be found under their firm's paragraph. If the firm has no paragraph (is not ranked) look at Other Notable Practitioners.

| Real Estate | |
|---|---|
| **Leading Firms** | |
| **Band 1** | |
| Conmy Feste Ltd | |
| Kennelly & O'Keeffe Attorneys | |
| Shaft, Reis & Shaft Ltd | |
| Vogel Law Firm | |

| Leading Individuals | |
|---|---|
| **Band 1** | |
| Bueide Daniel | *Vogel Law Firm* |
| Hubbard Paul | *Conmy Feste Ltd* |
| Stroup Robert L | *Kennelly & O'Keeffe Attorneys* |
| Wanner David | *Ohnstad Twichell PC (ONP)[†]* |
| **Band 2** | |
| Rindy Dean | *Kennelly & O'Keeffe Attorneys* |
| Shaft Grant | *Shaft, Reis & Shaft Ltd* |
| Smith Sean | *Tschider & Smith (ONP)[†]* |
| Thompson Greg | *Anderson, Bottrell, Sanden (ONP)[†]* |

[†]*ONP = Other Notable Practitioner*
*Alphabetical order within each band. Band 1 is the highest.*

## Band 1

### Conmy Feste Ltd
**THE FIRM** Peers identify this Fargo firm as a leader in the real estate market. The team regularly handles the full range financing matters for lenders, as well as acting for owners and developments. It also has capability in title insurance work and real estate foreclosures.
**KEY INDIVIDUALS Paul Hubbard** is known to have *"a great reputation in the state for real estate work."* He represents lenders and developers in a variety of real estate issues.

### Kennelly & O'Keeffe Attorneys
**THE FIRM** This firm has had a strong year with heavy involvement in a series of refinancing and redevelopment matters. Clients also praise the team's ability to handle significant title issues, and are impressed with the attorneys' passionate approach to meeting their needs.
**KEY INDIVIDUALS** Real estate specialist **Robert Stroup** has deep experience in the field. He focuses on all areas of real estate and the full range of related business issues on behalf of his clients. **Dean Rindy** is a favorite among clients for his strength in real estate title insurance issues. He offers clients extensive expertise in the purchase, sale and trade of property.

### Shaft, Reis & Shaft Ltd
**THE FIRM** This firm is known as a leader in the Grand Forks area and has a broad real estate offering. The team handles a range of real estate issues relating to both commercial and residential properties, and also offers expertise in title insurance matters.

**KEY INDIVIDUALS** Sources praise **Grant Shaft** as a strong player in the local real estate market, with particular knowledge and experience in title insurance.

### Vogel Law Firm
**THE FIRM** Clients are quick to praise this North Dakota staple, particularly its depth and expertise in the full variety of real estate issues. The group is frequently involved in major real estate development projects, and is able to turn its hand to transactional work as well as related litigation.
**KEY INDIVIDUALS** According to clients, **Daniel Bueide** *"is the go-to lawyer on commercial real estate deals."* He is known for his extensive expertise in sophisticated transactional real estate.

### Other Notable Practitioners
**David Wanner** of Ohnstad Twichell PC has a broad practice covering estate planning and probate work, as well as deep expertise in all aspects of real estate law. Experienced practitioner **Greg Thompson** of Anderson, Bottrell, Sanden & Thompson has a healthy reputation for acting for property owners on eviction matters and other landlord-tenant issues. **Sean Smith** of Tschider & Smith enters the rankings, having been recognized as an *"incredibly highly qualified individual"* when it comes to real estate work in North Dakota.

# Leaders' Profiles in North Dakota

**MORRISON, John**
Crowley Fleck PLLP, Bismarck
701 223 6585
jmorrison@crowleyfleck.com
*Featured in Litigation (North Dakota)*
**Practice Areas:** Natural resources, public utilities, commercial law.
**Professional Memberships:** Interstate Oil and Gas Compact Committee (North Dakota representative); American Bar Association; North Dakota State Bar Association.
**Career:** Bachelor of Arts from Mary College and Juris Doctorate for the University of North Dakota School of Law. AV Preeminent, Martindale-Hubbell; Best Lawyers since 1995; Super Lawyers since 2011.
**Publications:** Co-author of 'Lobbing, PAC's and Campaign Finance' West 1996-2012, author of numerous articles printed in special and annual institutes of the Rocky Mountain Mineral Law Foundation.

**REIERSON, Kent**
Crowley Fleck PLLP, Williston
701 572 2200
kreierson@crowleyfleck.com
*Featured in Litigation (North Dakota)*
**Practice Areas:** Litigation related to oil and gas matters, including all phases form defending and prosecuting title issues, defending damage claims and defense of serious injury and death claims arising from oil field and industrial activities. Experienced in working with government relations on a local and state level for development projects.
**Professional Memberships:** Board certified Civil Trial Advocate by the National Board of Trial Advocates.
**Career:** Admitted ND 1980. AV rated Martindale-Hubble.
**Personal:** Born 1954, JD and MPA University of North Dakota, 1980.

**WALLER, Michael**
Crowley Fleck PLLP, Bismarck
701 223 6585
mwaller@crowleyfleck.com
*Featured in Litigation (North Dakota)*
**Practice Areas:** Defense of medical malpractice and medical products claims. Also defends personal injury and wrongful death claims.
**Professional Memberships:** Defense Research Institute; State Bar Associations of North Dakota and Montana; American Bar Association; North Dakota Defense Lawyers Association
**Career:** Admitted to bar, 1985, Montana; 1986 US District Court, District of Montana; 1987, US Court of Appeals, Eighth Circuit; 1991, North Dakota and US District Court, District of North Dakota
**Personal:** Born October 22, 1957. Graduated University of Idaho College of Law (cum laude) - 1985. Leisure interests include golf, water skiing, hunting, fishing and reading.

## How lawyers are ranked

Every year we carry out thousands of in-depth interviews with clients in order to assess the reputations and expertise of business lawyers worldwide. The qualities we look for (and which determine rankings) include technical legal ability, professional conduct, client service, commercial awareness/astuteness, diligence, commitment, and other qualities most valued by the client. For details of our research team, see p.5.

**Contents:**

## BANKING & FINANCE

Commentary about individuals can be found under their firm's paragraph. If the firm has no paragraph (is not ranked) look at Other Notable Practitioners.

### Banking & Finance
### Leading Firms

**Band 1**
Jones Day
Squire Sanders (US) LLP *
Thompson Hine LLP *

**Band 2**
Calfee, Halter & Griswold LLP *
Porter Wright Morris & Arthur LLP *
Vorys, Sater, Seymour and Pease LLP *

**Band 3**
Benesch, Friedlander, Coplan & Aronoff LLP *
Frost Brown Todd LLC *
Ice Miller LLP
Kegler, Brown, Hill & Ritter *
McDonald Hopkins LLC
Taft Stettinius & Hollister LLP *

### Banking & Finance
### Leading Individuals

| Band 1 | |
|---|---|
| Barragate Brett | Jones Day * |
| Cicarella Thomas | Calfee, Halter & Griswold LLP * |
| Guinn Guy | Squire Sanders (US) LLP * |
| Mills Jr Osborne | Squire Sanders (US) LLP * |
| Miraldi Leslee W | Thompson Hine LLP * |
| Rawson Rachel | Jones Day |

| Band 2 | |
|---|---|
| Bedree Melvin | Vorys, Sater, Seymour and Pease LLP * |
| Grady Timothy | Porter Wright Morris & Arthur LLP * |
| Handlan Allen | Kegler, Brown, Hill & Ritter |
| Kallas Hani R | Vorys, Sater, Seymour and Pease LLP * |
| Kirchick Ross | Benesch, Friedlander, Coplan & Aronoff * |
| Rush Jeffery | Frost Brown Todd LLC * |

| Band 3 | |
|---|---|
| Barnhart Richard A | Ice Miller LLP |
| Beus Karl | Calfee, Halter & Griswold LLP * |
| Gates Martin S | Jones Day * |
| Johnston Gordon | Bricker & Eckler LLP (ONP) † |
| Kim Eduardo | Thompson Hine LLP * |
| Mauer Kimberly K | Frost Brown Todd LLC * |
| Schloemer Jeffrey S | Taft Stettinius & Hollister LLP * |
| Stief James | McDonald Hopkins LLC |
| Teplitzky Ronald J | Singerman, Mills, Desberg (ONP) † |
| Weimer John | Vorys, Sater, Seymour and Pease LLP * |

| Up-and-coming individuals | |
|---|---|
| Bojko Andrew | Porter Wright Morris & Arthur LLP * |
| Nazette Adam R | Thompson Hine LLP * |

| Associates to watch | |
|---|---|
| Hult Laura | Ice Miller LLP |

* Indicates firm / individual with profile.
† ONP = Other Notable Practitioner

## Band 1

### Jones Day
See profile on p.919

**THE FIRM** This international firm is widely acknowledged as a market leader for banking in Ohio. Its profile in Cleveland is complemented by its reputation nationwide, and the team stands out for its strength acting for borrowers and on private equity transactions. In highlights, it advised PolyOne on its $486 million acquisition of ColorMatrix Group. The team also handles lender-side work, acting for an enviable roster of financial institution clients, including KeyCorp, Bank of America and JPMorgan Chase.

**Sources say:** "*The level of service we have received from Jones Day has been superb, encompassing excellent legal advice, extreme responsiveness, unsurpassed attention to detail and, most importantly, the utmost attention to our needs and concerns.*" "*A flourishing borrower-side practice.*"

**KEY INDIVIDUALS Brett Barragate** (see p.2090) divides his time between Ohio and New York, and is admitted to practice in both jurisdictions. He is the joint leader of the firm's global banking and finance department, and regularly undertakes high-profile work. He led on the ColorMatrix transaction for PolyOne, and is sought out for his "*calm and unflappable*" manner and extensive financing experience. One source enthused: "*He is a phenomenal finance lawyer.*" **Rachel Rawson** is also admitted in New York and Ohio. She is best known for her deft legal and commercial skills in borrower work, in particular. Sources admire her keen eye for what is important in a deal, and describe her as "*very pleasant and knowledgeable.*" She acted for Atlas Resource Partners on its acquisition of $190 million energy reserves from Carrizo Oil & Gas. **Marty Gates** (see p.2097) is singled out for his expertise in asset-based lending, and recently advised JPMorgan Chase on a number of loan matters involving manufacturing and private equity interests.

### Squire Sanders (US) LLP
See profile on p.2129

**THE FIRM** This Cleveland-based practice is involved in substantial work for major household names in the banking world, including Key Bank, Fifth Third Bank and HSBC. The firm continues to grow its practice across the state, and is highly active in both syndicated and non-syndicated asset-based finance, leveraged capital finance and capital market note placements. It also advises on project finance and real estate loan work. The firm's international footprint makes it a strong choice for national and cross-border transactions. Notably, it assisted HCC Insurance Holdings with a restatement of its credit facility, involving the alignment of the US and UK-governed senior syndicate facilities terms.

**Sources say:** "*Leaders in the field.*"

**KEY INDIVIDUALS Guy Guinn** (see p.2098) co-heads the firm's worldwide banking and finance practice. He advises on high-yield and structured bank credit facilities, and is now admitted to practice in New York. Clients seek out his services on account of his practical and clear advice, remarking: "*He is very pragmatic in approach and* *explains the options clearly as well as the likely consequences of each path.* **Osborne Mills** (see p.2107) is one of the most highly respected lawyers in the state. His practice includes acting on substantial loan facilities and debtor-creditor work, and he recently advised Lassonde Industries on a $230 million term financing for the acquisition of Clement Pappas. He applies his flexible yet methodical approach to advise on both the borrower and bank sides. Sources agree he is a reliable choice for work that is *"thorough and of high quality,"* and say he is *"easily a top practitioner in Ohio."*

### Thompson Hine LLP
See profile on p.2131

**THE FIRM** This firm is distinguished in the Cleveland market for its extensive experience acting on the lender side, and is well known for its high-level work for institutional clients such as KeyBank. Interviewees are quick to highlight the team's high-quality service and deep experience in both secured and unsecured financings as strong assets for the practice. Its other high-end clients include Bank of America and JPMorgan Chase.

**Sources say:** *"A market leader in this area – they stand out for the depth of their experience, and ability to handle complex and simple transactions."*

**KEY INDIVIDUALS Leslee Miraldi** (see p.2107) is a key partner in the firm's dedicated commercial and public finance department. Clients laud her pragmatic and effective negotiation style, describing her as *"congenial, yet firm. She is focused and accountable, and has the ability to avoid games of 'one-upmanship' and to focus on the task at hand."* She is frequently engaged by KeyBank to advise on its numerous lending interests. **Eduardo Kim** (see p.2102) continues to develop his prowess in commercial lending, including advising on syndicated multiparty credit facilities. Sources say he is a pleasant professional to deal with. He is an increasingly popular choice for astute loan work for banking entities. **Adam Nazette** (see p.2108) was promoted to the partnership in 2012. He is described as *"very capable"* and *"very advanced technically"* in his work for banking clients. His clients include KeyBank.

### Band 2

### Calfee, Halter & Griswold LLP
See profile on p.2121

**THE FIRM** This firm is a highly respected name in Ohio for banking and finance work. With notable strength in Cleveland, the team is singled out for its representation of borrower clients. In highlights, it advised Applied Industrial Technologies on the refinancing of a senior unsecured revolving credit facility. Other key clients include FirstEnergy and American Greetings.

**Sources say:** *"They view each situation as an opportunity to develop a sound business strategy that can be executed and sustained successfully for the long-term gain of the client."*

**KEY INDIVIDUALS** Practice group chair **Thomas Cicarella** (see p.2092) is a longstanding and consistent feature of the Ohio banking and finance market. Sources

speak of his highly developed interpersonal skills, with one saying: *"I really like working with him – he is easy to work with and friendly."* Cicarella recently advised Invacare on a $525 million credit facility. The *"highly skilled"* **Karl Beus** (see p.2090) advised on the Applied Industrial Technologies matter. Sources speak of him as a *"very practical lawyer"* who continues to develop his name in this arena.

### Porter Wright Morris & Arthur LLP
See profile on p.2127

**THE FIRM** This firm has a strong profile for both borrower and lender representation in the Columbus market. It acts for big names including US Bank and American Eagle Outfitters. Work highlights include advising Huntington National Bank on a $46 million revolving credit facility to Stonehenge Capital Company.

**Sources say:** *"Practical, cost-effective counsel."* *"Talented professionals who speak business language."*

**KEY INDIVIDUALS Timothy Grady** (see p.2097) heads up the firm's banking and finance practice. He is lauded for his comprehensive knowledge and experience, and *"he knows all the ins and outs of banking and finance work, and can cut down to the important issues right away,"* say clients. **Andrew Bojko** (see p.2091) acted as lead partner on the Stonehenge Capital Company facility for Huntington National Bank. He is regarded as *"a good, solid attorney"* on account of his dedication to the task at hand. *"I appreciate his resolve to get the best possible solution,"* said one client.

### Vorys, Sater, Seymour and Pease LLP
See profile on p.2133

**THE FIRM** This firm is a regular feature on the banking and finance scene in Ohio. With offices in Cleveland, Cincinnati and Columbus, it is equally at home advising on either the lender or borrower side of transactions, and continues to grow its practice across the state. It acts for a wide range of household-name banking, manufacturing and retail clients, and has recently advised on derivatives matters and multimillion-dollar revolving credit facilities.

**Sources say:** *"They are very sophisticated attorneys."*

**KEY INDIVIDUALS Hani Kallas** (see p.2101) is a partner in the Cincinnati office, where he divides his time between commercial and real estate matters. *"He is pragmatic and smart, and focuses on getting the deal done,"* said one source, while others note his cooperative approach to deal-making, and that *"he works extremely well with opposing counsel."* **Melvin Bedree** (see p.2090) also practices out of Cincinnati, and frequently acts for lenders in areas such as mezzanine financing. According to sources, he is a *"very detail-oriented lawyer who is highly skilled in creditors' rights. He is very tenacious and always looks to represent his client in the strongest possible fashion."* **John Weimer** (see p.2117) heads up the firm's commercial finance practice from Columbus. Sources agree he is a cogent and effectual adviser, describing him as *"very practical and goal-oriented – it is easy to work with him and get a transaction consummated."* He recently advised a public company on negotiation for a revolving credit facility.

### Band 3

### Benesch, Friedlander, Coplan & Aronoff LLP
See profile on p.2120

**THE FIRM** Sources agree that this firm is a sound choice for counsel on the Ohio banking scene. It is commended for its cost-effective and accomplished service offering, and regularly advises regional banking clients on senior credit facilities, asset-based lending and syndicated financing deals, among other matters. Its client roster is impressive, and includes PNC Bank, Fifth Third Bank and Wells Fargo.

**Sources say:** *"Strong knowledge of middle market transactions at a reasonable price."*

**KEY INDIVIDUALS** Department head **Ross Kirchick** (see p.2102) counts a number of banks on his client list, as well as private equity entities. *"He is always professional, knowledgeable, and timely,"* according to highly satisfied interviewees.

### Frost Brown Todd LLC
See profile on p.1329

**THE FIRM** This firm operates a vibrant lending and commercial practice. With a strong core in Cincinnati, it acts for both lender and borrower clients on matters such as real estate finance, bond counseling and bank regulatory law. Key clients include entities from the insurance, healthcare and manufacturing sectors.

**KEY INDIVIDUALS** The experienced **Jeffery Rush** (see p.2111) maintains a notable profile on the Cincinnati scene. His skill set is broad, covering securitization, revolving credit and credit restructuring matters. **Kimberly Mauer** (see p.2106) divides her time between real estate and banking matters, and has made a strong name for herself in both areas. She also advises on New Markets Tax Credits, and on standard loan documentation and regulatory work.

### Ice Miller LLP

**THE FIRM** The Columbus arm of this regional firm is increasingly viewed as a top choice for corporate finance and banking work across the Midwest. Areas of expertise include mezzanine financing, loan restructuring, municipal finance, and senior and subordinated debt. The team is sought after by a number of banking and private equity clients, including Huntington National Bank, JPMorgan Chase and Stonehenge Partners.

**Sources say:** *"The firm has a strong culture to represent its clients in a very professional, customer-centric mode."*

**KEY INDIVIDUALS** The *"efficient and informed"* **Richard Barnhart** heads the banking and finance department in Ohio. Sources say he is *"hard-working and easily accessible,"* as well as *"extremely experienced and knowledgeable regarding any type of financing transaction."* **Laura Hult** is recognized as a highly skilled associate in the banking and finance group. Sources describe her as *"process-driven, organized and well versed on all aspects of the documentation."*

## Kegler, Brown, Hill & Ritter
See profile on p.2125

**THE FIRM** This local Ohio firm is well known for its prominence in the Columbus market. It acts for a broad client base, and its well-rounded skills make it an expedient adviser on both the lender and borrower sides of transactions. Key clients include WD Partners, Huntington National Bank and Wells Fargo.

**KEY INDIVIDUALS** Columbus-based firm director **Allen Handlan** heads the banking and commercial lending practice. His practice also includes associated real estate lending work. Sources describe him as *"a pro-business dealmaker who is very easy to work with."*

## McDonald Hopkins LLC

**THE FIRM** This firm is recognized for the quality of its banking and finance practice in Ohio. With offices in Cleveland and Columbus, it is a popular choice for mid-market, single bank, and asset-based lending work. The team advises its roster of global and national banking clients on significant revolving credit facilities, and on the trading of notes and warrants.

**KEY INDIVIDUALS** Cleveland-based **James Stief** is the lead firm member in the commercial finance department. Sources speak of him as a keen client advocate who *"has the deal in mind and does it well."* Global, national and merchant banks all feature prominently on his client list.

## Taft Stettinius & Hollister LLP
See profile on p.2130

**THE FIRM** This Cincinnati-based practice group is recognized for its strong regional relationships and cost-effective service. It continues to advise the likes of US Bank, Big Turtle Capital Partners and Federal Home Loan Bank of Cincinnati on a variety of secured lending matters.

**KEY INDIVIDUALS Jeffrey Schloemer** (see p.2112) cochairs the banking and finance practice from Cincinnati. He has longstanding relationships with a number of banks, who have come to rely on him for his *"high-quality work."* His client list includes US Bank, which he assists with real estate and other finance work.

### Other Notable Practitioners

**Ronald Teplitzky** of Singerman, Mills, Desberg & Kauntz Co LPA is acknowledged by sources as a proficient lawyer with a fine skill set in this arena. Based in Cleveland, his practice encompasses commercial lending, M&A and general business law. **Gordon Johnston** is a member of the creditors' rights and bankruptcy department at Bricker & Eckler LLP in Columbus. He is recommended for his expertise in distressed finance, and has a notable profile advising banks on midmarket, single-lender matters.

# BANKRUPTCY/RESTRUCTURING

Commentary about individuals can be found under their firm's paragraph. If the firm has no paragraph (is not ranked) look at Other Notable Practitioners.

## Bankruptcy/Restructuring
### Leading Firms

**Band 1**

Jones Day *
Squire Sanders (US) LLP *

**Band 2**

Baker & Hostetler LLP *
Dinsmore & Shohl LLP *
Frost Brown Todd LLC *
Hahn Loeser & Parks LLP *
McDonald Hopkins LLC
Thompson Hine LLP *
Vorys, Sater, Seymour and Pease LLP *

**Band 3**

Allen Kuehnle Stovall & Neuman LLP
Bricker & Eckler LLP
Calfee, Halter & Griswold LLP *
Ice Miller LLP
Keating Muething & Klekamp PLL *
Kegler, Brown, Hill & Ritter *
Porter Wright Morris & Arthur LLP *
Taft Stettinius & Hollister LLP *

## Band 1

### Jones Day
See profile on p.919

**THE FIRM** Jones Day receives high praise for its work on high-stakes matters in Ohio and further afield. Working primarily out of Cleveland, the team is well regarded nationwide for its expertise in matters such as restructuring and bankruptcy protection. It has a strong profile on the debtor side, where highlights saw the group advise on the widely reported Harry & David Chapter 11 filing, including the contentious termination of the company's

## Bankruptcy/Restructuring
### Leading Individuals

**Star individuals**

| | | |
|---|---|---|
| Heiman David G | Jones Day * | |
| Lepene Alan R | Thompson Hine LLP * | |
| Lerner Stephen D | Squire Sanders (US) LLP * | |

**Band 1**

| | |
|---|---|
| DeMarco Daniel A | Hahn Loeser & Parks LLP * |
| Gold Ronald | Frost Brown Todd LLC * |
| Hurley Timothy J | Taft Stettinius & Hollister LLP * |
| Hutchinson Jr Joseph F | Baker & Hostetler LLP * |
| Jackson Reginald W | Vorys, Sater, Seymour and Pease LLP * |
| Lennox Heather | Jones Day * |
| Lewis Kim Martin | Dinsmore & Shohl LLP |
| Meyer G Christopher | Squire Sanders (US) LLP * |
| Oscar Lawrence E | Hahn Loeser & Parks LLP * |
| Parobek Drew | Vorys, Sater, Seymour and Pease LLP * |
| Pigman Jack R | Porter Wright Morris & Arthur LLP * |
| Powers Victoria E | Ice Miller LLP |
| Riley Shawn | McDonald Hopkins LLC |

**Band 2**

| | |
|---|---|
| Allen Tom | Allen Kuehnle Stovall & Neuman LLP |
| Bash Brian A | Baker & Hostetler LLP * |
| Cavalieri Nick V | Bailey Cavalieri (ONP)† |
| Debbeler Michael | Graydon Head & Ritchey LLP (ONP)† |
| Gibbons M Colette | Ice Miller LLP |
| Goldman Matthew R | Baker & Hostetler LLP * |
| Irwin Kevin E | Keating Muething & Klekamp PLL * |
| Lawniczak James | Calfee, Halter & Griswold LLP * |
| Lutz Douglas L | Frost Brown Todd LLC * |
| Malloy Sean | McDonald Hopkins LLC |
| Marks Jeffrey A | Vorys, Sater, Seymour and Pease LLP * |
| Opincar Scott | McDonald Hopkins LLC |

| | |
|---|---|
| Robinson Tim J | Dinsmore & Shohl LLP |
| Sanker Robert G | Keating Muething & Klekamp PLL * |
| Solimine Louis F | Thompson Hine LLP * |

**Band 3**

| | |
|---|---|
| Folland Robert C | Thompson Hine LLP * |
| McClatchey Larry J | Kegler, Brown, Hill & Ritter |
| Oellermann Charles M | Jones Day * |
| Powar Lee | Hahn Loeser & Parks LLP * |
| Stovall Richard | Allen Kuehnle Stovall & Neuman LLP |
| Swetnam Dan | Ice Miller LLP |
| Valentine Nancy | Hahn Loeser & Parks LLP * |

**Band 4**

| | |
|---|---|
| Black Carl E | Jones Day * |
| Botti James | Porter Wright Morris & Arthur LLP * |
| Boydston Richard | Bingham Greenebaum Doll LLP (ONP)† * |
| Brody John | Kegler, Brown, Hill & Ritter |
| Campana Jeremy M | Thompson Hine LLP * |
| Cox Yvette | Bailey Cavalieri (ONP)† |
| Fisher J Matthew | Allen Kuehnle Stovall & Neuman LLP |
| Greenfield Harry | Buckley King (ONP)† |
| Johnson Kenneth | Bricker & Eckler LLP |
| LaTour Randall D | Vorys, Sater, Seymour and Pease LLP * |
| Lazear Sherri Blank | Baker & Hostetler LLP * |
| Miller W Timothy | Taft Stettinius & Hollister LLP * |
| Rhiel Susan | Rhiel & Associates (ONP)† |
| Wearsch Thomas M | Baker & Hostetler LLP * |
| Whittaker David M | Bricker & Eckler LLP |

**Associates to watch**

| | |
|---|---|
| Dahl Sherri | Squire Sanders (US) LLP * |
| Tuggle Curtis L | Thompson Hine LLP * |
| Wheatley Nathan | Calfee, Halter & Griswold LLP * |

\* Indicates firm / individual with profile.
† ONP = Other Notable Practitioner

pension plan. Other household-name clients include GM and Hostess Brands.

**Sources say:** *"They have an excellent knowledge of bankruptcy law, and the ability to be practical and incisive on key and difficult legal points. They are a pleasure to work with, being not only exceptional lawyers but extremely professional in their approach to getting deals done."*

**KEY INDIVIDUALS** Cleveland luminary **David Heiman** (see p.2100) chairs the bankruptcy and restructuring practice, having founded it in 1984. He is one of the state's most respected lawyers and continues to be involved in the largest and most high-profile matters of the day. He acted as lead counsel on the abovementioned Harry & David Chapter 11 matter. **Heather Lennox** (see p.2104) divides her time between New York and Cleveland. One client enthused: *"She is very helpful, knowledgeable and responsive to our needs. I was very pleased with my experience with her and I would not hesitate to work with her again."* Other sources deem Lennox to be *"smart, savvy and practical,"* and commend her impressive depth and breadth of understanding of the US Bankruptcy Code. She recently defended GM against a UAW action concerning a bankruptcy sale, and acted for Hostess Brands on its Chapter 11 case. In Columbus, of counsel **Charles Oellermann** (see p.2108) is *"really skilled and competent"* in this practice area, whether he is acting on restructuring, bankruptcy or asset sales. Recent work includes advising NRP Financial on the disposal of a broker-dealer business, and on associated aspects of potential insolvency. **Carl Black** (see p.2090) practices out of Cleveland, and sources agree he is a well-trained professional with the skills to handle matters effectively. He frequently acts on Chapter 11 debtor cases, and recently acted for Franciscan Communities St Mary of the Woods on the sale of its assets in connection with its Chapter 11 bankruptcy.

## Squire Sanders (US) LLP
See profile on p.2129

**THE FIRM** This international firm's Cincinnati and Cleveland offices continue to attract a market-leading following for bankruptcy and associated insolvency work. In highlights, it advised AmFin Financial and its affiliates on a series of Chapter 11 reorganizations, including protracted and high-stakes contentious work. On the creditor side, the firm represented FirstBank as the senior secured lender and DIP lender in the Chapter 11 case of Power Plus Electric in Kentucky. Other notable clients include Goodyear and PNC Bank.

**Sources say:** *"The team at Squire Sanders is skilled and efficient, and has a strong business sense." "They are excellent attorneys, who are well respected nationally at the bankruptcy bar."*

**KEY INDIVIDUALS Stephen Lerner** (see p.2104) splits his practice between Cincinnati and New York, where he chairs the firmwide restructuring and insolvency department. Clients say: *"He is not only a legal expert, but uses his tremendous business acumen to give us tailored best advice."* One source enthused: *"Stephen Lerner is one of the brightest, most knowledgeable lawyers I have ever dealt with."* Cleveland-based **Christopher Meyer** (see p.2107) assists a

broad range of clients with bankruptcy and insolvency matters. He is recognized for the *"great job"* he does in this area, and praised for his *"pragmatic approach as an advocate for his client."* His clients include AmFin Financial, Eaton Corporation and Specialty Minerals. **Sherri Dahl** (see p.2094) attracts increasing market attention for her keen work ethic and legal know-how. Sources describe her as *"very responsive and practical in her advice,"* and *"excellent to deal with."* She acted for AmFin Financial alongside Lerner and Meyer.

## Band 2

## Baker & Hostetler LLP
See profile on p.2119

**THE FIRM** This firm attracts substantial market attention for its continued bankruptcy and insolvency-related work associated with the Madoff scandal. Its partners have also been selected to act as trustee on a number of other high-profile insolvency proceedings. Additionally, the firm handles receivership matters and creditor-side work, and recently acted for the official committee of administrative claimants in connection with the Chapter 11 bankruptcy of LTV Steel. Interviewees regard the firm as a strong choice in this area, with the skills to handle large and national matters.

**Sources say:** *"They are very high profile in the state."*

**KEY INDIVIDUALS Joseph Hutchinson** (see p.2100) is the national leader of the firm's bankruptcy, restructuring and creditors' rights department. He is a well-known litigator and trial lawyer regarded for his highly effective input when insolvency matters turn contentious. He is a lead adviser to the firm's own Brian Bash as trustee in connection with the notorious Fair Finance Chapter 7 case. **Brian Bash** (see p.2090) is regularly engaged in high-profile, high-value matters. He was appointed as trustee in the widely reported Fair Finance Company Chapter 7 proceedings. **Matthew Goldman** (see p.2097) has a sound and respected reputation for his work in this area. He has been involved in a number of high-stakes matters, including the aforementioned LTV Steel case. **Sherri Lazear** (see p.2104) is a respected trial counsel who is described by sources as a *"solid lawyer"* with a *"professional approach"* to obtaining the best result. She continues to act for the SIPA Trustee in connection with the Madoff proceedings. **Thomas Wearsch** (see p.2116) recently acted as lead adviser to Swift-Cor Aerospace on its restructuring and sale to Impresa Aerospace.

## Dinsmore & Shohl LLP

**THE FIRM** This firm fields a number of skilled bankruptcy lawyers, with a strong core in Cincinnati and additional strength in Columbus and Dayton. It has built a respected profile for its involvement in midmarket matters in the local area and beyond, including acting for debtors on Chapter 11 and bankruptcy litigation defense. The team also represents creditors in formal bankruptcy proceedings and out-of-court workouts.

**KEY INDIVIDUALS Kim Martin Lewis** is regarded as the *"driving force"* behind the practice. Sources describe her as a *"very high-level practitioner – she works very hard and has a good reputation."* Deemed a *"tough opponent,"* she is also widely seen as a *"deal-maker"* and a *"first-rate debtor's lawyer."* **Tim Robinson** wins plaudits in the central Ohio market for being *"very bright"* and *"in his own right a strong first-chair lawyer."* He advises entities across the debtor, lender and unsecured creditor spectrum.

## Frost Brown Todd LLC
See profile on p.1329

**THE FIRM** This practice group is lauded as a popular and cost-effective choice for midmarket bankruptcy work, and is highlighted for the talent of its team in Cincinnati. Peers reserve special mention for its committed client advocacy combined with pragmatic commercial instinct. It represents debtors, special committees and senior secured lenders in matters across the state, in sectors as diverse as automotive, coal, real estate and manufacturing. Clients include private equity funds and local banks.

**KEY INDIVIDUALS Ronald Gold** (see p.2097) cochairs the bankruptcy and restructuring group, and is widely acclaimed for his market-leading command of this arena. Sources point to his *"commercial and practical"* approach, which makes him *"a very effective collaborator in negotiations."* Sources say: *"He is very good with clients and with difficult situations."* **Douglas Lutz** (see p.2105) is the other practice cochair. Source agree he is smart, hard-working, and a reliable choice for pragmatic and capable counsel in this market. He remains busy with receivership, restructuring and workout matters.

## Hahn Loeser & Parks LLP
See profile on p.2123

**THE FIRM** This firm is recognized for the strength of its creditors' rights, reorganization and bankruptcy practice. It is recommended for its experience in this field as counsel to a wide range of interests, including debtors, creditors, and other parties on matters at both the state and federal levels. Highlights include advising AgStar Financial Services on a number of loan transactions, and on the Chapter 11 reorganizations of Van Alphen Dairy and Vissers Dairy in Indiana. Other notable clients include Evans Oil, Twin City Hospital and the Attorney General of the State of Ohio.

**Sources say:** *"They are committed to representing clients in a manner that gets results."*

**KEY INDIVIDUALS** Practice group cochair **Daniel DeMarco** (see p.2094) is singled out for his *"exceptional attention to detail and great drafting,"* and sources note that he is a pragmatic yet keen fighter for his clients' rights. *"He can disagree without being disagreeable,"* say interviewees. He recently advised Evans Oil on its Chapter 11 bankruptcy filing and associated restructuring work. **Lawrence Oscar** (see p.2109) currently serves as the firm's CEO as well as cochair of the bankruptcy group. Sources praise him as a well-trained and effective professional who is easy to deal with. In highlights, he advised the creditors' committee of Amtrust Financial on its Chapter 11 plan. The experienced **Lee Powar** (see p.2110) remains a trusted adviser to a number of highly satisfied clients, who say: *"We call upon him to step in when issues are complex, deadlines are short, and we simply need to get it right."* **Nancy Valentine** (see p.2115) acted for AgStar Financial Services on the abovementioned matters, and is no stranger to contentious and high-value work. *"She works tirelessly to meet our needs and address our concerns. She is tough when she needs to be and knows the law, but doesn't lose sight of practical and business implications in the process."*

## McDonald Hopkins LLC

**THE FIRM** This firm benefits from a deep bench of experienced bankruptcy professionals with a strong Cleveland core. It has broad capabilities and is particularly well known for its work as debtor's counsel, as well as for its prominence on hospital bankruptcies and healthcare restructuring. Sources agree that the team works well with opposing counsel when handling difficult issues.

**KEY INDIVIDUALS** Cleveland managing partner **Shawn Riley** is lauded for his leadership in this field. He is praised for his commercial instincts, and sources say: *"He will fight really hard for his clients."* He regularly acts as debtor's counsel and has a strong profile in the healthcare sector, where highlights have seen him advise on bankruptcy and related asset sales. **Scott Opincar** advises on state and federal receiverships, creditors' rights and distressed M&A. He counts a number of banking entities on his client roster, and is described by sources as *"a very intellectually powerful lawyer"* who is *"very practical and pragmatic."* **Sean Malloy** has built a sound reputation for his advice to creditors' committees. Sources speak of him as a capable and effective counsel who is *"hard-working and very dedicated."*

## Thompson Hine LLP
See profile on p.2131

**THE FIRM** Thompson Hine has a strong reputation for its representation of creditor clients, acting for a number of household banking names, including KeyBank, Wells Fargo and JPMorgan Chase. It is regularly sought out on account of its efficient and pragmatic legal advice on Chapter 11 reorganizations, loan restructurings and creditors' rights, among other matters. The team has notable experience of cross-border matters, and recently represented the Law Debenture Trust Company of New York in connection with two series of senior guaranteed notes issued by Sino-Forest in its restructuring proceedings under the Companies' Creditors Arrangement Act in the Supreme Court of Ontario.

**KEY INDIVIDUALS Alan Lepene** (see p.2104) chairs the practice from Cleveland, and is highlighted for his *"very calm demeanor"* and his meticulous consideration of the facts before contentious negotiations. Interviewees describe him as *"excellent in every aspect of practice; an excellent advocate and litigator."* He acted for Carestream Health on various matters relating to the bankruptcy of Eastman Kodak. Cincinnati-based **Louis Solimine** (see p.2113) is considered *"an amazing resource"* on account of his legal knowledge and keen client service ethic. *"He listens to the question, knows the subject matter extremely well,*

*understands our business and provides practical legal advice,"* said one client. **Robert Folland** (see p.2096) recently advised CH2M Hill on defending a large claim brought by the liquidating trust of the Lyondell Chemical Company. Sources describe him as a detail-oriented and careful expert. **Jeremy Campana** (see p.2092) is no stranger to high-profile work, and had a lead role advising Qorval as the receiver of East Coast Gun Sales. He is recognized for his fine legal skills and affable manner. **Curtis Tuggle** (see p.2115) is an associate who is *"smart and hard-working,"* according to sources. He is noted for his keen attention to detail, and acted for the Law Debenture Trust Company of New York as indenture trustee in connection with the Sino-Forest case.

## Vorys, Sater, Seymour and Pease LLP
See profile on p.2133

**THE FIRM** This firm is well known in the Ohio bankruptcy market. It regularly acts on matters of regional significance across a wide range of sectors, including healthcare, manufacturing, media and entertainment. The team has a strong profile for its representation of creditor clients both in and out of court concerning debt restructuring, asset protection and corporate reorganization. The firm also acts for creditors' committees, debtors, trustees and receivers, among other parties of interest.

**KEY INDIVIDUALS Reginald Jackson** (see p.2100) receives wide acclaim as an *"excellent"* lawyer with an enviable amount of experience in this area, including creditors' committee work and section 363 asset sales. He also advises on receiverships and foreclosures. **Drew Parobek** (see p.2109) covers real estate as well as bankruptcy matters. Clients have come to rely on him as a *"very good and thoughtful lawyer,"* and praise the *"excellent quality of his work."* He is well known for his representation of secured lenders, and regularly acts for national, regional and local banks on workouts, reorganizations and restructurings, and other lending transactions. **Jeffrey Marks** (see p.2106) joined the firm's Cincinnati office from Squire Sanders in March 2012. Sources laud him as a constructive and communicative professional, and say *"he is excellent with the law and wonderful to deal with."* He continues to act for a supplier on a high-profile insolvency matter in the US Bankruptcy Court. Practice group leader **Randall LaTour** (see p.2103) is *"well regarded, very smart and practical,"* according to interviewees. His deep experience in this area includes advising on substantial debtor/creditor matters, as well as Bankruptcy Court proceedings and workouts.

## Band 3

## Allen Kuehnle Stovall & Neuman LLP

**THE FIRM** This Columbus-based practice group attracts increasing market attention for its work on the debtor side of bankruptcy. It regularly advises on out-of-court workouts, Chapter 11 restructurings and section 363 asset sales, among other matters, acting for clients including retirement communities, restaurant chains, financial institutions and utility companies.

**Sources say:** *"They are always extremely professional, prompt and thoughtful." "A really great small firm."*

**KEY INDIVIDUALS Tom Allen** is a *"fantastic lawyer"* who is a popular choice as debtor's counsel in Columbus. He is recognized for his holistic skills in this arena, and sources describe him as *"very bright, good in court and good on paper too."* **Richard Stovall** wins substantial recognition as a reliable and *"well-trained"* professional in this field. One peer described him as a *"bright, professional, gentlemanly lawyer who I am very comfortable referring reorganization work to."* Stovall has also developed a reputation for adroit and pragmatic advice, especially to debtor entities. **Matthew Fisher** is increasingly praised for his *"great command of this area."* One source noted that in the bankruptcy arena he *"really understands what it takes to practice law."*

## Bricker & Eckler LLP

**THE FIRM** This 13-strong Ohio practice group advises on Chapter 11 reorganizations and liquidation proceedings, as well as out-of-court workouts and creditors' rights. It acts on matters across the Midwest, with a strong focus on the midmarket. It also handles related contentious work, including recovery actions, involuntary petitions and lender liability suits.

**Sources say:** *"The firm understands the law very well and provides sound counsel."*

**KEY INDIVIDUALS Kenneth Johnson** heads the creditors' rights and bankruptcy group. He wins plaudits as a good and effective bankruptcy lawyer, particularly from a creditor and secured lender perspective. His expertise covers Chapter 7, Chapter 11 and Chapter 13 matters. **David Whittaker** has broad experience in this arena, which includes serving as a Chapter 11 trustee and acting as debtor's counsel on high-value matters. Sources describe him as *"highly competent,"* and say that *"he spends quality time explaining every step of the process, and the strategy used, to get the best results for us."*

## Calfee, Halter & Griswold LLP
See profile on p.2121

**THE FIRM** This full-service bankruptcy and restructuring practice group is sought out for its strategic planning and effective advice. With a strong emphasis on the midmarket, the firm represents a wide range of client types in Chapter 11 cases and court actions. In highlights, it advised the official committee of unsecured creditors in connection with the Chapter 11 proceedings of Cardinal Fastener. Other notable clients include Pacific Western Bank and New York Community Bancorp.

**Sources say:** *"They have the deep technical knowledge and the practical know-how to assist clients in formulating strategy and tactics during a bankruptcy proceeding."*

**KEY INDIVIDUALS James Lawniczak** (see p.2103) is the head of the firm's bankruptcy litigation department, and accordingly has a sound and quality profile for his contentious insolvency work. Sources see him as a technically proficient and keen client advocate, and describe him as a very *"bright guy."* He defended Broadvox against claims brought by the creditors of Infotelecom regarding Broadvox's proposed purchase of the company's business assets. **Nathan Wheatley** (see p.2117) is recognized by clients as "*an integral part of formulating our strategy and approach.*" Of note is his "*deep technical knowledge of the legal subject matter, with a practical view of how business and the world really work.*"

### Ice Miller LLP

**THE FIRM** The recent merger of Schottenstein Zox & Dunn and Ice Miller means this team is increasingly well placed to advise on all areas of midmarket bankruptcy and restructuring in Ohio and across the region. It remains busy with indenture trustee and bank work, among other matters, acting for such clients as Huntington National Bank and Access Media 3.

**KEY INDIVIDUALS** Columbus partner **Victoria Powers** chairs the bankruptcy and financial restructuring practice. She has acted for the Bank of New York Mellon Trust Company on various matters as indenture trustee. Sources describe her as "*a very good technician,*" and see her as a popular referral choice for her committed yet pragmatic manner. "*She is easy to work with and will go all the way for her client,*" sources say. The "*thorough and bright*" **Colette Gibbons** advises on state court insolvency matters and receivership work. Sources speak of her as a wonderful and easy lawyer to work with, even when matters turn contentious, describing her as "*very results-oriented – she wants to get the best result for all parties.*" She was lead adviser to the Chapter 7 Trustee of retail chain InkStop. **Dan Swetnam** is a sound choice for those seeking a detail-oriented and switched-on professional, according to sources. He continues to lead on high-profile matters, and advised RAK Corrosion Control on two separate bankruptcy filings by former employees. His broad skill set sees him act equally effectively for creditor as well as debtor clients.

### Keating Muething & Klekamp PLL
See profile on p.2124

**THE FIRM** This firm stands out for his unique focus on mass tort bankruptcy and settlement trusts. It continues to be heavily involved in post-bankruptcy asbestos settlement trusts arising out of a series of Chapter 11 cases. The team also advises on out-of-court workouts and creditors' rights litigation, among other areas of specialism. Clients include Cintas, Fifth Third Bank and First Financial Bank.

**Sources say:** "*I have been impressed by the understanding of the case by the lawyers – they understand the details better than I do.*"

**KEY INDIVIDUALS Kevin Irwin** (see p.2100) is considered a "*go-to guy*" for asbestos settlement trusts work and mass tort bankruptcy proceedings. Sources agree that he is a smart and able practitioner who can be relied upon for quality representation. **Robert Sanker** (see p.2111) wins plaudits for his legal skills and highly pragmatic approach.

"*He is not only a subject matter expert, but also applies his knowledge in a practical way that assists us in our business.*"

### Kegler, Brown, Hill & Ritter
See profile on p.2125

**THE FIRM** This firm has a strong reputation for its involvement in bankruptcy and restructuring, and related litigation. It acts for a range of trustees and financial institutions, including Ohio State Bank and CFBank. In other highlights, the team acts for Cardinal Health on its collection cases nationwide.

**Sources say:** "*They have extensive experience in this area.*"

**KEY INDIVIDUALS Larry McClatchey** co-heads the creditors' rights and bankruptcy group. He plays a key role in the Cardinal Health collection work, and is recognized as "*a talented attorney*" by sources. He is also highlighted for his trustee work in respect of Chapter 7 cases. **John Brody** cochairs the practice with McClatchey. His practice covers contentious work arising from bankruptcy as well as associated insurance matters. He advised United Bank on a loan default and surrender agreement with LA Pipeline Construction.

### Porter Wright Morris & Arthur LLP
See profile on p.2127

**THE FIRM** Porter Wright is recommended for its proficient advice on the lender side of bankruptcy matters in the local market. It acts for a strong stable of financial institution clients, including Fifth Third Bank and Huntington National Bank. Work highlights include acting for KeyBank on the restructuring of a $50 million construction loan facility to Columbus Campus and on other matters arising out of the Chapter 11 proceedings of the borrower.

**Sources say:** "*The firm has always been responsive to our needs.*"

**KEY INDIVIDUALS** Department head **Jack Pigman** (see p.2110) is "*an unquestioned market leader in this area,*" say sources. One interviewee enthused: "*His approach and experience have been instrumental in our success. His thoroughness and professionalism are impeccable.*" **James Botti** (see p.2091) is described by sources as "*extremely professional, very competent and good for difficult cases.*" He is particularly active on the lender side, and recently advised KeyBank on a significant global forbearance and subsequent receivership.

### Taft Stettinius & Hollister LLP
See profile on p.2130

**THE FIRM** This firm advises on both debtor and creditor work across the state. Of late, it has been particularly active in the representation of borrowers, including GE, US Steel and Philips Electronics North America. Work highlights

include notable state court receiverships and Chapter 11 matters involving the real estate and manufacturing sectors.

**Sources say:** "*It has a very experienced and knowledgeable team dedicated to this area of law.*"

**KEY INDIVIDUALS** Practice group leader **Timothy Hurley** (see p.2100) enjoys a rising profile as a high-level practitioner with a firm handle on matters both inside and outside the courtroom. Sources cite his "*good rapport with the bankruptcy judges*" and say he is "*committed to the best interests of his clients, a recognized expert in bankruptcy and insolvency law, and very personable and likeable.*" He recently advised on the restructuring of a commercial real estate project. **Timothy Miller** (see p.2107) wins plaudits from market sources as a "*logical yet creative thinker*" with a "*very professional demeanor.*" He recently advised a telecoms company on a notable and expedited Chapter 11 filing.

### Other Notable Practitioners

**Nick Cavalieri** practices out of Bailey Cavalieri's Columbus branch, where he chairs the commercial transactions and bankruptcy group. He is acclaimed as "*a smart guy who understands the issues, and will correctly analyze risks.*" Sources say of his interpersonal skills: "*He is great to deal with and great with clients.*" Also at Bailey Cavalieri, **Yvette Cox** enjoys a growing profile for her skilled negotiation of client interests, particularly on the debtor side. "*She was a quick study, and raised some matters other lawyers had not thought about. She is smart and gets things done,*" one source said. Cox's work includes advising on the restructuring of commercial real estate loans. **Michael Debbeler** of Graydon Head & Ritchey LLP is lauded as a "*great commercial brain*" who "*focuses on resolution.*" One source enthused: "*I have a great deal of respect for him. He is a gentleman with a professional approach.*" **Richard Boydston** (see p.2091) of Bingham Greenebaum Doll LLP has built a reputation as a trusted adviser on bankruptcy and restructuring. He represents local and non-local creditor interests, and sources say "*he doesn't miss a beat.*" **Harry Greenfield** of Buckley King garners substantial market acclaim as an experienced professional, and is described as "*incredibly knowledgeable about bankruptcy law and strategy.*" Sources also note that "*as an attorney he has that rare trait: he understands business.*" Banking and real estate companies feature on his client list. **Susan Rhiel** of Rhiel & Associates has developed a sound reputation for Chapter 7, receivership, and bankruptcy panel trustee work, and is no stranger to Chapter 11 matters. Sources describe her as an effective lawyer who can handle sophisticated work, and can be "*very tough*" when the need arises.

# CONSTRUCTION

Commentary about individuals can be found under their firm's paragraph. If the firm has no paragraph (is not ranked) look at Other Notable Practitioners.

## Construction
### Leading Firms

**Band 1**
Thompson Hine LLP *

**Band 2**
Benesch, Friedlander, Coplan & Aronoff LLP *
Bricker & Eckler LLP
Frantz Ward LLP *

**Band 3**
Calfee, Halter & Griswold LLP *
Frost Brown Todd LLC *
Ice Miller LLP
Kegler, Brown, Hill & Ritter *

**Band 4**
Hahn Loeser & Parks LLP *
Taft Stettinius & Hollister LLP *

## Construction
### Senior Statesmen

| Senior Statesmen: distinguished older practitioners | |
| --- | --- |
| Petro John J | Williams & Petro Co. LLC (ONP)[†] |

### Leading Individuals

**Star individuals**

| | |
| --- | --- |
| Appelbaum Jeffrey R | Thompson Hine LLP * |

**Band 1**

| | |
| --- | --- |
| Gregory Donald | Kegler, Brown, Hill & Ritter |
| Miller Barry | Benesch, Friedlander, Coplan & Aronoff * |
| Natale Andrew J | Frantz Ward LLP * |
| Rosati Jack | Bricker & Eckler LLP |

**Band 2**

| | |
| --- | --- |
| Kirkwood Thomas J | Thompson Hine LLP * |
| Leach Donald | Dinsmore & Shohl LLP (ONP)[†] |
| Remington Rob | Hahn Loeser & Parks LLP * |
| Tarullo Michael | Ice Miller LLP |

**Band 3**

| | |
| --- | --- |
| Comodeca Peter J | Calfee, Halter & Griswold LLP * |
| Frank Ian H | Frantz Ward LLP * |
| Friedman Steven A | Squire Sanders (US) LLP (ONP)[†] * |
| Paynter Craig | Taft Stettinius & Hollister LLP * |
| Reder Henry | Henry I. Reder (ONP)[†] |
| Sweeney Patrick J | Thompson Hine LLP * |
| Vickers F Thomas | Vickers Law Group (ONP)[†] |
| Welin Peter D | Welin O'Shaughnessy and Scheaf (ONP)[†] |

**Band 4**

| | |
| --- | --- |
| Crist Thomas O | Benesch, Friedlander, Coplan & Aronoff * |
| Dobrowski Stanley J | Calfee, Halter & Griswold LLP * |
| Evans Mark | Bricker & Eckler LLP |
| Fisher Kenneth | Fisher Law Firm (ONP)[†] |
| Gabelman Thomas | Frost Brown Todd LLC |
| Gurney Scott | Frost Brown Todd LLC * |
| Higgins John | Frost Brown Todd LLC * |
| Rhee Hansel H | Ice Miller LLP |
| Rosenberg Thomas L | Roetzel & Andress, LPA (ONP)[†] * |

**Up-and-coming individuals**

| | |
| --- | --- |
| Levasseur Eric | Hahn Loeser & Parks LLP * |
| Zarlenga Audra J | Thompson Hine LLP * |

**Associates to watch**

| | |
| --- | --- |
| Loftus Nora | Frantz Ward LLP * |

\* Indicates individual with profile.
[†]ONP = Other Notable Practitioner

## Band 1

### Thompson Hine LLP
See profile on p.2131

**THE FIRM** This firm has an enviable reputation and proven bench strength, and it remains a leading force in the state for construction work. Recent highlights include advising on construction of a retractable roof at Marlins Park baseball park in Miami. Other key clients of the practice include URS and Gilbane Building.
**Sources say:** *"Thomson Hine is a leader in this area."*
**KEY INDIVIDUALS Jeffrey Appelbaum** (see p.2089) has a superb reputation and a high profile. Clients consider him a key contributor to negotiating successful deals, describing him as *"instrumental in leading large construction projects; he is consistently able to find creative solutions to difficult questions."* He is also an *"excellent construction disputes mediator"* and a proficient, experienced trial lawyer. Cincinnati-based **Thomas Kirkwood** (see p.2102) has a practice covering construction work and commercial litigation. Sources describe him as a *"very good lawyer and very capable,"* and note his *"great people skills"* when he is negotiating on clients' behalves. He is also a high-profile mediator. **Patrick Sweeney** (see p.2114) has been actively representing educational institutions and manufacturing interests, negotiating the construction of new facilities as well as upgrades of old ones. Sources agree he is an experienced and effective lawyer who *"certainly understands the industry."* Clients praise his keen service ethic: *"He is very responsive to our needs."* **Audra Zarlenga** (see p.2118) is a younger partner in the Cleveland office. She continues to attract considerable market attention as *"very smart and professional."* Much of her practice includes contentious construction matters, and her client list includes URS.

## Band 2

### Benesch, Friedlander, Coplan & Aronoff LLP
See profile on p.2120

**THE FIRM** Sources recognize this firm's notable talents in the construction arena, especially on the contentious side. Sources describe a responsive practice that is equipped to handle aggressive and contentious litigation. Work highlights include advising Northeast Ohio Regional Sewer District on a multibillion-dollar contractor dispute arising from a tunneling project. It also counts Donley's and Eaton Corporation on its client roster.
**Sources say:** *"A leader in the construction industry."*
**KEY INDIVIDUALS Barry Miller** (see p.2107) chairs the firm's construction practice. His registered architect status affords him reassuring familiarity with the finer points of this practice area, and clients praise his all-around practical awareness of client pressures. *"He is very much in tune with what happens on a construction site; we did not have to train him,"* say sources. He acted as lead lawyer on the Northeast Ohio Regional Sewer District dispute. **Thomas Crist** (see p.2093) serves as the deputy head of the construction group. Sources describe him as a *"good and experienced lawyer,"* particularly in construction disputes. He is also a well-known arbitrator and mediator in this area. His clients include design professionals and manufacturers.

### Bricker & Eckler LLP

**THE FIRM** This firm has built a sound reputation in the market for public construction work in particular, including matters on behalf of school districts. Sources speak of its keen client advocacy and inventive approach to problem solving as key strengths. Highlights for the practice include acting for Avon Lake City School District on a replacement design and build project. It also counts OhioHealth and the City of Delaware on its client roster.
**Sources say:** *"It finds good ways around obstacles and does an excellent job."*
**KEY INDIVIDUALS** Columbus partner **Jack Rosati** serves as chair of the construction practice. He is acclaimed for his *"very well-rounded knowledge of all aspects of construction."* His interpersonal skills mean that he is equally effective at negotiating with all levels of interested parties. He acted as lead partner on the Avon Lake City School District matter. The West Chester-based **Mark Evans** brings a diligent and committed approach to his work, according to impressed sources. His former role as a project engineer puts him in good stead in the sector. His recent work includes acting as outside counsel to the City of Zanesville.

### Frantz Ward LLP
See profile on p.2122

**THE FIRM** This group is particularly well known for advising on matters local to the Cleveland area. Clients of the firm include infrastructure contractors. It has a repository of skills across both the contentious and transactional aspects of construction.
**Sources say:** *"Fabulous lawyers and a fabulous group."*
**KEY INDIVIDUALS Andrew Natale** (see p.2108) is a member of both the construction and litigation groups at the firm, and is a recognized trial lawyer. He enjoys a prominent reputation in construction, with many praising his ability to do an *"effective job."* The *"smart and hardworking"* **Ian Frank** (see p.2096) is acclaimed as a *"younger and effective"* member of the team. Sources praise him as a

proficient client advocate who contributes greatly to the strength of the overall practice. His clients include contractors, subcontractors and design professionals. **Nora Loftus** (see p.2105) is a senior associate. She is already visible in the market for her proficient and supportive role in the team.

## Band 3

### Calfee, Halter & Griswold LLP
See profile on p.2121

**THE FIRM** Calfee's construction practice has a solid name in the state, with a client list including FirstEnergy and Ohio Turnpike Commission, as well as casino operators. The team advises on bid documents and arbitrations, in connection with mixed-use developments and sewer projects, among other areas.
**Sources say:** *"They fit our needs and provide quality services for the best value."*
**KEY INDIVIDUALS** **Peter Comodeca** (see p.2093) is the chair of the dedicated construction practice. His skill set also includes energy matters, and sources recognize his ability to handle *"complex and challenging work."* He also comes recommended for his solid litigation skills. He recently advised FirstEnergy on a number of matters, including on issues relating to a power plant upgrade. *"Good adviser"* **Stanley Dobrowski** (see p.2094) wins plaudits for his commercial approach and his talent for coming up with practical resolutions. He recently advised the City of Westlake on the bid process surrounding a mixed-use development.

### Frost Brown Todd LLC
See profile on p.1329

**THE FIRM** This firm is noted for its representation of contractor and subcontractor interests in particular, as well as architects, and sources describe its lawyers as experienced and high quality. Its recent work highlights include representing four subcontractors in connection with the foreclosure of the Kenwood Towne Place shopping center.
**KEY INDIVIDUALS** The *"very capable"* **Scott Gurney** (see p.2098) wins praise from sources for being thorough as well as clear: *"His explanations are always such that, as a lay person, I completely understand what is going on."* He recently advised Superior Steel and Ben Hur Construction in a trial against an owner-developer and construction manager. **John Higgins** (see p.2100) is *"very professional and easy to deal with,"* according to sources. He is renowned as a litigator, particularly in the construction arena. He was lead attorney in the aforementioned Kenwood Towne Place matter. **Thomas Gabelman** recently joined the firm from Vorys, Sater, Seymour and Pease. Sources agree his work reflects a thorough understanding of the construction industry. Others laud his deal-focused attitude: *"He helps bring parties together to develop a project."*

### Ice Miller LLP
**THE FIRM** The legacy Schottenstein Zox and Dunn construction practice maintains its profile, following its merger into Ice Miller. It advises on contractual as well as litigation matters in this area, including arbitration and trial work.
**Sources say:** *"They do a very good job."*
**KEY INDIVIDUALS** **Michael Tarullo** is a lawyer and a qualified engineer. He calls on years of front-line experience in the construction industry. Sources agree: *"He has a great deal of construction expertise,"* and is *"pragmatic and results-oriented"* in his approach. He is also a recognized mediator. **Hansel Rhee** enjoys a rising profile as in this field. He advises on disputes, including trial work and mediation as well as litigation. *"He understands construction law very thoroughly,"* and is *"well prepared and capable."*

### Kegler, Brown, Hill & Ritter
See profile on p.2125

**THE FIRM** Interviewees respect this firm for its prowess in the construction area. Its enviable client base includes the American Subcontractors Association and Baker Concrete. Its recent highlights include advising a contractor on a high-value claim concerning the Ohio School Facilities Commission.
**Sources say:** *"The team was picked because of its expertise in construction, business and employment law."*
**KEY INDIVIDUALS** **Donald Gregory** heads up the construction practice group. He acts as general counsel to the American Subcontractors Association. Sources praise his capabilities as an *"excellent trial lawyer,"* and his *"always responsive and timely"* approach.

## Band 4

### Hahn Loeser & Parks LLP
See profile on p.2123

**THE FIRM** HL Construction Law is a distinct department within Hahn Loeser set up to advise construction clients. Interviewees speak of great value for money, and willingness of lawyers to fit in with client processes. The group's recent highlights include acting as lead counsel to manufacturer POET on a high-value dispute concerning an ethanol plant. Its client roster also includes Johnson Controls and Fidelity National Financial.
**Sources say:** *"It gives you big-firm service at a medium-firm price."*
**KEY INDIVIDUALS** **Rob Remington** (see p.2110) heads up the practice. He is lauded as a *"top-flight construction lawyer"* who looks to resolve issues as quickly as possible. *"He doesn't waste time and money,"* sources say. His litigation and contract negotiation skills prove invaluable to clients. **Eric Levasseur** (see p.2104) is an up-and-coming commercial dispute resolution lawyer who also acts on construction disputes. He recently provided input on the POET case, and also counts Fidelity National Financial as a client.

### Taft Stettinius & Hollister LLP
See profile on p.2130

**THE FIRM** Messer Construction and TriHealth are among this dedicated construction practice's key clients. The team's recent highlights include advising DCI Properties-DKY on negotiation and litigation concerning a mixed-use development on the Ohio River.
**KEY INDIVIDUALS** **Craig Paynter** (see p.2109) is characterized by his *"solid advice to clients,"* say sources. Interviewees also note his interpersonal skills, and speak of him as *"very personable and professional."* He has recently acted as special counsel to a number of entities, including the Ohio Attorney General and the City of Columbus.

### Other Notable Practitioners

**Donald Leach** cochairs Dinsmore & Shohl LLP's construction practice. He is described as a senior litigator and a strong personality who obtains good results for clients. *"He is a very knowledgeable and capable trial lawyer,"* interviewees add. He recently advised Franklin County Convention Facilities Authority on transactional aspects of acquisition of the Nationwide Arena. **Steven Friedman** (see p.2096) of Squire Sanders (US) LLP is best known for his handling of the contentious side of construction. Sources consider him highly knowledgeable, with an effective litigation style. He is also an experienced trial lawyer. **Henry Reder** is a registered architect as well as a lawyer, giving him almost unique insight into the issues surrounding construction. His practice includes advising on transactional as well as contentious matters. He acts for clients such as architects and engineers. **Thomas Vickers** is founder of, and lead counsel at, Vickers Law Group in Westlake. He is a recognized and experienced disputes lawyer in the construction arena. His admittance to practice in the Supreme Court allows him to advise when those contentious matters reach the appellate stage. **Peter Welin** left Thompson Hine to found Welin O'Shaughnessy and Scheaf LLC. His reputation is that of an astute adviser in major construction disputes. His prior academic study of construction engineering renders him a particularly advantageous choice of counsel. **Kenneth Fisher** is the name lawyer at Fisher Law Firm. He is a registered architect as well as a lawyer. He is highlighted for his role as special counsel to the Ohio Attorney General on construction contract matters. **Thomas Rosenberg** (see p.2111) of Roetzel & Andress, LPA remains particularly active in contentious construction matters. He is an American Arbitration Association arbitrator, as well as an experienced courtroom lawyer. His recent work includes advising suppliers and contractors on public construction disputes. **John Petro** is a name partner at Williams & Petro Co. LLC. He has a notable profile in the construction context for his bonding-related work. Sources speak of him as a *"preeminent expert"* and a *"practical, experienced, smart lawyer."*

# CORPORATE/M&A

Commentary about individuals can be found under their firm's paragraph. If the firm has no paragraph (is not ranked) look at Other Notable Practitioners.

## Band 1

### Baker & Hostetler LLP
See profile on p.2119

**THE FIRM** The practice benefits from the firm's enviable national profile and is particularly recognized in Ohio for its strength in the Cleveland market. It acts on a broad array of significant transactional and compliance work including public company, private equity and joint venture matters. Highlights for the practice include acting as transactional counsel to TransDigm on the $750 million acquisition of AmSafe Global Holdings. Its client roster also include The Progressive Corporation, OSI Restaurant Partners and Associated Estates Realty.

**Sources say:** "A strong relationship management approach offering not just legal advice, but business advice." "It doesn't over-lawyer the deals and tries to be mindful of the cost/benefit associated with getting a deal done."

**KEY INDIVIDUALS** "Leading business lawyer" **John Gherlein** (see p.2097) acted for TransDigm on the AmSafe Global Holdings acquisition matter. He heads up the business practice at the entire firm from the Cleveland office and has built a laudable reputation for his pragmatic advice across the transactional spectrum, including M&A and compliance counseling. Sources describe him as "so practical, he has a very good approach to getting things done; if one structure is not working, he will think of another." Cleveland partner **Suzanne Hanselman** (see p.2099) is a great choice, particularly for her deft command of the securities and capital markets aspects. She is a key lawyer in the securities and corporate governance practice. Sources speak of her as "very good and thorough" in her work. She was lead adviser to the firm's longtime client The Progressive Corporation concerning a $500 million debt

securities offering. **Robert Weible** (see p.2116) is a partner in the Cleveland office who heads up the firm's securities and corporate governance practice. He wins plaudits for being "extremely helpful" in navigating clients through the finer points of transactional work, especially securities and associated compliance issues. "His advice and counsel was sound and knowledgeable, and his past experiences were most appreciated," according to one happy client. His highlights include assisting on the $398 million sale of American Dental Partners to JLL Partners. **Steven Kestner** (see p.2102) is an executive partner in Cleveland who currently serves as the firm's CEO and remains engaged in private practice. His areas of expertise include transactional and securities work, and he is a trusted point of contact for a number of entities including The Progressive Corporation. **Ashley Hess** (see p.2100) is the Cincinnati office's highest-profile partner in this practice area. He is praised as being "a very good lawyer," and is increasingly recognized for his proficiency in the area. Clients he has advised include Humana, as well as Fortune 100 entities. **John Allotta** (see p.2089) is praised as "a good young M&A partner who can generate large output in short timeframes," according to enthusiastic sources, who also note his adroit handling of sometimes high-pressure deal demands. He recently assisted Lincoln Electric Holdings in a transactional matter.

### Jones Day
See profile on p.919

**THE FIRM** This Cleveland office remains a focal point for high-value transactional work, both in the state and beyond, nicely complementing the firm's national and international profile. Strengths of the practice include private equity and public company work. Recent highlights include acting for Goodrich on its $18.4 billion merger with United Technologies.

**Sources say:** "The level of service we have received from Jones Day has been superb, encompassing excellent legal advice, extreme responsiveness, unsurpassed attention to detail and, most importantly, the utmost attention to our needs and concerns."

**KEY INDIVIDUALS Lyle Ganske** (see p.2097) remains perhaps the most prominent M&A partner in the Cleveland office. He had a lead role on the Goodrich merger matter. Clients were keen to recommend his interpersonal and legal skills. He is described as "a very effective communicator," with a great line in "keeping the discussion at the right level," yet "without getting lost in the weeds on very technical legal nuances," according to sources. The "excellent" **Chuck Hardin** (see p.2099) is the Cleveland partner who heads the worldwide private equity practice at the firm. "He is an exceptional business lawyer himself and also does a wonderful job of making the considerable worldwide assets of the firm available to us 24/7." He recently advised the firm's long-term client The Riverside Company on the acquisition of Avatar International and

DentalPlans.com. Cleveland partner **John Saada** (see p.2111) has built a sound name for himself in venture capital and private equity, in particular. Accordingly, his client roster includes a number of big-name players in this sector, such as The Riverside Company, Goode Partners and Rockwood Equity Partners. **Mike Solecki** (see p.2113) is a younger partner in the Cleveland office. His skill set spans the corporate, finance and capital markets arenas, and his client base includes financial institutions. He provided input on Cliffs Natural Resources' CAD4.9 billion acquisition of Consolidated Thompson Iron Mines.

## Band 2

### Dinsmore & Shohl LLP

**THE FIRM** This firm's business, acquisitions and securities practice has garnered a high degree of attention, particularly via the recognized lawyers in its Cincinnati office. It boasts long and mutually productive relationships with leading household name clients including Procter & Gamble as well as Lexmark. It continues to proffer expedient and practical advice on high-value acquisitions and disposals, and recently assisted Lexmark on acquisition of software interests.
**Sources say:** *"They know what they're doing and are professional to work with."*
**KEY INDIVIDUALS** The *"very smart"* **George Vincent** is managing partner and chairman of the firm, and maintains an active presence in the market. He continues to be held in high regard as a top performer in this area. Clients are quick to describe him as *"extraordinarily attentive; he knows our company and culture, and is very responsive."* He recently advised on the purchase of assets of an online business. **Calvin Buford** is a key Cincinnati partner. Sources speak of his *"strong community connections"* and note his command of private company transactional work in particular. Other interviewees speak of his well-developed interpersonal skills, describing him as a *"good guy to deal with."* His broad skill set enables him to advise on associated financing work, as well. Cincinnati partner **Charles Hertlein** enjoys a rising market profile for his securities work in particular, including SEC regulatory matters. Sources paint a picture of a well-trained professional and a clear, polite communicator. **Clifford Roe** is one of the more senior lawyers in the Cincinnati office and remains engaged with the team. He gains high praise for his long commitment and substantial successes in areas including public company matters and banking.

### Keating Muething & Klekamp PLL
See profile on p.2124
**THE FIRM** This firm offers its clients skilled advice, detailed local knowledge and innovative strategies, according to highly enthusiastic interviewees. Highlights for the practice include advising Great American Financial Resources on the $295 million sale of its subsidiary to CIGNA Health. It also counts Duro Bag Manufacturing and Meridian Bioscience on its client roster.

**Sources say:** *"A results-oriented and business-focused practice, intent on solving business problems and not over-lawyering deals."*
**KEY INDIVIDUALS Edward Steiner** (see p.2114) is a key lawyer in the transactional group and acted as a lead counsel on the Great American Financial Resources deal. He advises on a broad range of corporate and commercial matters, including tax credit and private equity work. Sources were quick to point to his virtues, describing him as *"clearly a leader, and extremely talented."* **Robert Coletti** (see p.2093) is a partner who shines for his M&A prowess, in particular. Clients speak of his longtime experience and commercial ethos, praising his *"subject matter expertise combined with practical insight."* **Mark Reuter** (see p.2110) enjoys a rising profile for his high quality of work and for being excellent to deal with, according to sources. He has a long list of notable clients, including Fifth Third Bank and Multi-Color Corporation. **Gary Kreider** (see p.2103) is highly respected as one of the most senior figures at the Cincinnati Bar. He remains a leading partner in the firm and is recognized for his lengthy experience and know-how in securities regulatory and compliance work in particular.

### Kegler, Brown, Hill & Ritter
See profile on p.2125
**THE FIRM** The Columbus office is the focus for this firm's undoubted transactional capabilities. Interviewees underline the impressive level of service offered by the team, which is also particularly noted for its ability to handle healthcare-related matters. Highlights for the practice include advising IgniteHealth in an asset purchase. Other key clients include Cardinal Health, Commercial Vehicle Group and Logtec. In addition to its strong regional work, the firm also has significant cross-border expertise in Asia, Europe and Latin America.
**Sources say:** *"Switched-on and good to deal with."*
**KEY INDIVIDUALS Charles Kegler** is a well-known and senior deal lawyer in the Columbus market. He chairs the business and tax practice and enjoys a high profile in estate planning. Clients are *"very satisfied"* with his exemplary service and communication skills: *"He communicates very well and clearly, and is very concise and easily understandable."* **Martijn Steger** heads up the dedicated international commercial practice. He is recognized for his skill and effectiveness when working on domestic as well as cross-border matters, and clients speak of his keen communication and *"great service."* He recently advised a global services provider on structuring issues in Europe. **Todd Kegler** is a *"young, talented lawyer"* and chairs the firms M&A practice. He is a lead relationship lawyer for CareFusion. Sources speak favorably of his legal skills and note that he is also extremely cost-effective.

### Thompson Hine LLP
See profile on p.2131
**THE FIRM** This firm has an increasing national profile and remains a stalwart of the Ohio market. The dedicated corporate transactions and securities practice is managed out of Cincinnati, but the Cleveland office continues to

expand its reputation, with the Columbus and Dayton teams proving additional support. It advised Forest City Enterprises on a number of capital markets transactions, including a $350 million convertible senior notes offering under Rule 144A. Other key clients include Advance Pierre Foods and KeyCorp.
**Sources say:** *"They are very responsive and provide us with cost-effective, high-quality work on a timely basis."*
**KEY INDIVIDUALS Thomas Aldrich** (see p.2089) is a key partner in the Cleveland office. His areas of expertise include securities regulatory and joint venture matters. He continues to advise on high-profile work, including acting as lead counsel on the Forest City Enterprises matter. **David Willbrand** (see p.2117) brings his experience as a former technology industry executive to his role heading up the firm's emerging company subpractice. His skill set includes early-stage investor work, and sources speak of him as *"an exceptional attorney in the venture capital space."* He advised clinical informatics entity AssureRx Health on a $12.5 million Series C financing. **Frank Chaiken** (see p.2092) heads up the corporate transactions and securities practice. Sources are quick to point out his dedicated approach to client service: *"He is always available and responsive."* Recent work includes advising a manufacturing client on a multimillion-dollar acquisition of a related company.

### Vorys, Sater, Seymour and Pease LLP
See profile on p.2133
**THE FIRM** Sources were quick to point to this firm for its long experience in transactional work, especially via its Columbus office. Banking entities feature strongly on its client roster, but its work is by no means confined to this space, as it also acts for entities in the hospitality, real estate and educational sectors. Recent highlights for the practice include advising on formation of a new multimillion-dollar venture capital fund.
**Sources say:** *"Excellent work." "Having worked with many of the other top firms, I feel Vorys's approach to clients and the knowledge and experience of its partners are superior."*
**KEY INDIVIDUALS John Vorys** (see p.2115) is the chair of the corporate and finance practice group at the firm, and is based in the Columbus office. At the time of writing he was on sabbatical, but he still commands respect across the state for his experience and quality. **Roger Lautzenhiser** (see p.2103), who divides his time between the Cincinnati and Columbus offices, had a lead role on the venture capital fund formation matter mentioned above. Sources describe him as *"extremely responsive and knowledgeable,"* as well as *"able to communicate complex issues in a concise manner."* **Jeffery Smith** (see p.2113) is a corporate and finance partner who practices in Columbus. He attracts notable market recognition in the realm of financial institutions work, especially banking regulatory aspects of M&A. Several sources appreciatively note that he is *"good to work with."*

## Band 3

### Benesch, Friedlander, Coplan & Aronoff LLP
See profile on p.2120

**THE FIRM** This corporate and securities practice has found a strong niche in midmarket work in the state, especially in the large Cleveland market. It has proved itself highly capable in a range of matters, including M&A and venture capital financings. Highlights of the year include acting as sellers' co-counsel on Audax Group's $486 million sale of The ColorMatrix Corporation to PolyOne. Other clients include Crimson Investments and Royal Adhesives & Sealants.
**Sources say:** "Very active in private equity."
**KEY INDIVIDUALS James Hill** (see p.2100) is one of the leading lights in the Cleveland office. Clients report being "extremely happy" with his service, and praise him as "a credible and good negotiator – he understands the transactions." He counts Audax Group and Crimson Investments as key clients. **Ira Kaplan** (see p.2101) is the managing partner of the firm, and is very active in deals in the local Cleveland market. He brings his experience to bear when handling a wide range of complex matters. He provided input on Kitchen Basics' $40 million asset sale to McCormick & Co. **Megan Mehalko** (see p.2106) chairs the corporate and securities department from the Cleveland office. Sources respect her as a key name in the market who impresses with her adroit handling of transactional work.

### Calfee, Halter & Griswold LLP
See profile on p.2121

**THE FIRM** Clients are quick to praise this firm for its highly cost-effective service. It has proved itself more than capable of handling matters including public company and private equity work. Marquee clients of the practice include Invacare, KeyCorp and Cardinal Health. It acted as counsel to JM Smucker in a $400 million acquisition of a Sara Lee foodservice business.
**Sources say:** "Great value. I have seen them matched against Wall Street firms and they have done exceptionally well at a fraction of the cost." "A wonderful asset that we are so fortunate to have within the Cleveland business community."
**KEY INDIVIDUALS John Jenkins** (see p.2100) is a partner who can be relied upon for "excellent support," according to impressed clients, who note: "He has guided us through the difficult times." His areas of influence include securities work of both the debt and equity varieties. He recently advised JM Smucker on its $750 million 3.5% senior notes offering. **Michael Marhofer** (see p.2106) is a cochair of the M&A group. His broad practice includes counseling private equity entities as well as public companies, and he also serves on private company boards. He had a lead negotiating role in JM Smucker's acquisition listed above. **Steve Karzmer** (see p.2101) is a versatile attorney who is admitted to practice in New York and Massachusetts as well as Ohio. Sources were quick to point to him as "very able," adding that he is a "very smart guy who works hard." **Douglas Neary** (see p.2108) is co-head of the firm's M&A practice. Sources laud his keen client service ethos, describing him as "extremely responsive and sen-

sitive to the needs and wishes of general counsel." He advised Invacare in its acquisition of equity in Dynamic Medical Systems. **Thomas McKee** (see p.2106) is chairman of the firm, and is highly respected for his extensive experience and seniority in this space. He recently advised a number of underwriters on four public offerings for Health Care REIT. Clients describe him as an "excellent, trusted adviser in high-level business decisions." **Jennifer Vergilii** (see p.2115) enjoys a rising profile as "a practical, business-oriented M&A lawyer." Sources praise her can-do approach to deals: "She is very bright and just gets things done without fuss." She had a key role advising Cardinal Health on its acquisition of a pharmaceutical business.

### Hahn Loeser & Parks LLP
See profile on p.2123

**THE FIRM** Interviewees speak of the excellent levels of partner attention on offer from this Ohio stalwart. It is a reliable choice for pragmatic advice and highly cost-effective counsel in the region. Key clients for the practice include Jacobs Entertainment and Cliffs Natural Resources. It recently acted for Head USA as borrower on a $40 million senior secured credit facility.
**Sources say:** "Business-oriented and practical, and does not get bogged down in the legal nuances of every line in the agreement."
**KEY INDIVIDUALS Stanley Gorom** of the Cleveland office heads up the business group.

### Porter Wright Morris & Arthur LLP
See profile on p.2127

**THE FIRM** This firm has clients in a number of sectors, but has a particular profile in acting for banks and insurance companies in company financing and transactional matters. Its main reserve of lawyer talent practices out of the Columbus office. Highlights for the practice include advising The Crane Group on its $79 million disposal of its equity stake in Crane Plastics Siding, including related IP and indemnity issues.
**Sources say:** "Porter Wright seems to go the extra step." "Practical, cost-effective counsel."
**KEY INDIVIDUALS Mark Koogler** (see p.2103) heads up the M&A group and wins plaudits for getting on with the task at hand in an efficient and cost-effective manner. "While he charges a partner's rate, we save money working with him because he understands what needs to be done, how to do it, and has the skill and organization to make it happen fast," one client states. **Curtis Loveland** (see p.2105) is acclaimed as a "straight talker and hard worker. He is dedicated to resolving the problem as quickly and inexpensively as possible." His skill set includes securities as well as corporate matters. **Robert Tannous** (see p.2114) acted as lead partner on the Crane Group matter. Clients describe him as a "practical, get-it-done lawyer," citing his "calm, reassuring approach" and keen support as reasons to retain his counsel.

### Squire Sanders (US) LLP
See profile on p.2129

**THE FIRM** Interviewees agreed that the international profile of this firm means that it is well placed to advise on

large, high-value transactional work. It has offices in the three main Ohio cities, but has the highest profile via its Cleveland office. Highlights for the year include advising Telvent GIT in relation to its sale to Schneider Electric.
**KEY INDIVIDUALS David Zagore** (see p.2118) practices out of the Cleveland office and acted on the Telvent GIT matter. He is lead lawyer of the firm's Midwest corporate finance group. Sources praise him for being "accomplished and smart" in his dealings in the transactional space. Clients come to him for his broad skill set, which includes securities and capital markets advisory work.

### Taft Stettinius & Hollister LLP
See profile on p.2130

**THE FIRM** Transactions, corporate, credit agreement and securities work feature extensively on the work roster of this regional firm, especially in Cincinnati. The firm's merger with the Chester Willcox & Saxbe firm has also afforded it a recent boost. The firm recently advised One Equity Partners on its purchase of Aluprint and Grafo Regia, two Mexican packaging manufacturers.
**Sources say:** "An excellent fit for all business law needs of our firm."
**KEY INDIVIDUALS Gerald Greenberg** (see p.2098) chairs the M&A practice from the Cincinnati branch. He is an ideal choice for those seeking a "strong M&A and corporate attorney," according to clients. Sources cite his deep knowledge and long-time experience as reasons to retain his services. His client roster includes a number of venture capital fund managers, include Blue Chip Venture and Triathlon Medical Ventures.

## Other Notable Practitioners

**Mark Jahnke** is the CEO of Katz, Teller, Brant & Hild, and is highly regarded in the Cincinnati market for his adroit handling of transactional work. "He understands business and maintains good relationships with clients," according to sources. His clients include public and private companies as well as nonprofit entities. **Neil Ganulin** (see p.2097) is based at Frost Brown Todd LLC's Cincinnati office. Clients are quick to point to his high-level know-how of the transactional arena, describing him as "remarkably experienced, often demonstrating more knowledge and expertise than many of the New York firms we deal with." Clients he has assisted include entities from the manufacturing, healthcare and technology sectors. **Michael Hirschfeld** is an experienced corporate practitioner at Graydon Head & Ritchey LLP. Sources are keen to point to his high-level capabilities, and speak of him as "a lawyer's lawyer," saying also: "He is extremely knowledgeable and a gentleman." His talents include tax and M&A work. **Robert Ouellette** is a partner in the Columbus office of Ice Miller LLP, and serves as vice chair of the firm's business practice. Sources describe him as very talented in his handling of complex transactions, as well as a "strong negotiator." His key clients include private equity funds, and he recently advised Stonehenge Opportunity Fund III on a $45 million transaction.

# EMPLOYEE BENEFITS & EXECUTIVE COMPENSATION

Commentary about individuals can be found under their firm's paragraph. If the firm has no paragraph (is not ranked) look at Other Notable Practitioners.

## Employee Benefits & Executive Compensation Leading Firms

**Band 1**
Baker & Hostetler LLP *
Jones Day *
Thompson Hine LLP *
Vorys, Sater, Seymour and Pease LLP *

**Band 2**
Calfee, Halter & Griswold LLP *
Dinsmore & Shohl LLP
Porter Wright Morris & Arthur LLP *
Squire Sanders (US) LLP *
Taft Stettinius & Hollister LLP *
Ulmer & Berne LLP *

\* Indicates firm / individual with profile.
† ONP = Other Notable Practitioner

## Employee Benefits & Executive Compensation Leading Individuals

**Band 1**

| | |
|---|---|
| Hagen Daniel C | Jones Day * |
| Helmreich Richard J | Porter Wright Morris & Arthur LLP * |
| McGowan Jr John J | Baker & Hostetler LLP * |
| Mendel Linda | Vorys, Sater, Seymour and Pease LLP * |
| Starkey J Shane | Thompson Hine LLP * |
| Youngstrom Karen D | Thompson Hine LLP * |

**Band 2**

| | |
|---|---|
| Brown Timothy R | Thompson Hine LLP * |
| Ciriaco Anthony C | Vorys, Sater, Seymour and Pease LLP * |
| Dunsizer Jennifer | Vorys, Sater, Seymour and Pease LLP * |
| Fuchs Jack F | Thompson Hine LLP * |
| Kahn Ronald L | Ulmer & Berne LLP * |
| Laing Michael | Taft Stettinius & Hollister LLP * |
| Malone Raymond M | Baker & Hostetler LLP * |
| Peters Georgeann G | Baker & Hostetler LLP * |
| Shlonsky Patricia A | Ulmer & Berne LLP * |
| Stansbury Ronald C | Ulmer & Berne LLP * |
| Viviani Gregory J | Squire Sanders (US) LLP * |
| Wells Ben F | Dinsmore & Shohl LLP |
| Zimon Jeffrey D | Zimon LLC (ONP) † |

**Band 3**

| | |
|---|---|
| Appel John H | Frost Brown Todd LLC (ONP) † * |
| Caresani Ann M | Porter Wright Morris & Arthur LLP * |
| Clark Wade | Calfee, Halter & Griswold LLP * |
| Dakin Carol | Squire Sanders (US) LLP |
| Draucker Carl A | Squire Sanders (US) LLP * |
| Hauer Richard | Calfee, Halter & Griswold LLP * |
| Jochim Tim | Kegler, Brown, Hill & Ritter (ONP) † |
| Lazar Kathy | Jones Day * |
| Leavitt Jeffrey S | Jones Day * |
| Prior James | Porter Wright Morris & Arthur LLP * |
| Shaw Russell C | Walter & Haverfield LLP (ONP) † * |

**Up-and-coming individuals**

| | |
|---|---|
| Whaley David A | Dinsmore & Shohl LLP |

## Band 1

### Baker & Hostetler LLP
See profile on p.2119

**THE FIRM** This respected national firm has a notable Ohio presence in this field, offering carefully considered and pragmatic input on matters ranging from ERISA to medical benefit planning matters. Sources describe it as an extremely competent, high-end practice with a great partner foundation, particularly in the Cleveland office. Key clients include notable healthcare entities such as The Methodist Hospital, of Houston, Texas, and Teleflex. The team's recent highlights include advising Cardinal Health on due diligence work associated with the acquisition of Kinray.

**Sources say:** *"A very good firm." "A very strong national practice."*

**KEY INDIVIDUALS John McGowan** (see p.2106) is a Cleveland lawyer and a principal partner in the practice. He has a longstanding career acting for public and private companies, as well as plan fiduciaries, sponsors and beyond. He is a *"knowledgeable and well-prepared attorney,"* say sources, *"who works hard for clients."* The Cleveland-based **Raymond Malone** (see p.2105) recently completed 30 years of legal practice. He is recognized for his *"very strong"* input on matters in this arena. His recent highlights include advising the SEC as receiver, in connection with entities such as Michael Kenwood Group. He also has expertise in Taft-Hartley and COBRA matters. **Georgeann Peters** (see p.2109) is a key figure in the Columbus office, and recently acted on the Cardinal Health matter. Her broad skill set includes providing tax and nonprofit advice, as well as expertise in wider benefits issues. *"The quality and timeliness of her work are great,"* say sources, *"and she knows how to keep clients in compliance and out of trouble."*

### Jones Day
See profile on p.919

**THE FIRM** This firm receives recognition for its exceptional geographical reach and highly trained professionals. Its Cleveland team acts on a range of matters, including ESOP and high-level executive compensation work. The group has recently represented a number of public companies, including Macy's, in connection with executive compensation and employee benefits associated with the acquisition of May Department Stores. Other clients of the practice include STERIS.

**Sources say:** *"A great practice."*

**KEY INDIVIDUALS Daniel Hagen** (see p.2099) is the leader of the firm's dedicated employee benefits and executive compensation group. Sources point to his proven and deep expertise, as well as his interpersonal skills and

willingness to work with other counsel to obtain the right result. He has played a key role in marquee work, including in public company transactional work and executive compensation consultancy. **Jeffrey Leavitt** (see p.2104) is of counsel with the firm. He divides his time between pure employee benefits matters and tax-exempt work for nonprofit organizations. Sources agree he is a sound choice of counselor, and the right name for proficient service. Cleveland counsel **Kathy Lazar** (see p.2104) has years of experience gained from her time as in-house counsel for a public corporation before joining the firm. Sources speak of her as *"an excellent resource"* in areas including ERISA, deferred compensation and welfare benefits. She has acted for a number of impressive clients, including Macy's.

### Thompson Hine LLP
See profile on p.2131

**THE FIRM** Sources are quick to mention the superb bench strength and large lawyer head count of this firm's dedicated employee benefits and executive compensation group. The team's recent work includes advising Verizon Wireless on benefits and compensation matters arising from the company's multibillion-dollar acquisition of Alltel.

**Sources say:** *"The team has vast knowledge of issues, a deep bench, and is cost-effective."*

**KEY INDIVIDUALS Shane Starkey** (see p.2114) is managing partner of the firm's Cincinnati office, and is also the head of the executive compensation group. Sources paint a picture of a well-liked, proficient and communicative professional. **Karen Youngstrom** (see p.2118) is a key partner, lauded for being *"as good a technical lawyer as you will get in this area,"* according to enthusiastic sources. She *"obviously works very hard at knowing everything there is to know"* and *"always impresses."* She recently advised Eaton Corporation on its benefits and executive compensation matters. The *"excellent"* **Timothy Brown** (see p.2091) is admitted to practice in Georgia as well as in Ohio. He recently acted as lead partner on the Verizon Wireless/Alltel matter, and also counts Credit Suisse on his client list. He is known as an adept professional and *"technically very strong."* **Jack Fuchs** (see p.2096) uses his hybrid benefits and contentious legal skills to great effect, especially in his contentious ERISA practice. He is *"a very good litigator"* with long and enviable experience in the sector.

### Vorys, Sater, Seymour and Pease LLP
See profile on p.2133

**THE FIRM** This firm's superb benefits group is renowned for its capacity for getting to know clients thoroughly before dispensing advice, and for offering practical suggestions on the best way forward. The team counsels a number of household names on a range of employee benefits issues, including health and welfare matters. Key clients include Greif and Honda.

Sources say: *"The team is sensitive to the nature of our company's business and culture."* *"They are absolutely in tune with all legislative updates, and proactively contact us to provide information and education."*

**KEY INDIVIDUALS** Columbus lawyer **Linda Mendel** (see p.2107) is of counsel with the firm, and has a lead role on benefits work for Greif and Honda. She is described as *"always timely and responsive, and provides quality advice that takes into account clients' needs."* Sources go on to praise her *"exceptional abilities and attention to detail."* **Jennifer Dunsizer** (see p.2095) is also of counsel in the firm's Columbus office, and enjoys a rising market profile in this field. Clients speak of her as *"a great resource,"* and describe her service as *"extremely knowledgeable and helpful."* She is a principal relationship attorney for clients such as Big Lots, which she has counseled on a range of matters ranging from retirement to medical benefit issues associated with the acquisition of a Canadian subsidiary. **Anthony Ciriaco** (see p.2093) is the Columbus partner who heads up the firm's employee benefits practice in Ohio. Sources agree he is a reliable choice of counsel for efficient, well-considered legal advice, particularly in ERISA matters. His clients include Fortune 500 companies.

## Band 2

### Calfee, Halter & Griswold LLP
See profile on p.2121

**THE FIRM** The Cleveland branch of this regional firm stables a strong amount of notable talent in the benefits arena. Interviewees are impressed by the group's collaborative approach and its communicative attorneys, many of whom strike the right balance between client advocacy and consummating transactions. It has a number of ongoing relationships in this field, and acts for the likes of Medical Mutual of Ohio and FirstEnergy on their executive compensation, employee benefits and associated benefit plans. Sources say: *"It operates much as a partner, and its dedication and commitment to our business is outstanding."*

**KEY INDIVIDUALS** **Wade Clark** (see p.2093) wins plaudits for his intimate knowledge of relevant legislation, be it 401(k) or high-end executive compensation matters. **Richard Hauer** (see p.2099) heads up the employee benefits and executive compensation practice. He is the lead benefits lawyer for Medical Mutual of Ohio, and also counts FirstEnergy on his client list. He is well regarded for his adept command of the benefits area, and clients report *"fantastic"* experiences with him.

### Dinsmore & Shohl LLP

**THE FIRM** The practice has a strong showing in the Cincinnati market, and frequently acts on matters such as ESOP and plan compliance, as well as institutional trustee work. It advises entities across an array of sectors, including in the healthcare and restaurant industries. Key clients include Husky Energy and Health Services of the Virginias. Sources say: *"Well-regarded benefits lawyers."*

**KEY INDIVIDUALS** **Ben Wells** divides his time between the firm's DC and Cincinnati offices. He is a transactional partner who chairs the entire tax, benefits and wealth planning practice at the firm. He acts as the lead benefits lawyer for Husky Energy, and clients speak of him as a well-trained and adept practitioner: *"He is very professional and knows the subject matter."* The up-and-coming **David Whaley** is recommended as a *"very capable"* professional for benefits work. He is an expert in ESOP matters, and also has a broader practice encompassing health and welfare plans as well as defined benefit matters.

### Porter Wright Morris & Arthur LLP
See profile on p.2127

**THE FIRM** Porter Wright's Ohio team houses a broad spectrum of talent, ensuring it can advise seamlessly across qualified and nonqualified pension plans, deferred compensation issues and ERISA litigation. Key clients of the practice include American Electric Power, Children's Medical Center of Dayton and Dana Holding.

Sources say: *"I would consider the services and support we receive from Porter Wright to be superior in every way."*

**KEY INDIVIDUALS** **Richard Helmreich** (see p.2100) chairs the dedicated employee benefits practice at the firm. Clients seek out his services on account of his *"broad and deep understanding"* of the practice area. Other interviewees agree he is *"diligent, conscientious and provides excellent advice,"* and describe him as *"thorough, and extremely easy to work with."* **Ann Caresani** (see p.2092) enjoys a rising market profile for the quality of her work in this field. Her expertise covers plan formation, administration and wind-ups, as well as ESOP and COBRA work. Clients agree she is *"very well versed in the area of employee benefits."* **James Prior** (see p.2110) is praised for his *"quality legal work and his excellent client service."* Although his employee benefits practice is broad, he is praised by one client in particular for his *"very detailed understanding of ERISA; he lays out detailed guidance around particular issues and provides good step-by-step analysis."*

### Squire Sanders (US) LLP
See profile on p.2129

**THE FIRM** This international firm's dedicated taxation and benefits practice is enhanced by its reputation in high-end transactional work. The Cleveland office contains the bulk of the firm's strength in this arena, and it is a well-regarded and respected name. It has the resources to advise large multinational conglomerates on matters such as global employee stock plans.

**KEY INDIVIDUALS** **Carl Draucker** (see p.2095) is a Cleveland partner who recently completed 35 years of legal practice. His skill set is varied and includes tax-qualified plans, executive compensation and ESOP matters. Sources adjudge him to be a solid name in the market, and speak of his adept and reasonable manner in negotiations. Partner **Gregory Viviani** (see p.2115) enjoys a sound and respectable reputation in the Cleveland market in particular, advising on matters from ERISA to deferred compensation plans. His client roster includes major hospitals as well as tax-exempt entities. **Carol Dakin** is a senior partner who practices out of the Cleveland office. Sources describe her as *"certainly very competent, with lots of experience."*

Her clients include both public and private entities, which she advises on a broad spectrum of matters such as incentive compensation and COBRA issues.

### Taft Stettinius & Hollister LLP
See profile on p.2130

**THE FIRM** This firm's Cincinnati office in particular has a profile for quality employee benefits and executive compensation counsel via the firm's taxation department. Recent highlights for the practice include advising DPL in connection with its executive compensation arrangements relating to DPL's acquisition by AES.

**KEY INDIVIDUALS** Cincinnati partner **Michael Laing** (see p.2103) has a strong niche in taxation issues as they relate to benefits, and recently acted as lead lawyer on the DPL matter. Sources agree he is an impressive performer, and speak of his *"very strong analysis"* of complex issues.

### Ulmer & Berne LLP
See profile on p.2132

**THE FIRM** Ulmer & Berne offers quality of counsel across a range of benefits and compensation issues, including on plan formation, administration and transactional matters. The team is also particularly well versed in contentious benefits assignments. The group recently advised The Minster Machine Company in relation to a dispute over inclusion of allowances in pension calculations.

Sources say: *"They have a practical approach to providing legal advice."*

**KEY INDIVIDUALS** **Ronald Kahn** (see p.2101) is a senior figure backed by 40 years of experience in the sector. *"His approach is very detailed and thorough,"* said one source; *"we have always been extremely impressed."* His areas of expertise include ESOP matters. **Patricia Shlonsky** (see p.2112) divides her time between the firm's Cleveland and Cincinnati offices. She heads up the dedicated employee benefits, ERISA and executive compensation practice group, and had a lead role in the aforementioned Minster Machine Company litigation. Clients laud her *"amazing comprehension of both the US tax code and ERISA laws,"* and describe her advice as *"very cost-effective and, importantly, always correct."* **Ronald Stansbury** (see p.2113) wins recognition for being *"extremely knowledgeable about ERISA and benefit plans."* Clients also underline his *"unique combination of knowledge and leadership with a warm approachable personal style."* His clients include large local manufacturing companies, as well as key executives, who he advises on numerous issues, including on compensation packages.

### Other Notable Practitioners

**Jeffrey Zimon** left Benesch, Friedlander, Coplan & Aronoff LLP in 2012 to found Zimon LLC in Cleveland. Clients admire his legal knowledge and great commercial sense, leading one to exclaim: *"He's marvelous!"* His expertise covers a range of areas, including ERISA matters. Thompson Hine alumnus **Russell Shaw** (see p.2112) is a partner who leads the employee benefits practice at local Cleveland firm Walter & Haverfield LLP. Sources describe him as a *"very knowledgeable benefits lawyer"* with a long-standing and quality reputation in this arena. **John Appel** (see p.2089) of Frost Brown Todd LLC is a Cincinnati lawyer with a strong line in representing healthcare and corporate entities, among others. Sources point to his eye

for detail and his *"great experience"* in this field, and describe him as *"thorough and meticulous."* **Tim Jochim** is a firm director at Kegler, Brown, Hill & Ritter. He heads up the firm's ESOP and business succession group, and is recognized for his *"huge reputation in the ESOP area."* His

recent highlights include advising CTL Engineering on correction of a prohibited transaction related to a 401(k) plan.

# HEALTHCARE

Commentary about individuals can be found under their firm's paragraph. If the firm has no paragraph (is not ranked) look at Other Notable Practitioners.

### Healthcare
### Leading Firms

**Band 1**
Bricker & Eckler LLP
Jones Day *

**Band 2**
Baker & Hostetler LLP *
Benesch, Friedlander, Coplan & Aronoff LLP *
Frost Brown Todd LLC *
Ice Miller LLP
Porter Wright Morris & Arthur LLP *
Squire Sanders (US) LLP *
Taft Stettinius & Hollister LLP *
Vorys, Sater, Seymour and Pease LLP *

* Indicates firm / individual with profile.
†ONP = Other Notable Practitioner

### Healthcare
### Leading Individuals

| Band 1 | |
|---|---|
| Flynn James | *Bricker & Eckler LLP* |
| Gire Michael | *Bricker & Eckler LLP* |

| Band 2 | |
|---|---|
| Anthony Thomas | *Frost Brown Todd LLC* * |
| Daniels Anthea | *Calfee, Halter & Griswold LLP (ONP)† * * |
| Dutton Thomas E | *Jones Day* * |

| Band 3 | |
|---|---|
| Ballard Catherine | *Bricker & Eckler LLP* |
| Brown Harry M | *Benesch, Friedlander, Coplan & Aronoff* * |
| Dawley Kris | *Ice Miller LLP* |
| Dunlay Catherine | *Taft Stettinius & Hollister LLP* * |
| Feldkamp Janet | *Benesch, Friedlander, Coplan & Aronoff* * |
| Grauer David W | *Squire Sanders (US) LLP* * |
| Kahle Thomas W | *Baker & Hostetler LLP* * |
| Kapp Jeffrey L | *Jones Day* * |
| King Roger | *Jones Day* * |
| McAdams Robert | *Porter Wright Morris & Arthur LLP* * |
| Scrutton Suzanne | *Vorys, Sater, Seymour and Pease LLP* * |
| Signoracci Diane | *Bricker & Eckler LLP* |
| Terapak Rich | *Porter Wright Morris & Arthur LLP* * |
| Turcotte Claire | *Bricker & Eckler LLP* |

| Up-and-coming individuals | |
|---|---|
| Havens Jolie | *Vorys, Sater, Seymour and Pease LLP* * |

| Associates to watch | |
|---|---|
| Albers Matthew | *Vorys, Sater, Seymour and Pease LLP* * |

## Band 1

### Bricker & Eckler LLP

**THE FIRM** Sources laud Bricker & Eckler's 40-strong lawyer healthcare team for its prowess in this area. It has enviably close relationships with organizations ranging from large healthcare systems to smaller local community hospitals. Interviewees also praise the team's ability to call on substantial resources when necessary. Highlights include acting for the Ohio Hospital Association on the negotiation of a Medicaid Incentive Payment Program. Other key clients include OhioHealth and Nationwide Children's Hospital.

**Sources say:** *"They are very competent, timely and effective." "They have a complete working knowledge of the healthcare field."*

**KEY INDIVIDUALS** The *"bright and personable"* **James Flynn** is a well-established Columbus lawyer and chair of the firm's healthcare practice. He recently acted as lead counsel for the Ohio Hospital Association on the Medicaid matter. According to interviewees, he is *"tremendously responsive and forward-thinking; he acts as a collaborator and doesn't just provide legal guidance, but helps us work through the issues and develop plans and processes to better address issues."* The tremendously experienced **Michael Gire** is lauded as *"very thorough and detail oriented,"* as well as *"extremely client focused."* His recent highlights include advising Adena Health System on its affiliation with Pike Community Hospital. **Diane Signoracci**'s practice includes advising on healthcare regulatory and contentious work, such as Medicare reimbursement. One

impressed client said: *"Her expertise, guidance and commitment to ensuring we have the best contracts have been key to our business. If Diane has worked through a contract, it is an assurance that we are in good standing."* Columbus partner **Catherine Ballard** is vice chair of the healthcare practice and a director of the firm's affiliated healthcare consultancy. Sources highlight her as an experienced and highly skilled attorney, particularly in medical staff work. She recently led the team acting for Mount Carmel Health System on its multisite staff integration project. **Claire Turcotte** is commended as *"an important asset"* when large and important decisions need to be taken in the healthcare transactional arena, including in the recruitment of physicians and acquisition of healthcare groups. She played a key role in the Adena Health System/Pike Community Hospital matter.

### Jones Day
See profile on p.919

**THE FIRM** This is a go-to firm for the largest and most complex transactional work in the state and beyond, and its healthcare practice in Ohio is no exception. It is active on compliance and STARK work, and the team's access to the firm's deep resources enables it to advise on the full range of legal issues affecting this sector, including antitrust, compliance, and hospital-to-hospital affiliations. Key clients include Cleveland Clinic Foundation, Yale New Haven Health System and Stanford Hospital & Clinics.

**Sources say:** *"An exceptional firm in terms of breadth and depth of healthcare law skills."*

**KEY INDIVIDUALS** **Thomas Dutton** (see p.2095) is actively involved in high-level work in this field, for clients such as Yale New Haven Health System. Sources admire his interpersonal skills and impressive command of the law, describing him as *"great to work with"* as well as *"personable and knowledgeable,"* adding that *"he knows how to run big deals."* **Roger King** (see p.2102) is of counsel in the firm's Columbus branch. He has built a notable profile in advising on labor and employment issues pertaining to the healthcare sector, and has extensive experience in NLRA, ADA and employment grievance matters. *"We consider him a national expert and his counsel is valued very highly by us,"* said one delighted client. **Jeffrey Kapp** (see p.2101) is a key Cleveland partner in the healthcare practice. He is a transactional lawyer with a growing profile in hospital-to-hospital affiliation work, and in the disposal and acquisition of healthcare interests. Clients underline his keen and timely client service ethic, with one describing him as *"the most responsive attorney I have ever worked with; he will juggle his schedule to meet my needs whenever I call."*

## Band 2

### Baker & Hostetler LLP
See profile on p.2119

**THE FIRM** Sources praise the levels of insight and guidance on offer at this firm. The group is a reliable choice of counsel for a variety of clients, including University of Louisville Physicians, Mercy Medical Center and Holzer Clinic. It is prominent in the healthcare transactional area in particular, and also assists with Federal Insurance Contributions Act (FICA) and healthcare litigation, among other matters.

Sources say: *"Down-to-earth folks who are excellent at what they do!"*

**KEY INDIVIDUALS Thomas Kahle** (see p.2101) is praised for his sensitive and pragmatic approach to healthcare transactional work. *"He demonstrated wonderful maturity and the ability to work through issues with us,"* said one particularly impressed source.

## Benesch, Friedlander, Coplan & Aronoff LLP
See profile on p.2120

**THE FIRM** This 11-lawyer practice has established a number of mutually profitable relationships in the market, especially in the nursing home and senior care sector. Recent transactional work includes advising AccentCare on its acquisition of Senior Select and At Home Companions. Other key clients include Genesis HealthCare System, Blue Sky Therapy and Communicare Health Services.

Sources say: *"Excellent counsel." "Very knowledgeable."*

**KEY INDIVIDUALS Harry Brown** (see p.2091) is one of the principal names in the firm's Cleveland office, and is particularly known for his work on behalf of nursing homes. He handles a range of healthcare regulatory matters, such as healthcare reimbursement and Certificate of Need work. Columbus partner **Janet Feldkamp** (see p.2096) is also a registered nurse, and is highlighted for her *"wonderful insights which can bridge the clinical and legal professions."* Clients praise her great wealth of knowledge and attest that she is *"very articulate"* in her delivery of advice. Her areas of influence include long-term care matters.

## Frost Brown Todd LLC
See profile on p.1329

**THE FIRM** This firm is an excellent choice for healthcare matters, particularly in the Cincinnati market. In addition to its solid expertise in hospital work, the group has a high profile for quality representation of physician interests. Its recent highlights include advising a major metropolitan health system on establishing an integrated delivery system. Clients of the practice include local hospitals and suppliers to the healthcare industry.

**KEY INDIVIDUALS Thomas Anthony** (see p.2089) practices out of the firm's Cincinnati office, and leads the healthcare practice. He is a former healthcare industry executive, and benefits from extensive real-world experience of the sector. Sources describe him as *"a good lawyer who knows his stuff and advocates well for clients."*

## Ice Miller LLP

**THE FIRM** This practice continues to be highly respected in healthcare, especially for its contentious work. A number of hospitals seek out its services in areas including class action healthcare reimbursement litigation.

**KEY INDIVIDUALS Kris Dawley** is the principal healthcare lawyer here, and practices out of the Columbus office. His litigation background stands him in good stead when disputes arise, but he is also able to assist in transactional work. He is recognized for his quality advocacy and focused practice.

## Porter Wright Morris & Arthur LLP
See profile on p.2127

**THE FIRM** Sources praise Porter Wright's effective counsel in this arena, particularly from its Columbus office. It is highlighted as a reliable choice for up-to-date advice, and for its expertise in a range of reimbursement, regulatory and federal agency issues, among other areas. The team recently acted for a healthcare entity on establishing a clinically integrated group. Key clients include OhioHealth and Polaris Surgery Center.

Sources say: *"They have expert knowledge regarding healthcare issues." "The team stays abreast of trends in healthcare, and provides opinions based on a broad base of knowledge."*

**KEY INDIVIDUALS Robert McAdams** (see p.2106) is lauded as a *"talented and knowledgeable"* expert in the field. *"He really knows the business ins and outs of healthcare and is one of the most creative healthcare lawyers I have encountered to find legal solutions to complex regulatory problems,"* said one impressed client. McAdams's expertise covers both compliance and transactional matters in the industry. **Rich Terapak** (see p.2115) brings substantial financing experience to transactional work, as a former in-house bank counsel. Sources describe him as *"knowledgeable, capable, articulate and timely."*

## Squire Sanders (US) LLP
See profile on p.2129

**THE FIRM** Squire Sanders has one of the stronger practices in the state, highlighted in particular for its broad healthcare expertise encompassing hospital and managed care work, among other issues. Its strong national and international profile stands it in good stead for cross-state and cross-border work as well.

Sources say: *"We have deep respect for the team, and rely heavily upon it." "It has a very big healthcare presence."*

**KEY INDIVIDUALS** Columbus partner **David Grauer** (see p.2098) leads the firm's healthcare and life sciences practice. His professional credentials are impressive: he is a qualified pharmacist and also has experience in hospital management. Sources especially admire his impressive handling of contractual negotiations for hospitals.

## Taft Stettinius & Hollister LLP
See profile on p.2130

**THE FIRM** Sources agree this firm is a respected name in the healthcare arena. The 30-strong team has an impressive client list including health systems as well as physician groups, such as Kettering Health Network and Ohio State University Physicians. Recent highlights include representing TriHealth in its acquisition of a hospital and a surgery center.

**KEY INDIVIDUALS Catherine Dunlay** (see p.2095) co-heads the firm's health and life sciences group. She *"has a good presence in the local market,"* say sources, who add that *"she is extremely time responsive and a trusted source to simply take over a project."*

## Vorys, Sater, Seymour and Pease LLP
See profile on p.2133

**THE FIRM** Clients were quick to praise the high level of service on offer at this firm, as well as its deft handling of matters such as fraud and abuse, STARK issues, and complex contractual work. Other sources praise the broad spectrum of expertise here. The team's key clients include hospitals and retirement community management entities.

Sources say: *"I have used quite a few firms throughout the East Coast and I have to say that Vorys far exceeds any interactions with those firms."*

**KEY INDIVIDUALS Suzanne Scrutton** (see p.2112) has substantial prior healthcare and regulatory experience as a former chief legal counsel to the local government's alcohol and drug addiction service. Clients laud her skilled and commercial manner, with one saying: *"She approaches every engagement with knowledge, experience, and a pragmatic approach to attain the result we seek."* **Jolie Havens** (see p.2099) is recognized for her sterling contribution to the healthcare practice. Her key work includes acting as lead counsel to a major hospital system on the opening of a new hospital, including extensive associated compliance work. **Matthew Albers** (see p.2089) is a former in-house associate general counsel for a health system. Now in private practice, he is of counsel in the firm's Cleveland branch. Sources describe him as *"very knowledgeable and practical,"* with excellent first-hand experience of the pressures clients face.

## Other Notable Practitioners

**Anthea Daniels** (see p.2094) is a partner in Calfee, Halter & Griswold LLP's Cleveland office. She cochairs the healthcare and life sciences practice, and advises on the spectrum of healthcare transactional and regulatory matters. She wins acclaim for her winning combination of sound and effective legal and communication skills. *"She is great, very approachable and knowledgeable,"* according to sources.

# INTELLECTUAL PROPERTY

Commentary about individuals can be found under their firm's paragraph. If the firm has no paragraph (is not ranked) look at Other Notable Practitioners.

## Intellectual Property
### Leading Firms

**Band 1**
Jones Day *

**Band 2**
Calfee, Halter & Griswold LLP *
Frost Brown Todd LLC *
Wood, Herron & Evans, LLP

**Band 3**
Baker & Hostetler LLP *
Dinsmore & Shohl LLP
Thompson Hine LLP *

**Band 4**
Benesch, Friedlander, Coplan & Aronoff LLP *
Hahn Loeser & Parks LLP *
Kegler, Brown, Hill & Ritter *
Pearne & Gordon
Renner, Otto, Boisselle & Sklar LLP
Taft Stettinius & Hollister LLP *

## Band 1

### Jones Day
See profile on p.919

**THE FIRM** This indigenous Ohio firm's highly impressive national and global reach affords it a high profile in many practice areas, and IP is no exception. It is a popular choice for handling high-stakes matters on behalf of large business interests, including notable patent litigation in the chemical and technology arenas. Its client roster includes household names Procter & Gamble and Canon. Highlights for the practice include advising DePuy Spine on a high-value noncompete and trade secret dispute.
**Sources say:** "*Regularly trusted by Fortune 250 and 500 companies for mission-critical work.*"
**KEY INDIVIDUALS** Cleveland partner **Rob Ducatman** (see p.2095) coordinates the firm's Ohio IP work. His skill set includes patent and trademark disputes as well as trade secret matters, and he acted as lead counsel on the DePuy Spine trade secret litigation. Sources are in no doubt about his profile or the effectiveness of his counsel, with one interviewee remarking that "*he is certainly a main player and a good lawyer.*" **Cal Griffith** (see p.2098) earns considerable respect in the market for the quality of his patent work in particular, with sources noting that "*he is articulate and technically sound on what he is arguing, both legally and scientifically.*" **Jim Wamsley** (see p.2116) is admitted to practice before the USPTO as well as in Ohio. He is recognized for his prowess in the patent area, including court litigation involving hi-tech and software matters. Significant clients he has advised include Eastman Kodak and Sprint Nextel.

## Band 2

### Calfee, Halter & Griswold LLP
See profile on p.2121

**THE FIRM** This sizable, proficient and effective IP group is particularly noted for its patent prosecution talents. Key clients include famous household brands such as Procter & Gamble, Lincoln Electric and Owens Corning. Highlights for the group include advising Invacare on protracted patent litigation proceedings.
**Sources say:** "*Strong substantively in patent prosecution and patent litigation.*"
**KEY INDIVIDUALS John Cipolla** (see p.2093) is the chair of the firm's intellectual property practice. He is adjudged "*very capable*" in his legal practice, and has the know-how to handle both transactional and contentious work. He recently advised US Endoscopy Group on strategy and IP portfolio management, among other matters. **Charles Lyon** (see p.2105) is a senior counsel in the firm and is highly regarded for his depth of knowledge in this area. He had a lead role in the aforementioned Invacare matter.

### Frost Brown Todd LLC
See profile on p.1329

**THE FIRM** Market feedback confirms Frost Brown Todd to be a sound choice in IP matters. The team handles a variety of work, including patent prosecution, trademark matters and copyright counseling. Clients include Chiquita Brands, ClarkDietrich Building Systems and Kao Brands.
**Sources say:** "*The firm gives tailored advice to our business, consistent with our goals in protecting our IP.*"
**KEY INDIVIDUALS** Cincinnati lawyer **Steven Goldstein** (see p.2097) is vice chair of Frost Brown Todd's IP practice. He is well regarded in the market, with sources speaking favorably of his all-encompassing skill set in the contentious and portfolio management aspects of IP. In the words of one interviewee, "*he can take a case from complaint to trial, conduct discovery in between, argue motions and advise his clients.*" **David Schmit** (see p.2112) is admitted to practice before the USPTO as well as the Ohio state bar and the Supreme Court. His practice includes high-value, IP-related disputes work, and he has substantial litigation experience, including acting as first chair trial counsel in patent, trademark and trade secret matters. **Karlyn Schnapp** (see p.2112) gained a PhD in organic chemistry before training as a lawyer, making her ideally placed to appreciate the nuances of this practice area, particularly in the area of patent prosecution. **Ann Schoen** (see p.2112) heads the IP practice group. Clients greatly appreciate her strong understanding of the technical aspects of manufacturing, noting that "*we really do work in partnership with her.*"

## Intellectual Property
### Senior Statesmen

| Senior Statesmen: | distinguished older practitioners |
|---|---|
| Germain Kenneth B | Wood, Herron & Evans, LLP |
| Killworth Richard | Dinsmore & Shohl LLP |
| Lyon Charles | Calfee, Halter & Griswold LLP * |

### Leading Individuals

| Band 1 | |
|---|---|
| Ebling Louis K | Thompson Hine LLP * |
| Gillen Stephen E | Wood, Herron & Evans, LLP |
| Goldstein Steven J | Frost Brown Todd LLC * |
| Roesch Lynda E | Dinsmore & Shohl LLP |

| Band 2 | |
|---|---|
| Auvil Steven | Squire Sanders (US) LLP (ONP)† * |
| Cipolla John S | Calfee, Halter & Griswold LLP * |
| Ducatman Robert | Jones Day * |
| Gaunt Karen Kreider | Dinsmore & Shohl LLP |
| Griffith Calvin P | Jones Day * |
| Kozlowski Holly D | Porter Wright Morris & Arthur (ONP)† * |
| Lyman Beverly | Thompson Hine LLP * |
| Rector Susan D | Ice Miller LLP (ONP)† |
| Schmit David E | Frost Brown Todd LLC * |
| Schnapp Karlyn | Frost Brown Todd LLC * |
| Sopko Jeffrey J | Pearne & Gordon |
| Wamsley James | Jones Day * |
| Wentsler Stephen S | Pearne & Gordon |

| Band 3 | |
|---|---|
| Brinkman David | Wood, Herron & Evans, LLP |
| Dreitler Joseph R | Dreitler True, LLC (ONP)† |
| Garvin Michael | Hahn Loeser & Parks LLP * |
| Kirsch Kevin W | Baker & Hostetler LLP * |
| Krafte Lori E | Wood, Herron & Evans, LLP |
| Lawson Margaret | Taft Stettinius & Hollister LLP * |
| Levy Mark P | Thompson Hine LLP * |
| Lunn Gregory | Wood, Herron & Evans, LLP |
| Mancino David A | Baker & Hostetler LLP * |
| Mueller John M | Baker & Hostetler LLP * |
| Pingor James | Kegler, Brown, Hill & Ritter |
| Schoen Ann G. | Frost Brown Todd LLC * |
| Shunk Thomas H | Baker & Hostetler LLP * |
| Smith Kathryn | Wood, Herron & Evans, LLP |
| Watkins Mark A | Hahn Loeser & Parks LLP * |
| Weinberg James | Ulmer & Berne LLP (ONP)† * |
| Wilcox Deborah A | Baker & Hostetler LLP * |

### Up-and-coming individuals
| Barsotti Stephen C | Kegler, Brown, Hill & Ritter |
|---|---|

* Indicates firm / individual with profile.
† ONP = Other Notable Practitioner

## Wood, Herron & Evans, LLP

**THE FIRM** This respected IP boutique handles a range of patent, trademark and unfair competition work, all the way up to the courtroom level. Clients include household names such as Procter & Gamble, Walmart and Goodyear. **Sources say:** *"A deep firm with good people across the board in IP."*

**KEY INDIVIDUALS Stephen Gillen** ascends to the top tier of IP lawyers in Ohio after receiving strong recognition for his publishing, software and copyright-focused practice. Clients appreciate his careful counsel and keen appreciation of commercial pressures, with one interviewee noting: *"He comes from an approach of understanding our needs, with an eye towards cost versus benefit."* **David Brinkman** focuses his practice on the mechanical and electrical technology space, and is able to draw on his significant prior experience in the electronics testing industry to advise clients on all relevant IP matters. **Lori Krafte** has a notable profile in trademark and advertising work, including domain name advice and dispute resolution. *"She represents us well and allows us to avoid many common pitfalls,"* said one highly satisfied client. **Gregory Lunn** is admitted to practice in Kentucky as well as in Ohio. He uses his background in chemistry to good effect in the chemical patent prosecution area in particular. Sources praise his speed and skill in identifying the crux of the matter: *"He is good at grabbing onto the key issue and separating the wheat from the chaff."* **Kathryn Smith** is noted for her trademark work, with interviewees highlighting her pragmatic approach to IP dispute resolution. She also advises on the related areas of advertising, copyright and domain names. Of counsel **Kenneth Germain** is a senior figure in the Ohio IP bar and a recognized expert in trademark, trade dress and unfair competition cases.

## Band 3

### Baker & Hostetler LLP
See profile on p.2119

**THE FIRM** This respected firm continues to develop its IP practice in Ohio, with an emerging Cincinnati presence complementing its established Cleveland offering. The team is routinely involved in high-stakes litigation, recently advising Funai Electric and Funai Corporation on a number of patent infringement claims. Other key clients of the practice include Caterpillar, Cincinnati Bell and Google. **Sources say:** *"It has a decent profile, and is a very good firm."* **KEY INDIVIDUALS Thomas Shunk** (see p.2113) is perhaps best known in the Cleveland market for his astute handling of contentious IP work, particularly patent litigation. Sources praise his effectual litigation style, describing him as a *"very respectable litigator and a straight shooter."* He advised Graco Children's Products on an ITC complaint concerning alleged infringement of its patents. Cleveland partner **Deborah Wilcox** (see p.2117) has developed a respectable profile in the soft IP space. Her major highlights include acting as lead counsel for Bloomin' Brands in connection with trademark, advertising and

enforcement work. Clients were keen to recommend her, with one noting that *"she is very good – she cuts to the chase, and is very practical and easy to work with."* **Kevin Kirsch** (see p.2102) has a broad IP practice covering trademark, trade dress, copyright and patent litigation. Recent highlights include acting as first chair litigator on the Funai patent infringement dispute. **David Mancino** (see p.2105) practices in the Cincinnati office and is acclaimed for his patent prosecution and litigation work. He acted as lead technical counsel on a number of patent litigation matters for Funai companies. **John Mueller** (see p.2108) recently left Taft Stettinius & Hollister to join Baker Hostetler's Cincinnati branch as counsel. He is currently a key adviser to Big Lots Stores on trademark, patent and IP litigation, among other matters.

## Dinsmore & Shohl LLP

**THE FIRM** This IP team is noted for its handling of IP portfolios for high-profile clients in a range of industries, including automotive, manufacturing and publishing. It is particularly prominent in the Cincinnati and Dayton areas.

**KEY INDIVIDUALS** The *"very well-respected"* **Lynda Roesch** is one of the most prominent IP practitioners in Ohio, and is noted for her high-level trademark prosecution work. She is equally comfortable in contentious and noncontentious matters, and has substantial experience of trial and appellate work. **Karen Gaunt** is respected by the market for her broad skill set, which includes trademarks, branding and advertising work. She has experience in both transactional and contentious work, and has acted for household names such as Procter & Gamble. **Richard Killworth** is a senior partner in the firm's Dayton office and is rightly lauded for his outstanding contribution to the IP bar. Sources deem him a *"very good patent prosecutor,"* and highlight the frequency of his appearances as an expert witness as evidence of his enduring prominence.

## Thompson Hine LLP
See profile on p.2131

**THE FIRM** This respected regional firm is recognized for its patent prosecution and IP litigation capabilities, and is highly active in restrictive covenant and trade secret disputes. Clients include Thermo Fisher Scientific, Intercept Pharmaceuticals and Fruit of the Loom.

**KEY INDIVIDUALS** The highly experienced **Louis Ebling** (see p.2095) is noted by sources for his expertise in the trademark arena. He recently advised Hill-Rom Services on its ongoing trademark procurement and enforcement activities. **Beverly Lyman** (see p.2105) is an effective choice of counsel for patent work in the chemical, medical and life sciences arenas. Her client roster includes Thermo Fisher Scientific. **Mark Levy** (see p.2104) is a partner in the firm's Dayton office, and a former chair of the IP practice. He handles the management, prosecution and enforcement of all aspects of intellectual property.

## Band 4

### Benesch, Friedlander, Coplan & Aronoff LLP
See profile on p.2120

**THE FIRM** This firm has a solid profile for IP work in the Cleveland area, acting for high-caliber clients such as Eaton Corporation and Eastman Kodak. Recent highlights include a number of high-stakes IP disputes, such as acting for mowing equipment manufacturer Alamo Group on a keenly contested patent infringement action. **KEY INDIVIDUALS Mark Avsec** is a key contact.

### Hahn Loeser & Parks LLP
See profile on p.2123

**THE FIRM** Hahn Loeser & Parks has recognized IP strength in its Akron and Cleveland offices. The 29-strong Ohio team acts on joint development agreements, patents and design matters, among others. Clients include Lincoln Electric, Electrolux North America and Norco Industries. **KEY INDIVIDUALS Michael Garvin** (see p.2097) has a rising profile in the IP arena due to his adroit handling of patent litigation and trial work. He recently advised Techtronic Floor Care Technology on a high stakes patent litigation action. **Mark Watkins** (see p.2116) cochairs the IP and technology practice at the firm. Sources are quick to emphasize his keen client service ethic, with one interviewee noting that *"he has a consistent, no-nonsense approach to client interactions, and uses sound logic to guide and recommend actions designed to maximize our corporate legal budget."*

### Kegler, Brown, Hill & Ritter
See profile on p.2125

**THE FIRM** This firm's growing IP practice has a strong presence, acting on copyright disputes, trade secrets and patent prosecution from its offices in Columbus and Cleveland. The team is experienced in working across a range of sectors, including manufacturing, financial services, healthcare and software, and its impressive client roster includes Wells Fargo and NASA Glenn Research. **Sources say:** *"We appreciate their advice, their presentation to us and others, their 'off the clock' guidance... they are great collaborators."* **KEY INDIVIDUALS James Pingor**'s areas of influence include patent preparation, processing and prosecution. Clients appreciate his direct, communicative manner, with one source noting that *"he can communicate in layman's terms, and is very detailed and approachable when I have a concern or question."* **Stephen Barsotti** focuses on transactional advice related to the IP arena. Sources highlight his *"calm demeanor,"* and state that he is *"easy to work with and very responsive."* Recent highlights include advising restaurant chain The Piada Group.

### Pearne & Gordon

**THE FIRM** This long-established Cleveland boutique has been handling IP matters in Ohio since the early 20th century. It offers a comprehensive IP service, but is perhaps best known for its enviable patent prosecution practice. **Sources say:** *"A good, solid boutique."*

**KEY INDIVIDUALS Stephen Wentsler**'s areas of expertise include patent prosecution related to the mechanical engineering area. One source describes him as a *"very bright patent prosecutor,"* and *"one of the hardest workers I have seen."* **Jeffrey Sopko** is praised as a *"good-quality practitioner"* in the patent arena. His admission to practice in the Supreme Court enables him to advise seamlessly on related litigation and appellate work.

### Renner, Otto, Boisselle & Sklar LLP

**THE FIRM** This Cleveland IP boutique is one of the most-established firms in the state. Sources speak of the team's enviable skill set and fine reputation in areas such as patent prosecution and litigation.

**KEY INDIVIDUALS** Donald Otto is the firm's managing partner.

### Taft Stettinius & Hollister LLP
See profile on p.2130

**THE FIRM** This firm's 16-strong Ohio IP team handles IP prosecution and litigation for a number of notable clients, including Hershey and Oki Semiconductor. Recent highlights include advising CostQuest Associates on trademark and licensing matters.

**Sources say:** *"The firm is valued for its experience, quick response times and honesty."*

**KEY INDIVIDUALS Margaret Lawson** (see p.2103) heads up the IP practice from the Cincinnati office. Clients praise her effectual and pragmatic style, describing her as *"knowledgeable, responsive and well connected in overseas markets."*

### Other Notable Practitioners

**Holly Kozlowski** (see p.2103) of Porter Wright Morris & Arthur LLP is considered an astute adviser in areas such as patent validity and trade secret work. She draws warm praise from the market, with one source noting that *"she*

*combines technological and legal experience; many times her great understanding of both these areas has enabled us to understand difficult situations."* **Susan Rector** of Ice Miller LLP is recognized as a proficient and effective trademark practitioner. Her impressive client list includes Cleveland Track Material. **Joseph Dreitler** is a name partner of compact Columbus firm Dreitler True, LLC. He is acclaimed for his strong command of the IP arena, with sources agreeing that he *"is very tenacious and really knows his stuff."* **James Weinberg** (see p.2117) of Ulmer & Berne LLP is a litigator with a recognized focus on IP disputes work. Sources praise him as being *"responsive, diligent and cost conscious."* **Steven Auvil** (see p.2089) of Squire Sanders (US) LLP is noted for his aggressive and convincing performance in IP litigation. Sources emphasize his ability to concentrate on the key issues, with one interviewee revealing that *"he can really cut through to what is important; he is no-nonsense, and relates well to juries and clients."*

# LABOR & EMPLOYMENT

Commentary about individuals can be found under their firm's paragraph. If the firm has no paragraph (is not ranked) look at Other Notable Practitioners.

| Labor & Employment |
| --- |
| **Leading Firms** |
| **Band 1** |
| Baker & Hostetler LLP * |
| Frantz Ward LLP * |
| Frost Brown Todd LLC * |
| Porter Wright Morris & Arthur LLP * |
| Taft Stettinius & Hollister LLP * |
| **Band 2** |
| Denlinger, Rosenthal & Greenberg LPA |
| Dinsmore & Shohl LLP |
| Fisher & Phillips LLP * |
| Jackson Lewis LLP * |
| Jones Day * |
| Littler Mendelson, PC * |
| Ogletree, Deakins, Nash, Smoak & Stewart, PC * |
| Squire Sanders (US) LLP * |
| Vorys, Sater, Seymour and Pease LLP * |
| **Band 3** |
| Benesch, Friedlander, Coplan & Aronoff LLP * |
| Bricker & Eckler LLP |
| Kegler, Brown, Hill & Ritter * |

*Indicates firm with profile.*
*Alphabetical order within each band. Band 1 is the highest.*

## Band 1

### Baker & Hostetler LLP
See profile on p.2119

**THE FIRM** The number and caliber of lawyers dedicated to labor and employment law at this firm give it a remarkably strong profile in the state and beyond, including in notable work for entities with a public service nexus. Highlights for the practice include advising CSX

Transportation on a hotly contested EEOC case involving significant traditional labor issues. Other key clients include EW Scripps and the City of Columbus.

**Sources say:** *"It has a really good base from which it can launch its abilities across a national network."* *"The firm is intuitive and proactive, and dedicates the resources and time necessary to help us develop and maintain a positive labor relations environment, while positioning us to prevail when arbitrations or litigation arise."*

**KEY INDIVIDUALS John Lewis** (see p.2104) heads the firm's dedicated employment and civil rights class action group. He is a highly respected attorney who remains active in complex employment disputes in the state. He acted as lead adviser on the aforementioned CSX Transportation litigation. **Gregory Mersol** (see p.2107) wins plaudits for his command of the courtroom process. He has proven skills in multiparty litigation, including employment class and collective actions. *"He approaches cases cerebrally, analytically and tactically, with an eye toward procedural defenses,"* say sources; *"his work is consistently excellent."* **Ronald Linville** (see p.2105) was recently appointed managing partner of the firm's Columbus office. He is described as a *"highly skilled labor and employment lawyer"* who can be relied upon to do a *"typically top-notch job,"* both in employment litigation and traditional labor matters. He remains labor relations counsel to the Central Ohio Transit Authority (COTA). Cleveland partner **Stephen Sutton** (see p.2114) can call on well-developed legal and trial skills to advise employer clients effectively, whether inside or outside the courtroom. Sources highlight his excellent abilities in handling complex employment disputes across a number of arenas, including state and federal courts. **Martin Wymer** (see p.2118) co-leads the firm's national employment litigation group, and is recognized for his broad skill set covering employment

litigation, counseling and traditional labor matters. He is also admitted to practice in the US Supreme Court, enabling him to advise on keenly contested appellate matters. **Mike Asensio** (see p.2089) leads the firm's national labor relations practice, and is described as an effective management-focused union negotiator in his own right. Clients are quick to praise his communication and legal skills, referring to him as a *"talented employment defense litigator and labor lawyer who can interact effectively with all levels of the organization."* His clients include Cameron International.

### Frantz Ward LLP
See profile on p.2122

**THE FIRM** Frantz Ward remains a preeminent leader across all manner of labor and employment issues, and is recognized for its effective expansion of key related areas of expertise. Based in Cleveland, the firm has a remarkable profile throughout the state, and undertakes the full range of matters, including collective bargaining, wage and hour compliance and ERISA questions.

**Sources say:** *"A strong regional boutique."*

**KEY INDIVIDUALS** *"Outstanding"* name partner **Michael Frantz** (see p.2096) is *"very bright,"* and spends much of his time on contentious work as well as labor and employment. He earns praise for his interpersonal skills as well as his enviable command of both employment and traditional labor. **Merritt Bumpass** (see p.2091) heads up the firm's labor and employment practice group. Sources praise his efficient case management skills and his effectiveness in mitigating risks to employers. His wide experience includes federal and state court assignments, as well as traditional labor work such as collective bargaining. **Daniel Ward** (see p.2116) is recognized for bringing a pragmatic approach to the lawyer-client relationship. His

## Labor & Employment
### Leading Individuals

**Band 1**

| | | |
|---|---|---|
| Adams Deborah | Frost Brown Todd LLC * | |
| Barnard Thomas H | Ogletree, Deakins, Nash, Smoak & Stewart * | |
| Frantz Michael | Frantz Ward LLP * | |
| King Roger | Jones Day * | |
| Reilly Timothy P | Taft Stettinius & Hollister LLP * | |
| Rosenthal Daniel G | Denlinger, Rosenthal & Greenberg LPA | |
| Siegel Bradd N | Porter Wright Morris & Arthur LLP * | |
| Warner Charles C | Porter Wright Morris & Arthur LLP * | |

**Band 2**

| | |
|---|---|
| Bixenstine Barton A | Vorys, Sater, Seymour and Pease LLP * |
| Bumpass T Merritt | Frantz Ward LLP * |
| Canton Doreen | Taft Stettinius & Hollister LLP * |
| Feheley Lawrence F | Kegler, Brown, Hill & Ritter |
| Griffith Kevin | Porter Wright Morris & Arthur LLP * |
| Hastings Susan C | Squire Sanders (US) LLP * |
| Hawkins Michael | Dinsmore & Shohl LLP |
| Hearey Bruce G | Ogletree, Deakins, Nash, Smoak & Stewart * |
| Lawrence James K L | Frost Brown Todd LLC |
| Lewis John B | Baker & Hostetler LLP * |
| Linville Ronald G | Baker & Hostetler LLP * |
| Mersol Gregory V | Baker & Hostetler LLP * |
| Nolan William A | Barnes & Thornburg LLP (ONP)† * |
| Pressley Jr Fred G | Porter Wright Morris & Arthur LLP * |
| Rogers Gregory Parker | Taft Stettinius & Hollister LLP * |
| Stepaniak Mark J | Taft Stettinius & Hollister LLP * |
| Stephen John M | Porter Wright Morris & Arthur LLP * |
| Wolff Robert M | Littler Mendelson, PC * |
| Yund George | Frost Brown Todd LLC * |

**Band 3**

| | |
|---|---|
| Ayers G Randall | Keating Muething & Klekamp PLL (ONP)† * |
| Dimling Robert A | Frost Brown Todd LLC * |
| Douglas Sue | Littler Mendelson, PC * |
| Glassman Michael S | Dinsmore & Shohl LLP |
| Greenberg Gary | Denlinger, Rosenthal & Greenberg LPA |
| Hensel Jan E | Dinsmore & Shohl LLP |
| Hutton Lee J | Littler Mendelson, PC * |
| Kelly Brian | Frantz Ward LLP * |
| Knueve Mark | Vorys, Sater, Seymour and Pease LLP * |
| Lardakis Terry | Fisher & Phillips LLP * |
| Millisor Richard A | Fisher & Phillips LLP * |
| Millstone David J | Squire Sanders (US) LLP * |
| Nobil Steven M | Fisher & Phillips LLP * |
| Pace Stanley Dan | Ogletree, Deakins, Nash, Smoak & Stewart * |
| Roesch Charles M | Dinsmore & Shohl LLP |
| Sutton Stephen C | Baker & Hostetler LLP * |
| Ward Daniel A | Frantz Ward LLP * |

**Band 4**

| | |
|---|---|
| Asensio M.J. | Baker & Hostetler LLP * |
| Ashmus Keith A | Frantz Ward LLP * |
| Buck Frank W | Littler Mendelson, PC * |
| Cernelich John R | Calfee, Halter & Griswold LLP (ONP)† * |
| Croall David T | Porter Wright Morris & Arthur LLP * |
| Day Alison | Littler Mendelson, PC * |
| Drozdowski Jim | Hahn Loeser & Parks LLP (ONP)† * |
| Fricke Wade M | Ogletree, Deakins, Nash, Smoak & Stewart * |
| Hastings Kerry P | Taft Stettinius & Hollister LLP * |
| Keiper Jeffrey B | Jackson Lewis LLP * |
| Keller Donald | Bricker & Eckler LLP |
| Leukart Barbara | Jones Day * |
| Petrie James | Bricker & Eckler LLP |
| Porter Sue | Ice Miller LLP (ONP)† |
| Schreiner David E | Fisher & Phillips LLP * |
| Sheeran Timothy J | Squire Sanders (US) LLP * |
| Smith Andrew | Vorys, Sater, Seymour and Pease LLP * |
| Stone James | Jackson Lewis LLP * |
| Swift Betsy | Bricker & Eckler LLP |
| Underwood Michael | Porter Wright Morris & Arthur LLP * |
| Vaughn Jonathan R | Vorys, Sater, Seymour and Pease LLP * |
| Wymer Martin T | Baker & Hostetler LLP * |

**Up-and-coming individuals**

| | |
|---|---|
| Clark Eric | Thompson Hine LLP (ONP)† * |

\* Indicates individual with profile.

†ONP = Other Notable Practitioner

areas of expertise include employment counseling as well as employment litigation advice. **Keith Ashmus** (see p.2089) is well known in the local market. His employment law capabilities encompass several areas, including employment discrimination and litigation. He is a frequent participant in seminars and training for employers. **Brian Kelly** (see p.2102) is acclaimed for his input in contentious employment issues, including in defending charges of harassment and wrongful discharge. He is described as *"good and solid; he knows what he is doing,"* and can be relied upon to do a *"professional, all-around good job,"* according to sources.

### Frost Brown Todd LLC
See profile on p.1329

**THE FIRM** Frost Brown Todd's Cincinnati office houses one of the state's strongest and most respected labor and employment groups. Its expertise covers everything from worker compensation actions and OSHA investigations to labor arbitrations and collective bargaining. Key highlights include advising an educational institution on a collective bargaining agreement. The team also acts for clients from the manufacturing, energy and insurance sectors.

**Sources say:** *"The lawyers I work with are responsive and direct in providing advice."*

**KEY INDIVIDUALS Deborah Adams** (see p.2089) attracts particular praise for her effective employment litigation and trial skills in collective and class actions. Her clients include insurance companies. She is also admitted to the Kentucky Bar, enabling her to offer seamless service across the state line. Firm managing member **George Yund** (see p.2118) is *"an excellent resource for labor and employment matters."* Although experienced in employment matters, he is particularly well known for his skills in the traditional labor field, including in union negotiations and labor disputes. **James Lawrence** enters his 48th year of legal practice, making him one of the most experienced practitioners in the state. He is distinguished for his former role as an in-house trial counsel with the NLRB, and for his correspondingly deep insight into the traditional labor arena. He recently advised on the collective bargaining agreement for an educational institution. **Robert Dimling** (see p.2094) counts traditional labor and particularly OSHA work as key areas of expertise. *"His experience in this area is invaluable to us,"* said one impressed client. Dimling's recent highlights include advising a manufacturing entity on alleged OSHA record-keeping requirement violations.

### Porter Wright Morris & Arthur LLP
See profile on p.2127

**THE FIRM** A number of market sources agree this firm is thoroughly deserving of recognition in this field on account of its breadth of practice. The large number of prominent attorneys also stands out here, particularly in the Columbus office. The team has proved itself a reliable choice of counsel in HR compliance and training, as well as in traditional labor law. On the employment litigation side, it has the resources to defend national and multiparty actions in an aggressive and effective manner. Key clients include American Electric Power, Delta Air Lines and The Huntington National Bank.

**Sources say:** *"Very solid and strong lawyers."*

**KEY INDIVIDUALS** The *"scholarly"* and *"very bright"* **Bradd Siegel** (see p.2113) combines his commercially focused legal practice with *"a professorial view of the practice of law."* Sources agree he is a *"very smart and experienced guy"* in areas including wrongful discharge and employment discrimination. Columbus partner **Charles Warner** (see p.2116) has built a reputation in the market for his broad-based employment-related work. He recently represented TASC in responding to an allegation of wrongful discharge in federal court. Younger lawyer **Kevin Griffith** (see p.2098) practices out of the Columbus office. His practice includes high-stakes employment disputes, and he recently acted as lead counsel for a local company on defending a charge of age discrimination. **John Stephen** (see p.2114) is described as a *"practical, hard-working and bright lawyer."* His admission to the US Supreme Court enables him to advise on high-stakes labor and employment court disputes all the way up to the appellate level. He is also an effective counselor and has advised on regulatory compliance reviews, among other issues. **Fred Pressley** (see p.2110) chairs the firm's labor and employment practice, and is described as a *"knowledgeable and well-prepared attorney who works hard for his clients."* Other interviewees note his employment litigation skills in particular, and highlight his *"very strong wage and hour work."* He recently advised a healthcare-related entity on a state court dispute concerning alleged false statements. *"Very bright, conscientious and efficient,"* **Michael Underwood** (see p.2115) *"knows the law very well, and usually answers questions without lots of research,"* say sources. He counsels across a broad range of issues, including employment compliance and OSHA matters, and counts public bodies among his clients. **David Croall** (see p.2093) is admitted to practice in Kentucky as well as in Ohio. Sources laud him as *"a good counselor and smart as a whip."* He recently acted for Delta Air Lines on defending a charge of gender discrimination and wrongful termination.

## Taft Stettinius & Hollister LLP
See profile on p.2130

**THE FIRM** This firm is a major force in the Cincinnati labor and employment market, and its merger with Chester, Willcox & Saxbe in January 2012 served to bolster its Columbus-based capabilities. It provides solid counsel on discrete collective bargaining matters as well as wider employment disputes inside and outside the courtroom. The group's recent highlights include representing US Bank in a number of cases involving ERISA class actions, alleged breach of contract and charges of retaliation.
**Sources say:** *"The team does a tremendous job of understanding the client and meeting or exceeding their expectations. I count it as one of the best."*
**KEY INDIVIDUALS Timothy Reilly** (see p.2110) is of counsel in the Cincinnati office. He has a broad practice and is especially well versed in the traditional labor arena. *"Simply put, he is one of the finest and most diversified lawyers I have ever worked with,"* said one particularly impressed source; *"he is tenacious in negotiations and understands the client's needs."* Cincinnati partner **Doreen Canton** (see p.2092) is now in her 25th year of legal practice. She is a key labor and employment counsel to US Bank, and has advised on a number of high-stakes disputes of late, including one involving alleged disability discrimination. Clients praise her *"excellent work, excellent analysis and great timely client service."* She cochairs the firm's labor and employment practice group. Fellow practice group cohead **Gregory Rogers** (see p.2110) *"tries to understand what his client wants, then forms a strategy to accomplish that,"* say sources; *"he provides outstanding service, is very responsive, and listens well."* His key clients include AK Steel, for which he recently acted in a number of disputes concerning allegations of ERISA retiree benefits impropriety and disability discrimination. **Mark Stepaniak's** (see p.2114) practice includes acting for public sector entities such as school boards, and handling associated employment-related disputes. He is highlighted as a switched-on and well-trained practitioner with an effective command of the traditional labor area, in particular. **Kerry Hastings** (see p.2099) is a younger partner with a rising profile in the sector, especially for his traditional labor and union-related work. He has already appeared extensively for clients in front of the NLRB as well as in court.

## Band 2

## Denlinger, Rosenthal & Greenberg LPA

**THE FIRM** This is a sterling one-office Cincinnati labor and employment boutique. Despite its compact size, the firm houses some impressive and market-leading talent, acting for employer clients across the employment disputes and traditional labor arena. It advises a range of

clients, including retailers, public bodies and healthcare entities.
**Sources say:** *"A great reputation."*
**KEY INDIVIDUALS Daniel Rosenthal** is widely respected in the Cincinnati market for his long-term concentration on this practice area. Sources say he is *"very effective with clients,"* and can be relied upon for *"good advice."* **Gary Greenberg** is well known for acting for management on labor and employment matters. Sources highlight him as an intelligent practitioner and a sound adviser.

## Dinsmore & Shohl LLP

**THE FIRM** This firm is considered one of the stronger practices in the market, and is praised for its thought leadership and willingness to participate in sate Bar activities. Its Cincinnati office in particular fields some exceptional talent. The team advises a number of household names, including Procter & Gamble and Husky Energy. Highlights include leading the defense of Golden Living and GGNSC Equity Holdings in respective and hotly contested putative wage and hour actions under the FLSA.
**KEY INDIVIDUALS Michael Hawkins** has an excellent reputation in the Cincinnati market. His extensive experience allows him to advise on a number of areas, including traditional labor and appellate matters. He recently advised Paritec on an alleged wrongful termination claim. Key Cincinnati partner **Michael Glassman** heads up the firm's employment law practice. His key clients include Procter & Gamble, which he recently assisted in a dispute concerning alleged disability and national origin discrimination. Sources agree he is a sound choice for high-quality labor and employment work. **Jan Hensel** is known in the market for her employment counseling work as well as for her litigation skills. Sources deem her *"a good employment lawyer"* and a *"very experienced litigator."* She is no stranger to the trial process, having represented client interests in state and federal courts as well as the Supreme Court. She recently advised Kanji Japanese Restaurant on a collective wage and hour matter. The tremendously experienced **Charles Roesch** heads up the firm's labor and employment group. His extensive skill set includes advising on ADA, ERISA and wage and hour matters. His highlights include acting as lead counsel on the Golden Living class action matter.

## Fisher & Phillips LLP
See profile on p.1107

**THE FIRM** Sources admire the practitioners in the Cleveland office of this national labor and employment boutique firm. The team is able to call on the firm's extensive resources to assist management clients with the entire scope of labor and employment issues. Highlights include advising on collective bargaining, compliance counseling and FLSA litigation. Manufacturers, food processors and commercial law firms feature highly on its client list.
**Sources say:** *"Solid lawyers."*
**KEY INDIVIDUALS Terry Lardakis** (see p.2103) maintains a distinct and respected profile for his traditional labor work, and handles a range of collective bargaining agreements and union-organizing campaigns for his com-

mercial clientele. *"Clients absolutely love him; he is very good at client service and is very smart,"* according to sources. **Richard Millisor's** (see p.2107) key strengths lie in contentious employment work, where he has represented clients in cases all the way up to the Supreme Court. *"He is very diligent and thoughtful, and will not let an issue go until he has figured it out,"* say interviewees. He recently advised a well-known commercial law firm on an alleged employment discrimination matter. **Steven Nobil** (see p.2108) is the Cleveland office managing partner. He has been in practice for 40 years and is a senior and respected attorney, known for his adept counsel on union matters. Sources describe him as *"a traditional labor lawyer who offers strong client service."* **David Schreiner** (see p.2112) is highly regarded for his traditional labor relations counseling in particular. He acts for a range of clients, including manufacturing and vehicle dealer associations.

## Jackson Lewis LLP
See profile on p.1982

**THE FIRM** This nationwide labor and employment boutique firm has considerable strength in its Cleveland and Cincinnati offices. Backed by the firm's extensive resources and deep expertise, the Ohio group handles the entire range of labor and employment matters. Its recent highlights include representing UniFirst in a hotly contested jury trial concerning alleged age discrimination. Other key clients include JM Smucker and Caesar's Entertainment.
**Sources say:** *"The team is knowledgeable and responsive to our needs. It has access to a broad array of experts on all aspects of labor law, federal and state employment law, and equal employment topics."*
**KEY INDIVIDUALS Jeffrey Keiper** (see p.2101) played a lead role on the UniFirst matter, and also counts JM Smucker as a client. He is admitted to practice in a number of jurisdictions, including Washington and Illinois as well as Ohio, giving his employment litigation practice an enviable national reach. Sources describe him as *"very knowledgeable, with the ability to provide quick, accurate answers to questions and issues."* **James Stone** (see p.2114) is managing partner of the firm's Cleveland office. His practice includes employment disputes as well as union matters, and interviewees highlight his *"practical, businesslike approach to problem solving."* He recently counseled Caesar's Entertainment on traditional labor negotiations.

## Jones Day
See profile on p.919

**THE FIRM** Backed by the firm's vast network of resources and expertise, Jones Day's Ohio-based practice group undertakes cases of national prominence. Its client list includes venerable household names such as Verizon Communications, AstraZeneca and McDonald's. Interviewees praise its excellent broad-based experience, particularly in relation to traditional labor matters.
**Sources say:** *"Very responsive and thorough." "A robust practice."*
**KEY INDIVIDUALS Roger King** (see p.2102) is of counsel in the firm's Columbus branch, and is praised as *"one of the best in traditional labor."* He is highlighted in particular

for his strong expertise in union-related issues affecting the healthcare industry, leading interviewees to concur: *"He is terrific with labor relations work specific to hospitals and healthcare providers."* **Barbara Leukart** (see p.2104) is based in the Cleveland office, where she is of counsel. She has a longstanding reputation in both the traditional labor and employment litigation fields.

## Littler Mendelson, PC
See profile on p.688

**THE FIRM** Littler Mendelson's Ohio-based practice group attracts praise for its sterling levels of talent, particularly in its Cleveland office, and benefits from the firm's nation-wide specialized and labor and employment capabilities. Recent highlights include acting for Office Depot on an action against ex-employees for alleged violation of employment contract provisions. Other clients include OhioHealth and Goodyear.

**Sources say:** *"Very effective."* *"A tremendous resource to any inside counsel."*

**KEY INDIVIDUALS Robert Wolff** (see p.2118) recently acted as lead lawyer on the Office Depot matter. He cochairs the firm's healthcare practice and has a great profile in contentious work. *"He has tremendous jury appeal,"* according to interviewees, and is *"a sincere, smart and likable person with a lot of common sense."* **Sue Douglas** (see p.2095) is managing shareholder of the firm's Cleveland office, as well as cochair of the discrimination and harassment group. Her recent highlights include advising Alcon Laboratories on a high-value case concerning allegations of ADA and ERISA violations. Sources describe her as *"personable and bright."* **Lee Hutton** (see p.2100) brings well-developed litigation skills to the table, and has in-depth in-court experience. He has advised on matters ranging from jury trials to keenly contested multiparty disputes such as wage and hour matters. **Frank Buck** (see p.2091) is a sound choice of counsel for traditional labor work, according to sources. His areas of expertise include collective bargaining and FLSA matters. **Alison Day** (see p.2094) is a new entry to the rankings. She acts for a number of major retailers and healthcare clients, such as OhioHealth. Her recent highlights include advising on allegations of disability discrimination.

## Ogletree, Deakins, Nash, Smoak & Stewart, PC
See profile on p.1110

**THE FIRM** The Cleveland office of this national boutique labor and employment firm earns praise for its flexible and cost-effective service. Clients include Eaton Corporation and Progressive Insurance Company. In recent highlights, the group represented ExxonMobil in a keenly contested age discrimination case.

**Sources say:** *"It's good and responsive, and has lots of skills."* *"The firm provides quality services for the best value."*

**KEY INDIVIDUALS** The *"excellent"* **Thomas Barnard** (see p.2090) led in the aforementioned ExxonMobil matter, and earns client admiration for his vast experience in this field. He has an *"encyclopedic knowledge of the law, of local plaintiff's counsel and of local judges, and uses that*

knowledge to recommend case strategy in his engagements," said an impressed source. **Bruce Hearey** (see p.2099) practices out of the Cleveland office, but is able to advise across a multitude of jurisdictions, including New Jersey, New York and California. He is a recognized adviser and trial lawyer in employment litigation, and has had a number of successes in court. He recently advised DaVita on a high-stakes race discrimination matter. **Dan Pace**'s (see p.2109) key strengths include his long experience of traditional labor matters, including NLRB negotiation and arbitration. He recently acted for Lehigh Specialty Melting on labor arbitration involving alleged absenteeism. Cleveland shareholder **Wade Fricke** (see p.2096) stands out for his traditional labor work in particular. He was lead adviser to Mission Foods on a UFCW certification election campaign matter involving a number of languages.

## Squire Sanders (US) LLP
See profile on p.2129

**THE FIRM** This practice group has a raft of highly satisfied clients, and is recognized for its quality counsel to entities including public sector organizations. The team also benefits from the firm's extensive network of resources and its enviable national reputation in this practice area. Key clients include Cleveland Metropolitan School District Board of Education, Ohio Presbyterian Retirement Services and Cleveland Clinic.

**Sources say:** *"It has done so much with us to make sure we are compliant in all areas of labor law within our organization."*

**KEY INDIVIDUALS Susan Hastings** (see p.2099) has notable experience acting for public sector employers, which dovetails conveniently with her experience in education law. Her recent highlights include acting as chief negotiator in collective bargaining for a number of school districts. **David Millstone** (see p.2107) has been in practice for more than four decades, making him one of the most experienced practitioners in the area. His skills span the traditional labor and employment fields, and he has recently handled noncompete work and union negotiation matters. **Timothy Sheeran** (see p.2112) is recognized as *"one of the preeminent public sector labor lawyers"* in the Cleveland market, particularly for his representation of school districts across the litigation, traditional labor and counseling spheres. His recent highlights include acting for a public school client on matters relating to multiyear remuneration agreements.

## Vorys, Sater, Seymour and Pease LLP
See profile on p.2133

**THE FIRM** This regional firm's Columbus office is recognized for its skilled and well-established labor and employment talent. It also added a prominent lateral hire to its Cleveland office, lending it further traction in the market. High-stakes matters feature regularly in its workload, with highlights including acting for Stanley Steemer International on a multiplaintiff wage and hour action. Other key clients include ABX Air and Abercrombie & Fitch.

**Sources say:** *"It communicated well and dealt expertly with our case."* *"Very solid and strong lawyers."*

**KEY INDIVIDUALS Barton Bixenstine** (see p.2090) recently arrived at the firm from Ogletree Deakins. As well as undertaking employment counseling and litigation, he also handles alternative dispute resolution. *"He is very knowledgeable, very strategic, and a good advocate,"* said one particularly impressed source; *"he really homes in and addresses issues."* **Mark Knueve** (see p.2102) has a recognized profile for his expert handling of multiparty employment disputes. He led in the aforementioned Stanley Steemer International matter, and is described as *"a smart and hard-working employment litigator."* **Jonathan Vaughn** (see p.2115) has an excellent reputation as an accomplished adviser on the collective bargaining aspects of traditional labor, and has proved to be proficient in a variety of other areas, such as FLSA, employment and noncompetition. **Andrew Smith** (see p.2113) chairs the labor and employment practice group and has an extensive skill set spanning traditional labor as well as employment areas. He is increasingly recognized as a *"really good litigator"* on account of his effective handling of disputes for employers, including class and collective actions involving alleged sex, age and disability discrimination.

## Band 3

## Benesch, Friedlander, Coplan & Aronoff LLP
See profile on p.2120

**THE FIRM** This firm's Cleveland office fields a respected team of labor and employment lawyers. The practice is a fine complement to the firm's wider capabilities in commercial matters generally. Recent highlights include representing the National Association of Manufacturers in a challenge to an NLRB rule. Other key clients include Oak Harbor Freight and Eaton Corporation.

**KEY INDIVIDUALS Maynard Buck** heads the labor and employment practice.

## Bricker & Eckler LLP

**THE FIRM** This Ohio firm has accrued a strong following for its keen and responsive service in the field, most notably in Columbus. Clients praise the accommodating and forward-thinking professionals, who are able to assist on matters including harassment, EEOC and pay disputes. The team acts for a number of healthcare entities, including Ohio Hospital Association and Genesis HealthCare System. Nationwide Mutual Insurance is another key client.

**Sources say:** *"They have always been extremely helpful, knowledgeable and available when I have needed its assistance."*

**KEY INDIVIDUALS James Petrie** heads up the firm's labor and employment practice. Employment disputes are a key part of his practice. His recent highlights include advising on a high-value dispute concerning alleged age discrimination. *"He understands our business and acts like our partner in tackling tough issues,"* said an impressed client. **Donald Keller** exhibits notable skills in the traditional labor area, including in collective bargaining and union negotiations. Sources say: "*He has worked effectively within longstanding organizational negotiating norms yet provided strong, objective external support for the use of other strategies that lead to highly successful outcomes.*" **Betsy Swift** had a teaching career before coming to the law, and is praised as "*a gifted speaker*" as well as an intelligent counselor. She is respected for her "*common-sense approach – she understands that clients have to operate their business and works to minimize risk,*" sources say.

### Kegler, Brown, Hill & Ritter
See profile on p.2125

**THE FIRM** This quality labor and employment practice group is a noted presence in the Columbus market. A number of employers rely on its counsel, including the Catholic Diocese of Columbus, Crescent Manufacturing and Donatos Pizzeria. The team's expertise covers a broad range of issues, including FMLA compliance, noncompetition and OSHA matters.

**KEY INDIVIDUALS** Firm director **Lawrence Feheley** heads up the dedicated labor and employee relations prac-

tice from the Columbus office, and does "*does a fine job,*" according to sources. He is active in traditional labor issues, but is also a proficient and respected employment counselor and litigator. His key clients include the Catholic Diocese of Columbus.

### Other Notable Practitioners

**William Nolan** (see p.2108) is the founding and managing partner of Barnes & Thornburg LLP's Columbus office. He also heads up the labor and employment department there, and is described as "*always reliable and extremely responsive.*" His clients include Ashland University and the Center of Vocational Alternatives. **John Cernelich** (see p.2092) cochairs the labor and employment practice at Calfee, Halter & Griswold LLP in Cleveland. He is noted for his expert handling of employment litigation in particular, and is lauded as "*very good at helping clients with strategy, and being proactive in avoiding issues.*" Other sources highlight his "*great knowledge of the law, and where potential pitfalls may be.*" Cleveland attorney **Jim Drozdowski** (see p.2095) heads up the labor and employment practice

group at Hahn Loeser & Parks LLP. Clients agree that "*his expansive knowledge and attention to detail are always refreshing,*" while other sources describe him as "*efficient, expedient, and forceful when needed.*" His key work includes advising Cargill Meat Solutions on defending allegations of discrimination, retaliation and harassment. **Sue Porter** practices from the Columbus office of Ice Miller LLP. "*A very good litigator,*" she is lauded for her candid and efficient work style. **Eric Clark** (see p.2093) worked as in-house labor counsel before joining Thompson Hine LLP. "*Eric always gives the detail needed to address legal concerns on a national, state and local basis,*" say sources; "*he works as an extension of the client's human resources team.*" He recently advised Veyance Industrial Services on a class action alleging wage and hour violations in West Virginia. **Randall Ayers** (see p.2090) recently left Frost Brown Todd to join Keating Muething & Klekamp PLL's Cincinnati office. He is "*very successful*" and is highly regarded for his expertise in the traditional labor arena in particular, including in NLRB matters, collective bargaining and dispute resolution.

## LITIGATION

General Commercial p.2077;   Antitrust p.2078;   White-Collar Crime & Government Investigations p.2078

Commentary about individuals can be found under their firm's paragraph.  If the firm has no paragraph (is not ranked) look at Other Notable Practitioners.

### Litigation: General Commercial
#### Leading Firms

**Band 1**
Jones Day *

**Band 2**
Baker & Hostetler LLP *
Squire Sanders (US) LLP *
Ulmer & Berne LLP *
Vorys, Sater, Seymour and Pease LLP *
Zeiger, Tigges & Little LLP

**Band 3**
Bricker & Eckler LLP
Calfee, Halter & Griswold LLP *
Dinsmore & Shohl LLP
Faruki Ireland & Cox PLL
Hahn Loeser & Parks LLP *
Ice Miller LLP
Keating Muething & Klekamp PLL *
Kegler, Brown, Hill & Ritter *
Porter Wright Morris & Arthur LLP *
Taft Stettinius & Hollister LLP *
Thompson Hine LLP *
Tucker Ellis

**Band 4**
Carpenter Lipps & Leland LLP *
Roetzel & Andress, LPA *
Sebaly Shillito & Dyer

*Indicates firm with profile.*
*Alphabetical order within each band. Band 1 is the highest.*

### Band 1

#### Jones Day
See profile on p.919

**THE FIRM** The bench strength of this international firm is well respected, with a raft of recognized lawyers in its Cleveland office. It is further validated by its comprehensive skill set, enabling it to handle antitrust, white-collar criminal and general commercial litigation. High-profile clients in the state and beyond are a given, and include Abercrombie & Fitch and IBM. Recent highlights include advising Macy's in a high-stakes licensing and manufacturing dispute.

**Sources say:** "*Jones Day is always at the top of the list.*"

**KEY INDIVIDUALS Jack Newman** (see p.2108) is a key partner in the Cleveland office. His practice includes advising on securities and shareholder actions. Sources continue to praise his pragmatic manner, with peers describing an "*excellent lawyer*" who commands "*great respect.*" **Theodore Grossman** (see p.2098) is a former DOJ trial and appellate counsel, who is now resident in the firm's Cleveland office. He is experienced in leading high-stakes cases all the way up to trial, and led the team in the aforementioned Macy's litigation. Cleveland partner **Robert Walker** (see p.2116) offers clients his experience after 30 years of legal practice. He was recently successful on behalf of shopping center owner and developer DDR Corp during a five-week trial relating to a high-value breach of contract lawsuit. **David Adler** (see p.2089) has developed a sound reputation in the Cleveland market for his represen-

tation of commercial entities and financial institutions. His recent work includes advising a bank on a class action alleging unfair and deceptive trade practice. **Robert Faxon** (see p.2096) is a respected disputes lawyer in the Cleveland market with experience in a variety of work, including product liability and securities matters. He acted as lead trial counsel for RJ Reynolds in a high-value lawsuit concerning wrongful death. **Elizabeth Kessler** (see p.2102) is partner-in-charge of the Columbus office. She continues to develop her skills in commercial litigation, and sources adjudge her to be "*a fine trial lawyer with great promise.*" **Thomas Demitrack** (see p.2094) wins plaudits from the market, with one interviewee remarking that he is an "*extremely good lawyer: smart, articulate and he does a very good job in the courtroom.*" His contentious practice has a particular slant toward the regulatory aspects of commerce, and he is called an "*effective antitrust litigator.*" He acted as lead counsel to Experian Information Solutions concerning antitrust aspects relating to access to consumer credit information. **John Majoras** (see p.2105) is commended for his "*broad set of skills,*" with sources describing him as an "*able trial lawyer*" who exhibits "*good judgment.*" He was lead adviser to Sirius XM Radio in an antitrust dispute involving satellite radio subscription. Former US Attorney **Stephen Sozio** (see p.2113) practices from the Cleveland office, and is recognized for his work in government investigations and white-collar criminal matters. Sources note his "*practical and solid advice*" and ability to reach acceptable resolutions as necessary. Clients include notable healthcare entities and manufacturing interests.

## Litigation: General Commercial
### Senior Statesmen

**Senior Statesmen: distinguished older practitioners**

| | |
|---|---|
| Greer David | Bieser, Greer, & Landis LLP (ONP)[†] |
| Karp Marvin L | Ulmer & Berne LLP * |

### Leading Individuals

**Band 1**

| | |
|---|---|
| Burke James E | Keating Muething & Klekamp PLL * |
| Faruki Charles J | Faruki Ireland & Cox PLL * |
| Hill Thomas | Kegler, Brown, Hill & Ritter |
| Newman Jr John (Jack) M | Jones Day * |
| Ungar Michael N | Ulmer & Berne LLP * |
| Zeiger John W | Zeiger, Tigges & Little LLP |

**Band 2**

| | |
|---|---|
| Arnold James S | Law Office of James S Arnold (ONP)[†] |
| Blair Mitchell G | Calfee, Halter & Griswold LLP * |
| Buckley Daniel J | Vorys, Sater, Seymour and Pease LLP * |
| Carpenter Michael | Carpenter Lipps & Leland LLP |
| Fogarty Robert J | Hahn Loeser & Parks LLP * |
| Grossman Theodore | Jones Day * |
| Kaufman Steven S | Kaufman & Company, LLC (ONP)[†] |
| Lindsmith Quintin | Bricker & Eckler LLP |
| Mace Damond R | Squire Sanders (US) LLP * |
| O'Malley Anthony | Vorys, Sater, Seymour and Pease LLP * |
| Pitcairn Jr Robert | Katz, Teller, Brant & Hild (ONP)[†] |
| Tigges Steven W | Zeiger, Tigges & Little LLP |
| Vander Laan Mark A | Dinsmore & Shohl LLP |
| Whitaker Glenn | Vorys, Sater, Seymour and Pease LLP * |

**Band 3**

| | |
|---|---|
| Campbell Drew | Bricker & Eckler LLP |
| Dornette W Stuart | Taft Stettinius & Hollister LLP * |
| Dyer Jim | Sebaly Shillito & Dyer |
| Fitch Stephen | Taft Stettinius & Hollister LLP (ONP)[†] * |
| Freund Neil | Freund, Freeze & Arnold |
| Fry Roger | Rendigs, Fry, Kiely & Dennis, LLP (ONP)[†] |
| Gilligan John P | Ice Miller LLP |
| Goldfarb Steven A | Hahn Loeser & Parks LLP * |
| Ireland D Jeffrey | Faruki Ireland & Cox PLL * |
| Kamp David | White, Getgey & Meyer Co LPA (ONP)[†] |
| Kincaid Jr Robert M | Baker & Hostetler LLP * |
| Little Jr Marion H | Zeiger, Tigges & Little LLP |
| McDonald John | Ice Miller LLP |
| Ray Frank | Frank A Ray Co LPA (ONP)[†] |
| Robenalt James D | Thompson Hine LLP * |
| Scheier Michael L | Keating Muething & Klekamp PLL * |
| Sferra Anne Marie | Bricker & Eckler LLP |
| Sugarman Roger P | Kegler, Brown, Hill & Ritter |
| Trafford Kathleen M | Porter Wright Morris & Arthur LLP * |
| Trafford Robert W | Porter Wright Morris & Arthur LLP * |

| | |
|---|---|
| Wallace David H | Taft Stettinius & Hollister LLP * |
| Wallach Mark | Thacker Martinsek LPA (ONP)[†] * |
| Weaver Robin G | Squire Sanders (US) LLP * |

**Band 4**

| | |
|---|---|
| Adler David F | Jones Day * |
| Casarona Robert B | Roetzel & Andress, LPA (ONP)[†] * |
| Castrodale Joseph A | Ulmer & Berne LLP * |
| Chappelear Stephen | Hahn Loeser & Parks LLP * |
| Fairfield Mary Ellen | Vorys, Sater, Seymour and Pease LLP * |
| Faxon Robert S | Jones Day * |
| Gall John R | Squire Sanders (US) LLP * |
| Gurbst Richard | Squire Sanders (US) LLP * |
| Hinebaugh Jeffrey P | Dinsmore & Shohl LLP |
| Johnson Mark A | Baker & Hostetler LLP * |
| Kessler Elizabeth P | Jones Day * |
| Kessler Marc | Hahn Loeser & Parks LLP * |
| King Scott A | Thompson Hine LLP * |
| Knoth Richard M | Baker & Hostetler LLP * |
| Lane Patrick | Dinsmore & Shohl LLP |
| Lucchesi Thomas R | Baker & Hostetler LLP * |
| McKay Hugh E | Porter Wright Morris & Arthur LLP * |
| McLaughlin Patrick | McLaughlin, LLP (ONP)[†] |
| Meyer Jill P | Frost Brown Todd LLC (ONP)[†] * |
| Porter II William G | Vorys, Sater, Seymour and Pease LLP * |
| Reed Orville | Stark & Knoll (ONP)[†] |
| Remington Rob | Hahn Loeser & Parks LLP * |
| Ruehlmann Mark J | Squire Sanders (US) LLP * |
| Saxbe Charles | Taft Stettinius & Hollister LLP * |
| Sayre Russell S | Taft Stettinius & Hollister LLP * |
| Shadley Frederic X | Ulmer & Berne LLP * |
| Solomon Randall L | Baker & Hostetler LLP * |
| Sprader Bobbie | Bricker & Eckler LLP |
| Stanley Hugh | Tucker Ellis |
| Vargo Ernest E | Baker & Hostetler LLP * |
| Walker Robert | Jones Day * |
| Warren Daniel R | Baker & Hostetler LLP * |
| Warren Thomas D | Baker & Hostetler LLP * |
| Woodside III Frank C | Dinsmore & Shohl LLP |
| Zagrans Eric | Zagrans Law Firm LLC (ONP)[†] |

**Up-and-coming individuals**

| | |
|---|---|
| Fuhrer Loriann E | Kegler, Brown, Hill & Ritter |
| Sherman Ryan | Porter Wright Morris & Arthur LLP * |

## Litigation: Antitrust
### Senior Statesmen

**Senior Statesmen: distinguished older practitioners**

| | |
|---|---|
| Rawson Robert | Jones Day * |

### Leading Individuals

**Band 1**

| | |
|---|---|
| Collin Thomas J | Thompson Hine LLP * |
| Demitrack Thomas | Jones Day * |
| Donson Jack | Taft Stettinius & Hollister LLP * |
| Majoras John M | Jones Day * |
| Squeri Steve | Jones Day * |
| Wilson James | Vorys, Sater, Seymour and Pease LLP * |

## Litigation: White-Collar Crime & Government Investigations
### Senior Statesmen

**Senior Statesmen: distinguished older practitioners**

| | |
|---|---|
| Rotatori Robert J | Rotatori Bender Co LPA (ONP)[†] |
| Schwartz Niki Z | Schwartz, Downey & Co LPA (ONP)[†] |

### Leading Individuals

**Band 1**

| | |
|---|---|
| Cascarilla Ralph E | Walter & Haverfield LLP (ONP)[†] * |
| McLaughlin Patrick | McLaughlin Law, LLP |
| Sozio Stephen | Jones Day * |
| Synenberg Roger M | Synenberg & Associates (ONP)[†] |
| Wooley James | Jones Day * |

**Band 2**

| | |
|---|---|
| Kerger Richard | Kerger & Hartman LLC (ONP)[†] |
| McCaffrey John F | Tucker Ellis |
| Whitaker Glenn | Vorys, Sater, Seymour and Pease LLP * |

**Band 3**

| | |
|---|---|
| Brinkman Kathleen | Porter Wright Morris & Arthur LLP * |
| Kohnen Ralph | Taft Stettinius & Hollister LLP * |
| Kushner Philip | Kushner & Hamed (ONP)[†] |
| Leiken Jonathan | Jones Day * |
| Meeks William | Sole Practitioner (ONP)[†] |
| Scherzer Donald | Roetzel & Andress, LPA * |

* Indicates individual with profile.

[†]ONP = Other Notable Practitioner

## Band 2

### Baker & Hostetler LLP
See profile on p.2119

**THE FIRM** Clients are quick to point to the keen service levels on offer at this indigenous Cleveland firm, and note its increasing prominence in the Columbus market. The firm has won considerable plaudits for its extensive, continuing and high-profile work for Irving Picard, the Securities Investor Protection Act trustee for the liquidation of Bernard L Madoff Securities. Other high-profile work includes acting for Cardinal Health in a class action antitrust case against Abbott Laboratoriess.

**Sources say:** "The firm is very responsive and accommodating. There is a lot of depth."

**KEY INDIVIDUALS** Robert Kincaid (see p.2102) is described as a "standout trial lawyer, very analytical, with

James Wooley (see p.2118) is a former federal prosecutor now resident in the Cleveland office. He is noted for his excellence in white-collar crime and government investigatory matters. Sources describe him as "top-shelf," and add that he is "the guy you want in front of the jury in a trial." The "very knowledgeable" Steve Squeri (see p.2113) is of counsel in the Cleveland office. He has a rising profile for his antitrust work, and is an experienced and recognized trial lawyer. Jonathan Leiken (see p.2104) represents clients in white-collar criminal matters. Sources agree that he has a fine reputation as a capable adviser on Foreign Corrupt Practices Act and SEC-related matters. Clients include individuals, multinational companies and financial institutions. Robert Rawson (see p.2110) has proven skills as "a litigator with antitrust strength," according to sources. He is widely considered to be one of the leading figures of the Ohio antitrust Bar.

*an excellent demeanor on his feet."* He recently advised on a high-value claim involving allegations of breach of fiduciary duty. The highly respected **Randall Solomon** (see p.2113) focuses his practice on the defense of toxic tort cases, construction disputes and trade secrets. **Mark Johnson** (see p.2101) is based in the Columbus office. He includes securities litigation and appellate work in his skill set, and wins particular plaudits for his *"great depth of knowledge of class action work; he recalls case specifics and draws them together."* Recent highlights include advising an insurance client on a putative nationwide class action. **Richard Knoth** (see p.2102) offers clients in the Cleveland market more than 30 years of litigation experience. He has broad capabilities across the dispute resolution spectrum, and is noted as a proficient and recognized advocate at the trial and appellate levels. **Thomas Lucchesi** (see p.2105) is recognized for his effective litigation skills and practical approach. Highlights include the aforementioned two-year representation of Irving Picard. **Ernest Vargo** (see p.2115) leads the firm's national class action defense practice from the Cleveland office. He continues to advise clients in the insurance industry, and has also acted on antitrust matters. Sources relate that he is *"someone you look to as an expert in his area."* Former federal prosecutor **Thomas Warren** (see p.2116) divides his time between the Los Angeles and Cleveland offices. He remains cochair of the firm's nationwide appellate group, and has also been heavily involved in the Madoff litigation. **Daniel Warren** (see p.2116) is acclaimed as *"fine and capable"* by market observers. Sources agree that he is particularly effective in complex shareholder litigation. He is also an accomplished appellate lawyer.

### Squire Sanders (US) LLP
See profile on p.2129

**THE FIRM** This firm is well known for the quality of its work in the dispute resolution arena, with its Cleveland, Columbus and Cincinnati offices providing an impressive statewide presence. A client roster of high-profile household names includes Goodyear and BP, while recent highlights include the successful defense of AmFin Financial in a $765 million jury trial brought by the FDIC.
**Sources say:** *"They are prompt, understand the needs of their clients, and have the resources to handle any matter appropriately."*
**KEY INDIVIDUALS Damond Mace** (see p.2105) is applauded by clients as an *"outstanding litigation strategist."* He is an experienced trial lawyer whose highlights include representing clients in high-stakes product liability-related litigation. Cleveland partner **Robin Weaver** (see p.2116) has built a respected name for himself in this field over his 40 years of legal practice. Sources note his profile in appellate matters in particular. He has argued cases all the way to the Supreme Court. **Richard Gurbst** (see p.2098) acted as lead counsel on the FDIC jury trial matter, and has long experience with trial and litigation work. Sources reveal that he is a *"good, smart and hard-working"* advocate. **John Gall** (see p.2097) is a senior partner who practices from the Columbus office. His key clients include entities from the healthcare and financial services sectors,

while sources describe him as *"a fine trial lawyer."* **Mark Ruehlmann** (see p.2111) is the managing partner of the Cincinnati office. Sources agree that he is a talented attorney who enjoys *"a good reputation with the Ohio judiciary."* He focuses his commercial litigation practice on the representation of clients in the financial services sector.

### Ulmer & Berne LLP
See profile on p.2132

**THE FIRM** This firm is recognized for its broad litigation capabilities. The team represents clients from a host of industries in high-stakes disputes, and receives warm praise as a tenacious and formidable group of trial lawyers. The firm is particularly noted for its representation of clients in the banking and insurance sectors.
**Sources say:** *"Phenomenal. They are smart and super responsive."*
**KEY INDIVIDUALS Michael Ungar** (see p.2115) chairs the firm's litigation practice. He is described by sources as *"a very fine, aggressive lawyer"* who *"understands what you have to do to present your case well to the judge."* He is experienced in multiparty and complex commercial litigation, and he has acted for clients such as Citi and US Bank. **Joseph Castrodale** (see p.2092) is a partner in the Cleveland office, and heads up the business litigation practice at the firm. His areas of influence include multistate, multiparty actions and high-stakes federal court disputes. Partner **Frederic Shadley** (see p.2112) handles a broad range of business litigation, and is particularly noted for his focus on construction disputes. Other areas of excellence include environmental, IP and toxic tort litigation. **Marvin Karp** (see p.2101) is based in the Cleveland office and is one of the most experienced figures of the Ohio litigation Bar. Sources describe him as *"one hell of a lawyer!"*

### Vorys, Sater, Seymour and Pease LLP
See profile on p.2133

**THE FIRM** This firm remains strong in Ohio and is noted for its trial expertise in cases relating to antitrust, toxic tort, white-collar and complex commercial matters. The team recently successfully represented Walnut Private Equity Fund in a high-value dispute with Argo Tea.
**Sources say:** *"The quality of legal counsel we receive is outstanding."*
**KEY INDIVIDUALS** The *"talented"* **Daniel Buckley** (see p.2091) is a key litigation partner in the Cincinnati office. His broad experience includes derivatives and class action disputes, and he recently led the team in the aforementioned matter for Walnut Private Equity Fund. **Glenn Whitaker** (see p.2117) has built a respected profile in the white-collar criminal and False Claims Act arena, in addition to the general commercial litigation field. *"He leads very well and sets the standards,"* according to sources, one praising his *"exceptional knowledge."* **Anthony O'Malley** (see p.2109) is the managing partner of the firm's Cleveland branch. He remains active in disputes work particularly for banks, and recently acted for a financial institution in breach of fiduciary duty litigation. Sources describe him as a *"no-nonsense litigator who gets to the point. He sees what is important and what is not."* **Mary**

**Ellen Fairfield** (see p.2095) is based in the Columbus office. She has acted for a number of notable manufacturing interests in matters involving alleged product liability and employment discrimination. **William Porter** (see p.2110) is chair of the firmwide litigation practice. He brings substantial litigation experience to the table, including trial and advocacy skills. His recent clients include financial institutions. Columbus partner **James Wilson** (see p.2117) is lauded as *"the guy with the antitrust expertise. He is very smart, has good judgment, and knows the antitrust laws inside and out."*

### Zeiger, Tigges & Little LLP

**THE FIRM** This litigation boutique has built an impressively strong reputation in the Columbus market. The 11-strong team is active in matters from high-value contractual and trust disputes to shareholder actions. Its client list includes American Signature, Fifth Third Bank and Deloitte & Touche. Highlights for the practice include representing JPMorgan Chase in a trial concerning alleged breach of fiduciary duty.
**Sources say:** *"Great technical ability and great, commonsense, practical advice."*
**KEY INDIVIDUALS** Those seeking a *"very perceptive, thoughtful litigator"* who is *"smart and capable"* would do well to consider retaining **John Zeiger**, according to admiring sources. He recently acted as lead counsel on a hotly contested shareholder and breach of fiduciary duty action. **Steven Tigges** acted as lead trial counsel in the aforementioned matter for JPMorgan Chase. He is admired for his fearless yet thoughtful approach to getting the best result, with sources noting that *"he is not just a litigator – he is a talented strategist."* **Marion Little** enjoys a rising profile in the market for his wide-ranging and effective skills. Sources describe him as *"very creative and strategic,"* and note that *"he writes very well."*

### Band 3

### Bricker & Eckler LLP

**THE FIRM** This firm's litigation practice group continues to impress market observers. It is active on an array of high-value work, including medical malpractice, contractual and insurance disputes. It advised Nationwide Mutual Insurance on keenly contested litigation concerning Lehman Brothers credit default swap agreements. Other clients include OhioHealth and JPMorgan Chase.
**Sources say:** *"They understand our commercial objectives and are superb at handling complex issues."*
**KEY INDIVIDUALS** The *"outstanding"* **Quintin Lindsmith** acted as the lead lawyer on the aforementioned matter for Nationwide Mutual Insurance. Sources note that *"he can get to the bottom of the most complex business litigation."* **Drew Campbell** heads up the litigation practice group at the firm. His key clients include insurance companies and financial institutions. Source label him a *"high-quality and very talented litigator."* **Anne Marie Sferra** heads up the firm's dedicated appellate practice. She recently acted as lead counsel to a number of Ohio health-

care associations in a Supreme Court case concerning health insurance coverage. **Bobbie Sprader** garners significant praise from the market, with one commentator naming her *"detail-oriented and knowledgeable,"* and adding that *"she follows through without exception."* She concentrates her practice on healthcare litigation.

## Calfee, Halter & Griswold LLP
See profile on p.2121

**THE FIRM** This Ohio firm retains a solid presence in the Cleveland market. It advises on a variety of contentious work, including shareholder litigation, breach of contract and associated class actions. Clients include FirstEnergy, AT&T and KeyBank.

**Sources say:** *"We have deep respect for Calfee and rely heavily upon it."*

**KEY INDIVIDUALS Mitchell Blair** (see p.2090) ascends the rankings after receiving sterling market feedback. Sources reserve special mention for his *"great oratory and litigation skills in the courtroom,"* and note that *"he is an excellent cross-examiner."* He continues to advise the directors of Eaton Corporation on a shareholder derivative lawsuit.

## Dinsmore & Shohl LLP

**THE FIRM** This respected firm continues to win plaudits for the strength of its litigation team. The group is particularly noted for work with the financial services and pharmaceutical sectors, while it continues to be known for its historic ties to Procter & Gamble.

**KEY INDIVIDUALS** The highly experienced **Mark Vander Laan** chairs the litigation practice and is described as *"a fine lawyer"* by market sources. His clients have included Procter & Gamble and the Archdiocese of Cincinnati. **Jeffrey Hinebaugh** is a key litigation partner in the practice, regularly acting in mass tort claims and product liability cases. Clients are often drawn from the automotive sector, and have included industry giants such as GM, Mazda and American Suzuki. **Frank Woodside** handles product liability trial work and professional malpractice litigation. Clients include pharmaceutical and medical device manufacturers. Of counsel **Patrick Lane**'s broad practice straddles litigation and IP matters, with sources praising him as a *"very talented trial lawyer."* His prior experience as an in-house counsel with Procter & Gamble lends him an invaluable level of commercial awareness.

## Faruki Ireland & Cox PLL

**THE FIRM** This compact commercial dispute resolution boutique operates from offices in Dayton and Cincinnati. The team comes to market attention for its courtroom skills and high degree of professionalism. It has longstanding relationships with clients such as Procter & Gamble, while it recently advised Reed Elsevier in a class certification dispute.

**Sources say:** *"A top-quality firm that compares well with those from other markets such as New York, Chicago or Los Angeles."*

**KEY INDIVIDUALS Charles Faruki** (see p.2095) is a renowned trial lawyer who wins outstanding recognition

from the market. Sources say that *"he never loses sight of his client's goals,"* while one interviewee notes that *"he will not hesitate to give his impartial advice for the benefit of the client. He is a real craftsman."* Faruki led the team on the aforementioned matter for Reed Elsevier. **Jeffrey Ireland** (see p.2100) handles antitrust and general commercial litigation. Sources regard him as *"a hard worker who leaves no stone unturned,"* and observe that *"he is willing and able to throw legal punches when necessary."*

## Hahn Loeser & Parks LLP
See profile on p.2123

**THE FIRM** The Hahn Loeser & Parks litigation team is noted for its strength in complex commercial disputes, with market sources speaking highly of its efficiency and cost-effectiveness. The group successfully defended Chicago Title Insurance in a keenly contested jury trial concerning alleging breach of contract and tort claims in the energy sector.

**Sources say:** *"Big-firm service at a medium-firm price."*

**KEY INDIVIDUALS Robert Fogarty** (see p.2096) is admired for his long and deep experience of commercial disputes, and is an accomplished trial lawyer. He recently represented Aetna Better Health in a dispute concerning Medicaid contract awards. Sources name him *"a tough litigator."* **Steven Goldfarb** (see p.2097) counts a number of financial institutions and insurance companies among his clients, and led the team on the Chicago Title Insurance matter. **Rob Remington** (see p.2110) recently represented biofuel manufacturer POET in a multimillion-dollar contract dispute. Sources note: *"He understands both litigation and negotiating contracts, which helps him help us across all issues."* **Stephen Chappelear** (see p.2092) is an experienced trial lawyer and former partner in charge of the Columbus office. Interviewees praise his ability to manage high end, detail-heavy matters effectively, noting that he is *"good at simplifying the case for the jury."* **Marc Kessler** (see p.2102) represents clients in high-stakes disputes at trial and appellate level. He worked closely with Fogarty in the aforementioned Aetna litigation.

## Ice Miller LLP

**THE FIRM** Ice Miller continues its respected showing in the litigation arena following its 2011 merger with native Ohio firm Schottenstein Zox & Dunn. The litigation team handles a variety of work from product liability to securities disputes. The group recently represented Ramius Private Select in a high-value securities fraud claim by investors against a fund manager. Other clients include Pinnacle Data Systems and City of Dublin.

**Sources say:** *"In my opinion the representation we received was outstanding."*

**KEY INDIVIDUALS John Gilligan** is a highly experienced litigator in the firm's Columbus office. As a fellow of the American College of Trial Lawyers he is noted for his immaculate courtroom skills. **John McDonald** is an accomplished and highly experienced trial counsel whose practice is increasingly concentrated on arbitration and mediation. He recently acted for Pinnacle Data Systems in a shareholder derivative and securities class action.

## Keating Muething & Klekamp PLL
See profile on p.2124

**THE FIRM** This firm receives warm praise from market sources for its professional, client-oriented and result-driven service. Recent highlights for the practice include acting for Fifth Third Bank in a breach of fiduciary duty dispute and a securities class action. Other clients include Cincom Systems and American Financial Group.

**Sources say:** *"They understand our business and business needs."*

**KEY INDIVIDUALS James Burke** (see p.2091) played a key role in the aforementioned matters for Fifth Third Bank. Sources speak admiringly of him as a *"strong, widely respected litigator"* and *"one of the top business litigation attorneys in the state."* **Michael Scheier** (see p.2111) is described as an *"excellent lawyer who expresses professionalism at every turn."* He is also a trial lawyer with notable experience in the courtroom.

## Kegler, Brown, Hill & Ritter
See profile on p.2125

**THE FIRM** The 35-strong litigation team at this Columbus firm has a rising profile for antitrust litigation, in addition to its recognized skills in broader commercial disputes work. Key matters of late include shareholder litigation and insurance disputes. Clients include Alliance Data Systems, Cardinal Health and the Catholic Diocese of Columbus.

**KEY INDIVIDUALS** The highly respected **Thomas Hill** is called a *"great business lawyer"* by sources, who unanimously agree that he is deserving of top-tier recognition. Recent matters include securities litigation arising from claims of breach of contract and fraud. **Roger Sugarman** is a reliable and effective choice of counsel for litigation and trial work, according to interviewees. His practice has a particular slant toward professional liability matters, and his highlights include advising the CEO of a Fortune 500 company in a shareholder class action. **Loriann Fuhrer** is quickly establishing a fine reputation in the state Bar. Sources describe her as *"smart, extremely diligent and hardworking,"* and note that *"she is good with witnesses and in the courtroom."*

## Porter Wright Morris & Arthur LLP
See profile on p.2127

**THE FIRM** This firm continues to win admirers in the Ohio market, with sources citing an impressive breadth of practice and credibility with local courts. Key clients include household names such as Duke Energy, American Electric Power and Huntington National Bank. The team recently secured an $8.2 million jury verdict on behalf of Skurka Aerospace.

**Sources say:** *"They have talented professionals that speak business language."*

**KEY INDIVIDUALS Kathleen Trafford** (see p.2115) is chair of the firm's appellate practice and has built a sound reputation in the Columbus area. Areas of excellence include government and regulatory litigation. Columbus-based **Robert Trafford** (see p.2115) is the firm's managing partner and maintains an active business litigation practice at trial and appellate levels. His practice is often concentrated on securities litigation and corporate governance matters. **Kathleen Brinkman** (see p.2091) is a former federal prosecutor and a leading litigator in the firm's Cincinnati office. She recently acted on a high-stakes class action concerning food supplements. **Hugh McKay** (see p.2106) represents corporate clients and financial institutions in commercial litigation at state and federal level. He led the team in the aforementioned matter for Skurka Aerospace. **Ryan Sherman** (see p.2112) continues to emerge as one of the next generation of leading Ohio litigators. His areas of influence include IP and securities litigation.

### Taft Stettinius & Hollister LLP

See profile on p.2130

**THE FIRM** This firm's January 2012 merger with Chester Willcox & Saxbe has provided a boost to its litigation capabilities in the Columbus market. Clients report long, productive relationships with its lawyers, and delight in the aggressive client advocacy on offer. It has an impressive client list that includes the Cincinnati Bengals, American Municipal Power and Globalstar.

**Sources say:** *"Professional, very easy to work with and very responsive."*

**KEY INDIVIDUALS Stuart Dornette** (see p.2095) is based in the Cincinnati office, where he serves as cochair of the litigation practice group. He is *"very thorough and he understands the issues very well,"* according to sources. **Stephen Fitch** (see p.2096) is a vastly experienced partner in the Columbus office. He recently represented American Municipal Power in a lawsuit stemming from the cancellation of a power station project. **David Wallace** (see p.2116) cochairs the litigation practice from the Cleveland branch of the firm. He is adjudged a versatile practitioner who is equally comfortable handling litigation from IP disputes to construction and wider commercial matters. **Charles Saxbe** (see p.2111) receives warm praise from the market for his general business litigation practice. In addition, he is admitted to the Supreme Court, enabling him to advise seamlessly on appellate matters. Cincinnati partner **Jack Donson** (see p.2094) chairs the antitrust group at the firm, and is a well-known and respected practitioner in this area. Sources point to his *"vast experience and good judgment"* as key reasons to engage his services. **Ralph Kohnen** (see p.2103) is the firm's authority on white-collar criminal matters. He enters the rankings for the first time after receiving glowing feedback from the market, with one impressed interviewee noting: *"Ralph is without question at the top of the list of those I have dealt with. His approach is to seek out the truth and stand firmly."* **Russell Sayre** (see p.2111) has a rising profile in the Cincinnati market. Sources speak of him as *"thorough, very systematic and meticulous in his approach."*

### Thompson Hine LLP

See profile on p.2131

**THE FIRM** This firm's business litigation and product liability practice has a solid reputation in the Cleveland market. Recent highlights include defending Ford in a lawsuit alleging the defective design and manufacture of the 2005 Crown Victoria Police Interceptor. Other clients include Wells Fargo Bank, KeyCorp and JPMorgan Chase.

**Sources say:** *"I am absolutely impressed. They are excellent trial lawyers."*

**KEY INDIVIDUALS** Cleveland-based **James Robenalt** (see p.2110) is an experienced trial counsel and arbitrator whose broad practice encompasses professional malpractice, tax disputes and general business litigation. **Scott King** (see p.2102) impresses sources, with one interviewee noting that *"he has a very firm handle on the courtroom, and he is very good at communicating back to us."* Recent work includes ongoing mortgage-related litigation for a number of financial institutions. **Thomas Collin** (see p.2093) is recognized for his excellence in antitrust matters, with sources speaking highly of his collegiate and intellectual approach to the law. He recently advised Dayton Superior on a matter concerning alleged Robinson-Patman Act price discrimination matters.

### Tucker Ellis

**THE FIRM** The Tucker Ellis trial team is noted for its representation of Fortune 500 companies, and is known for its close ties with the medical device and pharmaceutical industries. The group recently represented PharmaJet on a nationwide putative class action concerning administration of medication. Other marquee clients include Johnson & Johnson, Pfizer and Electrolux.

**Sources say:** *"Outstanding. A very strong firm."*

**KEY INDIVIDUALS Hugh Stanley** focuses on commercial litigation pertaining to the corporate, banking and insurance sectors, and is noted for his class action experience in state and federal court. **John McCaffrey** is a former FBI special agent and public prosecutor. His practice has a particular slant toward high-stakes white-collar criminal matters such as securities fraud. Sources agree he is *"very good at what he does."*

### Band 4

### Carpenter Lipps & Leland LLP

**THE FIRM** This compact litigation boutique has built a sound reputation in the market for its wide spectrum of work and high-quality practice. Its areas of experience include banking disputes, product liability and regulatory matters.

**KEY INDIVIDUALS Michael Carpenter** is described by sources as a *"very effective"* litigator with *"great vision."* He is closely associated with the automotive, banking and consumer lending industries.

### Roetzel & Andress, LPA

See profile on p.2128

**THE FIRM** This firm remains visible in the Ohio market, recently handling a number of matters including insurance defense and white-collar criminal work. It has also advised on high-stakes arbitrations and enforcement work.

**KEY INDIVIDUALS Robert Casarona** (see p.2092) is chair of the firm's national litigation and government affairs group. His long activity in this field has seen him act for entities from the energy, utility and waste management sectors. **Donald Scherzer** (see p.2111) garners market respect for his handling of white-collar criminal matters. Sources describe him as a *"well-rounded litigator"* and a *"very effective communicator who works extremely well with co-counsel."*

### Sebaly Shillito & Dyer

**THE FIRM** Clients were quick to praise the keen service and effective litigation practice at this compact corporate and commercial firm. The firm has proved itself a force to contend with in matters such as insurance, environmental and ERISA litigation. Clients include MeadWestvaco and Barco.

**Sources say:** *"The quality of the firm's representation has met or exceeded the other Ohio firms."*

**KEY INDIVIDUALS Jim Dyer** is the chair of the litigation department at the firm. He advised MeadWestvaco on product liability matters related to an acquisition. Clients report that *"he has very good insight into our business and is genuinely interested in it."*

### Other Notable Practitioners

Sole practitioner **James Arnold** is admired for his litigation capabilities and his adroit case preparation. Sources describe him as a *"fabulous, standout trial lawyer."* His experience includes commercial and noncommercial matters, including probate and medical malpractice work. The *"outstanding"* **Ralph Cascarilla** (see p.2092) is a lawyer at Walter & Haverfield LLP in Cleveland. He is a white-collar crime specialist and is described as *"thorough, analytical, knowledgeable and experienced."* **Neil Freund** is a name partner at Dayton firm Freund, Freeze & Arnold. He enjoys a deservedly good reputation in matters such as product liability. **Roger Fry** is of counsel at Cincinnati firm Rendigs, Fry, Kiely & Dennis, LLP. Areas of excellence include insurance defense and commercial law. **David Greer** of Bieser, Greer, & Landis LLP is widely considered to be one of the leading figures of the Ohio litigation Bar. Sources call him *"an outstanding trial lawyer, with an excellent reputation in this part of the state."* **David Kamp** is the managing partner of White, Getgey & Meyer Co LPA in Cincinnati. Sources attest that *"he relates well to jurors and judges,"* and note that *"he makes sharp points without being obstreperous or difficult."* The *"very creative"* **Steven Kaufman** practices with Cleveland firm Kaufman & Company, LLC. Sources note the breadth of his experience in both plaintiff and defense representation. His clients include financial institutions. **Richard Kerger** of Kerger & Hartman LLC is a well-known lawyer in the Toledo market. He is noted for his expertise in white-collar criminal matters and wins the respect of market observers for his *"good common sense and great experience."* The *"very effective"* **Philip Kushner** of Kushner & Hamed is also noted for his expertise in the white-collar criminal arena. Sources point to him as an *"extremely aggressive and hard-working lawyer."* **Patrick McLaughlin** is the name partner at McLaughlin Law, LLP. He is an effective counsel in commercial litigation and white-collar criminal matters. Sources describe him as *"aggressive yet thoughtful."* Sole practitioner **William Meeks** enjoys a fine reputation for white-collar criminal defense work in Columbus and beyond. He can be relied upon to do a good job of representing clients, according to sources. **Jill Meyer** (see p.2107) is managing member of the Cincinnati office of Frost Brown Todd LLC. She is noted for her IP-related disputes work and enjoys a reputation as a skilled counselor in contentious matters. **Robert Pitcairn** is *"a great trial lawyer"* and head of litigation at Katz, Teller, Brant & Hild in Cincinnati. Areas of focus include securities litigation and high-stakes contract disputes. Columbus-based sole practitioner **Frank Ray** acts for commercial concerns and individuals. Interviewees praise his trial skills and cite his credibility before the judiciary. The highly experienced **Orville Reed** recently left Buckingham Doolittle & Burroughs to join Akron firm Stark & Knoll. His areas of expertise include personal injury and insurance and business litigation. **Robert Rotatori** is the managing partner of Cleveland firm Rotatori Bender Co LPA. Interviewees refer to him as a bright and highly capable litigator, with a notable profile in white-collar criminal matters. **Niki Schwartz** is a senior and name partner at Cleveland dispute resolution and criminal law boutique Schwartz, Downey & Co LPA. Interviewees describe him as a *"very effective advocate,"* and point to his *"wisdom and terrific judgment."* He is increasingly active in mediation work.

**Roger Synenberg** is a former Assistant US Attorney who now practices at Synenberg & Associates in Cleveland. He is a litigator and trial lawyer who spends a substantial amount of his time on white-collar criminal matters. Sources describe him as *"first-rate,"* and an *"experienced, well-regarded lawyer."* **Mark Wallach** (see p.2116) is a *"tenacious litigator"* at Thacker Martinsek LPA. He advised Northeast Ohio Regional Sewer District in a dispute concerning a stormwater management program. **Eric Zagrans** of Zagrans Law Firm LLC is lauded by sources for his *"honest, straight-talking and ethical"* approach. He handles complex commercial litigation, class actions and medical malpractice work.

# NATURAL RESOURCES & ENVIRONMENT

Commentary about individuals can be found under their firm's paragraph. If the firm has no paragraph (is not ranked) look at Other Notable Practitioners.

## Natural Resources & Environment
### Leading Firms

**Band 1**

Frost Brown Todd LLC *
McMahon DeGulis LLP *
Squire Sanders (US) LLP *
Thompson Hine LLP *
Vorys, Sater, Seymour and Pease LLP *

**Band 2**

Bricker & Eckler LLP
Jones Day *
Porter Wright Morris & Arthur LLP *
Roetzel & Andress, LPA *
Shumaker Loop & Kendrick LLP

**Band 3**

Baker & Hostetler LLP *
Eastman & Smith Ltd
Ice Miller LLP
Taft Stettinius & Hollister LLP *
Van Kley & Walker

## Band 1

### Frost Brown Todd LLC
See profile on p.1329

**THE FIRM** Interviewees praise this standout practice for its breadth of capabilities in the natural resources space, as well as its aptitude for high-value and complex litigation and transactional work. Highlights include advising on significant air permitting, site remediation and land redevelopment matters. Key clients include industrial, energy and manufacturing companies.

**Sources say:** *"Frost Brown Todd had a responsive and extensive breadth of knowledge, and I was never dissatisfied with their service, outcomes or approach."*

**KEY INDIVIDUALS William Hayes** (see p.2099) is a high-profile attorney who is praised by sources as a *"very good air lawyer."* He acted recently for a major automotive manufacturer on permitting aspects of a new manufactur-

## Natural Resources & Environment
### Senior Statesmen

**Senior Statesmen: distinguished older practitioners**

| | | |
|---|---|---|
| Brubaker Robert | Porter Wright Morris & Arthur LLP * | |
| Carson Van | Squire Sanders (US) LLP * | |
| Casper Jr Paul W | Frost Brown Todd LLC | |
| Hardy Michael L | Thompson Hine LLP * | |
| Tosi Louis | Shumaker Loop & Kendrick LLP | |

### Leading Individuals

**Band 1**

| | |
|---|---|
| Blattner Wray | Thompson Hine LLP * |
| Burke Kim | Taft Stettinius & Hollister LLP * |
| Farolino Shane A | Roetzel & Andress, LPA * |
| Hayes William D | Frost Brown Todd LLC * |
| Schraff Christopher | Porter Wright Morris & Arthur LLP * |

**Band 2**

| | |
|---|---|
| Barnes Geoffrey K | Squire Sanders (US) LLP * |
| Bott April | Bott Law Group (ONP)[†] |
| Brennan Maureen A | Baker & Hostetler LLP * |
| Cyphert Michael | Walter & Haverfield LLP (ONP)[†] * |
| Finn Terrence | Roetzel & Andress, LPA * |
| Haughey Stephen N | Frost Brown Todd LLC * |
| Kolesar Andrew L | Thompson Hine LLP * |
| McMahon Louis L | McMahon DeGulis LLP * |
| McMahon Michael S | McMahon DeGulis LLP * |
| McMurray Kevin N | Frost Brown Todd LLC * |
| Merrill Frank | Bricker & Eckler LLP |
| Nash David | McMahon DeGulis LLP * |
| Norman Mark A | Vorys, Sater, Seymour and Pease LLP * |
| Rego John A | Jones Day * |
| Reidy Joseph M | Ice Miller LLP |
| Samuels Stephen P | Ice Miller LLP |
| Sargeant Richard T | Eastman & Smith Ltd |
| Terp Thomas T | Taft Stettinius & Hollister LLP * |
| Van Kley Jack A | Van Kley & Walker |
| Walker Christopher A | Van Kley & Walker |
| Winters Karen A | Squire Sanders (US) LLP * |

**Band 3**

| | |
|---|---|
| Born Michael | Shumaker Loop & Kendrick LLP |
| DeGulis Gregory J | McMahon DeGulis LLP * |
| Doran Scott | Taft Stettinius & Hollister LLP * |
| Goldstein Heidi B | Thompson Hine LLP * |
| Habel Christopher S | Frost Brown Todd LLC * |
| Haynam Douglas | Shumaker Loop & Kendrick LLP |
| Jones Christopher | Calfee, Halter & Griswold LLP (ONP)[†] * |
| McWilliams Douglas A | Squire Sanders (US) LLP * |
| Patberg William L | Shumaker Loop & Kendrick LLP |
| Schmidt Jr Robert J | Porter Wright Morris & Arthur LLP * |
| Watt Kristin L | Vorys, Sater, Seymour and Pease LLP * |

**Band 4**

| | |
|---|---|
| Casarona Robert B | Roetzel & Andress, LPA * |
| Coughlin William E | Calfee, Halter & Griswold LLP (ONP)[†] * |
| Fay Terrence M | Thompson Hine LLP * |
| Fisher-Edwards Suzanne M | McMahon DeGulis LLP * |
| Gregg Joseph | Eastman & Smith Ltd |
| Gunsett Daniel J | Baker & Hostetler LLP * |
| Hoffman Timothy | Dinsmore & Shohl LLP (ONP)[†] |
| Keller John | Vorys, Sater, Seymour and Pease LLP * |
| Krassen Glenn | Bricker & Eckler LLP |
| Petricoff Howard | Vorys, Sater, Seymour and Pease LLP * |
| Pfefferle III Ben L | Baker & Hostetler LLP * |
| Russell Gregory | Vorys, Sater, Seymour and Pease LLP * |
| Stamp Vincent B | Dinsmore & Shohl LLP (ONP)[†] |
| Wesloh Steven | Frost Brown Todd LLC * |

* Indicates firm / individual with profile.
[†]ONP = Other Notable Practitioner

ing facility. **Stephen Haughey** (see p.2099) has built an enviable reputation for the quality of his work in Clean Water Act matters. He is a noted litigator who is *"very experienced in the courtroom,"* say sources. **Kevin McMurray** (see p.2106) heads up the firm's environmental practice. He is held in high regard for his *"very calm demeanor in approaching environmental issues that are especially problematic, and resolving them."* He applies his broad skill set to air and water disputes, and is an experienced trial advocate at both state and federal level. **Christopher Habel** (see p.2098) recently advised a logistics entity in a dispute concerning alleged contamination from a landfill site. Sources praise his commercial approach as well as his ability to simplify complicated matters and identify a clear progression plan. **Steven Wesloh** (see p.2117) can be relied upon for *"sound advice,"* say sources. He is recognized for his profile in air-related work. He recently led for a prominent manufacturer in an air emissions permitting matter. **Paul Casper** is the founder and former chair of the firm's environmental practice. He is an experienced and effective trial lawyer, and recently acted as lead counsel to a chemical company in a Superfund cost recovery action.

## McMahon DeGulis LLP
See profile on p.2126

**THE FIRM** This distinguished firm has one of the largest and most successful environmental practices in the state. The team is accomplished in transactional and contentious work, and routinely services clients of the caliber of Lockheed Martin, CSX and The Lincoln Electric Company. The group recently advised the Metropolitan Sewer District of Greater Cincinnati on environmental aspects of its multimillion-dollar wet weather improvement plan.

**Sources say:** *"They have carved out a good niche for environmental litigation, as well as transactional work. They have a very good reputation."*

**KEY INDIVIDUALS David Nash** (see p.2108) is *"a calm, cool and collected individual"* with *"a knack for anticipating the appropriate end game,"* sources report. He is an accomplished Superfund litigator, and enjoys a growing profile in the wind-powered energy sector. **Louis McMahon** (see p.2106) is *"a pleasure to deal with,"* according to interviewees. His practice includes water law and brownfield sites. Sources praise his *"excellent rapport with the local EPA officials,"* which enables him to negotiate the most favorable outcome. He was lead adviser on the wet weather improvement plan matter for the Metropolitan Sewer District of Greater Cincinnati. *"Good negotiator"* **Michael McMahon** (see p.2106) is the firm's managing partner. He is *"especially good in air issues,"* according to interviewees. Sources praise him as *"creative, thorough and resourceful. He examines each concern from many varied points of view, and helps us prepare our position to our best advantage."* **Gregory DeGulis** (see p.2094) heads up the firm's insurance recovery practice. He is a versatile and experienced lawyer who is admitted to practice in Massachusetts, New York and Ohio. He possesses *"impressive expertise in environmental law,"* according to clients. **Suzanne Fisher-Edwards** (see p.2096) brings a sound scientific understanding of envi-

ronmental issues to the table. She recently provided input on lease negotiations connected with water use.

## Squire Sanders (US) LLP
See profile on p.2129

**THE FIRM** Squire Sanders has a highly impressive environmental, safety and health practice, the influence of which extends far beyond the Ohio state lines. The team is adept at handling high-stakes litigation, compliance counseling and legislative issues, in addition to its noted expertise in licensing and transactional matters. Work highlights include acting for ArcelorMittal Cleveland in front of the appeals board of the EPA. Other key clients include the National Association of Flood & Stormwater Management Agencies and Enterprise Liquids Pipeline.

**Sources say:** *"The lawyers are very smart at what they do, very well connected, and very responsive."*

**KEY INDIVIDUALS Geoffrey Barnes** (see p.2090) is described by sources as a *"very tenacious"* advocate, whose practice comprises litigation and transactional work. He recently advised a manufacturer on state and federal regulatory actions concerning pollutants. **Karen Winters** (see p.2118) heads up the firm's global environmental, safety and health practice. Sources note that *"she is incredibly responsive"* and *"a great person to work with."* Litigator **Douglas McWilliams** (see p.2106) recently acted as lead counsel to a manufacturer concerning a federal action under the Clean Air Act. He has also previously advised the American Iron and Steel Institute. Senior counsel **Van Carson** (see p.2092) brings 46 years of experience to his commercial advisory work in air, water and Superfund matters. He recently acted for Goodyear on Superfund issues surrounding its prior disposal of a subsidiary.

## Thompson Hine LLP
See profile on p.2131

**THE FIRM** Interviewees are quick to laud this longstanding practice, and note its continuing prominence in the Ohio environmental arena. The team handles the full range of transactional, legislative and litigious matters, recently acting for Stanley Black & Decker and Goodrich Corporation in a Lower Passaic River Superfund matter. Other clients include Whirlpool and Waste Management.

**Sources say:** *"Thompson Hine stands out as having a very capable environmental practice."*

**KEY INDIVIDUALS Wray Blattner's** (see p.2090) practice includes government enforcement and private action work. Sources respect his broad skill set across air, water and waste work. *"He has great knowledge of the area, and is very levelheaded"* as well as *"a very accomplished litigator,"* say sources. **Heidi Goldstein** (see p.2097) has built a sound reputation in toxic tort and Superfund matters. She has anchored the firm's work for Goodrich in the matter described above. **Andrew Kolesar** (see p.2103) took a similar role for Stanley Black & Decker in the same matter. Sources say he is *"an excellent lawyer, as well as a very professional and knowledgeable advocate."* **Terrence Fay** (see p.2096) handles air and water matters, including EPA litigation. He recently advised American Landfill, a subsidiary of Waste Management, on a hotly contested environmen-

tal construction permitting appeal concerning the expansion of a landfill. **Michael Hardy** (see p.2099) is a respected senior figure in the environmental sphere. Sources declare him to be *"great to work with, and smart,"* and admire his ability to *"figure out how to get to a 'yes.'"*

## Vorys, Sater, Seymour and Pease LLP
See profile on p.2133

**THE FIRM** Vorys Sater has an excellent reputation in the environmental space, and a high profile in acting for entities from the energy and natural resources sectors. It recently advised a number of oil and gas producers on development of the Utica Shale. It has also acted for academic institutions, farms and manufacturers in a variety of litigious, permitting and transactional matters.

**KEY INDIVIDUALS Kristin Watt** (see p.2116) heads up the energy and environment practice. Sources agree she is *"a tenacious litigator"* who also provides solid and sound transactional advice. Her recent highlights include negotiating a number of environmental consent orders with the Ohio Attorney General's office. **Mark Norman** (see p.2108) has broad experience of contentious, transactional and emergency response work in the environmental arena. He recently acted as lead adviser to an energy company on the negotiation of a consent decree from the US Government. **John Keller** (see p.2101) is recognized for his expertise in oil and gas matters. He has provided ongoing advice to entities from the natural resources and energy sectors on the aforementioned Utica Shale development. One admiring client describes him as a *"guru of Appalachian oil and gas law."* **Gregory Russell** (see p.2111) is *"articulate and succinct,"* according to sources, and wins plaudits for his *"solid grasp of regulatory, contractual and administrative law."* **Howard Petricoff** (see p.2109) is a noted litigator who is experienced at trial level, as well as in matters before public permitting agencies such as the Federal Energy Regulatory Commission (FERC).

## Band 2

## Bricker & Eckler LLP

**THE FIRM** This firm is respected for its handling of a wide range of matters, including climate change and sustainable development issues, environmental litigation, and permitting and regulatory matters. A number of marquee clients seek out its services, including the Ohio Department of Natural Resources and JPMorgan Chase. It recently advised the Northeast Ohio Public Energy Council on a keenly contested rate plan dispute before the Public Utilities Council of Ohio (PUCO).

**KEY INDIVIDUALS** The *"very approachable and personable"* **Frank Merrill** serves as chair of the firm's energy, public utilities and environmental practice. He recently acted as the lead lawyer for an energy company in a Supreme Court landfill dispute. Sources report: *"Frank's style has allowed him to be able to network with people across industries and regulators. Those relationships pay dividends."* **Glenn Krassen** heads up the firm's shale, oil and gas practice. He was the lead lawyer on the aforementioned

Northeast Ohio Public Energy Council PUCO dispute. Clients say he is *"well informed in all aspects of utilities."*

## Jones Day
See profile on p.919

**THE FIRM** This firm has a sound reputation both in the region and beyond, and is known for its broad national footprint. The team handles the full range of environmental litigation, permitting and transactional work, and has recently advised on a number of hazardous waste disputes, including air and Superfund matters.
**Sources say:** *"A very capable environmental practice group."*
**KEY INDIVIDUALS** John Rego (see p.2110) is *"well known and highly regarded"* in the Ohio environmental sphere, say sources. He advises on air matters, rulemaking and emission standards.

## Porter Wright Morris & Arthur LLP
See profile on p.2127

**THE FIRM** This firm has a recognized prowess in a wide range of transactional and regulatory matters, and its noted for its strength in air pollution regulation. It recently advised a refinery company in a state action alleging air pollution in violation of local law. Key clients include American Electric Power, FirstEnergy and Procter & Gamble.
**Sources say:** *"Its rates are competitive among high-quality firms, and it is extremely efficient."*
**KEY INDIVIDUALS** Christopher Schraff (see p.2112) heads up the environmental law group. He is described by sources as *"one of the most respected water attorneys in Ohio."* His recent highlights include advising a large industrial company on regulatory permits and approvals connected with a proposed new manufacturing facility. **Robert Schmidt** (see p.2112) is *"very knowledgeable and efficient,"* according to sources. He was the lead lawyer on the aforementioned air pollution matter for the refinery company. **Robert Brubaker** (see p.2091) is a venerated figure in air matters. One interviewee reports: *"His immersion in the details, his tenacity, his ability to be an advocate without being offensive, and his dedication to securing workable outcomes for his clients are the traits that I most admire."*

## Roetzel & Andress, LPA
See profile on p.2128

**THE FIRM** This firm's environmental, energy, and health and safety practice continues to be respected by market observers for its handling of regulatory compliance and enforcement matters in the air and water spaces, as well as for its representation of oil and gas companies. Highlights include advising a recycling company on Superfund litigation concerning alleged river contamination. It has an enviable client list, including Speedway SuperAmerica, Anadarko Petroleum and Marathon Petroleum.
**KEY INDIVIDUALS** Shane Farolino (see p.2095) is chair of the practice, and is noted for his substantial environmental enforcement experience. *"He uses his unmatched technical expertise and negotiating prowess to resolve difficult environmental issues,"* according to sources. **Terrence Finn** (see p.2096) recently advised an energy company in an

EPA enforcement action alleging breach of the Clean Air Act. Sources point to his *"good advocacy skills and solid reputation"* as reasons to retain his services. **Robert Casarona** (see p.2092) chairs the firm's national litigation and government affairs practice. *"He is a skilled problem solver who can quickly ascertain collaborative solutions to complex problems,"* according to clients.

## Shumaker Loop & Kendrick LLP

**THE FIRM** This firm has a respected track record in the environmental space. It is experienced in representing clients before the EPA and other regulatory agencies, as well as both state and federal court. The group handles regulatory compliance and enforcement matters, and is particularly noted for its work in air pollution regulations. Clients include major utilities, petroleum refineries and interstate pipeline companies.
**KEY INDIVIDUALS** Michael Born is described as a *"very hard-working, hard-hitting and direct"* advocate. He advises on air and solid waste matters for clients which include utilities. **Douglas Haynam** is an environmental litigator whose practice includes notable Superfund work for manufacturers, real estate companies and waste management companies on his client list. **William Patberg** has achieved market prominence for the quality of his water and air work. *"He is very sharp and always respected,"* say sources. The *"well-regarded and well-known"* **Louis Tosi** heads up the firm's environmental group, and is a prominent lawyer in the Clean Air Act space.

## Band 3

## Baker & Hostetler LLP
See profile on p.2119

**THE FIRM** Clients appreciate the broad regional and national reach of this firm's environmental and energy practice. The team recently acted for AK Steel in a high-value permitting dispute concerning the Middletown Coke Company plant. The group acts for a number of impressive clients, including Hygenic, ConocoPhillips and Greif.
**Sources say:** *"When the issues are broader or involve multi-state jurisdictions, the firm's size and networking firepower have been incredibly helpful."*
**KEY INDIVIDUALS** Maureen Brennan (see p.2091) is praised as *"a great strategist"* who is *"tough, demanding, intelligent, organized and gets results."* Recent highlights include advising LRC Copley Investors on a 401 Water Quality Certification appeal. **Daniel Gunsett** (see p.2098) is noted for his transactional expertise in environmental matters. He recently advised an energy company on a joint venture concerning the Utica Shale development. **Ben Pfefferle** (see p.2109) is the national chair of the environmental and energy group. He was the lead lawyer in the AK Steel litigation described above.

## Eastman & Smith Ltd

**THE FIRM** This Toledo-headquartered firm is known for its consistency and stability in the environmental arena. The environmental practice group acts for Fortune 500

companies and municipalities in a range of permitting, lobbying and litigation work.
**KEY INDIVIDUALS** Richard Sargeant is well known for his solid waste work. He is described by sources as *"a solid lawyer"* who is *"easy to work with and very knowledgeable."* Sources *"think highly"* of **Joseph Gregg** for his handling of Superfund litigation and air permitting matters.

## Ice Miller LLP

**THE FIRM** This firm handles the full range of environmental matters, including litigation, regulatory compliance and enforcement, and transactional advice. The team is recognized for its handling of brownfield, Superfund and water matters. Key clients include Vertellus Specialties, BayernLB and CMA Corporation.
**KEY INDIVIDUALS** The *"very thorough"* **Joseph Reidy** wins praise for his astute command of brownfield matters. He is an experienced litigator who has represented clients before both state and federal court. **Stephen Samuels** is noted for his handling of water matters. Peers describe him as *"a dangerous opponent and a top-notch advocate."*

## Taft Stettinius & Hollister LLP
See profile on p.2130

**THE FIRM** This firm routinely acts on high-stakes litigation across the environmental spectrum, on both the plaintiff and defense sides. The group is experienced in handling regulatory permitting, compliance and enforcement actions, and is recognized for its handling of energy litigation and transactions. Its client list includes Cintas Corporation and American Municipal Power.
**KEY INDIVIDUALS** Kim Burke (see p.2092) cochairs the environmental practice group. He is well known for his Superfund work, and sources describe him as a *"solid, thorough and tough litigator."* **Thomas Terp** (see p.2115) is noted for his skilled handling of contentious Superfund work. Highlights include advising Soco West in connection with groundwater cleanup at the Lockwood Solvent Superfund site. **Scott Doran** (see p.2094) wins plaudits for the quality of his wetlands expertise. He has *"thorough knowledge of Ohio's environmental regulatory programs and extensive hands-on experience,"* say sources.

## Van Kley & Walker

**THE FIRM** This compact environmental boutique punches well above its weight in the Ohio market. Areas of expertise include litigation, permitting, transactional work and legislative matters. The firm has recognized capabilities in environmental issues affecting large-scale farming clients, in addition to its solid roster of industrial clients.
**Sources say:** *"The lawyers are very tenacious and very knowledgeable."*
**KEY INDIVIDUALS** Prominent litigator **Jack Van Kley** is commended by sources for his expertise in the environmental aspects of agricultural law. **Christopher Walker** is admired by sources for his strong showing in regulatory and Superfund work. Clients come from both the public and private sector, and include steel manufacturers and farms.

## Other Notable Practitioners

**April Bott** of Bott Law Group garners market attention for her broad environmental practice, which includes mining, shale gas and construction work. Sources emphasize her committed litigation style, describing her as a *"fierce advocate."* **Michael Cyphert** (see p.2094) of Walter & Haverfield LLP enjoys a rising profile in the market as an experienced and highly effective Superfund litigator. His work includes advising on matters concerning the manufacturing and automotive sectors. **Christopher Jones** (see p.2101) of Calfee, Halter & Griswold LLP is a former director of the Ohio EPA. Sources note that *"he brings good political sense to his practice."* His highlights include advising the City of Euclid on its sewer and water-related obligations. **Timothy Hoffman** is chair of Dinsmore & Shohl LLP's environmental practice. He is described as *"knowledgeable and good to deal with,"* and is recognized for his handling of high-stakes Superfund matters. **William Coughlin** (see p.2093) chairs the environmental practice group at Calfee Halter. Clients speak of his *"wide and deep experience litigating environmental matters."* He advised Union Carbide on environmental issues pertaining to a number of Ohio sites. **Vincent Stamp** is an environmental litigator at Dinsmore Shohl. He is considered an experienced and effective environmental lawyer, with a high profile for Superfund and associated cost-recovery work.

# REAL ESTATE

Real Estate p.2085   Zoning/Land Use p.2086

Commentary about individuals can be found under their firm's paragraph.  If the firm has no paragraph (is not ranked) look at Other Notable Practitioners.

## Real Estate
### Leading Firms

**Band 1**
Jones Day [*]
Thompson Hine LLP [*]
Vorys, Sater, Seymour and Pease LLP [*]

**Band 2**
Bricker & Eckler LLP
Frost Brown Todd LLC [*]

**Band 3**
Baker & Hostetler LLP [*]
Benesch, Friedlander, Coplan & Aronoff LLP [*]
Porter Wright Morris & Arthur LLP [*]

**Band 4**
Hurtuk & Daroff
Ice Miller LLP
Kegler, Brown, Hill & Ritter [*]
Singerman, Mills, Desberg & Kauntz Co LPA
Squire Sanders (US) LLP [*]
Taft Stettinius & Hollister LLP [*]
Ulmer & Berne LLP [*]

[*] *Indicates firm / individual with profile.*
[†] *ONP = Other Notable Practitioner*

*The editorial is in alpha order by firm name.*

## Baker & Hostetler LLP
### See profile on p.2119

**THE FIRM** Despite the departure of key lawyer Harlan Robins, this national firm is still noted for its depth of real estate talent. Interviewees admire its quality of service and appropriate fee structure. It has advised the Board of Church Extension of the Disciples of Christ on real estate portfolio management. Other clients include Forest City Enterprises and Playhouse Square Foundation.

**Sources say:** *"A very professional firm that understands how to balance market conditions and business requirements."*

**KEY INDIVIDUALS Amy Kellogg** (see p.2101) advises the Board of Church Extension of the Disciples of Christ on transactional property work, including loans and foreclosures. Sources describe her as *"a very good listener and communicator. She understands her profession and knows*

## Real Estate
### Senior Statesmen

**Senior Statesmen: distinguished older practitioners**
Strauss David J          *Baker & Hostetler LLP* [*]

### Leading Individuals

**Band 1**

| | |
|---|---|
| Baker David | *Bricker & Eckler LLP* |
| Buchenroth Stephen | *Vorys, Sater, Seymour and Pease LLP* [*] |
| Coyne Thomas J | *Thompson Hine LLP* [*] |
| McCreary Charles 'Dusty' | *Bricker & Eckler LLP* |
| Paris Zachary | *Jones Day* [*] |
| Striefsky Linda A | *Thompson Hine LLP* [*] |

**Band 2**

| | |
|---|---|
| Aronoff James B | *Thompson Hine LLP* [*] |
| Cadwallader John I | *Frost Brown Todd LLC* [*] |
| Conrad David | *Bricker & Eckler LLP* |
| Coscarelli Dianne S | *Thompson Hine LLP* [*] |
| Curry Robert M | *Thompson Hine LLP* [*] |
| Intihar Steve | *Bricker & Eckler LLP* |
| Oberschmidt E Richard | *Frost Brown Todd LLC* [*] |
| Ording Michael K | *Jones Day* [*] |
| Robins Harlan W | *Dickinson Wright PLLC (ONP)* [†] [*] |
| Steindler Howard | *Benesch, Friedlander, Coplan & Aronoff* [*] |
| Weir Bill | *Porter Wright Morris & Arthur LLP* [*] |
| Wellner John P | *Vorys, Sater, Seymour and Pease LLP* [*] |

**Band 3**

| | |
|---|---|
| Arndt Randall S | *Ice Miller LLP* |
| Daroff Charles | *Hurtuk & Daroff* |
| Desberg Gary | *Singerman, Mills, Desberg & Kauntz Co LPA* |
| Diller Edward D | *Taft Stettinius & Hollister LLP* [*] |
| Gagliano Bill J | *Ulmer & Berne LLP* [*] |
| Griffith Jr Stephen M | *Taft Stettinius & Hollister LLP* [*] |
| Gutmacher Norman | *Benesch, Friedlander, Coplan & Aronoff* [*] |
| Handlan Allen | *Kegler, Brown, Hill & Ritter* |
| Hunt Stephen | *Aronoff Rosen & Hunt (ONP)* [†] |
| Kellogg Amy E | *Baker & Hostetler LLP* [*] |

| | |
|---|---|
| Kuehnle Kenton | *Allen Kuehnle Stovall & Neuman (ONP)* [†] |
| Lindberg Lawrence V | *Baker & Hostetler LLP* [*] |
| Pearlman Samuel | *Singerman, Mills, Desberg & Kauntz Co LPA* |
| Phillips William | *Taft Stettinius & Hollister LLP* [*] |
| Saad Michael D | *Squire Sanders (US) LLP* [*] |
| Schreiner Joanne M | *Dinsmore & Shohl LLP (ONP)* [†] |
| Smith J Theodore (Ted) | *Vorys, Sater, Seymour and Pease LLP* [*] |
| Swank Christopher N | *Bricker & Eckler LLP* |

**Band 4**

| | |
|---|---|
| Bissinger Charles | *Vorys, Sater, Seymour and Pease LLP* [*] |
| Godby Herbert R | *Ice Miller LLP* |
| Haas Colleen | *Frost Brown Todd LLC* [*] |
| Haas Michael | *Jones Day* [*] |
| Hayes Jeffrey | *Porter Wright Morris & Arthur LLP* [*] |
| Hurtuk Edward | *Hurtuk & Daroff* |
| Kadish Scott P | *Ulmer & Berne LLP* [*] |
| Kreider Kenneth | *Keating Muething & Klekamp (ONP)* [†] [*] |
| Lemasters P Reid | *Frost Brown Todd LLC* [*] |
| Mixter Stephen | *Jones Day* [*] |
| Pauken Patrick J | *Baker & Hostetler LLP* [*] |
| Raker Keith | *Tucker Ellis (ONP)* [†] |
| Rogers Karla | *Calfee, Halter & Griswold LLP (ONP)* [†] [*] |
| Shuller Donald | *Vorys, Sater, Seymour and Pease LLP* [*] |
| Wild Jeffrey J | *Benesch, Friedlander, Coplan & Aronoff* [*] |
| Wilson W Russell | *Frost Brown Todd LLC* [*] |

**Up-and-coming individuals**

| | |
|---|---|
| Sosin Jeremy | *Hurtuk & Daroff* |

**Associates to watch**

| | |
|---|---|
| Oakes Jared E | *Thompson Hine LLP* [*] |
| Sullivan Peggy | *Frost Brown Todd LLC* [*] |
| Woeste Kristin | *Vorys, Sater, Seymour and Pease LLP* [*] |

*how to guide the discussion on the important items."* **Lawrence Lindberg** (see p.2105) has 40 years' experience in the real estate field, advising clients on real estate development, leasing, construction and financing matters. He continues to act as counsel to a prominent building and construction management company in a $350 million construction project. **Patrick Pauken** (see p.2109) acted as lead adviser and negotiator for a prominent logistics company on a significant lease acquisition. He also counts real estate developers amongst his clients. **David Strauss** (see

*The editorial is in alphabetical order by firm name.*

p.2114) is recognized for his timely and quality service in this area. He advised Play House Square Foundation on refurbishment and rehabilitation connected with the Middough Building Project.

## Benesch, Friedlander, Coplan & Aronoff LLP
See profile on p.2120

**THE FIRM** The dedicated real estate and environmental practice at this firm receives client praise for its keen service levels and cost-effective work. It acts for clients ranging from private equity firms to lenders and developers on all real estate and real estate financing matters.

**Sources say:** *"The lawyers are very thorough and very responsive to our needs."*

**KEY INDIVIDUALS** Howard Steindler (see p.2114) calls on 45 years of experience to offer *"excellent service,"* according to clients. He has a distinct profile in shopping center and residential development work. **Norman Gutmacher** (see p.2098) recently acted as borrower counsel to a developer of a multiple-unit residential complex in Ohio. His skill set includes commercial leasing, loan restructuring and workout matters, foreclosures, acquisitions and divestitures. **Jeffrey Wild** (see p.2117) is a younger partner who serves as vice chair of the real estate practice. He earns praise for his commercial instincts, and is described as *"a very good attorney with very good business sense."* His practice covers all aspects of commercial real estate, with a particular focus on financing.

## Berns, Ockner & Greenberger

**THE FIRM** This six-attorney Beachwood firm offers advice across the full spectrum of real estate and construction law, but is best known for its expertise in zoning and land use matters. It often acts for clients on promoting and opposing zoning and permitting applications.

**KEY INDIVIDUALS** Name member **Sheldon Berns** can call on 52 years of legal experience. He advises on eminent domain, construction and zoning, among other matters. Clients concur that his work is *"of a very high quality."* **Ben Ockner** is no stranger to commercial disputes, particularly those involving land use permitting and regulatory work. Market sources recommend him for his broad skills and experience.

## Bricker & Eckler LLP

**THE FIRM** This firm's real estate team has built an admirable profile for its work on behalf of lenders, including KeyBank and Huntington National Bank. It also advises general corporate and low-income housing clients. It recently counseled Episcopal Retirement Homes on HUD matters, acquisition and refurbishment of an affordable development worth $12 million.

**Sources say:** *"The team's knowledge of the local market and its expertise in the real estate sector are second to none."*

**KEY INDIVIDUALS** **David Baker** wins plaudits for his legal know-how and sensible commercial manner: *"He is very easy to work with and skilled."* He handles high-value leasing, real estate development and associated finance work with aplomb. His clients include Fortune 500 and local manufacturing companies. **Dusty McCreary** is noted as a *"preeminent real estate finance lawyer."* He is *"very knowledgeable and easy to work with,"* as well as *"efficient and cordial"* in his dealings, according to sources. His highlights include leading negotiations for a developer concerning a Florida mixed-use development worth in excess of $100 million. **Steve Intihar** chairs the firm's real estate practice, and is described as a *"very practical and solution-oriented lender counsel, who is good at finding ways to make deals happen."* Recent highlights include advising a developer on land acquisition for multifamily projects. **David Conrad** has built a great name for his representation of financial institutions. One particular client praised him as being *"instrumental in getting transactions resolved or closed while protecting the bank. He is very well respected and his opinion on matters is very influential."* Conrad's recent work includes negotiating shopping center refinancings and syndicated construction loans. **Christopher Swank** is a younger partner with notable expertise in the highly regulated low-income housing tax credit area. According to sources, he is *"a terrific young lawyer – an emerging talent."*

## Frost Brown Todd LLC
See profile on p.1329

**THE FIRM** This regional firm acts frequently for financial institutions, developers, owners, investors and real estate professionals on the full range of real estate transactions and financings. Its client roster also includes prominent entities from the retail, manufacturing and healthcare sectors. Interviewees praise the lawyers' experience and skills.

**Sources say:** *"The real estate group does lots of lender and development work."*

**KEY INDIVIDUALS** The *"very astute"* **John Cadwallader** (see p.2092) is a key member of the practice. He advises frequently on retail and shopping center-related matters, and recently had a lead role on negotiating the multimillion-dollar securitized refinancing of a notable regional shopping mall. **Richard Oberschmidt** (see p.2108) often counsels healthcare clients on their real estate matters. Clients laud the trouble he takes to analyze the cost-benefit ratio of a course of action. He recently advised a notable healthcare organization on the real estate issues surrounding the disposal of a number of hospital facilities. **Colleen Haas** (see p.2098) is a younger Cincinnati member who wins plaudits as a *"good technical lawyer who is very responsive and does a nice job."* She earns recognition for her command of the intricacies of tax-advantaged real estate work: *"These are very complex transactions, yet she handles them well."* **Reid Lemasters** (see p.2104) is described as *"a great team player"* with a keen eye for detail in his real estate transactional practice. His key clients include real estate investment companies. **Russell Wilson** (see p.2117) is an experienced lawyer who has advised on retail and office developments. He recently acted on the acquisition of a number of shopping centers, in a deal worth more than $100 million. **Peggy Sullivan** (see p.2114) is a managing associate in the firm's Cincinnati office. Notable mandates include advising on several acquisitions of shopping centers by a real estate investment company.

## Hurtuk & Daroff

**THE FIRM** This compact real estate boutique is based exclusively in Cleveland. Now in its 15th year, the firm has developed a notable profile for local and smaller transactional real estate matters.

**KEY INDIVIDUALS** Name partner **Charles Daroff** is praised as a strong real estate lawyer. He acts as legal adviser to B'nai Jeshurun Congregation in Pepper Pike, Ohio. According to interviewees, **Edward Hurtuk** is rated among the state's top real estate attorneys. Recent work highlights include advising lenders on real estate financing for apartment developments. **Jeremy Sosin** is recognized as a bright attorney with a contemplative and detailed approach to his work. His practice covers all aspects of real estate and real estate financing.

## Ice Miller LLP

**THE FIRM** This real estate practice has grown following the firm's merger with Schottenstein Zox & Dunn in January 2012. Clients include Circle Black Partners and ExactTarget.

**KEY INDIVIDUALS** **Randall Arndt** is described as a seasoned and experienced professional. He acts for a number of clients, including landlords, tenants and retailers, with key names including Columbus College of Art and Design. **Herbert Godby** is a seasoned lawyer who imbues a sense of confidence in those he deals with. Sources agree that he is *"very qualified and cordial."*

*The editorial is in alphabetical order by firm name.*

## Jones Day

See profile on p.919

**THE FIRM** This is a strong national firm with a respected real estate practice. It is recognized for successfully servicing large industrial and commercial clients, such as KeyBank National Association and Trammell Crow Residential. The team recently advised DDR on a $1.43 billion real estate joint venture and purchase agreement with Blackstone.

**Sources say:** *"This firm has a broad national real estate practice."*

**KEY INDIVIDUALS** Benefiting from 40 years of experience, **Zachary Paris** (see p.2109) heads up the firm's Cleveland real estate practice. Sources agree that he handles highly complex transactions successfully and effectually, and that *"he is always at the top of his game."* His recent work includes a lead role on a real estate joint venture and purchase agreement for DDR. **Michael Ording** (see p.2109) heads up the Columbus real estate practice. He advises on a range of real estate transactions, including financings and joint ventures. He counseled the Trammell Crow Company on a $430 million disposal of its interest in 22 apartment complexes. **Michael Haas** (see p.2098) acted on the DDR transaction, and also counts NRP Group among his clients. He has successfully built a profile in the real estate arena, advising on housing projects, investment and joint ventures. **Stephen Mixter** (see p.2108) advises on substantial real estate matters for corporate clients. He recently acted for KeyBank National Association on its acquisition of 37 bank branch offices in New York. He has also acted for Continental Airlines.

## Kegler, Brown, Hill & Ritter

See profile on p.2125

**THE FIRM** This real estate practice acts for prominent clients and has worked on some notable matters. Key clients include The Catholic Diocese of Columbus, Columbus Metropolitan Housing Authority and Huntington National Bank.

**Sources say:** *"It offers us a complete range of services related to real estate law."*

**KEY INDIVIDUALS** The *"very solid"* **Allen Handlan** heads up the firm's real estate practice. He recently advised The Catholic Diocese of Columbus on a number of transactional real estate matters. Sources particularly note his communication skills: *"He explains very clearly what the options and the results will be."*

## Porter Wright Morris & Arthur LLP

See profile on p.2127

**THE FIRM** This broad real estate practice has recognized strengths in land use as well as transactional matters. Highlights for the practice include advising AT&T on leasing and licensing contracts for antenna systems. Other marquee clients include Huntington National Bank and Genesis HealthCare System.

**KEY INDIVIDUALS** **Bill Weir** (see p.2117) has built a remarkable reputation for the quality of his lender representation. Sources report excellent relations with him, and he appears frequently in transactional matters. His key

clients include Wells Fargo. **Jeffrey Hayes** (see p.2099) heads up the real estate practice. Sources deem him to be a highly competent practitioner with easily transferable skills across the full spectrum of real estate law, as well as general corporate and business law. He acts as a lead adviser to a number of clients, including Casto and Huntington National Bank. **Robert Meyer** (see p.2107) was in-house general counsel for a home builder before returning to private practice. He is cochair of the firm's dedicated green practice group, and a primary port of call at the firm for land use issues. He advised Dominion Homes on an access dispute concerning a large residential-zoned plot. **Jeffrey McNealey** (see p.2106) is a senior and active lawyer on land use and regulatory work. He recently acted for Muskingum Iron & Metal on the proposed reuse of a former industrial site.

## Singerman, Mills, Desberg & Kauntz Co LPA

**THE FIRM** This compact commercial and real estate firm enjoys a rising profile for its proficient handling of real estate transactions. It has the resources to handle sophisticated work including tax credit financing, as well as the more common purchase and sale work.

**KEY INDIVIDUALS** Sources consider founding shareholder **Gary Desberg** a deal-oriented and solid transactional lawyer. He is particularly well known for advising on retail and shopping center industry work. **Samuel Pearlman** is of counsel to the firm. Sources agree he has a keen eye for detail and praise him as a reliable and experienced lawyer in the Cleveland market.

## Smith & Hale LLC

**THE FIRM** This compact boutique punches above its weight for land use and zoning matters in the Columbus area. Sources speak of it as a great practice, offering superb value for money and proven expertise.

**Sources say:** *"This is a team of great land use specialists."*

**KEY INDIVIDUALS** **Jeffrey Brown** has built a reputation as a leading attorney in zoning, land use and municipal law. His work ranges from advising on large-scale public projects to assisting small businesses, nonprofit organizations and homeowners with land use issues. **Ben Hale** is a name partner with a longstanding reputation. He assists commercial entities as well as nonprofit organizations with their land use and municipal law issues.

## Squire Sanders (US) LLP

See profile on p.2129

**THE FIRM** This strong national firm is recognized for its prowess in the real estate-related areas of tax credit and bond financing. Its client base includes prominent developers and investors.

**KEY INDIVIDUALS** Senior partner **Michael Saad** (see p.2111) is the firm's former real estate practice head. Sources praise his astute input on areas including tax credit and affordable housing work. He acts for investors and financial institutions.

## Taft Stettinius & Hollister LLP

See profile on p.2130

**THE FIRM** This old-line firm has bench strength in real estate transactional work, and is also effective on tax credit matters. It has boosted its lawyer headcount following its merger with another Ohio firm. Marquee clients of the practice include Cabot Properties, Stark Enterprises and Case Western Reserve University.

**KEY INDIVIDUALS** **Edward Diller** (see p.2094) is partner-in-charge of the Cincinnati office and a well-respected real estate professional. Sources describe him as a well-connected and proficient lawyer with a sound profile in developer representation. He also advises on construction contracts. **Stephen Griffith** (see p.2098) cochairs the real estate practice. Interviewees highlight his ability to protect clients while bringing negotiations to a successful conclusion, adding: *"He does a great job of listening, seeking compromise and holding firm when needed."* Fellow cochair **William Phillips** (see p.2109) notably acts for shopping center developers and retailers. He advised Visconsi Companies on the acquisition and development of a number of Walgreen retail outlets.

## Thompson Hine LLP

See profile on p.2131

**THE FIRM** The breadth and depth of this firm's real estate practice is well recognized, especially in Cleveland. Its enviable client list includes DDR, Verizon and KeyCorp. It recently advised a financial institution on a $25 million development, including associated financing and new market tax credit advice.

**Sources say:** *"The real estate group does high-quality work at very reasonable fees. It is very thorough and very responsive to our needs."*

**KEY INDIVIDUALS** **Thomas Coyne** (see p.2093) leads the firm's national real estate practice and recently had a lead advisory role on a $25 million development and financing matter. Interviewees note that he is highly skilled, with a practical approach to negotiation. *"He is certainly competent and very fair,"* according to sources. **Linda Striefsky** (see p.2114) cochairs the real estate finance group. Interviewees were enthusiastic about her legal prowess, describing her as *"top notch, efficient and very intelligent."* She acts for high end clients such as NYSE-listed REITs. She recently advised DDR on a number of financings and transactions. Cleveland partner-in-charge **James Aronoff** (see p.2089) heads up the real estate capital markets practice. He divides his time between real estate and general commercial transactional work. According to sources, he is *"hard-working and very attentive to the client."* He assisted DDR with the acquisition of an Arizona shopping center, and also counts the Richard E Jacobs Group as a key client. **Dianne Coscarelli** (see p.2093) is a knowledgeable and experienced finance lawyer, according to interviewees, who agree that she is *"very thorough"* in her work. She cochairs the real estate finance practice. Her clients include lenders as well as developers, and she has recently advised DDR on a number of matters. The *"very knowledgeable"* **Robert Curry** (see p.2094) is partner-in-charge of the Dayton office. Real estate financing is a key

*The editorial is in alphabetical order by firm name.*

aspect of his practice, and sources praise his activity in Ohio State Bar Association matters. He advised a healthcare entity on a $17.7 million new market tax credit financing for a new office building. **Jared Oakes** (see p.2108) is an associate in the Cleveland practice. Clients describe him as *"hard-working and very attentive."* His recent work includes counseling the Richard E Jacobs Group on transactions concerning shopping malls.

## Ulmer & Berne LLP
See profile on p.2132

**THE FIRM** This broad practice acts frequently on retail projects, leasing and permitting work. It recently advised the NRP Group on its acquisition of office buildings to be redeveloped for a new residential project. Other clients include Jo-Ann Stores and Yum! Brands.

**Sources say:** *"The team provides us with cost-effective, high-quality work on a timely basis."*

**KEY INDIVIDUALS Bill Gagliano** (see p.2097) is the real estate practice's lead lawyer. He advised on the NRP Group matter, and counts Yum! Brands on his client list. Sources describe him as *"practical, responsive and experienced."* **Scott Kadish** (see p.2101) wins plaudits as a cost-effective and responsive counselor in this field. He often advises on leasing work for retail and commercial landlord entities. *"He is very efficient at negotiating and drafting real estate leases, and he works seamlessly with our internal staff,"* said one interviewee. Kadish's key clients include Jo-Ann Stores. **Craig Miller** (see p.2107) heads up the public law practice, and is also a member of the real estate group. He is noted for his advice on land use matters, and led the team acting for John Carroll University on multifaceted zoning matters concerning a building and a stadium.

## Vorys, Sater, Seymour and Pease LLP
See profile on p.2133

**THE FIRM** This firm is virtually synonymous with high-value real estate work, such as large condominium developments. It also has a rising profile in the related energy and natural resources arenas. Interviewees agree it is a great choice for commercially focused advice. Recent highlights include high-value real estate refinancing and sale/leaseback transactions.

**Sources say:** *"The team provides good service, pragmatic counsel and reasonable fees."*

**KEY INDIVIDUALS Stephen Buchenroth** (see p.2091) is a key real estate lawyer in the firm's Columbus office, and a high-profile professional known for his breadth and depth of practice. Sources score him *"ten out of ten on every attribute; he is very responsive and extremely intelligent, puts lots into the Bar Association for the good of all, and is smart yet practical."* He recently acted for a developer on restructuring and refinancing a multimillion-dollar commercial property portfolio. **John Wellner** (see p.2117) is a former head of the firm's real estate group. Developers, lenders and owners feature extensively on his client list, and he has advised on mixed-use developments and urban redevelopment. He recently advised on the establishment of a privately owned parking facility. **Ted Smith** (see p.2113) is a member of the real estate and commercial practices. He *"has a great technical base and is very thorough,"* according to sources. His highlights include counseling a developer on a condominium project, including associated acquisition and construction financing. **Charles Bissinger** (see p.2090) has a good reputation across a broad range of real estate matters, and is particularly recognized for his advice on housing matters, including Department of Housing and Urban Development (HUD) work. He has also had a lead role on a number of recent real estate acquisitions and redevelopment projects. **Donald Shuller** (see p.2113) is a partner in the Cincinnati practice. He acts on a number of real estate transactions, including real estate financing work. Sources agree that he is a highly proficient counselor. **Kristin Woeste** (see p.2118) is based in the Cincinnati office, where she is an associate. She is a commercial and real estate lawyer who advises on matters ranging from deal negotiation to complicated financing, including multifamily financing matters. **Jill Tangeman** (see p.2114) has a notable profile for her real estate zoning and permitting practice. Clients praise her *"great blend of business sense with legal protection."* She advises on permitting issues surrounding multifamily projects and mixed-use developments.

## Other Notable Practitioners

**Richard Brahm** is a principal at compact Columbus firm Brahm & Cunningham, LLC. A substantial part of his practice is given over to advising on land use and zoning matters. **Don Plank** is the name partner of Plank Law Firm. His personal practice includes notable eminent domain and zoning work. **Harlan Robins** (see p.2110) left Baker Hostetler to help found Dickinson Wright PLLC's new Columbus office in June 2012. According to commentators, *"he is very smart – he identifies the issues and works through them."* His clients include Huntington National Bank and Hillspoint Group. **Richard Tranter** chairs the real estate practice at Dinsmore & Shohl LLP. He is a versatile lawyer as a member of the firm's corporate department, as well as a land use adviser. He is well versed in negotiating mutually agreeable deals on shopping centers, and sources report good relations with him. **Joanne Schreiner** heads up the commercial finance practice at Dinsmore Shohl, and is recognized as a *"strong lending attorney"* for her real estate finance work. *"She goes above and beyond with each closing that she handles,"* say interviewees. **Stephen Hunt** of Aronoff Rosen & Hunt is noted as an effective attorney who maintains cordial relations with opposing counsel. Sources say: *"You can trust him to take good care of matters and get them done efficiently."* He has advised developers, corporations and residential associations. **Kenton Kuehnle** of Allen Kuehnle Stovall & Neuman LLP is well known for his prowess in condominium law, a field where he has been instrumental in guiding policy in the state over the years. He is respected as a detail-oriented and smart professional. **Kenneth Kreider** (see p.2103) of Keating Muething & Klekamp PLL counts transactional real estate as a key part of his practice, and also has experience of tax-advantaged real estate matters. Sources agree he is a very knowledgeable attorney with enviable experience in the area. He advised Community Builders on its Choice Housing Program project. **Karla Rogers** (see p.2111) of Calfee, Halter & Griswold LLP has a hybrid real estate and finance practice. She acts for banks and Fortune 500 companies, among other clients, on negotiating leases as well as real estate finance. **Keith Raker** heads up the franchising and real estate practices at Tucker Ellis in Cleveland. He has acted for natural resources companies as well as financial institutions. Real estate financing, leasing and tax credit matters feature highly in his work.

# Leaders' Profiles in Ohio

**ADAMS, Deborah**
Frost Brown Todd LLC, Cincinnati
513 651 6705
dadams@fbtlaw.com
*Featured in Labor & Employment (Ohio)*
**Practice Areas:** Labor and employment. Represents management in EEO, tort and contract-based litigation, including class and collective actions. Develops/facilitates employers' personnel-law training programs.
**Professional Memberships:** Cincinnati and Ohio Bar Associations; Ohio Management Lawyers Association; College of Labor and Employment Lawyers; Management Labor and Employment Roundtable.
**Career:** Frost Brown Todd LLC 1982-present. Admitted Ohio 1982; Kentucky 1983.
**Publications:** Jury Dynamics of An EEO Case: A Defense Perspective; Discovery Issues in Employment Litigation; Harassment in the Modern Workplace.
**Personal:** Born May 7, 1955. University of Cincinnati, BA, 1977, Classics; Harvard University, MA, 1979, Classics; Harvard Law School, JD, 1982.

**ADLER, David F**
Jones Day, Cleveland
216 586 1344
dfadler@jonesday.com
*Featured in Litigation (Ohio)*
**Practice Areas:** Member of Jones Day's Financial Institutions Litigation and Regulation practice. He represents financial institutions and other businesses in complex commercial litigation, regulatory matters, and internal investigations. He has represented clients on matters throughout the United States pertaining to, among others, consumer financial products, financial instruments, securities fraud, accounting malpractice, and CFPB, OCC, SEC, and state attorney general investigations.
**Professional Memberships:** Member of the Ohio and New York Bars.
**Personal:** Board of Trustees, Cleveland Jewish Federation; Board of Trustees, Mount Sinai Healthcare Foundation.

**ALBERS, Matthew**
Vorys, Sater, Seymour and Pease LLP, Cleveland
216 479 6196
mealbers@vorys.com
*Featured in Healthcare (Ohio)*
**Practice Areas:** Partner who advises client in all areas of healthcare law, but focuses his practice on health care mergers and acquisitions activity. Also assists clients in other areas including physician and provider certification, registration, licensure, and accreditation; Medicare and Medicaid billing, coding, documentation, payment, and reimbursement; teaching physician and non-physician practitioner supervision and billing; federal and state fraud and abuse laws and related government investigations; HIPAA; EMTALA; and professional disciplinary actions.
**Career:** Admitted in Ohio and Texas.

**Personal:** Received his JD magna cum laude from Case Western Reserve University School of Law and BA from The Ohio State University.

**ALDRICH, Thomas A**
Thompson Hine LLP, Cleveland
216 566 5749
Tom.Aldrich@ThompsonHine.com
*Featured in Corporate/M&A (Ohio)*
**Career:** Tom is a partner in Thompson Hine's Corporate Transactions & Securities Practice. He focuses on domestic and international mergers and acquisitions and joint ventures, public and private offerings, securities law compliance and reporting and corporate governance. He works primarily with public companies and their directors and officers in a variety of manufacturing and service industries, including financial services, commercial real estate, electronics and industrial equipment.

**ALLOTTA, John J**
Baker & Hostetler LLP, Cleveland
216 861 7660
jallotta@bakerlaw.com
*Featured in Corporate/M&A (Ohio)*
**Career:** John Allotta focuses on private M&A and financing transactions. John advises private and public companies and private equity firms on structuring and negotiating business transactions, including domestic and international acquisitions, leveraged buyouts, recapitalizations, spinoffs, equity financings and restructurings. John's financing experience includes counseling clients in a variety of commercial financing transactions, including secured and unsecured credit, subordinated debt and acquisition facilities, debt restructuring and workout transactions. John also advises companies on day-to-day legal issues, including commercial arrangements, such as distribution, supply, contract manufacturing agreements, business-related issues and corporate governance.

**ANTHONY, Thomas**
Frost Brown Todd LLC, Cincinnati
513 651 6191
tanthony@fbtlaw.com
*Featured in Healthcare (Ohio)*
**Practice Areas:** Tom focuses on health care, corporate transactions, and regulatory. He is counsel to hospitals regarding clinically integrated networks, accountable care organizations, medical staff bylaws, physician relations, acquisition of medical groups, corporate governance, acquisitions of outpatient and ancillary facilities, strategic alliances and joint ventures, HOPD and provider-based facilities, executive employment agreements, Medicare compliance, contracting, and employment matters.
**Professional Memberships:** Cincinnati Bar Association, Ohio State Bar Association Health Care Law Committee, American Bar Association Health Care Section, Emerging Issues Seminar Committee, American Health Lawyers Association.

**Personal:** Case Western Reserve University School of Law, JD, 1977; Miami University, BS, 1974.

**APPEL, John H**
Frost Brown Todd LLC, Cincinnati
513 651 6830
jappel@fbtlaw.com
*Featured in Employee Benefits & Executive Compensation (Ohio)*
**Practice Areas:** Employee benefits and executive compensation, including extensive experience in defined benefit and contribution plans (including cash balance plans) and nonqualified deferred compensation plans.
**Professional Memberships:** Member of the Ohio, Cincinnati, and American Bar Associations.
**Career:** Joined Frost & Jacobs (now Frost Brown Todd LLC) in September of 1974, and have been with such firm for his entire career.
**Personal:** Born June 1, 1949. JD, Harvard University 1974, magna cum laude; BA, University of Cincinnati, 1971. Married, with three children.

**APPELBAUM, Jeffrey R**
Thompson Hine LLP, Cleveland
216 566 5548
Jeff.Appelbaum@ThompsonHine.com
*Featured in Construction (Ohio)*
**Career:** For 35 years, Jeff has provided distinguished service to public/private owners, design professionals, construction managers and contractors. He has served as trial counsel for multi-million dollar claims, and lead counsel or project management consultant for over 100 projects involving billions of dollars of construction, including 17 professional sports facilities; facilitated 175 partnering sessions; and mediated 200 complex construction disputes. He facilitated the Governor's Ohio Construction Reform Panel and participated in creating final legislation, effective January 2012, that dramatically modified public procurement in Ohio. In 2012, he became the first lawyer inducted into the Cleveland Engineering Society's Hall of Fame.

**ARONOFF, James B**
Thompson Hine LLP, Cleveland
216 566 5504
Jim.Aronoff@ThompsonHine.com
*Featured in Real Estate (Ohio)*
**Career:** Jim is a Partner in the Real Estate Group, Chair of the firm's Real Estate Capital Markets Practice and Partner-in-Charge of the firm's Cleveland office. He represents real estate investment trusts (REITs) and real estate equity funds both transactionally and in evaluating internal structures to maximize value. He also focuses on structuring partnerships, joint ventures, and LLCs; commercial real estate financing, shopping center development and construction; gaming and casino-related projects and acquisitions and divestitures of resort and other lodging properties. A frequent lecturer, Jim is a member of the Board of Governors of Ohio's Real Property Bar.

**ASENSIO, M.J.**
Baker & Hostetler LLP, Columbus
614 462 2622
masensio@bakerlaw.com
*Featured in Labor & Employment (Ohio)*
**Career:** National Chair of BakerHostetler's Labor Relations team, Mike Asensio is a nationally recognized labor and employment practitioner with experience managing employee relations for clients in the healthcare, aerospace, transportation, manufacturing and energy industries. Mike represents employers in union organizational drives, especially those involving very large or complex voting units. Mike is experienced in organizational development, work stoppages, strikes, negotiation, labor arbitration and administration of labor and employment contracts. Mike is also an experienced NLRB litigator, having represented clients in labor matters across the country before the Board's regional offices. Mike's practice also encompasses employment ligation, executive compensation and employment counseling.

**ASHMUS, Keith A**
Frantz Ward LLP, Cleveland
216 515 1609
kashmus@frantzward.com
*Featured in Labor & Employment (Ohio)*
**Practice Areas:** Represents employers in federal and state courts, federal and state administrative agencies, arbitration proceedings, and in collective bargaining negotiations. Counsels employers with respect to wide variety of employment matters, including SOX retaliation. Provides general business advice to entrepreneurs.
**Professional Memberships:** President (current), Ohio State Bar Foundation; Chairman (2009-10), National Small Business Association; President (2003-04), Ohio State Bar Association; Boards of the Salvation Army of Greater Cleveland; National Funders Association; Council of Smaller Enterprises.
**Publications:** Frequent publications on labor and employment-related issues. Co-author, Labor & Employment Law Navigator blog (www.laboremploymentlawnavigator.com).

**AUVIL, Steven**
Squire Sanders (US) LLP, Cleveland
216 479 8023
steven.auvil@squiresanders.com
*Featured in Intellectual Property (Ohio)*
**Practice Areas:** Trial and appellate lawyer in patent, copyright, trademark matters in courts and administrative agencies throughout the US. Negotiates IP agreements, prepares and prosecutes patent applications and advises clients regarding IP issues.
**Career:** Chair of Intellectual Property Practice Group. Has held leadership positions in bar associations. Former Partner at Fay Sharpe and started legal career as associate of Jones Day.
**Personal:** Cleveland State University, Cleveland-Marshall College of Law (JD, summa cum laude, 1993); University of Pennsylvania Law School

(1992); New York University School of Law (LLM, 1994); The Ohio State University (BSME, 1988).

## AYERS, G Randall
Keating Muething & Klekamp PLL, Cincinnati
513 579 6919
rayers@kmklaw.com
*Featured in Labor & Employment (Ohio)*
**Practice Areas:** Concentrates on traditional, management-side labor relations. Serves as Chief Negotiator for Fortune 500 corporations. Serves as Trial Counsel for employers in wrongful discharge and EEO matters. Significant steel industry experience in workforce and benefit restructuring labor negotiations. Handled hundreds of labor arbitrations in defense of management. Represents employers before National Labor Relations Board in unfair labor practice and representation trials and appeals.
**Personal:** JD, The Ohio State University, 1988. AB, Earlham College, 1984.

## BARNARD, Thomas H
Ogletree, Deakins, Nash, Smoak & Stewart, PC, Cleveland
216 241 6100
tom.barnard@ogletreedeakins.com
*Featured in Labor & Employment (Ohio)*
**Practice Areas:** Labor and employment, litigation.
**Professional Memberships:** ABA, OSBA (former chair, Labor & Employment Law section; member, Labor & Employment Law Specialty Board), Ohio Management Lawyer's Association founding Steering Committee, The College of Labor and Employment Lawyers.
**Career:** Admitted to practice in Ohio, US Supreme Court, US Courts of Appeals (4th, 6th, 7th, 8th, 11th, and DC). US District Courts, Ohio. Frequent national speaker on labor and employment matters. Adjunct Professor of Law, Case Western Reserve University School of Law.
**Publications:** Written extensively on employment matters.
**Personal:** University of Puget Sound (BA, 1961), Columbia University (JD, 1964).

## BARNES, Geoffrey K
Squire Sanders (US) LLP, Cleveland
216 479 8646
geoffrey.barnes@squiresanders.com
*Featured in Natural Resources (Ohio)*
**Practice Areas:** Partner with more than 25 years of experience in environmental law. Named in The Best Lawyers in America. Practice includes corporate counseling and litigation before state and federal courts and agencies involving matters under federal and state air, water, and solid and hazardous waste laws. Experienced with evaluation and reduction of environmental risk in business and property acquisitions; defense of enforcement claims; private party claims for cost recovery or diminution in property value; insurance claims for recovery of environmental cleanup costs; environmental criminal proceedings; employee exposure claims; and disputes over environmental indemnities.

## BARRAGATE, Brett
Jones Day, New York
212 326 3446
bpbarragate@jonesday.com
*Featured in Banking & Finance (Ohio), Banking & Finance (Nationwide)*
**Practice Areas:** Co-chairs Jones Day's Banking and Finance Practice. Substantial experience in all aspects of commercial financing, including the representation of financial institutions, hedge funds, and public and private companies in senior and subordinated debt facilities, and the representation of creditors and debtors in loan workouts, restructurings, and chapter 11 proceedings. Extensive experience with leveraged and acquisition finance transactions and other syndicated, multibank senior credit facilities; as well as asset-based and structured finance facilities; asset securitizations; acquisition financings; letter of credit facilities; foreign currency facilities; debtor-in-possession financings; and real estate financings.

## BASH, Brian A
Baker & Hostetler LLP, Cleveland
216 861 7581
bbash@bakerlaw.com
*Featured in Bankruptcy/Restructuring (Ohio)*
**Career:** Brian Bash represents businesses in bankruptcy proceedings and commercial law matters. Brian co-authored Banking Law, Volumes 7, 8 and 8A, published by Matthew Bender, and was an adjunct professor of commercial law at Cleveland-Marshall College of Law. He is a member of the Federal Court Mediation Panel, a Panel Trustee and member of the National Association of Bankruptcy Trustees and a member of the Ohio State and New York Bar Associations. He has been listed as a leading lawyer in bankruptcy and insolvency law by Euromoney Publications and Best Lawyers in America. Brian holds an AV rating from Martindale-Hubbell.

## BEDREE, Melvin
Vorys, Sater, Seymour and Pease LLP, Cincinnati
513 723 4023
mabedree@vorys.com
*Featured in Banking & Finance (Ohio)*
**Practice Areas:** Partner practicing commercial finance law. Represents national and regional asset based, structured finance and mezzanine lenders. Practice includes multi-borrower, multi-jurisdiction transactions, acquisition financing, asset sales out of bankruptcy, multi-lender (club) deals, capital expenditure financing, and negotiating subordinated debt and preferred stock arrangements with institutional providers of mezzanine and senior capital.
**Professional Memberships:** Ohio and American Bar Associations.
**Career:** Admitted to Ohio Bar, 1984; US District Court, Southern District of Ohio, 1984.
**Personal:** University of Cincinnati, JD, Order of the Coif, University of Cincinnati Law Review, Research Editor, 1984; DePauw University, BA, magna cum laude, 1981.

## BEUS, Karl
Calfee, Halter & Griswold LLP, Cleveland
216 622 8804
kbeus@calfee.com
*Featured in Banking & Finance (Ohio)*
**Practice Areas:** Commercial business and finance; bankruptcy, workout and creditors' rights.
**Professional Memberships:** Ohio State and Cleveland Metropolitan Bar Associations.
**Career:** Commercial and real estate financings and syndications; securitizations and restructurings; domestic and international commercial business transactions. Member, Executive Committee.
**Personal:** University of Idaho School of Law, JD, magna cum laude, 1992; University of Utah, BA, 1989.

## BISSINGER, Charles
Vorys, Sater, Seymour and Pease LLP, Cincinnati
513 723 4084
ccbissinger@vorys.com
*Featured in Real Estate (Ohio)*
**Practice Areas:** Partner representing lenders and borrowers in financing transactions, purchasers and sellers in real estate transfers; landlords and tenants in commercial leasing transactions; developers in commercial and residential development projects; and borrowers, lenders and investors in real estate workouts.Specializes in FHA-insured financings of multi-family properties and healthcare facilities.
**Professional Memberships:** Cincinnati and Kentucky Bar Associations; Eastern Lenders Association; Southeast Mortgagee Advisory Council; Western Mortgagee Advisory Council.
**Career:** Ohio, Massachusetts, Kentucky, US District Court for the Southern District of Ohio.
**Personal:** Harvard Law School, JD, cum laude, 1979; University of Michigan, BBA, High Distinction, Phi Beta Kappa, 1976.

## BIXENSTINE, Barton A
Vorys, Sater, Seymour and Pease LLP, Cleveland
216 479 6192
babixenstine@vorys.com
*Featured in Labor & Employment (Ohio)*
**Practice Areas:** Employment litigation and advice, immigration, alternative dispute resolution.
**Professional Memberships:** American Bar Association, Ohio State Bar Association, Cleveland Bar Association, American Arbitration Association (Member, Past Chair, Labor Advisory Committee).
**Career:** Partner at Duvin, Cahn and Hutton, 1985-95, Partner at Ulmer & Berne, 1996-2008, shareholder at Ogletree, 2008-11. Partner at Vorys, 2011-present.
**Publications:** 'Implementing a Program of Employment Alternative Dispute Resolution Under the American Arbitration Association' (2009); 'Immigration Compliance Watch 2009: I-9 Enforcement, E-Verify, No-Match Letters and State's Law' (2010).
**Personal:** Kent State University (BA, 1971), Indiana University (MA, 1973), Indiana University (PhD, 1977), University of Chicago (JD), 1981.

## BLACK, Carl E
Jones Day, Cleveland
216 586 7035
ceblack@jonesday.com
*Featured in Bankruptcy/Restructuring (Ohio)*
**Practice Areas:** Plays an active and leading role in Jones Day's representations of debtors, creditors' committees, lenders and other significant creditors in many of the nation's largest corporate restructurings. Has substantial experience counseling clients in fraudulent conveyance, illegal dividend, preferential transfer, fiduciary duty and insolvency related intellectual property and environmental issues. He has represented clients in out-of-court restructuring transactions and has extensive experience in bankruptcy-related litigation.
**Professional Memberships:** Ohio State Bar Association; Cleveland Bar Association; American Bankruptcy Institute.
**Publications:** Co-authored bankruptcy-related articles published in American Bankruptcy Institute Journal and Law Review and was a contributing co-author to Bankruptcy Business Acquisitions.

## BLAIR, Mitchell G
Calfee, Halter & Griswold LLP, Cleveland
216 622 8361
mblair@calfee.com
*Featured in Litigation (Ohio)*
**Practice Areas:** Business, corporate and commercial litigation; securities and derivative litigation; alternative dispute resolution proceedings.
**Professional Memberships:** Ohio State and Cleveland Metropolitan Bar Associations; Federal Bar Association.
**Career:** Co-Chair of the firm's Litigation Group, heads the Securities Litigation Practice, is a Member of the White-Collar Defense and Investigations Practice, and is a Member of the Management and Executive Committees. Litigates and tries complex disputes, with special emphasis on securities, class and derivative litigation and enforcement, and corporate investigations.
**Personal:** Marshall-Wythe School of Law of the College of William and Mary, JD, 1982; Union College, BA, magna cum laude, 1979.

## BLATTNER, Wray
Thompson Hine LLP, Dayton
937 443 6539
Wray.Blattner@ThompsonHine.com
*Featured in Natural Resources (Ohio)*
**Career:** Wray is a partner in Thompson Hine's Environmental Practice Group. His practice includes defense of federal, state and local government enforcement actions and private party environmental litigation, environmental permitting, site remediations, regulatory compliance counseling and environmental management systems, environmental audits, commenting on rulemakings, and counsel in connection with business and real estate acquisitions and sales. Wray received his undergraduate degree from Denison University and his law degree from Georgetown University Law Center.

## BOJKO, Andrew
Porter Wright Morris & Arthur LLP, Columbus
614 227 2007
abojko@porterwright.com
*Featured in Banking & Finance (Ohio)*
**Career:** Mr Bojko is a partner in Porter Wright's Corporate department in the Columbus office. He advises lenders and borrowers in matters involving commercial lending, asset-based financing, mezzanine debt and leveraged buyouts. Mr Bojko also handles a variety of real estate matters, with a particular emphasis on construction and permanent loans, leasing, and acquisitions and divestitures.

## BOTTI, James
Porter Wright Morris & Arthur LLP, Columbus
614 227 2178
jbotti@porterwright.com
*Featured in Bankruptcy/Restructuring (Ohio)*
**Career:** Mr Botti, chair of the firm's Bankruptcy and Reorganization Practice Group, has 30 years of experience representing lenders — financial institutions and otherwise. His practice focuses on negotiating and documenting complex commercial loan transactions and handling troubled loan or workout situations both inside and outside of bankruptcy, including representing special services of CMBS real estate loans. Mr Botti also represents commercial borrowers in negotiating complex commercial loan transactions and assisting them in troubled loan or workout situations. He is a recognized expert on provisional remedies such as replevin, attachment, creditor's bills and charging orders as well as receiverships.

## BOYDSTON, Richard
Bingham Greenebaum Doll LLP, Cincinnati
513 455 7663
rboydston@bgdlegal.com
*Featured in Bankruptcy/Restructuring (Ohio)*
**Practice Areas:** Mr Boydston practices in the areas of bankruptcy (including representation of creditors, debtors and of committees and bankruptcy litigation), receiverships, debtor/creditor relations, and commercial transactions and workouts.
**Professional Memberships:** American Bar Association; Kentucky Bar Association; Ohio Bar Association; Cincinnati Bar Association; American Bankruptcy Institute; Tri-State Association for Corporate Renewal.
**Personal:** AB, Harvard College, 1974 JD, University of Pennsylvania, 1977.

## BRENNAN, Maureen A
Baker & Hostetler LLP, Cleveland
216 861 7957
mbrennan@bakerlaw.com
*Featured in Natural Resources (Ohio)*
**Career:** Maureen Brennan works on matters under all major federal environmental statutes: Clean Air Act, Clean Water Act, Resource Conservation and Recovery Act, Comprehensive Environmental Response, Compensation and Liability Act (Superfund), Toxic Substances Control Act and Safe Drinking Water Act. She provides regulatory advice on matters involving wind-powered electrical generating facilities,

Brownfield developments, land acquisitions, coal mines, steel plants, municipal sewage treatment facilities, solid/hazardous waste landfills, inorganic chemicals plants, underground storage tanks, manufacturers of pumps, automotive parts, and furniture and various other consumer products. She has particular experience in water quality and wetlands issues under the Clean Water Act.

## BRINKMAN, Kathleen
Porter Wright Morris & Arthur LLP, Cincinnati
513 369 4258
kbrinkman@porterwright.com
*Featured in Litigation (Ohio)*
**Career:** Kathy joined Porter Wright after 24 years as an Assistant United States Attorney. Her prosecution specialties included white-collar, environmental, public corruption, and health care fraud crimes. She is a recognized authority in asset forfeiture and represents corporations and individuals who face investigation or charges by federal or state authorities or whose property the government seeks to forfeit, as well as fraud victims. Her honors include the 2011 John P. Kiely Professionalism Award (Cincinnati Bar Association), the 2005 Nettie Cronise Lutes Award (Ohio State Bar Association), and inclusion as a Fellow of the American College of Trial Lawyers.

## BROWN, Harry M
Benesch, Friedlander, Coplan & Aronoff LLP, Cleveland
216 363 4606
hbrown@beneschlaw.com
*Featured in Healthcare (Ohio)*
**Practice Areas:** Practice is focused on acquisition, disposition and financing of health care facilities and providers; Medicare and Medicaid reimbursement; physician and institutional joint ventures; licensure and certification; construction and financing; and Certificate of Need applications. He has extensive experience with skilled nursing and mental retardation facilities, physician practices, ambulatory surgical facilities, and provider practices.
**Personal:** New York University School of Law, 1972, JD Member; Yeshiva University, 1969, BA magna cum laude.

## BROWN, Timothy R
Thompson Hine LLP, Cincinnati
513 352 6800
Tim.Brown@ThompsonHine.com
*Featured in Employee Benefits & Executive Compensation (Ohio)*
**Career:** Tim is a member of the firm's Executive Committee and was leader of the Employee Benefits & Executive Compensation Practice Group for 12 years. He focuses his practice on employee benefits, executive compensation and ERISA, including benefit issues and liabilities in corporate transactions; creation, maintenance, compliance and termination of tax-qualified retirement plans and master trusts; development and compliance of non-qualified, bonus and equity compensation arrangements, including compliance with IRC 409A; welfare plan administration, compliance and documentation; IRS/DOL audits and PBGC matters; ERISA litigation; multi-

employer plans and withdrawal liability; governmental reporting obligations; ERISA fiduciary counseling, compliance and investment matters.

## BRUBAKER, Robert
Porter Wright Morris & Arthur LLP, Columbus
614 227 2033
rbrubaker@porterwright.com
*Featured in Natural Resources (Ohio)*
**Career:** Mr Brubaker advises manufacturers, utilities, small businesses, trade associations, and public sector clients with regard to Clean Air Act and other environmental legislative, regulatory, and litigation matters. He is the immediate past Chair of the ABA Section of Public Utility, Communications, and Transportation Law, a Fellow of the American College of Environmental Lawyers, a member of the Department of Energy's National Coal Council, a Fellow of the American Bar Foundation, and an Adjunct Professor at Capital University Law School.

## BUCHENROTH, Stephen
Vorys, Sater, Seymour and Pease LLP, Columbus
614 464 6366
srbuchenroth@vorys.com
*Featured in Real Estate (Ohio)*
**Practice Areas:** Real estate law; franchising.
**Professional Memberships:** Columbus (Board of Governors, 1986-94; President, 1992-93), Ohio State(Council of Delegates, 1986-88, 1991; Real Property Section, Board of Governors, 1990; Chair, 2003-05) Real Property Specialty Board, 2004; and American (Antitrust/Business Sections; Chairman, Small Business Committee's Franchising Subcommittee, 1991-92; Real Property, Probate and Trust Law; Forum Committee on Franchising) Bar Associations; American College of Real Estate Lawyers; Ohio Supreme Court Commission on Continuing Legal Education, 1994-2000, Chairman, 2000; Ohio Legal Assistance Foundation Board of Trustees, 2006-10.
**Career:** Ohio Bar (1974).
**Personal:** University of Chicago, JD, 1974; Wittenberg University, AB, cum laude, 1970.

## BUCK, Frank W
Littler Mendelson, PC, Cleveland
216 696 6137
fbuck@littler.com
*Featured in Labor & Employment (Ohio)*
**Practice Areas:** Labor relations.
**Professional Memberships:** Leadership Cleveland Class of 1998; Member, Board of Directors – MUSiC; Former Member, Board of Trustees - Achievement Centers for Children; Member, Cleveland Metropolitan Bar Association; Member, American Bar Association/Labor Section.
**Career:** Frank W Buck focuses his practice on labor relations and strategic advice for both private and public sector clients and has served as the chief negotiator for employers in hundreds of negotiations. Frank regularly represents clients before Federal Courts, the National Labor Relations Board, Department of Labor, OCRC, EEOC, and other state and federal agencies.

**Personal:** JD, University of Michigan, 1979; BA, University of Michigan, 1976, with distinction.

## BUCKLEY, Daniel J
Vorys, Sater, Seymour and Pease LLP, Cincinnati
513 723 4002
djbuckley@vorys.com
*Featured in Litigation (Ohio)*
**Practice Areas:** Partner in Litigation Group; extensive experience in business, healthcare, and probate and fiduciary, representing financial institutions, venture capital and accounting firms, inside and outside directors, pharmaceutical companies and hospitals in complex litigation.
**Professional Memberships:** American, Ohio State, Cincinnati Bar Associations.
**Career:** Admitted to Ohio Bar (1974), US Federal Court (1974), US Supreme Court (1982).
**Personal:** Fellow, American College of Trial Lawyers. Listed in legal publication under business, 'bet the company' and personal injury litigation. Ohio Wesleyan University, BA, Pi Sigma Alpha, 1971. University of Cincinnati College of Law, JD, 1974.

## BUMPASS, T Merritt
Frantz Ward LLP, Cleveland
216 515 1615
mbumpass@frantzward.com
*Featured in Labor & Employment (Ohio)*
**Practice Areas:** Responsibilities include: Chair, Frantz Ward Labor and Employment Group; represents employers in federal and state courts, federal and state administrative agencies, arbitration proceedings, and collective bargaining negotiations. Counsels employers with respect to a wide variety of employment matters, including union campaigns.
**Professional Memberships:** Ohio State Bar; North Carolina State Bar; Ohio Management Lawyers Association.
**Publications:** Several law review articles and frequent speaker on labor and employment related issues.
**Personal:** Dean's List, United States Military Academy; Dean's List and Comments Editor of the Law Review, Wake Forest University School of Law; Columbia University School of Law (LLM).

## BURKE, James E
Keating Muething & Klekamp PLL, Cincinnati
513 579 6428
jburke@kmklaw.com
*Featured in Litigation (Ohio)*
**Practice Areas:** Mr Burke's practice focuses on complex corporate and commercial litigation, including both trial and appellate practice, in state and federal court. He has significant experience in financial and transactional cases, commercial matters, class and derivative actions and actions arising under the federal securities laws.
**Personal:** JD, University of Cincinnati College of Law, 1978; magna cum laude; University of Cincinnati Law Review, Editorial Board, 1976-78; Order of the Coif. BA, Yale University, 1975. Fellow, American College of Trial Lawyers; American Board of Trial Advocates.

## BURKE, Kim
Taft Stettinius & Hollister LLP, Cincinnati
513 357 9369
kburke@taftlaw.com
*Featured in Natural Resources (Ohio)*

**Practice Areas:** Litigation, Sustainability Initiative, Environmental Transactional Services, Class Action and Multi-Party Litigation, E-Discovery, Environmental.
**Career:** Mr Burke is co-chair of the Environmental group. He has concentrated in a variety of environmental law areas, including Superfund defense and negotiation, development and implementation of hazardous substance remedial investigation and corrective measure plans, defense of toxic tort and other civil and criminal claims, real estate transfers, acquisitions and divestitures, government funding, including stimulus and brownfields, environmental insurance litigation, air permits and administrative proceedings before state and federal environmental agencies.
**Personal:** University of Pittsburgh School of Law (1980); Indiana University of Pennsylvania (1977).

## CADWALLADER, John I
Frost Brown Todd LLC, Columbus
614 464 1211
jcadwallader@fbtlaw.com
*Featured in Real Estate (Ohio)*

**Practice Areas:** Represents developers, owners, borrowers and lenders in structuring entity formation, acquisition, financing, leasing and development of commercial, retail, industrial, hotel and office properties.
**Professional Memberships:** Admitted in Ohio and Florida; American College of Real Estate Lawyers (Vice-Chair to the Hotels Committee); International Council of Shopping Centers; OSBA Real Property Council (Secretary to the Council); American Bar Association.
**Career:** One of the founding members of Frost Brown Todd LLC's Columbus office; Best Lawyers in America; Ohio Super Lawyers.
**Personal:** BA, Denison University; MA, University of Chicago (Rockefeller Foundation Fellow); JD, The Ohio State University.

## CAMPANA, Jeremy M
Thompson Hine LLP, Cleveland
216 566 5936
Jeremy.Campana@ThompsonHine.com
*Featured in Bankruptcy/Restructuring (Ohio)*

**Career:** Jeremy is a partner in the firm's Business Restructuring, Creditors' Rights & Bankruptcy Practice Group. He focuses his practice on commercial debtor and creditor rights, bankruptcy (primarily commercial Chapter 11 cases), workouts, business litigation, director and officer liability litigation, and other commercial law cases. In addition to secured lenders, creditor committees and debtors, Jeremy has represented a wide array of creditors and other parties involved in bankruptcy proceedings, including commercial equipment lessors and financiers, goods and service providers, trustees, insurers, purchasers, tenants and preference claim defendants.

## CANTON, Doreen
Taft Stettinius & Hollister LLP, Cincinnati
513 357 9387
canton@taftlaw.com
*Featured in Labor & Employment (Ohio)*

**Practice Areas:** Labor & Employment, Education - Litigation, Workplace Safety and Health, College and University Law.
**Career:** Ms Canton is co-chair of the Labor & Employment group. She has advised and represented private and public employers in all areas of labor and employment law. She has a great deal of jury trial experience and has tried many Title VII, Title IX and state law claims, including age, sex, race, disability, national origin discrimination, harassment, retaliation and contract claims.
**Personal:** University of Cincinnati College of Law (1988); State University of New York at Buffalo (1978); Columbia University (1973); Canisius College (1970).

## CARESANI, Ann M.
Porter Wright Morris & Arthur LLP, Cleveland
216 443 2570
acaresani@porterwright.com
*Featured in Employee Benefits & Executive Compensation (Ohio)*

**Career:** Ms Caresani represents employers in the design, administration and termination of employee benefit programs, including tax-qualified retirement plans, health and welfare plans, and executive compensation arrangements. She defends employers, plan administrators, trustees, banks, insurers, investment managers, and other fiduciaries/service providers in a broad range of ERISA litigation matters, including class action pension claims. She also helps employers navigate through health care reform. As editor of the firm's employee benefits blog, Employee Benefits Law Report, Ms Caresani consistently reviews recent cases, legislation, regulations, and other related legal developments and helps our clients understand how these changes may impact their organizations.

## CARSON, Van
Squire Sanders (US) LLP, Cleveland
216 479 8559
van.carson@squiresanders.com
*Featured in Natural Resources (Ohio)*

**Practice Areas:** Has more than 40 years' experience representing the interests of industrial and public clients in environmental matters. Particular expertise dealing with Clean Water Act, Clean Air Act and Superfund matters. Represents companies from the manufacturing, refining, steel, mining and chemical industries, as well as numerous public sector clients. Selected by his peers for inclusion in The Best Lawyers in America.
**Professional Memberships:** Ohio Chamber of Commerce, Executive Committee, Board of Directors, vice chair.

## CASARONA, Robert B
Roetzel & Andress, LPA, Cleveland
216 615 4841
rcasarona@ralaw.com
*Featured in Natural Resources (Ohio), Litigation (Ohio)*

**Practice Areas:** Mr Casarona is National Director of the firm's Litigation and Government Affairs practices. He focuses his practice on environmental litigation, including toxic torts, business and construction litigation. He has been the lead trial counsel in cases in Ohio, Florida, California and Utah, and has argued appeals in several districts and the Sixth Circuit Court of Appeals. He is AV Preeminent rated by Martindale & Hubbell, selected as one of the Best Lawyers in America since 2006, been a SuperLawyer since 2004 and has been selected as an Ohio Manufacturers Alliance Counsel. His clients include businesses of all types.

## CASCARILLA, Ralph E
Walter & Haverfield LLP, Cleveland
216 928 2908
rcascarilla@walterhav.com
*Featured in Litigation (Ohio)*

**Practice Areas:** Additional Practice Area: Complex Commercial Litigation.
**Professional Memberships:** American, Ohio and Cleveland Metropolitan Bar Associations.
**Career:** Managing Partner at Walter & Haverfield LLP, Ralph was formerly Chief of the White-Collar Crime Section of the United States Attorney's Office for the Northern District of Ohio. He heads the firm's White-Collar Criminal Defense Practice Group, and represents individuals and corporations in criminal investigations by governmental agencies encompassing environmental, healthcare, securities fraud, antitrust, tax and government procurement matters. Ralph is licensed to practice before the Supreme Courts of the United States, Ohio and Florida, and numerous Federal district and appellate courts.
**Personal:** T. M. Cooley School of Law, JD, 1976; University of Notre Dame, BA, 1971.

## CASTRODALE, Joseph A
Ulmer & Berne LLP, Cleveland
216 583 7342
jcastrodale@ulmer.com
*Featured in Litigation (Ohio)*

**Practice Areas:** A magna cum laude graduate of Harvard Law School, Joe chairs the firm's Business Litigation Group. Joe represents large corporate clients in complex litigation in federal and state courts, and in arbitrations throughout the country. Joe was recently recognized as a national leader for providing exceptional client service based on a survey of Fortune 1000 companies and other large corporations. He is routinely recognized by peer groups as one of the top litigators in the region.

## CERNELICH, John R
Calfee, Halter & Griswold LLP, Cleveland
216 622 8251
jcernelich@calfee.com
*Featured in Labor & Employment (Ohio)*

**Practice Areas:** Labor and employment litigation; labor and employment; health care reform.
**Professional Memberships:** Frequent speaker before human resources professionals and routinely conducts training sessions for clients concerning various legal considerations for the workplace. Member of the American, Ohio and Cleveland Bar Associations.
**Career:** John serves as co-chair of the firm's Labor and Employment group. He represents management in NLRB proceedings, union negotiations and arbitration hearings. Extensive experience defending claims of workplace discrimination, harassment and retaliation. Counsels as to wage and hour, FMLA, and affirmative action compliance.

## CHAIKEN, Frank D
Thompson Hine LLP, Cincinnati
513 352 6550
Frank.Chaiken@ThompsonHine.com
*Featured in Corporate/M&A (Ohio)*

**Career:** Frank is a partner in the firm and chair of the Corporate Transactions & Securities practice group. He also serves on the firm's International Practice committee. Frank focuses his practice on mergers and acquisitions, cross-border transactions and general corporate counseling, as well as startups, joint ventures and complex commercial agreements. Prior to joining Thompson Hine, Frank lived and worked in Switzerland for several years as in-house counsel to a multinational chemicals group. He is conversant in German and continues to work extensively with German and Swiss companies. Frank is based in Thompson Hine's Cincinnati office.

## CHAPPELEAR, Stephen
Hahn Loeser & Parks LLP, Columbus
614 233 5148
sechappelear@hahnlaw.com
*Featured in Litigation (Ohio)*

**Practice Areas:** Mr Chappelear has over 34 years of experience and 60 trials in the litigation of business, complex commercial, construction, intellectual property, and employment matters, among others; and dispute resolution and appeals.
**Professional Memberships:** President, National Conference of Bar Foundations; Past Chair, Trial Techniques Committee, American Bar Association Tort Trial and Insurance Practice Section; Past Chair, Litigation Section, Ohio State Bar Association; Past President, Ohio State and Columbus Bar Associations.
**Personal:** The Ohio State University Moritz College of Law (JD, 1977); The Ohio State University (BA, 1974).

## CICARELLA, Thomas
Calfee, Halter & Griswold LLP, Cleveland
216 622 8378
tcicarella@calfee.com
*Featured in Banking & Finance (Ohio)*

**Practice Areas:** Commercial business and finance; bankruptcy and creditors' rights.
**Professional Memberships:** American and Ohio State Bar Associations.
**Career:** Chair of the firm's Commercial Business and Finance Group and a member of the Executive and Management Committees. Has more than 30 years of experience counseling clients through the complexities of leveraged buyouts, domestic and international financing and workouts.

**Publications:** Author of chapters in Asset Based Financing, a Transactional Guide.
**Personal:** Indiana University, JD, magna cum laude, 1974; Indiana University, BA, 1971.

## CIPOLLA, John S
Calfee, Halter & Griswold LLP, Cleveland
216 622 8808
jcipolla@calfee.com
*Featured in Intellectual Property (Ohio)*
**Practice Areas:** Patent litigation, patent counseling, strategy and portfolio management. Trademark and copyright litigation. Licensing and transactions related to IP.
**Professional Memberships:** American Intellectual Property Law Association, Intellectual Property Owners Association, Cleveland Intellectual Property Law Association.
**Career:** Chair of Intellectual Property group; member of Calfee's Management Committee. Handles litigation, counseling and business strategy related to patents and patent portfolio management. Practices in several technological and product areas including consumer products, software, electronics and medical devices.
**Personal:** Cleveland-Marshall College of Law, JD, cum laude, 1989; Bowling Green State University, BS, cum laude, 1985. Board member, NAMI (National Alliance for Mental Illness).

## CIRIACO, Anthony C
Vorys, Sater, Seymour and Pease LLP, Columbus
614 464 6429
acciriaco@vorys.com
*Featured in Employee Benefits & Executive Compensation (Ohio)*
**Practice Areas:** Partner focusing predominantly on the regulatory side of the Employee Benefits Practice where he has counseled clients in qualified retirement plan areas, including both defined benefit and defined contribution plans, as well as, non-qualified deferred compensation, other forms of executive compensation and welfare plan areas. Focus on Employee Retirement Income Security Act (ERISA) and tax related aspects of employee benefit programs.
**Professional Memberships:** Columbus and Ohio State Bar Associations.
**Career:** Ohio Bar 1983.
**Personal:** University of North Carolina School of Law, JD, 1983; University of Virginia, BS, with distinction in accounting, Beta Gamma Sigma, Beta Alpha Psi, 1980.

## CLARK, Eric
Thompson Hine LLP, Cincinnati
513 352 6555
Eric.Clark@ThompsonHine.com
*Featured in Labor & Employment (Ohio)*
**Career:** Eric is a partner in the firm's Labor & Employment practice group. He is experienced in every facet of labor and employment law, including matters arising under the NLRA, ERISA, FLSA, Title VII, ADEA, ADA, FMLA, the Davis-Bacon Act, the Service Contract Act and prevailing wage laws. Eric regularly counsels clients regarding matters arising under these statutes and represents them before various state and federal

agencies and courts. He has first-chaired the defense of numerous single-plaintiff, class and collective actions. And, Eric regularly represents clients in labor arbitrations, collective bargaining agreement negotiations and union organizing campaigns.

## CLARK, Wade
Calfee, Halter & Griswold LLP, Cleveland
216 622 8389
wclark@calfee.com
*Featured in Employee Benefits & Executive Compensation (Ohio)*
**Practice Areas:** Employee Benefits and Executive Compensation; Health Care Reform.
**Professional Memberships:** Worldwide Employee Benefits Network.
**Career:** Partner in the Employee Benefits and Executive Compensation Group. Has worked with a range of companies and government employers in the design, administration and termination of qualified retirement plans, nonqualified plans, welfare plans, cafeteria plans and related funding vehicles. Provides counsel on matters regarding complex welfare plan designs, including employer group waiver plans, funding arrangements for welfare plans, plan governance and fiduciary responsibility provisions of ERISA, prohibited transactions and exemptions, IRS and DOL correction programs, and CMS, DOL and IRS audits.

## COLETTI, Robert E
Keating Muething & Klekamp PLL, Cincinnati
513 579 6560
rcoletti@kmklaw.com
*Featured in Corporate/M&A (Ohio)*
**Practice Areas:** Mr Coletti's practice is concentrated in the corporate, private equity, securities and financing areas where he has extensive experience in forming joint ventures, initial public offerings of securities, and mergers, acquisitions and divestitures representing both public and closely-held corporations and private equity firms. Mr Coletti serves in a general counsel capacity for several firm clients and represents investment partnerships and individuals in private equity investments and venture capital based transactions.
**Personal:** JD, University of Cincinnati College of Law, 1982; Order of the Barristers. BS, Miami University, 1979; Business, with honors.

## COLLIN, Thomas J
Thompson Hine LLP, Cleveland
216 566 5509
Tom.Collin@ThompsonHine.com
*Featured in Franchising (Nationwide), Litigation (Ohio)*
**Career:** Tom is head of the Antitrust, Competition and Distribution Practice in the firm's Business Litigation Practice Group. He concentrates on antitrust, dealer termination and unfair competition litigation, including price-fixing class actions, and advising on substantive antitrust, distribution and franchise matters, including compliance by distributors and agents with the Foreign Corrupt Practices Act. He has spoken and published widely on antitrust, dealership and franchise law and is an editor of books

published by the American Bar Association on antitrust and distribution law: Antitrust Law and Economics of Product Distribution (2006), and Antitrust Handbook for Franchise and Distribution Practitioners (2008).

## COMODECA, Peter J
Calfee, Halter & Griswold LLP, Cleveland
216 622 8830
pcomodeca@calfee.com
*Featured in Construction (Ohio)*
**Practice Areas:** Construction; construction litigation; government contracting.
**Professional Memberships:** Arbitrator, mediator in construction, commercial and international disputes, American Arbitration Association Blue Ribbon Panel; Inaugural Chairperson, Lex Mundi construction and infrastructure group.
**Career:** Chair, construction group; Co-Chair, Energy Group. Advises owners, contractors, subcontractors and design professionals on construction matters, from project planning through disputes. Advises on federal contracts; customs and agency regulation and commercial litigation and arbitration. Lecturer and published author. Regularly serves as arbitrator and mediator on complex international and domestic disputes.
**Personal:** Judge Advocate Generals' School, LLM, 1988; Harvard Law School, JD, 1984; United States Military Academy, BS, 1977.

## COSCARELLI, Dianne S
Thompson Hine LLP, Cleveland
216 566 5769
Dianne.Coscarelli@ThompsonHine.com
*Featured in Real Estate (Ohio)*
**Career:** Dianne is a Partner and co-chair of the firm's Real Estate Finance Team and Distressed Real Estate Response Team. She focuses her practice on all aspects of commercial real estate including financings, restructurings, acquisitions and dispositions, leasing and opinion letters. Dianne has served as chair of the Ohio State Bar Association's Real Property Section, and the ABA Real Property Section's Mortgage Lending, Construction Lending and Mezzanine Lending Committees, and is a member of the American College of Mortgage Attorneys (ACMA) and the American College of Real Estate Lawyers (ACREL), serving as a governor.

## COUGHLIN, William E
Calfee, Halter & Griswold LLP, Cleveland
216 622 8334
wcoughlin@calfee.com
*Featured in Natural Resources (Ohio)*
**Practice Areas:** Environmental Litigation; Business Litigation.
**Professional Memberships:** Chair, Georgetown University Northeast Ohio Undergraduate Alumni Admissions Committee. Chair, Loyola Club, Cleveland's Jesuit Alumni Network.
**Career:** Chair, Environmental Group and Environmental Litigation; successful representation in enforcement defense (air, water, hazardous waste), cost recovery, indemnity suits. Senior trial partner; won multimillion-dollar plaintiff and defense verdicts in tortious interference, breach of

contract, breach of fiduciary duty, fraud, product liability and minority shareholder oppression trials. Law Clerk, DC Circuit, 1983-84.
**Personal:** Georgetown University (AB, magna cum laude, Phi Beta Kappa, 1978; MSFS, 1983; JD, magna cum laude, 1983). Fulbright Scholar, Geneva, Switzerland, 1978-79.

## COYNE, Thomas J
Thompson Hine LLP, Cleveland
216 566 5781
Thomas.Coyne@ThompsonHine.com
*Featured in Real Estate (Ohio)*
**Career:** Tom leads the firm's national Real Estate Practice Group. He concentrates on commercial real estate transactions and planning on properties throughout the United States. Principal types of transactions include: acquisitions and sales, including distressed sales in foreclosure and bankruptcy; handling of troubled assets and workouts; asset management, including leasing and subleasing; corporate and institutional real estate; plant siting and relocation; government incentives; construction and development; joint ventures; complex easement agreements; financing; brownfields; real estate tax abatement and valuation reductions; and commercial real estate disputes. Asset classes include industrial, office, warehouse, retail, mixed use, arena, stadium and special use.

## CRIST, Thomas O
Benesch, Friedlander, Coplan & Aronoff LLP, Cleveland
216 363 6108
tcrist@beneschlaw.com
*Featured in Construction (Ohio)*
**Practice Areas:** Public and private construction law. Annually provides interim project counseling on projects exceeding $300,000,000 in contracts. Litigates in state and federal courts, and is a certified mediator/arbitrator.
**Career:** Co-Chair of Construction Law Group. Represents the gamut of participants on substantial projects, including sports stadiums and arenas, hospitals, marquee structures for one of the country's largest public universities, power plants, dams, bridges and highways. Representation includes every form and type of claim on most types of commercial, industrial and infrastructure improvements.
**Personal:** Capital University (JD, Order of the Curia, 1994); The Ohio State University (BA cum laude, 1992).

## CROALL, David T
Porter Wright Morris & Arthur LLP, Cincinnati
513 369 4240
dcroall@porterwright.com
*Featured in Labor & Employment (Ohio)*
**Career:** Mr Croall has represented employers in a wide variety of employment law matters for over 30 years. He focuses his practice on employment discrimination, wrongful discharge litigation, and preventive employment law counseling and training. Over the years, he has successfully assisted employers in all kinds of employment matters, has obtained summary judgment for many employers in discrimination/wrongful discharge matters, and has obtained numerous favorable verdicts from

juries in cases that have gone to trial. He has represented a variety of employers, including hospitals, manufacturers, airlines, universities, retailers and service providers. Mr Croall received his JD from Harvard Law School.

## CURRY, Robert M
Thompson Hine LLP, Dayton
937 443 6511
Bob.Curry@ThompsonHine.com
*Featured in Real Estate (Ohio)*
**Career:** Bob is partner-in-charge of Thompson Hine's Dayton office. His practice is focused on shopping center, office, industrial, residential and mixed use developments, mortgage loan transactions, commercial leases, broker/agency law and condominiums. His experience includes complex urban redevelopment projects, multi-tiered ownership structures, condominiums, master associations and governmental incentives. Bob is co-author of the treatise, Ohio Real Property Law and Practice, serves as chair of the Real Property Council of the Ohio State Bar Association, and is a member of ACREL.

## CYPHERT, Michael
Walter & Haverfield LLP, Cleveland
216 928 2897
mcyphert@walterhav.com
*Featured in Natural Resources (Ohio)*
**Professional Memberships:** American, Federal, Ohio and Cleveland Metropolitan Bar Associations.
**Career:** Mike concentrates his practice in the areas of environmental counseling and litigation, environmental violation defense, land disposal regulatory compliance, strategic planning and analysis of environmental issues in acquisitions and divestitures and evaluation of environmental due diligence investigations, litigation and defense of CAA, CWA, RCRA, CERCLA, TSCA and other federal and state environmental issues. He is licensed to practice in the United States Supreme Court, the State of Ohio, and a number of Federal district and appellate courts.
**Personal:** Case Western Reserve University School of Law, JD, 1973 (Order of the Coif); Case Western Reserve University, BA, 1970.

## DAHL, Sherri
Squire Sanders (US) LLP, Cleveland
216 479 8480
sherri.dahl@squiresanders.com
*Featured in Bankruptcy/Restructuring (Ohio)*

## DANIELS, Anthea
Calfee, Halter & Griswold LLP, Cleveland
216 622 8391
adaniels@calfee.com
*Featured in Healthcare (Ohio)*
**Practice Areas:** Health Care and Life Sciences; HIPPA; Mergers and Acquisitions.
**Professional Memberships:** American Health Lawyers Association (past President); Cleveland Metropolitan Bar Association Health Law Section, American Bar Association Health Law Section, Northeast Ohio Chapter/Healthcare Financial Management Association (past President). Anthea is a national speaker on health care.

**Career:** Anthea servers as co-chair of Health Care & Life Sciences group. Counsels healthcare providers, manufacturers and payors on fraud and abuse, false claims, compliance, Stark, mergers, Medicare, state licensing, HIPAA and contracting.
**Publications:** AHLA, Health Law Handbook.
**Personal:** Case Western Reserve University School of Law, JD, 1989; Denison University, BA, 1986.

## DAY, Alison
Littler Mendelson, PC, Columbus
614 463 4212
aday@littler.com
*Featured in Labor & Employment (Ohio)*
**Practice Areas:** Complex Litigation and Jury Trials, Discrimination and Harassment, Leaves of Absence and Disability Accommodation, Healthcare.
**Professional Memberships:** Member, Labor and Employment Section - Columbus, Ohio State Bar Association Member, Labor and Employment Section - Columbus Bar Association Member, Labor and Employment Section - American Bar Association Member, Human Resources Association of Central Ohio.
**Career:** Alison represents and counsels employers, from small businesses to Fortune 100 companies, with an emphasis on the healthcare and retail sectors. Alison also has extensive experience handling administrative charges before the Equal Employment Opportunity Commission, the Ohio Civil Rights Commission, the Department of Labor, and the NLRB.

## DEGULIS, Gregory J
McMahon DeGulis LLP, Cleveland
216 367 1403
gdegulis@mdllp.net
*Featured in Natural Resources (Ohio)*
**Practice Areas:** Extensive experience prosecuting and defending environmental and toxic exposure claims; cost recovery matters; environmental insurance coverage litigation; toxic tort litigation and the negotiation of administrative consent decrees. He leads the firm's insurance recovery practice and has extensive arbitration experience as an advocate and panel member with the American Arbitration Association.

## DEMARCO, Daniel A
Hahn Loeser & Parks LLP, Cleveland
216 274 2432
dademarco@hahnlaw.com
*Featured in Bankruptcy/Restructuring (Ohio)*
**Practice Areas:** Mr DeMarco, co-chair of the firm's Creditors' Rights, Reorganization & Bankruptcy Area, represents creditors, creditors' committees, indenture trustees, trustees and debtors in numerous reorganization proceedings. He is certified in the practice of business bankruptcy by the American Board of Certification.
**Professional Memberships:** Board of Trustees, Ohio Chapter of the Turnaround Management Association; Sixth Circuit Editor, ABA Bankruptcy & Insolvency Litigation Committee.
**Personal:** University of Michigan Law School (JD, 1983); University of Chicago (BA, Phi Beta Kappa, 1980).

## DEMITRACK, Thomas
Jones Day, Cleveland
216 586 3939
tdemitrack@jonesday.com
*Featured in Litigation (Ohio)*
**Practice Areas:** Co-ordinator of the Antitrust Practice in Jones Day's Cleveland Office. He has litigated numerous antitrust cases, including price fixing, monopolization, vertical restraints, and Robinson-Patman cases, as well as IP cases raising antitrust issues. Has substantial experience in supplier-distribution cases raising Robinson-Patman and other pricing issues and in antitrust class action cases in general. Listed as a leading lawyer in antitrust in Northeast Ohio's Inside Business magazine and in Ohio Super Lawyers. He has spoken on antitrust issues at Ohio State Bar Association and Federal Bar Association programs and on conflicts of interest issues at continuing legal education programs.

## DILLER, Edward D
Taft Stettinius & Hollister LLP, Cincinnati
513 357 9313
diller@taftlaw.com
*Featured in Real Estate (Ohio)*
**Practice Areas:** Real Property, Construction, Business & Finance, Emerging Companies, Nonprofit and Tax-Exempt Organizations, Corporate Finance, Banking and Institutional Finance, Health and Life Sciences, Education - Litigation.
**Career:** Mr Diller is Partner-in-Charge of the Cincinnati office and also a member of the Executive and Development Committees. He practices primarily in the areas of real estate, health care and general corporate law. He is a member of the boards of trustees of Cincinnati Museum Center, Mennonite Central Committee - US, Downtown Cincinnati Inc. and the Dan Beard Council, Boy Scouts of America.
**Personal:** Harvard Law School (1976); Bluffton University (1969).

## DIMLING, Robert A
Frost Brown Todd LLC, Cincinnati
513 651 6821
rdimling@fbtlaw.com
*Featured in Labor & Employment (Ohio)*
**Practice Areas:** Represents management in all aspects of labor and employment including workplace safety and health (OSHA), discrimination and wrongful discharge claims, administrative proceedings, arbitrations and collective bargaining.
**Professional Memberships:** American Bar Association, Ohio State Bar Association, Cincinnati Bar Association.
**Career:** Listed in The Best Lawyers in America; Named to Ohio Super Lawyers.
**Personal:** University of Michigan Law School (JD 1966), Bowling Green State University (1963).

## DOBROWSKI, Stanley J
Calfee, Halter & Griswold LLP, Columbus
614 621 7003
sdobrowski@calfee.com
*Featured in Construction (Ohio)*

**Practice Areas:** Construction; Construction Litigation; Public Law.
**Professional Memberships:** Chair, Industry Outreach Committee, former chair Owners & Lenders Division, American Bar Association Forum on Construction Industry; former chair, Ohio State Bar Association and Columbus Bar Association Construction Law Committees.
**Career:** Focuses on construction and contract documents, selection processes, agreements for architects, construction managers, design-builders. Former Ohio special counsel by Ohio Attorney General for standard bidding and construction documents.
**Publications:** Numerous articles; "Open Meetings and Public Records" chapter of "Ohio Municipal Law."
**Personal:** Ohio State University College of Law, JD, 1976; University of Notre Dame, BA, 1973.

## DONSON, Jack
Taft Stettinius & Hollister LLP, Cincinnati
513 357 9343
donson@taftlaw.com
*Featured in Litigation (Ohio)*
**Practice Areas:** Antitrust, Franchise and Distribution, Litigation, Class Action and Multi-Party Litigation.
**Professional Memberships:** American, Federal, Ohio State and Cincinnati Bar Associations.
**Career:** Mr Donson is chair of the Antitrust practice. He has tried both criminal and civil antitrust suits and has represented clients in numerous antitrust suits and investigations. This litigation experience covers all aspects of the antitrust laws and includes suits brought by the federal government, various state attorneys general and private plaintiffs.
**Personal:** University of Cincinnati College of Law (1971); The Ohio State University (1968).

## DORAN, Scott
Taft Stettinius & Hollister LLP, Columbus
614 334 6157
sdoran@taftlaw.com
*Featured in Natural Resources (Ohio)*
**Practice Areas:** Environmental, Litigation, Energy and Regulated Industries, Environmental Transactional Services.
**Professional Memberships:** Columbus and Ohio State Bar Associations, Ohio Home Builders Association, Ohio Oil and Gas Association.
**Career:** Mr Doran represents clients in all aspects of state and federal permitting and permit appeals, the defense of enforcement actions, rule-making, environmental regulation of land use, Brownfields redevelopment, hazardous waste regulation, CERCLA cost recovery claims, corporate transactions and environmental risk allocation, and toxic tort and property damage claims.
**Personal:** University of Cincinnati College of Law (1986); Miami University, MS in Toxicology (1983); Miami University, BA (1979).

## DORNETTE, W Stuart
Taft Stettinius & Hollister LLP, Cincinnati
513 357 9353
dornette@taftlaw.com
*Featured in Litigation (Ohio)*
**Practice Areas:** Securities - Litigation, Corporate Governance, Sports, Public Law, Nonprofit and Tax-Exempt Organizations, Education - Litigation, Campaign & Election Law, Class Action and Multi-Party Litigation, E-Discovery, Litigation.
**Career:** Mr Dornette is co-chair of the Litigation group. He has substantial personal experience in complex litigation – particularly involving financial, corporate and securities issues – in state and federal courts. He also has represented the Cincinnati Bengals in many aspects of their business operations and was involved in all aspects of the development and construction of the Paul Brown Football Stadium.
**Personal:** University of Virginia Law School (1975); Williams College (1972).

## DOUGLAS, Sue
Littler Mendelson, PC, Cleveland
216 696 6174
sdouglas@littler.com
*Featured in Labor & Employment (Ohio)*
**Practice Areas:** Discrimination and Harassment, Complex Litigation and Jury Trials.
**Professional Memberships:** Ohio State Bar Association Labor and Employment Law Specialty Certification Board, American Arbitration Association Employment Law Panel, Alternative Dispute Resolution Panel for the United States District Court for the Northern District of Ohio, Fellow – American Bar Foundation, Fellow - Akron Bar Association, Cleveland Bar Association.
**Career:** Ms Douglas is Cleveland Office Managing Shareholder, Co-Chair of the Discrimination & Harassment Practice Group and a member of the Firm's Diversity & Inclusion Council.
**Personal:** JD, Washington College of Law, American University, 1981; BA, Georgetown University, cum laude, 1976.

## DRAUCKER, Carl A
Squire Sanders (US) LLP, Cleveland
216 479 8766
carl.draucker@squiresanders.com
*Featured in Employee Benefits & Executive Compensation (Ohio)*
**Practice Areas:** Partner focused on tax-qualified retirement plans, deferred compensation plans and executive compensation. Practices before the Internal Revenue Service and US Tax Court. Extensive experience in employee benefits aspects of corporate and real estate transactions including acquisitions, dispositions and mergers, and employee stock ownership plans. Listed in The Best Lawyers in America since 2006 and named 2012 Cleveland Employee Benefits Lawyer of the Year by The Best Lawyers in America.
**Professional Memberships:** Akron Bar Association; Section of Taxation, American Bar Association.

## DROZDOWSKI, Jim
Hahn Loeser & Parks LLP, Cleveland
216 274 2553
jmdrozdowski@hahnlaw.com
*Featured in Labor & Employment (Ohio)*
**Practice Areas:** Mr Drozdowski chairs the firm's Labor & Employment Area. He is a Board Certified Ohio State Bar Association Labor and Employment Law Specialist and is also licensed in New York. He litigates complex cases, advises clients on employment laws and litigation avoidance strategies, and represents employers as chief negotiator for collective bargaining negotiations.
**Professional Memberships:** Federal Bar Association; L&E Section, American Bar Association; Lake/Geauga County Chapter, Society of Human Resource Managers; Cleveland Employment Inns of Court.
**Personal:** Case Western Reserve University School of Law (JD, magna cum laude, 1995); University of Cincinnati (BA, summa cum laude, 1992).

## DUCATMAN, Robert
Jones Day, Cleveland
216 586 7144
rducatman@jonesday.com
*Featured in Intellectual Property (Ohio)*
**Practice Areas:** Practices in the areas of litigation and intellectual property law, with considerable experience in the RICO area, patent and trademark infringement matters, trade secrets enforcement and defense, employment agreement enforcement and defense, commercial litigation, and cybersquatting.
**Professional Memberships:** Member of the Judge John M. Manos Inn of Court. Former Chairman of the RICO Subcommittee of the Trial Practice Committee of the ABA.
**Publications:** Authored jury instructions for the Ohio Judicial Conference for actions brought under the Ohio Corrupt Activities Act and has coauthored articles related to the use of RICO in intellectual property matters.

## DUNLAY, Catherine
Taft Stettinius & Hollister LLP, Columbus
614 220 0236
*Featured in Healthcare (Ohio)*
**Practice Areas:** Health and life sciences.
**Professional Memberships:** American Health Lawyers Association, Columbus Bar Association, Ohio State Bar Association.
**Career:** Ms Dunlay is co-chair of the Health & Life Sciences group. She represents hospitals, physicians and other health care organizations and professionals in mergers, acquisitions, joint ventures and contractual arrangements, including a variety of hospital physician relationships. She also counsels clients on operational and compliance matters, including Anti-Kickback and Stark physician self-referral laws and Medicare and Medicaid coverage and reimbursement issues.
**Personal:** The Ohio State University College of Law (1984); University of Cincinnati (1981).

## DUNSIZER, Jennifer
Vorys, Sater, Seymour and Pease LLP, Columbus
614 464 5631
jbdunsizer@vorys.com
*Featured in Employee Benefits & Executive Compensation (Ohio)*
**Practice Areas:** Of counsel in Labor and Employment Group; practice focuses on employee benefits and executive compensation plans. Former Managing Corporate Counsel for a large, publicly traded employer with extensive experience in retirement plans, deferred compensation, insurance benefits, short- and long-term cash and equity-based incentive plans, early retirement programs, public company disclosure obligations and merger and acquisition activity.
**Professional Memberships:** American, Columbus Bar Associations.
**Career:** Admitted to Ohio Bar (1993).
**Personal:** The Ohio State University Michael E. Moritz College of Law, JD, 1993; University of Rochester College of Arts and Science, dual BA degrees, cum laude, 1990.

## DUTTON, Thomas E
Jones Day, Columbus
614 281 3897
tedutton@jonesday.com
*Featured in Healthcare (Ohio)*
**Practice Areas:** Tom Dutton helps hospitals, health systems, insurance companies, and large physician groups successfully implement cutting-edge clinical integration and delivery strategies. He has developed numerous co-management arrangements, physician practice acquisitions and provider-based clinics, regulatory-compliant physician employment and PSA compensation models, physician-hospital organizations, and every type of physician-hospital joint venture (including cancer centers, ASCs and diagnostic imaging centers). Tom has led dozens of hospital, HMO, and insurance company mergers, acquisitions and joint ventures, including innovative whole hospital and service line revenue mergers and those involving distressed companies. He also advises on Stark Law matters.

## EBLING, Louis K
Thompson Hine LLP, Cincinnati
513 352 6527
Louis.Ebling@ThompsonHine.com
*Featured in Intellectual Property (Ohio)*
**Career:** Lou is a partner in the firm's Intellectual Property Practice Group. Lou's practice focuses on all aspects of US and international trademark law, as well as internet, advertising, data privacy and copyright issues. He has significant experience in global brand creation and portfolio management, IP transactions, licensing and global IP rights policing and enforcement. He is an active member of the International Trademark Association and presently serves on the Emerging Issues Committee.

## FAIRFIELD, Mary Ellen
Vorys, Sater, Seymour and Pease LLP, Columbus
614 464 6335
mefairfield@vorys.com
*Featured in Litigation (Ohio)*
**Practice Areas:** Partner whose practice includes the defense of all types of civil litigation, including business and commercial disputes; class actions and employment.
**Professional Memberships:** American, Ohio and Columbus Bar Associations; Federal, Ohio and Columbus Bar Foundations; American College of Trial Lawyers (1992); Adjunct Professor, Ohio State Moritz College of Law, 1985-95.
**Career:** Ohio, US Supreme Court, US Courts of Appeals for the Federal, Sixth and Ninth Circuits, US District Courts for the Northern and Southern Districts of Ohio.
**Personal:** Ohio State University Moritz College of Law, JD, cum laude, 1972; Purdue University, BA, with honors 1970.

## FAROLINO, Shane A
Roetzel & Andress, LPA, Akron
330 849 6680
sfarolino@ralaw.com
*Featured in Natural Resources (Ohio)*
**Practice Areas:** As Environmental, Energy and Health & Safety Practice Group Manager, Mr Farolino focuses his practice on environmental compliance counseling, permitting, and administrative, civil, and criminal litigation. He has extensive experience in handling Clean Water Act and Clean Air Act permitting projects, Emergency Response & Crisis Management events, the defense of environmental enforcement actions, and toxic tort litigation matters. His clients include major petroleum companies, manufacturing companies, commercial developers, and government entities. Before entering private practice, he served as an Assistant Attorney General in the Environmental Enforcement Section of the Ohio Attorney General's Office.

## FARUKI, Charles J
Faruki Ireland & Cox PLL, Dayton
937 227 3705
cfaruki@ficlaw.com
*Featured in Litigation (Ohio)*
**Practice Areas:** Business litigation, including intellectual property; antitrust; class actions.
**Professional Memberships:** Fellow, American College of Trial Lawyers; Member, American Board of Trial Advocates; fellow, American Bar Foundation; fellow, Ohio State Bar Foundation; Fellow, Litigation Counsel of America; past President, Dayton Bar Association; past President, Dayton Chapter, Federal Bar Association; Member Cincinnati, Dayton, Ohio State, Federal, American, and Federal Circuit Bar Associations.
**Career:** 1974-89, Smith & Schnacke (Partner, 1979-89); Founder and Managing Partner, Faruki Ireland & Cox PLL, 1989 to present. Repeatedly selected as one of Top Ten Lawyers in Ohio in SuperLawyers poll of all Ohio attorneys.

**Publications:** Numerous publications in law journals and legal press.

## FAXON, Robert S
Jones Day, Cleveland
216 586 7104
rfaxon@jonesday.com
*Featured in Litigation (Ohio)*

**Practice Areas:** Rob Faxon splits his practice between complex commercial/corporate matters and products liability/class action defense. Rob has appeared in courts throughout the country, including federal multidistrict litigation, the Delaware Chancery Court, and other complex state and federal litigations. In corporate and commercial litigation and arbitration, Rob has handled disputes involving corporate governance, Ohio's Control Share Acquisition Act, and business acquisitions. He has also defended companies in class action, product liability, consumer fraud, and medical device litigation. Most recently on the product liability side, Rob has been trial counsel for R.J. Reynolds in Florida fraud and product liability claims.

## FAY, Terrence M
Thompson Hine LLP, Columbus
614 469 3259
Terrence.Fay@ThompsonHine.com
*Featured in Natural Resources (Ohio)*

**Career:** Terry is a partner in the Environmental Practice Group with 35 years of experience. Before joining Thompson Hine, he was Chief Civil Attorney of the Environmental Enforcement Section of the Ohio Attorney General's Office, Chief Counsel to the Ohio Board on Unreclaimed Strip-Mined Lands, and clerked for the Chief Administrative Law Judge of the Ohio Power Siting Board. His honors include being named to American Counsel's 2012 list of top-rated energy, environmental and natural resource lawyers nationally, Ohio Super Lawyers, Who's Who in America, and 2013 Law360 Environmental MVP, one of only five in the entire country.

## FELDKAMP, Janet
Benesch, Friedlander, Coplan & Aronoff LLP, Columbus
614 223 9328
jfeldkamp@beneschlaw.com
*Featured in Healthcare (Ohio)*

**Practice Areas:** Health care law, including long-term care survey and certification, state and federal regulation, physician and nurse practice, and fraud and abuse involving hospitals, suppliers, insurers and physicians.

**Professional Memberships:** Past President, The American Association of Nurse Attorneys Member, American Health Lawyers Association Member, American College of Health Care Administrators National Editorial Advisory Committee Member, American Association of Nurse Executives Member, Sigma Theta Tau, National Nursing Honor Society Certified in Health Care Compliance, Health Care Compliance Certification Board.

**Personal:** Saint Louis University School of Law, 1990, JD cum laude; University of Missouri, 1978, BS, Nursing magna cum laude.

## FINN, Terrence
Roetzel & Andress, LPA, Akron
330 849 6605
tfinn@ralaw.com
*Featured in Natural Resources (Ohio)*

**Practice Areas:** Mr Finn focuses his practice on environmental compliance counseling and environmental litigation in administrative, state and federal forms. He defends clients in environmental enforcement actions brought by both state and federal agencies, prosecutes appeals before the Ohio Environmental Review Appeals Commission, counsels clients on brownfield clean-up and redevelopment projects in addition to a variety of environmental permitting matters, including wetland, storm water, NPDES, solid and hazardous waste matters. Clients include major corporations, small closely held businesses, national retailers, developers and municipalities. He was formerly an Assistant Attorney General for the State of Ohio, in the Environmental Enforcement Section.

## FISHER-EDWARDS, Suzanne M
McMahon DeGulis LLP, Columbus
614 678 5370
sfisher@mdllp.net
*Featured in Natural Resources (Ohio)*

**Practice Areas:** Environmental counseling regarding issues affecting real estate development and transactions; brownfield redevelopment; advise on PCB and lead-based paint compliance under TSCA; represent landowners in wind development projects and negotiate leases for oil and gas, as well as pipelines; negotiate leases and transmission easements as well as obtaining permits, licenses, siting authorizations and other regulatory approvals from federal, state and local agencies for proposed energy projects; cleanup of contaminated sites, including negotiation of orders and consent decrees with regulatory agencies.

## FITCH, Stephen
Taft Stettinius & Hollister LLP, Columbus
614 334 6120
sfitch@taftlaw.com
*Featured in Litigation (Ohio)*

**Practice Areas:** Litigation, ethics and professional responsibility.

**Professional Memberships:** American College of Trial Lawyers, American, Federal, Ohio State and Columbus Bar Associations.

**Career:** Mr Fitch's practice is focused on commercial litigation. He routinely represents clients in all aspects of civil trial and appellate litigation, alternative dispute resolution and professional responsibility. Mr Fitch is a fellow in the American College of Trial Lawyers and frequently serves as a court appointed mediator in the US District Court (Southern District).

**Personal:** The Ohio State University College of Law (1973); The Ohio State University (1970).

## FOGARTY, Robert J
Hahn Loeser & Parks LLP, Cleveland
216 274 2291
rjfogarty@hahnlaw.com
*Featured in Litigation (Ohio)*

**Practice Areas:** Mr Fogarty, co-chair of the firm's Litigation Area, has extensive experience in complex commercial litigation, class action, healthcare, antitrust and employment/non-compete agreements, among others. He has represented a Fortune 100 managed care organization for many years, and is currently defending one of the leading title insurance companies in the United States in class action litigation nationwide.

**Personal:** Assistant United States Attorney, Southern District of Ohio (1979-82); University of Cincinnati College of Law (JD, 1977); University of Cincinnati (BA, Phi Beta Kappa, 1974).

## FOLLAND, Robert C
Thompson Hine LLP, Cleveland
216 566 5813
Rob.Folland@ThompsonHine.com
*Featured in Bankruptcy/Restructuring (Ohio)*

**Career:** Rob is a partner in the firm's Business Restructuring, Creditors' Rights & Bankruptcy and Commercial & Public Finance Practice Groups. He focuses his practice on bankruptcy (primarily Chapter 11 reorganizations) and creditors' rights, out of court business restructurings, lender liability and consumer lending liability defense, and other financially distressed business issues. Rob has significant experience representing secured lenders, debtors, creditors' committees, indenture trustees, landlords, trade creditors and parties desiring to acquire assets in bankruptcy proceedings.

## FRANK, Ian H
Frantz Ward LLP, Cleveland
216 515 1633
ifrank@frantzward.com
*Featured in Construction (Ohio)*

**Practice Areas:** Dedicates entire practice to all facets of construction law. Counsels contractors, subcontractors, specialty trades, material and equipment manufacturers, design professionals and other project participants in developing, managing, resolving and litigating complex commercial construction disputes, including: differing/changed conditions claims, delay/disruption claims, bond claims, default/termination claims and bid disputes. Represents clients in diverse construction disciplines, including road, bridge and utility construction, heavy civil/tunneling work, structural steel fabrication/erection, and general trades/building construction.

**Professional Memberships:** ABA Forum on Construction Industry, Associated General Contractors of America, Ohio Contractors Association, Surety Association of Ohio, Northeast Ohio Chapter of US Green Building Council.

## FRANTZ, Michael
Frantz Ward LLP, Cleveland
216 515 1606
mfrantz@frantzward.com
*Featured in Labor & Employment (Ohio)*

**Practice Areas:** Focuses on labor and employment law, higher education, healthcare and manufacturing. Extensive experience in defense of labor and employment disputes. Has negotiated hundreds of contracts for employers in an array of industries involving every major union throughout the United States and Canada.

**Professional Memberships:** American Bar Association; Ohio Bar Association; Cleveland Bar Association; National Association of College and University Attorneys; American Arbitration Association Labor Advisory Council; Defense Research Institute, Labor Relations Committee; Journal College and University Law, Member of the Editorial Board, 1997-99; Ohio Management Lawyers Association.

**Publications:** Frequent author and speaker on labor and employment issues.

## FRICKE, Wade M
Ogletree, Deakins, Nash, Smoak & Stewart, PC, Cleveland
216 241 6100
wade.fricke@ogletreedeakins.com
*Featured in Labor & Employment (Ohio)*

**Practice Areas:** Focus on extensive issue avoidance and positive employment practices training and related work; significant experience negotiating labor agreements and assisting companies of all sizes administer labor agreements; extensive NLRB representation election experience.

**Professional Memberships:** Cleveland Metropolitan Bar Association, Ohio State Bar Association, Ohio Management Lawyers Association, American Employment Law Council.

**Career:** Admitted to practice in Ohio in 1989 and started with national law firm in Cleveland, Ohio office; partner in Cleveland's oldest law firm prior to joining Ogletree Deakins; one of three founding members of Cleveland office of Ogletree Deakins.

**Personal:** Princeton University (AB, 1984), Washington and Lee University (JD, 1989).

## FRIEDMAN, Steven A
Squire Sanders (US) LLP, Cleveland
216 479 8327
steven.friedman@squiresanders.com
*Featured in Construction (Ohio)*

**Practice Areas:** Partner and trial lawyer with extensive experience representing owners and contractors in construction projects including dispute resolution and trial work. Particular emphasis representing Ohio public entities in construction matters including bidding issues, contracting issues and dispute resolution. Also has substantial experience in complex commercial litigation matters and representing media in first amendment issues. Listed in The Best Lawyers in America.

## FUCHS, Jack F
Thompson Hine LLP, Cincinnati
513 352 6741
Jack.Fuchs@ThompsonHine.com
*Featured in Employee Benefits & Executive Compensation (Ohio)*

**Career:** Jack is a partner who focuses his practice on employee benefits, professional liability and securities litigation. He has handled numerous class actions involving a wide range of disputes, including investment manager, employee stock, 401(k) investments, modification and termination of retiree health benefits in both union and non-union contexts, termination of pension plans, cash balance whipsaw and age discrimination claims, interference with benefits under ERISA 510, and breach of fiduciary duties claims. Jack litigates claims involving the Department of Labor, third-party administrators, participants, beneficiaries and service providers.

### GAGLIANO, Bill J
Ulmer & Berne LLP, Cleveland
216 583 7047
bgagliano@ulmer.com
*Featured in Real Estate (Ohio)*
**Practice Areas:** Chair of the firm's Real Estate Group and a member of the firm's Management Committee, Bill represents property owners, tenants, contractors, and developers, as well as governmental entities. His expertise includes construction law, affordable housing, real estate development, leasing, property taxation, and abatement. In the corporate area, he concentrates on corporate governance issues and business counseling. Bill's litigation practice focuses on leasing matters, title insurance litigation, and construction claims.
**Professional Memberships:** Fellow - American College of Real Estate Lawyers and Member, Alumni Advisory Board, Center for Business Law & Regulation – CWRU Law School.

### GALL, John R
Squire Sanders (US) LLP, Columbus
614 365 2806
john.gall@squiresanders.com
*Featured in Litigation (Ohio)*
**Practice Areas:** Senior Partner in the Columbus office's litigation group. Has extensive trial and appellate practice involving commercial issues, including antitrust and unfair competition claims, business contract disputes, intellectual property rights, professional liability claims and corporate control contests. Clients include larger corporations and foundations, financial institutions and accounting firms. Consistently recognized in The Best Lawyers in America and Ohio Super Lawyers.
**Professional Memberships:** Member, United States Anti-Doping Agency Review Board and ITF/ATP/WTF Anti-Doping Review Board; Member, Ohio Supreme Court's Board of Bar Examiners.

### GANSKE, Lyle G
Jones Day, Cleveland
216 586 7264
lgganske@jonesday.com
*Featured in Corporate/M&A (Ohio)*
**Practice Areas:** Partner-in-Charge, Midwest Region. Lyle is an advisor to significant companies, focusing primarily on M&A, takeovers, takeover preparedness, corporate governance, executive compensation, and general corporate counseling. He frequently speaks on M&A, takeover preparedness, corporate governance issues, and has co-authored articles that have appeared in publications such as 'The Business Lawyer,' 'Director's Monthly,' and the 'New York Law Journal.' He has submitted comments to the Securities and Exchange Commission on various

proposed rules. One of four lawyers in the US to be named to the 2009 "Client Service Super All-Star Team: Truly Outstanding" survey conducted by BTI Consulting.

### GANULIN, Neil
Frost Brown Todd LLC, Cincinnati
513 651 6882
nganulin@fbtlaw.com
*Featured in Corporate/M&A (Ohio)*
**Practice Areas:** All aspects of business, transactional and finance law, securities regulation and compliance and Sarbanes Oxley/Dodd-Frank Act/corporate governance matters. Extensive experience in mergers and acquisitions and counseling executive management of publicly-traded and private corporations in the conduct of strategic business matters, board and shareholder responsibilities and duties, equity and debt issuances, regulatory matters, disclosure and reporting matters.
**Career:** Member, Frost Brown Todd LLC (1979-Present).
**Personal:** Juris Doctor, University of Michigan Law School, 1973; BA, University of Cincinnati, 1970, Magna Cum Laude, Phi Beta Kappa.

### GARVIN, Michael
Hahn Loeser & Parks LLP, Cleveland
216 274 2322
mjgarvin@hahnlaw.com
*Featured in Intellectual Property (Ohio)*
**Practice Areas:** Mr Garvin focuses his practice on intellectual property and technology litigation, particularly patent litigation. In addition to intellectual property and technology disputes, Mr Garvin has handled several other business-related cases, including those involving contracts, securities and other corporate law issues, and financial services.
**Professional Memberships:** Past co-chair, Intellectual Property Litigation Committee, Section of Litigation, American Bar Association.
**Personal:** College of William and Mary (JD, 1984); Miami University (BS, 1981).

### GATES, Martin S
Jones Day, Cleveland
216 586 7292
mgates@jonesday.com
*Featured in Banking & Finance (Ohio)*
**Practice Areas:** Focuses his practice on representing lending institutions, publicly and privately held companies and private equity groups in all types of secured and unsecured financing transactions, syndications, venture financings including SBIC financings, mezzanine and other subordinated debt financings, asset securitization transactions, commercial transactions, mergers, acquisitions, divestitures, leveraged buyouts, restructurings, debtor-in-possession financings, workouts, multi-currency financings and reorganizations.
**Professional Memberships:** Cleveland Metropolitan Bar Association; Ohio State Bar Association; American Bar Association.
**Personal:** JD University of Pittsburgh, School of Law, 1988; AB Princeton University, 1984.

### GHERLEIN, John M
Baker & Hostetler LLP, Cleveland
216 861 7398
jgherlein@bakerlaw.com
*Featured in Corporate/M&A (Ohio)*
**Career:** Firmwide Chair of BakerHostetler's Business Group, John Gherlein has extensive experience representing public and private companies in M&A transactions and counseling public companies regarding their compliance with disclosure and reporting obligations. He advises public and private companies on debt and equity offerings, including IPOs and regularly advises boards of directors and their committees on general corporate governance matters, as well as in special circumstances such as change of control settings and accounting inquiries. He has worked closely with the firm's White Collar Defense and Corporate Investigations Team in FCPA, options dating and other accounting inquiries.

### GOLD, Ronald
Frost Brown Todd LLC, Cincinnati
513 651 6156
rgold@fbtlaw.com
*Featured in Bankruptcy/Restructuring (Ohio)*
**Practice Areas:** Financial Restructuring, Corporate/Business; Workouts and Restructuring. Extensive experience in chapter 11 restructurings representing corporate debtors, lenders, landlords, official committees and purchasers of businesses.
**Professional Memberships:** Admitted to practice Illinois (1989) and Ohio (1993). Fellow in American College of Bankruptcy.
**Career:** Katten Muchin & Zavis (Chicago), 1989; Frost & Jacobs LLP (Cincinnati), 1992, became partner, 1996; Member Frost Brown Todd LLC, 2000-present.
**Personal:** Born Erie, Pennsylvania, 1964. The University of Michigan, AB, 1986; University of Pittsburgh School of Law, JD (magna cum laude, Order of the Coif), 1989.

### GOLDFARB, Steven A.
Hahn Loeser & Parks LLP, Cleveland
216 274 2314
sagoldfarb@hahnlaw.com
*Featured in Litigation (Ohio)*
**Practice Areas:** Mr Goldfarb, co-chair of the firm's Litigation Area, has a national litigation practice representing public companies in the title insurance, financial services and franchising industries. He defends class action litigation and non-compete/corporate raiding cases nationwide for clients like Fidelity National Financial, Inc., the largest title insurance company in the US, which has resulted in two jury trial victories named "Top 100 Verdicts" by The National Law Journal (2005 and 2006).
**Personal:** The Ohio State University Moritz College of Law (JD, 1985); Indiana University (BA, 1982).

### GOLDMAN, Matthew R
Baker & Hostetler LLP, Cleveland
216 861 7797
mgoldman@bakerlaw.com
*Featured in Bankruptcy/Restructuring (Ohio)*

**Career:** Matthew Goldman represents debtors, creditors and purchasers in bankruptcies and restructures across the United States. He was lead counsel for the LTV Steel Committee which won a D&O lawsuit and reversed the nation's largest failed industrial bankruptcy. Mr Goldman was named to the ABI Commission on Reform of Chapter 11 and is Reporter for its Administrative Claims committee. He is a past chair of the Cleveland Bar Association Bankruptcy Section, a member of its Executive Committee for ten years, and organized the O'Neill Regional Bankruptcy Institute for eight years.

### GOLDSTEIN, Heidi B
Thompson Hine LLP, Cleveland
216 566 5559
Heidi.Goldstein@ThompsonHine.com
*Featured in Natural Resources (Ohio)*
**Career:** Heidi is a partner in the firm's Environmental and Product Liability Litigation Practice Groups. She focuses her practice on environmental counseling in business, regulatory and legislative matters, environmental and toxic tort litigation, environmental enforcement actions, site remediation and compliance with environmental regulations. She is the chair of Thompson Hine's Firmwide Women's Initiative.

### GOLDSTEIN, Steven J
Frost Brown Todd LLC, Cincinnati
513 651 6131
sgoldstein@fbtlaw.com
*Featured in Intellectual Property (Ohio)*
**Practice Areas:** Vice-Chairman, Intellectual Property Department. Work includes patent prosecution, licensing, counseling and opinion work in chemical and pharmaceutical technologies. Extensive experience in portfolio management, patent strategy development and counseling corporate clients. Consultant on IP department management issues.
**Professional Memberships:** American Intellectual Property Law Association, AIPPI, Cincinnati Bar Association.
**Career:** Admitted to Ohio Bar in 1975 and USPTO bar in 1976. Former Associate General Counsel, Intellectual Property, at The Procter & Gamble Company. Since 1987, adjunct professor of law, University of Cincinnati College of Law.
**Personal:** Born September, 1951. Attended Massachusetts Institute of Technology and Boston University Law School.

### GRADY, Timothy
Porter Wright Morris & Arthur LLP, Columbus
614 227 2105
tgrady@porterwright.com
*Featured in Banking & Finance (Ohio)*
**Career:** Mr Grady chairs the firm's Banking and Finance Practice Group. He represents administrative agents and lenders as well as corporate borrowers in syndicated, large corporate, commercial and industrial, asset-based and middle-market credit extensions, loan restructuring, leveraged and acquisition financings, ESOP credit facilities, recapitalizations, and multi-state and cross-border financing. His experience encompasses a diverse group of industries and owners including health-

care, manufacturing, retail, energy and agribusiness. In addition, he advises clients regarding letters of credit and swap transactions, conducts seminars on secured transactions under Article 9 of the UCC and authored the Ohio Chapter of the ABA's Law of Guaranties.

## GRAUER, David W
Squire Sanders (US) LLP, Columbus
614 365 2786
david.grauer@squiresanders.com
*Featured in Healthcare (Ohio)*

## GREENBERG, Gerald
Taft Stettinius & Hollister LLP, Cincinnati
513 357 9670
greenberg@taftlaw.com
*Featured in Corporate/M&A (Ohio)*
**Practice Areas:** Banking and Institutional Finance, Emerging Companies, International, Structured Finance, Public Offerings, Private Equity & Venture Capital, Securities - Corporate, Public Company, Business Succession Planning, Employee Benefits & Executive Compensation, Corporate Governance, Corporate Finance, Business & Finance, Mergers & Acquisitions.
**Career:** Mr Greenberg is chair of the Mergers & Acquisitions practice. He advises corporations, LLCs and partnerships in general business and transactional matters, including M&A, venture capital, equipment leasing, project finance, bank loans, asset securitizations, leveraged buyouts, and public and private securities offerings.
**Personal:** Harvard Law School (1976); Dickinson College (1973).

## GRIFFITH, Calvin P
Jones Day, Cleveland
216 586 7050
cpgriffith@jonesday.com
*Featured in Intellectual Property (Ohio)*
**Practice Areas:** Trial attorney and counseling in all aspects of intellectual property matters. He has represented the following companies in intellectual property matters: Johnson & Johnson, DePuy Spine, Progressive Corporation, Canon, General Electric, Procter & Gamble, Eastman Kodak, Molten Metal Equipment, Lamson & Sessions, Bridgestone, The Firestone Tire & Rubber Co. and Martek Biosciences. Cal's technical training was in molecular genetics. In practice, he has worked with a wide array of technologies. As a lead trial attorney, Cal has won jury verdicts of $226 million, $52 million and $26 million in patent cases.

## GRIFFITH, Kevin
Porter Wright Morris & Arthur LLP, Columbus
614 227 2207
kgriffith@porterwright.com
*Featured in Labor & Employment (Ohio)*
**Career:** Mr Griffith focuses on employment and business competition litigation. He has defended hundreds of employment discrimination and wrongful termination cases, including seminal cases before the Ohio Supreme Court. He also has litigated hundreds of business competition cases, including corporate raiding and tortious interference claims, employment contract, trade secret, and covenant-not-to-compete claims. Mr Griffith

also counsels large corporations concerning mass layoffs, fraud investigations, executive employment contracts, severance agreements, and overall compliance with federal and state employment laws, including Dodd-Frank and SOX whistle-blower provisions, computer crime laws, Title VII, ADEA, ADAAA, and sexual harassment laws.

## GRIFFITH JR, Stephen M
Taft Stettinius & Hollister LLP, Cincinnati
513 357 9312
griffith@taftlaw.com
*Featured in Real Estate (Ohio)*
**Practice Areas:** Banking and Institutional Finance, Corporate Finance, Construction, State and Local Tax, Real Property.
**Career:** Mr Griffith is co-chair of the Real Estate group. He is primarily involved in the representation of lender, real property developer, investor, and corporate clients in various types of real property transactions, including acquisition, development, and zoning, zoning and land use litigation, construction contracts, design and engineering contracts, all forms of financing, real property loan workouts, retail, office and industrial leasing, and real property tax valuation proceedings.
**Personal:** College of William and Mary School of Law (1981); Northwestern University (1975).

## GROSSMAN, Theodore
Jones Day, Cleveland
216 586 7268
tgrossman@jonesday.com
*Featured in Products Liability (Nationwide), Litigation (Ohio)*
**Practice Areas:** Repeatedly cited as 'one of the nation's top litigators' by 'The National Law Journal' and called "America's top product liability attorney" by Japan's Nikkei newspapers, he has tried landmark cases and argued appeals in every section of the country. He has handled commercial and product liability litigation of all sorts, as well as constitutional and regulatory cases brought by or against virtually every federal department. He has been victorious lead counsel on behalf of all defendants in some of the largest class actions ever brought.
**Professional Memberships:** Fellow, American College of Trial Lawyers; Member, American Law Institute.

## GUINN, Guy
Squire Sanders (US) LLP, Cleveland
216 479 8360
guy.guinn@squiresanders.com
*Featured in Banking & Finance (Ohio)*
**Practice Areas:** Co-chair of Squire Sanders' Global Banking & Finance Practice Group. Focuses on US and cross-border leveraged commercial debt and real estate financings including mezzanine and second lien financings, asset based financings and note placements as well as related workouts and restructurings and debtor-in-possession and exit financings. Engagements as syndicate counsel and transaction counsel have involved a broad range of industries including manufacturing and industrial, retail, chemicals, transportation, mining and metals, energy and

renewable energy, international supply chain, technology, consumer, and construction products as well as public municipal and real estate development sectors.

## GUNSETT, Daniel J
Baker & Hostetler LLP, Columbus
614 462 2642
dgunsett@bakerlaw.com
*Featured in Natural Resources (Ohio)*
**Career:** Dan Gunsett's experience includes corporate counseling and environmental, class action and real estate litigation. He serves as general counsel for two electric cooperatives and general counsel for an integrated energy cooperative. For a number of years preceding a consolidation of airports, he served as general counsel for a port authority which operated a major airport facility in Columbus, Ohio, and developed major real estate resources for the airport. Dan has been on the Board of Directors of Greif, Inc., since 1996 and served on several Board committees. He also headed BakerHostetler's nationwide Energy and Environmental Practice for many years.

## GURBST, Richard
Squire Sanders (US) LLP, Cleveland
216 479 8607
richard.gurbst@squiresanders.com
*Featured in Litigation (Ohio)*

## GURNEY, Scott
Frost Brown Todd LLC, Cincinnati
513 651 6841
sgurney@fbtlaw.com
*Featured in Construction (Ohio)*
**Practice Areas:** Represents construction managers, general contractors, trade/specialty contractors, suppliers, sureties, and project owners in contract negotiation, risk management, and dispute resolution across Ohio, Kentucky, Indiana, Tennessee and West Virginia.
**Professional Memberships:** ABA Forum on the Construction Industry; ABA Committee on Construction Litigation; Past Chair of Cincinnati Bar Association Construction Law Committee; Allied Construction Industries (AGC- Cincinnati) Board of Directors (2008-09); AGC- Ohio Legislative Committee.
**Career:** Admitted to practice 1986. Elected Member Frost Brown Todd 1997.
**Publications:** Resolving Subcontractor Claims (Constructor Magazine).
**Personal:** Born 28 April 1961. JD Indiana University (Bloomington) 1986; BA Indiana University (Bloomington) 1983.

## GUTMACHER, Norman
Benesch, Friedlander, Coplan & Aronoff LLP, Cleveland
216 363 4591
ngutmacher@beneschlaw.com
*Featured in Real Estate (Ohio)*
**Practice Areas:** Commercial real estate, particularly real estate workouts, foreclosures, commercial leasing, acquisition, development and financing, wind farms, oil and gas leases, AIA contract matters.
**Professional Memberships:** Fellow of American College of Real Estate Lawyers (prior

Secretary, Co-Practice Technology Committee Co-Chair, Leasing Committee Chair, Executive Committee and Board of Governors member). Member of International Council of Shopping Centers.
**Career:** Represents national developers, restaurant chains and franchisees. Represents lenders and borrowers in workouts, foreclosures, construction and permanent financings. Advises on leasing, purchase and/or sale of local and regional shopping centers.
**Personal:** University of Cincinnati (JD, 1971); Ohio State University (BS, 1968).

## HAAS, Colleen
Frost Brown Todd LLC, Cincinnati
513 651 6414
chaas@fbtlaw.com
*Featured in Real Estate (Ohio)*
**Practice Areas:** Practice focuses on commercial real estate and construction financing. Includes use of new markets tax credits and historic tax credits to finance development in low-income communities. Chair of the firm's Community Outreach Committee.
**Professional Memberships:** Cincinnati, Ohio, and American Bar Associations; Commercial Real Estate Women (CREW).
**Career:** Admitted in Ohio and joined Frost & Jacobs (now Frost Brown Todd) in 1997. Elected to Member in 2009.
**Personal:** Originally from Los Angeles, California. Attended University of Notre Dame, BBA 1992 and Notre Dame Law School, JD 1997. Resides in Cincinnati, Ohio with her husband and three children.

## HAAS, Michael
Jones Day, Cleveland
216 586 1345
mjhaas@jonesday.com
*Featured in Real Estate (Ohio)*
**Practice Areas:** Represents clients in real estate, real estate finance, private equity, and real estate fund formation. Negotiates joint venture agreements and large portfolio transactions and counsels clients in relation to distressed assets and workouts and in connection with troubled joint ventures. Advises clients on the acquisition, disposition, leasing, and management of multifamily retail, industrial, office, and hotel properties. He is a frequent speaker on real estate and has been a guest commentator on Fox Business News.
**Professional Memberships:** Member of the International Council of Shopping Centers and the Cleveland Metropolitan Bar Association.

## HABEL, Christopher S
Frost Brown Todd LLC, Cincinnati
513 651 6993
chabel@fbtlaw.com
*Featured in Natural Resources (Ohio)*
**Practice Areas:** Chris Habel's practice is devoted to environmental, construction and hazardous materials transportation law. He counsels clients on a wide variety of environmental issues and represents them in environmental litigation. He conducts environmental audits and advises buyers, sellers, and lenders on environmental consid-

erations in real estate and corporate transactions. He is representing clients on complex brownfield redevelopment, ecosystem restoration and sustainable development projects. He applies his civil engineering and construction background that includes solid waste landfill design, and large scale industrial construction, to provide sound legal and technically-feasible solutions to client problems.

**HAGEN, Daniel C**
Jones Day, Cleveland
216 586 7159
dchagen@jonesday.com
*Featured in Employee Benefits & Executive Compensation (Ohio)*
**Practice Areas:** Chairs Jones Day's Employee Benefits and Executive Compensation Practice. He advises clients on all aspects of their executive compensation and employee benefits programs and in managing those programs through business and regulatory change. He handles senior level executives' employment agreements and severance arrangements, supplemental deferred compensation and retirement plans, and equity and other cash-based long-term incentive programs. Routinely handles benefits and compensation issues that arise in transactions including company mergers, tender offers, sales of large divisions, private equity fund leveraged buyouts, and joint ventures. Experienced in the personnel and employee benefits aspects of professional sports law as well.

**HANSELMAN, Suzanne K**
Baker & Hostetler LLP, Cleveland
216 861 7090
shanselman@bakerlaw.com
*Featured in Corporate/M&A (Ohio)*
**Career:** A member of the Securities and Corporate Governance Practice and Business Group Coordinator for BakerHostetler's Cleveland office, Suzanne Hanselman represents issuers, investors and underwriters in a variety of financings, including IPOs and other SEC-registered offerings, private placements of debt and equity and venture capital investments. She works with publicly held firm clients counseling on corporate governance and securities law compliance issues, including public disclosure and periodic reporting, executive compensation, proxy solicitations, shareholder proposals and transactions in issuer securities by officers and directors. Suzanne serves as an Adjunct Professor of securities and corporate law at Cleveland-Marshall College of Law.

**HARDIN, Charles**
Jones Day, Cleveland
216 586 7084
charleswhardin@jonesday.com
*Featured in Corporate/M&A (Ohio)*
**Practice Areas:** Chuck chairs Jones Day's worldwide Private Equity Practice. In over 25 years of practice, he has acted as principal outside lawyer on scores of completed PE and M&A transactions covering a wide range of matters across numerous industries. Representative private equity clients include The Riverside Company,

Brockway Moran & Partners, High Road Capital Partners, and Resilience Capital Partners, among others. He has also acted as lead lawyer in numerous high-profile strategic transactions, including International Steel Group's acquisition of Bethlehem Steel; Cooper Tire & Rubber's disposition of Cooper-Standard Automotive; and AssuraMed, Inc's. acquisition of Invacare Supply Group.

**HARDY, Michael L**
Thompson Hine LLP, Cleveland
216 566 5804
Mike.Hardy@ThompsonHine.com
*Featured in Natural Resources (Ohio)*
**Career:** Mike is a partner in Thompson Hine's Environmental Practice Group. His focus on environmental law began more than 35 years ago. While his primary work lies in environmental litigation, he also works extensively with clients in the development of business and strategic solutions to environmental problems arising from business transactions.

**HASTINGS, Kerry P**
Taft Stettinius & Hollister LLP, Cincinnati
513 357 9380
hastings@taftlaw.com
*Featured in Labor & Employment (Ohio)*
**Practice Areas:** Labor & Employment, Workplace Safety and Health, Appellate, Public Law, Construction.
**Professional Memberships:** Cincinnati Academy of Leadership for Lawyers (CALL) (Member, Class of 2006), Cincinnati Bar Association (Member, Labor and Employment Law Committee, Unauthorized Practice of Law Committee), DRI (Member).
**Career:** Mr Hastings represents employers in a broad range of labor and employment matters involving employment discrimination, sexual harassment, unfair labor practices, union organizing, contract negotiations, arbitrations, constitutional claims and other labor and employment related issues.
**Personal:** Harvard Law School (1996); University of Michigan (1993).

**HASTINGS, Susan C**
Squire Sanders (US) LLP, Cleveland
216 479 8723
susan.hastings@squiresanders.com
*Featured in Labor & Employment (Ohio)*
**Practice Areas:** Member, Squire Sanders Global Board; former chair, Squire Sanders' Labor and Employment Practice Group. Represents private and public sector employers in labor and employment matters including collective bargaining, arbitration, and federal and state agency proceedings. Significant experience in employment counseling and compliance training. Trial experience in federal and state courts. Represents boards of education in education law. Listed in The Best Lawyers in America and Ohio Super Lawyers.
**Professional Memberships:** American, Ohio State and Cleveland Metropolitan Bar Associations, Labor and Employment Law Sections; Ohio Council of School Board

Attorneys; National School Boards Association; Ohio Management Lawyers Association.

**HAUER, Richard**
Calfee, Halter & Griswold LLP, Cleveland
216 622 8430
rhauer@calfee.com
*Featured in Employee Benefits & Executive Compensation (Ohio)*
**Practice Areas:** Employee benefits; executive compensation.
**Professional Memberships:** Benefits Committee, US Chamber of Commerce.
**Career:** Chair, Employee Benefits and Executive Compensation Practice Group; Member, Executive Committee; advises employers, management, executives, boards of directors and compensation committees on current, deferred and change in control payment arrangements; experienced in compensation and benefits issues arising in business transactions including public and private equity fund deals and financially distressed and bankrupt businesses, including funding waivers, retention and post-bankruptcy executive compensation; special rabbi trust provisions.
**Personal:** Boston College, BA, magna cum laude, 1972; Case Western Reserve University School of Law, JD, Law Review Editor, 1975.

**HAUGHEY, Stephen N**
Frost Brown Todd LLC, Cincinnati
513 651 6127
shaughey@fbtlaw.com
*Featured in Natural Resources (Ohio)*
**Practice Areas:** Environmental, OSHA; representation in cleanup/compliance-related litigation, emphasis in Clean Water Act regulatory counseling, permitting, wetlands filling, rulemaking, enforcement defense and citizen suits. Involved in Superfund cleanups dating-back to Chem-Dyne litigation; public utilities planning, OSHA compliance counseling.
**Professional Memberships:** American, Ohio and Cincinnati Bar Associations; Sixth Circuit; Northern and Southern Districts of Ohio; Water Environment Federation; Ohio Water Association.
**Publications:** Best Lawyers 2003-13; Ohio Super Lawyers 2005-13; Past-Chair NKY and Greater Cincinnati Chambers of Commerce Environmental Committees; Chair 2010 & 2012 OSBA Environment, Energy and Resources Law Seminar.
**Personal:** JD University of Dayton; BS Environmental Health Wright State University.

**HAVENS, Jolie**
Vorys, Sater, Seymour and Pease LLP, Columbus
614 464 5429
jnhavens@vorys.com
*Featured in Healthcare (Ohio)*
**Practice Areas:** Partner specializing in hospital and physician contracting and alignment strategies, regulatory compliance and provider/supplier reimbursement (public and private payer). Routinely counsels providers of all types on day-to-day and complex healthcare issues. Also maintains an employee health benefits practice. Speaks

and publishes nationally on Affordable Care Act compliance and provider-based status.
**Professional Memberships:** American Health Lawyers Association.
**Career:** Ohio, Tennessee, Texas, US District Court for the Southern District of Ohio.
**Personal:** Ohio State University Michael E. Moritz College of Law, JD, with Honors, Ohio State Law Journal, Associate Editor, 2000; Ohio Wesleyan University, BA, magna cum laude, 1997.

**HAYES, Jeffrey**
Porter Wright Morris & Arthur LLP, Columbus
614 227 2261
jhayes@porterwright.com
*Featured in Real Estate (Ohio)*
**Career:** Mr Hayes, chair of the firm's Real Estate Practice Group, focuses on the areas of commercial real estate, general corporate and business law, with particular emphasis on mergers and acquisitions and other large transactions. He has negotiated and handled numerous purchases and sales of businesses, including financial institutions, utilities, manufacturing, service and technology businesses. He has represented developers in connection with the acquisition, financing, development and sale of large hospital, retail, office, commercial and residential real estate projects. Mr Hayes also counsels a wide range of clients on general corporate and transactional matters.

**HAYES, William D**
Frost Brown Todd LLC, Cincinnati
513 651 6827
whayes@fbtlaw.com
*Featured in Natural Resources (Ohio)*
**Practice Areas:** Partner, Environmental Group, Air Quality Issues.
**Professional Memberships:** Cincinnati (former Chair, Environmental Committee), Ohio State (Environmental Committee) Bar Associations; Air and Waste Management Association; Cincinnati Chamber of Commerce (Air Quality Committee); Ohio Small Business Clean Air Act Stationary Source Compliance Advisory Panel (appointed by Governor, former Chair); Southwest Ohio Air Quality Advisory Committee; Ohio EPA Permit Advisory Committee; Ohio Forestry Council.
**Career:** Ohio and US District Court, Southern District of Ohio (1986). Managing Attorney, Air and Water Divisions, Ohio EPA (1986-91).
**Personal:** Vermont Law School, LLM-Climate Change, 2012; Capital University, JD, 1986; Denison University, BA, 1983.

**HEAREY, Bruce G**
Ogletree, Deakins, Nash, Smoak & Stewart, PC, Cleveland
216 357 4734
bruce.hearey@ogletreedeakins.com
*Featured in Labor & Employment (Ohio)*
**Practice Areas:** Employment and Commercial Litigation. Advised clients on employment issues and handled numerous trials for 30 years in and outside of Ohio.
**Professional Memberships:** American Employment Law Council, Cleveland Bar

Association President-Elect, Manos Inn of Court, College of Labor and Employment Lawyers.

**Career:** Admitted Ohio, New Jersey, New York, California, US Supreme Court. Best Lawyers in America (Cleveland Labor & Employment Lawyer of Year 2013).

**Personal:** Wesleyan University (1972), Fordham University (JD, 1975), Leadership Cleveland, 1999.

### HEIMAN, David G
Jones Day, Cleveland
216 586 7175
dgheiman@jonesday.com

*Featured in Bankruptcy/Restructuring (Nationwide), Bankruptcy/Restructuring (Ohio)*

**Practice Areas:** Played a key role in many of the country's largest chapter 11 and out-of-court business restructuring matters, including, Chrysler LLC, Lehman Holdings, The Tribune Company, Federated Department Stores, Macy's, USG, Pillowtex, Burlington Industries, LTV Corporation, Oglebay Norton, Olympia & York, AHERF, Phar-Mor, Boscov's, Harry & David and multiple engagements for WL Ross & Co.

**Professional Memberships:** Chair, American College of Bankruptcy; American College of Commercial Finance Lawyers; American Bar Association (Past Chair, Commercial Financial Services); Editorial Advisory Board of the Journal of Bankruptcy Law and Practice; BTI Client Service All-Star.

### HELMREICH, Richard J
Porter Wright Morris & Arthur LLP, Columbus
614 227 2088
rhelmreich@porterwright.com

*Featured in Employee Benefits & Executive Compensation (Ohio)*

**Career:** Mr Helmreich counsels clients on business issues, including strategic growth initiatives, merger and acquisition opportunities and corporate finance prospects. As Chair of Porter Wright's Employee Benefits Practice Group, he advises employers on a range of employee benefit plan issues, including tax-qualified retirement plans, health and welfare plans, nonqualified plans, executive compensation arrangements, and equity-based incentive programs. He has substantial experience in mergers and acquisitions and securities laws related to employee benefit plans and has negotiated comprehensive covenants, representations and warranties in asset purchase and stock purchase agreements as well as performed due diligence of employee benefit plan liability issues.

### HESS, W Ashley
Baker & Hostetler LLP, Cincinnati
513 852 2621
ahess@bakerlaw.com

*Featured in Corporate/M&A (Ohio)*

**Career:** Ashley Hess is a partner in the Business Transactions Group and regularly advises clients on a full range of corporate matters, with an emphasis on middle-market mergers and acquisitions, joint ventures and private capital investments. Mr Hess's M&A experience includes stock, asset and merger transactions for public and private companies and advising privately-held busi-

ness owners on sell-side engagements, including pre-sale due diligence preparation and auction processes. Mr Hess has done transactional work in a wide range of industries, including automotive, healthcare, online media and multi-unit franchised restaurants. Additionally, Mr Hess has advised clients on large manufacturing joint venture deals.

### HIGGINS, John
Frost Brown Todd LLC, Columbus
513 651 6950
jhiggins@fbtlaw.com

*Featured in Construction (Ohio)*

**Practice Areas:** John Higgins specializes in national complex construction litigation and disaster projects. John's representation includes secured interests / priority disputes, in-house training, risk management, bidding issues, contract disputes, mechanics' liens and payment disputes, surety bond matters, delay and defect claims, and mediation.

**Professional Memberships:** Member, ABA Forum on Construction Industry; ABA Committee on Construction Litigation; Cincinnati Bar Association; Cincinnati Academy of Leadership for Lawyers; Ohio State Bar Association.

**Personal:** JD, cum laude, Cleveland Marshall College of Law at Cleveland State University; BS, cum laude, University of Cincinnati. Admitted to United States Supreme Court.

### HILL, James M
Benesch, Friedlander, Coplan & Aronoff LLP, Cleveland
216 363 4444
jhill@beneschlaw.com

*Featured in Corporate/M&A (Ohio)*

**Practice Areas:** Primarily handles mergers and acquisitions, public and private offerings of equity, and public and private offerings of debt. Represents private equity firms and hedge funds, mezzanine funds and publicly and privately held growth companies. Sits on numerous boards of directors as strategic advisor.

**Career:** Executive Chairman of the firm, Chair of the Private Equity Group and an active and practicing member of the firm's Corporate and Securities Practice Group. Member of the Executive Committee and past Managing Partner of the firm from 1999-2007.

**Personal:** Yale Law School (JD, 1978); University of Iowa (BS, summa cum laude, 1975).

### HURLEY, Timothy J
Taft Stettinius & Hollister LLP, Cincinnati
513 357 9341
hurley@taftlaw.com

*Featured in Bankruptcy/Restructuring (Ohio)*

**Practice Areas:** Banking and Institutional Finance, Litigation, Business Restructuring and Creditor Rights, Bankruptcy.

**Career:** Mr Hurley is co-chair of the Business Restructuring, Bankruptcy and Creditor Rights group. He has represented debtors, creditors, committees, indenture trustees, buyers, landlords, insurance companies and executors both in out-of-court work-out agreements and restructurings

and in Chapter 11 cases throughout the United States. These representations encompass all types of complex transactions and litigation involving financially-distressed businesses and assets.

**Personal:** St. Louis University School of Law (1976); Xavier University (1973).

### HUTCHINSON JR, Joseph F
Baker & Hostetler LLP, Cleveland
216 861 7701
jhutchinson@bakerlaw.com

**Career:** National Chair of BakerHostetler's Bankruptcy, Restructuring and Creditors' Rights Group, Joe Hutchinson concentrates his practice on commercial and bankruptcy law. He represents debtors, creditors' committees, trustees, the FDIC and secured lenders in large chapter 11 cases. He also specializes in commercial litigation involving contract disputes, constructive fraud, fraud recovery and failed LBOs. Joe has lectured extensively on bankruptcy and commercial law, as well as lender liability and fraudulent transfer issues. He is a member of the Akron, Cleveland Metropolitan, Ohio State and American Bar Associations, and past president of the Turnaround Management Association (Ohio Chapter).

### HUTTON, Lee J
Littler Mendelson, PC, Cleveland
216 696 6140
LHutton@littler.com

*Featured in Labor & Employment (Ohio)*

**Practice Areas:** Competition and Trade Secret Law, Complex Litigation and Jury Trials, Whistleblowing and Retaliation, Hiring, Performance Management and Termination, Wage and Hour.

**Professional Memberships:** Founder and Former President, Cleveland Employment Inn of Court; Member, American Bar Association; Member, Ohio State Bar Association.

**Career:** Lee J. Hutton has defended employers for more than thirty years, litigating, trying cases to verdict, and defending trial outcomes on appeal. Lee also provides practical solutions, strategic advice and compliance guidance in all traditional areas of employment law.

**Personal:** JD, University of Michigan, magna cum laude, 1975; AB, Ohio University, summa cum laude, 1972.

### IRELAND, D Jeffrey
Faruki Ireland & Cox PLL, Dayton
937 227 3710
djireland@ficlaw.com

*Featured in Litigation (Ohio)*

**Practice Areas:** Competitive litigation, including false advertising, trademarks and trade secrets; antitrust; employment; products liability; class actions and complex commercial cases.

**Professional Memberships:** American Bar Association; Ohio State Bar Association (Board of Governors, Antitrust Section); Dayton Bar Association; Cincinnati Bar Association; International Society of Barristers.

**Career:** 1980-89, Smith & Schnacke (Partner, 1987-89); Founding Partner, Faruki Ireland & Cox

PLL, 1989 to present; selected as Ohio Super Lawyer 2004-present in poll of all Ohio lawyers and 'Best of the Bar' in poll of Dayton lawyers.

**Publications:** Has lectured and written on all aspects of commercial litigation.

**Personal:** University of Dayton, College of Law (1980); Denison University (1976).

### IRWIN, Kevin E
Keating Muething & Klekamp PLL, Cincinnati
513 579 6426
kirwin@kmklaw.com

*Featured in Bankruptcy/Restructuring (Ohio)*

**Practice Areas:** Mr Irwin's practice is focused on the representation of parties in large mass tort bankruptcy proceedings. He heads a practice group that represents court-supervised, mass tort settlement trusts through-out the nation. His trust clients are among the largest settlement trusts in the country. He also represents creditor committees and court appointed representatives of future claimants in major mass tort bankruptcy proceedings. He regularly appears in bankruptcy courts throughout the United States.

**Personal:** JD, Cleveland-Marshall College of Law, 1977; magna cum laude, Law Review Executive Editor. BS, Miami University, 1973.

### JACKSON, Reginald W
Vorys, Sater, Seymour and Pease LLP, Columbus
614 464 5621
rwjackson@vorys.com

*Featured in Bankruptcy/Restructuring (Ohio)*

**Practice Areas:** Partner in the bankruptcy, workout and restructuring areas with emphasis on representing secured creditors, suppliers, franchisors, creditors' committees and debtors in Chapter 11 reorganization proceedings and workouts.

**Professional Memberships:** American Bankruptcy Institute (President, 2007-08, Board of Directors; Executive Committee; and former editor of the 'ABI Journal'), Columbus (former Chair, Bankruptcy Committee) and Ohio State (Member, Board of Governors, 2003-07) Bar Associations, Ohio State Bar Foundation (former President), American College of Bankruptcy (Fellow).

**Career:** Admitted to Ohio (1980).

**Personal:** Cornell University, BA, 1977; University of Pennsylvania Law School, JD, 1980.

### JENKINS, John
Calfee, Halter & Griswold LLP, Cleveland
216 622 8507
jjenkins@calfee.com

*Featured in Corporate/M&A (Ohio)*

**Practice Areas:** Securities; corporate; mergers and acquisitions.

**Professional Memberships:** American Bar Association.

**Career:** Partner in Securities and Capital Markets Group and member of the firm's Executive Committee. Represents issuers and underwriters in securities offerings and has extensive experience in corporate governance, mergers and acquisitions and representation of investment bankers. Also represents corporations and individuals in SEC

investigations. Teaches mergers and acquisitions law at Cleveland - Marshall College of Law.
**Personal:** The University of Virginia School of Law, JD, 1986; Canisius College, BA, magna cum laude, 1983.

### JOHNSON, Mark A
Baker & Hostetler LLP, Columbus
614 462 2698
mjohnson@bakerlaw.com
*Featured in Litigation (Ohio)*
**Career:** Mark Johnson has extensive experience defending complex class action lawsuits against a wide variety of businesses, having handled more than 70 class actions in state and federal courts across the country. Mark develops hands-on strategies to attack class certification, including measures to defeat class allegations early to limit costly discovery. He has the experience and resources available to leverage technology to manage the massive data typically involved in defending class actions. Mark is a frequent author and presenter on class actions and emerging trends in class certification to legislators, trade groups, corporate counsel, lawyers and law students.

### JONES, Christopher
Calfee, Halter & Griswold LLP, Columbus
614 621 7004
cjones@calfee.com
*Featured in Natural Resources (Ohio)*
**Practice Areas:** Environmental, government relations.
**Professional Memberships:** Former: President, Environmental Council of the States; Chairman, Lake Erie Commission; Member, Great Lakes Commission. Current: Board of Directors, Environmental Research Institute of the States; Nature Conservancy Board of Trustees, Ohio Chapter (Chair); Board of Directors, Greater Ohio Policy Center (Chair); Ohio and Columbus Bar Associations.
**Career:** Senior Counsel, Environmental and Government Groups. Former Director of Ohio Environmental Protection Agency and Chief of Ohio Attorney General's Environmental Enforcement Section; listed in Best Lawyers in America. AV Preeminent Rating from Martindale-Hubbell.
**Personal:** Georgetown University Law Center, JD, 1990; Ohio Wesleyan University, BA, 1979.

### KADISH, Scott P
Ulmer & Berne LLP, Cincinnati
513 698 5051
skadish@ulmer.com
*Featured in Real Estate (Ohio)*
**Practice Areas:** Chairing the firm's Shopping Center Group, Scott maintains the skills and expertise needed to represent landlords and tenants in the development and lease up of shopping centers on a national basis. He also counsels clients on a wide variety of real estate and business transactions, and general business law. Scott brings his leadership to the firm's Cincinnati office where he serves as partner-in-charge, overseeing its operations, business development, and client relationships. Scott also serves as a member of the firm's Management Committee.

### KAHLE, Thomas W
Baker & Hostetler LLP, Cincinnati
513 929 3414
tkahle@bakerlaw.com
*Featured in Healthcare (Ohio)*
**Career:** Thomas Kahle's practice has been focused on the transactional and financing needs of nonprofit providers for more than 35 years. He previously served as co-leader of BakerHostetler's Healthcare Industry Team. His experience includes coordinating the legal representation of healthcare entities in affiliation, purchase and sale transactions, including strategic planning and Board counseling; coordinating the consolidation of multiple academic physician practice plans into a single multi-specialty practice plan; coordinating general legal representation of hospitals, long-term care facilities, physician groups, senior living organizations and other providers of healthcare, medical and dental services and special borrower's and underwriter's counsel on healthcare financings.

### KAHN, Ronald L
Ulmer & Berne LLP, Cleveland
216 583 7018
rkahn@ulmer.com
*Featured in Employee Benefits & Executive Compensation (Ohio)*
**Practice Areas:** With over 30 years of experience, Ron's practice includes employee benefits (including ESOPs and IRAs), executive and incentive compensation, ERISA litigation (including MPPAA withdrawal liability assessments), employment and labor, nonprofit, succession planning, business, tax, health care transactions, and estate planning. Ron advises businesses of all sizes on the design and maintenance of employee pension and welfare benefit programs including guidance regarding fiduciary responsibility, prohibited transactions, and unrelated business income tax (UBIT) in connection with IRS and DOL exams.
**Professional Memberships:** The ESOP Association, The National Center of Employee Ownership, and Worldwide Employee Benefits Network (WEB).

### KALLAS, Hani R
Vorys, Sater, Seymour and Pease LLP, Cincinnati
513 723 4615
hrkallas@vorys.com
*Featured in Banking & Finance (Ohio)*
**Practice Areas:** Partner in the Commercial and Real Estate Group that practices in the areas of banking law, commercial law, general business law, and real estate law. Concentrates in the representation of lenders in complex financing transactions, with an emphasis on representing lenders in cash flow, asset-based and mezzanine loan originations.
**Career:** Admitted in Ohio (1994).
**Personal:** University of Cincinnati College of Law, JD, Order of the Coif, 1994. Miami University, BA, cum laude, 1991.

### KAPLAN, Ira C
Benesch, Friedlander, Coplan & Aronoff LLP, Cleveland
216 363 4567
ikaplan@beneschlaw.com
*Featured in Corporate/M&A (Ohio)*
**Practice Areas:** Represents private equity, subordinated debt and venture funds and portfolio companies of such funds. Focuses on mergers and acquisitions, public and private debt and equity financings. Represents publicly and privately held companies at various stages of growth and plans for growth companies, positioning them for private financing and anticipated public offerings.
**Career:** Managing Partner of firm and Member of Executive Committee. Member of firm's Polymer Group as well as the Diversity Initiative Committee. Past Co-Chair of firm's Corporate & Securities and Private Equity Groups.
**Personal:** The George Washington University Law School (JD, 1979); University of Rochester (BA, 1976).

### KAPP, Jeffrey L
Jones Day, Cleveland
216 586 7230
jlkapp@jonesday.com
*Featured in Healthcare (Ohio)*
**Practice Areas:** Jeff Kapp practices in the area of health care transactions and has substantial experience in mergers and acquisitions and various types of joint ventures, affiliations, and outsourcing transactions. Jeff also counsels various health providers and companies regarding compliance issues. Jeff's outsourcing practice focuses on negotiating and drafting customer-side transactions for information technology, benefit plan administration, and other administrative services.
**Professional Memberships:** Jeff is a member of American Health Lawyers Association and serves as a Vice Chair for the AHLA's Business Law and Governance Practice Group. He serves as president of the Society of Ohio Healthcare Attorneys.

### KARP, Marvin L
Ulmer & Berne LLP, Cleveland
216 583 7014
mkarp@ulmer.com
*Featured in Litigation (Ohio)*
**Practice Areas:** Partner and Chair Emeritus of the firm's Litigation Department, Marvin has over 50 years of trial and appellate experience in business, corporate, and insurance litigation. Marvin received the American ORT Jurisprudence Award for his contributions to the legal profession and the community, the Ohio State Bar Association's highest honor, The Ohio Bar Medal for "unusually meritorious service to the legal profession and the community," and the American Bar Association's 2010 Michael Franck Professional Responsibility Award.

### KARZMER, Steve
Calfee, Halter & Griswold LLP, Cleveland
*Featured in Corporate/M&A (Ohio)*
**Practice Areas:** General Corporate; Private Equity; Mergers and Acquisitions; Securities and Capital Markets; Information Technology.

**Professional Memberships:** Center for Entrepreneurship at The Ohio State University Fisher School of Business Advisory Board; Reservoir Ventures Partners II Advisory Board. New York, Massachusetts, Ohio and Columbus Bar Associations.
**Career:** Steve counsels clients regarding mergers and acquisitions, venture capital and private equity investments, mezzanine debt financings and business formation issues, particularly using limited liability companies; serves as outside general counsel to a number of private companies; and represents buyers and sellers of businesses in various transactions, including asset purchases, stock purchase, and mergers.

### KEIPER, Jeffrey B
Jackson Lewis LLP, Cleveland
216 750 4308
Jeffrey.Keiper@jacksonlewis.com
*Featured in Labor & Employment (Ohio)*
**Practice Areas:** Management side employment litigation, traditional labor law, counseling and training. Employment discrimination/retaliation/harassment claims under Title VII, ADEA, ADA, FMLA; labor arbitration; EEOC and NLRB charges; reductions-in-force.
**Professional Memberships:** American, Cleveland and Ohio State Bar Associations (Labor/Employment and Litigation Sections).
**Career:** Jones Day (Associate); McDonald Hopkins Co., LPA (Associate 1998-2000, Shareholder 2000-06); Jackson Lewis, LLP, Partner and Litigation Manager of Cleveland Office (2006 to present).
**Personal:** The Ohio State University Moritz College of Law, JD, with Honors and Law Journal, 1992; Indiana University, MA (English), 1989; The College of Wooster, BA, Phi Beta Kappa, Departmental Honors (1986).

### KELLER, John
Vorys, Sater, Seymour and Pease LLP, Columbus
614 464 6389
jkeller@vorys.com
*Featured in Natural Resources (Ohio)*
**Practice Areas:** A partner who provides general business representation, primarily to persons engaged in natural resources industries. He has significant experience in operational issues, real estate, litigation and arbitration, acquisitions, zoning, banking, and business planning. He acted as lead trial counsel in gas contract arbitration against a Fortune 100 company resulting in an award of more than $100 million.
**Professional Memberships:** Ohio and Columbus Bar Associations; Energy and Mineral Law Foundation; Rocky Mountain Mineral Law Foundation; Mountain States Legal Foundation.
**Career:** Ohio.
**Personal:** Duke University School of Law, JD, 1975; Indiana University, AB, 1972.

### KELLOGG, Amy E
Baker & Hostetler LLP, Cleveland
216 861 7982
akellogg@bakerlaw.com
*Featured in Real Estate (Ohio)*

**Career:** National co-chair of BakerHostetler's Real Estate Practice Group and Real Estate Practice Area Coordinator for the Cleveland office, Amy Kellogg is a problem-solver, offering clients creative solutions and assistance in helping them reach their goals concerning real estate ownership, leasing or expansion of current facilities. Known as an attorney who can get the deal done, she takes the mystery out of the real estate process and efficiently brings a transaction to its desired conclusion. Amy partners closely with clients, helping them through a variety of different real estate issues, effectively coping with challenges posed throughout the process.

## KELLY, Brian
Frantz Ward LLP, Cleveland
216 515 1620
bkelly@frantzward.com
*Featured in Labor & Employment (Ohio)*

**Practice Areas:** Partner with 16 years of experience counseling and representing employers before federal and state courts, administrative agencies, and labor and employment arbitrators in all facets of employment law in matters ranging from discrimination and harassment issues to overtime, non-compete and wrongful discharge cases. He has also successfully represented employers in union arbitrations, contract negotiations and strike situations. Routinely counsels employers on employee policies and manuals and on day to day employment issues.

## KESSLER, Elizabeth P
Jones Day, Columbus
614 281 3852
ekessler@jonesday.com
*Featured in Litigation (Ohio)*

**Practice Areas:** Liza Kessler has extensive experience in complex litigation with a particular focus on nationwide product liability cases. Her experience includes defending manufacturers of medical devices, cigarettes, recreational vehicles, paints, and chemicals. She appears in state and federal courts throughout the US and coordinates the defense for clients with co-defendants in joint defense groups. Liza's experience includes defending companies from allegations of environmental exposures leading to complex diseases, off-road vehicle injury litigation, and consumer litigation, including serving as lead counsel in mortgage servicing class actions involving issues ranging from claimed credit disparagement to consumer fraud.

## KESSLER, Marc
Hahn Loeser & Parks LLP, Columbus
614 233 5168
mjkessler@hahnlaw.com
*Featured in Litigation (Ohio)*

**Practice Areas:** Mr Kessler is chair of the litigation department in, and managing partner of, the firm's Columbus office. His practice is focused in business litigation, with an emphasis on complex commercial transactions, securities, business torts, real estate, product liability, construction, sports facilities, insurance, bankruptcy, health care and aviation issues. Mr Kessler provides strategic busi-

ness counsel to numerous large corporations headquartered in the Midwest.
**Professional Memberships:** Vice Chair, Certification of Attorneys as Specialists, Ohio Supreme Court Commission.
**Personal:** Capital Law School (JD, 1992), Dickinson College (BA, cum laude, 1989).

## KESTNER, R Steven
Baker & Hostetler LLP, Cleveland
216 861 7558
skestner@bakerlaw.com
*Featured in Corporate/M&A (Ohio)*

**Career:** As Executive Partner of Baker & Hostetler LLP, Steve Kestner serves as the firm's Chief Executive Officer, chairing all meetings of the Policy Committee—the governing body of the firm. Since joining the firm, Steve's leadership roles have included serving as a Policy Committee Member and Chair of BakerHostetler's national Business Group, while developing an active legal practice focusing primarily on transactions, financings and securities law. Steve advises and represents clients in domestic and foreign mergers and acquisitions and regularly works with public and private companies, private equity and venture capital firms, and emerging companies in obtaining venture capital financing.

## KIM, Eduardo
Thompson Hine LLP, Cleveland
216 566 5948
Eduardo.Kim@ThompsonHine.com
*Featured in Banking & Finance (Ohio)*

**Career:** Eduardo is a partner in the firm's Commercial & Public Finance Practice Group. He focuses his practice on commercial lending, representing banks and other financial institutions, and also private equity firms. Eduardo has significant experience with syndicated, multi-bank senior credit facilities, asset based and structured finance facilities, acquisition financing, and financing transactions involving multiple foreign jurisdictions and currencies. Prior to joining the Commercial & Public Finance Practice Group, Eduardo was a member of the Bankruptcy Practice Group.

## KINCAID JR, Robert M
Baker & Hostetler LLP, Columbus
614 462 4734
rkincaid@bakerlaw.com
*Featured in Litigation (Ohio)*

**Career:** A Fellow of the American College of Trial Lawyers, Robert Kincaid has broad experience in civil litigation, particularly in business and commercial litigation, fiduciary and trust litigation and employment litigation. His experience includes more than 38 civil jury trials to verdict. Rob has represented individuals and corporations in federal and state courts in 17 states in cases alleging breach of contract, fraud, breach of fiduciary duties by joint venturers, partners, officers, directors and shareholders. His representation includes both plaintiffs and defendants. Rob has been recognized by Chambers USA, Best Lawyers® (Bet-the-Company Litigation, Commercial Litigation and Fiduciary Litigation) and Super Lawyers®.

## KING, Roger
Jones Day, Columbus
614 281 3874
rking@jonesday.com
*Featured in Healthcare (Ohio), Labor & Employment (Ohio)*

**Practice Areas:** Labor and Employment Relations Practice, representing management in National Labor Relations Act, state and federal equal employment statutes, the Americans with Disabilities Act, the Family and Medical Leave Act, the Fair Labor Standards Act, Office of Federal Contract Compliance, employment contract, and covenant-not-to-compete matters. Represents employers in collective bargaining negotiations, grievance and arbitration matters, and labor and employment-related litigation in state and federal trial and appellate courts.
**Professional Memberships:** Fellow of The College of Labor and Employment Lawyers; SHRM; ASHHRA; ABA Labor Law Section; Labor Counsel HR Policy Association.
**Publications:** Contributing editor, HR advisor.

## KING, Scott A
Thompson Hine LLP, Dayton
937 443 6560
Scott.King@ThompsonHine.com
*Featured in Litigation (Ohio)*

**Career:** Scott is a partner in the firm's Business Litigation group. He focuses his practice on representing financial institutions, mortgage servicers and corporations in all forms of commercial litigation, including consumer class action defense, creditors' rights, lender liability and breach of fiduciary duty, commercial collection and foreclosure, as well as warranty, sales and intellectual property litigation. Scott is admitted to practice before Ohio courts, United States District Courts for the Southern and Northern Districts of Ohio and Eastern and Western Districts of Michigan, United States Circuit Courts of Appeal for the Fifth, Sixth and Federal Circuits, and United States Supreme Court.

## KIRCHICK, Ross
Benesch, Friedlander, Coplan & Aronoff LLP, Cleveland
216 363 4449
rkirchick@beneschlaw.com
*Featured in Banking & Finance (Ohio)*

**Practice Areas:** Bank and lender representation in senior and subordinated debt transactions, and borrower representation including for-profit and not-for-profit borrowers. Loan transactions experience includes healthcare lending, letters of credit and bond financings, syndications, asset-based lending, venture capital transactions and other leveraged buyout transactions, loan maintenance and modifications, and workouts and recapitalization.
**Career:** Chairman of the Commercial Finance and Banking Group and member of the Corporate and Securities Group.
**Personal:** Ohio State University (JD, with honors, 2000); University of Michigan (BA, with great distinction, 1996).

## KIRKWOOD, Thomas J
Thompson Hine LLP, Cincinnati
513 352 6728
Tom.Kirkwood@ThompsonHine.com
*Featured in Construction (Ohio)*

**Career:** Tom has handled private and public sector construction transactions and claims litigation for owners, developers, designers, CMs, and contractors since 1974. He has served as special counsel to such major developments as Cincinnati's $600 million Banks riverfront project. As a consultant in the firm's Project Management Consultants ancillary business, he has more than 130 construction disputes and has provided field level consulting to more than 150 projects with budgets totaling more than $7 billion.

## KIRSCH, Kevin W
Baker & Hostetler LLP, Cincinnati
513 929 3499
kkirsch@bakerlaw.com
*Featured in Intellectual Property (Ohio)*

**Career:** Kevin Kirsch has represented companies in more than 100 patent litigation matters and has testified before and advised members of the United States House of Representatives on various proposed patent reform legislative initiatives. A registered patent attorney, licensed to practice before the United States Patent & Trademark Office, Kevin is the primary author of the Patent Local Rules for the Southern District of Ohio, implemented in June 2010. He has been listed in Best Lawyers in America, rated AV® Preeminent in Intellectual Property law by Martindale-Hubbell and named an Ohio "Super Lawyer" in Intellectual Property Litigation.

## KNOTH, Richard M
Baker & Hostetler LLP, Cleveland
216 861 7412
rknoth@bakerlaw.com
*Featured in Litigation (Ohio)*

**Career:** Dick Knoth practices in the areas of complex commercial litigation, competition and intellectual property law. He has a wealth of trial experience on behalf of national and international companies in both jury and bench cases in federal and state courts throughout the United States. Dick has also argued many appellate cases throughout the federal and state courts. Given the breadth of his trial experience, Dick and his team are often also called upon to represent companies undergoing governmental investigations in many areas including advertising, trade practices, antitrust and corporate governance.

## KNUEVE, Mark
Vorys, Sater, Seymour and Pease LLP, Columbus
614 464 6387
maknueve@vorys.com
*Featured in Labor & Employment (Ohio)*

**Practice Areas:** Partner representing employers in complex wage and hour class actions and collective actions.
**Professional Memberships:** Veterans Consortium Pro Bono Program, 2002-present; Volunteer for numerous pro bono projects.

**Career:** Ohio (1996); US Court of Appeals for the Sixth, Eighth and Eleventh Circuits; US District Court, Eastern District of Michigan; US District Court, Northern and Southern Districts of Ohio; US District Court, Western District of Wisconsin; US District Court, Middle District of Florida; US District Court, District of Colorado; US Court of Appeals for Veterans Claims.
**Personal:** University of Virginia School of Law, JD, 1996; University of Virginia, BA, 1993.

### KOHNEN, Ralph
Taft Stettinius & Hollister LLP, Cincinnati
513 357 9618
kohnen@taftlaw.com
*Featured in Litigation (Ohio)*
**Practice Areas:** Antitrust, Securities - Litigation, FCPA and International Anti-Corruption, White Collar Criminal Defense.
**Professional Memberships:** Cincinnati Bar Association, Judicial Advisory Commission, Northern District of Ohio, Kentucky Bar Association, National Association of Criminal Defense Lawyers.
**Career:** Mr Kohnen is Chair of the White Collar Criminal Defense Practice. He spent much of his career in the United States Attorney's Office for the Southern District of Ohio as a federal prosecutor and then as Deputy Criminal Chief in charge of the criminal side of the US Attorney's Cincinnati office.
**Personal:** University of Cincinnati College of Law (1986); Ohio Wesleyan University (1983).

### KOLESAR, Andrew L
Thompson Hine LLP, Cincinnati
513 352 6545
Andrew.Kolesar@ThompsonHine.com
*Featured in Natural Resources (Ohio)*
**Career:** Andrew leads the Environmental Practice and co-chairs the Climate Change and Sustainable Business Solutions Group. He represents companies in matters across the US involving the defense of environmental enforcement actions, environmental litigation, permitting, and environmental, health and safety compliance matters; assisting with cleanups under state and federal programs; counseling on corporate, real estate transactions and brownfields development; and developing proactive environmental compliance programs. Andrew received his JD, cum laude, from Georgetown University, where he was a law and economics Olin Fellow and associate editor of the law journal. Before becoming a lawyer, Andrew worked as an environmental engineer.

### KOOGLER, Mark
Porter Wright Morris & Arthur LLP, Columbus
614 227 2133
mkoogler@porterwright.com
*Featured in Corporate/M&A (Ohio)*
**Career:** Mr Koogler is the firm's Mergers and Acquisition Practice Group leader. His extensive M&A experience includes the representation of publicly and privately held businesses and special committees. He has been lead counsel in approximately 100 M&A transactions of numerous forms in a wide range of industries, including insurance, asset management, manufacturing, pharmaceuti-

cal, hotels and restaurants. These transactions, including some of the most complex transactions in the insurance industry, have an aggregate value in excess of $9 billion. Mr Koogler regularly counsels businesses on general corporate matters, including corporate governance, compliance and general business matters.

### KOZLOWSKI, Holly D
Porter Wright Morris & Arthur LLP, Cincinnati
513 369 4224
hkozlowski@porterwright.com
*Featured in Intellectual Property (Ohio)*
**Career:** Ms Kozlowski's practice focuses on all stages of patent application preparation and prosecution, including reissue, reexamination, interference and patent term extension, and on trademark and copyright protection. She has extensive experience with international PCT and national foreign patent application filings and prosecution, including opposition proceedings around the world. Ms Kozlowski routinely provides inventor and corporate counseling on all patent-related issues including patentability, infringement, validity matters, related litigation and licensing matters. Her technical expertise includes organic and pharmaceutical chemistry, inorganic chemistry, polymer chemistry, biotechnology and chemical engineering and processing.

### KREIDER, Gary P
Keating Muething & Klekamp PLL, Cincinnati
513 579 6411
gkreider@kmklaw.com
*Featured in Corporate/M&A (Ohio)*
**Practice Areas:** Mr Kreider concentrates his practice in the areas of securities regulation compliance, public offerings, private offerings, mergers and acquisitions and business planning and formation.
**Personal:** JD, University of Cincinnati College of Law, 1964. MA, University of Cincinnati, 1961. BA, University of Cincinnati, 1960; with honors.

### KREIDER, Kenneth
Keating Muething & Klekamp PLL, Cincinnati
513 579 6579
kpkreider@kmklaw.com
*Featured in Real Estate (Ohio)*
**Practice Areas:** Mr Kreider helps business clients structure and close transactions involving the acquisition, development, finance or disposition of real estate. His diverse experience with tenant in common syndications, complex IRC 1031 transactions, real estate taxation, building and preservation code matters, and rail/utility rights of way is instrumental in achieving superior results in a variety of client transactions. He leads the KMK Green Team which focuses on sustainable building practices, related incentives, and climate change issues.
**Personal:** JD, University of Cincinnati College of Law, 1989; cum laude, Executive Editor, University of Cincinnati Law Review. BA, Kenyon College, 1986; cum laude.

### LAING, Michael
Taft Stettinius & Hollister LLP, Cincinnati
513 357 9385
laing@taftlaw.com
*Featured in Employee Benefits & Executive Compensation (Ohio)*
**Practice Areas:** Health and life sciences, employee benefits and executive compensation.
**Professional Memberships:** American Bar Association, American College of Employee Benefits Counsel.
**Career:** Mr Laing represents clients who maintain broad-based retirement plans, group welfare plans, and fringe benefit arrangements for their rank-and-file employees, as well as stock-based incentive plans, non-qualified deferred compensation plans, and other perquisites provided to executives. He is a Fellow of the American College of Employee Benefits Counsel and is a trustee of the Southern Federal Tax Institute.
**Personal:** University of Alabama School of Law (1986); University of Florida (1987); Auburn University (1983).

### LARDAKIS, Terry
Fisher & Phillips LLP, Cleveland
440 838 8800
tlardakis@laborlawyers.com
*Featured in Labor & Employment (Ohio)*
**Career:** Terry Lardakis is a partner in the Cleveland office. He has extensive experience in the negotiation of collective bargaining agreements and the representation of employers in union organizational campaigns and elections. Terry has represented employers in traditional labor matters including arbitrations, union decertification, craft severance, and unfair labor practice litigation. He has also handled matters involving wage/hour, family/medical leave and disability issues, and employment litigation matters in federal and state courts. His practice also includes an emphasis on third-party avoidance programs. He has developed personnel practice programs concentrating on employee selection and manager training to help avoid litigation.

### LATOUR, Randall D
Vorys, Sater, Seymour and Pease LLP, Columbus
614 464 8290
rdlatour@vorys.com
*Featured in Bankruptcy/Restructuring (Ohio)*
**Practice Areas:** Partner focusing on bankruptcy, debtor/creditor, collection, commercial, secured lending, real estate and commercial litigation with emphasis on bankruptcy proceedings and workouts.
**Professional Memberships:** Columbus Bar Association.
**Career:** Admitted in Ohio (1987); US Court of Appeals 4th Circuit (1990); US Court of Appeals 6th Circuit (1994); US District Court for the Northern (1997) and Southern Districts of Ohio (1988).
**Personal:** The Ohio State University College of Law, JD, with Honors, 1987; The Ohio State University, BA, with Honors, 1977.

### LAUTZENHISER, Roger
Vorys, Sater, Seymour and Pease LLP, Columbus
513 723 4091
relautzenhis@vorys.com
*Featured in Corporate/M&A (Ohio)*
**Practice Areas:** Partner in corporate/finance group focused on the representation of public and private companies in federal and state securities regulation, corporate law and governance, corporate financing and insurance law. Works with public companies on corporate reporting and disclosure; securities offerings; corporate governance and regulatory compliance; executive compensation; mergers and acquisitions; and financing and risk management. Has represented providers of capital(private equity and venture firms) and companies receiving such capital and has participated in financing and M&A transactions in a wide range of industries.
**Personal:** University of California at Los Angeles School of Law, JD; Stanford University, AB.

### LAWNICZAK, James
Calfee, Halter & Griswold LLP, Cleveland
216 622 8364
jlawniczak@calfee.com
*Featured in Bankruptcy/Restructuring (Ohio)*
**Practice Areas:** Bankruptcy, bankruptcy litigation and creditors' rights; commercial business and finance.
**Professional Memberships:** Member, former trustee of Cleveland Metropolitan Bar Association (2005-09), Chair of its Bankruptcy and Commercial Law Section (2003-04). Member, former trustee and committee Chair of Northern Ohio Chapter of Turnaround Management Association. Member, Finance Committee, Cleveland Legal Aid Society.
**Career:** Partner. Handles all aspects of corporate bankruptcy, workout proceedings. Represents secured and unsecured creditors, debtors, unsecured creditors committees.
**Publications:** Contributing author to Collier on Bankruptcy, 16th edition; other Lexis treatises on bankruptcy and debtor-creditor law.
**Personal:** University of Michigan School of Law, magna cum laude, 1977.

### LAWSON, Margaret
Taft Stettinius & Hollister LLP, Cincinnati
513 357 9388
lawson@taftlaw.com
*Featured in Intellectual Property (Ohio)*
**Practice Areas:** Emerging Companies, International, Mergers & Acquisitions, Health & Life Sciences, Business Succession Planning, Business & Finance, Franchise and Distribution, Intellectual Property, Trademark, Copyright and Trade Secret.
**Career:** Ms Lawson is co-chair of the Intellectual Property group. She has extensive experience in drafting and negotiating license agreements, technology transfer agreements and other contracts in areas that include biomedical technology, computer software and hardware, e-commerce, publishing and franchising. She oversees the registra-

tion and maintenance of trademark portfolios in the United States and foreign countries.
**Personal:** Harvard Law School (1982), Dartmouth College (1979).

### LAZAR, Kathy
Jones Day, Cleveland
216 586 7236
kplazar@jonesday.com
*Featured in Employee Benefits & Executive Compensation (Ohio)*

**Practice Areas:** Kathy Lazar has extensive experience in the areas of employee benefits and deferred compensation plans. She has counseled clients in all aspects of qualified and nonqualified retirement plans, welfare benefit plans, and compensation arrangements, including the employee benefit aspects of corporate acquisitions, mergers, and dispositions.
**Professional Memberships:** Kathy is a member of the Ohio State Bar Association, and is also a member of the WEB Worldwide Employee Benefits Network.
**Career:** Prior to joining Jones Day, Kathy was senior counsel for TRW Inc., a global corporation formerly headquartered in Cleveland, Ohio.

### LAZEAR, Sherri Blank
Baker & Hostetler LLP, Columbus
614 462 2631
slazear@bakerlaw.com
*Featured in Bankruptcy/Restructuring (Ohio)*

**Career:** Sherri Blank Lazear is a trial lawyer focusing on bankruptcy litigation, creditors' and debtors' rights, construction litigation and commercial law. Sherri has experience with litigation in bankruptcy courts, including the representation of secured and unsecured creditors, lenders, construction companies, landlords, officers and directors, and vendors. She handles matters including preference and fraudulent conveyance litigation, relief from stay, administrative claims and reclamation proceedings in bankruptcy courts throughout the country. Sherri has also advised members of Creditor's Committees in numerous Chapter 11 proceedings. Her bankruptcy litigation matters include litigation in the healthcare, airline, real estate, construction, steel and paper industries.

### LEAVITT, Jeffrey S
Jones Day, Cleveland
216 586 7188
jleavitt@jonesday.com
*Featured in Employee Benefits & Executive Compensation (Ohio)*

**Practice Areas:** With respect to ERISA plan asset issues, represents venture capital, private equity, investment banking and hedge fund clients in connection with the design and operation of investment funds. Represents corporate and governmental employers and institutional fiduciaries with respect to employee benefits, including compliance reviews of plans and their administration, benefits aspects of acquisitions, cash balance plan issues, and the insulation of Directors and other individuals from fiduciary liability through plan design and governance. Advises defined benefit plan sponsors regarding compliance with new

funding rules and defined contribution plan sponsors concerning fiduciary aspects of investment options, including employer stock.

### LEIKEN, Jonathan
Jones Day, Cleveland
216 586 7744
jleiken@jonesday.com
*Featured in Litigation (Ohio)*

**Practice Areas:** Jon Leiken represents businesses and individuals in significant government investigations, complex civil lawsuits, and at trial. He conducts internal investigations for boards of directors and senior management and defends clients before government agencies, including the DOJ, SEC, and other regulators. Jon represents financial institutions, manufacturers, universities, professional sports teams, private equity concerns in government inquiries, and litigation involving allegations of fraud, insider trading, and violations of anticorruption laws. He conducts inquiries for U.S. public companies, provides guidance on international acquisitions, and advises on compliance programs. Jon is a former federal prosecutor in the Southern District of New York.

### LEMASTERS, P. Reid
Frost Brown Todd LLC, Cincinnati
513 651 6178
rlemasters@fbtlaw.com
*Featured in Real Estate (Ohio)*

**Practice Areas:** Lender and Developer Representation; Structured Financings; Private Pension and Equity Funds; Oil, Gas, Coal and other Mineral Interests.
**Professional Memberships:** Ohio, Indiana, Kentucky, Cincinnati, and American Bar Associations; Ohio, Indiana, Kentucky, SW Ohio, and American Land Title Associations; International Council of Shopping Centers.
**Career:** Member, Frost Brown Todd LLC; Executive Manager, Multi-State Title Agency, LLC; The Best Lawyers in America® "Lawyer of the Year," Banking & Finance Law, 2013; OSBA Certified Specialist in Business, Commercial and Industrial Real Property.
**Personal:** Indiana University School of Law, JD, 1971; Indiana University, BA, 1968.

### LENNOX, Heather
Jones Day, New York
212 326 3837
hlennox@jonesday.com
*Featured in Bankruptcy/Restructuring (Nationwide), Bankruptcy/Restructuring (New York), Bankruptcy/Restructuring (Ohio)*

**Practice Areas:** Has lead representations of companies in distress, debtors, prepetition secured lenders, DIP lenders, and other significant creditors, in many of the nation's largest corporate restructurings, including Hostess, Metaldyne, Oglebay Norton and Dana Corp. Has substantial experience counseling clients in fraudulent conveyance, illegal dividend, fiduciary duty, and piercing the corporate veil issues. Has represented clients in out-of-court restructuring transactions and bankruptcy-related litigation.

**Professional Memberships:** National Bankruptcy Conference; American College of Bankruptcy; American Bankruptcy Institute.
**Publications:** Co-authored bankruptcy-related articles published in The Business Lawyer, the Journal of Bankruptcy Law and Practice, and the American College of Bankruptcy.

### LEPENE, Alan R
Thompson Hine LLP, Cleveland
216 566 5520
Alan.Lepene@ThompsonHine.com
*Featured in Bankruptcy/Restructuring (Ohio)*

**Career:** Alan is the leader of the firm's Business Restructuring, Creditors' Rights & Bankruptcy Practice Group and a former member of the Firm's Executive Committee. He focuses his practice on bankruptcy (primarily Chapter 11 reorganizations), workouts and commercial litigation. Alan has had significant experience representing senior lenders in major bankruptcy cases and workouts and creditors' committees and debtors in numerous cases under Chapter 11 of the Bankruptcy Code. Alan previously served as chair of the Banking, Commercial and Bankruptcy Law Committee of the Ohio State Bar Association and is a Fellow in the American College of Bankruptcy.

### LERNER, Stephen D
Squire Sanders (US) LLP, Cincinnati
513 361 1220
stephen.lerner@squiresanders.com
*Featured in Bankruptcy/Restructuring (Ohio)*

**Practice Areas:** Leads Squire Sanders' Restructuring and Insolvency Practice Group. Represents debtors, creditors' committees, lenders and other parties in Chapter 11 reorganization cases and out-of-court restructurings throughout the United States. Lead restructuring counsel for AmFin Financial, Special Litigation Committee of the Board of Station Casinos, Chrysler Committee of Affected Dealers and EnviroSolutions Creditors Committee. Sixth Circuit Regent of the American College of Bankruptcy. Perennial inclusion in The Best Lawyers in America and Ohio Super Lawyers. Frequent speaker on bankruptcy and restructuring issues.
**Professional Memberships:** American Bankruptcy Institute; Tri-State Association for Corporate Renewal; Midwest Regional Bankruptcy Seminar, Executive Committee.

### LEUKART, Barbara
Jones Day, Cleveland
216 586 7190
bjleukart@jonesday.com
*Featured in Labor & Employment (Ohio)*

**Practice Areas:** Represents management and counsels companies in all areas of labor and employment relations. Defends numerous cases at the administrative, trial, and appellate levels, including class and individual claims regarding sex, race, and age discrimination, ERISA, pay equity and employment torts. Advises companies on union matters and the creation of employment policies and practices. Serves on the Boards of Land Studio, Music from the Western Reserve, and as President of The Hudson Library and

Historical Society. Serves as a Mediator for the USDC, Northern District of Ohio.
**Professional Memberships:** Celebrezze Inn of Court; ABA.

### LEVASSEUR, Eric
Hahn Loeser & Parks LLP, Cleveland
216 274 2346
eblevasseur@hahnlaw.com
*Featured in Construction (Ohio)*

**Practice Areas:** Mr Levasseur has significant experience in a range of commercial and construction litigation matters, representing individuals and corporations in state and federal trial and appellate courts around the country. He represents design professionals, owners, general contractors, subcontractors and material suppliers in a variety of construction disputes in state and federal courts and AAA arbitrations, including considerable handling of mechanic's lien and bond claims on public and private projects.
**Professional Memberships:** Construction Litigation Committee, Litigation Section, American Bar Association.
**Personal:** Case Western Reserve University School of Law (JD, 2002), Colgate University (BA, 1999).

### LEVY, Mark P
Thompson Hine LLP, Dayton
937 443 6949
Mark.Levy@ThompsonHine.com
*Featured in Intellectual Property (Ohio)*

**Career:** Mark is a registered patent attorney and former leader of Thompson Hine's Intellectual Property Practice. He focuses on patent reexaminations and the management, prosecution and enforcement of all aspects of intellectual property, including technology transfer, licensing and joint venture agreements; patent and trademark validity and infringement opinions; intellectual property audits; patent application preparation; intellectual property litigation; foreign patents; and trade secrets. Mark is admitted to practice in Ohio and before the United States Patent and Trademark Office. Mark has negotiated multi-million dollar pharmaceutical development and license agreements and participated in significant and successful patent litigations.

### LEWIS, John B
Baker & Hostetler LLP, Cleveland
216 861 7496
jlewis@bakerlaw.com
*Featured in Labor & Employment (Ohio)*

**Career:** John Lewis concentrates on the resolution of complex employment, labor, civil rights and regulatory disputes. He is the Chair of BakerHostetler's Employment and Civil Rights Class Action Team, editor of the Class Actions Newsletter and a regular contributor to BakerHostetler's Employment Class Action Blog. The majority of John's time is devoted to litigation, appellate practice and alternative dispute resolution procedures involving anti-discrimination and fair housing laws, the Railway Labor Act, the Civil Rights Acts, the Federal Reserve Act, the Sarbanes-Oxley Act, the Employee Retirement Income Security Act and wrongful discharge, individual employment contract, trade secret, non-competition and work-related tort claims.

## LINDBERG, Lawrence V
Baker & Hostetler LLP, Cleveland
216 861 7483
llindberg@bakerlaw.com
*Featured in Real Estate (Ohio)*
**Career:** Lawrence Lindberg practices real estate law, with emphasis on matters pertaining to real estate development, leasing, construction and financing. He represents clients in a range of real estate activities, including national tenant leasing; hotel development, acquisition and sales; residential subdivision development, construction and sales; residential and commercial condominium development, construction, sales and management; multifamily apartment development and leasing; shopping center development, construction and leasing; renovation of historic office and apartment buildings and hotel properties; and acquisition and construction of manufacturing, warehousing and industrial facilities. Larry's practice includes real property taxation and exemption and environmental aspects of real estate development.

## LINVILLE, Ronald G
Baker & Hostetler LLP, Columbus
614 462 2647
rlinville@bakerlaw.com
*Featured in Labor & Employment (Ohio)*
**Career:** Managing Partner of BakerHostetler's Columbus office and former Chair of the nationwide Employment Group, Ron Linville's practice has focused on management labor and employment law for more than 32 years, representing public and private sector clients. His experience includes the negotiation and administration of over 250 labor contracts. A seasoned employment litigator, he has successfully tried a number of employment cases to juries for Fortune 100 clients in state and federal court. He defends complex employment discrimination/civil rights actions, wage-hour and other types of class actions, and disputes involving protection of trade secrets, unfair competition and unfair business practices.

## LOFTUS, Nora
Frantz Ward LLP, Cleveland
216 515 1665
nloftus@frantzward.com
*Featured in Construction (Ohio)*
**Practice Areas:** Nora is a senior associate focusing her practice in construction, from front-end contract review and claim avoidance through litigation, including contract disputes, professional negligence claims, bid protests, insurance coverage issues, and other construction-related litigation between owners, architects, engineers, general contractors, subcontractors, manufacturers, suppliers, and sureties. Nora also has unique experience advising clients on issues relating to federal contracting's small business set-aside programs. Nora has served as both first and second chair for numerous trials and arbitrations in Ohio and nationally, and has successfully mediated or resolved a significant number of other disputes.

## LOVELAND, Curtis
Porter Wright Morris & Arthur LLP, Columbus
614 227 2004
cloveland@porterwright.com
*Featured in Corporate/M&A (Ohio)*
**Career:** Mr Loveland practices corporate and securities law. His practice focuses on business organization, growth and finance, mergers and acquisitions, corporate governance, securities regulation, franchising and executive compensation. He represents publicly traded and privately held companies and investors in a range of transactions including venture capital and private equity investments as well as issuers in public and private offerings of equity and debt securities. Mr Loveland spends significant time counseling boards of directors, CEOs and executive management teams regarding strategic business/legal issues and has gained substantial experience as a member of several boards of directors of public and private corporations.

## LUCCHESI, Thomas R
Baker & Hostetler LLP, Cleveland
216 861 7672
tlucchesi@bakerlaw.com
*Featured in Litigation (Ohio)*
**Career:** Thomas Lucchesi has more than 28 years of experience as a trial lawyer representing clients in commercial disputes. He has represented plaintiffs and defendants in state and federal courts, including bankruptcy courts, throughout the United States. Tom has participated in more than 25 trials and in dozens of arbitration and mediation proceedings and has appeared before numerous state and federal appellate courts. His litigation experience includes contract, general commercial, landlord-tenant, intellectual property, construction, fraud, negligence, legal malpractice and bankruptcy issues involving a wide range of clients, from sophisticated financial institutions to individuals and entrepreneurs.

## LUTZ, Douglas L
Frost Brown Todd LLC, Cincinnati
513 651 6724
dlutz@fbtlaw.com
*Featured in Bankruptcy/Restructuring (Ohio)*
**Practice Areas:** Financial Restructuring-experience in: (a) restructurings representing debtors, trustees, secured lenders, landlords, official committees and purchasers of distressed businesses; and (b) insolvency/restructuring related litigation.
**Professional Memberships:** Admitted Ohio (1995). Member American Bankruptcy Institute. Board of Directors (2012-)Bankruptcy Section, 2007-12, The Best Lawyers in America and Ohio Super Lawyers, 2006-12.
**Career:** Law Clerk, Honorable James D. Gregg, Bankruptcy Court-Michigan, (1991); Dykema Gossett, 1993; Frost & Jacobs LLP (Cincinnati), 1995; Member, Frost Brown Todd LLC, 2000–present; Practice Group Leader, Bankruptcy & Restructuring Group, 2009–present.
**Personal:** Miami University, Ohio, 1987; Toledo College of Law (Managing Editor–Law Review), 1991.

## LYMAN, Beverly
Thompson Hine LLP, Cincinnati
513 352 6596
Beverly.Lyman@ThompsonHine.com
*Featured in Intellectual Property (Ohio)*
**Career:** Beverly is a life science and transactional patent attorney. Her focus is chemical, medical (device and therapeutics), and biotech protection and monetization, coordinated with regulatory strategy. She represents global corporations to startup companies to technology transfer offices. Invited presentations encompass strategies to protect technology, and all business aspects of global intellectual property. Representative experiences includes technology in- and out-licensing, apportioning a platform technology, co-ordinating US and European regulatory and patent issues, monetizing patent portfolios, and assessing IP rights. Beverly also practices in the firm's Atlanta office.

## LYON, Charles
Calfee, Halter & Griswold LLP, Cleveland
216 622 8510
clyon@calfee.com
*Featured in Intellectual Property (Ohio)*
**Practice Areas:** Intellectual property; intellectual property litigation.
**Professional Memberships:** Member, Northern District of Ohio Alternative Dispute Resolution Panel; acted as mediator or special master in intellectual property disputes; former Director of Cleveland Patent Law Association; Member of Intellectual Property Council, University of Akron Law School.
**Career:** Handles patent and trademark matters and litigates intellectual property cases. Has been involved in the full scope of intellectual property practice, including negotiating employment and licensing contracts, technology transfers and lawsuit settlements.
**Personal:** George Washington University Law School, JD, with honors, 1970; University of Oklahoma, BS in Mechanical Engineering, 1967.

## MACE, Damond R
Squire Sanders (US) LLP, Cleveland
216 479 8764
damond.mace@squiresanders.com
*Featured in Litigation (Ohio)*
**Practice Areas:** Trial lawyer with extensive experience in commercial contract disputes, class actions, commercial litigation, UCC, product liability and tort actions. Diverse litigation experience includes real estate, trade secrets, premises liability, environmental/pollution, construction, wrongful death, royalty disputes and antitrust. Successfully handled jury trials and appeals in state and federal courts, and arbitration, mediation and ADR proceedings. American College of Trial Lawyers, Ohio State Committee. Listed in The Best Lawyers in America, including "Bet-the-Company Litigation" designation; Chambers USA: America's Leading Business Lawyers; and Ohio Super Lawyers including top 100 ranking.
**Professional Memberships:** ABA, Litigation Section; Manos Inn of Court, Master Bencher.

## MAJORAS, John M
Jones Day, Washington, DC
202 879 7652
jmmajoras@jonesday.com
*Featured in Litigation (Ohio)*
**Practice Areas:** Coordinates Jones Day's Competition Law Litigation Practice worldwide. John has 25 years experience in general commercial litigation, with a particular focus on antitrust matters. He recently won two antitrust jury trials, including a class action. He advises clients in responding to global antitrust prosecutions and investigations, and he conducts internal investigations relating to competition concerns. He has handled a wide range of significant commercial disputes and he advises clients on antitrust and FDA regulatory issues, particularly in patent and pharmaceutical matters. He frequently speaks at national and international antitrust and litigation conferences.
**Professional Memberships:** Litigation and Antitrust Sections of the ABA.

## MALONE, Raymond M
Baker & Hostetler LLP, Cleveland
216 861 7879
rmalone@bakerlaw.com
*Featured in Employee Benefits & Executive Compensation (Ohio)*
**Career:** Ray Malone has more than 25 years' experience in all areas of employee benefits and executive compensation. He handles matters covering most aspects of tax qualified retirement plans, including multiemployer pension plans and tax-exempt organization plans. He has significant experience in executive incentive compensation programs, including Code Section 409A compliance, and in health and welfare plans, including the effects of Health Care Reform, principally affecting employers. The types of entities with which he has worked include corporations, partnerships, limited liability companies, venture capital funds, REITs, multiemployer pension plans and tax-exempt employers, including hospitals and universities.

## MANCINO, David A
Baker & Hostetler LLP, Cincinnati
513 929 3495
dmancino@bakerlaw.com
*Featured in Intellectual Property (Ohio)*
**Career:** Registered to practice before the United States Patent & Trademark Office, David Mancino's practice includes patent litigation, patent preparation and prosecution opinion work, IP and technology licensing and client counseling as it relates to intellectual property and technology. David's primary role in patent litigations is to oversee and handle technical issues and technical witnesses in patent litigation trials and depositions. David's patent litigation and prosecution experience includes electrical circuits, software, computer systems, semiconductor technologies, medical devices, prosthetic devices and implants, jet engine technologies, mechanical components and systems, printing systems and technologies, automotive components and commercial products.

## MARHOFER, Michael
Calfee, Halter & Griswold LLP, Cleveland
216 622 8536
mmarhofer@calfee.com
*Featured in Corporate/M&A (Ohio)*

**Practice Areas:** Mergers and acquisitions, joint ventures, general corporate.
**Professional Memberships:** Former member on the Advancement Council for The University of Akron College of Business Administration. Director and corporate secretary for several privately-held companies including NeuroTherm, Royal Bath, Hospitality Mints, Transpac Industries and Spartan Foods of America.
**Career:** Counsels private and public companies on general corporate and transactional matters, specifically contract matters, joint ventures, acquisitions, divestitures and reorganizations.
**Personal:** University of Akron School of Law, JD, magna cum laude, Law Review Managing Editor, 1991; The University of Akron, MBA, 1991; Miami University, BS, 1987.

## MARKS, Jeffrey A
Vorys, Sater, Seymour and Pease LLP, Cincinnati
513 723 4482
jamarks@vorys.com
*Featured in Bankruptcy/Restructuring (Ohio)*

**Practice Areas:** Partner focusing in the areas of bankruptcy, Chapter 11 reorganizations, debtors' and creditors' rights, out-of-court workouts and debt restructurings; represents secured lenders, creditors' committees, debtors, equity holders, lessors, contract counterparties and business acquirers.
**Professional Memberships:** Cincinnati Bar Association, Bankruptcy Law Committee, past chair; American Bankruptcy Institute; Tri-State Association for Corporate Renewal, past president; Advisory Committee for Local Rules of the US Bankruptcy Court, Southern District of Ohio, past member.
**Personal:** University of Cincinnati College of Law, JD, 1980; University of Cincinnati Law Review, Student Articles Editor, 1979-80; The Ohio State University, BA, 1977.

## MAUER, Kimberly K
Frost Brown Todd LLC, Cincinnati
513 651 6743
kmauer@fbtlaw.com
*Featured in Banking & Finance (Ohio)*

**Practice Areas:** Banking and finance. Represents financial institutions in a wide array of matters including bank regulation, loan documentation, and loan workouts. Also significant work in New Markets Tax Credits.
**Professional Memberships:** Cincinnati Bar Association, Ohio Bar Association, American Bar Association.
**Career:** Clerked for Iowa Supreme Court, 1984. Associate - Davis, Hockenberg, Wine, Brown, Koehn & Shors. Associate - Frost & Jacobs in 1987. General Counsel to PNC Bank, Ohio, National Association 1990-94. Rejoined Frost & Jacobs (now Frost Brown Todd) in 1994. Member.

**Personal:** Born June 28, 1959. Attended Drake Law School. Leisure interests include travel, reading, and cooking.

## MCADAMS, Robert
Porter Wright Morris & Arthur LLP, Columbus
614 227 2091
rmcadams@porterwright.com
*Featured in Healthcare (Ohio)*

**Career:** Mr McAdams has more than 25 years of experience advising healthcare organizations and providers about how to best navigate regulatory frameworks, resolve legal disputes and take advantage of business opportunities in today's ever-changing healthcare environment. He uses a combination of strong legal and business skills to successfully counsel healthcare entities in business transactions, contractual issues, regulatory matters, fraud and abuse issues, compliance matters, public and private payor billing issues, medical staff issues, provider clinical integration plans, pay-for-quality contracting, antitrust issues and pharmaceutical matters. Mr McAdams is recognized by his peers as one of the leading practitioners in the region.

## MCGOWAN JR, John J
Baker & Hostetler LLP, Cleveland
216 861 7475
jmcgowan@bakerlaw.com
*Featured in Employee Benefits & Executive Compensation (Ohio)*

**Career:** With nearly 30 years of experience advising and representing benefit plans, plan sponsors and plan fiduciaries, John McGowan has a history of handling the special challenges organizations and fiduciaries can face. John handles disputes involving plan-covered individuals, vendors and government agencies over such events as plan financial distress, failure of a trusted vendor or adviser, plan mis-administration, abandonment, prohibited transactions and tax-qualification issues. John also counsels and represents plans, plan sponsors and plan fiduciaries, and a variety of insurers and third party administrators, caught up in the health care reform process.

## MCKAY, Hugh E
Porter Wright Morris & Arthur LLP, Cleveland
216 443 2580
HMcKay@porterwright.com
*Featured in Litigation (Ohio)*

**Career:** Hugh serves as Partner-in-Charge of the Firm's Cleveland office and represents corporate clients and financial institutions in complex commercial litigation in state and federal courts. He has successfully represented several Fortune 500 companies in major litigation. A past President of the Cleveland Bar Association and active member for 30 years, Hugh's leadership extends to numerous Board, Committee, and Chairman roles. During his Presidency, Hugh developed the nationally recognized 3Rs Program with over 500 lawyers in every Cleveland City High School every month focusing on the law and careers.

## MCKEE, Thomas F
Calfee, Halter & Griswold LLP, Cleveland
216 622 8420
tmckee@calfee.com
*Featured in Corporate/M&A (Ohio)*

**Practice Areas:** Corporate; securities and capital markets; M&A; private equity; regulatory investigations.
**Professional Memberships:** American, Cleveland Bar Associations; Society of Corporate Secretaries and Governance Professionals.
**Career:** Chairman of firm; Member, Executive and Management Committees; Co-Chair, Business Transactions Department. Counsels public companies, investment banking firms on capital formation, M&A, compliance; private equity firms on fund formation, portfolio investment activities. Serves on Board of Directors, numerous public, private companies and Trustee of Case Western Reserve University and The Musical Arts Association.
**Personal:** Case Western Reserve University School of Law, JD, high honors, 1975; University of Michigan, BA, high distinction, 1970.

## MCMAHON, Louis L
McMahon DeGulis LLP, Cleveland
216 367 1407
lmcmahon@mdllp.net
*Featured in Natural Resources (Ohio)*

**Practice Areas:** Environmental issues relating to water law litigation, the Great Lakes and related public trust issues, brownfields redevelopment, and other environmental regulatory and legislative matters. Counsel a major metropolitan sewer district in the development a long term control plan that incorporates green infrastructure, which is recognized as a model of Integrated Planning. He is a frequent speaker on water law topics.

## MCMAHON, Michael S
McMahon DeGulis LLP, Cleveland
216 367 1402
mmcmahon@mdllp.net
*Featured in Natural Resources (Ohio)*

**Practice Areas:** Clean Air Act; Resource Conservation and Recovery Act; environmental management systems and auditing; environmental compliance counseling and permitting; enforcement actions; transportation of hazardous materials; environmental aspects of corporate and real estate transactions; complex air work and indemnity negotiation with predecessor operator at manufacturing facility in Ohio; negotiate Title V permits for facilities involved in coatings, batch processing, continuous processing and chemical manufacturing; defend facilities involved in air permit enforcement actions brought by US EPA/Ohio EPA; advise facilities confronting RACT/BACT/LEAR requirements.

## MCMURRAY, Kevin N
Frost Brown Todd LLC, Cincinnati
513 651 6160
kmcmurray@fbtlaw.com
*Featured in Natural Resources (Ohio)*

**Practice Areas:** Environmental law. Kevin Chairs the firm's Environmental Practice Group. He has broad experience in various environmental

programs, focusing on litigation and enforcement defense, regulatory counseling and audits, remediation of contaminated sites, and real estate and corporate transactions.
**Professional Memberships:** American, Ohio State and Cincinnati Bar Associations; Past Chair, CBA Environmental Law Committee; Member, American Institute of Chemical Engineers.
**Career:** Frost Brown Todd (1989 to present); Best Lawyers in America (2005-12); Ohio Super Lawyer (2005-12); Best Lawyers' 2013 Cincinnati Litigation - Environmental Lawyer of the Year.
**Personal:** JD, University of Cincinnati, (1989); BS Chemical Engineering, University of Cincinnati, (1986).

## MCNEALEY, J Jeffrey
Porter Wright Morris & Arthur LLP, Columbus
614 227 2074
jmcnealey@porterwright.com
*Featured in Real Estate (Ohio)*

**Career:** Mr McNealey has extensive experience assisting local, regional and national clients in the acquisition and development of industrial, commercial and multifamily properties, with a focus on zoning and land use planning matters, annexation, integration with regional or local governmental plans, environmental licensing, compliance with zoning and environmental regulations, environmental assessments and Brownfields redevelopments. Mr McNealey assists with tax abatements, incentive and other governmental programs, and deals with local citizen group demands that may arise in connection with real estate and industrial developments.

## MCWILLIAMS, Douglas A
Squire Sanders (US) LLP, Cleveland
216 479 8332
douglas.mcwilliams@squiresanders.com
*Featured in Natural Resources (Ohio)*

**Practice Areas:** Partner whose practice encompasses environmental counseling, rulemaking and litigation with an emphasis on the Clean Air Act. Utilizes deep industry sector experience in energy, metals/mining, paper and transportation to counsel clients on complex permitting and compliance challenges. Offers expertise in renewable energy credits, carbon trading and other market-based strategies. Assists clients to access and influence federal and state rule developments including judicial review of final adverse rules. Provides counsel services in multi-party hazardous waste sites. Listed in The Best Lawyers in America.
**Professional Memberships:** ABA, Environment, Energy and Resources Section; Ohio Bar Association; Cleveland Metropolitan Bar Association.

## MEHALKO, Megan
Benesch, Friedlander, Coplan & Aronoff LLP, Cleveland
216 363 4487
mmehalko@beneschlaw.com
*Featured in Corporate/M&A (Ohio)*

**Practice Areas:** Primarily handles mergers, acquisitions, divestitures, domestic and cross border strategic alliances and joint ventures, general business counseling, and distressed/insolvent

company acquisitions and restructurings. Has experience representing companies in the plastics, rubber, metal stamping and fabricating, healthcare, telecom, equipment manufacturing, logistics and financial services industries.
**Career:** Chair of Corporate & Securities and Polymer Practice Groups and Executive Committee member.
**Personal:** Case Western Reserve University (JD, 1990); Bucknell University (BA, 1987).

### MENDEL, Linda
Vorys, Sater, Seymour and Pease LLP, Columbus
lrmendel@vorys.com
*Featured in Employee Benefits & Executive Compensation (Ohio)*
**Practice Areas:** Employee benefits practice. Works with employers and multiemployer plans on health and welfare plan issues, including compliance with the Patient Protection and Affordable Care Act (PPACA), Employee Retirement Income Security Act (ERISA), Health Insurance Portability and Accountability Act (HIPAA) portability and privacy, and Consolidated Omnibus Budget Reconciliation Act (COBRA), employee communications, tax issues, and vendor contracting.
**Professional Memberships:** American Bar Association (Chair of Welfare Plans/EEOC Issues Subcommittee, Section of Taxation).
**Career:** Admitted to Ohio (1981).
**Personal:** The Ohio State University College of Law, JD, with Honors, 1981; Kent State University, BBA, 1978, magna cum laude.

### MERSOL, Gregory V
Baker & Hostetler LLP, Cleveland
216 861 7935
gmersol@bakerlaw.com
*Featured in Labor & Employment (Ohio)*
**Career:** Greg Mersol concentrates on the resolution of class action and other complex employment disputes. Greg defends employers in class and collective actions on topics such as wage and hour disputes; race, sex and age discrimination; public accommodations; constitutional claims; and employee benefits. He consults with employers on a range of complex employment matters, including restructuring and benefits disputes, as well as the use, preservation and production of electronic data in the litigation context.

### MEYER, G Christopher
Squire Sanders (US) LLP, Cleveland
216 479 8692
christopher.meyer@squiresanders.com
*Featured in Bankruptcy/Restructuring (Ohio)*
**Practice Areas:** Partner with significant experience in workouts, restructurings and bankruptcy reorganizations including representing debtors, creditors and committees in commercial cases; additional experience in real estate, commercial lending and troubled loan issues. Listed in Ohio SuperLawyers and Best Lawyers in America (named 2012 Cleveland Bankruptcy and Creditor-Debtor Lawyer of the Year by Best Lawyers in America).

**Professional Memberships:** American College of Bankruptcy (Chair, Board of Regents and Foundation Director); ABI; TMA (Past chapter president and 2011 inaugural winner of Chapter Lifetime Achievement Award); ABA; Cleveland Metropolitan Bar Association (board member and treasurer).

### MEYER, Jill P
Frost Brown Todd LLC, Cincinnati
513 651 6124
jmeyer@fbtlaw.com
*Featured in Litigation (Ohio)*
**Practice Areas:** Advertising, Intellectual Property, Media and First Amendment.
**Professional Memberships:** American Advertising Federation; ABA Forum on Communications Law; Media Law Resource Center, Advertising & Commercial Speech Committee.
**Career:** Concentrates on litigating advertising issues, including false advertising, unfair competition, deceptive trade practices, right of publicity, and intellectual property claims; and defending media companies' and other content creators' First Amendment rights against claims of defamation, invasion of privacy, and related claims. Also counsels advertising and media clients in the creative/pre-publication stage.
**Personal:** BA, magna cum laude, College of Mount St. Joseph; JD, magna cum laude, Salmon P. Chase College of Law.

### MEYER JR, Robert A
Porter Wright Morris & Arthur LLP, Columbus
614 227 2096
rmeyer@porterwright.com
*Featured in Real Estate (Ohio)*
**Career:** Mr Meyer has considerable experience in a wide variety of zoning and land development matters, having secured or directed the securing of zoning and other entitlement approvals for more than 30,000 residential units as well as numerous commercial and industrial developments. He has also represented clients in a variety of matters arising from the federal Clean Air Act and Ohio's air pollution statute, and rules and policies implementing both. Mr Meyer chairs the firm's Green Practice Group and is an Accredited Professional under the Leadership in Energy and Environmental Design (LEED®) green building program.

### MILLER, Barry
Benesch, Friedlander, Coplan & Aronoff LLP, Cleveland
216 363 4454
bmiller@beneschlaw.com
*Featured in Construction (Ohio)*
**Practice Areas:** Construction law, real estate, commercial litigation. Represents owners, general contractors, subcontractors, public owners, design professionals and sureties in construction disputes including bid protests, extra work disputes, delay, disruption and productivity disputes and post-acceptance building failures.
**Career:** Chairman of Construction Practice Group. Registered architect. Represents industry participants in dispute resolution forums at local,

state and federal levels. Litigates claims up to $30 million. Project Counsel for public and private projects up to $3 billion. Experienced large case arbitrator, mediator and dispute review Board Member.
**Personal:** Case Western Reserve University (JD, 1983); Kent State University (1979); Miami University (BED, 1977).

### MILLER, Craig S
Ulmer & Berne LLP, Cleveland
216 583 7048
cmiller@ulmer.com
*Featured in Real Estate (Ohio)*
**Practice Areas:** Chair of the Public Law Group and a member of the Real Estate Group, Craig has over 30 years of experience that integrates public law and public finance, urban redevelopment and financing, zoning and land use, and nonprofit corporations. He assists clients with major urban redevelopment projects involving land acquisition, public infrastructure, and complex public and private financing. He also advises private for-profit and not-for-profit developers on historic rehabilitation and new construction projects. Craig represents local and regional public agencies in public law matters.
**Professional Memberships:** Cuyahoga County Law Directors Association

### MILLER, W Timothy
Taft Stettinius & Hollister LLP, Cincinnati
513 357 9678
miller@taftlaw.com
*Featured in Bankruptcy/Restructuring (Ohio)*
**Practice Areas:** Banking and Institutional Finance, Mergers & Acquisitions, Business Restructuring and Creditor Rights, Bankruptcy, Business & Finance.
**Career:** Mr Miller is certified by the American Board of Certification in Business Bankruptcy Law and has extensive experience representing corporate debtors, official and unofficial creditors committees, financial institutions, trade creditors, investment funds and commercial real estate and equipment lessors in all aspects of complex Chapter 11 business bankruptcies and out-of-court restructurings. In addition, he has worked with derivatives, including interest rate swaps and repurchase agreements.
**Personal:** Cornell University Law School (1992); DePauw University (1989).

### MILLISOR, Richard A
Fisher & Phillips LLP, Cleveland
440 838 8800
rmillisor@laborlawyers.com
*Featured in Labor & Employment (Ohio)*
**Career:** Rich Millisor is a partner in the Cleveland office. He has extensive experience representing employers before state and federal courts and administrative agencies in all areas of employment law, including discrimination, wage and hour and unfair labor practice litigation. Rich also has an active traditional labor practice, where he represents employers in resolving grievances, prosecuting arbitrations and negotiating collective bargaining agreements. He also devotes a portion of his practice counseling clients to avoid employ-

ment and labor disputes and has substantial experience litigating collective and hybrid class actions under the Fair Labor Standards Act and state wage and hour laws.

### MILLS JR, Osborne
Squire Sanders (US) LLP, Cleveland
216 479 8343
osborne.mills@squiresanders.com
*Featured in Banking & Finance (Ohio)*
**Practice Areas:** Partner with broad experience in commercial and real estate lending, loan workouts, debtor-creditor issues and real estate law. Represents financial institutions in syndicated and bi-lateral, secured and unsecured, loan transactions, complex debt and mortgage financings, mezzanine debt transactions, venture capital transactions, loan restructurings, workouts and bankruptcy proceedings. Extensive experience in multifamily, commercial and industrial real estate transactions. Named Cleveland Banking Lawyer of the Year by The Best Lawyers in America 2012.
**Professional Memberships:** Ohio State Bar Association; Cleveland Metropolitan Bar Association, Corporation, Banking and Business Law Section, Bankruptcy and Commercial Law Section and Real Estate Section.

### MILLSTONE, David J
Squire Sanders (US) LLP, Cleveland
216 479 8574
david.millstone@squiresanders.com
*Featured in Labor & Employment (Ohio)*
**Practice Areas:** Partner and former labor and employment practice coordinator of 15 years. Significant experience in all aspects of labor and employment law including union relations, general employment counseling, employment litigation, international labor and employment issues, FLSA litigation, union avoidance, collective bargaining, arbitration, employment discrimination, employment termination, executive contracts, executive terminations, and merger and acquisition issues. Middle East editor, "International Restrictive Covenants and Trade Secrets in Employment," published by American Bar Association and BNA. Listed in The Best Lawyers in America.
**Professional Memberships:** American Bar Association, Labor and Employment Law Section; Ohio State Bar Association; Cleveland Metropolitan Bar Association.

### MIRALDI, Leslee W
Thompson Hine LLP, Cleveland
216 566 5508
Leslee.Miraldi@ThompsonHine.com
*Featured in Banking & Finance (Ohio)*
**Career:** Leslee is a partner in the Commercial & Public Finance Practice Group. She focuses on commercial lending, representing banks, financial institutions and public and private companies in connection with senior and subordinated debt facilities. She has extensive experience with syndicated, multi-bank senior credit facilities, asset based and structured finance facilities, international financing transactions (involving foreign borrowers and foreign collateral), acquisition financing, letter of credit facilities, foreign currency transactions, second lien lending and real estate

financing. Leslee also has extensive experience in the area of secured transactions, including both personal and real property. Her representation includes loan restructuring and workouts.

**MIXTER, Stephen**
Jones Day, Cleveland
216 586 1085
smixter@jonesday.com
*Featured in Real Estate (Ohio)*
**Practice Areas:** General real estate, particularly providing corporate real estate services to companies not primarily in the real estate industry which occupy properties as a necessity for their core businesses. His practice includes the acquisition, disposition, financing, development, leasing, and subleasing of commercial and industrial real estate. He has significant experience in dealing with the real estate aspects of major corporate acquisitions, dispositions, financings and bankruptcies, has been involved in numerous multi-asset transactions for Fortune 500 companies, and also has worked on several professional basketball and baseball facility and airport hub facility transactions.
**Professional Memberships:** President of CoreNet Ohio/Kentucky Chapter.

**MUELLER, John M**
Baker & Hostetler LLP, Cincinnati
513 929 3413
jmueller@bakerlaw.com
*Featured in Intellectual Property (Ohio)*
**Career:** John Mueller practices in all facets of intellectual property law, including patent, trademark, copyright and trade secret law. He prepares and prosecutes patent applications on a variety of subjects, in a variety of industries, with emphasis in the consumer products industry. John manages patent and trademark portfolios of large consumer products companies and issues patent and trademark clearance and non-infringement opinions. John has experience handling trademark disputes, including the filing and prosecution of Lanham Act, Uniform Dispute Resolution Policy and Anti-cybersquatting Consumer Protection Act actions, as well as opposition and cancellation proceedings before the Trademark Trial and Appeal Board.

**NASH, David**
McMahon DeGulis LLP, Cleveland
216 367 1401
dnash@mdllp.net
*Featured in Natural Resources (Ohio)*
**Practice Areas:** Advanced energy, emerging technologies, corporate sustainability, climate change, business and real estate transactions, regulatory matters and legislative matters, environmental litigation, and environmental enforcement actions; corporate mergers and acquisitions due diligence and environmental risk and contract negotiation and drafting. Counsel on renewable energy credits, energy efficiency, and carbon emission credit and offset projects and advised on real estate transactions, including lease counseling for landowners on wind farm and solar farm projects.

**NATALE, Andrew J**
Frantz Ward LLP, Cleveland
216 515 1602
anatale@frantzward.com
*Featured in Construction (Ohio)*
**Practice Areas:** Extensive experience in construction law, construction claims management, arbitration, mediation and litigation. Primarily engaged in construction law practice representing contractors, design/builders, subcontractors, specialty trades, developers, sureties, owners, and design professionals in all aspects of construction law.
**Publications:** Frequent author/lecturer on construction law, including: 'Ohio Construction Claims, Damages and Liability Theories'; 'Construction Claims Management and Avoidance'; 'Ohio Mechanics' Lien Law'; 'Ohio Construction Contracting for Public Entities'; 'Construction Law for Attorneys'; 'Creative Strategies for Project Completion and Litigation Avoidance'; 'Alternative Dispute Resolution in Construction'; 'Ohio Lien and Bond Law'; 'Construction Schedule Claims'; 'Construction Surety Law'; 'Competitive Bid Law'.

**NAZETTE, Adam R**
Thompson Hine LLP, Cleveland
216 566 5940
Adam.Nazette@ThompsonHine.com
*Featured in Banking & Finance (Ohio)*
**Career:** Adam is a partner in the Commercial & Public Finance practice group. He focuses his practice on representing financial institutions and other entities in secured and unsecured commercial financing transactions. He has significant experience with syndicated and bilateral credit facilities, senior and subordinated credit facilities, cross-border transactions, asset-based credit facilities, acquisition financing, real estate financing, loan restructurings, workouts and other complex financing transactions.

**NEARY, Douglas A**
Calfee, Halter & Griswold LLP, Cleveland
216 622 8285
dneary@calfee.com
*Featured in Corporate/M&A (Ohio)*
**Practice Areas:** Mergers and Acquisitions; General Corporate; Securities and Capital Markets; Private Equity; Health Care and Life Sciences.
**Career:** Chair of General Corporate practice; co-chair of M&A group. Doug's practice focuses on M&A, corporate governance, securities law compliance and commercial finance for public and private companies and financial sponsors and lenders. Advises on mergers, acquisitions and divestitures; capital formation; venture capital and SEC matters. Knowledgeable on general contracting issues, commercial transactions, joint ventures, strategic alliances. Longtime member of firm's Executive and Management Committees.
**Personal:** Board member or secretary of various privately held corporations and foundations. Executive committee of GCSC.

**NEWMAN JR, John (Jack) M**
Jones Day, Cleveland
216 586 7207
jmnewman@jonesday.com
*Featured in Litigation (Ohio)*
**Practice Areas:** His practice encompasses a variety of general business matters, with a substantial focus on shareholder actions, including securities, fiduciary and governance claims and related ERISA actions, and also encompasses banking services, bankruptcy, tax and accounting-related litigation, and other commercial controversies. Admitted to practice in Ohio, Illinois and California, and before the US Tax and Supreme Courts and numerous federal district courts and courts of appeals.
**Professional Memberships:** Fellow of the American College of Trial Lawyers; ABA; Los Angeles County Bar Association; Cleveland Metropolitan Bar Association.

**NOBIL, Steven M**
Fisher & Phillips LLP, Cleveland
440 838 8800
snobil@laborlawyers.com
*Featured in Labor & Employment (Ohio)*
**Career:** Steve Nobil is the managing partner in the Cleveland office. He devotes his practice to representing public and private sector employers in all areas of traditional labor law including union organizing campaigns, contract negotiations, arbitrations, union avoidance, supervisory training, and other related labor advice and counsel. He has an outstanding success record in countering union organizing attempts and he has been involved in many mergers and acquisitions from a labor and employment perspective. Steve also lectures extensively on developments in labor and employment law and their implications for employers.

**NOLAN, William A**
Barnes & Thornburg LLP, Columbus
614 365 2784
wnolan@btlaw.com
*Featured in Labor & Employment (Ohio)*
**Practice Areas:** Strives to bring energy, attentiveness, and clarity to bear on employment, contract, and other disputes, and on helping clients build teams, policies and processes to minimize the frequency and severity of disputes. Areas of particular experience include noncompetes and employee trade secrets, executive agreements, organizational privacy and technology, and managing employee health issues. Works in industries including manufacturing, education, construction, health care, and nonprofits. Opened and manages the firm's Columbus office.
**Personal:** Cornell University (BA 1984); Harvard University (JD 1989).

**NORMAN, Mark A**
Vorys, Sater, Seymour and Pease LLP, Cincinnati
513 723 4006
manorman@vorys.com
*Featured in Natural Resources (Ohio)*
**Practice Areas:** Partner. Represents business in environmental compliance, business transactions,

investigations, enforcement and litigation. Prosecutes, defends and negotiates private disputes and defends enforcement actions in state and federal courts. Major 'brownfields' redevelopment practice (including Ohio EPA Voluntary Action and Clean Ohio programs) and regulated government organizations practice. Multi-year 'Ohio Super Lawyer' and 'Best Lawyers in America'.
**Professional Memberships:** Ohio State and Cincinnati Bar Associations.
**Career:** Admitted to Ohio Bar (1983).
**Personal:** Georgetown University Law Center, JD, cum laude, 1983. George Washington University, BA, with honors, 1977, Phi Beta Kappa.

**OAKES, Jared E**
Thompson Hine LLP, Cleveland
216 566 5615
Jared.Oakes@Thompsonhine.com
*Featured in Real Estate (Ohio)*
**Career:** Jared practices in the firm's Real Estate Practice Group. He regularly represents real estate investment trusts, real estate operating companies, institutional investors, private equity funds and other public and private investors, developers and owners of commercial real estate, with a particular focus on retail/shopping center assets. This work includes counseling clients in the acquisition and sale of commercial properties, repositioning troubled assets, entity planning, leasing, development, asset management, commercial lending and debt restructuring. In addition, Jared devotes a significant portion of his practice to providing strategic counseling on corporate real estate matters and complex real estate litigation.

**OBERSCHMIDT, E Richard**
Frost Brown Todd LLC, Cincinnati
513 651 6887
roberschmidt@fbtlaw.com
*Featured in Real Estate (Ohio)*
**Professional Memberships:** Member, Cincinnati, Ohio State and American Bar Associations; Member, Board of Zoning Appeals, Anderson Township, Ohio; Member, Ohio Land Title Association.
**Career:** Admitted to Bar in Ohio, 1978; Practices in the real estate and lending services practice groups and is based in the Cincinnati, Ohio office; Member, Board of Managers of Multi-State Title Agency Ltd.
**Personal:** University of Virginia, JD, 1978; Miami University, BA, 1975; Phi Beta Kappa; Member of the Board of Trustees of the College of Mount St. Joseph; Member of Board of Trustees of the Physicians Charitable Foundation.

**OELLERMANN, Charles M**
Jones Day, Columbus
614 281 3948
coellermann@jonesday.com
*Featured in Bankruptcy/Restructuring (Ohio)*
**Practice Areas:** Oversees the Business Restructuring and Reorganization Practice in the Columbus Office. His practice focuses primarily on corporate bankruptcy, restructuring, and other insolvency related matters. He has represented

debtors, creditors' committees, and other parties in large corporate restructurings nationwide and has provided insolvency-related advice to clients in litigation and transactional contexts. He regularly counsels clients on fraudulent conveyance, illegal dividend, preferential transfer, fiduciary duty, and corporate veil piercing issues as well as the structuring and consummation of spin-offs, secured financings, distressed mergers and acquisitions, and other transactions.
**Professional Memberships:** American Bankruptcy Institute; Ohio State Bar Association; Columbus Bar Association.

### O'MALLEY, Anthony
Vorys, Sater, Seymour and Pease LLP, Cleveland
216 479 6159
ajomalley@vorys.com
*Featured in Litigation (Ohio)*
**Practice Areas:** Managing Partner of Vorys' Cleveland office. His practice focuses on complex business litigation, with particular expertise in class actions, corporate and banking law. Elected by peers as 'Ohio Super Lawyer' and listed in 'The Best Lawyers in America'.
**Professional Memberships:** John M Manos Inn of Court (Master Bencher); Life Member: Judicial Conference for Ohio's Eighth Appellate Judicial District and US Court of Appeals for the Sixth Circuit.
**Career:** Admitted to Ohio Bar 1984.
**Personal:** John Carroll University, BA, cum laude, (1980); Case Western Reserve University Law School, JD, (1984); Law Review: Case Western Law Review, Articles Editor, (1984).

### ORDING, Michael K
Jones Day, Columbus
614 281 3839
mkording@jonesday.com
*Featured in Real Estate (Ohio)*
**Practice Areas:** Real estate and real estate finance. Extensive experience with joint ventures, financings, acquisitions and dispositions, construction contracts, and workouts and distressed asset transactions. Extensive experience in the multifamily housing sector, including numerous financings using tax-exempt bonds and tax credits. Has represented clients in negotiating public/private partnerships and financing nontraditional real estate projects, such as sports arenas.
**Career:** Partner since 1987.
**Personal:** Ohio Northern University (BA 1977), The Ohio State University (JD summa cum laude, 1980).

### OSCAR, Lawrence E
Hahn Loeser & Parks LLP, Cleveland
216 274 2229
leoscar@hahnlaw.com
*Featured in Bankruptcy/Restructuring (Ohio)*
**Practice Areas:** Mr Oscar is Managing Partner and CEO of the firm and co-chair of its Creditors' Rights, Reorganization & Bankruptcy Area. He represents creditors, creditors' committees, debtors and trustees in reorganization and insolvency matters, including Chapter 11 proceedings. Mr Oscar represents financial institutions, ven-

dors and other creditor or debtor interests in connection with numerous workouts and restructurings, and negotiates and closes a variety of commercial transactions.
**Personal:** New York University School of Law (JD, 1981); Wharton School of the University of Pennsylvania (BS, cum laude, 1978).

### PACE, Stanley Dan
Ogletree, Deakins, Nash, Smoak & Stewart, PC, Cleveland
216 241 6100
stanley.pace@ogletreedeakins.com
*Featured in Labor & Employment (Ohio)*
**Practice Areas:** Represents employers in employee relations including negotiation, arbitration, NLRB representation elections and statutory compliance. Dan's practice involves structuring corporate policies in union/non-union facilities maximizing efficiency and productivity of employees including LEAN, Six Sigma, gain sharing, profit sharing and various other employee involvement programs. He has extensive experience in restructuring work systems and employee benefits in connection with acquisitions and restructuring failed businesses.
**Professional Memberships:** Cleveland, Ohio and American Bar Associations.
**Career:** Admitted in Ohio. Listed in Best Lawyers, Chambers' Leading Business Lawyers, Super Lawyers, Who's Who in America.
**Personal:** Denison University (BA, 1970), University of Toledo (JD, 1975).

### PARIS, Zachary
Jones Day, Cleveland
216 586 7275
ztparis@jonesday.com
*Featured in Real Estate (Ohio)*
**Practice Areas:** Practice focuses on real estate development, corporate real estate services, and the hospitality industry. Represented developers in commercial and industrial ownership and development, including the acquisition of land, the installation of improvements, the financing, construction and leasing of buildings, the negotiation of reciprocal easement agreements, and the acquisition of existing portfolios. His corporate real estate services work includes corporate headquarters projects, ground leases for industrial properties, and leases and financings for airport expansion projects. As co-leader of the firm's Hospitality Practice, he has been involved in the acquisition, sale, and/or financing of individual hotels and hotel portfolios.

### PAROBEK, Drew
Vorys, Sater, Seymour and Pease LLP, Cleveland
216 479 6162
dtparobek@vorys.com
*Featured in Bankruptcy/Restructuring (Ohio)*
**Practice Areas:** Partner in the Commercial Group with emphasis on bankruptcy, loan restructurings and workouts, commercial law and banking.
**Professional Memberships:** Cleveland Metropolitan Bar Association (Executive Committee; Trustee; Member, Bankruptcy and

Commercial Law Section); Trustee, Cleveland Metropolitan Bar Foundation; Ohio State Bar Association; Turnaround Management Association.
**Career:** Admitted to Ohio (1984); US District Court, Northern and Southern Districts of Ohio; US Court of Appeals, Sixth Circuit.
**Personal:** Vanderbilt University School of Law, JD, 1984; Vanderbilt University, BA, summa cum laude, Phi Beta Kappa, 1980. Former Trustee, Cleveland Zoological Society; Bay Rockets Association; Ohio Board of Bar Examiners.

### PAUKEN, Patrick J
Baker & Hostetler LLP, Cleveland
216 861 7289
ppauken@bakerlaw.com
*Featured in Real Estate (Ohio)*
**Career:** Pat Pauken teams with clients to plan and implement real estate strategies; negotiate, document and close transactions to acquire, develop, lease, finance, construct, operate, sell and exchange properties and projects; and manage risk and maximize real estate value. His experience includes real estate planning and transactions on behalf of developers, corporate and non-profit clients, and more than two decades as in-house counsel to a major national developer and manager of regional and community shopping centers, free-standing retail stores, restaurants, theatres, mixed-use projects, major urban and suburban office buildings, suburban office parks and full- and limited-service hotels.

### PAYNTER, Craig
Taft Stettinius & Hollister LLP, Columbus
614 334 6135
cpaynter@taftlaw.com
*Featured in Construction (Ohio)*
**Practice Areas:** Public Law, Construction, Construction Claims, Real Property, Labor and Employment, Litigation, Local Government, College & University Law.
**Career:** Mr Paynter has built a successful practice in the construction law area. He represents clients in all aspects of construction, with a particular emphasis on public sector litigation and contracting. Mr Paynter is a leading authority on eminent domain issues and currently serves as a Federal Civil Rule 71.1 Commissioner for eminent domain acquisitions related to an interstate natural gas pipeline project.
**Personal:** University of Akron School of Law (1982); Denison University (1979).

### PETERS, Georgeann G
Baker & Hostetler LLP, Columbus
614 462 4769
gpeters@bakerlaw.com
*Featured in Employee Benefits & Executive Compensation (Ohio)*
**Career:** Georgeann Peters has 30 years' experience in employee benefits and executive compensation law, ERISA compliance and tax-exempt organization law. She also works on mergers and acquisitions and federal tax matters, including tax controversies. Georgeann's employee benefits experience includes qualified and nonqualified retirement plans, profit-sharing and 401(k) plans,

ESOPs, health and welfare benefit plans (including Multiple Employer Welfare Arrangements of trade and industry organizations), as well as equity and incentive compensation plans and executive employment, severance and change in control agreements. She has extensive experience with "non-electing church" plans exempt from ERISA and plans subject to ERISA's requirements.

### PETRICOFF, Howard
Vorys, Sater, Seymour and Pease LLP, Columbus
614 464 5414
mhpetricoff@vorys.com
*Featured in Natural Resources (Ohio)*
**Practice Areas:** Partner in the energy and environmental group who advises/represents clients on energy, utility and environmental matters, including litigation in federal and state court as well as state public service commissions, the Federal Energy Regulatory Commission and various permitting boards/commissions. He is also an adjunct professor at Capital University Law School, teaching courses on energy law and natural resources.
**Professional Memberships:** Ohio State Bar Association, Ohio Bar Foundation, Energy & Mineral Law Foundation.
**Personal:** Mr Petricoff received his MPA from Harvard University, his JD from the University of Cincinnati College of Law and his BS from American University.

### PFEFFERLE III, Ben L
Baker & Hostetler LLP, Columbus
614 462 2601
bpfefferle@bakerlaw.com
*Featured in Natural Resources (Ohio)*
**Career:** Chair of BakerHostetler's nationwide Environmental and Energy team, Ben Pfefferle's practice includes class action defense; environmental compliance; shale plays; hazardous/toxic waste issues; Superfund litigation and private cost recovery; environmental permitting; and redevelopment, acquisition and divestiture of environmentally impaired property. A core member of the firm's Shale Plays team, Ben is at the forefront of the rapidly growing natural gas and oil industry in Ohio, Pennsylvania, West Virginia and New York. Ben defends companies in civil, criminal and administrative enforcement proceedings involving state and federal Clean Air Act, Clean Water Act, Solid Waste Disposal, RCRA (hazardous waste) and CERCLA (Superfund) actions.

### PHILLIPS, William
Taft Stettinius & Hollister LLP, Cleveland
216 706 3844
wphillips@taftlaw.com
*Featured in Real Estate (Ohio)*
**Practice Areas:** Real property.
**Professional Memberships:** Founding member of the Ohio International Council of Shopping Center Law Symposium, International Council of Shopping Centers, and American, California, Ohio State and Cleveland Bar Associations.
**Career:** Mr Phillips is co-chair of the Real Estate group. He represents a significant number of

national and regional shopping center developers. He also represents national and regional chain tenants and is fully conversant with issues regarding the development of retail projects in partnership with major anchor tenants.

**Personal:** The Ohio State University College of Law (1983); Miami University (1979).

## PIGMAN, Jack R
Porter Wright Morris & Arthur LLP, Columbus
614 227 2119
jpigman@porterwright.com
*Featured in Bankruptcy/Restructuring (Ohio)*

**Career:** Mr Pigman, former chair of the firm's Bankruptcy and Reorganization Practice Group, specializes in business reorganizations and creditor-debtor rights law. He represents debtor and creditor committees as well as financial institutions and syndicates in business workouts, loan restructuring and Chapter 11 cases. His business reorganization practice includes non-judicial workouts, the purchase and sale of businesses, receiverships and foreclosures. Mr Pigman serves as a mediator in commercial disputes and is a frequent speaker on various insolvency, bankruptcy and lender liability topics.

## PORTER II, William G
Vorys, Sater, Seymour and Pease LLP, Columbus
614 464 5448
wgporter@vorys.com
*Featured in Litigation (Ohio)*

**Practice Areas:** Chair of the firm's litigation group. He has extensive experience with complex business and commercial litigation, including directors and officers liability claims and class actions, involving a variety of entities, including banks, universities, pharmaceutical companies and design professionals.
**Professional Memberships:** American College of Trial Lawyers, Fellow (2011); American, Ohio and Columbus Bar Associations. Elected by peers as "Ohio Super Lawyer" and listed in "Best Lawyers In America."
**Career:** Admitted to Ohio Bar 1984.
**Personal:** Case Western Reserve University School of Law, JD, 1984; Amherst College, BA, cum laude, 1978.

## POWAR, Lee
Hahn Loeser & Parks LLP, Cleveland
216 274 2295
ldpowar@hahnlaw.com
*Featured in Bankruptcy/Restructuring (Ohio)*

**Practice Areas:** Mr Powar represents debtors, creditors' committees, creditors and indenture trustees in insolvency matters. He counsels bank lenders, commercial finance companies and agricultural lenders in complex, multi-lender loan workout transactions and loans to cutting-edge, high-tech borrowers. Mr Powar has also had extensive dealings in labor, pension and environmental issues, among others. In addition to his Ohio work, he is involved in workouts and bankruptcies of substantial South Florida businesses and real estate developments.
**Personal:** University of Michigan Law School (JD, 1963); Cornell University (BA, 1960).

## PRESSLEY JR, Fred G
Porter Wright Morris & Arthur LLP, Columbus
614 227 2233
fpressley@porterwright.com
*Featured in Labor & Employment (Ohio)*

**Career:** Mr Pressley is Chair of Porter Wright's Labor and Employment Department. For over 30 years, he has successfully represented clients in employment discrimination litigation, union avoidance campaigns, collective bargaining, and wage-and-hour matters around the country. His litigation experience also includes enforcing and defending employment contracts, trade secrets, and covenants-not-to-compete. He also helps clients avoid employee-relations difficulties by providing proactive advice and counsel on issues that arise during the course of an employment relationship. He regularly represents employers in employment discrimination, wage and hour, and contract-based litigation claims in both state and federal court and before various administrative agencies.

## PRIOR, James
Porter Wright Morris & Arthur LLP, Columbus
jprior@porterwright.com
614 227 2008
*Featured in Employee Benefits & Executive Compensation (Ohio)*

**Career:** Mr Prior represents clients in the design, implementation, administration, amendment, and termination of group health plan and other welfare plan benefits. In conjunction with this representation, he also assists clients with cafeteria plans, voluntary employees' beneficiaries associations, third-party administration agreements, COBRA administration, consumer-driven health care programs, wellness programs, domestic partner benefits, Medicare Secondary Payer issues, HIPAA privacy and security rule compliance, and compliance with the myriad other laws impacting health and welfare plans, including the Internal Revenue Code, ERISA, HIPAA and the Affordable Care Act (Health Care Reform). Mr Prior received his J.D. from The University of Virginia.

## RAWSON, Robert
Jones Day, Cleveland
216 586 7216
rrawson@jonesday.com
*Featured in Litigation (Ohio)*

**Practice Areas:** He counsels and litigates concerning antitrust and trade regulation issues. Recently led a team for R.J. Reynolds Tobacco to a defense jury verdict on a price discrimination claim seeking several billion dollars in damages. On the plaintiff's side, he won multimillions of dollars for Hospital Corporation of America in a conspiracy and monopolization case. Also has had successful appellate arguments in the Second, Seventh, Eighth, Ninth, Tenth, and Eleventh Circuits.
**Professional Memberships:** ABA; Ohio State Bar Association; Cleveland Bar Association; Bar Association of the District of Columbia.
**Personal:** Chaired Princeton University Board; currently chairs Cleveland State University Board.

## REGO, John A
Jones Day, Cleveland
216 586 7542
jrego@jonesday.com
*Featured in Natural Resources (Ohio)*

**Practice Areas:** Litigates on behalf of clients in governmental and private party environmental claims, including toxic tort, Superfund and natural resource damage litigation with federal and state trustees, RCRA, Clean Water Act, and environmental indemnification claims. Assists clients with rulemaking comments and administrative challenges. Routinely provides strategic environmental counseling on topics including brownfield redevelopment or divestment strategies, and environmental compliance. Founder and Executive Editor of The Climate Report, Jones Day's quarterly client advisory on climate change developments.
**Career:** Law clerk, Hon. Stanley Harris, US District Court, District of Columbia. Chemical engineer in product development, The Procter & Gamble Company.

## REILLY, Timothy P
Taft Stettinius & Hollister LLP, Cincinnati
513 357 9367
reilly@taftlaw.com
*Featured in Labor & Employment (Ohio)*

**Practice Areas:** Japan, Labor & Employment, Workplace Safety and Health.
**Professional Memberships:** American Bar Association, Cincinnati Bar Association, Cincinnati Law Library Association.
**Career:** Mr Reilly represents employers in all forms of employment litigation, including employment discrimination claims, disability claims under the ADA and state law, FMLA claims, non-compete and related claims, collective bargaining contract claims, picket line and strike injunction cases, and other employment-related litigation. He has also served as chief negotiator in over 250 collective bargaining negotiations, both initial and renewal contracts.
**Personal:** University of Cincinnati College of Law (1978); University of Notre Dame (1975).

## REMINGTON, Rob
Hahn Loeser & Parks LLP, Cleveland
216 274 2208
rrremington@hahnlaw.com
*Featured in Construction (Ohio), Litigation (Ohio)*

**Practice Areas:** Mr Remington co-chairs the firm's Litigation Area and chairs its Construction Practice Group. He serves as national construction counsel for a number of publicly-traded companies and represents a wide range of clients in construction related matters across the country. He is former chair of the ABA Section of Litigation Construction Litigation Committee, Member of the Fellows of the American Bar, and frequent speaker on construction law for the ABA, AAA and other organizations in the construction industry.
**Personal:** Cleveland-Marshall College of Law (JD, cum laude, 1988); College of Applied Science and Technology, Rochester Institute of Technology (BS, 1983).

## REUTER, F Mark
Keating Muething & Klekamp PLL, Cincinnati
513 579 6469
freuter@kmklaw.com
*Featured in Corporate/M&A (Ohio)*

**Practice Areas:** Mr Reuter advocates for business clients in transactions, proceedings and conflicts governed by federal and state securities regulations and stock exchange listing standards. He applies his experience in securities regulatory matters for the benefit of both publicly traded and privately owned clients in strategic transactions, executive compensation and equity arrangements, corporate governance, reporting, and administrative actions.
**Personal:** JD, University of Notre Dame Law, 1996; cum laude. BA, University of Notre Dame, 1992; magna cum laude.

## ROBENALT, James D
Thompson Hine LLP, Cleveland
216 566 5755
Jim.Robenalt@ThompsonHine.com
*Featured in Litigation (Ohio)*

**Career:** Jim is a partner in the Business Litigation Group. A trial lawyer his entire career, he handles complex commercial and intellectual property disputes and has tried major construction cases. Jim was co-lead counsel for a Fortune 500 company in a civil RICO case, resulting in an $81 million jury verdict against Taiwanese defendants that followed the first successful prosecution under the Economic Espionage Act of 1996. In 2004, he was Lead Counsel in an arbitration among pharmaceutical companies, ending in a $68 million award. He currently heads a team working on a multi-district litigation involving hormone replacement therapy drugs.

## ROBINS, Harlan W
Dickinson Wright PLLC, Columbus
614 744 2575
hrobins@dickinsonwright.com
*Featured in Real Estate (Ohio)*

**Practice Areas:** Harlan Robins is a member in the the Columbus Office and maintains a commercial real estate and general business practice, with emphasis on real estate and mezzanine lending, real estate development, commercial leasing, land use and general corporate real estate services. He assists in the acquisition of land, development and leasing for office, hotel and shopping centers and joint venture formation, with considerable experience in real estate healthcare issues. He also has extensive loan restructuring and workout experience and performs real estate-related counseling in corporate bankruptcies and reorganizations. Mr Robins received his juris doctor from Emory University School of Law, and a bachelor of arts from the University of Michigan.

## ROGERS, Gregory Parker
Taft Stettinius & Hollister LLP, Cincinnati
513 357 9349
rogers@taftlaw.com
*Featured in Labor & Employment (Ohio)*

**Practice Areas:** Employee Benefits & Executive Compensation, Construction, Class Action and

Multi-Party Litigation, ERISA Litigation, Labor & Employment, Workplace Safety and Health.
**Professional Memberships:** American Bar Association, American Employment Law Council.
**Career:** Mr Rogers is co-chair of the Labor & Employment group. He represents private and public employers in all aspects of labor and employment law, and he has substantial experience in sophisticated labor, employment and benefits litigation issues.
**Publications:** Contributor to "Employment Discrimination Law" (4th Edition) and "How Arbitration Works" (6th Edition).
**Personal:** Emory University School of Law (1989); Miami University (1986).

### ROGERS, Karla
Calfee, Halter & Griswold LLP, Cleveland
216 622 8616
krogers@calfee.com
*Featured in Real Estate (Ohio)*
**Practice Areas:** Real estate; commercial business and finance; mergers and acquisitions.
**Professional Memberships:** Cleveland Metropolitan Bar Association, Ohio Bar Association, Chicago Title Insurance Company Advisory Board Member; Board of Directors, Shoes and Clothes for Kids.
**Career:** Partner. Primary focus is real estate law and commercial business finance law. Experienced in property development, land use acquisitions, dispositions and leases involving corporate mergers, acquisitions and divestitures. Structures, negotiates and drafts real estate financing agreements and facilitates secured financing transactions. Negotiates and drafts commercial, industrial and retail leases.
**Personal:** Cleveland-Marshall College of Law, JD, cum laude, 1996; University of Akron, BS, cum laude, 1992.

### ROSENBERG, Thomas L
Roetzel & Andress, LPA, Columbus
614 723 2006
trosenberg@ralaw.com
*Featured in Construction (Ohio)*
**Practice Areas:** Mr Rosenberg focuses his practice on construction law and civil litigation. He represents owners, architects, engineers, contractors, subcontractors and suppliers in all aspects of construction law, as well as bidders for construction and purchase contracts on challenges to competitive bidding determinations and awards. He serves as a construction mediator and is an arbitrator with the American Arbitration Association. He has experience drafting contracts of construction for multi-million dollar construction projects undertaken by public and private owners in Ohio and elsewhere. In addition, Mr Rosenberg continues to serve in leadership positions for many construction law and trade organizations.

### RUEHLMANN, Mark J
Squire Sanders (US) LLP, Cincinnati
513 361 1210
mark.ruehlmann@squiresanders.com
*Featured in Litigation (Ohio)*
**Practice Areas:** Practice focuses on commercial and class action litigation, with an emphasis on

cases in the financial services sector, along with disputes involving healthcare, business interruption, product liability and trade secrets. Represents a variety of clients, ranging from Fortune 500 corporations to individual entrepreneurs, in federal and state trial and appellate courts. Recent experience includes representing The Christ Hospital in connection with its withdrawal from The Health Alliance of Greater Cincinnati and leading Squire Sanders' litigation representation of the Official Committee of Unsecured Creditors in the Enron bankruptcy.

### RUSH, Jeffery
Frost Brown Todd LLC, Cincinnati
513 651 6893
jrush@fbtlaw.com
*Featured in Banking & Finance (Ohio)*
**Practice Areas:** Banking, commercial law and real estate, including workouts and restructurings.
**Professional Memberships:** Admitted to practice in Ohio (1975). Member, Banking, Commercial Law and Bankruptcy Subcommittee of the Ohio State Bar Association and the Section of Business Law of the American Bar Association.
**Career:** Joined Frost Brown Todd, 1975; Member, 1982; former Head of Commercial Transactions and Real Estate Department; former Member of the Executive Committee.
**Personal:** Born 18 September 1950. JD, Vanderbilt University, 1975; BS (Economics), Wharton School of the University of Pennsylvania, 1972.

### RUSSELL, Gregory
Vorys, Sater, Seymour and Pease LLP, Columbus
614 464 5468
gdrussell@vorys.com
*Featured in Natural Resources (Ohio)*
**Practice Areas:** A partner representing clients in business and litigation matters related to the exploration, production, transportation, and marketing of oil, natural gas, and their constituents.
**Professional Memberships:** Ohio State Bar Association; Ohio Oil and Gas Association, Chair, Environmental Committee; Energy and Mineral Law Foundation, Board of Trustees; Rocky Mountain Mineral Law Foundation.
**Career:** Ohio, US Supreme Court, US Court of Appeals for the Sixth Circuit, US District Courts for the Northern District and Southern District of Ohio.
**Personal:** Harvard Law School, JD, 1992; Washington and Lee University, BA summa cum laude, 1988; TH Darmstadt, West Germany, 1989.

### SAAD, Michael D
Squire Sanders (US) LLP, Columbus
614 365 2735
michael.saad@squiresanders.com
*Featured in Real Estate (Ohio)*
**Practice Areas:** Partner and former leader of Squire Sanders' Real Estate Practice Group. Practice focuses on corporate banking, real estate, real estate finance, joint ventures, equity funds, low-income housing tax credits, rehabilitation tax credits and government housing law. Served on the management committee of Squire Sanders.

Listed in The Best Lawyers in America and Ohio Super Lawyers.
**Professional Memberships:** American Bar Association, Forum on Affordable Housing and Community Development; Ohio Housing Council; Columbus Bar Association, Financial Institutions, Bankruptcy and Real Properties Committees; Association of Foreign Investors in Real Estate.

### SAADA JR, John M
Jones Day, Cleveland
216 586 7089
johnmsaada@jonesday.com
*Featured in Corporate/M&A (Ohio)*
**Practice Areas:** Represents private equity funds and strategic investors in investment activities, including venture capital investments, leveraged buyouts, mergers and acquisitions, restructurings, joint ventures, mezzanine financings, and fund formation. He has extensive experience in the formation and governance of private investment funds and the organization and documentation of fund sponsors' internal firm arrangements. Also represents limited partners in their investments in private equity funds. He also advises private companies in sectors such as healthcare, technology, information services and consumer products. His work with these companies focuses on strategic counsel, mergers and acquisitions, joint ventures, financings, compensation and governance matters.

### SANKER, Robert G
Keating Muething & Klekamp PLL, Cincinnati
513 579 6587
rsanker@kmklaw.com
*Featured in Bankruptcy/Restructuring (Ohio)*
**Practice Areas:** Mr Sanker's practice is concentrated in the areas of bankruptcy, reorganization and creditors' rights. He has extensive experience in representing debtors, creditors, creditors' committees, lenders, investors and purchasers in Chapter 11 cases and in and out of court restructurings.
**Professional Memberships:** American Bankruptcy Institute, Tri-State Association for Corporate Renewal, Midwest Regional Bankruptcy Seminar Executive Committee.
**Personal:** JD, Georgetown University Law Center, 1987. BA, Xavier University, 1984; magna cum laude.

### SAXBE, Charles
Taft Stettinius & Hollister LLP, Columbus
614 334 6104
rsaxbe@taftlaw.com
*Featured in Litigation (Ohio)*
**Practice Areas:** Public Law, Litigation, College & University Law, Ethics & Professional Responsibility, School Public Finance, Campaign & Election Law, Government Relations.
**Career:** Charles R "Rocky" Saxbe is Partner-in-Charge of the Columbus office. He maintains an active litigation practice representing clients in all aspects of civil litigation. He has acted as principal litigation counsel in numerous complex litigation cases. He has also appeared in numerous jury trials and before the Ohio Supreme Court, Ohio

Courts of Appeals and the Sixth Circuit US Court of Appeals.
**Personal:** The Ohio State University College of Law (1975); Southern Methodist University (1969).

### SAYRE, Russell S.
Taft Stettinius & Hollister LLP, Cincinnati
513 357 9304
sayre@taftlaw.com
*Featured in Litigation (Ohio)*
**Practice Areas:** Litigation, First Amendment & Media Law, Emerging Companies, Ethics & Professional Responsibility, Class Action and Multi-Party Litigation, Securities - Litigation.
**Career:** Mr Sayre has represented corporate, business and individual clients in federal and state courts, in alternative dispute resolution, and before state administrative boards. He is admitted to practice in all Ohio courts, in the United States District Courts for the Southern District of Ohio and the Southern District of Indiana, and in the United States Courts of Appeals for the Third and Sixth Circuits.
**Personal:** University of Virginia School of Law (1990); Mary Washington College (1986).

### SCHEIER, Michael L
Keating Muething & Klekamp PLL, Cincinnati
513 579 6952
mscheier@kmklaw.com
*Featured in Litigation (Ohio)*
**Practice Areas:** Mr Scheier is a trial lawyer. His practice is concentrated in the areas of defending ERISA fiduciary duty claims, state law director and officer defense, and complex banking and creditor's rights disputes, including bankruptcy related litigation. He has served as the leader of the Litigation Group, Chair of the Diversity Committee and as a member of the Associates and Hiring Committees.
**Personal:** JD, University of Cincinnati College of Law, 1991; Order of the Coif, Editor-in-Chief of Law Review. BA, Hobart College, 1983.

### SCHERZER, Donald
Roetzel & Andress, LPA, Akron
216 615 7418
dscherzer@ralaw.com
*Featured in Litigation (Ohio)*
**Practice Areas:** Mr Scherzer is Practice Group Manager of the Business Litigation group. He focuses on white-collar crime, criminal and civil antitrust, securities, complex business, and commercial litigation. He has represented clients in both Foreign Corrupt Practices Act and international price fixing investigations regarding their activities in Asia and Europe, in addition to several significant SEC matters. His experience also includes civil and criminal bank, tax and health care fraud, common law fraud, and civil and criminal environmental matters. He is AV Preeminent rated by Martindale & Hubbell and selected as one of the Best Lawyers in America since 2005.

**SCHLOEMER, Jeffrey S**
Taft Stettinius & Hollister LLP, Cincinnati
513 357 9609
schloemer@taftlaw.com
*Featured in Banking & Finance (Ohio)*

**Practice Areas:** Emerging companies, international, structured finance, sports, private equity and venture capital, mergers and acquisitions, corporate governance, banking and institutional finance, business and finance, business succession planning, corporate finance.
**Professional Memberships:** Cincinnati Bar Association.
**Career:** Mr Schloemer is co-chair of the Business & Finance group. He practices primarily in the areas of banking and finance, mergers and acquisitions, and commercial and corporate law. He has broad-based experience in advising businesses on corporate, contractual, capital formation, business planning and regulatory matters.
**Personal:** Duke University School of Law (1983); University of Notre Dame (1980).

**SCHMIDT JR, Robert J**
Porter Wright Morris & Arthur LLP, Columbus
614 227 2028
rschmidt@porterwright.com
*Featured in Natural Resources (Ohio)*

**Career:** Mr Schmidt represents clients in environmental programs, including Clean Water Act, Clean Air Act, Superfund, and solid and hazardous waste. He frequently negotiates with state and federal environmental agencies on regulatory issues and enforcement matters. Mr Schmidt's practice includes significant representation of major utilities in the development and siting of utility facilities, including new generation and transmission facilities. He also assists clients with environmental considerations in real estate and business transactions, including drafting and reviewing commercial leases, asset purchase agreements and other commercial transactions. He represents coal, industrial mineral, and oil and gas companies in regulatory and enforcement matters.

**SCHMIT, David E**
Frost Brown Todd LLC, Cincinnati
513 651 6985
dschmit@fbtlaw.com
*Featured in Intellectual Property (Ohio)*

**Practice Areas:** David practices in all areas of intellectual property law, with particular concentration in patent, trademark, copyright, trade secret and unfair competition litigation. During his more than 30 year career he has acted as lead trial counsel in nearly 100 litigation cases, including 10 complex jury trials in which he was sole trial attorney.
**Professional Memberships:** Cincinnati Patent Law Association, Ohio State Bar Association, Mensa, USPTO.
**Career:** Chambers USA (2008-13); Ohio Super Lawyers (2008, 2012); The Best Lawyers in America (2008-13); The Best Lawyers in America Cincinnati Litigation-Intellectual Property Lawyer of the Year (2012); AV Rated, Martindale-Hubbell.

**SCHNAPP, Karlyn**
Frost Brown Todd LLC, Cincinnati
513 651 6865
kschnapp@fbtlaw.com
*Featured in Intellectual Property (Ohio)*

**Practice Areas:** Intellectual property law, in particular patent prosecution (chemical/pharma/bio), counseling, infringement, patentability and validity opinions and licensing.
**Professional Memberships:** Admitted in Ohio, US Patent and Trademark Office, Intellectual Property Law Association, Ohio Bar Association, Cincinnati Bar Association, American Chemical Society.
**Career:** Joined Frost Brown Todd in 2000; prior to joining was a professor of organic chemistry at Northern Kentucky University for nine and a half years.
**Personal:** BS (with honors in Chemistry), University of Cincinnati, 1984; PhD (organic chemistry) 1989, University of Cincinnati; JD 2000, Chase College of Law, Northern Kentucky University.

**SCHOEN, Ann G.**
Frost Brown Todd LLC, Cincinnati
513 651 6128
aschoen@fbtlaw.com
*Featured in Intellectual Property (Ohio)*

**Practice Areas:** Practice Group Leader of Intellectual Property Practice Group. Represents clients in intellectual property litigation and counsels clients on all aspects of intellectual property law, including patent prosecution, intellectual property portfolio management, and licensing.
**Professional Memberships:** Ohio State Bar Association; Federal Bar Association; American Intellectual Property Law Association; American Bar Association.
**Career:** Prior to joining Frost Brown Todd, worked as an engineer and then as in-house patent counsel at General Electric.
**Personal:** JD from Salmon P. Chase College of Law of Northern Kentucky University; Bachelor of Science degree in Chemical Engineering from the University of Notre Dame.

**SCHRAFF, Christopher**
Porter Wright Morris & Arthur LLP, Columbus
614 227 2097
cschraff@porterwright.com
*Featured in Natural Resources (Ohio)*

**Career:** Mr Schraff practices in the Firm's Environmental/Energy/Government Department. His areas of practice include the Federal Water Pollution Control Act, CERCLA and RCRA matters, wetlands regulation, pretreatment requirements, state and local environmental statutes and regulations, oil and gas regulatory matters, and lender and fiduciary liability issues. He regularly practices before the Public Utilities Commission's Ohio Power Siting Board where he is involved in the siting of electric transmission lines, electric generation facilities, and gas pipelines. He has extensive experience in negotiating and drafting environmental provisions for purchase agreements, loan documents, real estate documents, and other business documents.

**SCHREINER, David E**
Fisher & Phillips LLP, Cleveland
440 838 8800
dschreiner@laborlawyers.com
*Featured in Labor & Employment (Ohio)*

**Career:** Dave Schreiner is a partner in the Cleveland office. Although he has counseled employers in virtually all areas of labor and employment law, his primary focus is in the traditional labor relations area. He has extensive experience in successfully counteracting union organizing drives, developing programs designed to maintain union-free status, and obtaining favorable contract results at the bargaining table.

**SCRUTTON, Suzanne**
Vorys, Sater, Seymour and Pease LLP, Columbus
614 464 8313
sjscrutton@vorys.com
*Featured in Healthcare (Ohio)*

**Practice Areas:** Partner in the health care group. She has experience representing providers and trade associations in the fields of long term care, behavioral health and developmental disabilities. She also has extensive experience with regulatory issues, Medicaid reimbursement and regulations, as well as contract negotiations with various payor sources.
**Professional Memberships:** American Health Lawyers Association.
**Personal:** Capital University Law School, JD; Albion College, BA, cum laude, with honors.

**SHADLEY, Frederic X**
Ulmer & Berne LLP, Cincinnati
513 698 5014
fshadley@ulmer.com
*Featured in Litigation (Ohio)*

**Practice Areas:** Chair of the firm's Construction Group, with more than 30 years of trial experience and an engineering degree, Fritz's background in complex litigation includes construction disputes, product liability and environmental litigation, class action claims, and toxic tort litigation. In business litigation, his concentration is in contract and transactional disputes, professional liability, and intellectual property litigation, including copyright/trademark and trade secrets disputes.
**Professional Memberships:** Federation of Defense and Corporate Counsel, Defense Research Institute, and The Fellows of the American Bar Foundation.

**SHAW, Russell C**
Walter & Haverfield LLP, Cleveland
216 928 2888
rshaw@walterhav.com
*Featured in Employee Benefits & Executive Compensation (Ohio)*

**Professional Memberships:** American and Ohio State Bar Associations; International Foundation of Employee Benefit Plans.
**Career:** An employee benefits specialist since 1970, Russ chairs the firm's Employee Benefits Group and has a nationwide practice that includes all aspects of employee benefit plans, including retirement plans, welfare benefit plans, voluntary employee beneficiary associations, executive deferred compensation, Taft-Hartley Act plans, and 403(b) tax deferred annuities. He also advises charitable foundations and other exempt organizations. Russ is an Adjunct Professor of Law at Case Western Reserve University School of Law.
**Personal:** The Ohio State University, JD, 1965; The Ohio State University, BS in BA, 1962.

**SHEERAN, Timothy J**
Squire Sanders (US) LLP, Cleveland
216 479 8605
tim.sheeran@squiresanders.com
*Featured in Labor & Employment (Ohio)*

**Practice Areas:** Partner representing educational institutions in contract negotiations, grievance arbitration, litigation, education law, employment and wage issues and employment discrimination matters. For private sector clients, provides counsel on issues including equal employment opportunity litigation, wage-hour problems, class action litigation, employment of the disabled, private employment agreements, bankruptcy and pension matters. Listed in The Best Lawyers in America.
**Professional Memberships:** American Bar Association, Labor and Employment Section; Ohio State Bar Association, Labor and Employment Section; Cleveland Metropolitan Bar Association, Labor and Employment Section; National Council of School Attorneys; Ohio Council of School Attorneys; Education Law Association.

**SHERMAN, Ryan**
Porter Wright Morris & Arthur LLP, Columbus
614 227 2184
rsherman@porterwright.com
*Featured in Litigation (Ohio)*

**Career:** Mr Sherman is a Partner in Porter Wright's Litigation Department and serves as co-chair of the firm's Construction group. He concentrates his practice in complex commercial disputes, with a focus on construction matters, intellectual property litigation, securities and shareholder disputes, and health care litigation. Mr Sherman has successfully argued before the United States Court of Appeals for the Sixth Circuit, and has successfully represented clients in Federal District Courts for the Southern and Northern Districts of Ohio, and numerous Ohio state courts at the trial and appellate levels. Mr Sherman's practice also involves representing clients in emergency injunctive proceedings.

**SHLONSKY, Patricia A**
Ulmer & Berne LLP, Cleveland
216 583 7012
pshlonsky@ulmer.com
*Featured in Employee Benefits & Executive Compensation (Ohio)*

**Practice Areas:** Chair of the Employee Benefits Group, the Tax Practice Group, and a member of the Management Committee, Patty has experience assisting clients in the establishment, qualification, and maintenance of all types of employee benefit plans. She advises clients regarding employee benefit compliance issues, benefits issues associated with mergers and acquisitions, privacy and data

security issues under HIPAA, health benefit issues under the Affordable Care Act, executive compensation, and represents clients involved in governmental and private dispute resolution. Patty also handles all types of ERISA litigation.
**Professional Memberships:** Worldwide Employee Benefits Network, American Society of Pension Actuaries Benefits Counsel.

### SHULLER, Donald
Vorys, Sater, Seymour and Pease LLP, Cincinnati
513 723 4010
djshuller@vorys.com
*Featured in Real Estate (Ohio)*
**Practice Areas:** Partner representing developers, purchasers, sellers, landlords, tenants, and lenders with respect to all types of commercial real estate, including office, retail, industrial and multi-family residential transactions.
**Professional Memberships:** American, Ohio, and Cincinnati Bar Associations; National Association of Office and Industrial Parks;Philada Home Fund, Board Member, 1996-present; National Multiple Sclerosis Society, Ohio Valley Chapter, Board Chair, 1996-2006.
**Career:** Admitted to Ohio.
**Personal:** University of Virginia School of Law, JD, 1976; University of Virginia, BS, cum laude, 1973.

### SHUNK, Thomas H
Baker & Hostetler LLP, Cleveland
216 861 7592
tshunk@bakerlaw.com
*Featured in Intellectual Property (Ohio)*
**Career:** Thomas Shunk brings a corporate trial lawyer's perspective to patent, trade secret and other technology-focused IP litigation. Tom has tried more than forty cases as lead trial counsel throughout the United States, in fields as diverse as software for medical imaging, high-speed powered knife blades, groundwater pollution remediation methods and liquid crystal displays. He has litigated numerous copyright, trademark, trade dress and Lanham Act issues. Tom is a member of the Mediation Panel for the US District Court, Northern District of Ohio. He has argued orally before the Federal Circuit Court of Appeals on more than a dozen occasions.

### SIEGEL, Bradd N
Porter Wright Morris & Arthur LLP, Columbus
614 227 2238
bsiegel@porterwright.com
*Featured in Labor & Employment (Ohio)*
**Career:** Mr Siegel has over 30 years of experience in labor and employment litigation defending employers against claims brought under state and federal employment discrimination statutes, ERISA, Section 301 of the LMRA, and state wrongful discharge law, including class actions. He is a Fellow of the College of Labor and Employment Lawyers and a founding member of the Ohio Management Lawyers Association, and has served for many years on the Ohio Chamber of Commerce's Labor and Employment Law Advisory Committee. Mr Siegel received his JD from George Washington University Law School

(with honors) and his LLM from Georgetown University.

### SMITH, Andrew
Vorys, Sater, Seymour and Pease LLP, Columbus
614 464 5434
ACSmith@vorys.com
*Featured in Labor & Employment (Ohio)*
**Practice Areas:** Chair of the firm's labor and employment group. His practice focuses on all aspects of labor and employment law, including employment litigation, wrongful discharge, and wage and hour class actions. Mr Smith has represented employers in federal and state court proceedings across the country; administrative matters before federal and state agencies; and in traditional labor relations issues. His clients include national retailers, home builders, financial institutions, and international container manufacturers.
**Professional Memberships:** Ohio State and Columbus Bar Associations.
**Personal:** He received his JD from the University of Pittsburgh School of Law and BA from the College of Wooster.

### SMITH, J Theodore (Ted)
Vorys, Sater, Seymour and Pease LLP, Columbus
614 464 6232
jtsmith@vorys.com
*Featured in Real Estate (Ohio)*
**Practice Areas:** Partner concentrating his practice on construction contracts (domestic and international including Europe, Asia, and South America), condominium law, real estate acquisition and sales, real estate development, leasing, liens, evictions, foreclosures and real estate secured loans. Licensed title agent.
**Professional Memberships:** American Bar Association, Columbus Bar Association, National Association of Industrial & Office Properties, The Building Industry Association of Central Ohio, and International Council of Shopping Centers.
**Career:** Admitted to Ohio Bar.
**Personal:** University of Illinois College of Law, JD, magna cum laude, 1998. Purdue University, BS Civil Engineering, Chi Epsilon, 1992. Frequent speaker for real estate related seminars.

### SMITH, Jeffery
Vorys, Sater, Seymour and Pease LLP, Columbus
614 464 5436
jesmith@vorys.com
*Featured in Corporate/M&A (Ohio)*
**Practice Areas:** Partner in the the corporate and finance group. He has more than 30 years experience in financial institution regulatory and corporate matters, including mergers, acquisitions, divestitures, regulatory compliance, capital raising, securities matters, corporate governance matters, "troubled institution" issues and de novo bank and holding company formation. Throughout his career, Smith has represented multinational financial services holding companies as well as community bank organizations.
**Professional Memberships:** Ohio State, Indiana State, Columbus and Toledo Bar

Associations; Ohio Bankers League; Community Bankers Association of Ohio; Indiana Bankers Association.
**Personal:** University of Toledo College of Law, JD; University of Toledo, BA.

### SOLECKI, Mike
Jones Day, Cleveland
216 586 7103
mjsolecki@jonesday.com
*Featured in Corporate/M&A (Ohio)*
**Practice Areas:** Advises a diverse range of companies and financial institutions on corporate finance and corporate governance matters. His corporate finance practice includes public and private equity and debt offerings and restructurings, including Rule 144A offerings, tender offers, and exchange offers. He also regularly advises public companies on corporate governance, securities laws, stock exchange rules and regulations, and periodic reporting responsibilities.

### SOLIMINE, Louis F
Thompson Hine LLP, Cincinnati
513 352 6784
Louis.Solimine@ThompsonHine.com
*Featured in Bankruptcy/Restructuring (Ohio)*
**Career:** Louis is a partner in the firm's Business Restructuring, Creditors' Rights & Bankruptcy Practice Group and has extensive experience in significant Chapter 11 reorganizations, commercial workouts, foreclosure cases, receiverships and assignments for the benefit of creditors. He has represented debtors, creditors' committees, secured lenders, equipment lessors, landlords and tenants, trade creditors, health insurers, prospective acquirers, preference defendants, and other interested parties in numerous major Chapter 11 cases throughout the United States. Louis also focuses his practice on related matters arising under the UCC including sales, personal property leases, letters of credit, security agreements and secured party sales.

### SOLOMON, Randall L
Baker & Hostetler LLP, Cleveland
216 861 7327
rsolomon@bakerlaw.com
*Featured in Litigation (Ohio)*
**Career:** Randall Solomon, a Fellow in the American College of Trial Lawyers and past Chairman of the Litigation Section of the Cleveland Bar Association, is a "hands-on" trial lawyer who concentrates his practice in commercial litigation, the defense of mass toxic tort cases and the defense of legal malpractice claims. He has extensive experience in defending against and in the settlement of class actions, and has appeared before the Judicial Panel for Multidistrict Litigation. He is the Vice-Chair of the Ohio Commission on the Rules of Practice and Procedure and Chair of the Commission's Rules of Evidence Subcommittee.

### SOZIO, Stephen
Jones Day, Cleveland
216 586 7201
sgsozio@jonesday.com
*Featured in Litigation (Ohio)*

**Practice Areas:** His practice involves representing businesses, healthcare organizations and their executives during investigations by federal and local governmental authorities for potential criminal charges and civil claims; investigating and prosecuting and/or defending civil actions on behalf of clients involved with fraud, false claims, and other business-related wrongdoing; and advising corporate clients regarding compliance issues to avoid governmental sanctions. He has also conducted many internal and external investigations on behalf of Boards of Directors and senior management. Adjunct Professor at the Cleveland-Marshall College of Law of Cleveland State University where he has taught criminal procedure and corporate criminal law.

### SQUERI, Steve
Jones Day, Cleveland
216 586 7237
sjsqueri@jonesday.com
*Featured in Litigation (Ohio)*
**Practice Areas:** Steve Squeri litigates civil and criminal antitrust cases and other complex business cases in the areas of business torts and white-collar crime.
**Professional Memberships:** Steve is an active member of the ABA Antitrust Law Section and the Council of the Antitrust Section of the Ohio State Bar Association.
**Publications:** Steve is one of the two principal editors and authors of the ABA Criminal Antitrust Litigation Handbook (second edition).
**Personal:** Steve is chairman of the board of directors for the Center for Community Solutions and also serves on the board of directors for the United Way of Greater Cleveland.

### STANSBURY, Ronald C
Ulmer & Berne LLP, Cleveland
216 583 7016
rstansbury@ulmer.com
*Featured in Employee Benefits & Executive Compensation (Ohio)*
**Practice Areas:** Ron's practice focuses on employee benefits and executive compensation law, representing publicly and privately held corporations and tax exempt entities, their respective boards of directors and trustees and compensation committees, as well as individual executives. He helps clients develop executive compensation arrangements and all types of employee benefit plans, including, within the context of initial public offerings, mergers and acquisitions.
**Professional Memberships:** Internal Revenue Service TE/GE Advisory Council, Great Lakes Region, Worldwide Employee Benefits Network (WEB), and Cleveland Law Library Association (Board/Chair of the Strategic Planning Committee).
**Personal:** Alzheimer's Association Cleveland Chapter (Board, Chair of the Compensation Committee).

## STARKEY, J Shane
Thompson Hine LLP, Cincinnati
513 352 6737
Shane.Starkey@ThompsonHine.com
*Featured in Employee Benefits & Executive Compensation (Ohio)*
**Career:** Shane is the partner-in-charge of the firm's Cincinnati office. He advises public companies on the tax, corporate governance and securities law aspects of executive compensation. Shane designs various executive compensation arrangements such as equity incentive plans, bonus plans, fringe benefit programs, deferred compensation arrangements, employment and severance agreements. He counsels clients on the rules related to the $1 million deduction limit on executive pay and the executive compensation aspects of mergers and acquisitions, including the tax penalties imposed on golden parachute payments.

## STEINDLER, Howard
Benesch, Friedlander, Coplan & Aronoff LLP, Cleveland
216 363 4560
hsteindler@beneschlaw.com
*Featured in Real Estate (Ohio)*
**Practice Areas:** Leasing, acquisitions and divestitures, complex legal structures and multi-use projects, finance and construction, and general business and commercial law. Extensive experience with shopping malls, residential developments, shopping centers, mixed use developments, public company real estate, corporate headquarters developments, public projects, charitable gifts of real property transactions and urban projects.
**Career:** Past Chairman of Real Estate and Environmental Practice Group. Past Partner-in-Charge of the Cleveland office. Member of the American College of Real Estate Lawyers. Adjunct Lecturer of Law, Cleveland State University College of Law, 1980-85.
**Personal:** The Ohio State University (JD, cum laude, 1967); Miami University (BS, 1964).

## STEINER, Edward E
Keating Muething & Klekamp PLL, Cincinnati
513 579 6468
esteiner@kmklaw.com
*Featured in Corporate/M&A (Ohio)*
**Practice Areas:** The focus of Mr Steiner's practice is corporate, securities and financing law, where he has experience in mergers, acquisitions and divestitures representing both public and closely-held entities. He regularly represents investment limited partnerships in venture capital and private equity investment transactions, including investment partnerships that utilize New Markets Tax Credits and public/private partnerships. He has experience in initial and follow-on public offerings of securities, and in representing issuers and investors in private placements of securities.
**Personal:** JD, Yale University, College of Law, 1983. MA, Johns Hopkins University, 1980. BA, University of Virginia, 1977

## STEPANIAK, Mark J
Taft Stettinius & Hollister LLP, Cincinnati
513 357 9398
stepaniak@taftlaw.com
*Featured in Labor & Employment (Ohio)*
**Practice Areas:** Public Law, Health & Life Sciences, Education - Litigation, Labor & Employment, School Public Finance, Workplace Safety and Health.
**Career:** Mr Stepaniak represents employers in all aspects of labor and employment law, including litigation for employers in the federal and state courts involving wrongful discharge, sexual harassment, race and age discrimination, retaliatory discharge and wage and hour matters. He is experienced in trade secret and non-competition agreement litigation. He also has extensive experience negotiating collective bargaining agreements in various industries and for public sector employers.
**Personal:** University of Cincinnati College of Law (1980); Thomas More College (1977).

## STEPHEN, John M
Porter Wright Morris & Arthur LLP, Columbus
614 227 2193
jstephen@porterwright.com
*Featured in Labor & Employment (Ohio)*
**Career:** Mr Stephen has helped employers throughout the country solve virtually every kind of employment problem imaginable. He defends clients in adversarial proceedings, but also devotes considerable time partnering with in-house counsel and human resource officials to help avoid claims and reduce legal spend through strategic planning, policy development, crisis management and training. As an adjunct professor at Capital University Law and Graduate Center and coeditor of Ohio Employment Practices Law: A Practical Guide for Employers and Their Legal Counsel, Mr Stephen is constantly examining legal developments to help clients stay ahead of potential problems as well as the competition.

## STONE, James
Jackson Lewis LLP, Cleveland
216 750 0404
StoneJ@jacksonlewis.com
*Featured in Labor & Employment (Ohio)*
**Practice Areas:** Labor, employment litigation, wage/hour compliance; knowledgeable in manufacturing, transportation, automotive, health care, gaming, hospitality, steel.
**Professional Memberships:** ABA, Cleveland Metropolitan Bar Association, Ohio State Bar Association, SHRM, Northeast Ohio Human Resource Planning Society, Ohio Management Lawyers Association, Columbus Bar Association.
**Career:** Admitted in Ohio, Michigan, 6th Circuit Court of Appeals, 7th Circuit Court of Appeals, Northern District of Indiana, Eastern District of Michigan, Northern and Southern Districts of Ohio.
**Personal:** JD, Cleveland-Marshall College of Law (1986); BA, Ohio State University (1976); Cleveland Pops Orchestra, Trustee and Chairman, Human Resources Committee; Museum of

Contemporary Art (Cleveland), Board of Directors.

## STRAUSS, David J
Baker & Hostetler LLP, Cleveland
216 861 7472
dstrauss@bakerlaw.com
*Featured in Real Estate (Ohio)*
**Career:** David Strauss practices primarily in real estate transactions, partnership matters and tax planning. He focuses on tax-advantaged investments involving real estate, oil and gas, sport franchises and cable television, and has represented major developers, underwriters, general contractors, syndicators and individual investors in the structuring and planning of tax-advantaged investments, including historic tax credit and new market tax credit transactions. David has extensive experience in financing transactions, including conventional real estate financing, tax-exempt housing bonds and industrial revenue bond financing. In addition, he is skilled in structuring equity participation financing transactions for significant pension fund clients.

## STRIEFSKY, Linda A
Thompson Hine LLP, Cleveland
216 566 5733
Linda.Striefsky@ThompsonHine.com
*Featured in Real Estate (Ohio)*
**Career:** Linda is a Partner in the firm's Real Estate Practice Group. She is a past president of The American College of Real Estate Lawyers, the premier honorary organization for commercial real estate lawyers in the United States. Linda is the co-chair of the Real Estate Finance Team and chair of the Global Sourcing & Procurement Team. She focuses her practice on acquisitions and sales; real estate financing, including portfolio and multi-state financing transactions; corporate facilities management; sourcing contracts; leasing, easement and related agreements, including oil and gas leases; real estate taxes, including tax complaints, exemptions and abatement.

## SULLIVAN, Peggy
Frost Brown Todd LLC, Cincinnati
513 651 6763
msullivan@fbtlaw.com
*Featured in Real Estate (Ohio)*
**Practice Areas:** Represents lenders, developers, owners, and equity investors in transactions involving acquisitions, developments, financing, leasing, and the sale of real estate facilities.
**Professional Memberships:** Admitted to practice in Ohio and Kentucky. Former Fellow, ABA RPTE Section and Vice Chair Industrial Leasing Committee (2012-13); Member, International Council of Shopping Centers; American, Ohio, Kentucky and Cincinnati Bar Associations.
**Personal:** JD, University of Cincinnati, 2004; BA, University of Cincinnati, 2001.

## SUTTON, Stephen C
Baker & Hostetler LLP, Cleveland
216 861 6165
ssutton@bakerlaw.com
*Featured in Labor & Employment (Ohio)*
**Career:** Dedicated to assisting employers in resolving employment law issues, Stephen Sutton

has wide-ranging civil litigation experience in complex, multi-plaintiff and class action employment discrimination and wage and hour lawsuits. He represents employers before federal and state courts, administrative agencies and arbitrators in all facets of employment law in matters ranging from age, race, gender and disability discrimination to harassment issues. Steve counsels employers on FMLA and ADA compliance, noncompete and trade secrets matters and other areas of employment law. In addition to his successful trial court experience, he has obtained favorable results in state and federal courts of appeal.

## SWEENEY, Patrick J
Thompson Hine LLP, Cleveland
216 566 5793
Pat.Sweeney@ThompsonHine.com
*Featured in Construction (Ohio)*
**Career:** Pat is a partner in the firm's Construction and Real Estate Practice Groups. His transactional construction practice involves negotiation and preparation of construction and design professional agreements and project management and risk counseling on a variety of projects, such as regional shopping malls, industrial projects, offices, hotels, convention centers and major sports venues such as MLB parks, NFL stadiums, NBA arenas and NHL arenas. He has prepared and negotiated agreements on behalf of owners, contractors, architects and engineers. A significant portion of his practice also includes commercial real estate development, including purchases and sales, financing and leasing.

## TANGEMAN, Jill S
Vorys, Sater, Seymour and Pease LLP, Columbus
614 464 5608
jstangeman@vorys.com
*Featured in Real Estate (Ohio)*
**Practice Areas:** Partner in commercial and real estate group focusing in commercial real estate, with an emphasis on zoning, land use regulation and developer representation.
**Professional Memberships:** Board of Directors of the Junior League of Columbus, Ohio, LeaderSpark, Inc., Franklin County Residential Services, Inc., Board of Directors of Available Light Theater Co.
**Career:** Admitted to Ohio Bar, U.S. District Court for the Southern District of Ohio. Certified by the Ohio State Bar Association as a specialist in Business, Commercial and Industrial Real Property Law.
**Personal:** The Ohio State University College of Law, JD, 1996; Denison University, BA, 1993.

## TANNOUS, Robert
Porter Wright Morris & Arthur LLP, Columbus
614 227 1953
rtannous@porterwright.com
*Featured in Corporate/M&A (Ohio)*
**Career:** Mr Tannous represents clients in corporate matters and business transactions, providing counsel on securities registrations, reporting and compliance; proxy statements; stock exchange compliance; reforms under Sarbanes-Oxley; executive compensation; corporate governance; and

mergers and acquisitions. He represents companies and investors in numerous types of transactions including venture capital and private equity investments, and advises issuers in public and private offerings of equity and debt security. Mr Tannous also counsels oil and gas companies on corporate and financing issues relating to operating and transporting energy resources. He chairs Porter Wright's Corporate and Securities Practice Group, and serves as Chief Operating Partner.

### TERAPAK, Rich

Porter Wright Morris & Arthur LLP, Columbus
rterapak@porterwright.com
614 227 4301
*Featured in Healthcare (Ohio)*

**Career:** Mr Terapak devotes his practice to the healthcare industry. He represents several local hospitals' ambulatory surgery centers, a regional hospital system, and physician group practices and organizations in a variety of legal matters. He also closely monitors federal and state enforcement efforts, and their affect on the entire healthcare industry. Mr Terapak possesses an in-depth knowledge of commercial transactions gained while Senior Counsel with Bank One, and state and federal compliance issues through his directorship of the Ohio Ethics Commission. He serves as co-chair of Porter Wright's Health Care Practice Group and is the firm's Partner-in-Charge of Community Relations.

### TERP, Thomas T

Taft Stettinius & Hollister LLP, Cincinnati
513 357 9354
terp@taftlaw.com
*Featured in Natural Resources (Ohio)*

**Practice Areas:** Environmental, Litigation, Environmental Transactional Services.

**Professional Memberships:** Attorneys' Liability Assurance Society Ltd. ("ALAS").

**Career:** Mr Terp is chairman of the Executive Committee and Managing Partner of the firm. He has concentrated on commercial litigation and environmental matters. He has represented clients throughout the United States, frequently in precedent-setting litigation. He also has advised clients on environmental issues in connection with real estate transfers, loan transactions and mergers and acquisitions.

**Personal:** William and Mary School of Law (1973); Albion College (1969).

### TRAFFORD, Kathleen M

Porter Wright Morris & Arthur LLP, Columbus
614 227 1915
ktrafford@porterwright.com
*Featured in Litigation (Ohio)*

**Career:** Ms Trafford concentrates her practice in the area of governmental and regulatory litigation and constitutional law. She represents private parties in disputes with governmental agencies and also serves as special counsel to a number of state and local government agencies. She handles cases involving constitutional challenges to state and local laws or orders, First Amendment claims, rate making and price discrimination, licensing disputes, trademarks, professional ethics, public records, injunctions, and special writs in the Ohio

Supreme Court. In addition to representing parties in federal and state courts, Ms Trafford also has experience arbitrating disputes.

### TRAFFORD, Robert W

Porter Wright Morris & Arthur LLP, Columbus
614 227 2149
rtrafford@porterwright.com
*Featured in Litigation (Ohio)*

**Career:** Mr Trafford concentrates his practice in the area of complex business litigation, at both the trial and appellate levels, including securities fraud, director and officer liability and other corporate governance matters, attorney and accountant liability, trade secrets and consumer class actions. A Fellow in the American College of Trial Lawyers, Mr Trafford also serves as the Firm's Managing Partner.

### TUGGLE, Curtis L

Thompson Hine LLP, Cleveland
216 566 5904
Curtis.Tuggle@ThompsonHine.com
*Featured in Bankruptcy/Restructuring (Ohio)*

**Career:** Curtis is a partner in the Business Restructuring, Creditors' Rights & Bankruptcy Practice Group. He focuses his practice on commercial and creditors' rights, domestic and cross-border insolvency proceedings (primarily Chapter 11 reorganizations and Chapter 15 proceedings), workouts, preference action litigation, commercial litigation, Uniform Commercial Code controversies and other commercial law cases including secured transactions. He has significant experience representing senior lenders and indenture trustees in workouts, loan restructurings and major reorganization and liquidation proceedings throughout North America. He has considerable experience representing creditors' committees and debtors in Chapter 11 cases and directors and officers in fiduciary duty litigation.

### UNDERWOOD, Michael

Porter Wright Morris & Arthur LLP, Columbus
614 227 2274
munderwood@porterwright.com
*Featured in Labor & Employment (Ohio)*

**Career:** Mr Underwood has considerable experience representing employers in all major areas of labor and employment law. His practice includes defending employers against discrimination claims and wrongful discharge claims, as well as providing advice on collective bargaining and arbitration cases, OSHA, COBRA compliance and affirmative action. In addition to his clients in the private sector, Mr Underwood represents several municipal government employers for labor negotiations, public-sector union representation matters, and civil service law issues. Mr Underwood received both his law degree and his bachelor's degree, cum laude, from the University of Pittsburgh.

### UNGAR, Michael N

Ulmer & Berne LLP, Cleveland
216 583 7002
mungar@ulmer.com
*Featured in Litigation (Ohio)*

**Practice Areas:** Chair of the firm's Litigation Department, Mike's national business litigation

practice encompasses a broad range of general business disputes, with a focus on commercial, banking, professional liability, securities and broker-dealer matters, including arbitrations, class actions, and other types of litigation. Mike also frequently serves as a mediator and arbitrator in complex disputes.

**Professional Memberships:** Past President, Cleveland Metropolitan Bar Association, Mandel Jewish Community Center Board of Trustees, Appointment by Chief Justice Maureen O'Connor of the Supreme Court of Ohio to the Task Force on the Funding of Ohio Courts.

### VALENTINE, Nancy

Hahn Loeser & Parks LLP, Cleveland
216 274 2383
navalentine@hahnlaw.com
*Featured in Bankruptcy/Restructuring (Ohio)*

**Practice Areas:** Ms Valentine represents secured creditors, equipment lessors, landlords, asset-based lenders and general creditors, and debtors in bankruptcy and in federal and state court litigation proceedings (such as receiverships and complex collection matters). She protects the rights of creditors by instituting or representing creditors in federal and state court receiverships, and by recovering the property of lenders in foreclosure and complex collection actions.

**Personal:** The Ohio State University Moritz College of Law (JD, with honors, 1998); Vanderbilt University (BA, cum laude, with honors, 1994).

### VARGO, Ernest E

Baker & Hostetler LLP, Cleveland
216 861 7349
evargo@bakerlaw.com
*Featured in Litigation (Ohio)*

**Career:** Ernest Vargo defends clients against claims of international price fixing, bid rigging, customer allocation, output restrictions and other cartel activities. His antitrust cartel experience extends to several industries, including steel, vitamins, liquid crystal display panel, hair care and cosmetics, print and broadcast advertising, insurance and other financial services and scrap metal. Mr Vargo has specific experience in defending class actions against financial services companies regarding rate and discount practices, claims adjustment practices, commission structures, premium tax charges, refund of unearned premium, collateral protection programs, payments to third-party providers, agent relations and vanishing premium programs.

### VAUGHN, Jonathan R

Vorys, Sater, Seymour and Pease LLP, Columbus
614 464 5672
jrvaughn@vorys.com
*Featured in Labor & Employment (Ohio)*

**Practice Areas:** Partner in the labor and employment group. Defends clients in federal and state court litigation arising from employment discrimination laws. Also involved in all aspects of traditional labor law.

**Professional Memberships:** Ballet Met, Board of Trustees, Member, 2004-11; Executive Committee, 2006-11.

**Career:** Ohio (1982); US Supreme Court; US Court of Appeals for the 6th Circuit; US District Court for the Central District of Illinois; US District Court for the Eastern District of Michigan; US District Court for the Northern and Southern Districts of Ohio.

**Personal:** Vanderbilt University Law School, JD, 1982; Duke University, BS, 1979.

### VERGILII, Jennifer

Calfee, Halter & Griswold LLP, Cleveland
*Featured in Corporate/M&A (Ohio)*

**Practice Areas:** M&A, Corporate; Corporate Succession Planning.

**Career:** Jennifer counsels publicly and privately-held clients on a wide range of general business matters as well as acquisitions, divestitures and business combinations. Jennifer has extensive experience with commercial contracts, including sales, transition, distribution, employment and consulting agreements. Jennifer is a member of Calfee's Hiring Committee and transactional contact for Lex Mundi.

**Publications:** Jennifer has authored many articles over the years and is a regular speaker at legal and business seminars.

**Personal:** Jennifer is Secretary/Board member for the Achievement Centers for Children and Advisory Board member for Case Western Reserve Law LLM Program.

### VIVIANI, Gregory J

Squire Sanders (US) LLP, Cleveland
216 479 8622
gregory.viviani@squiresanders.com
*Featured in Employee Benefits & Executive Compensation (Ohio)*

**Practice Areas:** Partner focusing on employee benefits law and related income tax matters including ERISA requirements, tax-qualified retirement plans, nonqualified deferred compensation plans, fringe benefits and employment taxes. Particularly experienced in matters relating to governmental bodies and tax exempt organizations. Listed in The Best Lawyers in America. Frequent speaker at seminars held by the Ohio Association of School Business Officials, the Government Finance Officers Association and other organizations.

**Professional Memberships:** American Bar Association, Section of Taxation; Worldwide Employee Benefits Network.

### VORYS, John

Vorys, Sater, Seymour and Pease LLP, Columbus
614 464 6211
jcvorys@vorys.com
*Featured in Corporate/M&A (Ohio)*

**Practice Areas:** Partner and Chair of Corporate and Finance Group. Specializes in general corporate law, securities regulation law, and community bank law and regulations.

**Professional Memberships:** Columbus Museum of Art, Board of Trustees and President, 2005-present; Green Lawn Cemetery, Board of

Trustees, 2006-present; The Community Housing Network, Director and President, 1995-2006; Alzheimer's Association of Central Ohio, Director and President, 1999-2008; Capital University Law School, Board of Counselors, 2006-08.
**Career:** Admitted to Ohio Bar (1980).
**Personal:** Capital University Law School, JD, 1980, magna cum laude, Order of the Curia; Williams College, BA, 1975, cum laude.

## WALKER, Robert
Jones Day, Cleveland
216 586 7249
rswalker@jonesday.com
*Featured in Litigation (Ohio)*
**Practice Areas:** Extensive trial and litigation experience in product liability, personal injury, insurance coverage, real estate, trade secrets, breach of contract, IP, commercial law, ERISA, and labor matters. He has defended complex product liability claims in state and federal courts. He also defended class action and individual claims of violations of ERISA, Title VII, the ADEA, the ADA, reverse discrimination, and related tort claims of wrongful discharge.
**Professional Memberships:** The Cleveland Metropolitan Bar Association.

## WALLACE, David H
Taft Stettinius & Hollister LLP, Cleveland
216 706 3898
dwallace@taftlaw.com
*Featured in Litigation (Ohio)*
**Practice Areas:** Construction, construction claims, litigation.
**Professional Memberships:** International Association of Defense Counsel, The Defense Research Institute, Cleveland Metropolitan Bar Association (former trustee), Eighth District Judicial Conference (life member).
**Career:** Mr Wallace is co-chair of the Litigation group. He focuses his practice on complex business litigation, intellectual property litigation, employment litigation and construction law.
**Personal:** Case Western Reserve University School of Law (1986); Middlebury College (1983).

## WALLACH, Mark
Thacker Martinsek LPA, Cleveland
216 456 3848
mwallach@tmlpa.com
*Featured in Litigation (Ohio)*
**Practice Areas:** Business litigation; municipal litigation; accountants, consultants and other professional liability litigation; computer systems litigation; appellate practice; alternative dispute resolution proceedings, including acting as mediator and arbitrator.
**Professional Memberships:** American, Federal and Cleveland Metropolitan Bar Associations; Cuyahoga County Law Directors Association.
**Career:** Litigates and advises clients on complex business and public sector disputes and has particular expertise in representing corporations as plaintiffs. Substantial trial and appellate advocacy experience, including major jury trials and non-administered arbitrations.

**Personal:** Harvard Law School, JD, cum laude, 1974; Wesleyan University, BA, magna cum laude, Phi Beta Kappa, 1971.

## WAMSLEY, James
Jones Day, Cleveland
216 586 7251
jlwamsleyiii@jonesday.com
*Featured in Intellectual Property (Ohio)*
**Practice Areas:** Patent infringement litigation, typically involving electronics, telecommunications, digital imaging, semiconductors, computers and/or software technology. Extensive experience in complex multi-jurisdiction, multi-party and multi-patent infringement litigation involving parties based in the US, North America, Europe and/or Asia. Has represented clients in litigation in US District Courts in Ohio, New York, New Jersey, Delaware, Michigan, Texas, California, Wisconsin and Illinois, the US International Trade Commission, and the US Court of Appeals for the Federal Circuit. Experienced in foreign discovery proceedings.
**Career:** Partner since 1985.
**Personal:** University of Michigan Law School (JD, 1975); University of Virginia (BSEE, 1972).

## WARD, Daniel A
Frantz Ward LLP, Cleveland
216 515 1610
dward@frantzward.com
*Featured in Labor & Employment (Ohio)*
**Practice Areas:** Represents employers in federal and state courts, federal and state administrative agencies, arbitration proceedings, and in collective bargaining negotiations. Counsels employers with respect to wide variety of employment matters, including union-avoidance campaigns.
**Career:** Ohio State Bar; Pennsylvania State Bar; United States District Court, Northern District of Ohio; United States Court of Appeals, Sixth Circuit.

## WARNER, Charles C
Porter Wright Morris & Arthur LLP, Columbus
614 227 2013
cwarner@porterwright.com
*Featured in Labor & Employment (Ohio)*
**Career:** Mr Warner is an experienced attorney who has represented management clients in labor and employment law and litigation for over 40 years. He represents employers in discrimination charges, express and implied employment contract issues, employment practices and related tort and benefit claims. Mr Warner's wide litigation experience includes the defense of both opt-out and opt-in class actions. He also helps clients avoid employee-relations difficulties by providing proactive advice and counsel on day-to-day employment issues and is the principal founder and former Chair of the Ohio Management Lawyers Association. Mr Warner received his law degree from The Ohio State University.

## WARREN, Daniel R
Baker & Hostetler LLP, Cleveland
216 861 7145
dwarren@bakerlaw.com
*Featured in Litigation (Ohio)*

**Career:** Dan Warren focuses on large, complex business disputes. He frequently has the lead role in "bet the company" lawsuits. While many of his cases have been in the financial arena, he also has experience in a wide range of other matters. Dan maintains an active appellate practice, as well, having argued more than 20 appeals with three appellate victories in 2012. He has a strong interest in pro bono work, having obtained the reversal on appeal of the murder conviction of a 12-year-old boy who had falsely confessed as the result of a coercive interrogation.

## WARREN, Thomas D
Baker & Hostetler LLP, Cleveland
216 861 7528
twarren@bakerlaw.com
*Featured in Litigation (Ohio)*
**Career:** Co-Chair of BakerHostetler's nationwide Appellate team, Tom Warren focuses on the reversal of adverse jury awards and judicial decisions and the defense of important trial-court victories. Tom has been successful in reversing numerous jury verdicts and summary judgment decisions on appeal. He also serves as a strategic analyst and brief writer in bet-the-company litigation and other high-profile matters. Tom has been involved in appeals to federal and state courts on issues of class action law, insurance law, bankruptcy law, intellectual property and trade secret law, employment law, contract law and tort law.

## WATKINS, Mark A.
Hahn Loeser & Parks LLP, Akron
330 864 5550
mawatkins@hahnlaw.com
*Featured in Intellectual Property (Ohio)*
**Practice Areas:** Mr Watkins focuses his practice generally in the areas of patents, trademarks, trade secrets, and intellectual property litigation. Specifically, he spends considerable time on intellectual property based agreements, due diligence, portfolio management and the development, management and enforcement of brands, with a particular niche in the entertainment industry.
**Professional Memberships:** Project Team Leader, International Trademark Association; Past President, Cleveland Intellectual Property Law Association.
**Personal:** University of Akron School of Law (JD, 1988); Ohio Northern University (BS, Pharmacy, 1983).

## WATT, Kristin L
Vorys, Sater, Seymour and Pease LLP, Columbus
614 464 8398
klwatt@vorys.com
*Featured in Natural Resources (Ohio)*
**Practice Areas:** Partner representing clients in environmental administrative and enforcement actions, toxic tort suits, and environmental compliance matters. Regularly counsels clients on environmental considerations for corporate and commercial transactions.
**Professional Memberships:** Columbus and Ohio State Bar Associations; OSBA Environmental Law Committee, Chair; served as

Co-Chair of the Columbus Bar Association's Environmental Law Committee.
**Career:** Admitted to the Ohio Bar, US Court of Appeals Sixth Circuit and US District Court, Northern and Southern Districts of Ohio.
**Personal:** The Ohio State University College of Law, JD, 1989, with honors; The Ohio State University, BSBA, 1986, cum laude.

## WEARSCH, Thomas M
Baker & Hostetler LLP, Cleveland
216 861 7303
twearsch@bakerlaw.com
*Featured in Bankruptcy/Restructuring (Ohio)*
**Career:** Tom Wearsch has experience in a broad range of matters, including sophisticated corporate restructuring, bankruptcy, distressed mergers and acquisitions, general corporate, debt finance and commercial law. His practice focuses on advising both distressed and healthy corporations, financial institutions, equity funds, hedge funds, bondholders and investors in all types of transactions and restructurings related to troubled company situations. Tom has been corporate and transactional counsel to numerous corporations involved in Chapter 11 reorganizations, out-of-court restructurings and mergers and acquisitions. He practices with a particular emphasis on restructurings and sale transactions of distressed companies both inside and outside Chapter 11 proceedings.

## WEAVER, Robin G
Squire Sanders (US) LLP, Cleveland
216 479 8572
robin.weaver@squiresanders.com
*Featured in Litigation (Ohio)*
**Practice Areas:** Partner focusing exclusively on civil litigation including commercial, environmental and product liability. Represents clients in federal and state courts. Practice includes extensive appellate work in the US Court of Appeals for the Second, Third, Sixth, Seventh and Eleventh Circuits and Supreme Courts of several states.
**Professional Memberships:** American College of Trial Lawyers and International Society of Barristers, Fellow; Cleveland Metropolitan Bar Association, past president; Supreme Court of Ohio Board of Commissioners on Grievances and Discipline, master commissioner and past chair; United States Sixth Circuit Court of Appeals Judicial Conference and Eighth Appellate Judicial District Judicial Conference, life member.

## WEIBLE, Robert A
Baker & Hostetler LLP, Cleveland
216 861 7553
rweible@bakerlaw.com
*Featured in Corporate/M&A (Ohio)*
**Career:** Chair of BakerHostetler's nationwide Securities & Corporate Governance team, Rob Weible counsels boards of directors, board committees and executives on corporate governance, mergers and acquisitions, securities offerings and compliance and general business matters. He counsels boards and special board committees in conflict-of-interest transactions and other sensitive situations, and represents sellers and buyers in going-private transactions. Rob's industry experi-

ence includes automotive supply and other manufacturing, telecommunications and other media, restaurant chain operations, office supply, insurance brokerage and other retail products and services, oil and gas production, storage and transportation, commercial real estate and hospitality REITs, gaming, professional sports and public utilities.

**WEIMER, John**
Vorys, Sater, Seymour and Pease LLP, Columbus
614 464 8343
jbweimer@vorys.com
*Featured in Banking & Finance (Ohio)*
**Practice Areas:** Partner leading the firm's commercial finance practice group. He represents borrowers and lenders in all types of commercial finance transactions ranging from syndicated secured credit facilities to public notes offerings to securitization facilities to structured finance transactions to real estate transactions to receivables purchase transactions. Weimer negotiates and issues legal opinions in all types of financing transactions. He has experience negotiating and documenting all aspects of commercial finance transactions.
**Professional Memberships:** American and Columbus Bar Associations.
**Personal:** Southern Methodist University School of Law, JD; Southern Methodist University, MBA; Miami University, BA.

**WEINBERG, James**
Ulmer & Berne LLP, Cleveland
216 583 7076
jweinberg@ulmer.com
*Featured in Intellectual Property (Ohio)*
**Practice Areas:** Jim is an experienced litigator with a national practice who specializes in high stakes intellectual property litigation. He has extensive experience in all areas of intellectual property and unfair competitive practices law, including patents, trade secrets, trademarks, and copyrights. He has successfully litigated intellectual property cases involving a wide range of technologies and products, including communications technologies, networking software, DVD technologies, internet platforms, printing and imaging devices, DNA sequencing, medical devices, consumer health care products, natural gas drilling systems, railway and mass transit products and systems, motion pictures, and the logos of national sports teams.

**WEIR, Bill**
Porter Wright Morris & Arthur LLP, Cleveland
216 443 2540
wweir@porterwright.com
*Featured in Real Estate (Ohio)*
**Career:** Mr Weir represents a variety of banks, insurance companies, savings and loans, and other financial institutions in the areas of real estate lending. His areas of concentration are construction and permanent financing, CMBS loans, low income housing tax credit financings, historic tax credit financings, new market tax credit financings, and mezzanine and subordinate debt. He regularly represents lending institutions as lead

counsel in multi-million dollar construction loans on projects located throughout the United States. Mr Weir also represents financial institutions in real estate loan workouts and restructurings.

**WELLNER, John P**
Vorys, Sater, Seymour and Pease LLP, Columbus
614 464 5614
jpwellner@vorys.com
*Featured in Real Estate (Ohio)*
**Practice Areas:** Past Chair of the firm's Commercial/Real Estate Group. Concentrates his practice in the general real estate and real estate development areas. Represents developers, ventures, owners, operators, borrowers and lenders in structuring and concluding the acquisition, sale, leasing, financing and development of commercial real estate.
**Professional Memberships:** Columbus and Ohio State Bar Associations. International Council of Shopping Centers.
**Career:** Admitted to Ohio Bar 1979.
**Personal:** The Ohio State University College of Law, JD, Order of the Coif, with Honors, 1979; Indiana University of Pennsylvania, BS in Business Administration, 1973.

**WESLOH, Steven**
Frost Brown Todd LLC, Cincinnati
513 651 6911
swesloh@fbtlaw.com
*Featured in Natural Resources (Ohio)*
**Practice Areas:** Steve Wesloh's practice is devoted to environmental law with a focus on air emission counseling and enforcement defense. He routinely counsels clients on air permitting issues, such as negotiating construction and operation permits, including New Source Review and Title V permits; assessing applicability of air regulations due to potential source modifications, and interpreting regulatory obligations, including State Implementation Plan regulations, New Source Performance Standards, hazardous pollutant MACT standards, and emission trading program requirements. He has defended numerous Clean Air Act enforcement actions, including convincing US EPA on several occasions to not pursue New Source Review notices of violation.

**WHEATLEY, Nathan**
Calfee, Halter & Griswold LLP, Cleveland
216 622 8573
nwheatley@calfee.com
*Featured in Bankruptcy/Restructuring (Ohio)*
**Practice Areas:** Bankruptcy litigation; business, corporate and commercial litigation; business restructuring and insolvency; receiverships.
**Professional Memberships:** American Bar Association, American Bankruptcy Institute, Federal Bar Association, American Mensa.
**Career:** Senior Counsel in Business Restructuring and Insolvency Group with a concentration in complex commercial litigation and creditor's rights. Has represented manufacturers, utility and energy companies, mortgage companies, banking institutions, as well as state departments and municipalities. Has also represented debtors, unsecured creditors' committees in bank-

ruptcy proceedings, liquidation trustees, and court-appointed receivers. Writes and speaks extensively on bankruptcy matters.
**Personal:** University of Akron, JD, summa cum laude, 1999; Kent State University, BA, 1993.

**WHITAKER, Glenn**
Vorys, Sater, Seymour and Pease LLP, Cincinnati
513 723 4608
gwhitaker@vorys.com
*Featured in Litigation (Ohio)*
**Practice Areas:** Partner focusing on complex litigation in qui tam, false claims; environmental issues; construction law; toxic torts; healthcare fraud, abuse; government procurement, white collar criminal defense, antitrust violations.
**Professional Memberships:** American, Ohio, Cincinnati, Maryland and DC Bar Associations; Fellow, American College of Trial Lawyers; American Board of Trial Advocates; University of Cincinnati College of Law (Adjunct Professor); Potter Stewart American Inn of Court (Emeritus, Master of the Bench).
**Career:** Admitted to Maryland (1972), DC (1973), Ohio (1980).
**Personal:** Denison University, BA, magna cum laude, Phi Beta Kappa, 1969; George Washington University, JD, cum laude, Order of the Coif, 1972.

**WILCOX, Deborah A**
Baker & Hostetler LLP, Cleveland
216 861 7864
dwilcox@bakerlaw.com
*Featured in Intellectual Property (Ohio)*
**Career:** An experienced copyright and trademark lawyer, Deborah Wilcox manages complex copyright, trademark and e-commerce litigation, from contractual software disputes to cybersquatting to the ex parte seizures of counterfeit merchandise. She handles worldwide copyright, trademark and domain name selection, registration and licensing. Deborah works with Customs and designs international protection programs for properties. As Internet and mobile technologies develop, Deborah counsels clients regarding search engine optimization, online auction sites, blogs and social media sites, fraudulent coupons, and direct marketing to consumer via emails and text messaging. She handles take-down notices and other matters under the Digital Millennium Copyright Act.

**WILD, Jeffrey J**
Benesch, Friedlander, Coplan & Aronoff LLP, Cleveland
216 363 4544
jwild@beneschlaw.com
*Featured in Real Estate (Ohio)*
**Practice Areas:** Real Estate & Environmental Law. Focuses on commercial financing, leasing, acquisitions, dispositions and development. Has extensive experience in the negotiation of all types of development and financing documents.
**Career:** Vice-Chair of Real Estate & Environmental Practice Group.
**Personal:** Benjamin N. Cardozo School of Law (JD, 1997); Yeshiva University (BA, 1994).

**WILLBRAND, David**
Thompson Hine LLP, Cincinnati
513 352 6646
David.Willbrand@ThompsonHine.com
*Featured in Corporate/M&A (Ohio)*
**Career:** David leads the firm's Early Stage & Emerging Company practice. He represents entrepreneurs, emerging companies, early-stage investors and venture capital funds. David previously worked in the technology industry, holding the dual role of CFO and General Counsel at a series of venture-backed companies. His unique background is reflected in the creative assistance he provides his clients during their formation, financing, growth and exit. David combines corporate, finance, securities, compensation and intellectual property legal knowledge with a practical understanding of an emerging company's business needs. David is a frequent speaker on venture capital, entrepreneurship and mergers & acquisitions.

**WILSON, James**
Vorys, Sater, Seymour and Pease LLP, Columbus
614 464 5606
jawilson@vorys.com
*Featured in Litigation (Ohio)*
**Practice Areas:** Partner practicing in antitrust and business litigation. Represents clients in antitrust matters, including criminal investigations and trials, civil actions and Hart-Scott-Rodino investigations. Litigated cases involving deceptive trade practices, class actions, hostile takeovers, and dealer terminations.
**Professional Memberships:** Past Chair of the Antitrust Section of the American Bar Association; BNA Antitrust and Trade Regulation Reports, Advisory Board; Adjunct Professor, Ohio State Law School.
**Career:** Admitted to the Ohio Bar, US District Court Southern District of Ohio, Fourth and Sixth Circuit Courts of Appeals and the US Supreme Court.
**Personal:** Columbia Law School, JD, 1985; Miami University, AB, 1982.

**WILSON, W Russell**
Frost Brown Todd LLC, Cincinnati
513 651 6733
rwilson@fbtlaw.com
*Featured in Real Estate (Ohio)*
**Practice Areas:** Practice includes representation of owners and developers in development, leasing, financing, purchases, and sales of shopping centers and office buildings. Also represents homebuilders in acquisition and development of land. Plays an active role in complex real estate litigation.
**Career:** Admitted in 1983.
**Personal:** Born in 1957. Graduate of Princeton University and University of Cincinnati College of Law. Active in local civic and charitable boards, frequently serving in leadership positions. 2001 Ohio Chess Champion.

## WINTERS, Karen A
Squire Sanders (US) LLP, Columbus
614 365 2750
karen.winters@squiresanders.com
*Featured in Natural Resources (Ohio)*

**Practice Areas:** Leads Squire Sanders' Environmental, Safety and Health Practice Group. Experienced in all aspects of environmental law and litigation including federal and state and litigation, administrative law practice before state and federal agencies, corporate and municipal counseling, and government relations and legislative counseling. Listed in Best Lawyers in America each year since 2006. Included in Law & Politics list of Ohio Super Lawyers since 2004.
**Professional Memberships:** Environmental Law Committees, Ohio State and Columbus Bar Associations; Environment Committees, American Iron and Steel Institute and Ohio Manufacturer's Association; Energy and Environment Committee and Executive Committee, Ohio Chamber of Commerce.

## WOESTE, Kristin
Vorys, Sater, Seymour and Pease LLP, Cincinnati
513 723 4684
klwoeste@vorys.com
*Featured in Real Estate (Ohio)*

**Practice Areas:** Associate focused on real estate financing transactions and general real estate matters. Specific experience in representing lenders and borrowers in Fannie Mae multifamily financing transactions.
**Professional Memberships:** American and Cincinnati Bar Associations; Cincinnati Chamber of Commerce 2012 C-Change Class 7; Commercial Real Estate Women of Greater Cincinnati.
**Career:** Admitted in Ohio (2005). Clerk for Honorable Roger L. Gregory, US Court of Appeals for the Fourth Circuit (2005-06).
**Personal:** University of Cincinnati College of Law, JD, Order of the Coif (2005); University of Cincinnati Law Review, Editor in Chief (2005); Ohio University Honors Tutorial College, BS (2002).

## WOLFF, Robert M
Littler Mendelson, PC, Cleveland
216 696 6065
rwolff@littler.com
*Featured in Labor & Employment (Ohio)*

**Practice Areas:** Class Actions, Discrimination & Harassment, Trade Secrets, Wage & Hour, Co-Chair, Health Care Practice Group.
**Professional Memberships:** Chairman, Cuyahoga County Human Resources Commission; Chair elect, The Diversity Center of Northeast Ohio, Trustee, Bellefaire JCB.
**Career:** A seasoned trial attorney, Robert M. Wolff represents companies in the increasingly complex world of employment litigation. Formerly, Managing Partner, Duvin, Cahn & Hutton and Chief Assistant Director of Law, City of Cleveland.
**Personal:** JD, University of Illinois College of Law, cum laude, 1980; Harno Scholar; Editor, University of Illinois Law Review (1979-80); Illinois Governor's Fellow (1977); BA, Oberlin College, 1977.

## WOOLEY, James
Jones Day, Cleveland
216 586 7345
jrwooley@jonesday.com
*Featured in Litigation (Ohio)*

**Practice Areas:** Partner who focuses on white-collar and corporate criminal matters, representing corporations, business people, and professionals during federal, state, and local government criminal investigations and/or prosecutions. He also conducts and oversees investigations on behalf of clients victimized by fraud and other business crimes. In addition, he represents corporate clients and individuals in complex civil litigation. Mr Wooley has represented clients in matters involving a wide range of alleged criminal offenses, including antitrust, healthcare fraud and abuse, criminal tax, government contractor fraud, securities fraud, criminal copyright infringement, environmental crimes, Davis-Bacon Act violations, customs violations, election law violations, and public corruption.

## WYMER, Martin T
Baker & Hostetler LLP, Cleveland
216 861 6021
mwymer@bakerlaw.com
*Featured in Labor & Employment (Ohio)*

**Career:** Martin Wymer is the leader of the firm's national Employment Litigation team. Marty concentrates his practice in the representation of corporations in complex employment litigation and day-to-day counseling on general labor relations and employment matters. The majority of his time is dedicated to litigating wage and hour and discrimination class actions, as well as misappropriation of trade secrets cases. He also handles executive termination disputes and individual discrimination and whistleblower claims at both the trial and appellate levels. He represents businesses in a wide range of industries, with a particular emphasis on the information technology industry.

## YOUNGSTROM, Karen D
Thompson Hine LLP, Cleveland
216 566 5670
Karen.Youngstrom@ThompsonHine.com
*Featured in Employee Benefits & Executive Compensation (Ohio)*

**Career:** Karen is a partner in the firm's Employee Benefits & Executive Compensation Group. She focuses on pension investment matters; employee benefits in mergers and acquisitions; executive deferred compensation and 409A matters; cash balance plan design and controversy; tax-qualified retirement plans, including 401(k) program design and implementation; employee welfare benefits and healthcare reform; benefit arrangements for tax-exempt organizations; tax, labor and securities law compliance issues relating to benefit plans; and the design and implementation of employee stock ownership plans. She formerly chaired Thompson Hine's employee benefits practice and is a charter fellow of the American College of Employee Benefits Counsel.

## YUND, George
Frost Brown Todd LLC, Cincinnati
513 651 6824
gyund@fbtlaw.com
*Featured in Labor & Employment (Ohio)*

**Practice Areas:** National practice in management-side labor arbitration and litigation, labor negotiations and claims against unions for strike-related misconduct, and employment litigation including class and collective actions.
**Professional Memberships:** Ohio and United States Supreme Court; Courts of Appeals for the Fourth, Sixth, Ninth, Eleventh and DC Circuits.

**Career:** Joined Frost in 1977; Partner 1984; firm-wide Managing Member beginning 2009 with responsibilities for operational, personnel and finance matters.
**Personal:** Born 15 April 1952. JD (cum laude), University of Michigan School of Law, 1977; BA (summa cum laude), The Ohio State University, 1974.

## ZAGORE, David A
Squire Sanders (US) LLP, Cleveland
216 479 8610
david.zagore@squiresanders.com
*Featured in Corporate/M&A (Ohio)*

**Practice Areas:** Practice focuses on general business representation of public and private companies. Regularly advises boards of directors and management on M&As, securities law matters, financings, tender offers and corporate control contests, executive compensation and corporate governance. Listed in The Best Lawyers in America and Lawdragon's Leading Lawyers 2006. Recognized by Law & Politics magazine as an Ohio Super Lawyer. Named as one of 78 lawyers worldwide in BTI Consulting Group's 2001 survey of Fortune 1000 corporate counsel as providing superior client service. Serves as primary outside counsel to several public companies.

## ZARLENGA, Audra J
Thompson Hine LLP, Cleveland
216 566 5647
Audra.Zarlenga@ThompsonHine.com
*Featured in Construction (Ohio)*

**Career:** Audra is a partner in the Construction practice group who focuses her practice on representing contractors, owners, design professionals, construction managers, design/builders and developers. She provides counsel on claim prevention, dispute resolution, contract disputes, licensing compliance requirements and risk management. Her work includes construction cases involving electric transmission lines, power plants, underground pipelines, wastewater treatment plants, schools, health care facilities, marine construction, bid protests, federal procurement, mechanic's lien and bond disputes, and insurance issues. Audra also counsels clients on construction and design agreements and strategies for critical claim avoidance and preservation issues.

# BAKER & HOSTETLER LLP

www.bakerlaw.com **tel:** 216 621 0200 **fax:** 216 696 0740

**Executive Partner:** R Steven Kestner
Number of attorneys: 820

## Firm Overview:

BakerHostetler represents clients around the globe. With offices coast to coast, clients count on BakerHostetler to help grow and protect their businesses in a complex business and regulatory environment. Within the firm's five core practice groups (Litigation, Business, Employment, Intellectual Property and Tax) are several large specialty practices, including antitrust, bankruptcy, healthcare, energy, M&A, complex commercial litigation, privacy and data protection, patent prosecution and international tax. The firm distinguishes itself through its outstanding client service.

## Main Areas of Practice:

### Antitrust:
BakerHostetler's Antitrust practice is notable for having tried many antitrust and competition cases to verdict, representing plaintiffs and defendants in antitrust and competition litigation—including class action lawsuits—and helping clients navigate the US merger review process.

### Bankruptcy/Creditors' Rights:
BakerHostetler's Bankruptcy team is known for its work in fraud investigations, litigation, recovery and workouts. The firm plays major roles in significant US and international bankruptcy cases, capitalizing on extensive experience in business workouts, complex reorganizations and bankruptcy proceedings.

### Benefits/Executive Compensation:
BakerHostetler counsels employers on the design and implementation of all types of retirement, savings, health and welfare programs, as well as executive compensation, bonus and other incentive plans, deferred compensation arrangements, and retention and severance plans.

### Corporate/M&A:
A recognized leader in middle-market transactions, the firm counsels large organizations on multibillion-dollar transactions and provides experienced counsel to publicly traded and closely held businesses of all sizes.

### Employment:
BakerHostetler counsels clients on the full array of employment and labor issues, including employee benefits and labor matters involving unions and collective bargaining. The firm is known for its national counsel in the hospitality, media and healthcare industries.

### E-Discovery:
Business leaders turn to the firm's E-Discovery Advocacy and Management team for solutions to complex electronic discovery and data challenges. BakerHostetler recognizes that the risk and burden involved with e-discovery in litigation and government enforcement can most effectively be addressed through advocacy by seasoned litigators skilled in current discovery law and supported by litigation professionals and disciplined project management.

### Healthcare:
BakerHostetler provides comprehensive legal counsel to healthcare interests, focusing on transactions, structuring, finance, reimbursement, compliance, fraud/abuse, investigations, tax and employment law, as well as privacy issues related to data breaches. The firm is intimately familiar with the Affordable Care Act.

### Hospitality:
BakerHostetler's Hospitality practice is known for its representation of major brands and developers in worldwide hotel and resort projects and involvement in the creation and operation of vacation clubs.

### Intellectual Property:
The team guides clients through all phases of IP planning, from the formulation of initial strategies and "best practices" to securing IP rights, creating strategies for exploitation, privacy and data protection and IP litigation.

### International Trade:
BakerHostetler represents foreign and domestic clients in all manner of international trade, customs and immigration proceedings before US and foreign regulatory agencies, courts and dispute resolution panels, especially NAFTA.

### Litigation:
BakerHostetler's Litigation practice is regarded for its pre-litigation strategies and ability to prepare, try and win cases in such areas as antitrust, appellate, bankruptcy, class action, commercial, privacy and data protection, environmental, product liability, securities and white collar.

### Privacy:
BakerHostetler's Privacy and Data Protection team has helped clients recover from and minimize the impact of data breaches, including some of the nation's largest, most significant incidents to date. It has handled dozens of regulatory investigations and is lead defense counsel in several putative class action lawsuits.

### Real Estate:
With capabilities in finance, development, acquisition, disposition and leasing matters, the firm offers a full range of legal services to help clients meet their real estate objectives in an efficient and cost-effective manner.

### Tax & Private Wealth:
BakerHostetler's Tax group is one of the nation's largest, known for its ability to resolve tax controversy matters, implement global planning opportunities and resolve issues through the regulatory and legislative processes. The firm is also known for its sophisticated Private Wealth Planning practice.

### White Collar Crime/Corporate Investigations:
With significant trial and monitorship experience, BakerHostetler's White Collar Defense and Corporate Investigations practice is among the most seasoned in serving corporations and individuals facing government scrutiny.

## OFFICES

**OHIO**
**CLEVELAND:** PNC Center, 1900 E. 9th St., Ste. 3200, OH 44114
Tel: 216 621 0200  Fax: 216 696 0740

**CINCINNATI:** 312 Walnut St., Ste. 3200, OH 45202
Tel: 513 929 3400  Fax: 513 929 0303

**COLUMBUS:** Capitol Square, 65 E. State St., Ste. 2100, OH 43215
Tel: 614 228 1541  Fax: 614 462 2616

**CALIFORNIA**
**COSTA MESA:** 600 Anton Blvd., Ste. 900, CA 92626
Tel: 714 754 6600  Fax: 714 754 6611

**LOS ANGELES:** 12100 Wilshire Blvd., 15th Fl., Los Angeles, CA 90025
Tel: 310 820 8800  Fax: 310 820 8859

**COLORADO**
**DENVER:** 303 East 17th St., Ste. 1100, Denver, CO 80203
Tel: 303 861 0600  Fax: 303 861 7805

**DISTRICT OF COLUMBIA**
**WASHINGTON:** Washington Square, Ste. 1100, 1050 Connecticut Ave., NW, Washington, DC 20036
Tel: 202 861 1500  Fax: 202 861 1783

**FLORIDA**
**ORLANDO:** SunTrust Center, 200 S. Orange Ave., Ste. 2300, Orlando, FL 32801
Tel: 407 649 4000  Fax: 407 841 0168

**ILLINOIS**
**CHICAGO:** 191 N. Wacker Dr., Ste. 3100, Chicago, IL 60606
Tel: 312 416 6200  Fax: 312 416 6201

**NEW YORK**
**NEW YORK:** 45 Rockefeller Plaza, New York, NY 10111
Tel: 212 589 4200  Fax: 212 589 4201

**TEXAS**
**HOUSTON:** 1000 Louisiana Ave., Ste. 2000, TX 77002
Tel: 713 751 1600  Fax: 713 751 1717

# BENESCH, FRIEDLANDER, COPLAN & ARONOFF LLP

www.beneschlaw.com **tel:** 216 363 4500 **fax:** 216 363 4588

**Managing Partner:** Ira C Kaplan
**Chief Operating Officer:** John H Banks II
**Executive Chairman:** James M Hill
Number of partners: 93  Number of other lawyers: 74

**Firm Overview:**

Benesch's national client base includes public, middle market, and emerging companies as well as private equity funds and their portfolio companies, public entities, entrepreneurs, not-for-profit organizations, trusts and estates.

**Main Areas of Practice:**

**Business Reorganization:**

Handle bankruptcies and restructurings, and represent banks and creditors' committees in Chapter 11 reorganizations, distressed businesses, trustees for operating bankruptcy estates, equity security holder committees, hedge funds and distressed private equity firms.

**Business Succession Planning & Wealth Management:**

Counsel on estate and trust administrations, gift and estate taxation, charitable planned giving, business succession planning, guardianships and disputes over wills and trusts.

**China:**

Assist US companies in establishment of China-related strategic alliances and joint ventures for manufacturing, distribution, and business operations in China, and acquire shares or assets of China-based companies.

**Commercial Finance & Banking:**

Represent banks and other financial institutions in such matters as loan documentation, senior and subordinated debt, loan workouts, securitizations, letters of credit and other lending transactions.

**Construction:**

Represent owners, contractors and design professionals in all facets of the industry.

**Corporate & Securities:**

Represent business interests in corporate and transactional work including mergers, acquisitions, divestitures, recapitalizations, restructurings, joint ventures, strategic alliances, licensing and franchise arrangements.

**Energy/ Shale Oil & Gas:**

Assist energy sector businesses in matters such as licensing construction, operations, environmental compliance, financing and acquisitions. Assist with shale, oil and gas business opportunities and issues.

**Executive Compensation & Benefits:**

Offer counsel on deferred compensation techniques, present clients with highly specialized benefits/tax litigation, design executive compensation arrangements for public and private businesses, focus on sophisticated qualified retirement plan issues and assist in tax advice.

**Health Care:**

Represent healthcare providers, payors, managed care organizations and lenders in transactional, financing, regulatory and reimbursement matters. Represent private equity and venture capital firms in regulatory and transactional matters.

**Innovations, Information Technology & Intellectual Property:**

Secure and enforce patent, trademark, copyright and trade secret rights. Additionally counsel on matters such as intellectual property validity and infringement, valuations, licensing and technology transfer. Also specialize in intellectual property litigation.

**Labor & Employment:**

Provide representation in collective bargaining, arbitration, NLRB and SERB hearings, litigation of employment-related matters, immigration matters and workers' compensation defense. Counsel on complying with wage and hour laws, EFCA, FMLA, ADA, COBRA, OSHA, EEOC and DOL.

**Litigation:**

Represent clients in courtroom litigation and dispute resolution including business contract disputes, product liability claims, transportation, officer and director liability, takeovers and mergers, insurance coverage disputes, building construction and real estate disputes, professional liability, environmental liability and unfair competition matters.

**Not-For-Profit:**

Assist not-for-profit and tax exempt clients in matters such as fund-raising, tax matters, reimbursement, compliance, financing and development.

**Private Equity:**

Represent the unique needs of private equity firms, including leverage buyout firms, mezzanine funds, venture capital funds and portfolio companies, paired with a focus on middle-market companies creates an ideal partnership between the attorneys in this group and private equity firms.

## OFFICES

**OHIO**

**CLEVELAND:** 200 Public Square, Suite 2300, OH 44114
Tel: 216 363 4500  Fax: 216 363 4588

**COLUMBUS:** 41 South High Street, Suite 2600, OH 43215
Tel: 614 223 9300  Fax: 614 223 9330

**DELAWARE**

**WILMINGTON:** 222 Delaware Avenue, Suite 801, DE 19801
Tel: 302 442 7010  Fax: 302 442 7012

**INDIANA**

**INDIANAPOLIS:** One American Square, Suite 2300, IN 46282
Tel: 317 632 3232  Fax: 317 632 2962

**NEW YORK**

**NEW YORK:** White Plains Center, 50 Main Street, Suite 1000, White Plains, NY 10606
Tel: 914 682 6812  Fax: 914 682 2600

**PENNSYLVANIA**

**PHILADELPHIA:** One Liberty Place, 1650 Market Street, 36th Floor, PA 19103
Tel: 302 207 2947  Fax: 267 207 2949

### INTERNATIONAL OFFICES

The firm also has an office in Shanghai.

**Public Finance:**

Service clients in matters involving public works, infrastructure projects and bond issuances.

**Public Law/Government Relations:**

Registered representation on behalf of clients before local, state, and federal legislative bodies and executive branch decision makers, as well as representation before regulatory and administrative agencies and of public entities.

**Real Estate & Environmental:**

Represent clients in acquisitions, development, financing, leasing, construction and management of real property including shopping centers; commercial, industrial and office developments; hotels; recreational facilities; and condominium and residential developments.

**Tax:**

Tax planning and evaluation related to corporate reorganizations and restructurings, acquisitions, dispositions, debt and equity financings, start-up ventures, tax free exchanges and leasing arrangements.

**Transportation & Logistics:**

Represent users and providers of logistics services in areas such as negotiating an operating contract, pursuing or defending a cargo claim, dealing with government regulations, developing a strategic alliance or financing an acquisition.

# CALFEE, HALTER & GRISWOLD LLP

www.calfee.com **tel**: 216 622 8200 **fax**: 216 241 0816

**Managing Partner:** Brent D Ballard
**Chairman:** Thomas F McKee
Number of partners: 82
Number of other lawyers: 73

**Firm Overview:**
Founded in 1903, Calfee is one of the largest law firms in Ohio and provides a full range of legal services in all substantive areas of business law throughout the US and abroad. With more than 170 legal professionals, services encompass the entire spectrum of general business law. Calfee is a Founding Member of Lex Mundi, a worldwide consortium of more than 160 independent law firms.

**Main Areas of Practice:**

**Corporate/M&A:**
20 partners; 54 total professionals
This diverse practice spans every type of M&A and other corporate transactions, as well as securities and capital markets, commercial financing, recapitalizations, succession planning and more, and serves public and private businesses, investors and entrepreneurs.
- Represented J.M. Smucker in many transactions, including $3 billion+ acquisition of Folgers coffee business from Procter & Gamble, and $350 million+ acquisition of food service liquid coffee business from Sara Lee
- Represented Invacare Corporation in decades of transactions, including $150 million sale of ISG, $140 million+ acquisition of Scandinavian Mobility in Denmark, $225 million+ acquisition of Domus in Germany and many other healthcare equipment company acquisitions.
- Represented Linsalata Capital Partners in 98+ transactions, including acquisitions of NeuroTherm, Spartan Foods, Manhattan Beachwear and Eatem Foods and divestitures of Transtar, Lund and Stanton Carpet

**Key Clients:** J.M. Smucker; RPM International; Invacare; Linsalata Capital Partners; Chart Industries; American Greetings; Cardinal Health; KeyBank.
**Contact:** Doug Neary **Tel:** 216 622 8285
**Email:** dneary@calfee.com

**Government Relations:**
4 partners; 13 total professionals
Calfee's Government Relations and Legislation Practice is respected for its political savvy and effectiveness, legal expertise, honesty and relationships with local and state government on both sides of the political aisle.
- All lobbyists have served in governmental positions, including President of Ohio Senate, Mayor of Cincinnati, Director of Ohio EPA, Law Director for City of Cleveland, Municipal Court Judge and member of US Congress
- Work includes analyzing regulations, preparing arguments, developing compatible legislation, and assisting with permit and licensing applications

**Key Clients:** Alliance of Automobile Manufacturers, Case Western Reserve University, Dell, Diageo, FirstEnergy, International Council of Shopping Centers, Invacare, KeyCorp and subsidiaries, RPM International, T-Mobile
**Contact:** Leah Pappas Porner **Tel:** 614 621 7007
**Email:** lpappasporner@calfee.com

**Intellectual Property:**
16 partners; 38 professionals
One of the largest IP practices within a corporate law firm in the Midwest, with a full range of services, including complex patent and copyright litigation, domestic and international patent, copyright and trademark prosecution, and client counseling and opinions. Includes 27 Patent Attorneys with diverse technical backgrounds.
- Successful defense of Invacare Corp. in complex multi-patent litigation directed to medical technology for treating sleep disordered breathing
- Representation of Lincoln Electric Co. in complex multi-patent litigation directed to welding technology
- Representation of Fortune Brands entities, i.e. Moen and Master Lock, in multiple IP and patent enforcement actions
- Patent prosecution, patent litigation, IP strategy and management of patent portfolios for many $1 billion+ public and private corporations

**Key Clients:** Invacare; Master Lock; Moen; American Greetings; Owens Corning; Swagelok; Procter & Gamble; Bendix; The J.M. Smucker Company.
**Contact:** John Cipolla **Tel:** 216 622 8808
**Email:** jcipolla@calfee.com

**Litigation:**
19 partners; 34 total professionals
Calfee litigators have expertise ranging from complex corporate and securities litigation to IP/IT, ERISA, class action, product liability, regulatory, public law, banking, antitrust, white collar criminal defense and investigations, and more.
- Represent Northeast Ohio Regional Sewer District in ongoing declaratory judgment action brought by District to validate its proposed stormwater program
- Represent certain current and former outside directors of Eaton Corporation in shareholder derivative lawsuit
- Represent country's largest utility in numerous class actions
- Regularly represent KeyBank in complex litigation matters including, among other things, consumer class actions and shareholder derivative matters
- Regularly represent largest publicly held bank headquartered in Ohio in commercial and consumer lawsuits

**Key Clients:** Eaton Corporation; KeyBank; Northeast Ohio Regional Sewer District; Fifth Third Bank; First Energy; Rock Gaming; Invacare; RPM International.
**Contact:** Mitchell G Blair **Tel:** 216 622 8361
**Email:** mblair@calfee.com

**PRACTICE AREAS**
Antitrust & Trade Regulation
Business Restructuring & Insolvency
Commercial Business & Finance
Construction/Environmental
Corporate Investigations/White Collar Criminal Defense
Employee Benefits & Executive Compensation
Corporate, Estate & Succession Planning
General Corporate/Mergers & Acquisitions
Government Relations & Legislation
Healthcare & Life Sciences
Insurance Recovery
Intellectual Property/Information Technology/Bioscience
Labor & Employment
Litigation
Private Equity/Public Law & Finance/Tax
Real Estate
Securities & Capital Markets
Workers Compensation & OSHA

**OFFICES**
OHIO
**CLEVELAND:** The Calfee Building, 1405 East Sixth Street, OH 44114-1607
Tel: 216 622 8200  Fax: 216 241 0816
Email: info@calfee.com

**COLUMBUS:** 1100 Fifth Third Center, 21 East State Street, OH 43215-4243
Tel 614 621 1500  Fax 614 621 0010

**CINCINNATI:** 2800 First Financial Center, 255 East Fifth Street, OH 45202-4728
Tel: 513 693 4880  Fax: 513 842 7028

# FRANTZ WARD LLP

**www.**frantzward.com **tel:** 216 515 1660 **fax:** 216 515 1650

Number of partners: 39
Number of other lawyers: 26

**OFFICES**

OHIO

**CLEVELAND:** 2500 Key Center, 127 Public Square,
OH 44114-1230
Tel: 216 515 1660   Fax: 216 515 1650

## Firm Overview:

Founded in 2000, Frantz Ward LLP has quickly grown to become one of the premier law firms in the Midwest. The firm's growth to 65 attorneys, who provide a broad range of services, and its joining ALFA International, a global legal network of independent law firms across the United States and around the world, demonstrate its commitment to client service.

## Main Areas of Practice:

### Bankruptcy/Debtor & Creditor Rights:
The Bankruptcy/Debtor and Creditor Rights Group is highly skilled at representing debtors and creditors in bankruptcy proceedings and complex non-bankruptcy workouts; represents financial institutions and borrowers in troubled loan transactions and advises on restructuring obligations in anticipation or avoidance of bankruptcy.

### Class Actions:
The Class Actions Group defends clients throughout Ohio and other jurisdictions in lawsuits on a variety of issues, including alleged violations of consumer protection statutes, claims of deceptive trade practices, lender liability, product liability and breach of warranty, ERISA violations, insurance issues and employment discrimination disparate impact claims.

### Commercial Lending:
The Commercial Lending Group represents banks, thrifts, and other lending institutions throughout all phases of the negotiating, structuring, closing, and enforcing of a variety of lending transactions, and counsels clients on issues pertaining to lending matters and their ramifications.

### Competition Law:
The Competition Law Group advises and represents clients on competition issues and litigation affecting their businesses, including antitrust, franchise, intellectual property, business tort and consumer protection laws. The group also counsels companies in the development and implementation of compliance programs.

### Construction:
The Construction Group is recognized for their knowledge and experience in all aspects of construction law, including project conceptualization and planning, contract preparation, project financing, project management, construction contracts, construction litigation, construction claims prosecution and analysis, and alternative dispute resolution proceedings, including arbitration and mediation.

### Corporate/Business Law:
The Corporate/Business Law Group counsels clients in traditional corporate and transactional areas, including corporate governance, commercial finance transactions, mergers/acquisitions, public and private debt offerings and licensing, and represents both target and acquiring corporations in the buying and selling of their privately-held businesses.

### Employee Benefits:
The Employee Benefits Group advises clients on all aspects of design, implementation, administration and termination of tax-qualified retirement plans, nonqualified deferred compensation, health and other welfare benefit plans and fringe benefit programs. Represents clients before the Internal Revenue Service, Department of Labor, and Pension Benefit Guaranty Corporation.

### Environmental:
The Environmental Group is led by the former Director and Chief Legal Counsel for the Ohio EPA, this Group possesses the broad skills and knowledge essential for counseling clients in all aspects of environmental law; guiding them through the complex environmental regulations and requirements pertaining to their business activities.

### Estate Planning/Probate:
The Estate Planning/Probate Group provides a full range of estate planning services and advises clients regarding succession issues in closely held businesses. The firm's probate practice includes estate administration and other representation in probate-related proceedings.

### Healthcare:
The Healthcare Group guides healthcare organizations through regulatory compliance and operational matters, including employment/labor issues, risk management, medical malpractice/liability, governmental/third party billing and reimbursement, licensure and certification, survey and enforcement, managed care contracting, Medicare and Medicaid enrollment, HIPAA compliance and healthcare contracting.

### Labor & Employment:
The highly regarded Labor and Employment Group represents employers nationally with respect to litigation and issues arising in the ever-changing modern employment relationship. The group is adept at providing effective personnel management strategies, counseling and training to assist clients in avoiding costly litigation, lengthy government investigations, labor disputes, and other outside party intervention.

### Litigation:
Highly skilled trial lawyers represent clients nationally in federal, state and appellate courts, and in arbitrations, mediations and other dispute resolution procedures. The Litigation Group represents clients in disputes involving a wide range of business issues, including nationwide toxic tort cases, medical devices, pharmaceuticals, automobiles, industrial equipment, and consumer products, and serving as national coordinating counsel in multi-jurisdictional litigation.

### Real Estate:
The Real Estate Group represents businesses and individuals, whether property owners or property users, in all types of real estate transactions, including acquisition, development, lease and finance of real estate and related property interests, retail, industrial and office leasing and construction contracts and disputes.

### Clients:
The firm's client base is national in scope, encompassing individuals to small privately-held businesses to publicly-traded Fortune 500 companies.

# HAHN LOESER & PARKS LLP

www.hahnlaw.com **tel:** 877 424 6529

**Managing Partner:** Lawrence E Oscar, Esq
Number of partners: 78   Number of other lawyers: 40
Languages: *English, French, German, Indonesian, Italian, Japanese, Korean, Russian, Spanish*

**Firm Overview:**
Founded in 1920, Hahn Loeser & Parks LLP is a full-service law firm with offices in Cleveland, Columbus, and Akron, Ohio; Naples and Fort Myers, Florida; Indianapolis, Indiana and San Diego, California. It has more than 130 attorneys providing sophisticated and creative counsel to a wide spectrum of clients, both regionally and around the globe.

## Main Areas of Practice:

**Litigation:**
Represent clients in trial and appellate courts throughout the United States and in all manners of alternative dispute resolution. Known for particular expertise in complex commercial litigation, employment and non-competition agreements, intellectual property, and tort litigation. Proven track record serving as outside litigation counsel for publicly-traded companies, providing creative solutions for managing litigation costs.
**Contact:** Robert J Fogarty
**Email:** rjfogarty@hahnlaw.com

**Business:**
Counsel to businesses of all sizes, ranging from emerging closely held enterprises to long established family businesses to publicly-traded corporations. Recognized for excellence in mergers and acquisitions, financing, distribution, leasing, licensing, corporate and securities law, tax planning, structuring and employee benefits, transitioning of family-held enterprises and real estate transactions.
**Contact:** Stanley R Gorom III
**Email:** srgorom@hahnlaw.com

**Creditors' Rights & Insolvency:**
Represent creditors (secured and unsecured), creditors' committees, debtors and trustees in reorganization and insolvency matters, including Chapter 11 proceedings. Represent financial institutions, vendors and other creditor or debtor interests in connection with numerous workouts and restructurings, and troubled company mergers and acquisitions.
**Contact:** Lawrence E Oscar
**Email:** leoscar@hahnlaw.com

**Labor & Employment:**
Represent public and private employers in all aspects of their relationships with employees, unions and regulatory state and federal agencies, including the EEOC, NLRB and DOL. Regularly represent employers in litigation, before state and federal agencies, and in union negotiations throughout the United States.
**Contact:** James M Drozdowski
**Email:** jmdrozdowski@hahnlaw.com

**Intellectual Property:**
Counsel clients for patent, trademark, and copyright procurement and prosecution. Also litigate disputes related to domestic and international intellectual property, including patents, trademarks, copyrights, trade secrets, and technology licensing matters.
**Contact:** Mark A Watkins
**Email:** mawatkins@hahnlaw.com

**Construction:**
Practice Group of more than 25 experienced attorneys providing counsel on nearly every area of law impacting the construction industry today. Represent a wide range of clients throughout the Midwest, as well as nationally and internationally. Clients include owners, developers, contractors, material suppliers, and design professionals.
**Contact:** Rob Remington
**Email:** rrremington@hahnlaw.com

**Health Care & Nonprofit:**
Experienced in affiliations and joint ventures involving health care and nonprofit organizations, hospital mergers and acquisitions, hospital financings, provider contracts, medical staff and private practitioner contracts and governance issues. Nonprofit representation includes formation of public charities and private foundations, joint ventures, mergers, governance issues, probate and civil litigation on behalf of charitable organizations and trusts, planned giving, and sophisticated executive compensation arrangements.
**Contact:** Arthur L Cobb (Health Care)
**Email:** alcobb@hahnlaw.com
**Contact:** Stephen J Knerly, Jr (Nonprofit)
**Email:** sjknerly@hahnlaw.com

**Estate Planning:**
Counsel high-net worth individuals and owners of privately-held companies in developing comprehensive plans for the management of assets during life, the protection of assets in the event of disability and the tax-efficient transfer of wealth at death. Attorneys focus on the individual client's needs, goals and values, striving to minimize estate, gift, generation-skipping transfer and income taxes.
**Contact:** Mark F Swary
**Email:** mfswary@hahnlaw.com

## OFFICES

**OHIO**
**CLEVELAND:** 200 Public Square, Suite 2800, OH 44114
Tel: 216 621 0150  Fax: 216 241 2824

**COLUMBUS:** 65 East State Street, Suite 1400, OH 43215
Tel: 614 221 0240  Fax: 614 221 5909

**AKRON:** 300 GOJO Plaza, OH 44311
Tel: 330 864 5550  Fax: 330 864 7986

**FLORIDA**
**NAPLES:** 800 Laurel Oak Drive, Suite 600, FL 34108
Tel: 239 254 2900  Fax: 239 592 7716

**FORT MYERS:** 2400 East First Street, FL 33901
Tel: 239 337 6700  Fax: 239 337 6701

**INDIANA**
**INDIANAPOLIS:** 10150 Lantern Road, Suite 250, Fishers, IN 46037
Tel: 317 578 1400  Fax: 317 578 0207

**CALIFORNIA**
**SAN DIEGO:** 600 West Broadway, Suite 1500, CA 92101
Tel: 619 810 4300  Fax: 619 810 4301

**Government:**
Counsel government officials  and public and quasi-public entities on economic development policies and initiatives, employment matters, diversity issues, public-private transactions and private sector transactions. Conduct impartial investigations involving the expenditure of public funds.
**Contact:** Alan S Kopit
**Email:** askopit@hahnlaw.com

**International Work:**
Law firm of choice for companies doing business across the border or overseas and for companies venturing into the United States. The firm handles international matters as diverse as cross-border mergers and acquisitions, joint ventures, foreign direct investment, international distribution agreements and technology transfer.
**Contact:** Christopher S W Blake
**Email:** cswblake@hahnlaw.com

**Clients:**
Fidelity National Financial, Inc., Aetna Inc., Cargill, Inc., Great Lakes Cheese Co. Inc., BMW Financial Services, NA, Johnson Controls, Inc., Lincoln Electric Company, Cleveland Museum of Art, Head USA, Jacobs Entertainment, Inc., Nucor Corporation, HUGO BOSS USA, Cliffs Natural Resources Inc., Shearer's Foods, LLC, DeBartolo Holdings, Rochester General Health System, POET Design and Construction LLC, McNally/Kiewit LLP, Gerber's Poultry, AgStar Financial Services, Avis Budget Group, Emerson Network Power – Americas, and OM Group, Inc.

HAHN HL LOESER

# KEATING MUETHING & KLEKAMP PLL

www.kmklaw.com **tel:** 513 579 6400 **fax:** 513 579 6457

**Managing Partner:** Paul V Muething
**Executive Partner:** Rachael A Rowe
Number of senior partners: 14   Number of partners: 60
Number of of counsel: 5   Number of associates: 29
Total number of attorneys: 108

## Firm Overview:

Keating Muething & Klekamp (KMK®) is a Cincinnati-based law firm that represents clients of all sizes, from small start-up companies to *Fortune* 500 corporations. Founded in 1954, KMK has established a reputation for providing sophisticated legal services to business clients across the country.

## Main Areas of Practice

**Commercial Finance & Reorganization:**
7 partners; 3 associates
- Serve as general counsel to 11 asbestos and silica bankruptcy settlement trusts, advising them on trust administration, including claims resolution
- Represented purchaser of $36m mortgage loan and subsequent acquisition of development project via deed in lieu

**Contact:** John S Fronduti **Tel:** 513 639 3958
**Email:** jfronduti@kmklaw.com
**Contact:** Robert G Sanker **Tel:** 513 579 6587
**Email:** rsanker@kmklaw.com

**Corporate/M&A:**
26 partners; 3 of counsel, 8 associates
- Represented American Financial Group, Inc. in the sale of its Medicare Supplement and Critical Illness businesses to Cigna Corporation for approximately $295m in cash
- Represented the Armstrong World Industries, Inc. Asbestos Personal Injury Settlement Trust in a secondary public offering of shares of common stock of Armstrong World Industries. Inc. along with shares offered by Armor TGP Holdings, L.P., with a value of securities offered of $265m in the aggregate
- Represented American Financial Group, Inc. in an offering of $200m aggregate principal amount of 6.375% Senior Notes due 2042, and the simultaneous redemption of $113m of 7.5% Senior Notes due 2033 and of $88m of 7.25% Senior Notes due 2034

**Key Clients:** American Financial Group, Chiquita Brands International, Inc., Cintas Corporation, Meridian Bioscience, Inc.
**Contact:** James M Jansing **Tel:** 513 579 6439
**Email:** jjansing@kmklaw.com
**Contact:** Edward E Steiner **Tel:** 513 579 6468
**Email:** esteiner@kmklaw.com

**Employee Benefits:**
4 partners; 1 associate
- KMK's Employee Benefits Group provides sophisticated and practical legal advice to clients regarding a broad spectrum of matters including qualified retirement plans, non-qualified deferred compensation, and health and welfare benefits. KMK's diverse group of clients includes large publicly traded companies, smaller privately held businesses, non-profit organizations, and individuals

**Key Clients:** American Financial Group, Inc., Cintas Corporation, Fifth Third Bank.
**Contact:** Lisa Wintersheimer Michel **Tel:** 513 579 6462
**Email:** lmichel@kmklaw.com

**Intellectual Property:**
2 partners; 1 of counsel; 1 associate
- Represented *Fortune* 500 clients in mergers and acquisitions involving intellectual property rights
- Served as counsel for a Fortune 500 client, assuming responsibility for several major brands' trademark portfolios

**Key Clients:** Belcan Corporation, Cintas Corporation, Great American Insurance Co.; Procter & Gamble, Gardner Denver, Inc.
**Contact:** Cheryl S. Scotney **Tel:** 513 579 6942
**Email:** cscotney@kmklaw.com

**Labor & Employment:**
4 partners; 1 of counsel; 3 associates
- KMK represents a *Fortune* 1000 corporation in all labor and employment administrative and litigation matters nationwide, including successful enforcement of mandatory arbitration agreements
- Represented a large private corporation in a national class action lawsuit involving the Fair Labor Standards Act and related claims
- Represents *Fortune* 500 corporation in all aspects of labor negotiations, labor arbitrations and NLRB matters

**Key Clients:** AK Steel Corporation, Belcan Corporation, GE Aviation.
**Contact:** G Randall Ayers **Tel:** 513 579 6919
**Email:** rayers@kmklaw.com

**Litigation:**
21 partners; 13 associates
- Serrano/EEOC v. Cintas Corporation - KMK defended client on claims related to gender discrimination in hiring involving over 300 US facilities
- Eshe v. Fifth Third Bancorp - Currently defending client in consolidated securities class action litigation

**Key Clients:** Belcan Corporation; Cintas Corporation; Fifth Third Bank.
**Contact:** Joseph M Callow, Jr **Tel:** 513 579 6419
**Email:** jcallow@kmklaw.com
**Contact:** Daniel E Izenson **Tel:** 513 579 6480
**Email:** dizenson@kmklaw.com

**Private Client Services:**
6 partners
- KMK's Private Client Services Group works closely with clients and assists in developing creative and tax-efficient solutions for current and long-term estate planning and succession needs. KMK's lawyers have vast experience in sophisticated estate planning strategies and techniques and are very knowledgeable in business succession planning, administration of estates and trusts, matrimonial disputes (divorce and child custody), guardianships, and income and transfer tax matters for individuals, estates, trusts, and family businesses

**Contact:** Joseph P Rouse **Tel:** 513 579 6417
**Email:** jrouse@kmklaw.com

**Real Estate:**
13 partners; 2 of counsel; 3 associates
- Represented a *Fortune* 500 client in a series of land and property acquisitions in Ohio with values in the $5m-$15m range
- KMK handled major real estate tax reduction cases for GE Aircraft Engine plant and for Procter & Gamble
- Represented the joint venture including Al. Neyer and Towne Properties in the $84m U-Square development. KMK's public finance team helped to close this transaction incorporating TIF, Bonds and New Markets Tax Credits

**Key Clients:** Al.Neyer, Inc., Cincinnati Center City Development Corp. (3CDC), Macy's Inc.
**Contact:** Daniel P Utt **Tel:** 513 579 6564
**Email:** dutt@kmklaw.com

**PRACTICE AREAS:**
Banking, Finance & Financial Services
Business Representation & Transactions
Commercial Finance & Reorganization
Employee Benefits & Executive Compensation
Labor & Employment
Litigation
Private Client Services
Real Estate

**OFFICES**

OHIO
**CINCINNATI:** One East Fourth Street, Suite 1400, OH 45202
Tel: 513 579 6400  Fax: 513 579 6457
Email: info@kmklaw.com

# KEGLER, BROWN, HILL & RITTER

**www.**keglerbrown.com  **tel:** 614 462 5400  **fax:** 614 464 2634

**Managing Partner**: Michael E. Zatezalo
Number of partners: 40
Number of other lawyers: 23

**OFFICE**

OHIO
**COLUMBUS:** 65 East State Street, Suite 1800, OH 43215
Tel: 614 462 5400  Fax: 614 464 2634
www.keglerbrown.com

## Firm Overview:

Kegler Brown is one of the most consistently recognized law firms in Ohio due to its high-quality legal work, uniquely responsive client service and value among clients. Founded in Columbus, Ohio, in 1964, the firm's lawyers serve clients locally, nationally and globally. Widely known for its collection of highly specialized niche practice areas, including gaming law, construction law, mediation and arbitration, international business law, healthcare regulation and health information technology, and others, the firm practices generally in the areas of corporate and tax law, commercial litigation and government relations.

Kegler Brown has been consistently praised by Chambers USA, which states that "clients highlight the practice's adaptability and 'brilliant response times.'" It also asserts that "the firm is praised for its clear communication, timely advice and knowledge, and is particularly noted for its customer service…and deep-rooted client relationships."

## Main Areas of Practice

Kegler Brown offers full service counsel to clients around the world in the areas of corporate law, commercial litigation, government relations, administrative law, antitrust, banking and lending, business succession and ESOPs, construction, creditor's rights and bankruptcy, employee benefits and ERISA, energy and public utilities, estate planning, gaming, government and internal investigations, health care regulation and health information technology, intellectual property, global business, labor and employee relations, mediation and arbitration, mergers and acquisitions, professional responsibility, real estate, securities and corporate governance, tax, and workers' compensation.

## Global Business

Led by attorney Martijn Steger, Kegler Brown maintains a highly regarded global business practice that serves clients in the US and around the world in nearly every area of law. The practice is organized by team leaders who practice all aaround the world and spearhead practices in Europe, Latin America and the Caribbean, the Asia-Pacific region, the Eastern Mediterranean and Israel region, Middle East and North Africa.

## Clients

Kegler Brown represents global businesses of all sizes, from private mid-market entities to publicly traded multinational corporations. Some of the firm's most notable clients include Cardinal Health, CareFusion, Commercial Vehicle Group, Donatos, inVentiv Health, Time Warner Cable, WebMD and more.

**Contacts:**
**General:** Michael E Zatezalo  **Tel:** 614 462 5497
**Corporate:** Charles J Kegler  **Tel:** 614 462 5446
**Litigation:** Donald W Gregory  **Tel:** 614 462 5416
**Government Relations:** Steve Tugend  **Tel:** 614 462 5424

# MCMAHON DEGULIS LLP

**www.**mdllp.net **tel:** 216 621 1312 **fax:** 216 621 0577

Number of partners: 8
Number of lawyers: 16
Languages: *English*

### Firm Overview:

Since 1994, McMahon DeGulis LLP has offered an alternative to large firm environmental law departments by providing experienced and innovative legal representation in complex environmental matters.

The largest environmental law firm in Ohio, McMahon DeGulis attorneys have represented Fortune 500 corporations, real estate developers, governmental entities and partnerships in all facets of environmental law and litigation. Several firm members have over 25 years of experience in environmental, toxic tort and complex litigation. The attorneys concentrate their practice in environmental, energy and natural resources law and related litigation. The firm's litigation attorneys have had consistent success, including several defense verdicts and reported cases, defending product liability, toxic tort, intentional tort and environmental claims, including asbestos, benzene and other toxins.

The firm's attorneys have significant experience with all major federal environmental statutes and corresponding Ohio laws. Specific areas of focus include transactional, regulatory, enforcement and litigation concerning brownfields, stormwater, oil and gas leases (hydro-fracking), advanced and renewable energy, water infrastructure, environmental audits, TSCA, NEPA, EPCRA, CERCLA, RCRA, FIFRA, Clean Air Act, Clean Water Act and the Ohio Voluntary Action Program (brownfields).

The firm's attorneys have held leadership positions with the ABA and the Ohio State Bar Association and are frequent speakers at regional and national conferences. Clients value the firm's contacts with regulators and experience in newer areas of environmental law such as wind, solar and Ohio shale matters, in addition to the more traditional areas of environmental media such as air, water and hazardous waste.

### Main Areas of Practice:

**Environmental Law:**
6 Partners; throughout Ohio
Represent property owners, lending institutions and purchasers and sellers of real property with environmental contamination and assist clients in all facets of property and facility-related environmental issues – this includes recommending the right environmental consultant, assessing Ohio's Voluntary Action (Brownfields) Program, handling complex hazardous or solid waste issues and supervision of large-scale remediation projects.
Work with major and minor sources to obtain air pollution permits to install (PTI) and permits to operate (PTO) that allow a facility to function cost-effectively.
Significant experience defending enforcement actions and negotiating resolution with local, state and federal agencies and experience with negotiating consent orders and thorough application of EPA's "Integrated Planning Framework."
Assist clients in negotiating leases and obtaining permits, licenses, siting authorizations and other regulatory approvals from federal, state and local agencies for proposed energy projects.
Reduce environmental risk and liabilities in all types of transactions, including property transfers, leases, construction, refinancing and mergers and acquisitions.
Assist in compliance with UST regulations, respond to state inspections and Notices of Violation, maximize coverage under the state UST insurance fund and oversee the closure of USTs and contamination assessment of UST sites.
Experience with surface water issues and wetlands, National Pollutant Discharge Elimination System permits, Permits to Install, storm water construction permits, drinking and groundwater issues and public water system regulation.
Contribute value to regulatory developments, closely track proposed changes to rule and law, and advise clients doing business in shifting regulatory landscapes.
**Contact:** Michael S McMahon
**Tel:** 216 367 1402
**Email:** mmcmahon@mdllp.net

**Toxic Tort Litigation:**
2 partners, 11 attorneys and paralegals based in Cleveland
Decades of experience handling toxic tort cases. Successfully defended several corporate clients in jurisdictions around the United States; indeed it is McMahon DeGulis' extensive trial experience that sets it apart from other firms.
A thorough understanding of the massive body of sophisticated medical, scientific and epidemiological literature and concepts, an in-depth familiarity with the experts in all of these fields, and an organization capable of handling tens of thousands of ongoing matters are essential to successfully defend these cases.
**Contact:** Stephen H Daniels
**Tel:** 216 367 1405
**Email:** sdaniels@mdllp.net

### PRACTICE AREAS

Environment
Energy & Natural Resources
Environmental Litigation
Product Liability & Mass Torts

### OFFICES

OHIO
**CLEVELAND:** 812 Huron Road, Suite 650, OH 44115
Tel: 216 621 1312
Email: mmcmahon@mdllp.net

**COLUMBUS:** 1335 Dublin Road, Suite 216A, OH 43215
Tel: 614 849 0300
Email: sfisher@mdllp.net

**CINCINNATI:** 1055 St. Paul Place, OH 45202
Tel: 513 898 1542
Email: espitzig@mdllp.net

# PORTER WRIGHT MORRIS & ARTHUR LLP

**www.**porterwright.com **tel:** 614 227 2000 **fax:** 614 227 2100

**Managing Partner:** Robert W Trafford
Number of partners: 139  Number of other lawyers: 86

**Firm Overview:**
Porter Wright Morris & Arthur LLP traces its origins to 1846 in Ohio. The firm's lawyers combine their knowledge, skills and experience to represent a worldwide base of clients in complex legal issues and business opportunities.

**Main Areas of Practice:**

**Antitrust & Trade Regulation:**
Counseling, litigation and ADR support on complex antitrust matters.

**Banking & Finance:**
Bank formation and regulation, lease/loan financing, project financing, public finance, asset securitization and commercial law.

**Bankruptcy, Workout & Creditors' Rights:**
Bankruptcy and insolvency, including creditors' rights, business workouts, claims and loan restructuring.

**Bioscience:**
Represents biotech and medical device clients in formation, contracts, IP protection, licensing and strategic alliance agreements.

**Business Growth & Operation:**
Counsels entrepreneurial businesses and fast-growing companies in business formation, corporate governance and securities, succession planning and transactions.

**Construction:**
Advises owners, contractors, architects, engineers, lenders and insurers in construction-related issues.

**Employee Benefits:**
Advises on employee benefits and executive compensation including qualified retirement plans, nonqualified deferred compensation, and health and welfare benefits.

**Energy & Telecommunications:**
Represents utilities before regulatory commissions and courts at the trial and appellate level.

**Environmental Law:**
Clean Air Act, water pollution and wetlands, EPCRA, Superfund, and environmental assessment and remediation.

**Government & Regulatory Affairs:**
Economic development initiatives; election, PAC and ethics laws; government contracting; and legislative and regulatory advocacy. Government contract negotiations, DCAA audits, debarment/suspension proceedings and protests/claims.

**Green:**
Representation on sustainability initiatives, including alternative energy, development and waste recovery/reuse.

**Health Law:**
Serves physician practice groups, hospitals and other medical providers in formation, financing, fraud/abuse, Stark, HIPAA, antikickback and false claims.

**Immigration:**
Visas, work authorizations, naturalization and compliance with employment eligibility verification rules.

**Insurance:**
Corporate, regulatory, transactional and litigation services to insurance companies, mutual holding companies, insurance agencies, investment advisers, investment companies and regulators.

**Intellectual Property:**
Patent, trademark, copyright and trade secret arenas, as well as ancillary areas.

**International Business & Trade:**
Venture formation, agency and distribution relationships, licensing and franchise, customs, import/export controls, trade agreements/disputes, taxation, cross-border litigation and arbitration.

**Labor & Employment:**
Represents management clients in employment discrimination and wrongful discharge litigation, including class actions and ERISA, and employment law and regulation compliance. Works with union and nonunion clients to plan labor and employment aspects of business changes and manage labor relations issues.

**Litigation:**
Complex commercial, appellate, tort and regulatory matters before federal and state courts, administrative agencies, arbitration panels and ADR settings, including e-discovery services.

**M&A:**
Transaction structuring, tax planning, due diligence, mergers, stock/asset transactions, proxy statements, securities registration and Hart-Scott-Rodino Act compliance.

**Oil & Gas:**
Advises producers and affiliated industry businesses in

operational, governance, transactional, labor/contract issues, and litigation matters.

**Privacy & Data Security:**
Broad range of privacy and data security issue advice, including data breach situations.

**Product Liability:**
Represents product manufacturers/distributors in potential and actual claims of personal injuries and damages from use or exposure to industrial, motor vehicle, medical and various consumer products.

**Real Estate:**
Commercial matters including acquisition/development, financing, leasing, title insurance, mortgages, fair housing, architect/contractor agreements, zoning and land use.

**Securities:**
Private placements, public offerings, venture capital, private equity, joint ventures, licensing/franchising, SEC investigations, civil enforcement actions and criminal securities cases.

**Tax & Personal Wealth:**
Business planning and tax disputes, tax credits and experience in federal, state, local and international taxation. Estate planning, wealth transfer, charitable giving, adoptions and guardianships, antenuptial agreements and probate litigation.

**Technology:**
Acquisition, transfer and licensing; software development; outsourcing; litigation; research/development and joint ventures; internet/ecommerce; and open source software.

**Transportation & Logistics:**
Counsels industry entities in litigation, environmental, regulatory, corporate and employment law.

**White Collar Defense & Corporate Investigations:**
Represents businesses/individuals whose operations and activities are placed under government scrutiny or are subject to governmental enforcement actions.

**OFFICES**

**OHIO**
**COLUMBUS:** 41 South High Street, OH 43215
Tel: 614 227 2000  Fax: 614 227 2100
Email: columbus@porterwright.com
**CINCINNATI:** Tel: 513 381 4700
**CLEVELAND:** Tel: 216 443 9000
**DAYTON:** Tel: 937 449 6810

**DISTRICT OF COLUMBIA**
**WASHINGTON DC:** Tel: 202 778 3000

**FLORIDA**
**NAPLES:** Tel: 239 593 2900

*porter*wright

# ROETZEL & ANDRESS

www.ralaw.com **tel:** 330 376 2700 **fax:** 330 376 4577

**Chairman/CEO:** Jeffrey J Casto
Number of partners: 138  Number of other lawyers: 70

## Firm Overview:

With more than 200 attorneys and 13 offices located throughout Ohio and Florida, and in Chicago, New York, and Washington, D.C., Roetzel attorneys serve a broad spectrum of clients on a regional, national, and international basis. Roetzel is a full-service law firm that has been guided by the core values of innovation, client services, integrity, and excellence in practice since 1876.

## Main Areas of Practice:

### Bankruptcy & Creditors' Rights:

The Bankruptcy and Creditors' Rights Practice helps companies and individuals address the challenges and opportunities abound in today's credit-driven world by representing companies across the US that are engaged in a variety of industries, including banking, finance, manufacturing, transportation, distribution, air travel, healthcare, and retail. Clients are debtors, creditors, secured creditors, creditors' committees, trustees, real estate lessors, equipment lessors, licensors, licensees, distributors, vendors, customers, and potential purchasers of distressed businesses.

### Corporate & Business Services:

The Corporate and Business Services Practice provides experienced counsel throughout all stages of business strategy, development and corporate governance, including wealth transfer and succession planning. This practice group works with their clients and in-house counsel to address the challenges and opportunities associated with the formation, operation and growth of all types of organizations.

### Employment Services:

The labor and employment attorneys work co-operatively with in-house counsel, executive level managers, public officials, risk management professionals, union management and human resource departments to handle routine and complex regulatory compliance issues that affect the workplace. In addition, the group has extensive experience working with complex and potentially costly labor and employment litigation issues, including harassment, discrimination, wrongful termination, trade secrets, and confidentiality agreements, among others.

### Environmental, Energy & Health & Safety:

The Environmental, Energy and Health and Safety Practice provides counsel to clients regarding all aspects of environmental law. Attorneys in this group address the vast array of environmental laws and issues that impact the daily operations of businesses and public entities - from large corporations and small businesses to local governments and individuals.

### Intellectual Property:

The Intellectual Property Practice works closely with in-house counsel, executive leadership teams and technical professionals to develop comprehensive programs focused on the procurement, counseling, protection and enforcement of IP rights, including licensing, establishment of litigation positioning, creation and management of international patent and trademark portfolios, proactive approaches to the protection of clients' intangible assets, and the prosecution and defense of all types of IP actions.

### Litigation:

Litigation practice attorneys' primary objective is to win for their clients and, at the same time, minimize the costly interruptions to their businesses that litigation may cause. The attorneys have extensive experience in representing all types of litigation matters and approach each matter with an analytical, yet business-oriented perspective. Attorneys have represented clients, including individuals closely-held businesses, and *Fortune* 500 companies, in civil and criminal cases at the state, federal, and appellate levels.

### Oil & Gas:

The firm's experienced attorneys counsel oil and gas industry clients on a wide range of business, legislative, regulatory and litigation matters, including employment, land use and emergency response issues. Roetzel attorneys understand the oil and gas business and are in tune with capital costs, infrastructure, and manpower issues relating to the development of the Utica Shale region. Representative clients include producers, pipelines, gathering and local distribution companies, drilling and service companies, financial institutions, landowners, and end-use customers.

### Public Law & Public Finance:

The public law attorneys develop solutions for clients' immediate legal and government relations' issues at federal, state, and local levels. Clients include *Fortune* 200 companies, trade associations, counties, cities, villages, school districts, public utilities, universities, libraries, townships, port authorities, and other governmental entities. The public finance attorneys serve as nationally recognized bond counsel, underwriter's counsel, issuer's counsel and trustee's counsel.

### Real Estate:

The Real Estate Practice offers comprehensive representation to real estate developers, institutional lenders, commercial and institutional owners, and a myriad of established and growing businesses with real estate related needs. The attorneys provide the type of in-depth skills required by developers and lenders working on sophisticated retail, commercial, mixed use or residential development projects. In addition, they advise clients of alternative strategies for governmental permitting, expanding, renovating, financing, or disposing of existing real estate holdings.

### Risk Management & Liability Defense:

The Risk Management and Liability Defense Practice offers experienced, aggressive counsel to defend lawsuits brought against large or small corporations, insurance carriers and their insured clients, retail entities, and transportation providers in the trucking, bus, rail, and automotive sectors.

**OFFICES**

OHIO

**AKRON:** 222 South Main Street, OH 44308
Tel: 330 376 2700  Fax: 330 376 4577

**CLEVELAND:** 1375 East Ninth Street, One Cleveland Center, 9th Floor, OH 44114
Tel: 216 623 0150  Fax: 216 623 0134

**COLUMBUS:** 155 East Broad Street, PNC Plaza, 12th Floor, OH 43215
Tel: 614 463 9770  Fax: 614 463 9792

**CINCINNATI:** 310 Chiquita Center, 250 E. 5th Street, OH 45202
Tel: 513 361 0200  Fax: 513 361 0335

**TOLEDO:** One SeaGate, Suite 1700, OH 43604
Tel: 419 242 7985  Fax: 419 242 0316

DISTRICT OF COLUMBIA

**WASHINGTON DC:** 600 14th Street, NW, Suite 400, DC 20005
Tel: 202 625 0600  Fax: 202 338 6340

FLORIDA

**FORT LAUDERDALE:** 350 East Las Olas Boulevard, Last Olas Centre II. Suite 1150, FL 33301
Tel: 954 462 4150  Fax: 954 462 4260

**FORT MYERS:** 2320 First Street, Suite 1000, FL 33901
Tel: 239 337 3850  Fax: 239 337 0970

**NAPLES:** 850 Park Shore Drive, Trianon Centre, 3rd Floor, FL 34103
Tel: 239 649 6200  Fax: 239 261 3659

**ORLANDO:** 420 South Orange Avenue, CNL Center II, 7th Floor, FL 32801
Tel: 407 896 2224  Fax: 407 835 3596

**TALLAHASSEE:** 119 East Park Avenue, Suite 2E, FL 32301
Tel: 850 425 5021  Fax: 850 222 8222

ILLINOIS

**CHICAGO:** Two Financial Plaza, 20 South Clark Street, Suite 300, Chicago, IL 60603
Tel: 312 580 1200 Fax: 312 580 1201

NEW YORK

**NEW YORK:** 245 Park Avenue, 39th Floor, NY 10167
Tel: 212 803 8160  Fax: 212 372 8798

# SQUIRE SANDERS

**www.**squiresanders.com **tel:** 216 479 8500 **fax:** 216 479 8780

**Chair and Global CEO:** James J Maiwurm
Number of partners: 460
Number of lawyers: 1,300

## Firm Overview:

Squire Sanders combines sound legal counsel with knowledge of clients' businesses. The client base spans every type of business, both private and public, worldwide. In the private sector, they provide the full range of legal advice required to implement practical strategies and resolve disputes. In the public sector, Squire Sanders counsels governments on privatization of whole industries and on establishment of regulatory systems under which new private businesses can compete. The global practice also serves the regional needs of the countries and cities it calls home.

Whatever is needed, they are able to deliver the seamless cross-practice and industry-specific support that clients require for success in today's competitive markets.

Squire Sanders operates as a 'one-firm firm' rather than a loose confederation of separate offices or practices. With more than 1,300 lawyers in 39 offices located in 19 countries across Asia Pacific, Europe and the Americas, they are well established in the markets where their clients do business. Squire Sanders also has strong working relationships with independent firms in the Middle East, as well as the Squire Sanders Legal Counsel Worldwide Network, which includes independent firms across Latin America.

Squire Sanders' extensive collective knowledge and resources are shared throughout the global practice via one of the most robust technology platforms in the legal business, as well as through ongoing rotation of lawyers throughout their offices. They employ knowledge- and project-management tools to implement continual business process improvements and enhance the value of their legal services.

Squire Sanders emphasizes quality, efficiency and alignment with client goals as core standards to improve continually their service delivery and the value of what they do for clients. Squire Sanders encourages and manages processes and tools to improve pricing models, training and resource optimization, knowledge management and more, all centered on their core focus – delivering the services their clients want, when and where they want them and with the value they deserve.

## Main Areas of Practice:

Aerospace and defense; antitrust and competition; automotive; aviation; brands; capital markets; chemicals; communications; construction; corporate governance; corporate transactions, finance and governance; data protection and privacy; diversified industrials; eDiscovery and data management; education; energy and natural resources; environmental, safety and health; FCPA/UK Bribery Act and anticorruption; financial services; global compliance solutions; government contracts; healthcare; hospitality and leisure; immigration; insurance; intellectual property and technology; international dispute resolution; international trade and export controls; labor and employment; life sciences; litigation; media; mergers and acquisitions; mining; pensions; private equity and venture capital; project and infrastructure finance; public advocacy; public finance; public-private partnerships; real estate; restructuring and insolvency; retail; sourcing and procurement; sports and entertainment; taxation and benefits; transportation, shipping and logistics; and white collar defense and investigations.

## Global Initiative:

Companies and organizations are under an ever-intensifying burden to manage and comply with myriad global rules and regulations. Squire Sanders has the technical and practical expertise necessary to design and implement compliance solutions that are sensitive to each organization's culture, way of doing business and economic model. They work with organizations to help ensure that employees are properly educated and incentivized not to engage in infringing conduct without stifling efforts to grow the business. They also defend organizations in legal challenges to their compliance programs. Squire Sanders offers:
- Global coverage
- Best practices for compliance
- Expertise in corporate defense
- Customized, global efforts effectively implemented locally

Their compliance advice is efficiently and effectively coordinated – across practice groups, industries and borders – and delivered by a team tailored to individual client needs.

## OFFICES

**ARIZONA**
**PHOENIX:** Tel: 602 528 4000  Fax: 602 253 8129

**CALIFORNIA**
**LOS ANGELES:** Tel: 213 624 2500  Fax: 213 623 4581
**PALO ALTO:** Tel: 650 856 6500  Fax: 650 843 8777
**SAN FRANCISCO:** Tel: 415 954 0200  Fax: 415 393 9887

**DISTRICT OF COLUMBIA**
**WASHINGTON DC:** Tel: 202 626 6600  Fax: 202 626 6780

**FLORIDA**
**MIAMI:** Tel: 305 577 7000  Fax: 305 577 7001
**TAMPA:** Tel: 813 202 1300  Fax: 813 202 1313
**WEST PALM BEACH:** Tel: 561 650 7200
Fax: 561 655 1509

**NEW YORK**
**NEW YORK:** Tel: 212 872 9800  Fax: 212 872 9815

**OHIO**
**CINCINNATI:** Tel: 513 361 1200  Fax: 513 361 1201
**CLEVELAND:** Tel: 216 479 8500  Fax: 216 479 8780
**COLUMBUS:** Tel: 614 365 2700  Fax: 614 365 2499

**TEXAS**
**HOUSTON:** Tel: 713 546 5850  Fax: 713 546 5830

**VIRGINIA**
**NORTHERN VIRGINIA:** Tel: 703 720 7800
Fax: 703 720 7801

## INTERNATIONAL OFFICES

The firm also has offices in Australia, Belgium, China, Czech Republic, Dominican Republic, France, Germany, Hungary, Japan, Poland, Russia, Saudi Arabia, Singapore, Slovak Republic, South Korea, Spain, Ukraine and UK.

Squire Sanders also has ongoing working relationships with independent firms in the following locations: Beirut, Lebanon; Bogotá, Colombia; Bucharest, Romania; Buenos Aires, Argentina; Caracas, Venezuela; La Paz, Bolivia; Lima, Peru; Panamá, Republic of Panamá; and Santiago, Chile.

# TAFT STETTINIUS & HOLLISTER LLP

www.taftlaw.com **tel:** 513 381 2838 **fax:** 513 381 0205

**Managing Partner:** Thomas T Terp
Number of partners: 198  Number of other lawyers: 136

## Firm Overview:

Established in 1885, Taft is a nationally recognized firm with more than 330 attorneys and offices in Cincinnati, Cleveland, Columbus and Dayton, Ohio; Indianapolis, Indiana; Covington, Kentucky; and Phoenix, Arizona. Taft attorneys serve individuals and businesses worldwide, in both mature and emerging industries, in areas such as manufacturing, banking and finance, insurance, distribution, television and radio, professional sports, healthcare, life sciences, advanced technology, energy, transportation and real estate.

## Main Areas of Practice:

### Banking & Institutional Finance:
Advises clients in structuring credit transactions, preparing and negotiating appropriate documentation, administering the credit relationship throughout its life, and working out problem credits.

### Business Restructuring, Bankruptcy & Creditor Rights:
Represents debtors, lenders, committees, suppliers, real estate owners and developers, equipment lessors, receivers, trustees, buyers and sellers, and other parties in connection with a wide assortment of transactions and litigation.

### Corporate Finance & Securities:
Represents clients on structuring credit transactions, preparing and negotiating the appropriate documentation, administering relationships with lenders, and solving problem credits. Counsels clients on the structuring of public and private securities offerings.

### Corporate Governance:
Provides advice to public, private and non-profit clients on all aspects of corporate governance, including compliance regarding SEC rules and the Sarbanes-Oxley Act.

### Emerging Companies:
Represents start-up and high-growth companies throughout the United States, as well as numerous providers of capital to emerging companies.

### Employee Benefits & Executive Compensation:
Advises clients regarding retirement plans, group welfare plans and fringe benefit arrangements, as well as stock-based incentive plans and non-qualified deferred compensation plans.

### Energy & Regulated Industries:
Offers comprehensive counsel to corporations, associations, utilities and municipalities on a wide range of energy, natural resources and utility issues.

### Environmental:
Provides nationally recognized litigation, counseling and dispute resolution services for clients related to local, state, regional and federal environmental laws, as well as emerging issues.

### Government Contracts:
Represents Fortune 100, entrepreneurial, privately-held, non-profit and governmental clients in all aspects of the procurement process, including contract formation, performance and administration, payment and dispute resolution.

### Health & Life Sciences:
Advises individual and institutional healthcare providers, research institutions, and pharmaceutical, medical device and biotechnology clients in multiple areas of law, including business and finance, employment and labor relations, malpractice litigation, insurance, regulatory and administrative law, ERISA, third-party reimbursement and hospital financing.

### Intellectual Property:
Counsels and assists clients with patents, trademarks, copyrights, trade secrets, computer software, internet-related issues and IP litigation.

### Labor & Employment:
Represents clients in a wide range of legal services, including labor management relations, employment litigation, benefit plans and ERISA compliance, workplace safety and health, immigration and citizenship and workers' compensation.

### Litigation:
Represents clients in all phases of litigation in federal and state courts, before regulatory agencies and arbitration panels, and in alternative dispute resolution in a full range of matters, including antitrust, appellate, bankruptcy, construction, ERISA, education, estates, trusts and fiduciary, FCPA and international anti-corruption, First Amendment & media law, government contracts, insurance, patent, product liability and personal injury, securities, sports and white collar criminal defense.

### Mergers & Acquisitions:
Represents buyers and sellers in public and private transactions in a broad range of M&A activities.

### Non-Profit & Tax-Exempt Organizations:
Represents non-profit organizations, foundations and tax-exempt entities in all aspects of their organization and operation.

### Private Client Services:
Counsels owners of closely-held businesses in establishing organizational structures to satisfy current and long-term needs and to plan for the smooth and tax-effective transfer of the business to the next generation.

### Public Law:
Comprised of current and former elected officials, experienced public administrators and lawyers who have worked closely with public entities.

### Real Property:
Represents clients in all facets of real estate, including acquisition and development, leasing, financing, construction and management agreements, land use issues, tax disputes and appeals, litigation, arbitration and mediation, and environmental concerns. Advises industry participants, including owners, contractors, design-builders, subcontractors, special servicers and material suppliers, on all aspects of public and private construction projects and dispute resolution.

### Tax:
Represents public corporations, financial institutions, domestic joint ventures, new business ventures, non-profit and tax-exempt organizations, and individuals in tax matters such as business transactions, employee benefits and executive compensation, international taxation, mergers and acquisitions, state and local tax, and tax controversy and litigation.

## International Work:
The firm's Japan practice represents over 100 Japanese-affiliated companies in the United States. Taft also represents a number of US companies with operations abroad, and foreign enterprises that do business in the US.

**OFFICES**

**OHIO**

**CINCINNATI:** 425 Walnut Street, Suite 1800, OH 45202
Tel: 513 381 2838  Fax: 513 381 0205

**CLEVELAND:** 200 Public Square, Suite 3500, OH 44114
Tel: 216 241 2838  Fax: 216 241 3707

**COLUMBUS:** 65 East State Street, Suite 1000, OH 43215
Tel: 614 221 2838  Fax: 614 221 2007

**DAYTON:** 40 North Main Street, Suite 1700, OH 45423
Tel: 937 228 2838  Fax: 937 228 2816

**INDIANA**

**INDIANAPOLIS:** One Indiana Square, Suite 3500, IN 46204
Tel: 317 713 3500  Fax: 317 713 3699

**KENTUCKY**

**COVINGTON:** 1717 Dixie Highway, Suite 910, KY 41011
Tel: 859 331 2838  Fax: 513 381 6613

**ARIZONA**

**PHOENIX:** 2375 East Camelback Road, Suite 600, AZ 85016
Tel: 602 387 4081  Fax: 602 387 5001

# THOMPSON HINE LLP

www.thompsonhine.com  **email:** info@thompsonhine.com

**Managing Partner:** Deborah Z Read
Number of partners: 193  Number of other lawyers: 179

**Firm Overview:**

Established in 1911, Thompson Hine is a business law firm dedicated to providing superior client service. The firm has been recognized for more than ten consecutive years as a top law firm in the US for client service excellence in *The BTI Client Service A-Team: Survey of Law Firm Client Service Performance*. Thompson Hine serves premier businesses worldwide, including AkzoNobel, Chiquita Brands International, Formica, Goodyear, Jo-Ann Stores, Johnson & Johnson, KeyCorp, Parker Hannifin and Verizon.

**Main Areas of Practice:**

**Admiralty & Maritime:**
Represents carriers and shippers before state and federal courts and agencies as well as toxic tort litigation on behalf of ship owners.

**Antitrust, Competition & Distribution:**
Advises on trade restraint price discrimination, franchising and distribution, trade secrets, false advertising and fraud.

**Business Restructuring, Creditors' Rights & Bankruptcy:**
Represents lenders, creditors' committees, debtors and other parties in finance transactions, workouts and bankruptcy matters.

**Climate Change & Sustainable Business Solutions:**
Addresses issues related to global climate change, evolving energy markets and sustainable business practices.

**Commercial & Public Finance:**
Handles commercial finance transactions, public finance, corporate trust, asset securitizations and general bank regulatory law.

**Construction:**
Represents owners, design professionals, construction managers, contractors and sureties. Serves as project counsel at sites across the United States.

**Corporate Transactions & Securities:**
Represents businesses in transactions, from startup to IPOs, joint ventures, mergers, acquisitions and beyond.

**Emerging Technologies:**
Helps businesses realize the opportunities and manage the risks of electronic and technological commerce.

**Employee Benefits & Executive Compensation:**
Advises on benefit plans; ERISA issues; controversies with the IRS, DOL, PBGC and other agencies; incentive and equity-based compensation; and ESOPs.

**Energy:**
Advises on regulated (at state and federal levels) and non-regulated energy transactions for natural gas (including shale plays), electricity, renewable energy, water and waste energy.

**Environmental:**
Advises on the environmental aspects of business transactions, allocating risk and compliance obligations under local, federal and state laws.

**ERISA Litigation:**
Handles ERISA litigation, from defending pre-litigation DOL enforcement actions and IRS audits of plans to trials on fiduciary duty claims.

**FCPA & Other Anti-Bribery Laws:**
Advises on compliance with the FCPA and other antibribery laws; defends client interests before the DOJ and SEC.

**Global Sourcing & Procurement:**
Assists with the procurement of internal and external solutions to strengthen operations, facilities, infrastructure, product supply chain and distribution channels.

**Government Contracts:**
Advises on contract matters involving the majority of federal agencies, as well as a wide range of state and municipal agencies.

**Health Care:**
Represents physician groups, hospitals, clinical laboratories, diagnostic service providers, pharmaceutical and medical device manufacturers and health insurance providers.

**Insurance:**
Provides regulatory, transactional, government relations and litigation services to insurance companies and other financial services organizations.

**Intellectual Property:**
Assists with patent/trademark preparation/prosecution; patent/trademark post- and pre-grant proceedings; patent, trademark, trade secret and copyright litigation; due diligence and IP audit reviews; opinions and competitive analysis; and contract negotiation.

**International:**
Advises US clients on matters in all regions of the world, as well as non-US-based clients with interests in the US.

**International Arbitration & Dispute Resolution:**
Advises companies and governments involved in complex, high-stakes disputes around the globe, including WTO disputes.

**International Trade & Customs:**
Represents clients in penalty actions, investigations and audits before US import/export agencies; advises on trade agreements and trade remedy proceedings.

**Investment Management:**
Advises mutual funds, hedge funds, private equity funds, investment advisers, broker-dealers, fund service providers and independent directors and trustees.

**Labor & Employment:**
Advises on employment litigation, workers' compensation, immigration, collective bargaining, and proceedings before federal and state agencies.

**Life Sciences:**
Creates business solutions and manages legal and regulatory issues for companies engaged in the research, development and delivery of human and animal health products and services.

**Litigation:**
Handles class actions, real estate and land use disputes, financial services litigation, competition and consumer protection matters, white collar issues, government and internal investigations, fiduciary duty and IP litigation.

**Personal & Succession Planning:**
Assists in the management and transmission of wealth and the succession of businesses and other personal and family concerns.

**Privacy & Information Security:**
Advises corporations on privacy and data security issues.

**Product Liability Litigation:**
Represents manufacturers in product liability matters involving chemicals, plastics, pharmaceuticals, medical devices, aircraft, automobiles, emerging technologies, and other consumer and commercial products.

**Real Estate:**
Advises on development, corporate real estate, zoning and land use, real estate investment and financing, and REITs.

**Tax:**
Advises on transactions and financings; tax controversy; legislative and regulatory activities; international, state and local taxation; and foundation and exempt organization matters.

**Telecommunications:**
Provides guidance on the regulations and laws affecting telecommunications, broadcasting and other communications companies.

**Transportation:**
Represents shippers, logistics providers, air carriers and other transportation interests in regulatory, commercial, policy and litigation matters.

**OFFICES**
DISTRICT OF COLUMBIA
**WASHINGTON, DC:** Tel: 202 331 8800
GEORGIA
**ATLANTA:** Tel: 404 541 2900
NEW YORK
**NEW YORK:** Tel: 212 344 5680
OHIO
**CINCINNATI:** Tel: 513 352 6700
**CLEVELAND:** Tel: 216 566 5500
**COLUMBUS:** Tel: 614 469 3200
**DAYTON:** Tel: 937 443 6600

# ULMER & BERNE LLP

www.ulmer.com **tel:** 216 583 7000 **fax:** 216 583 7001

**Managing Partner:** Kip Reader
Number of partners: 102   Number of lawyers: 187

## Firm Overview:

Ulmer & Berne LLP, established in 1908, is a full-service law firm focused on exceeding client expectations and delivering superior, customized legal solutions. Known as a firm that provides value to clients with its highly competitive rate structure, culture of providing practical legal advice, and efficiency in staffing legal matters, Ulmer & Berne's commitment to quality is uncompromising. The firm represents publicly traded and privately held companies, financial institutions, hedge funds, private equity funds, pharmaceutical companies, international joint ventures and affiliations, investor groups, family offices, start-ups and emerging businesses, public bodies, and nonprofit organizations.

## Main Areas of Practice:

### Business Law:

Combining legal experience with business acumen, practicality, and creativity, the firm counsels a wide range of businesses and industries at every stage to deliver seamless service. Covering the full spectrum of transactions and matters important to organizations in today's global marketplace, Ulmer & Berne advises clients on almost every type of deal.

### Complex Business Litigation:

Ulmer & Berne handles complex business litigation of all kinds for large sophisticated companies in a manner that balances aggressive advocacy with practical, cost-effective representation. Many of the firm's business litigators are routinely recognized as preeminent in their field. Their practice is national in scope and the quality is unsurpassed, but it's the firm's personal service and value that sets them apart.

### Construction:

Ulmer & Berne has a strong history of handling construction-related claims throughout the United States in state and federal courts, arbitration hearings, and mediation proceedings. They represent all construction-project participants, including owners, designers, contractors, and sureties. The team has focused on construction issues for decades, representing businesses from multi-billion dollar conglomerates to mid-size contractors.

### Corporate Restructuring & Creditors' Rights:

Marked by significant experience representing creditors, debtors, lenders and trustees in reorganization and insolvency matters, the firm handles workouts and restructurings; troubled company acquisitions and asset dispositions; and adversary proceedings involving preferences and fraudulent transfers; directors and officers litigation; assumption and rejection of leases and contracts; use of cash collateral; objections to discharge; automatic stay violations; and claims objections.

### Employment & Labor:

Ulmer & Berne provides employers the full spectrum of employment and labor representation, ranging from proactive counseling to the defense of the most complex litigation matters, including claims involving allegations of wrongful termination and FLSA, OSHA, and ERISA non-compliance. The firm also counsels and defends employers dealing with unlawful discrimination and workers' compensation claims, unfair labor practice allegations, non-compete and trade secret matters, collective bargaining negotiations, and immigration challenges.

### Financial Services Litigation:

Ulmer & Berne attorneys provide in-depth expertise in all aspects of financial services litigation on a wide range of matters. The firm represents banks, brokers, and diversified financial services companies in complex and class action litigation matters across the country. They also defend national broker-dealers and futures commission merchants against claims including breach of fiduciary duty, fraud, unsuitable investments, churning, failure to supervise, and improper margin borrowing.

### Health Care:

The firm represents various providers in matters involving the Affordable Care Act, HIPAA, health care antitrust matters, health care fraud matters, federal and state physician self-referral laws, anti-kickback laws, false claims laws, civil monetary penalty laws, and various compliance requirements. They also represent providers in structuring acquisitions, investments, joint ventures, and other business transactions to ensure compliance with the laws and requirements.

### IP & Technology:

Recognized as a leader in the region, the firm represents clients in patent and other IP proceedings in courts nationwide, the ITC, and the US Patent & Trademark Office. The firm successfully counsels and helps clients secure valuable patents, trademarks, and copyrights to protect international brands and leading edge innovations. Additionally, they assist clients with data privacy compliance, protecting trade secrets, and implementing licensing and other IP monetization strategies.

### Product Liability:

Serving as national counsel to numerous pharmaceutical, medical device, and dietary supplement companies, Ulmer & Berne has one of the largest and most well respected products liability practices in the United States. The firm also has significant expertise in the defense of product liability claims representing manufacturers and distributors of many types of equipment and other products, including power plant components, heavy equipment, industrial systems and consumer goods.

### Real Estate:

Privately and publicly held corporations as well as individual investors around the country turn to Ulmer & Berne's real estate attorneys for assistance in all aspects of real estate law, including leasing, acquisitions, tax credit projects, multi-family development, residential and commercial construction, shopping center development, tackling difficult environmental issues, private and public financing, property taxation and abatements, zoning, and tax-deferred exchanges.

### Tax:

Ulmer & Berne's tax attorneys provide counsel regarding all aspects of federal, state, and local taxation, employee benefit, executive compensation, health and welfare and retirement plan matters; estate planning and probate; and tax controversies. The firm works closely with its clients in achieving tax-efficient structures in mergers and acquisitions, divestitures, and finance transactions.

### Clients:

Ulmer & Berne serves a diverse client base including Fortune 500 companies and other major business entities across the United States and increasingly abroad in both Asia and Europe.

## OFFICES

**OHIO**

**CLEVELAND:** Skylight Office Tower, 1660 West 2nd Street, Suite 1100, OH 44113-1448
Tel: 216 583 7000

**CINCINNATI:** 600 Vine Street, Suite 2800, OH 45202-2409
Tel: 513 698 5000

**COLUMBUS:** 88 East Broad Street, Suite 1600, OH 43215-3581
Tel: 614 229 0000

**ILLINOIS**

**CHICAGO:** 500 West Madison Street, Suite 3600, IL 60661-4587
Tel: 312 658 6500

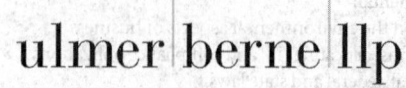
ulmer | berne | llp
ATTORNEYS

# VORYS, SATER, SEYMOUR AND PEASE LLP

**www.**vorys.com **tel:** 614 464 6400 **fax:** 614 464 6350

**Managing Partner:** Russell M Gertmenian
Number of partners: 170   Total number of attorneys: 361

## Firm Overview:

Vorys provides business and legal counsel to clients throughout the US and around the world. With attorneys in six offices, the firm represents thousands of clients, ranging from start-up businesses to *Fortune* 500 corporations and from individuals needing estate planning advice to defendants embroiled in multi-state class action litigation.

## Main Areas of Practice:

### Antitrust & Trade Regulation:
Vorys has represented clients in some of the most significant recent antitrust cases. The firm regularly represents clients in private civil litigation, in civil investigations brought by both federal and state governments, and in criminal grand juries and trials.

### Bankruptcy & Creditors' Rights:
Vorys lawyers have decades of practical experience and have represented clients in hundreds of matters addressing all aspects of bankruptcy law, corporate reorganizations, debt restructurings, asset protection and recovery, and debtor/creditor matters.

### Corporate & Business Organizations:
Vorys is a nationally recognized corporate law firm representing more than 2,000 public and private companies on corporate law matters. Vorys also provides legal services to a large number of banks, savings associations and holding companies.

### Environmental, Energy & Utilities:
Vorys environment, energy and utilities lawyers are among the most experienced in the Midwest. The firm represents all segments of the energy industry and provides clients with representation in regulatory affairs, commercial and corporate transactions and litigation, and in the emerging alternative energy fields of wind, solar and biofuel. The firm also has extensive experience in all aspects of oil and natural gas law.

### Government Relations:
Vorys assists clients in achieving their government relations objectives as efficiently as possible and with minimum expense and frustration. The firm offers representation before federal, state and local governments and many other organizations.

### Healthcare:
Vorys healthcare attorneys counsel clients on the legal and regulatory issues facing the healthcare industry. Vorys serves as outside counsel for many hospitals, health systems, nursing homes, skilled nursing facilities, and other healthcare institutional providers.

### Insurance:
Vorys handles the organization, capitalization and restructuring of insurance companies and agencies, mergers, mutual-to-stock conversions, admissions of domestic companies to other states and of foreign companies to Ohio, regulatory approvals of insurance policies and forms, negotiation of insurance and reinsurance contracts, and licensing and management of agents and brokers.

### Intellectual Property, Media & Entertainment:
Vorys guides clients through complex strategic planning, sensitive negotiations and other details of intellectual property protection. The firm has experience in the acquisition, protection, enforcement, and exploitation of patents, trademarks, copyrights and industrial designs.

### International Law:
Vorys advises US and foreign manufacturers, trading companies, importers, exporters, industrial consumers, and trade associations on a wide range of issues regarding trade remedy and import relief proceedings, customs laws and import compliance, export controls and sanctions programs and trade policy.

### Labor & Employment:
Vorys has expanded from traditional areas of union organizing campaigns and collective bargaining to encompass employee benefit plans and executive compensation issues, federal and state statutes that govern various aspects of the employer-employee relationship and workplace safety issues.

### Litigation:
Vorys represents clients in a wide range of disputes, whether it involves allegations of civil or criminal liability, concerns business issues, claimed violation of statutes, professional malpractice, or whether it is to be resolved in a trial court, on appeal or through other forms of alternative dispute resolution.

### Real Estate & Commercial:
Vorys provides services to local, regional, national and international clients in a variety of industries. The firm's lawyers draw upon industry-leading knowledge and experience to assist clients in planning, structuring and realizing their commercial and real estate goals.

### Taxation:
Vorys' experienced attorneys identify and achieve clients' objectives efficiently and cost-effectively in the federal, state and local tax arenas as well as in the growing field of economic development incentives.

### Technology, Advertising & Communications:
Vorys guides clients through strategic planning, contractual negotiations and compliance issues associated with use of technology. Vorys attorneys work with key providers, know the relevant tools and applications, and help clients to exploit the innovations driven by the internet and e-commerce.

### Trusts, Estates & Wealth Transfer:
Vorys attorneys assist individuals, families and fiduciaries to plan and prepare for the future transfer of wealth, carry out and administer clients' intentions as set forth in their written estate plans, and represent clients in litigation to preserve and protect their interests.

## PRACTICE AREAS

Antitrust & Trade Regulation
Bankruptcy & Creditors' Rights
Corporate & Business Organizations
Environmental, Energy & Utilities
Government Relations
Healthcare
Insurance
Intellectual Property
International Law
Labor & Employment
Litigation
Real Estate & Commercial
Taxation
Technology, Advertising & Communications
Trusts, Estates & Wealth Transfer

## OFFICES

**DISTRICT OF COLUMBIA**
**WASHINGTON, DC:** 1909 K Street NW, Suite 900, DC 20006
Tel: 202 467 8800   Fax: 202 467 8900

**OHIO**
**COLUMBUS:** 52 East Gay Street, OH 43215
Tel: 614 464 6400   Fax: 614 464 6350

**CINCINNATI:** 301 East Fourth Street, Suite 3500, Great American Tower, OH 45202
Tel: 513 723 4000   Fax: 513 723 4056

**CLEVELAND:** 1375 East Ninth Street, 2100 One Cleveland Center, OH 44114
Tel: 216 479 6100   Fax: 216 479 6060

**AKRON:** 106 South Main Street, Suite 1100, OH 44308
Tel: 330 208 1000   Fax: 330 208 1001

**TEXAS**
**HOUSTON:** 700 Louisiana Street, Suite 4100, TX 77002
Tel: 713 588 7000   Fax: 713 588 7050

## How lawyers are ranked

Every year we carry out thousands of in-depth interviews with clients in order to assess the reputations and expertise of business lawyers worldwide. The qualities we look for (and which determine rankings) include technical legal ability, professional conduct, client service, commercial awareness/astuteness, diligence, commitment, and other qualities most valued by the client. For details of our research team, see p.5.

# CORPORATE/COMMERCIAL

Commentary about individuals can be found under their firm's paragraph. If the firm has no paragraph (is not ranked) look at Other Notable Practitioners.

### Corporate/Commercial — Leading Firms

**Band 1**
Crowe & Dunlevy, a Professional Corporation *
McAfee & Taft *

**Band 2**
Commercial Law Group
Conner & Winters, LLP
Doerner, Saunders, Daniel & Anderson, LLP
Hall, Estill, Hardwick, Gable, Golden & Nelson, PC *
Hartzog Conger Cason & Neville, LLP *

\* Indicates firm with profile.
†ONP ≈ Other Notable Practitioner.

## Band 1

### Crowe & Dunlevy, a Professional Corporation
See profile on p.2157

**THE FIRM** This firm has expertise in the full range of corporate matters, and is particularly noted for its depth of experience in the banking and finance arena. The group recently represented RKI Exploration & Production in its joint venture with Chesapeake Energy. The team also serves clients including JPMorgan Chase, US Bancorp and BancFirst. Sources underscore the firm's bench strength and ability in surrounding states.
**Sources say:** *"The excellent talent and expertise that they have in a variety of fields is first rate."*
**KEY INDIVIDUALS James Holloman** is widely noted for his experience in tax and restructuring matters. Sources praise the *"great insight and direction"* that he brings to his work. Experienced practitioner **Karen Rieger** (see p.2153) continues to be considered a go-to lawyer for transactional work in the healthcare arena. Recent matters include leading the team in connection with a $100 million healthcare acquisition. **Roger Stong** (see p.2154) recently advised New Source Energy in connection with its $100 million IPO. A client attests that *"he's really top tier,"* and com-

### Corporate/Commercial — Leading Individuals

**Band 1**
| | |
|---|---|
| Coleman W Chris | McAfee & Taft * |
| Curry Robert A | Conner & Winters, LLP |
| Derrick Gary W | Derrick & Briggs LLP (ONP)† |
| Moore Lynnwood | Conner & Winters, LLP |
| Paliotta Armand | Hartzog Conger Cason & Neville, LLP * |
| Stong Roger A | Crowe & Dunlevy * |

**Band 2**
| | |
|---|---|
| Blalock Tom | Commercial Law Group |
| Cooper H Wayne | Doerner, Saunders, Daniel & Anderson * |
| Robertson John D | Hartzog Conger Cason & Neville, LLP* |
| Rockett D Joe | Andrews Davis Legg Bixler Milsten (ONP)† |
| Stringer N Martin | McAfee & Taft * |

**Band 3**
| | |
|---|---|
| Anderson Michael A | Anderson McCoy & Orta (ONP)† |
| Betow Gary | Conner & Winters, LLP |
| Chambers Lawrence | Doerner, Saunders, Daniel & Anderson * |
| Crum Bruce | McAfee & Taft * |
| Larimore James W | Crowe & Dunlevy * |
| Lees C. Ray | Commercial Law Group |
| Melgaard Robert J | Conner & Winters, LLP |

**Up-and-coming individuals**
| | |
|---|---|
| Smith Joshua D. | McAfee & Taft * |

**Associates to watch**
| | |
|---|---|
| Bentley Kassandra | Doerner, Saunders, Daniel & Anderson * |

ments that he has *"a brilliant mind."* **Kevin Gordon** is recognized for his expertise pertaining to the healthcare sphere. He chairs the firm's healthcare litigation practice group. **Cori Loomis** (see p.2151) has a broad practice in the healthcare sector. She is noted for her work on the transfer of information, policy compliance and regulatory compliance issues. Sources affirm that she is *"very well respected."* **James Larimore** (see p.2151) recently acted alongside Stong in the aforementioned New Source Energy

### Corporate/Commercial: Healthcare — Leading Individuals

**Band 1**
| | |
|---|---|
| Brennan Elise | Conner & Winters, LLP |
| Burkett Teresa M. | Conner & Winters, LLP |
| Joseph Michael E | McAfee & Taft * |
| Rieger Karen | Crowe & Dunlevy * |
| Scoggins Linda G. | Scoggins & Cross, PLLC (ONP)† |

**Band 2**
| | |
|---|---|
| Glass Robert | Glass & Wilkins (ONP)† |
| Gordon Kevin D | Crowe & Dunlevy |
| Loomis Cori H | Crowe & Dunlevy * |
| Tyrrell Elizabeth D | McAfee & Taft * |

**Up-and-coming individuals**
| | |
|---|---|
| Rogers Patricia A. | McAfee & Taft * |

### Corporate/Commercial: Tax — Senior Statesmen

**Senior Statesmen: distinguished older practitioners**
| | |
|---|---|
| Fuller Gary | McAfee & Taft * |

### Leading Individuals

**Band 1**
| | |
|---|---|
| Blake T Michael | McAfee & Taft * |
| Cason Len | Hartzog Conger Cason & Neville, LLP * |
| Davis Steven C | Hartzog Conger Cason & Neville, LLP * |
| Holloman Jr James H | Crowe & Dunlevy |
| Larason Timothy M | Andrews Davis Legg Bixler Milsten (ONP)† |
| Mock Randall D | Mock, Schwabe, Waldo, Elder (ONP)† |

**Up-and-coming individuals**
| | |
|---|---|
| Haines Spencer | McAfee & Taft * |

**Associates to watch**
| | |
|---|---|
| Hickey Matthew | Crowe & Dunlevy |

IPO. *"He's beyond his years when it comes to business acumen,"* reports one interviewee. **Matthew Hickey** is highly rated for his expertise in corporate, tax and securities law issues. One interviewee remarks that he "*secures the most value and protects our interests.*"

### McAfee & Taft
See profile on p.2162

**THE FIRM** This firm is widely recognized for the strength of its corporate practice. The team recently represented Dalea Partners in a highly complex matter involving the formation of a joint venture with Abraaj Capital, as well as in the ensuing acquisition of Viking Services from TransAtlantic Petroleum. The firm is also notable in the tax and healthcare sectors, recently advising Oklahoma Heart Hospital on a series of major commercial matters, including the expansion of its facilities. Other key clients include Chaparral Energy and the Oklahoma Publishing Company.

**Sources say:** "*The firm performed magnificently. Their work was on par with any firm in the country, including East and West Coast megafirms.*"

**KEY INDIVIDUALS Michael Blake** (see p.2146) handles tax and transactional work for corporate clients. He is highly lauded by the market, with one interviewee labeling him "*truly astounding*" and "*a super advocate for our company.*" **Chris Coleman** (see p.2148) is identified as "*an outstanding lawyer in all regards.*" He acts on transactional matters across a number of industries, including energy, real estate, financial services and communications. **Michael Joseph** (see p.2150) is an experienced healthcare practitioner. He recently acted for the Presbyterian Health Foundation Research Park in its sale to the University of Oklahoma. **Bruce Crum** (see p.2148) is noted for his expertise in banking and finance matters. He has significant experience working for banks, financial institutions and private equity groups. Sources describe him as "*a wonderful, thoughtful lawyer.*" **Gary Fuller's** (see p.2149) mastery of tax law is widely acknowledged by the Oklahoma market. Fuller has broad experience dealing with corporate tax issues. **Spencer Haines** (see p.2150) has a broad tax practice covering general tax planning, wealth transfer tax and tax structuring for a range of commercial bodies. **Patricia Rogers** (see p.2153) continues to be noted for her work in the healthcare sector. She assists a range of clientele, including hospitals, ambulatory surgery centers and other healthcare facilities, on transactional and regulatory issues. **Martin Stringer** (see p.2154) has a broad business law practice which includes M&A and securities law. His clients include Stage Stores and Oklahoma City Thunder. **Elizabeth Tyrrell** (see p.2155) is identified as "*a really great health lawyer*" by her peers. She has been closely involved in the aforementioned matters for Oklahoma Heart Hospital. "*Excellent transactional attorney*" **Joshua Smith** (see p.2154) is described as "*persuasive and creative in crafting solutions to solve complex problems*" by clients. He was involved in the Dalea matters described above.

## Band 2

### Commercial Law Group

**THE FIRM** This boutique firm focuses on corporate and commercial law. The group handles complex transactions and has garnered praise for its representation of major players in a number of industries, including energy and finance. Additional expertise includes workouts and commercial restructuring.

**KEY INDIVIDUALS Ray Lees** is highly regarded for his work as a commercial attorney to major energy companies. Sources describe him as "*a very good transactional attorney.*" **Tom Blalock** is considered "*an exceptional lawyer who is great at what he does*" by market observers. His practice covers a broad range of matters in the commercial sector, including corporate restructuring.

### Conner & Winters, LLP

**THE FIRM** This firm has a broad corporate and commercial practice and handles a range of matters, including securities, corporate governance and tax issues. The firm also impresses on the healthcare front, representing clients on a range of matters, including those related to the Health Insurance Portability and Accountability Act and corporate compliance. Noteworthy clients include Dover Corporation, Walmart and SemGroup Corporation.

**KEY INDIVIDUALS Gary Betow** is noted for his focus on commercial lending. He is described by peers as "*a wonderful lawyer,*" and is highly regarded for his analytical and meticulous approach. Sources identify him as "*a guru*" of commercial lending. **Robert Curry** is "*an outstanding lawyer*" with a broad practice covering mergers and acquisitions, equity and debt securities, international corporate matters and initial public offerings. Experienced healthcare attorney **Elise Brennan** is noted for her work on transactional and regulatory matters involving hospitals. **Teresa Burkett** also focuses her practice on the healthcare sector. She handles a range of matters, including corporate compliance and transactional work. **Lynnwood Moore** achieves significant praise for his long career in the corporate sector. Sources underscore his expertise in securities issues as well as his work with notable clients in the energy industry. "*He's someone I really admire,*" comments one interviewee. **Robert Melgaard** covers a range of corporate matters, and is noted for his expertise in securities. "*He has an outstanding reputation and always impresses,*" remarks one source.

### Doerner, Saunders, Daniel & Anderson, LLP

**THE FIRM** This firm provides a broad spectrum of corporate and commercial services. The transactional team has experience in structuring mergers, acquisitions, property exchanges and loans for parties on all sides of a transaction. Recent highlights include acting for Titan Propane in a multistate 1031 exchange of operation properties. Notable clients also include Navico, Hanley and Bird and Houston Interests.

**Sources say:** "*They always provide excellent counsel in everything from straight purchase orders to complicated aspects of sale and acquisition.*"

**KEY INDIVIDUALS Wayne Cooper** (see p.2148) receives high praise from clients and peers, who describe him as "*a very strong contracts attorney.*" Clients appreciate how "*he has a systematic way of thinking through legal issues*" and "*stays calm in times of crisis.*" **Larry Chambers** (see p.2148) is noted as "*an excellent attorney.*" He has a broad practice encompassing corporate and partnership finance, transactional matters, commercial lending, and public and private securities offerings. **Kassandra Bentley** (see p.2146) is a highly rated associate and a keen favorite among clients. Alongside her experience in transactional matters, she also has significant knowledge of tax, trust and estate planning. "*She is a good organizer, attentive, and has a good recall of transaction details,*" says one interviewee.

### Hall, Estill, Hardwick, Gable, Golden & Nelson, PC
See profile on p.2160

**THE FIRM** This firm enters the rankings this year following acclaim from both peers and clients. Sources identify the depth of the firm's oil and gas practice on both transactional and litigation matters, and also note experience in tax issues and commercial loan transactions. Clients include Dow Jones & Company and The Williams Companies.

**Sources say:** "*Prompt, timely and cost effective. They are good value for money.*"

**KEY INDIVIDUALS Michael Cooke** is the firm's managing partner and a key contact for corporate matters.

### Hartzog Conger Cason & Neville, LLP
See profile on p.2161

**THE FIRM** This compact Oklahoma City firm has experience in all stages of the commercial transaction process, and is noted for its handling of private placement securities offerings. In addition, the team's expertise covers tax credits and incentives, tax controversies, corporate financings and business structuring.

**Sources say:** "*A strong smaller firm.*"

**KEY INDIVIDUALS Len Cason** (see p.2147) is widely acclaimed for his ability as a tax attorney. He has experience working on the tax elements of major corporate transactions. Sources state that he is "*a really good practitioner.*" **Steven Davis** (see p.2149) is well known for his work on tax matters. Market observers widely agree that he is "*a wonderful lawyer.*" **Armand Paliotta** (see p.2152) is described as "*very analytical, strong and thorough.*" He is noted for his expertise in corporate transactions and corporate governance. **John Robertson** (see p.2153) has significant experience in transactional matters, securities and employment law.

## Other Notable Practitioners

**Timothy Larason** of Andrews Davis Legg Bixler Milsten & Price, A Professional Corporation is highly rated for his intelligence and experience as a tax attorney. His practice covers business structuring, and he has experience litigating major tax cases. The "*legendary*" **Joe Rockett**, also at Andrews Davis, has a broad practice that covers a wide range of corporate and commercial issues. Sources name him *"a fabulous attorney."* **Gary Derrick** of Derrick & Briggs LLP is noted for his expertise in corporate and securities law, as well as for his considerable experience in seeing through legislative changes. Sources describe him as *"one of the best lawyers in Oklahoma City."* Tulsa-based healthcare attorney **Robert Glass** of Glass & Wilkins has a

wealth of experience acting on transactional matters. He is particularly noted for his work with physicians' groups. **Randall Mock** of Mock, Schwabe, Waldo, Elder, Reeves & Bryant has extensive experience as a tax attorney. He provides tax counsel on a range of matters, including real estate and commercial transactions. Oklahoma City-based **Linda Scoggins** of Scoggins & Cross, PLLC is a respected

healthcare practitioner with a strong litigation practice. Sources describe her as *"very bright"* and *"a terrific lawyer."* The *"phenomenal"* **Michael Anderson** of Anderson McCoy & Orta enters the rankings this year. He has significant expertise acting for borrowers, documenting loan assumption transactions, and working on securitized loans in general.

# ENERGY & NATURAL RESOURCES

Commentary about individuals can be found under their firm's paragraph. If the firm has no paragraph (is not ranked) look at Other Notable Practitioners.

## Energy & Natural Resources
### Leading Firms

**Band 1**
Crowe & Dunlevy, a Professional Corporation *
Hall, Estill, Hardwick, Gable, Golden & Nelson, PC *
McAfee & Taft *

**Band 2**
Conner & Winters, LLP
GableGotwals

### Leading Individuals

**Band 1**

| | | |
|---|---|---|
| Christiansen Mark D | McAfee & Taft * | |
| Hardwick James C T | Hall, Estill, Hardwick, Gable, Golden * | |
| Pepper David E | Hartzog Conger Cason & Neville (ONP)[†] * | |
| Smith Michael E | Hall, Estill, Hardwick, Gable, Golden * | |
| Walker Mark L | Crowe & Dunlevy | |

**Band 2**

| | |
|---|---|
| Barrett Terry | McAfee & Taft * |
| Bomhoff Timothy J | McAfee & Taft * |
| Cottingham Dale E | GableGotwals |
| Griffin Jr John J | Crowe & Dunlevy * |
| Grove Roger A | Grove & Hulett (ONP)[†] |
| Hayes J Kevin | Hall, Estill, Hardwick, Gable, Golden * |
| Hulett Carrie | Grove & Hulett (ONP)[†] |
| Mahaffey Gregory L | Mahaffey & Gore (ONP)[†] |
| Ragsdale Terry D | GableGotwals |
| Redwine R Kevin | Conner & Winters, LLP |
| Stinson C David | McAfee & Taft * |

**Up-and-coming individuals**

| | |
|---|---|
| Banner Mark | Hall, Estill, Hardwick, Gable, Golden * |

## Band 1

### Crowe & Dunlevy, a Professional Corporation
See profile on p.2157

**THE FIRM** This firm remains a leader in the market, with clients praising its expertise and experience in energy and environmental matters. On the energy side, the group acts for major industry names including ExxonMobil, The Williams Companies and Devon Energy. In addition to addressing environmental regulatory matters, the firm also has a healthy renewables practice, having acted for a number of wind farm projects of late.

## Energy & Natural Resources: Environment
### Leading Individuals

**Band 1**

| | |
|---|---|
| Burnett LeAnne | Crowe & Dunlevy, a Professional Corporation * |
| Crook Martin Linda | Doerner, Saunders, Daniel (ONP)[†] * |
| Ternes Mary Ellen | McAfee & Taft * |

**Band 2**

| | |
|---|---|
| Joyce Robert | McAfee & Taft * |
| Landreth Lloyd | Landreth Law (ONP)[†] |
| Paul Chris A | McAfee & Taft * |
| Shandy Donald | Ryan Whaley Coldiron Shandy (ONP)[†] |
| Tolbert Miles | Crowe & Dunlevy * |
| Wofford Michael | Doerner, Saunders, Daniel (ONP)[†] * |

*\* Indicates firm / individual with profile.*
*[†]ONP = Other Notable Practitioner.*

**Sources say:** *"We are very pleased with the service. They're real good at thinking through the way to approach new things."*

**KEY INDIVIDUALS** The *"very personable, very motivated"* **LeAnne Burnett** (see p.2147) is considered one of Oklahoma's leading environmental attorneys. Though particularly well known in water law, she has a broad range of experience in environmental regulation and litigation, advising major energy companies on such issues. **Mark Walker** has *"a proven ability to understand oil and gas operations and the needs we have,"* according to sources. He has extensive experience in environmental and natural resources disputes and recently acted for GMX Resources in an arbitration concerning shale wells. Department head **John Griffin** (see p.2149) is held in high regard by clients, who value the *"huge experience"* and *"great perspective"* he brings to matters. Clients identify **Miles Tolbert** (see p.2155) as a skilled environmental attorney. He has recently acted for WPX Energy and The Williams Companies on significant environmental matters.

### Hall, Estill, Hardwick, Gable, Golden & Nelson, PC
See profile on p.2160

**THE FIRM** This firm is widely considered by peers to be a key competitor for work in this sector. The team is known for its litigation prowess and has acted for The Williams Companies and WPX on major contentious issues. The group has also recently worked on royalty class actions, antitrust issues and appellate matters both in Oklahoma

and across the USA. It is noted for its experience in litigation related to environmental issues, and has a healthy transactional and regulatory practice.

**Sources say:** *"We are been very pleased with the services they provide. Over the years they've been super – we couldn't ask for any more."*

**KEY INDIVIDUALS Michael Smith** (see p.2154) recently represented Flamingo Seismic Solutions in a high-value dispute. *"He has a very sound understanding of oil and gas matters, and takes a practical approach to problem solving,"* say clients. He is praised for his common-sense approach and experience in representing major energy companies. **James Hardwick** (see p.2150) is *"certainly well respected and has a broad range of experience,"* according to sources. He recently defended XTO Energy and Apache Corporation against class actions by royalty owners across Kansas and Texas. Head of department **Kevin Hayes** (see p.2150) was recently successful in the Oklahoma Court of Civil Appeals, reversing a trial court summary judgment regarding a pooling order entered by the Oklahoma Corporation Commission. *"He's super,"* according to clients. *"Well informed and knowledgeable about oil and gas matters,"* **Mark Banner** (see p.2146) is highly praised by clients and peers. He was lead attorney on a matter for Apache Corporation and also recently represented Frontier Gas Services.

### McAfee & Taft
See profile on p.2162

**THE FIRM** This firm is known for its work in the oil and gas sector, and is also heavily involved in the renewable energy field, with experience on significant wind energy projects. As well as its well-regarded strength in transactional work, the firm also houses expertise in dispute resolution. It has particular experience in spill response and remediation, and pipeline compliance. Noteworthy clients include Anadarko, Chesapeake Operating and Citgo Petroleum.

**Sources say:** *"I have been overwhelmed with their service. I was using them at a previous employer too. They're our preferred provider in Oklahoma. They are great."*

**KEY INDIVIDUALS Mary Ellen Ternes** (see p.2155) provides environmental guidance on a variety of matters undertaken by the firm. Sources underscore her outstanding reputation and impressive background in chemical engineering. The highly regarded **Mark Christiansen** (see p.2148) recently joined the firm from Crowe & Dunlevy.

Sources highlight his *"measured and thoughtful approach to problem solving."* He is expected to add considerable strength to the firm's work for energy sector clients. **Tim Bomhoff** (see p.2147) is highlighted for being *"very responsive and very easy to work with."* His practice focuses on oil and gas litigation, through which he represents several major energy companies. He recently acted for Devon Energy on various matters related to its oil and gas operations. Seasoned practitioner **David Stinson** (see p.2154) has a wealth of experience acting on transactional matters in the oil and gas industry. He recently acted for RAM Energy Resources in its sizable private offering of common stock. Sources praise his pragmatic approach. **Terry Barrett** (see p.2146) has a wealth of experience in the oil and gas sector. He has represented a number of companies on various transactions. and has acted for a number of major energy companies of late. **Robert Joyce** (see p.2150) has litigated extensively on environmental issues and continues to represent significant players in the energy industry. His recent work includes a case involving a renowned Superfund site in Oklahoma. **Chris Paul** (see p.2152) is noted for his work with midstream and downstream energy companies, as well as on environmental compliance issues.

## Band 2

### Conner & Winters, LLP
**THE FIRM** This firm is identified as a key player when it comes to transactional work in energy and natural resources. The team recently represented Dover Energy on several major acquisitions related to oil and gas production. The group also provides services for a range of client needs in this sector, including litigation and alternative dispute resolution. The firm also has an impressive environmental practice, acting on regulatory and litigation matters, as well as the environmental issues related to commercial transactions.

**Sources say:** *"Conner & Winters is very responsive and capable, which is why we continue using it."*

**KEY INDIVIDUALS Kevin Redwine** has extensive expertise in energy-related transactions. He is described by clients as *"timely and accurate with current, pertinent experience."* In addition to representing Dover Energy, he recently acted for BlueStone Natural Resources on significant corporate matters.

### GableGotwals
**THE FIRM** This highly regarded group has an impressive litigation bench, with practitioners active in both energy and environmental matters. The firm has acted for local and national energy players on complicated disputes. The team also impresses clients with its expertise in environmental issues, and has accrued extensive experience related to CERCLA, CAA and CWA issues, in addition to negotiations with public authorities, including the EPA.

**KEY INDIVIDUALS Dale Cottingham** is described as an *"outstanding energy litigator,"* but also has a widely respected water law practice. He has represented a range of clients including BP and ONEOK in various contentious matters, and has extensive expertise at the Oklahoma Corporation Commission. **Terry Ragsdale** has developed a strong practice in this sector, representing clients in matters related to work in Oklahoma, Texas, New Mexico, Colorado, Louisiana and North Dakota.

## Other Notable Practitioners

**Linda Crook Martin** (see p.2148) of Doerner, Saunders, Daniel & Anderson, LLP gets glowing reviews from clients and peers. Sources say she is *"one of the best environmental litigators in the state, and fun to be around."* The *"methodical and thorough"* **Michael Wofford** (see p.2156), also of Doerner Saunders, has a broad environmental practice covering water law, clean air, hazardous waste and Superfund issues. **David Pepper** (see p.2152) of Hartzog Conger Cason & Neville, LLP is known as a leader in the field for Oklahoma Corporation Commission work. Clients and peers commend his accessibility and expertise on regulatory matters. **Lloyd Landreth** of Landreth Law receives substantial praise from commentators for his environmental practice. He is noted for representing domestic airlines and airline fuel consortiums, as well as businesses in the oil and gas sector. Peers note that **Gregory Mahaffey** of Mahaffey & Gore assiduously pursues his clients' interests. He has broad experience in oil and gas litigation. **Donald Shandy** of Ryan Whaley Coldiron Shandy is noted as *"a smart, effective lawyer."* He is well known for his work on clean air issues. **Roger Grove** of Grove & Hulett is best known for his work at the Oklahoma Corporation Commission. He is *"excellent,"* according to sources. **Carrie Hulett**, also of Grove & Hulett, is widely acknowledged for her experience in title examination in the oil and gas field.

# INTELLECTUAL PROPERTY

Commentary about individuals can be found under their firm's paragraph. If the firm has no paragraph (is not ranked) look at Other Notable Practitioners.

| Intellectual Property |
| --- |
| **Leading Firms** |

**Band 1**

Crowe & Dunlevy, a Professional Corporation *

Dunlap Codding *

Hall, Estill, Hardwick, Gable, Golden & Nelson, PC *

McAfee & Taft *

**Band 2**

Fellers, Snider, Blankenship, Bailey & Tippens, P.C. *

| Intellectual Property |
| --- |
| **Senior Statesmen** |

**Senior Statesmen:** distinguished older practitioners

| Johnson Paul H. | GableGotwals (ONP)[†] |
| --- | --- |
| McCarthy Bill D. | Hall, Estill, Hardwick, Gable, Golden * |

**Leading Individuals**

**Band 1**

| Blue Rachel | McAfee & Taft * |
| --- | --- |
| Brockhaus Marc A | Dunlap Codding * |
| Free Jr Philip L | Hall, Estill, Hardwick, Gable, Golden * |
| Kenney John A | McAfee & Taft * |
| LaBrie Michael J | McAfee & Taft * |
| McCarthy Randall K | Hall, Estill, Hardwick, Gable, Golden * |
| Rouse Nicholas D | Dunlap Codding * |
| Sorocco Douglas J | Dunlap Codding * |
| Sullivan David | Crowe & Dunlevy * |

**Band 2**

| Breedlove Roy C | Fellers, Snider, Blankenship, Bailey |
| --- | --- |
| Dougherty, III Clifford C | McAfee & Taft * |
| Lee Mary M. | Law Office of Mary M. Lee (ONP)[†] |
| Millikin Margaret | Crowe & Dunlevy, PC * |
| Ozinga Martin G. | Phillips Murrah P.C. (ONP)[†] |
| Rahhal Anthony | McAfee & Taft * |

**Up-and-coming individuals**

| Deligans Julianna | Hall, Estill, Hardwick, Gable, Golden * |
| --- | --- |
| Harvey Derrick | Harvey Law (ONP)[†] |

**Associates to watch**

| Palmer Drew T | Crowe & Dunlevy * |
| --- | --- |
| Peterson Andrew | McAfee & Taft * |
| Smith Michael H | Hall, Estill, Hardwick, Gable, Golden * |

* Indicates firm / individual with profile.

[†]ONP = Other Notable Practitioner.

## Band 1

### Crowe & Dunlevy, a Professional Corporation
See profile on p.2157

**THE FIRM** This firm impresses a range of clients with its extensive experience and knowledge. It provides a range of services in the IP sector, ranging from traditional patent prosecution to cutting-edge and transactional IP work. The firm boasts significant expertise in matters relating to the oil and gas and renewables sectors, with noteworthy clients including The Williams Companies and Oilfield Improvements, as well as other major international companies. The group is also increasingly recognized for its handling of both regional and national engagements. **Sources say:** "They have gone above and beyond. We're very, very pleased!"

**KEY INDIVIDUALS** Clients enjoy working with **David Sullivan** (see p.2155), highlighting his up-to-date knowledge of new technologies and ability to produce a high-quality work product. He recently acted for Sonic Corp in various matters, including patent prosecution and IP litigation. "One of the finest IP lawyers I've worked with," one client enthuses. **Margaret Millikin** (see p.2152) is noted for her superb expertise and availability. "She's excellent – so caring and frank. Very, very good at what she does," say sources. Millikin has recently worked with a range of businesses and groups, and also has significant international experience. **Drew Palmer** (see p.2152) recently acted for a major client in litigation relating to trade secrets, trademark and copyright infringement. Clients appreciate his responsiveness and abilities as a negotiator.

### Dunlap Codding
See profile on p.2158

**THE FIRM** This firm receives high praise from clients spanning a number of industries, including mechanical, electrical and chemical engineering, oil and gas, and healthcare. The group comes highly recommended for its patent prosecution work, and has a growing soft IP practice, particularly involving the music and film sectors. The firm also boasts a convincing litigation bench. Key clients include the University of Oklahoma, the University of Central Florida and Siemens Healthcare Diagnostics. **Sources say:** "They were outstanding – they contributed to improving the patent and never dropped the ball."

**KEY INDIVIDUALS Marc Brockhaus** (see p.2147) is described as a "communicative, creative thinker" with an impressive technical background. He recently acted for Chesapeake NG Ventures in providing due diligence on the client's various ventures and acquisitions. "He's just great to work with," report interviewees. **Nicholas Rouse**'s (see p.2154) recent work highlights include representing Maxcess International in various IP issues, including in trademark registration, maintenance and policing. Sources highlight his charisma and quality work product, saying: "He really is a band-one guy!" **Douglas Sorocco** (see p.2154) is well liked by his clients, who say: "He really fosters a relationship with us." He was lead partner in the aforementioned Pictometry matter, and also acted for Unique Sea Farms in securing a favorable settlement in litigation.

### Hall, Estill, Hardwick, Gable, Golden & Nelson, PC
See profile on p.2160

**THE FIRM** This major Oklahoma-based firm provides the full gamut of intellectual property services. Its experienced bench is particularly noted for its work in IP litigation, as well as for its attorneys' experience at trial level. The team regularly acts for both defendants and plaintiffs in patent infringement disputes, and represents a range of clients such as Spirit Wing Aviation and Seagate Technology. The group also acts in patent prosecution for major international companies. In a recent highlight, the team prosecuted patents for Wikipad both in the USA and in several foreign jurisdictions. **Sources say:** "Technologically literate, informative and helpful."

**KEY INDIVIDUALS Philip Free** (see p.2149) is "an excellent patent litigator" and a lead attorney in a number of disputes for the firm. He recently defended The Bankers Bank against breach of contract and misappropriation of trade secrets claims. Highlights of **Randall McCarthy**'s (see p.2151) recent work include prosecuting the US and international patents for Seagate on a number of information storage technologies. "He's a solid hi-tech patent litigator," say sources. Senior statesman **Bill McCarthy** (see p.2151) is a veteran practitioner whose experience in the sector is widely acknowledged. Sources describe him as "a dean of the practice." **Julianna Deligans** (see p.2149) is considered a very sharp, organized practitioner. Recent highlights include her involvement in litigation relating to cybersquatting. **Michael Smith** (see p.2154) is a key IP associate at the firm. Sources describe him as "very cooperative and very responsive." He has recently worked on a range of disputes involving patent infringement and trade secret misappropriation.

### McAfee & Taft
See profile on p.2162

**THE FIRM** This state leader has a preeminent IP practice, with an extensive bench and a wealth of expertise. The team tackles a variety of matters, ranging from transactions to litigation. Recent transactional work includes acting for major companies in the oil and gas, food and drink, and chemical manufacturing industries. On the litigation side, the firm has recently undertaken a number of patent and trademark infringement disputes, acting for a range of clients, which include individual inventors and international companies. Notably, the firm defended the Professional Basketball Club, owners of the Oklahoma City Thunder NBA team, in a copyright infringement dispute brought against the company. **Sources say:** "We're very happy – they're technically strong, really proactive, punctual and responsive."

**KEY INDIVIDUALS** The "diligent, highly professional and competent" **Rachel Blue** (see p.2147) is widely commended for her expertise in trademarks. She recently represented Phoenix Software in a dispute relating to identical trademark registration. She also acts for a number of UK-based companies, advising them on US trademark matters. Seasoned practitioner **John Kenney** (see p.2151) is widely respected among peers. He continues to be a very active litigator, representing clients in patent infringement and trademark oppositions on behalf of both plaintiffs and defendants. Clients appreciate **Michael LaBrie**'s (see p.2151) ability *"to look at legal issues from a business perspective."* He acts for a broad range of clients, including the Professional Basketball Club, and a number of major food and drink companies. **Clifford Dougherty** (see p.2149) is described as *"a great strategist with strong customer focus."* His broad IP practice serves clients such as Chesapeake Corporation and Tyson Foods. He recently acted for Tyson Refrigerated Processed Meats in opposing the registration of various trademarks. **Anthony Rahhal** (see p.2153) maintains a broad practice covering patent and trademark prosecution and enforcement. Among his clients are Halliburton Energy Services, Specialty Retailers and

Carlisle FoodServe Products. **Andrew Peterson** (see p.2153) is highlighted for both his strong understanding of scientific issues and his availability. He has significant expertise in computer software matters.

## Band 2

### Fellers, Snider, Blankenship, Bailey & Tippens, P.C.
See profile on p.2159

**THE FIRM** This firm demonstrates both breadth and depth of expertise in IP matters, and has a notably strong litigation practice. The team has recently acted in multi-million-dollar IP cases involving copyright and inventorship issues. The firm has experience litigating in a variety of industries on IP matters, including in the chemical engineering, mechanical engineering and sports equipment sectors. Outside litigation, the firm has significant experience working on patents, trademarks, copyright, and technology licensing and transactional issues.

**KEY INDIVIDUALS Roy Breedlove** is particularly noted for his work in IP litigation. He has undertaken many cases involving patents, and also has experience working on trademark, copyright and trade secret issues.

## Other Notable Practitioners

**Paul Johnson** of GableGotwals is described as *"the dean of patent attorneys."* A tremendously experienced practitioner, he receives huge praise for his extensive expertise in the sector. *"We all look up to him,"* says one peer. *"Phenomenal – I think she's just brilliant!"* says one source of **Mary Lee** of the Law Office of Mary M. Lee. She is widely noted for her experience in acting for individual clients. **Martin Ozinga** of Phillips Murrah P.C. is increasingly recognized as a *"sharp, smart and really personable"* attorney. Clients commend his expertise in both patent prosecution and trademark matters. **Derrick Harvey** of Harvey Law is noted as being *"very bright and capable."* This up-and-comer is highlighted for his broad solo practice and his meticulous approach.

# LABOR & EMPLOYMENT

Commentary about individuals can be found under their firm's paragraph. If the firm has no paragraph (is not ranked) look at Other Notable Practitioners.

| Labor & Employment |
| --- |
| **Leading Firms** |
| **Band 1** |
| Conner & Winters, LLP |
| Crowe & Dunlevy, a Professional Corporation * |
| Hall, Estill, Hardwick, Gable, Golden & Nelson, PC * |
| McAfee & Taft * |
| **Band 2** |
| Doerner, Saunders, Daniel & Anderson, LLP |
| * Indicates firm with profile. |
| Alphabetical order within each band. Band 1 is the highest. |

## Band 1

### Conner & Winters, LLP

**THE FIRM** This top-tier firm impresses clients with its experienced bench and breadth of practice. In addition to offering a full range of general labor and employment services, the group also has a wealth of experience in dealing with employee benefits and compensation. Its attorneys are noted for their expertise in dealing with issues arising within the aviation industry, as well as for acting on behalf of major domestic and international airlines. The firm has an impressive geographic footprint, with teams stationed across Oklahoma, Arizona, Texas and DC.

**KEY INDIVIDUALS Ronald Petrikin** is a go-to name for union-related issues. A seasoned labor lawyer, he is partic-

ularly well known for his work in the transportation industry, and also has significant experience in ERISA issues. *"He's really top notch,"* says one interviewee. **David Cordell** is described by commentators as *"a quality lawyer with a broad spectrum of skills."* Winning unanimous praise from peers, he is identified as a keen litigator who represents a range of clients across a number of industries. His practice extends beyond employment issues to include energy-related litigation, among other types of matters. Oklahoma City-based **Victor Albert** is highlighted as a key trial attorney for labor and employment matters, with a wealth of experience in jury cases. He is additionally noted for his work with interstate trucking companies. The *"very smart"* **Nancy Vaughn** is identified for her experience working on policy and procedure issues. Her practice covers the gamut of workplace matters, from offer letters and employment contracts to separation agreements.

### Crowe & Dunlevy, a Professional Corporation
See profile on p.2157

**THE FIRM** This leading team impresses clients with its depth of experience across a spectrum of services in employment law, and is particularly noted for its work in litigation. Recent work highlights include successfully defending a range of employers against claims of wrongful termination, pre-amendment Americans with Disabilities Act (ADA) issues, and discrimination based on age, race and national origin. Its impressive client roster features a

number of key players in the healthcare industry, including Integris Hospital, Norman Regional Hospital and Epworth Villa Life Care Community.

**Sources say:** *"The firm demonstrated complete diligence in protecting our interests. It's just super!"*

**KEY INDIVIDUALS Leonard Court** is widely considered a mainstay of Oklahoma's labor and employment market. *"He's an expert in the field and is always dependable,"* clients enthuse. Of counsel **Gayle Barrett** has a superb practice representing management in employment litigation. Her recent work has included successfully defending employers against allegations of race and national origin discrimination, retaliation and Oklahoma public policy tort ('Burk torts'). The Tulsa-based **Randall Snapp** (see p.2154) is *"available, responsive and speaks in business terms,"* according to sources. He has experience working on a range of litigious employment matters, including workers' compensation issues. He cochairs the practice alongside **Adam Childers** (see p.2148). Based in Oklahoma City, Childers is described as *"intelligent, pragmatic and a great representative of client interests."* **Madelene Witterholt** is noted for her broad practice, with particular emphasis on workers' compensation cases. Sources highlight the depth of her experience and describe her as *"the hidden gem of the group, who cuts to the heart of any issue."* **Courtney Warmington** has successfully represented management clients on a range of different employment issues. Clients appreciate her work product, depth of knowledge and disposition. *"She's great to work with,"* say sources, who add that *"she really ensures our needs are met."*

## Hall, Estill, Hardwick, Gable, Golden & Nelson, PC
### See profile on p.2160
**THE FIRM** This firm is highlighted for its counseling services as well as for its sterling litigation practice. The team works for some of the largest companies in the world on employment issues, including energy titans such as The Williams Companies, ConocoPhillips and Global Power. The firm's experienced bench undertakes a range of work, including immigration, employee and management training, and general counseling, as well as union issues. On the litigation side, the firm has extensive expertise acting for employers and management in discrimination, ERISA, wrongful termination and workers' compensation mandates.
**Sources say:** *"The attorneys are always very capable over there."*

**KEY INDIVIDUALS Steven Broussard** (see p.2147) is adept at defending employers against a broad range of claims, and has significant experience working on labor issues. Clients commend him for his work on matters related to the Equal Employment Opportunity Commission (EEOC). *"He's been very, very helpful – an excellent lawyer,"* reports one interviewee. **Pat Cremin** (see p.2148) is lauded as a leading stalwart of the state's labor and employment arena. His recent work highlights include acting for Garmin in litigation relating to trade secrets and inevitable disclosure. In a career spanning nearly four decades, he has accrued a wealth of experience counseling and representing employers in litigation. He is *"possibly the most experienced attorneys working in this sector,"* according to interviewees. Clients underscore the pragmatism and experience of **Angelyn Dale** (see p.2148), while peers highlight her work for major international companies. Her broad practice covers the gamut of employment issues, including counseling, litigation, mediation and investigations. **Elaine Turner** (see p.2155) is described by clients as *"practical, responsive and helpful."* Her recent work includes consulting with a major energy company on employment issues and revising their employee handbook. She is also noted for her employment litigation practice.

## McAfee & Taft
### See profile on p.2162
**THE FIRM** This mammoth of the Oklahoma legal sector boasts breadth and depth of experience in labor and employment issues across an extensive range of industries. Peers laud the firm for its large ERISA/employee benefits practice, which deftly litigates and counsels for a range of major clients, including Chesapeake Energy and American Fidelity. Notably, the firm has undertaken benefits work for tribal clients, involving additional complexities such as sovereignty issues. The team has carried out a range of employment mandates, assisting clients with the implementation of the Patient Protection and Affordable Care Act, as well as discrimination matters, health and safety issues, and de-unionizing.
**Sources say:** *"We're always satisfied – the firm has a lot of excellent people."*
**KEY INDIVIDUALS Charles Plumb** (see p.2153) is noted as a key figure in the employment market. In addition to acting for clients in various discrimination claims, he has also represented a number of municipalities in Oklahoma in significant labor and employment issues. He is lauded as *"a top-shelf attorney and a great resource at the firm."* **Tony Puckett** (see p.2153) has also undertaken work for Oklahoma municipalities. He also recently acted for a construction company in settling an occupational health and safety administration citation. *"He does an absolutely outstanding job preparing for and briefing the case,"* mentions one particularly impressed interviewee. **Sam Fulkerson** (see p.2149) is described as a *"quality, levelheaded"* attorney. He has recently assisted clients with the termination of senior executive contracts, and also advised a major venture capital group on employment issues associated with the merger of multiple energy companies in advance of an IPO. **Kathy Neal** (see p.2152) *"has always been very highly*

*regarded,"* say sources. She is noted for representing a number of employers before the DOL in Fair Labor Standards Act claims, and recently acted for a large bottling company in relation to audits by the Office of Federal Contract Compliance Programs. The *"detailed and methodical"* **Nathan Whatley** (see p.2156) recently provided union avoidance training to a tribe-owned casino. He has also been active in contributing to state legislation. Clients underscore his excellent business acumen and responsiveness. Sources highlight **Michael Lauderdale** (see p.2151) for his work as a litigator in this sector. He has experience acting for employers in various matters, including in non-compete covenants, wage and hour disputes, discrimination and the Fair Labor Standards Act. *"I'm a big fan of his,"* mentions one impressed peer; *"he's super to work with."* **James Dudley Hyde** (see p.2150) has significant expertise in employee benefits and wider issues relating to tax. He is described as *"a great attorney and innovator in this field."* **Elizabeth Wood** (see p.2156) recently advised ProBuild on the employment aspects of its acquisition of Harbert Lumber Locations. She also continues her representation of Express Personnel Services in relation to EEOC and fair employment practice charges across the nation. Senior statesman **Peter Van Dyke** (see p.2155) is highlighted for his extensive career in labor law. He has a wealth of expertise in matters relating to unions, as well as in defending clients against unfair labor claims and in negotiating collective bargaining agreements. He is *"Very levelheaded – I would recommend him to anybody,"* reports one interviewee.

## Band 2

### Doerner, Saunders, Daniel & Anderson, LLP
**THE FIRM** This firm is best known its work counseling employers and management on labor and employment issues. The team covers a wide range of issues, including wage and hour, discrimination, drug and alcohol policies and testing, and nondisclosure matters. The firm also has a strong litigation practice. Recent work highlights include defending the City of Tulsa in a suit alleging age and sexual orientation discrimination.
**Sources say:** *"Very efficient at achieving good results."*
**KEY INDIVIDUALS** Practice group leader **Kristen Brightmire** (see p.2147) is noted for her understanding of the clients' perspectives and for working well with others. *"She's always there for us and is so responsive,"* says one client. Skilled in both litigious and nonlitigious matters, was lead attorney in representing the City of Tulsa. **Jon Brightmire** (see p.2147) is also noted for his work in this area. He recently defended a major company in an unpaid wages claim, and acted for the Public Service Company of Oklahoma in relation to alleged violations of the Racketeer Influenced and Corrupt Organizations Act. Sources describe him as a *"thoughtful, bright and articulate lawyer."* Clients appreciate how **Courtney Bru** (see p.2147) provides *"legal expertise coupled with practical advice in a timely, friendly, professional manner."* She impresses peers with her experience in a range of labor and employment issues.

## Other Notable Practitioners

**David Strecker** of Strecker & Associates is considered *"top drawer for union issues."* This Tulsa-based attorney is favored by clients from a range of industries, including healthcare, broadcasting and energy. **Kirk Turner** (see p.2155) of Newton, O'Connor, Turner & Ketchum has a broad base of expertise. His practice covers litigation and counseling on behalf of corporate clients, and he has additional expertise advising automobile dealerships in connection with industry-specific legal issues. **Paula Quillin** of Franden | Woodard | Farris | Quillin + Goodnight is described as *"very smart and reasonable."* Her prior experience as in-house counsel ensures she is well placed to understand the needs of clients.

# LITIGATION

Commentary about individuals can be found under their firm's paragraph. If the firm has no paragraph (is not ranked) look at Other Notable Practitioners.

## Litigation: General Commercial
### Leading Firms

**Band 1**
Crowe & Dunlevy, a Professional Corporation *
McAfee & Taft *

**Band 2**
Corbyn Hampton PLLC
GableGotwals
Hartzog Conger Cason & Neville, LLP *

**Band 3**
Fellers, Snider, Blankenship, Bailey & Tippens, P.C. *
Kirk & Chaney
Rhodes, Hieronymus, Jones, Tucker & Gable PLLC
Ryan Whaley Coldiron Shandy

## Litigation: Mediators
### Senior Statesmen

**Senior Statesmen: distinguished older practitioners**

| | |
|---|---|
| Davis Gary | *Crowe & Dunlevy* * |

### Leading Individuals

**Band 1**

| | |
|---|---|
| Barghols Steven L | *GableGotwals* |
| Burrage Michael | *Whitten, Burrage, Priest, Fulmer, Anderson* |
| Paulk Joseph H | *Dispute Resolution Consultants, Inc. (ONP)[†]* |
| Spears Larry | *The Spears Law Firm (ONP)[†]* |

**Band 2**

| | |
|---|---|
| Margo Robert C | *Law Office of Robert C. Margo (ONP)[†]* |
| Rothman John D | *Oklahoma Mediation/Arbitration Service (ONP)[†]* |

*\* Indicates firm / individual with profile.*
*[†] ONP = Other Notable Practitioner.*

## Litigation: General Commercial
### Senior Statesmen

**Senior Statesmen: distinguished older practitioners**

| | | | |
|---|---|---|---|
| Davis Gary | *Crowe & Dunlevy* * | Sturdivant James | *GableGotwals* |
| Meyers D Kent | *Crowe & Dunlevy* * | Tippens Terry W | *Fellers, Snider, Blankenship, Bailey* |

### Leading Individuals

**Band 1**

| | | | | |
|---|---|---|---|---|
| Abowitz Murray E | *Abowitz, Timberlake, Dahnke (ONP)[†]* | | Morgan III Mack J | *Crowe & Dunlevy* |
| Burrage Michael | *Whitten, Burrage, Priest, Fulmer (ONP)[†]* | | Morse Judy Hamilton | *Crowe & Dunlevy* |
| Corbyn George | *Corbyn Hampton PLLC* | | Murphy Brooke S | *Crowe & Dunlevy* |
| Hermes John N | *McAfee & Taft* * | | Nelon Robert D | *Hall, Estill, Hardwick, Gable, Golden (ONP)[†]* * |
| Kenney John A | *McAfee & Taft* * | | Robison Reid | *McAfee & Taft* * |
| Muchmore Clyde A | *Crowe & Dunlevy* * | | Rupert Anton | *Crowe & Dunlevy* |
| Neville Drew | *Hartzog Conger Cason & Neville, LLP* * | | Tucker John H | *Rhodes, Hieronymus, Jones, Tucker* * |
| Ryan Patrick M | *Ryan Whaley Coldiron Shandy* | | Webber Daniel | *Ryan Whaley Coldiron Shandy* |

**Band 2**

| | | | | |
|---|---|---|---|---|
| Bialick Mark | *Durbin, Larimore & Bialick PC (ONP)[†]* | | **Band 3** | |
| Bocock Joseph H | *McAfee & Taft* * | | Bickford IV Warren F | *Fellers, Snider, Blankenship, Bailey* |
| Bryant David L | *GableGotwals* | | Chaney James | *Kirk & Chaney* |
| Cooper Mary Quinn | *McAfee & Taft* * | | Dace Robert W | *McAfee & Taft* * |
| Dunagan Sidney G | *GableGotwals* | | Ellis, Jr. Harvey D | *Crowe & Dunlevy* * |
| Geister III Charles E | *Hartzog Conger Cason & Neville, LLP* * | | Folluo Dan S | *Rhodes, Hieronymus, Jones, Tucker* * |
| Goodman Jimmy | *Crowe & Dunlevy* * | | Giddens Jared D | *Conner & Winters, LLP (ONP)[†]* |
| Hampton Joe M | *Corbyn Hampton PLLC* | | Green James | *Conner & Winters, LLP (ONP)[†]* |
| Heatly John B | *Fellers, Snider, Blankenship, Bailey* | | Hix Richard P | *McAfee & Taft* * |
| Howard Oliver S | *GableGotwals* | | Kincaid James L | *Crowe & Dunlevy, PC* |
| Kirk James | *Kirk & Chaney* | | Leach William S | *McAfee & Taft* * |
| Leibrock Fred A | *Phillips Murrah P.C. (ONP)[†]* | | Phansalkar Kiran | *Conner & Winters, LLP (ONP)[†]* |
| McConnell-Corbyn Laura | *Hartzog Conger Cason & Neville, LLP* * | | Todd Jeff L | *McAfee & Taft* * |

**Up-and-coming individuals**

| | |
|---|---|
| Buchanan Brandon L | *McAfee & Taft* * |

## Band 1

### Crowe & Dunlevy, a Professional Corporation
**See profile on p.2157**
**THE FIRM** This firm is acknowledged for its bench of accomplished litigators with experience in representing plaintiffs, defendants and appellants at both state and federal level. The group acts for companies across a range of industries and practice sectors, including in healthcare, creditors' rights, intellectual property and general business litigation. The firm recently acted as convergence counsel for The Williams Companies, handling significant matters on a national basis. The group also represented Cox Communications in a multidistrict dispute involving a class action and alleged antitrust violations. The firm also demonstrates experience in Native American law, white-collar crime and banking disputes.
**Sources say:** *"They did an excellent job in both preparing us for trial and in negotiating settlements."*
**KEY INDIVIDUALS** *"Outstanding trial attorney"* **Jimmy Goodman** (see p.2149) recently acted for Hillerich & Bradsby in relation to allegations that its baseball bats had dangerous enhanced performance characteristics. He has litigated on a range of matters, including insurance, healthcare and labor law, and is noted for being *"very even keeled"* and *"a class act."* The *"amazing"* **Clyde Muchmore** (see p.2152) is highly respected for his experience as an appellate attorney. Over an accomplished career, he has been engaged in various litigations involving complicated business disputes. Sources describe him as *"top tier"* and *"a superb attorney."* Key partner **Anton Rupert** has a wealth of experience working on construction disputes, toxic torts and product liability litigation. He is praised for his great insight, efficiency and effective preparation of cases. *"Highly experienced, confident trial attorney"* **Judy Hamilton Morse** is head of the firm's litigation practice group. She has a practice spanning a range of commercial litigation matters, and recently successfully defended Avalon, a private prison company, against various claims brought by minority shareholders. She also has particular expertise in bankruptcy and creditors' rights issues. Interviewees highlight the superb *"strategy and levelheadedness"* of **Mack Morgan**. He consistently impresses both peers and clients with his experience in various intellectual property and employment disputes, among other matters. **Brooke Murphy** continues to be a key litigation attorney for clients such as Pre-Paid Legal Services, which she

recently defended against a major class action. Sources recommend her as *"an amazing litigator."* Tulsa-based attorney **James Kincaid** maintains a respected and broad commercial litigation practice, acting for a range of clients. He is identified as a seasoned practitioner with a depth of experience in litigation matters. **Harvey Ellis** (see p.2149) is also credited for being a key appellate lawyer. *"He is highly knowledgeable of this specialized area,"* say sources, who add that he *"does fantastic work."* He recently acted alongside Goodman in the aforementioned Hillerich & Bradsby mandate, and has experience in both federal and state courts. Senior statesman **Gary Davis** (see p.2148) is described as an *"exceptional mediator and trial lawyer."* He is widely recognized for his work in oil and gas matters, for which he receives significant respect from both peers and clients. **Kent Meyers** (see p.2152) continues to act as lead attorney in the aforementioned Cox Communications matter. Sources point to his wisdom and experience in litigation, identifying him as a *"wonderful, well-regarded attorney."*

## McAfee & Taft
### See profile on p.2162
**THE FIRM** This firm's preeminent litigation team is made up of practitioners with a wealth of trial experience who act on a broad spectrum of disputes. The group's size ensures that it has the capacity to deftly handle larger mandates, including those on regional and national scales. Its recent workload has included product liability cases, significant Superfund litigation and sizable class actions. In recent highlights, the team defended Ford and Kia Motors in separate manufacturer liability matters. It has also been involved in the complicated Superfund matters linked to the Tar Creek site in northeast Oklahoma.
**Sources say:** *"They acted for us as if we were their own company – how could you ask for more?"*
**KEY INDIVIDUALS** Premier litigator **John Hermes** (see p.2150) continues to be a dominant force in litigation. Impressing clients and peers, he is consistently described as *"an excellent litigator."* He recently defended MidFirst Bank against civil claims of facilitating fraud. His broad commercial litigation practice also encompasses oil and gas, real estate and healthcare matters, as well as general business disputes. **John Kenney** (see p.2151) has established a solid reputation as a go-to litigator. Sources widely acknowledge his expertise as an intellectual property litigator, specializing in trademark, patent and trade secrets litigation. He is *"highly successful and confident in the courtroom,"* note sources. **Mary Quinn Cooper** (see p.2148) has been especially active in product liability cases on behalf of Ford. *"She's phenomenal in the courtroom,"* enthuse clients. Sources also highlight her nationwide experience and nononsense manner. **Joseph Bocock** (see p.2147) stands out for his superb arbitration expertise. He has a wealth of experience in real estate, condemnation, oil and gas, and debtor-creditor disputes. *"He does a terrific job,"* say sources. The experienced **Reid Robison** (see p.2153) has a broad business litigation practice, and is widely acknowledged as a quality litigator by his peers. He acts for a range of companies in disputes across the nation. **Richard Hix**

(see p.2150) has recently acted in significant litigation in the oil and gas and energy sectors, and has accrued a wealth of experience across all manner of general commercial litigation. He has also undertaken cases involving tax, banking, environmental and antitrust disputes. **William Leach**'s (see p.2151) practice covers insurance, product liability and complex contract disputes. He was recently involved in achieving a summary judgment in favor of Kia Motors following manufacturer liability and negligence allegations. Clients underscore his approachability and responsiveness. Sources also appreciate the accessibility, concern and candor of **Jeff Todd** (see p.2155), whose recent work highlights include acting for agricultural producers in federal crop disputes around the country. He also litigates matters involving antitrust, intellectual property and real estate in both state and federal courts. *"He easily overcomes hurdles,"* say clients. **Robert Dace** (see p.2148) enters the rankings on the back of strong recommendations as *"an effective attorney who is good on his feet."* His litigation practice covers a variety of matters, including insurance, intellectual property and environmental disputes. **Brandon Buchanan** (see p.2147) is an up-and-coming litigation attorney with a broad practice encompassing commercial disputes, employment litigation and mass tort defense. Clients praise his diligence and efficiency.

## Band 2

## Corbyn Hampton PLLC
**THE FIRM** This effective boutique litigation firm remains a favorite of peers and clients for its impressive litigation practice. The group regularly undertakes complex business transactions for clients of all sizes, and is highlighted for its experience in oil and gas, legal malpractice, product liability and tax disputes. The firm also demonstrates strong arbitration and mediation capabilities.
**Sources say:** *"An absolute pleasure to work with."*
**KEY INDIVIDUALS George Corbyn** is hugely respected as a litigator and mediator in Oklahoma. Described as *"extremely knowledgeable and prepared"* as well as *"absolutely top notch,"* he has generated an impressive reputation over a long and distinguished career. His extensive expertise covers many subjects, including business torts, securities and complex commercial litigation. **Joe Hampton** has gained a wealth of experience in jury and non-jury trials. He has a broad litigation practice covering a range of commercial matters, as well as construction, franchising and personal injury cases. *"He does an excellent job,"* state interviewees; *"he's so communicative, and is always moving things forward."*

## GableGotwals
**THE FIRM** This firm has an established reputation for its impressive litigation practice. The group boasts a team of experienced attorneys working at both state and federal level, undertaking a broad range of complex business disputes. In addition to oil and gas expertise, the firm is also noted for its work involving Native American, environ-

mental and healthcare-related matters. It also displays strong capabilities in the appellate space.
**Sources say:** *"A standout firm for litigation."*
**KEY INDIVIDUALS Steven Barghols** is described as *"one of the best"* for commercial mediation. He is lauded by peers for his extensive experience, as well as for his knowledge of disputes involving the oil and gas sector. Tulsa-based **David Bryant** is widely respected for his abilities in banking disputes, as well as for his breadth and depth of experience in a range of commercial litigations. Sources consistently underscore his reputation and professionalism. Peers praise **Sidney Dunagan** for his expertise in a host of complex litigations. His experience extends to disputes involving oil and gas and aviation, as well as product liability matters. **Oliver Howard** is noted for achieving *"great successes on large matters."* He is best known for his work as an environmental litigator, and is identified by interviewees as *"highly intelligent and experienced."* He also acts on oil and gas disputes, and undertakes significant mandates from major petroleum corporations. Litigation veteran **James Sturdivant** *"always does a wonderful job,"* according to sources. Over a career spanning almost half a century, he has gathered experience on a range of business disputes, including securities, antitrust and trade regulation matters.

## Hartzog Conger Cason & Neville, LLP
### See profile on p.2161
**THE FIRM** This firm consistently impresses competitors in both litigious and transactional matters. It has experience working on a range of disputes, and has represented regional and national organizations. Its litigation bench demonstrates experience across the spectrum of commercial issues, as well as in white-collar crime and family law matters. Sources point to a quality set of accomplished litigators, well respected across the state.
**Sources say:** *"Fantastic trial lawyers – very industrious, committed, and they love what they do."*
**KEY INDIVIDUALS Drew Neville** (see p.2152) is identified as a leading white-collar crime attorney. He is *"practical, realistic and thoughtful,"* and demonstrates extensive courtroom experience and problem-solving abilities. In business litigation, Neville's practice has an emphasis on disputes involving federal securities. **Charles Geister** (see p.2149) acts for a range of client types across a variety of business and commercial disputes. Interviewees say that *"he's an excellent lawyer"* and *"a solid litigator."* His work also covers insurance, antitrust and product liability cases. Peers laud **Laura McConnell-Corbyn** (see p.2151), describing her as *"fantastic in family law."* She has a wealth of expertise in handling high-value divorces and issues arising from marital estates.

## Band 3

### Fellers, Snider, Blankenship, Bailey & Tippens, P.C.
See profile on p.2159

**THE FIRM** This firm boasts a long and established reputation in litigation. The group demonstrates particular strength in oil and gas disputes, though it is also noted for its work in employment matters, sports law and creditors' rights. Recent work highlights include successfully settling a multimillion-dollar intellectual property dispute in favor of the firm's client, as well as defending an insurer against bad faith allegations in multidistrict litigation.

**Sources say:** *"They really get involved and are always super-responsive."*

**KEY INDIVIDUALS** The *"experienced and well-respected"* **John Heatly** has a broad trial and appellate practice in commercial litigation matters. He has undertaken mandates related to bankruptcy litigation, as well as fraud, embezzlement and bad faith issues. His wide-ranging client base includes lenders, underwriters and hotel chains. **Warren Bickford** has a sterling and broad commercial litigation practice, and also undertakes substantial white-collar crime defense. He also has experience in dealing with class actions, regulatory matters and alternative dispute resolution mechanisms. Litigation veteran **Terry Tippens** continues to garner praise from his peers across Oklahoma. Over his long career he has experienced all manner of contentious issues, including disputes involving intellectual property, agriculture and environment. For a number of sources, *"he's the first name you think of"* at the firm.

### Kirk & Chaney

**THE FIRM** This litigation boutique based in Oklahoma City has a diverse practice encompassing contractual, oil and gas, employment, and family disputes, to name a few. Its bench of experienced trial attorneys acts for a broad range of clients on complex litigations and mediations. The firm has particular expertise acting on insurance defense and high-value family matters, as well as disputes involving healthcare and medical malpractice.

**KEY INDIVIDUALS** Sources describe **James Kirk** as *"a smooth operator."* His practice covers a range of commercial litigation matters, though he is best known for his work involving high-value divorces. He also has expertise in antitrust and securities litigation. **James Chaney** is identified as *"a bulldog in the courtroom."* Sources point to his active oil and gas practice, and attest that *"he's great at figuring out cases."*

### Rhodes, Hieronymus, Jones, Tucker & Gable PLLC

**THE FIRM** This Tulsa litigation boutique receives praise from clients and attorneys across the state. The team has experience working on major product liability cases, damage suits, employment and insurance matters. The firm has undertaken work for major national insurance companies, trucking companies and car manufacturers.

**KEY INDIVIDUALS** **John Tucker** (see p.2155) is described as *"a superb lawyer with a huge reputation,"* and is praised for his common-sense approach to dispute resolution. He recently acted for Cargill, successfully defending the company against allegations of environmental destruction as a result of poultry farming. **Dan Folluo** (see p.2149) recently successfully represented Suzlon Energy in a case relating to the death of a wind turbine engineer. He also acts for trucking companies in accident claims, and has experience in matters involving product and professional liability.

### Ryan Whaley Coldiron Shandy

**THE FIRM** This boutique firm is best known for its work in energy and environment litigation. However, it also has extensive experience in a range of commercial litigation matters, including securities and brokerage, employment, white-collar defense and toxic torts. The group is also highlighted for its work on behalf of plaintiffs.

**KEY INDIVIDUALS** **Patrick Ryan** is *"a really outstanding lawyer,"* according to interviewees. A seasoned practitioner, his practice spans both civil and criminal matters. He has acted on many high-profile cases, and was previously involved in the prosecution of the Oklahoma bombers. He is highly esteemed by peers, and is considered a premier litigation attorney. **Daniel Webber** is also particularly well regarded for his work in the white-collar arena. Sources laud his experience in the US Attorney's office, describing him as a *"very experienced practitioner."* Webber also has experience undertaking healthcare-related cases, and has acted for physicians in medical fraud matters.

## Other Notable Practitioners

**James Green** of Conner & Winters, LLP is *"definitely a quality lawyer,"* according to sources. His practice covers a range of personal injury and insurance matters. He also has experience with contentious issues arising from a number of industries, including construction, oil and gas, and transport. Also at Conner Winters, **Jared Giddens** has an established practice incorporating bankruptcy litigation and debt restructuring, frequently acting for both creditors and debtors. **Kiran Phansalkar**, also at Conner Winters, is noted for his work in financially distressed situations, and frequently undertakes matters involves litigation arising from debt restructuring. In addition to his litigation practice, he also has experience as a transactional attorney. **Murray Abowitz** of Abowitz, Timberlake, Dahnke & Gisinger, P.C. is a seasoned lawyer who is *"always effective for his clients."* Sources praise his dogged determination in the courtroom. He has acted extensively in both state and federal matters. **Michael Burrage** of Whitten, Burrage, Priest, Fulmer, Anderson & Eisel is lauded for his abilities in both litigation and mediation. A former judge, he is noted for his work for plaintiffs in insurance and personal injury disputes. **Joseph Paulk** of Dispute Resolution Consultants, Inc. receives plaudits for his work across a range of disputes, including employment, personal injury, real estate and construction matters. **Larry Spears** of The Spears Law Firm is identified as *"a top-notch mediator for family law."* He has experience working on divorce cases, and also represents victims in wrongful death, medical negligence and personal injury cases. **Mark Bialick** of Durbin, Larimore & Bialick PC has an excellent reputation for insurance disputes, and also has an active plaintiff-side practice. Peers also highlight his experience in matters involving bad faith. *"Fantastic litigator"* **Fred Leibrock** of Phillips Murrah P.C. has a practice encompassing complex multijurisdictional cases and class action suits. His diverse experience also includes real estate, employment, professional malpractice and product liability disputes. Oklahoma City-based **Robert Margo** of the Law Office of Robert C. Margo is highly regarded for his work in mediation and arbitration. He has accrued extensive experience in various legal fields, including in insurance, professional malpractice and commercial disputes. In a career spanning more than three decades, **Robert Nelon** (see p.2152) of Hall, Estill, Hardwick, Gable, Golden & Nelson, PC has built a solid media and communications litigation practice. Described by sources as *"a great trial lawyer,"* he has experience representing a number of major networks, including ABC, NBC and BBC America. The *"head-knockin', arm-twistin'"* **John Rothman** of Oklahoma Mediation/Arbitration Service is highly praised as a mediator. He has a wealth of experience in resolving commercial disputes.

# NATIVE AMERICAN LAW

Commentary about individuals can be found under their firm's paragraph. If the firm has no paragraph (is not ranked) look at Other Notable Practitioners.

## Native American Law
### Leading Firms

**Band 1**
Crowe & Dunlevy, a Professional Corporation *

**Band 2**
Hall, Estill, Hardwick, Gable, Golden & Nelson, PC *
McAfee & Taft *

### Senior Statesmen

**Senior Statesmen: distinguished older practitioners**
Echo-Hawk Walter R.    Crowe & Dunlevy

### Leading Individuals

**Star individuals**
McBride III Michael    Crowe & Dunlevy, PC

**Band 1**
Luthey Dean    GableGotwals (ONP)[†]
Rabon Bob    Rabon, Wolf & Rabon (ONP)[†]
Standing Bear Geoffrey    Law Offices of Geoffrey Standing Bear (ONP)[†]

**Band 2**
McCullough David    Doerner, Saunders, Daniel (ONP)[†*]
McMillin James C.    McAfee & Taft *
Pitchlynn Gary S.    Pitchlynn Law PLLC (ONP)[†]
Posey Tim    Hall, Estill, Hardwick, Gable, Golden *

**Band 3**
Black Amos    Sole Practitioner (ONP)[†]
Ward Stephen R.    Conner & Winters, LLP (ONP)[†]
Williams O. Joseph    O. Joseph Williams Law Office (ONP)[†]

**Up-and-coming individuals**
Huntsman Susan    Crowe & Dunlevy *

**Associates to watch**
Vaughn Christina M    McAfee & Taft *

[†] Indicates firm / individual with profile.
[†] ONP = Other Notable Practitioner.

## Band 1

### Crowe & Dunlevy, a Professional Corporation
See profile on p.2157

**THE FIRM** This firm is widely identified as a leader in Native American law, and has considerable expertise in addressing a range of issues relevant to tribes and those interacting with tribes. The Indian law and gaming practice group is supported by the firm's strength in other sectors, ensuring that it can meet the needs of tribes as their business interests expand. The many tribes represented by the firm include the Comanche Nation, the Sac and Fox Nation and the Eastern Shawnee Tribe of Oklahoma. **Sources say:** "*I'm always very impressed. They're the best in Oklahoma!*"

**KEY INDIVIDUALS Michael McBride** achieves a star ranking this year, following unanimous praise from peers and clients. He recently successfully obtained a judgment in favor of the Eastern Shawnee Tribe of Oklahoma against a financial services company and its principals following a breach of contract. Sources praise him as "*an outstanding trial attorney*" and "*a superstar gaming lawyer.*" **Walter Echo-Hawk** is described as "*a skilled practitioner.*" Sources note his long career and wealth of experience in Indian gaming law and water rights. Up-and-comer **Susan Huntsman** (see p.2150) is identified as "*a great lawyer*" and "*a smart attorney.*" She has worked extensively for a number of tribes, including the Eastern Shawnee Tribe of Oklahoma, and has additional expertise in oil and gas and appellate law.

## Band 2

### Hall, Estill, Hardwick, Gable, Golden & Nelson, PC
See profile on p.2160

**THE FIRM** This firm has acted extensively for clients in tribal court, as well as on matters related to Native American interests in state and federal court. The group acts for a number of key clients, including the Creek Nation and the Choctaw Nation, in addition to advising non-tribal clients on associated matters. Recent highlights include defending First Americans Insurance Group and its policyholders against various claims. The team has experience dealing with commercial matters, government relations and lobbying on behalf of tribal clients and those engaging with tribes.

**KEY INDIVIDUALS** Sources highlight the "*deep knowledge base and experience*" of **Tim Posey** (see p.2153). He cochairs the firm's Indian law practice group and his expertise covers a range of issues relevant to tribal law, including land rights and tribal disputes.

### McAfee & Taft
See profile on p.2162

**THE FIRM** This firm has an active Native American practice representing tribes and tribal business interests. The team's expertise covers both transactional matters and litigation, and it acts for a range of clients including the Chickasaw Nation and the United Keetoowah Band of Cherokee Indians in Oklahoma. In relation to the latter, the firm recently achieved a groundbreaking land trust decision from the Bureau of Indian Affairs in the Keetoowah Cherokees' favor. The firm has also acted on

business litigation related to economic development, and on employee benefits and tax issues for tribal clients.
**Sources say:** "*The firm helped us navigate some tricky issues and was very knowledgeable.*"
**KEY INDIVIDUALS James McMillin** (see p.2152) is extensively involved in the firm's representation of the United Keetoowah Band of Cherokee Indians, recently playing a leading role in the aforementioned land trust matter. Sources describe him as "*a good trial lawyer*" and note his "*great legal background.*" Associate-to-watch **Christina Vaughn** (see p.2155) is a key asset to the firm's practice. Sources praise her as "*a diligent, detail-oriented lawyer who is excellent at stripping things back to the issue at hand.*"

## Other Notable Practitioners

Sources widely agree that **Dean Luthey** will be a great asset to the developing tribal practice at GableGotwals. "*He's got a fantastic reputation,*" notes one interviewee. **David McCullough** (see p.2152) of Doerner, Saunders, Daniel & Anderson, LLP has both breadth and depth of experience in this sector. He recently acted for the Apache Tribe of Oklahoma on a dispute arising from election results. **Amos Black** is a sole practitioner working in Anadarko, and is noted for his long experience in this sector. "*He knows the Oklahoma tribes very well,*" says one source. **Stephen Ward** of Conner & Winters, LLP has significant experience working on nationwide matters and major financing issues for Oklahoma tribes. Sources highlight him as "*a good, smart lawyer.*" **Geoffrey Standing Bear** of Law Offices of Geoffrey M Standing Bear has long been a notable presence in this sector. He receives high praise from peers as "*a superb lawyer*" with strengths in tribal litigation and criminal law. The "*outstanding*" **Bob Rabon** of Rabon, Wolf & Rabon is lauded for his work with a number of tribes. Sources particularly highlight his work with the Choctaw and Chickasaw Nations. **Gary Pitchlynn** of Pitchlynn Law PLLC is "*a seasoned tribal lawyer.*" He has decades of experience in advising Native American organizations and tribes, and is well versed in representing the transactional and litigation needs of clients. Sole practitioner **Joseph Williams** is another key lawyer in this sector. Sources highlight his "*strong skill set and great demeanor.*" He has a broad advisory and litigation practice, handling gaming matters, tribal taxation and tribal code development.

# REAL ESTATE

Commentary about individuals can be found under their firm's paragraph. If the firm has no paragraph (is not ranked) look at Other Notable Practitioners.

## Real Estate
### Leading Firms

**Band 1**
Crowe & Dunlevy, a Professional Corporation *
McAfee & Taft *

**Band 2**
Mock, Schwabe, Waldo, Elder, Reeves & Bryant
Phillips Murrah P.C.
Spradling, Kennedy & McPhail LLP
The Center for Economic Development Law

### Senior Statesmen

Senior Statesmen: distinguished older practitioners
Hastie John D          Phillips Murrah P.C.

### Leading Individuals

**Band 1**

| | |
|---|---|
| Elder James | Mock, Schwabe, Waldo, Elder, Reeves |
| Hill Frank | McAfee & Taft * |
| Laird Michael S | Crowe & Dunlevy * |
| Riggs Richard A | McAfee & Taft * |
| Spradling T Scott | Spradling, Kennedy & McPhail LLP |

**Band 2**

| | |
|---|---|
| Allen Zachary W | Crowe & Dunlevy * |
| Batchelor Dan | The Center for Economic Development Law |
| Batchelor Leslie V | The Center for Economic Development Law |
| Berry Jennifer L. Ivester | Crowe & Dunlevy * |
| Box Dennis R. | Williams, Box, Forshee & Bullard (ONP)† |
| Garbrecht Robert L | McAfee & Taft * |
| Hasenfratz Sally A. | Phillips Murrah P.C. |
| Kennedy David D | Spradling, Kennedy & McPhail LLP |
| Latham Myrna | McAfee & Taft * |
| Rosser IV Malcolm E | Crowe & Dunlevy, PC * |
| Sargent Jr John E | McAfee & Taft * |
| Sharrock James W | McAfee & Taft * |

**Up-and-coming individuals**

| | |
|---|---|
| Hetrick Stephen M | McAfee & Taft * |
| Pomeroy Emily | The Center for Economic Development Law |

* Indicates firm / individual with profile.
† ONP = Other Notable Practitioner.

## Band 1

### Crowe & Dunlevy, a Professional Corporation
See profile on p.2157

**THE FIRM** This firm's impressive real estate bench demonstrates a wealth of expertise. The team's broad skill set caters to commercial clients from a number of industries, including healthcare, food services and renewable energy. Recent highlights include advising The Williams Companies on facilities matters across the nation, including acquisitions, leasing arrangements and large-scale construction. Other notable clients include Boeing and Ford. **Sources say:** *"They have been excellent. Outstanding!"*

**KEY INDIVIDUALS** Head of practice **Michael Laird** (see p.2151) is praised for his familiarity with the intricacies of commercial real estate. His major clients include the University of Oklahoma, BancFirst and a major American food conglomerate. **Jennifer Ivester Berry** (see p.2146) has recently undertaken major wind farm projects, as well as property construction, development, leasing and divestiture issues for various major clients. *"Her strengths are her thoroughness as well as her ability to immediately understand the transaction and our expectations, and also her responsiveness,"* say sources. Practice group leader **Zachary Allen** (see p.2146) has significant expertise working across a range of real estate matters, including engagements relating to shopping centers. He recently acted for TriGate Capital in acquisitions of real estate for its shopping center portfolio. He also has significant experience in financing transactions. **Malcolm Rosser** (see p.2153) is lauded for his expertise in complex real estate transactions, including in zoning and land use issues. He leads the firm's real estate team in Tulsa, and is described as *"fabulous on every aspect"* of real estate law by sources.

### McAfee & Taft
See profile on p.2162

**THE FIRM** This firm houses one of the largest real estate practice groups in Oklahoma. The team undertakes a broad range of sophisticated real estate transactions, and is increasingly highlighted for its work involving tax exemptions, notably those in the charitable healthcare and manufacturing sectors. The firm recently acted for Belgian manufacturer ASCO Industries in its acquisition of a sizable facility in Stillwater, Oklahoma. It also acted for both the buyer and seller in American Fidelity's acquisition of real estate from the Oklahoma Publishing Company. **Sources say:** *"A unanimously positive experience."*

**KEY INDIVIDUALS** Senior partner **Frank Hill** (see p.2150) is widely acclaimed by peers and clients for his wealth of experience in this sector. His expertise covers sales, acquisitions, exchanges, construction and business incentives. Sources describe him as *"a unique talent"* and *"a real deal-maker."* **Richard Riggs** (see p.2153) is noted for his crucial work on wind farm projects, and cochairs the firm's renewable and sustainable energy group. *"He's fabulous,"* says one source; *"he did great research, negotiated excellently and provided great advice."* Riggs currently advises Apex Wind Energy on wind projects in Oklahoma, and also advised a Fortune 100 company on its equity investment in the Chisholm View Wind Farm Project. Interviewees commend **Jim Sharrock** (see p.2154) for *"his varied practice and broad array of skills."* He has experience representing clients from a number of industries, including agriculture, banking and construction. He recently acted for Mayo 420 in the financing and development of the Mayo Building in Tulsa. **Robert Garbrecht** (see p.2149) offers a *"good, very responsive, high-quality service,"* according to interviewees. He is involved in the firm's representation of ASCO Industries, and also continues to act for various ProBuild entities on real estate matters across the country. His expertise includes acquisitions, sales, leasing and financing issues. **Myrna Latham** (see p.2151) comes highly recommended for her superb attention to detail. Her expertise encompasses a range of real estate matters, including leases and shopping center financing. **John Sargent** (see p.2154) is consistently highlighted for his expertise in condominium projects. He also has experience representing major tenants, developers and investors in various real estate matters, as well as in zoning engagements. Clients are impressed by up-and-comer **Stephen Hetrick** (see p.2150), whose practice covers an array of real estate transactions, including leases, development and acquisitions. Sources appreciate that he has *"experience well beyond his years."*

## Band 2

### Mock, Schwabe, Waldo, Elder, Reeves & Bryant

**THE FIRM** This small but extremely effective Oklahoma City firm offers a full range of services to real estate clients. The team acts on both litigation and transactional issues, and is commended for its handling of real estate financing matters. Peers highlight the firm's expertise, efficiency and reputation for work in this sector. **Sources say:** *"Terrific real estate lawyers."*

**KEY INDIVIDUALS James Elder** is highly regarded for his work in real estate finance, as well as in leasing and commercial transactions. He is lauded as *"absolutely one of the best in the state"* by his peers.

### Phillips Murrah P.C.

**THE FIRM** This firm has a superb breadth of expertise in the real estate sector, and represents architects, developers and financial institutions, among other parties. The group is noted for its experience with mixed-use projects, particularly in the leisure sector. Sources also highlight the firm's understanding of the business implications of PPP. **KEY INDIVIDUALS** Sources commend **Sally Hasenfratz** for her expertise in all manner of real estate transactions, including in tax issues. *"She is a quality lawyer,"* say interviewees. **John Hastie** has an outstanding reputation undertaking a full range of real estate matters, including project developments, financings, acquisitions and sales.

### Spradling, Kennedy & McPhail LLP

**THE FIRM** This firm has longstanding experience in state real estate laws. The group boasts expertise in many real estate issues, including purchase and sale agreements, insurance, loans and zoning matters.

**KEY INDIVIDUALS Scott Spradling** has a comprehensive real estate practice undertaking planning, finance, zoning and leasing work. He is also regularly highlighted for his work involving affordable housing. **David Kennedy** has a broad practice covering both litigation and transactional work. He acts for a broad range of clients, including those in the healthcare sector.

## The Center for Economic Development Law

**THE FIRM** This firm focuses on real estate development and redevelopment projects across the upper Midwest. The group most often undertakes matters on the public side of PPP developments, and frequently represents municipalities. The firm is also highlighted for its capabilities in urban renewal projects and tax increment financing. In addition to municipalities, its clients regularly include major developers and nonprofit organizations. **Sources say:** *"A highly respected firm undertaking sophisticated real estate matters."*

**KEY INDIVIDUALS** Cofounder and director of the firm's litigation practice **Leslie Batchelor** has significant experience representing public bodies, including public trusts, in matters involving public financing and issues associated with development projects. She is also highly active in PPP matters. Boasting decades of experience, **Dan Batchelor** is highly regarded across the real estate sector for his work on tax increment financing matters, among others. Sources highlight his extensive expertise in urban renewal matters. **Emily Pomeroy** is highlighted for her abilities in public-private redevelopment projects, as well as in related litigation issues.

## Other Notable Practitioners

**Dennis Box** of Williams, Box, Forshee & Bullard, P.C. is identified as a key practitioner for municipal zoning and land use matters.

# Leaders' Profiles in Oklahoma

### ALLEN, Zachary W
Crowe & Dunlevy, a Professional
Corporation, Oklahoma City
405 235 7728
zach.allen@crowedunlevy.com
*Featured in Real Estate (Oklahoma)*
**Practice Areas:** Mr Allen concentrates his practice in commercial real estate lending, leasing, development and sales transactions, in which he represents a diverse range of clients, including developers, purchasers, owners, tenants and lenders. He is licensed and actively practices in both Oklahoma and Texas and regularly handles multi-state matters.
**Professional Memberships:** State Bar of Oklahoma; Oklahoma County Bar Association; State Bar of Texas; Dallas Bar Association; American Bar Association. Board-certified in Commercial Real Estate Law - Texas Board of Legal Specialization.
**Personal:** University of Oklahoma (BBA, 1985); Southern Methodist University School of Law (JD, 1988).

### BANNER, Mark
Hall, Estill, Hardwick, Gable, Golden &
Nelson, PC, Tulsa
918 594 0432
mbanner@hallestill.com
*Featured in Energy & Natural Resources (Oklahoma)*
**Practice Areas:** Alternative dispute resolution, class action defense, energy and natural resources,

litigation, oil and gas, professional malpractice and liability.
**Professional Memberships:** Oklahoma Bar Association; Tulsa County Bar Association, American Inns of Court, Adjunct Settlement Judge for the Northern District of Oklahoma.
**Career:** Oklahoma (1988); Oklahoma Supreme Court, US District Court for the Eastern, Northern and Western Districts of Oklahoma, US Court of Appeals for the Tenth Circuit.
**Personal:** BA, Psychology, University of Oklahoma, 1983; JD, cum laude, Georgetown University Law Center, 1988.

### BARRETT, Terry
McAfee & Taft, Oklahoma City
405 552 2220
terry.barrett@mcafeetaft.com
*Featured in Energy & Natural Resources (Oklahoma)*
**Practice Areas:** Practice encompasses all aspects of energy law, including counseling on day-to-day operations, handling the acquisition and sales of assets, and representing clients in tax, litigation, environmental and other industry matters.
**Professional Memberships:** Oklahoma County Bar Association; Oklahoma Bar Association; Federal Energy Bar Association; American Association of Petroleum Landmen; Past Secretary, Vice President and President of Oklahoma City Mineral Lawyers Association.
**Career:** Oklahoma Bar (1973); All state and federal courts in Oklahoma; US Courts of Appeals

for the Fifth and Tenth Circuits; US Supreme Court.
**Personal:** BBA, University of Oklahoma, 1967 (Petroleum Land Management); JD, University of Oklahoma, 1973.

### BENTLEY, Kassandra
Doerner, Saunders, Daniel & Anderson, LLP,
Tulsa
918 591 5259
kbentley@dsda.com
*Featured in Corporate/Commercial (Oklahoma)*
**Practice Areas:** Kassandra M Bentley focuses her practice mainly in the areas of trust and probate litigation, estate planning, business formation, mergers and acquisitions, and business transactions. She was a recipient of the Craig Sterne Memorial Award for Estate Planning and Taxation and is a member of the Tulsa Tax Forum.
**Career:** Kassandra received her Juris Doctor, summa cum laude, from the University of Arkansas School of Law. While there, Kassandra served as a Note and Comment Editor for the Arkansas Law Review and president of the Christian Legal Society.

### BERRY, Jennifer L. Ivester
Crowe & Dunlevy, a Professional
Corporation, Oklahoma City
405 239 6638
jennifer.berry@crowedunlevy.com
*Featured in Real Estate (Oklahoma)*
**Practice Areas:** Concentration in commercial real estate, including project development, financ-

ing and leasing. Also involved with the development of alternative energy generation facilities.
**Professional Memberships:** Oklahoma Bar Association; American Bar Association; Commercial Real Estate Council of Oklahoma City; Urban Land Institute; Leadership Oklahoma City Class XXVII.
**Career:** Qualified in 2003. Named Director/Shareholder of Crowe & Dunlevy in 2011. Member of the Firm's Real Estate and Environmental Practice Groups.
**Publications:** Has co-authored "Acceleration of Rent in Oklahoma: What's a Landlord to Do? Framework for a Practical Approach."
**Personal:** Oklahoma City University (JD, 2003); University of Tulsa (BSBA, 1998).

### BLAKE, T Michael
McAfee & Taft, Oklahoma City
405 552 2317
mike.blake@mcafeetaft.com
*Featured in Corporate/Commercial (Oklahoma)*
**Practice Areas:** Practice is focused on tax and complex transaction planning and implementation for corporations, limited liability companies, partnerships and high net worth individuals. Special expertise in energy industry transactions, merger and acquisitions, and structuring tax-deferred Section 1031 reverse and "build-to-suit" exchanges.
**Professional Memberships:** Oklahoma County Bar Association; Oklahoma Bar Association; American Bar Association.

**Career:** Oklahoma Bar (1996); US Tax Court; Former leader of the firm's tax and family wealth practice group; Board Member, Oklahoma Lawyers for Children.
**Personal:** AB, Duke University, 1993 (Economics and English); JD, University of Oklahoma, 1996; LLM, New York University (Taxation).

### BLUE, Rachel
McAfee & Taft, Tulsa
918 574 3007
rachel.blue@mcafeetaft.com
*Featured in Intellectual Property (Oklahoma)*
**Practice Areas:** Trademark clearance and prosecution, opposition and cancellation proceedings and enforcement actions; licensing of IP and technology; coexistence and consent agreements; copyright prosecution and filing; and litigation of trade secrets, trademarks and copyrights. Franchise practice includes preparation and review of disclosure documents and franchise agreements, registration of franchises, and counseling of franchisees and franchisors.
**Professional Memberships:** Tulsa County, Oklahoma, and American Bar Associations; ABA Forum on Franchising; International Trademark Association.
**Career:** Examining Attorney, US Patent & Trademark Office; Missouri Bar; Oklahoma Bar.
**Publications:** Contributor, "Intellectual Property Licensing Strategies" by Aspatore.
**Personal:** BA, University of Texas; JD, University of Tulsa.

### BOCOCK, Joseph H
McAfee & Taft, Oklahoma City
405 552 2256
joseph.bocock@mcafeetaft.com
*Featured in Litigation (Oklahoma)*
**Practice Areas:** Practice concentrates in commercial litigation/arbitration advocacy with extensive experience in real estate, energy, securities, warehousing, manufacturing, debtor/creditor transactions and class actions.
**Professional Memberships:** Oklahoma Bar Association (Paralegal Committee; Chair since 2006), American Inns of Court (Master, Holloway Chapter; President 2008-09); Member, Public Investor Arbitration Bar Association.
**Career:** Oklahoma Bar (1978); Has tried substantial commercial arbitrations across the country regularly for over 20 years and has extensive experience in federal practice.
**Personal:** AB magna cum laude, highest distinction (Government), Dartmouth College, 1975; JD, Order of the Coif, Law Review, University of Oklahoma College of Law, 1978.

### BOMHOFF, Timothy J
McAfee & Taft, Oklahoma City
405 552 2339
tim.bomhoff@mcafeetaft.com
*Featured in Energy & Natural Resources (Oklahoma)*
**Practice Areas:** Commercial litigation practice includes representation of energy companies in a variety of disputes, including surface damages, environmental claims, quiet title actions, drilling costs, gas contracts, farmouts, joint operating agreements and lease disputes. Experience also

includes products liability, mass torts, securities arbitration, and representation of employers in employment litigation.
**Professional Memberships:** Oklahoma County, Oklahoma and Federal Bar Associations; Fellow, Litigation Counsel of America; Oklahoma City Mineral Lawyers Society.
**Career:** All state and federal courts in Oklahoma; US Court of Appeals for the Tenth Circuit.
**Personal:** BS, Oklahoma State University (1984); JD, University of Oklahoma (1988).

### BRIGHTMIRE, Jon
Doerner, Saunders, Daniel & Anderson, LLP, Tulsa
918 591 5258
jbrightmire@dsda.com
*Featured in Labor & Employment (Oklahoma)*
**Practice Areas:** Jon Brightmire focuses his practice on civil litigation. He has litigated cases in state and federal courts involving a wide range of issues, including employment, ERISA, contract, tort and intellectual property. He is one of the lead appellate attorneys for his firm, and has been involved in over 175 appeals in his career.
**Professional Memberships:** American, Oklahoma, and Tulsa County Bar Associations; American Inns of Court.
**Career:** Admitted in all state and federal courts in Oklahoma, the United States Supreme Court, and the United States Courts of Appeals for the Third, Fifth, Seventh, Tenth, and Eleventh Circuits.

### BRIGHTMIRE, Kristen
Doerner, Saunders, Daniel & Anderson, LLP, Tulsa
918 591 5204
kbrightmire@dsda.com
*Featured in Labor & Employment (Oklahoma)*
**Practice Areas:** Kristen Brightmire exclusively represents employers in all employment-law issues. In addition to representing clients in every step of the litigation process from the administrative agency through trial and appeal, she regularly counsels employers on contracts, policies, drug and alcohol testing, investigations, and related matters. She also assists her clients by drafting or reviewing policies, handbooks, employment contracts, severance programs, severance agreements, and relocation programs.
**Career:** Admitted to Oklahoma Bar, all federal courts in Oklahoma and Arkansas, 8th and 10th Circuit Courts of Appeals, United States Supreme Court. Was previously in-house labor, employment, and benefits Counsel for CITGO Petroleum Corporation.

### BROCKHAUS, Marc A
Dunlap Codding, Oklahoma City
405 607 8600
mbrockhaus@dunlapcodding.com
*Featured in Intellectual Property (Oklahoma)*
**Practice Areas:** Concentrates on intellectual property, technology, computer and patent law and counseling, transactions, litigation and prosecution before the USPTO. Has prosecuted patent applications in the United States and abroad in multiple categories in the electrical, software and

mechanical arts, including business method patents. Involved extensively in patent-related litigation and licensing efforts involving the enforcement of intellectual property rights.
**Professional Memberships:** USPTO; State Bar of Oklahoma; and Beta Gamma Sigma, an honor society marking academic achievement in the study of business.
**Personal:** JD and MBA, University of Oklahoma, 1997, and BS in Electrical Engineering, University of Oklahoma, 1993.

### BROUSSARD, Steven
Hall, Estill, Hardwick, Gable, Golden & Nelson, PC, Tulsa
918 594 0442
sbroussard@hallestill.com
*Featured in Labor & Employment (Oklahoma)*
**Practice Areas:** Labor and employment; immigration.
**Professional Memberships:** Tulsa County and Oklahoma Bar Associations; American Inns of Court; Defense Research Institute.
**Career:** Oklahoma (1988); United States Supreme Court; US Court of Appeals for the Tenth Circuit; US District Court of the Northern, Eastern and Western Districts of Oklahoma.
**Personal:** BS, Vanderbilt University, 1984; JD, University of Tulsa, 1988.

### BRU, Courtney
Doerner, Saunders, Daniel & Anderson, LLP, Tulsa
918 591 5339
cbru@dsda.com
*Featured in Labor & Employment (Oklahoma)*
**Practice Areas:** Represents employers, human resource personnel and managers on matters arising under state and federal laws; develops policies and practices designed to protect against employment-related claims; represents unionized employers in arbitration of grievances. In addition to her employment practice, she has consistently devoted a portion of her practice to commercial and civil litigation in state and federal trial and appellate courts.
**Career:** Admitted in Georgia (2005), including all state courts and US District Court for Northern District of Georgia; admitted in Oklahoma (2006), including all state and federal courts; admitted to 10th Circuit Court of Appeals; previously worked for Littler Mendelson, P.C.

### BUCHANAN, Brandon L
McAfee & Taft, Oklahoma City
405 552 2307
brandon.buchanan@mcafeetaft.com
*Featured in Litigation (Oklahoma)*
**Practice Areas:** State and federal litigation practice is focused on business and commercial litigation with specific experience in the areas of products liability defense, mass torts, contract and insurance disputes, professional negligence, wrongful death claims, and litigation involving healthcare, insurance, oil and gas, and complex construction disputes.
**Professional Memberships:** Oklahoma County Bar Association, Oklahoma Bar Association, Oklahoma Association of Defense

Counsel, Defense Research Institute, International Association of Defense Counsel, Luther J. Bohanon American Inn of Court.
**Career:** Admitted to all state and federal courts in Oklahoma.
**Personal:** BA, cum laude, University of Oklahoma; JD, University of Oklahoma.

### BURNETT, LeAnne
Crowe & Dunlevy, a Professional Corporation, Oklahoma City
405 239 6610
leanne.burnett@crowedunlevy.com
*Featured in Energy & Natural Resources (Oklahoma)*
**Practice Areas:** Experienced trial lawyer in environmental and energy complex litigation and regulation.
**Professional Memberships:** Fellow of American College of Environmental Lawyers; Oklahoma Bar Association Environmental Law Section founding member, with service as Section Chairperson and Environmental Law Handbook Editor.
**Career:** 1971 Southern Methodist University BA; 1989 Oklahoma University JD; Crowe & Dunlevy since 1989; currently Shareholder, Director.
**Publications:** "The Potential Federal Regulation of Hydraulic Fracturing," The Oklahoma Bar Association's Environmental Law CLE, October 2011; "The Fracking Face-Off," The Oklahoma Bar Journal, February 11, 2012.
**Personal:** Raised six children and other wildlife on Oklahoma farm. Oklahoma Lawyers for Children volunteer.

### CASON, Len
Hartzog Conger Cason & Neville, LLP, Oklahoma City
405 235 7000
lcason@hartzoglaw.com
*Featured in Corporate/Commercial (Oklahoma)*
**Practice Areas:** Tax; trusts and estates; business and financial transactions. Listed in Best Lawyers in America in corporate law, tax law, and trusts and estates.
**Professional Memberships:** Fellow, American College of Trust and Estate Counsel; Fellow, American College of Tax Counsel. Member of Bars of Oklahoma, California and Texas. Past Chairman Tax Section Okla Bar Association.
**Career:** Founding Partner, 1979. Adjunct Professor of Law in Taxation, University of Oklahoma since 1981. Captain, United States Air Force JAG, 1972-76. LLM in Taxation. Attorney with Rain Harrell Emery Young and Doke, Dallas, TX 1976-9.
**Publications:** Various publications in the Oklahoma Bar Journal, Texas Bar Journal and Prentice Hall. Most recently, 'Maximizing Funding of Credit Shelter Trust With Non-Ira Assets' (in the June 2002 edition of Estate Planning); IRS approves Poorer Spouse Funding Technique (in the May 2004 edition of Estate Planning); and The 'Just Enough' Funding Technique: An Innovative New Strategy (in the June 2008 edition of Estate Planning). Numerous articles in Leimberg and Commentator on Leimberg Board of Commentators.

**Personal:** Oklahoma Medical Research Foundation (Chairman of the Board of Directors)since 2001. Director, InvesTrust N.A.

## CHAMBERS, Lawrence
Doerner, Saunders, Daniel & Anderson, LLP, Tulsa
918 591 5207
lchambers@dsda.com
*Featured in Corporate/Commercial (Oklahoma)*
**Practice Areas:** Larry Chambers counsels clients in the areas of business formation, corporate finance, mergers and acquisitions, oil and gas and real estate. He has experience in domestic and international transactions in areas as diverse as Azerbaijan, Canada, South Korea, Venezuela, and the United Arab Emirates. Larry has over 40 years of experience, and he has been a trusted advisor in the formation and growth of companies from their early investment stage through public offerings and beyond.
**Professional Memberships:** American Bar Association; Oklahoma Bar Association; Tulsa County Bar Association; Oklahoma Bar Corporation Act Committee.
**Career:** BBA 1967 and JD 1972 University of Oklahoma, Order of the Coif, Law Review.

## CHILDERS, Adam W
Crowe & Dunlevy, a Professional Corporation, Oklahoma City
405 235 7741
adam.childers@crowedunlevy.com
*Featured in Labor & Employment (Oklahoma)*
**Practice Areas:** Labor and employment.
**Professional Memberships:** Co-Chair of firm's Labor & Employment Section; Administrative Law Judge, Oklahoma Department of Labor; Journal Record's "Achievers Under 40 – Class VI"; Phi Beta Kappa; Order of the Barristers; Board of Visitors, OU College of Arts and Sciences; Graduate, Leadership Norman 2008; Member, OKConnect Class 2; Chairman, 2013 OBA Labor & Employment Section; "BV" peer review rating, LexisNexis Martindale-Hubbell; "Rising Star" in October 2008, 2010, 2011 and 2012 "Super Lawyers" magazine.
**Career:** Crowe & Dunlevy (2000).
**Personal:** Bachelor of Arts (1997) and Juris Doctorate (2000), both with honors, from University of Oklahoma.

## CHRISTIANSEN, Mark D
McAfee & Taft, Oklahoma City
*Featured in Energy & Natural Resources (Oklahoma)*
**Practice Areas:** Mr Christiansen works for clients in the energy industry in litigation matters of all types and in transactional matters, including the defense of statewide, multistate and nationwide class action lawsuits, lawsuits over operations, contractual and transactional projects, and advice as to energy law.
**Professional Memberships:** Executive Committee for the Dallas-based Center for American and International Law (2000-Present); Executive Committee for Denver-based Rocky Mountain Mineral Law Foundation (2005-07 and 2011-13).

**Publications:** Board of Editors, Oil & Gas Reporter. Author of Annual Energy Litigation Reports for American Bar Association and Rocky Mountain Mineral Law Foundation Journal.

## COLEMAN, W Chris
McAfee & Taft, Oklahoma City
405 552 2234
chris.coleman@mcafeetaft.com
*Featured in Corporate/Commercial (Oklahoma)*
**Practice Areas:** Practice involves the representation of businesses in a broad range of business transactions, including mergers, acquisitions and divestitures; securities offerings and public reporting; contract negotiations; public and private financing; structuring and capitalizing new entities; and reorganizing existing entities.
**Professional Memberships:** Oklahoma County, Oklahoma and American Bar Associations.
**Career:** Oklahoma Bar (1982). Has represented businesses engaged in virtually every major industry, including real estate, energy, financial services, engineering, software, food manufacturing and distribution, communications and sales.
**Personal:** BA with distinction, Phi Beta Kappa, University of Oklahoma, 1979; JD, University of Oklahoma College of Law, 1982.

## COOPER, H Wayne
Doerner, Saunders, Daniel & Anderson, LLP, Tulsa
918 591 5228
hwcooper@dsda.com
*Featured in Corporate/Commercial (Oklahoma)*
**Practice Areas:** Securities law, mergers and acquisitions, corporate and limited liability company financing, franchising law and oil and gas. Has taught Business Organizations – Planning and Drafting and Entrepreneurial Law as an adjunct instructor at the University of Tulsa College of Law.
**Career:** BS, Mechanical Engineering, University of Oklahoma (1968); MBA, University of Nevada (Las Vegas) (1972); JD, The University of Tulsa College of Law (with highest honors) (1975); Law clerk for Hon William J Holloway, Jr, Circuit Judge, United States Court of Appeals, Tenth Circuit (1975-76); United States Air Force, Development Engineer (1968-72).
**Publications:** Co-author of Business Organizations, Vernon's Oklahoma Forms 2d (Thompson West).

## COOPER, Mary Quinn
McAfee & Taft, Tulsa
918 574 3065
maryquinn.cooper@mcafeetaft.com
*Featured in Litigation (Oklahoma)*
**Practice Areas:** Serves as national trial counsel for major corporations, including Ford and General Motors, and defends high-exposure products liability claims and class actions across the country. Practice includes complex commercial litigation and professional liability defense.
**Professional Memberships:** Tulsa County, Oklahoma and American Bar Associations; American Board of Trial Advocates; American Inns of Court; Defense Research Institute;

Oklahoma Association of Defense Counsel; International Association of Defense Counsel; Products Liability Advisory Counsel; Oklahoma Bar Foundation.
**Career:** All state and federal courts in Oklahoma, US Tenth Circuit Court of Appeals, US Supreme Court. Frequent speaker on trial practice issues.

## CREMIN, Pat
Hall, Estill, Hardwick, Gable, Golden & Nelson, PC, Tulsa
918 594 0594
Pcremin@hallestill.com
*Featured in Labor & Employment (Oklahoma)*
**Practice Areas:** Labor/employment litigation and counseling; ERISA claims; management training; employment counseling; employment and class action.
**Professional Memberships:** American, Oklahoma, Oklahoma County and Tulsa County Bar Associations; Master, American Inns of Court; Northern District of Oklahoma Adjunct Settlement Program, Sr Adjunct Settlement Judge; American College of Trial Lawyers, Outreach Committee State Liaison.
**Career:** Oklahoma (1974); US Supreme Court; US Circuit Courts, Tenth, Fifth, Sixth and Eighth Circuits; Oklahoma Supreme Court; US District Court, Northern, Eastern and Western Districts of Oklahoma; US District Court for the Eastern District of Michigan.
**Personal:** BS, University of Tulsa, 1966; JD, University of Tulsa, 1974.

## CROOK MARTIN, Linda
Doerner, Saunders, Daniel & Anderson, LLP, Tulsa
918 591 5307
lmartin@dsda.com
*Featured in Energy & Natural Resources (Oklahoma)*
**Practice Areas:** Linda C Martin works with state and federal regulatory agencies regularly to assist clients, including municipal entities, in finding environmentally sound, cost effective remedies to alleged violations of environmental laws. Linda is also an experienced first chair trial lawyer in environmental cases, and zealously represents firm clients in the most cost effective manner possible while still maintaining the high quality of legal representation firm clients have come to expect.
**Professional Memberships:** Fellow, American College of Environmental Lawyers; American Bar Association Section on Environment, Energy and Resources; Oklahoma Bar Association Environmental Law Section and Women in Law Committee; Tulsa Women Lawyers Association.
**Career:** University of Tennessee - BA, 1972 and JD, 1980.

## CRUM, Bruce
McAfee & Taft, Oklahoma City
405 552 2220
bruce.crum@mcafeetaft.com
*Featured in Corporate/Commercial (Oklahoma)*
**Practice Areas:** Practice is primarily concerned with regulatory and transactional matters affecting banks, bank holding companies and other financial institutions. Also represents purchasers and sellers in private equity capital leveraged

transactions involving financial as well as strategic parties.
**Professional Memberships:** Oklahoma Bar Association.
**Career:** Oklahoma Bar (1977); Gubernatorial appointee to Incentive Review Committee for the State of Oklahoma.
**Personal:** AB with honors, Colgate University, 1972; MBA, Columbia University, 1974; JD, University of Oklahoma, 1977.

## DACE, Robert W
McAfee & Taft, Oklahoma City
405 552 2268
bob.dace@mcafeetaft.com
*Featured in Litigation (Oklahoma)*
**Practice Areas:** Practice involves litigation of complex business cases, including those involving intellectual property, oil and gas, environmental issues, insurance coverage, and other technical and scientific issues. Has tried cases, arbitrations and administrative proceedings throughout the US.
**Professional Memberships:** Oklahoma County, Oklahoma, and American Bar Associations; Robert J. Turner American Inn of Court; Mineral Lawyers Society of Oklahoma.
**Career:** Oklahoma Bar (1983); Federal courts in Arkansas, Illinois, North Dakota, Texas and Wisconsin; US Courts of Appeals for the Seventh, Eighth and Tenth Circuits; US Tax Court; US Supreme Court.
**Personal:** BS, US Military Academy, West Point; JD, University of Oklahoma.

## DALE, Angelyn
Hall, Estill, Hardwick, Gable, Golden & Nelson, PC, Tulsa
918 594 0558
adale@hallestill.com
*Featured in Labor & Employment (Oklahoma)*
**Practice Areas:** Labor and employment litigation; class action defense; employee and management training.
**Professional Memberships:** American Bar Association; Oklahoma Bar Association; Tulsa County Bar Association; Executive Committee and Master for the Johnson Sontag Chapter, American Inns of Court; Tulsa Women Lawyers Association.
**Career:** Oklahoma (1984); US Court of Appeals, Tenth Circuit; US District Court for the Northern, Western and Eastern Districts of Oklahoma; Oklahoma Supreme Court.
**Personal:** BBA, Statistics, with high honors, University of Oklahoma, 1981; JD Southern Methodist University Dedman School of Law, 1984.

## DAVIS, Gary
Crowe & Dunlevy, a Professional Corporation, Oklahoma City
405 235 7798
gary.davis@crowedunlevy.com
*Featured in Litigation (Oklahoma)*
**Practice Areas:** Mr Davis practices in the areas of oil, gas, energy, litigation, trial, commercial transactions law, mediation and Bet-the-Company litigation.

**Professional Memberships:** Admitted Oklahoma and Kansas (1957); American Petroleum Institute; Governor's Special Advisory Commission on oil and gas (1979-82); American Bar Association; Oklahoma Bar Association.
**Career:** Joined Crowe & Dunlevy in 1982.
**Publications:** Chapter: 'Energy Litigation, Business and Commercial Litigation in Federal Courts' (1998) and other notable works published in the Oil and Gas Analyst and The Oil Daily (1983).
**Personal:** University of Kansas School of Law (JD, 1957; BA, 1953).

### DAVIS, Steven C
Hartzog Conger Cason & Neville, LLP, Oklahoma City
405 235 7000
sdavis@hartzoglaw.com
*Featured in Corporate/Commercial (Oklahoma)*
**Practice Areas:** Tax, business transactions, estates and trusts.
**Professional Memberships:** ABA; OBA (former Chairman, Vice-Chair and Secretary-Treasurer, Section of Taxation). Oklahoma Society of Certified Public Accountants.
**Publications:** Various continuing legal education articles and materials; articles in Oklahoma Law Review, Oklahoma Bar Journal, and selected tax publications.
**Personal:** American Heart Association (Past Chairman and director, Oklahoma Affiliate). Oklahoma City Community Foundation (trustee; Investment Committee Chairman). First Commercial Bank (Chairman of the Board).

### DELIGANS, Julianna
Hall, Estill, Hardwick, Gable, Golden & Nelson, PC, Oklahoma City
405 553 2810
jdeligans@hallestill.com
*Featured in Intellectual Property (Oklahoma)*
**Practice Areas:** Intellectual property and information technology; copyrights; licensing; patents; trademarks; trade secrets; intellectual property litigation.
**Professional Memberships:** Oklahoma, Oklahoma County & American Bar Associations; American Intellectual Property Law Association; International Trademark Association.
**Career:** Oklahoma (2003); US District Court for the Western and Northen Districts of Oklahoma
**Personal:** BS, Cell & Molecular Biology, with honors, University of Oklahoma, 2000; JD University of Oklahoma College of Law, 2003.

### DOUGHERTY, III, Clifford C
McAfee & Taft, Oklahoma City
405 552 2302
cliff.dougherty@mcafeetaft.com
*Featured in Intellectual Property (Oklahoma)*
**Practice Areas:** Cliff has practiced exclusively in all aspects of intellectual property law (including patent, trademark and copyright law) and intellectual property litigation his entire career. He serves as exclusive IP counsel for numerous private and public companies ranging from Fortune 100 corporations to small family partnerships.

**Professional Memberships:** Oklahoma Bar Association, American Bar Association, International Trademark Association and American Intellectual Property Law Association.
**Career:** Registered in US Patent and Trademark Office as patent agent, 1984, and patent attorney in 1985. Oklahoma Bar, 1985.
**Personal:** BS (chemistry) (1982) and JD, with distinction (1985), both from the University of Oklahoma.

### ELLIS, JR., Harvey D.
Crowe & Dunlevy, a Professional Corporation, Oklahoma City
405 235 7743
harvey.ellis@crowedunlevy.com
*Featured in Litigation (Oklahoma)*
**Practice Areas:** Appellate practice, constitutional law, professional ethics.
**Professional Memberships:** American Bar Association, Oklahoma Bar Association, Oklahoma County Bar Association, admitted to Fifth Circuit, Ninth Circuit, Tenth Circuit, Federal Circuit, US Supreme Court, Oklahoma Supreme Court, and Northern, Eastern and Western federal districts in Oklahoma.
**Career:** Chairman of Crowe & Dunlevy Ethics Committee, member of Western District of Oklahoma Local Rules Committee, past member of Oklahoma Bar Association Civil Procedure Committee.
**Publications:** Ellis and Muchmore, Oklahoma Appellate Practice (West) Muchmore and Ellis, Oklahoma Civil Procedure Forms and Practice (Lexis).

### FOLLUO, Dan S.
Rhodes, Hieronymus, Jones, Tucker & Gable PLLC, Tulsa
918 582 1173
dfolluo@rhodesokla.com
*Featured in Litigation (Oklahoma)*
**Practice Areas:** Chair of the Firm's transportation litigation group. Folluo concentrates on defense cases with an emphasis in trucking law, extra contractual defense and professional liability. Major recent matters involved accidents and disputes involving commercial trucking, tractor trailers, mass highway casualties and oil field accidents in Oklahoma and surrounding states.
**Career:** Past-President of the Oklahoma Association of Defense Counsel (1998); 2012 Oklahoma President for the American Board of Trial Advocates.

### FREE JR, Philip L
Hall, Estill, Hardwick, Gable, Golden & Nelson, PC, Oklahoma City
405 553 2878
pfree@hallestill.com
*Featured in Intellectual Property (Oklahoma)*
**Practice Areas:** Intellectual property litigation and counseling; right of publicity; patent and patent litigation.
**Professional Memberships:** Oklahoma Bar Association; American Bar Association, American Intellectual Property Lawyers Association, and the International Trademark Association.

**Career:** Oklahoma (1993); US Supreme Court; US Patent & Trademark Office; US Court of Appeals for the Federal and Tenth Circuits.
**Publications:** Co-authored 'Intellectual Property Litigation: Are OK Courts Missing the Mark(man)?', 69 Okla. B.J. 792, 1998.
**Personal:** BS, Chemistry, cum laude, Southwestern Oklahoma State University, 1988; JD. University of Oklahoma College of Law, 1993.

### FULKERSON, Sam
McAfee & Taft, Oklahoma City
405 552 2369
sam.fulkerson@mcafeetaft.com
*Featured in Labor & Employment (Oklahoma)*
**Practice Areas:** Represents management in all employment areas, including litigation, arbitration and administrative practice. Past chair, Firm's Labor & Employment Group and OBA's Employment Law Section. Frequent author and lecturer. Co-editor, Oklahoma Employment Law Letter. Also listed in Best Lawyers, Oklahoma Super Lawyers (Top 50).
**Professional Memberships:** Oklahoma and American Bar Associations, Oklahoma Bar Foundation, Federal Bar Association.
**Career:** Oklahoma Bar (1991); Federal courts (Oklahoma, Texas); US Court of Appeals, Tenth and Fourth Circuits; US Supreme Court.
**Personal:** BA, magna cum laude, Phi Beta Kappa, University of Oklahoma; MA, honors, University of North Carolina; JD, honors, University of Oklahoma.

### FULLER, Gary
McAfee & Taft, Oklahoma City
405 552 2227
gary.fuller@mcafeetaft.com
*Featured in Corporate/Commercial (Oklahoma)*
**Practice Areas:** Practice is primarily concentrated in corporate, tax and estate planning law.
**Professional Memberships:** Oklahoma County Bar Association, Oklahoma Bar Association, State Bar of Texas, American Bar Association.
**Career:** Oklahoma Bar (1959); Texas Bar (1963). Judge Advocate General Corps, USAF, (1959-62). Lectured extensively to lawyer groups on tax planning subjects and has been an instructor at the University of Oklahoma College of Law.
**Personal:** BBA, University of Oklahoma, 1957; studied law at the Academy of International Law, The Hague, Netherlands; received LLB from University of Oklahoma, 1959; LLM, Yale Law School, 1963.

### GARBRECHT, Robert L
McAfee & Taft, Oklahoma City
405 552 2254
rob.garbrecht@mcafeetaft.com
*Featured in Real Estate (Oklahoma)*
**Practice Areas:** Commercial transactions attorney who principally practices in the areas of business acquisitions, finance, real estate, technology and state and local taxation law. Has substantial experience in structuring and negotiating business acquisitions and strategic alliances and other unique business relationships, as well as in entity organization and governance matters.

**Professional Memberships:** Oklahoma Bar Association, American Bar Association, Oklahoma Society of Certified Public Accountants, American Institute of Certified Public Accountants.
**Career:** Oklahoma Bar (1990). Inactive Certified Public Accountant. Adjunct Professor at the University of Oklahoma College of Law.
**Personal:** BBA, University of Oklahoma, 1986; JD, University of Oklahoma, 1990.

### GEISTER III, Charles E
Hartzog Conger Cason & Neville, LLP, Oklahoma City
405 235 7000
cgeister@hartzoglaw.com
*Featured in Litigation (Oklahoma)*
**Practice Areas:** Litigation: commercial disputes; securities and antitrust cases; class actions; products liability; insurance; employment.
**Professional Memberships:** ABA; OBA (Civil Procedure Committee, 1995-2000); OCBA (President, 2007-08). US Courts, Western, Northern and Eastern Districts, Oklahoma. 10th Circuit Court of Appeals.
**Career:** Named to Best Lawyers in America: Bet-the-Company Litigation; Commercial Litigation; Litigation-Antitrust; Litigation-Securities; Litigation-Labor & Employment; Insurance Law. Best Lawyers' 2011 Lawyer of the Year-Oklahoma City/Insurance. Named as an Oklahoma Super Lawyer.
**Publications:** Oklahoma law regarding Statutes of Limitation and Repose, Liability for Off-Label use of Pharmaceutical Products. Lectured in areas of civil procedure, trial practice and insurance law.

### GOODMAN, Jimmy
Crowe & Dunlevy, a Professional Corporation, Oklahoma City
405 235 7717
jimmy.goodman@crowedunlevy.com
*Featured in Litigation (Oklahoma)*
**Practice Areas:** Mr Goodman specializes in high-stakes litigation. His trials include business tort and contract litigation; Indian gaming/economic development; federal false claims; class actions; insurance bad faith defense; construction; real estate; product liability; Medicare fraud; restraining orders and injunction; unfair competition.
**Professional Memberships:** Oklahoma's ABA delegate. Past Member, ABA Litigation Section Council, ABA Council on Racial and Ethnic Justice, ABA Commission on Racial and Ethnic Diversity. Chair, Fellows of the American Bar Foundation. Former Member, ABF Board of Directors.
**Career:** Best Lawyers and Superlawyers. Chairman/Past President of firm.
**Personal:** Stanford Law School (JD, 1971); University of Oklahoma (BA, 1968).

### GRIFFIN JR, John J
Crowe & Dunlevy, a Professional Corporation, Oklahoma City
405 235 7718
john.griffin@crowedunlevy.com
*Featured in Energy & Natural Resources (Oklahoma)*

**Practice Areas:** Energy and natural resources law; oil and gas law; water law.
**Career:** Chairman, Energy and Natural Resources Department. Mr Griffin has practiced in the area of Energy and Natural Resources Litigation for more than 35 years, representing major oil companies, independent producers and mining companies in multi-state class action litigation, complex commercial litigation, and regulatory proceedings. His cases have involved royalty payments, gas purchase contracts, gas processing agreements, operating agreements, mineral conveyances, production taxes, environmental damage, water rights, and mining regulation.
**Personal:** New York University School of Law (JD 1975) Root Tilden Scholar; University of Oklahoma (BA With Special Distinction 1972).

**HAINES, Spencer**
McAfee & Taft, Oklahoma City
405 552 2298
spencer.haines@mcafeetaft.com
*Featured in Corporate/Commercial (Oklahoma)*
**Practice Areas:** Practice is focused on complex transaction planning for corporations, limited liability companies, partnerships, and high net worth individuals; wealth transfer tax planning; local, state and federal taxation; and structuring tax-deferred (Section 1031) transactions.
**Professional Memberships:** Oklahoma Bar Association.
**Career:** Oklahoma Bar (2004); US District Court, Western District of Oklahoma; US Tax Court.
**Personal:** BS, Oklahoma State University, 1998 (Accounting); JD, with highest honors, University of Oklahoma, 2004; LLM, New York University, 2007 (Taxation).

**HARDWICK, James C T**
Hall, Estill, Hardwick, Gable, Golden & Nelson, PC, Tulsa
918 594 0434
jhardwick@hallestill.com
*Featured in Energy & Natural Resources (Oklahoma)*
**Practice Areas:** Energy/natural resources; oil/gas; land rights; natural resources and energy transactions; pipeline regulatory; utilities; partnership/unincorporated entity; federal/state energy regulatory.
**Professional Memberships:** American, Oklahoma and Tulsa County Bar Associations; Board, Oklahoma Law Review; Oklahoma Reporter, Mineral Law Newsletter, RMMLF; Trustee, RMML Foundation; Executive Committee Vice-Chair of the Advisory Board of the Institute for Energy Law of The Center for American and International Law.
**Career:** Oklahoma (1963); US Court of Appeals, Tenth and Eighth Circuits; Oklahoma Supreme Court; US District Court, Northern and Western Districts of Oklahoma; DC Court of Appeals.
**Personal:** BS, Oklahoma University, 1960; LLB, Oklahoma University, 1963.

**HAYES, J Kevin**
Hall, Estill, Hardwick, Gable, Golden & Nelson, PC, Tulsa
918 594 0460
KHayes@HallEstill.Com
*Featured in Energy & Natural Resources (Oklahoma)*
**Practice Areas:** Corporate/commercial litigation; energy and natural resources; energy transactions; land rights; natural resources transactions; oil and gas; pipeline regulatory; utilities.
**Professional Memberships:** Oklahoma Bar Association; Oklahoma County Bar Association; Tulsa County Bar Association; Council Oak Chapter, American Inns of Court (Master).
**Career:** Oklahoma (1975); United States Supreme Court; US Court of Appeals for the Tenth Circuit; Oklahoma Supreme Court; US District Court for the Northern, Eastern and Western Districts of Oklahoma.
**Personal:** BS University of Tulsa, 1972; JD, University of Tulsa, 1974.

**HERMES, John N**
McAfee & Taft, Oklahoma City
405 552 2258
john.hermes@mcafeetaft.com
*Featured in Litigation (Oklahoma)*
**Practice Areas:** Practice concentrates on commercial and business litigation.
**Professional Memberships:** American College of Trial Lawyers, American Law Institute, American Inn of Court CV, Oklahoma Bar Association, Oklahoma Bar Foundation, American Bar Association, American Bar Foundation, Federal Bar Association.
**Career:** Oklahoma Bar (1975); all state and federal district courts in Oklahoma; US Fifth, Tenth and Federal Circuit Courts of Appeals; US Tax Court; US Court of Claims; US Supreme Court.
**Personal:** AB, Ripon College, 1968; JD, University of Oklahoma, 1975.

**HETRICK, Stephen M**
McAfee & Taft, Tulsa
918 574 3029
stephen.hetrick@mcafeetaft.com
*Featured in Real Estate (Oklahoma)*
**Practice Areas:** Practice encompasses a broad range of complex business transactions, including the acquisition, development, leasing, management and financing of real estate; the organization, financing, acquisition, reorganization and divestiture of all types of entities; and state and local taxation matters. Also advises clients on numerous organizational and operational matters, including legal and regulatory compliance, corporate strategy and fiduciary duties.
**Professional Memberships:** Oklahoma County Bar Association, Oklahoma Bar Association.
**Career:** Oklahoma Bar (2003); US District Court for the Western District of Oklahoma.
**Personal:** BS, summa cum laude, University of Central Oklahoma, 2000; JD, with highest honors, University of Oklahoma, 2003.

**HILL, Frank**
McAfee & Taft, Oklahoma City
405 552 2259
frank.hill@mcafeetaft.com
*Featured in Real Estate (Oklahoma)*
**Practice Areas:** Commercial transactions, including real estate and finance; acquisitions, sales, exchanges and other dispositions; construction and development; public-private partnerships; tax planning; tax-exempt organizations, and debt settlement transactions.
**Professional Memberships:** American Bar Association; American College of Real Estate Lawyers.
**Career:** Texas Bar, Oklahoma Bar, US Tenth Circuit Court of Appeals, US District Court for the Western District of Oklahoma, US Tax Court, US Court of Claims. Judge Advocate General's Corps, US Army.
**Personal:** BBA, University of Oklahoma, 1963; LLB, University of Texas at Austin, 1966; LLM in Taxation, The George Washington University, 1969.

**HIX, Richard P**
McAfee & Taft, Tulsa
918 574 3016
richard.hix@mcafeetaft.com
*Featured in Litigation (Oklahoma)*
**Practice Areas:** Federal and state court trial practice concentrating in commercial litigation, including breach of contract, business torts, oil and gas, environmental and class action. Expertise extends to all phases of civil litigation, including appeals.
**Professional Memberships:** Oklahoma and American Bar Associations; State Bar of Texas.
**Career:** Texas Bar (1977); Oklahoma Bar (1978); Federal district courts in Oklahoma; US Court of Appeals for the Tenth Circuit; US Supreme Court. Adjunct Settlement Judge, US District Court for the Northern District of Oklahoma.
**Personal:** US Air Force (1967-1970); BA, University of Oklahoma, 1974; JD, Duke University, 1977.

**HUNTSMAN, Susan**
Crowe & Dunlevy, a Professional Corporation, Oklahoma City
918 592 9866
susan.huntsman@crowedunlevy.com
*Featured in Native American Law (Oklahoma)*
**Practice Areas:** Susan Huntsman's practice focuses on appellate law and issues particularly affecting tribes, those doing business in Indian country, and natural resources.
**Professional Memberships:** Admitted in Oklahoma (1999); Illinois (2004); Wisconsin (2007); and Arkansas (2013).
**Career:** Joined Crowe & Dunlevy in 2000. Previously served as a law clerk for Judge Terence C. Kern, United States District Court for the Northern District of Oklahoma.
**Personal:** Harvard Law School (JD, cum laude, 1999); University of Arkansas (BA, summa cum laude, 1996).

**HYDE, James Dudley**
McAfee & Taft, Oklahoma City
405 552 2229
dudley.hyde@mcafeetaft.com
*Featured in Labor & Employment (Oklahoma)*
**Practice Areas:** Entire range of employee benefits services, including retirement plans, executive compensation, health and welfare plans, COBRA, and deferred compensation matters.
**Professional Memberships:** Oklahoma County Bar Association, Oklahoma Bar Association, American Bar Association, SouthWest Benefits Association (Former President), IRS Dallas Key District EP/EO Council, Department of Labor Southwest Practitioners Group, and Charter Fellow of the American College of Employee Benefits Council.
**Career:** Admitted in Oklahoma and Texas. Frequent speaker at SouthWest Benefits Association, Western States Pension Conference, and numerous trade and professional organizations.
**Personal:** BA, University of Oklahoma; JD, Southern Methodist University; LLM (Taxation), The George Washington University.

**JOSEPH, Michael E**
McAfee & Taft, Oklahoma City
405 235 9621
mike.joseph@mcafeetaft.com
*Featured in Corporate/Commercial (Oklahoma)*
**Practice Areas:** Diverse business practice with extensive experience representing clients in a broad range of complex business, corporate, healthcare, and franchising transactions. Represents privately owned businesses in joint ventures, acquisitions, strategic and business planning, corporate finance.
**Professional Memberships:** Founder and Past President, Oklahoma Health Lawyers Association; Former Chair, Health Law Section, Oklahoma Bar Association; American Health Lawyers Association; ABA Sections of Corporate, Health, and Antitrust Law.
**Personal:** Director of numerous foundations and charitable organizations involved in healthcare, economic development, medical research, arts and cultural, social services, education, civic improvement, and leadership development

**JOYCE, Robert**
McAfee & Taft, Tulsa
918 574 3040
robert.joyce@mcafeetaft.com
*Featured in Energy & Natural Resources (Oklahoma)*
**Practice Areas:** Environmental and toxic tort litigation, regulatory compliance and enforcement and transactional matters, with particular expertise in issues affecting refineries, gas processing, pipelines and other midstream and downstream oil and gas facilities, as well as manufacturing and aviation/aerospace facilities.
**Professional Memberships:** Tulsa County, Oklahoma and American Bar Associations; Defense Research Institute; American Institute of Chemical Engineers; Master, Hudson Hall Wheaton American Inn of Court.

**Career:** Oklahoma Bar (1988); All federal district courts in Oklahoma; Tenth Circuit Court of Appeals; Former chemical engineer for OXY USA.
**Personal:** BS, Chemical Engineering (1981) and JD (1988), University of Tulsa.

### KENNEY, John A
McAfee & Taft, Oklahoma City
405 552 2244
john.kenney@mcafeetaft.com
*Featured in Intellectual Property (Oklahoma), Litigation (Oklahoma)*
**Practice Areas:** Trial practice concentrating on cases involving intellectual property and other technical and scientific issues. Has tried cases, arbitrations, and administrative proceedings and hearings in the US, US Virgin Islands, and several foreign countries.
**Professional Memberships:** Oklahoma Bar Association, American Bar Association, American College of Trial Lawyers, Federal Bar Association.
**Career:** Texas Bar (1975)(inactive); Oklahoma Bar (1981); Numerous federal trial and appellate courts and US Supreme Court. Worked as an engineer prior to law school. Inventor on six US Patents.
**Personal:** BSIE with distinction, University of Oklahoma, 1971; JD, University of Oklahoma, 1975.

### LABRIE, Michael J.
McAfee & Taft, Oklahoma City
405 552 2305
michael.labrie@mcafeetaft.com
*Featured in Intellectual Property (Oklahoma)*
**Practice Areas:** Mike is a registered patent attorney whose practice encompasses all aspects of intellectual property law, including patent, trademark and copyright law and related litigation. He serves as chief IP counsel for numerous public and private companies and has extensive experience with patent and trademark portfolio management, opinions and licensing.
**Professional Memberships:** Oklahoma Bar Association (Past President, IP Section), Oklahoma County Bar Association, AIPLA, INTA, National Society of Professional Engineers, Oklahoma Society of Professional Engineers, Association of University Technology Managers.
**Publications:** Author, "State Trademark and Unfair Competition Law".
**Personal:** BS (Mechanical Engineering), University of Oklahoma; JD, Oklahoma City University.

### LAIRD, Michael S
Crowe & Dunlevy, a Professional Corporation, Oklahoma City
405 239 6623
michael.laird@crowedunlevy.com
*Featured in Real Estate (Oklahoma)*
**Practice Areas:** Mr Laird practices in commercial real estate, large project development, project finance, construction and leasing, energy generation facilities, wind energy, healthcare facilities and the hospitality industry. He currently serves as the co-chair of the firm's Real Estate Practice Group.

**Professional Memberships:** Fellow, American College of Mortgage Attorneys; Member, ABA Forum on the Construction Industry; Past President, Commercial Real Estate Council of Oklahoma City; Executive Committee Member, Urban Land Institute - Oklahoma.
**Publications:** Numerous articles on real estate and construction issues for industry groups and attorneys.
**Personal:** University of Oklahoma College of Law (JD, 1979); Harvard University (BA, 1973).

### LARIMORE, James W
Crowe & Dunlevy, a Professional Corporation, Oklahoma City
405 239 6643
james.larimore@crowedunlevy.com
*Featured in Corporate/Commercial (Oklahoma)*
**Practice Areas:** Mr Larimore's practice focuses on multiple aspects of business and commercial transactions, from entity formation and organizational matters to debt and equity capital-raising activities, mergers and acquisitions, corporate governance, securities law compliance and tax planning. He has significant experience representing publicly-held and private clients in joint ventures, acquisitions, divestitures, securities offerings and the negotiation of various other transactions.
**Personal:** The University of Texas School of Law (JD, with honors, 2001); The University of Oklahoma (BBA, with special distinction, 1997).

### LATHAM, Myrna
McAfee & Taft, Oklahoma City
405 552 2278
myrna.latham@mcafeetaft.com
*Featured in Real Estate (Oklahoma)*
**Practice Areas:** Real estate and other commercial transactions, including finance, acquisitions, sales, leasing, exchanges and other dispositions.
**Professional Memberships:** Oklahoma County Bar Association, Oklahoma Bar Association, Oklahoma Commercial Real Estate Council, Oklahoma Business Ethics Consortium (Director and General Counsel), American Bar Association.
**Career:** Oklahoma Bar (1985); US District Courts for the Western and Northern Districts of Oklahoma; US Tenth Circuit Court of Appeals. Previous experience includes representation of businesses in commercial litigation as well as transactional matters.
**Personal:** BA, Southern Nazarene University, 1978; JD with honors, University of Oklahoma College of Law, 1985.

### LAUDERDALE, Michael F
McAfee & Taft, Oklahoma City
405 552 2257
michael.lauderdale@mcafeetaft.com
*Featured in Labor & Employment (Oklahoma)*
**Practice Areas:** Represents management in all phases of employment law, including litigation before federal and state courts, regulatory and administrative agencies and in arbitration. Also commercial litigation with an emphasis on franchise and healthcare litigation. Frequent author and presenter.

**Professional Memberships:** Oklahoma Bar Association.
**Career:** Oklahoma Bar; federal district courts in Oklahoma and Texas; US Court of Appeals for the Tenth Circuit, US Supreme Court.
**Personal:** BBA, with special distinction, University of Oklahoma, 1987; JD with honors, University of Oklahoma College of Law, 1990 and Order of the Coif. Former ALJ, Oklahoma Department of Labor, 2003-05.

### LEACH, William S
McAfee & Taft, Tulsa
918 574 3063
bill.leach@mcafeetaft.com
*Featured in Litigation (Oklahoma)*
**Practice Areas:** Tried nearly 100 cases to verdict. Practice concentrated on insurance disputes, product liability defense, mass torts and class actions, MDL and complex business litigation.
**Professional Memberships:** Tulsa County and Oklahoma Bar Associations, State Bar of Texas, Oklahoma Association of Defense Counsel, Texas Association of Certified Civil Trial Attorneys, Texas Association of Defense Counsel, American Board of Trial Advocates.
**Career:** Texas Bar, Oklahoma Bar, all federal courts in Oklahoma and Texas, Fifth and Tenth Circuit Courts of Appeal, US Supreme Court. Adjunct settlement judge, Eastern District of Oklahoma and adjunct professor of trial advocacy. Frequent speaker on trial practice.

### LOOMIS, Cori H
Crowe & Dunlevy, a Professional Corporation, Oklahoma City
405 234 3238
cori.loomis@crowedunlevy.com
*Featured in Corporate/Commercial (Oklahoma)*
**Practice Areas:** Focus on the representation of health care providers with transactional, compliance, reimbursement, legislative and regulatory compliance issues. Member Health Care Practice Group.
**Professional Memberships:** American Bar Association, Oklahoma Bar Association, American Health Lawyers Association.
**Career:** Crowe & Dunlevy, P.C., Advisory Director (2008 to present); Private Practice (2006); Oklahoma State Medical Association, General Counsel (2003-06); University of Oklahoma, Director of Compliance and Privacy Official (2001); Crowe & Dunlevy, P.C., Associate(1994-2001).
**Personal:** University of Texas School of Law (JD 1994), University of Oklahoma (BS 1991), Oklahoma Board of Nursing, Church of the Servant Administrative Council, Prevent Blindness Oklahoma Board Member.

### MCCARTHY, Bill D.
Hall, Estill, Hardwick, Gable, Golden & Nelson, PC, Oklahoma City
405 553 2302
BMcCarthy@HallEstill.com
*Featured in Intellectual Property (Oklahoma)*
**Practice Areas:** Intellectual property and information technology; intellectual property litigation; patents and patent litigation.

**Professional Memberships:** American & Oklahoma Bar Associations; National Society of Professional Engineers; Oklahoma Society of Professional Engineers.
**Career:** Oklahoma (1972).
**Personal:** BS Chemical Engineering, University of Oklahoma, 1957; MS Chemical Engineering, University of Oklahoma; JD, Oklahoma City University School of Law, 1972.

### MCCARTHY, Randall K.
Hall, Estill, Hardwick, Gable, Golden & Nelson, PC, Oklahoma City
405 553 2300
RMcCarthy@HallEstill.com
*Featured in Intellectual Property (Oklahoma)*
**Practice Areas:** Intellectual property and information technology; intellectual property litigation; patents and patent litigation.
**Professional Memberships:** American & Oklahoma Bar Associations; American Intellectual Property Association.
**Career:** Oklahoma (1995); US District Court for the Western District of Oklahoma; US Court of Appeals for the Federal Circuit; US Patent & Trademark Office.
**Publications:** Co-Author, Intellectual Property Litigation: Are Oklahoma Courts Missing the Mark(man)? 69 Okl. B.J. 792 (1998).
**Personal:** BSEE, University of Oklahoma, 1987; JD, summa cum laude, Oklahoma City University School of Law, 1995.

### MCCONNELL-CORBYN, Laura
Hartzog Conger Cason & Neville, LLP, Oklahoma City
405 235 7000
lmcconnell@hartzoglaw.com
*Featured in Litigation (Oklahoma)*
**Practice Areas:** Family law, employment law, general and commercial litigation.
**Professional Memberships:** ABA; Oklahoma Bar Association, Oklahoma County Bar Association (Past-President), ABA Fellow, OBA Fellow, American Academy of Matrimonial Lawyers, 2010 OBA Mona Salyer Lambird Spotlight Award, 2010 OBA Oklahoma Justice Award, Board of Directors, Legal Aid Services of Oklahoma; Oklahoma City Fundraising Committee of Legal Aid Services of Oklahoma.
**Career:** Listed in Best Lawyers in America (Family Law), Oklahoma Super Lawyers.
**Publications:** Redman v. Cauthen, 2009 OK CIV APP 46, 211 P.3d 233, deSilva v. Pitts, 481 F. 3d 1279 (10th Cir. 2007,) Kerby v. Kerby, 2007 OK 36, 164 P.3d 1053, Kerby v. Kerby, 2007 OK 35, 164 P.3d 1049, Smith v. Smith, 2003 OK CIV APP 28, 67 P.3d 351, Myers v. Lashley, 2002 OK 4, 44 P.3d 553, Dorn v. Heritage Trust Co., 2001 OK CIV APP 64, 24 P.3d 886, In the Matter of the Adoption of CDM, 2001 OK 103, 39 P.3d 802, Smith v. Spelegene, 1999 OK CIV APP 95, 990 P. 2d 312, Robinson v. City of Edmond, 160 F. 3d 1275 (10th Cir. 1998), Robinson v. City of Edmond, 68 F. 3d 1226 (10th Cir. 1995), Horton v. State of Oklahoma, 1996 OK 137, 915 P. 2d 352, Crysco Oilfield Services, Inc. v. Hutchinson-Hayes International, 913 F. 2d 850 (10th Cir. 1990).

**Personal:** Two children, ages 26 and 24.

## MCCULLOUGH, David
Doerner, Saunders, Daniel & Anderson, LLP, Oklahoma City
918 319 3501
dmccullough@dsda.com
*Featured in Native American Law (Oklahoma)*

**Practice Areas:** Mr McCullough practices Native American Law providing advice and representation to Native American tribes as well as to individuals and entities desiring to do business with tribes or within tribal reservations. He advises and litigates on behalf of tribes on issues ranging from tribal sovereignty to business development, including gaming development and management.

**Professional Memberships:** American Bar Association, Oklahoma Bar Association.

**Career:** University of Oklahoma (BA, 1977); University of Oklahoma (JD, 1984).

## MCMILLIN, James C.
McAfee & Taft, Oklahoma City
405 552 2280
james.mcmillin@mcafeetaft.com
*Featured in Native American Law (Oklahoma)*

**Practice Areas:** Practice concentrates in representing Indian tribes in litigation with the federal government and complex commercial litigation.

**Professional Memberships:** Association of the Bar, City of New York; District of Columbia Bar Association; Oklahoma Bar Association; Master Emeritus, Holloway American Inn of Court.

**Career:** New York Bar (1977); Oklahoma Bar (1997); Has tried cases in 17 states and appeared before four US Courts of Appeal as well as several international arbitrations.

**Personal:** Root-Tilden Scholar, New York University School of Law.

## MEYERS, D Kent
Crowe & Dunlevy, a Professional Corporation, Oklahoma City
405 235 7729
kent.meyers@crowedunlevy.com
*Featured in Litigation (Oklahoma)*

**Practice Areas:** Mr Meyers practices in the areas of commercial litigation and antitrust law.

**Professional Memberships:** Admitted to practice in Oklahoma (1964). Fellow of the American College of Trial Lawyers and selected for Order of Barristers (1982).

**Career:** Active practice of Law. Adjunct Professor of Law at the University of Oklahoma College of Law, the University of Tulsa Law School and the Oklahoma City University Law School.

**Personal:** Co-founder of Oklahoma Lawyers for Children, non-profit group providing volunteer lawyers representing deprived children in Juvenile Court. University of Oklahoma College of Law (JD, 1964); Harvard Law School (LLM 1976).

## MILLIKIN, Margaret
Crowe & Dunlevy, PC, Tulsa
918 592 9820
margaret.millikin@crowedunlevy.com
*Featured in Intellectual Property (Oklahoma)*

**Practice Areas:** Intellectual property procurement, transactions and litigation; M&A; antitrust; export control.

**Professional Memberships:** ABA, OBA, TCBA, Society of Women Engineers.

**Career:** Director and Co-Chair of the Intellectual Property and Technology Group. Registered patent attorney practicing in all phases of intellectual property law. Helps people create, protect and exploit intellectual assets to maximize the value of their IP spend in everyday operations and in specialized transactions. Creates strategies for managing IP as business assets and has managed the global portfolios for international businesses. In-house with Owens Corning, Honeywell and Hercules and managed the US IP Office for Basell N.V.

## MUCHMORE, Clyde A
Crowe & Dunlevy, a Professional Corporation, Oklahoma City
405 235 7734
clyde.muchmore@crowedunlevy.com
*Featured in Litigation (Oklahoma)*

**Practice Areas:** Mr Muchmore specializes in civil litigation and appellate practice, communications and media law litigation, and constitutional law.

**Professional Memberships:** Admitted to practice in Oklahoma (1967); American Academy of Appellate Lawyers; American College of Trial Lawyers; Oklahoma and American Bar Associations.

**Career:** Joined Crowe & Dunlevy in 1967. Firm President, 1989-91.

**Publications:** Oklahoma Appellate Practice (West) and Oklahoma Civil Procedure Forms-Practice (Lexis).

**Personal:** University of Oklahoma College of Law (JD, Honors, 1967); Rice University (BA, 1964). Lecturer: University of Oklahoma College of Law in Appellate Practice, Constitutional Law and Federal Practice. Adjunct Professor: Oklahoma City University College of Law.

## NEAL, Kathy R
McAfee & Taft, Tulsa
918 574 3020
kathy.neal@mcafeetaft.com
*Featured in Labor & Employment (Oklahoma)*

**Practice Areas:** Represents management in all phases of employment law and labor relations including counseling on compliance with state and federal employment laws, litigation, and union negotiations. Experience includes representation of federal contractors with respect to OFCCP proceedings, defense of Department of Labor wage and hour claims and defense of Fair Housing claims.

**Professional Memberships:** Tulsa County Bar Association and Oklahoma Bar Association.

**Career:** Oklahoma Bar (1982); Alberta Bar (2001); All federal courts in Oklahoma; US Court of Appeals, Tenth Circuit; US Supreme Court.

**Personal:** BA in Letters, University of Oklahoma, 1979; JD, University of Tulsa College of Law, 1982.

## NELON, Robert D
Hall, Estill, Hardwick, Gable, Golden & Nelson, PC, Oklahoma City
405 553 2805
bnelon@hallestill.com
*Featured in Litigation (Oklahoma)*

**Practice Areas:** Media law; first amendment law; commercial litigation; intellectual property litigation.

**Professional Memberships:** American Bar Association, Forum on Communications Law; American Judicature Society; Oklahoma Bar Association, Communications Committee; Oklahoma County Bar Association, Treasurer; Oklahoma County Bar Foundation, Treasurer; Media Law Resource Center, President, Defense Counsel Section.

**Career:** Oklahoma (1971); US Supreme Court; US Court of Appeals for the Second, Eighth and Tenth Circuits; US District Court of the Northern, Eastern, Western Districts of Oklahoma; US Court of Appeals for the Armed Services.

**Personal:** BA, Political Science, Northwestern University, 1968; JD, University of Oklahoma College of Law, 1971.

## NEVILLE, Drew
Hartzog Conger Cason & Neville, LLP, Oklahoma City
405 225 7000
dneville@hartzoglaw.com
*Featured in Litigation (Oklahoma)*

**Practice Areas:** Complex litigation in both civil and criminal cases in state and federal court.

**Professional Memberships:** US Supreme Court; US Court of Appeals for the Fifth, Seventh, Tenth and Eleventh Circuits; US District Court for the Western, Northern and Eastern Districts of Oklahoma, Southern District of New York; Northern and Southern Districts of Texas; Southern District of Florida, District of Colorado; and the Oklahoma Supreme Court. American College of Trial Lawyers. Past President, Federal Bar Association, Oklahoma City. ABA; OBA; OCBA.

**Career:** Director/Shareholder since 2000; Partner, Linn & Neville, 1976-2000.

**Publications:** Written extensively on complex litigation.

## PALIOTTA, Armand
Hartzog Conger Cason & Neville, LLP, Oklahoma City
405 235 7000
apaliotta@hartzoglaw.com
*Featured in Corporate/Commercial (Oklahoma)*

**Practice Areas:** Corporate, securities, tax planning and tax controversies and general business transactions, including mergers and acquisitions, private securities offerings, contract negotiations, and structuring, capitalizing and reorganizing entities.

**Professional Memberships:** Oklahoma County and Oklahoma Bar Associations.

**Career:** Recognized in Best Lawyers in America in corporate law, mergers and acquisitions, securities law, and corporate governance and compliance law. Appointed by Governor Brad Henry as a Commissioner on the Oklahoma Securities Commission (Chairperson 2009-10). Adjunct Professor of Law in mergers and acquisitions, corporations, and business planning at Oklahoma City University and Adjunct Professor of Law in business entities at the University of Oklahoma.

**Personal:** BBA with distinction, University of Oklahoma, 1989; JD, University of Oklahoma College of Law, 1992 (with highest honors).

## PALMER, Drew T.
Crowe & Dunlevy, a Professional Corporation, Oklahoma City
405 234 3234
drew.palmer@crowedunlevy.com
*Featured in Intellectual Property (Oklahoma)*

**Practice Areas:** Trademark litigation, patent litigation, copyright litigation, trade secret litigation, patent prosecution, trademark prosecution, copyright prosecution, information technology law, domain name law.

**Professional Memberships:** American Bar Association, Federal Bar Association, Oklahoma Bar Association.

**Career:** Mr Palmer's practice focuses on intellectual property litigation and sofware licensing and compliance. Prior to his legal career, Mr Palmer ran the maintenance renewal department for an enteprise software company and was a consultant and programmer specializing in implementation of complex enterprise software applications.

## PAUL, Chris A
McAfee & Taft, Tulsa
918 574 3037
chris.paul@mcafeetaft.com
*Featured in Energy & Natural Resources (Oklahoma)*

**Practice Areas:** Chris concentrates his practice on complex transactional and regulatory matters, including pre-transaction due diligence, risk assessment and evaluation, contracts, and post-transaction implementation, with a focus on clients in the energy, transportation, and manufacturing industries. Regulatory work primarily in environmental, safety, risk communications, security, compliance, emergency response, and transportation.

**Career:** Admitted in Oklahoma, Arkansas, Kansas, and Pennsylvania, and various district courts and the US Supreme Court. Served as US Army JAGC and Special Assistant United States Attorney, 1984-87.

**Personal:** JD, College of William and Mary, 1983; BA, Dickinson College, 1980. National speaker on regulatory issues affecting the midstream industry.

## PEPPER, David E
Hartzog Conger Cason & Neville, LLP, Oklahoma City
405 235 7000
dpepper@hartzoglaw.com
*Featured in Energy & Natural Resources (Oklahoma)*

**Practice Areas:** Energy and natural resources; oil and gas regulatory and litigation.

**Professional Memberships:** Oklahoma Bar Association, American Bar Asociation; Okla Mineral Lawyers Association; US District Court Northern, Eastern and Western Districts.

**Career:** Director/shareholder since 2000; Partner Linn & Neville 1984-2000.
**Publications:** Various continuing legal education article; numerous decisions from Okla Supreme Court and Okla Court of Appeals.
**Personal:** Married Leslie; 3 children.

### PETERSON, Andrew
McAfee & Taft, Oklahoma City
405 552 2333
andy.peterson@mcafeetaft.com
*Featured in Intellectual Property (Oklahoma)*
**Practice Areas:** Andy is a registered patent attorney whose practice focuses on all aspects of intellectual property law. He represents clients in a wide range of licensing and registration issues and has assisted clients in complex litigation matters, including intellectual property rights involving trademark, copyright, trade secret and patent disputes.
**Professional Memberships:** Oklahoma Bar Association.
**Career:** Oklahoma Bar, US Patent and Trademark Office, United States District Court for the Western District of Oklahoma, US Court of Appeals for the Federal Circuit, US Supreme Court.
**Personal:** BA in Spanish and BS in Biochemistry, University of Oklahoma; JD, University of Oklahoma.

### PLUMB, Charles S
McAfee & Taft, Tulsa
918 574 3003
charlie.plumb@mcafeetaft.com
*Featured in Labor & Employment (Oklahoma)*
**Practice Areas:** Represents management in all phases of employment law and labor relations including counseling on compliance with state and federal employment laws, litigation, and union negotiations.
**Professional Memberships:** Tulsa County Bar Association, Oklahoma Bar Association (Labor Council), American Bar Association (Labor and Employment Law Section), Employers Counsel Network.
**Career:** Oklahoma Bar (1982); All federal courts in Oklahoma; US Court of Appeals for the Tenth Circuit; Frequent speaker and author on workplace issues; Co-editor of the Oklahoma Employment Law Letter.
**Personal:** BBA, Southern Methodist University, 1979; JD, The Ohio State University, 1982.

### POSEY, Tim
Hall, Estill, Hardwick, Gable, Golden & Nelson, PC, Tulsa
918 594 0669
tposey@hallestill.com
*Featured in Native American Law (Oklahoma)*
**Practice Areas:** Administrative law; corporate/commercial; Indian law; litigation.
**Professional Memberships:** Tulsa County, Oklahoma, Muscogee (Creek) and Cherokee Bar Associations.
**Career:** Oklahoma (1989); United States Supreme Court; US Court of Appeals for the Tenth Circuit; US District Court of the Northern,

Eastern and Western Districts of Oklahoma; Muscogee (Creek) Nation and Cherokee Nation.
**Personal:** BA, University of Oklahoma, 1986; JD, University of Oklahoma, 1989.

### PUCKETT, Tony G
McAfee & Taft, Oklahoma City
405 552 2251
tony.puckett@mcafeetaft.com
*Featured in Labor & Employment (Oklahoma)*
**Practice Areas:** Represents management in all phases of employment-related matters, including litigation before federal and state courts, regulatory and administrative agencies, and union avoidance issues and labor negotiations and arbitrations.
**Professional Memberships:** Oklahoma County Bar Association; Oklahoma Bar Association (Past Chair, Labor & Employment Section); American Bar Association; Oklahoma Association of Municipal Attorneys; Society for Human Resources Management; Oklahoma Bar Foundation.
**Career:** Oklahoma Bar (1988); all federal courts in Oklahoma; US Courts of Appeals, Eighth and Tenth Circuits; US Supreme Court. Author and frequent speaker on employment law and arbitration.
**Personal:** BA, Colorado College, 1983; JD, University of Oklahoma, 1988.

### RAHHAL, Anthony
McAfee & Taft, Oklahoma City
405 552 2306
anthony.rahhal@mcafeetaft.com
*Featured in Intellectual Property (Oklahoma)*
**Practice Areas:** Tony is a registered patent attorney whose practice, which is global in scope, encompasses all areas of intellectual property law, including patent, trademark, copyright, trade secret and Internet law. He also serves as IP counsel for numerous companies.
**Professional Memberships:** Oklahoma County Bar Association, Oklahoma Bar Association (Past President and Director, IP Section), American Bar Association, International Trademark Association.
**Career:** Engineer for Rockwell International, 1984-88; Registered patent attorney since 1993. Adjunct professor of patent law, University of Oklahoma.
**Personal:** BS (Mechanical Engineering), Oklahoma State University; JD, with highest honors, University of Oklahoma.

### RIEGER, Karen
Crowe & Dunlevy, a Professional Corporation, Oklahoma City
405 235 7788
karen.rieger@crowedunlevy.com
*Featured in Corporate/Commercial (Oklahoma)*
**Practice Areas:** Transactional and regulatory practice for healthcare providers.
**Professional Memberships:** Director and past president — Oklahoma Health Lawyers Association; Past chair and current secretary — OBA Health Law Section; Associate Bar Examiner, OBA.

**Career:** Best Lawyers: Oklahoma City Lawyer of the Year — Health Care (2012); Corporate Compliance (2013); healthcare (since 1991), corporate compliance, corporate governance, corporate law, non-profit/charities law;Super Lawyers (2006-present).
**Publications:** "Healthcare Entity Bylaws and Related Documents: Navigating the Medical Staff/Healthcare Entity Relationship" (with Eric S. Fisher) AHLA Guidebook (2011).
**Personal:** Board member: Oklahoma Cerebral Palsy Commission; Catholic Foundation of Oklahoma, Canterbury Choral Society.

### RIGGS, Richard A
McAfee & Taft, Oklahoma City
405 552 2265
richard.riggs@mcafeetaft.com
*Featured in Real Estate (Oklahoma)*
**Practice Areas:** Real estate, renewable energy and other commercial transactions, including projects utilizing state and local governmental incentives. Representation of borrowers in credit transactions.
**Professional Memberships:** American, Oklahoma and Oklahoma County Bar Associations; American College of Real Estate Lawyers; Urban Land Institute; Commercial Real Estate Council.
**Career:** Oklahoma Bar (1974). Author and presenter at continuing legal education seminars on real estate acquisition and finance, commercial real estate leasing, wind energy and secured transactions. Former adjunct professor, University of Oklahoma College of Law.
**Personal:** BA, University of Oklahoma, 1971; JD, University of Michigan, 1974. Former President, Oklahoma Bar Foundation.

### ROBERTSON, John D
Hartzog Conger Cason & Neville, LLP, Oklahoma City
405 235 7000
jrobertson@hartzoglaw.com
*Featured in Corporate/Commercial (Oklahoma)*
**Practice Areas:** Business transactions, corporate law, securities law and employment law.
**Professional Memberships:** Member of American Bar Association and Oklahoma Bar Association.
**Career:** Managing Partner of Firm since 2002. Recognized in Best Lawyers in America in the areas of: Mergers & Acquisitions Law, Securities Law and Corporate Law.
**Personal:** Oklahoma State University (BS, Business Administration, 1983;) University of Oklahoma, College of Law (JD, 1986); Member of the Board of Education of Deer Creek Schools since 2007.

### ROBISON, Reid
McAfee & Taft, Oklahoma City
405 552 2260
reid.robison@mcafeetaft.com
*Featured in Litigation (Oklahoma)*
**Practice Areas:** Business-related litigation, including antitrust, securities, products liability, tax, white-collar criminal, and multi-district and

other complex litigation in courts throughout the US.
**Professional Memberships:** Oklahoma County Bar Association (Past President); Oklahoma and American Bar Associations; American Inn of Court (Past President); Oklahoma Bar Foundation; International Academy of Trial Lawyers (State Chair).
**Career:** Oklahoma Bar (1968); Colorado Bar (1971); US Fifth, Eighth, Tenth, and Eleventh Circuit Courts of Appeals; US Tax Court; US Claims Court; US Supreme Court. Judge Advocate General Corps, USAF, (1968-72).
**Personal:** BA, University of Oklahoma, 1966; JD, University of Oklahoma College of Law, 1968.

### ROGERS, Patricia A.
McAfee & Taft, Oklahoma City
405 552 2233
pat.rogers@mcafeetaft.com
*Featured in Corporate/Commercial (Oklahoma)*
**Practice Areas:** Focused on healthcare regulatory matters affecting hospitals, physicians, and other healthcare facilities and professionals. Advise clients on compliance with Stark and federal anti-kickback statute, joint ventures, licensure, Medicare enrollment and certification, accreditation, state CON requirements, HIPAA, EMTALA, physician contracting, and medical staff matters.
**Professional Memberships:** Oklahoma Bar Association; American Health Lawyers Association; Oklahoma Health Lawyers Association.
**Career:** Oklahoma Bar (1999); Past President, Oklahoma Bar Association Health Law Section.
**Personal:** BA, University of Pittsburgh, 1983; MHS, The Johns Hopkins University School of Hygiene and Public Health, 1985; USAF Medical Service Corps Officer, 1985-89; JD, Oklahoma City University, 1999.

### ROSSER IV, Malcolm E
Crowe & Dunlevy, PC, Tulsa
918 592 9838
mac.rosser@crowedunlevy.com
*Featured in Real Estate (Oklahoma)*
**Practice Areas:** Commercial real estate transactions including commercial real estate acquisitions, finance and lending, zoning and land use, leasing, eminent domain and loan workouts.
**Professional Memberships:** Oklahoma Bar Association (Chair, Real Property Law Section, 1994-95); Tulsa Title and Probate Lawyers. Urban Land Institute. Leadership Oklahoma.
**Career:** Joined Crowe & Dunlevy 1992; Co-chair of Real Estate Section.
**Publications:** 'Adverse Possession: An Idea Whose Time Has Come and Gone?', Oklahoma Bar Journal (2000). Oklahoma Bar Association Golden Quill Award for outstanding scholarly article.
**Personal:** University of Oklahoma College of Law (JD, 1981); Oklahoma State University (BS Architectural Engineering, 1977).

**ROUSE, Nicholas D**
Dunlap Codding, Oklahoma City
405 607 8600
nrouse@dunlapcodding.com
*Featured in Intellectual Property (Oklahoma)*
**Practice Areas:** Managing Director, Dunlap Codding. Practice includes patent counseling, preparation, prosecution, portfolio management, validity and infringement opinions, evaluations of new designs, and licensing strategy. Experience with multiple technologies in the mechanical and electro-mechanical arts. Practice includes all aspects of trademark planning, management, prosecution, licensing and enforcement.
**Professional Memberships:** Past President of the Intellectual Property Law Section of the Oklahoma Bar Association. American Intellectual Property Law Association. Admitted to practice before the USPTO.
**Career:** Admitted to practice in 1990. Shareholder at Dunlap Codding since 2000.
**Personal:** BS in Petroleum Engineering, University of Oklahoma, 1987; JD, University of Oklahoma, 1990.

**SARGENT JR, John E**
McAfee & Taft, Oklahoma City
405 552 2252
john.sargent@mcafeetaft.com
*Featured in Real Estate (Oklahoma)*
**Practice Areas:** Practice concentrated in commercial and real estate law. Represents developers, users, major tenants and investors in all phases of transactions involving the financing, construction, sales, purchase, leasing and zoning of commercial real estate, as well as the negotiation of construction contracts and architectural contracts on behalf of owners.
**Professional Memberships:** Oklahoma County Bar Association, Oklahoma Bar Association.
**Career:** Oklahoma Bar (1971). Prior to law school, served as a lieutenant in the US Navy.
**Personal:** BS, Villanova University, 1965; JD, University of Oklahoma, 1971.

**SHARROCK, James W**
McAfee & Taft, Oklahoma City
405 552 2272
jim.sharrock@mcafeetaft.com
*Featured in Real Estate (Oklahoma)*
**Practice Areas:** Diverse business practice includes acquisition, development, management and sale of real property and related financing transactions; contracting to provide architectural and engineering services; mergers and acquisitions; commercial financing transactions; organization and restructuring of business entities; and joint ventures.
**Professional Memberships:** Oklahoma County and Oklahoma Bar Associations; State Bar of Texas; Commercial Real Estate Council.
**Career:** Oklahoma (1973); Texas (1973); US Courts of Appeals for the Fifth and Eleventh Circuits; US District Court for the Northern District of Texas.

**Personal:** BA, University of Oklahoma, 1970; JD, University of Oklahoma, 1973; Artillery Officer, US Army Reserves, 1970-78.

**SMITH, Joshua D.**
McAfee & Taft, Oklahoma City
405 552 2301
josh.smith@mcafeetaft.com
*Featured in Corporate/Commercial (Oklahoma)*
**Practice Areas:** Mergers and acquisitions, other commercial transactions, and real estate. Has represented clients in mergers and stock and asset acquisitions and sales of all sizes and various other transactions, including private equity and venture capital investments and financings, real estate transactions, securities offerings, and commercial lending transactions.
**Professional Memberships:** Oklahoma Bar Association.
**Career:** Oklahoma Bar Association (2005), US District Court for the Western District of Oklahoma (2005).
**Personal:** BA, University of Oklahoma, 2002, JD, with highest honors, University of Oklahoma, 2005; Order of the Coif; Oklahoma Law Review.

**SMITH, Michael E**
Hall, Estill, Hardwick, Gable, Golden & Nelson, PC, Oklahoma City
405 553 2821
mesmith@hallestill.com
*Featured in Energy & Natural Resources (Oklahoma)*
**Practice Areas:** Corporate/commercial litigation; class action litigation; energy and natural resources; environmental; oil and gas.
**Professional Memberships:** American Bar Association; American Bar Foundation; Oklahoma County Bar Association; Association of Trial Lawyers of America; American Inns of Court - Master; Oklahoma Bar Association, Member, Professional Responsibility Commission.
**Career:** Oklahoma (1975); Hawaii (1976); United States Supreme Court; US Court of Appeals for the Tenth Circuit; US District Court of the Northern, Eastern and Western Districts of Oklahoma; District of Hawaii; US Court of Military Appeals.
**Personal:** BS, US Military Academy, West Point, 1969; JD, University of Oklahoma, 1975.

**SMITH, Michael H**
Hall, Estill, Hardwick, Gable, Golden & Nelson, PC, Oklahoma City
405 553 2803
mhsmith@hallestill.com
*Featured in Intellectual Property (Oklahoma)*
**Practice Areas:** Intellectual property and information technology; intellectual property litigation; licensing; patents and patent litigation; trade secrets; trademarks; copyrights.
**Professional Memberships:** Oklahoma Bar Association; American Intellectual Property Association; Licensing Executives Society.
**Career:** Oklahoma (2001); US District Court for the Western District of Oklahoma; US Patent & Trademark Office.
**Personal:** BS, Biology, Oklahoma Baptist University, 1991; JD, University of Oklahoma College of Law, 2001.

**SNAPP, Randall J**
Crowe & Dunlevy, PC, Tulsa
918 592 9855
randall.snapp@crowedunlevy.com
*Featured in Labor & Employment (Oklahoma)*
**Practice Areas:** Mr Snapp practices labor and employment law, workers' compensation, and commercial litigation. Mr Snapp is the Co-Chair of Crowe & Dunlevy's Labor & Employment practice group.
**Professional Memberships:** American Bar Association; Oklahoma Bar Association Employment Law Section and Workers' Compensation Section. Admitted to practice in Oklahoma, the Federal District Courts for the Northern, Eastern, and Western Districts in Oklahoma, the United States Court of Appeals, Tenth Circuit, and the United States Supreme Court.
**Career:** Joined Crowe & Dunlevy in 1993. Adjunct Instructor: Human Resources Law, Tulsa Community College.
**Personal:** University of Kansas (JD 1985, MBA, 1885, BA 1981).

**SOROCCO, Douglas J**
Dunlap Codding, Oklahoma City
405 607 8600
dsorocco@dunlapcodding.com
*Featured in Intellectual Property (Oklahoma)*
**Practice Areas:** Counseling and transactional matters involving all aspects of intellectual property. Scientific background of biotechnology, chemistry and life sciences Significant experience in providing strategic and tactical intellectual property counsel to individual clients, universities, pharmaceutical and research institutions as well as manufacturing entities, and early stage biotechnology companies. Developed a proprietary process for the identification of patenting opportunities used in facilitated sessions with technical and business personnel of major client company, currently tracking over 100 companies and approximately 1,000 intellectual property documents.
**Professional Memberships:** Registered to practice before the USPTO. Member: State Bar of Oklahoma. Admitted to practice in Oklahoma and Illinois and before the US District Court for the Western District of Oklahoma and the US Court of Appeals for the Federal Circuit.
**Career:** Adjunct faculty member at the Oklahoma City University School of Law and in the Physiology Department at Oklahoma University Health Sciences Center. Shareholder at Dunlap Codding since 2000.
**Publications:** Editor and an author of Dunlap Codding's award winning and innovative intellectual property legal blog and resource center, PHOSITA(R).
**Personal:** University of Dayton School of Law, JD, 1996; Northwestern University School of Law, Visiting Student 1995-96; Butler University, BS, 1993, Chemistry. Named as an inaugural Member of the Butler University 50 Under 50 in 2004. Recipient of 2008 Leadership in Law Award, Oklahoma Bar. Listed in The Journal Record's 2008 Achievers Under 40. Chairman of the Board

of Directors of the Spina Bifida Association of America (2004-07). Served as Oklahoma Chairman of the Licensing Executives Society.

**STINSON, C David**
McAfee & Taft, Oklahoma City
405 552 2266
david.stinson@mcafeetaft.com
*Featured in Energy & Natural Resources (Oklahoma)*
**Practice Areas:** Representation of clients engaged in oil and gas exploration, production, gathering, transportation and marketing. Practice encompasses commercial and corporate transactions and counseling on industry matters, including mergers, acquisitions and dispositions; financing arrangements; partnerships and joint ventures; pipeline and gathering agreements; sale and purchase contracts; and strategic counseling.
**Professional Memberships:** Oklahoma Bar Association and American Bar Association.
**Career:** Oklahoma Bar (1976); US District Courts for the Western and Northern Districts of Oklahoma; US Court of Appeals for the Tenth Circuit; US Supreme Court.
**Personal:** BA, Oklahoma State University, 1969; JD, University of Oklahoma, 1976.

**STONG, Roger A**
Crowe & Dunlevy, a Professional Corporation, Oklahoma City
405 239 6614
roger.stong@crowedunlevy.com
*Featured in Corporate/Commercial (Oklahoma)*
**Practice Areas:** Corporate and securities, mergers and acquisitions and bankruptcy.
**Professional Memberships:** American Bar Association. Oklahoma Bar Association (Chairman, Business and Corporate Law Section, 2002-03). Oklahoma County Bar Association. Oklahoma State Chamber of Commerce (director since 2006).
**Career:** Admitted to bar in 1986. Joined Crowe & Dunlevy in 1986 (Shareholder in 1993). Firm president (2008-12). Chairman of Business Department and Corporate and Securities Section.
**Publications:** Author of articles on arbitration and healthcare law.
**Personal:** Born 1962. University of Virginia (BA 1983). Indiana University (JD 1985). University of Oklahoma (MBA 1986).

**STRINGER, N Martin**
McAfee & Taft, Oklahoma City
405 552 2284
martin.stringer@mcafeetaft.com
*Featured in Corporate/Commercial (Oklahoma)*
**Practice Areas:** Experienced negotiator in the fields of business, financial institutions and governmental relations and strategic planner in complex business litigation. Legal practice concentrated in business law, with emphasis on negotiating and structuring business combinations, including acquisitions, mergers and other private and public securities transactions, including professional sports.
**Professional Memberships:** Oklahoma Bar Association; American Bar Association.

**Career:** Oklahoma Bar (1964); All federal courts in Oklahoma; US Court of Appeals for the Tenth Circuit; US Supreme Court. Frequent lecturer and past recipient of Oklahoma Bar Association's "Outstanding Service Award."

**Personal:** BS, University of Oklahoma; LLB, University of Oklahoma.

### SULLIVAN, David
Crowe & Dunlevy, a Professional Corporation, Oklahoma City
405 234 3236
david.sullivan@crowedunlevy.com
*Featured in Intellectual Property (Oklahoma)*

**Practice Areas:** David Sullivan is a registered patent attorney and a Co-Chair of the firm's Intellectual Property and Technology Group. Mr Sullivan's practice is primarily directed at obtaining and enforcing patent and trademark rights for his clients, who range from Fortune 500 companies to small start-ups with emerging technology. Mr Sullivan also manages several large trademark portfolios and frequently advises clients on software licensing matters.

**Publications:** Author of chapter entitled 'Minimizing Risk of Trademark Registration Fraud', published in 2009 Recent Trends in Trademark Protection in the Inside the Minds series published by Aspatore (a Thomson/Reuters publication).

### TERNES, Mary Ellen
McAfee & Taft, Oklahoma City
405 552 2303
maryellen.ternes@mcafeetaft.com
*Featured in Energy & Natural Resources (Oklahoma)*

**Practice Areas:** Environmental practice in compliance and mitigation strategies, enforcement/litigation defense, due diligence, transactions. Special expertise in air, hazardous waste, and citizen suits.

**Professional Memberships:** Oklahoma, South Carolina, Arkansas, D.C., and American Bar Associations; AIChE; ACOEL.

**Career:** Chemical engineer USEPA (emergency response/site remediation; hazardous waste incineration), industry (permitting and compliance, commercial hazardous waste incineration); law clerk, USEPA Office of General Counsel Air and Radiation Division.

**Publications:** Author, "EPA's Mandatory Greenhouse Gas Reporting Rule," LexiNexis; Coauthor, "New Source Review," Chapter 6, Clean Air Act Handbook.

**Personal:** BE, (Chemical Engineering), Vanderbilt University 1980; JD, high honors, University of Arkansas Little Rock, 1995.

### TODD, Jeff L
McAfee & Taft, Oklahoma City
405 552 2269
jeff.todd@mcafeetaft.com
*Featured in Litigation (Oklahoma)*

**Practice Areas:** Business, real estate, eminent domain, oil and gas, healthcare, intellectual property and tax litigation, as well as of legal matters affecting the agricultural and equine industries, including crop insurance litigation, landowner rights, wind energy and syndications.

**Professional Memberships:** Oklahoma County and Oklahoma Bar Associations, American Agricultural Law Association.

**Career:** Oklahoma Bar (1997); US District Courts for the Western and Northern Districts of Oklahoma, Northern and Southern Districts of Texas, and District of Colorado; US Court of Appeals for the Tenth Circuit; US Federal Court Circuit; US Tax Court.

**Personal:** BA, Northwestern Oklahoma State University; JD, University of Oklahoma.

### TOLBERT, Miles
Crowe & Dunlevy, a Professional Corporation, Oklahoma City
405 235 7700
Miles.Tolbert@crowedunlevy.com
*Featured in Energy & Natural Resources (Oklahoma)*

**Practice Areas:** Environmental law, water law, administrative law, regulated utilities.

**Professional Memberships:** Federal Bar Association (Board Member, Energy, Environment and Natural Resources Section); Oklahoma Bar Association (Past-Chair, Environmental Law Section); Oklahoma County Bar Association; Oklahoma City Mineral Lawyers Society.

**Career:** Environmental Practice Group Chair at Crowe & Dunlevy 2008-present; Secretary of the Environment 2003-08; Advisory Director, Crowe & Dunlevy, 2001-03; Chief of the Environmental Protection Unit, Office of the Attorney General, 1996-2001; Trial Attorney, US Department of Justice 1993-96.

**Personal:** Harvard Law School 1991; Stanford University 1987.

### TUCKER, John H
Rhodes, Hieronymus, Jones, Tucker & Gable PLLC, Tulsa
918 582 1173
jtucker@rhodesokla.com
*Featured in Litigation (Oklahoma)*

**Practice Areas:** All facets of general civil and commercial litigation. Tucker focuses on disputes involving high damages exposure. Recent major matters include litigation over failed business acquisitions, products liability involving national class action elements, mass toxic tort defense, directors and officers liability; surplus and excess lines insurance disputes.

**Professional Memberships:** Fellow, Past Regent, Committee and State Chairman, American College of Trial Lawyers; Fellow, International Academy of Trial Lawyers. Member, Judicial Nominating Commission for the State of Oklahoma. Senior Adjunct Settlement Judge, Special Projects, US District Court, Northern District of Oklahoma.

**Career:** Tenth Circuit Advisory Committee, Oklahoma Delegate, 2000-04. Chairman, Civil Justice Reform Act Advisory Committee, N.D. Okla.

**Personal:** Enrolled member, Choctaw Nation of Oklahoma.

### TURNER, Elaine R
Hall, Estill, Hardwick, Gable, Golden & Nelson, PC, Oklahoma City
405 553 2804
eturner@hallestill.com
*Featured in Labor & Employment (Oklahoma)*

**Practice Areas:** Labor and employment litigation; class action defense; employee and management training.

**Professional Memberships:** American Bar Association; Oklahoma Bar Association; Oklahoma County Bar Association; Member, Oklahoma City University School of Law Executive Board.

**Career:** Oklahoma (1989); US Supreme Court; US Court of Appeals for the Tenth Circuit; Oklahoma Supreme Court; US District Court for the Northern, Eastern and Western Districts of Oklahoma.

**Personal:** BBB, Finance, with distinction, University of Oklahoma, 1985; JD, Oklahoma City University School of Law, 1989.

### TURNER, W Kirk
Newton, O'Connor, Turner & Ketchum, Tulsa
918 587 0101
kturner@newtonoconnor.com
*Featured in Labor & Employment (Oklahoma)*

**Practice Areas:** Represents management in all areas of employment law and labor relations, provides preventive counsel and employment practices training to managers, supervisors and employees in the areas of effective and legal communication, legal compliance and other workplace challenges.

**Professional Memberships:** Has served for 18 years as the Vice President and General Counsel, Tulsa Area Human Resources Association ("TAHRA"); Legislative Director, Oklahoma State Council for Human Resources Management; and General Counsel, Tulsa Better Business Bureau, Workforce Tulsa, and the Tulsa Automobile Dealers Association; Chair, Tulsa Metro Chamber of Commerce Labor and Human Resources Task Force; former Chair, Oklahoma Bar Association, Labor and Employment Law Section.

**Career:** Founder, Shareholder and Director of Newton, O'Connor, Turner & Ketchum, P.C.; admitted in 1989 to all state and federal courts in Oklahoma and Arkansas; admitted to United States Court of Appeals for the Tenth Circuit; United States Tax Court; United States Supreme Court.

**Personal:** JD, University of Arkansas School of Law (1989); recipient of TAHRA's President's and Excellence Awards, and the Oklahoma State Council for Human Resources Management Excellence Award for outstanding contributions to the human resources profession; AV Preeminent, Martindale-Hubbell; Best Lawyers in America; Super Lawyers; and Oklahoma's Top-Rated Lawyers.

### TYRRELL, Elizabeth D
McAfee & Taft, Oklahoma City
405 552 2217
elizabeth.tyrrell@mcafeetaft.com
*Featured in Corporate/Commercial (Oklahoma)*

**Practice Areas:** Regulatory and transactional matters affecting the healthcare industry; representing physicians, hospitals and other healthcare facilities, both for-profit and charitable, in organization, development of facilities, acquisitions and mergers, affiliations and joint ventures, secured and unsecured lending, business contracts, and advising regarding fraud and abuse, self-referrals, Stark law, reimbursement, and physician compensation arrangements.

**Professional Memberships:** Oklahoma Bar Association; American Bar Association; American Health Lawyers Association; Oklahoma Health Lawyers Association.

**Career:** Oklahoma Bar (1985); Leader of the firm's healthcare practice group; Officer, Oklahoma Bar Association Health Law Section.

**Personal:** BA, University of Virginia, 1981; JD, Southern Methodist University, 1985.

### VAN DYKE, Peter
McAfee & Taft, Oklahoma City
405 552 2211
peter.vandyke@mcafeetaft.com
*Featured in Labor & Employment (Oklahoma)*

**Practice Areas:** Represents management in all labor and employment related matters, including litigation, arbitrations, union avoidance issues, labor negotiations, federal and state administrative agency practice, supervisory and employee training, and regular consultation. Also a mediator, arbitrator and Oklahoma Department of Labor administrative law judge.

**Professional Memberships:** Oklahoma and American Bar Associations.

**Career:** New York Bar; Oklahoma Bar; US Supreme Court; US Courts of Appeals for the Tenth and Fifth Circuits; Federal district courts in Oklahoma and Texas.

**Personal:** BS, University of Rhode Island; JD with honors, Albany Law School of Union University; LLM in Labor Laws, The George Washington University.

### VAUGHN, Christina M
McAfee & Taft, Tulsa
918 574 3004
christina.vaughn@mcafeetaft.com
*Featured in Native American Law (Oklahoma)*

**Practice Areas:** Litigation practice representing clients in federal, state, and tribal courts, administrative actions and arbitration, with Native American law focus. Native American law practice includes litigation and transactional work, including gaming, self-governance and self-determination, trust acquisitions, trust litigation, trust land leasing and easements, and environmental.

**Professional Memberships:** Tulsa County, Oklahoma, and Federal Bar Associations; Hudson-Hall-Wheaton American Inn of Court.

**Career:** All state and federal courts in Oklahoma, US District Court-District of Columbia, US Court of Federal Claims, US Tenth Circuit Court of Appeals, Muscogee (Creek) Nation, Pawnee Nation of Oklahoma.

**Personal:** BA, Northeastern State University; JD, University of Tulsa.

## WHATLEY, Nathan L
McAfee & Taft, Oklahoma City
405 552 2365
nathan.whatley@mcafeetaft.com
*Featured in Labor & Employment (Oklahoma)*

**Practice Areas:** Practice focuses on labor and employment and the representation of management in all phases of litigation.

**Professional Memberships:** Oklahoma County Bar Association, Oklahoma Bar Association, American Bar Association, Oklahoma City Metro Employer Council, Sooner Human Resources Society, Society for Human Resources Management.

**Career:** Oklahoma Bar (1992); US District Courts for the Western, Northern and Eastern Districts of Oklahoma; US District Court for the Northern District of Texas; US Court of Appeals for the Tenth Circuit; US Supreme Court. Frequent author and speaker on workplace issues.

**Personal:** BA, University of Oklahoma, 1989; JD, University of Oklahoma, 1992.

## WOFFORD, Michael
Doerner, Saunders, Daniel & Anderson, LLP, Oklahoma City
405 319 3504
mwofford@dsda.com
*Featured in Energy & Natural Resources (Oklahoma)*

**Practice Areas:** Environmental law, including energy, natural resources, permitting, and protection; general business law and litigation.

**Professional Memberships:** Environmental Federation of Oklahoma, Vice-Chairman.

**Career:** Redlands Community College, Adjunct Professor of Political Science; ConocoPhillips Alaska Gas Pipeline Project, Environment Regulatory and Land Manager; Phillips Petroleum Company, Senior Attorney; Oklahoma State Department of Health, Attorney; Office of Governor David Boren, Assistant General Counsel.

**Publications:** People v. General Motors – NPDES Permit Shield – OBA Environmental Law Newsletter; Safe Drinking Water Act – Oklahoma Municipal League Conf. on Municipal Law; Sections on Environmental Insurance and on Health, Safety and Environment Compliance Audits, Oklahoma Environmental Law Handbook.

## WOOD, Elizabeth Scott
McAfee & Taft, Oklahoma City
405 552 2270
elizabeth.wood@mcafeetaft.com
*Featured in Labor & Employment (Oklahoma)*

**Practice Areas:** Represents employers in litigation and before regulatory and administrative agencies. Counsels companies regarding compliance with antidiscrimination, wage and hour, workplace safety, mandatory leave, employee benefits and all other federal and state employment laws and regulations. Also provides management training in all areas affecting the employer/employee relationship and assistance in connection with reductions in force and other business adjustments.

**Professional Memberships:** Oklahoma County, Oklahoma and American Bar Associations.

**Career:** All state and federal courts in Oklahoma; US Court of Appeals for the Tenth Circuit; US Supreme Court. American Arbitration Association's Employment and Commercial Rosters of Arbitrators and Mediators.

# CROWE & DUNLEVY, A PROFESSIONAL CORPORATION

www.crowedunlevy.com

**Firm President:** Kevin D Gordon
Number of attorneys: 130

**Firm Overview:**
Crowe & Dunlevy is one of the largest firms in Oklahoma with offices in the state's two largest cities: Oklahoma City and Tulsa. The firm, founded in 1902 represents clients in all aspects of the general practice of law, including complex business transactions, litigation in both state and federal courts, and all types of alternative dispute resolution.
**Legal Alliances:** The firm is the sole Oklahoma member of Lex Mundi, the Employment Law Alliance and State Law Resources.

## Main Areas of Practice:

**Aviation/Aircraft:**
The firm features a well known practice group for commercial aviation transactions, including aircraft title examination and aircraft transfers. The attorneys routinely assist major airlines as well as business clients and individuals with importing and exporting aircraft, US registration of foreign-owned aircraft and escrow and documentation needs.
**Contact:** J Robert Kalsu

**Corporate & Securities/M&A:**
The firm assists a broad and diverse group of business clients, both public and private, in matters ranging from complex transactional work to day-to-day business counseling. Representative transactions include public and private securities offerings, Sarbanes-Oxley and other securities compliance issues, asset and stock sales of large and small businesses and organizational consulting.
**Contact:** Roger A Stong

**Energy & Natural Resources:**
The firm has broad experience in energy law providing a wide range of legal services to major energy companies, oil and gas producers, purchasers, contractors and others.
**Contact:** John J Griffin, Jr

**Financial Institutions/Finance:**
Crowe & Dunlevy is well known in the representation of financial institutions of all types of services including loan negotiation and documentation, bank and bank holding company organizations, acquisitions and sales, and regulatory enforcement and compliance matters.
**Contact:** Scott A Meacham

**Healthcare:**
The firm represents hospitals, physicians and physician groups, clinics, HMOs and other managed care groups, long-term care facilities, home health agencies, hospices, academic medical centers and other entities that provide or pay for healthcare services.
**Contact:** Karen S Rieger

**Indian Law & Gaming:**
The firm represents Indian tribal governments and Alaskan native entities on matters relating to sovereignty, economic development and governmental objectives, tribal corporations, affiliated entities and non-tribal clients who work with them.
**Contact:** D Michael McBride III

**Intellectual Property & Technology:**
Crowe & Dunlevy represents national, regional and local companies in patent, trademark, trade secret, copyright and other transactional and litigation intellectual property matters.
**Contacts:** David M Sullivan, Margaret Millikin

**Labor & Employment:**
The firm represents management in all facets of labor and employment law, including collective bargaining, employment discrimination, wrongful discharge, workers' compensation, employee benefits and administrative practices.
**Contact:** Randall J Snapp, Adam W Childers

**Litigation & Trial Practice:**
Half of the firm's attorneys regularly represent clients in litigation matters. This includes virtually all aspects of litigation in federal, state and appellate courts, as well as all types of alternative dispute resolution. The firm's litigation clients range from individuals and small businesses, to national and international companies.
**Contact:** Judy Hamilton Morse

**Real Estate:**
Crowe & Dunlevy represents regional, national and international clients in all areas of commercial real estate, including acquisitions, sales, project development, leasing and financing, title matters, zoning and governmental issues, construction processes, environmental concerns and tax and organizational planning.
**Contact:** Michael S Laird

**Securities Litigation:**
Crowe & Dunlevy provides services to national, regional and local securities firms and securities agents jointly and to investment advisors in proceedings involving sales practices, employment and investment products. It also provides representation before various securities regulatory organizations including the SEC, FINRA and the various state securities agencies.
**Contact:** Bruce W Day, Tara A LaClair

**Taxation:**
Crowe & Dunlevy represents taxpayers on all facets of taxation law issues.
**Contact:** James H Holloman, Jr

**Trusts & Estates:**
Crowe & Dunlevy estate planning attorneys assist individuals in all aspects of trusts and estates and wealth planning. The firm also handles issues involving charitable transfers to tax-exempt entities, such as foundations and charitable trusts.
**Contact:** Cynda C Ottaway

**OFFICES**

OKLAHOMA

**OKLAHOMA CITY:** 20 N. Broadway, Suite 1800, OK 73102-8273
Tel: 405 235 7700   Fax: 405 239 6651

**TULSA:** 500 Kennedy Building, 321 South Boston Avenue, OK 74103-3313
Tel: 918 592 9800   Fax: 918 592 9801

# DUNLAP CODDING

www.dunlapcodding.com

**Managing Shareholder:** Nicholas D Rouse
**Equity Shareholders:** Nicholas D Rouse, Marc A Brockhaus, Douglas J Sorocco
Number of shareholders: 3
Number of other lawyers: 16
Number of patent agents: 1
Languages: *Bulgarian, English, Spanish*

**PRACTICE AREAS**

Intellectual Property
Litigation

**OFFICES**

OKLAHOMA
**OKLAHOMA CITY:** 609 W Sheridan Avenue, OK, 73102
Tel: 405 607 8600

## Firm Overview:

Established in 1957 as Oklahoma's original intellectual property firm, Dunlap Codding offers personalized, strategic, pragmatic, and responsive legal counsel in all intellectual property practice areas. Clients include research and academic institutions, multinational technology and manufacturing organizations and start-up companies. On behalf of its sophisticated clients, it has for the past 50 years obtained more patents, trademarks, and copyrights than any other firm in the region.

## Main Areas of Practice:

### Biotechnology & Life Science Patents:

The firm prosecutes more than 100 technologies and improvements a year on immunology-linked inventions alone. It secured intellectual property protection for the first process for producing individual endogenously loaded soluble HLA molecules and on the first recombinant methods for producing hyaluronic acid, chondroitin, and heparin. Dunlap Codding routinely assists clients in the acquisition and exploitation of patent portfolios of cutting edge research in the areas of pharmaceuticals, life sciences, medical devices, immunology proteomics, and genomics.

### Chemical Patents:

The firm is the preferred provider to some of the world's largest chemical companies, writing and prosecuting patents on front line chemical engineering technologies and providing strategic planning and facilitated innovation services to help clients maintain their technological leads. It conducts complex freedom to operate analyses, and provides infringement and invalidity opinions. The firm provides due diligence analyses in connection with capital investments. Using an in-house proprietary process, it provides facilitated patent strategy sessions and identifies market-entry opportunities.

### Mechanical Patents:

The firm provides new approaches to patenting mechanical inventions, writing and patenting in nearly every mechanical field, including machines of less than five parts as well as those having thousands of parts. Dunlap Codding has, since 1980, represented the most prolific living inventor in the US. Its mechanical practice has been recognized as one of the top two practices in the United States.

### Electrical & Software Patents:

The firm develops defensible and likely to be infringed portfolios, with more electrical and software patents that have withstood the rigors of litigation than any

other firm in the region, and has patented sensor designs for sampling data underground as well as preparing patent applications on communication methodologies and protocols which can be used for communicating between underground equipment and a surface location. It has represented clients in patenting computer programs, electronic and/or optical (including nano-optical) equipment for use in the telecommunications industry. The firm wrote, prosecuted and obtained the fundamental patents that covered the downloading of 'digital data' on the internet. These patents were successfully litigated and deemed to be valid and enforceable by the United States Court of Appeals for the Federal Court and subsequently licensed to companies such as Apple, IBM, and Microsoft. The firm has obtained and enforced patents for Pictometry International Corp., the market leader in aerial imagery, against US and foreign-based infringers and has helped Pictometry develop a worldwide portfolio of patents that have been used to keep all significant competitors out of the marketplace.

### Trademarks, Copyrights, Trade Secrets, Internet & E-Commerce:

Dunlap Codding's work includes collaborative counseling on clearance searches, infringement analysis, licenses and agreements, and litigation. The firm works closely with its clients to create proactive strategies to protect and manage international and US portfolios.

### Litigation:

Dunlap Codding is experienced in setting realistic case budgets and conducting early case assessments, handling complex commercial cases for Fortune 1000 companies and start-ups, involving contract disputes, business torts, product liability, and all areas of intellectual property law. Dunlap Codding represented Pictometry in a precedent-setting unanimous decision handed down by the Connecticut Supreme Court in January 2013. This case is the first in the US to examine the interplay between a citizen's access to public records and the limitations placed upon such access by federal copyright law. The firm also litigated one of the first trademark

infringement cases involving the issue of genericism and the scope of trademark protection afforded to generic product configuration and trade dress.

### Licensing:

The firm's practice includes licensing intellectual property across technological, geographical and governmental boundaries. It assists clients with acquiring, managing and commercializing a business-driven intellectual property portfolio. It is experienced with licensing in and licensing out, joint development agreements among international corporations, development of 'licensing packages' built around platform technologies, cross licensing as a resolution of patent and other disputes, complex license agreement negotiations, including front-end engineering packages, patents, and technical information in support of the design, construction and commissioning of large scale chemical manufacturing facilities and licensing in connection with acquisitions and divestitures.

### International Work:

The firm has licensed complex process technology and engineering packages to licensee/manufacturers in India, China, and Brazil. The firm's work has included acquisition and divestiture of numerous businesses with global assets: transferring corresponding US and non-US patent, trademark, and technology portfolios with negotiated grant-back, non-assert, confidentiality, patent/TM maintenance and other related contractual obligations and restrictions. The firm works with counsel throughout the world to obtain and exploit its clients' patent and trademark portfolios.

### Clients:

Ashland Inc., Chesapeake NG Ventures, Cristal US Inc., DePuy Synthes, DuPont, EKC Technology, Highland Supply Corporation, Hyalose L.L.C., Infinera Corporation, Pictometry International Corp., QuiBids, Schlumberger Etudes Et Production SA, SDC Technologies, Inc., Siemens Healthcare Diagnostics, The University of Oklahoma, The University of Central Florida.

# FELLERS, SNIDER, BLANKENSHIP, BAILEY & TIPPENS

www.**FellersSnider**.com

**President:** Kevin R Donelson
Number of attorneys: 51

## Firm Overview:

Founded in 1963, Fellers Snider Blankenship Bailey & Tippens has strong litigation and transactional practices. The firm boasts a broad and diverse range of expertise on a national, regional and local scope. Attorneys at Fellers Snider are active within the local and legal communities. Its founder, James D Fellers, is a past President of the American Bar Association. The firm has had two presidents of the Oklahoma Bar Association.

## Main Areas of Practice:

**Banking & Bank Regulations:**
Extensive experience representing all categories of banks in matters from lender liability, Regulation Z, formation and merger, to regulatory proceedings.

**Bankruptcy & Insolvency:**
Experience and expertise in complex and small bankruptcy cases. Attorneys represent debtors in possession, creditors, committees, equity holders and Chapter 11 trustees in the bankruptcy context. Provides innovative legal services to borrowers and lenders in handling troubled loans, out-of-court restructuring (workouts) and officer and director liability issues. The firm is skilled in commercial foreclosures, repossession and liquidation of collateral and defense of lender liability claims.

**Business, Corporate & Securities:**
Comprehensive representation of clients in virtually all facets of business, corporate law, and use of limited liability companies and limited partnerships including choice of entity, financing and structuring sales, mergers and acquisitions, leveraged buyouts, proxy contests and tender offers, buy/sell agreements, asset purchases and sales, stock purchases and sales, and executive compensation. It also has substantial experience in the formation, operation, governance, dissolution, and liquidation corporate entities.

**Employment & Labor Law:**
Representation of both the public and private sectors in employment litigation and workers' compensation claims. Representation of state, county and local government in constitutional and civil rights litigation. Additionally, the firm does extensive pre-litigation resolution of workplace disputes and formulation of personnel policies and guidelines to address evolving employment issues.

**Energy, Environmental & Natural Resources:**
Representation in energy transactions, energy marketing and trading, natural gas, wind power, energy litigation and administrative/regulatory matters. Negotiation and drafting of agreements; advice and counseling on pre-transaction activities; development and negotiation of complex transactions. Energy, environmental and toxic tort litigation are handled for the petroleum and petrochemical industry, as well as litigation of enforcement actions, natural resource damage claims, citizens suits, common law, and statutory provisions for remediation and cost recovery related to exploration and production, refining, processing, retail, transportation, storage and disposal facilities.

**Intellectual Property:**
Handles intellectual property – trademark, copyright, and patent – issues both domestically and internationally for virtually all technologies. Active Trademark Practice is well versed in procurement, prosecution and defense of trademarks. The IP Group has valuable experience in obtaining copyright registrations and patents, and structuring acquisition, development and license agreements. They also advise and counsel clients on corporate intellectual property matters. The firm is highly proficient in enforcement of IP law.

**Litigation:**
Fellers Snider has a national reputation for the quality of its Litigation Practice with a concentration on commercial litigation on behalf of both plaintiffs and defendants. Its attorneys try cases nationwide, primarily involving complex commercial and business litigation, as well as personal injury and other tort and property damage litigation. The firm has many attorneys with jury trial experience in oil and gas, insurance, intellectual property, antitrust, real estate and banking. The firm also represents both individuals and corporations in a variety of white collar criminal proceedings at all levels of the criminal process. Attorneys at the firm have represented clients before federal and state administrative agencies. Fellers Snider has an active appellate practice, having received a favorable ruling from the Supreme Court of the United States most recently in November 2012.

**Real Estate & Commercial Transactions:**
The firm's Real Estate and Transactional Practice serves national and local clients in matters ranging from significant real estate and commercial transactions to normal business and personal transactions. It represents businesses and individuals in acquiring, financing, developing, selling and leasing real estate. This firm frequently serves as local counsel for major national corporations in conjunction with nationwide transactions.

**Regulatory Matters:**
The firm has attorneys who have expertise in representing telecommunication and utility companies before the Oklahoma Corporation Commission in all regulatory matters.

**Tax, Trusts, Probate & Estate Planning:**
The firm handles estate plans for clients with multi-million dollar estates. The firm prepares federal and state estate and gift tax returns for large estates and successfully defends them through the audit process both by the IRS and state agencies. It regularly represents charitable organizations in the handling and administration of charitable gifts, trust departments on numerous matters, beneficiaries in the protection of their interests, creditors and others in estate and trust matters. The firm also handles major probates, will contests and other similar litigation.

**Clients:**
The clients of this firm range from national retail, manufacturing and service organizations whose names are household words, to government agencies and entities, to local businesses and individuals. The unique talents and backgrounds of its lawyers enable the firm to counsel clients in a range of areas such as aircraft title and financing, white collar criminal defense, election and campaign finance, agricultural law and workers compensation. Client's needs are met and problems solved with the integrity, creativity and dedication upon which the firm's reputation for service and quality has been built.

## OFFICES

OKLAHOMA

**OKLAHOMA CITY:** Chase Tower, 17th Floor, 100 N. Broadway, OK 73102-9211
Tel: 405 232 0621  Fax: 405 232 9659

**TULSA:** The Kennedy Building, 321 South Boston Avenue, Suite 800, OK 74103-3318
Tel: 918 599 0621  Fax: 918 583 9659

# HALL ESTILL

www.hallestill.com

**Managing Partner/President:** Michael D Cooke
Number of partners: 84  Number of attorneys: 120
Languages: *English*

## Firm Overview:

One of Oklahoma's largest and most trusted law firms since 1967, Hall Estill delivers powerful results to its clients regionally, nationally and internationally. With a client-first mentality that provides friendly, attentive client service, the firm delivers results through creative, cost-effective solutions. Hall Estill attorneys represent clients from *Fortune* 500 corporations and medium-sized companies, to non-profit organizations, emerging businesses and individuals. Hall Estill attorneys are leaders in their respective fields and in their communities; regularly publishing and lecturing in their areas of expertise, continuing to build on the firm's reputation of excellence. Hall Estill is nationally recognized and highly respected for a wide range of expertise and depth of legal knowledge.

## Main Areas of Practice:

### Business Finance & Restructuring:

- Representation of numerous clients in successfully defending preference cases all across the country with amounts at issue in some cases of over one million dollars

**Key Clients:** Level 3 Communications, Saber Acceptance, GE Capital Corporation
**Contact:** Steven W Soulé  **Tel:** 918 594 0466
**Email:** ssoule@hallestill.com

### Corporate Services:

- Lead counsel in acquisition of the assets of a transportation company whose purchase price was approximately $35 million

**Key Clients:** Syntroleum, HollyFrontier, WPX
**Contact:** Michael D Cooke  **Tel:** 918 594 0414
**Email:** mcooke@hallestill.com

### Energy & Natural Resources:

- Successful defense of class action claims of class royalty owners in Oklahoma and Kansas. Royalty owners asserted claims for underpayment of royalties against natural gas producer by obtaining order from court removing class representatives and class counsel and decertifying class

**Key Clients:** ConocoPhillips, Williams, Burlington Resources
**Contact:** J Kevin Hayes  **Tel:** 918 594 0460
**Email:** khayes@hallestill.com

### Environmental Services:

- The Environmental Practice Group continues to assist clients in matters of environmental enforcement, compliance and litigation, including working with a client on an air permit appeal at the state level. It is also assisting chemical manufacturing clients in matters of water quality/permitting and waste investigation/ remediation at the state and federal levels

**Key Clients:** CP Kelco, Bailey Bark Materials, Atlas Pipeline Partners
**Contact:** Garry L Keele, II  **Tel:** 918 594 0553

**Email:** gkeele@hallestill.com

### Family Services:

- Over the last two years Hall Estill handled in excess of 100 new domestic matters which ranged up to $100 million. Cases involve complex valuation and separate property issues with valuation issues running the gamut from medical groups to IPOs

**Contact:** Bradley A Grundy  **Tel:** 918 594 0452
**Email:** bgrundy@hallestill.com

### Indian Law:

- Representation of the Stockbridge-Munsee Community, a federally recognized Indian tribe, and its liability insurance carrier, First Americans Insurance Group, Inc., in an off-reservation personal injury matter filed against the firm's clients in Wisconsin state court

**Key Clients:** Muscogee (Creek) Nation, San Pasqual Band of Mission Indians, Oklahoma Indian Gaming Commission
**Contact:** Timothy W Posey  **Tel:** 918 594 0669
**Email:** tposey@hallestill.com

### Intellectual Property & Information Technology:

- Judgment received in the US District Court for the Northern District of Texas in a landmark case. In Goforit Entertainment, LLC v. Digimedia.com L.P.; Cyberfusion.com, L.Pl; Happydays, Inc.; Digimedia.com Management Inc. and Scott Day, judgment was entered awarding damages, fees and costs for the defendants on counterclaims against plaintiff. This is the first successful reverse domain name hijacking claim ever

**Contact:** Phillip L Free, Jr  **Tel:** 405 553 2878
**Email:** pfree@hallestill.com

### Labor & Employment:

- Successfully defended JM Manufacturing Company, Inc. in a wrongful discharge matter before a jury trial. Former employee has since appealed a portion of the district court's order granting partial summary judgment to the firm's client. That appeal is currently

pending with the 10th Circuit Court of Appeals
**Key Clients:** Best Buy, St. Paul Travelers, Tenaska Operations, Chubb Insurance
**Contact:** J Patrick Cremin  **Tel:** 918 594 0594
**Email:** pcremin@hallestill.com

### Litigation:

- Defended Random House, John Grisham, and others in defamation, false light invasion of privacy, and intentional infliction suit in federal court based on the Grisham book The Innocent Man. Obtained judgment for defendants on motion to dismiss

**Key Clients:** Hiland Partners, AES Shady Point, Orchids Paper Products
**Contact:** J Kevin Hayes  **Tel:** 918 594 0460
**Email:** khayes@hallestill.com

### Tax/Trusts & Estate Planning:

- Hall Estill assists clients in the tax/trusts and estate planning areas whose net worth exceeds $1 million

**Key Clients:** The Baptist Foundation of Oklahoma, The AYCO Company
**Contact:** Kenneth L Hunt  **Tel:** 918 594 0420
**Email:** khunt@hallestill.com

# HARTZOG CONGER CASON & NEVILLE

**www.**hartzoglaw.com **tel:** 405 235 7000 **fax:** 405 996 3403

**Managing Partner:** John D Robertson
Number of partners: 20
Number of other lawyers: 17

**OFFICES**

OKLAHOMA

**OKLAHOMA CITY:** 201 Robert S. Kerr Avenue, 1600 Bank
of Oklahoma Plaza, OK 73102
Tel: 405 235 7000   Fax: 405 996 3403

## Firm Overview:

Hartzog Conger Cason & Neville is known for its results oriented style of representation and its commitment to unsurpassed client service and responsiveness. The firm has 37 lawyers and is growing in size and capacity to meet the needs of its clientele. The firm expects its lawyers to have strong academic credentials as well as interpersonal skills necessary to communicate effectively with clients and others. Clients include businesses and business owners, high net worth individuals and families and Section 501(c)(3) organizations.

## Main Areas of Practice:

### Business & Financial Transactions, Securities & Business Law:

Hartzog Conger Cason & Neville represents publicly-held corporations, privately-held businesses, entrepreneurs and successful business owners in all aspects of business law, including merger and acquisition transactions, capital formation activities and securities law matters. This practice area also includes commercial banking and lending transactions, business reorganizations and litigation resulting from these types of commercial transactions.
**Contacts:** Len Cason, Armand Paliotta, John D Robertson

### Litigation:

Hartzog Conger Cason & Neville has an established Trial and Appellate Practice in state and federal courts. The Litigation Practice includes civil cases involving antitrust law, insurance disputes, professional malpractice, securities litigation, shareholders' derivative actions, products liability, unfair trade practices, agency and licensing board proceeding, general commercial and business litigation and appeals, as well as white-collar criminal matters. Although the firm represents both plaintiffs and defendants, most of the litigation practice is defense-oriented. During the past five years, the Litigation Practice Group has defended claims in excess of $2 billion. One partner of the firm is a member of the American College of Trial Lawyers. Two partners of the firm are individually listed in Chambers among the top business litigators in Oklahoma. Others are recognized in Best Lawyers in America and in Oklahoma Super Lawyers.
**Contact:** Drew Neville, Charles E Geister, William A Johnson, Ryan S Wilson

### Employment Law:

The lawyers in this practice group provide legal services and litigation representation in matters concerning all aspects of employment relationships, including employment contracts, personnel policies, employee manuals, drug and alcohol testing, employment termination, sexual harassment, EEOC investigations, executive compensation, hiring and employment of persons with disabilities, wage and hour disputes, health and safety issues and employee benefits matters.
**Contacts:** Charles E Geister, Ryan S Wilson

### Family Law:

The firm handles a variety of family law matters that usually have significant financial issues, including divorce trials and appeals, post-decree enforcement and modification and child support and child custody disputes. The firm has been successful in helping clients reach favorable settlements in complex family disputes. One of the firm's partners is a Fellow of the American Academy of Matrimonial Lawyers and is listed in Best Lawyers in America in family law.
**Contact:** Laura H McConnell-Corbyn

### Oil & Gas:

This practice group performs oil and gas litigation and handles title matters, property acquisition contracts, operating agreements, environmental matters, and also has an extensive practice before the Oklahoma Corporation Commission.
**Contact:** David E Pepper

### Real Estate Law:

The Real Estate Practice Group represents a diverse group of clients in connection with real estate acquisitions and sales, management and leasing activities, real estate development, multiparty tax-deferred and tenancy-in-common exchanges, environmental law and a wide variety of complex real estate financing transactions. The firm routinely represents owners, developers, lenders and brokers.
**Contact:** Joseph P Hogsett

### Tax Planning & Tax Controversies:

Hartzog Conger Cason & Neville's Tax Planning and Tax Controversies Group, which includes two certified public accountants, has a wealth of experience in federal, state and local tax matters, some of which are routine but many of which are unique or special. The firm is regularly involved in ongoing tax planning services for many clients and often is engaged to handle special tax projects, such as criminal tax matters. The firm regularly maintains an extensive tax controversy docket in tax controversies with the state and federal taxing authorities, usually involving business or investment issues. The group regularly assists taxpayer-clients in audits, protest filings, administrative appeals and court proceedings. Two partners of the firm are individually listed in Chambers among the top tax attorneys in Oklahoma. The firm also has an extensive practice in state and federal tax credit projects.
**Contact:** Steven C Davis

### Wealth Transfer Planning, Trusts & Estates:

The firm has a significant practice in representing high net worth individuals and families in wealth transfer planning and business succession plans, as well as representing charitable and philanthropic organizations. This practice group is experienced in all aspects of complex estate and trust planning, estate and gift tax, estate and trust administration, and in the creation and administration of charitable foundations and trusts. Three partners of the firm are Fellows in the American College of Trust and Estate Counsel (ACTEC); one partner is also a Fellow in the American College of Tax Counsel; and four partners are listed in the 'Best Lawyers in America' in the trusts and estates practice area.
**Contacts:** Len Cason, Steven C Davis, Amy J Sine, J Leslie LaReau

### Tax Credit Finance & Business Incentives:

The firm's tax credit finance and business incentives group has extensive experience assisting clients to achieve the maximum return on their business development and financing. This group regularly utilizes federal historic tax credits, federal new markets tax credits, federal energy tax credits and federal low-income housing tax credits. In addition, the firm has developed an expertise in various state and local tax credits and development incentives.
**Contact:** J Christian Guzzy

### Appellate Practice:

This practice group, which includes former district court and appellate law clerks, utilizes its knowledge, expertise and research and writing skills to handle all aspects of an appeal, from filing, to briefing, to oral argument.

# MCAFEE & TAFT

www.mcafeetaft.com **tel:** 405 235 9621 **fax:** 405 235 0439

**Managing Partner:** Richard D Nix
Number of partners: 95
Number of other lawyers: 85

**OFFICES**

OKLAHOMA

**OKLAHOMA CITY:** Two Leadership Square, 10th Floor, 211 North Robinson, OK 73102
Tel: 405 235 9621    Fax: 405 235 0439

**TULSA:** 1717 S. Boulder, Suite 900, OK 74119
Tel: 918 587 0000    Fax: 918 599 9317

## Firm Overview:

McAfee & Taft has distinguished itself by being an industry leader in developing innovative legal solutions for business for more than 60 years and ranks as Oklahoma's largest law firm. McAfee & Taft is also the sole Oklahoma member of TerraLex® and the Employers Counsel Network.

## Main Areas of Practice:

### Aviation:

Located just miles from the FAA in Oklahoma City, McAfee & Taft has one of the largest and most experienced FAA aviation groups in the nation. Its attorneys represent local, national and international clients of all sizes on aviation matters, including the documentation of aircraft transactions, aircraft title and registration matters, aircraft title insurance, escrow closings, closing and post-recordation opinions, and the Cape Town Convention and International Registry.

### Banking & Finance:

McAfee & Taft has extensive experience serving the unique legal needs of commercial banks, thrifts and other providers of financial services. In addition to representing clients in a wide variety of banking and corporate transaction matters, the firm's lawyers counsel clients on specific federal and state regulatory and compliance issues.

### Business Law:

The firm has significant depth and expertise in representing clients in all aspects of business law, including entity formation, administrative law, agricultural law, bankruptcy and creditors' rights, business restructuring and workouts, commercial contracts, financing, franchising and licensing, Native American law and gaming, and project finance.

### Corporate & Securities:

The firm advises clients on corporate governance and compliance, mergers and acquisitions of private and public entities, divestitures, joint ventures, venture capital and private equity investments, public and private offerings of securities, tender offers, and other forms of financing.

### Employee Benefits:

McAfee & Taft's premier Employee Benefits Practice offers specialized legal solutions in all major areas, including legal compliance, qualified plan design and implementation, multi-employer plans, collectively bargained plans, welfare plans and flexible benefits, executive compensation, plan terminations and surplus assets, plan investments, funding and taxation, plan

fiduciary counseling, ERISA litigation, and health care reform compliance.

### Energy, Oil & Gas:

The firm's Oil and Gas Practice involves the structuring and negotiation of purchase, sale, financing, capital infusion, AMI, farmout, lease, drilling, and similar transactions with respect to oil and gas properties and oil and gas businesses, including securities offerings for oil and gas drilling programs and funds. The firm also represents clients involved in renewable and sustainable energy projects.

### Environmental Law:

The firm offers in-depth expertise in issues arising in environmental permitting, compliance, enforcement and litigation involving the Clean Air Act, Clean Water Act, Resource Conservation and Recovery Act, Solid Waste Disposal Act, Comprehensive Environmental Response, Compensation and Liability Act, Hazardous Materials Transportation Act, OSHA, Oil Pollution Act, PATRIOT Act, and Emergency Planning and Community Right-to-Know Act.

### Healthcare:

The firm represents physicians, hospitals, and other healthcare facilities and institutions in joint ventures, facilities development, financing transactions, payer contracting, affiliations and network development, regulatory compliance, investigations, medical staff matters, legal proceedings, risk management, and legal liability protection.

### Intellectual Property:

McAfee & Taft represents clients in transactions and disputes involving trademarks, copyrights, patents, domain names, trade secrets, counterfeiting, rights of privacy, internet liability, unfair competition and false advertising claims, as well as entertainment law and multimedia rights. The firm's transactional experience includes the registration, licensing, sale and acquisition of complex intellectual property rights.

### Labor & Employment:

McAfee & Taft represents management in all areas of labor and employment law. Its practice includes drafting and negotiating labor agreements, resolving

labor disputes through arbitration, defending unfair labor practice charges before regulatory agencies, designing and implementing preventive workplace practices, ensuring state and federal compliance, representing management before administrative agencies, and litigating employment claims in state and federal courts. The firm is actively involved in designing workplace arbitration agreements and arbitrating employment-related cases.

### Litigation & Appellate:

Firm trial lawyers represent clients in all types of business and commercial disputes, including complex litigation and arbitration involving banking, bankruptcy, class actions, healthcare, insurance, intellectual property, mass torts, oil and gas, pharmaceuticals, products liability, real estate, securities, and tax.

### Real Estate:

The firm has significant experience handling a variety of real estate transactions, including sales, purchases, financing and leasing transactions, as well as representing borrowers in secured and unsecured credit arrangements. The firm also has developed a particular expertise in structuring transactions to take advantage of various tax credits and government incentives.

### Tax & Family Wealth:

The firm has long been a leader in providing sophisticated tax advice to individuals, tax-exempt organizations and the business community. It provides assistance in connection with all forms of estate and tax planning, including commercial and private transactions, mergers and acquisitions, oil and gas operations, real estate transactions, like-kind exchanges, business succession planning, deferred compensation arrangements, gift and estate planning, foreign transactions and state and local tax issues.

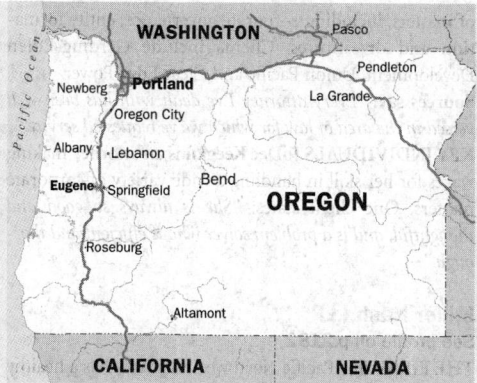

## How lawyers are ranked

Every year we carry out thousands of in-depth interviews with clients in order to assess the reputations and expertise of business lawyers worldwide. The qualities we look for (and which determine rankings) include technical legal ability, professional conduct, client service, commercial awareness/astuteness, diligence, commitment, and other qualities most valued by the client. For details of our research team, see p.5.

## Contents:

# CORPORATE/M&A

Commentary about individuals can be found under their firm's paragraph. If the firm has no paragraph (is not ranked) look at Other Notable Practitioners.

| Corporate/M&A |
| --- |
| **Leading Firms** |
| **Band 1** |
| Perkins Coie LLP |
| Stoel Rives LLP |
| **Band 2** |
| Davis Wright Tremaine LLP * |
| Lane Powell PC * |
| Tonkon Torp LLP * |
| **Band 3** |
| Ater Wynne LLP |
| Dunn Carney Allen Higgins & Tongue LLP |
| Miller Nash LLP * |
| Schwabe, Williamson & Wyatt |

## Band 1

### Perkins Coie LLP
See profile on p.2548

THE FIRM The Portland office of this leading firm offers one of the premier corporate practices in the state. The 12-partner team provides expertise in all facets of corporate and M&A law, and in particular represents clients from the emerging growth and technology spheres. Clients include TriQuint Semiconductor, Endeavour Capital and Microsoft. Recent highlights include representing PacifiCorp in a $650 million mortgage bond offering.

KEY INDIVIDUALS **Roy Tucker** has a wide-ranging corporate practice which covers M&A, public offerings and restructurings. He recently advised Micro Power Electronics on its $60 million sale to Electrochem Solutions. The highly regarded **Brentley Bullock** represents clients from the technology and emerging company spaces in all aspects of corporate and M&A law, including venture capital and angel financings, strategic partnerships and debt and equity financings. **David Matheson** advises domestic and foreign clients on a variety of corporate matters, such as SEC and national securities exchange compli-

ance, raising capital, and the restructuring and disposal of assets. **John Thomas** attracts compliments for his corporate expertise, with clients lauding his dedication to their interests and creativity in finding solutions. **Patrick Simpson** is commended for his longstanding experience in M&A and corporate law, with areas of expertise including capital formation, federal securities laws compliance and corporate governance.

### Stoel Rives LLP

THE FIRM This Portland-headquartered national firm has a market-leading corporate and M&A practice. The group offers clients the depth and expertise to handle all aspects of related matters, and is particularly known for representing a large number of public companies. Clients include Precision Castparts and Schnitzer Steel. The team recently acted for JELD-WEN Holding on an $871 million investment by Onex.

KEY INDIVIDUALS **Todd Bauman** is chair of the firm's technology ventures group. He represents a number of emerging growth and technology companies in a wide variety of corporate law matters. He recently represented Agilyx in its $25 million stock financing. **Ruth Beyer** represents some of the practice's biggest clients in key M&A transactions, and wins admiration from peers for her talent and experience. She earns market praise for her prowess in high-value acquisitions. **Henry Hewitt** is well known and highly respected in the market for his deep experience in corporate law, which encompasses corporate governance, public company work and general business advice. **Robert Moorman** counsels clients on public and private financings, securities law compliance and the sale and acquisition of businesses. **Margaret Hill Noto** is admired for her corporate practice, which includes securities, M&A and corporate governance matters for some of the firm's biggest clients. **Steven Hull** represents technology, manufacturing and public companies in a broad range of corporate and M&A matters, including venture capital financings, securities transactions and governance matters.

**Mark Norby** is a specialist in corporate matters particularly relating to the forest and agribusiness industries. He is praised by sources as an efficient and effective negotiator. **Margaret Kushner** has a vast knowledge of the structure and formation of business entities, partnership matters and joint ventures.

## Band 2

### Davis Wright Tremaine LLP
See profile on p.2544

THE FIRM The Portland branch of this full-service firm is commended by clients, many of whom highlight the team's superb expertise and customer service. The group offers a comprehensive corporate practice undertaking a range of matters, including securities, corporate governance and M&A for public and private clients. Clients include Starbucks, Renewal Partners and Willamette Valley Vineyards.

Sources say: *"They show themselves to be reliable, never promising more than they can deliver, and often delivering more than they promised."*

KEY INDIVIDUALS **Michael Phillips** is a trusted adviser to US and foreign clients in corporate matters including securities law compliance, joint venture formation and public and private offerings. One client enthuses: *"His support is rock-solid and he always looks out for the best interests of my business."* **Jesse Lyon** is appreciated for his knowledge of corporate matters relating to the food, wine, beverage and agribusiness industries. One client remarks: *"He is prompt, knowledgeable, efficient and strategic in his thinking."*

### Lane Powell PC
See profile on p.2547

THE FIRM This established Pacific Northwest firm has a thriving corporate practice in Oregon that attracts praise from clients for the quality of its work. The team represents clients from the banking, retail, energy and aviation industries in all facets of business and M&A matters, with key names including Wells Fargo, Nordstrom and Iberdrola Renewables. The group recently represented Lithia Motors in establishing a new primary credit facility worth $650 million.

**Sources say:** *"Our experience is that they are a dedicated group of highly capable professionals who provide a broad range of legal services."*

**KEY INDIVIDUALS Jeffrey Wolfstone** (see p.2179) generates praise from clients, who are impressed with his knowledge of a wide range of corporate and M&A matters. Sources describe him as someone who *"brings business sense with his legal expertise,"* and who is *"a fabulous adviser and exceptional in identifying resources within the firm to address specific, technical matters."* **Benjamin Lenhart** (see

p.2176) is recognized for his skill in corporate matters relating to securities, M&A and commercial finance.

## Tonkon Torp LLP
See profile on p.2183
**THE FIRM** This well-respected Portland firm has a strong group which is adept at handling an extensive range of corporate and M&A matters, including complex transactions, restructurings and private equity investments. The firm also has expertise in handling the affairs of fast-growing and dynamic software companies. Clients include Nike, Endeavour Capital and Portland General Electric.

**Sources say:** *"We get great value and at a reasonable cost. Plus the lawyers are professional and easy and pleasant to work with."*

**KEY INDIVIDUALS Kurt Ruttum** (see p.2178) wins praise for his ability to negotiate complex financial transactions. *"He has the intellectual horsepower and ability to identify creative solutions to resolve issues, and he has a good practical sense about business and legal risks,"* states an appreciative client. **Sherrill Corbett** (see p.2176) is chair of the firm's M&A practice group, and has an extremely strong reputation in the market for her expertise in deep securities matters and detailed transactional work. **Ronald Greenman** (see p.2176) is known for his skill and practicality in handling transactional and corporate matters such as venture capital financings, corporate governance and public offerings. **Thomas Palmer** (see p.2177), chair of the firm's corporate finance practice group, is held in high esteem for his deep knowledge of corporate and securities law, including M&A transactions, corporate governance issues and counseling. The distinguished **Kenneth Stephens** (see p.2179), a founding partner of the firm, is admired for his vast experience in corporate matters, particularly those relating to the financial services industry.

## Band 3

## Ater Wynne LLP
**THE FIRM** This Pacific Northwest firm has a corporate practice which is especially respected for its expertise in handling the affairs of emerging businesses, as well as several prominent and established Oregon firms. Clients include T-Mobile USA, Northwest Pipe and Planar Systems.

**Sources say:** *"Very hard-working, responsive and service-oriented."*

**KEY INDIVIDUALS Brenda Meltebeke** is a specialist in corporate matters affecting startups and emerging companies. Clients particularly praise her attentiveness to their needs. **Gregory Struxness** draws plaudits from his clients for his corporate and securities practice. He has recently played a lead role in the firm's representation of Northwest Pipe.

## Dunn Carney Allen Higgins & Tongue LLP
**THE FIRM** The 13-partner corporate and M&A team at this Oregon firm joins the rankings this year following strong client endorsements. It is proficient in a wide range

of matters, including corporate governance, entity formation and divestitures. Clients include Gerding-Edlen Development, Union Pacific and Clear Edge Power.

**Sources say:** *"Every attorney I've dealt with has been well versed in the area of law for which we've requested service."*

**KEY INDIVIDUALS JoDee Keegan** is an attorney making waves for her skill in handling a wide variety of corporate matters. One client states: *"She is always so good and thoughtful, and is a problem solver who is efficient and thorough."*

## Miller Nash LLP
See profile on p.2182
**THE FIRM** This Pacific Northwest mainstay has a healthy corporate practice which is active in advising clients from the manufacturing, forest products, agriculture and technology industries on a broad range of corporate matters. Clients include Cascade Corporation, Bank of the Pacific and Craft Brew Alliance.

**Sources say:** *"They have done an excellent job for us."*

**KEY INDIVIDUALS** The *"detail-oriented"* and *"really knowledgeable"* **Mary Ann Frantz**, head of the firm's business practice group, is well respected in the market for her practice, which emphasizes debt and equity offerings, M&A and SEC reporting compliance. **Erich Merrill** (see p.2177) has a corporate practice which covers entity choice and formation, sales and acquisitions of businesses and corporate strategy. He recently co-represented eScreen in the sale of its business to a strategic buyer.

## Schwabe, Williamson & Wyatt
**THE FIRM** The corporate practice at this notable Pacific Northwest firm is comprised of offices in Portland, Bend and Salem. The group has expertise in representing clients from the manufacturing, technology and forest product industries, with timber law being a particular area of strength. It acts for a number of significant clients including Coaxis, Columbia Forest Products and Greenwood Resources.

**KEY INDIVIDUALS Carmen Calzacorta** has deep experience of corporate law, particularly in securities and M&A law compliance, corporate governance and counseling.

## Other Notable Practitioners
The highly respected **Mark von Bergen** (see p.2179) of Holland & Knight LLP is a specialist in a wide range of corporate matters, particularly public offerings, M&A and venture capital transactions. He frequently represents clients from the investment management and startup arenas. **Brendan McDonnell** (see p.2177) of K&L Gates has a vast knowledge of corporate matters, in particular venture capital transactions, public and private financings, and matters affecting private equity funds. According to clients, *"he is a fantastic attorney and has an understanding of how to get deals done."*

# ENVIRONMENT

Commentary about individuals can be found under their firm's paragraph. If the firm has no paragraph (is not ranked) look at Other Notable Practitioners.

## Environment
### Leading Firms

**Band 1**
Perkins Coie LLP
Stoel Rives LLP

**Band 2**
Cable Huston Benedict Haagensen & Lloyd LLP
Davis Wright Tremaine LLP *
Schwabe, Williamson & Wyatt
Tonkon Torp LLP *

**Band 3**
Jordan Ramis PC
Landye Bennett Blumstein LLP

### Leading Individuals

**Band 1**

| | | |
|---|---|---|
| Blount David L | Landye Bennett Blumstein LLP | |
| Dost Patricia | Pearl Legal Group, PC (ONP)† | |
| Glick Richard M | Davis Wright Tremaine LLP | |
| Lindley Tom | Perkins Coie LLP | |
| Morford J Mark | Stoel Rives LLP | |
| Pagel Martha O | Schwabe, Williamson & Wyatt | |
| Powers Claudia K | Ater Wynne LLP (ONP)† | |
| Snyder Joan P | Stoel Rives LLP | |
| Wood Thomas R | Stoel Rives LLP | |

**Band 2**

| | |
|---|---|
| Benedict James E | Cable Huston Benedict Haagensen & Lloyd |
| Bledsoe David | Perkins Coie LLP |
| Burke Lawrence B | Davis Wright Tremaine LLP |
| Campbell Michael R | Stoel Rives LLP |
| Filippi David E | Stoel Rives LLP |
| Miller Jr Max M | Tonkon Torp LLP * |
| Rich Christopher W | Perkins Coie LLP |
| Shropshire Steven L | Jordan Ramis PC * |

**Band 3**

| | |
|---|---|
| Allan Richard H | Marten Law PLLC (ONP)† |
| Ashworth John P | Kell Alterman & Runstein, LLP (ONP)† |
| Balfour Clark I | Cable Huston Benedict Haagensen & Lloyd |
| Craig Barbara | Stoel Rives LLP |
| Gates Jennifer L | Landye Bennett Blumstein LLP |
| Mohr Peter | Tonkon Torp LLP * |
| O'Leary Daniel | Davis Wright Tremaine LLP |
| Reive Chris | Jordan Ramis PC * |
| Ring Jeffrey | Wrenn Bender (ONP)† |

\* Indicates firm / individual with profile.
† ONP = Other Notable Practitioner.

## Band 1

### Perkins Coie LLP
See profile on p.2548

**THE FIRM** Perkins Coie has one of the finest environmental practices in the state and offers clients a broad base of expertise which also encompasses energy and resources work. The team is heavily involved in a range of water quality issues, ocean and coastal law and matters stemming from the Endangered Species Act. Recent highlights include acting for Pacific Wood Preserving of Oregon on its environmental compliance issues. Other key clients include Boeing, Jordan Cove Energy Project, and Oregon International Port of Coos Bay.

**KEY INDIVIDUALS** The much-admired **Tom Lindley** has a broad-ranging environmental practice. Sources laud the breadth and depth of his experience and responsiveness to client needs. **Christopher Rich** concentrates his practice on environmental cleanup compliance and litigation. He acts as general outside counsel to the Washington Demilitarization Company, and in particular assists it with complex permitting and compliance issues. **David Bledsoe** is a litigator held in high regard for his skill in trying cases involving environmental disputes. He has deep expertise in the Clean Water Act, the Endangered Species Act and Superfund issues.

### Stoel Rives LLP

**THE FIRM** Stoel Rives's formidable Oregon environmental group is comprised of 16 partners, which makes the practice one of the state's largest in this field. The team has prowess in a wide range of matters, such as National Environmental Policy Act and Clean Air Act issues, regulatory compliance and litigation, and land use permitting. Clients include JELD-WEN, Evraz and The Northwest Pulp & Paper Association.

**KEY INDIVIDUALS Mark Morford** earns high praise for his longstanding experience in environmental law. His broad practice includes complex regulatory compliance and permitting, hazardous materials management and expertise issues relating to industrial operations such as metals and forest products facilities. **Joan Snyder** has a wide-ranging environmental practice which includes all aspects of environmental, natural resources and health and safety law. She has recently advised Evraz on regulatory aspects related to the multiparty Portland Harbor Superfund site. **Thomas Wood** is an attorney known for his expertise in air quality issues and hazardous waste permitting and compliance. **Michael Campbell** is a respected specialist in water quality regulation and permitting matters, including wastewater and stormwater discharge permits, and assisting hydroelectric facilities to obtain section 401 certifications. **David Filippi** concentrates his practice on water rights and water quality, project facility siting and fish and wildlife law. Clients appreciate his deep knowledge of specialized water rights, the Endangered Species Act and other regulatory matters. **Barbara Craig** focuses her practice on federal environmental and natural resources law, with particular areas of expertise including the National Forest Management Act, the Marine Mammal Protection Act and the Endangered Species Act.

## Band 2

### Cable Huston Benedict Haagensen & Lloyd LLP

**THE FIRM** This impressive Portland firm is respected in the market for a strong practice which is proficient in all facets of environmental law. The team is adept in matters such as waste cleanup and management issues, environmental assessments and impact statements, and complex environmental litigation.

**KEY INDIVIDUALS James Benedict** is renowned as being "*technically astute with a good reputation.*" His practice is particularly focused on energy, natural resources and hazardous waste law. **Clark Balfour** is an expert in the environmental issues that municipalities and special districts face, such as surface water management and sanitary sewer issues. He also represents local governments in state and federal regulatory permit proceedings.

### Davis Wright Tremaine LLP
See profile on p.2544

**THE FIRM** This Portland environmental group wins high praise from clients, who appreciate it's client service and depth of expertise. The team is particularly proficient in matters relating to the Clean Water Act, Superfund and state cleanup sites, as well as environmental due diligence and National Environmental Policy Act compliance. The team recently acted for Idaho Power on regulatory issues. Other major clients include the City of Bend and Mitsubishi.

**Sources say:** "*They are professional, thorough, timely and practical.*"

**KEY INDIVIDUALS Richard Glick** is described by sources as being "*very knowledgeable in his area of the law and extremely professional.*" He has expertise in assisting clients with a wide range of environmental issues, including regulatory compliance, endangered species and environmental impact reviews and water rights. The "*excellent and very experienced*" **Lawrence Burke** is particularly renowned for his contamination-related environmental work involving issues involving the Clean Air Act, the Clean Water Act, stormwater runoff and groundwater contamination. The well-respected **Daniel O'Leary** is a litigator who handles environmental issues and related insurance coverage cases. He is particularly adept in litigating cases involving natural resources, Superfund law and the Endangered Species Act.

### Schwabe, Williamson & Wyatt

**THE FIRM** This well-regarded Pacific Northwest firm has a healthy environmental practice which is particularly admired for its attorneys' experience in air and water quality compliance, insurance coverage claims and environmental criminal defense. The firm recently acted as lead Oregon counsel regarding water supply, land use and permitting in the development of major client Facebook's first remote data center.

**KEY INDIVIDUALS Martha Pagel** is commended by sources for her water law practice, which includes water rights, the Endangered Species Act and waterway ownership. She is also an expert in natural resources law and advises clients from the mining, agriculture and farming industries on related matters.

## Tonkon Torp LLP
See profile on p.2183

**THE FIRM** This Portland mainstay is renowned for its representation of clients from the metals manufacturing, timber and renewable energy industries in issues relating to hazardous materials and environmental permitting. Other areas of expertise include regulatory reviews, PCB cleanups and natural resource damages issues. Recent highlights include acting for Gunderson on the potential high-value remediation of the Portland Harbor Superfund site.

**Sources say:** *"They have a real commitment to a client's success beyond any individual legal matter. They choose solutions that are in the client's best interests, and are conscious on costs and strong on value."*

**KEY INDIVIDUALS Max Miller** (see p.2177) focuses on regulatory environmental matters, advising clients on natural resources, land use and energy issues before federal, state and local regulators. He has recently advised Gunderson on a feasibility study for the remediation of the Portland Harbor Superfund site. **Peter Mohr** (see p.2177) has a wide-ranging environmental practice that includes water law, environmental regulatory compliance and natural resource acquisition and development. Clients say: *"It was a very pleasant experience working with him – he's knowledgeable and effective."*

## Band 3

### Jordan Ramis PC
**THE FIRM** Jordan Ramis has a comprehensive natural resources and environmental law practice that is supported by its real estate, land use and construction groups. The team has expertise in Clean Water Act and Clean Air Act permitting, issues related to the Portland Harbor Superfund site, and water rights acquisitions, sales, and leases. Clients include Siltronic Corporation, Oregon Association of Nurseries and Dyno Nobel.

**KEY INDIVIDUALS Steven Shropshire** (see p.2178) is particularly admired for his skill in water law. He is also an expert in a wide variety of other natural resources and environmental matters, including regulatory advice, issues related to the Endangered Species Act, and real estate and land use matters. **Chris Reive** (see p.2178) is respected for his wide-ranging environmental practice which encompasses environmental risk management, insurance coverage issues and industrial cleanup projects.

### Landye Bennett Blumstein LLP
**THE FIRM** This firm, with offices in Portland and Anchorage, is experienced in a broad range of environmental and natural resources matters, including the Magnuson-Stevens Act, insurance coverage and wildlife protection. The team is particularly known for its work on brownfield development projects in Oregon, which is ably aided by the firm's real estate practice.

**KEY INDIVIDUALS David Blount** chairs the firm's environmental practice and is respected for his deep experience as a litigator. He is a specialist in issues relating to contaminated brownfield sites, environmental insurance coverage, and negotiations with regulatory agencies. *"Very strong*

*lawyer"* **Jennifer Gates** counsels clients on a variety of environmental matters, including compliance, Portland Harbor Superfund issues and site remediation.

## Other Notable Practitioners

The much-admired **Patricia Dost** of Pearl Legal Group, PC is complimented as being *"excellent – one of the best lawyers in the environmental field."* She has particular expertise in water quality, hazardous waste and regulatory matters. **Claudia Powers** of Ater Wynne LLP is held in high regard for her environmental practice in which she advises clients from the chemical, utility and solid waste industries on issues related to contaminated properties, Superfund sites and redevelopment and sustainability. **John Ashworth** of Kell Alterman & Runstein, LLP is respected for his skill as an environmental litigator, and handles cases involving issues such as environmental compliance, contractual disputes, and multiple Superfund sites across the Pacific Northwest. **Jeffrey Ring** of Wrenn Bender is appreciated for his vast knowledge of environmental law, which covers ocean, mining and administrative law, as well as for his broad litigation practice which includes natural resource issues. **Richard Allan** of Marten Law PLLC is described by sources as *"a very good environmental practitioner"* who *"does a fine job."* He focuses on land use, permitting and development issues relating to projects, as well as the litigation of cases concerning water rights and environmental enforcement. He recently joined the firm from Ball Janik.

# INTELLECTUAL PROPERTY

Commentary about individuals can be found under their firm's paragraph. If the firm has no paragraph (is not ranked) look at Other Notable Practitioners.

| Intellectual Property |
| --- |
| **Leading Firms** |

**Band 1**
Klarquist Sparkman, LLP
Stoel Rives LLP

**Band 2**
Marger Johnson & McCollom PC
Perkins Coie LLP
Tonkon Torp LLP *

**Band 3**
Schwabe, Williamson & Wyatt

*Indicates firm with profile.*
*Alphabetical order within each band. Band 1 is the highest.*

## Band 1

### Klarquist Sparkman, LLP
**THE FIRM** This dedicated IP boutique is universally acknowledged as one of the strongest in the state, and is also involved in representing significant clients across the nation. Clients laud the team's deep expertise across all facets of IP work, including trade secrets, copyright procurement, patent prosecution and IP litigation.

**Sources say:** *"They have some outstanding lawyers. The quality is good across the board – it's a high-quality firm."*

**KEY INDIVIDUALS William Noonan** heads the firm's biotechnology group and is described by sources as an *"outstanding patent prosecutor."* He utilizes his background in medicine to assist clients from a broad range of scientific industries, including the molecular biochemistry, medical devices and pharmacology spheres. **John Vandenberg** is a highly prized litigator who represents some of the Pacific Northwest's biggest companies in cases around the

country. Sources describe him as a *"terrific lawyer, very intelligent, and very skilled in patent litigation."* **Scott Davis** is a litigator who represents clients from the computer arts, chemicals and mechanical fields in cases around the country.

### Stoel Rives LLP
**THE FIRM** This market-leading Oregon firm has one of the state's premier IP practices, allowing it to represent the state's biggest companies in all types of matters. The team is exceptionally adept at patent and trademark portfolio management, IP litigation and domain name and trademark disputes. Recent highlights include representing Electro Scientific Industries in a range of issues relating to semiconductors.

**KEY INDIVIDUALS Paul Angello** is a well-regarded patent attorney who has deep knowledge of patent prosecution, infringement and litigation related to various technologies. **John Rafter** uses his background in mechanical engineering in his practice as a patent prosecutor. He is particularly adept at handling client patent portfolios, filing for and prosecuting patent and trademark applications, and defending intellectual property rights. Patent prosecutor **Kassim Ferris** handles domestic and international patent prosecution, trademark registration and IP dispute resolution for clients from a wide range of industries. **Randolph Foster** is a litigator with vast experience in IP law. He has recently handled a series of significant trademark infringement and licensing issues on behalf of high-profile clients. **Gary Glisson** is cochair of the firm's technology ventures group and an expert in trademarks and licensing law. He represents clients from the software, renewable resources and e-commerce industries. **Wally Van Valkenburg** focuses his IP practice on transactions and business counseling, representing a wide range of clients in matters such as strategic alliances, technology

transfers and M&A. **Anne Glazer** is a respected attorney who concentrates her practice on intellectual property licensing issues such as trademarks, software and patents, as well as IP enforcement and dispute resolution.

## Band 2

### Marger Johnson & McCollom PC

**THE FIRM** This boutique is one of Portland's most established patent law firms. The team is particularly recognized for its skill in patent prosecution involving computer software, hardware and electronics. The firm is also experienced in IP litigation, licensing matters, portfolio strategy and alternative dispute resolution.

**Sources say:** "They have distinguished themselves by focusing on hi-tech software. They have a specialty, and they're successful at that."

**KEY INDIVIDUALS Alexander Johnson** is a patent attorney with longstanding experience in the field. He is skilled in patent infringement issues, summary judgments and jury trials.

### Perkins Coie LLP
See profile on p.2548

**THE FIRM** This leading national firm's Oregon branch has a deep knowledge of IP law, with particular experience in the Hatch-Waxman Act, trademark litigation and patents relating to mobile device applications. The firm's roster of clients includes Icebreaker, adidas and Google.

**KEY INDIVIDUALS** IP litigator **Scott Eads** is experienced in trying cases involving the Hatch-Waxman Act, semiconductor and mechanical technologies, and trademark infringements.

### Tonkon Torp LLP
See profile on p.2183

**THE FIRM** This established Portland firm has a strong IP practice with expertise in all areas of the law, including trademark prosecution and protection, disputes and protection, and licensing transactions. Clients include Oregon Health & Science University, Laika and Key Technology. The group recently represented Apeldyn in two patent infringement actions totaling more than $500 million.

**Sources say:** "They're approachable, they communicate clearly, and they're incredibly responsive."

**KEY INDIVIDUALS Vicki Ballou** (see p.2175) concentrates her IP practice on enforcement, licensing work and agreements. Clients describe her as "a personable, hardworking lawyer who gives good client service." **David Aman** (see p.2175) chairs the firm's IP practice group and is held in high regard for his work, which combines business and IP litigation. He represents both plaintiffs and defendants in a variety of cases, including patent, trademark and copyright infringement matters.

## Band 3

### Schwabe, Williamson & Wyatt

**THE FIRM** This Pacific Northwest firm continues to impress with an IP practice that is adept at handling both litigation and patent prosecution, with the former being a particular area of strength. The team's litigators are licensed to practice in states across the region, and represent clients from the electronics, aerospace and entertainment industries.

**KEY INDIVIDUALS Peter Heuser** is admired in the market for his deep experience as an IP attorney. He conducts both patent prosecution and litigation, frequently representing both plaintiff and defendant clients in jury trials. **David Axelrod** practices both business and IP litigation. He represents a number of prominent clients from the computer, semiconductor and telecom industries in patent and trade secret lawsuits.

## Other Notable Practitioners

**Jacob Vilhauer** of Chernoff, Vilhauer, McClung & Stenzel is a longstanding practitioner of IP law, and is particularly adept at advising manufacturers of mechanical and electrical industrial equipment on matters such as patent procurement, enforcement and infringement defense, licensing, and joint technology development. **Peter Staples**, also of Chernoff, Vilhauer, McClung & Stenzel, is well respected for his broad IP practice. One admiring source states: "He's a guy I respect a lot. He's a good lawyer who covers the gamut of IP work."

## LABOR & EMPLOYMENT

Commentary about individuals can be found under their firm's paragraph. If the firm has no paragraph (is not ranked) look at Other Notable Practitioners.

### Labor & Employment
### Leading Firms

**Band 1**
Barran Liebman LLP *
Stoel Rives LLP

**Band 2**
Buchanan Angeli Altschul & Sullivan LLP
Bullard Law *
Davis Wright Tremaine LLP *
Littler Mendelson, PC *

**Band 3**
Fisher & Phillips LLP *
Schwabe, Williamson & Wyatt
Tonkon Torp LLP *

**Band 4**
Lane Powell PC *
Miller Nash LLP *
Ogletree, Deakins, Nash, Smoak & Stewart, PC *

\* Indicates firm / individual with profile.
†ONP = Other Notable Practitioner.

*The firms are in alphabetical order by firm name.*

## Barran Liebman LLP
**See profile on p.2180**

**THE FIRM** This Portland-based boutique firm is acknowledged as one of the state's premier labor and employment firms. The 16-strong team is proficient in all facets of labor and employment law, including employee benefits, labor relations, employment litigation and counseling. Clients include Umpqua Bank, Portland Schools Foundation and Hoffman Construction.

**Sources say:** *"They operate as true professionals, with both the knowledge and skills to offer sound legal advice. They are responsive, and communicate in layman's terms for employers to address and understand."*

**KEY INDIVIDUALS** The *"excellent"* and *"outstanding"* **Paula Barran** (see p.2175) is lauded by sources for her longstanding labor and employment practice, which includes management training, employment arbitrations and complex litigation in both state and federal courts. **Edwin Harnden** (see p.2176) is universally recognized as one of the state's best labor and employment lawyers. One client remarks: *"He's great, and an excellent resource. He's very professional and timely, strives to understand the issues, and provides you with a clear path to resolve concerns coupled with risks."* The *"top-flight"* **Richard Liebman** (see p.2177) is a highly experienced attorney who is respected for his skill in labor and employment matters. Sources state: *"He's excellent – an obvious leader."*

### Labor & Employment
### Senior Statesmen

**Senior Statesmen: distinguished older practitioners**

| | |
|---|---|
| Jernstedt Kenneth | *Bullard Law* |

### Leading Individuals

**Band 1**

| | |
|---|---|
| Barran Paula | *Barran Liebman LLP* * |
| Bernick Carol | *Davis Wright Tremaine LLP* |
| Buchanan Paul | *Buchanan Angeli Altschul & Sullivan LLP* |
| Harnden Edwin | *Barran Liebman LLP* * |
| Joseph Pedersen Amy | *Stoel Rives LLP* |
| Kisch Victor J | *Stoel Rives LLP* |
| Liebman Richard | *Barran Liebman LLP* * |

**Band 2**

| | |
|---|---|
| Amburgey Larry | *Littler Mendelson, PC* * |
| Angeli Courtney | *Buchanan Angeli Altschul & Sullivan LLP* |
| Belnavis Clarence | *Fisher & Phillips LLP* * |
| Carey Robert | *Tonkon Torp LLP* * |
| Creps Clay | *Tonkon Torp LLP* * |
| Grinfas Dan | *Buchanan Angeli Altschul & Sullivan LLP* |
| Kitchel Chris | *Stoel Rives LLP* |
| Lively Leah C | *Ogletree, Deakins, Nash, Smoak & Stewart* * |
| Martin Chrys | *Davis Wright Tremaine LLP* |
| Meneghello Richard | *Fisher & Phillips LLP* * |
| Peck Kathy A | *Williams, Zografos & Peck (ONP)*† |
| Ryan Sarah J | *Jackson Lewis LLP (ONP)*† * |
| Schleuning Elizabeth A | *Schwabe, Williamson & Wyatt* |
| Symes David PR | *Ogletree, Deakins, Nash, Smoak & Stewart* * |
| Wilson David H | *Bullard Law* |

**Band 3**

| | |
|---|---|
| Alli Jr Richard J | *Bullard Law* |
| Altschul Andrew | *Buchanan Angeli Altschul & Sullivan LLP* |
| Brainard Barbara A | *Stoel Rives LLP* |
| Damm Jacqueline | *Bullard Law* |
| Garone Michael | *Schwabe, Williamson & Wyatt* |
| Keith Calvin L | *Perkins Coie LLP (ONP)*† |
| Kramer Thomas I | *Bullard Law* |
| Krueger Allyson S | *Dunn Carney Allen Higgins & Tongue (ONP)*† |
| Leachman Tamsen L | *Fisher & Phillips LLP* * |
| Mooney Jenna L | *Davis Wright Tremaine LLP* |
| O'Connor Karen L | *Stoel Rives LLP* |
| Reeves Edward | *Stoel Rives LLP* |
| Rubin Howard | *Littler Mendelson, PC* * |
| Yelnosky Maryann | *Bullard Law* |

**Band 4**

| | |
|---|---|
| Alpern Amy | *Littler Mendelson, PC* * |
| Barnwell Francis T | *Bullard Law* |
| Hindman Kathryn M | *Bullard Law* |
| Hosenpud David | *Lane Powell PC* * |
| Janove Jathan | *Ogletree, Deakins, Nash, Smoak & Stewart* * |

### Labor & Employment: Immigration
### Leading Firms

**Band 1**
Black Helterline LLP
Parrilli Renison
Tonkon Torp LLP *

### Leading Individuals

**Band 1**

| | |
|---|---|
| Butte Dagmar | *Parker, Butte & Lane PC (ONP)*† |
| Hribernick Paul R | *Black Helterline LLP* |
| Maier Bradley | *Schwabe, Williamson & Wyatt* |
| Owren Turid | *Tonkon Torp LLP* * |
| Renison Brent | *Parrilli Renison* |

**Band 2**

| | |
|---|---|
| Donaldson Robert W | *Black Helterline LLP* |
| Mei James M | *Davis Wright Tremaine LLP* |
| Morrissey Jennifer M | *Black Helterline LLP* |
| Newhall David G | *Black Helterline LLP* |
| Parrilli Tifani | *Parrilli Renison* |
| Perkins Alan Curtis | *Tonkon Torp LLP* * |

## Black Helterline LLP

**THE FIRM** This Portland firm has an acclaimed immigration practice which aids businesses in issues such as obtaining temporary work visas, labor certifications and counseling on avoiding employer sanctions and discrimination claims. The firm also has a thriving labor and employment practice, which includes expertise in matters including wage and hour regulations, incentive compensation programs and employment discrimination.

**KEY INDIVIDUALS Jennifer Morrissey** attracts plaudits for her skill in a broad range of immigration matters affecting executives and management-level employees from the hi-tech, education and marketing industries. The well-respected **Paul Hribernick** is an expert in all manner of business immigration issues, including extraordinary ability petitions, labor certifications and nonimmigrant visas. **Robert Donaldson** is an experienced attorney who concentrates his practice on immigration issues such as employment-based immigrant visas, nonimmigrant visas and labor certifications. **David Newhall**, chair of the firm's immigration practice group, is a well-regarded attorney who specializes in obtaining a variety of nonimmigrant and immigrant visas. He represents a broad range of clients, including those from the construction, creative and mining industries.

## Buchanan Angeli Altschul & Sullivan LLP

**THE FIRM** This impressive boutique, consisting of eight attorneys, is dedicated solely to labor and employment law. The team is experienced in all types of related law, including litigation, counseling and mediation. Clients include BendBroadband, JELD-WEN and L'Oréal. Recent highlights include successfully representing Standard Insurance in an ERISA dispute.

**Sources say:** *"Their service is top-notch. Their diversity and depth of experience provide us with the resources and answers we need. We are very pleased with how the group operates, and we refer colleagues to them anytime we get the opportunity."*

**KEY INDIVIDUALS** The highly respected **Paul Buchanan** has deep experience litigating employment cases throughout the Pacific Northwest. Clients say: *"He's responsive, practical and efficient. We can always reach him."* The *"excellent"* **Courtney Angeli** is an employment litigator who represents some of the firm's biggest clients in key cases in both state and federal courts. She also provides training and counseling to employers. **Dan Grinfas** is singled out by clients as someone who is *"extremely customer focused"* and who has *"an encyclopedic regulatory knowledge. Rather than looking something up, I just call him."* He is a specialist in wage and hour and family medical leave issues. **Andrew Altschul** is an expert in ERISA litigation, frequently appearing in cases across the country. He also offers clients advice on other employment issues, such as collective bargaining, wage and hour issues, and employee training.

### Bullard Law
See profile on p.2181

**THE FIRM** This well-regarded labor and employment boutique has one of the deepest benches for its practice area in the state. The team has the ability to handle the full range of labor and employment matters, and is well known for representing companies from the healthcare and hospitality industries, as illustrated by its recent representation of Hilton Hotels and Salem Health.

**KEY INDIVIDUALS** **Kenneth Jernstedt** is held in high regard for his labor and employment practice, which focuses on traditional labor law. One peer states: *"His reputation is really sound and has been for many years. I wouldn't hesitate to refer the right case to him."* **Richard Alli** concentrates on traditional labor law, and is experienced in areas such as collective bargaining, NLRB and ERB proceedings, and strike operations. He counsels many of the firm's hospitality clients in matters such as union negotiations and preventive advice. The well-respected **David Wilson** is a longtime practitioner of labor and employment law, with appellate work being a particular area of expertise. **Jacqueline Damm** concentrates her practice on traditional labor law, representing both public and private sector employers in union avoidance issues, labor arbitrations and collective bargaining negotiations. **Maryann Yelnosky** is a labor and employment litigator much admired in the market, who utilizes her background in medical malpractice defense to represent the firm's many healthcare clients. **Thomas Kramer** is a respected specialist in employee benefits law, with ERISA law and 401(k) plan issues being particular areas of expertise. **Francis Barnwell** has over 30 years' experience as a litigator of labor and employment law, including frequently conducting class action litigation defense. He also offers preventive counseling, as well as acting as general counsel for some of the firm's largest clients. **Kathryn Hindman** has an

employment-related advice practice, which consists of litigation prevention and counseling on issues such as complex leave, workplace harassment and discrimination, and family medical leave.

### Davis Wright Tremaine LLP
See profile on p.2544

**THE FIRM** The Portland office of this full-service firm offers a comprehensive labor and employment practice with expertise in the full scope of related issues. Class actions, wage and hour matters, and employee benefits are particular specialties for the team. The office also has a thriving immigration practice which is experienced in a wide range of complicated issues. The firm's labor and employment clients include Whole Foods, Les Schwab Tire Centers and Alaska Airlines, while Daimler Trucks North America and REC Silicon are among the immigration practice's clients.

**Sources say:** *"I am very impressed with the support I receive from this law office. They have top-rate client service and are always willing to take the extra step to help me."*

**KEY INDIVIDUALS** The *"excellent"* **Carol Bernick** earns high praise from peers and clients for her employment trial and class action litigation defense practice, which focuses on the healthcare and financial industries. The well-regarded **Chrys Martin** has a broad labor and employment practice which covers litigation, counseling and training. According to sources: *"There's been nothing she can't help with."* **James Mei** is an immigration lawyer who is especially proficient in international business transactions and Chinese joint venture law. One client marvels: *"Since I have been working with Jim he has taught me so much about the immigration process. He is a pleasure to work with and is always readily available to take my calls."* **Jenna Mooney** has an employment litigation and counseling practice which encompasses wage and hour matters, trade secret and noncompetition litigation, and training in diversity and harassment issues.

### Fisher & Phillips LLP
See profile on p.1107

**THE FIRM** The Portland office of this national firm is staffed with 11 attorneys who are adept in all aspects of labor and employment law. The team is especially commended for its expertise in wage and hour class actions, as well as cases involving disability discrimination and retaliation claims. Clients include Taco Bell, Legacy Health System and DHL Express.

**KEY INDIVIDUALS** **Clarence Belnavis** (see p.2176) has a wide-ranging labor and employment litigation practice which covers wrongful discharge, employment class actions and sexual harassment. One client states: *"He's creative, knows the law, and is responsive, detail-oriented and cost-effective."* **Tamsen Leachman** (see p.2176) is a well-regarded labor and employment attorney who represents employers in matters including grievances, arbitrations and collective bargaining. **Richard Meneghello** (see p.2177) is a recognized specialist in disability discrimination issues, while other areas of expertise include wage and hour issues, injured worker discrimination, and family and

medical leave discrimination. According to sources: *"He is a blend of assertiveness and wisdom – he has a great balance."*

### Lane Powell PC
See profile on p.2547

**THE FIRM** Lane Powell's Oregon labor and employment group consists of nine attorneys who are able to handle the full spectrum of related law. The team is especially adept in union issues, arbitrations, and wage and hour matters. Clients include Nordstrom, Wells Fargo and Pendleton Woolen Mills.

**KEY INDIVIDUALS** **David Hosenpud** (see p.2176) is a litigator whose practice combines labor and employment and general litigation. Areas of expertise include the defense of discrimination claims, wrongful discharge and class actions.

### Littler Mendelson, PC
See profile on p.688

**THE FIRM** The Oregon branch of this specialized labor and employment giant continues to command respect across the region. The team is experienced in the full range of labor and employment law, including labor management relations, HR counseling, and class action prevention and litigation. It serves a wide variety of clients both in the Pacific Northwest and nationwide.

**KEY INDIVIDUALS** **Larry Amburgey** (see p.2175) is admired in the market for his acumen in labor and employment advice law. He counsels management on issues such as unfair labor practice matters, union organizing campaigns, and discrimination and wrongful discharge claims. **Howard Rubin** (see p.2178) focuses his labor and employment practice on traditional labor law, such as labor arbitrations, union organizing and negotiations. He often appears before federal and state administrative agencies, including the NLRB and the ERB. **Amy Alpern** (see p.2175) is an employment litigator complimented by one source as *"a very good, very smart lawyer."* She litigates cases involving race discrimination, sexual harassment and disability discrimination issues.

### Miller Nash LLP
See profile on p.2182

**THE FIRM** This Pacific Northwest stalwart has a broad labor and employment practice which is particularly renowned for its representation of clients from the education, manufacturing and financial industries, as well as Native American tribes and public entities. The team handles matters such as NLRB proceedings, union issues and discrimination cases. Clients include Portland Public Schools, ESCO and Cascade Corporation.

**Sources say:** *"They have a lot of expertise and give very good service. It provides me with the bandwidth to do a more robust job."*

**KEY INDIVIDUALS** Department head **Wayne Landsverk** is the firm's practice contact.

## Ogletree, Deakins, Nash, Smoak & Stewart, PC
See profile on p.1110

**THE FIRM** The Portland office of this international labor and employment firm is still relatively new, but has made an impression on the market with its team's talent and experience. The nine-strong group represents significant clients throughout the Pacific Northwest, California, Utah and Alaska, including Home Depot, Rite Aid and Frontier Management.

**KEY INDIVIDUALS Leah Lively** (see p.2177) is admired for her talent as a labor and employment litigator, and is admitted to practice in Oregon, California and Idaho. She recently represented Home Depot in Oregon against non-class claims of harassment, discrimination, retaliation, and wage and hour violations. **David Symes** (see p.2179) is respected for his wide-ranging labor and employment practice, which covers litigation and arbitration issues, as well as the enforcement and defense of noncompetition and nonsolicitation agreements. He frequently handles class action, wage and hour, and disability litigation matters. **Jathan Janove** (see p.2176) is a seasoned attorney and former litigator who now concentrates his practice on labor and employment advice, counseling and training.

## Parrilli Renison

**THE FIRM** This compact boutique has a stellar reputation as one of the state's best immigration practices. The team counsels domestic and international clients from a variety of industries in immigration matters, such as visa issues and immigration compliance.

**KEY INDIVIDUALS Brent Renison** enjoys a healthy reputation for his skill as an immigration lawyer, and is considered an expert in naturalization and residency applications, as well as conducting litigation and class action suits. **Tifani Parrilli** is a specialist in business immigration issues such as labor certification applications, immigrant and nonimmigrant visas, and extraordinary ability petitions.

## Schwabe, Williamson & Wyatt

**THE FIRM** The Portland office of this Pacific Northwest firm has a labor and employment team respected in the market for its skill across the gamut of employment law matters. The group is especially adept in wage and hour cases, wrongful termination cases and arbitrations. Clients include Morgan Stanley Smith Barney, Columbia Forest Products and Thompson Metal Fabrication.

**KEY INDIVIDUALS Bradley Maier** is a highly regarded immigration attorney who represents foreign and domestic clients in a variety of matters. He has particular expertise in obtaining H-1B, E-1/E-2 and O-1 nonimmigrant visas, as well being adroit in I-9 employment verification compliance. Practice chair **Elizabeth Schleuning** is an experienced litigator who is especially skilled in discrimination cases as well as wage and hour class action lawsuits. The well-respected **Michael Garone** has over three decades of experience in traditional labor law. He is an expert in arbitration law, as well as being a seasoned litigator who has appeared in federal and state courts in the Pacific Northwest at both trial and appellate level.

## Stoel Rives LLP

**THE FIRM** This key Pacific Northwest player has an impressive labor and employment group which is adept at handling all aspects of related law. Areas of expertise include wage and hour and discrimination class action defense, ERISA law, and employment law compliance advice. The firm regularly acts for a series of major organizations, including Costco, Nike and Gunderson.

**KEY INDIVIDUALS Amy Joseph Pedersen** is a seasoned labor and employment attorney who has a litigation and counseling practice. **Victor Kisch** is held in high regard for his labor and employment practice. He focuses on traditional labor law, employment litigation, and training and risk analysis. **Chris Kitchel** is a widely respected trial lawyer with deep experience. She is an expert in employment law matters, and is particularly experienced in the labor and employment issues health organizations face. She has represented the Kaiser Health Plan Foundation in all of its Northwest employment litigation. **Barbara Brainard** is experienced in representing employers in a wide range of labor and employment issues, including sexual harassment, class actions and wrongful discharge cases. She is particularly admired by peers for her expertise in workers' compensation law. **Karen O'Connor** draws praise from across the board for her wide-ranging labor and employment practice. **Edward Reeves** has a labor and employment counseling practice which focuses on advising management. He also acts as a mediator and arbitrator.

## Tonkon Torp LLP
See profile on p.2183

**THE FIRM** Tonkon Torp is commended for an impressive level of client service across its labor and employment and immigration practices. The labor and employment team handles all types of related law, such as traditional labor issues, litigation and employee benefits, while the immigration group is expert in temporary business immigration visas and employment-based permanent residence petitions. Clients include Georgia-Pacific and Stimson Lumber Company.

**Sources say:** *"They're a terrific team, and they know their stuff. I can rely on them for their expertise and legal prowess."*
**KEY INDIVIDUALS** The *"responsive"* and *"personable"* **Turid Owren** (see p.2177) is an immigration attorney who attracts glowing praise from clients, with one stating that *"she's really good about engaging our organization and knowing our people. She's very professional and knowledgeable."* **Robert Carey** (see p.2176) is a well-regarded labor and employment litigator and arbitrator who handles wrongful discharge, wage and hour, and whistle-blower cases. He also regularly acts as a mediator on employment and benefits cases. The *"terrific"* **Clay Creps** (see p.2176) is admired for his labor and employment litigation and counseling practice, which includes COBRA law, wage and overtime issues and discrimination cases. According to clients: *"He is masterful at explaining tricky employment concepts to our front-line managers."* Immigration attorney **Alan Perkins** (see p.2177) assists employers with a range of such issues. He also counsels clients on employment matters such as those arising from M&A involving employees who are foreign nationals.

## Other Notable Practitioners

The well-respected **Allyson Krueger** of Dunn Carney Allen Higgins & Tongue LLP has a broad labor and employment practice which covers litigation, advice, policy review and investigations into workplace misconduct. **Dagmar Butte** of Parker, Butte & Lane PC has a combined immigration and corporate practice. She is regarded by peers as one of the state's finest practitioners in the immigration space. **Kathy Peck** of Williams, Zografos & Peck is renowned for her labor and employment practice. She represents both public and private employers in a wide variety of labor matters, such as collective bargaining and interest arbitration proceedings. Employment litigator **Calvin Keith** of Perkins Coie LLP is head of the group's Portland employment law practice, and frequently handles class action, wage and hour, and unlawful competition cases. His clients include UPS, Boise and Weyerhaeuser. Former Ball Janik partner **Sarah Ryan** (see p.2178) of Jackson Lewis LLP attracts praise for her employment law practice. One source remarks: *"I attribute the top-notch service, expertise, practical approach and cost-effective strategy that I received to Sarah."*

# LITIGATION GENERAL COMMERCIAL

Commentary about individuals can be found under their firm's paragraph. If the firm has no paragraph (is not ranked) look at Other Notable Practitioners.

## Litigation: General Commercial
### Leading Firms

**Band 1**
Markowitz, Herbold, Glade & Mehlhaf PC
Perkins Coie LLP
Stoel Rives LLP
Stoll Berne

**Band 2**
Davis Wright Tremaine LLP *
Miller Nash LLP *
Schwabe, Williamson & Wyatt
Tonkon Torp LLP *

**Band 3**
Ater Wynne LLP
Ball Janik LLP
Dunn Carney Allen Higgins & Tongue LLP
Lane Powell PC *

*\* Indicates firm / individual with profile.*
*†ONP = Other Notable Practitioner.*

## Band 1

### Markowitz, Herbold, Glade & Mehlhaf PC

**THE FIRM** This firm is recognized by peers as one of the region's finest trial and litigation boutiques. It has the ability to handle a wide variety of litigation types, including high-stakes business disputes, business torts, unfair competition and contractual rights. The team recently defended The Progressive Group of Insurance Companies in a putative class action alleging breach of contract. Other clients include Evraz Oregon Steel, Portland General Electric and the State of Oregon.

**Sources say:** *"I would recommend Markowitz Herbold highly for complex business litigation."*

**KEY INDIVIDUALS David Markowitz** is a trial lawyer who commands respect from the market, with one source stating: *"He's an excellent attorney who is very well prepared."* He recently represented the State of Oregon against Philip Morris in the collection of payments from major tobacco companies. **Peter Glade** is an expert in complex commercial litigation, and recently acted on behalf of The Progressive Group of Insurance Companies in the class action dispute. **Renée Rothauge** is a well-respected attorney who has a thriving intellectual property and business litigation practice. **Kerry Shepherd** focuses his practice on representing the firm's financial and banking clients in matters such as securities fraud, business torts and lender liability disputes.

### Perkins Coie LLP

See profile on p.2548

**THE FIRM** This eminent national firm with strong Pacific Northwest roots has a market-leading litigation practice in Oregon. The Portland office, consisting of 26 attorneys, is skilful in all types of litigation, with areas of particular expertise being class actions, corporate governance and product liability. Recent highlights include representing Les Schwab Tire Centers in a $140 million class action dispute.

**KEY INDIVIDUALS** Known as a top litigator and savvy pracitioner, **Stephen English** enjoys a reputation as one of the state's leading trial lawyers. He has experience in trade secrets, commercial torts and high-stakes matters. **Paul Fortino** is a much-admired trial lawyer who concentrates his practice on intellectual property and patent cases, as well as complex business torts. He is known among commentators to have a longstanding reputation as a leading litigator. **James Gidley** is a well-respected litigator with deep experience in areas such as real estate litigation, insurance coverage disputes and work site accidents. Sources know him to be an excellent trial lawyer. Rising star **Thomas Johnson** handles a wide variety of complex business disputes, including antitrust and corporate governance litigation.

### Stoel Rives LLP

**THE FIRM** Portland stalwart Stoel Rives has one of the state's most illustrious litigation practices, as well as the breadth and resources to tackle most types of dispute. Class actions and arbitrations are notable areas of expertise for the team, which is particularly experienced in representing companies from the forestry, life sciences and renewable energy industries. The group's prominence in significant matters is exemplified by its recent representation of ESCO in an ICC arbitration against its licensee involving $2 billion in damages.

**KEY INDIVIDUALS Joel Mullin** is a prominent trial lawyer who attracts glowing praise from clients for his tactical skills. **Lois Rosenbaum** is held in high regard in the market for her longstanding experience as a litigator, with areas of expertise including securities and product liability litigation. She recently represented Mentor Graphics and its board in a class action filed by a shareholder. **Gregory Mowe** attracts acclaim for his real estate and business litigation practice, and is recognized as a specialist in condemnation cases. **Randolph Foster** has a combined business and intellectual property litigation practice. He represents clients from the advertising, software and petroleum products industries in a wide variety of matters.

### Stoll Berne

**THE FIRM** Stoll Berne is noted for having one of the state's premier litigation practices. The group is best known for its prowess in complex business, securities, intellectual property and class action litigation. Clients includes Columbia Sportswear Company, Oregon Public Employees' Retirement Systems and Paulson Investment, and the firm enjoys a healthy reputation for both plaintiff-side and defense work.

**Sources say:** *"They are a tremendous team of aggressive, smart litigators. They're highly professional and easy to deal with."*

**KEY INDIVIDUALS Gary Berne** is an expert in securities, partnership and class action litigation, and is experienced in representing clients before the SEC and FINRA. Complimented as *"a fine lawyer who gets right to the heart of the matter,"* **Keith Ketterling** handles complex business

## Litigation: General Commercial
### Senior Statesmen

| Senior Statesmen: | distinguished older practitioners |
|---|---|
| Crow William | Schwabe, Williamson & Wyatt |
| Houser Douglas | Bullivant Houser Bailey PC (ONP)† |
| Skerritt Daniel | Tonkon Torp LLP * |
| Stoll Robert | Stoll Berne |

### Leading Individuals

**Star individuals**

| | |
|---|---|
| English Stephen | Perkins Coie LLP |
| Markowitz David | Markowitz, Herbold, Glade & Mehlhaf PC |
| Tongue Thomas H | Dunn Carney Allen Higgins & Tongue LLP |

**Band 1**

| | |
|---|---|
| Berne Gary | Stoll Berne |
| Blackhurst Steven | Ater Wynne LLP |
| Fortino Paul | Perkins Coie LLP |
| Martson Jr William F | Tonkon Torp LLP * |
| Mullin Joel A | Stoel Rives LLP |
| Rosenbaum Lois O | Stoel Rives LLP |

**Band 2**

| | |
|---|---|
| Arellano Joseph C | Kennedy, Watts, Arellano & Ricks (ONP)† |
| Dulcich Thomas | Schwabe, Williamson & Wyatt |
| Gidley James | Perkins Coie LLP |
| Glade Peter | Markowitz, Herbold, Glade & Mehlhaf PC |
| Haglund Michael E | Haglund Kelley Jones & Wilder LLP (ONP)† |
| Ketterling Keith A | Stoll Berne |
| McDermott James T | Ball Janik LLP |
| McGrory John F | Davis Wright Tremaine LLP |
| Mowe Gregory | Stoel Rives LLP |
| Newell Robert D | Davis Wright Tremaine LLP |
| Petranovich Milo | Lane Powell PC * |
| Richter Peter | Miller Nash LLP * |
| Rothauge Renée | Markowitz, Herbold, Glade & Mehlhaf PC |
| Sand Thomas C | Miller Nash LLP * |
| Shepherd Kerry | Markowitz, Herbold, Glade & Mehlhaf PC |
| Shlachter Robert A | Stoll Berne |

**Band 3**

| | |
|---|---|
| Axelrod David W | Schwabe, Williamson & Wyatt |
| Ernst David A | Davis Wright Tremaine LLP |
| Foster Randolph | Stoel Rives LLP |
| Larson Steve D | Stoll Berne |
| Neupert John | Miller Nash LLP * |
| O'Leary Daniel | Davis Wright Tremaine LLP |
| Rawlinson Dennis P | Miller Nash LLP * |
| Stride Jon P | Tonkon Torp LLP * |

**Up-and-coming individuals**

| | |
|---|---|
| Johnson Thomas | Perkins Coie LLP |

litigation, securities class actions and financial fraud matters. **Robert Shlachter** is deeply respected in the market for his business litigation practice, which includes intellectual property, unfair competition and complex litigation. **Steve Larson** has a broad complex business litigation practice, and is recognized for his expertise in class actions, wage and hour matters, and consumer cases. Founding partner **Robert Stoll** has extensive experience as a trial lawyer, and is admired for his impressive track record in trials within Oregon and across the West Coast.

## Band 2

### Davis Wright Tremaine LLP
See profile on p.2544

**THE FIRM** The Oregon litigation team at this renowned national firm has a deep bench of 34 attorneys who can effectively handle all varieties of litigation. The group is particularly renowned for its appellate practice, its experience in food and beverage litigation, and its acumen in complex commercial litigation. The firm recently acted for major client Comcast on a dispute concerning revenue taxation for internet access.

**Sources say:** *"Everyone we have worked with at the firm has been extraordinarily focused and committed."*

**KEY INDIVIDUALS** The *"excellent"* **John McGrory** is a much-respected litigator who focuses on securities, antitrust and shareholder matters. One client states: *"He was completely committed. We achieved our goals because of his integrity and determination, and I have nothing but the highest regard for him."* **David Ernst** is respected for his expertise in class actions relating to the food and beverage industries, and frequently represents national restaurant chains, food producers and distributors in litigation within Oregon and across the state. **Daniel O'Leary** is a trial lawyer well known in the state for his longstanding experience in environmental matters and related insurance coverage cases. He also offers an alternative dispute resolution service covering torts and real estate. The well-respected **Robert Newell** is a commercial litigator experienced in cases involving trade secrets, securities and unfair competition. He is particularly adept at representing healthcare and software companies in contentious matters.

### Miller Nash LLP
See profile on p.2182

**THE FIRM** Miller Nash has a strong track record in handling a wide variety of litigation types, with complex corporate litigation, securities issues and professional liability claims being strong areas for the team. The practice is particularly expert in handling litigation for clients from the banking, financial services and insurance industries.

**Sources say:** *"I have a high regard for all of the lawyers there."*

**KEY INDIVIDUALS** **Peter Richter** (see p.2178) is described by commentators as a *"strong, solid trial lawyer."* His practice focuses on a wide range of areas, including insurance, partnership, creditors' rights and timber law. *"Excellent"* litigator **Thomas Sand** (see p.2178) is well

regarded by peers. He primarily focuses on securities issues, and frequently tries jury cases in federal and state courts across Oregon and Washington. **John Neupert** (see p.2177) is acclaimed for his practice, which has spanned over three decades. He handles class actions, corporate governance, lender liability defense and tax litigation. **Dennis Rawlinson** (see p.2178) is experienced in handling trials and arbitrations concerning a wide variety of matters, such as shareholder disputes, professional negligence and breach of contract.

### Schwabe, Williamson & Wyatt

**THE FIRM** Schwabe is able to offer clients a fully statewide litigation service thanks to its offices in Portland, Bend and Salem. The team represents a variety of companies from the corporate, financial and timber products industries in a vast array of disputes. Major clients include KeyBank, HSBC and Columbia Forest Products.

**KEY INDIVIDUALS** **David Axelrod** is regarded as an expert in patent, trade secret and complex business litigation. One source states: *"He really knows his stuff – he's a very fine lawyer."* The *"terrific"* **Thomas Dulcich** has forged a reputation as a litigator adept at handling a wide array of subjects, including business and securities litigation, wrongful death suits and discrimination cases. The eminent **William Crow** commands respect for his longstanding practice, which includes antitrust, commercial and environmental litigation. He also has an active mediation and arbitration practice which covers a great variety of cases.

### Tonkon Torp LLP
See profile on p.2183

**THE FIRM** The litigation team at this prominent Portland firm is particularly admired for its skill in matters involving securities, professional liability, and product liability and torts. The group is renowned for representing clients from the banking, investment securities and technology industries, among others, with key clients including The Greenbrier Companies, Nike and Stimson Lumber Company.

**Sources say:** *"They are very high quality – very responsive and technically very strong."*

**KEY INDIVIDUALS** *"Top-notch"* trial lawyer **William Martson** (see p.2177) is much admired for his commercial litigation practice, which includes experience of securities, shareholder rights and commercial contract dispute litigation. **Jon Stride**'s (see p.2179) commercial litigation practice emphasizes intellectual property issues, such as patent infringement claims and trade secrets. Described as a *"top litigator"* who *"does an excellent job,"* **Daniel Skerritt** (see p.2179) has a commercial litigation practice that involves the representation of plaintiffs and defendants in a wide variety of complex litigation matters.

## Band 3

### Ater Wynne LLP

**THE FIRM** This well-regarded West Coast firm has a robust litigation practice in Oregon which is comprised of 15 attorneys. The team is particularly experienced in product liability defense, breach of contract issues and class action lawsuits. Clients include Northwest Pipe Company, FLIR Systems and Siemens Wind Power.

**Sources say:** *"They are professional and personable. They mix cutting-edge capability and leadership and experience."*

**KEY INDIVIDUALS** The *"excellent"* **Steven Blackhurst** is celebrated for his commercial litigation practice, which has spanned over 30 years. One source states: *"I think very highly of Steve. He's a problem solver, very professional and very smart."*

### Ball Janik LLP

**THE FIRM** This established Pacific Northwest firm is recognized for its litigation practice, with clients particularly commending the team's responsiveness and skill. The group is especially proficient in insurance coverage matters, class actions and real estate litigation. Clients include Johnson & Johnson, Oregon Health & Science University and Lone Star Funds.

**Sources say:** *"They go above and beyond what is expected. They provide top-notch service."*

**KEY INDIVIDUALS** **James McDermott** is a business litigator and trial lawyer who is a specialist in insurance coverage matters. According to clients: *"He's on top of his game when it comes to strategy."*

### Dunn Carney Allen Higgins & Tongue LLP

**THE FIRM** This Portland firm has a litigation practice particularly known for its expertise in insurance coverage disputes. Other areas of strength include professional malpractice, appellate and natural resources litigation. Clients come from a range of industrial sectors, and include major names such as Allstate Insurance, Wal-Mart and Union Pacific Railroad.

**KEY INDIVIDUALS** Trial lawyer **Thomas Tongue** attracts widespread praise and respect for his complex civil litigation and health law practice. Sources say that he is *"one of the most honorable and best lawyers that I know, and one that I have great confidence in."*

### Lane Powell PC
See profile on p.2547

**THE FIRM** The Portland office of this Pacific Northwest firm is staffed by a deep bench of 33 attorneys. The group has a strong reputation for litigation in the financial services, securities and class action spheres, and also has a thriving mortgage litigation practice. Major clients such as Wells Fargo, JPMorgan and Chartis Insurance emphasize the firm's prominence in the financial sector.

**Sources say:** *"I was very pleased with the level of service and attention to my case."*

**KEY INDIVIDUALS** **Milo Petranovich** (see p.2178) is held in high regard for his complex civil and corporate litigation practice, with sources declaring him *"a very fine lit-*

igator." He has deep experience of cases involving corporate governance, white-collar criminal defense and securities fraud.

## REAL ESTATE

Commentary about individuals can be found under their firm's paragraph. If the firm has no paragraph (is not ranked) look at Other Notable Practitioners.

### Other Notable Practitioners

**Joseph Arellano** of Kennedy, Watts, Arellano & Ricks LLP handles securities work and professional liability defense. According to sources: "*He's very highly respected and easy to work with.*" **Michael Haglund** of Haglund Kelley Jones & Wilder LLP is widely respected for his expertise in antitrust

cases and maritime law. "*His reputation as a litigator is sharp, tough and professional. He's very good,*" say commentators. The "*excellent*" **Douglas Houser** of Bullivant Houser Bailey PC is particularly respected for his skill in handling insurance defense claims. "*He's been an extremely highly regarded litigator in this community for a long time,*" according to interviewees.

### Real Estate
#### Leading Firms

**Band 1**
Stoel Rives LLP

**Band 2**
Ball Janik LLP
Davis Wright Tremaine LLP *
Dunn Carney Allen Higgins & Tongue LLP
Perkins Coie LLP

**Band 3**
Bateman Seidel Miner Blomgren Chellis & Gram, P.C.
Lane Powell PC *
Radler White Parks & Alexander
Schwabe, Williamson & Wyatt
Tonkon Torp LLP *

**Band 4**
McEwen Gisvold LLP
Zupancic Rathbone Law Group, P.C.

### Real Estate
#### Senior Statesmen

**Senior Statesmen: distinguished older practitioners**

| | |
|---|---|
| Cantlin Richard | *Perkins Coie LLP* |
| Gisvold Dean P | *McEwen Gisvold LLP* |

#### Leading Individuals

**Star individuals**

| | |
|---|---|
| Janik Stephen | *Ball Janik LLP* |

**Band 1**

| | |
|---|---|
| Feuerstein Howard | *Stoel Rives LLP* |
| Green David W | *Stoel Rives LLP* |
| Hauck Terry | *Schwabe, Williamson & Wyatt* |
| Miller Bradley | *Ball Janik LLP* |
| Page Thomas | *Stoel Rives LLP* |
| Parker Gilbert E | *Dunn Carney Allen Higgins & Tongue LLP* |
| Radler Barbara | *Radler White Parks & Alexander* |

**Band 2**

| | |
|---|---|
| Antell Kenneth S | *Dunn Carney Allen Higgins & Tongue LLP* |
| Bateman Randall | *Bateman Seidel Miner Blomgren Chellis* |
| Bennett J David | *Landye Bennett Blumstein LLP (ONP)[†]* |
| Carter Don G | *McEwen Gisvold LLP* |
| Goodling Jonathon L | *Miller Nash LLP (ONP)[†] *|
| Grant Eugene L | *Davis Wright Tremaine LLP* |
| Guinasso John | *Schwabe, Williamson & Wyatt* |
| Keeney Jeffrey H | *Tonkon Torp LLP *|
| Lokting David | *Stoll Berne (ONP)[†]* |
| Parks Timothy M | *Radler White Parks & Alexander* |
| Rathbone Coni S | *Zupancic Rathbone Law Group, P.C.* |
| Russell III P Stephen | *Landye Bennett Blumstein LLP (ONP)[†]* |
| Smith Thomas S | *Davis Wright Tremaine LLP* |
| Voboril Joseph | *Tonkon Torp LLP *|

**Band 3**

| | |
|---|---|
| Alexander Dina E | *Radler White Parks & Alexander* |
| Dagle Paul | *Dagle Law Office, LLC (ONP)[†]* |
| Gram Chresten | *Bateman Seidel Miner Blomgren Chellis* |
| Ledoux Stephen R | *Davis Wright Tremaine LLP* |
| Manulik Mark | *Schwabe, Williamson & Wyatt* |
| Powell Bryan | *Lane Powell PC *|
| Silvey Michael | *Lane Powell PC *|
| Solomon Andrew | *Perkins Coie LLP* |
| Stayer Mark | *Schwabe, Williamson & Wyatt* |

\* Indicates firm / individual with profile.
[†]ONP = Other Notable Practitioner.

### Real Estate: Zoning/Land Use
#### Leading Individuals

**Star individuals**

| | |
|---|---|
| Janik Stephen | *Ball Janik LLP* |

**Band 1**

| | |
|---|---|
| Abel Steven W | *Stoel Rives LLP* |
| Hathaway Gregory S | *Hathaway Koback Connors LLP (ONP)[†]* |
| Pfeiffer Steven L | *Perkins Coie LLP* |
| Ramis Timothy V | *Jordan Ramis PC (ONP)[†] *|
| Robinson Michael C | *Perkins Coie LLP* |
| Sullivan Edward J | *Garvey Schubert Barer (ONP)[†]* |

**Band 2**

| | |
|---|---|
| Connors Michael | *Hathaway Koback Connors LLP (ONP)[†]* |
| Grillo Phillip E | *Davis Wright Tremaine LLP* |
| Whitlow Mark | *Perkins Coie LLP* |

**Associates to watch**

| | |
|---|---|
| Hultberg Steven P | *Radler White Parks & Alexander* |

## Band 1

### Stoel Rives LLP

**THE FIRM** The Oregon real estate and land use practice of Stoel Rives stands head and shoulders above any other in the state. Its talented practitioners are admired for their expertise in a wide range of matters, including land use law and real estate transactions. The group's recent work includes acting for Gramor Development on all aspects of two recent projects, including financing and construction. Additional clients include JPMorgan Asset Management, Fred Meyer and Jantzen Dynamic.
**KEY INDIVIDUALS Steven Abel** is highly respected by sources for his skill in negotiating Oregon's complex land use laws. Well respected in the community, he represents Fred Meyer in land use matters in numerous cities across Oregon. **David Green** is admired for his expertise as a real estate and financial transactions attorney. He recently represented Sizzler Restaurants in several leases, including that of its new headquarters in California. **Howard Feuerstein** is a well-established expert in real estate developments such as resorts, planned communities and condominiums. **Thomas Page** has expertise in matters such as real estate transactions, finance and development. His recent work includes acting for clients such as JPMorgan Asset Management on commercial leaseback transactions.

## Band 2

### Ball Janik LLP

**THE FIRM** The real estate arm of Ball Janik remains a key player in the Oregon market. It handles the full spread of matters for its broad client base, and operates in both the commercial and residential space. Recent highlights include counseling Mill Creek Residential Trust on the acquisition, financing and development of several residential communities.
**Sources say:** "*They have a high caliber and culture that is very customer focused, and I have never felt like we are on the clock. The highest compliment is that I have referred them to a number of friends in the industry.*"
**KEY INDIVIDUALS** The "*super-talented*" **Stephen Janik** commands enormous respect for his broad-based real estate and land use practice. One client enthuses: "*He has been outstanding. He has lots of experience, he's thorough, and is always extremely well prepared.*" **Bradley Miller** is a "*very talented*" real estate attorney, who has deep experience in representing clients in real estate leasings, financing and acquisitions. Sources say: "*He has a lot of clients, but makes us feel like we are the only one. He has a great brain that creates solution-oriented results.*"

### Davis Wright Tremaine LLP
**See profile on p.2544**
**THE FIRM** This firm's Portland office has the bench strength and resources to handle all types of real estate and

land use matters. The 12-strong team works with clients from a wide range of industries, reflecting its broad-based expertise in transactional and developmental matters. Its recent work includes acting for Powell Real Estate on its development of a new student community.

**KEY INDIVIDUALS Eugene Grant** is a land use and real estate lawyer with a broad transactional practice which includes leasing work and project development. He led in the Powell Real Estate matter. **Phillip Grillo** is well regarded in the market for his extensive land use practice. He represents clients from numerous industries in matters such as planning and permitting. **Thomas Smith** has expertise across the board in real estate development, financing and transactions. Sources state: *"He's very knowledgeable and extremely professional."* The *"brilliant"* **Stephen Ledoux** enters the rankings this year on the strength of his real estate and land use practice, which includes expertise in mixed-use developments and hotels.

## Dunn Carney Allen Higgins & Tongue LLP

**THE FIRM** The real estate and land use team at this venerable Portland firm is adept at handling a broad range of matters, including representing clients in cases involving condemnation, distressed assets, and planning and zoning. It works with clients such as Providence Health & Services, Gerding Edlen Development and Retail Opportunity Investment Corporation.

**Sources say:** *"They are top-rate. We wouldn't keep using them if they were not. Their knowledge is tremendous."*

**KEY INDIVIDUALS** The *"first-rate"* **Gilbert Parker** attracts glowing praise for his widespread expertise in this area. According to one client: *"He's a top partner for us, an integral part of our business. We don't make any major decisions without him."* **Kenneth Antell** offers experience in a wide range of matters, including real estate leasing and construction transactions, and entity structurings. He recently led the acquisition of ten shopping centers on behalf of a REIT.

## Perkins Coie LLP
### See profile on p.2548

**THE FIRM** This respected firm's Oregon office has an experienced and talented real estate and land use group able to handle all aspects of related law. Its areas of expertise include obtaining land use and environmental permits, representing clients in major real estate transactions, and working on complex development projects. Jordan Cove Energy, Providence Health & Services and the Port of Portland all count among the group's client base.

**KEY INDIVIDUALS Steven Pfeiffer** has expertise across a wide array of land use matters. He is advising Jordan Cove Energy on the development of its $3.5 billion liquefied natural gas terminal and energy production facility in Coos Bay, along with **Mark Whitlow**. Whitlow is a highly regarded land use attorney whose practice focuses on matters pertaining to environment, energy and resources. **Michael Robinson** frequently represents energy providers, industrial developers, hospitals and municipal clients in a wide variety of land use issues. **Andrew Solomon** is highly praised for his strength in handling transactional real

estate matters. He has recently worked with clients such as CWCapital Asset Management and Pacific Realty Associates (PacTrust). **Richard Cantlin** draws on extensive experience in complex real estate transactions, and is held in high regard in the Oregon market.

## Band 3

### Bateman Seidel Miner Blomgren Chellis & Gram, P.C.

**THE FIRM** This highly regarded Portland firm attracts plaudits for its real estate practice, with leasing, financing and tax-oriented work being particular areas of strength for the team. The firm is particularly experienced in representing clients from the financial, banking and life insurance industries.

**Sources say:** *"I really respect them."*

**KEY INDIVIDUALS** The *"very smart and knowledgeable"* **Randall Bateman** has a combined real estate and commercial finance practice. He offers particular expertise in representing lenders. **Chresten Gram** concentrates his practice on transactional real estate matters, and also has experience in business and corporate law.

### Lane Powell PC
#### See profile on p.2547

**THE FIRM** This national firm has a robust real estate and land use practice in Oregon. The team is especially expert in matters relating to urban and retail redevelopment, senior housing and assisted living facilities. It also has particular expertise in the development of arenas and stadiums. Its clients include Home Depot, Wells Fargo and VillaSport.

**Sources say:** *"They are very responsive and timely, and keep clients' best interests in mind at all times. We really did get value for money."*

**KEY INDIVIDUALS Michael Silvey** (see p.2178) is *"highly intelligent, creative and thorough,"* and earns praise for his comprehensive commercial real estate practice. He represents a wide range of investors, businesses and developers. **Bryan Powell** (see p.2178) handles matters involving mixed-use developments, senior housing projects and real estate transactions. *"He has a good, solid reputation,"* according to market commentators.

### Radler White Parks & Alexander

**THE FIRM** This new real estate and land use firm was set up by several former partners of Ball Janik. It has deep experience in a wide variety of matters, including commercial and residential developments, as well as loan restructuring and workouts. It also houses a full-service hospitality practice. Clients include Polygon Northwest Company, Provenance Hotels and the City of Portland.

**Sources say:** *"They are a good group of people."* *"This firm operates very well."*

**KEY INDIVIDUALS Barbara Radler** is admired for her experience in this space, and has notable expertise in handling commercial leasings and complicated real estate transactions. **Timothy Parks** recently advised Provenance

Hotels on its $25 million acquisition and renovation of the historic Governor Hotel. One source states: *"He is very responsive with the services he provides, and he knows what he is doing in all areas of the advice we get from him."* **Dina Alexander** is respected in the market for her expertise in real estate matters, particularly regarding transactions and large-scale development projects. **Steven Hultberg** is a versatile land use and real estate specialist, whose expertise encompasses zoning matters, land use entitlement, and purchase and sale agreements.

### Schwabe, Williamson & Wyatt

**THE FIRM** This Oregon and Washington-based firm has a strong real estate practice and a deep bench of experienced attorneys. The group is recognized for its expertise in a wide range of areas, including leasing, matters related to the timber industry, and resort development.

**Sources say:** *"They have a really strong real estate group."*

**KEY INDIVIDUALS John Guinasso** is renowned for his leasing work, which involves office, retail, industrial and mixed-use projects. He also handles a range of transactional matters. **Mark Manulik** represents a large variety of clients in commercial real estate and lending matters, and is praised by sources for his longstanding experience in the field. **Mark Stayer** is singled out by peers for his work as a highly specialized timber lawyer. He also has expertise in a broad range of transactional real estate matters. The *"terrific"* **Terry Hauck** attracts widespread acclaim for his respected real estate and land use practice. One peer states: *"I've done a number of deals with him, and have a lot of respect for him."*

### Tonkon Torp LLP
#### See profile on p.2183

**THE FIRM** The real estate and land use branch of this Portland powerhouse has a solid reputation in the state, and represents a number of the city's large corporations. The team is strong in a wide variety of areas, including commercial and industrial leasings, and development, acquisition, and financing of alternative energy facilities. Clients include Hawthorn Development, Stimson Lumber and Washington Capital Management.

**Sources say:** *"They understand our business needs and deliver results. They often work not only on legal issues, but also on general business advice, which is important and critical to our success."*

**KEY INDIVIDUALS Jeffrey Keeney** (see p.2176) is held in high regard in the market for his experience across the board in land use and real estate matters. One source remarks: *"We often call on him for his expertise and insight."* **Joseph Voboril** (see p.2179) has notable experience in commercial real estate transactions and land use regulation. His recent work includes successfully representing Gunderson in appealing an ordinance issued by the City of Portland to the Oregon Land Use Board of Appeals.

## Band 4

### McEwen Gisvold LLP

**THE FIRM** This esteemed Portland boutique is respected in the market for its real estate and land use practice, with the team offering experience in a variety of matters, including development, financing, and acquisitions and sales. The firm also has a strong history of representing lenders and life insurance companies in related matters.
**Sources say:** "*It is a good firm and does a broad range of work.*"
**KEY INDIVIDUALS Don Carter** is admired for his broad and longstanding real estate practice. Sources describe him as "*very well known and respected in the community,*" and state that he is "*very knowledgeable and easy to work with.*" **Dean Gisvold** is a "*very talented*" senior partner at the firm, and draws on extensive experience in handling transactional real estate matters.

### Zupancic Rathbone Law Group, P.C.

**THE FIRM** This compact yet highly effective firm focuses on a wide range of real estate and land use matters, as well as general business law. Its areas of strength include real estate finance and securities, condemnations and sustainable development. Recent work includes acting as national leasing counsel to clients such as Clearwire Corporation and XO Communications.
**Sources say:** "*They are extremely knowledgeable, and very effective in both a courtroom setting and in dealing with clients.*"
**KEY INDIVIDUALS Coni Rathbone** is widely admired for her expertise in real estate matters, as well as in corporate and securities law. Sources describe her as "*the ultimate deal maker, who understands the process,*" while another states that she is "*timely, responsive and extremely knowledgeable.*"

## Other Notable Practitioners

The eminent **Edward Sullivan** of Garvey Schubert Barer is described by sources as "*one of the deans of the Oregon land use system,*" as well as "*an encyclopedia of land use law.*" He has extensive experience in this arena. **Timothy Ramis** (see p.2178) of Jordan Ramis PC primarily focuses his practice on land use law, and has practiced in the region for over 30 years. Peers praise his expertise in this space, with one declaring: "*I've lots of respect for his abilities as a land use lawyer.*" **David Lokting** is head of Stoll Berne's business law and real estate practices, and handles a wide variety of transactional real estate matters. **David Bennett** and **Stephen Russell**, both of Landye Bennett Blumstein LLP, are well-regarded real estate lawyers whose practice includes a focus on homeowner association and condominium projects. They also offer notable experience across a broad spread of real estate transactions and development matters. The "*super*" **Jonathon Goodling** (see p.2176) of Miller Nash LLP has widespread experience in handling sophisticated transactions. One admiring source remarks that "*he is our go-to counsel, and has the enviable ability to translate complicated situations into understandable language. He is fast, efficient, and available anytime we call.*" **Paul Dagle** of Dagle Law Office, LLC is particularly recognized for his expertise in financing for public and low-income housing. He also handles a wider range of transactional and tax-related matters. **Gregory Hathaway** of Hathaway Koback Connors LLP is a land use attorney who is held in high regard for his experience in this area. One client comments: "*He's highly knowledgeable, with excellent communication skills. He is adept at finding solutions that ultimately allow a project to move forward.*" **Michael Connors** is another much-admired land use attorney at Hathaway Koback Connors LLP. According to sources: "*He possesses an incredible wealth of knowledge of land use law, as well as the intricacies of the process from a jurisdictional point of view. He is never taken off guard.*"

# Leaders' Profiles in Oregon

**ALPERN, Amy**
Littler Mendelson, PC, Portland
503 221 0309
AAlpern@littler.com
*Featured in Labor & Employment (Oregon)*
**Practice Areas:** Complex litigation and jury trials; e-discovery; discrimination/harassment; competition/trade secret law.
**Professional Memberships:** Oregon and Washington State Bars; Arbitrator, Multnomah County; Mentor, Multnomah Bar Association.
**Career:** Before joining Littler, Amy was a shareholder with Amburgey & Rubin, focused on litigation. Prior to that she served as a deputy district attorney for Multnomah County and then joined another Portland firm.
**Publications:** "Oregon Employment Law Developments: Meal Periods, Family Leave and Smokefree Rules," 2009; "Oregon Supreme Court Puts the 'Breaks' on Rest Period Claims," 2008.
**Personal:** JD, Northwestern School of Law of Lewis and Clark College; BA, University of Southern California. Legal Aid Volunteer - Domestic Violence Project. Fundraiser - Campaign for Equal Justice & Muscular Dystrophy Association. Portland office representative for Littler's Women's Initiative.

**AMAN, David S.**
Tonkon Torp LLP, Portland
503 802 2053
david.aman@tonkon.com
*Featured in Intellectual Property (Oregon)*
**Practice Areas:** Maintains a business litigation and intellectual property practice. Chair of the firm's Intellectual Property practice group. Has extensive experience representing plaintiffs and defendants in cases involving patent infringement, trademark infringement, copyright infringement, trade secrets, non-competition provisions and other business disputes.
**Professional Memberships:** Oregon State Bar (current Executive Committee Member, Intellectual Property Section) (former Executive Committee Member of the Antitrust, Trade Regulation, and Unfair Business Practice Section); Federal Bar Association; American Intellectual Property Law Association.
**Career:** Joined firm in 1996.
**Personal:** JD, summa cum laude, Lewis and Clark Law School, 1996; BA, Lewis and Clark College, 1993.

**AMBURGEY, Larry**
Littler Mendelson, PC, Portland
503 221 0309
lamburgey@littler.com
*Featured in Labor & Employment (Oregon)*
**Practice Areas:** Labor Management Relations, including Labor Negotiations/Arbitration; Discrimination and Harassment; Training - Compliance, Ethics, Leadership; Policies, Procedures and Handbooks; Hiring, Performance Management and Termination.
**Professional Memberships:** Member, Civil Rights Section and Labor Law Section - Oregon Bar Association.
**Career:** Prior to Littler, Larry was a practicing lawyer at Amburgey & Rubin, which he co-founded in 1989.
**Publications:** Co-author of the Oregon State Bar Labor and Employment Law publication, "The Americans with Disabilities Act and Employment Issues".
**Personal:** JD, Northwestern School of Law of Lewis and Clark College, magna cum laude, 1975; BA, Whitman College, 1969.

**BALLOU, Vicki A**
Tonkon Torp LLP, Portland
503 802 2028
vicki.ballou@tonkon.com
*Featured in Intellectual Property (Oregon)*
**Practice Areas:** Past Chair of firm's Intellectual Property Practice Group. Focuses on licenses, joint development agreements, and co-branding agreements. Advises in open source intellectual property ownership and indemnity issues.
**Professional Memberships:** Oregon State Bar.
**Career:** Joined firm in 1986.
**Personal:** JD, with honors, University of Texas at Austin School of Law; BA, with honors, Walla Walla College. Enjoys hiking, fly fishing, and reading. Resident of Banks, Oregon.

**BARRAN, Paula**
Barran Liebman LLP, Portland
503 228 0500
pbarran@barran.com
*Featured in Labor & Employment (Oregon)*
**Practice Areas:** Labor and employment law; Higher Education Compliance since 1980.
**Professional Memberships:** Listed in Best Lawyers and Super Lawyers; American Bar Foundation; American Bar Association; Defense Research Institute; Regional Drug Foundation; Oregon State Bar; Oregon Women Lawyers; American Association of University Women; Association of Title IX Administrators; American College of Labor & Employment Attorneys.
**Career:** Admitted to Oregon; Washington; US Court of Appeals, Ninth Circuit; District of Oregon, Eastern and Western Districts of Washington; US Supreme Court. Willamette University, Adjunct Professor (2000-01).
**Personal:** PhD, UBC; MA, Cornell University; JD, Osgoode Hall Law School, York University; MBA, University of Oregon.

## BELNAVIS, Clarence
Fisher & Phillips LLP, Portland
503 242 4262
cbelnavis@laborlawyers.com
*Featured in Labor & Employment (Oregon)*

**Career:** Clarence Belnavis is a Partner in the Portland, Oregon office. He has extensive experience handling various types of employment litigation, including disability, racial, and gender discrimination; retaliation; sexual harassment; and wrongful discharge. He also represents employers in wage and hour claims and employment class actions. Belnavis received a JD from Howard University School of Law in Washington, DC and began his legal career as a law clerk in the Office of the General Counsel for the Department of the Navy.

## CAREY, Robert
Tonkon Torp LLP, Portland
503 802 2032
bob.carey@tonkon.com
*Featured in Labor & Employment (Oregon)*

**Practice Areas:** Chair, Labor and Employment Practice Group. Practices employment litigation and provides counseling on employment-related issues. Has substantial jury trial experience in Oregon and Washington, defending wrongful discharge, discrimination, sexual harassment, wage and hour, and whistleblower cases. Has defended ERISA lawsuits, been on both sides of post-termination cases with non-competition, trade secret and related claims, and defended numerous labor disputes in arbitration and before the NLRB.
**Professional Memberships:** Oregon, Washington, and District of Columbia State Bars, Oregon Association of Defense Counsel, Federal Bar Association.
**Career:** Joined firm, 2006.
**Personal:** JD, Willamette University College of Law; BA, Harvard University.

## CORBETT, Sherrill A
Tonkon Torp LLP, Portland
503 802 2049
sherrill.corbett@tonkon.com
*Featured in Corporate/M&A (Oregon)*

**Practice Areas:** Partner in the firm's Mergers & Acquisitions Practice Group. Represents companies in mergers, acquisitions and divestitures, corporate finance transactions and structuring complex joint ventures. Represents public companies on securities compliance and corporate governance matters.
**Professional Memberships:** Oregon State Bar, State Bar of California, American Bar Association, Society of Corporate Secretaries & Governance Professionals.
**Career:** Joined Tonkon in 1999. Previously with Heller Ehrman White & McAuliffe LLP and Graham & James LLP.
**Personal:** JD, magna cum laude, Order of the Coif, University of California, Hastings College of the Law; BA, summa cum laude, Saint Mary's College of California.

## CREPS, Clay
Tonkon Torp LLP, Portland
503 802 2059
clay.creps@tonkon.com
*Featured in Labor & Employment (Oregon)*

**Practice Areas:** Partner in firm's Labor & Employment practice group. Has litigated and taken to trial cases involving all aspects of employment law including discrimination, harassment, wage and overtime claims, severance agreements, noncompete agreements, the Older Worker Benefit Protection Act (OWBPA), COBRA, FMLA/OFLA, defamation and wrongful discharge.
**Professional Memberships:** Oregon State Bar, State Bar of Michigan, State Bar of Montana.
**Career:** Joined firm in 2011.
**Personal:** JD, Harvard Law School, cum laude, 1985; BA, University of Notre Dame, summa cum laude, Phi Beta Kappa, 1982.

## GOODLING, Jonathon L
Miller Nash LLP, Portland
503 205 2522
jon.goodling@millernash.com
*Featured in Real Estate (Oregon)*

**Practice Areas:** Commercial real property and commercial-lending transactions, representing lenders, borrowers, developers, owners, tenants, landlords, purchasers, and sellers.
**Professional Memberships:** Partner, Miller Nash LLP. Former Chair of the Oregon State Bar Real Estate and Land Use Section ("RELU") and the Oregon State Bar's Financial Institutions Committee. Member of the American College of Mortgage Attorneys' (ACMA) Board of Regents and the American Bar Association. Member of Opinion Letter Committee for RELU and ACMA.
**Personal:** Earned Bachelor's Degree in Political Science and Law Degree at the University of Oregon and was a member of the Order of the Coif.

## GREENMAN, Ronald L
Tonkon Torp LLP, Portland
503 802 2006
ron.greenman@tonkon.com
*Featured in Corporate/M&A (Oregon)*

**Practice Areas:** Ron's business law practice emphasizes business transactions and corporate finance, management buyouts, joint ventures and counseling to senior management and boards of directors with respect to equity and compensation plans and corporate governance matters.
**Professional Memberships:** Oregon State Bar, State Bar of California.
**Career:** San Francisco large firm practice 1974-1978; joined firm in 1978.
**Personal:** JD, Order of the Coif, University of Oregon School of Law; BS, University of Oregon, Phi Beta Kappa.

## HARNDEN, Edwin
Barran Liebman LLP, Portland
503 228 0500
eharnden@barran.com
*Featured in Labor & Employment (Oregon)*

**Practice Areas:** Managing Partner with over 35 years of experience maintaining an employment law practice.
**Professional Memberships:** Fellow, American College of Trial Lawyers and College of Labor & Employment Lawyers; Judge Learned Hand Lifetime Humanitarian Achievement Awardee; Henry Hewitt Access to Justice Awardee; Listed in Best Lawyers & Super Lawyers; Past President of the OSB & PLF; Federal, American, Oregon & Multnomah Bar committees; American Bar Foundation Fellow.
**Career:** Admitted to Oregon; Washington; Idaho; District of Columbia; US Court of Appeals, Ninth Circuit; and US Supreme Court.
**Personal:** JD ('72) & BA ('69), Columbia University.

## HOSENPUD, David
Lane Powell PC, Portland
503 778 2141
hosenpudd@lanepowell.com
*Featured in Labor & Employment (Oregon)*

**Practice Areas:** David Hosenpud's employment and complex commercial litigation practice involves the defense of class action and individual discrimination suits in both federal and state courts, as well as cases involving breach of contract and fiduciary duties, and claims involving tortious interference and misappropriation confidential/trade secret information. He has extensive trial experience with over 85 jury and court trials.
**Career:** Shareholder since 1989.
**Publications:** Speaker: Labor and employment, and wage and hour issues. Published: "Witness Competency," Oregon State Bar Evidence Handbook, 1986 (Co-author).
**Personal:** University of Oregon, Editor-in-chief (JD, 1983); University of California in Santa Barbara (BA, Highest Honors, 1978).

## JANOVE, Jathan
Ogletree, Deakins, Nash, Smoak & Stewart, PC, Portland
503 552 2140
jathan.janove@ogletreedeakins.com
*Featured in Labor & Employment (Oregon)*

**Practice Areas:** Management training, coaching and consulting to improve workplace leadership, accountability and employee engagement.
**Professional Memberships:** National Speakers Association, Society for Human Resource Management, American Society of Training & Development, Oregon HR Specialist (Editor); Management Labor & Employment Roundtable, HR Magazine (frequent contributor).
**Career:** Admitted to practice: Oregon, Idaho, New York, Utah, Washington.
**Publications:** The Star Profile: A Management Tool To Unleash Employee Potential (Davies-Black Publishing 2008); Managing To Stay Out Of Court: How To Avoid The 8 Deadly Sins Of Mismanagement (Berrett-Koehler Publishers & SHRM 2005). Editor of SHRM book series on HR, labor and employment law.
**Personal:** Indiana University (BA, 1979), University of Chicago (JD, 1982).

## KEENEY, Jeffrey H
Tonkon Torp LLP, Portland
503 802 2025
jeff.keeney@tonkon.com
*Featured in Real Estate (Oregon)*

**Practice Areas:** Practice concentrated on representation with local, regional, national property owners and developers in transactional matters. Significant experience in purchase and sale transactions, loan transactions and office, retail, industrial leasing. Represents alternative energy clients in connection with siting, development and financing of wind energy projects. Immediate past Chair of firm's Real Estate and Land Use Group.
**Professional Memberships:** Oregon State Bar; Board Member of the LaSalle Catholic College Preparatory Educational Foundation and The Wetlands Conservancy.
**Career:** Joined the firm in 1983.
**Personal:** JD, cum laude, Lewis and Clark Law School, 1983; BA, University of Vermont, 1980, Phi Beta Kappa.

## LEACHMAN, Tamsen L
Fisher & Phillips LLP, Portland
503 205 8095
tleachman@laborlawyers.com
*Featured in Labor & Employment (Oregon)*

**Career:** Tamsen Leachman is a partner in the Portland office. She represents employers in a wide variety of employment-related lawsuits, administrative hearings, grievances, arbitrations, unfair labor practices, and collective bargaining. She also provides counsel to employers regarding the laws governing the employment relationship with an emphasis on prevention through compliance and the development of strategic, system-driven solutions. Tamsen develops training programs targeted at human resource professionals, managers, executives, and in-house counsel. These programs begin with root-cause analysis, move to development of programs to eliminate core problems, and conclude with educational training to ensure new solutions and tools are used effectively.

## LENHART, Benjamin
Lane Powell PC, Portland
503 778 2052
lenhartb@lanepowell.com
*Featured in Corporate/M&A (Oregon)*

**Practice Areas:** Mergers and acquisitions, corporate finance and securities transactions (including angel, venture and private equity), commercial finance, and corporate governance. Regularly counsels both public and private companies, and capital sources that finance these businesses.
**Career:** Shareholder since 2004.
**Publications:** Speaker: Securities laws; going-private transactions; Published: Business periodicals and 'Advising Oregon Businesses.'
**Personal:** Lewis and Clark College, Northwestern School of Law (JD, cum laude, 1996); Whitman College (BA, 1991). Board Chair, The Children's Course/The First Tee of Greater Portland.

**LIEBMAN, Richard**
Barran Liebman LLP, Portland
503 228 0500
rliebman@barran.com
*Featured in Labor & Employment (Oregon)*
**Practice Areas:** Founding Partner with experience in labor and employment law since 1972.
**Professional Memberships:** Listed in Best Lawyers and Super Lawyers; Fellow, College of Labor and Employment Lawyers; Former EEO Instructor, PSU; Past Chair, Oregon State Bar Labor Law Section; Board Member, Oregon State Bar Civil Rights Section; NW EEO/Affirmative Action Association; Mangement Editor (1990-Present), Labor and Employment Law (OSB book).
**Career:** Admitted to Oregon; Hawaii; Washington; US Court of Appeals, Seventh Circuit; US Court of Appeals, Ninth Circuit; US Court of Appeals, District of Columbia.
**Personal:** JD (1972) and BA (1969) from the University of California at Berkeley.

**LIVELY, Leah C**
Ogletree, Deakins, Nash, Smoak & Stewart, PC, Portland
503 552 2140
leah.lively@ogletreedeakins.com
*Featured in Labor & Employment (Oregon)*
**Practice Areas:** Exclusively defends employers from claims of discrimination, retaliation, wrongful discharge, and wage and hour violations, including class actions. Leah has tried more than 40 jury trials in multiple states and jurisdictions. She advises employers on employment related issues and policies.
**Professional Memberships:** Oregon State Bar Association, Labor & Employment Section; California State Bar, Labor & Employment Section.
**Career:** Admitted in Oregon, California and Idaho.
**Publications:** Lectured, authored, and trained on multiple employment-law related topics.
**Personal:** Northwestern School of Law of Lewis and Clark College (JD, 1996); California Polytechnic State University at San Luis Obispo (BS, 1993).

**MARTSON JR, William F**
Tonkon Torp LLP, Portland
503 802 2005
rick.martson@tonkon.com
*Featured in Litigation (Oregon)*
**Practice Areas:** Partner with wide range of commercial litigation experience, including securities, shareholder rights, corporate governance, natural resources-based and environmental litigation. Tried over 200 cases, more than 75 injunctive proceedings, has substantial experience in business work for private timber companies.
**Professional Memberships:** International Society of Barristers (President 2009-10); Oregon State Bar, Federal Bar Association, Member, Congress of Fellows of the Center for International Legal Studies.
**Career:** One of first Tonkon Torp associates hired, 1974.

**Personal:** JD, magna cum laude, Order of the Coif, University of Michigan Law School; BA, magna cum laude, Phi Beta Kappa, Washington and Jefferson College.

**MCDONNELL, Brendan**
K&L Gates, Portland
503 226 5710
brendan.mcdonnell@klgates.com
*Featured in Corporate/M&A (Oregon)*
**Practice Areas:** Partner Brendan McDonnell counsels corporate clients on a variety of business issues including strategic planning, financings, mergers and acquisitions, securities laws, general corporate law, fiduciary duties, executive compensation and general contracting. Mr McDonnell provides strategic advice to multinational clients with respect to their global business issues, including market entry and international M&A and commercial transactions. He also represents some of the region's most active private equity firms in portfolio company acquisitions and operations.

**MENEGHELLO, Richard**
Fisher & Phillips LLP, Portland
503 242 4262
rmeneghello@laborlawyers.com
*Featured in Labor & Employment (Oregon)*
**Career:** Rich Meneghello is the Managing Partner of the Portland, Oregon office. He has focused much of his practice on defending and advising employers on disability discrimination issues. Rich has maintained this focus since 1999, when he was the lead associate attorney before the US Supreme Court in the case of Albertsons v. Kirkinburg, a unanimous decision interpreting the Americans with Disabilities Act in favor of employers. He commonly appears in court defending claims of sexual harassment, gender discrimination, injured worker discrimination, race discrimination, retaliation, wage and hour violations, and family and medical leave discrimination.

**MERRILL, Erich**
Miller Nash LLP, Portland
503 205 2504
erich.merrill@millernash.com
*Featured in Corporate/M&A (Oregon)*
**Practice Areas:** Business; business governance; intellectual property; mergers and acquisitions.
**Professional Memberships:** Member, Oregon State Bar; Admitted to practice before United States Patent & Trademark Office. Past chair, Emerging Business Committee, American Electronics Assoc.; Steering committee member, Organization for Corporate Governance.
**Career:** Works with company management on corporate policy and strategy, entity choice and formation, raising funds from investors, negotiating and writing contracts, sales and acquisitions of businesses, and IP protection and licensing.
**Publications:** "Building a Better Board of Directors," Daily Journal of Commerce (July 16, 2012).
**Personal:** Bachelor's Degree, summa cum laude, Vanderbilt University; Law Degree, Harvard Law School.

**MILLER JR, Max M**
Tonkon Torp LLP, Portland
503 802 2030
max.miller@tonkon.com
*Featured in Environment (Oregon)*
**Practice Areas:** Chairs the firm's Environmental and Natural Resources Practice Group. Assists businesses in all matters concerning the environment, natural resources, renewable energy, sustainable practices, and land use.
**Professional Memberships:** Oregon State Bar; American Bar Association; Oregon Lawyers for a Sustainable Future.
**Career:** Joined Tonkon Torp LLP in 1988, following 4 1/2 years with Garvey Schubert & Barer.
**Personal:** JD, Lewis and Clark Law School, 1983; BA, Economics, Pitzer College, 1979. Serves on several boards and committees related primarily to arts education, and sustainability.

**MOHR, Peter**
Tonkon Torp LLP, Portland
503 802 5759
peter.mohr@tonkon.com
*Featured in Environment (Oregon)*
**Practice Areas:** Practice covers environmental, energy, land use, and natural resources law with focus on water law. Emphasizes: state water quantity, federal and state water quality, endangered species protection compliance and permitting issues; securing, purchasing and protecting water rights for power generation, municipal, industrial, commercial, and agricultural uses; performing due diligence on water rights and related assets for investors and lenders.
**Professional Memberships:** American Bar Association; Colorado Bar Association; Oregon State Bar; Oregon Business Association.
**Career:** Joined firm 2009; Solo practice, Oregon, 2002-09; Colorado firm, 1998-2001.
**Personal:** JD, Vermont Law School; BA, Connecticut College. Bar Admissions: Colorado (1998); Oregon (2001).

**NEUPERT, John**
Miller Nash LLP, Portland
503 205 2461
john.neupert@millernash.com
*Featured in Litigation (Oregon)*
**Practice Areas:** Practice involves complex commercial litigation, including banking, trade regulation, business torts, tax, intellectual property, and corporate governance.
**Professional Memberships:** Member of the Oregon State Bar, the Washington State Bar, the American Bar Association, and the Multnomah Bar Association and participates in various litigation sections' activities. Is admitted in Oregon and Washington and has been admitted pro hac vice to many federal and state courts nationwide.
**Career:** Through his professional corporation, is a Partner of Miller Nash LLP.
**Personal:** Earned Law Degree from the University of Oregon and was a Member of the Order of the Coif.

**OWREN, Turid**
Tonkon Torp LLP, Portland
503 802 2045
turid.owren@tonkon.com
*Featured in Labor & Employment (Oregon)*
**Practice Areas:** Chair of the firm's Immigration Practice Group. Advises domestic and international companies and individuals on employment-related immigration and naturalization. Member, AILA Service Center Operations Committee 2012-13 (serving as liaison to the USCIS Administrative Appeals Office); AILA Business Immigration Committee 2012-13.
**Professional Memberships:** American Immigration Lawyers Association (AILA); Oregon State Bar; Multnomah Bar Association.
**Career:** Joined the firm in 1999; began practicing immigration law in 1988.
**Personal:** JD, Lewis and Clark Law School; BA, Reed College.

**PALMER, Thomas**
Tonkon Torp LLP, Portland
503 802 2018
tom.palmer@tonkon.com
*Featured in Corporate/M&A (Oregon)*
**Practice Areas:** Tom Palmer is Chair of Tonkon Torp's Corporate Finance Practice Group with a practice emphasizing securities and general corporate matters, including mergers and acquisitions, joint ventures, initial public offerings, other equity and debt offerings, and private placements. Also skilled in corporate governance and international transactions.
**Professional Memberships:** Oregon State Bar; District of Columbia Bar; New York State Bar; New York City Bar Association.
**Career:** Joined the firm in 1988.
**Personal:** JD, Cornell Law School; BA, Hamilton College.

**PERKINS, Alan Curtis**
Tonkon Torp LLP, Portland
503 802 2127
alan.perkins@tonkon.com
*Featured in Labor & Employment (Oregon)*
**Practice Areas:** A partner in the firm's Immigration Practice Group focusing on employment-based immigration, including temporary visas, permanent residence and naturalization. Advises clients, from large corporations to start-ups, on the employment of foreign nationals in the United States, including Form I-9 employment eligibility verification. Member, American Immigration Lawyers Association. Member, Oregon State Bar International Law Section Executive Committee.
**Professional Memberships:** Oregon State Bar, California State Bar, American Immigration Lawyers Association.
**Career:** Joined the firm in 2007.
**Personal:** JD, Vanderbilt University Law School, 1997; BA, summa cum laude, Willamette University, 1993.

## PETRANOVICH, Milo
Lane Powell PC, Portland
503 778 2114
petranovichm@lanepowell.com
*Featured in Litigation (Oregon)*
**Practice Areas:** Commercial litigation, including securities, antitrust and trade regulation; government investigations and white collar criminal defense.
**Professional Memberships:** Oregon State Bar, ABA Antitrust Section, Oregon State Bar Association sections of: Antitrust and Trade Regulation, Securities, Business Litigation, and Alternative Dispute Resolution.
**Career:** Shareholder since 1983.
**Publications:** Speaker: 'Developments in Securities Litigation: Private Internal Investigations and Parallel Government Investigations,''Private Securities Actions after StoneRidge,''Recent Development in Health Care Antitrust: Dominant Hospitals and Exclusive Contracts,''The Foreign Corrupt Practices Act and Doing Business in China.'
**Personal:** University of Michigan (JD, 1976); American University (BA, magna cum laude, 1973).

## POWELL, Bryan
Lane Powell PC, Portland
503 778 2189
powellb@lanepowell.com
*Featured in Real Estate (Oregon)*
**Practice Areas:** Private/public and mixed use development; seniors housing projects; office, retail, industrial and hotel acquisitions, sales and leasing; business, joint venture and deal structuring; real estate finance and workouts. Common sense approach to finding solutions for projects that are difficult to build and finance.
**Professional Memberships:** Member, Oregon, Washington and California State Bar Associations. Portland State University Center for Real Estate, Advisory Board Member; NAIOP (former Oregon Board Member).
**Career:** Shareholder; Co-chair, Real Estate and Land Use Group 1998-2012; Executive Committee, 2002-08.
**Personal:** University of California, Hastings College of the Law (JD, 1988); University of Washington (BA, 1982).

## RAMIS, Timothy V
Jordan Ramis PC, Lake Oswego
503 598 7070
Tim.Ramis@jordanramis.com
*Featured in Real Estate (Oregon)*
**Practice Areas:** For more than 30 years, Tim Ramis has focused his practice on the business of land development. Tim's extensive experience includes land use and transportation planning, local government applications, Goal 5 applications, wetland permitting, Land Use Board of Appeals (LUBA) petitions, Court of Appeals and Supreme Court cases, and legislative drafting. His knowledge enables collaboration with planning, engineering, transportation, wetlands, habitat, economic, and other technical consultants and

permits him to interface well with local planning staff.
**Professional Memberships:** Multnomah County Bar Association, Oregon City Attorneys Association, US Supreme Court Bar.
**Personal:** BA, Stanford University, 1972; JD, University of Oregon, 1975.

## RAWLINSON, Dennis P
Miller Nash LLP, Portland
503 205 2406
dennis.rawlinson@millernash.com
*Featured in Litigation (Oregon)*
**Practice Areas:** Numerous cases involving bet-the-company litigation, breach of contract, commercial torts, construction/design, shareholder disputes, lender liability, real estate, professional negligence, employment, trademark disputes.
**Professional Memberships:** 2006 President, Oregon State Bar; Council (Board) and Division Director, ABA Section of Litigation.
**Career:** Top List Oregon Super Lawyer, Business Litigation; Recommended Commercial Litigation Lawyer, Assoc. of Corp. Counsel and Chambers USA, 2006-present; Inclusion in Oregon Super Lawyers, 2006-present; American Board of Trial Advocates; Best Lawyers in America, 2005-present.
**Publications:** Numerous.
**Personal:** Bachelor's Degree, magna cum laude, University of Notre Dame; MBA, and JD Degrees, cum laude, Cornell University.

## REIVE, Chris
Jordan Ramis PC, Lake Oswego
503 598 7070
chris.reive@jordanramis.com
*Featured in Environment (Oregon)*
**Practice Areas:** Chris regularly assists businesses, individuals, and local governments in recognizing and solving the many issues that arise from environmental concerns, including environmental risk management and allocation in business transactions, waste management and disposal on job sites, obtaining insurance coverage for environmental issues, permitting and reporting to regulatory agencies, spill and release response, and worker safety.
**Professional Memberships:** American Bar Association, Oregon State Bar Association, Washington State Bar Association.
**Personal:** BS, Biology, University of Michigan, 1973; MPH, Environmental Health, University of Michigan School of Public Health, 1976; JD, Lewis and Clark College, Northwestern School of Law, 1983.

## RICHTER, Peter
Miller Nash LLP, Portland
503 205 2366
peter.richter@millernash.com
*Featured in Litigation (Oregon)*
**Practice Areas:** Has helped hundreds of clients solve their legal problems favorably, economically, efficiently, and professionally in numerous legal areas through negotiation, mediation, arbitration, and jury trials.
**Professional Memberships:** American Board of Trial Advocates (Oregon Chapter President 2007-08), International Association of Defense

Counsel, Oregon Association of Defense Counsel, Fellow, American Bar Foundation. Admitted in US Supreme Court and all Oregon courts.
**Career:** Named one of Oregon's ten best litigators and in several publications as leading litigator. Lewis and Clark Law School, Adjunct Professor (1988-present). Oregon State Bar lecturer on advocacy and co-founder of Oregon State Bar Trial Advocacy College (1999-current).

## RUBIN, Howard
Littler Mendelson, PC, Portland
503 221 0309
hrubin@littler.com
*Featured in Labor & Employment (Oregon)*
**Practice Areas:** Labor management relations, including labor arbitrations/agreement administration, negotiations, union organizing; discrimination and harassment; hiring, performance management and termination.
**Professional Memberships:** Member, Civil Rights Law/Labor Relations Law sections - Oregon State Bar.
**Career:** Prior to Littler, Howard was a practicing lawyer at Amburgey & Rubin, which he co-founded in 1989.
**Publications:** "Legislative Lowdown" DJC-Oregon, 2009-Present; "Oregon's Job Applicant Fairness Act Update - BOLI Issues Final Rules," 2010; "New Oregon Law Prohibits Credit Checks," 2010; "Employer Speech in Oregon's Workplaces, the Impact of SB 519," 2009.
**Personal:** JD, Northwestern School of Law of Lewis and Clark College; BA, Northwestern University.

## RUTTUM, Kurt W
Tonkon Torp LLP, Portland
503 802 2043
kurt.ruttum@tonkon.com
*Featured in Corporate/M&A (Oregon)*
**Practice Areas:** Practice emphasizes mergers and acquisitions, private equity, public and private securities offerings and general corporate counseling. Has extensive experience in public offerings, commercial loans and private placements of debt and equity securities. Represents buyers and sellers of public and private companies.
**Professional Memberships:** Oregon and Washington State Bars.
**Career:** Joined firm in 1986, left for four years to be an executive at two publicly traded companies, including CFO of software services company. Returned to practice of law in 2000.
**Personal:** JD, University of Chicago Law School; BA magna cum laude, University of Colorado at Boulder, Phi Beta Kappa.

## RYAN, Sarah J
Jackson Lewis LLP, Portland
503 229 0404
Sarah.Ryan@jacksonlewis.com
*Featured in Labor & Employment (Oregon)*
**Practice Areas:** Defense of employment claims, including harassment, discrimination and retaliation, wrongful termination, wage and hour. Advice to identify creative solutions to personnel issues that reduce risk.

**Professional Memberships:** Oregon, Washington and District of Columbia Bar Associations, Federal Bar Association.
**Career:** In practice for almost 30 years, focusing on defense of employment claims. Before joining Jackson Lewis, chaired Labor and Employment Group at Portland-based law firm.
**Publications:** Chapters in Inside the Minds: Dealing with Employee Lawsuits (Thomson West, 2005) and Federal Civil Litigation in Oregon Manual (Oregon State Bar).
**Personal:** University of Oregon (JD, 1982), University of Nebraska (cum laude).

## SAND, Thomas C
Miller Nash LLP, Portland
503 205 2475
tom.sand@millernash.com
*Featured in Litigation (Oregon)*
**Practice Areas:** Civil litigation, with emphasis on securities, employment, and commercial law. Tried numerous cases in several state and federal courts; argued appeals in Ninth Circuit Court of Appeals, Oregon Supreme Court, Oregon Court of Appeals.
**Professional Memberships:** Member of the American Bar Association Securities Litigation section, Oregon State Bar, and Washington State Bar Association.
**Career:** Managing partner of Miller Nash (1999-2007). Selected for The Best Lawyers in America (2006-present), and Oregon Super Lawyer (2006-present, Top 10 ranking in 2008).
**Personal:** BA University of Oregon; JD Lewis & Clark Law School. 2004 Distinguished Graduate Award, Lewis & Clark Law School.

## SHROPSHIRE, Steven L
Jordan Ramis PC, Lake Oswego
503 598 7070
steve.shropshire@jordanramis.com
*Featured in Environment (Oregon)*
**Practice Areas:** For nearly two decades Steve has helped his clients understand and navigate the complex legal environment that governs natural resources and environmental matters. He advises clients in a wide variety of contexts including transactions, administrative proceedings, and legislation. Steve is a seasoned litigator who effectively represents his clients before state agencies as well as state and federal courts, having served as counsel on several cases involving water rights issues of first impression before Oregon, Colorado, and federal courts.
**Professional Memberships:** Oregon State Bar, Washington State Bar.
**Personal:** Universität Regensburg, Germany, 1988-89; BA University of Colorado, 1991; JD Northwestern School of Law at Lewis & Clark College, 1994;

## SILVEY, Michael
Lane Powell PC, Portland
503 778 2195
silveym@lanepowell.com
*Featured in Real Estate (Oregon)*
**Practice Areas:** Real estate, construction, land use, financial institutions, public/private partnerships, education.

**Professional Memberships:** Member, Oregon, Washington, California and Idaho State Bars; National Association of Industrial and Office Properties; Counselors of Real Estate; Board Member, Proud Ground; Commercial Association of Brokers; American Bar Association.
**Career:** Shareholder since 1993. Major projects include: Rose Garden Arena, Seahawks Stadium, Miami Heat Arena, Mirabella CCRC Washington Convention Center Expansion, Sale of JELD-WEN's destination resorts.
**Personal:** UC Hastings (JD, 1971); University of California, Santa Barbara (AB, History, with honors, 1967); Adjunct Professor, Portland State University.

**SKERRITT, Daniel**
Tonkon Torp LLP, Portland
503 802 2024
dan.skerritt@tonkon.com
*Featured in Litigation (Oregon)*
**Practice Areas:** Recognized for trial excellence over the past 35 years. Represents directors, officers and companies in corporate governance issues. Skilled in defense of securities class actions and derivative claims and other complex commercial cases. Has achieved some of Oregon's largest awards and settlements.
**Professional Memberships:** Fellow, American College of Trial Lawyers (State Chair 2010-12); Fellow, International Society of Barristers; Oregon State Bar; Oregon Association of Defense Counsel.
**Career:** Joined the firm in 2003.
**Personal:** JD, summa cum laude, Willamette University College of Law; LLM, George Washington University; BA, Willamette University.

**STEPHENS, Kenneth**
Tonkon Torp LLP, Portland
503 802 2008
ken.stephens@tonkon.com
*Featured in Corporate/M&A (Oregon)*
**Practice Areas:** Practice emphasizes corporate and securities matters. Has extensive experience in corporation finance, mergers and acquisitions and

corporate conflicts and governance. Represents issuers in private and public financings, mergers, acquisitions and divestitures.
**Professional Memberships:** Oregon State Bar; Society of Corporate Secretaries & Governance Professionals; The American Law Institute; Association for Advanced Life Underwriting.
**Career:** Founding partner of the firm (1974). US Senate, Committee on Banking, Housing & Urban Affairs, Securities Industry Study (1971-72).
**Personal:** JD, University of Oregon School of Law (Order of the Coif); BS, University of Oregon.

**STRIDE, Jon P**
Tonkon Torp LLP, Portland
503 802 2034
jon.stride@tonkon.com
*Featured in Litigation (Oregon)*
**Practice Areas:** Partner experienced in intellectual property litigation and cases involving trade secrets and noncompete agreements. Litigates copyright, trademark and patent infringement claims. Also represents clients in a broad range of commercial disputes, including business interference claims. Former Chair of the firm's Managing Board.
**Professional Memberships:** Oregon State Bar; Washington State Bar; Oregon Association of Defense Counsel; admitted to Oregon and Washington federal courts; admitted to Federal Circuit.
**Career:** Joined firm in 1990.
**Personal:** JD, University of Oregon School of Law; Order of the Coif, Editor in Chief, Oregon Law Review; MS, Oregon State University/Western Oregon; BS Western Oregon University.

**SYMES, David PR**
Ogletree, Deakins, Nash, Smoak & Stewart, PC, Portland
503 552 2140
david.symes@ogletreedeakins.com
*Featured in Labor & Employment (Oregon)*

**Practice Areas:** David PR Symes represents employers and management in employment-related litigation across many industries, including financial services, airline manufacturers and carriers, telecommunications, transportation services, manufacturing, and emerging growth technology. Mr Symes's practice covers complex, multiple plaintiff, and class action litigation involving the full range of legal issues facing employers. He has has successfully handled jury and bench trials involving such workplace topics as equal employment opportunities, wage and hour law, and family and medical leave law. Mr Symes also has successfully handled numerous cases involving non-competition agreements and trade secrets misappropriation, including first-chair responsibilities in over 10 injunction hearings.

**VOBORIL, Joseph**
Tonkon Torp LLP, Portland
503 802 2009
joe.voboril@tonkon.com
*Featured in Real Estate (Oregon)*
**Practice Areas:** Practice is concentrated on complex commercial real estate transactions and land use matters. He has extensive experience in deal negotiation, documentation and project financing. He assists clients in securing land use approvals, negotiation of architect services agreements and construction contracts for large commercial projects, and restructuring financial arrangements.
**Professional Memberships:** Oregon and Washington State Bar Associations; former Board Member of Portland Public Schools, Portland City Planning Commission. Current Board Member of Portland Art Museum.
**Personal:** JD, University of Michigan, 1973; BS University of Nebraska, Phi Beta Kappa, 1970. Listed in 'Best Lawyers in America' for Real Estate law.

**VON BERGEN, Mark**
Holland & Knight LLP, Portland
503 243 2300
mark.vonbergen@hklaw.com
*Featured in Corporate/M&A (Oregon)*
**Career:** Mr von Bergen is a Partner in the Business Section and Executive Partner of the Portland office. He practices in the areas of business and securities law, mergers and acquisitions (US and cross-border), corporate governance, and venture capital transactions. For more than 30 years, Mr von Bergen has represented businesses ranging from small, start-up entities to major public companies. He has served as lead counsel to both issuers and underwriters in numerous registered offerings, has represented public and private companies in mergers and acquisitions, and has advised on corporate governance issues.

**WOLFSTONE, Jeffrey**
Lane Powell PC, Portland
503 778 2153
wolfstonej@lanepowell.com
*Featured in Corporate/M&A (Oregon)*
**Practice Areas:** Corporate finance, securities, mergers and acquisitions, corporate law and governance, venture capital and private equity, sustainability, and nonprofit corporations. Lead counsel to entrepreneurs, companies and investors on a broad array of business matters, including debt and equity financings, M&A and going private transactions, special committee issues, securities offerings and compliance, executive employment agreements and compensation, and entity formation and restructuring.
**Career:** Co-chair of Corporate Finance/M&A Practice.
**Publications:** Speaker: mergers and acquisitions, corporations, partnerships, LLCs and sustainability. Published in business periodicals and 'Advising Oregon Businesses.'
**Personal:** UC Berkeley School of Law; Stanford University.

# BARRAN LIEBMAN LLP

**www.**barran.com **tel:** 503 228 0500 **fax:** 503 274 1212

**Managing Partner:** Edwin Harnden
Number of partners: 9  Number of attorneys: 17
Languages: *English, Spanish*

## Firm Overview:

Barran Liebman LLP is an Oregon partnership dedicated to representing employers and finding solutions for their labor management and employment law needs. The firm consists of 17 specialized attorneys who offer clients seamless assistance and responsiveness. To assist employers in preventing problems, the firm provides a full range of tools including 'Food for Thought' breakfast seminars held throughout the year, their award winning Annual Employment, Labor and Benefits Law Seminar held every September, and customized onsite trainings to meet the individual needs of employers with regard to their industry and experience. As a special service, the firm also provides valuable Electronic Alerts free of charge. These updates summarize new case law and statutes that impact businesses. Training videotapes, 'Train the Trainer' materials and CD-Roms are also available.

## Main Areas of Practice:

Barran Liebman attorneys focus on five practice areas: employment law advice, employment litigation, protection of intellectual property, labor relations and employee benefits advice.

### Employment Law Advice:

The firm counsels employers on preventative practices, focusing on how to properly maintain low-risk work environments, training them to adapt to legal changes, and ultimately, working to reduce the risk of litigation. The majority of the firm's employment work is in equal employment opportunity, wage and hour, and protected leave. Each year, the firm handles approximately 150 Oregon Civil Rights Division, EEOC, OFCCP and Washington Human Rights Commission charges and defends dozens of court actions in Oregon and Washington. This high volume of work allows the firm's lawyers to stay abreast of fast-developing case law, including knowledge of unreported new decisions, an ability which is extraordinarily valuable at a critical time. The attorneys participate in rules development for administrative agencies and in the legislative process, and prepare amicus briefs in employment EEO and employment-at-will cases in state appellate courts. The wide range of employment law issues the firm can address include: discrimination, including ADA, ADEA and Title VII; substance abuse issues in the workplace; compensation issues; ethics and compliance; employee handbooks and manuals; employee status and clarification; employee theft; employment contracts; equal employment opportunity matters; family medical leave; general employment dispute resolution; hiring and performance management; internal investigations for clients; policy and procedure reviews; privacy issues in the workplace; retaliation claims; sexual harassment; violence in the workplace; wage and hour issues; workplace investigations; wrongful termination claims; complex executive disputes over termination; and separation benefits.

### Employment Litigation:

Should litigation become necessary, Barran Liebman's attorneys are equipped with extensive experience before state, federal and appellate courts, as well as administrative agencies. The attorneys are committed to achieving favorable, efficient resolutions and limiting client exposure. The firm focuses on understanding what motivates the dispute and evaluating whether offering counseling, retraining, retirement packages or other benefits might assist the parties in resolving a matter on mutually beneficial terms.

### Protection of Intellectual Property:

The firm assists employers whose employees misuse confidential business information. For example, without proper internal protections a former employee can start a competing business, solicit clients and customers, recruit employees away or use key competitive assets. The firm has expertise in preparing non-competition agreements and protecting against misappropriation of trade secrets issues. It also offers training on proper drafting and use of non-competition and trade secret agreements.

### Labor Relations:

The firm represents employers in public, private and non-profit sectors, offering counsel in both union and non-union environments. Five partners at Barran Liebman maintain a substantial labor relations practice including: Nelson Atkin, Paula Barran, Richard Hunt, Richard Liebman and Todd Lyon.

### Employee Benefits:

The firm represents employers in the drafting, design and growth of retirement and health plans, as well as executive compensation and §409A compliance. Jeffrey Robertson and Iris Tilley counsel private employers, municipalities and multi-employer pension and benefit trusts in all aspects of the design, tax qualification and ERISA compliance of retirement plans, executive compensation and health and welfare benefit plans.

### Clients:

Barran Liebman attorneys represent clients in the following industries: academic institutions, chemical businesses, civic agencies, communications and media organizations, construction, architectural and engineering firms, energy companies, financial institutions, food and consumer products companies, healthcare organizations, hi-tech companies, law firms, hospitality businesses, manufacturers, non-profits, printers, professional sport organizations, real estate developers, religious institutions, retail, cities and counties, banking, advertising, trade associations and transportation companies.

## PRACTICE AREAS

Advice
Litigation
Labor, Employment, Employee Benefits

## OFFICES

OREGON
**PORTLAND:** 601 SW 2nd Ave, Suite 2300, OR 97204
Tel: 503 228 0500   Fax: 503 274 1212
Email: clientservices@barran.com

BARRAN LIEBMAN LLP
ATTORNEYS
Employment | Labor | Benefits
www.barran.com | 503.228.0500

# BULLARD LAW

**www.**bullardlaw.com **tel:** 503 248 1134 **fax:** 503 224 8851

**President:** Francis T Barnwell
**Managing Partners:** Executive Committee
Number of partners: 23
Number of lawyers: 27
Languages: *English, Spanish*

## Firm Overview:

Since 1977, Bullard Law® has partnered with employers providing them with services in labor law, public sector labor and employment law, employment litigation and employee benefits law. A Pacific Northwest leader, Bullard's exceptional performance includes employment defense verdicts in tough discrimination litigation cases as well as active participation to prevent "would-be" claims. The firm's labor, employment and benefits law experience spans across all industries and remains extensive. Its capacity for private and public sector bargaining and NLRB work is unmatched. Bullard Law® attorneys work side-by-side with clients to minimize risks and avoid problems before they happen.

**Affiliation with WORKLAW® Network:** The firm is proud to be a member of the Worklaw® Network, a nationwide network of highly regarded independent management-side labor and employment law firms. Worklaw® Network (www.worklawnetwork.com) currently has over 350 attorneys practicing in 35 firms nationwide. This network provides access to a common computer data bank of briefs and research giving clients up-to-date and time saving information that is needed to make important decisions.

## Main Areas of Practice:

### Labor Law:

- Collective bargaining negotiations
- Grievance and arbitration
- Legal strategic advice to company negotiators
- Contract disputes
- Numerous petitions and unfair labor practice charges in Oregon, Washington and California
- All aspects of the NLRA, including unfair labor practice proceedings, union election campaigns, strike management and decertification efforts
- Public sector labor law
- Contract administration

### Employment Litigation:

- Employment discrimination and harassment claims, with extensive experience before state, federal and appellate courts as well as administrative agencies
- Claims arising out of pre-employment tests, screening procedures and drug and alcohol testing
- Wrongful discharge litigation and related "tort and contract claims" brought by employees and unions
- Whistleblower and retaliation claims
- Wage and hour claims, advice and defense including unsurpassed class/collective suit experience

- Reductions in force
- ERISA, PERS, and fringe benefit litigation
- Complex employment-related business litigation
- Family and medical leave, disability accommodation, and injured worker claims
- Appellate cases
- Non-compete agreements and departing employee disputes
- Private sector and public sector labor-related claims and litigation before the NLRB, ERB and federal courts

### Employee Benefits:

- Document drafting – plan documents and summaries, trust documents, forms and notices for retirement plans, executive compensation and health and welfare plans
- Advice regarding plan administration and fiduciary duties, taxation and reporting requirements
- Regulatory issues with the IRS, US Dept. of Labor and Health & Human Services, state Labor Bureaus and Insurance Divisions
- Employee benefit plan litigation
- Designing benefit and compensation packages
- HIPAA compliance and documentation for portability, privacy and security rules

## PRACTICE AREAS

Labor Law
Employment Litigation
Employee Benefits
Preventative Employment Advice
Training

## OFFICES

OREGON
**PORTLAND:** 200 SW Market Street, Suite 1900, OR 97201
Tel: 503 248 1134   Fax: 503 224 8851
Email: laborlaw@bullardlaw.com

### Preventative Employment Advice & Training:

- Employment law advice and training
- State and federal regulations of employment
- Employee handbooks, personnel policies and practice
- Trade Secrets, Confidentiality and Non-Compete Agreements
- Employment, independent contractor and Separation Agreements

### Clients:

Bullard Law represents public and private employers in a variety of industries including but not limited to: hospitals and healthcare facilities; Oregon and Washington cities, counties and local governments; financial and professional service firms; fire districts; non-profits; manufacturing; agriculture and food processing; consumer goods; retail; utilities; and transportation.

# MILLER NASH LLP

www.millernash.com **tel:** 503 224 5858 **fax:** 503 224 0155

**Chairman:** Dennis P Rawlinson
**Managing Partner:** Kieran J Curley
Number of partners: 69  Number of lawyers: 110

### Firm Overview:

Miller Nash LLP is one of the Pacific Northwest's largest and most respected multiservice law firms, offering comprehensive, creative, and innovative services to its business clients since 1873. The firm serves a wide range of leading businesses, public entities, nonprofit organizations, and individuals. The firm's clients work in a variety of significant industries, including banking, biotech, communications, construction, education, energy, finance, government, hospitality, manufacturing, real estate, nonprofits, retail, transportation, and utilities.

### Main Areas of Practice:

#### Bankruptcy & Creditor's Rights:

Miller Nash's bankruptcy and creditor's rights attorneys represent creditors, creditors' committees, trustees, and debtors in nonbankruptcy workouts, as well as in reorganization and liquidation bankruptcy cases. The firm also provides counsel on financing, securities, commercial lending, leasing, bonds, credit administration, letters of credit, cross-border financing, import-export, and other international transactions.

#### Business:

Miller Nash serves businesses of all sizes and in all stages of development. The firm's attorneys offer their expertise in multiple specialties, including business governance; contracts; emerging business and start-ups; technology protection and acquisition; entity structuring; mergers, acquisitions, and dispositions; public and private offerings of equity and debt securities; state, federal, and international tax issues; and corporation law, including director, officer, and shareholder matters.

#### Business Litigation:

Miller Nash's business litigation attorneys regularly try, mediate, negotiate, or arbitrate "bet the company" disputes as well as claims in the areas of corporate governance, complex insurance coverage, tax, lender liability, real estate, and international transactions. The firm also has extensive experience with securities fraud claims under federal and state securities laws, as well as suitability, churning, and breach-of-fiduciary-duty claims against broker-dealers.

#### Construction Litigation:

Miller Nash provides many construction law services. The firm's primary clients are owners, developers, public entities, general contractors, and subcontractors. Clients range from local and regional companies to national and international contractors doing business in the Northwest, involved in projects in the private and public sectors.

#### Employee Benefits:

Businesses, trusts, institutions, and individuals seek Miller Nash's counsel on employee benefits matters. The firm's attorneys work on all types of plans to help clients in all aspects of benefits work and represent them before the Internal Revenue Service, the US Department of Labor, the Pension Benefit Guaranty Corporation, and other federal agencies.

#### Employment Law & Labor Relations:

Miller Nash provides complete employment law and labor relations services to private- and public-sector employers, in both union and nonunion environments. The firm works with clients in proactively solving problems in today's rapidly changing employment environment, and defends employers when disputes arise. Miller Nash is also the worldwide Employment Law Alliance member firm in the states of Oregon and Washington.

#### Finance & Financial Institutions:

Miller Nash has long been the premier provider of counsel to financial institutions in the Pacific Northwest. Services provided by the firm in this area include counsel on financing, securities, commercial lending, leasing, bonds, credit administration, letters of credit, cross-border financing, import-export, and other international transactions.

#### Intellectual Property:

Intellectual property rights are often the most valuable assets of a company. Safeguarding those rights requires a comprehensive understanding of legal protections. Miller Nash represents clients in intellectual property matters involving patents, copyrights, trademarks, trade dress, and trade secrets.

#### Native American Tribes & Organizations:

Miller Nash serves Native American tribes and organizations on a diverse range of issues from legislative concerns to gaming and economic development. The firm offers assistance with government relations and lobbying on their behalf, including drafting legislation and ongoing advocacy, as well as providing counsel on Indian Civil Rights Act issues, advising tribes on organizational issues under the Indian Reorganization Act, and drafting and revising tribal constitutions and bylaws, ordinances, and codes.

#### Real Estate, Land Use & Environmental:

The firm's real estate, land use, and environmental lawyers assist clients in the buying, selling, financing, development, leasing, and construction of residential, commercial, industrial, and institutional properties. Miller Nash helps individuals and businesses structure, document, and obtain government approvals for all types of real estate transactions and developments.

#### Regulatory & Government Affairs:

Miller Nash's regulatory and government affairs attorneys work with clients in the oil, tribal, gaming, telecommunications, cable, broadcasting, computer, financial, construction, transportation, energy, education, medical, and insurance industries. Firm attorneys have extensive experience interacting with the legislative, judicial, and executive branches of state governments, as well as with federal, state, and local agencies and commissions.

#### Tax, Trusts & Estates & Nonprofit Organizations:

Attorneys in the firm's tax, trusts and estates, and nonprofit organizations practice help clients attain their business objectives while minimizing taxes and complying with local, state, and federal tax laws. The firm's wealth-management practice combines estate planning, will and trust preparation, and estate and trust administration.

#### International Work:

Miller Nash handles cross-border transactional work and international trade issues and cases. The firm has experience with litigation in US courts involving cross-border issues, as well as ICC, AAA, CIETAC, WIPO, and other international arbitrations. It is active in the IBA and the ABA International Section.

## OFFICES

**OREGON**

**PORTLAND:** 111 SW Fifth Avenue, Suite 3400, OR 97204
Tel: 503 224 5858  Fax: 503 224 0155
Email: clientservices@millernash.com

**BEND:** 1567 SW Chandler Avenue, Suite 204, OR 97702
Tel: 541 383 5857  Fax: 541 383 3968

**WASHINGTON**

**SEATTLE:** 4400 Two Union Square, 601 Union Street, WA 98101
Tel: 206 622 8484  Fax: 206 622 7485

**VANCOUVER:** 500 Broadway, Suite 400, WA 98660
Tel: 360 699 4771  Fax: 360 694 6413

# TONKON TORP LLP

www.tonkon.com **tel:** 503 221 1440

**Managing Partner:** Michael M. Morgan
Number of partners: 59
Number of Lawyers: 87
Languages: *Danish, Farsi, French, German, Italian, Mandarin Chinese, Norwegian, Russian, Spanish, Swedish, Tagalog*

**Firm Overview:**
Tonkon Torp LLP is a leading business and litigation law firm in Portland, Oregon serving public companies, substantial private enterprises, entrepreneurial businesses and individuals throughout the Pacific Northwest.

**Main Areas of Practice:**

**Bankruptcy & Creditors' Rights:**
The firm has nationally recognized expertise in reorganizations and debt restructuring, representing debtors in Chapter 7 and Chapter 11 proceedings, sales and acquisitions of troubled companies, real estate foreclosures, and commercial and collection litigation in state and federal court.

**Corporate Finance:**
Advice on venture capital and angel investor financing, initial and secondary public equity offerings, rule 144A and regulation S private placements, offshore private placements, corporate debt offerings, syndicated and secured loans, fund formation, and ongoing compliance and transactions for unregistered collective investment vehicles.

**Corporate Governance:**
Disclosure obligations, director fiduciary responsibilities, audit committee responsibilities, controlling shareholder responsibilities, use of special committees, and compliance and document retention policies.

**Energy Law:**
Regularly advise both renewable and traditional energy generators, manufacturers and utilities. Represent traditional utilities in finance, permitting and ownership issues, and the firm also advises clients in the wind, solar and other renewable energy sectors.

**Environment & Natural Resources:**
Counsel landowners, lenders, local governments and non-profit entities on issues ranging from acquisition of water rights to cleanup of contaminated property. Experience in compliance, litigation, permitting, certification, green building, and all aspects of water law.

**Financial Services:**
Leading provider of comprehensive legal services for institutions and professionals in the financial services industry. Counsel on federal and state securities and banking laws, and also on the rules and regulations of the SEC, FINRA, FDIC, FRB, OCC, various securities exchanges, and state banking and securities regulators.

**Government Relations & Public Policy:**
Strategy, advocacy and lobbying services on state, local, regional and national policy and legislative issues.

**Immigration:**
Nationally recognized immigration team provides services for domestic and international companies and individuals. Lawyers counsel and assist business clients with temporary and permanent visa applications and extensions, the preparation and filing of nonimmigrant and immigrant petitions, and citizenship proceedings.

**Intellectual Property:**
Identify and protect trademarks, service marks and copyrights; negotiate technology transfer and licensing agreements; negotiate software development and licensing; copyright compliance programs; perform due diligence in merger and acquisition transactions; protecting inventions, creations and trade secrets; develop privacy policies.

**Labor & Employment:**
Defend employment litigation matters and advise clients on union activities. Experience with the full range of labor and employment issues, including wage and hour practices, compliance with state and federal leave requirements; employment contracts, executive compensation and employee benefits; and non-compete and nondisclosure agreements.

**Litigation:**
Litigation expertise in commercial law, contract disputes, antitrust and trade regulations, constitutional law, corporate and securities litigation, debtor and creditor issues, intellectual property and trademark litigation, labor and employment, real estate, environmental and land use matters, business owner disputes, insurance coverage litigation, trust and probate litigation, and construction litigation.

**Mergers & Acquisitions:**
Counsel on corporate control transactions including mergers and acquisitions, joint ventures and strategic alliances, management buyouts, proxy contests, sales and acquisitions of troubled companies, spin-offs and asset sales, and going private transactions.

**Real Estate & Land Use:**
Advise on complex transactions involving land use and development matters, environment and natural resources issues, sales and acquisitions of developed and undeveloped real estate, and leasing matters.

**Taxation:**
Structure businesses and transactions to minimize tax liability while ensuring compliance with the various local, state and federal tax regimes. Advise on entity formation and structure, mergers and acquisitions, domestic and international joint ventures, executive compensation and benefits, investment and research credits, tax-exempt organizations, employee stock ownership plans, and tax-qualified plans.

**PRACTICE AREAS**

Accountant & Professional Liability
Administrative & Regulatory Law
Antitrust Advice & Litigation
Appeals
Bankruptcy & Creditor's Rights
Business Immigration
Business Law
Civil Rights & Constitutional Law
Construction Litigation
Commercial Litigation
Corporate Finance
Corporate Governance
Energy Law & Litigation
Environmental & Natural Resources Advocacy
Estate & Wealth Planning
Executive Compensation & Employee Benefits
Financial Services & Investment Management
Financial Services Litigation
Government Relations & Public Policy
Information Privacy & Security
Insurance Coverage
Intellectual Property Advice & Litigation
Labor & Employment
Media Law Litigation & Advice
Mediation & Arbitration Services
Mergers & Acquisitions
Nonprofit & Tax-Exempt Entities
Products Liability & Complex Torts
Real Estate & Land Use
Securities & SEC Enforcement
Taxation
Trust & Probate Litigation
Water Law

**OFFICES**

OREGON
PORTLAND: 888 SW 5th Avenue, Ste. 1600, OR 97204
Tel: 503 221 1440

## How lawyers are ranked

Every year we carry out thousands of in-depth interviews with clients in order to assess the reputations and expertise of business lawyers worldwide. The qualities we look for (and which determine rankings) include technical legal ability, professional conduct, client service, commercial awareness/astuteness, diligence, commitment, and other qualities most valued by the client. For details of our research team, see p.5.

# ANTITRUST

Commentary about individuals can be found under their firm's paragraph. If the firm has no paragraph (is not ranked) look at Other Notable Practitioners.

## Antitrust
### Leading Firms

**Band 1**
Dechert LLP *

**Band 2**
Berger & Montague PC
Buchanan Ingersoll & Rooney PC *
Fine, Kaplan and Black, RPC
Pepper Hamilton LLP *

**Band 3**
Ballard Spahr LLP *
Cozen O'Connor *
Kohn Swift & Graf, PC
Langer, Grogan & Diver PC
Morgan, Lewis & Bockius LLP *
Reed Smith LLP

## Band 1

### Dechert LLP
See profile on p.1969
THE FIRM This firm is highly regarded for its deep bench and broad antitrust practice. The group has expertise across a range of industries including life sciences, commodities and the food and beverage sector. Recent work highlights include successful representation of Whole Foods in a class certification matter, and continued victories defending high-profile client Dean Foods. Clients are particularly impressed with the high standard of service offered by the team.
Sources say: *"The best antitrust practice I have seen – proactive, flexible, cost-effective and they're doing discovery in cutting-edge ways."*
KEY INDIVIDUALS Clients laud standout performer **Joseph Tate** (see p.2231) as a *"strong negotiator"* who *"will go to the ends of the earth for his client."* He recently represented FMC Corporation in litigation regarding alleged price-fixing in the hydrogen peroxide industry. Litigator

**Stephen Brown** (see p.2212) is described by commentators as *"very active"* and *"an excellent lawyer."* He has recently continued his representation of Commercial Metals in direct and indirect purchaser antitrust actions. Pharmaceuticals expert **George Gordon** (see p.2217) is cochair of the firm's life sciences industry group and antitrust/competition group. Clients find him to be *"very knowledgeable and professional."* Recent highlights include leading litigation for Anaheim Manufacturing in an antitrust and unfair competition matter. **Christine Levin** (see p.2223) has a broad practice with particular emphasis on civil and criminal litigation across a wide range of industries. She recently successfully defended Whole Foods in a class certification action brought by Kottaras. The deeply experienced **Stephen Stack** (see p.2231) is adept at handling a wide variety of antitrust issues and regularly advises clients in the chemical and pharmaceutical industries. **Carolyn Feeney** (see p.2215) has been involved in multiple matters defending Dean Foods including a putative class action brought by supermarket chain Food Lion.

## Band 2

### Berger & Montague PC
THE FIRM This boutique is held in high regard in Pennsylvania, particularly for its representation of plaintiffs in significant antitrust litigations. The firm continues to have a strong presence in antitrust matters within the pharmaceutical industry. For example, recent highlights include the representation of Louisiana Wholesale Drug in relation to high-profile litigation surrounding the drug K-Dur. The firm also continues to act on behalf of a proposed class in a complex antitrust case against Visa and MasterCard.
Sources say: *"Outstanding lawyers who have gotten fantastic results."*
KEY INDIVIDUALS **Laddie Montague** is favorably described as *"a bright guy, a real gentleman and a very, very*

## Antitrust
### Senior Statesmen

Senior Statesmen: distinguished older practitioners
Black Allen    *Fine, Kaplan and Black, RPC*

### Leading Individuals

**Star individuals**

| | |
|---|---|
| Mather Barbara W | *Pepper Hamilton LLP* * |
| Tate Joseph A | *Dechert LLP* * |

**Band 1**

| | |
|---|---|
| Bizar Steven E | *Buchanan Ingersoll & Rooney PC* * |
| Langer Howard | *Langer, Grogan & Diver PC* |
| Liebenberg Roberta D | *Fine, Kaplan and Black, RPC* |
| Montague Jr H Laddie | *Berger & Montague PC* |
| Sicalides Barbara T | *Pepper Hamilton LLP* * |

**Band 2**

| | |
|---|---|
| Booker Daniel I | *Reed Smith LLP* |
| Brown Stephen D | *Dechert LLP* * |
| Cramer Eric | *Berger & Montague PC* |
| Davidoff Merrill | *Berger & Montague PC* |
| Gordon George G | *Dechert LLP* * |
| Kohn Joseph | *Kohn Swift & Graf, PC* |
| Levin Christine C | *Dechert LLP* * |
| Scher Howard D | *Buchanan Ingersoll & Rooney PC* * |
| Stack Jr Stephen A | *Dechert LLP* * |

**Band 3**

| | |
|---|---|
| Dever Gerard | *Fine, Kaplan and Black, RPC* |
| Feeney Carolyn | *Dechert LLP* * |
| Newell Francis Patrick | *Cozen O'Connor* * |
| Newton Wendelynne J | *Buchanan Ingersoll & Rooney PC* * |
| Saint-Antoine Paul | *Drinker Biddle & Reath LLP (ONP)* † * |
| Sorensen David F. | *Berger & Montague PC* |
| Sumner Robin P | *Pepper Hamilton LLP* * |

\* Indicates firm / individual with profile.
†ONP = Other Notable Practitioner.

*good lawyer.*" Notable transactions include representing a proposed class of plaintiffs in an action brought against Visa and MasterCard in relation to alleged price-fixing of the interchange fee. **Eric Cramer** recently represented Rochester Drug Co-Operative in an alleged monopolization action against hypodermic product manufacturer and seller Becton, Dickinson & Company. Sources say he is *"an effective antitrust lawyer and litigator with a good deal of integrity."* **Merrill Davidoff** recently led the team representing a class of plaintiffs in an action brought against American Express alleging multiple antitrust violations including inflation of foreign transaction fees. **David Sorensen** counseled Louisiana Wholesale Drug, purchasers of the drug K-Dur, in a high-profile 'pay for delay' deal. Sources describe him as a *"fantastic lawyer, incredibly fierce."*

### Buchanan Ingersoll & Rooney PC
See profile on p.2236

**THE FIRM** This full-service firm has an impressive antitrust practice and offers its services across an array of matters including compliance, M&A counseling and both civil and criminal litigation. Notable recent highlights include acting as co-counsel in the defense of LM Ericsson. The group actively represents organizations spanning numerous sectors ranging from healthcare to pharmaceutical and manufacturing companies.
**Sources say:** *"Outstanding. They're very practical, very knowledgeable about the law and very knowledgeable about our business."*
**KEY INDIVIDUALS** Favorably described as *"the perfect business lawyer,"* **Steven Bizar** (see p.2211) is praised by clients for his *"great intellectual firepower."* He is identified by sources as a genuine go-to practitioner for sophisticated business antitrust issues. **Howard Scher** (see p.2229) is described as *"courteous and professional"* with *"great intelligence and toughness."* Notable transactions this year include defending a price-fixing claim brought against chemical manufacturer Arkema. The *"extremely practical and very knowledgeable"* **Wendelynne Newton** (see p.2226) was instrumental in reaching a settlement in a lawsuit brought against client West Penn Multi-List. Clients praise her deep understanding of their issues.

### Fine, Kaplan and Black, RPC
**THE FIRM** This boutique antitrust firm continues to focus on complex litigation, with an emphasis on the representation of plaintiffs in class action disputes. The group also houses expertise in white-collar antitrust matters. The firm has recently been handling significant class actions surrounding the chemical products industry and involving major organizations in that field. The team is also able to represent defendants in the full range of antitrust issues.
**Sources say:** *"An excellent firm and excellent lawyers."*
**KEY INDIVIDUALS** The *"very insightful"* **Roberta Liebenberg** is regularly lauded as one of the leading antitrust practitioners in the state. She concentrates her practice on class action and commercial litigation and is widely recognized for her expertise in handling complex antitrust matters. **Gerard Dever** is identified by commentators as a *"very talented lawyer, very smart and very capa-*

*ble."* He regularly litigates cases in both state and federal court and handles civil and criminal antitrust violations. *"An excellent lawyer and an honorable practitioner,"* **Allen Black** has extensive experience in litigating complex class action disputes. Peers recognize him as *"the top scholar in antitrust law."*

### Pepper Hamilton LLP
See profile on p.2248

**THE FIRM** This full-service firm has a robust antitrust practice with a particular specialty in antitrust matters relating to the healthcare and pharmaceutical industries. Recent highlights include the successful representation of West Penn Allegheny Health System in a sophisticated competition antitrust dispute. The team has also acted for high-profile client GlaxoSmithKline in a class action revolving around pay-for-delay issues raised in the controversial K-Dur decision.
**Sources say:** *"They are willing to ask the right questions and they are very thorough."*
**KEY INDIVIDUALS** *"Top-notch"* practitioner **Barbara Mather** (see p.2224) is held in the highest regard by market commentators. Notable highlights include the representation of pharmaceutical giant GlaxoSmithKline in a class action brought against it by direct purchasers of Lamictal. The *"very smart, savvy and articulate"* **Barbara Sicalides** (see p.2230) is admired for her litigation skills. She recently led the team defending Advanced Urethane Technologies in an action alleging price-fixing among manufacturers. **Robin Sumner** (see p.2231) is appreciated by clients, who find her to be *"very accomplished and really very important to the team."* She recently assisted in the Processed Egg Products antitrust litigation involving a series of putative class actions.

## Band 3

### Ballard Spahr LLP
See profile on p.2234

**THE FIRM** This practice serves an impressive client roster spanning a range of industries. The antitrust group at Ballard Spahr has significant expertise in the pharmaceutical sector, representing high-profile clients such as GlaxoSmithKline. The group has also represented global client DuPont in several antitrust matters. The team has recently been involved in a series of complex class action disputes on behalf of its clients.
**Sources say:** *"The right mix of experience and the right strategy."*
**KEY INDIVIDUALS** Leslie John is the department head and key practice contact.

### Cozen O'Connor
See profile on p.2237

**THE FIRM** This established Pennsylvania presence has a comprehensive antitrust practice which can advise clients on all aspects of antitrust. The team is active in both civil and criminal litigation across a range of industrial sectors. Recent highlights include the representation of Premier

Chemicals in the defense of several antitrust class action claims. Other key clients include Kitchen Pride Mushroom Farms, Love's Travel Stops and Apotex.
**Sources say:** *"They know the facts and learn about our company and how we fit into the industry."*
**KEY INDIVIDUALS** The *"incredibly proactive"* **Francis Newell** (see p.2226) is held in high regard by his clients, who say: *"He helped us craft a strategy to negate our concerns, which was magnificent."*

### Kohn Swift & Graf, PC
**THE FIRM** This Philadelphia boutique is respected for its antitrust practice, particularly in the representation of plaintiffs. The firm represents both individuals and businesses in a variety of antitrust issues including price-fixing matters, anticompetitive trade practices and monopolization cases.
**KEY INDIVIDUALS** **Joseph Kohn** is praised by sources for his calm and rational approach to contentious issues. He focuses his practice on major civil litigation for a wide array of clients.

### Langer, Grogan & Diver PC
**THE FIRM** This compact team specializes in antitrust and highly complex commercial litigation. Market commentators recognize the group as an active presence in the state and particularly note its work in class action disputes. The practice also has a strong focus on pharmaceutical patent antitrust litigation.
**KEY INDIVIDUALS** The *"very smart and tenacious"* **Howard Langer** is highly regarded for antitrust. He has litigated major cases in the field and has notable experience in the pharmaceutical industry.

### Morgan, Lewis & Bockius LLP
See profile on p.2246

**THE FIRM** This firm has a global reach and is able to serve both national and international clients in both civil and criminal antitrust litigation. The Pennsylvania group is active across a broad range of industries, with particular strength in the life sciences and financial services sectors. Notable highlights include continued representation of Comdata in relation to allegations of monopolization.
**Sources say:** *"They were outstanding in so many ways, it was a pleasure for me; they are really some of the best lawyers I have ever worked with."*
**KEY INDIVIDUALS** Steven Reed is based in the Philadelphia office and cochairs the practice.

### Reed Smith LLP
**THE FIRM** This Pittsburgh practice benefits from the firm's global presence and international capabilities. The group is particularly active in the manufacturing and financial services sector. Recent highlights for the team include its ongoing representation of US Steel in several antitrust matters related to issues ranging from M&A to class action cartel litigation.
**KEY INDIVIDUALS** **Daniel Booker** continues to serve as lead counsel to US Steel in multiple litigations including an industrywide class action. Sources say he is an *"exceptionally talented lawyer."*

## Other Notable Practitioners

**Paul Saint-Antoine** (see p.2229) of Drinker Biddle & Reath LLP is described as *"very competent"* and *"a bright and capable antitrust lawyer."* He represents clients across a wide range of industries and has significant experience handling class action disputes.

# BANKING & FINANCE

Commentary about individuals can be found under their firm's paragraph. If the firm has no paragraph (is not ranked) look at Other Notable Practitioners.

### Banking & Finance
#### Leading Firms

**Band 1**
Blank Rome LLP *
Reed Smith LLP

**Band 2**
Ballard Spahr LLP *
Drinker Biddle & Reath LLP *

**Band 3**
Buchanan Ingersoll & Rooney PC *
Stradley Ronon Stevens & Young LLP

#### Senior Statesmen

Senior Statesmen: distinguished older practitioners
| Lesser Bruce | Blank Rome LLP * |

#### Leading Individuals

**Band 1**
| Bronson Jill E | Drinker Biddle & Reath LLP * |
| Flick II Lawrence | Blank Rome LLP * |
| Fridy Carl H | Ballard Spahr LLP * |
| Kabnick Lisa D | Reed Smith LLP |

**Band 2**
| Congdon Charles B | Drinker Biddle & Reath LLP * |
| Forman Harvey I | Blank Rome LLP * |
| Graziano Michael C | Blank Rome LLP * |
| Heryford Craig S | Buchanan Ingersoll & Rooney PC * |
| Lawlor James S | Reed Smith LLP |
| Miller Steven M. | Ballard Spahr LLP * |
| Pedrick Michael J | Morgan, Lewis & Bockius LLP (ONP) * |
| Perelman Richard S | Ballard Spahr LLP * |
| Rabinowitz Mark I | Blank Rome LLP * |
| Reich Judith E | Drinker Biddle & Reath LLP * |
| Stern Joan N | Blank Rome LLP * |

**Band 3**
| Chiafullo James D. | Cohen & Grigsby PC (ONP) |
| Harvey Calvin R. | Buchanan Ingersoll & Rooney PC * |
| Meyer Dianne A | Duane Morris LLP (ONP) |
| Zucker Richard M | Stradley Ronon Stevens & Young LLP |

**Up-and-coming individuals**
| Surbeck David | Reed Smith LLP |

### Banking & Finance: Mainly Regulatory
#### Leading Individuals

**Band 1**
| Bernstein Leonard A | Reed Smith LLP |
| Bleier Michael E | Reed Smith LLP |
| Kaplinsky Alan S | Ballard Spahr LLP * |
| Rosenblum Jeremy T | Ballard Spahr LLP * |
| Schieber Paul H | Stevens & Lee PC (ONP) |

**Associates to watch**
| Furletti Mark J. | Ballard Spahr LLP * |

*\* Indicates firm / individual with profile.*
*†ONP = Other Notable Practitioner.*

## Band 1

### Blank Rome LLP
#### See profile on p.2235

**THE FIRM** This full-service firm represents a range of financial institutions and public and private companies across a variety of industries, including healthcare, energy and real estate. It is often singled out as a leader in the public finance field, receiving praise from peers and clients alike. Recent highlights include assisting PNC Bank with numerous transactions, including a complex multijurisdictional financing matter which also involved foreign tax issues.

**Sources say:** *"They combine the highest professional standards with solid business acumen and a practical approach to issues as they arise."*

**KEY INDIVIDUALS Lawrence Flick** (see p.2216) is praised for his ability to handle complex negotiations. He recently led the team in a multifaceted transaction, providing counsel to long-standing client PNC Bank. Clients find him to be *"really knowledgeable"* and *"very impactful."* **Harvey Forman** (see p.2216) is well known and respected for his work in the banking and finance sector. Sources recognize him as a *"very strong"* and seasoned practitioner. Highly regarded in the financial services sector, **Bruce Lesser** (see p.2223) has extensive experience representing financial institutions and borrowers. **Mark Rabinowitz** (see p.2227) is widely praised by clients for his outstanding performance and *"extensive legal background."* According to commentators, *"his real magic is being able to provide practical business advice."* *"Tremendously good attorney"* **Joan Stern** (see p.2231) led the team advising Raymond James on a transaction relating to the financing of energy facilities for the Revel Casino and Resort in Atlantic City.

Sources note that she is *"extremely knowledgeable, well versed in the law and easy to work with."* **Michael Graziano** (see p.2217) recently represented PNC Bank in a complex revolving credit facility involving numerous foreign jurisdictions. Clients praise him as *"a practical businessman and an excellent strategic thinker."*

### Reed Smith LLP

**THE FIRM** The Pennsylvania headquarters of this well-reputed global firm is regarded highly for its ability to represent lenders in the large midmarket. The team has an established presence in numerous jurisdictions and is particularly active in Europe as well as across the USA. Recent highlights include handling multiple complex transactions for Bank of America, and successfully closing a lengthy matter for Fox Chase Cancer Center.

**Sources say:** *"They are outstanding – very responsive and usually ahead of the game."*

**KEY INDIVIDUALS Leonard Bernstein** is chair of the firm's financial services regulatory group. He has extensive experience representing financial institutions and regularly advises on federal and state regulations. Sources find **Lisa Kabnick** to be *"insightful and perceptive,"* with an *"excellent ability to explain legal issues."* She has represented Bank of America in numerous transactions of late. Clients appreciate that she is *"very professional and user-friendly."* **James Lawlor** is praised by clients as *"hard-working, smart and very creative."* He recently represented Fox Chase Cancer Center in a $125 million transaction. **David Surbeck** has assisted on various cases for major client Bank of America. He is well liked by clients, with one source noting: *"Nobody knows the guts of a credit agreement better."* **Michael Bleier** is highly regarded for his expertise on regulatory matters.

## Band 2

### Ballard Spahr LLP
#### See profile on p.2234

**THE FIRM** This firm maintains a diverse banking and finance practice with specific expertise across public, transactional and consumer finance services. The team's strong presence in the public finance sector is exemplified by its counsel to numerous banks, including First Niagara and Huntington National. Recent highlights include representing Grupo Salinas in a complex project relating to its acquisition of short-term loan provider Advance America. **Sources say:** *"They are experts and they know their business very well. They are very responsive and very good to work with."* **KEY INDIVIDUALS Carl Fridy** (see p.2216) leads the firm's transactional finance practice and is praised as being *"top-notch"* and *"standout."* He regularly represents commercial banks and has a wealth of experience dealing with both secured and unsecured loans. **Alan Kaplinsky** (see p.343) heads the consumer financial services team. He is highly regarded for providing counsel to financial institutions on transactional and regulatory matters. **Steven Miller** (see p.2225) is *"terrific and extremely well respected,"* according to sources. He has significant experience representing lenders in transactional finance matters. **Jeremy Rosenblum** (see p.395) has a strong regulatory finance practice and recently led the team advising Grupo Salinas on consumer finance service laws. **Richard Perelman** (see p.2227) has an extensive practice representing lenders and borrowers in a wide array of transactional finance matters. He is praised by clients for his *"patient, very smart and client-focused"* approach. **Mark Furletti** (see p.318) is an associate in the firm's business and finance department. He recently assisted on a complex transaction for First Niagara, and was also an active member of the team advising Grupo Salinas on regulatory matters.

## Drinker Biddle & Reath LLP
See profile on p.2238

**THE FIRM** This highly regarded practice has extensive experience counseling clients on a variety of corporate finance matters, ranging from senior bank debt to mezzanine debt and tax-exempt bonds. The team recently represented Morgan Stanley in connection with public offerings of taxable bonds and tax-exempt bonds. The firm is notably strong in Rule 144A debt issuances.

**KEY INDIVIDUALS** Peers speak highly of corporate finance team head **Jill Bronson** (see p.2212), and clients find her to be *"extremely knowledgeable and a good negotiator."* She has vast experience dealing with a range of finance transactions and has represented a variety of major lending institutions. **Charles Congdon** (see p.2213) is held in high regard for his work in the bond market and regularly represents issuers and underwriters. Recent highlights include advising underwriters Merrill Lynch on University of Pennsylvania bonds. **Judith Reich** (see p.2227) is well respected in the banking and finance arena and has a great deal of experience dealing with commercial loan transactions. Peers find her easy to deal with, and she is recognized as *"a team player who knows how to see the big picture."*

### Band 3

## Buchanan Ingersoll & Rooney PC
See profile on p.2236

**THE FIRM** This Pittsburgh-based firm has expanded its team over the past year with numerous significant additions. The firm offers a broad selection of financial services and is adept at handling multibank transactions. The team represents institutions across a range of industries, including healthcare and natural resources. Notable highlights include acting as bank counsel for RBS Citizens on a $29.9 million revenue bonds matter.

**Sources say:** *"It has been a great relationship for a long time. They have distinguished themselves in the way they bring deals together and their interpersonal skills."*

**KEY INDIVIDUALS Craig Heryford** (see p.2219) deals with a range of corporate finance matters, and has particular expertise in venture capital transactions. Clients appreciate his *"business sense and financial acumen,"* and praise his ability to make good business sense out of com-

plicated deals. Seasoned practitioner **Calvin Harvey** (see p.2219) is highly regarded for his expertise in real estate finance and syndicated loan transactions.

## Stradley Ronon Stevens & Young LLP

**THE FIRM** This firm is expanding its practice and has the ability to represent a wide range of clients in a variety of areas within the banking and finance remit, including regulatory, creditors' rights, and interstate and international banking matters. The team has recently been involved in a range of acquisition and financing transactions.

**Sources say:** *"We like the experience and capacity they have to handle the size and number of transactions."*

**KEY INDIVIDUALS Richard Zucker** is well regarded for his representation of commercial lenders and has a particularly strong reputation with regards to asset-based financing and real estate transactions.

### Other Notable Practitioners

**Paul Schieber** of Stevens & Lee PC is well known in the market for his regulatory practice in the banking and finance sector. He has specific expertise in mortgaging. **Michael Pedrick** (see p.2227) of Morgan, Lewis & Bockius LLP *"is reasonable and smart, and knows how to get a deal done,"* according to impressed interviewees. He focuses on representing borrowers. **James Chiafullo** of Cohen & Grigsby PC is hailed by market commentators as a *"very talented and very pragmatic"* lawyer. **Dianne Meyer** of Duane Morris LLP is highly regarded by both peers and clients, with sources noting that she is *"efficient,"* *"timely"* and *"always very responsive."* Recent highlights include representing the lender in a $75 million credit facility to a piping systems manufacturer.

# BANKRUPTCY/RESTRUCTURING

Bankruptcy/Restructuring p.2188

Commentary about individuals can be found under their firm's paragraph. If the firm has no paragraph (is not ranked) look at Other Notable Practitioners.

### Band 1

## Blank Rome LLP
See profile on p.2235

**THE FIRM** Blank Rome has a sterling reputation across both the commonwealth and the country for its Philadelphia-based bankruptcy practice. It represents all parties involved in bankruptcy and restructuring matters, while gaining particularly praise for its work with creditors. Recent highlights include representing the unsecured creditors' committee in Lower Bucks Hospital's Chapter 11 bankruptcy. The group has also been active in litigation, and is acting as co-counsel to USGen New England in a Fourth Circuit appeal following the firm's prior handling of the company's reorganization.

**Sources say:** *"The best thing about them is that their technical skills and capabilities are very, very good. What sets them apart is their responsiveness; they work very hard to be available 24/7. Whenever you need them they are willing and able to make themselves available and contribute whatever I need."*

**KEY INDIVIDUALS Thomas Biron** (see p.2211) is known as a tireless advocate for his clients, who describe him as *"extremely knowledgeable and very common-sensical."* He advises numerous big-name clients, including many leading financial institutions, on their involvement in Chapter 11 bankruptcies, as well as a full suite of related litigation. One client says of **Regina Stango Kelbon** (see p.2220): *"It's obvious to everyone that she knows what she's talking about. She's passionate about her work. She's conscientious of the work that she's doing and conscious about the cost that's*

incurred." Her recent successes include leading on the aforementioned Lower Bucks Hospital matter. **Michael Schaedle** (see p.2229) is another client favorite, and receives enthusiastic feedback from all corners for his committee work. One source comments that he is *"great and very knowledgeable. He's very concise and informative, he framed questions very well and explained difficult legal theories very articulately."* **Raymond Shapiro** (see p.2230) is *"a classy senior practitioner"* and *"a true statesman,"* according to many impressed market sources. He remains a leading light in the firm's practice and leads on the USGen New England work mentioned above. **Joel Charles Shapiro** (see p.2230) is praised for his knowledge of bankruptcy and aviation finance, and represented Pennsylvania banking giant PNC Bank as lender in the workout and disposition of nine aircraft. One client enthuses that he is *"top shelf, very pragmat-*

## Bankruptcy/Restructuring
### Leading Firms

**Band 1**
Blank Rome LLP *
Reed Smith LLP

**Band 2**
Dilworth Paxson LLP
Duane Morris LLP *
Hangley Aronchick Segal Pudlin & Schiller *

**Band 3**
Cozen O'Connor *
Drinker Biddle & Reath LLP *
Fox Rothschild LLP *
Klehr Harrison Harvey Branzburg LLP
Pepper Hamilton LLP *

**Band 4**
Ballard Spahr LLP *
Buchanan Ingersoll & Rooney PC *
Campbell & Levine
Eckert Seamans Cherin & Mellott, LLC *
McCarter & English, LLP *
McElroy, Deutsch, Mulvaney & Carpenter, LLP *
Morgan, Lewis & Bockius LLP *
Saul Ewing LLP *
Stradley Ronon Stevens & Young LLP

*\* Indicates firm / individual with profile.*
*†ONP = Other Notable Practitioner.*

## Bankruptcy/Restructuring
### Senior Statesmen

**Senior Statesmen: distinguished older practitioners**

| | | | |
|---|---|---|---|
| Shapiro Raymond | Blank Rome LLP * | Temin Michael L | Fox Rothschild LLP * |

### Leading Individuals

**Star individuals**

| | |
|---|---|
| Dworetzky Joseph A | Hangley Aronchick Segal Pudlin & Schiller * |
| Kassner Andrew C | Drinker Biddle & Reath LLP * |
| McMichael Esq Lawrence | Dilworth Paxson LLP |

**Band 1**

| | |
|---|---|
| Biron Thomas E | Blank Rome LLP * |
| Kleban Barry | McElroy, Deutsch, Mulvaney & Carpenter * |
| Reed Margery N | Duane Morris LLP |
| Singer Paul | Reed Smith LLP |
| Springer Claudia Z | Reed Smith LLP |

**Band 2**

| | |
|---|---|
| Barson Leon R | Blank Rome LLP * |
| Campbell Douglas A | Campbell & Levine |
| Clark Peter | Reed Smith LLP |
| Colton Neal | Cozen O'Connor * |
| Di Massa Jr Rudolph J | Duane Morris LLP |
| Karalis Aris J | Maschmeyer Karalis PC (ONP)† |
| Kelbon Regina Stango | Blank Rome LLP * |
| Lapowsky Robert | Stevens & Lee PC (ONP)† |
| Lawall Francis J | Pepper Hamilton LLP * |
| Levine Stanley E | Campbell & Levine |
| Matour James M | Hangley Aronchick Segal Pudlin & Schiller * |
| Menkowitz Michael | Fox Rothschild LLP * |
| Ramsey Natalie D | Montgomery, McCracken, Walker (ONP)† |
| Schaffer Eric A | Reed Smith LLP |
| Schorling William H | Buchanan Ingersoll & Rooney PC * |
| Shapiro Joel Charles | Blank Rome LLP * |
| Weis Martin J | Dilworth Paxson LLP |

**Band 3**

| | |
|---|---|
| Bloom Michael | Morgan, Lewis & Bockius LLP |
| Branzburg Morton R | Klehr Harrison Harvey Branzburg LLP |

| | |
|---|---|
| Bressler Barry E | Schnader Harrison Segal & Lewis (ONP)† |
| Bressler Gary D | McElroy, Deutsch, Mulvaney & Carpenter * |
| Chan Ashely M | Hangley Aronchick Segal Pudlin & Schiller * |
| Hampton Jeffrey C | Saul Ewing LLP * |
| Holman James J | Duane Morris LLP |
| Kotler Lawrence J | Duane Morris LLP |
| Kurtzman Jeffrey | Klehr Harrison Harvey Branzburg LLP |
| Marriott III Vincent J | Ballard Spahr LLP * |
| Packer Rosetta B | McCarter & English, LLP * |
| Patterson Paul | Stradley Ronon Stevens & Young LLP |
| Reed Michael H | Pepper Hamilton LLP * |
| Schaedle Michael B. | Blank Rome LLP * |
| Schildhorn Gary M | Eckert Seamans Cherin & Mellott, LLC |
| Turner Kitt | Eckert Seamans Cherin & Mellott, LLC |

**Band 4**

| | |
|---|---|
| Aaronson Anne Marie | Dilworth Paxson LLP |
| Baker Derek J | Reed Smith LLP |
| Ciardi Albert | Ciardi & Ciardi (ONP)† |
| Cordone Michael J | Stradley Ronon Stevens & Young LLP |
| Goodchild John | Morgan, Lewis & Bockius LLP * |
| Hamermesh Matthew A | Hangley Aronchick Segal Pudlin & Schiller * |
| Hughes Peter C | Dilworth Paxson LLP |
| Isenberg Adam H | Saul Ewing LLP |
| Santamour Gretchen M | Stradley Ronon Stevens & Young LLP |
| Vuocolo Diane E | Greenberg Traurig, LLP (ONP)† * |

**Up-and-coming individuals**

| | |
|---|---|
| Flame Andrew J | Drinker Biddle & Reath LLP * |
| Gellert Ronald | Gellert Scali Busenkell & Brown (ONP)† |
| Klein Joshua T | Fox Rothschild LLP * |

**Associates to watch**

| | |
|---|---|
| Mintz Josef | Blank Rome LLP * |

---

ic and responsive to the particular matter at hand. He's respectful of our strategy and opinion, but he's not afraid to voice his thoughts." **Josef Mintz** (see p.2225) is the group's most promising associate and has impressed clients across the board. One states that he has *"great potential and a great demeanor. He managed the case and did an outstanding job keeping everyone in the loop. He was always on top of things. I was very impressed with him."* **Leon Barson** (see p.2211) recently moved from Pepper Hamilton. Sources consider him to be *"very strong, really smart and very pragmatic."* Notable transactions undertaken in his previous role include representing plastic cutlery manufacturer Jet Plastica Industries in the divestment of its assets.

### Reed Smith LLP

**THE FIRM** This firm fields a team with tremendous depth and experience, which is sought out by clients from across the country to advise on any and all matters pertaining to bankruptcy and restructuring. The group has had a number of impressive and diverse mandates of late, including representing hedge fund New Stream Capital and some of its affiliates in their bankruptcy proceedings. On the creditors' side, Reed Smith acted for the creditors' committee of the Philadelphia Orchestra on its Chapter 11 bankruptcy. Other sectors of activity include hospitality, energy and natural resources.

**Sources say:** *"Very responsive, deep bench, excellent customer service." "I use them whenever I possibly can – they're definitely my first call if I have a new case."*

**KEY INDIVIDUALS** *"Great all-around practitioner"* **Paul Singer** is a market leader for creditor representation, and is

singled out by a number of peers as their top choice for referral in case of a conflict. He is the founder of the practice and has several decades' experience in the market. Healthcare bankruptcy expert **Claudia Springer** is *"excellent, and inspires a great deal of respect."* She represents Siemens Medical Solutions USA as creditor in numerous hospital bankruptcies involving tens of millions of dollars in claims. Outside of that industry, she also led on the Philadelphia Orchestra matter listed above. Clients are full of praise for **Peter Clark**, who they describe as *"one of the top workout and creditors' rights attorneys in the Northeast. We often rely on him to help us with significant commercial workout matters."* He acted for Wells Fargo in a large government contracting healthcare company's Delaware receivership action. **Eric Schaffer** is a top choice for creditors across a wide spread of industries and locations. He currently represents Wells Fargo as the largest unsecured creditor in Jefferson County, Alabama's Chapter 9 bankruptcy, the largest of its kind in US history. **Derek Baker's** universally positive reviews move him up in the tables this year. He assisted Claudia Springer on the Philadelphia Orchestra case, and is *"clearly a rising star."*

## Band 2

### Dilworth Paxson LLP

**THE FIRM** This Philadelphia stalwart punches above its weight in this area, and is often called upon to act on high-profile, high-value bankruptcies. The firm regularly advises debtors, creditors and lenders across the full spectrum of insolvency-related work. It is presently acting as debtor's counsel in the Philadelphia Orchestra's bankruptcy, and has already successfully settled with the Kimmel Center, the Musicians' Union and other creditors in the matter. Other highlights include advising the trustee in Proliance International's Chapter 7 case.

**Sources say:** *"Very creative lawyers." "Very active and unique."*

**KEY INDIVIDUALS** The *"excellent"* **Lawrence McMichael** is widely regarded for his *"high-end debtor work."* He effectively combines expertise in bankruptcy and skills as a strong advocate to successfully represent his clients. He is the lead partner on the Philadelphia Orchestra's bankruptcy. **Martin Weis** advises both creditors and debtors, and sources recommend him for his work across industries and in international mandates. **Peter Hughes** has been active on matters including the representation of George L Miller, Proliance's Chapter 7 trustee. He is praised for his advisory services, as well as his litigation skills. Sources praise the *"very smart"* **Anne Marie Aaronson**, who comes particularly highly rated for her work on Chapter 11 reorganizations. Among other recent highlights, she acted with McMichael on the Philadelphia Orchestra mandate.

### Duane Morris LLP
See profile on p.2239

**THE FIRM** Duane Morris is highlighted for the depth of its bankruptcy department and its prominence in this field. The firm has a strong profile for its representation of both secured and unsecured creditors, and also frequently acts for a range of other parties in both national and international bankruptcy proceedings. Recent highlights include acting for the Italian trustee in a bankruptcy case pending in Italy and the USA.
**Sources say:** *"A very strong and well-established firm with a good bankruptcy practice."*
**KEY INDIVIDUALS Margery Reed** has a broad practice, with a focus on insurance insolvency and commercial finance. She has advised both property and casualty insurance companies in connection with the Chapter 11 bankruptcies of such companies as Residential Capital, Hostess Brands and Chrysler. *"She is terrific,"* sources agree. **Rudolph Di Massa** chairs the firm's business reorganization and financial restructuring group, and comes highly recommended for his experience in contentious bankruptcy matters, including in relation to cross-border insolvency. He acted as counsel to the Italian trustee of Think3 on the aforementioned case in Bologna, Italy and Austin, Texas. **James Holman** divides his time between Philadelphia and Wilmington, Delaware, where he operates a strong lender-side practice. Recent highlights include work for Principal Life Insurance and UBS in connection with the restructuring of loan facilities in relation to Chapter 11 reorganization proceedings. **Lawrence Kotler** acted for the Executive Sounding Board Associates as the liquidating trustee in the bankruptcy of Metaldyne.

### Hangley Aronchick Segal Pudlin & Schiller
See profile on p.2243

**THE FIRM** This highly respected Philadelphia firm is acclaimed for its focus on Chapter 11 cases in Pennsylvania, New Jersey and Delaware. Best known for its work as debtors' counsel, the team also acts for creditors and a range of other interests, including investors and insurers in matters arising out of bankruptcy cases. It recently acted for NCR Corporation in connection with the prosecution of trust claims relating to the bankruptcy of GM.
**Sources say:** *"They are very responsive, creative, reasonable and very knowledgeable – I give them a solid A."*
**KEY INDIVIDUALS** The *"exceedingly bright and intuitive"* **Joseph Dworetzky** (see p.2215) is *"a brilliant human being,"* who operates at a very high level in this field. One peer commented: *"He is the finest lawyer I know – the first*

*person I would refer work to."* **James Matour** (see p.2224) chairs the firm's bankruptcy department, and is well regarded for his debtor side representation. He recently assisted a Philadelphia-based dog and cat grooming facility with the reorganization of approximately $8 million in secured and unsecured debt. **Ashely Chan** (see p.2212) is a *"very, very strong practitioner"* who is one to watch in this space, according to interviewees. She recently defended Citibank in two separate lawsuits relating to the bankruptcy of Universal Marketing. **Matthew Hamermesh** (see p.2218) advised Prince Music Theater on its Chapter 11 bankruptcy. One client enthused: *"He is an excellent writer and a very quick study. I like the work he does and I like him."*

## Band 3

### Cozen O'Connor
See profile on p.2237

**THE FIRM** This team is actively involved in the Pennsylvania bankruptcy and restructuring scene as counsel to debtors, creditors, trustees and other clients in a range of insolvency issues. Notably, the firm advised the Commonwealth of Pennsylvania in connection with the dismissal of the bankruptcy of the City of Harrisburg. Other key clients include Wilmington Trust and the Honickman Group.
**KEY INDIVIDUALS Neal Colton** (see p.2213) is a senior member of the bankruptcy Bar, who is lauded by both peers and clients for his work in this field. Sources say: *"He is outstanding – everyone has the utmost confidence in him."*

### Drinker Biddle & Reath LLP
See profile on p.2238

**THE FIRM** This strong team focuses on the representation of lenders and distressed debt funds in secured creditor facility restructurings. Highlights include acting for Textron Financial as the senior lender in the restructuring of the timeshare resort developer of Split Rock and Mount Laurel resorts. It also regularly acts for midmarket creditor companies, and recently advised Pennsylvania and Alabama-based Plumbing Holdings on its Chapter 11 filing.
**Sources say:** *"They really get good results in high-level cases."*
**KEY INDIVIDUALS Andrew Kassner** (see p.2220) is *"a fabulous strategic partner and a wonderful spokesperson who knows what to say as much as what not to say. Nobody comes close,"* one client enthused. Peers comment: *"He is a stellar attorney. He is an adversary you can trust; he has been around a long time and deserves a lot of respect."* **Andrew Flame** (see p.2215) is commended for his *"fine performance"* in corporate restructuring, insolvency and related litigation. Alongside Kassner, he advised Penske Truck Leasing as the creditor or preference claim defendant in more than 20 bankruptcy cases across the USA.

### Fox Rothschild LLP
See profile on p.2242

**THE FIRM** The Philadelphia arm of this nationwide team has had a strong year acting for creditors' committees,

trustees and debtors on a range of well-known Chapter 7, Chapter 11 and receivership proceedings. Recent highlights include its representation of the Chapter 7 trustee in the bankruptcy of Bionol Clearfield, which incorporated a multiparty bid and auction for the successful $10 million sale of its production facility.
**KEY INDIVIDUALS** Department head **Michael Menkowitz** (see p.2225) is *"a terrific lawyer"* and, according to a peer, *"a good opponent, who is very knowledgeable and practical in terms of getting to solutions."* Rising star **Joshua Klein** (see p.2221) continues to solidify his reputation in this market. He recently represented the creditors' committee in connection with the reorganization of a multiphase and residential real estate development. The distinguished **Michael Temin** (see p.2231) is a seasoned bankruptcy practitioner who earns widespread acclaim for his contributions to this field.

### Klehr Harrison Harvey Branzburg LLP

**THE FIRM** This established team is acknowledged for its coverage of midmarket bankruptcy and collection matters in Pennsylvania. It regularly advises banks and other lenders on a range of matters, including troubled loans, workouts and state court collection procedures.
**KEY INDIVIDUALS** Practice group cochair **Morton Branzburg** is a well-known and deeply experienced lawyer who comes highly recommended for his work with creditors' committees. **Jeffrey Kurtzman** represents real estate investment trusts, landlords, public companies and other clients in Chapter 11 cases.

### Pepper Hamilton LLP
See profile on p.2248

**THE FIRM** This solid ten-partner bankruptcy and restructuring practice is a significant presence in the Pennsylvania market. Recent highlights for this firm include representation of Nassau Broadcasting debtors in a significant Chapter 11 bankruptcy case. Other key clients include ExxonMobil, Lindenmeyr Munroe and Jet Plastica Industries.
**Sources say:** *"Well regarded in this market for a very long time. A high-level firm, and I think they do excellent work"*
**KEY INDIVIDUALS Francis Lawall** (see p.2222) recently acted on behalf of Exelon and PECO Energy defending a class action in a bankruptcy proceeding. Sources regard him as a *"very seasoned, very smart attorney"* who *"commands an awful lot of respect."* The experienced **Michael Reed** (see p.2227) comes highly recommended for his diverse bankruptcy and insolvency practice.

## Band 4

### Ballard Spahr LLP
See profile on p.2234

**THE FIRM** New entry Ballard Spahr is recognized for its high-level bankruptcy practice in this jurisdiction. The team in Philadelphia focuses on the representation of secured creditors, as well as on the nationwide representation of landlords in retail tenant bankruptcies. Other areas of expertise include asset purchases and sales, bankruptcy litigation and municipal recovery.

**Sources say:** *"Ballard has many outstanding attorneys who are regarded as preeminent in their particular area of the law."*

**KEY INDIVIDUALS** Vincent Marriott (see p.2224) is head of the firm's bankruptcy, reorganization and capital recovery group. Peers highlight his *"great credentials"* as counsel to financial institutions and other clients in a range of insolvency-related proceedings and litigation.

## Buchanan Ingersoll & Rooney PC
See profile on p.2236

**THE FIRM** This firm's bankruptcy team is highly regarded for its representation of secured lenders. Its impressive client roster includes the likes of PNC Bank, RBS Citizens and Bank of America. Notable matters handled by the group include a complex transaction valued at over $300 million for real estate giant LNR Partners.

**Sources say:** *"Their knowledge and efficiency are second to none."*

**KEY INDIVIDUALS** William Schorling (see p.2229) is held in high regard by market commentators. Sources say he *"has the magical combination of traits necessary for workout business."*

## Campbell & Levine

**THE FIRM** This Pittsburgh boutique is recognized as a go-to firm for debtors in possession, and is particularly active in industrial cases. The firm also regularly represents creditors' committees, with notable expertise in the asbestos sector as well as experience in retail and healthcare.

**KEY INDIVIDUALS** Douglas Campbell is described as being *"a very good lawyer, both for his legal knowledge and from a personality standpoint."* Stanley Levine is noted as *"a go-to guy"* and a *"very good practitioner."* He focuses his practice on debtors' and creditors' rights.

## Eckert Seamans Cherin & Mellott, LLC
See profile on p.2241

**THE FIRM** This Pittsburgh firm works extensively in the hospitality industry. Operating primarily in the midmarket, the firm has a thriving international aviation practice. Recent highlights include work for Zurich American Insurance and representing the interests of overseas carriers, including Dragonair and Cathay Pacific Airways.

**Sources say:** *"Creative, determined, skillful and successful."*

**KEY INDIVIDUALS** Gary Schildhorn recently acted on behalf of Bancorp Bank in connection with a reorganization for Saxby's Coffee Worldwide. Kitt Turner is described as a tenacious and confident attorney. Recent highlights include advising Zurich American Insurance on a variety of bankruptcy matters.

## McCarter & English, LLP
See profile on p.1759

**THE FIRM** This Philadelphia group focuses largely on commercial workouts and court litigation on behalf of lenders. The team regularly represents high-profile financial institutions, including First Niagara and Wells Fargo.

Recent highlights include representing CE Capital Asset management in connection with a foreclosure on a retail shopping center.

**Sources say:** *"They are good at working to maintain their relationship with us."*

**KEY INDIVIDUALS** Rosetta Packer (see p.2226) is head of the department at McCarter & English. Clients say: *"She's a very strong negotiator, and someone you want to have on your side."*

## McElroy, Deutsch, Mulvaney & Carpenter, LLP
See profile on p.1760

**THE FIRM** This practice represents a broad array of clients, ranging from debtors and creditors to equity holders and buyers. The group is active in numerous bankruptcy courts and also handles a significant number of out-of-court settlements. Work highlights include wrapping up a Chapter 11 proceeding on behalf of Midland Food Services.

**KEY INDIVIDUALS** Barry Kleban (see p.2221) *"brings a level of diplomacy and calm to very difficult situations,"* according to commentators. He recently represented the creditors' committee in relation to the bankruptcy of The Hyman Companies. Sources comment that Gary Bressler (see p.2212) is *"very professional and very knowledgeable,"* and appreciate his practical approach. Notable matters include the representation of Capital One Bank.

## Morgan, Lewis & Bockius LLP
See profile on p.2246

**THE FIRM** The Pennsylvania bankruptcy practice at this full-service giant has particular strength in relation to Chapter 11 proceedings. The team represents a variety of high-profile banks, as well as large debtors and trade creditors. A significant international footprint ensures the team also has extensive capabilities in relation to cross-border transactions and complex multinational restructurings.

**Sources say:** *"They always find a person with the deepest knowledge for the issue we're addressing, and there's always great follow-up."*

**KEY INDIVIDUALS** The *"very professional and incredibly knowledgeable"* Michael Bloom *"does a very competent job on complex matters,"* according to sources. He recently led a pro bono restructuring for the Child Welfare League of America. John Goodchild (see p.2217) recently acted on behalf of Air Products & Chemicals in connection with the bankruptcy of Qimonda Richmond, LLC. Clients laud his *"complete grasp of the subject matter."*

## Saul Ewing LLP
See profile on p.2249

**THE FIRM** This firm's bankruptcy and restructuring group is primarily renowned for representing debtors and unsecured creditors in all aspects of bankruptcy proceedings. The group also regularly acts on behalf of committees, and often serves as conflicts counsel. Highlights include the representation and successful reorganization of Lower Bucks Hospital.

**Sources say:** *"They were very attentive to the engagement and pleasant to work with. They are knowledgeable of insol-*

*vency law and the bankruptcy process, and they have a hands-on approach."*

**KEY INDIVIDUALS** Highlights for Jeffrey Hampton include representing US Foods on a variety of bankruptcy-related matters. He is considered to be *"a very effective leader"* who *"has a very strong financial background."* Adam Isenberg is held in high regard by commentators. He recently co-led the team representing Lower Bucks Hospital with regards to Chapter 11 bankruptcy proceedings and reorganization.

## Stradley Ronon Stevens & Young LLP

**THE FIRM** This firm's financial restructuring group represent lenders in a broad spectrum of bankruptcy and restructuring matters. The team regularly represents commercial finance companies as well as regional and national banks. The firm has experience and depth in many different areas, with significant expertise in creditors' rights litigation.

**KEY INDIVIDUALS** Cochair of the department Paul Patterson is recognized as *"a super lawyer and a stand-up guy."* He has particular expertise in Chapter 11 business bankruptcy. Michael Cordone represents debtors, creditors and purchasers in bankruptcy-related matters, and has also acted for banks in connection with loan workouts and restructurings. Gretchen Santamour represents clients across the broad spectrum of bankruptcy transactions.

## Other Notable Practitioners

Aris Karalis of Maschmeyer Karalis PC is highly regarded in the bankruptcy arena and garners significant praise from commentators. One source states that he is *"extraordinarily successful, extraordinarily dependable, and somebody who is greatly respected."* Natalie Ramsey of Montgomery, McCracken, Walker & Rhoads, LLP is recognized as a *"strong practitioner"* with a *"super reputation"* in bankruptcy work. She represents a broad range of clients in relation to all aspects of bankruptcy matters. Robert Lapowsky of Stevens & Lee PC is considered by sources to be *"very knowledgeable"* and *"very effective."* He regularly represents financial institutions as well as debtors and creditors' committees in insolvency matters. Barry Bressler of Schnader Harrison Segal & Lewis LLP is noted as a *"terrific"* lawyer who takes a *"very active role on behalf of his clients."* He recently represented TD Bank in relation to the foreclosure and bankruptcy of Harrisburg Mall. Albert Ciardi of Ciardi & Ciardi is regarded as *"very competent"* and a *"very good debtor lawyer."* His practice includes a focus on acting for Chapter 7 trustees and secured lenders. Diane Vuocolo (see p.2232) of Greenberg Traurig, LLP has particular expertise in aviation bankruptcy matters. She advises a variety of clients on issues ranging from business reorganization and restructurings to foreclosure litigation. Ronald Gellert recently moved from Eckert Seamans Cherin & Mellott to Gellert Scali Busenkell & Brown, LLC. In his former role, he represented ConAgra Foods in connection with the bankruptcy of Hostess Brands. He remains a well-regarded figure in this space, and has handled a wide range of Chapter 11 proceedings.

# CORPORATE/M&A & PRIVATE EQUITY

Commentary about individuals can be found under their firm's paragraph. If the firm has no paragraph (is not ranked) look at Other Notable Practitioners.

## Corporate/M&A & Private Equity
### Leading Firms

**Band 1**
Dechert LLP *
Morgan, Lewis & Bockius LLP *

**Band 2**
Blank Rome LLP *
Drinker Biddle & Reath LLP *
Duane Morris LLP *
Pepper Hamilton LLP *

**Band 3**
Ballard Spahr LLP *
Buchanan Ingersoll & Rooney PC *
Cozen O'Connor *
Fox Rothschild LLP *
K&L Gates *

## Corporate/M&A: Securities
### Leading Individuals

| Star individuals | |
| --- | --- |
| Abelson Barry M | Pepper Hamilton LLP * |

| Band 1 | |
| --- | --- |
| Klein Justin P | Ballard Spahr LLP * |
| McKenzie James | Morgan, Lewis & Bockius LLP * |
| Shargel Jason M | Cozen O'Connor * |
| Singer Alan | Morgan, Lewis & Bockius LLP * |

| Band 2 | |
| --- | --- |
| Busis Richard J | Cozen O'Connor * |
| Friedman Michael H | Pepper Hamilton LLP * |
| Genkin Barry H | Blank Rome LLP * |
| Guarcini Gerald J | Ballard Spahr LLP * |
| Katz Brian M | Pepper Hamilton LLP * |
| McLean Michael | K&L Gates * |
| Raymond III F Douglas | Drinker Biddle & Reath LLP * |
| Silfen Richard A | Duane Morris LLP |
| Soslow Joanne R | Morgan, Lewis & Bockius LLP * |

\* Indicates individual with profile.
†ONP = Other Notable Practitioner.

## Corporate/M&A & Private Equity
### Senior Statesmen

| Senior Statesmen: distinguished older practitioners | |
| --- | --- |
| Blume Fred | Blank Rome LLP * |
| Goodman Stephen M | Morgan, Lewis & Bockius LLP |

### Leading Individuals

| Star individuals | |
| --- | --- |
| Abelson Barry M | Pepper Hamilton LLP * |
| Winokur Barton J | Dechert LLP * |

| Band 1 | |
| --- | --- |
| Gerson David | Morgan, Lewis & Bockius LLP * |
| Nassau Henry N | Dechert LLP * |
| O'Donnell G Daniel | Dechert LLP * |
| Zeiger Alan L | Blank Rome LLP * |

| Band 2 | |
| --- | --- |
| Dubow Steven | Blank Rome LLP * |
| Klein Justin P | Ballard Spahr LLP * |
| Lawlor William G | Dechert LLP * |
| Lebovitz James A | Dechert LLP * |
| Libson Jeffrey P | Pepper Hamilton LLP * |
| Myers Marlee | Morgan, Lewis & Bockius LLP * |
| Raymond III F Douglas | Drinker Biddle & Reath LLP * |
| Romano Carmen J | Dechert LLP * |
| Shay Kathleen M | Duane Morris LLP |

| Band 3 | |
| --- | --- |
| Aldridge Richard B | Morgan, Lewis & Bockius LLP * |
| Braemer Richard J | Ballard Spahr LLP * |
| Buchanan Thomas G. | Buchanan Ingersoll & Rooney PC * |
| Gitlin David | Greenberg Traurig, LLP (ONP)† * |
| Godshall Craig L | Dechert LLP * |
| Haimm Neil K | Drinker Biddle & Reath LLP * |
| Harrington Michael S | Fox Rothschild LLP * |
| Heller Michael | Cozen O'Connor * |
| Jaffe Richard P | Duane Morris LLP |
| Juelke Robert C | Drinker Biddle & Reath LLP * |
| Sinatra Geraldine | Dechert LLP * |
| Thompson Thomas M | Buchanan Ingersoll & Rooney PC * |
| Zinn Robert P | K&L Gates * |

| Band 4 | |
| --- | --- |
| Agran Raymond | Saul Ewing LLP (ONP)† |
| Burdumy Stephen T | Drinker Biddle & Reath LLP * |
| Coogan John | Duane Morris LLP |
| Denious David S | Drinker Biddle & Reath LLP * |
| Doerner Brian D | Ballard Spahr LLP * |
| Genkin Barry H | Blank Rome LLP * |
| Laubach Larry P | Cozen O'Connor * |
| Miller Christopher S | Pepper Hamilton LLP * |
| Schuler Ronald W | Spilman Thomas & Battle, PLLC (ONP)† * |
| Tucci Peter J. | Fox Rothschild LLP * |

| Associates to watch | |
| --- | --- |
| Romaszewski Sandra | Fox Rothschild LLP * |
| Seltzer Greg | Ballard Spahr LLP * |

## Band 1

### Dechert LLP
**See profile on p.1969**

**THE FIRM** This leading corporate practice continues to focus on the high end of the Pennsylvania market, representing high-profile, long-standing clients such as Crown Holdings and Schramm. The firm has a broad global footprint and is expanding its international reach with many recent transactions involving cross-border elements. Recent highlights for the team include representing Randstad Holding in relation to its $770 million acquisition of SFN Group.
**Sources say:** "We found all members of the team to be very easy to deal with and very professional in their approach."
**KEY INDIVIDUALS** The "exceptional" and "extraordinarily well-respected" **Barton Winokur** (see p.2233) recently acted as lead partner representing NCO Group in connection with its merger with APAC. Sources recognize **Henry Nassau** (see p.2226) as a "standout lawyer" and "true professional." Notable recent highlights include acting as key partner in an acquisition for Versa Capital Management. Sources note that **William Lawlor** (see p.2222) "doesn't miss anything" and is "not intimidated by anybody." He recently represented Siemens in its acquisition of eMeter. **Carmen Romano** (see p.2228) is highly reputed as an "extraordinarily good lawyer." He recently played a lead role in advising Select Medical on its $1.15 billion refinancing. Notably active in the healthcare sector, **Craig Godshall** (see p.2217) recently led the team representing Court Square Capital Partners in connection with its acquisition of outpatient services provider Physiotherapy Associates Holdings. **James Lebovitz** (see p.2222) is praised by clients as "smart, down to earth and very talented." Highlights include acting for Adolor in relation to its sale to Cubist Pharmaceuticals, a transaction valued at $415 million. **Geraldine Sinatra** (see p.2230) has a good reputation

among peers and regularly advises private equity sponsors. She recently co-led the team representing Capital Square Partners in its acquisition of PRV Aerospace. **Daniel O'Donnell** (see p.2226) is recognized as a "terrific lawyer" with extensive experience. He recently acted on behalf of Court Square Capital Partners in relation to its acquisition of Encompass Digital Media Group.

### Morgan, Lewis & Bockius LLP
**See profile on p.2246**

**THE FIRM** This full-service firm has a thriving corporate practice in Pennsylvania. Numerous additions have been made to the team in the past year, which has led to a corresponding increase in the volume of transactions. The group has notable experience in providing counsel to corporations and has expanded its presence overseas. Recent work highlights include advising GSI Commerce in connection with its $2.4 billion merger with eBay.
**Sources say:** "We have been very impressed with their skills and how they approach things, and they are commercially aware."
**KEY INDIVIDUALS Marlee Myers** (see p.2226) is described by sources as "extraordinarily dedicated, tenacious and very smart." She recently represented EverPower in the significant acquisition of a California wind project. **James McKenzie** (see p.2224) is praised by clients for "keeping the work product practical and aligned with the underlying business objectives." His recent highlights include representing The Pep Boys in a merger valued at $1 billion. **Alan Singer** (see p.2230) is considered an expert in the securities arena. His diverse practice ranges from advising companies in relation to SEC matters to representing clients with respect to public and nonpublic offerings. The

well-respected **David Gerson** (see p.2217) recently acted as lead partner on an acquisition for long-term private equity client Sun Capital. **Joanne Soslow** (see p.2231) has been praised for her *"excellent business sense."* Work highlights include playing a key role in a $343 million transaction for Susquehanna Bancshares. **Richard Aldridge** (see p.2210) is lauded for his *"really great long-term thinking"* and impressive ability to manage sophisticated projects. Notable transactions include representing Lightwire in its sale to Cisco Systems, a matter valued at $271 million. **Stephen Goodman** is recognized as a *"superb lawyer,"* with sources finding him to be *"smart and practical with excellent interpersonal and client skills."*

## Band 2

### Blank Rome LLP
See profile on p.2235

**THE FIRM** This established firm focuses primarily on middle-market transactions, representing clients ranging from entrepreneurs to private equity funds and family-owned businesses. The team has an industry presence across a variety of areas including life sciences, energy and medical devices. Noteworthy highlights include representing Accutome in a cross-border acquisition by British company Halma Investment Holdings.

**Sources say:** *"You never want for a lawyer with a particular skill or expertise. They're very responsive, they manage their relationships very well and they communicate well."*

**KEY INDIVIDUALS** Sources describe **Alan Zeiger** (see p.2233) as an *"extremely smart, soft-spoken gentleman"* and a *"tremendous attorney."* Recent highlights include representing the founder of Yodle, Nathaniel Stevens, in relation to the redemption of his equity shares in the company. An *"exceptionally good business lawyer,"* **Barry Genkin** (see p.2216) is favorably described as being *"very versatile, very responsive and a delight to deal with."* Notable transactions include his representation of Sabre Industries in a cross-border joint venture with Brametal. **Steven Dubow** (see p.2215) is well thought of by both peers and clients. Sources praise his *"extremely good judgment, very good lawyer skills and ability to stay cool and calm under pressure."* He led a transaction for private equity fund Blue 9 Fund I in connection with its purchase of a minority interest in Hirtle Callaghan. Seasoned practitioner **Fred Blume** (see p.2211) is highly respected in the corporate arena. He advises a variety of public and private companies on a wide range of corporate matters.

### Drinker Biddle & Reath LLP
See profile on p.2238

**THE FIRM** This nationally acclaimed firm is well regarded for its corporate and securities practice in Pennsylvania. The team has experience across a range of industries with specific expertise in insurance, life sciences, healthcare and financial services to name but a few. The group regularly acts on behalf of a series of major organizations including Urban Outfitters, Endo Pharmaceuticals and Enstar.

**Sources say:** *"They've been terrific. As responsive as any firm I have ever worked with. Their attention to detail and quality control has been excellent."*

**KEY INDIVIDUALS Neil Haimm** (see p.2218) is recognized by peers as a strong practitioner in the field. He has extensive experience in joint venture transactions and regularly represents companies in the life sciences and technology sectors. Clients have nothing but praise for **Douglas Raymond** (see p.2227), describing him as *"devoted, incredibly responsive and wise."* He led the firm's team representing Charming Shoppes in its $890 million sale to Ascena Retail. **Stephen Burdumy** (see p.2212) is praised for his *"great practical sense."* Recent highlights include representing a medical device company in a high-value IPO. **David Denious** (see p.2214) regularly represents private equity sponsors and advises clients across a diverse range of corporate transactions. He has significant experience on matters within the healthcare sector and pharmaceutical industry. **Robert Juelke** (see p.2220) is described by commentators as *"terrific, with an excellent working knowledge of the law."*

### Duane Morris LLP
See profile on p.2239

**THE FIRM** This firm has worked to significantly expand its corporate department in the past twelve months, while maintaining its principal focus on middle-market private equity transactions. With expertise across a wide array of industries the team is well equipped to provide clients with high-quality legal advice at competitive rates.

**Sources say:** *"Not only have they done very good legal work, they have also been extremely good at helping with business aspects as well."*

**KEY INDIVIDUALS Kathleen Shay** is widely praised by clients for her practical approach and *"tremendous legal acumen."* Sources note she is *"very diligent, very thorough and makes herself available whenever needed."* Shay recently led the team negotiating a $40 million transaction for Agile Therapeutics. **Richard Silfen** heads the capital markets group at the practice. Highly regarded for his securities work, he advises clients on M&A and regularly counsels companies in relation to debt and equity securities offerings. Clients appreciate that **Richard Jaffe** *"understands the business side of the equation"* and note that he is *"always available, very responsive and very thoughtful."* Recent highlights include representing Point Judith Capital in connection with investment in a portfolio company. **John Coogan** represents clients across a range of corporate transactions including M&A, venture capital financings and securities offerings. He recently advised Sure Fit in the acquisition of its outdoor line from Trilink.

### Pepper Hamilton LLP
See profile on p.2248

**THE FIRM** This firm's corporate department provides expert advice and representation on a variety of transactions. The team is active in the healthcare sector and is particularly well regarded for its robust life sciences practice. Recent highlights include representing First Niagara Financial Group in its acquisition of 195 branches from

HSBC as well as its divestment of branches to KeyBank and Five Star Bank.

**Sources say:** *"Very responsive, very capable and very skilled on the private equity front."*

**KEY INDIVIDUALS** The *"bright, professional and intellectually strong"* **Barry Abelson** (see p.2210) is recognized as *"one of the most highly regarded corporate lawyers in Philadelphia."* He recently led the team advising leading financial services company DFC Global. **Michael Friedman** (see p.2216) *"gets transactions done and he's collegial to work with."* He represented First Niagara in its acquisition of multiple branches from HSBC. **Brian Katz** (see p.2220) is identified by sources as a standout practitioner. He recently represented Marsh & McLennan in its acquisition of Progressive Benefits Solutions as well as insurance agency Seitlin & Company. **Christopher Miller** (see p.2225) is described as *"very helpful, highly competent and responsive,"* with *"a good dose of common sense."* Recent highlights include representing Internet Pipeline and its investors in connection with investment by Technology Crossover Ventures. **Jeffrey Libson** (see p.2223) has extensive experience in the life sciences sector and has acted on behalf of numerous nonprofit clients that support the industry. He has been favorably described by clients and peers alike as being *"good to work with,"* *"very responsive"* and an *"absolute gentleman."*

## Band 3

### Ballard Spahr LLP
See profile on p.2234

**THE FIRM** This firm has a strong middle-market M&A practice with industry focus in the life sciences, aerospace and gaming sectors. It has formed strategic cross-border partnerships in order to facilitate M&A transactions with a foreign element. The corporate team also has significant experience in the insurance sector and recently represented Harleysville Mutual Insurance in connection with its $1.6 billion merger with Nationwide Mutual Insurance.

**Sources say:** *"They have done an excellent job and deliver great value."*

**KEY INDIVIDUALS** Client favorite **Justin Klein** (see p.2221) earns regular plaudits for his *"great business judgment"* and *"unbelievably intelligent"* approach. He recently led the team assisting Harleysville Mutual Insurance in two mergers. **Gerald Guarcini** (see p.2218) earns praise for his deep expertise in the corporate field. He recently acted on behalf of LEAF Commercial Capital in connection with an equity investment from Eos Partners. **Richard Braemer** (see p.2212) regularly represents both buyers and sellers in M&A transactions. According to commentators, he is *"very, very smart, capable and handles people well."* Sources note **Brian Doerner** (see p.2214) is a *"very knowledgeable M&A lawyer"* who *"does a great job."* He has particular expertise in life sciences and technology, and also handles securities transactions. **Greg Seltzer** (see p.2230) recently assisted on a $50 million growth equity investment in LEAF Commercial Capital. Sources are particularly impressed with his *"very practical"* approach.

## Buchanan Ingersoll & Rooney PC
See profile on p.2236

THE FIRM This Pittsburgh firm serves a diverse client base ranging from Fortune 500 public companies to venture funds and startup companies. The corporate department has experience handling transactions across a broad spectrum of industries and has notably strengthened its expertise in the energy sector. Recent highlights for the group include counseling Kennametal in relation to its acquisition of Deloro Stellite Group from a UK-based private equity firm.

Sources say: *"They are superb. The service level I get out of these guys is extraordinary. I trust them implicitly."*

KEY INDIVIDUALS Thomas Buchanan (see p.2212) heads the corporate department and is praised for his ability to *"interpret issues well and give very unbiased support and advice."* Recent highlights include providing counsel to Solideal USA in connection with its acquisition of Forklift Tires of America. Thomas Thompson (see p.2232) represents clients across a range of transactions including corporate acquisitions and venture capital financings. Clients comment he is *"always responsive, very practical"* and note that *"you can always count on Tom."*

## Cozen O'Connor
See profile on p.2237

THE FIRM This corporate group represents both buyers and sellers as well as family-owned business on a wide range of transactions spanning numerous industries including healthcare, telecommunications and manufacturing. Clients appreciate the team's responsiveness and competitive rates. The team recently represented Sony in connection with its acquisition of medical equipment developer Micronics.

Sources say: *"They are all very competent and knowledgeable and are very timely in their response and proactive in their communications."*

KEY INDIVIDUALS Michael Heller (see p.2219) recently represented long-term client Portico Systems in a $90 million equity raising transaction. He has specific expertise on

venture capital transactions and is well regarded for his representation of entrepreneurs. Larry Laubach (see p.2222) is held in excellent regard by his clients, who say: *"His skills are superb, his judgment is superb and so is his responsiveness and managing style."* He recently led the firm's representation of Sony in its acquisition of Micronics. Leading securities player Jason Shargel (see p.2230) remains a key presence in the market, particularly in private equity transactions. He has taken a lead role in a number of such deals in the past year, along with various other high-value matters. Richard Busis (see p.2212) is head of the firm's securities practice. He has particular expertise representing emerging companies in a range of transactions within the technology industry.

## Fox Rothschild LLP
See profile on p.2242

THE FIRM With five Pennsylvania offices, Fox Rothschild has a robust corporate presence throughout the state. The group see a significant amount of activity on the seller side and continues to represent clients in the mid to high midmarket. The team has been particularly active in transactions on behalf of technology, pharmaceutical and biotechnology companies.

Sources say: *"Fantastic. What you would hope to get out of a long-term attorney-client relationship. They anticipate issues for us and allow things to run smoothly."*

KEY INDIVIDUALS *"Valued adviser"* Michael Harrington (see p.2219) is extremely active in the life sciences and technology industries. Notable transactions include representation of Nitric BioTherapeutics in a $6 million follow-on financing. Clients praise his *"really good business sense."* Sandra Romaszewski (see p.2228) is held in the highest regard by clients, who say she is *"always available and always provides high-quality work."* Peter Tucci (see p.2232) recently acted for Harleysville Mutual Insurance in its acquisition by Nationwide Mutual Insurance. Sources say he is *"extremely smart"* and *"brings lots and lots of authoritative experience, which is incredibly helpful."*

## K&L Gates
See profile on p.2245

THE FIRM This Pittsburgh-based firm offers a full range of corporate services covering M&A, private equity and capital markets as well as joint ventures and public and private debt offerings. The firm has a global reach and is extremely active in cross-border transactions. It continues to represent clients across a diverse range of industries including financial services, natural resources and technology. The team recently acted as counsel to mobile payments technology company TxVia in relation to its acquisition by internet giant Google.

Sources say: *"They understand our business and provide answers tailored to the level of risk we're addressing."*

KEY INDIVIDUALS Securities attorney Michael McLean (see p.2225) represents corporations across a wide range of industries including oil and gas, media and technology. He regularly represents a diverse group of clients in debt and equity offerings as well as venture capital transactions. Robert Zinn (see p.2233) heads the firm's corporate practice and is held in fine regard as a business lawyer. One source notes: *"His level of communication with his clients is unbelievable, as is his level of expertise."*

## Other Notable Practitioners

David Gitlin (see p.321) of Greenberg Traurig, LLP is well renowned for his expertise in cross-border transactions and has particular experience representing Israeli clients. He regularly handles matters within the technology and life sciences industries. With significant experience across a broad range of corporate matters, Raymond Agran of Saul Ewing LLP is recognized for his expertise in M&A transactions involving cross-border issues. Ronald Schuler (see p.2229) of Spilman Thomas & Battle, PLLC is highly regarded for his extensive experience in the biotechnology sector, regularly advising medical device companies on corporate matters. Sources note he is *"a great resource."*

# ENVIRONMENT

Commentary about individuals can be found under their firm's paragraph. If the firm has no paragraph (is not ranked) look at Other Notable Practitioners.

| Environment Leading Firms | |
| --- | --- |
| **Band 1** | |
| Babst, Calland, Clements and Zomnir | |
| Manko, Gold, Katcher & Fox LLP | |
| **Band 2** | |
| Ballard Spahr LLP * | |
| Drinker Biddle & Reath LLP * | |
| Greenberg Traurig, LLP * | |
| K&L Gates * | |
| **Band 3** | |
| Fox Rothschild LLP * | |
| Hangley Aronchick Segal Pudlin & Schiller * | |
| Morgan, Lewis & Bockius LLP * | |
| Saul Ewing LLP * | |
| **Band 4** | |
| Buchanan Ingersoll & Rooney PC * | |
| Dechert LLP * | |

\* Indicates firm / individual with profile.
†ONP = Other Notable Practitioner.

| Environment Senior Statesmen | | |
| --- | --- | --- |
| **Senior Statesmen: distinguished older practitioners** | | |
| Manko Joseph M | Manko, Gold, Katcher & Fox LLP | |

| Leading Individuals | | |
| --- | --- | --- |
| **Band 1** | | |
| Babst III Chester | Babst, Calland, Clements and Zomnir | |
| Barnett Bonnie Allyn | Drinker Biddle & Reath LLP * | |
| Calland Dean | Babst, Calland, Clements and Zomnir | |
| Fox Robert | Manko, Gold, Katcher & Fox LLP | |
| Gold Marc | Manko, Gold, Katcher & Fox LLP | |
| Mandelbaum David G | Greenberg Traurig, LLP * | |
| Meloy Michael M | Manko, Gold, Katcher & Fox LLP | |
| Miano Steven T | Hangley Aronchick Segal Pudlin & Schiller * | |
| Weston R Timothy | K&L Gates * | |
| Woelfling Maxine | Morgan, Lewis & Bockius LLP * | |
| **Band 2** | | |
| Bergère Timothy J | Montgomery, McCracken, Walker (ONP)† | |
| Bluedorn II Donald C | Babst, Calland, Clements and Zomnir | |
| Bolstein Joel | Fox Rothschild LLP * | |
| Burcat Joel R | Saul Ewing LLP | |
| Buzzell David W | Land Air Water Legal Solutions LLC (ONP)† | |
| Carroll John W | Pepper Hamilton LLP (ONP)† * | |
| Cassidy Bart | Manko, Gold, Katcher & Fox LLP | |
| Cohen Abbi L | Dechert LLP * | |
| Collings Robert L | Schnader Harrison Segal & Lewis (ONP)† | |
| Collins Brendan K | Ballard Spahr LLP * | |
| Garber Kevin J | Babst, Calland, Clements and Zomnir | |
| Hinerman Philip L | Fox Rothschild LLP * | |
| Judge John P | Land Air Water Legal Solutions LLC (ONP)† | |
| McKinstry Jr Robert B | Ballard Spahr LLP * | |
| Miller Alan S | Picadio Sneath Miller & Norton (ONP)† | |
| Naugle Louis | Reed Smith LLP (ONP)† | |

| | | |
| --- | --- | --- |
| Sarachan Ronald A | Drinker Biddle & Reath LLP * | |
| Unterberger Glenn L | Ballard Spahr LLP * | |
| Warren Kenneth J | Warren Glass LLP (ONP)† | |
| Wein Howard J | Buchanan Ingersoll & Rooney PC * | |
| Wilson Craig P | K&L Gates * | |
| **Band 3** | | |
| Boyle Christopher W | Drinker Biddle & Reath LLP * | |
| Everett Carl B | Saul Ewing LLP | |
| Howard Lindsay | Babst, Calland, Clements and Zomnir | |
| Komoroski Kenneth S | Fulbright & Jaworski LLP (ONP)† * | |
| McAleese III John J | Morgan, Lewis & Bockius LLP * | |
| Reinhart Joe | Babst, Calland, Clements and Zomnir | |
| Roe Christopher M | Fox Rothschild LLP * | |
| Weiss Harry R | Ballard Spahr LLP * | |
| **Band 4** | | |
| Corson Samantha R | Greenberg Traurig, LLP * | |
| Gullace John | Manko, Gold, Katcher & Fox LLP | |
| Ix John | Dechert LLP * | |
| McCabe Carol | Manko, Gold, Katcher & Fox LLP | |
| Overstreet David | K&L Gates * | |
| Rader Kermit L | Hamburg, Rubin, Mullin, Maxwell (ONP)† | |
| Spergel Jonathan | Manko, Gold, Katcher & Fox LLP | |
| Stuart Glen R | Morgan, Lewis & Bockius LLP * | |
| Thomson Robert | Babst, Calland, Clements and Zomnir | |
| Toll Curtis B | Greenberg Traurig, LLP * | |
| **Up-and-coming individuals** | | |
| McIntyre Paul R | Greenberg Traurig, LLP * | |

## Band 1

### Babst, Calland, Clements and Zomnir, A Professional Corporation

**THE FIRM** This Pittsburgh boutique has a sophisticated environmental group with a deep bench of attorneys. The team handles a wide variety of environmental issues, ranging from air pollution and waste management to complex remediation including brownfields. Recent highlights include representing FirstEnergy Generation in negotiating a consent decree relating to the ultimate closure of Little Blue Run disposal facility.

**Sources say:** *"One of my go-to firms. It has a high degree of environmental expertise."*

**KEY INDIVIDUALS Chester Babst** is highly regarded for his experience in a wide range of environmental matters. He has particular expertise in dealing with CAA issues. *"A true leader of the practice,"* **Dean Calland** recently served as counsel to a Fortune 500 company on the sale of a large chemical business. **Donald Bluedorn** is described as a *"very knowledgeable"* attorney with a *"good grasp of the issues."* He recently acted as lead negotiator for FirstEnergy Generation. **Kevin Garber** is well regarded in the environmental community and has particular expertise in natural resources law. He regularly advises oil and gas and mining companies on a range of issues. Sources say he is *"very conscientious, very timely, punctual and capable."* **Lindsay Howard** has a wealth of experience in Superfund issues at both state and federal levels. He is well regarded for his practice in relation to natural resource damage claims. **Joe Reinhart** has extensive experience dealing with complex permitting and enforcement matters. His practice focuses on coal mining, oil and gas well development, and matters relating to the Marcellus Shale. *"Very reasonable and prac-*

*tical,"* **Robert Thomson** has a wide-ranging environmental practice. Sources note that he *"always gives good advice and is very prompt."*

### Manko, Gold, Katcher & Fox LLP

**THE FIRM** This firm handles all aspects of environmental law, from large Superfund cases to site remediation and brownfields development. The team has specific expertise in air regulation matters, and a notably active practice in relation to Marcellus Shale issues. The firm also has an active environmental litigation practice.

**Sources say:** *"I think they're fantastic. They're my number one. Incredibly reliable and responsive, and extremely knowledgeable."*

**KEY INDIVIDUALS** *"Smart and savvy,"* **Robert Fox** has extensive experience counseling on a range of environmental issues, including hazardous and municipal waste regulations and brownfields redevelopment. **Marc Gold** is recognized for his expertise in water pollution control and management. One source notes: *"He's got a wealth of expe-*

*rience; he's a very practical guy. A lawyer at the top of his game."* *"Incredibly detailed"* and *"very smart,"* **Michael Meloy** is widely praised by clients for his *"very deep understanding of the law"* and *"valuable technical insight."* **Bart Cassidy** is appreciated for his *"depth and breadth of knowledge,"* particularly in relation to air quality control issues. **Carol McCabe** focuses her practice on air-related environmental matters and regularly represents clients before the Pennsylvania Environmental Hearing Board. **Jonathan Spergel** advises clients on a broad spectrum of environmental issues, with a notable focus on the redevelopment of brownfield sites. Experienced negotiator and litigator **John Gullace** represents clients across a range of industries, including chemical, waste and telecommunications. Clients find him to be *"incredibly knowledgeable, very articulate and very responsive."* **Joseph Manko** is highly respected by peers and has extensive experience counseling clients on a wide range of environmental issues, particularly in relation to real estate development.

## Band 2

### Ballard Spahr LLP
See profile on p.2234

THE FIRM The environmental group at this full-service firm offers expertise across a broad spectrum of issues, including natural resources, brownfield redevelopment, permitting support and regulatory compliance. The group also has an active litigation practice, and has recently defended the Philadelphia Regional Port Authority. Sources say: *"They deliver excellent service of the first order. They did a first-rate job."*

KEY INDIVIDUALS The *"reasonable and thoughtful"* **Brendan Collins** (see p.2213) recently led the team acting for Exelon and a number of clean energy companies in litigation regarding Mercury and Air Toxics Standards. Sources note him to be extremely *"knowledgeable and practical."* **Robert McKinstry** (see p.2224) is recognized for his expertise in climate change. He recently co-led the team advising Exelon on numerous federal regulations. **Glenn Unterberger** (see p.2232) is praised for his *"in-depth knowledge of air quality regulations."* He recently represented Lehigh University in connection with land acquisition and related environmental matters. Sources note him to be *"very practical and effective in working out solutions."* A talented litigator, **Harry Weiss** (see p.2232) recently represented and counseled JPMorgan Chase and individual clients on natural resources and oil and gas rights.

### Drinker Biddle & Reath LLP
See profile on p.2238

THE FIRM Attorneys at this full-service firm are highly regarded for their expertise in Superfund matters. The firm's environmental practice covers litigation, regulatory and transactional work for clients ranging from pharmaceutical and manufacturing companies to solid waste companies and brownfields redevelopers. Notable highlights for the firm include defending Maxus Energy and Tierra Solutions in complex litigation involving Superfund issues. Sources say: *"Extremely effective and extremely reasonable."*

KEY INDIVIDUALS **Bonnie Allyn Barnett** (see p.2210) is highly regarded as *"one of the top players in Superfund law."* She is hailed as a *"terrific litigator,"* and clients appreciate that *"she knows how to think on her feet and she's very responsive."* **Ronald Sarachan** (see p.2229) is *"very knowledgeable and very smart, with good instincts,"* say interviewees. He assisted the team in defending Maxus Energy and Tierra Solutions, as mentioned above. Clients praise **Christopher Boyle**'s (see p.2212) efficiency, effectiveness and problem-solving abilities. One source notes: *"He's extremely knowledgeable. He understands how to come to a resolution, and gets to the crux of an issue."*

### Greenberg Traurig, LLP
See profile on p.1024

THE FIRM This highly reputed firm recently acted for EFG Brownfield Partners in a complex transaction involving the remediation and redevelopment of Globeville Smelter, a copper smelting facility in Colorado. The firm continues to expand its environmental practice, and coun-

sels clients on Superfund and brownfield matters, among others, including permitting and enforcement issues relating to natural resources. Sources say: *"They have senior expert attorneys and great second-tier associates that are a pleasure to work with."*

KEY INDIVIDUALS An *"exceptional attorney and preeminent in his field,"* **David Mandelbaum** (see p.2224) recently counseled Seneca Resources and is described as a *"thoughtful technician."* **Samantha Corson** (see p.2213) is recognized for her transactional work in the environmental arena. She recently advised Landbank Properties on the establishment of a wildlife conservation bank in California. **Curtis Toll** (see p.2232) regularly represents developers and corporations in a range of transactions concerning environmental matters relating to real estate. He recently advised LNR Property on the transfer of the remaining land at South Weymouth Naval Air Station into the developer's ownership. **Paul McIntyre** (see p.2224) led the team representing Rockpoint Group in acquisition and financing transactions involving numerous environmental elements. Sources are impressed by his ability to accomplish deals, and note him to be *"extremely good at what he does."*

### K&L Gates
See profile on p.2245

THE FIRM This Pittsburgh-based firm has strong presence and international reach. Its broad-based environmental practice covers a range of issues, including compliance counseling, enforcement defense and project development. The team is particularly strong in regulatory matters and has a robust practice handling Marcellus Shale issues. Sources say: *"Its attorneys are always accessible, and they are very flexible – not only with their time, but in their approach to addressing issues of interest."*

KEY INDIVIDUALS The *"highly skilled and experienced"* **Timothy Weston** (see p.2232) is widely respected by peers for his expertise in water matters. Clients describe him as *"extremely sharp, extremely competent and very good to work with."* **Craig Wilson** (see p.2233) *"incorporates his legal advice within a business context."* His practice focuses on regulatory matters and representing natural gas developers. An experienced administrative litigator, **David Overstreet** (see p.2226) is *"strategically oriented in his legal advice."* Clients appreciate his responsiveness and find him to be *"very knowledgeable, smart and sensitive to his clients' needs."*

## Band 3

### Fox Rothschild LLP
See profile on p.2242

THE FIRM The environmental group at Fox Rothschild has a strong litigation practice covering a wide range of issues, including toxic torts, product liability claims and air pollution matters. Notable highlights for the group include providing outside counsel to Clean Earth on permitting and compliance issues. The team has a deep bench with expertise across the gamut of environmental law, including

Superfund, waste management, water and air, as well as climate change and greenhouse gases.

KEY INDIVIDUALS **Joel Bolstein** (see p.2211) regularly advises clients on permitting matters and brownfields redevelopment. Recent highlights include providing counsel to Schreiber Foods on transactional and permitting matters relating to the expansion of its yogurt manufacturing facility. **Philip Hinerman** (see p.2219) has extensive experience in federal and state regulatory litigation and counseling, land use and sustainable building. He recently successfully represented Philadelphia Housing Authority in a contamination lawsuit against petroleum refiners. **Christopher Roe** (see p.2228) is hailed by clients as *"very responsive, very knowledgeable and very competent."* One source notes: *"He advocated very strongly on our behalf and accommodated all our needs. He really explained issues in an understandable way."*

### Hangley Aronchick Segal Pudlin & Schiller
See profile on p.2243

THE FIRM This compact group is highly regarded in the environmental arena and regularly counsels clients on compliance and permitting matters. Skilled in environmental litigation and Superfund matters, attorneys at Hangley Aronchick regularly advise major Fortune 100 companies. The group also has significant expertise in handling all aspects of water resource and brownfields redevelopment issues. Sources say: *"Vigorous advocates."*

KEY INDIVIDUALS *"A very articulate communicator,"* **Steven Miano** (see p.2225) earns praise from peers and clients alike. Sources say he *"is very bright and very experienced, and moves very easily from the big picture to detail."*

### Morgan, Lewis & Bockius LLP
See profile on p.2246

THE FIRM With a geographic presence across Pennsylvania and a strong national reputation, this full-service firm has an extensive environmental practice handling transactional and regulatory matters. The group's core focus is in handling complex litigation across a broad spectrum of environmental matters. Highlights for the team include representing DuPont in a complex lawsuit concerning a diverse range of environmental claims. Sources say: *"Very responsive – really great customer service."*

KEY INDIVIDUALS **Maxine Woelfling** (see p.2233) is a member of the Environmental Hearing Board, and is highly respected in the Pennsylvania environmental community. She recently represented global energy company ConocoPhillips in the spin-off of its businesses into a new company. *"Very confident, very helpful"* and *"always available,"* **John McAleese** (see p.2224) is an experienced environmental litigator. His notable transactions include representing Exelon in connection with complex environmental issues relating to the sale of Maryland Clean Coal. **Glen Stuart** (see p.2231) is lead counsel to AstraZeneca on a number of matters, including the Delaware Sand and Gravel Superfund Site. Sources note that *"he consistently provides high-quality and efficient support."*

## Saul Ewing LLP
See profile on p.2249

THE FIRM This firm's environmental group provides counsel at local, state and federal levels, advising clients on regulatory, transactional and litigation matters. The group has significant experience working with government agencies, and collaborates with colleagues across numerous practice areas to provide interdisciplinary advice to clients. Attorneys at Saul Ewing represent a range of clients, from waste management, power and energy companies to property owners and developers.

KEY INDIVIDUALS **Joel Burcat** is highly respected by peers in the field. He has significant experience representing clients in the oil and gas industry, and recently represented Spectra Energy in litigation relating to its pipelines. **Carl Everett** has a broad-based practice with particular expertise in Superfund matters. He regularly counsels clients on permitting issues under both state and federal law.

## Band 4

### Buchanan Ingersoll & Rooney PC
See profile on p.2236

THE FIRM This Pittsburgh-based firm offers environmental counseling and handles litigation relating to regulatory and land use matters, as well as real estate and corporate transactions. The distinguished multidisciplinary group has a strong renewable energy practice. Attorneys are also active in advising clients in the continually emerging Marcellus Shale arena.

KEY INDIVIDUALS *"Top-notch lawyer"* **Howard Wein** (see p.2232) has a strong reputation in the environmental field and regularly advises clients from a variety of industries, including energy, oil and gas and natural resources.

## Dechert LLP
See profile on p.1969

THE FIRM The team at Dechert is highly regarded for its transactional advice on environmental issues, particularly in relation to sophisticated real estate finance transactions. The firm has a wide reach, handling national and international matters. Notable highlights include providing environmental counsel to Bank of America on the financing of a California resort constructed on the site of an oil and gas processing facility.

**Sources say:** *"They are extremely knowledgeable and user-friendly. They help us assess the risk first and translate it into layman's terms."*

KEY INDIVIDUALS The *"very client-oriented and very commercial"* **Abbi Cohen** (see p.2213) recently acted as lead counsel for Bank of America. One source notes: *"She gets through all the issues and articulates potential solutions and our risks around them."* **John Ix** (see p.2219) was lead environmental counsel representing RAF Industries in connection with the sale of WI Holdings. He is described as *"extremely responsive, very good to deal with and extremely quick."*

## Other Notable Practitioners

**Timothy Bergère** of Montgomery, McCracken, Walker & Rhoads, LLP is described as *"a very capable attorney who's very thorough and very deliberate in what he does."* **John Judge** of Land Air Water Legal Solutions LLC has significant technical expertise in science and engineering. He is described as *"a sharp lawyer"* and regularly provides environmental counsel to clients in the pharmaceutical and chemical industries. At the same firm, the *"very smart and capable"* **David Buzzell** has a respected environmental practice specializing in solid and hazardous waste matters. The *"hard-working"* **John Carroll** (see p.2212) of Pepper Hamilton LLP is praised by clients for his excellent negotiating skills. He recently represented Tilden Township in negotiating a complex municipal sewer agreement. **Robert Collings** of Schnader Harrison Segal & Lewis LLP is *"a very respected litigator and a very highly regarded environmental lawyer."* He has extensive regulatory and litigation experience, particularly with regards to hazardous substance issues. **Alan Miller** of Picadio Sneath Miller & Norton is lauded as *"a very fine lawyer"* who has a broad practice handling numerous aspects of environmental law, including Superfund, contamination issues, and air and water pollution regulatory enforcement actions. **Kenneth Komoroski** (see p.2221) of Fulbright & Jaworski LLP is recognized for his oil and gas practice and regularly advises on Marcellus Shale matters. **Louis Naugle** of Reed Smith LLP has a strong reputation and regularly counsels clients on compliance and permitting issues across a diverse range of environmental matters. **Kermit Rader** of Hamburg, Rubin, Mullin, Maxwell & Lupin focuses his practice on remediation, compliance and enforcement, and is particularly experienced in the oil and gas sector. He is viewed as *"a smart guy and a great litigator – very knowledgeable."* **Kenneth Warren** recently left Hangley Aronchick to form Warren Glass LLP. He is highly regarded in the environmental field, and is described as *"very practical and a great counselor."* One source states: *"He's brilliant and insightful, and gives excellent advice."*

# INTELLECTUAL PROPERTY

Intellectual Property p.2197

Commentary about individuals can be found under their firm's paragraph. If the firm has no paragraph (is not ranked) look at Other Notable Practitioners.

## Band 1

### Woodcock Washburn LLP
See profile on p.2250

THE FIRM This boutique firm is highly regarded in Pennsylvania for its capabilities across all aspects of IP matters, ranging from patent, copyright and trademark procurement to litigation, licensing and transactions. The group has industry expertise across a variety of sectors including life sciences, medical devices technology and software. Recent highlights include reaching a settlement in its continued representation of Microsoft in a patent infringement case relating to the Android operating system.

**Sources say:** *"They offer both quality of services and attention for clients."*

KEY INDIVIDUALS *"Solid practitioner"* **Dale Heist** (see p.2219) led the team in its representation of Microsoft in a patent infringement dispute and has continued to represent it in a declaratory judgment action against DataTern. **Steven Rocci** (see p.2228) is described as *"a very gracious person and really a pleasure to interact with."* His notable representations include bringing a lawsuit on behalf of Stertil-Koni USA in connection with infringement issues relating to heavy-duty vehicle lifts. **David Wolfsohn** (see p.2233) is lead counsel for DuPont in a high-value lawsuit brought against Medtronic for breach of a patent license agreement. He is praised as *"a very good communicator"* and *"an extraordinarily intelligent lawyer."* **Joseph Lucci** (see p.2223) acted for the University of Pennsylvania in a bench trial relating to the ownership of patents by the Alzheimer's Institute of America. Sources note him to be *"a good, solid, sound attorney"* who is *"especially good at complex reexamination."* **Nancy Frandsen** (see p.2216) has a solid reputation among peers. She recently led the firm's representation of First Service Networks in a trademark infringement matter. The *"very sharp"* **Aleksander Goranin** (see p.2217) is recognized as a *"fabulous lawyer and a really smart guy."* He recently co-led the firm's representation of Crown Packaging Technology in patent infringement cases against Ball Metal Beverage Container. Recent highlights for **John Donohue** (see p.2214) include representing Frontline Technologies in a patent infringement matter against CRS. He is held in high regard by his peers.

## Band 2

### Caesar, Rivise, Bernstein, Cohen & Pokotilow Ltd

THE FIRM This well-known boutique is highly regarded in Philadelphia and offer clients a full range of IP services. The group is experienced across a broad spectrum of

## Intellectual Property
### Leading Firms

**Band 1**
Woodcock Washburn LLP *

**Band 2**
Caesar, Rivise, Bernstein, Cohen & Pokotilow Ltd
Drinker Biddle & Reath LLP *
Panitch Schwarze Belisario & Nadel LLP *

**Band 3**
Akin Gump Strauss Hauer & Feld LLP *
Dechert LLP *
Duane Morris LLP *
Eckert Seamans Cherin & Mellott, LLC *
K&L Gates *
Pepper Hamilton LLP *
RatnerPrestia
Volpe and Koenig, PC

**Band 4**
Ballard Spahr LLP *
Buchanan Ingersoll & Rooney PC *
Flaster Greenberg PC
Reed Smith LLP
The Webb Law Firm

*\* Indicates firm / individual with profile.*
*† ONP = Other Notable Practitioner.*

## Intellectual Property
### Senior Statesmen

**Senior Statesmen: distinguished older practitioners**

| | | | |
|---|---|---|---|
| Cohen Stanley H | *Caesar, Rivise, Bernstein, Cohen* | Prestia Paul F | *RatnerPrestia* |

### Leading Individuals

**Star individuals**

| | |
|---|---|
| Pokotilow Manny D | *Caesar, Rivise, Bernstein, Cohen* |

**Band 1**

| | |
|---|---|
| Elderkin Dianne B | *Akin Gump Strauss Hauer & Feld LLP* * |
| Heist Dale M | *Woodcock Washburn LLP* * |
| Jacobs-Meadway Roberta | *Eckert Seamans Cherin & Mellott, LLC* |

**Band 2**

| | |
|---|---|
| Alstadt Lynn J | *Buchanan Ingersoll & Rooney PC* * |
| Beck Paul | *Beck & Thomas, PC (ONP)† * |
| Belisario Martin G | *Panitch Schwarze Belisario & Nadel LLP* * |
| Black Martin J | *Dechert LLP* * |
| Byrne Richard L | *The Webb Law Firm* |
| Casey Kevin | *Stradley Ronon Stevens & Young PC (ONP)† * |
| Colen Frederick H | *Reed Smith LLP* |
| Cronk Peter J | *Duane Morris LLP* |
| Donohue Jr John P | *Woodcock Washburn LLP* * |
| Doyle Kathryn R | *Riverside Law Firm PC (ONP)† * |
| Gundersen Glenn A | *Dechert LLP* * |
| Kyper James R | *K&L Gates* * |
| LaVine Jordan A | *Flaster Greenberg PC* |
| Lavorgna Gregory J | *Drinker Biddle & Reath LLP* * |
| Leace Benjamin | *RatnerPrestia* |
| Marshall John | *Drinker Biddle & Reath LLP* * |
| Nadel Alan S | *Panitch Schwarze Belisario & Nadel LLP* * |
| Nigon Kenneth | *RatnerPrestia* |
| Panitch Ronald L | *Panitch Schwarze Belisario & Nadel LLP* * |
| Rocci Steven J | *Woodcock Washburn LLP* * |
| Tillery M Kelly | *Pepper Hamilton LLP* * |
| Wolfsohn David J | *Woodcock Washburn LLP* * |

**Band 3**

| | |
|---|---|
| Calderone Lynda | *Flaster Greenberg PC* |

| | |
|---|---|
| DeLuca Mark | *Pepper Hamilton LLP* * |
| Faigus Martin | *Caesar, Rivise, Bernstein, Cohen* |
| Flannery Kevin M | *Dechert LLP* * |
| Frandsen Nancy | *Woodcock Washburn LLP* * |
| Jablon Clark | *Panitch Schwarze Belisario & Nadel LLP* * |
| Koons Jr Robert A | *Drinker Biddle & Reath LLP* * |
| Miller Camille | *Cozen O'Connor PC (ONP)† * |
| Rzonca Lynn E | *Ballard Spahr LLP* * |
| Schwarze William W | *Panitch Schwarze Belisario & Nadel LLP* * |
| Silver Robert S | *Caesar, Rivise, Bernstein, Cohen* |
| Stein Barry | *Caesar, Rivise, Bernstein, Cohen* |
| Volpe Anthony S | *Volpe and Koenig, PC* |

**Band 4**

| | |
|---|---|
| Baldauf Sr Kent E | *The Webb Law Firm* |
| Baron Jr Robert R | *Ballard Spahr LLP* * |
| Cannuscio Robert | *Drinker Biddle & Reath LLP* * |
| Cohen Barry L | *SorinRand LLC PC (ONP)† * |
| Driscoll Stephen J | *Saul Ewing LLP PC (ONP)† * |
| Fletman Abbe F | *Flaster Greenberg PC* |
| Jacobs Hara K | *Ballard Spahr LLP* * |
| Kennedy Paul J | *Pepper Hamilton LLP* * |
| Lucci Joseph | *Woodcock Washburn LLP* * |
| McElhinny Patrick | *K&L Gates* * |
| McIlvaine III John W | *The Webb Law Firm* |
| McNichol William J | *Reed Smith LLP* |
| Milcetic Paul B | *Kessler Topaz Meltzer & Check PC (ONP)† * |
| Monaco Daniel A | *Drinker Biddle & Reath LLP* * |
| Peirce Richard | *Eckert Seamans Cherin & Mellott, LLC* |

**Up-and-coming individuals**

| | |
|---|---|
| Goranin Aleksander J | *Woodcock Washburn LLP* * |

industries including financial services, telecommunications and medical devices. The firm also has extensive knowledge of the pharmaceutical sector and is widely acknowledged for its expertise in Abbreviated New Drug Application (ANDA) litigation. Highlights for the team include an action for trademark infringement and unfair competition on behalf of the American Diabetes Association.

**KEY INDIVIDUALS** *"First-rate attorney"* **Manny Pokotilow** is described as a *"true gentleman and very smart guy."* He has extensive expertise in patent, trademark and copyright enforcement litigation. **Martin Faigus** has a broad practice with particular focus on the prosecution of patent and trademark applications. Sources find him to be *"very experienced and very capable."* **Robert Silver** has an extensive litigation practice representing US and international companies across a wide range of industries. He has specific expertise in ANDA litigation. **Barry Stein** is highly respected in the sector. His practice places particular emphasis on IP in the technology fields including computer systems, e-commerce and communications. **Stanley Cohen** is highly regarded as a leader in this practice area and noted to be an *"outstanding practitioner"* and a *"terrific guy."* He continues to counsel with a specific focus on trademark and copyright law.

### Drinker Biddle & Reath LLP
See profile on p.2238
**THE FIRM** The group at Drinker Biddle offers clients the full range of IP services. The team is skilled in transactional work, litigation and general counseling and is well regarded for its expertise in the biotechnology and life sciences industries. Notable transactions include handling a

diverse array of IP matters ranging from trademark concerns to patent infringement suits for SafeNet both in the USA and internationally.

**Sources say:** *"Very effective in getting the objective as well as proposing strategies to maximize our likelihood of success."*
**KEY INDIVIDUALS Gregory Lavorgna** (see p.2222) is lead partner for SafeNet handling the company's entire IP portfolio. He assists a range of clients worldwide. **John Marshall** (see p.2224) focuses his practice on civil litigation in trademark, copyright and patent matters. He is described as *"very professional"* and *"very accomplished."* The *"extraordinarily responsive"* **Robert Koons** (see p.2221) represents both US and foreign clients across a range of industries. Recent highlights include handling a patent infringement case for ORBCOMM. Clients appreciate his *"very good business mind"* and find him to be *"very intelligent, accessible and reliable."* **Robert Cannuscio** (see p.2212) *"does an excellent job. He is very knowledgeable, very efficient and he responds quickly,"* according to sources. He recently represented Globus Medical in its IPO. **Daniel Monaco** (see p.2225) concentrates his practice on patents within the biotechnology and chemistry sectors. Sources

note he is *"extremely knowledgeable in the area of law and within science."*

### Panitch Schwarze Belisario & Nadel LLP
See profile on p.2247
**THE FIRM** This boutique firm is recognized for its strength in handling a broad range of IP transactions, particularly patent application prosecutions. The team represents clients across the full spectrum of industries including technology, pharmaceutical and medical devices. Highlights from the past year include acting on behalf of MorphoSys in connection with a trademark infringement action. The firm also represents high-profile client AMI Entertainment Network.

**Sources say:** *"We have a very high success rate with them. They understand our business and they understand the technology behind the business."*
**KEY INDIVIDUALS Martin Belisario** (see p.2211) has an active prosecution practice. Clients appreciate that he is *"very conscientious about doing work efficiently."* Founding partner and *"outstanding lawyer"* **Alan Nadel** (see p.2226) is admired by peers and is noted to be *"a pleasure to work*

*against."* **Ronald Panitch** (see p.2226) is held in high regard by his peers and brings a wealth of experience in IP matters. Sources view him as *"a trusted professional in this area"* and comment: *"He's good at addressing and resolving issues."* **Clark Jablon** (see p.2219) is lauded as *"outstanding at getting patents issued quickly."* Clients note he *"has the ability to be very persuasive"* and is *"extremely knowledgeable about patent laws, procedures and practice."* **William Schwarze** (see p.2229) recently represented World Pac International in relation to a patent prosecution matter. Clients appreciate that he *"goes the extra mile for you."*

## Band 3

### Akin Gump Strauss Hauer & Feld LLP
See profile on p.904

**THE FIRM** This firm's IP group has a strong reputation for its ability to deal with complex patent matters. The team has particular expertise within the life sciences, pharmaceutical and medical device industries. The firm is adept at handling patent infringement disputes for high-profile clients. For example, the group recently provided counsel to Google in several infringement actions.
**KEY INDIVIDUALS** *"Creative and knowledgeable"* practitioner **Dianne Elderkin** (see p.2215) is praised by market commentators. One source notes: *"She's cool, very solid and very stable."*

### Dechert LLP
See profile on p.1969

**THE FIRM** This Philadelphia practice regularly handles significant and complex patent litigation, and has particular expertise in Abbreviated New Drug Application issues. The IP practice has international capabilities with matters spanning across the globe including Germany and Japan. The group recently represented Japanese manufacturer Teikoku and its US distributor Endo Pharmaceuticals in a high-stakes dispute.
**Sources say:** *"Very thorough and thoughtful, always a top-notch job."*
**KEY INDIVIDUALS** **Martin Black** (see p.2211) recently represented Hitachi and its licensing agent in a patent enforcement action. He is lauded as *"absolutely top-notch as a strategist and a technical lawyer. Very creative and willing to think outside the box."* **Glenn Gundersen** (see p.2218) is highly regarded by peers and widely acknowledged for his trademark practice. Work highlights for **Kevin Flannery** (see p.2216) include playing a key role in a patent infringement litigation for global pharmaceutical giant GlaxoSmithKline. He enjoys a solid reputation among peers.

### Duane Morris LLP
See profile on p.2239

**THE FIRM** This well-reputed firm has experience across a broad range of IP matters including patents, copyrights and trade secrets, with particular focus on patent and trademark prosecution cases. Its attorneys have backgrounds in a variety of areas including biosciences, chem-

icals and telecommunications, providing expertise across a range of industries.
**KEY INDIVIDUALS** The *"bold, strong and experienced"* **Peter Cronk** recently handled a trademark and unfair competition dispute for CertainTeed.

### Eckert Seamans Cherin & Mellott, LLC
See profile on p.2241

**THE FIRM** This full-service firm provides a full range of IP services for a series of long-standing clients across numerous industries. Recent work highlights for the group include the representation of Drew Estates in a trademark infringement matter. The group is strong in relation to licensing and technology; it is also active within the retail industry and has acted on behalf of Spencer Gifts in multiple IP actions.
**Sources say:** *"Their advice has been very helpful and effective. We are very pleased with the quality and efficiency of their representation."*
**KEY INDIVIDUALS** **Roberta Jacobs-Meadway** is widely respected for her trademark expertise. Clients find her to be *"very responsive"* and *"a tough negotiator."* One source notes she is *"very pragmatic and thinks like a businessperson."* **Richard Peirce** led the team on a cybersquatting action on behalf of Washington National Insurance. According to clients he is *"very knowledgeable and efficient, he follows up promptly"* and provides *"thoughtful, effective representation."*

### K&L Gates
See profile on p.2245

**THE FIRM** This internationally recognized firm has a clear presence within the Pennsylvania IP market. The Pittsburgh group has an extensive prosecution practice as well as capabilities in patent, trademark and copyright litigation. Their expertise spans a range of industries including technology, electronics and science.
**KEY INDIVIDUALS** **James Kyper** (see p.2222) has extensive experience advising clients on a broad range of IP-related matters and has an active litigation practice regularly handling trademark, patent and copyright disputes. **Patrick McElhinny** (see p.2224) has specific expertise in relation to insurance coverage for IP claims. He has significant trial experience and concentrates his practice on patent litigation.

### Pepper Hamilton LLP
See profile on p.2248

**THE FIRM** This full-service firm has a deep IP practice with particular strength in the life sciences sector. The group regularly handles complex patent litigation as well as trademark and copyright actions. Its client roster includes high-profile companies such as Comcast and Motorola. Recent highlights include the representation of Saint-Gobain Performance Plastics in connection with multiple trade secrets and patent infringement claims.
**Sources say:** *"They're very responsive. They have a depth of knowledge, particularly for trademark work, where they provide a lot of insight."*

**KEY INDIVIDUALS** According to sources, **Mark DeLuca** (see p.2214) *"has a great deal of experience and seems to anticipate problems; he thinks a couple of steps ahead."* One client comments: *"The advice he gives is very good and I think his analytical skills are extraordinary."* **Paul Kennedy** (see p.2221) is appreciated by clients and praised for his *"good insight into the business practicalities for applying and protecting trademarks."* **Kelly Tillery** (see p.2232) is well respected among his peers. Recent highlights include representing Nest International in relation to trade secret and copyright infringement claims.

### RatnerPrestia

**THE FIRM** This compact boutique offers sophisticated representation on a full range of IP matters. The group has strong technological background and capabilities counseling on transactions involving cross-border elements, particularly within Europe and Asia. The team regularly represents major clients across many industries including Endo Pharmaceuticals, Porsche and Arkema.
**Sources say:** *"Thorough and adept. I feel comfortable when they tell me something that it will be accurate and good advice."*
**KEY INDIVIDUALS** Chair of the firm's litigation group, **Benjamin Leace** is described as *"quick on his feet and able to give thorough answers that clients understand."* **Kenneth Nigon** counsels clients across the full range of IP matters. He has significant expertise in patent prosecution. **Paul Prestia** is praised as *"very helpful, approachable and available."* He has extensive experience in the life sciences field.

### Volpe and Koenig, PC

**THE FIRM** This boutique firm has expertise across a range of industries and specializes in IP matters within the technology sector. The firm also has cross-border affiliations and handles matters involving foreign jurisdictions such as Germany and Japan. Notable highlights include providing counsel to InterDigital on a $375 million patent transaction.
**KEY INDIVIDUALS** The well-respected **Anthony Volpe** is a seasoned practitioner and *"very client-oriented."*

## Band 4

### Ballard Spahr LLP
See profile on p.2234

**THE FIRM** This full-service firm has a substantial IP department with capabilities ranging from counseling to complex litigation. The group regularly handles a diverse array of IP matters including patent, trademark and copyright actions on a national and international level. Recent representations include serving as IP counsel to the American Board of Internal Medicine (ABIM) in numerous disputes.
**Sources say:** *"Very responsive, very practical and a very good sense of finding solutions to difficult situations from both a legal and business standpoint."*
**KEY INDIVIDUALS** **Lynn Rzonca** (see p.2229) has a strong reputation in the IP space. Her work highlights

include representing Limited Brands in patent litigation and other IP matters. IP department vice chair **Robert Baron** (see p.2210) is well respected by clients. One source described him as *"a brilliant tactician in the litigation arena."* **Hara Jacobs** (see p.2220) is lead counsel for ABIM in connection with numerous disputes. Sources note she is *"tenacious and smart, works hard and is fast and savvy."*

### Buchanan Ingersoll & Rooney PC
See profile on p.2236
**THE FIRM** This group has enjoyed impressive results recently, including securing a summary judgment in favor of client Pitt Ohio Express in a patent infringement action. The team also represented Black Box Corporation and BB Technologies in a trademark opposition matter. The firm has specialized practice groups devoted to IP matters across specific industries including chemical, biotech and electrical. The group is particularly active in patent prosecution.
**Sources say:** *"Excellent and very professional. They take into consideration the business aspects of every legal situation."*
**KEY INDIVIDUALS Lynn Alstadt** (see p.2210) represents high-profile client Siemens International. He is noted as *"fantastic at the law"* and *"very responsive."* One source adds: *"I always get really excellent advice from Lynn."*

### Flaster Greenberg PC
**THE FIRM** Acting on behalf of clients such as The New York Times and The Northface Apparel, this firm's IP department is adept at handling complex matters for significant organizations. The group assists clients on a wide variety of IP concerns ranging from transactional matters to patent prosecution and litigation. Notable highlights include the prosecution of multiple patent applications for American Standard Brands.
**Sources say:** *"They are technically very strong in our areas of concern and provide excellent guidance in constructing new IP as well as prosecuting other IP."*

**KEY INDIVIDUALS Jordan LaVine** served as primary counsel to The New York Times in connection with trademark and copyright issues. Clients find him to be *"responsive and prompt with advice,"* and *"very pragmatic."* **Lynda Calderone** is praised as *"meticulous and self-driven."* Clients appreciate that she *"delivers service in a cost-effective and timely manner."* Recent representations include providing counsel to Greene, Tweed of Delaware in relation to numerous patent applications. **Abbe Fletman** is favorably described as *"extremely competent, highly skilled, incredibly intelligent and practical."* She recently served as lead partner on a trademark matter for Members 1st Federal Credit Union.

### Reed Smith LLP
**THE FIRM** This internationally renowned firm has a significant Pennsylvania IP practice with a focus on patent litigation. The team has an impressive client roster including GE, GlaxoSmithKline and Siemens. It is active across a wide range of industries and recently succeeded in defending a lengthy patent infringement litigation for Altair Eyewear.
**KEY INDIVIDUALS Frederick Colen** has extensive experience dealing with both US and foreign IP matters including copyright, trademark and patent actions. He is described as *"a true gentleman and a very honorable person."* **William McNichol** focuses his practice on the representation of clients in the technology industry. He is well regarded for his experience and *"solid judgment."*

### The Webb Law Firm
**THE FIRM** This Pittsburgh boutique provides counsel on all matters related to IP, ranging from patent innovation, trademark and copyright protection to full-scale litigation services. With significant technical backgrounds, its attorneys are able to offer expertise across a variety of industries including life sciences, medical devices and manufacturing. Clients range from startup companies to Fortune 100 corporations.
**KEY INDIVIDUALS Richard Byrne** is widely acknowledged to be a *"very good practitioner."* His deep experience has provided him with expertise across the full spectrum of IP-related matters. Experienced IP practitioner **Kent Baldauf** also has particular expertise within the engineering industry. He is known as a prominent market player among peers. **John McIlvaine** has an extensive patent litigation practice. Sources say he is *"very knowledgeable and very good in court."*

### Other Notable Practitioners

**Paul Beck** of Beck & Thomas, PC is well regarded by peers for his experience and skill in IP law. **Camille Miller** (see p.2225) of Cozen O'Connor chairs the firm's IP practice. She actively litigates a wide range of IP-related actions. **Paul Milcetic** of Kessler Topaz Meltzer & Check, LLP regularly represents clients in complex patent litigation and has significant expertise in the technology sector. **Kathryn Doyle** of Riverside Law Firm is held in high regard by commentators. Sources praise her *"ability to get the job done and to communicate."* **Stephen Driscoll** of Saul Ewing LLP is an experienced IP litigator and is held in high esteem for his expertise in patent infringement matters. The *"hardworking and smart"* **Barry Cohen** of SorinRand LLC has particular expertise in trade secret litigation. Sources know him to be *"very knowledgeable."* **Kevin Casey** of Stradley Ronon Stevens & Young LLP enjoys *"a very strong reputation for being an excellent IP attorney."*

# LABOR & EMPLOYMENT

Commentary about individuals can be found under their firm's paragraph. If the firm has no paragraph (is not ranked) look at Other Notable Practitioners.

| Labor & Employment Leading Firms | |
|---|---|
| **Band 1** | |
| Morgan, Lewis & Bockius LLP * | |
| **Band 2** | |
| Ballard Spahr LLP * | |
| Buchanan Ingersoll & Rooney PC * | |
| Reed Smith LLP | |
| **Band 3** | |
| Blank Rome LLP * | |
| Cozen O'Connor * | |
| Duane Morris LLP * | |
| Littler Mendelson, PC * | |
| Pepper Hamilton LLP * | |
| **Band 4** | |
| Cohen & Grigsby PC | |
| Dechert LLP * | |
| Drinker Biddle & Reath LLP * | |

*\* Indicates firm / individual with profile.*
*Alphabetical order within each band. Band 1 is the highest.*

| Labor & Employment Leading Individuals | |
|---|---|
| **Band 1** | |
| Banks Michael L | Morgan, Lewis & Bockius LLP * |
| Berkowitz Alan D | Dechert LLP * |
| D'Angelo Jr Alfred J | Buchanan Ingersoll & Rooney PC * |
| Giotto Thomas S | Buchanan Ingersoll & Rooney PC * |
| Haller Anthony | Blank Rome LLP * |
| Langel John B | Ballard Spahr LLP * |
| Wall Steven R | Morgan, Lewis & Bockius LLP * |
| **Band 2** | |
| Bender Jr Thomas J | Littler Mendelson, PC |
| Bevan III William | Reed Smith LLP |
| Brown James B | Cohen & Grigsby PC |
| Connors Eugene | Reed Smith LLP |
| Cooper Scott | Blank Rome LLP * |
| Costello Joseph J | Morgan, Lewis & Bockius LLP * |
| Davis Doreen | Jones Day PC (ONP)[†] * |
| Foley Mark J | Cozen O'Connor * |
| Fritton Karl | Reed Smith LLP |
| Fryman David S | Ballard Spahr LLP * |
| Malloy Elizabeth A | Buchanan Ingersoll & Rooney PC * |
| Munsch Martha Hartle | Reed Smith LLP |
| Murphy Terrence H | Littler Mendelson, PC * |
| Ossip Michael J | Morgan, Lewis & Bockius LLP * |
| Pasek Jeffrey | Cozen O'Connor * |
| Servodidio Thomas G | Duane Morris LLP * |
| **Band 3** | |
| Barton Thomas J | Drinker Biddle & Reath LLP * |
| Hanlon Michael J | Blank Rome LLP * |
| Jarin Kenneth M | Ballard Spahr LLP * |
| Kresge Raymond | Cozen O'Connor * |
| Pedrow Brian D | Ballard Spahr LLP * |
| **Band 4** | |
| Bouchard Sarah | Morgan, Lewis & Bockius LLP * |
| Farmer Shannon D | Ballard Spahr LLP * |
| Furman Marc | Cohen Seglias Pallas Greenhall PC (ONP)[†] |
| Kelly Sarah A | Cozen O'Connor * |
| Ryan Casey | Reed Smith LLP |
| Satinsky Barnett | Fox Rothschild LLP PC (ONP)[†] * |
| Segal Jonathan A | Duane Morris LLP |
| **Up-and-coming individuals** | |
| Hale-Eagland Jennifer | Blank Rome LLP * |
| Johns Daniel V. | Ballard Spahr LLP * |

| Labor & Employment: Employee Benefits & Compensation Leading Individuals | |
|---|---|
| **Band 1** | |
| Abramowitz Robert | Morgan, Lewis & Bockius LLP * |
| Jones David F | Dechert LLP * |
| Lichtenstein Robert J | Morgan, Lewis & Bockius LLP * |
| Rudolph Andrew J | Pepper Hamilton LLP * |
| **Band 2** | |
| Clark Jonathan A | Pepper Hamilton LLP * |
| Kaplan David M | Pepper Hamilton LLP * |
| Klein Barry L | Blank Rome LLP |
| Leeds Edward I | Ballard Spahr LLP * |
| Martini John D | Reed Smith LLP |
| Pinheiro Brian M | Ballard Spahr LLP * |
| Spencer Steven D | Morgan, Lewis & Bockius LLP * |
| Zabriskie Mims Maynard | Morgan, Lewis & Bockius LLP * |
| **Band 3** | |
| Dougherty Brian | Morgan, Lewis & Bockius LLP * |
| **Up-and-coming individuals** | |
| Pocino Kelly Amy | Morgan, Lewis & Bockius LLP * |

## Band 1

### Morgan, Lewis & Bockius LLP
See profile on p.2246

**THE FIRM** This nationally acclaimed firm has a highly skilled and much-admired labor and employment practice. The deep bench of attorneys represents clients across the gamut of industries, from insurance and retail to pharmaceuticals and technology. Notable highlights include representing Dell in complex sex discrimination and retaliation litigation. The firm also acts for Philips, illustrating its strong employee benefits and executive compensation practice.

**Sources say:** *"They represent not just the best quality but also the best value. They are able to handle big, complicated and sensitive class actions very effectively."*

**KEY INDIVIDUALS Robert Abramowitz** (see p.2210) is an experienced and highly respected employee benefits and executive compensation practitioner. He counsels clients on all aspects of employment benefits law, including ERISA concerns. *"Very experienced and very smart,"* **Michael Banks** (see p.2210) recently represented Hewlett-Packard in restrictive covenant litigation. **Robert Lichtenstein** (see p.2223) recently co-led the team advising the executive management of AmWINS Group on its compensation and employment agreement in connection with its partnership with New Mountain Capital. Sources say he is *"a brilliant lawyer – very energetic, very insightful and very capable."* *"Very smart, wise and experienced,"* **Steven Wall** (see p.2232) is well respected by peers and clients. He has extensive employment litigation experience and particular expertise in union corporation campaigns. **Joseph Costello** (see p.2213) represents employers in a wide range of litigation and regularly handles complex class action cases. Clients find him to be *"supremely responsive."* The

*"highly articulate"* **Michael Ossip** (see p.2226) is well versed in all areas of employee relations law. He is particularly recognized for his significant experience advising employers on wage and hour compliance. **Steven Spencer** (see p.2231) recently represented the Philadelphia Orchestra Association with regards to collective bargaining on pension and benefit plans. In the words of one source, he is *"remarkable – he can make an extremely complicated subject understandable."* *"Worthy of very high regard,"* **Mims Maynard Zabriskie** (see p.2233) regularly counsels

Fortune 500 companies on all aspects of employee benefits and executive compensation law. She routinely assists clients in negotiating employment agreements and designing executive compensation programs. Recent highlights for **Brian Dougherty** (see p.2214) include advising Philips on employee benefits and executive compensation in connection with a variety of projects. **Sarah Bouchard** (see p.2212) has a strong reputation among peers in the labor and employment field. Notable cases include co-leading the representation of Hewlett-Packard in restrictive covenant litigation. **Amy Pocino Kelly** (see p.2227) has a growing practice and regularly advises tax-exempt organizations and public and private companies, among other clients, on a broad array of benefit and compensation issues.

## Band 2

### Ballard Spahr LLP
See profile on p.2234

**THE FIRM** Based in Philadelphia, this full-service firm has a significant number of attorneys dedicated to labor and employment law. It has a broad remit with a highly regarded traditional labor practice as well as a leading employee benefits and compensation group. Its impressive client portfolio includes high-profile names such as Johnson & Johnson and DuPont. Ballard Spahr has particular expertise in the healthcare sector, as illustrated by its recent representation of Temple University Health System and West Penn Allegheny Health System in collective and class action cases related to the FLSA.

**Sources say:** *"Their performance was outstanding. They provide terrific service on every level. "*

KEY INDIVIDUALS **John Langel** (see p.2222) provides ongoing labor advice to Temple University Health System. According to interviewees, he *"is responsive and thoughtful, and can give some very practical guidance."* **David Fryman** (see p.2216) is described as *"a good strategic thinker"* and an *"outstanding lawyer."* Notable highlights include representing West Penn Allegheny Health System. **Edward Leeds** (see p.2223) is an experienced employee benefits and executive compensation practitioner. His practice has a strong emphasis on health and welfare issues. **Brian Pinheiro** (see p.2227) is lauded as *"responsive and very knowledgeable, with excellent communication skills."* He recently provided employee benefits and executive compensation advice to Ricoh Americas. **Kenneth Jarin** (see p.2220) has recently co-led multiple arbitrations on behalf of the City of Philadelphia. He routinely litigates labor relations matters, including wage and hour disputes and employment discrimination actions. **Shannon Farmer** (see p.2215) is *"excellent as a person to work with and in terms of the quality of her advice and advocacy,"* say interviewees. She advises American Red Cross on traditional labor and employment issues. **Daniel Johns** (see p.2220) is an experienced litigator and regularly handles the gamut of labor and employment litigation. He has particular expertise in representing and advising higher education institutions. **Brian Pedrow** (see p.2227) concentrates his practice on representing management in a broad range of employment litigation, including discrimination, harassment, trade secret and noncompetition actions.

## Buchanan Ingersoll & Rooney PC
See profile on p.2236

THE FIRM With a deep bench of attorneys, this highly regarded firm has an extensive employment practice. The team handles all aspects of traditional labor relations, including contract negotiations, arbitration and mediation. Buchanan Ingersoll also has a robust employee benefits practice covering ERISA litigation, employment agreements and executive compensation arrangements.

Sources say: *"They understand our business and they understand what is going on in the industry so they are very efficient, very effective and very practical. They keep on top of the trends and we really value this."*

KEY INDIVIDUALS **Alfred D'Angelo** (see p.2214) is well regarded in the employment arena. He regularly handles collective bargaining negotiations as well as litigation before the NLRB. *"Very practical,"* **Elizabeth Malloy** (see p.2223) represents employers in a wide range of litigation matters, including sexual harassment and disability and age discrimination actions. She is described as *"knowledgeable, savvy and efficient."* *"A super smart lawyer,"* **Thomas Giotto** (see p.2217) has a broad traditional labor practice encompassing many aspects of employment law, including collective bargaining and union matters.

## Reed Smith LLP

THE FIRM Notable highlights for this internationally recognized firm include counseling Verizon on unemployment compensation benefit claims by employees on strike. The labor and employment practice has unique expertise in the higher education arena. In addition to traditional labor law matters, attorneys at Reed Smith offer clients interdisciplinary advice on employee benefits and executive compensation. The team operates across numerous industries and represents a diverse range of clients, including private equity firms and nonprofit institutions.

Sources say: *"They are outstanding – clearly experts in their field, as well as easy to work with. They are responsive and very helpful to us."*

KEY INDIVIDUALS **William Bevan** *"has a great depth of knowledge"* and concentrates his practice on representing employers in the construction and manufacturing industry. He has particular expertise in the NLRA. **Eugene Connors** has represented employers in all aspects of traditional labor law across the gamut of industries. He is hailed for his communication skills, and sources note his popularity among clients. **Karl Fritton** has a strong reputation in the traditional labor law arena. He currently acts as lead negotiator on labor agreements for Clear Channel Media & Entertainment. Respondents say that *"clients really hold him in high regard."* **John Martini** has specific expertise in employee benefits and executive compensation matters, including complex ERISA litigation. His clients span numerous industries, from life sciences to financial services. **Martha Hartle Munsch** is described as a *"very strong employment litigator"* with *"a tremendous level of experience."* She concentrates on representing higher education and nonprofit clients. *"A very hard worker and a good litigator,"* **Casey Ryan** routinely litigates a broad range of employment disputes, including discrimination, harassment and wrongful dismissal. *"We really respect and value her guidance and opinion,"* said one client.

---

## Band 3

## Blank Rome LLP
See profile on p.2235

THE FIRM Practitioners at this Philadelphia-based practice counsel clients on all aspects of employment law, ranging from collective bargaining and union relations to HR policy design and development. Attorneys at Blank Rome have a strong reputation for their litigation abilities. The team represents clients in all types of employment litigation, including ERISA cases and wage and hour actions. Recent highlights include representing medical device manufacturer Synthes in an action against competing company Emerge Medical.

Sources say: *"The advice was spot-on and timely, and very helpful."*

KEY INDIVIDUALS Described as *"very talented"* and *"extremely knowledgeable,"* **Anthony Haller** (see p.2218) has represented Synthes in a number of matters, including a wage and hour putative class claim. **Scott Cooper** (see p.2213) recently acted as lead trial counsel for the City of Reading in connection with its interest arbitration against the City's Police Union. One client comments: *"His communication skills are superb and he's very strategic. He looks at all the possible angles and finds the most advantageous approach."* **Barry Klein** (see p.2221) recently defended Lord

Baltimore Employee Retirement Income Account Plan in an ERISA action brought by a former employee relating to a breach of fiduciary duty. **Michael Hanlon** (see p.2218) provides strategic labor and employment advice to a number of high-profile clients, including U.S. Security Associates and the School District of Philadelphia. **Jennifer Hale-Eagland** (see p.2218) led the team representing Foxwood Development Company in employment litigation involving breach of contract issues. Sources find her *"very practical,"* with one adding: *"She gives good advice and looks for the best answer for our company. She understands our business and understands our needs. She has good judgment."*

## Cozen O'Connor
See profile on p.2237

THE FIRM Cozen O'Connor has a deep bench of attorneys representing a diverse range of employers, including public and private sector companies, nonprofit organizations and universities. The group has broad industry expertise and routinely litigates all types of claims, including sexual harassment, discrimination, wage and hour, and wrongful dismissal actions. Attorneys are well versed in employee benefits matters and highly experienced at handling union-related issues and disputes.

Sources say: *"An exceptional group of attorneys. I trust them wholeheartedly with all legal issues I bring to them. They are very good at assessing the legal aspects as well as the business aspects. Their advice is always relevant and very good."*

KEY INDIVIDUALS **Jeffrey Pasek** (see p.2227) is praised for his analytical ability and is described as *"highly responsive, very patient and very diplomatic."* Clients appreciate his *"ability to take a very complex concept and break it down."* Well reputed for his traditional labor law practice, **Mark Foley** (see p.2216) has extensive experience handling a broad range of issues under local, state and federal law. His practice focuses on representing management in labor and employment disputes. **Raymond Kresge** (see p.2222) has extensive experience handling ERISA litigation, and routinely defends clients in individual and class action cases. His expertise includes disability, retirement, and health and life benefit denial cases. **Sarah Kelly** (see p.2220) concentrates her practice on discrimination and sexual harassment litigation in the context of employment law. One source comments: *"She has an acute understanding of employment law and is very good at getting to the heart of the issue quickly."*

## Duane Morris LLP
See profile on p.2239

THE FIRM Attorneys at this nationally recognized firm cover the gamut of labor and employment legal-related issues, including union matters and all aspects of workplace litigation ranging from restrictive covenants to wrongful dismissal and wage and hour actions. This is complemented by a robust and all-encompassing employee benefits and executive compensation practice. The group represents a wide range of clients, including healthcare systems and software companies.

**Sources say:** *"Really remarkable, immediately responsive and absolutely available to us. They provide great advice and really do focus on us and our needs when we need them."* **KEY INDIVIDUALS Thomas Servodidio** is active in all aspects of employment litigation, and also regularly represents clients in proceedings before the NLRB. Sources say: *"He's terrific. He's smart, a great communicator and a great trial attorney."* *"Remarkable and immediately responsive,"* **Jonathan Segal** recently worked with Princeton HealthCare System on developing employment policies and providing guidance on a range of labor and employment issues. Interviewees say: *"He is highly pragmatic, pays attention to detail and is customer-oriented."*

## Littler Mendelson, PC
See profile on p.688

**THE FIRM** This nationally acclaimed labor and employment firm has a strong geographic presence across Pennsylvania. The group handles complex litigation across a variety of industries, from retail to healthcare, and has an impressive client roster including high-profile names such as AstraZeneca and Rite Aid. In addition to a strong traditional labor law practice, Littler has a significant group of attorneys specializing in employee benefits and executive compensation matters.
**Sources say:** *"Super lawyers doing a great job for their clients."*
**KEY INDIVIDUALS Thomas Bender** is described as *"a good person to work and interact with, and an excellent lawyer who does a good job for his clients."* He regularly represents clients in ERISA and benefit plan litigation. *"Deliberate, thoughtful and meticulous,"* **Terrence Murphy** (see p.2226) *"has broad and deep experience."* He recently acted for Precision Drilling on a purported nationwide class action.

## Pepper Hamilton LLP
See profile on p.2248

**THE FIRM** Recent work highlights for this group include representing Siemens Medical Systems in a noncompete matter against a former senior executive. The group has extensive experience representing healthcare clients, and has advised long-standing client Main Line Health on a variety of labor and employment matters. The team also recently defended Albert Einstein Healthcare Network in putative collective and class action cases. Pepper Hamilton is also highly regarded for its strong employee benefits and executive compensation practice.

**Sources say:** *"Very good. I found it to have consistent high-level quality among all of its practice areas. Very responsive and quality work product."*
**KEY INDIVIDUALS Andrew Rudolph** (see p.2228) is recognized for his *"breadth of experience and knowledge."* Notable transactions include serving as lead outside counsel to Comcast and NBCUniversal in connection with the redesign of retirement programs. Employee benefits group cochair **Jonathan Clark** (see p.2213) recently advised Lafayette College on its retirement and health and welfare programs. The *"very dedicated and very prompt"* **David Kaplan** (see p.2220) is praised for his technical approach and responsiveness. Clients appreciate his ability to explain complicated matters in an understandable manner. He recently advised NutriSystem on executive compensation matters.

## Band 4

### Cohen & Grigsby PC

**THE FIRM** This Pittsburgh-based labor and employment group counsels clients on a broad range of employment-related issues, including contracts, litigation and workers' compensation. Of late the team has been involved in a high-profile sexual harassment action. Attorneys at Cohen & Grigsby are recognized for their expertise in handling union issues, including collective bargaining, arbitration and litigation.
**Sources say:** *"They've been exceptional, they've gone above and beyond, and they know our organization very well, which is incredibly helpful."*
**KEY INDIVIDUALS** Clients appreciate **James Brown**'s *"pragmatic approach."* Sources say he is *"very knowledgeable, a great person to work with and always highly responsive."*

### Dechert LLP
See profile on p.1969

**THE FIRM** This international firm has a wide-reaching labor and employment practice handling all aspects of employment litigation, including sexual harassment, non-competition and wage and hour cases. The firm also has an active employee benefits and executive compensation practice regularly dealing with ERISA and WARN Act litigation. Recent highlights include representing Advanta in ERISA and securities actions.

**Sources say:** *"Very good at delivering excellent counsel. They are thorough, complete and extremely timely. They make themselves available whenever I need them."*
**KEY INDIVIDUALS Alan Berkowitz** (see p.2211) is praised by clients for his *"excellent knowledge of the law"* and *"common-sense business approach to legal matters."* His recent highlights include representing Siemens Industry in a putative prevailing wage class action. **David Jones** (see p.2220) works extensively on employee benefits and executive compensation matters. Sources find him *"very personable"* and easy to work with.

## Drinker Biddle & Reath LLP
See profile on p.2238

**THE FIRM** This full-service firm handles all aspects of labor and employment law, with a strong focus on litigation. The group represents a diverse range of clients, including manufacturers, retailers and healthcare organizations. Notable highlights from the past year include successfully representing Urban Outfitters in connection with sexual discrimination and harassment claims.
**Sources say:** *"They've been great – their approach to litigation has been very reasonable and measured. They're not overly aggressive – they're very logical and pragmatic."*
**KEY INDIVIDUALS** *"Smart, creative and practical,"* **Thomas Barton** (see p.2211) *"tries to find a solution for his clients."* He handles all aspects of employment law, including employment discrimination and wrongful termination litigation.

## Other Notable Practitioners

**Doreen Davis** (see p.2214) of Jones Day has deep experience across a range of industries, including healthcare, manufacturing and energy. *"An exceptional lawyer,"* she focuses her practice on NLRB advice and litigation. **Marc Furman** of Cohen Seglias Pallas Greenhall & Furman, PC is favorably described as *"very personable, very professional and very knowledgeable."* Sources note: *"He goes out of his way to look out for the best interests of his clients."* **Barnett Satinsky** (see p.2229) of Fox Rothschild LLP has a broad labor and employment practice spanning a range of industries and handling a variety of issues, including contract negotiation, employment litigation and employee benefits.

# LITIGATION

Commentary about individuals can be found under their firm's paragraph. If the firm has no paragraph (is not ranked) look at Other Notable Practitioners.

## Litigation: General Commercial
### Leading Firms

**Band 1**
Dechert LLP *
Morgan, Lewis & Bockius LLP *
Pepper Hamilton LLP *

**Band 2**
Ballard Spahr LLP *
Conrad O'Brien
Drinker Biddle & Reath LLP *
Duane Morris LLP *
Hangley Aronchick Segal Pudlin & Schiller *

**Band 3**
Blank Rome LLP *
Buchanan Ingersoll & Rooney PC *
Cozen O'Connor *
Fox Rothschild LLP *
Harkins Cunningham LLP *
Schnader Harrison Segal & Lewis LLP

**Band 4**
Jones Day *
K&L Gates *
Reed Smith LLP
Saul Ewing LLP *
Stradley Ronon Stevens & Young LLP

\* Indicates firm / individual with profile.
† ONP = Other Notable Practitioner.

## Litigation: General Commercial
### Senior Statesmen

**Senior Statesmen: distinguished older practitioners**

| | | | |
|---|---|---|---|
| Harkins Jr John G | Harkins Cunningham LLP * | Wycoff William | Thorp Reed & Armstrong, LLP PC (ONP)† |
| Marion David H | Archer & Greiner PC (ONP)† * | | |

### Leading Individuals

**Star individuals**

| | |
|---|---|
| Cooney Jr J Gordon | Morgan, Lewis & Bockius LLP * |

**Band 1**

| | | | |
|---|---|---|---|
| Gellman Nancy J | Conrad O'Brien | Ellison John N | Reed Smith LLP |
| Gussack Nina M | Pepper Hamilton LLP * | Ellsworth Laura | Jones Day * |
| Hangley William T | Hangley Aronchick Segal Pudlin & Schiller * | Feirson Steven B | Dechert LLP * |
| Heim Robert C | Dechert LLP * | Griesing Francine Friedman | Griesing Law, LLC PC (ONP)† |
| Hickok Robert L | Pepper Hamilton LLP * | Griffith James | Fox Rothschild LLP * |
| Mather Barbara W | Pepper Hamilton LLP * | Guernsey John (Jack) | Conrad O'Brien * |
| Reich Esq Abraham C | Fox Rothschild LLP * | Klein Howard M | Conrad O'Brien PC (ONP)† * |
| Sonnenfeld Marc | Morgan, Lewis & Bockius LLP * | Lutsky Jeffrey A | Stradley Ronon Stevens & Young LLP |
| Suplee Dennis R | Schnader Harrison Segal & Lewis LLP | Magaziner Fred T | Dechert LLP * |
| Tate Joseph A | Dechert LLP * | Miller Gregory P | Drinker Biddle & Reath LLP * |
| | | O'Dea Jr Joseph F | Saul Ewing LLP |

**Band 2**

| | | | |
|---|---|---|---|
| Ainslie Elizabeth K | Schnader Harrison Segal & Lewis LLP | Pagliaro James | Morgan, Lewis & Bockius LLP * |
| Aronchick Mark Alan | Hangley Aronchick Segal Pudlin & Schiller * | Pittinsky David H | Ballard Spahr LLP * |
| Devine III Francis P | Pepper Hamilton LLP * | Scott Michael T | Reed Smith LLP |
| Ginensky Amy B | Pepper Hamilton LLP * | Smith James T | Blank Rome LLP * |
| Kastenberg Stephen J | Ballard Spahr LLP * | Soroko John J | Duane Morris LLP |
| Laupheimer Ann Blair | Blank Rome LLP * | Summers John | Hangley Aronchick Segal Pudlin & Schiller * |
| Lavelle Jr John P | Morgan, Lewis & Bockius LLP * | Taylor Matthew A | Duane Morris LLP |
| Makadon Arthur | Ballard Spahr LLP * | Vernick Scott | Fox Rothschild LLP * |
| Scher Howard D | Buchanan Ingersoll & Rooney PC * | Zanic Michael G | K&L Gates * |
| Schiller Ronald P | Hangley Aronchick Segal Pudlin & Schiller * | | |
| Segal Daniel | Hangley Aronchick Segal Pudlin & Schiller * | | |

**Band 3**

| | | | |
|---|---|---|---|
| Birsic Thomas E | K&L Gates * | | |
| Bizar Steven E | Buchanan Ingersoll & Rooney PC * | | |
| Black Allen | Fine, Kaplan and Black, RPC PC (ONP)† | | |
| Coran Michael | Klehr Harrison Harvey Branzburg PC (ONP)† | | |
| Crawford Joseph C | Pepper Hamilton LLP * | | |
| Danoff Diane S | Dechert LLP * | | |

**Band 4**

| | |
|---|---|
| Bixler Albert G | Eckert Seamans Cherin & Mellott PC (ONP)† |
| Centrella Nicholas M | Conrad O'Brien |
| Fiebach H Robert | Cozen O'Connor * |
| Kerr Alexander | McCarter & English, LLP PC (ONP)† * |
| Klinges Dana B | Duane Morris LLP |
| Kraeutler Eric | Morgan, Lewis & Bockius LLP * |
| Landau David E | Duane Morris LLP |
| Pohl Paul M | Jones Day * |
| Powell Roy A | Jones Day * |
| Resnick Stephanie | Fox Rothschild LLP * |
| Sproul Gayle | Levine Sullivan Koch & Schulz PC (ONP)†* |

## Band 1

### Dechert LLP
See profile on p.1969

**THE FIRM** This premier litigation practice routinely handles complex and high-stakes matters for significant clients, with highlights including representing Advanta in a securities class action litigation. The team represents clients across a broad range of industries, including financial services, pharmaceuticals and manufacturing. With a deep bench of litigators, Dechert maintains a strong reputation across the gamut of substantive areas, including general commercial, product liability, securities, white-collar crime and government investigations litigation.
**Sources say:** "*They are outstanding. The quality of the written work product is the best I have ever seen. They understand our business and know us very well.*"
**KEY INDIVIDUALS Steven Feirson** (see p.2215) recently defended Advanta in class action litigation. Sources find him "*very engaging, bright and perceptive,*" and describe him as a "*very clever, very skilled lawyer.*" **Robert Heim** (see p.2219) recently represented Nationwide Mutual Insurance in a putative class action relating to its merger with Harleysville Mutual Insurance. Sources praise him as

"*an outstanding trial lawyer*" and note that he is "*extremely knowledgeable of the law and very well respected by the courts.*" **Thomas Lee** (see p.2222) is renowned for his expertise in white-collar and government investigations litigation. Sources describe him as "*extremely bright and very careful.*" **Joseph Tate** (see p.2231) is a "*very accomplished litigator*" with expertise in a broad range of areas, including antitrust, white-collar, class actions and complex commercial litigation. **Michael Kichline** (see p.2221) has a strong reputation in the securities litigation arena, and recently represented the board members of Education Management in two derivative suits. One client notes: "*He*

knows the law and he's responsive." **Diane Danoff** (see p.2214) has a sophisticated IP litigation practice encompassing patent, copyright, trademark, trade secrets and unfair competition matters. **Fred Magaziner** (see p.2223) has a broad litigation practice, and is experienced in handling multijurisdictional mass torts, corporate governance disputes and contractual disputes. He also has extensive experience acting on behalf of both plaintiffs and defendants in medical malpractice cases.

## Morgan, Lewis & Bockius LLP

See profile on p.2246

**THE FIRM** This national powerhouse has a highly reputed litigation practice with deep bench strength and expertise across a broad range of industries. The group has extensive experience representing clients in the financial services, life sciences and medical device sectors. Highlights for the commercial litigation group include representing Toys R Us in a premises liability case. In addition, Morgan Lewis has a premier securities practice complemented by a leading white-collar and government investigations team.

**Sources say:** "They have excellent skills and, more importantly, excellent judgment about how to manage complex litigation. An extraordinary depth of experience and talent."

**KEY INDIVIDUALS Gordon Cooney** (see p.2213) provides "excellent advice" and has extensive experience handling class actions, as illustrated by his recent representation of Teva in two putative nationwide class actions. One client notes that "his experience and perspective have been exceedingly helpful on class-related issues." **John Dodds** (see p.2214) is well respected in the government investigations space. His recent highlights include representing pharmaceutical giant AstraZeneca in investigations relating to the Seroquel drug. According to interviewees, he is "viewed as a terrific advocate by prosecutors and clients." Impressed sources describe **Eric Sitarchuk** (see p.2230) as "a talented lawyer and a good advocate." He recently represented Guthrie Health Systems in a whistle-blower case alleging healthcare fraud. **Marc Sonnenfeld** (see p.2231) is recognized as being "preeminent in his field of securities litigation and derivatives litigation." Notable representations include handling a stockholder derivative action for Hewlett-Packard. **John Lavelle** (see p.2222) is a "very well-regarded litigator" within the fields of product liability and complex commercial litigation. Highlights include representing medical technology company Medtronic in personal injury claims and product liability suits. **James Pagliaro** (see p.2226) continues to represent National Gypsum in connection with product liability matters, and recently acted for Philips in an arbitration. **Eric Kraeutler** (see p.2222) heads the Philadelphia litigation practice and is "very smart, very focused on what needs to be done and an absolute delight to work with." He has recently represented the University of Pennsylvania in a number of matters, including IP issues.

## Pepper Hamilton LLP

See profile on p.2248

**THE FIRM** This full-service firm's nationally acclaimed commercial litigation practice is complemented by a robust white-collar team. The group is adept at handling complex class action defense cases, including antitrust, securities and product liability litigation. In addition, Pepper Hamilton has an active First Amendment litigation practice as illustrated by the team's representation of Lancaster Newspapers. The group also has a significant presence in the healthcare sector, and recently represented the Albert Einstein Healthcare Network.

**Sources say:** "Excellent – professional and responsive, with good legal advice."

**KEY INDIVIDUALS** "Very bright and very well respected," **Robert Hickok** (see p.2219) recently led the team representing ADT Security Services in a class action brought under the Telephone Consumer Protection Act. He is lauded by sources as "a tremendous civil litigator and securities litigator – one of the best in the country." Interviewees describe **Barbara Mather** (see p.2224) as "really smart and a very good lawyer." Her recent cases include defending Covidien in a breach of contract suit brought against it by GE. **Nina Gussack** (see p.328) handles civil litigation with a focus on the defense of pharmaceutical and medical device companies. Sources agree that "she has great judgment and great skill." **Francis Devine** (see p.2214) recently represented TRO Avenue of the Arts as owner/landlord in a high-value unpaid rent dispute with The Art Institute of Philadelphia. Sources note his "personal attention, ingenuity and hard work," and comment on his "aggressiveness in pursuing outside-the-box solutions." **Thomas Gallagher** (see p.2216) is chair of the firm's white-collar litigation and investigations practice group. He represents businesses and individuals in white-collar criminal matters and corporate investigations. **Amy Ginensky** (see p.2217) has significant expertise in First Amendment litigation. Sources say: "She is a terrific lawyer who understands her clients. She can fashion arguments to make courts receptive to them." **Joseph Crawford** (see p.2213) assisted in the ADT Security Services litigation and is described favorably as a "very skilled civil trial attorney." **Michael Schwartz** (see p.2229) is described as an "incredibly talented and experienced young white-collar lawyer." He enters the white-collar table, having received outstanding feedback from the market.

### Band 2

## Ballard Spahr LLP

See profile on p.2234

**THE FIRM** Ballard Spahr is well positioned to represent high-profile clients in complex litigation proceedings. The team is well versed in the law across a range of sectors, including pharmaceuticals, insurance and financial services, with an impressive client roster including blue-chip clients such as Penn Treaty American, Harleysville Mutual Insurance and NASDAQ OMX Group.

**Sources say:** "The lawyers are oriented to business advice and not just legal advice, and that's what we value."

**KEY INDIVIDUALS Norman Goldberger** (see p.2217) recently represented Penn Millers Holding in high-profile litigation. "He always brings a level of experience and sophistication to proceedings," said one interviewee. **Henry Hockeimer** (see p.2219) concentrates his practice on white-collar criminal defense and has significant experience handling securities fraud and official corruption investigations. He is praised as a "very strong litigator" with a "terrific reputation." **Stephen Kastenberg** (see p.2220) has recently represented NASDAQ in numerous individual and putative class actions. One client notes: "He's very bright and very business-oriented, and is able to give us the strategic advice that we look for." The "first-rate" **Arthur Makadon** (see p.2223) has extensive trial experience and is recognized as a "really talented lawyer." He regularly handles antitrust, securities and ERISA litigation. **David Pittinsky** (see p.2227) is favorably described as "a good strategist and a very smart guy." He recently represented Harleysville Mutual Insurance in relation to an attempt by policyholders to prevent a merger with Nationwide Mutual Insurance.

## Conrad O'Brien

**THE FIRM** This boutique firm has an impressive reputation for its litigation capabilities in Pennsylvania. Its enviable client roster spans a wide range of industries, including chemical, energy and technology. Recent highlights include representing the Archdiocese of Philadelphia in a highly publicized matter involving alleged sexual abuse by priests and employees. The group also has extensive experience representing law firms in professional liability and malpractice cases, as illustrated by its representation of WolfBlock LLP. Other clients include ExxonMobil, Transamerica and Dow Chemical.

**Sources say:** *"They've been outstanding. Their dedication, tenacity, integrity and legal acumen impress me."*

**KEY INDIVIDUALS Nancy Gellman** is widely praised by peers and clients. One source notes that *"she pays great attention to detail and she's extremely responsive,"* while another highlights her as *"a very practical, pragmatic lawyer."* **James Rohn** (see p.2228) is hailed by clients as a *"highly skilled, highly professional, highly competent lawyer."* He played a central role in the aforementioned matters for the Archdiocese of Philadelphia. Sources note that *"his judgment is outstanding."* **Jack Guernsey** (see p.2218) concentrates on complex commercial litigation across a broad range of practice areas, including IP, toxic torts, insurance coverage and product liability. He routinely represents clients in federal and state courts. The *"very knowledgeable"* **Howard Klein** (see p.2221) has significant experience dealing with commercial, construction or medical malpractice litigation. **Nicholas Centrella** recently represented WolfBlock LLP in a legal malpractice suit. One interviewee comments that *"he's a strong trial lawyer – he has an engaging personality and he really works hard for his clients."*

### Drinker Biddle & Reath LLP
See profile on p.2238

**THE FIRM** This firm's Philadelphia litigation group offers a strong bench of attorneys across the full range of areas, including complex commercial, white-collar defense and securities litigation. Notable highlights include representing long-standing client Johnson & Johnson in extensive litigation relating to the antipsychotic medication Risperdal. Other clients include AT&T Mobility and Comcast.

**Sources say:** *"They are very attentive and very service-oriented, they understand the service business and they're focused on getting good results for clients."*

**KEY INDIVIDUALS** The *"very astute"* and *"very skilled"* **Gregory Miller** (see p.2225) recently represented ExxonMobil in a tort claim following an injury at one of its former plants. One source reports: *"He can summarize issues quickly and communicate them. He helps not only from a legal point of view but also from a practical point of view."*

### Duane Morris LLP
See profile on p.2239

**THE FIRM** This highly regarded firm has a broad litigation practice and a strong reputation across an array of industry sectors, from software development to real estate and pharmaceuticals. Recent highlights for the team include representing EMD Serono in connection with a collaboration agreement dispute with Pfizer.

**Sources say:** *"They are focused, confident and aggressive advocates, but fair and professional. They recognize that time is money."*

**KEY INDIVIDUALS John Soroko** has an extensive corporate and securities litigation practice. One source notes that *"he's the consummate professional – an excellent litigator with great litigation sense and great client service."* **Dana Klinges** continues to provide securities counsel to clients like Cohen & Co Securities. One sources states: *"She has provided us with really important guidance for some difficult cases."* **David Landau** recently represented internet-based company AcademyOne in a complicated IP dispute with CollegeSource. Sources praise him as *"a good litigator."* **Matthew Taylor** is chair of the trial practice group at Duane Morris and is described as *"accessible and responsive"* by interviewees. Recent cases include handling a contractual dispute for Lockheed Martin Transportation Security Solutions.

### Hangley Aronchick Segal Pudlin & Schiller
See profile on p.2243

**THE FIRM** This boutique firm offers clients a deep bench of highly skilled and experienced litigators. The team regularly represents other law firms in sophisticated legal malpractice matters, and actively handles all aspects of commercial litigation and related appellate work. Recent work highlights include representing Executive Risk Indemnity in an insurance coverage dispute with CIGNA.

**Sources say:** *"They are excellent litigators; very effective. They can try cases and they're very good analysts and strategists in terms of preparing cases well."*

**KEY INDIVIDUALS** Founding partner **William Hangley** (see p.2218) is a highly respected trial lawyer with a broad litigation practice. Sources say: *"He's an excellent lawyer and a good advocate, and has significant presence in the courtroom."* **Ronald Schiller** (see p.2229) is praised as a *"high performer"* by market sources. He led the team in the aforementioned matter for Executive Risk Indemnity. The *"extremely accomplished"* **Mark Aronchick** (see p.2210) is described as a *"high-quality top-level lawyer."* He recently represented Ate Kays Company in a condemnation case. **Daniel Segal** (see p.2230) co-led the team acting for the Commonwealth of Pennsylvania in multiple suits brought by the Pennsylvania Medical Society and the Hospital & Healthsystem Association of Pennsylvania. Sources attest that he is *"a wonderful lawyer: very smart, very engaging and very collegial."* **John Summers** (see p.2231) recently led the team defending Shire in an action brought by GlaxoSmithKline relating to breach of a co-promotion agreement. Sources name him *"a really fine litigator."*

## Band 3

### Blank Rome LLP
See profile on p.2235

**THE FIRM** Blank Rome has a thriving litigation practice handling a diverse range of criminal, civil and administrative matters. Attorneys are experienced across a wide variety of areas, including securities, white-collar defense, financial services and environmental litigation. Clients include Synthes, Wells Fargo and Facebook.

**Sources say:** *"Attorneys were extremely responsive to our needs and were always available to address our concerns. They were very attentive to the unique aspects of our claim, and diligently worked to develop effective defensive strategies. The written materials developed by Blank Rome were exceptional."*

**KEY INDIVIDUALS Ann Laupheimer** (see p.2222) has a broad corporate litigation practice. She is described as *"an unbelievably skilled litigator who is a client's best advocate."* **James Smith** (see p.2231) is noted for his expertise in complex commercial litigation. Sources report that he is *"a very serious litigator with very good instincts. He has very good judgment and he's very skillful in crafting a strategy."*

### Buchanan Ingersoll & Rooney PC
See profile on p.2236

**THE FIRM** With offices in Philadelphia, Harrisburg and Pittsburgh, this firm has a strong presence across Pennsylvania. Its litigation practice covers a broad range of industries, including energy, healthcare and manufacturing. Recent highlights for the team include obtaining a successful arbitration verdict for Foresight Energy. Other notable clients include Pittsburgh Steelers Sports, Arkema and Xcoal Energy & Resources.

**Sources say:** *"Outstanding, timely, responsive, very thorough and very knowledgeable."*

**KEY INDIVIDUALS Thomas Bergstrom** (see p.2211) has broad litigation experience and regularly handles antitrust, securities and white-collar criminal cases. Sources say that *"he has an incredibly effective presence in the courtroom."* *"Outstanding lawyer"* **James Becker** (see p.2211) has significant expertise in representing clients across a range of sectors in connection with government investigations. **Howard Scher** (see p.2229) is described as a *"very accomplished litigator."* He regularly handles major high-stakes litigation including commercial disputes, class actions and mass tort cases. He is also noted for his expertise in securities litigation. The *"superb"* **Steven Bizar** (see p.2211) led the team defending Arkema against breach of contract suits.

### Cozen O'Connor
See profile on p.2237

**THE FIRM** This litigation team offers skilled representation across a broad range of practice areas, including securities litigation, product liability, antitrust and IP. Highlights include successfully representing the Commonwealth of Pennsylvania in its bid to block the declaration of bankruptcy of the City of Harrisburg.

**Sources say:** *"Very responsive, great substantive knowledge and a great ability to manage matters in multiple jurisdictions at one time."*

**KEY INDIVIDUALS William Winning** (see p.2233) is chair of the firm's criminal defense and government investigations practice group. Sources comment that he is *"a fabulous professional"* who is *"very respected."* **Robert Fiebach** (see p.2215) is praised for his *"extraordinary knowledge of the law,"* and is highly regarded for his extensive trial experience. One source notes that *"he's a great trial lawyer and a wonderful strategist and tactician."*

## Fox Rothschild LLP
See profile on p.2242
THE FIRM Notable highlights for this litigation group include representing First Data Merchant Services and Wells Fargo in connection with the defense of a putative class action regarding overcharging for the processing of credit card transactions. Litigators at Fox Rothschild handle complex lawsuits for clients of all sizes from a wide variety of industries, including financial services, healthcare and technology.
Sources say: *"They do very good work. They have very good knowledge of procedural issues but more importantly they are very strategic."*
KEY INDIVIDUALS Abraham Reich (see p.2228) is commended for his broad business litigation practice. Sources note that he is a *"very well-known, well-regarded litigator in Pennsylvania."* James Griffith (see p.2217) represents both plaintiffs and defendants in a wide variety of matters, including insurance coverage, product liability and antitrust. Scott Vernick (see p.2232) recently acted for Euphrates on claims alleging a diversion of corporate opportunity and a breach of fiduciary duty. One source notes that *"he is very knowledgeable, appropriately aggressive and strategic."* Stephanie Resnick (see p.2228) is chair of the firm's litigation group. She has a broad practice and regularly handles shareholder disputes, corporate governance matters and class actions.

## Harkins Cunningham LLP
See profile on p.2244
THE FIRM This compact firm offers extensive trial experience and has a solid reputation in the market. Attorneys at the firm are well equipped to handle all aspects of complex commercial litigation, including antitrust, contractual disputes and appellate work.
KEY INDIVIDUALS John Harkins (see p.2218) is extremely well respected and highly regarded by peers in the litigation space. Sources report that he is a *"very credible, very persuasive advocate with tremendous judgment,"* and *"a wonderful strategist."*

## Schnader Harrison Segal & Lewis LLP
THE FIRM Attorneys at this reputable firm have extensive litigation experience and regularly handle sophisticated matters for a broad client base. The team has established a reputation for its expertise in the aviation industry, and recently represented Landow Aviation and its insurer Chartis Aerospace in litigation arising from the collapse of an aircraft hangar following heavy snowfall. Other notable clients include Rohm and Haas, Teva and Wells Fargo.
Sources say: *"A very good firm – highly professional, highly competent and very responsive, and I find my interactions with them to always be pleasant and professional."*
KEY INDIVIDUALS Dennis Suplee recently led the team handling an array of complex claims brought against chemical company Rohm and Haas. He is a *"very skilled senior litigation lawyer,"* say clients. Philadelphia-based Elizabeth Ainslie is a highly experienced trial lawyer whose broad litigation practice is often focused on the

financial services sector. Sources attest that she is *"a terrific, gifted lawyer."*

## Band 4

## Jones Day
See profile on p.919
THE FIRM This globally recognized firm has a solid litigation presence in the state. Notable highlights of late include representing the University of Pittsburgh Medical Center in connection with a number of high-profile matters, including breach of contract claims and allegations of false advertising. Other clients include Education Management and US Steel.
Sources say: *"We are very happy. They have deep expertise, they are good litigators and they are a good resource."*
KEY INDIVIDUALS Laura Ellsworth (see p.2215) is praised by clients as *"very responsive, smart and very good at summarizing complex information and making it easy to understand."* She recently represented Education Management in a number of lawsuits, including a securities class action. Paul Pohl (see p.385) heads the firm's business and tort litigation practice. Clients appreciate that he *"responds very quickly"* and *"does a nice job in terms of analysis of the legal issues."* Roy Powell (see p.2227) recently represented Nationwide Realty Investors in claims relating to construction defects. He is described as *"a collegial lawyer and very smart."*

## K&L Gates
See profile on p.2245
THE FIRM The Pittsburgh office of this internationally renowned firm has a large number of litigators skilled and experienced in a wide variety of disciplines, including product liability, securities, white-collar crime and antitrust matters.
KEY INDIVIDUALS Michael Zanic (see p.2233) represents energy, construction and manufacturing companies. He regularly litigates cases in the areas of product liability, environmental law and insurance coverage. One source notes that *"he's very responsive to client concerns."* The *"outstanding"* Thomas Birsic (see p.2211) heads up the firm's litigation practice. He has extensive trial experience and regularly litigates complex commercial and insurance coverage cases.

## Reed Smith LLP
THE FIRM Reed Smith litigators provide expert advice to clients across a range of disciplines. The team is recognized for its capabilities within the life sciences and financial services industries, and also routinely handles insurance coverage litigation on behalf of policyholders. Clients include Bayer, The Bank of New York Mellon and Verizon.
Sources say: *"Outstanding. It's probably the most responsive law firm I have ever dealt with. It is a very customer-oriented firm."*
KEY INDIVIDUALS Thomas Suddath recently led the team representing medical device company DJO Global during an industrywide criminal and civil investigation

into bone growth stimulators. Sources praise him as *"a strong white-collar lawyer"* with a *"solid reputation."* John Ellison concentrates on representing policyholders in insurance coverage matters. He regularly represents a broad range of clients, including Fortune 50 companies. Michael Scott has extensive experience in the life sciences field, particularly relating to product liability litigation. One interviewee singles him out as *"one of the finest litigators that I've ever worked with."*

## Saul Ewing LLP
See profile on p.2249
THE FIRM Litigators at Saul Ewing are adept at representing clients across a wide variety of industries, including construction, education and real estate. The firm also has an active insurance practice and recently represented Foremost Insurance in a putative class action. Other clients include Tanner Industries and Investment Management Advisory Group.
Sources say: *"Excellent. They were capable of integrating elements of various matters into a single cohesive strategy."*
KEY INDIVIDUALS Joseph O'Dea is praised by interviewees as a *"very experienced high-level legal thinker who operates comfortably at the highest level of our business."* His notable highlights include representing The Pennsylvania State University in high-profile civil litigation brought by victims of sexual abuse. Christopher Hall (see p.2218) leads the white-collar practice group. Recent cases include developing a defense strategy for chemical company Tanner Industries in connection to a government investigation. Sources appreciate his *"ability to see through complexities to give clear and practical advice in challenging areas."*

## Stradley Ronon Stevens & Young LLP
THE FIRM This litigation group has a strong reputation for its representation of clients in the financial services industry. Attorneys at the firm handle complex commercial litigation across a wide array of areas, including product liability, IP, and labor and employment disputes. The firm also has an impressive securities litigation practice and deals with securities regulatory investigations.
Sources say: *"Absolutely top-notch. They are very responsive, approachable, collegial and respectful."*
KEY INDIVIDUALS Jeffrey Lutsky represents clients from a wide range of industries in significant and complex litigation. He is described as a *"sound, well-grounded, trustworthy counselor."*

## Other Notable Practitioners

Sole practitioner and former federal prosecutor Creed Black has a strong reputation in Pennsylvania for his white-collar criminal defense work. David Marion (see p.2224) of Archer & Greiner, A Professional Corporation is well regarded for his litigation capabilities, often with respect to antitrust, securities and professional liability matters. Allen Black of Fine, Kaplan and Black, RPC *"well regarded in the community"* and has extensive experience dealing with all aspects of commercial litigation.

Commercial litigator **Francine Friedman Griesing** of Griesing Law, LLC receives high praise from both peers and clients. Sources highlight her *"extraordinary brilliance."* **Albert Bixler** of Eckert Seamans Cherin & Mellott, LLC is involved in a wide variety of litigation, including insurance coverage, toxic tort and personal injury claims. He regularly represents clients in the pharmaceutical industry in product liability and class action litigation. **Howard Bruce Klein** (see p.2221) of Law Offices Of Howard Bruce Klein is a *"very strong communicator"* who is *"always professional and well prepared,"* say sources. He is noted for his representation of businesses and individuals in white-collar criminal defense matters. **Alexander Kerr** (see p.2221) of McCarter & English, LLP has extensive experience in a broad range of litigation, including insurance coverage disputes and antitrust matters. Sources attest that he is a *"knowledgeable and invaluable"* asset in the

most complex of contentious matters. **Robert Welsh** of Welsh & Recker has a strong reputation within the white-collar criminal defense field, and regularly handles fraud cases and criminal tax matters. At the same firm, **Catherine Recker** is a highly experienced defense practitioner and *"a good solid litigator."* She often handles Foreign Corrupt Practices Act cases and public corruption charges. **William DeStefano** chairs the white-collar defense and investigations group at Stevens & Lee PC. He handles a range of cases, including antitrust and trade regulation litigation. **Richard Sprague** of Sprague & Sprague has over 30 years' experience in both civil and criminal litigation. He is highly regarded for his skill and expertise across a wide range of cases. **William Wycoff** of Thorp Reed & Armstrong, LLP concentrates his practice on commercial litigation disputes and has recently defended law firms in professional negligence cases. **Richard Scheff** of

Montgomery, McCracken, Walker & Rhoads, LLP focuses his practice on government investigations and has significant experience handling matters within the medical device, pharmaceutical and financial services industries. Sources report that he is *"well respected and a good advocate."* The *"very competent and bright"* **David Comerford** (see p.2213) of Akin Gump Strauss Hauer & Feld LLP handles a wide variety of matters and has extensive experience in securities litigation and class actions. **Michael Coran** of Klehr Harrison Harvey Branzburg LLP focuses on corporate and securities litigation, and regularly represents clients in state and federal courts. He is cochair of the firm's litigation department. **Gayle Sproul** (see p.2231) of Levine Sullivan Koch & Schulz LLP is *"extremely intelligent and very easy to work with – an excellent lawyer"* who *"turns out consistently excellent work product."* She is highly regarded for her First Amendment litigation practice.

# REAL ESTATE

Real Estate p.2207;   Zoning/Land Use p.2208

Commentary about individuals can be found under their firm's paragraph. If the firm has no paragraph (is not ranked) look at Other Notable Practitioners.

## Real Estate
### Leading Firms

**Band 1**
Ballard Spahr LLP *
Cozen O'Connor *

**Band 2**
Blank Rome LLP *
Drinker Biddle & Reath LLP *
Saul Ewing LLP *

**Band 3**
Klehr Harrison Harvey Branzburg LLP
Morgan, Lewis & Bockius LLP *

**Band 4**
Dechert LLP *
Duane Morris LLP *
Fox Rothschild LLP *
Hangley Aronchick Segal Pudlin & Schiller *
Schnader Harrison Segal & Lewis LLP
Stradley Ronon Stevens & Young LLP

* Indicates firm with profile.
Alphabetical order within each band. Band 1 is the highest.

## Band 1

### Ballard Spahr LLP
See profile on p.2234

**THE FIRM** This nationally renowned firm has a deep bench of high-quality real estate practitioners. The dedicated team offers a full range of services to its impressive and extensive client base. Attorneys regularly handle complex transactions including acquisitions, leasing and financing. Notable highlights for the group include representation of restaurant franchise company The Rose

Group in a system-wide refinancing. In addition to traditional real estate matters, Ballard Spahr also enjoys a strong reputation for its capabilities in relation to zoning and land use issues.

**Sources say:** *"They have been wonderful to work with. They bring to the table a strong real estate group with knowledge of not only the finance aspect but also the actual nuts and bolts of real estate law."*

**KEY INDIVIDUALS David Gifford** (see p.2217) is considered preeminent in his field and described by one interviewee as *"tremendous"* and *"a real star."* He recently represented Drexel University with regards to the development of a student housing and retail space. **Michael Sklaroff** (see p.2230) is an authority in transactional real estate work and land use and zoning issues. He recently assisted Pennsylvania Real Estate Investment Trust in a leasing matter stemming from the relocation of the Philadelphia Inquirer. Sources note that he is *"an excellent lawyer"* who *"maintains a professional relationship with opposing counsel."* **Neil Sklaroff** (see p.2230) has significant expertise in land use and zoning matters. He recently represented Radnor Property Group in connection with zoning issues. Sources note that *"he represents his clients well"* and *"argues very fine legal points."* The *"experienced and proactive"* **Philip Korb** (see p.2222) is praised by sources as *"absolutely brilliant,"* *"just extraordinary"* and *"really top of the profession."* He was recently involved in the aforementioned refinancing for The Rose Group. **Dominic De Simone** (see p.2214) is a *"very effective lawyer"* who *"knows how to get transactions done,"* say sources. He heads up the firm's commercial real estate recovery group, and is noted for his expertise in real estate finance and distressed real estate acquisitions. Sources praise **Tina Makoulian** (see p.2223) as *"incredibly hard-working, extremely smart and very cre-*

*ative."* Highlights include leading the team in negotiating the purchase and sale agreement of multifamily properties in Virginia on behalf of BPG Properties. The *"extremely capable and reliable"* **Bart Mellits** (see p.2225) has a strong development practice as illustrated by his representation of Parkway Corporation in the development of Hilton Home2 Suites. **Mark DePillis** (see p.2214) is renowned for his expertise in construction law and litigation. Sources report: *"He's practical and down to earth and he's very, very smart and able to foresee and solve problems before they become big problems."* **Matthew McClure** (see p.2224) has a broad practice and is described by sources as a *"very fine attorney"* and a *"very capable and fair individual."* He recently represented Pennrose Development in connection with the first LGBT-friendly senior housing project in Philadelphia. **Alan Ritterband** (see p.2228) focuses the real estate element of his practice on transactional matters including acquisitions, sales, leasing and financing. He recently represented The Ingerman Group in relation to the construction of St. Maron Senior Apartments. In addition, Ritterband is a noted authority on construction law.

### Cozen O'Connor
See profile on p.2237

**THE FIRM** This high-quality real estate practice has a national scope encompassing a broad spectrum of matters ranging from property acquisitions and dispositions to leasing transactions and equity and debt financing. In addition the group is adept in handle zoning and land use matters. Significant representations this year have included acting for MIM-Hayden Real Estate Fund in connection with its acquisition of Five Tower Bridge. Other clients include Wolfson Group and TD Bank.

## Real Estate
### Senior Statesmen

**Senior Statesmen:** distinguished older practitioners

| | |
|---|---|
| Ebby Stuart F | *Hangley Aronchick Segal Pudlin & Schiller* * |

### Leading Individuals

**Star individuals**

| | |
|---|---|
| Fala Herman C | *Cozen O'Connor* * |

**Band 1**

| | |
|---|---|
| Gifford David B | *Ballard Spahr LLP* * |
| Lord Craig | *Blank Rome LLP* * |
| Sklaroff Michael | *Ballard Spahr LLP* * |

**Band 2**

| | |
|---|---|
| Broderick JJ | *Morgan, Lewis & Bockius LLP* |
| Burg Michael S | *Saul Ewing LLP* |
| Cherken Jr Harry S | *Drinker Biddle & Reath LLP* * |
| Finkelstein Joseph | *Blank Rome LLP* * |
| Korb Philip B | *Ballard Spahr LLP* * |
| Kutler Marilyn | *Schnader Harrison Segal & Lewis LLP* |
| Silverman Robert A | *Cozen O'Connor* * |
| Stern Eric L | *Morgan, Lewis & Bockius LLP* |
| Strober Frederick D | *Saul Ewing LLP* |

**Band 3**

| | |
|---|---|
| Brookman Marc D | *Duane Morris LLP* |
| De Simone Dominic | *Ballard Spahr LLP* * |
| Ebby David A | *Drinker Biddle & Reath LLP* * |
| Forti David W | *Dechert LLP* * |
| Galante Linda Ann | *Stradley Ronon Stevens & Young LLP* |
| Glazer Ronald B | *Kaplin Stewart Meloff Reiter & Stein (ONP)* † |
| Gosfield Gregory G | *Klehr Harrison Harvey Branzburg LLP* |
| Jones Richard D | *Dechert LLP* * |
| Krouse Bradley A | *Klehr Harrison Harvey Branzburg LLP* |
| Makoulian Tina R | *Ballard Spahr LLP* * |
| Mellits Bart | *Ballard Spahr LLP* * |
| Pierce John P | *Saul Ewing LLP* |
| Ritterband Alan | *Ballard Spahr LLP* * |
| Rodak Ralph | *Drinker Biddle & Reath LLP* * |
| Rosenfeldt Philip | *Blank Rome LLP* * |
| Scolnic David | *Hangley Aronchick Segal Pudlin & Schiller* * |
| Williams James R | *Cozen O'Connor* * |

**Band 4**

| | |
|---|---|
| Augustin David R | *Duane Morris LLP* |
| DePillis Mark S | *Ballard Spahr LLP* * |
| Goodman Jerald M | *Drinker Biddle & Reath LLP* * |
| Kroculick George J | *Duane Morris LLP* |
| Leonard Jeffrey A | *Cozen O'Connor* * |
| McClure Matthew N | *Ballard Spahr LLP* * |
| Morris Mark L | *Fox Rothschild LLP* * |
| Robins Jon S | *Klehr Harrison Harvey Branzburg LLP* |
| Steele Tracy L | *Morgan, Lewis & Bockius LLP* |

**Up-and-coming individuals**

| | |
|---|---|
| Bishop Jeannine T | *Morgan, Lewis & Bockius LLP* |

\* *Indicates individual with profile.*
† *ONP = Other Notable Practitioner.*

## Real Estate: Zoning/Land Use
### Leading Individuals

**Band 1**

| | |
|---|---|
| Kelsen Peter Foster | *Blank Rome LLP* * |
| Primavera Carl | *Klehr Harrison Harvey Branzburg LLP* |
| Sklaroff Michael | *Ballard Spahr LLP* * |
| Sklaroff Neil | *Ballard Spahr LLP* * |
| Witt Thomas | *Cozen O'Connor* * |

**Band 2**

| | |
|---|---|
| Forte Anthony P | *Saul Ewing LLP* |

**Sources say:** *"They are just terrific lawyers and they look out for you. We have a lot less to worry about when they represent us. They are thorough, smart and very experienced at getting stuff done."*

**KEY INDIVIDUALS Herman Fala** (see p.2215) enjoys an outstanding reputation in the Pennsylvania real estate marketplace and is described as *"wonderful to work with, smart, creative, ethical, and someone you can trust in a deal."* He cochairs the firm's real estate group and has a broad transactional experience that includes portfolio acquisitions, joint venture arrangements and project finance transactions. **Thomas Witt** (see p.2233) is *"recognized as in the zoning elite"* by impressed market observers. He is widely noted for the strength of his knowledge of state and local government procedure, and is prized by clients for his ability to navigate the maze of land use laws and regulations. **Robert Silverman** (see p.2230) is a *"very good negotiator"* who is *"extremely knowledgeable and experienced,"* say sources. He represents owners, lenders and developers in a variety of complex property transactions. **James Williams** (see p.2232) has represented GE Pension Trust/GE Asset Management in a variety of matters this year. One source reports: *"Jim is the consummate legal professional. Always wise in his advice, creative in structuring deals, precise in drafting and completely committed to his clients' objectives."* **Jeffrey Leonard** (see p.2223) is incredibly *"well known and well respected in the community,"* say market observers. He led the team in the aforementioned matter for MIM-Hayden Real Estate Fund.

## Band 2

### Blank Rome LLP
See profile on p.2235

**THE FIRM** Blank Rome has a leading real estate practice offering a diversity of expertise ranging from transactional work to zoning and land use matters. The team has a broad client roster including public and private owners and operators, REITs, private equity funds and housing authorities. Notable highlights of late include providing zoning counsel to the Church of Latter Day Saints with regards to the development of a Mormon temple in Philadelphia. Other clients include Wells Fargo, Capital Automotive and AEGON.
**Sources say:** *"They are accessible, available and effective, and they got the job done. They're experienced, smart and competent."*

**KEY INDIVIDUALS Peter Foster Kelsen** (see p.2220) recently served as lead counsel to Barnes Foundation in relation to a high-profile development of an art gallery. He is praised as *"responsive, knowledgeable, levelheaded and insightful."* **Craig Lord** (see p.2223) recently represented iStar Financial on a foreclosure matter. He receives strong praise from the market, with one interviewee reporting his *"stellar reputation"* and a second commenting that he is *"very capable and well versed in deal-making."* Notable highlights for **Joseph Finkelstein** (see p.2215) include a complex $1.64 billion acquisition for Simon Property Group as well as a $77 million construction project for Toll Brothers. He handles all aspects of commercial real estate work. **Philip Rosenfeldt** (see p.2228) has extensive experience representing clients in all aspects of real estate, ranging from sales and acquisitions to leasing and financing.

### Drinker Biddle & Reath LLP
See profile on p.2238

**THE FIRM** Drinker Biddle has a deep bench of attorneys in its real estate team. The group is particularly experienced in leasing work as illustrated by its recent representation of Endo Pharmaceuticals with regards to the lease of its new headquarters. The team routinely handles financing and lending work and is renowned for its expertise representing clients on large and complex transactions in the retail industry. Other clients include Urban Outfitters and Jackson National Life Insurance.
**Sources say:** *"They're very professional, their substantive knowledge is good, the partners are very fair in billing and they work hard to try and serve our needs."*
**KEY INDIVIDUALS Harry Cherken** (see p.2213) recently led the team in its handling of the acquisition, leasing and construction of headquarters for retail giant Urban Outfitters. One client notes: *"When I have a complex issue he is the first person I call. He has substantive knowledge of real estate law that is almost unparalleled."* **David Ebby** (see p.2215) is praised as an *"extraordinary, outstanding lawyer"* by admiring commentators. Highlights over the past year include handling a high-profile office lease for Metropolis Investment Holdings with regards to new headquarters for the Cozen O'Connor law firm. The *"extremely knowledgeable"* **Ralph Rodak** (see p.2228) is praised as *"dedicated, hard-working, extremely responsive and very efficient"* by market observers. Notable transactions include the representation of Citizens Bank of Pennsylvania in connection with a construction loan for a dining and entertainment venue in Philadelphia. **Jerald Goodman** (see p.2217) recently represented Main Line Health System in connection with numerous real estate issues including leasing and zoning matters. Sources relate that *"he's resourceful, he gets the job done and understands what needs to be done."*

### Saul Ewing LLP
See profile on p.2249

**THE FIRM** This firm is highly regarded in the Pennsylvania market for its impressive real estate practice. Attorneys regularly represent developers, owners and major institutions in all of their real estate matters. In addition to a robust transactional practice, Saul Ewing has an active real estate litigation practice and offers standout advice on zoning, land use and permitting issues. Highlights include the representation of Philadelphia Regional Port Authority on a number of matters ranging from lease negotiations to infrastructure development. **Sources say:** "*They've got a very good group of attorneys who work hard to serve the client, are responsive and have excellent substantive skills in the area they practice.*" **KEY INDIVIDUALS Michael Burg** wins accolades from clients for his extensive experience and "*knowledge of the industry.*" He handles significant transactions for clients including campus relocations and headquarter leases. Sources note that he is "*responsive and easy to work with.*" Zoning expert **Anthony Forte** is described by sources as "*knowledgeable, diligent, timely and pragmatic.*" He regularly represents clients before the Philadelphia Planning Commission. The "*practical, creative, responsive and hardworking*" **Frederick Strober** handles large development projects, construction matters, acquisitions and leasing. One client remarks that "*he's a very smart lawyer, he's thoughtful and will help find solutions.*" **John Pierce** is chair of the firm's transactional real estate group. He has a broad client portfolio including BPG Properties and Lower Bucks Hospital. Sources say: "*He's deeply experienced, with a breadth of knowledge and gets deals done. He understands the big picture and he's got a very comprehensive understanding of real estate transactions.*"

## Band 3

### Klehr Harrison Harvey Branzburg LLP

**THE FIRM** This reputable firm represents the full spectrum of clients ranging from individual investors to institutional lenders and REITs. The group is particularly active representing developers and handling zoning and land use matters. Notable highlights over the last twelve months include the representation of Pennsylvania Real Estate Investment Trust in connection with the refinancing of a Cherry Hill Mall. **Sources say:** "*We get great service. They're not a huge national firm but they have all the expertise we need and we don't get lost in a large firm bureaucracy.*" **KEY INDIVIDUALS Carl Primavera** is a "*very fine attorney,*" say sources. Recent highlights include representation of Brandywine Realty Trust in a zoning and land use matter. **Gregory Gosfield** recently handled a transaction involving the development and construction of nursing home facilities for Genesis Healthcare. He is favorably described as a "*smart, thoughtful lawyer.*" **Bradley Krouse** recently represented student housing developer Campus Apartments in connection with the development and construction of over 1,000 units. Sources note that "*he's methodical in his approach and he's a critical thinker.*" **Jon Robins** has a broad practice encompassing a wide range of real estate transactions. He has particular expertise representing lenders including banks, insurance companies and private equity funds.

### Morgan, Lewis & Bockius LLP
See profile on p.2246

**THE FIRM** This group focuses primarily on corporate real estate, REITs, real estate funds and private equity. The firm has an impressive client portfolio including Pfizer and CubeSmart. The team recently represented Subaru of America in connection with its lease of a distribution center in New Jersey. The team is able to draw on the firm's broad interdisciplinary resources to provide comprehensive multifaceted advice to clients. **Sources say:** "*They're prompt in responding, they're easy to work with and their advice and guidance has proven to be valuable and on target.*" **KEY INDIVIDUALS JJ Broderick** "*cares about his clients and cares deeply about getting a project done the right way,*" according to interviewees. He recently handled the aforementioned lease transaction for Subaru of America. Clients appreciate that **Eric Stern** is "*proactive in following up*" and find him "*extremely responsive, easy to get along with and good to work with.*" He represents real estate investors and owners in the full range of transactional matters. **Tracy Steele** "*helps a transaction get done quickly,*" say sources, who also describe her as "*a good negotiator*" and "*very responsive.*" She deals with all aspects of real estate law and regularly works with energy companies on their real estate matters. **Jeannine Bishop** represented REIT CubeSmart in connection with a $560 million acquisition of self-storage facilities. Clients find her to be a "*very efficient real estate transactional attorney.*"

## Band 4

### Dechert LLP
See profile on p.1969

**THE FIRM** This internationally renowned firm has a complete national real estate practice. The Pennsylvania practice group focuses on real estate finance with a specialization in capital markets and securitization. The team is adept at handling a broad array of large and complex commercial transactions including acquisitions, dispositions and loan securitization. **Sources say:** "*The strength of the Dechert team has always been the quality of the partners, as well as the senior and more junior associates, which has enabled Dechert to provide terrific counsel for all types of real estate transactions in which we have engaged.*" **KEY INDIVIDUALS David Forti** (see p.2216) is lauded by clients as "*very practical and good at arriving at creative solutions to bridge the gap between parties in disagreements.*" He concentrates his practice on real estate finance and securitization. **Richard Jones** (see p.1907) is cochair of the firm's finance and real estate group. He deals principally with mortgage finance and capital markets.

### Duane Morris LLP
See profile on p.2239

**THE FIRM** This full-service firm has a significant real estate team with a focus on transactional work. Attorneys regularly assist investors, owners and real estate funds with the acquisition and sale of real estate. The team handles a wide variety of transactions including educational and medical projects and recently dealt with a number of condemnation matters. **Sources say:** "*They are very responsive, they get right back to you, they're efficient and they get things done.*" **KEY INDIVIDUALS Marc Brookman** has recently been involved in a smart-growth multifamily project. Sources note that "*he's got great expertise and knows real estate well.*" **David Augustin** handles a range of real estate issues including financings, commercial acquisitions and real estate development. He is described as "*bright and extraordinarily hard-working.*" **George Kroculick** is praised as a "*very competent real estate attorney.*" One client notes that "*he's punctual, prompt, responsive and gets back to us within an hour regardless of the matter.*"

### Fox Rothschild LLP
See profile on p.2242

**THE FIRM** This group has a strong presence in Pennsylvania, routinely assisting clients with the acquisition and development of real estate in the area. The firm has a strong land use and zoning practice and is also well versed in leasing, financing and condemnation. Notable transactions include representing Teva in relation to zoning, land use and development work regarding its distribution facility. **Sources say:** "*They do a fantastic job.*" **KEY INDIVIDUALS Mark Morris** (see p.2225) is described by sources as "*practical and business-minded.*" He recently handled a matter for Pinnacle Hotel Management involving the negotiation of loan transactions. Clients report: "*He's terrific. He's personable, compassionate and very, very bright. Really great to work with.*"

### Hangley Aronchick Segal Pudlin & Schiller
See profile on p.2243

**THE FIRM** Significant transactions this year have included the redevelopment of Cherry Hill Mall, involving extensive land use matters. Attorneys at Hangley Aronchick also serve as lead real estate counsel to retail company Aldi, handling lease and acquisition work. The group deals with transactions involving a wide variety of commercial and residential properties including office buildings, hospitals, hotels and industrial facilities. **Sources say:** "*Representation has been excellent. The timeliness and focus on the projects is particularly impressive.*" **KEY INDIVIDUALS David Scolnic** (see p.2229) recently represented Select Medical in connection with numerous real estate matters including construction projects and leasing issues. Sources note that he is "*effective at managing the deal process.*" The highly experienced **Stuart Ebby** (see p.2215) is well versed in all aspects of the law and represents a wide range of clients in all areas of real estate practice. Sources describe him as "*a great lawyer*" and "*a gentleman among gentlemen.*"

### Schnader Harrison Segal & Lewis LLP

**THE FIRM** Recent highlights for this firm's real estate practice group include the representation of The Wistar

Institute in connection with a $100 million expansion of a scientific research institute. Other notable clients include the City of Philadelphia and the University of Pennsylvania. The group represents a diverse range of clients across the full gamut of real estate transactions.
**KEY INDIVIDUALS Marilyn Kutler** recently handled the restructuring and refinancing of a downtown car parking facility for Parametric Garage Associates. She is highly experienced in complex development projects in both private and public sectors.

## Stradley Ronon Stevens & Young LLP

**THE FIRM** This firm covers all aspects of real estate law and regularly represents a broad array of clients including buyers, sellers, tenants and landlords. In addition to a comprehensive real estate transactional and financing practice, the group at Stradley Ronon also represents REITs, advises on land use and zoning issues and handles condominium work. Clients include Camelot Schools and OmniVest Properties.
**Sources say:** *"The firm is practical and efficient."*
**KEY INDIVIDUALS** Clients appreciate that **Linda Ann Galante** *"understands the whole picture and how to make a*

*deal move on business terms."* She focuses on investment and development matters in commercial and residential property.

## Other Notable Practitioners

**Ronald Glazer** of Kaplin Stewart Meloff Reiter & Stein, PC is highly regarded by peers and is renowned for his particular expertise in the field of condominiums. Sources note that he is *"a very good lawyer."*

# Leaders' Profiles in Pennsylvania

**ABELSON, Barry M**
Pepper Hamilton LLP, Philadelphia
215 981 4282
abelsonb@pepperlaw.com
*Featured in Corporate/M&A (Pennsylvania)*
**Practice Areas:** Partner; Chair Emeritus; past Chairman, Executive Committee. Experienced in securities; venture capital; mergers/acquisitions of public and private companies; public and private offerings of equity and debt securities. Represents issuers, underwriters and venture capitalists. Counsels boards of directors, independent board committees and management on governance, disclosure and transactions.
**Professional Memberships:** Board of Directors, Children's Crisis Treatment Center; Board of Directors, Institute for Law and Economics of the University of Pennsylvania; Board of Directors and Executive Committee, Greater Philadelphia Alliance for Capital and Technologies.
**Personal:** JD, magna cum laude, 1971 University of Pennsylvania Law School; BA 1968 Dartmouth College.

**ABRAMOWITZ, Robert**
Morgan, Lewis & Bockius LLP, Philadelphia
215 963 4811
rabramowitz@morganlewis.com
*Featured in Labor & Employment (Pennsylvania)*
**Practice Areas:** Robert L Abramowitz is a partner in Morgan Lewis's Employee Benefits and Executive Compensation Practice, counseling clients in all aspects of employee benefits and executive compensation law, including fiduciary aspects of ERISA, qualified pension, welfare benefit and profit-sharing plans, executive and deferred compensation arrangements, and flexible compensation programs.
**Professional Memberships:** He is a Fellow of the American College of Tax Counsel and a Charter Fellow of the American College of Employee Benefits Counsel.

**Personal:** Mr Abramowitz graduated from Harvard Law School (1974, JD) and Yale University (1971, BA). He is admitted to practice in Pennsylvania and New Jersey.

**ALDRIDGE, Richard B**
Morgan, Lewis & Bockius LLP, Philadelphia
215 963 4829
raldridge@morganlewis.com
*Featured in Corporate/M&A (Pennsylvania)*
**Practice Areas:** Richard B. Aldridge is the co-chair of Morgan Lewis's Mergers and Acquisitions Practice. Mr Aldridge counsels clients in a wide range of complex business law matters, with an emphasis on both public and private company merger and acquisition transactions. He regularly advises clients with respect to takeover preparedness matters, corporate governance issues and obligations under securities laws, particularly in connection with acquisitions of publicly and privately held companies and public and private securities offerings, in addition to other general corporate matters.
**Personal:** University of Pennsylvania Law School, 1993, JD; Duke University, 1989, AB.

**ALSTADT, Lynn J**
Buchanan Ingersoll & Rooney PC, Pittsburgh
412 562 1632
lynn.alstadt@bipc.com
*Featured in Intellectual Property (Pennsylvania)*
**Career:** Lynn is a Shareholder in the firm's Intellectual Property Section. He has experience in all areas of patent, trademark, copyright and unfair competition law, including litigation, patent solicitation, licensing, patent interferences, trademark cancellation and opposition proceedings, International Trade Commission investigations, registration of trademarks and copyrights, and related exclusion proceedings. His work involves a wide range of technical subjects, including mechanical, electrical, electronic, e-commerce, biotech, chemical, metallurgical and computer. He earned his JD from the University of Pittsburgh School of Law and is an adjunct professor of

patent law at the University of Pittsburgh and Duquesne University.

**ARONCHICK, Mark Alan**
Hangley Aronchick Segal Pudlin & Schiller, Philadelphia
215 496 7002
maronchick@hangley.com
*Featured in Litigation (Pennsylvania)*
**Practice Areas:** Commercial, civil/white-collar criminal matters involving healthcare, professional malpractice, finance, accounting, tax, insurance, government, civil rights, unfair trade practices, and real estate.
**Professional Memberships:** Fellow, American College of Trial Lawyers. Member, Lawyers Advisory Committee, US Court of Appeals for the Third Circuit. Member, Judicial Conduct Board, Commonwealth of Pennsylvania. Member, Judicial Council, Commonwealth of Pennsylvania. Philadelphia Bar Association: Chancellor, 1998; Member, Board of Governors, 1990-92; treasurer, 1986-89; Co-Chair, Committee to Elect Qualified Judges, 1993-95; Co-Chair, Trial Advocacy Program, 1987-91. Philadelphia Bar Foundation: President, 1996; secretary, 1993; trustee, 1990; treasurer, 1986-89. Past Member, House of Delegates, Pennsylvania Bar Association. Past Member, Bench Bar Relations Task Force, US Court of Appeals for the Third Circuit. Past Judge Pro Tem, Court of Common Pleas of Philadelphia County. Past Chair, Hearing Committee, Disciplinary Board of Supreme Court of Pennsylvania. Past Member, Civil Rules Committee, Supreme Court of Pennsylvania.
**Career:** Founder and Shareholder, Hangley Aronchick Segal Pudlin & Schiller, 1994 to present. Shareholder, 1986-94, Hangley Connolly Epstein Chicco Foxman & Ewing. Partner, 1983-86; associate, 1974-79, Wolf, Block Schorr and Solis-Cohen. Philadelphia City Solicitor, 1983; first deputy city solicitor, 1980-82. University of Chicago Law School, JD with highest honors; University of Pennsylvania, BA, cum laude.

**BANKS, Michael L**
Morgan, Lewis & Bockius LLP, Philadelphia
215 963 5387
mbanks@morganlewis.com
*Featured in Labor & Employment (Pennsylvania)*
**Practice Areas:** Michael L. Banks is a partner in the Firm and has litigated a wide range of employment, benefits, trade secret, commercial, professional liability, and tort claims in state and federal courts. He has tried more than 30 cases and has handled several dozen class action and multi-plaintiff cases around the country for some of the firm's largest and most sophisticated clients.
**Personal:** Attended Columbia University Law School, 1981, JD; Cornell University, 1978, AB.

**BARNETT, Bonnie Allyn**
Drinker Biddle & Reath LLP, Philadelphia
215 988 2916
Bonnie.Barnett@dbr.com
*Featured in Environment (Pennsylvania)*
**Practice Areas:** Managing Partner, Chair of the firm's Environment and Energy Practice. Combines an active litigation practice with general counseling on regulatory compliance issues, environmental implications of business and real estate transactions and development and implementation of sustainable business solutions.
**Professional Memberships:** Admitted in Pennsylvania (1982) and New Jersey (1996). Former Co-Chair of Philadelphia Bar Association Environmental Law Committee. Helped charter the Delaware Valley Environmental Inn of Court. Frequent lecturer on environmental law.
**Career:** Joined Drinker Biddle in 1984, after federal clerkship.
**Personal:** JD (summa cum laude), Temple University School of Law, 1982; BA (summa cum laude) Temple University, 1979.

**BARON JR, Robert R**
Ballard Spahr LLP, Philadelphia
215 864 8335
baron@ballardspahr.com
*Featured in Intellectual Property (Pennsylvania)*

**Practice Areas:** Mr Baron, Vice Chair of the Intellectual Property Department, regularly prosecutes and defends cases involving patent, copyright, trademark, and trade dress infringement; theft of trade secrets; breach of contract; breakdown of commercial acquisitions and related investments; partnership disputes; unfair competition; business terminations; and licensing disputes.

**Professional Memberships:** Philadelphia Bar Association (Past Chair, Business Litigation Committee); Philadelphia County Court of Common Pleas (Judge Pro Team, Commerce Litigation Division); University of Pennsylvania Inn of Court (Barrister, 2002-2004).

**Career:** Admissions: New Jersey, Pennsylvania

**Personal:** George Washington University Law School (JD 1992) Brown University (BA 1988).

### BARSON, Leon R
Blank Rome LLP, Philadelphia
215 569 5576
LBarson@BlankRome.com
*Featured in Bankruptcy/Restructuring (Pennsylvania)*

**Practice Areas:** Leon Barson focuses his practice on corporate reorganizations, workouts, debtors' and creditors' rights, and corporate transactions. He has represented parties in the restructuring, reorganization, or sale of complex businesses in a variety of industries, including automotive, telecommunications, healthcare, manufacturing, hospitality, real estate, apparel, and retail. Mr Barson has extensive experience representing and advising companies, buyers and investors in all aspects of distressed and insolvency situations. He also counsels boards of directors and senior management with respect to their duties and obligations to financially-challenged companies. For more information: www.BlankRome.com/LBarson

### BARTON, Thomas J
Drinker Biddle & Reath LLP, Philadelphia
215 988 2834
thomas.barton@dbr.com
*Featured in Labor & Employment (Pennsylvania)*

**Practice Areas:** Partner and Co-Chair of the firm's Labor and Employment Practice Group. Tom represents employers in all aspects of labor and employment law, including employment discrimination and wrongful termination litigation, preventive advice and counseling, manager and employee training and internal employee investigations and audits. Significant experience with non-competition and trade secret litigation, wage & hour and EEO class actions and labor management and collective bargaining and disputes.

**Professional Memberships:** Admitted in Pennsylvania and New Jersey.

**Personal:** Boston College Law School, JD 1987 (magna cum laude, Boston College Law Review); The College of William & Mary, BA 1984.

### BECKER, James M
Buchanan Ingersoll & Rooney PC, Philadelphia
215 665 5366
james.becker@bipc.com
*Featured in Litigation (Pennsylvania)*

**Career:** James is a Shareholder in the firm's Litigation Section and represents companies and individuals at all stages of government enforcement proceedings, whether criminal, civil or administrative. His clients are from health care, environmental, government procurement, tax, securities and antitrust fields. Jim was previously an Assistant United States Attorney for the Eastern District of Pennsylvania. Jim earned his JD from the George Washington University Law School with honors. He frequently lectures on white-collar crime and serves on the Advisory Committee to the Committee on Model Criminal Jury Instructions of the United States Court of Appeals for the Third Circuit.

### BELISARIO, Martin G
Panitch Schwarze Belisario & Nadel LLP, Philadelphia
215 965 1303
mbelisario@panitchlaw.com
*Featured in Intellectual Property (Pennsylvania)*

**Practice Areas:** Martin Belisario practices intellectual property and technology law, including representation before the United States Patent and Trademark Office and foreign patent offices, technology licensing, portfolio counseling and litigation. His practice focuses primarily on the mechanical and electrical arts. His experience includes litigating patent disputes, providing opinions on patent infringement and validity, and supervising prosecution of both US and foreign patents for large high technology portfolios.

**Professional Memberships:** Philadelphia Bar Association; Philadelphia Intellectual Property Law Association; Pennsylvania Bar.

**Personal:** BSME, Drexel University; JD, Widener University School of Law.

### BERGSTROM, Thomas A
Buchanan Ingersoll & Rooney PC, Pittsburgh
215 665 3955
thomas.bergstrom@bipc.com
*Featured in Litigation (Pennsylvania)*

**Career:** Thomas is Of Counsel in the firm's Litigation Section. He focuses his practice on white-collar criminal defense in federal and state courts. Tom has defended hundreds of businesses, professionals and individuals in all stages of enforcement proceedings. He has also conducted internal corporate investigations. He has substantial experience in antitrust, securities, tax, fraud and environmental criminal cases and regularly represents medical, legal and accounting professionals in high-profile criminal investigations, trials and appeals. He earned his JD from the University of Iowa and frequently lectures on white collar topics.

### BERKOWITZ, Alan D
Dechert LLP, Philadelphia
215 994 2170
alan.berkowitz@dechert.com
*Featured in Labor & Employment (Pennsylvania)*

**Practice Areas:** Mr Berkowitz represents employers in employment litigation disputes alleging discrimination, breach of contract, employment torts, non-compete violations, and wage and hour violations. He frequently handles unfair labor practices proceedings before the NLRB.

**Professional Memberships:** Member, Pennsylvania Bar; admitted to practice before the US Supreme Court and numerous federal courts

**Publications:** Author, treatise on Pennsylvania Employment Law; co-author, The Landrum-Griffin Act: Twenty Years of Federal Protection of Union Members' Rights and The NLRB and Secondary Boycotts.

**Personal:** Cornell University (BS, 1977); University of Pennsylvania Law School (JD, 1980, summa cum laude, Member, Law Review)

### BIRON, Thomas E
Blank Rome LLP, Philadelphia
215 569 5562
Biron@BlankRome.com
*Featured in Bankruptcy/Restructuring (Pennsylvania)*

**Practice Areas:** Tom Biron focuses on challenges, defenses, remedies and opportunities presented by financial distress typically caused by insolvency, fraud, leverage or insufficient capital. He represents stakeholders, managers, purchasers, investors, finance sources and victims in insolvency proceedings, transactions and litigation. For more information: www.BlankRome.com/Biron

### BIRSIC, Thomas E
K&L Gates, Pittsburgh
412 355 6538
thomas.birsic@klgates.com
*Featured in Litigation (Pennsylvania)*

**Practice Areas:** As Co-Leader of K&L Gates' global Litigation and Dispute Resolution Practice Area, Mr Birsic maintains an active trial, arbitration and counseling practice focused principally on complex commercial and insurance coverage litigation. He has extensive jury and bench trial experience involving complex, plaintiff-oriented commercial cases. He has also tried numerous international and US-based commercial arbitrations to conclusion. He is a Fellow of the American College of Trial Lawyers and the International Academy of Trial Lawyers.

### BIZAR, Steven E
Buchanan Ingersoll & Rooney PC, Philadelphia
215 665 3826
steven.bizar@bipc.com
*Featured in Antitrust (Pennsylvania), Litigation (Pennsylvania)*

**Career:** Steven's practice concentrates on litigation related to antitrust and trade regulation, securities, contracts and business torts, and government investigations. Steven has significant experience in the trial defense of multidistrict class actions. Steven also represents clients in government antitrust and securities fraud investigations and enforcement proceedings and related civil proceedings. He regularly represents clients in courts throughout the country and before arbitration panels in a wide range of contract and tort disputes arising from their commercial activities, including "bet the company" lawsuits. He earned his JD from the Columbia University Law School and was a Harlan Fiske Stone Scholar.

### BLACK, Martin J
Dechert LLP, Philadelphia
215 994 2664
martin.black@dechert.com
*Featured in Intellectual Property (Pennsylvania)*

**Practice Areas:** Mr Black, co-chair of Dechert's intellectual property group, focuses on patent, trademark, copyright, trade secret, and software litigation. He has handled patent cases concerning technologies as diverse as molecular genetics, electronic games, mobile computers, septic systems, and chip technology. He also helps clients monetize their patent portfolios and advises on complex matters at the interface of antitrust and intellectual property law.

**Professional Memberships:** Member, Pennsylvania and New Jersey Bars; admitted to practice before numerous federal courts.

**Personal:** University of Pennsylvania (BSE, 1985, cum laude, Benjamin Franklin Scholar); University of Chicago Law School (JD, 1988, cum laude).

### BLUME, Fred
Blank Rome LLP, Philadelphia
215 569 5512
Blume@BlankRome.com
*Featured in Corporate/M&A (Pennsylvania)*

**Practice Areas:** Fred Blume advises senior executives and owners of publicly-held, family-owned and closely-held companies in their business needs, including mergers, acquisitions and divestitures and capital-raising activities. He also serves as a mediator in corporate disputes. Mr Blume is the Chairman Emeritus of Blank Rome. For more information please visit: www.BlankRome.com/Blume.

### BOLSTEIN, Joel
Fox Rothschild LLP, Warrington
215 918 3555
jbolstein@foxrothschild.com
*Featured in Environment (Pennsylvania)*

**Practice Areas:** Environmental law, brownfields redevelopment, business transactions, permitting, compliance counseling/litigation, Marcellus Shale exploration/development.

**Professional Memberships:** American Bar Association.

**Career:** Co-Chair, Marcellus Shale Working Group, Fox Rothschild; Former PADEP Deputy Secretary; Three terms - USEPA's National Advisory Council for Environmental Policy and Technology.

**Publications:** PA Brownfields & Environmental Law Blog (http://pabrownfieldsenvironmentallaw.foxrothschild.com); 'PA Marcellus Legislation Brings Several Hammers Down on Local Ordinances', In the Zone (2012); 'PA Governor-Elect Tom Corbett Lays Out Environmental Priorities', In the Zone (2010).

**Personal:** Included in list of 'Best Lawyers in America,' Environmental Law (2003-11) and in 'Super Lawyers,' Philadelphia Magazine/Law & Politics Magazine (2004-10).

## BOUCHARD, Sarah
Morgan, Lewis & Bockius LLP, Philadelphia
215 963 5077
sbouchard@morganlewis.com
*Featured in Labor & Employment (Pennsylvania)*
**Practice Areas:** Sarah Bouchard is a partner in Morgan Lewis's Labor and Employment Practice and a co-leader of the Sarbanes-Oxley subpractice. Sarah has extensive experience in a variety of disciplines, including litigating complex employment class and collective actions, non-competition and trade secret matters, and whistleblower/Sarbanes-Oxley/Dodd Frank actions. She also provides strategic representation and counseling in areas of wrongful discharge, employment contracts, sexual harassment, discrimination, whistleblower issues, severance agreements, noncompetition and trade secret protections, reductions in force, and a variety of other employment matters.
**Personal:** Attended Villanova University School of Law, 1995, JD; Pennsylvania State University, 1992, BA Phi Beta Kappa.

## BOYLE, Christopher W
Drinker Biddle & Reath LLP, Philadelphia
215 988 2962
Christopher.Boyle@dbr.com
*Featured in Environment (Pennsylvania)*
**Practice Areas:** Partner, Vice-Chair Environment and Energy Practice, licensed professional engineer. Focuses on environmental M&A transactions; Brownfield and energy development, permitting and regulatory enforcement; skilled in remediation, construction and risk management.
**Professional Memberships:** Admissions: Pennsylvania and New Jersey. Former Chair, Philadelphia Bar Association Environmental Law Committee; Member, National Civil Engineering Honor Society, National Engineering Society and American Society for Testing and Materials Committee E-50 on Environmental Assessments.
**Career:** Previously, Senior Project Engineer, O'Brien & Gere, Inc.
**Personal:** JD, Villanova University School of Law, 1991; MCE, Villanova University, 1988; MBA Program, Drexel University, 1982-85; BCE, Villanova University, 1982.

## BRAEMER, Richard J
Ballard Spahr LLP, Philadelphia
215 864 8899
braemer@ballardspahr.com
*Featured in Corporate/M&A (Pennsylvania)*
**Practice Areas:** Richard J. Braemer is senior counsel in the Business and Finance Department. He practices in the areas of mergers and acquisitions (representing sellers and buyers), corporate and real estate financings, corporate restructurings, private equity investments, joint ventures, and executive compensation. He is involved in general corporate and corporate governance issues, including the representation of directors of public companies and independent committees of boards of directors.
**Career:** Admissions: Pennsylvania.

**Personal:** Yale Law School (LLB 1965) Amherst College (BA 1962).

## BRESSLER, Gary D
McElroy, Deutsch, Mulvaney & Carpenter, LLP, Philadelphia
215 557 2971
gbressler@mdmc-law.com
*Featured in Bankruptcy/Restructuring (Pennsylvania)*
**Practice Areas:** Mr Bressler's areas of practice include business bankruptcy and insolvency. He has represented Secured Creditors, Equity Security Holders' Committees, Creditors' Committees, Chapter 11 Debtors, and Chapter 7 Trustees.
**Professional Memberships:** Mr Bressler is a member of the Philadelphia, Pennsylvania and American Bar Associations, the Eastern District of Pennsylvania Bankruptcy Conference and the American Bankruptcy Institute. He is also a member of the Turnaround Management Association and the National Association of Bankruptcy Trustees. Mr Bressler has served on various committees of the Eastern District of Pennsylvania Bankruptcy Conference.
**Personal:** Villanova University School of Law (JD); University of Pennsylvania (BA).

## BRONSON, Jill E
Drinker Biddle & Reath LLP, Philadelphia
215 988 2665
Jill.Bronson@dbr.com
*Featured in Banking & Finance (Pennsylvania)*
**Practice Areas:** Partner in the Corporate and Securities Practice and leader of the Corporate Finance Team. Jill has experience handling a wide range of financing transactions, both as counsel to the agent/lender and as counsel to the borrower/issuer. She has represented major regional and national banks and other financial institutions in diverse types of financing matters across a wide range of industries. Additionally, she represents public and private companies and private equity groups in a variety of financing matters.
**Personal:** University of Pennsylvania, BA, 1975, magna cum laude; University of Pennsylvania, BS, 1975; University of Pennsylvania Law School, JD 1979.

## BROWN, Stephen D
Dechert LLP, Philadelphia
215 994 2240
stephen.brown@dechert.com
*Featured in Antitrust (Pennsylvania)*
**Practice Areas:** Mr Brown focuses his practice on internal investigations and complex criminal and civil cases relating to fraud, RICO, antitrust, and legal malpractice issues. He is recognized for his handling of prisoner civil rights cases.
**Professional Memberships:** Member, Pennsylvania and Massachusetts Bars; admitted to practice before several federal courts; co-chair, Prisoner Civil Rights Panel of the US District Court, Eastern District of Pennsylvania; former vice-chair, ABA Section, Antitrust Law Criminal Practice and Procedure Subcommittee
**Personal:** Williams College (BA, 1971); Villanova University School of Law (JD, 1976, editor-in-

chief, Villanova University Law Review, Order of the Coif)

## BUCHANAN, Thomas G.
Buchanan Ingersoll & Rooney PC, Pittsburgh
412 562 1380
thomas.buchanan@bipc.com
*Featured in Corporate/M&A (Pennsylvania)*
**Career:** Thomas is a member of the firm's Advisory Committee and Co-chair of the Corporate Section, as well as a member of the section's Executive Committee. Tom has nearly 25 years of experience representing clients in corporate transactions, including mergers, acquisitions, dispositions, venture capital financings and joint ventures. He is a trusted advisor to his clients, often serving as general counsel for companies that do not have in-house counsel. Tom also regularly counsels companies on their compliance obligations under the Hart-Scott-Rodino Antitrust Improvements Act of 1976. He earned his JD (with honors) from Template University Beasley School of Law.

## BURDUMY, Stephen T
Drinker Biddle & Reath LLP, Philadelphia
215 988 2880
Stephen.Burdumy@dbr.com
*Featured in Corporate/M&A (Pennsylvania)*
**Career:** Partner in the Corporate and Securities and Investment Management Groups and Managing Partner, Steve Burdumy handles all aspects of business transactions, including financing, divestitures, securities, mergers and acquisitions. He represents acquirers and targets in private and public mergers and acquisitions, issuers and underwriters in public and private securities offerings, venture capital, private equity and hedge funds and emerging companies in formation, investments and acquisitions. He also has managed internal and SEC investigations, defense of securities class action claims, and counsels clients on corporate governance issues.
**Personal:** Georgetown University, BSFS, cum laude; University of San Francisco Law School, JD.

## BUSIS, Richard J
Cozen O'Connor, Philadelphia
215 665 2756
rbusis@cozen.com
*Featured in Corporate/M&A (Pennsylvania)*
**Practice Areas:** Richard counsels public and private companies, ranging from startup companies seeking venture capital to NASDAQ and NYSE-listed companies, in a variety of corporate and securities transactions. His practice has a particular emphasis on securities offerings and mergers and acquisitions. Richard represents not only issuers, but also underwriters, placement agents, venture funds and private equity funds. He also has particular expertise in Israeli investments.
**Professional Memberships:** Florida Bar Association, International Bar Association, Pennsylvania Bar Association, Philadelphia Bar Association.
**Career:** Chair, US Securities Practice Group.
**Personal:** Harvard Law School, JD, 1984; University of Pennsylvania, MA, 1980; University of Pennsylvania, BA, 1975.

## CANNUSCIO, Robert
Drinker Biddle & Reath LLP, Philadelphia
215 988 3303
Robert.Cannuscio@dbr.com
*Featured in Intellectual Property (Pennsylvania)*
**Practice Areas:** Experienced in intellectual property law (patents, trademarks, copyrights, trade secrets and trade dress) with an emphasis on prosecution, opposition practice, litigation, technology licensing (including software licensing) and client counseling including IP portfolio development.
**Career:** Involved in intellectual property matters related to mechanical and electro-mechanical devices, material and system processing, manufacturing operations, medical devices and procedures, computer and Internet technologies, and design and manufacture of aircraft structures, propulsion systems and flight controls. Prior Vice Chair of the IP Group.
**Personal:** Pace University School of Law, JD 1994; Polytechnic Institute of New York, MSME 1989 and BSME 1985; Professional Engineer.

## CARROLL, John W
Pepper Hamilton LLP, Harrisburg
717 255 1159
carrollj@pepperlaw.com
*Featured in Environment (Pennsylvania)*
**Practice Areas:** Partner; Chairman, Environmental Practice Group. Experienced in energy and natural resources litigation, counseling, transactional representation and government relations. Has represented clients in Clean Air Act enforcement litigation instituted by EPA; manufacturers in water pollution matters; waste generators/transporters/landowners in CERCLA matters; land developers in wetlands and permitting matters; buyers/sellers of contaminated property in negotiation of sales agreements, and negotiation of clean-up agreements with state and federal agencies.
**Professional Memberships:** Former Member, Pennsylvania Environmental Hearing Board Rules Committee.
**Career:** Former Chief Counsel, Pennsylvania Department of Environmental Resources.
**Personal:** JD 1972 University of Pennsylvania Law School; BA 1969 University of Pennsylvania.

## CHAN, Ashely M
Hangley Aronchick Segal Pudlin & Schiller, Philadelphia
215 496 7050
achan@hangley.com
*Featured in Bankruptcy/Restructuring (Pennsylvania)*
**Practice Areas:** Bankruptcy and creditor rights.
**Professional Memberships:** Eastern District of Pennsylvania Bankruptcy Conference Steering Committee (2010-); Vice-Chair, Bankruptcy Committee of the Philadelphia Bar Association (2010-); Board Member (2007 to present), Secretary (2010), and Legal Coordinator (2001 to present), Homeless Advocacy Project; Leadership, Inc. Philadelphia, Class of 2012; Eastern District of Pennsylvania Planner for Commercial Panels, PBI Bankruptcy Institute (2012).

**Career:** Shareholder, Hangley Aronchick Segal Pudlin & Schiller, 2001 to present. Associate, Morgan Lewis & Bockius LLP, 1997-2001. Law clerk, the Honorable Gloria M Burns, 1996-97. Rutgers Law School-Camden, graduated with tax honors and received the Pro Bono Publico Award.

### CHERKEN JR, Harry S
Drinker Biddle & Reath LLP, Philadelphia
215 988 2721
harry.cherken@dbr.com
*Featured in Real Estate (Pennsylvania)*

**Practice Areas:** Represents publicly-traded and closely-held corporations, partnerships, investors and developers, particularly in the acquisition, construction, development, financing, leasing, management, consolidation and disposition of commercial real estate.

**Professional Memberships:** Member, American College of Real Estate Lawyers; Former Member, Advisory Board, Advanced Commercial Leasing Institute, Georgetown University Law Center. Selected for The Best Lawyers in America, Who's Who Legal: USA Real Estate, International Who's Who of Real Estate Lawyers, and the Guide to the World's Leading Real Estate Lawyers.

**Personal:** JD, Villanova University School of Law, 1976; MLA, University of Pennsylvania, 2010; BA, Lafayette College, 1971.

### CLARK, Jonathan A
Pepper Hamilton LLP, Philadelphia
215 981 4436
clarkja@pepperlaw.com
*Featured in Labor & Employment (Pennsylvania)*

**Practice Areas:** Partner; Co-Chair, Employee Benefits Practice Group. Experienced in a variety of employee benefits, executive compensation and related securities law matters, including benefits and compensation issues arising during transactions, including plan asset transfers, management investment in leveraged buyouts, ESOPs and other employee ownership vehicles; equity-based compensation arrangements for directors and executives, including stock option, restricted stock and phantom stock programs; design, implementation, operation, communication and termination of qualified retirement plans.

**Personal:** JD 1994 University of Chicago Law School; BA 1991 Johns Hopkins University.

### COHEN, Abbi L
Dechert LLP, Philadelphia
215 994 2352
abbi.cohen@dechert.com
*Featured in Environment (Pennsylvania)*

**Practice Areas:** Ms Cohen focuses her practice on evaluating environmental liabilities concerning corporate, real estate, and financing transactions—including with respect to renewable energy—and providing permitting and regulatory compliance advice. She counsels clients on structuring transactions to minimize environmental liabilities and has assisted in siting and permitting industrial facilities.

**Professional Memberships:** Member, Pennsylvania Bar; member, BNA Environmental Due Diligence Advisory Board; member, Environmental Policy Committee of the Real

Estate Round Table; participated in EPA's negotiated rulemaking on "All Appropriate Inquiry" rule.

**Personal:** Barnard College (BA, 1980, high honors in economics, magna cum laude); University of Pennsylvania Law School (JD, 1983).

### COLLINS, Brendan K
Ballard Spahr LLP, Philadelphia
215 864 8106
collins@ballardspahr.com
*Featured in Environment (Pennsylvania)*

**Practice Areas:** Brendan K. Collins, a partner in the Environmental Group, represents clients in environmental litigation involving permit appeals, enforcement actions, citizen suits, and toxic torts in civil, criminal, and administrative matters at all levels. He has appeared before the US Supreme Court and the Supreme Court of Pennsylvania. He assists clients with regulatory and government affairs.

**Professional Memberships:** American Bar Association Vice Chair, Toxic Torts and Environmental Law Committee Philadelphia Bar Association.

**Career:** Sierra Club v. Wellington Development (USDC WDPa).

**Publications:** Author, Settlement Consideration, ABA Toxic Tort Practitioner's Handbook Contributing author, Environmental Regulation Essentials, John Wiley & Sons.

### COLTON, Neal
Cozen O'Connor, Philadelphia
215 665 2060
ncolton@cozen.com
*Featured in Bankruptcy/Restructuring (Pennsylvania)*

**Practice Areas:** Neal focuses his practice on sophisticated international and domestic insolvency, creditors' rights, bankruptcy, restructuring, reorganization, liquidation, internal investigation, and fraud matters, as well as non judicial restructurings. He represents corporate debtors, creditors, creditors' committees, foreign representatives, landlords, equipment lessors, and investors in chapter 11.

**Professional Memberships:** American Bankruptcy Institute, American Bar Association, Fellow: American Bar Foundation and American College of Bankruptcy, Pennsylvania Bar Association, Turnaround Management Association.

**Career:** Chair Bankruptcy, Insolvency, & Restructuring department (1995-2011).

**Personal:** Temple University Beasley School of Law, JD, 1970 Columbia University, MBA, 1967 University of Pittsburgh, AB, 1965.

### COMERFORD, David L
Akin Gump Strauss Hauer & Feld LLP, Philadelphia
215 965 1324
dcomerford@akingump.com
*Featured in Litigation (Pennsylvania)*

**Practice Areas:** Partner in charge, Philadelphia office. Focuses on complex class actions and commercial litigation involving business torts, contracts, accountants' liability, lender liability, securities, antitrust, RICO, ERISA, insurance, trade

secrets. Lectures on securities litigation, accountants' liability, class actions, trade secrets, litigation avoidance and in-house counsel liability risks. Named one of '50 On The Fast Track' in 2002 by The Legal Intelligencer and Pennsylvania Law Weekly, which noted, "David's reputation as an excellent litigator and advocate for some of the most prestigious clients is well deserved."

**Personal:** BA, University of Virginia (1989); JD, with honors, Rutgers University (1992).

### CONGDON, Charles B
Drinker Biddle & Reath LLP, Philadelphia
215 988 2659
Charles.Congdon@dbr.com
*Featured in Banking & Finance (Pennsylvania)*

**Practice Areas:** Partner in the Corporate and Securities Practice with a wide range of experience in corporate and governmental finance. Charlie's practice experience includes all facets of governmental and quasi-governmental financing, including general obligation and revenue bonds, tax-exempt finance for nonprofit institutions, including higher education and healthcare, healthcare and healthcare-related transactional work, and emerging practice in tribal government and gaming finance.

**Professional Memberships:** Admitted to practice in Pennsylvania.

**Personal:** University of Pennsylvania, BA 1979; Villanova University School of Law, JD 1984 magna cum laude, Villanova Law Review.

### COONEY JR, J Gordon
Morgan, Lewis & Bockius LLP, Philadelphia
215 963 4806
jgcooney@morganlewis.com
*Featured in Litigation (Pennsylvania)*

**Practice Areas:** Managing Partner of firm's Philadelphia office, and co-chair of firm's Class Action Working Group. Practice focuses on commercial and civil litigation; particular emphasis on state and federal court class actions, including consumer, product liability, deceptive trade practice, RICO, antitrust, and securities class actions. Represented John Thompson in the landmark case that eventually exonerated Thompson of involvement in a carjacking and murder, and released him from death sentence and prison after 18 years. Retained as co-counsel by Third Circuit Judicial Council with regard to high-profile allegations of judicial misconduct.

**Professional Memberships:** Fellow of the American College of Trial Lawyers.

### COOPER, Scott
Blank Rome LLP, Philadelphia
215 569 5487
Cooper@BlankRome.com
*Featured in Labor & Employment (Pennsylvania)*

**Practice Areas:** Scott Cooper litigates employment matters throughout the United States. He represents significant employers in both the private and public sectors. His practice emphasizes restrictive covenants and trade secrets litigation; defending race, disability, age, medical, leave and gender discrimination matters; overtime and wage payment issues; public and private labor relations, including contract negotiations and arbitrations;

electronic surveillance; social media, technology and privacy policies; professional sports; and reductions in force. Mr Cooper is the Past President/Chancellor of the Philadelphia Bar Association and President-Elect of the Temple University Alumni Association. He holds local elected office and is a frequent lecturer. www.BlankRome.com/Cooper.

### CORSON, Samantha R
Greenberg Traurig, LLP, Philadelphia
215 988 7842
CorsonS@gtlaw.com
*Featured in Environment (Pennsylvania)*

**Practice Areas:** Environmental; climate change; green building/sustainable development.

**Professional Memberships:** Member, Task Force on Government Submissions for the Real Property Division of the American Bar Association (2010-11, 2011-12, 2012-13 Terms); Chair (2009-10, 2010-11 Terms), Vice-Chair (2008-09 Term), Environmental Committee of the Real Property, Trust and Estate Law Section of the American Bar Association; Master Member, Delaware Valley Environmental American Inn of Court (2005-present).

**Career:** US Green Building Council LEED Accredited Professional (LEED AP).

**Personal:** JD, University of Pennsylvania Law School; MA, Philosophy, University of Pennsylvania; BA, cum laude, Philosophy, Hamilton College.

### COSTELLO, Joseph J
Morgan, Lewis & Bockius LLP, Philadelphia
215 963 5295
jcostello@morganlewis.com
*Featured in Labor & Employment (Pennsylvania)*

**Practice Areas:** Joseph J. Costello is the practice group leader of Morgan Lewis's Labor and Employment Practice. He is responsible for the strategic and day-to-day management of these operations across each of the firm's offices. Within his legal practice, Joe represents employers in a broad range of employment and ERISA litigation matters and administrative agency proceedings, and provides counseling on human resources, benefits and whistleblower/retaliation issues.

**Personal:** Attended Stanford Law School, 1985, JD; Cornell University, 1980, MILR; Pennsylvania State University, 1978, BA.

### CRAWFORD, Joseph C
Pepper Hamilton LLP, Philadelphia
215 981 4409
crawfordjc@pepperlaw.com
*Featured in Litigation (Pennsylvania)*

**Practice Areas:** Partner. Experienced in complex commercial litigation; civil litigation; antitrust and competition; directors' and officers' liability; defamation; First Amendment law; product liability; securities class action. Has tried numerous cases to jury verdicts, including breach of contract and other commercial litigation cases, a securities class action case, defamation cases and product liability cases. Conducted numerous non-jury trials and commercial arbitration cases in many areas.

**Professional Memberships:** Fellow, American College of Trial Lawyers; former Member, Board of Governors, Philadelphia Bar Association.
**Personal:** JD, cum laude, 1979 University of Pennsylvania Law School; BS, cum laude, 1976 St Joseph's College.

### D'ANGELO JR, Alfred J
Buchanan Ingersoll & Rooney PC, Philadelphia
215 665 5304
alfred.dangelo@bipc.com
*Featured in Labor & Employment (Pennsylvania)*
**Career:** Alfred is a Shareholder and member of the Executive Committee of the firm's Labor & Employment Section. Fred has concentrated his practice on the representation of management in labor and employment law since 1974, including representing employers in both traditional labor relations and employment litigation. This experience includes representing employers on union prevention campaigns, collective bargaining negotiations and labor contract administration. He earned his JD from Villanova University School of Law (cum laude, Order of the Coif), is a frequent speaker on labor and employment matters, and is actively involved in many charitable organizations in the community.

### DANOFF, Diane S
Dechert LLP, Philadelphia
215 994 2179
diane.danoff@dechert.com
*Featured in Litigation (Pennsylvania)*
**Practice Areas:** Ms Danoff concentrates her practice in intellectual property litigation. She has extensive experience with trade secret, non-compete, trademark, patent, copyright, unfair advertising, and invasion of privacy matters. She has represented clients in a variety of industries including medical devices, specialty chemicals, and financial services.
**Professional Memberships:** Member of Pennsylvania Bar; admitted to practice before numerous federal courts.
**Personal:** Harvard University (AB, 1981, magna cum laude); University of Chicago Law School (JD, 1984).

### DAVIS, Doreen
Jones Day, New York
212 326 3833
ddavis@jonesday.com
*Featured in Labor & Employment (Pennsylvania)*
**Practice Areas:** Doreen is a Partner in the NY office of Jones Day. She practices nationwide, concentrating in NLRB advice and litigation, union organizational activities, and collective bargaining. Her experience spans many industries, including traditional manufacturing, healthcare, hospitality, gaming, retail, construction, and energy.
**Career:** Prior to joining Jones Day in 2012, Doreen successfully litigated one of the largest cases ever to emanate from the Philadelphia region at the NLRB. She also made new law in a secondary boycott case, establishing that noise alone can constitute coercion.

**Personal:** Attended Temple University School of Law, 1978, JD; Pennsylvania State University, 1974, BA.

### DE SIMONE, Dominic
Ballard Spahr LLP, Philadelphia
215 864 8704
desimone@ballardspahr.com
*Featured in Real Estate (Pennsylvania)*
**Practice Areas:** Dominic J. De Simone is a partner in the Real Estate Department and Practice Leader of the Commercial Real Estate Recovery Group, which oversees the firm's distressed real estate practice and focuses on real estate debt and equity matters, including joint venture and CMBS transactions. He practices general real estate law, focusing on debt and equity transactions and distressed real estate matters on behalf of lenders, special servicers, investors, and borrowers.
**Professional Memberships:** American College of Mortgage Attorneys.
**Career:** Admissions: New Jersey Pennsylvania.
**Personal:** Education: Temple University James E. Beasley School of Law (JD 1995) Drexel University (BS 1988).

### DELUCA, Mark
Pepper Hamilton LLP, Berwyn
610 640 7855
delucam@pepperlaw.com
*Featured in Intellectual Property (Pennsylvania)*
**Practice Areas:** Partner. All areas of intellectual property, including patent procurement, infringement and validity studies, licensing and intellectual property management. Counsels large pharmaceutical companies, biotechnology companies, universities and nonprofit institutions in the areas of patent protection, the development of global patent strategies, technology transfer matters, and intellectual property portfolio management and analysis. Also counsels software and other technology companies in the area of standards licensing.
**Professional Memberships:** Member, American Intellectual Property Association; Member, Philadelphia Property Law Association.
**Personal:** JD 1988 Franklin Pierce Law Center; BS 1982 State University of New York at Stony Brook.

### DENIOUS, David S
Drinker Biddle & Reath LLP, Philadelphia
215 988 2529
David.Denious@dbr.com
*Featured in Corporate/M&A (Pennsylvania)*
**Practice Areas:** Partner in the Corporate and Securities Practice. Dave Denious advises clients on leveraged acquisitions and dispositions and corporate finance transactions. He has represented a wide variety of private equity sponsors on leveraged buyout, "going private," recapitalization, and other control transactions and the debt and equity financing relating to such transactions. He also advises sponsors and issuers in PIPE, growth capital, venture capital, and other equity investments.
**Professional Memberships:** Member, American Bar Association's Private Equity and Venture Capital Committee.

**Personal:** Amherst College, BA, magna cum laude, 1986; University of Virginia School of Law, JD, 1992, Order of the Coif.

### DEPILLIS, Mark S
Ballard Spahr LLP, Philadelphia
215 864 8731
depillis@ballardspahr.com
*Featured in Real Estate (Pennsylvania)*
**Practice Areas:** Mark S. DePillis is a partner in the Real Estate Department and Practice Leader of the Construction Group. His practice focuses on complex commercial development, design and construction contracting and secured lending.
**Professional Memberships:** American Bar Association, Forum on the Construction Industry Philadelphia Bar Association International Council of Shopping Centers General Building Contractors Association LEED Accredited Professional, as certified by the US Green Building Council.
**Career:** Admissions: Massachusetts Pennsylvania.
**Publications:** Co-author, On-line Fifty-State Survey of Mechanics Lien Law, Pennsylvania chapter of Lien Law On-Line.
**Personal:** Education: Boston College Law School (JD 1990) Tufts University (BA 1987).

### DEVINE III, Francis P
Pepper Hamilton LLP, Philadelphia
215 981 4230
devinef@pepperlaw.com
*Featured in Litigation (Pennsylvania)*
**Practice Areas:** Partner; former Co-Chairman, Litigation and Dispute Resolution Department. Experienced in complex business and commercial disputes, products liability, insurance coverage, professional liability and malpractice, directors and officers liability, and intellectual property disputes. Experienced in resolving disputes through negotiation, mediation, arbitration and litigation.
**Professional Memberships:** Former Chancellor, Philadelphia Bar Association; Fellow, International Academy of Trial Lawyers; Fellow, American College of Trial Lawyers; Member and past President, Philadelphia Association of Defense Council; Co-Founder, Member, Executive Committee, and former Chair, Board of Directors, Philadelphia Volunteers for the Indigent Program.
**Personal:** JD 1973 Villanova University School of Law; BS 1970 University of Pennsylvania.

### DODDS, John C
Morgan, Lewis & Bockius LLP, Philadelphia
215 963 4942
jdodds@morganlewis.com
*Featured in Litigation (Pennsylvania)*
**Practice Areas:** Co-leader, Pharmaceutical Litigation Practice. Representation of organizations and individuals in white collar matters, government investigations, internal investigations and litigation involving claims of fraud and abuse. Acted as lead counsel for major pharmaceutical companies and other entities in government investigations, class action litigation, and claims by state attorneys general involving the marketing and pricing of products, promotional activities and FDA regulations.

**Professional Memberships:** Fellow, American College of Trial Lawyers.
**Career:** Former Assistant US Attorney in the Criminal Division of the US Attorney's Office for the Eastern District of Pennsylvania; Former Special Deputy Attorney General for the Commonwealth of Pennsylvania.

### DOERNER, Brian D
Ballard Spahr LLP, Philadelphia
215 864 8615
doerner@ballardspahr.com
*Featured in Corporate/M&A (Pennsylvania)*
**Practice Areas:** Brian D. Doerner is a partner in the Business and Finance Department and Practice Leader of the Life Sciences/Technology Group. He represents public and private companies in mergers/acquisitions, restructurings, and cross-border transactions. He handles securities offerings, including private placements, venture capital transactions, and initial public offerings, and has been involved in strategic alliances, licensing, and co-promotion agreements for life sciences, technology, and other companies.
**Professional Memberships:** Philadelphia Bar Association, Business Law Section Entrepreneurs' Forum, past President and Director.
**Career:** Admissions: Pennsylvania.
**Personal:** University of Pennsylvania Law School (JD 1987) University of Michigan (MBA 1982) University of Delaware (BA 1980).

### DONOHUE JR, John P
Woodcock Washburn LLP, Philadelphia
215 564 8367
donohue@woodcock.com
*Featured in Intellectual Property (Pennsylvania)*
**Practice Areas:** Litigation, counseling involving computers, computer software, digital and analog electronics, telecommunications, robotics, medical imaging, specialty materials, and trademarks.
**Professional Memberships:** Member, Pennsylvania Bar, Federal Circuit Bar Association, ABA's Litigation Section, AIPLA's Special ITC Committee, Federal Litigation, Electronic, and Computer Law Committees, INTA Enforcement Committee; President, Benjamin Franklin American Inn of Court, 2002-03.
**Career:** Joined Woodcock Washburn, 1987.
**Publications:** Recognized in Chambers USA since 2003. Named in Pennsylvania Super Lawyers and Best Lawyers in America.
**Personal:** LLM, Trial Advocacy, Temple University Law School (1997), JD, New England School of Law (1977), BEE, University of Dayton (1974).

### DOUGHERTY, Brian
Morgan, Lewis & Bockius LLP, Philadelphia
215 963 4812
bdougherty@morganlewis.com
*Featured in Labor & Employment (Pennsylvania)*
**Practice Areas:** Brian J. Dougherty is a partner in Morgan Lewis's Employee Benefits and Executive Compensation Practice and is the co-leader of the practice's Plan Sponsor Task Force. His practice involves all aspects of employee benefits and ERISA, including compliance, plan design

and administration, litigation and executive compensation.

**Professional Memberships:** He is a Fellow of the American College of Employee Benefits Counsel and a Senior Editor of BNA's Employee Benefits Law.

**Personal:** Mr Dougherty graduated from Harvard Law School (1980, JD, cum laude) and Bucknell University (1977, BS, summa cum laude). He is admitted to practice in Pennsylvania.

### DUBOW, Steven
Blank Rome LLP, Philadelphia
215 569 5755
Dubow@BlankRome.com
*Featured in Corporate/M&A (Pennsylvania)*
**Practice Areas:** Steven Dubow concentrates his practice in mergers and acquisitions, capital formation, financing agreements, private equity funds and their portfolio companies, venture capital, joint ventures and shareholder disputes. For more information: www.BlankRome.com/Dubow.

### DWORETZKY, Joseph A
Hangley Aronchick Segal Pudlin & Schiller, Philadelphia
215 496 7014
jad@hangley.com
*Featured in Bankruptcy/Restructuring (Pennsylvania)*
**Practice Areas:** Bankruptcy, creditors rights, commercial litigation, governmental.
**Professional Memberships:** Member, Philadelphia School Reform Commission; Board of Directors (2008-present), 3rd Circuit Regent (2002-08), American College of Bankruptcy; adjunct Professor, Bankruptcy, Temple Law School (2005-06); Chair, Lawyers Advisory Committee, Third Circuit Court of Appeals (2008).
**Career:** Shareholder, Hangley Aronchick Segal Pudlin & Schiller, 1997 to present. City solicitor, city of Philadelphia, 1994-96. Managing Partner 1992-93; Partner 1984-93; associate 1978-84, Drinker Biddle & Reath. Law clerk, Honorable Ellsworth Van Graafeiland, US Court of Appeals for the Second Circuit, 1977-78. Villanova Law School, summa cum laude.

### EBBY, David A
Drinker Biddle & Reath LLP, Philadelphia
215 988 2496
David.Ebby@dbr.com
*Featured in Real Estate (Pennsylvania)*
**Practice Areas:** Partner and Vice Chair, Real Estate Practice Group. Practice is national in scope and focuses on commercial real estate. Represents developers and lenders in acquisition, leasing, construction and financing. Represents companies in financing, leasing, management and operation of high-rise office towers, retail shopping centers and industrial/flex and multi-family properties. Handles real estate litigation, including workouts, foreclosures, landlord/tenant matters and disputes involving brokerage commissions, partnerships and agreements of sale.
**Career:** Joined Drinker Biddle in 1989; Admitted to Bars of Pennsylvania and New Jersey.
**Personal:** JD (cum laude), Villanova University School of Law, 1989; BA (cum laude), Amherst College, 1985.

### EBBY, Stuart F
Hangley Aronchick Segal Pudlin & Schiller, Philadelphia
215 496 7017
sfe@hangley.com
*Featured in Real Estate (Pennsylvania)*
**Practice Areas:** Mr Ebby has more than 45 years' experience representing lenders, developers, investors, brokers, and title insurers in selling, buying, developing, mortgaging, leasing and managing commercial and industrial real estate. He frequently serves as an expert witness in cases involving Pennsylvania real estate law and practice.
**Professional Memberships:** Member, American College of Real Estate Lawyers; Adjunct Professor of Law, Temple University; Lecturer-in-Law, University of Pennsylvania.
**Career:** Shareholder, Hangley Aronchick Segal Pudlin & Schiller, 2001 to present. Harvard Law School, LLB, 1961; Harvard College, AB, 1958.

### ELDERKIN, Dianne B
Akin Gump Strauss Hauer & Feld LLP, Philadelphia
215 965 1340
delderkin@akingump.com
*Featured in Intellectual Property (Pennsylvania)*
**Practice Areas:** Litigates patent infringement actions nationwide and counsels clients on patent issues involving a wide range of technologies, especially biologic therapeutics, pharmaceuticals, medical devices, diagnostic methods and devices and consumer products. Has successfully tried cases to the bench and to juries, argued appeals to the Court of Appeals for the Federal Circuit and represented clients in numerous arbitrations.
**Professional Memberships:** Fellow, American College of Trial Lawyers; Chair, American Intellectual Property Law Association's Patent Litigation Committee.
**Personal:** George Washington University Law School, JD with high honors (1978), Bucknell University, BS (1975).

### ELLSWORTH, Laura
Jones Day, Pittsburgh
412 394 7929
leellsworth@jonesday.com
*Featured in Litigation (Pennsylvania)*
**Practice Areas:** Partner-in-Charge, Pittsburgh Office. Handles a wide range of complex litigation matters, including toxic tort, product liability, intellectual property, and commercial matters. Several of her cases have resulted in significant appellate rulings on novel issues such as market share liability and public nuisance. Routinely coordinates and litigates nationwide matters and has appeared in federal and state courts throughout the US. Listed in Best Lawyers in America (commercial litigation), as "leader in the law" by Legal Intelligencer, and as a top female litigator in Pennsylvania by Pennsylvania Law Weekly. Named by Pennsylvania Governor as a "Top 50 Women in Business."

### FALA, Herman C
Cozen O'Connor, Philadelphia
215 665 4643
hfala@cozen.com
*Featured in Real Estate (Pennsylvania)*
**Practice Areas:** Herman has represented banks, pension funds, publicly traded companies, insurance companies, REITs, and real estate developers. He handles local and national transactions, including acquisitions, mergers, financings, joint ventures, leases, project finance transactions, syndications, public and private debt and equity placements, and transactions involving the development and management of hotels, office buildings, and other projects. In addition, he has experience in the management, financing, acquisition, development, and franchising of hotels.
**Professional Memberships:** Pennsylvania Bar Association Philadelphia Bar Association Urban Land Institute American College of Real Estate Lawyers.
**Career:** Co-chair, Real Estate.
**Personal:** Harvard Law School, JD, 1974 University of Notre Dame, BS, 1971.

### FARMER, Shannon D
Ballard Spahr LLP, Philadelphia
215 864 8221
farmers@ballardspahr.com
*Featured in Labor & Employment (Pennsylvania)*
**Practice Areas:** Shannon D Farmer handles traditional labor matters, including labor arbitrations, collective bargaining negotiations, interest arbitrations, and labor relations proceedings. She defends employers in all aspects of employment law, including discrimination claims, as well as wage and hour, civil rights, contract, and tort claims.
**Professional Memberships:** Immediate Past President of, and a current member of the Personnel Committee for, the Board of Directors of The Birth Center.
**Career:** Pennsylvania.
**Publications:** Co-author, "The ADA Amendments Act: A Real Older Workers Protection Act?" The Legal Intelligencer, February 22, 2010.
**Personal:** University of Pennsylvania Law School (JD 1998) Stanford University (BA 1993).

### FEENEY, Carolyn
Dechert LLP, Philadelphia
215 994 2247
carolyn.feeney@dechert.com
*Featured in Antitrust (Pennsylvania)*
**Practice Areas:** Ms Feeney focuses her practice on antitrust and other complex civil litigation, including class actions and multi-district litigation. Her experience includes litigation involving the airline, graphite electrodes, chemical, building products and pharmaceutical industries.
**Professional Memberships:** Member, Pennsylvania and New York Bars; admitted to practice before the US Supreme Court and numerous federal courts; member, American Bar Association's Section of Antitrust Law
**Personal:** Princeton University (AB, 1991, cum laude); Columbia Law School (JD, 1994, Harlan Fiske Stone Scholar, head articles editor, Columbia Human Rights Law Review)

### FEIRSON, Steven B
Dechert LLP, Philadelphia
215 994 2489
steven.feirson@dechert.com
*Featured in Litigation (Pennsylvania)*
**Practice Areas:** Mr Feirson, deputy chair of the firm, focuses his practice on litigating large, complex cases in the securities, financial services and corporate governance areas. He has represented clients in a wide array of industries including energy, oil and gas, and financial services. He has also devoted a significant portion of his career to handling appellate matters.
**Personal:** University of Pennsylvania (BA, 1972); University of Chicago Law School (JD, 1975).

### FIEBACH, H Robert
Cozen O'Connor, Philadelphia
215 665 4166
rfiebach@cozen.com
*Featured in Litigation (Pennsylvania)*
**Practice Areas:** Robert has an active trial practice, and handles appeals in the Pennsylvania Superior and Supreme Courts, the US Courts of Appeals for the Second, Third, Fourth, and Fifth Circuits, and the Federal Court of Appeals. Represents lawyers, law firms and other clients in professional liability, ADR, appellate, class action & multidistrict litigation, commercial litigation, and securities & financial services litigation. Fellow, American College of Trial Lawyers.
**Professional Memberships:** American College of Trial Lawyers; American Bar Association; Pennsylvania Bar Association, Past President; Philadelphia Bar Association.
**Personal:** University of Pennsylvania Law School, L.L.B., 1964; University of Pennsylvania, BS, 1961.

### FINKELSTEIN, Joseph
Blank Rome LLP, Philadelphia
215 569 5382
JFinkelstein@BlankRome.com
*Featured in Real Estate (Pennsylvania)*
**Practice Areas:** Joseph Finkelstein concentrates his practice in commercial real property transactions, including acquisitions, sales, leasing, joint ventures, expansions, redevelopment and repositioning of retail properties and shopping centers and other commercial properties, real estate financing, title insurance and other real property matters. He represents developers, institutional investors, REITs, pension funds, financial institutions, insurance companies, national and regional retailers, property owners, landlords and tenants, homebuilders, brokers and title insurance companies. For more information: www.BlankRome.com/JFinkelstein.

### FLAME, Andrew J
Drinker Biddle & Reath LLP, Wilmington
302 467 4214
andrew.flame@dbr.com
*Featured in Bankruptcy/Restructuring (Pennsylvania)*
**Practice Areas:** Partner in the Corporate Restructuring Practice Group, Andrew has appeared in bankruptcy courts throughout the

country representing secured creditors, lessors, creditors committees and purchasers. Andrew counts NYSE listed lenders among his clients and has represented creditors and purchasers in, among others, the Kmart and Philadelphia Newspapers bankruptcy cases, receivership proceedings and assignments for benefit of creditors. Andrew represents lenders in complex commercial foreclosures in many jurisdictions and in gas and oil industry collection/bankruptcy matters and has managed $30+ million UCC sales.
**Personal:** Temple University Beasley School of Law, JD magna cum laude, Pennsylvania State University, BS with Distinction.

### FLANNERY, Kevin M
Dechert LLP, Philadelphia
215 994 2814
kevin.flannery@dechert.com
*Featured in Intellectual Property (Pennsylvania)*
**Practice Areas:** Mr Flannery litigates complex patent and trade secret cases across a wide spectrum of technology areas including medical devices, pharmaceuticals, electronics, computer software, and consumer products. He has also represented clients under the Hatch Waxman Act and in ANDA matters.
**Professional Memberships:** Member, Pennsylvania Bar; admitted to practice before the US Court of Appeals for the Federal Circuit, the US District Court for the Eastern District of Pennsylvania, and the US Patent and Trademark Office.
**Personal:** Virginia Polytechnic Institute and State University (BS, Aerospace and Ocean Engineering, 1986); Villanova University School of Law (JD, 1991).

### FLICK II, Lawrence
Blank Rome LLP, Philadelphia
215 569 5556
Flick@BlankRome.com
*Featured in Banking & Finance (Pennsylvania)*
**Practice Areas:** Lawrence Flick has built a national reputation as a leading attorney in the area of general business and corporate law. He represents some of the nation's largest financial institutions and private equity funds and serves clients in areas such as commercial lending, asset-based financing, mergers and acquisitions, securitizations and structured finance, leveraged lease transactions and reorganization. He serves on the Board of Governors of the Commercial Finance Association's Education Foundation and was honored by the organization with its 2010 Harry H. Chen Memorial Instructor Award of Excellence for his outstanding contributions to CFA's education programs. More information: www.BlankRome.com/Flick

### FOLEY, Mark J
Cozen O'Connor, Philadelphia
215 665 6904
mfoley@cozen.com
*Featured in Labor & Employment (Pennsylvania)*
**Practice Areas:** Mark represents employers in all aspects of labor and employment law and has experience in a range of matters under local, state, and federal law, including the NLRA, the LMRA,

Title VII, the ADEA, the ADA, the FLSA, whistle-blower laws, restrictive covenants and trade secrets, and executive transition issues.
**Professional Memberships:** Economy League of Greater Philadelphia; The American Red Cross; The National Constitution Center Corporate Council; Pennsylvania and Philadelphia Bar Associations.
**Career:** Chair, Labor and Employment Group
**Personal:** Villanova University School of Law, JD, 1987, Villanova Law Review, Order of the Coif; Pennsylvania State University Park, BA, 1984

### FORMAN, Harvey I
Blank Rome LLP, Philadelphia
215 569 5516
Forman@BlankRome.com
*Featured in Banking & Finance (Pennsylvania)*
**Practice Areas:** Harvey Forman has more than 40 years of experience representing institutional lenders, including banks, commercial finance companies, mortgage companies, and insurance companies. He serves clients in areas such as asset-based financing and commercial lending; secured transactions and creditors' rights; loan syndications and participations; loan restructurings and workouts; intercreditor relationships; lender liability prevention and defense; debtor-in-possession financing; and bankruptcy and reorganizations. For more information: www.BlankRome.com/Forman.

### FORTI, David W
Dechert LLP, Philadelphia
215 994 2647
david.forti@dechert.com
*Featured in Real Estate (Pennsylvania)*
**Practice Areas:** Mr Forti focuses on real estate finance and securitization. He represents lenders, issuers, funds, master servicers, and special servicers in transactions involving loan origination, mezzanine financing, fund formation, CMBS securitization, post-closing modifications, workouts, and foreclosures.
**Professional Memberships:** Member, Pennsylvania and New York Bars; member, CRE Finance Council; member, Mortgage Bankers Association
**Personal:** University of Pittsburgh (BA, 1992, cum laude; MBA,1995); University of Pittsburgh School of Law (JD, 1995, magna cum laude, editor of the University of Pittsburgh Law Review and the Journal of Law and Commerce, Order of the Coif)

### FRANDSEN, Nancy
Woodcock Washburn LLP, Philadelphia
215 564 1223
nfrandsen@woodcock.com
*Featured in Intellectual Property (Pennsylvania)*
**Practice Areas:** Trademark/copyright.
**Professional Memberships:** INTA (Committee: Information Resources); Copyright Society of the USA (Former Chair, Philadelphia Chapter); Philadelphia Bar Association (IP Law Committee); Pennsylvania Bar Institute (IP Advisory Committee); AIPLA.
**Career:** 1983-2001: Seidel, Gonda, Lavorgna & Monaco, PC, Philadelphia, PA; 2001-07: Drinker

Biddle & Reath, LLP, Philadelphia, PA; 2007-Present: Woodcock Washburn LLP, Philadelphia, PA.
**Publications:** Co-author, What The General Practitioner Should Know About Trademarks and Copyrights, 6th Edition, ALI-ABA (1992); What the General Practitioner Should Know About Bad Faith UDRP Proceedings, IP Law Newsletter, 2002.
**Personal:** Ohio University, BA (1975), Temple University, JD (1986).

### FRIDY, Carl H
Ballard Spahr LLP, Philadelphia
215 864 8726
fridy@ballardspahr.com
*Featured in Banking & Finance (Pennsylvania)*
**Practice Areas:** Carl H. Fridy is a partner in the Business and Finance Department and Practice Leader of the Transactional Finance Group. Mr Fridy has extensive experience in secured and unsecured commercial lending, real estate and construction finance, letter-of-credit-backed and other tax-exempt bond financings, and the workout and restructuring of troubled loans.
**Professional Memberships:** American Bar Association Member; Business Law Section, Commercial Financial Services Subcommittee; member, Real Property, Probate and Trust Law Section, Real Property Division American College of Commercial Finance Lawyers, Regent.
**Career:** Admissions: Pennsylvania.
**Personal:** Duke University School of Law (JD 1973) Trinity College (BA 1969).

### FRIEDMAN, Michael H
Pepper Hamilton LLP, Philadelphia
215 981 4563
friedmanm@pepperlaw.com
*Featured in Corporate/M&A (Pennsylvania)*
**Practice Areas:** Partner; past Co-Chairman, Commercial Department; past Chairman, Corporate and Securities Practice Group. Experienced in mergers and acquisitions; corporate finance; corporate securities; joint ventures and real estate investment trusts (REITs). Counsels boards of directors and senior management of companies on governance, disclosure, regulatory compliance (Sarbanes-Oxley), transactional matters and audit committee issues.
**Professional Memberships:** Board Member, The Council for Relationships.
**Personal:** JD 1982 University of Virginia School of Law; MA 1979 University of Chicago; BA, summa cum laude, 1978 Hamilton College.

### FRYMAN, David S
Ballard Spahr LLP, Philadelphia
215 864 8105
fryman@ballardspahr.com
*Featured in Labor & Employment (Pennsylvania)*
**Practice Areas:** David Fryman, Practice Leader of the Labor and Employment Group, represents employers in all types of labor and employment matters, including labor arbitrations and employment litigation, union campaigns and unfair labor practice proceedings, ERISA/benefits litigation, restrictive covenant and trade secret cases, and advice and training on human resource issues.

**Professional Memberships:** People's Emergency Center Board of Directors, Chair Arden Theatre Company Board of Directors, Member.
**Career:** Pennsylvania New Jersey US Court of Appeals for the Fifth Circuit.
**Publications:** Chapter author, "The Complex World of ERISA Preemption," ERISA: A Comprehensive Guide, Third Edition.
**Personal:** George Washington University Law School (JD) Lafayette College (AB).

### FURLETTI, Mark J.
Ballard Spahr LLP, Philadelphia
215 864 8138
furlettim@ballardspahr.com
*Featured in Financial Services Regulation (Nationwide), Banking & Finance (Pennsylvania)*
See under Nationwide for profile.

### GALLAGHER, Thomas M
Pepper Hamilton LLP, Philadelphia
215 981 4068
gallaghert@pepperlaw.com
*Featured in Litigation (Pennsylvania)*
**Practice Areas:** Partner; Chair, White Collar Litigation and Investigations Practice Group. Represents clients in white collar criminal matters, corporate investigations and complex civil litigation. National practice is primarily focused in the health care industry. Represents pharmaceutical companies, medical device companies, hospitals, providers, physicians and other individuals. Also represents businesses and individuals facing investigation by federal and state law enforcement authorities, government regulatory agencies and congressional committees.
**Career:** Former Assistant US Attorney: United States Attorney's Office, Eastern District of Pennsylvania, Criminal Division (Philadelphia, PA).
**Personal:** JD 1989 Villanova University School of Law; BA 1982 University of Pennsylvania.

### GENKIN, Barry H
Blank Rome LLP, Philadelphia
215 569 5514
Genkin@BlankRome.com
*Featured in Corporate/M&A (Pennsylvania)*
**Practice Areas:** Barry Genkin has more than 30 years' experience and serves as a trusted advisor to public-company clients (US and Asian) in public and private offerings of equity and debt securities; mergers, carve-outs, acquisitions, divestitures and joint ventures. His experience includes capital-formation transactions, including US and Hong Kong listings; cross-border M&A; private equity, venture capital and other early-stage transactions; proxy contests and defensive planning; securities law and compliance; take-overs and anti-takeover defenses, including rights plans; going private transactions; complex outsourcing arrangements; corporate governance; and special board committee representations and investigations. For more information: www.BlankRome.com/Genkin.

## GERSON, David
Morgan, Lewis & Bockius LLP, Pittsburgh
412 560 3300
dgerson@morganlewis.com
*Featured in Corporate/M&A (Pennsylvania)*
**Practice Areas:** David A. Gerson is the leader of Morgan Lewis's Philadelphia Business and Finance Practice. Mr Gerson advises private equity funds and public and private company clients in mergers and acquisitions and securities matters, with a particular emphasis on complex acquisitions, dispositions, and securities transactions. He counsels clients on a variety of matters, including mergers and acquisitions, mezzanine finance, securities offerings and compliance, and general corporate law. Mr Gerson represents private equity sponsors and their portfolio companies in domestic and international mergers and acquisitions and in ongoing corporate finance matters.
**Personal:** Harvard Law School, JD; University of Pennsylvania, BA.

## GIFFORD, David B
Ballard Spahr LLP, Philadelphia
215 864 8703
gifford@ballardspahr.com
*Featured in Real Estate (Pennsylvania)*
**Practice Areas:** David B. Gifford is a partner in the Real Estate Department. His practice is concentrated in real estate and related corporate and general business matters, including extensive experience with commercial, industrial, and residential planning, acquisition, development, construction, leasing, and operations; franchise operations and agreements; partnership and corporate organization and operation; real estate syndication; dispute resolution; construction and permanent loan financing; troubled project work-outs; bankruptcy planning; and zoning and subdivision.
**Professional Memberships:** American Bar Association Pennsylvania Bar Association Philadelphia Bar Association.
**Career:** Admissions: Maryland Pennsylvania.
**Personal:** Education: William & Mary Law School (JD 1979) Temple University (BA 1975).

## GINENSKY, Amy B
Pepper Hamilton LLP, Philadelphia
215 981 4315
ginenskya@pepperlaw.com
*Featured in Litigation (Pennsylvania)*
**Practice Areas:** Partner; Chair, Commercial Litigation Practice Group; leader, Media and Communications Practice. Handles class action and commercial litigation matters; media and communications practice focuses on First Amendment, defamation and other media-related areas. Represents newspapers and radio and television broadcasters. Defends the rights of reporters and editors in libel and privacy cases. Handled hundreds of First Amendment matters, including jury trials representing the media.
**Professional Memberships:** Fellow, American College of Trial Lawyers; Past President, Board of Trustees, Philadelphia Bar Foundation.
**Personal:** JD 1977 University of Virginia School of Law; AB, magna cum laude, 1974 Mount Holyoke College. Phi Beta Kappa.

## GIOTTO, Thomas S
Buchanan Ingersoll & Rooney PC, Pittsburgh
412 392 2068
thomas.giotto@bipc.com
*Featured in Labor & Employment (Pennsylvania)*
**Career:** Thomas is a Shareholder in the firm's Labor & Employment Section. He concentrates his practice on representing management in many aspects of labor, employment and employment-related litigation, and he counsels clients in a wide range of industries and business sectors. His traditional labor practice includes representing employers during union-organizing campaigns, collective bargaining and grievance arbitrations. He has represented employers in litigation involving discrimination and against claims alleging violations of the Fair Labor Standards Act, Family and Medical Leave Act, restrictive covenants, wrongful discharge and related common law claims. He earned his JD from Duquesne University School of Law.

## GITLIN, David
Greenberg Traurig, LLP, Philadelphia
215 988 7850
GitlinD@gtlaw.com
*Featured in Investment Funds (Nationwide),*
*Corporate/M&A (Pennsylvania)*
See under Nationwide for profile.

## GODSHALL, Craig L
Dechert LLP, Philadelphia
215 994 2491
craig.godshall@dechert.com
*Featured in Corporate/M&A (Pennsylvania)*
**Practice Areas:** Mr Godshall, a partner in the corporate and securities, private equity, and mergers and acquisitions groups, handles public and private transactions across a wide range of industries, including healthcare, industrial and utilities. He structures transactions on behalf of leading private equity fund sponsors with a focus on accomplishing successful exits. He is also involved in building Dechert's Asian corporate and securities practice.
**Professional Memberships:** Member, Pennsylvania Bar; Registered Foreign Lawyer, Hong Kong.
**Personal:** Columbia College (BA, 1980); University of Michigan (JD, 1983, Order of the Coif, member, University of Michigan Law Review; MA, economics, 1985).

## GOLDBERGER, M Norman
Ballard Spahr LLP, Philadelphia
215 864 8850
goldbergerm@ballardspahr.com
*Featured in Litigation (Pennsylvania)*
**Practice Areas:** Mr Goldberger concentrates his practice on complex commercial matters, including securities litigation, consumer fraud class actions, restrictive covenants, derivative actions, internal investigations, False Claims Act litigation, RICO litigation, and issues relating to the availability of insurance coverage for commercial litigation matters. He represents Fortune 500 public clients across industries, including financial, investment/securities, banking, accounting, and real estate. He also represents clients in NASD and NYSE arbitration proceedings on securities matters.
**Professional Memberships:** American Bar Association Pennsylvania Bar Association Philadelphia Bar Association.
**Career:** Admissions: Pennsylvania.
**Personal:** Education: University of Pennsylvania Law School (JD 1978) University of Pennsylvania (BA 1975).

## GOODCHILD, John
Morgan, Lewis & Bockius LLP, Philadelphia
215 963 5020
jgoodchild@morganlewis.com
*Featured in Bankruptcy/Restructuring (Pennsylvania)*
**Practice Areas:** Partner in the Business and Corporate Litigation Practice. Practice focuses on bankruptcy and insolvency litigation. Has represented defendants in actions brought by receivers, liquidators, and bankruptcy trustees. Has represented trustees, debtors, official committees, and creditors in US and international bankruptcy and insolvency cases. Practice also includes disputes relating to real estate and real estate valuation.

## GOODMAN, Jerald M
Drinker Biddle & Reath LLP, Philadelphia
215 988 2563
Jerald.Goodman@dbr.com
*Featured in Real Estate (Pennsylvania)*
**Practice Areas:** Partner, Real Estate Practice Group. Practice focuses on complex real estate matters, including acquisitions, dispositions, office, retail and ground leases, development, land use and zoning approvals, construction and design agreements, joint ventures and real estate secured finance. Represents universities, health systems, REITs, developers, lending institutions, landlords and tenants.
**Professional Memberships:** Admitted in Pennsylvania (1984) and Florida (1986). Member, American, Pennsylvania, Florida and Philadelphia Bar Associations.
**Career:** Joined Drinker Biddle in 2003.
**Personal:** JD, cum laude, University of Miami School of Law, 1984; BA, cum laude, Temple University, 1981.

## GORANIN, Aleksander J.
Woodcock Washburn LLP, Philadelphia
215 564 8915
agoranin@woodcock.com
*Featured in Intellectual Property (Pennsylvania)*
**Practice Areas:** Patent litigation, copyright litigation, and licensing.
**Professional Memberships:** Fellow, Temple Academy of Advocacy; Member, American Intellectual Property Law Association, Model Patent Jury Instruction Subcommittee; Member, Licensing Executives Society
**Career:** Alex has litigated numerous patent cases in both district court and before the International Trade Commission. Alex also has considerable experience at the appellate level. He has successfully represented clients before the US Courts of Appeal for the Third Circuit and the Federal Circuit.
**Personal:** University of Virginia School of Law, JD, 2000; University of Maryland, BA summa cum laude in Economics and Government & Politics, 1997.

## GORDON, George G
Dechert LLP, Philadelphia
215 994 2382
george.gordon@dechert.com
*Featured in Antitrust (Pennsylvania)*
**Practice Areas:** Mr Gordon is co-chair of both the antitrust/competition and life sciences practices. He focuses on antitrust litigation, counseling and government investigations. He handles cases involving monopolization, price discrimination, group boycotts, and predatory pricing. He also represents clients in non-public government investigations.
**Professional Memberships:** Member, Pennsylvania and New Jersey Bars; member, ABA Sections of Antitrust and Litigation.
**Publications:** Testified in connection with the FTC/DOJ intellectual property/antitrust hearings at the request of the FTC.
**Personal:** Brandeis University (BA, 1988, cum laude); University of Pennsylvania Law School (JD, 1991); London School of Economics and Political Science (1987, High Commendation).

## GRAZIANO, Michael C
Blank Rome LLP, Philadelphia
215 569 5387
Graziano@BlankRome.com
*Featured in Banking & Finance (Pennsylvania)*
**Practice Areas:** Michael Graziano concentrates his practice in financial services, representing banks, commercial finance companies, second lien lenders and other institutional lenders in areas such as commercial lending, asset-based financing, second lien transactions, acquisition financing, debtor-in-possession financing, and mergers and acquisitions. For more information: www.BlankRome.com/Graziano.

## GRIFFITH, James
Fox Rothschild LLP, Philadelphia
215 965 1324
jgriffith@foxrothschild.com
*Featured in Litigation (Pennsylvania)*
**Practice Areas:** All aspects of litigation, including antitrust, insurance coverage, intellectual property, class actions, banking, lender liability cases, commercial litigation, professional liability, environmental matters and product liability.
**Professional Memberships:** Pennsylvania, New Jersey and New York Bar Associations; Pennsylvania Trial Lawyers Association; Philadelphia Bar Association; Philadelphia Trial Lawyers Association.
**Career:** Appointed Judge Pro Tempore by Pennsylvania Supreme Court.
**Publications:** Published articles in legal and medical periodicals and lectured at law schools, medical schools, hospitals and national meetings for lawyers and industry groups.
**Personal:** Graduate of Villanova University School of Law (1965) and St. Francis College (1962).

## GUARCINI, Gerald J
Ballard Spahr LLP, Philadelphia
215 864 8625
guarcini@ballardspahr.com
*Featured in Corporate/M&A (Pennsylvania)*
**Practice Areas:** Gerald J. Guarcini is Practice Leader of the Mergers and Acquisitions/Private Equity Group. He specializes in securities and corporate law, including business acquisitions and dispositions, private equity, and venture capital transactions. His securities work focuses on public and private offerings of debt and equity securities, including IPOs, tender offers, and private investments in public equity (PIPEs), as well as securities law compliance issues.
**Professional Memberships:** Philadelphia Bar Association, Business Law Section.
**Career:** Admissions: Pennsylvania.
**Personal:** Education: Villanova University School of Law (JD 1987, cum laude) Member, Villanova Law Review Wharton School of University of Pennsylvania (BS 1982).

## GUERNSEY, John (Jack)
Conrad O'Brien, Philadelphia
215 864 8066
jguernsey@conradobrien.com
*Featured in Litigation (Pennsylvania)*
**Practice Areas:** He tries and has tried numerous injunctive based and jury trials involving complex commercial disputes regarding restrictive covenants, trade secrets, fiduciary duty, contract disputes, patent infringement, construction defects and ERISA benefits.
**Professional Memberships:** Fellow, American College of Trial Lawyers.
**Career:** Captain, US Army 1969-1974; Colonel, Massachusetts/Delaware National Guards, 1974-99 (part-time).
**Personal:** BS, United States Military Academy - with distinction (1969) JD, Harvard Law School (1977) Admitted to practice in federal and state Courts in Pennsylvania and New Jersey and the Federal Circuit Court of Appeals.

## GUNDERSEN, Glenn A
Dechert LLP, Philadelphia
215 994 2183
glenn.gundersen@dechert.com
*Featured in Intellectual Property (Pennsylvania)*
**Practice Areas:** Mr Gundersen has significant experience in trademark and copyright law and intellectual property transactions. He advises clients on prosecution, fair use, licensing, IP acquisitions, opposition and cancellation proceedings, infringement disputes, advertising, and right of publicity law.
**Professional Memberships:** Member, Pennsylvania Bar; member, International Trademark Association; founder, Copyright Society of the USA's Philadelphia chapter
**Publications:** Author, Trademark Searching (1st & 2d. Ed.); co-author, Intellectual Property Assets in Mergers & Acquisitions.
**Personal:** The College of William and Mary (BA, 1976); University of Virginia School of Law (JD, 1980).

## GUSSACK, Nina M
Pepper Hamilton LLP, Philadelphia
215 981 4950
gussackn@pepperlaw.com
*Featured in Products Liability (Nationwide), Litigation (Pennsylvania)*
See under Nationwide for profile.

## HAIMM, Neil K
Drinker Biddle & Reath LLP, Philadelphia
610 993 2219
Neil.Haimm@dbr.com
*Featured in Corporate/M&A (Pennsylvania)*
**Practice Areas:** Partner in the corporate and securities practice with more than 25 years' experience. Neil's practice focuses primarily on acquisitions and divestitures, joint ventures and other strategic transactions, and venture capital and private equity investments, with particular emphasis on the life sciences and technology industries.
**Professional Memberships:** Admitted to practice in Pennsylvania, New Jersey and New York. Member of the Board of Directors of the Association for Corporate Growth in the Philadelphia region.
**Personal:** University of Pennsylvania, BA, 1977 magna cum laude; New York University School of Law, JD, 1980; New York University School of Law, LLM, Taxation 1985.

## HALE-EAGLAND, Jennifer
Blank Rome LLP, Philadelphia
215 569 5321
HaleEagland@BlankRome.com
*Featured in Labor & Employment (Pennsylvania)*
**Practice Areas:** Jennifer Hale Eagland's practice focuses on representing employers in all aspects of employment law, including matters involving the Americans with Disabilities Act, Title VII, the Age Discrimination in Employment Act, the Family and Medical Leave Act, and the Fair Labor Standards Act. Ms Eagland's practice also focuses on strategic counseling and training on a variety of employment and labor-related issues, including wage and hour compliance, discrimination and harassment matters, reductions in force, plant closings, protecting corporate assets, drafting and negotiating employment and severance agreements, administration of personnel policies, social media and litigation avoidance strategies. More information: www.BlankRome.com/HaleEagland.

## HALL, Christopher R
Saul Ewing LLP, Philadelphia
215 972 7180
CHall@saul.com
*Featured in Litigation (Pennsylvania)*
**Practice Areas:** Chair, Government Investigations Practice: compliance, investigations, and defense of criminal allegations and civil enforcement actions.
**Professional Memberships:** Co-Chair, ABA Criminal Justice Section Qui Tam Subcommittee; Vice-President, Federal Bar Association - Philadelphia, Criminal Law Committee; Vice Chair, White Collar Crime Committee, NACDL.
**Career:** Former federal prosecutor, US Attorney's Office, Eastern District of Pennsylvania.

**Publications:** "The Most Effective Opening Statement Ever Given?" The Champion, November 2012, NACDL False Claims Act, Pharmaceutical and Medical Device Compliance Manual, 2012, AHLA, FDLI, Seton Hall Law Center.
**Personal:** JD, Georgetown University Law Center, 1985 (Editor, American Criminal Law Review); BA, Amherst College, 1981, cum laude.

## HALLER, Anthony
Blank Rome LLP, Philadelphia
215 569 5690
Haller@BlankRome.com
*Featured in Labor & Employment (Pennsylvania)*
**Practice Areas:** Anthony Haller chairs Blank Rome's Employment, Benefits and Labor group. His practice covers all aspects of labor and employment law, including preventative counseling, complex litigation, trial and appellate work. He represents clients in areas including counseling on strategic labor relations and employment issues; handling multiple plaintiff, class, and representative actions involving civil rights and employment claims; counseling and litigating labor relations issues; and designing and enforcing policies to protect confidentiality and non-solicitation and post-employment competition, and litigating claims for breach of non-compete agreements, misappropriation of trade secrets, breach of fiduciary duty, and related torts. For more information: www.BlankRome.com/Haller

## HAMERMESH, Matthew A
Hangley Aronchick Segal Pudlin & Schiller, Philadelphia
215 496 7054
mhamermesh@hangley.com
*Featured in Bankruptcy/Restructuring (Pennsylvania)*
**Practice Areas:** Bankruptcy litigation, including insolvency and debtor-creditor matters and general commercial litigation.
**Professional Memberships:** Philadelphia Bar Association, Appellate Courts Committee; Eastern District of Pennsylvania Bankruptcy Conference, 2001 – Present; American Bar Association, Litigation and Business Law Sections; American Bankruptcy Institute, 2001 – Present.
**Career:** The University of Michigan Law School, Ann Arbor, Michigan, 1998, JD, magna cum laude, Order of the Coif; Yale University, New Haven, Connecticut, 1994, BS; Law clerk, the Honorable Edward R. Becker, United States Court of Appeals for the Third Circuit, 1998 – 1999.

## HANGLEY, William T
Hangley Aronchick Segal Pudlin & Schiller, Philadelphia
215 496 7001
whangley@hangley.com
*Featured in Litigation (Pennsylvania)*
**Practice Areas:** General business litigation; professional responsibility, legal malpractice and counseling law firms; intellectual property; First Amendment; securities; antitrust.
**Professional Memberships:** Member, United States Judicial Conference Advisory Committee on Evidence Rules, 2006-present; Member, Third Circuit Judicial Conference Committee, 2006-

present; Chair, Lawyers Advisory Committee, Third Circuit Judicial Council, 2011-present; Fellow, American College of Trial Lawyers, 1987-present; Chair, Pennsylvania IOLTA Board; Fellow, American Bar Foundation; Member, American Law Institute; Founding Member and Master of the Bench, University of Pennsylvania Inn of Court; Judge Pro Tem, Philadelphia Court of Common Pleas, 1990-2000; Member, ABA Section of Litigation; Member, Philadelphia Bar Association; Member, Community Legal Services Leadership Council, 2004-present; Board of Advisors, Public Interest Law Center of Philadelphia, Board of Advisors, 1995-2009.
**Career:** Founder, Chair, Hangley Aronchick Segal Pudlin & Schiller, 1994 to present. Founder (Chair 1983-94) Hangley Connolly Epstein Chicco Foxman & Ewing and predecessor firms, 1969-94. Associate, Schnader, Harrison, Segal & Lewis, 1966-69. University of Pennsylvania Law School, JD, cum laude, University of Pennsylvania Law Review, 1966; State University of New York, Fredonia, BS, 1963.

## HANLON, Michael J
Blank Rome LLP, Philadelphia
215 569 5652
Hanlon@BlankRome.com
*Featured in Labor & Employment (Pennsylvania)*
**Practice Areas:** Michael Hanlon has a diverse, high-level practice counseling large publicly traded corporations, government entities, and other employers in all areas of employment law as well as strategic legal issues. He provides counsel to clients on issues arising from transactions including mergers and acquisitions and governmental takeovers. His practice includes all areas of traditional labor and employment law, executive compensation, employment discrimination and public education. He counsels clients on compliance with federal and state employment laws; planning for and execution of transactions; and advising Boards of Directors and negotiating executive employment agreements; and various litigation matters. More information: www.BlankRome.com/Hanlon.

## HARKINS JR, John G
Harkins Cunningham LLP, Philadelphia
215 851 6701
jharkins@harkinscunningham.com
*Featured in Litigation (Pennsylvania)*
**Practice Areas:** Throughout his career, John Harkins has been engaged in complex litigation involving issues of corporate, securities and antitrust law, contracts, intellectual property and ERISA, frequently arguing such cases in appellate courts. Mr Harkins has also served as an advisor on a wide variety of corporate issues and transactions. He has advised directors on their fiduciary and other duties, corporate clients on disclosure issues, special committees in the investigation of alleged corporate wrongdoing, and corporations on the defenses available to them under Pennsylvania law against hostile takeover bids. He has also appeared on behalf of defendants in many derivative actions.

**Professional Memberships:** Fellow, American College of Trial Lawyers; Member, American Law Institute.
**Career:** Partner, Harkins Cunningham LLP; Member of the Bars of the Commonwealth of Pennsylvania; the Supreme Court of the United States; the United States Courts of Appeals for the Second, Third, Fourth, Fifth, Seventh, Ninth, Tenth and Eleventh Circuits; and the United States District Court for the Eastern District of Pennsylvania and other districts.
**Personal:** University of Pennsylvania, LLB, summa cum laude, 1958; University of Pennsylvania, BA, cum laude, 1953.

### HARRINGTON, Michael S
Fox Rothschild LLP, Exton
610 458 4957
mharrington@foxrothschild.com
*Featured in Corporate/M&A (Pennsylvania)*
**Practice Areas:** Represents early/growth stage, technology, life science, clean-tech and traditional companies in corporate finance, private equity, mergers, acquisitions, venture capital, securities, technology law, leveraging intellectual property, taxation and general corporate matters.
**Professional Memberships:** Board of Directors, Greater Philadelphia Alliance for Capital and Technologies and Ideas and Innovations Network.
**Career:** Chair of Corporate Department; Member of Executive Committee; Founding Member of firm's Technology and Venture Finance Practice.
**Personal:** Selected as '40 Under 40' and 'Leader in Law' by The Philadelphia Business Journal; Recipient, '2010 Life Sciences Award' in category of Best Consultant (Later Stage) by The Philadelphia Business Journal.

### HARVEY, Calvin R.
Buchanan Ingersoll & Rooney PC, Pittsburgh
412 562 8902
calvin.harvey@bipc.com
*Featured in Banking & Finance (Pennsylvania)*
**Career:** Calvin is a Senior Counsel in the firm's Financial Services Section. He is the former Chair of the firm's Financial Institutions/Real Estate/Bankruptcy & Creditors' Rights Section and served as managing partner of the Pittsburgh office for 10 years. He works primarily in the area of financial transactions, including syndicated loan transactions, complex project and real estate finance and development, affordable housing and tax-exempt financing. His clients are major, super-regional and regional banking institutions; real estate development companies; universities; non-profit organizations; and many western Pennsylvania entrepreneurs and investors. He earned his JD from the George Washington University Law School.

### HEIM, Robert C
Dechert LLP, Philadelphia
215 994 2570
robert.heim@dechert.com
*Featured in Products Liability (Nationwide), Litigation (Pennsylvania)*

**Practice Areas:** Mr Heim, a nationally known trial lawyer, handles antitrust, securities, product liability, and other complex commercial litigation and is regarded for his skill in alternative dispute resolution.
**Professional Memberships:** Member, Pennsylvania Bar; admitted to practice before numerous federal courts; chair, Advisory Committee to the Third Circuit Court of Appeals; chair, Pennsylvania's Continuing Legal Education Board; Fellow, American College of Trial Lawyers and the International Academy of Trial Lawyers.
**Personal:** University of Pennsylvania (BS, 1964); The College of William and Mary (MBA, 1968); University of Pennsylvania Law School (JD, 1972).

### HEIST, Dale M
Woodcock Washburn LLP, Philadelphia
215 564 8939
heist@woodcock.com
*Featured in Intellectual Property (Pennsylvania)*
**Practice Areas:** Litigated more than 100 patent/IP cases in diverse fields, including robotics, polymers, medical products, and computer software.
**Professional Memberships:** Member, Pennsylvania Bar; Fellow, American College of Trial Lawyers; Member, American Bar Association, AIPLA, PIPLA, and NYIPLA.
**Career:** Joined Woodcock Washburn, 1977.
**Publications:** Recognized in Chambers USA since 2003; Named by BTI for Client Service All Star Team; Recognized as finalist for Lawdragon's 500 Leading Lawyers; Pennsylvania Super Lawyers and The Best Lawyers in America; Martindale-Hubbell, A/V (preeminent) Peer Review Rating; IAM Strategy 250; IAM Patent Litigation 250.
**Personal:** BS, Electrical Engineering (1970) and JD (1976) from Villanova University.

### HELLER, Michael
Cozen O'Connor, Philadelphia
215 665 4141
mheller@cozen.com
*Featured in Corporate/M&A (Pennsylvania)*
**Practice Areas:** Michael heads the firm's emerging business & venture capital practice. He represents clients in the formation/business planning stage; forming, structuring and negotiating joint ventures and strategic alliances; technology licensing, transfer and development; and negotiating and structuring all types of angel, venture, and other capital-raising transactions, mergers and acquisitions and initial public offerings. Michael also represents venture capital funds and angel investor groups in all forms of capital-raising transactions.
**Professional Memberships:** Pennsylvania and Philadelphia Bar Associations, numerous for profit and nonprofit boards
**Career:** Chief Executive Officer.
**Personal:** Villanova University School of Law, JD, 1989, Pennsylvania State University, BS, 1986.

### HERYFORD, Craig S
Buchanan Ingersoll & Rooney PC, Pittsburgh
412 392 2157
craig.heryford@bipc.com
*Featured in Banking & Finance (Pennsylvania)*

**Career:** Craig is a Shareholder and member of the Executive Committee of the firm's Corporate Section and Co-chair of the firm's Merger and Acquisition and Private Equity Practice Groups. His practice is concentrated in the area of mergers and acquisitions and in representing mature and emerging businesses in venture capital matters and corporate finance matters. He has experience in a wide variety of commercial transactions, including merger and acquisition transactions, private equity transactions, and numerous corporate finance and venture capital funding transactions involving equity and debt. He earned his JD (cum laude) from the Duquesne University School of Law.

### HICKOK, Robert L
Pepper Hamilton LLP, Philadelphia
215 981 4583
hickokr@pepperlaw.com
*Featured in Litigation (Pennsylvania)*
**Practice Areas:** Partner; Co-Chair, Litigation and Dispute Resolution Department. Experienced in antitrust, securities, white-collar and criminal, insurance sales practices litigation; corporate investigations; class action defense; application of economic analysis in antitrust (product/market definition; pricing) federal securities law (efficient capital market theory) and commercial contract cases; application of technology to information/litigation management.
**Professional Memberships:** Fellow, American College of Trial Lawyers; Member and past President, Executive Committee, Harvard Law School Association of Philadelphia.
**Career:** Former Assistant US Attorney, Eastern District of Pennsylvania.
**Personal:** JD, magna cum laude, 1978 Harvard Law School; AM, magna cum laude, 1978 Harvard University; BA 1974 Lehigh University.

### HINERMAN, Philip L
Fox Rothschild LLP, Philadelphia
215 299 2066
phinerman@foxrothschild.com
*Featured in Environment (Pennsylvania)*
**Practice Areas:** Litigation, real estate and corporate acquisition related to environmental issues.
**Professional Memberships:** Environmental and Energy Law Section of the Pennsylvania Bar Association; Executive Committee Member, Pennsylvania Environmental Council; Member, Rules Committee of the Pennsylvania Environmental Hearing Board; Founding Board Member, Delaware Valley Green Building Council.
**Career:** Martindale-Hubbell 'AV' rated; Included in list of 'Super Lawyers' Philadelphia Magazine/Law & Politics Magazine, 2006, 2009, 2010.
**Personal:** Diploma, Wines and Spirits , WSET ; 1979 graduate, Washington & Lee University School of Law; 1975 graduate, Marshall University; LEED accredited professional; Certified Specialist, Society of Wine Educators.

### HOCKEIMER JR, Henry E
Ballard Spahr LLP, Philadelphia
215 864 8204
hockeimerh@ballardspahr.com
*Featured in Litigation (Pennsylvania)*
**Practice Areas:** Mr Hockeimer, Practice Leader of the White Collar/Investigations Group, defends individuals and corporations involved in federal criminal investigations, including allegations of public corruption, securities fraud, FCPA violations, computer fraud, financial crimes, antitrust price-fixing matters, health care fraud, and tax fraud. He directs internal investigations and responds to DOJ/SEC inquiries. Mr Hockeimer has extensive jury trial experience in private practice and as a federal prosecutor.
**Professional Memberships:** American Bar Association, American Red Cross.
**Career:** Admissions: District of Columbia, Pennsylvania, Virginia.
**Personal:** Education Catholic University of America Columbus School of Law (JD 1989) Miami University (BA 1985).

### IX, John
Dechert LLP, Philadelphia
215 994 2995
john.ix@dechert.com
*Featured in Environment (Pennsylvania)*
**Practice Areas:** Mr Ix counsels clients on environmental regulatory compliance issues, litigates environmental disputes, negotiates environmental terms in business transactions, and develops cost-effective solutions to site remediation and permitting.
**Professional Memberships:** Member, New Jersey, New York and Pennsylvania Bars
**Career:** Previously, he worked as a geologist at an environmental consulting firm.
**Personal:** Colgate University (BA, 1988); Indiana University School of Public and Environmental Affairs (MS, Environmental Science, 1994); Indiana University Mauer School of Law (JD, 1994, magna cum laude, articles editor of the Indiana Law Journal, Order of the Coif).

### JABLON, Clark
Panitch Schwarze Belisario & Nadel LLP, Philadelphia
215 965 1293
cjablon@panitchlaw.com
*Featured in Intellectual Property (Pennsylvania)*
**Practice Areas:** Mr Jablon is a registered patent attorney and focuses his practice on all phases of patent prosecution in the fields of electronics, computer hardware and software, internet technologies and computer-implemented business methods.
**Career:** Mr Jablon has more than 29 years of experience in patent law, including eight years in the public sector as a Patent Examiner with the United States Patent and Trademark Office.
**Personal:** Mr Jablon received his BE with honors in electrical engineering from the State University of New York at Stony Brook and his JD from the Temple University James E. Beasley School of Law.

## JACOBS, Hara K
Ballard Spahr LLP, Philadelphia
215 864 8209
jacobsh@ballardspahr.com
*Featured in Intellectual Property (Pennsylvania)*
**Practice Areas:** Ms Jacobs is a partner in the Litigation and Intellectual Property Departments. She has successfully litigated a wide variety of IP matters for media personalities, a sports figure, and for companies in the e-commerce, technology, medical, retail, and financial services fields.
**Professional Memberships:** International Trademark Association.
**Career:** Admissions: New Jersey New York Pennsylvania.
**Publications:** Co-author, "IP Twitter-Style: Understanding Practical And Legal Risks in Promoting A Brand Through Social Media," The Pennsylvania Bar Association Quarterly, Volume LXXXI, No. 2, April 2010.
**Personal:** Education: Duke University School of Law, JD University of Michigan, BA.

## JARIN, Kenneth M
Ballard Spahr LLP, Philadelphia
215 864 8135
jarink@ballardspahr.com
*Featured in Labor & Employment (Pennsylvania)*
**Practice Areas:** Kenneth Jarin represents both public and private employers in matters relating to labor relations, contract negotiations, interest arbitration, and employment litigation. He has participated in administrative proceedings before the NLRB and various state agencies. He has served as chief labor negotiator/arbitrator for various cities, states, and municipalities. He also provides legal and strategic guidance to clients who work with government entities at legislative, regulatory, and policy levels.
**Career:** Pennsylvania.
**Personal:** Temple University James E. Beasley School of Law (JD 1975) Duke University (BA 1972).

## JOHNS, Daniel V.
Ballard Spahr LLP, Philadelphia
215 864 8107
johns@ballardspahr.com
*Featured in Labor & Employment (Pennsylvania)*
**Practice Areas:** Daniel V. Johns represents employers and management in labor and employment issues including discrimination, harassment, and other civil rights litigation; interest and grievance arbitrations; collective bargaining; and unfair labor practice litigation. Mr Johns is Practice Leader of the Higher Education Group.
**Career:** Admissions: Pennsylvania US District Court for the District of Colorado US District Courts for the Eastern and Middle Districts of Pennsylvania US Court of Appeals for the Third and Fourth Circuits US Supreme Court.
**Personal:** Education: University of Virginia School of Law, JD University of Notre Dame, BA.

## JONES, David F
Dechert LLP, Philadelphia
215 994 2822
david.jones@dechert.com
*Featured in Labor & Employment (Pennsylvania)*

**Practice Areas:** Mr Jones, co-chair of the employee benefits and executive compensation group, represents both public and private corporations, private equity investors, and hedge funds with respect to qualified and nonqualified retirement plans, executive compensation, and employee welfare benefit matters. He also assists clients with their employee benefit programs following significant acquisitions.
**Professional Memberships:** Member, Pennsylvania Bar.
**Personal:** Temple University (BBA, 1979 cum laude); Temple University Beasley School of Law (JD, 1982, cum laude, business editor of Temple Law Review); New York University School of Law (LLM in Taxation, 1984).

## JONES, Richard D
Dechert LLP, New York
212 698 3844
richard.jones@dechert.com
*Featured in Real Estate (New York), Real Estate (Pennsylvania)*
See under New York for profile.

## JUELKE, Robert C
Drinker Biddle & Reath LLP, Philadelphia
215 988 2759
Robert.Juelke@dbr.com
*Featured in Corporate/M&A (Pennsylvania)*
**Practice Areas:** Partner and Chair of the Corporate and Securities Practice. Bob focuses his practice on acquisitions and divestitures, securities offerings and the general representation of public reporting companies and private growth companies. Bob has significant experience in the financial services industry, having handled transactions involving insurance companies, investment advisors and commercial banks. He has also represented registered investment companies.
**Professional Memberships:** Admitted to practice in Pennsylvania and New Jersey.
**Personal:** University of Virginia, BS, 1990 with distinction; William & Mary School of Law, JD, 1993, William and Mary Law Review.

## KAPLAN, David M
Pepper Hamilton LLP, Philadelphia
215 981 4620
kapland@pepperlaw.com
*Featured in Labor & Employment (Pennsylvania)*
**Practice Areas:** Partner; Co-Chair, Employee Benefits Practice Group. Experience in all areas of employee benefits law and executive compensation; emphasis on design, negotiation and documentation of stock-based compensation arrangements, deferred compensation arrangements and senior executive employment, change in control and separation agreements; public company executive compensation disclosures; required and best practices regarding the grant of stock-based compensation; design and operation of ERISA plans; benefits and compensation aspects of corporate transactions. Represents corporations, the compensation committees of their boards of directors and financial investors.
**Personal:** JD 1994 George Washington University Law School; BS 1991 University of Pennsylvania, The Wharton School.

## KAPLINSKY, Alan S
Ballard Spahr LLP, Philadelphia
215 864 8544
kaplinsky@ballardspahr.com
*Featured in Financial Services Regulation (Nationwide), Banking & Finance (Pennsylvania)*
See under Nationwide for profile.

## KASSNER, Andrew C
Drinker Biddle & Reath LLP, Philadelphia
215 988 2554
Andrew.Kassner@dbr.com
*Featured in Bankruptcy/Restructuring (Pennsylvania)*
**Practice Areas:** Firm executive partner and Chair of the Corporate Restructuring Practice Group. Andy's practice is concentrated in workouts, complex Chapter 11 cases and related bankruptcy litigation. Andy has represented debtors, secured creditors, significant unsecured creditors and interested parties in over 400 Chapter 11 cases in over 30 federal jurisdictions.
**Professional Memberships:** Admitted New York, Pennsylvania, Delaware; Member - Delaware, Pennsylvania, Philadelphia Bar Associations; Fellow - American College of Bankruptcy; Board - Mid-Atlantic Section, American Bankruptcy Institute; Board Member - Consumer Bankruptcy Assistance Project.
**Personal:** University of Pennsylvania, BA, 1980; New York School of Law, JD (cum laude), 1983.

## KASTENBERG, Stephen J
Ballard Spahr LLP, Philadelphia
215 864 8122
kastenberg@ballardspahr.com
*Featured in Litigation (Pennsylvania)*
**Practice Areas:** Mr Kastenberg focuses on complex business litigation with an emphasis on antitrust and corporate governance. He handles matters involving monopolization, collusive dealing, price discrimination, RICO violations, securities claims, breach of fiduciary duty, derivative actions, and putative class actions.
**Professional Memberships:** American Bar Association, New Jersey State Bar Association, Pennsylvania Bar Association, Philadelphia Bar Association.
**Career:** Admissions: New Jersey, Pennsylvania, Supreme Court of New Jersey and Pennsylvania, US District Court for the Eastern District of Pennsylvania and New Jersey, US Court of Appeals for the Third Circuit.
**Personal:** Harvard Law School (JD 1992) Princeton University (AB 1988).

## KATZ, Brian M
Pepper Hamilton LLP, Philadelphia
215 981 4193
katzb@pepperlaw.com
*Featured in Corporate/M&A (Pennsylvania)*
**Practice Areas:** Partner; Chair, Corporate and Securities Practice Group. Concentrates practice in securities, mergers and acquisitions, venture capital and general corporate representation. Handles all types of business transactions, including public and private securities offerings, venture capital transactions, mergers and acquisitions, joint venture relationships, electronic commerce matters and compensation issues. Represents

issuers and underwriters in initial and secondary public offerings. Also assists clients in complying with their federal and state reporting and disclosure requirements as public companies.
**Personal:** JD 1992 Temple University School of Law; BA 1988 University of Pennsylvania; BSE1988 University of Pennsylvania, The Wharton School.

## KELBON, Regina Stango
Blank Rome LLP, Philadelphia
215 569 5507
Kelbon@BlankRome.com
*Featured in Bankruptcy/Restructuring (Delaware), Bankruptcy/Restructuring (Pennsylvania)*
**Practice Areas:** Regina Stango Kelbon chairs the twenty-six lawyer Business Restructuring and Bankruptcy Group. Ms Kelbon is admitted in Delaware, Pennsylvania and New Jersey and handles bankruptcy, business reorganizations and workouts, along with banking and commercial lending matters. She represents creditors' committees, debtors, institutional lenders, lender groups, creditors, executory contract parties, equipment lessors, plan of reorganization proponents and asset purchasers. She is Chair of the Subcommittee on Corporate Governance of the Business Bankruptcy Section of the American Bar Association. Ms Kelbon is a Bankruptcy Mediator and holds leadership positions in the Philadelphia Chapter of the Turnaround Management Association. www.BlankRome.com/Kelbon.

## KELLY, Sarah A
Cozen O'Connor, Philadelphia
215 665 5536
skelly@cozen.com
*Featured in Labor & Employment (Pennsylvania)*
**Practice Areas:** Sarah has more than 25 years of experience at leading law firms and as in-house counsel. She advises, counsels on and litigates all issues of employment law; conducts internal investigations; negotiates employment law issues in corporate transactions and drafts employment agreements; and develops and advises on employment policies. She is expert in reductions-in-force and waivers under OWBPA and ADA accommodation.
**Professional Memberships:** American Bar Association, Equal Employment Opportunity Committee; American Employment Law Council; Fellow, College of Labor and Employment Lawyers.
**Personal:** Tufts University, BA, 1977; University of Pennsylvania Law School, JD, 1985.

## KELSEN, Peter Foster
Blank Rome LLP, Philadelphia
215 569 5655
Kelsen@BlankRome.com
*Featured in Real Estate (Pennsylvania)*
**Practice Areas:** Peter Kelsen concentrates his practice in land use and real estate development. He serves as counsel to a wide range of clients, including developers, owners, financial institutions, and municipal agencies in an equally diverse range of industries. Mr Kelsen advises clients on the complexities of their transactions in the area of zoning and land use; real estate tax assess-

ment/exemption litigation; commercial development and condemnation. He served as Vice Chairman of the Zoning Code Commission of the City of Philadelphia and Chair of its work plan committee. He is the editor of the Philadelphia Zoning Code Publication Project. www.BlankRome.com/Kelsen.

**KENNEDY, Paul J**
Pepper Hamilton LLP, Philadelphia
215 981 4194
kennedyp@pepperlaw.com
*Featured in Intellectual Property (Pennsylvania)*
**Practice Areas:** Partner; Co-Chair, Intellectual Property Litigation Practice Group. Experienced in trademark, counterfeit, trade name, trade secrets, unfair competition, copyright, license, assignments, advertising and right of publicity matters. Prosecution and defense of numerous infringement claims, including injunction actions in federal courts and opposition proceedings before the Trademark Trial and Appeal Board.
**Professional Memberships:** Member, Board of Directors and Advisory Board, The Legal Clinic for the Disabled, Inc.
**Personal:** JD 1983 Villanova University School of Law; MS 1979 London School of Economics; BA 1978 American University.

**KERR, Alexander**
McCarter & English, LLP, Philadelphia
215 979 3868
akerr@mccarter.com
*Featured in Litigation (Pennsylvania)*
**Career:** Mr Kerr is experienced in handling complex commercial litigation, including securities class actions and private equity matters. He has successfully defended corporations and individual officers and directors against alleged violations of the securities laws and breaches of fiduciary duty. He is one of the few attorneys who have tried a securities class action through to a favorable jury verdict. His career includes service as a Deputy Attorney General in the Pennsylvania Department of Justice. Mr Kerr regularly teaches courses in trial advocacy. He is a Fellow of the American College of Trial Lawyers. For full bio: http://www.mccarter.com/Alexander-Kerr/.

**KICHLINE, Michael L**
Dechert LLP, Philadelphia
215 994 2439
michael.kichline@dechert.com
*Featured in Litigation (Pennsylvania)*
**Practice Areas:** Mr Kichline represents clients in high-stakes complex litigation. His experiences spans a range of areas including securities class actions, derivative suits, M&A disputes, bankruptcy trustee matters and litigation arising from corporate, finanicial, commericial and/or consumer transactions.
**Professional Memberships:** Member, Pennsylvania Bar; admitted to practice before the US Supreme Court and several federal courts; member, Board of Trustees, Philadelphia Bar Foundation.
**Personal:** Temple University (BA, 1988, magna cum laude); Temple University Beasley School of

Law (JD, 1991, magna cum laude, Moot Court Honor Society)

**KLEBAN, Barry**
McElroy, Deutsch, Mulvaney & Carpenter, LLP, Philadelphia
215 557 2945
bkleban@mdmc-law.com
*Featured in Bankruptcy/Restructuring (Pennsylvania)*
**Practice Areas:** Mr Kleban practices in the areas of business bankruptcy, insolvency, and commercial transactions with emphasis in representing businesses and their owners in out-of-court reorganizations and debtors and creditors' committees in business bankruptcies.
**Professional Memberships:** Mr Kleban is a Member of the Philadelphia, Pennsylvania and American Bar Associations, the American Bankruptcy Institute and the Eastern District of Pennsylvania Bankruptcy Conference, on which he is a Member of the Steering Committee. Mr Kleban has also served on the Boards of Directors of the Miquon School and the Consumer Bankruptcy Assistance Project.
**Personal:** University of Pennsylvania (JD); Pennsylvania State University (BA).

**KLEIN, Barry L**
Blank Rome LLP, Philadelphia
215 569 5403
Klein-B@BlankRome.com
*Featured in Labor & Employment (Pennsylvania)*
**Practice Areas:** Barry L. Klein advises employers and executives with respect to their employee benefits and executive compensation arrangements. Previously, he served as an attorney at the National Office of the IRS and as in-house counsel for two major employers and employee benefits providers. He regularly advises employers with respect to benefits aspects of mergers and acquisitions, and plan fiduciaries with respect to administrative procedures and investment policy statements. He represents employers in connection with IRS audits and DOL proceedings. Mr Klein has significant experience advising financial services clients with respect to their obligations under ERISA. For more information: www.BlankRome.com/Klein-B.

**KLEIN, Howard Bruce**
Law Offices Of Howard Bruce Klein, Philadelphia
215 972 1411
klein@hbklein.com
*Featured in Litigation (Pennsylvania)*
**Practice Areas:** White-collar criminal defense: trials, grand jury investigations, internal investigations, and parallel civil False Claims Act litigation. Representation of corporate executives, individuals, and corporate entities in the areas of healthcare fraud, tax, securities, antitrust, pharmaceutical litigation, bank fraud, environmental litigation, defense contracting, public corruption and other fraud matters.
**Professional Memberships:** Philadelphia, American and Federal Bar Associations(founder and former Chairman, Criminal Law Committee); Pennsylvania Association of Criminal Defense Lawyers; Conducts litigation skills training pro-

grams for law firms and government agencies for American Law Institute-CLE.
**Career:** Law clerk, Justice Robert Hansen, Wisconsin Supreme Court; Assistant United States Attorney and former Chief of the Criminal Division, U.S Attorney's Office for the Eastern District of Pennsylvania; Blank, Rome LLP, Litigation Partner (1987-1996)—Former Chairman, Litigation Department; Adjunct Professor of Evidence and Trial Advocacy—Temple University Law School.
**Publications:** Deposition Guidebook,(ALI-ABA,2007); Medicare/Medicaid Fraud and Abuse Enforcement, Physician's News Digest; Use of the Deposition at Trial, The Practical Litigator, Volume 19, No. 5, September, 2008; Fighting Corruption in the Philadelphia Police Department: The Death Knell of the Conspiracy of Silence, 60 Temple Law Quarterly 103-115.
**Personal:** Georgetown University Law School, JD; 1976 Undergraduate: Northwestern University and University of Wisconsin, BA, 1972 (With High Honors).

**KLEIN, Howard M**
Conrad O'Brien, Philadelphia
215 864 8068
hklein@conradobrien.com
*Featured in Litigation (Pennsylvania)*
**Practice Areas:** Shareholder, Conrad O'Brien PC. He has been Lead Counsel and tried cases in state and federal courts. His practice includes products liability, mass torts, medical and legal malpractice, construction and commercial litigation.
**Professional Memberships:** Pennsylvania and American Bar Associations, Defense Research Institute, Pennsylvania Defense Institute and Philadelphia Association of Defense Counsel.
**Career:** Law Clerk, Honorable Alfred L Luongo (ED Pa., 1980-82); President - Philadelphia Association of Defense Counsel (1999-2000).
**Personal:** BA, State University of New York at Binghamton (1977); JD, Magna Cum Laude, Villanova University (1980); Research Project Editor of Villanova Law Review.

**KLEIN, Joshua T**
Fox Rothschild LLP, Philadelphia
215 299 2723
jklein@foxrothschild.com
*Featured in Bankruptcy/Restructuring (Pennsylvania)*
**Practice Areas:** Practice encompasses areas related to corporate restructuring, insolvency and bankruptcy; Certified Mediator.
**Professional Memberships:** American Bankruptcy Institute, INSOL International.
**Publications:** Frequent writer on insolvency and bankruptcy topics. Editor/Author: American Bankruptcy Institute Journal and American Bankruptcy Institute's Third Circuit Case Update; Recent articles: "Heritage Highgate, Inc.: Second Liens, Valuation & Strategy," Bloomberg BNA (2012), "Elimination of Junior Liens, Valuation Issues and Burden of Proof for Secured Claim Valuations," ABI Journal (2012), "Plan Confirmation and Lien Extinguishment in

Greater American Land Resources," ABI Journal (2012).
**Personal:** JD, Widener University School of Law, 2001; BA, Moravian College, 1997.

**KLEIN, Justin P**
Ballard Spahr LLP, Philadelphia
+1 215 864 8606
kleinj@ballardspahr.com
*Featured in Corporate/M&A (Pennsylvania)*
**Practice Areas:** Justin P. Klein is partner in the Business and Finance Department and Practice Leader of the Securities Group. He focuses on securities matters, including public and private offerings, representing boards and committees of public companies and parties in regulatory and enforcement proceedings.
**Professional Memberships:** National Association of Securities Dealers (now FINRA) Past Chair and Member, National Arbitration and Mediation Committee Pennsylvania Securities Commission, Attorney Advisory Committee.
**Career:** Past Assistant Director, SEC Division of Corporation Finance Admissions: District of Columbia Maryland Pennsylvania.
**Personal:** Education: George Washington University Law School (JD 1972) University of Pennsylvania (BA 1969).

**KOMOROSKI, Kenneth S**
Fulbright & Jaworski LLP, Canonsburg
724 416 0420
kkomoroski@fulbright.com
*Featured in Environment (Pennsylvania)*
**Practice Areas:** Environmental; Litigation; Oil and Gas.
**Professional Memberships:** Member of the District of Columbia, Ohio, Pennsylvania, and West Virginia Bars.
**Career:** Ken is Partner-In-Charge of the Pittsburgh office. He has active oil and gas and environmental practices. In his oil and gas practice, he represents producers and midstream companies in a variety of areas including land use and zoning, permitting, environmental, water usage, wastewater treatment, litigation and local ordinances. He also represents businesses in environmental matters, including steel, wood treating, chemical and power generating concerns.
**Personal:** JD, University of Pittsburgh School of Law; BS, Environmental Engineering, Pennsylvania State University.

**KOONS JR, Robert A**
Drinker Biddle & Reath LLP, Philadelphia
215 988 3392
Robert.Koons@dbr.com
*Featured in Intellectual Property (Pennsylvania)*
**Practice Areas:** Focuses on all areas of intellectual property counseling, licensing and transactional matters. Litigates patent and trademark disputes. Prosecutes patent applications before the USPTO in numerous areas, including chemical processes, asset intelligence, transportation technology and electronic communications.
**Professional Memberships:** Philadelphia Intellectual Property Law Association; American Intellectual Property Law Association; American

Society of Mechanical Engineers; Society of Automotive Engineers.

**Personal:** JD Temple University, 1983, magna cum laude; MBA, University of Pennsylvania, The Wharton School, 2001, with honors; BSME, 1972; Master of Engineering, 1974 University of South Carolina.

## KORB, Philip B
Ballard Spahr LLP, Philadelphia
215 864 8709
korb@ballardspahr.com

*Featured in Real Estate (Pennsylvania)*

**Practice Areas:** Philip B. Korb is a partner in the Real Estate Department and Practice Leader of the Planned Communities and Condominiums Group. His practice includes real estate development, real estate acquisitions and financings, real estate taxation, leasing, condominium and planned community development, workouts, and general real estate matters.
**Professional Memberships:** Pennsylvania Bar Association Philadelphia Bar Association American College of Real Estate Lawyers.
**Career:** Admissions: Pennsylvania.
**Publications:** Pennsylvania Condominiums Model Forms & Commentary,' Pennsylvania Bar Institute Press.
**Personal:** Education: Temple University James E. Beasley School of Law (JD 1975, magna cum laude) Johns Hopkins University (BA 1969).

## KRAEUTLER, Eric
Morgan, Lewis & Bockius LLP, Philadelphia
215 963 4840
ekraeutler@morganlewis.com

*Featured in Litigation (Pennsylvania)*

**Practice Areas:** Leader of Philadelphia Litigation Practice. Practice focuses on trials and appeals involving complex commercial cases, intellectual property disputes, and white collar criminal matters and government investigations. Lead trial lawyer in civil and criminal jury trials, civil bench trials, and arbitrations including international arbitrations. Appellate experience includes having argued numerous cases before the US Courts of Appeals for the Third, Ninth, and Federal Circuits, as well as state appellate courts.
**Professional Memberships:** Fellow, American College of Trial Lawyers (induction pending).
**Career:** Criminal Division of the US Attorney's Office for the Eastern District of Pennsylvania; Special Pennsylvania Deputy Attorney General.

## KRESGE, Raymond
Cozen O'Connor, Philadelphia
215 665 2128
rkresge@cozen.com

*Featured in Labor & Employment (Pennsylvania)*

**Practice Areas:** Ray has extensive experience in litigation and counseling on a variety of labor and employment matters. Ray's employment litigation experience includes the defense of a wide range of employment discrimination claims and other statutory employment claims (e.g., FMLA; FLSA), and the defense of general employment contract and tort claims. Ray has extensive experience in traditional labor litigation in Federal Courts, before the NLRB or in labor arbitration. Ray also

has experience in employee benefits litigation under ERISA, defending plans and administrators in individual and class action ERISA cases.
**Personal:** Harvard Law School, JD, 1984; Haverford College, BA, 1981.

## KYPER, James R
K&L Gates, Pittsburgh
412 355 6542
james.kyper@klgates.com

*Featured in Intellectual Property (Pennsylvania)*

**Practice Areas:** A trial lawyer and client counselor, Mr Kyper focuses on intellectual property litigation, including patent, trademark, trade secret, and other complex commercial matters, in the state and federal courts. He has represented clients in litigations involving a variety of products and technologies, including steel framing, safety equipment, automobiles, ceramic cutting tools, software, pitch controls systems for wind turbines, optical communication systems, control valves, cellular phones and entertainment properties. He also has experience in both Court annexed, AAA and ICC arbitrations and mediations.

## LANGEL, John B
Ballard Spahr LLP, Philadelphia
215 864 8227
langel@ballardspahr.com

*Featured in Labor & Employment (Pennsylvania)*

**Practice Areas:** John B. Langel chairs the firm's Litigation Department, after leading the Labor and Employment Group for nearly 30 years. He represents employers in employment litigation, including discrimination and FLSA class actions, restrictive covenant/trade secret, and breach of employment contract cases. He also represents employers in unfair labor practices, representation matters, jurisdictional disputes, labor negotiations and arbitrations, and other labor matters.
**Professional Memberships:** American Society for Healthcare Human Resources Administration National Association of College and University Attorneys.
**Career:** Admissions: Pennsylvania New Jersey.
**Personal:** Temple University James E. Beasley School of Law (JD 1974) Marietta College (BA 1970).

## LAUBACH, Larry P
Cozen O'Connor, Philadelphia
215 665 4666
llaubach@cozen.com

*Featured in Corporate/M&A (Pennsylvania)*

**Practice Areas:** Larry has more than 30 years of experience in mergers and acquisitions, as well as venture capital and other minority investments, private placements, limited partner investments in private funds, senior and mezzanine financings, corporate governance matters, and general corporate and contractual matters. He represents large and middle market companies, strategic and financial buyers and sellers, and family office and other institutional investors.
**Professional Memberships:** American Bar Association, Pennsylvania Bar Association and its Title 15 Committee.
**Career:** Chair, Corporate Practice Group.

**Personal:** University of Pennsylvania Law School, JD, 1980; Franklin & Marshall College, BA, 1977.

## LAUPHEIMER, Ann Blair
Blank Rome LLP, Philadelphia
215 569 5758
Laupheimer@BlankRome.com

*Featured in Litigation (Pennsylvania)*

**Practice Areas:** Ann Laupheimer concentrates her practice on corporate litigation, including insurance coverage and insolvency; complex business disputes arising from M&A, joint ventures, and corporate dissolutions; corporate liability—director, officer, professional, and general partner liability; securities; shareholder disputes; banking and financial institutions litigation; and bankruptcy-related litigation. For more information: www.BlankRome.com/Laupheimer.

## LAVELLE JR, John P
Morgan, Lewis & Bockius LLP, Philadelphia
215 963 4824
jlavelle@morganlewis.com

*Featured in Products Liability (Nationwide), Litigation (Pennsylvania)*

**Practice Areas:** Partner, Litigation Practice, and co-chair of firm's Product Liability and Mass Torts Litigation Practice. Practice includes product liability, complex commercial and class action litigation, and election law. Twenty years of trial and appellate litigation experience, focusing on defense of medical device and pharmaceutical product liability claims. Product liability experience includes cases concerning pacemakers, cardiodefibrillators, drug pumps, neurostimulators, stents, knee and hip replacements, vaccines, pharmaceuticals, industrial equipment, consumer products, nutritional supplements, and chemicals.
**Career:** Special Master appointed by the US District Court for the Eastern District of Pennsylvania.

## LAVORGNA, Gregory J
Drinker Biddle & Reath LLP, Philadelphia
215 988 3309
Gregory.Lavorgna@dbr.com

*Featured in Intellectual Property (Pennsylvania)*

**Practice Areas:** Assists in protecting, enforcing, and capitalizing on intellectual property assets. Litigates intellectual property disputes. Advises on patentability, patent infringement and patent validity; trademark and copyright registration and infringement; trade secrets and employee agreements; licensing.
**Professional Memberships:** American and Philadelphia Bar Associations; Philadelphia and American Intellectual Property Law Associations; Benjamin Franklin Inn of Court (founding Member); American Law Institute.
**Career:** Former Managing Partner; former Chair, Intellectual Property Practice.
**Publications:** Numerous, including What the General Practitioner Should Know About Patent Law and Practice (fifth and sixth editions).
**Personal:** JD (cum laude), Temple University School of Law, MSEE, BSEE, Drexel University.

## LAWALL, Francis J
Pepper Hamilton LLP, Philadelphia
215 981 4481
lawallf@pepperlaw.com

*Featured in Bankruptcy/Restructuring (Pennsylvania)*

**Practice Areas:** Partner. Concentrates in national bankruptcy and reorganization matters, including the representation of major oil companies in bankruptcy proceedings throughout the United States. Also has broad experience in the reorganization of companies plagued with massive toxic tort liabilities, as well as companies in the textile, automotive, clothing and construction materials industries. Has represented numerous buyers and sellers of assets in and out of bankruptcy proceedings.
**Professional Memberships:** Board Member, International Energy Credit Association, Inc.
**Personal:** JD 1985 Temple University School of Law; MA 1982 Temple University; BA 1981 Temple University.

## LAWLOR, William G
Dechert LLP, Philadelphia
215 994 2823
william.lawlor@dechert.com

*Featured in Corporate/M&A (Pennsylvania)*

**Practice Areas:** Mr Lawlor represents corporate clients, boards of directors, and special committees in domestic and cross-border mergers and acquisitions, including negotiated and contested transactions. He also advises clients on securities offerings, proxy contests, and general corporate matters.
**Professional Memberships:** Member, Pennsylvania Bar; admitted to practice before the Supreme Court of Pennsylvania; Advisory Board, DealLawyers.com.
**Personal:** University of Pennsylvania (BA,1977); Stanford Law School (JD, 1980).

## LEBOVITZ, James A
Dechert LLP, Philadelphia
215 994 2510
james.lebovitz@dechert.com

*Featured in Capital Markets (Nationwide), Corporate/M&A (Pennsylvania)*

**Practice Areas:** Mr Lebovitz represents corporate clients in domestic and international corporate finance and M&A transactions. He handles securities transactions, mergers and acquisitions, strategic alliances, and general corporate matters. Mr Lebovitz serves as chair of the firm-wide lawyer hiring committee.
**Career:** Served as general counsel of a national, publicly traded, physician practice management company.
**Personal:** Yale College (BA, 1979, editor-in-chief, Yale Daily News); University of Virginia School of Law (JD, 1982, notes editor, The Virginia Journal of International Law); University of Cambridge (LLM, 1983).

## LEE II, Thomas H
Dechert LLP, Philadelphia
215 994 2994
thomas.lee@dechert.com

*Featured in Litigation (Pennsylvania)*

**Practice Areas:** Mr Lee represents companies and individuals involved in criminal and other government investigations and related civil litigation, including matters arising under the False Claims Act; the Food, Drug and Cosmetic Act; the Medicare/Medicaid Anti-Kickback Statute; and state consumer fraud statutes.
**Professional Memberships:** Member, Pennsylvania and Massachusetts Bars; admitted to practice before numerous federal courts.
**Career:** US Attorney's Office, Eastern District of Pennsylvania (1981-1990): chief of the Major Crimes Section, chief of the Criminal Division, first assistant US Attorney.
**Personal:** Williams College (BA, 1973, magna cum laude); Harvard University Law School (JD, 1976, cum laude).

**LEEDS, Edward I**
Ballard Spahr LLP, Philadelphia
215 864 8419
leeds@ballardspahr.com
*Featured in Labor & Employment (Pennsylvania)*
**Practice Areas:** Edward I. Leeds concentrates his practice on issues relating to the design, administration, and taxation of health and other welfare benefits plans. He has represented employers in the negotiation and drafting of contracts with insurers, third-party administrators, and other vendors in documenting and communicating welfare benefits plans, and in complying with state and federal laws, including health care reform mandates, HIPAA/HITECH, COBRA, and the rules applicable to cafeteria-plans, wellness initiatives, and government benefit programs.
**Career:** Pennsylvania.
**Publications:** Frequent author on numerous benefits law topics.
**Personal:** Harvard Law School (JD 1984) Haverford College (BA 1980).

**LEONARD, Jeffrey A**
Cozen O'Connor, Philadelphia
215 665 4157
jleonard@cozen.com
*Featured in Real Estate (Pennsylvania)*
**Practice Areas:** Jeff represents a range of clients, including real estate private equity funds; lenders, including banks and life insurance companies; investors in and owners of multifamily housing properties; and investors and owners of retail shopping malls and centers, and office buildings. His work includes financing, distressed debt, work-outs, acquisitions, sales, leasing, joint venture transactions and portfolio acquisitions and dispositions.
**Professional Memberships:** Executive Board Member, Penjerdel Council, ICSC, Pennsylvania and Philadelphia Bar Association.
**Career:** Chair, Business Law Department. Co-chair, Real Estate Group. Member, Firm Management Committee.
**Personal:** Georgetown University Law Center, JD, 1985 Lafayette College, AB, 1982.

**LESSER, Bruce**
Blank Rome LLP, Philadelphia
215 569 5339
BLesser@BlankRome.com
*Featured in Banking & Finance (Pennsylvania)*
**Practice Areas:** Bruce Lesser represents lenders and borrowers in the structuring and documentation of financing transactions and in the areas of loan workouts, bankruptcy and business law. He also has significant experience in the real estate industry and in private equity investments and fundings. Mr Lesser has represented financial institutions and other lenders in numerous complex transactions for over thirty years. His experience also includes the representation of privately-held companies in acquisitions and divestitures. For more information:
www.BlankRome.com/BLesser.

**LEVIN, Christine C**
Dechert LLP, Philadelphia
215 994 2421
christine.levin@dechert.com
*Featured in Antitrust (Pennsylvania)*
**Practice Areas:** Ms Levin focuses on complex civil and criminal litigation, including antitrust and consumer fraud class action matters. Her antitrust experience has spanned multiple industries including newspapers, chemicals, technology and pharmaceuticals. She has handled class actions alleging price-fixing, false advertising and product liability claims.
**Professional Memberships:** Member, Pennsylvania Bar; admitted to practice before the US Supreme Court and numerous federal courts
**Personal:** Duke University (BA, 1976, magna cum laude); University of Pennsylvania Law School (JD, 1982, cum laude, Order of the Coif).

**LIBSON, Jeffrey P**
Pepper Hamilton LLP, Berwyn
610 640 7825
libsonj@pepperlaw.com
*Featured in Corporate/M&A (Pennsylvania)*
**Practice Areas:** Partner; Head, Life Sciences Practice Group. Practice is devoted primarily to the areas of securities law, venture financing, mergers and acquisitions, corporate governance and the commercialization, licensing and acquisition of intellectual property. Represents a number of publicly traded and closely held life science companies in ongoing representations as outside general counsel. Also represents a number of non-profit entities that support the life sciences industry.
**Professional Memberships:** Member, Board of Directors, Pennsylvania Biotechnology Association; Member, Board of Directors, Japan America Society of Greater Philadelphia.
**Personal:** JD 1981 Duke University School of Law; BA 1976 Oberlin College.

**LICHTENSTEIN, Robert J**
Morgan, Lewis & Bockius LLP, Philadelphia
215 963 5726
rlichtenstein@morganlewis.com
*Featured in Labor & Employment (Pennsylvania)*
**Practice Areas:** Robert Lichtenstein is a partner in Morgan Lewis's Employee Benefits and

Executive Compensation Practice. He provides counseling to employers, boards of directors, and individuals on all facets of executive compensation and employee benefits, including equity and incentive compensation, employment and retention arrangements, ERISA compliance, qualified retirement, and pension and profit-sharing.
**Personal:** Graduated from New York University School of Law (1974, LLM), University of Pittsburgh School of Law (1973, JD), and University of Pennsylvania (1969, BS). Admitted to practice in Pennsylvania and before the US Tax Court. Adjunct professor of law at University of Pennsylvania and Villanova Law Schools.

**LORD, Craig**
Blank Rome LLP, Philadelphia
215 569 5496
Lord@BlankRome.com
*Featured in Real Estate (Pennsylvania)*
**Practice Areas:** Craig Lord has extensive experience in nearly every aspect of real estate law. He helps clients navigate the complexities of acquisition and sales; partnerships and joint ventures; development and leasing; financing; and construction and design agreements. Mr Lord served as a judge in the Trial Division of the Philadelphia Court of Common Pleas from 1988 through 1997. He represents clients in commercial litigation, focusing in real estate related commercial litigation. For more information:
www.BlankRome.com/Lord.

**LUCCI, Joseph**
Woodcock Washburn LLP, Philadelphia
215 564 8370
lucci@woodcock.com
*Featured in Intellectual Property (Pennsylvania)*
**Practice Areas:** Patent litigation, prosecution, interference, and counseling; especially involving pharmaceuticals and medical devices.
**Professional Memberships:** Member, American Bar Association, AIPLA, PIPLA, IPO.
**Career:** Joe has practiced patent law for over 20 years, and is a trusted advisor to some of the world's leading corporations, including Fortune 100 companies. He is a member of Woodcock Washburn's Policy Committee and Chair of the firm's Finance Committee.
**Publications:** Frequent lecturer on IP Law.
**Personal:** Boston College Law School, JD, cum laude (1989), University of Pennsylvania, MS Organic Chemistry (1985), Georgetown University, BS Chemistry (1983).

**MAGAZINER, Fred T**
Dechert LLP, Philadelphia
215 994 2587
fred.magaziner@dechert.com
*Featured in Litigation (Pennsylvania)*
**Practice Areas:** Mr Magaziner is a trial lawyer and litigator, having served as lead defense lawyer in several mass tort multidistrict litigations. He also has tried a variety of other types of cases, including patent infringement, breach of contract, commercial fraud, corporate governance, will contests, and medical malpractice matters.
**Professional Memberships:** Member, Pennsylvania Bar; admitted to practice before

numerous federal courts; Fellow, American College of Trial Lawyers; member, American Law Institute; member, Temple University Academy of Advocacy Advisory Board.
**Personal:** Columbia University (BA, 1969); Columbia Law School (JD, 1976, notes and comments editor of Columbia Law Review).

**MAKADON, Arthur**
Ballard Spahr LLP, Philadelphia
215 864 8200
makadon@ballardspahr.com
*Featured in Litigation (Pennsylvania)*
**Practice Areas:** Mr Makadon, former firm Chair, has tried more than 35 jury trials to verdict and an equal number of nonjury trials. He represents public officials and publicly traded corporations in grand jury matters and other government investigations, and defends against violations under securities, antitrust, ERISA, and consumer protection laws. Mr Makadon is engaged for appellate work nationwide and in complex, high-profile litigation matters generally. He counsels corporations and special committees on corporate governance.
**Professional Memberships:** American Bar Association, Pennsylvania Bar Association.
**Career:** Pennsylvania.
**Personal:** University of Pennsylvania Law School (LLB 1967) Pennsylvania State University (BA 1964).

**MAKOULIAN, Tina R**
Ballard Spahr LLP, Philadelphia
215 864 8713
makoulian@ballardspahr.com
*Featured in Real Estate (Pennsylvania)*
**Practice Areas:** Tina R. Makoulian is a partner in the Real Estate Department and Practice Leader of the Zoning and Land Use Group. She focuses on complex real estate development; acquisition and disposition of commercial properties; commercial leasing; zoning and land use; and representing developers of hotels, office buildings, shopping centers, and medical, educational, and parking facilities.
**Professional Memberships:** Pennsylvania Bar Association American College of Real Estate Lawyers, Fellow Commercial Real Estate Women (CREW), National Board of Directors, Past President, Philadelphia Chapter.
**Career:** Admissions: Pennsylvania.
**Personal:** Villanova University School of Law (JD 1993) University of Pennsylvania (BA 1990).

**MALLOY, Elizabeth A**
Buchanan Ingersoll & Rooney PC, Philadelphia
215 665 5310
elizabeth.malloy@bipc.com
*Featured in Labor & Employment (Pennsylvania)*
**Career:** Elizabeth is a Shareholder in the firm's Labor & Employment Section and a member of the firm's Board of Directors. She focuses her practice on employment litigation, trial and appellate work, and preventive counseling. She has represented employers in various litigation matters, including cases related to discrimination, sexual harassment, the Fair Labor Standards Act, the

Family and Medical Leave Act, wrongful discharge and retaliation. Liz earned her JD from Villanova University School of Law (cum laude, Order of the Coif, Phi Beta Kappa). She is a member of the Course Planning Committee of the Pennsylvania Bar Institute's Employment Law Institute.

## MANDELBAUM, David G
Greenberg Traurig, LLP, Philadelphia
215 988 7813
MandelbaumD@gtlaw.com
*Featured in Environment (Pennsylvania)*

**Practice Areas:** Co-Chair, National Environmental Practice.
**Professional Memberships:** Chair, Delaware Valley Environmental American Inn of Court; Vice-Chair Pennsylvania Statewide Water Resources Committee; Past Chair, PBA environmental section; former committee chair, ABA SEER; Planner, Pennsylvania Environmental Law Forum.
**Career:** Chambers USA, 2003-13, Environmental Law, Top Band; Best Lawyers in America. Adjunct Professor, Temple Law School. Clerkship: Hon. Louis H. Pollak, USDC ED Pa.
**Publications:** 'Regulation of Unconventional Natural Gas Development', 25 Probate & Property No. 5 at 44 (2011); monthly columnist, Pa. L. Weekly.
**Personal:** JD, magna cum laude, Harvard Law School, 1983; AB, summa cum laude, Harvard College, 1980.

## MARION, David H
Archer & Greiner, A Professional Corporation, Philadelphia
215 246 3131
dmarion@archerlaw.com
*Featured in Litigation (Pennsylvania)*

**Practice Areas:** DAVID MARION is widely known for successful trial practice, concentrating in business litigation, antitrust, securities, class actions, professional liability and communications. A former Philadelphia Bar Association Chancellor, Mr Marion has acted as plaintiff and defense counsel in major antitrust, ERISA, securities and RICO actions and class actions. He successfully argued in the US Supreme Court in a landmark libel law case (Philadelphia Newspapers v. Hepps) and represented another newspaper in a Pennsylvania Supreme Court case which liberalized standards for grant of summary judgment. He has served as federal court-appointed Receiver in a case involving more than $300 million.

## MARRIOTT III, Vincent J
Ballard Spahr LLP, Philadelphia
215 864 8236
Marriott@ballardspahr.com
*Featured in Bankruptcy/Restructuring (Pennsylvania)*

**Practice Areas:** Vincent J. Marriott III is Practice Leader of the Bankruptcy, Reorganization and Capital Recovery Group. He is experienced in representing financial institutions, indenture trustees, trade creditors, creditor's committees, avoidance action defendants, trustees, debtors, and sellers and acquirers of distressed assets in workouts, reorganizations, recapitalizations, and

liquidations, both inside and outside of formal insolvency proceedings.
**Professional Memberships:** American Bar Association.
**Career:** Admissions: Georgia Pennsylvania.
**Personal:** Duke University School of Law (JD 1982) Dartmouth College (AB 1979).

## MARSHALL, John
Drinker Biddle & Reath LLP, Philadelphia
215 988 2731
John.Marshall@dbr.com
*Featured in Intellectual Property (Pennsylvania)*

**Practice Areas:** Of Counsel in the Intellectual Property Practice. Practice is concentrated in civil litigation involving patent, trademark and copyright infringement, representation of patent and trademark applications before domestic and foreign governments, and advice to clients on intellectual property matters.
**Professional Memberships:** Admitted in Pennsylvania and before the USPTO. Member of the American Intellectual Property Association, the American Bar Association, the Philadelphia Intellectual Property Law Association and the Benjamin Franklin AIC.
**Career:** Joined Drinker Biddle in 2001.
**Personal:** JD (cum laude) Villanova University School of Law, 1979; MS, University of West Florida, 1970; BS, US Naval Academy, 1969.

## MATHER, Barbara W
Pepper Hamilton LLP, Philadelphia
215 981 4895
matherb@pepperlaw.com
*Featured in Antitrust (Pennsylvania), Litigation (Pennsylvania)*

**Practice Areas:** Partner; General Counsel; past Co-Chair, Litigation and Dispute Resolution Department; past Executive Partner. Experienced in antitrust, securities, professional malpractice, commercial litigation. Represented co-counsel for plaintiff LePage's in trial and appeals in monopolization claim that awarded $65 million after trebling, defendant's petition for certiorari before US Supreme Court denied in 2004; bathroom/kitchen fixtures and fittings manufacturer in allegations of price fixing; various entities in shareholder class actions; major law firms in malpractice allegations.
**Professional Memberships:** Fellow, American College of Trial Lawyers.
**Career:** Former City Solicitor, Philadelphia, PA.
**Personal:** JD 1968 University of Chicago Law School; BA 1965 Swarthmore College.

## MATOUR, James M
Hangley Aronchick Segal Pudlin & Schiller, Philadelphia
215 496 7016
jmatour@hangley.com
*Featured in Bankruptcy/Restructuring (Pennsylvania)*

**Practice Areas:** Bankruptcy, creditors rights, M&A, commercial litigation.
**Professional Memberships:** American Bankruptcy Institute, Healthcare Insolvency Committee; Eastern District of Pennsylvania Bankruptcy Conference; Turnaround Management Association; Founding Board

Member, Consumer Bankruptcy Assistance Project; contributing editor, The Bankruptcy Strategist (1983-97); Mediator, Eastern District of Pennsylvania Bankruptcy Court (1988-present).
**Career:** Hangley Aronchick Segal Pudlin & Schiller, Shareholder (2000-present). Middleman & Matour, PC, Founder & Chairman (1994-2000). Wolf, Block, Schorr & Solis-Cohen, Partner (1991-94), associate (1986-91). White and Williams, associate (1980-86). Delaware Law School, 1980, cum laude, Law Review, Moot Court Honor Society.

## MCALEESE III, John J
Morgan, Lewis & Bockius LLP, Philadelphia
215 963 5094
jmcaleese@morganlewis.com
*Featured in Environment (Pennsylvania)*

**Practice Areas:** Focuses on environmental matters, including representing corporate clients in civil and administrative environmental litigation such as cost recovery actions under CERCLA (Superfund) and analogous state statutes, enforcement actions by federal and state environmental agencies, permit appeals, and toxic torts relating to environmental contamination. He advises clients on environmental issues that arise in business transactions involving real estate; on compliance with federal, state, and local environmental laws and regulations; and represents clients in negotiations with environmental regulatory agencies. Also counsels clients on issues regarding insurance coverage for environmental risks.

## MCCLURE, Matthew N
Ballard Spahr LLP, Philadelphia
215 864 8771
mcclure@ballardspahr.com
*Featured in Real Estate (Pennsylvania)*

**Practice Areas:** Matthew N. McClure is a partner in the Real Estate Department. He counsels numerous developers, nonprofits, and universities in connection with a full range of real estate matters. His practice includes heavy emphasis on development, land use, zoning, and historic preservation matters. His land use experience involves high profile matters before local administrative boards, as well as appellate advocacy.
**Professional Memberships:** Pennsylvania Bar Association Philadelphia Bar Association Lambda Alpha International Society for Advancement of Land Economics.
**Career:** Admissions: New Jersey, Pennsylvania.
**Personal:** Education: Villanova University School of Law (JD 1999) Loyola College (BA 1994).

## MCELHINNY, Patrick
K&L Gates, Pittsburgh
412 355 6334
patrick.mcelhinny@klgates.com
*Featured in Intellectual Property (Pennsylvania)*

**Practice Areas:** Mr McElhinny concentrates his practice on patent litigation, handling major cases involving an array of technologies. He co-led the litigation team that won 2012's largest verdict in the US, as reported by the National Law Journal. The $1.2 billion verdict was the third largest ever in a patent case. He has handled litigation of

trademarks and copyrights, misappropriation of trade secrets, and breaches of non-competition agreements. Many of those cases involved claims for preliminary injunctive relief. He has 25 years of trial experience in IP disputes and complex commercial litigation and is registered to practice before the USPTO.

## MCINTYRE, Paul R.
Greenberg Traurig, LLP, Philadelphia
215 988 7856
McIntyrePR@gtlaw.com
*Featured in Environment (Pennsylvania)*

**Practice Areas:** Transactional and regulatory environmental matters, including environmental due diligence, environmental insurance, brownfields remediation and financing, and related regulatory counseling, environmental tax credits.
**Professional Memberships:** Member: American Bar Association; Pennsylvania Bar Association; Philadelphia Bar Association; President of Board of Trustees of West Nottingham Academy in Colora, Maryland.
**Career:** Team Member, a Law360 'Real Estate Practice Group of the Year', 2011-12. Member, Winning Team, 2010 Chambers and Partners USA Award for Excellence in Real Estate. Named, 'Rising Star', Philadelphia Magazine and Pennsylvania Super Lawyers, 2012.
**Personal:** JD, Vermont Law School, 2001; MSEL, Vermont Law School, 2001; BA, Elon University, 1996.

## MCKENZIE, James
Morgan, Lewis & Bockius LLP, Philadelphia
215 963 5134
jmckenzie@morganlewis.com
*Featured in Corporate/M&A (Pennsylvania)*

**Practice Areas:** James W. McKenzie, Jr. is a partner in Morgan Lewis's Mergers & Acquisitions and Securities Practices. He advises clients on public offerings, private placements, mergers and acquisitions and venture capital investments. As the former general counsel of a public company, he has extensive experience advising boards of directors and serves as the primary outside counselor in most of his client relationships. He has particular experience working with clients in the pharmaceutical services, life sciences, technology, retail, REIT, and finance industries.
**Personal:** University of Pennsylvania Law School, JD; Wharton School of Business, MBA; Dartmouth College, AB.

## MCKINSTRY JR, Robert B
Ballard Spahr LLP, Philadelphia
215 864 8208
mckinstry@ballardspahr.com
*Featured in Climate Change (Nationwide), Environment (Pennsylvania)*

**Practice Areas:** Robert B. McKinstry, Jr., advises on and litigates the spectrum of environmental issues. He heads the firm's Climate Change and Sustainability Initiative, focusing on regulatory initiatives and corporate, municipal, and nonprofit programs to reduce greenhouse gas emissions.
**Professional Memberships:** Center for Climate Strategies, Senior Advisor ABA

Sustainable Development and Ecosystems Committee, Vice Chair.
**Career:** Admissions: Pennsylvania.
**Publications:** 'Biodiversity Conservation Handbook: State, Local, and Private Protection of Biological Diversity' (ELI 2006).
**Personal:** Lifetime Achievement Award, PBA Environmental and Energy Law Section Yale Law School (JD 1979) Yale School of Forestry and Environmental Studies (M.F.S. 1979) Swarthmore College (BA 1975).

### MCLEAN, Michael
K&L Gates, Pittsburgh
412 355 6458
michael.mclean@klgates.com
*Featured in Corporate/M&A (Pennsylvania)*
**Practice Areas:** Mr McLean has represented corporations, partnerships and other entities across a variety of industries in numerous domestic and international business and securities transactions. He has provided counsel on corporate governance, securities and related matters. Mr McLean has represented corporations and underwriters in over 150 debt and equity offerings (including IPOs, carve-outs and spin-offs) as well as sponsors of venture capital funds and venture funds in equity and mezzanine debt investments. Additionally, he has represented parties in mergers and acquisitions, in takeover situations, management buyouts, ESOP leveraged transactions and recapitalization transactions.

### MELLITS, Bart
Ballard Spahr LLP, Philadelphia
215 864 8701
mellits@ballardspahr.com
*Featured in Real Estate (Pennsylvania)*
**Practice Areas:** Bart I. Mellits is a partner in and Vice Chair of the Real Estate Department. He has extensive experience in leasing, acquisition, development, financing, and restructuring transactions. He has represented landlords and tenants in retail, office, and industrial leases; headquarters facilities; and built-to-suit and financing leases. He also has worked with developers and investors in the acquisition, development, and financing of research and office parks and mixed-use developments, with a focus on working with universities and other institutions.
**Career:** Admissions: New Jersey New York Pennsylvania.
**Personal:** Education: George Washington University Law School (JD 1984) Georgetown University (BA 1981).

### MENKOWITZ, Michael
Fox Rothschild LLP, Philadelphia
215 299 2756
mmenkowitz@foxrothschild.com
*Featured in Bankruptcy/Restructuring (Pennsylvania)*
**Practice Areas:** Represents secured and unsecured creditors, creditors' committees, trustees and debtors in financial restructuring and bankruptcy issues. Extensive experience representing automobile dealers in a variety of matters.
**Professional Memberships:** American Bankruptcy Institute; Pennsylvania Bar

Association; National Association of Dealer Counsel.
**Career:** Chair, Financial Restructuring & Bankruptcy Practice; Co-Chair, Automotive Practice; Member, Executive Committee; Martindale-Hubbell 'AV' rated; Included in list of 'Super Lawyers' by Philadelphia Magazine/Law & Politics Magazine (2006-12) and in SmartCEO Legal Elite list.
**Personal:** Boston University School of Management (MBA 1991). Boston University School of Law (JD 1990). Princeton University (AB 1987).

### MIANO, Steven T
Hangley Aronchick Segal Pudlin & Schiller, Philadelphia
215 496 7025
smiano@hangley.com
*Featured in Environment (Pennsylvania)*
**Practice Areas:** Environmental law, including Clean Water Act, Clean Air Act, Resource Conservation and Recovery Act, CERCLA, Toxic Substances Control Act, and brownfields redevelopment laws. Former Assistant Regional Counsel for US Environmental Protection Agency, Region III, Hazardous Waste Branch.
**Professional Memberships:** Executive Committee, American Bar Association Section of Environment, Energy and Resources; Pennsylvania Bar Association Natural Resources Section; Philadelphia Bar Association Environmental Law Committee; Member, Organizing Committee for Pennsylvania Brownfields Conference; Former Member, Board of Trustees of Support Center for Child Advocates.
**Career:** The University of New Hampshire School of Law, JD, 1985; George Washington University, BS, 1982.

### MILLER, Camille
Cozen O'Connor, Philadelphia
215 665 7273
cmiller@cozen.com
*Featured in Intellectual Property (Pennsylvania)*
**Practice Areas:** Camille practices in all aspects of intellectual property, specifically trademark, trade dress, copyright, unfair competition, right of privacy, right of publicity, domain names, counterfeiting, licensing, trade secret and franchising law, as well as all areas of intellectual property litigation, including patent, trademark, copyright, and trade secret.
**Professional Memberships:** American Bar Association American Intellectual Property Association Copyright Society of the USA, Inns of Court Intellectual Property Owners Association International Trademark Association Pennsylvania Bar Association Philadelphia Chapter of the Copyright Society Philadelphia Intellectual Property Law Association.
**Career:** Co-chair, Intellectual Property.
**Personal:** Chicago-Kent College of Law, Illinois Institute of Technology, JD, 1991 Franklin and Marshall College, BA, 1987.

### MILLER, Christopher S
Pepper Hamilton LLP, Berwyn
610 640 7837
millerc@pepperlaw.com
*Featured in Corporate/M&A (Pennsylvania)*
**Practice Areas:** Partner. Concentrates practice in the areas of mergers and acquisitions, private equity, venture capital, securities, technology law and general corporate matters. Regularly represents US and foreign public and private companies and private equity funds in merger and acquisition transactions. Also represented private equity funds and emerging companies in venture capital, growth equity and debt financing transactions, including numerous financings of LLCs. Represents companies in private and public securities offerings, as well as public companies in ongoing reporting and compliance matters.
**Personal:** JD 1992 University of Miami; BA 1988 College of William & Mary.

### MILLER, Gregory P
Drinker Biddle & Reath LLP, Philadelphia
215 988 1103
Gregory.Miller@dbr.com
*Featured in Litigation (Pennsylvania)*
**Practice Areas:** Partner in Commercial Litigation Department and a Managing Partner of the firm. Focuses on white-collar criminal defense and corporate investigations and securities and corporate governance litigation.
**Professional Memberships:** Admitted to practice in Pennsylvania. Member, Criminal Justice Act Panel Selection Committee, US District Court, Eastern District of PA; Fellow, American College of Trial Lawyers.
**Career:** Officer, US Navy, Judge Advocate General's Corps; federal prosecutor, US Attorney's Office, Philadelphia (Chief, Criminal Division); Partner, Miller Alfano & Raspanti, PC prior to joining Drinker Biddle, January 2008.
**Personal:** JD, Case Western Reserve University School of Law, 1975. BA, Mount Union College, 1972.

### MILLER, Steven M.
Ballard Spahr LLP, Philadelphia
215 864 8310
millersm@ballardspahr.com
*Featured in Banking & Finance (Pennsylvania)*
**Practice Areas:** Steven M. Miller is a partner in the Business and Finance Department and a member of the Transactional Finance Group. Mr Miller concentrates his practice on counseling both lenders and borrowers in financing and restructuring transactions, with a particular emphasis on secured and asset-based lending, as well as syndicated credit facilities.
**Professional Memberships:** Pennsylvania Bar Association Association of Commercial Finance Attorneys Association of Corporate Growth Commercial Finance Association Turnaround Management Association.
**Career:** Admissions: New Jersey Pennsylvania.
**Personal:** Temple University James E. Beasley School of Law (JD 1987) Pennsylvania State University (BA 1978).

### MINTZ, Josef
Blank Rome LLP, Philadelphia
215 569 5528
Mintz@BlankRome.com
*Featured in Bankruptcy/Restructuring (Pennsylvania)*
**Practice Areas:** Josef Mintz concentrates his practice in the areas of business restructuring, creditors' rights, bankruptcy litigation and commercial finance. Mr Mintz represents debtors, trustees, secured and unsecured creditors, asset purchasers and lenders. Mr Mintz regularly works on matters concerning restructuring, bankruptcy litigation, plan negotiations, asset sales and out-of-court workouts. He serves on the Board of Directors for the Philadelphia Chapter of the Turnaround Management Association. For more information: www.BlankRome.com/Mintz.

### MONACO, Daniel A
Drinker Biddle & Reath LLP, Philadelphia
215 988 3312
Daniel.Monaco@dbr.com
*Featured in Intellectual Property (Pennsylvania)*
**Practice Areas:** Partner in the Intellectual Property Practice, with a concentration on patent practice. Has prepared and/or prosecuted thousands of US and foreign patent applications, primarily in chemistry and biotechnology. Provides strategic counseling on patent portfolio development and freedom to operate. Experienced in representing universities and start-up companies, particularly in life sciences.
**Professional Memberships:** Admitted in Pennsylvania (1981), New Jersey (1983) and before the USPTO. Member: Philadelphia, Pennsylvania and American Bar Associations; American Chemical Society.
**Publications:** Co-author, 'What the General Practitioner Should Know About Patent Law and Practice'.
**Personal:** JD, Wake Forest University, 1981; BA, University of Pennsylvania, 1977.

### MORRIS, Mark L
Fox Rothschild LLP, Philadelphia
215 299 2828
mlmorris@foxrothschild.com
*Featured in Real Estate (Pennsylvania)*
**Practice Areas:** Experienced real estate practitioner, focus on hospitality industry. Routinely handles acquisitions, development, joint ventures, leasing and finance. Lead attorney in more than 30 transactions annually involving sale, acquisition, development and management of full-service and limited-service hotels throughout US
**Career:** Member, firm's Executive Committee; Managing Partner, firm's Philadelphia office; Co-chair, firm's Hospitality Practice; Former Chair, firm's Real Estate Department. Frequent author/speaker on matters of interest to executives in hospitality industry and shopping center owners/tenants.
**Personal:** JD, cum laude, Boston University School of Law, 1983; BA, magna cum laude, State University of New York at Albany, 1980.

## MURPHY, Terrence H
Littler Mendelson, PC, Pittsburgh
412 201 7621
TMurphy@littler.com
*Featured in Labor & Employment (Pennsylvania)*
**Practice Areas:** Labor and Employment Law, Labor Relations, Employment Litigation, Employment Class and Collective Action Litigation, Human Resource and Employee Relations Counseling, Fair Labor Standards Act (Overtime Pay) Matters, Acquisitions and Divestitures, Affirmative Action and OFCCP Matters.
**Professional Memberships:** Fellow, College of Labor and Employment Lawyers; Labor and Employment Law Section (EEO Committee) and Litigation Sections, American Bar Association; Section on Labor and Employment Law, New York Bar Association; American Employment Law Council; American Health Lawyers Association.
**Personal:** JD, University of Pittsburgh School of Law, 1975; MS, Cornell University, 1977; BA, University of Rochester, 1972.

## MYERS, Marlee
Morgan, Lewis & Bockius LLP, Pittsburgh
412 560 3310
msmyers@morganlewis.com
*Featured in Corporate/M&A (Pennsylvania)*
**Practice Areas:** Marlee S Myers is the managing partner of the Pittsburgh, Pennsylvania office of Morgan, Lewis & Bockius LLP. Her practice focuses on mergers and acquisitions, corporate governance, venture finance, initial and follow-on public offerings, securities compliance, joint ventures, international business transactions and general corporate counseling. Ms Myers represents major publicly traded companies and emerging companies in growth industries such as e-commerce, clean energy, information technology, social networking, and health care.
**Personal:** University of Pittsburgh School of Law, 1977, JD; University of Pittsburgh, 1974, BA.

## NADEL, Alan S
Panitch Schwarze Belisario & Nadel LLP, Philadelphia
215 965 1280
anadel@panitchlaw.com
*Featured in Intellectual Property (Pennsylvania)*
**Practice Areas:** Represents domestic and foreign corporate clients of all sizes, academic and research institutions, individual physicians and other researchers in all aspects of patent matters involving bioscience, chemical and mechanical inventions, including patent preparation, prosecution, licensing, counseling and litigation. Provides analysis and opinions concerning patent validity, infringement and due diligence, including negotiating, advising and preparing licensing, confidentiality, technology transfer, trade secret and consulting agreements. Devises practical solutions to intellectual property problems.
**Professional Memberships:** Former President, Philadelphia Intellectual Property Law Association; Member Philadelphia Bar Association Intellectual Property Committee; Pennsylvania Bar.

**Personal:** BS (chemistry), JD (honors), The George Washington University.

## NASSAU, Henry N
Dechert LLP, Philadelphia
215 994 2138
henry.nassau@dechert.com
*Featured in Private Equity (Nationwide), Corporate/M&A (Pennsylvania)*
**Practice Areas:** Mr Nassau chairs Dechert's corporate and securities group. He focuses on mergers, acquisitions, public offerings, private equity, and venture capital transactions. He also advises clients in the areas of corporate governance and compliance.
**Professional Memberships:** Member, Pennsylvania Bar.
**Career:** Former chief operating officer, general counsel, and secretary of Internet Capital Group.
**Personal:** University of Pennsylvania (BS, 1976, cum laude; MA, 1976, Benjamin Franklin Scholar); Penn State University, Dickinson School of Law (JD, 1979, magna cum laude, managing editor of the Dickinson Law Review).

## NEWELL, Francis Patrick
Cozen O'Connor, Philadelphia
215 665 2000
fnewell@cozen.com
*Featured in Antitrust (Pennsylvania)*
**Practice Areas:** Frank Newell is an accomplished litigator with broad-based experience handling complex and class action litigation. He also conducts internal corporate investigations, negotiates on his clients' behalf with federal and state regulatory agencies, and represents companies and individuals who are subject to criminal grand jury investigations.
**Professional Memberships:** Chairman, Rules Advisory Committee (E.D. Pa.); Board of Governors, Philadelphia Bar Association; Director, American Counsel Association.
**Career:** Co-chair, Antitrust; US Department of Justice, Antitrust Division, Honors Program
**Personal:** Pennsylvania State University, BS, cum laude, 1972; Villanova University School of Law, JD, 1975, Editorial Board, Law Review.

## NEWTON, Wendelynne J,
Buchanan Ingersoll & Rooney PC, Pittsburgh
412 562 8932
wendelynne.newton@bipc.com
*Featured in Antitrust (Pennsylvania)*
**Career:** Wendelynne is a Shareholder in the firm's Litigation Section and Chair of the Antitrust and Trade Regulation Practice Group, and she serves on the Executive Management Team of the firm. Her practice focuses on antitrust issues in the litigation (including class actions), transaction and counseling contexts. In the last 10 years, she has handled the antitrust aspects of more than 80 mergers and acquisitions in the health care, chemicals, industrial pipe, retail, aluminum extrusions, tooling, railroad, pharmaceuticals, mining and construction and other industries. She earned her JD (cum laude) from the University of Pittsburgh School of Law.

## O'DONNELL, G Daniel
Dechert LLP, Philadelphia
215 994 2762
daniel.odonnell@dechert.com
*Featured in Private Equity (Nationwide), Corporate/M&A (Pennsylvania)*
**Practice Areas:** Mr O'Donnell, chief executive officer of the firm and a member of the firm's policy committee, focuses his practice on mergers, acquisitions, corporate restructuring, and corporate governance matters. His clients include private equity fund sponsors, corporations, and financial institutions as well as company management, boards of directors, and special committees.
**Professional Memberships:** Member, Pennsylvania Bar; member, Board of Advisors, Penn Wharton Institute for Law and Economics
**Personal:** University of Notre Dame (BA, 1973, summa cum laude); University of Pennsylvania Law School (JD, 1976, Order of the Coif; member, University of Pennsylvania Law Review).

## OSSIP, Michael J
Morgan, Lewis & Bockius LLP, Philadelphia
215 963 5761
mossip@morganlewis.com
*Featured in Labor & Employment (Pennsylvania)*
**Practice Areas:** Michael Ossip is the General Counsel and a partner in Morgan Lewis's Labor and Employment Practice. He exclusively represents management in all facets of employee relations, including litigation of employment discrimination, wage and hour, and wrongful discharge claims in federal and state courts. He has tried to verdict numerous jury and nonjury cases. He provides advice regarding wage and hour, FMLA and ADA issues, reductions in force, human resources policies, and sexual harassment prevention and investigations.
**Personal:** Attended University of Pennsylvania Law School, 1979, JD, Magna Cum Laude, Order of the Coif; Cornell University, 1976, BS, With Honors.

## OVERSTREET, David
K&L Gates, Pittsburgh
412 355 8263
david.overstreet@klgates.com
*Featured in Environment (Pennsylvania)*
**Practice Areas:** David Overstreet is licensed in Pennsylvania and Ohio and focuses his administrative law and litigation practice on energy and environmental matters. He counsels clients, including state and national trade associations and natural gas production and midstream companies, with respect to permitting, enforcement, regulatory compliance and local land use matters. Mr Overstreet litigates leasehold disputes, tort claims and contract matters arising in connection with the development of shale gas in Pennsylvania and Ohio. He appears before state and federal regulatory agencies and boards and has served as lead counsel in jury and non-jury trials in state and federal courts.

## PACKER, Rosetta B
McCarter & English, LLP, Philadelphia
215 979 3840
rpacker@mccarter.com
*Featured in Bankruptcy/Restructuring (Pennsylvania)*
**Career:** Ms Packer's practice includes loan restructuring, lender liability prevention and defense, and intercreditor relationships. Ms Packer has represented secured lenders in major Chapter 11 cases in the Eastern District of Pennsylvania and the District of Delaware. She has negotiated and documented complex real estate restructured transactions and asset-based facilities and has tried cases in both federal and state courts in complex commercial matters and lease finance transactions. Ms Packer has also represented creditors' committees, including the unsecured Creditors Committee of Coudert Brothers. For full bio: http://www.mccarter.com/Rosetta-B-Packer/.

## PAGLIARO, James
Morgan, Lewis & Bockius LLP, Philadelphia
215 963 5668
jpagliaro@morganlewis.com
*Featured in Litigation (Pennsylvania)*
**Practice Areas:** Firm Managing Partner and Leader of Product Liability and Mass Tort Practice. Practice includes commercial, mass tort, and product liability litigation. Acted as national coordinating and trial counsel for Fortune 500 companies and international corporations. Led defense teams in jury trials across the US in complex litigation involving class action allegations, large mass tort filings, and serious bodily injury claims. Mass tort matters include personal injury, medical monitoring, and property damage claims. Lead counsel for international companies in diverse industries including oil/gas, chemical, pharmaceutical, medical device, construction, technology, and manufacturing.
**Professional Memberships:** Fellow, American College of Trial Lawyers.

## PANITCH, Ronald L
Panitch Schwarze Belisario & Nadel LLP, Philadelphia
rpanitch@panitchlaw.com
*Featured in Intellectual Property (Pennsylvania)*
**Practice Areas:** Mr Panitch's expertise is in patent and trademark licensing and in reaching creative settlements of contentious matters. He frequently serves as an expert witness in contested proceedings. He was named Best Lawyers' 2011 Philadelphia Intellectual Property "Lawyer of the Year," and twice named "Best Lawyer" by the Philadelphia Magazine.
**Professional Memberships:** Philadelphia and American Bar Associations; Philadelphia Intellectual Property Law Association; American Intellectual Property Law Association; American Law Institute (elected); Pennsylvania Bar.
**Personal:** BSME, New Jersey Institute of Technology, received the 2001 Distinguished Alumni Medal for Outstanding Achievement; JD, Georgetown University, Associate Editor of the Law Review.

## PASEK, Jeffrey
Cozen O'Connor, Philadelphia
215 665 2072
jpasek@cozen.com
*Featured in Labor & Employment (Pennsylvania)*
**Practice Areas:** Jeff concentrates his practice in representing management in all facets of labor and employment law such as litigation and counseling on wrongful discharge and employment discrimination claims, maintaining a union-free environment, collective bargaining, occupational safety and health, whistleblower claims, wage and hour, affirmative action compliance, workplace torts, and employee benefits litigation. He also handles employment contract negotiations and non-compete litigation involving senior corporate executives.
**Professional Memberships:** Pennsylvania Chamber of Business and Industry, Board of Directors and Executive Committee.
**Personal:** University of Pennsylvania Law School, JD, 1976 University of Pittsburgh, BA, 1973.

## PEDRICK, Michael J
Morgan, Lewis & Bockius LLP, Philadelphia
215 963 4808
mpedrick@morganlewis.com
*Featured in Banking & Finance (Pennsylvania)*
**Practice Areas:** Michael J. Pedrick is a partner in Morgan Lewis's Business and Finance Practice, focusing in the Finance and the Mergers and Acquisitions areas. Mr Pedrick's finance practice includes the representation of borrowers and lenders in a wide range of financing transactions including syndicated credits, asset based lending, leveraged acquisition financing and structured financings involving senior and mezzanine tranches. He has significant experience in the use of limited recourse and bankruptcy-remote financing vehicles as well as experience addressing financing issues in restructurings, workouts and bankruptcies.
**Personal:** University of Virginia School of Law, JD; University of Virginia, BA.

## PEDROW, Brian D
Ballard Spahr LLP, Philadelphia
215 864 8108
pedrow@ballardspahr.com
*Featured in Labor & Employment (Pennsylvania)*
**Practice Areas:** Brian D. Pedrow's practice consists primarily of representing management in employment-related litigation, including discrimination and harassment, labor arbitrations and negotiations, and employment contract, wrongful discharge, and tort claims. He advises clients regarding compliance with employment and benefit laws such as Title VII, ADA, ADEA, OSHA, FMLA, and drug testing.
**Professional Memberships:** American Bar Association Pennsylvania Bar Association Pennsylvania Bar Institute, Planning Committee.
**Career:** Pennsylvania.
**Publications:** Supreme Court and legislative/regulatory reporter, Employment and Labor Relations Law (ABA newsletter).

**Personal:** Georgetown University Law Center (JD 1988) Dickinson College (BA 1985).

## PERELMAN, Richard S
Ballard Spahr LLP, Philadelphia
215 864 8118
perelman@ballardspahr.com
*Featured in Banking & Finance (Pennsylvania)*
**Practice Areas:** Richard S. Perelman is a partner in the Business and Finance Department and a member of the Transactional Finance Group. He represents financial institutions and borrowers in a wide variety of financing transactions, including secured and unsecured revolving credit facilities, term loans, asset-based loans, acquisition financing, and second-lien and mezzanine loans, including syndicated credit facilities and special purpose financing.
**Professional Memberships:** Pennsylvania Bar Association New York State Bar Association.
**Career:** Admissions: New York Pennsylvania.
**Personal:** University of Pennsylvania Law School (JD 1984) University of Pennsylvania, The Wharton School (MBA 1984) University of Pennsylvania (BS 1979).

## PINHEIRO, Brian M
Ballard Spahr LLP, Philadelphia
215 864 8511
pinheiro@ballardspahr.com
*Featured in Labor & Employment (Pennsylvania)*
**Practice Areas:** Brian M. Pinheiro is Chair-elect of Ballard Spahr's Business and Finance Department and Practice Leader of the Employee Benefits and Executive Compensation Group. He represents employers on matters relating to executive compensation, including Section 409A and the Section 280G golden parachute rules; tax-qualified retirement plans, including cash balance pension plans and tax-sheltered annuity programs; and health and welfare benefit plans.
**Professional Memberships:** American Bar Association Pennsylvania Bar Association.
**Career:** Pennsylvania District of Columbia.
**Personal:** Catholic University of America Columbus School of Law (JD 1995) Georgetown University Law Center (LLM 1997) Boston College (BA 1992).

## PITTINSKY, David H
Ballard Spahr LLP, Philadelphia
215 864 8117
pittinsky@ballardspahr.com
*Featured in Litigation (Pennsylvania)*
**Practice Areas:** During more than 45 years of litigation practice, Mr Pittinsky has been involved in almost every aspect of complex commercial litigation. He has extensive experience in defending and prosecuting complex commercial, antitrust, federal securities, ERISA, merger and acquisition, qui tam, trade secret, and contract claims commenced in federal and state courts.
**Professional Memberships:** Philadelphia Bar Association.
**Career:** Admissions: California, Pennsylvania, US Court of Appeals for the First, Second, Third, Fourth, and Ninth Circuits, US Supreme Court.
**Personal:** Yale Law School (LLB 1966) Columbia University (AB 1963).

## POCINO KELLY, Amy
Morgan, Lewis & Bockius LLP, Philadelphia
215 963 5042
akelly@morganlewis.com
*Featured in Labor & Employment (Pennsylvania)*
**Practice Areas:** Amy Pocino Kelly is a partner in Morgan Lewis's Employee Benefits and Executive Compensation Practice, advising plan sponsors regarding design, governance, operation, and compliance of all types of employee benefit plans. She also advises companies regarding employee benefits issues in mergers and acquisitions and has represented senior management teams in leveraged buyout transactions.
**Personal:** Ms Kelly is a graduate of Rutgers University School of Law (1999, JD) and Boston University (1996, BA). She is admitted to practice in Pennsylvania, the District of Columbia, and Virginia. Amy serves on the boards of Robins' Nest, Inc. and Women Against Abuse.

## POHL, Paul M
Jones Day, Pittsburgh
412 394 7900
pmpohl@jonesday.com
*Featured in Products Liability (Nationwide), Litigation (Pennsylvania)*
See under Nationwide for profile.

## POWELL, Roy A
Jones Day, Pittsburgh
412 394 7922
rapowell@jonesday.com
*Featured in Litigation (Pennsylvania)*
**Practice Areas:** Roy Powell's practice is devoted to complex commercial disputes and counseling, with an emphasis on construction industry and energy and infrastructure. He is co-chair of Jones Day's Global Construction Practice. He has been named in The Best Lawyers in America in both Commercial Litigation and Construction categories and a Pennsylvania Super Lawyer in multiple categories.
**Publications:** Roy has written articles and book chapters for Aspen Publishers, the Pennsylvania Bar Institute, and other legal and business journals, and has participated as a faculty member for the Construction Superconferences and the National Institute of Trial Advocacy.

## RABINOWITZ, Mark I
Blank Rome LLP, Philadelphia
215 569 5629
MRabinowitz@BlankRome.com
*Featured in Banking & Finance (Pennsylvania)*
**Practice Areas:** Mark Rabinowitz concentrates his practice on commercial and corporate finance, equipment leasing and finance, and loan workouts and restructurings. He serves a wide range of clients in areas such as cash flow lending; asset-based financing; secured transactions and creditors' rights; healthcare finance; equipment leasing and finance; loan syndications and participations; asset securitization; junior debt, mezzanine, and tranche B financing; intercreditor relationships; lender liability prevention and defense; and bankruptcy, reorganizations, debt restructuring, and workouts. For more information: www.BlankRome.com/MRabinowitz.

## RAYMOND III, F Douglas
Drinker Biddle & Reath LLP, Philadelphia
215 988 2548
Douglas.Raymond@dbr.com
*Featured in Corporate/M&A (Pennsylvania)*
**Practice Areas:** Partner. Transactional practice focused on M&A, securities offerings and joint ventures. Cultivates strong client relationships with deep understanding of their businesses, industries, objectives, and strategy. Advises public and private companies, boards and committees on governance matters, including conflicts of interest, changes in control, corporate investigations and risk management. Writes and speaks frequently on governance and other corporate matters.
**Career:** Joined Drinker Biddle: 1986; Managing Partner: 1999-2004; Chair, corporate and securities practice: 2000-10. Previously was a commercial lender.
**Personal:** Harvard University, AB (cum laude), 1980; University of Pennsylvania, JD (magna cum laude), 1985; Admitted to practice in Pennsylvania, 1985.

## REED, Michael H
Pepper Hamilton LLP, Philadelphia
215 981 4416
reedm@pepperlaw.com
*Featured in Bankruptcy/Restructuring (Pennsylvania)*
**Practice Areas:** Partner. Experienced in bankruptcy, creditor's rights and insolvency law. Served as special bankruptcy counsel to Commonwealth of Pennsylvania in LTV bankruptcy and represented amici curiae in litigation that resulted in US Second Circuit landmark decision in environmental and bankruptcy law.
**Professional Memberships:** Fellow, American College of Bankruptcy; Member, American Bankruptcy Institute; Member, American Law Institute; former President, Pennsylvania Bar Association; Board of Advisors, Public Interest Law Center of Philadelphia; Member, Pennsylvania Interest on Lawyers Trust Account Board; Member, Board of Directors, United Way of Southeastern Pennsylvania.
**Personal:** JD 1972 Yale Law School; BA 1969 Temple University.

## REICH, Judith E
Drinker Biddle & Reath LLP, Philadelphia
609 716 6566
Judith.Reich@dbr.com
*Featured in Banking & Finance (Pennsylvania)*
**Practice Areas:** Partner in the Corporate and Securities Group, Judith's practice focuses on banking, bankruptcy and creditor-debtor relations. She structures, negotiates and documents commercial loan transactions, from widely syndicated, multicurrency credit facilities to fully secured asset-based loans, and represents lenders and borrowers in out-of-court workouts and restructurings.
**Professional Memberships:** Member of the American Bar Association Business Law Section, the New Jersey Bar Association Bankruptcy Law and Banking Sections, and the Eastern District of Pennsylvania Bankruptcy Conference.
**Career:** Joined Drinker Biddle in 1990.

**Personal:** Newhouse School of Public Communications at Syracuse University, BS, 1984; University of Pennsylvania Law School, JD, 1987.

## REICH ESQ, Abraham C
Fox Rothschild LLP, Philadelphia
215 299 2090
areich@foxrothschild.com
*Featured in Litigation (Pennsylvania)*

**Practice Areas:** Business litigation, antitrust, securities, trade secrets, IP matters, legal ethics and professional responsibility and alternative dispute resolution.
**Professional Memberships:** Fellow, American College of Trial Lawyers; Member, American Bar Association's House of Delegates; Chancellor, Philadelphia Bar Association (1995); Lecturer In Law, University of Pennsylvania Law School – Ethics and Advocacy.
**Career:** Co-Chair, Fox Rothschild; Member, firm's Executive Committee.
**Publications:** Co-author, Ethics Chapter, 'Successful Partnering Between Inside and Outside Counsel,' West Services, Inc., 2009; Co-author, Chapter, Pennsylvania Ethics Handbook, Pennsylvania Bar Institute, 2011.
**Personal:** Temple University School of Law, 1974 (Law Review); University of Connecticut, 1971 (Phi Beta Kappa).

## RESNICK, Stephanie
Fox Rothschild LLP, Philadelphia
215 299 2082
sresnick@foxrothschild.com
*Featured in Litigation (Pennsylvania)*

**Practice Areas:** Complex business litigation including D&O liability, IP, unfair business practices and competition, misappropriation of trade secrets, corporate governance, shareholder and partnership disputes, breach of fiduciary duty, employment-related litigation, ethics, physician and insurance issues.
**Professional Memberships:** American Bar Association (former member of the ABA Standing Committee for the Federal Judiciary - Third Circuit Representative), American Law Institute, Pennsylvania Bar Association, Philadelphia Bar Association (former Chair and Member of Board of Governors, former Chair of Commission on Judicial Selection and Retention), NJ and NY State Bar Associations.
**Career:** Chair, Litigation Department; Chair, Directors' and Officers' Liability and Corporate Governance Practice; Member, Executive Committee; Member, Diversity Committee.
**Personal:** Recipient, Sandra Day O'Connor Award, Philadelphia Bar Association (2010); appointed as Third Circuit Representative to ABA Standing Committee on Federal Judiciary (2009); Appointed and currently serves on Justice William J Brennan Jr Distinguished Jurist Award Committee of PBA (2009); appointed to Philadelphia Mayor's Advisory Task Force on Ethics and Campaign Finance Reform (2008); 2004 Women of Distinction (Philadelphia Business Journal); Top 50 Female Attorneys in Pennsylvania (Law & Politics and Philadelphia Magazine) (2004-12) and one of 10 women rec-

ognized as "Top 100 Lawyers in Pennsylvania" by Philadelphia Magazine (2011); Selected as a "Litigation Star" in the state of Pennsylvania of Benchmark Litigation: 2011 and 2012 Guide to America's Leading Litigation Firms and Attorneys; Listed as one of the "Top 250 Female Litigators" in America by Benchmark Litigation; Selected for inclusion in the Martindale-Hubbell® Bar Register of Preeminent Women Lawyers™, which includes less than 5 percent of women lawyers (2012-13); Included in "The Best Lawyers in America" in the area of Commercial Litigation (2013); Included in a list of "Super Lawyers" by Philadelphia Magazine and Law & Politics Magazine (2004-2012); Recognized as a "Leader in Law" by the Philadelphia Business Journal (2009-2011).

## RITTERBAND, Alan
Ballard Spahr LLP, Philadelphia
215 864 8716
ritterband@ballardspahr.com
*Featured in Real Estate (Pennsylvania)*

**Practice Areas:** Alan S. Ritterband is a partner in the Real Estate Department and Practice Leader of the Construction Group. He has extensive experience in complex transactional matters, including real estate acquisitions and sales, leasing, and real estate financing. He also frequently negotiates design, construction, and design-build agreements on behalf of owners and developers.
**Professional Memberships:** American Bar Association, Forum on the Construction Industry American College of Mortgage Attorneys, Fellow LEED Accredited Professional, as certified by the US Green Building Council.
**Career:** Admissions: Pennsylvania.
**Personal:** Education: University of Pennsylvania Law School (JD 1984) Dartmouth College (AB 1981).

## ROCCI, Steven J
Woodcock Washburn LLP, Philadelphia
215 564 8364
rocci@woodcock.com
*Featured in Intellectual Property (Pennsylvania)*

**Practice Areas:** Patent litigation, counseling in electronics, computer science, telecommunications, encryption and compression technologies, internet technologies, consumer products.
**Professional Memberships:** Member, Pennsylvania, American, and Philadelphia Bar Associations. PIPLA and AIPLA.
**Career:** Former chair of firm's Management Committee. Adjunct Professor, Patent Law and Patent Litigation at Drexel University's Earle Mack School of Law. Distinguished Practice Professor of IP Law at Earle Mack School of Law.
**Publications:** Recognized in Chambers USA since 2003, Pennsylvania Super Lawyers since 2004, Best Lawyers in America since 2006, and the Legal 500.
**Personal:** Temple University School of Law, JD (1981), Drexel University, BS, cum laude (1977).

## RODAK, Ralph
Drinker Biddle & Reath LLP, Philadelphia
215 988 2710
Ralph.Rodak@dbr.com
*Featured in Real Estate (Pennsylvania)*

**Practice Areas:** Ralph Rodak is a partner in Drinker Biddle's Real Estate Practice Group. He represents developers, investors and lenders in real estate related matters, with primary emphasis on transactional work such as sales and acquisitions, leases, financings and joint ventures. A significant portion of his practice revolves around the financing of real estate, representing both lenders and borrowers in new loan originations and the resolution of problem loans, as well as counseling property owners in their real estate investment portfolios.
**Personal:** University of Pennsylvania Law School, JD 1979 Rutgers University, BA 1976.

## ROE, Christopher M
Fox Rothschild LLP, Exton
610 458 4987
croe@foxrothschild.com
*Featured in Environment (Pennsylvania)*

**Practice Areas:** Environment, chemical handling, exposure and compliance, transactions, risk allocation, litigation.
**Professional Memberships:** Past president, Delaware Valley Environmental American Inn of Court; member, ASTM Subcommittee on Real Estate Assessment; Subcommittee advising Pennsylvania on vapor guidance; Chair, HR Committee, Legal Clinic for Disabled.
**Career:** Frequent speaker on vapor intrusion from experience in multiple states; Helped replace ASTM Standard Practice for vapor intrusion; Focus Group leader in revision of ASTM Standard Practice for Phase I assessments.
**Publications:** Vapor Intrusion: State of Science and Law, ELI's Environmental Law Reporter (2013).
**Personal:** JD, Temple University School of Law; BA, George Washington University.

## ROHN, James J
Conrad O'Brien, Philadelphia
215 864 8074
jrohn@conradobrien.com
*Featured in Litigation (Pennsylvania)*

**Practice Areas:** Chairman, Conrad O'Brien PC. He has tried and been involved as Lead Counsel in civil RICO cases, class actions, complex commercial litigation, white-collar grand jury investigations, internal corporate investigations and regulatory compliance, antitrust, insurance, securities, asset recovery, environmental, and legal malpractice cases.
**Professional Memberships:** Fellow, American College of Trial Lawyers.
**Career:** Law Clerk, Hon Louis C Bechtle (EDPa); assistant United States Attorney (1978-82), first assistant United States Attorney (1983-86), Eastern District of Pennsylvania.
**Personal:** BA and JD, Villanova University (1972) and Villanova University School of Law (1975), Member of Law Review.

## ROMANO, Carmen J
Dechert LLP, Philadelphia
215 994 2971
carmen.romano@dechert.com
*Featured in Corporate/M&A (Pennsylvania)*

**Practice Areas:** Mr Romano represents private equity firms in mergers and acquisitions across a wide variety of industries, including health care, education, food and beverage, transportation, industrial and consumer products.
**Professional Memberships:** Member, Pennsylvania Bar.
**Personal:** The Wharton School of the University of Pennsylvania (BS, 1977, summa cum laude); Columbia Law School (JD, 1980, note editor of the Columbia University Law Review).

## ROMASZEWSKI, Sandra
Fox Rothschild LLP, Warrington
215 918 3543
sromaszewski@foxrothschild.com
*Featured in Corporate/M&A (Pennsylvania)*

**Practice Areas:** Corporate, insurance and international matters for public and private companies, including mergers & acquisitions, corporate finance, securities and private placements, corporate governance, joint ventures, and insurance regulatory matters. Advises businesses from formation to sale or dissolution.
**Professional Memberships:** Member, American Bar Association, Pennsylvania Bar Association, Bucks County Bar Association; Director and Corporate Secretary, Boys & Girls Clubs of Philadelphia, Inc.; Director, Bridesburg Boys & Girls Club; Trustee, Henry Reed Hatfield Nicetown Playground; Member, Paralegal Studies Program Advisory Committee for Peirce College.
**Personal:** JD, The Thomas M. Cooley Law School, 2007; BA, cum laude, Temple University, 1998.

## ROSENBLUM, Jeremy T
Ballard Spahr LLP, Philadelphia
215 864 8505
rosenblum@ballardspahr.com
*Featured in Financial Services Regulation (Nationwide), Banking & Finance (Pennsylvania)*
See under Nationwide for profile.

## ROSENFELDT, Philip
Blank Rome LLP, Philadelphia
215 569 5686
Rosenfeldt@BlankRome.com
*Featured in Real Estate (Pennsylvania)*

**Practice Areas:** Philip Rosenfeldt maintains a national practice counseling clients in all facets of real estate transactions. Mr Rosenfeldt has 30 years of experience representing clients in ground up development; sales and acquisitions; financing; leasing; and entity structuring and restructuring for many types of projects including retail developments, office and industrial buildings and residential and mixed use projects. For more information: www.blankrome.com/Rosenfeldt

## RUDOLPH, Andrew J
Pepper Hamilton LLP, Philadelphia
215 981 4749
rudolpha@pepperlaw.com
*Featured in Labor & Employment (Pennsylvania)*

**Practice Areas:** Partner; former Chair, Employee Benefits Practice Group. Experienced in employee benefits/ERISA; executive compensation, related tax and corporate law issues for public and private companies. Practice focuses on the

development of programs that link compensation and benefits to the employer's performance; qualified and non-qualified retirement plans; executive employment and severance agreements; benefits and compensation aspects of corporate transactions. Represents clients before US Internal Revenue Service and Department of Labor.
**Professional Memberships:** Fellow, American College of Employee Benefits Counsel.
**Personal:** JD, magna cum laude, 1982 University of Pennsylvania Law School; 1978 BA, cum laude, University of Pennsylvania.

---

**RZONCA, Lynn E**
Ballard Spahr LLP, Philadelphia
215 864 8109
rzoncal@ballardspahr.com
*Featured in Intellectual Property (Pennsylvania)*
**Practice Areas:** Ms Rzonca is a partner in the Litigation and Intellectual Property Departments. Ms Rzonca is a registered patent attorney. She litigates patent, trademark, trade secret, false advertising, and copyright issues before federal courts and the US Trademark Trial and Appeal Board. She counsels clients on IP protection strategies and helps clients bring new products to market by assessing new trademarks, branding, and advertising.
**Career:** Admissions: Illinois Pennsylvania USPTO.
**Personal:** Education: Northwestern University School of Law, JD Loyola University Chicago, MA Loyola University Chicago, BA.

---

**SAINT-ANTOINE, Paul**
Drinker Biddle & Reath LLP, Philadelphia
215 988 2990
Paul.Saint-Antoine@dbr.com
*Featured in Antitrust (Pennsylvania)*
**Practice Areas:** Partner in the firm's Litigation Department and Co-Head of the firm's Antitrust Practice Group. Practice includes both antitrust litigation and counseling, with an emphasis on antitrust disputes involving pharmaceuticals and hi-tech industries.
**Professional Memberships:** Admitted to practice in Pennsylvania (1989) and New Jersey (1989). Vice Chair of the Health Care and Pharmaceuticals Committee of the ABA's Antitrust Section.
**Career:** Joined Drinker Biddle in 1989.
**Publications:** Editor-in-Chief of 'Federal Antitrust Guidelines for the Licensing of Intellectual Property, Origins and Applications' (second edition).
**Personal:** JD, Columbia University, 1989; AB, Kenyon College, 1986.

---

**SARACHAN, Ronald A**
Drinker Biddle & Reath LLP, Philadelphia
215 988 1122
Ronald.Sarachan@dbr.com
*Featured in Environment (Pennsylvania)*
**Practice Areas:** Partner, Commercial Litigation Practice Group. Team Leader, White Collar and Internal Investigations. Focuses on white collar defense, regulatory enforcement, False Claims Act and environmental litigation.

**Professional Memberships:** Co-chair, White Collar Crime Section, Environmental Crimes Subcommittee, American Bar Association; Federal Bar Association, Criminal Law Committee; Pennsylvania Bar Association.
**Career:** Served as Assistant US Attorney, Eastern District of Pennsylvania, senior litigation counsel and chief of major crimes. Served as chief of environmental crimes section, US Department of Justice, Washington, DC.
**Personal:** JD magna cum laude, University of Michigan Law School; BS magna cum laude, Brown University.

---

**SATINSKY, Barnett**
Fox Rothschild LLP, Philadelphia
215 299 2088
bsatinsky@foxrothschild.com
*Featured in Labor & Employment (Pennsylvania)*
**Practice Areas:** Broad employment practice handling union avoidance, contract negotiation, labor arbitration, employment discrimination, employment litigation, restrictive covenants, employee benefits and wage and hour law. Represents clients in industries including health care, education, electronics, manufacturing, public utilities, transportation and agriculture. Also focuses on energy and public utilities matters.
**Professional Memberships:** American Bar Association, Louis D Brandeis Law Society, National Association of College and University Attorneys, Pennsylvania Bar Association.
**Career:** Has served as Chief Counsel, Pennsylvania Public Utility Commission and Deputy Attorney General, Pennsylvania Department of Justice.
**Personal:** JD, Villanova School of Law; AB, Brown University.

---

**SCHAEDLE, Michael B.**
Blank Rome LLP, Philadelphia
215 569 5762
Schaedle@BlankRome.com
*Featured in Bankruptcy/Restructuring (Pennsylvania)*
**Practice Areas:** Michael Schaedle concentrates his practice on bankruptcy, reorganizations and workouts, debt and equity restructuring, and commercial and public debt transactions, including creditors' committees, debtors, plan-of-reorganization proponents, and asset purchasers. Representative engagements include: Centaur Gaming (creditors' committee), Mortgage Lenders Network (creditors' committee), Marco Polo Seatrade (creditors' committee), Trans World Airlines (creditors' committee), USGen New England (debtors), Nova Biosource Fuels (debtors), Philadelphia Rittenhouse (secured creditor), and Alliance Bancorp, Inc. (trustee). For more information:
www.BlankRome.com/Schaedle

---

**SCHER, Howard D**
Buchanan Ingersoll & Rooney PC,
Philadelphia
215 665 3920
howard.scher@bipc.com
*Featured in Antitrust (Pennsylvania), Litigation (Pennsylvania)*

**Career:** Howard is a Shareholder in the firm's Litigation Section. He is a fellow of the International Academy of Trial Lawyers and the American College of Trial Lawyers, the nation's two most prestigious, invitation-only, trial lawyer organizations. He specializes in trial – presenting complex law and facts to courts throughout the United States. He has a national reputation for achieving victories in the prosecution and defense of complex and sophisticated litigation. Howard is a frequent author on trial related subjects and earned his JD from Rutgers School of Law and his undergraduate degree at Brandeis University.

---

**SCHILLER, Ronald P**
Hangley Aronchick Segal Pudlin & Schiller,
Philadelphia
215 496 7020
rschiller@hangley.com
*Featured in Litigation (Pennsylvania)*
**Practice Areas:** Complex commercial litigation, particularly large insurers in sophisticated coverage, bad faith and reinsurance disputes, technology companies in disputes with public and private entities, and financial institutions in transactional disputes.
**Professional Memberships:** American Bar Association; Philadelphia Bar Association: Business Litigation Section and Insurance Committee.
**Career:** Ron has represented the world's largest insurers in coverage, bad faith, and reinsurance disputes. He has represented commercial online services, telecommunication companies, and backbone and equipment providers in cellular communications in First Amendment, IP, E911, online, and general civil litigation.
**Personal:** University of Pennsylvania Law School, JD; Temple University, BBA.

---

**SCHORLING, William H**
Buchanan Ingersoll & Rooney PC,
Philadelphia
215 665 5326
william.schorling@bipc.com
*Featured in Bankruptcy/Restructuring (Pennsylvania)*
**Career:** William is the Chair of the firm's Bankruptcy & Creditors' Rights group. He practices in the area of bankruptcy and corporate reorganization and has represented debtors, indenture trustees, creditors' committees, and secured and unsecured creditors in bankruptcy proceedings and restructurings outside bankruptcy. Bill has also represented debtors in a number of national Chapter 11 cases. Bill has been actively involved in the bankruptcy legislative process starting with the 1994 Bankruptcy Amendments Act and lectures frequently on the topics of bankruptcy, the Uniform Commercial Code and lending law. He earned his JD (cum laude) from the University of Michigan.

---

**SCHULER, Ronald W**
Spilman Thomas & Battle, PLLC, Pittsburgh
412 325 3302
rschuler@spilmanlaw.com
*Featured in Corporate/M&A (Pennsylvania)*
**Practice Areas:** Corporate, securities and commercial transactions with special emphasis on

mergers & acquisitions, public offerings, private placement financings, and contracts for clients within the energy, software, biotechnology and telecommunications industries.
**Professional Memberships:** Independent Petroleum Association of America; Allegheny County and American Bar Associations.
**Career:** Member in charge of Pittsburgh office. Formerly, Senior VP - Corporate Development, PGMT Energy; Partner, McGuireWoods; Shareholder/Associate and founding Co-Chair of Biotechnology Group, Buchanan Ingersoll.
**Personal:** Pomona College, BA, cum laude; Cornell Law School, JD.

---

**SCHWARTZ, Michael**
Pepper Hamilton LLP, Philadelphia
215 981 4494
schwartzma@pepperlaw.com
*Featured in Litigation (Pennsylvania)*
**Practice Areas:** Partner; Co-Chair, Litigation and Dispute Resolution Department. Focuses practice in criminal defense and counseling, internal corporate investigations, corporate compliance programs and First Amendment matters. Represents businesses and individuals facing investigation by federal and state law enforcement authorities, government regulatory agencies and congressional committees. Also represents businesses and individuals who have been victims of crimes.
**Career:** Former Assistant US Attorney: United States Attorney's Office for the Eastern District of Pennsylvania (Philadelphia).
**Personal:** JD 1990 Yale Law School; BA 1987 Pennsylvania State University.

---

**SCHWARZE, William W**
Panitch Schwarze Belisario & Nadel LLP,
Philadelphia
215 965 1270
wschwarze@panitchlaw.com
*Featured in Intellectual Property (Pennsylvania)*
**Practice Areas:** Mr Schwarze chairs the Chemical and Foreign Patent Practices in the firm. Fluent in German, he counsels many German and Japanese companies in patent matters. He has many clients in the medical arts and focuses his practice on patent prosecution, licensing and opinion work.
**Professional Memberships:** Pennsylvania Bar; Philadelphia and American Bar Associations; Philadelphia Intellectual Property Law Association; US Court of Appeals for the Federal Circuit; United States Patent and Trademark Office.
**Personal:** BChE, Yale University (1965); LLB, University of Pennsylvania (1968).

---

**SCOLNIC, David**
Hangley Aronchick Segal Pudlin & Schiller,
Philadelphia
215 496 7046
dscolnic@hangley.com
*Featured in Real Estate (Pennsylvania)*
**Practice Areas:** International real estate and corporate matters, including acquisition, development, construction, financing, investment, leasing and management. Represents developers,

investors, lenders, brokers and governments, as well as non-industry companies. Corporate practice includes acquisitions, sales, financing, and contracts. Serves as outside general counsel to clients.
**Professional Memberships:** Member, Pennsylvania and New Jersey Bars; ABA Section on Real Property, Probate and Trust Law.
**Career:** Hangley Aronchick Segal Pudlin & Schiller, Shareholder, 1997-present, associate, 1995-97; Drinker Biddle & Reath, 1986-95, associate; New York University, School of Law, JD, 1986; University of Pennsylvania, MCP, 1983, BA, 1982.

### SEGAL, Daniel
Hangley Aronchick Segal Pudlin & Schiller, Philadelphia
215 496 7003
dsegal@hangley.com
*Featured in Litigation (Pennsylvania)*
**Practice Areas:** Civil/commercial litigation involving defamation, First Amendment, intellectual property, health care, professional ethics, education, civil rights, securities, antitrust, academic research misconduct, and employment.
**Professional Memberships:** Juvenile Law Center; University of Pennsylvania Inn of Court; American, Pennsylvania, and Philadelphia Bar Associations; Vice President, Hillel of Greater Philadelphia; International Member, New Israel Fund.
**Career:** Founder, Hangley Aronchick Segal Pudlin & Schiller, 1994 to present; shareholder, Hangley Connolly Epstein Chicco Foxman and Ewing, 1979-94; assistant Law Professor, University of Pennsylvania Law School, 1976-79; clerk, Hon. Thurgood Marshall, US Supreme Court, 1975-76; clerk, Hon. David L Bazelon, US Court of Appeals, DC Circuit, 1974-75; Harvard Law School, JD, magna cum laude; London School of Economics, MSc; Yale College, BA, magna cum laude.

### SELTZER, Greg
Ballard Spahr LLP, Philadelphia
215 864 8142
seltzerg@ballardspahr.com
*Featured in Corporate/M&A (Pennsylvania)*
**Practice Areas:** Gregory L. Seltzer is a transactional attorney in the Business and Finance Department who utilizes legal, accounting, and business disciplines to provide business law services to clients. He concentrates his practice on public and private merger and acquisitions transactions. He also handles a multitude of securities matters, including public and private securities offerings, capital-raising transactions and disclosure issues, private equity and venture capital transactions, and corporate governance and general contract matters.
**Career:** Admissions: Pennsylvania.
**Personal:** Temple University James E. Beasley School of Law (JD 1992) Temple University (MBA 2003) Pennsylvania State University (BS 1998).

### SHAPIRO, Joel Charles
Blank Rome LLP, Philadelphia
215 569 5746
Shapiro-JC@BlankRome.com
*Featured in Bankruptcy/Restructuring (Pennsylvania)*
**Practice Areas:** Joel Shapiro concentrates his practice on bankruptcy, reorganizations and workouts and other banking and commercial lending matters, including loan restructuring, debtor-in-possession financing, intercreditor relationships and lender liability prevention and defense, primarily representing institutional lenders, lender groups, creditors, creditors' committees, debtors, plan of reorganization proponents, and asset purchasers. For more information: www.BlankRome.com/Shapiro-JC.

### SHAPIRO, Raymond
Blank Rome LLP, Philadelphia
215 569 5569
Shapiro@BlankRome.com
*Featured in Bankruptcy/Restructuring (Pennsylvania)*
**Practice Areas:** Raymond Shapiro is a member of the National Bankruptcy Conference and the International Insolvency Institute. He is former Chair of the American College of Bankruptcy. He primarily represents institutional lenders and lender syndicates, creditors and creditors' committees, debtors, plan-of-reorganization proponents, and asset purchasers. He regularly advises corporations in areas such as bankruptcies and creditors' rights; reorganizations and workouts; loan and debt restructuring; debtor-in-possession financing; and intercreditor relationships. For more information: www.BlankRome.com/Shapiro.

### SHARGEL, Jason M
Cozen O'Connor, Philadelphia
215 665 6914
jshargel@cozen.com
*Featured in Corporate/M&A (Pennsylvania)*
**Practice Areas:** Jason has more than 30 years of experience in the private practice of corporate and securities law. Having begun his career in the SEC's Enforcement Division, his practice includes mergers and acquisitions, as well as the representation of issuers and funds in venture capital and growth capital financings. He has also represented issuers in a wide variety of public and private offerings of debt and equity securities.
**Personal:** University of Pennsylvania Law School, JD, 1977 Columbia University, BA, 1974.

### SICALIDES, Barbara T
Pepper Hamilton LLP, Philadelphia
215 981 4783
sicalidesb@pepperlaw.com
*Featured in Antitrust (Pennsylvania)*
**Practice Areas:** Partner; Head of Antitrust Section of Commercial Litigation Group. Experienced in antitrust counseling and litigation; Hart-Scott-Rodino filings/proceedings. Represented UK flat glass manufacturer in treble damage class action; tobacco company in Robinson-Patman Act and distributor termination; bathroom/kitchen fixtures/fittings manufacturer in allegations of price fixing.

**Professional Memberships:** President, Board of Trustees, Community Legal Services of Philadelphia; Co-Chair, Antitrust Committee, and Member, Executive Committee, Business Law Section, Philadelphia Bar Association; Board of Directors/past President, Philadelphia Volunteers for the Indigent Program; Chair, Steering Committee, Philadelphia LawWorks.
**Personal:** JD, cum laude, 1989 Temple University School of Law; BA 1983 Barnard College, Columbia University.

### SILVERMAN, Robert A
Cozen O'Connor, Philadelphia
215 665 4620
rsilverman@cozen.com
*Featured in Real Estate (Pennsylvania)*
**Practice Areas:** Bob represents developers, lenders (including mezzanine lenders), and owners in a variety of sophisticated transactions, including joint venture transactions, distressed loan purchases, and the sale, purchase and development of office buildings, shopping centers, hotels, apartment buildings, warehouse/industrial properties, and condominiums. His practice also includes the representation of residential developers and homebuilders, opportunistic purchasers of commercial real estate, buyers and sellers of investment quality properties, and borrowers and lenders in workout and foreclosure situations. He also actively participates in real estate litigation matters.
**Personal:** University of Pennsylvania Law School, JD, 1981 Franklin and Marshall College, BA, 1978.

### SINATRA, Geraldine
Dechert LLP, Philadelphia
215 994 2824
geraldine.sinatra@dechert.com
*Featured in Corporate/M&A (Pennsylvania)*
**Practice Areas:** Ms Sinatra advises private equity sponsors in their domestic and cross-border acquisitions of portfolio companies and related financing transactions. She also represents sponsors and their portfolio companies in subsequent add-on acquisitions or dispositions, financings, dividend recapitalization transactions, and restructurings.
**Professional Memberships:** Member, Pennsylvania and New Jersey Bars.
**Personal:** Ohio State University (BS, 1988, summa cum laude); Ohio State University College of Law (JD, 1991, summa cum laude; Order of the Coif; managing editor, Ohio State Law Journal).

### SINGER, Alan
Morgan, Lewis & Bockius LLP, Philadelphia
215 963 5224
asinger@morganlewis.com
*Featured in Corporate/M&A (Pennsylvania)*
**Practice Areas:** Alan Singer is a partner in Morgan Lewis's Securities Practice. Mr Singer advises companies on a wide range of corporate and securities matters. He counsels public companies with respect to annual and periodic Securities and Exchange Commission (SEC) filings, proxy statements, executive compensation disclosure, and beneficial ownership reporting. He also pro-

vides advice to companies regarding corporate governance, compliance with stock exchange listing standards and other SEC regulatory and corporate matters. In addition, Mr Singer has represented companies and investment bankers in public and non-public offerings. He has been listed in Chambers since its first US publication in 2003.

### SITARCHUK, Eric W
Morgan, Lewis & Bockius LLP, Philadelphia
215 963 5840
esitarchuk@morganlewis.com
*Featured in Litigation (Pennsylvania)*
**Practice Areas:** Chair, White Collar Litigation and Government Investigations Practice. Focuses on white collar criminal defense and related civil litigation including False Claims Act/qui tam actions. Handles government/internal investigations, and litigation involving alleged healthcare, defense contract, securities, and tax fraud; FCPA, antitrust, environmental, and export violations; trade secrets theft; official corruption; ponzi schemes; and other offenses. Counsels on internal compliance/ethics programs, and the FCPA.
**Professional Memberships:** Fellow of the American College of Trial Lawyers.
**Career:** Former Assistant US Attorney, Criminal Division, US Attorney's Office, Philadelphia; Former Special Assistant United States Attorney, US Attorney's Office, Public Corruption Section, Washington, DC.

### SKLAROFF, Michael
Ballard Spahr LLP, Philadelphia
215 864 8700
sklaroff@ballardspahr.com
*Featured in Real Estate (Pennsylvania)*
**Practice Areas:** Michael Sklaroff chairs the Real Estate Department and manages the firm's real estate practice, one of the largest in the nation. Mr Sklaroff's practice encompasses development, property tax, condemnation, land use, and serving as counsel to cultural institutions.
**Professional Memberships:** American College of Real Estate Lawyers College of Physicians of Philadelphia Counselors of Real Estate Development Workshop, Inc. Philadelphia, Pennsylvania, and American Bar Associations.
**Career:** Admissions: Pennsylvania.
**Personal:** Education: University of Pennsylvania Law School (LLB 1967, magna cum laude) Editor, 'University of Pennsylvania Law Review' Columbia College (AB 1964).

### SKLAROFF, Neil
Ballard Spahr LLP, Philadelphia
215 864 8514
sklaroffn@ballardspahr.com
*Featured in Real Estate (Pennsylvania)*
**Practice Areas:** Neil Sklaroff, a partner in the Real Estate Department, focuses his practice on zoning and land use and other real estate-related matters. He represents developers, institutions, universities, and municipalities in land use matters before agencies and courts. Recently, he established the primacy of Philadelphia's Historical Commission in historic preservation matters. Turchi v. Board of License and Inspection Review, 20 A.3d 586 (Pa. Cmwlth. 2011).

**Career:** Admissions: Pennsylvania US District Court for the Eastern District of Pennsylvania US Court of Appeals for the Third Circuit.
**Personal:** Education: Temple University School of Law (JD 1973) Emory University (BA 1969).

## SMITH, James T
Blank Rome LLP, Philadelphia
215 569 5643
Smith-JT@BlankRome.com
*Featured in Litigation (Pennsylvania)*
**Practice Areas:** James T. Smith has more than 30 years experience in complex commercial litigation and white collar criminal defense, nationwide. He chairs the Firm's Litigation Department where he oversees 200 attorneys included within nine practice groups in ten cities. Mr Smith serves both corporate and individual clients in a wide variety of industries including technology, transportation, healthcare, aerospace and defense, in disputes involving fraud and abuse, intellectual property, corporate governance, government and internal investigations, white collar criminal defense, breach of contract and related claims and many other areas. For more information: www.BlankRome.com/Smith-JT.

## SONNENFELD, Marc
Morgan, Lewis & Bockius LLP, Philadelphia
215 963 5572
msonnenfeld@morganlewis.com
*Featured in Litigation (Pennsylvania)*
**Practice Areas:** Securities Litigation Group Leader, Philadelphia. Practice focuses on defending securities and shareholder litigation and related regulatory and enforcement proceedings, defending shareholder class and derivative litigation challenging public company acquisitions, and counseling directors, officers, and board committees on corporate governance issues. Served as counsel for board of directors' special litigation committees for several public companies. Successfully defended shareholder class and derivative actions against public and private corporations, controlling shareholders, directors and officers, and underwriters arising under federal and state law. Appellate practice includes appearing as amicus curiae in several significant cases.
**Professional Memberships:** Fellow, American College of Trial Lawyers.

## SOSLOW, Joanne R
Morgan, Lewis & Bockius LLP, Philadelphia
215 963 5262
jsoslow@morganlewis.com
*Featured in Corporate/M&A (Pennsylvania)*
**Practice Areas:** Joanne R. Soslow is a partner in Morgan Lewis's Business and Finance Practice. Focused on corporate and securities matters, Ms Soslow is dedicated to working with public companies and emerging growth businesses primarily in the biotechnology, financial services, technology, medical device and specialty pharmaceutical sectors. Ms Soslow's transactional practice is focused on complex public and private equity and debt securities, venture capital and mergers and acquisitions transactions. In addition, she regularly advises clients in all aspects of their growth cycle, from business plan development and start-

up structuring to exit strategies, including IPOs and change in control transactions.

## SPENCER, Steven D
Morgan, Lewis & Bockius LLP, Philadelphia
215 963 5714
sspencer@morganlewis.com
*Featured in Labor & Employment (Pennsylvania)*
**Practice Areas:** Steven D. Spencer is the leader of Morgan Lewis's Employee Benefits and Executive Compensation Practice. His practice focuses on collectively bargained employee benefit plans, particularly as they are affected by various labor and employment laws. He regularly advises employers that contribute to multiemployer pension and welfare trust funds regarding withdrawal liability and the Pension Protection Act of 2006.
**Personal:** Graduated from Columbia University Law School (1978, JD) and Cornell University (1975, BS). Admitted to practice in Pennsylvania and New York. He also teaches Employee Benefit Law at the University of Pennsylvania and Villanova University Law Schools.

## SPROUL, Gayle
Levine Sullivan Koch & Schulz LLP, Philadelphia
215 988 9782
gsproul@lskslaw.com
*Featured in Litigation (Pennsylvania)*
**Practice Areas:** Almost 30 years experience representing media in libel, invasion of privacy, copyright and First Amendment cases. Recently won press subpoena decision in Baker v. Goldman Sachs in Second Circuit and argued for open government in Levy v. Senate in Pennsylvania Supreme Court. In 2010, won unanimous jury verdict for Pennsylvania newspaper in defamation case. Member of firm's Executive Committee.
**Publications:** "Privilege Paves the Road to Dismissal in Defamation Cases," Communications Lawyer.
**Personal:** Born 13 December 1954. JD, Villanova University, Managing Editor, Villanova Law Review; Law Clerk to Hon. John P. Fullam (E.D. Pa.).; Masters in Journalism, Temple University.

## STACK JR, Stephen A
Dechert LLP, Philadelphia
215 994 2660
stephen.stack@dechert.com
*Featured in Antitrust (Pennsylvania)*
**Practice Areas:** Mr Stack has extensive experience handling a full range of antitrust activities ranging from preventive counseling to litigation. He regularly represents clients on antitrust issues relating to intellectual property and mergers.
**Professional Memberships:** Member, Pennsylvania Bar; admitted to practice before numerous federal courts; member, American Bar Association Antitrust Section.
**Career:** Mr Stack served on the Justice Department's advisory committee of President George W. Bush's Transition Team.
**Publications:** Author, "Handbook of US Antitrust Sources," ABA Antitrust Section
**Personal:** Yale University (BA, 1967, cum laude); University of Pennsylvania School of Law (JD, 1970, cum laude).

## STERN, Joan N
Blank Rome LLP, Philadelphia
215 569 5526
Stern@BlankRome.com
*Featured in Banking & Finance (Pennsylvania)*
**Practice Areas:** Joan N. Stern concentrates her practice in all areas of public finance law in Pennsylvania and throughout the country, including general government, education, transportation and utilities, tax and revenue anticipation financing, healthcare and housing finance, refinancing and working capital, and distressed credits. She serves as bond, underwriter's, issuer's, credit enhancement, swap, and trustee's counsel and represents public and private entities in P3 matters. She also represents clients in enforcement matters involving the SEC and IRS. Ms Stern has drafted significant debt and finance legislation for Pennsylvania and other states. For more information: www.BlankRome.com/Stern.

## STUART, Glen R
Morgan, Lewis & Bockius LLP, Philadelphia
215 963 5883
gstuart@morganlewis.com
*Featured in Environment (Pennsylvania)*
**Practice Areas:** Complex commercial litigation practice focusing on environmental law, toxic torts, and pharmaceutical matters. Successfully defended and tried private cost recovery actions; pursued and defended third-party contribution claims; defended property diminution claims; negotiated consent decrees, including two of the first CERCLA response actions funded through mixed funding; represented companies in defense of NRD claims. Provide counsel to Trusts and Steering Committees through all phases of Superfund remediation. Actively involved in defense of water company's groundwater contamination claim and defense of another law firm in legal malpractice claim arising out of environmental litigation.

## SUMMERS, John
Hangley Aronchick Segal Pudlin & Schiller, Philadelphia
215 496 7007
jsummers@hangley.com
*Featured in Litigation (Pennsylvania)*
**Practice Areas:** Complex civil and white-collar criminal defense, healthcare, ERISA, professional malpractice, class actions.
**Professional Memberships:** American Law Institute; Philadelphia Bar Foundation, former treasurer and secretary; The Reinvestment Fund, Vice-Chairman and Executive Committee Member; Disciplinary Board of the Supreme Court of Pennsylvania, past Chair of Hearing Panel.
**Career:** Hangley Aronchick Segal Pudlin & Schiller, Shareholder, 1994 to present. Hangley Connolly Epstein Chicco Foxman & Ewing, 1986-94. Law clerk, Honorable Thomas N O'Neill, Jr, US District Court, Eastern District of Pennsylvania, 1984-86. University of Pennsylvania Law School, JD, Editor, Law Review. Wesleyan University, BA, magna cum laude.

## SUMNER, Robin P
Pepper Hamilton LLP, Philadelphia
215 981 4652
sumnerr@pepperlaw.com
*Featured in Antitrust (Pennsylvania)*
**Practice Areas:** Partner. Antitrust/competition law, securities law and complex civil litigation, including class actions and multi-district litigation. Has significant experience litigating a variety of cases in the healthcare industry, including cases alleging violations of antitrust laws and False Claims Act. Represents cooperatives and trade association in a series of putative class actions alleging an industry-wide supply restriction scheme to fix the prices of eggs and egg products sold in the United States during an eight year period.
**Personal:** JD 1998 University of California, Berkeley, Boalt Hall School of Law; AB, magna cum laude, 1992 Brown University.

## TATE, Joseph A
Dechert LLP, Philadelphia
215 994 2350
joseph.tate@dechert.com
*Featured in Antitrust (Pennsylvania), Litigation (Pennsylvania)*
**Practice Areas:** Mr Tate defends US and foreign corporations, executives, lawyers, and others against allegations of white collar crime, with particular emphasis on antitrust, patent fraud, and other regulatory issues. His practice also involves complex civil litigation and class actions.
**Professional Memberships:** Member, Pennsylvania and Massachusetts Bars; fellow, American College of Trial Lawyers; faculty member, Philadelphia Bar Association's Trial Advocacy Program; member, Board of Consultors of Villanova Law School.
**Career:** Former prosecutor, US Department of Justice, Antitrust Division.
**Personal:** Villanova University, (AB, 1963); Villanova University School of Law, (LLB, 1966, member, Villanova University Law Review).

## TEMIN, Michael L
Fox Rothschild LLP, Philadelphia
215 299 3835
mtemin@foxrothschild.com
*Featured in Bankruptcy/Restructuring (Pennsylvania)*
**Practice Areas:** Bankruptcy and Ethics. Advises, consults and represents participants and others in restructuring of insolvent businesses.
**Professional Memberships:** Adjunct Professor, University of Pennsylvania Law School (20+ years). Former Scholar in Residence and current Fellow, American College of Bankruptcy. Former Chair, Eastern District of Pennsylvania Bankruptcy Conference. Former Co-Chair, Legal Ethics & Professional Responsibilities Committee (PBA).
**Career:** Admitted to PA and DE.
**Publications:** Contributing author, Collier on Bankruptcy, Collier Bankruptcy Practice Guide. Co-editor, Pennsylvania Ethics Handbook.
**Personal:** Received BA, magna cum laude, from Yale University in 1954; and LLB, cum laude, from University of Pennsylvania in 1957.

**THOMPSON, Thomas M**
Buchanan Ingersoll & Rooney PC, Pittsburgh
412 562 8855
thomas.thompson@bipc.com
*Featured in Corporate/M&A (Pennsylvania)*
**Career:** Thomas is a Shareholder in the firm's Corporate Section. Drawing on more than 40 years of legal experience, Tom works primarily in the areas of corporate acquisitions, corporate governance, private placements and venture capital financings. Among others, Tom has represented manufacturing companies, venture capital funds, insurance companies, radio stations, restaurant chains, oil and gas companies, regional investment banking firms, public companies, family businesses, management groups and investors. A published author, Tom has made many presentations and written extensive materials on letters of intent, opinion letters, and mergers and acquisitions. He earned his JD (cum laude) from Harvard University.

**TILLERY, M Kelly**
Pepper Hamilton LLP, Philadelphia
215 981 4401
tilleryk@pepperlaw.com
*Featured in Intellectual Property (Pennsylvania)*
**Practice Areas:** Partner. Experienced in intellectual property litigation; known for work in anti-counterfeiting actions, especially injunctions and seizure orders; individual, national and facility injunctions to protect the trademarks and copyrights of performing artists as well as major software, novelty, jewelry and designer manufacturers from around the world; commercial litigation.
**Professional Memberships:** Arbitrator, World Intellectual Property Organization; arbitrator, Intellectual Property Panel, National Arbitration Forum; Member, Philadelphia Intellectual Property Law Association; Member, Copyright Society of the USA, Philadelphia Chapter; former Member, Board of Directors, International Anti-Counterfeiting Coalition.
**Personal:** JD 1979 University of Pennsylvania Law School; BA, high honors, 1976 Swarthmore College.

**TOLL, Curtis B.**
Greenberg Traurig, LLP, Philadelphia
215 988 7804
TollC@gtlaw.com
*Featured in Environment (Pennsylvania)*
**Practice Areas:** Environmental; real estate; retail; global energy and infrastructure.
**Professional Memberships:** Member, Board of Counselors, Penn State University's Dickinson School of Law.
**Career:** Listed: Chambers USA Guide, 2005-06, 2008-13; Best Lawyers in America, 2012-13. Member, Winning Team, 2010 Chambers and Partners USA Award for Excellence in Real Estate. Team Member, a Law360 'Real Estate Practice Group of the Year', 2011-12.
**Publications:** Author, 'Trash to Treasure-The Evolution of Brownfield Development and Renewable Energy Opportunities on

Contaminated Property', Lexicon, Penn State The Dickinson School of Law Magazine, Spring 2011.
**Personal:** JD, The Dickinson School of Law; BS, University of Pittsburgh.

**TUCCI, Peter J.**
Fox Rothschild LLP, Philadelphia
215 918 3562
ptucci@foxrothschild.com
*Featured in Corporate/M&A (Pennsylvania)*
**Practice Areas:** International and corporate matters: mergers and acquisitions; insurance and reinsurance transactions; private equity transactions; corporate finance; joint ventures.
**Professional Memberships:** American Society of the French Legion of Honor; International, American, Pennsylvania and Philadelphia Bar Associations.
**Career:** Chair, Fox Rothschild International Practice; member of Fox Rothschild's Executive Committee; Named a Chevalier (Knight) of the French Legion of Honor by the President of the Republic of France, Jacques Chirac; Pennsylvania "Super Lawyers" (2004 through 2012); Philadelphia Business Journal's "40 Under 40" award (2001); "Super Lawyers" International (2010).
**Personal:** JD, Georgetown University Law Center; BSFS, cum laude, Georgetown University.

**UNTERBERGER, Glenn L**
Ballard Spahr LLP, Philadelphia
215 864 8210
unterberge@ballardspahr.com
*Featured in Environment (Pennsylvania)*
**Practice Areas:** Glenn L. Unterberger is partner leader of the Environmental Group. He represents energy, large industrial, and finance clients on environmental issues related to permitting, compliance activities, strategic planning, and business and real estate transactions. He is a former national enforcement program manager with the US Environmental Protection Agency.
**Professional Memberships:** Pennsylvania Chamber of Business and Industry Co-chair, Air Quality Work Group Federal Bar Association.
**Career:** Admissions: District of Columbia Maryland Pennsylvania.
**Publications:** "Primer on Air Pollution Control Issues, Including Permitting and Climate Change," chapter in 2011/2012 Guidebook on Complying with Pennsylvania Environmental Laws and Regulations.

**VERNICK, Scott**
Fox Rothschild LLP, Philadelphia
215 299 2860
svernick@foxrothschild.com
*Featured in Litigation (Pennsylvania)*
**Practice Areas:** Scott has a national trial practice focusing on technology, pharmaceutical and healthcare. His practice emphasizes intellectual property, licensing and technology transfer agreements, trade secrets, electronic payments, mergers and acquisitions, corporate changes of control, privacy and data security, software and hardware service agreements, government contracting and procurement, FCRA, FDCPA and TIL.

**Publications:** Guest Commentary – "Steven Tyler Act' Legal?' The Willis Report (March 2013); 'To Catch a Hacker, Companies Start To Think Like One,' Law360 (February 2013); 'As Sales of Drones Increase So Do Privacy Concerns,' WPVI-TV ABC News (February 2013); 'Data Privacy: Television Interview,' WPHL-TV (February 2013); 'Data Privacy Day: Attorneys Call for Better Online Protection,' ABC News Radio (January 2013); 'Stormy Weather: The Pitfalls of Cloud Computing,' Philadelphia Business Journal (January 2013); 'UK Fine Likely Just the Start of Sony's Breach Woes,' Law360 (January 2013); 'Privacy Regulation and Legislation to Watch in 2013,' Law360 (January 2013); 'Balancing the Fight Against Piracy Versus Free Speech,' The Willis Report (January 2012).
**Personal:** JD, cum laude, Georgetown University, 1987; BA, Trinity College, 1983.

**VUOCOLO, Diane E**
Greenberg Traurig, LLP, Philadelphia
215 988 7803
VuocoloD@gtlaw.com
*Featured in Bankruptcy/Restructuring (Pennsylvania)*
**Practice Areas:** Business reorganization and financial restructuring.
**Professional Memberships:** Mediator for the Delaware bankruptcy courts; Former Chair, Bankruptcy Law Section, New Jersey State Bar Association. Member: American Bar Association; Pennsylvania Bar Association; American Bankruptcy Institute; Association of Insolvency and Restructuring Advisors; and Organization of Insolvency Lawyers of the Third Circuit.
**Career:** Appointed to Judicial Merit Selection Committee for the US Bankruptcy Court-D.N.J., 2006; appointed Member, Lawyers' Advisory Committee to the US Bankruptcy Court for the District of New Jersey, 1997-2000, 2003-04, 2006-08.
**Personal:** JD, Temple University James E. Beasley School of Law; MPP, Rutgers University; BA, Rutgers University.

**WALL, Steven R**
Morgan, Lewis & Bockius LLP, Philadelphia
215 963 4928
swall@morganlewis.com
*Featured in Labor & Employment (Pennsylvania)*
**Practice Areas:** Steven Wall is Morgan Lewis's global Managing Partner of Practice and a senior partner in the Labor and Employment Practice. Steven is responsible for working with the firm's practice group and industry sector leaders on strategic business planning, talent management, and practice management. He served as the practice leader of the global Labor and Employment Practice from 2003 to 2009. His client service centers on traditional labor strategic advice, class-based employment litigation, and executive compensation and employment agreements.
**Personal:** Cornell Law School, 1983, JD; Cornell University, 1979, BS.

**WEIN, Howard J**
Buchanan Ingersoll & Rooney PC, Pittsburgh
412 392 2160
howard.wein@bipc.com
*Featured in Environment (Pennsylvania)*
**Career:** Howard is a Shareholder in the firm's Energy Section. His environmental practice focuses on water quality, waste management, mining and air quality matters at the state and federal levels. He has handled major environmental litigation in Federal Court, Commonwealth Court and Pennsylvania's Environmental Hearing Board. His environmental litigation clients are in the oil, gas, energy and natural resources industries. In addition, Howard has handled complex transactions involving permitting and environmental issues on behalf of buyers and sellers of industrial properties and other clients. He earned his JD from the University of Pittsburgh School of Law.

**WEISS, Harry R**
Ballard Spahr LLP, Philadelphia
215 864 8129
weiss@ballardspahr.com
*Featured in Environment (Pennsylvania)*
**Practice Areas:** Harry Weiss litigates environmental matters in state and federal courts, and before regulatory agencies. He represents the Philadelphia Regional Port Authority in the Delaware River Main Channel Deepening dispute. Mr Weiss is also active in matters involving natural gas exploration and development in the Marcellus Shale formation.
**Professional Memberships:** American Bar Association Section of Energy and Environmental Resources, Permanent Committee on Environmental Transactions and Brownfields.
**Career:** Admissions: New Jersey Pennsylvania.
**Publications:** Co-author, "The Future of Oil, Gas Drilling in the Delaware River Basin," BNA's Daily Report for Executives, January 23, 2012.

**WESTON, R Timothy**
K&L Gates, Harrisburg
717 231 4504
tim.weston@klgates.com
*Featured in Environment (Pennsylvania)*
**Practice Areas:** With over 41 years experience in a practice focused on environmental regulation and litigation, energy and infrastructure development, and water and natural resources management, Mr Weston is co-practice group coordinator of the firm's global energy practice. He has handled a broad range of complex project development, transactional, public-private partnership, regulatory, and environmental regulatory matters. Prior to joining K&L Gates, Mr Weston served for 15 years in the Pennsylvania Department of Environmental Resources as an Assistant Attorney General and later Associate Deputy Secretary for Resources Management, overseeing a broad spectrum of natural resource and environmental protection programs.

**WILLIAMS, James R**
Cozen O'Connor, Philadelphia
215 665 4698
jrwilliams@cozen.com
*Featured in Real Estate (Pennsylvania)*

**Practice Areas:** James is a member of the firm's Real Estate Group, representing financial institutions and developers in real estate transactions, with a particular emphasis on transactions involving tax-exempt financial institutions. His practice encompasses a broad range of real estate matters, including financing, acquisitions, sales, leasing, and development in a number of major metropolitan areas.
**Professional Memberships:** Pennsylvania Bar Association.
**Personal:** New York University School of Law, JD, 1982 University of Pennsylvania, BA, 1978.

## WILSON, Craig P
K&L Gates, Harrisburg
717 231 4509
craig.wilson@klgates.com
*Featured in Environment (Pennsylvania)*
**Practice Areas:** Craig Wilson concentrates his practice in the areas of energy, the environment and natural resources, and serves as co-coordinator of the firm's Environmental, Land and Natural Resources practice group. Mr Wilson has counseled clients who are exploring for, producing and transporting natural gas, clients who are developing and operating energy projects and other commercial and industrial projects, clients who are seeking environmental permits and zoning and land development approvals from government agencies, and clients who are parties to business transactions or litigation involving potential environmental liabilities.

## WINNING JR, William J
Cozen O'Connor, Philadelphia
610 941 5400
wwinning@cozen.com
*Featured in Litigation (Pennsylvania)*
**Practice Areas:** Bill concentrates his practice in the representation of individuals and corporations under investigation for, or charged with, violations of federal and state criminal law and has tried numerous cases to verdict in both federal and state courts. Bill also has significant experience representing clients in a variety of regulatory and government compliance matters.
**Professional Memberships:** American Bar Association, American College of Trial Lawyers, National Association of Criminal Defense Lawyers, Pennsylvania Association of Criminal Defense Lawyers.
**Career:** Chair, Criminal Defense and Government Investigations.
**Personal:** Villanova University School of Law, JD, 1973; La Salle University, BA, 1970.

## WINOKUR, Barton J
Dechert LLP, Philadelphia
215 994 2505
barton.winokur@dechert.com
*Featured in Corporate/M&A (Pennsylvania)*
**Practice Areas:** Mr Winokur is the former chief executive officer of the firm. He concentrates his practice on representing public and private companies, leveraged buyout sponsor funds, and venture capital firms in complex corporate transactions including mergers, acquisitions, divestitures, joint ventures, and restructurings. He also advises boards and special committees of public companies on corporate governance matters.
**Professional Memberships:** Member, Pennsylvania and New York Bars; former chair, Board of Trustees, Brandeis University; member, Board of Trustees, Cornell University; member, Council on Foreign Relations.
**Personal:** Cornell University (AB, 1961); Harvard Law School (LLB, 1964, editor of the Harvard Law Review).

## WITT, Thomas
Cozen O'Connor, Philadelphia
215 665 5578
twitt@cozen.com
*Featured in Real Estate (Pennsylvania)*
**Practice Areas:** Tom has extensive experience in commercial real estate transactions, including sales, leasing, financing, brokers licensing, zoning, and land development regulation. His subspecialties include zoning, land use, and historic preservation for projects in Philadelphia, including the Comcast Center (tallest building in the city), the luxury condominium 1706 Rittenhouse Square, and the National Museum of American Jewish History. Additional subspecialties are sale leaseback transactions and the representation of office tenants in leasing.
**Professional Memberships:** American Bar Association, Pennsylvania Bar Association, Philadelphia Bar Association.
**Personal:** Temple University School of Law, JD, 1975 Harvard University, MA, 1969 La Salle University, BA, 1968.

## WOELFLING, Maxine
Morgan, Lewis & Bockius LLP, Harrisburg
717 237 5065
mwoelfling@morganlewis.com
*Featured in Environment (Pennsylvania)*
**Practice Areas:** Practice focuses on environmental law and involves permitting, compliance counseling, litigation of permitting and enforcement issues before state and federal administrative and judicial tribunals, and environmental issues in business and financial transactions and bankruptcy. It encompasses a broad range of environmental subjects, including air quality, solid and hazardous waste, water quality, wetlands and waterways obstructions, surface and deep coal mining, gas drilling, and environmental remediation. She has been extensively involved in counseling clients regarding management of legacy coal mining discharges and permitting of conventional and alternative energy projects, including coal, waste coal, natural gas, wind, and solar.

## WOLFSOHN, David J
Woodcock Washburn LLP, Philadelphia
215 564 2222
wolfsohn@woodcock.com
*Featured in Intellectual Property (Pennsylvania)*
**Practice Areas:** Patent, copyright, trade secret, trademark, licensing, unfair competition, and noncompete litigation.
**Professional Memberships:** Past Co-Chair of the Trial Evidence Committee, ABA Section of Litigation; Past President of the Federal Bar Association, ED Pa Chapter; Copyright Society of the USA.
**Career:** Served on Woodcock Washburn's Policy Committee (governance body); Co-Chair of Pro Bono Committee.
**Publications:** Frequent lecturer on trial strategies, e-discovery, deposition techniques, and intellectual property.
**Personal:** University of Chicago Law School, JD, cum laude, Order of Coif (1988), Manhattan School of Music, Doctor of Musical Arts (1984), Villa Schifanoia Graduate School of Fine Arts, Florence, MM (1976).

## ZABRISKIE, Mims Maynard
Morgan, Lewis & Bockius LLP, Philadelphia
215 963 5036
mzabriskie@morganlewis.com
*Featured in Labor & Employment (Pennsylvania)*
**Practice Areas:** Mims Maynard Zabriskie is a partner in Morgan Lewis's Employee Benefits and Executive Compensation Practice. She counsels clients with respect to all aspects of employee benefits, including executive compensation arrangements, equity compensation plans, change in control arrangements and tax-qualified retirement plans.
**Professional Memberships:** She has been active in a variety of professional and civic organizations, and lectures for continuing legal education programs on executive compensation and equity compensation issues.
**Personal:** Graduated from University of Virginia School of Law (1979, JD) and Vanderbilt University (1976, BA). Admitted to practice in Pennsylvania and Virginia and before the US Supreme Court.

## ZANIC, Michael G
K&L Gates, Pittsburgh
412 355 6219
michael.zanic@klgates.com
*Featured in Litigation (Pennsylvania)*
**Practice Areas:** A co-leader of K&L Gates' global Energy, Infrastructure and Resources practice area, Michael Zanic has focused his practice on providing strategic advice to energy, manufacturing and construction companies, including in the areas of insurance coverage and innovative solutions to toxic-tort-related problems. He has litigated major environmental, asbestos, product liability, property damage and business interruption insurance coverage cases, under property and general liability insurance policies, in courts across the US, having recovered in excess of $1.75 billion in insurance coverage claims for policyholders he has represented. Additionally, he has represented companies in business operations or disputes throughout the world.

## ZEIGER, Alan L
Blank Rome LLP, Philadelphia
215 569 5754
Zeiger@BlankRome.com
*Featured in Corporate/M&A (Pennsylvania)*
**Practice Areas:** Alan Zeiger chairs Blank Rome's Business Department consisting of more than 190 attorneys practicing globally in numerous industries. He represents public and private companies and private equity funds, as well as entrepreneurs. He frequently counsels clients in mergers and acquisitions, early-stage seed capital, private equity/venture capital, joint venture transactions and capital formation. For more information: www.BlankRome.com/Zeiger.

## ZINN, Robert P
K&L Gates, Pittsburgh
412 355 8687
robert.zinn@klgates.com
*Featured in Corporate/M&A (Pennsylvania)*
**Practice Areas:** Global head of K&L Gates' M&A practice and a firmwide leader of the corporate and transactional practice areas, Mr Zinn provides general corporate, transactional and strategic counsel to owners, boards of directors, management, financial institutions, private equity firms, and investment banks on a national and global basis. His transactional experience includes mergers & acquisitions, private equity, securities offerings, strategic and venture capital investments, joint ventures, recapitalizations and financial restructurings. He advises public and private companies across an array of industries, including representing some of the world's largest corporations, as well as middle-market, emerging growth companies, and investment firms.

# BALLARD SPAHR LLP

www.ballardspahr.com **tel:** 215 665 8500 **fax:** 215 864 8999

**Chairman:** Mark S Stewart
Number of partners: 226
Numbers of lawyers: 506

**Firm Overview:**

Ballard Spahr is a national firm with 13 offices. Attorneys provide counseling and advocacy in more than 40 practice areas. The firm's mission: to provide nothing less than excellence in every legal representation.

## Main Areas of Practice:

**Business & Finance:**

The Business and Finance Department serves regional, national, and international clients. They include financial institutions, government entities, and nonprofit organizations, as well as life science, energy, and health care companies.

In the M&A/private equity area, attorneys structure, negotiate, and close transactions for buyers, sellers, and related parties, including venture capital firms.

Securities attorneys advise on development and capital-raising activities and compliance with public reporting and proxy obligations.

Attorneys in the firm's consumer financial services practice advise on regulatory matters, assist in the design and documentation of credit products, and represent clients in class actions, regulatory enforcement proceedings, and other lawsuits.

Employee benefits and executive compensation attorneys help design and implement benefits packages that comply with all regulatory requirements.

The energy and project finance practice handles the development, acquisition, and financing of energy assets and regulatory compliance. Attorneys represent producers and distributors of electricity from renewable and other sources, operators of regional wholesale energy markets, natural gas producers, and large industrial consumers of natural gas. Clients also include underwriters, private issuers, banks, and investors.

**Intellectual Property:**

Ballard Spahr work nationally and internationally to identify, secure, and protect clients' intellectual property. Many attorneys hold PhDs or other advanced degrees. The firm's attorneys provide the spectrum of IP representation, including copyright and trademark clearance and counsel, patent counseling and procurement, licensing, branding services, and

litigation. They also counsel on unfair competition, trade secret, and trade dress matters. Attorneys offer strategic due diligence guidance during mergers and acquisitions and portfolio restructuring, and work with early-stage growth companies and entrepreneurs in commercializing IP assets.

**Litigation:**

Litigation is the firm's largest department, with more than 200 attorneys. They handle complex litigation, from securities class actions and contractual disputes to federal and state appeals, for regional, national, and international clients. A dedicated group handles eDiscovery and data management issues.

Labor and employment attorneys counsel and defend against discrimination, harassment, and retaliation claims. They also handle issues involving family and medical leave, whistle-blowing, ERISA, and noncompetition agreements. Attorneys have significant experience in class and collective action litigation.

White collar lawyers conduct internal investigations and represent clients facing government enforcement. They also represent clients in False Claims Act and other civil fraud litigation and administrative proceedings.

**Public Finance:**

Ballard Spahr have one of the premier public finance practices in the nation. Clients include state and local governments and authorities throughout the country, underwriters, borrowers, investors, financial institutions, nonprofit organizations, and trustees. Attorneys regularly act as bond counsel, disclosure counsel, underwriter's counsel, issuer's counsel, special tax counsel, borrower's counsel, lender and credit enhancer's counsel, and trustee's counsel. They also advise on defaults, restructurings, tax audits, and securities investigations, as well as arbitrage rebate and post-issuance compliance.

## OFFICES

**PENNSYLVANIA**
**PHILADELPHIA (HEAD OFFICE):** Tel: 215 665 8500

**ARIZONA**
**PHOENIX:** Tel: 602 798 5400

**CALIFORNIA**
**LOS ANGELES:** Tel: 424 204 4400
**SAN DIEGO:** Tel: 619 696 9200

**COLORADO**
**DENVER:** Tel: 303 292 2400

**DELAWARE**
**WILMINGTON:** Tel: 302 252 4465

**DISTRICT OF COLUMBIA**
**WASHINGTON, DC:** Tel: 202 661 2200

**GEORGIA**
**ATLANTA:** Tel: 678 420 9300

**MARYLAND**
**BALTIMORE:** Tel: 410 528 5600
**BETHESDA:** Tel: 301 664 6200

**NEVADA**
**LAS VEGAS:** Tel: 702 471 7000

**NEW JERSEY**
**NEW JERSEY:** Tel: 856 761 3400

**UTAH**
**SALT LAKE CITY:** Tel: 801 531 3000

The firm's experience covers matters in municipal, tax, securities, transportation, economic development, real estate, affordable housing, environmental, public utilities, energy, health care, education, banking, administrative, and corporate areas.

**Real Estate:**

The Real Estate Department, one of the most prominent in the nation, serves a diversified client base. Representations include acquisitions and equity participations; securitized and balance-sheet loans; construction and design contracts; mixed-use development and research parks; public/private ventures; leasing; housing development and finance; industrial facilities; condominium and planned community development; hotel, resort, and fractional interests; and workouts, restructurings, and foreclosures.

Clients include owners, lenders, investors, and developers, as well as government agencies, colleges and universities, and hospitals.

# BLANK ROME LLP

www.BlankRome.com **tel:** 215 569 5500 **fax:** 215 569 5555

**Chairmen:** Alan J Hoffman and T Michael Dyer
**Managing Partner:** Alan J Hoffman
Number of partners: 247   Number of lawyers: 488

**Firm Overview:**

Blank Rome LLP is a global law firm recognized for providing outstanding legal advice and service to its clients, which range from Fortune 500 companies to start-up entities. Founded in 1946, Blank Rome advises clients on all aspects of their businesses, including business restructuring and bankruptcy; business tax; commercial and corporate litigation; consumer financial services; employment, benefits and labor; environmental litigation; financial services; government relations; intellectual property; international litigation and alternative dispute resolution; maritime, international trade and procurement; matrimonial; mergers and acquisitions and private equity; products liability; public companies and capital formation; public finance; real estate; trusts and estates; and white collar defense and investigations. Blank Rome also represents pro bono clients in a wide variety of cases and matters. Blank Rome has 12 offices, 10 in the US, and an international presence in Shanghai and Hong Kong.

**Main Areas of Practice:**

**Litigation:**
125 partners; 145 additional fee earners

- Won a precedent-setting victory that definitively secured the immunity of 911 call takers in the Appellate Division of the New Jersey Superior Court for the firm's client, the City of Jersey City
- Won a landmark victory that successfully challenged a municipality's attempt to withhold condemnation funds by rezoning
- Served as lead counsel in the two largest natural resource damage cases in the United States
- Ongoing representation of Marine Spill Response Corporation with regard to the Deepwater Horizon clean-up operations, and follow-on litigation
- Ongoing trial court and appellate representation in various suits in state and federal courts in Pennsylvania and Florida involving one of Philadelphia's most prominent families and multi-million dollar disputes over family trusts, estates and commercial transactions
- Secured a ground-breaking victory protecting trade secrets in software code development

**Additional Key Clients:** Aetna, Aramark, Audi, Bank of America, Burlington Coat Factory, Casella/ DBA (Yellow Tail), Facebook, Heraeus Incorporated, Lyondell, Marine Spill Response Corporation, Prudential Financial Inc., Siemens, SunGard Data Systems, Inc., Synthes, Wells Fargo Bank, N.A.
**Contact:** James T Smith **Tel:** 215 569 5643
**Email:** Smith-JT@BlankRome.com

**Banking, Bankruptcy & Finance:**
34 partners; 32 additional fee earners

- Representation of Revolving Agent and 2nd lien Term Loan Collateral Agent in a $102,000,000 acquisition and asset based lending working capital facility to support the acquisition of a publicly held specialty manufacturer

- Counsel to the Official Committee of Unsecured Creditors in the Solyndra bankruptcy case in Delaware
- Representation of the underwriters in connection with the issuance by the Allentown Neighborhood Improvement Zone Development Authority of its $183,955,000 Tax Revenue Bonds, Series 2012 A and its $40,425,000 Tax Revenue Bonds, Series 2012B (Federally Taxable), the original issuance of publicly offered bonds under a new State law

**Additional Key Clients:** PNC Bank, N.A., Wells Fargo Bank, N.A., Bank of America, RBS Citizens, N.A., People's United Bank, Janney Montgomery Scott, Merrill Lynch, UBS Securities LLC, Citigroup Global Markets LLP, Morgan Stanley
**Contact:** Lawrence F Flick II **Tel:** 212 885 5556
**Email:** Flick@BlankRome.com
**Contact:** Regina Stango Kelbon **Tel:** 302 425 6424
**Email:** Kelbon@BlankRome.com

**Real Estate: Dirt & Finance:**
25 partners; 18 additional fee earners

- Representation of Simon Property Group L.P. in a $1.5 billion acquisition of the interests of its financial partner, Farallon Capital Management, in a portfolio of 26 retail properties located throughout the US
- Representation of DRA Advisors LLC in a $600 million joint venture acquisition with Westcore Properties Inc. of an 11.1 million-square-foot industrial property portfolio consisting of 110 properties located throughout three states
- Closed more than 250 loans in 2012 totaling in excess of $4 billion involving real estate financing and secondary financing transactions for sale to Fannie Mae and Freddie Mac

**Additional Key Clients:** Aegon, Guggenheim, Morgan Properties, Philadelphia Eagles, PNC Multifamily, Toll Brothers, Wells Fargo Bank, N.A.
**Contact:** Martin Luskin **Tel:** 212 885 5311
**Email:** MLuskin@BlankRome.com

**Corporate Finance/M&A/Private Equity:**
63 partners; 46 additional fee earners

- General Cable Corporation in its private offering of $600 million in aggregate principal amount of senior notes and in its $150 million acquisition of the North American portion of Alcan Cable
- BrightPoint, Inc. in its $849 million acquisition by Ingram Micro Inc.
- 180 Medical Holdings, Inc., a portfolio company of Cortec Group, in connection with the company's sale to ConvaTec Inc.

**Additional Key Clients:** Lincoln Financial Group, SunGard Data Systems, Inc., Iconix Brand Group, Inc., J.F. Lehman & Company, First Energy Corp., Dorman Products
**Contact:** Alan Zeiger **Tel:** 215 569 5754
**Email:** Zeiger@BlankRome.com

# BUCHANAN INGERSOLL & ROONEY

**www.**bipc.com **tel:** 412 562 8800 **fax:** 412 562 1041

**CEO & Managing Director:** John A Barbour
Number of partners: 208  Number of lawyers: 444
Languages: *English, Arabic, Armenian, Chinese, Farsi, French, German, Gujarati, Hebrew, Hindi, Italian, Japanese, Korean, Russian, Spanish, Swedish, Ukrainian*

## Firm Overview:

Buchanan Ingersoll & Rooney, founded in 1850, has nearly 450 attorneys and government relations professionals in 15 offices. The firm is dedicated to building a deep understanding of its clients and their businesses and industries.

## Main Areas of Practice:

### Corporate:

Buchanan is nationally recognized by Corporate Counsel as a "Go-To" firm for corporate law and was recently ranked the #1 corporate law firm by directors and general counsel in its headquarter metropolitan market in a study published by Corporate Board Member. The corporate team structures, negotiates, documents and completes transactions essential to the objectives of its business clients.

### Energy:

Buchanan's integrated energy team includes more than 80 lawyers and professionals in the areas of corporate finance, environmental, regulatory, tax, litigation, labor and employment, intellectual property, real estate and government relations. The firm has handled more than $15 billion in energy-related transactions in the past two years. From natural gas, oil and coal to renewable energy, firm clients are leaders in the energy arena.

### Financial Services:

Buchanan's financial services lawyers count among clients most of the largest financial institutions in the country. It also represents federal and state-chartered bank and thrift institutions, unregulated lenders, municipal authorities, equipment lessors and lessees and borrowers in bilateral transactions.

### Health Care:

Buchanan's health care team members have both regulatory and legal depth in the industry. Many of the members have professional degrees in health care disciplines and have held senior agency and congressional positions. The firm's experience creates a distinct advantage in dealing with the policies, practices and procedures that govern the industry.

### Intellectual Property:

Buchanan's Intellectual Property Section is a full-service, collaborative team of more than 60 attorneys and professionals, many of whom possess specialized technical degrees. The firm is also active in leadership roles in several IP industry trade associations.

### Labor & Employment:

Buchanan's Labor & Employment Section draws upon its experience and collaborative knowledge to resolve issues for clients in a wide variety of industries in the private and public sectors. The firm's knowledge of state and federal laws helps its clients navigate these risks to achieve client objectives.

### Litigation:

Buchanan's lawyers regularly handle bet-the-company litigation, as well as routine disputes for Fortune 500 companies and high-growth businesses. The firm has handled high-stakes litigation, major class actions, mass tort and other complex litigation in state and federal courts and before administrative agencies and arbitral tribunals.

### Real Estate:

Buchanan's real estate practice encompasses acquisition, disposition, leasing and asset management, land use, construction and development, real estate finance and tax planning for real estate investments.

### Regulatory & Government:

Buchanan's lobbyists have collective experience and bi-partisan relationships that span 40 years. From Washington DC and throughout Pennsylvania, the team draws upon their backgrounds in the highest levels of state and federal government to help clients navigate the regulatory and legislative issues that impact their businesses.

### FDA/Pharmaceuticals:

Buchanan was one of the first law firms with a dedicated Food and Drug Administration practice. The firm understands this highly regulated sector and its scientific disciplines. The FDA/Pharmaceuticals Group uses this knowledge to defend clients' products through wide-ranging efforts in all the arenas that affect the industry – FDA, CMS, Congress, DEA and AHRQ.

### Tax:

Buchanan's tax attorneys have experience with federal, state, local and international tax issues, including business and financial transactions, general tax planning, tax controversies and litigation and estate planning. The firm also serves as the technical editors of the Bloomberg/BNA Tax Management portfolios and journals.

## OFFICES:

**CALIFORNIA**
**SAN DIEGO:** Downtown, 600 West Broadway, Suite 1100, CA 92101-3387
Tel: 619 239 8700  Fax: 619 702 3898

**DELAWARE**
**WILMINGTON:** 1105 North Market Street, Suite 1900, DE 19801-1054
Tel: 302 552 4200  Fax: 302 552 4295

**DISTRICT OF COLUMBIA**
**WASHINGTON, DC:** 1700 K Street, NW, Suite 300, DC 20006-3807
Tel: 202 452 7900  Fax: 202 452 7989

**FLORIDA**
**AVENTURA:** Country Club Center, 19950 W. Country Club Drive, Suite 101, FL 33180-2402
Tel: 305 933 5600  Fax: 305 933 2350

**MIAMI:** Miami Tower, 100 S.E. Second Street, Suite 3500, FL 33131-2158
Tel: 305 347 4080  Fax: 305 347 4089

**TAMPA:** SunTrust Financial Centre, 401 E. Jackson Street, Suite 2500, FL 33602-5236
Tel: 813 222 8180  Fax: 813 222 8189

**NEW JERSEY**
**NEWARK:** 550 Broad Street, Suite 810, NJ 07102-4582
Tel: 973 273 9800  Fax: 973 273 9430

**PRINCETON:** 700 Alexander Park, Suite 300, NJ 08540-6347
Tel: 609 987 6800  Fax: 609 520 0360

**NEW YORK**
**BUFFALO:** Key Center at Fountain Plaza, 50 Fountain Plaza, Suite 1230, NY 14202-2212
Tel: 716 853 2330  Fax: 716 854 4227

**NEW YORK:** 1290 Avenue of the Americas, 30th Floor, NY 10104-3001
Tel: 212 440 4400  Fax: 212 440 4401

**NORTH CAROLINA**
**CHARLOTTE:** Carillon Building, 227 West Trade Street, Suite 1920, NC 28202
Tel: 704 444 3300  Fax: 704 444 3490

**PENNSYLVANIA**
**HARRISBURG:** 409 North Second Street, Suite 500, PA 17101-1357
Tel: 717 237 4800  Fax: 717 233 0852

**PHILADELPHIA:** Two Liberty Place, 50 S. 16th Street, Suite 3200, PA 19102-2555
Tel: 215 665 8700  Fax: 215 665 8760

**PITTSBURGH (MAIN OFFICE):** One Oxford Centre, 301 Grant Street, 20th Floor, PA 15219-1410
Tel: 412 562 8800  Fax: 412 562 1041

**VIRGINIA**
**ALEXANDRIA:** 1737 King Street, Suite 500, VA 22314-2727
Tel: 703 836 6620  Fax: 703 836 2021

Buchanan Ingersoll & Rooney PC
Attorneys & Government Relations Professionals

# COZEN O'CONNOR

www.cozen.com **tel:** 215 665 2000

**Chief Executive Officer:** Michael J Heller
**Managing Partner:** Vincent R McGuinness
**Founder & Chairman:** Stephen A Cozen
**Founder & Vice Chairman:** Patrick J O'Connor
Number of lawyers: 575

**OFFICES**

PENNSYLVANIA
**PHILADELPHIA:** 1900 Market Street, PA 19103
Tel: 215 665 2000

**ADDITIONAL OFFICES:** Washington, DC, New York, NY, Chicago, IL, Los Angeles and San Diego, CA, Wilmington, DE, Houston and Dallas, TX, Seattle, WA, Atlanta, GA, Cherry Hill, NJ, Miami, FL, Denver, CO, Charlotte, NC, and Harrisburg, Wilkes Barre, and West Conshohocken, PA, and internationally in Toronto, Canada and London, UK.

## Firm Overview:

Established in 1970 and ranked among the 100 largest law firms in the United States, Cozen O'Connor has more than 575 attorneys who help clients manage risk and make better business decisions. The firm counsels clients on their most sophisticated legal matters in all areas of the law, including litigation, transactions, and regulatory law.

## Main Areas of Practice:

### Antitrust:

This practice involves both corporate transactions and litigation. With capacity in Washington, DC, and Philadelphia, it is well positioned to deal with regulatory approvals, government investigations, and private litigation.

### Bankruptcy, Insolvency & Restructuring:

The firm's Bankruptcy Practice represents clients in a broad range of commercial litigation and transactional matters, with emphasis in domestic and international insolvency, creditors' rights, bankruptcy, restructuring, and reorganization.

### Commercial Litigation:

The firm's Litigation Department includes trial-tested lawyers who regularly prosecute and defend a diverse caseload of construction litigation, complex corporate and partnership disputes, product liability and mass torts, securities and financial services litigation, trusts and estates litigation, e-discovery disputes, environmental claims, class action defense, and real estate matters.

### Corporate:

The firm's corporate attorneys counsel clients on matters related to organization, structure, and governance, provide advice on matters arising in day-to-day operations, assist in negotiating and documenting financing and business expansion transactions, and provide guidance in acquisitions, sales, mergers and acquisitions, and divestitures.

### Criminal Defense & Government Investigations:

The attorneys in this group are a highly skilled team of former federal prosecutors and veteran defense lawyers who can fight zealously for the firm's clients in pre-trial negotiations with prosecutors, criminal jury trials, and any necessary appeals.

### Employee Benefits & Executive Compensation:

The firm's lawyers are experienced in all issues relating to employee benefit plans and executive compensation, including qualified and non-qualified plans, retirement plans, executive compensation programs, health and welfare benefits, and ERISA.

### Energy, Environmental & Public Utilities:

The firm's lawyers offer integrated public utility and environmental regulatory services to entities in the electricity, gas, water, real estate development, and manufacturing sectors. It provides clients with traditional legal services in addition to emerging areas such as electric competition counseling, renewable energy siting, and market-based pollution trading counseling.

### Health Law:

The firm's Health Law Practice provides varied regulatory and litigation services including Medicare, Medicaid and other third-party reimbursement issues, fraud and abuse and Federal False Claims Act issues, compliance program development, and confidentiality and other HIPAA-related compliance issues.

### Insurance Coverage Claims/Litigation:

The firm provides clients with sound and sophisticated advice on the rights and obligations of the respective parties to insurance contracts and assists them in resolving claims in accordance with the contract provisions and the law.

### Intellectual Property:

The IP Practice works with clients to develop and implement protection and enforcement strategies for patents, trademarks, trade names, domain names, service marks, trade dress, copyrights, trade secrets, rights of publicity and privacy, and franchising.

### Labor & Employment:

This group takes a comprehensive view of workplace problems, including counseling and litigation. The firm's attorneys help clients structure their personnel policies and business transactions to enhance productivity, comply with legal requirements, and avoid litigation.

### Public & Project Finance:

The firm has one of the most active practices in the mid-Atlantic region. Its team is experienced in tax-exempt and taxable financings, debt restructurings, off-balance sheet financings, securitizations, and municipal swaps.

### Public Strategies:

Cozen O'Connor Public Strategies is a bipartisan government relations firm. These professionals offer a full complement of government affairs services, including legislative and executive branch advocacy, policy analysis, assistance with government procurement and funding, and crisis management.

### Real Estate:

This group has experience in virtually every facet of the real estate business, including complex commercial acquisitions, dispositions and development, partnerships and joint ventures, leasing, sale/leasebacks, senior debt and mezzanine debt financings, loan restructuring and workouts, and land use and zoning.

### Subrogation & Recovery:

This group of attorneys handle more substantial property damage and other first-party subrogation claims than any other law firm in the United States. These claims arise from casualties such as fires, explosions, structural collapses, equipment failures, gas and water leaks, and natural disasters such as wildfires, windstorms, and floods.

### Tax:

The firm's tax attorneys assist businesses and individuals with minimizing the consequences of federal, state and local taxes. They have experience in such matters as mergers and acquisitions, financings, purchase or sale of businesses, negotiation and structuring of joint ventures, client representations and real estate matters.

### Transportation & Logistics:

This team offers broad experience in the transportation sector, practicing in the areas of corporate, commercial, transactional, regulatory, litigation, public and private contracting, and financing. Its work regularly involves cargo and passenger transportation, towage, dredging, terminals, offshore energy, fisheries, and marine construction.

# DRINKER BIDDLE & REATH LLP

www.drinkerbiddle.com  **tel:** 215 988 2700  **fax:** 215 988 2757

**Chairman:** Alfred W Putnam, Jr
Number of partners worldwide: 271  Number of other lawyers worldwide: 368

## Firm Overview:

With 650 lawyers in 11 U.S. offices and an affiliation with the World Law Group, Drinker Biddle & Reath LLP provides clients with unparalleled service. The firm's priorities are knowing its clients' business and providing the value they need so that the firm can be an integral part of their success.

## Main Areas of Practice:
Drinker Biddle's national practices include:

### Commercial Litigation:
The practice encompasses a diverse caseload, including antitrust, appellate, class actions, entertainment, construction and real estate, pharmaceutical and medical device, accountant and professional services liability, securities and corporate governance, and white collar defense and corporate investigations.

### Communications Litigation:
The firm represents top companies in the wireless, wireline and cable industries in matters involving consumer class actions, federal preemption, state and municipal regulation, commercial litigation, and shareholder and corporate governance issues.

### Corporate & Securities:
The group's core practice includes mergers, acquisitions and complex joint ventures, securities compliance, insurance regulatory matters, advice for public companies, commercial lending, corporate finance and private equity, including venture capital, investment vehicles and portfolio companies.

### Corporate Restructuring:
Located in three of the country's largest bankruptcy venues (New York/New Jersey, Chicago and Delaware), the group represents creditors' and bondholders' committees and handles business workouts, restructurings and various insolvency proceedings. It also represents secured and unsecured creditors, bankruptcy trustees, debtors and potential acquirers, as well as indenture trustees and bondholder interests.

### Employee Benefits & Executive Compensation:
This full-service practice handles virtually every aspect of employee benefits, executive compensation and ERISA issues. The practice handles Sec. 401(k), pension, cash balance, profit-sharing and stock bonus plans, as well as clients' incentive stock option, non-qualified stock option, stock grant, employee stock purchase, stock appreciation rights and phantom stock plans.

### Environment & Energy:
This diverse practice includes litigators, regulatory counselors, scientists, engineers, strategists, project advisors and transactional lawyers. It counsels clients from an array of industries and backgrounds on the full spectrum of environmental and energy regulation issues.

### Government & Regulatory Affairs:
This group encompasses several practices, including communications regulation, customs and trade counseling, education, Indian tribal governments and pharmaceutical consortia, in addition to a government affairs practice that ranges from handling significant legislative and regulatory activity for clients interested in state and local matters to representing clients' interests before Congress and federal agencies, especially in the health care arena.

### Health Care:
This group serves providers, vendors, professional associations, provider-sponsored managed care organizations, group purchasing organizations and pharmaceutical companies.

### Insurance Coverage:
This group represents insurance industry leaders, including property and casualty, health and accident families of companies, as well as agents, brokers and reinsurers. The firm is known for its practice in directors' and officers' liability, employment practices liability, general liability, errors and omissions, fidelity and commercial crime liability and lawyers' professional liability.

### Intellectual Property:
One of the country's largest IP groups housed in a full-service firm, the group handles patents, trademarks, copyrights, trade secrets, litigation, information technology, licensing and outsourcing, life sciences and biotechnology, legislative affairs, advertising and promotions, online and e-commerce initiatives and portfolio assessment and management. The group also counsels clients on the America Invents Act.

### Investment Management:
This group serves a wide range of national and multinational financial institutions, including investment companies, registered hedge funds, exchange-traded funds and private funds (offshore and domestic, including hedge funds and private equity funds). It also serves investment advisers, commodity trading advisers, broker-dealers, commodity pool operators, trust companies, and insurance companies and related insurance products.

### Labor & Employment:
The group represents employers, often serving as national counsel, handling individual and class action cases involving matters such as FMLA, ADA and state law disability retaliation, discrimination, wrongful discharge, wage-and-hour, non-competition/non-solicitation and whistleblower claims.

### Life Insurance & Annuities:
This practice provides counsel on all phases of life insurance and financial services operations, including the rapidly evolving structured settlement, STOLI and annuity litigation arena.

### Private Client Group:
This practice covers a range of needs, including fiduciary matters and litigation, issues related to tax-exempt entities for individual and foundation clients, and the traditional notion of trust and estates.

### Products Liability & Mass Tort:
This group defends alleged class actions across a broad range of products litigation, especially in the pharmaceutical and medical device industries. The group also handles toxic torts and chemical exposure matters, Daubert motions and punitive damages claims.

### Real Estate:
The firm represents clients for which real estate is their primary business, as well as clients for which real estate is an important asset. Clients include developers, lenders, investors, manufacturing companies, retailers and non-profit institutions.

## OFFICES

**PENNSYLVANIA**

**PHILADELPHIA:** One Logan Square, Suite 2000, PA 19103-6996
Tel: 215 988 2700  Fax: 215 988 2757
The firm has additional offices in Albany, N.Y.; Chicago; Florham Park, N.J.; Los Angeles; Milwaukee; New York; Princeton, N.J.; San Francisco; Washington, D.C.; and Wilmington. Del.

**DrinkerBiddle**

# DUANE MORRIS LLP

**www.**duanemorris.com **tel:** 215 979 1000 **fax:** 215 979 1020

**Chairman:** John J Soroko

## Firm Overview:

Duane Morris LLP, a global law firm with more than 700 attorneys in offices across the United States and around the world, is asked by a broad array of clients to provide innovative solutions to today's legal and business challenges.

## Main Areas of Practice:

**Business Reorganization & Financial Restructuring:**
Attorneys in Duane Morris' Business Reorganization and Financial Restructuring Group represent clients in all aspects of financial reorganization and bankruptcy. They work closely with clients to develop and implement the most effective plan of action for achieving the client's goal, even under difficult and changing circumstances. Business publication The Deal regularly ranks the bankruptcy practice, which focuses primarily on complex commercial chapter 11 cases, as among the most active in the United States. Duane Morris frequently serves as counsel to debtors, trustees, creditors and equity holders during the bankruptcy and reorganization processes and in cases of litigation, provides legal counsel throughout.
**Contact:** Rudolph J Di Massa, Jr., Practice Group Chair
Tel: 215 979 1506 Email: DiMassa@duanemorris.com

**Construction:**
Duane Morris' Construction Group is nationally ranked by Chambers USA and U.S. News-Best Lawyers, which named Duane Morris "2013 Law Firm of the Year." The group's lawyers across the nation provide a full range of legal services to clients in all aspects of construction and government contracting. Attorneys assist clients in addressing the legal challenges of engaging in the design, development, financing, performance and management of major construction and government procurement contracts and has special experience working on complex, high-visibility projects in New York and other cities.
**Contact:** Robert A Prentice, Practice Group Chair,
Tel: 215 979 1130 Email: RAPrentice@duanemorris.com

**Corporate:**
The Corporate Practice group counsels clients in every step of the business cycle, from company start-up to establishing long-term growth strategies, including navigating the complex venture capital and private equity markets. Attorneys around the globe provide guidance on agreements of all kinds, licensing, compliance and regulatory requirements and have experience in assisting clients in a wide range of industries, such as life sciences, fashion, manufacturing, biotechnology, renewable/alternative energy, healthcare and financial services. Members of the Corporate team bring a wealth of experience in managing joint ventures and alliances; corporate governance; mergers and acquisitions; private equity and venture capital; and securities law and litigation.
**Contact:** George J Nemphos, Practice Group Chair
Tel: 410 949 2910 Email: gjnemphos@duanemorris.com

**Employment, Labor, Benefits & Immigration:**
Duane Morris' employment lawyers offer practical counseling designed to help clients achieve their business objectives and resolve potentially disruptive labor and employment disputes. Lawyers aggressively promote client interests before state and federal courts and in mediation and arbitration proceedings, as well as before the Equal Employment Opportunity Commission, the Department of Labor, the federal Wage and Hour Division, and all other state and federal agencies. Duane Morris attorneys have experience assisting employers in responding to union organizing efforts and regularly defend employers against unfair labor practice charges filed with the National Labor Relations Board. Duane Morris' employee benefits attorneys provide clients with the full range of benefits-related legal services. Immigration attorneys have a comprehensive knowledge of the legal, political and business context in which immigration and naturalization concerns arise and have a reputation for responsiveness and efficiency.
**Contact:** Thomas G Servodidio, Practice Group Chair
Tel: 215 979 1844
Email: TGServodidio@duanemorris.com

**Energy, Environment & Resources:**
Duane Morris, as both advisor and advocate, guides clients through complex legal, financial, practical and political issues. Attorneys help clients navigate complicated rules and regulations, fluctuating market conditions, and surging demand for various energy sources. With the capabilities of a full-service firm, attorneys are able to manage environmental issues at the local, national and international levels. The group has been involved in multibillion-dollar transactions and litigated significant cases on complex regulatory issues before various government agencies and state and federal courts, and regularly interacts with agencies, committees, commissions and associations whose regulations and decisions affect clients.
**Contact:** Stephen L Teichler, Co-Chair
Tel: 202 776 7830 Email: SLTeichler@duanemorris.com

## PRACTICE AREAS

Business Reorganization & Financial Restructuring
Construction
Corporate
Employment, Labor, Benefits & Immigration
Energy, Environment & Resources
Health Law
Insurance
Intellectual Property
International
Litigation & Alternative Dispute Resolution
Real Estate
Wealth Planning

## OFFICES

### CALIFORNIA
**LOS ANGELES:** 865 South Figueroa Street, Suite 3100, CA 90017-5450
Tel: 213 689 7400 Fax: 213 689 7401

**SILICON VALLEY:** 490 South California Avenue, Suite 200, CA 94306-2068
Tel: 650 847 4150  Fax: 650 847 4151

**SAN DIEGO:** 750 B Street, Suite 2900, CA 92101-4681
Tel: 619 744 2200 Fax: 619 744 2201

**SAN FRANCISCO:** One Market Plaza, Spear Tower, Suite 2200, CA 94105-1127
Tel: 415 957 3000 Fax: 415 957 3001

**LAKE TAHOE:** 11149 Brockway Road, Suite 100, CA 96161
Tel: 530 550 2050 Fax: 530 550 8619

### DELAWARE
**WILMINGTON:** 222 Delaware Avenue, Suite 1600, DE 19801-1659
Tel: 302 657 4900 Fax: 302 657 4901

### DISTRICT OF COLUMBIA
**WASHINGTON, DC:** 505 9th Street, N.W., Suite 1000, DC 20004-2166
Tel: 202 776 7800 Fax: 202 776 7801

### FLORIDA
**MIAMI:** 200 South Biscayne Boulevard, Suite 3400, FL 33131-2318
Tel: 305 960 2200 Fax: 305 960 2201

**BOCA RATON:** 5100 Town Center Circle, Suite 650, FL 33486-9000
Tel: 561 962 2100 Fax: 561 962 2101

### GEORGIA
**ATLANTA:** 1075 Peachtree Street NE, Suite 2000, GA 30309
Tel: 404 253 6900 Fax: 404 253 6901

### ILLINOIS
**CHICAGO:** 190 South LaSalle Street, Suite 3700, IL 60603-3433
Tel: 312 499 6700 Fax: 312 499 6701

### MARYLAND
**BALTIMORE:** 111 South Calvert Street, Suite 2000, MD 21202
Tel: 410 949 2900 Fax: 410 949 2901

## Health Law:

Duane Morris attorneys understand the demands of the market and create business and legal value in all situations—transactional, regulatory and litigation. Services are tailored in order to better meet the multifaceted needs of sectors such as the evolving information technology and Health and telemedicine industries. The healthcare practice focuses on developing innovative and creative ways to help clients increase profitability and protect their assets. A diverse concentration of healthcare specialties includes: insurance reimbursement; physician-hospital transactions; sale/acquisition of facility assets; long-term care; governance issues; healthcare fraud and abuse; and licensure and credentialing, among others.

Contact: David E Loder, Practice Group Chair
Tel: 215 979 1834 Email: DELoder@duanemorris.com

## Insurance:

Repeatedly recognized as having one of the best Insurance practices in the United States, Duane Morris attorneys have been engaged in representations of insurance industry interests for years, having served as counsel to numerous property/casualty insurance companies, life insurance companies, reinsurance companies, HMOs and PPOs, rating bureaus, captive insurers offshore, and alternative market entities and guaranty associations. The firm has also represented underwriters of public offerings of insurance securities. Duane Morris' background in the industry contributes to the firm's ability to address client concerns effectively. Attorneys have an in-depth understanding of actuarial, underwriting and policy coverage matters affecting the business and legal issues of insurance industry clients. The firm has handled matters affecting financial examinations, market conduct examinations and other regulatory issues, as well as general corporate matters.

Contact: Max H Stern, Practice Group Chair
Tel: 415 957 3129 Email: MHStern@duanemorris.com

## Intellectual Property:

The Intellectual Property Practice is recognized as one of the leading IP groups in the United States by national publications such as U.S. News and World Report, Intellectual Property Today and IP Law360. Duane Morris' IP attorneys focus on leveraging their clients' intellectual property to help achieve success in the marketplace, and provide counsel on the most effective methods of establishing and developing IP holdings and protecting IP rights. Highly-trained attorneys, many of whom hold advanced degrees in technical areas, utilize cutting edge technology to better serve clients, who range from large multinational corporations to individual inventors, authors and owners of creative works. Duane Morris offers counsel on all aspects of patents, trademarks, copyrights, trade secrets, unfair competition and intellectual property litigation, with strong capabilities in matters related to generic

pharmaceuticals, ITC Section 337 litigation, technology transactions and life sciences.

Contact: L Norwood 'Woody' Jameson, Practice Group Chair
Tel: 404 253 6915 Email: WJameson@duanemorris.com

## Litigation & Alternative Dispute Resolution:

Duane Morris attorneys understand a client's needs and objectives, and fully evaluate appropriate strategies and tactics, whether litigation or alternative dispute resolution may be the best course of action. In either scenario, the practice group is well-versed and can offer experienced perspectives on approaching either a trial or some form of dispute resolution. Duane Morris attorneys have represented parties in arbitrations, mediations, and other forms of ADR and also served as third-party neutrals, mediators and arbitrators. When litigation is required, the firm offers comprehensive services in securities, class action, commercial, technology, financial, franchise, healthcare, insurance and other categories of litigation, with an interdisciplinary, cross-office approach to best serve the clients.

Contact: Matthew A Taylor, Practice Group Chair
Tel: 215 979 1140 Email: MATaylor@duanemorris.com

## Real Estate:

Duane Morris has a national and regional practice and with experience in virtually all real estate and development matters. Attorneys represent clients in a broad range of sophisticated and complex real estate transactions and offer services related to the purchase, sale, leasing, development, financing, joint venture, syndication, securitization, use and management of real property and real estate portfolios. Representations include work relating to lease agreements, financing and loan documents, restructurings and workouts, condemnation, eminent domain, valuation and tax issues, purchase and sale agreement negotiations, real estate development and real estate portfolio management.

Contact: George J.Kroculick, Practice Group Co-Chair,
Tel: 215 979 1386 Email:
GJKroculick@duanemorris.com
Contact: Chester P Lee, Practice Group Co-Chair
Tel: 212 692 1018 Email: cplee@duanemorris.com

## Wealth Planning:

Duane Morris provides estates, trusts, asset planning and related litigation services to individuals, business owners, charitable organizations and fiduciaries. For each client, attorneys listen to business and personal needs and understanding what the client desires in order to achieve the necessary peace of mind. Based on specific goals, the team tailors a plan and apply appropriate and sophisticated tax techniques as required, minimizing tax exposure and implementing creative strategies to preserve capital and transfer resources within the client's family and to next generations. Attorneys work with individuals on all aspects of personal tax planning,

including income, estate and gift taxes and charitable giving and counsel business owners on tax, estate planning, management succession, allocating benefits and various techniques for shifting value.

Contact: Michael D Grohman, Practice Group Chair
Tel: 212 692 1040
Email: MDGrohman@duanemorris.com

## International Work

Duane Morris has offices across the United States and around the world, including, most recently, a joint law venture opened in Oman. The Dr. Said Al Mashaikhi and Partner Law Firm— A GCC representative office of Duane Morris— is the firm's first office in the Middle East and further expanding its geographic reach. The firm has two offices in Vietnam and in Singapore, its joint law venture Duane Morris & Selvam serves clients in and with business interests in southeast Asia. In Mexico, Duane Morris has an alliance with Mexico City law firm Miranda & Estavillo, S.C. formalizing and strengthening a longtime referral and networking relationship between the two independent firms. The International Practice integrates the services of attorneys from all of the firm's offices and across all practice areas of the firm, creating a global infrastructure of experienced advisors available to represent clients in all types of cross-border and international matters. The international reach of the firm allows attorneys to leverage resources on both local and international levels to address the needs of clients in an increasingly global economy.

# ECKERT SEAMANS CHERIN & MELLOTT, LLC

**www.**eckertseamans.com   **tel:** 412 566 6000   **fax:** 412 566 6099

**Chief Executive Officer:** Timothy P Ryan

Number of partners: 229

Number of other lawyers: 120

**OFFICES**

PENNSYLVANIA

**PITTSBURGH:** 600 Grant Street, 44th Floor, PA 15219
Tel: 412 566 6000   Fax: 412 566 6099
Email: info@eckertseamans.com

## Firm Overview:

Eckert Seamans Cherin & Mellott, LLC, a national law firm with 10 offices throughout the eastern United States and internationally through its affiliation with Lex Mundi, provides a full range of legal services nationwide to businesses of all sizes, institutions, municipalities, colleges and universities, government agencies and individuals. Eckert Seamans has offices in Pittsburgh, Harrisburg, Philadelphia, and Southpointe, PA; Wilmington, DE; Charleston, WV; Boston, MA; Richmond, VA; Washington, DC and White Plains, NY.

## Main Areas of Practice:

**Aviation Law:**
Represents airlines in regulatory compliance, commercial transactions and litigation as well as regulatory proceedings, audits and investigations.

**Bankruptcy & Restructuring:**
Represents debtors, creditors' committees, equity holder committees, trustees and creditors in turnarounds, loan workouts, collections and bankruptcy proceedings.

**Commercial Litigation:**
Represents clients in state and federal courts, regulatory proceedings, grand jury proceedings, arbitrations and alternative dispute resolution proceedings.

**Construction:**
Represents public and private owners, developers, contractors, subcontractors, suppliers, design professionals and bonding companies in all phases of construction, both nationally and internationally.

**Corporate & Business Counseling:**
Represents multinational corporations, emerging and growing businesses, non-profit institutions, municipalities and government agencies.

**Employee Benefits:**
Designs, implements and administers employee benefit plans, including qualified retirement plans, trust agreements, health and other welfare plans, deferred compensation arrangements, stock, stock option and other equity-based compensation arrangements.

**Environmental:**
Represents full range of industries with compliance, enforcement, government rulemaking, responding to information requests, strategic planning and other matters.

**Estates & Trusts:**
Provides range of estate planning and administration services to individuals, entrepreneurs, owners of family businesses, charitable and nonprofit organizations.

**Gaming:**
Represents gaming manufacturers, gaming employees, and vendors.

**Hospitality:**
Represents real estate funds, lenders, owners, developers, franchisors and management companies in acquisitions and sales of hotel and resort real estate, joint venture agreements, management agreements, franchise agreements, public and private financing arrangements, and mergers and acquisitions.

**Immigration:**
Assists employers maneuver through complex immigration laws and regulations, as well as the multitude of procedures enforced by various U.S. agencies.

**Insurance:**
Furnish insurance business and regulatory compliance services to insurance companies that underwrite property, casualty, life, health and credit insurance products, and fraternal benefit societies.

**Intellectual Property:**
Represents clients in United States and foreign patent, trademark, copyright, trade secret and unfair competition law, and negotiates, prepares and enforces a variety of related agreements including license, assignment, consulting, employment, nondisclosure and joint venture, as well as college and university patent policies.

**Labor & Employment:**
Represents employers in all facets of employment and labor relations, including employment litigation, union/management relations and litigation-preventive counseling. Aggressively defends management's decisions and prerogatives in the courtroom.

**Mass Tort Litigation:**
Has served as national co-ordinator for the defense of claims involving medications, chemical products and asbestos-containing products.

**Product Liability:**
Defends product liability suits and counsels corporate clients to avoid claims. Representation has spanned local, regional and national product litigation involving diverse industries and products.

**Professional Liability:**
Defends claims against professionals, including claims of professional malpractice, breach of fiduciary duty, negligence, securities violations and accounting wrongdoings, among many other issues.

**Public Finance:**
Represents issuers, underwriters, lenders, trustees and investors in nearly every type of municipal offering from general obligation debt to private activity revenue issues.

**Real Estate:**
Represents a broad spectrum of clients in real estate-related transactions, from assisting in structuring the transaction to preparing and negotiating the operative documents.

**Tax:**
Provides services in all areas of federal, state and local tax, tax planning, partnership and hybrid-entity taxation, individual income tax, compliance and litigation.

**Transportation:**
Represents clients on issues and claims before the U.S. Departments of Transportation and Labor, various state departments and agencies, and state and federal courts.

**Energy, Utilities & Telecommunications:**
Represents major telecommunications, energy, natural gas and water utility companies before state and federal regulatory agencies. Experienced in compliance and licensing issues involving all types of regulated companies.

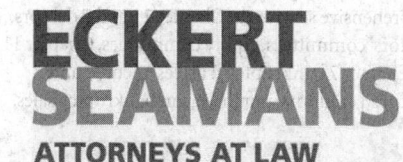

# FOX ROTHSCHILD LLP

www.foxrothschild.com

**Managing Partners:** Abraham C Reich (Co-Chair of the firm), Phillip E Griffin (Co-Chair of the firm), Mark L Silow (Firmwide Managing Partner)

**OFFICES**

Los Angeles, San Francisco, CA; Denver, CO; Stamford, CT; Wilmington, DE; Washington, DC; West Palm Beach, FL; Las Vegas, NV; Atlantic City, Princeton, Roseland, NJ; New York, NY; Blue Bell, Exton, Philadelphia, Pittsburgh, Warrington, PA

**Firm Overview:**

With more than 500 attorneys located in 17 offices nationwide, Fox provides a full range of legal services to public and private business entities, charitable, medical and educational institutions and individuals throughout the country. Attorneys and staff are supported by sophisticated technologies that link offices and promote rapid communication and collaboration among firm members. Clients have access to the full resources of its attorney network and to the depth of experience available firmwide in more than 45 practice areas.

**Main Areas of Practice:**

**Corporate:**
Fox attorneys help clients navigate the full range of business challenges they encounter (corporate formation, management, growth, acquisitions and transfers) as they transition through the corporate life cycle. Services include general business representation and assistance with mergers and acquisitions, securities issues, public finance, technology and venture finance, infrastructure, franchising, gaming law, insurance and international transactions.
**Contact:** Michael S Harrington

**Entertainment:**
Fox assists both individual and corporate clients in devising innovative and sophisticated strategies to develop and capitalize brands using a variety of delivery platforms and digital media outlets. Services include various business agreements, including artist management, co-production, development, distribution, motion picture, television and music development and production financing, as well as contract negotiations and general and entertainment litigation.
**Contact:** Darrell D Miller

**Environmental:**
The firm's Environmental Practice has a national record of strong results on behalf of clients in such areas as environmental litigation, environmental aspects of transactions and due diligence, permitting, compliance and enforcement, site remediation, product and take-back requirements and sustainable 'green' development.

**Financial Restructuring & Bankruptcy:**
Fox attorneys provide comprehensive services in the insolvency and distressed business contexts for businesses suffering financial distress and for their owners and managers. The firm also offers comprehensive services to Chapter 11 and 7 debtors, creditors' committees, equity committees, Chapter 11 and Chapter 7 bankruptcy trustees, secured and unsecured creditors, purchasers in bankruptcy sales, investors in distressed assets and securities and parties in bankruptcy litigation, including preference and other avoidance actions.
**Contact:** Michael G Menkowitz

**Health Law:**
The firm's Health Law Practice provides general representation to all types of healthcare providers. Services include representation in general corporate matters; mergers, acquisitions and joint ventures; legislative and policy advocacy; regulatory issues; medical staff issues; labor and employment; real estate; tax; and litigation and white-collar criminal defense.

**Intellectual Property:**
With more than 80 members – more than half of whom are registered patent attorneys and more than a dozen who possess advanced degrees in specific technical disciplines – Fox IP attorneys provide comprehensive counseling and litigation services related to patents, trademarks, copyrights, trade secrets, technology, licensing and domain names. They also perform due diligence reviews in connection with corporate transactions and conduct IP audits and evaluations. Clients trust in the team's knowledge of the science, technology and principles that drive the development and creation of new ideas, inventions and works.
**Contact:** Gerard P Norton, PhD

**Labor & Employment:**
Fox attorneys represent employers in the spectrum of legal matters arising in both the union and non-union workplace. Services include counseling and representation in connection with labor relations, immigration, human resource issues, employee benefits, training, corporate restructurings and class actions and compliance with and defense of claims arising under federal, state and local employment laws.
**Contacts:** James A Matthews III, Stanley L Goodman

**Litigation:**
Clients call on Fox to handle emergent matters and rely on the firm's record of obtaining injunctive relief as well as its deep experience to help design case strategies that position them for the best possible outcomes. The firm's litigation services include intellectual property; media, defamation and privacy law; environmental; white collar compliance and defense; securities law; construction; tax controversy and litigation; insurance; eminent domain/condemnation; probate and trust law litigation and international matters.
**Contact:** Stephanie Resnick

**Real Estate:**
Fox's team of real estate professionals is well-versed in key areas (acquisitions, sales, leasing, financing, zoning, land use, construction, tax appeals and condemnation). Attorneys assist owners, developers, investors, lenders, real estate professionals, design professionals, landlords, tenants, financial institutions, syndicators, insurance companies and many other clients with real estate opportunites and help to identify and address risks to solve clients' real estate needs.
**Contact:** Robert W Gundlach, Jr

**Taxation & Wealth Planning:**
Fox attorneys help clients navigate tax laws governing businesses and individuals. Attorneys continually assess developments that arise regarding federal and state income laws, administrative announcements, regulations and case law, and integrate those updates into evaluations of business and personal situations. Specific tax services include business and international taxation; employee benefits and compensation planning; family business and succession planning; federal estate and gift tax planning; nonprofit organizations; probate and trust law litigation; tax controversy and litigation; and trust and estate law and administration.
**Contacts:** Jerald David August, Michael C McBratnie

# HANGLEY ARONCHICK SEGAL PUDLIN & SCHILLER

**www.**hangley.com  **tel:** 215 568 6200  **fax:** 215 568 0300

**OFFICES**

PENNSYLVANIA
**PHILADELPHIA:** One Logan Square, 27th Floor, PA
19103-6933
Tel: 215 568 6200   Fax: 215 568 0300
**HARRISBURG:** 4400 Deer Path Road, Suite 200, PA
17110
Tel: 717 364 1030   Fax: 717 364 1020
**NORRISTOWN:** 401 DeKalb Street, 4th Floor, PA 19401
Tel: 610 313 1670   Fax: 610 313 1689

NEW JERSEY
**CHERRY HILL:** 20 Brace Road, Suite 201, NJ 08034-2634
Tel: 856 616 2100   Fax: 856 616 2170

## Firm Overview:

Hangley Aronchick Segal Pudlin & Schiller is proud to be recognized by Chambers USA in various practice areas. Founded in 1994, the 52 lawyer firm is known for the sophistication of its matters, the roster of its clients and the quality of its work. In the Delaware Valley, the firm is unparalleled in its ability to attract the most highly qualified attorneys, both at the entry level and laterally. The firm includes former Philadelphia City Solicitors, Fellows of the American College of Trial Lawyers, the American College of Bankruptcy and the American College of Real Estate Lawyers, members of judicial advisory committees, members of the American Law Institute, and adjunct faculty members at area law schools. For further information on the firm's practice areas and outstanding lawyers, readers are invited to visit the firm's website.

## Main Areas of Practice:

### Litigation:

Clients and referring counsel seek out Hangley Aronchick for cases that will actually have to be tried. The firm has represented some of the country's largest corporations, the Commonwealth of Pennsylvania, the City of Philadelphia, major universities and healthcare complexes, and the Pennsylvania Bar Association. Lawsuits the firm is currently handling or has recently handled include the following:

**Antitrust:** Representing national pharmacy chains in suits against pharmaceutical manufacturers; representing product manufacturers in price-fixing suits against them.
**Appellate:** Conducting successful appellate litigation in state and federal courts throughout the country, resulting in significant precedents in the areas of shareholder litigation, estates litigation, education law, insurance coverage law, municipal government law, professional responsibility, jurisdiction and the limits of discovery.
**Civil Rights:** Representing, in a federal class action, 5,000 juveniles who were victims of a judicial scandal in Luzerne County, Pennsylvania, in which two judges were secretly paid millions of dollars by the owners of two private detention facilities.
**Criminal & Investigative:** Representing subjects and targets in criminal investigations of commercial and financial affairs; assisting in internal investigations for publicly held companies.
**Education Law:** Providing representation in litigation and other matters to school districts, independent schools, colleges, universities and educational service providers in both the public and for-profit sectors.
**Employment Law:** Representing an options trading house in 'garden leave' litigation against a departing employee; representing executives or companies in trade secrets/restrictive covenants disputes.
**Finance:** Defending banks and credit card companies in class and non-class litigation with card holders; representing private equity fund managers in litigation; representing Ponzi scheme victims in negotiations and litigation with lender banks.
**Franchisee Rights:** Representing New Jersey and Pennsylvania beverage distributors in improper-

termination cases.
**First Amendment:** Representing city officials, media personalities, and newspapers in defamation cases.
**Healthcare:** Representing leading health maintenance organizations, hospitals, and healthcare service providers in class actions, parallel criminal and civil actions, and complex civil disputes.
**Intellectual Property:** Litigating on behalf of patent holders or alleged infringers; defending a pediatric research institution against charges of corporate espionage.
**Lawyers' Professional Responsibility:** Representing major Philadelphia and national law firms in business-related malpractice and fiduciary duty litigation.
**Public Affairs:** Representing the Governor of Pennsylvania and other executive officials in litigation; representing the Commonwealth of Pennsylvania in a constitutional challenge to the transfer of over $800 million to help resolve Pennsylvania's 2009 budget crisis
**Securities & Corporate Law:** Representing companies in litigation over mergers and securities offerings; representing individual officers and directors in securities fraud claims.
**Trusts & Estates:** Defending executors and estates against claims of would-be beneficiaries; representing trust beneficiaries in negligence claims against trustees.

### Insurance Law:

The firm's insurance coverage team handles all facets of coverage disputes on behalf of many of the world's largest insurers in virtually all lines of insurance, including Managed Care E&O, D&O, General Liability in both the first and third party context, bankruptcy-related coverage disputes, and Professional Liability. The firm prides itself in having one of the few coverage groups in the country with a thriving trial and appellate practice.

### Environmental Law:

The firm's environmental lawyers provide the full range of legal services in environmental regulatory, transactional and litigation matters. The firm regularly counsels clients on compliance with federal and state regulations and permits involving management of water discharges, waste handling and disposal and air

emissions. It also represents private and public clients regarding use of water resources, and the purchase or sale of contaminated properties and regulated facilities.

### Real Estate:

The firm's Real Estate Practice covers all aspects of commercial real estate: acquisition, financing, construction, development, leasing, and management of high rise office towers, suburban corporate facilities, hotels, national and regional shopping centers, industrial facilities, apartment complexes and residential subdivisions. The practice concentrates in the following areas:
**Finance:** Representing national and regional institutional lenders and borrowers in connection with permanent and construction loans on all types of real estate.
**Leasing:** Representing city and suburban developers and building owners in connection with leases and management agreements.
**Companies & Their Real Estate:** Representing owner and tenant clients, in connection with their businesses and facilities.
**Development:** Representing clients in the construction and development of new buildings, including development agreements, construction contracts, architect's contracts, agreements of sale and financing.
**Land Use/Zoning:** Representing clients before zoning and planning boards and other governmental bodies.

### Bankruptcy & Insolvency:

The firm's Bankruptcy and Insolvency Group combine business law, negotiation, litigation and problem-solving skills to help business debtors and creditors in sensitive restructuring situations. It represents clients who must manage their businesses (or collect claims from other businesses) in the crisis atmosphere of insolvency, regularly handling out-of-court liquidations, restructurings and pre-packaged and pre-arranged proceedings as well as cases under Chapters 7 and 11 of the Bankruptcy Code, purchasing and selling assets in distress circumstances, advancing competing or 'hostile' reorganization plans, and prosecuting and defending bankruptcy litigation.

# HARKINS CUNNINGHAM LLP

www.harkinscunningham.com **tel:** 215 851 6700 **fax:** 215 851 6710

**Presiding Partner:** John G Harkins, Jr
Number of partners: 7
Number of other lawyers: 7

## Firm Overview:

Harkins Cunningham LLP was founded in 1992 as a small firm with a highly sophisticated legal practice dedicated to resolving difficult problems using a team approach. From its inception, Harkins Cunningham has been one of the firms of choice for clients seeking lawyers who can tackle complex disputes successfully and efficiently. The firm's Litigation Practice includes antitrust, anti-takeover, intellectual property, securities fraud defense, professional malpractice, white-collar criminal defense, and other complex matters at both the trial and appellate levels. The firm also has extensive experience advising clients with respect to economic regulation, competition law, internal and governmental investigations, corporate governance and risk management across a broad range of industries.

## Main Areas of Practice:

### Commercial Litigation:

The firm helps business entities, organizations and individuals resolve challenging controversies through court or agency litigation and appeals, or through alternative dispute resolution. The firm's lawyers are frequently involved in federal multi-district litigation and in class action litigation in both federal and state courts.

### Antitrust:

The firm's Antitrust Practice has five principal components: 1) litigating antitrust actions in court and administrative regulatory proceedings; 2) assisting clients with competition issues that arise in the context of mergers and acquisitions and other business activity; 3) developing antitrust compliance programs; 4) responding to criminal and civil investigations by state and federal authorities; and 5) helping clients that operate in or are served by regulated industries successfully utilize competition law and principles in the context of state and federal regulation.

### Appellate Practice:

The firm has an active Appellate Practice. Its engagements have covered a wide range of areas of law, including those where the firm is not regularly engaged at the trial court level but for which experience and credibility in the appellate courts is critically important. The firm's attorneys have appeared before the Supreme Court of the United States as well as the United States Courts of Appeals for the District of Columbia and for the Second, Third, Fourth, Fifth, Sixth, Ninth, Tenth and Eleventh Circuits. In Pennsylvania, the firm has represented clients in the state Supreme Court and in the intermediate appellate courts.

### Corporate Counseling:

The firm advises public and private companies and other institutions and their directors on matters of corporate governance and the fiduciary duties of directors and officers; and advises public companies on their disclosure obligations under the federal securities laws. The firm also counsels early stage companies in their organization and financing.

### Corporate Investigations:

The firm's lawyers conduct internal corporate investigations for both institutions and committees of boards of directors, and negotiate with civil and criminal enforcement officials in matters of great sensitivity and importance to its clients.

### Railroads & other Regulated Industries:

The firm handles a broad range of matters for clients in the railroad industry and other regulated industries. In the railroad industry it has represented major (Class I) railroads as merger parties in five different railroad mergers proceedings; provided counsel to congressional committees, railroads, groups of railroads and the Association of American Railroads in a variety of legislative, administrative and judicial proceedings relating to the formation of the current scheme of railroad regulation; and regularly represents clients in rulemakings and related appellate proceedings.

### Clients:

The firm's clients are business and public entities, boards and committees of directors, industry coalitions, law firms and other professional organizations, universities and individuals with significant business interests. From its offices in Philadelphia and Washington, the firm's lawyers regularly work with other law firms and with a variety of experts to serve its clients throughout North America effectively and efficiently.

**OFFICES**

PENNSYLVANIA

**PHILADELPHIA:** 4000 Two Commerce Square, 2001 Market Street, PA 19103-7044
Tel: 215 851 6700   Fax: 215 851 6710

DISTRICT OF COLUMBIA

**WASHINGTON:** Suite 400, 1700 K Street, NW, DC 20006-3804
Tel: 202 973 7600   Fax: 202 973 7610

# K&L GATES LLP

**www.**klgates.com   **tel:** 412 355 6500   **fax:** 412 355 6501

**Chairman and Global Managing Partner:** Peter J Kalis
Number of lawyers worldwide: 2,000

## Firm Overview:

K&L Gates has more than 2,000 lawyers practicing in 48 fully integrated offices across five continents. The firm has one of the largest contingents of lawyers and offices across the United States (26) of any law firm and strong local presence in key capital cities and world commercial and financial centers. Their extensive network includes approximately 300 lawyers in Europe's largest economies. When K&L Gates combined with Australian national law firm Middletons in early 2013, the firm not only expanded its global platform to five continents, but now also has the largest Asia-Pacific presence among US law firms with more than 400 legal professionals across 11 offices. The firm's offices in the Asia-Pacific market, Australia, Germany, the Greater China market, Japan, the Middle East, Poland, and the United Kingdom all rank in the Top 10 of US-based firms in those markets.

## Main Areas of Practice:

### Corporate & Transactional:
K&L Gates' highly regarded corporate and transactional practice each year completes hundreds of M&A transactions and public and private debt and equity offerings. In 2013, K&L Gates was named "Law Firm of the Year" by Mergers & Acquisitions magazine for its strong performance, global approach to middle market mergers and acquisitions, as well as its own continued growth. Their private equity lawyers handle transactions from formation to investment to exit. The firm has a sophisticated global finance practice in structured finance; securitization; derivatives; structured products; real estate finance; municipal finance; and mezzanine, leveraged, and acquisition finance.

### Energy, Infrastructure & Resources:
K&L Gates leverages experience from a wide variety of legal disciplines to serve clients in the global energy, infrastructure, and resources space, including climate change and carbon finance. They advise on the financing, development, permitting, and construction needed to build large infrastructure, the operational issues of power generation and resource extraction activities, joint ventures, capital markets transactions and mergers and acquisitions of infrastructure and resource companies, and litigation and arbitration related to business activities of clients in this sector.

### Financial Services:
Offering one of the largest and most highly regarded investment management groups in the US, K&L Gates is noted for its work in the investment management and professional investor communities. In addition to representing major financial institutions and securities firms in a variety of disciplines, the firm has a diverse national and international bankruptcy/insolvency practice that serves a broad range of clients on both the debtor and creditor side. Their consumer financial services group is highly regarded for its representation of depository institutions, mortgage banks, consumer finance companies, loan servicers, broker dealers and investment banks in regulatory compliance, government enforcement, public policy and governmental affairs matters.

### Litigation & Dispute Resolution:
K&L Gates' dispute resolution practice includes international arbitrations, civil and criminal trials, class actions, multi-district and multi-national litigations, and appellate work. Their highly regarded litigators have resolved disputes in the most nuanced and complex areas, including commercial contracts, construction law, product liability, employment, toxic tort, antitrust and trade regulation, and securities enforcement. The firm partners with clients to resolve conflicts through arbitration, mediation, or other alternative dispute resolution methods and handles arbitrations under all the major institutional rules. K&L Gates also has one of the world's largest policyholder-side insurance coverage practices.

### Policy & Regulatory:
K&L Gates' policy and regulatory lawyers counsel companies on matters involving financial services, public policy, government enforcement, healthcare, antitrust/competition, telecommunications, environmental, food and drug, education, government contracts and international trade, as well as corporate compliance, internal investigations, and white-collar crime. Their more than 200 regulatory lawyers, many with governmental backgrounds or experience in regulated industries, guide clients through the regulatory processes at all jurisdictional levels. K&L Gates consistently ranks among the nation's most influential law firms in lobbying and government policy work.

### Intellectual Property:
K&L Gates' advises prominent global companies, helping to develop and protect their intellectual property assets worldwide and handling complex, high-stakes litigation. A K&L Gates IP litigation team won a hard fought $1.17 billion jury verdict in a patent infringement suit in 2012, the largest jury verdict in the country last year. More than 200 lawyers and 100 USPTO-registered professionals devote their practices to protecting and commercializing IP assets in the form of patents, trademarks, copyrights, or trade secrets. Patent lawyers, many with PhDs, handle cases involving biotechnology innovations, hospital equipment, and medical devices, computer networking equipment, sports equipment, and outdoor clothing. K&L Gates is one of the top filers of patent and trademark applications in the US. Their IP litigation teams have handled cases in 50 states and the District of Columbia and have extensive experience in the leading IP venues.

### Real Estate:
As one of the largest, most diversified real estate practices of any global law firm, K&L Gates has extensive experience in handling large and complex real estate transactions spanning multiple jurisdictions and nationalities in the US, Europe, the Middle East, and key markets in the Asia-Pacific region. They advise clients on their real estate needs related to land use, planning and zoning, development and construction, acquisitions, dispositions, financing and leasing, tax advice, joint venture structuring, and real estate-related litigation.

### Clients:
K&L Gates represents leading global corporations in every major industry, capital market participants, and ambitious middle-market and emerging growth companies, as well as public sector entities, educational institutions, philanthropic organizations, and individuals.

## OFFICES

**PENNSYLVANIA**

**PITTSBURGH:** K&L Gates Center, 210 Sixth Avenue, PA 15222-2613
Tel: 412 355 6500   Fax: 412 355 6501

The firm has offices in Anchorage, Alaska; Austin, Dallas, Fort Worth and Houston, Texas; Boston, Massachusetts; Charlotte, Raleigh and Research Triangle Park, North Carolina; Charleston, South Carolina; Chicago, Illinois; Los Angeles, Orange County, Palo Alto, San Diego and San Francisco, California; Miami, Florida; Newark, New Jersey; New York, New York; Portland, Oregon; Harrisburg and Pittsburgh, Pennsylvania; Seattle and Spokane, Washington; Washington, DC; and Wilmington, Delaware.

## INTERNATIONAL OFFICES

The firm maintains 11 offices in the Asia-Pacific region, located in Beijing, Brisbane, Hong Kong, Melbourne, Perth, Seoul, Shanghai, Singapore, Sydney, Taipei and Tokyo; eight offices in Europe, located in Berlin, Brussels, Frankfurt, London, Milan, Moscow, Paris and Warsaw; two offices in the Middle East, located in Doha, Qatar and Dubai, United Arab Emirates; and one office in South America located in São Paulo, Brazil.

# K&L GATES

# MORGAN, LEWIS & BOCKIUS LLP

www.morganlewis.com

**Firm Chair:** Francis M Milone
Number of partners worldwide: 492   Number of other lawyers worldwide: 933
Languages: *Arabic, Chinese (Mandarin), Dutch, English, French, German, Greek, Hebrew, Hindi, Indonesian, Italian, Japanese, Kazakh, Korean, Portuguese, Russian, Spanish, and Turkish.*

**Firm Overview:**
Morgan Lewis provides comprehensive litigation, corporate, transactional, regulatory, intellectual property, and labor and employment legal services to clients of all sizes - from globally established industry leaders to just-conceived start-ups. Founded in 1873, Morgan Lewis offers some 1,600 legal professionals in 24 offices across the United States, Europe, and Asia. The firm counts nearly half the Global 25, some two-thirds of the Fortune 100, and many top emerging businesses as clients.

**Main Areas of Practice:**

**Antitrust:**
Morgan Lewis attorneys regularly practice before antitrust enforcement agencies and courts around the world and bring critical insight to the strategic handling of complex transactions and bet-the company litigation.

**Corporate Affairs & Transactions:**
The firm serves as outside general counsel to global industry leaders, offering pragmatic, sophisticated representation in all aspects of their business planning. Morgan Lewis lawyers broker and close deals ranging from multibillion-dollar industry game-changers to discreet but significant transactions crucial to clients' business strategies, representing sellers, buyers, and investors; banks; funds; lenders; and independent director committees and management groups across all industries.

**Energy:**
For more than a century, major domestic and international entities in the electric, nuclear, oil and natural gas, water, and renewable energy sectors have turned to Morgan Lewis for their corporate, finance, transactional, regulatory and litigation needs.

**Latin America:**
With clients in virtually every Latin American country, the firm has an indepth understanding of the nuances of the region's business practices, laws and cultures. Lawyers on the Latin America Team assist clients across many industries on a variety of matters, including international tax, real estate, capital markets, labor and employment, immigration, litigation and international arbitration.

**Life Sciences & Healthcare:**
With lawyers in the US, London, Brussels, Frankfurt, and Tokyo, the firm's international life sciences and healthcare practices cover the complete life sciences product lifecycle as well as all matters related to healthcare products and services.

**Litigation:**
The firm's approximately 700 litigators include high-level government alumni, former top counsel to global businesses, and a deep bench of trial lawyers renowned for winning against the odds and breaking new legal ground in high-profile matters critical to the industries the firm serves.

**Intellectual Property:**
Ranked a Top Five Intellectual Property Law Firm by Law360 in 2012 and a Top Patent Firm by IP Today in 2012, the firm's full-service IP Practice comprises more than 150 lawyers and professionals, many with advanced degrees in engineering and the sciences.

**Labor & Employment:**
A hallmark practice for the firm with an international platform and a reputation for results, Morgan Lewis offers historical perspective, depth of resources, and command of virtually all workforce-related issues - with top-rated litigation, immigration, and benefits services and workplace training resources.

**China Practice & Morgan Lewis-TMI:**
The firm's China Practice guides clients through the complex business landscape in Greater China, focusing on mergers and acquisitions; securities; regulatory issues; private equity and venture capital transactions; and intellectual property counseling and litigation in China, Taiwan, and Hong Kong. In Tokyo, Morgan Lewis-TMI brings together one of the largest US law firms and one of the largest Japanese law firms to advise Japanese clients on a wide range of corporate and operational matters.

**Russia & CIS Practice:**
The firm's attorneys in Moscow, Russia and Almaty, Kazakhstan, working in close coordination with its European and Asia offices, represent international and domestic clients across the Russian Federation, the Republic of Kazakhstan, and the Commonwealth of Independent States (CIS), including Central Asia and the Caspian.

## OFFICES

### CALIFORNIA
**IRVINE:** 5 Park Plaza, Suite 1750, CA 92614-3508
Tel: 949 399 7000   Fax: 949 399 7001

**LOS ANGELES:** 300 South Grand Ave, 22nd Fl., CA 90071-3132
Tel: 213 612 2500   Fax: 213 612 2501

**SAN FRANCISCO:** One Market, Spear Street Tower, CA 94105-1596
Tel: 415 442 1000   Fax: 415 442 1001

**PALO ALTO:** 2 Palo Alto Square, 3000 El Camino Real, Suite 700, CA 94306-2121
Tel: 650 843 4000   Fax: 650 843 4001

### DELAWARE
**WILMINGTON:** The Nemours Building, 1007 N. Orange Street, Suite 501, DE 19801
Tel: 302 574 3000   Fax: 302 574 3001

### DISTRICT OF COLUMBIA
**WASHINGTON DC:** 1111 Pennsylvania Ave., NW, DC 20004-2541
Tel: 202 739 3000   Fax: 202 739 3001

### FLORIDA
**MIAMI:** 200 S. Biscayne Blvd., Suite 5300, FL 33131-2339
Tel: 305 415 3000   Fax: 305 415 3001

### ILLINOIS
**CHICAGO:** 77 West Wacker Dr., IL 60601-5094
Tel: 312 324 1000   Fax: 312 324 1001

### MASSACHUSETTS
**BOSTON:** 225 Franklin Street, 16th Floor, MA 02110-4104
Tel: 617 341 7700   Fax: 617 341 7701

### NEW JERSEY
**PRINCETON:** 502 Carnegie Center, NJ 08540-6289
Tel: 609 919 6600   Fax: 609 919 6701

### NEW YORK
**NEW YORK:** 101 Park Avenue, NY 10178-0060
Tel: 212 309 6000   Fax: 212 309 6001

### PENNSYLVANIA
**HARRISBURG:** 17 N. Second St., 14th Fl., PA 17101-1601
Tel: 717 237 5000   Fax: 717 237 5001

**PHILADELPHIA:** 1701 Market St., PA 19103-2921
Tel: 215 963 5000   Fax: 215 963 5001

**PITTSBURGH:** One Oxford Centre, Thirty-Second Floor, PA 15219-6401
Tel: 412 560 3300   Fax: 412 560 7001

### TEXAS
**DALLAS:** 1717 Main St., Suite 3200, TX 75201-7347
Tel: 214 466 4000   Fax: 214 466 4001

**HOUSTON:** 1000 Louisiana St., Suite 4000, TX 77002-5006
Tel: 713 890 5000   Fax: 713 890 5001

## INTERNATIONAL OFFICES
Almaty, Brussels, Beijing, Frankfurt, London, Moscow, Paris, Tokyo

## International Work:
Serving and working within Europe, Asia, Russia and the Commonwealth of Independent States, Latin America, Africa and the Middle East.

# PANITCH SCHWARZE BELISARIO & NADEL LLP

www.panitchlaw.com **tel:** 215 965 1330 **fax:** 215 965 1331

**Managing Partners:** William W Schwarze, Martin G Belisario
Number of partners: 12  Number of lawyers: 22
Number of patent agents: 1
Languages: *include Chinese, German, Gujarati and Spanish*

**Firm Overview:**
An intellectual property firm based in Philadelphia, PA, Panitch Schwarze Belisario & Nadel LLP provides litigation, licensing, and counseling services related to patents, trademarks, copyrights, and trade secrets. With an experienced and highly talented team of intellectual property professionals, the firm has successfully represented a variety of clientele, ranging from individual inventors to *Fortune* 500 companies. PSB&N has long-standing relationships with a network of foreign associates in countries around the world, allowing it to provide clients with comprehensive global protection of their intellectual property assets. With such experience and technical expertise, PSB&N is able to address each client need with the responsiveness and personal attention characteristic of a sophisticated boutique firm.

**Main Areas of Practice:**
Attracting clients from throughout the world as well as from the United States, PSB&N works hard to assist individuals and companies in all matters relating to intellectual property. The firm's core practice areas include:

**Patents:**
8 partners; 17 fee-earners
With the rapid advancement of new technologies in virtually all areas of science, patents continue to be one of the most important ways to protect intellectual property rights. PSB&N attorneys recognize this and rely on their wealth of experience and knowledge to successfully guide clients through the patent process. This broad range of expertise includes the preparation and prosecution of original, ex parte re-examination and inter partes re-examination patent applications in the US Patent and Trademark Office and foreign patent offices, new product clearance, due diligence and patentability analyses.
**Contact:** Martin G Belisario **Tel:** 215 965 1303
**Email:** mbelisario@panitchlaw.com

**Trademarks:**
2 partners; 5 fee-earners
The firm's team of five dedicated trademark attorneys focus their practice on advising clients as to the availability and adoption of trademarks, and the management and enforcement of domestic and international trademark portfolios. The firm's trademark attorneys possess an extensive amount of experience representing clients in connection with opposition and cancellation proceedings before the US Patent and Trademark Office's Trademark Trial and Appeal Board and various US District Courts, internet and domain name disputes, trademark licensing, and the acquisition and auditing of trademark portfolios.
**Contact:** Michael J Leonard **Tel:** 215 965 1390
**Email:** mleonard@panitchlaw.com

**Copyrights:**
2 partners; 5 fee-earners
The firm's attorneys possess a wide variety of experience in counseling clients on the registration, licensing and policing of copyrights. Their copyright attorneys not only specialize in the acquisition of protection for creative works in media such as software, literature, art and music, but they are well skilled at identifying and enforcing violations. The firm possess an extensive amount of experience in working with internet-based and digital technology clients who disseminate and share information around the globe. It provides clients with clear guidance and creative solutions for the protection of copyrighted works as it fully appreciates how copyright protection frequently overlaps with other forms of intellectual property protection, such as patents and trademarks.
**Contact:** Laura A Genovese **Tel:** 215 965 1348
**Email:** lgenovese@panitchlaw.com

**Litigation:**
5 partners; 10 fee-earners
Relying on their professional experiences, PSB&N attorneys have successfully litigated all types of intellectual property cases before administrative agencies, state courts, and federal courts, including litigation involving patent, trademark, copyright, trade secret, and trade dress cases. The firm's widely respected litigation practice has attracted a worldwide clientele. In addition to representing many North American companies, PSB&N attorneys also represent a wide array of companies from around the globe. For many PSB&N clients, US litigation represents only a portion of a much broader global dispute. The firm's attorneys are accustomed to coordinating a multinational approach and are adept at working with counsel in other countries to ensure that litigation efforts both in the US and abroad are successful.
**Contact:** John D Simmons **Tel:** 215 965 1268
**Email:** jsimmons@panitchlaw.com

**Licensing:**
10 partners; 22 fee-earners
In an increasingly fast-paced and ever-changing technological world, licenses represent an important method for protecting intellectual property rights and guarding against possible infringement claims. With extensive licensing experience in both the US and international markets, PSB&N is well positioned to guide clients in maximizing the value of their intellectual property.
**Contact:** Ronald L Panitch **Tel:** 215 965 1300
**Email:** rpanitch@panitchlaw.com

**Trade Secrets:**
7 partners; 22 fee-earners
Trade secret protection can serve as a valuable way to protect certain intellectual property rights. Such protection can last indefinitely, and thus, trade secrets can offer an advantage over patent protection, which only lasts for a specifically limited period of time. However, through methods such as reverse engineering, trade secrets can also be lost. PSB&N attorneys understand these complexities and rely on their experience and skill to tailor legal strategies that will afford the best possible intellectual property protection for each client.
**Contact:** Frederick A Tecce **Tel:** 215 965 1294
**Email:** ftecce@panitchlaw.com

**International Work:**
The firm provides comprehensive intellectual property representation for a worldwide clientele. Recently, for example, the firm has represented a German company in an ANDA litigation, a Japanese company enforcing its patent for pharmaceutical equipment in the US, an opposition for an Ecuadoran company in Australia and is handling eight reexamination applications involving patents in litigation for a large company in Taiwan.

**PRACTICE AREAS**
Patents
Trademarks
Copyrights
Licensing
Litigation
Trade Secrets

**OFFICES**
PENNSYLVANIA
**PHILADELPHIA:** One Commerce Square, 2005 Market Street, Suite 2200, PA 19103
Tel: 215 965 1330   Fax: 215 965 1331
Email: info@panitchlaw.com

PANITCH SCHWARZE BELISARIO & NADEL LLP
Intellectual Property Law

# PEPPER HAMILTON LLP

www.pepperlaw.com

**Chairman:** Louis J Freeh
**Executive Partner:** Thomas J Cole Jr

**Firm Overview:**

Pepper Hamilton LLP is a multi-practice law firm with more than 500 lawyers nationally providing corporate, litigation and regulatory legal services to US and international businesses, governmental entities, non-profit organizations and individuals. Pepper was founded in 1890.

**Main Areas of Practice:**

**Commercial Litigation:**
Represents clients in complex contract, corporate governance, securities, ERISA and antitrust litigation and alternative dispute resolution, in the single case, class action and MDL context.
**Contact:** Amy B Ginensky

**Construction:**
Represents contractors, public and private owners, developers, subcontractors, architects, engineers and sureties in contract negotiations, arbitration, mediation and litigation.
**Contact:** Bruce W Ficken

**Corporate Restructuring & Bankruptcy:**
Represents creditors, debtors, trustees, commercial lenders, examiners and other parties in insolvencies.
**Contact:** Robert S Hertzberg, David B Stratton

**Corporate & Securities:**
Represents public and private companies in M&A activities, corporate governance, disclosure, securities compliance and enforcement, and other business matters; private equity and venture funds in fund formation, investments, buyouts and other transactions.
**Contact:** Brian M Katz

**Employee Benefits:**
Benefits and executive compensation counseling, plan drafting and administration; and benefits/ compensation aspects of transactions; ERISA litigation.
**Contact:** Jonathan A Clark, David M Kaplan

**Environmental & Energy:**
Represents manufacturers, public and private utilities, insurance companies, renewable energy developers, trade associations, land owners, large institutional organisations, oil and gas producers with environmental, regulatory and commercial issues.
**Contact:** John W Carroll

**Financial Services:**
Represents sophisticated institutional lenders and borrowers in leveraged transactions, secured financings, securitizations and litigation; investment advisory fund formation and regulation.
**Contact:** Richard P Eckman

**Health Effects Litigation:**
Risk management, regulatory counseling and litigation related to alleged adverse health effects from pharmaceuticals, medical devices, radiation, chemicals and environmental substances; product liability litigation involving consumer goods and industrial equipment; civil and criminal matters related to clinical trials.
**Contact:** Nina M Gussack

**Intellectual Property:**
Procures intellectual property rights and resolves disputes, including patents, copyrights, trademarks, trade secret protection, unfair competition, false advertising, and defamation, publicity and privacy issues.
**Contact:** Vincent V Carissimi, William D Belanger

**International:**
Represents major national and multinational corporations, emerging businesses, foreign governments, trade associations, nonprofit organizations, entrepreneurs and individuals.
**Contact:** James D Rosener

**Labor & Employment:**
Represents employers in all aspects of labor and employment law, from management counseling to complex employment litigation.
**Contact:** Matthew V DelDuca

**Real Estate:**
Represents major developers in financing, leasing and construction of commercial and residential developments.
**Contact:** Norman B Berlin, Matthew J Swett

**Tax:**
Structures businesses and transactions to improve local, state, national and international tax efficiency.
**Contact:** Joan C Arnold

**Trusts & Estates:**
Represents individuals and businesses in wealth preservation issues and family-owned businesses.
**Contact:** Mark S Blaskey

**OFFICES**

**CALIFORNIA**
**IRVINE:** Suite 1200, 4 Park Plaza, CA 92614-5955
Tel: 949 567 3500   Fax: 949 863 0151

**LOS ANGELES:** Suite 1670, 333 South Grand Avenue, CA 90071
Tel: 213 293 3130 Fax: 213 628 8690

**DELAWARE**
**WILMINGTON:** Hercules Plaza, Suite 5100, 1313 Market Street, PO Box 1709, DE 19899-1709
Tel: 302 777 6500   Fax: 302 421 8390

**DISTRICT OF COLUMBIA**
**WASHINGTON DC:** Hamilton Square, 600 Fourteenth Street, NW, DC 20005-2004
Tel: 202 220 1200   Fax: 202 220 1665

**MASSACHUSETTS**
**BOSTON:** 19th Floor, High Street Tower, 125 High Street, MA 02110-2736
Tel: 617 204 5100   Fax: 617 204 5150

**MICHIGAN**
**SOUTHFIELD:** Suite 1800, 4000 Town Center, MI 48075-1505
Tel: 248 359 7300   Fax: 248 359 7700

**NEW JERSEY**
**PRINCETON:** Suite 400, 301 Carnegie Center, NJ 08543-5276
Tel: 609 452 0808   Fax: 609 452 1147

**NEW YORK**
**NEW YORK:** The New York Times Building, 37th Floor, 620 Eighth Avenue, NY 10018-1405
Tel: 212 808 2700   Fax: 212 286 9806

**PENNSYLVANIA**
**BERWYN:** 400 Berwyn Park, 899 Cassatt Road, PA 19312-1183
Tel: 610 640 7800   Fax: 610 640 7835

**HARRISBURG:** Suite 200, 100 Market Street, PO Box 1181, PA 17108-1181
Tel: 717 255 1155   Fax: 717 238 0575

**PHILADELPHIA:** 3000 Two Logan Square, Eighteenth and Arch Streets, PA 19103-2799
Tel: 215 981 4000   Fax: 215 981 4750

**PITTSBURGH:** Suite 5000, 500 Grant Street, PA 15219-2507
Tel: 412 454 5000   Fax: 412 281 0717

**White Collar Litigation & Investigations:**
Team includes former FBI director and a highly skilled group of former judges, federal and state prosecutors, and experienced corporate counsel with unparalleled expertise in white collar defense and regulatory enforcement, corporate investigations, compliance and ethics.
**Contact:** Thomas M Gallagher

**Pepper Hamilton LLP**
Attorneys at Law

# SAUL EWING LLP

**www.saul.com  tel:** 215 972 7777  **fax:** 215 972 7725

**Managing Partner:** David S Antzis
Number of partners: 144
Number of other lawyers: 95

**Firm Overview:**
Founded in 1921, Saul Ewing provides a broad array of legal services to businesses from its offices located throughout the east coast.

## Main Areas of Practice:

**Bankruptcy:**
Representing companies in cases under the bankruptcy laws, as well as in other matters relating to corporate reorganization, creditors' rights and insolvency.

**Litigation:**
Representing corporations and corporate officers and directors in commercial disputes including shareholder derivative actions, securities fraud claims and other actions to enforce or defend legal or contractual rights.

**Business & Finance:**
Providing legal services to corporations and corporate officers and directors on issues related to the operation of their businesses including corporate formation, corporate governance, business transactions, corporate financings and capitalization, intellectual property rights and other legal matters that face businesses in today's economy.

**Real Estate:**
Representing owners, developers, REITs and other investors in the development and construction of new projects, in the acquisition and leasing of existing facilities and in matters related to the ownership of land generally.

**Public Finance:**
Serving as bond counsel, issuers counsel and underwriters counsel in transactions involving the issuance and sale of tax-exempt state and local government bonds.

**Insurance:**
Advising corporations in the insurance industry on issues related to the operation and regulation of companies in the insurance business including licensing, capitalization and solvency, and the marketing and sale of insurance products. The firm also represents clients in litigation related to the business of insurance.

**Environment:**
Advise clients on matters related to compliance with state and federal environmental regulations and help to structure real estate and corporate transactions to minimize environmental liability. The firm also represents corporations and corporate officers in litigation related to environmental and regulatory liabilities.

**Personal Wealth, Estates & Trusts:**
Representing wealthy individuals, trusts and institutions in matters related to wealth preservation and management including tax, estate and retirement planning, business succession and executive compensation and charitable giving.

**Labor:**
Representing clients in collective bargaining agreements, labor relations, procedures and protocols, employment, pay practices to comply with federal and state wage and hour laws and affirmative action plans and programs.

**Higher Education:**
Handling a wide range of legal matters for large public and private universities, small independent colleges and universities, community colleges and a myriad of institutions affiliated with higher education.

**Energy & Utilities:**
Providing comprehensive advice and representation on energy (electricity, natural gas, liquefied natural gas, steam, and hot and chilled water), water, wastewater, telecommunications and transportation issues. Attorneys represent clients before local, state and federal regulatory agencies, as well as in state and federal courts.

**Clients:**
Saul Ewing serves a broad range of regional, national, and international clients from across the business spectrum. The firm's clients include businesses of all sizes, nonprofits, academic institutions and governments and their agencies. Clients value Saul Ewing for its industry knowledge and the responsiveness of its attorneys.

## PRACTICE AREAS

Bankruptcy
Litigation
Business & Finance
Real Estate
Public Finance
Insurance
Intellectual Property
Life Sciences
Environment
Health Law
Personal Wealth, Estates & Trusts
Labor
Higher Education
Energy & Utilities

## OFFICES

**DELAWARE**
**WILMINGTON:** 222 Delaware Avenue, Suite 1200, DE 19899
Tel: 302 421 6800  Fax: 302 421 6813

**DISTRICT OF COLUMBIA**
**WASHINGTON DC:** 1919 Pennsylvania Avenue, NW, Suite 550, DC 20006-3434
Tel: 202 333 8800  Fax: 202 337 6065

**MARYLAND**
**BALTIMORE:** Lockwood Place, 500 East Pratt Street, Suite 900, MD 21202-3171
Tel: 410 332 8600  Fax: 410 332 8862

**MASSACHUSETTS**
**BOSTON:** 131 Dartmouth Street, Suite 501, MA 02116
Tel: 617 723 3300  Fax: 617 723 4151

**NEW JERSEY**
**NEWARK:** One Riverfront Plaza, Suite 1520, NJ 07102-5426
Tel: 973 286 6700  Fax: 973 286 6800

**PRINCETON:** 750 College Road East, Suite 100, NJ 08540-6617
Tel: 609 452 3100  Fax: 609 452 3122

**NEW YORK**
**NEW YORK:** 555 Fifth Avenue, Suite 1700 NY 10017
Tel: 212 980 7200  Fax: 212 980 7209

**PENNSYLVANIA**
**HARRISBURG:** Penn National Insurance Plaza, 2 North Second Street, 7th Floor, PA 17101-1619
Tel: 717 257 7500  Fax: 717 238 4622

**PHILADELPHIA:** Centre Square West, 1500 Market Street, 38th Floor, PA 19102-2186
Tel: 215 972 7777  Fax: 215 972 7725

**PITTSBURGH:** One PPG Place, Suite 3010, PA 15222
Tel: 412 209 2500  Fax: 412 209 2570

**WAYNE:** 1200 Liberty Ridge Drive, Suite 200, PA 19087-5569
Tel: 610 251 5050  Fax: 610 651 5930

# WOODCOCK WASHBURN

www.woodcock.com

**Policy Committee:** David Bailey, Gary Levin, David Wolfsohn

### Firm Overview:

Woodcock Washburn recognizes the importance of intellectual property to business enterprises. As the firm likes to say, "Intellectual property isn't just something we do… it's all we do."® The firm has built a superb reputation and a wealth of experience in patent, trademark, copyright, and trade secret law for more than 60 years. Its 80-lawyer boutique is one of the largest intellectual property law firms in the United States and the largest in Pennsylvania, New Jersey, and Delaware. With offices in Atlanta, Philadelphia, and Seattle, the firm is uniquely positioned to serve national and international clients. Woodcock Washburn has consistently been recognized as a leader in providing intellectual property legal services. In Corporate Counsel, a survey of *Fortune* 250 companies recognized Woodcock Washburn as one of the "go-to" firms for intellectual property procurement and enforcement. Of the first twelve "Inventor of the Year" awards, three went to Woodcock Washburn clients. And formative work for firm clients became the basis for the first U.S. software patents.

**Legal Expertise:** IP Law & Business recognized Woodcock Washburn as one of the top firms nationwide for protecting intellectual property in America. Clients routinely rely on Woodcock Washburn for advice in cases involving damages claims over $100 million.

**Technical Expertise:** Most Woodcock Washburn patent attorneys have a technical degree in biotechnology, chemistry, chemical, electrical, or mechanical engineering, or computer science. Many have advanced degrees, including PhDs and even a Doctor of Veterinary Medicine.

**In-House Perspective:** Woodcock Washburn attorneys understand their clients' needs since many previously served as in-house counsel for companies such as AT&T, Coca-Cola, DuPont, the Recording Industry Association of America, Rohm & Haas, QVC, and Unisys.

**Diversity:** The Vault recognized the firm as being "very accommodating to women" and "very welcoming to all racial and ethnic minorities." The firm has received an award from the Pennsylvania Bar Association's Women in the Profession Committee for promoting women lawyers to leadership positions within the firm. Woodcock Washburn is a Sponsor of the American Intellectual Property Law Education Foundation which promotes diversity in the intellectual property bar, and of the American Bar Association's Judicial Intern Opportunity Program, which promotes diversity for judicial interns.

## Main Areas of Practice:

### Lawyers as Scientists & Engineers:

Woodcock Washburn lawyers are not just intellectual property lawyers, they are all business lawyers who understand that meeting the clients' strategic goals is paramount. And most of Woodcock Washburn's attorneys are also scientists and engineers, schooled in such demanding disciplines as biotechnology, chemistry, electrical and mechanical engineering, and computer science. As technology specialists, the firm's lawyers possess a unique understanding of the issues faced by clients, and they present those issues in clear and meaningful ways to judges, juries, and government examiners around the world.

### Industry Focused Practice:

Woodcock Washburn represents clients in many industries. The firm has successfully represented clients in diverse biotechnology and chemistry fields that include agricultural chemicals, drug delivery compositions, genetically engineered plants, food additives, monoclonal antibodies, organic chemistry, genomics, nanotechnology, pharmaceuticals, small molecule chemistry, and vaccines. The firm also represents clients in mechanical, electrical, and computer sciences, offering services in business methods, financial services, computer hardware, digital rights management, encryption/decryption, medical and dental devices, optics, packaging, robotics, semiconductors, smart cards, telecommunications and wireless technology, among others.

### Effective Litigation Strategies:

The firm's litigators have litigated in nearly every federal court in the United States and most appeals courts. On behalf of plaintiffs, the firm's litigators have achieved numerous judgments and settlements in the tens of millions of dollars, and on behalf of defendants, verdicts of no liability. Most importantly, the firm's litigators make the client's strategic business goals paramount—using innovative techniques of project management, alternative fee agreements, outside-the-box strategizing, and the full range of ADR techniques to align the firm's goals with those of its clients.

### Clients:

Woodcock Washburn represents *Fortune* 100 and 500 companies in diverse, technology-driven industries. The firm's clients have repeatedly sought Woodcock Washburn to handle their complex matters in patent prosecution, patent litigation, trademarks, trade secrets, copyrights, and licensing. Some of the firm's valued clients include Johnson & Johnson, Microsoft, DuPont, Crown Holdings, SAP, AT&T, National Institutes of Health, The Weather Channel, The University of Pennsylvania, Synthes, Morphotek, Elster, ISIS Pharmaceuticals, and TruePosition. For a more detailed client listing, please view the firm's website at www.woodcock.com.

### International Work:

Woodcock Washburn's experience extends beyond the United States to other countries – an important capability in today's global economy. The firm's lawyers are familiar with the complexities of patent, trademark, copyright, trade secrets, and unfair competition laws across jurisdictions worldwide. Guided by its history of practicing intellectual property law and its dedication to quality client service, Woodcock Washburn LLP protects the ideas that will shape the future.

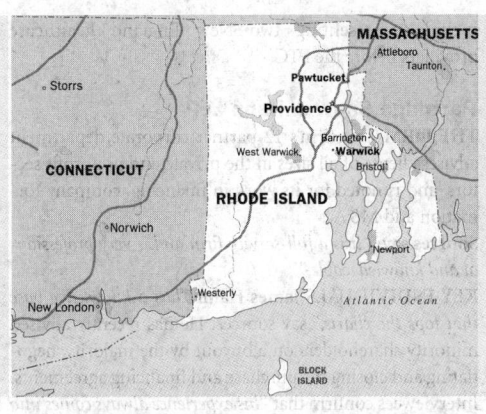

## How lawyers are ranked

Every year we carry out thousands of in-depth interviews with clients in order to assess the reputations and expertise of business lawyers worldwide. The qualities we look for (and which determine rankings) include technical legal ability, professional conduct, client service, commercial awareness/astuteness, diligence, commitment, and other qualities most valued by the client. For details of our research team, see p.5.

# CORPORATE/COMMERCIAL

Commentary about individuals can be found under their firm's paragraph. If the firm has no paragraph (is not ranked), look at Other Notable Practitioners.

### Corporate/Commercial
### Leading Firms

**Band 1**
Adler Pollock & Sheehan PC *
Edwards Wildman Palmer *

**Band 2**
Duffy & Sweeney, Ltd
Hinckley, Allen & Snyder LLP
Partridge Snow & Hahn LLP

### Senior Statesmen
**Senior Statesmen: distinguished older practitioners**

| | |
|---|---|
| Carlotti Stephen J | Hinckley, Allen & Snyder LLP |
| Johnson V Duncan | Edwards Wildman Palmer * |

### Leading Individuals

**Band 1**

| | |
|---|---|
| Geanacopoulos Stephen | Adler Pollock & Sheehan PC * |
| Gilden David M | Partridge Snow & Hahn LLP |
| Hahn James H | Partridge Snow & Hahn LLP |
| Hood Roger W | Duffy & Sweeney, Ltd |
| Skeffington James J | Edwards Wildman Palmer * |
| Sweeney Michael F | Duffy & Sweeney, Ltd |

**Band 2**

| | |
|---|---|
| Cameron E Colby | Cameron & Mittleman LLP (ONP)[†] |
| Duffell David K | Weil, Gotshal & Manges LLP (ONP)[†] * |
| Farrell Margaret D | Hinckley, Allen & Snyder LLP |
| Graham Christopher | Edwards Wildman Palmer * |
| Gray Douglas G | Edwards Wildman Palmer * |
| Partridge John J | Partridge Snow & Hahn LLP |
| Reed Walter G D | Edwards Wildman Palmer * |

**Band 3**

| | |
|---|---|
| Dowling Sarah T | Adler Pollock & Sheehan PC * |
| Lundsten E Hans | Adler Pollock & Sheehan PC * |
| Myers Elizabeth Murdock | Hinckley, Allen & Snyder LLP |

* Indicates firm / individual with profile.
[†] ONP = Other Notable Practitioner.

### Corporate/Commercial: Banking & Finance
### Senior Statesmen
**Senior Statesmen: distinguished older practitioners**

| | |
|---|---|
| Farmer III Malcolm | Hinckley, Allen & Snyder LLP |

### Leading Individuals

**Band 1**

| | |
|---|---|
| Chlebus Andrew J | Edwards Wildman Palmer * |
| McCann Gail E | Edwards Wildman Palmer * |

**Band 2**

| | |
|---|---|
| Marcello III Matthew T | Hinckley, Allen & Snyder LLP |

### Corporate/Commercial: Intellectual Property
### Leading Individuals

**Band 1**

| | |
|---|---|
| Ottaviani John E | Edwards Wildman Palmer * |

**Band 2**

| | |
|---|---|
| Campellone Paul | Adler Pollock & Sheehan PC * |
| Sweeney Michael F | Duffy & Sweeney, Ltd |

## Band 1

### Adler Pollock & Sheehan PC
See profile on p.2259

**THE FIRM** This mid-sized regional firm has offices in both Providence and Boston, in addition to a satellite office in New Hampshire. The firm's deep corporate and commercial expertise makes it a favorite among its impressive portfolio of national and international clients. Recent work highlights include advising Cookson Group on the sale of its US precious metals business to Richline Group.
**Sources say:** *"The best firm in the region."*
**KEY INDIVIDUALS** The *"very dedicated and enthusiastic"* **Stephen Geanacopoulos** (see p.2257) heads the firm's business and corporate law department. He recently advised Ingenico on its strategic investment in Roam Data. **Sarah Dowling** (see p.2257) *"is very knowledgeable in her areas of expertise,"* say sources. She is head of the firm's

healthcare department, and routinely advises physician practice groups on the financing, expansion and sale to hospital practices. The highly experienced **Paul Campellone** (see p.2256) continues to be noted for his expertise in public finance, intellectual property and M&A. He recently advised the State of Rhode Island on the issuance and sale of general obligation bonds. Tax attorney **Hans Lundsten** (see p.2257) advises private and public sector clients on a plethora of tax issues. He recently worked alongside Geanacopoulos on the aforementioned work for Ingenico.

### Edwards Wildman Palmer
See profile on p.1520

**THE FIRM** The 2011 merger between Edwards Angell Palmer & Dodge LLP and Wildman, Harrold, Allen & Dixon LLP continues to bear dividends, with the resultant firm's Rhode Island business law department going from strength to strength. Key clients include Bank of America, Amtrol and DAK Americas.
**Sources say:** *"The firm has broadened and added sophistication to its practice this year."*
**KEY INDIVIDUALS Duncan Johnson** (see p.2257) continues to practice as a high-level general corporate legal adviser to financial institutions. He has expertise on both corporate and regulatory legal issues affecting financial firms. **John Ottaviani** (see p.2258) focuses on business law and intellectual property matters and has recently handled worldwide trademark protection and enforcement on behalf of Five Star Fragrances. **James Skeffington** (see p.2258) continues to command a fine reputation in the Providence business community and beyond. Sources describe him as *"one of the best lawyers in New England."* **Andrew Chlebus** (see p.2256) advises financial institutions on the provision of loans to entities in a broad spectrum of industries, most prominent of which are the media and entertainment sectors. He is also noted for his knowledge of the state's consumer finance laws. **Christopher Graham** (see p.2257) is co-head of the firm's

Providence office and focuses his practice on the venture capital and private equity space. Clients include R3 Education and Wedgewood Waterford. Clients name **Douglas Gray** (see p.2257) *"a fine lawyer and a talented man."* He cochairs the firm's corporate counseling and business transaction group, and has recently advised Amtrol on a wide range of general corporate law matters. **Walter Reed** (see p.2258) recently stepped down as managing partner, but continues to serve the firm as a partner advising on corporate law. He has deep experience in M&A, joint ventures and partnerships. **Gail McCann** (see p.2257) recently represented Bank of America in an auction sale of bulk loans to third parties, and has extensive experience in handling financing transactions.

## Band 2

### Duffy & Sweeney, Ltd

**THE FIRM** The Duffy & Sweeney business law team maintains a fine reputation among the Providence business community. Its broad skill set ensures that it can cover a wide range of corporate and commercial matters, and it is particularly noted for its ability to handle licensing and IP-related work. Clients include RBS Citizens NA, NumArk Industries and Astro-Med.

**Sources say:** *"I think it is very business savvy as a firm of lawyers."*

**KEY INDIVIDUALS Roger Hood** has recent experience advising in the technology and healthcare sectors. Sources say: *"He handles things in a practical way and gets a result that is appropriate."* Firm cofounder **Michael Sweeney**

advises a host of midmarket companies on corporate law matters and is noted for his knowledge of M&A, securities law, private equity and venture capital. *"He is a smart guy and a good lawyer,"* say sources.

### Hinckley, Allen & Snyder LLP

**THE FIRM** This regional firm has a sizable corporate department that handles a broad range of general corporate matters, including M&A work and tax planning. The firm continues to be trusted by clients of the caliber of Bancorp Rhode Island, Astro-Med and AT Cross Company.

**Sources say:** *"A full-service firm that has very talented staff in most segments of law so as to provide full and comprehensive support for public companies."*

**KEY INDIVIDUALS Stephen Carlotti** is an immensely experienced corporate lawyer with knowledge of both the public and private sectors. Sources relate that *"his experience and his broad base of corporate representation make him stand out."* The similarly venerated **Malcolm Farmer** advises financial institutions and corporate entities on a broad swathe of business matters, and is noted for his knowledge of the nonprofit sector. **Margaret Farrell** earns extensive praise for her exceptional technical expertise in corporate law. She has recently been involved in advising on the $1.6 billion acquisition of NewAlliance Bancshares by First Niagara Financial Group. **Matthew Marcello** concentrates his practice on banking, real estate finance and corporate matters. Sources confirm that *"he has a business-oriented mindset."* The deeply experienced **Elizabeth Murdock Myers** has a broad-ranging practice covering corporate, healthcare and antitrust law. Recent matters

include representing two New England healthcare providers before the FTC.

### Partridge Snow & Hahn LLP

**THE FIRM** This firm's 12-partner corporate department advises clients of all sizes in the private and nonprofit sectors, and is noted for its work in financing, company formation and M&A.

**Sources say:** *"It is a full-service firm and is very professional and knowledgeable."*

**KEY INDIVIDUALS James Hahn** *"has a knowledge base that tops the charts,"* say sources. He has recently advised minority shareholders on a buyout by the majority, negotiating and closing the purchase and financing agreements. Interviewees confirm that *"his experience always comes into play and he is a great negotiator."* **John Partridge** continues to act as counsel to a major general hospital on general corporate matters, including bank financing and M&A. Managing partner **David Gilden** handles banking and finance matters, and is noted for his expertise in real estate finance transactions.

### Other Notable Practitioners

**David Duffell** (see p.2257) of Weil, Gotshal & Manges LLP continues to attract praise from clients, who value his indefatigable attitude as a senior transactional attorney and his deep private equity experience. **Colby Cameron** of Cameron Mittleman LLP *"is a good lawyer and a good businessman,"* say sources. He advises corporate clients in a range of sectors, including sports, healthcare and media.

# LABOR & EMPLOYMENT

Commentary about individuals can be found under their firm's paragraph. If the firm has no paragraph (is not ranked), look at Other Notable Practitioners.

## Labor & Employment
### Leading Firms

**Band 1**
Adler Pollock & Sheehan PC *
Nixon Peabody LLP *

**Band 2**
Hinckley, Allen & Snyder LLP
Partridge Snow & Hahn LLP

**Band 3**
Edwards Wildman Palmer *

### Leading Individuals

**Band 1**

| | | |
|---|---|---|
| Brooks Robert | Adler Pollock & Sheehan PC * | |
| Collier Stacie B | Nixon Peabody LLP * | |
| Gamboli Michael | Partridge Snow & Hahn LLP | |
| Prescott Andrew | Nixon Peabody LLP * | |
| Whelan Joseph D | Whelan & Siket (ONP)[†] | |

**Band 2**

| | |
|---|---|
| Chittick Michael D | Adler Pollock & Sheehan PC * |
| Kasle Jeffrey | St Peter & Kasle (ONP)[†] |
| Kinder Daniel K | Little Medeiros Kinder Bulman (ONP)[†] |
| Kraemer Michael F | Hinckley, Allen & Snyder LLP |
| McNamara Neal J | Nixon Peabody LLP * |
| Pogue Mark | Edwards Wildman Palmer * |

*\* Indicates firm / individual with profile.*
*[†]ONP = Other Notable Practitioner.*

## Band 1

### Adler Pollock & Sheehan PC
See profile on p.2259

**THE FIRM** The labor and employment practice at this firm covers a broad range of issues, including discrimination litigation, union negotiations and employee relationship consultations, and is lauded for its work with private and public sector employers. An impressive roster of clients includes PepsiCo, the City of Pawtucket and National Grid.
**Sources say:** *"This is a firm that has become stronger and stronger of late."*
**KEY INDIVIDUALS Robert Brooks** (see p.2256) heads the firm's labor and employment team and is respected by peers as a lawyer who *"is practical and appropriately aggressive."* He recently advised the City of Pawtucket on a case regarding non-adherence to a collective bargaining con-

tract. **Michael Chittick** (see p.2256) is a respected employment litigator whose skills are valued by clients in the public and private sectors. He recently defended PepsiCo subsidiary Frito-Lay with respect to overtime pay claims.

### Nixon Peabody LLP
See profile on p.1526

**THE FIRM** Nixon Peabody's highly regarded labor and employment practice continues to go from strength to strength in Rhode Island. The team receives strong praise from the market for its handling of labor relations and high-stakes employment litigation, and is further commended for its provision of counseling and training services to employers. Clients include Concord Hospital, Providence Housing Authority and Fidelity Investments.
**Sources say:** *"The lawyers at this firm are highly professional experts giving excellent service."*
**KEY INDIVIDUALS Stacie Collier** (see p.2256) ascends to the top tier of employment attorneys after receiving strong accolades from sources, who confirm that she is *"very pragmatic in litigation and discrimination cases."* She is an experienced trial lawyer and a recognized trainer in employment matters. The highly experienced **Andrew Prescott** (see p.2258) is consistently lauded for his knowledge of labor relations. He continues to handle high-value labor, wage and hour and discrimination litigation, and is described by sources as *"an expert in his field"* who *"knows his law very, very well."* **Neal McNamara** (see p.2257) *"is very good at advising on labor issues,"* say sources. He recently represented an energy industry client in employment litigation stemming from the FMLA.

## Band 2

### Hinckley, Allen & Snyder LLP

**THE FIRM** This regional firm is noted for its work in discrimination cases, labor relations and other employment litigation matters. The team is highly prized by employers in a range of sectors, including construction, technology and manufacturing, and is able to offer clients tailored and industry-specific advice.
**KEY INDIVIDUALS Michael Kraemer**, of counsel, offers wide-ranging labor and employment expertise to private and public sector clients. Areas of excellence include union avoidance, collective bargaining and wrongful discharge compliance and litigation.

### Partridge Snow & Hahn LLP

**THE FIRM** This respected firm offers counseling and litigation expertise across a spectrum of employment matters, including noncompetition, employee benefits, discrimination and termination. The team is experienced before state and federal courts and regulatory agencies such as the NLRB and the EEOC.
**Sources say:** *"High-quality work and a personalized service."*
**KEY INDIVIDUALS Michael Gamboli** *"is a terrific lawyer,"* according to one impressed source, while a second interviewee describes him as *"business-oriented and practically minded."* He continues to act for an impressive roster of quality clients on a variety of employment disputes.

## Band 3

### Edwards Wildman Palmer
See profile on p.1520

**THE FIRM** The Providence office of this international firm is well placed to offer a full labor and employment service to its roster of national and international clients. The team is well versed in matters concerning ERISA litigation, wage and hour disputes and noncompetition.
**KEY INDIVIDUALS Mark Pogue**'s (see p.2258) broad practice covers both employment and commercial litigation. In addition to his expertise before state and federal courts and state regulatory agencies, he is noted for the quality of his preventive counseling on employment matters and labor relations.

## Other Notable Practitioners

**Joseph Whelan** of Whelan & Siket is noted for his expertise in collective bargaining negotiations, employment litigation and business breakups. Sources relate that he *"quickly engenders the trust of the client,"* and confirm that he is *"a smart litigator and good on his feet."* **Daniel Kinder** heads the labor and employment practice at Little Medeiros Kinder Bulman & Whitney, PC. Areas of excellence within a broad practice include ERISA litigation and discrimination cases. The respected **Jeffrey Kasle** of St Peter & Kasle continues to be a strong presence in the Rhode Island business community and is trusted by employers for his labor and employment acumen.

# LITIGATION GENERAL COMMERCIAL

Commentary about individuals can be found under their firm's paragraph. If the firm has no paragraph (is not ranked), look at Other Notable Practitioners.

## Litigation: General Commercial

### Leading Firms

**Band 1**

Adler Pollock & Sheehan PC *

Edwards Wildman Palmer *

Hinckley, Allen & Snyder LLP

**Band 2**

Blish & Cavanagh, LLP

Duffy & Sweeney, Ltd

Partridge Snow & Hahn LLP

**Band 3**

Little Medeiros Kinder Bulman & Whitney, PC

Nixon Peabody LLP *

**Band 4**

Olenn & Penza

Scott & Bush Ltd

### Leading Individuals

**Star individuals**

| | |
|---|---|
| Cavanagh Jr Joseph V | Blish & Cavanagh, LLP |
| Tarantino John | Adler Pollock & Sheehan PC * |

**Band 1**

| | |
|---|---|
| Duffy Robert | Duffy & Sweeney, Ltd |
| Freel Mark W | Edwards Wildman Palmer * |
| Petros Gerald J | Hinckley, Allen & Snyder LLP |
| Pogue Mark | Edwards Wildman Palmer * |

**Band 2**

| | |
|---|---|
| Brenner Jeffrey S | Nixon Peabody LLP * |
| Bulman John | Little Medeiros Kinder Bulman & Whitney |
| Flanders Jr Robert G | Hinckley, Allen & Snyder LLP |
| Green Rachelle R | Duffy & Sweeney, Ltd |
| Nakasian Stacey | Duffy & Sweeney, Ltd |
| Rocha Patricia | Adler Pollock & Sheehan PC * |
| Snow Steven E | Partridge Snow & Hahn LLP |

**Band 3**

| | |
|---|---|
| Bush Christine K | Scott & Bush Ltd |
| DeMaria Gerald C | Higgins, Cavanagh & Cooney LLP (ONP)† |
| Denehy Mark O | Adler Pollock & Sheehan PC * |
| Little Christopher | Little Medeiros Kinder Bulman & Whitney |
| Medeiros Matthew F | Little Medeiros Kinder Bulman & Whitney, |
| Merten Howard | Partridge Snow & Hahn LLP |
| Olenn J Renn | Olenn & Penza |
| Pelczarski Karen A | Blish & Cavanagh, LLP |
| Penza Jr Joseph F | Olenn & Penza |
| Poore William A | Poore & Rosenbaum (ONP)† |
| Scott Craig M | Scott & Bush Ltd |
| Wollin David A | Adler Pollock & Sheehan PC * |

*\* Indicates firm / individual with profile.*

*Alphabetical order within each band. Band 1 is the highest.*

## Band 1

### Adler Pollock & Sheehan PC
See profile on p.2259

**THE FIRM** This firm has a fine reputation in southeast New England and handles a range of business disputes, including antitrust, tort and securities litigation. The group prides itself on providing high-quality litigation advice for reasonable fees. Its superior reputation is reflected in its impressive client list, which includes Hasbro, Tufts Medical and ARCO.

**Sources say:** *"A high-profile, enviable litigation practice."*

**KEY INDIVIDUALS** The acclaimed **John Tarantino** (see p.2258) is widely considered to be in the leading rank of Rhode Island trial lawyers. Sources commend his legal stature, remarking that *"he symbolizes the best that the state has to offer."* He recently defended Southern Union in relation to environmental criminal charges. **Patricia Rocha** (see p.2258) chairs the firm's litigation group and is a recognized authority on trial advocacy. She recently worked closely alongside Tarantino on representing Southern Union. **David Wollin** (see p.2258) recently represented New England Medical Center as plaintiff in a high-value dispute with Lifespan. His litigation practice covers a wide variety of matters, including environmental law, toxic tort and insurance defense. **Mark Denehy** (see p.2256) focuses his practice on environmental insurance coverage disputes and high-value product liability cases.

### Edwards Wildman Palmer
See profile on p.1520

**THE FIRM** The increased national footprint that this firm has enjoyed since the 2011 merger between Wildman, Harrold, Allen and Dixon and Edwards, Angell, Palmer and Dodge has served to enhance the reputation of its respected team of Rhode Island litigators. An enviable client roster includes Delta Airlines, Ernst & Young and Textron.

**Sources say:** *"A high-profile firm that provides good service at reasonable fees."*

**KEY INDIVIDUALS Mark Freel** (see p.2257) is an *"impressive advocate"* who represents high-quality clients in relation to a broad range of business and IP disputes. Sources suggest that he is *"very detailed in his analysis and very thorough in his evaluation of a case."* **Mark Pogue** (see p.2258) is highly regarded by the Providence business community and is recognized by sources for his *"outstanding"* level of general commercial litigation advocacy in addition to his respected employment litigation offering. In the words of one appreciative client, he did *"an excellent job of understanding our industry and focusing our language."*

### Hinckley, Allen & Snyder LLP

**THE FIRM** The highly respected litigation department at Hinckley, Allen & Snyder continues to go from strength to strength. The team's broad litigation expertise covers real estate, environment, insurance, intellectual property and white-collar crime defense, among others. Sources are adamant in their praise of the firm's quality counsel. Clients include GE, RBS Citizens and ExxonMobil.

**Sources say:** *"A very strong group of lawyers."*

**KEY INDIVIDUALS Gerald Petros** *"is a lawyer you can have candid discussions with,"* sources say. He is considered to be among the leading litigators in Rhode Island and has recently advised the Center for Toxicology and Environmental Health on a number of issues relating to the BP Gulf Oil spill. **Robert Flanders** is chair of the firm's litigation group and cochair of its white-collar defense team. He recently represented RBS Citizens in claims stemming from the bank's forced placement of flood insurance on certain mortgaged properties.

## Band 2

### Blish & Cavanagh, LLP

**THE FIRM** This quality regional firm's litigation team continues to draw praise from market sources. Its trial lawyers handle a wide variety of cases from many different industry clients. Their industry-specific expertise covers construction, media, employment, insurance and personal injury, among other matters.

**KEY INDIVIDUALS Joseph Cavanagh** *"is one of the best attorneys in the state,"* said one impressed interviewee, and accordingly takes his place at the pinnacle of the rankings. He is praised for his level-headed analysis as a trial lawyer and continues to feature prominently as a high-profile legal talent in Rhode Island. **Karen Pelczarski** is lauded by peers for her *"outstanding"* practice. She is respected for her abilities at trial and appellate level, representing plaintiffs and defendants in a broad range of business litigation.

### Duffy & Sweeney, Ltd

**THE FIRM** This firm continues to develop its reputation as a boutique IP and commercial litigation practice. Asset protection, patents and licensing are core practice areas for the litigation team, and the firm also distinguishes itself in the area of financial litigation, including matters concerning securities, shareholders' rights and fiduciary duty.

**KEY INDIVIDUALS Robert Duffy** advises clients on soft and hard IP matters and complex business litigation. He is described by sources as *"an excellent attorney with a prominent practice."* **Rachelle Green** recently handled a high-value case for Inland American Retail Management concerning a breach of lease claim. She is noted for the tenacity of her representations at state and federal level. **Stacey Nakasian** is praised by sources for her *"dogged and determined"* attitude toward complex commercial litigation. Areas of excellence include fiduciary liability, construction disputes and insurance coverage disputes.

## Partridge Snow & Hahn LLP

**THE FIRM** This expanding litigation practice impresses with its innovative approach to client service, as evidenced by a recently established E-Discovery group whose focus is the preservation and collection of electronic data. Clients include Bank of America and Pilgrim Title Insurance Company.

**KEY INDIVIDUALS Steven Snow** handles a broad range of cases, including antitrust, banking, commercial/corporate and constitutional law. He is admitted to the Bar in both Rhode Island and Massachusetts. **Howard Merten** recently represented Pilgrim Title Insurance Company in a high-value case regarding improper conduct in relation to life assurance policy sales. His areas of expertise include insurance and intellectual property.

## Band 3

## Little Medeiros Kinder Bulman & Whitney, PC

**THE FIRM** This boutique firm is noted for its expertise in construction and business disputes, and continues to handle an impressive array of complex lawsuits. Clients include Brown University, Narragansett Bay Commission and Citadel Broadcasting Company.

**KEY INDIVIDUALS John Bulman** is a respected trial lawyer whose practice spans construction and complex commercial disputes. He recently acted for Certified Power Systems on high-value claims, including breach of contract and misrepresentation. Founding partner **Christopher Little** successfully represented Quaker Towers Associates in a multimillion-dollar case claiming breach of fiduciary

duties. He has more than 30 years' experience in advising on construction law and general business law. The highly experienced **Matthew Medeiros** is noted for his broad commercial litigation acumen. He represents plaintiffs and defendants in matters ranging from antitrust and securities litigation to shareholder disputes.

## Nixon Peabody LLP

See profile on p.1526

**THE FIRM** This firm's Rhode Island litigation team continues to draw praise from peers and clients. The group is adept at handling complex business disputes across a wide variety of industry sectors, and is able to draw on its enviable geographical footprint to offer a seamless service to clients engaged in multijurisdictional litigation. Clients include TransCanada Energy, Rhode Island Public Transit Authority and Dunkin' Brands.

**KEY INDIVIDUALS Jeffrey Brenner** (see p.2256) is *"a no-nonsense guy whose work is nothing short of brilliant,"* say sources. He focuses his practice on complex commercial litigation and arbitration. *"His questioning skills and legal arguments were impressive,"* said one client.

## Band 4

## Olenn & Penza

**THE FIRM** This respected Warwick litigation boutique represents clients in litigation and arbitration across a broad swathe of business areas, including construction, admiralty and professional liability. The compact team is noted for the quality of its advice and the depth of its trial experience.

**KEY INDIVIDUALS Renn Olenn** has advised on a broad range of cases and is noted for his expertise in maritime law and professional liability. **Joseph Penza** has represented clients at both state and federal level, and has noted experience in arbitration and mediation. His practice revolves around professional liability and the defense of claims against the police.

## Scott & Bush Ltd

**THE FIRM** This litigation boutique is recognized for its work in intellectual property and complex commercial litigation. Clients include companies in the technology, manufacturing and construction sectors.

**KEY INDIVIDUALS Christine Bush** is accomplished in advising clients on IP issues, construction disputes and shareholder disputes. **Craig Scott** represents clients at trial and appellate level in both state and federal courts. Areas of focus include commercial litigation and patent, trademark and copyright cases.

## Other Notable Practitioners

**Gerald DeMaria** of Higgins, Cavanagh & Cooney LLP advises clients on civil litigation matters, with a focus on complex commercial and product liability cases. Sources relate that he is *"a great defense attorney."* **William Poore** of Poore & Rosenbaum has a broad practice covering insurance, zoning, and personal injury and negligence law. He is experienced in arbitration and mediation.

# REAL ESTATE

Commentary about individuals can be found under their firm's paragraph. If the firm has no paragraph (is not ranked), look at Other Notable Practitioners.

| Real Estate Leading Firms | |
|---|---|
| **Band 1** | |
| Hinckley, Allen & Snyder LLP | |
| **Band 2** | |
| Adler Pollock & Sheehan PC * | |
| Partridge Snow & Hahn LLP | |

| Real Estate Leading Individuals | | |
|---|---|---|
| **Band 1** | | |
| Batty E Jerome | Hinckley, Allen & Snyder LLP | |
| Kanter Stanley | Adler Pollock & Sheehan PC * | |
| McCann Gail E | Edwards Wildman Palmer (ONP)† * | |
| Rubin David J | Hinckley, Allen & Snyder LLP | |
| Stolzman Robert | Adler Pollock & Sheehan PC * | |
| Tracy David J | Hinckley, Allen & Snyder LLP | |
| **Band 2** | | |
| DiStefano Joseph R | Adler Pollock & Sheehan PC * | |
| Gilden David M | Partridge Snow & Hahn LLP | |
| **Band 3** | | |
| Noonan Elizabeth McDonough | Adler Pollock & Sheehan PC * | |

\* Indicates firm / individual with profile.
†ONP = Other Notable Practitioner.

## Band 1

## Hinckley, Allen & Snyder LLP

**THE FIRM** This firm continues to be recognized as the leading shop for real estate expertise in Rhode Island. The team covers all aspects of commercial real estate work, including leasing, acquisition and disposition, land use and real estate finance. It recently advised Bucci Development on the Dowling Village shopping center development in North Smithfield.

**Sources say:** *"A very good experience. The attorneys are knowledgeable and easy to work with."*

**KEY INDIVIDUALS** The highly experienced **Jerome Batty** advises developers, construction companies and financial institutions on all aspects of commercial real estate work. He is particularly noted for his knowledge of

leasing and real estate finance. Interviewees award *"high marks"* to **David Rubin**, the head of the firm's real estate department. He advises clients on financing, leasing, acquisition and development. **David Tracy** led the team in the aforementioned work for Bucci Development and completes the firm's triumvirate of outstanding real estate talent. He is noted for his work on big box retail developments and office leasing.

## Band 2

## Adler Pollock & Sheehan PC

See profile on p.2259

**THE FIRM** This firm handles the full range of commercial real estate matters, including financing, leasing, acquisition and development. Recent highlights include advising Wells Fargo on the $65 million refinancing of a Florida hotel.

**KEY INDIVIDUALS Stanley Kanter** (see p.2257) is noted for his expertise in all aspects of real estate work, including development and title insurance commitments. He recently represented Fall River Ready Mix in its purchase of an operating concrete plant in Massachusetts. **Robert Stolzman** (see p.2258) is able to draw on his prior experience as corporate counsel to the Rhode Island Economic Development Corporation and the Rhode Island Senate Committees on Finance and Corporations to advise clients on development matters, land use and municipal land law. He recently advised Eaton on the refit and relocation of an aerospace manufacturing plant. **Elizabeth Noonan** (see p.2257) focuses her practice on real estate litigation, zoning and land use. She represents the developers of commercial and residential properties. **Joseph DiStefano** (see p.2256) advises commercial developers and clients in the health-care and education sectors in relation to real estate transactions.

## Partridge Snow & Hahn LLP

**THE FIRM** This team advises clients on conveyancing, land use, development and real estate transactions. In addition to its solid roster of commercial clients in the construction, development and financial industries, it is noted for its representation of municipal and state entities. **Sources say:** *"An incredibly good, well-respected law firm."* **KEY INDIVIDUALS** Managing partner **David Gilden** is widely respected for the real estate element of his broad commercial practice. He represents financial institutions, developers and other parties in all commercial real estate matters.

### Other Notable Practitioners

**Gail McCann** (see p.2257) of Edwards Wildman Palmer handles real estate matters as part of a broader commercial practice. She is particularly noted for her knowledge of real estate finance, and sources confirm that she is held *"in very high regard"* by the market.

# Leaders' Profiles in Rhode Island

### BRENNER, Jeffrey S
Nixon Peabody LLP, Providence
401 454 1042
jbrenner@nixonpeabody.com
*Featured in Litigation (Rhode Island)*
**Practice Areas:** Jeffrey Brenner is a litigation Partner and Team Leader of the firm's Real Estate Litigation and Construction Team. He concentrates his practice on commercial litigation, construction disputes, complex real estate issues, and tort litigation in Rhode Island and Massachusetts. Jeff frequently represents clients with commercial and construction disputes in federal court, state court, arbitrations, and mediations. Jeff regularly lectures on business litigation topics and is a contributing author in three national publications. Jeff was a member of the Barrington Zoning Board for twelve years and was a member of the Barrington Town Council for the past eight years.

### BROOKS, Robert
Adler Pollock & Sheehan PC, Providence
401 274 7200
rbrooks@apslaw.com
*Featured in Labor & Employment (Rhode Island)*
**Practice Areas:** Labor and employment, alternative dispute resolution, construction, governmental and legislative.
**Professional Memberships:** Rhode Island Bar Association, Labor Law Committee.
**Career:** Managing Partner and Chairman of the Labor and Employment Law Group, he represents management in all facets of labor relations and employment law in public and private sectors. He has successfully represented employers in employment discrimination matters, and counsels employers on complex administrative law issues. He regularly handles collective bargaining negotiations and defense of union organizing campaigns.
**Personal:** Former Deputy Chief of Staff to the Mayor of Providence; President, Board of Governors, Boys & Girls Club of Providence.

### CAMPELLONE, Paul
Adler Pollock & Sheehan PC, Providence
401 274 7200
pcampellone@apslaw.com
*Featured in Corporate/Commercial (Rhode Island)*
**Practice Areas:** Business and corporate, commercial finance, public finance, mergers and acquisitions, intellectual property.
**Professional Memberships:** Rhode Island Bar Foundation; National Association of Bond Lawyers.
**Career:** Paul has a broad-based corporate, banking, public finance and commercial practice that includes mergers, acquisitions, dispositions, secured and unsecured financing, issuance of bonds and notes by municipalities and other governmental authorities, governance issues for companies, formation of domestic and international joint ventures, distribution and supply arrangements and technology transfers for the firm's clients.
**Personal:** Executive Committee, Junior Achievement of Rhode Island, Inc.

### CHITTICK, Michael D
Adler Pollock & Sheehan PC, Providence
401 274 7200
mchittick@apslaw.com
*Featured in Labor & Employment (Rhode Island)*
**Practice Areas:** Labor and employment, alternative dispute resolution.
**Professional Memberships:** Rhode Island Bar Association, Labor Law Committee.
**Career:** Shareholder in the Labor and Employment Law Group, handling all facets of labor and employment law and related litigation in both the public and private sectors. He has successfully represented employers in numerous matters including collective bargaining negotiations, alleged unfair labor practices, wage-hour laws, medical leave, reductions-in-force, OSHA compliance, labor arbitration and employment discrimination cases.
**Publications:** Contributing editor, 7th and 8th editions of BNA publication, How to Take a Case

Before the NLRB, and 2011 supplement to same publication.

### CHLEBUS, Andrew J
Edwards Wildman Palmer, Providence
401 276 6473
achlebus@edwardswildman.com
*Featured in Corporate/Commercial (Rhode Island)*
**Practice Areas:** During the past 35 years, Andy has represented at least 10 different banks and commercial finance companies in structuring and closing loans to customers in the radio, television, cable television, billboard, publishing and related media industries. In addition to traditional secured loan transactions, Andy has experience in non-traditional areas of finance including consignments of gold and other precious metals to manufacturers.
**Professional Memberships:** American Bar Association, Business Law Section; Rhode Island Bar Association; Rhode Island Bar Foundation, Fellow.
**Personal:** Harvard Law School, JD; Brown University, AB, magna cum laude, Phi Beta Kappa.

### COLLIER, Stacie B
Nixon Peabody LLP, Providence
401 454 1018
sbcollier@nixonpeabody.com
*Featured in Labor & Employment (Rhode Island)*
**Practice Areas:** Counsels employers on all labor and employment topics (i.e. discrimination, harassment, hiring/firing, wage-hour, privacy, etc.). Drafts and revises employment agreements, policies and handbooks. Provides training for all areas of labor and employment law compliance. Represents employers in state and federal courts and before administrative agencies.
**Professional Memberships:** Member, Rhode Island Bar Association, Labor and Employment Section. Board member, St. Mary's Home for Children and Louminati Youth Leadership Foundation.
**Personal:** JD, University of Connecticut School of Law. BA, Syracuse University, magna cum laude, Phi Beta Kappa. Admitted to practice in

Rhode Island, Connecticut, Massachusetts and New Hampshire.

### DENEHY, Mark O
Adler Pollock & Sheehan PC, Providence
401 274 7200
mdenehy@apslaw.com
*Featured in Litigation (Rhode Island)*
**Practice Areas:** Insurance, environmental, criminal white/collar defense, litigation, products liability and toxic tort.
**Professional Memberships:** Rhode Island and American Bar Associations, Member, Board of Directors of the R.I. Public Expenditure Council.
**Career:** Trial counsel in noted national Superfund cases and toxic tort and environmental insurance coverage litigation, Mark Denehy has successfully represented manufacturers and others in a wide range of complex, high stakes product liability matters involving asbestos, Silica, DES, radiation exposure, toxic shock litigation and more.
**Personal:** Shareholder.

### DISTEFANO, Joseph R
Adler Pollock & Sheehan PC, Providence
401 274 7200
jdistefano@apslaw.com
*Featured in Real Estate (Rhode Island)*
**Practice Areas:** Business and corporate, governmental and legislative, real estate.
**Career:** Partner who handles major commercial real estate transactions. He was instrumental in the redevelopment of Downtown Providence, and as one of the originators of the Capital Center Project, he spearheaded the development of several major downtown office buildings.
**Personal:** Previous State Senator and President of the Senate. Member of the Board of Trustees of Salve Regina University, Previous Chair of the RI Board of Elections for over 15 years, former Chair of the RI Convention Center Authority. Serves on the Board of CharterCare Health Partners.

**DOWLING, Sarah T**
Adler Pollock & Sheehan PC, Providence
401 274 7200
sdowling@apslaw.com
*Featured in Corporate/Commercial (Rhode Island)*
**Practice Areas:** Commercial finance, business and corporate, healthcare, higher education, mergers and acquisitions.
**Professional Memberships:** Rhode Island Bar Association, American Bar Association, Former chair, of Rhode Island Supreme Court Ethics Advisory Panel and Rhode Island Board of Governors for Higher Education.
**Career:** She counsels privately held businesses, individuals, and government agencies on private equity and hedge fund investments, acquisitions, divestitures, financings, business succession, governance and other corporate matters. She represents lenders and borrowers in complex financing transactions, non-profit hospitals in affiliations, nursing homes and numerous medical group practices.
**Personal:** Recipient, Rhode Island College Honorary Doctor of Public Service.

**DUFFELL, David K**
Weil, Gotshal & Manges LLP, Providence
401 278 4710
david.duffell@weil.com
*Featured in Private Equity (Nationwide),*
*Corporate/Commercial (Rhode Island)*
**Practice Areas:** David Duffell represents private equity funds in investments and mergers and acquisitions. Recently he represented Providence Equity Partners in the sale of its stake in Hulu, Providence Equity Partner, as part of an investor group comprising Ontario Teachers' Pension Plan, Madison Dearborn Partners, and BCE Inc., in the group's C$1.1 billion acquisition of Q9 Networks, and AmSafe Global Holding (a portfolio company of Berkshire Partners and Greenbriar Equity Group) in its $750 million acquisition by Transdigm Group.
**Personal:** Brown University (AB, 1969); Boston University School of Law (JD, 1972 and LLM tax, 1976).

**FREEL, Mark W**
Edwards Wildman Palmer, Providence
401 276 6681
mfreel@edwardswildman.com
*Featured in Litigation (Rhode Island)*
**Practice Areas:** Mark has experience in matters involving shareholder disputes, construction and real estate disputes, unfair competition, trademarks and trade secrets, covenants not to compete, and probate and family business disputes. He advises on intellectual property and proprietary business information, and in product liability actions involving a wide variety of products.
**Professional Memberships:** Defense Research Institute, RI Manufacturers' Association, Rhode Island Bar Association.
**Publications:** Mark writes for such publications as For the Defense, DRI, and the Rhode Island Bar Journal.
**Personal:** University of Connecticut School of Law, JD, highest honors; University of New

Hampshire, MA; University of New Hampshire, BA.

**GEANACOPOULOS, Stephen**
Adler Pollock & Sheehan PC, Providence
401 274 7200
sgeanacopoulos@apslaw.com
*Featured in Corporate/Commercial (Rhode Island)*
**Practice Areas:** M&A (domestic and international/cross border), private equity, securities, venture capital, general corporate and commercial law.
**Professional Memberships:** Rhode Island Bar Association and American Bar Association, Business and International Law Sections.
**Career:** Steve is Chair of the Corporate Department and plays a leading role in the representation of some of the firm's largest and most sophisticated clients.
**Publications:** Author of 'Resales of Securities', Amerercian Bar Association's Business Law Today, Vol 7, No 2, Nov/Dec 1997.
**Personal:** Dartmouth College, AB cum laude 1974; Boston College, JD 1979; Teaching Fellow, Athens College, Athens, Greece, 1975-76; Dartmouth Alumni Council Class Representative.

**GRAHAM, Christopher**
Edwards Wildman Palmer, Providence
401 276 6579
cgraham@edwardswildman.com
*Featured in Corporate/Commercial (Rhode Island)*
**Practice Areas:** Chris, Co-Partner-In-Charge of the Providence office and Co-Chair of the Firm's Business Law Department, negotiates acquisitions, dispositions and management buyouts for buyers and sellers, private equity funds and management teams. He represents borrowers in financing transactions, including highly-leveraged financings in private equity buyouts. He also counsels start-up enterprises and assists in capital formation, represents emerging companies and private equity investors in their equity financings, and advises companies at all stages on matters of corporate and business law.
**Professional Memberships:** Rhode Island Bar Association.
**Personal:** University of Pennsylvania Law School, JD; Brown University, BA, magna cum laude.

**GRAY, Douglas G**
Edwards Wildman Palmer, Providence
401 276 6673
dgray@edwardswildman.com
*Featured in Corporate/Commercial (Rhode Island)*
**Practice Areas:** Douglas, a member of the firm's Business Law Department and Co-Chair of the Corporate Counseling & Business Transactions practice, concentrates his practice in areas of mergers, acquisitions, corporate governance, strategic alliances, and commercial ventures. He acts as general outside counsel to a number of clients, ranging from large multinational companies to local manufacturers to newly formed companies as well as non-profit entities. Douglas' practice involves representation of corporate entities, individuals, management

teams, and private equity firms as buyers and sellers.
**Personal:** University of Notre Dame, JD; Yale University, BA.

**JOHNSON, V Duncan**
Edwards Wildman Palmer, Providence
401 276 6477
djohnson@edwardswildman.com
*Featured in Corporate/Commercial (Rhode Island)*
**Practice Areas:** Duncan's practice has been in the general corporate area with a specific focus on the financial services industry. He led the firm's bank regulatory and mergers and acquisitions practice for a number of years. He served as principal outside counsel for FleetBoston Financial Corporation in substantially all of its acquisitions. He has, in addition, represented a variety of other regional financial services firms in corporate and regulatory matters.
**Professional Memberships:** Rhode Island Bar Association.
**Personal:** Harvard Law School, LLB; Harvard University, AB, cum laude.

**KANTER, Stanley**
Adler Pollock & Sheehan PC, Providence
401 274 7200
skanter@apslaw.com
*Featured in Real Estate (Rhode Island)*
**Practice Areas:** Real estate, financial and estate planning.
**Professional Memberships:** Rhode Island Bar Association, Title Standards Committee.
**Career:** Chair, Real Estate Group, representing clients in domestic and international matters in all aspects of purchase, development, leasing, financing and sale of real estate. Represents builders and lenders in all phases of project development. Well versed in intricacies of title insurance policies and conservation and development easements, including analysis and resolution of complicated transactions.
**Personal:** Fellow & State Chair, American College of Mortgage Attorneys; Fellow, American College of Trust and Estate Counsel; Real Estate Council of Cornell University;International Council of Shopping Centers.

**LUNDSTEN, E Hans**
Adler Pollock & Sheehan PC, Providence
401 274 7200
hlundsten@apslaw.com
*Featured in Corporate/Commercial (Rhode Island)*
**Practice Areas:** Tax, business and corporate, mergers and acquisitions, financial and estate planning.
**Professional Memberships:** Rhode Island Bar Association, Tax Section, American Bar Association.
**Career:** Chair of the Tax Group and Co-chair of the Financial and Estate Planning Group, he advises owners of closely held businesses, corporations, governmental entities, universities, and movie production companies. Sucessfully argued numerous significant state taxation cases before state courts, including the Rhode Island Supreme Court.

**MCCANN, Gail E**
Edwards Wildman Palmer, Providence
401 276 6527
gmccann@edwardswildman.com
*Featured in Real Estate (Rhode Island),*
*Corporate/Commercial (Rhode Island)*
**Practice Areas:** Has served as chair of the firm's Real Estate Department and has particular knowledge in a wide variety of construction and project financing, including affordable housing, apartments, hotels, power retail centers, office and industrial space, and assisted living and other healthcare facilities. Has extensive experience in commercial loan restructurings, workouts, foreclosures, note sales, and REO sales.
**Professional Memberships:** American College of Mortgage Attorneys; Rhode Island Bar Association; Rhode Island Bar Foundation.
**Personal:** University of Pennsylvania Law School, JD; Brown University, AB, magna cum laude.

**MCNAMARA, Neal J**
Nixon Peabody LLP, Providence
401 454 1019
nmcnamara@nixonpeabody.com
*Featured in Labor & Employment (Rhode Island)*
**Practice Areas:** Practice focuses on litigation and counseling. Handles matters involving employment related statutes: Title VII, ADEA, ADA, FMLA, and ERISA, and state law employment issues and non-compete and confidentiality agreements. Counsels clients on a wide range of employee issues in order to prevent matters from reaching litigation. He has developed employment handbooks and policies, conducted internal investigations and regularly conducts client training on employment law topics.
**Professional Memberships:** ABA; Rhode Island Bar Association.
**Career:** Partner since 2006; previously a Partner with Holland & Knight.
**Personal:** University of Pennsylvania, BA, 1977; Columbia University, MA, 1979; New York University, JD, 1982.

**NOONAN, Elizabeth McDonough**
Adler Pollock & Sheehan PC, Providence
401 274 7200
bnoonan@apslaw.com
*Featured in Real Estate (Rhode Island)*
**Practice Areas:** Real estate, litigation, environmental, governmental and legislative.
**Professional Memberships:** RI Women's Bar Association.
**Career:** Shareholder who represents developers of commercial and residential properties in all phases of development, from acquisition to permitting and construction. She has been involved in several significant property rights cases. She also handles commercial, tax and construction litigation, and has represented national clients in successfully challenging state and local tax levies. Major clients include Cox Cable, Cumberland Farms, Rite Aid Pharmacy,Walmart and Stop & Shop.

**Personal:** Past President of RI Women's Bar Association; former delegate to 1996 and 2008 Democratic National Convention.

## OTTAVIANI, John E
Edwards Wildman Palmer, Providence
401 276 6405
jottaviani@edwardswildman.com
*Featured in Corporate/Commercial (Rhode Island)*
**Practice Areas:** Represents clients in a variety of intellectual property and business matters including the protection of trademarks, copyrights and trade secrets, the acquisition and sale of technology companies, the Internet, electronic commerce, the use and exploitation of technology, and investments in technology companies. He also advises emerging technology and other privately held businesses on organizational, operational and financing matters.
**Professional Memberships:** Rhode Island Bar Association, Massachusetts Bar Association, American Bar Association, American Intellectual Property Law Association, Computer Law Association, International Trademark Association.
**Personal:** Columbia University School of Law, JD; Bowdoin College, AB, magna cum laude.

## POGUE, Mark
Edwards Wildman Palmer, Providence
401 276 6491
mpogue@edwardswildman.com
*Featured in Labor & Employment (Rhode Island), Litigation (Rhode Island)*
**Practice Areas:** Mark's practice is focused on commercial and employment litigation. He appears frequently in state and federal courts in Rhode Island and Massachusetts, and before the Rhode Island Commission (successfully) the first case ever tried to a jury verdict under the federal Family and Medical Leave Act. In addition to handling litigation, Mark advises clients on commercial and tax matters.
**Professional Memberships:** Rhode Island Bar Association, Massachusetts Bar Association, Employment Law Alliance.
**Personal:** Harvard Law School, JD, cum laude; Williams College, BA, summa cum laude; United States Department of Justice, Trial Attorney, 1983-86.

## PRESCOTT, Andrew
Nixon Peabody LLP, Providence
401 454 1016
aprescott@nixonpeabody.com
*Featured in Labor & Employment (Rhode Island)*
**Practice Areas:** Represents employers in labor, wage and hour, and discrimination matters. His practice includes unfair labor practice charge hearings, collective bargaining, and grievance and interest arbitration. He represents employers nationally in various industries, including gas transmission/energy, transportation, manufacturing, healthcare, construction, finance, and human services.
**Publications:** Andrew provides training on various subjects, including sexual and other forms of harassment and strategies for avoiding employment liability. He regularly gives presentations and is featured in the media on developments in employment and labor law.
**Personal:** Washington & Lee University School of Law, JD, cum laude; University of Massachusetts/Amherst, BA, magna cum laude.

## REED, Walter G D
Edwards Wildman Palmer, Providence
401 276 6647
wreed@edwardswildman.com
*Featured in Corporate/Commercial (Rhode Island)*
**Practice Areas:** With nearly 35 years of experience as a corporate lawyer, Walter serves as "outside" general counsel to a number of major business clients and concentrates in corporate transactions including mergers and acquisitions, joint ventures, partnerships and private equity investments. Walter served as Managing Partner for the firm from April 2008 to February 2012, and as Chairman of the Executive Committee from 2005 to 2008.
**Professional Memberships:** Rhode Island Bar Association, past Chairman, Committee on Corporations and Partnerships.
**Personal:** Columbia University School of Law, JD; Chancellor Kent Scholar and Harlan Stone Scholar; Harvard University, BA, magna cum laude.

## ROCHA, Patricia
Adler Pollock & Sheehan PC, Providence
401 274 7200
procha@apslaw.com
*Featured in Litigation (Rhode Island)*
**Practice Areas:** Litigation, healthcare, criminal/white-collar defense, labor and employment.
**Professional Memberships:** International Academy of Trial Lawyers; American College of

Trial Lawyers; Litigation Counsel of America; Defense Counsel of Rhode Island.
**Career:** Shareholder and Chair of the firm's Litigation Group. She has tried and defended cases ranging from product liability and toxic tort, employment discrimination, redistricting legislation, to bribery, wire fraud, honest services and conspiracy. She has also successfully represented healthcare providers in acquiring regulatory approvals and in civil and criminal investigations. Chair, Committee on Character and Fitness; Member, Commission on Judicial Tenure and Discipline; Superlawyers Top 50 Women - New England.

## SKEFFINGTON, James J
Edwards Wildman Palmer, Providence
401 276 6560
jskeffington@edwardswildman.com
*Featured in Corporate/Commercial (Rhode Island)*
**Practice Areas:** Jim focuses his practice in the areas of development, financing, syndication, leasing projects for governmental and private enterprise and management of civil and employment litigation for large multi-state corporations.
**Publications:** Frequent lecturer at various national conferences on revenue bond financings for public and private projects as well as on state/local legislative initiatives to stimulate economic development.
**Personal:** Georgetown University Law Center, JD; Boston University School of Law, LLM, Taxation; Boston College, BS.

## STOLZMAN, Robert
Adler Pollock & Sheehan PC, Providence
401 274 7200
rstolzman@apslaw.com
*Featured in Real Estate (Rhode Island)*
**Practice Areas:** Real estate, business and corporate, governmental and legislative, public finance.
**Professional Memberships:** Fellow, American College of Real Estate Attorneys.
**Career:** As Shareholder, he focuses his practice in land use, real estate transactions, small business and governmental relations. He has shepherded projects for national and local clients through regulatory and governmental agencies. A registered lobbyist for trade associations and private businesses, he has also drafted and assisted with the passage of a wide range of business legislation. Recent projects include site development for a national restaurant chain, landfill gas powerplant approvals and shopping center acquisitions.

## TARANTINO, John
Adler Pollock & Sheehan PC, Providence
401 274 7200
jtarantino@apslaw.com
*Featured in Litigation (Rhode Island)*
**Practice Areas:** Litigation, ADR, products liability/toxic tort, white collar defense, insurance, appellate.
**Professional Memberships:** ABA, RI Bar Association (President 1997-98), N.E. Bar Association (President 2002-03), MA Bar Association, RI Bar Foundation (President 2005-11), DRI, American College of Trial Lawyers, International Academy of Trial Lawyers, International Society of Barristers; ABOTA.
**Career:** Shareholder in the Litigation Group, Counsel in numerous high profile cases, representing clients in sophisticated civil and criminal litigation, including successful defense of client in precedent-setting RI lead paint trial.
**Personal:** 2002 Lawyer of the Year, Lawyers Weekly USA; 2005-12 Top 500 Lawyers in US, Lawdragon Magazine.

## WOLLIN, David A
Adler Pollock & Sheehan PC, Providence
401 274 7200
dwollin@apslaw.com
*Featured in Litigation (Rhode Island)*
**Practice Areas:** Litigation, appellate, products liability/toxic tort, insurance.
**Professional Memberships:** Federation of Defense & Corporate Counsel; International Association of Defense Counsel; Defense Research Institute; Claims and Litigation Management Alliance; Rhode Island Bar Association; Federal Bar Association.
**Career:** Shareholder of the firm, handling all aspects of civil litigation, including mediations, arbitrations, trials and appellate proceedings in federal and state courts. Substantial track record in commercial and insurance defense litigation, product liability/personal injury defense and appellate law includes successfully defending multinational and US clients in high-stakes litigation.
**Publications:** Co-author, Rhode Island Civil and Appellate Procedure with Commentaries.

# ADLER POLLOCK & SHEEHAN P.C.

**www. apslaw.com tel:** 401 274 7200 **fax:** 401 571 0604

**Founding Partners:** Walter Adler (1896-1991),
Bernard R Pollock (1926-1984),
William J Sheehan (1917-1999)
**Managing Partner:** Robert P Brooks
Number of attorneys: 74

## Firm Overview:

For over 50 years, Adler Pollock & Sheehan P.C. has delivered client focused, business law services designed to achieve cost-effective solutions for today's complex challenges. AP&S successfully combines the depth and breadth of expertise of a large law firm with the advantages of responsive and direct personal service by partners found in smaller firms. AP&S is a full-service law firm featuring sophisticated Corporate and Labor Practices and a nationally-renowned Litigation Practice. AP&S services clients in 43 jurisdictions throughout New England, across the country and around the world.

NETWORK: AP&S has the distinction of having been selected to be a member of three prominent law firm networks: Lex Mundi, State Capital Group and the USLAW Network. Membership is by invitation only to select firms that have demonstrated the highest quality service and industry leadership. These strategic relationships allow AP&S to call upon resources all over the world to serve its clients to the utmost expectation. Member firms of these three law firm networks practice independently and not in a relationship for the joint practice of law.

## Main Areas of Practice:

### Litigation:

Among the largest and most experienced in New England, the AP&S Litigation Department is recognized nationally for its high quality and cost effectiveness. AP&S has assembled the largest litigation group in Rhode Island, which includes a diverse and broad-based civil and whitecollar criminal practice. AP&S serves as national coordinating counsel in mass-tort litigation. Recent high profile cases include the landmark lead paint lawsuit brought by the State of Rhode Island Attorney General in which the firm successfully defended Atlantic Richfield Company at trial and on appeal; the defense of a major tobacco company in the first New England case brought by the family of a deceased smoker; the defense of the former Rhode Island Senate President on ethics charges; the defense of the former Mayor of Providence's Chief of Staff on bribery charges; the defense of a Chinese pharmaceutical company on criminal charges relating to the importation of human growth hormone; the defense of a national utility company on environmental criminal charges; and the defense of several public companies on security laws and ERISA class actions. Finance Monthly Magazine named AP&S Commercial Litigation Law Firm of the Year - USA, 2011.

### Labor & Employment:

The Labor & Employment Group represents and counsels public and private sector employers in connection with virtually every aspect of the employment relationship, including discrimination and wrongful discharge matters, labor-management relations and collective bargaining. AP&S has successfully represented clients before all federal and state labor and employment agencies, including the EEOC, NLRB, OSHA and the U.S. Department of Labor.

### Business & Corporate:

The Business and Corporate Group has a practice which is local, regional, national and increasingly global in reach. It offers a broad range of sophisticated business counseling and transactional services to a diverse clientele, including foreign based multinationals, US-based public companies, emerging companies, family-owned businesses, entrepreneurs, high net worth individuals, government and economic development agencies, financial institutions, utilities, colleges and universities and other nonprofit organizations. The firm's practice focuses on mergers and acquisitions, joint ventures and strategic alliances, securities, taxation and business planning, public finance, economic development, trusts and estates, energy and communications and general corporate and commercial law.

### Healthcare:

The Healthcare Group serves as counsel to New England's premier hospitals and healthcare facilities, including freestanding surgi-centers and nursing homes. The firm's attorneys also represent regional and national hospital networks on interstate healthcare acquisitions, assist healthcare providers to obtain necessary regulatory approvals, as well as provide defense to healthcare providers on compliance and fraud investigations. In addition, the Healthcare Group has assisted physician group practices in the sale of their practices to national provider groups, hospital affiliates and other group practices.

### Environmental:

The Environmental Group boasts nationally-recognized lawyers who have helped define environmental standards in New England. AP&S has served as lead counsel for many cases with long-term effects on current environmental law-from the defense of multi-million dollar EPA fines and compliance actions to the initiation and management of Superfund cost recovery actions of over 100 parties for *Fortune* 100 companies.

### Governmental Relations:

The Government Relations Group is comprised of skilled legislative and regulatory advocates who provide astute counsel on governmental issues, lending hands-on experience and a unique understanding of governmental processes.

### Real Estate:

The Real Estate Group represents developers, multinational corporations, family-owned businesses, contractors and individuals in every aspect of industrial, commercial and residential real estate, including permitting, financing, leasing, and development of major retail commercial centers, office buildings, golf courses, assisted living facilities, hotels, apartments and condominiums; and is well versed in conservation and development easements and the intricacies of title insurance policies. The Real Estate Group, in conjunction with the Litigation Department, has also successfully addressed numerous appeals of excessive tax valuations of high-end residential, recreational, commercial and industrial properties.

### Clients:

The firm's ability to create and execute winning strategies has earned AP&S national recognition and a growing roster of loyal clients, from publicly-held *Fortune* 500 and *Fortune* 100 companies to small businesses, individuals and organizations. The firm represents clients such as The Dow Chemical Company, Atlantic Richfield, Cookson Group plc, Precision Engineered Products Group, Rhode Island State Investment Commission, Windmoeller & Hoelscher Corporation, Textron Inc., Hasbro, Inc. Rhode Island Airport Corporation, Colbea Enterprises, LLC, Rhode Island Health and Education Building Corporation, Johnson & Wales University, Rhode Island Convention Center Authority, Twin River Worldwide Holdings, Inc., Cox Communications, National Grid, Westerly Hospital, Chartis Insurance and CharterCare Health Partners among others.

## How lawyers are ranked

Every year we carry out thousands of in-depth interviews with clients in order to assess the reputations and expertise of business lawyers worldwide. The qualities we look for (and which determine rankings) include technical legal ability, professional conduct, client service, commercial awareness/astuteness, diligence, commitment, and other qualities most valued by the client. For details of our research team, see p.5.

## CORPORATE/M&A

Commentary about individuals can be found under their firm's paragraph. If the firm has no paragraph (is not ranked) look at Other Notable Practitioners.

### Corporate/M&A
**Leading Firms**

**Band 1**
Haynsworth Sinkler Boyd PA
McNair Law Firm PA
Nelson Mullins Riley & Scarborough LLP *
Nexsen Pruet, LLC *

**Band 2**
Womble Carlyle Sandridge & Rice, LLP *
Wyche, P.A. *

*The firms are in alphabetical order by firm name.*

### Haynsworth Sinkler Boyd PA

**THE FIRM** This firm is regarded as one of the finest among the state's business community for its corporate and banking expertise. The group's corporate practice covers corporate governance, mergers and acquisitions, tax, and transactions. The firm is particularly noted for its finance and securities offering, and is a go-to choice for clients looking to retain bond counsel.

**Sources say:** *"Some of the premier bond attorneys in the state. They have a lot of expertise in derivatives, derivative contracts and new market tax credits."*

**KEY INDIVIDUALS George King** is highly regarded for his financial services practice. He often handles M&A and securities-related work on behalf of commercial banks. **Kathleen McKinney** is highly sought after by South Carolina's leading public entities for her bond, tax and securities expertise. She is hailed as *"the dean of bond lawyers in the state"* by sources. **William Boyd** offers a wealth of experience in the corporate arena, representing clients in complex transactions and counseling them on business strategies.

### McNair Law Firm PA

**THE FIRM** This firm continues to impress with noted strength in the corporate M&A arena, and enjoys a stellar reputation in the banking and finance space. The firm has

### Corporate/M&A
**Senior Statesmen**

**Senior Statesmen:** distinguished older practitioners
| | | |
|---|---|---|
| Boyd William | | *Haynsworth Sinkler Boyd PA* |
| Warren III John | | *Warren & Sinkler LLP (ONP)†* |

**Leading Individuals**

**Band 1**
| | |
|---|---|
| Currie John Withers | *McNair Law Firm PA* |
| Dixon Augustus M | *Nelson Mullins Riley & Scarborough LLP* |
| King Jr George S | *Haynsworth Sinkler Boyd PA* |
| Knight G Marcus | *Nexsen Pruet, LLC* |
| Menzie Edward G | *Nexsen Pruet, LLC* |

**Band 2**
| | |
|---|---|
| Fritze Daniel J | *Nelson Mullins Riley & Scarborough LLP* |
| Grayson Neil E | *Nelson Mullins Riley & Scarborough LLP* * |
| Grumbine D Allen | *Womble Carlyle Sandridge & Rice, LLP* |
| Hall Jr Cary H | *Wyche, P.A.* * |
| Hogue Jr P Mason | *Nelson Mullins Riley & Scarborough LLP* * |

**Band 3**
| | |
|---|---|
| Amstutz Eric B | *Wyche, P.A.* * |
| Bruce James S. | *K&L Gates (ONP)† * |
| DuBose Jones | *Nexsen Pruet, LLC* |
| Few Jr Richard L | *Smith Moore Leatherwood LLP (ONP)† * |
| Jennings John M. | *Nelson Mullins Riley & Scarborough LLP* * |
| Musser William | *McNair Law Firm PA* |
| Temple Elizabeth O | *Womble Carlyle Sandridge & Rice, LLP* |

**Up-and-coming individuals**
| | |
|---|---|
| Davis Lux Melinda | *Wyche, P.A.* * |

been recognized by peers and clients as one of the preeminent firms in the state for tax, securities and bond work, representing some of the largest players in the state's business and banking community.

**Sources say:** *"Their performance is exemplary. McNair is a top firm in South Carolina for tax-exempt issues."*

**KEY INDIVIDUALS John Withers Currie** is described as a *"superstar,"* and represents clients in banking, corporate

### Corporate/M&A: Banking & Finance
**Leading Firms**

**Band 1**
Haynsworth Sinkler Boyd PA
McNair Law Firm PA
Nelson Mullins Riley & Scarborough LLP *
Nexsen Pruet, LLC *
Womble Carlyle Sandridge & Rice, LLP *

**Leading Individuals**

**Band 1**
| | |
|---|---|
| Grayson Neil E | *Nelson Mullins Riley & Scarborough LLP* * |
| King Jr George S | *Haynsworth Sinkler Boyd PA* |
| Lipsitz Alan M | *Nexsen Pruet, LLC* |
| McKinney Kathleen | *Haynsworth Sinkler Boyd PA* |
| Moore John T | *Nelson Mullins Riley & Scarborough LLP* * |
| Musser William | *McNair Law Firm PA* |

* Indicates firm / individual with profile.
†ONP = Other Notable Practitioner.

finance, M&A and securities issues. **William Musser** is praised as a *"very talented lawyer,"* and is highly regarded in the corporate and public finance spaces. He is often retained as bond counsel by municipalities and other issuers.

### Nelson Mullins Riley & Scarborough LLP
See profile on p.2276

**THE FIRM** This large regional firm garners high praise from peers and clients as a well-established corporate practice. The group retains immense talent in the corporate, M&A, securities and finance spaces with attorneys that cover counseling, contracts, public offerings and venture capital financings. The firm's breadth of experience allows it to serve a roster of clients across a range of industries, including banking, investment, healthcare and technology.

**Sources say:** *"They were very efficient professional, and provided invaluable advice during the process. Their depth of knowledge and experience in this area was evident."*

*The editorial is in alphabetical order by firm name.*

**KEY INDIVIDUALS Augustus Dixon** has a broad corporate practice, and is particularly well regarded for his M&A and corporate finance work. Sources say: *"He's excellent – great attention to detail, great work ethic, and high integrity."* **Neil Grayson** (see p.2269) has an excellent reputation in the corporate finance and banking arena, and is sought after by many financial institutions for his securities and M&A expertise. **John Moore** (see p.2271) leads the financial institutions team and is highly regarded for his bankruptcy and creditors rights practice. The well-regarded **Daniel Fritze** (see p.2269) concentrates on the areas of corporate, M&A, finance and securities law, with particular expertise in corporate formations and governance. **Mason Hogue** (see p.2270) is an experienced corporate attorney who is also well-versed in IP and technology law. Sources say: *"He has led our negotiations, and I have found he is very helpful and easy to work with."* **John Jennings** (see p.2270) has a broad corporate practice which encompasses securities offerings, M&A, regulatory compliance and executive compensation.

### Nexsen Pruet, LLC
See profile on p.2277

**THE FIRM** This firm retains a 34-strong team across its corporate and financial services groups, giving it remarkable bench strength to serve its institutional clients. The group is recognized for its corporate, M&A and finance expertise, with specialties in complex loan transactions, new market tax credits, public finance, and secured lending transactions. The group has the ability to draw on its real estate and creditors' rights teams to offer a seamless service to clients.

**Sources say:** *"We work with Nexsen Pruet on all corporate matters, and we have found that there is always an attorney on staff with the particular skillset we may need."*

**KEY INDIVIDUALS** Practice group leader **Marcus Knight** is praised as a *"superb corporate lawyer,"* and focuses on corporate, M&A and securities law. **Alan Lipsitz** is

highly regarded for his finance practice, which covers the commercial, public and real estate spaces. A source says: *"He's always very professional, very insightful, and does a great job in representing his client."* **Edward Menzie** has expertise in real estate, securities and corporate law. Sources note that: *"His strengths include an in-depth knowledge of the M&A industry and an ability to apply business principles to legal documents."* **Jones DuBose** is described as *"an excellent lawyer,"* and his corporate practice centers on governance, company formation, M&A and securities matters.

### Womble Carlyle Sandridge & Rice, LLP
See profile on p.2049

**THE FIRM** This firm is held in high esteem by its clients, and is widely recognized for its ability in the corporate, banking and finance spaces. The group consists of 55 dedicated attorneys handling complex business transactions on behalf of the state's leading banks and financial institutions. Areas of expertise include public offerings, venture capital financings and M&A. Recent work includes representing Transcend services in a $350 million merger with Nuance Communications. The firm's clients also include Crescent Financial Bancshares and BNC Bancorp.

**KEY INDIVIDUALS Allen Grumbine** is renowned for his bankruptcy and workouts expertise, and represents businesses, banks and other institutions in complex lending transactions. According to clients: *"He does a really, really good job on any workout or bankruptcy situation."* **Elizabeth Temple** focuses her practice in the public finance and M&A spaces. She is particularly well regarded for her expertise in securities law. Clients praise her *"very good subject matter knowledge."*

### Wyche, P.A.
See profile on p.2280

**THE FIRM** This South Carolina firm has a sophisticated corporate practice, adept in handling M&A, corporate finance, venture capital and private equity transactions. The group is also able to utilize its attorneys with expertise in IP, tax and technology to service clients such as Milliken, TD Bank, Span-America Medical Systems and SOMA Access System.

**Sources say:** *"I continue to be very impressed with their performance – both the legal knowledge tempered by business acumen as well as professionalism."*

**KEY INDIVIDUALS Cary Hall** (see p.2269) is praised as a *"really outstanding"* attorney and is noted for his expertise in tax law, which complements his well-regarded corporate practice. **Eric Amstutz** (see p.2267) has a broad corporate practice, and is particularly well regarded for handling complex agreements, M&A and securities work. Sources say: *"He is really, really smart, and has an amazing ability to grasp very complicated concepts."* **Melinda Davis Lux** (see p.2268) focuses her practice on M&A, representing clients in the manufacturing, distribution and chemical industries. A source describes her as *"outstanding, knowledgeable, bright and very sharp."*

### Other Notable Practitioners

**Richard Few** (see p.2268) of Smith Moore Leatherwood LLP has a broad corporate practice which includes acquisitions, securities and commercial and public financings. He has recently represented Greenville ONE in a complex project involving the negotiation of ownership, financial governance documents, and New Market Tax Credit financing. **James Bruce** (see p.2267) of K&L Gates concentrates on corporate reorganizations, counseling, M&A and joint ventures. The highly respected **John Warren** of Warren & Sinkler LLP has extensive experience in corporate, banking, securities and commercial real estate law.

# LABOR & EMPLOYMENT

Commentary about individuals can be found under their firm's paragraph. If the firm has no paragraph (is not ranked) look at Other Notable Practitioners.

| Labor & Employment | | |
| --- | --- | --- |
| **Leading Firms** | | |
| **Band 1** | | |
| Fisher & Phillips LLP * | | |
| Ogletree, Deakins, Nash, Smoak & Stewart, PC * | | |
| **Band 2** | | |
| FordHarrison LLP * | | |
| Gignilliat, Savitz & Bettis LLP | | |
| Jackson Lewis LLP * | | |
| Nexsen Pruet, LLC * | | |
| **Band 3** | | |
| Constangy, Brooks & Smith, LLP | | |
| Turner, Padget, Graham & Laney, P.A. * | | |
| Wyche, P.A. * | | |

## Band 1

### Fisher & Phillips LLP
See profile on p.1107

**THE FIRM** This group continues to stand out thanks to its exceptional ability to handle union avoidance issues and employment litigation on behalf of clients. The team has a strong bench in the Columbia office with extensive trial experience in wage and hour, discrimination and breach of contract disputes. The group also provides high-quality advice on issues involving labor relations, employment counseling and collective bargaining, making it a top choice for leading employers in the state.
**Sources say:** *"Their skill sets are truly refined in that they work not on hard technical approaches to managing union threat or campaign, but more on a soft side. They helped us develop strategies, training programs and communication techniques that help us remain union-free."*
**KEY INDIVIDUALS Hagood Tighe** (see p.2273) earns high praise from peers and clients, and focuses on employment litigation and union-related matters. One source comments: *"He is best of all in terms of practical application. He gets it – he understands how businesses operate."* **Jonathan Pearson** (see p.2271) is described as a *"very good"* attorney and covers the full scope of employment litigation in addition to traditional labor law issues. **Michael Carrouth** (see p.2268) is well regarded for his labor law specialty, assisting clients in responses to union organization on a national scale. Sources say: *"He has a masterful grasp of law."* **Stephen Mitchell** (see p.2271) handles traditional labor law and employment litigation issues. *"He gives excellent advice,"* say interviewees. **Fred Manning** (see p.2271) focuses his practice on employment litigation. According to commentators, *"Fred is outstanding at keeping you informed and has a real strong grasp of the law. His legal knowledge is top-notch."* The highly regarded **Daniel Ellzey** (see p.2268) has a wealth of experience in the labor and employment arena. He is known for his expertise in employment litigation, union avoidance and preventive employee relations plans.

### Ogletree, Deakins, Nash, Smoak & Stewart, PC
See profile on p.1110

**THE FIRM** This highly regarded boutique is known as one of the strongest labor and employment firms in the country. With a team of 62 attorneys across its offices in Charleston, Columbia and Greenville, it offers unparalleled bench strength and breadth of expertise. The group is particularly recognized for its work in employee benefits and employment litigation, and handles complex disputes and class actions for clients such as Michelin, Security Finance and SCANA.
**Sources say:** *"They are well versed in the law, knowledgeable of the courts and very efficient."*
**KEY INDIVIDUALS** The *"outstanding"* **Gray Geddie** (see p.2269) has extensive experience as a trial lawyer and is adept in handling various kinds of disputes, in addition to employment litigation. The *"excellent"* **Charles Speth** (see p.2272) is an experienced trial lawyer with a national employment litigation practice. **Fred Suggs** (see p.2272) has vast experience in labor and employment law, with particular expertise in discrimination and union-related issues. **Leigh Nason** (see p.2271) is noted for her affirmative action expertise and focuses on handling OFCCP-related compliance issues on behalf of federal contractors and subcontractors. **Katherine Dudley Helms** (see p.2269) is experienced in advising public and private sector clients on various employment issues. She has particular expertise in the healthcare industry. **Mike Shetterly** (see p.2272) focuses on representing clients in employment litigation, and on providing proactive advice and management training. The highly regarded **Lewis Smoak** (see p.2272) is one of the firm's founding partners and is known for his expertise in traditional labor law issues, including union-organization campaigns and preventive labor relations. The *"outstanding"* **Hamilton Stewart** (see p.2272) continues to be a key individual at the firm, and has experience across the full spectrum of labor and employment matters. **Bernhard Mueller** (see p.2271) concentrates on immigration law, assisting clients with visa-related issues, government investigations and immigration compliance.

## Band 2

### FordHarrison LLP
See profile on p.1108

**THE FIRM** This established group is known for its trade secrets, noncompetition and employment litigation capabilities, with added specialties in discrimination-related issues. The group is also adept in wage and hour, class actions and immigration issues, and is able to draw on the firm's nationwide presence to provide a seamless service to clients. The team has acted for major organizations including CommScope, Coca-Cola Bottling and National Healthcare Corporation.
**Sources say:** *"We have found them to be most professional, compassionate, and understanding."*

| Labor & Employment | | |
| --- | --- | --- |
| **Senior Statesmen** | | |
| Senior Statesmen: distinguished older practitioners | | |
| Ellzey Daniel | Fisher & Phillips LLP * | |
| Smoak Lewis T | Ogletree, Deakins, Nash, Smoak & Stewart * | |
| Stewart III J Hamilton | Ogletree, Deakins, Nash, Smoak & Stewart * | |

| Leading Individuals | | |
| --- | --- | --- |
| **Band 1** | | |
| Ballard Wade E | FordHarrison LLP * | |
| Geddie Jr J L Gray | Ogletree, Deakins, Nash, Smoak & Stewart * | |
| Speth II Charles T | Ogletree, Deakins, Nash, Smoak & Stewart * | |
| Suggs Jr Fred W | Ogletree, Deakins, Nash, Smoak & Stewart * | |
| **Band 2** | | |
| Bettis Vance J | Gignilliat, Savitz & Bettis LLP | |
| Carrouth Michael | Fisher & Phillips LLP * | |
| Coleman IV J Walker | K&L Gates (ONP)† * | |
| Dubberly David E | Nexsen Pruet, LLC | |
| Helms Katherine Dudley | Ogletree, Deakins, Nash, Smoak * | |
| McCormack David B | Womble Carlyle Sandridge & Rice (ONP)† | |
| Nason Leigh M | Ogletree, Deakins, Nash, Smoak & Stewart * | |
| Pearson Jonathan | Fisher & Phillips LLP * | |
| Satterfield Jr Andreas N | Jackson Lewis LLP * | |
| Savitz Stephen | Gignilliat, Savitz & Bettis LLP | |
| Shuler Jr Franklin G | Turner, Padget, Graham & Laney, P.A. * | |
| Stephenson Thomas | Nexsen Pruet, LLC | |
| Tighe J Hagood | Fisher & Phillips LLP * | |
| Warren J Steve | Constangy, Brooks & Smith, LLP | |
| **Band 3** | | |
| Abel Ashley B | Jackson Lewis LLP * | |
| Bakker Mark W | Wyche, P.A. * | |
| Edwards Linda Pearce | Gignilliat, Savitz & Bettis LLP | |
| Foster III William H | Nelson Mullins Riley & Scarborough (ONP)† * | |
| Gentry J. Theodore | Wyche, P.A. * | |
| Harper Sue Erwin | Nelson Mullins Riley & Scarborough LLP * | |
| Henthorne D. Michael | Littler Mendelson, PC (ONP)† * | |
| Keim Clay | FordHarrison LLP * | |
| Keim Jr Thomas H | FordHarrison LLP * | |
| Lewis Stephanie | Jackson Lewis LLP * | |
| Magargle M. Brian | Constangy, Brooks & Smith, LLP | |
| Manning Fred | Fisher & Phillips LLP * | |
| McWilliams Susan | Nexsen Pruet, LLC | |
| Mitchell Stephen C | Fisher & Phillips LLP * | |
| Mueller Bernhard | Ogletree, Deakins, Nash, Smoak & Stewart * | |
| Shetterly Mike M | Ogletree, Deakins, Nash, Smoak & Stewart * | |
| **Up-and-coming individuals** | | |
| Belcher Reginald G. | Turner, Padget, Graham & Laney, P.A. * | |

\* Indicates individual with profile.
†ONP = Other Notable Practitioner.

KEY INDIVIDUALS **Wade Ballard** (see p.2267) is an experienced trial attorney, having handled various labor and employment disputes in state and federal courts. *"He is an excellent, very smart, very fine lawyer,"* said one interviewee, adding: *"I can't say anything but positive things about his skills and professionalism."* **Clay Keim** (see p.2270) has a broad range of expertise, including in the areas of union avoidance, employment contracts, noncompetition, trade secrets and discrimination. The experienced **Thomas Keim** (see p.2270) handles traditional labor law and employment litigation, and has significant experience in the healthcare industry.

### Gignilliat, Savitz & Bettis LLP

THE FIRM This South Carolina boutique handles a range of labor and employment matters, including wage and hour, discrimination, employee benefits, litigation and union avoidance. The group is particularly known for its representation of public sector managers in employment-related disputes.

KEY INDIVIDUALS **Vance Bettis** is an experienced trial lawyer concentrating on employment disputes. Peers laud him as *"the best public employment lawyer in the state."* **Stephen Savitz** specializes in wage and hour law and also handles affirmative action, collective bargaining and equal employment issues. **Linda Pearce Edwards** is an experienced employment lawyer with expertise in FLSA, FMLA and wrongful discharge issues. She represents both public and private clients.

### Jackson Lewis LLP
See profile on p.1982

THE FIRM This labor and employment boutique retains a sophisticated team in its Greenville office, and its national coverage and broad expertise allow the group to provide top-quality services to clients. The team is recognized for its employment litigation strength in particular, and is also praised for its labor law, ERISA and discrimination work. The firm's impressive list of clients includes BMW Manufacturing, Nestlé USA and Pfizer.

Sources say: *"Excellent performance as a firm. Not only are they well versed in law and very intelligent, but they are also very reasonable, well respected and responsive."*

KEY INDIVIDUALS **Andreas Satterfield** (see p.2272) handles a variety of employment issues, including discrimination, harassment and breach of contracts, and has experience in a diverse set of industries. Sources say: *"He is incredibly responsive and provides practical advice that is geared toward business operations."* **Ashley Abel** (see p.2267) is an experienced trial lawyer, focusing on employment and ERISA-related litigation. **Stephanie Lewis** (see p.2270) has a well-regarded employment litigation practice and specializes in issues pertaining to harassment and

discrimination. Sources say she is *"aggressive, smart and results-oriented."*

### Nexsen Pruet, LLC
See profile on p.2277

THE FIRM This firm covers a host of labor and employment services, including immigration, discrimination, benefits, union and wage and hour issues. The group is noted for its strength in employment-related litigation, and serves clients such as Verizon Wireless, Honda, Coastal Healthcare Resources and Tidelands Bancshares.

Sources say: *"They have always acted professionally and expeditiously to ensure we have what we need as quickly as possible."*

KEY INDIVIDUALS **David Dubberly** heads the labor and employment practice and has expertise in employment litigation, government investigations and mediation. Sources describe him as *"excellent, talented, intelligent and very committed to his work."* **Thomas Stephenson** has extensive experience in labor law issues as well as employment litigation, and is hailed as *"an outstanding mediator."* **Susan McWilliams** is an experienced trial lawyer whose practice has a significant emphasis on employment-related disputes.

## Band 3

### Constangy, Brooks & Smith, LLP

THE FIRM This labor and employment boutique maintains a strong presence across the Southeast, and its national presence allows it to service management clients across the country. The group is particularly noted for its work involving labor relations, employee benefits and discrimination lawsuits, representing clients such as UPS Freight, US Airways, BMW Manufacturing and Averitt Express.

KEY INDIVIDUALS **Steve Warren** is a well-regarded labor and employment lawyer whose practice includes counseling employers on union, employment and collective bargaining issues. **Brian Magargle** has a broad employment practice with significant experience in employee benefits, ERISA and discrimination-related matters.

### Turner, Padget, Graham & Laney, P.A.
See profile on p.2279

THE FIRM This firm has a solid employment practice with core focuses in employment litigation and compliance matters, including contracts, handbooks and managerial training. The team has been praised for its work involving employee benefits and FLSA issues, representing clients such as Columbia College and South Carolina Bank.

KEY INDIVIDUALS **Franklin Shuler** (see p.2272) is noted for his ERISA expertise and his mediation skills. According to interviewees, he is *"an outstanding individual and a great mediator."* Rising star **Reginald Belcher** (see p.2267) focuses primarily on employment litigation and *"is truly an outstanding attorney,"* say sources.

### Wyche, P.A.
See profile on p.2280

THE FIRM Wyche is recognized for its strong employment practice, which covers the full scope of issues including discrimination, harassment, ERISA, employment torts and litigation. The team represents employers from a range of industries; clients include Blue Cross/Blue Shield, Presbyterian College and Milliken & Company.

KEY INDIVIDUALS **Mark Bakker** (see p.2267) is an experienced commercial trial lawyer who focuses on employment law issues. *"He's an outstanding attorney, very knowledgeable, very accessible and does a great job handling all our legal needs,"* say satisfied clients. *"Outstanding guy"* **Theodore Gentry** (see p.2269) concentrates on complex litigation matters, with a significant focus on employment-related disputes.

### Other Notable Practitioners

**Sue Erwin Harper** (see p.2269) of Nelson Mullins Riley & Scarborough LLP is praised as *"an excellent lawyer."* She concentrates her practice on employment litigation in relation to discrimination, trade secrets and wage and hour issues. **William Foster** (see p.2268) of Nelson Mullins Riley & Scarborough LLP is described as *"a very bright guy"* with an employment practice that centers on employee benefits and immigration matters. **David McCormack** of Womble Carlyle Sandridge & Rice, LLP has extensive experience in employment litigation and is recognized for his mediation expertise. Sources say: *"He is an excellent attorney and a great mediator."* **Michael Henthorne** (see p.2269) of Littler Mendelson, PC earns high praise from clients and focuses on employment litigation. Sources say: *"He is a pleasure to deal with – prompt, thorough and creative in legal analysis and strategy."* **Walker Coleman** (see p.2268) of K&L Gates is a well-regarded trial lawyer focusing on employment-related litigation. According to commentators, he is *"very impressive in his knowledge of employment law subject matter and a very skilled litigator."*

# LITIGATION GENERAL COMMERCIAL

Commentary about individuals can be found under their firm's paragraph. If the firm has no paragraph (is not ranked) look at Other Notable Practitioners.

## Litigation: General Commercial
### Leading Firms

**Band 1**
Nelson Mullins Riley & Scarborough LLP *
Nexsen Pruet, LLC *
Wyche, P.A. *

**Band 2**
Gallivan, White & Boyd, PA *
Sowell Gray Stepp & Laffitte LLC *
Womble Carlyle Sandridge & Rice, LLP *

**Band 3**
Haynsworth Sinkler Boyd PA
Hood Law Firm, LLC *
McNair Law Firm PA
Pratt-Thomas Walker PA
Smith Moore Leatherwood LLP *
Turner, Padget, Graham & Laney, P.A. *
Young Clement Rivers LLP

## Band 1

### Nelson Mullins Riley & Scarborough LLP
See profile on p.2276

**THE FIRM** This regional firm is recognized as having one of the finest litigation practices in the state. The group's size and scope of expertise make it a formidable force, providing top-quality advice and counsel in areas including commercial, employment, products liability and technology litigation. The team is also able to cover complex disputes and class actions on behalf of its clients in areas such as healthcare, consumer products and the automotive industries.
**KEY INDIVIDUALS** The well-regarded **David Dukes** (see p.2268) handles business and patent litigation, with expertise in drug and devices law. **Stephen Morrison** (see p.2271) is known to be a *"top-notch"* attorney, with a varied practice which includes technology law, business and securities litigation and products liability. **Mark Phillips** (see p.2271) concentrates on products liability lawsuits and is regarded as an *"excellent"* attorney for this area of expertise. **Marvin Quattlebaum** (see p.2272) is hailed as an *"outstanding lawyer,"* and focuses on products liability and commercial litigation.

### Nexsen Pruet, LLC
See profile on p.2277

**THE FIRM** Nexsen Pruet continues to assert itself as a frontrunner in the market with a deep bench of over 50 attorneys. The group offers a litigation practice that has a national reach and expertise in an impressive array of areas. In particular, the team is noted for its commercial litigation, products liability and professional liability work on behalf of a varied client base which includes Progress Energy and Roper Saint Francis Healthcare System.

**KEY INDIVIDUALS Thomas Stephenson** is highly regarded for his expertise in the labor and employment arena, and has experience in handling many employment-related lawsuits. The reputable **William Wilkins** concentrates in the areas of white-collar crime and appellate litigation, and also has a significant practice in business-related disputes. **Marc Manos** focuses his practice on civil litigation, and is well regarded for his ability to tackle various complex cases. **Susan McWilliams** is praised as an *"outstanding lawyer with an excellent track record"* and is experienced in dealing with commercial suits, including business torts, products liability and professional liability. **Marvin Infinger** is a business litigator who handles complex disputes and has a niche expertise in admiralty and maritime law.

### Wyche, P.A.
See profile on p.2280

**THE FIRM** This South Carolina firm houses a 19-strong team in its litigation department, and continues to offer top-class advice to large companies and local municipalities. The group covers the full scope of civil litigation matters, and is particularly rated by clients for its work involving real estate, corporate, and complex commercial disputes. The firm's impressive list of clients include Metso Paper USA, TD Bank, The Bank of New York Mellon, Florence County Council and LG Display.
**Sources say:** *"The Wyche attorneys are a unique collection of highly skilled and very intelligent people, who are also very personable. Their performance has been stellar on the matters they have handled."*
**KEY INDIVIDUALS** The *"outstanding"* **Wallace Lightsey** (see p.2270) has a wealth of trial experience and a practice which covers various complex disputes, including corporate, securities and IP. **Henry Parr** (see p.2271) garners high praise from clients, and is an experienced trial lawyer who focuses on complex litigation. **Troy Tessier** (see p.2273) has a varied litigation practice which includes personal injury, products liability, IP and other commercial disputes.

## Band 2

### Gallivan, White & Boyd, PA
See profile on p.2274

**THE FIRM** This well-regarded firm has a strong presence across the region, and is highly sought after by clients in the pharmaceutical and healthcare industries. The group's skill in products liability, toxic torts, and drug and medical device litigation gives it a competitive niche in the South Carolina market. The team also has expertise in transportation law pertaining to the railroad and trucking industries.

## Litigation: General Commercial
### Senior Statesmen

**Senior Statesmen:** distinguished older practitioners

| | | |
|---|---|---|
| Linton John | | Duffy & Young, LLC (ONP) [†] |

### Leading Individuals

**Band 1**

| | | |
|---|---|---|
| Dukes David E | Nelson Mullins Riley & Scarborough LLP * |
| Gray Elizabeth Van Doren | Sowell Gray Stepp & Laffitte LLC * |
| Lightsey Wallace K | Wyche, P.A. * |
| Morrison Stephen G | Nelson Mullins Riley & Scarborough LLP * |
| Stephenson Thomas | Nexsen Pruet, LLC |
| Stepp Robert E | Sowell Gray Stepp & Laffitte LLC * |
| Walker Trenholm G | Pratt-Thomas Walker PA |
| Wilkins William | Nexsen Pruet, LLC |

**Band 2**

| | |
|---|---|
| Cleveland III William | Womble Carlyle Sandridge & Rice, LLP |
| Hood Robert | Hood Law Firm, LLC * |
| Jones Celeste | McNair Law Firm PA |
| Manos Marc | Nexsen Pruet, LLC |
| McWilliams Susan | Nexsen Pruet, LLC |
| Outten Samuel W. | Womble Carlyle Sandridge & Rice, LLP |
| Parr, Jr Henry L | Wyche, P.A. * |
| Phillips G Mark | Nelson Mullins Riley & Scarborough LLP * |
| Smith Joel H | Bowman and Brooke LLP (ONP) [†] * |
| Smythe Jr Henry B | Womble Carlyle Sandridge & Rice, LLP |
| Sowell Thornwell F | Sowell Gray Stepp & Laffitte LLC * |
| White Daniel B | Gallivan, White & Boyd, PA * |
| Young Jr Rutledge | Duffy & Young, LLC (ONP) [†] |

**Band 3**

| | |
|---|---|
| Cox David S | Womble Carlyle Sandridge & Rice, LLP |
| Farrar Steven E | Smith Moore Leatherwood LLP * |
| Gibson Jr C Allen | Womble Carlyle Sandridge & Rice, LLP |
| Giese Michael J | Smith Moore Leatherwood LLP * |
| Quattlebaum Jr A Marvin | Nelson Mullins Riley & Scarborough * |
| Summerall IV Charles P | Womble Carlyle Sandridge & Rice, LLP |
| Tessier Troy A | Wyche, P.A. * |
| Watson J Calhoun | Sowell Gray Stepp & Laffitte LLC * |
| Wilkerson John | Turner, Padget, Graham & Laney, P.A. * |

**Band 4**

| | |
|---|---|
| Carter J. Kenneth | Turner, Padget, Graham & Laney, P.A. * |
| Craig Molly Hood | Hood Law Firm, LLC * |
| Infinger Marvin D | Nexsen Pruet, LLC |
| Lay John T. | Gallivan, White & Boyd, PA * |
| Lesemann Ellis R | Harvey & Vallini, LLC (ONP) [†] |

**Up-and-coming individuals**

| | |
|---|---|
| Hood James | Hood Law Firm, LLC * |

*Indicates firm / individual with profile.*
[†]ONP = Other Notable Practitioner.

**KEY INDIVIDUALS Daniel White** (see p.2273) has a wide-ranging practice which includes commercial litigation, products liability law and mass torts. **John Lay** (see p.2270) is noted as *"a well-versed litigator,"* and has extensive experience in complex business disputes.

## Sowell Gray Stepp & Laffitte LLC
**THE FIRM** This Columbia boutique receives high praise from peers for its talented group of litigators. Attorneys at this firm are adept at dealing with disputes at state and federal level and retain skills in a range of areas, including construction, healthcare, workers compensation, products liability and business litigation.
**Sources say:** *"It's amazing the number of excellent lawyers they have."*
**KEY INDIVIDUALS** The highly regarded **Elizabeth Van Doren Gray** (see p.2269) is noted for her expertise in professional liability claims, and also handles business-related disputes. **Robert Stepp** (see p.2272) is hailed as a *"top-flight litigator"* and concentrates his practice in the areas of professional liability, appellate law and commercial disputes. **Thornwell Sowell** (see p.2272) has a broad litigation practice which includes construction, healthcare and business disputes. Sources also note he is a *"great mediator."* **Calhoun Watson** (see p.2273) is skilled in the areas of commercial litigation and professional liability, as well as being able to handle mediation and arbitration.

## Womble Carlyle Sandridge & Rice, LLP
**THE FIRM** This strong regional firm possesses remarkable bench strength in its litigation practice group, assisting clients in a variety of complex commercial disputes. Areas of expertise include antitrust, IP, products liability and business litigation, and the team has recently handled work involving breach of contracts, fraudulent conveyance and trade secrets. Clients include Product Data Integration Technologies, Colonial Properties Trust and Trammell Crow Residential.
**Sources say:** *"I worked with them for many hours, and what impressed me is that it is not just a case to them – they are personally dedicated."*
**KEY INDIVIDUALS William Cleveland** has extensive experience in the business litigation arena and also mediates complex business disputes. **Samuel Outten** is lauded as an *"excellent litigator,"* and works with clients in various industries on business litigation, commercial disputes and products liability cases. **Henry Smythe** is highly sought after for his mass tort and products liability defense work, representing companies at regional and national level. **David Cox** concentrates his practice in the products liability area, and manages disputes on behalf of a host of manufacturers. **Allen Gibson** is an experienced trial lawyer, and specializes in representing clients in the construction industry. **Charles Summerall** focuses on business litigation with a specialty in bankruptcy law. Sources say he is *"very responsive, very proactive, and focused on making sure things run smoothly. He's been a tremendous asset."*

## Band 3

### Haynsworth Sinkler Boyd PA
**THE FIRM** This firm has a solid business litigation practice consisting of 26 attorneys, giving it a strong bench to cater to its corporate clients in commercial disputes. The group is also able to draw on attorneys who are skilled in products liability, professional liability and personal injury to offer a greater capacity to service a broad range of industry sectors.
**Sources say:** *"An old South Carolina firm with a very good reputation."*
**KEY INDIVIDUALS** Donald Sellers heads the firm's business litigation team.

### Hood Law Firm, LLC
**THE FIRM** This litigation boutique has expertise in a variety of areas, including commercial, employment and construction disputes as well as products liability, professional liability and toxic torts, allowing clients to benefit from the team's broad knowledge base. The firm's clientele includes Yamaha Motor Corporation, Medical Protective Company and Altec Industries.
**Sources say:** *"They are extremely competent attorneys."*
**KEY INDIVIDUALS Robert Hood** (see p.2270) handles commercial disputes and corporate litigation. A source says: *"He has great political contacts in the state – familiar with every judge, knows every plaintiff lawyer. It's invaluable to have his experience."* **Molly Hood Craig** (see p.2268) concentrates on professional liability and products liability, as well as pharmaceutical and medical device lawsuits. Sources say: *"She's very professional, speaks well, and is very knowledgeable."* **James Hood** (see p.2270) has a varied practice which includes products liability defense and commercial disputes.

### McNair Law Firm PA
**THE FIRM** This firm offers a solid litigation practice with a strong statewide presence, allowing it to service clients on both a local and national level. The group covers bankruptcy, environmental, commercial, construction and healthcare litigation, and is also known for its ability to mediate various disputes.
**Sources say:** *"They always seem to possess the skillsets needed and have the expert for the task at hand."*
**KEY INDIVIDUALS** The *"excellent"* **Celeste Jones** is an experienced trial lawyer who specializes in disputes relating to the healthcare industry.

### Pratt-Thomas Walker PA
**THE FIRM** This Charleston boutique firm concentrates in the areas of complex commercial disputes and civil litigation. The group is able to handle lawsuits in a diverse range of industries, with skills that cover land use and development, healthcare matters and products liability claims.
**KEY INDIVIDUALS Trenholm Walker** garners high praise from peers as an experienced litigator noted for his mediation and arbitration skills.

## Smith Moore Leatherwood LLP
**THE FIRM** This firm has a broad-based litigation practice which includes handling complex commercial disputes, construction litigation and products liability. The team is particularly well regarded among clients in the insurance and transportation industries, serving companies such as Estes Express Lines, Chartis Insurance and CH Robinson Worldwide.
**Sources say:** *"Smith Moore has always provided top-notch representation, and is known to be a very professional and reputable firm."*
**KEY INDIVIDUALS** The *"excellent"* **Steven Farrar** (see p.2268) centers his practice on handling complex disputes, which includes products liability, business, and construction litigation. **Michael Giese** (see p.2269) has extensive trial experience, and is well regarded for his commercial litigation practice.

## Turner, Padget, Graham & Laney, P.A.
**THE FIRM** This South Carolina firm has offices across the state, offering clients an integrated litigation practice. Areas of focus for the team include commercial litigation and employment disputes, and it also receives praise for its medical malpractice work. The group also has a longstanding relationship with Ford, acting as outside counsel on a series of matters.
**Sources say:** *"They have a great deal of credibility with the courts, other counsel and mediators."*
**KEY INDIVIDUALS John Wilkerson** (see p.2273) has a diverse litigation practice and is particularly noted for his work involving bad faith and contractual liability issues. Sources say he is *"extremely thorough and knowledgeable, dedicated to his clients, well respected by the judiciary, and responsive."* **Kenneth Carter** (see p.2268) gains high praise from clients, and handles disputes in the construction, transportation and products liability areas.

## Young Clement Rivers LLP
**THE FIRM** This firm remains a solid presence in the South Carolina litigation arena with an experienced group of trial lawyers practicing in a variety of areas. The team is well versed in banking litigation, business torts, construction disputes and insurance defense, as well as having a notable appellate law practice.
**KEY INDIVIDUALS** Stephen Brown is chair of the firm's commercial litigation and appellate practice group.

## Other Notable Practitioners

The experienced **Joel Smith** (see p.2272) of Bowman and Brooke LLP concentrates on products liability defense, with specialties in pharmaceutical and automotive-related disputes. **Rutledge Young** of Duffy & Young, LLC is described as a *"very good"* attorney, and focuses his practice on complex business disputes. The highly regarded **John Linton** of Duffy & Young, LLC has a wealth of experience in handling civil litigation matters. **Ellis Lesemann** of Harvey & Vallini, LLC has a broad practice which

# REAL ESTATE

Commentary about individuals can be found under their firm's paragraph. If the firm has no paragraph (is not ranked) look at Other Notable Practitioners.

## Band 1

### McNair Law Firm PA

**THE FIRM** This firm is held in high esteem by the business community and boasts one of the finest real estate practices in South Carolina, with offices across the state. Focusing on commercial real estate transactions, the group is particularly well known for its ability to handle all stages involved in the development process with expertise in the mixed-use, retail and resort development spaces.
**Sources say:** *"We use the McNair firm for our bond counsel and real estate transactions. Both areas have provided excellent advice and service."*
**KEY INDIVIDUALS Sidney Boone** is a highly regarded real estate lawyer who focuses his practice on land acquisition, rezoning and development contracts. **Joel Gottlieb** is praised as an *"outstanding lawyer."* He is known for his commercial real estate practice, with extensive experience handling retail and office development projects. **Judith McInnis** is able to bring her expertise in commercial lending and workouts to her commercial real estate practice. She focuses on real estate development projects involving retail, resort and mixed-use developments.

### Nexsen Pruet, LLC
See profile on p.2277

**THE FIRM** Nexsen Pruet is known to retain a wealth of talent in the real estate space, with 17 dedicated attorneys across its South Carolina offices. The firm's breadth of experience enables it to cater to various client needs, representing institutional lenders, developers and investors. The group provides transactional real estate services in addition to offering a strong litigation practice to handle related disputes. Clients include Estates Management Company, Realty Income Corporation, Southeastern Freight Lines and Garden & Gun.
**Sources say:** *"The firm's skill base is broad and detailed. In all areas we have been exceedingly pleased."*
**KEY INDIVIDUALS** The *"outstanding"* **Edward Menzie** has a broad practice with corporate and securities expertise in addition to his highly regarded real estate practice. **David Gossett** specializes in the real estate, lending and economic development fields, often representing banks and other financial institutions in complex real estate, construction and development loan transactions. The experienced **Neil Robinson** concentrates on complex real estate transactions and handles permitting and zoning issues relating to commercial, mixed-use, industrial and resort development projects. Client favorite **Franklin Daniels** chairs the firm's real estate practice. Sources say he is *"a tough, savvy attorney fully capable of leading and closing the most complex legal transaction, while ensuring his client's best interest at all times."* **Leighton Lord** is known for his expertise in economic development, real estate financing, land sale and leasing. A source describes him as *"extremely*

responsive, very accommodating and very in touch with the political and administrative scene in South Carolina."*

### Womble Carlyle Sandridge & Rice, LLP
See profile on p.2049

**THE FIRM** Clients give high praise to Womble Carlyle's real estate practice, which consists of a team of 38 attorneys offering unparalleled bench strength and breadth of experience in South Carolina. Recent highlights include assisting Foster Creek in the development of a large mixed-use project and acting for TD Bank as lead arranger in a loan transaction financing the development of the first new office tower since the 2008 recession.
**Sources say:** *"WCSR assists us with all our real estate needs, and in all of these areas they have much experience and extensive expertise. They are very competent at what they do."*
**KEY INDIVIDUALS Larry Estridge** is described as a *"great lawyer"* and is highly experienced in real estate development, particularly with issues involving land use and zoning. Sources say: *"He has a vast array of real estate knowledge and knows exactly how to navigate a transaction from beginning to end."* **Foster Gaillard** concentrates his practice on complex real estate transactions as well as business and banking law. He often represents developers of retail, mixed-use, industrial and condominium projects. **Lindsay Smith** garners high praise from peers and clients for his commercial real estate, financing and secured transactions expertise. A source says: *"He has a very deep knowledge of real estate and real estate issues, especially in South Carolina. He has been doing it a long time, is good to rely on and gets to the heart of issues."* **Susan Smythe** has a wide-ranging practice which includes real estate, M&A, finance and insurance, regularly handling complex transactions on behalf of clients. **Morris Ellison** handles commercial real estate transactions and is also an experienced litigator and banking lawyer. An admiring source says: *"He's very knowledgeable of the law, very loyal, very tenacious and very professional."*

## Band 2

### Haynsworth Sinkler Boyd PA

**THE FIRM** This well-regarded South Carolina firm retains a strong real estate practice with expertise in commercial real estate development as well as in the land use and zoning spaces. The firm is particularly recognized for its ability to handle real estate financings on behalf of institutional lenders.
**KEY INDIVIDUALS Anne Ellefson** has vast experience in handling commercial real estate transactions including zoning, permitting and financing elements. A source comments: *"She is as experienced as they come and well respected."* **John McArthur** focuses his practice on real estate lending, often representing banks and other lenders in

transactions for various development projects. **David Swanson** represents real estate owners and developers offering advice and counsel on commercial and residential property matters.

## Band 3

### Smith Moore Leatherwood LLP
See profile on p.2048

**THE FIRM** This firm presents a solid real estate offering focusing on all aspects of the commercial development process. The team is also able to utilize the firm's corporate and tax departments to cover all bases in a real estate transaction. Recent highlights include representing Greenville ONE in a $100 million retail and office project in downtown Greenville.

**KEY INDIVIDUALS Michele Lyerly** (see p.2271) heads the real estate department and focuses on commercial real estate development and leasing of retail, office and mixed-use projects. **Marvin Quattlebaum** (see p.2271) is described as *"a great lawyer"* and has expertise in the areas of industrial, residential and commercial real estate and lending.

### Wyche, P.A.
See profile on p.2280

**THE FIRM** This South Carolina firm offers a sophisticated real estate practice with a focus on commercial real estate acquisitions, development, finance and leasing. Recent work includes representing Con-Pearl in the establishment of its first North American production facility, a $14.25 million investment. Major clients also include Lehman Brothers, Michelin and TD Bank.

**Sources say:** *"Wyche tries to match up their lawyers' skills that best align with client needs. I have worked with several different lawyers in the practice and each seems to be very professional and competent in their field."*

**KEY INDIVIDUALS James Warren** (see p.2273) is head of the commercial real estate group and is experienced in handling the development of retail, industrial and commercial real estate projects. Rising star **Maurie Lawrence** (see p.2270) focuses on commercial real estate transactions and leasing, with a niche expertise in sustainable real estate. *"She's really good and very measured in her approach,"* say sources.

### Other Notable Practitioners

**Matthew Norton** (see p.2271) of K&L Gates has an international commercial real estate practice with notable expertise on developments in the resorts and hospitality industry. A source says: *"He really gives great advice, he has very good understanding of what is in the best interest of clients, and fights for what we may need for the future."* **Allen Jeffcoat** (see p.2270) of Turner Padget Graham and Laney P.A. has extensive legal experience and can bring environmental, corporate, foreclosure and bankruptcy expertise to his broad real estate practice. **Simpson Fant** of Parker Poe Adams & Bernstein LLP focuses his practice on the development and financing of residential real estate and housing projects. Sources say he *"does a wonderful job"* and *"has demonstrated an unparalleled understanding of the HUD regulations and nuances."* **Mark Sharpe** of Warren & Sinkler LLP complements his commercial real estate practice with banking and bankruptcy expertise and is considered as *"a very well-rounded, thoughtful and bright attorney"* by commentators. The *"excellent"* **John Warren** of Warren & Sinkler LLP is a highly regarded corporate attorney with a significant commercial real estate practice.

# Leaders' Profiles in South Carolina

### ABEL, Ashley B
Jackson Lewis LLP, Greenville
864 232 7000
AbelA@jacksonlewis.com
*Featured in Labor & Employment (South Carolina)*
**Practice Areas:** Employment, employee benefits. Certified by South Carolina Supreme Court as Specialist in Labor and Employment Law. Practices before federal /state courts, EEOC, other administrative agencies in 20+ states. Chairs ERISA Litigation Practice Group.
**Professional Memberships:** South Carolina Bar; Greenville County Bar Association; Defense Research Institute, American Bar Association.
**Career:** Partner 2001-present. General partner 2008. Joined 1998.
**Publications:** 'Jumping the Hurdles of the HIPAA Privacy Rule', South Carolina Lawyer, July 2003; 'Hiring, Firing & Discipline in South Carolina', 4th edition, South Carolina Chamber of Commerce, 2006.
**Personal:** University of South Carolina, JD, 1987; South Carolina Honors College, BA, 1983.

### AMSTUTZ, Eric B
Wyche, P.A., Greenville
864 242 8201
eamstutz@wyche.com
*Featured in Corporate/M&A (South Carolina)*
**Practice Areas:** Corporate; mergers and acquisitions.
**Career:** For over 30 years, Eric has concentrated his practice in the representation of publicly traded and privately held companies; the drafting and negotiation of complex agreements, including business mergers, acquisitions, dispositions, spin-offs and joint ventures; board governance; and transactional practice assistance in litigation matters.
**Personal:** Eric received his JD from Yale Law School in 1978 and was a law clerk to Gerhard Gesell, US District Court for the District of Columbia, and to associate Justice Potter Stewart, US Supreme Court. Eric was named "Greenville Best Lawyers Corporate Lawyer of the Year" in 2009.

### BAKKER, Mark W
Wyche, P.A., Greenville
864 242 8299
MBakker@Wyche.com
*Featured in Labor & Employment (South Carolina)*
**Practice Areas:** Employee benefits litigation; employment; entrepreneur services; alternative dispute resolution; litigation.
**Professional Memberships:** Certified Civil Court Mediator.
**Career:** Mark Bakker has developed an employment law emphasis in his commercial litigation practice. He provides proactive employment advice and counsel on a wide range of employment issues to human resource personnel and management in established companies, in addition to entrepreneurs and start-up companies.
**Personal:** In 1995, Mr Bakker earned his JD from the University of North Carolina School of Law, with high honors. Mark is also recognized in Best Lawyers of America for his employment work.

### BALLARD, Wade E
FordHarrison LLP, Spartanburg
864 699 1127
wballard@fordharrison.com
*Featured in Labor & Employment (South Carolina)*
**Practice Areas:** Labor and employment.
**Career:** Wade Ballard represents management in labor and employment matters in the courts, in arbitration, and before government agencies, including the EEOC, the US DOL, the North and South Carolina DOL, the South Carolina Human Affairs Commission, and other agencies at the federal, state and local level. He counsels businesses on the entire range of workplace issues and frequently conducts management training and continuing legal education on employment law, wage and hour law, discrimination, harassment, and other issues of concern to employers and the bar. He earned his JD from Duke University School of Law.

### BELCHER, Reginald G.
Turner, Padget, Graham & Laney, P.A., Columbia
803 227 4314
rbelcher@turnerpadget.com
*Featured in Labor & Employment (South Carolina)*
**Practice Areas:** Employment counseling and litigation.
**Professional Memberships:** Certified by the South Carolina Supreme Court as a Specialist in Employment and Labor Law; Certified Mediator.
**Career:** Mr Belcher represents management in employment litigation throughout the state, having successfully handled and argued cases before the US Circuit Court of Appeals for the Fourth Circuit. While maintaining an active litigation practice, Reggie also provides clients with practical and proactive advice designed to minimize the risk of litigation.
**Personal:** JD University of South Carolina, 1996; Masters of Human Resources, University of South Carolina, 1996; BS, West Virginia University, summa cum laude, 1992.

### BRUCE, James S.
K&L Gates, Charleston
843 579 5622
jamie.bruce@klgates.com
*Featured in Corporate/M&A (South Carolina)*
**Practice Areas:** James Bruce focuses his practice in the areas of mergers and acquisitions, joint ventures, and general corporate matters. He advises Fortune 500 companies as well as middle-market and emerging growth companies in a variety of industries, and his transactional experience includes mergers and acquisitions, private equity, cross-border transactions, strategic and venture capital investments, joint ventures, debt purchases and recapitalizations. Mr Bruce also has significant experience representing real estate developers

and owners and operators of golf, hotel, and resort properties.

## CARROUTH, Michael
Fisher & Phillips LLP, Columbia
803 255 0000
mcarrouth@laborlawyers.com
*Featured in Labor & Employment (South Carolina)*

**Career:** Mike Carrouth is a Partner in the Columbia office. He is certified as a Specialist in Employment and Labor Law by the South Carolina Supreme Court. Mike has represented clients in successfully responding to union organizing efforts in 27 states. This work includes successfully defending against multi-site and multi-state national organizing blitzes and card-check/neutrality campaigns. Mike also has represented clients in numerous litigation matters, including jury trials, involving FMLA, Title VII, breach of employment contract, and non-compete enforcement. Mike is also a frequent speaker at seminars on labor and employment and litigation matters.

## CARTER, J. Kenneth
Turner, Padget, Graham & Laney, P.A., Columbia
803 227 4279
kcarter@turnerpadget.com
*Featured in Litigation (South Carolina)*

**Practice Areas:** Litigation, including: construction, product liability, trucking, drug and medical device, and personal injury.

**Professional Memberships:** Business Counsel, Inc. (Board of Directors, 1999-Present, Chairman, 2012-Present), South Carolina Defense Trial Attorneys Association, Defense Research Institute (1989-Present), Richland County Bar Association, American Bar Association (Torts and Insurance Practice Section), South Carolina Bar.

**Career:** Mr Carter serves as state and regional counsel for automotive manufacturers, trucking and transportation companies, construction and building product manufacturers, and medical device companies. His practice involves defense of his clients' most high exposure cases in both state and federal courts.

**Personal:** JD, University of South Carolina, 1989; BS, University of South Carolina, 1984.

## COLEMAN IV, J Walker
K&L Gates, Charleston
843 579 5627
walker.coleman@klgates.com
*Featured in Labor & Employment (South Carolina)*

**Practice Areas:** An experienced labor and employment litigator, Walker Coleman handles cases for regional, national, and international companies in the banking, chemical, construction, environmental, government contracts, health care, insurance, manufacturing, medical product, pharmaceutical, retail, resort and hospitality, software, steel, transportation, technology, and telecommunications industries, among others. He defends employers in litigation involving employment discrimination, harassment, wage and hour, wrongful termination, and retaliation claims; defends and prosecutes trade secret claims; represents employers before state and federal employment

and labor boards and departments; and counsels employers on various employment matters and the sale and acquisition of domestic and foreign businesses.

## CRAIG, Molly Hood
Hood Law Firm, LLC, Charleston
843 577 1215
molly.craig@hoodlaw.com
*Featured in Litigation (South Carolina)*

**Practice Areas:** Ms Craig's trial work involves products and professional liability, pharmaceutical/medical device and employment litigation on a local, regional and national basis.

**Professional Memberships:** Ms Craig is the President-Elect of the International Association of Defense Counsel, Immediate Past President of the South Carolina Defense Trial Attorneys' Association, current Board member of the Defense Research Institute (The Voice of the Defense Bar), current Board member of Lawyers for Civil Justice, former member of the Executive Council for the Association of Defense Trial Attorneys, member of the American Board of Trial Advocates, member of the Federation of Defense and Corporate Counsel, and member of the Attorneys Committee for the National Center of State Courts.

**Career:** Ms Craig is the former managing partner of the Hood Law Firm, LLC where she has practiced for nineteen years. Honors include listing as one of South Carolina's Top 25 Super Lawyers, Best Lawyers in America, and the recipient of the Gold Compleat Lawyer Award given by the USC School of Law Alumni Association. Ms Craig was appointed National Coordinator for iCivics by Justice Sandra Day O'Connor (Ret.) in 2010 and also currently serves as South Carolina's State Coordinator for iCivics.

**Personal:** Ms Craig received her BA from the University of the South (Sewanee, Tennessee) and her JD from the University of South Carolina School of Law. Ms Craig and her husband have three children and live in Charleston, South Carolina.

## DAVIS LUX, Melinda
Wyche, P.A., Greenville
864 242 8223
mlux@wyche.com
*Featured in Corporate/M&A (South Carolina)*

**Practice Areas:** Corporate; entrepreneur services; mergers and acquisitions; securities and corporate finance.

**Career:** Melinda is a corporate lawyer who focuses her practice on complex business deals, including mergers and acquisitions, joint ventures, and financing transactions. Melinda teaches an entrepreneurial law course to MBA students at Clemson University, where she received her MBA. Melinda received her JD from Yale Law School and is currently pursuing her LLM in Taxation.

**Personal:** Melinda was named a "Rising Star" by South Carolina Super Lawyers in 2012 and "Young Professional of the Year" by the Greenville Chamber of Commerce in 2009.

## DUKES, David E
Nelson Mullins Riley & Scarborough LLP, Columbia
803 255 9451
david.dukes@nelsonmullins.com
*Featured in Litigation (South Carolina), Products Liability (Nationwide)*

**Practice Areas:** Pharmaceutical, patent, and business litigation; coordination of national litigation.

**Professional Memberships:** David is a past president of DRI, a national professional organization of lawyers who defend companies and individuals in civil litigation. He is past chair of Lawyers for Civil Justice.

**Career:** David is a Partner in Nelson Mullins Riley & Scarborough, LLP. He has been recognized as one of the top products liability lawyers by 'The Guide to the World's Leading Products Liability Lawyers'. He has served as national trial counsel in the pharmaceutical, computer and consumer products industries. David has tried cases throughout the United States.

## ELLZEY, Daniel
Fisher & Phillips LLP, Columbia
803 255 0000
dellzey@laborlawyers.com
*Featured in Labor & Employment (South Carolina)*

**Career:** Dan Ellzey is a Partner in the Columbia office. He counsels clients on all state and federal employment laws, major staff reductions and facility closures, labor law implications of mergers and acquisitions, OSHA compliance, and wage and hour matters. Dan litigates cases involving discrimination, wrongful discharge, ERISA, non-compete, and other employment-related matters. He also represents companies before the Occupational Safety and Health Administration. In the labor area, Dan advises companies across the nation on union avoidance and proactive employee relations plans. Dan is certified as a Specialist in Employment and Labor Law by the Supreme Court of South Carolina.

## FARRAR, Steven E
Smith Moore Leatherwood LLP, Greenville
864 240 2443
steve.farrar@smithmoorelaw.com
*Featured in Litigation (South Carolina)*

**Practice Areas:** Mr Farrar is an experienced trial lawyer, routinely working on complex cases involving complicated business litigation, professional liability defense, and major products liability issues. He has tried numerous cases including, among others, fighting charges of securities fraud and improper corporate activity, defending accountants and lawyers in malpractice actions, and defending automobile manufacturers from product liability exposure. In addition, he has served as counsel for a federally appointed Receiver in a criminal action, and in that role he helped recover millions of dollars for defrauded investors. Mr Farrar is also a Certified Public Accountant and a certified civil mediator.

## FEW JR, Richard L
Smith Moore Leatherwood LLP, Greenville
864 240 2473
richard.few@smithmoorelaw.com
*Featured in Corporate/M&A (South Carolina)*

**Practice Areas:** Mr Few is a Member of the firm's Business Group and his practice includes mergers and acquisitions, strategic and tax planning in structuring business ventures, and commercial and public/private financings. In addition, he represents businesses seeking economic development and tax incentives for relocations or expansions in South Carolina and serves on the South Carolina Chamber of Commerce Tax Committee which promotes pro-business laws in the state. Mr Few served as Managing Director of Leatherwood Walker Todd & Mann, P.C. from 2001 through 2008 until its merger with the firm.

## FOSTER III, William H
Nelson Mullins Riley & Scarborough LLP, Greenville
864 250 2222
bill.foster@nelsonmullins.com
*Featured in Labor & Employment (South Carolina)*

**Practice Areas:** Labor and employment; non-compete litigation; ERISA and employee benefits; OSHA; immigration; government relations and administrative law.

**Professional Memberships:** American Bar Association; South Carolina Bar; Greenville County Bar; South Carolina Defense Trial Attorneys Association; Admitted: Fourth Circuit Court of Appeals; US District Court, District of South Carolina.

**Career:** For the past fifteen years, Mr Foster's practice has focused on advising and defending management on all issues of employment law, employee benefits, immigration and human relations on a local, regional and national basis. Mr Foster advises and defends employers in a variety of employment-related matters, including, among other areas: all forms of discrimination under federal and state laws; wrongful discharge; employee benefits litigation under ERISA; immigration compliance; non-compete and trade secret litigation; and contract disputes. He has tried jury and non-jury cases in both state and federal courts throughout the Southeast, and has argued cases in both the federal and state courts of appeal. Since 1993, Mr Foster has also successfully defended firm clients on numerous employment law and employee benefits class actions. Prior to joining Nelson Mullins, Mr. Foster served as a law clerk for US District Court Judge G Ross Anderson, Jr of South Carolina.

**Publications:** A frequent public speaker, Mr Foster is the author of numerous articles regarding employment law and has been invited to provide the annual Fourth Circuit and South Carolina legal update for the South Carolina/North Carolina Joint Labor & Employment Law Section Annual Meeting on several occasions.

## FRITZE, Daniel J
Nelson Mullins Riley & Scarborough LLP, Columbia
803 255 9584
dan.fritze@nelsonmullins.com
*Featured in Corporate/M&A (South Carolina)*

**Practice Areas:** Corporate, mergers and acquisitions, finance.

**Professional Memberships:** A Member of the South Carolina Bar, Mr Fritze served as the Chairman of the Corporate, Banking and Securities Law Section of the South Carolina Bar from 2002-03.

**Career:** Mr Fritze is a Partner in the firm's Columbia, South Carolina, office, with experience in mergers and acquisitions, corporate formation and governance issues, private placements, corporate finance, and commercial and supply contracts.

**Personal:** Mr Fritze earned a Juris Doctor from Wake Forest University School of Law in 1991 and a Bachelor of Arts in accounting, magna cum laude, from Wofford College in 1984.

## GEDDIE JR, L Gray
Ogletree, Deakins, Nash, Smoak & Stewart, PC, Greenville
864 271 1300
gray.geddie@ogletreedeakins.com
*Featured in Labor & Employment (South Carolina)*

**Practice Areas:** Labor and employment, class action defense, litigation.

**Professional Memberships:** American Bar Association, Greenville Bar Association, Federal Bar Association, Defense Research Institute, South Carolina Defense Trial Lawyers Association, Fellow, College of Labor and Employment Lawyers, Certified Specialist in Labor and Employment Law by South Carolina Supreme Court.

**Career:** Mr Geddie was the Managing Shareholder of Ogletree Deakins from January, 2001 until January, 2010. He is admitted to practice in South Carolina, the District of Columbia and the United States Supreme Court.

**Personal:** Furman University (BA, 1966), University of South Carolina School of Law (JD, 1969).

## GENTRY, J. Theodore
Wyche, P.A., Greenville
864 242 8270
tgentry@wyche.com
*Featured in Labor & Employment (South Carolina)*

**Practice Areas:** Antitrust and trade regulation; appellate; class action litigation; colleges and universities; employment; governmental representation; litigation.

**Career:** For 20+ years, Ted Gentry has focused his practice on complex litigation, involving employment, commercial and financial matters, in both state and federal courts. He has extensive appellate experience, including cases before the SC Court of Appeals, the SC Supreme Court, the US Court of Appeals for the Fourth Circuit, and the US Supreme Court.

**Personal:** In 1987, Ted earned his JD from the Yale School of Law. Ted is also recognized in

South Carolina Super Lawyers and Best Lawyers in America.

## GIESE, Michael J
Smith Moore Leatherwood LLP, Greenville
864 240 2493
mike.giese@smithmoorelaw.com
*Featured in Litigation (South Carolina)*

**Practice Areas:** Mr Giese was law clerk to Honorable Clement F Haynsworth, Jr, Chief Judge, US Court of Appeals, Fourth Circuit. Mr Giese served as a member of the Board of Commissioners on Grievances and Discipline, South Carolina Supreme Court (1990-93), served as a Member of its Executive Committee (1993-97), and is presently a Member of the South Carolina Commission on Lawyer Conduct. He is a Fellow of the American College of Trial Lawyers, an Advocate of the American Board of Trial Advocates, a permanent Member of the Fourth Circuit Judicial Conference, and a Fellow of the American Bar Foundation.

## GRAY, Elizabeth Van Doren
Sowell Gray Stepp & Laffitte LLC, Columbia
803 231 7827
egray@sowellgray.com
*Featured in Litigation (South Carolina)*

**Practice Areas:** Commercial litigation, probate and estate litigation, and professional liability and ethics.

**Professional Memberships:** American Bar Association; South Carolina Bar; South Carolina Women Lawyers Association.

**Career:** Fellow, American College of Trial Lawyers; Member, Chief Justice's Commission on the Profession; Past President of the South Carolina Bar; Permanent Member, Fourth Circuit Judicial Conference; Compleat Lawyer Award Gold Medallion, 1997; Jean Galloway Bissell Award, 2000; South Carolina "Super Lawyers" Business Litigation (2008-13), Top 10 List (2009, 2013), Top 25 List (2008-10, 2013); Best Lawyers in America Commercial Litigation (2005-13), Bet-the-Company Litigation (2009-13),Columbia's Bet-the-Company Litigator of the Year (2009); Benchmark Litigation, Local Litigation Star (2009-13); Fellow, Litigation Counsel of America.

**Personal:** University of South Carolina, BA, 1970; University of South Carolina School of Law, JD, cum laude, 1976; Order of Wig and Robe, South Carolina Law Review, Comments Editor.

## GRAYSON, Neil E
Nelson Mullins Riley & Scarborough LLP, Greenville
864 250 2235
neil.grayson@nelsonmullins.com
*Featured in Corporate/M&A (South Carolina)*

**Practice Areas:** Securities, bank regulatory, and corporate governance.

**Professional Memberships:** Mr Grayson is licensed to practice in Georgia, New York, and South Carolina.

**Career:** Mr Grayson focuses on securities, bank regulatory, and corporate governance matters, emphasizing: Banks and other financial services companies; emerging growth companies and private equity funds; public companies and private

companies with outside investors. Previously, Mr Grayson practiced securities and corporate law in New York with Cravath, Swaine & Moore. Mr Grayson is the head of the firm's Financial Institutions Practice Group.

**Personal:** University of South Carolina Law School, cum laude, 1987; Wofford College, 1984.

## HALL JR, Cary H
Wyche, P.A., Greenville
864 242 8255
chall@wyche.com
*Featured in Corporate/M&A (South Carolina)*

**Practice Areas:** Corporate; entrepreneur services; environmental; estate planning and probate; mergers and acquisitions; outside general counsel; securities and corporate finance; and tax.

**Career:** Cary Hall has been practicing law with Wyche for more than 35 years and is a certified specialist in taxation law. Mr Hall's practice is evenly divided between tax law and general corporate and transactional matters, such as mergers and acquisitions, securities transactions, private equity, and venture capital.

**Personal:** Cary earned his JD from Harvard School of Law, graduating cum laude. He was named Greenville's "Tax Law Lawyer of the Year" by Best Lawyers in 2011.

## HARPER, Sue Erwin
Nelson Mullins Riley & Scarborough LLP, Columbia
803 255 5544
corky.harper@nelsonmullins.com
*Featured in Labor & Employment (South Carolina)*

**Practice Areas:** Labor and employment; business litigation; certified specialist in employment and labor law.

**Professional Memberships:** Ms Harper is certified by the Supreme Court of South Carolina as a Specialist in Employment and Labor Law. She is a Member of the South Carolina Bar, and is admitted to practice before the US Supreme Court, the US Court of Appeals for the Fourth Circuit, and the US District Court for the District of South Carolina. She is a Member of the Fourth Circuit Judicial Conference, John Belton O'Neall Inn of Court (President, 1990-91), the Commission on Continuing Legal Education & Specialization of the Supreme Court of South Carolina (Chair, 2010-13) and the South Carolina Women Lawyers Association (President, 1993-95). She is listed in the 2003-12 editions of The Best Lawyers in America. Ms Harper has served on the South Carolina State Ethics Commission, the Supreme Court of South Carolina Board of Commissioners on Grievances and Discipline, the Board of the South Carolina Bar and the South Carolina Bar Foundation.

**Career:** Before entering private practice, Ms Harper was a law clerk for US District Judge Robert F Chapman of South Carolina. She leads the Firm's labor and employment practice in Columbia.

**Personal:** In 1979, Ms Harper earned a Juris Doctor from the University of South Carolina School of Law where she was Notes Editor of South Carolina Law Review and served as a legal

writing instructor. She earned a Bachelor of Arts in Political Science from Queens College in 1972.

## HELMS, Katherine Dudley
Ogletree, Deakins, Nash, Smoak & Stewart, PC, Columbia
803 252 1300
kathy.helms@ogletreedeakins.com
*Featured in Labor & Employment (South Carolina)*

**Practice Areas:** Employment, litigation, alternative dispute resolution.

**Professional Memberships:** South Carolina Women Lawyers Association, National Association of Women Lawyers, American Bar Association, South Carolina Bar, State Bar of Georgia, Arkansas Bar Association, American Health Lawyers Association, ASHHRA/SHRM, Fellow in the Litigation Counsel of America, Women Lawyers Alliance.

**Career:** Admitted to practice in Georgia, South Carolina, Arkansas, US Court of Appeals (Fourth Circuit), US Supreme Court.

**Publications:** Notes & Comments Editor, Georgia State Law Review (1985). Frequent speaker/trainer on employment law issues including FMLA, retaliation, discrimination, and issues regarding physician conduct in the workplace.

**Personal:** University of Arkansas (BA, 1979), Georgia State University College of Law (JD, cum laude, 1985).

## HENTHORNE, D. Michael
Littler Mendelson, PC, Columbia
803 231 2500
mhenthorne@littler.com
*Featured in Labor & Employment (South Carolina)*

**Practice Areas:** Complex litigation and jury trials; discrimination and harassment; wage and hour; leaves of absence and disability accommodation; alternative dispute resolution.

**Professional Memberships:** Member, South Carolina Bar Association Member, Defense Research Institute Member, Labor and Employment/Litigation sections - American Bar Association Member, Society for Human Resource Management Member, Midlands Society for Human Resource Management Member, Committee of 100, Central SC Alliance Former member, Board of Directors - WORKLINK Former member, Board of Directors - New Foundation Children and Family Services For member, Board of Directors - Partners for a Healthy Community.

**Publications:** Confronting Workplace Violence: A Priority for Employers May 2011; For the Defense, Defense Research Institute Pleading Plausibility: Applying Twombly and Iqbal to Employment Litigation March 2010; For the Defense, Defense Research Institute Experts in Employment Litigation 2010; Litigators on Experts: Strategies for Managing Expert Witnesses from Retention through Trial, American Bar Association.

**Personal:** Univerity of South Carolina, JD, 1994; Furman University, BS, 1987.

## HOGUE JR, P Mason
Nelson Mullins Riley & Scarborough LLP, Columbia
803 255 9417
mason.hogue@nelsonmullins.com
*Featured in Corporate/M&A (South Carolina)*

**Career:** Mr Hogue practices in the areas of corporate law, intellectual property law, and economic development. Mr Hogue has devoted a significant part of his practice to representing entrepreneurs and other companies, with a particular focus on computer software and technology companies with respect to corporate, venture capital, mergers and acquisitions, strategic alliance, outsourcing and licensing matters.
**Personal:** In 1992, Mr Hogue was First Honor Graduate when he earned a Juris Doctor, magna cum laude, from the University of South Carolina School of Law where he served as Editor-in-Chief of the South Carolina Law Review.

## HOOD, James
Hood Law Firm, LLC, Charleston
843 577 4435
James.Hood@hoodlaw.com
*Featured in Litigation (South Carolina)*

**Practice Areas:** Mr Hood focuses his civil litigation practice in the following areas: commercial litigation, products liability, admiralty, professional negligence, and insurance coverage litigation. Mr Hood handles cases in state and federal courts throughout South Carolina, serving as local and national counsel for corporations and insurance companies.
**Professional Memberships:** Mr Hood is a member of the South Carolina Defense Trial Attorneys Association (Board of Directors, 2010 - present), the International Association of Defense Counsel, the Association of Defense Trial Attorneys, Defense Research Institute, and Claims and Litigation Management Alliance.
**Career:** Mr Hood is admitted to practice in the United States District Court, District of South Carolina and the United States Court of Appeals, Fourth Circuit, and all South Carolina State Courts.
**Personal:** Mr Hood received his BA from the University of The South (Sewanee, Tennessee), his JD from the University of South Carolina School of Law and his LLM in Admiralty Maritime Law from Tulane University. Mr Hood and his wife have three children and live in Charleston, South Carolina.

## HOOD, Robert
Hood Law Firm, LLC, Charleston
843 577 4435
bobby.hood@hoodlaw.com
*Featured in Litigation (South Carolina)*

**Practice Areas:** Mr Hood handles a wide variety of litigation services in state and federal courts throughout South Carolina and the United States. His practice areas include commercial and corporate litigation, construction, general civil litigation, insurance litigation, intellectual property, medical and legal malpractice, personal injury,and product liability.

**Professional Memberships:** He is a member of the South Carolina Bar, South Carolina Defense Trial Attorneys' Association (Past President), Association of Defense Trial Attorneys (Past President), a Permanent Member of the Fourth Circuit Judicial Conference, Federation of Defense and Corporate Counsel, International Association of Defense Counsel, American Board of Trial Advocates, Defense Research Institute, American Bar Association, Network of Trial Law Firms, Litigation Counsel of America, and Product Liability Advisory Council.
**Career:** Mr Hood was Assistant Attorney General of the State of South Carolina from 1969 to 1970. He is admitted to practice before the Supreme Court of the United States, the United States Court of Appeals, Fourth Circuit, the United States District Court, District of South Carolina and the Supreme Court of South Carolina. Mr Hood has been admitted pro hoc in most state and federal courts of the United States.
**Personal:** Mr Hood received his BA from the University of the South (Sewanee, Tennessee) and his JD from the University of South Carolina. Mr Hood and his wife have four children and ten grand children and live in Charleston, South Carolina.

## JEFFCOAT III, Otis Allen
Turner Padget Graham and Laney P.A., Myrtle Beach
843 213 5532
ajeffcoat@turnerpadget.com
*Featured in Real Estate (South Carolina)*

**Practice Areas:** Business litigation; commercial financing; bankruptcy; real estate; community associations; environmental law; probate administration and litigation; estate planning.
**Professional Memberships:** South Carolina Bar, American Bankruptcy Institute, South Carolina Bankruptcy Law Association, Grand Strand Area Estate Planning Council.
**Career:** Mr Jeffcoat assists clients in the areas of real estate, environmental law, corporate law, foreclosures, estate planning, and consumer and business bankruptcy. He is a licensed real estate agent and has qualified as an expert witness in state and federal court in real estate matters.
**Personal:** JD University of South Carolina, 1973; AB, Princeton University, magna cum laude, 1970.

## JENNINGS, John M.
Nelson Mullins Riley & Scarborough LLP, Greenville
864 250 2207
john.jennings@nelsonmullins.com
*Featured in Corporate/M&A (South Carolina)*

**Practice Areas:** Corporate/M&A; securities; private equity; joint ventures.
**Professional Memberships:** SC Bar's Corporate, Banking & Securities Law Section Council; ABA M&A Market Trends Subcommittee, Committee on Negotiated Acquisitions, American Bar Association's Section of Business Law.
**Career:** Represents clients in public and private M&A transactions, initial public offerings, PIPE transactions, and shelf take-downs; advises clients

regarding banking regulatory, fiduciary duty and corporate governance issues, proxy contests, and periodic disclosure.
**Personal:** Juris Doctor, magna cum laude, from Northwestern University School of Law; Masters in Business Administration degree, with distinction, Northwestern University Kellogg School of Management; Bachelor of Arts, University of Virginia.

## KEIM, Clay
FordHarrison LLP, Spartanburg
864 699 1136
ckeim@fordharrison.com
*Featured in Labor & Employment (South Carolina)*

**Practice Areas:** Labor and employment.
**Career:** Clay Keim represents employers in a wide-range of matters involving breach of contract, including breach of non-compete, non-solicitation, and non-disclosure covenants, misappropriation of trade secrets, unfair competition, and employment discrimination and harassment. He also has extensive experience in labor law matters, including opposing union organizing campaigns, and litigating unfair labor practice charges. Clay counsels businesses on the entire range of workplace issues and frequently conducts management training on employment law, labor law, and other issues of concern to employers. He received his JD from University of South Carolina School of Law in 1995.

## KEIM JR, Thomas H
FordHarrison LLP, Spartanburg
864 699 1129
tkeim@fordharrison.com
*Featured in Labor & Employment (South Carolina)*

**Practice Areas:** Labor and employment.
**Career:** Tom Keim has practiced exclusively in the areas of management labor and employment law since 1987. He represents clients in federal and state courts in many jurisdictions throughout the United States. His experience ranges from the representation of clients in employment litigation to union campaigns, strikes, and other employment-related matters. He also advises clients on the full spectrum of workplace issues. Tom is a South Carolina Supreme Court Certified Specialist in Employment and Labor Law. He received his JD from the University of South Carolina School of Law in 1987.

## LAWRENCE, Maurie
Wyche, P.A., Greenville
864 242 8319
mlawrence@wyche.com
*Featured in Real Estate (South Carolina)*

**Practice Areas:** Colleges and universities; commercial real estate; economic incentives; environmental and sustainability.
**Professional Memberships:** CREW Upstate South Carolina, Former President.
**Career:** Maurie works with a broad range of clients on all types of commercial property transactions. She often represents private companies across many industries, colleges, significant non-profits, developers and property management companies. Maurie is also involved with sustainable business practices.

**Personal:** Maurie received her JD from Georgetown University Law Center in 2003.Maurie was named one of South Carolina's ten "Emerging Legal Leaders" by South Carolina Lawyers Weekly in 2011.

## LAY, John T.
Gallivan, White & Boyd, PA, Columbia
803 779 1833
jlay@gwblawfirm.com
*Featured in Litigation (South Carolina)*

**Practice Areas:** Business and commercial; appellate; litigation and dispute resolution; banking and finance; insurance litigation; drug and medical device; product liability; toxic and mass torts; class action; professional negligence.
**Professional Memberships:** South Carolina Bar; Richland County Bar; Defense Research Institute; International Association of Defense Counsel; South Carolina Defense Trial Attorneys' Association; American Bar Association; American Board of Trial Advocates; John B. O'Neill Inn of Court; Litigation Counsel of America, Fellow Association of Defense Trial Attorneys
**Career:** John T Lay has over 20 years of experience managing complex, high-stakes litigation for clients, and has tried more than 100 cases to verdict.

## LEWIS, Stephanie
Jackson Lewis LLP, Greenville
864 672 8048
LewisS@jacksonlewis.com
*Featured in Labor & Employment (South Carolina)*

**Practice Areas:** Employment litigation on behalf of management, including discrimination, harassment, and fair pay and glass ceiling claims.
**Professional Memberships:** Board of Directors, Federal Bar Association; Council Member, Employment and Labor Law Section: South Carolina Bar; other professional memberships.
**Career:** Law Clerk, Judge Williams, Fourth Circuit Court of Appeals (2000-02); Law Clerk, Judge Duffy, United States District Court (SC) (2002-04); Partner, Jackson Lewis since 2008.
**Publications:** Multiple publications: employment law topics and EEOC enforcement procedures,
**Personal:** University of North Carolina School of Law, JD, with High Honors (2000); Order of the Coif (2000); North Carolina State University, BA (1997.)

## LIGHTSEY, Wallace K
Wyche, P.A., Greenville
864 242 8207
wlightsey@wyche.com
*Featured in Litigation (South Carolina)*

**Practice Areas:** Appellate; architectural works copyright infringement litigation First Amendment; intellectual property; commercial litigation; media and communications.
**Career:** Wallace is a skilled litigator with 25+ years experience and well over 50 jury trials, and has argued numerous appeals in state and federal appellate courts. Wallace earned his JD from Harvard Law School and was law clerk to Judge

John Wisdom, US Court of Appeals, and Chief Justice Warren Burger, US Supreme Court.
**Personal:** In 2012, Wallace was named Greenville's "Bet-the-Company Litigation Lawyer of the Year" by Best Lawyers and one of the "Top 25 Lawyers in SC" by SC Super Lawyers.

### LYERLY, Michele
Smith Moore Leatherwood LLP, Greenville
864 240 2429
michele.lyerly@smithmoorelaw.com
*Featured in Real Estate (South Carolina)*
**Practice Areas:** Michele Lyerly represents developers and investors in the acquisition, construction, financing, development, leasing and sale of shopping centers, office buildings and mixed-use developments. Michele has significant experience in the land acquisition for large-scale retail, mixed-use and "lifestyle" developments and in the preparation and negotiation of retail tenant leases. Her experience also includes negotiating and drafting purchase, sale, operating and joint venture agreements, easements, restrictive covenants, development agreements, management agreements, ground, retail and office leases. Her practice also includes real estate financing including traditional acquisition and construction loans, new market tax credit financing and tax-deferred exchanges.

### MANNING, Fred
Fisher & Phillips LLP, Columbia
803 255 0000
fmanning@laborlawyers.com
*Featured in Labor & Employment (South Carolina)*
**Career:** Fred Manning is a partner in the Columbia office. He has extensive experience litigating employment law matters involving civil rights, contracts, and wrongful termination claims. He regularly provides advice and assistance to employers regarding the drafting and enforcement of restrictive covenants, employment contracts and corrective action. Fred has assisted employers throughout the United States in union related matters. He also has extensive experience in representing private colleges and universities in matters relating to employment and faculty and student issues.

### MITCHELL, Stephen C
Fisher & Phillips LLP, Columbia
803 255 0000
smitchell@laborlawyers.com
*Featured in Labor & Employment (South Carolina)*
**Career:** Steve Mitchell is a Partner in the Columbia office. His practice emphasizes employment litigation as well as traditional labor law. He has handled administrative charges and lawsuits in state and federal courts involving wrongful discharge, Title VII, ADA, ADEA, ERISA, FMLA, FLSA, and other types of employment based claims. Steve has also assisted employers in handling class action litigation. In the traditional labor law arena, Steve has represented employers throughout the United States in a broad variety of union related matters. Steve is certified by the South Carolina Supreme Court as a Specialist in Employment and Labor Law.

### MOORE, John T
Nelson Mullins Riley & Scarborough LLP, Columbia
803 255 9415
john.moore@nelsonmullins.com
*Featured in Corporate/M&A (South Carolina)*
**Practice Areas:** John T Moore is a partner of Nelson Mullins Riley & Scarborough LLP in Columbia and practices in the areas of debtor and creditors' rights, financial institutions, and consumer compliance law.
**Professional Memberships:** General Counsel, South Carolina Bankers Association (1989 – present); General Counsel, South Carolina Student Loan Association (2005 – present); General Counsel, Young Men's Christian Association of Columbia; General Counsel, Riverbanks Zoo; American Bar Association; Past Chairman, S.C. Bar Corporation, Banking and Securities Section (1986-87); Past Chairman, S.C. Bar Consumer Law Section (1985-86); South Carolina Bar; Richland Bar Association.

### MORRISON, Stephen G
Nelson Mullins Riley & Scarborough LLP, Columbia
803 255 9410
steve.morrison@nelsonmullins.com
*Featured in Litigation (South Carolina), Products Liability (Nationwide)*
**Practice Areas:** Technology law and litigation; business litigation; product liability; securities litigation.
**Professional Memberships:** Member, American Bar Association; Defense Research Institute (Former President); International Association of Defense Counsel; Lawyers for Civil Justice (Former President); Product Liability Advisory Council; SC Defense Trial Attorneys Association.
**Career:** Has tried more than 240 cases and 60 appeals; member of the firm's Executive Committee; experienced in litigation and negotiation with the Federal Trade Commission (FTC).
**Personal:** Juris Doctor, University of South Carolina School of Law, 1975; Bachelor of Business Administration, University of Michigan, 1971; Advanced Management Program, Harvard Business School, 1997.

### MUELLER, Bernhard
Ogletree, Deakins, Nash, Smoak & Stewart, PC, Columbia
803 227 0844
bernhard.mueller@ogletreedeakins.com
*Featured in Labor & Employment (South Carolina)*
**Practice Areas:** Immigration law compliance, international labor and employment law, and business immigration. Bernhard Mueller assists employers with US immigration law compliance matters and government investigations / litigation resulting from immigration compliance and employment law matters. He assists companies in obtaining work visas for employees. He counsels companies on international employment law matters.
**Professional Memberships:** South Carolina Bar, North Carolina Bar Association, North Carolina State Bar, American Immigration Lawyers Association.
**Career:** Admitted in South Carolina and North Carolina.
**Personal:** University of South Carolina (BA 1995), University of South Carolina Moore School of Business (MIBS 2001), University of South Carolina School of Law (JD 2001).

### NASON, Leigh M
Ogletree, Deakins, Nash, Smoak & Stewart, PC, Columbia
803 252 1300
leigh.nason@ogletreedeakins.com
*Featured in Labor & Employment (South Carolina)*
**Practice Areas:** Affirmative action/government contracting, labor and employment law.
**Professional Memberships:** Certified Specialist in Employment and Labor Law (South Carolina), American Bar Association; Society for Human Resources Management, South Carolina Industry Liaison Group.
**Career:** Admitted to practice in South Carolina, US Court of Appeals (Fourth Circuit), US District Court (District of South Carolina).
**Publications:** Co-Editor," Labor and Employment Law for South Carolina Lawyers (S.C. Bar 1st-4th eds. 1999-2011); "Executive Order 11,246," Understanding Employment Discrimination (LEXIS/NEXIS 2008).
**Personal:** Wake Forest University (BA, 1982), University of South Carolina School of Law (JD, 1988).

### NORTON, Matthew J
K&L Gates, Charleston
843 579 5634
matt.norton@klgates.com
*Featured in Real Estate (South Carolina)*
**Practice Areas:** Partner Matt Norton's practice focuses on commercial real estate, private equity real estate, and real estate development, including real estate acquisitions and sales, portfolio transactions, joint ventures, and project and loan workouts and restructurings. He also has an extensive international practice in the field of Resort, Hospitality and Leisure and regularly represents clients in connection with resort planned communities, hotels, private clubs, golf courses, condominiums and strata title projects, condo hotels, branded residences, timeshares, and marinas.

### PARR, JR, Henry L
Wyche, P.A., Greenville
864 242 8209
hparr@wyche.com
*Featured in Litigation (South Carolina)*
**Practice Areas:** Arbitration; antitrust and trade regulation; appellate; class action litigation; commercial and corporate litigation; product liability.
**Career:** Henry has represented clients, plaintiffs and defendants, in complex litigation in state and federal trial and appellate courts for more than 30 years. Henry has also represented clients before administrative law judges and arbitrators and serves as an arbitrator for the American Arbitration Association. Henry received his JD from the University of Virginia in 1976 and was law clerk for Clement Haynsworth, Chief Judge

US Ct. Appeals 4th Circuit, and Chief Justice Warren Burger of the US Supreme Court.

### PEARSON, Jonathan
Fisher & Phillips LLP, Columbia
803 255 0000
jpearson@laborlawyers.com
*Featured in Labor & Employment (South Carolina)*
**Career:** Jonathan Pearson is the Managing Partner in the Columbia office. His practice emphasizes traditional labor law, as well as a wide range of employment litigation including Title VII, ADA, ADEA, FMLA and FLSA. He also frequently assists employers in union contract negotiations and in dealing with strike-related issues. Jon is certified as a specialist in labor and employment law by the South Carolina Supreme Court and is past Chairman of the Labor and Employment Section of the South Carolina Bar.

### PHILLIPS, G Mark
Nelson Mullins Riley & Scarborough LLP, Charleston
843 720 4383
mark.phillips@nelsonmullins.com
*Featured in Litigation (South Carolina)*
**Practice Areas:** Mr Phillips engages in trial work in product liability, personal injury, premises liability, construction, and commercial cases. Mr Phillips has tried asbestos personal injury cases to verdict in Florida, Georgia, Illinois, Ohio, Pennsylvania, South Carolina, Tennessee, Texas, Washington state, and West Virginia.
**Professional Memberships:** Mr Phillips is a Fellow in the American College of Trial Lawyers, an Advocate-level member of the American Board of Trial Advocates, a Permanent Member of the Fourth Circuit Judicial Conference, and a recent Past-President of the South Carolina Defense Trial Attorneys' Association.
**Career:** Mr Phillips was first admitted to practice in 1986. He is admitted to practice before the Supreme Court of the United States, the 4th US Circuit of Appeals, the US District Court for the District of South Carolina, the Supreme Court of South Carolina, and the Supreme Court of Florida.
**Publications:** Published quarterly "President's Message" in The Defense Line while President of the South Carolina Defense Trial Attorneys' Association in 2006.
**Personal:** Born on 20 July 1961. Mr Phillips attended British Studies at Oxford at St. John's College of Oxford University during the Summer of 1981, received a BA from The University of the South (Sewanee, Tennessee) in 1983, and received a JD from the University of South Carolina in 1986. He is a recent President and Chairman of the Coastal Carolina Council for the Boy Scouts of America.

### QUATTLEBAUM, Marvin
Smith Moore Leatherwood LLP, Greenville
864 240 2420
marvin.quattlebaum@smithmoorelaw.com
*Featured in Real Estate (South Carolina)*
**Practice Areas:** Mr Quattlebaum represents purchasers, sellers and developers of commercial, industrial and agricultural real estate, as well as

local and national lending institutions financing real estate transactions. He also has experience in representation of landlords, tenants, and lenders in leasing transactions involving real property for commercial and industrial development and use. Clients include, in addition, local special purpose districts, and he is involved with state governmental law issues relating to that representation. Mr Quattlebaum is an approved attorney and agent for the Chicago Trust Insurance Company, Lawyers Title Insurance Corporation, and First American Title Insurance Company.

### QUATTLEBAUM JR, A Marvin
Nelson Mullins Riley & Scarborough LLP, Greenville
864 250 2209
marvin.quattlebaum@nelsonmullins.com
*Featured in Litigation (South Carolina)*
**Practice Areas:** Marvin Quattlebaum is a partner in the Greenville office of Nelson Mullins Riley & Scarborough LLP. He serves as the Business Litigation Practice Group co-chair and as a member of the Firm's management group. Mr Quattlebaum practices in the areas of product liability litigation, business litigation, and other complex civil litigation.
**Professional Memberships:** South Carolina Bar President (2011-12), American Board of Trial Advocates, Products Liability Advisory Counsel, Super Lawyers, Best Lawyers in America, Litigation Counsel of America.

### SATTERFIELD JR, Andreas N
Jackson Lewis LLP, Greenville
864 232 7000
SatterA@jacksonlewis.com
*Featured in Labor & Employment (South Carolina)*
**Practice Areas:** Employment litigation, counseling on behalf of management.
**Professional Memberships:** South Carolina Bar (Chairman, Employment & Labor Law Section, 1998-99); District of Columbia Bar; South Carolina Chamber of Commerce, Board of Directors ( Human Resources Committee) 2011-2013.
**Career:** Joined Jackson Lewis 2007; Nelson Mullins Riley & Scarborough (2004-07); Haynsworth Baldwin Johnson & Greaves (1988-2004); Judicial clerk to Hon. John L. Napier, US Court of Federal Claims (1987-88).
**Personal:** University of South Carolina School of Law (1985); University of Georgia (1981); South Carolina Super Lawyers; Best Lawyers In America, "2012 Greenville Litigation – Labor and Employment Lawyer of the Year."

### SHETTERLY, Mike M
Ogletree, Deakins, Nash, Smoak & Stewart, PC, Greenville
864 271 1300
mike.shetterly@ogletreedeakins.com
*Featured in Labor & Employment (South Carolina)*
**Practice Areas:** Labor and employment, including ADA/FMLA compliance, employment policies and practices, termination issues, reorganizations, employment contracts, handbooks. Litigation concerning discrimination, retaliation,

wrongful discharge. Construction and business litigation for clients.
**Professional Memberships:** Leadership Greenville, Riley Institute Diversity Leadership Academy, Team Spartanburg (Chairman), International Center for the Upstate (Chairman), Spartanburg Area Chamber of Commerce.
**Career:** Admitted, South Carolina - 1996; Finkel & Altman until 2000. Ogletree Deakins Law Firm - 2000. Shareholder - 2005. Managing Shareholder Greenville since 2010.
**Publications:** Authored/co-authored several articles and/or books on employment and construction.
**Personal:** Wofford College (BA, 1993); South Carolina School of Law (JD, 1996).

### SHULER JR, Franklin G
Turner, Padget, Graham & Laney, P.A., Columbia
803 227 4242
fshuler@turnerpadget.com
*Featured in Labor & Employment (South Carolina)*
**Practice Areas:** Employment; dispute resolution.
**Career:** For over 30 years, Mr Shuler has handled all aspects of labor and employment law, including litigation. He spends significant time protecting his clients before litigation arises. When litigation is unavoidable, Frank protects his clients' interests with an eye towards their long-term goals.
**Personal:** Prior to practicing law, Mr Shuler served with the US Marine Corps. JD Samford University, 1983; BS Georgia Tech, 1977.

### SMITH, Joel H
Bowman and Brooke LLP, Columbia
803 726 7422
joel.smith@bowmanandbrooke.com
*Featured in Litigation (South Carolina), Products Liability (Nationwide)*
**Practice Areas:** With over 30 years of experience, Joel Smith focuses his national trial practice on the defense of product liability claims, with an emphasis on automotive and pharmaceutical cases. As a first-chair trial lawyer, he has extensive experience defending high-profile, catastrophic exposure claims and class actions, as well as experience in congressional investigations and recalls.
**Professional Memberships:** He is a fellow of the American College of Trial Lawyers and member of the Product Liability Advisory Council.
**Career:** Mr Smith has represented manufacturers of automobiles, tires, forklifts and other equipment as well as consumer products and pharmaceuticals nationwide.
**Personal:** Best Lawyers in America named Mr Smith as their "South Carolina Lawyer of the Year" for Product Liability Litigation in 2010 and 2011 and in 2012 he was named "South Carolina Lawyer of the Year" for Personal Injury Litigation. He is named in the International Who's Who of Product Liability Defence Lawyers. Joel has taught trial advocacy at the University of South Carolina since 1992, and lectures nationally.

### SMOAK, Lewis T
Ogletree, Deakins, Nash, Smoak & Stewart, PC, Greenville
864 271 1300
lewis.smoak@ogletreedeakins.com
*Featured in Labor & Employment (South Carolina)*
**Practice Areas:** Management, labor and employment law.
**Professional Memberships:** Greenville, South Carolina, District of Columbia, and American Bar Associations, Fourth Circuit Judicial Conference.
**Career:** Admitted in South Carolina, District of Columbia, and US Supreme Court. Founding partner Ogletree, Deakins, Nash, Smoak & Stewart (1977). Best Lawyers in America, Fellow of the College of Labor and Employment Lawyers, Who's Who in American Law.
**Publications:** Nationwide labor relations study of the construction industry.
**Personal:** Furman University (BA, 1966), University of South Carolina (JD, 1969); Ellis Island Medal of Honor (2006); South Carolina First Steps (Vice-Chair 2003-09); Furman University Trustee (1990-94).

### SOWELL, Thornwell F
Sowell Gray Stepp & Laffitte LLC, Columbia
803 231 7835
bsowell@sowellgray.com
*Featured in Litigation (South Carolina)*
**Practice Areas:** Mr Sowell practices in the areas of commercial litigation and business dispute litigation, contruction litigation, alternative dispute resolution.
**Professional Memberships:** American Bar Association; Former member, South Carolina Bar House of Delegates; Federation of Defense and Corporate Counsel; American Board of Trial Advocates; South Carolina Defense Trial Attorneys' Association.
**Career:** Best Lawyers in America (Woodward/White, 2001-13), Business Litigation Category; Best Lawyers in America (Woodward/White, 2009-13), Bet-the-Company Litigation, Bet-the-Company Lawyer of the Year (2013); Chambers USA America's Leading Lawyers for Business (2003-13); Fellow of the American Bar Foundation.
**Personal:** Clemson University, BA, 1973; University of South Carolina School of Law, JD, 1976 - President of the Student Bar Association, South Carolina Law Review.

### SPETH II, Charles T
Ogletree, Deakins, Nash, Smoak & Stewart, PC, Columbia
803 252 1300
ted.speth@ogletreedeakins.com
*Featured in Labor & Employment (South Carolina)*
**Practice Areas:** Employment, class action litigation, healthcare.
**Professional Memberships:** South Carolina Bar Association (Chair, Employment and Labor Law Section, 1990-91), Richland County Bar Association, American Bar Association, American Board of Trial Advocates (President, South Carolina Chapter, 2006-07), Greater Columbia Chamber of Commerce (Chair, 2007-08).

**Career:** Admitted to practice in South Carolina, US Supreme Court and US Court of Appeals (Fourth, Fifth and Seventh Circuits). Listed in 2001-12 editions of The Best Lawyers in America.
**Personal:** Duke University (AB, 1973), University of South Carolina School of Law (JD, 1979).

### STEPP, Robert E
Sowell Gray Stepp & Laffitte LLC, Columbia
803 231 7836
rstepp@sowellgray.com
*Featured in Litigation (South Carolina)*
**Practice Areas:** Mr Stepp practices in the areas of constitutional and commercial litigation, professional liabitliy and ethics, and appellate advocacy.
**Professional Memberships:** American Bar Association, Litigation Section; Richland County Bar Association; South Carolina Defense Trial Attorneys' Association; John Belton O'Neall Inn of Court.
**Career:** Fellow, American College of Trial Lawyers; American Board of Trial Advocates; Best Lawyers in America (Woodward/White, 2005-13), Business Litigation Category; Compleat Lawyer Gold Award (2004); Board of Directors and Former President, South Carolina Philharmonic.
**Personal:** University of South Carolina, BA, 1972; University of South Carolina School of Law, JD, 1977, Order of Wig and Robe, South Carolina Law Review.

### STEWART III, J Hamilton
Ogletree, Deakins, Nash, Smoak & Stewart, PC, Greenville
864 271 1300
jimmie.stewart@ogletreedeakins.com
*Featured in Labor & Employment (South Carolina)*
**Practice Areas:** Representing management: positive employee relations; labor matters; corporate campaigns.
**Professional Memberships:** SCBA, TBA, DC Bar, ABA
**Career:** Ogletree Deakins Founder/Of Counsel. Certified Specialist (SC); Best Lawyers in America. Fellow, College of Labor and Employment Lawyers.
**Publications:** NLRB Regulations of Election Conduct (1985-1997) (Olin Institute). "Neutrality" and "Card Checks": Union Assaults on Employee Rights and the Integrity of the NLRB (Journal of Labor Research - Fall 2006).
**Personal:** Presbyterian College (AB, 1965), University of South Carolina (JD, 1969).

### SUGGS JR, Fred W
Ogletree, Deakins, Nash, Smoak & Stewart, PC, Greenville
864 271 1300
fred.suggs@ogletreedeakins.com
*Featured in Labor & Employment (South Carolina)*
**Practice Areas:** Labor and employment.
**Professional Memberships:** American, Alabama, Florida, and South Carolina (Past President) Bars; Certified Specialist in Labor and Employment Law (SC), Member, Fourth Circuit Judicial Conference, and Fellow of the College of Labor and Employment Lawyers.

**Career:** Admitted to the United States, Alabama, Florida, and South Carolina Supreme Courts, US District Courts (various), and US Courts of Appeal (various).

**Publications:** Has lectured and written extensively on labor and employment matters and is frequently quoted in publications for lawyers and various newspapers.

**Personal:** Kansas State University (BS, 1970), University of Alabama (JD, 1975).

---

**TESSIER, Troy A**
Wyche, P.A., Greenville
864 242 8219
ttessier@wyche.com

*Featured in Litigation (South Carolina)*

**Practice Areas:** Architectural works copyright infringement litigation; construction; First Amendment; intellectual property; commercial and corporate litigation; plaintiff's personal injury practice; product liability; whistleblower and False Claims Act litigation.

**Career:** Troy Tessier is a skilled litigator with experience in many different areas, including the conduct of 50+ jury or bench trials to verdict. Troy earned his JD from Harvard Law School, cum laude, and served in the US Marines as a Judge Advocate and as an Assistant US Attorney.

**Personal:** He has been recognized as in Best Lawyers in America since 2008 and in South Carolina Super Lawyers since 2010.

---

**TIGHE, J Hagood**
Fisher & Phillips LLP, Columbia
803 255 0000
htighe@laborlawyers.com

*Featured in Labor & Employment (South Carolina)*

**Career:** Hagood Tighe is a partner in the Columbia office. He represents management in union matters and employment litigation. Hagood also has successfully handled and argued cases before the United States Circuit Court of Appeals for the Fourth Circuit. While he maintains an active litigation practice, he also focuses on providing practical and proactive advice designed to minimize the risk of litigation. He provides training for supervisors and managers on harassment, EEO compliance, the Family and Medical Leave Act, and many other areas. He is certified by the South Carolina Supreme Court as a Specialist in Employment and Labor Law.

---

**WARREN III, James I**
Wyche, P.A., Greenville
864 242 8320
jwarren@wyche.com

*Featured in Real Estate (South Carolina)*

**Practice Areas:** Commercial real estate; economic incentives; tax.

**Career:** Jim Warren leads Wyche's commercial real estate and economic incentives practice groups. He represents developers, public and private companies, lenders and investors in a wide variety of sophisticated real estate transactions, including the development, acquisition, disposition and tax-deferred exchange and contribution of properties, as well as leases for retail, commercial and industrial projects.

**Personal:** In 1991, Jim earned his JD from the Vanderbilt University School of Law. Jim was named the 2013 Real Estate "Lawyer of the Year" for Greenville by Best Lawyers In America.

---

**WATSON, J Calhoun**
Sowell Gray Stepp & Laffitte LLC, Columbia
803 231 7839
cwatson@sowellgray.com

*Featured in Litigation (South Carolina)*

**Practice Areas:** Commercial litigation, class actions, and professional negligence.

**Professional Memberships:** International Association of Defense Counsel; SC Bar (President-Elect 2013-14; Treasurer 2012-13; Secretary 2011-12); ABA; John Belton O'Neall Inn of Court (President 2010-11); SC Defense Trial Attorneys' Association; DRI.

**Career:** Judicial clerk, Honorable Robert Chapman, Judge, United States Court of Appeals, Fourth Circuit, 1987-88; SC Bar Board of Governors, 1997-2000, 2009-present; SC Bar House of Delegates, 1997-present; SC Access to Justice Commission, 2006-11; President, SC Bar Foundation, 2006-07; Editorial Board of SC Lawyer Magazine, 2000-07; President, SC Bar Young Lawyers Division, 1997-98; Best Lawyers in America Commercial Litigation, Professional Malpractice Law and Bet-the-Company Litigation Categories; SC 'Super Lawyers' for Business Litigation and Professional Liability Defense; Compleat Lawyer Award Silver Medallion, 2001.

**Personal:** Wofford College, BA, summa cum laude, 1984; Phi Beta Kappa; President of the Student Body; USC School of Law, JD, cum laude, 1987; Order of the Coif; Order of Wig and Robe; Student Works Editor, SC Law Review.

---

**WHITE, Daniel B**
Gallivan, White & Boyd, PA, Greenville
864 271 5342
dwhite@gwblawfirm.com

*Featured in Litigation (South Carolina)*

**Practice Areas:** Civil litigation (commercial, products liability, pharmaceutical, class action and mass torts).

**Professional Memberships:** South Carolina Bar; International Association of Defense Counsel; Association of Defense Trial Counsel; Litigation Counsel of America.

**Career:** Senior Litigation Partner at Gallivan, White and Boyd, P.A. White served as Lead Counsel for a national rail carrier in the In Re Graniteville Train Derailment litigation, the largest non-natural disaster in S.C. history. White has also served as national and regional counsel for product manufacturers in numerous toxic tort and mass tort matters.

**Personal:** Married, 2 children; 1st Lt, US Army (1971-73); Vietnam veteran.

---

**WILKERSON, John**
Turner, Padget, Graham & Laney, P.A., Charleston
843 576 2801
jwilkerson@turnerpadget.com

*Featured in Litigation (South Carolina)*

**Practice Areas:** Business litigation; insurance coverage/bad faith.

**Professional Memberships:** Past president of the South Carolina Defense Trial Attorneys Association and a member of The American Board of Trial Advocates (Advocate Rank) and the Federation of Defense and Corporate Counsel.

**Career:** Mr Wilkerson has extensive experience as a trial lawyer, having served as lead counsel in over 150 jury trials. He represents companies and individuals in cases involving insurance coverage/bad faith, employment, professional liability, drug and medical devices, and business and probate litigation.

**Personal:** JD, University of South Carolina, 1979; BA, Furman University, 1976.

# GALLIVAN WHITE & BOYD PA

www.GWBlawfirm.com  **tel:** 864 271 9580  **fax:** 864 271 7502

**Managing Partner:** C William McGee
Number of partners: 34   Number of other lawyers: 29

### Firm Overview:

Gallivan, White and Boyd, P.A. (GWB) is one of the Southeast's leading commercial and complex litigation law firms founded 65 years ago in Greenville, South Carolina. With 63 attorneys GWB has the strength to tackle complex issues and the agility to change fields quickly when necessary. The firm's negotiation and litigation experience is excellent. GWB attorneys are reliable problem solvers who lead their clients through challenges and opportunities great and small. GWB is proud of its history of growth and the results the firm's attorneys have achieved for its clients over the years. Like GWB clients, the firm's attorneys are future-focused and concerned about being stronger tomorrow than they are today. In 2011, GWB opened offices in Charlotte, NC and Columbia, SC. GWB's team of attorneys is now able to serve all of South Carolina and North Carolina. The firm's scope and capabilities are greater than ever.

### OFFICES

**NORTH CAROLINA**
**CHARLOTTE:** 6805 Morrison Blvd., Suite 200, PO Box 12250, NC 28220
Tel: 704 552 1712   Fax: 864 271 7502

**SOUTH CAROLINA**
**COLUMBIA:** 1201 Main Street, Suite 1200, PO Box 7368, SC 29202
Tel: 803 779 1833   Fax: 864 271 7502
**GREENVILLE:** 55 Beattie Place, Suite 1200, PO Box 10589, SC 29603
Tel: 864 271 9580   Fax: 864 271 7502

## Main Areas of Practice:

### Banking, Bankruptcy & Creditors' Rights:
The firm represents banks, thrifts, and their holding companies in regulatory matters, commercial lending transactions, and problem asset workouts.

### Business & Commercial Litigation:
GWB represents clients in arbitration and litigation involving business torts, contracts, corporate finance, securities, insurance, shareholder disputes, derivative actions, real estate and land use issues, trade secrets, and covenants not to compete within a variety of industries. Additionally, GWB has class action experience within several industries, including healthcare, commercial transportation, products liability, insurance and unfair trade practices, as well as in electronic discovery matters.

### Corporate & Business Planning & Real Estate:
GWB advises clients concerning the formation and operation of businesses, and negotiates and prepares operating agreements, partnership agreements, buy-sell agreements, and contracts for all types of business transactions. The firm also has extensive experience representing individuals, corporations, developers, and financial institutions in franchising transactions, real estate law and finance matters including the acquisition, sale, leasing, and development of real estate.

### Design & Construction:
GWB's Design and Construction Team represents a wide variety of clients who are involved in the construction process. The firm offers a broad array of legal services to developers and owners of commercial and industrial properties, to general and trade contractors, and to design professionals. The firm has represented local, national and international architectural and engineering firms, contractors, subcontractors, design/builders, bonding companies and suppliers in construction matters.

### Drug & Medical Device:
GWB represents many well known domestic and foreign manufacturers and distributors of pharmaceuticals, medical devices, biologics, foods, and cosmetics.

### Healthcare & Benefits:
GWB represents healthcare providers including professionals and facilities, health plans, employers, and third-party administrators as well as insurers providing life, health and accidental death coverage. The firm has handled class actions, arbitrations, contract actions, reimbursement disputes, bad faith actions, actions relating to fiduciary responsibilities and actions involving administration of employee benefit plans. Additionally, the firm handles all stages of ERISA litigation and other benefits disputes.

### Insurance Practice:
GWB has extensive experience handling a variety of matters, including personal, commercial, excess and umbrella policies. The Insurance Coverage Team specializes in handling litigated first party claims and bad faith claims, as well as assisting in the investigation and handling of pre-suit claims involving property losses, fire and theft losses, arson and potentially fraudulent claims.

### Product Liability:
GWB has extensive experience in products liability matters, including post-accident investigation and in all aspects of litigation. Fortune 500 corporations retain the firm to defend product liability claims in federal and state courts in the Southeast.

### Professional Negligence:
GWB defends malpractice actions on behalf of physicians, hospitals, accountants, attorneys, and numerous other professionals. Additionally, the firm has substantial experience representing long term care providers, including nursing homes, assisted living facilities, hospice and continuing care retirement.

### Tort & Personal Injury:
The Tort and Personal Injury Team defends insurers, self-insured corporations and third-party risk managers in both state and federal courts.

### Toxic & Mass Torts:
The firm has extensive experience in handling toxic and mass tort cases involving exposure to substances such as benzene, silica, heavy metals, asbestos, PCBs, lead, latex, mold, chlorine, Chinese drywall, and many others.

### Transportation Law & Litigation:
GWB has represented national railroads for more than four decades and has extensive experience defending crossing accidents, FELA claims, real estate and contract disputes, occupational claims and toxic tort claims. The firm also handles trucking accident investigations, emergency response to accident scenes, transportation contract issues and cargo and freight claims.

### Workplace Practices:
GWB defends employers, insurance carriers, and third party administrators in employment and workers' compensation matters.

### Clients:
Representative clients include:  Amsted Industries; Baxter Healthcare Corporation; Bayer Corporation; Beretta USA; Biomet, Inc.; Blue Cross Blue Shield of South Carolina; Building Materials Corporation of America d/b/a GAF; Canal Insurance Company; Chartis; City of Greenville; CSX Transportation, Inc; DirecTV, Inc; Edens and Avant; Emeritus Corporation; First Citizens Bank; General Electric; Greenville Airport Commission; Home Depot; Laurel Baye Healthcare; Michelin North America, Inc.; Minnesota Lawyers Mutual; Nationstar Mortgage; Norfolk Southern Corporation; Nutricia USA, Inc; Palmetto Bank; Prime, Inc.; Schneider Electric; South Carolina Bank & Trust; SunTrust Bank; Swift Transportation; Target; Teva Pharmaceuticals; Textron; TLC Vision Corp.; UBS; Zurich North America.

Gallivan, White & Boyd, P.A.
ATTORNEYS AT LAW

# HOOD LAW FIRM LLC

www.hoodlaw.com  **tel:** 843 577 4435  **fax:** 843 722 1630

**Managing Partner:** Robert H Hood, Jr
Number of partners: 12
Number of other lawyers: 13

**Firm Overview:**

The Hood Law Firm, LLC is a defense trial law firm comprised of twenty-five attorneys who practice as national and statewide trial counsel for major corporations and insurers. Over the past twenty-five years, the firm has consistently maintained its focus on trial practice, trying literally hundreds of cases to verdict. Success is obtained through collaboration with the client in a team approach to achieve the desired goal.

**Main Areas of Practice:**

**Litigation:**

Hood Law Firm, LLC represents clients in trial, appeals, arbitrations and complex civil litigation throughout South Carolina and the United States. The firm's practice focuses on admiralty and maritime law, business litigation, construction litigation, drug and medical device, employment litigation, insurance coverage, mass tort litigation, product liability, professional negligence, and transportation law and litigation.

**Clients:**

Representative clients include: Altec Industries; Chartis Insurance; OneBeacon Insurance Group; ACE (USA); Detyens Shipyards; Hubbell, Inc.; AstraZeneca, USA; First Citizens Bank; Gould Pumps, Inc.; LifeCare Centers of America; LifeCare Centers of Charleston; Yamaha Motor Corp, USA; Zurich, US; South Carolina Medical JUA; Selective Insurance Company; The Sherwin Williams Company; Primerica Insurance Co.; MAG Mutual Insurance Company; Medical Protective Company; Medtronics, Inc.; Liberty Mutual Insurance Company; HCR Manor Care; Insurance Reserve Fund; AIG Claim Services; Admiral Insurance Company; CAN Insurance Company; Markel; Community First Bank; American Southern Insurance Company; Pennsylvania Lumberman Mutual Insurance; Shell Oil Company; Fortune Brands Home & Office, Inc.; Premier Behavioral Solutions.

# NELSON MULLINS RILEY & SCARBOROUGH LLP

www.nelsonmullins.com  **tel:** 803 799 2000  **fax:** 803 256 7500

**Managing Partner:** James K Lehman
**Marketing Partner:** Gus Dixon
Number of partners: 282  Number of other lawyers: 178

## Firm Overview:

Founded in 1897, Nelson Mullins maintains offices in Georgia, North Carolina, South Carolina, Florida, Massachusetts, Tennessee, West Virginia and Washington, DC. With more than 470 attorneys and government relations professionals practicing in 13 offices, the firm has more than 50 diversified practice areas and represents a wide variety of clients ranging from start-up technology companies to *Fortune* 500 corporations.

## Main Areas of Practice:

### Financial Services:

Attorneys in this group provide counsel throughout the United States in the areas of business, securities and financial fraud, business torts, antitrust matters, lending liability claims, contract disputes, and other areas.

### Corporate Finance:

Firm attorneys handle a broad range of securities, finance and regulatory matters for development stage private companies and large publicly held companies in a wide range of industries.

### Intellectual Property:

These attorneys and technical specialists provide comprehensive patent, trademark, and copyright services to a large base of domestic and international corporations.

### Pharmaceuticals & Medical Devices:

Firm attorneys have extensive knowledge in many areas of science and technology and effectively handle claims regarding clients' products and services. The attorneys have experience with mass torts and multi-district litigation, requiring co-ordination with attorneys from across the United States.

### Healthcare:

Firm attorneys provide comprehensive client services to healthcare clients in corporate transactions, regulatory and governmental affairs, litigation, finance, and tax.

### Mass Tort Litigation:

Firm attorneys are equipped to handle or co-ordinate the defense of mass tort claims on an individual, regional or national basis, and serve as national trial and coordinating counsel for leading US companies.

### Government Relations:

These attorneys have extensive experience with a wide range of clients in many areas of lobbying and legislative analysis.

### Labor & Employment:

This diverse group of attorneys defends companies in all facets of labor and employment disputes.

### International Work:

The Nelson Mullins International Practice Group serves clients around the world in international business, commercial and trade matters, business immigration, and matters before federal courts, international agencies, and tribunals.

## PRACTICE AREAS

Business Litigation
Corporate Finance
Intellectual Property
Pharmaceuticals & Medical Devices
Government Relations
Healthcare
Mass Tort Litigation
Labor & Employment

## OFFICES

### SOUTH CAROLINA

**COLUMBIA:** Meridian, 17th Floor, 1320 Main Street, SC 29201
Tel: 803 799 2000  Fax: 803 256 7500

**CHARLESTON:** Liberty Center, Suite 600, 151 Meeting Street, SC 29401-2239
Tel: 843 853 5200  Fax: 843 722 8700

**GREENVILLE:** Poinsett Plaza, Suite 900, 104 South Main Street, SC 29601
Tel: 864 250 2300  Fax: 864 232 2925

**MYRTLE BEACH:** BNC Bank Corporate Center, Suite 300, 3751 Robert M Grissom Parkway, SC 29577
Tel: 843 448 3500  Fax: 843 448 3437

### MASSACHUSETTS

**BOSTON:** One Post Office Square, 30th Floor, MA 02109-2127
Tel: 617 573 4700  Fax: 617 573 4710

### DISTRICT OF COLUMBIA

**WASHINGTON DC:** 101 Constitution Avenue, NW, Suite 900, DC 20001
Tel: 202 712 2800  Fax: 202 712 2860

### FLORIDA

**TALLAHASSEE:** 3600 Maclay Blvd. South, Suite 202, FL 32312-1267
Tel: 850 907 2500  Fax: 850 907 2501

### GEORGIA

**ATLANTA:** Atlantic Station, 201 17th Street NW, Suite 1700, GA 30363
Tel: 404 322 6000  Fax: 404 322 6050

### NORTH CAROLINA

**CHARLOTTE:** Bank of America Corporate Center, 42nd Floor, 100 North Tryon Street, NC 28202-4007
Tel: 704 417 3000  Fax: 704 377 4814

**RALEIGH:** GlenLake One, Suite 200, 4140 Parklake Avenue, NC 27612
Tel: 919 877 3800  Fax: 919 877 3799

**WINSTON SALEM:** The Knollwood, Suite 530, 380 Knollwood Street, NC 27103
Tel: 336 774 3300  Fax: 336 774 3299

### TENNESSEE

**NASHVILLE:** 315 Deaderick Street, Suite 1800
Tel: 615 664 5300  Fax: 615 664 5399

### WEST VIRGINIA

**HUNTINGTON:** 949 Third Avenue, Suite 200, WV 25701
Tel: 304 526 3500  Fax: 304 526 3599

# Nelson Mullins.

**Nelson Mullins Riley & Scarborough LLP**

# NEXSEN PRUET LLC

**www.**nexsenpruet.com **tel:** 803 771 8900 **fax:** 803 253 8277

**Managing Partner:** John A Sowards
Number of partners: 104
Number of other attorneys: 87

## Firm Overview:

Nexsen Pruet, LLC is one of the largest law firms in the Carolinas, with more than 190 attorneys and offices in Columbia, Charleston, Greenville, Hilton Head, and Myrtle Beach, SC. as well as Charlotte, Greensboro, and Raleigh, NC. Founded in 1945, Nexsen Pruet provides a broad range of legal services to the business community and represents companies and other entities in local, state, national, and international venues.

## Main Areas of Practice:

### Financial Services:

The group has experience in corporate/commercial finance transactions involving debt and equity markets as well as representing lenders and borrowers in middle market, asset-based, mezzanine and other types of debt financing. The group has extensive experience in workouts, restructures, modifications and general debt restructures.

### Litigation:

The firm's broad litigation experience includes antitrust and unfair trade practices, appellate, asbestos, aviation, business disputes, catastrophic injury, civil rights defense, class actions, commercial/contracts, computer, internet and technology, creditors' rights and bankruptcy, document review capabilities, health care, insurance coverage, insurance bad faith defense, intellectual property, international arbitrations, labor and employment, lender liability and business torts, maritime, products liability, public utilities, securities, toxic tort, transportation and trucking, truck accident defense, workers' compensation and more.

### Construction:

The Construction Team's experience includes pre-construction planning, bid-packaging, employment issues, procurement, environmental permitting, project financing, contract drafting and review, claims preparation, and litigation. The firm represents public and private owners, developers, design professionals, contractors, subcontractors, and suppliers as well as working with national bonding companies.

### Corporate:

The firm serves local and start-up companies as well as major institutional businesses with multi-state and international operations. Activities include banking and financial services, insurance, manufacturing, transportation, textiles, computers and other technologies, wholesale and retail sales, distribution services, construction, real estate development and management and natural resources development.

### Employment & Labor:

The group's diverse services include arbitrations/mediations, business immigration, discrimination, retaliation, harassment claims, employee benefits design/administration, employee benefits litigation, executive contracts and compensation, FMLA issues, individual employee and class action suits, reductions in force and plant closings, trade secret protection /litigation, union representation elections and unfair labor practices, wage and hour compliance/litigation, whistleblower investigations/lawsuits, and workers' compensation.

### Environmental:

The firm handles licensing, permitting and enforcement transactions, siting, permitting, and operation of industrial, manufacturing, service, or research and development facilities, the purchase of and lending for commercial or industrial properties, and environmental insurance coverage litigation.

### Healthcare:

The group represents several hundred physicians and more than twenty hospitals on an on-going basis throughout South Carolina and North Carolina. The firm is also called upon for special projects by many other healthcare clients.

### Intellectual Property:

The firm represents clients with a broad range of intellectual property issues, including internet law, patent, trademark and copyright matters, intellectual property litigation and dispute resolution, licensing, technology transfer, employer/employee rights in intellectual property, and issues important in the buying and selling of businesses such as due diligence and valuation.

### Real Estate:

The group represents buyers, sellers, landlords, tenants, lenders, borrowers, developers, and investors, and serves businesses of all types and size. The firm's lawyers combine an understanding of real estate transactions with years of experience in issues such as project structuring, land assemblage, financing, zoning, permitting and land-use.

### Tax:

The firm represents clients in buying and selling businesses; state and local taxation; corporate distributions and reorganizations; tax aspects of buying, selling and leasing, including tax-free exchange transactions, general and limited partnership taxation, including tax opinions for real estate offerings, pension and profit-sharing plans, stock option and other employee benefit plans, deferred compensation arrangements, income, estate and gift tax planning for individuals, and the taxation of estates and trusts.

### International Work:

The firm represents over 100 Asian, European, and Latin American companies with expansions in the Southeastern US, advising them on economic development incentives, site acquisition and zoning approvals, corporate and tax issues, employment and labor law matters, environmental issues; mergers and acquisitions, terms of sale, international distribution, joint venture, or licensing arrangements, foreign supplier arrangements and enforcing and terminating such arrangements. Various attorneys and staff are fluent in French, German, Italian, Portuguese, Russian and Spanish.

### Clients:

The firm's domestic and international clients include companies in the agriculture, automotive, aviation, chemistry, franchise, biotechnology, pharmaceutical, construction, economic development, energy, health care, hospitality and tourism, manufacturing, real estate, telecommunications and transportation industries. The firm offers significant advantages in terms of outstanding individual lawyers, a depth of talent, and extensive experience in many areas.

## OFFICES

### SOUTH CAROLINA

**COLUMBIA:** 1230 Main Street, Suite 700, SC 29201
Tel: 803 771 8900  Fax: 803 253 8277

**CHARLESTON:** 205 King Street, Suite 400, 29401
Tel: 843 577 9440  Fax: 843 720 1777

**GREENVILLE:** 55 E. Camperdown Way, Suite 400, 29601
Tel: 864 370 2211  Fax: 864 282 1177

**HILTON HEAD ISLAND:** 400 Main Street Office Campus, Suite 100A, 29926
Tel: 843 689 6277  Fax: 843 682 1577

**MYRTLE BEACH:** 1101 Johnson Avenue, Suite 300, 29577
Tel: 843 213 5400  Fax: 843 213 5407

### NORTH CAROLINA

**CHARLOTTE:** 227 West Trade Street, Suite 1550, NC 28202
Tel: 704 339 0304  Fax: 704 338 5377

**GREENSBORO:** 701 Green Valley Road, Suite 100, 27408
Tel: 336 373 1600  Fax: 336 273 5357

**RALEIGH:** 4141 Parklake Avenue, Suite 200, NC 27612
Tel: 919 755 1800  Fax: 919 653 0435

NEXT CHALLENGE. NEXT LEVEL.

# NEXSEN|PRUET

# SOWELL GRAY STEPP & LAFFITTE, LLC

www.sowellgray.com **tel:** 803 929 1400

**Managing Partner:** J Calhoun Watson
Number of partners: 9
Number of other lawyers: 12

**OFFICES**

SOUTH CAROLINA
**COLUMBIA:** 1310 Gadsden St, 29201, PO Box 11449, SC 29211
Tel: 803 929 1400

**Firm Overview:**

Sowell Gray Stepp & Laffitte, LLC is a full service litigation firm representing clients from across the State of South Carolina in all phases of legal disputes. The firm was founded in 1996 by a group of lawyers who worked together for many years at South Carolina's largest law firm. The firm enjoys an excellent reputation in the legal community and beyond as one of the state's premier litigation firms.

**Main Areas of Practice:**

**Administrative & Regulatory:**
The firm represents clients before a wide range of regulatory agencies and administrative courts on a variety of matters ranging from disciplinary proceedings, to permitting issues, to actions opposing rate increases. The firm also serves municipalities and companies seeking to do business with local government.

**Alternative Dispute Resolution:**
Some of the firm's lawyers serve as mediators, bringing their extensive litigation and trial experience to the cases they mediate. Cases mediated include personal injury, workers' compensation, and complex business disputes.

**Appellate Advocacy:**
Sowell Gray's Appellate Practice Group is comprised of lawyers who have served as appellate court law clerks and who have extensive litigation experience. The firm handles appeals in cases originating in the firm and cases tried by other lawyers. The firm has successfully litigated numerous appeals before state and federal courts.

**Commercial Litigation & Business Dispute Resolution:**
Sowell Gray's business litigators handle a wide variety of business issues, focusing both on complex commercial litigation and resolution of commercial disputes. The firm's experience ranges from securities litigation, banking and financial services litigation, class actions, intellectual property, insurance disputes, business torts, real property and title insurance, to all types of commercial disputes and corporate counseling. The firm's lawyers defended one of the longest non-jury trials in South Carolina history.

**Commercial Transportation & Trucking:**
Sowell Gray has extensive experience handling the investigation of trucking and other transportation accidents, and enlists the services of experienced accident-reconstruction experts, engineers, transportation consultant experts and adjusters when necessary. The firm's lawyers serve as Rapid Response

Counsel for several trucking and bus companies, and provide legal advice to companies needing assistance with compliance issues involving federal and state laws and regulations.

**Construction Litigation:**
The firm prosecutes and defends construction claims brought by or against owners, developers, contractors, subcontractors, construction managers, suppliers, manufacturers, design professionals, builders risk insurers, and sureties. The firm has served as counsel in cases involving synthetic stucco systems and roofing systems, and has helped clients in the negotiation and drafting phase of construction projects.

**Healthcare Litigation:**
Sowell Gray has a group of lawyers committed to defending physicians, hospitals, extended care facilities, and all types of health care professionals and institutions in matters involving medical malpractice, nursing home defense, medical devices, pharmaceutical litigation, and partnership and corporate disputes. This practice group handles claims arising from alleged professional negligence and malpractice, disciplinary actions before the South Carolina Medical Board, and disputes regarding hospital credentialing privileges. The firm also handles cases involving serious injury or wrongful death and assists healthcare professionals in resolving disputes before litigation is filed.

**Probate & Estate Litigation:**
Sowell Gray's lawyers handle a wide range of disputes involving probate and estate matters regarding challenges to a will or trust, life insurance disputes, actions to reform trusts, and disputes surrounding the conduct of fiduciaries. The firm has represented various parties in probate and estate litigation, including beneficiaries and potential beneficiaries, personal representatives, trustees, and holders of powers of attorney.

**Products Liability:**
The firm represents clients in cases involving industrial equipment, pharmaceutical and medical devices, household appliances, deer tree stands, automotives,

logging equipment, and chain and skill saws, to name a few. The firm also serves as local counsel for clients who have national or regional counsel.

**Professional Liability & Ethics:**
The firm defends lawyers and law firms confronting legal malpractice claims, and represents lawyers during investigations and subsequent proceedings involving the South Carolina Office of Disciplinary Counsel. The firm also represents directors and officers, accountants, brokers, real estate professionals and engineers in lawsuits alleging malpractice, fraud, negligence, breach of fiduciary duty, breach of contract, and conspiracy.

**Workers' Compensation:**
The firm's workers' compensation team represents employers, insurance carriers, self-insureds, and third-party administrators in all phases of claim defense, from the initial strategy sessions, through discovery, and into the trial and appellate levels. The leader of this practice group is the co-author of The Law of Workers' Compensation Insurance in South Carolina, regarded as the most comprehensive treatise on South Carolina workers' compensation law, and the firm is the sole South Carolina representative of the National Workers' Compensation Defense Network.

**Clients:**
Corporations, individuals, banks, elected officials, state and local government, state agencies, insurance companies, lawyers, law firms, hospitals, physicians, healthcare professionals, employers, officers and directors, accountants, brokers, real estate professionals and engineers.

**SOWELL GRAY STEPP & LAFFITTE, LLC**
Litigation is our Business.

# TURNER PADGET GRAHAM & LANEY PA

www.turnerpadget.com **tel:** 803 254 2200 **fax:** 803 799 3957

**Chief Executive Officer:** Edward W Laney, IV
**Executive Committee:** Michael Roberts, Wayne Byrd, John Wilkerson and Rhonda Amick
Number of shareholders: 57 Number of lawyers: 92
Languages: *English*

## Firm Overview:

Founded in 1929, Turner Padget serves clients throughout South Carolina and has five offices across the state. With over 90 attorneys handling a broad range of business and litigation matters, Turner Padget meets the legal needs of clients ranging from individuals to Fortune 500 corporations with state, national and international issues.

## Main Areas of Practice:

### Business Litigation:

With nearly 75% of the firm's attorneys having litigation experience, Turner Padget's litigation group handles a broad range of matters, from general business litigation to professional liability and insurance coverage.

### Employment:

Turner Padget provides litigation and transactional services to management in all employment and labor related matters. The firm's clients range from Fortune 500 companies to state colleges and universities and smaller, private employers in the credit unions. The attorneys in the group have significant mediation experience, and two attorneys are certified by the South Carolina Supreme Court as specialists in Employment and Labor Law.

### Product Liability:

Turner Padget serves as statewide and regional counsel for product manufacturers, including long-standing representation of a Big 3 auto company. The firm also represents drug and medical device manufacturers in product defect claims. The firm has successfully defended clients in numerous multi-week trials in both state and federal court.

### Commercial Real Estate:

Turner Padget provides clients with a full range of real estate-related legal services, with particular emphasis on commercial real estate development, local counsel/opinion letter services and lender and borrower financing transactions. Recent projects include working with developers to acquire, build or renovate office buildings, retail shopping centers, single tenant properties and mixed-use centers from inception to completion, from securing loans to leasing outparcels.

### Class Actions:

Turner Padget has over 20 years of frontline experience in class action litigation, primarily defending product liability and environmental cases. The firm's attorneys understand every facet of class action litigation, from the critical opening challenges involving jurisdiction and certification to the end game of settlement or trial.

### Intellectual Property:

Turner Padget provides transactional and litigation services related to patents, copyrights and trademarks. The firm's depth, resources, tools and capabilities rival large litigation practices, but Turner Padget provides the personal client responsiveness of an IP boutique. The firm's attorneys have transactional experience in directing complex technical matters, which makes the firm a strong advocate for clients before the United States Patent and Trademark Office, the Trademark Trial and Appeal Board and in federal and state court.

## PRACTICE AREAS

Administrative, Regulatory & Municipal Law
Appellate
Business Entity Planning
Business Litigation
Class Actions
Commercial Real Estate Transactions & Litigation
Community Associations & Private Clubs
Construction Litigation
Dispute Resolution
Economic Development Incentives
Employment Counseling & Litigation
Healthcare Law
Hospitality Law
Insurance Litigation
Intellectual Property & Litigation
Medical Malpractice
Mergers & Acquisitions
Nonprofit Organizations
Probate Administration & Litigation
Product Liability
Professional Liability
Tax Counseling & Litigation
Toxic & Mass Torts
Trucking Litigation
White Collar Crime & Corporate Investigations
Wills, Trusts & Estates
Workers' Compensation

## OFFICES

**SOUTH CAROLINA**

**COLUMBIA:** 1901 Main St., Suite 1700, SC 29201
Tel: 803 254 2200 Fax: 803 799 3957
Email: info@turnerpadget.com

**CHARLESTON:** 40 Calhoun St., Suite 200, SC 29401
Tel: 843 576 2800 Fax: 843 577 3369

**FLORENCE:** 319 South Irby St., SC 29501
Tel: 843 662 9008 Fax: 843 667 0828

**GREENVILLE:** 200 E. Broad St., Suite 250, SC 29601
Tel: 864 552 4600 Fax: 864 552 4620

**MYRTLE BEACH:** 2411 N, Oak St., Suite 301, SC 29577
Tel: 843 213 5500 Fax: 843 213 5555

**TURNER PADGET**
TURNER PADGET GRAHAM & LANEY P.A.
BUSINESS·LITIGATION·SOLUTIONS

# WYCHE, P.A.

www.wyche.com **tel:** 864 242 8200 **fax:** 864 235 8900

**Firm Management:** Executive Committee
Number of members: 23   Total number of lawyers: 36

## Firm Overview:

Wyche has practiced law and served the community for more than 90 years. In that time, Wyche has participated in landmark litigation, served as counsel on cutting-edge transactions, and provided community leadership that has helped shape and drive the region's growth and success.

Wyche lawyers are handpicked, one by one, to join the firm because each has the skills and accomplishments to be part of the firm's effort to provide unmatched service to its clients. Wyche attorneys have law degrees from Harvard, Yale, the University of Virginia, Columbia, and other leading law schools, where many served on law review. Collectively, the firm's attorneys have earned a bounty of academic honors. Many have held clerkships in the United States District Courts, Courts of Appeals, and the United States Supreme Court. The firm recognizes, however, that such distinctions alone are not enough to be successful in the practice of law: Wyche attorneys have the real-world experience and wisdom that can only be acquired through years of practice.

Wyche is the South Carolina member of Lex Mundi, the world's leading association of independent law firms.

## Main Areas of Practice:

### Antitrust & Trade Regulation:

Wyche provides both compliance counseling and representation in litigation, and its practice has included both civil and criminal antitrust matters. Wyche has given compliance advice on antitrust and distribution matters in a wide variety of industries, including paving, television broadcasting, newspapers, textiles, chemicals, groceries, soft drink bottling, power tools, apparel, home furnishings, hospitals, physician services, construction, recycling, and waste disposal.

### Commercial Real Estate:

The Real Estate Practice includes commercial development, asset-based lending purchases and sales, construction contracts, leases, and fee-in-lieu-of-taxes transactions. Through its subsidiary, Camperdown Title Services, Inc., the firm provides title insurance services and acts as agent for four major title insurance companies.

### Corporate/M&A:

Wyche regularly assists regional, national, and multinational companies in investigating, structuring, and consummating sophisticated transactions. Wyche's Corporate/M&A Practice includes leveraged buyouts, recapitalizations, public and private offerings, securities compliance, debt refinancings, and mergers and acquisitions. These transactions range from relatively small transactions to billion dollar deals.

### Employment:

Wyche attorneys handle employment litigation in federal and state courts. They have successfully argued a complex ERISA case on behalf of a client before the United States Supreme Court; persuaded the South Carolina Court of Appeals to affirm summary judgment for a client in an employee handbook case; and obtained favorable interpretations of the South Carolina Payment of Wages Act in the South Carolina Supreme Court.

Members of the practice also provide general counseling for human resources personnel and management.

### Entrepreneur Services:

Wyche has a rich history of serving as legal counsel to start-ups, many of which are now successful, established businesses. The firm continues to grow its practice to serve the expanded needs of today's entrepreneurs, who are building some of the most dynamic and successful companies in the Southeast. Wyche works with clients from initial formation, through the various phases of growth, to maturity and success.

### Environmental & Sustainability:

Environmental law is a rapidly changing field in which risks are often difficult to assess. Wyche's Environmental Practice assists clients in navigating the complex maze of environmental laws and offers solutions to improve business practices.

### Governmental Representation:

Wyche has a long history of providing legal services to South Carolina's counties, cities, and state government and also to private clients with governmental needs. As a full-service firm with a deep bench, Wyche can quickly and deftly handle a wide range of issues from constitutional challenges and politically sensitive matters to everyday matters, such as drafting and reviewing contracts, and providing proactive advice and counseling.

### Intellectual Property:

The Intellectual Property Practice involves both counseling with respect to the protection of intellectual property, as well as representing clients in litigation concerning infringement or misappropriation of intellectual property. Wyche attorneys have litigated virtually every aspect of intellectual property, including copyrights, trademarks, patents, trade secrets, confidentiality agreements, electronic commerce and common law proprietary information.

## PRACTICE AREAS

Antitrust & Trade Regulation
Commercial Real Estate
Corporate/M&A
Employment
Entrepreneur Services
Environmental & Sustainability
Intellectual Property
Litigation

## OFFICES

SOUTH CAROLINA

**GREENVILLE:** 44 East Camperdown Way, SC 29601
Tel: 864 242 8200   Fax: 864 235 8900

**COLUMBIA:** 801 Gervais Street, Suite B, SC 29201
Tel: 803 254 6542   Fax: 803 254 6544

### Litigation:

Wyche litigators are the lawyers of choice for big case litigation and matters presenting novel questions of law. The firm engages in complex civil litigation in state and federal courts, including substantial class action work. It regularly handles matters in areas such as antitrust, First Amendment, securities, insurance practices, and patent and trade secrets. In addition to the areas just mentioned, the firm advises and litigates on behalf of clients in numerous areas, including bankruptcy, communications, construction, employment, employee benefits, environmental, financial institutions, health care, municipal bonds, probate, commercial real estate, taxation, intellectual property and trade regulation.

### Clients:

The firm's clients are diverse. They include major pharmaceutical companies, multinational corporations, entrepreneurs and start-ups, electronics manufacturers, hospitals, real estate developers, engineering and architectural firms, newspapers and television stations, colleges and universities, and even other lawyers and law firms. Specific clients include Delta Apparel, JPS Industries, LG Display, Co. LTD, Louis Berger Services, Metso Paper USA, Michelin, N.A., Milliken & Company, Span-America Medical Systems, TD Bank, N.A., The Bank of New York Mellon, and TIC Properties Management, LLC.

W Y C H E
Attorneys at Law

## How lawyers are ranked

Every year we carry out thousands of in-depth interviews with clients in order to assess the reputations and expertise of business lawyers worldwide. The qualities we look for (and which determine rankings) include technical legal ability, professional conduct, client service, commercial awareness/astuteness, diligence, commitment, and other qualities most valued by the client. For details of our research team, see p.5.

# CORPORATE/COMMERCIAL

Commentary about individuals can be found under their firm's paragraph. If the firm has no paragraph (is not ranked) look at Other Notable Practitioners.

### Corporate/Commercial Leading Firms

**Band 1**
Davenport, Evans, Hurwitz & Smith LLP
Woods, Fuller, Shultz & Smith PC

**Band 2**
Bangs, McCullen, Butler, Foye & Simmons, LLP
Boyce, Greenfield, Pashby & Welk LLP
Cadwell Sanford Deibert & Garry LLP
Cutler & Donahoe LLP
Gunderson, Palmer, Nelson & Ashmore, LLP
Murphy, Goldammer & Prendergast LLP

## Band 1

### Davenport, Evans, Hurwitz & Smith LLP

**THE FIRM** This firm houses lawyers with expertise in all areas of corporate law and works with a range of partnerships, limited companies and nonprofit organizations. The firm maintains its strength in handling matters related to the issue of prepaid cards and the restructuring of credit card products. Its recent work includes acting for University National Bank on matters pertaining to prepaid cards and financial product compliance issues.

**Sources say:** "Davenport is very business oriented. Their application of law in a business context and provision of advice to a client is remarkable."

**KEY INDIVIDUALS Jonathan Brown** specializes in sales transactions and business planning. He is commended by sources for his negotiation skills, and his practice also includes a focus on real estate matters. **Keith Gauer** is highly regarded for his dedicated representation of financial institutions in a range of corporate and bankruptcy matters. He advises clients on matters related to payment systems and financial product arrangements. One source praises him as someone who "gives highly practical suggestions." **Charles Gullickson**'s practice is concentrated on insurance regulatory and insolvency matters. His recent work includes serving as general counsel and executive

### Senior Statesmen

**Senior Statesmen: distinguished older practitioners**

| | |
|---|---|
| Cutler Richard A | Cutler & Donahoe LLP |

### Leading Individuals

**Band 1**

| | |
|---|---|
| Brown Jonathan | Davenport, Evans, Hurwitz & Smith LLP |
| Damgaard Roger | Woods, Fuller, Shultz & Smith PC |
| Goetzinger Patrick | Gunderson, Palmer, Nelson & Ashmore |
| Goldammer Vance RC | Murphy, Goldammer & Prendergast LLP |
| Gullickson Charles D | Davenport, Evans, Hurwitz & Smith LLP |
| Hajek Douglas J | Davenport, Evans, Hurwitz & Smith LLP |
| Hayes Robert E | Davenport, Evans, Hurwitz & Smith LLP |
| Wiederrich James | Woods, Fuller, Shultz & Smith PC |

**Band 2**

| | |
|---|---|
| Gauer Keith A | Davenport, Evans, Hurwitz & Smith LLP |
| Greenfield Gregg S | Boyce, Greenfield, Pashby & Welk LLP |
| Grossenburg Bradley C | Woods, Fuller, Shultz & Smith PC |
| Magnuson Lee A | Lindquist & Vennum LLP (ONP)[†] |
| Perrenoud Scott | Cadwell Sanford Deibert & Garry LLP |
| Prendergast Terry N | Murphy, Goldammer & Prendergast LLP |
| Raforth John H | Bangs, McCullen, Butler, Foye & Simmons |
| Sanford Steven | Cadwell Sanford Deibert & Garry LLP |

**Band 3**

| | |
|---|---|
| Donohue P Daniel | Davenport, Evans, Hurwitz & Smith LLP |
| Hieb Dixie | Davenport, Evans, Hurwitz & Smith LLP |
| Lust David E | Gunderson, Palmer, Nelson & Ashmore |
| Palmer Crisman | Gunderson, Palmer, Nelson & Ashmore |
| Rotert Sherri | Novellus Law, PC (ONP)[†] |
| Sarbacker Steve | Cutler & Donahoe LLP |
| Walz Monte | Davenport, Evans, Hurwitz & Smith LLP |

**Up-and-coming individuals**

| | |
|---|---|
| Taylor Ryan J | Cutler & Donahoe LLP |

director for the South Dakota Life & Health Insurance Guaranty Association. **Douglas Hajek** focuses on banking and corporate law, and also offers expertise in renewable energy ventures and public finance. His recent work includes representing Bel Brands USA in matters related to

### Corporate/Commercial: Bankruptcy/Restructuring Leading Individuals

**Band 1**

| | |
|---|---|
| Damgaard Roger | Woods, Fuller, Shultz & Smith PC |
| Gauer Keith A | Davenport, Evans, Hurwitz & Smith LLP |
| Hayes Robert E | Davenport, Evans, Hurwitz & Smith LLP |
| Perrenoud Scott | Cadwell Sanford Deibert & Garry LLP |

[†]ONP = Other Notable Practitioner
Alphabetical order within each band. Band 1 is the highest.

its expansion. **Robert Hayes**'s extensive experience in the field of creditors' rights means he remains a popular choice with clients in this area. He is also a highly experienced bankruptcy attorney. **Monte Walz** advises his banking clients on a range of regulatory issues and credit-based financial products. His broad-based practice also includes an emphasis on healthcare law and eminent domain-related matters. Sources enthuse that **Daniel Donohue** is "an experienced practitioner and brings his years of experience to the discussion. He is very seasoned and insightful." He focuses his practice on trust formation and administration. **Dixie Hieb** is held in high esteem by clients for her expertise in trust planning, formation and management. She is characterized as "very knowledgeable" and as someone who "understands time pressure and constraints."

### Woods, Fuller, Shultz & Smith PC

**THE FIRM** This large corporate practice is highly regarded in the area for its wide-ranging commercial experience and sophistication in M&A matters. The firm also boasts expertise in banking law and represents clients in regulatory compliance, bankruptcy and workout matters.

**Sources say:** "They probably have the largest and best of the business practice groups in the state, and their reputation is excellent."

**KEY INDIVIDUALS Roger Damgaard** focuses his respected practice on commercial and bankruptcy issues. Sources say he is "very knowledgeable and practical, and gets *to the problem quickly."* **James Wiederrich** is particularly noted for his expertise in the agricultural arena. He advises clients on a range of structural, taxation and general corporate matters. Sources recommend **Bradley Grossenburg** for his firm command of taxation issues. He also has vast experience in business law and trust matters.

## Band 2

### Bangs, McCullen, Butler, Foye & Simmons, LLP

**THE FIRM** This broad-based corporate and commercial practice advises its business clients on an array of matters, including compliance issues, M&A and tax liability. The team's wide range of experience sees it represent clients from several different industry sectors.

**KEY INDIVIDUALS John Raforth** focuses his practice on business strategy, taxation issues and trust law. He is highly thought of by market commentators for the breadth of his expertise.

### Boyce, Greenfield, Pashby & Welk LLP

**THE FIRM** This highly respected Sioux Falls firm has a wide-ranging corporate and commercial practice which spans banking and financial matters, transactions and estate planning. The team is recognized by peers as a top choice for referral work.

**KEY INDIVIDUALS Gregg Greenfield** is a highly regarded expert in business law, and is particularly experienced in matters related to real estate and environmental law.

### Cadwell Sanford Deibert & Garry LLP

**THE FIRM** This firm is based in Sioux Falls and handles the full range of corporate and commercial issues faced by clients. Its areas of focus include banking, creditors' rights

and real estate, and it is adept at handling matters with a nationwide scope.

**KEY INDIVIDUALS Scott Perrenoud** is highly regarded by sources for his experience in corporate and commercial matters. He is also noted for his bankruptcy expertise, and recently extended his focus to include business and estate planning. **Steven Sanford** maintains an impressive breadth of expertise across the commercial arena, advising on a variety of business-related legal issues. He is characterized by market commentators as being *"very experienced and much sought after."*

### Cutler & Donahoe LLP

**THE FIRM** This firm enjoys a long-standing reputation and notable client loyalty from its base in Sioux Falls. Its broad-based practice advises a range of clients on business strategy and transactional matters. It has also represented clients in investment property matters.

**Sources say:** *"I have been very impressed with the firm. Responsiveness is high and they take the time to get to know us personally."*

**KEY INDIVIDUALS Steve Sarbacker** is highly regarded for his M&A expertise. Sources state that *"he is good at establishing his position and representing the client very, very strongly."* **Richard Cutler**'s esteemed practice focuses on advising on corporate strategy and M&A matters. Sources exclaim that he *"is an outstanding lawyer"* and celebrate his *"experience as a businessperson, which gives him a great perspective."* **Ryan Taylor** is recognized for his ability to handle a wide range of corporate and commercial matters. He is also particularly noted for his expertise in the telecoms industry.

### Gunderson, Palmer, Nelson & Ashmore, LLP

**THE FIRM** This Rapid City-based corporate and commercial practice offers knowledge and experience across a wide

range of fields, including business strategy planning, risk assessments, contracts and M&A work.

**KEY INDIVIDUALS Patrick Goetzinger** centers his business and real estate practice on representing smaller businesses and private individuals. He leads the business and estate planning group. **David Lust** advises a range of companies and individuals on taxation, business planning and M&A-related matters. His practice also includes a focus on business litigation. **Crisman Palmer** is experienced across a range of different practice areas, including product liability, insurance and banking-related issues. He is also noted for his expertise in handling contentious matters.

### Murphy, Goldammer & Prendergast LLP

**THE FIRM** This popular business team is recommended for its skill in advising clients on a range of corporate, banking and taxation matters. The firm is also recommended for its M&A expertise, and has recently developed a greater emphasis on transactions within the energy sector.

**KEY INDIVIDUALS Vance Goldammer** is recognized as a leading corporate and commercial attorney whose depth of knowledge in this area is particularly highlighted. He is also noted for his focus on real estate law. **Terry Prendergast** is experienced across a broad range of practice areas in the corporate space. His areas of focus include estate planning and wealth management.

## Other Notable Practitioners

**Lee Magnuson** recently joined Lindquist & Vennum LLP from Lynn, Jackson, Shultz & Lebrun, to continue his highly regarded M&A practice. He is praised for his broad-based corporate expertise. **Sherri Rotert** of Novellus Law, PC brings her extensive experience to bear on a range of corporate and M&A transactions. Her clients include local venture capitalists, universities and private companies.

# LABOR & EMPLOYMENT

Commentary about individuals can be found under their firm's paragraph. If the firm has no paragraph (is not ranked) look at Other Notable Practitioners.

| Labor & Employment Leading Firms | |
|---|---|
| **Band 1** | |
| Boyce, Greenfield, Pashby & Welk LLP | |
| Davenport, Evans, Hurwitz & Smith LLP | |
| Woods, Fuller, Shultz & Smith PC | |
| **Band 2** | |
| Gunderson, Palmer, Nelson & Ashmore, LLP | |
| Lynn, Jackson, Shultz & Lebrun PC | |

| Leading Individuals | |
|---|---|
| **Band 1** | |
| Bender Jean | Davenport, Evans, Hurwitz & Smith LLP |
| Casey Richard D | Lynn, Jackson, Shultz & Lebrun PC |
| Marso Lisa Hansen | Boyce, Greenfield, Pashby & Welk LLP |
| **Band 2** | |
| Anderson Robert | May, Adam, Gerdes & Thompson (ONP)[†] |
| Hanson Sandra | Davenport, Evans, Hurwitz & Smith LLP |
| Knudsen Donald P | Gunderson, Palmer, Nelson & Ashmore |
| Kroon David | Woods, Fuller, Shultz & Smith PC |
| Sogn Jon C | Lynn, Jackson, Shultz & Lebrun PC |
| Springer Heather R | Boyce, Greenfield, Pashby & Welk LLP |
| Thimsen Gary | Woods, Fuller, Shultz & Smith PC |

| Labor & Employment: Workers' Compensation Leading Individuals | |
|---|---|
| **Band 1** | |
| Ashmore Daniel E | Gunderson, Palmer, Nelson & Ashmore |
| Haraldson Comet | Woods, Fuller, Shultz & Smith PC |
| McKnight Michael S | Boyce, Greenfield, Pashby & Welk LLP |
| Orr Rick W | Davenport, Evans, Hurwitz & Smith LLP |
| Shultz Jeff | Woods, Fuller, Shultz & Smith PC |
| **Band 2** | |
| Anderson Robert | May, Adam, Gerdes & Thompson, L.L.P. |
| Holm Kristi Geisler | Davenport, Evans, Hurwitz & Smith LLP |
| Larson Charles | Boyce, Greenfield, Pashby & Welk LLP |

[†]ONP = Other Notable Practitioner
*Alphabetical order within each band. Band 1 is the highest.*

## Band 1

### Boyce, Greenfield, Pashby & Welk LLP

**THE FIRM** This firm's ability to offer legal expertise in all areas of employment law makes it a market leader in South Dakota. The team regularly represents employers and their insurers, and also acts in workers' compensation matters. Its client base continues to grow, and is representative of the breadth of its practice.

**Sources say:** *"They see the big picture, understand our perspective and get the best results."*

**KEY INDIVIDUALS Lisa Marso** is highly regarded as a leading practitioner in the field who offers extensive experience in representing a wide range of employers. Her practice includes acting for clients in discrimination claims and matters related to workers' compensation. Sources praise her dedicated approach, stating that *"she works hard for her clients."* Clients praise **Michael McKnight** for his significant employment law expertise and excellent customer service. He concentrates primarily on workers' compensation cases and is also recommended for his experience in acting as a mediator. **Charles Larson** is praised by sources for his *"willingness to take on the fight and go with it."* His broad practice spans all areas of employment law and workers' compensation. **Heather Springer** is recognized for her experience in representing employers across a broad spread of regulatory and advisory matters. She is also particularly noted for her expertise in the healthcare arena and its intersection with employment law.

### Davenport, Evans, Hurwitz & Smith LLP

**THE FIRM** This highly acclaimed Sioux Falls-based firm advises on an array of employment law matters, including contract drafting, employment handbook reviews and acting in employment law litigation. It continues working with Sanford Health and The First National Bank in Sioux Falls and also acts on behalf of Midwest Railcar Repair and First PREMIER Bank.

**Sources say:** *"I've been impressed with this firm – they are responsive, knowledgeable, down-to-earth and easy to work with."*

**KEY INDIVIDUALS** The *"fantastic"* **Jean Bender** provides general employment counseling for her broad base of clientele. Her expertise also extends to matters arising from employee benefits plans. One source commented: *"I have taken sensitive matters to her and she handles them respectfully and professionally."* **Rick Orr** is known for his expertise in litigation on workers' compensation defense and on a range of other civil disputes. Sources say he is a *"hard-working, bright guy who always impresses"* and note that he *"brings a wealth of experience to the system."* **Kristi Geisler Holm**'s impressive client list includes Sanford Health and ESIS. She focuses her practice on workers' compensation claims. **Sandra Hanson** is noted for her expertise in representing employers in a range of discrimination claims and proceedings relating to workers' compensation. Her recent work includes the successful representation of Sanford against sex discrimination claims brought in a federal court.

### Woods, Fuller, Shultz & Smith PC

**THE FIRM** This highly acclaimed Sioux Falls employment group deals regularly with a wide array of matters for a large client base. It represents employers in employment discrimination litigation, ERISA compliance and disputes, and matters relating to employee benefits. Its expertise also includes advising clients on more general employment law matters.

**KEY INDIVIDUALS Comet Haraldson** brings his comprehensive experience to bear on workers' compensation matters, and is also highly regarded for his wider litigation practice. **Jeff Shultz** is a renowned litigator whose expertise in matters relating to ERISA and workers' compensation is particularly impressive. He works with a range of employers and insurers across the state. **David Kroon** is known for his effective counseling in all areas of employment law for his clients, and also focuses on healthcare-related matters. **Gary Thimsen** garners praise for his experience in representing employers in a range of employment law cases. His practice also includes a broader focus on matters such as civil rights defense and aviation law.

## Band 2

### Gunderson, Palmer, Nelson & Ashmore, LLP

**THE FIRM** This strong employment group encompasses a broad spread of matters in its respected practice. Its experience includes acting on behalf of employees and employers in disputes arising from immigration status, discrimination and harassment, among other focus areas.

**KEY INDIVIDUALS Daniel Ashmore** is highly regarded for his experience in workers' compensation matters. He also offers expertise in insurance defense cases and construction law, and is praised for his *"knowledgeable"* and client-friendly approach. **Donald Knudsen** is particularly noted for his litigation expertise, and maintains a strong focus on employment law. His practice also extends to issues arising from discrimination and sexual harassment claims.

### Lynn, Jackson, Shultz & Lebrun PC

**THE FIRM** This respected employment practice is run from offices in both Rapid City and Sioux Falls. The team is known for its representation of plaintiffs in litigation cases as well as its expertise in a variety of employment issues, including discrimination and harassment matters.

**KEY INDIVIDUALS Richard Casey** is *"enjoyable to work with"* and is a *"good advocate on behalf of employees."* His practice centers on employment discrimination matters. **Jon Sogn** is a recommended employment practitioner whose expertise also extends to commercial litigation. One source states: *"Clients respect him and appreciate his thoughtful advice."*

### Other Notable Practitioners

**Robert Anderson** of May, Adam, Gerdes & Thompson, L.L.P. specializes in advising on federal employment matters and has particular experience of working with government entities. Sources comment that he *"brings to the table a lot of good, common-sense advice and input."*

# LITIGATION

Commentary about individuals can be found under their firm's paragraph. If the firm has no paragraph (is not ranked) look at Other Notable Practitioners.

## Litigation: General Commercial
### Leading Firms

**Band 1**
Boyce, Greenfield, Pashby & Welk LLP
Cadwell Sanford Deibert & Garry LLP
Davenport, Evans, Hurwitz & Smith LLP
Johnson, Heidepriem & Abdallah, LLP

**Band 2**
Bangs, McCullen, Butler, Foye & Simmons, LLP
Gunderson, Palmer, Nelson & Ashmore, LLP
Lynn, Jackson, Shultz & Lebrun PC
May, Adam, Gerdes & Thompson, L.L.P.
Murphy, Goldammer & Prendergast LLP
Woods, Fuller, Shultz & Smith PC

### Leading Individuals

**Band 1**

| | |
|---|---|
| Anderson Robert | May, Adam, Gerdes & Thompson, L.L.P. |
| Evans Edwin E | Davenport, Evans, Hurwitz & Smith LLP |
| Fritz Thomas G | Lynn, Jackson, Shultz & Lebrun PC |
| Fuller William P | Fuller & Sabers, LLP (ONP)[†] |
| Garry William C | Cadwell Sanford Deibert & Garry LLP |
| Johnson Steven | Johnson, Heidepriem & Abdallah, LLP |
| Landon Stephen | Cadwell Sanford Deibert & Garry LLP |
| Luce Michael L | Murphy, Goldammer & Prendergast LLP |
| Moore James E | Woods, Fuller, Shultz & Smith PC |
| Palmer Crisman | Gunderson, Palmer, Nelson & Ashmore |
| Pashby Gary | Boyce, Greenfield, Pashby & Welk LLP |
| Sanford Steven | Cadwell Sanford Deibert & Garry LLP |
| Schaffer Michael | Schaffer Law Office Prof LLC (ONP)[†] |
| Sudbeck Roger | Boyce, Greenfield, Pashby & Welk LLP |
| Thimsen Gary | Woods, Fuller, Shultz & Smith PC |
| Turbak Nancy J | Turbak Law Offices (ONP)[†] |
| Welk Thomas | Boyce, Greenfield, Pashby & Welk LLP |

**Band 2**

| | |
|---|---|
| Ashmore Daniel E | Gunderson, Palmer, Nelson & Ashmore |
| Carpenter Edward | Costello Porter Hill Heisterkamp (ONP)[†] |
| Deibert Doug | Cadwell Sanford Deibert & Garry LLP |
| Hickey Michael | Bangs, McCullen, Butler, Foye & Simmons |
| Hieb Jack H | Richardson, Wyly, Wise, Sauck (ONP)[†] |
| Schulte Eric | Davenport, Evans, Hurwitz & Smith LLP |
| Sogn Jon C | Lynn, Jackson, Shultz & Lebrun PC |
| Taylor William | Woods, Fuller, Shultz & Smith PC |

**Band 3**

| | |
|---|---|
| Abdallah Scott | Johnson, Heidepriem & Abdallah, LLP |
| Goodsell Verne | Goodsell Quinn (ONP)[†] |
| Magnuson Lee A | Lindquist & Vennum LLP (ONP)[†] |
| Parsons Ron | Johnson, Heidepriem & Abdallah, LLP |
| Peterson R Alan | Lynn, Jackson, Shultz & Lebrun PC |

**Up-and-coming individuals**

| | |
|---|---|
| Bollweg Pamela | Johnson, Heidepriem & Abdallah, LLP |

*Alphabetical order within each band. Band 1 is the highest.*

## Litigation: Medical Malpractice Defense
### Leading Individuals

**Star individuals**

| | |
|---|---|
| Evans Edwin E | Davenport, Evans, Hurwitz & Smith LLP |

**Band 1**

| | |
|---|---|
| Braun Lonnie R | Thomas Braun Bernard & Burke (ONP)[†] |
| Duffy Daniel F | Bangs, McCullen, Butler, Foye & Simmons |
| Haigh Mark W | Davenport, Evans, Hurwitz & Smith LLP |
| Rasmussen Reed | Siegel, Barnett & Schutz LLP (ONP)[†] |
| Sudbeck Roger | Boyce, Greenfield, Pashby & Welk LLP |

**Band 2**

| | |
|---|---|
| Hinton Melissa | Davenport, Evans, Hurwitz & Smith LLP |
| Hurd Jeffrey G | Bangs, McCullen, Butler, Foye & Simmons |

[†]ONP = Other Notable Practitioner
*Alphabetical order within each band. Band 1 is the highest.*

## Band 1

### Boyce, Greenfield, Pashby & Welk LLP

**THE FIRM** This market-leading Sioux Falls firm boasts a large, highly skilled team specializing in litigation. The group's recent work includes defending a large class action dealing with issues in gasoline regulation. It also has experience in handling litigation involving medical malpractice claims and actions arising from the construction industry. **Sources say:** "*The practice has some incredible lawyers in this area.*"

**KEY INDIVIDUALS** Sources commend **Roger Sudbeck's** provision of "*an excellent service*" and consider him a leading litigator. He maintains a wide practice, handling general commercial, medical malpractice and construction litigation disputes. **Gary Pashby** offers a specialist focus on construction litigation, although his broad-based practice incorporates all aspects of general commercial litigation, mediation and arbitration. **Thomas Welk** focuses on a wide range of litigation matters and is particularly praised for his analytical approach to disputes. His recent work includes handling legal malpractice cases, divorce proceedings involving high net worth individuals and administrative law matters.

### Cadwell Sanford Deibert & Garry LLP

**THE FIRM** This highly regarded Sioux Falls litigation practice is renowned for its skill in undertaking commercial litigation on behalf of its business and insurance clients. The firm also specializes in personal injury litigation claims.

**KEY INDIVIDUALS** Sources praise **William Garry** as "*extremely effective and someone who doesn't leave a stone unturned.*" He centers his practice around a range of litigation, including insurance defense, construction disputes and general commercial matters. **Stephen Landon** represents clients in a full range of commercial litigation disputes. His practice includes handling matters involving IP

and product liability disputes, and his clients range from small, local businesses to national corporations. **Steven Sanford** is an esteemed practitioner whose litigation experience extends to an array of commercial matters, encompassing insurance, construction and healthcare cases among others. **Doug Deibert** acts for clients on a full range of commercial litigation matters. His practice also includes a focus on appellate work and insurance defense.

### Davenport, Evans, Hurwitz & Smith LLP

**THE FIRM** This large litigation practice offers its clients in-depth knowledge across the board in civil litigation issues. The team is renowned for its success at both state and federal level, and in trial and appellate work. The firm's impressive client list includes Avera Heart Hospital, Daktronics and Brown Clinic.

**KEY INDIVIDUALS** **Edwin Evans** is highly respected for his vast knowledge and experience in medical malpractice litigation. One source commented that "*he is very, very good at thinking through strategies and is a very solid trial attorney.*" His expertise also includes a focus on wider civil litigation. **Melissa Hinton** is also recognized for her successes in medical malpractice defense work and sources praise her assured demeanor and "*strong communication skills*" at trial. **Mark Haigh** is particularly praised by sources for his expertise as a trial attorney. He focuses on medical malpractice litigation and has significant experience in dealing with class action cases in this field. Sources say **Eric Schulte** "*gets great results*" in his highly regarded civil litigation practice. His areas of specialty include personal injury and property damage. His recent work includes successfully defending Blue Cloud Abbey in a Supreme Court case.

### Johnson, Heidepriem & Abdallah, LLP

**THE FIRM** This highly respected firm maintains its dedicated focus on litigation and brings a wealth of experience to the table. The group is able to act on both sides of a dispute, and has carved a particular niche in the area of sports law through its long-term relationship with a number of professional athletes and local sports teams. Other clients include Charles Rose Architects and American Family Insurance Group.

**KEY INDIVIDUALS** One source describes **Steven Johnson** as "*one of the best litigation lawyers in the state,*" due to his good preparation and thoroughness. He recently represented numerous Sioux Falls property owners in a certified class action against the city, a $3 million matter. **Scott Abdallah** is recognized for his broad civil litigation practice. His recent work includes bringing claims of over $1 million against insurers on behalf of an individual client. **Ron Parsons** leads the firm's appellate practice and he has experience in dealing with a wide range of civil and criminal cases. His practice also extends to representing clients before the appellate stage. **Pamela Bollweg** recently represented the plaintiffs in an action relating to the use of tobacco products in state institutions during religious ceremonies. Her experience extends to a wide range of criminal and civil litigation matters.

## Band 2

### Bangs, McCullen, Butler, Foye & Simmons, LLP

**THE FIRM** This firm has offices in both Rapid City and Sioux Falls, and offers clients a full range of commercial litigation services. Its respected practice also has a focus on healthcare, insurance and product liability disputes, among a range of other practice areas.

**KEY INDIVIDUALS Daniel Duffy** remains highly regarded for his strength in hospital and medical malpractice defense. Clients are impressed by his holistic approach to problem-solving. **Michael Hickey** maintains an impressively extensive litigation practice. He handles a broad range of matters involving natural resources and water law, and administrative and employment law. **Jeffrey Hurd**'s clients range from small startup companies to large regional businesses. He handles a range of commercial litigation matters and is an experienced trial lawyer.

### Gunderson, Palmer, Nelson & Ashmore, LLP

**THE FIRM** This Rapid City team maintains a strong reputation as a litigation specialist in a broad spread of areas, including insurance defense and commercial liability. It also has a wealth of experience in workers' compensation matters.

**KEY INDIVIDUALS Crisman Palmer** continues to impress as a highly experienced litigator. One source described him as *"one of the top defense litigators in the state. He's polished, cordial and extremely effective."* **Daniel Ashmore** is recognized for his broad experience in litigating cases across a wide range of practice areas. His focus includes disputes related to insurance defense, workers' compensation and construction law.

### Lynn, Jackson, Shultz & Lebrun PC

**THE FIRM** This reputable firm works out of Sioux Falls and Rapid City and is a notable force in the litigation field. Its practice includes insurance defense, workers' compensation and professional liability matters, and it is also adept at handling a broad spread of commercial disputes.

**KEY INDIVIDUALS Thomas Fritz** shines in a variety of civil litigation cases. He is also well known for his success in personal injury litigation and product liability matters. **Jon Sogn** handles a variety of matters for clients and is noted for his experience as a litigator. His practice covers a broad spread of commercial, labor and personal injury cases. **Alan Peterson** is based in the Sioux Falls office and is an experienced litigator whose civil practice focuses on a range of different matters. He offers expertise in areas such as professional liability and workers' compensation.

### May, Adam, Gerdes & Thompson, L.L.P.

**THE FIRM** The firm is highlighted for its extensive litigation practice, which includes expertise at the trial and appellate levels. Its experience in representing a broad spread of agricultural clients is particularly noted, as is its strength in regulatory and administrative government law matters.

**KEY INDIVIDUALS Robert Anderson** remains one of the eminent litigation lawyers in the state, with a wealth of experience in matters involving fire damage, feed storage systems and product liability. Sources confirm that he is *"a very solid litigation lawyer."*

### Murphy, Goldammer & Prendergast LLP

**THE FIRM** This valued practice provides clients with the entire range of litigation services, including appellate work. The team boasts significant experience in both state and federal litigation cases.

**KEY INDIVIDUALS Michael Luce** is held in high regard for his mediation and litigation practice. His notable experience sees him handle a broad spread of cases that draw on his expertise in areas as diverse as commercial litigation and civil rights disputes.

### Woods, Fuller, Shultz & Smith PC

**THE FIRM** This firm is noted for its considerable depth of litigation expertise, and represents clients across a range of disputes. It is able to offer experience at the appellate and trial level, and houses attorneys licensed to practice in several different states. It has a strong focus on defense work within a range of areas, and works with clients representative of multiple sectors.

**KEY INDIVIDUALS James Moore**'s skill in civil rights and governmental liability matters makes him a leader in this field. He also has a wealth of experience in appellate cases. **Gary Thimsen** covers a variety of practice areas in

his leading litigation practice, including disputes involving employment, civil rights and aviation law. He is also noted for his expertise as a trial lawyer. **William Taylor** is well respected by sources for his comprehensive litigation experience. His practice focuses on a range of matters, including those involving environmental, real estate and construction law.

## Other Notable Practitioners

**Lonnie Braun** of Thomas Braun Bernard & Burke, LLP is highly praised for his *"wonderful experience"* as a trial lawyer and ability to build strong working relationships with clients. His practice includes a wide range of matters, and he is particularly noted for his medical malpractice defense work. Esteemed defense lawyer **William Fuller** of Fuller & Sabers, LLP is experienced at handling a wide range of cases at federal and state level. He is licensed to practice in Minnesota and South Dakota. **Michael Schaffer** of Schaffer Law Office Prof LLC is applauded for his expertise in trying a wide range of cases. He is highly adept at handling work on behalf of plaintiffs and defendants. Alongside general commercial disputes, **Edward Carpenter** of Costello Porter Hill Heisterkamp Bushnell & Carpenter LLP also tries a range of other cases, including construction and professional negligence disputes. **Jack Hieb** of Richardson, Wyly, Wise, Sauck & Hieb, LLP is noted for his expertise in business and insurance defense litigation. He is also adept at handling cases involving construction and water law, among other matters. **Lee Magnuson** recently moved to Lindquist & Vennum PLLP, where he continues his recognized litigation practice from the Sioux Falls office. He is also an experienced transactional lawyer. **Verne Goodsell** of Goodsell Quinn maintains a notable litigation practice, specializing in medical malpractice and bad faith insurance claims. His experience also extends to matters involving business planning and personal injury. **Reed Rasmussen** of Siegel, Barnett & Schutz LLP is commended as being *"well respected and highly experienced"* by sources. He deals in a full range of litigation areas and is noted here for his medical malpractice expertise. **Nancy Turbak** of Turbak Law Offices offers clients extensive experience across a wide range of litigation matters from her offices in Watertown. She is particularly noted for her work representing individuals in cases involving insurance companies.

# REAL ESTATE

Commentary about individuals can be found under their firm's paragraph. If the firm has no paragraph (is not ranked) look at Other Notable Practitioners.

## Real Estate
### Leading Firms

**Band 1**

Bangs, McCullen, Butler, Foye & Simmons, LLP

Davenport, Evans, Hurwitz & Smith LLP

Woods, Fuller, Shultz & Smith PC

**Band 2**

Boyce, Greenfield, Pashby & Welk LLP

Cutler & Donahoe LLP

**Band 3**

DeMersseman Jensen Tellinghuisen & Huffman, LLP

Gunderson, Palmer, Nelson & Ashmore, LLP

Murphy, Goldammer & Prendergast LLP

### Senior Statesmen

**Senior Statesmen:** distinguished older practitioners

| Cutler Richard A | Cutler & Donahoe LLP |
|---|---|

### Leading Individuals

**Band 1**

| Brown Jonathan | Davenport, Evans, Hurwitz & Smith LLP |
|---|---|
| Donohue P Daniel | Davenport, Evans, Hurwitz & Smith LLP |
| Goldammer Vance RC | Murphy, Goldammer & Prendergast LLP |
| Greenfield Gregg S | Boyce, Greenfield, Pashby & Welk LLP |
| Hayes Robert E | Davenport, Evans, Hurwitz & Smith LLP |
| Jensen Curtis S | DeMersseman Jensen Tellinghuisen & |
| Riter Charles | Bangs, McCullen, Butler, Foye & Simmons |
| Wiederrich James | Woods, Fuller, Shultz & Smith PC |

**Band 2**

| Goetzinger Patrick | Gunderson, Palmer, Nelson & Ashmore |
|---|---|
| Raforth John H | Bangs, McCullen, Butler, Foye & Simmons |
| Stuck Haven L | Lynn, Jackson, Shultz & Lebrun (ONP)[†] |

[†]ONP = Other Notable Practitioner

*Alphabetical order within each band. Band 1 is the highest.*

## Band 1

### Bangs, McCullen, Butler, Foye & Simmons, LLP

**THE FIRM** This first-class firm runs its real estate practice from offices in Rapid City and Sioux Falls. It is highly commended for its proficiency across a broad spread of matters, including commercial leasing, workouts and environmental issues. Its clients include a range of local businesses, corporations, banks and individuals.

**KEY INDIVIDUALS Charles Riter** combines extensive tax expertise with significant estate planning knowledge to strengthen his real estate practice. **John Raforth** advises clients on a range of real estate issues, and offers notable expertise in estate planning and tax-related issues. One source commented: *"He is very good and very thorough – I would certainly give him very high marks."*

### Davenport, Evans, Hurwitz & Smith LLP

**THE FIRM** This preeminent real estate practice is based in Sioux Falls and is highly experienced in a wide range of commercial real estate matters. It handles all aspects of the sale and acquisition of property, and has expertise in dealing with regulators and environmental compliance. The team also offers notable experience in commercial leasing. **Sources say:** *"I think their knowledge and competence is outstanding and for that reason you don't get bogged down in irrelevancies – they cut to the chase."*

**KEY INDIVIDUALS Jonathan Brown** acts on behalf of a variety of real estate clients, including developers, lenders and manufacturers. He advises on all aspects of the real estate process. Sources say he is *"extremely capable, knowledgeable and expeditious in his approach."* **Daniel Donohue** is held in high regard for his experience in tax evaluation and trust law, and also offers significant expertise in wider real estate matters. Sources applaud **Robert Hayes** for his excellent command of real estate matters, particularly in foreclosure and real property law. He is highly regarded for his broader experience in bankruptcy-related issues.

### Woods, Fuller, Shultz & Smith PC

**THE FIRM** This esteemed real estate practice is highly active in the areas of construction law, condominium law and transactional matters, as well as land use and zoning issues. The team focuses in particular on rural and agricultural real estate.

**KEY INDIVIDUALS James Wiederrich** represents a wide range of clients in all aspects of real estate transactions. He brings his agricultural background to bear in all areas of his practice, and sources commend his in-depth knowledge of real estate law.

## Band 2

### Boyce, Greenfield, Pashby & Welk LLP

**THE FIRM** This Sioux Falls firm acts on behalf of a range of clients, including investors, owners and developers. Its impressive real estate practice covers the full range of matters, including property redevelopment, trust administration and construction projects.

**KEY INDIVIDUALS Gregg Greenfield** is recognized as a leader in the real estate arena. He is experienced across a wide range of development and redevelopment transactions, and is also highlighted for his expertise in issues arising from brownfield properties and water development.

### Cutler & Donahoe LLP

**THE FIRM** This dynamic team is recommended for its real estate work on behalf of a variety of clients, including investment institutions, developers and landlords. The practice has experience in dealing with a range of intricate commercial transactions among, other matters.

**KEY INDIVIDUALS Richard Cutler** is held in high esteem by peers for his extensive experience and knowledge of all areas of real estate practice. He is also highly regarded in the fields of business planning and taxation.

## Band 3

### DeMersseman Jensen Tellinghuisen & Huffman, LLP

**THE FIRM** This notable practice works on large commercial transactions and is often seen representing lenders in a range of loan-related matters. The team also has significant experience in acting as local counsel for clients outside South Dakota.

**KEY INDIVIDUALS Curtis Jensen** deals with all aspects of real estate law for his clients, including sales and acquisitions of commercial property and advising on commercial lending.

### Gunderson, Palmer, Nelson & Ashmore, LLP

**THE FIRM** This comprehensive team is based in Rapid City and has notable experience in agricultural and residential real estate matters. It also brings its knowledge on zoning and environmental issues to the table in complex commercial transactions.

**KEY INDIVIDUALS Patrick Goetzinger** is highly experienced in a wide range of real estate matters. His practice also includes a focus on several other practice areas, including estate planning and corporate transactions.

### Murphy, Goldammer & Prendergast LLP

**THE FIRM** This robust practice covers the full range of real estate services, and is noted for its additional litigation expertise. Its caseload has recently included large, complex transactions involving agricultural real estate.

**KEY INDIVIDUALS** Sources highly respect **Vance Goldammer** for his knowledge and experience in real estate law. His expertise in corporate and commercial transactional work is also particularly noted.

## Other Notable Practitioners

Sources praise **Haven Stuck** of Lynn, Jackson, Shultz & Lebrun PC as *"an excellent and very experienced attorney"* in the world of real estate. He handles a range of transactional matters, and also offers extensive experience in business planning, taxation and real estate disputes.

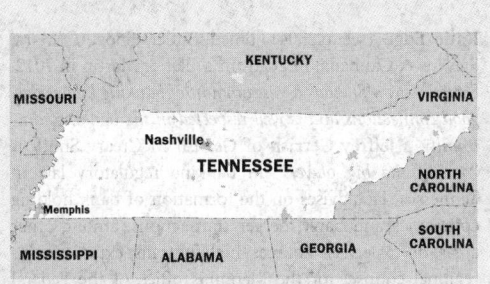

## How lawyers are ranked

Every year we carry out thousands of in-depth interviews with clients in order to assess the reputations and expertise of business lawyers worldwide. The qualities we look for (and which determine rankings) include technical legal ability, professional conduct, client service, commercial awareness/astuteness, diligence, commitment, and other qualities most valued by the client. For details of our research team, see p.5.

**Contents:**

# BANKING & FINANCE

Commentary about individuals can be found under their firm's paragraph. If the firm has no paragraph (is not ranked) look at Other Notable Practitioners.

### Banking & Finance
#### Leading Firms

**Band 1**
Bass, Berry & Sims PLC *

**Band 2**
Baker, Donelson, Bearman, Caldwell & Berkowitz, PC *
Bradley Arant Boult Cummings LLP *
Stites & Harbison PLLC *
Waller Lansden Dortch & Davis *

#### Leading Individuals

**Band 1**

| | |
|---|---|
| Bibb Julian L | Stites & Harbison PLLC * |
| Murdock III John E | Bradley Arant Boult Cummings LLP |
| Myers II John W | Bradley Arant Boult Cummings LLP |
| Sellers Cynthia N | Bass, Berry & Sims PLC * |
| Tate Jr James S | Bass, Berry & Sims PLC * |
| Thompson Bob F | Bass, Berry & Sims PLC * |

**Band 2**

| | |
|---|---|
| Dowsley III Felix R | Bass, Berry & Sims PLC * |
| Eisen Steven J | Baker, Donelson, Bearman, Caldwell * |
| Harris Robert L | Waller Lansden Dortch & Davis * |
| Mace Gerald F | Waller Lansden Dortch & Davis * |
| Prester Jackie | Baker, Donelson, Bearman, Caldwell * |

**Up-and-coming individuals**

| | |
|---|---|
| Hannon Bob | Bradley Arant Boult Cummings LLP |

## Band 1

### Bass, Berry & Sims PLC
See profile on p.2314

**THE FIRM** This firm has excellent credentials both in commercial banking and finance and in banking regulatory law. Highlights of 2012 were acting on a number of healthcare finance and project finance transactions, including the negotiation of a $20 million, 120-unit senior living community on behalf of Brookdale Senior Living. In

### Banking & Finance: Regulatory
#### Leading Individuals

**Band 1**

| | |
|---|---|
| Edge Kathryn (Katie) Reed | Butler, Snow, O'Mara (ONP)† * |
| Eisen Steven J | Baker, Donelson, Bearman, Caldwell * |
| Thompson Bob F | Bass, Berry & Sims PLC * |

**Band 2**

| | |
|---|---|
| Gerrish Jeffrey | Gerrish McCreary Smith (ONP)† |
| Small Daniel W | Daniel W. Small & Company (ONP)† |
| Wilson Virginia B | Butler, Snow, O'Mara, Stevens (ONP)† * |

*  Indicates firm / individual with profile.
† ONP = Other Notable Practitioner

other notable work, it represented Healthways in connection with a $400 million senior secured credit facility led by SunTrust Bank, and advised Citizens State Bank on the regulatory approvals required for its acquisition of four branch locations of Peoples State Bank of Commerce.
**Sources say:** *"They have very experienced lawyers, and have proven themselves on large and complex legal matters."*
**KEY INDIVIDUALS Cynthia Sellers** (see p.2309) represented Brown-Forman in the negotiation of an $800 million five-year credit agreement. She has significant experience representing both administrative agents and borrowers in large corporate transactions. **James Tate** (see p.2310) is active in real estate and commercial lending. Notable work includes the successful closing of a $785 million revolving credit facility for Corrections Corporation of America. Sources highlight **Bob Thompson's** (see p.2311) wealth of experience in banking and regulatory issues. He represented Merchants & Marine Bank in its acquisition of the assets of Heritage Bank. **Felix Dowsley** (see p.2303) was instrumental in Gaylord Entertainment's REIT conversion subsequent to its long-term management agreement for its four convention hotels with Marriott International.

## Band 2

### Baker, Donelson, Bearman, Caldwell & Berkowitz, PC
See profile on p.2313

**THE FIRM** This firm impresses market sources with its heavyweight banking regulatory expertise. It is frequently counsel to both community and regional banks, and has been called upon to provide regulatory advice at both the federal and state level, as well as assisting in enforcement actions. Notable highlights include its role in Magna Bank's privatization process.
**Sources say:** *"They are very competent, well known in the state and understand the environment that we are working in."*
**KEY INDIVIDUALS Steven Eisen** (see p.2304) advises on regulatory law and corporate governance, as well as on M&A and asset sales. Recent experience includes advising banks on expansion and branch acquisition activities. Sources note his strong, even-handed manner in negotiations. **Jackie Prester** (see p.2309) is *"responsive and effective in communication; she would just pick up the phone and tell us if we were on the wrong page."* She recently advised a regional bank on securities registrations and SEC Exchange Act filings.

### Bradley Arant Boult Cummings LLP
See profile on p.476

**THE FIRM** This firm is widely recognized for its finance and commercial lending practice. Its substantial experience working with banks and financial institutions is reflected in recent loan closings for Avenue Bank and First Bank. The team also advises on commercial real estate, M&A and regulatory matters.
**Sources say:** *"They are able to undertake sophisticated transactions that are negotiated on a national level, as well as handle local deals that have more sensitive issues related to our community."*

**KEY INDIVIDUALS John Murdock** represents clients in both debt and equity lending transactions. Recent work includes financings in the retail, healthcare and specialty lending sectors. **John Myers** is described as *"very diligent and efficient."* He acts for lenders on matters ranging from the restructuring of mezzanine funds to loans secured by auction rate securities and private equity investments. **Bob Hannon** is recognized for his involvement in commercial real estate lending transactions. One source said: *"Bob is a top-notch attorney – he provides sound legal advice and is very responsive."*

## Stites & Harbison PLLC
See profile on p.1331

**THE FIRM** This team regularly advises on M&A transactions and has an active practice in commercial lending. Other noted areas of expertise include bond financing, loan syndications and loan transactions. The firm also provides banking regulatory advice.

**KEY INDIVIDUALS Julian Bibb** (see p.2301) *"is a phenomenal person and a phenomenal lawyer,"* one peer enthused. Clients comment: *"He is not only technically competent, but has a good business sense. He has a good skill set to deal with difficult and high-profile situations – he is the*

*sort of person I want on my side."* He advises on the full array of loan types and financings.

## Waller Lansden Dortch & Davis
See profile on p.2320

**THE FIRM** This firm offers a comprehensive suite of financing and securities advisory services. It is especially active in healthcare finance transactions, where notable work includes advising Church Street Health Management in relation to a debtor-in-possession credit agreement subsequent to Church Street's 2012 Chapter 11 bankruptcy. In other highlights, the team acted for BancorpSouth on a $109.3 million common stock offering. Other key clients include MidCap Financial and Cressey & Company.

**Sources say:** *"They are among a small group of go-to firms for us. We consider them a key and strong partner."*

**KEY INDIVIDUALS Robert Harris** (see p.2305) successfully closed a $210 million senior credit facility for Encompass Home Health. *"He knows the market cold, and has invested in a relationship with our firm beyond any particular transaction,"* one client commented. **Gerald Mace** (see p.2307) recently advised Acadia Healthcare on the expansion of an existing loan which involved outstanding high-yield notes. He also acts for financial institutions on commercial finance transactions.

## Other Notable Practitioners

**Katie Edge** (see p.2304) joined Butler, Snow, O'Mara, Stevens & Cannada, PLLC from Miller & Martin in 2012. Sources say: *"She has a vast amount of banking knowledge, good connections and is well respected in the banking community."* **Jeffrey Gerrish** of Gerrish McCreary Smith is *"one of the big players"* in banking regulatory law in Tennessee. He advises on the formation of bank holding companies and bank merger transactions, among other areas of expertise. Sources highlight his experience as regional counsel for the Memphis office of the Federal Deposit Insurance Corporation. **Daniel Small** of Daniel W. Small & Company operates a well-respected regulatory practice, acting for solid base of financial institutions clients. **Virginia Wilson** (see p.2312) of Butler, Snow, O'Mara, Stevens & Cannada, PLLC is recognized for her expertise in financial services regulation and compliance. She advised the Community Bank of East Tennessee on a change in control transaction involving a private investor group.

# CORPORATE/M&A

| Corporate/M&A | |
| --- | --- |
| **Leading Firms** | |
| **Band 1** | |
| Bass, Berry & Sims PLC * | |
| Waller Lansden Dortch & Davis * | |
| **Band 2** | |
| Baker, Donelson, Bearman, Caldwell & Berkowitz, PC * | |
| Harwell Howard Hyne Gabbert & Manner, PC | |
| **Band 3** | |
| Bradley Arant Boult Cummings LLP * | |
| Miller & Martin PLLC * | |
| Sherrard & Roe PLC | |

*\* Indicates firm / individual with profile.*
*†ONP = Other Notable Practitioner*

| Corporate/M&A | |
| --- | --- |
| **Leading Individuals** | |
| **Star individuals** | |
| Cheek III James H | *Bass, Berry & Sims PLC* * |
| **Band 1** | |
| Cole J Chase | *Waller Lansden Dortch & Davis* |
| Manner Mark | *Harwell Howard Hyne Gabbert & Manner* |
| Sherrard III Thomas J | *Sherrard & Roe PLC* |
| Walker Jr F Mitchell | *Bass, Berry & Sims PLC* * |
| **Band 2** | |
| Burnstein Matthew R | *Waller Lansden Dortch & Davis* * |
| Cox David | *Harwell Howard Hyne Gabbert & Manner* |
| Davidson J Page | *Bass, Berry & Sims PLC* * |
| Heiter Matthew S | *Baker, Donelson, Bearman, Caldwell* * |
| Lamar III Howard H | *Bass, Berry & Sims PLC* * |
| **Band 3** | |
| DelPriore Robert J | *Baker, Donelson, Bearman, Caldwell* * |
| Franck Douglas C | *Bradley Arant Boult Cummings LLP* |
| Good John A | *Bass, Berry & Sims PLC* * |
| Kemp Kris | *Harwell Howard Hyne Gabbert & Manner* |
| Overby J Allen | *Bass, Berry & Sims PLC* * |
| Rolapp Todd J | *Bass, Berry & Sims PLC* * |
| Sharber Hugh | *Miller & Martin PLLC* * |
| Titus John | *Bradley Arant Boult Cummings LLP* |

## Band 1

## Bass, Berry & Sims PLC
See profile on p.2314

**THE FIRM** This practice group is acclaimed for its work at both the state and national level as counsel to a large number of public companies. Its depth of resources enables it to provide an extensive range of corporate-related advice. The team recently represented Luminex in its acquisition by merger of GenturaDx, a British Virgin Islands company with a number of international subsidiaries. Other notable clients include HCA and Coventry Health Care.

**Sources say:** *"One of the most significant practices in the state."*

**KEY INDIVIDUALS James Cheek** (see p.2302) is held in high regard as an *"exceptional practitioner"* who is *"the best of the best."* He is well known for his expertise in securities

law and corporate governance, and continues to act as disclosure counsel to the audit committee of the board of directors of Bank of America regarding an SEC settlement. **Howard Lamar** (see p.2306) represented HealthSpring in connection with its high-profile $3.8 billion merger with Cigna. He regularly advises different types of investment entities as well as corporate boards and committees. **Allen Overby** (see p.2307) is highlighted by peers for his expertise in securities law, and works alongside Cheek as counsel to the board of directors of Bank of America. He also acted for Applied Systems on its cross-border acquisition of Canada's Compu-Quote. Sources say: *"He is a trusted adviser and always has his client's best interests at heart."* **Page Davidson** (see p.2303) advised O'Charley's on its $221 million acquisition by Fidelity National Financial. *"He is extraordinarily detailed, responsive, and thoughtful,"* say interviewees. Memphis partner **John Good** (see p.323) is widely known for his expertise in REITs, and recently advised AmREIT on its IPO and listing on the NYSE. He also advised AutoZone on its $500 million senior note offering. One source enthused: *"He is the best REIT lawyer on the planet."* Firm managing partner **Todd Rolapp** (see p.2309) regularly acts for a variety of different players on public and private M&A. He also advises on fund formation and SEC reporting. Peers describe **Mitchell Walker** (see p.2311) as a *"practical, strong and very smart lawyer."* Recent highlights saw him represent J Alexander's in a challenging merger by public tender offer. He also acts for corporate clients on public offerings.

## Waller Lansden Dortch & Davis
See profile on p.2320

THE FIRM This firm's highly reputed corporate practice acts for a strong and diverse list of clients. The team is especially well known for its representation of healthcare industry clients such as LifePoint Hospitals and Capella Healthcare. In highlights, it acted for Acadia Healthcare Company on its acquisition of an inpatient behavioral healthcare facility in Chicago. In addition to M&A, the firm also advises on securities offerings, venture capital financings and corporate restructurings.

Sources say: "*They provide excellent service and understand how regulations apply in the context of investments and acquisitions – they get us to yes.*"

KEY INDIVIDUALS **Chase Cole** has a strong reputation among peers. He represented the firm's longtime client Capstone Turbine in a $23.1 million common stock offering. **Matthew Burnstein** (see p.2302) is "*good at strategy and framing risks*," and is "*very smart on his feet*," say sources. He recently advised HCA affiliate Health Insight Capital on its investment in mobile patient software developer AirStrip Technologies.

## Band 2

### Baker, Donelson, Bearman, Caldwell & Berkowitz, PC
See profile on p.2313

THE FIRM This firm is rated for its broad industry sector and regional coverage. It had an active year advising on the acquisition and establishment of startup companies, and also experienced an uptick in energy-related work, for clients such as Eco Energy and Advanced BioEnergy. Other areas of expertise include securities compliance and debt refinancings.

KEY INDIVIDUALS **Matthew Heiter** (see p.2305) "*is outstanding – his knowledge of the applicable law is extensive and his personality is wonderful*," say clients. Recent highlights include emerging companies work, including representing technology and biotechnology investors and com-

panies. **Robert DelPriore** (see p.2303) is "*very detail-oriented and responsive.*" He acted for Monogram Food Solutions on its acquisition of a manufacturing facility and on the restructuring of its senior secured credit facilities.

### Harwell Howard Hyne Gabbert & Manner, PC

THE FIRM This firm has a strong profile in Tennessee for corporate/M&A work, leveraged by its eminent healthcare services practice. In line with the rise of group buying transactions, the team acted for Navigator Group Purchasing on its sale to Managed Healthcare Associates. It is also recognized for its strength in the private equity arena.

Sources say: "*A very good firm offering all the specialties a medium to large company would need from external counsel.*"

KEY INDIVIDUALS **Mark Manner** is described as "*a very bright lawyer with very good people skills.*" He is a key adviser to the firm's major healthcare industry clients. Sources commend **David Cox** for his ability to "*use good common sense in negotiations – he does not try to 'win' every deal point.*" He has been heavily engaged in healthcare private equity work of late. Department head **Kris Kemp** advised Agilum Healthcare Intelligence on a preferred stock offering with a matching investment from the Tennessee INCITE Co-Investment Fund. "*His style helps to break down walls,*" one source noted.

## Band 3

### Bradley Arant Boult Cummings LLP
See profile on p.476

THE FIRM This 24-strong team acts on a diverse portfolio of corporate transactions. It has a significant presence in the healthcare space, and recently represented e+ Healthcare in its acquisition of a provider of radiation oncology services. The firm also represents venture capital and financial services sector clients, as well as technology and emerging companies and manufacturing businesses.

KEY INDIVIDUALS **Douglas Franck** represents corporate borrowers in recapitalizations in a variety of industries. Additional expertise includes senior secured credit facility transactions and preferred equity financings. Department head **John Titus** "*is great to work with and has a good demeanor,*" say sources. He advises on a range of commercial financing transactions involving bank lenders and private equity investors.

### Miller & Martin PLLC
See profile on p.2317

THE FIRM This firm is recognized for its strong focus on private equity transactions. It advises on private equity M&A and fund formation, and has recently advised on transactions involving significant cross-border components. Notably, it acted for Philadelphia-based Larsen MacColl Partners on the sale of its majority stake in roller coaster manufacturer S&S Worldwide to a company based in Japan.

Sources say: "*I have been impressed with the firm's skillful and practical approach.*"

KEY INDIVIDUALS Chattanooga-based **Hugh Sharber** (see p.2309) represented the shareholders of Krystal Holdings in its sale to two private equity companies. One client said: "*He is someone I can rely on if I have any kind of significant problem.*"

### Sherrard & Roe PLC

THE FIRM This Nashville-based team commands respect from both clients and peers for its high-quality work and service offering. The firm is well known for its representation of healthcare industry clients, and has seen increasing activity in the digital space of late.

Sources say: "*They have a good knowledge base and strong client service orientation.*"

KEY INDIVIDUALS **Thomas Sherrard** is highlighted by peers for his "*impeccable reputation.*" He has a background in acting as general and outside corporate counsel, and his clients include a number of preeminent Tennessee-based enterprises.

# ENVIRONMENT

Commentary about individuals can be found under their firm's paragraph. If the firm has no paragraph (is not ranked) look at Other Notable Practitioners.

## Band 1

### Bass, Berry & Sims PLC
See profile on p.2314

**THE FIRM** This environmental law group provides day-to-day operational assistance and corporate transactional support to a range of industry clients. It has developed notable strength in enforcement actions, including complex government investigations. The team counts GlaxoSmithKline, Bridgestone Americas Tire Operations and Resolute Forest Products among its clients.

**Sources say:** *"They have been terrific and reliable. They consider the realities of the business on top of legal theories and evaluations, and arrive at solutions."*

**KEY INDIVIDUALS Andrew Goddard** (see p.2304) has an active practice with a strong focus on clean air, assisting clients with self-disclosure and compliance inquiries. *"I don't know if there is anyone better – he assesses information, guides us quickly and can walk us through any situation,"*

one client said. **Scott Thomas** (see p.2310) specializes in brownfields redevelopment, waste management and underground storage. Sources say: *"He is results-driven and pragmatic, and understands client needs."*

### Waller Lansden Dortch & Davis
See profile on p.2320

**THE FIRM** This team advises on the full range of environmental matters and is acclaimed for the breadth of its expertise in this field. The firm represents both public and private sector clients in connection with site development and brownfields, permitting, litigation, environmental management and regulatory compliance. It recently assisted Austin Powder with permit applications relating to its new manufacturing facility in Tennessee.

**KEY INDIVIDUALS James Weaver** (see p.2311) is best known for his government relations practice. He works alongside state legislators and advises on major project developments. He is currently advising the Rogers Group on litigation involving the operation of a quarry in Rutherford County, and in relation to the relocation of a portion of Richland Creek in Nashville for a quarry expansion project. Department head **Edward Callaway** (see p.2302) has significant experience advising on landfill and waste management, among other areas of expertise. He acts as nationwide counsel to Tractor Supply Company, advising on the environmental issues arising from its store development program. New to the rankings, **Michael Stagg** (see p.2310) is noted by sources for his expertise in air and water matters. He advised six counties in Tennessee on their levels of ozone pollution pursuant to EPA-revised standards.

## Band 2

### Baker, Donelson, Bearman, Caldwell & Berkowitz, PC
See profile on p.2313

**THE FIRM** This firm advises on both transactions and compliance as well as regulatory law, enforcement and litigation. The ten-strong team in Tennessee regularly handles citizen suit claims, brownfields redevelopment, permitting and Superfund cleanup matters. Clients include Ford and Nestlé Waters North America.

**KEY INDIVIDUALS Robert Steele** (see p.2310) represents clients in transactional and compliance matters. Of late, he has acted on facilities acquisitions entailing environmental permitting and related agreements. His client base includes consumer appliance manufacturers and hospital operators, and reflects his varied industry sector experience.

**Gary Shockley** (see p.2310) has a broad commercial litigation practice and undertakes significant work in the environmental arena. He also has expertise in construction, healthcare and personal injury cases. *"He is an excellent practitioner,"* peers comment.

### Luna Law Group PLLC

**THE FIRM** This local law firm is noted for its representation of small businesses and government authorities. It has a strong practice at the county level, where team members provide advice on environmental due diligence in transactions, compliance and permitting for property development.

**KEY INDIVIDUALS J W Luna** is highly regarded by market commentators, who highlight his previous tenure as a commissioner where he oversaw the passage of significant environmental legislation in Tennessee. His areas of expertise include government relations and regulatory compliance. **Michael Pearigen** regularly represents state and local government entities. He also advises businesses and individuals on permitting and enforcement actions.

### Stites & Harbison PLLC
See profile on p.1331

**THE FIRM** The environmental law team at Stites & Harbison provides statutory guidance to clients on the CAA, CERCLA and the CWA. Besides advising on compliance strategies, it also has experience litigating before state and federal trial and appellate courts, as well as specialist tribunals.

**KEY INDIVIDUALS William Penny** (see p.2308) is *"an excellent attorney who has broad experience and knows the regulators well."* His portfolio of expertise includes advising on brownfield redevelopment and low-level radioactive waste. **Greg Young** (see p.2312) is noted for his expertise in waste management actions. His practice includes representing clients in citizen suits and actions brought by the Tennessee Department of Environment and Conservation.

## Other Notable Practitioners

**David Bullock** joined Tune, Entrekin & White in 2012, where he continues his practice as an environmental litigator. He further assists purchasers and vendors in assessing environmental risks incidental to property transactions. **Darlene Marsh** of Burr & Forman LLP primarily advises on environmental compliance issues that relate to commercial real estate. She represents clients in cleanup actions arising from leaks and contamination in underground storage.

# HEALTHCARE

Commentary about individuals can be found under their firm's paragraph. If the firm has no paragraph (is not ranked) look at Other Notable Practitioners.

## Healthcare
### Leading Firms

**Band 1**
Bass, Berry & Sims PLC *
Bradley Arant Boult Cummings LLP *
Waller Lansden Dortch & Davis *

**Band 2**
Baker, Donelson, Bearman, Caldwell & Berkowitz, PC *
Butler, Snow, O'Mara, Stevens & Cannada, PLLC *

**Band 3**
Harwell Howard Hyne Gabbert & Manner, PC
Sherrard & Roe PLC

### Leading Individuals

**Band 1**

| | |
|---|---|
| Bishop III George W | Waller Lansden Dortch & Davis * |
| Braun Stephen T | Bradley Arant Boult Cummings LLP |
| Cowart Richard | Baker, Donelson, Bearman, Caldwell * |
| Hill J Reginald | Waller Lansden Dortch & Davis * |
| Reisz Cynthia Y | Bass, Berry & Sims PLC * |
| Voigt John | Sherrard & Roe PLC |
| Walton Leigh | Bass, Berry & Sims PLC * |

**Band 2**

| | |
|---|---|
| Burks Ashby Q | Baker, Donelson, Bearman, Caldwell * |
| Hardcastle Jay | Bradley Arant Boult Cummings LLP |
| Manner Mark | Harwell Howard Hyne Gabbert & Manner |
| McSween Philip | Baker, Donelson, Bearman, Caldwell * |

**Band 3**

| | |
|---|---|
| Campbell Kevin B | Bradley Arant Boult Cummings LLP |
| Folk Mark D | Limbo |
| Hill Michael R | Harwell Howard Hyne Gabbert & Manner |
| Holt III Berry | Bradley Arant Boult Cummings LLP |
| Humphreys Angela | Bass, Berry & Sims PLC * |
| Powell Tracy | Sherrard & Roe PLC |
| Rayson G Scott | Waller Lansden Dortch & Davis * |
| Watson Lampley Julie | Butler, Snow, O'Mara, Stevens & Cannada * |
| Youngberg Angela C. | Rainey, Kizer, Reviere & Bell PLC (ONP)† |

**Up-and-coming individuals**

| | |
|---|---|
| Browder Brian R | Waller Lansden Dortch & Davis * |

* Indicates firm / individual with profile.

†ONP = Other Notable Practitioner

## Healthcare: Regulatory
### Senior Statesmen

**Senior Statesmen: distinguished older practitioners**

| | |
|---|---|
| Powers Patricia O | Waller Lansden Dortch & Davis * |

### Leading Individuals

**Band 1**

| | |
|---|---|
| Bartrum Thomas E | Baker, Donelson, Bearman, Caldwell * |
| Burke Denise D | Butler, Snow, O'Mara, Stevens & Cannada * |
| Campbell Kevin B | Bradley Arant Boult Cummings LLP |
| Hardcastle Jay | Bradley Arant Boult Cummings LLP |
| Holt III Berry | Bradley Arant Boult Cummings LLP |
| Liggett Nora L | Waller Lansden Dortch & Davis * |
| Miley Claire F | Bass, Berry & Sims PLC * |
| Reisz Cynthia Y | Bass, Berry & Sims PLC * |

## Healthcare: Government Investigations & Fraud
### Leading Individuals

**Band 1**

| | |
|---|---|
| Curley Matthew M | Bass, Berry & Sims PLC * |
| Roark Brian D. | Bass, Berry & Sims PLC * |
| Sawyer Sheila | Waller Lansden Dortch & Davis * |
| Westling Richard | Waller Lansden Dortch & Davis * |

## Band 1

### Bass, Berry & Sims PLC
See profile on p.2314

**THE FIRM** This team offers a comprehensive range of transactional, operational and compliance assistance. It has recently advised healthcare providers on private equity investments, and assisted with the development of new lines of business. Practitioners have also handled an increased amount of healthcare investigations, fraud and enforcement actions.

**Sources say:** *"Each of their attorneys has excellent credentials and experience. They genuinely care about the success and wellbeing of their clients."*

**KEY INDIVIDUALS Cindy Reisz**'s (see p.2309) recent transactional experience includes acting for Anesthesia Medical Group on a merger with Excellere Capital. She is praised as *"superb and consistent,"* and highlighted for her *"wide-ranging skill set."* She also advises on healthcare regulatory issues. *"Phenomenal"* **Leigh Walton** (see p.2311) is a *"brilliant, friendly"* attorney, say interviewees. She represented Health Management Associates in relation to its joint venture with INTEGRIS Health. **Angela Humphreys** (see p.2305) is active in corporate healthcare transactions across the region. She was part of the team advising Coventry Health Care on its $5.7 billion acquisition by Aetna. Experienced attorney **Claire Miley** (see p.2307) acts on joint venture and management relationship concerns, reimbursement analyses and physician self-referral issues. **Matthew Curley** (see p.2303) specializes in healthcare fraud and abuse matters. He advised IASIS Healthcare on a False Claims Act investigation. **Brian Roark** (see p.2309) leads the firm's healthcare fraud task force and assists healthcare providers in dealing with investigations by regulators and agencies. He counts Erlanger Medical Center and HealthSpring among his clients.

### Bradley Arant Boult Cummings LLP
See profile on p.476

**THE FIRM** This team remains a top choice among heavyweight clients in the healthcare industry. It has been extensively involved in advising on the creation of accountable care organizations, and also assists with facilities acquisitions, joint ventures and licensing concerns. Highlights include advising Longview Regional Medical Center Hospital on acquiring a sizable physician practice, with facilities across 18 locations. Key clients include Tennessee Health Management, Surgical Care Affiliates and HealthSouth.

**Sources say:** *"They are efficient and do not cut corners. They do what needs to be done."*

**KEY INDIVIDUALS Stephen Braun** receives unanimous praise from sources for his skills as a transactional healthcare lawyer. His clients include Community Health Systems and Ardent Health Services, both of which he recently advised on out-of-state hospital acquisitions. **Jay Hardcastle** *"focuses on the outcomes,"* observe clients. His practice is built around expertise in both transactional and regulatory issues, and *"he is always a pleasure to work with."* **Kevin Campbell** *"does a fine job of making sure that we don't miss anything prescribed by the rules and regulations,"* said one source. Campbell has assisted Fresenius Medical with its national accountable care organization initiative. Interviewees appreciate **Berry Holt**'s *"tremendous experience"* and *"cool, levelheaded"* approach. He represented Saint Thomas Health in establishing a rural healthcare joint venture with Capella.

### Waller Lansden Dortch & Davis
See profile on p.2320

**THE FIRM** This firm's impressively skilled bench of attorneys can meet every need associated with healthcare law. The team has been heavily involved with acquisitions of late, including representing Duke LifePoint Healthcare in the $483 million purchase of Marquette General Hospital in Michigan, and advising on the formation of the Health Innovation Specialists physician network. Members of the team with a regulatory background have also been advising on healthcare employment, self-disclosure issues and investigations.

**Sources say:** *"They are very knowledgeable about the industry."*

**KEY INDIVIDUALS George Bishop** (see p.2301) led the team representing RegionalCare Hospital Partners in its merger with Essent Healthcare. *"He is brilliant in finding solutions and managing transactions – a joy to work with,"* remarks an interviewee. Clients note that **Reginald Hill** (see p.2305) *"has a knack for building relationships with other parties and makes sure that the transaction is closed with the relationship intact."* He has experience of advising major healthcare operators on regulatory compliance. **Patricia Powers** (see p.2308) is known for her regulatory expertise in industry transactions and antikickback compliance issues. *"I can be sure that she will provide the right workable solutions,"* said one interviewee. **Brian Browder** (see p.2302) frequently advises clients on regional transactions. He recently acted for LifePoint Hospitals on its joint venture with Kentucky-based Norton Healthcare. Sources praise **Nora Liggett** (see p.2307) as *"a very levelheaded regulatory lawyer."* She advises on compliance matters arising from M&A activity and joint venture formations. *"Very smart"* attorney **Scott Rayson** (see p.2309) advises on healthcare acquisitions and divestitures. He is also conversant on tax incentives relating to the development of healthcare facilities. **Sheila Sawyer** (see p.2309) represents both healthcare companies and executives with respect to litigation and investigatory matters. **Richard Westling** (see p.2311) offers wide experience of government investigations and enforcement actions. *"He can anticipate what the other side is going to think,"* remarked one interviewee. **Mark Folk** recently arrived from Shutts & Bowen. He is a broad-based transactional healthcare expert who is described by clients as *"approachable, efficient and always available."*

## Band 2

### Baker, Donelson, Bearman, Caldwell & Berkowitz, PC
See profile on p.2313

THE FIRM This healthcare group has had a busy year acting for clients on transactional matters, including multiple consolidations of hospital groups. It also houses an expanding regulatory practice and is active in healthcare litigation. Clients include key industry players such as therapy clinics, medical spas and university medical centers.
KEY INDIVIDUALS **Thomas Bartrum** (see p.2301) is praised as *"a truly excellent lawyer"* for healthcare regulatory matters. He assists clients with the implementation of compliance strategies as well as fraud and abuse investigations. **Richard Cowart** (see p.2302) took a lead role representing Memphis-based Baptist Memorial Healthcare in the purchase of an interest in North Mississippi. His trans-

actional experience is complemented by an ability to advise on policy and governance matters. **Ashby Burks** (see p.2302) has had a busy year acting on the sale and purchase of hospital assets. He also represented a client in the refinancing of loan facilities. **Philip McSween** (see p.2307) assists clients with employment agreements and due diligence issues, in addition to corporate transactions. He is also outside general counsel to various hospitals and physician groups.

### Butler, Snow, O'Mara, Stevens & Cannada, PLLC
See profile on p.1613

THE FIRM This practice remains a key adviser on regulatory healthcare concerns. A significant development has been its recent appointment as Federal Monitor of Wright Medical Technology, delivering reports to the Attorney General on antikickback fraud, abuse and corporate investigations. Attorneys here also provide certificate and licensing advice.
Sources say: *"Very positive and responsive. Extremely capable and easy to work with on all levels."*
KEY INDIVIDUALS **Denise Burke** (see p.2302) is noted for her regulatory expertise. She has advised Tennessee Health Management and Baptist Memorial Healthcare on compliance programs in the past year. **Julie Watson Lampley** (see p.2311) continues to advise healthcare providers on transactions, contractual issues and regulatory compliance.

## Band 3

### Harwell Howard Hyne Gabbert & Manner, PC
THE FIRM This firm has had an active year thanks to its involvement in a series of significant healthcare transactions. Most notably, the team represented HealthSpring in

its sale to Cigna for $3.8 billion. It also acts for healthcare providers on LBOs and spin-offs.
Sources say: *"A solid command of their areas of expertise. Rarely do I not get an immediate answer when needed."*
KEY INDIVIDUALS **Mark Manner** is recommended for his *"extraordinary knowledge and experience in the healthcare sector."* He regularly plays a key role in some of the firm's most high-profile and complex transactions. **Michael Hill** led the team advising Acadia Healthcare on its purchase of three psychiatric hospitals. *"He gets through matters efficiently and is able to explain them clearly and promptly,"* observes one client.

### Sherrard & Roe PLC
THE FIRM This healthcare team wins acclaim from clients for its good value and high-quality advice. Practitioners have a strong focus on providing hospitals and physician groups with transactional and regulatory advice. The group is experienced in handling critical structural issues, joint venture agreements and operational matters.
Sources say: *"Their advice is always spot on."*
KEY INDIVIDUALS **John Voigt** remains the go-to lawyer for matters affecting physician practices. Clients praise him as *"an exceptionally gifted healthcare and business attorney who always offers sage advice on even the most delicate matters."* He represented the shareholders of Anesthesia Medical Group in a $68 million sale of stock. **Tracy Powell** is recommended by sources as *"a bright lawyer who works hard."* He advises healthcare providers on integration and regulatory issues.

### Other Notable Practitioners
Sources praise **Angela Youngberg** of Rainey, Kizer, Reviere & Bell PLC for her skill in handling transactions and healthcare employment concerns.

# LABOR & EMPLOYMENT

Commentary about individuals can be found under their firm's paragraph. If the firm has no paragraph (is not ranked) look at Other Notable Practitioners.

## Labor & Employment
### Leading Firms

**Band 1**
Bass, Berry & Sims PLC *
FordHarrison LLP *
Littler Mendelson, PC *

**Band 2**
Baker, Donelson, Bearman, Caldwell & Berkowitz, PC *
Butler, Snow, O'Mara, Stevens & Cannada, PLLC *
Jackson Lewis LLP *
Kramer Rayson LLP *
Ogletree, Deakins, Nash, Smoak & Stewart, PC *
Waller Lansden Dortch & Davis *

**Band 3**
Constangy, Brooks & Smith, LLP
King & Ballow
Miller & Martin PLLC *

## Labor & Employment
### Leading Individuals

| **Band 1** | |
|---|---|
| Boston Robert E | Waller Lansden Dortch & Davis * |
| Jaqua David P | Butler, Snow, O'Mara, Stevens & Cannada * |
| Ozier William N | Bass, Berry & Sims PLC * |
| Phillips Edward G | Kramer Rayson LLP * |
| Prather Paul E | Littler Mendelson, PC * |

| **Band 2** | |
|---|---|
| Blue Jr William A | Constangy, Brooks & Smith, LLP |
| Britt III Louis P | FordHarrison LLP * |
| Crenshaw Jr Waverly D | Waller Lansden Dortch & Davis * |
| Frazier Keith D | Ogletree, Deakins, Nash, Smoak & Stewart * |
| Garrett Tim K | Bass, Berry & Sims PLC * |
| Gerson Herb | FordHarrison LLP * |
| Kaplan Jonathan E | Littler Mendelson, PC * |
| Kiesewetter Jay W | Littler Mendelson, PC * |
| Kramer Steven E | Kramer Rayson LLP * |
| Mulroy II James R | Jackson Lewis LLP * |
| Robinson Jennifer B | Littler Mendelson, PC * |
| Sisk Bart N | Butler, Snow, O'Mara, Stevens & Cannada * |
| Wayland R Eddie | King & Ballow |
| Young Edward R | Baker, Donelson, Bearman, Caldwell * |

| **Band 3** | |
|---|---|
| Bult Teresa Rider | Constangy, Brooks & Smith, LLP |
| Crider Marcus | Waller Lansden Dortch & Davis * |
| Graham Stanley E | Waller Lansden Dortch & Davis * |
| Horton Bob | Bass, Berry & Sims PLC * |
| Keller Jennifer P | Baker, Donelson, Bearman, Caldwell * |
| McConnell Timothy | Baker, Donelson, Bearman, Caldwell * |
| Moschel Michael | Bass, Berry & Sims PLC * |
| Oliver Craig | Bradley Arant Boult Cummings LLP (ONP)† |
| Palmer Timothy A | Ogletree, Deakins, Nash, Smoak & Stewart * |
| Perl Arnold E | Glankler Brown, PLLC (ONP)† * |
| Shea Kara E. | Butler, Snow, O'Mara, Stevens & Cannada * |
| Swafford Thomas Anthony (Tony) | Adams and Reese (ONP)† * |
| Trent Steven H | Baker, Donelson, Bearman, Caldwell * |
| Vance Kim | Baker, Donelson, Bearman, Caldwell * |
| Weintraub Jeff | Fisher & Phillips LLP (ONP)† * |

| **Up-and-coming individuals** | |
|---|---|
| Dohner Smith Mary | Constangy, Brooks & Smith, LLP |

\* Indicates firm / individual with profile.
†ONP = Other Notable Practitioner

## Band 1

### Bass, Berry & Sims PLC
See profile on p.2314

**THE FIRM** This established firm houses one of the preeminent labor and employment teams in Tennessee. The team's litigation experience includes age discrimination and FMLA actions, and its reputation for expertise in labor generated an uptick in handbook reviews and on-site investigations. Clients include Vanderbilt University and IASIS Healthcare.

**Sources say:** *"They consistently provide great-quality product at a reasonable price." "Very caring and professional in their relationships, work ethic and commitment."*

**KEY INDIVIDUALS William Ozier** (see p.2308) defends employers in breach of contract and discrimination claims. *"He walked me through the entire matter, pointing out the issues and expectations. A well-documented and focused process,"* comments one appreciative client. **Tim Garrett** (see p.2304) handles cases ranging from noncompete litigation to FMLA retaliation discharges. He also acts as national labor and employment counsel to various companies. **Michael Moschel** (see p.2307) is identified by sources as *"a good traditional labor practitioner."* He has been advising an out-of-state client on unfair labor practice charges. Clients appreciate **Bob Horton**'s (see p.2305) *"strong trial persona"* and his ability to *"connect with the jury."* He negotiated a settlement over a collective action brought under FLSA regulations on behalf of Gibson Guitar.

### FordHarrison LLP
See profile on p.1108

**THE FIRM** Attorneys here have had a busy year handling EEOC lawsuits. The team recently obtained summary judgment in a discrimination action alleging infringe-ments of the ADA, ERISA, Rehabilitation Act and FMLA. FordHarrison offers experience of acting for both public and private sector clients, including defending against claims made by former executives.

**Sources say:** *"They gave us phenomenal help during a critical time. They knew exactly what we needed and how to provide it."*

**KEY INDIVIDUALS Louis Britt** (see p.2301) achieved successful results for the Shelby County government regarding a race discrimination claim and, separately, a challenge to the moving of three Homeland Security personnel to another department. *"He does not waste time and will utilize every resource to give the most appropriate advice."* **Herb Gerson** (see p.2304) advises and counsels corporate clients on union matters, including handling negotiations with workforces.

### Littler Mendelson, PC
See profile on p.688

**THE FIRM** This practice is fast becoming a popular adviser to employers in Tennessee. It successfully sought summary judgment in the Court of Appeals for River Park Hospital over a retaliatory discharge claim brought under the Tennessee Public Protection Act. Clients appreciate the time and cost-saving advantages the team brings as part of the Littler Mendelson network.

**Sources say:** *"The thing about this firm is that they will always have a practitioner who knows the answer to your queries."*

**KEY INDIVIDUALS** *"Knowledgeable, personable and easy to work with,"* **Paul Prather** (see p.2309) is held in high regard by sources. His range of advice reaches from wrongful discharge to wage issues. **Jonathan Kaplan** (see p.2306) assists employers with the development of hiring and termination procedures. He also represents management in discrimination and harassment claims. **Jay Kiesewetter** (see p.2306) is widely regarded as *"a veteran practitioner"* in the traditional labor sphere. Clients highlight his union avoidance expertise in particular. **Jennifer Robinson** (see p.2309) has gained significant experience as lead counsel in heavyweight wage and hour class actions. One source notes that *"she gets the nuances of our business and keeps us abreast of developments."*

## Band 2

### Baker, Donelson, Bearman, Caldwell & Berkowitz, PC
See profile on p.2313

**THE FIRM** This team possesses a strong statewide reputation for representing its clients on a mix of interests. An increase in work relating to FLSA collective actions has particularly supplemented its employment litigation capacity. It also retains practitioners dedicated to traditional labor and union matters as well as experts in corporate training.

**KEY INDIVIDUALS Edward Young** (see p.2312) has had an active year serving as lead counsel to corporate employers in union campaigns across the nation. He also successfully obtained summary judgment for a client in a race discrimination suit brought by the EEOC. **Timothy McConnell** (see p.2307) has much experience in employment litigation. Besides his involvement in a sex discrimination matter, he has also advised on employment issues arising from the Dodd-Frank Act. **Kim Vance** (see p.2311) is described by a sources as *"a terrific problem solver."* She is noted for her impressive counseling and defense of management teams before the EEOC and the Tennessee Human Rights Commission. Head of practice **Jennifer Keller** (see p.2306) is particularly experienced in preventive initiatives such as union avoidance, as well as harassment and discrimination issues. **Steven Trent** (see p.2311) represents employers facing race discrimination claims. He also has experience of successfully acting in constructive discharge claims.

## Butler, Snow, O'Mara, Stevens & Cannada, PLLC
See profile on p.1613

**THE FIRM** This firm has amassed solid experience in handling all types of employment claims. The team also provides traditional labor counseling and assistance on related litigation. Key clients include West Fraser and Chickasaw Nation Industries.

**Sources say:** *"Established, highly qualified and easy to deal with."*

**KEY INDIVIDUALS David Jaqua** (see p.2306) recently defended U-Haul International in an EEOC racial harassment and retaliatory discharge claim. Clients remark that *"he is very skillful in handling matters and good at maintaining relations with the opposite party."* One source describes traditional labor practitioner **Bart Sisk** (see p.2310) as *"very cooperative and easy to work with."* He was instrumental in obtaining the dismissal of a union election petition for Weyerhaeuser. **Kara Shea** (see p.2310) has boosted the team with her experience of wage and hour actions and sexual harassment claims since joining from Miller & Martin. Clients outline her forte in *"presenting available options clearly to non-attorneys."*

## Jackson Lewis LLP
See profile on p.1982

**THE FIRM** In recent months this team has been increasingly busy, especially in dealing with allegations of FMLA and ADA violations. The team also handles employer immigration matters, and represents key clients from the automotive, healthcare and financial services industries.

**Sources say:** *"The firm is of a very high caliber when it comes to labor and employment law."*

**KEY INDIVIDUALS James Mulroy** (see p.2307) is praised by sources as a *"smart, aggressive and very tactical"* trial lawyer. Key recent cases include handling noncompete and trade secret disputes. He has also defended clients from EEOC charges brought by employees.

## Kramer Rayson LLP
See profile on p.2316

**THE FIRM** This practice distinguishes itself in employment disputes through its representation of both plaintiffs and defendants. Areas of expertise include handling whistle-blower cases and discrimination claims. It also acts on behalf of employers in relation to labor and union matters. **KEY INDIVIDUALS Edward Phillips** (see p.2308) earns strong praise from fellow practitioners for his work for

employers on litigation avoidance strategies. **Steven Kramer**'s (see p.2306) practice focuses on traditional labor relations and labor arbitrations. He also handles noncompete disputes.

## Ogletree, Deakins, Nash, Smoak & Stewart, PC
See profile on p.1110

**THE FIRM** This firm boasts an impressive record in employment litigation, including both class actions and single-plaintiff claims. Of note is its work in successfully defending employers in a number of physical abuse and assault claims. Representative clients include Electrolux Home Products and Eastman Chemical.

**Sources say:** *"Outstanding. They were my first outside counsel hire and I've never regretted it."*

**KEY INDIVIDUALS Keith Frazier** (see p.2304) has a background in defending FLSA and discrimination actions. *"He is very prompt and practical with his advice,"* notes one source. **Timothy Palmer** (see p.2308) recently arrived from the firm's Birmingham, Alabama office. He has notable expertise in employment disputes and has been representing Dunn Construction in a case concerning disparate pay and charges of harassment.

## Waller Lansden Dortch & Davis
See profile on p.2320

**THE FIRM** Research suggests that this team is called on to handle employment litigation involving novel points of law. It remains a go-to firm for healthcare employment matters, servicing such clients as HCA and Blue Cross Blue Shield of Tennessee. Practitioners offer recent experience of defending employers in FMLA, FLSA and ERISA claims.

**Sources say:** *"I have been impressed by their caring and conscientious approach to, and their knowledge of, our business and people."*

**KEY INDIVIDUALS Robert Boston** (see p.2301) is regarded as an *"incredibly skilled lawyer"* with a *"great reputation."* He has taken lead roles in high-profile matters relating to the treatment of employees. **Waverly Crenshaw** (see p.2302) continues to represent healthcare operators across Tennessee in FMLA and ERISA disputes. **Marcus Crider** (see p.2303) has particular experience in representing family-owned businesses and startup companies. He advises on the negotiation of noncompete clauses, as well as Title VII and ADA litigation. **Stanley Graham** (see p.2304) acts on matters involving strong technical concerns, including cases brought under the Tennessee Human Rights Act. *"He is always responsive and accessible,"* observes one client.

## Band 3

## Constangy, Brooks & Smith, LLP
**THE FIRM** This team is active on wage and hour actions, discrimination claims and lawsuits brought under the ADA. It also has a strong workers' compensation defense practice. Clients include Metropolitan Nashville Airport Authority and Pirelli Tire.

**Sources say:** *"Good, responsive lawyers who are results-driven."*

**KEY INDIVIDUALS William Blue** is a litigator who is also in demand for his employer training advice. He represented an amicus curiae before the Tennessee Court of Appeals and the Tennessee Supreme Court regarding the selection of state appellate court judges. *"Very knowledgeable"* **Teresa Rider Bult** is identified by clients as *"an excellent advocate."* She defended Toho Tenax of America in a race discrimination claim. **Mary Dohner Smith** gains recognition as a *"strong, aggressive litigator"* who handles a range of statutory and breach of contract claims.

## King & Ballow
**THE FIRM** This team has a long tradition of providing labor and employment advice to management teams. Attorneys bring experience of litigating before the NLRB and handling employee benefits and privacy rights matters.

**KEY INDIVIDUALS** Peers regard **Eddie Wayland** as *"one of the most knowledgeable people"* in the market. He counts wage and hour cases and NLRB litigation as key to his practice.

## Miller & Martin PLLC
See profile on p.2317

**THE FIRM** This team operates from the firm's Chattanooga office, advising clients on both traditional labor and general employment matters. Recently, the team acted as sole legal counsel to Tennessee State Bank in a sex and age discrimination claim. It also regularly advises clients from the hospitality and food and beverage industries.

**KEY INDIVIDUALS** Head of department John Bode is a key contact.

## Other Notable Practitioners

**Craig Oliver** of Bradley Arant Boult Cummings LLP is noted by clients for *"making practical, sound business judgments."* He represented Vaco in a dispute over the hiring of an employee of a company client. **Arnold Perl** (see p.2308) of Glankler Brown, PLLC is a veteran practitioner and adviser to a number of corporate organizations. He works with management in developing employee relations strategies. *"Effective attorney"* **Tony Swafford** (see p.2310) of Adams and Reese LLP brings expertise of representing clients from the transportation industry. Based in Memphis, **Jeff Weintraub** (see p.2311) of Fisher & Phillips LLP is known among sources as a *"very bright and capable attorney."* His practice focuses on whistle-blower claims, discrimination and harassment cases.

# LITIGATION

Commentary about individuals can be found under their firm's paragraph. If the firm has no paragraph (is not ranked) look at Other Notable Practitioners.

## Litigation: General Commercial
### Leading Firms

**Band 1**
Bass, Berry & Sims PLC *
Riley Warnock & Jacobson, PLC *
Walker, Tipps & Malone *

**Band 2**
Baker, Donelson, Bearman, Caldwell & Berkowitz, PC *
Bradley Arant Boult Cummings LLP *
Neal & Harwell, PLC
Sherrard & Roe PLC

**Band 3**
Burch, Porter & Johnson PLLC
Butler, Snow, O'Mara, Stevens & Cannada, PLLC *
Harwell Howard Hyne Gabbert & Manner, PC *
Miller & Martin PLLC *

## Band 1

### Bass, Berry & Sims PLC
See profile on p.2314

**THE FIRM** This full-service firm retains real prowess in an array of litigation, from major class actions to antitrust cases and loan disputes. The team also has experience in advising on corporate securities disputes and healthcare fraud cases. Clients appreciate the group's knowledgeable, cost-effective approach. Highlights include representing O'Charley's in defending allegations of a breach of fiduciary duty over the $220 million sale of the company.
**Sources say:** "*They are very professional, strategic thinkers. Cooperative collaboration within the firm definitely enhances outcomes, and client communication is a strength.*"
**KEY INDIVIDUALS Lee Barfield** (see p.2301) handles a mix of medical malpractice defense and healthcare litigation. Sources praise him as an "*outstanding*" practitioner. **Michael Dagley** (see p.2303) is active in corporate and securities litigation. He recently defended Morgan Keegan in relation to various claims arising from investment fund losses. **Wallace Dietz** (see p.2303) is praised for his "*top-shelf experience and seasoned judgment.*" As well as his experience in handling shareholder class actions, he frequently takes a lead role in acting on internal investigations and healthcare fraud claims. **Overton Thompson** (see p.2311) has "*a very pragmatic view of litigation and will listen to the client,*" say sources. He recently defended Green Bankshares (now Capital Bank) against claims of violations of federal securities laws. **Dale Grimes** (see p.2304) counsels clients on premerger notification and exclusionary practices, as well as pricing and joint venture issues. **Brook Lathram** (see p.2306) has more than 40 years' experience in commercial litigation concerning breach of contract, antitrust and product liability claims. Clients value **John Speer**'s (see p.2310) "*extremely good judgment.*" He

## Litigation: General Commercial
### Leading Individuals

**Star individuals**

| | |
|---|---|
| Walker Robert | Walker, Tipps & Malone |

**Band 1**

| | |
|---|---|
| Bearman Jr Leo | Baker, Donelson, Bearman, Caldwell * |
| Boston Robert E | Waller Lansden Dortch & Davis * |
| Feibelman Jef | Burch, Porter & Johnson PLLC |
| Harbison William L | Sherrard & Roe PLC |
| Riley Steven A | Riley Warnock & Jacobson, PLC |
| Sanders James F | Neal & Harwell, PLC |

**Band 2**

| | |
|---|---|
| Barfield II H Lee | Bass, Berry & Sims PLC * |
| Belz Saul | Glankler Brown, PLLC (ONP) [†] * |
| Campbell II L Webb | Sherrard & Roe PLC |
| Dagley Michael L | Bass, Berry & Sims PLC * |
| Davidson Paul S | Waller Lansden Dortch & Davis * |
| Dickson Roger W | Miller & Martin PLLC * |
| Dietz Wallace W | Bass, Berry & Sims PLC * |
| Doran Jr James M | Waller Lansden Dortch & Davis * |
| Fardon D Alexander | Harwell Howard Hyne Gabbert & Manner |
| Funk Samuel | Sherrard & Roe PLC |
| Hicks John S | Baker, Donelson, Bearman, Caldwell * |
| Jacobson John R | Riley Warnock & Jacobson, PLC |
| Malone Jr Gayle | Walker, Tipps & Malone |
| Noel Randall D | Butler, Snow, O'Mara, Stevens & Cannada * |
| Patterson Robert S | Bradley Arant Boult Cummings LLP |
| Reid Jr Glen G | Wyatt, Tarrant & Combs, LLP (ONP) [†] * |
| Thompson III Overton | Bass, Berry & Sims PLC * |
| Tipps Mark | Walker, Tipps & Malone |
| Urness Thor | Bradley Arant Boult Cummings LLP |
| Woodruff Joseph A | Waller Lansden Dortch & Davis * |

**Band 3**

| | |
|---|---|
| Chase III Lee James | Glankler Brown, PLLC (ONP) [†] * |
| Cody W J Michael | Burch, Porter & Johnson PLLC |
| Grimes Dale | Bass, Berry & Sims PLC * |
| Harwell Jr Aubrey B | Neal & Harwell, PLC |
| Hayworth John | Walker, Tipps & Malone |
| Lathram Brook | Bass, Berry & Sims PLC * |
| Pera Lucian | Adams and Reese LLP (ONP) [†] * |
| Shockley Gary C | Baker, Donelson, Bearman, Caldwell * |
| Speer John | Bass, Berry & Sims PLC * |

**Associates to watch**

| | |
|---|---|
| Bowen James N | Riley Warnock & Jacobson, PLC |

advises financial services companies on real estate and commercial loans litigation. **Paul Jennings** (see p.2306) is described as a "*top-notch*" lawyer in bankruptcy litigation, where he represents both creditors and corporate debtors. He is also noted for his collegial manner among fellow practitioners.

## Litigation: Medical Malpractice Defense
### Leading Individuals

**Band 1**

| | |
|---|---|
| Barfield II H Lee | Bass, Berry & Sims PLC * |
| Gideon CJ | Gideon, Cooper & Essary PLC (ONP) [†] |
| Trentham Robert | Butler, Snow, O'Mara, Stevens & Cannada * |
| Wellford Buckner | Baker, Donelson, Bearman, Caldwell * |
| Wiseman Tom | Wiseman Ashworth Law Group PLC |

## Litigation: Bankruptcy
### Senior Statesmen

**Senior Statesmen:** distinguished older practitioners

| | |
|---|---|
| Ahern III Lawrence R | Burr & Forman LLP (ONP) [†] |

### Leading Individuals

**Band 1**

| | |
|---|---|
| Childress, Jr E Franklin | Baker, Donelson, Bearman, Caldwell * |
| Gabbert Jr Craig V | Harwell Howard Hyne Gabbert & Manner |
| Goodrich Robert | Stites & Harbison PLLC (ONP) [†] * |
| Jennings Paul G | Bass, Berry & Sims PLC * |
| Kelley James R | Neal & Harwell, PLC |
| Norton III William L | Bradley Arant Boult Cummings LLP |
| Rose Glenn B | Harwell Howard Hyne Gabbert & Manner |

**Band 2**

| | |
|---|---|
| Bucy Rhea | Gullett, Sanford, Robinson & Martin (ONP) [†] |
| Forrester Thomas | Gullett, Sanford, Robinson & Martin (ONP) [†] |
| Holmes Barbara | Harwell Howard Hyne Gabbert & Manner |
| Jones Roger | Bradley Arant Boult Cummings LLP |
| Lawless Thomas | Thomas W. Lawless (ONP) [†] * |

\* Indicates firm / individual with profile.
[†] ONP = Other Notable Practitioner

### Riley Warnock & Jacobson, PLC
See profile on p.2318

**THE FIRM** This team is a trusted adviser to major corporate clients across many different types of claims, receiving considerable praise from sources for the quality of advice it provides. Recent highlights include successfully representing Universal Health Services in dismissing an action brought by an insurer under the False Claims Act. Other areas of strength include securities and healthcare employment litigation.
**Sources say:** "*A top-notch litigation firm.*"
**KEY INDIVIDUALS Steven Riley** has been defending Qwest Communications in a class action challenging its placing of fiber-optic cables along railway rights of way. "*He is very smart and good on his feet in the courtroom,*" observes one interviewee. Managing partner **John Jacobson** has handled extensive litigation work for healthcare clients over the past year. He is also experienced in dealing with disputes in the entertainment and financial services industries. **James Bowen** is highlighted for his "*impressive writing skills.*" He recently assisted Dollar

General in defending allegations of a breach to an executive severance package.

## Walker, Tipps & Malone
See profile on p.2319

**THE FIRM** This team of litigation specialists is renowned for its skill in handling complex commercial disputes for clients from the healthcare, banking and aviation industries. Attorneys have substantial experience of handling a wide spectrum of contentious issues, from securities claims to insurance coverage disputes. The team is also active in the mediation and arbitration fields.
**Sources say:** *"A fine firm." "They are very nimble. Strong litigation work."*
**KEY INDIVIDUALS Robert Walker** is unanimously recognized as *"a fantastic trial lawyer"* and *"the big name that comes to mind in Tennessee."* Throughout his extensive career he has acted on a number of complex business fraud claims and hostile takeover suits. **Gayle Malone** has a strong reputation in alternative dispute resolution, and is also highlighted as *"a well-respected mediator."* He has expertise in handling insurance and construction litigation. **Mark Tipps** is praised by market sources for his *"solid skills"* and *"real strength as a counselor."* He advises clients on multiple areas of commercial litigation. **John Hayworth** is increasingly recognized for his work on niche matters such as SEC enforcement actions and corporate investigations.

## Band 2

## Baker, Donelson, Bearman, Caldwell & Berkowitz, PC
See profile on p.2313

**THE FIRM** This firm has in-depth expertise in advising on major disputes covering bankruptcy, healthcare and a full range of commercial concerns. Attorneys also handle niche environmental litigation, property damage and personal injury claims. Representative clients include the Regents of the University of New Mexico and CSX Transportation.
**KEY INDIVIDUALS** The *"outstanding"* **Leo Bearman** (see p.2301) is based in Memphis and represents clients in multiple aspects of business litigation, ranging from class action defense to shareholder disputes. Besides dealing with commercial interests in the courtroom, he also has recent experience acting for public bodies. **John Hicks's** (see p.2305) recent experience includes representing Rock Ivy in post-trial matters and in an appeal regarding breach of fiduciary duty claims. He has also been defending Assurance Group against unpaid commission fee claims. *"Very intellectual"* **Gary Shockley** (see p.2310) specializes in handling cases involving complex environmental issues, and is noted for his experience in jury trials. He also handles antitrust and healthcare litigation. **Franklin Childress** (see p.2302) has had a busy year acting for institutional lenders in a series of loan and guarantor disputes. He is also adept at representing clients in objecting to Chapter 11 filings. **Buckner Wellford's** (see p.2311) litigation expertise extends to medical malpractice defense and

advising medical groups on regulatory violations. Over the past year he has successfully defended practitioners in wrongful death allegations involving the use of anticoagulants.

## Bradley Arant Boult Cummings LLP
See profile on p.476

**THE FIRM** This strong group of attorneys is noted for its industry knowledge and vast experience of handling pharmaceutical, healthcare and financial services disputes. Recent cases of note include acting for Education Networks of America on the award of a government contract by the state of Idaho.
**Sources say:** *"The team is very effective at pushing towards a resolution and not allowing cases to languish."*
**KEY INDIVIDUALS Robert Patterson** is recognized for his extensive trial experience. *"He is good at devising intelligent litigation strategies,"* remarks one interviewee. **Thor Urness** is described as a *"strategic and thoughtful"* litigator. He achieved a successful result for American National Property and Casualty in a complex claim involving misrepresentation, interference and conspiracy allegations. **William Norton** is a key member of the bankruptcy team. His major work highlights include representing the lenders group in the Chapter 11 filing of Citizens Corporation. **Roger Jones** represents creditors' interests across all aspects of insolvency work. Sources highlight his skills as *"a thorough writer."*

## Neal & Harwell, PLC

**THE FIRM** This practice is a formidable force when it comes to handling Tennessee disputes. Attorneys have particular expertise in such areas as white-collar criminal defense, product liability and bankruptcy representation. Key clients include high-profile local and national corporate organizations.
**KEY INDIVIDUALS** Market sources regard **James Sanders** as a leading white-collar defense lawyer. He also has experience in acting for major companies such as GM and ExxonMobil. Veteran practitioner **Aubrey Harwell** has acted in a number of high-profile commercial litigation cases. He is also known for his role as counsel to public sector officials. **James Kelley** represents creditors and debtors alike in bankruptcy litigation. *"He is a brilliant litigator – one of the few who can speak the language of tax codes and bankruptcy law,"* says one source.

## Sherrard & Roe PLC

**THE FIRM** Litigators at Sherrard & Roe have substantial experience in handling a range of commercial disputes. Clients also benefit substantially from the team's wide-ranging industry experience. The team has recently been active in antitrust and estates litigation. Clients include UBS Financial Services and Belmont University.
**Sources say:** *"Their litigators are very smart and good at what they do."*
**KEY INDIVIDUALS** Sources regard **William Harbison** as *"an excellent trial lawyer."* He continues to represent clients in high-value claims. **Webb Campbell** advises clients from the healthcare and financial services industries. His experi-

ence includes shareholder and securities disputes, as well as insurance coverage issues. Practice chair **Samuel Funk** *"gives very solid advice,"* according to interviewees. He handles a wide array of commercial disputes.

## Waller Lansden Dortch & Davis
See profile on p.2320

**THE FIRM** This firm has solid experience of acting as litigation counsel for a wide range of clients. As well as securing roles in employment and healthcare disputes, the team has handled intellectual property litigation, bankruptcy and publicity rights claims in the past year.
**Sources say:** *"Very solid and well balanced."*
**KEY INDIVIDUALS Robert Boston** (see p.2301) is an established litigator with experience of employment disputes. One interviewee enthusiastically praises him as *"a go-to trial lawyer who is regarded as one of the best."* **Paul Davidson's** (see p.2303) *"quiet demeanor masks his aggressive representation of clients,"* observes one source. Davidson handles antitrust, securities and intellectual property litigation. **James Doran** (see p.2303) is renowned for his expertise in product liability actions. He has been defending an engineering company in a claim alleging defective helicopter engine components were provided to the US military. **Joseph Woodruff** (see p.2312) oversees the firm's financial services litigation team. Sources are impressed with his ability to *"bring a case to a resolution."*

## Band 3

## Burch, Porter & Johnson PLLC

**THE FIRM** This Memphis-based firm regularly assists clients in arbitration proceedings, as well as pre-litigation and court-mandated arbitration actions. It remains active in patent, noncompete and trade secret litigation.
**KEY INDIVIDUALS Jef Feibelman** has a solid track record in the arbitration arena, bolstered by several recent breach of contract cases. He also has recent experience of arguing before the Tennessee Supreme Court. **Michael Cody** handles commercial litigation, internal investigations and regulatory claims. He has experience in alternative dispute resolution.

## Butler, Snow, O'Mara, Stevens & Cannada, PLLC
See profile on p.1613

**THE FIRM** This practice remains heavily involved in representing banks and other financial institutions. It recently defended Pinnacle National Bank over claims relating to the conversion of checks and alleged violations of the Bank Secrecy Act. The team also acted for a major healthcare insurance provider on a significant antitrust matter.
**KEY INDIVIDUALS** Peers cite **Robert Trentham** (see p.2311) as a top choice for referrals when it comes to medical malpractice litigation. He acts on behalf of hospitals and physicians. **Randall Noel** (see p.2307) covers the areas of toxic tort defense and product liability. He also has experience of representing clients at appellate level.

## Harwell Howard Hyne Gabbert & Manner, PC

**THE FIRM** This firm is well known for its extensive bankruptcy and restructuring expertise. In one recent matter, the team advised the federal receiver of Vivid Restaurant on claims arising from the company's sale as a going concern. Litigators also advise on intellectual property disputes and commercial fraud claims.

**Sources say:** *"Their lawyers are extremely well trained, analytical and inventive."*

**KEY INDIVIDUALS** Sources remark positively on **Alexander Fardon**'s *"great reputation and experience."* He has litigated in professional malpractice claims as well as contractual disputes. **Craig Gabbert** is *"one of the premier restructuring and bankruptcy lawyers,"* comment interviewees. He advised a real estate developer on claims relating to a $40 million Chapter 11 bankruptcy. **Glenn Rose** is noted for his work with companies in distressed financial situations. *"He has great judgment and instincts,"* observes one interviewee. **Barbara Holmes** has an extensive record of involvement in restructuring and bankruptcy disputes. Sources highlight her *"irreproachable skills and ethics."*

## Miller & Martin PLLC

See profile on p.2317

**THE FIRM** This firm remains a force in Eastern Tennessee through its work on class actions, healthcare disputes and intellectual property litigation. Its representation of Federal Deposit Insurance Corporation as receiver of Colonial Bank also demonstrates expertise in financial disputes as well as the ability to handle matters crossing state boundaries.

**KEY INDIVIDUALS Roger Dickson** (see p.2303) is praised for his *"good, practical advice on sensitive issues."* He defended US Xpress Enterprises in an action alleging violation of the Fair Credit Reporting Act.

### Other Notable Practitioners

Memphis-based **Saul Belz** (see p.2301) of Glankler Brown, PLLC receives commendations for his litigation and client management skills. His experience covers a wide array of claims, including class actions and employment disputes. **Glen Reid** (see p.2309) of Wyatt, Tarrant & Combs, LLP advises on product liability litigation and white-collar criminal defense cases. He recently advised in a medical equipment dispute. **Lee Chase** (see p.2302) of Glankler Brown, PLLC advises on healthcare and construction litigation, including such matters as contract disputes and personal injury claims. **Lucian Pera** (see p.2308) of Adams and Reese LLP is well regarded in the area of legal ethics and negligence claims. *"He is tremendous in answering ethics questions,"* remarks one peer. Senior statesman

**Lawrence Ahern** of Burr & Forman LLP is a bankruptcy litigation expert. He is admired for his ability to *"identify and focus efforts on key issues as opposed to the minutiae."* **Rhea Bucy** of Gullett, Sanford, Robinson & Martin PLLC handles claims arising from Chapter 11 bankruptcy filings and reorganizations. As well as creditors and debtors, **Thomas Forrester**, also of Gullett, Sanford, Robinson & Martin PLLC, acts for receivers and trustees on insolvency matters. *"He has a great hand on the details and a sense for the case – extraordinarily high quality,"* says one client. **Robert Goodrich** (see p.2304) of Stites & Harbison PLLC is recommended by market sources for being *"very good at getting results,"* particularly during complex bankruptcy disputes. Sole practitioner **Thomas Lawless** (see p.2306) is *"not only excellent in the courtroom, but also a good negotiator and he has a sound business mind,"* comment clients. He recently acted for the First National Bank of McMinnville in a disputed Chapter 11 reorganization. In the area of medical malpractice defense, **CJ Gideon** of Gideon, Cooper & Essary PLC is *"as good as they come,"* according to sources. He is highlighted for his lengthy experience and dedication to the field. **Tom Wiseman** of Wiseman Ashworth Law Group PLC continues to be highlighted for his experience of healthcare and medical malpractice cases.

# MEDIA & ENTERTAINMENT

Commentary about individuals can be found under their firm's paragraph. If the firm has no paragraph (is not ranked) look at Other Notable Practitioners.

| Media & Entertainment Leading Firms |
| --- |
| **Band 1** |
| Adams and Reese LLP * |
| Milom Hornsell Crow Rose Kelley PLC |
| **Band 2** |
| Bradley Arant Boult Cummings LLP * |
| Harris Martin Jones P.A. |
| Waller Lansden Dortch & Davis * |

| Media & Entertainment Leading Individuals | |
| --- | --- |
| **Star individuals** | |
| Milom W Michael | Milom Hornsell Crow Rose Kelley PLC |
| **Band 1** | |
| Almon Orville | Almon Law, PLLC (ONP)[†] |
| Del Casino Casey | Law Office of F. Casey Del Casino (ONP)[†] |
| Edell Howard Linda | Adams and Reese LLP * |
| Jones Russell A. | Harris Martin Jones P.A. |
| Lipshie Samuel D | Bradley Arant Boult Cummings LLP |
| **Band 2** | |
| Harris II James H | Harris Martin Jones P.A. |
| Harvey Robb S | Waller Lansden Dortch & Davis * |
| Hornsell Chris | Milom Hornsell Crow Rose Kelley PLC |
| Mimms Malcolm | Malcolm L Mimms Jr, Attorney-at-law (ONP)[†] |
| Morrow Lynn | Adams and Reese LLP * |
| Norwood E Andrew | Waller Lansden Dortch & Davis * |
| Zumwalt Jim | Shackelford, Zumwalt & Hayes (ONP)[†] |
| **Up-and-coming individuals** | |
| Crow David | Milom Hornsell Crow Rose Kelley PLC |
| Rose Natalya | Milom Hornsell Crow Rose Kelley PLC |

\* Indicates firm / individual with profile.

[†]ONP = Other Notable Practitioner

## Band 1

### Adams and Reese LLP

See profile on p.1372

**THE FIRM** This Nashville-based team has firmly established itself at the heart of the media and entertainment world in Tennessee, not only through its geographical location on Nashville's celebrated Music Row, but also through a steadfast reputation for first-class work. The group focus on a multiplicity of matters, including IP, entertainment, new media and e-commerce, and its clients range from songwriters, producers and music publishers to illustrators and graphic artists.

**Sources say:** *"Great firm!"*

**KEY INDIVIDUALS** *"Top lawyer"* **Linda Edell Howard** (see p.2303) continues to maintain a transactional focus to her work, representing numerous high-profile recording artists, producers, publishers and authors. She is particularly noted for her expertise on IP matters, both on a national and international level. **Lynn Morrow** (see p.2307) is well known for her work with Christian and country music clients. She is a much-noted litigator and receives high praise from peers, who say: *"She is knowledgeable and she understands the dispute resolution aspect of entertainment issues."*

## Milom Hornsell Crow Rose Kelley PLC

**THE FIRM** This boutique firm enjoys a fine reputation for media, entertainment and IP work and its team of experienced attorneys take a dedicated approach to advising their clients, who span the spectrum of the entertainment and publishing industries. The group handles matters from brand and trademark protection to distribution contracts and tour agreements. In a recent highlight, it has recently advised The Band Perry on numerous issues including recording contracts, sponsorship deals and merchandise agreements.

Sources say: *"World-class work. They are collaborative and attack every situation with a thoughtful, pragmatic approach – gold standard!"*

**KEY INDIVIDUALS Michael Milom** is regarded as a luminary in the field, with peers and clients quick to recognize him as *"the king of entertainment law"* and part of the *"fabric of the music industry."* He continues to represent an enviable list of clients, including top recording artists, authors and producers. Sources identify **Chris Horsnell** as an excellent transactional lawyer and reserve particular praise for his efficiency and ability to get the job done. Recent work includes negotiating licensing and recording contracts for country music band Rascal Flatts. **David Crow** is regarded as a rising star in the market, with sources hailing him as being *"at the top of the list"* for his age group and also commending his *"almost encyclopedic knowledge"* of entertainment law. He works with a medley of high-profile clients such as The Band Perry and Daily & Vincent. **Natalya Rose** is known for her expertise on IP matters as they relate to the media and entertainment world, including patent protection and trademark and copyright issues. Clients describe her as a *"pleasure to work with,"* and single out her responsiveness, industrious work ethic and ability to find practical answers as being among her key attributes.

## Band 2

### Bradley Arant Boult Cummings LLP
See profile on p.476

**THE FIRM** This firm is particularly noted for its litigation savvy and is a go-to for First Amendment cases, but is also recognized as a fine choice for clients seeking advice on transactional matters. It represents a host of high-profile

media and entertainment clients such as Clint Black, Randy Travis and Broken Bow Records.

Sources say: *"The firm ranks very highly in terms of its no-nonsense approach to litigation."*

**KEY INDIVIDUALS** Sources identify **Samuel Lipshie** as *"one of the finest lawyers in Tennessee."* He is primarily a litigator, handling complex disputes for a variety of high-profile clients. He recently acted for The Songwriters Guild of America in copyright royalty litigation.

### Harris Martin Jones P.A.

**THE FIRM** Harris Martin Jones is a stalwart of the Tennessee music and entertainment scene. As well as advising on copyright, trademark and contract issues, the firm also provides an assortment of more traditional legal services, including family law, corporate, estate planning and dispute resolution. Its distinguished client roster includes entertainers, songwriters and producers.

**KEY INDIVIDUALS Russell Jones** has carved out a fine reputation for his work in the entertainment industry, acting for a number of celebrity artists such as the Dixie Chicks and Garth Brooks. **James Harris** is particularly noted for his expertise in music law, in addition to matters concerning copyright and trademarks. He is also particularly singled out by sources for his litigation strengths.

### Waller Lansden Dortch & Davis
See profile on p.2320

**THE FIRM** This firm offers clients a cross-disciplinary approach to media and entertainment, covering trial and appellant, IP and tax matters. Waller continues to distinguish itself as excellent IP and First Amendment litigators, and this promises to flourish further with the recent addition of Kelly Hollowell to the team. Clients include individuals and companies from the music, television and film

industries. The team won recent acclaim when it represented a coalition of media bodies in the In re Hansen case, which led to the triumphant opening of court records to the public.

Sources say: *"Innovative, proactive and extremely service-oriented."*

**KEY INDIVIDUALS Robb Harvey** (see p.2305) is an excellent litigator particularly praised for his inventive approach and collegial relationship with clients. Harvey has achieved numerous successes this year in IP and access to information litigation. **Andrew Norwood** (see p.2307) is particularly noted for his expertise in IP and book publishing. Sources particularly single out his business understanding and thoughtful approach to matters.

## Other Notable Practitioners

**Orville Almon** of Almon Law, PLLC is an experienced and highly respected practitioner in the media and entertainment space. He works with clients from all corners of the industry, with a particular focus in music publishing. In the eyes of peers he is *"excellent, organized, thorough and a good negotiator."* Sources describe sole practitioner **Casey Del Casino** as an *"excellent lawyer"* who *"understands the industry in ways others do not."* He is a much-noted expert in copyright law. Fellow sole practitioner **Malcolm Mimms** receives a wealth of praise from peers, not least for his fine judgment and practical approach to matters. He remains particularly admired for his depth of experience and level of understanding of the music business. **Jim Zumwalt** of Shackelford, Zumwalt & Hayes is a seasoned attorney with over 35 years of experience in the media and entertainment space. He represents some of the biggest names in show business and elicits much praise for his ability to get deals done.

# REAL ESTATE

Commentary about individuals can be found under their firm's paragraph. If the firm has no paragraph (is not ranked) look at Other Notable Practitioners.

## Band 1

### Baker, Donelson, Bearman, Caldwell & Berkowitz, PC
See profile on p.2313

**THE FIRM** This real estate group has established a strong reputation in Tennessee. With four offices statewide, the firm is well placed to advise a range of local and national clients on such matters as property acquisitions and sales, leasing and financing transactions. The team represents major financial institutions such as First Tennessee Bank, as well as insurance companies, Fortune 500 companies, hospitals and real estate investment trusts.

Sources say: *"A very professional firm that is able to provide backup when I need it."* *"They provide excellent results."*

**KEY INDIVIDUALS Robert Liddon** (see p.2306) has a versatile practice that covers multiple areas of real estate

law. He advises on expansion and improvement initiatives, and also has experience acting on behalf of financial institutions and healthcare facilities on acquisitions and refinancings. **Pete Ezell** (see p.2304) is recommended for his expertise in REIT taxation. Recent work includes payment-in-lieu-of-tax transactions (PILOTs) and borrower-side financing mandates. **Mary Aronov** (see p.2301) frequently advises on asset-based lending and commercial real estate loan transactions. *"She is very thorough, hard-working and accessible,"* clients comment. Besides representing institutional lenders, she also represents healthcare clients in acquisitions and refinancings. **John Gupton** (see p.2305) acted for AO Smith on its $390 million purchase of a manufacturing facility. Sources comment: *"He is very practical and understands the time sensitivity of this business."*

### Bass, Berry & Sims PLC
See profile on p.2314

**THE FIRM** This firm earns glowing praise from its strong corporate client base for its real estate practice in Tennessee. The team regularly advises on retail development projects and also handles REIT work. It recently advised AmREIT on a $75 million syndicated unsecured loan facility provided by five separate lenders. Notably, it also advised the City of Bristol in relation to a border region retail development. The team has also acted on various redevelopments and PPP projects.

Sources say: *"The firm is highly regarded, reputable and held in high esteem in the legal profession."*

**KEY INDIVIDUALS Dewees Berry** (see p.2301) is *"very well versed in real estate litigation,"* say sources. His knowledge of land use, boundary and lease disputes complements additional experience in transactions. **John**

## Real Estate
### Leading Firms

**Band 1**
Baker, Donelson, Bearman, Caldwell & Berkowitz, PC *
Bass, Berry & Sims PLC *
Bradley Arant Boult Cummings LLP *
Sherrard & Roe PLC
Waller Lansden Dortch & Davis *

**Band 2**
Glankler Brown, PLLC

**Band 3**
Adams and Reese LLP *
Burch, Porter & Johnson PLLC
Butler, Snow, O'Mara, Stevens & Cannada, PLLC *
Harkavy Shainberg Kaplan & Dunstan PLC
Stites & Harbison PLLC *

## Real Estate
### Leading Individuals

**Band 1**

| | |
|---|---|
| Berry IV C Dewees | Bass, Berry & Sims PLC * |
| Brown Kim | Sherrard & Roe PLC |
| Campbell Jr Robert R | Waller Lansden Dortch & Davis * |
| Cargile Ann Peldo | Bradley Arant Boult Cummings LLP |
| Liddon Robert C | Baker, Donelson, Bearman, Caldwell * |
| Stemmler John A | Bass, Berry & Sims PLC * |
| Trent Tom | Bradley Arant Boult Cummings LLP |
| Warren Jr Richard F | Bradley Arant Boult Cummings LLP |

**Band 2**

| | |
|---|---|
| Aronov Mary L | Baker, Donelson, Bearman, Caldwell * |
| Bibb Julian L | Stites & Harbison PLLC * |
| Calk Jeffrey A | Waller Lansden Dortch & Davis * |
| Carver Mark | Sherrard & Roe PLC |
| Ezell Jr Kenneth P (Pete) | Baker, Donelson, Bearman, Caldwell * |
| Gupton III John A | Baker, Donelson, Bearman, Caldwell * |
| Harkavy Ronald | Harkavy Shainberg Kaplan & Dunstan PLC |
| Harris Matthew T | Waller Lansden Dortch & Davis * |
| Haynes John | Bradley Arant Boult Cummings LLP |
| Houk D Reed | Adams and Reese LLP * |
| Humphreys Hunter | Glankler Brown, PLLC * |
| Peek Michael S | Bass, Berry & Sims PLC * |
| Raines Richard C | Wyatt, Tarrant & Combs, LLP (ONP)[†] |
| Reasor Jr Charles B | White & Reasor, PLC (ONP)[†] |
| Roe Jr John H | Sherrard & Roe PLC |
| Scott W Rowlett | Burch, Porter & Johnson PLLC |
| Wood Robert | Bradley Arant Boult Cummings LLP |

**Band 3**

| | |
|---|---|
| Cates C Thomas | Burch, Porter & Johnson PLLC |
| Earthman B Douglas | Glankler Brown, PLLC * |
| Feldman Ron | Husch Blackwell LLP (ONP)[†] |
| Gumbert Gregg C | Butler, Snow, O'Mara, Stevens & Cannada * |
| Marsh Darlene T | Burr & Forman LLP (ONP)[†] |
| Marshall Cox LeeAnne | Burch, Porter & Johnson PLLC |
| Papel Laurence M | Nelson Mullins Riley (ONP)[†] * |
| Rutter David | Bradley Arant Boult Cummings LLP |
| Shainberg Raymond | Harkavy Shainberg Kaplan & Dunstan PLC |
| Sheets D Mark | Bass, Berry & Sims PLC * |
| Spore III Richard R | Bass, Berry & Sims PLC * |
| Weathersby E Woods | Evans & Petree PC (ONP)[†] |
| Yarbro Jason G | Butler, Snow, O'Mara, Stevens & Cannada * |

## Real Estate: Zoning/Land Use
### Leading Individuals

**Band 1**

| | |
|---|---|
| Berry IV C Dewees | Bass, Berry & Sims PLC * |
| Harkavy Ronald | Harkavy Shainberg Kaplan & Dunstan PLC |
| Murphy III James L | Bradley Arant Boult Cummings LLP |
| White Thomas V | Tune, Entrekin & White (ONP)[†] |

* Indicates firm / individual with profile.
[†] ONP = Other Notable Practitioner

---

**Stemmler** (see p.2310) had an active year acting for property investors on a series of sales and acquisitions. *"John is a very experienced and levelheaded attorney. He worked through very sensitive issues and got the results we wanted,"* said one client. **Richard Spore** (see p.2310) *"is very thorough, very good to work with and is well liked by clients,"* sources say. He advised Loeb Properties on the acquisition and redevelopment of Overton Square in Memphis. **Michael Peek** (see p.2308) is recognized for his work for real estate developers. In highlights, he advised Alex S Palmer & Company on the development of two office towers at West End Summit. Department head **Mark Sheets** (see p.2310) acted for O'Charley's on a sale and leaseback facility of a number of restaurants in multiple states. His practice also covers healthcare, industrial and office real estate matters.

## Bradley Arant Boult Cummings LLP
See profile on p.476

**THE FIRM** This practice group is acclaimed for its multi-faceted expertise in real estate, and provides the full spectrum of services to its clients in Tennessee. In 2012, the firm acted on purchase and sale transactions both in and out of state, as well as on joint ventures, financings, land use matters and related litigation. The team advised Knoxville Properties Partnership on its purchase of several commercial properties. Other clients include Wells Fargo, Greenfield Partners and the City of Clarksville.

**Sources say:** *"I'd give them the highest marks we can give. They are very cost effective and are always available to us; they are willing to work around their clients." "I don't think anybody in Nashville is better than they are."*

**KEY INDIVIDUALS Richard Warren**'s recent work for Stiles Corporation on the formation of a joint venture and the negotiation of the financing for a high-rise luxury apartment reflects his impressive expertise in commercial real estate. He also advises on tax increment financing and PILOTs. Peers are unanimous in their praise for **Ann Peldo Cargile**, who is best known for her forte in leasing and lending matters. She advised Commerce Street Associates on the $47 million sale of a Nashville office building to Sun Life Assurance Company of Canada. **Tom Trent** is an

*"extraordinarily detailed and thoughtful lawyer,"* sources enthuse. He advises a variety of clients, including insurance and healthcare companies, on real estate matters. His practice also covers construction and economic development. **John Haynes** represents international clients in property sales and purchases. *"He is very good at protecting our interests,"* say sources. The *"knowledgeable and pleasant"* **David Rutter** advises owners of commercial real estate throughout the entire development process, and is often involved in multistate transactions. Land use and zoning lawyer **James Murphy** successfully defended the City of Clarksville in a lawsuit challenging its adoption of a temporary land use moratorium. He also has experience handling challenges concerning the validity of zoning regulations. **Robert Wood** regularly advises lenders on real estate transactions. He has experience dealing with different loan structures which are secured by commercial properties.

## Sherrard & Roe PLC

**THE FIRM** This firm comes highly recommended by market sources for the high quality of its work in this field. It advises a wide range of clients, including real estate developers, hospitality companies, REITs, shopping center owner-operators and high net worth individuals on all manner of real estate project types, including PPP and residential and mixed-use developments. The firm also advises on land use and zoning and title insurance. Representative clients include City Development and Nashville Bank & Trust.

**Sources say:** *"A highly respected and well-regarded firm." "I think they are the best firm in our market – I use them because of their thoroughness, timeliness and the value they bring to my business."*

**KEY INDIVIDUALS Kim Brown** advises on real estate development and financing. *"He is one of the best – he manages to strike a good balance between business acumen and legalities,"* said one source. **Mark Carver** earns praise for being *"fair, reasonable and extremely knowledgeable."* He focuses on development work as well as real estate brokerage. **John Roe** advises on commercial real estate, municipal finance and international law. He also advises on private equity transactions, and has a strong focus on multifamily condominium project development.

## Waller Lansden Dortch & Davis
See profile on p.2320

**THE FIRM** This group is recognized for the diversity of its real estate practice, and attracts significant roles acting for clients with large property portfolios in Tennessee and further afield. In recent highlights, it represented Carter-Haston Real Estate in a series of property acquisitions and dispositions totaling $136 million. It also has experience dealing with state and city incentives as well as development issues. The nature of properties handled by the group ranges from retail locations to automobile manufacturing facilities.

**KEY INDIVIDUALS** Practice group leader **Robert Campbell** (see p.2302) acted for Covenant Capital Group on its investment in ten properties worth over $100 million. *"He represents a good variety of clients and is always a pleasure to work with,"* said one source. **Jeffrey Calk** (see p.2302) has been handling various real estate matters for the firm's long-term client HCA, including the acquisition of hospital sites and development of new facilities.

Matthew Harris (see p.2305) has a varied practice that includes leasing matters and real estate financing. Recent work includes acting for Tractor Supply on the acquisition and negotiation of development agreements for its new corporate headquarters.

## Band 2

### Glankler Brown, PLLC

THE FIRM This real estate group enjoys a fine reputation among peers and clients alike. The team handles a high volume of real estate sales and acquisitions, and represented the City of Memphis in its acquisition and redevelopment of Overton Square. The firm also acted on the sale of The Mall at Green Hills to Taubman Centers. Other clients include the Memphis-Shelby County Airport Authority and Elvis Presley Enterprises.

Sources say: *"They are quality attorneys who are very responsive to their clients."*

KEY INDIVIDUALS Hunter Humphreys (see p.2305) *"is very good technically, and does a good job managing clients,"* one source said. He handles property management agreements, leases and receiverships for LEDIC Management Group. Douglas Earthman (see p.2303) is commended by peers for his combined experience in real estate and municipal bond transactions. Alongside Humphreys, he acted for the City of Memphis regarding the leasing of the Pyramid Arena and on its subsequent redevelopment.

## Band 3

### Adams and Reese LLP
See profile on p.1372

THE FIRM This regional firm offers a comprehensive range of real estate-related legal services. Core areas of practice include commercial leasing, property acquisitions and related real estate financing. The team also advises on construction transactions and economic development, as well as on litigation, licensing and compliance.

KEY INDIVIDUALS Reed Houk (see p.2305) is recognized for his representation of banks and other lenders in real estate financings. He also advises on bankruptcy and reorganizations and on related litigation. *"He's excellent,"* sources say.

### Burch, Porter & Johnson PLLC

THE FIRM The Memphis-based team has a longstanding reputation for real estate throughout Tennessee. It regularly advises a variety of land-owners including developers and small family businesses on commercial transactions. Additionally, the team provides guidance on land use and zoning regulation as well as environmental compliance.

Sources say: *"A very fine real estate group."*

KEY INDIVIDUALS Thomas Cates has an active real estate transactions practice in Memphis, and has been involved in sales and acquisitions of property across the country. Rowlett Scott's commercial real estate work encompasses leasing and property acquisitions. Commercial lending is another area of his practice. Sources say: *"He works extremely hard."* LeeAnne Marshall Cox represents both lenders and borrowers in real estate financings. She has acted on a wide variety of real estate projects, including residential subdivisions, hotel and resort developments, and government-assisted projects.

### Butler, Snow, O'Mara, Stevens & Cannada, PLLC
See profile on p.1613

THE FIRM This firm's real estate department benefited from several lateral hires in its Nashville office in 2012, and is recognized for its increasing activity throughout Tennessee. Notable work includes advising West Tennessee Healthcare on the lease for a wellness center in Jackson, financed through new markets tax credits.

KEY INDIVIDUALS Jason Yarbro (see p.2312) acted for American Health Companies on the refinancing of a $55 million senior credit facility. Gregg Gumbert (see p.2304) acted for IBERIABANK on the financing of the purchase of Overton Square Entertainment District by Loeb Properties.

### Harkavy Shainberg Kaplan & Dunstan PLC

THE FIRM This Memphis firm has a long history in the real estate market. The team is well known for its expertise in land use and zoning, and also handles landlord-tenant disputes and leasing matters on behalf of property management companies throughout Tennessee.

KEY INDIVIDUALS The experienced Ronald Harkavy operates a strong real estate practice that covers land use and zoning matters as well as commercial transactions. Raymond Shainberg is *"an exceptionally bright attorney with a strong roster of clients."* He represents developers and lenders and has extensive experience advising hotel operators.

### Stites & Harbison PLLC
See profile on p.1331

THE FIRM This firm is well known for its representation of real estate lenders such as SunTrust Bank and Regions Bank. Other areas of focus include real estate development and redevelopment, where the group regularly acts on the purchase and refinancing of a variety of real estate assets including residential, commercial and mixed-use properties. It also advises on land use and zoning as well as related litigation.

KEY INDIVIDUALS Peers view Julian Bibb's (see p.2301) banking background as an asset to his representation of various interests in property transactions. He has additional expertise in real estate law advising clients on historic preservation and conservation easements.

## Other Notable Practitioners

The highly respected Thomas White of Tune, Entrekin & White specializes in land use, zoning and construction law. He has significant experience before the Metropolitan Nashville Planning Commission and the Metropolitan Board of Zoning Appeals. Darlene Marsh of Burr & Forman LLP *"is thorough in her work, communicates clearly and precisely, and understands our business requirements."* She focuses on real estate finance and environmental law, acting for such clients as US Bank and First American Title Insurance. Laurence Papel (see p.2308) is the managing partner of Nelson Mullins Riley & Scarborough LLP's Nashville office. He advises on both real estate and general corporate commercial law. Woods Weathersby of Evans & Petree PC represents commercial developers and corporate users of real estate in a wide range of real estate transactions, including acquisitions, tax incentives and PILOTs. Ron Feldman of Husch Blackwell LLP has acted on numerous transactions involving the purchase, sale, redevelopment and expansion of shopping centers and office buildings. Sources say: *"His knowledge is vast and varied – he is able to condense complex legal issues into a format that the client can understand, which greatly facilitates our ability to make business decisions."* Richard Raines (see p.2309) of Wyatt, Tarrant & Combs, LLP represents property owners in the negotiation of contracts, title evaluations and leasing matters. His prior experience as in-house counsel to a large regional bank is a strong asset to his real estate lending practice. Charles Reasor of White & Reasor, PLC advises on commercial workouts in the context of real estate. He has acted on behalf of a variety of local, national and international clients.

# Leaders' Profiles in Tennessee

**ARONOV, Mary L**
Baker, Donelson, Bearman, Caldwell &
Berkowitz, PC, Memphis
901 577 2223
maronov@bakerdonelson.com
*Featured in Real Estate (Tennessee)*
**Practice Areas:** Practice concentrated in commercial real estate, commercial lending and financial transactions. Extensive experience in real estate and asset-based loan transactions, purchases and sale of commercial real estate, mergers and acquisitions, multi-state lending transactions, leases, corporate finance operations, loan modifications and work-outs, foreclosures and other commercial transactions.
**Professional Memberships:** Member of American Bar Association (commercial law, real estate and probate sections), Tennessee and Memphis Bar Associations. Former Chairperson, Memphis and Shelby County Air Pollution Control Board. Authored articles in several legal publications.
**Career:** Licensed in Tennessee since 1984.

**BARFIELD II, H Lee**
Bass, Berry & Sims PLC, Nashville
615 742 6202
lbarfield@bassberry.com
*Featured in Litigation (Tennessee)*
**Practice Areas:** Business litigation and healthcare law. Handles broad variety of litigation, including business disputes, healthcare, class actions, insurance, commercial law, malpractice, government relations and constitutional law.
**Professional Memberships:** American, Tennessee and Nashville Bar Associations.
**Career:** Joined the firm in 1974. Served as President of Board of Law Examiners for the State of Tennessee, 1986-2000. Adjunct professor, Vanderbilt Law School, since 2000.
**Publications:** "Providing a Safe Harbor for Those Who Play by the Rules: The Case for a Strong Regulatory Compliance Defense," Utah Law Review (Vol. 2008. No. 1, 2008).
**Personal:** BA (1968) and JD (1974), Vanderbilt University.

**BARTRUM, Thomas E**
Baker, Donelson, Bearman, Caldwell &
Berkowitz, PC, Nashville
615 726 5641
tbartrum@bakerdonelson.com
*Featured in Healthcare (Tennessee)*
**Practice Areas:** Thomas Bartrum concentrates his practice in health care regulatory, transactional and government investigation matters, including structuring and advising regarding hospital-physician joint ventures and accountable care organizations, day to day compliance advice, responding to government fraud and abuse investigations, whistleblower actions, and overpayment issues.
**Professional Memberships:** Tennessee, Kentucky and American Bar Associations. American Health Lawyers Association, Health Care Financial Management Association.

**Career:** Licensed in Tennessee and Kentucky. Listed in The Best Lawyers in America® in Health Law.
**Personal:** Loyola University Chicago School of Law, LLM, Health Law, 1997. University of Kentucky, JD, 1993, with distinction. Bellarmine College, BA, 1989.

**BEARMAN JR, Leo**
Baker, Donelson, Bearman, Caldwell &
Berkowitz, PC, Memphis
901 577 2220
lbearman@bakerdonelson.com
*Featured in Litigation (Tennessee)*
**Practice Areas:** Fifty years' experience representing local, regional and national companies as well as city and county governments in class action defense, antitrust matters, insurance defense litigation, products liability defense, intellectual property litigation, professional liability and general commercial litigation.
**Professional Memberships:** Fellow, American College of Trial Lawyers. Member, American Academy of Appellate Lawyers. Life Member, Fellows of the American Bar Foundation. Member, Tennessee and Memphis Bar Associations. Member, American Board of Trial Advocates. Adjunct Professor of law, University of Memphis Cecil C Humphreys School of Law.
**Career:** Licensed in Tennessee since 1960 and United States Supreme Court since 1973.

**BELZ, Saul**
Glankler Brown, PLLC, Memphis
901 576 1741
sbelz@glankler.com
*Featured in Litigation (Tennessee)*
**Practice Areas:** Business litigation, commercial disputes, complex litigation, appeals, employment law, mediation and alternative dispute resolution.
**Professional Memberships:** American Bar Association; Memphis Bar Association (Director, 1987-88); Tennessee Justice Center (Director, 2001-06); Center for Southern Studies at the University of Mississippi (Past Director); Memphis Zoological Society (Past Director); Supreme Court of the State of Tennessee Advisory Commission on the Rules of Practice and Procedure; Memphis Area Legal Services Fundraising Campaign Chairman 2009.
**Career:** Admitted to practice 1967, Texas & 1968, Tennessee; The Best Lawyers in America, Bet-the-Company litigation, business litigation, banking & finance; The Best Lawyers in America, Memphis Best Lawyers, Securities Lawyer of the Year 2011; Benchmark Litigation, Litigation Star in Tennessee; Chambers & Partners, America's Leading Lawyers for Business; Best 101 Lawyers in Tennessee, Business TN magazine; Fellow, American College of Trial Lawyers; Mid South SuperLawyers; Rule 31 Certified Mediator, Tennessee.
**Publications:** Contributing co-author of the American Bar Association, Section of Litigation, Survey of State Class Action Law, A Report of the State Laws Subcommittee of the Class Actions and

Derivative Suits Committee (ABA 1999) for the State of Tennessee; Also published in the 2001 Supplement to Newberg on Class Actions (West Group 2001); Federal Tax Rulings: Procedure and Policy, 21 Vand. L. Rev. 78 (1967) and co-author of Limitations on Employer Conduct During Union Organizational Campaigns - A Survey, 19 Vand. L. Rev. 438 (1966)
**Personal:** Born 1942; University of Texas, BA degree, with honors, 1964; Vanderbilt University, JD degree, 1967 (Order of the Coif, Legislation Editor, Vanderbilt Law Review).

**BERRY IV, C Dewees**
Bass, Berry & Sims PLC, Nashville
615 742 6215
cberry@bassberry.com
*Featured in Real Estate (Tennessee)*
**Practice Areas:** Litigates real estate disputes. Advises clients concerning restrictive covenant, planning, zoning, and other land use issues. Has extensive transactional experience including purchases and sales, financings, leasing and all other aspects of commercial real estate.
**Professional Memberships:** Rule 31 Listed General Civil Mediator; past President, Nashville Bar Association; Fellow, American College of Real Estate Lawyers.
**Career:** Joined the firm in 1981. Editor, Tennessee Real Estate Law Letter. Instructor in Real Property Law, Nashville School of Law.
**Personal:** BA (1973) and JD (1976), Vanderbilt University.

**BIBB, Julian L**
Stites & Harbison PLLC, Nashville
615 782 2227
julian.bibb@stites.com
*Featured in Banking & Finance (Tennessee), Real Estate (Tennessee)*
**Practice Areas:** (1) Banking and finance: broad range of finance, banking, financial institution, and related matters, including syndicated bank financing, structured credit facilities, and workout transactions. (2) Real estate: extensive experience in commerical real estate, planning and zoning, lease transactions, historic preservation, land conservation and financing.
**Professional Memberships:** Licensed in Tennessee since 1977. American, Tennessee, Nashville and Williamson County Bar Associations; Lawyers Association for Women; Tennessee Bar Foundation, Fellow; Nashville Bar Foundation, Fellow; NAIOP.
**Career:** Member, Stites & Harbison. Chair, Real Estate and Banking Service Group; Member, Tennessee Board of Law Examiners.
**Personal:** JD, Vanderbilt University Law School, 1977; BA, University of the South, 1973

**BISHOP III, George W**
Waller Lansden Dortch & Davis, Nashville
615 850 8623
george.bishop@wallerlaw.com
*Featured in Healthcare (Tennessee)*

**Practice Areas:** Corporate law with nearly 40 years' experience in healthcare mergers and acquisitions, joint ventures, syndications, antitrust, regulatory compliance, securities and venture capital financings. Lead counsel for investor-owned and tax-exempt healthcare providers in approximately 200 transactions throughout the United States.
**Professional Memberships:** American Health Lawyers Association; Nashville Bar Association, Initial Chair - Health Law Committee; Tennessee Bar Association, Founder And Initial Chair - Health Law Section
**Career:** Licensed in Tennessee since 1976. Joined Waller in 1976.
**Personal:** JD, with highest honors, 1975, University of Tennessee; MA, 1973, University of Oxford; BA, cum laude, 1970, University of the South.

**BOSTON, Robert E**
Waller Lansden Dortch & Davis, Nashville
615 850 8953
bob.boston@wallerlaw.com
*Featured in Labor & Employment (Tennessee), Litigation (Tennessee)*
**Practice Areas:** Represents retailers, domestic and international manufacturers, nationwide service providers and multi-site hospital systems in complex commercial litigation and labor and employment litigation and dispute resolution. Advises on employer/employee related issues, including day-to-day management, labor relations and business litigation.
**Professional Memberships:** Fellow, Nashville, Tennessee and American Bar Associations. Fellow, Nashville Bar Foundation. Fellow, American College of Trial Lawyers. Approved arbitrator for National Association of Securities Dealers, National Futures Association.
**Career:** Licensed in Tennessee since 1982. Joined Waller in 1982. Former member of Waller's Board of Directors.
**Personal:** JD, with high honors, 1981, University of Tennessee; BA, 1979 Vanderbilt University.

**BRITT III, Louis P**
FordHarrison LLP, Memphis
901 291 1516
lbritt@fordharrison.com
*Featured in Labor & Employment (Tennessee)*
**Practice Areas:** Labor and Employment
**Career:** Louis Britt concentrates his practice on employment litigation and advice, representing private and public employers in a broad range of employment matters. He handles employment discrimination and harassment cases (Title VII, ADA, ADEA and FMLA), wage/hour matters, enforcement and defense of restrictive covenants contained in employment agreements, and employment-related torts. He is experienced in complex and class action litigation, and has tried cases in state and federal courts across the country. Louis has extensive experience in public sector representation in both litigation and collective bargaining. He received his JD from Tulane University Law School.

## BROWDER, Brian R
Waller Lansden Dortch & Davis, Nashville
615 850 8636
brian.browder@wallerlaw.com
*Featured in Healthcare (Tennessee)*
**Practice Areas:** M&A and corporate law. Represents investor-owned and tax-exempt hospitals, health systems and other healthcare providers in mergers and acquisitions and other complex corporate transactions including joint ventures, dispositions, leveraged/management buyouts, venture capital and private equity investments. Assists public and private companies, not-for-profit healthcare systems and governmental providers. Chairs Waller's interdisciplinary Healthcare Department of more than 70 attorneys.
**Professional Memberships:** Nashville, Tennessee and American Bar Associations; ABA Business Law, Business Law and Health Law Sections; American Health Lawyers Association.
**Career:** Licensed in Tennessee since 1994. Joined Waller in 1997.
**Personal:** JD, 1994, Vanderbilt University; BSBA, 1991, Georgetown University.

## BURKE, Denise D
Butler, Snow, O'Mara, Stevens & Cannada, PLLC, Memphis
901 680 7321
denise.burke@butlersnow.com
*Featured in Healthcare (Tennessee)*
**Practice Areas:** Healthcare law; government investigations; regulatory compliance counsel and advice.
**Professional Memberships:** American Health Lawyers Association; Medical Group Managers Association; Healthcare Financial Management Association; American Health Information Management Association; Healthcare Compliance Association; American Bar Association; Tennessee Bar Association (Executive Counsel, Health Law section); Memphis Bar Association.
**Career:** AV-rated, Martindale-Hubbell; The Best Lawyers in America, Lawyer of the Year (Health Care Law); Mid-South Super Lawyers (Health Care Law); Fellow, American Bar Foundation; Registered Health Information Management Administrator.
**Personal:** Memphis State University, JD, 1993; University of Tennessee, BS, with honors, 1986.

## BURKS, Ashby Q
Baker, Donelson, Bearman, Caldwell & Berkowitz, PC, Nashville
615 726 5626
aburks@bakerdonelson.com
*Featured in Healthcare (Tennessee)*
**Practice Areas:** Mr Burks' practice emphasizes mergers and acquisitions, joint ventures and other business transactions. He has served as Counsel in the purchase, sale or joint venture of more than 100 hospitals and other investor-owned and not-for-profit healthcare businesses. He was previously Vice President, Secretary and General Counsel of Quorum Health Group, Inc. and served as Vice President and Assistant General Counsel of Hospital Corporation of America.

**Professional Memberships:** Virginia, Tennessee and American Bar Associations. Phi Beta Kappa.
**Career:** Licensed in Tennessee since 1985, Virginia since 1982.
**Personal:** Columbia University School of Law, JD, 1982. University of Virginia, BA, 1979.

## BURNSTEIN, Matthew R
Waller Lansden Dortch & Davis, Nashville
615 850 8110
matt.burnstein@wallerlaw.com
*Featured in Corporate/M&A (Tennessee)*
**Practice Areas:** Acquisitions, venture capital investments and private equity transactions for businesses ranging from public companies to start-ups. Extensive healthcare experience including ambulatory surgery, imaging and stereotactic radiosurgery, acute care medical and surgical hospitals, behavioral healthcare, and physician joint ventures.
**Professional Memberships:** Nashville, Tennessee and American Bar Associations; ABA Business Law and Health Law Sections; American Health Lawyers Association; Director, Nashville Capital Network.
**Career:** Licensed in Alabama since 1996, in Tennessee since 1997. Joined Waller in 1997. Former member, Waller Board of Directors.
**Personal:** JD, Order of the Coif, 1996, Vanderbilt University; BA, magna cum laude, 1993, Vanderbilt University.

## CALK, Jeffrey A
Waller Lansden Dortch & Davis, Nashville
615 850 8129
jeff.calk@wallerlaw.com
*Featured in Real Estate (Tennessee)*
**Practice Areas:** Commercial real estate, healthcare and general corporate law. Advises healthcare providers, REITs and other investors on regulatory issues related to complex real estate transactions involving acute care and behavioral hospitals, senior housing facilities, medical office buildings and physician practices.
**Professional Memberships:** Nashville, Tennessee, Georgia and American Bar Associations; Vice Chair, Healthcare Facility Operations Interest Group, Health Law Section of the American Bar Association; American Health Lawyers Association.
**Career:** Licensed in Georgia since 1991, Tennessee since 1993. Joined Waller in 1997.
**Personal:** JD, with high honors, 1991, University of Tennessee; BS, magna cum laude, 1985, Belmont University.

## CALLAWAY, Edward M
Waller Lansden Dortch & Davis, Nashville
615 850 8470
ed.callaway@wallerlaw.com
*Featured in Environment (Tennessee)*
**Practice Areas:** Environmental law, including site development, regulatory compliance, state and local permitting. Represents solid waste disposal and hazardous waste treatment companies on compliance, enforcement defense, permitting, site contamination and remediation. Provides environmental due diligence assessments in transac-

tions within the healthcare, wireless communications, and other industries.
**Professional Memberships:** Nashville, Tennessee and American Bar Associations; Former Chair, Environmental Law Sections of NBA and TBA; Board Member, Volunteer Section, Solid Waste Association of North America.
**Personal:** JD, cum laude, 1993, Vermont Law School; BA, cum laude, 1990, Dartmouth College.

## CAMPBELL JR, Robert R
Waller Lansden Dortch & Davis, Nashville
615 850 8469
robert.campbell@wallerlaw.com
*Featured in Real Estate (Tennessee)*
**Practice Areas:** Real estate development and financing, corporate and commercial transactions involving banks and financial institutions. Had primary responsibility for all secured real estate transactions and credit facilities exceeding $1 billion for a publicly traded operator of privatized governmental facilities. Coordinated the real estate and related incentive package for the North American headquarters relocation of one of the world's largest automobile manufacturers.
**Professional Memberships:** Nashville, Tennessee and American Bar Associations.
**Career:** Licensed in Tennessee since 1983. Joined Waller in 2005. Co-chairs Waller's Real Estate practice.
**Personal:** JD, with high honors, 1983, University of Tennessee; BA, 1980, Wake Forest University.

## CHASE III, Lee James
Glankler Brown, PLLC, Memphis
901 576 1729
lchase@glankler.com
*Featured in Litigation (Tennessee)*
**Practice Areas:** Tort, health and construction law with an emphasis on litigation, concerning personal injuries, medical malpractice, commercial disputes and construction contracting.
**Professional Memberships:** Journal Club; Chairman, The Assisi Foundation of Memphis, Inc.; American, Tennessee and Memphis (Director, 1984-85 & 2009-10, 2011-13) Bar Associations; Tennessee and Memphis Bar Foundations.
**Career:** Listed, The Best Lawyers in America; Strathmore Who's Who; Chambers USA Leaders in their Field.
**Personal:** Born 1942; BA, LLB, Vanderbilt University, 1967.

## CHEEK III, James H
Bass, Berry & Sims PLC, Nashville
615 742 6223
jcheek@bassberry.com
*Featured in Corporate/M&A (Tennessee)*
**Practice Areas:** Represents public and private companies and investment banking firms in capital raising and merger and acquisition activities. Counsels boards on matters relating to corporate governance and legal compliance. Also serves as the Regulatory Auditor of the NYSE.
**Professional Memberships:** American Bar Association (past Chair, Section of Business Law and Federal Regulation of Securities Committee); National ABA Task Force on Corporate

Responsibility (past Chair); San Diego Securities Regulation Institute (executive committee and past Chair).
**Career:** Joined the firm in 1970.
**Personal:** BA, (1964), Duke University; JD, (1967), Vanderbilt University; LLM, (1968), Harvard University.

## CHILDRESS, JR, E Franklin
Baker, Donelson, Bearman, Caldwell & Berkowitz, PC, Memphis
901 577 2147
fchildress@bakerdonelson.com
*Featured in Litigation (Tennessee)*
**Practice Areas:** Experienced in representation of secured/unsecured creditors and debtors in reorganization, liquidation; representation in purchases/sales of assets; litigation (preference, avoidance actions, bank, secured transaction); trustee and creditor's committee representation; creditors' rights; loan workouts; and general commercial litigation.
**Professional Memberships:** Fellow: American College of Bankruptcy; Member: Commercial Law League; Turnaround Mgt. Association; American; TN Bar Associations; American Bankruptcy Institute; and Past President, Mid-South Commercial Law Institute.; Memphis and Tennessee Bar Foundations. Board of Directors, Porter-Leath.
**Career:** Licensed in Tennessee, 1980.
**Personal:** Cumberland School of Law, Samford University, JD-1980. University of Tennessee (Martin), BS-1977

## COWART, Richard
Baker, Donelson, Bearman, Caldwell & Berkowitz, PC, Nashville
615 726 5660
dcowart@bakerdonelson.com
*Featured in Healthcare (Tennessee)*
**Practice Areas:** Chair, Baker Donelson's Health Law Department and Public Policy Department. Past President of the American Health Lawyers Association. Practice concentrated in advising senior management regarding policy, regulatory and business issues related to healthcare. Serves as strategic counsel to health care companies (for-profit and not-for-profit). National columnist and frequent speaker on health law topics.
**Professional Memberships:** Recipient, David R. Greenburg Award for Lifetime Service to Health Law; Editorial Board, Journal of Life Science and Health Law.
**Career:** Licensed in Mississippi since 1978, Tennessee since 1999.
**Personal:** University of Southern Mississippi, BA, 1975. University of Mississippi Law School, JD, 1978.

## CRENSHAW JR, Waverly D
Waller Lansden Dortch & Davis, Nashville
615 850 8909
waverly.crenshaw@wallerlaw.com
*Featured in Labor & Employment (Tennessee)*
**Practice Areas:** Complex employment matters, including multi-plaintiff and class action discrimination, harassment, and retaliation cases, as well as wage and hour collective actions. Broad indus-

try experience, including: logistics, healthcare, higher education, hospitality, insurance, manufacturing, non-profit organizations, public utilities, religious organizations, retail and telecommunications.
**Professional Memberships:** Fellow, Napier-Looby, Nashville and Tennessee Bar Foundations; Life Member, Conference of the Sixth Judicial Circuit of the United States; Charter member, Harry Phillips American Inns of Courts.
**Career:** Licensed in Tennessee since 1982. Joined Waller in 1990. Serves on Waller Board of Directors and Diversity Committee.
**Personal:** JD, 1981, Vanderbilt University; BA, 1978, Vanderbilt University.

**CRIDER, Marcus**
Waller Lansden Dortch & Davis, Nashville
615 850 8067
marcus.crider@wallerlaw.com
*Featured in Labor & Employment (Tennessee)*
**Practice Areas:** Represents some of the world's largest employers in manufacturing, healthcare, transportation, retail and grocery and hospitality as well as start-up companies and family-owned businesses in labor, employment and non-compete disputes and related business litigation. Trial experience includes alleged violations of the ADEA, FMLA, ADA and USERRA.
**Professional Memberships:** Nashville, Tennessee and Arkansas Bar Associations; Human Resources Committee; Tennessee Chamber of Commerce and Industry; Board Member, Tennessee Hospitality Association.
**Career:** Licensed in Arkansas since 1996, in Tennessee since 1997. Joined Waller in 2003.
**Personal:** JD, 1996, University of Arkansas; BA, 1993, Northwestern Louisiana State University.

**CURLEY, Matthew M**
Bass, Berry & Sims PLC, Nashville
615 742 7790
mcurley@bassberry.com
*Featured in Healthcare (Tennessee)*
**Practice Areas:** Represents clients in connection with internal and governmental investigations and related criminal and civil proceedings, including False Claims Act litigation.
**Professional Memberships:** AHLA; ABA, Co-Chair – Class Actions Subcommittee; Tennessee Bar Association, Litigation Section Executive Council.
**Career:** Bass, Berry & Sims; Adjunct Professor – Vanderbilt Law School, Health Care Fraud and Abuse. Served previously as Assistant US Attorney and Civil Chief, US Attorney's Office - MD Tenn. Law Clerk: Hon. Royce Lamberth, US District Court for the District of Columbia; Hon. Michael Kanne, US Court of Appeals for the Seventh Circuit.
**Personal:** JD, Vanderbilt University; BA, SUNY Albany.

**DAGLEY, Michael L**
Bass, Berry & Sims PLC, Nashville
615 742 7729
mdagley@bassberry.com
*Featured in Litigation (Tennessee)*

**Practice Areas:** Focuses in the areas of complex litigation with a special emphasis in securities, healthcare and internal investigations. Represents both plaintiffs and defendants in major commercial litigation.
**Professional Memberships:** Member of the Nashville, Tennessee and American Bar Associations; Member of the Harry Phillips American Inn of Court; Past chair of the Nashville Bar Association's Federal Court Committee.
**Career:** Joined the firm in 1999.
**Personal:** BA (1978), Middle Tennessee State University; JD (1981), Vanderbilt University.

**DAVIDSON, J Page**
Bass, Berry & Sims PLC, Nashville
615 742 6253
pdavidson@bassberry.com
*Featured in Corporate/M&A (Tennessee)*
**Practice Areas:** Focuses his practice on mergers and acquisitions of both public and private companies, strategic relationships, such as joint ventures and corporate partnerships, and offerings representing both issuers and underwriters. Counsels public and private companies on a variety of other corporate and securities matters, including corporate governance, public company disclosure, shareholder activism and consideration of various strategic alternatives.
**Professional Memberships:** American and Nashville Bar Associations; American Health Lawyers Association.
**Career:** Joined the firm in 1985.
**Personal:** BA (1982), with honors, Vanderbilt University; JD (1985), Duke University School of Law.

**DAVIDSON, Paul S**
Waller Lansden Dortch & Davis, Nashville
615 850 8942
paul.davidson@wallerlaw.com
*Featured in Litigation (Tennessee)*
**Practice Areas:** Represents corporations, healthcare providers, and individual corporate officers and directors in complex litigation and dispute resolution. Extensive experience includes antitrust, securities, intellectual property litigation, business torts and commercial litigation. Currently serving as co-lead trial counsel for plaintiffs in the bankruptcy of Jefferson County, Alabama, the largest U.S. municipal bankruptcy ever filed.
**Professional Memberships:** Nashville, Tennessee and District of Columbia Bar Associations; American Health Lawyers Association; Fellow, Nashville Bar Foundation and Tennessee Bar Foundation.
**Career:** Licensed in Tennessee since 1986. Joined Waller in 2005.
**Personal:** JD, 1980, Vanderbilt University; LLM, 1981, University College London; BA, 1976, Syracuse University.

**DELPRIORE, Robert J**
Baker, Donelson, Bearman, Caldwell & Berkowitz, PC, Memphis
901 577 8228
rdelpriore@bakerdonelson.com
*Featured in Corporate/M&A (Tennessee)*

**Practice Areas:** Focuses on securities offerings and other corporate finance matters, mergers and acquisitions, corporate governance and compliance and the general representation of public and private companies. Regularly counsels boards on matters related to corporate governance and legal compliance.
**Professional Memberships:** Memphis, Tennessee (Chair of Business Law Section, 2011 and 2012) and American Bar Associations (M&A Subcommittee).
**Personal:** BA (1990), Vanderbilt University; JD (1993) magna cum laude, Order of the Coif, University of Tennessee.

**DICKSON, Roger W**
Miller & Martin PLLC, Chattanooga
423 785 8330
rdickson@millermartin.com
*Featured in Litigation (Tennessee)*
**Practice Areas:** Roger Dickson concentrates his practice on litigation with an emphasis on complex commercial disputes, white collar crime, health care, personal injury, and products liability. He has handled major civil litigation for the world's largest soft drink bottling company and has served as lead national counsel defending publicly traded consumer products companies in hundreds of pharmaceutical product liability cases. He also represents a publicly traded construction materials company in its litigation in Tennessee and one of the nation's largest disability insurance companies in its complex litigation.

**DIETZ, Wallace W**
Bass, Berry & Sims PLC, Nashville
615 742 6276
wdietz@bassberry.com
*Featured in Litigation (Tennessee)*
**Practice Areas:** Complex business and commercial litigation and internal investigations, including False Claims Act, FCPA, healthcare, securities, fiduciary duty and corporate governance cases, class action defense, RICO, and financial services.
**Professional Memberships:** Nashville, Tennessee and American Bar Associations; Past President and Chair, Nashville Pro Bono, Inc.
**Career:** Joined the firm in 1983. Chair of firm's Compliance and Government Investigations Group. Legislative assistant and media aide to former US Senator Jim Sasser, 1977-81; Law Clerk to US District Judge Thomas A Wiseman Jr, 1982-83.
**Personal:** BA (1977), Emory University; JD (1982), cum laude, Georgetown University.

**DORAN JR, James M**
Waller Lansden Dortch & Davis, Nashville
615 850 8843
jim.doran@wallerlaw.com
*Featured in Litigation (Tennessee)*
**Practice Areas:** Defends pharmaceutical, medical device, aviation, automotive, chemical and other manufacturers in complex products liability claims, mass tort litigation, and other commercial and contract disputes.
**Professional Memberships:** American Board of Trial Advocates; Past President, Tennessee Defense Lawyers Association; Civil Justice Reform

Act Advisory Panel, Middle District Tennessee; IADC (Executive Committee; Director, Trial Academy; Past Chair, Product Liability Committee); DRI (Board Directors; Chair, Amicus Curiae Committee). Fellow, American College of Trial Lawyers, International Academy of Trial Lawyers.
**Career:** Licensed in Tennessee since 1968. Joined Waller in 1998.
**Personal:** JD, 1968, University of Tennessee; BS, 1966, Tennessee Technological University.

**DOWSLEY III, Felix R**
Bass, Berry & Sims PLC, Nashville
615 742 6228
fdowsley@bassberry.com
*Featured in Banking & Finance (Tennessee)*
**Practice Areas:** Focuses on commercial lending, secured transactions, real estate and general commercial law. Negotiation and documentation of a variety of financing and real estate transactions, including asset-based financings, syndicated revolving credit and term loan facilities, mezzanine and subordinated loans, construction loans and work-outs and restructures of credit facilities, as well as the sale and leasing of commerical real estate.
**Career:** Joined the firm in 1984.
**Personal:** BS (1981) and JD (1984), University of Tennessee.

**EARTHMAN, B Douglas**
Glankler Brown, PLLC, Memphis
901 576 1707
dearthman@glankler.com
*Featured in Real Estate (Tennessee)*
**Practice Areas:** Real estate and secured lending; municipal bonds and tax-exempt financing; business transactions.
**Professional Memberships:** Member, American Bar Association (Real Property, Probate and Trust Law Section); Member, Tennessee Bar Association (Real Estate Section, Chairman 1987-88); Member, Memphis Bar Association (Real Estate/Environmental Section); Member, National Association of Bond Lawyers.
**Career:** Admitted to practice in Tennessee; Glankler Brown, PLLC (2006-present); Armstrong Allen, PLLC (1999-2005); Servicemaster Diversified Health Services, LP (Senior Vice President, Senior Living Services) (1995-99); Waring Cox (1974-94). Listed, Best Lawyers in America; Listed, Mid-South SuperLawyers.
**Personal:** Born November 26, 1949, Kingsport, TN; JD, University of Memphis, 1973 (Law Review); BE, cum laude (Mechanical Engineering), Vanderbilt University, 1971.

**EDELL HOWARD, Linda**
Adams and Reese LLP, Nashville
615 341 0068
linda.edellhoward@arlaw.com
*Featured in Media & Entertainment (Tennessee)*
**Practice Areas:** Partner: entertainment/new media, intellectual property/technology, e-commerce.
**Professional Memberships:** Member of the Tennessee, Nashville, New York, and New Jersey Bar Associations.

**Career:** Entertainment/New Media Practice Team Leader. Experienced in all areas of entertainment, new media/technology and domestic/international copyright law. Transaction-based practice focuses on entertainment/new technology contracts, advocacy for creators and protection for copyright and other rights holders. Ms Edell Howard has an extensive client list including recording artists, key industry executives, music publishers, songwriters, producers, authors and related industry players.
**Personal:** JD, Seton Hall University School of Law, 1985; BA, Rutgers University, 1982.

## EDGE, Kathryn (Katie) Reed
Butler, Snow, O'Mara, Stevens & Cannada, PLLC, Nashville
615 503 9103
katie.edge@butlersnow.com
*Featured in Banking & Finance (Tennessee)*
**Practice Areas:** Represents banks and other financial institutions in regulatory, corporate, mergers/acquisitions, and securities matters; has assisted in the organization of more than 25 new commercial banks, trust companies and bank holding companies.
**Professional Memberships:** American, Tennessee, Nashville Bar associations; Tennessee Lawyers Association for Women; Marion Griffin Lawyers Association for Women.
**Career:** Financial Institutions Practice Group Leader 2000-date; Commercial Department Chairman 2007-2010.
**Publications:** Frequent contributor to Tennessee Bar Journal; contributing author for Tennessee Practice Legal Forms.
**Personal:** Graduated George Peabody College for Teachers, 1967 (BA English); Nashville School of Law, 1983 (JD); one son.

## EISEN, Steven J
Baker, Donelson, Bearman, Caldwell & Berkowitz, PC, Nashville
615 726 5718
sjeisen@bakerdonelson.com
*Featured in Banking & Finance (Tennessee)*
**Practice Areas:** Concentrates practice in corporate and securities transactions with emphasis in banking and financial institution law. Experience includes mergers and acquisitions, regulatory compliance, new corporate, LLC, and bank formation, equity and debt offerings, state and federal securities laws registration and exemptions, copyrights and trademarks, computer and technology, and general corporate law.
**Professional Memberships:** American Bar Association (Banking Law Committee); Tennessee Bankers Association (formerly Chairman, Lawyer's Committee; member, Government Relations Committee and Insurance Task Force).
**Career:** Licensed in Tennessee since 1983. Frequent author/speaker for national publications/seminars.
**Personal:** Vanderbilt Law School, JD, 1983. Vanderbilt University, MBA, 1983. Northwestern University, BA, 1979.

## EZELL JR, Kenneth P (Pete)
Baker, Donelson, Bearman, Caldwell & Berkowitz, PC, Nashville
615 726 5721
pezell@bakerdonelson.com
*Featured in Real Estate (Tennessee)*
**Practice Areas:** Commercial real estate transactions, including portfolio sales and acquisitions, development, leasing and financing. Also engages in conduit tax-exempt financings, serving as Bond Counsel, Issuer Counsel, Trustee Counsel and Credit Provider Counsel.
**Professional Memberships:** Fellow, American College of Real Estate Lawyers (Past Chair, Attorneys Opinions Committee). Past Chair, Committee on Legal Opinions in Real Estate Transactions; Real Property, Probate and Trust Section of the American Bar Association. Steering Committee, Working Group on Legal Opinions.
**Career:** Licensed in Tennessee since 1979.
**Personal:** BA, The University of the South, 1971; MBA, National University, 1976; JD, Vanderbilt University, 1979.

## FRAZIER, Keith D
Ogletree, Deakins, Nash, Smoak & Stewart, PC, Nashville
615 687 2231
keith.frazier@ogletreedeakins.com
*Featured in Labor & Employment (Tennessee)*
**Practice Areas:** Labor and employment, litigation.
**Professional Memberships:** American Bar Association (Section Delegate - House of Delegates, 2009 - ; Council Member, Labor and Employment Section, 2007 - present; Fellow,, ABA/YLD; Fellow, American Bar Foundation), Tennessee Bar Association (YLD: President, 1994-95; Fellow of the TBA/YLD), Nashville Bar Association (Fellow, Nashville Bar Foundation); Fellow, College of Labor and Employment Lawyers.
**Career:** Admitted to practice in Tennessee, U.S. Court of Appeals (Fifth ,Sixth and Eleventh Circuits) and various U.S. District Courts. Listed in Best Lawyers in America.
**Personal:** University of Tennessee (BS, 1982), University of Tennessee College of Law (JD, 1985).

## GARRETT, Tim K
Bass, Berry & Sims PLC, Nashville
615 742 6270
tgarrett@bassberry.com
*Featured in Labor & Employment (Tennessee)*
**Practice Areas:** Former Chair of the labor and employment practice area. Represents employers in all aspects of employment discrimination counseling and litigation (both class actions and individual claims) and traditional labor law counseling and litigation, including union avoidance, responding to unfair labor practices, grievance and arbitration matters, contract interpretation, wage and hour claims (collective actions and individual claims), ERISA litigation, OSHA/TOSHA proceedings, covenants not to compete and FMLA.
**Career:** Joined the firm in 1986.

**Personal:** BA (1983), summa cum laude, University of the South; JD (1986), Order of the Coif, Vanderbilt University.

## GERSON, Herb
FordHarrison LLP, Memphis
901 291 1530
hgerson@fordharrison.com
*Featured in Labor & Employment (Tennessee)*
**Practice Areas:** Labor and Employment
**Career:** Herb Gerson is co-managing partner of FordHarrison. He focuses his practice on managing all areas related to traditional labor and employment matters. He devotes much of his practice to counseling clients on avoiding employment discrimination claims and developing a positive work environment. Herb earned his JD from Emory University School of Law in 1973 and is licensed in Georgia and Tennessee. He is a Fellow of the College of Labor and Employment Lawyers and a Fellow of Litigation Counsel of America.

## GODDARD, J. Andrew
Bass, Berry & Sims PLC, Nashville
615 742 6224
dgoddard@bassberry.com
*Featured in Environment (Tennessee)*
**Practice Areas:** Practices in all areas of environmental law, including air, water, solid and hazardous waste, site remediation and environmental transaction due diligence. Significant environmental litigation experience, including citizen suit and toxic tort defense, enforcement actions and permit appeals. Has negotiated numerous consent decrees with the US EPA and state environmental agencies.
**Professional Memberships:** American College of Environmental Lawyers, Environmental Sections of American, Tennessee and Nashville Bar Associations.
**Career:** Joined the firm in 1978.
**Personal:** BE (1975) Vanderbilt University, Tau Beta Pi; JD (1978) Duke University, Order of the Coif.

## GOOD, John A
Bass, Berry & Sims PLC, Memphis
901 543 5901
jgood@bassberry.com
*Featured in Corporate/M&A (Tennessee), Capital Markets (Nationwide)*
See under Nationwide for profile.

## GOODRICH, Robert
Stites & Harbison PLLC, Nashville
615 782 2231
robert.goodrich@stites.com
*Featured in Litigation (Tennessee)*
**Practice Areas:** Creditors' rights, bankruptcy, and business litigation.
**Professional Memberships:** American, Tennessee and Nashville Bar Associations, American Bankruptcy Institute, Turnaround Management Association.
**Career:** Member, Stites & Harbison. Designated specialist in business bankruptcy. Best Lawyers in America (Bankruptcy), 1997-present. AV Rated in Martindale-Hubbell®.
**Publications:** "Performance Anxiety: The Nondebtor's Dilemma Under § 365," Norton

Bankruptcy Law Adviser, Issue No. 5, May 2009; and "TOUSAworld: Everything You Know About Fraudulent Conveyance Law Is Wrong (Maybe)," Norton Bankruptcy Law Adviser, Issue No. 6, June 2011.
**Personal:** JD, Vanderbilt Law School, 1983, Elliot Cheatham Scholar; BA, University of Virginia, 1978.

## GRAHAM, Stanley E
Waller Lansden Dortch & Davis, Nashville
615 850 8935
stan.graham@wallerlaw.com
*Featured in Labor & Employment (Tennessee)*
**Practice Areas:** Represents employers in retail, automotive, hospitality, information services, and manufacturing industries. Experience includes Family and Medical Leave Act, Civil Rights Acts of 1866 and 1964, Fair Labor Standards Act, Labor Management Relations Act and state civil rights laws as well as ERISA litigation, non-compete disputes, medical peer review actions, drug testing and medical inquiries, and business disputes.
**Professional Memberships:** Steering Committee, DRI Employment Law Section; Past Chair, Tennessee Bar Association Labor and Employment Law Section.
**Career:** Licensed in Alabama, Georgia and Tennessee. Joined Waller in 1998.
**Personal:** JD, cum laude, 1996, Samford University; BS, 1991, University of Florida.

## GRIMES, Dale
Bass, Berry & Sims PLC, Nashville
615 742 6244
dgrimes@bassberry.com
*Featured in Litigation (Tennessee)*
**Practice Areas:** Civil litigation in state and federal trial and appellate courts focusing on antitrust, consumer fraud, telecommunications, energy and water, including utility regulation; complex and class actions.
**Professional Memberships:** Chair, Lex Mundi Antitrust Practice Group; Member, American, Tennessee and Nashville Bar Associations; Fellow, Nashville and American Bar Foundations.
**Career:** Leader, firm's Antitrust and Trade Practices group. Editor, Federal Chapter, ABA's Price Discrimination Handbook; Editor, Tennessee chapter of ABA's State Antitrust Practice and Statutes (4th ed); Past Chair, Civil Justice Reform Act Advisory Group for the Middle District of Tennessee.
**Personal:** BA- University of the South; JD- University of Tennessee.

## GUMBERT, Gregg C
Butler, Snow, O'Mara, Stevens & Cannada, PLLC, Memphis
901 680 7307
gregg.gumbert@butlersnow.com
*Featured in Real Estate (Tennessee)*
**Practice Areas:** Commercial transactions; commercial real estate; finance; new markets tax credits; mergers and acquisitions.
**Professional Memberships:** International Association of Attorneys and Executives in Corporate Real Estate; American Bar Association (Business Law and Real Property and Probate Law

sections); Tennessee Bar Association; Memphis Bar Association.

**Career:** Mid-South Super Lawyers (Real Estate, Securities and Corporate Finance, Business/Corporate); Representation of local, regional and national lenders and borrowers in a variety of real estate and asset-based loan transactions, including loan syndications and participations; former Senior Attorney in Business Transactions Group of Federal Express, 2005-06.
**Personal:** Emory University, JD, 1999; Kenyon College, BA, 1991.

### GUPTON III, John A
Baker, Donelson, Bearman, Caldwell & Berkowitz, PC, Nashville
615 726 7351
jgupton@bakerdonelson.com
*Featured in Real Estate (Tennessee)*

**Practice Areas:** Practice concentrated in commercial real estate and mortgage lending. Represents several life insurance companies, developers, commercial real estate owners, brokers and contractors. Extensive experience in the formation, development, financing, acquisition, disposition and leasing of commercial real estate projects and properties.
**Professional Memberships:** Member, American (Real Property Section), Tennessee (Real Property Section) and Nashville Bar Associations. Fellow, American College of Mortgage Attorneys.
**Career:** Licensed in Tennessee since 1976.
**Personal:** University of Virginia, BA. University of Memphis Cecil C Humphreys School of Law, JD.

### HARRIS, Matthew T
Waller Lansden Dortch & Davis, Nashville
615 850 8906
matt.harris@wallerlaw.com
*Featured in Real Estate (Tennessee)*

**Practice Areas:** Commercial real estate for local, regional, national and international companies. Represents developers, institutional real estate clients and companies in the communications, supply-chain and healthcare industries in the acquisition, disposition, development, financing and leasing of office, industrial and retail properties for public and private companies. Experience in land use and zoning law, and commercial real estate lending.
**Professional Memberships:** Nashville, Tennessee and American Bar Associations; National Association of Industrial and Office Properties; American Health Lawyers Association.
**Career:** Licensed in Tennessee since 1984. Joined Waller in 1997.
**Personal:** JD, 1984, University of Tennessee; BA, with honors, 1980, University of Tennessee.

### HARRIS, Robert L
Waller Lansden Dortch & Davis, Nashville
615 850 8467
rob.harris@wallerlaw.com
*Featured in Banking & Finance (Tennessee)*

**Practice Areas:** Assists companies, investors and entrepreneurs in achieving strategic objectives through mergers, acquisitions, joint ventures,

recapitalizations as well as public and private equity and debt financing. Clients include healthcare companies, private equity firms, banks, and healthcare specialty lenders throughout the United States and abroad.
**Professional Memberships:** American Health Lawyers Association; Tennessee, New York and District of Columbia Bar Associations.
**Career:** Licensed in District of Columbia, New York and Tennessee. Joined Waller in 1997. Serves on Waller's Board of Directors.
**Personal:** JD, 1993, Columbia University; BA, magna cum laude, 1990, Dartmouth College.

### HARVEY, Robb S
Waller Lansden Dortch & Davis, Nashville
615 850 8859
robb.harvey@wallerlaw.com
*Featured in Media & Entertainment (Tennessee)*

**Practice Areas:** Complex intellectual property, media, commercial and franchise litigation involving substantial damages claims in federal and state courts across the country. Lead counsel in precedent-setting IP and media cases including reporters' privilege, fair use, and access.
**Professional Memberships:** Media Law Resource Center (past chair, Trial Committee), ABA Forums on Communications Law and Franchising, Nashville Bar Media (former chair) and IP Committees; State's Advisory Committee on Open Records; founding/board member of Tennessee Coalition for Open Government.
**Career:** Licensed in Tennessee since 1985. Joined Waller in 2000.
**Personal:** JD, 1985, Vanderbilt University; BS, magna cum laude, 1982 Vanderbilt University.

### HEITER, Matthew S
Baker, Donelson, Bearman, Caldwell & Berkowitz, PC, Memphis
901 577 8117
mheiter@bakerdonelson.com
*Featured in Corporate/M&A (Tennessee)*

**Practice Areas:** Shareholder in the Memphis office, member and former chair of firm's Securities/Corporate Governance Practice Group. Focuses his practice on public and private securities offerings, mergers and acquisitions, venture capital financing, corporate governance and business planning and organization. Experienced in the representation of emerging companies and investors in the biotechnology and technology industries.
**Professional Memberships:** Listed in Best Lawyers in America since 2005; Mid-South Super Lawyers, 2006-08 and 2010.
**Career:** Licensed in Tennessee, 1985.
**Personal:** Vanderbilt University School of Law, JD, 1985. University of Mississippi, BA, 1982, summa cum laude.

### HICKS, John S
Baker, Donelson, Bearman, Caldwell & Berkowitz, PC, Nashville
615 726 7337
jhicks@bakerdonelson.com
*Featured in Litigation (Tennessee)*

**Practice Areas:** Practice concentrated in corporate, business and commercial litigation, health

law litigation, class action defense, ADR, insurance coverage, professional liability and banking litigation. Experienced in creditors' rights and business reorganizations.
**Professional Memberships:** Member, American (litigation, health law, dispute resolution, tort trial and insurance practice sections and Center for Professional Responsibility), Tennessee (litigation, dispute resolution and health care law sections) and Nashville (Federal Court Practice and ethics and professional service committees) Bar Associations. Member, American Health Lawyers Association, Tennessee Defense Lawyers Association, Defense Research Institute and International Association of Defense Counsel.
**Career:** Tennessee license, 1983.

### HILL, J Reginald
Waller Lansden Dortch & Davis, Nashville
615 850 8473
reggie.hill@wallerlaw.com
*Featured in Healthcare (Tennessee)*

**Practice Areas:** Healthcare mergers and acquisitions, joint ventures, syndications, regulatory compliance, securities and venture capital financings. Extensive transactional experience involving hospitals, health systems, outpatient health services and physician practices. Advises Boards of Directors on corporate governance matters, including Sarbanes-Oxley.
**Professional Memberships:** Nashville, Tennessee and American Bar Associations; ABA Business Law and Health Law sections; American Health Lawyers Association; AHLA Fraud and Abuse, Hospitals and Health Systems, and Business Law and Governance Practice Groups.
**Career:** Licensed in Tennessee since 1980. Joined Waller in 1982.
**Personal:** JD, 1980, Order of the Coif, University of Tennessee; BS, 1977, University of Tennessee - Martin.

### HORTON, Bob
Bass, Berry & Sims PLC, Nashville
615 742 7708
rhorton@bassberry.com
*Featured in Labor & Employment (Tennessee)*

**Practice Areas:** Litigates and advises clients regarding employment matters, including hiring, discipline, compensation, promotion, and discharge issues, unlawful discrimination, harassment, and retaliation claims, whistleblower claims and non-competition agreements. Assists clients with DOL Wage & Hour investigations, OFCCP audits, disability and leave issues under the ADA and FMLA, transactional issues and union avoidance. Obtained favorable jury verdicts across the country in various employment lawsuits including age, sex, race, and national origin discrimination claims, harassment, and retaliatory discharge claims.
**Career:** Joined the firm in 1999.
**Personal:** BA (1984) Louisiana State University; MDiv (1987) Southern Baptist Theological Seminary; JD (1991) University of Tennessee.

### HOUK, D Reed
Adams and Reese LLP, Nashville
615 259 1450
reed.houk@arlaw.com
*Featured in Real Estate (Tennessee)*

**Practice Areas:** Real estate, banking and finance. Represents public and private companies in negotiation and documentation of a broad range of real estate transactions involving commercial, industrial and residential properties. Represents lenders and borrowers in connection with financing transactions secured by real estate. Has also represented owners and lenders in multi-state acquisition, disposition and financing transactions involving real estate.
**Professional Memberships:** Member, Nashville, Tennessee (Chairman, Real Estate Law Section, 1997-98) and American Bar Associations.
**Career:** Admitted to Tennessee Bar, 1979. Partner in the firm and its predecessors since 1984.
**Personal:** University of Tennessee, BS, magna cum laude, 1976; JD, 1979.

### HUMPHREYS, Angela
Bass, Berry & Sims PLC, Nashville
615 742 7852
ahumphreys@bassberry.com
*Featured in Healthcare (Tennessee)*

**Practice Areas:** Focuses practice on representing healthcare companies in mergers and acquisitions, creation of joint ventures, public debt and equity offerings, private placements of securities, and corporate governance and public company disclosure matters.
**Professional Memberships:** Nashville, Tennessee and American Bar Associations (Chair, ABA Health Care M&A Committee); American Health Lawyers Association; Nashville Health Care Council's Leadership Health Care (Board of Directors); Tennessee Society of Certified Public Accountants; Healthcare Information and Management Systems Society, Tennessee Chapter (Board of Directors); Women Business Leaders of the U.S. Health Care Industry Foundation.
**Personal:** BS (1991) University of Tennessee; JD (1996), University of Tennessee.

### HUMPHREYS, Hunter
Glankler Brown, PLLC, Memphis
901 576 1744
hhumphreys@glankler.com
*Featured in Real Estate (Tennessee)*

**Practice Areas:** Real estate and secured lending. Mr Humphreys represents numerous investors, developers, lenders and participants in real estate, secured lending and other business transactions.
**Professional Memberships:** Admitted to practice in Tennessee. Adjunct Professor, University of Memphis School of Law (Real Estate Transactions). President-Elect and Board Member of the University of Memphis Law School Alumni Association. Past Board Member of the Estate Planning Council of Memphis. Member of Tennessee Bar Association Real Estate Section UPL Subcommittee. Member, Tennessee Bar Association (Real Estate Section; District 9 Committee on Moral Fitness for Admission to the Bar). Member, Memphis Bar Association (Former

member, CLE Committee; Former Chairman, University of Memphis Law School Liaison Committee).

**Career:** Lawler, Humphreys, Dunlap & Wellford (1977-85); Glankler Brown, PLLC (1985-present), Member, Chair of Real Estate Section. Named to Best Best 150 Lawyers in the State of Tennessee, (2004-10) and 150 Most Influential Individuals in Commercial Real Estate (2005) by Business TN magazine; Mid South SuperLawyers (2006-12), SuperLawyers Top 100 Lawyers in the State of Tennessee (2009-10); Chambers and Partners Leaders in their Fields (2004-12); and Best Lawyers in America (2007-13).

**Personal:** Born 24 November 1951, Memphis, TN; JD, University of Memphis, 1977; BA, University of North Carolina (Chapel Hill), 1974.

### JAQUA, David P
Butler, Snow, O'Mara, Stevens & Cannada, PLLC, Memphis
901 680 7343
david.jaqua@butlersnow.com
*Featured in Labor & Employment (Tennessee)*

**Practice Areas:** Employment Litgation (Defense); Arbitration and Mediation; Traditional Labor Practice, including Representation Campaigns, NLRB hearings and Negotiations; Management Counseling and Training.

**Professional Memberships:** American Bar Association (Labor and Employment Section); Tennessee Bar Association (Labor and Employment Section); Mississippi Bar.

**Career:** AV-Rated, Martindale-Hubbell; The Best Lawyers in America, Labor and Employment Law; Chambers USA, Americas Leading Lawyers for Business, Labor and Employment; Mid-South Super Lawyers, Employment and Labor; Fellow, Tennessee Bar Foundation; Fellow, American Bar Foundation.

**Personal:** University of Mississippi; JD, with honors, 1976; United States Naval Academy, BS, Mathematics, 1973.

### JENNINGS, Paul G
Bass, Berry & Sims PLC, Nashville
615 742 6267
pjennings@bassberry.com
*Featured in Litigation (Tennessee)*

**Practice Areas:** Restructuring, bankruptcy and related commercial litigation. Represents creditors including institutional creditors in corporate bankruptcies, counsel to significant corporate debtors in Chapter 11, creditors committees and Chapter 11 trustees. Handles related litigation including preferences, fraudulent transfers and fiduciary duty matters. Has handled numerous §363 purchases from bankruptcy.

**Professional Memberships:** American Bankruptcy Institute; Nashville Bar Association; Tennessee Bar Association (past president of Section of Commercial, Bankruptcy and Banking Law); Mid-South Commercial Law Institute (former director).

**Career:** Joined the firm in 1990.

**Personal:** BS (1987), Middle Tennessee State University; JD (1990), with high honors, University of Tennessee (Order of the Coif).

### KAPLAN, Jonathan E
Littler Mendelson, PC, Memphis
901 795 6695
jkaplan@littler.com
*Featured in Labor & Employment (Tennessee)*

**Practice Areas:** Labor & Employment

**Professional Memberships:** Member, ABA Labor and Employment Law Section, Practice and Procedure Under the NLRA Committee. Past Co-Chair, ABA Subcommittee on Drug and Alcohol Abuse in the Workplace. Past Chair, Tennessee Bar Association, Labor and Employment Law Section. Member, Memphis Bar Association.

**Career:** Jonathan practices before the NLRB, and his practice spans litigation, training, and consulting in more than 40 states and Canada.

**Publications:** Chapter Editor, 'How To Take A Case Before The NLRB' Eighth Edition (BNA, 2008).

**Personal:** JD, University of Memphis, 1982; BA, Rhodes College, 1979.

### KELLER, Jennifer P
Baker, Donelson, Bearman, Caldwell & Berkowitz, PC, Johnson City
423 928 0181
jkeller@bakerdonelson.com
*Featured in Labor & Employment (Tennessee)*

**Practice Areas:** Shareholder and Chair of firm's Labor and Employment Department. Practice focused in employment litigation and counseling. Regularly appears before administrative agencies, including the Department of Labor, EEOC, Tennessee Human Rights Commission and NLRB. Experienced in representation of employers with regard to claims based on Civil Rights Acts, FMLA, ADA, FLSA, NLRA, state workers' compensation laws and state-specific employment laws.

**Professional Memberships:** Tennessee, North Carolina, Washington County and American Bar Associations; Defense Research Institute.

**Career:** Licensed in Tennessee, 1996; North Carolina, 1997.

**Personal:** University of Tennessee School of Law, JD, 1996. University of Tennessee (Knoxville), BS, 1993.

### KIESEWETTER, Jay W
Littler Mendelson, PC, Memphis
901 795 6695
jkiesewetter@littler.com
*Featured in Labor & Employment (Tennessee)*

**Practice Areas:** Labor & Employment.

**Professional Memberships:** Member ABA, Section of Labor and Employment Law (Committees on Development of the Law Under the NLRA; Practices & Procedures Before the NLRB).

**Career:** Mr Kiesewetter counsels employers in union-free management and advises non-union companies facing union organizing activity; represents employers in unfair labor practice and representational proceedings before the NLRB and the U.S. Courts of Appeal; and works with companies that have unions to improve union-management relations and represents management in contract negotiations, arbitrations, and labor disputes. Mr

Kiesewetter develops preventive strategies to reduce exposure to future legal/human relations problems.

### KRAMER, Steven E
Kramer Rayson LLP, Knoxville
865 525 5134
skramer@kramer-rayson.com
*Featured in Labor & Employment (Tennessee)*

**Practice Areas:** Steven Kramer's practice principally involves employment and labor law, corporate law and sports law.

**Professional Memberships:** Mr Kramer is a Member of the Knoxville and Kingsport (Tennessee) Bar Associations and the American Bar Association. He is listed in the 2004-12 editions of Chambers USA: America's Leading Lawyers for Business and from 2007-11 in Mid-South Super Lawyers published by Law and Politics Media. Mr Kramer has been a frequent speaker at seminars on a variety of legal topics in his practice areas. He is a Member of the Regional Board of Directors for First Tennessee Bank. He served as Chairman of the Kingsport Economic Development Board for 10 years and is a member of the Board of Directors for the Northeast State Community College Foundation and the Boys and Girls Club.

**Career:** Mr Kramer joined Kramer Rayson LLP in 2003. He previously served as Vice President of Human Resources and General Counsel for AGC Glass, Inc from 1992-2003. Prior to joining AGC, Mr Kramer spent 10 years in private practice as a Partner at Hunter, Smith & Davis and Baker Donelson law firms.

### LAMAR III, Howard H
Bass, Berry & Sims PLC, Nashville
615 742 6209
hlamar@bassberry.com
*Featured in Corporate/M&A (Tennessee)*

**Practice Areas:** Focuses on counseling publicly held and sophisticated privately held companies in corporate finance, governance, operating matters and complex transactions, such as mergers and acquisitions, public offerings of equity and debt securities and private equity and venture capital financings (equity and subordinated debt). Counsels companies on a variety of corporate and securities matters, including balance sheet structuring, corporate governance, shareholder activism and special committee matters, disclosure issues, strategic analysis and start-up concerns.

**Professional Memberships:** American and Nashville Bar Associations.

**Career:** Joined firm in 1989.

**Personal:** BA (1983), JD (1989), Order of the Coif, Vanderbilt University.

### LATHRAM, Brook
Bass, Berry & Sims PLC, Memphis
901 543 5905
blathram@bassberry.com
*Featured in Litigation (Tennessee)*

**Practice Areas:** Focuses his practice on federal criminal trials and internal investigations; on complex business and commercial litigation, including antitrust, business tort and breach-of-

contract cases; and on the defense of product liability claims.

**Professional Memberships:** Fellow, American College of Trial Lawyers; Tennessee Bar Association; American Bar Association; Memphis Bar Association; Defense Research Institute; Tennessee Defense Lawyers Association.

**Career:** Joined Bass, Berry & Sims PLC in May 2011. Prior to joining the firm, Brook spent his entire career at Burch, Porter & Johnson PLLC in Memphis.

**Personal:** JD (1972) Columbia University; BA (1969) Vanderbilt University.

### LAWLESS, Thomas
Thomas W. Lawless, Nashville
615 351 7839
tomlawless@comcast.net
*Featured in Litigation (Tennessee)*

**Practice Areas:** Creditors' rights and bankruptcy litigation practice which is limited to representation of financial institutions and mortgage lenders.

**Professional Memberships:** Admitted to practice in the United States Supreme Court, the Court of Appeals for the Sixth Circuit and the Federal Circuit and all state and federal courts in Tennessee. Member of the International Bar Association, American Bar Association, Federal Circuit Bar Association, Tennessee Bar Association and Nashville Bar Association (serving as Chair of the Professionalism and Ethics Committee). Member of the National Association of Chapter 13 Trustees, National Association of Bankruptcy Trustees and American Bankruptcy Institute.

**Career:** Certified Creditors' Rights Specialist by the American Board of Certification and the Tennessee Commission on CLE and Specialization. Designated by the State of Tennessee as a certified Mediator. Sole practitioner with AV Rating in the Martindale-Hubbell Law Directory and listed in the Bar Register of Preeminent Lawyers in America.

**Publications:** "Proposed Amendments to Tennessee Supreme Court Rule 9-Attorney Discipline an Overview," Lorman Education Services, December 2012; "Residential Foreclosure: Inside and Outside of Bankruptcy" Mid-South Commercial Law Institute, December 2009; "Collection Law from Start to Finish," National Business Institute, January 2007; "Collection Techniques and Law in Tennessee," Lorman Education Services, July 2006.

**Personal:** BS (1976) Middle Tennessee State University; JD (1980) Nashville School of Law. Chairman of the Board of Zoning Appeals for the City of Oak Hill, TN; Chairman of the Judicial Nominating Commission of the State of Tennessee and Secretary of the Board of Judicial Conduct for the State of Tennessee.

### LIDDON, Robert C
Baker, Donelson, Bearman, Caldwell & Berkowitz, PC, Memphis
901 579 3122
rliddon@bakerdonelson.com
*Featured in Real Estate (Tennessee)*

**Practice Areas:** Practice concentrated in real estate, lending and financing. Experience includes commercial real estate acquisitions/ dispositions, real estate leasing for office, commercial and industrial facilities, site location issues, tax and other incentives in plant locations, credit and financing, banking law, construction contracts, asset based finance, workouts, and foreclosures.
**Professional Memberships:** Member, American, Tennessee, Mississippi and Memphis Bar Associations. Member, Phi Beta Kappa.
**Career:** Licensed in Tennessee since 1975 and Mississippi since 1976.
**Personal:** BA, Vanderbilt University, 1972; JD, Columbia University, 1975.

### LIGGETT, Nora L
Waller Lansden Dorch & Davis, Nashville
615 850 8908
nora.liggett@wallerlaw.com
*Featured in Healthcare (Tennessee)*
**Practice Areas:** Represents healthcare providers with regulatory compliance issues, including Medicare fraud and abuse, federal Stark law and other physician self-referral prohibitions. Assists physician groups, hospitals, surgery centers, imaging centers and other provider facilities with licensing, certificate of need (CON) applications and other state regulatory issues. Extensive experience developing Stark-compliant income distribution plans.
**Professional Memberships:** American Health Lawyers Association; Nashville, Tennessee and American Bar Associations; Health Law Sections of the American and Tennessee Bar Associations.
**Career:** Licensed in Tennessee since 1989. Joined Waller in 1995.
**Personal:** JD, 1989, Washington and Lee University; BA, cum laude, 1986, University of the South.

### MACE, Gerald F
Waller Lansden Dorch & Davis, Nashville
615 850 8912
gerry.mace@wallerlaw.com
*Featured in Banking & Finance (Tennessee)*
**Practice Areas:** Commercial finance. Represents both borrowers and lenders in senior and subordinated credit facilities, corporate debt issuances and public finance transactions. Experienced in healthcare, manufacturing, aviation and other industries. Counsels banks, financial institutions, specialty lenders and indenture trustees in workout, restructuring and bankruptcy situations. International practice covering the United States, Europe, Central and South America, and the Pacific Rim.
**Professional Memberships:** Nashville, Tennessee and American Bar Associations; National Association of Bond Lawyers.
**Career:** Licensed in Tennessee since 1985. Joined Waller in 2000.
**Personal:** JD, 1985, Vanderbilt University; BA, 1982, University of Virginia.

### MCCONNELL, Timothy
Baker, Donelson, Bearman, Caldwell & Berkowitz, PC, Knoxville
865 971 5166
tmcconnell@bakerdonelson.com
*Featured in Labor & Employment (Tennessee)*
**Practice Areas:** Defends clients in matters arising under Title VII, the ADA, ADEA, FMLA, FLSA, Sarbanes-Oxley and state-specific employment laws before administrative agencies (Department of Labor, EEOC, Tennessee Human Rights Commission, OSHA) and in cases filed in federal and state courts. Advises employers on matters including union avoidance and campaigns, FMLA administration, reductions in force, wage and hour issues, employee handbooks and workplace harassment.
**Professional Memberships:** Knox County, Tennessee, American Bar Associations.
**Career:** Tennessee-1998. U.S. Court of Appeals for Sixth Circuit-(2008); U.S. District Court, Eastern District of Tennessee-(1999).
**Personal:** University of Memphis Cecil C Humphreys School of Law, (JD-1997).

### MCSWEEN, Philip
Baker, Donelson, Bearman, Caldwell & Berkowitz, PC, Nashville
615 726 7334
pmcsween@bakerdonelson.com
*Featured in Healthcare (Tennessee)*
**Practice Areas:** Shareholder and chair of the firm's health law group. Counsel to nonprofit and for-profit health care providers including hospitals, specialty providers and physician groups on a national basis. He concentrates his practice primarily in health care mergers and acquisitions and joint ventures. Experienced in negotiating joint ventures, stock and asset purchases, mergers and share exchanges, non-competition agreements, and employment agreements and assessing due diligence issues.
**Professional Memberships:** Member: Law360 Health Editorial Advisory Board. Member: Tennessee and American Health Lawyers Associations.
**Career:** Tennessee, 1990.
**Personal:** University of Virginia School of Law, JD, 1990.

### MILEY, Claire F
Bass, Berry & Sims PLC, Nashville
615 742 7847
cmiley@bassberry.com
*Featured in Healthcare (Tennessee)*
**Practice Areas:** Devotes her practice exclusively to health law and concentrates on fraud and abuse analyses; coordinated care models; reimbursement analyses; joint ventures and management relationships; hospital contracting and operational issues; physician group practice and compensation issues; long-term care providers; and specialty providers.
**Career:** Numerous author and speaker credits, including for national presentations and publications of the American Health Lawyers Association. Has served as chair of Health Law Sections of both the Tennessee and Nashville Bar Associations.

**Personal:** Phi Beta Kappa; BA/BS (1980), Miami University (summa cum laude); JD (1983), Northwestern University (member of editorial board of law review).

### MORROW, Lynn
Adams and Reese LLP, Nashville
615 341 0068
lynn.morrow@arlaw.com
*Featured in Media & Entertainment (Tennessee)*
**Practice Areas:** Partner, entertainment and new media; intellectual property and technology.
**Professional Memberships:** Tennessee Bar Association, Entertainment and Sports Law Section, Former Chair; Nashville Bar Association, Entertainment and Sports Law Section, Former Chair; California Bar, Entertainment and Sports Law; Gospel Music Association; Country Music Association.
**Career:** She has extensive experience in representing clients in the music industry, representing many of the top country and contemporary Christian artists, producers and songwriters, as well as the Nashville Symphony.
**Personal:** LLM International Business Law, University of Exeter, England, 1989; JD, Pepperdine University School of Law, 1985; BA, University of California, Irvine, 1982.

### MOSCHEL, Michael
Bass, Berry & Sims PLC, Nashville
615 742 6297
mmoschel@bassberry.com
*Featured in Labor & Employment (Tennessee)*
**Practice Areas:** Successfully represented employers in union-organizing campaigns, labor contract negotiations, work-stoppage counseling, and unfair labor practice proceedings before the National Labor Relations Board. Litigated cases which resulted in several published decisions in the United States Courts of Appeal. Experience includes Section 301 and federal WARN Act claims. Litigates and advises clients regarding various employment issues, including restrictive covenants agreements, wage and hour compliance, discipline and discharge, reductions in force, discrimination and civil rights, sexual harassment and I-9 compliance.
**Career:** Joined the firm in 1996.
**Personal:** BA (1991) Univeristy of Rochester; JD (1994) Vanderbilt University.

### MULROY II, James R
Jackson Lewis LLP, Memphis
901 462 2601
MulroyJ@jacksonlewis.com
*Featured in Labor & Employment (Tennessee)*
**Practice Areas:** Workplace litigation and counseling on behalf of management, including class actions, discrimination, wage and hour, DOT compliance and non-competition agreements.
**Professional Memberships:** Fellow, College of Labor and Employment Lawyers; American, Tennessee and Arkansas Bar associations; Director, Tennessee Chamber of Commerce.
**Career:** Navy JAG Corps; Federal Express Corporation, Managing Attorney 1989-2000; Partner, Jackson Lewis LLP; AV Rated by Martindale Hubbell since 1988; Listed: Best

Lawyers since 2005; Super Lawyers since 2006 including Top 100 Tennessee Lawyers 2011, 2012, Top 50 Memphis Lawyers 2012.
**Personal:** BA - Rhodes College; MBA – University of Memphis; JD – University of Tennessee.

### NOEL, Randall D
Butler, Snow, O'Mara, Stevens & Cannada, PLLC, Memphis
901 680 7346
randy.noel@butlersnow.com
*Featured in Litigation (Tennessee)*
**Practice Areas:** Business litigation; product liability; toxic tort defense; healthcare litigation.
**Professional Memberships:** American Counsel Association (former President); Tennessee Bar Association (former President); Tennessee Legal Community Foundation (former President); Southern Conference of Bar Presidents (former President); American Bar Association (State Delegate for House of Delegates, Litigation Section); American Judicature Society; ALI-ABA CLE Board; Tennessee Defense Lawyers Association; Mississippi Bar.
**Career:** AV-rated, Martindale-Hubbell; Best Lawyers in America (Commercial Litigation); Mid-South Super Lawyers (Business Litigation); Fellow, American Bar Foundation; Who's Who in American Law; Fellow, Memphis Bar Foundation; Fellow,Tennessee Bar Foundation; Lawdragon 3000.
**Personal:** University of Mississippi, JD, 1978.

### NORWOOD, E Andrew
Waller Lansden Dorch & Davis, Nashville
615 850 8491
andy.norwood@wallerlaw.com
*Featured in Media & Entertainment (Tennessee)*
**Practice Areas:** Intellectual property law, with an emphasis on copyright, trademark, trade secret, and related licensing issues. Extensive experience assisting hospitals and health systems in contract and licensing matters related to computer software and information systems. Has represented over 50 publishing houses in a wide range of transactions, from simple author contracts to corporate mergers and acquisitions.
**Professional Memberships:** Nashville, Tennessee, American and Federal Bar Associations; American Health Lawyers Association.
**Career:** Licensed in Tennessee since 1989. Joined Waller in 1994.
**Personal:** JD, 1987, University of Alabama; BA, cum laude, 1984, University of Alabama.

### OVERBY, J Allen
Bass, Berry & Sims PLC, Nashville
615 742 6211
aoverby@bassberry.com
*Featured in Corporate/M&A (Tennessee)*
**Practice Areas:** Chair of the firm's Corporate and Securities Practice Group. Concentrates his practice on corporate, M&A, and securities law matters, including cross-border M&A transactions. Emphasizes public company representations, including special and other board commit-

tees. Also conducts internal investigations and defends SEC enforcement matters.

**Professional Memberships:** Chamber's Economic Development Committee; Member, Business Law Section of the American Bar Association.

**Career:** Joined the firm in 1996. Former Senior Counsel, U.S. Securities and Exchange Commission.

**Personal:** BA (1985), Millsaps College; JD (1987), University of Mississippi; LLM (1993) Georgetown University.

## OZIER, William N
Bass, Berry & Sims PLC, Nashville
615 742 6232
bozier@bassberry.com
*Featured in Labor & Employment (Tennessee)*

**Practice Areas:** Represents management in all types of labor and employment matters including union avoidance, union relations, negotiation of union contracts, labor arbitration, defense of age, gender, disability and race discrimination claims, retaliatory discharge claims under federal and state laws, defense of FLSA claims, and enforcement and defense of non-compete agreements. Represents academic institutions in employment and student-related litigation.

**Professional Memberships:** Fellow, American College of Labor and Employment Lawyers; Chair, Tennessee Chamber of Commerce and Industry (2012, 2013).

**Career:** Joined the firm in 1969. Served as Managing Partner, 1987-92.

**Personal:** BA (1966) and JD (1969), Vanderbilt University.

## PALMER, Timothy A
Ogletree, Deakins, Nash, Smoak & Stewart, PC, Nashville
615 254 1900
timothy.palmer@ogletreedeakins.com
*Featured in Labor & Employment (Tennessee)*

**Practice Areas:** Labor and employment, class action defense, litigation.

**Professional Memberships:** American Bar Association, State Bar Associations of Alabama and Tennessee, Alabama Defense Lawyer's Association.

**Career:** Admitted to practice in the states of Alabama and Tennessee, United States Supreme Court, United States Court of Appeals for the Eleventh Circuit, United States District Courts of Alabama, Northern, Middle and Southern Division, Alabama Supreme Court, Tennessee Supreme Court.

**Personal:** Lipscomb University (BA, summa cum laude, 1985), Vanderbilt University School of Law (JD, 1988; associate Justice Moot Court Board and Moot Court Champion).

## PAPEL, Laurence M
Nelson Mullins Riley & Scarborough LLP, Nashville
*Featured in Real Estate (Tennessee)*

**Practice Areas:** Concentrates primarily in corporate law, mergers and acquisitions and real estate development, including commercial transactions, entity and capital formation, private

offerings, complex financings, joint ventures. Nashville Office Managing Partner.

**Professional Memberships:** American (Corporate, Real Estate Sections), Tennessee and Nashville Bar Associations.

**Career:** Licensed in Tennessee, and federal courts,1980.

**Personal:** Trinity College (BA-1977). Vanderbilt University School of Law, (JD-1980). Past President, Rotary Club of Nashville. Past Chairman, Arts and Business Council of Greater Nashville. Board Member: Nashville Zoo; Nashville Public Library Foundation; Nashville Civic Design Center; Arts and Business Council of Greater Nashville.

## PEEK, Michael S
Bass, Berry & Sims PLC, Nashville
615 742 6231
mpeek@bassberry.com
*Featured in Real Estate (Tennessee)*

**Practice Areas:** Practices primarily in commercial real estate development, banking and commercial lending, tax increment finance and general commercial law. Devotes the majority of professional time to the negotiation and documentation of a variety of commercial lending and real estate transactions, including commercial real estate developments, hospital and medical office building developments, construction loans, and tax increment financings.

**Professional Memberships:** American, Tennessee and Nashville Bar Associations.

**Career:** Joined the firm in 1974. Former Managing Partner. Former member of the Vanderbilt Law School Alumni Board.

**Personal:** BA (1970), Murray State University; JD (1974), Vanderbilt University.

## PENNY, William
Stites & Harbison PLLC, Nashville
615 782 2308
bill.penny@stites.com
*Featured in Environment (Tennessee)*

**Practice Areas:** Environmental law, administrative law, natural resources law.

**Professional Memberships:** American Bar Association (Vice Chair, Section of Environment, Energy & Resources)Tennessee Bar Association (founding chair Environmental Section), Nashville Bar Association (founding chair, Environmental Committee, Harry Phillips Inns of Court.

**Career:** Tennessee State Comptroller's Office, State Auditor (1975-1980); Department of Environment and Conservation, General Counsel(1982-92; Manier, Herod, Hollabaugh & Smith,PC, Partner (1992-1998); Wyatt, Tarrant & Combs, PLLC, Managing Partner of Nashville office (1998-2005); Stites & Harbison, PLLC, Partner (2005 - ).

**Publications:** 'A Practical Guide To Tennessee Environmental Law', 'A Practical Guide to Tennessee Administrative Law', BNA Due Diligence Guide (Tenn. Editor), ABA 'Brownfields Book' (est. 2010, Tenn. Editor), ABA 'Use of Institutional Controls' (est. 2010, Tenn. Editor).

**Personal:** DOB: 4 September 1953, University of Tennessee, Knoxville, BA, 1975; Nashville School of Law, JD, 1981; Admitted to practice in the United States Supreme Court, East, Middle and West United States District Courts and all state and local courts in Tennessee.

## PERA, Lucian
Adams and Reese LLP, Memphis
901 524 5278
lucian.pera@arlaw.com
*Featured in Litigation (Tennessee)*

**Practice Areas:** Partner, litigation, commercial dispute resolution, media law, professional liability, ethics.

**Professional Memberships:** American Bar Association, Chairman, Standing Committee on Technology and Information Systems, Media Law Resource Center, Fellow in Tennessee Bar Foundation, American Bar Foundation, American Law Institute and Association of Professional Responsibility Lawyers.

**Career:** Practices primarily in the civil trial arena, including a wide variety of commercial, media, intellectual property, and personal injury litigation. Also counsels and represents lawyers, law firms, and others on questions of legal ethics and the professional responsibility of lawyers.

**Personal:** JD, Vanderbilt University School of Law, 1985; AB, Princeton University, 1982.

## PERL, Arnold E
Glankler Brown, PLLC, Memphis
901 576 1758
aperl@glankler.com
*Featured in Labor & Employment (Tennessee)*

**Practice Areas:** Labor and employment.

**Career:** Arnold Perl focuses his practice on labor and employment law. He has successfully argued many cases before various United States Courts of Appeals, and is admitted to practice before the United States Supreme Court. He has extensive experience counseling organizations on positive employee relations. He leads a uniquely effective leadership development program for all levels of management. In 2006, Arnold co-authored, Simple Solutions, with Tom Schmitt from FedEx and published by John Wiley & Sons. The book offers guidance and real-world insight on making collaboration work, tailoring leadership styles to fit team needs, assembling great teams and inspiring people. Representing the Tennessee Chamber of Commerce and Industry, Arnold was the lead witness in a 2011 two-day hearing before the National Labor Relations Board regarding proposed rule changes designed to speed elections for unionization of companies.

**Personal:** Chairman Emeritus, Memphis-Shelby County Airport Authority; Who's Who Memphis Magazine Top 100 Influential Leaders; Best Lawyers in America (30 years, serves on Advisory Board); International Who's Who of Management Labour and Employment Lawyers; Super Lawyers (Top 100 Lawyers in Tennessee); MBQ Power Players, 2008-2012; PRSSA 2005 Communicator of the Year; Order of the Rising Sun, Gold Rays with Rosette, conferred by the Emperor of Japan and Japanese government (2nd highest award

conferred upon a civilian); Airport Minority Advisory Council (AMAC) Hall of Fame; Diversity Memphis Humanitarian of the Year; Fellow, Memphis & Shelby County Bar Foundation.

## PHILLIPS, Edward G
Kramer Rayson LLP, Knoxville
865 525 5134
ephillips@kramer-rayson.com
*Featured in Labor & Employment (Tennessee)*

**Practice Areas:** Mr Phillips' practice principally involves employment and labor law.

**Professional Memberships:** Mr Phillips is a past Chairman of the Labor and Employment Section of the Tennessee Bar Association. He is listed in the 2004-13 editions of Chambers USA: America's Leading Lawyers for Business, from 2000-13 in the Best Lawyers in America for his employment law practice, and from 2006-13 in Mid-South Super Lawyers published by Law and Politics Media. Mr Phillips writes a regular column in the Tennessee Bar Journal and frequently speaks at seminars on a variety of employment law topics.

**Career:** Mr Phillips is the former Managing Partner of the firm. He has practiced labor and employment law for over 34 years, representing management exclusively. His labor and employment practice includes counseling involving union avoidance, collective bargaining, employment discrimination, wrongful discharge, harrassment, employment policies, and wage and hour issues. His litigation experience includes employment discrimination, retaliation and harassment cases in federal and state courts, defending multi-plaintiff and class-action cases, FLSA, ERISA and USERRA actions, civil service trials, and similar proceedings representing management. His clients include many of the major private and public employers in East Tennessee.

## POWERS, Patricia O
Waller Lansden Dortch & Davis, Nashville
615 850 8808
patsy.powers@wallerlaw.com
*Featured in Healthcare (Tennessee)*

**Practice Areas:** Advises surgery centers, psychiatric facilities and acute care hospitals on regulatory and operations issues, structuring joint ventures and facility acquisitions with respect to regulatory compliance, fraud and abuse matters, state and federal anti-kickback regulations, self-referral prohibitions, Medicare enrollment and reimbursement matters.

**Professional Memberships:** Nashville, Tennessee and American Bar Associations; TBA Health Law Section; American Health Lawyers Association; Director, Tennessee Pediatric Society Foundation; Director, Siloam Family Health Center.

**Career:** Licensed in Tennessee since 1991. Joined Waller in 1991.

**Personal:** JD, 1991, University of Tennessee; BS, 1984, Vanderbilt University.

**PRATHER, Paul E**
Littler Mendelson, PC, Memphis
901 795 6695
pprather@littler.com
*Featured in Labor & Employment (Tennessee)*
**Practice Areas:** Labor & Employment.
**Professional Memberships:** Member,
American Bar Association, Labor & Employment
& Litigation Sections; Fellow, American College of
Labor and Employment Lawyers; Defense
Research Institute; past Chair of the Memphis and
Tennessee Bar Associations Labor and
Employment Section; American Employment Law
Counsel; Management Labor and Employment
Roundtable; Tennessee Commission on
Continuing Legal Education and Specialization.
**Career:** Nationally recognized employment claim
jury trial lecturer.
**Publications:** Executive editor 'Healthcare
Employment Law Letter'; contributing editor,
'Annual Review of Developments in Business and
Corporate Litigation' (ABA 2007).
**Personal:** JD, University of Memphis, 1982.

**PRESTER, Jackie**
Baker, Donelson, Bearman, Caldwell &
Berkowitz, PC, Memphis
901 577 8114
jprester@bakerdonelson.com
*Featured in Banking & Finance (Tennessee)*
**Practice Areas:** Shareholder who practices in
the corporate and securities areas, with particular
experience representing financial institutions, bro-
ker-dealers and investment advisers. Serves as lead
counsel for public companies registered under the
Securities Exchange Act of 1934, providing regular
advice regarding compliance with SEC disclosure
requirements and corporate governance issues.
**Professional Memberships:** Member -
Memphis and Tennessee Bar Associations.
Adjunct Professor - Cecil C. Humphreys School of
Law.
**Career:** Tennessee, 1996.
**Personal:** University of Memphis Cecil C.
Humphreys School of Law, JD, 1996, with highest
honors. Rhodes College, BA, 1987, cum laude.

**RAINES, Richard C**
Wyatt, Tarrant & Combs, LLP, Memphis
901 537 1020
rraines@wyattfirm.com
*Featured in Real Estate (Tennessee)*
**Practice Areas:** Mr Raines represents financial
institutions in transactional practice, including
commercial asset based and real estate loans, work
outs and foreclosures. Also represents real estate
developers and leasing and acquisition entities on
a national basis, possessing experience in contract
negotiation, title and survey evaluations and tenant lease matters.
**Professional Memberships:** Memphis, Shelby
County and Tennessee Bar Associations.
**Career:** Formerly, General Counsel, Union
Planters Bank (now Regions Bank), a $140 billion
financial institution.
**Publications:** Lectures at educational seminars
on real estate, banking and contract law topics.

**Personal:** 1974 - JD, University of Memphis;
1971 - BBA, University of Memphis.

**RAYSON, G Scott**
Waller Lansden Dortch & Davis, Nashville
615 850 8489
scott.rayson@wallerlaw.com
*Featured in Healthcare (Tennessee)*
**Practice Areas:** Corporate law with extensive
experience in acquisitions and divestiture of businesses, including hospitals and other healthcare
businesses. Assists publicly traded and privately
held companies across all industries in corporate
and business relocations involving corporate
headquarters, hospital and other healthcare facili-
ties, major manufacturing facilities and professional sports franchises.
**Professional Memberships:** Nashville,
Tennessee and American Bar Associations; Fellow,
Nashville Bar Foundation; Health Law Sections of
the Nashville, Tennessee and American Bar
Associations; American Health Lawyers
Association.
**Career:** Licensed in Tennessee since 1981. Joined
Waller in 1981.
**Personal:** JD, 1981, Washington and Lee
University; BA, cum laude, 1978, Duke University.

**REID JR, Glen G**
Wyatt, Tarrant & Combs, LLP, Memphis
901 537 1057
greid@wyattfirm.com
*Featured in Litigation (Tennessee)*
**Practice Areas:** Glen Reid is Partner in Charge
of Wyatt's Memphis office. He concentrates his
practice in the areas of banking litigation, com-
mercial litigation, products liability litigation,
white collar criminal defense, and patent and
intellectual property litigation.
**Professional Memberships:** Memphis and
Tennessee Bar Associations, Director of the MBA;
Memphis and Tennessee Bar Foundations; Fellow,
American College of Trial Lawyers; Fellow,
International Academy of Trial Lawyers; Master,
American Board of Trial Advocates.
**Career:** Assistant United States Attorney for the
Western District of Tennessee (1971-77), Barrister
in the American Board of Trial Advocates, Master
in the American Inns of Court.

**REISZ, Cynthia Y**
Bass, Berry & Sims PLC, Nashville
615 742 6283
creisz@bassberry.com
*Featured in Healthcare (Tennessee)*
**Practice Areas:** Represents hospital systems,
ancillary service providers and large physician
groups in transactions and regulatory/operational
matters. Assists clients in structuring acquisitions,
joint ventures and other strategic arrangements
for compliance with fraud and abuse laws.
Reviews operational issues applicable to healthcare facilities, such as licensing, Medicare certification, Medicare reimbursement and corporate
compliance matters.
**Professional Memberships:** Member, Sections
on Business Law and Health Law, American Bar
Association; Memphis Bar Association (Board
Member, Health Law Section); Member, American

Health Lawyers Association (Chair, Planning
Committee, 2013 Physicians Institute; Past Chair,
Physician Organizations Practice Group).
**Career:** Joined firm in 1986.
**Personal:** BA (1980), magna cum laude,
Vanderbilt University; JD (1986), Order of the
Coif, Vanderbilt University.

**ROARK, Brian D.**
Bass, Berry & Sims PLC, Nashville
615 742 7753
broark@bassberry.com
*Featured in Healthcare (Tennessee)*
**Practice Areas:** Head of the firm's Healthcare
Fraud Task Force; represents clients in the health-
care industry facing governmental investigations
from U.S. Department of Justice, U.S. Attorney's
Offices, States' Attorneys General, and various reg-
ulatory agencies; significant experience defending
False Claims Act lawsuits; also represents health-
care clients in overpayment disputes and self-dis-
closure matters.
**Professional Memberships:** American,
Tennessee and Nashville Bar Associations;
American Health Lawyers Association; Health
Care Compliance Association.
**Career:** Joined Bass, Berry & Sims in 2001.
**Personal:** JD (1999) University of North
Carolina; BA (1995) Lipscomb University.

**ROBINSON, Jennifer B**
Littler Mendelson, PC, Nashville
615 383 3033
JenRobinson@littler.com
*Featured in Labor & Employment (Tennessee)*
**Practice Areas:** Class Actions; Wage and Hour;
Discrimination and Harassment
**Professional Memberships:** Member,
American Bar Association - Labor and
Employment Section Member, State Bar of
California - Labor and Employment Section
Member, Tennessee Bar Association Member,
Lawyers' Association for Women Member,
Nashville Bar Association.
**Publications:** New Tennessee Attorney General's
Opinion Opens Door to Wage Claims by
Employees Serving Jury Duty Wage & Hour
Counsel; October 17, 2011.
**Personal:** JD, Vanderbilt University School of
Law, 1990; BA, University of Virginia, 1986.

**ROLAPP, Todd J**
Bass, Berry & Sims PLC, Nashville
615 742 6288
trolapp@bassberry.com
*Featured in Corporate/M&A (Tennessee)*
**Practice Areas:** Managing partner. Focuses on
general corporate and securities law, including
representation of issuers, underwriters and
investors in public and private securities offerings
and the representation of both public and private
buyers and sellers in M&A transactions. Regularly
counsels clients on matters of corporate governance and heads the firm's Executive
Compensation Group and the Corporate and
Securities Group.
**Career:** Joined the firm in 1996.
**Personal:** BA (1991), Brigham Young University;
JD (1994), Duke University.

**SAWYER, Sheila**
Waller Lansden Dortch & Davis, Nashville
615 850 8949
sheila.sawyer@wallerlaw.com
*Featured in Healthcare (Tennessee)*
**Practice Areas:** Represents companies and
executives in healthcare, pharmaceutical, defense,
financial services and other industries in govern-
ment investigations and complex civil litigation.
Served as General Counsel and Chief
Administrative Officer of $160 million healthcare
company, where she was a member of the company's Board of Directors and responsible for the
Human Resources, Licensing and Credentialing
and Training departments.
**Professional Memberships:** Boston, Nashville,
American and Federal Bar Associations; American
Health Lawyers Association; National Association
of Criminal Defense Lawyers.
**Career:** Licensed in Massachusetts, New York
and Tennessee. Joined Waller in 2006.
**Personal:** JD, 1988, Fordham University; BA,
magna cum laude, Cornell University.

**SELLERS, Cynthia N**
Bass, Berry & Sims PLC, Nashville
615 742 6255
csellers@bassberry.com
*Featured in Banking & Finance (Tennessee)*
**Practice Areas:** Over 20 years of experience
working on financial transactions, representing
banks, private and public companies and investors
in a variety of transactions, including syndicated
senior credit facilities, mezzanine finance deals,
asset based loans and real estate-based corporate
financings. Extensive experience in healthcare
finance and matters uniquely effecting regulated
borrowers.
**Career:** Joined the firm in 2006. Prior to joining
the firm, she was a member of Farris, Warfield &
Kanaday, now Stites& Harbison. Cindy also
worked in the legal department of Bank of
America as an assistant general counsel.
**Personal:** BS (1982) Meredith College; JD (1985)
University of Tennessee.

**SHARBER, Hugh**
Miller & Martin PLLC, Chattanooga
423 785 8212
hsharber@millermartin.com
*Featured in Corporate/M&A (Tennessee)*
**Practice Areas:** Hugh Sharber practices business law with an emphasis on mergers and acquisitions and securities transactions. He handles
acquisitions and sales of businesses in the healthcare, consumer products, restaurant and financial
services industries, among others. He also advises
clients on securities offerings, including initial
public offerings, secondary public offerings, senior
subordinated and convertible senior note offerings under Rule 144A and the issuance of registered common stock to acquire publicly and privately held companies and handles private placements of securities.

## SHEA, Kara E.
Butler, Snow, O'Mara, Stevens & Cannada, PLLC, Nashville
615 503 9112
kara.shea@butlersnow.com
*Featured in Labor & Employment (Tennessee)*
**Practice Areas:** Advises employers in a variety of industries including: financial services, healthcare, and transportation. Assists with wage and hour compliance, employee leave and accommodation issues, and workplace investigations. Also represents employers before administrative agencies and in litigation, including defending employers in discrimination, whistleblower, FMLA, noncompete, and wage and hour cases, including class actions. Regularly speaks on employment-related topics and provides supervisory training on topics including FMLA and FLSA compliance, conducting workplace investigations, and implementing employee discipline.
**Publications:** Co-author of a comprehensive guide to wage and hour compliance; Editor of the Tennessee Employment Law Letter.

## SHEETS, D Mark
Bass, Berry & Sims PLC, Nashville
615 742 6258
msheets@bassberry.com
*Featured in Real Estate (Tennessee)*
**Practice Areas:** Focuses on commercial real estate with substantial experience in virtually all aspects of acquisition, disposition, financing, sale-leaseback, development, leasing and ground leasing of a wide variety of commercial properties. Specific areas of emphasis include retail development, healthcare real estate, office and industrial and distressed assets.
**Professional Memberships:** Nashville Bar Association; International Council of Shopping Centers; NAIOP; and American Health Lawyers Association.
**Career:** Joined the firm in 1990.
**Personal:** BA (1987), Centre College; JD (1990), with honors, University of Kentucky.

## SHOCKLEY, Gary C
Baker, Donelson, Bearman, Caldwell & Berkowitz, PC, Nashville
615 726 5704
gshockley@bakerdonelson.com
*Featured in Environment (Tennessee), Litigation (Tennessee)*
**Practice Areas:** Chair of the firm's Government Regulatory Actions Group. Experience includes environmental, personal injury, class action, antitrust, health care and construction cases. Also represents businesses and individuals in white collar criminal investigations and prosecutions and has conducted numerous internal investigations.
**Professional Memberships:** American (Litigation, Environmental and Antitrust Sections), Tennessee (Chair of Litigation Section, 2005-06; Chair of Environmental Law Section, 1994-95; House of Delegates, 1987-1996) and Nashville Bar Associations. Fellow, Nashville Bar Foundation. Certified Civil Trial Specialist, Tennessee Commission on CLE and Specialization and NBTA.
**Career:** Licensed in Tennessee, 1982.

**Personal:** University of Tennessee, JD-1982. University of Tennessee, BA-1979.

## SISK, Bart N
Butler, Snow, O'Mara, Stevens & Cannada, PLLC, Memphis
901 680 7342
bart.sisk@butlersnow.com
*Featured in Labor & Employment (Tennessee)*
**Practice Areas:** Traditional labor practice including representation campaigns, union decertifications, NLRB hearings; business immigration law; management consulting and training; Collective Bargaining, Labor Arbitrations.
**Professional Memberships:** American Bar Association (Labor and Employment section); American Immigration Lawyers Association; Louisiana Bar Association; Tennessee Bar Association; Memphis Bar Association.
**Career:** AV-rated, Martindale-Hubbell; Represented employers across the United States, Puerto Rico, and the Caribbean faced with union organizing, including multi-facility organizing and corporate campaigns.
**Personal:** University of Tennessee, JD, with honors, 1984; Memphis State University, BBA, cum laude, 1981.

## SPEER, John
Bass, Berry & Sims PLC, Memphis
901 543 5919
JSpeer@bassberry.com
*Featured in Litigation (Tennessee)*
**Practice Areas:** Representation of clients, primarily in financial services and banking industries, in complex commercial litigation and disputes arising from lending transactions and troubled or defaulted loan issues. Litigates in federal and state courts across the country and represents clients in connection with regulatory and administrative investigations and proceedings.
**Professional Memberships:** Member of American Bar Association, Business Law Section's Business and Corporate Litigation Committee; Tennessee Bankers Association Bank Lawyer Committee.
**Career:** Admitted to United States Supreme Court, 5th, 6th and 8th US Courts of Appeals.
**Personal:** University of Kentucky, BA, 1969; University of Kentucky JD, 1973, Order of the Coif.

## SPORE III, Richard R
Bass, Berry & Sims PLC, Memphis
901 543 5902
rspore@bassberry.com
*Featured in Real Estate (Tennessee)*
**Practice Areas:** Devotes his practice in the areas of commercial real estate development, finance and leasing; business planning for business and real estate owners; partnerships and joint ventures; and business divorces.
**Professional Memberships:** Member of the Tennessee Bar Association; Member of the Memphis Bar Association.
**Career:** Joined the firm in 1999.
**Personal:** BA (1984), University of the South; JD (1987), University of Virginia; MBA, Christian Brothers University (1992).

## STAGG, Michael
Waller Lansden Dortch & Davis, Nashville
615 850 8876
michael.stagg@wallerlaw.com
*Featured in Environment (Tennessee)*
**Practice Areas:** Represents manufacturers, utilities, and local governments in environmental matters, including actions brought by Tennessee Department of Environment and Conservation, US Environmental Protection Agency, citizen and environmental groups, and federal, state, and local governmental agencies. Advises companies on compliance with federal, state, and local environmental statutes such as the Clean Water Act and the Clean Air Act. Served in Environment and Natural Resources Division of the U.S. Department of Justice.
**Career:** Licensed in Tennessee since 1995. Joined Waller in 1996.
**Personal:** JD, 1994, University of Tennessee; LLM, with highest honors, 1998, George Washington University; BS, 1982, Colorado State University.

## STEELE, Robert M.
Baker, Donelson, Bearman, Caldwell & Berkowitz, PC, Nashville
615 726 5741
rsteele@bakerdonelson.com
*Featured in Environment (Tennessee)*
**Practice Areas:** Shareholder with a broad federal and state environmental, energy, and resources law practice, with special emphases in all types of site remediation; in environmental liability counseling and documentation for business acquisitions, financial transactions, and real estate transfers; and in environmental permitting, compliance, auditing and enforcement for varied facilities including water and utility projects.
**Professional Memberships:** American (Section of Environment, Energy and Resources Law), Tennessee (Environmental Law Section), Nashville (Environmental Law Committee) Bar Associations, and The Florida Bar (Environmental and Land Use Law Section).
**Career:** Licensed, 1981.
**Personal:** Vanderbilt University School of Law, JD, 1981. Furman University, BA, 1978.

## STEMMLER, John A
Bass, Berry & Sims PLC, Memphis
901 543 5908
jstemmler@bassberry.com
*Featured in Real Estate (Tennessee)*
**Practice Areas:** Has more than 40 years of experience in commercial transactions, real estate and corporate law. Advises clients in mergers and acquisitions, commercial and residential real estate development and commercial lending. Extensive experience in the hospitality and multi-family residential markets. Represents borrowers in multi-property, multi-state hotel and apartment community financings and acquisitions.
**Professional Memberships:** American, Tennessee and Memphis Bar Associations. Former Chair, Corporation and Business Law Section, Tennessee Bar Association.

**Career:** Joined the firm in 2000. Former Member of firm's Executive Committee and current Managing Partner of the firm's Memphis office.
**Personal:** BA (1968) and JD (1971), Vanderbilt University.

## SWAFFORD, Thomas Anthony (Tony)
Adams and Reese LLP, Nashville
615 259 1518
tony.swafford@arlaw.com
*Featured in Labor & Employment (Tennessee)*
**Practice Areas:** Represents national and regional clients in labor and employment-related matters. Represents carriers, shippers and brokers in transportation-related matters. Represents corporate clients in class action litigation. Heavily involved in national and local pro bono efforts.
**Professional Memberships:** American, Tennessee Bar Associations; Transportation Lawyers Association; Association for Transportation Law, Logistics and Policy.
**Career:** Adams and Reese Transportation and Logistics Practice Team Leader.
**Publications:** Frequent writer, lecturer for number of bar associations, professional associations and seminar producers.
**Personal:** Graduated (High Honors) University of Tennessee, 1990 (BS, Accounting); cum laude, Case Western Reserve University, 1995 (JD). Married, three sons.

## TATE JR, James S
Bass, Berry & Sims PLC, Nashville
615 742 6235
jtate@bassberry.com
*Featured in Banking & Finance (Tennessee)*
**Practice Areas:** Concentrates practice in areas of banking and commercial lending, secured transactions, real estate, creditors' rights and general commercial law. Devotes majority of professional time to the negotiation and documentation of a variety of corporate financing, commercial lending and real estate transactions including revolving credit and term loan facilities, asset-based financings, construction and term real estate loans and real estate development projects.
**Career:** Joined the firm in 1980.
**Personal:** BA (1976), Vanderbilt University; JD (1980), Vanderbilt University. Order of the Coif, Vanderbilt University.

## THOMAS, G. Scott
Bass, Berry & Sims PLC, Nashville
615 742 6243
sthomas@bassberry.com
*Featured in Environment (Tennessee)*
**Practice Areas:** Practices primarily in environmental, energy and natural resource law. Represents owners, buyers, sellers and mortgagees of property in wide range of environmental transactions, enforcement actions and other disputes, including brownfield agreements. Drafted and supported numerous environmental regulatory amendments and legislative bills.
**Professional Memberships:** TBA and NBA. Co-chair of Remediation Subcommittee, Tennessee Chamber of Commerce and Industry.
**Career:** Joined firm in 1982. Best Lawyers in America. Super Lawyers.

Personal: BA (1975), UAH; JD (1982), Washington and Lee School of Law.

## THOMPSON, Bob F
Bass, Berry & Sims PLC, Nashville
615 742 6262
bthompson@bassberry.com
*Featured in Banking & Finance (Tennessee)*
**Practice Areas:** Focuses on financial institutions, securities regulation and mergers and acquisitions. Serves as principal corporate and securities counsel for public companies in the banking, managed care and healthcare information industries. Represents clients in bank regulatory matters, acquisitions, initial public offerings and private placements.
**Professional Memberships:** Nashville, Tennessee and American (Banking Law Committee; Federal Regulation of Securities Committee) Bar Associations; Tennessee Bankers Association (Lawyers Committee).
**Career:** Joined the firm in 1975. US Navy, 1969-72.
**Personal:** BA (1969), Princeton University; JD (1975), Harvard.

## THOMPSON III, Overton
Bass, Berry & Sims PLC, Nashville
615 742 7730
othompson@bassberry.com
*Featured in Litigation (Tennessee)*
**Practice Areas:** Focuses his practice on complex business litigation, including cases involving securities and shareholder class action defense, derivative actions, officer and director liability, intellectual property and patent litigation, breach of contract, business fraud, corporate and partnership dissolutions, and trust and estates litigation.
**Professional Memberships:** Member of the Nashville Bar Association Board of Directors; Past Chair of the Tennessee Bar Association Litigation Section and the Nashville Bar Association Dispute Resolution Committee.
**Personal:** BA (1981), University of the South; JD (1984), Vanderbilt University.

## TRENT, Steven H
Baker, Donelson, Bearman, Caldwell & Berkowitz, PC, Johnson City
423 928 0181
strent@bakerdonelson.com
*Featured in Labor & Employment (Tennessee)*
**Practice Areas:** Office Managing Shareholder of Firm's Johnson City, TN office. Practice includes defending claims related to Americans With Disabilities Act, Title VII, age discrimination, Fair Labor Standards Act and related collective actions, whistleblower, Equal Pay Act, FMLA, breach of contract, and retaliation. Advises employers on matters including union avoidance, FMLA administration, reductions in force, wage and hour issues, employee handbooks, employment contracts and workplace harassment.
**Professional Memberships:** Member, Washington County, Tennessee, Virginia and American Bar Associations; Federalist Society.
**Career:** Licensed in Tennessee (1993) and Virginia (1994).

Personal: David Lipscomb University, BA, 1990; Vanderbilt University Law School, JD, 1993.

## TRENTHAM, Robert
Butler, Snow, O'Mara, Stevens & Cannada, PLLC, Nashville
615 503 9106
bob.trentham@butlersnow.com
*Featured in Litigation (Tennessee)*
**Practice Areas:** Product liability law
**Professional Memberships:** Nashville, Tennessee and American Bar Associations; Life Member of the Judicial Conference of the Sixth Circuit, U.S. Court of Appeals; Fellow of the American College of Trial Lawyers.
**Career:** Fellow, Tennessee Bar Foundation; Fellow, American College of Trial Lawyers; The Best Lawyers in America® (Medical Malpractice Law and Personal Injury Litigation); Listed in Nashville Business Journal's 2012 Best of the Bar; AV-Rated, Martindale-Hubbell; Mid-South Super Lawyers® (Personal Injury Defense: Medical Malpractice)
**Personal:** Received a BA in 1969 and a JD in 1972 from Vanderbilt University.

## VANCE, Kim
Baker, Donelson, Bearman, Caldwell & Berkowitz, PC, Nashville
615 726 5674
kvance@bakerdonelson.com
*Featured in Labor & Employment (Tennessee)*
**Practice Areas:** Ms Vance represents management in every aspect of labor and employment law. She defends companies in employment litigation; presents in-house management training programs to reduce employment related legal risks; counsels management clients through auditing human resources policies and practices; and develops pre-litigation strategies to improve available defenses. She has represented management clients in State and Federal Courts and in defense of administrative proceedings.
**Professional Memberships:** Nashville, Tennessee and American Bar Associations.
**Career:** Licensed in Tennessee since 1986.
**Personal:** University of Arkansas at Little Rock Law School, JD, 1986. University of Central Arkansas, BA, 1983.

## WALKER JR, F Mitchell
Bass, Berry & Sims PLC, Nashville
615 742 6275
mwalker@bassberry.com
*Featured in Corporate/M&A (Tennessee)*
**Practice Areas:** Represents public companies and underwriters in public offerings and in mergers and acquisitions. Works with issuers and underwriters on public offerings of both equity and debt securities. Advises boards of directors or special committees on corporate governance issues, corporate restructurings, management led buy outs and investigations of accounting irregularities. Counsels clients on acquisitions or divestitures of operating subsidiaries or divisions and often coordinates an acquisition with raising the necessary capital to finance the purchase price.
**Career:** Joined the firm in 1982.

Personal: AB (1979), cum laude, Harvard University; JD (1982), Vanderbilt University.

## WALTON, Leigh
Bass, Berry & Sims PLC, Nashville
615 742 6201
lwalton@bassberry.com
*Featured in Healthcare (Tennessee)*
**Practice Areas:** Concentrates her practice in healthcare, corporate and securities law matters. Represents public companies in securities, mergers and acquisitions, and corporate governance matters. Handles acquisitions of, and joint ventures among, healthcare services providers.
**Professional Memberships:** American, Tennessee and Nashville Bar Associations; Past Chair, ABA Mergers & Acquisitions Committee; Member, American Health Lawyers Association; Fellow, American and Tennessee Bar Foundations.
**Career:** Joined the firm in 1979.
**Personal:** BA (1973), magna cum laude, Randolph-Macon Woman's College; JD (1979), Order of the Coif, Vanderbilt University.

## WATSON LAMPLEY, Julie
Butler, Snow, O'Mara, Stevens & Cannada, PLLC, Nashville
615 503 9041
julie.watson@butlersnow.com
*Featured in Healthcare (Tennessee)*
**Practice Areas:** Healthcare law; commercial contracting; antitrust; mergers and acquisitions
**Professional Memberships:** American Bar Association; Tennessee Bar Association (Health Law Section); Nashville Bar Association; Chattanooga Bar Association.
**Career:** Representation of physician groups, physician practice management companies, pharmaceutical companies, provider networks, hospitals, home healthcare providers, durable medical equipment providers and ambulatory surgery centers.
**Personal:** University of Southern Mississippi, BMEd, with honors, 1978; University of Tennessee, JD, with honors (first in class), 1987

## WEAVER, James M
Waller Lansden Dortch & Davis, Nashville
615 850 8482
james.weaver@wallerlaw.com
*Featured in Environment (Tennessee)*
**Practice Areas:** Assists clients in state and local government relations and regulatory matters. Extensive experience in the areas of incentives, real estate development, mining, environmental, insurance, construction, healthcare, professional sports, waste management, telecommunications, transportation and economic development.
**Professional Memberships:** Nashville, Tennessee and American Bar Associations; General Counsel, Tennessee Road Builders Association; Government Relations Chair, United Way of Metropolitan Nashville; Former General Counsel, Tennessee Chamber of Commerce and Industry; Former Vice-Chair, Government Relations, Nashville Chamber of Commerce; Fellow, Tennessee Bar Foundation.
**Career:** Licensed in Tennessee since 1988. Joined Waller in 1989.

Personal: JD, 1988, University of Memphis; BA, 1984, Vanderbilt University.

## WEINTRAUB, Jeff
Fisher & Phillips LLP, Memphis
901 526 0431
jweintraub@laborlawyers.com
*Featured in Labor & Employment (Tennessee)*
**Career:** Jeff Weintraub is the managing partner of the Memphis office. He is a trial attorney who has represented employers in more than 59 jury and bench trials in the private and public sectors in employment-harassment/discrimination and retaliatory discharge lawsuits. He also handles EEOC charges, wage and hour cases, labor cases, and enforcing non-competes in federal and state courts and agencies, various Courts of Appeals, and the U.S. Supreme Court. Jeff also represents employers in union-related matters, and he has handled more than 80 labor arbitrations. He provides training for employers in avoiding harassment charges and employment litigation.

## WELLFORD, Buckner
Baker, Donelson, Bearman, Caldwell & Berkowitz, PC, Memphis
*Featured in Litigation (Tennessee)*
**Practice Areas:** Shareholder and chair of the Health Care Advocacy Group. Represents hospitals, physicians and medical groups in health care litigation, regulatory, peer review, contract and employee matters. Experienced in jury and bench trials in state and federal courts in Tennessee, Mississippi and Arkansas, involving defense of health care providers in medical malpractice or regulatory matters, product liability, breach of contract and employment disputes, civil rights and fraud claims.
**Professional Memberships:** Listed in Best Lawyers in America, Mid-South Super Lawyers. "150 Best Lawyers" (Business Tennessee–2009).
**Career:** Licensed in Tennessee.
**Personal:** Washington & Lee (JD-1981, Burks Scholar), Vanderbilt University (BA-1978).

## WESTLING, Richard
Waller Lansden Dortch & Davis, Nashville
615 850 8481
richard.westling@wallerlaw.com
*Featured in Healthcare (Tennessee)*
**Practice Areas:** Represents companies and individuals in government investigations, high-profile enforcement actions, or those facing the prospect of severe criminal, civil, or administrative sanctions. Experience includes white collar defense, healthcare compliance and operations, False Claims Act, Foreign Corrupt Practices Act, environmental litigation, and tax litigation.
**Professional Memberships:** American Bar Association Litigation, Health Law, Criminal Justice and Taxation Sections; American Health Lawyers Association; Health Care Compliance Association; National Association of Criminal Defense Lawyers.
**Career:** Licensed in District of Columbia, Louisiana, Maryland, New Jersey, Tennessee. Joined Waller in 2011.
**Personal:** JD, cum laude, 1988, Tulane University; BA, 1985, University of the South.

## WILSON, Virginia B
Butler, Snow, O'Mara, Stevens & Cannada, PLLC, Memphis
901 680 7313
virginia.wilson@butlersnow.com
*Featured in Banking & Finance (Tennessee)*
**Practice Areas:** Banking and financial services regulation and activities; corporate transactions; mergers and acquisitions; securities/public finance; estate planning.
**Professional Memberships:** American Bar Association; Mississippi Bar; Tennessee Bar Association; Memphis Bar Association.
**Career:** AV-rated, Martindale-Hubbell; Mid-South Super Lawyers (Banking); Mississippi and Tennessee editor for HouseLaw; representation of area banks and other financial institutions.
**Personal:** University of Mississippi, BA, magna cum laude, 1979; MBA, with honors, 1981; JD, 1989.

## WOODRUFF, Joseph A
Waller Lansden Dortch & Davis, Nashville
615 850 8485
joseph.woodruff@wallerlaw.com
*Featured in Litigation (Tennessee)*
**Practice Areas:** Business and tort litigation involving financial services, healthcare, manufac-turing, real estate, professional sports and enter-tainment. Represented State of Tennessee in suc-cessful efforts to return $100,000,000 Maddox Foundation to Tennessee after controversial move to Mississippi. Retired at the rank of Lieutenant Colonel in the US Army Reserve after more than 30 years of active and reserve military duty.
**Professional Memberships:** Fellow, Nashville Bar Foundation; Fellow, Litigation Counsel of America.
**Career:** Licensed in Alabama since 1981, in Tennessee since 1987. Joined Waller in 1987.
**Personal:** JD, Order of the Coif, 1981, University of Alabama; BA, 1974, University of Alabama.

## YARBRO, Jason G
Butler, Snow, O'Mara, Stevens & Cannada, PLLC, Memphis
901 680 7306
jason.yarbro@butlersnow.com
*Featured in Real Estate (Tennessee)*
**Practice Areas:** Real estate; corporate and secu-rities; government contracts and investigations.
**Professional Memberships:** American Bar Association (Real Property and Probate Sections); Tennessee Bar Association (Business Law section and Limited Liability Company Act Drafting Committee).
**Career:** Mid-South Rising Stars (Real Estate); representations of local, regional and national developers in acquisition development, financing, ownership, operation and disposition of various real estate projects.
**Personal:** University of Memphis, JD, 1996; University of Tennessee, BA, 1993.

## YOUNG, Edward R
Baker, Donelson, Bearman, Caldwell & Berkowitz, PC, Memphis
901 577 2341
eyoung@bakerdonelson.com
*Featured in Labor & Employment (Tennessee)*
**Practice Areas:** Nationwide practice represent-ing public and private management in all phases of labor relations and employment law, including litigation, union avoidance, and collective bargain-ing. Over 40 years' experience representing clients in state and federal courts on issues dealing with EEOC, NLRB, and US Department of Labor. Has litigated matters in over 20 states and Canada.
**Professional Memberships:** Memphis, Tennessee and American Bar Associations.
**Career:** Admitted before US Courts of Appeals (Fifth, Sixth, Eighth, Eleventh, and DC Circuits), US Supreme Court, Tennessee Supreme Court.
**Personal:** University of Memphis, BS, 1963; Vanderbilt University, JD, 1966. Listed in Best Lawyers in America.

## YOUNG, Greg
Stites & Harbison PLLC, Nashville
615 782 2264
greg.young@stites.com
*Featured in Environment (Tennessee)*
**Practice Areas:** Environmental, Administrative, Natural Resources
**Professional Memberships:** American, Tennessee & Nashville Bar Associations
**Career:** Stites & Harbison (2010 - ); Bass, Berry & Sims (2001-10).
**Publications:** The Clean Water Act's Impact on Project Development, Construction Executive; Water Law in Tennessee, Professional Development Seminars; Stormwater Issues in Tennessee, Lorman Education Services; TDEC Compliance & Enforcement Strategies, TAUD; Stream & Wetland Mitigation Banking Primer.
**Personal:** DOB: February 12, 1976; Mississippi College, BA magna cum laude (1998); Tulane University School of Law, JD cum laude (2001); Admitted in Eastern, Middle & Western US District Courts and all state and local Tennessee courts.

# BAKER, DONELSON, BEARMAN, CALDWELL & BERKOWITZ, PC

www.bakerdonelson.com **tel:** 901 526 2000 **fax:** 901 577 2303

**Chairman & CEO:** Ben C Adams, Jr
**COO:** Jerry Stauffer
Shareholders: 313
Other lawyers: 342 (attorneys and public policy advisors)

## Firm Overview:

For more than 120 years, Baker Donelson has built a reputation for achieving results for clients on a wide range of legal matters. Clients know it's not just what the firm does, but how they do it that makes the difference. The firm commits to a deep understanding of a client's business, anticipating clients' needs and assisting in their decision making processes. Because Baker Donelson offers consistent, knowledgeable guidance based on specific goals and objectives, clients view the firm as a valued business partner. This allows them to focus on the growth and success of their business, confident their legal issues will be handled by an attentive, responsive team.

## Main Areas of Practice:

The 72nd largest law firm in the US, Baker Donelson, is a full-service firm that gives clients access to a team of more than 630 attorneys and public policy advisors representing more than 30 practice areas, all seamlessly connected across 18 offices to serve virtually any legal need.

- Admiralty & Maritime
- ADR – Center for Dispute Resolution
- Antitrust
- Broker-Dealer/Registered Investment Adviser
- Business Technology
- Commercial Real Estate Recovery Team
- Construction
- Corporate Compliance, Ethics and Crisis Management
- Defense
- Disaster Recovery and Government Services
- Economic Development
- Emerging Companies
- Eminent Domain
- Employee Benefits & Executive Compensation
- Environmental
- Estate Planning/Probate
- Exempt Organizations
- Financial Institutions
- Gaming
- Global Business
- Government Contracts
- Health Law
- Hospitality, Franchising and Distribution
- Immigration
- Insurance Regulatory
- Intellectual Property
- Labor & Employment
- Litigation
- Mergers and Acquisitions
- Oil & Gas
- Pro Bono
- Product Liability and Mass Tort
- Public Finance
- Public Policy - Federal and State
- Real Estate
- Residential Mortgage Lending and Servicing
- Securities and Corporate Governance
- Sports Law
- Taxation
- Transportation
- White Collar Crime and Government Investigations

## OFFICES

### TENNESSEE
**MEMPHIS:** 165 Madison Avenue, Suite 2000, TN 38103
Tel: 901 526 2000 Fax: 901 577 2303

### ALABAMA
**BIRMINGHAM:** 420 20th Street N, 1400 Wells Fargo Tower, AL 35203
Tel: 205 328 0480 Fax: 205 322 8007

**MONTGOMERY:** 614 South Hull Street, AL 36104
Tel: 334 262 2000 Fax: 334 263 0960

### FLORIDA
**ORLANDO:** 390 North Orange Avenue, Suite 1875, FL 32801
Tel: 407 422 6600 Fax: 407 841 0325

### GEORGIA
**ATLANTA:** Monarch Plaza, Suite 1600, 3414 Peachtree Road NE, GA 30326
Tel: 404 577 6000 Fax: 404 221 6501

**MACON:** Gateway Plaza, Suite 201, 300 Mulberry Street, GA 31201
Tel: 478 750 0777 Fax: 478 750 1777

### LOUISIANA
**NEW ORLEANS:** 201 St. Charles Ave., Suite 3600, LA 70170
Tel: 504 566 5200 Fax: 504 636 4000

**MANDEVILLE:** 3 Sanctuary Blvd., Suite 201, LA 70471
Tel: 985 819 8400 Fax: 985 819 8484

**BATON ROUGE:** 450 Laurel Street, Chase Tower North, 20th Floor, LA 70801
Tel: 225 381 7000 Fax: 225 343 3612

### MISSISSIPPI
**JACKSON:** 4268 I-55 North, Meadowbrook Office Park, MS 39211
Tel: 601 351 2400 Fax: 601 351 2424

### TENNESSEE
**CHATTANOOGA:** 633 Chestnut Street, 1800 Republic Centre, TN 37450
Tel: 423 756 2010 Fax: 423 756 3447

**HUNTSVILLE:** One Courthouse Square, TN 37756
Tel: 423 663 9148 Fax: 423 663 2076

**JOHNSON CITY:** 100 Med Tech Parkway, Suite 200, TN 37604
Tel: 423 928 0181 Fax: 423 928 5694

**KNOXVILLE:** 265 Brookview Centre Way, Suite 600, Knoxville, TN 37919
Tel: 865 549 7000 Fax: 865 525 8569

**MEMPHIS:** 6060 Poplar Ave., Suite 440, Memphis, TN 38119
Tel: 901 579 3100 Fax: 901 577 3111

**NASHVILLE:** Baker Donelson Center, 211 Commerce Street, Suite 800, Nashville, TN 37201
Tel: 615 726 5600 Fax: 615 726 0464

### TEXAS
**HOUSTON:** 1301 McKinney Avenue, Suite 3700, TX 77010
Tel: 713 650 9700 Fax: 713 650 9701

### WASHINGTON, DC
**WASHINGTON:** 920 Massachusetts Ave, NW, Suite 900, Washington, DC 20001
Tel: 202 508 3400 Fax: 202 508 3402

# BASS, BERRY & SIMS PLC

www.bassberry.com **tel:** 615 742 6200

**Managing Partner:** Todd J Rolapp
Number of partners: 119
Number of other lawyers: 94

## Firm Overview:

Bass, Berry & Sims PLC is principal corporate counsel to more than 40 public companies and is a leader in corporate governance, healthcare and complex litigation.

## Main Areas of Practice:

### Corporate & Securities:

Nationally known for its extensive experience in mergers and acquisitions, securities transactions, private equity and venture capital, corporate governance and compliance, executive compensation, special committee assignments, going private transactions, proxy contests, reorganizations and tax issues.

### Healthcare:

Counsels public and private healthcare companies in complex mergers and acquisitions; joint ventures and syndications; fraud and abuse investigations; regulatory, contracting and operational matters; and government enforcement and compliance. The firm represents for-profit and nonprofit hospitals and health systems; outpatient service providers; long-term care facilities; managed care organizations; disease management; and healthcare information technology companies.

### Securities & Shareholder Litigation:

Defends complex securities class actions and merger-related litigation, including corporate governance matters arising under federal and state securities laws.

### Compliance & Investigations:

Advises clients on securities, healthcare and public corruption-related investigations. Conducts internal investigations and manages client exposure before, during, and after governmental inquiries. Negotiates with governmental officials and defends clients in civil, criminal, administrative and regulatory proceedings.

### FCPA:

Advises public and private companies on FCPA and other foreign anti-corruption laws including conducting international anti-corruption investigations and risk assessments. Develops cost-effective FCPA compliance programs and conducts international due diligence, and assists in the navigation of anti-corruption compliance issues in international mergers, acquisitions, joint ventures, sourcing, contracting and distributing.

### Antitrust:

Provides antitrust litigation and counseling for issues arising under federal and state antitrust laws. Particular focus in the healthcare industry. Representations include managing collaborations between competitors and joint ventures, relationships with suppliers and customers, HSR Act pre-merger clearance, interlocking directorates, pricing issues, market allocation, licensing and distribution, bid-rigging, and the development of effective compliance programs.

### Healthcare Fraud Litigation:

Provides healthcare clients with counsel and support for civil and criminal exposure, including matters relating to the Stark Law and Anti-Kickback Statute, the False Claims Act, various criminal statutes, and Medicare and Medicaid audits.

### Real Estate Capital Markets:

Counsels real estate investment trusts on corporate, compliance, mergers and acquisitions, securities and tax matters. The firm represents issuers and underwriters in transactions involving REITs in the student housing, multi-family, self-storage, office, retail, healthcare, hotel, commercial and industrial sectors.

### Commercial Transactions & Real Estate:

Focuses on acquisition, development, construction, leasing, disposition and management of a wide variety of commercial real estate for developers, investors and corporate clients. The firm advises clients in commercial lending and debt transactions, including senior credit facilities, mezzanine financings, public finance, tax increment financings, equipment financing and leasing, asset based lending and project/construction finance.

### Employee Benefits:

Experienced in design, drafting, implementation, amendment, termination and administration of all types of employee benefit plans and compensation arrangements. Experienced in employee benefits litigation, ERISA fiduciary advice, advice related to the PPACA, and executive compensation advice.

### Environmental:

Routinely handles litigation and administrative actions, transactions, permitting, enforcement and general counsel on environmental matters, including air/water pollution, hazardous and solid waste, toxic materials, Superfund, USTs, brownfields, sustainability and NEPA.

### Financial Institutions:

Assists in the organization of new banks, insurance companies and HMOs; capital raising and securities law compliance; regulatory compliance; acquisitions of or by banks, thrifts, insurance companies or their holding companies; branch purchases and acquisitions of failed institutions; advice concerning permissible non-bank activities; and enforcement proceedings against institutions or their officers and directors.

### Intellectual Property:

Experienced in intellectual property protection, prosecution and enforcement, including IP litigation, commercialization of IP, portfolio management, software and technology transactions, healthcare information technology, licensing, due diligence and audits, outsourcing transactions and advertising and promotion issues.

### Labor & Employment:

Experienced in management side labor practice and employment law litigation and counseling, including (1) informational and decertification campaigns, contract negotiations and arbitrations; (2) retaliation, discrimination and whistleblower claims; (3) FLSA DOL investigations and class/collective actions; and (4) a myriad of other issues including FMLA and state law leaves of absence, I-9 compliance, independent contractor classification and non-competes.

### Public Finance:

Experienced in all types of tax-exempt and taxable governmental bond, private activity bond and economic development transactions; serving as counsel to issuers, underwriters and lenders.

### Tax:

Comprehensive counseling in transactional tax, state and local tax, business and personal tax planning.

## OFFICES

**TENNESSEE**

**NASHVILLE:** 150 Third Avenue South, Suite 2800, TN 37201
Tel: 615 742 6200

**KNOXVILLE:** 1700 Riverview Tower, 900 S. Gay Street, TN 37902
Tel: 865 521 6200

**MEMPHIS:** The Tower at Peabody Place, 100 Peabody Place, Suite 900, TN 38103
Tel: 901 543 5900

**DISTRICT OF COLUMBIA**

**WASHINGTON:** 1201 Pennsylvania Avenue NW, Suite 300, DC 20004
Tel: 202 827 2950

# BURR AND FORMAN LLP

**www.**burr.com   **tel:** 800 GET BURR

**Chairman:** Lee Thuston
Managing Partners: 9   Number of partners: 178   Number of lawyers: 288

**Firm Overview:**
Burr & Forman is a full service law firm with a long history of serving clients in Alabama, Florida, Georgia, Mississippi and Tennessee. The firm's forward-thinking approach allows it to provide legal solutions appropriate to the needs of its clients. With nearly 300 attorneys, Burr & Forman offers a wide range of business and litigation services to diverse clients with local, national and international interests.

**Main Areas of Practice:**

**Automotive:**
Represents automotive dealerships in claims associated with franchise agreements, breach of contract, sales and acquisitions, non-competes and wrongful termination.

**Banking & Finance:**
Represents lenders of all types in lending and financial transactions for working capital needs, refinancings, specific personal and real property asset acquisitions and development and company acquisitions in the middle and large corporate markets.

**Commercial Litigation:**
Represents financial institutions, businesses and officers and directors in complex commercial disputes and securities litigation.

**Corporate & Tax:**
Represents businesses and not-for-profits of all sizes and in all stages of development in complex business matters, mergers and acquisitions, capital raises and regulatory compliance issues.

**Creditors' Rights & Bankruptcy:**
Represents financial services institutions, asset-based lenders and local, regional and national banks in significant and complex bankruptcy proceedings.

**Construction:**
Represents owners, contractors, suppliers and design professionals in all construction-related transactional matters and in the litigation or dispute resolution of all construction claims.

**Economic Development:**
Leading economic development firm in the Southeast. Projects reflect a diversity of industries and represent over $16 billion of capital investment and over 25,000 new jobs created.

**Environmental:**
Represents industries, developers, financial institutions and individuals in environmental matters related to business strategy, permitting and regulatory compliance, litigation, sustainability, and administrative proceedings.

**Financial Services Litigation:**
Represents banks, mortgage, finance and credit card companies in all types of litigation involving deceptive loan origination, predatory lending, wrongful foreclosure, mortgage fraud and statutory violation claims.

**Health Care:**
Represents all types of health care organizations in a variety of litigation, regulatory, compliance, licensure and corporate law matters.

**Insurance Regulatory:**
Represents all types of businesses and insurance entities in connection with structuring solutions to their business insurance needs and maintaining regulatory compliance.

**Labor & Employment:**
Represents employers of all sizes in matters ranging from drafting policies and handbooks to defending against the entire gamut of employment-related claims.

**Maritime & Transportation:**
Represents clients whose businesses are in, around or near navigable waters with all types of litigation claims, financing activities, contract negotiations, employment matters and other regulatory issues.

**Products Liability:**
Represents clients in all industries with products and premises liability, personal injury, industrial and construction site accidents, pharmaceuticals, medical devices, mass torts and toxic tort cases.

**Real Estate:**
Represents commercial real estate development companies in land planning, entitlement and development, governmental incentives, title matters, acquisition and disposition and performing and distressed assets.

**Securities Litigation:**
Represents broker-dealers and investment bankers in disputes, such as mutual-fund class-actions, derivative contracts trials, government enforcement actions and constitutional challenges to municipal securities rules.

**Technology:**
Represents businesses in protection of, and licensing strategies for, intellectual property, contract negotiation,

growth, investment and acquisition strategies.

**OFFICES**

**TENNESSEE**
**NASHVILLE:** 700 Two American Center, 3102 West End Avenue, TN 37203
Tel: 615 724 3200   Fax: 615 724 3290

**ALABAMA**
**BIRMINGHAM:** 420 North 20th Street, Suite 3400, AL 35203
Tel: 205 251 3000   Fax: 205 458 5100

**MOBILE:** RSA Tower, 11 North Water Street, Suite 22200, AL 36602
Tel: 251 344 5151   Fax: 251 344 9696

**MONTGOMERY:** RSA Tower, 201 Monroe Street, Suite 1950, AL 36104
Tel: 334 241 7000   Fax: 334 262 0020

**FLORIDA**
**FT. LAUDERDALE:** Las Olas Centre I, 450 East Las Olas Boulevard, Suite 700, FL 33301
Tel: 954 414 6200   Fax: 954 414 6201

**ORLANDO:** 200 South Orange Avenue, Suite 800, FL 32801
Tel: 407 540 6600   Fax: 407 540 6601

**TAMPA:** One Tampa City Center, Suite 3200, FL 33602
Tel: 813 221 2626   Fax: 813 221 7335

**GEORGIA**
**ATLANTA:** 171 17th Street, NW Suite 1100, GA 30363
Tel: 404 815 3000   Fax: 404 817 3244

**MISSISSIPPI**
**JACKSON:** The Heritage Building, 401 E Capitol Street, Suite 100, MS 39201
Tel: 601 355 3434   Fax: 601 355 5150

**Clients:**
American Cast Iron Pipe Company; ADTRAN; American Suzuki Motor Corporation; Assuranceforeningen Gard-gjensidig; Bank of America; Bank of Tampa; Brasfield and Gorrie General Contractors; Brice Building Company; Budgetext; Capital One; Charles Schwab & Co., Inc.; Circle K; Citibank; City of Tampa; Coastal Forest Products; Coca-Cola Enterprises; CVS Caremark; Daniel Realty Company; Dillard's; East Alabama Medical Center; First American; Founders Insurance Company; Gray Construction; HealthSouth Corporation; Laboratory Corporation of America; Mercedes-Benz U.S. International, Inc.; M/I Homes; Millard Maritime; Morgan Keegan & Co.; National Steel Car; Nissan Motors of America, Inc.; Nutech Medical Inc.; Nu Tech Spine, Inc.; ProAssurance; RockTenn Company; Rinnai; Standard Insurance; Southpace Properties; SunTrust Mortgage; Synovus Bank; Tacala; Tenet Healthcare Corporation; Guardian Life; ThyssenKrupp; Time Insurance Company; TriNovus Capital, LLC; UAB Health Services Foundation; United States Steel; Wells Fargo Bank; Wells Fargo Advisors; Whirlpool

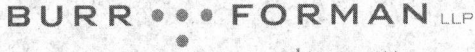

BURR ••• FORMAN LLP
*results matter*

# KRAMER RAYSON LLP

www.kramer-rayson.com **tel:** 865 525 5134 **fax:** 865 522 5723

**Managing Partner:** John E Winters

### Firm Overview:

Since its inception in Knoxville in 1948, Kramer Rayson has dedicated itself to the representation of businesses and business owners in Tennessee. The firm is committed to providing superior, cost-effective legal services covering the gamut of issues its business clients face. Kramer Rayson has 26 attorneys with significant practices in labor and employment law, healthcare, corporate/business, government relations, tax, estate/planning/probate, litigation and insurance coverage. The firm is regularly employed by corporate counsel, government agencies, and public and private entities, as well as individuals either doing business or involved in litigation in Tennessee.

### Main Areas of Practice:

**Labor & Employment:**

Kramer Rayson's thirteen labor and employment attorneys represent management in employment discrimination litigation; unfair competition disputes; harassment and whistleblower cases; traditional labor law, including union campaigns, collective bargaining, arbitration and NLRB practice; human resources counseling and training; and ADR-mediation processes. The firm has one of the largest management-side employment practices in East Tennessee and has successfully litigated through trial and appeal many high profile matters. Decisions can be viewed at www.kramer-rayson.com.

**Key Clients:** G4S Governement Solutions, Inc., Knoxville Utilities Board, Babcock & Wilcox Technical Services Y-12, LLC, UT Battelle, LLC, East Tennessee Children's Hospital, University of Tennessee
**Contact:** Edward G Phillips **Tel:** 865 525 5134
**Email:** ephillips@kramer-rayson.com
**Contact:** Steven E Kramer **Tel:** 865 525 5134
**Email:** skramer@kramer-rayson.com

**Healthcare:**

Kramer Rayson's five healthcare attorneys have successfully represented and counseled clients ranging from major hospitals and practice groups to independent practitioners on a complete range of matters spanning business-related issues, licensing, certificates of need, compliance plans/audits, Medicare reimbursement, HIPPA compliance, fraud/abuse, Stark, anti-kickback and false claims.
**Key Clients:** Tennova Healthcare, St. Thomas Health Services
**Contact:** Warren L Gooch **Tel:** 865 525 5134
**Email:** wgooch@kramer-rayson.com

**Corporate/Business/Real Estate:**

Kramer Rayson's nine corporate/business attorneys maintain a strong practice in traditional corporate and transactional areas including corporate governance, start-up ventures, purchase, sale merger or acquisitions, financing and credit arrangements and related commercial transactions, creditor's rights, business planning, real estate transactions, zoning, loan workouts and other commercial transactions.
**Key Clients:** US Cellular, Blalock Companies, CROET
**Contact:** Thomas M Hale **Tel:** 865 525 5134
**Email:** tomhale@kramer-rayson.com
**Contact:** Jackson G Kramer **Tel:** 865 525 5134
**Email:** jgkramer@kramer-rayson.com

**Government Relations:**

Kramer Rayson's four government relations attorneys have extensive experience representing clients' interests before federal, state and local governmental decision-makers, boards and public bodies.
**Key Clients:** Town of Farragut, City of Townsend, Loudon County
**Contact:** Thomas M Hale **Tel:** 865 525 5134
**Email:** tomhale@kramer-rayson.com
**Contact:** Robert L Bowman **Tel:** 865 525 5134
**Email:** rlbowman@krame-rayson.com

**Tax:**

Kramer Rayson's three tax attorneys have practices that include work in the areas of estate, gift, state and local tax (including sales, use and property taxes), corporate, partnership, tax exempt entities, and individuals in their personal tax planning and various other tax issues. One of the firm's partners has a highly regarded reputation representing major businesses in ad valorem, property and sales and use tax planning and litigation.
**Key Clients:** General Motors, Alcoa, UT Battelle
**Contact:** Wayne R Kramer **Tel:** 865 525 5134
**Email:** wrkramer@kramer-rayson.com

**Estate Planning/Probate:**

Kramer Rayson's five estate/planning/probate attorneys provide a full range of estate planning services and advises clients with respect to succession issues and closely held businesses.
**Contact:** Charles M Finn **Tel:** 865 525 5134
**Email:** cmfinn@kramer-rayson.com
**Contact:** Jackson G Kramer **Tel:** 865 525 5134

## PRACTICE AREAS

Labor & Employment
Healthcare
Corporate/Business
Government
Tax
Estate/Planning/Probate
Litigation

## OFFICES

**TENNESSEE**

**KNOXVILLE:** 800 S. Gay Street, Suite 2500, TN 37929
Tel: 865 525 5134   Fax: 865 522 5723

**OAK RIDGE:** 105 Donner Drive, Suite A TN 37830
Tel: 865 220 5134   Fax 865 220 5132

**Email:** jgkramer@kramer-rayson.com
**Contact:** Wayne R Kramer **Tel:** 865 525 5134
**Email:** wrkramer@kramer-rayson.com

**Litigation:**

Kramer Rayson's nine litigation attorneys represent a broad array of clients in commercial litigation, unfair competition, construction law, insurance defense, insurance coverage, personal injury litigation, condemnation, worker's compensation, product liability litigation, government contract disputes, ERISA litigation, arbitration, mediation and appellate practice, as well as administrative matters including in tax and related forums.
**Key Clients:** TFMIC, Grange Insurance, Functional Pathways, Auto Owners Insurance, State Farm
**Contact:** John T Johnson, Jr **Tel:** 865 525 5134
**Email:** jtjohnson@kramer-rayson.com
**Contact:** John E Winters **Tel:** 865 525 5134
**Email:** jwinters@kramer-rayson.com

## KRAMER RAYSON LLP
ATTORNEYS AT LAW

# MILLER & MARTIN PLLC

**www.**millermartin.com **tel:** 1 800 275 7303

**Chairman:** James M Haley IV
Number of partners: 86  Number of lawyers: 130

**Firm Overview:**

Miller & Martin lawyers are dedicated to efficient, responsive and reliable counsel and service. Attorneys in the firm partner with clients to forge long-lasting business relationships. For more than145 years, a focus on service, relationships and results has set Miller & Martin apart from other law firms.

**Main Areas of Practice:**

**Corporate/M&A:**

- Represented a privately-held trucking company in an acquisition of assets of Kinard Trucking, Inc.
- Represented a gas appliance company in its sale to an affiliate of Aterian Investment Partners. Entities involved were from US, UK, Turkey, Mexico and France. This deal was selected as a finalist transaction for the 2012 M&A Advisory Summit.
- Represented a national portrait company in its sale to the photography industry's largest employee-owned company.
- Served as special counsel and represented the shareholders of a restaurant company in the sale of stock to two private equity firms for $175 million.
- Represented Larsen MacColl Partners, L.P., a private equity firm, in connection with the sale of a majority stake in its portfolio company, S&S Worldwide, Inc., one of the leading amusement ride and roller coaster manufacturers in the world.
- Represented Mayne Pharma Group Limited, a publicly held company based in Melbourne, Australia, in the acquisition of Metrics, Inc., a North Carolina based pharmaceuticals company.

**Key Clients:** River Associates Investments, LLC; Larsen MacColl Partners, L.P.; Playcore; Cadillac Jack, Inc.; Harbert Mezzanine Partners II SBIC, L.P.; Chattem, Inc.; Independent Healthcare Properties, LLC; Dixie Group, Inc.; Craftworks Restaurants & Breweries Group, Inc.

**Contact:** Pat Murphy  Tel. 423 785 8339
**Email:** pmurphy@millermartin.com
**Contact:** Ward Nelson  Tel: 423 785 8250
**Email:** wnelson@millermartin.com

**Commercial:**

- Represented a national real estate development company in receiving approval for first ever Tax Increment Financing (TIF) project for construction of a $9,000,000 mountain road and related infrastructure as part of a $500+ million dollar, 3000 acre mixed use development project.
- Represented a developer in an $80 million sale of apartment complexes.
- Represented multinational polysilicon manufacturer in connection with the Chapter 11 bankruptcy of a

customer filed in the United States Bankruptcy Court for the District of Delaware and in connection with the associated avoidance claims asserted by the Court appointed indenture trustee.
- Represented senior secured lender in successful modification and renewal of $50,000,000+ commercial credit facilities extended to multi-location automotive enterprise.
- Successfully represented North Chickamauga Creek Conservancy in coordinating the acquisition of a seven-mile trail corridor across the Cumberland Plateau by the State of Tennessee.  This seven-mile corridor will incorporate into the larger Cumberland Trail project, stretching from the Cumberland Gap on the Kentucky border all of the way across the state to its present terminus on Signal Point near the Georgia border.

**Key Clients:** CraftWorks Restaurants & Breweries Group, Inc.; Wacker Polysilicon North America, LLC
**Contact:** Bill DuPre  Tel. 404-962-6418
**Email:** bdupre@millermartin.com

**Labor & Employment:**

- Representation of the Atlanta Regional Commission—governmental support and planning services for the most heavily populated counties in the State of Georgia.
- Representation of international manufacturer/distributor in a large, multiple-plaintiff race discrimination lawsuit.
- Representation of U.S. Xpress, Inc. in a class action case alleging violations of the Fair Credit Reporting Act.
- Representation of banking institution in a multiple plaintiff age discrimination lawsuit.

**Key Clients:** Coca-Cola Refreshments USA, Inc.; Chattem, Inc.; Covenant Transportation Group, Inc.
**Contact:** John Bode  Tel: 423 785 8320
**Email:** jbode@millermartin.com
**Contact:** Jimmy Daniel  Tel: 404 962 6426
**Email:** jpdaniel@millermartin.com

**Litigation:**

- Representation of Life Care Centers of America, Inc. in False Claims Act litigation brought by the U.S. Department of Justice challenging legitimacy of charges relating to therapy.
- Representation of a major health insurer as defendant in a lawsuit filed by seven hospitals and medical centers

owned by a national healthcare service provider, which sought additional reimbursement for out-of-network healthcare provided to members of the client's particular network.  The lawsuit combines over 6,000 individual claims.
- Representation of FDIC as receiver in connection with the professional liability, accountant malpractice, fidelity bond, investigations and in resulting litigation following the sixth largest bank failure in U.S. history.
- Representation of SunLife Assurance Company (U.S.) defending securities and consumer protection claims by 55 plaintiffs from 10 states arising from the sale of various annuities.

**Key Clients:** Acella Pharmaceuticals, LLC; BlueCross BlueShield of Tennessee, Inc.; Coca-Cola Refreshments USA, Inc.; Sun Life Assurance Company of Canada (U.S.); Life Care Centers of America, Inc.
**Contact:** Travis McDonough  Tel. 423 785 8328
**Email:** tmcdonough@millermartin.com

**International Work:**

Clients benefit from the firm's membership in the World Law Group, an international network of 51 leading independent law firms with more than 315 offices in major commercial centers worldwide. The firm's lawyers regularly secure incentives and abatements for international companies establishing operations in the US as well as assisting companies seeking to do business overseas. The firm has represented clients involved in a variety of international joint ventures and in international litigation including appearing before the US-Iranian Claims Tribunal in The Hague and the London Arbitration Council. The firm represented an Australian pharmaceutical company in the acquisition of a North Carolina drug company for $115,000,000 which closed November 14, 2012.

---

**PRACTICE AREAS**

Corporate/M&A
Commercial
Labor & Employment
Litigation

**OFFICES**

**GEORGIA**

**ATLANTA:** Suite 800, 1170 Peachtree Street, NE, GA 30309-7706
Tel: 404 962 6100  Fax: 404 962 6300
Email: info@millermartin.com

**TENNESSEE**

**CHATTANOOGA:** Suite 1000, Volunteer Building, 832 Georgia Avenue, TN 37402-2289
Tel: 423 756 6600  Fax: 423 785 8480
Email: info@millermartin.com

**NASHVILLE:** 1200 One Nashville Place, 150 Fourth Avenue North, TN 37219-2433
Tel: 615 244 9270  Fax: 615 256 8197
Email: info@millermartin.com

# RILEY WARNOCK & JACOBSON PLC

**www.rwjplc.com** **tel:** 615 320 3700 **fax:** 615 320 3737

**Managing Partner:** John R Jacobson
Number of partners: 12
Number of other lawyers: 7

**OFFICES**

TENNESSEE

**NASHVILLE:** 1906 West End Avenue, TN 37203
Tel: 615 320 3700   Fax: 615 320 3737

## Firm Overview:

Riley Warnock & Jacobson, PLC was founded more than 16 years ago when its founding members left one of Tennessee's largest full-service law firms to concentrate on litigation. The firm's goal is to provide the highest quality legal services in the most responsive and cost-effective manner available. The firm focuses its practice on litigation but defines 'litigation' broadly to encompass dispute resolution in all forums, including state and federal courts, appellate courts, arbitration and mediation. Equally as important, the firm works to advise clients and to resolve disputes before initiating formal legal proceedings. The firm's lawyers have extensive litigation experience in jury and non-jury trials in state and federal court as well as in arbitration and other forms of alternate dispute resolution. The firm employs attorneys who are licensed in multiple states, including Alabama, Arkansas, California, Florida, Georgia, Kentucky, New York and Tennessee, to ensure proper representation of its clients no matter the location of the dispute. The firm's commitment is to design and execute an appropriate strategy to accomplish each client's goals.

## Main Areas of Practice:

### Commercial & Business Litigation:

The firm's lawyers have in-depth experience resolving a wide array of complex business and commercial disputes, including matters involving antitrust, healthcare, securities, mergers and acquisitions, financial accounting, business torts, unfair competition, trade secrets, contract, employment law, insurance, bankruptcy, banking, product liability, construction and real estate, among others. The firm has extensive experience in class action litigation, both in state and federal court. Many of the nations' major industries have a presence in Tennessee. In Nashville, these include major financial, healthcare and entertainment entities, and the firm has particular expertise in these areas.

### Securities & Corporate Governance:

The firm has extensive experience in defending securities class actions, derivative litigation, and the lawsuits that typically follow the announcement of public company mergers and going private transactions. The firm's clients have included *Fortune* 500 companies involved in 'stock drop' securities class action lawsuits and related derivative cases; both acquirers and acquirees in merger and acquisition-related litigation; accounting firms large and small in complex matters of tax and financial accounting; and numerous financial institutions. The firm represents large public corporations, as well as privately held entities and closely-held corporations. The firm regularly engages in extensive and fast-paced discovery, preliminary injunction proceedings and dispositive motion practice in many of these cases. Members of the firm also have a great deal of experience representing clients in connection with SEC enforcement actions, CFTC and other governmental agency investigations, and FINRA and NFA arbitrations, which include broker recruiting cases and retail brokerage sales practice defense actions.

### Healthcare:

The firm combines its litigation expertise with a comprehensive knowledge of the ever-growing healthcare industry to represent and advise numerous healthcare companies, hospitals, facilities and professionals in resolving complex problems and disputes. The firm's understanding of the regulatory and business climate in which its healthcare clients operate allows attorneys to provide counsel in governmental and managed care issues, qui tam actions, certificate-of-need applications, healthcare fraud matters, physician recruitment and general business and commercial issues.

### Intellectual Property & Entertainment:

The firm represents and advises a variety of businesses, including music, media, technology and book-publishing clients, with respect to copyright, trademark, trade dress, domain name and other intellectual property issues. The firm's intellectual property clients include book publishers, film companies, major and independent record labels, music publishers, musical instrument manufacturers, computer software and hardware manufactures and a variety of other technology firms, artist and business managers, booking agencies and other entities and individuals with intellectual property needs at the heart of their businesses.

## Clients:

Riley Warnock & Jacobson, PLC focuses its practice on resolving complex problems for local, regional, national and international clients. The firm represents corporate and individual clients, plaintiffs and defendants. The firm's experience includes resolving legal issues unique to many of the nation's major industries. Representative clients include Ameriprise Financial Services, Inc., Avondale Partners, LLC, Brinker International, Inc., The Coca-Cola Company, Community Health Systems, Inc., Covenant Health, Dollar General Corporation, Erlanger Health System, First Data Corporation, Gaylord Entertainment Company, Gibson Guitar Corp., HCA Inc., J. Alexander's Corporation, Kohlberg Kravis Roberts & Co., MB Trading Holdings, LLC, Morgan Stanley Smith Barney LLC, National Renal Alliance, LLC, PricewaterhouseCoopers, LLP, Shoney's North America Corp., Sony Music Entertainment, Thomas Nelson, Inc., Unum Group, Universal Health Services, Vanderbilt University, Walgreen Co., Warner Music Group and many other businesses and individuals.

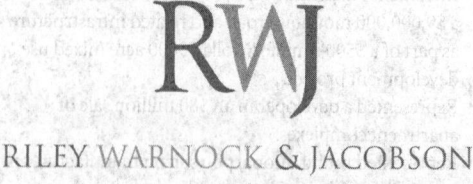

# WALKER, TIPPS & MALONE PLC

**www.**walkertipps.com

**Managing Partner:** John C Hayworth
**Senior Partner:** Robert J Walker
Number of lawyers: 15

### Firm Overview:

Walker, Tipps & Malone PLC was formed by a group of trial lawyers in January 2000. Since its formation, the firm's focus has been civil litigation and dispute resolution. With Ed Yarbrough joining the firm in June 2010, after serving almost three years as United States Attorney for the Middle District of Tennessee, WTM's lawyers now have a broad range of experience in both civil and criminal litigation, as is illustrated by four of the firm's seventeen lawyers having been inducted as Fellows of the American College of Trial Lawyers.

WTM represents individuals, small businesses and corporations, including corporations based in Nashville, in Tennessee, and throughout the United States, in complex commercial, business and contractual disputes, litigation matters, and internal corporate investigations. Among other types of corporate litigation, WTM has significant experience handling class actions, corporate dissolutions, securities fraud claims, antitrust claims, government regulations or contracts, fraud and compliance, conflicts of interest, ethics violations, construction or property-related claims, condemnation, regulatory and peer review actions. By way of example, the firm served as lead counsel for The Finish Line, Inc. in its highly publicized dispute with Genesco, Inc. over their billion dollar plus merger agreement; represented The Nashville Hockey Club Limited Partnership (Nashville Predators) in its contractual disputes with Gaylord Entertainment Company; and has performed a number of internal corporate investigations for large and small public companies involving, among other matters, securities law, governance, and insider dealing.

WTM represents individuals as plaintiffs in cases asserting professional negligence, including engineering and medical, and individuals as plaintiff in cases involving catastrophic personal injury and wrongful death with particular emphasis in litigation involving nursing homes, building design and maintenance, fire, the design and manufacture of motor vehicles, aviation, many other types of product liability actions, insurance law, and tractor-trailer and automobile collision litigation. WTM also represents individuals and business entities, as plaintiffs, in business-related claims involving economic injury and loss.

### Main Areas of Practice:

**Commercial Litigation:**
The firm's commercial litigation includes defense of class action and non-class action suits in securities, private and public corporate governance (including proxy fights and takeover litigation), products liability defense, complex commercial and business disputes, and other commercial matters.

**Personal Injury:**
The firm is well-known for its abilities in the defense of medical malpractice litigation, but also defends personal injury suits in other areas. Additionally, WTM has developed a plaintiff's personal injury practice in selected cases and has recovered several multi-million-dollar results for its clients.
**Contact:** Scott Sims

**Dispute Resolution:**
Two of the firm's partners are Rule 31-listed Civil Mediators.

**Contact:** Gayle Malone, Mark Tipps

**Complex Business Litigation:**
**Contact:** Bob Walker, Mark Tipps, John Hayworth

**Financial Institutions/Insurance:**
**Contact:** Mark Tipps, Joe Welborn

**Governmental Relations (Federal):**
**Contact:** Mark Tipps

**Personal Injury/Plaintiff:**
**Contact:** Gayle Malone, Joe Welborn

**Product Liability:**
**Contact:** Gayle Malone

**Securities & Corporate Governance:**
**Contact:** Bob Walker, John Hayworth

**Prisoner Rights Litigation:**
**Contact:** Joe Welborn

### PRACTICE AREAS

Commercial Business/Litigation
Personal Injury/Professional Liability, Defense
Personal Injury/Plaintiff

### OFFICES

TENNESSEE
**NASHVILLE:** 2300 One Nashville Place, TN 37219
Tel: 615 313 6000   Fax: 615 313 6001
Email: info@walkertipps.com

### Clients:
The firm's clients include individuals, teaching hospitals, commercial banks, insurance and other financial institutions, venture capital and private equity firms, industrial and service corporations, partnerships, and myriad businesses clients in the fields of healthcare, private prison management and ownership, accounting, and other service industries.

### International Work:
The firm has represented a number of international companies engaged in civil litigation in the United States.

WALKER TIPPS AND MALONE

# WALLER

www.wallerlaw.com **tel:** 615 244 6380 **fax:** 615 244 6804

**Chairman:** John C Tishler
Number of partners: 89
Number of other lawyers: 84

## Firm Overview:

Time and again clients derive extraordinary value from the length and depth of their relationships with Waller attorneys and the firm as a whole. Waller's focus on providing cost-effective solutions that support the clients' business goals has earned the firm recognition for robust legal analysis and creativity. As a result, Waller has ranked among "America's Best Corporate Law Firms" by Corporate Board Member magazine since 2000.
**Industries Served:** In addition to healthcare, Waller has deep experience in the automotive and manufacturing, banking and financial services, real estate, telecommunications, franchise, hospitality, media and entertainment and utilities industries, as well as government relations and crisis management.
**Commitment to Diversity:** Waller has a long history of commitment to diversity, which continues today. Since 2000, the firm has grown approximately 50 percent while the number of women and minority attorneys has increased by more than 70 percent. This growth was accomplished by actively seeking minority candidates through a variety of strategic recruiting efforts. And the firm continues to strive to achieve greater diversity; in 2012, 100 percent of the firm's leadership appointments were women, which increased the overall percentage of diverse leaders within the firm to 28 percent.

## Main Areas of Practice:

### Healthcare Services:

Waller has earned a national reputation as a trusted adviser to many of the leading companies in the highly regulated healthcare industry. In fact, Modern Healthcare has ranked the firm among the nation's ten largest healthcare law firms for the past six years. Many of the nation's largest publicly traded and privately owned healthcare companies, as well as tax-exempt and municipal hospitals and systems, rely on Waller's healthcare attorneys for advice and counsel on mergers and acquisitions, joint ventures, physician alignment, Medicare reimbursement issues, Stark and anti-kickback compliance, patient privacy regulations, government investigations, commercial and securities, real estate transactions, employment issues and intellectual property matters.

### Litigation & Dispute Resolution:

The firm has compiled a successful track record in trial and appellate litigation in state and federal courts across the country. Waller trial attorneys analyze and place legal conflicts in their proper context early, often leading to favorable results through negotiation or alternative dispute resolution. Some disputes, however, need court intervention. Waller attorneys help a client determine which resolution technique is most appropriate and then work to achieve a result consistent with the client's business goals.

### Corporate:

The firm regularly works with top companies on governance and transactional matters involving mergers and acquisitions, joint ventures, divestitures, commercial finance, securities, restructuring, real estate, tax and the expansion or relocation of business operations.

### Environmental:

Waller assists clients with environmental litigation, permitting and regulatory and compliance issues. Additionally, the group's lawyers have deep experience in defense matters involving state and federal statutes, as well as environmental due diligence in transactional matters.

### Finance & Restructuring:

The firm's bankruptcy and corporate restructuring work is national in scope. Waller attorneys have a well-earned reputation for developing practical, proactive, cost-effective solutions to the legal and business issues involved in corporate bankruptcies, restructurings and workouts.

### Intellectual Property:

Waller provides counsel on intellectual property issues ranging from licensing and outsourcing agreements, trade secrets and non-compete agreements to the registration and protection of trademarks, copyrights and patents.

### Labor & Employment:

The firm provides counseling and litigation services to employers for wage and hour (FLSA), discrimination, class action, ERISA, and labor matters.

### Real Estate:

Waller represents owners, acquirers, developers and investors in negotiations and documentation of sophisticated real estate transactions, and represents owners in the preparation of construction agreements.

### Government Investigations & Crisis Management:

Waller's team of high-profile attorneys (including the 80th US Attorney General and several former federal prosecutors), represents corporations and individuals in complex federal and state criminal investigations, confidential internal investigations and related civil and regulatory proceedings.

### Government Relations:

The firm regularly represents the interests of clients before a broad range of state and local decision-makers. Firm attorneys also monitor and track state legislation.

### Tax:

Waller's tax group advises clients in the following major areas: corporate partnership, estate, gift, state and local, tax-exempt entities, deferred compensation plans, qualified and nonqualified personal tax planning and tax controversies.

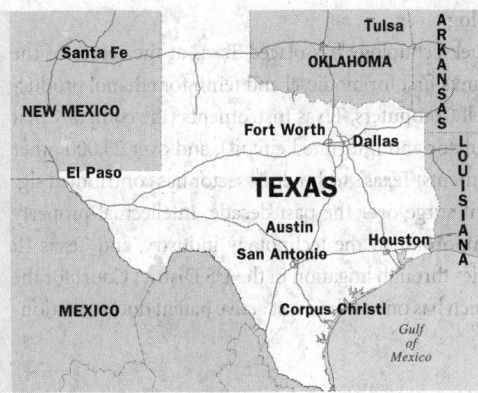

## How lawyers are ranked

Every year we carry out thousands of in-depth interviews with clients in order to assess the reputations and expertise of business lawyers worldwide. The qualities we look for (and which determine rankings) include technical legal ability, professional conduct, client service, commercial awareness/astuteness, diligence, commitment, and other qualities most valued by the client. For details of our research team, see p.5.

# TEXAS: An Introduction

## Contributed by Gardere Wynne Sewell LLP

Texas is a state with a storied history, amplified by Hollywood, including its unique attribute of having been an independent republic for nine years prior to joining the United States. Texas has a vibrant economy, a low-tax and low-cost environment, a relatively light regulatory regimen, business organization statutes favorable to management, well-developed infrastructure, and a solid workforce. It has a diversified economy, including agriculture, aviation, energy, healthcare, high-tech/computers, insurance, manufacturing, telecommunications, space and tourism industries. All of these industries afforded Texas the ability to record the largest US job increase of any state in 2012.

Aside from cowboys, Texas is best known for its energy industry and is generally recognized as the energy capital of the Western Hemisphere, if not the world. Texas is home to the corporate headquarters of 52 of the Fortune 500 companies (28 of which are energy industry companies), and the energy industry is interwoven into the fabric of the state in many different ways.

As a result of its long history with the energy industry, Texas has an abundance of resources to address all aspects of industry opportunities and challenges: technical, research, financial and legal expertise, along with extensive fossil fuel energy resources. Although the state's connection with the energy industry may have started with the oil and gas industry, beginning with the famed 1901 discovery at "Spindletop", it has expanded dramatically over the last century to involve every sector of the modern energy industry – upstream (exploration and production), midstream (pipelines, gathering and processing), downstream (refining and petrochemicals), power (electrical general and distribution), renewables and alternative energy (wind, solar, biomass, etc.), and energy services.

### Upstream

The exploration and production (E&P) of oil and natural gas has a long history in Texas, both onshore and offshore. Texas leads the nation in crude oil production (and has almost 25% of US reserves) and natural gas production (with some 30% of US reserves). The upstream sector has been bolstered in recent years by substantial acquisition and drilling activity in the "shale plays" – particularly in the Barnett Shale of east and north central Texas, and the Eagle Ford Shale of south Texas. The shale plays involve a hydraulic fracturing process ("fracking") that has come under increased scrutiny in the last year due to environmental concerns. Horizontal drilling procedures and associated fracking have also resulted in prolific natural gas production in many other areas in the US (and in other parts of the world), to the extent that some believe the US will become a net exporter of natural gas. Offshore E&P activities in the shallow and deeper waters of the Gulf of Mexico (GOM) were greatly curtailed following the mid-2010 GOM oil spill; however, activity increased in 2011 and 2012 and economic activity has been rebounding across all GOM states. Unlike most other coastal states that own their land out to three nautical miles, Texas's ownership extends to 10.3 nautical miles.

### Midstream

Pipelines and gathering systems have undergone significant expansions over the past five years as the midstream sector attempts to keep pace with increased production. Texas now has over 365,000 miles of pipelines. In particular, and due to pricing differentials between oil and gas, areas with so-called "wet" gas (or gas with sufficiently high concentrations of natural gas liquids) have become valuable and have resulted in a build-up of gas processing plants and fractionation facilities.

### Downstream

Texas has a substantial complement of refineries and other petrochemicals facilities that produce a wide variety of products. Texas is the leader in US refining capacity with over 26% of the total amount. Crude oil is refined into hundreds of products such as gasoline, diesel, jet fuel, heating oil, lubricants, and liquid petroleum gases such as butane and propane. Crude oil byproducts are used as petrochemical feedstocks to make plastics, chemicals and pharmaceuticals. Texas chemical manufacturers account for 50% of all US chemicals and petrochemicals production.

## Power

Texas leads the nation in generation and consumption of electricity and is the only state that has its own power grid (ERCOT), though parts of the state are included within neighboring power grids. Texas is also one of a handful of states with a well-functioning retail electricity market. Texas power plants are fueled primarily by natural gas and coal. Texas is a major producer of coal, particularly lignite coal, and has five of the nation's largest coal mines. The two nuclear power facilities in Texas (Comanche Peak and South Texas) produce less than 10% of the state's power generation.

## Renewables and Alternative Energy

Texas leads the nation in wind energy generation and has been the leading state for installed wind capacity for the past five years (over 12,200 MW at the end of December 2012). It has a Renewable Portfolio Standard which encourages renewable energy usage and has also adopted an accelerated approval process for large transmission lines to move wind-generated power. Seven of the ten largest wind farms in the US are located in Texas. Solar energy facilities are on the increase, as well as biofuels and biomass facilities. Texas is the nation's leading producer of biodiesel.

## Energy Services

Naturally accompanying the high levels of activity in all of the other sectors, Texas has an extremely well-developed, sophisticated, innovative services industry, including many multinational companies that provide engineering, construction and other services worldwide.

## Technology and Biotechnology

The desire for alternative fuel technology has placed Texas at the center of the biotech industry, where it ranks first for biodiesel and tenth for ethanol production nationally. Home to Dell Computers, Texas Instruments (the company that invented the handheld calculator and integrated circuit), and over 25,000 other high-tech industry establishments, Texas's technology sector has contributed significantly to an employment surge over the past decade. Intellectual property (IP) rights are especially important to the technology industry, and Texas IP lawyers often guide companies through litigation in the US District Court for the Eastern District of Texas, which has one of the most active patent dockets nationwide.

## Aerospace, Aviation and Defense

Texas maintains six of the 50 busiest US airports and is home base for Southwest Airlines and American Airlines. Texas is also an epicenter of government-related aviation, with NASA's Johnson Space Center in Houston, 15 active military bases, and almost 246,000 active duty, reservist and civilian personnel.

*Disclaimer*

*The Texas Overview is a publication of Gardere Wynne Sewell LLP for general information purposes only, does not create an attorney-client relationship and should not be construed as legal advice on any specific facts or circumstances.*

# ANTITRUST

Commentary about individuals can be found under their firm's paragraph. If the firm has no paragraph (is not ranked) look at Other Notable Practitioners.

| Antitrust |
| --- |
| **Leading Firms** |
| **Band 1** |
| Fulbright & Jaworski LLP * |
| Gibson, Dunn & Crutcher LLP * |
| Haynes and Boone, LLP * |
| Susman Godfrey LLP |
| **Band 2** |
| Andrews Kurth LLP * |
| Thompson & Knight LLP * |
| **Band 3** |
| Baker Botts LLP * |
| Cox Smith Matthews Incorporated |
| Gardere Wynne Sewell LLP * |
| Jones Day * |
| McDermott Will & Emery LLP * |
| Vinson & Elkins LLP * |

\* *Indicates firm with profile.*
*Alphabetical order within each band. Band 1 is the highest.*

## Band 1

### Fulbright & Jaworski LLP
See profile on p.2435
THE FIRM This group's reputation as a preeminent antitrust practice in Texas is complemented by its outstanding expertise in the energy and healthcare sectors. Sources are quick to note the firm's strong track record in antitrust litigation, and its additional experience in mergers, strategic alliances, class actions and government investigations. Recent highlights include representing CHRISTUS Health in a nationwide class action brought by nurses in four cities concerning an alleged wage-fixing conspiracy. The firm also defended GCC Alliance Concrete against claims of price-fixing brought by purchasers of ready-mix concrete.
Sources say: *"An extremely talented group across the board – they are very knowledgeable about antitrust law and its nuances."*
KEY INDIVIDUALS Star individual **Layne Kruse** (see p.2400) is described as *"very sharp and very practical,"* and praised for his abilities in the courtroom. He has more than 30 years' experience in antitrust and securities litiga-

tion, and commentators say they *"would trust him with anything."* **William Pakalka** (see p.2408) is a litigator who *"knows how to handle himself in front of judges"* and is seen to be *"right up there at the top"* by peers. An antitrust and broad civil practitioner, he recently defended Memorial Hermann Healthcare System against claims of an alleged boycott of a failed startup hospital by major managed care companies. **Anne Rodgers** (see p.2413) has a strong reputation as a general commercial litigator, with substantial experience in antitrust matters, including work on a recent case alleging anticompetitive conduct in the steel production market. Of counsel **Richard Carrell** (see p.2383) is seen as a *"go-to litigator on the defense side."* He recently acted for a petroleum company in a case concerning an alleged breach of the Sherman Act by OPEC.

### Gibson, Dunn & Crutcher LLP
See profile on p.682
THE FIRM Gibson, Dunn & Crutcher offers impressive bench strength and is highly rated by its peers for the quality of its antitrust practice. The nationwide firm is recognized for the investment it has made in its team in Texas, and for its strength in IP-related work, litigation and gov-

ernment investigations. It acts for a plethora of big-name clients, and recently represented Estée Lauder in an antitrust suit brought by Duty Free Americas. The firm also acted for 3M on a case brought by Avery Dennison involving claims of false advertising and unfair competition concerning reflective materials on road signs.

**Sources say:** *"One of the best antitrust litigation practices in the country."*

**KEY INDIVIDUALS Sean Royall** (see p.2414) is an *"exceptionally good lawyer"* who is *"very savvy and experienced,"* according to sources. An extremely skilled attorney with vast experience across the antitrust spectrum, he is praised for his *"ability to distil complex information into*

easily digestible pieces." He recently represented Sanofi in two cases concerning the drug Lovenox, and advised The Williams Companies on its unsolicited – eventually unsuccessful – attempt to acquire Southern Union. **Brian Robison** (see p.2413) has been involved in a number of high-profile government investigations and class action cases, and recently obtained a dismissal with prejudice in a price-fixing class action on behalf of the United Potato Growers of Canada. Sources praise his *"very strong intellect and organizational skills."* The *"excellent"* **Robert Walters** (see p.2420) is seen by peers as one of the leading commercial litigators in the state, with experience in antitrust, securities and tort cases. He was lead counsel for the firm in the Estée Lauder suit. **Veronica Lewis** (see p.2401) has a broad commercial practice encompassing IP and securities in addition to antitrust law. She represented Aetna in a complaint brought against Blue Cross Blue Shield Michigan concerning its use of most-favored-nation contracts at hospitals.

## Haynes and Boone, LLP
See profile on p.444

**THE FIRM** This firm benefits from tremendous resources in antitrust law, and remains one of Texas's strongest groups in this field. It focuses primarily on litigation, and has also had notable success outside the courtroom. In highlights, the team advised international freight forwarder CEVA Logistics on a DOJ investigation into the freight forwarding industry, which involved coordinating responses to competition authorities in Brazil, New Zealand, Japan and across the EU. The firm also represented the Sacramento Kings in its dispute with the NBA, and acted for AT&T on the antitrust matters relating to its proposed $39 billion acquisition – subsequently abandoned – of T-Mobile USA.

**Sources say:** *"They have real strength in Texas." "They do an excellent job."*

**KEY INDIVIDUALS** The *"phenomenally talented"* **Barry McNeil** is recognized by peers as one of the leading antitrust attorneys in Texas. A former DOJ lawyer, he continues to work extensively on criminal antitrust cases and related civil and class actions. Sources say he is *"very strategic, organized and experienced."* Described as *"very knowledgeable in the antitrust field,"* **Ronald Breaux** heads the firm's litigation section, which includes the antitrust practice group. He also undertakes a wide array of complex commercial litigation. **Kathleen Beasley** is a *"professional, friendly and responsive"* antitrust practitioner whom one source calls a *"straight shooter."* She played an active part in advising CEVA Logistics on the DOJ investigation.

## Susman Godfrey LLP

**THE FIRM** This litigation boutique earns its place at the top of the list of antitrust firms in Texas, and is widely acclaimed for its unrivalled plaintiff-side practice. It also handles some defense work, and has developed a strong presence nationwide. With no fewer than 100 attorneys across its five offices, it is well placed to advise on claims involving a wide range of industries, including medical devices, airlines, dairy, steel and telecommunications.

**Sources say:** *"The strongest plaintiff firm in the state, and one of the top in the country."*

**KEY INDIVIDUALS Stephen Susman** has long been regarded as a preeminent plaintiff lawyer in the state of Texas and nationwide, and sources commend his *"incredible energy."* He divides his time between Houston and New York. **Lee Godfrey** is a highly experienced and adept trial lawyer, with a strong general commercial practice which includes antitrust work. *"He is a magician in the courtroom,"* sources say. **Barry Barnett** is also well regarded for his trial expertise, which covers a wide range of areas including antitrust, business fraud and class actions. **Harry Susman** operates a broad commercial litigation practice, and represents both plaintiffs and defendants in antitrust suits.

## Band 2

### Andrews Kurth LLP
See profile on p.2426

**THE FIRM** Andrews Kurth has a strong reputation for its broad antitrust practice, with notable expertise in merger clearance work, Hart-Scott-Rodino filings and government investigations. Recent highlights saw the firm represent Cheniere Energy Partners in respect of a $2 billion equity investment by Blackstone Partners, and act for Air New Zealand on a DOJ investigation concerning the price of fuel surcharges on flights coming into the USA.

**Sources say:** *"They are very responsive and professional."*

**KEY INDIVIDUALS Jerry Beane** (see p.2380) is seen as *"one of the top antitrust lawyers"* in Texas and is highlighted for his ability to provide *"practical, business-savvy advice."* He is a specialist defense attorney with an antitrust practice encompassing litigation and counseling. In recent work, he acted for National Dairy as a defendant in the Southeastern Milk antitrust litigation. **Kay Lynn Brumbaugh** (see p.2382) is acclaimed as a *"smart, creative and plain-spoken"* antitrust lawyer with *"great subject matter knowledge."* She has extensive experience in litigation, and has recently been heavily engaged in a high volume of Hart-Scott-Rodino filing and merger work. Notably, she represented Provident Energy in its $3.1 billion merger with Pembina Pipeline.

## Thompson & Knight LLP
See profile on p.2458

**THE FIRM** Thompson & Knight has a strong reputation for antitrust litigation, and is a regular feature on class actions and cases before the FTC. In recent work, it defended chemicals manufacturer Voltaix against various allegations of monopolization. Other recent clients include Gruma and Star Pipe Products.

**Sources say:** *"They are able to look at things from your point of view, rather than just offering a pure opinion."*

**KEY INDIVIDUALS** *"One of the leading antitrust lawyers in the state,"* **Gregory Huffman** (see p.2396) is described as a *"savvy, smart and knowledgeable attorney who focuses on the client's needs."* He is a seasoned litigator with substantial experience across the board in antitrust and complex commercial litigation. **William Katz** (see p.2398) is a hardworking and *"very knowledgeable"* attorney whose *"legal writing is excellent."* He was heavily involved in the Voltaix case, and also advises on international arbitration and energy issues. **James Berglund** (see p.2380) is a litigator with a wide array of antitrust expertise covering civil and criminal cases, as well as complex commercial litigation and healthcare fraud.

## Band 3

### Baker Botts LLP
See profile on p.2427

**THE FIRM** This firm has long experience advising on antitrust litigation at both the state and federal level, and continues to grow its practice in this field. Within Texas, its strength in energy matters is evidenced by its work for such clients as ConocoPhillips, Halliburton and Marathon Oil. Other notable highlights include successfully defending Actelion Pharmaceuticals against conspiracy claims under California's Cartwright Act.

**Sources say:** *"We've been impressed with their responsiveness and the depth and insight that they bring."*

**KEY INDIVIDUALS David Rodi** (see p.2413) is developing a strong reputation among peers and clients alike, who agree that *"he's extremely practical"* and *"knows the law exceptionally well."* He continues to represent Actelion Pharmaceuticals before the California Court of Appeal.

### Cox Smith Matthews Incorporated

**THE FIRM** This San Antonio-based firm is a leading name for antitrust in south Texas. It has seen a high volume of work related to healthcare M&A, and also has substantial expertise in energy-related antitrust. In other notable work, the team continues to represent Pedernales Electric Cooperative in an independent investigation into its operations. The firm also advises clients on competition and antitrust law in Canada, Latin America and the EU.

**Sources say:** *"They have been fantastic, responsive and cost-effective."*

**KEY INDIVIDUALS Michael Ferrill** is a strong presence in south Texas, and *"knows compliance law as well as anyone in the country,"* say sources. A seasoned antitrust, securities and compliance expert, he is a regular feature on many of the firm's larger recent cases.

### Gardere Wynne Sewell LLP
See profile on p.2436

**THE FIRM** This group has a long-standing reputation in Texas and is proficient in both civil and criminal antitrust matters. It specializes in work relating to the insurance industry and has a particular niche in cases involving the civil RICO statute. It recently defended Chartis, a subsidiary of AIG, against a claim brought by one of its clients concerning the overpayment of insurance rates.

**Sources say:** *"They were efficient and responsive, and they had an obvious command of the subject."*

**KEY INDIVIDUALS Curtis Frisbie** (see p.2389) has 41 years' experience as a trial lawyer in antitrust and commercial litigation, and is well regarded for his ability to *"boil down information into layman's terms."* He recently achieved a settlement on behalf of Jordan Reses Supply against claims of alleged conspiracy. Commentators describe **Mark Bayer** (see p.2380) as an insightful attorney who is *"thorough, comprehensive and decisive."* In highlights, he helped to obtain dismissal on behalf of National Union Fire Insurance and AIG in a class action relating to accidental death benefit insurance. **Randy Gordon** (see p.2392) is highly regarded for the quality of his written briefs and his client-friendly approach. He recently brought his expertise in RICO claims to bear in the National Union Fire Insurance case alongside Bayer.

### Jones Day
See profile on p.919

**THE FIRM** Jones Day has a substantial antitrust merger clearance practice and has worked on a range of notable deals, including Texas Instruments' acquisition of National Semiconductor. It undertakes a broad array of antitrust matters, and owing to its international standing counts high-profile names such as Dell and Chevron among its clients.

**Sources say:** *"They have a deep and talented group of antitrust lawyers with significant global reach and broad subject matter expertise."*

**KEY INDIVIDUALS Bruce McDonald** (see p.2404) has *"exceptional judgment and substantive knowledge,"* and is praised by sources for his outstanding preparation. He has a broad antitrust practice, with notable expertise in the energy and telecom sectors. In highlights, he represented Level 3 Communications in its $3 billion acquisition of Global Crossing. **Thomas Jackson** (see p.2397) is an experienced general commercial litigator with a strong antitrust aspect to his practice. He provided antitrust counseling to Texas Instruments regarding resale price maintenance.

### McDermott Will & Emery LLP
See profile on p.1258

**THE FIRM** This compact group was boosted by the addition of Allan Van Fleet from Greenberg Traurig in May 2012. It undertakes work across the criminal and civil antitrust litigation spectrum, with particular experience in IP and energy matters. Highlights include advising Anadarko Petroleum on a breach of contract lawsuit relating to a drilling platform in the Gulf of Mexico.

**KEY INDIVIDUALS Allan Van Fleet** (see p.2419) is a *"first-rate lawyer"* for antitrust in Texas. With substantial experience in litigation, he has an excellent reputation for intellectual property-related antitrust law. **Alison Smith** (see p.2416) has anchored the McDermott antitrust practice since 2010. Sources call her an *"extremely smart, hardworking and indefatigable"* lawyer, and note her client-handling skills and the quality of her advice.

### Vinson & Elkins LLP
See profile on p.2459

**THE FIRM** Vinson & Elkins handles antitrust matters across the board, including in such areas as energy and healthcare. It has substantial experience in monopolization and price-fixing cases, and represented Huntsman International in antitrust suits concerning polyurethane and titanium dioxide. Other big-name clients include Shell and United Airlines.

**Sources say:** *"We were impressed by the way they worked."*

**KEY INDIVIDUALS James Reeder** (see p.2412) co-heads the antitrust department and has an active and varied antitrust practice across a number of industries, including healthcare and aviation. Commentators say he has *"lots of experience and good judgment."* Sources hold **Harry Reasoner** (see p.390) *"in very high regard"* for the depth and breadth of his trial experience, which spans some 50 years and encompasses antitrust and other complex commercial litigation, both at first instance and on appeal.

## Other Notable Practitioners

**James Nelson** (see p.2406) of DLA Piper LLP *"knows his area, is levelheaded and works extremely hard,"* according to sources. He is seen as being *"as tough as nails,"* and recently represented Reddy Ice Holdings in the packaged ice antitrust litigation as well as in a Hart-Scott-Rodino merger approval filing. A new addition to the rankings, **Bruce Blefeld** (see p.2381) of Jackson Walker LLP is a *"thoughtful and practical"* antitrust lawyer who has 20 years' experience in a range of antitrust and complex commercial litigation. **Michael Warnecke** joined Akin Gump Strauss Hauer & Feld LLP from Haynes & Boone in 2012, and wins plaudits for his responsiveness and practicality. One source enthused: *"I know with him that I'm going to get good advice."*

# BANKING & FINANCE

Commentary about individuals can be found under their firm's paragraph. If the firm has no paragraph (is not ranked) look at Other Notable Practitioners.

## Banking & Finance
### Leading Firms

**Band 1**
Bracewell & Giuliani LLP *

**Band 2**
Baker Botts LLP *
Haynes and Boone, LLP *
Latham & Watkins LLP *
Vinson & Elkins LLP *
Weil, Gotshal & Manges LLP *

**Band 3**
Andrews Kurth LLP *
Thompson & Knight LLP *

**Band 4**
Mayer Brown LLP *
Simpson Thacher & Bartlett LLP *

**Band 5**
Fulbright & Jaworski LLP *
Jones Day *
Locke Lord LLP *
Porter Hedges LLP *
Winstead PC *

* Indicates firm / individual with profile.
†ONP = Other Notable Practitioner

## Senior Statesmen

**Senior Statesmen: distinguished older practitioners**

| | |
|---|---|
| Barbour Larry G | Vinson & Elkins LLP * |
| Evans Mark C | Bracewell & Giuliani LLP * |
| Murray Craig | Vinson & Elkins LLP * |

## Leading Individuals

**Band 1**

| | |
|---|---|
| Fontana Angela L | Weil, Gotshal & Manges LLP * |
| Goyne Roderick | Baker Botts LLP * |
| McKellar James W | Thompson & Knight LLP * |
| Niebruegge Michael E | Cadwalader, Wickersham & Taft (ONP)† * |
| Rabalais Robert René | Simpson Thacher & Bartlett LLP * |
| Rain John W | Thompson & Knight LLP * |

**Band 2**

| | |
|---|---|
| Barbour David | Andrews Kurth LLP * |
| Bradley III Francis 'Frank' R | Greenberg Traurig, LLP (ONP)† * |
| Dybala Kelly M | Weil, Gotshal & Manges LLP * |
| Gonsoulin Jr Dewey J | Bracewell & Giuliani LLP * |
| Hilliard Michael | Winstead PC * |
| Kornreich Craig | Latham & Watkins LLP |
| Littlejohn James R | Winstead PC * |
| Marcus Courtney | Fulbright & Jaworski LLP * |
| Ozdogan Catherine | Latham & Watkins LLP |
| Propst Tristan | Mayer Brown LLP |
| Sorensen Nick H | Porter Hedges LLP * |

**Band 3**

| | |
|---|---|
| Anderson Kenneth M | Sidley Austin LLP (ONP)† * |
| Boren Alison C | Baker Botts LLP * |
| Bos William | Vinson & Elkins LLP * |
| Brown Heather L | Bracewell & Giuliani LLP * |
| Clark Gary | Fulbright & Jaworski LLP * |
| Flint Andrew P | Thompson & Knight LLP * |
| Hart Jr Bill | Mayer Brown LLP |
| Keyes David | Kelly Hart & Hallman LLP (ONP)† |
| Night Scott G | Haynes and Boone, LLP |
| Perich Thomas J | Andrews Kurth LLP * |
| Powers Timothy | Haynes and Boone, LLP |
| Rafte G Alan | Bracewell & Giuliani LLP * |
| Weedon Luke A | Baker Botts LLP * |

**Band 4**

| | |
|---|---|
| Einhorn Theresa A | Haynes and Boone, LLP |
| Ettredge Katherine | Jones Day * |
| Haas Buddy | Locke Lord LLP * |
| Kaminsky Neal | Porter Hedges LLP * |
| Markus James A | Vinson & Elkins LLP * |
| Neeley Karen | Cox Smith Matthews (ONP)† |
| Rendell Robert | Patton Boggs LLP (ONP)† |
| Song Stephanie Koo | Bracewell & Giuliani LLP * |
| Weinstock Peter G | Hunton & Williams LLP (ONP)† * |

**Up-and-coming individuals**

| | |
|---|---|
| Day Kate | Bracewell & Giuliani LLP * |
| Hamner Herschel | Baker Botts LLP |
| Mott Cassandra | Jones Day * |
| Yang Emeline | Winstead PC * |

**Associates to watch**

| | |
|---|---|
| Wommack Trevor | Bracewell & Giuliani LLP * |

## Band 1

### Bracewell & Giuliani LLP
See profile on p.2429

**THE FIRM** Texas stalwart Bracewell & Giuliani maintains its preeminent position in the field of banking and finance. The firm's impressive bench provides a wide range of expertise, enabling it to offer a full array of services on both the borrower and lender sides. Specific strengths include energy finance, restructurings, acquisition finance and syndicated lending. BNP Paribas, Wells Fargo and Citibank are all key clients. The firm has spent substantial time of late on a variety of complex, high-value credit facilities, and is particularly noted for its representation of ConocoPhillips in an aggregate $23 billion deal involving various credit and loan facilities.
**Sources say:** "Creative, high-caliber lawyers with great market knowledge."
**KEY INDIVIDUALS Dewey Gonsoulin** (see p.2391) has "prodigious market knowledge," and maintains a stellar reputation for his broad lender-side work. Described as "a proven expert in energy finance," his specialty in this field attracts regular work from clients seeking experienced representation in the energy market. Respected for her "commercial awareness and ability to achieve practical solutions," **Heather Brown** (see p.2382) has enjoyed success of late on various complex financial transactions, including representing ConocoPhillips in the $23 billion matter. Acknowledged for his expertise in energy-related finance, **Alan Rafte** (see p.389) continues to handle project finance work, specifically in the upstream oil and gas arena. **Mark**

Evans (see p.2388) has a vital role in maintaining the firm's client relationships. As managing partner, he continues to attract new business, as well as being a primary contact for a number of the firm's leading clients. Commended for her "intelligence and knowledge," **Kate Day** (see p.2387) represents a broad range of clients in complex financial transactions. Recent highlights include acting for both Wells Fargo and Citibank on revolving credit facilities. Clients praise **Trevor Wommack's** (see p.2422) "diligent, hard-working and meticulous nature." His key strengths include work in energy finance and reserves-based loans. With her "decisive nature" and "impressive negotiating skills," **Stephanie Koo Song** (see p.2416) has acted on several of the firm's stand-out deals of late, including advising Wells Fargo on several revolving credit facilities totaling $1.2 billion.

## Band 2

### Baker Botts LLP
See profile on p.2427

**THE FIRM** Houston-born firm Baker Botts demonstrates impressive skills in the banking and finance arena. The group is particularly recognized for its strengths in intellectual property, technology and energy-related finance, among other areas. It acts for both borrowers and lenders, and provides a full range of expertise across the general financial services spectrum. Highlights include advising Prudential Insurance on a series of complex senior notes offerings, and representing JPMorgan Chase in several sophisticated, high-value credit agreements with firms from the energy industry.
**Sources say:** "They consistently do a standout job."
**KEY INDIVIDUALS** Sources describe **Herschel Hamner** as an "incredibly smart and detail-oriented individual." Key strengths include syndicated bank finance and high-yield debt offerings. He recently advised Marathon Oil on a $2.5 billion revolving credit facility. **Roderick Goyne** (see p.2392) is noted as "the consummate legal professional." His "depth of knowledge and tremendous experience" are greatly valued by interviewees. As well as a significant dedication to syndicated finance, other recent focuses include increased private placement work for clients such as AIG. Well respected by market observers, **Alison Boren** (see p.2381) is admired for her "strong negotiating skills," which ensure her clients' "complete confidence." She is particularly admired for her debt work. The "energetic and skillful," **Luke Weedon** (see p.2421) is a growing presence in the banking and finance arena. Notable work includes representing Citibank and JPMorgan Chase in relation to credit facilities of, respectively, $700 million and $1.5 billion.

### Haynes and Boone, LLP
See profile on p.444

**THE FIRM** This practice maintains an outstanding reputation for its core finance strengths, primarily syndicated loan transactions, energy finance and corporate lending.

The group works with an impressive array of the nation's leading financial institutions, including Bank of America, Citibank and Wells Fargo, as well as foreign-based clients such as RBS. A standout recent transaction was advising all lead arrangers, co-syndication agents and the administrative agent on $11.8 billion of credit facilities in connection with the spin-off of a large, independent oil refining company.

**Sources say:** "*The attorneys' market experience is extremely valuable as it allows them to take a very commercial approach to legal issues and provide great advice from a business perspective.*"

**KEY INDIVIDUALS** Praised for his "*impressive technical skill set,*" **Scott Night** continues to represent lenders and borrowers in corporate and commercial lending. **Timothy Powers** is noted for his "*strong, consultative approach and calming, collaborative nature.*" Clients also value "*his effective ability to resolve problems.*" He focuses on international banking and finance, and demonstrates particular expertise in representing foreign investors in the US. Highly valued by interviewees, **Theresa Einhorn** is applauded for her style. One source says: "*She is thoughtful in discussions and represents us and our interests so well. She is always very cognizant of whom she is representing. She streamlines deals for us and always brings the full force of the firm to the table. When I have a deal I want her on it.*"

## Latham & Watkins LLP
See profile on p.446

**THE FIRM** Still a relative newcomer to the state, this expanding, high-quality group continues to make its presence known in the Texas market. With a specific focus on syndicated finance transactions, primarily within the energy industry, the firm is frequently involved in complex credit facility work, representing major companies and financial institutions involved in energy finance, among other areas. Recent deals include acting for Wells Fargo on a highly complex $1.1 billion term loan and revolving credit facility matter involving a theme park operator.

**Sources say:** "*Excellent – great experience, smart, and creative.*"

**KEY INDIVIDUALS** Sources describe **Catherine Ozdogan** as a "*tough, smart and commercially focused lawyer.*" Her stellar reputation in the energy finance field continues to attract work on market-leading deals. Clients say **Craig Kornreich**'s "*greatest assets are his strong commercial sense and his flexible, creative solutions.*" He has worked on a large number of syndicated financings of late, including a $2.2 billion term loan and revolving credit facility for Energy Transfer Equity to be used in the acquisition of a large natural gas company.

## Vinson & Elkins LLP
See profile on p.2459

**THE FIRM** Respected for its presence in energy finance, this group demonstrates strong capabilities on a wide range of financial transactions. The firm works with prominent market lenders including Wells Fargo, JPMorgan Chase and Bank of America on credit facility transactions. Alongside this it utilizes close ties with existing corporate clients to generate significant work on the borrower side. It has recently worked with Oncor Electric Delivery Company on a $2.4 billion senior secured credit facility, and represented Endeavour in a number of financings secured by its assets in the North Sea.

**Sources say:** "*The firm has business understanding in abundance.*"

**KEY INDIVIDUALS** With a practice focused on commercial lending, **William Bos** (see p.2381) is praised by clients for "*his sharpness, commercial mindset, strong judgment and attentiveness.*" Lately he has worked on a number of prominent transactions, including representing Wells Fargo as administrative agent in a $1 billion senior secured credit facility. **Larry Barbour** (see p.2379) continues to play a valuable role at the firm as a vital source of information and experience in all areas of energy, acquisition and structured finance as well as syndicated bank transactions. **Craig Murray** (see p.2406) is also a well-respected figure in the market and is particularly recognized for his knowledge of both corporate and energy-related finance. **James Markus** (see p.2403) is valued for his experience in commercial lending. His clients include financial institutions such as Bank of America as well as regional and foreign banks active in the market.

## Weil, Gotshal & Manges LLP
See profile on p.2015

**THE FIRM** With a firm focus on borrower side representation, this practice specializes in private equity finance, where it retains a stellar reputation among market observers. It is adept at handling a wide scope of transactions in areas such as high-level acquisition finance, subordinated debt finance and asset-based lending. The practice frequently represents private equity clients in transactions with a national scope, and sources highlight the team's invaluable knowledge in that space. It is also well known for its strength in bankruptcy work, offering an array of expertise in workout and restructuring matters.

**Sources say:** "*The firm has very talented lawyers whose expertise and leading market knowledge are admirable.*"

**KEY INDIVIDUALS Angela Fontana** (see p.2389) is consistently singled out as one of the major players in sponsor-side representation. Clients say she is "*the leading expert in her field of finance. Her experience and knowledge just make it unfair for the opposition.*" **Kelly Dybala** (see p.2388) is also highly rated, with sources saying she is "*an excellent attorney who is thorough, detail-oriented and hard-working.*" She has acted on a number of high-value financial transactions of late, including representing Thomas H Lee Partners in revolving credit facilities of over $1.5 billion to finance its acquisition of a majority stake in Party City.

## Band 3

## Andrews Kurth LLP
See profile on p.2426

**THE FIRM** This broad practice is noted for its representation of both borrowers and lenders in a wide range of areas, including syndicated lending, securitization and energy finance. The practice has been particularly active for energy lending clients of late, having worked on a number of complex transactions. Highlights include advising NuStar Energy and NuStar Logistics on revolving credit facility matters, and representing KBR in a $1 billion financing.

**Sources say:** "*The attorneys are always thinking five steps ahead of the deal. To have that forethought is incredible.*"

**KEY INDIVIDUALS David Barbour** (see p.2379) is valued by clients for "*his creativity and incredible breadth of experience.*" He has a broad range of expertise in commercial transactions, and recently represented Ashford Hospitality Trust in its common stock offering. Firm chairman **Thomas Perich** (see p.2409) is an experienced figure in the banking and finance arena. He often advises clients on a range of loan matters in a number of industry sectors, including real estate, energy and construction.

## Thompson & Knight LLP
See profile on p.2458

**THE FIRM** Thompson & Knight continues to focus on the demands of the regional market, and has well-established experience in the oil, gas and energy fields. With industry-specific expertise across the firm, the finance team has the capability to provide clients with seamless service in energy-focused deals. It recently worked on several high-value energy-based syndicated loans on behalf of borrowers and lenders active in the market.

**Sources say:** "*A very experienced firm with very strong lawyers.*"

**KEY INDIVIDUALS** Commentators highlight **James McKellar** (see p.2404) for his vast experience, particularly in the energy lending arena. He focuses on advising clients on a range of transactions in the corporate, energy and financial services fields. **John Rain** (see p.2411) is also recognized by market observers, who say: "*He is outstanding, there is no way around that.*" He is experienced in handling volumetric production payments and structuring matters. Sources describe **Andrew Flint** (see p.2389) as "*very practical and a supersmart lawyer.*" He is particularly active in the energy and oil and gas markets, and consistently provides clients with a full range of services in financial lending transactions.

## Band 4

## Mayer Brown LLP
See profile on p.1257

**THE FIRM** This well-established practice has an impressive background in energy-based finance. With the ability to utilize global resources, the firm offers a diverse range of services in secured and unsecured lending, project finance and acquisition finance. The firm is traditionally known as lender's counsel, and frequently represents leading financial institutions such as Deutsche Bank and JPMorgan Chase in energy-related transactions. Highlights include representing JPMorgan in its role as administrative agent and arranger in a $2 billion credit facility for EP Energy's acquisition of oil and gas assets.

Sources say: "*The experience they bring in the energy space has been critical to us.*"

**KEY INDIVIDUALS Tristan Propst**'s practice is focused on traditional commercial bank lending, specifically within the energy market, where clients value his substantial experience. He is said to be "*sharp on technical matters and he knows all the nuances that are vital to energy work in this field.*" A new addition to the firm, **Bill Hart** is noted for his vast experience in a wide range of financial transactions, specifically in industries such as energy and manufacturing, where he continues to impress market observers.

### Simpson Thacher & Bartlett LLP
See profile on p.2006

**THE FIRM** The Houston office of this New York powerhouse continues to make inroads into the Texas market. With a focus on energy finance, it dedicates substantial attention to representing lenders active in the oil and gas markets, as well as some large privately owned energy companies. The practice's location and the addition of one of the state's finest oil and gas lawyers has ensured the team attracts energy-based finance work from regular Simpson Thacher client JPMorgan Securities. It has recently represented the institution in a variety of financings, including a $1.7 billion bank and bond acquisition finance.

Sources say: "*A very capable group. They know the business and know how to get things done.*"

**KEY INDIVIDUALS** Sources describe **Robert Rabalais** (see p.2411) as "*one of the best in the business.*" Clients say his "*key strengths are his ability to focus on the primary issues and his acumen in breaking these issues down to negotiate both the legal and business points.*" His highlights include working with Credit Suisse on the $9.4 billion acquisition of Southern Union Company by Energy Transfer Equity, and representing BNP Paribas as administrative agent in a $750 million financing.

### Band 5

### Fulbright & Jaworski LLP
See profile on p.2435

**THE FIRM** This team offers services in asset-based, acquisition and leveraged finance, among other areas. It has a particular focus on the energy industry, representing clients on both the borrower and lender side, and is also active in strategic M&A work including acquisitions and debt facilities. The firm recently represented oilfield services company Weatherford International in an unsecured multicurrency $2.25 billion revolving credit agreement.

Sources say: "*We are a very demanding and high-pace company and they perfectly align with us. They understand urgency and have great insight into the market.*"

**KEY INDIVIDUALS** Sources say **Courtney Marcus** (see p.2403) "*is always thinking of the company and consistently offers good advice.*" She mainly focuses on representing borrowers in a wide range of financial transactions. **Gary Clark** (see p.2384) focuses considerable time on representing lender clients who are active in the energy market. He

is experienced in acquisition financing as well as exploration and production financing for the energy industry.

### Jones Day
See profile on p.919

**THE FIRM** This practice has a range of expertise in financial transactions. As well as taking a share of the vast amount of energy-related finance work in the state, this team is also well versed in a number of other sectors, including construction, consumer products, healthcare and insurance. It represented the purchasers, including Jefferies & Company, in an offering of $775 million senior secured first lien notes.

Sources say: "*The firm does excellent work – they are very hands-on and detail-oriented, and their great view of the market is really valuable in negotiations.*"

**KEY INDIVIDUALS Katherine Ettredge** (see p.2388) is highly valued by clients, one of whom said: "*Her technical knowledge is amazing and I trust her implicitly.*" Ettredge regularly works closely with the firm's M&A team on acquisition matters, and represented Samson Investment Company in its acquisition by an investor group in a $7.2 billion LBO. Sources say **Cassandra Mott** (see p.2406) is an "*exceptional practitioner with great business sense.*" She has comprehensive experience in senior and subordinated financing facilities.

### Locke Lord LLP
See profile on p.2443

**THE FIRM** This 40-strong practice offers a wide scope of transactional experience. It specializes in a range of financial litigation matters, representing banks and institutions in lender-liability actions and corporate trustee representation. Clients value its strong experience across several industries, including real estate and healthcare. Historically known for its lender-side representation, the firm continues to represent institutions such as JPMorgan Chase, Bank of America and Wells Fargo.

**KEY INDIVIDUALS Buddy Haas** (see p.2393) is recognized for his experience in lending matters and his knowledge of the energy market. Lately he has regularly represented JPMorgan Chase in its role as agent lender on various secured syndicated credit facilities.

### Porter Hedges LLP
See profile on p.2450

**THE FIRM** With roots in midmarket finance work, this practice demonstrates a broad range of expertise in areas including asset-based lending, syndicated transactions and project finance. The firm is also acknowledged for its experience in the energy industry. Representing both borrowers and lenders, the firm's client list includes financial institutions such as ING Capital and Bank of America. Highlights of late include representing ING Capital in a credit facility matter involving a planned gas storage infrastructure project.

Sources say: "*They are good at keeping perspective and advising us on what is important rather than overloading on the irrelevant. Their people work hard and are very knowledgeable.*"

**KEY INDIVIDUALS** As the lead partner on several of the firm's major deals over the past year, **Nick Sorensen** (see p.2417) stands out for his experience in commercial lending. He is also acknowledged for his workout and restructuring abilities. Sources say: "*The work he does is exemplary.*" **Neal Kaminsky** (see p.2398) continues to work on a broad range of financial and corporate transactions. Lately he has worked closely with Iberiabank on amending and restating credit agreements.

### Winstead PC
See profile on p.2460

**THE FIRM** This 19-strong banking and finance practice is recognized for its work in syndicated transactions, the energy arena and midmarket deals. It is particularly valued by leading financial institutions, which frequently utilize the firm's expertise in syndication work, turning to Winstead for a range of services in commercial lending and debt capital markets. Other strengths include accomplished workout and restructurings skills.

Sources say: "*A very professional team with a high level of service. They are really strong when it comes to closing a deal – at that point they run with it and work well with other firms.*"

**KEY INDIVIDUALS James Littlejohn** (see p.2402) is highly valued by clients, who say: "*He has so much experience and is a very practical lawyer. It is obvious that he loves the law and his work.*" Large syndicated transactions within the region remain a particular focus of his practice, and his impressive abilities in this arena are highly regarded by fellow practitioners. Attracting significant praise from interviewees, **Michael Hilliard** (see p.2396) is highlighted as an attorney whose clients "*have so much confidence in him – there is nothing he has not seen. We see him like our in-house counsel. He is great at building relationships and giving his opinion when we need it.*" **Emeline Yang** (see p.2423) regularly works with both lenders and borrowers on a range of commercial transactions.

### Other Notable Practitioners

**Frank Bradley** (see p.2382) of Greenberg Traurig, LLP is valued for his "*great ability to understand commercial angles, paired with his thorough command of legal concepts.*" He is regularly involved in investment grade financings, representing both borrowers and lenders in credit facility matters that often involve an international element. At the same firm, **Peter Weinstock** (see p.2421) represents a variety of financial institutions in corporate and regulatory matters. Clients praise him as "*a technician who knows regulations inside and out.*" **Karen Neeley** of Cox Smith Matthews Incorporated is acknowledged for her expertise in compliance and regulatory matters, where clients recognize her as "*a top-notch attorney and an absolute expert in her field.*" **Robert Rendell** of Patton Boggs LLP regularly works with both domestic and foreign clients. He has experience in a range of areas, such as project finance, oil and gas lending and energy-related finance. **Kenneth Anderson** (see p.2378) of Sidley Austin LLP is highly regarded for his work with borrowers and lenders, which he frequently represents in syndicated financings. **David Keyes** of Kelly Hart & Hallman LLP has a broad practice that includes a swathe of financial transactions. He is experienced in a range of industries, including energy and technology. **Michael Niebruegge** (see p.2407) of Cadwalader, Wickersham & Taft LLP attracts overwhelming praise from sources, who describe him as *"one of the top banking and finance lawyers in Texas – an outstanding attorney."* His recent highlights include representing Barclays Capital in a ten-year, $850 million volumetric production payment which involved new approaches to allow the gas producer a lower cost of capital.

# BANKRUPTCY/RESTRUCTURING

Commentary about individuals can be found under their firm's paragraph. If the firm has no paragraph (is not ranked) look at Other Notable Practitioners.

## Bankruptcy/Restructuring
### Leading Firms

**Band 1**
Baker Botts LLP *
Fulbright & Jaworski LLP *
Haynes and Boone, LLP *
Vinson & Elkins LLP *
Weil, Gotshal & Manges LLP *

**Band 2**
Akin Gump Strauss Hauer & Feld LLP *
Bracewell & Giuliani LLP *
Gardere Wynne Sewell LLP *
Jones Day *
Thompson & Knight LLP *

**Band 3**
Andrews Kurth LLP *
Cox Smith Matthews Incorporated
Forshey Prostok LLP *
Greenberg Traurig, LLP *
Kane Russell Coleman & Logan PC *
King & Spalding LLP *
Munsch Hardt Kopf & Harr, P.C. *
Porter Hedges LLP *

\* *Indicates firm / individual with profile.*
† *ONP = Other Notable Practitioner*

## Bankruptcy/Restructuring
### Senior Statesmen

**Senior Statesmen: distinguished older practitioners**

| | |
|---|---|
| Kinzie Jack L | Baker Botts LLP * |

### Leading Individuals

**Band 1**

| | | | | |
|---|---|---|---|---|
| Albergotti Robert | Haynes and Boone, LLP | | Heath Paul E | Vinson & Elkins LLP * |
| Beckham, Jr. Charles A. | Haynes and Boone, LLP | | Howley Thomas A | Jones Day * |
| Campbell Rhett G | Thompson & Knight LLP * | | Kurtz Marcy E | Bracewell & Giuliani LLP * |
| Gerber Toby L | Fulbright & Jaworski LLP * | | Lee James J | Vinson & Elkins LLP * |
| Gibbs Charles R | Akin Gump Strauss Hauer & Feld LLP | | Melko John P | Gardere Wynne Sewell LLP * |
| Higgins John | Porter Hedges LLP * | | Munsch Russell L | Munsch Hardt Kopf & Harr, P.C. |
| Kaim Henry | King & Spalding LLP | | Pezanosky Stephen | Haynes and Boone, LLP |
| Perez Alfredo R | Weil, Gotshal & Manges LLP * | | Prostok Jeff | Forshey Prostok LLP * |
| Phelan Robin | Haynes and Boone, LLP | | Ruckman Deirdre B | Gardere Wynne Sewell LLP * |
| Roberson Richard M | Gardere Wynne Sewell LLP * | | Stricklin Samuel M | Bracewell & Giuliani LLP * |
| Sosland Martin | Weil, Gotshal & Manges LLP * | | Tarpley George | Cox Smith Matthews Incorporated |
| Stewart Dan | Vinson & Elkins LLP * | | White Bruce H | Greenberg Traurig, LLP * |
| Strubeck Lou | Fulbright & Jaworski LLP * | | | |
| Wallander William | Vinson & Elkins LLP * | | **Band 4** | |

**Band 2**

| | | | | |
|---|---|---|---|---|
| Bennett David M | Thompson & Knight LLP * | | Epstein Joseph G | Winstead PC (ONP)† * |
| Brookner Jason S | Andrews Kurth LLP * | | Friedman Joseph | Kane Russell Coleman & Logan PC * |
| Coleman Joseph M | Kane Russell Coleman & Logan PC * | | Hughes Patrick L | Haynes and Boone, LLP |
| Daniel Josiah | Vinson & Elkins LLP * | | Jordan Shelby | Jordan, Hyden, Womble, Culbreth (ONP)† |
| Esserman Sander L | Stutzman, Bromberg, Esserman (ONP)† | | Kilmer Brian | Okin Adams & Kilmer LLP (ONP)† |
| Gordon Gregory M | Jones Day * | | Mayer Sylvia | Weil, Gotshal & Manges LLP * |
| Greendyke William | Fulbright & Jaworski LLP * | | McDowell C. Luckey | Baker Botts LLP * |
| Jessup Jr Clifton R | Greenberg Traurig, LLP * | | Morris E Lee | Munsch Hardt Kopf & Harr, P.C. |
| Neligan Jr Patrick J | Neligan Foley LLP (ONP)† | | Parham David | Baker & McKenzie (ONP)† * |
| O'Neil Holland N | Gardere Wynne Sewell LLP * | | Prince James | Baker Botts LLP * |
| Perrin Harry | Vinson & Elkins LLP * | | Rochelle Michael | Rochelle, Hutcheson & McCullough (ONP)† |
| Ray Hugh M | McKool Smith (ONP)† * | | Ross Judith | Baker Botts LLP * |
| Russell Robin | Andrews Kurth LLP * | | Rothberg Edward L | Hoover Slovacek LLP (ONP)† |
| Spears Berry | Fulbright & Jaworski LLP * | | Ruzinsky Bruce | Jackson Walker LLP (ONP)† * |
| Wielebinski Joseph J | Munsch Hardt Kopf & Harr, P.C. | | Spiers Jeffrey E | Andrews Kurth LLP * |
| Williamson Deborah | Cox Smith Matthews Incorporated | | Stohner Ken | Jackson Walker LLP (ONP)† * |
| Wood III William A | Bracewell & Giuliani LLP * | | Vaughn Matthew | Porter Hedges LLP * |
| Youngman Stephen A | Weil, Gotshal & Manges LLP * | | Warner Michael | Cole, Schotz, Meisel, Forman (ONP)† * |
| | | | Wege Mark | King & Spalding LLP * |
| **Band 3** | | | Zdunkewicz David A | Andrews Kurth LLP * |
| Andrews Mark | Cox Smith Matthews Incorporated | | | |
| Clement Zack | Fulbright & Jaworski LLP * | | **Up-and-coming individuals** | |
| Davis Tony | Baker Botts LLP | | McFaul Duston | Vinson & Elkins LLP * |
| Forshey J Robert | Forshey Prostok LLP | | Peck Ian | Haynes and Boone, LLP |
| | | | Protopapas Lydia | Weil, Gotshal & Manges LLP * |
| | | | Schultz Sarah | Akin Gump Strauss Hauer & Feld LLP |

## Band 1

### Baker Botts LLP
See profile on p.2427

**THE FIRM** Baker Botts has risen to prominence in recent years on the back of its acclaimed work in cases of national repute. The firm utilizes its deep bench to undertake large-scale matters across the spectrum of bankruptcy representations. The team is particularly known for its exemplary track record in bankruptcy litigation, and for its expertise in advising on the acquisition of distressed assets. Highlights of the past year include the ongoing representation of Ralph Janvey, the court-appointed receiver in the highly publicized $8 billon receivership of Allen Stanford and the companies that he owned.

**KEY INDIVIDUALS** The *"tremendous"* **Jack Kinzie** (see p.2399) chairs the firm's bankruptcy and restructuring group. He has immense experience representing a diverse range of clients, including institutional lenders, creditors, debtors and distressed asset acquirers. He has developed particular expertise in advising on prepackaged mass tort bankruptcies. **Tony Davis** has particular expertise in real estate, environmental and insurance-related bankruptcies.

He recently advised the receiver during the Stanford receivership. **James Prince** (see p.2411) is often recognized for his litigation expertise but has a broad-ranging practice, with peers quick to identify him as a *"real and complete bankruptcy lawyer."* He recently completed the firm's representation of Pride International, the largest creditor in the Seahawk Drilling Chapter 11 bankruptcy. **Judith Ross** (see p.2414) is acknowledged for her exemplary knowledge of bankruptcy law, and is also adept in conducting bankruptcy-related litigation matters, including trial and appellate litigation. She recently represented lenders during satellite television provider Raser Technologies' Chapter 11 proceedings. Peers are impressed with **Luckey McDowell**'s (see p.2404) courtroom presence. He regularly acts for hedge fund and private equity clients, and recently represented YA Global Investments in the California bankruptcy of Cobalis.

## Fulbright & Jaworski LLP
See profile on p.2435

**THE FIRM** Fulbright & Jaworski continues to field one of the more formidable bankruptcy and insolvency groups in Texas. Its bench strength and experience are integral factors to this reputation, and clients praise the team's ability to manage complex issues. The team is particular recognized for its sophisticated bankruptcy litigation work. Key clients include JPMorgan Chase Bank, AT&T and Vitro America.

**Sources say:** *"The group is very strong and is coming on even more so." "Broad experience, depth of knowledge and responsiveness. Their advice on legal strategy has been excellent."*

**KEY INDIVIDUALS Lou Strubeck** (see p.2418) heads Fulbright's global restructuring, bankruptcy and insolvency group. He is one of the most widely respected practitioners in Texas, and his reasoned approach to matters continues to impress clients. *"He is very accessible and gives good solid advice,"* say sources, who add: *"He understands business issues without overwhelming clients and uses the legal information to inform business decisions."* **Toby Gerber** (see p.2390) provides *"decades of experience and excellent strategic thinking"* to numerous bank group and lender clients. He has immense knowledge across the spectrum of bankruptcy and reorganization matters, with particular expertise in the transportation and airline sectors. **William Greendyke** (see p.2392) has developed a superb practice covering a broad range of bankruptcy and reorganization matters since his move from the Bench in 2004. He earns respect among those in the industry, with peers singling out his in-depth understanding of the bankruptcy process as a contributing factor. He continues to play a major role in the Vitro America bankruptcy. **Berry Spears** (see p.2417) is partner-in-charge of Fulbright's Austin office. He offers expertise across the electric utility, telecom, real estate and oil and gas industries, among others. Commentators note: *"His courtroom presence is magnificent; the way he navigates among all constituents really brings value to the situation."* A *"superb bankruptcy attorney,"* **Zack Clement** (see p.2385) earns praise for his eminent experience: *"He has been around and seen so many situations; he just immediately gets it."* He has broad-ranging expertise covering business reorganizations, insolvency litigation and acquiring distressed assets.

## Haynes and Boone, LLP
See profile on p.444

**THE FIRM** Haynes and Boone fields a formidable team of bankruptcy and restructuring experts, many of whom serve clients throughout the country. The group is experienced in all manner of bankruptcy situations but of late has developed particular expertise in conducting distressed real estate acquisitions on behalf of private equity funds. Recent highlights include acting for BOH Park Highland on Land Investors' Chapter 11 proceedings, and representing Crédit Agricole CIB in the South Edge bankruptcy. The group also offers expertise in the aviation sector, and was recently assigned as conflicts counsel in the Chapter 11 bankruptcy of AMR, the parent company of American Airlines.

**Sources say:** *"They have done a very good job. They understand the strategies and issues in bankruptcy." "The team is very proactive in looking forward and anticipating developments. The back-up and associates are very good and we are pleased with the service – timeliness and availability are strengths."*

**KEY INDIVIDUALS Robert Albergotti** *"is a great strategist,"* according to sources, who add: *"He is very practical and knows what can and can't be said; he knows the best use of time and what is worth a client's time."* He is immensely experienced across all areas of bankruptcy issues, and has focused of late on the firm's representation of AMR. **Charles Beckham** brings over 25 years' bankruptcy experience to negotiations, where clients note that he is *"good in terms of analyzing a situation and communicating what is important."* He continues to act for Crédit Agricole CIB on the South Edge Chapter 11 case. **Stephen Pezanosky** leads Haynes and Boone's bankruptcy and business restructuring group from its Fort Worth office. He has been advising on distressed M&A issues of late, and recently represented BOH Park Highland in the bankruptcy of Las Vegas-based Land Investors. **Patrick Hughes** is an expert in representing secured creditors, debtors and court-appointed committees. He is particularly adept in conducting complex litigation matters, and has conducted a number of cases recently in the oil and gas sector, where he has built a reputation as a highly capable and reliable practitioner. **Robin Phelan** is widely acknowledged as one of the *"deans of the Texas Bar,"* with clients commenting that he is *"always impressive."* He is a seasoned authority whose knowledge remains integral to many in the bankruptcy law sector: *"He is a recognized genius in the legal field – the guy you go to if you have a question you can't answer."* **Ian Peck** is renowned for his debtor-focused bankruptcy practice. He has developed a strong reputation in this field and continues to advise large companies in distressed situations. He acted for Guaranty Financial during its 2011 Chapter 11 bankruptcy.

## Vinson & Elkins LLP
See profile on p.2459

**THE FIRM** This firm's bankruptcy and restructuring department has galvanized its reputation as one of the premier practices in the state. The group focuses predominantly on complex, high-profile debtor-side engagements but can advise on any aspect of business restructuring and insolvency work, thanks to a large bench of bankruptcy experts. The team is increasingly recognized for acting for private equity funds on distressed asset acquisitions. Recent highlights include representing DE Shaw Direct Capital as the DIP lender to the publicly traded Seahawk Drilling. The team is also acting for Stan Springel as trustee on the $650 million Chapter 11 bankruptcy of Innovative Communication.

**Sources say:** *"An excellent reputation in Texas; responsiveness, appropriate staffing and strong client communication skills."*

**KEY INDIVIDUALS William Wallander** (see p.2420) leads Vinson & Elkins's restructuring and reorganization practice group. He is well versed in all aspects of bankruptcy law and works across a range of industry sectors, including energy, healthcare, manufacturing, real estate and transportation. Clients note that Wallander drives cases with his *"analytical, strategic thinking."* **Dan Stewart** (see p.2417) is one of the founding members of Vinson's bankruptcy practice. He has over 35 years of bankruptcy experience spanning all aspects of debtor and creditor-side matters, and commentators commend his *"long-lasting, outstanding reputation."* **Josiah Daniel** (see p.2386) is described as *"a real southern gentleman, who is well respected and very good at working with the other side to get an amicable resolution."* He is experienced across the spectrum of bankruptcy-related situations, and has gained particular acclaim for his ongoing representation of BI-LO during its Chapter 11 bankruptcy and post-confirmation litigation. **Harry Perrin** (see p.2410) is acclaimed for his litigation expertise, especially as it relates to energy and oil and gas matters. Clients praise his ability to take a case by the reins and drive towards a practical solution for all parties. **James Lee** (see p.2401) is the group's go-to lawyer when complex bankruptcy litigation arises. He has conducted trials nationwide, in both state and federal courts. His experience includes litigating fraudulent transfers, valuation contests, avoidance actions and objections to plan confirmation, among many other issues. **Paul Heath** (see p.2394) has developed a reputation for representing lenders and investors in distressed acquisitions. He is currently playing a leading role in acting for GE Business Financial Services, the senior secured lenders of over $50 million in the Chapter 11 bankruptcy of Levelland/Hockley County Ethanol. Up-and-comer **Duston McFaul** (see p.2404) is quickly making his mark in the bankruptcy law market. He continues to increase his first chair experience and has gained a reputation among clients as a *"thoughtful, responsive and creative thinker who easily adapts to client requests and needs."*

## Weil, Gotshal & Manges LLP
See profile on p.2015

**THE FIRM** Weil Gotshal's Texas-based bankruptcy group is an essential component of the firm's leading international business finance and restructuring practice. Some of the firm's most significant matters have involved leading roles for Texas partners, including the debtor-side representations of Lehman Brothers, Dallas Stars and DSI Holdings. The team is currently playing a prominent role for American Airlines' parent company AMR during its high-profile Chapter 11 case. Weil is renowned for its debtor-side expertise but is not limited to such engagements, having recently advised Macquarie Capital on the Reddy Ice Chapter 11 bankruptcy.

**Sources say:** *"They clearly have a lot of resources and very experienced restructuring lawyers who are known and respected by judges; that is very important to us."*

**KEY INDIVIDUALS Alfredo Perez** (see p.2409) leads the business finance and restructuring group in Weil's Houston office. Clients note that he is *"outstanding – one of the best in the country."* He takes key leadership roles in many of the biggest bankruptcies filed in the USA, and is advising AMR on the American Airlines bankruptcy. Sources highlight his expertise during negotiations. **Martin Sosland** (see p.2417) heads the Dallas team. He has outstanding debtor-side abilities, and is praised for his technical ability and strategic leadership. He recently acted for Macquarie Capital during the Reddy Ice Chapter 11 bankruptcy, where Macquarie provided a substantial credit facility and new equity investments. **Stephen Youngman** (see p.2423) is adept across the bankruptcy law spectrum, regularly advising on reorganizations, refinancings, debtor issues and creditors' rights. He recently worked alongside Alfredo Perez on advising AMR on the American Airlines bankruptcy. *"Stephen has organized the troops and is running things in the background; he has done a really good job with his advice,"* says one satisfied client. **Sylvia Mayer** (see p.2404) represents parties in all areas of bankruptcy, and has been especially active of late in providing recovery and resolution planning for financial institutions. She is praised for her leadership skills, with one source noting: *"Sylvia's strength is that when she works with boards and management teams she makes sure everyone is communicating and understands their roles and duties."* **Lydia Protopapas** (see p.2411) is fast gaining a reputation for her prominence in representing debtors and acquirers of distressed assets. *"She understands the nuances and intersections of federal and state law,"* according to sources, who add: *"No one is better prepared or can write better briefs – she boils down issues to what is easily understood, and judges love her for that."*

## Band 2

### Akin Gump Strauss Hauer & Feld LLP
See profile on p.904

**THE FIRM** This firm's Dallas-based bankruptcy team has experienced a stellar year at a time when traditional bankruptcy filings have been low on the ground. The team mirrors the firm's national focus and exemplary reputation in representing creditors and creditors' committees, with a strong localized niche in the oil and gas industry. Clients appreciate that the team is able to draw on the firm's abundant resources in other areas of law. Highlights include representing the official noteholders' committee in the Chapter 11 proceedings of mortgage company RE Loans. The group also acted for the official equity holders committee in the now concluded Chapter 11 bankruptcy of Seahawk Drilling.

**Sources say:** *"A well-integrated practice." "An excellent team, from trial attorneys to 'nuts and bolts' bankruptcy attorneys. I haven't had a case with them that has turned out badly."*

**KEY INDIVIDUALS Charles Gibbs** has fast built a reputation as one of the premier bankruptcy practitioners in the state, and is praised as *"a master of his craft."* He is equally described as an advocate who *"brings a lot of credibility to the table"* in court, and as *"a great strategist who can provide a good road map for how the case will progress."* He led the firm's representation of committees in both the RE Loans and Seahawk Drilling Chapter 11 bankruptcies. Up-and-coming attorney **Sarah Schultz** is *"effective in the business side of the restructurings and very knowledgeable on the Bankruptcy Code and procedure."* She has recently acted for a number of committees in various New York-based bankruptcy proceedings. Clients note that Schultz has *"impressed judges with her knowledge and fluency, which is helpful in establishing credibility."*

### Bracewell & Giuliani LLP
See profile on p.2429

**THE FIRM** This sterling financial restructuring practice balances representations of debtor and creditor clients. The team has significant expertise in the energy sector, in which it acts for a number of exploration and production companies. Recent highlights include advising the agent for senior and junior secured creditors on the ongoing $50 million Chapter 11 proceedings of Cano Petroleum. The team is also advising power provider PPL as the largest unsecured creditor in the bankruptcy of Southern Montana Electric Generation.

**Sources say:** *"A very fine group with talented lawyers."*

**KEY INDIVIDUALS Trey Wood** (see p.2423) heads the Texas financial restructuring practice and has more than two decades' experience in all aspects of the industry, particularly in relation to the energy sector. He led the firm's creditor representations during both the Cano Petroleum and Southern Montana Electric Generation bankruptcies. **Marcy Kurtz** (see p.2400) is regularly praised for her dedication to her clients' interests, especially in conducting complex litigation matters. She primarily advises banks and other lenders on creditors' rights issues. **Samuel Stricklin** (see p.2418) is immensely experienced in representing creditor committees in bankruptcies. He is especially capable within the real estate, retail and restaurant industries. He is also praised for his poise in litigious matters, with one gracious opponent conceding: *"He pays attention to details – he wasn't very fun to negotiate with! He held his positions very well."*

### Gardere Wynne Sewell LLP
See profile on p.2436

**THE FIRM** This firm's superb bankruptcy and business reorganization group represents a steady base of both debtor and creditor clients. The practice offers a deep bench of experienced practitioners operating out of offices in Dallas and Houston. It has industry-specific expertise within the oil and gas, healthcare, construction, utilities, and transportation sectors. In recent highlights, the team represented RE Loans, RE Future and Capital Salvage during their respective Chapter 11 bankruptcies. On the creditor side, the team also acts for the Official Committee of Unsecured Creditors in the bankruptcy of the Gerald Champion Regional Medical Center.

**Sources say:** *"I have always found that it is a very personalized service." "They have the talent levels and experience to maneuver through any bankruptcy and educate the client properly on all avenues that one should take."*

**KEY INDIVIDUALS Rich Roberson** (see p.2413) is chair of the firm's bankruptcy and business reorganization group. He is tremendously experienced, and has particular expertise in energy-related bankruptcy work. Clients note that he has *"the ability to stay calm in extreme distressed situations."* He is currently acting as special counsel to the debtors in the ongoing Vitro Asset bankruptcy. **Holly O'Neil** (see p.2408) is described as a *"top-notch lawyer"* with a *"very good practice."* She is praised for her presence in court and is also recommended for her sports industry expertise. O'Neil is currently lead counsel in the firm's representation of RE Loans and associated companies in their respective Chapter 11 proceedings. **Deirdre Ruckman** (see p.2414) acts for a variety of debtor and creditor clients. She is widely admired for her *"tremendous knowledge base, not only in bankruptcy law but also in healthcare law; it is great to work with her."* She represents the unsecured creditors' committee in the Gerald Champion Regional Medical Center bankruptcy. **John Melko** (see p.2405) is highly respected in the bankruptcy arena, especially within the oil and gas sector. He recently represented cable TV operator Broadstripe in its Delaware-based Chapter 11 proceedings.

### Jones Day
See profile on p.919

**THE FIRM** Jones Day's tremendously strong Texas-based restructuring and reorganization group is praised by peers, both locally and nationally. While the team operates independently, it also actively supports Jones Day's prominent national and international practice. As such, it benefits from the seamless interconnection of resources between the firm's various offices and experts. Recent highlights include representing the Official Creditors' Committee of international intellectual property business Qimonda during its complex Chapter 11 case in Delaware. Jones Day also represents Bondex International and chemical products manufacturer Specialty Products in their Delaware-based Chapter 11 bankruptcies.

**KEY INDIVIDUALS Gregory Gordon** (see p.2391) leads Jones Day's Texas restructuring and reorganization offering. He is praised for his expert litigation capabilities and his experience across a range of industries, and is currently representing Bondex International and Specialty Products in their Chapter 11 proceedings. **Thomas Howley** (see p.2396) represents private equity funds, lenders and bondholders in bankruptcy situations. He has been highly active of late advising clients on the acquisitions of distressed assets.

## Thompson & Knight LLP
See profile on p.2458

**THE FIRM** Thompson & Knight's corporate reorganization and creditors' rights group is renowned for its oil and gas sector expertise. It has particular experience in conducting upstream oil and gas reorganizations, and is also well regarded for its regular representation of indenture trustees and bondholders. Recent highlights include its ongoing representation of Vitro SAB de CV in the Mexican company's high-profile Chapter 15 proceedings. The team is also acting for Cano Petroleum and affiliates on their Chapter 11 cases.

**Sources say:** *"The firm is very experienced in all forms of credit and restructuring but is particularly good in cases involving energy and oil and gas."*

**KEY INDIVIDUALS** Of counsel **Rhett Campbell** (see p.2383) maintains an exemplary reputation in the sector. One source noted: *"He is one of the finest attorneys I have ever seen; he is very experienced and really is the expert on oil and gas bankruptcies and creditor's rights."* Campbell recently represented Hercules Offshore in its Section 363 acquisition of the debtor's drilling rig assets from Seahawk Drilling. **David Bennett** (see p.2380) was recently appointed as leader of the firm's corporate reorganization and creditors' rights group. He mirrors the firm's reputation for preeminent oil and gas expertise, and continues to lead the team representing Vitro SAB de CV.

## Band 3

## Andrews Kurth LLP
See profile on p.2426

**THE FIRM** This strong regional group is well regarded across the bankruptcy spectrum and in recent times has developed a strong practice in distressed asset acquisition and corporate risk assessment. It also has formidable experience in the energy sector and has represented a number of debtors in that area of late. Highlights include a role as counsel to HSH Nordbank as agent for the secured lenders in the bankruptcy proceedings of Greek shipping company Omega Navigation Enterprises.

**Sources say:** *"Andrews Kurth has always provided me with services that equal or exceed my expectations. Their resourcefulness and quick response times continue to be prime motivators for this continuing relationship."*

**KEY INDIVIDUALS** Group head **Robin Russell** (see p.2414) is deeply experienced in all manner of business reorganization matters, and is renowned for her litigation expertise. Interviewees praise her strong negotiation skills and unflappable demeanor. She has been highly active assessing bankruptcy risk for large corporate clients of late. The *"very versatile"* **Jason Brookner** (see p.2382) *"is attentive, and knows his area and all the relevant pitfalls that may arise."* He has a broad-ranging practice, and recently represented Centerbridge Partners in relation to funding provided to bankrupt entity Reddy Ice Holdings. **Jeffrey Spiers** (see p.2417) is a long-established bankruptcy expert, widely admired by fellow practitioners. His recent highlights include representing Dune Energy in its out-of-

court restructuring. **David Zdunkewicz** (see p.2424) is primarily recognized as a bankruptcy litigation specialist, although his practice stretches to many other disciplines. *"He is a very talented lawyer,"* say sources, with one adding: *"He is smart as a whip and has been involved in very big bankruptcies in significant roles."*

## Cox Smith Matthews Incorporated

**THE FIRM** This regional bankruptcy and creditors' rights group is renowned for its expertise in the energy, real estate and retail sectors. The team is strong in conducting litigation, with a reputation among clients for steadfastly representing their interests in negotiations. Its successful year has included acting as local counsel for the Official Committee of Unsecured Creditors of Reddy Ice. It also recently acted for construction company JC Evans on its Chapter 11 proceedings.

**Sources say:** *"The knowledge, experience and level of integrity that Cox Smith provide have been major factors in our decision to use this firm."*

**KEY INDIVIDUALS** **Deborah Williamson** is immensely experienced in a range of bankruptcy-related matters. She is praised for her excellent foresight and strategic ability. **Mark Andrews** leads the bankruptcy and creditors' rights group, and is an expert in representing both debtors and lenders in Chapter 11 cases. He and **George Tarpley** led the firm's representation of JC Evans in its bankruptcy proceedings. The *"detailed and analytical"* Tarpley is most regularly recognized for his expertise in the insurance and healthcare sectors, in addition to having a reputation for bankruptcy litigation work.

## Forshey Prostok LLP
See profile on p.2434

**THE FIRM** Forshey Prostok remains a go-to firm for large-scale, complex bankruptcy work in the Fort Worth area. The boutique practice operates across the spectrum of bankruptcy and restructuring work, and has also recently added an office in Dallas. Recent highlights include acting as co-counsel to an ad hoc group of noteholders in the Chapter 15 cross-border restructuring of Mexican glass maker Vitro SAB de CV.

**Sources say:** *"They're smart and have been around long enough to understand the most practical aspects of resolving case problems."*

**KEY INDIVIDUALS** **Robert Forshey** *"continues to be the guiding light of the firm,"* say sources; *"he also has an outstanding work ethic and is extremely knowledgeable."* He is renowned for his litigation expertise, and is noted for rigorously defending his clients. **Jeff Prostok** (see p.2411) is noted for his collaborative, deal-oriented approach. *"His main strength is his demeanor and ability to take a contentious situation and take the emotion out of it and reach a consensual resolution,"* according to respondents. Prostok leads the firm's role as co-counsel in the Vitro SAB de CV Chapter 15 bankruptcy.

## Greenberg Traurig, LLP
See profile on p.1024

**THE FIRM** Greenberg Traurig's Texas-based business reorganization and financial restructuring group is spread between offices in Dallas and Houston, with further resources and expertise readily available through the firm's extensive international network. The team is distinguished in acting for secured lenders on bankruptcies and workouts, and for representing buyers of distressed assets. The team's highlights include acting for the indenture trustee for the senior secured bond debt on the $230 million bankruptcy of The Clare at Water Tower.

**Sources say:** *"Great lawyers."*

**KEY INDIVIDUALS** **Clifton Jessup** (see p.2397) is renowned for his work across all sides of bankruptcy, and particularly for his lender-side representations and in matters in the real estate and energy sectors. He acts for the indenture trustee in the bankruptcy of The Clare at Water Tower. **Bruce White** (see p.2421) works in unison with Jessup, and also retains a commendable practice in his own right. Sources praise him as *"a smart lawyer who does a good job of guiding his clients through complicated problems."*

## Kane Russell Coleman & Logan PC
See profile on p.2442

**THE FIRM** This bankruptcy and creditors' rights practice is making significant gains in the Texas bankruptcy market. The team acts for all parties involved in bankruptcy matters, and has developed an excellent reputation for representing creditors' committees in particular. It is also well known for its expertise in the automobile, healthcare, sports and retail industries. It recently acted as debtor's counsel in the $66 million Chapter 11 bankruptcy of All Smiles Dental Center.

**Sources say:** *"A very good, thorough and efficient practice. They are tireless when it comes to promoting their clients' interests in cases."*

**KEY INDIVIDUALS** **Joseph Coleman** (see p.2385) is a founding director of the firm and chair of the bankruptcy and creditors' rights group. He is acclaimed for his experience representing creditors' committees, and as an attorney who *"will work until the very end of the case to get every dollar he can for his clients."* *"Polished courtroom lawyer"* **Joseph Friedman** (see p.2389) is well regarded for his litigation expertise. *"He has a great demeanor for these situations and thinks outside the box,"* say interviewees. He recently represented All Smiles Dental Center as debtor's counsel in the company's bankruptcy proceedings.

## King & Spalding LLP
See profile on p.445

**THE FIRM** King & Spalding continues to provide clients with quality advice across the full range of bankruptcy and reorganization matters. The team offers expertise in representing debtors in restructurings, both in and out of court, and also acts for various lender entities in DIP financings and distressed asset acquisitions. Its industry experience spans energy, real estate, healthcare, telecom and manufacturing. Highlights from the past year include acting for

Montana Resources in a lawsuit involving a copper mine ownership dispute connected with formerly bankrupt entity Asarco.

**Sources say:** *"They have been very good to work with, and the support staff has always been responsive."*

**KEY INDIVIDUALS Henry Kaim** has more than 30 years' experience in this industry and garners immense respect among both colleagues and adversaries. He leads in many of the group's most high-profile cases, with clients noting that *"he is very aware of bankruptcy law and is good in the courtroom."* **Mark Wege** (see p.2421) is a talented practitioner with expertise in acting for secured creditors, and comprehensive knowledge of the oil and gas industry. He led the firm's high-profile debtor representation of SpectraWatt in its recently completed bankruptcy. He *"has a good reputation and is well thought of,"* say market commentators.

## Munsch Hardt Kopf & Harr, P.C.
See profile on p.2448

**THE FIRM** Munsch Hardt's insolvency, restructuring and creditors' rights practice is traditionally acknowledged for its strength in representing creditor and bondholder committees. However, as one of the larger groups in the state, it is well versed in all manner of bankruptcy matters. The team has been involved in a large number of real estate and hospitality cases of late, as well as fostering a growing reputation for cross-border work. This is highlighted by its role in the Chapter 15 bankruptcy of Stanford International Bank in Antigua, where the firm represents the joint liquidators.

**KEY INDIVIDUALS Joseph Wielebinski** advises various entities on both domestic and international matters. He is currently acting for the liquidators on the cross-border Chapter 15 case of Stanford International Bank. Founding partner **Russell Munsch** earns respect for his tremendous experience in the industry. His practice has focused in recent years on acting for bank groups, creditors and financial institutions on loan workouts, restructurings and bankruptcies. **Lee Morris** has an outstanding reputation among fellow practitioners for his effective and efficient work, particularly in relation to bankruptcy litigation. He is currently representing the liquidation trustee in the Chapter 11 plan of Guaranty Financial Group.

## Porter Hedges LLP
See profile on p.2450

**THE FIRM** This compact bankruptcy, restructuring and creditors' rights group specializes in debtor, creditor and trustee representations. The team can handle any aspect of bankruptcy work, and is particularly adept at guiding companies through reorganization, both out of court and in Chapter 11 cases. Matters arising in the oil and gas sector are a particular specialty. The team is currently acting as counsel for H Malcolm Lovett Jr, the plan agent under the confirmed plan of liquidation for former underwater construction and commercial diving company Superior Offshore International.

**KEY INDIVIDUALS John Higgins** (see p.2395) is acknowledged as an expert in corporate reorganizations, restructurings and acquisitions, especially those pertaining to the oil and gas sector. One peer praises him as *"the most conscientious and thorough lawyer that I know; he leaves no stone unturned."* Others note that he *"will zealously represent his client but won't push the envelope too far; he has a good sense of how to set up a case and then reach a resolution on the best terms possible for his clients."* Interviewees are quick to point out that **Matthew Vaughn** (see p.2419) *"can be aggressive when he has to be but doesn't make people feel bad; he never burns bridges."* He has excellent expertise in acting for publicly traded entities and creditors during complex Chapter 11 cases.

## Other Notable Practitioners

**David Parham** (see p.2408) of Baker & McKenzie's Dallas office is recognized for his excellent and broad-ranging bankruptcy expertise. He is described as *"a dynamic individual, whose problem-solving skills have been very useful, particularly when formulating complicated litigation strategies."* **Michael Warner** (see p.2420) enters the rankings as the head of Cole, Schotz, Meisel, Forman & Leonard's bankruptcy offering in Fort Worth, where he focuses on reorganizations and out-of-court workouts. He has garnered considerable praise among sources for his *"ability to see beyond the legal issue and focus on the business issues."* He is *"very effective and has a good working relationship with judges."* **Sander Esserman** of Stutzman, Bromberg, Esserman & Plifka operates a widely respected practice

focusing on mass tort and asbestos-related bankruptcies on a national scale. **Patrick Neligan** is the founding partner of Neligan Foley LLP, and has developed a reputation for having *"a great practice"* encompassing debtor and creditor-side representations. **Hugh Ray** (see p.2412) is praised for developing a strong bankruptcy practice at McKool Smith. He is a nationally respected lawyer specializing in bankruptcy litigation and trial work. Commentators note that he is *"deeply knowledgeable,"* and has the *"expertise to strategize in very large cases."* **Brian Kilmer** of Okin Adams & Kilmer LLP receives praise for being *"understanding of the business needs and goals of the client; he has a good grasp of the law and picks things up really quickly in the industry."* His recent highlights include advising an ad hoc group of first and second lien noteholders on the Chapter 11 bankruptcy of Reddy Ice holdings. *"Outstanding bankruptcy lawyer"* **Michael Rochelle** of Rochelle, Hutcheson & McCullough, LLP is an expert in bankruptcy matters relating to the oil and gas industry. **Joseph Epstein** (see p.2388) of Winstead PC is broadly experienced in many aspects of bankruptcy law, with strong recent involvement in out-of-court restructurings and distressed asset acquisitions. He recently acted for Wells Fargo as a senior secured lender in the bankruptcy of shopping center Moore Sorrento. **Bruce Ruzinsky** (see p.2414) of Jackson Walker LLP has an established presence in the Texas bankruptcy market. He is an expert in advising lenders and creditors on reorganizations and bankruptcy proceedings. Sources are quick to praise his *"technical knowledge coupled with practical application."* The *"capable and experienced"* **Ken Stohner** (see p.2418) is also at Jackson Walker LLP. He has been practicing bankruptcy for more than two decades and is well regarded by his fellow practitioners. **Edward Rothberg** is head of Hoover Slovacek's bankruptcy practice. He is an oil and gas expert and represents clients across the full spectrum of insolvency and restructuring matters. **Shelby Jordan** of Jordan, Hyden, Womble, Culbreth & Holzer, P.C. enters the rankings as a prominent bankruptcy specialist in Corpus Christi. Commentators admire his efficiency and note that *"you would be well advised to look up Shelby as local counsel"* should a matter be filed in Corpus Christi.

# CAPITAL MARKETS DEBT & EQUITY

Commentary about individuals can be found under their firm's paragraph. If the firm has no paragraph (is not ranked) look at Other Notable Practitioners.

## Capital Markets: Debt & Equity
### Leading Firms

**Band 1**
Latham & Watkins LLP *
Vinson & Elkins LLP *

**Band 2**
Andrews Kurth LLP *
Baker Botts LLP *

**Band 3**
Bracewell & Giuliani LLP *
Haynes and Boone, LLP *
Jones Day *
Mayer Brown LLP *
Porter Hedges LLP *
Thompson & Knight LLP *

### Leading Individuals

**Band 1**

| | |
|---|---|
| Finnegan IV William N | Latham & Watkins LLP |
| Oelman David | Vinson & Elkins LLP * |
| O'Leary Michael | Andrews Kurth LLP * |

**Band 2**

| | |
|---|---|
| Davidson Joshua | Baker Botts LLP * |
| Dillard Michael E | Latham & Watkins LLP |
| Kelly T Mark | Vinson & Elkins LLP * |
| Reedy Robert | Porter Hedges LLP * |
| Telle Michael S | Bracewell & Giuliani LLP * |

**Band 3**

| | |
|---|---|
| Chambers J Michael | Latham & Watkins LLP |
| Chapman Jeffrey A | Gibson, Dunn & Crutcher LLP * (ONP)† |
| Goodgame John | Akin Gump Strauss Hauer & Feld * (ONP)† |
| Heller William | Thompson & Knight LLP |
| Jewell Robert V | Andrews Kurth LLP * |
| Prince James M | Vinson & Elkins LLP * |
| Young Guy | Haynes and Boone, LLP |

**Up-and-coming individuals**

| | |
|---|---|
| Wheeler Sean T | Latham & Watkins LLP |

\* Indicates firm / individual with profile.

†ONP = Other Notable Practitioner

## Band 1

### Latham & Watkins LLP
See profile on p.446

THE FIRM Latham's Houston office opened in 2010 and has become a major force in the market for its representation of issuers and underwriters in debt and equity capital market transactions. It has a notable focus on transactions related to MLPs. Recent highlights include representing the initial purchaser, RBS Securities, in Linn Energy's offering of 6.25% senior notes due 2019. Other notable clients include Green Field Energy Services, Citigroup Global Markets and Wells Fargo Securities.
**Sources say:** *"They are very high-quality."*
**KEY INDIVIDUALS** The *"highly thoughtful"* and *"practical"* **William Finnegan** is a *"constructive"* lawyer who

*"leaves no stone unturned,"* sources say. He is recommended for his representation of issuers and underwriters in energy transactions. **Michael Dillard** is managing partner of the Houston office. Sources say he is *"a strong strategic thinker,"* and a *"hard worker"* who *"rigorously represents his clients."* **Michael Chambers** is *"very thoughtful and practical"* and is further recommended for his problem-solving abilities. He recently advised Barclays, the lead purchaser, on a 9.625% senior notes offering by midstream natural gas company NGPL Pipe. **Sean Wheeler** is *"highly capable"* and has a particularly good reputation for his work on MLP transactions. He is cochair of the oil and gas team.

### Vinson & Elkins LLP
See profile on p.2459

THE FIRM This team has a superb reputation for its work on the full range of transactions in the energy sector, with notable strength in MLP-related transactions. Recent highlights include representing Energy Transfer Partners on a $2 billion senior notes offering. Other names on its client roster include Anadarko, Southwest Airlines and Riverstone.
**Sources say:** *"Their technical strength, which is important to this market, is second to none."*
**KEY INDIVIDUALS** The *"terrific"* **David Oelman** (see p.2407) *"has good judgment"* and a *"practical business approach to getting deals done,"* impressed sources say. He recently represented Plains All American Pipeline on a $455 million common units offering and a $1.250 billion offering of senior notes. **Mark Kelly** (see p.2399) recently represented Ute Energy on a $250 million IPO and a $300 million debt offering. Sources say he is a *"practical"* and *"outstanding attorney."* **James Prince** (see p.2411) is *"knowledgeable,"* *"thorough"* and *"hard-working,"* sources say. His recent highlights include representing Wells Fargo Securities on Berry Petroleum's offering of $600 million of high-yield senior notes.

## Band 2

### Andrews Kurth LLP
See profile on p.2426

THE FIRM This firm wins strong market endorsement for its expertise across all aspects of the energy sector. Sources speak with admiration of its astute representation of underwriters and MLPs.
**KEY INDIVIDUALS Michael O'Leary** (see p.2407) is an *"accomplished lawyer"* with *"tremendous experience"* who is *"good about focusing on the big issues and resolving them in a practical way,"* sources say. He is cochair of the corporate/securities practice. **Robert Jewell** (see p.2397) has notable expertise advising clients in the energy services and refining industries sectors. He is the managing partner of the firm.

### Baker Botts LLP
See profile on p.2427

THE FIRM This team frequently handles a range of transactions for issuers and underwriters including IPOs, secondary offerings, Rule 144A offerings and shelf registrations. It recently represented Berry Petroleum on a $600 million senior notes offering. Other notable clients include Transocean, Morgan Stanley and CenterPoint Energy.
**Sources say:** *"A tremendous practice."*
**KEY INDIVIDUALS** *"MLP expert"* **Joshua Davidson** (see p.2386) is *"highly meticulous"* and *"does a very good job,"* impressed sources report. His clients include Maxum Energy Logistics and EQT Midstream Partners.

## Band 3

### Bracewell & Giuliani LLP
See profile on p.2429

THE FIRM This team is held in high esteem for its representation of issuers and underwriters on a range of transactions in the energy sector. Recent highlights include representing Kinder Morgan in the sale of some $2 billion of common stock. The group also advises ConocoPhillips, Chesapeake Energy and Apache.
**KEY INDIVIDUALS Michael Telle** (see p.2419) recently advised the hydraulic fracturing company Frac Tech International – now FTS International – on its $1.15 billion IPO. Sources speak with admiration of his diligence in representing issuers on a range of deals.

### Haynes and Boone, LLP
See profile on p.444

THE FIRM This team is a highly respected option for representing public companies of all sizes and underwriters on the full range of capital markets matters. It recently represented Lighting Science Group on a $140 million sale of convertible preferred stock. InterOil, HCC Insurance and Trinity Industries are among others that the team has recently advised.
**Sources say:** *"They are extremely responsive on projects."*
**KEY INDIVIDUALS Guy Young** is *"very knowledgeable and good to work with,"* sources say. He represented EV Energy on the issue of $200 million in senior unsecured notes due 2019.

### Jones Day
See profile on p.919

THE FIRM This team has a strong reputation for its advice to clients on matters including US high-yield and global bond offerings, and equity transactions. It recently represented Kaiser Aluminum on its $225 million issue of senior notes. Among other leading clients are Chuy's, PMFG and Viasystems.
**Sources say:** *"They have great expertise in the securities field and they also have very user-friendly professionals."*

**KEY INDIVIDUALS** James O'Bannon is a key contact in the Dallas office.

## Mayer Brown LLP
See profile on p.1257

**THE FIRM** This team is recognized for its representation of clients in the energy sector, including exploration and production, oilfield service and integrated oil companies, in the full array of capital markets transactions. Recent highlights include representing RBC Capital Markets on Rowan Companies' $500 million senior notes issue. The firm advises issuers and underwriters, including Bonanza Creek Energy, Merrill Lynch and Talos Energy.

**Sources say:** *"I am impressed; they made a process that can be painful a lot easier."*

**KEY INDIVIDUALS** Robert Gray is the main contact at the Houston office.

## Porter Hedges LLP
See profile on p.2450

**THE FIRM** This Houston-based team is highly regarded by market sources for its expertise in representing clients in the upstream, midstream, alternative and oilfield services sectors. It acted for Johnson Rice on the $220 million IPO of Sanchez Energy. Other notable clients include Mission Resources, Allied Waste Industries and Encysive Pharmaceuticals.

**KEY INDIVIDUALS** Robert Reedy (see p.2412) is *"personable and knowledgeable,"* impressed sources say. He recently represented Luca Technologies in its $100 million IPO.

## Thompson & Knight LLP
See profile on p.2458

**THE FIRM** Market sources speak with particular admiration of this team's expertise in representing issuers and underwriters on capital markets transactions in the energy industry. Recent highlights include advising Halcón

Resources on its $750 million issue of senior unsecured notes. Other clients of the firm include Amegy Bank, Petrohawk Energy and Noble Energy.

**KEY INDIVIDUALS** William Heller is a *"levelheaded"* attorney, sources say. His recent highlights include representing Petrohawk in its $600 million Rule 144A senior notes offering.

## Other Notable Practitioners

**Jeffrey Chapman** (see p.2384) of Gibson, Dunn & Crutcher LLP recently represented Del Frisco's Restaurant in its $100 million IPO. He is well known and well respected for his representation of issuers and underwriters in an array of debt and equity transactions. **John Goodgame** (see p.2391) of Akin Gump Strauss Hauer & Feld LLP is well regarded by peers for his astute handling of a range of capital markets transactions, with notable expertise in representing MLPs. His areas of expertise include upstream, downstream, midstream and power.

# CONSTRUCTION

Commentary about individuals can be found under their firm's paragraph. If the firm has no paragraph (is not ranked) look at Other Notable Practitioners.

| Construction |
| --- |
| **Leading Firms** |
| **Band 1** |
| Andrews Myers PC |
| Cokinos, Bosien and Young |
| Ford Nassen & Baldwin, P.C. |
| Porter Hedges LLP * |
| Winstead PC * |
| **Band 2** |
| Allensworth and Porter, L.L.P |
| Canterbury, Elder, Gooch, Surratt, Shapiro & Stein, P. C. * |
| Coats Rose Yale Ryman Lee |
| Griffith Nixon Davison, PC |
| **Band 3** |
| Fisk & Fielder |
| Gardere Wynne Sewell LLP * |
| Haynes and Boone, LLP * |
| Jackson Walker LLP * |
| King & Spalding LLP * |

## Band 1

### Andrews Myers PC

**THE FIRM** Andrews Myers remains a leading player in the Texas construction arena. Over the past year the team has seen an increase in work related to the energy and industrial spheres and continues to benefit from the firm's history of acting for municipal and government clients. A significant highlight has seen it act on behalf of the MLN Company, defending a claim for damages in relation to flooding of the 33-story Memorial Hermann Hospital Tower. Other key clients include Odebrecht Construction, Toshiba and BIS TEPSCO.

**Sources say:** *"They are effective communicators and keep the client's best interests at heart."*

**KEY INDIVIDUALS Thomas Myers** is regarded as *"a first-rate lawyer,"* with sources particularly praising his *"wisdom, expertise and strategic vision."* He is particularly noted for his wealth of experience in litigation, arbitration and risk management. Sources think highly of the *"excellent"* **Jason Walker**, who has particular expertise in construction liens and work for subcontractors. **William Westcott** is well known for his strengths in construction litigation. Recently, he has been involved in the high-profile Reliant Stadium litigation, defending both the insulators and the mechanical contractors, in connection with the stadium's air conditioning system. **William Andrews** remains a much-admired figure in the Texas construction industry, particularly for his wide-ranging litigation experience. Sources also single out his *"poise, confidence and advocacy."*

### Cokinos, Bosien and Young

**THE FIRM** This firm remains a key player in the Texas construction market, and comes highly regarded by peers across the board. The group is equally adept on both the transactional side and in litigation, and is well equipped to provide the gamut of legal services to project managers, subcontractors, general contractors and sureties, among others.

**Sources say:** *"On litigation they're very good – a good courtroom firm."*

**KEY INDIVIDUALS Gregory Cokinos** comes highly recommended, with sources quick to describe him as *"a first-rate trial lawyer in construction."* He operates out of the firm's Houston office alongside the *"very knowledgeable"* **Richard Flake**. Flake continues to draw praise for his work as a mediator. **Patrick Wielinski** is noted for his expertise

in the areas of risk management and insurance coverage relating to construction, and regularly speaks on these matters. He splits his time between the Dallas and Fort Worth offices. The *"very experienced"* **Stanley Curry** continues to enjoy a fine reputation in the Texas market, particularly for his trial skills. He is based in San Antonio.

### Ford Nassen & Baldwin, P.C.

**THE FIRM** With offices in Austin, Dallas and Houston, this highly rated construction boutique remains a leading presence in the state. It is well versed in handling complex, multiparty claims on state, national and international levels, and regularly acts on behalf of a diverse clientele, including owners, contractors and suppliers in both the public and private sector.

**Sources say:** *"A very good firm."*

**KEY INDIVIDUALS** Based in the firm's Austin office, **George Baldwin** has a wealth of experience in the construction arena, and is recognized for his varied litigation and dispute resolution strengths. **John Nassen** is similarly noted for his skill in construction litigation, arbitration and other forms of dispute resolution. He represents owners, specialty subcontractors and sureties, among others, and works out of the firm's Dallas office, alongside **Jeffrey Ford**. Ford has experience across the full spectrum of construction matters, acting for a range of developers, manufacturers and general contractors.

### Porter Hedges LLP
See profile on p.2450

**THE FIRM** The team at Porter Hedges offers experience across a broad array of construction matters, acting for a range of contractors, design professionals, suppliers and lenders. A recent highlight was acting for the City of

## Construction

Houston on defending a breach of contract claim made by Southern Electrical Services relating to public wage rates

on an airport construction project. Other key clients include KBR, IBC Bank and Durotech Construction.

**Sources say:** *"A very strong firm."*

**KEY INDIVIDUALS** Head of the department **David Peden** (see p.2409) has a *"fabulous reputation"* in the construction market. He recently successfully acted on behalf of Brasfield & Gorrie on a $50 million construction defects and delays case. **Allison Snyder** (see p.2416) is a well-known construction expert and is particularly recognized for her experience in complex litigation. A highlight of the past year saw her represent ISI in a claim for unpaid costs relating to the Lubbock City jail project.

### Winstead PC
See profile on p.2460

**THE FIRM** Winstead's well-regarded construction team works closely with the firm's real estate and banking and finance groups to provide a seamless service on a variety of complex construction projects and disputes to lenders, developers and owners. In a recent highlight the practice acted on behalf of Parkland Health & Hospital System on the construction of the new $1.2 billion New Parkland hospital campus. It also counts HC Beck, Trademark Construction and The University of Houston System as clients.

**Sources say:** *"The service is always excellent: they are responsive, creative in their solutions, and very knowledgeable in all substantive areas of law."*

**KEY INDIVIDUALS** The *"well-respected"* **Robert Bass** (see p.2380) continues to act as chief counsel for publicly traded REIT Weingarten Realty Investors on all its nationwide construction projects, encompassing large shopping center developments as well as smaller tenant finish out projects. **Mark Guthrie** (see p.2393) enjoys a fine reputation in the construction arena and in a recent highlight successfully settled a case for Harris Country Hospital District concerning a claim for $1.75 million by a contractor who was terminated from a $14 million hospital construction contract. **Michelle Rieger** (see p.2412) is singled out as *"extremely pleasant to work with"* by client sources, who also admire her ability to bring *"a very common-sense approach to everything."* **Stewart Whitehead** (see p.2422) chairs the firm's construction practice and in recent work has acted on behalf of Hays County on its dispute with PBS&J over nonpayment for design documents.

### Band 2

### Allensworth and Porter, L.L.P

**THE FIRM** This Austin-based construction boutique acts for clients in all areas of the construction industry, including contractors, municipalities and developers. The team has particular strength in construction litigation, handling matters such as defect claims, payment issues and defective design, among others.

**Sources say:** *"A very solid firm."*

**KEY INDIVIDUALS** *"Great attorney"* **Matthew Ryan** has substantial experience in construction disputes, and is also highly sought for his expertise in mediation and arbitra-

tion matters. The *"well-respected"* **William Allensworth** remains a luminary in the field. He is much noted for his vast wealth of knowledge and experience in construction matters and continues to enjoy a fine track record acting for design professionals.

### Canterbury, Elder, Gooch, Surratt, Shapiro & Stein, P. C.
See profile on p.2431

**THE FIRM** The key focus of this Dallas-based firm continues to be on construction law and litigation. The group acts for a varied client base made up of owners, subcontractors, general contractors and sureties.

**KEY INDIVIDUALS** Founding partner **Joseph Canterbury** is, as one source notes, *"the dean of Texas construction law."* Recently he has been particularly involved in the mediation and arbitration of construction-related disputes. **Kyle Gooch** continues to enjoy an excellent reputation for his skillful approach to construction-related litigation.

### Coats Rose Yale Ryman Lee

**THE FIRM** This highly regarded construction practice offers a comprehensive service to clients from all areas of the construction industry and is well equipped to handle matters on both a national and international level. In a highlight, it advised the Houston Independent School District on the drafting and negotiation of Energy Performance Contract forms for districtwide energy-saving retrofits.

**Sources say:** *"Very good service: I think what I like most is that they have lawyers with a lot of experience in the areas that they're practicing in."*

**KEY INDIVIDUALS** The *"very knowledgeable"* **Thomas Barber** (see p.2379) *"has considerable experience in construction practices"* and is *"very easy to work with,"* commentators are quick to assert. He has been advising the City of Sugar Land on the $40 million construction of a new professional baseball stadium. Barber operates out of the firm's Dallas office alongside **William Short** (see p.2415). Short has four decades of experience across a broad range of construction matters, acting for a variety of lenders, owners, contractors, sureties and design professionals on both public and private sector construction matters.

### Griffith Nixon Davison, PC

**THE FIRM** This construction boutique continues to make significant strides in the industry and garners particular praise for its strengths in handling complex litigation, as well as mediation and arbitration. In one recent highlight the team has been representing AECOM in defending a claim over damage to a multifamily development, allegedly due to negligent design.

**Sources say:** *"As their client, I feel that they care about me and my business as if it was their own, and their commitment to remaining price-competitive is much appreciated." "Extremely valuable to have on our side."*

**KEY INDIVIDUALS** The *"very, very intelligent and extremely experienced"* **Scott Griffith** is regarded as *"a great* *leader with good vision and commitment.*" He has recently been representing PRA SE Construction in litigation concerning extensive water damage in an apartment complex, of which the client was the general contractor. **Kimberly Davison** is "*extremely well organized, and has a razor-sharp train of thought.*" Sources also appreciate her "*tough but very well-balanced*" approach to matters. Sources note that **Anthony Jach** is "*personable and a pleasure to work with,*" and especially highlight his "*impressive skills of recall and stellar judgment.*" He played a leading role in the AECOM matter and has also been working alongside Griffith in the PRA SE Construction litigation.

## Band 3

### Fisk & Fielder

**THE FIRM** This boutique is recognized for its expertise in insurance and civil defense litigation, with a core focus on construction litigation. The group regularly acts for a client base of engineers, contractors, subcontractors and architects.

**KEY INDIVIDUALS** **Hollye Fisk** maintains a highly regarded construction litigation practice and is singled out by commentators as "*very diligent and effective – he's always on top of things.*"

### Gardere Wynne Sewell LLP
See profile on p.2436

**THE FIRM** The construction group at Gardere Wynne Sewell offers the benefits of a boutique practice within the framework of a larger firm, providing a comprehensive legal service to a range of clients, including general contractors, home builders and alternative energy developers. Recently, the group has been acting on behalf of Museum Tower on the construction of a $180 million condominium skyscraper.

**Sources say:** "*They do a really good job of balancing legal issues with our business issues.*"

**KEY INDIVIDUALS** **Steven Henry** (see p.2395) wins praise from clients for possessing "*a keen business mind as well as a legal mind.*" Recent highlights include acting on behalf of EMJ Corporation. According to interviewees, **Gregory Harwell** (see p.2394) is "*an analytical machine,*" and he elicits further plaudits for his ability to "*take complex construction and design issues and distill them into layman terms.*" Recently he has been involved in work for Austin Industries.

### Haynes and Boone, LLP
See profile on p.444

**THE FIRM** This firm's construction practice works closely alongside its real estate group to provide a seamless service on related contentious matters. The team acts for a diverse mix of clients, including contractors, engineers and architects, handling disputes concerning shopping centers, hotels, pipelines and industrial complexes, among other matters.

**KEY INDIVIDUALS** **Bruce Merwin** has over three decades of experience in the industry, and in a recent highlight represented a developer in the construction and leasing of a multimillion-dollar medical complex, also handling the financing and land acquisition documentation.

### Jackson Walker LLP
See profile on p.2441

**THE FIRM** This construction practice acts for clients on all aspects of residential, public and commercial disputes, and provides legal services from a project's inception through to final completion. Recently, the team successfully defended GRI Preston Hollow, Glenbrook Residential and Guy E. Brignon in a $10 million lawsuit concerning construction defects on a luxury condominium development. Other key clients include Fort Worth Transportation Authority and RamJack Construction.

**Sources say:** "*All of the attorneys at Jackson Walker are extremely responsive – they promptly complete legal tasks and provide excellent customer service.*"

**KEY INDIVIDUALS** Sources note that **Michael Moran** (see p.2406) is an "*unbelievable trial attorney*" who has so much experience that he "*could be a tour guide for construction litigation.*" In addition to being part of the team acting for GRI Preston Hollow, Glenbrook Residential and Guy E. Brignon in the construction defects lawsuit, he has recently been involved in advising the Lower Colorado River Authority on a contract dispute.

### King & Spalding LLP
See profile on p.445

**THE FIRM** This firm's construction practice acts for developers, lenders and project owners on a state, national and international platform. The group has particular expertise in LNG projects and has been busy representing Anadarko in its multibillion-dollar LNG export facility in Mozambique. Other key clients include Duke Energy, Cheniere Energy and Exelon.

**Sources say:** "*They have a very high level of service and they're extremely responsive.*"

**KEY INDIVIDUALS** **Scott Greer** (see p.2392) leads the firm's construction practice, acting for developers and owners on a range of matters. He impresses clients particularly with his knowledge of LNG projects and his "*thorough and tireless*" approach to matters.

## Other Notable Practitioners

**Michael Albers** (see p.2377) at Hunton & Williams LLP represents developers, contractors, and public and private owners, in project acquisition, development and financing activities, as well as in dispute resolution. **Michael Johnson** (see p.2397) of Goins, Underkofler, Crawford & Langdon LLP is recognized for his strengths in construction litigation, while name partner **Paul Underkofler** is widely regarded for his mediation expertise. Capshaw & Associates's **Richard Capshaw** has a wealth of experience in litigation matters, representing owners, design professionals and contractors in both defense and prosecution. **Lee Haag** recently joined Reed Smith LLP from Fulbright & Jaworski. He is an experienced trial lawyer who often acts on cases concerning petrochemicals, energy and healthcare, in addition to construction-based disputes. He is "*a good strategist and very good at executing that strategy for his clients,*" a source notes. Houston-based sole practitioner **Gavin McGee** is noted for his expertise in litigation, arbitration and mediation. He is also well versed on the transaction side and is routinely called upon to advise on matters concerning construction and design defects. **Donald Pratt** of Pratt & Yungblut, PC has over 20 years of construction mediation experience, and has dealt with payment disputes, defective designs, delays and other operational problems. At the same firm, **Stephen Yungblut** represents owners, contractors and engineers, among others, utilizing his extensive experience in construction litigation and surety matters. **Stephen Miller** (see p.2405) of Jones Walker Waechter Poitevent Carrère & Denègre L.L.P. offers significant experience in energy and electrical power infrastructure project development and finance. The Gardner Law Firm's **William Sommers** practices extensively in construction, as well as commercial law. He often represents clients involved in complex, multiparty construction disputes. **Phillip Sampson** (see p.2414) of Bracewell & Giuliani LLP focuses on complex business and commercial litigation, with sources describing him as "*a very accomplished, intelligent and diligent attorney.*"

# CORPORATE/M&A

Commentary about individuals can be found under their firm's paragraph. If the firm has no paragraph (is not ranked) look at Other Notable Practitioners.

## Corporate/M&A
### Leading Firms

**Band 1**
Baker Botts LLP *
Vinson & Elkins LLP *

**Band 2**
Andrews Kurth LLP *
Latham & Watkins LLP *
Weil, Gotshal & Manges LLP *

**Band 3**
Bracewell & Giuliani LLP *
Gibson, Dunn & Crutcher LLP *
Haynes and Boone, LLP *
Jones Day *
Locke Lord LLP *
Thompson & Knight LLP *

**Band 4**
Akin Gump Strauss Hauer & Feld LLP *
Fulbright & Jaworski LLP *
Mayer Brown LLP *
Porter Hedges LLP *

**Band 5**
Gardere Wynne Sewell LLP *
Jackson Walker LLP *

\* Indicates firm / individual with profile.
†ONP = Other Notable Practitioner

## Corporate/M&A
### Senior Statesmen

**Senior Statesmen: distinguished older practitioners**

| | | |
|---|---|---|
| Boone Michael | Haynes and Boone, LLP | |
| Marston III Edgar J | Bracewell & Giuliani LLP * | |
| Schoenbrun Larry | Gardere Wynne Sewell LLP * | |

### Leading Individuals

**Star individuals**

| | |
|---|---|
| Chapman Jeffrey A | Gibson, Dunn & Crutcher LLP * |

**Band 1**

| | |
|---|---|
| Baker Andrew M | Baker Botts LLP * |
| Finnegan IV William N | Latham & Watkins LLP |
| Jewell Robert V | Andrews Kurth LLP * |
| Kelly T Mark | Vinson & Elkins LLP * |
| Kirkland David | Baker Botts LLP * |
| Massad Stephen A | Baker Botts LLP * |
| O'Leary Michael | Andrews Kurth LLP * |
| Tabor Jay | Weil, Gotshal & Manges LLP * |
| West Glenn D | Weil, Gotshal & Manges LLP * |
| Wortley Michael | Vinson & Elkins LLP * |
| Wulfe Scott | Vinson & Elkins LLP * |

**Band 2**

| | |
|---|---|
| Betzen Mark E | Jones Day * |
| Buck David | Andrews Kurth LLP * |
| Cohen R Scott | Jones Day * |
| Dillard Michael E | Latham & Watkins LLP |
| Gray Robert F | Mayer Brown LLP |
| Hainsfurther A Michael | Munsch Hardt Kopf & Harr, P.C. (ONP)† |
| Hettinger Glen | Fulbright & Jaworski LLP * |
| Korby Mary | K&L Gates (ONP)† * |
| LaFollette Christine B | Akin Gump Strauss Hauer & Feld LLP * |
| Lemon Neel | Baker Botts LLP * |
| Oelman David | Vinson & Elkins LLP * |
| Saslaw Michael A | Weil, Gotshal & Manges LLP * |
| Swanstrom Bill | Locke Lord LLP * |

**Band 3**

| | |
|---|---|
| Bayouth Frank E | Skadden, Arps, Slate, Meagher (ONP)† * |
| Conlon Michael W | Fulbright & Jaworski LLP * |
| Fullenweider Keith | Vinson & Elkins LLP * |

| | |
|---|---|
| Glendenning Don M | Locke Lord LLP * |
| Kimball Robert L | Vinson & Elkins LLP * |
| O'Bannon James E | Jones Day * |
| Oshman Gene | Baker Botts LLP |
| Paris Ted W | Baker Botts LLP * |
| Prince James M | Vinson & Elkins LLP * |
| Sharry Janice V | Haynes and Boone, LLP |
| Zlotky Jeffrey A | Thompson & Knight LLP * |

**Band 4**

| | |
|---|---|
| Asmus David | Morgan, Lewis & Bockius (ONP)† * |
| Blumrosen Eric A | Gardere Wynne Sewell LLP * |
| Bogdanow Alan J | Vinson & Elkins LLP * |
| Bopp Gregory M | Bracewell & Giuliani LLP * |
| Dahlson Richard | Jackson Walker LLP * |
| Floyd Jeffery B | Vinson & Elkins LLP * |
| Friedlander D Gilbert | Weil, Gotshal & Manges LLP * |
| Hall Lawrence A | Thompson & Knight LLP * |
| Lewis Troy B | Jones Day * |
| Little Robert B | Gibson, Dunn & Crutcher LLP * |
| Menges Kenneth | Akin Gump Strauss Hauer & Feld LLP * |
| Nathan Arthur M | Haynes and Boone, LLP * |
| Newton Geoff | Baker Botts LLP * |
| Orloff Gary W | Bracewell & Giuliani LLP * |
| Parker Dallas | Mayer Brown LLP * |
| Perkins Alan | Gardere Wynne Sewell LLP * |
| Reedy Robert | Porter Hedges LLP * |
| Rose Kelly Brunetti | Baker Botts LLP * |
| Telle Michael S | Bracewell & Giuliani LLP * |

**Up-and-coming individuals**

| | |
|---|---|
| Parel S Scott | Weil, Gotshal & Manges LLP * |
| Wheeler Sean T | Latham & Watkins LLP |

## Band 1

### Baker Botts LLP
See profile on p.2427

**THE FIRM** This team maintains a leading position in the Texas market, playing a significant role in some of the year's biggest transactions. Energy remains a dominant focus for the team, with technology-related transactions also featuring regularly on the deal list. Recent highlights include representing Pride International throughout its $8.7 billion acquisition by Ensco, reflecting the team's market-leading capabilities. Other high-profile clients include Marathon Oil and Halliburton.

**Sources say:** "*The firm has a strong group of lawyers in every practice area relevant to our business, and they are very responsive to our requests for assistance.*"

**KEY INDIVIDUALS** The "*very talented*" **Andrew Baker** (see p.2379) is identified by market observers as a well-known figure in the market. Based in the Houston office, he is the firm's managing partner and continues to serve a variety of public and private companies on corporate matters. **David Kirkland** (see p.2399) attracts praise for his "*outstanding*" practice. He recently led on the Pride acquisition, and has handled several matters for client Imperial Sugar Company over the past year. **Stephen Massad** (see p.2403) acted for Lazard as financial adviser to Progress Energy on its high-profile all-stock merger with Duke

Energy, a $13.7 billion transaction. Peers highlight **Neel Lemon** (see p.2401) as a "*really top-notch guy*" in this space. He has a broad practice advising investment banking and corporate clients on a range of issues. **Gene Oshman** represented StarTex Power in its $142.5 million acquisition by Constellation Energy. He is a highly experienced corporate attorney with knowledge of public offerings, securities offerings, M&A and corporate governance. **Ted Paris** (see p.2408) recently led the team acting for EP Energy on its $7.15 billion acquisition by Apollo Global Management. Well-respected **Geoff Newton** (see p.2407) is praised as "*a very smart attorney.*" He handles a healthy volume of work from private equity clients, especially from those funds focusing on the energy and real estate sectors.

**Kelly Rose** (see p.2413) is highly active in the market, with sources saying she is "*on the rise*" in this area.

### Vinson & Elkins LLP
See profile on p.2459

**THE FIRM** This firm has a long history in the state and distinguishes itself from competitors through its high-level representation of both private equity and public company clients. It has recently been deployed on a series of transactions for key client TPG Capital, including an acquisition of $1.25 billion of preferred interests in Chesapeake Cleveland-Tonkawa. The team's enviable client list also includes Duke Energy, Warburg Pincus and The Shaw Group.

Sources say: *"They have a commercial perspective, they know the energy space very well and they are able to get to the drivers of a question very effectively."*

KEY INDIVIDUALS Firm chairman **Mark Kelly** (see p.2399) has a robust reputation in the state, having served as counsel to clients in the region for many years. He has represented companies from a range of industries, including oil and gas, medical technology and investment banking. **Michael Wortley** (see p.2423) is regarded as a *"great guy and a good lawyer"* in the Texas market. His practice maintains a strong emphasis on representing private equity funds. Sources agree that **Scott Wulfe** (see p.2423) deserves to be recognized as a *"very fine lawyer."* He acted for Warburg Pincus on its joint investment, with several other private equity firms, of $1.125 billion in Venari Resources. Peers identify **David Oelman** (see p.2407) as a strong practitioner in this area. He has specific expertise in transactions within the exploration and production industry, which complements his broad knowledge of corporate and securities transactions. Sources are quick to highlight **Keith Fullenweider**'s (see p.2390) qualities, describing him as *"very commercial and very effective."* He is highly active in the Texas market and has spearheaded the team's work for TPG Capital over the past year. **Robert Kimball** (see p.2399) *"is one of the handful of lawyers you can call and ask any question and almost every time he will have the answer,"* according to an impressed interviewee. **James Prince** (see p.2411) is a long-standing figure in the Texas market and is highly capable of advising clients on the full spectrum of corporate and M&A matters, including joint ventures, private placements and secured financings. **Alan Bogdanow** (see p.2381) earns praise for his well-established practice based out of the firm's Dallas office. He has been involved in some of the state's most significant corporate financing and M&A transactions in his career. **Jeffery Floyd** (see p.2389) is recognized as being *"extremely responsive"* and able to *"cut through a lot of bureaucracy"* in order to achieve the best results for his clients.

## Band 2

### Andrews Kurth LLP
See profile on p.2426

THE FIRM This corporate team receives glowing endorsements from market sources, who highlight its hard-working approach. By virtue of its longstanding position in the state, the firm has developed highly productive relationships with key clients such as Apax Partners, Bridas and Trinity Hunt Partners. A recent highlight saw lawyers act as local counsel for Apax Partners on its $6.3 billion purchase of Kinetic Concepts.

Sources say: *"They are very thorough and offer outstanding service."*

KEY INDIVIDUALS **Robert Jewell** (see p.2397) is lauded by sources who *"respect and admire"* him as an attorney. He recently represented the Special Committee of DCP Midstream Partners in the $240 million purchase of an interest in DCP Southeast Texas Holdings. The *"outstanding"* **Michael O'Leary** (see p.2407) *"did whatever it took to*

meet deadlines and provide best legal advice,"* said one interviewee. He is further noted as being *"thorough,"* and for *"offering ways to get things done instead of offering roadblocks."* Sources highlight **David Buck**'s (see p.2383) strength in corporate and M&A matters, with one enthusiastic client saying: *"He focuses on doing the best deals possible."*

### Latham & Watkins LLP
See profile on p.446

THE FIRM Latham & Watkins has been building on its initial success in the Texas market, wasting no time in cultivating an impressive and diverse client base. The team is lauded by market observers for its energetic and proactive attitude, and is already enjoying a significantly increased market share. It recently acted for major client Energy Transfer Partners on the $5.3 billion acquisition of Sunoco. Other key clients include Red Leaf Resources and Suburban Propane Partners.

Sources say: *"Experienced attorneys who are responsive to our needs."* *"They are becoming an increasing factor in the marketplace and moving up rapidly."*

KEY INDIVIDUALS **William Finnegan** is renowned as a *"very fine lawyer."* He has handled much of the team's major work for Energy Transfer Partners over the past year, and continues to have a considerable impact on the Texas market. **Michael Dillard** has been deployed on several significant matters of late owing to his stellar reputation as an *"experienced M&A attorney."* Of particular note, he advised Red Leaf Resources on the formation of a $450 million joint venture with TOTAL E&P USA. **Sean Wheeler** enters the rankings following resounding endorsements from market observers for his *"really exceptional talent."* Suburban Propane Partners recently engaged his services as counsel on its $1.8 billion acquisition of Inergy Propane.

### Weil, Gotshal & Manges LLP
See profile on p.2015

THE FIRM Due to the firm's impressive global network, this team can call on considerable resources to support its clients in complex high-stakes transactions. It acted for the acquirer on one of the past year's largest Texas-based transactions, the $38 billion acquisition of El Paso by Kinder Morgan. The team also acts for significant players on the private equity side, and has an excellent reputation in that field.

Sources say: *"They are power players thanks to the sheer talent that exists there."*

KEY INDIVIDUALS Based in the firm's Dallas office, **Jay Tabor** (see p.2418) is very well reputed for his work in the corporate M&A space in Texas. He served as lead partner on Kinder Morgan's highly publicized acquisition of El Paso. The *"outstanding"* **Glenn West** (see p.2421) attracts praise for his robust and wide-ranging corporate practice. He recently advised the Special Committee of the Board of Directors of Continental Resources on the company's $340 million acquisition of Wheatland Oil's oil assets. **Michael Saslaw** (see p.2414) and **Gilbert Friedlander** (see p.2389) are both highlighted by interviewees as talented attorneys in the sphere. Saslaw recently handled two strategic acqui-

sitions for Trimble Navigation, including the $235 million purchase of PeopleNet Communications. Friedlander maintains a strong practice on the corporate governance side. **Scott Parel** (see p.2408) has cultivated a standout practice in this area, representing key client OMERS Private Equity throughout its purchase of GEDC Super Holdings from Audax Private Equity.

## Band 3

### Bracewell & Giuliani LLP
See profile on p.2429

THE FIRM Buoyant levels of transactional activity in the energy sector have generated a significant amount of work for the team at Bracewell & Giuliani of late. Lawyers here represented longstanding client Kinder Morgan in its acquisition of El Paso, and have further demonstrated their prowess in mergers, joint ventures and private equity investments through a diverse series of transactions.

Sources say: *"We're very happy with the support they provide."* *"They are fantastic in Houston."*

KEY INDIVIDUALS **Gregory Bopp** (see p.2381) cochairs the department and was a major player in the Kinder Morgan acquisition. He has lately guided several other clients through complicated corporate deals, including Evercore Partners and Apache Corporation. **Gary Orloff** (see p.2408) demonstrates strong proficiency in M&A through his representation of Encore Energy Partners in its $544.8 million sale to Vanguard Natural Resources. **Michael Telle** (see p.2419) possesses a strong grasp of corporate and securities issues, and has particular experience advising energy clients on both the public and private side. Rightly recognized for his distinguished reputation, **Edgar Marston** (see p.2403) has a wealth of experience in the corporate arena.

### Gibson, Dunn & Crutcher LLP
See profile on p.682

THE FIRM This firm has made great strides in the Texas market over the past year, combining a strong energy sector focus with broad capabilities in all aspects of corporate and M&A work. In a highly publicized transaction, lawyers acted for American Airlines on the multibillion-dollar purchase of 260 aircraft from Airbus in 2011. Other clients include Energy Future Holdings, Lone Star US Acquisitions and EXCO Resources.

Sources say: *"They have vast experience with a diverse client base and in so many different arenas. They have creativity and sophistication."*

KEY INDIVIDUALS The *"responsive and creative"* **Jeffrey Chapman** (see p.2384) is elevated in the rankings this year, having received extensive positive feedback from peers and clients alike. *"He makes certain that the team takes care of the client. As a counselor he is unmatched in both business and legal terms, at all levels,"* enthuses one impressed source. **Robert Little** (see p.2401) has also attracted a raft of glowing comments, with one interviewee noting: *"He is very personable and one of the best lawyers I've seen in negotiations at keeping the relationship with the other side good.*

*He is a fantastic lawyer with great commercial and interpersonal skills."*

## Haynes and Boone, LLP
See profile on p.444

**THE FIRM** This highly acclaimed practice has had a strong presence in Texas for many years, and consistently handles sophisticated and high-value matters for clients. Recent highlights have included advising Wingate Partners on its disposal of Industrial Container Services, and representing watchmaker Fossil in its $225 million acquisition of Skagen Design. Clients benefit from the input and support of other strong departments within the firm, including bankruptcy and tax.

**Sources say:** *"Very creative, thoughtful, practical and effective legal advisers."*

**KEY INDIVIDUALS** **Janice Sharry** is described as *"a brilliantly gifted corporate lawyer and a strategic thinker who can think in three or four dimensions at the same time."* She has a broad corporate finance practice and can draw on considerable experience when advising clients. **Arthur Nathan** is a founder member of the Houston office and has cultivated a diverse practice. He can advise on business owner and shareholder disputes, alongside transactional matters. By virtue of his long-standing reputation in the state, **Michael Boone** is held in high esteem by peers and is consistently recognized as an excellent attorney by market observers.

## Jones Day
See profile on p.919

**THE FIRM** Lawyers at Jones Day have proved adept at utilizing the firm's impressive global footprint to attract some of the most high-profile mandates in the region. The team's extensive clientele is drawn from a broad range of industries, and includes Texas Instruments, Chesapeake Midstream Partners and PepsiCo. Recently, the team guided Samson Investment through its acquisition by an investment group led by KKR, a $7.2 billion deal.

**Sources say:** *"They are extremely bright lawyers who are down to earth and service-oriented."*

**KEY INDIVIDUALS** *"Business-savvy and practical,"* **Scott Cohen** (see p.2385) has received much enthusiastic praise, with one interviewee declaring him to be *"the most intelligent, practical lawyer I know. He brings the voice of reason to every situation and is my go-to lawyer for any question I have, regardless of the practice area."* **Mark Betzen** (see p.2381) recently advised the Special Committee of the Board of Directors of EXCO Resources on a proposed $4.4 billion buyout offer. He is lauded as a *"fine technical lawyer."* **James O'Bannon** (see p.2407) has been highly active of late for several of the firm's key clients in this area. One highlight saw him engaged by Sprint Nextel to advise on a $4 billion note issue. **Troy Lewis** (see p.2401) has wide-ranging knowledge of M&A transactions and is a longstanding and respected member of the firm. He spearheaded the team guiding The Weir Group through its $675 million purchase of Seaboard Holdings.

## Locke Lord LLP
See profile on p.2443

**THE FIRM** Locke Lord has a strong track record in the state for corporate and M&A work. Continuing to focus on the energy sector, the team recently acted for El Paso during its $7.15 billion sale of EP Energy to a group of private equity companies, demonstrating its ability to seamlessly integrate with other departments in the firm, including tax, environment and ERISA.

**Sources say:** *"A very, very fine regional firm."*

**KEY INDIVIDUALS** Sources agree that **Bill Swanstrom** (see p.2418) is a *"very good lawyer"* in this area, and particularly highlight his skill on the private equity side. In a busy year, he has acted for numerous clients from the energy industry, including representing The Energy & Minerals Group in its disposal of a joint venture interest for $2 billion. **Don Glendenning** (see p.2391) led the team acting for Southern Union on its $9.7 billion merger with Energy Transfer Equity, having previously acted for Southern Union on its equity valuation agreement.

## Thompson & Knight LLP
See profile on p.2458

**THE FIRM** This team serves as counsel to some of the state's most active energy clients, including Halcón Resources and Noble Energy, and impresses market observers with its coverage of the sector. In a major recent transaction, it represented Brigham Exploration in its sale to Statoil ASA for an equity value of some $4.4 billion. Thompson & Knight's corporate team is highly capable of acting on both a domestic and cross-border basis in M&A transactions, and also has excellent practical experience of private equity matters.

**Sources say:** *"Detail-oriented, focused lawyers."*

**KEY INDIVIDUALS** **Jeffrey Zlotky** (see p.2424) has *"made quite a mark recently and he's very well regarded,"* say interviewees. His private equity experience makes him an excellent choice for clients considering investment transactions, mergers, acquisitions or dispositions. **Lawrence Hall** (see p.2393) continues to concentrate his practice largely on representing oil and gas companies, and has proved very capable of handling a broad range of transactions on their behalf.

## Band 4

### Akin Gump Strauss Hauer & Feld LLP
See profile on p.904

**THE FIRM** This highly reputed team is well versed in all aspects of corporate and securities law, and has particular knowledge of debt financing transactions. Attorneys here are consistently recognized for their responsiveness and ability to view deals from a business perspective. The team recently advised Wexford Capital on the sale of Great White Energy Services to Archer Limited, a $630 million transaction.

**Sources say:** *"They're very responsive and very quick."*

**KEY INDIVIDUALS** Sources appreciate **Christine LaFollette's** (see p.2400) *"wonderful"* leadership of the corporate practice. She recently assisted energy client Laredo Petroleum with its $1 billion acquisition of Broad Oak Energy. **Kenneth Menges** is a talented corporate governance practitioner and is also able to guide clients through M&A transactions on both a cross-border and domestic basis.

## Fulbright & Jaworski LLP
See profile on p.2435

**THE FIRM** Fulbright & Jaworski is acknowledged as having a robust presence in the region, with three offices across Texas handling significant levels of corporate and M&A work. Attorneys frequently coordinate matters across domestic and international offices, and can adopt an interdepartmental approach to assist clients. A recent highlight saw the team engaged by Brinks Home Security on its $2 billion sale to Tyco International.

**KEY INDIVIDUALS** Interviewees identify **Glen Hettinger** (see p.2395) as a *"great guy."* He played a key role in the team acting for Highland Bancshares on its merger with Viewpoint Financial Group, and maintains a wide-ranging corporate practice. **Michael Conlon** (see p.2385) receives accolades from peers for his work in M&A and corporate finance transactions. He has a wealth of experience in the area and has represented clients from a variety of industries, including manufacturing, energy and retail.

## Mayer Brown LLP
See profile on p.1257

**THE FIRM** This international powerhouse continues to attract high-quality mandates from clients in the energy sector, and is praised for its extensive knowledge and experience in this area. The team assists high-profile clients such as Talos Energy, NGP Capital Resources and Halliburton with corporate and M&A matters.

**Sources say:** *"They really helped manage negotiations with the buyers."*

**KEY INDIVIDUALS** Sources are *"very impressed"* by **Robert Gray's** performance. He recently acted for Sumitomo during the purchase by its subsidiaries of a minority interest in a manufacturing company. **Dallas Parker** represented SK Energy in its $2.4 billion sale of SK do Brasilia, coordinating closely with Mayer Brown's associated firm in Brazil on the cross-border detail.

## Porter Hedges LLP
See profile on p.2450

**THE FIRM** Porter Hedges maintains a highly visible presence throughout the state from its Houston base, representing both public and private companies in a range of corporate transactions and across many industries. In the past year, attorneys have acted for Noble Energy on forming a significant $3.4 billion joint venture with CONSOL Energy, in order to establish a presence in the vibrant Marcellus Shale.

**KEY INDIVIDUALS** Several interviewees highlight **Robert Reedy** (see p.2412) as a key figure in this space. He is the managing partner of the firm and maintains an active practice advising both emerging private companies and public companies on a range of corporate matters.

## Band 5

### Gardere Wynne Sewell LLP
See profile on p.2436

**THE FIRM** Consistently recognized as a solid player in Texas, this firm has recently handled a considerable amount of corporate work for BP America, including the $1.2 billion sale of Hugoton Assets to Linn Energy, and the $575 million sale of Wattenberg Gas Plant to Anadarko Petroleum. The team is renowned for its ability to develop and maintain close working relationships with its clients.
**Sources say:** *"They provide extremely good negotiating support in transactions."*
**KEY INDIVIDUALS Eric Blumrosen** (see p.2381) has forged a reputation as an *"extremely versatile"* lawyer. He has considerable experience in a broad spectrum of corporate, securities and private equity matters. Sources note that **Alan Perkins** (see p.2410) consistently *"does a remarkably good job"* for his clients. He has a strong track record on M&A transactions. **Larry Schoenbrun** (see p.2415) deserves continued recognition, according to market

observers. For more than 40 years he has been a trusted adviser to numerous medium and large corporations.

### Jackson Walker LLP
See profile on p.2441

**THE FIRM** A new entrant to the rankings this year, Jackson Walker has long been a presence in the state and has been highly visible in the market of late. The team has handled healthy levels of cross-border work, and regularly assists investment fund clients with M&A matters. Notable recent transactions include acting for the Teacher Retirement System of Texas in a major series of investments, and for Exelon on its $305 million purchase of Wolf Hollow power plant.
**Sources say:** *"What I like best is that they are good business attorneys. They don't throw up obstacles that keep you from completing deals – they try to help you solve problems."*
**KEY INDIVIDUALS Richard Dahlson** (see p.2386) leads the corporate and securities group at Jackson Walker and has built a strong practice, focusing particularly on emerging growth companies and the technology and telecom industries.

### Other Notable Practitioners

The *"very smart, analytical and practical"* **Michael Hainsfurther** of Munsch Hardt Kopf & Harr, P.C. is praised for his *"really professional"* approach to M&A matters. *"He is extremely responsive. He is always very much our advocate and does whatever it takes to meet our needs,"* adds one impressed source. **Frank Bayouth** (see p.2380) is based in the Houston office of Skadden, Arps, Slate, Meagher & Flom LLP & Affiliates. He has been highly active on significant transactions of late, including advising JPMorgan as financial adviser to AmeriGas on its $2.4 billion acquisition of a propane distribution business. An *"experienced attorney with a great deal of knowledge,"* **David Asmus** (see p.274) of Morgan, Lewis & Bockius LLP is *"a real force of nature in terms of his expertise,"* according to sources. **Mary Korby** (see p.2399) recently joined K&L Gates from Weil, Gotshal & Manges. She is a recognized figure in the Texas market and is commended for consistently having her *"ear to the ground"* and being well informed on market trends.

# ENERGY STATE REGULATORY & LITIGATION

State Regulatory & Litigation (Oil & Gas) p.2341
Commentary about individuals can be found under their firm's paragraph. If the firm has no paragraph (is not ranked) look at Other Notable Practitioners.

| Energy: State Regulatory & Litigation (Electricity) |
| --- |
| **Leading Firms** |
| **Band 1** |
| Andrews Kurth LLP * |
| Baker Botts LLP * |
| Duggins Wren Mann & Romero, LLP |
| Lloyd Gosselink Rochelle & Townsend, P.C. |
| Vinson & Elkins LLP * |
| **Band 2** |
| Brown McCarroll, L.L.P. * |
| Haynes and Boone, LLP * |
| Jackson Walker LLP * |
| Parsley Coffin Renner, LLP |
| **Band 3** |
| Bracewell & Giuliani LLP * |
| Sutherland Asbill & Brennan LLP |

\* Indicates firm with profile.
Alphabetical order within each band. Band 1 is the highest.

*The editorial is in alphabetical order by firm name.*

### Andrews Kurth LLP
See profile on p.2426

**THE FIRM** This prestigious and highly regarded 12-strong team offers one of the deepest benches in the Texas energy sphere. It handles work for clients of the caliber of Texas Industrial Energy Consumers, a trade association comprising the 40 largest commercial energy users in the state. The team's widespread representation of this group includes

matters before the Public Utility Commission of Texas (PUCT) relating to a variety of contested rate proceedings.
**Sources say:** *"They know the law and the regulatory issues. They have good connections that are effective when they work with the regulators. They have a great track record."*
**KEY INDIVIDUALS Lino Mendiola** (see p.2405) is an expert litigator who handles commercial and public law cases. He has a deep knowledge of electricity litigation and is an acknowledged authority on electric utility law. Sources relate that he is *"on top of the issues,"* with one client appreciating that he *"anticipates my interests and needs."* **Rex VanMiddlesworth** (see p.2419) is a renowned courtroom lawyer whose practice also includes administrative law and alternative dispute resolution. He is particularly known for his work in electric rate cases, and regularly represents clients before the PUCT. **Tammy Cooper** (see p.2386) concentrates her practice on representing large industrial energy consumers, and is recognized for her work with landowner clients in transmission line routing cases before the PUCT. Sources note that she is *"diligent and thorough,"* and that she is *"always well prepared and knowledgeable in electrical regulatory law."* **Phillip Oldham** (see p.2407) is at the *"top in his field"* for power and energy issues, according to impressed sources. He is a noted lobbyist who regularly provides strategic counseling to clients. As one source sums up, *"this guy hits it out of the park every time for us."*

### Baker Botts LLP
See profile on p.2427

**THE FIRM** This experienced team continues to operate at the high end of the market, and is noted for its representation of industry giant CenterPoint Energy in cases before both the PUCT and the Texas State Court. The group also successfully represented Marathon GTF in a high-value breach of contract dispute before the Delaware Chancery Court.
**KEY INDIVIDUALS James Barkley** concentrates on representing public utilities in matters ranging from smart meters to contested rate cases. He is praised for his *"extremely deep knowledge of state regulation."* **William Kroger** is a highly regarded litigator with a focus on regulatory matters. Clients praise his *"excellent rate-setting skills"* and his *"ability to walk us through the process and plan what's needed."* He was lead partner in a recent nuisance case involving a wind farm for BP Alternative Energy North America.

### Bracewell & Giuliani LLP
See profile on p.2429

**THE FIRM** The Bracewell & Giuliani energy team represents clients in matters involving power generation regulation, licensing and rate cases. It has extensive experience acting for public, investor-owned and independent power entities in Texas. Clients include American Electric Power.
**KEY INDIVIDUALS Phil Ricketts** (see p.2412) is highly experienced in dealing with electric utility regulatory matters. Recent highlights include assisting Southwestern Electric Power in a PUCT application to increase rates.

*The editorial is in alphabetical order by firm name.*

## Energy: State Regulatory & Litigation (Electricity)

### Leading Individuals

**Band 1**

| | |
|---|---|
| Barkley James | *Baker Botts LLP* |
| Baron Steven | *Steven Baron Consulting (ONP)*[†] |
| Carroll Marianne | *Brown McCarroll, L.L.P.* |
| Liebmann Diana | *Haynes and Boone, LLP* |
| Mendiola III Lino | *Andrews Kurth LLP* * |
| Moss Ron H | *Winstead PC* * |
| Ricketts Phil F | *Bracewell & Giuliani LLP* * |
| Tomsu Michael | *Vinson & Elkins LLP* * |
| VanMiddlesworth Rex D | *Andrews Kurth LLP* * |
| Wren William C | *Duggins Wren Mann & Romero, LLP* |

**Band 2**

| | |
|---|---|
| Adams Richard | *Vinson & Elkins LLP* * |
| Arnold John K | *Winstead PC* * |
| Brocato Thomas L. | *Lloyd Gosselink Rochelle & Townsend, P.C.* |
| Cooper Tammy | *Andrews Kurth LLP* * |
| Cowlishaw Patrick R | *Jackson Walker LLP* * |
| Duggins David C. | *Duggins Wren Mann & Romero, LLP* |
| Gay Geoffrey M | *Lloyd Gosselink Rochelle & Townsend, P.C.* |
| Henry Matthew C | *Vinson & Elkins LLP* * |
| Kroger William | *Baker Botts LLP* |
| LaValle Kathleen | *Jackson Walker LLP* * |
| McGrath Kerry | *Duggins Wren Mann & Romero, LLP* |
| Noland Richard P | *Sutherland Asbill & Brennan LLP* |
| Oldham Phillip G | *Andrews Kurth LLP* * |
| Parsley Julie | *Parsley Coffin Renner, LLP* * |
| Sullivan Patrick J. | *Haynes and Boone, LLP* |
| Townsend Lambeth | *Lloyd Gosselink Rochelle & Townsend, P.C.* |
| Webking Catherine | *Gardere Wynne Sewell LLP (ONP)*[†] * |

**Up-and-coming individuals**

| | |
|---|---|
| Brewster Christopher L. | *Lloyd Gosselink Rochelle & Townsend* |

**Associates to watch**

| | |
|---|---|
| Diffen Becky H | *Vinson & Elkins LLP* * |

## Brown McCarroll, L.L.P.
**See profile on p.2430**

**THE FIRM** This compact team is adept at representing clients before bodies such as the PUCT and the Electric Reliability Council of Texas (ERCOT). Recent highlights for the team include obtaining certification from the PUCT on behalf of Source Power & Gas. Other clients include Exelon, Calpine, BP Wind Energy and Shell Energy.

**Sources say:** *"For me, it is the firm's responsiveness and practicality that make it stand out."*

**KEY INDIVIDUALS** Marianne Carroll helps clients in rulemaking proceedings and contested cases before the PUCT. She was lead partner for the team's recent work for Exelon during its acquisition of Constellation Energy, with work including due diligence analysis and post-merger compliance activities.

## Duggins Wren Mann & Romero, LLP

**THE FIRM** With significant expertise in both electricity and oil and gas, this team covers the gamut of energy regulatory needs in Texas. The team represents many electric

## Energy: State Regulatory & Litigation (Oil & Gas)

### Leading Firms

**Band 1**
Duggins Wren Mann & Romero, LLP
McElroy, Sullivan & Miller LLP
McGinnis Lochridge & Kilgore LLP
Parsley Coffin Renner, LLP
Scott, Douglass & McConnico LLP

**Band 2**
Jackson, Sjoberg, McCarthy & Wilson, LLP
Lloyd Gosselink Rochelle & Townsend, P.C.

**Band 3**
Winstead PC *

### Leading Individuals

**Band 1**

| | |
|---|---|
| Coffin Ann M | *Parsley Coffin Renner, LLP* * |
| George Tim | *McGinnis Lochridge & Kilgore LLP* |
| Mann James E | *Duggins Wren Mann & Romero, LLP* |
| Nielson Jamie | *Jamie Nielson Attorney At Law (ONP)*[†] |
| Sullivan, P.E. Brian R | *McElroy, Sullivan & Miller LLP* |
| Whitworth H. Philip | *Scott, Douglass & McConnico LLP* |

**Band 2**

| | |
|---|---|
| Camp John W | *Scott, Douglass & McConnico LLP* |
| Gay Geoffrey M | *Lloyd Gosselink Rochelle & Townsend, P.C.* |
| Jackson David | *Jackson, Sjoberg, McCarthy & Wilson, LLP* |
| Johnson Glenn E | *Kelly Hart & Hallman LLP (ONP)*[†] |
| Osborn William Sheffield | *Osborn & Griffith (ONP)*[†] |

\* *Indicates firm / individual with profile.*
[†] *ONP = Other Notable Practitioner*

companies, including both regulated and unregulated utilities. On the oil and gas side it has earned a sensational reputation for its work on pipelines and regularly represents clients before the FERC and the Texas Commission on Environmental Quality (TCEQ).

**KEY INDIVIDUALS** Leading natural gas lawyer **James Mann** is highly regarded for his work relating to midstream and interstate pipelines. He is also a recognized expert in eminent domain issues. **Casey Wren** maintains a broad practice, which encompasses both the electricity and natural gas spheres. He has extensive experience of representing clients in front of the PUCT and the Railroad Commission of Texas (RRC). **David Duggins** is an experienced appellate lawyer who frequently helps clients in hearings and appeals covering all aspects of civil law. **Kerry McGrath** represents clients, typically electric utilities, in litigation matters such as regulatory, trial and appellate proceedings. He frequently appears before the PUCT in cases ranging from the formation of joint venture transmission companies to contesting competition transition charges.

## Haynes and Boone, LLP
**See profile on p.444**

**THE FIRM** This firm's energy practice group is noted for its electric power regulatory compliance work before bodies such as the PUCT and ERCOT. The team has appeared before ERCOT for a variety of clients recently, and advised

Hill Country Wind Power on regulatory approvals for operating as a retail electric provider. Other clients include ConocoPhillips and EDP Renewables.

**Sources say:** *"We appreciate their professionalism, their quick turnaround times, and the thoroughness of their analysis."*

**KEY INDIVIDUALS Diana Liebmann**'s practice encompasses both transactional and regulatory work. She is *"incredibly thorough and precise in her understanding of the law,"* say clients. She led the team on the Hill Country Wind Power matter. **Patrick Sullivan** advises clients on state and federal regulatory requirements. He was recently involved with the team's work for Fulcrum Retail Holdings, successfully helping the client obtain PUCT approval for the sale of two retail electric providers.

## Jackson, Sjoberg, McCarthy & Wilson, LLP

**THE FIRM** This seven-member firm is noted for its representation of oil and gas clients in contentious matters before the state. Areas of expertise include operating agreement disputes, landowner/producer disputes, and lease and royalty disputes. The team also handles permitting and compliance matters before regulatory bodies such as the RRC.

**KEY INDIVIDUALS David Jackson** maintains a broad oil and gas practice with a focus on real estate and transactional matters before the RRC.

## Jackson Walker LLP
**See profile on p.2441**

**THE FIRM** This compact and experienced team assists clients before the PUCT and ERCOT in a variety of litigation matters. It acts for electric power clients such as transmission and distribution utilities, landowners and power generation companies. Recent matters include representing E.ON Climate & Renewables in a state court dispute with Direct Energy concerning Production Tax Credits.

**Sources say:** *"Jackson Walker gives us great, great service in Texas."*

**KEY INDIVIDUALS Patrick Cowlishaw** (see p.2386) assists clients in contested proceedings before the PUCT and ERCOT. He was recently lead counsel for RES America Developments in PUCT proceedings to develop Competitive Renewable Energy Zones and improve transmission infrastructure. **Kathleen LaValle** (see p.2401) is noted for her skill in high-stakes energy litigation. Recent highlights include leading the team in the E.ON Climate & Renewables matter.

## Lloyd Gosselink Rochelle & Townsend, P.C.

**THE FIRM** This team is highly regarded for its representation of clients before the PUCT, the TCEQ and the RRC. It is particularly strong in the electricity arena, but is also widely noted for its work with the oil and gas industries. The firm is particularly well known for its representation of municipalities as consumers of energy.

**Sources say:** *"It is the go-to municipal representation firm."*

**KEY INDIVIDUALS Thomas Brocato** focuses on representing municipalities in matters that involve electric power or natural gas utilities. **Geoffrey Gay** is chair of the

*The editorial is in alphabetical order by firm name.*

energy and utility practice group, and advises both cities and coalitions of local governments on issues dealing with franchises, energy and utilities. **Lambeth Townsend** maintains a broad practice covering all types of utilities. He is experienced before state and federal courts and administrative tribunals. **Christopher Brewster** is frequently seen in front of the PUCT, where he primarily represents city coalitions. He is praised for his litigation skills and is *"thoughtful and moderate in his opinion,"* with sources noting that *"he represents his clients very effectively."*

## McElroy, Sullivan & Miller LLP

**THE FIRM** This Austin-based group has an outstanding reputation for its work pertaining to regulation, litigation and transactions. The team counsels clients in a wide array of matters, including natural gas storage, land use and surveying disputes and carbon sequestration.

**Sources say:** *"A leading firm with great lawyers."*

**KEY INDIVIDUALS Brian Sullivan** is an experienced oil and gas attorney who *"is just outstanding,"* according to impressed sources. He is particularly recognized in regulatory and litigation matters.

## McGinnis Lochridge & Kilgore LLP

**THE FIRM** This venerable Texan firm has offices in both Austin and Houston, and advises clients on arbitration, litigation and dispute resolution in the energy arena. The team is particularly well regarded for its work with the oil and gas industry.

**KEY INDIVIDUALS Tim George** is *"a very prominent individual"* with his *"finger on the pulse,"* according to industry observers. He is highly regarded for his representation of clients before the RRC.

## Parsley Coffin Renner, LLP

**THE FIRM** This young firm is now well established as one of the state's top boutiques for utilities work. The small team is noted for the depth of its regulatory agency experience and the strength of its relationships with agency professionals, and counts many of the state's largest gas and electric utilities among its clients.

**KEY INDIVIDUALS Ann Coffin** (see p.2385) is *"one of the finest practitioners in this area,"* reveal impressed interviewees. She represents both gas and electric utilities. **Julie Parsley** (see p.2409) concentrates her practice on representing electric utilities, and is noted for her past experience as a commissioner at the PUCT.

## Scott, Douglass & McConnico LLP

**THE FIRM** This esteemed firm has a long history in oil and gas work, frequently representing clients before state and federal court and regulatory bodies such as the RRC. The team assists clients in a wide variety of matters, including claims relating to operation, exploration and regulation.

**Sources say:** *"They have a great cadre of people."*

**KEY INDIVIDUALS Philip Whitworth** is highly respected for his deep experience on all issues relating to the litigation and regulation of oil and gas utilities. Sources confirm that he is *"a great name"* in the energy arena. **John Camp** is also highly rated for his work pertaining to oil and gas. Areas of focus include pipeline-to-pipeline rate charges, pipeline safety matters and service disputes.

## Sutherland Asbill & Brennan LLP

**THE FIRM** This group is noted for its representation of electric power clients in a variety of issues, including rate restructuring, certification and complaint proceedings before the PUCT and ERCOT. Clients include Sharyland Utilities.

**KEY INDIVIDUALS Richard Noland** continues to represent key client Sharyland Utilities in a range of regulatory matters. Other clients include power marketers, independent power producers and retail electric providers.

## Vinson & Elkins LLP

### See profile on p.2459

**THE FIRM** This firm is a potent force in the Texas market, and is best known for its work on behalf of electric utilities. The team acts for clients in rate-making cases, and rule-making and transmission line certification proceedings, among others. It continues to represent key client Oncor in a variety of matters, including disputes involving interconnections.

**KEY INDIVIDUALS Michael Tomsu** (see p.2419) is well respected for his work following the deregulation of electric utilities in Texas. Clients remark: *"He is brilliant in terms of both legal representation and the integrity that he brings to his practice."* **Richard Adams** (see p.2377) is *"a wonderful appellate lawyer,"* say sources. He counsels clients on a variety of matters, ranging from regulatory issues arising from M&A to antitrust matters. He is described as *"a pragmatic attorney with amazing business sense."* **Matt Henry** (see p.2395) anchors the firm's relationship with Oncor. He *"is very bright and knowledgeable,*

*and has excellent litigation skills,"* according to sources. His recent highlights include successfully defending an appeal in front of the PUCT on behalf of Energy Future Holdings. Associate **Becky Diffen** (see p.2387) has a burgeoning practice counseling clients on Texan regulatory law. She played a key role in advising Duke Energy on compliance with PUCT protocols.

## Winstead PC

### See profile on p.2460

**THE FIRM** This team is recognized for its expertise in regulatory and litigious matters. It regularly handles disputes concerning hydraulic fracking, condemnation and eminent domain as well as regulatory matters. Clients include the Texas Oil and Gas Association, Devon Energy Production and XTO Energy.

**KEY INDIVIDUALS Ron Moss** (see p.2406) is a renowned litigator and regulatory compliance counselor. He was part of the team representing new service provider SiEnergy in its bid to attain approval for natural gas distribution systems in Texas. **John Arnold** (see p.2378) assists clients in litigation, compliance and enforcement matters. One impressed source relates that he *"is one of the best lawyers I have ever had the pleasure to work with."*

## Other Notable Practitioners

**Steven Baron** of Steven Baron Consulting & Legal Services is a significant player in the electric utilities regulatory sector. He offers clients a long history of experience with state and federal regulatory agencies. **Jamie Nielson** of Jamie Nielson Attorney At Law is well known for his work before the RRC. Sources note that he is *"very well known in the litigation arena."* **William Osborn** of Osborn & Griffith is praised by sources as a *"deep thinker."* He assists oil and gas clients in regulatory proceedings before the RRC. **Catherine Webking** (see p.2421) of Gardere Wynne Sewell LLP advises electric utility clients on their state regulatory needs. She is highly regarded for her work in rerouting and rate setting cases, and is described by one grateful client as *"a trusted and needed resource for us."* **Glenn Johnson** of Kelly Hart & Hallman LLP is an experienced litigator who frequently appears before the RRC in cases involving oil and gas development and pipeline regulations.

# ENVIRONMENT

Commentary about individuals can be found under their firm's paragraph. If the firm has no paragraph (is not ranked) look at Other Notable Practitioners.

## Environment
### Leading Firms

**Band 1**
Baker Botts LLP *
Vinson & Elkins LLP *

**Band 2**
Bracewell & Giuliani LLP *
Brown McCarroll, L.L.P. *
Fulbright & Jaworski LLP *
Guida, Slavich & Flores, P.C.
Haynes and Boone, LLP *
Locke Lord LLP *
Thompson & Knight LLP *

**Band 3**
Kelly Hart & Hallman LLP
Lloyd Gosselink Rochelle & Townsend, P.C.
Winstead PC *

**Band 4**
Andrews Kurth LLP *
Beveridge & Diamond PC *
Connelly Baker Wotring LLP
Gardere Wynne Sewell LLP *
Jackson Walker LLP *
King & Spalding LLP *
Pillsbury Winthrop Shaw Pittman LLP *
Porter Hedges LLP *

\* Indicates firm / individual with profile.
† ONP = Other Notable Practitioner

## Environment
### Leading Individuals

**Star individuals**

| | |
|---|---|
| Civins Jeff | Haynes and Boone, LLP |
| Dinkins Carol | Vinson & Elkins LLP * |
| Giblin Pamela | Baker Botts LLP * |

**Band 1**

| | |
|---|---|
| Braddock James D | Haynes and Boone, LLP |
| Burgin Sara | Baker Botts LLP * |
| Cagle Molly | Baker Botts LLP * |
| Finn Braddock Patricia | Fulbright & Jaworski LLP * |
| Fromm O'Brien Eva | Fulbright & Jaworski LLP * |
| Morriss III James C | Thompson & Knight LLP * |

**Band 2**

| | |
|---|---|
| Amandes Christopher B | Morgan, Lewis & Bockius LLP (ONP)† |
| Axe Albert | Winstead PC * |
| Baker Debra | Connelly Baker Wotring LLP |
| Connelly Michael | Connelly Baker Wotring LLP |
| Faulk Richard O | Gardere Wynne Sewell LLP * |
| Groten Eric | Vinson & Elkins LLP * |
| Guida Joseph | Guida, Slavich & Flores, P.C. |
| Harris James B | Thompson & Knight LLP * |
| Higdon Gerald D | Locke Lord LLP * |
| Hopson Keith | Brown McCarroll, L.L.P. |
| Johnson Rodman C | Brown McCarroll, L.L.P. |
| Kuryla Matthew | Baker Botts LLP * |
| Mattox Sharon | Vinson & Elkins LLP * |
| McDonald Derek | Baker Botts LLP * |
| Nettles Larry | Vinson & Elkins LLP * |
| Phillips Frances E | Gardere Wynne Sewell LLP * |
| Ramirez Kenneth R | Law Offices of Ken Ramirez (ONP)† |
| Seals Paul | Guida, Slavich & Flores, P.C. |
| Slavich John | Guida, Slavich & Flores, P.C. |
| Smith James E | Porter Hedges LLP * |
| Wilkins Timothy A | Bracewell & Giuliani LLP * |
| Worrell Danny | Brown McCarroll, L.L.P. |

**Band 3**

| | |
|---|---|
| Bell Christopher L | Sidley Austin LLP (ONP)† * |

| | |
|---|---|
| Bishop Cynthia J | C Bishop Law PC (ONP)† |
| Bohannon Paul | Andrews Kurth LLP * |
| Chernekoff Michael A | Jones Walker LLP (ONP)† * |
| Courtney Keith | Winstead PC * |
| Deatherage Scott D | Gardere Wynne Sewell LLP * |
| Eldridge John R | Haynes and Boone, LLP |
| Keane Jennifer | Baker Botts LLP * |
| Lewis Edward | Fulbright & Jaworski LLP * |
| Mack Elizabeth E | Locke Lord LLP * |
| Mendoza Mary S | Haynes and Boone, LLP |
| Pels Gerald J | Locke Lord LLP * |
| Ross Jerry W | Pillsbury Winthrop Shaw Pittman LLP * |
| Schick Robert M | Vinson & Elkins LLP * |
| Shelton Lisa | Andrews Kurth LLP * |
| Stewart Robert | Kelly Hart & Hallman LLP |

**Band 4**

| | |
|---|---|
| Dugdale John | Burford & Ryburn, L.L.P. (ONP)† |
| Gosselink Paul | Lloyd Gosselink Rochelle & Townsend, P.C. |
| Henrichs Ragna | Porter Hedges LLP * |
| Jackson William | Jackson Gilmour & Dobbs, PC (ONP)† |
| Moore Bryan | Beveridge & Diamond PC * |
| Nasi Michael | Jackson Walker LLP * |
| Paulson Matthew | Katten Muchin Rosenman LLP (ONP)† |
| Renfroe Tracie | King & Spalding LLP * |
| Rentz Rebecca J | Winstead PC * |
| Riley John A | Bracewell & Giuliani LLP * |
| Roska Kay | Thompson & Knight LLP * |
| Smiley Cynthia M | Smiley Law Firm (ONP)† |
| Sniff Kirk F | Strasburger & Price LLP (ONP)† |
| Vineyard Daniel | Jackson Walker LLP * |

**Up-and-coming individuals**

| | |
|---|---|
| Cobb Bill | Jackson Walker LLP * |
| Seal Derek | Winstead PC * |

**Associates to watch**

| | |
|---|---|
| Rainey Susan M | Locke Lord LLP * |

## Band 1

### Baker Botts LLP
See profile on p.2427

**THE FIRM** This environmental practice is widely regarded as one of the strongest in the state. The group has extensive experience across a variety of environmental issues, including upstream oil and gas, electric generation, renewable energy and petrochemicals. A recent work highlight saw it represent the BCCA Appeal Group in a challenge to the EPA's actions on rules submitted for approval by the State of Texas, concerning the state's implementation of the CAA. Other significant clients include ExxonMobil, BP and Targa Resources.
**Sources say:** "I think that the service has been terrific." "They're a great shop of lawyers."
**KEY INDIVIDUALS** Sources describe **Pamela Giblin** (see p.2391) as "an extraordinary lawyer" and "a legend of the Texas Bar." She recently advised Waste Control Specialists on the development and licensing of a radioactive waste disposal facility. **Sara Burgin** (see p.2383) elicits particular praise from interviewees for her strengths in the water quality space. She is also recommended for her expertise in matters concerning Superfunds, wetlands, and solid and hazardous waste. **Molly Cagle** (see p.2383) recently joined the team from Vinson & Elkins and brings experience across a broad spectrum of issues, including permitting,

regulation and environmental disputes. **Matthew Kuryla** (see p.2400) recently acted for BP in litigation brought against its Texas City refinery by the State of Texas on a claim for civil penalties, as well as a permanent injunction for alleged violations of the Texas CAA and Texas Commission on Environmental Quality (TCEQ) regulations. **Jennifer Keane** (see p.2398) focuses on environmental regulation, with a particular emphasis and expertise in CAA issues. **Derek McDonald** (see p.2404) represented Texas Oil and Gas Association in preventing the listing of the dunes sagebrush lizard as an endangered species, successfully obtaining a six-month extension on the decision, and drafting the Texas Conservation Plan for the lizard.

### Vinson & Elkins LLP
See profile on p.2459

**THE FIRM** The team at Vinson & Elkins continues to demonstrate strength in the area of catastrophic events, helping clients to develop effective preparation and responses to such disasters. The group is also well known for its work securing and defending contested water, wetlands and air permits for clients' development projects, such as power plants and other industrial establishments. The impressive client list includes Sunflower Electric Power, El Paso Electric and Sandy Creek Energy Associates.
**Sources say:** "They have a terrific team." "A top firm."
**KEY INDIVIDUALS** Department head **Carol Dinkins** (see p.2387) is "obviously a superstar," according to sources. She maintains a diverse environmental practice, which includes counseling on permit matters, business transactions and civil litigation. Sources are quick to describe **Eric**

Groten (see p.2392) as *"a terrific air lawyer."* He recently represented the Coalition for Responsible Regulation in an application for judicial review of the EPA's greenhouse gas control scheme. **Sharon Mattox** (see p.2403) recently acted for White Stallion Energy Center on obtaining all the relevant environmental authorizations for a proposed 1,200 MW coal and petroleum coke-fired power project for Matagorda County. **Robert Schick** (see p.2415) is an environmental litigation expert with more than three decades of experience. His particular areas of expertise include pharmaceutical, complex tort and class-wide litigation. **Larry Nettles** (see p.2406) recently acted for Caiman Energy on its $2.5 billion sale of Caiman Eastern midstream, handling all the environmental elements, which were critical for the success of the transaction.

## Band 2

### Bracewell & Giuliani LLP
See profile on p.2429

**THE FIRM** This experienced environmental group has been boosted with the recent lateral hiring of two partners from Vinson & Elkins. The practice covers the full spectrum of matters, including climate change, regulatory enforcement and compliance matters, in addition to handling work concerning contamination and energy policy. In recent highlights, the team acted for midstream energy firm Energy Transfer on successfully obtaining EPA permits for greenhouse gas emissions. Other key clients include Cabot Oil & Gas, Kinder Morgan and Halliburton. **Sources say:** *"They're exceptional."* *"They've always done an excellent job for us."*
**KEY INDIVIDUALS John Riley** (see p.2413) recently joined the team from Vinson & Elkins, and is described as *"an excellent lawyer and an excellent advocate."* He has particular expertise in matters concerning air, water and waste media permitting and enforcement. The *"very thoughtful"* **Timothy Wilkins** (see p.2422) is *"a fabulous lawyer and his leadership is excellent,"* note sources, who also admire his ability to *"remain calm and analytical in a crisis."* Wilkins led on the Energy Transfer matter.

### Brown McCarroll, L.L.P.
See profile on p.2430

**THE FIRM** This firm's environmental practice is highly regarded in the local market, and has key contacts at the regulatory agencies and team members with notable industry-specific backgrounds, in engineering, geology and geophysics. The group acts for manufacturing and electric generating companies and municipalities, among others, and recently represented Tenaska in litigation concerning a dispute over its application for air quality permits for a coal-fired electric generating facility.
**Sources say:** *"The firm is solid in all areas."* *"I would recommend them to any and all who need legal counsel. Excellent firm."*
**KEY INDIVIDUALS Rodman Johnson** is *"absolutely an air specialist,"* according to sources, who also praise his wealth of business knowledge and common-sense

approach to matters. **Keith Hopson** is highlighted as *"an excellent hazards waste lawyer."* In recent work, he represented Arkansas Waste to Energy Warehouse in an order to remove hazardous substance containers from an abandoned warehouse site. Sources agree that **Danny Worrell** is *"a phenomenal person"* to have on your side, not least because he *"is extremely intelligent, has common sense, and cares personally about his clients."* He recently represented Lerin Hills Municipal Utility District, defending an appeal against its application for a wastewater discharge permit.

### Fulbright & Jaworski LLP
See profile on p.2435

**THE FIRM** The environmental team at Fulbright & Jaworski offers expertise in a broad range of issues, including climate change, hydraulic fracturing, shale development, and civil and criminal enforcement. A recent highlight saw the group represent Chinese client Sinopec International Petroleum and Exploration Company in its acquisition of an interest in the Tuscaloosa Marine Shale in Mississippi. Other important clients include CITGO Petroleum, EOG Resources and Delta Airlines.
**KEY INDIVIDUALS Patricia Finn Braddock** (see p.2388) specializes in permitting and enforcement matters before regulatory agencies at both the state and federal level. Recently, she has been working with Samsung Austin Semiconductor on the environmental issues concerning a potential expansion of its Austin site. The *"very effective"* **Eva Fromm O'Brien** (see p.2390) recently represented Monroe Energy, a subsidiary of Delta Air Lines, in negotiations for the $180 million purchase of a Philadelphia crude oil refinery. **Edward Lewis** (see p.2401) elicits praise for his *"detail-oriented"* approach to matters. He has been busy of late acting for CITGO Petroleum, defending a case brought against it by the US government relating to a 2006 oil release in Louisiana.

### Guida, Slavich & Flores, P.C.

**THE FIRM** This environmental boutique is highly regarded in the Texas market. The group covers a broad spectrum of matters, including deal structuring, brownfield development and waste management, for a diverse client base. It guides clients in the oil and gas, aerospace and alternative energy industries through the complexities of environmental law so that they can effectively execute their business objectives.
**Sources say:** *"They're extremely competent regulatory and compliance lawyers."*
**KEY INDIVIDUALS** The *"highly respected"* **Joseph Guida** has a wealth of experience in air and water quality control matters, Superfund work and issues pertaining to hazardous waste management. **John Slavich** advises clients on all aspects of environmental matters concerning corporate and real estate transactions. He also has particular expertise in risk management, climate change and brownfield redevelopment. Experienced litigator **Paul Seals** focuses his practice on environmental public law and policy, and compliance and licensing matters.

### Haynes and Boone, LLP
See profile on p.444

**THE FIRM** This firm's environmental offering provides a complete range of services, from regulatory matters to litigation, but is particularly well known for its expertise in the energy sector. It recently advised Panda Power Infrastructure Fund on environmental matters involved in the development of a 710 MW natural gas-fired power plant. Other notable clients include Shell, ConcocoPhillips and KMG Chemicals.
**Sources say:** *"They have an excellent environmental practice."* *"Talented, knowledgeable, and friendly."*
**KEY INDIVIDUALS** Department head **Jeff Civins** is regarded as *"a legend of the Texas Bar"* by sources. He recently represented Aruba Petroleum in regulatory and litigation matters relating to its production activities in the Barnett Shale. *"He always pulls together a team with the particular skills we need,"* notes one enthusiastic source. The highly regarded **James Braddock** has a wealth of experience acting for oil and gas operations, refineries, airports and asphalt plants, representing them in both transactional matters and litigation. **Mary Mendoza** focuses on environmental and administrative law, and led the team on the Panda Power Infrastructure Fund matter. **John Eldridge** recently successfully represented El Paso in litigation relating to the Turtle Bayou Superfund site.

### Locke Lord LLP
See profile on p.2443

**THE FIRM** Locke Lord's environmental practice is especially highly regarded for its expertise in energy-related environmental work. Recent highlights include handling a number of environmental permitting matters for Riviana Foods. Other key clients include Cooper Industries, Tyco International and Behringer Harvard REITs.
**Sources say:** *"A well-respected firm that provides a broad base of legal specialties."* *"An outstanding firm and the one we recommend for all our projects."*
**KEY INDIVIDUALS** Department head **Elizabeth Mack** (see p.2402) is praised as being *"very thorough, essential in negotiations with seller or buyers"* and a *"solid team member in collaboration with the rest of my development team."* Interviewees single out **Gerald Pels** (see p.2409) as *"an extraordinary negotiator"* who is *"very creative in attacking problems, extremely knowledgeable and a pleasure to work with."* He played a significant role in the Riviana Foods matter. **Gerald Higdon** (see p.2395) *"is very well versed in both the process and environmental regulations,"* and his ability *"to take a practical common-sense approach"* is much valued by clients. **Susan Rainey** (see p.2411) is lauded by interviewees for her *"solid technical background and ability to assimilate large amounts of technical material."*

### Thompson & Knight LLP
See profile on p.2458

**THE FIRM** The environmental practice at Thompson & Knight offers a broad spectrum of services, but is especially well known for its work on Superfund matters and in the energy and petrochemical industries. It represents a variety of clients in issues including risk management, permitting, litigation and brownfield redevelopment. An enviable client list includes BNSF, BHP Billiton and Dow Chemical. **Sources say:** *"A very reputable firm with very skilled attorneys."*

**KEY INDIVIDUALS James Harris** (see p.2394) offers expertise in Superfund and litigation matters. He represented Pace Petroleum in a dispute with Navarro County Landowners concerning the drilling and completion of an oil well. Harris *"has a lot of depth and experience and capability,"* according to interviewees. Department head **James Morriss** (see p.2406)recently acted for Pasadena Refining System on successfully negotiating a reduced order from the TCEQ relating to alleged violations of air quality regulations. He maintains an outstanding reputation in Austin, according to interviewees, who also praise his thorough approach to matters. **Kay Roska** (see p.2413) earns praise for her broad experience and her wealth of knowledge in the oil and gas industry and the OSHA. *"In addition to being competent and responsive, she endeavors to understand our business and provide tailored legal advice relevant to our business needs,"* asserts one impressed client.

## Band 3

### Kelly Hart & Hallman LLP

**THE FIRM** This Austin-based group offers a wide range of environmental services, including regulatory assistance, compliance counseling and transactional advice. The team also has notable strength in environmental litigation, and provides representation in civil, administrative and criminal proceedings. Specific areas of expertise include special waste management, oil and gas exploration, endangered species, and mining and minerals matters.

**KEY INDIVIDUALS** The highly regarded **Robert Stewart** focuses on toxic torts, air pollution control and environmental criminal investigations. An experienced litigator, he represents a variety of commercial and industrial clients at both the state and federal level.

### Lloyd Gosselink Rochelle & Townsend, P.C.

**THE FIRM** This environmental boutique is very highly regarded in the Texas market, particularly for its government-related work. With a number of the firm's attorneys having previously worked at institutions including the Texas Legislature, the Texas Attorney General's Office and the TCEQ, the team has excellent contacts and a wealth of experience much valued by clients.

**Sources say:** *"A solid group of attorneys." "An extraordinary law firm."*

**KEY INDIVIDUALS** The highly regarded **Paul Gosselink** is chair of the firm's air and waste practice, and has particular expertise in the area of municipal solid waste compliance and permitting.

### Winstead PC

See profile on p.2460

**THE FIRM** This firm's environmental practice maintains a strong presence in the Texas market, representing a variety of clients, including electric generation, petroleum and

chemical companies, across a broad spectrum of issues from transactions to litigation. A recent highlight saw the group defend Goodyear in Superfund cost recovery litigation. Other key clients include ExxonMobil, Waste Management, Inc and Texas Oil & Gas Association.

**Sources say:** *"An excellent team." "A good, strong Texas firm."*

**KEY INDIVIDUALS** The terrific **Albert Axe** (see p.2379) is a much-respected and well-liked attorney, whom clients describe as an *"excellent sounding board for a wide range of environmental issues."* He is valued for his wealth of experience and excellent contacts. Axe is particularly well known for his expertise in state permitting matters, and led the team on the Goodyear matter. **Keith Courtney** (see p.2386) receives much praise for his *"very diligent and detail-oriented"* approach to matters. He has recently been representing ExxonMobil in a CAA citizen suit. **Rebecca Rentz** (see p.2412) has been representing Matagorda Partnership in opposing EPA's proposal to designate Matagorda County as part of the Houston–Galveston–Brazoria Ozone Nonattainment Area. Sources praise the *"young and energetic"* **Derek Seal** (see p.2415) for his *"incredible ability to foresee issues and work on a team basis with in-house counsel."* During the past year he represented Corix in its $20 million acquisition of water and wastewater assets.

## Band 4

### Andrews Kurth LLP

See profile on p.2426

**THE FIRM** The environmental group at Andrews Kurth is particularly well known for its strength in litigation. It recently represented Southwestern Energy in two class action suits concerning claims of pollution from the process of hydraulic fracturing. Other notable clients include Invesco, Alloy Polymers and Pattern Energy.

**KEY INDIVIDUALS Lisa Shelton** (see p.2415) is noted for her expertise in environmental transactions, and recently represented Barclays Capital and Goldman Sachs in their role as underwriters of the Kinder Morgan IPO, handling all the environmental elements of the deal. Interviewees regard **Paul Bohannon** (see p.2381) as *"a very strong litigator."* He has a wealth of experience in oil and gas matters, and acted as the lead partner on the two Southwestern Energy suits mentioned above.

### Beveridge & Diamond PC

See profile on p.907

**THE FIRM** This boutique offers a full roster of environmental services and regularly handles complex hydraulic fracturing, greenhouse gas permitting and flaring issues for clients from a range of industries, including pharmaceuticals, oil and natural gas exploration, and petroleum refining. Key clients include Valero Energy, BASF and Luminant Energy.

**Sources say:** *"I do not think I could do my job without their advice and guidance." "They have a wealth of experience and expertise."*

**KEY INDIVIDUALS** *"Excellent lawyer"* **Bryan Moore** (see p.2406) specializes in water and landfill issues, and recently represented Oak Grove Management Company in the successful defense of the grant of a wastewater permit by the TCEQ.

### Connelly Baker Wotring LLP

**THE FIRM** The environmental group at Connelly Baker Wotring is arguably best known for its expertise and skill in environmental disputes, but also offers a wealth of experience on the regulatory and transactional sides. The team has a particularly strong track record in representing clients in Superfund matters, as well as contaminated waterways, enforcement issues and multi-tenant and co-located facility issues.

**Sources say:** *"A great environmental litigation firm."*

**KEY INDIVIDUALS Michael Connelly** has extensive litigation experience, with specific expertise in mass toxic tort cases, mass community suits and government cost recovery actions. He receives high praise from sources, with one commenting: *"He's one of the finest environment trial lawyers in the country."* **Debra Baker** is well regarded by sources, who describe her as *"a smart lawyer who does a good job for her clients."* She has experience across the full range of environmental issues, with particular expertise in complex multiparty cases and Superfund matters.

### Gardere Wynne Sewell LLP

See profile on p.2436

**THE FIRM** Gardere Wynne Sewell's environmental team includes a wealth of talented trial and appellate specialists, and consequently focuses on complex litigious matters, most notably in the land, air and water spheres. It recently defended ExxonMobil against a claim for damages made against the company relating to alleged damage and diminution caused to a Houston office building. Other clients include American Chemistry Council, LyondellBasell and D.R. Horton.

**Sources say:** *"The quality of work is consistently exceptional." "They're responsive to client needs – they try to understand client objectives and help them achieve those objectives."*

**KEY INDIVIDUALS Richard Faulk** (see p.2388) is popular among sources, who describe him as *"a strategic thinker who is responsive to clients' needs and aligned with client objectives."* Faulk is particularly renowned for his toxic tort work, with one interviewee stating: *"If you want somebody by your side in complex toxic tort cases then he's the guy."* Commentators enjoy working with the *"wonderful"* **Frances Phillips** (see p.2410), and single out her punctuality, knowledge and contacts within the state and federal system as being among her key attributes. **Scott Deatherage** (see p.2387) recently joined the firm from Patton Boggs. He focuses on compliance, permitting and environmental litigation, representing clients at both state and federal level. Sources comment: *"He's the real McCoy – a fabulous environmental lawyer."*

## Jackson Walker LLP
See profile on p.2441

**THE FIRM** The environmental group at Jackson Walker includes experts in a range of areas, including air and water quality, Superfund issues, and mining and energy matters. In the past year the team represented Mahard Egg Farm in a $3.9 million CWA enforcement brought by EPA and the DOJ. Other notable clients include BP America, South Power and Exelon.

**Sources say:** *"They have an amazing understanding of the letter of the law, and also of the inner workings of the regulatory institutions and how the state functions."*

**KEY INDIVIDUALS Michael Nasi** (see p.2406) offers expertise in regulatory permitting across a wide variety of environmental areas, including water, air and waste programs. *"He brings a very good perspective on legal and business decisions; he's very well-spoken, and has excellent contacts in the political and regulatory industry,"* notes one appreciative source. **Daniel Vineyard** (see p.2420) has a wealth of experience handling Superfund matters, having been involved in more than 300 sites nationally. Chevron Chemical and Wyeth Pharmaceuticals are among his key clients. **William Cobb** (see p.2385) recently rejoined the firm after serving as Special Counsel to the Attorney General. Sources praise his *"extraordinary ability to articulate intricate issues and fact patterns."* Interviewees also highlight his *"unique perspective on state regulation, which is respected by all regulating entities in Texas."*

## King & Spalding LLP
See profile on p.445

**THE FIRM** This group is well known for its litigation expertise and includes attorneys with extensive experience as lead trial counsel. In a highlight of the past year, the team represented Halliburton in class action litigation concerning perchlorate contamination of ground water, arising from Halliburton's historical activities in Oklahoma. Shell, ConocoPhillips and Chevron are among its other key clients.

**KEY INDIVIDUALS Tracie Renfroe** (see p.2412) is highlighted for her abilities in environmental disputes. She acts as national counsel for Shell Oil on its TCP drinking water litigation, involving the defense of wrongful death, personal injury and property damage claims.

## Pillsbury Winthrop Shaw Pittman LLP
See profile on p.2000

**THE FIRM** This firm's environmental team is noted for its regulatory and permitting strengths, and also maintains considerable expertise in high-stakes litigation, such as oil spills and explosions. Over the past year, the group continued to represent the Mitsui family of companies in all liabilities arising from the Deepwater Horizon oil spill, helping them to develop and implement a global strategy. Other notable clients include Marathon Oil, Teck Metals and Tesoro.

**KEY INDIVIDUALS** The highly regarded **Jerry Ross** (see p.2413) recently represented Valero Energy in an inherited $20 million environmental liabilities dispute with Motiva.

## Porter Hedges LLP
See profile on p.2450

**THE FIRM** The environmental group at Porter Hedges offers a wide variety of services, from advice on due diligence to compliance and enforcement counseling. Its diverse client base is made up of real estate developers, oil and gas producers, waste service providers and construction companies, among others. The team recently represented Noble Energy in its $3.2 billion acquisition of Marcellus shale oil and gas assets from CONSOL, and in its joint development agreement with the company. Other key clients include Cameron International, Dow Chemical and KBR.

**Sources say:** *"I would highly recommend them to anyone seeking environmental assistance or legal defense of environmental lawsuits or actions."*

**KEY INDIVIDUALS** *"Excellent environmental lawyer"* **James Smith** (see p.2416) elicits particular praise from market sources for his *"very methodical approach"* to matters, as well as for his contract negotiating skills. He led on the Noble Energy matter. Sources applaud **Ragna Henrichs**'s (see p.2395) *"incredible legal insight"* and describe him as a *"great strategist."* *"He expertly translates 'legalese' into plain English,"* notes one enthusiastic commentator.

## Other Notable Practitioners

**John Dugdale** of Burford & Ryburn, L.L.P. maintains a fine reputation for his federal work and is much valued by sources as being among *"the best federal environment lawyers."* *"Fabulous lawyer"* **Cynthia Smiley** of Smiley Law Firm is well known in the market and is praised by interviewees for being *"very skilled, very levelheaded and very thoughtful."* **Kirk Sniff** at Strasburger & Price LLP is *"very smart,"* and is recommended for his expertise in environmental and toxic tort litigation. Sole practitioner **Cynthia Bishop** has been representing Southwest Airlines in the filing of an application to facilitate the cleanup of Love Field airport. Sources highlight her *"ability to home in on the most important issues and solve complex legal problems under tight deadlines."* *"Very smart and enthusiastic,"* **Michael Chernekoff** (see p.2384) of Jones Walker Waechter Poitevent Carrère & Denègre L.L.P. has a broad practice that covers a variety of environmental matters, but he is particularly noted for his expertise in toxic tort defense and environmental litigation. Jackson Gilmour & Dobbs, PC's **William Jackson** is an environmental litigation expert. He has been busy over the past year representing the State of New Jersey in connection with the Passaic River cleanup. *"He's very bright, very hardworking, and extremely organized,"* notes one enthusiastic source. **Christopher Bell** (see p.2380) has been busy over the past year developing Sidley Austin LLP's environmental presence in Texas. Commentators note that he is *"up to date on emerging issues and developments,"* and also praise his ability to *"work through issues and challenges promptly and efficiently."* Sole practitioner **Kenneth Ramirez** has a fine reputation in the market, not least for his strengths in water litigation. **Matthew Paulson** recently joined Katten Muchin Rosenman LLP to head its environmental practice, having previously worked at Baker Botts. He is recognized for his litigation expertise, in addition to his compliance and permitting experience. The *"superlative"* **Christopher Amandes** (see p.2378) recently joined Morgan, Lewis & Bockius LLP from Vinson & Elkins. Amandes focuses on environmental issues that arise in transactions, as well as compliance counseling and environmental dispute resolution.

# HEALTHCARE

Commentary about individuals can be found under their firm's paragraph. If the firm has no paragraph (is not ranked) look at Other Notable Practitioners.

| Healthcare Leading Firms | |
|---|---|
| **Band 1** | |
| Fulbright & Jaworski LLP * | |
| **Band 2** | |
| Baker & Hostetler LLP * | |
| Brown McCarroll, L.L.P. * | |
| Reed, Claymon, Meeker & Hargett, PLLC | |
| King & Spalding LLP * | |
| **Band 3** | |
| Locke Lord LLP * | |
| Strasburger & Price LLP * | |
| **Band 4** | |
| Greenberg Traurig, LLP * | |
| Jackson Walker LLP * | |
| Munsch Hardt Kopf & Harr, P.C. * | |
| Thompson & Knight LLP * | |

\* Indicates firm / individual with profile.
† ONP = Other Notable Practitioner

| Healthcare Leading Individuals | |
|---|---|
| **Band 1** | |
| Bell Jerry | Fulbright & Jaworski LLP * |
| Eiland Gary | King & Spalding LLP * |
| Hilgers David W | Brown McCarroll, L.L.P. |
| Johnstone Debbi M | Fulbright & Jaworski LLP * |
| Reed Kevin A | Reed, Claymon, Meeker & Hargett, PLLC * |
| **Band 2** | |
| Clark Donna S | Baker & Hostetler LLP * |
| Darling William Duane | Strasburger & Price LLP |
| Genecov Lisa | Locke Lord LLP * |
| Geraci Joseph V | Brown McCarroll, L.L.P. |
| Harris Susan Feigin | Baker & Hostetler LLP * |
| Jones Wilson G | Thompson & Knight LLP * |
| Morrison Edgar C | Jackson Walker LLP * |
| Poppitt Kathy L | Cox Smith Matthews Incorporated (ONP)† |
| Puig Yvonne Karen | Fulbright & Jaworski LLP * |
| Rogers Elizabeth N | Waller Lansden Dortch & Davis (ONP)† * |
| Wood Ivan | Strasburger & Price LLP |
| **Band 3** | |
| Bredehoft Patrick | Thompson & Knight LLP * |
| Brown Fletcher | Waller Lansden Dortch & Davis (ONP)† * |
| Carter Diane T. | Brown McCarroll, L.L.P. |
| Claymon Jennifer | Reed, Claymon, Meeker & Hargett, PLLC * |
| DeMeo Chris | Munsch Hardt Kopf & Harr, P.C. |
| Katz Hal | Brown McCarroll, L.L.P. |
| Malone Michael L | Greenberg Traurig, LLP * |
| Scott Dwight | Munsch Hardt Kopf & Harr, P.C. |
| Sheeder III Frank E | DLA Piper LLP (US) (ONP)† * |
| Wolin Robert M | Baker & Hostetler LLP * |
| **Up-and-coming individuals** | |
| Coniglio Joseph F. | Greenberg Traurig, LLP * |
| McBride B. Scott | Baker & Hostetler LLP * |
| **Associates to watch** | |
| Barnes John Kelly | Greenberg Traurig, LLP * |

## Band 1

### Fulbright & Jaworski LLP
See profile on p.2435

THE FIRM Fulbright's market-leading healthcare group regularly acts for a broad variety of industry clients, including hospitals and pharmaceutical organizations. The group has been active on a series of high-value sales and acquisitions of health systems of late, as well as dealing with complex healthcare disputes. Key clients include Baylor College of Medicine, Methodist Hospitals of Dallas and the Texas Hospital Association. The firm also acts for physicians and industry trade associations.
Sources say: "A wonderful healthcare practice."
KEY INDIVIDUALS Health law business and regulatory department head **Jerry Bell** (see p.2380) represents healthcare organizations in both transactional and regulatory issues. He is described as "one of the best" by market commentators. The "very bright" **Debbi Johnstone** (see p.2397) is considered a leading player in the market by both clients and peers. Her practice has a particular focus on regulatory compliance issues, and she has recently been involved in a number of healthcare transactions. **Yvonne Karen Puig** (see p.2411) represents healthcare providers in various disputes. She recently led the firm's representation of Tenet in its lawsuit filed against Humana. Interviewees "find her style and knowledge to be very good."

## Band 2

### Baker & Hostetler LLP
See profile on p.2119

THE FIRM This healthcare practice is able to draw on the firm's wider expertise in labor and IP to offer clients the benefit of full-service legal representation. The team is par-

ticularly involved in the legal issues relating to children's health, and continues to advise Texas Children's Hospital on a range of regulatory issues. Healthcare data breach issues is another area of expertise for the team. Key clients include DaVita, National Cardiovascular Partners and MD Anderson Cancer Center.
Sources say: "They are very responsive. Wherever they are and whatever they are doing they respond to e-mails and calls quickly."
KEY INDIVIDUALS **Susan Feigin Harris** (see p.2394) has led the firm's representation of Texas Children's Hospital and is known for her expertise in regulatory issues. According to clients, "her knowledge of healthcare public policy is one of the best in the country and for sure in Texas." Clients are quick to praise **Robert Wolin** (see p.2422), particularly for his expertise in corporate structuring and regulatory compliance. He is "very knowledgeable on healthcare contract law and healthcare policy," say sources. **Donna**

**Clark** (see p.2384) earns market acclaim for her knowledge of referral law compliance. According to commentators, she is an "excellent technical lawyer" who is considered a go-to attorney in the state for Stark issues. Rising star **Scott McBride** (see p.2404) handles a range of investigations and reviews for healthcare providers, and is held in high regard by peers for his impressive expertise in this area.

### Brown McCarroll, L.L.P.
See profile on p.2430

THE FIRM This firm acts on behalf of a series of healthcare providers and is involved in a range of regulatory compliance issues and significant transactions. The team recently acted for Austin Regional Clinic on the establishment of its professional services agreement with a local hospital. Other significant clients include Greater Houston Health Network, Lifepoint Hospital System and Dallas Nephrology Associates.
Sources say: "A great base of knowledge and in-depth experience related to healthcare."
KEY INDIVIDUALS **David Hilgers** represents healthcare providers and individuals in corporate and administrative issues. Clients say he is "professional, very accessible, customer service-oriented," and "one of the top healthcare lawyers in the country." Clients are quick to praise **Joseph Geraci**'s "very accessible and customer service-oriented" approach. He has recently been involved in a series of regulatory compliance issues for healthcare organizations. Practice head **Diane Carter** has a particular focus on corporate and transactions matters relating to healthcare. She is lauded by commentators for her "detail-oriented, knowledgeable, thorough" approach. "Great lawyer" **Hal Katz** advises clients on the full range of healthcare matters, including transactional and regulatory work as well as public policy issues. He has recently been involved in high-value transactions on behalf of healthcare providers.

### Reed, Claymon, Meeker & Hargett, PLLC

THE FIRM Davis & Wright recently changed its name from Davis & Wilkerson, and remains a key player in the Texas healthcare legal market. The team is particularly known for its work on behalf of independent, rural and smaller community hospitals across the state, offering them a broad range of legal services including sale and purchase transactions, M&A and regulatory compliance.
Sources say: "Fantastic healthcare lawyers."
KEY INDIVIDUALS The "excellent" **Kevin Reed** (see p.2412) is regarded as one of the state's premier healthcare practitioners. He regularly acts for both healthcare organizations and individual physicians in transactions, regulatory matters and hearings. **Jennifer Claymon** (see p.2384) is held in high regard by clients for her expertise in employment issues relating to healthcare organizations. She also handles a range of regulatory issues on behalf of healthcare clients.

## King & Spalding LLP

See profile on p.445

THE FIRM This global firm's Houston practice forms a significant part of its healthcare offering. The group is regularly involved in a series of high-value matters, particularly involving Medicare and Medicaid services. For example, it recently acted for Nueces County Hospital District on supplementary Medicaid payments worth up to $1.07 billion. Other key clients include The University of Texas System, Odyssey HealthCare and CHRISTUS Health.

Sources say: "King & Spalding's access to various resources is a huge asset. They have many in-house experts as well as rapid access to multiple regulatory agencies. They are extremely resourceful."

KEY INDIVIDUALS Experienced practitioner Gary Eiland (see p.2388) has a strong focus on regulatory issues related to healthcare providers. "Gary gives wonderful counsel. He is incredibly responsive and really thoughtful in the way he approaches problems," say clients.

## Band 3

## Locke Lord LLP

See profile on p.2443

THE FIRM This well-established firm is known among market competitors as a significant healthcare player in Texas, and clients are quick to praise its in-depth understanding of regulatory compliance issues and cost-effective approach. The group recently represented NewLight Healthcare in the establishment of accountable care organizations in Texas and Oklahoma. Other major clients include Humana, Baylor Health Care System and First Street Surgical.

Sources say: "Impressive timeliness and huge expertise and attention to detail."

KEY INDIVIDUALS Practice cochair Lisa Genecov (see p.2390) regularly takes a lead role on the firm's most significant healthcare engagements. According to clients, she "is very client-centric and quick to respond, and understands client needs."

## Strasburger & Price LLP

See profile on p.2455

THE FIRM Peers recognize Strasburger & Price as a solid local practice with a particular focus on handling regulatory compliance issues for a range of healthcare organizations in Texas. The firm has remained active in advising clients on how to respond to the various healthcare reforms that will affect their operations.

KEY INDIVIDUALS William Duane Darling is regarded among peers as a leading practitioner in the Texas healthcare arena. As well as handling the range of regulatory compliance issues, he has particular experience in establishing managed care organizations. Ivan Wood is an experienced corporate practitioner who is respected in the

market for his prowess in sophisticated healthcare transactions. He is also known for his Medicare fraud and abuse expertise.

## Band 4

## Greenberg Traurig, LLP

See profile on p.1024

THE FIRM The ten-attorney Texas practice at this global firm joins the rankings this year following extensive endorsement from across the healthcare industry. The group has recently acted on behalf of the Emergency Medical Services Corporation on corporate litigation. It also represents organizations such as Dental Professionals of Texas, Universal Health Services and PICA.

Sources say: "Their strengths are expertise, prompt response and availability. As a client, waiting is not an option."

KEY INDIVIDUALS Michael Malone (see p.2402) is praised by commentators for his transactional and financial expertise as it relates to healthcare. He earns particular praise from clients for his "deep knowledge set." New entry Joseph Coniglio (see p.2385) is known for his presence in healthcare disputes, but is also expanding his practice into related transactional activity. Clients say he is "friendly, responsive, competent and great to work with." Associate Kelly Barnes (see p.2379) is a favorite among clients, who say: "His help has been extraordinary" on transactional and regulatory issues.

## Jackson Walker LLP

See profile on p.2441

THE FIRM Jackson Walker enters the rankings this year having earned strong feedback from clients, praising its levels of service and transactional expertise. Peers also identify the firm as a target for referrals in healthcare matters. The team recently handled the full restructuring of Memorial Hermann Healthcare System, and assisted Forest Park Medical Center with the growth of its physician-owned business model.

Sources say: "Highly knowledgeable, competent and pleasant to deal with."

KEY INDIVIDUALS "Excellent lawyer" Edgar Morrison (see p.2406) is known for his regulatory expertise. He regularly acts for a variety of healthcare providers and pharmacies.

## Munsch Hardt Kopf & Harr, P.C.

See profile on p.2448

THE FIRM This firm debuts in the rankings this year thanks to ringing endorsement from clients. It earns particular acclaim for its expertise in regulatory issues and its ability to assist clients in navigating through the full range of sophisticated compliance issues. Key clients include the Hospital Corporation of America, Solis Women's Health and Diamond Respiratory.

Sources say: "Each individual lawyer has strong specific specialty knowledge and keeps you in the loop very closely all the time."

KEY INDIVIDUALS Practice head Dwight Scot has a broad healthcare practice covering regulatory compliance and related healthcare litigation. He earns praise from clients for his calm and measured approach in disputes. Chris Demeo enters the rankings this year, with clients quick to praise his regulatory expertise. He is described as an "excellent and very responsive" practitioner.

## Thompson & Knight LLP

See profile on p.2458

THE FIRM This firm focuses particularly on healthcare litigation and regularly acts for a range of hospital and pharmaceutical companies on high-value disputes. The team also has expertise in regulatory compliance issues and earns extensive praise from clients for its work across the board in healthcare.

Sources say: "The lawyers are excellent with their expertise and very strong at what they do."

KEY INDIVIDUALS Department head Wilson Jones (see p.2397) is involved in many of the firm's most significant healthcare engagements. He is active across the board, with expertise in regulatory compliance and contentious matters. Sources say he is "very knowledgeable regarding business, the healthcare industry and the legal field in general." New entry Patrick Bredehoft (see p.2382) advises on regulatory issues and related disputes. Sources describe him as "a very good litigator with a wealth of information on multiple areas."

## Other Notable Practitioners

Elizabeth Rogers (see p.2413) of Waller Lansden Dortch & Davis is highlighted by sources as being "extremely thorough, a good listener and an expert in managed care." Her practice focuses on transactional and regulatory healthcare issues. Rogers is joined at the firm by Fletcher Brown (see p.2382), a recent arrival from Reed Claymon. He focuses extensively on regulatory compliance, particularly with regard to Start and the Health Insurance Portability and Accountability Act (HIPAA). He is also heavily involved in healthcare-related transactions, including financings and contract negotiation and drafting. Kathy Poppitt of Cox Smith Matthews Incorporated is lauded by clients as an "extremely professional and knowledgeable" practitioner. She regularly handles healthcare disputes and regulatory compliance issues. Frank Sheeder (see p.2415) chairs the DLA Piper LLP (US) healthcare enforcement and compliance practice. He focuses his healthcare work on regulatory compliance and related litigation. According to clients, he is "professional, knowledgeable and fun to work with."

# IMMIGRATION

Commentary about individuals can be found under their firm's paragraph. If the firm has no paragraph (is not ranked) look at Other Notable Practitioners.

## Band 1

### Berry Appleman & Leiden LLP

**THE FIRM** Berry Appleman & Leiden maintains a strong reputation in the marketplace as a large and sophisticated boutique practice. The firm offers a full range of services to clients and lately has been particularly busy running programs for companies, and dealing with compliance issues. With offices in Dallas and Houston, the firm is still growing in manpower and also benefits from resources in partner offices nationally and internationally, including in Sydney, Brazil, London and Singapore.
**Sources say:** *"They're the best, a notch above everyone else."*
**KEY INDIVIDUALS Steven Ladik** *"has good connections and is very responsive and reliable,"* according to sources. He is recognized for his expertise in forming strategies for corporate clients, and for developing compliance programs. He also has considerable experience acting for athletes on immigration matters. **Shawn Orme** has particular skills in dealing with immigration issues arising out of corporate and M&A work. He also advises clients on a range of other matters, including investment in the USA, and aliens of extraordinary ability. **Paige Taylor** is praised for being very accessible and responsive. Sources say that she *"knows how to simplify complicated topics and is direct and easy to work with."* She focuses on representing a variety of clients in the telecom, electronics, technology and engineering industries and other sectors.

## Band 2

### Cox Smith Matthews Incorporated

**THE FIRM** Cox Smith provides a full service to clients in immigration matters. The group has been involved in many cases regarding worksite compliance and enforcement of late. Clients benefit from extra support for outbound services through the firm's membership of TAGLaw and Lawyers Associated Worldwide.
**Sources say:** *"I've always received excellent service and I enjoy working with them. They address problems immediately and are available for me 24/7."*
**KEY INDIVIDUALS Edward Rios** concentrates on developing immigration strategies for multinational companies, and has expertise in cross-border investments. Observers describe him as *"phenomenal"* and *"professional, timely, and very patient with people who don't have the experience level he's used to working with."* **Kathleen Walker** is highly respected and *"good at keeping her eye on the ball."* She has a broad range of expertise in immigration matters, including worksite compliance, citizenship and naturalization, security checks and consular processing. Sources note that Walker is *"very service-oriented and responsive."*

### FosterQuan, LLP

**THE FIRM** FosterQuan offers the full breadth of immigration services to clients. The group has recently undertaken a significant number of cases involving foreign investors and setting up EB-5 regional centers. The team has developed expertise in advising clients in various industries, including IT and oil and gas.
**KEY INDIVIDUALS** Practice cochairs **Charles Foster** and **Gordon Quan** are well known and respected in the immigration law community for their longstanding presence in the market. Observers note that they are *"both really big names in Houston."* **Judy Lee** is commended by interviewees for being extremely responsive. Sources comment that she *"really knows her stuff and can communicate that knowledge to clients."* **John Meyer** has a strong reputation in dealing with immigration matters, and is described as a *"very solid practitioner"* by sources.

### Law Offices of Richard A Gump Jr PC

**THE FIRM** This boutique firm is recognized for its excellence in providing a vast array of immigration services, including worksite compliance, foreign investment visas and other employment-based visas. The group also has a strong reputation in the immigration law community.
**Sources say:** *"Excellent immigration lawyers."*
**KEY INDIVIDUALS** Sources comment that **Richard Gump** offers a *"good depth of knowledge and a lot of personalized attention."* He has particular expertise in corporate strategies for immigration matters, investor visas and immigration issues brought about by M&A. **Charla Truett** does *"outstanding work,"* according to sources. She represents a wide variety of clients and has considerable experience in undertaking immigration work for small and family businesses, and for IT companies.

### Miley & Brown PC

**THE FIRM** This greatly respected, longstanding Dallas-based firm handles the gamut of immigration matters. The team handles family, business and deportation matters with equal prowess.
**KEY INDIVIDUALS Craig Miley** is well known and regarded as a solid immigration practitioner. He is active in the community and has a wealth of experience in immigration and nationality law.

## Band 3

### Jackson Lewis LLP
**See profile on p.1982**

**THE FIRM** Jackson Lewis specializes in labor and employment law, and has expanded its capabilities in immigration. The group's immigration workplace and I-9 compliance, training and defense work are of particular note, providing a natural fit alongside the firm's other services.

Clients include Whole Foods Market and Texas Gulf Energy.

**Sources say:** "*Very professional and quick to respond, with a wealth of information related to immigration.*"

**KEY INDIVIDUALS Harry Joe** (see p.2397) is "*a force to be reckoned with*" and has an excellent longstanding reputation owing to his wealth of knowledge and experience in immigration law. Clients appreciate **Rebecca Massiatte**'s (see p.2403) timely advice, and sources describe her as "*creative and excellent.*" She assists individuals, their families and companies with obtaining visas and developing internal immigration policies.

### Shivers & Shivers

**THE FIRM** This well-known boutique immigration firm offers a range of immigration and nationality services to clients, and is often called upon by detainees. Serving both individuals and businesses, the group is highly recommended for its broad range of expertise.

**Sources say:** "*A wonderful firm.*"

**KEY INDIVIDUALS Robert Shivers** is held in high regard for his work on family immigration and removal matters. **Nancy Shivers** handles both business and family-related immigration cases. She is also noted among commentators

for her community involvement and speaking engagements.

## Other Notable Practitioners

Commentators describe **Peter Williamson** of Chamberlain, Hrdlicka, White, Williams & Aughtry as "*tough and not afraid to speak out in favor of justice,*" and "*a major player in Texas.*" He has a broad range of experience and takes on the full spectrum of immigration and nationality cases. **Victoria Garcia** (see p.2390) of Bracewell & Giuliani LLP offers a broad range of immigration services and has a particularly fine understanding of the energy sector. She has recently acted for Valero Energy and China Communications Construction, and for members of the Association of Mexican Entrepreneurs, on a range of immigration matters. **Cindy Kang Ansbach** (see p.2398) of Fulbright & Jaworski LLP represents domestic and international companies in a range of immigration matters. She has experience acting for clients from a wide range of industries, and has particular expertise in the oil and gas sector. **Leigh Ganchan** (see p.2390) of Ogletree, Deakins, Nash, Smoak & Stewart, PC has a healthy reputation in the market. She advises professionals and employers on various immigration matters, including I-9 and E-

Verify compliance and H-1B visas. **Irina Plumlee** of Munsch Hardt Kopf & Harr, P.C. focuses on business immigration and has particular expertise in specialized planning for corporate clients. Recent clients include Cambridge-Lee Industries, WorldVentures Holdings and Good Shepherd Medical Center. **Brian Graham** of Strasburger & Price LLP offers a wide range of immigration and naturalization services, and has been particularly busy representing foreign investors and other individuals, and setting up EB-5 regional centers. Sole practitioner **Paul Parsons** undertakes both family-based and employment-based immigration work. He has recently assisted a number of religious workers, researchers, engineers and teachers, among others, with their immigration needs. Sources say he is "*very dedicated and devoted to his clients and to the profession.*" **Brian Bates** of Reina Bates & Kowalski is a "*brilliant lawyer*" and "*one of the best writers and thinkers,*" according to sources. He is particularly well known for his litigation work and representation of clients in deportation and immigration-related criminal proceedings. **Harry Gee** of Law Office of Harry Gee Jr & Associates is the "*grandfather of immigration law,*" according to sources, thanks to his fine longstanding reputation in the industry and an abundance of experience in immigration law and related litigation.

# INSURANCE

**Regulation Senior Statesmen and Eminent Partners p.2351**

Commentary about individuals can be found under their firm's paragraph. If the firm has no paragraph (is not ranked) look at Other Notable Practitioners.

| Insurance | | | |
| --- | --- | --- | --- |
| **Leading Firms** | | | |
| **Band 1** | | | |
| Gardere Wynne Sewell LLP * | | | |
| Haynes and Boone, LLP * | | | |
| Martin, Disiere, Jefferson & Wisdom, LLP * | | | |
| Thompson, Coe, Cousins & Irons, LLP * | | | |
| **Band 2** | | | |
| Brown & Kornegay LLP | | | |
| Cooper & Scully PC * | | | |
| Fulbright & Jaworski LLP * | | | |
| Shidlofsky Law Firm PLLC | | | |
| Winstead PC * | | | |
| **Band 3** | | | |
| Hall Maines Lugrin, P.C. | | | |
| Phelps Dunbar LLP * | | | |
| Shannon, Gracey, Ratliff & Miller LLP * | | | |
| Tollefson Bradley Ball & Mitchell, LLP | | | |
| **Band 4** | | | |
| Akin Gump Strauss Hauer & Feld LLP * | | | |
| Beirne Maynard & Parsons, LLP * | | | |
| Cox Smith Matthews Incorporated | | | |
| Porter Hedges LLP * | | | |
| Roach & Newton, L.L.P. | | | |
| Sutherland Asbill & Brennan LLP | | | |

* *Indicates firm with profile.*
*Alphabetical order within each band. Band 1 is the highest.*

## Band 1

### Gardere Wynne Sewell LLP
**See profile on p.2436**

**THE FIRM** This established Texas firm features a diverse practice spanning various insurance coverage and regulatory issues. The team represents policyholders in a range of coverage disputes, but also handles regulatory work for a host of entities including insurers, reinsurers and brokers. As well as representing major national and international clients, the group remains a mainstay in the state thanks to major offices in Austin, Dallas and Houston acting for organizations including Schlumberger, Pacific Drilling Services and McDermott.

**Sources say:** "*There is no better insurance regulatory work anywhere.*"

**KEY INDIVIDUALS James Cooper** (see p.2385) is renowned for his extensive experience serving policyholders in high-value coverage disputes. He has recently acted for major US home builder Lennar on a construction defect coverage case. **Kimberly Yelkin** (see p.2423) chairs the insurance regulatory group and is recognized nationally as an expert in government affairs. Commentators appreciate her "*good relationships and long history within the industry*" and note that she possesses "*great political instincts.*" **Samantha Trahan**'s (see p.2419) impressive profile continues to rise in the insurance coverage sector. She is described by clients as "*really knowledgeable.*"

### Haynes and Boone, LLP
**See profile on p.444**

**THE FIRM** Haynes and Boone is considered to be the go-to firm for policyholder representation in Texas. Market sources single it out as experts in insurance coverage litigation, having dealt with a variety of issues including general liability, property damage and catastrophe claims among others. The practitioners are also adept at handling cases across a range of different industries, evidenced by their range of current clients such as Atmos Energy, East Texas Medical Center and Dallas Stars.

**Sources say:** "*I like to be associated with them. They're good people.*"

**KEY INDIVIDUALS** Lead partner **Ernest Martin** enjoys a stellar reputation as one of the leading policyholder lawyers in Texas. Commentators regard him as "*an excellent subject matter expert*" who is "*very responsive, easy to work with, organized and great at bringing relevant issues to the table.*" **Werner Powers** has deep litigation experience which he applies to his broad insurance practice. He primarily handles complex coverage issues, and also deals with insurance torts and other disputes. Associate **Micah Skidmore** is gaining prominence in the insurance area representing policyholders. Market commentators are impressed with his successful results and rapidly growing skill set.

## Insurance
### Senior Statesmen

**Senior Statesmen: distinguished older practitioners**

| | |
|---|---|
| Geiger Richard S | Thompson, Coe, Cousins & Irons, LLP |

### Leading Individuals

**Band 1**

| | |
|---|---|
| Brown David H | Brown & Kornegay LLP * |
| Cooper Brent | Cooper & Scully PC |
| Huddleston Michael | Shannon, Gracey, Ratliff & Miller LLP |
| Lawless J Mark | McGuireWoods LLP (ONP)† |
| Martin Brian S | Thompson, Coe, Cousins & Irons, LLP |
| Martin Christopher W | Martin, Disiere, Jefferson & Wisdom, LLP |
| Martin Ernest | Haynes and Boone, LLP |
| Morgan Vincent E | Pillsbury Winthrop Shaw Pittman (ONP)† * |
| Pate Stephen | Fulbright & Jaworski LLP * |
| Shidlofsky Lee H | Shidlofsky Law Firm PLLC |

**Band 2**

| | |
|---|---|
| Bradley Beth D | Tollefson Bradley Ball & Mitchell, LLP |
| Brown Reagan | Fulbright & Jaworski LLP * |
| Cooper James | Gardere Wynne Sewell LLP * |
| Cornell James L | Cornell & Pardue LLP (ONP)† |
| Hall III J Clifton | Hall Maines Lugrin, P.C. |
| Higgins Roger | Thompson, Coe, Cousins & Irons, LLP |
| Keller Mary | Winstead PC * |
| Roach Jr Robert M | Roach & Newton, L.L.P. |
| Rosenblum Rick | Akin Gump Strauss Hauer & Feld LLP * |
| Stuart III Claude | Phelps Dunbar LLP |
| Wielinski Patrick J | Cokinos, Bosien and Young (ONP)† |

**Band 3**

| | |
|---|---|
| Alleman Thomas B | Cox Smith Matthews Incorporated |
| Brown Jay W | Winstead PC * |
| Burgess Linda J | Winstead PC * |
| Cunningham Robert J | Roach & Newton, L.L.P. |
| Dedman Linda | Dedman & Handschuch (ONP)† |
| Disiere David D | Martin, Disiere, Jefferson & Wisdom, LLP |
| Garcia Rodrigo | Thompson, Coe, Cousins & Irons, LLP |
| Holub Cynthia A | Porter Hedges LLP * |
| Nicholson Barclay R | Fulbright & Jaworski LLP * |
| Nolan Peter A | Winstead PC * |
| Parsons Jeffrey R | Beirne Maynard & Parsons, LLP * |
| Powers Werner | Haynes and Boone, LLP |
| Roberts Steven L | Sutherland Asbill & Brennan LLP |
| Schenkkan Pete | Graves, Dougherty, Hearon & Moody (ONP)† |
| Thompson Jay | Thompson, Coe, Cousins & Irons, LLP |
| Tollefson John | Tollefson Bradley Ball & Mitchell, LLP |
| Trahan Samantha | Gardere Wynne Sewell LLP * |

### Up-and-coming individuals

| | |
|---|---|
| Johnson Daniel | Sutherland Asbill & Brennan LLP |
| Kornegay Nancy | Brown & Kornegay LLP * |
| Van Meir Ellen M | Thompson, Coe, Cousins & Irons, LLP |

### Associates to watch

| | |
|---|---|
| Skelley Douglas | Shidlofsky Law Firm PLLC |
| Skidmore Micah | Haynes and Boone, LLP |

## Martin, Disiere, Jefferson & Wisdom, LLP
See profile on p.2445

**THE FIRM** As a celebrated litigation boutique, this Texas outfit is well equipped to handle insurance coverage and bad faith litigation. Its practitioners are particularly experienced defending insurers and carriers against class actions. The team has recently represented major carrier Liberty Mutual in a significant insurance dispute that emerged in the aftermath of the Deepwater Horizon oil spill and environmental disaster.
**Sources say:** "*They live and breathe insurance.*" "*They are perfect for complicated or dangerous cases.*"
**KEY INDIVIDUALS** Known as "*one heck of a lawyer*," **Christopher Martin** is head of the firm's insurance department. Commentators particularly highlight his trial skills: "*He possesses very rare qualities in that he is softly spoken but can be aggressive and very good in court.*" Experienced practitioner **David Disiere** focuses his practice on complex insurance coverage and first-party litigation. He has recently been involved in the representation of Liberty Mutual in a large lawsuit.

## Insurance: Regulation
### Senior Statesmen

**Senior Statesmen: distinguished older practitioners**

| | |
|---|---|
| Davis Will | Thompson, Coe, Cousins & Irons, LLP |

### Leading Individuals

**Band 1**

| | |
|---|---|
| Bond Thomas J | Greenberg Traurig, LLP (ONP)† * |
| Keller Mary | Winstead PC * |
| Thompson Jay | Thompson, Coe, Cousins & Irons, LLP |

**Band 2**

| | |
|---|---|
| Gonzales Alex | Winstead PC * |
| Perkins Michael | Sneed, Vine & Perry (ONP)† |
| Yelkin Kimberly A | Gardere Wynne Sewell LLP * |

\* Indicates individual with profile.
†ONP = Other Notable Practitioner

## Thompson, Coe, Cousins & Irons, LLP
See profile on p.2457

**THE FIRM** This firm earns positive recognition for its wide array of insurance services, which include regulatory and transactional matters and coverage claims. The team regularly represents some of the country's most prominent insurers, with a particular emphasis on catastrophe claims. The practitioners are adept at handling a multitude of claims including construction and builders' risk, life and health claims and professional liability. Recent highlights include defending a major insurer against over 900 lawsuits arising after Hurricane Ike.
**Sources say:** "*Extensive knowledge of insurance coverage issues, high-quality work product, outstanding trial skills, extremely fair and reasonable billing practices, and easy to work with.*"
**KEY INDIVIDUALS Brian Martin** is identified as "*probably the best coverage lawyer in Texas*" and garners an overwhelming amount of respect. Commentators agree he is "*an outstanding speaker and writer.*" He successfully defended North River Insurance in a $72 million lawsuit regarding the distribution of Chinese drywall products. **Jay Thompson** is regarded by market sources as "*a premier insurance industry lobbyist and regulatory counsel*" who is held in high regard by sources. He recently represented

Progressive County Mutual Insurance and other insurers before the Texas Attorney General in advertising issues. **Roger Higgins** specializes in defending insurers against catastrophe claims. This expertise is illustrated by his continued representation of a major insurer against multiple Hurricane Ike lawsuits. Sources add that he is "*premier for bad faith insurance class actions.*" **Rodrigo Garcia** is acknowledged as an impressive insurance coverage litigator, handling issues involving construction defects, D&O liability, property liability, environmental pollution and personal injury claims. He is known to be "*very knowledgeable and effective in all phases of litigation.*" The deeply experienced **Will Davis** is a significant asset to the team and regularly handles regulatory and transactional matters for insurance companies. **Richard Geiger** continues to provide insurance organizations with sound advice and support regarding regulatory issues. **Ellen Van Meir** is a new addition to the rankings and comes highly recommended by her peers. She represents insurance carriers against a variety of coverage claims.

## Band 2

### Brown & Kornegay LLP

**THE FIRM** This compact litigation boutique is praised for its impressive output in insurance disputes. The team exclusively represents policyholders in coverage claims, serving a diverse cross-section of clients from industries including energy, real estate, petrochemicals and transportation. The firm has recently been particularly engaged with Hurricane Ike property claims.
**Sources say:** "*Up there with any of the massive full-service firms that I have used in the past. Nothing is too complex.*"
**KEY INDIVIDUALS David Brown** (see p.2382) garners high praise as a widely respected insurance coverage lawyer. Sources enthuse about his "*encyclopedic knowledge of insurance law,*" saying also: "*His advocacy skills are absolutely superb*" and "*he has the ability to take something that's very complex and explain it in a simple way.*" **Nancy Kornegay** (see p.2399) has thoroughly impressed both clients and peers with her "*smart and practical demeanor*" when representing policyholders. One client noted: "*Nancy's instincts, preparation and strategic choices were correct over and over again.*"

### Cooper & Scully PC
See profile on p.2433

**THE FIRM** Consistently touted as one of the leading insurance firms, Cooper & Scully specializes in insurance coverage and represents both policyholders and insurers. The team is adept at handling a range of insurance issues including general and professional liability claims. The practitioners also frequently defend bad faith claims against insurance carriers.
**Sources say:** "*They have a dominant presence in the insurance world.*"
**KEY INDIVIDUALS** Hailed as one of the go-to insurance lawyers in Texas, **Brent Cooper** is highly regarded for his broad commercial litigation practice. His deep experience

enables him to represent clients effectively in a range of sophisticated coverage disputes.

## Fulbright & Jaworski LLP
See profile on p.2435

THE FIRM This Texas giant is predominantly known for representing major insurance companies in coverage disputes. However, the team is also equally capable in handling transactional and regulatory matters. The group's impressive clientele includes many large insurance organizations, including Lexington and Farmers Group. The team has also represented Chartis in multiple insurance class action disputes.

Sources say: *"A strong litigation practice."*

KEY INDIVIDUALS Practice head **Stephen Pate** (see p.2409) has built a commendable reputation for dispute resolution, which includes representing major insurers in complex cases. This is illustrated by his recent representation of United States Fire Insurance in a number of claims emerging from property damage caused by Hurricane Ike. **Reagan Brown** (see p.2382) has a successful track record defending carriers in lawsuits across a multitude of areas, including personal injury, automobiles and health insurance. Sources also attest to his expert appellate practice. **Barclay Nicholson** (see p.2407) is described as a *"very diligent, bright guy"* who continues to make headway in the market. He has recently been heavily involved in the firm's key representation of Chartis.

## Shidlofsky Law Firm PLLC

THE FIRM This compact Austin boutique is able to consistently punch above its weight when representing policyholders against major insurance companies. The team regularly acts on behalf of a range of corporations on a range of liability issues including D&O, E&O, general liability and business interruption claims.

Sources say: *"Major players in coverage litigation."*

KEY INDIVIDUALS Firm founder **Lee Shidlofsky** is regarded as an expert policyholder lawyer who handles many varying coverage issues, yet places particular emphasis on claims concerning construction defects and product liability. According to sources, he is *"a creative thinker"* who does *"outstanding work"* and is *"a good guy to work with."* Senior associate **Douglas Skelley** is a rising star in policyholder representation across a range of insurance coverage cases. Market sources describe him as *"a very sharp guy."*

## Winstead PC
See profile on p.2460

THE FIRM This Texas stalwart is renowned for its superior regulatory practice which acts on behalf of a series of insurance brokers and agents. The team also has an active insurance dispute resolution presence, having recently represented Arrowood Surplus Lines Insurance in a $7.3 million lawsuit involving property damage. Other significant clients include OneBeacon Insurance, First American Title Insurance and Zurich American Insurance Company.

Sources say: *"Excellent and proactive. They think about the client's needs and are very effective with insurance work."*

KEY INDIVIDUALS **Mary Keller** (see p.2398) has spent over 25 years in government employment, and is consequently regarded as a leading insurance regulation expert. She also dedicates part of her practice to litigating related disputes. Transactional specialist **Alex Gonzales** (see p.2391) serves as managing partner of the Austin office. He represents major insurance companies and financial institutions in compliance and regulatory matters. Clients appreciate that *"he's well connected on all levels of government in Texas and knowledgeable about the specific laws and regulations that affect the company."* Insurance litigation specialist **Linda Burgess** (see p.2383) enters the rankings this year following strong market feedback. *"She is very dedicated, detail-oriented and diligent,"* say sources. **Jay Brown** (see p.2382) is known for his successful record on behalf of insurers across a range of disputes including bad faith, catastrophic accidents, contract disputes and fraud. Notable highlights include the successful dismissal of a $75 million property claim arising from Hurricane Ike. Market sources are full of praise for **Peter Nolan** (see p.2407), who is known for taking on complex disputes. Commentators also mention his impeccable trial skills, saying he has *"a very good demeanor in front of a jury."*

## Band 3

### Hall Maines Lugrin, P.C.

THE FIRM Hall Maines Lugrin offers a diverse range of services, including insurance and reinsurance and coverage disputes spanning an assortment of industries such as construction, oil and gas and the energy sector in particular. The firm is also singled out as one of the go-to firms for London market insurers. For example, the firm currently represents various London market insurers in a matter arising from the Deepwater Horizon incident in the Gulf of Mexico.

Sources say: *"They have good, knowledgeable, commercial lawyers."*

KEY INDIVIDUALS **Clifton Hall** concentrates on representing insurers within the energy sector who are faced with insurance coverage disputes. He is characterized as *"charismatic and very good in court."*

### Phelps Dunbar LLP
See profile on p.1383

THE FIRM Phelps Dunbar is best known for its significant work for the London market, notably representing underwriters at Lloyd's. The team takes on most aspects of coverage disputes, including professional liability and general liability, property, energy and marine insurance matters. Clients specifically appreciate the firm's focus on commerciality and industry knowledge. Current clients feature Aspen Insurance UK, Great American Insurance and Scottsdale Insurance.

Sources say: *"They display consistent professionalism in all of their contact with our organization and in their representation of our company when dealing with anyone outside the organization."*

KEY INDIVIDUALS **Claude Stuart** regularly represents insurers in major coverage litigation concerning a variety of first and third-party claims. According to sources, *"the advice he provides is considered and thoughtful."*

### Shannon, Gracey, Ratliff & Miller LLP
See profile on p.2453

THE FIRM With offices in Dallas, Houston, Fort Worth, Arlington and Austin this integrated practice group offers a truly local service to any company with operations in Texas. The team traditionally represents policyholders, but also has some involvement on the carrier side. The firm's diverse caseload consists of specialized problems relating to regulation and fraud, as well as broader matters relating to coverage disputes.

KEY INDIVIDUALS **Michael Huddleston** is described as *"one of the best and most brilliant coverage lawyers in the state."* He takes on extensive amounts of coverage work, but also handles bad faith claims and reinsurance issues.

### Tollefson Bradley Ball & Mitchell, LLP

THE FIRM This respected Dallas-based boutique specializes in representing insurers in coverage disputes, bad faith claims and also offers regulatory services. The team displays notable experience defending liability claims, and also handles property claims, excess and reinsurance matters.

KEY INDIVIDUALS **Beth Bradley** impresses peers with her remarkable track record defending insurers in coverage disputes and also has a strong appellate practice. New entry **John Tollefson** is regarded as *"very smart, balanced and resourceful"* by market sources. Alongside his recognized insurance coverage practice, he is also a respected mediator.

## Band 4

### Akin Gump Strauss Hauer & Feld LLP
See profile on p.904

THE FIRM This international firm is noted for its ability to handle the larger, more complex insurance issues. Its sizable team is well equipped to deal with sophisticated transactions and disputes regarding sales practices, bad faith claims and class actions, and also takes on regulatory matters. The group has represented Lloyd's underwriters in a dispute over an alleged $8 billion Ponzi scheme.

KEY INDIVIDUALS **Rick Rosenblum** (see p.2413) is hailed as *"wonderful, very competent and mild-mannered yet aggressive."* He has recently been heavily involved in the firm's representation of the London market.

### Beirne Maynard & Parsons, LLP
See profile on p.2428

THE FIRM This Texas firm has a significant insurance presence. The practice is focused on advising and representing carriers, insureds and insurers in coverage disputes concerning the range of professional liability and insurance bad faith claims.

**KEY INDIVIDUALS** Founding partner **Jeffrey Parsons** (see p.2409) is respected for his expertise and experience in class actions and complex coverage disputes concerning property liability, environmental lawsuits and IP claims, among others.

## Cox Smith Matthews Incorporated

**THE FIRM** This firm is regarded as a go-to firm for environmental coverage issues. The firm has recently expanded its service to better cater for clients in the energy industry, with a specific emphasis on oil and gas production. The team handles a broad range of matters on behalf of a series of major national insurance companies including Hartford Life Accident Insurance, Great American Insurance and Fireman's Fund.

**KEY INDIVIDUALS Thomas Alleman** is described as a *"really tenacious guy who leaves no rock unturned."* His practice particularly focuses on sophisticated environmental and energy coverage issues.

## Porter Hedges LLP
See profile on p.2450

**THE FIRM** This firm exclusively represents policyholders in an array of insurance coverage matters. Although the team has a strong focus on construction issues, it also houses expertise in cases involving professional and general liability, property insurance and environmental coverage. Key clients include Kellogg Brown & Root and Continental Carbon.

**Sources say:** *"Efficient, always cordial and always available."*

**KEY INDIVIDUALS** Head of department **Cynthia Holub** (see p.2396) specializes in insurance coverage litigation and matters relating to construction. She is held in high regard in this field by market commentators.

## Roach & Newton, L.L.P.

**THE FIRM** This compact group continues to concentrate on insurance coverage issues and appellate law in insurance cases. The firm has built a strong presence in Texas, with offices in Beaumont, Austin and Houston.

**KEY INDIVIDUALS Robert Roach** has a healthy appellate practice, enhanced by his extensive experience in the insurance field. He also handles mediations and arbitrations concerning insurance coverage. **Robert Cunningham** is described by market sources as *"very scholarly"* and impresses peers with his smooth handling of complex insurance and commercial disputes.

## Sutherland Asbill & Brennan LLP

**THE FIRM** This established firm is particularly known for its expertise in offshore energy and marine insurance coverage issues. Recent highlights include its representation of Transocean in insurance cases arising from the BP oil spill in the Gulf of Mexico. The group also has a significant presence in the London market, working on behalf of underwriters at Lloyd's.

**KEY INDIVIDUALS Steven Roberts** is singled out for his strong advocacy skills and ability to handle complex litigation. He has led the firm's representation of Transocean and is also active in the London market. **Daniel Johnson** is widely regarded as a rising star in insurance law. Market sources praise his practical approach to providing business-related advice.

## Other Notable Practitioners

**Pete Schenkkan** of Graves, Dougherty, Hearon & Moody, P.C. is regarded as *"a brilliant guy"* and *"incredibly bright"* by commentators. He has a broad practice, handling regulatory and administrative issues alongside his work in other areas such as environmental and antitrust law. **Thomas Bond** (see p.2381) of Greenberg Traurig, LLP is considered to be one of the leading lights in the regulatory field. Sources laud his *"depth and breadth of knowledge of the Texas legislative process."* **Vincent Morgan** (see p.2406) of Pillsbury Winthrop Shaw Pittman LLP is hailed as *"a great asset to the insurance community"* by commentators. He regularly represents corporate policyholders in a wide variety of insurance coverage disputes. **James Cornell** of Cornell & Pardue LLP is regarded by commentators as a leading representative of policyholders in insurance coverage work. He also has a strong commercial litigation practice. **Michael Perkins** of Sneed, Vine & Perry, A Professional Corporation regularly handles significant work on behalf of numerous insurance companies in regulatory issues. He is experienced dealing with matters concerning life insurance, property, casualty, accident and health insurance. **Patrick Wielinski** of Cokinos, Bosien and Young specializes in coverage matters concerning the construction industry. Sources note he is particularly adept at handling difficult coverage issues. **Linda Dedman** of Dedman & Handschuch enjoys *"a great reputation for representing policyholders in coverage matters."* She handles both first and third-party claims for clients from an array of industries. **Mark Lawless** is managing partner of McGuireWoods LLP's Austin office. He is celebrated as *"one of the best lawyers in the state,"* whose *"policyholder representation is truly exceptional."* He handles a diverse range of coverage disputes including issues concerning employment practices, asbestos and the environment.

# INTELLECTUAL PROPERTY

Commentary about individuals can be found under their firm's paragraph. If the firm has no paragraph (is not ranked) look at Other Notable Practitioners.

## Intellectual Property — Leading Firms

**Band 1**
Baker Botts LLP *
Fish & Richardson PC
McKool Smith *

**Band 2**
Fulbright & Jaworski LLP *
Haynes and Boone, LLP *
Jones Day *
Sidley Austin LLP *
Thompson & Knight LLP *
Vinson & Elkins LLP *
Weil, Gotshal & Manges LLP *

**Band 3**
Baker & McKenzie *
Bracewell & Giuliani LLP *
Cox Smith Matthews Incorporated
Locke Lord LLP *
Morgan, Lewis & Bockius LLP *
Pirkey Barber LLP
Susman Godfrey LLP

**Band 4**
Akin Gump Strauss Hauer & Feld LLP *
Conley Rose, PC
DLA Piper LLP (US) *
Heim, Payne & Chorush LLP *
Munck Wilson Mandala LLP *
Sutton McAughan Deaver, PLLC *
Winston & Strawn LLP *

## Intellectual Property: Trade Mark & Copyright — Leading Individuals

**Star individuals**

| | |
|---|---|
| Pirkey Louis | Pirkey Barber LLP |

**Band 1**

| | |
|---|---|
| Barber Bill | Pirkey Barber LLP |
| Becker Jeffrey | Haynes and Boone, LLP |
| Buck Richard Molly | Richard Law Group (ONP)[†] |

**Band 2**

| | |
|---|---|
| Berryman Cathryn A | Winstead PC (ONP)[†] * |
| Huff Pamela B | Cox Smith Matthews Incorporated |
| Vale Shannon | Pirkey Barber LLP |

**Band 3**

| | |
|---|---|
| Boulware Margaret A | Boulware & Valoir (ONP)[†] |
| Cotropia Charles S | Sidley Austin LLP * |
| Groos Richard J | Fulbright & Jaworski LLP * |
| Rawls III John C. | Baker Williams Matthiesen (ONP)[†] |

*  Indicates firm / individual with profile.
[†]ONP = Other Notable Practitioner

## Intellectual Property — Leading Individuals

**Band 1**

| | |
|---|---|
| Baxter Samuel F | McKool Smith * |
| Cawley Douglas | McKool Smith * |
| Healey David J | Fish & Richardson PC |
| LaFuze William L | Vinson & Elkins LLP * |
| McCombs David | Haynes and Boone, LLP |
| McKool Mike | McKool Smith * |
| Partridge Scott | Baker Botts LLP * |
| Schuurman Willem | Vinson & Elkins LLP * |
| Showalter Barton E | Baker Botts LLP * |
| Slusser William C | Fulbright & Jaworski LLP * |

**Band 2**

| | |
|---|---|
| Barzoukas Nicolas G | Weil, Gotshal & Manges LLP * |
| Bradley James P | Sidley Austin LLP * |
| Clonts David R | Akin Gump Strauss Hauer & Feld LLP * |
| Galvan Hilda | Jones Day * |
| Heim Michael F | Heim, Payne & Chorush LLP * |
| Israel Sharon | Mayer Brown LLP (ONP)[†] |
| Keville John | Winston & Strawn LLP * |
| Krieger Paul | Morgan, Lewis & Bockius LLP * |
| Kudlac Kevin | Weil, Gotshal & Manges LLP * |
| McAughan Jr Robert J | Sutton McAughan Deaver, PLLC |
| Melsheimer Tom | Fish & Richardson PC |
| Parker David L | Parker Highlander PLLC (ONP)[†] |
| Sostek Bruce S | Thompson & Knight LLP * |
| Stevenson III Theodore | McKool Smith * |
| Susman Stephen D | Susman Godfrey LLP |
| White T Gordon | McKool Smith * |

**Band 3**

| | |
|---|---|
| Albright Alan D | Bracewell & Giuliani LLP * |
| Baker Charles S | Fulbright & Jaworski LLP * |
| Barr Jr John H | Bracewell & Giuliani LLP * |
| Burgert David | Porter Hedges LLP (ONP)[†] * |
| Chen Li | Sidley Austin LLP * |
| Dodd Jeff | Andrews Kurth LLP (ONP)[†] * |
| Farney Bryan | Farney Daniels (ONP)[†] |
| Govett Brett C | Fulbright & Jaworski LLP * |

| | |
|---|---|
| Guaragna John M | DLA Piper LLP (US) * |
| Hammond Herbert J | Thompson & Knight LLP * |
| Jordan Carey | McDermott Will & Emery LLP (ONP)[†] * |
| Kimball Jr Albert B | Bracewell & Giuliani LLP * |
| Levy David | Morgan, Lewis & Bockius LLP * |
| Meek Kevin J | Baker Botts LLP * |
| Mims Peter E | Vinson & Elkins LLP * |
| Nation Floyd | Winston & Strawn LLP * |
| Philbin Phillip B | Haynes and Boone, LLP |
| Spears L Gene | Baker Botts LLP * |
| Sutton Michael O | Sutton McAughan Deaver, PLLC * |
| Tobor Ben D | Greenberg Traurig, LLP (ONP)[†] * |
| Turner Robert W | McDole, Kennedy & Williams (ONP)[†] |

**Band 4**

| | |
|---|---|
| Cagle Steve | Winston & Strawn LLP * |
| Emerson J. Russell | Haynes and Boone, LLP |
| Flaim John G | Baker & McKenzie |
| Hall Eric B. | Fulbright & Jaworski LLP * |
| Hewitt Lester L | Akin Gump Strauss Hauer & Feld LLP |
| Huffman Bart W | Locke Lord LLP * |
| Kubehl Douglas M | Baker Botts LLP |
| Lukin Mitch | Baker Botts LLP |
| Malin Steven | Sidley Austin LLP * |
| McSpadden William | Baker & McKenzie |
| Munck William A | Munck Wilson Mandala LLP |
| Repass James | Fulbright & Jaworski LLP * |
| Rose David A | Conley Rose, PC |
| Stephens Garland | Weil, Gotshal & Manges LLP * |
| Tribble Max | Susman Godfrey LLP |
| Walker Charles | Fulbright & Jaworski LLP * |
| Weaver David | Vinson & Elkins LLP * |
| Whittle Jeffrey S | Bracewell & Giuliani LLP * |
| Zembek Richard S. | Fulbright & Jaworski LLP * |

**Up-and-coming individuals**

| | |
|---|---|
| Burgess Kevin | McKool Smith * |

**Associates to watch**

| | |
|---|---|
| Fountain Aaron | DLA Piper LLP (US) * |

## Band 1

### Baker Botts LLP
See profile on p.2427

**THE FIRM** Baker Botts has one of the most dynamic and extensive IP practices in the Southwest, and can now be said to enjoy a nationwide reputation for its lawyers' work in the discipline. The Texas group has a deep pool of resources on hand to tackle any legal issue concerning all categories of IP rights, regardless of scale or international scope. Major clients include Dell, Halliburton Company and BlackBerry.
**Sources say:** "A very formidable force to have on your side."
**KEY INDIVIDUALS Scott Partridge** (see p.2409) is a "very strong trial lawyer" with significant victories to his name, and is a fixture in the courts of the Eastern District of Texas, one of the nation's most active battlegrounds for IP litigation. He has tried cases centering on hard and soft IP rights. **Barton Showalter**'s (see p.2416) standing at the Texas IP Bar is such that fellow attorneys "refer defense case clients to him in a flash." He is the firmwide IP department chair, and has particular expertise in electronics, semiconductors, communications and software. **Kevin Meek** (see p.2405) heads the IP team at the firm's Austin office. His "very diverse, rich practice" takes in patent, trademark and copyright work, both contentious and noncontentious. **Gene Spears** (see p.2417) specializes mainly in the prosecution and enforcement of chemical patents. He has litigated cases concerning chemical, genetic engineering, diagnostic and mechanical technologies. **Douglas Kubehl**

is praised by big-name clients for his conscientiousness and affability to work with. He litigates patent cases involving technologies of all kinds, and is also an expert in IP licensing and the management of patent portfolios. **Mitch Lukin** (see p.2402) has an admirably broad IP practice, which includes transactions and agreements involving IP rights of all kinds, as well as portfolio development, counseling and infringement litigation.

## Fish & Richardson PC

**THE FIRM** This venerable technology and IP-focused firm has offices in Austin, Dallas and Houston, and a market-leading nationwide presence for patent, trademark and copyright legal services. A powerhouse for counseling and litigation, the firm's principal focuses are on computer hardware, internet, software, telecom and transport technologies. Clients include Adobe Systems, iRobot and Velcro USA.

**Sources say:** "*This wide breadth of expertise makes Fish & Richardson attractive to our company, which is involved in offering products across numerous different markets.*"

**KEY INDIVIDUALS** Described variously as a "*commanding presence in court*" and "*always a gentleman,*" **David Healey** is an accomplished trial lawyer with an excellent track record of litigating patent and related antitrust cases in multiple jurisdictions. **Tom Melsheimer** heads the firm's Dallas office, as well as that office's trial practice. He recently led the firm in its successful defense of United, Continental, Delta, US Airways, Virgin, Ticketmaster, Live Nation and TicketsNow in a patent suit filed by CEATS regarding aircraft ticketing software.

## McKool Smith

**See profile on p.2446**

**THE FIRM** McKool Smith is widely regarded as one of the leading firms for IP and particularly patent litigation, in a state that remains a prime venue for such disputes. As well as representing defendants in patent and other IP right infringement cases, the firm is also well known for its work representing plaintiffs bringing claims. Areas of strength include computer and software technology, telecom, pharmaceuticals and medical devices.

**Sources say:** "*Enormously talented trial lawyers.*"

**KEY INDIVIDUALS Samuel Baxter** (see p.2380) is one of the firm's most effective trial attorneys, and is described by a source as "*the real deal.*" Primarily a patent litigator, he is a seasoned veteran of the Eastern District of Texas courts. **Douglas Cawley** (see p.2384) is roundly considered to be a "*superb*" IP litigator in the pantheon of contemporary Texas-based trial attorneys. He has had a number of recent successes for plaintiffs, acting against household names in consumer technology. **Theodore Stevenson** (see p.2417) acts for globally recognized clients in significant patent cases. He is particularly renowned for his understanding of computer, software and telecom technology, as well as oil-field equipment and medical devices. **Gordon White** (see p.2422) is the principal in charge of the firm's Austin office. He has a long-established reputation as a persuasive and highly successful trial lawyer in cases of great technical complexity, often regarding electrical engineering patents.

**Kevin Burgess** (see p.2383) is a veteran patent litigator with a PhD in electrical engineering. He has excelled in defense and plaintiff infringement actions, frequently involving very complex technical applications. **Mike McKool** (see p.2405) is lauded by all commentators, with one saying: "*He is a great leader of the firm and has encouraged its growth very deftly.*" A leading trial lawyer, McKool is sought by companies needing a powerful and effective litigator for their most sensitive cases.

## Band 2

## Fulbright & Jaworski LLP

**See profile on p.2435**

**THE FIRM** This Texan firm gone global has offices in Austin, Dallas, Houston and San Antonio, and more than 100 attorneys experienced in IP, making it well placed to serve technology-heavy companies with operations in the state. The firm's comprehensive IP offering takes in patent, trademark, copyright, design and trade secret matters, and is as adept at high-stakes litigation as it is at non-contentious counseling and portfolio management.

**KEY INDIVIDUALS William Slusser** (see p.2416) is based in the Houston office and is described as "*vigorous, focused and motivated.*" As a seasoned hand at highly complex patent suits, it is said with understatement that he "*knows his way around a courtroom.*" **Charles Baker** (see p.2379) is an all-round IP litigator, having led cases centering on patents, trademark, copyright, trade secret issues, and related antitrust law questions. He is particularly sought for cases involving computer hardware, software, internet and telecom technology. **Brett Govett** (see p.2392) has a comprehensive IP infringement trial and litigation practice. He is known for his skills in the courtroom and for his effectiveness before a jury. **Richard Groos** (see p.2392) is an expert in the registration and commercial exploitation of copyright, trademarks and domain names. He is, according to sources, "*consummately professional, composed and a good adviser to clients.*" **Eric Hall** (see p.2393) is widely known for his expertise in patent law relating to telecom and IT technologies. His practice takes in litigation and prosecution as well as commercial agreements and transactions. **James Repass** (see p.2412) chairs the firmwide IP and technology department. He is well regarded for his expertise in handling the IP aspects of transactions such as licensing agreements, joint ventures and M&A, and also for his skill at patent, trademark and copyright disputes. **Charles Walker** (see p.2420) heads the Houston office's IP and technology team. His areas of focus include patent, trademark, copyright, trade secrets and false advertising litigation. He recently won an important jury verdict for Louis Vuitton in an action against a commercial landlord accused of letting premises to traders in counterfeit luxury goods. **Richard Zembek** (see p.2424) is adept at all manner of transactional IP matters, such as technology transfers, licensing agreements, patent licenses and software development. He is also an accomplished litigator with experience of cases involving all kinds of IP rights.

## Haynes and Boone, LLP

**See profile on p.444**

**THE FIRM** This leading Texan powerhouse has in recent years expanded beyond the state lines and is now considered to have a formidable national practice in IP as well as other practice areas. The group within Texas comprises attorneys who are well versed in the commercial as well as legal facets of IP rights, many of whom have previous experience as research scientists and as in-house counsel at technology companies working across the spectrum of scientific and technical matters.

**Sources say:** "*A very talented group.*"

**KEY INDIVIDUALS Jeffrey Becker** is an all-around soft IP specialist whose practice takes in registration, portfolio management, litigation and transactional work centering on trademarks, copyright, trade secrets, domain names and patent prosecution. **David McCombs** is praised by sources for his "*great technical understanding and practical manner.*" He is above all a patent specialist, and conducts litigation as well as drafting, prosecution and USPTO proceedings. He also handles IP-related transactions and agreements. **Russell Emerson** is a patent trial lawyer and litigator with deep experience in acting for household-name blue-chips, often in actions concerning digital technology and internet-related patents. **Phillip Philbin** is well regarded for his skills as a "*strong trial lawyer*" and a "*very good advocate for his clients.*" He is best known for trying patent suits, and also has extensive experience litigating matters concerned with copyright, trade dress, trademark and trade secrets.

## Jones Day

**See profile on p.919**

**THE FIRM** Jones Day's Texas offices, located in Dallas and Houston, have in recent years expanded to offer expert IP services relevant to technologies beyond the firm's consistently strong emphasis on electronic and software rights. The firm is widely known for the effectiveness of its patent litigation work, and for the quality of its noncontentious prosecution and portfolio management services. Clients include Dell, GM and Hyundai.

**KEY INDIVIDUALS Hilda Galvan** (see p.2390) has carved an admirable reputation for her formidable representation of clients in business-critical patent disputes, very often multidefendant cases. Her principal areas of expertise include computing, electronics and software actions.

## Sidley Austin LLP

**See profile on p.1264**

**THE FIRM** Sidley Austin continues to go from strength to strength in its IP presence in Texas, where it has offices in Dallas and Houston. Patent litigation is a universally acknowledged strong suit, with a particular focus on hi-tech patents for electronic engineering, telecom and semiconductors, as well as pharmaceutical, medical devices and biologics.

**KEY INDIVIDUALS James Bradley** (see p.2382) heads the IP department in the Dallas office. His primary area of focus is patent litigation, typically relating to rights to developments in semiconductor, telecom and oilfield technologies. **Li Chen** (see p.2384) is a widely respected lead litigator and trial lawyer with *"good strategic vision."* He mainly specializes in patent disputes, and also advises on IP transactions and strategy. In addition, he is much sought for advice concerning Far Eastern technology markets. **Charles Cotropia** (see p.2386) is best known for his longstanding expertise and success in managing copyright, trademark and trade dress litigation and trials brought before the federal courts and the USPTO. **Steven Malin** (see p.2402) is admired for his ability to assimilate and simplify complex technological details in IP disputes of all kinds – hard and soft IP – and litigates cases across an admirable range of technology and industry sectors.

### Thompson & Knight LLP
See profile on p.2458

**THE FIRM** Thompson & Knight owes its enviable reputation to the sheer range and depth of its attorneys' knowledge and experience across the range of IP matters, both contentious and noncontentious. As well as having a good name in IP litigation, the Texas group has sophisticated capabilities in patent, trademark and copyright registration, prosecution, and transactional and portfolio management.

**Sources say:** *"They brought a lot of knowledge and creativity to the table."*

**KEY INDIVIDUALS Bruce Sostek** (see p.2417) is variously described as a *"very strategic thinker"* and as being *"very personable and tenacious."* He is foremost a patent litigator with much experience practicing before the courts of the crucial Eastern District of Texas circuit. **Herbert Hammond**'s (see p.2393) IP practice is impressively comprehensive, taking in the litigation and arbitration of hard and soft IP rights, as well as transactions such as licensing agreements and counseling on IP strategy.

### Vinson & Elkins LLP
See profile on p.2459

**THE FIRM** This Texas institution excels in its representation of clients in the life sciences, pharmaceuticals, hi-tech electronics, online and digital media sectors. Litigation is above all the focus of the practice, which deals mainly with patent cases but also a variety of trademark, copyright and trade secrets actions. The group also counsels on portfolio management, commercial agreements and the treatment of IP in M&A transactions.

**Sources say:** *"They are attuned to our commercial interests and understand the need for balance between legal and commercial issues."*

**KEY INDIVIDUALS William LaFuze** (see p.2400) is roundly considered a hard-working and talented attorney. His practice focuses on patent litigation on behalf of electronics, computing, online and oilfield technology companies. **Willem Schuurman** (see p.2415) has an impressive track record as a patent and trade secrets litigator and trial lawyer, and has tried cases involving biotechnology, electronics, software and pharmaceutical patents. His background in patent registration and prosecution strongly informs his approach to cases. **Peter Mims** (see p.2405)

*"cuts to the chase, understands issues well and knows how to resolve matters."* He is an accomplished trial lawyer and litigator who handles patent, trademark, trade secrets and copyright disputes for clients in the chemicals, medical devices, computing, healthcare and fossil fuel extraction sectors. **David Weaver** (see p.2421) specializes in patent litigation. His technical background is in aerospace engineering, and he handles numerous semiconductor, internet and digital media disputes. *"What impresses me is that he is a technical guy who can translate difficult concepts into normal language,"* said one interviewee.

### Weil, Gotshal & Manges LLP
See profile on p.2015

**THE FIRM** The IP team at Weil, Gotshal & Manges concentrates exclusively on patent litigation in the two primary areas of hi-tech and pharmaceuticals. The team notably acted as trial counsel for Amazon and Yahoo!, obtaining a Texas federal jury verdict in their favor upholding their challenges to the validity of patents held by the plaintiff, Eolas Technologies.

**KEY INDIVIDUALS Nicolas Barzoukas** (see p.2380) is a patent litigator specializing in pharmaceuticals and, more specifically, Hatch-Waxman Act cases in which allegations of infringement are made by branded pharmaceutical concerns against generic drugs companies. **Kevin Kudlac** (see p.2400) handles patent litigation concerning the alleged infringement of complex computing, hardware, software and electronics technology, as well as matters related to medical devices. **Garland Stephens** (see p.2417) is a seasoned trial lawyer who concentrates mainly on patent cases focused on sophisticated electrical engineering and computer technology.

### Band 3

### Baker & McKenzie
See profile on p.435

**THE FIRM** Baker & McKenzie's Texas IP team makes up a significant proportion of the firm's nationwide offering, reflected in the range and scale of work undertaken from Dallas and Houston. The two offices have strong patent and soft IP capabilities, and run global anticounterfeiting campaigns on behalf of clients. The team has a good name for IP litigation, and for patent prosecution and strategic counseling.

**KEY INDIVIDUALS John Flaim** chairs the firm's global IP practice and is above all an IP litigator known for his *"good workmanship."* A large portion of his case load is devoted to representing financial institutions and service providers in patent actions. **William McSpadden** concentrates on patent litigation, counseling, opinion and prosecution work. He has particular expertise in patents relating to financial systems, medical devices, semiconductors, software and telecom.

### Bracewell & Giuliani LLP
See profile on p.2429

**THE FIRM** Bracewell & Giuliani's IP team in Texas stands out for its up-to-the-minute knowledge and experience representing energy sector companies and natural resources extraction technology manufacturers. It also acts for giants in the hi-tech and consumer electronics fields, as well as e-commerce and biomedical science-reliant entities. Clients include Google, Hewlett-Packard and Lockheed Martin.

**Sources say:** *"Experienced and consummate professionals."*

**KEY INDIVIDUALS Alan Albright** (see p.2377) is highly sought by sophisticated clients in the technology sector. His comprehensive practice covers licensing agreements, patent litigation, licensing, protection and enforcement of trade secrets, as well as the variety of issues faced by technology companies. **John Barr** (see p.2379) concentrates mainly on IP and oil and gas-related disputes. His strengths include patent actions, trademark, copyright and trade secrets litigation, and Abbreviated New Drug Application cases. **Albert Kimball** (see p.2399) litigates and tries patent suits for defendants and plaintiffs, and often acts for major US and international corporations. He also counsels on the treatment and transfer of IP rights in M&A transactions and commercial agreements. **Jeffrey Whittle** (see p.2422) heads the firm's technology practice and advises technology clients and IP-heavy businesses on acquisitions, mergers, licensing agreements and joint ventures. He also advises on IP planning, strategy, licensing and patent filing. He has particular expertise in electronics and software as applied to geology and the extractive industries.

### Cox Smith Matthews Incorporated

**THE FIRM** This firm has five offices throughout Texas and handles all manner of litigious, commercial and transactional IP work. The firm is particularly appreciated for its attorneys' skill in matters concerning trademarks, copyright and soft IP rights. The firm has also expanded its patent and IP litigation capability, and is increasing its representation of oil and gas technology clients.

**KEY INDIVIDUALS Pamela Huff** is well regarded for her trademark and soft IP work, and has further experience on patent matters. She specializes in international portfolio management and licensing work, and related litigation.

### Locke Lord LLP
See profile on p.2443

**THE FIRM** With offices in Austin, Dallas and Houston, Locke Lord has a strong presence in Texas as well as nationally. The team is well equipped to handle all manner of patent, trademark, trade secret and copyright matters. It includes a number of specialists with extensive experience in handling matters before the USPTO, and in Hatch-Waxman patent infringement claims.

**KEY INDIVIDUALS Bart Huffman** (see p.2396) has vast knowledge of the issues surrounding e-commerce, data and privacy, and the internet, owing in part to his background as a systems engineer.

## Morgan, Lewis & Bockius LLP
See profile on p.2246

**THE FIRM** This firm's Texas IP team is based in Houston and is best known for its panache in patent litigation. It has a distinguished record in the courtrooms of the state's Eastern District. Clients include Hewlett-Packard, LG Electronics and United Continental Holdings.

**KEY INDIVIDUALS Paul Krieger** (see p.2400) is a hard-hitting patent litigator with *"excellent legal and commercial sense."* He has also tried cases regarding copyright, trademarks and trade secrets, and is engaged for nonlitigious IP counseling. The *"particularly impressive"* **David Levy** (see p.2401) chairs the group's litigation practice. A significant proportion of his practice is taken up with IP work, including patent cases, and he has particular strength in wireless, internet and computer technology cases.

## Pirkey Barber LLP

**THE FIRM** This specialist firm, based in Austin, is renowned for having one of the best trademark and soft IP offerings in Texas, and indeed the country. It also excels in the related field of unfair competition law. It represents a truly global client base in litigation and USPTO actions, domain name disputes, registration and portfolio management.

**Sources say:** *"An excellent trademark litigation boutique."*
**KEY INDIVIDUALS** Firm cofounder **Louis Pirkey** is acknowledged as being one of the foremost authorities on trademark law in the USA. He handles litigation and non-contentious work, and one interviewee noted that they had heard *"nothing but spectacular things"* about him. Fellow cofounder **Bill Barber** is renowned for his skills at trademark cases in federal courts nationwide and before the USPTO. He is currently president of the American Intellectual Property Law Association. **Shannon Vale** handles trademark and copyright litigation, license agreements, portfolio management and the treatment of IP rights and assets in M&A and corporate transactions.

## Susman Godfrey LLP

**THE FIRM** From offices in Dallas and Houston, Susman Godfrey represents defendants and plaintiffs in actions concerning copyright and trademark infringement, misuse of trade secrets, patent litigation and unfair competition. The attorneys' experience in plaintiff litigation is particularly highly commended by sources.

**KEY INDIVIDUALS Stephen Susman** is *"tenacious and fearless, and always exceedingly well prepared,"* say interviewees. He continues to be regarded as a *"force of nature"* in IP litigation. **Max Tribble** is esteemed as a litigator and trial lawyer in patent and complex IP cases, often concerning computer software and systems, video games, GPS technology and seismology.

## Band 4

### Akin Gump Strauss Hauer & Feld LLP
See profile on p.904

**KEY INDIVIDUALS** This firm's IP practice in Texas has five offices across the state and specializes in complex and high-stakes IP litigation for Fortune 500 companies. The team has consolidated its strength in patent litigation, and is also adept in actions concerning copyright, trademarks, trade secrets and internet domain names.

**KEY INDIVIDUALS David Clonts** (see p.2385) is probably best known for his abilities as a trial lawyer and litigator in patent cases involving semiconductors, communications and electronic engineering, although he is also much appreciated for his counsel to clients on long-term, strategic IP issues. **Lester Hewitt** is thought of as a dean of the Texas patent Bar, and has accrued victory after victory over the years, particularly in cases surrounding oilfield and oil-processing technology.

### Conley Rose, PC

**THE FIRM** With offices in Austin, Dallas and Houston, Conley Rose is one of the state's largest and most distinguished IP boutiques. A leader in patent, soft IP and internet-related litigation, the firm has a large number of patent agents and technical advisers forming the backbone of its well-regarded prosecution and registration practice.

**KEY INDIVIDUALS David Rose** is a seasoned litigator and counselor in all facets of IP law. He has particularly commanding authority in matters concerning oilfield equipment and technology.

### DLA Piper LLP (US)
See profile on p.1971

**THE FIRM** This international firm's IP teams in Austin and Houston continue to grow and attract acclaim. The Texas group has an impressive number of active patent cases before the state's courts at any one time, and is further strengthened by the firm's national and worldwide platforms. Clients include Hewlett-Packard, Motorola Mobility and Samsung Electronics.

**Sources say:** *"They more than exceeded our expectations."*
**KEY INDIVIDUALS John Guaragna** (see p.2392) handles sophisticated patent, indemnity, trademark and trade secret actions before US Federal courts and the USPTO. According to one source, he *"showed a level of care and concern for the client that was very impressive."* **Aaron Fountain** (see p.2389) is considered *"very bright, capable"* and *"super nice"* by senior legal sources. He is fast blazing a trail in patent litigation and is considered to be one of the most promising litigators of his generation.

### Heim, Payne & Chorush LLP
See profile on p.2440

**THE FIRM** This widely respected boutique firm operates from offices in Austin and Houston, and focuses exclusively on IP and technology-related antitrust litigation on behalf of defendants and plaintiffs. The range of technologies handled is impressively broad, taking in software,

hardware and microprocessors, pharmaceuticals and natural resources extraction and processing equipment.

**KEY INDIVIDUALS Michael Heim** (see p.2395) is praised for his deep technical understanding. He is a trial lawyer with an accomplished record in patent cases relating to software, hardware and consumer electronics.

### Munck Wilson Mandala LLP
See profile on p.2447

**THE FIRM** This firm is in the main a litigation shop, although it retains a thriving patent prosecution and counseling practice. It mainly acts for clients from the defense, computer science, semiconductor and telecom industries, and is taking on ever more work in expanding sectors such as energy and electronic gaming technologies.

**Sources say:** *"Excellent organizational and administrative infrastructure."*
**KEY INDIVIDUALS William Munck** is renowned for his skills at strategic patent analysis in judging the enforceability of patents infringement claims. His background as a software engineer makes him an excellent resource for legal and highly technical advice.

### Sutton McAughan Deaver, PLLC
See profile on p.2456

**THE FIRM** This Houston firm is dedicated to IP law, managing litigation, strategic counseling and portfolio management, and transactions such as license agreements. The team handles all aspects of IP, from consumer and industrial electronics through pharmaceuticals and energy production technologies to children's products and architectural copyright.

**KEY INDIVIDUALS Robert McAughan** has a varied and comprehensive IP practice that takes in transactional, advisory and litigious work in copyright, patents, trademarks, trade dress and trade secrets. **Michael Sutton** (see p.2418) handles the full range of IP litigation, leading on cases in which the infringement or defense of copyright, trademarks, trade secrets and patents is in issue.

### Winston & Strawn LLP
See profile on p.1267

**THE FIRM** The IP team at this firm's Houston office is noted for its formidable patent litigation offering, which has been impressively bolstered by a targeted expansion in recent years. It handles almost all areas of technology and IP rights, and has enjoyed successes in cases relating to consumer products, computing, oil and gas technologies and pharmaceuticals.

**Sources say:** *"A very effective group."*
**KEY INDIVIDUALS** Clients from household-name blue-chips *"can't say enough good things"* about **John Keville** (see p.2399), who is widely acknowledged as a *"top-notch attorney"* in patent litigation. **Floyd Nation** (see p.2406) is praised by clients and lawyers alike for his knowledge and judgment. He is an accomplished patent litigator and trial lawyer, specializing mainly in cases concerning chemistry, biotechnology, business methods and electronics. Sources describe **Steve Cagle** (see p.2383) as an *"excellent lawyer,"* adding that working with him is *"always a positive experi-*

*ence.*" He engages in patent litigation and also advises on patent prosecution and noncompete agreements.

## Other Notable Practitioners

**Margaret Boulware** of Boulware & Valoir has a much-admired and comprehensive IP practice, which includes contentious and noncontentious patent, copyright and trademark work. In patents, her strength lies in rights concerned with technologies in the fields of chemistry and biotechnology. **Molly Buck Richard** of Richard Law Group is considered by fellow professionals to be "*at the top of any good list*" of the most able trademark law specialists in Texas and beyond. Clients praise her capacity to get to know their businesses and their objectives. **Robert Turner** of McDole, Kennedy & Williams, PC has a universally acknowledged command of IP law in all its guises, having had experience with all rights and in advisory and adversarial situations. **John Rawls** of Baker Williams Matthiesen specializes mainly in litigation concerning brand protec-

tion, copyright, false advertising and trademarks. Sources remark on his "*impressive*" abilities and client base. **Bryan Farney** of Farney Daniels has fought patent actions at all levels of the US judiciary and is one of the most seasoned patent trial lawyers in the state. He has tried cases regarding chemical, mechanical engineering, consumer electronics, medical devices and pharmaceutical patents. **David Parker** has left his role as practice head at Fulbright to establish new IP boutique Parker Highlander PLLC. He has been heavily involved in a variety of patent infringement disputes on behalf of biotechnology and pharmaceutical companies. At Andrews Kurth LLP, **Jeff Dodd**'s (see p.2387) IP practice focuses mainly on the transactional end of the discipline in licensing and outsourcing matters, as well as handling questions of data security and online trading and business activities. **Cathryn Berryman** (see p.2381) of Winstead PC has a broad and sophisticated transactional IP practice, centering on technology development, distribution and license agreements of all kinds, as well as helping businesses of all sizes register, exploit and

protect their IP rights. **David Burgert** (see p.2383) of Porter Hedges LLP is an IP litigator who has shown himself to be unafraid to go to trial. As well as high-stakes patent cases, he also tries trademark suits and has a subspecialty in internet cyber-squatting and piracy-related matters. **Carey Jordan** (see p.2397) of McDermott Will & Emery LLP specializes in assembling and managing patent portfolios for large and emerging businesses, and guides these entities through their overall IP strategy. She also handles commercial licensing deals and leads the firm's alternative energy branding group. At Mayer Brown LLP, **Sharon Israel** focuses predominantly on patent litigation concerned with technologies invented for the oilfield services, electronics and telecom industries. Sources think of her as an extremely capable attorney who earns the respect and admiration of her clients. **Ben Tobor** (see p.2419) of Greenberg Traurig, LLP has a long and distinguished track record advising on copyright, patent and trademark matters, particularly those concerning the acquisition, licensing, enforcement and management of such rights.

# LABOR & EMPLOYMENT

Commentary about individuals can be found under their firm's paragraph. If the firm has no paragraph (is not ranked) look at Other Notable Practitioners.

| Labor & Employment |
| --- |
| **Leading Firms** |
| **Band 1** |
| Fulbright & Jaworski LLP * |
| Morgan, Lewis & Bockius LLP * |
| Ogletree, Deakins, Nash, Smoak & Stewart, PC * |
| **Band 2** |
| Littler Mendelson, PC * |
| Vinson & Elkins LLP * |
| **Band 3** |
| Bracewell & Giuliani LLP * |
| Haynes and Boone, LLP * |
| Kemp Smith LLP |
| Thompson & Knight LLP * |
| **Band 4** |
| Constangy, Brooks & Smith, LLP |
| Cozen O'Connor * |
| Hunton & Williams LLP * |
| Jackson Walker LLP * |
| Jones Day * |
| Seyfarth Shaw LLP * |

\* *Indicates firm with profile.*
*Alphabetical order within each band. Band 1 is the highest.*

## Band 1

### Fulbright & Jaworski LLP
See profile on p.2435
**THE FIRM** This substantial labor and employment team comprises ten partners and is dispersed across four Texas offices. The group is warmly regarded for its labor work, including wage and hour filings. On the employment front, it represents companies in benefits and contract dis-

putes. Recently, the team has acted for Enterprise Products Partners on an FLSA collective action relating to barge employees' wages being paid on a day rate.
**Sources say:** "*A strong team with resources to leverage for larger matters. They have an incredibly strong work ethic.*"
**KEY INDIVIDUALS** The "*extremely experienced and capable*" **Brian Greig** (see p.2392) handles a range of employment litigation, including discrimination and retaliation claims. His status in the Texas labor and employment market is indisputable, with sources confirming that "*he commands a great deal of respect.*" He recently served as lead attorney representing the defendant in Dannellia Gladden-Green v Freescale Semiconductor, a sex discrimination and retaliation case. **Carter Crow** (see p.2386) is praised for providing "*excellent and insightful advice.*" He has recently been defending Service Corporation International against an alleged nationwide class action in which the plaintiffs claim discrimination against African Americans in hiring and promotion. **Shauna Clark** (see p.2384) is Houston-based and handles a range of contentious and noncontentious labor and employment matters. "*She is a tremendous lawyer – I can't say that enough,*" a market observer notes. Located in San Antonio, **Philip Pfeiffer** (see p.2410) predominantly focuses on traditional labor matters, although he is also expert in civil rights and discrimination issues. A client lauds **Shafeeqa Watkins Giarratani** (see p.2420) for "*holding nothing back when preparing for trial.*" She has recently been acting on behalf of Freescale Semiconductor alongside Greig.

### Morgan, Lewis & Bockius LLP
See profile on p.2246
**THE FIRM** This group, which spans offices in Houston and Dallas, is composed of 16 dedicated labor and employ-

ment attorneys. It has a reach that is truly national, with its lawyers often appearing in class and collective actions filed outside Texas. Of late, the group has acted on civil rights, equal pay, FLSA and wage and hour claims. Recent clients include Dow Chemical, Dollar General and American Airlines.
**Sources say:** "*Their work is superior, in my view. They have been instrumental in resolving complex matters.*"
**KEY INDIVIDUALS** **Nancy Patterson** (see p.2409) is known as "*one of the best and brightest*" in Texas. She recently represented Dow Chemical in an FLSA suit regarding overtime pay. **Ron Manthey** (see p.2403) has a diverse practice that covers matters such as wage and hour class actions, FLSA collective actions and discrimination claims. He was the lead partner defending Dollar General in a nationwide class action involving claims by female store managers that they were paid less than their male counterparts. **Ann Marie Painter** (see p.2408) impresses with her work on big-ticket matters. During the past year she acted for a major telecom company on an FLSA wage and hour collective action. **John Harper** (see p.2393) is a seasoned practitioner with a top-notch labor and employment pedigree. He has recently been active on ERISA claims, but he is also adept at representing employers in other matters, including NLRB, FLSA and ADA filings.

### Ogletree, Deakins, Nash, Smoak & Stewart, PC
See profile on p.1110
**THE FIRM** This dynamic national labor and employment boutique is making waves in the Lone Star State. With 28 partners in Texas, this firm advises on the full spectrum of labor and employment matters. Noted areas of expertise include traditional labor issues, FMLA filings and non-

## Labor & Employment

### Senior Statesmen

**Senior Statesmen:** distinguished older practitioners

| | |
|---|---|
| Harper A John | Morgan, Lewis & Bockius LLP * |
| Pfeiffer Philip J | Fulbright & Jaworski LLP * |
| Strock William | Haynes and Boone, LLP |

### Leading Individuals

**Star individuals**

| | |
|---|---|
| Greig Brian | Fulbright & Jaworski LLP * |

**Band 1**

| | |
|---|---|
| Fox Michael W | Ogletree, Deakins, Nash, Smoak & Stewart * |
| High Jr Charles C | Kemp Smith LLP |
| Jansonius John V | Jackson Walker LLP * |
| Jordan W. Carl | Vinson & Elkins LLP * |
| Londa Jeffrey C | Ogletree, Deakins, Nash, Smoak & Stewart * |
| Patterson Nancy L | Morgan, Lewis & Bockius LLP * |
| Sheeder Robert E | Bracewell & Giuliani LLP * |

**Band 2**

| | |
|---|---|
| Carter Arthur | Haynes and Boone, LLP |
| Crow Carter | Fulbright & Jaworski LLP * |
| Duffy Dennis P | Baker & Hostetler LLP (ONP)† * |
| Fink Stephen F | Thompson & Knight LLP * |
| Hamel Douglas | Vinson & Elkins LLP * |
| Headley Linda | Littler Mendelson, PC * |
| Manthey Ron | Morgan, Lewis & Bockius LLP * |
| Maslanka Michael | Constangy, Brooks & Smith, LLP |
| Meyer Theodore D | Meyer Moser Lang LLP (ONP)† |
| Shank Mark | Gruber Hurst Johansen Hail Shank (ONP)† * |
| Valderrama Teresa S | Jackson Lewis LLP (ONP)† * |
| Wickliff Jr A Martin | Cozen O'Connor * |
| Williamson Holly H | Hunton & Williams LLP * |

**Band 3**

| | |
|---|---|
| Bacon Christopher V | Vinson & Elkins LLP * |
| Burns C B | Kemp Smith LLP |
| Chapman Jr Ron | Ogletree, Deakins, Nash, Smoak & Stewart * |
| Clark Shauna | Fulbright & Jaworski LLP * |
| Halevy Amy Karff | Bracewell & Giuliani LLP * |
| McCown Steven R | Littler Mendelson, PC * |
| McDonald Scott | Littler Mendelson, PC * |
| Steinfield Arlene | Cox Smith Matthews Incorporated (ONP)† |
| Wilson Thomas H | Vinson & Elkins LLP * |

**Band 4**

| | |
|---|---|
| Banes Bryant | Neel, Hooper & Banes, P.C. (ONP)† * |
| Fischer A Robert | Jackson Lewis LLP (ONP)† * |
| Gaswirth Ronald M | Gardere Wynne Sewell LLP (ONP)† * |
| Griffith Vanessa | Vinson & Elkins LLP * |
| Kizziar Jr James H | Bracewell & Giuliani LLP * |
| Lambert Arthur | Kane Russell Coleman & Logan PC (ONP)† * |
| McQueen Michael D. | Kemp Smith LLP |
| Painter Ann Marie | Morgan, Lewis & Bockius LLP * |
| Ramón Jaime | K&L Gates (ONP)† * |
| Roppolo Stephen | Fisher & Phillips LLP (ONP)† * |
| Schartz Elizabeth A. | Thompson & Knight LLP * |
| Wells J Tullos | Bracewell & Giuliani LLP * |
| Wilson Jonathan | Littler Mendelson, PC * |

**Associates to watch**

| | |
|---|---|
| Watkins Giarratani Shafeeqa | Fulbright & Jaworski LLP * |

†ONP = Other Notable Practitioner

competition cases. In the past year, the group represented Compass Bank in an FMLA termination suit.

**Sources say:** "*I feel the group operates at a very high level; I've had nothing but outstanding experiences working with Ogletree.*"

**KEY INDIVIDUALS** The "*customer-oriented and responsive*" **Michael Fox** (see p.2389) impressed this year in FMLA cases. His peers describe him as "*a real bright spot*" and "*a dynamo.*" **Jeffrey Londa** (see p.2402) is considered to be "*one of the absolute best*" in Texas. He represented Continental Airlines in a Uniformed Services Employment and Reemployment Rights Act (USERRA) class action about the way flights were assigned and pensions given. Dallas-based **Ron Chapman** (see p.2384) covers the full spectrum of labor and employment litigation. He recently acted for DR Horton on an alleged NLRB violation.

## Band 2

### Littler Mendelson, PC
See profile on p.688

**THE FIRM** This labor and employment boutique moves up the rankings following strong feedback this year. The group is substantial, with 32 partners spread across two Texas offices. Its work is a mixed bag, and includes discrimination, retaliation, noncompete, and wage and hour issues. The team recently represented the defendant in Sewell-Aker v Sysco, regarding FMLA retaliation claims.

**Sources say:** "*I think the group works very well together. The firm's marketing and legal update services are the best around and much appreciated!*"

**KEY INDIVIDUALS Linda Headley** (see p.2394) has a broad practice that covers unfair competition, workers' compensation, discrimination and harassment issues. One impressed client reports: "*She is a master in this area. She has an incredible personal touch on every case and is careful to make sure she uses her time efficiently.*" **Scott McDonald** (see p.2404) is praised for being "*smart, thorough and efficient.*" He places particular emphasis on unfair competition disputes, employment contracts and wrongful termination matters. **Steven McCown** (see p.2404) is well liked and widely regarded as an expert in OSHA and MSHA issues. **Jonathan Wilson** (see p.2422) recently joined the team from Haynes and Boone. He has a broad labor and employment practice, with a definite focus on wage and hour suits. His peers hail him as "*an outstanding lawyer.*"

### Vinson & Elkins LLP
See profile on p.2459

**THE FIRM** This six-partner employment, labor and OSHA practice punches above its weight. Noted areas of employment expertise include discrimination, FLSA, OSHA and wage and hour issues. On the traditional labor side, the group excels in NLRB, noncompetition and whistle-blower matters. In the past year, the team has acted for US Virgin Islands giant HOVENSA on a suit concerning yearly incentive bonuses.

**Sources say:** "*They are very plugged in on current litigation.*"

**KEY INDIVIDUALS** With more than 30 years in practice, **Carl Jordan** (see p.2398) is considered to be "*one of the deans in Texas.*" He recently acted as lead attorney on the team's representation of HOVENSA. **Douglas Hamel** (see p.2393) frequently represents companies in matters including FLSA, shareholder and ERISA matters. Sources praise his intelligence and note that he is one of the most widely recognized names in the market. **Christopher Bacon** (see p.2379) dedicates his practice to civil rights and employment matters, as well as the overlap between the two. He recently helped represent BP in major OSHA proceedings in Toledo, Ohio. **Thomas Wilson** (see p.2422) brings 25 years' experience to a mix of employment and traditional labor counseling and litigation. He also acted on the BP OSHA proceedings. **Vanessa Griffith** (see p.2392) handles a range of labor and employment matters, such as wage and hour, OSHA and FLSA. She acted with Carl Jordan on the HOVENSA suit.

## Band 3

### Bracewell & Giuliani LLP
See profile on p.2429

**THE FIRM** This substantial group is well known for defending and counseling sizable companies in employment matters, although it is also active on traditional labor disputes. The team handles nationwide class and collective actions, as well as multiparty and single plaintiff cases. Of late, the team acted for the defendant in Powell et al v The Dallas Morning News on a fraud, ERISA and discrimination case.

**Sources say:** "*I am very impressed with their communication, attentiveness and client relations.*"

**KEY INDIVIDUALS Robert Sheeder** (see p.2415) is a veteran attorney known for his litigation abilities. He recently acted on The Dallas Morning News case. Sources note that **Amy Karff Halevy** (see p.2393) "*is a very committed lawyer – she is so impressive.*" She recently provided employment advice to BHP Billiton during its acquisition of Petrohawk Energy. San Antonio-based **Tullos Wells** (see p.2421) frequently acts for sports teams, media outlets and entertainment venues. He is known for being an "*experienced and consummate professional.*" Although **Jim Kizziar** (see p.2399) has a broad labor and employment practice, he is particularly noted for his advice to healthcare advisers on the Patient Protection and Affordable Care Act.

### Haynes and Boone, LLP
See profile on p.444

**THE FIRM** This team benefits from the firm's impressive geographical network of six offices in the state. It covers the range of labor and employment matters, including traditional labor relations, ERISA and FLSA matters, OSHA compliance and unfair competition cases. Recently, the group acted for American Airlines on an ERISA claim regarding alleged denial of benefits.

**Sources say:** "*The group provides practical legal advice while taking into account business realities.*"

**KEY INDIVIDUALS Arthur Carter** is warmly regarded for his counseling and advisory work. However, he also handles issues such as wage and hour claims and health and safety claims. Of late, he represented ASARCO in a wage classification and rates arbitration that involved seven unions. **William Strock** is a veteran of the labor and employment space. His work on discrimination cases is particularly well known.

## Kemp Smith LLP

**THE FIRM** This august firm has the preeminent labor and employment offering in El Paso, and is growing a smaller outpost in Austin. The group enjoys the lion's share of the labor and employment market in west Texas, and often deals with issues that cross the Mexican border. Areas of focus include OSHA filings, mining litigation and labor relations.

**Sources say:** *"They are the kings of El Paso."*

**KEY INDIVIDUALS Charlie High** is a labor and employment luminary, and is described as *"excellent"* and *"very accomplished"* by a number of market sources. **C B Burns** is known as an *"outstanding practitioner."* She is noted for her work on FMLA, discrimination and OSHA matters. **Michael McQueen** is a seasoned practitioner who is highly regarded for his OSHA and NLRB-related work.

## Thompson & Knight LLP

See profile on p.2458

**THE FIRM** This dedicated, ten-strong group acts for a diverse range of clients, from charitable organizations to energy companies. The practice spans four offices in Texas and represents clients on matters including noncompetition, EEOC and FLSA violations, and discrimination and retaliation claims. Recently, the group has acted for BNSF Railway on several matters, including a case regarding an EEOC subpoena.

**KEY INDIVIDUALS Stephen Fink** (see p.2388) has a broad labor and employment practice, and often wins plaudits for his litigation abilities. A peer comments that Fink is a *"fantastic lawyer. I have nothing but good things to say."* **Elizabeth Schartz** (see p.2414) continues to impress on litigious and regulatory matters. She has a specialty in advising companies on the labor and employment issues surrounding M&A.

## Band 4

## Constangy, Brooks & Smith, LLP

**THE FIRM** This group joins the rankings following some impressive feedback and a growing geographical footprint in Texas. The boutique labor and employment firm concentrates solely on representing employers, with a caseload that often consists of discrimination, retaliation, NLRB, noncompete and ERISA matters.

**Sources say:** *"They operate very efficiently and are client-focused."*

**KEY INDIVIDUALS Michael Maslanka** is a veteran of the Texas labor and employment market. He is particularly

well regarded for his thought leadership and litigation prowess.

## Cozen O'Connor

See profile on p.2237

**THE FIRM** This compact team comprises five partners in Texas, and advises employers from an array of sectors. Contentious matters such as discrimination, retaliation, breach of contract and wage and hour claims are bread and butter for the group. It is equipped to handle single-plaintiff claims as well as class and collective actions. Of late, the team has acted for McDonald's, Celgene and CITGO.

**KEY INDIVIDUALS Martin Wickliff** (see p.2422) is *"outstanding"* and *"has a great practice,"* according to sources. He recently represented Celgene in opposing a multimillion-dollar claim involving alleged breach of contract, several business torts and promissory estoppel.

## Hunton & Williams LLP

See profile on p.2517

**THE FIRM** Hunton & Williams's Texas team dedicates the bulk of its time to employment advice and litigation, although the group also has traditional labor capabilities. It has been involved in a number of big-ticket wage and hour class actions, including the game-changing Brinker case. The group also often handles discrimination, ADA and retaliation cases.

**KEY INDIVIDUALS** The *"amazing"* **Holly Williamson** (see p.2422) is based out of Hunton & Williams's Houston office, and is known for representing corporates before administrative employment bodies.

## Jackson Walker LLP

See profile on p.2441

**THE FIRM** This team impresses thanks to an expanded labor and employment offering. It excels in labor matters, such as collective bargaining and unfair labor practices negotiations. Employment litigation also forms a significant part of the group's work, and includes harassment, breach of contract, discrimination and OSHA matters. It recently represented Reynolds Nationwide Trucking in a unionizing campaign and attendant NLRB proceedings.

**Sources say:** *"The group is well run and on top of things."*

**KEY INDIVIDUALS John Jansonius** (see p.2397) made waves in the Texas labor and employment community by joining Jackson Walker from Akin Gump in 2012, with a peer citing the move as *"the biggest thing in Texas."* He is valued for his formidable litigation skills, and sources describe him as *"a legend"* and *"really fantastic."*

## Jones Day

See profile on p.919

**THE FIRM** This labor and employment group is made up of nine lawyers spread between offices in Dallas and Houston. Of late, the group has been involved in substantial wage and hour litigation. It successfully acted for the defendant on Banks v IBM, a case concerning employees allegedly working off the clock and not being compensated.

**Sources say:** *"The group provides consistent advice and excellent representation."*

**KEY INDIVIDUALS** Dallas-based Brian Jorgensen is a key contact.

## Seyfarth Shaw LLP

See profile on p.1262

**THE FIRM** This Houston-based team, which has grown significantly in recent years, is also supported by the firm's leading nationwide network of labor and employment offices. The six Texas partners act on a range of matters, although they have particular strength in wage and hour litigation. The group recently represented Wells Fargo in a class and collective action revolving around alleged unpaid overtime.

**Sources say:** *"The attorneys are extremely responsive, even after regular business hours. They seek to understand the client's culture and offer guidance to match."*

**KEY INDIVIDUALS** Timothy Watson leads the Texas labor and employment department.

## Other Notable Practitioners

**Dennis Duffy** (see p.2387) moved to Baker Hostetler from Baker Botts this past year. He is known as a *"very, very bright guy"* who is *"an expert"* on labor and employment matters. Meyer White LLP's **Ted Meyer** is recognized throughout the state for his employment litigation expertise. Sources note that *"he brings big-firm experience to bear."* At Gruber Hurst Johansen Hail Shank LLP, **Mark Shank** (see p.2415) excels in investigations, trials and arbitration. His employment work focuses heavily on wage and hour, discrimination and retaliation claims. The *"amazing"* **Teresa Valderrama** (see p.2419) is based in Jackson Lewis LLP's Houston office and focuses on employment matters, including whistle-blower, noncompetition and discrimination cases. **Arlene Steinfield** of Cox Smith Matthews Incorporated applies more than 30 years' experience to workplace disputes and discrimination claims. She also deftly represents lawyers in union and nonunion arbitrations. Neel, Hooper & Banes, P.C.'s **Bryant Banes** (see p.2379) is praised for being *"extremely capable, responsible and creative."* He has a broad litigation practice, but routinely advises on workplace disputes. Austin-based **Robert Fischer** (see p.2388) of Jackson Lewis LLP concentrates on trade secret and noncompete litigation. At Gardere Wynne Sewell LLP, **Ronald Gaswirth** (see p.2390) is a senior attorney active on a range of labor and employment matters, including union, wage and hour and OSHA issues. **Arthur Lambert** (see p.2400) of Kane Russell Coleman & Logan PC represents clients in issues concerning trade secrets, FLSA claims and civil rights violations. *"He definitely stays on top of current issues,"* states a source. **Jaime Ramón** (see p.2411) of K&L Gates has a diverse employment practice that encompasses wrongful discharge, Title VII, affirmative action and OFCCP matters. Peers deem **Stephen Roppolo** (see p.2413) of Fisher & Phillips LLP a *"very good practitioner who deserves recognition."* He often advises on matters involving such issues as harassment, breach of contract and discrimination.

# LITIGATION

Appellate p.2362;   Energy p.2362;   Securities p.2362

Commentary about individuals can be found under their firm's paragraph. If the firm has no paragraph (is not ranked) look at Other Notable Practitioners.

## Litigation: General Commercial
### Leading Firms

**Band 1**
Beck Redden LLP
Gibbs & Bruns LLP *
Susman Godfrey LLP
Vinson & Elkins LLP *

**Band 2**
Baker Botts LLP *
Fulbright & Jaworski LLP *
Lynn Tillotson Pinker & Cox, LLP *
McKool Smith *
Yetter Coleman LLP *

**Band 3**
Haynes and Boone, LLP *
Jones Day *
King & Spalding LLP *
Locke Lord LLP *
Reynolds, Frizzell, Black, Doyle, Allen & Oldham, LLP *
Smyser Kaplan & Veselka LLP *
Weil, Gotshal & Manges LLP *

**Band 4**
Bracewell & Giuliani LLP *
Carrington, Coleman, Sloman & Blumenthal, LLP
Gibson, Dunn & Crutcher LLP *
Jackson Walker LLP *
Morgan, Lewis & Bockius LLP *
Rose Walker, L.L.P.
Thompson & Knight LLP *

\* Indicates firm / individual with profile.

†ONP = Other Notable Practitioner

## Litigation: General Commercial
### Senior Statesmen

Senior Statesmen: distinguished older practitioners

| | | | | |
|---|---|---|---|---|
| Coleman James | Carrington, Coleman, Sloman & Blumenthal | | Reasoner Harry M | Vinson & Elkins LLP * |
| Gunter III J Clifford | Bracewell & Giuliani LLP * | | Terrell Irv | Baker Botts LLP * |
| Mow Jr Robert H | K&L Gates (ONP)† * | | Yarbrough Fletcher L | Carrington, Coleman, Sloman & Blumenthal |

### Leading Individuals

**Band 1**

| | |
|---|---|
| Babcock Charles | Jackson Walker LLP * |
| Beck David J | Beck Redden LLP |
| Bramblett Jr George W | Haynes and Boone, LLP |
| Fogler Murray | Beck Redden LLP |
| Gibbs Robin C | Gibbs & Bruns LLP * |
| Godfrey H Lee | Susman Godfrey LLP |
| McKool Mike | McKool Smith * |
| Patrick Kathy | Gibbs & Bruns LLP * |
| Phelan Rod | Baker Botts LLP * |
| Susman Stephen D | Susman Godfrey LLP |

| | |
|---|---|
| Dillard Stephen C | Fulbright & Jaworski LLP * |
| Frizzell Jean C | Reynolds, Frizzell, Black, Doyle, Allen * |
| Harvin David | Vinson & Elkins LLP * |
| Karen James | Jones Day * |
| Leahy James R | Locke Lord LLP * |
| McCormick Timothy R | Thompson & Knight LLP * |
| McNiel D Ferguson | Vinson & Elkins LLP * |
| Meadows Robert E | King & Spalding LLP * |
| Powell Michael V | Locke Lord LLP * |
| Rose Martin | Rose Walker, L.L.P. |
| Sayles Richard A 'Dick' | Sayles Werbner, PC (ONP)† |
| Shipley George | Shipley Snell Montgomery Droog (ONP)† |
| Susman Harry | Susman Godfrey LLP |
| Tillotson Jeff | Lynn Tillotson Pinker & Cox, LLP * |
| Voyles Robb L | Baker Botts LLP * |
| Wawro Mark | Susman Godfrey LLP |
| Werbner Mark | Sayles Werbner, PC (ONP)† |

**Band 2**

| | |
|---|---|
| Acker Rodney | Fulbright & Jaworski LLP * |
| Baxter Samuel F | McKool Smith * |
| Brown Reagan | Fulbright & Jaworski LLP * |
| Dawson William B | Gibson, Dunn & Crutcher LLP * |
| Denny Otway | Fulbright & Jaworski LLP * |
| Glasser Mark K | Sidley Austin LLP (ONP)† * |
| Kaplan Lee | Smyser Kaplan & Veselka LLP * |
| LeClair Lewis | McKool Smith * |
| Lynn Mike | Lynn Tillotson Pinker & Cox, LLP * |
| Manne Neal | Susman Godfrey LLP |
| Ostolaza Yvette | Weil, Gotshal & Manges LLP * |
| Reasoner Barrett | Gibbs & Bruns LLP * |
| Redden Joe | Beck Redden LLP |
| Reynolds Chris | Reynolds, Frizzell, Black, Doyle, Allen * |
| Sims William D | Vinson & Elkins LLP * |
| Smyser Craig | Smyser Kaplan & Veselka LLP * |
| Walton Gib | Hogan Lovells US LLP (ONP)† |
| Yetter R Paul | Yetter Coleman LLP * |

**Band 4**

| | |
|---|---|
| Carter Leon | Carter Stafford Arnett Hamada (ONP)† |
| Carter Jr Winstol D | Morgan, Lewis & Bockius LLP * |
| Clements Jerry K | Locke Lord LLP * |
| Crain Stephen B | Bracewell & Giuliani LLP * |
| Cunningham Ross | Rose Walker, L.L.P. |
| Dameris Thad | Hogan Lovells US LLP (ONP)† |
| Dawson Alistair | Beck Redden LLP |
| Edwards Brady | Morgan, Lewis & Bockius LLP * |
| Gorman Sean | Ahmad, Zavitsanos, Anaipakos (ONP)† * |
| Harrison Geoffrey | Susman Godfrey LLP |
| Hedges Daniel K | Porter Hedges LLP (ONP)† * |
| Johnston Kenneth C | Kane Russell Coleman & Logan (ONP)† * |
| Josephson Richard | Baker Botts LLP * |
| Kruse C Thomas | Baker & Hostetler LLP (ONP)† * |
| Marks Kenneth S | Susman Godfrey LLP |
| Pinker Eric | Lynn Tillotson Pinker & Cox, LLP * |
| Schick Robert M | Vinson & Elkins LLP * |
| Walters Robert | Gibson, Dunn & Crutcher LLP * |

**Band 3**

| | |
|---|---|
| Ajamie Thomas | Ajamie LLP (ONP)† |
| Anaipakos John | Baker Botts LLP * |
| Barnett Barry C | Susman Godfrey LLP |
| Bayko Tom | Hogan Lovells US LLP (ONP)† |
| Bishop Doak | King & Spalding LLP * |
| Cox Trey | Lynn Tillotson Pinker & Cox, LLP * |

## Band 1

### Beck Redden LLP

**THE FIRM** This standout litigation practice deals with business litigation and appellate matters, among other areas. The team prides itself on being ready for trial at short notice and this capability was evidenced when the firm's litigation practice took on the case of Asif Said v Azhar Said just two months before the trial date. The team's notable clients include Cameron International, ExxonMobil and Altria.

**Sources say:** *"Beck Redden is fantastic."*

**KEY INDIVIDUALS** Sources comment that **David Beck** *"is an absolutely phenomenal lawyer."* He is leading the team on behalf of Cameron International in the multimillion-dollar Deepwater Horizon litigation. The *"excellent"* **Murray Fogler** is recognized by sources for his expertise in both general commercial litigation and litigation relating to energy and natural resources. Commentators note that he is *"a wonderful lawyer."* **David Gunn** is recognized for his preeminence in civil appeals in both state and federal courts. One source said: *"I've always been very impressed with David Gunn."* **Russell Post** is similarly deemed a solid attorney in appellate litigation matters. Sources note that he *"does tremendous work – a very, very fine talent."* **Joe Redden** is renowned in the market as *"a top-notch trial lawyer."* He deals in a variety of general commercial litigation matters, and acted on behalf of Pathfinder Exploration this year on a case involving breach of contract, fraud and breach of fiduciary duty. **Alistair Dawson** focuses his well-regarded practice on general commercial litigation. He is also well versed in professional liability and class action cases.

### Gibbs & Bruns LLP

See profile on p.2437

**THE FIRM** This outstanding litigation practice is praised for its expert command of litigation in areas including complex commercial, energy-related and professional malpractice litigation. The team has handled matters for

## Litigation: Appellate
### Leading Individuals

**Band 1**

| | |
|---|---|
| Cortell Nina | Haynes and Boone, LLP |
| Gunn David M | Beck Redden LLP |
| Hatchell Mike A | Locke Lord LLP * |
| Keltner David | Kelly Hart & Hallman LLP (ONP)† |
| Phillips Thomas R | Baker Botts LLP * |
| Simpson Reagan | Yetter Coleman LLP * |
| Yeates Marie | Vinson & Elkins LLP * |

**Band 2**

| | |
|---|---|
| Alexander Douglas W | Alexander Dubose & Townsend (ONP)† * |
| Brister Scott | Andrews Kurth LLP (ONP)† * |
| Dubose Kevin | Alexander Dubose & Townsend (ONP)† |
| Frost Claudia Wilson | DLA Piper LLP (US) (ONP)† * |
| Hankinson Deborah G | Hankinson LLP (ONP)† * |
| Harris Warren W | Bracewell & Giuliani LLP * |
| Ho Allyson N | Morgan, Lewis & Bockius LLP * |
| Jung P Michael | Strasburger & Price LLP (ONP)† |
| Liberato Lynne | Haynes and Boone, LLP |
| Stokes Macey Reasoner | Baker Botts LLP * |
| Townsend Roger | Alexander Dubose & Townsend LLP * |

**Band 3**

| | |
|---|---|
| Cohen Murry B | Akin Gump Strauss Hauer & Feld (ONP)† * |
| Enoch Craig T | Enoch Kever PLLC (ONP)† |
| Ho James | Gibson, Dunn & Crutcher LLP * |
| Post Russell | Beck Redden LLP |
| Precella Karen S | Haynes and Boone, LLP |

**Associates to watch**

| | |
|---|---|
| Young Evan | Baker Botts LLP * |

## Litigation: Energy & Natural Resources
### Senior Statesmen

| **Senior Statesmen:** distinguished older practitioners | |
|---|---|
| Gunter III J Clifford | Bracewell & Giuliani LLP * |
| Reasoner Harry M | Vinson & Elkins LLP * |

### Leading Individuals

**Band 1**

| | |
|---|---|
| Beck David J | Beck Redden LLP |
| Copeland Gregory | Baker Botts LLP * |
| Fogler Murray | Beck Redden LLP |
| Gibbs Robin C | Gibbs & Bruns LLP * |
| Godfrey H Lee | Susman Godfrey LLP |
| Pierce Jesse | Pierce & O'Neill, LLP (ONP)† * |
| Ratliff Shannon H. | Ratliff Law Firm PLLC (ONP)† |
| Wood William | Fulbright & Jaworski LLP * |

**Band 2**

| | |
|---|---|
| Bayko Tom | Hogan Lovells US LLP |
| Harvin David | Vinson & Elkins LLP * |
| Lipe Guy | Vinson & Elkins LLP * |
| McClure Daniel M | Fulbright & Jaworski LLP * |
| Meadows Robert E | King & Spalding LLP * |
| Reasoner Barrett | Gibbs & Bruns LLP * |
| Reynolds Chris | Reynolds, Frizzell, Black, Doyle, Allen * |
| Simpson Reagan | Yetter Coleman LLP * |
| Thompson James D | Vinson & Elkins LLP * |
| Watt Dick | Watt, Beckworth, Thompson (ONP)† * |

**Band 3**

| | |
|---|---|
| Beatty J Robert | Locke Lord LLP * |
| Dye Jr Phillip B | Vinson & Elkins LLP * |
| Harvey Grant J | Gibbs & Bruns LLP * |
| Haynes Craig A | Thompson & Knight LLP * |
| Knull William H | Mayer Brown LLP (ONP)† |
| Pecht Gerard | Fulbright & Jaworski LLP * |
| Powell Michael V | Locke Lord LLP * |
| Schiffer Adam P | Schiffer Odom Hicks & Johnson (ONP)† |
| Whitman W Ray | Baker & Hostetler LLP (ONP)† * |

## Litigation: Securities
### Leading Individuals

**Band 1**

| | |
|---|---|
| Fletcher N Scott | Jones Day * |
| Harrison III Orrin L | Akin Gump Strauss Hauer (ONP)† |
| Patrick Kathy | Gibbs & Bruns LLP * |
| Schwartz Charles | Skadden, Arps, Slate, Meagher (ONP)† * |
| Sterling David | Baker Botts LLP * |
| Villareal Patricia J | Jones Day * |

**Band 2**

| | |
|---|---|
| Cooper Samuel W | Paul Hastings LLP (ONP)† * |
| Held Kenneth P | Schiffer Odom Hicks & Johnson (ONP)† |
| Maloney James | Andrews Kurth LLP (ONP)† * |
| Nickens Jacks C | McGuireWoods LLP (ONP)† |
| Pecht Gerard | Fulbright & Jaworski LLP * |

**Band 3**

| | |
|---|---|
| Marks Kenneth S | Susman Godfrey LLP |

* Indicates individual with profile.
† ONP = Other Notable Practitioner

---

clients in the technology, banking and healthcare industries. The team's clients include BlackRock, PIMCO and Pioneer Natural Resources.

**Sources say:** *"The firm's strong points are a rare combination of knowledge, competence and practical, strategic thinking. Their edge is being forward-thinking and tactical while not sacrificing superb legal scholarship."*

**KEY INDIVIDUALS** The *"outstanding"* **Kathy Patrick** (see p.2409) has a top-flight reputation in both securities and general commercial litigation. Sources say that *"her combination of empathy for her clients and the degree of preparedness and understanding of precedents is just remarkable."* **Robin Gibbs** (see p.2391) comes highly recommended in both general commercial and energy and natural resources litigation. Sources say he is *"highly thought of and very talented."* **Barrett Reasoner** (see p.2412) enjoys a great reputation in all aspects of general commercial litigation and in energy-related disputes. Commentators note that *"his understanding of his field is really excellent and, importantly, he is efficient; he doesn't take an army to do something, he just gets the matter done."* Acting alongside Gibbs, **Grant Harvey** (see p.2394) wins special recognition for his successful lead in a number of high-profile energy-related cases. These include the D Bobbitt Noel Jr v Devon Energy Holdings LLC, et al case relating to fraud and breach of fiduciary duty.

## Susman Godfrey LLP

**THE FIRM** This thriving litigation boutique has seen rapid growth within the firm in the past year. The team deals with litigation across various states, on behalf of both plaintiffs and defendants. The group's recent list of high-profile matters has included disputes involving complex mortgage-backed securities, patents, arbitration and class action issues.

**Sources say:** *"Absolutely top-notch." "Good lawyers, good results, very successful."*

**KEY INDIVIDUALS** The highly experienced **Lee Godfrey** remains a favorite with clients, many of whom praise his personable nature. He is acknowledged as a leader in complex commercial litigation, and possesses in-depth experience of handling matters in the energy industry. **Stephen Susman** is renowned for his expertise with plaintiff representations. One source commented: *"I liked his straightforward manner, it's so refreshing."* Managing partner **Neal Manne** is praised for his presentation skills. *"He's very easy to talk to, very clear in his manner of speech,"* said an interviewee. Acting for both plaintiffs and defendants, his wide-

ranging litigation practice encompasses energy, mass tort, labor and employment and general business disputes. The *"very strong"* **Barry Barnett** handles a broad range of commercial litigation and antitrust matters. **Kenneth Marks** enjoys a high-profile position within the firm's commercial litigation team. Sources know him as *"a great lawyer,"* and he is praised for his solid expertise in securities litigation. **Harry Susman** is commended for his excellent approach to practice. He represents both plaintiff and defendant clients in commercial litigation cases. **Mark Wawro** has worked on a variety of high-profile cases, including contract disputes. Commentators state: *"He's phenomenal"* and that he is *"very much a go-to litigator for either plaintiff or defense."* Peers are *"really impressed"* by **Geoffrey Harrison**, a new entry in this year's tables. *"He's very smart,"* say sources, and he comes highly recommended for his commercial litigation expertise across multiple arenas, including antitrust, oil and gas, and arbitration.

## Vinson & Elkins LLP
See profile on p.2459

**THE FIRM** This sizable litigation team maintains its preeminent position as a leading group for litigation claims arising from the energy industry. The team handles cases in a variety of jurisdictions, and also demonstrates exceptional capabilities across the gamut of antitrust, securities and white-collar defense work. The team recently represented Anadarko in opposing claims of royalty underpayments, and also acted for Antero Resources on obtaining the dismissal of claims concerning a court order relating to a toxic tort case involving drilling and fracturing activities.

**Sources say:** *"They did a wonderful job and we were very impressed."*

**KEY INDIVIDUALS Harry Reasoner** (see p.390) is *"something of a legend"* in this sector. He maintains a significant and enduring reputation in complex commercial, energy, contract, antitrust and insurance disputes. The *"phenomenal"* **Marie Yeates** (see p.2423) has cultivated an exceptional appellate practice. She recently evidenced her prowess by successfully representing The Port of Houston

Authority in an appeal on an ongoing contractual claim. **William Sims** (see p.2416) is renowned for being strong across the board of litigation issues. Notably, he recently played a key part in the trial team representing The Port of Houston Authority in its prolonged contractual dispute against Zachry Construction. According to sources, he is *"remarkably good: always ready, very thoughtful and very smart."* **David Harvin** (see p.2394) is a *"fabulous lawyer,"* say interviewees. He exhibits superb expertise in general commercial and energy litigation. He also maintains an excellent reputation for his experience in antitrust, securities and class action litigation. **Guy Lipe** (see p.2401) upholds a strong focus on energy-related cases. He led on behalf of Anadarko in the royalty underpayment matter. The extremely knowledgeable **James Thompson** (see p.2419) focuses on litigation arising from the energy industry. His recent highlights include representing Antero Resources in a major toxic tort case. The *"superb"* **Phillip Dye** (see p.2388) centers his highly regarded practice on international litigation matters. As such, he has a particular specialty in multijurisdictional and forum non conveniens issues, and in representing foreign clients. **Ferguson McNiel** (see p.2405) handles a full range of general commercial litigation, including construction and energy industry matters for his esteemed clients. **Robert Schick** (see p.2415) distinguishes himself in some of the firm's most high-profile cases. He was recently involved in litigation on behalf of Antero Resources arising from the process of accessing natural gas wells in a residential area.

## Band 2

### Baker Botts LLP
See profile on p.2427

**THE FIRM** Baker Botts is firmly established as a solid choice for international matters, patent, bankruptcy, appellate and securities litigation. The team services clients across the energy, financial and professional services industries, to name but a few. Its attorneys are well connected and clients applaud their ability to anticipate issues in a case. The firm's esteemed clients include Ernst & Young, Halliburton and ExxonMobil.

**KEY INDIVIDUALS** *"Wonderful trial attorney"* **Gregory Copeland** (see p.2386) is a key litigator on behalf of ExxonMobil. He has expertise in energy litigation, and is highly regarded for his work in antitrust, competition law and complex corporate litigation. **Rod Phelan** (see p.2410) has a superb, broad-based commercial litigation practice. He recently litigated on behalf of law firm Orrick, Herrington & Sutcliffe in a professional liability case brought by a number of plaintiffs from Highland Capital Management. The preeminent appellate attorney **Thomas Phillips** (see p.2410) is lauded as *"very intelligent, respected and well connected."* **David Sterling** (see p.2417) has an excellent reputation in securities litigation, and recently led in a shareholder dispute on behalf of Imperial Sugar. **Macey Reasoner Stokes** (see p.2418) has a prominent appellate practice and has represented clients in both state and federal courts, including the Texas Supreme Court.

She had a notable victory recently in representing an eminent energy industry client. *"Excellent litigator"* **Robb Voyles** (see p.2420) recently acted on behalf of Halliburton on disputes with a former subsidiary regarding a tax sharing agreement. He chairs the firm's litigation practice group. **Richard Josephson** (see p.2398) is well known for his general commercial litigation practice, and has particular experience in life sciences and pharmaceutical litigation. He regularly represents large pharmaceutical companies, such as Merck, in complex litigation cases. **John Anaipakos** (see p.2378) is admired for his broad-based commercial practice, and is known as being *"good all-around."* He also possesses expertise in the areas of energy and professional litigation. *"Excellent lawyer"* **Irv Terrell**'s (see p.416) practice is based largely on complex business litigation, although he regularly homes in on the areas of antitrust, securities and IP disputes. Senior associate **Evan Young** (see p.2423) is known by sources as *"supersmart and very responsive."* His excellent reputation is reflected in his appointment as amicus curiae by the Supreme Court in a recent groundbreaking pro bono matter.

### Fulbright & Jaworski LLP
See profile on p.2435

**THE FIRM** This international firm boasts a large and diverse litigation practice run from offices across Texas. The team's impressive client list include Bank of America Merrill Lynch, BP and Vulcan Materials. Attorneys in this practice are renowned for their comprehensive experience in the energy arena, particularly in the oil and gas sectors, and are involved in cutting-edge litigation relating to fracking disputes.

**Sources say:** *"The firm is efficient and responsive."*

**KEY INDIVIDUALS** A leading light in the energy litigation space, **William Wood** (see p.2423) has led in a number of the group's cutting-edge cases. He recently represented Shell and Pecten Orient in a matter involving disputed payments and acreage issues relating to oil and gas operations in Syria. **Rodney Acker** (see p.2377) handles a variety of commercial litigation, with a focus on securities litigation and working on behalf of clients from the banking and finance industry. He recently acted on behalf of Oppenheimer in an auction rate securities case. Sources describe him as *"a smart guy, and very smooth."* **Otway Denny**'s (see p.2387) advocacy skills are highly praised by sources. He recently worked on behalf of Kinder Morgan in a case involving a fatality resulting from a pipeline explosion. Clients hold **Daniel McClure** (see p.2404) in high esteem for his *"very analytical"* style. He demonstrates particular expertise in dealing with class actions in the energy sector. **Gerard Pecht** (see p.2409) is renowned for his excellent energy and securities litigation practice. His recent highlights include representing DCP Midstream in a major case relating to alleged undermeasurement of natural gas by pipeline and gathering companies over the course of 40 years. **Reagan Brown**'s (see p.2382) outstanding reputation has been built over a considerable career. He has a broad-based practice with extensive experience in commercial litigation. **Stephen Dillard** (see p.2387) is relied upon by clients for his niche experience in fracking

issues as well as toxic tort cases. Sources call him *"efficient and easy to work with."*

### Lynn Tillotson Pinker & Cox, LLP
See profile on p.2444

**THE FIRM** This boutique litigation group is lauded for its efforts with patent infringement strategy cases and energy litigation matters arising from the energy sector. The last year has seen the team branch out into additional international matters and represent an increasing number of overseas clients.

**Sources say:** *"They have some of the brightest litigation minds around." "In tune with clients' interests and goals." "An amazing array of talented individuals."*

**KEY INDIVIDUALS Mike Lynn** (see p.2402) is an immensely respected litigator who has been particularly active in matters involving the mining sector. Sources are impressed by his advocacy skills and note that *"Mike is tenacious"* and *"a ferocious litigator."* **Trey Cox** (see p.2386) continues to build upon his sterling reputation for complex litigation. He has a commercial litigation focus and is kept busy working on contract disputes. He is considered a future star of the sector, and sources state that *"he's got a great career ahead of him."* **Jeff Tillotson** (see p.2419) is well versed in the intricacies of multiparty litigation matters. He is *"a very fine trial lawyer with a lot of courtroom presence – he's very savvy,"* say sources. One commentator said of **Eric Pinker** (see p.2410): *"Eric is the single best litigator I have ever worked with. I would say that this is not limited to a single aspect of his practice – his preparation, writing skills, success at depositions, skill in the courtroom, litigation strategy and ease of interaction with the businesspeople are unmatched."*

### McKool Smith
See profile on p.2446

**THE FIRM** This large litigation practice has a reputation for fielding high-quality lawyers and working on high-profile general commercial litigation. The team has experience in dealing with joint venture litigation, IP litigation and bankruptcy matters. The firm's impressive client list includes Ericsson, Freedom Medical and Lennox International.

**Sources say:** *"It's a firm that is always extremely well prepared. They take their task very seriously and have great attention to detail." "For a bet-the-company, or a case you have to win, they're unquestionably the firm to hire."*

**KEY INDIVIDUALS Mike McKool** (see p.2405) maintains an eminent reputation for his work in general commercial litigation. *"Mike McKool is the best litigator in the city, he's great,"* say sources, with one commentator in particular mentioning: *"I have tons of respect for him; he's a warrior in the courtroom."* **Samuel Baxter** (see p.2380) is highly regarded for his management of IP and antitrust litigation. *"Incredibly impressed"* observers label him *"a giant of the Texas litigation Bar."* **Lewis LeClair** (see p.2401) is renowned for being *"capable and smart,"* and for having *"a great eye for detail"* in general commercial litigation matters. One source noted: *"He has great intuition for what will* *and won't work; he is able to anticipate what the other side will do in ways I've not seen before."*

## Yetter Coleman LLP
See profile on p.2461

**THE FIRM** This Houston and Austin-based litigation boutique deals with a range of general commercial litigation, including antitrust disputes, matters arising from asbestos claims, and breach of contract cases. The team's enviable client list includes American Airlines, CenterPoint Energy and ConocoPhillips.

**Sources say:** *"A fabulous law firm." "Very, very smart people."*

**KEY INDIVIDUALS Paul Yetter** (see p.2423) is recommended as *"a formidable trial attorney"* who is *"doing excellent work and working very hard."* He has superb expertise in complex commercial litigation, and recently led the team acting as trial counsel for American Airlines on a number of antitrust lawsuits totaling some $1 billion. **Reagan Simpson** (see p.2416) is a leading authority in the appellate space, and in matters pertaining to energy and natural resources. Sources note: *"He's got a great reputation and does a good job."*

## Band 3

## Haynes and Boone, LLP
See profile on p.444

**THE FIRM** This proficient litigation practice is respected as a go-to team for a wide array of litigation types, including IP, antitrust and bankruptcy. However, it is for its expertise in real estate, energy, securities and class action disputes that the group wins most praise. The firm's enviable client list contains the NFL, AT&T and Shell, among others. The firm recently represented Halliburton in a matter involving trade secret issues, breach of contract and breach of fiduciary duty.

**Sources say:** *"They've been outstanding; really good about providing us with great counsel."*

**KEY INDIVIDUALS** Sources have the utmost confidence in **George Bramblett**'s litigation prowess. He has been instrumental in working on behalf of Texas Capital Bank in a breach of contract and fraud case recently. **Nina Cortell** is *"great,"* say sources; *"definitely a standout lawyer – she is charming, experienced, has good judgment, no ego and does very solid work."* She is a preeminent appellate attorney, and recently represented NextEra Energy in an appeal seeking to reverse an opinion relating to power purchase agreements for wind energy. Sterling litigation lawyer **Lynne Liberato** has been especially active on behalf of Shell. She is commended as a go-to lawyer by many of her peers, while clients are particularly appreciative of her personable approach during tense situations. The *"technically proficient"* **Karen Precella** recently worked on behalf of ARGO Data Resource in a successful appeal launched by the litigation team relating to a shareholder dispute.

## Jones Day
See profile on p.919

**THE FIRM** The highly respected Texas litigation arm of this international firm offers a range of general commercial litigation services. The team has comprehensive business litigation experience, including a history of regularly acting on bet-the-company litigation, and is especially well regarded for its securities litigation expertise. Clients of the team include Century Aluminum, Chevron, Ernst & Young and Expedia.

**Sources say:** *"A strong practice."*

**KEY INDIVIDUALS** The eminent **Scott Fletcher** (see p.2389) centers his practice on securities litigation, although he is a renowned corporate litigator in a wide range of areas. He recently defended Holly Corporation against numerous shareholder lawsuits relating to the company's proposed $7 billion merger with Frontier Oil. **Patricia Villareal** (see p.2420) is the partner in charge of the firm's Dallas offices. She is similarly hailed as a leading securities litigator. Peers are especially impressed with her abilities in both the boardroom and the courtroom. **James Karen** (see p.2398) regularly represents large companies, including publicly traded companies, in their most complex disputes. Notably, he recently represented Expedia in a case relating to occupancy taxes.

## King & Spalding LLP
See profile on p.445

**THE FIRM** This high-quality litigation group offers a broad range of general commercial litigation services. The team is highly active in handling litigation arising from the energy industry, including the gas, oil and electricity sectors, and also handles securities litigation. Clients include Fortune 100 companies, such as Chevron, Shell Chemical and Valero Energy.

**Sources say:** *"An incredibly substantial litigation and arbitration practice."*

**KEY INDIVIDUALS Robert Meadows** (see p.2405) has cultivated a venerable national energy and general commercial litigation practice. His recent highlights include representing Chevron in numerous major climate change litigation cases. **Doak Bishop** (see p.283) is much admired for his general litigation practice. He also has a highly regarded international arbitration practice.

## Locke Lord LLP
See profile on p.2443

**THE FIRM** This celebrated litigation team boasts expertise in pharmaceutical, appellate, securities, banking and a vast range of general business litigation. The attorneys represent a range of clients, from small, privately held firms to large, Fortune 500 companies. The client roster includes American Airlines, Johnson & Johnson and Bank of America Home Loans. The group is especially well known for its work involving financial institutions.

**Sources say:** *"Good across the board."*

**KEY INDIVIDUALS** The *"terrific"* **Mike Hatchell** (see p.2394) leads the firm's appellate practice group. As such, he is a leading figure in the appellate sphere, and is consistently highlighted for his experience acting before the

Texas Supreme Court. The *"impressive"* **Michael Powell** (see p.2411) undertakes significant litigation matters in the energy sector. One source said: *"Mike is our attorney of choice in Texas for oil and gas litigation matters of any significance – a great trial lawyer and appellate lawyer too."* **Robert Beatty** (see p.2380) remains busy litigating in cases involving energy and natural gas issues. He acts on behalf of ConocoPhillips on litigation relating to gas and oil leasing and drilling. Sources are impressed by **James Leahy**'s (see p.2401) efficiency and ability to get great results. He regularly handles commercial disputes and has particular expertise in the energy sector. **Jerry Clements** (see p.2385) is prized as a *"solid attorney"* in acting on behalf of a variety of clients, including large multinational companies, on complex litigation matters. Her expertise spans a variety of industries, including hi-tech-related matters.

## Reynolds, Frizzell, Black, Doyle, Allen & Oldham, LLP
See profile on p.2451

**THE FIRM** This commercial litigation boutique attracts praise for its work in representing plaintiffs and defendants in a range of cases, including contract disputes, securities litigation, IP litigation and class actions. The team also boasts expertise in litigating on behalf of clients in the energy industry. MetroNational, Seashore Investment Management Trust and ExxonMobil appear on the team's impressive client list.

**Sources say:** *"They have given us confidence that they truly understand what we need and expect. They have a very good grasp of law and legal procedure and how to go forward with a case."*

**KEY INDIVIDUALS Jean Frizzell** (see p.2389) is currently defending a private equity fund in an action involving the challenge of various corporate decisions made by directors of the company. Damages claimed in the case exceed $300 million. Clients hold him in high esteem, with one source mentioning: *"He has a memory like a trap; he really gets into the case and he knows the facts better than us."* **Chris Reynolds** (see p.2412) has a broad-based commercial litigation practice. He brings his engineering background to bear on an array of construction cases and also has particular expertise in energy litigation.

## Smyser Kaplan & Veselka LLP
See profile on p.2454

**THE FIRM** This distinguished firm works on all areas of complex commercial litigation, including securities, patent disputes and medical malpractice matters. The team has gained experience in guiding a range of clients, including Fortune 500 companies, multinational energy companies and joint ventures, through the intricacies of the most complex litigation.

**Sources say:** *"They did an excellent job; we got the outcome we wanted." "The quality of their legal analysis is among the best I've ever seen."*

**KEY INDIVIDUALS** The tremendously experienced **Lee Kaplan** (see p.2398) has extensive trial expertise and is praised for his work involving IP and hi-tech issues. His recent highlights include representing WesternGeco, an affiliate of Schlumberger, in a major patent infringement case. **Craig Smyser** (see p.2416) has a broad-ranging commercial litigation practice that encompasses medical malpractice cases and energy issues. Sources say: *"He's a remarkably impressive lawyer; you can give him a bare amount of detail and he can isolate the ultimate issue and find a good solution."*

### Weil, Gotshal & Manges LLP
See profile on p.2015

**THE FIRM** This robust litigation group is highlighted for its excellence in significant bankruptcy-related litigation, shareholder disputes and insurance litigation on behalf of a range of prominent clients hailing from an array of jurisdictions. Anadarko, Kerr-McGee, American Airlines and Deutsche Bank are among the firm's key clients.
**Sources say:** *"The whole team is fantastic. I've worked with a lot of firms over the years and I've never had such a good firm."*
**KEY INDIVIDUALS Yvette Ostolaza** (see p.2408) has a much-admired commercial litigation practice, and has been particularly active in the securities space of late. Sources note that *"Yvette has an incredible ability to understand the people involved, who's on the other side, their strengths and weaknesses – she doesn't look for the usual cookie-cutter, classic legal responses and solutions."*

### Band 4

### Bracewell & Giuliani LLP
See profile on p.2429

**THE FIRM** This versatile team undertakes a broad array of litigation cases, including energy, appellate, banking and construction. The group is highlighted in particular this year for its appearance in international disputes, including its role on behalf of oil and gas exploration company Eni in litigation surrounding gas production at the Devils Tower Spar oil and gas platform.
**KEY INDIVIDUALS Warren Harris** (see p.2394) leads the firm's appellate practice group and has tremendous trial experience, including matters before the Texas Supreme Court. The impressive **Stephen Crain's** (see p.2386) recent highlights include representing Tide Natural Gas Storage in a dispute arising from fraudulent representations made prior to the sale of a gas storage company to the client. Sources agree that seasoned authority **Clifford Gunter** (see p.2393) *"does a wonderful job on energy disputes."* He maintains ongoing relationships with high-profile clients and remains particularly active litigating in the energy sector.

### Carrington, Coleman, Sloman & Blumenthal, LLP

**THE FIRM** This results-driven, Dallas-based firm is applauded for its work in business litigation, bankruptcy matters, energy and securities litigation. However, the group is perhaps best known for its expertise with RICO, legal malpractice and fraud issues.
**KEY INDIVIDUALS** The superb and tremendously experienced **Fletcher Yarbrough** is particularly active in major

arbitration assignments as well as a broad range of commercial litigation roles. The highly respected **James Coleman** has a vast amount of experience in all areas of business litigation. He also has a stellar reputation in arbitrating cases.

### Gibson, Dunn & Crutcher LLP
See profile on p.682

**THE FIRM** This significant litigation practice handles appellate, general commercial and securities litigation matters for an impressive client roster. This includes the likes of Luminant Energy, Viacom, MTV and Country Music Television. The team's strength in appellate matters was highlighted recently with its successful representation of Oncor Electric Delivery in one of the most prominent appeals affecting the energy industry in recent years.
**KEY INDIVIDUALS William Dawson** (see p.2387) recently defended Dallas County judge Clay Jenkins in a suit brought by a number of Dallas County constables and deputy constables. He regularly handles IP and technology licensing claims in addition to professional liability and malpractice matters. A former Texas solicitor general, **James Ho** (see p.2396) manages appeal work and has constitutional litigation expertise. Recent highlights include representing a number of media companies, led by Belo, as amicus curiae before the Fifth Circuit. Sources laud him as a *"good strategic thinker, and a very good appellate advocate."* **Robert Walters** (see p.2420) focuses on general commercial litigation, although he has impressive skills in the areas of antitrust litigation and trade regulation. Notably, he recently successfully defended Tenet Healthcare against an unsolicited takeover offer by Community Health Systems. Clients are especially enamored of his holistic and intuitive knowledge of their goals.

### Jackson Walker LLP
See profile on p.2441

**THE FIRM** This quality firm has the ability to handle complex business litigation in numerous jurisdictions. The team handles matters in the energy, media and aviation sectors and comprises highly experienced lawyers. The firm's impressive client list includes Google, JPMorgan Chase and Farmers.
**Sources say:** *"It's an excellent firm. They're very focused on client service and delivering the work product quickly, efficiently and economically."*
**KEY INDIVIDUALS** Sources acknowledge that *"superstar"* **Charles Babcock** (see p.276) is very highly regarded in First Amendment-related litigation. Interviewees go on to describe him as *"very engaging, extremely likable and professional, and easily relatable to a jury so you get the benefit of a good mind with mental sharpness but with an amiable exterior too."*

### Morgan, Lewis & Bockius LLP
See profile on p.2246

**THE FIRM** This Houston-based team has an excellent general commercial litigation practice and exhibits solid expertise in product liability and patent litigation. The team's impressive client list includes several Fortune 500

companies from a variety of sectors, including energy, aviation and entertainment. Hewlett-Packard, CenterPoint Energy and Toyota Motor Sales are all included on its roster.
**KEY INDIVIDUALS Allyson Ho** (see p.2396) is highly respected for her superb appellate practice. Sources label her as *"intellectually brilliant,"* highlighting her impeccable work ethic and client-friendly approach. **Winstol Carter** (see p.2383) has an impressive complex commercial litigation practice, and is highly regarded as an expert in the IP litigation field. **Brady Edwards** (see p.2388) is hailed as *"a great modern and technically advanced lawyer."* He has expertise in the areas of product liability and toxic tort litigation, as well as a vast array of experience in a range of commercial litigation matters.

### Rose Walker, L.L.P.

**THE FIRM** Clients are impressed with this thriving general commercial litigation boutique. The team also possesses particular IP expertise. Notably, the team recently represented a client in a complex trust litigation matter, concerning the question of whether an independent trustee breached its fiduciary duty to the beneficiary.
**Sources say:** *"They're wonderful. They're very responsive and very collaborative in the way they approach things. They take direction very well from us, but are good at giving us alternatives to think about."*
**KEY INDIVIDUALS Martin Rose** has expertise across a variety of complex commercial litigation cases. He has in-depth knowledge of contract disputes and litigation surrounding hi-tech issues. *"He's very thoughtful in his approach,"* say sources, who add: *"He always has his eyes on the best resolution for the client and is very creative in the way he does things."* **Ross Cunningham** has a solid general commercial practice, which also encompasses IP disputes. Sources note that *"he's really focused on the best, most efficient resolution to a case."*

### Thompson & Knight LLP
See profile on p.2458

**THE FIRM** This reputable firm operates a large Texas-wide litigation team. The groups handles a range of general commercial litigation including antitrust, and energy, environment and aviation-related disputes. Key clients include Allegiance Telecom, BNSF Railway and Mitsubishi Heavy Industries.
**KEY INDIVIDUALS Craig Haynes** (see p.2394) maintains a well-reputed energy and natural resources litigation practice, and actively represents esteemed oil and gas clients in multimillion-dollar disputes. The *"really solid"* **Timothy McCormick** (see p.2404) focuses on general commercial litigation, in particular centering his practice on antitrust matters and securities litigation.

### Other Notable Practitioners

Sources have nothing but praise for **Thomas Ajamie** of Ajamie LLP. He is described as a *"stupendous litigator with a winning attitude and work ethic."* **Douglas Alexander** (see p.2378) of Alexander Dubose & Townsend LLP continues to develop his established and long-standing appellate practice, with great results. **Tom Bayko** of Hogan Lovells US LLP represents clients in a range of general commercial litigation, and has particular expertise in energy-related matters. He recently represented a key energy client in significant matters pertaining to a pipeline explosion. **Scott Brister** (see p.2382) is head of the appellate practice group at Andrews Kurth LLP. He brings his experience in the Texas Supreme Court to bear on matters in his successful appellate practice. Sources *"have a great deal of respect for his ability,"* and particularly laud his impressive intelligence. **Leon Carter** of Carter Stafford Arnett Hamada & Mockler is widely recognized for the impressive range of disputes he undertakes, with sources noting his adroit handling of everything from employment to IP matters. He is praised as *"a very, very capable, intelligent and hard-working individual."*

The sterling **Kevin Dubose** of Alexander Dubose & Townsend LLP is similarly known by peers as *"a great, great appellate lawyer."* **Craig Enoch** of Enoch Kever PLLC is a highly regarded appellate lawyer. His experience as a Justice of the Texas Supreme Court provides him with invaluable perspective and experience in complex trials. The impressive **Claudia Wilson Frost** (see p.2390) of DLA Piper LLP (US) has a successful appellate practice in the firm's Houston office. She is also known for her patent litigation skills. The highly experienced **Mark Glasser** (see p.2391) of Sidley Austin LLP has a respected and varied litigation practice encompassing general business, securities and energy-related disputes. According to interviewees: *"He has excellent presence, and is very good with judges, and*

**Murry Cohen** (see p.2385) leads the Texas appellate practice group at Akin Gump Strauss Hauer & Feld LLP. He maintains a reputable appellate practice, backed by his in-depth experience, having been a judge on the Court of Appeals for the First District of Texas for more than 19 years. Interviewees describe **Samuel Cooper** (see p.2385) of Paul Hastings LLP as *"a really fine lawyer; he's warp-speed smart, has a great sense of humor and great personality."* He is renowned in the field of securities litigation, and also undertakes a range of business litigation matters. Cooper recently joined the firm from Baker Botts. **Thad Dameris** at Hogan Lovells US LLP maintains a solid general commercial litigation practice. He has been representing Carnival Corporation in all litigation relating to insurance losses arising from the grounding of the 'Costa Concordia' off Italy.

juries like him." The *"highly competent and successful"* **Sean Gorman** (see p.2392) of Ahmad, Zavitsanos, Anaipakos, Alavi & Mensing P.C. recently represented key client Intercontinental Terminals in antitrust litigation. One pleased client said: *"Sean has been like a miracle worker."* A former Justice on the Fifth District Court of Appeals, **Deborah Hankinson** (see p.2393) of Hankinson LLP has a great deal of experience in appellate litigation. She is known by sources, who respect her advocacy skills and writing style, as a tenacious attorney. The *"wonderful"* **Orrin Harrison** of Akin Gump Strauss Hauer & Feld LLP is lauded by sources as a *"first-rate"* attorney, particularly in the securities field. He is commended for his skills in litigation relating to securities, and for having recently represented Gregory Wallace, the former CFO of SemGroup, in a significant securities class action case. The extensively experienced **Daniel Hedges** (see p.2394) of Porter Hedges LLP is highly regarded for his broad-based commercial litigation practice. He has tremendous experience in dealing with both public and private clients as well as government entities.

**Kenneth Held** of Schiffer Odom Hicks & Johnson PLLC has an impressive litigation practice representing financial industry clients in securities matters. **Kenneth Johnston** (see p.2397) of Kane Russell Coleman & Logan PC continues his highly reputed general commercial litigation and class action practice. He has particular expertise in bankruptcy-related litigation and matters occurring in the financial services arena. Impressed clients describe him as *"very responsive, and very client-oriented."* **Michael Jung** of Strasburger & Price LLP has built upon his highly regarded appellate practice and continues to impress sources, one of whom noted: *"He's terrific, he is a star; one of the finest appellate lawyers in Dallas."* The *"terrific"* **David Keltner** of Kelly Hart & Hallman LLP is heralded by sources for his extensive experience in appellate litigation. One commentator said: *"I think very highly of him and always have. A very fine appellate lawyer."*

Acknowledged energy litigation expert **William Knull** cochairs the international arbitration practice group at Mayer Brown LLP. He continues to work on significant commercial litigation matters as well as maintaining his highly regarded arbitration practice. Solid lawyer **Thomas Kruse** (see p.2400) leads the commercial litigation group at Baker Hostetler. He handles a broad range of commercial litigation on behalf of clients, and has experience in energy litigation. **James Maloney** (see p.2403) recently

joined Andrews Kurth LLP from Baker Botts. He is highly regarded for his work in an array of securities litigation assignments. **Robert Mow** (see p.2406) of K&L Gates has in-depth experience in commercial litigation. Sources *"think the world of him,"* and admire his spectacular career. **Jacks Nickens** of McGuireWoods LLP deals with a range of complex litigation matters for a variety of clients, including governmental agencies, and has a particular focus on securities litigation. The venerable **Jesse Pierce** (see p.2410) of Pierce & O'Neill, LLP maintains an outstanding reputation in energy and natural resources litigation, and brings his extensive experience to bear on a range of commercial matters. Sources praise the eminent **Shannon Ratliff** of Ratliff Law Firm PLLC and note that he is *"a wonderful, fabulous trial attorney, especially in the energy sector."* **Dick Sayles** of Sayles Werbner, PC brings his impressive experience to bear on a range of general commercial litigation matters. Sources say he is *"a very good lawyer, very successful and very accomplished."*

**Adam Schiffer** of Schiffer Odom Hicks & Johnson PLLC has cultivated an impressive and highly active energy litigation practice. He is well known in the state as a solid advocate with a wealth of trial experience. **Charles Schwartz** (see p.2415) leads the Houston office and its litigation practice at Skadden, Arps, Slate, Meagher & Flom LLP & Affiliates. He is a preeminent securities litigator. Client are especially impressed with his presentation skills, with one source mentioning: *"He does a great job in presenting in a thorough and relaxed manner."* **George Shipley** of Shipley Snell Montgomery Droog LLP is applauded for his supreme advocacy skills. *"He is extremely calm under fire,"* say sources, who add: *"He's steadfast and can think extremely well on his feet."* Commentators label **Roger Townsend** (see p.2419), of Alexander Dubose & Townsend LLP, as a *"very fine attorney."* He is renowned across the state for his successful appellate practice. **Dick Watt** (see p.2420) of Watt, Beckworth, Thompson & Henneman acts on behalf of both plaintiffs and defendants on a range of gas and energy-related litigation. He possesses expertise in both trial and appellate matters. The highly proficient **Mark Werbner**, of Sayles Werbner, PC, has a well-respected practice encompassing a range of general commercial litigation. **Ray Whitman** (see p.2422) leads Baker Hostetler LLP's national litigation practice. He is recognized for his skill in representing energy and natural resources clients, in particular, in a range of litigation matters. Sources commend his *"consistently excellent work."*

# REAL ESTATE

Commentary about individuals can be found under their firm's paragraph. If the firm has no paragraph (is not ranked) look at Other Notable Practitioners.

## Real Estate
### Leading Firms

**Band 1**
Baker Botts LLP *
Haynes and Boone, LLP *
Thompson & Knight LLP *
Vinson & Elkins LLP *
Winstead PC *

**Band 2**
Andrews Kurth LLP *
Bracewell & Giuliani LLP *
Greenberg Traurig, LLP *
Locke Lord LLP *
Mayer Brown LLP *

**Band 3**
Akin Gump Strauss Hauer & Feld LLP *
Baker & Hostetler LLP *
DLA Piper LLP (US) *
Fulbright & Jaworski LLP *
Gardere Wynne Sewell LLP *
Hunton & Williams LLP *
Jackson Walker LLP *
Jones Day *
Munsch Hardt Kopf & Harr, P.C. *

\* Indicates firm / individual with profile.
†ONP = Other Notable Practitioner

## Real Estate
### Senior Statesmen

**Senior Statesmen: distinguished older practitioners**

| | | | |
|---|---|---|---|
| Dow Melvin | Haynes and Boone, LLP | Katz M Marvin | Mayer Brown LLP |
| Dunlop Fred | Baker Botts LLP * | Roberts Jr Harry M | Thompson & Knight LLP * |
| Hollyfield John S | Fulbright & Jaworski LLP * | | |

### Leading Individuals

**Star individuals**

| | | | |
|---|---|---|---|
| Dunlay Jon | Baker Botts LLP * | Santos Ralph G | Greenberg Traurig, LLP * |
| Jurgensmeyer Randy R | Vinson & Elkins LLP * | Sloan Mark M | Thompson & Knight LLP * |
| Wallenstein James H | Glast, Phillips & Murray PC | | |
| Weiner Sanford A | Vinson & Elkins LLP * | **Band 3** | |
| | | Alletag Gary M | Baker & Hostetler LLP * |
| **Band 1** | | Arnold Mark | Andrews Kurth LLP * |
| Hicks Jr M Lawrence | Thompson & Knight LLP * | Bailey K Brock | Bracewell & Giuliani LLP * |
| Jenkins Steve | Haynes and Boone, LLP | Bast Cynthia | Locke Lord LLP * |
| Newsome J Kent | Greenberg Traurig, LLP * | Boyd Michael | Andrews Kurth LLP * |
| Nondorf Kurt | Jackson Walker LLP * | Campbell Andrew | Andrews Kurth LLP * |
| Stanton Patricia | Baker Botts LLP * | Dow T Andrew | Winstead PC * |
| Wasserstrom Neil | Mayer Brown LLP (ONP)† | Giese Jeffrey W | Hunton & Williams LLP * |
| Weller Philip D | DLA Piper LLP (US) * | Gunning Vicky | Locke Lord LLP * |
| Wilson Robert | Haynes and Boone, LLP | Halsey Susan A | Jackson Walker LLP * |
| Wright Robert | Baker Botts LLP * | Harris Martha | Thompson & Knight LLP * |
| | | Inoff Darren | Andrews Kurth LLP * |
| **Band 2** | | Kane Raymond J | Kane Russell Coleman (ONP)† * |
| Alessio Michael | Winstead PC * | Kopf Rick O | Munsch Hardt Kopf & Harr, P.C. |
| Boulden Michael R | Vinson & Elkins LLP * | Lowery David | Jones Day * |
| Cavanaugh Jr William (Chip) T | Munsch Hardt Kopf & Harr, P.C. | Martin Richard | Haynes and Boone, LLP |
| Erwin Greg | Winstead PC * | Meyerson Alfred M | Thompson & Knight LLP * |
| Hailey Jay | DLA Piper LLP (US) * | Nolan John | Winstead PC * |
| Ingrum Andrew A | Thompson & Knight LLP * | Pappert Michael J | Baker & Hostetler LLP * |
| Jacobs Stephen C | Locke Lord LLP * | Schreiber Howard | Hunton & Williams LLP * |
| Kelley Kevin L | Gardere Wynne Sewell LLP * | Shoss Ronald | Mayer Brown LLP |
| Lee Carl B | Akin Gump Strauss Hauer & Feld LLP | Smith Jane S | Fulbright & Jaworski LLP * |
| Martin Paul | Vinson & Elkins LLP * | Stein Pamela B | Greenberg Traurig, LLP * |
| Peterson Edward | Winstead PC * | Sullivan Kevin A | Winstead PC * |
| Ratner Randall M | Akin Gump Strauss Hauer & Feld LLP | Taylor Consuella Simmons | Baker Botts LLP * |
| Risman Clifford J | Gardere Wynne Sewell LLP * | Taylor Timothy C. | Jackson Walker LLP * |
| Ross Joel L | Vinson & Elkins LLP * | Weibel Mark | Thompson & Knight LLP * |
| Saegert Ann | Haynes and Boone, LLP | Wilson Reid | Wilson, Cribbs & Goren, P.C. (ONP)† |

## Band 1

### Baker Botts LLP
**See profile on p.2427**

**THE FIRM** This well-established real estate practice remains a key player in the Texas market, and specializes in joint venture transactions, acquisitions, disposals and complex commercial real estate development. Highlights of the past year include representing key client Hines in the $1 billion redevelopment of mixed use site CityCenterDC. The impressive client list also includes Clarion, Crescent Real Estate and E2M Partners.

**Sources say:** "*They're absolutely the best advisers – 24/7 service, very hard-working and always available.*"

**KEY INDIVIDUALS** The well-respected **Jon Dunlay** (see p.2387) is described as "*an excellent lawyer and gentleman,*" and further praised for being "*easy to get along with.*" He has recently been involved in representing Hines in the development of a Houston high-rise office tower for Apache Corporation. **Patricia Stanton** (see p.2417) offers expertise in debt and equity financing, restructurings and workouts. Sources regard her as "*a dynamo*" and also single her out as being "*incredibly diligent, thoughtful, and a tireless worker.*" **Robert Wright** (see p.2423) has a fine reputation among peers and remains highly sought by clients across the country to handle developments, acquisitions and disposals of substantial real estate projects, including

hotels and shopping centers. **Connie Taylor** (see p.2418) wins enthusiastic praise from commentators who laud her as "*very personable – she can get her point across with no inkling of arrogance.*" **Fred Dunlop** (see p.2388) has more than 40 years' experience in real estate matters, and concentrates his practice on sophisticated commercial transactions for investors, developers and institutional lenders.

### Haynes and Boone, LLP
**See profile on p.444**

**THE FIRM** This highly regarded real estate group offers expertise across the full spectrum of matters, including leasing, development and financing. It recently advised Bank of America on a $120 million loan for the construction and rehabilitation of a Hawaiian resort hotel. Other

key clients include Frost National Bank, Hillwood Development and Bentall Kennedy.

**Sources say:** "*The firm is top tier.*"

**KEY INDIVIDUALS Steve Jenkins** is highly regarded for his experience in setting up private and public REITs, and in structuring joint ventures, private equity investments and other ownership vehicles. **Robert Wilson** is another leading figure in the practice and is commended as "*a good, well-rounded attorney*" with "*a lot of experience.*" **Richard Martin** remains an excellent choice for his expertise in investment and debt restructuring. He is also highly sought after for his experience in the acquisition of distressed debt. The "*excellent*" **Ann Saegert** is popular among sources, who describe her as "*thoughtful, thorough and tough.*" She regularly represents pension plans, funds and REITs in a whole range of real estate transactions. Of counsel **Melvin Dow** continues to be a leading figure in the market and is an expert in handling complex commercial transactions for investor and developer clients.

## Thompson & Knight LLP
See profile on p.2458

**THE FIRM** The top-notch real estate team at Thompson & Knight is particularly renowned for its work on the finance side, and offers substantial experience in workouts, loan restructurings and the disposal of distressed assets. A recent work highlight saw the practice act for Trigild on its role as chief restructuring officer in the SCI Bankruptcy. Other notable clients include Wells Fargo, Transwestern and Comerica.

**Sources say:** *"They've been a delight to work with." "An excellent firm."*

**KEY INDIVIDUALS Lawrence Hicks** (see p.2395) is particularly singled out by commentators for his wealth of experience and skill as a lawyer. He handles a broad spectrum of real estate matters for a number of institutional clients, including leasing, foreclosures and workouts. **Andrew Ingrum** (see p.2396) is well versed in the acquisition, development, management and disposal of real estate. In a recent highlight, he represented the City of Austin in a high-profile $750 million mixed-use development, involving the disposal of five riverfront city blocks. The *"very talented"* **Mark Sloan** (see p.2416) splits his practice between acting for lenders and developers. In the past year he has represented Wells Fargo as lead agent in a $250 million credit facility for the redevelopment of the Ward Centers in Honolulu. The highly regarded **Martha Harris** (see p.2394) regularly represents lenders in real estate-related financings, including multifamily, retail and office projects. **Alfred Meyerson** (see p.2405) works out of the Houston office and offers expertise in all areas of transactions related to commercial real estate. He recently acted for Cadence Bank on successfully closing a sophisticated $25 million advancing term loan. **Mark Weibel** (see p.2421) recently joined the firm and is described as *"a great addition"* to the practice. He has substantial experience in capital markets, and is well known for his expertise in representing special servicers in the CMBS market. **Harry Roberts** (see p.2413) is a stalwart in the industry and uses his extensive experience to effectively represent institutional lenders and investors.

## Vinson & Elkins LLP
See profile on p.2459

**THE FIRM** Vinson & Elkin's highly regarded real estate practice has continued to develop its strength in the energy sphere over the past year, with particular emphasis on renewable energy sources. The group has a broad base of experience across all elements of real estate, and acts for clients from a variety of industries, including developers, insurance companies and banks, on a national level. One recent highlight saw the team act for a private equity investor on the acquisition of 1,800 acres of land through a contested Bankruptcy Code Section 363 auction.

**Sources say:** *"Excellent in real estate – they are one of the best."*

**KEY INDIVIDUALS Randy Jurgensmeyer** (see p.2398) is a luminary in the Texas real estate community. Sources are quick to describe him as *"a very, very smart and well-rounded attorney,"* and particularly single out his *"excellent ability to work with private equity funds."* He led the team acting for a private equity investor on the bankruptcy auction acquisition. **Sanford Weiner** (see p.2421) maintains a similarly eminent reputation in the market, with interviewees hailing him as *"a phenomenal lawyer and a great human being."* He remains a noted authority on the financing of real estate transactions. Department head **Michael Boulden** (see p.2381) *"has a very deep understanding of real estate and a lot of expertise in the real estate world,"* according to sources, who also appreciate that *"he's very pleasant and a very even-keeled person to work with."* He represents an excellent choice of counsel for private equity fund clients. **Paul Martin** (see p.2403) acts on behalf of a number of substantial property managers and developers, and is particularly recommended for his leasing work. **Joel Ross** (see p.2414) continues to enjoy a fine reputation in the commercial real estate market and is much sought by a varied list of clients, including developers, REITs and private equity sources.

## Winstead PC
See profile on p.2460

**THE FIRM** The well-respected real estate group at Winstead is one of the largest in the state, and has successfully established a full-service approach to the practice area. Key areas of expertise include mixed-use developments and complex lending arrangements, and the team has also established a particular niche handling real estate matters for a range of sports facilities. In a recent highlight, it represented the State of Georgia in the proposed development and lease of a new stadium for the Atlanta Falcons.

**Sources say:** *"The firm is one of the best in Texas and has very competent people from top to bottom."*

**KEY INDIVIDUALS** *"Good, well-rounded attorney"* **Michael Alessio** (see p.2378) is recognized for his experience across a broad range of real estate issues, and offers particular expertise in multifamily transactions. According to sources, the *"excellent"* **Kevin Sullivan** (see p.2418) is *"as good as it gets from a lender lawyer standpoint."* He has experience across the full spectrum of real estate finance matters, and plays a pivotal role in maintaining a number of the group's key client relationships. **Greg Erwin** (see p.2388) has more than three decades of experience in the real estate market. In a recent highlight, he represented Timothy Horan, founder of Mesa Real Estate Partners, in the formation of the private equity fund and the subsequent acquisition of 36 net-leased properties. **Andrew Dow** (see p.2387) recently acted for TRT Holdings on the development of a new 170,000 sq ft headquarters in Dallas, which included a ten-year tax abatement from the City. He cochairs the firm's healthcare and real estate industry practice groups. Fellow real estate cochair **John Nolan** (see p.2407) acts for clients ranging from local businesses and state governments to Fortune 500 companies. He recently

represented Paragon Outlet Partners in the $210 million acquisition and development of two outlet malls. **Edward Peterson** (see p.2410) wins acclaim from sources, with one impressed commentator asserting: *"He is very knowledgeable and a great source of information and contacts."* During the past year, Peterson has been representing Southern Methodist University in the $350 million construction of the George W. Bush Presidential Center.

## Band 2

## Andrews Kurth LLP
See profile on p.2426

**THE FIRM** Andrew Kurth's real estate group regularly acts for a varied mix of clients, including equity investors, institutional lenders and corporate owners, on large-scale projects such as international hotel chains and corporate headquarters. Recent highlights include representing Red Roof Inns in the $250 million acquisition of interests in 240 service hotels. Other notable clients include Invesco, Landry's Restaurants and Anadarko Petroleum.

**Sources say:** *"There's a continuation of the same level of service from top to bottom." "I think they have a phenomenal practice."*

**KEY INDIVIDUALS Andrew Campbell** (see p.2383) has particular expertise in advising on the acquisition, financing and development of commercial properties for private investor funds. He recently acted for Invesco on the $300 million development of two new Washington, DC office buildings. **Mark Arnold** (see p.2378) focuses on all aspects of commercial real estate, and is particularly sought for his experience handling substantial public projects. A recent highlight saw him representing Harris County-Houston Sports Authority in the $75 million construction of the new MLS Soccer Stadium in Houston. **Michael Boyd** (see p.2382) elicits particular praise for his thoroughness and dedication to clients. He recently acted for Anadarko on the $200 million expansion of its headquarters in The Woodlands. **Darren Inoff** (see p.2396) has a wealth of experience across a broad range of real estate matters and is a fine choice for clients seeking counsel on the development of office buildings, retail projects, hotels and entertainment arenas, among others. During the past year he represented PinPoint Commercial in the $37 million development of three assisted living facilities in Texas and Georgia.

## Bracewell & Giuliani LLP
See profile on p.2429

**THE FIRM** This real estate practice is particularly well known for its skill in project development matters, as well as energy-related transactions. It recently represented Shell Oil in the lease renewal of its corporate headquarters in Houston, comprising two office buildings covering 1.2 million sq ft. The impressive client list includes Kinder Morgan, BP and Apache.

**Sources say:** *"The firm brings the right depth and breadth of legal talent to each project."*

**KEY INDIVIDUALS Brock Bailey** (see p.2379) is popular among sources as *"a practical deal maker who knows how to solve problems and get a deal done, all while recognizing and fighting for what is important to the client."* Interviewees also appreciate his ability to *"stay on top of the most complicated deal and retain his good humor and easygoing sensibility throughout."*

## Greenberg Traurig, LLP
See profile on p.1024

**THE FIRM** The Texas offering of this global real estate practice is well equipped to provide expertise in commercial lending, acquisitions, leasing and disposals. In a recent highlight, it represented Trammell Crow in the sale of Hess Tower. Other key clients include Southwestern Energy, Duty Free Americas and Baker Hughes.

**Sources say:** *"Lots of horsepower and options across all disciplines." "They can handle work on a national level."*

**KEY INDIVIDUALS Kent Newsome** (see p.2407) chairs the Houston real estate group and is regularly called upon by developers and owners to handle a variety of property matters. He elicits much praise from the market, with interviewees particularly highlighting his pragmatism. **Ralph Santos** (see p.2414) is recommended for his expertise in mortgage lending, and also maintains a fine track record in hospital acquisitions and disposals. Sources are quick to laud his *"excellent work ethic and interpersonal skills."* **Pamela Stein** (see p.2417) is applauded for being *"not only very knowledgeable, but also very good at negotiating and applying the right amount of diplomacy when needed."* She offers particular expertise in leasing and land developments, as well as acquisitions and sales of commercial property.

## Locke Lord LLP
See profile on p.2443

**THE FIRM** This real estate team continues to be seen as a key player in the area of affordable housing, with clients citing Locke Lord as the 'go-to' firm for that type of work. Particular areas of expertise include multifamily and single family housing, tax-exempt bond financing, and special needs housing. A recent highlight saw the team represent Verde Realty in a $290 million acquisition from investment funds of ten industrial warehouse properties.

**Sources say:** *"Excellent." "Very competent and professional."*

**KEY INDIVIDUALS Stephen Jacobs** (see p.2397) is noted for his skill in real estate contract negotiations. His practice includes representing retail users, landlords and tenants, and telecom companies in matters ranging from developments to leasings and acquisitions. **Cynthia Bast** (see p.2380) recently assisted Beaumont Housing Authority with closing four sources of financing for the construction of a 140-unit multifamily housing property. One enthusiastic source was keen to name her *"the most outstanding affordable housing lawyer in Texas."* **Vicky Gunning** (see p.2392) concentrates on advising venture capital companies and financial institutions on a range of real estate-related matters, including secured loans, foreclosures and debt restructurings.

## Mayer Brown LLP
See profile on p.1257

**THE FIRM** Mayer Brown's real estate practice continues to increase its presence in the Texas market and has established itself as an excellent choice of counsel for complex, high-value matters. In a highlight from the past year the group acted on behalf of one leading client on a 400,000 sq ft San Francisco office lease. Other key clients include Clarion, AmREIT and Wells Fargo.

**Sources say:** *"They have such an amazing amount of experience and talent. They're all masterful negotiators." "They are very good at protecting my interests but understand my ultimate goal is to get the deal done."*

**KEY INDIVIDUALS Neil Wasserstrom** is noted for his wealth of experience and acts for clients including home builders, REITs and investors. As one source asserts, he *"understands the need to get the deal done while protecting the client and is adept at formulating win/win solutions."* **Ronald Shoss** heads the Texas real estate group and *"knows the market inside and out,"* according to interviewees. He has a diverse practice acting for institutional property owners on acquisitions, leasing, financing and development. The *"very knowledgeable"* **Marvin Katz** is senior counsel at the firm and focuses on corporate issues, probate and estate planning relating to real estate matters.

## Band 3

## Akin Gump Strauss Hauer & Feld LLP
See profile on p.904

**THE FIRM** This group has particular strength in the field of real estate finance and offers expertise across the whole range of CMBS-related matters. It represents developers, funds, banks and REITs, among others, and recently acted for VWI Partners on the acquisition of the Crowne Plaza East in Florida. Key clients include Element Power, FelCor Lodging Trust and MeriStar Hospitality.

**Sources say:** *"They're wonderfully helpful."*

**KEY INDIVIDUALS** Sources laud **Carl Lee**'s ability to *"take a complex legal issue and break it down into bite-size pieces."* He recently represented renewable energy project developer Element Power in the sale of a 14,000 acre Texas wind power project. **Randall Ratner** has a wealth of experience in real estate-related matters, and recently acted for Behringer Harvard REIT on the $340 million financing of a seven-property portfolio.

## Baker & Hostetler LLP
See profile on p.2119

**THE FIRM** The real estate group at Baker Hostetler handles the full spectrum of real estate matters, including workouts, leasing, financings and restructurings, for a diverse client base of funds, lenders and developers, among others. During the past year, the team has been acting for TPCO on the $1 billion construction of a seamless pipe fabricating facility in Gregory, Texas. Other notable clients include Palletized Trucking, Creek Meadow Partners and Metropolitan Life.

**Sources say:** *"Baker Hostetler does a terrific job for us."*

**KEY INDIVIDUALS Michael Pappert** (see p.2408) is *"exceedingly thorough and conscientious,"* according to interviewees, who also note that he is *"a pleasure to deal with."* In the past year, Pappert represented Beacon Acquisitions in the $50 million acquisition and finance of two Dallas office buildings. Department head **Gary Alletag** (see p.2378) handles a mix of commercial transactions for both businesses and individuals and, in addition to leading on the TPCO matter, has recently been representing Creek Meadow Partners in a $20 million Brazos County residential development project.

## DLA Piper LLP (US)
See profile on p.1971

**THE FIRM** DLA Piper is well known for its strength in both national and cross-border real estate work, and its Texas team regularly handles substantial out-of-state matters as well as local ones. A highlight of the past year saw the group act for Greystar on the $170 million acquisition of a Southern California multifamily apartment portfolio. The team counts Dave & Busters, Redleaf Properties and Bain & Company among its other key clients.

**Sources say:** *"They do a great job and have the ability to skillfully handle all types of transactions."*

**KEY INDIVIDUALS** Sources describe **Philip Weller** (see p.2421) as *"truly an expert"* and *"great to work with."* He recently represented Bain & Company in a lease transaction for 40,000 sq ft in a LEED-certified building in Uptown Dallas. **Jay Hailey** (see p.2393) offers expertise across the full range of real estate issues. During the past year he acted for Redleaf Properties on the $39 million acquisition of the last parcel of land comprising the Highland Mall in Austin.

## Fulbright & Jaworski LLP
See profile on p.2435

**THE FIRM** Fulbright & Jaworski's real estate practice offers expertise across the whole spectrum of services, including leasing, construction, financing and workouts. It works with the firm's other leading practice groups, including tax, securities, environmental law, IP and litigation, to provide a seamless service to a diverse client base of owners, contractors, investors and lenders. Recently, the team has been representing Toyota in the development and construction of a $200 million-plus 2,000 acre manufacturing plant in San Antonio.

**Sources say:** *"Very good, higher level negotiating and structuring."*

**KEY INDIVIDUALS Jane Smith** (see p.2416) represented EPN in the sale of a $1.43 billion portfolio of 46 shopping centers to a joint venture. Sources describe her as *"extremely professional, detailed and good at seeing the bigger picture."* The *"top-notch"* **John Hollyfield** (see p.2396) is of counsel at the firm. He has more than four decades of experience in real estate, focusing on lending, leasing and construction matters, among other areas.

## Gardere Wynne Sewell LLP
See profile on p.2436

**THE FIRM** This group covers the whole range of real estate-related matters, and is especially well known for its work on large-scale transactions such as retail centers, residential developments and office buildings. The team regularly acts on behalf of funds, developers, purchasers and financial institutions on projects across the USA, as well as in Canada, Mexico and the Caribbean.

**Sources say:** *"They're great to work with."*

**KEY INDIVIDUALS** The *"high-quality"* **Kevin Kelley** (see p.2399) has a wealth of experience in acting for lenders, developers and owners on real estate matters. He wins much praise from interviewees, who are particularly keen to single out his understated approach to matters. **Clifford Risman** (see p.392) represents clients in issues related to resort, hotel and mixed-use properties on an international level. He chairs the firm's hospitality industry team and is described as *"very practical and always accessible."* He also elicits praise for his *"calm demeanor."*

## Hunton & Williams LLP
See profile on p.2517

**THE FIRM** Hunton & Williams's real estate department offers particular expertise in the area of complicated workouts and structured financings. Over the past year the team represented 111 Realty Group in the $198 million acquisition of 110 natural gas drilling sites covering over 400 acres. Other notable clients include Baylor Hospital, Beal Bank and H&R Real Estate Trust.

**Sources say:** *"A very good firm."*

**KEY INDIVIDUALS Howard Schreiber** (see p.2415) ticks many boxes for clients, being described as *"detail-oriented, organized, responsive and efficient."* He also elicits praise for his *"extensive knowledge of different transaction types."* He led on the 111 Realty Group matter. **Jeffrey Giese** (see p.2391) is described as *"an all-around good lawyer."* In addition to a varied real estate practice, he is also noted for his capital markets expertise.

## Jackson Walker LLP
See profile on p.2441

**THE FIRM** The group at Jackson Walker provides expertise across the full spectrum of real estate matters, and is particularly noted for its expertise in issues relating to office buildings. A recent highlight saw the team act for The Lionstone Group on the $180 million acquisition of two office building portfolios. An enviable client list also includes IKEA, Skanska and JPMorgan Chase.

**Sources say:** *"They provide excellent legal services and good value." "A really high-quality firm."*

**KEY INDIVIDUALS** The *"very personable"* **Kurt Nondorf** (see p.2407) maintains an excellent reputation in the Texas real estate market. He played a leading role in The Lionstone Group's acquisition. **Susan Halsey** (see p.2393) receives particular praise for her *"extensive knowledge of real estate."* She chairs the firm's real estate practice group and recently acted for JPMorgan Chase on several lease transactions in Texas. **Timothy Taylor** (see p.2418) represented The University of Texas System in the ground lease of a block of land which is to be developed into a large mixed-use facility. Sources find him bright and easy to work with.

## Jones Day
See profile on p.919

**THE FIRM** This real estate group acts for investors, owners, private equity funds and investment banks, handling sales and acquisitions of portfolios on a national level. It also has an active borrower practice, advising on loan restructurings, workouts and other financings. During the past year the team represented Rockpoint Group in the formation of a new private equity fund of over $800 million. Other key clients include Behringer Harvard, Mill Creek Residential and Morgan Stanley Realty.

**Sources say:** *"We think very highly of Jones Day and enjoy the breadth of its resources."*

**KEY INDIVIDUALS** Department head **David Lowery** (see p.2402) *"is an extremely experienced real estate lawyer with outstanding deal judgment,"* according to sources. He has recently been advising Mill Creek Residential on a series of apartment complex-secured financings totaling more than $110 million.

## Munsch Hardt Kopf & Harr, P.C.
See profile on p.2448

**THE FIRM** This group is well regarded in the Texas market and represents developers, lenders, investors and owners in a range of real estate matters. The firm has recently expanded its services in reaction to the current market, and now offers real estate expertise in healthcare, affordable housing and student housing developments. Of note is its recent representation of FelCor Lodging Trust in the $100 million sale of six hotels located in several states. The group also counts Crow Holdings, Teachers Insurance & Annuity and Hall Financial Group among its notable clients.

**Sources say:** *"An excellent real estate firm."*

**KEY INDIVIDUALS** The highly regarded **Chip Cavanaugh** heads the real estate department. In a recent highlight, he was part of the team that advised The Sammons Companies on the sale of Grove Park Inn, Golf Course and Condominiums in North Carolina. He also led on the FelCor Lodging Trust matter. **Rick Kopf** offers particular expertise in real estate finance. He recently represented Hall Financial Group in the $60 million refinancing of four Texas office buildings.

## Other Notable Practitioners

**James Wallenstein** of Glast, Phillips & Murray PC focuses on commercial matters and is regarded by interviewees as a *"dean of Texas real estate."* Sources add: *"He never gets in the way of making a deal work and can always come up with great ideas and solutions."* **Raymond Kane** (see p.2398) at Kane Russell Coleman & Logan PC recently represented Trammell Crow in the $100 million acquisition of a Pennsylvania office park. Sources applaud his *"uncanny ability for quickly understanding all of the nuances of a particular matter."* **Reid Wilson** heads the real estate team at Wilson, Cribbs & Goren, P.C., and is renowned for his expertise in land use matters.

# TAX

Commentary about individuals can be found under their firm's paragraph. If the firm has no paragraph (is not ranked) look at Other Notable Practitioners.

| Tax | |
|---|---|
| **Leading Firms** | |
| **Band 1** | |
| Baker Botts LLP * | |
| Vinson & Elkins LLP * | |
| **Band 2** | |
| Andrews Kurth LLP * | |
| Fulbright & Jaworski LLP * | |
| Thompson & Knight LLP * | |
| **Band 3** | |
| Akin Gump Strauss Hauer & Feld LLP * | |
| Bracewell & Giuliani LLP * | |
| Locke Lord LLP * | |
| Meadows, Collier, Reed, Cousins, Crouch & Ungerman, L.L.P. | |
| **Band 4** | |
| Baker & McKenzie * | |
| Chamberlain, Hrdlicka, White, Williams & Aughtry * | |
| Gardere Wynne Sewell LLP * | |
| Haynes and Boone, LLP * | |
| Hunton & Williams LLP * | |
| Jones Day * | |
| McDermott Will & Emery LLP * | |
| Winstead PC * | |

| Tax | |
|---|---|
| **Senior Statesmen** | |
| **Senior Statesmen:** distinguished older practitioners | |
| Hughes Vester T | K&L Gates (ONP)[†] * |
| Osterberg Edward | Vinson & Elkins LLP * |
| **Leading Individuals** | |
| **Band 1** | |
| Allender John R | Fulbright & Jaworski LLP * |
| Bowers William | Fulbright & Jaworski LLP * |
| Ford Jr Thomas W | Andrews Kurth LLP * |
| Nelson Gregory | Paul Hastings LLP (ONP)[†] |
| Wheat R David | Thompson & Knight LLP * |
| **Band 2** | |
| Allison Christopher F | Locke Lord LLP * |
| Micciche Daniel J | Akin Gump Strauss Hauer & Feld LLP |
| Rusman Jared M | Weil, Gotshal & Manges LLP (ONP)[†] * |
| Sinak David | Gibson, Dunn & Crutcher LLP (ONP)[†] * |
| **Band 3** | |
| Bopp Gregory M | Bracewell & Giuliani LLP * |
| Caudill William H | Fulbright & Jaworski LLP * |
| Clifton R Brent | Winstead PC |
| Cowling David | Jones Day * |
| Fenn Tim | Latham & Watkins LLP (ONP)[†] |
| Helfand Thomas | Winstead PC * |
| Marcus Stephen | Baker Botts LLP * |
| McNamara Robert J | Andrews Kurth LLP * |
| Stone Susan | Baker & McKenzie |
| **Band 4** | |
| Aksamit Roger D | Thompson & Knight LLP * |
| Blissard Judith M | Vinson & Elkins LLP * |
| Craig III Allen B | Gardere Wynne Sewell LLP * |
| Devetski Tim | Vinson & Elkins LLP * |
| Drablos Scott | Haynes and Boone, LLP |
| Fijolek Richard M | Haynes and Boone, LLP |
| Kontrimas Andrius | Fulbright & Jaworski LLP * |
| Lynch John Edward | Vinson & Elkins LLP * |
| O'Daniel Patrick | Fulbright & Jaworski LLP * |
| Popplewell Thomas | Andrews Kurth LLP * |
| Scofield George W | Fulbright & Jaworski LLP * |
| Thomason Kevin | Elliot & Thomason, LLP (ONP)[†] |
| **Associates to watch** | |
| Carney Ryan Kenneth | Vinson & Elkins LLP * |

| Tax: Litigation | |
|---|---|
| **Senior Statesmen** | |
| **Senior Statesmen:** distinguished older practitioners | |
| Hall Charles | Fulbright & Jaworski LLP * |
| **Leading Individuals** | |
| **Band 1** | |
| Albright Val J | Gardere Wynne Sewell LLP * |
| Campagna Larry A | Chamberlain, Hrdlicka, White, Williams |
| Gerachis George Matthew | Vinson & Elkins LLP * |
| Lowell Cym H | McDermott Will & Emery LLP * |
| Meadows Jr Charles M | Meadows, Collier, Reed, Cousins, Crouch |
| Parker Emily A | Thompson & Knight LLP * |
| Taylor Jasper | Fulbright & Jaworski LLP * |
| **Band 2** | |
| Jones Jr Lawrence R | Townsend & Jones (ONP)[†] |
| Lee William S | Fulbright & Jaworski LLP * |
| Lyda Kirk R | Jones Day * |
| Martin Mark R | McDermott Will & Emery LLP * |
| McNulty Mary A | Thompson & Knight LLP * |
| Ohlenforst Cynthia | K&L Gates (ONP)[†] * |
| Porter John | Baker Botts LLP * |
| Townsend John A | Townsend & Jones (ONP)[†] |
| Ungerman Josh O | Meadows, Collier, Reed, Cousins, Crouch |
| Welty Todd | Dentons (ONP)[†] * |

\* Indicates firm / individual with profile.

[†]ONP = Other Notable Practitioner

## Band 1

### Baker Botts LLP
See profile on p.2427

**THE FIRM** This large tax practice continues to be held in high regard by market commentators, who laud its strategic tax analysis, collaboration skills, advisory techniques, depth and experience. Its lawyers are known for advising businesses in both the technology and energy sectors, and handle tax controversy, oil and gas tax, international tax, Subchapter C, Subchapter K and MLP tax issues. Clients include EQT Midstream Partners and CenterPoint Energy. The team recently acted for The Energy & Minerals Group on a $1.8 billion matter relating to Tallgrass Energy Partners' acquisition of Midstream Assets from Kinder Morgan Energy Partners.

**Sources say:** "A top-notch firm with a lot of depth and a lot of experience."

**KEY INDIVIDUALS John Porter**'s (see p.386) highly regarded practice tends to focus on estate and gift litigation work, in addition to fiduciary issues, the valuation of business interests and income tax disputes. He is also known for his litigation and dispute work in relation to the IRS. "Outstanding practitioner" **Stephen Marcus** (see p.2403) is praised by peers, particularly for his dispute work. He is adept at handling tax planning and issues relating to federal income tax law.

### Vinson & Elkins LLP
See profile on p.2459

**THE FIRM** This Texas powerhouse has an excellent reputation for taking on national tax work of the highest level of sophistication, with peers quick to praise its transactional prowess. The team is able to call on marked expertise and experience in MLP formation and operation, and regularly represents private equity funds in fund formation, LBOs and M&A. Energy taxation is a noted area of specialization, and the group recently represented CON-

SOL Energy and Devon Energy in joint venture shale plays with values of up to $6 billion. Other clients include BG Group, Pioneer Natural Resources and Riverstone Holdings.

**Sources say:** "They have a national tax practice that is well known and respected." "The entire firm really understands client service."

**KEY INDIVIDUALS** Department head **George Matthew Gerachis** (see p.2390) is particularly recognized by peers for his controversy work. He regularly handles matters for US and non-US based multinational companies in addition to global high net worth individual audits. He is also experienced in tax planning issues, including transfer pricing, foreign direct investment and joint ventures. Client favorite **Tim Devetski** (see p.2387) earns particular praise for his energy and corporate tax work. He has handled a number of MLP IPOs of late, for clients including Oiltanking Partners, Hi-Crush Proppants and Seadrill. "Very good lawyer" **John Edward Lynch** (see p.2402) is well versed in advising energy clients on both tax planning and transactional matters. He has handled a swathe of recent MLP IPOs for Inergy, Citi and Northern Tier Energy. Respectful peers acknowledge that **Edward Osterberg** (see p.2408) is "an outstanding tax partner," and recognize his continued prominence, particularly as a consultant. His vast experience and body of work includes M&A, divestments and a special focus on international transactions and corporate and partnership taxation. Clients praise associate **Ryan Kenneth Carney** (see p.2383) as *"an excellent tax lawyer who can communicate complex tax matters in a way non-tax persons can understand."* His recent work highlights include involvement on various MLP IPOs, and advising Caiman Energy on its sale of Caiman Eastern Midstream to Williams Partners. **Judith Blissard** (see p.2381) tends to focus on tax planning at both domestic and international levels in addition to business transactions, with her work in these areas attracting praise from her contemporaries. She regularly represents public and privately held companies in a number of diverse tax matters.

## Band 2

### Andrews Kurth LLP
See profile on p.2426

**THE FIRM** This firm's tax team is split into four groups, enabling it to handle any number of tax matters that may arise. The practice's 23 lawyers are spread across the areas of general tax, tax-exempt, trust and estates and executive compensation, and market sources are particularly quick to call attention to its MLP, partnership and corporate transactional expertise. The team recently acted for Kinder Morgan Energy Partners on its acquisition of interests in an El Paso/KKR joint venture, and represented the underwriters in the $600 million IPO of PetroLogistics.
**Sources say:** *"They have a very fine corporate transactional practice."*
**KEY INDIVIDUALS Thomas Ford** (see p.2389) is a *"very good energy lawyer doing complex work,"* according to peers, who hold him up as a practitioner at the top of his game. His recent highlights include representing Cordillera Energy Partners III in its $3.1 billion acquisition by Apache. **Robert McNamara** (see p.2405) focuses on advising domestic businesses on federal income tax matters and transactional planning. He is also well versed in counseling MLPs on all manner of tax issues. **Thomas Popplewell**'s (see p.2411) recent work includes representing Consumer Portfolio Services in its $141.5 million issue of asset-backed notes. He is highly skilled and experienced in real estate income tax matters, domestic and international asset securitization and corporate M&A.

### Fulbright & Jaworski LLP
See profile on p.2435

**THE FIRM** Fulbright is known for its massive presence across Texas, and its considerable tax team has a large number of highly respected practitioners able to handle the full range of domestic and international tax matters. The group regularly handles tax planning and controversy issues in addition to various consultation roles, and recently represented National Oilwell Varco in its $2.5 billion acquisition of Robins & Myers. Other notable clients include Magnum Hunter Resources, Armand Hammer Foundation and Prospector Offshore Drilling.
**Sources say:** *"They have a good group with good quality people."*

**KEY INDIVIDUALS** Sources praise **William Bowers** (see p.2382) as *"the partnership guru,"* and are keen to highlight his Subchapter K work. He recently advised Magnum Hunter Resources on an issue of senior notes and shares of common stock. Department head **John Allender** (see p.2378) is an *"outstanding lawyer,"* according to peers impressed with his healthy corporate M&A practice and expertise in warranties, covenants and tax indemnity clauses. He recently led on National Oilwell Varco's acquisition of Robins & Myers. **Jasper Taylor** (see p.2418) is held in high regard by peers for his handling of tax litigation and controversy matters, as well as energy and corporate governance issues. He regularly appears before the grand jury, the US Tax Court and the US Court of Federal Claims. Clients say **William Lee** (see p.2401) is *"a very gracious individual, but firm when he has to be. He is very serious-minded and professional."* He has been heavily involved in a number of complex tax controversy issues, including litigation, IRS examinations and Appeals Office proceedings. *"Excellent lawyer"* **William Caudill**'s (see p.2383) general tax practice covers a substantial range of issues, with financially troubled businesses, partnerships, commercial transactions and oil and gas law all featuring heavily. He also regularly appears before the IRS. **Andrius Kontrimas** (see p.2399) wins plaudits for his international tax work in particular, an area in which peers regard him to be a *"very good lawyer."* His other areas of expertise include contested tax matters, such as IRS audits and civil litigation, joint ventures, transfer pricing and private equity transactions. San Antonio-based **George Scofield** (see p.2415) can turn his hand to a range of tax matters that regularly cross over with his other areas of specialism, such as general business and healthcare law. He has a wealth of experience in federal, state and local tax matters, and internal tax compliance reviews and audits. Interviewees highlight esteemed practitioner **Charles Hall** (see p.328) as *"the dean there. He is truly a phenomenal tax lawyer."* Tax law and litigation, estate planning, international matters and corporate issues form the core of his practice. **Patrick O'Daniel** (see p.2407) recently acted for the City of Houston on a matter relating to tax-exempt and taxable public improvement refunding bonds. The bulk of his workload focuses on tax and public law aspects of municipal finance, as well as structured and project finance.

### Thompson & Knight LLP
See profile on p.2458

**THE FIRM** This international group is especially well known for its considerable capabilities and depth in the energy sphere, with oil and gas tax and tax litigation high on its agenda. The team represents a series of MLP companies, and transactional work also features prominently, particularly in the form of M&A, private equity fund formations, UPREIT IPOs and natural resource production payments. Major clients include Chevron, Noble Energy and the Texas Department of Transportation.
**Sources say:** *"The quality of their work is excellent."*
**KEY INDIVIDUALS** As a litigator of some renown, the *"excellent"* **Emily Parker** (see p.2408) regularly represents taxpayers before the IRS, and advises clients on federal

income tax and Texas tax planning. She has recently represented Chevron subsidiary Texaco in two cases docketed in the Court of Federal Claims. The *"outstanding"* **David Wheat** (see p.2421) is noted by peers as a leading player in oil and gas and MLP matters. He recently represented the majority holder of Frac Tech Services in the $3.7 billion equity sale to a consortium led by Singaporean fund Temasek Capital. **Mary McNulty** (see p.2405) has recently been involved in representing EnCap Investments in tax issues arising from the formation of private equity funds and the sale of oil and gas properties and midstream and gathering assets, worth in excess of $5 billion. Market commentators think highly of **Roger Aksamit** (see p.2377). He regularly represents energy clients in M&A, joint venture transactions and financing, and is well known for the wider tax planning and transactional aspects of his practice.

## Band 3

### Akin Gump Strauss Hauer & Feld LLP
See profile on p.904

**THE FIRM** This team earns considerable praise for providing a full-service tax offering to a wide range of clients. Offices in the Middle East, Asia and Europe provide the perfect platform for the firm to handle any number of cross-border transactional cases, while controversy, private client, ERISA matters and IRS appeals constitute much of its workload. In addition, various M&A and real estate deals feature prominently.
**KEY INDIVIDUALS Daniel Micciche** is a highly experienced attorney and has represented a range of clients in federal and state tax controversy matters. He is also active in IRS audits and appeals and M&A deals.

### Bracewell & Giuliani LLP
See profile on p.2429

**THE FIRM** This group's ability to handle significant upstream work and its expertise and focus on the energy sector are noted and admired by peers and clients alike. Its client roster includes major international energy companies such as Kinder Morgan, Phillips 66 and Chesapeake Energy, and this sector provides a significant portion of the practice's cases. MLPs and tax matters related to these also feature heavily, with other work coming from private investment funds, corporate and international transactions, financial products and bankruptcy.
**KEY INDIVIDUALS Gregory Bopp**'s (see p.2381) practice is predominantly energy-related, with a great deal of M&A work. He is also adept at handling MLP-related matters. Sources say: *"He is an outstanding tax lawyer who does a very good job of serving his clients."*

### Locke Lord LLP
See profile on p.2443

**THE FIRM** This large and experienced practice group fields 34 tax lawyers in Texas. It is able to handle tax planning and controversy matters for a variety of businesses, including IRS cases, as well as M&A and oil and gas trans-

actions. The team also handles significant healthcare-related matters, including a series of M&A transactions on behalf of Humana. Other major clients include Comstock Resources, Tenet Healthcare and High Sierra Energy.
**Sources say:** "*It is a full-service tax firm and does very nice work.*"
**KEY INDIVIDUALS** Experienced partner **Christopher Allison** (see p.2378) is "*extraordinarily good,*" according to sources. He advises on a broad range of tax issues, from corporate work to partnerships, and his impressive client roster includes names like Humana, New Vision Television and Torchmark.

## Meadows, Collier, Reed, Cousins, Crouch & Ungerman, L.L.P.

**THE FIRM** Market commentators are quick to praise this group's controversy expertise, especially in the civil tax and white-collar areas, while also highlighting the work it undertakes in the fields of estate tax and planning. The boutique's litigation prowess is particularly lauded, with income tax litigation and estate and gift litigation prominent features of the practice.
**Sources say:** "*They have expertise in civil tax controversy and in the white-collar criminal area.*"
**KEY INDIVIDUALS** The highly experienced **Charles Meadows** is well known in the Texas tax sphere, with peers particularly commending his white-collar criminal defense work. He has represented various taxpayers in tax controversies, including corporate and individual income tax and estate and gift tax matters. **Josh Ungerman** is praised for his handling of highly complex tax controversies. His sophisticated practice also incorporates both international and domestic tax disputes before a variety of courts.

## Band 4

### Baker & McKenzie
See profile on p.435

**THE FIRM** The tax capability of this international firm's Dallas and Houston offices is supported by a rich global network, meaning clients benefit from the firm's ability to take on international matters. Texas-based clients seek out the team for its expertise in complex multijurisdictional tax planning, M&A, transfer pricing and restructuring matters, and the group also advises clients from outside the state on doing work within it.
**Sources say:** "*They are great at international deals.*"
**KEY INDIVIDUALS** Houston practice chair **Susan Stone** has been heavily involved in a number of high-profile matters over the past year. Her practice tends to focus on tax issues arising from foreign oil, gas and energy projects, and she has considerable experience in international tax and business transactions.

### Chamberlain, Hrdlicka, White, Williams & Aughtry
See profile on p.2432

**THE FIRM** This 12-partner tax planning and controversy boutique has offices in Houston and San Antonio, and handles all matters that may arise in these areas at both domestic and international levels. Its lawyers regularly deal with issues before the IRS and federal and state courts. Key clients include Western Refining and Discovery Couer d'Alene Investors.
**KEY INDIVIDUALS Larry Campagna** is held in high regard among his fellow professionals for contentious tax work. His practice covers white-collar criminal defense, federal, state and local tax controversies, and business litigation matters.

### Gardere Wynne Sewell LLP
See profile on p.2436

**THE FIRM** Gardere's tax group is spread across offices in Dallas, Houston and Mexico City. The team is particularly known for its tax planning, transfer pricing, tax controversy and international capabilities. The energy sector provides the firm with a significant amount of activity, exemplified by its involvement in the high-value sale of Western International Gas & Cylinders. The group has also recently handled a number of cases before the IRS.
**KEY INDIVIDUALS Val Albright** (see p.2378) is "*a strong controversy guy,*" according to commentators. He heads the tax litigation practice and has led on a number of high-value matters in this area over the past year. He is experienced in representing clients before the IRS and in federal courts, and also in advising clients on US domestic and international tax matters. Of counsel **Allen Craig** (see p.2386) is best known for his considerable experience in business and tax planning matters. He also represents individuals and closely held businesses in tax matters before the IRS, and handles trusts and estates, and international, federal and state tax work.

### Haynes and Boone, LLP
See profile on p.444

**THE FIRM** This respected tax group is able to undertake a number of transactional matters both domestically and internationally. A broad range of M&A work forms the core of the practice, with the energy, manufacturing and healthcare sectors all being areas of focus. A great deal of nationwide work is handled from Texas, while its cross-border capabilities are also considerable. Other areas covered include tax controversy, REITs and real estate tax, trust and estate administration, state and local tax and corporate tax.
**KEY INDIVIDUALS** Sources laud **Scott Drablos** for the high level of controversy work, tax planning and transactional matters he undertakes. He often assists clients with international and domestic tax planning, while the bulk of his practice is focused on real estate tax, partnership and LLC tax, joint ventures, private equity and investment fund matters. **Richard Fijolek** is "*a very good lawyer,*" according to peers. His varied practice ranges across the energy and real estate sectors, and he has commendable expertise in private client and estate planning, international tax, venture capital and emerging company issues.

### Hunton & Williams LLP
See profile on p.2517

**THE FIRM** This practice is known for its expertise in transactional tax work, and also has expertise in controversy, litigation and administration issues. Its lawyers have forged healthy national reputations in a broad range of specialist areas, including REITs, corporate M&A, project finance, partnerships and joint ventures, tax audits and litigation.
**Sources say:** "*They are outstanding because they are able to achieve, over several matters and years, outstanding results with difficult challenges.*"
**KEY INDIVIDUALS** Patrick Mitchell is a key practice contact in Dallas.

### Jones Day
See profile on p.919

**THE FIRM** State and local tax and controversy work is the focal point of Jones Day's four-partner Dallas tax practice. Private and publicly held corporations and partnerships are regularly represented in a range of matters and areas, from bankruptcy transactions, energy and real estate to M&A, structured finance and private equity. The team regularly represents a series of household names, including Amazon.com, Expedia and Goldman Sachs.
**KEY INDIVIDUALS** Tax litigator **Kirk Lyda** (see p.2402) has handled a range of local and state taxation, controversies and tax audit, M&A, real estate and private equity taxation matters. He has recently been involved in a Texas franchise hearing, representing a large oil and gas company. **David Cowling**'s (see p.2386) peers regard him as "*one of the leading experts in state and local tax work.*" He has handled a broad range of transactional and tax controversy matters, while also dealing with private equity, real estate and M&A taxation, in addition to franchising and distribution.

### McDermott Will & Emery LLP
See profile on p.1258

**THE FIRM** McDermott Will & Emery's Houston-based tax group has a dedicated transfer pricing practice, and is known nationwide for its prowess in the area. Tax planning, controversy and litigation are also prominent aspects of the team's workload, allied to the undertaking of a wide variety of international tax matters. Clients include multinational companies, high net worth individuals and domestic and foreign-based individuals.
**Sources say:** "*It compares very favorably with the other firms we have recently dealt with in the Texas market.*"
**KEY INDIVIDUALS** Peers are effusive in their appraisals of **Cym Lowell** (see p.2402), with one lauding him as "*the best thing going.*" He regularly advises both domestic and international high net worth individuals and multinational companies on all manner of controversy and tax planning matters. Clients are quick to laud transfer pricing practice head **Mark Martin** (see p.2403), highlighting his "*subject matter expertise and knowledge, and his timely, efficient and exceptional service.*" He regularly handles tax controversy and international transfer pricing matters for multinational enterprises.

## Winstead PC

See profile on p.2460

**THE FIRM** Winstead is able to provide a sophisticated full-service tax offering to its clients. The team has considerable expertise in tax planning at the federal and international levels, tax controversy and litigation, business M&A, business structuring and work related to tax-exempt organizations. Major clients include the Dallas Cowboys, Rice University and Forbes Energy.

**Sources say:** *"They are of a very high caliber, and they are very responsive."*

**KEY INDIVIDUALS** Dallas-based **Thomas Helfand** (see p.2395) is *"a very talented guy,"* according to peers, and clients appreciate *"his very impressive understanding of the tax code and his crafting of business decisions."* His broad practice takes in tax controversies, state tax planning, bankruptcy reorganizations and restructurings. **Brent Clifton** recently joined the firm from Locke Lord. The core of his practice revolves around joint venture transactions relating to real estate, in which he represents sponsors and developers as well as institutional investors.

## Other Notable Practitioners

**Cynthia Ohlenforst** (see p.2407) of K&L Gates is praised for her expertise in state and local and federal taxation matters. She also handles controversy, litigation, transactions and tax-related legislative and administrative projects. Also at K&L Gates, experienced practitioner **Vester Hughes** (see p.2396) is known as the *"dean of the tax Bar in Texas."* Tax planning and litigation are his specialist areas, and he has handled a considerable number of federal taxation matters, including gift, excise, estate and income. Clients laud the performance of Gibson, Dunn & Crutcher LLP corporate tax partner **David Sinak** (see p.2416), calling him *"wonderful"* and *"a structuring expert extraordinaire."* His oil and gas industry expertise is well noted, and he has recently represented a series of energy companies in tax issues. **Tim Fenn** chairs Latham & Watkins LLP's Houston department and is recognized *"as one of the top authorities on MLPs."* Recent clients include Energy Transfer Partners, Rentech and Pacific Coast Energy. **Kevin Thomason** of Elliot & Thomason, LLP is recognized for his expertise in partnership tax. He also handles real estate and corporate tax issues, with like-kind

exchanges, REITs and MLPs being the key areas of focus. The *"terrific"* **Gregory Nelson** chairs Paul Hastings LLP's Houston office. His practice centers on federal income taxation issues, particularly those pertaining to partnerships and corporations in both the real estate and energy sectors. Dallas-based **Lawrence Jones** of Townsend & Jones is a noted tax controversy and IRS specialist, with audits and appeals featuring prominently in his practice. He has considerable tax case trial experience, and regularly represents taxpayers in litigation against the IRS. **John Townsend** of Townsend & Jones is acknowledged by peers for his deep subject expertise. Federal income tax controversy matters, especially IRS audits and appeals and litigation in all federal courts, form the crux of his practice. **Jared Rusman** (see p.2414) of Weil, Gotshal & Manges LLP is a *"fine lawyer"* who is well known for his involvement on big deals. He is a corporate and partnership tax specialist, and handles all manner of issues in this area. He recently advised Kinder Morgan on the tax aspects of its $38 billion acquisition of El Paso. **Todd Welty** (see p.2421) of Dentons is based in Dallas and is known for his work in tax controversy issues in both the civil and criminal spheres. He also regularly represents taxpayers in IRS challenges.

# TECHNOLOGY CORPORATE & COMMERCIAL

Commentary about individuals can be found under their firm's paragraph. If the firm has no paragraph (is not ranked) look at Other Notable Practitioners.

| Technology: Corporate & Commercial Leading Firms |
| --- |
| **Band 1** |
| Andrews Kurth LLP * |
| Baker Botts LLP * |
| DLA Piper LLP (US) * |
| Wilson Sonsini Goodrich & Rosati * |
| **Band 2** |
| Fulbright & Jaworski LLP * |
| Vinson & Elkins LLP * |
| **Band 3** |
| Bracewell & Giuliani LLP * |
| Jones Day * |
| Mayer Brown LLP * |

*Indicates firm with profile.*
*Alphabetical order within each band. Band 1 is the highest.*

## Band 1

### Andrews Kurth LLP

See profile on p.2426

**THE FIRM** This high-caliber firm maintains its prominent position in the market, and acts for an array of industry leaders such as Javelin Semiconductor and Nuventix. Interviewees are effusive in their praise of the Austin office, which is supported by teams in Houston and Dallas. Its lawyers offer expertise across the full range of corporate and commercial transactions, and handle financings, public offerings and acquisitions. They also bring their indus-

try knowledge to bear in advising on the formation and operation of companies.

**Sources say:** *"Solid command of the issues related to early and growth-stage technology companies, and excellent representation in both venture fund and portfolio company engagements."*

**KEY INDIVIDUALS Carmelo Gordian** (see p.2391) is a well-established figure, lauded for the deep knowledge he has acquired over three decades of practice. He is commended for his expertise in the private equity and venture capital field, and advises funds focused on energy, life sciences and technology. Work highlights include acting for United Biologics on its acquisition by a syndicate. Clients describe **Matthew Lyons** (see p.2402) as *"a superior attorney, whose execution has been outstanding."* He has extensive experience in representing entrepreneurs and startups, and offers expert guidance on acquisitions, divestitures and raising capital. In standout matters, he advised Drilling Info on its sale of control to a syndicate led by Insight Venture Partners. **Alan Bickerstaff** (see p.2381) is widely regarded as *"a very fine lawyer."* Sources note that he has an extremely good rapport with clients, as well as a strong work ethic and impressive attention to detail. He also has valuable experience in advising emerging companies across a range of industries. Practice highlights include representing Mavenir Systems in a Series E financing and acquisition.

### Baker Botts LLP

See profile on p.2427

**THE FIRM** This practice is well known as one of the strongest teams in Texas, whose talented experts attract a variety of plaudits. Clients value the team's appreciation of business requirements, and its understanding of the commercial impact of legal developments. The interdisciplinary group offers a wide range of experience, and represents leading names from the software, consumer electronics and academic research fields. Highlights include advising international clients such as Accenture, AT&T and Raytheon.

**Sources say:** *"Customer-focused, and results- and value-oriented."*

**KEY INDIVIDUALS** Department head **John Martin** (see p.2403) can draw on extensive experience in business-critical transactions, and is a valued adviser on M&A deals. Sources have high praise for his well-rounded service, and assert that *"his knowledge is top-flight, but his ability to communicate and guide negotiations is nothing short of amazing."* One client enthused: *"He is hands-down one of the best outside counsels I have ever worked with."* **Don McDermett** (see p.2404) has established a well-respected practice that attracts leading clients such as Samsung Telecommunications America and GENBAND. His wide-ranging knowledge of corporate transactions includes valuable expertise in complex acquisitions and strategic alliances, and clients appreciate his *"timely, practical and strategic advice."* **Charles Szalkowski** (see p.2418) remains a highly regarded figure who *"provides inspiration and*

## Technology: Corporate & Commercial

### Senior Statesmen

### Leading Individuals

*leadership*" to the rest of the legal community. Market commentators praise the wealth of experience he has accumulated during his exemplary career.

## DLA Piper LLP (US)

See profile on p.1971

**THE FIRM** DLA Piper retains its dominant position in Austin, winning praise from interviewees across the board. The firm's extensive network means that clients can call on experienced practitioners across the globe, as well as the impressive expertise housed within the Texas office. Its client base includes a number of leading venture capital funds, and technology entrepreneurs can benefit from its flat-fee Foundations Program. Austin Ventures and HelioVolt are among those using the firm's services. **KEY INDIVIDUALS Paul Hurdlow** (see p.2396) is *"an important figure"* within the field, who cochairs the emerging growth and venture capital group. His long experience includes a variety of corporate and securities matters. **Philip Russell**'s (see p.2414) transactional expertise continues to attract complex M&A mandates, and he is commended for his impressive technical abilities. Work highlights include representing Silicon Laboratories in its acquisition of SpectraLinear. The *"fantastic"* **Sam Zabaneh** (see p.2424) maintains his strong reputation, and is described as a *"stellar attorney whose practice is skyrocketing."* He acted for WhaleShark Media on its acquisition of eConversions. Managing partner **James Montgomery** (see p.2405) is a highly respected practitioner who offers deep knowledge and experience in the technology field. His workload includes a number of transactions involving emerging technology companies, and he represented Austin Ribbon and Computer Supplies in its takeover by Pivot Acquisition. Peers are enthusiastic in their praise for **John Gilluly** (see p.2391), who is commended for his active funds practice and his deal-focused attitude. He is singled out as a smart attorney who is *"so good with clients."*

## Wilson Sonsini Goodrich & Rosati

See profile on p.700

**THE FIRM** This firm is deeply entrenched in the technology sector, and has a long-standing reputation as a leader in the venture capital field. Its lawyers are recognized for their ability to provide expert advice at all stages of a company's development, and advise both emerging names and high-profile international corporations. Sources praise the volume of high-value matters within the practice's impressive caseload. Clients are drawn from a variety of industries and include Active Power, RealPage and National Instruments.

**Sources say:** *"A number-one firm, with a tremendous reputation in the smaller growth company space."*

**KEY INDIVIDUALS Brian Beard** is widely held to be a leading expert in the technology arena, and has valuable knowledge of the life cycle of emerging growth companies. His experience includes a broad range of M&A matters and public offerings. **Paul Tobias** is a well-known name regarded as an *"exceptional lawyer."* He assists a number of growth companies seeking to raise funds via private and public offerings, and also acts on behalf of venture capital investors. **Robert Suffoletta** has established a strong reputation in the corporate and securities field, and works with various technology companies and venture capital funds. He has impressive expertise in M&A transactions, and is a knowledgeable adviser on public offerings and corporate governance matters. **Derek Willis** is respected as *"a fantastic attorney,"* and is lauded for his strength in M&A transactions and venture capital financings. He regularly advises leading companies in the cleantech, life sciences and software sectors.

## Band 2

## Fulbright & Jaworski LLP

See profile on p.2435

**THE FIRM** Fulbright & Jaworski offers a notable breadth of corporate and commercial expertise in the technology arena. The firm is well versed in guiding companies through the various stages of their development, and is called on by both entrepreneurial and established entities. High-profile clients such as AT&T and GeoScape Analytics entrust the team with crucial transactions, including a number of corporate financing deals. In standout matters, the team represented Merrick Systems in its sale to HiTecVision.

**KEY INDIVIDUALS** Well-respected practitioner **Charles Powell** (see p.2411) is praised for the valuable perspective he brings to transactions. Practice highlights include advising Senscient on the issue of Series C and D convertible preferred stock. **Daryl Lansdale** (see p.2401) leads the San Antonio corporate and securities team, and represented Encore Capital Group in the disposal of its software tracking business and bankruptcy service, Ascension Capital Group. Houston corporate practice head **David Peterman** (see p.2410) has wide-ranging experience in corporate and securities mandates on both a domestic and an international scale.

## Vinson & Elkins LLP

See profile on p.2459

**THE FIRM** Vinson & Elkins's technology practice wins plaudits for its depth of experience in venture capital and private equity transactions. Commentators also appreciate the team's knowledge of the issues faced by growing technology companies in M&A transactions. The team's sector-spanning client base includes big names such as Pharos Capital and Austin Ventures, and Dell instructed the team in its acquisition of Force10 Networks. High-profile companies value the firm's pragmatic approach to legal advice.

**Sources say:** *"They offer a combination of practical legal guidance and expertise in the areas that we consult them on – they add value to the company."*

**KEY INDIVIDUALS William Volk** (see p.2420) maintains his status as *"a dean,"* and is highly respected by peers for the breadth and depth of his knowledge. Interviewees value his mastery of all facets of corporate and commercial transactions, and he is *"never at a loss for advice."* **Wesley Jones** (see p.2397) enters the rankings after receiving excellent feedback for his talents in the technological arena. He is prized by clients for his understanding of *"the commercial aspects of software and technology companies, and the practical realities of deal-making."* Practice highlights include representing BMC Software in its acquisition of Numara Software.

## Band 3

### Bracewell & Giuliani LLP
See profile on p.2429

**THE FIRM** Bracewell & Giuliani is widely commended for the in-depth knowledge of its technology specialists. Interviewees attest to the high quality of advice provided by the interdisciplinary team, and value its appreciation of the commercial realities of transactions. The practice is noted for its strength across a range of industries, including life sciences, software and the internet. A diverse client base includes the University of Texas Office of Technology Commercialization and Next Step Capital Partners. **Sources say:** "*The firm brings the right depth and breadth of legal talent to each project, and facilitates deal execution by advising not only from a pure legal perspective but also according to what is reasonable in the market.*"

**KEY INDIVIDUALS** Market commentators are enthusiastic in their praise of practice leader **Edward Cavazos** (see p.2384). He is valued for his years of experience in private practice and as a general counsel, which "*make him an invaluable resource on numerous topics.*" He is also well known for his expertise in IP licensing transactions. Highlights include representing WhaleShark Media in a series of strategic technology deals. Associate **Andrew Gajkowski** (see p.2390) continues to be singled out as "*a highly skilled lawyer who understands the nature of our business and delivers strategic and practical advice.*" He wins praise for his hands-on approach, and is highly commended for his skills in contract negotiation and drafting.

### Jones Day
See profile on p.919

**THE FIRM** Jones Day has experience across the full range of corporate and commercial matters, advising companies on early-stage financing and licensing issues as well as substantial M&A and joint venture transactions. Big-ticket funds and technology companies call on the team for high-value mandates. It was retained by Texas Instruments in its $6.5 billion acquisition of National Semiconductor; other clients from the technology and telecom sectors include Micron Technology and Sprint Nextel.

**KEY INDIVIDUALS** Michael Weinberg is a key contact for technology-related transactions.

### Mayer Brown LLP
See profile on p.1257

**THE FIRM** This firm has established an impressive technology transactions practice. The experienced team guides clients through a range of issues, such as data protection, outsourcing and service agreements, and also advises on open source software compliance. In standout matters, it represented Armorlogic in its sale to Alert Logic, and acted for INX on its merger with Presidio.

**KEY INDIVIDUALS** The highly respected **Robert Gray** cochairs the firm's corporate and securities practice.

Clients benefit from his wealth of experience, which spans a broad range of industries. **Dallas Parker** maintains a strong reputation in the technology field. He is well known for the depth of his M&A experience, and is regularly retained by international clients in transactional mandates. Leading companies also look to him for advice on corporate governance.

### Other Notable Practitioners

**Nixon Fox** of DuBois, Bryant, Campbell & Schwartz LLP is "*a fantastic attorney*" who wins plaudits for his technical ability. He has considerable experience in advising early-stage technology clients. **Wilson Chu** (see p.2384) of K&L Gates is a respected name in the corporate field and well known for his deep industry knowledge. His client base includes a number of high-profile national and international names. **Peter Vogel** (see p.2420) of Gardere Wynne Sewell LLP is a "*fine lawyer*" with a long background in the technology industry. He is a hit with clients, with one reporting: "*He is very attentive to our needs and schedules, and knowledgeable about our technology and the market in which we operate.*" **Darrell Windham** (see p.2422) is co-managing partner of Greenberg Traurig LLP's Austin office, and offers expert guidance on complex M&A deals, joint ventures and strategic alliances.

# TECHNOLOGY OUTSOURCING

Commentary about individuals can be found under their firm's paragraph. If the firm has no paragraph (is not ranked) look at Other Notable Practitioners.

| Technology: Outsourcing — Leading Firms | |
| --- | --- |
| **Band 1** | |
| K&L Gates * | |
| **Band 2** | |
| Akin Gump Strauss Hauer & Feld LLP * | |
| Baker Botts LLP * | |
| Haynes and Boone, LLP * | |
| Dentons * | |
| **Band 3** | |
| Thompson & Knight LLP * | |

\* Indicates firm / individual with profile.
Alphabetical order within each band. Band 1 is the highest.

## Band 1

### K&L Gates
See profile on p.2245

**THE FIRM** This firm is lauded by market commentators for the impressive strength of its outsourcing team, which includes several market-leading practitioners. Its superb reputation has been further bolstered by the arrival of two highly regarded specialists from Jones Day. The group has extensive experience in advising both vendors and customers, and offers expert guidance on BPO, ITO and vari-ous technology agreements. High-profile clients include Ericsson and American Express.
**Sources say:** "*There is just nobody else in Texas that touches them.*"

| Technology: Outsourcing — Leading Individuals | | |
| --- | --- | --- |
| **Star individuals** | | |
| Howell John E | K&L Gates * | |
| **Band 1** | | |
| Andrews Jeffrey B | Bracewell & Giuliani LLP (ONP)† * | |
| Brito Michael James | Akin Gump Strauss Hauer & Feld LLP | |
| Guedry David N | K&L Gates * | |
| Krieser Jason D | K&L Gates * | |
| **Band 2** | | |
| Fisher Todd A | K&L Gates * | |
| Helms Shawn C | K&L Gates * | |
| King Chad W | K&L Gates * | |
| Martin John | Baker Botts LLP * | |
| **Band 3** | | |
| Colson Randall E | Haynes and Boone, LLP | |
| Harvey Dean William | Andrews Kurth LLP (ONP)† * | |
| Henchey Brian | Baker Botts LLP * | |
| Herman Jordan J | Baker Botts LLP | |
| Kline Scott | Dentons | |

†ONP = Other Notable Practitioner

**KEY INDIVIDUALS John Howell** (see p.337) is a highly respected figure within the outsourcing field, and sources assert: "*His main strength is his incredible depth of knowledge and experience in outsourcing.*" Highlights include representing Travelport in a long-term agreement with Japan Airlines and its subsidiary Axess International Network. Sources consider **David Guedry** (see p.327) to be "*one of the best in the field of outsourcing.*" He is prized for his ability to "*stay current on trends in the industry, so as to provide excellent practical advice.*" Interviewees are also keen to praise his negotiating skills. His workload includes a number of significant transactions handled on behalf of Fujitsu. The "*excellent*" **Jason Krieser** (see p.2400) is valued by clients for his quick understanding and in-depth knowledge of technology acquisitions. He represented Sprint Nextel in the purchase of wireless infrastructure equipment and implementation services. **Chad King** (see p.2399) maintains a wide-ranging transactional practice, and has considerable expertise in licensing issues. **Shawn Helms** (see p.2395) is "*an exceptional lawyer*" with "*tremendous subject matter expertise, judgment and client focus.*" Interviewees also praise his practical, business-oriented approach. **Todd Fisher** (see p.2389) remains a strong presence in the outsourcing field, advising clients on a range of international mandates. He continues to represent Deere & Company in its outsourcing projects.

## Band 2

### Akin Gump Strauss Hauer & Feld LLP
See profile on p.904

**THE FIRM** Akin Gump Strauss Hauer & Feld has a well-established practice, with ten partners offering specialist advice on outsourcing issues. The team is known for its high-volume caseload, which includes strategic disposals, ITO and BPO agreements. A prestigious client base features market leaders from the financial, telecom and manufacturing industries.

**KEY INDIVIDUALS Michael Brito** has a stellar reputation for his broad outsourcing experience. He is regularly called on for advice on complex, high-value matters requiring deep industry knowledge.

### Baker Botts LLP
See profile on p.2427

**THE FIRM** This practice is held in high regard for the breadth of its capabilities. Sources are impressed by the deep expertise of its lawyers across a range of transactions, including complex ITO and BPO arrangements. The firm is highly active in work for both vendors and customers, and represents big-ticket names such as Accenture and Dell.

**Sources say:** *"This team is able to draw on a lot of talent."*

**KEY INDIVIDUALS** The highly respected **John Martin** (see p.2403) chairs the firm's technology department. Sources draw attention to his impressive command of the technology market, which enables him to take on high-value transactions. Market commentators are quick to remark on the strength of **Brian Henchey**'s (see p.2395) outsourcing practice. He continues to work for a number of clients from the healthcare industry, as well as advising financial and energy companies on their outsourcing needs. **Jordan Herman** is entrusted with various business-

critical mandates, and is well known for his work for high-profile suppliers.

### Dentons
See profile on p.449

**THE FIRM** This firm's Texas office has established a highly respected team of outsourcing experts, which is commended by peers and clients alike for the quality of its advice. The group is singled out for its recognition of clients' business needs, and its strategic, results-driven approach. It regularly acts for a range of multinational companies on complex ITO and BPO transactions. The team is viewed as a leading presence, despite the recent departure of key partner John Funk.

**Sources say:** *"Their client service is very good and they act as an extension of our internal legal department." "A very strong presence."*

**KEY INDIVIDUALS** The *"fantastic"* **Scott Kline** is well known for his prolific transactional practice. Clients value his responsiveness and understanding of their needs.

### Haynes and Boone, LLP
See profile on p.444

**THE FIRM** This practice provides specialist expertise at every stage of the outsourcing process. The team is particularly well known for its in-depth knowledge of the licensing and IP elements of deals. Market commentators note the firm's active presence in the field and commend its ability to take on the full range of transactions, including complex international arrangements.

**KEY INDIVIDUALS Randall Colson** leads the information technology and business process outsourcing group. He combines a wealth of sector experience with extensive legal expertise to tackle substantial transactional work for industry leaders.

## Band 3

### Thompson & Knight LLP
See profile on p.2458

**THE FIRM** Thompson & Knight maintains a solid reputation in the outsourcing sector. Market commentators praise the firm's ability to understand not just the legal aspects of outsourcing agreements, but also the practical and technical concerns of their clients. The outsourcing transactions practice group handles a broad spectrum of matters on a national and international scale, and offers vast experience in negotiating deals at every stage of the outsourcing process.

**Sources say:** *"The attorneys are experienced in their area of expertise, and are proactive in providing excellent client service."*

**KEY INDIVIDUALS** Stephen Stein is a key contact for this team

### Other Notable Practitioners

**Dean Harvey** (see p.2394) is a standout member of the technology transactions group at Andrews Kurth LLP. He is well regarded as a BPO and strategic alliance expert, and has valuable experience in both domestic and international outsourcing arrangements. Clients include 7-Eleven and Parallon Business Solutions. **Jeffrey Andrews** (see p.2378) of Bracewell & Giuliani LLP stands out as *"a tough negotiator who knows his subject matter extremely well."* He is prized by clients for his experience on both the vendor and customer side of transactions. Described as one of the best outsourcing lawyers in the field, he wins plaudits for *"his enthusiastic work style and his attention to detail."* He

# Leaders' Profiles in Texas

**ACKER, Rodney**
Fulbright & Jaworski LLP, Dallas
214 855 7466
racker@fulbright.com
*Featured in Litigation (Texas)*
**Practice Areas:** Litigation.
**Professional Memberships:** ABOTA; Fellow, ACTL; IATL; International Society of Barristers.
**Career:** Partner Rodney Acker focuses on trying cases in state and federal courts across the US with experience in all areas of civil commercial litigation, including securities litigation, oil and gas, antitrust, breach of contract/fraud and banking. Best Lawyers in America, Texas Super Lawyers, Law Dragon 3000, Board Certified in Civil Trial Law, Texas Board of Legal Specialization.
**Personal:** JD, with honors, Order of the Coif, Law Review, Texas Tech University School of Law (1974); BA, Business Administration, University of Texas at Arlington (1971).

**ADAMS, Richard**
Vinson & Elkins LLP, Dallas
214 220 7725
radams@velaw.com
*Featured in Energy & Natural Resources (Texas)*
**Practice Areas:** Partner in Energy Regulatory Practice. Practice primarily involves the regulation of electric and natural gas utilities. Experience in administrative and civil litigation involving rate, antitrust, regulatory compliance and environmental issues.
**Professional Memberships:** Dallas Bar Association.
**Career:** Admitted to Texas Bar 1978, Missouri and Florida Bars 1975. Joined Vinson & Elkins as a partner in 2008.
**Personal:** Southeast Missouri State University, BA 1972 and University of Missouri, JD 1974.

**AKSAMIT, Roger D**
Thompson & Knight LLP, Houston
713 951 5885
Roger.Aksamit@tklaw.com
*Featured in Tax (Texas)*
**Professional Memberships:** American College of Trust and Estate Counsel; American and Houston Bar Associations; Houston and American Bar Foundations.
**Personal:** SMU Dedman School of Law (LLM, 1987); University of Texas School of Law (JD, 1978); Southern Methodist University (BBA, with honors, 1975).

**ALBERS, Michael F**
Hunton & Williams LLP, Dallas
214 468 3302
malbers@hunton.com
*Featured in Construction (Texas)*
**Practice Areas:** Mr Albers' practice focuses on construction law and commercial and industrial real-estate development. He represents owners,

developers, lenders and contractors in construction transactions, documentation and dispute resolution proceedings, as well as project acquisition, financing and development activities. His clients include national industrial and manufacturing companies, real estate developers, mass transit authorities and general contractors. Mike is also an Adjunct Professor at Southern Methodist University School of Law and on the faculty of the Design-Build Institute of America, and the American Arbitration Association's Roster of Neutrals.

**ALBRIGHT, Alan D**
Bracewell & Giuliani LLP, Austin
512 494 3620
alan.albright@bgllp.com
*Featured in Intellectual Property (Texas)*
**Practice Areas:** Heads the firm's IP litigation practice. He routinely counsels clients regarding patent litigation, licensing, protection and enforcement of trade secrets, as well as other

issues faced by technology companies. Has civil jury trial experience in both state and federal courts, where he has litigated disputes involving patents, trade secrets, employment cases, breach of contract, and Internet-related claims. Also has experience handling antitrust and first amendment issues.

**Career:** Former United States Magistrate Judge in the Austin Division of the Western District of Texas.

**Personal:** JD, The University of Texas School of Law, 1984; BA, with honors, Trinity University, 1981.

## ALBRIGHT, Val J
Gardere Wynne Sewell LLP, Dallas
214 999 4825
valbright@gardere.com
*Featured in Tax (Texas)*

**Practice Areas:** Tax, tax litigation, transfer pricing.

**Professional Memberships:** State Bar of Texas, American and Dallas Bar Associations.

**Career:** Val Albright represents clients in tax matters before the Internal Revenue Service (IRS) and in federal courts, and advises clients concerning domestic and international tax planning. He previously worked for the IRS Office of Chief Counsel in Chicago and Dallas. Mr Albright is active in Gardere's Energy Industry Team and Transfer Pricing and International Tax Specialty Practice Group.

**Personal:** LLM, Southern Methodist University Dedman School of Law, 1986; JD, University of Arkansas School of Law, 1977; BA, University of Arkansas, 1971.

## ALESSIO, Michael
Winstead PC, Dallas
214 745 5144
malessio@winstead.com
*Featured in Real Estate (Texas)*

**Practice Areas:** Mike's areas of practice involve a variety of commercial real estate transactions, including the acquisition and disposition of investment-grade property, commercial development, office and retail leasing and a broad range of financing transactions. Michael works with multi-site/jurisdictional portfolio acquisitions and related debt and equity structuring on behalf of long-term public and private equity investors. He represents developers and investors in all stages of development projects, and institutional lenders and banks in connection with debt and equity transactions, financing, and securitized mortgage lending.

## ALEXANDER, Douglas W
Alexander Dubose & Townsend LLP, Austin
512 482 9301
dalexander@adtappellate.com
*Featured in Litigation (Texas)*

**Practice Areas:** Civil appeals, with majority of practice devoted to proceedings before supreme Court of Texas.

**Professional Memberships:** Fellow, American Academy of Appellate Lawyers; former Chair, State Bar of Texas Appellate Section.

**Career:** Partner, Alexander Dubose & Townsend 2003-present; Board Certified in Civil Appellate Law by Texas Board of Legal Specialization since 1990; Law Clerk, former Chief Judge John R. Brown, United States Court of Appeals, Fifth Circuit 1980-81.

**Publications:** 'The Petition for Review,' Texas Supreme Court Practice Manual, Chapter 7 (2005); Co-Editor, 'Guide to the New Texas Rules of Appellate Procedure' (State Bar of Texas 1997).

## ALLENDER, John R
Fulbright & Jaworski LLP, Houston
713 651 5664
jallender@fulbright.com
*Featured in Tax (Texas)*

**Practice Areas:** Taxation.

**Professional Memberships:** Former chair, Taxation Section of the State Bar of Texas and Houston Bar Association.

**Career:** As Head of Fulbright's Tax Department, Allender's practice focuses on federal income taxation and corporate matters. He is involved in the negotiation and planning of complex business transactions, often related to Fulbright's substantial mergers and acquisition practice. In addition, he is frequently involved in tax and business matters for wealthy individuals and their closely held businesses.

**Personal:** LLM in Tax, New York University School of Law (1976); JD, cum laude, University of San Diego (1975); BS, Iowa State University (1972).

## ALLETAG, Gary M
Baker & Hostetler LLP, Houston
713 646 1356
galletag@bakerlaw.com
*Featured in Real Estate (Texas)*

**Career:** Business Group Coordinator for BakerHostetler's Houston office, Gary Alletag has represented individuals and businesses in a variety of transactions, with a focus in the areas of real estate and energy. He has represented lenders, sellers and purchasers in the financing, sale and purchase of office buildings, hotels, hospitals, apartments, shopping centers, industrial warehouses and office and residential condominiums. He has advised developers in the acquisition, development and marketing of commercial and residential properties, including shopping centers, industrial parks and residential subdivisions. Gary has negotiated ground leases, office leases and shopping center, mall and warehouse leases, representing both lessors and lessees.

## ALLISON, Christopher F
Locke Lord LLP, Dallas
214 740 8692
callison@lockelord.com
*Featured in Tax (Texas)*

**Practice Areas:** Chairs Firm's Tax Practice Group. Advises publicly-held corporations on the tax consequences of taxable and tax-free merger, acquisition, spin-off and joint venture transactions. Provides tax advice on corporate formations, liquidations, distributions, reorganizations and recapitalizations; partnership taxation; taxation of limited liability companies; and taxation of

S corporations. Works on issues related to investments by tax-exempt entities and on federal tax controversies.

**Professional Memberships:** ABA; State Bar of Texas; Dallas Bar Association.

**Career:** Partner since 1984.

**Personal:** New York University School of Law (LLM, 1981); University of South Carolina School of Law (JD, 1977); Davidson College (BA, cum laude, 1974).

## AMANDES, Christopher B
Morgan, Lewis & Bockius LLP, Houston
713 890 5735
camandes@morganlewis.com
*Featured in Environment (Texas)*

**Practice Areas:** Principal area of practice is environmental law, with emphasis on compliance counseling, enforcement defense, transactional environmental issues, and contractual disputes involving environmental issues. Listed: in a leading legal publication in America in environmental law, since 1995.

**Professional Memberships:** Co-Chair: City of Houston's Brownfield Redevelopment Committee, 1996-2000; ABA Annual Conference on Environmental Law (Keystone), 2004-06. Member: City of Houston Planning Commission.

**Career:** Admitted to practice: Texas, 1985. Joined Vinson & Elkins, 1986; admitted to partnership, 1994. Registered Professional Engineer (Inactive), Texas.

**Personal:** Rice University, BA, 1976; Masters of Environmental Engineering, 1978; University of California at Los Angeles, JD, 1985.

## ANAIPAKOS, John
Baker Botts LLP, Houston
713 229 1154
john.anaipakos@bakerbotts.com
*Featured in Litigation (Texas)*

**Practice Areas:** Tried 20+ civil cases to juries in Texas; argued appeals to the Fifth Circuit, Texas Supreme Court and intermediate appellate courts; tried cases before administrative tribunals, arbitrators and judges. Matters include complex business litigation, energy, oil and gas, professional liability, employment and catastrophic injury/death. Represents clients in the energy industry and accounting profession, among others.

**Career:** Joined Baker Botts after clerkship with Judge Edith Jones, US Court of Appeals, Fifth Circuit. Former Chair, Houston Litigation Department; ABOTA, Associate.

**Personal:** JD (cum laude), Harvard Law School, 1993; Editor, Harvard Law Review; BA (summa cum laude), Economics, Trinity University, 1990.

## ANDERSON, Kenneth M
Sidley Austin LLP, Houston
713 495 4503
kanderson@sidley.com
*Featured in Banking & Finance (Texas)*

**Practice Areas:** Partner in Sidley's Houston office, primarily representing arrangers and borrowers in syndicated financings. His national practice includes experience in a broad spectrum of syndicated financing transactions, including oil and gas (upstream and midstream), master limit-

ed partnership (MLP), merger and acquisition, private equity, structured, project and multicurrency financings with a particular emphasis on energy.

**Professional Memberships:** American Bar Association Syndicated Finance Subcommittee of the Developments in Business Law Committee, Business Law Section (Past Chair).

**Personal:** Brigham Young University Law School (JD, with honors, 1982); Brigham Young University (BS, Accounting, 1979).

## ANDREWS, Jeffrey B
Bracewell & Giuliani LLP, Houston
713 221 1439
jeff.andrews@bgllp.com
*Featured in Outsourcing (Nationwide), Technology (Texas)*

**Practice Areas:** Broad transactional practice focuses on outsourcing, sourcing and technology transactions. Best known for structuring and negotiating complex domestic and international information technology and business process outsourcing agreements. Has assisted clients in outsourcing all major business functions and operations. Has negotiated opposite every major multinational and Indian outsourcing service provider. Clients span a wide range of industries, including energy, financial services, consumer products, retail, manufacturing, pharmaceuticals, commercial aviation, and telecommunications.

**Personal:** JD, The University of Texas School of Law, 1997; BA, Trinity University, 1994.

## ARNOLD, John K
Winstead PC, Houston
713 650 2628
jkarnold@winstead.com
*Featured in Energy & Natural Resources (Texas)*

**Practice Areas:** John Arnold is a shareholder in Winstead's Energy & Environmental Law Practice Group. He represents energy companies in a broad range of regulatory matters including litigation, compliance, and enforcement as well as due diligence and counseling for project development and business transactions. John serves clients in the gas and power industries before the Public Utility Commission of Texas, the Railroad Commission of Texas, and the Federal Energy Regulatory Commission. He represents natural gas local distribution companies, intra- and interstate pipelines and storage companies, retailers of electricity, industrial customers of electricity, developers of wind generation, and multinational energy companies.

## ARNOLD, Mark
Andrews Kurth LLP, Houston
713 220 3938
markarnold@andrewskurth.com
*Featured in Real Estate (Texas)*

**Practice Areas:** Mark represents and advises clients in public and private project development and financing transactions, and mergers and acquisitions, with an emphasis on convention centers, hotels and casinos, sports, recreation and entertainment facilities and educational facilities. He also has extensive experience in structuring and implementing creative economic development solutions such as Chapter 380/381 grants, 4A/4B financings, tax increment financing and tax abatements. Mark is well versed in all aspects of commercial real estate development, financing, leasing and construction on behalf of both public entities and private owners and developers.

### ASMUS, David
Morgan, Lewis & Bockius LLP, Houston
713 890 5718
dasmus@morganlewis.com
*Featured in Corporate/M&A (Texas), Energy & Natural Resources (Nationwide), Projects (Nationwide)*
See under Nationwide for profile.

### AXE, Albert
Winstead PC, Austin
512 370 2806
aaxe@winstead.com
*Featured in Environment (Texas)*
**Practice Areas:** Al has experience representing business and industrial clients in environmental, administrative, related litigation and legislative matters. He has provided legal advice to clients in these industries: construction, pulp, paper and forestry, electronic, semiconductor, nonferrous metals, chemical (including agricultural chemicals), petroleum refinery, flexographic printing, lime and cement, beef slaughtering and processing, waste disposal and mining. He advises clients with regards to federal, state and local regulation of air pollutants, wastewater discharges, hazardous waste management facilities, injection wells, fuel blending plants and cement plants that burn waste derived fuels. He handles business and regulatory-related litigation, including superfund and toxic-tort cases.

### BABCOCK, Charles
Jackson Walker LLP, Houston
713 752 4210
cbabcock@jw.com
*Featured in First Amendment Litigation (Nationwide), Litigation (Nationwide), Litigation (Texas)*
See under Nationwide for profile.

### BACON, Christopher V
Vinson & Elkins LLP, Houston
713 758 1148
cbacon@velaw.com
*Featured in Labor & Employment (Texas)*
**Practice Areas:** Employment litigation, labor law, OSHA, MSHA, international labor law, class action litigation.
**Career:** Chris has tried over 30 (mostly jury) cases and argued a dozen times before appellate courts. Chris also has considerable experience advising clients on cross-border and international assignment issues in Europe and Latin America. Chris is an Adjunct Professor at the University of Houston where he teaches courses on employment law including a course on sexual orientation and the law.
**Personal:** University of Houston, BA summa cum laude, in 1979 and MEd in mathematics education, 1982; Harvard School of Law, JD cum laude, 1990.

### BAILEY, K Brock
Bracewell & Giuliani LLP, Dallas
214 758 1076
brock.bailey@bgllp.com
*Featured in Real Estate (Texas)*
**Practice Areas:** Serves as managing partner of the firm's Dallas office. Represents and counsels clients in the acquisition, development, financing, and divestiture of large commercial and industrial projects. His real estate experience includes office, industrial, multifamily, mixed use, and retail real estate projects. He focuses on all aspects of real estate development, zoning and land use, project finance and infrastructure development, as well as construction, leasing, acquisition and disposition matters. He also advises clients on the formation and dissolution of partnerships, joint ventures and corporations.
**Personal:** JD, Southern Methodist University Dedman School of Law, 1996; BBA, Southern Methodist University, 1992.

### BAKER, Andrew M
Baker Botts LLP, Houston
713 229 1198
andrew.baker@bakerbotts.com
*Featured in Corporate/M&A (Texas)*
**Practice Areas:** Managing Partner (Firmwide); previously Chair: Dallas Corporate Section. Practice areas: general corporate, mergers, acquisitions, corporate finance/securities and government and internal investigations. Practice emphasizes development of close, value-added relationships with public and private entities. Counseled with senior management/boards of directors/audit and compensation committees on numerous matters, and led transaction teams in complex mergers and acquisitions and corporate finance transactions involving a variety of industries around the world.
**Personal:** BA, summa cum laude, State University of New York at Albany, 1976; JD, magna cum laude, Cornell Law School, 1979.

### BAKER, Charles S
Fulbright & Jaworski LLP, Houston
713 651 8396
csbaker@fulbright.com
*Featured in Intellectual Property (Texas)*
**Practice Areas:** Mr Baker's forte for the past 25 years has been trying intellectual property and complex commercial litigation matters throughout the US. He regularly handles patent and trademark infringement lawsuits in Texas, including the Eastern District, and has extensive experience in precedent copyright matters (he represented StreamCast in the noteworthy US Supreme Court case MGM v Grokster). Mr Baker has also handled several ITC matters.
**Professional Memberships:** Mr Baker is a Member the American Bar Association, Houston Bar Association, INTA, American Intellectual Property Law Association, Houston Intellectual Property Association and a Houston Bar Foundation Life Fellow.

### BANES, Bryant
Neel, Hooper & Banes, P.C., Houston
713 629 1800
bbanes@nhblaw.com
*Featured in Labor & Employment (Texas)*
**Practice Areas:** Managing Partner. Specialization in labor and employment with emphasis in the government contracting, petrochemical, and steel industries. He is also a recognized expert in government contracts and fiscal law, including litigation, compliance, and investigations. Mr Banes provides clients with business-minded, proactive solutions.
**Professional Memberships:** Licensed by the Texas Board of Legal Specialization in Labor and Employment Law. Member of the ABA's Public Contract Law Section and the National Contract Management Association, Space City Chapter. Rated AV Preeminent by Martindale Hubbell. Board Certified in Labor and Employment Law by the Texas Board of Legal Specialization. Fellow, Litigation Counsel of America, Member, Wage &; Hour Defense Institute. Member, WorkLaw Network.
**Career:** Admitted to the Louisiana Bar in 1990 and the Texas Bar in 2002. Admitted to the Fifth Circuit Court of Appeals and the Court of Appeals for Federal Circuit. Practices before all Texas federal courts and in all government contract related forums, including the U.S. Court of Federal Claims. Served as a Trial Attorney in the U.S Department of Justice from 1998-2002. Joined Neel, Hooper & Banes in 2003, becoming managing partner in 2006. Retired from the United States Army Reserve in December 2010, finishing his career as a lieutenant colonel in the Army General Counsel's Office. Served as the Chief of Procurement and Fiscal Law and Legal Advisor to the Chief Engineer in Iraq in 2004, and was awarded the Bronze Star Medal, the Combat Action Badge, and the Meritorious Unit Citation.
**Personal:** Born July 6, 1965. Graduated Kansas State University in 1987, Louisiana State University law school in 1990, and the Command and General Staff College in 2005.

### BARBER, Thomas R
Coats Rose Yale Ryman Lee, Houston
713 653 5755
trbarber@coatsrose.com
*Featured in Construction (Texas)*
**Practice Areas:** Thomas Barber's practice focuses on representing owners, sureties, general contractors, subcontractors, and suppliers emphasizing the investigation and administration of construction contract and subcontract defaults on behalf of owners, sureties and general contractors, complex construction case workouts, lien and bond claims, and contract document preparation.
**Career:** Mr Barber has presented over eighty lectures and seminars to industry groups, Bar Associations and client groups. His professional recognitions include an AV Peer Review rating by Martindale-Hubbell, being named a Super Lawyer every year since the inception of the distinction, and recognition by Chambers USA.

### BARBOUR, David
Andrews Kurth LLP, Dallas
214 659 4444
dbarbour@andrewskurth.com
*Featured in Banking & Finance (Texas)*
**Practice Areas:** David's practice includes experience in various commercial transactions on a national and international basis. He represents issuers and underwriters in public and private offerings of equity and debt securities, with an emphasis in structured and restructured debt issuances of mortgage-backed and asset-backed securities. He also advises clients regarding the negotiation and structuring (and restructuring) of various corporate and real estate financings and asset and stock acquisitions. Finally, David is experienced in handling a variety of other general corporate, mortgage banking, real estate and securities transactions.

### BARBOUR, Larry G
Vinson & Elkins LLP, Houston
713 758 2126
lbarbour@velaw.com
*Featured in Banking & Finance (Texas)*
**Practice Areas:** Finance, including project, structured, acquisition and mezzanine finance. Has extensive experience in international finance transactions and complex syndicated bank transactions, representing either the lender or the borrower. Worked on all aspects of energy finance.
**Career:** Came to the firm in 1977 and was admitted to partnership in October 1985.
**Personal:** Graduated from Princeton University, AB in Economics with honors in 1972, New York University, MBA in Finance in 1974, and The University of Texas, JD with high honors, in 1977. (Chancellors; Order of the Coif.)

### BARNES, John Kelly
Greenberg Traurig, LLP, Dallas
214 665 3730
BarnesKe@gtlaw.com
*Featured in Healthcare (Texas)*
**Practice Areas:** Health and FDA business (transactions, regulatory).
**Professional Memberships:** American Health Lawyers Association; State Bar of Texas, Health Law Section; District of Columbia Bar, Health Law Section; ABA.
**Career:** Chambers USA, 2013.
**Publications:** Author, 'Are You Ready for New and Upcoming Prescription Drug Legislation? Recent Trends in State Prescription Drug Laws', Journal of Health Care Compliance, March/April 2008. Contributing Author, 'Phase III Regulations Result in Dramatic Changes to Stark Law', BNA's Health Law Reporter, Oct. 11, 2007.
**Personal:** JD, University of Houston Law Center, 2006; MBA, Texas Tech University, 2000 (Health Organization Management Certification); BBA, Texas Tech University, 1999.

### BARR JR, John H
Bracewell & Giuliani LLP, Houston
713 221 1242
john.barr@bgllp.com
*Featured in Intellectual Property (Texas)*

**Practice Areas:** Commercial litigator with particular skill in disputes involving patent litigation and other intellectual property issues such as patent infringement, breach of patent assignment, indemnity for patent infringement liability, misappropriation of trade secrets and trademark infringement. Also represents and counsels clients in general commercial litigation involving breaches of corporate contracts and agreements, including non-compete and stock purchase agreements, employment issues and product liability defense.
**Personal:** JD, Texas Tech University School of Law, 1992; BA, The University of the South, 1989.

## BARZOUKAS, Nicolas G
Weil, Gotshal & Manges LLP, Houston
713 546 5058
nicolas.barzoukas@weil.com
*Featured in Intellectual Property (Texas)*
**Practice Areas:** Nicolas Barzoukas' practice is devoted to intellectual property litigation, including patent and trade secret litigation. He concentrates on patent litigation in the pharmaceutical field. His practice, in addition to Hatch-Waxman Act lawsuits, has involved suits challenging the interpretation of the patent statute by federal agencies, and the constitutionality of certain provisions of the patent statute. He also counsels clients on intellectual property enforcement matters, defensive and offensive litigation strategy, freedom to operate, settlement negotiations and licensing.
**Personal:** Baylor University (BS, 1986); Baylor University (MBA, 1989); University of Texas School of Law (JD, 1992).

## BASS JR, Robert C
Winstead PC, Austin
512 370 2852
rbass@winstead.com
*Featured in Construction (Texas)*
**Practice Areas:** Robert represents Winstead's real estate development, lending, bond underwriting and construction industry clients on a wide range of issues based on his extensive, practical experience in litigating construction disputes and in drafting and negotiating both large and small construction contracts. Robert has extensive experience in drafting and negotiating construction documents for owners and contractors on commercial construction projects, including sports venue, multi-family residential, condominium, high-rise office, and shopping center projects. Additionally, as one of Texas' leading lobbyists on construction-related issues, Robert has a direct hand in the development of construction law for Winstead's clients.

## BAST, Cynthia
Locke Lord LLP, Austin
512 305 4707
cbast@lockelord.com
*Featured in Real Estate (Texas)*
**Practice Areas:** Chair of the Affordable Housing Section and recognized as a preeminent attorney in affordable housing finance. Serves clients with her vast experience in finance transactions, governmental advocacy, regulatory compli-

ance, and repositioning assets and is a frequent speaker at conferences nationwide.
**Professional Memberships:** ABA (Affordable Housing and Community Development Law Forum); National Association of Home Builders Housing Credit Group; Former Chair, Texas Community Building With Attorney Resources.
**Career:** Co-Chair of Firm's Board of Directors. Partner since 1999.
**Personal:** The University of Texas School of Law (JD, with honors, 1991); University of Tulsa (MBA, 1988; BA, magna cum laude, 1987).

## BAXTER, Samuel F
McKool Smith, Dallas
903 923 9000
sbaxter@mckoolsmith.com
*Featured in Intellectual Property (Texas), Litigation (Texas)*
**Practice Areas:** Intellectual property and complex commercial litigation.
**Career:** Sam Baxter is a former Texas State District Judge and Harrison County District Attorney who has secured victories worth hundreds of millions of dollars for clients. Two of these victories are included in the National Law Journal's listing of the top 100 jury verdicts. Sam was named one of Law360's "10 Most Admired Intellectual Property Attorneys," and the 2011 Dallas Intellectual Property "Lawyer of the Year" by Best Lawyers.
**Personal:** University of Texas School of Law (JD, 1970); University of Texas (BA, 1967).

## BAYER, Mark W
Gardere Wynne Sewell LLP, Dallas
214 999 4521
mbayer@gardere.com
*Featured in Antitrust (Texas)*
**Practice Areas:** Trial [alternative dispute resolution, antitrust and trade regulation, appellate, class action, commercial litigation, intellectual property, securities litigation].
**Professional Memberships:** State Bar of Texas, American and Dallas Bar Associations.
**Career:** Mark Bayer focuses on antitrust, securities, privacy, RICO, theft of trade secrets, intellectual property, class actions and other complex litigation. He has appeared in state and federal courts, and represented clients in connection with investigations by the DOJ, the FTC, the SEC, and the Texas Attorney General. Mr Bayer is a member of Gardere's Antitrust Specialty Practice Group.
**Personal:** JD, Columbia Law School, 1981; AB, Bowdoin College, 1979.

## BAYOUTH, Frank E
Skadden, Arps, Slate, Meagher & Flom LLP & Affiliates, Houston
713 655 5115
frank.bayouth@skadden.com
*Featured in Corporate/M&A (Texas)*
**Practice Areas:** Frank Bayouth is a corporate attorney, concentrating in the areas of mergers and acquisitions, private equity, corporate finance and general corporate law. He has substantial experience advising companies in the oil and gas and financial services industries and is recognized in business and legal publications for his corpo-

rate expertise. Mr Bayouth represents public and private companies, private equity firms and hedge funds, as well as investment banks and financing sources in a variety of US and international transactions.
**Career:** JD, University of Texas Law School, 1990 (high honors); BBA, Accounting, Texas Tech University, 1987 (cum laude).

## BEANE, Jerry
Andrews Kurth LLP, Dallas
214 659 4520
jerrybeane@andrewskurth.com
*Featured in Antitrust (Texas)*
**Practice Areas:** Jerry Beane's practice focuses on antitrust and commercial litigation and antitrust counseling. He has more than 45 years of experience in federal and state antitrust cases and governmental investigations in the banking, construction, energy, explosives, food, beverage, health care, home furnishings, insurance, logistics, printing and transportation industries. He also handles patent, trademark, securities, contract and breach of fiduciary duty cases. Jerry's antitrust representation includes work on mergers and acquisitions in the energy, beverage, food, healthcare, transportation, manufacturing and telecommunications industries. He counsels clients on distribution, HSR, joint venture, pricing, trade association and compliance issues.

## BEATTY, J Robert
Locke Lord LLP, Dallas
214 740 8530
jrbeatty@lockelord.com
*Featured in Litigation (Texas)*
**Practice Areas:** Has 30+ years of experience in commercial dispute resolution, primarily in the energy and oil and gas industries. His activities span litigation, arbitration and mediation, and include False Claims Act qui tam royalty claims, crude oil and natural gas contract disputes, price re-determinations, energy taxation, working interest owner claims, lease and title disputes and surface damages claims.
**Professional Memberships:** Center for American and International Law; Rocky Mountain Mineral Law Foundation; Dallas Bar Association (Energy Law Section).
**Career:** Partner since 1985.
**Personal:** The University of Texas School of Law (JD, 1979); Southern Methodist University (BS, magna cum laude, 1976).

## BELL, Christopher L
Sidley Austin LLP, Houston
713 495 4508
cbell@sidley.com
*Featured in Environment (Texas)*
**Practice Areas:** Represents clients in civil and criminal litigation, investigations and compliance counseling under all of the major environmental statutes, and assists on environmental cleanups and the environmental aspects of transactions. He advises on climate change, product and chemicals regulation and supply chain management (including TSCA, REACH, CLP, WEEE/ROHS), international movement of materials and waste, and sustainable development. He evaluates and imple-

ments environmental management systems (including ISO 14001), and corporate compliance and ethics programs and codes of conduct under the Sentencing Guidelines.
**Personal:** University of Michigan Law School, JD, 1985; Michigan State University, BA, 1981. Admissions: District of Columbia, Texas.

## BELL, Jerry
Fulbright & Jaworski LLP, Austin
512 536 4596
jbell@fulbright.com
*Featured in Healthcare (Texas), Healthcare (Nationwide)*
**Practice Areas:** Health.
**Professional Memberships:** Board certified by the Texas Board of Legal Specialization; Chair, Health Law Section of the State Bar of Texas (1994-95); Board of Directors, American Health Lawyers Association (1997-2001); Board of Directors, American Academy of Health Care Attorneys (1995-97).
**Career:** Bell, head of Fulbright's Health Law Business and Regulatory Department, has handled major healthcare transactions. He is an adjunct professor at The University of Texas School of Law, where he has taught 'Business and Regulatory Aspects of Health Law' for 15 years.
**Personal:** JD, University of Texas School of Law (1977); BA, University of Texas (1974).

## BENNETT, David M
Thompson & Knight LLP, Dallas
214 969 1486
David.Bennett@tklaw.com
*Featured in Bankruptcy/Restructuring (Texas)*
**Practice Areas:** Mr Bennett's expertise includes both transactions and litigation involving distressed and insolvent businesses. His clients include debtors, creditors, committees, capital providers, and other counter-parties in loan restructurings, out-of-court plans, and plans of reorganization in bankruptcy. He has been named one of The Best Lawyers in America (2006-present) and one of the Texas Super Lawyers (2003-present).
**Professional Memberships:** State Bar of Texas; Dallas Bar Association; American Bankruptcy Institute; Turnaround Management Association.
**Career:** Partner since 1992.
**Personal:** University of Texas School of Law (JD, with high honors, 1986); University of Texas at Austin (BA, with high honors, 1983).

## BERGLUND II, James
Thompson & Knight LLP, Dallas
214 969 1385
James.Berglund@tklaw.com
*Featured in Antitrust (Texas)*
**Practice Areas:** Mr Berglund focuses his practice on matters involving complex business claims, civil and criminal antitrust litigation, contract issues, fiduciary duty issues, healthcare fraud investigations, class action litigation, securities litigation, products liability, dram shop liability, and aviation law. In addition, he counsels clients in the areas of commercial risk management, antitrust compliance programs, government investigations,

joint ventures, securities fraud, and derivative claims.

**Professional Memberships:** State Bar of Texas, Antitrust and Business Litigation Section Chair; American Bar Association; Dallas Bar Association; Texas Association of Defense Counsel; Defense Research Institute (DRI).

**Personal:** University of Kansas (JD, 1992; BS, 1986).

### BERRYMAN, Cathryn A
Winstead PC, Dallas
214 745 5172
cberryman@winstead.com
*Featured in Intellectual Property (Texas)*

**Practice Areas:** Cathryn's practice focuses on domestic and international intellectual property licensing and transactional work for computer software and systems integration, procurement and outsourcing, Internet and electronic commerce, privacy and security, trademarks and branding, domain name registrations and disputes, visual art, entertainment and multimedia, hospitals, health care and medical device manufacturing, transportation and supply chain management, semiconductor chip manufacturing, banking and financial institutions, technology development and distribution, consumer devices, software and related services, and intellectual property aspects of corporate transactions and related litigation (including mergers and acquisitions, policies and procedures, due diligence and audits).

### BETZEN, Mark E
Jones Day, Dallas
214 969 3704
mbetzen@jonesday.com
*Featured in Corporate/M&A (Texas)*

**Practice Areas:** Co-Chairs Jones Day's Mergers and Acquisitions Practice in the Texas region. Extensive experience in mergers, acquisitions, and dispositions involving publicly traded and closely held companies and in public offerings and private placements of equity and debt securities. Also counsels clients with respect to corporate governance, fiduciary duties and securities law compliance.

**Professional Memberships:** State Bar of Texas; Dallas Bar Association.

**Career:** Partner since 1993.

**Publications:** Member of the Editorial Board of The Corporate Compliance & Regulatory Newsletter.

**Personal:** Texas Tech University (National Merit Scholar; BBA 1981); University of Texas School of Law (JD with honors 1984).

### BICKERSTAFF, Alan
Andrews Kurth LLP, Austin
512 320 9229
abickerstaff@andrewskurth.com
*Featured in Technology (Texas)*

**Practice Areas:** Alan Bickerstaff is a Corporate and Securities partner who focuses on representing entrepreneurs and public and private emerging growth companies on formation, operations and corporate governance matters; securities law reporting and compliance matters; private equity

and venture capital financings; public offerings and mergers and acquisitions. He represents companies in a wide variety of industries, including the software, internet, energy, semiconductor, renewable energy, clean technology, life sciences, and telecommunications industries.

### BISHOP, Doak
King & Spalding LLP, Houston
713 751 3205
dbishop@kslaw.com
*Featured in International Arbitration (Nationwide), Litigation (Texas)*
See under Nationwide for profile.

### BLEFELD, Bruce
Jackson Walker LLP, Houston
713 752 4207
bblefeld@jw.com
*Featured in Antitrust (Texas)*

**Practice Areas:** Bruce A Blefeld is a trial lawyer who concentrates his practice on antitrust litigation and other complex commercial litigation matters.

**Career:** Mr Blefeld successfully defended a major global health care device and supply company in a $1 billion antitrust suit; he also successfully defended the largest health care group purchasing organization in a $600 million antitrust suit. Mr Blefeld has represented energy, technology, healthcare, and chemical companies in antitrust cases, and has represented companies in oil and gas, healthcare, ERISA, and other business litigation matters.

### BLISSARD, Judith M
Vinson & Elkins LLP, Houston
713 758 2374
jblissard@velaw.com
*Featured in Tax (Texas)*

**Practice Areas:** Judith's principal areas of practice are business transactions and domestic and international tax planning.

**Professional Memberships:** American Bar Association, Taxation Section; Committee on US Activities of Foreigners and Tax Treaties; State Bar of Texas; Houston Bar Association; International Fiscal Association; Houston Tax Roundtable.

**Career:** Admitted to practice: Texas, 1987; United States Tax Court.

**Personal:** University of Houston, BBA summa cum laude, 1984 (Beta Alpha Psi); University of Houston Law Center, JD cum laude, 1987 (Order of the Barons; Order of the Coif).

### BLUMROSEN, Eric A
Gardere Wynne Sewell LLP, Houston
713 276 5533
eblumrosen@gardere.com
*Featured in Corporate/M&A (Texas)*

**Practice Areas:** Corporate, mergers and acquisitions (M&A), private equity, securities.

**Professional Memberships:** State Bar of Texas, American and Houston Bar Associations, National Association of Corporate Directors, Association for Corporate Growth - Houston.

**Career:** Eric Blumrosen has more than 28 years of experience handling securities offerings, M&A transactions, re-capitalizations, governance matters, joint ventures, and private equity matters for

numerous clients, including public and private companies, boards of directors, board committees, officers, underwriters, entrepreneurs, and private equity funds and portfolio companies.

**Personal:** JD, The University of Texas School of Law, 1984; BA, The University of Texas at Austin, magna cum laude, 1981.

### BOGDANOW, Alan J
Vinson & Elkins LLP, Dallas
214 220 7857
abogdanow@velaw.com
*Featured in Corporate/M&A (Texas)*

**Practice Areas:** Primary areas of practice are mergers and acquisitions, public and private financings, and corporate control and governance matters. Represents public and private acquirers, targets, sellers, special committees, and investment bankers in a broad range of merger and acquisition and capital markets transactions.

**Career:** Admitted to New York Bar in 1972 and Texas Bar in 1977. Came to the firm as a Partner in 2001.

**Personal:** Graduated cum laude from Brown University, AB in 1968 and Columbia Law School, JD in 1971, served as editor of the 'Columbia Law Review'.

### BOHANNON, Paul
Andrews Kurth LLP, The Woodlands
713 220 4193
pbohannon@andrewskurth.com
*Featured in Environment (Texas)*

**Practice Areas:** Paul handles environmental litigation and related regulatory matters, with particular emphasis on groundwater, surface water, and sediment issues. He has substantial jury and bench trial experience in federal and state courts involving groundwater and surface water claims, cost recovery, nuisance, and trespass, having gone to final verdict in numerous cases. He has considerable downhole litigation experience in the energy industry. He is a Member of the AAA National Energy Panel. From early groundwater to sediment to fracing issues, he is consistently at the forefront of developing courtroom issues.

### BOND, Thomas J
Greenberg Traurig, LLP, Austin
512 320 7202
BondT@gtlaw.com
*Featured in Insurance (Texas)*

**Practice Areas:** Co-Chair, Insurance Regulatory and Transactions Group. Chair, National Governmental Affairs Practice.

**Professional Memberships:** Founding Board Member, Federation of Regulatory Counsel.

**Career:** Selected: Chambers USA Guide, 2008-13; Best Lawyers in America, 2007-13; Texas' Best Lawyers, 2009-10; 'Austin Insurance Lawyer of the Year', Best Lawyers, 2011. Rated, AV® Preeminent™ 5.0 out of 5.

**Publications:** Co-Author, 'The Children's Health Insurance Program Reauthorization Act and The Future of The SChip Program in Today's Economic Climate', Federation of Regulatory Counsel, Inc., February 2009.

**Personal:** JD, with honors, University of Texas; MFA, Bowling Green State University; BA, Baylor University.

### BOPP, Gregory M
Bracewell & Giuliani LLP, Houston
713 221 1511
greg.bopp@bgllp.com
*Featured in Corporate/M&A (Texas), Tax (Texas)*

**Practice Areas:** Co-chair of the firm's business and regulatory practice and serves as a member of the firm's management committee. Has experience in tax and corporate matters related to mergers and acquisitions, joint ventures and capital markets transactions. Clients include master limited partnerships (MLPs), foreign and domestic public corporations, investment banks and private investment funds. Practice involves energy related assets and businesses, including pipelines, oil and gas properties, processing facilities, terminal facilities, storage facilities, oilfield services and retail distribution systems.

**Personal:** JD, South Texas College of Law, 1995; BBA, Accounting, The University of Texas, 1989.

### BOREN, Alison C
Baker Botts LLP, Dallas
214 953 6827
alison.boren@bakerbotts.com
*Featured in Banking & Finance (Texas)*

**Practice Areas:** Financing transactions and debt restructurings, including investment grade lending, acquisition financing, debtor-in-possession financing, exit financing, letter of credit facilities, cash flow lending, asset-based lending, bridge financing, equity and subordinated debt financing, and workouts and restructurings. She represents both borrowers and financial institutions, and has been involved in a wide variety of financing transactions in both the United States and abroad.

**Personal:** SMU Dedman School of Law (JD, 1983); SMU (BA, 1980 and BBA, 1980).

### BOS, William
Vinson & Elkins LLP, Houston
713 758 3688
wbos@velaw.com
*Featured in Banking & Finance (Texas)*

**Practice Areas:** Will's practice focuses on leveraged financings and investments in the energy industry with a particular focus on transactions within the upstream, midstream and oil field service sectors. He represents arranger banks, corporate borrowers, private equity sponsors and alternative lenders in syndicated loan facilities, mezzanine investments and other commercial lending transactions.

**Career:** Admitted to New York and Texas Bar.

**Personal:** University of Vermont, BA, 1993; The Johns Hopkins University, MA, 1999; The University of Virginia School of Law, JD, 2002.

### BOULDEN, Michael R
Vinson & Elkins LLP, Dallas
214 220 7840
mboulden@velaw.com
*Featured in Real Estate (Texas)*

**Practice Areas:** Experience includes construction and permanent lending on commercial real estate; real estate joint ventures; acquisitions and dispositions of commercial properties; commercial leases; restructuring mortgage and mezzanine financings; joint venture buy-outs and restructuring; servicing agreements; and US and foreign investment by private equity funds.

**Professional Memberships:** American Bar Association; State Bar of Texas; Dallas Bar Association; Dallas Real Estate Council.

**Career:** Admitted to Texas Bar, 1977. Came to the firm as a Partner, 1994.

**Personal:** Graduated from Rice University, BA in 1973, and Southern Methodist University, JD in 1977.

### BOWERS, William
Fulbright & Jaworski LLP, Dallas
214 855 3903
bbowers@fulbright.com
*Featured in Tax (Texas)*

**Practice Areas:** Tax.

**Professional Memberships:** American Bar Association, Past Chair Committee on Tax Accounting Problems; Texas Bar Association, Past Chair Tax Section; Dallas Bar Association, Past Chair Tax Section; Fellow American College of Tax Counsel.

**Career:** Bowers focuses on federal income tax planning for complex transactions involving corporations, partnerships and REITS. He served as senior counsel in the Office of Tax Policy of the Treasury Department where he was responsible for the development of administrative guidance and legislative initiatives for pass-through entities.

**Personal:** LLM, Tax, Georgetown University (1979); JD, Southern Methodist University (1975); BBA, with honors, Texas A&M University (1972).

### BOYD, Michael
Andrews Kurth LLP, Houston
713 220 3921
mboyd@andrewskurth.com
*Featured in Real Estate (Texas)*

**Practice Areas:** Michael's practice involves all aspects of commercial real estate development and finance and commercial leasing. Michael has represented developers, operators and institutional investors and lenders in joint ventures, acquisitions, developments, leases and financing transactions across a broad spectrum of real estate asset classes.

### BRADLEY, James P
Sidley Austin LLP, Dallas
214 981 3306
jbradley@sidley.com
*Featured in Intellectual Property (Texas)*

**Practice Areas:** Managing partner in Sidley's Dallas office, practicing in intellectual property litigation. He focuses his practice on patents and has over 30 years of experience in trying intellectual property cases in district courts and before the International Trade Commission. His litigated patent cases have involved a variety of technologies including semiconductor devices, semiconductor process technology, telecommunications, oil drilling apparatus, metal detectors and medical devices.

**Professional Memberships:** The Fellows of the American Bar Foundation; AIPLA; Texas Bar Foundation; Dallas Bar Foundation.

**Personal:** Southern Methodist University, JD, 1970; University of Notre Dame, BS, 1967; University of Notre Dame, BA, 1966.

### BRADLEY III, Francis 'Frank' R
Greenberg Traurig, LLP, Houston
713 374 3630
BradleyF@gtlaw.com
*Featured in Banking & Finance (Texas)*

**Practice Areas:** Financial institutions and banking; energy and natural resources; corporate and securities; oil and gas.

**Professional Memberships:** Texas Association of Bank Counsel; Sustaining Life Fellow, Texas Bar Foundation. Member, Houston Bar Association.

**Career:** Selected: Chambers USA Guide, Banking/Finance, 2007-13; Super Lawyers magazine and Texas Super Lawyers magazine, Texas Rising Star, 2006-08. Rated, AV® Preeminent™ 5.0 out of 5. Listed: The Best Lawyers in America, 2013; Houston Business Journal 'Who's Who in Energy', 2012.

**Personal:** JD with honors, The University of Houston Law Center; BBA, with honors, Dean's List, The University of Texas at Austin.

### BREDEHOFT, Patrick
Thompson & Knight LLP, Dallas
214 969 1395
Patrick.Bredehoft@tklaw.com
*Featured in Healthcare (Texas)*

**Practice Areas:** Patrick focuses his practice primarily on complex healthcare and commercial litigation. He represents clients on matters involving federal and state false claim acts, fraud and abuse issues, physician and hospital compliance issues, and malpractice disputes. He also advises providers and clients in the pharmaceutical and medical device industries on regulatory compliance, business entity formation, risk management systems, and reimbursement issues.

**Professional Memberships:** American Health Lawyers Association; American and Dallas Bar Associations; State Bar of Texas; State Bar of California.

**Personal:** The University of Texas School of Law (JD, with honors, 1992); Colorado State University (BS, 1986).

### BRISTER, Scott
Andrews Kurth LLP, Austin
512 320 9220
scottbrister@andrewskurth.com
*Featured in Litigation (Texas)*

**Practice Areas:** Scott is head of the firm's appellate section and practices all aspects of litigation and arbitration. He returned to Andrews Kurth in 2009 after 20 years of judicial service — six years as a Justice on the Texas Supreme Court, three years on the First and Fourteenth Courts of Appeals (the first person ever to serve on both courts), and 11 years as a trial judge of a district court in Houston. Scott is triple board-certified in civil appellate, civil trial, and personal injury trial law. He is an honors graduate of Duke University and Harvard Law School.

### BROOKNER, Jason S
Andrews Kurth LLP, Dallas
214 659 4457
jbrookner@andrewskurth.com
*Featured in Bankruptcy/Restructuring (Texas)*

**Practice Areas:** Jason's practice concentrates on transactional, restructuring and litigation matters, both in and out of court. Jason has broad experience representing debtors, trustees, committees, individual creditors and sellers/purchasers of assets. Recent representations include: Baytown/Omega Navigation, Counsel to senior secured lenders; Dynegy, Counsel to Subordinated Noteholder; FiberTower Corporation, Counsel to debtors; NextMedia Group, Inc., Counsel to debtors; Pilgrim's Pride Corporation, Counsel to Official Committee of Unsecured Creditors; Kitty Hawk, Inc., Counsel to debtors; Romacorp, Inc. (Tony Roma's), Counsel to debtors; Mirant Corporation, Counsel to Official Committee of Unsecured Creditors; and NextWave Personal Communications, Inc., Counsel to debtors.

### BROWN, David H
Brown & Kornegay LLP, Houston
713 528 3703
dbrown@bkllp.com
*Featured in Insurance (Texas)*

**Practice Areas:** Represents policyholders in insurance coverage disputes and related commercial litigation. Has represented a variety of business enterprises, including energy and transportation companies, and healthcare providers, in insurance litigation, appeals and arbitration matters under both first party and liability policies. Represents the Port of Houston Authority in litigation matters.

**Professional Memberships:** Member: Houston Bar Association; Texas Bar Foundation; Maritime Law Association.

**Career:** Admitted to practice: Texas, 1976. Joined Vinson & Elkins, 1977; admitted to partnership, 1984; co-founded Brown & Kornegay in March, 2008.

**Personal:** Northwestern University, BS, 1972; The University of Texas School of Law, JD with honors, 1975.

### BROWN, Fletcher
Waller Lansden Dortch & Davis, Austin
512 328 9323
fletcher.brown@wallerlaw.com
*Featured in Healthcare (Texas)*

**Practice Areas:** Counsels hospitals, health systems, physician practices and other providers on regulatory issues ranging from contract negotiations to Stark and anti-kickback compliance. Advises on policies and procedures, physician contracting, board governance, and patient privacy issues. Recognized for precedent-setting work with Texas Medicaid 1115 Waiver helping over 45 healthcare providers receive additional funding for risk-based managed care statewide.

**Professional Memberships:** Board Certified, Health Law by Texas Board of Legal Specialization; American Health Lawyers Association; Austin Bar Association, Health Law Section.

**Career:** Licensed in Texas since 1991. Joined Waller in 2013.

**Personal:** JD, 1991, Baylor University; BBA, 1985, Baylor University.

### BROWN, Heather L
Bracewell & Giuliani LLP, Houston
713 221 1419
heather.brown@bgllp.com
*Featured in Banking & Finance (Texas)*

**Practice Areas:** Focuses on complex financial transactions and a variety of other commercial transactions, with emphasis on the energy industry. Represents both lenders and borrowers in large, syndicated and bilateral, secured and unsecured, and traditional and structured financings, including acquisition and working capital facilities, bond financing credit enhancement, project financings, contract monetizations and forward sale transactions.

**Personal:** JD, magna cum laude, The University of Houston Law Center, 1994; BA, Rice University, 1991.

### BROWN, Jay W
Winstead PC, Houston
713 650 2706
jbrown@winstead.com
*Featured in Insurance (Texas)*

**Practice Areas:** Jay has achieved an exemplary record of jury verdicts and judgments in a variety of industries, including contract disputes, fraud, wrongful death, energy, insurance bad faith, deceptive trade practices, civil rights, toxic tort, catastrophic accidents and other cases. Highly regarded in the insurance industry, Jay has skillfully navigated numerous commercial property insurers and adjusters through the murky waters of first party bad faith disputes, including catastrophes involving habitational properties, office buildings, retail complexes, and refineries.

### BROWN, Reagan
Fulbright & Jaworski LLP, Houston
713 651 5469
rbrown@fulbright.com
*Featured in Insurance (Texas), Litigation (Texas)*

**Practice Areas:** Trial and appellate litigation, insurance, legal malpractice, ERISA and products liability.

**Professional Memberships:** ACTL (Fellow); ABOTA; Admitted to practice before US Supreme Court; the Second, Fifth and Ninth Circuit Courts of Appeals, multiple districts and state courts in Texas.

**Career:** Fulbright Partner since 1990; tried over 90 cases and arbitration proceedings with over 50 jury cases to verdict. Argued over 35 appeals to state, federal courts. Certified by the TBLS in Civil Trial Law, Civil Appellate Law and Personal Injury Trial Law.

**Personal:** BS, BA, summa cum laude, Southern Methodist University (1978); JD, honors, University of Texas (1981).

### BRUMBAUGH, Kay Lynn
Andrews Kurth LLP, Dallas
214 659 4702
kaylynnbrumbaugh@andrewskurth.com
*Featured in Antitrust (Texas)*

**Practice Areas:** Kay Lynn represents clients in all areas of antitrust and competition matters, including complex litigation, counseling, civil and criminal government antitrust investigations and merger clearances. Kay Lynn has provided representation for clients in many industries including energy, food and beverage, hospitality, franchising and distribution, consumer products, defense contracting, solid waste, manufacturing, health care and insurance. Recent antitrust litigation includes the defense of National Dairy Holdings, LP in the Southeastern Milk Antitrust litigation, and recent merger clearance work includes defending Hilcorp Alaska, LLC in its acquisition of assets in the Cook Inlet of Alaska from Marathon Alaska Production LLC.

**BUCK, David**
Andrews Kurth LLP, Houston
713 220 4301
dbuck@andrewskurth.com
*Featured in Corporate/M&A (Texas)*
**Practice Areas:** All areas of corporate and securities law, emphasizing transactional and governance matters. Corporate finance practice representing issuers and investment banks in IPOs, other public and private equity and debt offerings and consent solicitations. Mergers and acquisitions practice (public and private) representing companies, special committees and financial advisors. Counsels public clients regarding compliance with periodic reporting, proxy solicitation, corporate governance matters and requirements of the federal securities laws, including exchange rules and Sarbanes-Oxley Act. Expertise with energy and oilfield service companies, master limited partnerships and royalty trusts, including M&A transactions in these industries and with these types of entities.

**BURGERT, David**
Porter Hedges LLP, Houston
713 226 6668
dburgert@porterhedges.com
*Featured in Intellectual Property (Texas)*
**Practice Areas:** David Burgert has tried over 50 cases to a jury verdict as Lead Counsel, and has argued appeals before the Texas appellate courts and the Fifth, Eighth, and Federal Circuit Courts of Appeal. His practice has been devoted to intellectual property disputes, representing both patent holders and accused patent infringers, and litigating various aspects of licensing, trademark and internet law.
**Professional Memberships:** Mr Burgert is Board Certified in Civil Trial Law by the Texas Board of Legal Specialization, is a Member of the American Board of Trial Advocates, and a Member of the American Intellectual Property Lawyers Association.

**BURGESS, Kevin**
McKool Smith, Dallas
512 692 8700
kburgess@mckoolsmith.com
*Featured in Intellectual Property (Texas)*
**Practice Areas:** Intellectual property litigation.

**Professional Memberships:** American, Federal Circuit, and Travis County Bar Associations; AIPLA.
**Career:** Kevin Burgess specializes in complex technical cases with a particular emphasis on patent matters. Prior to joining McKool Smith, he served as a Judicial Clerk to Hon. William C. Bryson, U.S. Court of Appeals for the Federal Circuit. His case work includes securing a $290 million judgment for i4i Inc. against Microsoft (named "Patent Case of the Year" by Managing IP).
**Personal:** Ohio State University (JD, summa cum laude, 1998; PhD, Electrical Engineering, 1995; MSEE, 1992; BSEE, 1990).

**BURGESS, Linda J**
Winstead PC, Dallas
512 370 2881
lburgess@winstead.com
*Featured in Insurance (Texas)*
**Practice Areas:** Linda Burgess' practice is focused on litigation in state and federal courts at both the trial and appellate levels. She also has significant experience in trying contested cases before the State Office of Administrative Hearings. Linda has represented individual and corporate clients in matters involving a wide range of issues, including contract, insurance "bad faith" and coverage, administrative law, open records, government investigation and enforcement, fiduciary duty, usury, lender liability, deceptive trade practice and antitrust, and premium and retaliatory tax.

**BURGIN, Sara**
Baker Botts LLP, Austin
512 322 2649
sara.burgin@bakerbotts.com
*Featured in Environment (Texas)*
**Practice Areas:** Practice focuses on regulatory aspects of environmental law, particularly Clean Water Act issues. Counsels primarily industrial clients on wastewater permitting, compliance and enforcement matters and regulatory developments.
**Professional Memberships:** State Bar of Texas - Environmental and Natural Resources Section, American Bar Association - Environment, Energy and Resources Section; Water Quality Committee.
**Personal:** JD (with honors), University of Houston Law Center (1982), Associate Editor, Houston Law Review, MS, Texas A&M University (1977), BA, The University of Texas (1973).

**CAGLE, Molly**
Baker Botts LLP, Houston
512 322 2535
molly.cagle@bakerbotts.com
*Featured in Environment (Texas)*
**Practice Areas:** Molly counsels clients on virtually every kind of environmental matter and represents them before various agencies and in federal and state courts. She has particular interest in water issues.
**Professional Memberships:** State Bar of Texas; Administrative and Public Law, and Environmental and Natural Resources Law Sections, State Bar of Texas; Board of Directors of

the Texas Water Conservation Association, 1999; Fellow, American College of Environmental Lawyers
**Personal:** JD (with honors), The University of Texas School of Law; 1981 BS (magna cum laude), textile technology and textile chemistry, Texas Tech University, 1978.

**CAGLE, Steve**
Winston & Strawn LLP, Houston
713 651 2648
scagle@winston.com
*Featured in Intellectual Property (Texas)*
**Practice Areas:** He has been involved in patent and trade secret litigation for the past 35 years, most of which has involved chemistry and mechanical devices involved in oil and gas exploration and recovery. His experience also includes counseling clients on mergers and acquisitions, opinions, licensing, and portfolio maintenance and all other aspects of intellectual property counseling and management. He is a member of the State Bars of Texas, Ohio, Indiana, and the Patent Bar.
**Professional Memberships:** American Bar Association; American Intellectual Property Law Association; Federal Circuit Bar Association; Texas Bar Association; Houston Bar Association; Houston Intellectual Property Law Association.

**CAMPBELL, Andrew**
Andrews Kurth LLP, Dallas
214 659 4511
acampbell@andrewskurth.com
*Featured in Real Estate (Texas)*
**Practice Areas:** Andrew's experience includes the representation of institutional owners in multi-state acquisitions, asset management, joint venture developments and equity recapitalization of existing joint ventures. He also advises private investor funds in the acquisition, development and financing of commercial properties.

**CAMPBELL, Rhett G**
Thompson & Knight LLP, Houston
713 653 8660
Rhett.Campbell@tklaw.com
*Featured in Bankruptcy/Restructuring (Texas)*
**Practice Areas:** Mr Campbell represents clients in corporate reorganization and business and commercial litigation, with an emphasis on creditors' rights and bankruptcy matters in the energy industry. He is Board Certified in Business Bankruptcy Law and Civil Trial Law by the Texas Board of Legal Specialization and a Fellow of the American College of Bankruptcy. He has been named to The Best Lawyers in America, Texas Super Lawyers, Houston's Top Lawyers (H Texas Magazine), and Who's Who Legal: Texas for multiple years.
**Personal:** SMU Dedman School of Law (JD, cum laude, 1973); Southern Methodist University (BA, magna cum laude, 1970).

**CARNEY, Ryan Kenneth**
Vinson & Elkins LLP, Houston
713 758 4720
rcarney@velaw.com
*Featured in Tax (Texas)*

**Practice Areas:** Extensive experience with tax structuring and advising publicly traded partnerships or master limited partnerships (MLPs) in capital market transactions, initial public offerings, private placements, mergers and acquisitions, and with private letter rulings from the IRS regarding qualifying income under section 7704 of the Internal Revenue Code. Regularly advises public and private companies and private equity firms in transactional matters.
**Career:** Admitted in Texas; joined Vinson & Elkins LLP, 2005. Recognized in Texas Rising Stars, 2009-12.
**Personal:** Texas A&M University, B.B.A., 2001; Southern Methodist University School of Law, JD, magna cum laude, 2005 (Order of the Coif).

**CARRELL, Richard**
Fulbright & Jaworski LLP, Houston
713 651 5447
rcarrell@fulbright.com
*Featured in Antitrust (Texas)*
**Practice Areas:** Antitrust, business litigation, securities litigation, contracts, and oil and gas litigation.
**Professional Memberships:** The Houston and the American Bar Associations and the State Bar of Texas. Emeritus Trustee of Baylor College of Medicine and Trustee of the Kelsey Foundation for Research.
**Career:** Admitted Texas Bar (1970). Partner, Fulbright & Jaworski L.L.P., where Mr Carrell has served as a member of the Firm's Executive and Policy Committees.
**Personal:** BA, Washington & Lee University (1965); JD, The University of Virginia (1970).

**CARTER JR, Winstol D**
Morgan, Lewis & Bockius LLP, Houston
713 890 5000
wcarter@morganlewis.com
*Featured in Litigation (Texas)*
**Practice Areas:** Winn Carter has more than 30 years of experience trying complex commercial cases in federal and state courts and before arbitration panels. He has tried nearly 100 cases to verdict and has litigated thousands of disputes. He has represented corporations and individuals in the aviation, energy, health, and telecommunications industries. He has handled cases involving trade secrets, shareholder disputes, air carrier disasters, products liability. He also has handled patent litigation involving computer software and hardware, telecommunications, wireless technology, medical device and life sciences, and energy-related technology.
**Personal:** Louisiana State University, 1979, JD; Southern Methodist University, 1976, BBA.

**CAUDILL, William H**
Fulbright & Jaworski LLP, Houston
713 651 5292
wcaudill@fulbright.com
*Featured in Tax (Texas)*
**Practice Areas:** Tax, bankruptcy and insolvency, commercial transactions, oil and gas, nonprofit organizations.
**Professional Memberships:** Former Chair, State Bar of Texas Tax Section; ABA Tax Section,

Former Chair, Committee on Partnerships and LLCs; Elected Member, Council of the Section; Liaison to IRS LB&I Division, Elected Officer, Vice Chair - Continuing Legal Education; Fellow, ACTC.
**Career:** Caudill, a Partner in Fulbright's Houston office since 1986, has a tax practice, involving partnerships, oil and gas, real estate and tax-exempt organizations and works with the IRS.
**Personal:** 1977-MPA, 1978-JD, The University of Texas (Chancellors, Order of the Coif); 1973-BSBA, University of Arkansas.

## CAVAZOS, Edward A
Bracewell & Giuliani LLP, Austin
512 494 3633
ed.cavazos@bgllp.com
*Featured in Technology (Texas)*

**Practice Areas:** Heads the firm's technology transactions practice. Represents clients in business and corporate transactions with an emphasis on complex technology-related intellectual property deals. Counsels clients regarding licensing arrangements, development contracts, sales and distribution arrangements, and a variety of other issues faced by technology companies. Also has civil jury trial experience in both state and federal courts, litigating disputes involving patents, trade secrets, copyright, trademarks, breach of contract, and Internet-related claims.
**Career:** Adjunct professor at The University of Texas School of Law
**Personal:** JD, The University of Texas School of Law, 1993; BA, The University of Texas at Austin, 1990.

## CAWLEY, Douglas
McKool Smith, Dallas
214 978 4000
dcawley@mckoolsmith.com
*Featured in Intellectual Property (Texas)*

**Practice Areas:** Intellectual property litigation.
**Professional Memberships:** AIPLA; American, Federal Circuit, and Dallas Bar Associations.
**Career:** Douglas Cawley recently won a $368m verdict for VirnetX Holding Corporation against Apple in 2012. His victories also include a $290m judgment for i4i Inc. against Microsoft; a $105m verdict for VirnetX against Microsoft; a $21m verdict for Anascape Ltd. against Nintendo, and a $156m verdict for TGIP Inc. against AT&T. These verdicts were all named "Top 100 Verdicts" by the National Law Journal.
**Personal:** University of Texas School of Law (JD, with honors, 1975); University of Texas (BA, with high honors, 1972).

## CHAPMAN, Jeffrey A
Gibson, Dunn & Crutcher LLP, Dallas
214 698 3120
JChapman@gibsondunn.com
*Featured in Corporate/M&A (Texas), Capital Markets (Texas)*

**Practice Areas:** Co-Chair of the firm's M&A practice group. Represents publicly and privately held corporations in wide variety of merger and acquisition transactions. Advises executives and Boards of Directors regarding sensitive corporate matters and transactions, including takeover

defenses, acquisition inquiries, fiduciary duties, and disclosure obligations. Represents issuers, underwriters and investors in public and private securities transactions, including equity and debt offerings. Extensive experience in corporate reorganizations.
**Career:** Admitted to Texas Bar, 1983. Came to firm as Partner, 2011.
**Personal:** JD, Harvard Law School, 1983, cum laude. BBA, University of Iowa, 1979, highest distinction.

## CHAPMAN JR, Ron
Ogletree, Deakins, Nash, Smoak & Stewart, PC, Dallas
214 987 3800
ron.chapman@ogletreedeakins.com
*Featured in Labor & Employment (Texas)*

**Practice Areas:** Labor and employment, including discrimination, harassment, retaliation, wage/hour, class/collective actions, restrictive covenants, unfair labor practices, union campaigns, collective bargaining, employment agreements, and HR counseling. Significant trial/arbitration experience.
**Professional Memberships:** City of Dallas Civil Service Board (Former Chairman); North Dallas Chamber of Commerce (Former Chairman).
**Career:** Member of Firm's Board of Directors. Board Certified in labor and employment law, Texas Board of Legal Specialization. Defended clients in over 25 states, received numerous recognitions, distinctions.
**Publications:** Lectured and published extensively on labor and employment topics.
**Personal:** SMU School of Law (JD, cum laude, 1995); Rice University (BA, cum laude, 1992).

## CHEN, Li
Sidley Austin LLP, Dallas
214 981 3385
lchen@sidley.com
*Featured in Intellectual Property (Texas)*

**Practice Areas:** Dallas partner, practices intellectual property litigation, complex commercial litigation, and technology transactions. Served as lead or co-lead counsel in over twenty litigation matters, and appeared in patent disputes before the International Trade Commission in DC, and district courts in California, Delaware, Illinois, Indiana, Michigan, Missouri, Ohio, Texas and Utah. Recent trial before the ITC, where the administrative law judge, based on admissions Li secured during cross examination, found non-liability in favor of firm client Realtek Semiconductor.
**Personal:** University of Houston Law Center, JD, 1997; University of Houston, MBA, 1997; University of Houston, BS. in Electrical Engineering, 1992.

## CHERNEKOFF, Michael A
Jones Walker LLP, Houston
713 437 1827
mchernekoff@joneswalker.com
*Featured in Environment (Texas)*

**Practice Areas:** Environmental and toxic torts, class action defense, and energy.

**Professional Memberships:** Louisiana State Bar Association (Environmental Law Section, Chairman, 1993-94), American Bar Association (Sections on Environment, Energy and Resources, Vice-Chair, Environmental Enforcement and Crimes Committee, 2005-13; Torts and Insurance Practice, Toxic Tort and Environment Law Committee; Litigation, Environmental Litigation Committee); DRI (Toxic Torts and Environmental Law Committee); District of Columbia Bar; New Orleans Bar Association; Houston Bar Association; State Bar of Texas.
**Career:** Mr Chernekoff started his career at the US Environmental Protection Agency in Washington, DC as an attorney advisor in the Office of Air, Mobile Source Enforcement from 1981 until joining Jones Walker in May 1982.
**Publications:** Mr Chernekoff has written and presented on a variety of environmental topics including: criminal enforcement; civil enforcement; compliance auditing; due diligence; Brownfield reclamation projects; CERCLA, RCRA, Oil Pollution Act, Clean Air Act and Clean Water Act programs.
**Personal:** Admitted to Bar, 1980, District of Columbia; 1982, Louisiana; 2006, Texas. Mr Chernekoff can also be reached in the firm's New Orleans office at 504 582 8264.

## CHU, Wilson
K&L Gates, Dallas
214 939 5688
wilson.chu@klgates.com
*Featured in Technology (Texas)*

**Practice Areas:** Highly regarded for his experience in M&A and private equity transactions, Wilson Chu represents clients in a broad range of industries, with a heavy-weighting in technology and healthcare. He also has significant experience in cross-border investments, particularly involving Asia. Two of Mr Chu's acquisitions made the "Top Ten Storage Acquisitions for 2010" list in the leading storage website, www.infostor.com. Mr Chu is widely-recognized for creating the influential "M&A Deal Points Study" used by M&A lawyers and advisors in the US and globally. The study is now a centerpiece publication of the ABA's Mergers & Acquisitions Committee.

## CLARK, Donna S
Baker & Hostetler LLP, Houston
713 646 1302
dclark@bakerlaw.com
*Featured in Healthcare (Texas)*

**Career:** Donna Clark represents healthcare providers in federal and state regulatory matters, with emphasis on compliance with referral laws. Her clients include academic medical centers, hospitals and hospital systems, physicians and physician groups, imaging facilities, pharmaceutical and medical device manufacturers, ambulatory surgery centers, home health agencies and dialysis providers. Donna advises clients on structuring joint ventures and contractual relationships in compliance with laws governing referral relationships, including anti-kickback, Stark and civil money penalties laws. Donna performs internal audits and investigations for healthcare providers

examining relationships with referral sources for compliance with the referral laws and with Medicare and Medicaid billing requirements.

## CLARK, Gary
Fulbright & Jaworski LLP, Houston
214 855 7460
gclark@fulbright.com
*Featured in Banking & Finance (Texas)*

**Practice Areas:** Corporate finance; energy.
**Professional Memberships:** State Bar of Texas; State Bar of New York; Texas Association of Bank Counsel; Dallas Bar Association.
**Career:** For over 25 years, partner Gary Clark has represented borrowers and lenders in the negotiation and documentation of secured and unsecured loans with a emphasis on acquisition financing for leveraged buyouts and exploration, production and midstream financing for the energy industry. He represents banks and investment funds in single bank and syndicated cash-flow and asset-based credit facilities and subordinated debt agreements and related warrant investments.
**Personal:** JD, University of Alabama School of Law (1982); BS, magna cum laude, University of Alabama (1979).

## CLARK, Shauna
Fulbright & Jaworski LLP, Houston
713 651 5601
sclark@fulbright.com
*Featured in Labor & Employment (Texas)*

**Practice Areas:** Labor and employment law.
**Professional Memberships:** National and American Bar Associations; Houston Lawyers Association.
**Career:** Clark is Partner-in-Charge of the Houston office of Fulbright & Jaworski. She represents management in all aspects of employment law matters including jury and non-jury trials, mediation and arbitration. Texas Monthly magazine named her a 'Texas Super Lawyer' (2005-present). She is also recognized by Best Lawyers in America (2009-present) and was named a 'Lawyer on the Fast Track' by H Texas magazine(2004).
**Personal:** JD, Tulane Law School (1994); BA, Louisiana State University (1990).

## CLAYMON, Jennifer
Reed, Claymon, Meeker & Hargett, PLLC, Austin
512 482 0614
jclaymon@dwlaw.com
*Featured in Healthcare (Texas)*

**Practice Areas:** Primary area of practice is health law. Also represents employers in personnel issues and employee disputes.
**Career:** Admitted to Texas Bar, 1998. Board Certified, Health Law by Texas Board of Legal Specialization.
**Personal:** Graduated from Texas A&M University, summa cum laude, BA in 1994 and the University of Texas School of Law, with honors, JD in 1998. Has been recognized as a "Texas Rising Star" (2005-09, 2011-12) in the Health Law Field by Texas Monthly and Law & Politics Magazines.

**CLEMENT, Zack**
Fulbright & Jaworski LLP, Houston
713 651 5434
zclement@fulbright.com
*Featured in Bankruptcy/Restructuring (Texas)*
**Practice Areas:** Bankruptcy, reorganization and creditor's rights.
**Professional Memberships:** American College of Bankruptcy; International Insolvency Institute; ABA; American Bankruptcy Institute; State Bar of Texas; HBA.
**Career:** Zack has represented Chapter 11 debtors with an aggregate value of over $50 billion; been involved in billions of dollars of sales by, loans to and exit financings for Chapter 11 debtors. He is licensed to practice law in Texas, New York and the US Supreme Court.
**Personal:** JD, University of Virginia School of Law, 1975; US Navy Air Intelligence Officer, 1972; AB, cum laude, Public and International Affairs (Economics), Princeton University, 1970.

**CLEMENTS, Jerry K**
Locke Lord LLP, Austin
512 305 4723
jclements@lockelord.com
*Featured in Litigation (Texas)*
**Practice Areas:** Serves as Chair of the Firm. Handles contract disputes, fraud claims, trade secret litigation, covenants not to compete litigation, oil/gas litigation, high technology litigation, environmental insurance coverage disputes, class actions.
**Professional Memberships:** Member, Baylor University Board of Regents; American College of Trial Lawyers; Business Counsel, Inc. Board of Governors; American Board of Trial Advocates; International Society of Barristers; Litigation Counsel of America; ABA; State Bar of Texas; Austin/Dallas Bar Associations; American/Texas/Dallas Bar Foundations.
**Career:** Chair since 2006; Partner since 1994.
**Personal:** Baylor University School of Law (JD, cum laude, 1981); Texas Christian University (BS, magna cum laude, 1975).

**CLONTS, David R**
Akin Gump Strauss Hauer & Feld LLP, Houston
713 220 5886
dclonts@akingump.com
*Featured in Intellectual Property (Texas)*
**Practice Areas:** A Member of Akin Gump's Patent Litigation Practice Group, Mr Clonts focuses on patent litigation and intellectual property counseling for large US and international companies in the electronics, telecommunications, software, medical device and business method fields.
**Personal:** BSEE, Georgia Institute of Technology (1987); JD, University of Texas (1991).

**COBB, Bill**
Jackson Walker LLP, Austin
512 236 2326
bcobb@jw.com
*Featured in Environment (Texas)*
**Career:** Bill Cobb is best known for his success challenging—and enforcing—environmental and insurance regulations. As Texas' Deputy Attorney General for Civil Litigation, Mr Cobb spearheaded Texas' opposition to the EPA's greenhouse gas regulations and was Texas' lead trial counsel in the historic 26 State constitutional challenge to the new federal health insurance law. He also negotiated an unprecedented $50 million settlement enforcing Texas' Clean Air Act, quarterbacked trial teams obtaining record-breaking jury verdicts and settlements in Medicaid insurance fraud litigation, and successfully defended Texas' Flexible (air) Permit program at oral arguments before the 5th Circuit.

**COFFIN, Ann M**
Parsley Coffin Renner, LLP, Austin
512 879 0915
ann.coffin@pcrllp.com
*Featured in Energy & Natural Resources (Texas)*
**Practice Areas:** Ms Coffin represents some of the largest energy and utility companies in the United States, with an emphasis on the regulation of natural gas, electricity and telecommunications before Texas state agencies and courts. Ms Coffin advises clients on regulatory implications and risks to their business, and regularly undertakes first-chair responsibilities in utility rate proceedings and other regulatory matters. Ms Coffin's past experience includes serving as a Hearings Examiner with the Railroad Commission of Texas, as well as Director of Enforcement and Assistant General Counsel with the Public Utility Commission of Texas. Ms Coffin is repeatedly recognized both nationally and within Texas as a leading lawyer providing energy-related services.

**COHEN, Murry B**
Akin Gump Strauss Hauer & Feld LLP, Houston
713 220 5866
mcohen@akingump.com
*Featured in Litigation (Texas)*
**Practice Areas:** Justice Cohen served for 20 years on the Court of Appeals for the First District of Texas before joining Akin Gump Strauss Hauer & Feld as Head of its Texas Appellate Practice Group. He is a board certified specialist in civil appeals, has been an Adjunct Professor at two law schools, and regularly argues before Texas and federal trial and appellate courts.
**Career:** Justice, Court of Appeals for the First District of Texas (1983-2002); Life Fellow, Texas Bar Foundation and Houston Bar Foundation.
**Personal:** BA, George Washington University; JD, University of Texas.

**COHEN, R Scott**
Jones Day, Dallas
214 969 5060
scohen@jonesday.com
*Featured in Corporate/M&A (Texas)*
**Practice Areas:** Concentrates primarily in public and private domestic and international mergers and acquisitions for corporate and private equity clients. Experience also includes restructurings, recapitalizations, corporate governance issues, and debt and equity financings. Broad industry experience, including technology, energy and energy services, manufacturing, and consumer products.

Mr Cohen has led major transactions for such clients as Fluor Corporation, International Wire Group, Latrobe Specialty Steel, Samson Resources, Taiwan Semiconductor Manufacturing Company, Texas Instruments, Tokyo Electron and Viasystems Group.
**Personal:** University of Texas at Arlington, BBA, 1976; Southern Methodist University School of Law, JD, 1979.

**COLEMAN, Joseph M**
Kane Russell Coleman & Logan PC, Dallas
214 777 4200
jcoleman@krcl.com
*Featured in Bankruptcy/Restructuring (Texas)*
**Practice Areas:** Joe Coleman has extensive experience in all aspects of bankruptcy, out-of-court restructurings and creditor rights. He has represented private and publicly traded debtors, over 36 creditors committees (in 15 states), financial institutions, equity funds, examiners, equity holders, lessors, and virtually all constituencies in complex Chapter 11 reorganization cases. Mr Coleman also represents parties to adversary proceedings and other litigation related to bankruptcy and insolvency matters.
**Professional Memberships:** American Bankruptcy Institute; Trial Advocacy Program, Faculty Member; American Bar Association, Business Law Section; Dallas Bar Association; Corporate Reorganization, Creditor Rights Section, Bankruptcy and Business Litigation Sections; State Bar of Texas; Business Law Section, Bankruptcy Reorganization Committee; Turnaround Management Association.
**Career:** Licensed to practice in 1985. Founded the firm in 1992 and is a shareholder, director and officer. The bankruptcy and creditor rights practice was recognized as part of the firm's selection by The National Law Journal for its Midsize Hot List (2012). Listed in Best Lawyers in America (1999-2012). Named in Texas Super Lawyers® and Texas Monthly magazines as one of the top bankruptcy & creditor/debtor attorneys in Texas (2003-12).
**Publications:** Frequent author and speaker on bankruptcy and creditors' rights issues, including publications by Mathew Bender, Callaghan and the Uniform Commercial Code Law Journal.
**Personal:** Southern Methodist University School of Law, JD (1985), law journal; Creighton University, BSBA (1982), Beta Alpha Psi Accounting Honor Society; Solon E. Summerfield Scholar.

**CONIGLIO, Joseph F.**
Greenberg Traurig, LLP, Dallas
214 665 3678
ConiglioJ@gtlaw.com
*Featured in Healthcare (Texas)*
**Practice Areas:** Health and FDA business; regulatory compliance; and health care litigation.
**Professional Memberships:** Member: State Bar of Texas; American Bar Association, Antitrust Section; College of the State Bar of Texas; Texas Young Lawyers Association; American Health Lawyers Association; Dallas Bar Association, Health Law Section. Fellow, Texas Bar Foundation.

**Career:** Listed, The Best Lawyers in America, 2013.
**Publications:** Co-Author, 'Centers for Medicare & Medicaid Services to Release Proposed Rule Relating to Accountable Care Organizations (ACOs) in Medicare', GT Alert, March 2011.
**Personal:** JD, cum laude, Texas Tech University School of Law, 1997; BBA, Southern Methodist University, 1994.

**CONLON, Michael W**
Fulbright & Jaworski LLP, Houston
713 651 5427
mconlon@fulbright.com
*Featured in Corporate/M&A (Texas)*
**Practice Areas:** Corporate securities, governance and M&A.
**Career:** His general corporate practice involves the representation of publicly held corporations in matters involving securities offerings and routine reporting, corporate governance and compliance matters, disclosure issues, secured and unsecured borrowing, and mergers, acquisitions and dispositions. He has represented special committees of boards of directors connected with takeover offers and corporate restructurings.
**Personal:** JD, Order of Coif, Duke University (1971); BA, magna cum laude and Phi Beta Kappa, Catholic University of America (1968).

**COOPER, James**
Gardere Wynne Sewell LLP, Houston
713 276 5884
jcooper@gardere.com
*Featured in Insurance (Texas)*
**Practice Areas:** Insurance coverage, commercial litigation.
**Professional Memberships:** State Bar of Texas, American Bar Association and Houston Bar Associations, Texas Annotated Insurance Code [Contributing Editor].
**Career:** Jim Cooper co-chairs Gardere's Policyholder Insurance Coverage Group and has more than 25 years of experience working on insurance matters. He represents policyholders in the resolution of multi-million dollar insurance coverage disputes. Mr Cooper co-authored a chapter on handling complex insurance coverage matters in 'Inside the Minds: Legal Strategies for the Insurance Industry' (Aspatore Books).
**Personal:** JD, Tulane University School of Law, cum laude, 1984; BA, Wabash College, 1981.

**COOPER, Samuel W**
Paul Hastings LLP, Houston
*Featured in Litigation (Texas)*
**Practice Areas:** Commercial trial lawyer focusing on securities and business litigation and government investigations. Has tried cases to decision before juries, judges, and arbitrators. Represents audit committees and corporate boards conducting internal investigations.
**Professional Memberships:** ABA; SBOT; HBA.
**Career:** Partner since 2001.
**Publications:** "Jury Selection," V. Hale Starr and Mark McCormick (4th ed.), 2009 (chapter author).

**Personal:** Stanford Law School (JD 1993, Order of the Coif); Harvard College (AB 1990, summa cum laude, Phi Beta Kappa); Managing Editor Stanford Law Review (1992-93); Law Clerk to the Honorable J Harvie Wilkinson III, US Court of Appeals for the Fourth Circuit (1993-94).

### COOPER, Tammy
Andrews Kurth LLP, Austin
512 320 9244
tammycooper@andrewskurth.com
*Featured in Energy & Natural Resources (Texas)*

**Practice Areas:** Tammy's practice focuses on representing clients in state and federal regulatory proceedings. Tammy also advises clients on a wide range of energy-related issues. She has broad-based experience in both electric and telecommunications regulation as well as Texas administrative law. Tammy began her career at the Public Utility Commission of Texas, where she held a variety of legal/management positions. Immediately prior to joining Andrews Kurth, she served as the Director of Commission Advising.

### COPELAND, Gregory
Baker Botts LLP, Houston
713 229 1301
greg.copeland@bakerbotts.com
*Featured in Litigation (Texas)*

**Practice Areas:** Represents clients in the energy industry in complex litigation, covering an expansive array of matters involving the production, storage, transmission and sale of electricity, oil, gas, lignite, coal and nuclear fuels. Represents clients in state and federal courts throughout the United States, and in arbitration proceedings, mediations and administrative hearings. Representative Cases: Oil and Gas Industry: antitrust, lease disputes, JOA disputes, gas sales, contract disputes, FCA; Electric Utility: construction disputes; Refining: environmental, PMPA, UCC, "open price" disputes; Gas Storage: damage claims, JOA disputes; Power & Gas Marketing: antitrust, market manipulation; Services Industry: rig contract disputes.

### COTROPIA, Charles S
Sidley Austin LLP, Dallas
214 981 3305
ccotropia@sidley.com
*Featured in Intellectual Property (Texas)*

**Practice Areas:** Senior Counsel in Sidley's Dallas office, Mr Cotropia has over 39 years of litigation experience. In the last 24 years, he has been lead counsel in patent, trademark, trade dress and copyright disputes litigated in federal courts and the United States Patent and Trademark Office. Mr Cotropia has represented clients with products and services in many diverse areas, including automobile equipment, aerospace, electronics, the Internet, oil and gas equipment, wearing apparel and consumer products.
**Personal:** Cornell Law School, JD, 1973; University of Texas, BSAE, 1968, with honors. Admission: Texas.

### COURTNEY, Keith
Winstead PC, Austin
512 370 2813
kcourtney@winstead.com
*Featured in Environment (Texas)*

**Practice Areas:** Keith has significant experience representing industrial and business clients in various environmental matters, including air quality and hazardous and solid waste counseling; permitting and enforcement; agency rulemaking and legislation development; spill and release counseling and enforcement; site assessment and remediation; environmental permitting, rulemaking, and enforcement litigation; environmental auditing and due diligence; and climate change.

### COWLING, David
Jones Day, Dallas
214 969 2991
decowling@jonesday.com
*Featured in Tax (Texas)*

**Practice Areas:** David Cowling has extensive transactional and controversy experience with taxing authorities. He chairs the Firm's State and Local Tax and e-Commerce Tax Practices. David resolved one of the largest e-commerce company assessments in the US and is integrally involved in numerous pending audits and lawsuits involving online travel and other e-commerce companies. David represents diverse financial services, entertainment, petroleum, e-commerce, wholesaling, distribution, technology, retailing, and services industry taxpayers.
**Professional Memberships:** Bloomberg BNA State Tax Advisory Board, State Bar of Texas, District of Columbia Bar.

### COWLISHAW, Patrick R
Jackson Walker LLP, Dallas
214 953 6049
pcowlishaw@jw.com
*Featured in Energy & Natural Resources (Texas)*

**Practice Areas:** Patrick Cowlishaw conducts a complex business litigation and regulatory practice.
**Career:** Mr Cowlishaw helps energy, utility, and other clients find winning solutions to difficult business and regulatory disputes. He serves as first-chair advocate and advisor on the spectrum of issues that come before the Texas PUC and ERCOT, representing a variety of market participants. His litigation practice concentrates on serious commercial disputes and regulatory enforcement matters. After thirty years, as one client says, "he has this way of taking very complex issues and presenting them in a really smooth way, almost like he is telling a story."

### COX, Trey
Lynn Tillotson Pinker & Cox, LLP, Dallas
214 981 3813
tcox@lynnllp.com
*Featured in Litigation (Texas)*

**Career:** Trey Cox has been helping his clients resolve large, complicated, and often high-profile business disputes for nearly 20 years. His jury trial experience and courtroom success have earned him the distinction of being double Board Certified by the National Board of Trial Advocacy.

Trey represents Fortune 500 corporations, entrepreneurs and leading firms in a wide array of industries. "We have built our firm on a singular pursuit of courtroom excellence in the service of our clients," he says. Progressive and innovative, Trey has earned a reputation as a pioneer in combining technology and neuroscience to maximize jury communication and persuasion. He serves on the faculties of Southern Methodist University Law School and the National Institute for Trial Advocacy. He has lectured throughout the country and authored numerous legal articles, white papers and books. His latest book is The Texas Jury Rules. Trey received a BA, magna cum laude, from Washington & Lee University, and his JD, with honors, from the University of Virginia School of Law.

### CRAIG III, Allen B
Gardere Wynne Sewell LLP, Houston
713 276 5570
acraig@gardere.com
*Featured in Tax (Texas)*

**Practice Areas:** Federal, state, and international tax, trusts and estates.
**Professional Memberships:** State Bar of Texas, American and Houston Bar Associations.
**Career:** Allen Craig is member of Gardere's Tax Practice Group and is certified in Taxation Law by the Texas Board of Legal Specialization. He focuses his practice on business and tax planning, including mergers and acquisitions, reorganizations, company and state tax planning, and international transactions. Mr Craig also handles income and estate planning for individuals and closely-held businesses.
**Personal:** JD, University of Texas School of Law, 1971; BS, Washington & Lee University, with special attainments, 1968.

### CRAIN, Stephen B
Bracewell & Giuliani LLP, Houston
713 221 1305
stephen.crain@bgllp.com
*Featured in Litigation (Texas)*

**Practice Areas:** Leader of Bracewell's energy litigation practice. Focuses predominantly on matters arising in the energy industry (including representing power developers and producers, power traders, and suppliers to the energy industry) disputes involving alleged violations of securities laws (including representing public companies, officers and directors, and special committees), and large-scale construction disputes.
**Personal:** JD, The University of Texas School of Law, 1990; AB, Duke University, 1987.

### CROW, Carter
Fulbright & Jaworski LLP, Houston
713 651 5218
mcrow@fulbright.com
*Featured in Labor & Employment (Texas)*

**Practice Areas:** Employment litigation, wage and hour, executive contract/compensation, non-compete and trade secrets.
**Professional Memberships:** Houston Management Lawyers Forum, Past President; Houston Bar Association, Director; Texas Bar Association, Life Fellow.

**Career:** Carter represents companies in employment litigation, including disputes with executives/partners, collective/class and multi-plaintiff actions under FLSA and Title VII, employee bonus/compensation disputes, whistleblower cases and commercial disputes. Carter is Chair of Fulbright's Unfair Competition Group, which focuses on non-compete/trade secret matters. He consults with companies and executives on employment policies, practices and contracts.
**Personal:** BS, Oklahoma State University (1988); JD, University of Oklahoma College of Law with Honors (1991).

### DAHLSON, Richard
Jackson Walker LLP, Dallas
214 953 5896
rdahlson@jw.com
*Featured in Corporate/M&A (Texas)*

**Career:** Richard ("Rick") Dahlson manages Jackson Walker's Corporate & Securities practice group, which comprises over 100 attorneys. His practice is transactional in nature and includes representing both purchasers and sellers in leveraged buy-outs and mergers and acquisitions, as well as representing entrepreneurs, investors and investment funds (equity funds, hedge funds and venture funds). Mr Dahlson has extensive international transaction experience, and his corporate practice is complemented by extensive experience in securities matters, including public offerings, private placements, and public reporting compliance. He has represented both companies and investment bankers in over 30 initial public offerings and over 40 PIPE transactions.

### DANIEL, Josiah
Vinson & Elkins LLP, Dallas
214 200 7718
jdaniel@velaw.com
*Featured in Bankruptcy/Restructuring (Texas)*

**Practice Areas:** Represents debtors, secured lenders, asset purchasers, unsecured creditors, and equity owners in corporate restructurings and Chapter 11, including: plan formulation and confirmation; fraudulent transfer, preference, and other insolvency-related litigation; mass torts; resolution of claims; Section 363 asset acquisitions; post petition financing; leases and executory contracts; bankruptcy settlements; workouts.
**Professional Memberships:** American Law Institute; Business Bankruptcy Committee, American Bar Association; State Bar of Texas; Texas Association of Bank Counsel; Texas Law Review Association; Texas Bar Foundation.
**Career:** Partner, 1999. Admitted to Texas Bar, 1978.
**Personal:** University of the South, BA, 1973; University of Texas School of Law, JD, 1978.

### DAVIDSON, Joshua
Baker Botts LLP, Houston
713 229 1527
joshua.davidson@bakerbotts.com
*Featured in Capital Markets (Texas), Energy & Natural Resources (Nationwide)*

**Practice Areas:** Concentrates on a wide range of corporate and securities work and is nationally recognized for expertise in all types of master lim-

ited partnership (MLP) transactions. Represents issuers and underwriters in initial public offerings and follow-on offerings of both equity and debt; issuers and purchasers in private placements; purchasers, sellers and financial advisors in acquisitions; issuers in their ongoing corporate and securities work; and special committees of boards of directors in asset dropdowns, mergers and reorganizations.
**Personal:** JD, cum laude, Harvard Law School, 1985; BA, summa cum laude, History, Yale University, 1981.

### DAWSON, William B
Gibson, Dunn & Crutcher LLP, Dallas
214 698 3132
WDawson@gibsondunn.com
*Featured in Litigation (Texas)*
**Practice Areas:** Leads trial teams in intellectual property lawsuits, including patent infringement, patent licensing disputes, and trademark and dilution litigation. Defends auditors and lawyers. Handles energy litigation, including cases involving pipeline safety.
**Professional Memberships:** Fellow, The American College of Trial Lawyers (Past-Chair Science and Technology in the Courts Committee); Fellow, International Academy of Trial Lawyers; American Law Institute, currently an Advisor, Restatement of the Law Third, Torts: Liability for Economic Harm; Board of Trustees, Center for American and International Law.
**Career:** Admitted, Texas, 1975.
**Personal:** Texas Tech University, BBA, 1972; JD with highest honors, 1975.

### DAY, Kate
Bracewell & Giuliani LLP, Houston
713 221 1581
kate.day@bgllp.com
*Featured in Banking & Finance (Texas)*
**Practice Areas:** Represents lenders, borrowers, and sponsors in secured and unsecured credit transactions, including senior and subordinated debt financings, acquisition financings, project financings, term loans, working capital loans, cross-border financings, bond credit enhancement facilities, and financial asset securitizations, and in connection with interbank relationships involved in syndicated loan transactions, as well as loan restructurings and workouts. Has experience in leveraged buyouts, secured asset-based loans, oil and gas reserve-based financing, and complex or non-traditional forms of financing, including off-balance sheet transactions and synthetic letter of credit facilities.
**Personal:** JD, University of Virginia School of Law, 1997; BA, Rice University, 1993.

### DEATHERAGE, Scott D
Gardere Wynne Sewell LLP, Dallas
214 999 4979
sdeatherage@gardere.com
*Featured in Environment (Texas)*
**Practice Areas:** Environmental [climate change task force, environmental litigation], Mexico and Latin America.
**Professional Memberships:** State Bar of Texas, American and Dallas Bar Associate, International

Energy Institute, Dallas Chamber of Commerce Environmental Task Force, Richardson Chamber of Commerce Environmental Committee, Principal Solar Advisory Board.
**Career:** Scott Deatherage's practice focuses on environmental-related permitting, compliance, administrative law and judicial litigation, including air emissions, wetlands, wastewater discharges, hazardous/toxic waste, water rights and supply, endangered species, and environmental disclosure. He is a member of Gardere's Energy Industry Team.
**Personal:** JD, Harvard Law School, cum laude, 1987; BA, University of Oklahoma, with highest honors, 1984.

### DENNY, Otway
Fulbright & Jaworski LLP, Houston
713 651 5588
odenny@fulbright.com
*Featured in Products Liability (Nationwide), Litigation (Texas)*
**Practice Areas:** Product liability, personal injury, commercial, and professional liability litigation; mass and toxic tort litigation.
**Professional Memberships:** Past President, Houston Bar Association; Fellow, International Academy of Trial Lawyers and American College of Trial Lawyers.
**Career:** Denny has litigated cases in state and federal courts, including products liability cases involving chemicals, construction equipment, automobiles and other vehicles. He has experience in the defense of personal injury claims and other tort matters, and has handled cases involving large refinery explosions, professional liability litigation and commercial litigation.
**Personal:** JD, cum laude, Baylor University (1973); BA, Texas A&M University (1971).

### DEVETSKI, Tim
Vinson & Elkins LLP, Houston
713 758 2222
tdevetski@velaw.com
*Featured in Tax (Texas)*
**Practice Areas:** Practice consists primarily of tax planning for business transactions, including private equity, mergers and acquisitions, and capital markets. Significant experience working with multinational corporations in cross-border transactions.
**Professional Memberships:** Tax Sections of Texas, New York, and American Bar Associations.
**Career:** Admitted to practice Texas, US Tax Court; author and lecturer on taxation matters.
**Personal:** University of Houston, BA 1990, Northwestern University, JD 1993, New York University, LLM (Taxation) 1995.

### DIFFEN, Becky H
Vinson & Elkins LLP, Austin
512 542 8737
bdiffen@velaw.com
*Featured in Energy & Natural Resources (Texas)*
**Practice Areas:** Practice focuses on energy transactions, project development, and energy regulatory law in the renewable energy, power generation, and natural gas industries. Experience in regulatory proceedings before the Public Utility

Commission of Texas and complex transactions including mergers and acquisitions, joint ventures, and project finance. Background in wind power development.
**Career:** Joined V&E in 2009. Adjunct Professor, University of Texas School of Law, Electric Power Law Seminar.
**Publications:** Texas Wind Law (LexisNexis) (co-author).
**Personal:** Carleton College, BA magna cum laude, 2004; University of Texas School of Law, JD with honors, 2009.

### DILLARD, Stephen C
Fulbright & Jaworski LLP, Houston
713 651 5507
sdillard@fulbright.com
*Featured in Litigation (Texas)*
**Practice Areas:** Complex commercial litigation; environmental litigation; toxic tort litigation.
**Professional Memberships:** Fellow, American College of Trial Lawyers, International Academy of Trial Lawyers; Advocate, American Board of Trial Advocates; Life Fellow, Texas Bar Foundation; Former Chair, Pattern Jury Charge Committee of the State Bar of Texas; Defense Research Institute; International Association of Defense Counsel; Texas Association of Defense Counsel.
**Career:** Former Chair of the firm's global Litigation Department, was among 'The Best Lawyers in America,' named a Texas Super Lawyer (2003-12) and named among 'Top 100 Lawyers in Texas' (2012).
**Personal:** JD, cum laude (1971), and BA (1968), Baylor University.

### DINKINS, Carol
Vinson & Elkins LLP, Houston
713 758 2528
cdinkins@velaw.com
*Featured in Environment (Texas)*
**Practice Areas:** Chairs Vinson & Elkins' Environmental Law Practice. Practice includes client counseling on business transactions, compliance, enforcement and regulatory matters; civil litigation, mediation, and criminal defense.
**Professional Memberships:** American Bar Association; American College of Environmental Lawyers; American Law Institute.
**Career:** Admitted to practice: Texas, 1971. Joined Vinson & Elkins, 1973; admitted to partnership, 1980. Served as: Assistant Attorney General in charge of the Environment and Natural Resources Division of the Department of Justice, 1981-83; Deputy Attorney General of the United States, 1984-85.
**Personal:** The University of Texas, BS, 1968; University of Houston, JD, 1971.

### DODD, Jeff
Andrews Kurth LLP, Houston
713 220 4736
jeffdodd@andrewskurth.com
*Featured in Intellectual Property (Texas)*
**Practice Areas:** Jeff has extensive experience with various domestic and international intellectual property and information transactions, including licensing, development, transfer, com-

mercialization, outsourcing, and e-commerce arrangements. His experience includes structuring, documenting and negotiating strategic ventures and alliances where intellectual property is the core asset; counseling as to intellectual property commercialization strategies; structuring and negotiating technology acquisition and transfer transactions; counseling as to privacy, regulatory and data protection requirements; and representing various parties in planning, design and implementation of e-commerce strategies. He is Co-Author of Modern Licensing Law, published by Thomson West.

### DOW, T Andrew
Winstead PC, Dallas
214 745 5387
adow@winstead.com
*Featured in Real Estate (Texas)*
**Practice Areas:** Andy Dow maintains a reputation of more than fifteen years in forming efficient solutions to a variety of complex real estate issues. Andy represents developers, pension funds and other investors in all stages of development, acquisition and disposition of real estate; property owners and managers in connection with negotiating property management agreements and providing advice on operating income producing properties; corporations utilizing their real estate assets; and institutional lenders and borrowers in a broad range of debt and equity financing transactions. He also has significant experience in forming and structuring real estate entities, transaction structures and strategies.

### DUFFY, Dennis P
Baker & Hostetler LLP, Houston
713 646 1364
dpduffy@bakerlaw.com
*Featured in Labor & Employment (Texas)*
**Career:** Dennis Duffy represents management in all aspects of labor and employment law, including defending allegations of discrimination, unfair labor practices, wage and hour, OSHA claims, whistleblowing complaints and wrongful discharge; counseling and training to employers on managing workplace issues and preventing employment lawsuits. Dennis has strategic and advisory legal experience in handling global corporate human resources issues and in collaborating with businesses to provide counsel and training on how to prevent and/or manage workplace legal issues and avoid escalation and litigation. He handles acquisition/divestiture employment issues, including due diligence, pre-merger planning and post-merger integration issues.

### DUNLAY, Jon
Baker Botts LLP, Dallas
214 953 6711
jon.dunlay@bakerbotts.com
*Featured in Real Estate (Texas)*
**Practice Areas:** Practice focuses on commercial real estate transactions, with significant involvement in the acquisition, financing, including debt and equity, leasing and disposition of shopping centers, hotels, office buildings, apartments, and land in Texas and other parts of the country.
**Professional Memberships:** State Bar of Texas.

**Career:** Baker Botts LLP since 1982.
**Personal:** JD, with honors, from the University of Maryland School of Law, 1982; AB, cum laude, from Princeton University, 1979.

## DUNLOP, Fred
Baker Botts LLP, Houston
713 229 1273
fred.dunlop@bakerbotts.com
*Featured in Real Estate (Texas)*
**Practice Areas:** Represents clients in complex commercial real estate transactions for major developers, institutional lenders and investors. Works with insurance companies and other institutional investors to structure their investments, including long-term mortgage loans for apartment, office, hotel, and shopping center projects; and represents clients in workouts, foreclosures, and a variety of restructurings.
**Professional Memberships:** American College of Real Estate Lawyers; State Bar of Texas.
**Personal:** JD from Vanderbilt University School of Law, 1971; BA from Vanderbilt University, 1968.

## DYBALA, Kelly M
Weil, Gotshal & Manges LLP, Dallas
214 746 7898
kelly.dybala@weil.com
*Featured in Banking & Finance (Texas)*
**Practice Areas:** Partner in the Banking & Finance Practice. Practice consists primarily of financing transactions and debt restructurings. Represents borrowers, private equity sponsors and financial institutions, concentrating on acquisition financing, asset-based lending, dividend recaps, mezzanine financing and subordinated debt financing, and is also experienced in workouts and debtor-in-possession financings. Representative clients include Advent International, Avista Capital Partners, Berkshire Partners, Lindsay Goldberg, Summit Partners, Providence Equity Partners, THL Partners, Fortegra Financial, Vantiv, Pier 1 Imports and Univision Communications.
**Personal:** Oklahoma State University (BA, 1995); University of Texas (JD, 1998).

## DYE JR, Phillip B
Vinson & Elkins LLP, Houston
713 758 2048
pdye@velaw.com
*Featured in Litigation (Texas)*
**Practice Areas:** Complex civil litigation and arbitration practice, with a particular expertise in representing non-US based corporations who are sued in the Courts of the United States; in the handling of matters in which foreign governments or their institutions are involved; and in the law of personal jurisdiction.
**Professional Memberships:** ABA, International Bar Association, International Association of Defense Counsel, Maritime Law Association. Licensed: Texas and Louisiana.
**Career:** Partner since 1993.
**Publications:** Has lectured extensively on the law of personal jurisdiction and transnational litigation.

**Personal:** Louisiana State University (BS, 1982; JD with honors, 1986).

## EDWARDS, Brady
Morgan, Lewis & Bockius LLP, Houston
713 890 5000
bedwards@morganlewis.com
*Featured in Litigation (Texas)*
**Practice Areas:** Brady Edwards focuses his practice in the areas of product liability, complex mass tort and toxic tort litigation. In his mass tort and toxic tort practice, he serves as national and regional counsel for a wide variety of corporate defendants. He has defended a wide variety of corporate clients in claims involving occupational exposure to aromatic hydrocarbons, pesticides and nematicides, asbestos, silica, industrial adhesives and solvents, paints, welding fumes, and numerous other substances.
**Personal:** Baylor University Law School, 1995, JD, Cum Laude; University of Texas, 1991, BA.

## EILAND, Gary
King & Spalding LLP, Houston
713 751 3207
geiland@kslaw.com
*Featured in Healthcare (Texas), Healthcare (Nationwide)*
**Practice Areas:** Represents healthcare providers and academic medical centers in handling fraud and abuse, Stark, and False Claims Act matters; compliance matters including internal risk assessments, self-disclosures, and pursuit of advisory opinions; structuring business transactions; medicare/ medicaid and other federal and state regulatory issues and controversies.
**Professional Memberships:** State Bar of Texas (former Chair, Health Law Section); Charter Member, Health Law Exam Commission, Texas Board of Legal Specialization; AHLA (former President; Recipient, AHLA's David J Greenburg Award).
**Career:** Admitted to practice: Texas, 1976.
**Personal:** The University of Texas, BBA with honors, 1973, JD with honors, 1976.

## EPSTEIN, Joseph G
Winstead PC, Houston
713 650 2740
jepstein@winstead.com
*Featured in Bankruptcy/Restructuring (Texas)*
**Practice Areas:** Joe's experience spans all areas of business reorganization, creditors' rights, energy, municipal insolvency, and representing asset purchasers, landlords and other stakeholders in reorganization matters. His strategic focus enables him to identify possible alternatives and consequences and recommend the most effective strategy. His strong interpersonal skills and commitment to personal service also extend to teaming efficiently with clients' financial advisors and consultants. Joe is a frequent speaker and writer for continuing education seminars in the areas of bankruptcy, real estate, small businesses, business reorganization and insolvency law.

## ERWIN, Greg
Winstead PC, Houston
713 650 2781
gerwin@winstead.com
*Featured in Real Estate (Texas)*
**Practice Areas:** Greg Erwin is Co-Chair of Winstead's Real Estate Development and Investments Practice Group. With more than 30 years of experience as a real estate practitioner, Greg handles sophisticated real estate deals for clients such as New York Stock Exchange REITs, privately held development firms and wealthy individuals. Grounded with a sound analytical background and well-versed in the substantive areas of complex real estate transactions, Greg is known for his ability to get deals done, while always watching out for his clients' best interests. Applying Winstead's traditional team approach to real estate deals, he is efficient and effective.

## ETTREDGE, Katherine
Jones Day, Dallas
214 969 3714
kettredge@jonesday.com
*Featured in Banking & Finance (Texas)*
**Practice Areas:** Specializes in banking and finance, with experience representing financial institutions, corporate borrowers, and private equity funds in connection with debt investments, debt restructuring transactions, commercial term loan and revolving credit facilities of all types (including syndicated and single lender, secured and unsecured, multicurrency, acquisition and working capital financings) and related counseling. Such experience spans a wide array of industries, such as retail, telecommunications, energy/oil and gas, healthcare, technology outsourcing, manufacturing, real estate, insurance and aircraft and other transportation industries.
**Personal:** The University of Texas at Austin (BBA in Accounting with highest honors, 1993; JD with honors, 1996).

## EVANS, Mark C
Bracewell & Giuliani LLP, Houston
713 221 1300
mark.evans@bgllp.com
*Featured in Banking & Finance (Texas)*
**Practice Areas:** Managing Partner of Bracewell & Giuliani. Represents French, Dutch, Scottish, Japanese, and US banks and other lenders in complex commercial finance transactions. Represented the agent in syndicated loans, revolving credit and term loans, leveraged transactions, structured transactions, subordinated and mezzanine investments, credit enhancement for commercial paper and bond transactions, letters of credit and commercial paper facilities, production payment and other oil- and gas-related credits, project finance, bankruptcy and restructurings.
**Personal:** JD, The University of Texas School of Law, 1977; BBA, The University of Texas at Austin, 1974.

## FAULK, Richard O
Gardere Wynne Sewell LLP, Houston
713 276 5651
rfaulk@gardere.com
*Featured in Environment (Texas)*

**Practice Areas:** Environmental litigation, toxic tort litigation, climate change, public policy litigation.
**Professional Memberships:** State Bar of Texas, American and Houston Bar Associations, Texas Association of Civil Trial and Appellate Specialists.
**Career:** Rick Faulk chairs Gardere's Litigation Department and Environmental Practice Group, and leads Gardere's Climate Change Task Force. He has extensive experience as trial and appellate counsel for complex environmental litigation, including class actions and mass torts. He is certified in Civil Appellate Law by the Texas Board of Legal Specialization.
**Personal:** JD, Southern Methodist University Dedman School of Law, 1977; BA, University of North Texas, 1974.

## FINK, Stephen F
Thompson & Knight LLP, Dallas
214 969 1120
Stephen.Fink@tklaw.com
*Featured in Labor & Employment (Texas)*
**Practice Areas:** Mr Fink has an active commercial litigation practice, with special emphasis on trial and appeals in the area of employment contracts and employment discrimination, unfair competition, and regulatory and constitutional law issues. He also counsels clients and conducts investigations in the same areas as his litigation practice. He is Board Certified in Labor and Employment Law by the Texas Board of Legal Specialization and a member of the American Law Institute.
**Personal:** University of Texas School of Law (JD, 1974); Pennsylvania State University (BA, 1971).

## FINN BRADDOCK, Patricia
Fulbright & Jaworski LLP, Austin
512 536 4547
pbraddock@fulbright.com
*Featured in Environment (Texas)*
**Practice Areas:** Environmental law; toxic torts.
**Professional Memberships:** Fellow, American Bar Foundation and Texas Bar Foundation; American College of Environmental Lawyers; American Bar Association-Natural Resources Section; Texas Bar Association-Environmental and Administrative Law Sections; and Air and Waste Management Association International.
**Career:** Co-chair of the firm's Climate Change Practice; handles permitting and enforcement matters before federal and state regulatory agencies in all environmental media, with a focus on air pollution control.
**Personal:** JD, St. Mary's University College of Law (1974); BA American University, (1971). Certified in Administrative Law by the Texas Board of Legal Specialization.

## FISCHER, A Robert
Jackson Lewis LLP, Austin
512 362 7404
FischerA@jacksonlewis.com
*Featured in Labor & Employment (Texas)*
**Practice Areas:** Employment contract (non-compete and other) drafting and litigation; employment law counseling and litigation.

**Professional Memberships:** Fellow, Litigation Counsel of America; Association for Corporate Growth; Texas Hedge Fund Association.
**Career:** National Co-Chair of firm's Non-Competes and Protection Against Unfair Competition practice group. Previously, Mobil Oil Corporation, 1983-86; Day, Berry & Howard, 1986-93.
**Personal:** Born April 21, 1957. University of Texas School of Law, JD, 1983; The University of Texas at El Paso, BBA with honors, 1980. The Best Lawyers in America, 2006 – present and Austin's Employment Litigator of the Year, 2013; AV rated by Martindale-Hubbell, 2001 - present.

### FISHER, Todd A
K&L Gates, Dallas
214 939 5793
todd.fisher@klgates.com
*Featured in Outsourcing (Nationwide), Technology (Texas)*
**Practice Areas:** Todd Fisher assists established and emerging companies in negotiating and structuring outsourcing, information technology, and services agreements, including large-scale IT, business process, and managed network outsourcing agreements and technology licensing agreements. He is the co-founder of the Association of Technology Law Professionals, an organization he helped form to allow in-house lawyers to share best practices and discuss trends and issues in technology, outsourcing, and other complex commercial transactions. Mr Fisher also founded Legal Cloud Central, www.legalcloudcentral.com, a blog focused on cloud computing issues.

### FLETCHER, N Scott
Jones Day, Houston
832 239 3846
sfletcher@jonesday.com
*Featured in Litigation (Texas)*
**Practice Areas:** Scott Fletcher has extensive experience defending corporations and their officers and directors in merger litigation, shareholder actions, commercial disputes, FCPA and SEC enforcement matters, and internal investigations. He has tried cases before federal and state courts and arbitrators throughout the country. Admitted to practice in Delaware, DC, Pennsylvania, and Texas.
**Career:** Law clerk for Justice Andrew Moore, Delaware Supreme Court, 1989-90. Associate, Wilmer Cutler & Pickering, 1990-93; associate, Partner, Co-Chair of Securities Litigation and Enforcement Group, Vinson & Elkins, 1993-2010.
**Personal:** Harvard College, 1984 (with honors); Tulane Law School, 1989 (Order of the Coif; Tulane Law Review).

### FLINT, Andrew P
Thompson & Knight LLP, Houston
713 217 2844
Andrew.Flint@tklaw.com
*Featured in Banking & Finance (Texas)*
**Practice Areas:** Mr Flint's practice consists of structuring, negotiating, and documenting business financial and lending transactions, including workouts and restructurings. His work focuses primarily on syndicated secured and unsecured

senior and subordinated energy and oil and gas upstream/midstream credit facilities and drilling rig and oil field service fleet financings. His experience also includes acquisition financing, off balance sheet financings, specialized structured finance transactions, and debt financings with equity kickers.
**Professional Memberships:** Texas Association of Bank Counsel; State Bar of Texas; American and Houston Bar Associations.
**Personal:** Tulane University Law School (JD, magna cum laude, 1989); Dartmouth College (BA, 1984).

### FLOYD, Jeffery B
Vinson & Elkins LLP, Houston
713 758 2194
jfloyd@velaw.com
*Featured in Corporate/M&A (Texas)*
**Practice Areas:** Practice is focused on mergers, acquisitions and divestitures, corporate and securities law, corporate governance, and advising public companies and boards of directors. Specializes in public mergers and acquisitions and has extensive experience in representing issuers in capital markets transactions.
**Career:** Admitted to Texas Bar, 1984; joined Vinson & Elkins, 1984; admitted to the partnership in January 1992.
**Personal:** Graduated from The University of South Carolina, BA cum laude, 1981 (Phi Beta Kappa; Omicron Delta Kappa) and Georgetown University, JD cum laude, 1984 (Editor, The Tax Lawyer).

### FONTANA, Angela L
Weil, Gotshal & Manges LLP, Dallas
214 746 7895
angela.fontana@weil.com
*Featured in Banking & Finance (Texas), Banking & Finance (Nationwide)*
**Practice Areas:** Co-head of US Banking & Finance Practice. Extensive experience in a broad spectrum of financing transactions and debt restructurings including investment grade, cash flow and asset-based lending, leveraged acquisitions, recapitalizations, bridge and mezzanine financing, and domestic and cross-border workouts and restructurings. Represents private equity funds including Advent International, Berkshire Partners, Brazos, CCMP Capital Advisors, Centerbridge, CVC Capital Partners, Genstar Capital, Ontario Teachers' Pension Plan, Providence Equity Partners and THL Partners, and corporations including General Growth Properties, Darling International and Generac Power Systems.
**Personal:** University of Iowa (BBA, 1987); University of Iowa College of Law (JD, 1989).

### FORD JR, Thomas W
Andrews Kurth LLP, Houston
713 220 4498
tford@andrewskurth.com
*Featured in Tax (Texas)*
**Practice Areas:** Tom's practice includes extensive experience in the federal income taxation of business transactions and business entities, including formations, mergers, securities offerings

and operations of publicly traded 'master limited partnerships'; joint ventures and dispositions of interests therein; formation and operation of private partnerships, including issuance of equity to management; mergers, acquisitions and spin-offs of corporations; acquisition, ownership, exploration, development and disposition of oil and gas and other mineral interests; royalty trusts; real estate investment trusts; and financially troubled entities, including financial institutions.

### FOUNTAIN, Aaron
DLA Piper LLP (US), Austin
512 457 7190
aaron.fountain@dlapiper.com
*Featured in Intellectual Property (Texas)*
**Practice Areas:** Patent litigation.
**Career:** He handles a broad range of patent and technology matters, with an emphasis on patent litigation. He has experience representing clients in federal district court and before the USPTO, as well as experience in acquisition and licensing transactions. Prior to attending the University of Houston, he was a research scientist focusing on instrumentation and instrument specific method development for proteomics research.
**Personal:** JD, University of Houston Law Center (summa cum laude); BS, Pepperdine University.

### FOX, Michael W
Ogletree, Deakins, Nash, Smoak & Stewart, PC, Austin
512 344 4711
michael.fox@ogletreedeakins.com
*Featured in Labor & Employment (Texas)*
**Practice Areas:** Employment litigation.
**Professional Memberships:** Fellow, College of Labor and Employment Lawyers; American and Texas Bar Associations; Management Labor & Employment Roundtable.
**Career:** Texas Labor and Employment Lawyers, Chambers USA Client Guide (since 2004); Best Lawyers in America (since 1999); Super Lawyer by Texas Monthly (since 2003); Austin Employment Law – Management Lawyer of the Year (2012).
**Publications:** Jottings By an Employer's Lawyer, first employment law related blog; Editor, HR Specialist, Texas Employment Law monthly newsletter ((National Institute of Business Management publication).
**Personal:** University of Texas (JD, with high honors, 1975); Stephen F. Austin State University (BA, with honors, 1972).

### FRIEDLANDER, D Gilbert
Weil, Gotshal & Manges LLP, Dallas
214 746 8178
gil.friedlander@weil.com
*Featured in Corporate/M&A (Texas)*
**Practice Areas:** Gilbert Friedlander's practice focuses on corporate (including corporate governance, corporate investigations and mergers and acquisitions), securities and general business law. He has more than 30 years of experience advising boards and board committees in connection with various governance issues, as well as generally, in respect to corporate, securities and crisis management matters.

**Personal:** University of Texas (BS); University of Texas School of Law (JD).

### FRIEDMAN, Joseph
Kane Russell Coleman & Logan PC, Dallas
214 777 4287
jfriedman@krcl.com
*Featured in Bankruptcy/Restructuring (Texas)*
**Practice Areas:** Insolvency bankruptcy and creditor rights; financial services; distressed assets.
**Professional Memberships:** Dallas Bar Association; American Bankruptcy Institute (Trade Creditor Newsletter Editor, 2010-present).
**Career:** Licensed to practice in 1991; Named in Texas Super Lawyers® and Texas Monthly magazines as one of the top bankruptcy & creditor/debtor attorneys in Texas selected by Law & Politics (2009-12).
**Publications:** Speaker, "Gone Broke: Issues in Bankruptcy," 37th Annual Advanced Family Law Course, Family Law Section, State Bar of Texas (August 2011). Co-Author, "Cut the Middle Man: Court Prohibits Use of Client for Indirect Solicitations," American Bankruptcy Institute Unsecured Trade Creditors Newsletter (Vol. 9, No. 2, May 2011) regarding attorney solicitations of unsecured creditors committees. Co-Author, "Defending Preferences and Preserving Data in an ESI World," American Bankruptcy Institute Trade Creditors Committee Newsletter (Vol. 9, No. 1, Feb. 2011). Speaker, "Financial Crisis: Selected Issues in Bankruptcy," Advanced Family Law Course, Family Law Section, State Bar of Texas (2010).
**Personal:** Southern Methodist University, JD cum laude, 1991; Tulane University, BS cum laude, 1985.

### FRISBIE JR, Curtis L
Gardere Wynne Sewell LLP, Dallas
214 999 4757
cfrisbie@gardere.com
*Featured in Antitrust (Texas)*
**Practice Areas:** Antitrust, commercial litigation, intellectual property litigation.
**Professional Memberships:** State Bar of Texas, American and Dallas Bar Associations.
**Career:** Curt Frisbie has more than 40 years of trial experience handling major antitrust and other commercial litigation matters in many states. He has substantial experience defending class action cases involving antitrust, RICO, insurance and other claims. Mr Frisbie also advises businesses on distributor agreements and antitrust corporate compliance programs. He is a former chair of the Texas and Dallas Bar Antitrust Sections, and former captain, US Marine Corps.
**Personal:** JD, St. Mary's University, 1971; BS, University of Alabama, 1966.

### FRIZZELL, Jean C
Reynolds, Frizzell, Black, Doyle, Allen & Oldham, LLP, Houston
713 485 7200
jfrizzell@reynoldsfrizzell.com
*Featured in Litigation (Texas)*
**Practice Areas:** Focuses practice on complex commercial and business litigation in a wide range of areas, including breach of contract, oil

and gas, securities, patent, trade secret, trademark, copyright, environmental, director liability, and partnership disputes. Routinely handles matters for both plaintiffs and defendants in state and federal court.
**Professional Memberships:** American Board of Trial Advocates, Texas Bar Foundation, Houston Bar Foundation.
**Career:** Joined Gibbs & Bruns LLP in 1990 and made Partner in 1995. Recognized by Chambers USA and Best Lawyers in America in the areas of commercial litigation and securities law. Listed as Texas Super Lawyer (Top 100 Lawyers in Houston) by Law and Politics. Recognized by Benchmark Litigation in the area of General Commercial.
**Personal:** Born in New Jersey, 1965. BA, Rice University, 1987; JD, with honors, The University of Texas School of Law, 1990; Member, Texas Law Review.

### FROMM O'BRIEN, Eva
Fulbright & Jaworski LLP, Houston
713 651 5321
eobrien@fulbright.com
*Featured in Environment (Texas)*
**Practice Areas:** Environmental law, civil and criminal enforcement, mergers and acquisitions, permits, and environmental litigation.
**Professional Memberships:** Fellow, American College of Environmental Lawyers. Past Chair, Vice-Chair and secretary of the Houston Bar Association's Environmental Law Section.
**Career:** Admitted to Texas Bar (1985). Partner at Fulbright & Jaworski L.L.P. joining the firm in 1986. Heads the Environmental Law Department and is a member of the Firm's Executive Committee.
**Personal:** Received a BS in Chemical Engineering in 1978 from Syracuse University and a JD in 1985 from the University of Houston.

### FROST, Claudia Wilson
DLA Piper LLP (US), Houston
713 425 8450
claudia.frost@dlapiper.com
*Featured in Litigation (Texas)*
**Practice Areas:** Litigation: appellate.
**Professional Memberships:** Fellow, American Academy of Appellate Lawyers.
**Career:** She handles federal and state trials, arbitrations, and administrative proceedings, including Section 337 actions in the ITC. Her recent trial experience is in the areas of intellectual property, oil and gas, products liability and healthcare. Her appellate experience includes appeals to the Texas intermediate appellate courts and the Texas Supreme Court and to various United States Courts of Appeals, as well as the United States Supreme Court.
**Personal:** JD, University of Houston Law Center (magna cum laude), Editor-in-Chief Houston Law Review; BA, University of Texas at Austin.

### FULLENWEIDER, Keith
Vinson & Elkins LLP, Houston
713 758 3838
kfullenweider@velaw.com
*Featured in Corporate/M&A (Texas), Energy & Natural Resources (Nationwide)*
**Practice Areas:** Practice is focused on mergers and acquisitions, private equity, joint venture and domestic and international energy and power transactions. Head of the firm's M&A Practice Group and Management Committee member.
**Career:** Admitted to Texas Bar in 1988. Joined Vinson & Elkins LLP in 1988, admitted to the partnership in January 1997.
**Personal:** Graduated from Princeton University, AB summa cum laude, 1985 and The University of Texas, JD with high honors in 1988 (Chancellors, Texas Law Review and Order of the Coif).

### GAJKOWSKI, Andrew J
Bracewell & Giuliani LLP, Houston
512 494 3627
andrew.gajkowski@bgllp.com
*Featured in Technology (Texas)*
**Practice Areas:** His practice focuses on representing clients in business and corporate transactions, specifically technology and intellectual property related deals. Has experience counseling clients on licensing transactions and other intellectual property matters, mergers and acquisitions, securities offerings, labor and employment, and business litigation issues. As well as in copyright, trademark, media and entertainment law, with an emphasis on digital/interactive media, wireless technologies and content licensing. He has has represented founders, companies and investors in connection with numerous startup company formations and venture capital financings.
**Personal:** JD, Columbia University School of Law, 2003; BA, The University of Texas at Austin, 1998.

### GALVAN, Hilda
Jones Day, Dallas
214 969 4556
hcgalvan@jonesday.com
*Featured in Intellectual Property (Texas)*
**Practice Areas:** Focuses on intellectual property litigation, including patent, trademark, copyright, trade secret, and unfair competition. She has represented some of the leading technology companies in patent litigation involving a broad range of technologies, including telecommunications, digital signal processors, semiconductor processing and packaging, computer software, and seismic data acquisition equipment. Provides strategic counseling to clients in enforcement and licensing of patent portfolios. She has been a speaker at a number of seminars on topics relating to patent licensing and litigation.
**Personal:** BSEE, University of Texas El Paso (1985); JD, UT School of Law (1993).

### GANCHAN, Leigh
Ogletree, Deakins, Nash, Smoak & Stewart, PC, Houston
713 655 5754
leigh.ganchan@ogletreedeakins.com
*Featured in Immigration (Texas)*
**Practice Areas:** Business immigration and compliance. International employment.
**Professional Memberships:** Texas State Bar; American Immigration Lawyers Association; HR Houston Board; Greater Houston Partnership, Women's Leadership Committee.
**Career:** Board Certified, Immigration and Nationality Law, Texas Board of Legal Specialization; Admitted: Texas.
**Publications:** AILA Handbook on Immigration for Entertainers, Artists, Athletes; HR Magazine "The Perils Of Multistate Employment"; Practical Law Company "U.S. Immigration Sponsorships and Third-party Worksites"; Texas Bar Journal "Managing U.S. Immigration Risks"; AILA Consular Practice Handbook; Texas Law Books "Party Talk: Answers to Everyday Legal Questions for Texas Lawyers."
**Personal:** JD, American University, 1996; Université de Paris-X, 1996; University of Vienna, Austria, 1992; University of Alabama, 1991.

### GARCIA, Victoria M
Bracewell & Giuliani LLP, San Antonio
210 299 3546
victoria.garcia@bgllp.com
*Featured in Immigration (Texas)*
**Practice Areas:** Managing Parter of the firm's San Antonio office. Provides clients with comprehensive legal guidance regarding business immigration matters, including (i) obtaining nonimmigrant and immigrant visas for foreign employees, (ii) responding to inquiries, investigations and mismatch letters from the Department of Homeland Security, the Internal Revenue Service, the Social Security Administration and Department of Labor, and (iii) complying with U.S. immigration laws in the hiring, retention and management of domestic workforces.
**Personal:** JD, The University of Texas School of Law, 1989; M. Public Affairs, The University of Texas at Austin, 1989; BS, Georgetown University, 1985.

### GASWIRTH, Ronald M
Gardere Wynne Sewell LLP, Dallas
214 999 4601
rgaswirth@gardere.com
*Featured in Labor & Employment (Texas)*
**Practice Areas:** Labor, employment litigation.
**Professional Memberships:** State Bars of Texas and Georgia, American and Dallas Bar Associations.
**Career:** Ron Gaswirth is the founding partner of Gardere's Labor & Employment Practice and chairs Gardere's Retail Industry Team. He has more than 40 years of experience trying individual and class action discrimination litigation in state and federal courts, and related Department of Labor matters (OSHA, wage and hour, OFCCP). Mr Gaswirth advises employers on all labor-related union issues, and serves as national and/or regional labor counsel for multiple clients. Mr Gaswirth is a former Regional Solicitor of the US Department of Labor.
**Personal:** LLM, SMU Dedman School of Law, with honors, 1978; JD, University of Houston Law Center, 1968; BA, University of Houston, 1965.

### GENECOV, Lisa
Locke Lord LLP, Dallas
214 740 8418
lgenecov@lockelord.com
*Featured in Healthcare (Texas)*
**Practice Areas:** Chairs Healthcare Practice Group. Concentrates on healthcare, securities, financings, mergers and acquisitions and general corporate matters. Counsels providers on formation of healthcare networks, physician alignment strategies, accountable care organizations, joint ventures and management services organizations, and choice of entity and governance matters.
**Professional Memberships:** Center for Women in Law-The University of Texas School of Law (Co-Founder); American Health Lawyers Association; ABA Health Law Section; ABA Foundation; Women Business Leaders of the US Healthcare Industry Foundation.
**Career:** Partner since 1998.
**Personal:** The University of Texas School of Law (JD, with honors, 1984); Stanford University (BA, with distinction, 1980).

### GERACHIS, George Matthew
Vinson & Elkins LLP, Houston
713 758 1056
ggerachis@velaw.com
*Featured in Tax (Nationwide), Tax (Texas)*
**Practice Areas:** Chair of the firm's Taxation Practice and leader of its Tax Controversy and Litigation Group. Practice consists primarily of tax planning and resolution of complex domestic and international tax disputes for individuals and companies. Counsels multinationals in the energy, technology, financial and other industries on 'inbound' and 'outbound' issues, including transfer pricing.
**Professional Memberships:** American Bar Association, Section of Taxation; International Fiscal Association.
**Career:** Admitted to practice US Tax Court, US District Courts for Northern and Southern Districts of Texas; 5th Circuit Appeals Court; frequent lecturer.
**Personal:** University of Virginia, BA 1979, JD 1983. Languages: German and Spanish.

### GERBER, Toby L
Fulbright & Jaworski LLP, Dallas
214 855 7171
tgerber@fulbright.com
*Featured in Bankruptcy/Restructuring (Texas), Bankruptcy/Restructuring (Nationwide)*
**Practice Areas:** Bankruptcy; transportation; commercial litigation.
**Professional Memberships:** American Bankruptcy Institute, Texas Association of Bank Counsel, American College of Bankruptcy.
**Career:** Gerber primarily represents financial institutions in troubled loans and insolvencies across several industries. He was lead debtor's

counsel in the successful restructuring of a major Yellow Pages publisher's $10 billion debt, and has represented an international transportation association in global insolvency matters. He is experienced in reorganization and troubled debt workouts, as well as representing financial institutions and non-bank lenders on bankruptcy and commercial litigation.

**Personal:** JD, Georgetown University (1975); BA and BJ, with honors, University of Missouri-Columbia (1972).

### GIBBS, Robin C
Gibbs & Bruns LLP, Houston
713 751 5217
rgibbs@gibbsbruns.com
*Featured in Litigation (Nationwide), Litigation (Texas)*

**Practice Areas:** Robin Gibbs has over four decades of experience in handling high-stakes commercial litigation, including securities, director and officer liability, contract disputes, fraud and fiduciary claims, energy litigation, construction litigation, antitrust litigation, legal and professional malpractice, and partnership disputes.

**Professional Memberships:** American College of Trial Lawyers; International Academy of Trial Lawyers; American Board of Trial Advocates; International Society of Barristers; The American Law Institute; International Network of Boutique Law Firms; University of Texas Law School Foundation, Trustee.

**Career:** Joined Vinson & Elkins in 1971; formed Wood, Campbell, Moody & Gibbs P.C. in 1974; formed Gibbs & Bruns (formerly Gibbs & Ratliff) in 1983. Gibbs & Bruns is nationally-recognized, premier litigation boutique, renowned for its signature lean trial teams and representation of both plaintiffs and defendants. The Financial Times named Gibbs & Bruns the "Top US Litigation Firm" in its "US Innovative Lawyers 2012." The National Law Journal named Gibbs & Bruns to its inaugural "Litigation Boutiques Hot List 2012" and to its "Plaintiffs Hot List." The American Lawyer named the firm one of the top four US litigation boutiques, 2009. International Commercial Litigation named Gibbs & Bruns a top 15 litigation firm in the US Robin was named TEX-ABOTA's (American Board of Trial Advocates) Trial Lawyer of the Year, 2012; Best Lawyers' Houston Litigation – Securities Lawyer of the Year 2012 and Bet-the-Company Litigator of the Year 2011. He is named to the: Top 25 US Litigator list by Expert Guides; Top 15 US Trial Lawyers list, International Commercial Litigation; Legal Media Group's World's Leading Litigation Lawyers list; Leading Commercial Litigators in the World list by Who's Who Legal. He is recognized by Best Lawyers in America, Chambers USA, Chambers Global, Legal 500 – Leading US Trial Lawyers, Texas Super Lawyers, and Benchmark Litigation.

### GIBLIN, Pamela
Baker Botts LLP, Austin
512 322 2509
pam.giblin@bakerbotts.com
*Featured in Environment (Texas)*

**Practice Areas:** Extensive environmental counseling; strategic permitting; and enforcement defense.

**Professional Memberships:** Board Certified Administrative Law; Texas Bar; First woman recipient Travis County Bar Association's Distinguished Lawyer Award.

**Career:** General Counsel Texas Air Control Board; former Chair Austin Commission on Electric Rates.

**Personal:** University of Texas, BA, with honors, JD, 1970; fluent in Spanish; frequent seminar and conference speaker; Best Lawyers in America; 'Texas Super Lawyer'; serves on Environmental Protection Agency's Federal Clean Air Act Advisory Committee; member of the American College of Environmental Lawyers.

### GIESE, Jeffrey W
Hunton & Williams LLP, Dallas
jgiese@hunton.com
*Featured in Real Estate (Texas)*

**Practice Areas:** Mr Giese's practice focuses on complex multi-property, multi-state real estate acquisitions, dispositions and financings, legal due diligence and acquisitions, financings and dispositions of performing and non-performing loan portfolios and related asset management, real estate development, syndications and sale-leaseback transactions, and private equity investment, structuring and entity formation. His clients include global private equity firms, opportunity funds, and national, regional and local developers and banks.

**Professional Memberships:** Member, American Bar Association; Member, Dallas Bar Association; Member, Texas State Bar Association.

**Personal:** JD, Southern Methodist University, 1986; BBA, Finance, University of Iowa, 1983.

### GILLULY III, John J
DLA Piper LLP (US), Austin
512 457 7090
john.gilluly@dlapiper.com
*Featured in Technology (Texas)*

**Practice Areas:** Technology: corporate and commercial.

**Career:** He is the managing partner of the Austin office, heads the firm's Corporate and Securities practice in Texas and is a member of firm's Policy Committee and Opinion Committee. He represents clients across a range of industries and focuses on capital markets transactions; SEC reporting and compliance; mergers and acquisitions, private equity and venture capital transactions and corporate governance matters. He has been listed in the Best Lawyers in America since 2005.

**Personal:** JD, University of Texas; BA, Rhodes College, cum laude.

### GLASSER, Mark K
Sidley Austin LLP, Houston
713 495 4502
mglasser@sidley.com
*Featured in Litigation (Texas)*

**Practice Areas:** Partner in Sidley's Houston office, Mr Glasser brings 35 years of experience to the prosecution and defense of energy, securities, and professional liability litigation. He represents energy industry participants in a wide variety of matters; financial institutions, accounting firms, and issuers of securities in the defense of derivative and securities class action litigation; as well as a wide variety of disputes for plaintiffs and defendants in trade secret litigation.

**Professional Memberships:** Member, American Board of Trial Advocates.

**Personal:** The University of Texas School of Law, JD, 1976; Columbia University, BA, 1973, with honors.

### GLENDENNING, Don M
Locke Lord LLP, Dallas
214 740 8623
dglendenning@lockelord.com
*Featured in Corporate/M&A (Texas)*

**Practice Areas:** Represents public and private companies in asset sales; stock sales; mergers; spin-offs and going-private transactions; advises issuers, investors concerning corporate governance and securities law disclosure and filing requirements. Extensive experience in federal and state securities law, representing issuers, underwriters in compliance; private placements; and reporting, disclosure requirements. Serves clients across private equity, finance, defense, technology, manufacturing, healthcare, oil/gas, agribusiness, restaurants and retail sales industries.

**Professional Memberships:** Texas Bar Foundation; Dallas Bar Foundation.

**Career:** Dallas Managing Partner for several years; Partner since 1985.

**Personal:** Stanford Law School (JD, 1979); Rice University (BA, magna cum laude, 1976).

### GONSOULIN JR, Dewey J
Bracewell & Giuliani LLP, Houston
713 221 1110
dewey.gonsoulin@bglip.com
*Featured in Banking & Finance (Texas)*

**Practice Areas:** Head of the firm's finance practice and serves on the firm-wide management committee. Represents lenders in financing transactions including working capital loans, revolving credit and letter of credit facilities, syndicated loans, acquisition loans, energy securitizations, and project finance. Has worked on credit facilities in upstream energy including base credit facilities, off-balance sheet volumetric production payments and hedging arrangements. Has also worked on mezzanine loan and equity transactions for oil and gas producers, handles financings for oilfield services and midstream sectors.

**Personal:** JD, The University of Texas School of Law, 1991; BBA, The University of Texas at Austin, 1988.

### GONZALES, Alex
Winstead PC, Austin
512 370 2887
agonzales@winstead.com
*Featured in Insurance (Texas)*

**Practice Areas:** Alex is managing shareholder of Winstead's Austin office. With more than 22 years of experience, Alex represents insurance companies and other financial institutions in compliance and regulatory matters, including government enforcement actions, mergers and acquisitions, corporate financing, reinsurance and licensing. Alex's client base includes many of the nation's top insurance companies and financial institutions. He has represented insurers and acquiring parties in acquisitions and other corporate regulatory matters before insurance departments in Texas, New York, Louisiana, Massachusetts, Missouri, Michigan and Arizona. Alex is a former Associate Commissioner of Insurance (Legal and Compliance) at the Texas Department of Insurance.

### GOODGAME, John
Akin Gump Strauss Hauer & Feld LLP, Houston
713 220 8144
jgoodgame@akingump.com
*Featured in Capital Markets (Texas)*

**Practice Areas:** Mr Goodgame regularly represents buyers, sellers and financial advisors in strategic transactions, including public-public and private acquisitions and divestitures. He also represents sophisticated parties in joint ventures and other strategic relationships and investments.

### GORDIAN, Carmelo
Andrews Kurth LLP, Austin
512 320 9290
carmelogordian@andrewskurth.com
*Featured in Technology (Texas)*

**Practice Areas:** Carmelo is known as a leader in the Texas venture capital and private equity community. Carmelo's primary focus is on life science, software, telecommunications, semiconductor and energy sector companies. His practice includes advising companies and boards of directors on corporate governance issues, representing issuers and investment banking firms in public offerings and private financings, and representing acquirers and targets in a broad variety of domestic and international mergers, acquisitions and other business combination transactions. Carmelo also has an active practice representing General Partners and Limited Partners of hedge, private equity, venture capital and real estate funds.

### GORDON, Gregory M
Jones Day, Dallas
214 969 3759
gmgordon@jonesday.com
*Featured in Bankruptcy/Restructuring (Texas)*

**Practice Areas:** Oversees the Dallas Office restructuring practice. Has over 25 years experience in complex business restructurings, in and out of court, distressed M&A, and commercial litigation. Has lectured on professional retention in bankruptcy, complex chapter 11 issues, valuations in bankruptcy, and restructuring mass tort liability.

**Publications:** Co-authored 'Overview of Issues Related to Professional Retention in Bankruptcy Cases', AIRA Journal (January 2009), Present Value Discounting of Claims in Bankruptcy', Norton Journal of Bankruptcy Law and Practice (February 2008), 'Innovative Approaches to Complex Restructurings', The Metropolitan Corporate Counsel (September 2006), and

'Retaining Key Employees in Bankruptcy', Texas Lawyer (October 16, 2006).

## GORDON, Randy D
Gardere Wynne Sewell LLP, Dallas
214 999 4527
rgordon@gardere.com

*Featured in Antitrust (Texas)*

**Practice Areas:** Antitrust, RICO, class actions.
**Professional Memberships:** American Law Institute, WS Society, State Bars of Texas and Oklahoma.
**Career:** Randy Gordon handles complex litigation nationwide and advises clients on distribution plans and antitrust implications of transactions. He is an SMU adjunct professor, past-chair of the State Bar Antitrust Section and former General Counsel of the Global Semiconductor Alliance.
**Publications:** Rehumanizing Law [Toronto UP]; recent articles on antitrust, class actions, copyright, international arbitration, and RICO in journals of Columbia, Florida, Loyola, San Francisco, SMU, Southwestern, Suffolk, Tulane and Vermont.
**Personal:** PhD, Edinburgh; LLM, Columbia; JD, Washburn; PhD, MA, BA, Kansas.

## GORMAN, Sean
Ahmad, Zavitsanos, Anaipakos, Alavi & Mensing P.C., Houston
713 655 1101
sgorman@azalaw.com

*Featured in Litigation (Texas)*

**Career:** Sean Gorman, an acclaimed litigator and former managing partner of a national law firm's Houston office, focuses on aggressive advocacy in high-risk and high-value US and international business disputes. Mr Gorman has extensive experience in complex business litigation and arbitration matters, including contract, fraud, energy, real estate and intellectual property matters, for both plaintiffs and defendants. He has represented clients based in the US, Europe, Asia, Latin America and the Middle East in the energy, chemical, petrochemical, steel, communications, oil field services, medical products, software, accounting, financial services, construction, real estate and manufacturing industries. www.azalaw.com

## GOVETT, Brett C
Fulbright & Jaworski LLP, Dallas
214 855 8118
bgovett@fulbright.com

*Featured in Intellectual Property (Texas)*

**Practice Areas:** Commercial litigation, patent infringement litigation.
**Career:** Govett is Board Certified in Civil Trial Law by the Texas Board of Legal Specialization and is a registered patent attorney with extensive experience in commercial and patent infringement matters. His trial wins have been featured in the National Law Journal, Texas Lawyer, Dallas Business Journal, Dallas Morning News and numerous other publications. Govett was recognized among 250 "World's Leading Patent Litigators" by IAM Magazine and has been named a "Texas Super Lawyer" annually since 2003.

**Personal:** JD, with honors, Texas Tech University (1990); BA in Chemistry, with honors, The Citadel (1987).

## GOYNE, Roderick
Baker Botts LLP, Dallas
214 953 6527
rick.goyne@bakerbotts.com

*Featured in Banking & Finance (Texas)*

**Practice Areas:** Chair: Finance Section (firmwide). Has broad experience in syndicated credit agreements, private placements, Rule 144A debt offerings, mezzanine financings, first lien/second lien financings and bridge loans as well as financing leases, structured financings, debt restructurings and intercreditor arrangements.
**Personal:** JD, cum laude, Harvard Law School, 1974; BA, with highest honors, history, The University of Texas at Arlington, 1971.

## GREENDYKE, William
Fulbright & Jaworski LLP, Houston
214 855 8204
wgreendyke@fulbright.com

*Featured in Bankruptcy/Restructuring (Texas)*

**Practice Areas:** Bankruptcy and insolvency, representing secured and unsecured lenders, debtors, creditors, creditor committees and other clients in connection with restructuring, bankruptcy, and related litigation matters.
**Professional Memberships:** Fellow, American College of Bankruptcy; Houston and Dallas Bar Associations; National Conference of Bankruptcy Judges; State Bar of Texas.
**Career:** Before joining Fulbright, he served as Chief Judge of the United States Bankruptcy Court for the Southern District of Texas sitting in Houston. He was appointed to the bankruptcy bench by the Fifth Circuit on September 1, 1987.
**Personal:** Baylor University (BS, 1976); Baylor Law School (JD, with honors, 1979).

## GREER, Scott A
King & Spalding LLP, Houston
713 751 3264
sgreer@kslaw.com

*Featured in Construction (Texas)*

**Practice Areas:** Focuses on practice of construction law and construction litigation. Represents clients in all aspects of a construction project, including structuring, drafting, modifying and negotiating of construction, engineering, architectural and development agreements, and negotiating, mediating, arbitrating and litigating claims on construction defects, delay, design deficiencies, wrongful termination, non-payment and surety bonds. Focuses on the representation of owners and developers. Extensive experience in LNG matters.
**Professional Memberships:** American Bar Association; American Concrete Institute; Atlanta Bar Association; State Bar of Georgia.
**Personal:** BS, Oklahoma State University, 1987; MS, University of Illinois, Champaign-Urbana, 1988; JD, Emory University, 1995.

## GREIG, Brian
Fulbright & Jaworski LLP, Austin
512 536 4510
bgreig@fulbright.com

*Featured in Labor & Employment (Texas)*

**Practice Areas:** Employment and traditional labor, trade secrets, non-competes, federal practice, technology, commercial and construction litigation.
**Career:** Partner since 1983, resident in Fulbright & Jaworski L.L.P.'s Austin office, where he heads the firm's international Labor and Employment Practice.
**Publications:** Editor-in-Chief, 'Texas Employment Law Handbook - A Guide for Employers', published annually by the Texas Association of Business; contributor, 'The Developing Labor Law' by the Labor and Employment Law Section of the ABA.
**Personal:** JD, The University of Texas School of Law (1975); BA, Economics, Washington & Lee University, (1972). Board Certified in Labor and Employment Law.

## GRIFFITH, Vanessa
Vinson & Elkins LLP, Dallas
214 220 7713
vgriffith@velaw.com

*Featured in Labor & Employment (Texas)*

**Practice Areas:** Represents management in all aspects of employment and labor litigation and counseling with a focus on class and collective action defense. Also represents management and executives in restrictive covenant and trade secret litigation. Board certified in labor and employment law by the Texas Board of Legal Specialization.
**Career:** Admitted to practice: 1994. Law clerk to the Honorable David Hittner, United States District Judge, Southern District of Texas: 1994 - 1996. Joined Vinson & Elkins, 1996; admitted to partnership, 2004.
**Personal:** Rice University, BA, 1988. University of Texas School of Law, JD, 1994 (Chancellors; Order of the Coif).

## GROOS, Richard J
Fulbright & Jaworski LLP, Austin
512 536 3007
rgroos@fulbright.com

*Featured in Intellectual Property (Texas)*

**Practice Areas:** Intellectual property, trademark, copyright.
**Professional Memberships:** International Trademark Association-Internet Committee/Online Use Subcommittee; IPO & LES, Member; IPO Committee, Member.
**Career:** Mr Groos handles IP matters including trademark disputes and litigation, copyright and trademark clearance and registration and internet and domain name disputes. He specializes in solutions to IP issues and the preparation and implementation of IP strategies. He's been in Chambers USA (2007-12), "IP Luminaries" (2007), "The Legal 500 United States" (2007-12) and "Best Lawyers in America" (2005-12).
**Personal:** JD, The University of Texas School of Law (1984); BES, The University of Texas (1981).

## GROTEN, Eric
Vinson & Elkins LLP, Austin
512 542 8709
egroten@velaw.com

*Featured in Environment (Texas)*

**Practice Areas:** Serves industrial and utility clients in managing their environmental issues, principally air quality, including permit application proceedings, defense of enforcement actions, environmental audits and investigations, compliance counseling, transaction of emission rights, advocacy in state and federal rulemakings and related litigation. Specially recognized by Texas Lawyer as one of the state's leading 'legal innovators' for facilitating the first-ever air emissions trading program across the Texas/Mexico border. Author of "Treatment of Greenhouse Gases under the Clean Air Act" (LexisNexis 2010).
**Career:** JD, The University of Texas School of Law, 1985; BA, Chemistry and Environmental Studies, Baylor University, 1981.

## GUARAGNA, John M
DLA Piper LLP (US), Austin
512 457 7125
john.guaragna@dlapiper.com

*Featured in Intellectual Property (Texas)*

**Practice Areas:** Intellectual property; patent litigation.
**Professional Memberships:** Austin Intellectual Property Law Association; Eastern District of Texas Bar Association; Federal Bar Association; American Intellectual Property Law Association.
**Career:** A trial lawyer who concentrates his practice on litigation of patent infringement and other intellectual property-related lawsuits, he has represented clients (both plaintiffs and defendants) in numerous patent infringement matters relating to computer hardware and software technology pending throughout the US. He has extensive experience relating to the intersection between intellectual property and antitrust law.
**Personal:** JD, University of San Diego; BA, Villanova University.

## GUEDRY, David N
K&L Gates, Dallas
214 939 5402
david.guedry@klgates.com

*Featured in Outsourcing (Nationwide), Technology (Texas)*

See under Nationwide for profile.

## GUNNING, Vicky
Locke Lord LLP, Dallas
214 740 8638
vgunning@lockelord.com

*Featured in Real Estate (Texas)*

**Practice Areas:** Represents financial institutions and venture capital companies in asset based and real estate secured loans, syndicated credits, mezzanine debt and debt restructurings and foreclosures. Counsels owners and developers in negotiating financing and the acquisition, development, leasing and disposition of commercial real estate, including raw land, healthcare facilities, senior housing, office and apartment properties, retail centers and warehouse facilities.

**Professional Memberships:** State Bar of Texas; Dallas Bar Association; Dallas Commercial Real Estate Women (Past-President).
**Career:** Partner since 1998.
**Personal:** Southern Methodist University School of Law (JD, magna cum laude, 1990); University of Oklahoma (BS, Accounting, with highest honors, 1987).

---

### GUNTER III, J Clifford
Bracewell & Giuliani LLP, Houston
713 221 1213
clifford.gunter@bgllp.com
*Featured in Litigation (Texas)*
**Practice Areas:** Heads the firm's antitrust litigation practice. Has devoted nearly 40 years of practice to providing strategic, effective trial representation to energy and a diverse array of other, major industrial and financial clients in complex, high stakes, multiple-party litigation, both internationally and domestically. Experience includes cases tried to conclusion, cases settled during trial and before trial, appellate arguments, federal grand jury investigations and arbitrations.
**Professional Memberships:** Fellow, American College of Trial Lawyers; Advocate, American Board of Trial Lawyers.
**Personal:** LLB, The University of Texas School of Law, 1967; BA, The University of Texas at Austin, 1965.

---

### GUTHRIE, Mark C
Winstead PC, Houston
713 650 2730
mguthrie@winstead.com
*Featured in Construction (Texas)*
**Practice Areas:** Mark's practice concentration is in construction-related transactions and disputes, insurance and reinsurance issues and disputes and other complex commercial litigation and arbitration. His specific areas of practice include representation of construction managers, contractors, subcontractors, sureties and developer/owners in construction and EPC contract negotiation and dispute resolution, including lien and bond claims, claims for extra time and money, delay claims, and related insurance coverage and claims issues. Mark has significant experience with transactions and disputes involving the design and construction of large power generation, petrochemical and hazardous material incinerator projects designed and constructed pursuant to EPC contracts.

---

### HAAS, Buddy
Locke Lord LLP, Houston
713 226 1247
bhaas@lockelord.com
*Featured in Banking & Finance (Texas)*
**Practice Areas:** Lending, real estate and related transactions law. Works with lenders and borrowers on energy, real estate and general commercial loan transactions, both secured and unsecured. Experienced in working with syndicated and participated credits and subordinated indebtedness, multi-state and shared collateral lending issues, acquisitions, sales, financing and management of assets, loan workouts and lender liability issues and leasing issues.

**Professional Memberships:** Houston Bar Association; State Bar of Texas; Texas Association of Bank Counsel.
**Career:** Partner since 1985.
**Personal:** The University of Texas School of Law (JD, with honors, 1979); Princeton University (AB, magna cum laude, 1976).

---

### HAILEY, Jay
DLA Piper LLP (US), Austin
512 457 7050
jay.hailey@dlapiper.com
*Featured in Real Estate (Texas)*
**Practice Areas:** Real estate.
**Professional Memberships:** Fellow, American Bar Foundation; Life Fellow, Texas Bar Foundation, ACREL, American Bar Association; State Bar of Texas.
**Career:** He represents clients in complex transactions, including the structuring of partnerships, limited liability companies, ground leases, tenancies-in-common, condominium regimes, and other forms of ownership for mixed use projects and master planned communities; the purchase, sale, financing, zoning, development, and construction of office, industrial, retail, and residential projects; the creation of public-private partnership; and the negotiation of financial incentives and development agreements.
**Personal:** JD, University of Texas School of Law, BA, Southern Methodist University.

---

### HALEVY, Amy Karff
Bracewell & Giuliani LLP, Houston
713 221 1329
amy.halevy@bgllp.com
*Featured in Labor & Employment (Texas)*
**Practice Areas:** Represents businesses in all areas of employment law. Specifically, she guides her business clients in the preparation and application of employment policies and procedures. She also represents employers in litigation in state and federal court, and in administrative proceedings before the Equal Employment Opportunity Commission (EEOC) and the Texas Workforce Commission, Human Rights Division.
**Personal:** JD, University of Houston Law Center, 1987; BA, Wesleyan University, 1984.

---

### HALL, Charles
Fulbright & Jaworski LLP, Houston
713 651 5268
chall@fulbright.com
*Featured in Tax (Nationwide), Tax (Texas)*
See under Nationwide for profile.

---

### HALL, Eric B.
Fulbright & Jaworski LLP, Houston
713 651 5627
ehall@fulbright.com
*Featured in Intellectual Property (Texas)*
**Practice Areas:** Intellectual property, telecommunications.
**Professional Memberships:** Houston Intellectual Property Lawyers Association; Senior Member of IEEE.
**Career:** Eric's practice focuses on patent law and communication technology issues including patent prosecution, litigation and transactions. He represents clients in the wireless, media, software

and industrial technology industries. He has successfully represented numerous telecommunications and wireless technology companies in patent infringement actions. Eric was formerly a professor of electrical engineering at SMU in Dallas, Texas.
**Personal:** JD, High Honors, The University of Texas Law School; PhD, Electrical Engineering, The University of Texas; MS, Electrical Engineering, The University of Texas; BS, cum laude, Electrical Engineering, Rice University.

---

### HALL, Lawrence A
Thompson & Knight LLP, Dallas
214 969 1635
Larry.Hall@tklaw.com
*Featured in Corporate/M&A (Texas)*
**Practice Areas:** Mr Hall focuses his practice on corporate, energy, and finance matters. With a primary emphasis on the representation of oil and gas companies (including those backed by private equity), he represents clients in mergers, acquisitions, and divestments; private equity funding transactions (both from the private equity provider and management team perspectives); exploration and development participation arrangements; and traditional and non-traditional financings.
**Professional Memberships:** State Bar of Texas; American and Oklahoma Bar Associations.
**Personal:** Harvard University (JD, 1990); University of Oklahoma (BBA, with highest honors, 1987).

---

### HALSEY, Susan A
Jackson Walker LLP, Fort Worth
817 334 7203
shalsey@jw.com
*Featured in Real Estate (Texas)*
**Career:** Susan Halsey has over 29 years of experience in real estate law and is the statewide chair of Jackson Walker's Real Estate practice group. She represents companies, partnerships, individuals, and financial institutions in real estate transactions and financial matters, including the acquisition, development, and sale of commercial, industrial, and residential real estate and other assets; structuring and negotiating financial relationships for lenders and borrowers; drafting office, industrial park, and shopping center leases for landlords and tenants; advising landlords on property management issues; and drafting restrictive covenants and forming homeowners associations and condominium regimes for commercial/residential developments.

---

### HAMEL, Douglas
Vinson & Elkins LLP, Houston
713 758 2036
dhamel@velaw.com
*Featured in Labor & Employment (Texas)*
**Practice Areas:** Representing management in labor and employment law, civil rights law, ERISA litigation and related issues. Represented clients in connection with numerous class action employment discrimination lawsuits involving issues of disparate treatment and disparate impact. Also regularly appears before federal and state agencies including NLRB, EEOC, and OFCCP.

**Career:** Partner since 1983; Employment Litigation and Labor, and chairs firm's Benefit Plans Administrative Committee.
**Personal:** University of Virginia, (BA, 1972; JD, 1976).

---

### HAMMOND, Herbert J
Thompson & Knight LLP, Dallas
214 969 1607
Herbert.Hammond@tklaw.com
*Featured in Intellectual Property (Texas)*
**Practice Areas:** Herb represents clients in intellectual property matters focusing on litigation, licensing, and counseling in patent, trademark, copyright, trade secret, computer, and entertainment matters. He also acts as an arbitrator, mediator, and expert witness in intellectual property/high-tech cases. He has been named to The Best Lawyers in America (2003-present) and Texas Super Lawyers (2003-present). He is author of the Texas Intellectual Property Handbook (2nd edition) published by Juris.
**Professional Memberships:** State Bar of Texas; Dallas Bar Association; American Intellectual Property Law Association; Licensed by the USPTO.
**Personal:** New York University (JD, 1976); University of New Mexico (BS, 1973).

---

### HANKINSON, Deborah G
Hankinson LLP, Dallas
214 754 9190
dhankinson@hankinsonlaw.com
*Featured in Litigation (Texas)*
**Practice Areas:** Formerly a Justice on the Supreme Court of Texas and the Fifth District Court of Appeals in Dallas, Deborah Hankinson is an appellate lawyer, strategist, arbitrator and mediator. In addition to appellate work, Deborah works with clients in conflict situations to resolve issues prior to litigation and collaborates with trial teams to set strategies. In mediations, Deborah uses a unique approach to foster positive outcomes. She sits on the Board of the American Arbitration Association and serves as a neutral in arbitration proceedings. Deborah is Board Certified in Civil Appellate Law by the Texas Board of Legal Specialization.

---

### HARPER, A John
Morgan, Lewis & Bockius LLP, Houston
713 890 5199
aharper@morganlewis.com
*Featured in Labor & Employment (Texas)*
**Practice Areas:** A John Harper II is senior counsel in Morgan Lewis's Labor and Employment Practice. His practice includes the exclusive representation of employers in labor and employment law matters and litigation under the National Labor Relations Act, the Fair Labor Standards Act, Title VII of the Civil Rights Act of 1964, the Age Discrimination in Employment Act, the Employee Income Retirement Security Act, the Americans with Disabilities Act, Railway Labor Act, and other state and federal laws impacting employment relations.
**Personal:** Attended Southern Methodist University School of Law, 1967, LLB cum laude; University of North Texas, 1964, BA.

## HARRIS, James B
Thompson & Knight LLP, Dallas
214 969 1102
James.Harris@tklaw.com
*Featured in Environment (Texas)*
**Practice Areas:** Mr Harris assists clients in environmental regulation compliance, including running compliance audits and developing corporate policies, as well as due diligence. His environmental litigation expertise includes cost recovery actions, enforcement actions, contested permits, bankruptcy claims, regulation challenges, debarment proceedings, and criminal actions. He also represents clients in litigation challenging local government ordinances, permit decisions, and zoning actions, as well as in property tax litigation regarding challenges to valuation, situs determinations, and right to exemptions.
**Personal:** University of Texas School of Law (JD, with honors, 1978); Southern Methodist University (BAS in Environmental Systems, with high honors, 1975).

## HARRIS, Martha
Thompson & Knight LLP, Dallas
214 969 1610
Martha.Harris@tklaw.com
*Featured in Real Estate (Texas)*
**Practice Areas:** Ms Harris represents interim and permanent lenders in connection with financings secured by or involving real estate, including retail, office, and multi-family projects, with an emphasis on senior housing projects and medical office buildings.
**Professional Memberships:** American College of Mortgage Attorneys; American Bar Association; Dallas Bar Association; State Bar of Texas; Attorneys Serving the Community; Board Member, Chiapas International.
**Personal:** Texas Tech University School of Law (JD, 1984); Texas Tech University (BS, 1975).

## HARRIS, Susan Feigin
Baker & Hostetler LLP, Houston
713 646 1307
sharris@bakerlaw.com
*Featured in Healthcare (Texas)*
**Career:** Susan Feigin Harris has represented the healthcare industry for 25 years, providing comprehensive legal services to health industry clients, including hospitals and hospital systems, physicians and physician groups, academic medical centers, rehabilitation facilities, ambulatory surgery centers and dialysis providers. Susan advises on Medicare and Medicaid reimbursement issues, including graduate medical education, upper payment limit disproportionate share hospital payment and licensure and certification issues. Susan represents clients before state legislatures, Congress and the Administration concerning Medicaid entitlement reform, CHGME and delivery reform. She also helps to craft new delivery reform models with her clients and CMS and CMMI.

## HARRIS, Warren W
Bracewell & Giuliani LLP, Houston
713 221 1490
warren.harris@bgllp.com
*Featured in Litigation (Texas)*
**Practice Areas:** Heads the firm's appellate practice. Certified in civil appellate law by Texas Board of Legal Specialization. Handled hundreds of appeals in Texas Supreme Court, US Supreme Court, and state and federal courts of appeals. Assists in trial strategy, preservation of error, preparing jury charges, post-verdict proceedings, and analysis of trial record for appeal.
**Career:** Served as adjunct professor at The University of Texas School of Law and The University of Houston Law Center and served as a briefing attorney for the Supreme Court of Texas.
**Personal:** JD, University of Houston Law Center, 1988; BBA, University of Houston, 1985.

## HARVEY, Dean William
Andrews Kurth LLP, Dallas
214 659 4736
deanharvey@andrewskurth.com
*Featured in Technology (Texas)*
**Practice Areas:** Dean's practice focuses on technology, communications and business process-related commercial transactions, such as BPO and IT outsourcing, licensing, strategic alliances, IP acquisitions, and joint ventures. He also advises clients on offshoring, healthcare IT, mobile technology and applications, and cloud computing in industries such as retail, healthcare, entertainment, energy, technology and government. As part of his practice, he routinely counsels clients on data privacy and security, and assists clients in protecting, acquiring and developing technology, software and other technology.

## HARVEY, Grant J
Gibbs & Bruns LLP, Houston
713 751 5267
gharvey@gibbsbruns.com
*Featured in Litigation (Texas)*
**Practice Areas:** Practice focuses on complex commercial litigation with an emphasis on contractual disputes involving fiduciary relationships and allegations of fraud, partnership disputes, and professional malpractice. Extensive arbitration practice, both domestic and international, including matters administered by the ICC, AAA, NASD, and JAMS.
**Professional Memberships:** Texas Bar Foundation, Fellow; Houston Bar Association, Member; Boys and Girls Harbor, Board of Directors - Board Chair (2007-09).
**Career:** Recognized as Leading US Trial Lawyer by Legal 500, 2012. Listed in: Chambers USA for Energy Litigation, Legal 500 for Energy Litigation, Best Lawyers in America for Commercial Litigation, Benchmark Litigation, and Texas Super Lawyers.

## HARVIN, David
Vinson & Elkins LLP, Houston
713 758 2368
dharvin@velaw.com
*Featured in Litigation (Texas)*

**Practice Areas:** Principal areas of practice include energy litigation, business litigation, class actions, securities, corporate and antitrust litigation.
**Professional Memberships:** Fellow of the American College of Trial Lawyers; listed since 1987 in the area of Business Litigation in a leading legal US publication.
**Career:** Admitted to Texas Bar in 1970. Joined Vinson & Elkins in 1971; admitted to partnership, 1977. Served on Management Committee, 2000-05; Chair, Litigation Section, 1998-2007.
**Personal:** Yale University, BA magna cum laude, 1967 (Phi Beta Kappa); University of Texas School of Law, JD, high honors, 1970 (Chancellors; Order of the Coif; articles editor, 'Texas Law Review').

## HARWELL, Gregory A
Gardere Wynne Sewell LLP, Dallas
214 999 4581
gharwell@gardere.com
*Featured in Construction (Texas)*
**Practice Areas:** Construction, government contracts, products liability.
**Professional Memberships:** State Bar of Texas, Dallas Bar Association, Texas Association of Builders.
**Career:** Greg Harwell's practice focuses on commercial construction, residential construction, and government contracting-related issues. He devotes his time to litigating and arbitrating disputes arising from construction and procurement projects, and to negotiating and drafting contracts, project records, and program documents for the development, design, and construction of all types of projects. He is a senior leader in Gardere's Construction Industry Team.
**Personal:** JD, Texas Tech University School of Law, cum laude, 1990; BS, Texas Tech University, magna cum laude, 1987.

## HATCHELL, Mike A
Locke Lord LLP, Austin
512 305 4752
mahatchell@lockelord.com
*Featured in Appellate Law (Nationwide), Litigation (Texas)*
**Practice Areas:** Chairs the Firm's Appellate Practice Group. Argued 49 cases in the Texas Supreme Court, obtained relief for clients in 71 reported decisions of that Court, handled more than 350 appeals in all 14 Courts of Appeals in Texas, twice argued en banc to federal Fifth Circuit Court of Appeals.
**Professional Memberships:** American Academy of Appellate Lawyers; Texas Supreme Court Advisory Committee; Past President and Founding Member, State Bar of Texas Appellate Practice and Advocacy Section.
**Career:** Of Counsel since 2004.
**Personal:** The University of Texas School of Law (LLB, 1964); The University of Texas at Austin (BBA, 1961).

## HAYNES, Craig A
Thompson & Knight LLP, Dallas
214 969 1239
Craig.Haynes@tklaw.com
*Featured in Litigation (Texas)*

**Practice Areas:** Craig represents major oil companies, independents, gas plant owners, and other interest owners in royalty owner litigation, class action litigation, pricing disputes, take-or-pay issues, operational issues, development and drainage claims, pooling and unitization issues, litigation of administrative disputes, and disputes between working interest owners. He has represented energy industry clients in actions in Texas, Oklahoma, Wyoming, New Mexico, Louisiana, and Alaska. He also handles a range of non-energy related complex commercial litigation in state/federal courts throughout Texas.
**Personal:** The University of Texas School of Law (JD, with high honors, 1985); Texas Tech University (BA, summa cum laude, 1981).

## HEADLEY, Linda
Littler Mendelson, PC, Houston
713 652 4772
lheadley@littler.com
*Featured in Labor & Employment (Texas)*
**Practice Areas:** Discrimination and harassment; labor management relations; competition and trade secret law; class actions.
**Professional Memberships:** State Bar of Texas; Committee for Employment Law - Fifth Circuit Pattern Jury Charge; Employee Rights and Responsibilities Committee - American Bar Association.
**Career:** Linda focuses her practice on employment litigation, client counseling and unfair competition issues. She represents employers in all labor and employment-related matters, including litigation in federal and state courts and administrative proceedings before the Equal Employment Opportunity Commission, Wage and Hour Division of the Department of Labor, the Occupational Safety and Health Administration, and related Texas state agencies.

## HEATH, Paul E
Vinson & Elkins LLP, Dallas
214 220 7976
pheath@velaw.com
*Featured in Bankruptcy/Restructuring (Texas)*
**Practice Areas:** Regularly represents public and private companies and advises their respective Boards of Directors and senior management on developing solutions for reorganizing capital structures and business operations. Devotes a significant portion of practice to the representation of senior secured lenders in out of court workouts and chapter 11 restructurings. Represents strategic and financial purchasers of assets from financially distressed companies. Clients include companies in a range of industries, including energy, distribution, manufacturing, and utilities.
**Career:** Admitted to Texas Bar, 1987; Came to firm as Partner, 1999.
**Personal:** Graduated from The University of Texas, BBA, 1984; JD with honors, 1987.

## HEDGES, Daniel K
Porter Hedges LLP, Houston
713 226 6641
dhedges@porterhedges.com
*Featured in Litigation (Texas)*

**Practice Areas:** Dan Hedges is a partner in the litigation practice at Porter Hedges. He has litigated a wide range of business cases including shareholder derivative suits, qui tam suits, alleged healthcare fraud, and energy contractual disputes. He also represents individuals and business entities in white collar criminal investigations and has conducted and participated in numerous internal corporate investigations. Prior to joining the firm, Mr Hedges served as the United States Attorney for the Southern District of Texas from 1981-85. He has been recognized for several years as one of the top business crimes lawyers in Texas.

### HEIM, Michael F
Heim, Payne & Chorush LLP, Houston
713 221 2000
mheim@hpcllp.com
*Featured in Intellectual Property (Texas)*
**Practice Areas:** Michael Heim specializes exclusively in intellectual property litigation and antitrust lawsuits involving intellectual property. Mr Heim represents plaintiffs and defendants throughout the United States in patent litigation in a wide range of technologies including microprocessors, computer architecture, memory control systems, cellular telephone systems, data transmission systems, online gaming systems, database caching software, logging-while drilling systems, and a host of other hi-tech technologies. He has expertise in evaluating patent portfolios and developing strategies to enforce and license those portfolios. He also is a skilled courtroom litigator, able to understand and explain highly complex technical and legal issues to both judges and jurors. Mr Heim has a Bachelor of Science degree in Electrical Engineering received from the University of Missouri with numerous academic honors. His ability to understand complex technical issues in the electrical arts is unparalleled. He received his JD degree from The George Washington University Law School, also with Honors. While in law school, he served three years as a Patent Examiner at the US Patent and Trademark Office, specializing in electrical communications and computer software and hardware. Mr Heim and his law firm often represent their clients on some form of contingency basis, thereby sharing in the client's risks and rewards. The willingness to align his interests with that of his clients typically results in a more synergistic relationship. Mr Heim has received recognition throughout the patent community in the United States for his abilities and for the significant results he has achieved on behalf of his clients.
**Professional Memberships:** Texas Intellectual Property Law Section (President, 2001-02); Houston Intellectual Property Law Association (President, 1998-99); American Bar Association; American Intellectual Property Law Association; Houston Bar Association and Federal Circuit Bar Association.
**Personal:** JD, Honors, 1986. The George Washington University Law School BS, Electrical Engineering, 1983 University of Missouri Honors: National Merit Scholar, University Scholar, Member of Tau Beta Pi and Eta Kappa Nu.

### HELFAND, Thomas
Winstead PC, Dallas
214 745 5342
thelfand@winstead.com
*Featured in Tax (Texas)*
**Practice Areas:** Tom has represented a broad range of clients in a wide variety of areas of the tax law. He has been very active professionally, giving speeches and writing articles on a broad array of topics reflecting his practice. Tom also serves as outside general counsel for several major clients. He has served in numerous leadership and management roles at Winstead since the commencement of his career in 1977, most recently serving on Winstead's executive committee and as the firm's chief operating officer and Dallas managing shareholder. He is currently chair of Winstead's Business & Transactions department.

### HELMS, Shawn C
K&L Gates, Dallas
214 939 5599
shawn.helms@klgates.com
*Featured in Outsourcing (Nationwide), Technology (Texas)*
**Practice Areas:** Shawn Helms has broad experience in the areas of outsourcing, information technology and telecommunications. His practice is focused on complex technology and intellectual property-centric transactions, including information technology outsourcing, business process outsourcing, technology licensing, cloud computing, technology development/customization, strategic sourcing, alliances, electronic commerce and data privacy. Previously, he served as in-house counsel at Sprint Corporation and served as an Adjunct Technology Professor at the University of Virginia. Shawn is the co-author of a legal treatise on outsourcing law titled "Outsourcing: Law and Business" published by Law Journal Press / American Lawyer Media.

### HENCHEY, Brian
Baker Botts LLP, Dallas
214 953 6576
brian.henchey@bakerbotts.com
*Featured in Technology (Texas)*
**Practice Areas:** Experienced in information technology and business process outsourcing transactions for both customers and service providers. Extensive experience in other types of technology-related commercial transactions, including joint ventures, licensing and distribution agreements, marketing alliances, and mergers and acquisitions involving significant intellectual property components. Active practice in public company representation in day to day securities matters.
**Career:** Baker Botts LLP (1999 to present).
**Personal:** Cornell Law School (JD cum laude, 1999); University of North Carolina (BS, 1992).

### HENRICHS, Ragna
Porter Hedges LLP, Houston
713 226 6602
rhenrichs@porterhedges.com
*Featured in Environment (Texas)*
**Practice Areas:** Ms Henrichs concentrates her practice exclusively in the field of environmental

law and has had extensive experience with compliance, regulatory counseling, litigation and due diligence. She has represented members of the manufacturing, chemical, energy, oil and gas, development, construction and waste management industries, as well as airlines and utilities, in environmental matters ranging from enforcement to permit proceedings and remediation to strategic planning and environmental insurance.
**Professional Memberships:** Ms Henrichs is a Member of the environmental sections of the American, Houston, Texas and New York bar associations, and of the New York State Bar Association's Environmental Section Council.

### HENRY, D Steven
Gardere Wynne Sewell LLP, Dallas
214 999 4838
shenry@gardere.com
*Featured in Construction (Texas)*
**Professional Memberships:** State Bar of Texas, Dallas Bar Association, National Association of Homebuilders, TEXO, America's Leading Builders, NAHB Construction Law Attorney Forum [Steering Committee].
**Career:** Steve Henry leads Gardere's Construction Industry Team. He serves as national counsel for a number of high-profile public and privately-held general contractors, homebuilders, engineering/architectural firms, developers, and construction materials manufacturing companies. He provides construction industry-related representation in the areas of risk and corporate management, contracting/contract management programs, strategic litigation, intellectual property, legislative affairs, and environmental matters.
**Personal:** JD, Texas Tech School of Law with honors, 1984; BS, Texas A&M University, with honors, 1981.

### HENRY, Matthew C
Vinson & Elkins LLP, Dallas
214 220 7726
mhenry@velaw.com
*Featured in Energy & Natural Resources (Texas)*
**Practice Areas:** State & Federal Regulation of Electricity, Natural Gas, and Coal Mining; Energy-Related Litigation; Energy-Related Transactions; Substantial Experience in Litigating High Value Cases and Advising on Energy Commercial and M&A Transactions.
**Career:** Partner, Vinson & Elkins LLP (2008-Present); Partner, Hunton & Williams LLP (2002-08); Associate, Worsham Forsythe Wooldridge LLP (1994-2002).
**Personal:** SMU Dedman School of Law, JD cum laude (1994) (Order of the Coif; Sumners Scholar); Howard Payne University, BS cum laude (1991).

### HETTINGER, Glen
Fulbright & Jaworski LLP, Dallas
214 855 7444
ghettinger@fulbright.com
*Featured in Corporate/M&A (Texas)*
**Practice Areas:** Corporate; securities; mergers and acquisitions; corporate governance.
**Career:** Hettinger heads the corporate practice for the firm's Dallas office. He has broad experi-

ence in M&A, securities law, corporate governance, spin-offs, capital markets, joint ventures, internal investigations and restructurings. Named to 'The Best Lawyers in America' in Corporate, M&A and Capital Markets(2007-13); Named among 'Texas Super Lawyers' by Texas Monthly magazine (2006-12) and among 'Best Lawyers in Dallas' by D Magazine (2005, 2007-13).
**Personal:** JD, Columbia University School of Law (1984); Editor, Columbia Law Review; BA, magna cum laude, Brigham Young University (1981).

### HICKS JR, M Lawrence
Thompson & Knight LLP, Dallas
214 969 1627
Larry.Hicks@tklaw.com
*Featured in Real Estate (Texas)*
**Practice Areas:** Mr Hicks is the Firm's Administrative Partner and Dallas Office Leader, and his practice encompasses multi-state real estate lending transactions, including workout agreements and foreclosures, purchases and sales, ground leases, and all aspects of shopping center development, ownership and financing. His expertise includes conveyances, leases, reciprocal easements, operating agreements, management agreements, loan documents, and reviewing title reports, surveys, zoning ordinances, and other regulations affecting the intended use of real estate.
**Professional Memberships:** Former President, American College of Mortgage Attorneys; International Council of Shopping Centers.
**Personal:** University of Texas School of Law (JD, 1970); Duke University (BA, 1967).

### HIGDON, Gerald D
Locke Lord LLP, Houston
713 238 3709
jhigdon@lockelord.com
*Featured in Environment (Texas)*
**Practice Areas:** Environmental law. Enforcement defense; counseling on climate change regulation, carbon capture and sequestration, and hydraulic fracturing; brownfields redevelopment; environmental permitting; citizen protest actions; environmental counseling and strategic planning with respect to the upstream, midstream, downstream, and renewable/alternative energy sectors; representation of potentially responsible parties at federal/state superfund facilities.
**Professional Memberships:** Houston Bar Association; State Bar of Texas; Association of Chemical Industry of Texas.
**Career:** Partner at Locke Lord (2009-Present; 2004-06; 1998-2001).
**Personal:** The University of Texas School of Law (J.D., with honors, 1990); Texas Tech University (BBA, Finance, magna cum laude, 1985).

### HIGGINS, John
Porter Hedges LLP, Houston
713 226 6648
jhiggins@porterhedges.com
*Featured in Bankruptcy/Restructuring (Texas)*
**Practice Areas:** Mr Higgins has represented clients for over 25 years in workouts and Chapter

11 bankruptcy cases across the country. He focuses on corporate reorganizations, restructurings, acquisitions and litigation. He has extensive experience in representing debtors, secured creditors, creditors' committees, boards of directors and members, and Chapter 11 and 7 Trustees.
**Professional Memberships:** Mr Higgins is Board Certified in Business Bankruptcy Law, serves on the Turnaround Management Association (Houston chapter) board of directors, served as an adjunct professor of bankruptcy law at the University of Houston Law Center and is a Certified Mediator.

## HILLIARD, Michael
Winstead PC, Houston
713 650 2727
mhilliard@winstead.com
*Featured in Banking & Finance (Texas)*
**Practice Areas:** Mike's more than 35 years of experience covers the full range of financial services, banking issues and credit transactions. His principal emphasis is on complex lending transactions, workouts, leveraged leasing, credit products and project finance. Mike represents financial services industry members, including lenders, in a full range of debt financings covering many industries; financial institutions in a broad range of business, corporate and regulatory matters; lenders, lessees, trustees and equity participants in leveraged lease and project finance transactions; and also developers, buyers and sellers in project development and asset and stock transactions.

## HO, Allyson N
Morgan, Lewis & Bockius LLP, Dallas
713 890 5000
aho@morganlewis.com
*Featured in Appellate Law (Nationwide), Litigation (Texas)*
**Practice Areas:** Allyson Ho co-chairs the firm's US Supreme Court and Appellate Litigation Practice. Recognized in Chambers as "a superstar young appellate lawyer" and by Texas Lawyer as one of Texas' top 20 "winning women" litigators, she has successfully litigated high-stakes cases for Fortune 500 clients in state and federal trial and appellate courts nationwide.
**Career:** Special Assistant to the President, 2005-06; Counselor to the Attorney General, 2004-05; Law clerk to Justice Sandra Day O'Connor, US Supreme Court, 2002-03
**Personal:** University of Chicago Law School, with high honors, 2000, JD; Rice University, 1994, MA, PhD; Duke University, 1988, BA.

## HO, James
Gibson, Dunn & Crutcher LLP, Dallas
214 698 3264
JHo@gibsondunn.com
*Featured in Litigation (Texas)*
**Practice Areas:** Experienced appellate, business, and constitutional litigator, prevailing in over 75% of his arguments in courts across the country, including the US Supreme Court, Texas Supreme Court, and US Court of Appeals for the Fifth Circuit.
**Career:** Decade of experience in all three branches of government. Solicitor General of Texas, the

State's chief appellate litigator. Chief Counsel, U.S. Senator John Cornyn, Senate Judiciary Committee. Office of Legal Counsel and Civil Rights Division, US Department of Justice. Law Clerk to Justice Clarence Thomas, US Supreme Court, and Judge Jerry E. Smith, US Court of Appeals for the Fifth Circuit.

## HOLLYFIELD, John S
Fulbright & Jaworski LLP, Houston
713 651 3717
jhollyfield@fulbright.com
*Featured in Real Estate (Texas)*
**Practice Areas:** Real estate.
**Professional Memberships:** Past Chair, Real Estate Law Section of the Houston Bar Association; Past Chair of Real Property, Probate and Trust Law Section of the American Bar Association; Past President, American College of Real Estate Lawyers; Past President, Anglo-American Real Property Institute.
**Career:** Hollyfield focuses his practice on real estate matters, including mortgage lending, leasing, real estate development, construction, sale and purchase of raw land, commercial and industrial properties, real estate brokerage and management, joint venture partnerships, mortgage foreclosures and loan workouts.
**Personal:** LLB, with honors (1968), and BBA (1961), The University of Texas.

## HOLUB, Cynthia A
Porter Hedges LLP, Houston
713 226 6607
cholub@porterhedges.com
*Featured in Insurance (Texas)*
**Practice Areas:** Cindy Holub is a partner in the litigation section of Porter Hedges. She represents both plaintiffs and defendants in a wide variety of litigation. Her practice focuses on construction and insurance coverage disputes. She has handled appeals in Texas appellate courts and in the Fifth Circuit Court of Appeals. She received her BBA degree in finance, cum laude, from the University of Texas in 1992 and her JD degree, cum laude, from the University of Houston Law Center in 1996. She is a member of the Insurance and Construction Sections of the State Bar of Texas.

## HOWELL, John E
K&L Gates, Dallas
214 939 5461
john.howell@klgates.com
*Featured in Outsourcing (Nationwide), Technology (Texas)*
See under Nationwide for profile.

## HOWLEY, Thomas A
Jones Day, Houston
832 239 3790
tahowley@jonesday.com
*Featured in Bankruptcy/Restructuring (Texas)*
**Practice Areas:** Advises clients involved in financially distressed situations throughout the US. He represents hedge funds, distressed investors, special situation lenders, banks, ad hoc committees, official committees of creditors, and companies in need of restructuring advice, in distressed corporate acquisitions and divestitures, lit-

igation, workouts, reorganizations, and chapter 11 bankruptcy cases.
**Professional Memberships:** Past treasurer, vice president and current President of the Bankruptcy Law Section of the State Bar of Texas and is a past president and current board member of the Houston Chapter of the Turnaround Management Association. He is a member of the American Bankruptcy Institute.

## HUFFMAN, Bart W
Locke Lord LLP, Austin
512 305 4746
bhuffman@lockelord.com
*Featured in Intellectual Property (Texas)*
**Practice Areas:** Experienced in a wide range of privacy and data security matters. Clients rely on his advice in connection with strategy and policy issues and initiatives, Internet-based commercial services and other transactional matters, compliance, and privacy and intellectual property litigation.
**Professional Memberships:** International Association of Privacy Professionals, Certified Information Privacy Professional; Visiting Fellow, Center for Information Technology Policy, Princeton University (2011-12); Registered Patent Attorney.
**Career:** Joined Locke Lord as Partner in 2012.
**Personal:** The University of Texas School of Law (JD, with honors, 1994); Princeton University (BSE, Civil Engineering/Operations Research, Certificate in Engineering and Management Systems, cum laude, 1988).

## HUFFMAN, Gregory S C
Thompson & Knight LLP, Dallas
214 969 1144
Gregory.Huffman@tklaw.com
*Featured in Antitrust (Texas)*
**Practice Areas:** Mr Huffman's practice focuses on antitrust, complex commercial litigation, criminal investigations, and mergers and acquisitions. He has been named one of the Nation's Top 10 Antitrust Lawyers by United States Lawyer Rankings (2007-12) and named to The Best Lawyers in America, Texas Super Lawyers, Who's Who Legal: Texas, and D Magazine's 'Best Lawyers in Dallas' for multiple years.
**Professional Memberships:** American College of Trial Lawyers; American Board of Trial Advocates; American and Dallas Bar Associations; Texas and Dallas Bar Foundations.
**Personal:** Harvard Law School (JD, 1973); London School of Economics (graduate study, 1971-72); Stanford University (BA, 1969).

## HUGHES, Vester T
K&L Gates, Dallas
214 939 5433
vester.hughes@klgates.com
*Featured in Tax (Texas)*
**Practice Areas:** Vester T Hughes is prominently regarded for his counsel to corporations and individuals on federal taxation issues. Long noted for his litigation skills, he has argued cases before the United States Supreme Court, the Texas Supreme Court, US Courts of Appeals, and the US Claims Court. On several occasions he has successfully

lobbied Congress on behalf of clients to amend the federal tax laws. The Treasury Department and Congressional tax-writing committees from time to time seek out his views on tax policy and pending legislation.

## HURDLOW, Paul E
DLA Piper LLP (US), Austin
512 457 7020
paul.hurdlow@dlapiper.com
*Featured in Technology (Texas)*
**Practice Areas:** Corporate; technology; intellectual property; venture capital.
**Professional Memberships:** State Bar of California; State Bar of Texas; Austin Entrepreneur Foundation (founding member, board of directors); Texas Angel Investors, Steering Committee.
**Career:** He is co-chair of the firm's Emerging Growth and Venture Capital practice, and represents public and private companies, many in the technology sector. He has experience in emerging compliance issues related to corporate governance, public disclosure, and Sarbanes-Oxley regulations. His clients include public companies in software, semiconductor, gaming technology, investment banks, and venture capital firms.
**Personal:** JD, University of California at Berkeley.

## INGRUM, Andrew A
Thompson & Knight LLP, Dallas
214 969 1279
Andrew.Ingrum@tklaw.com
*Featured in Real Estate (Texas)*
**Practice Areas:** Mr Ingrum represents clients in virtually every facet of commercial real estate financing and development, including real estate acquisition/dispositions, loan originations, redevelopments, workouts, and leasing in almost every segment of commercial real estate such as office, industrial, retail, flex, hi tech, and senior housing. Mr Ingrum currently serves as Practice Leader for the Real Estate and Banking Practice Area and member of the Technology Steering Committee.
**Professional Memberships:** State Bar of Texas; American Bar Association.
**Personal:** University of Oklahoma College of Law (JD, 1996); University of Texas at Austin (BA, 1992).

## INOFF, Darren
Andrews Kurth LLP, Houston
713 220 3841
dinoff@andrewskurth.com
*Featured in Real Estate (Texas)*
**Practice Areas:** Darren's real estate practice includes the leasing of office buildings, retail projects and industrial warehouses, and advising on the acquisition and disposition of raw land and income producing properties. Darren offers comprehensive counsel on the construction and development of office buildings, retail shopping centers, assisted living facilities, research and technology facilities, entertainment arenas, hotels, cardiac catheterization laboratories and ambulatory surgery centers. Darren also handles construction and permanent loans and other structured financings. Finally, Darren counsels his clients on business formation issues, including choice of entities,

and negotiates and drafts limited liability company agreements and limited partnership agreements.

**JACKSON, Thomas R**
Jones Day, Dallas
214 969 2978
trjackson@jonesday.com
*Featured in Antitrust (Texas)*

**Practice Areas:** Tom's practice focuses on complex commercial litigation in the securities, intellectual property, and antitrust areas. He represents clients on claims of monopolization, distribution practices, takeovers, mergers, section 10(b) lawsuits, derivative actions, intellectual property disputes, and governmental investigations. Tom also represents clients in a variety of commercial disputes, including breach of contract, fraud, director and officer liability, and prudency issues involving the activities of regulated utilities.
**Professional Memberships:** American Bar Association; Dallas Bar Association.

**JACOBS, Stephen C**
Locke Lord LLP, Houston
713 226 1382
sjacobs@lockelord.com
*Featured in Real Estate (Texas)*

**Practice Areas:** Real estate development, ownership and acquisition and formation of business organizations associated with real estate development and ownership. Represents landlords and tenants in office and retail leasing, and large retail users in developing retail facilities. Represents developers of master planned residential projects, multi-family developments and high-density, mixed-use developments. Works with leisure industry in developing resort properties. Represents and serves as general counsel to governmental authorities in public-private partnership, and other real estate development matters.
**Career:** Partner since 1987.
**Personal:** The University of Texas School of Law (JD, 1981); Tulane University (BA, 1978).

**JANSONIUS, John V**
Jackson Walker LLP, Dallas
214 953 5970
jjansonius@jw.com
*Featured in Labor & Employment (Texas)*

**Practice Areas:** Board Certified, Labor & Employment Law, Texas Board of Legal Specialization. Defends employment discrimination claims, wrongful discharge claims, L&E arbitration cases, unfair labor practice claims under NLRA, plan administration and denial of benefits claims under ERISA and collective/individual actions under FLSA. Has represented defense in jury and non-jury trials in state/federal court and presented oral arguments to US Supreme Court and several federal courts of appeals.
**Professional Memberships:** Chair, Labor and Employment Section, State Bar of Texas (2004-05); Board of Directors, State Bar of Texas (2008-11); Fellow, College of Labor and Employment Lawyers (2006-present); Member, American Employment Law Council; Chair, North American Transportation Employee Relations Association (2010); President, Industrial Relations

Research Association, North Texas Chapter (1987-88); Chapter Update Chair, ABA Employment Discrimination Law (2010-present); Chair, State Bar of Texas Client Security Fund (2010-11); Vice-Chair, State Bar of Texas Grievance Committee, District 6 (2011-present); Vice-Chair, Dallas Bar Association, Judiciary Committee (2012-present).
**Personal:** BA, Drake University; JD, Southern Methodist University.

**JESSUP JR, Clifton R**
Greenberg Traurig, LLP, Dallas
214 665 3638
JessupC@gtlaw.com
*Featured in Bankruptcy/Restructuring (Texas)*

**Practice Areas:** Business reorganization and financial restructuring; bankruptcy; business; creditors' rights; corporate reorganization.
**Professional Memberships:** Fellow, American College of Bankruptcy. Former Board Member, North Texas Regional Mental Health Board; Board of Trustees Member, Oakwood University, Huntsville, Alabama; Member, American Bar Association.
**Career:** Selected: Chambers USA Guide, 2006-13; Best Lawyers in America, 1999-2012; One of America's Top Black Lawyers in Black Enterprise Magazine, November 2003; Super Lawyers magazine, 2003-12. Master in the John C. Ford American Inns of Court. Rated, AV® Preeminent™ 5.0 out of 5.
**Personal:** JD, University of Michigan Law School; BA, summa cum laude, Oakwood College.

**JEWELL, Robert V**
Andrews Kurth LLP, Houston
713 220 4358
bjewell@andrewskurth.com
*Featured in Corporate/M&A (Texas), Capital Markets (Texas)*

**Practice Areas:** Bob Jewell is the Managing Partner of the firm, Chair of the Executive Committee and a Member of the Policy Committee. Bob's principal areas of practice are mergers and acquisitions (both domestic and foreign), corporate governance and capital markets transactions. In over 30 years of practice, Bob has particular experience relating to the energy services industry, the refining industry, master limited partnerships, real estate investment trusts, the forest products industry, and representing special committees of boards of directors.

**JOE, Harry**
Jackson Lewis LLP, Dallas
214 273 5060
joeh@jacksonlewis.com
*Featured in Immigration (Texas)*

**Practice Areas:** Employment based immigration law; nationality law; employer work verification compliance and worksite enforcement defense.
**Professional Memberships:** American Immigration Lawyers Association; State Bar of Texas; Dallas Bar Association, Dallas Asian American Bar Association.
**Career:** Jenkens and Gilchrist PC ( 1986-2007 ); Winstead PC ( 2007-09 ) Jackson Lewis LLP ( 2009 – present .)

**Publications:** Verification of Employment Authorization: Avoiding Criminal and Civil Liability and Immigration Related Employment Discrimination, Texas Employment Law Handbook, 2009-11 Ed.
**Personal:** JD, Washington University School of Law , 1975; BA, University of North Texas,1970. Board Certified , Immigration Law, Texas Board of Legal Specialization.

**JOHNSON, Michael R**
Goins, Underkofler, Crawford & Langdon LLP, Dallas
214 253 4100
mrj@gucl.com
*Featured in Construction (Texas)*

**Practice Areas:** Construction, litigation. Extensive experience in multi-party litigation and arbitrations.
**Career:** Board certified in civil trial law by the Texas Board of Legal Specialization; law clerk US District Court, Southern District of Texas (1973-75).
**Personal:** University of Virginia, BA, 1970; University of Texas School of Law, JD, 1973.

**JOHNSTON, Kenneth C**
Kane Russell Coleman & Logan PC, Dallas
214 777 4222
kjohnston@krcl.com
*Featured in Litigation (Texas)*

**Practice Areas:** Commercial litigation, with emphasis on financial services, insolvency and creditor rights. Represents financial institutions in a variety of matters, including general bank operations, material defensive litigation, and credit risk management. Represents parties on both sides of cases involving oil and gas, partnerships, securities, and corporate governance, as well as investor groups in Ponzi scheme matters.
**Professional Memberships:** Dallas Bar Association; Pro Bono College of the State Bar of Texas; American Bankruptcy Institute; Texas Association of Bank Counsel; Texas Young Lawyers Association; Dallas Association of Young Lawyers.
**Career:** Licensed to practice in 1991. Joined the firm in 1994 and is a director and shareholder.
**Publications:** "Overdraft Update, Litigation and Regulatory Developments," Strafford (July 2012); "Tough Times on the Auction Block," Texas Lawyer (May 2008); "The Subprime Morass: Past, Present and Future," 12 NC Banking Inst. 125 (March 2008); "How the Takeover of Fannie Mae and Freddie Mac Will Fuel New Credit Crisis Litigation," Andrews Financial Crisis Litigation Reporter, ANFCLR 4 20081016 (October 16, 2008); "Ponzi Schemes and Litigation Risks: What Every Financial Services Company Should Know," 14 N.C. Banking Inst. 29 (2010).
**Personal:** University of Mississippi, BBA (1988); JD (1991).

**JOHNSTONE, Debbi M**
Fulbright & Jaworski LLP, Houston
713 651 5335
djohnstone@fulbright.com
*Featured in Healthcare (Texas), Healthcare (Nationwide)*

**Practice Areas:** Health Law–Transactions, Regulatory and Compliance.
**Professional Memberships:** American Health Lawyers Association; ABA, Health Law Section; Houston Bar Association, Health Law Section (Chair 2004-05); State Bar of Texas, Health Law Section; Texas Board of Legal Specialization Health Law Exam Commission.
**Career:** Admitted to practice: Indiana, 1980 (inactive); Texas, 1982; Board Certified in Health Law by the Texas Board of Legal Specialization.
**Publications:** Various speeches and articles on health law issues.
**Personal:** Northwestern University, BA, 1977; Indiana University School of Law, JD, cum laude, 1980.

**JONES, J Wesley**
Vinson & Elkins LLP, Austin
512 542 8703
wjones@velaw.com
*Featured in Technology (Texas)*

**Practice Areas:** Represents public and private companies in corporate transactions, emphasizing private equity transactions and mergers and acquisitions in the software and hardware technology, energy, and life sciences industries.
**Career:** Clerk to The Honorable Walter J. Cummings, US Court of Appeals for the Seventh Circuit, 1995-96; Admitted to Texas Bar, 1996; joined Vinson & Elkins, 1996; admitted to partnership, 2008; General Counsel of private, then publicly-traded, software company, 1999-2005.
**Personal:** The University of Texas School of Law, JD with honors, 1995 (Secretary of the Chancellors; Order of the Coif; Texas Law Review) and The University of Texas, BBA Finance, 1992.

**JONES, Wilson G**
Thompson & Knight LLP, Dallas
214 969 1400
Wilson.Jones@tklaw.com
*Featured in Healthcare (Texas)*

**Practice Areas:** Mr Jones focuses his practice on corporate health law with an emphasis on compliance and investigations, health industry transactions, and federal and state regulatory, administrative, and litigation-related health law matters. He has assisted clients in preventing and responding to investigations, managing Medicare and Medicaid reimbursement issues, analyzing arrangements under state and federal fraud and abuse statutes, and establishing and maintaining compliance programs.
**Professional Memberships:** Secretary, State Bar of Texas Health Law Section; Dallas Bar Association.
**Personal:** The University of Texas School of Law (JD, 1992); Texas Tech University (BA, 1988).

**JORDAN, Carey**
McDermott Will & Emery LLP, Houston
713 653 1782
ccjordan@mwe.com
*Featured in Intellectual Property (Texas)*

**Practice Areas:** Practice focused on patent prosecution, transactions and strategic portfolio management in the chemical, energy and alternative energy sectors. Develops worldwide intellectu-

al property portfolios for both start-up and established companies, including establishing and formulating patent procurement strategies; obtaining domestic and foreign patents; handling complex prosecution procedures, such as reexaminations. **Professional Memberships:** Admitted to practice in Texas and registered to practice before the US Patent and Trademark Office; American Intellectual Property Law Association.
**Personal:** University of Houston Law Center, JD (magna cum laude), 1997; Clemson University, MS, 1994; Clemson University, BS (magna cum laude), 1993.

## JORDAN, W. Carl
Vinson & Elkins LLP, Houston
713 758 2258
cjordan@velaw.com
*Featured in Labor & Employment (Texas)*
**Practice Areas:** Focuses on representing management in employment, ERISA and labor-related trial and appellate work and counseling, focusing on systemic and other complex matters, including whistleblower cases. Certified in labor and employment law by the Texas Board of Legal Specialization.
**Professional Memberships:** Member: Labor and Employment Section and Section's Committee on Equal Employment Opportunity Law, American Bar Association. Fellow: American College of Labor and Employment Lawyers. Director, American Employment Law Council.
**Career:** Admitted to practice: Texas, 1974. Joined Vinson & Elkins, 1974; admitted to Partnership, 1981.
**Personal:** Baylor University, BA, 1971; Harvard Law School, JD, 1974.

## JOSEPHSON, Richard
Baker Botts LLP, Houston
713 229 1460
richard.josephson@bakerbotts.com
*Featured in Litigation (Texas)*
**Practice Areas:** Has litigated securities, business, drug products liability, antitrust, consumer class actions, attorney general investigations, legal malpractice defense, mass and toxic tort, and other complex commercial disputes for over 35 years.
**Professional Memberships:** State Bar of Texas, American College of Trial Lawyers, American Board of Trial Advocates.
**Career:** Recognized by Best Lawyers in America 2001 to present, The International Who's Who of Business Lawyers 2002 to present, Chambers USA Guide 2006-present.
**Personal:** JD, summa cum laude, University of Houston Law Center, 1973 (Order of the Barons, Phi Delta Phi); BS, University of Missouri, 1970.

## JURGENSMEYER, Randy R
Vinson & Elkins LLP, Dallas
214 220 7790
rjurgensmeyer@velaw.com
*Featured in Real Estate (Texas)*
**Practice Areas:** Practice areas include business and finance, concentrating on complex transactions involving real estate. Randy has extensive involvement representing private equity funds and

other investors in forming joint ventures and strategic alliances, portfolio transactions, merger transactions, and acquiring, developing, financing, restructuring, selling and leasing shopping centers, office buildings, hotels, industrial parks and apartment complexes.
**Professional Memberships:** American Bar Association; Texas Bar Association; Dallas Bar Association.
**Career:** Admitted Texas Bar, 1986. Came to firm as Partner, 1996.
**Personal:** University of Missouri, BA magna cum laude, 1982; Southern Methodist University School of Law, JD, 1985. Member of Phi Beta Kappa.

## KAMINSKY, Neal
Porter Hedges LLP, Houston
713 226 6698
nkaminsky@porterhedges.com
*Featured in Banking & Finance (Texas)*
**Practice Areas:** Neal Kaminsky represents clients in financial and corporate transactions, including cash flow and asset based credit facilities and letter of credit facilities in corporate, middle market and high net worth wealth management markets, as well as loan workouts and restructuring, debtor-in-possession financings, real estate acquisition and construction loans, project finance, mezzanine and subordinated debt facilities, debt offerings, mergers, asset and stock acquisitions and divestitures. His practice further includes entity formation and governance agreements.
**Professional Memberships:** Mr Kaminsky is a Member of the American Bar Association, State Bar of Texas, Houston Bar Association, and Turnaround Management Association, Houston Chapter.

## KANE, Raymond J
Kane Russell Coleman & Logan PC, Dallas
214 777 4290
rkane@krcl.com
*Featured in Real Estate (Texas)*
**Practice Areas:** Real Estate – Development, leasing and lending matters; business and corporate; Federal and State income taxation; financial services; restaurant and hospitality.
**Professional Memberships:** Dallas Bar Association; International Council of Shopping Centers; NAIOP; NTCAR; The Real Estate Council.
**Career:** Licensed to practice in 1983. Founded the firm in 1992 and is a Director and Shareholder. Firm selected by The National Law Journal for the Midsize Hot List (2012). Listed in Best Lawyers in American (2012). Named in Texas Super Lawyers® and Texas Monthly magazines as one of the top real estate attorneys in Texas (2003-12). Identified by Corporate Counsel magazine's annual survey of FORTUNE 500® companies as a Go-To Law Firm® (2011 & 2012), nominated by Home Depot U.S.A., Inc.
**Publications:** "Lease Accounting & Real Estate Law Changes You Need to be Aware of in 2011," Kinsman Equity Partners Investor Breakfast (January, 2011). "Distressed Assets: Understanding

the Opportunities & Challenges in Today's Commercial Market," North Texas Commercial Association of Realtors and Real Estate Professionals (April 2010).
**Personal:** Southern Methodist University, LLM in taxation (1988). University of Oklahoma, BBA with distinction (1980); JD (1983).

## KANG ANSBACH, Cindy
Fulbright & Jaworski LLP, Dallas
214 855 7499
ckang@fulbright.com
*Featured in Immigration (Texas)*
**Practice Areas:** Immigration and nationality law.
**Professional Memberships:** American Immigration Lawyers Association; National Asian Pacific American Bar Association.
**Career:** Kang Ansbach joined Fulbright in Dallas as a partner in 2007. Head of the firm's immigration practice group, she has extensive experience representing clients in a range of industries. Clients include domestic, foreign and international companies in the airline, health care, logistics, transportation, oil and gas and technology industries. She frequently provides presentations to corporate clients and human resources personnel.
**Personal:** JD, University of Texas School of Law (1995); BA, magna cum laude, Political Science & Philosophy, Boston College (1992).

## KAPLAN, Lee
Smyser Kaplan & Veselka LLP, Houston
713 221 2300
lkaplan@skv.com
*Featured in Litigation (Texas)*
**Practice Areas:** Trials, arbitrations, and appeals; including fraud and contract disputes, patent and trademark infringement, unfair competition, shareholder rights, securities and antitrust, insurance disputes, other business torts, Foreign Corrupt Practices Act and white-collar criminal matters.
**Professional Memberships:** American Board of Trial Advocates, American Law Institute, American Bar Association, State Bar of Texas, Houston Bar Association, American Intellectual Property Law Association, Houston Intellectual Property Law Association, Bar of the US Supreme Court, Fifth Circuit, Eleventh Circuit, Federal Circuit, and the US District Courts for the Southern, Eastern, Northern and Western Districts of Texas.
**Career:** Law clerk, Hon Joe M Ingraham, US Court of Appeals for the Fifth Circuit, 1976-77; Baker Botts LLP, associate 1977-84, Partner 1985-95; Founding Partner Smyser Kaplan & Veselka LLP, 1995 to present.
**Publications:** 'Drafting Common Sense Patents for Judges and Juries', IP Litigator, March-April 2006 (co-author).
**Personal:** University of Texas Law School, JD with honors, 1976; Princeton University, AB, Woodrow Wilson Scholar, 1973. Eagle Scout; married to Diana M Hudson; son William (born 04/15/90).

## KAREN, James
Jones Day, Dallas
214 969 5027
jkaren@jonesday.com
*Featured in Litigation (Texas)*
**Practice Areas:** Serves as the Head of Litigation in the Dallas office. His practice encompasses the full range of general litigation matters, with particular emphasis in the areas of complex corporate and commercial litigation and class actions. Has significant experience in jury and bench trials, injunction matters, and arbitrations. He has tried numerous lawsuits and arbitrations throughout the United States. In addition, he has handled preliminary injunction hearings, class certification hearings, and state and federal appellate arguments.

## KATZ JR, William M
Thompson & Knight LLP, Dallas
214 969 1330
William.Katz@tklaw.com
*Featured in Antitrust (Texas)*
**Practice Areas:** Mr Katz focuses his practice on antitrust, securities, corporate governance, class action, and complex commercial litigation and arbitration. He also has expertise in internal investigations and the representation of audit committees. He is Co-Chair of the Firm's Securities and Complex Commercial Litigation Practice Group and has been named to The Best Lawyers in America, Texas Super Lawyers, and Who's Who Legal: Texas.
**Professional Memberships:** State Bars of Texas, New York, and DC; American Bar Association; Dallas Bar Association; American, Texas, and Dallas Bar Foundations.
**Personal:** Georgetown University (JD, 1994; BSBA, 1991).

## KEANE, Jennifer
Baker Botts LLP, Austin
512 322 2594
jennifer.keane@bakerbotts.com
*Featured in Environment (Texas)*
**Practice Areas:** Broad expertise in environmental permitting, compliance, acquisitions, and state and federal enforcement with focus on energy, chemical, and manufacturing sectors. Special expertise in complex Clean Air Act matters.
**Professional Memberships:** State Bar of Texas.
**Career:** Admitted to Texas Bar, 1990. Baker Botts Partner since 1999.
**Personal:** JD (with honors), The University of Texas School of Law (1989), Order of the Coif, Phi Delta Phi; MS, BS, BA, University of South Carolina (1986, 1984). Listed: Best Lawyers in America, Chambers, International Who's Who of Environmental Lawyers.

## KELLER, Mary
Winstead PC, Austin
512 370 2840
mkeller@winstead.com
*Featured in Insurance (Texas)*
**Practice Areas:** Mary brings 25 years of government experience to Winstead's Corporate, Securities/Mergers & Acquisitions and Insurance practice. Mary was the Chief Deputy for litigation

at the Texas Attorney General's Office and First Assistant to Attorney General Jim Mattox. In 1993, she became the Senior Associate Commissioner for Legal and Compliance for the Texas Department of Insurance, where she acted as senior policy advisor to the Commissioner and oversaw all enforcement activity of the Department. Mary has been retained as an insurance expert in a number of multi-million dollar lawsuits involving the interpretation of insurance statutes and regulations.

### KELLEY, Kevin L
Gardere Wynne Sewell LLP, Dallas
214 999 4503
kkelley@gardere.com
*Featured in Real Estate (Texas)*
**Practice Areas:** Real estate.
**Professional Memberships:** State Bar of Texas, American and Dallas Bar Associations.
**Career:** Kevin Kelley chairs Gardere's Real Estate Practice Group and is board certified in Commercial Real Estate Law by the Texas Board of Legal Specialization. He represents owners, developers, lenders, and investors in all facets of commercial real estate transactions. Mr Kelley's clients include individuals, private businesses, Fortune 500 companies, institutional lenders, and equity funds. Mr Kelley is also a member of Gardere's Hospitality Industry Team.
**Personal:** JD, St. Mary's University School of Law, 1985; BBA, Texas Christian University, with honors, 1981.

### KELLY, T Mark
Vinson & Elkins LLP, Houston
713 758 4592
mkelly@velaw.com
*Featured in Corporate/M&A (Texas), Capital Markets (Texas), Capital Markets (Nationwide)*
**Practice Areas:** Chairman of the firm and a member of the firm's Management Committee. Practice focuses on mergers and acquisitions and public and private offerings. Serves as principal outside counsel to several public and private companies in the exploration and production, oilfield service, insurance and manufacturing industries, and also represents a number of major investment banks. Extensive experience in merger and acquisition transactions, representing clients in transactions totaling over $35 billion in the last two years. Has represented clients in over 150 domestic and cross-border debt and equity offerings since 2008.
**Professional Memberships:** Director, State Bar of Texas; Past President, Houston Bar Association; Past Chair, Houston Bar Foundation; Past President, Houston Young Lawyers Association; Past Director, Texas Young Lawyers Association; Trustee and Executive Committee Member, Houston Museum of Natural Science; Board of Visitors, MD Anderson Cancer Center; Board Member, Greater Houston Partnership.
**Career:** Joined Vinson & Elkins in May 1981 and admitted to partnership in January 1989. Recognized as one of 12 corporate lawyers in the United States as Dealmaker of the Year by a leading legal publication. Also listed: International Who's Who of Business Lawyers in Oil and Gas,

2009-10; Best Lawyers in America in Corporate Law, 2003-12; Texas Lawyer 'Go To' Lawyer in corporate law, 2002-11; Texas Monthly's Top 100 Lawyers, 2003-11; Best Lawyers, "Lawyer of the Year" (Mergers & Acquisitions-Houston), 2011.
**Personal:** Texas A&M University, BBA, Magna Cum Laude, 1978; Southern Methodist University, JD, 1981. Editor of SMU Law Review.

### KEVILLE, John
Winston & Strawn LLP, Houston
713 651 2659
jkeville@winston.com
*Featured in Intellectual Property (Texas)*
**Practice Areas:** John Keville heads the firm's Houston office and serves as lead counsel for both plaintiffs and defendants in IP litigation involving a wide range of technologies, including oilfield tools, cellular telephone systems, software, drilling fluids and many others. He counsels clients on protecting their intellectual property and has litigated trade secret, copyright and trademark cases, as well as other commercial and contract disputes.
**Professional Memberships:** ABA, Life Fellow of the Texas Bar Foundation, American and Houston Intellectual Property Law Associations.
**Career:** Member, Winston's Executive Committee.
**Personal:** St. John's University (JD 1995) New York Institute of Technology (BSME 1988).

### KIMBALL, Robert L
Vinson & Elkins LLP, Dallas
214 220 7860
rkimball@velaw.com
*Featured in Corporate/M&A (Texas)*
**Practice Areas:** Practice primarily involves securities offerings, mergers and acquisitions, corporate governance, private equity, and other investment activities in US and international settings.
**Professional Memberships:** American Bar Association; J Reuben Clark Law Society.
**Career:** Admitted to Texas Bar, 1988. Came to firm as Partner, 1995.
**Personal:** Graduated from Brigham Young University, BA magna cum laude, 1983, and The University of Chicago, JD, 1986 (Comment Editor, University of Chicago Law Review).

### KIMBALL JR, Albert B
Bracewell & Giuliani LLP, Houston
713 221 1377
albert.kimball@bgllp.com
*Featured in Intellectual Property (Texas)*
**Practice Areas:** Represents litigants in patent infringement litigation, either patentees or alleged infringers. Has also successfully represented clients before the Federal Circuit Court, dealing with appeals in patent cases. Represents companies in acquiring and transferring rights in intellectual property and technology in a variety of acquisitions and transactions. Represents domestic and multinational companies acquiring and seeking to protect intellectual property assets around the world. In appropriate patent litigation cases, has served as an expert witness.
**Personal:** LLM, The George Washington University Law School, 1972; LLB, The University

of Texas at Austin, 1968; BSEE, The University of Texas at Austin, 1962.

### KING, Chad W
K&L Gates, Dallas
214 939 5631
chad.king@klgates.com
*Featured in Technology (Texas)*
**Practice Areas:** Chad King advises companies in industries such as financial services, retail, media, manufacturing, and healthcare on technology transactions, licensing, Internet and e-commerce law, cloud computing, software development, outsourcing, intellectual property, mobile technology, and privacy issues. He frequently counsels companies on the licensing, acquisition and use of mission-critical technology and professional services. He has founded several websites covering privacy, the Internet, and legal technology tools. Mr King currently maintains a blog focused on cloud computing at www.legalcloud-central.com. He also co-founded the Association of Technology Law Professionals, a networking and educational group for in-house technology and outsourcing lawyers.

### KINZIE, Jack L
Baker Botts LLP, Dallas
214 953 6727
jack.kinzie@bakerbotts.com
*Featured in Bankruptcy/Restructuring (Texas)*
**Practice Areas:** Represents debtors, lenders, acquirers, creditors, directors, and parent companies in chapter 11 cases.
**Career:** Innovated prepackaged mass tort bankruptcies as Dyncorp's counsel in the bankruptcy case of its subsidiary, Fuller-Austin Insulation Company and as Halliburton's counsel in the Dresser Industries and KBR bankruptcy cases. Served as debtor's counsel to ASARCO LLC which paid its creditors in full. The presiding judge described the case as perhaps the most successful complex chapter 11 case in bankruptcy history.
**Personal:** University of Oklahoma College of Law; Order of the Coif; Editor, Oklahoma Law Review.

### KIRKLAND, David
Baker Botts LLP, Houston
713 229 1101
david.kirkland@bakerbotts.com
*Featured in Corporate/M&A (Texas)*
**Practice Areas:** Chair: Corporate Department (firmwide); Member: Executive Committee. Concentrates on mergers and acquisitions, securities offerings and corporate control and governance issues. Represents parties and investment bankers in mergers and acquisitions, including negotiated acquisitions and dispositions, controlled auctions, tender offers and related financings. Involved in many of the largest mergers in the oilfield service sector and participates in numerous contested takeovers and proxy fights. Represents issuers, underwriters and shareholders in capital markets transactions.
**Professional Memberships:** Member, American Law Institute.
**Personal:** JD, Yale Law School, 1983; BA, summa cum laude, Economics, Yale College, 1980.

### KIZZIAR JR, James H
Bracewell & Giuliani LLP, San Antonio
210 299 3526
James.Kizziar@bgllp.com
*Featured in Labor & Employment (Texas)*
**Practice Areas:** Represents and counsels the managers and owners of diverse companies and business entities in all aspects of labor and employment law, before federal and state agencies and the courts. His practice includes litigation and preventive counseling of management on issues such as discrimination, harassment, union organizing and wage-hour issues. Conducts employment law training for executives, managers and supervisors.
**Personal:** JD, Duke University School of Law, 1976; BA, Ohio Wesleyan University, 1973.

### KONTRIMAS, Andrius
Fulbright & Jaworski LLP, Houston
713 651 5482
akontrimas@fulbright.com
*Featured in Tax (Texas)*
**Practice Areas:** Tax.
**Professional Memberships:** Taxation Section, American Bar Association; United States Supreme Court Bar Association; International Fiscal Association; Federalist Society.
**Career:** Kontrimas, a Fulbright partner, has more than 27 years of experience in tax and business law working with both domestic and foreign business matters, counseling clients on global tax planning, transfer pricing, joint ventures, private equity transactions, international mergers and acquisitions, financial derivatives, contested tax matters, corporate counseling, non-profit and exempt organizations and art law.
**Personal:** JD, University of California, Los Angeles, School of Law (1985); BA, University of California, Berkeley 1982.

### KORBY, Mary
K&L Gates, Dallas
214 939 4906
mary.korby@klgates.com
*Featured in Corporate/M&A (Texas)*
**Practice Areas:** Mary Korby's practice focuses on mergers and acquisitions, including complex crossborder public and private transactions, restructurings and bankruptcy-related acquisitions and divestitures in the biofuels, rendering, chemicals, aviation and manufacturing industries. She is representing AMR Corporation in connection with its $11 billion merger with US Airways, creating the largest airline in the United States, and has represented Darling International in its $840 million acquisition of Griffin Industries, Lone Star Technologies in its $2 billion disposition to US Steel, and General Growth in its Howard Hughes Corporation spin-off.

### KORNEGAY, Nancy
Brown & Kornegay LLP, Houston
713 528 3705
nkornegay@bkllp.com
*Featured in Insurance (Texas)*
**Practice Areas:** Practices primarily in the areas of commercial litigation and insurance-policyholder representation. Represents energy and

transportation companies, medical and manufacturing facilities, and technology-sector businesses in insurance coverage disputes, litigation, appeals, and arbitrations.
**Professional Memberships:** Member of the Federal Bar Association; American Bar Association; Houston Bar Association.
**Career:** Admitted to practice in Texas in 2001. Joined Vinson & Elkins in 2001. Co-founded Brown & Kornegay in March 2008.
**Publications:** D&O Policies: Giving Notice of "Circumstances," Fall 2008; Prima Paint to First Options: The Supreme Court's Procrustean Approach to the Federal Arbitration Act and Fraud, 38 Houston Law Review 335 (2001).
**Personal:** University of Houston Law Center, 2001 JD, with honors; University of Houston, Houston, Texas, 1997, BA, summa cum laude.

## KRIEGER, Paul
Morgan, Lewis & Bockius LLP, Houston
713 890 5160
pkrieger@morganlewis.com
*Featured in Intellectual Property (Texas)*
**Practice Areas:** Paul Krieger has more than 40 years of intellectual property law prosecution, licensing, counseling, and litigation experience. He has been lead counsel in more than 50 patent, trademark, trade secret, and copyright lawsuits in courts throughout the United States and is a frequent lecturer and author on intellectual property issues in the US, Europe, India and China. He is an adjunct professor at the University of Houston teaching trademark and trade secret law.
**Personal:** George Washington University Law School, 1971, LLM; University of Maryland School of Law, 1968, LLB; University of Pittsburgh, 1964, BS.

## KRIESER, Jason D
K&L Gates, Dallas
214 939 5423
jason.krieser@klgates.com
*Featured in Outsourcing (Nationwide), Technology (Texas)*
**Practice Areas:** Jason Krieser represents companies in outsourcing, technology transactions and general corporate matters. Technology transactions include information technology and business process outsourcing, licensing, distribution arrangements for software and hardware, joint ventures, strategic alliances, and technology service arrangements, such as cloud computing services. He also represents clients in IP asset transfers and in service arrangements relating to mergers and acquisitions. He counsels clients on day to day technology operational issues, such as advice on strategic customer and supplier relationships, privacy issues, data security issues, product distribution channels, software development, and software implementation.

## KRUSE, C Thomas
Baker & Hostetler LLP, Houston
713 646 1365
tkruse@bakerlaw.com
*Featured in Litigation (Texas)*
**Career:** Tom Kruse heads BakerHostetler's Complex Commercial Litigation group.

Recognized by his peers as an experienced trial and arbitration lawyer, he has been listed in The Best Lawyers in America and as a "Top 100 in Texas" lawyer in Texas Super Lawyers. His expertise is reflected in more than 20 years of experience of practices in federal and state courts, including trials and appeals, and in arbitrations before national and international bodies. Mr Kruse focuses his practice in energy, engineering and construction, financial issues, intellectual property, and an array of complex issues for clients in the US and abroad.

## KRUSE, Layne
Fulbright & Jaworski LLP, Houston
713 651 5194
lkruse@fulbright.com
*Featured in Antitrust (Texas)*
**Practice Areas:** Antitrust and trade regulation; securities litigation; government investigations; international litigation and arbitration; class actions; energy.
**Professional Memberships:** ABA Antitrust Section; Texas State Bar; Texas Association of Civil Trial Specialists; Certified in Civil Trial Law by the Texas Board of Legal Specialization.
**Career:** Head, Fulbright's Houston Litigation Department; Co-Head, Fulbright's Antitrust and Competition Practice Group; former judicial clerk for Chief Judge John R. Brown, US Court of Appeals, Fifth Circuit.
**Personal:** JD, Yale Law School (1977); MSc, London School of Economics (1974); BA, Texas A&M University (economics) (1973).

## KUDLAC, Kevin
Weil, Gotshal & Manges LLP, Houston
713 546 5020
kevin.kudlac@weil.com
*Featured in Intellectual Property (Texas)*
**Practice Areas:** Kevin Kudlac's practice focuses on patent disputes involving complex electrical and computer-related technology. He has handled cases involving operating system software, telecommunications software and hardware, financial transaction software, Word Processing Systems and Software, microprocessors, PC chipsets, computer memory, semiconductor processing technology, analog-to-digital converters and video software. He also handled cases in other technologies including: medical devices; food processing; and electrical appliances. He has extensive experience with litigating intellectual property matters in Asia and Europe. Prior experience as a software engineer at Schlumberger Industries.
**Personal:** University of Dayton (BS, 1987); Georgia State University College of Law (JD, 1991).

## KURTZ, Marcy E
Bracewell & Giuliani LLP, Houston
713 221 1206
marcy.kurtz@bgllp.com
*Featured in Bankruptcy/Restructuring (Texas)*
**Practice Areas:** Advises banks and other lenders on creditors' rights issues and represents clients in litigation, both within and outside the bankruptcy context. Also provides pre-bankruptcy advice to debtors, including debt restructuring

and maximizing use of exemption laws and other safe harbors, and advises corporate clients on bankruptcy implications of various corporate merger and acquisition transactions. Also handles complex commercial and collection litigation cases in state and federal courts. She has acquired particular experience in fraud litigation and preferential transfer and other avoidance action litigation.
**Personal:** JD, The University of Houston Law Center, 1981; BBA, The University of Texas, 1977.

## KURYLA, Matthew
Baker Botts LLP, Houston
713 229 1114
matthew.kuryla@bakerbotts.com
*Featured in Environment (Texas)*
**Practice Areas:** Environmental regulatory litigation, compliance counseling, project authorization and permitting.
**Professional Memberships:** State Bar of Texas, Houston Bar Association, Houston Bar Foundation (Fellow), Houston/Galveston Air Quality Leadership Group, Greater Houston Partnership Environment Committee, Texas Industry Project.
**Career:** Environmental practice encompasses regulatory counseling, transactional advice, litigation and alternative dispute resolution. Represents clients before state and federal courts in a variety of environmental actions. Coordinated litigation, regulatory negotiation and rulemaking as counsel to several Texas industry coalitions responding to emerging air quality requirements.
**Personal:** JD, University of Virginia School of Law (1989); BA (with highest distinction), University of Virginia (1986).

## LAFOLLETTE, Christine B
Akin Gump Strauss Hauer & Feld LLP, Houston
713 220 5896
clafollette@akingump.com
*Featured in Corporate/M&A (Texas), Energy & Natural Resources (Nationwide)*
**Practice Areas:** Represents issuers/underwriters in public and private offerings of equity/debt securities, restructurings, financings, including MLPs. Represents clients in M&A/dispositions, particularly in the energy industry. Represents boards of directors in securities and corporate governance matters. Partner-in-Charge, Houston Office.
**Professional Memberships:** Sustaining Fellow, Houston Bar Association and Texas Bar Foundation; Member of Advisory Council Tahirih Justice Center; Director of National Association of Corporate Directors Texas Tricities Chapter; former Chair of Corporate Counsel Section; former Director of Houston Bar Foundation and Houston World Affairs Council.
**Personal:** BS (highest honors), University of Texas; JD (honors), Loyola University.

## LAFUZE, William L
Vinson & Elkins LLP, Houston
713 758 2595
wlafuze@velaw.com
*Featured in Intellectual Property (Texas)*

**Practice Areas:** Practices in all areas of intellectual property law, with emphasis on computer, internet, electronics, and computer-related patent litigation. He has handled patent litigation in District Courts in the Eastern District of Texas and throughout the United States, as well as appeals to the United States Court of Appeals for the Federal Circuit.
**Professional Memberships:** Former President: American Intellectual Property Law Association. Past Chair: American Bar Association, Section of Intellectual Property Law. Former Member: Patent Public Advisory Committee, United States Patent and Trademark Office Law. Past Member: Presidential Transition Team Task force on the United States Patent Office; Past Chair, State Bar of Texas, Intellectual Property Law Section.
**Career:** Partner, Intellectual Property Section, Vinson & Elkins; Admitted to practice: Texas, 1973. Joined Vinson & Elkins, 1973.
**Publications:** Authored over 100 articles on IP Law and Litigation.
**Personal:** University of Texas, BS in Physics, 1969; Southern Methodist University, MS in Applied Science, 1971; University of Texas, JD, 1973.

## LAMBERT, Arthur
Kane Russell Coleman & Logan PC, Dallas
214 777 4225
alambert@krcl.com
*Featured in Labor & Employment (Texas)*
**Practice Areas:** Litigation with an emphasis in labor and employment law.
**Professional Memberships:** Dallas Bar Association; American Bar Association.
**Career:** Licensed to practice in 1989. Certified by the Texas Board of Legal Specialization in Labor and Employment Law. Joined the firm in 2005 and is a director. Named in Texas Super Lawyers® and Texas Monthly magazines (2006-13).
**Publications:** Regularly publishes articles on a variety of legal topics in national and regional publications such as Best's Review, "The Best Defense," Insurance Journal, "Steer Your Clients Away from Risk of Sexual Harassment Claims," WARD'S DealerBusiness, "Danger in the Dealership," Business First (Buffalo, NY) "Helping to Combat Sexual Harassment," Dallas Business Journal, "Sexual Harassment Training Pays Dividends," Houston Business Journal, "Basic Steps to Reduce Sexual Harassment, Texas Lawyer, "Praying for Answers – Religion in the Workplace and Workplace Ministries" (March 7, 2005), "Religion in the Workplace, How Far Can it Go? Dallas Bar Headnotes" (August 1, 2006). Numerous Op-Ed articles and quotes in publications such as Texas Lawyer, Lawyers USA and the Dallas and Houston Business Journals; gives seminars on a variety of topics including EEOC and management training.
**Personal:** State University of New York at Stony Brook, BA (1982), Phi Beta Kappa. University of Virginia School of Law, JD (1989).

**LANSDALE, Daryl**
Fulbright & Jaworski LLP, San Antonio
210 270 9367
dlansdale@fulbright.com
*Featured in Technology (Texas)*
**Practice Areas:** Corporate and securities; mergers and acquisitions; private equity and investment funds; venture capital; technology and emerging companies.
**Professional Memberships:** American Bar Association; State Bar of Texas.
**Career:** Head of Mergers/Acquisitions and Corporate and Securities department in the firm's San Antonio office. Named to 'The Best Lawyers in America' and "Texas Super Lawyer" by Texas Monthly magazine.
**Personal:** JD, Southern Methodist University School of Law (1992); BBA, magna cum laude, The University of Texas (1989).

**LAVALLE, Kathleen**
Jackson Walker LLP, Dallas
214 953 6144
klavalle@jw.com
*Featured in Energy & Natural Resources (Texas)*
**Career:** Kathleen McElroy LaValle has dedicated her career to achieving quality results in high-stakes legal disputes. She handles a wide range of complex litigation in areas including antitrust, lender liability, energy, health care, securities fraud, business tort, intellectual property, environmental, and telecommunications. She also has been actively involved in high-profile state regulatory dockets involving energy and telecommunications. She is a past chair of the Texas State Bar Antitrust and Business Litigation Section and taught Texas pretrial and trial and appellate procedure as an adjunct professor at SMU law school.
**Personal:** JD, Southern Methodist University; BA, University of Notre Dame.

**LEAHY, James R**
Locke Lord LLP, Houston
713 226 1125
jleahy@lockelord.com
*Featured in Litigation (Texas)*
**Practice Areas:** Chair of the Firm's Energy Litigation Practice Group. He has substantial experience in general civil litigation proceedings in federal/state courts in the oil and gas industry and in commercial and business disputes, lender liability, white collar criminal defense and internal investigations, securities litigation, fraud, insurance, deceptive trade practices and actions.
**Professional Memberships:** ABA; Texas Bar Foundation; American College of Trial Lawyers (Fellow); State Bar of Texas; American Board of Trial Advocates.
**Career:** Partner at Locke Lord since 2005.
**Personal:** The University of Texas School of Law (JD, 1971); The University of Texas at Austin (BBA, 1968).

**LECLAIR, Lewis**
McKool Smith, Dallas
214 978 4000
lleclair@mckoolsmith.com
*Featured in Litigation (Texas)*

**Practice Areas:** Complex commercial litigation and intellectual property litigation.
**Professional Memberships:** State Bar of Texas, Dallas Bar Association, Texas Bar Foundation.
**Career:** Lew LeClair has been a trial lawyer for more than 30 years representing both plaintiffs and defendants in complex commercial and IP disputes. He is Board Certified in Civil Trial Law by the Texas Board of Legal Specialization. Mr LeClair is consistently recognized by leading legal directories, including Chambers USA, Best Lawyers, and Lawdragon.
**Personal:** University of Texas School of Law (JD, with honors, 1976); University of Texas (BBA, with honors, 1973).

**LEE, James J**
Vinson & Elkins LLP, Dallas
214 220 7744
jimlee@velaw.com
*Featured in Bankruptcy/Restructuring (Texas)*
**Practice Areas:** Insolvencies, reorganizations, workouts, and creditor's rights, with special emphasis on complex commercial and bankruptcy litigation, including arbitrations and mediations. Board Certified in Civil Trial Law, Texas Board of Legal Specialization. Litigation experience includes creditors' rights, lender liability, securities fraud, class actions, fraudulent transfers, and all forms of business torts. Extensive litigation experience in complex bankruptcy cases on behalf of secured lenders, debtors, creditors' committees, equity sponsors, and trustees.
**Professional Memberships:** American Bar Association.
**Career:** Admitted to Texas Bar, 1976. Came to firm as Partner, 2000.
**Personal:** Tulane University, BA, 1973; University of Virginia School of Law, JD, 1976.

**LEE, William S**
Fulbright & Jaworski LLP, Houston
713 651 5633
wlee@fulbright.com
*Featured in Tax (Texas)*
**Practice Areas:** Tax.
**Career:** Bill Lee concentrates his practice on all phases of federal tax controversy, including representation of individual taxpayers, partnerships, estates, and corporations in IRS examinations, before the IRS Appeals Office, and in litigation in the Tax Court, the Court of Federal Claims, District Courts, and the Courts of Appeals. He has spoken at programs sponsored by many of the nation's premier tax associations and institutes.
**Personal:** LLM, Taxation, New York University School of Law (1979); LLB, The University of Texas Law School (1975); BBA, The University of Texas(1972); Certified Public Accountant.

**LEMON, Neel**
Baker Botts LLP, Dallas
214 953 6954
neel.lemon@bakerbotts.com
*Featured in Corporate/M&A (Texas)*
**Practice Areas:** Head of Dallas Office Corporate Department. Represents public and private corporate and investment banking clients in mergers and acquisitions, securities offering

transactions and corporate finance. Counsels companies in connection with corporate governance, fiduciary duties, Sarbanes-Oxley compliance, securities law disclosure and compliance, and SEC and other governmental investigations. A frequent speaker on legal issues.
**Personal:** JD, with honors, Texas Tech University School of Law,1979 ; BBA, finance, Texas Tech University, 1976.

**LEVY, David**
Morgan, Lewis & Bockius LLP, Houston
713 890 5000
dlevy@morganlewis.com
*Featured in Intellectual Property (Texas)*
**Practice Areas:** David Levy leads the Houston office's Litigation Practice and is co-chair of the Firm's Technology Industry Client Initiative. He focuses on complex commercial and intellectual property disputes in technology, energy and other industries. He advises clients on crisis management and international litigation, and is editor of the ABA's book on international litigation. He has tried commercial cases in Texas state and federal courts as well as before domestic and international arbitration tribunals, and has tried patent cases in the Eastern District of Texas.
**Personal:** Harvard Law School, 1991, JD; University of Texas, 1987, BA, Highest Honors/Phi Beta Kappa.

**LEWIS, Edward**
Fulbright & Jaworski LLP, Houston
713 651 3760
elewis@fulbright.com
*Featured in Environment (Texas)*
**Practice Areas:** Environmental law.
**Professional Memberships:** Board of Directors, Houston-Galveston Air Emissions Reduction Credit Organization.
**Career:** Lewis focuses his practice in the environmental law area, including environmental litigation, enforcement actions, compliance counseling, climate change, remediation, permitting, auditing, and transactional matters. His practice frequently involves legal issues in which complex technical issues are at the forefront. Prior to joining Fulbright, Eddie worked as a chemical engineer.
**Personal:** JD, with honors, University of Texas (1992); BS, Texas A & M University (1988).

**LEWIS, Troy B**
Jones Day, Dallas
214 969 3721
tblewis@jonesday.com
*Featured in Corporate/M&A (Texas)*
**Practice Areas:** Co-Head of the M&A Practice in the Texas region. Handles M&A, private equity and capital markets transactions, regional, national and international in scope, across a variety of industries, including the basic materials, energy, health care, manufacturing, and technology sectors, on behalf of corporate and private equity clients. Extensive experience with distressed M&A transactions. Regularly advises on corporate governance, fiduciary duties, executive compensation, and disclosure and other securities law matters. Recently represented Arctic Glacier, Fluor Corporation, Kaiser Aluminum, Micron

Technology, Patriarch Partners, Weir Group, and Zoran Corporation in significant transactions.
**Professional Memberships:** State Bar of Texas.

**LEWIS, Veronica**
Gibson, Dunn & Crutcher LLP, Dallas
214 698 3320
vlewis@gibsondunn.com
*Featured in Antitrust (Texas)*
**Practice Areas:** Broad experience in highly complex civil litigation matters, including antitrust; business tort; false claims act; false advertising; patent; trademark, and copyright infringement; securities; and theft of trade secret. Lead or co-lead counsel for principal defendant in Processed Egg Products and Rail Freight Fuel Surcharge Antitrust Litigations. Obtained unanimous defense verdict for Tyler Perry in EDTX copyright infringement matter.
**Professional Memberships:** American Bar Association, Antitrust Section. Dallas Bar Association. Center for American and Internal Law, Board of Trustees.
**Career:** Former General Counsel for healthcare GPO Novation, LLC.
**Personal:** SB, MIT, 1983, Chemical Engineering. JD, Harvard Law School, 1986.

**LIPE, Guy**
Vinson & Elkins LLP, Houston
713 758 1109
glipe@velaw.com
*Featured in Litigation (Texas)*
**Practice Areas:** Guy is an experienced trial lawyer who has extensive experience representing companies in the energy industry both in courts and arbitration in connection with all types of commercial disputes. He has particular expertise handling upstream and midstream oil and gas litigation, including royalty disputes, and in representing non-US parties sued in the United States. Guy chairs Vinson & Elkins' Energy Litigation Practice Group.
**Professional Memberships:** Past Co-Chair, International Litigation Committee, ABA Section of International Law.
**Career:** Partner since 1991.
**Personal:** University of Texas School of Law (JD 1983); Texas A&M University (BBA 1980).

**LITTLE, Robert B**
Gibson, Dunn & Crutcher LLP, Dallas
rlittle@gibsondunn.com
214 698 3260
*Featured in Corporate/M&A (Texas)*
**Practice Areas:** Focuses on corporate transactions, including mergers and acquisitions, securities offerings, joint ventures, investments in public and private entities, and commercial transactions. Also advises business organizations regarding matters such as securities law disclosure, corporate governance, and fiduciary obligations. Represents investment funds and their sponsors along with investors in such funds, as well as clients in a variety of industries, including energy, retail, technology, transportation, manufacturing, and financial services.
**Personal:** Former law clerk to Patrick Higginbotham, US Court of Appeals for the Fifth

Circuit. JD, University of Texas, 1998, highest honors, Order of the Coif, Articles Editor, Texas Law Review.

## LITTLEJOHN, James R
Winstead PC, Dallas
214 745 5197
jlittlejohn@winstead.com
*Featured in Banking & Finance (Texas)*
**Practice Areas:** Jim Littlejohn has more than 30 years of experience in finance and banking, and has primarily represented lenders in various types of corporate and commercial lending. He represents and counsels agents, bank groups, individual lenders and borrowers in structuring and documenting secured and unsecured commercial and corporate credit facilities, including multilender syndicated credits, multi-currency financings, acquisition financings, letter of credit facilities and asset-based facilities. He also represents lending parties in financial transactions in varied industries, and is involved in facilities with multiple debt levels, with extensive involvement with subordinated debt and inter-creditor issues.

## LONDA, Jeffrey C
Ogletree, Deakins, Nash, Smoak & Stewart, PC, Houston
713 655 5750
jeffrey.londa@ogletreedeakins.com
*Featured in Labor & Employment (Texas)*
**Practice Areas:** Labor and employment.
**Professional Memberships:** Texas Association of Business (Chair (1993-2010), State Employment Relations Committee; Board of Directors), American Arbitration Association (Panel of Arbitrators), American Public Transit Association Legal Affairs/13(c) Committee.
**Career:** Listed, "Lawyer of the Year" in Best Lawyers in America, Fellow, the College of Labor and Employment Lawyers. Adjunct Professor at Thurgood Marshall School of Law, TSU.
**Publications:** Author, O'Connor's Texas Employment Codes Plus (Jones McClure Pub.); Author, O'Connor's Federal Employment Codes Plus (Jones McClure Pub.); Executive Editor, Texas Labor Letter (1991-2000).
**Personal:** University of Texas at Austin (BA with honors, 1972), SMU (JD, 1975).

## LOWELL, Cym H
McDermott Will & Emery LLP, Houston
972 232 3063
clowell@mwe.com
*Featured in Tax (Texas)*
**Practice Areas:** Focuses on assisting clients on transfer pricing, international tax Advance Pricing Agreements and Competent Authority matters. Has advised the US House Committee on Ways and Means, and served as expert witness for the United States in treaty responsibility litigation.
**Professional Memberships:** OECD Business and Industry Advisory Committee (Paris), Taxation Commission of International Chamber of Commerce (Paris), US Council of International Business.
**Personal:** JD, Duke University Law School, 1972; BS, Indiana University, 1969.

## LOWERY, David
Jones Day, Dallas
214 969 3710
djlowery@JonesDay.com
*Featured in Real Estate (Texas)*
**Practice Areas:** Co-chairs Jones Day's Real Estate Practice and leads the Real Estate Capital Markets Practice. Represents clients in complex real estate transactions, focusing on acquisitions, dispositions, M&A, financings, and joint ventures. He has significant experience in international real estate transactions, as well as distressed asset transactions, workouts, and bulk sales of nonperforming loans and real estate owned, and frequently speaks on real estate private equity topics. Clients include Morgan Stanley, Mill Creek, TriGate Capital, HighBrook Investment Management, GreenOak Real Estate Partners, Whitman Peterson, and Behringer Harvard.
**Professional Memberships:** Member of the National Association of Real Estate Investment Trusts.

## LUKIN, Mitch
Baker Botts LLP, Houston
713 229 1733
mitch.lukin@bakerbotts.com
*Featured in Intellectual Property (Texas)*
**Practice Areas:** Primary expertise in intellectual property transactions and litigation. Represents clients in licensing and other intellectual property transactions. Counsels clients on intellectual property asset management, including technology transfer, transaction due diligence, evaluation of intellectual property assets and evaluation and minimization of litigation risks. Represents both plaintiffs and defendants in intellectual property litigation.
**Professional Memberships:** Houston, Texas and American Bar Associations.
**Personal:** JD, with high honors, University of Houston Law Center, 1982; Bachelor of Electrical Engineering (1972) and MSEE (1976), Georgia Tech.

## LYDA, Kirk R
Jones Day, Dallas
214 969 5013
klyda@jonesday.com
*Featured in Tax (Texas)*
**Practice Areas:** Concentrates his practice on state tax litigation, controversies, and planning. For more than a decade, he has handled state tax controversies ranging from elimination of audit risk via voluntary disclosures and letter rulings, to field audits, administrative hearings, lawsuits, and appeals. He regularly advises clients on the state tax implications of restructuring their domestic business operations. He speaks routinely at conferences on a variety of state tax topics. He co-authored Accounting and Finance for Lawyers, a Harcourt publication, and Business Purpose: What Is It? How Much Is Enough?, a NYU Institute publication. Internet: http://www.jonesday.com/klyda/

## LYNCH, John Edward
Vinson & Elkins LLP, Houston
713 758 1050
jlynch@velaw.com
*Featured in Tax (Texas)*
**Practice Areas:** Partner in the firm's Tax Section focusing on federal income tax aspects of domestic and international transactions.
**Career:** Admitted to Texas Bar, 1986. John came to the Firm in 1986 and was admitted to the partnership in January 1995.
**Personal:** Graduated from Baylor University, BBA in Accounting with honors, 1983; The University of Texas School of Law, JD with honors, 1986 (Order of the Coif).

## LYNN, Mike
Lynn Tillotson Pinker & Cox, LLP, Dallas
214 981 3800
mlynn@lynnllp.com
*Featured in Litigation (Texas)*
**Career:** Mike Lynn brings unmatched experience to the practice of law. He has tried to verdict more than 97 civil and criminal jury trials and handled over 100 non-jury, arbitration and injunction matters in his distinguished career, winning well over $300 million for his clients. Mr Lynn, the founder of the firm, believes one of the keys to his firm's success is that "[w]e are an elite, highly-motivated group of business trial lawyers. We are the 'special forces of litigation.' We are prepared, experienced, tough and creative." Mike has published numerous articles and is a frequent speaker on legal topics. He has taught law classes at SMU, is active in a number of professional organizations including the ALI, has served as Co-Chair of a number of Committees of the ABA, most recently the Federal Rules Task Force and was co-editor of the Litigation Section's Business Tort Jury Instruction Project, 2nd Edition. Mike served as a Council Member of the Litigation Section of the ABA, and is presently serving as co-chair of the Litigation Institute of Trial Training. He is married to the Honorable Barbara M.G. Lynn, United States District Judge, Northern District of Texas. He received his undergraduate degree from the University of Virginia and his law degree from SMU.

## LYONS, J Matthew
Andrews Kurth LLP, Austin
512 320 9284
mlyons@andrewskurth.com
*Featured in Technology (Texas)*
**Practice Areas:** Matt represents entrepreneurial private and public technology, cleantech, life science and other emerging growth companies along with those that invest in them. Matt advises companies, entrepreneurs and investors on forming and operating businesses, raising capital through private and public offerings, and buying and selling companies. He regularly counsels companies and boards on compliance with federal securities laws, corporate governance and executive compensation matters. He represents and maintains relationships with numerous venture capital, private equity and investment banking firms. He also counsels institutional investors in their invest-

ments in onshore and offshore private equity, venture capital and hedge funds.

## MACK, Elizabeth E
Locke Lord LLP, Dallas
214 740 8598
emack@lockelord.com
*Featured in Environment (Texas)*
**Practice Areas:** Chairs the Firm's Environmental Section, making her the leader of one of the largest groups of dedicated environmental practitioners in a major law firm. Has substantial experience in environmental compliance, environmental litigation and environmental transactional work. Employs creative solutions to environmentally-challenged projects. Is leading site remediation efforts in 11 states.
**Professional Memberships:** State Bar of Texas (Past Chair, Litigation Section); Texas Appleseed (Board of Directors); Dallas and Texas Bar Foundations; Texas Supreme Court Task Force to Expand Legal Services Delivery to the Poor.
**Career:** Partner since 1995.
**Personal:** Harvard Law School (JD, 1988); Northwestern University (BA, 1985).

## MALIN, Steven
Sidley Austin LLP, Dallas
214 981 3386
smalin@sidley.com
*Featured in Intellectual Property (Texas)*
**Practice Areas:** A seasoned litigator with over twenty trials in his career, most recently including: a 2012 patent defense victory for an optical fiber manufacturer in a jury case; a 2011 patent defense victory in the ITC on behalf of an Asian semiconductor manufacturer; a successful award in 2010 of domain name rights to the world's largest publicly funded museum in a jury case (the case settling after Mr Malin's cross examination of the opponent's corporate representative); and a seven figure recovery in 2009 on behalf of shareholders in a jury case (the case settling after Mr Malin's opening statement).

## MALONE, Michael L
Greenberg Traurig, LLP, Dallas
214 665 3691
MaloneM@gtlaw.com
*Featured in Healthcare (Texas)*
**Practice Areas:** Health and FDA business; corporate and securities; public finance; financial institutions; antitrust; capital markets and securities; financial institutions litigation; health litigation; health public policy practice; health transactions; mergers/acquisitions; public finance/municipal bonds; structured finance; Texas regulatory.
**Professional Memberships:** Life Fellow, Texas Bar Foundation. Member: American Health Lawyers Association; Health Law Section, State Bar of Texas; American Bar Association.
**Career:** Selected: Best Lawyers in America, 1991-2013; Texas' Best Lawyers, 2009-10; Chambers USA Guide, 2004, 2011-13. Rated, AV® Preeminent™ 5.0 out of 5.
**Personal:** JD, The University of Texas School of Law, 1973; BA, Texas Christian University, 1970.

**MALONEY, James**
Andrews Kurth LLP, Houston
713 229 1255
james.maloney@bakerbotts.com
*Featured in Litigation (Texas)*
**Practice Areas:** Trial practice involving securities transactions; takeover disputes; defense of individual, derivative, and class action claims against business institutions, officers, and directors; corporate investigations; representation of audit and special committees; complex commercial litigation; and trade secret litigation. He has tried cases all over Texas, and in the states of Delaware, California, Nevada, New Jersey, and New York.
**Career:** Best Lawyers in America, Texas Super Lawyers, profiled in 'Big Suits', The American Lawyer, January, 2006.
**Personal:** JD, Harvard Law School, 1975; BA cum laude, Yale University, 1972; Board of Trustees, Museum of Fine Arts, Houston.

**MANTHEY, Ron**
Morgan, Lewis & Bockius LLP, Dallas
214 466 4111
ron.manthey@morganlewis.com
*Featured in Labor & Employment (Texas)*
**Practice Areas:** Ronald E Manthey is a partner in Morgan Lewis's Labor and Employment Practice and co-chair of the Noncompete and Trade Secrets Practice. He has represented Fortune 500 companies in class actions and other complex litigation involving national and state wide discrimination claims. He has litigated and tried numerous nationwide and regional FLSA collective actions. He has tried cases in all areas of employment law, including unfair competition cases, having tried over 30 employment law jury and bench trials and arbitrations.
**Personal:** Attended University of Virginia School of Law, 1979, JD; University of Southern Mississippi, 1976 BA.

**MARCUS, Courtney**
Fulbright & Jaworski LLP, Dallas
214 855 7464
cmarcus@fulbright.com
*Featured in Banking & Finance (Texas)*
**Practice Areas:** Banking and finance; private equity; investment funds.
**Professional Memberships:** State Bar of Texas; Dallas Bar Association; State Bar of New York; American Bar Association.
**Career:** Co-head of the Dallas Corporate Finance practice; licensed in Texas and New York. Ms Marcus has extensive experience in a variety of debt financing and restructuring transactions, representing private equity firms, corporate borrowers, financial institutions and other investors in leveraged acquisition and recapitalization transactions, bridge and mezzanine financing, cash flow and asset-based lending, domestic and cross-border financings, debtor-in-possession financing and loan restructurings.
**Personal:** JD, St. Mary's University (1998); BA, Economics, Vanderbilt University (1995).

**MARCUS, Stephen**
Baker Botts LLP, Dallas
214 953 6533
steve.marcus@bakerbotts.com
*Featured in Tax (Texas)*
**Practice Areas:** Provides tax related structuring and counseling in connection with the formation of, investment in, and the acquisition and disposition of investments by, private equity funds, MLPs and REITs. Advises on project acquisition and disposition by, and mergers, acquisitions, recapitalizations, formations, restructurings, roll-ups, and liquidations of, limited partnerships and other pass-through entities involved in the oil and gas and real estate industries.
**Professional Memberships:** State Bar of Texas; certified public accountant.
**Career:** Joined Baker Botts in 1986; admitted to partnership 1995.
**Personal:** The University of Texas, BBA, with honors, 1983; Southern Methodist University School of Law, JD, 1986.

**MARKUS, James A**
Vinson & Elkins LLP, Dallas
214 220 7836
jmarkus@velaw.com
*Featured in Banking & Finance (Texas)*
**Practice Areas:** Jim's practice focuses on commercial lending, corporate finance, loan workouts and restructurings. He has over 30 years of experience representing financial institutions and borrowers in numerous types of financings, with a special emphasis on syndicated loans. Jim has special expertise in asset-based lending, leveraged acquisitions and debtor in possession financing.
**Professional Memberships:** Member: Turnaround Management Association; Commercial Financial Services Committee, Business Law Section, American Bar Association; Texas Association of Bank Counsel.
**Career:** Cornell Law School, JD, 1977; Yale University, BA cum laude with special distinction in History, 1974 (John Addison Porter Prize in American History).

**MARSTON III, Edgar J**
Bracewell & Giuliani LLP, Houston
713 221 1315
edgar.marston@bgllp.com
*Featured in Corporate/M&A (Texas)*
**Practice Areas:** Has practiced law for more than 40 years, with an emphasis on asset acquisitions, business combinations and divestitures, securities offerings, and contests for corporate control. Clients have included companies engaged in oil and gas, cement production, computer manufacturing, telecommunications, biotech, heating and air conditioning manufacturing and retail sales businesses. Served as a senior officer and member of the board of directors for a major NYSE company. Has also been legal counsel to special committees of boards of directors and controlling stockholders in public companies.
**Personal:** LLB, The University of Texas School of Law, 1964; BA, Brown University, 1961.

**MARTIN, John**
Baker Botts LLP, Dallas
214 953 6757
john.martin@bakerbotts.com
*Featured in Outsourcing (Nationwide), Technology (Texas)*
**Practice Areas:** Mergers and acquisitions, corporate finance/securities, outsourcing, and joint ventures. Represents purchasers and sellers in complex M&A transactions, acquisitions, divestitures, leveraged buyouts, and spin-offs. Represents issuers and underwriters in public offerings. Extensive experience with venture capital and private equity fund transactions. Represents industry leaders in wide variety of technology transactions, including complex BPO/ITO outsourcings. Counsels senior management, boards of directors and special committees on corporate governance, disclosure, Sarbanes Oxley and compliance issues. Significant client concentration in technology sector.
**Personal:** JD, with honors, The University of Texas School of Law, 1984; BA, summa cum laude, political science, Baylor University, 1981.

**MARTIN, Mark R**
McDermott Will & Emery LLP, Houston
713 653 1719
mrmartin@mwe.com
*Featured in Tax (Texas)*
**Practice Areas:** Head of the Firm's Transfer Pricing Practice. Represents multinational enterprises and other clients in international transfer pricing and tax controversy matters relating to cross-border operations, investments and transactions. Regularly advises clients on competent authority cases, negotiates advance pricing agreements, and provides guidance on FIN 48 (FASB ASC 740-10) matters, with a particular focus on their effect on transfer pricing, permanent establishment and other international tax issues.
**Professional Memberships:** State Bar of Texas; American Bar Association.
**Personal:** LLM, Washington University School of Law, 1993; JD, University of Toledo College of Law, 1992, BA, University of Cincinnati, 1989.

**MARTIN, Paul**
Vinson & Elkins LLP, Dallas
214 220 7875
pmartin@velaw.com
*Featured in Real Estate (Texas)*
**Practice Areas:** Experience includes representation of a wide variety of clients engaged in many types of real estate, financing and other business transactions, as well as institutional lenders in the acquisition and sale of commercial property and the restructuring of existing credit facilities. Experience in commercial leasing and general corporate representation.
**Professional Memberships:** American Bar Association; Real Property, Probate, and Trust Section of the Texas Bar Association; Dallas Bar Association.
**Career:** Admitted to Texas Bar in 1991.
**Personal:** Graduated from Stanford University, BA with highest honors, 1988; and The University of Texas School of Law, JD with honors, 1991.

**MASSAD, Stephen A**
Baker Botts LLP, Houston
713 229 1475
stephen.massad@bakerbotts.com
*Featured in Corporate/M&A (Texas)*
**Practice Areas:** Chair: Houston Corporate Department (1994-2002); Member: Executive Committee (1995-2001). Practice is concentrated in corporate, securities, M&A, corporate governance and joint ventures. Has substantial experience in M&A transactions and related financings, including negotiated acquisitions, tender offers, proxy contests and takeover defense. Much of his practice has involved representing major participants in the restructuring and consolidation of the oil and gas, power and chemicals sectors. Additional areas of emphasis include capital markets transactions and audit committee and other investigations.
**Personal:** JD, cum laude, Harvard Law School, 1975; AB, summa cum laude, Princeton University, 1972.

**MASSIATTE, Rebecca**
Jackson Lewis LLP, Dallas
214 520 2400
MassiatteR@jacksonlewis.com
*Featured in Immigration (Texas)*
**Practice Areas:** Immigration and nationality law. Assists private, corporate and non-profit organizations obtain permanent and temporary visas. Advise on the foreign labor certification process, effective immigration policies and compliance.
**Professional Memberships:** American Immigration Lawyers Association; National Association of Women Lawyers, State Bar of Texas, Attorneys Serving the Community.
**Career:** U.S. DOJ- Executive Office for Immigration Review, San Antonio & Harlingen, TX Immigration Court (2002-03); Jenkens & Gilchrist (2003-07); Winstead PC (2007-09); Jackson Lewis LLP (2009 to present).
**Personal:** Washington University in St. Louis, JD / MSW, 2002; Texas State University, BSW, 1997.

**MATTOX, Sharon**
Vinson & Elkins LLP, Houston
713 758 4598
smattox@velaw.com
*Featured in Environment (Texas)*
**Practice Areas:** Principal areas of practice are environmental law and environmental litigation. Is a Fellow of the Texas Bar Foundation and is listed in a leading legal US publication in environmental law.
**Career:** Admitted to Texas Bar in 1981. Joined Vinson & Elkins in 1981; admitted to the partnership in 1990.
**Personal:** Graduated from Emporia State University, BA in 1974, The University of Texas, PhD in Botany, 1978, and The University of Texas School of Law, JD in 1981 (Order of Barristers, Order of the Coif).

## MAYER, Sylvia
Weil, Gotshal & Manges LLP, Houston
713 546 5087
sylvia.mayer@weil.com
*Featured in Bankruptcy/Restructuring (Texas)*
**Practice Areas:** Ms Mayer specializes in work-outs, bankruptcy and restructuring engagements for debtors, as well as recovery and resolution planning for financial institutions. She has represented debtors, committees, trustees, creditors and acquirers in chapter 11 cases and out of court restructurings. Currently representing LodgeNet Interactive in its prepackaged chapter 11 case, she also advises systemically important financial institutions on recovery and resolution planning under Dodd-Frank and has represented debtors such as Highland Hospitality, in an out-of-court transaction, and General Growth Properties, in its successful solvent company chapter 11 cases.
**Personal:** Washington University (BA); University of Houston Law Center (JD).

## MCBRIDE, B. Scott
Baker & Hostetler LLP, Houston
713 646 1390
smcbride@bakerlaw.com
*Featured in Healthcare (Texas)*
**Career:** Scott McBride concentrates on providing legal services to the healthcare industry, including representing and advising hospitals, academic medical centers, physician groups and other healthcare clients. He represents and advises clients in government and private payor investigations and reviews, including False Claims Act investigations and defense, as well as other regulatory enforcement proceedings, including matters related to Medicare and Medicaid billing compliance, Civil Monetary Penalties, Stark and anti-kickback laws, corporate oversight and exclusions from federal and state healthcare programs. He also counsels clients in comprehensive corporate compliance matters, including assisting and advising clients on internal investigations, self-disclosures and repayment matters.

## MCCLURE, Daniel M
Fulbright & Jaworski LLP, Houston
713 651 5159
dmcclure@fulbright.com
*Featured in Energy & Natural Resources (Nationwide), Litigation (Texas)*
**Practice Areas:** Litigation; energy; class actions; qui tam; healthcare.
**Professional Memberships:** Executive Committee, Institute for Energy Law; Texas Board of Legal Specialization - certified in Civil Trial Law.
**Career:** McClure has extensive first-chair jury trial experience in civil litigation matters. His practice currently focuses on complex commercial litigation, including class actions, energy, antitrust, business torts, qui tam actions, healthcare and government investigations. Twice named to national BTI Client Service All-Star Team. Chair, Fulbright Global Class Action practice group; Co-chair, Energy Litigation practice group.

**Personal:** JD, cum laude, Harvard Law School(1978); BA, highest honors, University of Oklahoma(1974).

## MCCORMICK, Timothy R
Thompson & Knight LLP, Dallas
214 969 1103
Timothy.McCormick@tklaw.com
*Featured in Litigation (Texas)*
**Practice Areas:** Mr McCormick chairs the firm's Securities and Complex Commercial Litigation Practice Group, which includes the Internal Investigations, Foreign Corrupt Practices Act, and White Collar Crime practices. He represents clients in corporate governance issues and has an active Securities Litigation, Complex Business Litigation, and SEC Enforcement practice.
**Professional Memberships:** State Bars of Texas, New York, and DC; American College of Trial Lawyers; International Society of Barristers; Texas and Dallas Bar Foundations.
**Personal:** SMU Dedman School of Law (JD, 1975); University of Texas Arlington (BA, 1973).

## MCCOWN, Steven R
Littler Mendelson, PC, Dallas
214 880 8101
smccown@littler.com
*Featured in Labor & Employment (Texas)*
**Practice Areas:** Workplace Safety and Health (OSHA); Class Actions; Complex Litigation and Jury Trials; Wage and Hour; Labor Management Relations.
**Professional Memberships:** Certified in labor and employment law by the State Bar of Texas Board of Legal Specialization.
**Career:** Has extensive experience in both traditional labor law and representing employers in employment law jury trials. Led successful defense of a Fortune 100 company in a nationwide sex discrimination class action. Successfully defended wage and hour collective actions, defeating class certification in several national collective actions.
**Personal:** JD, Southern Methodist University School of Law, 1975; Undergraduate degree, Business Management, University of Texas at Austin, 1972.

## MCDERMETT JR, Don J
Baker Botts LLP, Dallas
214 953 6454
don.mcdermett@bakerbotts.com
*Featured in Technology (Texas)*
**Practice Areas:** Mergers and acquisitions, corporate finance, venture capital, SEC compliance, corporate governance, joint ventures. Significant client concentration in the IT and telecom industries.
**Professional Memberships:** ABarA, State Bar of Texas, Society of Corporate Secretaries and Governance Professionals, Texas Business Law Foundation.
**Career:** Former Senior Vice-President, General Counsel and secretary of Sterling Software, Inc.; partner at Baker Botts since May 2000.
**Personal:** JD, with honors, University of Texas School of Law, 1984 (Texas Law Review, Order of

the Coif); BBA, with highest honors, finance, University of Texas 1981.

## MCDONALD, Bruce
Jones Day, Washington, DC
832 239 3822
bmcdonald@jonesday.com
*Featured in Antitrust (District of Columbia), Antitrust (Texas)*
**Practice Areas:** Represents energy, transportation, and telecommunications companies in antitrust government investigations and enforcement actions, merger reviews, and antitrust private litigation. Has worked extensively in related petroleum, chemicals, aviation, and technology sectors.
**Career:** Served as deputy assistant attorney general with the US Department of Justice (2003-07), responsible for civil antitrust enforcement. Appointed to the Electric Energy Competition Task Force created by Congress and to the US delegation that negotiated the "open skies" agreement between the US and European Union.
**Publications:** Active in writing and speaking, bar leadership, adjunct teaching, and pro bono matters for church, civic, and youth organisations.

## MCDONALD, Derek
Baker Botts LLP, Austin
512 322 2667
derek.mcdonald@bakerbotts.com
*Featured in Environment (Texas)*
**Practice Areas:** Practices in the areas of environmental law and litigation, concentrating on matters relating to the permitting of high-profile projects and remediation. Mr McDonald's litigation experience includes representing clients in complex environmental litigation in Texas state and federal courts, as well as before the ICC International Court of Arbitration.
**Professional Memberships:** Member, State Bar of Texas.
**Career:** Admitted to Texas Bar in 1993. Joined Baker Botts in 1994; admitted to partnership 2001.
**Personal:** University of Texas, BA, with honors, 1989; JD, with honors, 1992.

## MCDONALD, Scott
Littler Mendelson, PC, Dallas
214 880 8107
smcdonald@littler.com
*Featured in Labor & Employment (Texas)*
**Practice Areas:** Competition and trade secret law, staffing and contingent workers, class actions, transportation.
**Professional Memberships:** Texas State Employee Relations Committee - Texas Association of Business; American Law Institute.
**Career:** Board Certified by the Texas Board of Legal Specialization in employment and labor law; Helped design a creative trade secret protection argument establishing a test for pre-lawsuit deposition actions in Texas.
**Publications:** "Covenants Not to Compete: State by State Survey," BNA, 1995 – present; "Employee Duty of Loyalty," BNA, 1996 to present.

**Personal:** JD, University of Texas School of Law, 1987; BA, University of Texas at El Paso, Honors Program, 1984.

## MCDOWELL, C. Luckey
Baker Botts LLP, Dallas
214 953 6571
luckey.mcdowell@bakerbotts.com
*Featured in Bankruptcy/Restructuring (Texas)*
**Practice Areas:** Bankruptcy and workouts, corporate practice.
**Professional Memberships:** State Bar of Texas; United States Court of Appeals for the Ninth Circuit; United States District Courts for the Northern, Southern, Eastern, and Western Districts of Texas; Dallas Association of Young Lawyers; Dallas Bar Association.
**Career:** Corporate reorganization, bankruptcy and insolvency-related litigation. Mr McDowell represents debtors, creditors, hedge funds and asset acquirers in corporate reorganization cases and out-of-court workouts, as well as in bankruptcy and related state court litigation.
**Personal:** JD, Duke University School of Law, 2001; BBA (cum laude), economics and insurance, Baylor University, 1999.

## MCFAUL, Duston
Vinson & Elkins LLP, Houston
713 758 4740
dmcfaul@velaw.com
*Featured in Bankruptcy/Restructuring (Texas)*
**Practice Areas:** Extensive experience in restructurings, complex Chapter 11 cases, business litigation, and negotiated workouts.
**Professional Memberships:** American Bankruptcy Institute; Texas Bar Life Fellow, Chapter Board, TMA; American Bar Association and HBF Fellow; Moller-Foltz American Inn of Court; Best Lawyers in America; Duke Advisory Committee.
**Career:** Partner with Vinson & Elkins LLP; Admitted, Texas, 1997; New York, 2008; US Courts for Fifth Circuit, Southern, Northern, Eastern, and Western Districts of Texas, and pro hac admissions with other states and USVI.
**Personal:** Duke University with honors; University of Texas School of Law, Presidential Scholarship; family of five based in Houston, Texas.

## MCKELLAR, James W
Thompson & Knight LLP, Dallas
214 969 1605
James.McKellar@tklaw.com
*Featured in Banking & Finance (Texas)*
**Practice Areas:** Mr McKellar advises clients in structuring, negotiating, and documenting business transactions with an emphasis on capital markets, energy, and financing transactions. His experience also includes counseling clients in connection with workouts, restructurings, bankruptcy, and creditors' rights; energy commodity purchases and derivative transactions; and general corporate matters. He has been named to The Best Lawyers in America, Texas Super Lawyers, and Who's Who Legal: Texas for multiple years.
**Professional Memberships:** American College of Investment Counsel; Texas Association of Bank

Counsel; Independent Petroleum Association of America.
**Personal:** SMU Dedman School of Law (JD, 1978); Southern Methodist University (BS, 1975).

### MCKOOL, Mike
McKool Smith, Dallas
214 978 4000
mmckool@mckoolsmith.com
*Featured in Litigation (Nationwide), Intellectual Property (Texas), Litigation (Texas)*
**Practice Areas:** Complex commercial litigation and intellectual property litigation.
**Professional Memberships:** American Board of Trial Advocates; Advisory Board for the Patent Case Management Judicial Guide; International Network of Boutique Law Firms, National Vice President; University of Texas Law School Alumni Association, Executive Committee.
**Career:** As Chairman and founder of McKool Smith, Mike McKool has served as trial counsel for some of the word's leading corporations. During his legal career of more than 30 years, he has built a reputation for superlative trial skills that have helped the firm earn verdicts and settlements worth billions of dollars for clients. He has been consistently recognized as a top lawyer in his field by leading legal directories, including Chambers USA, Best Lawyers, Benchmark Litigation, and Lawdragon.
**Personal:** University of Texas School of Law (JD, with honors, Order of the Coif, 1974); University of Notre Dame (BA, magna cum laude, 1971).

### MCNAMARA, Robert J
Andrews Kurth LLP, Houston
713 220 4413
rmcnamara@andrewskurth.com
*Featured in Tax (Texas)*
**Practice Areas:** Robert's principal area of practice is federal income tax law with an emphasis on domestic business transaction planning. He has significant experience advising publicly-traded partnerships (MLPs) on capital formation and acquisition activities and has served as tax counsel to both issuers and underwriters in connection with numerous debt offerings. Robert also advises clients on federal income and Texas state tax issues in mergers and acquisitions, including tax-free reorganizations and like-kind exchanges.

### MCNIEL, D Ferguson
Vinson & Elkins LLP, Houston
713 758 3882
fmcniel@velaw.com
*Featured in Litigation (Texas)*
**Practice Areas:** Practice concentrates on commercial litigation, construction, toxic tort, and product liability. Certified: civil trial law and personal injury trial law by Texas Board of Legal Specialization.
**Professional Memberships:** Fellow of the American College of Trial Lawyers; International Society of Barristers; American Board of Trial Advocates; International Association of Defense Counsel; Defense Research Institute; American Bar Association; Texas Association of Defense Counsel; Houston Bar Association. Fellow: Texas Bar Foundation; Houston Bar Foundation.

**Career:** Admitted to practice: Texas, 1980. Joined Vinson & Elkins, 1980; admitted to partnership, 1990.
**Personal:** University of Arkansas, BSBA, 1977; University of Arkansas, JD, 1980.

### MCNULTY, Mary A
Thompson & Knight LLP, Dallas
214 969 1187
Mary.McNulty@tklaw.com
*Featured in Tax (Texas)*
**Practice Areas:** Mary represents corporate and partnership taxpayers in IRS audits, appeals, and tax litigation and provides tax planning for partnerships, limited liability companies, and S corporations. She specializes in Federal tax procedural issues, including statutes of limitations, interest, penalties, privilege, TEFRA partnerships, and in partnership tax issues relating to private equity, oil and gas, wind energy, real estate, and exempt organizations.
**Professional Memberships:** American Bar Association Tax Section, Council; State Bar of Texas, Former Chair; Dallas Bar Association, Former Chair.
**Personal:** SMU Dedman School of Law (JD, Order of the Coif); University of Notre Dame (BBA, with highest honors).

### MEADOWS, Robert E
King & Spalding LLP, Houston
713 276 7370
rmeadows@kslaw.com
*Featured in Litigation (Texas)*
**Practice Areas:** Represents clients in litigation throughout the United States, including trials in state and federal courts, international and domestic arbitrations, summary jury trials and other forms of alternative dispute resolution. Trial experience includes both commercial and tort litigation.
**Professional Memberships:** Inducted into the American College of Trial Lawyers, the American Board of Trial Advocates, the International Association of Defense Counsel, and the Texas Association of Defense Counsel.
**Personal:** JD, University of Houston MPA, Lyndon B. Johnson School of Public Affairs, University of Texas BA, University of Texas.

### MEEK, Kevin J
Baker Botts LLP, Austin
512 322 5471
kevin.meek@bakerbotts.com
*Featured in Intellectual Property (Texas)*
**Practice Areas:** Mr Meek is the Chair of the firm's Austin office IP Department. He has broad experience in high technology patent litigation, prosecution, licensing, and software licensing and disputes. He also handles a variety of corporate transactions centering on technology transfers and intellectual property rights.
**Professional Memberships:** State Bar of Texas; US Patent and Trademark Office.
**Career:** Joined Baker Botts in 1990; admitted to partnership 1997.
**Personal:** Texas A&M University, BSEE, 1985; University of Texas School of Law, JD, 1988.

### MELKO, John P
Gardere Wynne Sewell LLP, Houston
713 276 5727
jmelko@gardere.com
*Featured in Bankruptcy/Restructuring (Texas)*
**Practice Areas:** Bankruptcy, business reorganization.
**Professional Memberships:** State Bar of Texas [Council Member, Bankruptcy Section], International Bar Association, Houston Bar Association, American Bankruptcy Institute, US Mexico Bar Association [Director], Turnaround Management Association [Board Member, Houston Chapter].
**Career:** John Melko has a broad-based practice including financial and business restructurings, complex bankruptcies, and acquisition and sale transactions. He represents borrowers and debtors in possession, creditors and creditors' committees, securitized noteholders, trustees, investors, and buyers in and out of restructuring or bankruptcy settings.
**Personal:** JD, South Texas College of Law, 1984; BS, Widener College, 1976; BA, Widener College, 1976.

### MENDIOLA III, Lino
Andrews Kurth LLP, Austin
512 320 9210
linomendiola@andrewskurth.com
*Featured in Energy & Natural Resources (Texas)*
**Practice Areas:** Lino practices commercial litigation in federal and state courts and before administrative agencies. He specializes in energy litigation. He is also the lead outside lawyer on public contracting matters for various clients and regularly advises municipalities, counties, transportation authorities and other entities on procurement matters. He represents clients in commercial litigation throughout Texas and other states and has particular expertise in South Texas litigation.

### MEYERSON, Alfred M
Thompson & Knight LLP, Houston
713 951 5870
Alfred.Meyerson@tklaw.com
*Featured in Real Estate (Texas)*
**Practice Areas:** Mr Meyerson focuses his practice on real estate investments, acquisitions, dispositions, development, and leasing, as well as various lending transactions and workouts. He has represented equity investors, borrowers and lenders in all types of loans, including construction, mezzanine, permanent, and revolving loan facilities, and both landlords and tenants in negotiating leases. He also represents financial institutions in connection with syndicated loan transactions.
**Professional Memberships:** ICSC; Texas Association of Bank Counsel; Houston Real Estate Lawyers Council; Interlaw North America Real Estate Group (Past Chair); State Bar of Texas.
**Personal:** University of Texas (JD, 1984; BA, 1981; Phi Beta Kappa).

### MILLER, Stephen
Jones Walker LLP, The Woodlands
281 296 4428
smiller@joneswalker.com
*Featured in Construction (Texas)*
**Practice Areas:** Business and commercial transactions; commercial lending and finance; construction; disaster preparedness and recovery; energy; energy, environment and natural resources; green law and sustainability; international; project development and finance; real estate: land use, development and finance; electric power-generation and transmission.
**Professional Memberships:** American Bar Association (member of the Project Finance and Development Committee); Houston Bar Association; Inter-American Bar Association; New York State Bar Association; The South Montgomery County Woodlands Economic Development Partnership (Partner Member); State Bar of Texas.
**Career:** Mr Miller is a partner in the firm's Real Estate Practice Group. He is a transactional attorney with a broad business practice in real estate and energy transactions, and he has advised clients in connection with the purchase, sale, and leasing of commercial and industrial properties. He has experience in a wide range of energy projects, which include upstream E&P, midstream, and downstream projects, as well as electric power projects, both inside and outside the United States.
**Personal:** He is a native of Santurce, Puerto Rico, and is conversant in Portuguese, as well as fluent in Spanish.

### MIMS, Peter E
Vinson & Elkins LLP, Houston
713 758 2732
pmims@velaw.com
*Featured in Intellectual Property (Texas)*
**Practice Areas:** Partner, Intellectual Property Section. Expertise in litigation and counseling involving patents, trade secrets, trademarks, and copyrights. Represents clients in bench and jury trials in federal and state courts in the US and in arbitrations.
**Professional Memberships:** Admitted to practice in Texas, 1985; United States Patent and Trademark Office; United States Court of Appeals for the Federal Circuit; and various federal district courts.
**Personal:** University of Texas School of Law, JD with honors, 1985; Rice University, BSChE (1978); MChE (1979).

### MONTGOMERY, James L
DLA Piper LLP (US), Austin
512 457 7100
jim.montgomery@dlapiper.com
*Featured in Technology (Texas)*
**Practice Areas:** Corporate and technology.
**Career:** His practice focuses on high growth, technology companies (Internet, software, microchip and life science) in formation, funding, growth and exit. He has represented technology companies in private placement offerings and has extensive experience in venture fund structures

and formations. He has structured and formed venture and private equity funds and represented various venture funds in fund investments, completing over 200 venture financings as either fund counsel or company counsel.

**Personal:** JD, Case Western Reserve University; BS, Bowling Green State University (Sydney Fohman Scholar).

## MOORE, Bryan
Beveridge & Diamond PC, Austin
512 391 8030
bmoore@bdlaw.com
*Featured in Environment (Texas)*

**Practice Areas:** Practice includes a wide range of environmental matters, from waste, water, and air permitting and compliance counseling, to enforcement defense and litigation. In matters arising under nearly every major federal and Texas environmental program, Mr Moore has represented clients in federal and state courts and before various agencies.

## MORAN, Michael W.
Jackson Walker LLP, Dallas
214 953 6040
mmoran@jw.com
*Featured in Construction (Texas)*

**Practice Areas:** Michael W Moran is a business litigation attorney whose practice focuses on construction litigation and transactions, surety bonds, corporate litigation, and business fraud.

**Career:** Throughout his 15-year career, Mr Moran has handled a wide assortment of construction lawsuits and transactions. He is currently the head of the Jackson Walker's Construction section. Mr Moran also represents businesses and financial institutions in disputes and litigation involving business torts, contracts, fraud, lender liability, real estate, tortious interference, and fiduciary duties. Additionally, he provides representation concerning loan workouts, including litigation related to those matters.

## MORGAN, Vincent E
Pillsbury Winthrop Shaw Pittman LLP, Houston
713 276 7625
vincent.morgan@pillsburylaw.com
*Featured in Insurance (Texas)*

**Practice Areas:** Mr Morgan represents corporate policyholders in litigation and arbitration concerning a wide range of insurance coverage matters involving first party and third party policies. Apart from handling coverage disputes, his consulting practice includes advising clients on insurance and risk management issues before losses occur. Mr Morgan is currently the Chair of the Insurance Law Section of the State Bar of Texas and a Member of the Editorial Board of West Publishing's 'Insurance Litigation Reporter.'

**Personal:** JD, University of Texas School of Law, 2000 (with honors); BA, Economics and Finance, University of Texas at Dallas, 1995 (summa cum laude).

## MORRISON, Edgar C
Jackson Walker LLP, San Antonio
210 978 7780
jmorrison@jw.com
*Featured in Healthcare (Texas)*

**Career:** Edgar ("Jed") C Morrison, Jr has practiced health care law since 1981. He specializes in the regulatory and transactional aspects of health care law and is Board Certified in health law by the Texas Board of Legal Specialization. Formerly Chairman of the Texas State Bar Health Law Section, Mr Morrison has extensive background in Medicare and Medicaid regulatory and reimbursement issues, antitrust, fraud and abuse, physician referral legislation (including recruitment contracts and joint ventures), and managed care issues. He represents physicians, hospitals, nursing homes, medical equipment suppliers, pharmacies, and other health care providers.

## MORRISS III, James C
Thompson & Knight LLP, Austin
512 469 6130
James.Morriss@tklaw.com
*Featured in Environment (Texas)*

**Practice Areas:** Mr Morriss focuses on environmental permitting, compliance counseling, and administrative and judicial litigation before local, state, and federal environmental agencies, state, and federal courts. He counsels clients, many of which are in the energy sector, in environmental risk management, including design/implementation of environmental auditing programs and environmental management systems, and in the investigation and disclosure of environmental liabilities and contingencies.

**Professional Memberships:** State Bar of Texas; Austin and American Bar Associations; Executive Committee, US Business Council for Sustainable Development.

**Personal:** University of Texas School of Law (JD, with honors, 1976); Southern Methodist University (BSME, with high honors, 1973).

## MOSS, Ron H
Winstead PC, Austin
512 370 2867
rhmoss@winstead.com
*Featured in Energy & Natural Resources (Texas)*

**Practice Areas:** Ron Moss focuses his practice on litigation, both in the courts and before administrative agencies. His primary practice is utility law, with emphasis on representing utilities before regulatory commissions and in court appeals. Ron also counsels utility clients regarding regulatory impacts of business decisions. He has had extensive experience with the 1999 legislation introducing retail competition in the Texas electric market. In addition to utility matters, Ron has represented clients in environmental litigation and business litigation.

## MOTT, Cassandra
Jones Day, Houston
832 239 3782
cgmott@jonesday.com
*Featured in Banking & Finance (Texas)*

**Practice Areas:** Cassandra Mott represents capital providers and borrowers in a broad range of finance transactions across an array of industries, including energy, health care, insurance, consumer products, and manufacturing. She has structured, negotiated, and documented senior and subordinated financing facilities, including general working capital, investment-grade credit, asset-based, multijurisdictional and multicurrency, and syndicated facilities. She also advises energy clients on collateral support and intercreditor matters relating to hedge transactions. Her practice includes advising clients on in-court and out-of-court debt restructurings, as well as on intercreditor issues, helping structure and negotiate transactions with multiple debt tranches and lien priorities.

## MOW JR, Robert H
K&L Gates, Dallas
214 939 5448
bob.mow@klgates.com
*Featured in Litigation (Texas)*

**Practice Areas:** A highly regarded trial lawyer, Mr Mow has tried more than 85 cases to jury verdict, including significant legal malpractice cases; trade secret and intellectual property disputes; fiduciary duty; estates litigation; and complex commercial and injury cases. A Fellow of the American College of Trial Lawyers, he has been selected as Dallas Bar's "Trial Lawyer of the Year," and a "Trial Legend" by the Dallas Bar's TIPS section. In 2011, he was chosen for the Ronald D. Secrest Outstanding Trial Lawyer award. He is a graduate of the University of Missouri and the SMU Dedman School of Law.

## MURRAY, Craig
Vinson & Elkins LLP, Houston
713 758 2008
cmurray@velaw.com
*Featured in Banking & Finance (Texas)*

**Practice Areas:** Business transactions, finance, including mezzanine finance, structured and project finance and mergers and acquisitions. Has extensive experience in complex syndicated transactions, representing either the lenders or the borrower. Has worked on all aspects of commerical finance and energy finance.

**Career:** Came to the firm in 1976 and was admitted to the partnership in October 1983.

**Personal:** Graduated from Rhodes College, BA in English, 1969 and Louisiana State University, JD with high honors in 1976. (Order of the Coif; Managing Editor, 'Louisiana Law Review').

## NASI, Michael
Jackson Walker LLP, Austin
512 236 2216
mnasi@jw.com
*Featured in Environment (Texas)*

**Practice Areas:** Mike Nasi practices environmental law in areas of air, water, reclamation and waste management and manages Jackson Walker's air quality practice.

**Career:** Mr Nasi has been practicing before state and federal environmental and energy agencies and the Texas Legislature for more than 19 years in Austin. He regularly secures environmental permits for and is active in state and federal policy development on behalf of corporations, governmental entities, and cooperatives in the electric power generation, mining, oil and gas, steel manufacturing, and recycling industries.

## NATION, Floyd
Winston & Strawn LLP, Houston
713 651 2661
fnation@winston.com
*Featured in Intellectual Property (Texas)*

**Practice Areas:** Over 35 years trying patent cases in all areas of technology including medical devices, semiconductor, software, internet, food processing, mechanical devices, and biotechnology. Experience in license negotiation, validity and infringement opinions and appeals to Federal Circuit.

**Professional Memberships:** ABA; AIPLA; State Bar of Texas; Louisiana State Bar; Registered US Patent Office.

**Career:** Arnold, White & Durkee 1974-2000; Howrey LLP 2000-11; Winston & Strawn 2011-present.

**Personal:** University of Texas Law School - JD with honors 1974; Georgia Institute of Technology - BME 1968; US Marine Corps (Res) 1969-75.

## NELSON, James R
DLA Piper LLP (US), Dallas
214 743 4512
jr.nelson@dlapiper.com
*Featured in Antitrust (Texas)*

**Practice Areas:** Litigation, antitrust.

**Career:** He heads the firm's Litigation practice in Texas and focuses on complex commercial litigation, including class actions, and defense of government investigations. He represents clients in investigations and litigation relating to federal and state antitrust laws and the federal securities laws, and in disputes regarding unfair competition and trade secrets. He has significant experience in conducting internal investigations and uses his experience as a prosecutor and in private practice to advise clients regarding compliance plans and training.

**Personal:** JD, Southern Methodist University School of Law; BA, Kansas Wesleyan University.

## NETTLES, Larry
Vinson & Elkins LLP, Houston
713 758 4586
lnettles@velaw.com
*Featured in Environment (Texas)*

**Practice Areas:** Extensive experience in all areas of environmental law, including site remediation, facility permitting, civil and criminal enforcement defense, land development, environmental due diligence for transactions, and dispute resolution. Has defended clients in more than three dozen criminal enforcement proceedings.

**Professional Memberships:** Life fellow, Texas Bar Foundation; fellow, Houston Bar Foundation; founder, Houston Bar Association Environmental Law Section.

**Career:** Joined V&E, 1981; admitted to partnership, 1990.

**Publications:** "Carbon Dioxide Sequestration — Transportation, Storage and Other Infrastructure Issues," Texas Journal of Oil, Gas & Energy Law, 2008.

**Personal:** Rice University, BS Civil Engineering,1978; University of Texas, JD with Honors, 1981.

## NEWSOME, J Kent
Greenberg Traurig, LLP, Houston
713 374 3659
NewsomeK@gtlaw.com
*Featured in Real Estate (Texas)*
**Practice Areas:** Chair, Houston Office Real Estate Practice.
**Professional Memberships:** Member, Houston and American Bar Associations and the State Bar of Texas; fellow, Houston Bar Foundation and Member of the American College of Real Estate Lawyers; voting member, National Academy of Recording Arts and Sciences.
**Career:** Listed in Euromoney Institutional Investor's Real Estate Expert Guide. Selected, Best Lawyers in America; Chambers USA Guide; Super Lawyers magazine and Texas Super Lawyers magazine. Rated, AV® Preeminent™ 5.0 out of 5.
**Personal:** JD, Vanderbilt University; BA, cum laude, Wake Forest University.

## NEWTON, Geoff
Baker Botts LLP, Dallas
214 953 6753
geoffrey.newton@bakerbotts.com
*Featured in Corporate/M&A (Texas)*
**Practice Areas:** Represents purchasers and sellers in connection with mergers and acquisitions involving public and private companies. Advises private equity funds and their sponsors regarding the establishment of the funds and the conduct of their investment activities. Counsels issuers and underwriters with respect to registered public offerings - including initial public offerings and offerings by seasoned issuers - as well as private placements of debt and equity securities. He also handles corporate governance matters, including audit committee assignments.
**Personal:** JD, Yale Law School, 1987, AB (magna cum laude), politics, Princeton University, 1984.

## NICHOLSON, Barclay R
Fulbright & Jaworski LLP, Houston
713 651 3662
bnicholson@fulbright.com
*Featured in Insurance (Texas)*
**Practice Areas:** Complex commercial litigation; energy litigation.
**Career:** Barclay's practice focus is energy and commercial disputes. He has represented a broad range of clients from Fortune 500 Companies to smaller energy start-up companies. He has significant experience in handling energy litigation, representing some of the world's major oil and gas producing and refining companies and some of the nation's biggest drilling and E&P companies. Barclay has handled billion dollar commercial cases and has represented clients in numerous proceedings both in the United States and abroad.
**Personal:** JD, magna cum laude, University of Houston (1999); BA, The University of Texas (1995).

## NIEBRUEGGE, Michael E
Cadwalader, Wickersham & Taft LLP, Houston
713 343 7560
michael.niebruegge@cwt.com
*Featured in Banking & Finance (Texas), Banking & Finance (Nationwide)*
**Practice Areas:** Represents lenders and arrangers in negotiating and documenting secured lending and structured agreements with corporations, master limited partnerships, and trusts engaged in energy and mining, including project loans, syndicated loans, and first lien/second lien finance. Has extensive experience in the oil and gas sector, representing producers and purchasers in onshore matters, including joint operating agreements, lease acquisitions, farm outs and farm ins, NPIs and volumetric production payments.
**Professional Memberships:** Admitted in Texas, Illinois, and before US District Court for the Southern District of Texas and for the Northern District of Illinois.
**Career:** Gulf Coast Royalty, Vice President and General Counsel, Houston, 1981-82. Northwestern University, Lecturer in Business Law, Chicago, 1979-80.
**Personal:** JD, Cornell University (Note and Comment Editor, Cornell Law Review). AB, cum laude, Harvard College.

## NOLAN, John
Winstead PC, Dallas
214 745 5251
jnolan@winstead.com
*Featured in Real Estate (Texas)*
**Practice Areas:** John's broad-based real estate practice encompasses development, workouts, portfolio/equity investments and financing for clients located across the United States and for international companies investing in the United States. He is known for his thorough analysis and knowledge of complex business transactions. The combination of these skills with John's financial background enables him to quickly evaluate his clients' business objectives and create a team, or compile the necessary resources, to formulate and execute his clients' plans.

## NOLAN, Peter A
Winstead PC, Austin
512 370 2885
pnolan@winstead.com
*Featured in Insurance (Texas)*
**Practice Areas:** Peter has represented local businesses, Fortune 500 companies, insurance companies and other regulated industries, and state governments in state, federal and bankruptcy courts and administrative hearings throughout the United States. The range of his representation has varied from rule and ratemaking hearings concerning regulated industries before administrative law judges to cases involving billions of dollars in damages in federal court. His areas of concentration are government enforcement and regulatory actions, complex commercial litigation and insurance regulatory litigation and defense. He has even defended the Alamo.

## NONDORF, Kurt
Jackson Walker LLP, Houston
713 752 4402
knondorf@jw.com
*Featured in Real Estate (Texas)*
**Career:** Kurt Nondorf has diverse experience in real estate transactions law, including the representation of institutional clients in connection with the acquisition, sale, financing, and leasing of office buildings, apartment complexes, raw land, warehouses, and hotels. His most frequent assignments involve work in the commercial capital and leasing markets, representing buyers and sellers of improved properties and landlords and tenants in commercial leases. Most recently, Mr Nondorf has spent a considerable portion of his practice on office building acquisitions, sales and financings for multiple fund clients and on sale/leaseback transactions. He is also managing partner of Jackson Walker's Houston office.

## O'BANNON, James E
Jones Day, Dallas
214 969 3766
jeobannon@jonesday.com
*Featured in Corporate/M&A (Texas)*
**Practice Areas:** Heads the Capital Markets Practice for the firm's Texas region. Practices in the areas of corporate and securities laws, with emphasis on representing issuers in public and private offerings of equity and debt securities and mergers and other acquisitions and dispositions of corporate securities and assets. Extensively engaged in counseling activities with respect to SEC disclosure issues, corporate governance, directors' and officers' fiduciary duties, tender offers and other contests for corporate control.
**Personal:** The University of Texas at Austin (BBA in Finance with highest honors 1978; MBA 1980); Southern Methodist University (Order of the Coif; JD 1983).

## O'DANIEL, Patrick
Fulbright & Jaworski LLP, Austin
512 536 5264
podaniel@fulbright.com
*Featured in Tax (Texas)*
**Practice Areas:** Tax; public finance.
**Career:** Patrick O'Daniel serves as a trusted business and tax advisor to clients efficiently solving their legal problems as part of their business team. A large portion of his practice is dedicated to the tax and public law aspects of municipal finance and structured project finance. He advises on a wide variety of international and domestic issues concerning the formation, operation, acquisition, merger, combination, liquidation and disposition of partnerships, limited liability companies and corporations, as well as various funding structures.
**Personal:** JD, University of Texas School of Law (1992); BBA, University of Texas (1989).

## OELMAN, David
Vinson & Elkins LLP, Houston
713 758 3708
doelman@velaw.com
*Featured in Corporate/M&A (Texas), Capital Markets (Texas), Capital Markets (Nationwide)*

**Practice Areas:** Co-Chair of the Capital Markets Practice. Focuses on corporate and securities transactions, including representation of public and private companies and investment banking firms; advising boards on corporate governance; public offerings and private placements of equity and debt; publicly traded limited partnerships; mergers and acquisitions; and private equity investments.
**Career:** Admitted to Texas Bar (1991); joined the firm as a Partner (2000).
**Publications:** Princeton University, Woodrow Wilson School of Public and International Affairs, BA (Summa Cum Laude, Phi Beta Kappa), 1987; The University of Texas School of Law, JD (Chancellors, Order of the Coif), 1990.

## OHLENFORST, Cynthia
K&L Gates, Dallas
214 939 5512
cindy.ohlenforst@klgates.com
*Featured in Tax (Texas)*
**Practice Areas:** Ms Ohlenforst, who represents multiple Fortune 100 companies, has engaged in a broad tax practice with extensive experience in state and federal planning, controversy, and legislative matters. Her practice includes substantial dispute resolution work (administrative proceedings before state tax agencies and litigation), including work defending against putative class actions by taxing jurisdictions. In addition to multi-state and local tax issues, with respect to sales, franchise, income and other taxes, she also handles transactional work related to e-commerce and Internet-related tax issues, leasing transactions, and other deal work.

## OLDHAM, Phillip G
Andrews Kurth LLP, Austin
512 320 9237
phillipoldham@andrewskurth.com
*Featured in Energy & Natural Resources (Texas)*
**Practice Areas:** As an energy and administrative law practitioner, much of Phillip's practice focuses on providing strategic counseling on regulatory matters and on significant transactions and infrastructure development projects. Phillip also has substantial representations before various state and federal agencies, and has handled numerous litigated matters involving all aspects of the energy and electric industries. Phillip is also a registered lobbyist in Texas with substantial representations before the Texas Legislature.

## O'LEARY, Michael
Andrews Kurth LLP, Houston
713 220 4360
moleary@andrewskurth.com
*Featured in Corporate/M&A (Texas), Capital Markets (Texas), Energy & Natural Resources (Nationwide)*
**Practice Areas:** Represents public and private companies and investment banking firms in corporate finance and M&A transactions, including: dispositions; public offerings, including IPOs; private placements of equity and debt; formations of partnerships and joint ventures; spin-offs and split-offs; redemptions and consent solicitations; royalty trusts and VPP financings. Counsels Boards of Directors and committees on fiduciary

duties; joint bidding arrangements; counsels clients on SOX and corporate governance matters. Particular expertise in upstream and midstream energy and oilfield service companies, joint ventures and joint development arrangements (among strategic companies or representing private equity or infrastructure funds); gas and liquids pipeline transportation.

## O'NEIL, Holland N
Gardere Wynne Sewell LLP, Dallas
214 999 4961
honeil@gardere.com
*Featured in Bankruptcy/Restructuring (Texas)*
**Practice Areas:** Bankruptcy, business reorganization.
**Professional Memberships:** State Bars of Texas and Arizona, American and Dallas Bar Associations, American Bankruptcy Institute, Turnaround Management Association, International Women's Insolvency and Restructuring Confederation.
**Career:** Holly O'Neil has a comprehensive practice including complex bankruptcies, restructurings and workouts, acquisitions of distressed assets, and bankruptcy litigation. She represents clients in all aspects of turnarounds and restructurings. Ms O'Neil's clients include debtors in possession, creditors' committees, examiners, creditors, and trustees, as well as clients interested in acquiring assets from troubled companies.
**Personal:** JD, Texas Tech University School of Law, 1987; BBA, University of Texas at Austin, 1983.

## ORLOFF, Gary W
Bracewell & Giuliani LLP, Houston
713 221 1306
gary.orloff@bgllp.com
*Featured in Corporate/M&A (Texas)*
**Practice Areas:** Has experience in domestic and foreign transactions, with specific emphasis on the legal and business implications of business plans and strategies, particularly in the areas of corporate and project finance. He is equally knowledgeable regarding mergers, acquisitions and divestitures, including management and leveraged buy-outs. Advises corporate clients, master limited partnerships and other entities on governance, fiduciary duties and change of control.
**Personal:** JD, University of Houston Law Center, 1973; BBA, The University of Texas at Austin, 1970.

## OSTERBERG, Edward
Vinson & Elkins LLP, Houston
713 758 2192
eosterberg@velaw.com
*Featured in Tax (Texas)*
**Practice Areas:** Federal income taxation with emphasis on international transactions, mergers and acquisitions, and partnerships and joint ventures.
**Professional Memberships:** President-elect, International Fiscal Association USA Branch; Past President, International Tax Forum of Houston.
**Publications:** 'Use of Series Companies in International Tax Planning,' International Tax

Journal, December 2009; 'Basic US Tax Considerations in Buying or Selling a Non-US Business,' Tax Notes, June 2, 2003; 'International Joint Ventures: Basic Tax Goals and Structures,' Tax Notes International, April 30, 2001.
**Personal:** BA, JD Cum Laude, Northwestern University; LLM in Taxation, Southern Methodist University.

## OSTOLAZA, Yvette
Weil, Gotshal & Manges LLP, Dallas
214 746 7805
yvette.ostolaza@weil.com
*Featured in Litigation (Texas)*
**Practice Areas:** Yvette Ostolaza, Co-head of Weil's 190+ lawyer Complex Commercial Litigation Practice and a member of the firm's Management Committee, is a nationally acclaimed litigator. Her practice encompasses: trying and managing complex litigation in US state and federal trial and appellate courts and before arbitration tribunals; leading investigations on behalf of companies, boards, and special committees; and serving as litigation counsel on corporate transactions. She handles the full spectrum of disputes, including cases involving business torts, fraud, constitutional, contracts, employment, insurance, fiduciary duty, purchase price adjustments, consumer class actions, advertising/sweepstakes, insurance, and products liability issues, and also focuses on Latin America-related disputes. She has extensive experience with multi-jurisdictional and class action litigation. She recently was selected as one of 20 "Most Powerful & Influential Women" in Texas by the Texas Diversity Council; named one of the "Top 250 Women in Litigation" by Benchmark; and named a "Defender" – a top-15 business defense attorney in the Dallas-Fort Worth metroplex – by Dallas Business Journal.
**Professional Memberships:** Admitted to Practice in New York and Texas; Former Director, State Bar of Texas; Roster of Neutral Arbitrators for AAA.
**Personal:** University of Miami (BA with general honors); University of Miami School of Law (JD, magna cum laude, Order of the Coif); fluent in Spanish.

## PAINTER, Ann Marie
Morgan, Lewis & Bockius LLP, Dallas
214 466 4121
annmarie.painter@morganlewis.com
*Featured in Labor & Employment (Texas)*
**Practice Areas:** Ann Marie Painter is a partner in Morgan Lewis's Labor and Employment Practice. Ms Painter focuses her practice on defending employers in employment litigation matters, including wage and hour compliance, all categories of alleged discrimination and harassment and retaliation, wrongful termination, breach of contract, and unfair competition. She regularly litigates in state and federal courts, and participates in mediations before some of the nation's best alternative dispute resolution practitioners.
**Personal:** Attended University of Tennessee College of Law, 1992, JD, High Honors ; Carson-Newman College, 1988, BA, Summa Cum Laude.

## PAKALKA, William
Fulbright & Jaworski LLP, Houston
713 651 5208
wpakalka@fulbright.com
*Featured in Antitrust (Texas)*
**Practice Areas:** Complex commercial litigation; antitrust (competition law); trade regulation; white-collar crime.
**Professional Memberships:** ABA; State Bar of Texas; Houston Bar Association; College of the State Bar of Texas; Life fellow, Texas and Houston Bar Foundations.
**Career:** A former Partner in the firm's Houston office, now Of Counsel, his Litigation Practice focuses on civil and criminal antitrust and general business litigation. Law clerk to Judge Irving L. Goldberg, U.S. Fifth Circuit Court of Appeals (1972-73).
**Personal:** JD, with honors, The University of Texas School of Law (1972); BA, The University of Texas at Austin (1969); Order of St. John 2003.

## PAPPERT, Michael J
Baker & Hostetler LLP, Houston
713 646 1371
mpappert@bakerlaw.com
*Featured in Real Estate (Texas)*
**Career:** Michael Pappert assists clients in creating and implementing strategies for business transactions. He is involved in the acquisition, development, leasing, management, financing and sale of commercial and residential real estate, including shopping centers, industrial warehouse projects, office buildings, hotel and recreational developments, and multi- and single-family properties. Mike represents lenders and borrowers, including financial institutions, mortgage companies, institutional investors, developers and publicly held companies in lending and financing transactions, and he has experience in mortgage and asset-based lending, loan workout and restructuring, and refinancing matters. He represents clients in the purchase, sale, restructuring and reorganization of business ownership and assets.

## PAREL, S Scott
Weil, Gotshal & Manges LLP, Dallas
214 746 7779
scott.parel@weil.com
*Featured in Corporate/M&A (Texas)*
**Practice Areas:** S Scott Parel maintains offices in both Dallas and New York. His practice focuses on complex corporate and transactional matters, primarily representing private equity sponsors and their portfolio companies in connection with leveraged acquisitions, minority investments, divestitures, joint ventures and restructurings. He has represented a wide range of private equity clients, including OMERS Private Equity, Avista Capital Partners, Alberta Investment Management Corp. and Lindsay Goldberg.
**Personal:** University of California, Los Angeles (BA, 1992); Southern Methodist University School of Law (JD, 1997).

## PARHAM, David
Baker & McKenzie, Dallas
214 978 3034
David.Parham@bakermckenzie.com
*Featured in Bankruptcy/Restructuring (Texas)*
**Practice Areas:** David Parham has experience representing corporate and partnership debtors, creditor committees, equity holders, secured and unsecured creditors, lessors and trustees in bankruptcy proceedings and workouts. Mr Parham has represented clients in restructuring cases involving many industries, including, agriculture, sports, aviation, telecommunications, distribution, retail, manufacturing, energy, mining, insurance and real estate. Mr Parham has also handled a variety of commercial litigation matters in bankruptcy courts and in federal and state courts. These representations include prosecution and defense of claims against directors and officers, cases involving allegations of fraud, fraudulent conveyance, preference and, in general, contract and business tort cases.

## PARIS, Ted W
Baker Botts LLP, Houston
713 229 1838
ted.paris@bakerbotts.com
*Featured in Corporate/M&A (Texas)*
**Practice Areas:** Mergers, acquisitions, securities offerings, corporate control and governance issues and joint ventures. Represents parties in negotiated acquisitions and dispositions, controlled auctions, tender offers and related financings. Also represents domestic and foreign issuers, underwriters and selling shareholders in public offerings and in Rule 144A transactions and other private placements. Substantial experience in a wide variety of industries, including oil and gas, oilfield services, shipping, manufacturing, industrial services and consumer products and services.
**Personal:** JD with honors, The University of Texas School of Law, 1988; MBA and BBA-Accounting, Texas A&M University - Corpus Christi, 1983.

## PARKER, Emily A
Thompson & Knight LLP, Dallas
214 969 1502
Emily.Parker@tklaw.com
*Featured in Tax (Texas)*
**Practice Areas:** Ms Parker is the firm's Managing Partner. She represents taxpayers in IRS audits and appeals proceedings, state tax audits and hearings, and federal and state tax refund and deficiency litigation. She was named 2012 Outstanding Texas Tax Lawyer by the State Bar of Texas Tax Section and is Board Certified in Tax Law by the Texas Board of Legal Specialization.
**Professional Memberships:** American College of Tax Counsel; American Bar Association.
**Career:** Acting Chief Counsel/Deputy Chief Counsel for the IRS, 2002-04.
**Personal:** SMU Dedman School of Law (JD, 1973); Stephen F. Austin University (BA, 1970).

**PARSLEY, Julie**
Parsley Coffin Renner, LLP, Austin
512 879 0980
julie.parsley@pcrllp.com
*Featured in Energy & Natural Resources (Texas)*
**Practice Areas:** A former Commissioner of the Public Utility Commission of Texas, Ms Parsley specializes in energy-related legal and consulting services, with a particular focus on wholesale markets and transmission issues in Texas and the Southwest Power Pool. Ms Parsley is also a former Solicitor General of Texas with the Office of the Attorney General, is Board Certified in Civil Appellate Law by the Texas Board of Legal Specialization, and enjoys an appellate practice in conjunction with her energy practice. A Fellow of the Texas Bar Foundation, she has been recognized as a leading lawyer providing energy-related services.

**PARSONS, Jeffrey R**
Beirne Maynard & Parsons, LLP, Houston
713 960 7302
jparsons@bmpllp.com
*Featured in Insurance (Texas)*
**Practice Areas:** Jeff Parsons has over 35 years of trial experience. His work includes the first Superfund Site lawsuit tried in Texas; major class actions; securities litigation; major construction cases; complex insurance coverage disputes; energy industry cases; fidelity and surety claims; intellectual property cases; fraud and civil RICO lawsuits; products liability claims; and, a myriad of wrongful death and bodily injury cases.
**Professional Memberships:** He is a Member of the State Bar of Texas, Director (2002-05); International Association of Defense Counsel; The Network of Trial Law Firms, Chair (1993-94); Houston Bar Association; American Bar Association; Defense Research Institute; Texas Association of Defense Counsel; American Bar Foundation; Houston Bar Foundation; Texas Bar Foundation; American Bar Foundation; College of the State Bar of Texas.
**Career:** Admitted to Bar, 1973, Texas; US Supreme Court, 1979; US Court of Appeals, Fifth and Second Circuits; US District Courts, Northern, Southern, Eastern, and Western Districts of Texas; admitted pro hac vice to practice before various state and federal courts throughout the US.
**Publications:** Mr Parsons speaks at numerous continuing legal education seminars, regarding trial strategies and tactics and principles of jury management. Publications available upon request.
**Personal:** BA History, 1969, Hamilton College; JD, 1972, Boston University.

**PARTRIDGE, Scott**
Baker Botts LLP, Houston
713 229 1569
scott.partridge@bakerbotts.com
*Featured in Intellectual Property (Texas)*
**Practice Areas:** Senior partner in Intellectual Property Department. Thirty years experience litigating patents, trade secrets, copyright matters in technology fields. Represents clients in federal and state courts and before the US International Trade Commission.
**Professional Memberships:** American Bar Association, House of Delegates; ABA Board of Governors and IP Section Counsel; past Chair, Science and Technology Section; Section Officers Conference, Executive Committee. International Trade Commission Trial Lawyers Association, Executive Council and past President. Admitted in DC, Virginia, Texas. Former adjunct professor at Georgetown Law and frequent IP law lecturer.
**Personal:** JD, Georgetown University, 1974; BS, electrical engineering, University of Cincinnati, 1969.

**PATE, Stephen**
Fulbright & Jaworski LLP, Houston
713 651 5132
spate@fulbright.com
*Featured in Insurance (Texas)*
**Practice Areas:** First-party insurance, commercial insurance, coverage, extracontractual and bad faith litigation, construction litigation.
**Professional Memberships:** Member, American Board of Trial Advocates; Member, American Law Institute; Texas and Houston Young Lawyers Associations.
**Career:** Pate, Chair of Fulbright's Insurance Litigation Practice Group, is a frequent speaker on bad faith and property insurance issues, and has spoken before the DRI, ABA and Mealy's. He is an editor of the Bad Faith Litigation Reporter and co-authored 'The Property Insurance Litigators Handbook' (2007) and 'Toxic Mold Litigation' (Lawyers & Judges Publishing Co. 2005).
**Personal:** JD, Vanderbilt (1983); BA, magna cum laude, Vanderbilt (1980).

**PATRICK, Kathy**
Gibbs & Bruns LLP, Houston
713 751 5253
kpatrick@gibbsbruns.com
*Featured in Securities (Nationwide), Litigation (Texas)*
**Practice Areas:** Kathy Patrick focuses her practice on complex commercial litigation, with an emphasis on securities law, creditor recovery litigation, and institutional investor litigation. Representative clients include: Huntsman Corporation, PIMCO, BlackRock, Trust Company of the West, Invesco, Western Asset Management, Ambac Assurance, the former outside directors of Enron Corporation and the State of Arizona. Kathy recently secured an $8.5 billion settlement with Bank of America on behalf of 22 institutional investors in connection with 530 securitization pools that issued over $424 billion of Countrywide-issued mortgage-backed securities. The Wall Street Journal profiled Kathy in an article entitled, "An Unlikely Bulldog for Mortgage Investors," and Forbes magazine called her "the woman Wall Street fears most."
**Career:** National recognition includes being named: a "Top Ten Change Agent" by the Financial Times in its feature, "US Innovative Lawyers 2012"; "Overall Female Litigator of the Year" and "Texas Litigator of the Year" by Benchmark Litigation, 2012; "Best in Litigation" at the inaugural Euromoney Legal Media Group Americas Women in Business Law Awards, 2012. She is named to Legal 500's national "Leading Trial Lawyer" shortlist; Legal Media's World's Leading Litigation Lawyers list; Chambers USA's Nationwide Securities Litigation Leading Lawyers list; Best Lawyers in America in the areas of Bet-the-Company Litigation, Securities Law and Commercial Litigation; and Benchmark Litigation in the areas of Complex Commercial, Securities and Legal Malpractice. Texas Lawyer named Kathy in its features "Winning Women 2011" and the inaugural "Extraordinary Women in Texas Law," 2008.

**PATTERSON, Nancy L**
Morgan, Lewis & Bockius LLP, Houston
713 890 5195
npatterson@morganlewis.com
*Featured in Labor & Employment (Texas)*
**Practice Areas:** Nancy L Patterson is a partner in Morgan Lewis's Labor and Employment Practice. She is Board Certified in Civil Trial Law and focuses her practice in the healthcare, energy, financial services, technology, transportation and chemical manufacturing industries. She frequently represents clients before administrative regulatory agencies, including the Equal Employment Opportunity Commission, the Texas Commission on Human Rights, the Texas Workforce Commission, the National Labor Relations Board, the US Department of Labor Wage and Hour Division, and the Occupational Safety and Health Administration.
**Personal:** Attended Southern Methodist University School of Law, 1988, JD; University of Missouri, 1985, BA.

**PECHT, Gerard**
Fulbright & Jaworski LLP, Houston
713 651 5243
gpecht@fulbright.com
*Featured in Litigation (Texas)*
**Practice Areas:** Energy, securities, business and international litigation; class actions and international anti-bribery investigations.
**Professional Memberships:** Fellow, Texas Bar Foundation; Life Fellow, Houston Bar Association; Antitrust and Business Litigation Section of the State Bar of Texas.
**Career:** A partner in Fulbright's Houston and Dallas offices and Chairman of the firm's Securities Litigation Investigations and Enforcement Group, Pecht practices in the Litigation section. He concentrates his practice on complex business and commercial litigation, including securities litigation and enforcement, antitrust, energy litigation, internal investigations, international litigation and arbitration.
**Personal:** JD with honors, University of Cincinnati (1978); BA, Georgetown University (1975).

**PEDEN, David**
Porter Hedges LLP, Houston
713 226 6622
dpeden@porterhedges.com
*Featured in Construction (Texas)*
**Practice Areas:** David Peden has extensive experience in litigation and arbitration of construction, insurance, surety and commercial issues. He represents general contractors, subcontractors, design professionals, lenders, and owners in disputes, litigation, mediation, trials and appeals. He has negotiated and drafted construction contracts in Texas and many other states.
**Professional Memberships:** David served as Chair of the State Bar of Texas Construction Law Section. He is a member of the panel of arbitrators of the American Arbitration Association, Construction and Litigation Sections of the Federal, American, Texas and Houston Bar Associations and the Houston Chapter of the Association of General Contractors.

**PELS, Gerald J**
Locke Lord LLP, Houston
713 226 1402
gpels@lockelord.com
*Featured in Environment (Texas)*
**Practice Areas:** Environmental litigation; agency negotiations; contested air, water, solid waste permitting; defending enforcement actions; and counseling clients regarding multimedia regulatory compliance. Represents PRP groups, individual parties at Superfund sites, assists with corporate environmental and sustainability policy development, stakeholder analyses, community relations plans and securities disclosures. Works extensively with heavy industry and energy concerns, including power plants, petrochemical facilities, drilling and E&P concerns, refineries, manufacturers, solid/hazardous waste facilities, recyclers and food processors.
**Career:** Partner, 1990-present.
**Personal:** Vanderbilt University Law School (JD, 1983); St. Joseph's University (AB, summa cum laude, 1980).

**PEREZ, Alfredo R**
Weil, Gotshal & Manges LLP, Houston
212 310 8510
alfredo.perez@weil.com
*Featured in Bankruptcy/Restructuring (Texas), Bankruptcy/Restructuring (Nationwide)*
**Practice Areas:** Mr Perez heads the Business Finance & Restructuring Department's Houston office and concentrates his practice in the representation of chapter 11 debtors and other diverse claimants, including secured and unsecured creditors in all aspects of corporate restructurings. He has also represented acquirers of assets from bankruptcy estates and companies in financial distress. Mr Perez has played a significant role in many major bankruptcies including AMR, Lehman, BearingPoint, and WorldCom. Mr Perez is a native Spanish speaker and has extensive experience in cross-border and transnational insolvency matters.
**Personal:** Haverford College (BA, 1977); University of Chicago Law School (JD, 1980).

**PERICH, Thomas J**
Andrews Kurth LLP, Houston
713 220 4268
tperich@andrewskurth.com
*Featured in Banking & Finance (Texas)*
**Practice Areas:** Tom centers his practice in banking and finance and counsels clients on mat-

ters including documentation of domestic and international commercial, construction, real estate, power and infrastructure development and energy (focusing on upstream and E&P) loans; leasing and project finance; monetization and structured finance, including off-balance-sheet financing, production payments, prepaid forward contracts, and credit insurance; bank regulatory issues; workouts and restructurings, with extensive experience in creditors' rights and bankruptcy, lender liability and usury. He represents banks and bank holding companies before state and federal regulatory and administrative agencies, and in the acquisition and disposition of banks and bank assets.

## PERKINS, Alan
Gardere Wynne Sewell LLP, Dallas
214 999 4683
aperkins@gardere.com
*Featured in Corporate/M&A (Texas)*
**Practice Areas:** Corporate, mergers and acquisitions (M&A), securities.
**Professional Memberships:** State Bar of Texas, Dallas Bar Association.
**Career:** Since 1978, Alan Perkins has represented buyers and sellers in hundreds of public and private merger and acquisition transactions involving a wide variety of industries. His practice also includes all types of general corporate and securities matters, including public and private securities issuances and private equity and venture capital financings. In addition, Mr Perkins serves as counsel to Special Committees and represents senior executives in complex employment and severance arrangements.
**Personal:** JD, Emory University School of Law, 1978; BA, Northwestern University, 1975.

## PERRIN, Harry
Vinson & Elkins LLP, Houston
713 758 2548
hperrin@velaw.com
*Featured in Bankruptcy/Restructuring (Texas)*
**Practice Areas:** Extensive experience as an attorney and as an investment banker/ financial advisor in restructurings and complex Chapter 11 cases.
**Professional Memberships:** Houston Bar Association; American Bankruptcy Institute; American College of Bankruptcy.
**Career:** CPA-Texas 1977; Admitted to Texas Bar, 1980; Joined V&E as a Partner in 2007; Prior to joining V&E, was co-head of restructuring arm of a Houston-based investment banking firm, previously a partner in the Houston office of a national law firm, and co-founding partner of a Houston-based business bankruptcy firm.
**Personal:** University of Houston, JD magna cum laude, 1980; University of Texas, BBA with Honors, 1975.

## PETERMAN, David
Fulbright & Jaworski LLP, Houston
713 651 3635
dpeterman@fulbright.com
*Featured in Technology (Texas)*
**Practice Areas:** Corporate, securities and transactions.

**Career:** Peterman has represented clients in numerous corporate, securities and business law matters, in numerous industries including the energy, private equity, manufacturing, distribution, telecom, automobile, technology, hospitality, and staffing industries. His experience includes representing a broad range of domestic and international buyers, sellers, issuers, underwriters, and investors in a number of substantial acquisitions and corporate finance transactions, including acquisitions and dispositions of stock, assets and business divisions, and public and private securities transactions.
**Personal:** 1982 - BBA, University of Texas-Austin; 1985 - JD, with honors, University of Texas School of Law, Austin.

## PETERSON, Edward
Winstead PC, Dallas
214 745 5642
epeterson@winstead.com
*Featured in Real Estate (Texas)*
**Practice Areas:** Ed represents institutional clients, including insurance companies, pension plans (public and private) and banks in their corporate real estate transactions on a national basis. He represents developers of real estate and investors in the acquisition and disposition of real estate portfolios and condominium developers in high rise, mixed-use and commercial condominium projects. He has represented institutions in numerous real estate restructures, including those involving multistate portfolios and significant office and retail projects in Texas and other jurisdictions.

## PFEIFFER, Philip J
Fulbright & Jaworski LLP, San Antonio
210 270 7117
ppfeiffer@fulbright.com
*Featured in Labor & Employment (Texas)*
**Practice Areas:** Labor and employment law.
**Professional Memberships:** American Bar Association's Equal Employment Opportunity Committee; Past Co-Chair, ABA's EEO Liaison Committee for South Texas; Former Editor-in-Chief, Second Supplement to Lindemann and Grossman, Employment Discrimination Law; Member, College Labor and Employment Lawyers.
**Career:** Pfeiffer focuses his legal practice on labor and employment matters, emphasizing complex civil rights and employment discrimination cases; employment torts, alternative dispute resolution, employment contracts, and Employment Retirement Income Security Act litigation. He serves as a mediator in employment and civil rights cases.
**Personal:** JD, Southern Methodist University (1972); BS, Sam Houston State University (1969).

## PHELAN, Rod
Baker Botts LLP, Dallas
214 953 6609
rod.phelan@bakerbotts.com
*Featured in Litigation (Nationwide), Litigation (Texas)*
**Practice Areas:** Commercial litigation, primarily defending claims of professional malpractice (against lawyers and accountants), representing

parties on both sides of cases involving oil and gas, partnerships, intellectual property, antitrust, securities, tax and corporate governance. Clients are professional service firms, national and local business entities, and their principals.
**Career:** 35+ years of experience. Member, American College of Trial Lawyers, International Academy of Trial Lawyers, International Society of Barristers, American Board of Trial Advocates.
**Personal:** JD, cum laude, Duke University School of Law, 1973; Order of the Coif; Editorial Board, Duke Law Journal; BA, cum laude, Vanderbilt University, 1970.

## PHILLIPS, Frances E
Gardere Wynne Sewell LLP, Dallas
214 999 4803
fphillips@gardere.com
*Featured in Environment (Texas)*
**Practice Areas:** Environmental law and policy: business transactions; risk transfer; air, water, stormwater, hazardous waste and climate change permitting/compliance, including NEPA compliance; munitions remediation/claims; administrative, civil, and criminal enforcement matters; litigation.
**Professional Memberships:** American, D.C., Texas and Dallas Bar Associations, Texas and Dallas Bar Foundations.
**Career:** Fran Phillips' experience includes 15 years in senior executive positions at the US Environmental Protection Agency. She has practiced law in Dallas, Houston, and Washington, DC, and served as a visiting scholar/professor at the SMU Dedman School of Law.
**Personal:** JD, University of Texas School of Law, 1972; BA, Baylor University, with honors, 1969.

## PHILLIPS, Thomas R
Baker Botts LLP, Austin
512 322 2565
tom.phillips@bakerbotts.com
*Featured in Appellate Law (Nationwide), Litigation (Texas)*
**Practice Areas:** Appellate and dispute resolution.
**Professional Memberships:** Board Certified Civil Trial Law; American Law Institute; CPR Texas Panel of Distinguished Neutrals; Conference of Chief Justices.
**Career:** State District Judge, 1981-88; Chief Justice, Supreme Court of Texas, 1988-2004; Visiting Professor, South Texas College of Law and SMU Law School, 2004-05.
**Personal:** BA, Baylor 1971; JD, Harvard, 1974.

## PIERCE, Jesse
Pierce & O'Neill, LLP, Houston
713 634 3600
jpierce@pierceoneill.com
*Featured in Litigation (Texas)*
**Practice Areas:** Commercial disputes litigation; energy litigation; toxic tort litigation; environmental litigation; appellate litigation; trade secrets and non-compete litigation; domestic arbitration/ADR; securities litigation.
**Professional Memberships:** Litigation Counsel of America; American Board of Trial Advocates; The Center for American and International Law -

Oil & Gas Practice Committee; Council of the Oil, Gas & Energy Resources Law Section of the State Bar of Texas; American Bar Association; Houston Bar Association.
**Career:** Jesse Pierce has more than thirty-five years of litigation experience and has tried many types of cases in state and federal courts of Texas, as well as other states. He specializes in the trial of complex energy and commercial cases. Mr Pierce is Board Certified in Civil Trial Law by the Texas Board of Legal Specialization and is a Commercial Arbitrator for American Arbitration Association. He is licensed to practice in Texas, Oklahoma, Arkansas, Michigan and Pennsylvania.
**Publications:** "Recent Developments in Oil and Gas Law," 8th Annual Energy Litigation Conference, The Institute for Energy Law, 2009; "Protecting Company Secrets and Rights to Compete: When Employer and Employees Clash in the Oilfield," 60th Annual Conference on Oil and Gas Law, Institute for Energy Law, 2009; "Termination of Oil, Gas, and Mineral Leases: Savings Clauses and Defensive Doctrines," Advanced Oil, Gas and Energy Resources Law Course, Texas State Bar Association, 2008; "Current Issues in Gas Royalty Litigation," Arkansas State Bar Association Oil, Gas & Energy Law Seminar, 2005; "Termination of Oil, Gas & Mineral Leases: The Temporary Cessation of Production & Production in Paying Quantities Doctrines," State Bar of Texas Oil, Gas and Energy Resources Law Section Report, Vol. 27, No. 4, June 2003; "Common Law Claims in Environmental Contamination cases," Advanced Environmental Law Course, State Bar of Texas, 1997; "Standards of Appellate Review," Houston Bar Association Appellate Practice Institute, 1996; "Current Issues in Controversies Between Royalty Owners and Energy Companies," Section of Natural Resources, Energy, and Environmental Law, American Bar Association, 1993.

## PINKER, Eric
Lynn Tillotson Pinker & Cox, LLP, Dallas
214 981 3800
epinker@lynnllp.com
*Featured in Litigation (Texas)*
**Career:** Board certified in civil trial advocacy by the prestigious National Board of Trial Advocacy, Eric Pinker represents clients in a wide range of complex commercial and intellectual property disputes throughout the country. "Our extensive courtroom experience, judgment, and careful planning give us the advantage in every case," he says, "and that's reflected in the results we obtain for our clients." While in private practice, Mr Pinker has recovered more than $200 million for his clients and protected defendants from claims valued at more than $500 million. Mr Pinker is also a sought-after speaker on a wide range of legal topics and is active in Bar and community service activities, including serving on the Board of the Dallas Bar Association's Trial Skill Section (2003-12) and serving as a Master in Dallas' newly-formed Intellectual Property Inn of Court (2011-present). He received both his undergraduate degree in Plan II and his JD from The University of Texas at Austin.

## POPPLEWELL, Thomas
Andrews Kurth LLP, Dallas
214 659 4480
tpopplewell@andrewskurth.com
*Featured in Tax (Texas)*
**Practice Areas:** Tom is experienced in income tax aspects of mergers and acquisitions, real estate income tax matters, renewable energy tax matters, and structuring and implementation of US and international REMIC and other asset securitizations. He also advises clients on Texas taxes, and on federal income taxation issues and their impact on partnerships, limited liability companies, corporations, S corporations, special forms of debt, real estate investment trusts, hedging and other derivatives, and bankruptcy matters. In these matters Tom often represents pension fund advisors, tax-exempt organizations, real estate investment trusts, private equity firms and hedge funds.

## PORTER, John
Baker Botts LLP, Houston
713 229 1597
john.porter@bakerbotts.com
*Featured in Tax (Nationwide), Wealth Management (Nationwide), Tax (Texas)*
See under Nationwide for profile.

## POWELL, Charles D
Fulbright & Jaworski LLP, Houston
713 651 5431
cpowell@fulbright.com
*Featured in Technology (Texas)*
**Practice Areas:** Corporate, technology and emerging companies, e-commerce, information technology, private equity, investment funds.
**Professional Memberships:** Houston Technology Center-Advisory Board of Directors, Chairman(2002-08), Vice Chairman (2007-08); Rice Alliance for Technology and Entrepreneurship-Faculty & Business Plan Judge (2006-11).
**Career:** Chuck handles venture capital, angel capital, private equity financings and public offerings. His clients are venture capital funds, technology companies, and businesses involved in energy technology, life sciences and information technology. Chuck has closed over 320 seed, angel, venture capital, private equity and IPO transactions from $500k to $600m.
**Personal:** JD, The University of Texas School of Law (1979); BA, Columbia (1976).

## POWELL, Michael V
Locke Lord LLP, Dallas
214 740 8520
mpowell@lockelord.com
*Featured in Litigation (Texas)*
**Practice Areas:** Mr Powell has many years of experience as a lead trial and appellate lawyer. Works on trial and appellate matters pertaining to the oil and gas industry, aviation, products liability and other forms of complex contract, tort, professional malpractice, statutory and constitutional litigation. Experienced in handling class actions and appeals in both federal and state courts.
**Professional Memberships:** American College of Trial Lawyers (Fellow).
**Career:** Partner since 1980.

**Personal:** The University of Texas School of Law (JD, with high honors, 1974); The University of Texas at Austin (MA, Public Administration, 1972); Davidson College (AB, 1968).

## PRINCE, James
Baker Botts LLP, Dallas
214 953 6612
jim.prince@bakerbotts.com
*Featured in Bankruptcy/Restructuring (Texas)*
**Practice Areas:** Represents a diverse range of asset acquirers, lenders, creditors, debtors, officers and directors, and parent companies in virtually every aspect of complex chapter 11 cases, as well as out-of-court workouts and pre-packaged reorganization plans. He has particular experience in mass tort bankruptcies.
**Professional Memberships:** State Bar of Texas; American Bankruptcy Institute, Dallas Bankruptcy Bar.
**Career:** Reorganization, bankruptcy; creditors' rights; debtor/creditor remedies; federal court appeals.
**Personal:** JD, Berkeley Law, University of California, Berkeley, 1992; BS, finance, Oklahoma State University, 1989.

## PRINCE, James M
Vinson & Elkins LLP, Houston
713 758 3710
jprince@velaw.com
*Featured in Corporate/M&A (Texas), Capital Markets (Texas)*
**Practice Areas:** Partner, Capital Markets Group. Represents publicly traded and private companies in various capacities and major investment banking firms in capital markets transactions, including equity and high yield debt finance. Corporate practice includes SEC compliance, corporate governance, secured and high yield debt finance, capital markets, private placements, master limited partnerships, joint ventures, M&A, and oil and gas matters. Has broad experience in the energy industry.
**Professional Memberships:** Houston Bar Association.
**Career:** Admitted to Texas Bar, 1980. Joined V&E as a partner, 2000.
**Personal:** The University of Texas, BBA, 1976; The University of Texas School of Law, JD, 1980.

## PROSTOK, Jeff
Forshey Prostok LLP, Fort Worth
817 877 4223
jprostok@forsheyprostok.com
*Featured in Bankruptcy/Restructuring (Texas)*
**Practice Areas:** Bankruptcy - restructuring.
**Career:** Jeff Prostok is a Partner in the firm with over 29 years of experience in the areas of business reorganization, workouts, and creditors' rights. Mr Prostok has successfully represented a wide range of clients from the debtors in the largest Texas bankruptcy reorganization case to small companies seeking reorganization relief. Mr Prostok has been recognized as a "Texas Super Lawyer" since the inception of such recognition by Texas Monthly. He was a recent recipient of the Fort Worth Business Press 2012 Power Attorney Award and is Board Certified in Business

Bankruptcy by the Texas Board of Legal Specialization.

## PROTOPAPAS, Lydia
Weil, Gotshal & Manges LLP, Houston
713 546 5322
lydia.protopapas@weil.com
*Featured in Bankruptcy/Restructuring (Texas)*
**Practice Areas:** Ms Protopapas focuses on business reorganizations, debtors' and creditors' rights, and insolvency. She has represented debtors, creditors, and acquirors of assets from bankruptcy estates including: Adobe Energy, American General Financial Center, Anadarko Petroleum Corporation, Cajun Electric Power, Cal-Dive International, Coastal Plains, Inc., Crescent Resources, Encompass Services Corporation, GE Franchise Finance, Global Crossing Limited, Integrated Electrical Services, Inc., Jazzland Inc., Macquaire Capital Funds, Simmons Bedding Company, Six Flags, Sterling Chemicals, Inc., Toyobo Company, Ltd ,TXCO Resources, Verizon Business, Viasystems, Inc. and WorldCom Inc.
**Personal:** University of Houston (BBA); University of Illinois (MBA); University of Houston Law Center (JD).

## PUIG, Yvonne Karen
Fulbright & Jaworski LLP, Austin
512 536 2450
ypuig@fulbright.com
*Featured in Healthcare (Texas)*
**Practice Areas:** Health law and litigation.
**Professional Memberships:** American Board of Trial Advocates;American Health Lawyers Association;Texas Association of Defense Counsel.
**Career:** Puig practices in the healthcare area, representing hospitals, HMOs, medical schools and other institutional health care providers. She has extensive experience in a variety of health law regulatory matters, including EMTALA, credentialing, due process hearings, and Joint Commission accreditation and compliance. Her trial experience includes complex litigation, such as representation of hospital systems, manufacturers and sellers of medical devices, and commercial litigation involving the health industry.
**Personal:** BA University of Texas (1975); JD,University of Texas School of Law (1978).

## RABALAIS, Robert René
Simpson Thacher & Bartlett LLP, Houston
713 821 5610
rrabalais@stblaw.com
*Featured in Banking & Finance (Texas)*
**Practice Areas:** Practice consists of secured and unsecured syndicated finance transactions, capital markets and privately placed debt securities.
**Professional Memberships:** Texas Bar Association, Louisiana Bar Association.
**Career:** Admitted to practice law in Louisiana (1989) and Texas (1990); admitted to partnership in 1998.
**Publications:** 'The Challenges of Acquiring Energy Assets from Distressed Sellers,' Project Finance International, October 2002 (with Mark Laufman); 'Banking & Lending Institution Forms',

Chapter 1.1A - Oil and Gas Lending (contributing editor).
**Personal:** Louisiana State University, BS, 1986; Louisiana State University, JD, 1989.

## RAFTE, G Alan
Bracewell & Giuliani LLP, Houston
713 221 1411
alan.rafte@bgllp.com
*Featured in Banking & Finance (Texas), Energy & Natural Resources (Nationwide), Projects (Nationwide)*
See under Nationwide for profile.

## RAIN, John W
Thompson & Knight LLP, Dallas
214 969 1644
John.Rain@tklaw.com
*Featured in Banking & Finance (Texas), Energy & Natural Resources (Nationwide)*
**Practice Areas:** Mr Rain represents capital providers and capital users in private debt or investment transactions, with an emphasis on the energy industry. He has special experience in structuring and negotiating volumetric production payments, royalties, and other deals involving the combination of property or commodity sales with derivative contracts.
**Professional Memberships:** American College of Investment Counsel; Texas Association of Bank Counsel; Independent Petroleum Association of America; State Bar of Texas; Dallas Bar Association; Dallas Bar Foundation.
**Personal:** University of Texas Law School (JD, with high honors, 1978); Gordon-Conwell Theological Seminary (graduate study, 1974-75); Amherst College (BA, with honors, 1973).

## RAINEY, Susan M
Locke Lord LLP, Dallas
214 740 8559
srainey@lockelord.com
*Featured in Environment (Texas)*
**Practice Areas:** Analyzes environmental risks and liabilities in real estate, lending and corporate transactions. Assists clients in redeveloping brownfield sites, conducting environmental assessments and remediation and pursuing closure through voluntary cleanup and other regulatory programs. Experience includes environmental regulatory work, and building environmental management issues including vapor intrusion, PCBs, asbestos, lead based paint and mold.
**Professional Memberships:** Dallas Bar Association; Commercial Real Estate Women.
**Career:** Associate since 2005; Project Manager at Texas Commission on Environmental Quality, 1999-2002.
**Personal:** The University of Texas School of Law (JD, with honors, 2005); Boston University (BA, Environmental Science and Biology, summa cum laude, 1996).

## RAMÓN, Jaime
K&L Gates, Dallas
214 939 4902
jaime.ramon@klgates.com
*Featured in Labor & Employment (Texas)*
**Practice Areas:** Jaime Ramón has counseled and litigated on behalf of employers in every

aspect of the employer/employee relationship, including Title VII, ADEA, ADA, FLSA, EPA, Service Contract Act, OFCCP, affirmative action, wrongful discharge and employment contracts. With prior government service as Director of the Office of Federal Contract Compliance Programs for the US Department of Labor and as General Counsel for the US Office of Personnel Management, he is an experienced practitioner on employment law, affirmative action plans and federal, state, and municipal government contract compliance issues. He is a frequent speaker on employment law policies, practices, and legislation.

### RAY, Hugh M
McKool Smith, Houston
713 485 7300
hray@mckoolsmith.com
*Featured in Bankruptcy/Restructuring (Texas)*
**Practice Areas:** Bankruptcy and restructuring.
**Professional Memberships:** Texas Board of Legal Specialization; American Board of Bankruptcy Certification; American College of Bankruptcy; American Law Institute; Chair, ABA Business Law Section's Business Bankruptcy Committee.
**Career:** For more than 40 years, Mr Ray has played a lead role in some of the country's most recognizable bankruptcy proceedings. He was among the first called before Congress to testify on proposed amendments to the Federal Bankruptcy Code. Prior to private practice, Mr Ray worked as an Assistant US Attorney in Houston.
**Personal:** Vanderbilt University Law School (LLB, 1967); Vanderbilt University (BS, 1965)

### REASONER, Barrett
Gibbs & Bruns LLP, Houston
713 751 5244
breasoner@gibbsbruns.com
*Featured in Litigation (Texas)*
**Practice Areas:** Represents both plaintiffs and defendants in complex commercial litigation, including breach of contract, securities, energy, oil and gas, legal and professional malpractice, construction, and intellectual property.
**Professional Memberships:** International Society of Barristers; State Bar of Texas, Board of Directors; Houston Bar Association, President (2009-10); American Law Institute; Houston Volunteer Lawyers Program, Past Board Chair; American Judicature Society, Board Member.
**Career:** Assistant District Attorney for Harris County, Texas, 1990-92. Joined Gibbs & Bruns in 1992 and became partner in 1996. Recognized in Legal 500, Chambers USA, Best Lawyers in America, Benchmark Litigation, Who's Who Legal, and Texas Super Lawyers.

### REASONER, Harry M
Vinson & Elkins LLP, Houston
713 758 2358
hreasoner@velaw.com
*Featured in Antitrust (Texas), Litigation (Nationwide), Litigation (Texas)*
See under Nationwide for profile.

### REED, Kevin A
Reed, Claymon, Meeker & Hargett, PLLC, Austin
512 482 0614
kreed@dwlaw.com
*Featured in Healthcare (Texas)*
**Practice Areas:** Health law.
**Career:** Admitted to Texas Bar, 1979. Board Certified, Administrative Law and Health Law by Texas Board of Legal Specialization. Former Chair, Health Law Section, State Bar of Texas; former Chair of the Exam Commission, Health Law, Texas Board of Legal Specialization.
**Personal:** Graduated from Salem College, cum laude, BA, 1976, University of Texas School of Law, JD, 1979. Recognized as a "Super Lawyer" by Texas Monthly and Law & Politics Magazines (2003-11); "The Best Lawyers in America" in Health Care Law, Best Lawyers, 2009; and as the "Go To Lawyer in Health Law in the State of Texas," Texas Lawyer in Go-To-Guide (October 2008). General Counsel, Texas Organization of Rural and Community Hospitals (1991-Present).

### REEDER JR, James A
Vinson & Elkins LLP, Houston
713 758 2202
jreeder@velaw.com
*Featured in Antitrust (Texas)*
**Practice Areas:** Complex commercial litigation, antitrust, healthcare litigation.
**Professional Memberships:** ABA Section of Litigation, Antitrust Section, State Bar of Texas, Antitrust Section, Houston Bar Association, Antitrust Committee, Healthcare Committee, American Health Lawyers Association.
**Career:** Admitted to practice: Texas, US District Courts for the Southern, Eastern, Western and Northern Districts of Texas, US Court of Appeals for the Fifth and Fourth Circuits, United States Court of Claims, United States Supreme Court.
**Personal:** Harvard University, AB with honors, 1984; University of Texas School of Law, JD with honors, 1989.

### REEDY, Robert
Porter Hedges LLP, Houston
713 226 6674
rreedy@porterhedges.com
*Featured in Corporate/M&A (Texas), Capital Markets (Texas)*
**Practice Areas:** Rob Reedy is Porter Hedges' managing partner and a partner in the corporate practice group. He is involved in a wide variety of corporate, securities and merger/acquisition transactions. His practice focuses on public companies and emerging privately held entities that are building their business through acquisitions and financings such as public offerings and private equity transactions. His clients include businesses involved in energy exploration, production, service and transmission, alternative energy, technology, biotech and manufacturing/distribution. Mr Reedy also represents investment banking firms who specialize in public and private securities offerings for companies in all phases of the energy industry.

### RENFROE, Tracie
King & Spalding LLP, Houston
713 751 3214
trenfroe@kslaw.com
*Featured in Environment (Texas)*
**Practice Areas:** Maintains national practice focusing on environmental and toxic tort litigation and product liability disputes, including federal and state class actions and multi-district litigation. Has significant experience in contaminated groundwater and drinking water cases. Serves as national coordinating Counsel for several oil companies in MTBE contamination litigation. Has handled cases involving petroleum hydrocarbons, solvents, chlorinated compounds, oxygenates and radioactive materials. Has litigated actions under CERCLA, RCRA, Safe Drinking Water Act and state and local statutes. Has litigated deep injection well disputes, personal injury and chemical exposure suits.
**Personal:** JD, Baylor University School of Law; BA, Baylor University.

### RENTZ, Rebecca J
Winstead PC, Houston
713 650 2776
rrentz@winstead.com
*Featured in Environment (Texas)*
**Practice Areas:** Rebecca is recognized as a leading lawyer in the environmental field with experience in the service of both government and private clients. She has extensive knowledge of air toxics issues, environmental enforcement, particulate emissions requirements, and ozone control requirements under the Houston-area State Implementation Plan including associated transportation conformity requirements. She also has experience defending state and federal Superfund matters, assisting clients with environmental permitting, regulations that impact production and midstream operations and handling the environmental aspects of real estate and financial transactions. She advises clients on a wide variety of environmental regulatory, liability and public policy issues.

### REPASS, James
Fulbright & Jaworski LLP, Houston
713 651 3623
jrepass@fulbright.com
*Featured in Intellectual Property (Texas)*
**Practice Areas:** Intellectual property, patent litigation.
**Professional Memberships:** American Bar Association; American Intellectual Property Law Association; Houston Intellectual Property Law Association, former president.
**Career:** Repass heads the Intellectual Property Department. His practice focuses on intellectual property transactions and disputes for global companies. His 25 years of experience includes managing transactions, including stock and asset deals, due diligence, joint development agreements and licensing arrangements. He was named to the BTI Client Service All-Stars, an elite group of attorneys nominated by clients.

Personal: JD, honors, George Washington University Law School; BS, summa cum laude, Chemical Engineering, University of Tennessee.

### REYNOLDS, Chris
Reynolds, Frizzell, Black, Doyle, Allen & Oldham, LLP, Houston
713 485 7200
creynolds@reynoldsfrizzell.com
*Featured in Litigation (Texas)*
**Practice Areas:** Practice focuses on complex commercial and business litigation, including securities fraud, engineering and construction disputes, oil and gas litigation, and every variety of intellectual property case. Represents both plaintiffs and defendants.
**Professional Memberships:** American College of Trial Lawyers, Fellow; American Board of Trial Advocates, Associate; Texas Bar Foundation, Fellow; Tau Beta Pi and Chi Epsilon engineering honor societies, Member.
**Career:** Began career with Wood, Campbell, Moody & Gibbs, PC (predecessor firm). Joined Gibbs & Bruns LLP (formerly Gibbs & Ratliff, LLP) in October of 1983, and was made a Partner in 1987. Recognized by Chambers USA, Benchmark Litigation, Best Lawyers in America, BTI Consulting, Texas Super Lawyers (Top 100 Lawyers in Houston), and H Texas Magazine.
**Publications:** Has written and presented on the following topics: the use of statistics in litigation; piercing the corporate veil; and how lawyers can avoid liability when deals 'go bad.'
**Personal:** Born 1959. BS, with honors, The University of Texas, 1980; JD, with honors, The University of Texas School of Law, 1982 - Order of the Coif; Member, Texas Law Review. Married with two children; enjoys deep sea fishing and fox hunting.

### RICKETTS, Phil F
Bracewell & Giuliani LLP, Austin
512 494 3630
phil.ricketts@bgllp.com
*Featured in Energy & Natural Resources (Texas)*
**Practice Areas:** Represents energy and telecommunications clients in rate cases, mergers, acquisitions, power sales and other regulatory matters, with particular focus on contested cases and rule-making proceedings at the Public Utility Commission of Texas. Also has experience in judicial appeals of these proceedings' determinations. He also has participated in regulatory proceedings in several other states.
**Personal:** JD, The University of Texas School of Law, 1973; BA, Baylor University, 1967.

### RIEGER, Michelle I
Winstead PC, Dallas
214 745 5416
mrieger@winstead.com
*Featured in Construction (Texas)*
**Practice Areas:** Michelle has a dual transactional/controversy practice focused on the construction industry. For more than 20 years, Michelle has represented Winstead's real estate owner, developer and contractor clients in a myriad of construction disputes, litigating construction issues through the trial and appellate process

and in various alternative dispute resolution procedures throughout the State of Texas. Michelle has extensive experience in drafting and negotiating all kinds of critical contracts for use on many commercial, hospital, airport and multi-family construction projects.

### RILEY, John A
Bracewell & Giuliani LLP, Houston
512 542 2108
john.riley@bgllp.com
*Featured in Environment (Texas)*

**Practice Areas:** Represents clients in permitting and enforcement matters in the air, water and waste media. Advises entities in the power generation, hydraulic fracturing, manufacturing and waste disposal sectors in matters before the Texas Commission on Environmental Quality (TCEQ) and the US Environmental Protection Agency. Regularly represents clients in contested case hearings in permit and enforcement matters before TCEQ at the State Office of Administrative Hearings in Texas.
**Personal:** JD, Boston University School of Law, 1983; BS, Cornell University, 1979.

### RISMAN, Clifford J
Gardere Wynne Sewell LLP, Dallas
214 999 4287
crisman@gardere.com
*Featured in Leisure & Hospitality (Nationwide), Real Estate (Texas)*
See under Nationwide for profile.

### ROBERSON, Richard M
Gardere Wynne Sewell LLP, Dallas
214 999 4955
rroberson@gardere.com
*Featured in Bankruptcy/Restructuring (Texas)*

**Practice Areas:** Bankruptcy, business reorganization.
**Professional Memberships:** State Bar of Texas, American and Dallas Bar Associations, American Bankruptcy Institute, Turnaround Management Association.
**Career:** Richard Roberson chairs Gardere's Bankruptcy and Business Reorganization Practice Group. His comprehensive practice includes the representation of secured lenders, debtors, trustees, and creditors' committees. Mr Roberson's practice also encompasses all litigation arising from his bankruptcy and creditors' rights matters. His clients include major banks, asset-based lenders, trustees, creditors' committees, receivers, creditors, and debtors in a variety of industries.
**Personal:** JD, St. Mary's University School of Law, with honors, 1978; BBA, Southern Methodist University, cum laude, 1975.

### ROBERTS JR, Harry M
Thompson & Knight LLP, Dallas
214 969 1616
Harry.Roberts@tklaw.com
*Featured in Real Estate (Texas)*

**Practice Areas:** Mr Roberts' practice focuses primarily on real estate transactions involving permanent and construction loan work; purchase and sale of commercial real estate; development of real property; leasing; loan servicing, including modification agreements and assumption agree-

ments; management agreements; reciprocal and other easements; limited partnerships; local counsel opinions; loan workouts; foreclosures; and usury analysis.
**Professional Memberships:** American College of Real Estate Lawyers; College of the State Bar of Texas; State Bar of Texas; Dallas Bar Association; American, Texas, and Dallas Bar Foundations.
**Career:** Adjunct Professor, SMU Dedman Law School.
**Personal:** Harvard Law School (JD, 1963); Southern Methodist University (BBA, 1960).

### ROBISON, Brian E
Gibson, Dunn & Crutcher LLP, Dallas
214 698 3370
brobison@gibsondunn.com
*Featured in Antitrust (Texas)*

**Practice Areas:** Antitrust and complex civil litigation. Experience includes bid rigging, price fixing, market allocation, supply control, predatory pricing, monopolization, and price discrimination cases. Counsels clients on the antitrust implications of business arrangements. Represents clients in federal and state antitrust investigations.
**Professional Memberships:** Council of the Antitrust & Business Litigation Section, Texas State Bar. Council of the Antitrust & Trade Regulation Section, Dallas Bar. Antitrust Section, ABA.
**Career:** Law clerk, John Cornyn, Texas Supreme Court.
**Personal:** JD, University of Texas Law School, 1995, with honors, Order of the Coif, Notes Editor, Texas Law Review.

### RODGERS, Anne
Fulbright & Jaworski LLP, Houston
713 651 3797
arodgers@fulbright.com
*Featured in Antitrust (Texas)*

**Practice Areas:** Business litigation, antitrust and competition, securities, class actions and appeals.
**Career:** Anne Rodgers has more than 20 years of experience as a trial and appellate lawyer in federal and state courts across the US and internationally, winning many precedent-setting victories for clients. She facilitates business solutions to problems, and provides counseling to help clients avoid problems in the first place. Anne represents clients throughout the energy, banking and finance, manufacturing, entertainment, and health care industries in traditional lawsuits, class actions, derivative suits, and investigations.
**Personal:** JD, University of Chicago Law School; BS, University of Houston.

### RODI, David
Baker Botts LLP, Houston
713 229 1139
david.rodi@bakerbotts.com
*Featured in Antitrust (Texas)*

**Practice Areas:** Antitrust litigation; energy litigation; investigations.
**Professional Memberships:** Federal Bar Association, Southern District of Texas Chapter, President, 2012; Houston Bar Association, Antitrust Section, Chair, 2007-08.

**Career:** Represents energy, pharmaceutical, and manufacturing clients in antitrust litigation, regulatory matters, and FCPA investigations. Has handled cases in trial courts and appeals across the United States. Represents refiners in PMPA and downstream commercial cases.
**Personal:** JD, University of Texas School of Law (Order of the Coif), 1996; Executive Editor, Texas Law Review; BA (highest honors; special honors in French), Plan II, University of Texas, 1993; law clerk to US District Judge Barefoot Sanders.

### ROGERS, Elizabeth N
Waller Lansden Dortch & Davis, Austin
512 328 9301
elizabeth.rogers@wallerlaw.com
*Featured in Healthcare (Texas)*

**Practice Areas:** Healthcare law. Advises hospitals, health systems, academic medical centers and other providers in regulatory, legislative and transactional matters plus critical issues related to healthcare reform, including emerging reimbursement and healthcare delivery models such as bundled payments, value-based purchasing initiatives and ACOs. Extensive experience with participation and reimbursement matters – including certification and licensure – under commercial and governmental programs, including Medicare and Medicaid programs.
**Professional Memberships:** Chair, Health Law Council, State Bar of Texas.
**Career:** Licensed in Texas since 1991. Joined Waller in 2012.
**Personal:** JD, 1990, University of Texas; BA, with high honors, 1978, University of Texas.

### ROPPOLO, Stephen
Fisher & Phillips LLP, Houston
713 292 0150
sroppolo@laborlawyers.com
*Featured in Labor & Employment (Texas)*

**Career:** Steve Roppolo is the Managing Partner of the Houston office. He has extensive experience litigating all types of employment claims in federal and state court on behalf of employers. He has defended companies of various sizes in cases involving allegations of sexual harassment, discrimination, defamation, breach of employment contract, and other employment torts. His counseling and litigation practice includes extensive work with independent schools and hospitality clients. Steve counsels large and small companies regarding day-to-day employment matters. He also helps employers by and conducting training for managers and developing policies and procedures designed to minimize exposure to litigation claims.

### ROSE, Kelly Brunetti
Baker Botts LLP, Houston
713 229 1796
kelly.rose@bakerbotts.com
*Featured in Corporate/M&A (Texas)*

**Practice Areas:** Experience advising on mergers and acquisitions, including negotiated acquisitions and divestitures, tender offers, exchange offers and corporate reorganizations. Also counsels clients on an ongoing basis on disclosure issues, compliance with federal securities laws, corporate governance,

state corporate law issues and general corporate concerns. Ms Rose is head of the Corporate Department in Houston.
**Professional Memberships:** State Bar of Texas; Houston Bar Association; Houston Bar Foundation, Fellow.
**Career:** Recognized as a "Top Female Deal Maker" by Law360, 2011.
**Personal:** JD (with honors), University of Florida Levin College of Law, 1991; BA, Chinese, Wellesley College, 1988.

### ROSENBLUM, Rick
Akin Gump Strauss Hauer & Feld LLP, San Antonio
210 281 7123
rrosenblum@akingump.com
*Featured in Insurance (Texas)*

**Practice Areas:** Mr Rosenblum litigates high-stakes disputes involving insurance, reinsurance and insurer insolvency. Recent representations include a Bermuda reinsurer in arbitration and litigation over a multi-year aggregate stop loss treaty; a domestic P&C company in litigation against state insurance department regarding hurricane claims; D&O insurers in litigation involving an alleged multi-national Ponzi scheme; a domestic cedent in a dispute with a special deputy receiver in Texas's first ever insurer rehabilitation; a domestic life insurer in a putative ERISA class action; and, serving as an expert in a Q/S reinsurance dispute at the High Court of Justice-Queen's Bench Division-Commercial Court, UK.

### ROSKA, Kay
Thompson & Knight LLP, Dallas
214 969 1342
Kay.Roska@tklaw.com
*Featured in Environment (Texas)*

**Practice Areas:** Kay's practice includes environmental compliance; permitting; soil, air, water contamination; risk and liability management; and administrative proceedings at local, state, and federal environmental agencies. She advises clients regarding compliance with health and safety requirements under OSHA and comparable state laws. Her practice includes assisting clients in auditing their compliance with environmental, health, and safety requirements and developing programs to maintain compliance. Kay also advises on the purchase/sale of businesses subject to environmental, health, and/or safety requirements.
**Personal:** SMU Dedman School of Law (JD, 1990); Marquette University (PhD, Immunology, 1977; MS, Biology, 1974); Southern Methodist University (BS, Biology, 1971).

### ROSS, Jerry W
Pillsbury Winthrop Shaw Pittman LLP, Houston
713 276 7620
jerry.ross@pillsburylaw.com
*Featured in Environment (Texas)*

**Practice Areas:** Mr Ross has handled numerous complex rulemaking and adjudicatory regulatory proceedings, as well as private party litigation. These matters include significant cost recovery actions, challenges to government clean up orders, regulatory enforcement actions, citizen suits, piercing the corporate veil claims and bankruptcy matters. Mr Ross also has extensive experience handling environmental issues associated with mergers and acquisitions.

**Professional Memberships:** Admitted to practice: State of California, State of Texas.

**Personal:** JD, University of Notre Dame Law School, 1978; MS, University of Notre Dame, 1977; BS, Stanford University, 1973.

### ROSS, Joel L
Vinson & Elkins LLP, Dallas
214 220 7769
Jross@velaw.com
*Featured in Real Estate (Texas)*

**Practice Areas:** Joel's principal areas of practice are real estate law and finance law. He has been involved in all facets of the real estate industry, including acquisitions, dispositions, equity arrangements, partner buyouts, debt/equity workouts, development, leasing, and management. Real estate clients include both local and national developers, private equity sources, and real estate investment trusts.

**Career:** Admitted to Texas Bar, 1979. Came to firm as Partner, 1996.

**Personal:** Graduated from The University of Texas of the Permian Basin, BS with highest honors, 1976, and Texas Tech University, JD with honors, 1979.

### ROSS, Judith
Baker Botts LLP, Dallas
214 953 6605
judith.ross@bakerbotts.com
*Featured in Bankruptcy/Restructuring (Texas)*

**Practice Areas:** Represents a diverse range of asset acquirers, lenders, creditors, debtors, officers and directors in all aspects of complex chapter 11 cases and out-of-court workouts. She is also a certified mediator, specializing in the mediation of complex business and bankruptcy disputes.

**Professional Memberships:** Member, ABA Business Bankruptcy Committee; Trustees/Examiners Subcommittee of the ABA Business Bankruptcy Committee, Co-Chair; Business Division of the Bankruptcy Law Section of the State Bar of Texas, Vice-President; Chair of Dallas Bar Association Bankruptcy Section, 2000.

**Personal:** JD, The University of Texas School of Law, 1985; MA, University of Texas, 1981; BA, Miami University, 1979.

### ROYALL, M Sean
Gibson, Dunn & Crutcher LLP, Dallas
214 698 3256
sroyall@gibsondunn.com
*Featured in Antitrust (Texas)*

**Practice Areas:** Co-Chair, Antitrust & Trade Regulation and Information Technology/Data Privacy Practice Groups. Specializes in litigation and government investigations in complex antitrust and consumer protection matters; antitrust counseling in M&A, joint-venture, distribution, and IP contexts; representations involving privacy, data security, advertising, and other consumer protection issues.

**Professional Memberships:** ABA Section of Antitrust Law (1994-present).

**Career:** Deputy Director, FTC Bureau of Competition (2001-03); Clerk, Higginbotham, J., Fifth Circuit Court of Appeals (1990-91).

**Publications:** Editor, Von Kalinowski Antitrust Treatise (1996-present); Chair, Antitrust Law Journal (1997-2000); Editor, Antitrust Magazine (2006-present).

**Personal:** JD, University of Chicago, 1990, with honors, Managing Editor of Law Review.

### RUCKMAN, Deirdre B
Gardere Wynne Sewell LLP, Dallas
214 999 4250
druckman@gardere.com
*Featured in Bankruptcy/Restructuring (Texas)*

**Practice Areas:** Bankruptcy, business reorganization.

**Professional Memberships:** State Bar of Texas, American and Dallas Bar Associations, American Bankruptcy Institute.

**Career:** Deirdre Ruckman has over 35 years of experience in the financial services sector. She is the former chair of Gardere's Bankruptcy Practice Group and specializes in representation of debtors and creditors in business reorganizations involving private and/or public debt. Ms Ruckman has held numerous management positions in the firm and is active in several of Gardere's specialty groups, including Asset Securitization, Hospitality, Retail, and Health Care.

**Personal:** JD, SMU Dedman School of Law, 1975; BS, Chestnut Hill College, 1970.

### RUSMAN, Jared M
Weil, Gotshal & Manges LLP, Dallas
214 746 8193
jared.rusman@weil.com
*Featured in Tax (Texas)*

**Practice Areas:** Jared Rusman's practice spans all aspects of corporate and partnership tax matters, with particular emphasis on the tax aspects of private and public companies, domestic and cross-border mergers, acquisitions, joint ventures, divestitures, and spin-offs and split-offs.

**Career:** Partner, Weil, Gotshal & Manges LLP (since 2007); Partner, Wachtell, Lipton, Rosen & Katz (2002-07).

**Personal:** Georgetown University (BSBA, 1991, summa cum laude); New York University School of Law (JD, Order of the Coif, 1994). Mr Rusman was a Notes and Comment Editor of the New York University Law Review.

### RUSSELL, Philip
DLA Piper LLP (US), Austin
512 457 7015
philip.russell@dlapiper.com
*Featured in Technology (Texas)*

**Practice Areas:** Technology, corporate, mergers and acquisitions, venture capital.

**Career:** He counsels technology and other emerging-growth companies with respect to mergers and acquisition, SEC compliance, public offerings, and venture capital financings. His clients include public and private companies in the semiconductor, software, hardware, wireless, business process outsourcing, and communications indus-

tries. He also has significant experience representing venture capital firms and underwriters with respect to financing transactions.

**Personal:** JD, University of Texas; BA, Yale University.

### RUSSELL, Robin
Andrews Kurth LLP, Houston
713 220 4086
rrussell@andrewskurth.com
*Featured in Bankruptcy/Restructuring (Texas)*

**Practice Areas:** Robin's practice combines a depth of experience in bankruptcy restructuring and litigation with financial transaction work. She represents clients throughout the US in in-and out-of-court corporate restructuring and reorganization as well as providing strategic advice to corporate clients and independent boards on legal risks associated with counterparty insolvency and the structuring of corporate acquisitions to minimize economic risks in the event of a counterparty's subsequent financial distress. Clients include debtors, statutory and plan trustees, official and ad hoc creditor committees, secured lenders, DIP lenders, private equity funds, contract counterparties, landlords, trade creditors and buyers and sellers of assets.

### RUZINSKY, Bruce
Jackson Walker LLP, Houston
713 752 4204
bruzinsky@jw.com
*Featured in Bankruptcy/Restructuring (Texas)*

**Practice Areas:** Bruce Ruzinsky chairs Jackson Walker's bankruptcy section and heads the Houston office litigation section. He focuses his practice primarily on representing financial institutions, corporations, and other business entities in workout/restructure efforts, chapter bankruptcy proceedings, and litigation.

**Career:** Mr Ruzinsky has approximately 29 years' experience representing creditors, creditors' committees, trustees, debtors, landlords, and asset purchasers in various industries and business environments. He was extensively involved in representing large creditors in the North American Petroleum, Enron, Seahawk Drilling, Osyka Permian, Kimball Trading, R&R Marine, Sonrisa Realty and HDD Rotary cases.

### SAMPSON, Phillip L
Bracewell & Giuliani LLP, Dallas
713 221 1307
phillip.sampson@bgllp.com
*Featured in Construction (Texas)*

**Practice Areas:** Focuses on complex commercial and business litigation. Has experience representing plaintiffs and defendants in state courts, federal courts, and before arbitration panels, and has successfully tried jury and non-jury cases in state and federal courts. Has successfully handled appeals at the state and federal level. Has prosecuted and defended cases involving complex contract and payment issues, trade secret and intellectual property rights, fraud, construction and products liability, real estate and landlord/tenant issues, securities fraud, defamation, employment claims, insurance claims and personal injury.

**Personal:** JD, South Texas College of Law, 1993; BA, Washington and Lee University, 1990.

### SANTOS, Ralph G
Greenberg Traurig, LLP, Dallas
214 665 3631
SantosR@gtlaw.com
*Featured in Real Estate (Texas)*

**Practice Areas:** Co-Regional Operating Shareholder, Texas Region. Real estate; foreclosures, workouts, loan restructures; commercial real estate; commercial mortgage lending; construction and design professional contracts; formation of investment partnerships, joint ventures between for-profit and non-profit hospital operators; hospital acquisitions, dispositions; commercial leasing; business law.

**Professional Memberships:** Member: Dallas Bar Association; Real Estate Council; Dallas Committee on Foreign Relations.

**Career:** Selected: Best Lawyers in America, 2007-13; Super Lawyers magazine, 2003-12; a Law360 'Real Estate Practice Group of the Year', 2011-12. Rated, AV® Preeminent™ 5.0 out of 5.

**Personal:** JD, William & Mary Law School; MA, Vanderbilt University; BA, University of South Carolina.

### SASLAW, Michael A
Weil, Gotshal & Manges LLP, Dallas
214 746 8117
mike.saslaw@weil.com
*Featured in Corporate/M&A (Texas)*

**Practice Areas:** Michael Saslaw's primary practice areas include mergers and acquisitions, securities offerings, financings, restructurings and corporate counseling. He has extensive experience counseling businesses in a variety of industries, including energy, technology, media, retail, consumer products and manufacturing. His representative clients include Abraaj Capital, Anadarko Petroleum Corporation, EQT Partners, General Electric Company, Consolidated, Inc., J.C. Penney Company, Inc., Prudential Insurance Company, Quicksilver Energy, L.P., Tower Three Partners, Trimble Navigation Limited, and WL Ross.

**Personal:** Miami University (BS Accounting, 1979); University of Pennsylvania Law School (JD, 1982).

### SCHARTZ, Elizabeth A.
Thompson & Knight LLP, Dallas
214 969 1737
Elizabeth.Schartz@tklaw.com
*Featured in Labor & Employment (Texas)*

**Practice Areas:** Ms Schartz is the firm's Employment and Labor Practice Group Leader. She represents management in client counseling and litigation of employment and labor matters. Her expertise includes litigating discrimination, whistleblower, wage-and-hour, and employment-related contract and tort claims; handling sensitive workplace investigations; advising on employee classification issues; drafting and litigating executive compensation, change-in-control, and separation arrangements; drafting and litigating non-competition and related covenants; OSHA/MSHA matters.

**Professional Memberships:** State Bar of Texas; Dallas and American Bar Associations; Board Certified in Labor and Employment Law by the Texas Board of Legal Specialization.
**Personal:** University of Kansas School of Law (JD, 1988).

### SCHICK, Robert M
Vinson & Elkins LLP, Houston
713 758 4582
rschick@velaw.com
*Featured in Environment (Texas), Litigation (Texas)*
**Practice Areas:** Over 30 years of experience in all aspects of products liability, environmental and toxic tort litigation, representing domestic and foreign corporations throughout Texas and in eight other states.
**Professional Memberships:** American College of Trial Lawyers; American Board of Trial Advocates; Product Liability Advisory Council; IADC; DRI.
**Career:** Partner since 1989. Texas Board certified since 1987 in Civil Trial Law and Personal Injury Law. Listed, Best Lawyers in America, 2003-06.
**Publications:** Co-author: Hampton, Schick & McGehee's Texas Civil Practice and Remedies Code Annotated, Thompson West 2002-04.
**Personal:** Princeton University (AB 1976), University of Houston (JD 1981).

### SCHOENBRUN, Larry
Gardere Wynne Sewell LLP, Dallas
214 999 4703
lschoenbrun@gardere.com
*Featured in Corporate/M&A (Texas)*
**Practice Areas:** Corporate, mergers and acquisitions (M&A), securities.
**Professional Memberships:** State Bar of Texas, American and Dallas Bar Associations, Texas Business Law Foundation.
**Career:** Larry Schoenbrun has more than 45 years of experience serving as corporate advisor for numerous large and medium-sized corporations. He has represented buyers and sellers in various corporate acquisitions and dispositions, corporations and investment bankers in public and private offerings, and venture capitalists in their investments. Mr Schoenbrun is active in Gardere's Private Equity Industry Team and Retail Industry Team.
**Personal:** LLB, University of Texas School of Law, 1965; BA, University of Texas, 1962.

### SCHREIBER, Howard
Hunton & Williams LLP, Dallas
214 468 3376
hschreiber@hunton.com
*Featured in Real Estate (Texas)*
**Practice Areas:** Howard Schreiber's practice focuses on commercial real estate transactions and financings. Experienced in all sectors of the commercial real estate industry, with particular concentration in commercial real estate lending and loan workouts, office leasing, and asset dispositions. He is a member of the American College of Mortgage Attorneys and the head of his firm's Commercial Real Estate Practice Group in Dallas.
**Professional Memberships:** Member, American Bar Association; Member, Dallas Bar

Association; Member Real Estate, Probate and Trust Law Section of the State Bar of Texas; American College of Mortgage Attorneys.
**Personal:** JD, Duke University School of Law, 1984; BA, Dickinson College, 1981.

### SCHUURMAN, Willem
Vinson & Elkins LLP, Austin
512 542 8663
bschuurman@velaw.com
*Featured in Intellectual Property (Texas)*
**Practice Areas:** Bill is a seasoned patent litigator with experience in a vast array of technical fields. Known for early development of winning strategies in patent litigations, Bill has an exceptional record of success in Markman hearings, trials, and appeals to the Court of Appeals for the Federal Circuit. Bill has been recognized as a leading intellectual property lawyer in Chambers USA (2006-12), Chambers Global (2006-10) and IAM Patent Litigation 250 (2011-12).
**Career:** South Texas College of Law, JD, magna cum laude, 1981; University of Cape Town, LLB 1964; BS 1962.
**Publications:** O'Connor's Federal Intellectual Property Codes Plus, co-author.

### SCHWARTZ, Charles
Skadden, Arps, Slate, Meagher & Flom LLP & Affiliates, Houston
713 655 5160
charles.schwartz@skadden.com
*Featured in Litigation (Texas)*
**Practice Areas:** Heads the Litigation practice in Skadden's Houston office. Has extensive experience in all aspects of business litigation. Practice focuses on defending companies and directors in securities and fiduciary duty cases, environmental, consumer, and other class actions, antitrust cases and commercial disputes.
**Professional Memberships:** Former Chairman of the Board of the State Bar of Texas; Member of the Texas Commission for Lawyer Discipline.
**Career:** LLM, Harvard University, 1980; MA, University of Texas, 1980; JD, University of Texas, 1977 (with honors); BS, University of Texas, 1975 (with highest honors).

### SCOFIELD, George W
Fulbright & Jaworski LLP, San Antonio
210 270 7189
gscofield@fulbright.com
*Featured in Tax (Texas)*
**Practice Areas:** Tax; health; general business.
**Career:** George Scofield has extensive experience in multi-hospital joint ventures, mergers, acquisitions and joint operating agreements involving tax-exempt organizations; exempt hospital and physician joint ventures; exempt organization tax compliance planning, internal reviews and IRS audits; charitable giving; sophisticated tax-exempt finance for municipally owned utility and water systems, cities, counties, school districts and other issuers, and IRS audits of tax-exempt bonds; tax partnership planning; private mergers and acquisitions; and sophisticated executive incentive compensation planning.
**Personal:** LLM, Taxation, New York University School of Law (1981); JD, Louisiana State

University (1980); BS, Louisiana State University (1977)

### SEAL, Derek
Winstead PC, Dallas
512 370 2807
dseal@winstead.com
*Featured in Environment (Texas)*
**Practice Areas:** Derek Seal has over 20 years of regulatory and legislative experience, and is a part of Winstead's Energy & Environmental Law Practice Group. Derek is a former General Counsel of the Texas Commission on Environmental Quality (TCEQ). Prior to this position, he was Counsel to former TCEQ Chairman Kathleen Hartnett White. Before joining the TCEQ in November 2002, he served in the combined roles of General Counsel in the Texas Legislature for the House Committee on Environmental Regulation and General Counsel and Chief of Staff for Representative Warren Chisum, who was the Chairman of that committee.

### SHANK, Mark
Gruber Hurst Johansen Hail Shank LLP, Dallas
214 855 6846
mshank@ghjhlaw.com
*Featured in Labor & Employment (Texas)*
**Practice Areas:** Labor and employment and business litigation.
**Professional Memberships:** Former director, State Bar of Texas; president of Dallas Bar Association; number of other legal and civic affiliations.
**Career:** Represents clients in labor and employment and business litigation matters across a number of industries. Work includes disputes involving contracts, officer and director liability, employment discrimination, wage and hour, retaliation, executive compensation and related issues. Board Certified in Civil Trial Law and Labor and Employment Law by the Texas Board of Legal Specialization; arbitrator for the American Arbitration Association. www.ghjhlaw.com
**Personal:** Recipient of numerous honors for professional, civic service.

### SHEEDER, Robert E
Bracewell & Giuliani LLP, Dallas
214 758 1643
robert.sheeder@bgllp.com
*Featured in Labor & Employment (Texas)*
**Practice Areas:** Heads the firm's labor practice. Represents management in all aspects of labor and employment law before state,federal agencies and courts. Practice includes litigation, counseling management on discrimination, harassment, collective and class actions, union organizing and wage-hour issues.
**Career:** Former Editor-in-Chief of the Texas Labor Letter. On the faculty of the Jury Trials of Employment Claims Course; participated in the Advanced Course. Charter member of the Management and Employment Law Roundtable. Fellow - College of Labor and Employment Laws.
**Personal:** JD, University of Michigan Law School, 1976; BA, University of Virginia, 1973.

### SHEEDER III, Frank E
DLA Piper LLP (US), Dallas
214 743 4560
frank.sheeder@dlapiper.com
*Featured in Healthcare (Texas)*
**Practice Areas:** Healthcare.
**Career:** He is chair of the firm's Health Care Enforcement and Compliance practice and has defended clients against civil and criminal fraud allegations brought by the government and other hostile third-party litigants – especially whistleblowers – for more than 20 years. He focuses on defending against government enforcement initiatives, complex health care litigation and regulatory compliance. He has appeared before multiple federal and state courts and represents clients opposite a multitude of federal and state agencies, whistleblowers and other plaintiffs.
**Personal:** JD, Boston University School of Law; BA, Duke University (cum laude).

### SHELTON, Lisa
Andrews Kurth LLP, Austin
512 320 9222
lisashelton@andrewskurth.com
*Featured in Environment (Texas)*
**Practice Areas:** Lisa focuses on environmental, health and safety counseling, compliance and liability. She has experience analyzing environmental, health and safety issues associated with business transactions as well as corporate and securities matters such as contaminated property redevelopment. Lisa covers a wide range of industries and businesses: power plant; oil and gas production, transportation and storage; refineries, chemical, windpower, solarpower and semiconductor companies; and real estate development. Lisa's experience includes negotiation of environmental insurance policies. She works with industry associations and companies to address air, waste, water, endangered species, wetlands and toxics issues in permitting, enforcement and regulatory forums.

### SHORT JR, William B
Coats Rose Yale Ryman Lee, Houston
972 982 8458
wshort@coatsrose.com
*Featured in Construction (Texas)*
**Practice Areas:** William Short represents lenders, owners, sureties, contractors, subcontractors, and design professionals in public and private construction projects. His practice focuses on commercial and construction litigation, involving contract interpretation, design defects, negligence and insurance claims, real estate transactions and bond claims. He also maintains an alternative dispute resolution practice.
**Career:** Mr Short has been a panel speaker and moderator at the annual State Bar of Texas Construction Law Conference since 1988. His professional recognitions include Texas Super Lawyer, Best Lawyers of America, Martindale Hubbell AV rating, Chambers USA and Who's Who Legal.

**SHOWALTER, Barton E**
Baker Botts LLP, Dallas
214 953 6509
bart.showalter@bakerbotts.com
*Featured in Intellectual Property (Texas)*
**Practice Areas:** Firm wide Chair of IP Department. Practice focused on patent litigation, licensing, and procurement for high technology companies. Significant experience litigating and licensing patents in fields of telecommunications, electronics, software, semiconductors, computers, and others. Also provides strategic counseling to maximize research and development investments. Develops and implements innovative processes and tools for patent portfolio management, enforcement, licensing, and IP risk mitigation.
**Personal:** BS and MS in Aerospace Engineering, MIT; Adjunct Professor, SMU School of Law; Governing Board, Perot Museum of Nature and Science; Board, Dallas Theater Center.

**SIMPSON, Reagan**
Yetter Coleman LLP, Houston
512 533 0150
rsimpson@yettercoleman.com
*Featured in Litigation (Texas)*
**Practice Areas:** Handles a wide variety of trial and appellate matters, including litigation involving personal injury, commercial torts, mass torts, media law and defamation, and products liability. Has active appellate and trial practice in both state and federal courts.
**Professional Memberships:** American Board of Trial Advocates; American College of Trial Lawyers; Federation of Insurance and Corporate Counsel; Houston Bar Association; State Bar of Texas.
**Publications:** Principal author of the first edition and co-author of the second edition of Effective Amicus Practice.
**Personal:** BA, highest honors, University of Texas, 1974; JD, high honors, University of Texas, 1977.

**SIMS, William D**
Vinson & Elkins LLP, Dallas
214 220 7703
bsims@velaw.com
*Featured in Litigation (Texas)*
**Practice Areas:** Represents plaintiffs and defendants in state and federal courts throughout Texas and the southwest. Trials have involved a wide range of business disputes, including securities, antitrust, breach of fiduciary duties, fraud, contracts, patents, copyrights, unfair competition, RICO, libel, ERISA, products liability (pharmaceutical), tortious interference with contractual relations, intentional infliction of emotional distress, oil and gas, and municipal finance.
**Professional Memberships:** International Academy of Trial Lawyers; Center for American and International Law.
**Career:** Admitted to Texas Bar, 1972. Came to firm as Partner, 1992.
**Personal:** Graduated from the University of Mississippi, BA, 1969; and Harvard University, JD, 1972.

**SINAK, David**
Gibson, Dunn & Crutcher LLP, Dallas
214 698 3100
dsinak@gibsondunn.com
*Featured in Tax (Texas)*
**Practice Areas:** Focuses on federal income taxation of corporations, partnerships, limited liability companies and investment securities. Involved in tax planning for private equity funds and their institutional investors (specializing in oil and gas funds), corporate and partnership M&A, financings, solvent/insolvent restructurings, tax-free spin-offs, tax free corporate reorganizations, partnership structuring and reorganizations, debt/equity offerings, and foreign investments in US. Experienced in obtaining private letter rulings from IRS and handling IRS audit appeals.
**Professional Memberships:** American Bar Association, State Bar of Texas, Dallas Bar Association.
**Personal:** JD, cum laude, Boston College, 1979; Articles Editor, 'Boston College Law Review'.

**SLOAN, Mark M**
Thompson & Knight LLP, Dallas
214 969 1574
Mark.Sloan@tklaw.com
*Featured in Real Estate (Texas)*
**Practice Areas:** Mark's practice includes real estate lending transactions, and real estate acquisitions, dispositions, and development focusing on retail, multifamily, and industrial properties. He has represented lenders in originations of real estate financings, including construction loans, interim bridge loans, mezzanine loans, permanent loans, CMBS loans, and revolving credit facilities, as well as in connection with real estate loan workouts and foreclosures. He has represented multiple financial institutions in their capacity as both administrative agent and participant in connection with syndicated loan transactions.
**Personal:** SMU Dedman School of Law (JD, cum laude, 1990); University of Iowa (BBA, with highest distinction, 1985).

**SLUSSER, William C**
Fulbright & Jaworski LLP, Houston
713 651 5500
slusser@fulbright.com
*Featured in Intellectual Property (Texas)*
**Practice Areas:** Jury trial experience in patent, antitrust, ERISA, general business and products liability cases.
**Professional Memberships:** American College of Trial Lawyers; American Law Institute; State Bar of Texas; American Bar Association; American and Houston Intellectual Property Lawyers Associations.
**Career:** Admitted Texas Bar, 1973. Baker Botts (1973-99) including Executive Committee and head of the Trial Department;Slusser Wilson & Partridge LLP (1999 to 2011); Fulbright & Jaworski, LLP (2011 to present).
**Personal:** JD, honors, University of Texas School of Law, 1972. Bachelor of Science in Electrical Engineering, University of Texas-Arlington, 1970.

**SMITH, Alison L**
McDermott Will & Emery LLP, Houston
713 653 1753
alsmith@mwe.com
*Featured in Antitrust (Texas)*
**Practice Areas:** Practices in the area of complex business litigation, including private class action litigation in antitrust, securities, ERISA, and shareholder derivative actions. She also represents corporations and individuals in criminal and regulatory matters, including antitrust, Foreign Corrupt Practices, and export trade violation investigations. Provides antitrust counseling to corporations on mergers and acquisitions, joint ventures and distribution arrangements.
**Professional Memberships:** Admitted to practice in Texas; American Law Institute; Antitrust Section of the American Bar Association; Litigation Section of the American Bar Association.
**Personal:** University of Texas, JD, (with honors), 1977; University of Texas, BJ, (with highest honors), 1974

**SMITH, James E**
Porter Hedges LLP, Houston
713 226 6608
jsmith@porterhedges.com
*Featured in Environment (Texas)*
**Practice Areas:** Jim Smith is a partner in the environmental section of Porter Hedges. His practice principally focuses on environmental matters, in counseling, supporting transactions, and trying cases. He primarily represents companies in refining, petrochemical and other resource related industries. He counsels corporate and individual clients on a variety of environmental issues, in addition to trying and arguing appeals in both civil and criminal matters and in both state and federal courts. Mr Smith has appeared before the US Environmental Protection Agency (EPA), the Texas Commission on Environmental Quality (TCEQ) and other administrative agencies in permitting and enforcement matters.

**SMITH, Jane S**
Fulbright & Jaworski LLP, Austin
512 536 5238
jsmith@fulbright.com
*Featured in Real Estate (Texas)*
**Practice Areas:** Commercial real estate transactions and disputes.
**Professional Memberships:** International Council of Shopping Centers; CREW Network (2013 Foundation Chair); Center for Women in Law (Founder); American College of Real Estate Lawyers; ULI.
**Career:** Jane advises pension funds, REITS and other institutional investors in equity and debt investments, including multiple $1b+ national portfolio acquisitions and dispositions. She also has expertise in shopping centers, handling transactions involving more than 130 million-plus s.f. centers in over 34 states.
**Personal:** JD, Emory University; MS Vanderbilt University; BS, College of William and Mary; Stephen Minister; "Women Leaders in Law," The American Lawyer Magazine (2013).

**SMYSER, Craig**
Smyser Kaplan & Veselka LLP, Houston
713 221 2300
csmyser@skv.com
*Featured in Litigation (Texas)*
**Practice Areas:** Trials, international and domestic arbitrations and appeals; including securities fraud class actions, intellectual property disputes, breach of contract claims, executive-company employment disputes, high net-worth individual trust and family disputes, legal and medical malpractice claims, individual and mass toxic tort claims, constructive disputes, and defamation lawsuits.
**Professional Memberships:** American, Texas and Houston Bar Associations, Fifth Circuit Court of Appeals, Bar of the Texas Supreme Court, Bar of the US Supreme Court, the US District Courts for the Southern, Eastern, Northern and Western Districts of Texas, American Board of Trial Advocates, Houston, Texas and American Bar Associations; Texas, Houston and American Bar Foundations, Texas Board of Legal Specialization.
**Career:** Vinson & Elkins, L.L.P., associate 1980-87, Partner 1988-95; Founding Partner Smyser Kaplan & Veselka, L.L.P. 1995-present.
**Publications:** "Texas Contract Law", West Publishing, 2005 (co-author).
**Personal:** University of Texas Law School, JD, 1980, Chair, Board of Advocates, Outstanding Advocate, 1980 Class; B.A., with honors, Phi Beta Kappa, University of Texas (1973). Married to Kathryn Smyser; daughters Claire (born 03/13/85), Georgiana (born 06/24/88)and son James Craig (born 03/02/91).

**SNYDER, Allison**
Porter Hedges LLP, Houston
713 226 6622
asnyder@porterhedges.com
*Featured in Construction (Texas)*
**Practice Areas:** Allison Snyder is a partner in the litigation section of Porter Hedges. She has more than 27 years of experience representing companies and individuals in complex business and construction disputes involving fraud, breach of contract, negligence, noncompetition issues, business torts, and matters involving emergency injunctive relief.
**Professional Memberships:** State Bar of Texas and the Houston Bar Association, Past Chairperson, Construction Sections; Arbitrator for the American Arbitration Association (construction and commercial panels); Texas Bar Foundation, Houston Bar Foundation and College of the State Bar, Fellow.

**SONG, Stephanie Koo**
Bracewell & Giuliani LLP, Houston
713 221 1542
stephanie.song@bgllp.com
*Featured in Banking & Finance (Texas)*
**Practice Areas:** Counsels and represents domestic and foreign financial institutions, other lenders and borrowers in all types of secured and unsecured credit transactions, including asset based lending, senior and subordinated debt financings, cross-border financings, debt restruc-

turings, project and acquisition financings, letter of credit facilities, term loans, working capital loans, bond credit enhancement facilities, securitization and conduit lending transactions, oil and gas secured financings, as well as loan restructures and workouts and other various interbank relationships involved in syndicated loan transactions. **Personal:** JD, The University of Texas School of Law, 1999; BA, The University of Texas at Austin, 1994.

**SORENSEN, Nick H**
Porter Hedges LLP, Houston
713 226 6677
nsorensen@porterhedges.com
*Featured in Banking & Finance (Texas)*
**Practice Areas:** Nick Sorensen represents both lenders and borrowers in commercial, corporate, reserve based, and asset based lending transactions. He also represents lessors and lessees in lease financing transactions. Mr Sorensen's practice also includes loan workouts and restructurings, representing buyers and sellers in corporate mergers and acquisitions, and representing buyers and sellers in commercial real estate transactions. **Professional Memberships:** Mr Sorensen is a Member of the American Bar Association, State Bar of Texas, Houston Bar Association, Texas Association of Bank Counsel and has served as a member of the Texas State Bar Commercial Code Committee.

**SOSLAND, Martin**
Weil, Gotshal & Manges LLP, Dallas
214 746 7730
martin.sosland@weil.com
*Featured in Bankruptcy/Restructuring (Texas), Bankruptcy/Restructuring (Nationwide)*
**Practice Areas:** Mr Sosland concentrates his practice in the area of business reorganizations, debtor and creditors' rights and refinancings and acquisitions of troubled companies. Mr Sosland led the firm's representation in several major chapter 11 debtor cases, including Dallas Stars, SemGroup, Crescent Resources, Texas Rangers Baseball Partners, and Blockbuster. He also represented AHMSI, a W. L. Ross portfolio company, in its acquisition of Option One Mortgage from H&R Block. Mr Sosland has represented statutory creditors' committees including Diagnostic Health Systems, Inc., First Republicbank Corporation and National Gypsum Company. **Personal:** Rice University (BA); University of Texas School of Law (JD).

**SOSTEK, Bruce S**
Thompson & Knight LLP, Dallas
214 969 1237
Bruce.Sostek@tklaw.com
*Featured in Intellectual Property (Texas)*
**Practice Areas:** Mr Sostek's practice focuses on intellectual property litigation and counseling, including IP strategies and valuation. He has extensive patent litigation experience with microelectronics, telecommunications, hardware, software, and energy matters, and also practices sports, media, and entertainment law. He has tried IP cases in federal courts throughout the country, at the International Trade Commission, and has

been involved in national and international arbitrations. **Professional Memberships:** American College of Trial Lawyers; Dallas Intellectual Property Inn of Court; Federal Circuit Bar Association; AIPLA. **Personal:** Emory University (JD, 1981); State University of NY at Albany (MA, 1977); Union College (BA, 1975).

**SPEARS, Berry**
Fulbright & Jaworski LLP, Austin
512 536 5246
bspears@fulbright.com
*Featured in Bankruptcy/Restructuring (Texas)*
**Practice Areas:** Partner-in-Charge of Fulbright's Austin office. Assists clients in bankruptcy and insolvency, non-bankruptcy reorganizations and liquidations, debtor-in-possession financing arrangements and all types of bankruptcy litigation and related matters. Advises lenders, creditors and creditor committees, debtors and related parties. Counsels agent and lenders/institutions in syndicated multi-lender credit facilities and banks/participants under participation agreements. **Professional Memberships:** American College of Bankruptcy;American Bankruptcy Institute;Turnaround Management Association;International Bar Association. **Personal:** The University of Texas School of Law, JD, 1982. Austin College, BA, 1979. Named to "Best Lawyers"(2006-13);Texas Super Lawyer,(2003-12); Central Texas Top' 50 Lawyers,(2003-08);Top 100 Attorneys in Houston(2010-12) and Top 100 Attorneys in Texas(2008).

**SPEARS, L Gene**
Baker Botts LLP, Houston
713 229 1590
gene.spears@bakerbotts.com
*Featured in Intellectual Property (Texas)*
**Practice Areas:** Patent enforcement and counseling; trade secret and copyright litigation. Has represented clients in federal courts throughout the United States and before the International Trade Commission. **Professional Memberships:** AIPLA, HIPLA. **Career:** Clerk to the Honorable Helen W Nies, Court of Appeals for the Federal Circuit; associated with Arnold, White & Durkee until 2001. **Publications:** Has spoken often on intellectual property related topics. **Personal:** BA, Rice University (1987); JD, University of Texas (1991).

**SPIERS, Jeffrey E**
Andrews Kurth LLP, Houston
713 220 4103
jspiers@andrewskurth.com
*Featured in Bankruptcy/Restructuring (Texas)*
**Practice Areas:** Jeff's practice includes extensive experience in out of court workouts and restructurings as well as in commercial bankruptcy proceedings for a wide variety of lending and borrowing clients throughout the US, including representation of official and unofficial creditors' committees, bondholders and debenture-holders, banks and institutional investors, and borrowers

and debtors-in-possession. Jeff's experience also includes advising purchasers of assets in bankruptcy proceedings and providing advice as to the implications of potential subsequent counterparty financial distress in the structuring of transactions. Jeff's experience includes representations in the energy, real estate, technology and restaurant/hospitality industries, among others.

**STANTON, Patricia**
Baker Botts LLP, Dallas
214 953 6704
pat.stanton@bakerbotts.com
*Featured in Real Estate (Texas)*
**Practice Areas:** Partner in Charge of Baker Botts' Dallas Office. Represents owners and developers of commercial real estate projects worldwide, including transactions in India, UAE, South America and Europe. Handles every aspect of commercial real estate development, including land acquisition, debt/equity financing, tenant leases, construction contracts, management agreements and easement and development agreements. Represents sellers, investors and purchasers in the acquisition and disposition of commercial properties, and has experience with fund formation and the special concerns of pension funds and real estate investment trusts. **Personal:** Ohio State University, BSN, with honors, 1979; Cleveland-Marshall College of Law JD, with honors, 1983.

**STEIN, Pamela B**
Greenberg Traurig, LLP, Dallas
214 665 3630
SteinP@gtlaw.com
*Featured in Real Estate (Texas)*
**Practice Areas:** Real estate (acquisitions, development, finance, leasing). **Professional Memberships:** President-Elect (2014) Commercial Real Estate Women of Dallas. Member: Urban Land Institute, Dallas Chapter; Programs Committee; Mixed-Use Local Product Council; Urban Plan classroom initiative. Member, Dallas Bar Assoc., Real Property Section. **Career:** Member: Law360 'Real Estate Practice Group of the Year', 2011-12; Winning Team, 2010 Chambers and Partners USA Award for Excellence in Real Estate. Rated, AV® Preeminent™ 5.0 out of 5. **Personal:** JD, cum laude, Southern Methodist University Dedman School of Law; MRP, Land Use and Environmental Planning, University of North Carolina at Chapel Hill; BA, Wellesley College.

**STEPHENS, Garland**
Weil, Gotshal & Manges LLP, Houston
713 546 5011
garland.stephens@weil.com
*Featured in Intellectual Property (Texas)*
**Practice Areas:** Garland Stephens is a trial lawyer who focuses on high-technology patent matters in the electronics and computer industries. His experience includes many cases involving many of the most well-known computer, consumer electronics, and software products. He received his law degree from the University of Missouri Law School, an MS in Electrical

Engineering from Columbia University, and a BS in Mathematics from the University of Chicago. After graduating from law school he served as a judicial clerk to Chief Judge William H. Billings of the Missouri Supreme Court and Judge R. Kenton Musgrave at the Court of International Trade.

**STERLING, David**
Baker Botts LLP, Houston
713 229 1946
david.sterling@bakerbotts.com
*Featured in Litigation (Texas)*
**Practice Areas:** Companies and their directors in class action securities fraud suits, derivative actions and breach of fiduciary claims; cases challenging mergers; broker-dealers in securities lawsuits and arbitrations; special committees; and other major commercial litigation. **Professional Memberships:** Securities Industry Association; State Bar of Texas. **Career:** Mr Sterling is a Senior Partner at Baker Botts, LLP. **Personal:** Mr Sterling graduated from Williams College in 1980 and The University of Texas Law School in 1984. He and his wife, Kimberly, who heads a consulting firm for nonprofit institutions, have three children.

**STEVENSON III, Theodore**
McKool Smith, Dallas
214 978 4000
tstevenson@mckoolsmith.com
*Featured in Intellectual Property (Texas)*
**Practice Areas:** Intellectual property litigation. **Professional Memberships:** National Institute of Trial Advocacy; AIPLA; American, Federal Circuit, Dallas and E.D. of Texas Bar Associations. **Career:** Mr Stevenson is a trial lawyer and registered patent attorney with nearly 20 years of experience. He has won courtroom victories in patent cases involving diverse technologies, including wireless email, balloon angioplasty catheters, integrated circuits, and prepaid calling cards, among others. He also has tried and won non-patent cases alleging Internet metatag misuse, trade secret violations, and other matters. **Personal:** University of Virginia School of Law (JD, 1988); Northwestern University (BS, 1985).

**STEWART, Dan**
Vinson & Elkins LLP, Dallas
214 220 7761
dstewart@velaw.com
*Featured in Bankruptcy/Restructuring (Texas), Bankruptcy/Restructuring (Nationwide)*
**Practice Areas:** Practice spans all aspects of debtor/creditor relationships. Major creditor representations include agent banks, bank groups, and creditor committee representations in connection with bankruptcy proceedings for major corporations. Served as Lead Counsel for borrowers in some of the largest workouts and reorganizations in Texas for over 35 years. Served as Bankruptcy Trustee in hundreds of Chapter 7 and Chapter 11 cases under the Bankruptcy Act and Code. **Professional Memberships:** Dallas Bar Association.

**Career:** Admitted to Texas Bar, 1972. Came to firm as Partner, 1999.
**Personal:** Graduated from Brown University, BA (1969), and Duke University School of Law, JD (1972).

## STOHNER, Ken
Jackson Walker LLP, Dallas
214 953 5904
kstohner@jw.com
*Featured in Bankruptcy/Restructuring (Texas)*
**Career:** Kenneth Stohner, Jr has over 35 years' experience representing clients in a wide variety of bankruptcy and reorganization matters. He has represented financial institutions and other secured creditors, creditor committees, debtors and trustees in numerous bankruptcy cases, including large and complex proceedings involving billions of dollars in claims. Mr Stohner's practice includes significant involvement in bankruptcy related litigation. He has extensive experience in a broad range of industries, especially in the energy, real estate and financial services sector. He has been named a "Top Lawyer in Dallas" by LexisNexis and a "Best Lawyer in Dallas" by D Magazine.

## STOKES, Macey Reasoner
Baker Botts LLP, Houston
713 229 1369
macey.stokes@bakerbotts.com
*Featured in Litigation (Texas)*
**Practice Areas:** Civil appellate practice in federal and Texas state court.
**Professional Memberships:** Fellow, American Law Institute; Secretary, Bar Association, Fifth Federal Circuit; Treasurer, Appellate Section, State Bar of Texas; Executive Committee Member and Trustee, Texas Supreme Court Historical Society; Board Certified in Civil Appellate Law by Texas Board of Legal Specialization.
**Career:** Partner; Chair, Appellate Practice; Briefing Attorney to Chief Justice Thomas R. Phillips, Supreme Court of Texas, 1993-94.
**Personal:** JD, University of Texas, 1993 (high honors; Chancellors; Order of the Coif; Associate Editor, Texas Law Review); BA, Yale, 1989 (summa cum laude; Phi Beta Kappa).

## STRICKLIN, Samuel M
Bracewell & Giuliani LLP, Dallas
214 758 1095
sam.stricklin@bgllp.com
*Featured in Bankruptcy/Restructuring (Texas)*
**Practice Areas:** He has represented clients in contested hearings before more than 40 bankruptcy judges in 17 states, as well as cross-border restructurings in Canada and Europe. Has led a wide range of business bankruptcy cases, representing debtors, trustees, creditors' committees, secured creditors, other bankruptcy professionals and purchasers of assets. Has confirmed Chapter 11 plans of reorganization, including several heavily contested confirmations involving competing plans of reorganization.
**Career:** Board certified in business bankruptcy law by the State Bar of Texas.
**Personal:** JD, University of Houston Law Center, 1987; BA, Texas A&M University, 1984.

## STRUBECK, Lou
Fulbright & Jaworski LLP, Dallas
214 855 8040
lstrubeck@fulbright.com
*Featured in Bankruptcy/Restructuring (Texas), Bankruptcy/Restructuring (Nationwide)*
**Practice Areas:** Bankruptcy law, debtor/creditors' rights, emphasis on representation of financial institutions, institutional lenders, hedge funds, investors and creditors in complex workouts and Chapter 11 bankruptcy reorganization and related litigation on a nation-wide basis.
**Professional Memberships:** Fellow, American College of Bankruptcy; Member, American Bankruptcy Institute; Dallas and American Bar Associations; State Bar of Texas and New York.
**Career:** Partner in Fulbright's Dallas office since 1992 and current chair of the firm's global Financial Restructuring practice.
**Personal:** BA, College of Charleston (1980); JD, Temple University (1983).

## SULLIVAN, Kevin A
Winstead PC, Dallas
214 745 5292
ksullivan@winstead.com
*Featured in Real Estate (Texas)*
**Practice Areas:** Chairman and CEO Kevin Sullivan heads the firm's Real Estate Structured Finance Practice Group. He has extensive experience in all areas of real estate finance. His direct involvement in client relationships and management of multi-attorney teams for the benefit of clients ensures a responsive, quality product on a competitively priced basis. He serves on committees of various industry groups and is a frequent contributor by way of both articles and speeches to new industry issues.

## SUTTON, Michael O
Sutton McAughan Deaver, PLLC, Houston
713 800 5701
msutton@smd-iplaw.com
*Featured in Intellectual Property (Texas)*
**Practice Areas:** All facets of intellectual property litigation, including patent, trademark, trade secret, and copyright.
**Professional Memberships:** ABA; HBA (Sustaining Fellow); AIPLA; HIPLA (Past President); Houston IP American Inns of Court (Founding Member).
**Career:** Mr Sutton has nearly 40 years of experience in all facets of intellectual property litigation. He has been rated by Chambers USA since 2007 and was recently described as a "top-notch litigator." Two of Mr Sutton's recent verdicts, including a trade secret case and a patent case, were recognized as Top Texas Verdicts by Texas Lawyer. Mr Sutton also won the largest-ever attorneys' fees award in a copyright case. Immediately prior to founding Sutton McAughan Deaver PLLC in 2012, Mr Sutton was the firm-wide head of the IP Department at an AmLaw 100 firm. Earlier in his career, Mr Sutton was the head of the Litigation Section at a different AmLaw 100 firm that specialized in IP.
**Personal:** George Washington University Law School (JD, with honors, 1973); The University of

Alabama (BS, Aerospace Engineering, cum laude, 1969).

## SWANSTROM, Bill
Locke Lord LLP, Houston
713 226 1143
bswanstrom@lockelord.com
*Featured in Corporate/M&A (Texas)*
**Practice Areas:** Co-chairs the firm's Energy Practice Group. Over 20 years of experience working with energy companies in their significant acquisition, divestiture, project development and finance activities. Substantial experience in energy private equity transactions, representing both investors and companies.
**Professional Memberships:** Global Energy Management Institute (Executive Committee); Greater Houston Energy Collaborative (Executive Committee); Institute for Energy Law (Board of Directors).
**Career:** Co-Vice Chair of the firm. Partner since 1995.
**Personal:** The University of Texas School of Law (JD, with high honors, 1988); Texas Law Review; Southern Methodist University (BA, English and Economics, summa cum laude, 1984).

## SZALKOWSKI, Charles
Baker Botts LLP, Houston
713 229 1480
charles.szalkowski@bakerbotts.com
*Featured in Technology (Texas)*
**Practice Areas:** Private equity transactions, mergers, acquisitions, general corporate, venture capital, public and private financings. Represents private equity funds and venture capitalists, emerging growth and public companies, investment bankers, and investors in, such companies, hedge funds, institutional investors, insurance companies, universities and endowments. Represents software and telecommunications companies, consumer and industrial products manufacturers, oil, gas and energy service companies, consolidators in various industries and other ventures with value embodied in intellectual property, including biotechnology, medical devices, and internet content.
**Personal:** JD and MBA, Harvard University, 1975; BA and BS Accounting, Rice University, 1971.

## TABOR, Jay
Weil, Gotshal & Manges LLP, Dallas
214 746 7889
jay.tabor@weil.com
*Featured in Corporate/M&A (Texas)*
**Practice Areas:** Mr Tabor handles complex corporate transactions. He was selected as AmLaw Daily's "Dealmaker of the Week" and "Dealmaker of the Month" for representing Kinder Morgan in its groundbreaking $38 billion acquisition of El Paso Corporation—creating the largest pipeline company in North America. He also advised Kinder Morgan on El Paso's $7.15 billion sale of EP Energy Corporation and in its $5 billion acquisition of Copano Energy. Mr Tabor also regularly advises private equity firms and portfolio companies in their corporate transactions.

**Personal:** Oklahoma Christian University (BS, 1986); Harvard Law School (JD, magna cum laude, 1990).

## TAYLOR, Consuella Simmons
Baker Botts LLP, Houston
713 229 1650
connie.simmons.taylor@bakerbotts.com
*Featured in Real Estate (Texas)*
**Practice Areas:** Real estate, global projects practice.
**Professional Memberships:** State Bar of Texas; Louisiana State Bar; Houston Bar Association; National Bar Association, International Council of Shopping Centers, Commercial Real Estate Women - Houston, Texas Executive Women.
**Career:** Connie Simmons Taylor primarily handles commercial real estate transactions, primarily representing developers, but with some tenant representation. She advises clients in a wide variety of matters relating to office and retail leasing; sale, acquisition and development of property; and financing, including joint ventures.
**Personal:** JD (magna cum laude), Tulane Law School, 1994; BA (magna cum laude), English, University of Houston, 1991.

## TAYLOR, Jasper
Fulbright & Jaworski LLP, Houston
713 651 5670
jtaylor@fulbright.com
*Featured in Tax (Nationwide), Tax (Texas)*
**Practice Areas:** Tax litigation and tax controversy.
**Professional Memberships:** Past Chair, Section of Taxation Committee on Court Procedure, American Bar Association; Past Chair, Section of Taxation of the State Bar of Texas.
**Career:** Taylor, a lawyer and certified public accountant, has an active practice in tax controversy, including representation of taxpayers in both administrative proceedings and litigation. He has served a wide range of clients and litigated in Texas district courts, federal district courts, the US Tax Court, the US Court of Federal Claims and predecessors, and respective appellate courts.
**Personal:** JD, Duke University (1978); BBA, University of Florida (1973).

## TAYLOR, Timothy C.
Jackson Walker LLP, Austin
512 236 2390
ttaylor@jw.com
*Featured in Real Estate (Texas)*
**Career:** Tim Taylor focuses his practice primarily on real estate and lending transactions. He represents individuals and businesses ranging from local investors to public companies in all aspects of real estate, from acquisition and development, to ownership, leasing, and management, and to subdivision and disposition. Mr Taylor devotes a significant amount of his practice to land acquisition and development, particularly with respect to residential subdivisions and mixed-use developments, and he works with local governments on land use and development issues for his clients. He also represents financial institutions in a wide variety of lending transactions.

**TELLE, Michael S**
Bracewell & Giuliani LLP, Houston
713 221 1327
michael.telle@bgllp.com
*Featured in Corporate/M&A (Texas), Capital Markets (Texas)*
**Practice Areas:** Represents issuers, underwriters and investors, in public offerings and other registered and unregistered offerings of debt and equity securities, in merger and acquisition transactions, and in other corporate and financing transactions. Also assists clients in securities law compliance, corporate governance and general corporate matters. Has experience advising clients involved in the energy industry, including public and private upstream exploration and production companies, public and private midstream companies, including several master limited partnerships, and oilfield service companies.
**Personal:** JD, South Texas College of Law, 1994; MS, Finance, Texas Tech University, 1991; BBA, Economics, Texas Tech University, 1990.

**TERRELL, Irv**
Baker Botts LLP, Houston
713 229 1231
irv.terrell@bakerbotts.com
*Featured in Litigation (Nationwide), Litigation (Texas)*
See under Nationwide for profile.

**THOMPSON, James D**
Vinson & Elkins LLP, Houston
713 758 4502
jthompson@velaw.com
*Featured in Litigation (Texas)*
**Practice Areas:** Jim's practice is complex commercial litigation and arbitration, with an emphasis on energy-related matters. Jim appears in state and federal courts throughout the United States and in domestic and international arbitration proceedings.
**Professional Memberships:** Texas Association of Defense Counsel; Sections of Litigation and Oil and Gas Law, ABA and State Bar of Texas; International Bar Association; London Court of International Arbitration.
**Career:** Admitted to practice: Texas, 1986. Joined Vinson & Elkins, 1986; admitted to partnership, 1993.
**Personal:** Texas A&M University, BS, Petroleum Engineering, 1981; South Texas College of Law, JD with honors, 1986.

**TILLOTSON, Jeff**
Lynn Tillotson Pinker & Cox, LLP, Dallas
214 981 3838
jtillotson@lynnllp.com
*Featured in Litigation (Texas)*
**Career:** Few lawyers in the country have as much complex litigation experience as Jeff Tillotson; even fewer have as much actual trial experience in complex multi-party cases. Over the past few years alone, Mr Tillotson has been the lead trial lawyer in over a dozen major multi-party cases brought in courts in nine different states for clients as diverse as the nation's largest consumer finance company, its third largest bank, its second largest credit card issuer and 40 of the nation's leading industrial concerns. These cases involved

all possible aspects of complex litigation – multiple parties, competing venues, extensive discovery, complex strategy and intense media scrutiny. Mr Tillotson has tried to a jury scores of other cases, including class action lawsuits, business disputes and large commercial matters. Mr Tillotson is a graduate of Georgetown University's School of Foreign Service, the London School of Economics and the University of Texas School of Law.

**TOBOR, Ben D**
Greenberg Traurig, LLP, Houston
713 374 3568
ToborB@gtlaw.com
*Featured in Intellectual Property (Texas)*
**Practice Areas:** Intellectual property and technology.
**Professional Memberships:** Member, International Trademark Association; Life Fellow, Texas and Houston Bar Foundations; Board of Directors and Secretary, Center for Medicine After the Holocaust.
**Career:** Selected, Chambers USA Guide, Intellectual Property, 2004-13; Best Lawyers in America, Intellectual Property, 2007-13; Texas Super Lawyers 2006-12. Recognized, IP Worldwide in 2001 in 'Patent Plums' for the most valuable US patents and the lawyers who nurtured them and again in 2002 among the lawyers who obtained one of the '10 Patents That Changed The World'.
**Personal:** JD, Georgetown University Law Center; BSME, The University of Texas at Austin.

**TOMSU, Michael**
Vinson & Elkins LLP, Austin
mtomsu@velaw.com
*Featured in Energy & Natural Resources (Texas)*
**Practice Areas:** Energy regulation. Energy transactions. Experience includes assistance with construction of, and sales and purchases of, power generation facilities; development and permitting of renewable energy projects, including wind, solar, hydroelectric and geothermal generation; transmission certification; negotiation of energy commodity supply and purchase agreements; nuclear decommissioning; representation of clients and counseling clients on compliance with ERCOT Protocols.
**Professional Memberships:** Board Certified in Administrative Law, Texas Board of Legal Specialization.
**Career:** Admitted to Texas Bar, 1987. Partner, Vinson & Elkins LLP.
**Personal:** BA, Chemistry, University of Texas, 1982; JD, University of Texas School of Law, 1986; MBA, University of Texas, 1986.

**TOWNSEND, Roger**
Alexander Dubose & Townsend LLP, Houston
713 523 2358
rtownsend@adtappellate.com
*Featured in Litigation (Texas)*
**Practice Areas:** Civil Appellate Practice; analysis of complex legal issues; managing complex litigation; licensed in US Supreme Court; 2nd, 4th, 5th, 9th, and 11th Federal Circuits; and all Texas state courts.

**Professional Memberships:** President of American Academy of Appellate Lawyers 2013; Bar Association of the Fifth Federal Circuit; Defense Research Institute; American Bar Association (Council of Appellate Lawyers; Appellate Advocacy Committees of Tort & Insurance Practice and Litigation Sections); Chair, Appellate Practice Section (State Bar of Texas 1989-90).
**Career:** Partner, Alexander Dubose & Townsend LLP 2003-present; Partner, Hogan Dubose & Townsend LLP 1995-2003; Partner and Head of Appellate Group, Fulbright & Jaworski 1987-95; J.D. Harvard Law School (1979).
**Publications:** National Editor, 'Superseding and Staying Judgments: A National Compendium' (ABA TIPS 2007); Editor-in-Chief, 'Texas Appellate Practice Manual' (State Bar of Texas 2d ed 1993); Author 'Stays and Supersedeas' in Appellate Practice in Federal and State Courts (Law Journal Press 2011); 'Focusing on Litigation Results: The Role of the Case Manager', in The Docket (Association of Corporate Counsel March 2006); 'Brief-writing: The Appellee's Perspective', in A Defense Lawyer's Guide to Appellate Practice (DRI 2004).
**Personal:** Selected as Houston Appellate Lawyer of the Year for 2012 by Best Lawyers in America; Awarded Certicate of Merit by State Bar of Texas in 1993 for outstanding contribution to legal profession.

**TRAHAN, Samantha**
Gardere Wynne Sewell LLP, Houston
713 276 5010
strahan@gardere.com
*Featured in Insurance (Texas)*
**Practice Areas:** Insurance coverage, commercial litigation.
**Professional Memberships:** State Bar of Texas, Texas Young Lawyers Association.
**Career:** Samantha Trahan helps manage policyholder risks through the effective use of insurance. Pre-loss, she conducts searches for historical policies, helps with policy renewals and provides counsel on insurance due diligence for corporate transactions. Post-loss, she helps clients evaluate claims, prepares coverage opinions and assists in processing claims. When commercial approaches fail, Ms Trahan litigates disputed claims.
**Personal:** JD, The University of Texas School of Law, with honors, 2000; BS, University of St. Thomas, cum laude, 1996.

**VALDERRAMA, Teresa S**
Jackson Lewis LLP, Houston
713 568 7868
ValderrT@jacksonlewis.com
*Featured in Labor & Employment (Texas)*
**Practice Areas:** Experience in all aspects of workplace law: Trade secret litigation, noncompetition, discrimination claims, torts, contract disputes, wage/hour, union avoidance, labor arbitration, whistleblowers. Conducts investigations, management training.
**Professional Memberships:** Texas State Bar: Executive Council member—L&E Section; ABA; HBA.

**Career:** Baker Botts LLP, 1988-2008. Jackson Lewis LLP, 2008–present. Houston Office Litigation Manager 2009-present.
**Publications:** "Assessing & Responding to Workplace Violence Risks," Executive Legal Advisor (Jan/Feb 2009); multiple CLE publications.
**Personal:** "Texas Super Lawyer," 2003+; Best Lawyers in America, 1999+. Certified, Labor and Employment Law, Texas Board of Legal Specialization, 1993+. University Houston Law, JD, summa cum laude, 1988.

**VAN FLEET, G Allan**
McDermott Will & Emery LLP, Houston
713 653 1703
avanfleet@mwe.com
*Featured in Antitrust (Texas)*
**Practice Areas:** Antitrust and trade regulation; litigation; international dispute resolution; intellectual property litigation; technology litigation; energy and natural resources.
**Professional Memberships:** Chair, ABA Section of Antitrust Law, 2010-11; Commissioner, Texas Supreme Court Permanent Judicial Commissions for Children, Youth and Families (2009-present).
**Career:** Principle drafter of the Unfair Competition Law of Ukraine. Selected: Best Lawyers in America, PLC's Dispute Resolution Handbook, 20 Highly Recommended Litigation Counsel in Texas; Texas Super Lawyers; International Who's Who of Competition Lawyers and Economists; Chambers USA. Rated, AV® Preeminent™ 5.0 out of 5.
**Personal:** JD, Columbia University School of Law; BA, summa cum laude, Rice University.

**VANMIDDLESWORTH, Rex D**
Andrews Kurth LLP, Austin
512 320 9292
rexvanmiddlesworth@andrewskurth.com
*Featured in Energy & Natural Resources (Texas)*
**Practice Areas:** Rex's practice includes commercial litigation, administrative law, energy and alternative dispute resolution. He has tried cases in state court, federal court, before arbitration panels, and before state and federal agencies. He has also argued appeals in the Fifth Circuit, the Texas Supreme Court, and various Texas Courts of Appeals. Rex has represented numerous public and private entities in breach of contract disputes, tortious interference cases and other forms of commercial litigation and arbitration. He handles all types of contested proceedings before state agencies and the State Office of Administrative Hearings, including licensing and rate setting disputes.

**VAUGHN, Matthew**
Porter Hedges LLP, Houston
713 226 6687
mvaughn@porterhedges.com
*Featured in Bankruptcy/Restructuring (Texas)*
**Practice Areas:** Matt Vaughn is a partner in the bankruptcy and corporate sections of Porter Hedges. His experience includes representation of clients in numerous Chapter 11 bankruptcy cases in Texas and across the country. His practice

focuses on corporate reorganizations and restructurings, acquisitions within the bankruptcy context, and creditors' rights with experience representing large, publicly traded entities in their Chapter 11 cases, and institutional and corporate creditors in some of the country's largest Chapter 11 cases to date.

## VILLAREAL, Patricia J
Jones Day, Dallas
214 969 2973
pjvillareal@jonesday.com
*Featured in Litigation (Texas)*

**Practice Areas:** Dallas Office head, Pat Villareal was previously co-head of the Firm's securities litigation and SEC enforcement practice. Pat represents public companies, directors and officers facing securities, M&A, and corporate governance litigation. She also leads internal investigations for boards and audit committees. Pat has been recognized consistently in Chambers Band 1 in securities and related litigation, named as one of the Top 50 Women Lawyers in Texas and Top 100 Lawyers in Texas, as well as included in The Best Lawyers in America, Texas Super Lawyers, D Magazine's "Best Women Lawyers," and Lawdragon's Leading Lawyers.

## VINEYARD, Daniel
Jackson Walker LLP, Houston
713 752 4277
dvineyard@jw.com
*Featured in Environment (Texas)*

**Career:** Dan Vineyard's practice focuses on environmental advice and litigation. Mr Vineyard has represented clients at more than 200 Superfund sites in all Environmental Protection Agency regions and has been lead trial counsel in many environmental cases and arbitrations. He has represented both plaintiffs and defendants in federal (CERCLA) cost recovery and contribution actions and in state environmental cases, and he has defended clients against government enforcement actions under the Resource Conservation and Recovery Act. He represents clients in complex, multi-party construction and commercial cases, and provides counsel on oil and gas, permitting and environmental legal issues.

## VOGEL, Peter S
Gardere Wynne Sewell LLP, Dallas
214 999 4422
pvogel@gardere.com
*Featured in Technology (Texas)*

**Practice Areas:** Internet, information technology (IT), intellectual property (IP), and eDiscovery.
**Professional Memberships:** Texas Supreme Court Judicial Committee on Information Technology [Founding Chair], State Bar of Texas, Dallas Bar Association.
**Career:** Peter Vogel is a trial lawyer who focuses his practice on Internet, IT, and IP litigation and licensing. He is an Arbitrator and eDiscovery Special Master. Mr Vogel is Chair of Gardere's eDiscovery Group, and Chair of Gardere's Internet, eCommerce, and Technology Team.
**Personal:** MS, Computer Science, American University, 1972; JD, St Mary's University, 1976; BBA, University of Texas at Austin, 1969.

## VOLK, William R
Vinson & Elkins LLP, Austin
512 542 8609
wvolk@velaw.com
*Featured in Technology (Texas)*

**Practice Areas:** Partner, M&A/Private Equity Practice Group. Practice includes venture capital and private equity financing, public offerings, mergers and acquisitions, joint ventures and strategic alliances and general corporate counseling and advice.
**Professional Memberships:** State Bar of Texas (Venture Capital Committee, Section of Business Law); American Bar Association; Sustaining Life Fellow, Texas Bar Foundation.
**Career:** Vanderbilt University, BA, 1972; The University of Texas School of Law, JD, with honors, 1975.

## VOYLES, Robb L
Baker Botts LLP, Dallas
214 953 6949
robb.voyles@bakerbotts.com
*Featured in Litigation (Texas)*

**Practice Areas:** Litigation Department Chair. His practice focuses on commercial, securities and FCPA litigation. He represents major accounting and law firms in professional liability litigation, and technology companies in disputes involving government contracts, trade secrets, noncompetition agreements, computer software and the performance of computer systems, and other high-tech products and services.
**Career:** 25+ years of practice. Partner-in-Charge of Austin office (1994-2005). Member of the firm's Executive Committee (2000 to date).
**Personal:** JD (magna cum laude), University of Michigan Law School, 1982. Order of the Coif. Contributing editor, Michigan Law Review. BBA (summa cum laude), Accounting, University of Dayton, 1979.

## WALKER, Charles
Fulbright & Jaworski LLP, Houston
713 651 5151
cwalker@fulbright.com
*Featured in Intellectual Property (Texas)*

**Practice Areas:** Intellectual property.
**Career:** Walker heads Fulbright's Houston Intellectual Property and Technology section and is experienced in patent, trade secret and trademark litigation across various industries. As lead counsel, he obtained two multi-million dollar jury verdicts and secured two appellate decisions in favor of his client, enforcing a patent covering offshore drilling technology. Recently, he obtained a multi-million dollar verdict against a landlord for contributing to trademark counterfeiting, and arbitrated a claim for patent infringement involving hydraulic fracturing.
**Personal:** JD, honors, The University of Texas School of Law; BS, Materials Science and Engineering, electronics option, Rice University.

## WALLANDER, William
Vinson & Elkins LLP, Dallas
214 220 7905
bwallander@velaw.com
*Featured in Bankruptcy/Restructuring (Texas)*

**Practice Areas:** Experience includes representation of creditors, committees, trustees, and debtors in restructuring, exchange offers, remedies enforcement, prepackaged plans, and bankruptcy cases.
**Professional Memberships:** American Bar Association; Dallas Bar Association; Dallas Bankruptcy Bar Association; Texas Banker's Association; American Bankruptcy Institute; Turnaround Management Association; Keeton Fellow, University of Texas School of Law; Dean's Roundtable, University of Texas School of Law.
**Career:** Admitted, Texas, 1984; New York, 2008. Joined firm as Partner, 1999.
**Personal:** University of Pittsburgh, BA magna cum laude, 1981; The University of Texas School of Law, JD, 1984; and University of Phoenix, MBA summa cum laude, 2001.

## WALTERS, Robert
Gibson, Dunn & Crutcher LLP, Dallas
214 698 3114
rwalters@gibsondunn.com
*Featured in Antitrust (Texas), Litigation (Texas)*

**Practice Areas:** Nationally recognized trial lawyer with extensive experience in antitrust, securities, class action, and business tort litigation. Lead trial counsel in many high-profile matters, including in multi-billion dollar antitrust litigation against Blockbuster and major Hollywood studios brought by independent video retailers claiming revenue-sharing agreements violated antitrust laws and in successful takeover defense litigation for Tenet Healthcare in an approximately $7 billion hostile tender offer.
**Career:** Former Executive Vice President/General Counsel, Energy Future Holdings (fka TXU Corp.); former partner and management committee member of Vinson & Elkins.
**Personal:** JD, University of Texas at Austin, 1983, cum laude, Texas Law Review.

## WARNER, Michael
Cole, Schotz, Meisel, Forman & Leonard, P.A., Fort Worth
817 810 5265
mwarner@coleschotz.com
*Featured in Bankruptcy/Restructuring (Texas)*

**Practice Areas:** Member of the Bankruptcy & Corporate Restructuring Department. Nationwide bankruptcy practice focuses exclusively on representing clients in mergers and acquisitions, reorganization cases and out of court workouts. His education and experience as an accountant offer clients invaluable counsel in today's highly complex business environment. Mr Warner approaches client representation with business sense and an eye toward resolution and results rather than prolonged disputes and litigation. He has significant experience in the negotiation and structuring of complex business transactions as well as the ability to litigate to protect client rights.
**Personal:** Southwestern University School of Law, JD, 1984.

## WATKINS GIARRATANI, Shafeeqa
Fulbright & Jaworski LLP, Austin
512 536 2488
sgiarratani@fulbright.com
*Featured in Labor & Employment (Texas)*

**Practice Areas:** Labor and employment; appellate; litigation.
**Professional Memberships:** San Antonio Industry Liaison Group; Austin Bar Association; Texas Young Lawyers Association; American Bar Association; Fulbright & Jaworski L.L.P. Recruiting Committee.
**Career:** Shafeeqa represents employers in federal and state court and before administrative agencies such as the Equal Employment Opportunity Commission and the Texas Workforce Commission. She has represented management in civil rights, wrongful discharge, Family and Medical Leave Act, Fair Labor Standards Act, employment tort, defamation, breach of contract, tortious interference and other employment-related charges and litigation.
**Personal:** JD, with honors, Harvard Law School; AB, with honors, Government, Harvard University.

## WATT, Dick
Watt, Beckworth, Thompson & Henneman, Houston
713 333 9101
dwatt@wattbeckworth.com
*Featured in Litigation (Texas)*

**Practice Areas:** Oil and gas litigation, commercial arbitration, commercial litigation.
**Professional Memberships:** State Bar of Texas, Houston Bar Association, American Bar Association, Fifth Federal Circuit Bar Association.
**Career:** Dick Watt has represented clients in all phases of the upstream exploration and production sector, including handling disputes about marketing and processing of natural gas, royalty calculation issues on behalf of both producers and royalty owners, oil and gas leases and joint operating agreements, drilling contracts and contractors, well blowouts, pipeline issues, offshore operations and facilities, and virtually all types of oil and gas agreements used in the E&P sector. Mr Watt is an author and speaker at numerous legal and oil and gas industry related seminars and he is licensed to practice before the United States District Court for the Southern District of Texas. He is the immediate past Chair of the State Bar of Texas Oil, Gas, and Energy Resources Law Section and Co-Chair of its Pattern Jury Charge Project. He was named a "Texas Super Lawyer" by Law and Politics/Texas Monthly for 2005-09 and a Lawdragon 500 Member by Lawdragon Magazine for 2005-06. Dick has represented parties or served as an arbitrator in approximately 15 arbitrations tried to conclusion and numerous arbitrations that either were settled or otherwise resolved prior to hearing. His international energy cases include a dispute over a pipeline construction contract for an offshore pipeline built in the Arabian Sea and a dispute over the provisions of a foreign concession in Jordan. Dick is an active participant in the oil and gas and ranching business.

## WEAVER, David
Vinson & Elkins LLP, Austin
512 542 8651
dweaver@velaw.com
*Featured in Intellectual Property (Texas)*
**Practice Areas:** David is a skilled litigator who has served as lead counsel in a wide range of patent litigation matters, particularly in the areas of electrical, semiconductor, software, mechanical and chemical technologies. As a former NASA-Johnson Space Center Design Engineer, David brings deep technical knowledge to his cases and has been tapped as a technical advisor to the court in several patent litigations in the District Court for the Eastern District of Texas.
**Career:** South Texas College of Law, JD magna cum laude, 1994; University of Kansas, MS Aerospace Engineering, (1987) and BS (1984); Assistant US Attorney 1999-2000.

## WEBKING, Catherine
Gardere Wynne Sewell LLP, Austin
512 542 7036
cwebking@gardere.com
*Featured in Energy & Natural Resources (Texas)*
**Practice Areas:** Corporate, energy [administrative and regulatory, appellate, commercial litigation, environmental, power and electricity], telecommunications.
**Professional Memberships:** State Bar of Texas, Travis County Bar Association, Gulf Coast Power Association.
**Career:** Catherine Webking focuses on infrastructure development, products, and services that are subject to economic regulation. She represents electric and telecommunications companies in contract negotiations, arbitrations, contested cases, litigation/appeals, rulemaking proceedings, and legislative initiatives. Ms Webking offers daily counseling on public utility regulatory issues. She is active in Gardere's Energy Industry Team.
**Personal:** JD, The University of Texas at Austin School of Law, with honors, 1991; BS, Texas A&M University, 1985.

## WEEDON, Luke A
Baker Botts LLP, Dallas
214 953 6970
luke.weedon@bakerbotts.com
*Featured in Banking & Finance (Texas)*
**Practice Areas:** Represents commercial banks, investment banking firms, asset-based lenders, insurance companies, other institutional lenders and investors, as well as borrowers and issuers of debt securities, in a wide range of financing transactions. Mr Weedon's practice focuses on secured and unsecured syndicated credit facilities, acquisition financings, bridge loans, first/second lien financings, private placements, Rule 144A debt offerings, project financings, letter of credit facilities, debt restructurings and workouts.
**Professional Memberships:** State Bar of Texas; Dallas Bar Association; American College of Investment Counsel.
**Personal:** SMU Dedman School of Law (JD, magna cum laude, 2001); Texas A&M University (BS, 1997).

## WEGE, Mark
King & Spalding LLP, Atlanta
713 751 3246
mwege@kslaw.com
*Featured in Bankruptcy/Restructuring (Texas)*
**Practice Areas:** Represents entities in corporate reorganizations, including out-of-court restructurings, and formal bankruptcy proceedings in a wide variety of industries. Practiced in financial restructuring for 21 years, representing companies in industries such as oil and gas exploration and production, petrochemicals, refining, electrical generation and transmission, oil field service and supply, transportation, telecommunication, retail grocery and convenience store, wholesale product production and distribution, retail restaurant, commercial real estate and healthcare.
**Personal:** JD, Baylor University BBA, with high honors, University of Texas.

## WEIBEL, Mark
Thompson & Knight LLP, Dallas
214 969 1111
Mark.Weibel@tklaw.com
*Featured in Real Estate (Texas)*
**Practice Areas:** Mark focuses on commercial real estate finance transactions, including representation of special servicers in the CMBS market, and provides transactional support when bankruptcy and litigation occur. He has unparalleled experience in the capital markets, providing a unique benefit to his clients for their commercial real estate, commercial real estate finance and complex business transactions. Mark counsels financial institutions, private-equity groups, and Fortune 100 companies with projects including capital structuring, financing, acquisitions, development and dispositions.
**Professional Memberships:** Commercial Real Estate Finance Council; CREFC Hi-Yield Forum.
**Personal:** Oklahoma City University School of Law (JD, 1991); University of Oklahoma (BBA, 1985).

## WEINER, Sanford A
Vinson & Elkins LLP, Houston
713 758 2558
sweiner@velaw.com
*Featured in Real Estate (Texas)*
**Practice Areas:** Real estate transactions and finance law.
**Professional Memberships:** Member: American College of Real Estate Lawyers (President 2003); Anglo-Amercian Real Property Institute; Lifetime Achievement Award, Texas Bar Real Property Section (2007).
**Career:** Admitted to Texas Bar, 1971. Joined Vinson & Elkins, LLP 1971, became Partner in 1978 and Of Counsel in 2013.
**Publications:** Introduction: 'Making Choice of Law a Contact Sport: Contractual Choices of Law in Texas', 54 'Texas Bar Journal' 262 (1991).
**Personal:** Born August 21, 1946. Graduated The University of Texas, BA in 1968 (Cum Laude, Phi Beta Kappa), and Harvard University, JD in 1971 (Cum Laude).

## WEINSTOCK, Peter G.
Hunton & Williams LLP, Dallas
214 468 3395
pweinstock@hunton.com
*Featured in Banking & Finance (Texas)*
**Practice Areas:** Mr Weinstock's practice focuses on corporate and regulatory representation of financial institutions.
**Professional Memberships:** Past President-The Family Place; Founding Board Member-The Family Place Foundation.
**Career:** Joined Hunton & Williams in 2007. Nationally recognized author and speaker (over 150 banking conferences and seminars). Since 1997, co-editor of ICBA's "Subchapter S: THE NEXT GENERATION" newsletter. His article, "Acquisitions of Failed Banks – Present Risk and Opportunity," was recognized by The Risk Managers Association in 2011.
**Personal:** JD, Duke University School of Law, 1985; BA, State University of New York, 1982.

## WELLER, Philip D
DLA Piper LLP (US), Dallas
214 743 4502
phil.weller@dlapiper.com
*Featured in Real Estate (Texas)*
**Practice Areas:** Real estate, construction.
**Professional Memberships:** ACREL.
**Career:** A well known real estate practitioner in Texas, he focuses on real estate acquisitions, dispositions, finance, development, general finance transactions, and private equity transactions. He has been involved in structuring equity investments, forming REITs, financings, development, planned community development, project finance, mortgage finance, and acquisitions and dispositions of office, retail, industrial, and multi-family properties. His clients include equity investors, sponsors, developers, interim lenders, long-term debt providers, banks, REITs, and insurance companies.
**Personal:** JD, Bates College of Law, University of Houston (with highest honors); BS, Bowling Green University (summa cum laude).

## WELLS, J Tullos
Bracewell & Giuliani LLP, San Antonio
210 299 3528
tullos.wells@bgllp.com
*Featured in Labor & Employment (Texas)*
**Practice Areas:** Represents management in labor and employment matters. Routinely handles a broad array of legal issues for professional and amateur sports franchises, broadcast television and radio stations, and major entertainment venues. Has experience in union avoidance and relationships, collective bargaining and handling unfair labor practice charges, including federal and state court trials, arbitrations and proceedings before the National Labor Relations Board and other administrative agencies.
**Career:** Board certified in labor and employment law by Texas Board of Legal Specialization.
**Personal:** JD, The University of Texas School of Law, 1974; BA, The University of Texas at Austin, 1971.

## WELTY, Todd
Dentons, Dallas
214 259 0953
todd.welty@dentons.com
*Featured in Tax (Nationwide), Tax (Texas)*
**Practice Areas:** Todd is the US Head of Tax Controversy and Litigation for legacy Dentons, and is a member of the American College of Tax Counsel. Todd focuses on US tax controversies, representing a broad range of clients in all stages of federal civil and criminal tax proceedings. He has extensive experience resolving high stakes domestic and international tax matters at all stages of a tax dispute, including Internal Revenue Service examinations, administrative appeals, alternative dispute resolution techniques and litigation, if necessary.
**Personal:** Southern Methodist University, JD.

## WEST, Glenn D
Weil, Gotshal & Manges LLP, Dallas
214 746 7780
gdwest@weil.com
*Featured in Private Equity (Nationwide), Corporate/M&A (Texas)*
**Practice Areas:** Glenn West is Managing Partner of Weil's Dallas office and is a dual-qualified US lawyer and English solicitor. He regularly represents private equity firms in acquiring and making investments in public and private companies. He also represents public and private companies (including the portfolio companies of private equity firms) in acquisitions and financings; and he is regularly called upon to provide general corporate and crisis management advice to boards and their management. He has also developed an expertise in the acquisition and financing of sports teams and their facilities.

## WHEAT, R David
Thompson & Knight LLP, Dallas
214 969 1468
David.Wheat@tklaw.com
*Featured in Tax (Texas)*
**Practice Areas:** Mr Wheat's practice focuses on federal income taxation, including corporate tax, mergers, acquisitions, transactions involving partnerships and LLCs, and tax controversies. He provides transactional planning and advice and preparation of tax opinions on federal and state tax implications of business transactions, including corporate mergers and acquisitions and the formation and operation of partnerships and limited liability companies.
**Professional Memberships:** American College of Tax Counsel, College of the State Bar of Texas, American and Dallas Bar Associations, Dallas and Texas Bar Foundations.
**Personal:** New York University (LLM, Taxation, 1989); Louisiana State University (JD, 1988; BS, with honors, 1985).

## WHITE, Bruce H
Greenberg Traurig, LLP, Dallas
214 665 3643
WhiteB@gtlaw.com
*Featured in Bankruptcy/Restructuring (Texas)*
**Practice Areas:** Business reorganization and financial restructuring.

**Professional Memberships:** Member: John C. Ford American Inn of Court (Bankruptcy). American Bankruptcy Institute; Turnaround Management Association; J. Reuben Clark Law Society; American Bar Association.
**Career:** Selected, Best Lawyers in America, 2006-13; Chambers USA Guide, 2007-13. Member, Winning Team, U.S. News - Best Lawyers "Law Firm of the Year" in Bankruptcy & Creditor Debtor Rights / Insolvency & Reorganization Law and Litigation – Bankruptcy, 2013. Rated, AV® Preeminent™ 5.0 out of 5.
**Publications:** Contributing Editor, American Bankruptcy Institute Journal.
**Personal:** JD, Creighton University School of Law; BS, Utah State University.

### WHITE, T Gordon
McKool Smith, Austin
512 692 8700
gwhite@mckoolsmith.com
*Featured in Intellectual Property (Texas)*
**Practice Areas:** Intellectual property litigation.
**Professional Memberships:** State Bar of Texas; AIPLA; Austin and American Bar Associations.
**Career:** Gordon White represents plaintiffs and defendants in complex patent litigation involving a broad range of technologies. Recently, he won a $200 million jury verdict plus $90 million in enhanced damages in i4i v. Microsoft (named 2011 "Patent Case of the Year" by Managing IP). He is consistently recognized by leading legal directories, including Chambers USA, Best Lawyers, and Legal 500.
**Personal:** University of Houston Law Center (JD, 1976); University of Texas (MSEE, with honors, 1967; BSEE, with honors, 1965).

### WHITEHEAD, Stewart
Winstead PC, Austin
512 370 2854
swhitehead@winstead.com
*Featured in Construction (Texas)*
**Practice Areas:** Stewart is chair of the firm's Construction Practice Group. He has successfully served as lead counsel in construction trials and arbitrations in Texas and beyond. Stewart has obtained multimillion dollar verdicts and has negotiated multimillion dollar settlements in favor of his clients. Stewart's experience includes representing clients in projects such as commercial and residential construction and development, transportation and drainage, governmental buildings and developments, public works projects, industrial and warehouse facilities, hospitals and health care facilities, schools, multi-family housing, surety claims and defense, environmental remediation projects, and employee injury investigations.

### WHITMAN, W Ray
Baker & Hostetler LLP, Houston
713 646 1367
rwhitman@bakerlaw.com
*Featured in Litigation (Texas)*
**Career:** Group Chair of BakerHostetler's Litigation Group, Co-Chair of the firm's Shale team and a Policy Committee member, Ray Whitman represents energy, oilfield service and technology companies in a variety of litigation

and business-related issues involving: international, national and local contractual disputes; Fracking; bad faith pooling; theft of trade secrets and noncompete violations; wrongful death claims involving catastrophic events; earn-out provisions; seismic licensing disputes; arbitrations and other matters. In addition, he has worked in the oil and gas industry as a geophysicist, gaining experience in oil and gas exploration, seismic acquisition and drilling and production practices.

### WHITTLE, Jeffrey S
Bracewell & Giuliani LLP, Houston
713 221 1185
jeffrey.whittle@bgllp.com
*Featured in Intellectual Property (Texas)*
**Practice Areas:** Serves as head of the firm's technology practice. Has experience representing clients in licenses, agreements for technology development, transfer, acquisition, joint development, product development, strategic alliance, collaboration, and product distribution, in the software, e-commerce, energy, telecommunications, mechanical/electrical, financial, and medical industries. Also has experience in patent, trademark and copyright preparation and prosecution, mergers and acquisitions, due diligence investigations and opinions, strategic planning, portfolio analysis, various types of intellectual property, litigation and client counseling.
**Personal:** JD, Wake Forest University School of Law, 1991; MBA, Wake Forest University, 1991; BS, Electrical Engineering, Vanderbilt University, 1984.

### WICKLIFF JR, A Martin
Cozen O'Connor, Houston
713 750 3110
awickliff@cozen.com
*Featured in Labor & Employment (Texas)*
**Practice Areas:** Marty has 39 years of litigation and trial experience as a labor and employment lawyer, representing energy, retail, pharmaceutical, grocery, communication and hospitality. A noted jury trial lawyer, Marty has been inducted in the American Board of Trial Advocates.
**Professional Memberships:** American Bar Association, American Board of Trial Advocates, Houston Bar Association, International Association of Defense Counsel, National Association of Railroad Trial Counsel Association, National Bar Association, Texas State Bar.
**Career:** Member, Houston office.
**Personal:** Texas Southern University—Thurgood Marshall School of Law, JD, cum laude, 1973. New York University School of Law, LLM, 1974. University of St. Thomas, BA, 1970.

### WILKINS, Timothy A
Bracewell & Giuliani LLP, Austin
512 542 2134
timothy.wilkins@bgllp.com
*Featured in Environment (Texas)*
**Practice Areas:** Heads the firm's environmental practice and serves as managing partner of the Austin office. Designs and manages corporate environmental governance systems and compliance audit programs. Identifies and resolves environmental issues for transactions and new proj-

ects. Defends environmental enforcement in all media. Clients include power, energy, chemicals, cement and real estate.
**Career:** Teaches Corporate Environmental Law at The University of Texas School of Law and has long served as an adjunct professor at the University of Houston Law Center.
**Personal:** JD, Harvard Law School, 1993; MPP, Harvard Kennedy School of Government, 1993; BA, Trinity University, 1988.

### WILLIAMSON, Holly H
Hunton & Williams LLP, Houston
713 229 5717
hwilliamson@hunton.com
*Featured in Labor & Employment (Texas)*
**Practice Areas:** Litigates claims under FLSA, ADEA, Title VII, state human rights acts, employment torts, ADA, FMLA, ERISA, privacy laws, and of unfair competition, noncompetes, trade secret thefts, and Computer Fraud and Abuse Act. Trial and appellate experience includes wage/hour class/collective actions, contracts, all areas of employment law, SOX, unfair competition, OSHA. Practice includes training, coaching, assistance with RIFs, contracts, WARN Act, contingent workforces, investigations.
**Professional Memberships:** Fellow, Texas and Houston Bar Foundations.
**Personal:** BBA (honors), Texas State University; JD (magna cum laude), South Texas College of Law; Clerk, Edith Hollan Jones, US Court of Appeals for the 5th Circuit.

### WILSON, Jonathan
Littler Mendelson, PC, Dallas
214 880 8174
jcwilson@littler.com
*Featured in Labor & Employment (Texas)*
**Practice Areas:** Labor management relations; wage and hour; whistleblowing and retaliation; discrimination and harassment; competition and trade secret law.
**Career:** Board Certified as a Specialist in Labor and Employment Law by the State Bar of Texas, Board of Legal Specialization. One of his primary focuses has been defending employers in wage-hour cases. In addition, he defends clients in discrimination and whistle-blower lawsuits, executive contract disputes, and fiduciary and unfair competition claims. He has also successfully represented employers in union organizing drives, unfair labor practice and representation cases before the National Labor Relations Board, negotiations of collective bargaining agreements, and labor arbitrations.

### WILSON, Thomas H
Vinson & Elkins LLP, Houston
713 758 2042
twilson@velaw.com
*Featured in Labor & Employment (Texas)*
**Practice Areas:** Tom's practice includes international employment issues, labor/employment issues in business transactions, OSHA inspections and litigation, traditional labor matters, and assisting non-US companies establish their employment practices in the US. Tom is V&E's

Employment, Labor and OSHA practice group leader.
**Professional Memberships:** American Bar Association, Committees on International Labor and Employment Law and OSHA; Practical Law Company's Advisory Board; Labor Relations Advisory Committee; American Health Lawyers Association; Interamerican Bar Association.
**Publications:** 'OSHA Guide for Healthcare Facilities', Thompson Publishing; 'Norwegian labor law chapter of ABA International Labor Law Treatise', (2006).
**Personal:** Drake University, BA, 1982; University of Tennessee, JD, 1985.

### WINDHAM, Darrell R
Greenberg Traurig, LLP, Austin
512 320 7273
WindhamD@gtlaw.com
*Featured in Technology (Texas)*
**Practice Areas:** Co-Managing Shareholder, Austin Office. Corporate/securities; emerging technology.
**Professional Memberships:** Member: Securities and VC Committees of State Bar of Texas and ABA Business Law sections. Board Member, Austin Development Nature Conservancy; Director, Austin Chapter of the College Football Hall of Fame Foundation.
**Career:** Selected: Chambers USA Guide, 2009-10, 2012-13; Best Lawyers in America, 1999-2013; Super Lawyers magazine, Law & Politics, 2009; 'Texas' Top Rated Lawyers', 2012. Rated, AV® Preeminent 5.0 out of 5. President/Chairman, Texas Exes (2007-09).
**Personal:** JD, with honors, The University of Texas School of Law, 1978; BBA, with highest honors, Accounting, The University of Texas-Austin, 1975.

### WOLIN, Robert M
Baker & Hostetler LLP, Houston
713 646 1327
rwolin@bakerlaw.com
*Featured in Healthcare (Texas)*
**Career:** Board certified in Health Law by the Texas Board of Legal Specialization, Bob Wolin maintains an active healthcare and business practice with an emphasis on counseling clients in the healthcare industry. These clients include dialysis providers, long-term care providers, corporate health and medical departments, assisted living facilities, home health agencies, ancillary service providers, IDTFs, physicians, joint ventures, hospitals, pharmaceutical distributors, pharmacies, medical device distributors and manufacturers and healthcare-related aviation service providers. Bob also advises clients regarding a variety of business and regulatory issues, from corporate structuring to compliance with the complex regulatory scheme facing clients in the healthcare industry.

### WOMMACK, Trevor
Bracewell & Giuliani LLP, Houston
713 221 1444
trevor.wommack@bgllp.com
*Featured in Banking & Finance (Texas)*

**Practice Areas:** Focuses his practice on financial transactions, representing financial institutions, other lenders and borrowers in all types of secured and unsecured credit facilities, working capital and acquisition loans, syndicated loan transactions, debt restructurings, and project finance. Experience includes syndicated credit facilities secured by upstream and midstream oil and gas assets, including pipelines and onshore and offshore reserves, as well as personal property and real estate.
**Personal:** JD, The University of Texas School of Law, 2006; BA, Economics, University of North Carolina at Chapel Hill, 2003.

## WOOD, William
Fulbright & Jaworski LLP, Houston
713 651 5537
wwood@fulbright.com
*Featured in Litigation (Texas)*
**Practice Areas:** Litigation and arbitration, domestic and international.
**Professional Memberships:** Past-president, University of Houston Law Alumni Association; Current board member and Immediate Past-President, University of Houston Law Foundation; Elected member, ABOTA.
**Career:** Wood is a leader in Fulbright's Energy, Energy Litigation and Latin America Practice Groups and serves on the Policy Committee. He has a trial and arbitration practice, concentrating on the defense and prosecution of business litigation matters with an emphasis on energy industry controversies.
**Personal:** BBA, Accounting, Texas A&M; JD, University of Houston Law Center, 1984, Houston Law Review associate editor. Chambers USA, Legal 500 US, Best Lawyers.

## WOOD III, William A
Bracewell & Giuliani LLP, Houston
713 221 1166
trey.wood@bgllp.com
*Featured in Bankruptcy/Restructuring (Texas)*
**Practice Areas:** Has more than 20 years of experience in representing debtors, creditors, committees and other parties in interest in all facets of the bankruptcy process and out of court restructurings, including plan creation and confirmation, asset purchases and sales, environmental claims, claim allowance and complex bankruptcy litigation. Has appeared in bankruptcy courts throughout the United States and is a frequent speaker on a variety of bankruptcy and restructuring topics.
**Personal:** JD, South Texas College of Law, 1989; BBA, Southern Methodist University, 1986.

## WORTLEY, Michael
Vinson & Elkins LLP, Dallas
214 220 7732
mwortley@velaw.com
*Featured in Corporate/M&A (Texas)*
**Practice Areas:** Primary area of practice is corporate and securities law. Experience in the food, telecommunications, oil and gas, REITs, manufacturing, healthcare, biotechnology, and high technology industries. Clients include issuers, underwriters, and private equity and other investors in

public and private securities and M&A transactions.
**Professional Memberships:** American Bar Association and Dallas Bar Association.
**Career:** Admitted to Texas Bar, 1978. Came to the firm as a Partner, 1995.
**Personal:** Graduated from Southern Methodist University, BA with highest honors, 1970, the University of North Carolina at Chapel Hill, Masters of Regional Planning, 1973, and Southern Methodist University, JD with honors, 1978.

## WRIGHT, Robert
Baker Botts LLP, Houston
713 229 1237
bob.wright@bakerbotts.com
*Featured in Real Estate (Texas)*
**Practice Areas:** Represents clients in Texas and multi-state acquisitions and divestitures, financing, workouts, development, leasing of commercial real estate, as well as wind, geothermal, carbon sequestration, fossil fuel and nuclear projects, chemical plants and pipelines. Counsels clients on transactional environmental issues, including contractual risk allocation, insurance issues, assessments, remediation, voluntary cleanup programs and claims.
**Professional Memberships:** Anglo-American Real Property Institute; American College of Real Estate Lawyers (former governor); State Bar of Texas (former section chair); Houston Bar Association (former section chair); Houston Real Estate Lawyers Council.
**Personal:** JD, Columbia University, 1975 (Stone Scholar); AB, magna cum laude, Princeton University, 1972.

## WULFE, Scott
Vinson & Elkins LLP, Houston
713 758 2750
swulfe@velaw.com
*Featured in Corporate/M&A (Texas)*
**Practice Areas:** Partner in the M&A/ Private Equity Practice Group, Managing Partner of the firm and a member of the firm's Management Committee. Specializes in private equity transactions, as well as public and private mergers and acquisitions. Also has extensive experience in representing issuers in initial public offerings.
**Career:** Admitted to Texas Bar, 1983; joined Vinson & Elkins, 1983; admitted to the partnership in January 1991.
**Personal:** Graduated from The University of Texas, Plan II BA with highest honors in 1979 (Phi Beta Kappa) and JD in 1983 with high honors (Chancellors).

## YANG, Emeline
Winstead PC, Dallas
214 745 5687
eyang@winstead.com
*Featured in Banking & Finance (Texas)*
**Practice Areas:** Emeline has been a member of Winstead's Finance & Banking practice since she joined the firm in 1997. She represents and advises financial institutions and borrowing entities in all types of business finance transactions including acquisition financings, secured and unsecured financings, single lender and syndicate lending,

participations, debtor-in-possession financings, debt workouts and restructures, mezzanine financing, complex intercreditor and subordination arrangements, and middle market and asset-based financings. Further, she represents clients in a variety of industries, including manufacturing, real estate, sports, financial services, retail, restaurants, energy, sports, media and telecommunications, insurance and healthcare.

## YEATES, Marie
Vinson & Elkins LLP, Houston
713 758 4576
myeates@velaw.com
*Featured in Appellate Law (Nationwide), Litigation (Texas)*
**Practice Areas:** Chairs V&E Appellate Practice. Certified, civil appellate law by Texas Board of Legal Specialization. Named by 'National Law Journal' as one of top 50 women litigators in US. In 2001, named by 'Texas Lawyer' as one of top 20 women litigators in Texas.
**Professional Memberships:** American Academy of Appellate Lawyers, American Law Institute.
**Career:** Louisiana, 1980; Texas, 1982. Joined V&E: 1981; admitted to partnership: 1988.
**Personal:** Louisiana State University, BS, 1977 (summa cum laude); Louisiana State University School of Law, JD, 1980 (first in class); Editor-in-Chief, 'Louisiana Law Review'; clerk US Fifth Circuit Judge Alvin Rubin, 1980-81.

## YELKIN, Kimberly A
Gardere Wynne Sewell LLP, Austin
512 542 7001
kyelkin@gardere.com
*Featured in Insurance (Texas)*
**Practice Areas:** Insurance regulation, government affairs, administrative law, healthcare law.
**Professional Memberships:** State Bars of Texas and Nebraska, American Bar Association, Federation of Regulatory Counsel, Inc.
**Career:** Kim Yelkin is the Executive Partner of the Austin office in charge of Gardere's Government Affairs Practice Group. Ms Yelkin has over 30 years of expertise in insurance and health care issues, having formerly served as senior government affairs counsel for the St. Paul Companies and associate counsel for the American Insurance Association. She is a recognized expert in government affairs and provides counsel on and assists her clients in solving complex problems, including high-profile legislative issues, litigation avoidance, and regulatory matters before various state agencies. Ms Yelkin routinely coordinates mulit-state regulatory and legislative projects to maximize her clients' long-term competitive advantage and defend against governmental action adverse to their interests. Her practice concentration is before the Texas Legislature, the Department of Insurance, the Office of Attorney General, the Texas Department of Health, the Texas Department of Health and Human Services, the Texas Comptroller, the Office of Consumer Credit Commissioner, the Texas Department of Licensing and Regulation and other state agencies.

**Personal:** JD, Creighton University School of Law, 1980; BA, Duke University, 1977.

## YETTER, R Paul
Yetter Coleman LLP, Houston
713 632 8000
pyetter@yettercoleman.com
*Featured in Litigation (Texas)*
**Practice Areas:** Represents plaintiffs and defendants in industries including energy, transportation, mining, utility, telecommunications, and financial services, and in all manner of litigation, including antitrust, IP, securities, business torts, contract, and injury/death suits. Paul has been lead counsel in lawsuits and arbitrations around the US, and appeals in many federal and state appellate courts.
**Career:** Managing partner and head of the firm's trial practice. Paul previously clerked for Judge John Brown on the US Fifth Circuit Court of Appeals.
**Personal:** University of Texas at El Paso, BA, 1980; Columbia University, JD, 1983.

## YOUNG, Evan
Baker Botts LLP, Austin
512 322 2506
evan.young@bakerbotts.com
*Featured in Litigation (Texas)*
**Practice Areas:** Young, a trial and appellate litigator, has argued and won cases in both the US and Texas Supreme Courts. Ranging from those courts to state trial courts, he represents clients at every judicial level.
**Professional Memberships:** State Bar of Texas; Chair, Judicial CLE Committee, State Bar of Texas Business Law Section; US Supreme Court; US Courts of Appeals, Fifth and Ninth Circuits; US District Court, Eastern District of Texas; American Bar Association; Austin Bar Association; US Supreme Court Historical Society; Texas Supreme Court Historical Society.
**Personal:** JD, Yale, 2004; BA, Oxford, 2001; AB (summa cum laude), Duke, 1999.

## YOUNGMAN, Stephen A
Weil, Gotshal & Manges LLP, Dallas
214 746 7758
stephen.youngman@weil.com
*Featured in Bankruptcy/Restructuring (Texas)*
**Practice Areas:** Concentrates in the area of business reorganizations and debtors' and creditors' rights focusing on the restructuring of companies in various industries, including retailers, distributors and finance companies. He has led or had major involvement in a number of the firm's debtor representations, including American Airlines, Pilgrim's Pride Corp., and General Growth Properties and was involved in the firm's representation of American Airlines' acquisition of substantially all of the assets of Trans World Airlines, Inc. He has also represented General Electric in various debtor-in-possession/exit loan transactions, including Mirant Corporation.
**Personal:** Northwest Missouri University (BS); Southern Methodist University (JD).

## ZABANEH, Sam
DLA Piper LLP (US), Austin
512 457 7126
samer.zabaneh@dlapiper.com
*Featured in Technology (Texas)*

**Practice Areas:** Technology, corporate, mergers and acquisitions; venture capital.

**Career:** He practices corporate and securities law, primarily in the context of entrepreneurial and emerging growth companies. He advises clients regarding general corporate matters and handles various capital raising and liquidity event transactions, including private and public equity financing and mergers and acquisition. He advises clients with respect to corporate governance and periodic reporting requirements of publicly held companies.

**Personal:** JD (with honors); BA (Plan Honors II, summa cum laude, Special Honors), BBA (with honors), University of Texas.

## ZDUNKEWICZ, David A
Andrews Kurth LLP, Houston
713 220 4128
dzdunkewicz@andrewskurth.com
*Featured in Bankruptcy/Restructuring (Texas)*

**Practice Areas:** David, a Bankruptcy/Restructuring Partner, has been associated with Andrews Kurth since 1989, handling a wide range of bankruptcy, litigation and transactional matters. His bankruptcy experience includes representations of debtors, creditors' committees, creditors, asset purchasers, and equity committees in the bankruptcy cases of Arcapita Bank, The Great Atlantic & Pacific Tea Company, Delta Petroleum Corporation, Banning Lewis Ranch Company, Energy Partners, LP, Tronox Inc., New Century Energy Corp., Lyondell Chemicals, Mirant, Enron, and Mobile Energy Services Company, LLC. He also has extensive experience in providing bankruptcy and insolvency advice involving complex financial transactions and asset acquisitions.

## ZEMBEK, Richard S.
Fulbright & Jaworski LLP, Houston
713 651 5283
rzembek@fulbright.com
*Featured in Intellectual Property (Texas)*

**Practice Areas:** Intellectual property.

**Career:** Richard's practice centers on intellectual property disputes. He defends clients across the country, and he helps companies protect, license, and monetize patents. His cases involve telecommunication, computer, semiconductor, e-commerce, and Internet technologies, and he's tried both jury and arbitration cases. He's handled significant matters involving industry standards and related IPR Policies, multiple defendants, and MDL proceedings. His broad-based transactional experience includes acquisitions, licenses, technology transfers, and freedom to operate studies.

**Personal:** JD, Vanderbilt University School of Law; BS, cum laude, Electrical Engineering, Union College, Eta Kappa Nu, Tau Beta Pi. Admitted to practice: Texas; USPTO.

## ZLOTKY, Jeffrey A
Thompson & Knight LLP, Dallas
214 969 1384
Jeffrey.Zlotky@tklaw.com
*Featured in Corporate/M&A (Texas)*

**Practice Areas:** Jeff's practice includes representation of private equity funds, public and private companies, capital funding sources, financial institutions, and investors regarding domestic and international transactions. His experience includes structuring, formation, and capitalization of private equity funds and their portfolio companies on behalf of sponsors, investors, and management teams. He structures financing and investment transactions and mergers, acquisitions, and dispositions of securities and assets. He is adept at the organization of joint ventures through a variety of legal structures.

**Professional Memberships:** American and Dallas Bar Associations.

**Personal:** The University of Texas School of Law (JD, 1985); Princeton University (AB, 1982).

# AHMAD, ZAVITSANOS, ANAIPAKOS, ALAVI & MENSING P.C. (OR AZA)

www.azalaw.com **tel:** 713 655 1101 **fax:** 713 655 0062

**OFFICES**

TEXAS

**HOUSTON:** 1221 McKinney Street, Suite 3460, TX 77010
Tel: 713 655 1101  Fax: 713 655 0062

**Managing Partner:** John Zavitsanos
Number of Partners: 8
Number of lawyers: 28
Languages: *Bengali, English, Greek, Mandarin, Russian, Spanish, Ukrainian*

## Firm Overview:

AZA is home to true courtroom lawyers who provide a formidable track record in complex commercial litigation and intellectual property disputes, among other areas. AZA specialties include energy law, patents, business disputes, trade secrets, covenants not to compete and corporate investigations. This lean boutique offers efficient, top-grade legal advice. AZA was named First-Tier in Commercial Litigation in Houston by U.S. News & World Report and The Best Lawyers in America. In U.S. surveys of corporate counsel, AZA has been cited both for being an "awesome opponent" in court and for excellent client service. AZA won three of Texas' Top 2011 Verdicts.

## Main Areas of Practice:

### Complex Commercial Litigation:

Clients call AZA when the stakes are high. AZA's eight partners have tried hundreds of cases, most of them commercial matters representing Fortune 1,000 companies, including extensive work in the energy industry. The firm handles all types of commercial cases, from breach of contract, warranty, indemnity, construction, real estate and business tort lawsuits to shareholder oppression, partnership and fiduciary litigation. Many AZA clients are former adversaries. Five firm lawyers have been named among the top attorneys in the nation by U.S. News & World Report and The Best Lawyers in America. Five firm partners are Board-Certified by the Texas Board of Legal Specialization. AZA is regularly hired on the eve of trial. One example: An oilfield supplier facing more than $35 million in exposure hired AZA shortly before trial. After getting the case continued, AZA filed a counterclaim. Nine months later, AZA's opponent ended up paying the firm's client a multimillion-dollar cash settlement.

**Key Clients:** AZA commercial litigation clients include Plains All American Pipeline in all types of energy-related commercial litigation; CITGO in a variety of energy litigation; Air Liquide in all types of commercial litigation; and Total in all types of contract and business tort cases.
**Contact:** John Zavitsanos
**Email:** jzavitsanos@azalaw.com
**Contact:** Sean Gorman
**Email:** sgorman@azalaw.com
**Contact:** Amir Alavi
**Email:** aalavi@azalaw.com

### Intellectual Property:

AZA has successfully represented clients in IP cases in the Eastern District of Texas and throughout the world.

The firm does not shy away from IP trials, and has tried three to verdict since 2011, including one that ended in a $391 million win for a patent client and another that defeated a $10 million trademark claim. AZA represents companies and inventors in the energy, automotive, software and financial industries. The firm's IP lawyers include two attorney/engineers, an attorney/chemist, and two U.S. Patent and Trademark Office-licensed attorneys, including one with extensive experience as a patent special master and mediator.
**Key Clients:** AZA's IP clients include Versata, in one of the nation's largest patent verdicts in 2011, and now in Dubai, Italy and Japan; Mistras Group in the successful defense of a trademark case; Acacia Research Group in patent infringement lawsuits; Core Laboratories in patent litigation; and American Automobile Association (AAA) in patent and trademark cases.
**Contact:** Demetrios Anaipakos
**Email:** danaipakos@azalaw.com
**Contact:** Steven Mitby
**Email:** smitby@azalaw.com

### Trade Secrets/ Covenant Not to Compete:

AZA is nationally recognized in covenant not to compete and trade secret litigation through work for numerous energy, technology and financial companies. AZA secured a unanimous defense verdict in a high-profile, $30 million trade secret lawsuit in Houston after being called in on the eve of trial.
**Key Clients:** AZA trade secret/covenant not to compete clients include Mistras Group, successful defense in trade secrets case; and A&B Valve and Supply (A&B), successful defense in nationally publicized case filed by National Oilwell Varco, which then hired AZA to represent the company in two trade secret cases.
**Contact:** Joseph Ahmad
**Email:** joeahmad@azalaw.com
**Contact:** Todd Mensing
**Email:** tmensing@azalaw.com

## Clients:

AAA Life Insurance Company; A&B Valve and Piping Systems; Advanced Technologies; Air Liquide America; American Alternative Insurance Corporation; Aon Risk Services; American Automobile Association; Andon Specialties Inc.; Antar Inc.; AT&T; CITGO; Columbia Gulf Transmission Co.; Comsys/Venturi Partners; CorEnergy; CHUBB Specialty Insurance; DeepFlex Inc.; DiCentral Corporation; Ecumenical Patriarchate of the Eastern Orthodox Church; Enbridge Inc.; Executive Lodging Limited; Fort Bend County; Genuine Parts Company; GreyStar Corporation; Group 1 Automotive Inc.; P & R Guzman Interests; Halliburton; Harris County; Healix Infusion Therapy Inc.; Houston Fertility Institute; Houston Pulmonary Medicine; Houston Radiology Associates; Key Energy Services Inc.; Liquidity Partners LLC; Lusk Properties Inc.; Lyondell Chemical Company; The Lancaster Hotel; Mercedes-Benz USA; Mi-Jack Products Inc.; Mistras Inc.; MJMC Inc.; Millennium Interests; Motion Industries Inc.; Munich Reinsurance America Inc.; METCO; National Oilwell Varco; Nevada Gold & Casinos Inc.; NAPA Auto Parts; NiSource; Noble Energy Inc.; Orthopedic Associates; Plains All American Pipeline L.P.; Prime Natural Resources Inc.; PSC; Ramex Inc.; Sheridan Healthcare Inc.; St. James Capital Partners L.P.; UTEC Survey Inc.; Versata Inc.; Willis Group.

AHMAD
ZAVITSANOS
ANAIPAKOS
ALAVI
MENSING

*Tough Name. Tougher Opponent.*

# ANDREWS KURTH LLP

www.andrewskurth.com **tel:** 713 220 4200 **fax:** 713 220 4285

**Chairman:** Thomas J Perich
**Managing Partners:** Robert V Jewell (firm-wide), Rex D VanMiddlesworth (Austin), Hong Irwin and Timothy J Unger (Beijing), Mark S Solomon (Dallas), Robin Russell (Houston), David Barbour and Geoffrey K Walker (London), Lynne M Fischman Uniman (New York), James V Mahon (Durham), Craig L Stahl (The Woodlands), Shemin V Proctor (Washington, DC)
Number of partners: 205  Number of other lawyers: 199
Languages: *Bengali, Chinese, English, French, German, Hindi, Japanese, Mandarin, Portuguese, Spanish, Taiwanese*

**Firm Overview:**
For more than a century, Andrews Kurth LLP, an international law firm with over 400 lawyers, has built its multidisciplinary practice on the belief that "straight talk is good business.®"
Andrews Kurth embraces diversity and inclusion as a business imperative and an ethical responsibility. The firm strives to be a leader in the legal profession by building a high performance team of diverse individuals to create a positive experience for the firm's clients.

**Main Areas of Practice:**

**Corporate & Securities:**
48 partners, 94 lawyers
- Represented Composite Engineering Inc. in its acquisition by Kratos Defense & Security Solutions Inc., which was honored as the 2012 Aerospace & Defense Services Deal of the Year at the M&A Atlas Awards
- Represented the underwriters in more than $12 billion of security issuances by Kinder Morgan, Inc. and its subsidiaries
**Key Clients:** Enterprise Products Partners L.P.
**Contact:** David Buck, co-chair **Tel:** 713 220 4301
**Email:** dbuck@andrewskurth.com
**Contact:** Mike O'Leary, co-chair **Tel:** 713 220 4360
**Email:** moleary@andrewskurth.com

**Financial Restructuring:**
11 partners, 24 lawyers
- Represented the official unsecured Creditor Committee in FairPoint Communications' Chapter 11 reorganization, which was honored as the Telecom Technology Turnaround of the Year at the 2012 Global M&A Network Turnaround Atlas Awards, and currently representing the post-confirmation litigation trust pursuing $2 billion in fraudulent transfers
**Key Clients:** Credit Suisse, Appaloosa Partners, Bank of New York, Wilmington Trust
**Contact:** Robin Russell, co-chair **Tel:** 713 220 4086
**Email:** rrussell@andrewskurth.com
**Contact:** Paul Silverstein, co-chair **Tel:** 212 850 2819
**Email:** paulsilverstein@andrewskurth.com

**Energy – Oil & Gas (Transactional):**
49 partners, 83 lawyers
- Represented Cordillera Energy Partners III, LLC in its $2.6 billion acquisition by Apache Corporation
- Advised Nucor Energy Holdings Inc. in connection with a $3 billion drilling program with Encana Oil & Gas (USA) Inc
**Key Clients:** Hilcorp Resources, Duke Energy

Corporation
**Contact:** Mike O'Leary **Tel:** 713 220 4360
**Email:** moleary@andrewskurth.com

**Energy – Oil & Gas (Regulatory & Litigation):**
4 partners, 10 lawyers
- Representation of clients in connection with rates, accounting, certificates and commission-initiated investigations
**Key Clients:** Great Lake Gas Transmission, Northern Border Pipeline Company
**Contact:** Kenneth L Wiseman **Tel:** 202 662 2715
**Email:** kwiseman@andrewskurth.com

**Intellectual Property:**
10 partners, 16 lawyers
- Represents Sony Mobile Communications as primary litigation counsel in IP matters relating to cellular telephony and in US and international licensing and negotiation
**Key Clients:** Fortune Brands/Master Lock Company
**Contact:** Jeff Dodd **Tel:** 713 220 4736
**Email:** jeffdodd@andrewskurth.com

**Litigation:**
59 partners, 110 lawyers
- Represents BP as Texas counsel in litigation arising out of Macondo oil spill, and represents BP as local counsel in shareholder litigation allegedly related to spill
- Successfully represented Aetna in a 10-year legal battle involving prompt pay penalties
**Key Clients:** Aetna, BP Corporation, Noble Energy
**Contact:** Tom Taylor **Tel:** 713 220 3991
**Email:** ttaylor@andrewskurth.com
**Contact:** John Shely **Tel:** 713 220 4105
**Email:** jshely@andrewskurth.com

**Tax:**
9 partners, 19 lawyers
- Tax counsel to Rose Rock Midstream, L.P. in its purchase of a 33.3% interest in SemCrude Pipeline, L.L.C., which owns 51% of the White Cliffs Pipeline

## OFFICES

**TEXAS**
**AUSTIN:** 111 Congress Avenue, Suite 1700, TX 78701
Tel: 512 320 9200  Fax: 512.320.9292

**DALLAS:** 1717 Main Street, Suite 3700, TX 75201
Tel: 214 659 4400  Fax: 214 659 4401

**HOUSTON:** 600 Travis, Suite 4200, TX 77002
Tel: 713 220 4200  Fax: 713 220 4285

**THE WOODLANDS:** Waterway Plaza Two, 10001 Woodloch Forest Drive, Suite 200, TX 77380
Tel: 713 220 4800  Fax: 713 220 4815

**NEW YORK**
**NEW YORK:** 450 Lexington Avenue, NY 10017
Tel: 212 850 2800  Fax: 212 850 2929

**NORTH CAROLINA**
**RESEARCH TRIANGLE PARK:** 4819 Emperor Boulevard, Suite 400, Durham, NC 27703
Tel: 919 313 4827

**DISTRICT OF COLUMBIA**
**WASHINGTON DC:** 1350 I Street, NW, Suite 1100, Washington, DC 20005
Tel: 202 662 2700  Fax: 202 662 2739

**CHINA**
**BEIJING:** Room 2007, Capital Mansion, No. 6 Xin Yuan Nan Lu, Chao Yang District, 100004
Tel: +86 10 8486 2699  Fax: +86 10 8486 8565

**UNITED KINGDOM**
**LONDON:** Level 16, City Tower, 40 Basinghall Street, EC2V 5DE
Tel: +44 20 7382 0550  Fax: +44 20 7614 0012

- Represents issuers and underwriters in billions of US dollars of public security offerings
**Key Clients:** Enterprise Products Partners, L.P. NuStar Energy, L.P.
**Contact:** Tom Ford **Tel:** 713 220 4498
**Email:** tford@andrewskurth.com
**Contact:** Terri Lacy **Tel:** 713 220 4482
**Email:** tlacy@andrewskurth.com

**Real Estate:**
29 partners, 53 lawyers
- Representation of various corporate clients in the acquisition, financing and construction of commercial properties throughout the United States
**Key Clients:** Invesco Real Estate, Capmark Finance, Inc.
**Contact:** Kathleen Wu **Tel:** 214 659 4448
**Email:** kwu@akllp.com
**Contact:** Michael Boyd **Tel:** 713 220 3921
**Email:** mboyd@andrewskurth.com

**International:**
22 partners, 33 lawyers
- Primary development counsel and primary finance counsel to AEI and Pattern Energy Group LP in the $245 million development and financing of Parque Eólico El Arrayán SpA's 115 MW wind power project
**Key Clients:** Inter-American Development Bank, Sinopec, AEI, Pattern Energy Group LP
**Contact:** Timothy J Unger **Tel:** 713 220 4370
**Email:** tunger@andrewskurth.com

# BAKER BOTTS

www.bakerbotts.com **tel:** 713 229 1234 **fax:** 713 229 1522

**Managing Partner:** Andrew M Baker
Number of partners worldwide: 285
Number of other lawyers worldwide: 415
Languages: *Arabic, Chinese (Cantonese, Mandarin), English, Russian, Spanish*

## Firm Overview:

Baker Botts is a leading international law firm recognised for its service to clients across three key business sectors – energy, technology and life sciences – and throughout 14 offices located in the US, Europe, Russia, the Middle East and China. Dating back to 1840, Baker Botts lawyers and staff have worked on complex legal issues, including energy projects, intellectual property arguments, litigation, corporate transactions, environmental compliance challenges and tax disputes. As one of the largest law firms in the United States, the firm has worked on behalf of clients in more than 100 countries, and the firm regularly consults on matters that have a local, regional and global impact.

## Main Areas of Practice:

### Global Projects Department:

53 partners, 64 other lawyers
Global Projects lawyers provide clients with in-depth legal advice in the world's major energy-producing regions. Areas include: oil and gas, project development and finance, real estate, energy regulatory and international trade. These focus on energy and infrastructure projects in both development and operational stages, as well as advisement in respect to regulatory, import/export, finance and commercial business transactions often required after these projects commence.

### Intellectual Property Department:

45 partners, 91 other lawyers
The firm offers a national and international practice including patent litigation, patent procurement, patent licensing and due diligence. Other areas of practice include strategic IP counseling, trademark acquisition, trademark and copyright litigation, franchise and distribution and other intellectual property transactions. With the skill set to protect and advance clients goals, combined with technical knowledge and industry experience, firm lawyers are able to work with clients facing complex technology issues.

### Litigation Department:

84 partners, 133 other lawyers
Litigators handle commercial, securities, professional liability, product liability, patent, white-collar, antitrust, international arbitration and energy litigation, as well as the appellate issues that arise from these matters. The firm's representations reflect the broad litigation practice, with matters ranging from wins in high-profile cases to precedent setting victories. The firm's lawyers excel in courtrooms across the United States and internationally, helping resolve clients legal problems in a variety of industries.

### Corporate Department:

67 partners, 75 other lawyers
Corporate lawyers handle complex matters, advising clients on a full range of corporate, securities and financing matters, including public offerings and private placements of equity and debt for both issuers and underwriters or placement agents. In addition, the firm's corporate lawyers have extensive experience in private equity and venture capital fund transactions and specialised financing in domestic and international contexts.

### Environmental Department:

14 partners, 23 other lawyers
The firm has one of the largest and most diverse environmental practices among general practice firms. Lawyers advise on matters relating to the environmental aspects of major energy, industrial and infrastructure projects, including LNG, pipeline, electric power and refinery. In addition, environmental lawyers handle nearly every type of counselling and transactional matters, as well as offering full service litigation capabilities.

### Tax Department:

19 partners, 29 other lawyers
Comprised of four sections, including income tax, state tax, employee benefits and executive compensation and private clients services, the tax department provides advice to clients across the spectrum of business activities and investments. Lawyers develop plans and structures to achieve clients' objectives while minimising the impact of federal, state and international taxes. The firm also features a substantial employee benefits and executive compensation practice, and provides counseling to individuals, families and entrepreneurs on wealth transfer and succession planning tax issues.

## OFFICES

### TEXAS

**AUSTIN:** 98 San Jacinto Boulevard, Suite 1500, TX 78701-4078
Tel: 512 322 2500  Fax: 512 322 2501
Email: joe.knight@bakerbotts.com

**DALLAS:** 2001 Ross Avenue, TX 75201-2980
Tel: 214 953 6500  Fax: 214 953 6503
Email: pat.stanton@bakerbotts.com

**HOUSTON:** One Shell Plaza, 910 Louisiana, TX 77002-4995
Tel: 713 229 1234  Fax: 713 229 1522
Email: maria.boyce@bakerbotts.com

### NEW YORK

**NEW YORK:** 30 Rockefeller Plaza, NY 10112-4498
Tel: 212 408 2500  Fax: 212 408 2501
Email: lee.charles@bakerbotts.com

### CALIFORNIA

**PALO ALTO:** 1001 Page Mill Road, Building One, Suite 200, CA 94304-1007
Tel: 650 739 7500  Fax: 650 739 7699
Email: bryant.c.boren@bakerbotts.com

### DISTRICT OF COLUMBIA

**WASHINGTON DC:** The Warner, 1299 Pennsylvania Avenue, NW, DC 20004-2400
Tel: 202 639 7700  Fax: 202 639 7890
Email: john.taladay@bakerbotts.com

# BAKER BOTTS

# BEIRNE, MAYNARD & PARSONS, LLP

www.bmpllp.com

Number of partners: 42
Number of other lawyers: 31

## Firm Overview:

Founded in 1987, Beirne, Maynard & Parsons, LLP has become a nationally significant force in civil trial and appellate work. With a long tradition of excellent litigation results, the firm has pursued a growth path based on general litigation and industry specialization. As specialists, the firm has developed one of the nation's leading energy practices, along with prestigious national practice teams serving the transportation and insurance industries. As generalists, the firm serves a diverse range of Fortune 500 companies locally, nationally and internationally. Because the firm specializes in winning trials, all of its lawyers are trained to practice in court, which has enabled Beirne, Maynard & Parsons to attract attorneys who might not otherwise obtain courtroom experience working at larger firms. The firm's arbitration specialists have vast experience before national and international tribunals. The Arbitration/Alternative Dispute Resolution Group (AADR) has successfully resolved disputes through mediation, national and international arbitration and other resolution forums. Beirne, Maynard & Parsons understands that going to court may not always be in the client's best interest and that there are many avenues for dispute resolution. Thus, the firm's trial lawyers are also trained to recognize when matters are best resolved through other mechanisms.

## Main Areas of Practice:

### Civil Trials, Appeals & Arbitration:

As one of the nation's leading litigation firms, Beirne, Maynard & Parsons is distinguished for both breadth and depth. Beirne, Maynard & Parsons represents hundreds of diverse corporations and other clients in cases ranging from energy-related disputes to insurance coverage and defense to representation of sovereign states. The firm's energy litigation specialty represents clients in an array of disputes, including interest owner, operational, production and marine construction, as well as contract and commercial litigation, environmental matters and more. In addition to energy, product liability and transportation, the firm includes significant practices in election law, aviation, intellectual property, coverage, bankruptcy, construction and computer sciences. Because Texas is a plaintiff-friendly jurisdiction, *Fortune* 500 companies throughout the country retain the firm when they are sued in the state.

## Clients:

Clients are often national and international companies seeking outside litigation counsel in capacities ranging from local or regional counsel to national coordinating counsel, from individual cases to dockets involving thousands of plaintiffs. The firm's energy client list includes: ConocoPhillips; ATP Oil & Gas Corporation;

Baker Hughes; Brazos Electric Power; Cooperative, Inc.; Wood Group; ONEOK, Inc.; Marathon Oil Corporation; CenterPoint Energy Corp.; FMC Technologies, Inc.; GreenEarth Fuels; Green Mountain Energy Services, Inc.; GEXA Energy; Superior Energy Services, Inc.; and Vaquillas Energy, LLC.

The firm's fabled transportation client list includes such companies as: American Suzuki Motor Corporation; Aviation Office of America; The Cessna Aircraft Company; Ferrari North America; Ford Motor Company; Global Aerospace; Hyundai North America; Maserati North America; Mazda North America; Mercedes-Benz Truck Company; Mitsubishi Motor Sales of America, Inc.; Orion Bus Industries; Porsche Cars North America; Pratt & Whitney of Canada; and Volvo North American Corporation.

Chemical company clients include Air Liquide Corporation and Chevron Phillips Chemical Company.

In healthcare, the firm represents Baylor College of Medicine, Christus health care, and Wyeth.

Among the many prominent insurance companies represented are: AIG, ACE USA, CNA Insurance, Fireman's Fund Insurance Companies, Global

## PRACTICE AREAS

Civil Trials, Appellate & Arbitration

## OFFICES

### TEXAS

**HOUSTON:** 1300 Post Oak Boulevard, Suite 2500, TX 77056
Tel: 713 623 0887  Fax: 713 960 1527
Email: info@bmpllp.com

**DALLAS:** 1700 Pacific Avenue, Suite 4400, TX 75201
Tel: 214 237 4300  Fax: 214 237 4340

**AUSTIN:** 401 West 15th Street, Suite 845, TX 78701
Tel: 512 623 6700  Fax: 512 623 6701

**SAN ANTONIO:** 112 East Pecan Street, Suite 2750, TX 78205
Tel: 210 582 0220  Fax: 210 582 0231

### LOUISIANA

**NEW ORLEANS:** 601 Poydras Street, Suite 2200, LA 70130
Tel: 504 586 1241  Fax: 504 584 9142

**BATON ROUGE:** 301 Main Street, Suite 1100, LA 70825
Tel: 225 387 5068  Fax: 225 387 4995

Aerospace Underwriting Managers Ltd., Zurich North America, and The Travelers Insurance Companies.

International sovereign state clients include The People's Republic of China and The Republic of Estonia.

Other client companies from various industries include Corrections Corporation of America; David Weekley Homes; Marriott Corporation; Newell Rubbermaid, Inc.; Procter & Gamble; Matthews International; Cushman Wakefield; and Service Corporation International.

# BRACEWELL & GIULIANI LLP

www.bgllp.com **tel:** 713 223 2300 **fax:** 713 221 1212

**Chairman:** Patrick C Oxford
**Managing Partner:** Mark C Evans
Number of partners: 203  Number of lawyers: 460
Languages: *Arabic, Bulgarian, Cantonese, Chinese, Croatian, Czech, English, French, German, Greek, Hebrew, Hindi, Indonesian, Italian, Korean, Latin, Malayalam, Mandarin, Polish, Portuguese, Russian, Serbian, Spanish, Tagalog, Thai, Vietnamese*

**Firm Overview:**
Bracewell & Giuliani LLP is a global law firm with 460 attorneys in Texas, New York, Washington, DC, Connecticut, Seattle, Dubai, and London. The firm has earned a reputation for delivering practical, cost-effective and relationship-driven client service in the energy, technology and finance sectors. The firm and its practice groups have been recognized for excellence by a number of global legal and business publications and organisations. The 2012 *Chambers and Partners USA: America's Leading Lawyers for Business* singled out 58 Bracewell attorneys as leaders and 23 practice areas.

**Main Areas of Practice:**

**Energy:**
67 partners, 121 total fee earners based in Texas, Seattle, New York and Washington, DC
- Represented ConocoPhillips in the $23 billion spin-off of Phillips 66, now an independent downstream energy company with industry-leading businesses in refining and marketing, midstream and chemicals
- Represented Kinder Morgan, Inc. in the acquisition of all outstanding shares of El Paso Corporation for approximately $38 billion
**Key Clients:** Kinder Morgan, Inc., Chesapeake Energy Corporation, ConocoPhillips, Apache Corporation
**Contact:** G Alan Rafte **Tel:** 713 221 1411
**Email:** alan.rafte@bgllp.com

**Technology:**
15 partners, 39 total fee earners based in Texas, Seattle and Washington, DC
- Represents Green Source Energy on strategic alliance agreements and key transactions involving technology development and intellectual property licensing
- Primary licensing and technology transaction counsel for Xtreme Power, Inc., a venture capital–backed company that manufactures and operates large-scale digital power systems for use in renewable energy and micro-grid applications
- Represented WhaleShark Media, Inc. in a number of technology deals, including the high-profile launch of card-linked coupon technology that identifies card-linked coupons on the receipt at the point of purchase – an industry first – during South by Southwest Interactive 2012
**Key Clients:** Google, HTC, Hewlett-Packard and Dow Corning
**Contact:** Jeffrey S Whittle **Tel:** 713 221 1185
**Email:** jeffrey.whittle@bgllp.com

**Finance:**
34 partners, 68 total fee earners based in Texas, Seattle, Washington, DC, New York and Connecticut
- Represented Wells Fargo Bank's Charlotte NC, Houston, TX, and San Francisco, CA offices in its purchase of the North American energy lending unit of BNP Paribas
- Represented Chesapeake Energy Corporation, as primary borrower's counsel in a $4 billion unsecured term loan facility
- Represented Citibank, N.A., as Administrative Agent, in an unsecured $1 billion revolving credit facility for international oil and gas company Marathon Oil Corporation
**Key Clients:** Wells Fargo Bank, Société Genérale, Bank of America, Citibank
**Contacts:** Mark C Evans **Tel:** 713 221 1300
**Email:** mark.evans@bgllp.com

**Litigation:**
69 partners, 138 total fee earners based in Texas, Seattle, Washington, DC, New York and Connecticut
- Represents Halliburton in the federal criminal and administrative investigations arising from the Deepwater Horizon oil spill
- Represents Chart, a leading manufacturer of equipment used in gas processing, defendants are former independent sales agents for Chart who violated their sales representative agreements by forming a side company to compete with Chart and developing technology that competes with Chart
- Represents Tide Natural Gas Storage; defendants are Falcon Gas Storage Company, Inc. and Arcapita Bank. The dispute arises out of a $500 million sale of a gas storage business to Tide and certain fraudulent representations discovered subsequent to closing
**Key Clients:** Halliburton, Baker Hughes, Powerex Corp.
**Contact:** Glenn A Ballard, Jr **Tel:** 713 221 1454
**Email:** glenn.ballard@bgllp.com

## PRACTICE AREAS
Broker-Dealer & Market Regulation
Corporate & Securities
Educational Institutions
Energy
Environmental Strategies
Finance
Financial Institutions
Financial Restructuring
Government
Intellectual Property
Internal Investigations
International Practice
Labor & Employment
Litigation
Private Investment Funds
Public Finance
Real Estate & Projects
Strategic Communications
Tax
Technology
White Collar Defense, Internal Investigations & Regulatory Enforcement

## OFFICES
**TEXAS**
**HOUSTON:** 711 Louisiana Street, Suite 2300, TX 77002-2770
Tel: 713 223 2300  Fax: 713 221 1212

**AUSTIN:** 111 Congress Avenue, Suite 2300, TX 78701-4061
Tel: 512 472 7800  Fax: 512 472 9123

**DALLAS:** 1445 Ross Avenue, Suite 3800, TX 75202-2711
Tel: 214 468 3800  Fax: 214 468 3888

**SAN ANTONIO:** 106 S. St Mary's Street, Suite 800, TX 78205-3603
Tel: 210 226 1166  Fax: 210 226 1133

**CONNECTICUT**
**HARTFORD:** 225 Asylum Street, Suite 2600, CT 06103-1516
Tel: 860 947 9000  Fax: 860 246 3201

**DISTRICT OF COLUMBIA**
**WASHINGTON DC:** 2000 K Street NW, Suite 500, DC 20006-1872
Tel: 202 828 5800  Fax: 202 223 1225

**NEW YORK**
**NEW YORK:** 1251 Avenue of the Americas, 49th Floor NY 10020-1104
Tel: 212 508 6100  Fax: 212 508 6101

**WASHINGTON**
**SEATTLE:** 701 Fifth Avenue, Suite 6200, WA 98104-7043
Tel: 206 204 6200  Fax: 206 204 6262

## INTERNATIONAL OFFICES
The firm also has offices in Dubai and London

# BRACEWELL &GIULIANI

# BROWN MCCARROLL

**www.**brownmccarroll.com **tel:** 512 472 5456 **fax:** 512 479 1101

**Chairman:** David Hilgers
**Managing Partner:** Adam Hauser
Number of partners: 51
Number of lawyers: 63
Languages: *English, Spanish*

## Firm Overview:

Founded in 1938, Brown McCarroll is a multi-disciplinary law firm with offices in Austin, Dallas and Houston, Texas. The firm prides itself on its commitment to client service and the practical solutions it offers its clients.

## Main Areas of Practice:

### Bankruptcy & Business Restructuring:

5 partners, 1 associate: Brown McCarroll is focused on developing the most effective and creative solutions for its clients. The firm counsels on all aspects of Chapter 11 reorganizations, Chapter 7 liquidations and out-of-court restructurings. Brown McCarroll represents owner and executive debtors, secured and unsecured creditors, financial institutions and other corporate clients, trustees, creditor committees, vendors, insurers, and buyers of distressed assets.
**Contact:** Stephen W Lemmon **Tel:** 512 479 1148
**Email:** slemmon@brownmccarroll.com

### Litigation:

17 partners, 4 associates: Brown McCarroll has had a vibrant litigation practice for over 70 years. Whether it's "bet-the-company" litigation or routine disputes, the firm's collective wisdom is a tactical advantage it leverages for its clients. Brown McCarroll's clients range from start-ups to Fortune 500 companies across many industries. The firm handles business disputes of all types, including breach of contract disputes, business torts, false claims / qui tam, non-compete controversies, partnership disputes, collections, class actions, Racketeer Influenced Corrupt Organizations Act (RICO) matters, professional liability allegations, banking and finance litigation, construction disputes, intellectual property litigation and labor and employment disputes.
**Contact:** Rick A Illmer **Tel:** 214 999 6112
**Email:** rillmer@brownmccarroll.com

### Electricity:

6 partners: Brown McCarroll attorneys have been at the forefront of electric market development and restructuring for over 25 years, providing strategic guidance and effective counsel to a variety of companies and financial institutions interested in the Texas electric markets. As the "go to" firm for wholesale electric providers and investors in Texas utility infrastructure assets, Brown McCarroll offers innovative solutions and a full range of services for generation development, asset management, power marketing, and mergers and acquisitions. The firm's attorneys understand not only the legal issues, but also the commercial issues their clients confront.
**Contact:** J Christopher Hughes **Tel:** 512 479 1173
**Email:** chughes@brownmccarroll.com

### Environmental:

4 partners, 1 of counsel: Brown McCarroll environmental attorneys have over two decades of experience which means they have seen, challenged, and negotiated a myriad of environmental issues. As a result, they are capable of providing effective counseling quickly, without having to become educated on the issues at their client's expense. From strategic planning, to compliance questions, to contested hearings, they have the resources and depth of counseling and litigation skills to represent clients throughout the course of their projects.
**Contact:** Danny Worrell **Tel:** 512 479 1151
**Email:** dworrell@brownmccarroll.com

### Governmental & Legislative Affairs

8 partners: Brown McCarroll represents clients at each step in the governmental affairs process and has a particular emphasis on representing health care and electricity clients before the Texas Legislature and various state agencies. The key to Brown McCarroll's success is the relationships it has built with public policy makers that give it credibility and allows the firm to help shape new legislation and serve as effective advocates in the agency rulemaking process.
**Contact:** J Christopher Hughes **Tel:** 512 479 1173
**Email:** chughes@brownmccarroll.com

### Health Care:

20 partners, 3 associates, 1 of counsel
Brown McCarroll has one of the largest dedicated health care practices in the Southwest. The firm represents all types of health care providers, including practitioners, hospitals, and allied health professionals, home health agencies, surgery centers, nursing home and other long term acute care hospitals, comprehensive outpatient rehabilitation facilities, residential treatment centers, imaging centers, medical device manufacturing companies and laboratories. In short, the firm offers a boutique health care law firm's attention within a full-service law firm that can address a full range of client needs.
**Contact:** Diane Carter **Tel:** 512 703 5738
**Email:** dcarter@brownmccarroll.com

### Real Estate

13 partners, 2 associates: Brown McCarroll's real estate team helps clients get deals done. Whether the transaction involves land acquisition, land use approval, financing, development, construction, leasing, or disposition, the firm's lawyers have the necessary capabilities. Brown McCarroll attorneys have the experience to help structure and negotiate the best deals, then guide the clients through documentation and closing of the transaction. Clients in this area draw upon the firm's interdisciplinary strengths in handling corporate, environmental, tax and other challenges that often arise in real estate transactions. Brown McCarroll is a single source that can see any size real estate project through to completion.
**Contact:** Charles W. Morris **Tel:** 214 999 6124
**Email:** cmorris@brownmccarroll.com

## PRACTICE AREAS

Appellate
Banking & Finance
Bankruptcy & Business Restructuring
Climate Change & Renewable Resources
Commercial Litigation
Construction
Corporate & Tax
Electricity
Environmental
Estate Planning & Probate
Governmental & Legislative Affairs
Health Care
Intellectual Property
Labor & Employment
Litigation
Nonprofit Organizations
Privately-Held Companies
Professional Liability
Real Estate
Startups & Early-Stage Companies
White Collar Criminal Defense

## OFFICES:

TEXAS
**AUSTIN:** 111 Congress Avenue, Suite 1400, TX 78701-4093
Tel: 512 472 5456  Fax: 512 479 1101
Email: inquiries@brownmccarroll.com

**DALLAS:** 2001 Ross Avenue, Suite 2000, TX 75201-2995
Tel: 214 999 6100  Fax: 214 999 6170
Email: inquiries@brownmccarroll.com

**HOUSTON:** 15333 JFK Blvd., Suite 100, TX 77032
Tel: 713 529 3110  Fax: 512 479 1101
Email: inquiries@brownmccarroll.com

# CANTERBURY, ELDER, GOOCH, SURRATT, SHAPIRO, & STEIN, P.C.

**www.**canterburylaw.com **tel:** 972 239 7493 **fax:** 972 490 7739

**Chairman:** Joseph F Canterbury, Jr
**Managing Partner:** Patricia Stein
Number of partners: 8
Number of attorneys: 10
Languages: *English*

**OFFICES**

TEXAS
**DALLAS:** Occidental Tower, 5005 LBJ Freeway, Suite 1000,
TX 75244-6136
Tel: 972 239 7493   Fax: 972 490 7739
Email: info@canterburylaw.com

## Firm Overview:

Established 30 years ago, the firm has extensive knowledge of construction law and labor and employment law as related to the construction industry. Over the years, the firm's practice has expanded into the areas of real estate, corporate, public project construction and construction insurance law. Members of the firm routinely assist clients in drafting and negotiating complex contracts, and in preparing and defending construction claims. Some of the attorneys are frequent speakers before national, state and local construction industry associations. The firm has two named directors, Joseph F Canterbury, Jr and W Kyle Gooch as members of the American College of Constructions Lawyers. Three members of the firm are also active in arbitration and mediation of construction disputes. Additionally, Mr Canterbury and Robert J Shapiro are authors of the Texas Construction Law Manual, 3rd Edition, a standard reference for the construction industry.

## Main Areas of Practice:

### Construction:

The firm has expertise and experience in the construction industry. Members of the firm represent developers, owners, contractors, subcontractors and suppliers in construction disputes and other legal problems of construction and development including commercial, industrial, highway, power plant, pipeline and public projects. The firm also has specialized knowledge of perfecting lien and bond claims for both public and private projects.

### Labor & Employment:

The firm represents employers in labor and employment matters, including defense of discrimination allegations and Occupational Safety and Health Act and the National Labor Relations Act issues. Two members of the firm have extensive experience in advising clients regarding union-related matters, personnel situations and wage and hour claims.

### Corporate/Real Estate:

The firm provides corporate services in entity organization and corporate reorganizations such as mergers and conversions by analyzing innovative business solutions. Members of the firm serve as counselors and negotiators for developers, buyers, sellers, landlords and tenants in office and industrial properties.

### Alternative Dispute Resolution:

The firm provides dispute resolution services in the construction industry through three experienced mediators, Joe Canterbury, Kyle Gooch and Robert Shapiro. Mr Canterbury and Mr Gooch also have extensive arbitration experience.

## Recent Work:

- Representing a client in an alleged chilled water piping failure at a stadium in Texas. This matter is in excess of $7 million and has involved extensive pre-trial discovery
- Representing a client on a pipeline project in Mississippi. The $15 million dispute involves disputes over payment and alleged defective work. This matter is currently in discovery and trial preparation stage
- Representing a client in a dispute with an owner over final payment and allegations of constructions defects. Multiple parties involved as design firms and subcontractors have been added. This $12.5 million matter is in discovery stage
- Representing a client in a dispute involving a large clearwell water reservoir in Oklahoma City
- Representing a client with respect to an extra work claim of approximately $4.5 million on a fresh water lake pumping station
- Representing a client with respect to alleged parking garage failures in a major airport
- Representing a school district with respect to a significant foundation failure
- Representing clients in defense of derivative action. This action involves claims of breach of fiduciary duty and usurpation of partnership opportunities
- Representing a client in a merger and acquisition transaction in excess of $10 million involving water treatment patents

Joe Canterbury served on a construction panel of arbitrators in four major construction disputes in three states. The firm has also prepared and filed amicus briefs in three appellate cases on behalf of the AGC of Texas which advanced positions important to Texas contractors. Kyle Gooch drafted major contracts for the contractors of a large housing unit, numerous office buildings and condominium projects. Rick Gover has represented employers in situations involving the Occupational Safety and Health and National Labor Relations Acts. Patricia Stein drafted substantial joint venture agreements for contractors on several projects including a hospital project and was involved in several land purchase and sale transactions for industrial clients. She also drafted and negotiated substantial construction contracts on behalf of clients. Robert Elder has prepared major EPC contracts.

## Clients:

AGC of Texas; All American Construction; Allen Butler Construction, Inc.; American Fire Sprinkler Association; Anderson Paving; Bob Moore Construction; Campbell Construction Co.; Dallas Demolition Co.; Driver Pipeline Company, Inc.; Gallagher Construction Co.; G. Greenstreet, Inc.; Gracon Construction; Haley Greer, Inc.; ICI Construction, Inc.; Lee Lewis Construction, Inc.; Manhattan Construction Company; Miller Sierra Contractors, Inc.; N.C. Sturgeon, L.P.; Odyssey Residential Construction; Oscar Renda Contracting; Panattoni Construction, Inc.; Panda Energy; Sandia Construction, Inc.; Templeton Construction; The Ridgemont Company.

Canterbury,
Elder,
Gooch,
Surratt,
Shapiro &
Stein

# CHAMBERLAIN, HRDLICKA, WHITE, WILLIAMS & AUGHTRY

www.chamberlainlaw.com **tel:** 713 658 1818 **fax:** 713 658 2553

**Managing Partner:** Wayne A Risoli
Number of partners: 65  Number of other lawyers: 47

**Firm Overview:**
Founded in 1965 by attorneys from the Tax Division of the United States Department of Justice as a boutique firm specializing in tax planning, controversy and litigation, Chamberlain Hrdlicka has grown to over 100 attorneys, servicing a wide variety of practice areas. Today, the firm's tradition of personalized service continues to be valued by clients from the smallest start-up ventures to the largest multinational companies.

**Main Areas of Practice:**

**Tax:**
Chamberlain Hrdlicka's nationally ranked tax section is a core strength of the firm's diversified law practice. The firm's tax section represents domestic and foreign multinational companies in cross-border financial transactions, international structuring, global tax minimization, including transfer pricing and contract manufacturing arrangements, foreign tax credit management and planning, section 199 deductions, accounting method issues, including inventory methods and capitalization issues, and advising on the application of FIN 48 to domestic and international tax issues. The firm also provides counsel on all phases of the tax controversy process, from the beginning of the tax audit, to the preparation of tax protests and negotiation with IRS Appeals, to litigation in the federal tax courts and representation on appeal. Similarly, at the state level, the firm represents taxpayers in all phases of the tax litigation process. Chamberlain Hrdlicka is also the sole United States law firm belonging to the International Tax Group ('ITG'), an elite group of international tax lawyers from five continents.

**Corporate, Securities & Finance:**
The firm represents a broad spectrum of public and private business entities involved in initial public offerings and secondary offerings of equity and debt securities; private placements; mergers and acquisitions; venture capital financing; international project finance; swaps and financial derivative transactions; corporate bonds and asset-backed securities; conventional loans; leveraged buy-outs; exchange offers; tender offers; roll-up consolidations, and other business combinations and reorganizations; technology licensing, equity incentive and compensation programs; supply chain management; and ongoing corporate and securities counseling of both public and private companies as well as their directors and executive officers.

**Energy:**
The firm's Energy Practice encompasses expertise in power development, project financing, industry mergers and acquisitions, dispute resolution, with emphasis on gas to power marketing and trading, asset development and financing, energy management agreements, gas supply agreements, power purchase and sale agreements, fuel transportation agreements, transmission queue position swaps, electrical and fuel interconnection agreements.

**Litigation:**
The firm provides comprehensive litigation services in a wide variety of specialized areas, including antitrust, insurance, business fraud, consumer law, deceptive trade practices, contract disputes, environmental law, federal multi-district litigation, products liability, toxic torts, IP rights infringement, white collar crime and other areas.

**Construction:**
The firm's representation of clients extends from the beginning of projects through their conclusion, from the negotiation of contracts and preparation of bids to the resolution of construction disputes. The firm assists clients in project administration, job close-outs and settlement, and 'privatization' matters, performs disaster and injury investigations, and provides a full range of services with respect to government (federal, state and local) contracts, including bid protests and board of contract appeals claims.

**Real Estate:**
The firm's expertise includes development, financing, purchase and sale of a wide variety of real estate assets, including residential and commercial office and retail complexes, manufacturing facilitates, resort facilities and land development. The firm handles negotiation and drafting of real estate contracts and leases, title and survey review and curative actions, closing agreements and documentation, workouts and foreclosures, and eminent domain and condemnation proceedings.

**Admiralty & Maritime:**
The firm handles claims and litigation matters for offshore drilling and production companies, marine transportation companies, marine construction companies, dredging contractors, inland barge lines, towing companies, shipping companies, commercial diving contractors, commercial fishing companies, and their cargo, hull, P&I, and general liability underwriters.

**Employee Benefits & Executive Compensation:**
The firm's Employee Benefits section represents public companies, large and closely-held private companies, tax-exempt organizations, and the fiduciaries who oversee those entities' employee benefit plans. From qualified retirement plans, to executive compensation, to fiduciary advice, to health and welfare programs, to mergers and acquisitions, to ERISA litigation.

**Labor & Employment:**
The firm's labor and employment attorneys specialize in protecting the interests of employers from executive stock and bonus plans, to hourly dispute resolution plans. The firm also has extensive experience in successfully resolving labor and employment litigation matters.

**Estate Planning & Administration:**
The firm's Estate Planning and Administration section provides legal counsel on wills, planning for incapacity, gifting strategies, life insurance planning, trust planning, charitable giving, succession planning, family limited partnerships, marital property agreements, estate administration and probate, preparation and filing of returns, representation in estate and gift tax audits.

**International & Immigration:**
The firm expertise includes outbound planning for US-based clients; inbound planning for foreign clients; cross-border business support and counsel; personal planning for 'citizens of the world'; resolving tax controversies involving international issues; and obtaining appropriate US immigration status.

**OFFICES**

**COLORADO**
**DENVER:** 600 17th Street, Suite 2800 South, CO 80202
Tel: 303 820 0831  Fax: 303 260 6401

**GEORGIA**
**ATLANTA:** 191 Peachtree Street NE, 34th Floor, GA 30303
Tel: 404 659 1410  Fax: 404 659 1852

**PENNSYLVANIA**
**PHILADELPHIA:** 300 Conshohocken State, Rd, Suite 570, PA 19428
Tel: 610 772 2300  Fax 610 772 2305

**TEXAS**
**HOUSTON:** Two Allen Center, 1200 Smith, Suite 1400, TX 77002
Tel: 713 658 1818  Fax: 713 658 2553

**SAN ANTONIO:** 112 East Pecan Street, Suite 1450, TX 78205
Tel: 210 253 8383  Fax: 210 253 8384

# COOPER & SCULLY PC

**www.**cooperscully.com **tel:** 214 712 9500 **fax:** 214 712 9540

**Named Shareholders:** R Brent Cooper, John A Scully
Number of partners: 17  Number of lawyers: 38

**Firm Overview:**
Cooper & Scully, P.C. is known for its vast experience in trial and appellate work and for providing aggressive representation. In addition to litigating complex cases from their inception, clients and other law firms retain the firm on the eve of trial to try cases prepared by other lawyers and to handle post-verdict or appellate phases of cases tried by other counsel. Cooper & Scully, P.C. has extensive experience litigating virtually all areas of law. The firm represents private and public entities in a broad range of litigation and other legal matters, including complex multiparty and class-action lawsuits before federal and state courts. The firm also handles federal and state regulatory and agency proceedings and alternative dispute resolution matters, such as arbitration, summary jury trial and mediation.

**Main Areas of Practice:**

**Appellate:**
Cooper & Scully appellate attorneys have experience in all aspects of appellate practice including evaluating potential appeals and original proceedings as well as perfecting appeals preparing briefs and petitions for writ of mandamus, and oral argument. The firm's appellate attorneys have briefed and argued landmark cases in the Texas Supreme Court, Texas intermediate appellate courts, and federal appeals courts, creating both procedural and substantive law. As a result, clients and other attorneys frequently ask Cooper & Scully to take over cases on appeal. Additionally, the firm's appellate section provides support for trial teams throughout litigation to protect the clients' interests in the event of an appeal. The appellate attorneys draft and argue complex discovery motions, dispositive motions, expert challenges, trial briefs, and jury charges. They also assist with preservation of error at trial, post-verdict motions, preparation of the judgment, and perfection of any appeal.

**Commercial:**
Cooper & Scully represents entities in litigation that has become a prevalent part of today's business climate. The firm's attorneys represent multinational companies, small partnerships, and individuals in prosecuting and defending business tort claims, contract disputes, trade-secret claims, breach of fiduciary duty claims, real estate disputes, and other business matters.

**Construction:**
The firm represents commercial contractors, subcontractors and residential builders in cases involving alleged construction defects, personal injury matters, and contract and commercial disputes.

**Healthcare:**
Cooper & Scully's attorneys are at the forefront of this highly regulated and rapidly evolving industry, maintaining a comprehensive healthcare practice encompassing virtually every aspect of healthcare law. Cooper & Scully represents hospital systems, academic centers, physicians, physician groups, managed care organizations, nursing homes, pharmaceutical companies, and other healthcare entities. Cooper & Scully's attorneys have successfully represented clients in complex commercial litigation, class actions, provider reimbursement litigation, medical malpractice lawsuits, managed care litigation, medical staff and peer review disputes, and ERISA-related litigation. The firm serves as coordinating counsel for one of the nation's largest healthcare organizations and has served as national counsel on birth injury litigation for several hospital systems. Cooper & Scully also counsels clients on state and federal regulation, including Stark and Anti-Kickback compliance, Medicare reimbursement, survey and certification, Medicare Advantage, HIPAA, IJCAHO accreditation, and EMTALA.

**Insurance:**
Cooper & Scully's insurance attorneys are at the forefront in the development of Texas law in the area of bad faith. The firm's attorneys have successfully tried numerous bad faith cases. They have the experience to analyze and evaluate the exposure presented by these cases and to advise clients on how to minimize risks. Cooper & Scully understands the most complex insurance matters. The firm represents insurers and insureds in disputes over coverage afforded by various policies. In addition, Cooper & Scully is among a relatively small number of firms that are equipped to represent reinsurers on various matters.

**Intellectual Property Litigation:**
The firm represents businesses and individuals in intellectual property litigation. It has represented nationwide retailers and local specialty stores in trademark, trade dress and trade secret actions. The firm provides representation concerning insurance coverage aspects of intellectual property disputes. The firm's attorneys have negotiated and drafted licensing agreements and have handled domain name disputes and disputes involving trademark or copyright infringements arising from website content.

**Labor & Employment:**
The firm offers transactional, litigation, and risk-assessment services in employment law. Its transactional services include severance, non-disclosure, and non-compete agreements.

**Products Liability:**
The firm's attorneys have litigated complex matters involving a variety of products such as medical devices, pharmaceuticals, gasoline additives, fuels, toxic chemicals, breast implants, asbestos, motor vehicles, helmets, tires and tire rims, underground gas storage tanks, and construction products. The firm has significant experience in representing makers of medical equipment and pharmaceutical products.

**Transportation:**
The firm's attorneys are experienced and knowledgeable about the transportation industry and understand the vital importance of early investigation and evaluation in issues of losses. Additionally, it uses state of the art technology to investigate and reconstruct accidents.

**Premises Liability:**
Cooper & Scully advises its property management clients on preventing litigation through risk assessment and risk strategy review. The firm focuses on providing adequate security and other safety training to management and administrative personnel. The firm also represents residential and commercial clients in personal injury lawsuits, suits arising out of third-party criminal acts committed on the clients' property, and lease disputes.

**OFFICES**

CALIFORNIA
**SAN FRANCISCO:** 100 California Street, Suite 850, CA 94111
Tel: 415 956 9700  Fax: 415 391 2074

TEXAS
**DALLAS:** 900 Jackson Street, Suite 100, TX 75202
Tel: 214 712 9500  Fax: 214 712 9540

**HOUSTON:** 700 Louisiana Street, Suite 3850, TX 77002
Tel: 713 236 6800  Fax: 713 236 6880

**SHERMAN:** 250 East Evergreen Street, TX 75090
Tel: 903 813 3900  Fax: 903 868 1919

# FORSHEY PROSTOK

www.forsheyprostok.com **tel:** 817 877 8855 **fax:** 817 877 4151

**Contact Partner:** Jeff Prostok
**Partners:** J Robert (Bobby) Forshey, Michelle V Larson
Partners: 3 Associates: 4 Counsel: 2

## Firm Overview:

FORSHEY PROSTOK has the experience, knowledge and skill to represent clients in all aspects of financial restructuring and insolvency matters, including complex bankruptcy-related litigation. The firm has extensive experience representing debtors, creditors, official and unofficial creditors' committees in bankruptcy cases and in out-of-court financial restructurings. The firm's practice is centralized in Dallas and Fort Worth, Texas and remains ideally positioned to respond to both regional and national representations. The firm's size and dedicated focus on financial restructuring allows it to give clients the close, individual attention they deserve throughout every aspect of the restructuring process. FORSHEY PROSTOK is honored to be the only Fort Worth based firm recognized by Chambers USA in 2012 for its expertise in bankruptcy and restructuring. The breadth of the firm's representations has varied from the largest case ever filed in Texas to mid-level Chapter 11 reorganization cases and sophisticated creditor representations.

## Clients:

**Vitro SAB:** FORSHEY PROSTOK served as co-counsel representing an Ad Hoc group of bondholders with claims exceeding $700m in the Vitro S.A.B. bankruptcy case pending in the Northern District of Texas. There, FP successfully assisted the bondholders in preventing Vitro from enforcing its Mexican concurso plan in the United States, thereby allowing important subsidiary guaranties to be preserved and enforceable domestically. On appeal, FP assisted the bondholders in obtaining a favorable decision from the Fifth Circuit Court of Appeals. The Fifth Circuit decision is expected to have a significant impact on international commercial transactions as well as on future cross-border financing and restructuring.

**Outsource Holdings, Inc.:** FORSHEY PROSTOK represented Outsource's bankruptcy sale/merger of its 100% interest in Jefferson Bank, a Texas bank with five branch locations in DFW Metroplex. The transaction was the first of its kind in Texas.

**Texas Rangers Baseball Club:** FORSHEY PROSTOK, acting as conflicts counsel, represented the Texas Rangers Baseball Partners in a chapter 11 bankruptcy case pending in Fort Worth, Texas. FORSHEY PROSTOK actively participated in facilitating an auction for the Major League baseball team and confirming a plan of reorganization for the Texas Rangers Baseball Club. The representation is one of the most unique and high-profile bankruptcies ever filed in Texas.

**Majestic Liquor Stores, Inc.:** FORSHEY PROSTOK serves as debtor's counsel for Majestic Liquor Stores. Through the firm's efforts, Majestic Liquor Stores, which operated 46 retail stores and three wholesale locations with gross sales in excess of $150,000,000 annually, was able to successfully confirm a plan of reorganization allowing for a sale of substantially all of its assets and a significant distribution to creditors.

**Movie Gallery, Inc. and Affiliates:** FORSHEY PROSTOK was retained by the Board of Directors of Movie Gallery, Inc., to represent its interests in the companies' bankruptcies filed in the Eastern District of Virginia. As of the commencement of the bankruptcies, the Movie Gallery debtors were one of the largest North American home entertainment specialty retailers and the debtors operated approximately 2,600 retail stores. In 2009, annual revenues of the debtors exceeded $1.4 billion.

**Heartland Automotive Holdings, Inc.:** FORSHEY PROSTOK served as debtors' co-counsel for Heartland Automotive Holdings, Inc. and its affiliate debtors. With approximately $396,000,000 in aggregate debt and $334,000,000 in aggregate assets, the Heartland bankruptcy was, at the time of filing, the largest case filed in the Northern District of Texas in 2008. Heartland's plan was confirmed in January 2009, with 100% recovery to creditors. FORSHEY PROSTOK took the lead on numerous claim objections in the case.

**Mirant Lovett, LLC:** FORSHEY PROSTOK successfully confirmed a full-pay plan of reorganization for Mirant Lovett, a Mirant Corporation power generation subsidiary with scheduled assets exceeding $200m. Prior to confirmation, FORSHEY PROSTOK was instrumental in bringing an 11 year property tax dispute regarding Mirant Lovett and another Mirant Corporation subsidiary to a favorable conclusion.

**Mirant NY-Gen, LLC:** FORSHEY PROSTOK filed and confirmed a separate plan of reorganization for Mirant Corporation subsidiary, Mirant NY-Gen, which provided for the sale of the company to a third-party purchaser. FORSHEY PROSTOK strategically structured the sale of the Mirant NY-Gen equity interests to allow various stages of bidding and raised funds to pay all prepetition creditor claims in full.

**MC Asset Recovery, LLC:** FORSHEY PROSTOK currently represents MC Asset Recovery, LLC, ("MCAR"), a subsidiary of Mirant Corporation created pursuant to Mirant's bankruptcy plan to pursue bankruptcy-related litigation for the benefit of Mirant's unsecured creditors and former equity holders. FORSHEY PROSTOK acts as plaintiff's counsel for MCAR in suits to recover more than $150m from a consortium of foreign-based lenders, including Commerzbank AG, and General Electric.

**The Bombay Company, Inc.:** FORSHEY PROSTOK served as local counsel for the Official Committee of Unsecured Creditors of The Bombay Company, Inc., et al., one of the largest retail bankruptcy cases ever filed in Texas. With the firm's assistance, the Committee and debtors confirmed a joint plan of liquidation, which resulted in payment of a significant dividend to unsecured creditors.

**TrueStar Barnett, LLC a/k/a Trinity Barnett, LLC:** FORSHEY PROSTOK, acting as debtor's counsel, successfully obtained confirmation of a plan of liquidation for the debtor.

**INSpire Insurance Solutions, Inc.:** FORSHEY PROSTOK represented the Liquidating Trust formed in the bankruptcy cases of INSpire Insurance Solutions, Inc. and INSpire Claims Management, Inc. INSpire Insurance Solutions offered complete insurance policy and claims administration outsourcing, IT outsourcing, and software services. FORSHEY PROSTOK handled a complex international litigation matter for the Liquidating Trustee against Sul America Companhia National Seguros, a large Brazilian insurance company, resulting in a favorable settlement of Sul America's $5.2m claim against the Trust. Through the claim objection process, including claim objections filed against IBM, Tokio Marine Management and Connecticut General Insurance Company, FORSHEY PROSTOK reduced overall claims in the bankruptcy cases from more than $30m to allowable claims of $2.3m.

**XTO Energy, Inc.:** FORSHEY PROSTOK currently represents XTO Energy, Inc., a creditor in various bankruptcy related matters throughout Texas.

## PRACTICE AREAS
Bankruptcy/ Restructuring

## OFFICES
TEXAS

**FORT WORTH:** 777 Main Street, Suite 1290, Fort Worth, TX 76102
Tel: 817 877 8855  Fax: 817 877 4151

**DALLAS:** 500 Crescent Court, Suite 240, TX 75201
Tel: 214 716 2100  Fax: 817 953 3215

# FULBRIGHT & JAWORSKI LLP

www.fulbright.com **email:** info@fulbright.com

**Managing Partner:** Kenneth L Stewart
Number of partners: 340
Number of other lawyers: 465

## Firm Overview:

Founded in 1919, Fulbright & Jaworski LLP is a leading full-service international law firm, with more than 800 lawyers in 17 locations in Austin, Beijing, Dallas, Denver, Dubai, Hong Kong, Houston, London, Los Angeles, Minneapolis, Munich, New York, Pittsburgh-Southpointe, Riyadh, San Antonio, St Louis and Washington, DC. Fulbright provides a full range of legal services to both domestic and foreign clients worldwide. *Corporate Board Member* magazine consistently names Fulbright among the top 20 corporate law firms in the US in its survey of general counsels and directors of public companies. Fulbright was the first law firm to receive the Client Choice Award for 'Excellence in Client Service' in the US by the International Law Office and the only law firm chosen on multiple occasions. Fulbright's excellent client service was recognized when the firm was named in the *BTI Client Service 30*. Fulbright also was recognized by Acritas as one of the leading US Law Firm Brands in 2012. On June 1, 2013, Fulbright will join forces with Norton Rose, creating a global legal practice with significant depth of experience across Africa, Asia, Australia, Canada, Europe, Latin America, the Middle East, Central Asia and the United States.

## Main Areas of Practice:

### Bankruptcy:

Fulbright's Bankruptcy and Insolvency Practice Group is one of the largest and most experienced groups in this practice area in the country. Fulbright's bankruptcy lawyers have substantial experience in representing parties complex insolvency matters. Experience includes secured and unsecured creditors, committees (both official and ad hoc), bondholders, asset purchasers, equity sponsors, debtors, trustees and other parties involved in financial restructuring transactions and cases, both in and out of court.

### Corporate:

Fulbright provides a broad array of corporate legal services to a diverse client base that ranges from start-up ventures to large multinational companies. The firm carefully guides its clients through the legal issues that affect their ability to maintain and expand their operations in today's highly competitive, high-speed business environment, including matters related to mergers and acquisitions, financings and corporate governance. The firm's skill and commitment to service span many industries including energy, healthcare, media, financial services, insurance software and hardware, biotechnology, telecommunications, information technology, transportation, business services, manufacturing, retail, ecommerce and consumer products.

### Energy:

Fulbright is recognized as a premier energy firm with a diversified practice that serves the needs of the global energy industry. With more than 50 years of experience in energy matters, the firm has accumulated a wealth of experience and valuable knowledge in both international and domestic energy matters involving energy litigation, transactions, regulatory issues and dispute resolution. In the transaction area, Fulbright attorneys are well versed in the development, financing and construction of energy projects, as well as acquisitions. Fulbright regulatory attorneys serve the needs of clients engaged in the pipeline, oil and gas production, and electric power industries. The firm provides a full range of services in federal and state regulatory matters. In addition, the firm is ranked internationally among the best in litigation and arbitration. That ranking stems in large part from the experience and successes of the firm's energy litigation and arbitration attorneys.

### Environmental:

Fulbright's Environmental Law Practice Group includes some of the most experienced lawyers in enforcement proceedings, contested permit hearings and environmental litigation. Knowledgeable in all aspects of environmental law, environmental litigation, mass tort, toxic tort and class action suits, Fulbright lawyers offer extensive experience in environmental auditing, enforcement actions, permitting and approvals, superfund actions, real estate and business transactions, land development restrictions, legislation and rulemaking.

### Healthcare:

Fulbright's Health Law Practice Group is widely known for strengths in its transactional practice, professional liability and medical malpractice, operational credentialing, and peer review matters, general tort and commercial litigation, and administration and regulatory representation. Fulbright has more than 50 years of experience representing healthcare clients in a wide range of issues, including business and corporate matters, tax matters, federal and state compliance issues, and commercial and professional malpractice claims. The firm has been deeply involved in the development of both large and small healthcare providers as well as community health clinics ever since Fulbright attorneys helped establish the Texas Medical Center.

## PRACTICE AREAS:

Bankruptcy
Corporate
Energy
Environmental
Healthcare
Intellectual Property & Technology
International
Labor & Employment Law
Litigation
Public Finance
Tax

## OFFICES

CALIFORNIA
**LOS ANGELES:** 555 South Flower Street, Forty-First Floor, Los Angeles, CA 90071
Tel: 213 892 9200  Fax: 213 892 9494

COLORADO
**DENVER:** 1200 Seventeenth Street, Suite 1000, Denver, CO 80202
Tel: 303 801 2700  Fax: 303 801 2777

DISTRICT OF COLUMBIA
**WASHINGTON:** Market Square, 801 Pennsylvania Avenue, NW, Washington, DC 20004-2623
Tel: 202 662 0200  Fax: 202 662 4643

MINNESOTA
**MINNEAPOLIS:** 2100 IDS Center, 80 South Eighth Street, Minneapolis, MN 55402-2112
Tel: 612 321 2800  Fax: 612 321 2288

MISSOURI
**ST LOUIS:** 190 Carondelet Plaza, Suite 1690, St Louis, MO 63105
Tel: 314 505 8800  Fax: 314 505 8899

NEW YORK
**NEW YORK:** 666 Fifth Avenue, New York, NY 10103-3198
Tel: 212 318 3000  Fax: 212 318 3400

PENNSYLVANIA
**PITTSBURGH-SOUTHPOINTE:** Southpointe Energy Complex, 370 Southpointe Blvd., Suite 300, Canonsburg, PA 15317-8572
Tel: 724 416 0400  Fax: 724 416 0404

TEXAS
**AUSTIN:** 98 San Jacinto Blvd, Suite 1100, Austin, TX 78701-4255
Tel: 512 474 5201  Fax: 512 536 4598

**DALLAS:** 2200 Ross Avenue, Suite 2800, Dallas, TX 75201-2784
Tel: 214 855 8000  Fax: 214 855 8200

**HOUSTON:** Fulbright Tower, 1301 McKinney, Suite 5100, Houston, TX 77010-3095
Tel: 713 651 5151  Fax: 713 651 5246

**SAN ANTONIO:** 300 Convent Street, Suite 2100, San Antonio, TX 78205-3792
Tel: 210 224 5575  Fax: 210 270 7205

# GARDERE WYNNE SEWELL LLP

www.gardere.com **tel:** 214 999 3000 **fax:** 214 999 4667

**Managing Partners:** Stephen D Good
Number of partners: 141   Number of lawyers: 235 (includes partners)

## Firm Overview:

For over 100 years, Gardere has been providing comprehensive litigation and business solutions to leading domestic and international companies. With more than 230 lawyers in four offices, complex challenges are crafted into sustainable solutions for clients across a broad spectrum of industries, including energy, hospitality, retail, private equity, construction, real estate, technology, financial services, and manufacturing. The firm's distinguishing traits–integrity, excellence, competitiveness and tireless service–make the difference when it comes to delivering the best results. Gardere creates and maintains client relationships that go beyond providing legal counsel. Gardere attorneys work to become a strategic partner, integral to clients' success.

## Main Areas of Practice:

**Bankruptcy & Business Reorganization:**
Represents debtors and creditors in dealing with problem loans, business reorganizations, workouts and private and public debt restructuring, Chapter 11 reorganizations, asset purchases from bankrupt estates, and creditor representation across a range of industries, including airlines, oil and gas, health care, technology, real estate, restaurants and retail.
**Contact:** Richard M Roberson

**Corporate:**
Counsels clients on strategic planning, outsourcing and a full range of issues involving business operations. Attorneys are recognized for their aggressive approach to finding meaningful solutions, and provide counsel in the areas of investment partnerships, major business transactions, public and private offerings, start-up ventures and private equity transactions, among others.
**Contacts:** Lawrence B Goldstein; Daniel L Cohen

**Energy:**
Utilizes multidisciplinary backgrounds of 60 attorneys with experience and skills specific to the energy industry. The team understands nearly every segment of energy and represents a range of participants from multinational corporations to individuals, well-head to burner tip and turbine to power plug.
**Contact:** Douglas K Eyberg

**Environmental:**
Includes team members from varied backgrounds including federal and state environmental agencies, the judiciary, Fortune 500® companies and academia, and contains a specialized Climate Change Task Force assisting clients with due diligence related to compliance issues.
**Contact:** Richard O Faulk

**Government Affairs:**
Navigates the bureaucracy to ensure clients have a voice in government and achieve results. The firm's lobby and legal team, recognized among the best in Texas, has extensive experience representing clients in Texas and across the country before state legislatures, regulatory agencies, courts, county and city governments and local boards and commissions.
**Contact:** Kimberly A Yelkin

**Intellectual Property:**
Handles domestic and global patent law issues, IP litigation and general IP matters, including trademark, copyright, licensing, trade secret, antitrust and unfair competition. The group's collective background includes business, science and engineering, providing clients with legal advisors who possess a unique understanding of complex IP issues and the strategic experience necessary to achieve results.
**Contact:** Kenneth R Glaser

**Labor & Employment:**
Provides counsel and litigation expertise on a national basis involving the National Labor Relations Act, Fair Labor Standards Act and individual and class action employment discrimination suits. Attorneys advise clients on the implications of corporate reductions in force, reorganizations, acquisitions and relocations, as well as employment forms, contracts, executive compensation, severance agreements, non-competes and employment policies. This group includes a full-service immigration practice.
**Contact:** Douglas D Haloftis

**Real Estate & Construction:**
Leads clients through changes in the real estate market and the varied sources for capital and development growth in domestic and international markets. The team is at the forefront of these changes, playing major roles in portfolio acquisitions, dispositions and financings in North America and around the world.
**Contact:** D Steven Henry; Kevin L Kelley; John W Slates

**Tax:**
Assists clients in all areas of local, state, federal and international tax in connection with reorganizations, spin-offs, mergers, asset acquisitions, employee benefits and executive compensation issues, partnerships, tax-exempt entities, real estate, oil & gas, bankruptcy and other matters. The group also provides unique expertise in international transfer pricing matters.
**Contact:** Keith V Novick

**Trial:**
Focuses on litigation in U.S. district courts and all state courts, as well as appellate matters in federal and state courts of appeal and the U.S. Supreme Court. Service also includes representation before various state, national and international arbitration boards. Practice areas within the section include antitrust, appellate, class action, construction, family law, energy, technology, construction, environmental/toxic tort, government contracts, IP, maritime, Medicaid fraud, oil and gas, products liability, securities, insurance and labor and employment.
**Contacts:** Mark W Bayer; Geoffrey H Bracken; Scott L Davis; Dwight M Francis; John W Slates; T Michael Wall

## International Work:

Gardere was one of the first US law firms to open a full-service Mexico office. Established in 1995, Gardere, Arena y Asociados, S.C. provides comprehensive legal services to clients involved in cross-border business. Experience includes: assisting Mexican and foreign clients in acquisitions, joint ventures, private equity, and other investments; development of infrastructure projects with the Mexican government and private sector entities involving the privatization or operations of public assets; hospitality and real estate; energy; and international tax planning and litigation.

## PRACTICE AREAS

Bankruptcy & Business Reorganization
Corporate
Energy
Environmental
Government Affairs
Intellectual Property
Labor & Employment
Real Estate & Construction
Tax
Trial

## OFFICES

**AUSTIN:** One American Center, Suite 3000, 600 Congress Avenue, TX 78701-3056
Tel: 512 542 7000   Fax: 512 542 7100

**DALLAS:** Thanksgiving Tower, Suite 3000, 1601 Elm Street, TX 75201-4757
Tel: 214 999 3000   Fax: 214 999 4667

**HOUSTON:** Wells Fargo Plaza, Suite 3400, 1000 Louisiana, TX 77002-5011
Tel: 713 276 5500   Fax: 713 276 5555

The firm also has an office in Mexico City, Mexico

# GARDERE

# GIBBS & BRUNS LLP

**www.gibbsbruns.com** **tel:** 713 650 8805 **fax:** 713 750 0903

**Founding Partner:** Robin C Gibbs
**Managing Partner:** Scott A Humphries
**Client Relations:** Tanya K Urban
Number of partners: 16
Number of other lawyers: 15

## Firm Overview:

Gibbs & Bruns LLP is a premier boutique law firm engaging in high-stakes business and commercial litigation.
The firm is renowned for its signature lean trial teams and representation of both plaintiffs and defendants in
complex matters, including significant securities and institutional investor litigation, director and officer liability,
contract disputes, fraud and fiduciary claims, energy litigation, construction litigation, trust and estate litigation,
antitrust litigation, legal and professional malpractice, and partnership disputes.
The Financial Times named Gibbs & Bruns the top U.S. Litigation Firm in its "US Innovative Lawyers 2012"
special report. The National Law Journal named Gibbs & Bruns to its inaugural "Litigation Boutiques Hot List,"
2012. The American Lawyer named Gibbs & Bruns one of the top four litigation boutiques in the U.S., 2009.
Gibbs & Bruns was twice-named to The National Law Journal's "Plaintiffs Hot List."

## Main Areas of Practice:

### High-Stakes Commercial Litigation:

- **$8.5 Billion Settlement with Bank of America for Institutional Investors.**
Secured an $8.5 billion settlement with Bank of America on behalf of 22 institutional investors in connection with 530 securitization pools that issued Countrywide-affiliated mortgage-backed securities. As has been disclosed in the national media, the firm is pursuing similar claims against other banks and issuers on behalf of its clients.
- **17 Institutional Investors Obtain Agreement From ResCap Debtors to Stipulate to $8.7 Billion Allowed Claim for RMBS Trusts in ResCap Bankruptcy.**
17 institutional investors (RMBS Holders) represented by Gibbs & Bruns and Ropes & Gray achieved an agreement with Residential Capital LLC and its affiliated debtors to grant an $8.7 billion allowed claim to 392 residential mortgage backed securities trusts issued by affiliates of the Debtors during the period from 2004 to 2008. The RMBS Holders hold, or manage investments for holders of, more than $13 billion in outstanding RMBS securities issued by over 350 of the Covered Trusts. The Debtors filed a motion to approve the settlement agreement within days of the petition date. The Debtors believe this settlement

is in the best interests of the Debtors, their estates, their creditors, and other stakeholders, will avoid all-consuming litigation, and will assist in the orderly confirmation of a chapter 11 plan. The matter is set for an approval hearing in March 2013.
- **$1.7 Billion Settlement for Huntsman in Fraud and Tortious Interference Case.**
Achieved a mid-trial $1.7 billion settlement win for client Huntsman Corporation on claims of tortious interference and fraud in connection with Huntsman's failed merger with Hexion. This settlement included the largest cash settlement ever paid in a failed leveraged buyout. Under the terms of the settlement, Credit Suisse and Deutsche Bank paid Huntsman $632 million cash and provided Huntsman with $1.1 billion of favorable financing through issuance of notes and bonds.
- **$600+ million in Settlements - In re National Century Financial Enterprises, Inc.**
Prosecuting $1.6 billion in securities fraud claims on behalf of 26 groups of institutional investors against accountants, trustees, and investment banks involved in the issuance of the debt securities of National Century Financial Enterprises. See In re National Century Financial Enterprises Litigation, 541 F. Supp. 2d 986 (S.D. Ohio 2007). To date, the firm achieved

over $600 million in settlements on behalf of its clients, and the case remains pending against Credit Suisse and the founders of NCFE.
- **$196 million Judgment in Fraud Case.**
Secured a $196 million judgment for Plaintiff client against Dallas billionaire Trevor Rees-Jones and energy giant Devon Energy Production Company, L.P. The fraud and breach of fiduciary duty judgment was based on a verdict reached by a Houston jury in March 2011 following a five-week trial. Defendants appealed. Following oral arguments in the 14th Court of Appeals, the parties reached a confidential, mutually-acceptable settlement that fully resolved the matter.

**Contact:** Scott Humphries, Managing Partner
**Tel:** 713 751 5248
**Email:** shumphries@gibbsbruns.com

### PRACTICE AREAS

Commercial Litigation
Securities Litigation
Energy Litigation
Appellate
Arbitration

### OFFICES

TEXAS

**HOUSTON:** 1100 Louisiana, Suite 5300, 77002
Tel: 713 650 8805  Fax: 713 750 0903

# GRUBER HURST JOHANSEN HAIL SHANK LLP

www.ghjhlaw.com

**OFFICES**

TEXAS

**DALLAS:** 1445 Ross Avenue, Suite 2500, TX 75202
Tel: 214 855 6800   Fax: 214 855 6808
Email: smacey@ghjhlaw.com

## Firm Overview:

Gruber Hurst Johansen Hail Shank LLP has built a highly regarded reputation based on understanding the business needs of its clients when facing or pursuing litigation. Aligning those operational strategies with legal strategies often results in greater efficiencies in preparing for trial and resolving disputes, both in the courtroom and at the bargaining table. This approach also means that the firm has the flexibility and freedom to work with clients on various fee structures, sharing in the risk and rewards by maintaining a stake in the outcome. This philosophy formed the foundation of the firm in 2006, and speaks to the collective experience and support of each of the firm's attorneys to practice law in a fundamentally different way.

## Main Areas of Practice:

The firm concentrates on complex business litigation, handling a wide range of commercial cases involving contract disputes, fraud and breach of fiduciary duty claims, securities, labor and employment, intellectual property, products liability and other claims for both defendants and plaintiffs. While this work typically encompasses jury trials, bench trials, and summary judgments, the firm's attorneys also handle arbitrations before the American Arbitration Association and the Financial Industry Regulatory Authority. Clients include leading companies – large and small – and individuals in industries as varied as financial services, private equity, real estate, manufacturing, professional services, insurance, energy, retail and technology.
The examples of the firm's work for clients in these key areas of practice and industries include:

### Commercial Litigation:

- Representation in claims involving a breach of a non-disclosure and confidentiality agreement on behalf of an entrepreneur against a publicly traded financial company, fund managers and venture capitalists
- Representation of a physician practice for breach of a service agreement and conversion against radiology center and physician practice management company
- Defense of a large retail/wholesale product manufacturer against hotel chain that claimed the manufacturer's products were defective
- Representation of a publicly traded food manufacturer/distributor in defending claims and prosecuting counterclaims related to the acquisition of a subsidiary company
- Arbitration on behalf of the purchaser of steel company against seller of the company related to post-acquisition covenants and seller misrepresentations
- Defense of a publicly traded software manufacturer and seller against claims of defective product filed by large employment organization
- Represented Hollywood actor, director and producer in high profile litigation in Los Angeles Superior Court. Case was ancillary to litigation between motion picture production company and European file distribution company involving claims of breach of contract and fraud concerning multi-picture distribution agreement
- Represented hospital in arbitration proceeding involving negligent audits of hospital resulting in $30 million overstatement of accounts receivable
- Represented prominent nationally known entrepreneur/business executive in well-publicized case arising from merger of two public technology companies in which the plaintiff alleged damages of $1 billion; obtained summary judgment for client
- Representation of several major developers on an ongoing basis in all types of litigation
- Representation of a telecom company in a multi-million dollar dispute with a service provider

### Employment Litigation:

- Defense of a large retail chain in age and FMLA claims
- Defense of a large executive search firm in FLSA claims
- Defense of FLSA class action including call centers
- Representation of labor unions in various matters, including member representation for the Texas Municipal Police Association
- Defense of a large equipment seller in sexual harassment and intentional infliction claims
- Representation of employees related to employee stock option agreements
- Representation of a terminated CEO in action for breach of severance agreement
- Defense of class action involving FLSA claims

### Energy Litigation:

- Representation of a Fortune 100 oilfield services company in cases involving the largest land-based well blowout in US history
- Representation of a Fortune 100 oilfield services company in cases involving deaths from oilfield blowouts
- Representation of various corporate entities in disputes involving ownership of large offshore wells
- Representation of oil well services companies that faced federal and state workplace safety citations and disciplinary proceedings
- Representation of a major Texas retail electric provider relating to the purchase and retail sale of electric power

### Intellectual Property Litigation:

- Representation of a developer of a graphics software file format in patent enforcement litigation
- Representation of a food product corporation in litigation regarding construction and permitted use of the company's trademark on other products
- Representation of an NFL team and its head coach and president, in defense of a copyright infringement lawsuit
- Representation of a leading national provider of telecommunications services to the inmate correctional industry in multiple patent infringement lawsuits
- Representation of specialized medical services provider in trademark infringement and false advertising litigation

### Securities Litigation:

- Representation of a publicly-traded building product manufacturer and its directors in shareholder derivative class action litigation concerning merger agreement and Shareholder Rights Plan
- Representation of a telecommunications company in defense of securities fraud litigation
- Representation of corporate officers in a 10b(5) fraud and fraudulent misrepresentation claim
- Representation of the former officers of a medical practice management company in adversary proceedings in bankruptcy court

### Clients:

Success on behalf of its clients has brought ongoing recognition for the firm and its individual attorneys. Each of the five name partners has achieved top verdicts in Texas state and federal courts and in arbitrations. Each is consistently recognized in the top tier of attorneys in Texas by their legal and business colleagues and in various publications. The firm continues to attract talented lawyers as associates and partners – lawyers who also believe in focusing on the delivery of services around the specific and distinctive interests of each client. Clients include: Aegis Communications, Inc., Capital Metropolitan Transportation Authority, CBRE/Trammell Crow, Crow Holdings, Hunt Consolidated, Jones Lang LaSalle, Kaye/Bassman International, Nabors Industries, Neiman Marcus Group, Nokia/Siemens, Oxy, Inc. and Occidental Chemical Corp., Pappas Bros., Ryan, Stream Energy, Texas Capital Bank.

GRUBER | HURST | JOHANSEN | HAIL | SHANK

# HANKINSON LLP

**www.**hankinsonlaw.com **tel:** 214 754 9190 **fax:** 214 754 9140

**Name Partner:** Deborah Hankinson
**Managing Partner:** Rick Thompson
Number of attorneys: 8

**OFFICES**

TEXAS
**DALLAS:** 750 North St. Paul Street, Suite 1800, TX 75201
Tel: 214 754 9190   Fax: 214 754 9140
Email : info@hankinsonlaw.com

## Firm Overview:

Dallas-based Hankinson LLP, the preeminent civil appellate firm in the Southwest, was founded in 2008 to represent national and regional companies, governmental bodies and individuals in trial and appellate matters, in addition to providing mediation and arbitration services. Outstanding briefing and oral advocacy skills are mainstays of the firm. Led by name partner Deborah Hankinson, the firm's attorneys include Carl Cecere, Ryan Clinton, Brett Kutnick, Joseph Morris, Stephanie Nelson, Jennifer Stagen and Rick Thompson, with each attorney bringing a unique and valuable perspective to the practice of appellate law. Ms Hankinson, Mr Clinton, Mr Kutnick and Mr Thompson are all Board Certified in Civil Appellate Law by the Texas Board of Legal Specialization. Only attorneys who have proven the highest standards of professional expertise qualify to receive board certification in their chosen field of practice. Ms Hankinson is a former justice of the Supreme Court of Texas and Texas 5th District Court of Appeals in Dallas, providing her with invaluable insights into how an appellate judge views issues. In addition to her appellate practice, she is a neutral in arbitration proceedings and is a sought-after mediator. Assisting in all stages of the litigation and appeals process, as well as in arbitrations, is Joseph Morris, a respected retired Texas 5th Court of Appeals justice and former district court judge. During his 25 years on the bench, he authored more than 2,000 judicial opinions covering countless legal issues related to property rights, corporate governance, contract rights, employee-employer relations, torts, and statutory claims.

## Main Areas of Practice:

### Appeals:

One of the most well-known and respected appellate firms in Texas, Hankinson LLP advocates for clients by presenting persuasive and successful arguments before the Supreme Court of Texas and intermediate Texas appellate courts, as well as the US Courts of Appeals and the US Supreme Court. The firm represents Fortune 500 companies, regional organizations and partnerships, governmental bodies and individuals in a variety of matters, including complex business and contractual disputes, oil and gas issues, intellectual property matters, professional liability issues, and concerns unique to governmental entities. In addition to former Justice Deborah Hankinson and retired Justice Joseph Morris, Hankinson LLP attorneys include Ryan Clinton and Rick Thompson, both former Texas Assistant Solicitors General, Carl Cecere, Brett Kutnick, Stephanie Nelson, and Jennifer Stagen. The firm's highly skilled attorneys provide unique expertise and judicial knowledge that enable them to strategically position legal issues on appeal, craft meticulous briefs, and present each client's case with force and precision. With a broad-based reputation for ingenuity and excellence, the firm often works in tandem with trial teams from other law firms in the trial courts to consult on appellate strategy and briefs, or to assist in preparation for oral argument. The firm's attorneys also handle and consult on procedures that originate at the appellate level, including mandamus petitions and writs of certiorari. For critically important cases, the firm will consider filing or contributing to amicus curiae briefs.

### Pretrial & Trial Strategy:

Hankinson LLP frequently is retained to help shape cases for trial and to ensure a strong foundation in the event of an appeal. Working in collaboration with these outside trial teams, the firm's attorneys bring an added dimension to trial strategy and the litigation process by leveraging their deep courtroom experience and appellate expertise. During the pretrial process, Hankinson LLP attorneys often are called on to draft, respond to, and provide arguments on major dispositive motions, including summary judgment and Daubert motions. They also consult on preservation of error, crafting trial briefs, and drafting jury charges or findings of fact and conclusions of law. In addition, the firm offers ongoing guidance on obtaining evidence that provides context for the storylines that help set the stage for success in the event of an appeal. Deborah Hankinson and Joseph Morris draw on their judicial experience in helping trial counsel anticipate court rulings in order to develop effective trial and appellate strategies. Once a trial has concluded, they are frequently responsible for developing or responding to post-trial motions and ensuring record preservation. Hankinson LLP also provides additional circumscribed services to potential litigants and trial teams. Before a lawsuit is filed, the firm evaluates potential claims at both the trial and appellate levels for the benefit of litigants or their trial counsel.

### Mediation & Arbitration:

The firm's mediation and arbitration practice is focused on fully understanding the needs and goals of parties involved in litigation as well as pre-suit conflict resolution. This provides the groundwork for working creatively towards mutually beneficial solutions in complex, multi-party mediations relating to diverse industries, businesses, and circumstances. Deborah Hankinson and Joseph Morris both excel at untangling difficult, multifaceted issues and providing parties with evaluative insights and options that break deadlocks and move them forward. Their work is guided by the foundational precepts of speed, economy, and justice that apply to arbitration proceedings and ensure the overall integrity of the process. Ms Hankinson, an American Arbitration Association (AAA) neutral and frequent arbitrator, is an experienced chair of arbitration panels whose opinions are clear and thoroughly address the parties' contentions. The group frequently consults on and assists in evaluating settlement options and negotiating strategies both before a lawsuit is filed and during the pendency of a lawsuit.

# HEIM, PAYNE & CHORUSH, LLP

www.hpcllp.com **tel:** 713 221 2000 **fax:** 713 2212021

Number of partners: 6
Number of associates: 4

## Firm Overview:

Heim, Payne & Chorush L.L.P. specializes exclusively in intellectual property litigation and antitrust lawsuits involving intellectual property. Mr Heim and Mr Payne have been named in *H Texas Magazine*'s "Best Lawyers in Houston" edition, and each of the partners in the firm has been named a Super Lawyer or a Rising Star by *Texas Monthly* magazine. The firm's Partners have previously worked together for several years on patent and antitrust cases at a predecessor firm, the result of which was the resolution of several nationally publicized cases. The firm takes pride in its ability to partner with other attorneys and firms to bring the best possible trial team together for the benefit of the client.

The firm represents plaintiffs and defendants in patent and antitrust litigation in a broad range of technologies including microprocessors, computer architecture, memory control systems, cellular telephone systems, data transmission systems, Internet radio, database caching software, on-line gaming systems, computer controlled lighting, pharmaceuticals, drilling and other downhole systems, stents and natural gas conversion systems. Their attorneys have a wide variety of technical backgrounds allowing them to handle all facets of intellectual property litigation. They handle every aspect of the most complicated patent disputes for some of the largest energy and technology firms. In addition, they often represent individuals and smaller companies against behemoths of industry.

The firm prefers to share the risks and rewards with its clients, thereby aligning its interests with its clients to produce a more synergistic relationship. They devote most of their time to litigation under fee agreements that link their fees to the results they achieve. They have developed fee arrangements with clients that range from partial contingent fees that reduce their hourly rates for a stake in the outcome, to full contingent arrangements where they receive no hourly fees. On the defense side, the firm is open to using reverse contingent fee arrangements where the amount it saves its clients determines its compensation.

They have found that their experience in handling contingent fee cases enables them to more efficiently manage hourly work. They treat every case as a representative model of their abilities and integrity. That is why so many clients and co-counsel contact them when they have a new case.

## Main Areas of Practice:

### Intellectual Property Litigation:

The firm provides counsel to large and small business entities as well as individuals at both the state and federal levels regarding intellectual property litigation. This includes patent infringement, patent licensing, trade secret and unfair competition matters, as well as antitrust lawsuits. The firm employs attorneys holding various types of technical degrees, and having the legal and technical expertise to handle highly complex cases.

### Michael F Heim - Partner

Specializes exclusively in intellectual property litigation and antitrust lawsuits involving intellectual property. Mr Heim represents plaintiffs and defendants throughout the United States in patent litigation in a wide range of technologies including microprocessors, computer architecture, memory control systems, cellular telephone systems, data transmission systems, on-line gaming systems, database caching software, logging-while drilling systems and a host of other high-tech technologies. He has expertise in evaluating patent portfolios and developing strategies to enforce and license those portfolios. He's a skilled courtroom litigator, able to understand and explain highly complex technical and legal issues to judges and jurors.

Mr Heim has received recognition throughout the patent community for his abilities and for the significant results he has achieved on behalf of his clients.

### Leslie V Payne - Partner

Specializes in prosecuting and defending actions in Federal and State courts (at the trial and appellate levels) in the areas of patent infringement, unfair competition, trademark infringement, copyright infringement, trade secret misappropriation, breach of contract, non-compete covenants, tortuous interference, fraud and other areas. Mr Payne also has extensive experience negotiating intellectual property contracts, including patent licenses, technology transfer agreements, supply and manufacturing agreements and research and development agreements. In addition, Mr Payne has represented clients in many reexamination proceedings at the U.S. Patent and Trademark Office. He has represented clients in many different engineering and science disciplines, including the mechanical, electrical, computer and chemical arts. Mr Payne is admitted to practice before the U.S. Patent and Trademark Office, various United States District Courts, the U.S. Court of Appeals for the Federal circuit and the Texas State Courts.

### Russell A Chorush - Partner

Dr Chorush specializes in patent infringement and antitrust cases in the pharmaceutical industry. While Mr Chorush has represented clients in many different engineering and science disciplines, his specialty lies in the chemical arts. He has prosecuted and defended clients in the technology arena ranging from patent infringement, unfair competition, trade secret misappropriation, breach of contract, non-compete covenants, tortious interference and other areas. Dr chorush is admitted to practice before the United States Patent and Trademark office, the United States District Courts for the Southern and Eastern Districts of Texas and the Texas State Courts.

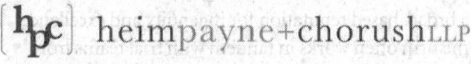

# JACKSON WALKER LLP

**www.**jw.com   **tel:** 214 953 6000   **fax:** 214 953 5822

**Managing Partner:** C Wade Cooper
Number of partners: 235
Number of lawyers: 345
Languages: *Chinese (Mandarin), English, French, Greek, Indonesian, Portuguese, Russian, Spanish*

## Firm Overview:

Jackson Walker LLP is a Texas-based law firm with a national presence and global reach. The firm was founded in 1887 and for more than 125 years has represented companies that have changed the face of Texas business. Today, the firm has 340+ attorneys and represents Fortune 500 companies, multinational corporations, major financial institutions, and a wide range of publicly traded corporations and closely held businesses.

### Committed to client service:

Jackson Walker attorneys don't see clients as interchangeable. They take the time to understand their clients' business goals, challenges, and opportunities, and they tailor their legal services to what works best for each. That's one reason Jackson Walker's clients are so loyal. One-third of the firm's legal work comes from clients who have been with the firm for ten or more years. They keep coming back to Jackson Walker because they trust in the quality of the work and they appreciate the commitment to individualized client service.

### Delivering value:

Jackson Walker provides clients comprehensive services in a broad range of practice areas, and the firm's reach extends around the globe. In fact, Jackson Walker attorneys have represented clients in more than 85 countries and territories, and the firm is a member of Globalaw, a worldwide network of law firms with offices throughout the US and in over 160 cities internationally.

Because the firm has chosen to keep its offices in Texas, it has lower overhead costs than just about every firm its size or larger. In fact, both PricewaterhouseCoopers and Citi Research have cited Jackson Walker as a Best Practice model in overhead cost structure compared to peers. The firm passes that value along to clients by keeping its rates competitive. Jackson Walker's cost structure also means the firm attracts and retains top-notch talent, so clients get the benefit of top-tier legal expertise without breaking their budgets.

### Providing expertise:

It's been said that great lawyers are made by great clients. Jackson Walker knows its clients, knows their businesses, and remembers every day what a privilege it is to help them achieve their business goals. Jackson Walker's attorneys also pride themselves on being the kind of lawyers clients enjoy working with. In fact, the firm has always been and remains today a very collegial place. Its longtime unofficial motto is: "We take our work seriously, but not ourselves."

Jackson Walker's attorneys believe that the service, value, and expertise they provide for clients speak for themselves. And sometimes, their clients speak for them, as in these excerpts from client reviews:

- "Jackson Walker lawyers are very efficient in how they perform and very attuned to the needs of the client."
- "They know me better than I know myself."
- "There was never a time they weren't brilliantly prepared with every detail."
- "I would use no one else."
- "They get great results."
- "First-rate service that was both strategic and cost effective…"
- "Truly interested in our business…"
- "An excellent combination of expertise, professionalism, and results…"

## PRACTICE AREAS

Bankruptcy
Corporate & Securities
Energy
Environmental & Legislative
Employee Benefits & Executive Compensation
Finance
Healthcare
Intellectual Property
Labor & Employment
Land Use
Litigation
Real Estate
Tax
Wealth Planning

## OFFICES

**TEXAS**

**AUSTIN:** 100 Congress Avenue, Suite 1100, TX 78701
Tel: 512 236 2000   Fax: 512 236 2002
Email: mdow@jw.com

**DALLAS:** 901 Main Street, Suite 6000, TX 75202
Tel: 214 953 6000   Fax: 214 953 5822
Email: dmoran@jw.com

**FORT WORTH:** 777 Main Street, Suite 2100, TX 76102
Tel: 817 334 7200   Fax: 817 334 7290
Email: shalsey@jw.com

**HOUSTON:** 1401 McKinney Street, Suite 1900, TX 77010
Tel : 713 752 4200   Fax : 713 752 4221
Email: knondorf@jw.com

**SAN ANGELO:** 301 W. Beauregard Avenue, Suite 200, TX 76903
Tel : 325 481 2550   Fax : 325 481 2552
Email: dgriffis@jw.com

**SAN ANTONIO:** 112 E. Pecan Street, Suite 2400, TX 78205
Tel : 210 978 7700   Fax : 210 978 7790
Email: ptobin@jw.com

**TEXARKANA:** 6004 Summerfield Drive, TX 75503
Tel: 903 255 3250   Fax: 903 255 3265
Email: dfolsom@jw.com

JW | JACKSON WALKER L.L.P.
TEXAS BASED. GLOBAL REACH.

# **KANE RUSSELL COLEMAN & LOGAN PC**

www.krcl.com **tel:** 214 777 4200  **fax:** 214 777 4299

**Chairman:** Raymond J Kane
**Managing Partners/Board of Directors:** Raymond J Kane, Kenneth C Johnston, Zachary T Mayer, Lawrence T Bowman, Bruce M Flowers, Forrest M Smith, Robert N LeMay, George H Barber
Number of partners: 46   Number of lawyers: 85
Languages: *Chinese (Cantonese and Mandarin), English, Spanish*

**Firm Overview:**
KRCL is a full service business law firm with offices in Dallas and Houston. Formed in 1992 with five lawyers, today KRCL has 85 lawyers. The firm provides professional services for clients ranging from Fortune 500 companies to small cap public and private companies and entrepreneurs. KRCL handles transactional, litigation and bankruptcy matters throughout the US and China. The firm's philosophy is to build long-term relationships by providing high-caliber legal representation in a cost-effective, client-responsive manner. Maintaining this philosophy for over twenty years, the marketplace has recognized KRCL as one of the top midsize business law firms in the US.

**Main Areas of Practice:**

**Insolvency, Bankruptcy & Creditor Rights:**
4 Partners; 6 Associates
- Represented second lienholder in northeast automotive retail bankruptcy, which significantly increased the Debtor's value by causing the cessation of operations
- Represented 36 Official Unsecured Creditor Committees in fifteen states
- Represented Regions Bank in extensive pre-bankruptcy and post-bankruptcy negotiations leading to significant reduction in debt and restructured loan terms with debtor
**Key Clients:** MEMA Financial Services Group, Inc.; Pentair Inc., Regions Bank
**Contact:** Joseph M Coleman **Tel:** 214 777 4280
**Email:** jcoleman@krcl.com

**Commercial Real Estate:**
10 Partners; 8 Associates
- Represented the purchaser and condominium declarant and unit owners in the acquisition of a 530,000 square foot office complex in Irving, Texas, including related formation of office condominium regime and lease of approximately 300,000 square feet for the headquarters of a credit tenant
- Represented Trammell Crow Company-affiliate in the acquisition of an office park located in Malvern Pennsylvania, construction of office complex (including $50m construction loan), and 300,000 square foot office lease for headquarters for a publicly-traded pharmaceutical company
**Key Clients:** Home Depot U.S.A., Inc.; Trammell Crow Company; Citigroup, Inc
**Contact:** Raymond J Kane **Tel:** 214 777 4290
**Email:** rkane@krcl.com

**Litigation: Commercial & Business:**
29 Partners; 27 Associates
- Represented banks and a bank holding company in debit card class-action litigation. In Re Checking Account Overdraft Litigation (MDL 2036)
- Represented a multitude of lenders and other parties in connection with the defense of claims and other issues in the Stanford Ponzi fallout. In Re Stanford Entities Securities Litigation (MDL 2099)
- Represented a bank in an appeal related to an unconstitutional taking of property by an equity receiver in an SEC proceeding
- Represented multiple banks in class actions alleging that ATM networks did not comply with ADA requirements
**Key Clients:** BBVA Compass Bank; Branch Banking & Trust Company; Capital One; Comerica Bank; Regions Bank; Trustmark National Bank
**Contact:** Kenneth C Johnston **Tel:** 214 777 4222
**Email:** kjohnston@krcl.com

**Business, Corporate Finance & Transactions:**
12 Partners; 3 Associates
- Represented an international energy company in a multi-party acquisition with an aggregate value of $150m involving eight foreign jurisdictions
- Represented Chinese investors in the investment of $50m in US based oil and gas properties
- Represented the European purchaser in a $630m acquisition of control of three office buildings, two in Chicago and one in New York City, each consisting of approximately 1,000,000 square feet
**Key Clients:** Renovo Capital, LLC; MTS Energy LLC; Trinity Regional Development, LLC
**Contact:** Patrick V Stark **Tel:** 214 777 4260
**Email:** rstark@krcl.com

**Human Resources & Employment:**
2 Partners; 2 Associates
- Represented a company in a suit brought to contain the theft and misuse of confidential information by an ex-employee wherein the firm obtained a contested temporary restraining order and obtained an agreement to not use any information nor solicit clients
- Represented a court reporting service company in a lawsuit filed under the Fair Labor Standards Act alleging unfair pay practices with potential industry wide consequences
- Represented a law firm in a lawsuit seeking to hold the client and a partner liable for alleged violations of civil rights based on actions taken in furtherance of their services to a client
**Key Clients:** Plustar, Inc.; TriVest Residential, LLC; Etheridge Printing Company
**Contact:** Arthur V Lambert **Tel:** 214 777 425
**Email:** alambert@krcl.com

**Banking & Financial Services:**
23 Partners; 11 Associates
- Represented bank in resolution of Go-Zone bond hospitality transactions in the amount of $50m
- Represented bank in syndicated credit for development of public and private improvements of prominent local town square in the aggregate amount of approximately $65m
- Represented banks in mortgage warehouse participation purchase and loan facilities in the aggregate amount of approximately $120m
- Represented banks in phased industrial development transactions in the aggregate amount of $55m
**Key Clients:** BBVA Compass Bank; Branch Banking & Trust Company; Capital One; Green Bank; Regions Bank; Trustmark National Bank
**Contact:** Gordon B Russell **Tel:** 214 777 4283
**Email:** grussell@krcl.com

# LOCKE LORD LLP

www.lockelord.com **tel:** 214 740 8000 **fax:** 214 740 8800

**Chair:** Jerry K Clements
Number of partners: 317  Number of lawyers: 645
Languages: *Arabic, Chinese (Cantonese, Mandarin), English, Farsi, Finnish, French, German, Hebrew, Hindi, Italian, Japanese, Korean, Polish, Portuguese, Russian, Spanish, Urdu, Vietnamese*

**Firm Overview:**
Locke Lord LLP is a full-service international law firm with offices in 11 US cities, London and Hong Kong. The firm has developed its London office into a comprehensive team of more than 30 lawyers and continues strategic growth efforts in the UK and Asia. Locke Lord attorneys have earned a solid reputation in complex litigation, regulatory and transactional work, building collaborative relationships with clients and crafting creative solutions to meet clients' long-term strategic goals. Firm clients range from *Fortune* 500 and middle market public and private companies to start-ups and emerging businesses.

## Main Areas of Practice:

### Corporate & Transactional:
101 partners; 213 total attorneys
Locke Lord attorneys represent US and foreign companies in a wide variety of corporate transactions. They have experience advising clients in the areas of capital markets, mergers and acquisitions, corporate trust, corporate governance, franchise, global investment, investment adviser and fund management, private equity, public finance and tax. The firm's transactional practice spans a wide range of industries, including energy, insurance, banking and financial services, healthcare, real estate and REITs, entertainment and media, technology and education.
**Contact:** Don M Glendenning **Tel:** 214 740 8623
**Email:** dglendenning@lockelord.com
**Contact:** Michael K Renetzky **Tel:** 312 443 1823
**Email:** mrenetzky@lockelord.com

### Finance, Banking & Real Estate:
46 partners; 72 total attorneys
Working closely with the firm's bankruptcy, restructuring and insolvency, tax, REIT and other practice groups, Locke Lord's Real Estate and Finance Team focuses on acquisitions and divestitures, construction, environmental, hospitality, creditors' rights, entity formation, land use and development, leasing and management, sales and purchases and transportation matters. They have closed transactions in all US jurisdictions, as well as a number of cross-border transactions. The firm's attorneys also regularly represent banks and financial institutions in transactional, regulatory and litigation-related matters. Locke Lord represents organizations in lending and finance transactions, as well as their regulatory, structuring and corporate matters.
**Contact:** Louis S Cohen **Tel:** 312 443 0298
**Email:** lcohen@lockelord.com

### Litigation & Dispute Resolution:
141 partners; 294 total attorneys
Locke Lord attorneys provide counseling, mediation, arbitration and litigation experience in all major areas of law that impact business, including contracts, labor and employment, environmental, fraud, antitrust, tax, technology, trademark, securities, intellectual property, class action defense, consumer finance, insolvency, insurance and reinsurance, white collar criminal defense and internal investigations and most other types of disputes. Firm attorneys try cases in federal, state and local courts across the country and represent clients before state and federal agencies. They arbitrate disputes in private proceedings and before organizations such as the AAA, ICC and FINRA. In addition, Locke Lord is home to a recognized appellate team with decades of experience in handling appeals and developing strategies for clients.
**Contact:** Thomas J Cunningham **Tel:** 312 443 1731
**Email:** tcunningham@lockelord.com
**Contact:** John P McDonald **Tel:** 214 740 8758
**Email:** jpmcdonald@lockelord.com

### Intellectual Property:
29 partners; 63 total attorneys
Locke Lord's intellectual property attorneys provide assistance to companies in a wide range of industries in the acquisition, development, protection and enforcement of IP rights. The firm regularly counsels clients in all aspects of patent, trademark, trade secret, copyright, licensing and technology law, and has a nationwide team experienced in social media, advertising and e-commerce matters. In addition, Locke Lord's IP attorneys have extensive experience with respect to Hatch-Waxman patent infringement litigation involving pharmaceuticals.
**Contact:** John F Sweeney **Tel:** 212 415 8625
**Email:** jsweeney@lockelord.com

## PRACTICE AREAS

Appellate
Bankruptcy, Restructuring & Insolvency
Business Litigation & Dispute Resolution
Consumer Finance
Corporate
Employee Benefits
Energy
Environmental
Financial Services
Healthcare
Insurance & Reinsurance
Intellectual Property
Labor & Employment
Public Law
Real Estate
Regulatory

## OFFICES

### CALIFORNIA
**LOS ANGELES:** 300 S. Grand Avenue, Suite 2600, CA 90071
Tel: 213 485 1500  Fax: 213 485 1200

**SACRAMENTO:** 500 Capitol Mall, Suite 1800, CA 95814
Tel: 916 930 2500  Fax: 916 930 2501

**SAN FRANCISCO:** 44 Montgomery Street, Suite 2400, CA 94104
Tel: 415 318 8810  Fax: 415 676 5816

### DISTRICT OF COLUMBIA
**WASHINGTON DC:** 701 8th Street, N.W., Suite 700, DC 20001
Tel: 202 220 6900  Fax: 202 220 6945

### GEORGIA
**ATLANTA:** Terminus 200, Suite 1200, 3333 Piedmont Road NE, GA 30305
Tel: 404 870 4600  Fax: 404 872 5547

### ILLINOIS
**CHICAGO:** 111 South Wacker Drive, IL 60606
Tel: 312 443 0700  Fax: 312 443 0336

### LOUISIANA
**NEW ORLEANS:** 601 Poydras Street, Suite 2660, LA 70130
Tel: 504 558 5100  Fax: 504 558 5200

### NEW YORK
**NEW YORK:** Three World Financial Center, NY 10281-2101
Tel: 212 415 8600  Fax: 212 303 2754

### TEXAS
**AUSTIN:** One American Center, 600 Congress, Suite 2200, TX 78701
Tel: 512 305 4700  Fax: 512 305 4800

**DALLAS:** 2200 Ross Avenue, Suite 2200, TX 75201
Tel: 214 740 8000  Fax: 214 740 8800

**HOUSTON:** 2800 JPMorgan Chase Tower, 600 Travis, TX 77002
Tel: 713 226 1200  Fax: 713 223 3717

## INTERNATIONAL OFFICES
The firm also has offices in Hong Kong and London

# LYNN TILLOTSON PINKER & COX LLP

www.lynnllp.com **tel:** 214 981 3800 **fax:** 214 981 3839

**Managing Partner:** Eric W Pinker
**Senior Partners:** Michael P Lynn, Jeffrey M Tillotson, Eric W Pinker, John T (Trey) Cox III
Number of partners: 13
Number of lawyers: 26
Languages: *English, German, Hebrew, Italian, Portuguese, Spanish, Swahili*

### Firm Overview:

Lynn Tillotson Pinker & Cox, LLP is a nationally-recognized commercial litigation boutique in Dallas, Texas. LTPC offers a level of commercial trial experience that few firms can match. The attorneys of LTPC regularly handle 'bet-the-company' commercial litigation. In fact, LTPC attorneys have taken more than 150 complex commercial cases to trial or arbitration since its inception in 1993. All of LTPC's partners and associates have extensive actual courtroom experience.

### Main Areas of Practice:

**Business Litigation:**
13 partners; 34 fee earners
- Representation of ACS and board members in litigation seeking to enjoin Xerox's approximately $9 billion merger with ACS
- Successful representation of GE Capital to recover money embezzled from GECC and then distributed as part of an effort to repay investors in a *Ponzi* scheme. This case posed a significant obstacle to recovery because the money was quickly distributed to third parties after it was embezzled
- Representation of the primary layer of insurers syndicated by Certain Underwriters at Lloyd's of London in connection with multiple insurance coverage and bad faith claims made by policyholders in connection with the 2008 landfall of Hurricane Ike.
- Successful defense of law firm against claims that former attorneys were owed millions of dollars in bonuses based on their work in a patent licensing matter. One matter resulted in an arbitration award for the law firm, while the other matter was disposed of on summary judgment
- Recovered more than $45 million in connection with successful representation of bankruptcy trustee in suit to recover dividends and set aside related-party transactions

**Key Clients:** XTO; Energy Transfer Partners; Certain Underwriters at Lloyd's of London; Citadel Investment Group, LLC; Frito-Lay; GE Capital Corp.; Inppamet, SA; Nexstar Broadcasting Group; ORIX USA Corp.; Rent-A-Center; Southwest Airlines Co.; The TCW Group, Inc.; Time-Warner Cable.
**Contact:** Trey Cox **Tel:** 214 981 3813
**Email:** tcox@lynnllp.com

**IP Litigation:**
7 partners; 15 fee earners
- Representation of Mary Kay Inc. against unauthorized re-seller of cosmetic products on the Internet. The firm obtained a $1.3 million jury verdict after two weeks of trial. In addition to the jury verdict, the court awarded permanent injunctive relief in Mary Kay's favor against the defendants
- Representation of Mannatech, Inc. in enforcing a patent portfolio that supports its principal product line (AmbrotoseTM), which has accounted for more than $1 billion in total sales. The firm obtained a judgment in Mannatech's favor after a jury trial, enjoining the defendant from falsely advertising the nature, characteristics, and/or qualities of their client's products
- Representation of Motorola, Inc. in an international patent dispute with Research In Motion involving more than one dozen telecommunications-related patents

**Key Clients:** Mannatech, Inc.; Mary Kay Inc. Motorola, Inc.
**Contact:** Eric Pinker **Tel:** 214 981 3837
**Email:** epnker@lynnllp.com

LynnTillotsonPinkerCox

**PRACTICE AREAS**
Business Litigation
IP Litigation

**OFFICES**
TEXAS
**DALLAS:** 2100 Ross Avenue, Suite 2700, TX 75201
Tel: 214 981 3800 Fax: 214 981 3839
Email: mlynn@lynnllp.com

# MARTIN, DISIERE, JEFFERSON & WISDOM, LLP

www.mdjwlaw.com **tel:** 713 632 1700 **fax:** 713 222 0101

**Senior Partner:** Christopher W Martin
**Managing Partner:** Levon Hovnatanian
Number of partners: 25
Number of other lawyers: 50

## Firm Overview:

Martin, Disiere, Jefferson & Wisdom, LLP has literally redefined the parameters of Texas insurance law. The firm is a rapidly growing Texas litigation boutique with an impressive track record of solving clients' problems in first party insurance lawsuits in Texas and particularly those lawsuits alleging extra-contractual causes of action or involving complex coverage issues. The firm's lawyers have extensive experience in handling lawsuits and disputes arising out of commercial and professional liability policies including environmental and products coverage issues, primary and excess disputes and defense/indemnity coverage questions. The firm also has extensive experience defending lawsuits arising out of homeowner policies with particular expertise in SIU claims (arson, alleged theft, etc), storm (hail, hurricane, etc.) and water damage claims. Additionally, the firm regularly handles liability disputes arising out of auto, homeowner, commercial and professional policies including Stowers disputes and, has extensive experience in UM/UIM value disputes and property claims.

Matters entrusted to the firm encompass a wide range of lawsuits from large class-action insurance lawsuits and multiparty coverage disputes, to individual property damage claims, from problematic life insurance claims to pre-existing health issue-related claims. For some insurers, the firm also defends third-party claims against their insureds and, some matters involving injuries to non-subscribers' employees. These third party liability cases usually involve fatalities, mass torts, severe personal injuries or other catastrophe damage claims. In many instances, the firm is called upon to assist local and other counsel when major issues of concern for the insurance industry arise in remote parts of the state or before the various state and federal courts of appeal. In these instances the firm provides briefing, support and helps develop a litigation strategy to either resolve the lawsuit or position the matter to enhance the possibility of bringing it to a successful conclusion.

The firm is not only its clients' go-to firm in Texas, but a valued member of their state and nationwide litigation teams. The firm's Labor and Employment Section adds another dimension to the firm with three partners board certified in labor and employment law by the Texas Board of Legal Specialization and with extensive experience in representing employers in a wide variety of employment and labor disputes and lawsuits. They also provide consultation, advice and training to employers on a wide variety of topics including drug testing, hiring and termination practices, RIFs, OSHA investigations and employment training and compliance. Martin, Disiere, Jefferson & Wisdom, LLP addresses your legal problems from a different perspective – yours. They try those cases that need to be tried, help you settle those cases that need to be settled and provide advice and counsel to help avoid problems before they get started.

## Main Areas of Practice:

### IInsurance Coverage & Litigation:

The firm is one of Texas' premier first party coverage and insurance litigation firms with its lawyers handling complex coverage matters, extra-contractual lawsuits and declaratory judgment actions in Texas and in multiple jurisdictions across the country.
**Contact:** Christopher Martin or David Disiere

### Appellate:

The firm has an impressive track record of successfully handling appeals before the Texas Supreme Court, the intermediate appellate courts of Texas and the Fifth Circuit Court of Appeals. The partner in charge of the firm's Appellate Section is Levon G. Hovnatanian, who is board certified in civil appellate law and a former Chief Staff Attorney for the First Court of Appeals. Other attorneys in the section have similar impressive credentials and experience.
**Contact:** Levon Hovnatanian

### Employment & Labor:

Under the leadership of three partners who are board certified in labor and employment law by the Texas Board of Legal Specialization, the firm provides sound advice and defends employers against claims alleging discrimination, wrongful discharge, harassment, affirmative action, privacy violations, non-competition agreements, wage and hour disputes, OSHA compliance, Title VII violations and ADEA compliance.
**Contact:** JackWisdom

### Commercial Litigation:

The firm represents a host of public and private companies in litigation involving business torts, partnership disputes, real estate transactions, First Amendment violations, fiduciary duty claims and indemnity obligations. They also defend lawyers and other firms in lawsuits alleging legal malpractice and other wrongful acts.
**Contact:** Dale Jefferson

## PRACTCE AREAS

Insurance Coverage & Litigation
Appellate
Commercial Litigation
Employment & Labor

## OFFICES

**TEXAS**

**HOUSTON:** 808 Travis, 20th Floor, TX.77002
Tel: 713 632 1700   Fax: 713 222 0101
Email: martin@mdjwlaw.com

**AUSTIN:** 900 S Capital of Texas Hwy, Suite 425, TX 78746
Tel: 512 610 4400   Fax: 512 610 4401
Email: farrell@mdjwlaw.com

**DALLAS:** 1600 N. Dallas Parkway, Suite 800, TX 75248
Tel: 214 420 5500   Fax: 214 420 5501
Email: dyer@mdjwlaw.com

## Clients:

The firm's impressive client list includes some of the largest property, casualty, life and health insurers in the world and a wide array of businesses and corporations.

# MCKOOL SMITH

www.mckoolsmith.com

**Managing Principal:** Mike McKool
Number of partners: 89
Number of lawyers: 185

## Firm Overview:

With more than 180 trial lawyers working across offices in Austin, Dallas, Houston, Los Angeles, Marshall, New York, Silicon Valley, and Washington, DC, McKool Smith has established a reputation as one of America's leading trial firms. The firm has won more National Law Journal and VerdictSearch "Top 100 Verdicts" over the last five years than any other law firm. McKool Smith represents leading clients across a broad range of practice areas, including complex commercial litigation, intellectual property, bankruptcy, and white collar defense.

## Main Areas of Practice:

### Complex Commercial Litigation:

McKool Smith's commercial litigators are experienced in all facets of complex commercial litigation, including matters involving antitrust; appellate; arbitration; bankruptcy; business and stock valuation; class actions; contract; corporate governance; energy; fiduciary duty; mergers and acquisitions; real estate; securities; and whistleblower actions, among others. The firm's attorneys have represented clients in complex commercial litigation in every available forum, including state and federal trials and appeals, and domestic and international mediations and arbitrations.

### Intellectual Property Litigation:

McKool Smith's courtroom track record in intellectual property cases is unrivaled. The firm represents clients in all aspects of intellectual property litigation, including patent litigation; ITC/Section 337 disputes and investigations; copyright, trademark and false advertising litigation; and trade secret disputes. McKool Smith employs skilled and experienced trial lawyers with the legal and technical expertise necessary to persuade judges and juries who decide technologically complex issues. Many of the firm's attorneys hold technical degrees and have previously worked as engineers or scientists, which offers clients an enhanced perspective in complex technological matters. Additionally, the firm's attorneys include 10 former Federal Circuit clerks. In 2012, McKool Smith was named the top patent litigation firm in the south by Managing IP. The firm has also been named an "IP Firm of the Year" by Law360.

### Bankruptcy Litigation:

McKool Smith's bankruptcy litigation practice focuses on the defense and prosecution of complex lawsuits arising under bankruptcy and related state and federal laws on behalf of debtors, creditors' committees, and other parties. The firm also represents clients in complex reorganization proceedings and out-of-court restructurings. McKool Smith's attorneys have litigated complex multi-party disputes in courtrooms and forums throughout the United States, and were among the first called before congress to provide insights on proposed changes to the Federal Bankruptcy Code.

### White Collar Defense:

McKool Smith's white collar defense practice is led by former federal prosecutors with decades of experience in virtually every type of government investigation and prosecution. The firm's attorneys have represented both companies and individuals in a variety of white collar matters, including allegations involving securities fraud, insider trading, bank fraud, tax violations, antitrust violations, racketeering, the Foreign Corrupt Practices Act (FCPA), environmental violations, Office of Foreign Assets Control (OFAC), government procurement violations, insurance fraud, political corruption, and criminal antitrust investigations. The firm's attorneys also effectively guide major corporations, boards, and committees through sensitive internal investigations.

### INTERNATIONAL WORK:

McKool Smith represents international clients in U.S. courts and international arbitration proceedings. The firm has represented many international businesses in countries across the globe, including Canada, Germany, the Netherlands, Sweden, Switzerland, Taiwan, and the United Kingdom.

## OFFICES

### TEXAS

**DALLAS:** 300 Crescent Court, Suite 1500, Dallas, TX 75201
Tel: 214 978 4000 Fax: 214 978 4044

**AUSTIN:** 300 W 6th Street, Suite 1700, Austin, TX 78701
Tel: 512 692 8700 Fax: 512 692 8744

**HOUSTON:** 600 Travis Street, Suite 700, Houston, TX 77002
Tel: 713 485 7300 Fax: 713 485 7344

**MARSHALL:** 104 E Houston Street, Suite 300, Marshall, TX 75670
Tel: 903 923 9000 Fax: 903 923 9099

### CALIFORNIA

**LOS ANGELES:** 865 South Figueroa Street, Suite 2900, Los Angeles, CA 90017
Tel: 213 694 1200 Fax: 213 694 1234

**SILICON VALLEY:** 255 Shoreline Drive, Suite 500, Redwood City, CA 94065
Tel: 650 394 1400 Fax: 650 394 1422

### NEW YORK

**NEW YORK:** One Bryant Park, 47th Floor, New York, NY 10036
Tel: 212 402 9400 Fax: 212 402 9444

### WASHINGTON, DC

**WASHINGTON, DC:** 1999 K Street, NW, Suite 600, Washington, DC 20006
Tel: 202 370 8300 Fax: 202 370 8344

## CLIENTS

McKool Smith clients have included Affiliated Computer Systems; American Airlines; Ericsson, Inc.; Federal Home Loan Mortgage Corporation (Freddie Mac); HM Capital; Hunt Oil; KB Home; Koch Industries; Halliburton; Hunter Douglas; Lennox International, Inc.; Lockheed Martin; Massachusetts Institute of Technology (MIT); Medtronic, Inc.; Novartis; Oaktree Capital Management; Rambus, Inc.; State of New Mexico; TiVo, Inc.; Toll Brothers; US Synthetic Corp.; and Versata Software, among others.

# MCKOOL SMITH

# MUNCK WILSON MANDALA, LLP

www.munckwilson.com

**Managing Partner:** William A Munck
Number of partners: 22
Number of other lawyers: 28

## Firm Overview:

Munck Wilson Mandala is a technology-focused law firm headquartered in Dallas, Texas with a branch office in Marshall, Texas. The firm provides legal services within the areas of complex litigation and trials, corporate and technology transactions, employment and intellectual property.

## Main Areas of Practice:

### Intellectual Property:

In addition to traditional patent, trademark and copyright preparation and prosecution, Munck Wilson Mandala has extensive experience in the development of comprehensive corporate IP strategies. Through technology assessment techniques and applied research, Munck Wilson Mandala helps clients improve business performance and institute organizational and strategic change for competitive advantage.

### IP Licensing, Audits & Legal Opinions:

Munck Wilson Mandala represents domestic, foreign and multinational companies in developing and executing offensive and defensive licensing strategies. The firm routinely performs intellectual property audits on specific licenses, trademarks, patents or technologies to determine whether any rights are or could be protected or exploited. The firm also investigates the validity of issued patents, registrations, contracts, designs and filings to be certain all avenues are explored and all proper precautions are in effect. The firm's attorneys often are engaged to investigate enforcement and validity issues, develop and render legal opinions and offer testimony regarding the same.

### Complex Commercial / IP Litigation:

Munck Wilson Mandala maintains a nationwide complex commercial and IP litigation, appellate, and arbitration practice. The firm's trial lawyers have expertise in a wide variety of legal disputes involving intellectual property, including patent infringement, trademarks, copyrights and trade secrets. The firm's complex commercial litigation practice spans a broad range of industries and subject matters, including commercial lending, securities litigation, oil and gas, telecommunications, representation of governmental agencies, labor and employment litigation, election law, first amendment law, bankruptcy and adversary proceedings and insurance. The litigation practice is focused on clients' business objectives. Through intelligent case development and pre-trial preparation, Munck Wilson Mandala attorneys provide legal strategies that are most likely to yield maximum value to clients.

### Corporate Transactions / Securities:

Attorneys from the Corporate Transactions and Securities Practice Group help the firm's clients achieve their business objectives in the areas of corporate finance, mergers and acquisitions, securities compliance, corporate governance and general transactional representation. Attorneys have advised clients in transactions ranging in size from relatively modest transactions for family-owned businesses and early-stage companies to complex matters involving billions of dollars for large, multinational public corporations. The firm represents companies in private placements and public offerings of equity, debt, direct participation and hybrid securities. Firm attorneys have counseled clients at all stages of the financing process, from 'friends and family' and seed funding, through angel and venture capital rounds, to bank financing, IPOs and follow-on public offerings. The firm represents both buyers and sellers in mergers, asset and stock purchases, strategic alliances and joint ventures, corporate restructurings, exchange offers, private equity investments, going-private transactions and hostile and friendly tender offers. The firm regularly provides counsel on federal and state securities law reporting and compliance matters, corporate governance issues and corporate 'best practices'.

### Employment:

The firm's Employment Practice Group represents employers in claims of discrimination, harassment and retaliation in court and before federal, state and local administrative agencies; prosecutes and defends claims alleging theft of trade secrets and breach of non-competition agreements, confidentiality agreements and non-solicitation agreements; conducts audits of FLSA exempt vs. nonexempt and contractor vs. employee classifications; defends companies in Fair Labor Standards Act collective action lawsuits and Department of Labor Investigations alleging failure to pay wages; trains managers and advises HR/in-house legal departments on pro-active measures to avoid litigation; prepares and updates key employment documents including employment agreements with restrictive covenants and employee handbooks to

reflect variations in state and local law; and prepares affirmative action plans for government contractors and subcontractors.

### Insurance Subrogation:

Munck Wilson Mandala prosecutes large-property subrogation matters across the country, and has a proven track record of successful recoveries under the most difficult of circumstances. As a result, some of the most respected insurance carriers in the world entrust their most important subrogation cases to Munck Wilson Mandala.

### International Work:

Munck Wilson Mandala routinely represents domestic, foreign and multinational companies in all areas of intellectual property and technology, and assists companies in protecting and asserting intellectual property assets worldwide.

### Clients:

The firm's clients range from start-ups to Fortune 50 international technology companies. The firm also works with foreign associate firms in the areas of patent preparation and prosecution.

# MUNSCH HARDT KOPF & HARR PC

www.munsch.com **tel:** 214 855 7500 **fax:** 214 855 7584

**Chairman:** Glenn B Callison
Number of partners: 74
Number of lawyers: 112
Languages: *Croatian, Russian, Spanish*

## OFFICES

**TEXAS**
**AUSTIN:** 401 Congress Avenue, Suite 3050, 78701-4071
Tel: 512 391 6100  Fax: 512 391 6149
**DALLAS:** 3800 Lincoln Plaza, 500 N. Akard Street, 75201-6659
Tel: 214 855 7500  Fax: 214 855 7584
**HOUSTON:** 700 Louisiana Street, Suite 4600, 77002-2845
Tel: 713 222 1470  Fax: 713 222 1475

## Firm Overview:

In 1985, six attorneys left one of the largest law firms in Dallas, Texas to form Munsch Hardt. Their idea was to create a new type of law firm, one that did not operate like the old guard firms. They envisioned a firm that was more energetic, agile and responsive; a firm that focused on the practice groups, industries and needs critical to a new generation of business leaders. Building on the philosophy of their founders, the firm is now one of the dominant players in Texas with more than 110 attorneys in three offices. Today, Munsch Hardt is truly the ... Right Firm. Right Now.®

## Main Areas of Practice:

### Business Litigation:

Is guided by two fundamental concepts. As trial lawyers they focus on what matters most to clients – producing the best outcome in the most efficient manner. That focus drives the second fundamental concept – an understanding that litigation is rarely an effective business strategy. Clients want sensible businesssolutions with accurate case evaluation, efficient staffing, targeted discovery and motion practices.

### Corporate & Securities:

The firm's lawyers represent a wide array of industries including high technology, telecommunications, manufacturing, renewable energy, entertainment, banking, financial services, health care and retail services. The firm provides assistance in corporate finance; leveraged capital and true leasing; tax planning, off-balance-sheet and tax-advantaged transactions; takeovers; contracts; franchising and distributorships; immigration; employment issues and general business matters.

### Employment & Labor:

The firm litigates cases in federal and state courts and proactively advises clients on compliance issues involving various governmental agencies such as the National Labor Relations Board, Equal Employment Opportunity Commission, Occupational Safety and Health Administration, Department of Labor, Office of Federal Contract Compliance Programs and Texas Workforce Commission .The firm helps clients build and maintain collaborative environments for today and tomorrow.

### Energy & Environmental:

The firm's energy clients' interests consist of virtually every aspect of the industry – from exploration and development to refining, transmission, renewable energy and marketing. The firm's experience in the environmental arena includes civil and criminal environmental proceedings in state and federal courts, before agencies, in permit proceedings and enforcement actions. The firm performs due diligence investigations, audits and analysis of environmental related issues in a variety of corporate and real estate transactions.

### Finance:

Provides counsel to a broad clientele from regulated financial institutions to private companies engaged in lending and other banking activities. In addition to handling a wide spectrum of banking, consumer lending, corporate finance, real estate and leasing transactions, the firm is experienced with the state and federal rules and regulations governing the various types of financial products and loans. Munsch Hardt assists domestic and global clients with compliance issues involving operations, licensing, electronic funds transfer and payment processing.

### Health Care:

Represents hospitals; health care facilities; physicians, nurses and health care professionals; physician and management service organizations; health care companies; insurers and others in a broad spectrum of matters involving state and federal health care laws including the physician self-referral law, anti- kickback statute, False Claims Act and Health Insurance Portability and Accountability Act .The firm counsels on regulatory compliance and other matters impacting strategic planning, development, entity formation, contracting, operations and litigation. Munsch Hardt attorneys advise clients on the wave of new health care legislation.

### Immigration:

Assists corporations, investors and start-up companies with obtaining the proper work permits and visas for hiring, transferring, and training employees in the US temporarily and permanently. Attorneys coordinate with foreign immigration specialists to obtain the proper work permits and visas for transferring US employees abroad, and counsel corporate clients on I-9 issues,hiring and termination decisions with regard to foreign nationals, and employer sanctions and anti-discrimination issues. Munsch Hardt assists clients with family based immigration, green card and naturalization applications.

### Insolvency, Restructuring & Creditors' Rights:

Engages in all phases of insolvency, reorganization, restructuring, creditors' rights, bankruptcy and commercial law. The firm has participated in many of the largest bankruptcy and restructuring cases throughout Texas and the United States. The firm's clients include debtors, secured and unsecured creditors, ad hoc and official creditor and equity committees, lenders and bank groups, asset purchasers, landlords, equipment lessors, vendors, investors, insurers and trustees. Munsch Hardt attorneys are intimately familiar with virtually every facet of bankruptcy, reorganization and the workout process.

### Real Estate:

The firm has one of the largest real estate groups in the Southwest. The firm's integrated approach helps clients restructure troubled transactions or capitalize on market opportunities. Munsch Hardt's clients include national real estate companies, private equity funds, developers, investors, individuals and corporations forprojects located in Texas, around the country and outside the United States.

### Tax:

Direct clients how to effectively navigate this difficult terrain by developing creative, practical and cost effective business and tax solutions. Drawing upon strong technical experience, Munsch Hardt advises closely held and publicly traded corporations, partnerships, limited liability companies and individuals on the manner in which they can achieve optimum federal, state and local tax efficiencies in conducting business.

**MUNSCH HARDT KOPF & HARR** PC
ATTORNEYS & COUNSELORS

# NEEL, HOOPER & BANES, P.C

www.nhblaw.com **tel:** 713 629 1800 **fax:** 713 629 1812

**Managing Partner:** Bryant S Banes
Number of partners: 2
Number of other lawyers: 5
Languages: *English, Turkish*

**PRACTICE AREAS**
Labor & Employment Law
Government Contracts
Civil Litigation
Corporate Structuring & Transactions

**OFFICES**
TEXAS
**HOUSTON:** 1800 West Loop South, Suite 1750, 77027-3272
Tel: 713 629 1800 Fax: 713 629 1812

## Firm Overview:

The firm was established in 1972 and focuses on the representation of employers and government contractors. The firm prides itself on providing individualized, cost-effective legal services. Two of the firm's attorneys are Board Certified in labor and employment law by the Texas Board of Legal Specialization. The firm's depth of knowledge and experience covers virtually every aspect of labor and employment law and government contracts. Additionally, the firm's representation of employers and corporate clients has evolved to include commercial litigation and corporate transactions. Neel, Hooper & Banes, P.C. is also a member of the Worklaw® Network. Consequently, the firm works with offices throughout the US so that it may further service clients with diverse geographical needs.

## Main Areas of Practice:

### Traditional Labor:
The firm assists non-union clients in remaining union free, advises and counsels employers that are the subject of union organizing drives, and represents unionized clients in collective bargaining negotiations, arbitration proceedings and unfair labor practice cases.

### Employment Litigation:
The firm represents clients, at both trial and appellate levels, in cases involving alleged sex, age, race, national origin, disability, and retaliation discrimination; alleged breaches of employment contracts; alleged discriminatory or retaliatory treatment; claimed breaches of covenants not-to-compete; theft of trade secrets and alleged tortious interference with contractual relationships; and wage and hour lawsuits.

### Wage & Hour:
The firm assists clients to achieve compliance with the minimum wage, overtime, wage payment (vacation pay, deductions, commissions, etc.) and recordkeeping requirements of all federal and state wage and hour laws. The firm also conducts preventive audits.

### Training & Counseling:
The firm also advises on employee handbooks and provides training seminars for companies.

### Fiscal and Procurement Methods Advice:
The firm assists government entities and the bidding public on how to structure procurements in such a manner that satisfies fiscal and procurement laws. NHB attorneys have years of experience inside and outside of government in performing such tasks.

### Business Development & Compliance Counseling:
The firm helps clients understand the government's requirements to increase the competitiveness of their proposals. This includes reviewing proposals, bids, or quotations to make sure all necessary information is included; drafting and implementing compliance programs; developing policies and procedures; and reviewing solicitations and related documents for risks, ambiguities, rights in technical data, protection of confidential or proprietary information, pricing issues, and compliance problems. The firm also assists clients with developing teaming agreements and creating business plans to obtain necessary financing. Additionally, the firm has expertise in export control and ITAR compliance.

### Government Contract Litigation & Alternative Dispute Resolution:
The firm helps clients analyze, prepare, present, and negotiate claims against governmental agencies. NHB attorneys have extensive experience in the litigation of highly complex protests and contract disputes before the federal boards of contract appeals, the US Court of Federal Claims, and the US Court of Appeals for the Federal Circuit. Moreover, attorneys have extensive experience handling such claims via alternative dispute resolution.

### Government Relations, Audits & Investigations:
The firm advises and assists contractors in responding to audits and investigations, and in avoiding the pitfalls that often accompany them. The firm minimizes the expense and disruption by participating in audits as an integral part of clients' audit response team. Because this team has extensive public and private sector experience, the firm has an integral and working knowledge of government operations and commercial business.

### Administrative Agency Representation:
The firm has considerable experience representing employers and companies before administrative agencies. This includes charges brought before the Equal Employment Opportunity Commission and other state fair employment practice agencies and handling claims brought before other administrative agencies such as the Department of Labor, National Labor Relations Board, Occupational Safety and Health Administration and Texas Workforce Commission. In addition, the firm has significant experience before the Government Accountability Office, Small Business Administration and Office of Federal Contract Compliance programs.

### Industries Served:
The firm represents clients involved in a wide range of industries including: aerospace, petrochemical, restaurant and food service, banking and finance, construction, insurance, manufacturing, property management, logistics, healthcare, telecommunications, municipal government, transportation carriers, consumer products, employee providers, oil and gas, and engineering.

# PORTER HEDGES LLP

www.porterhedges.com **tel:** 713 226 6000 **fax:** 713 228 1331

**Managing Partner:** Robert G Reedy
Number of partners: 51
Number of other lawyers: 98

**OFFICES**

TEXAS

**HOUSTON:** 1000 Main Street, 36th Floor, TX 77002
Tel: 713 226 6000 Fax: 713 228 1331

## Firm Overview:

Porter Hedges is recognized as one of the premier business law firms based in Texas. Key areas of the firm include energy transactions, corporate/M&A, litigation, banking and finance, bankruptcy and construction, with additional experience in tax, real estate, intellectual property and environmental, among other areas. The firm assists clients from small start-ups to large national and multinational organizations and provides practical, cost-effective solutions in all areas of business law.

## Main Areas of Practice:

### Energy Transactions:

Porter Hedges provides clients with a cross-practice team of attorneys who have handled more than $30 billion in energy transactions. The firm's clients include public and private exploration and production companies, oilfield service companies, reservoir engineering firms, commercial banks, mezzanine lenders, private equity companies, natural gas pipelines and gathering systems and natural gas storage companies, among others. The team has particular experience advising oil and gas companies on the formation of joint venture agreements in the domestic shale plays.
**Contact:** Robert H Thomas

### Corporate/M&A:

The firm has one of the most sophisticated corporate practices in Texas with lawyers who have counseled growth-oriented public and private companies ranging in size from New York Stock Exchange-listed companies to start-ups. The firm has handled hundreds of public and private offerings of equity and debt securities, mergers and acquisitions, venture capital financings, institutional and private placements, leveraged buyouts, joint ventures and exchange offers.
**Contact:** Robert G Reedy

### Litigation:

The firm's trial lawyers have both the experience and resources to meet the complex litigation needs of large national and multinational corporations, as well as those of small to mid-sized companies and individuals, from pre-litigation negotiation through appeal. The firm handles all types of commercial disputes, including the interpretation and enforcement of complex contracts, disputes regarding the ownership of various forms of businesses, business torts, banking matters, representation of lenders and borrowers, fraud, real estate, breach of fiduciary duty, employment-related disputes and cases concerning the respective rights of buyers and sellers.
**Contact:** Brad M Whalen

### Banking & Finance:

The firm has a diverse and broad-based finance practice which is concentrated in the middle market but covers all tiers of the market and crosses many industries. The firm advises financial institution clients as lenders, corporate trustees, collateral agents, issuers, underwriters, and credit enhancers and has a proven ability to handle both complex and routine transactions where controlling legal costs is essential. On the borrower side, the firm assists clients in sectors including oil field service, transportation, distribution, pipeline services, retail, technology, co-location services, manufacturing, pharmaceutical, healthcare, and hospitality services.
**Contact:** Nick H Sorensen

### Bankruptcy:

The firm represents debtors, creditors, trustees, creditors' committees, institutional lenders and investors in connection with out-of-court debt restructurings, acquisitions, and financings in addition to Chapter 7, 9, and 11 bankruptcy cases. The firm's lawyers also have substantial litigation experience in bankruptcy courts, federal district courts and federal appellate courts. In addition, the bankruptcy attorneys have developed special skills in facilitating asset purchases from bankruptcy estates.
**Contact:** John F Higgins

### Construction:

Equipped with a broad understanding of the construction process and experience on all sides of the table, Porter Hedges lawyers handle the most complex private and public development projects. The firm represents prime contractors, public and private owners, developers, lenders, construction managers, sub-contractors, architects and engineers, sureties, vendors and suppliers in regards to litigation, arbitration and contracts.
**Contact:** David D Peden

### Tax:

The firm's tax group regularly assists public and private enterprises with the federal, state and international tax aspects of acquisitions, dispositions, restructurings and financings of corporate and partnership ventures. They have significant experience in the tax aspects of upstream oil & gas transactions involving tax partnerships, carried interests, like kind exchanges and other tax matters unique to the oil and gas exploration business.
**Contact:** John M Ransom

### Intellectual Property:

Porter Hedges provides the full range of services, including portfolio preparation and management; freedom-to-operate, clearance, invalidity and non-infringement opinion work; transactional matters, including licensing and due diligence support; and IP litigation, including patent, trademark, trade secret, unfair competition and antitrust litigation. The firm also specializes in patent, trademark and copyright preparation and prosecution with specific experience in patent preparation and prosecution supporting the energy, chemical, petrochemical and oilfield services industries.
**Contact:** Timothy S Westby

### Real Estate:

The firm represents developers, investors, lenders, owners and tenants in a range of real estate transactions and financing. Porter Hedges' lawyers advise on every aspect of real estate projects, including pre-development planning and financing, entity selection and structure, acquisitions and sales of improved and unimproved properties, construction contracts, commercial leases, operating agreements, and restrictive covenant agreements.
**Contact:** George S Craft

### Environmental:

Porter Hedges handles environmental compliance, controversies and due diligence for companies in the chemical, manufacturing, real estate development, waste collection and disposal, oil and gas, pipeline, transportation and other industries. Lawyers counsel clients on state and federal environmental laws and regulations and represent them in all aspects of environmental litigation.
**Contact:** Ragna Henrichs

# REYNOLDS, FRIZZELL, BLACK, DOYLE, ALLEN & OLDHAM, LLP

www.reynoldsfrizzell.com **tel:** 713 485 7200 **fax:** 713 485 7250

Number of partners: 6
Number of lawyers: 13
Languages: *English, German, Spanish*

## Firm Overview:

Founded in 2009, Reynolds, Frizzell, Black, Doyle Allen & Oldham L.L.P. is a boutique law firm focused on high-stakes complex commercial litigation. The firm brings to bear extensive jury trial experience in state and federal courts, domestic and international arbitration and numerous courts of appeal.

The firm is recognized for its representation of both plaintiffs and defendants, and it frequently undertakes cases on a contingent or other alternate fee basis in order to share risk with its clients.

The firm is comprised of 13 top-in-class lawyers, and firm partners have been recognized by the Country's most prestigious trial attorney organizations such as the American College of Trial Lawyers and the American Board of Trial Advocates. All of the firm's associates completed at least one Federal judicial clerkship before joining the firm.

## Main Areas of Practice:

The firm's practice includes energy, antitrust, product liability, contract disputes, business torts, securities, intellectual property, executive compensation, patent infringement, trade secret theft, insurance, class action and multi-district litigation, construction, lender liability, director liability, professional malpractice, products liability, trust and estate litigation and partnership disputes.

Some examples of recent work include the following cases:

- Matthew Minnis and Cullen 130 LLC v. Citrin Holdings LLC and Jacob Citrin, Case No. 2006-78939: After a 3-week jury trial, the firm obtained a unanimous jury verdict in favor of the firm's clients in a suit involving the breakup of a partnership to develop and own air and sea cargo facilities across the United States. The jury awarded the firm's clients more than $29 million in actual damages and $14 million in punitive damages.
- Toby Shor and Seashore Investments v. PBF Investments, Ltd; Paul Black, BNP Holdings, Ltd; BNP Commercial Properties: AAA No. 70 198 Y 00161 19 03: After a two-week arbitration hearing, the firm obtained an award in favor of defendants/counterclaimants Toby Shor and the Seashore Investments Management Trust. The claimants filed arbitration seeking to recover more than $64 million in a dispute involving jointly-owned oil and gas and real estate businesses. A panel of 3 arbitrators awarded the claimants nothing on their claims, and instead found in favor of the clients on all counterclaims. The panel awarded the clients more than $31 million, including $5 million in punitive damages and $2.5 million for attorneys' fees and expenses.
- Zachry Construction Corp. n/k/a Zachry Industrial, Inc. v. Port of Houston Authority of Harris County, Texas:

Served as trial counsel for plaintiff Zachry Construction Corp. in its breach-of-contract suit against the Port of Houston Authority of Harris County, Texas arising out of Zachry's construction of the Port of Houston's Bayport terminal wharf facility. Following a 3-month trial, the jury rendered a verdict entitling Zachry to a judgment for $23,443,719 in actual damages on its claim for breach of contract and denying the Port's $15 million counterclaim for attorney fees.

- Huntsman Corporation v. Credit Suisse Securities (USA), L.L.C., et al.: Several of the firm's partners were key members of the trial team representing plaintiff Huntsman in the record-setting case against Credit Suisse and Deutsche Bank in connection with failure to fund a $15 billion merger between Huntsman and Hexion of Columbus, Ohio. During trial, Huntsman obtained a $1.7 billion settlement package that included $632 million in cash and $1.1 billion in financing through issuance of notes and bonds on favorable terms.
- St. James Capital Partners, L.P., et al v. St. James Capital Corporation, et al.: Counsel for defendants/counterclaimants in a partnership dispute in which plaintiffs claimed breach of fiduciary duties in 14 separate transactions. Following 6 weeks of pretrial and 8 weeks of trial, the firm obtained a jury finding that all 14 transactions were "entirely fair." The verdict rejected the plaintiffs' claims and awarded nothing on plaintiffs' claims seeking $47 million in alleged damages, $50 million in disgorgement, and $60 million in punitive damages. The jury found in favor of clients on all counterclaims, including findings of malice and punitive damages, and clients collected $11 million.
- Duke Energy Field Services, LP v. Exxon Mobil Corporation: After close of discovery, the firm was hired to defend ExxonMobil at trial against claims filed by Plaintiff Duke Energy Field Services arising out of

ExxonMobil's role as unit operator of the Conroe Field Unit. Duke claimed that ExxonMobil had made accounting errors that caused Duke to overpay $4.4 million to other working interest owners and sought to recover damages in the amount of all un-recouped overpayments plus more than $2 million in attorney fees. After a 2-week trial, the jury returned a verdict rejecting all of Duke's claims.

The firm has, in addition, achieved dozens of highly favorable settlements for parties that the firm represented as plaintiffs or defendants over the last three years, but the terms of those settlements require confidentiality.

## Clients:

Henkels & McCoy, Port Freeport, Exxon Mobil, Hudson Advisors, Balli Trading, Furie Petroleum, Mustang Engineering, Wood Group, Huntsman Corporation, MetroNational Corporation

## International Work:

In conjunction with co-counsel, some of the firm's lawyers have litigated high stakes disputes in Canada, the United Kingdom, and Trinidad.

**Contact:** Chris Reynolds **Tel:** 713 485 7200
**Email:** creynolds@reynoldsfrizzell.com
**Contact:** Jean Frizzell **Tel:** 713 485 7200
**Email:** jfrizzell@reynoldsfrizzell.com

**PRACTICE AREAS**
Commercial Litigation
Construction
Securities
Professional Malpractice Defense
Intellectual Property
Patent

**OFFICES**
TEXAS
**HOUSTON:** 1100 Louisiana, Suite 3500, TX 77002
Tel: 713 485 7200  Fax: 713 485 7250

Reynolds
Frizzell
Black
Doyle
Allen
Oldham
L.L.P.

# SCHIFFER ODOM HICKS & JOHNSON PLLC

www.sohjlaw.com **tel:** 713 357 5150  **fax:** 713 357 5160

Number of partners: 5
Number of lawyers: 14

## Firm Overview

Schiffer Odom Hicks & Johnson (SOHJ) is a commercial litigation and arbitration boutique with national and international reach. Known for providing excellent representation at competitive rates, the firm's lawyers routinely go to trial, handling large, complex cases for some of the largest corporations in the world. In addition to broad subject matter expertise, the firm has an excellent record of courtroom success.

## Main Areas of Practice:

### Trial Practice:

SOHJ attorneys are all experienced litigators from major international law firms, who offer large firm experience with boutique specialization and personal attention. Firm lawyers regularly try cases throughout the U.S. before federal and state courts, representing clients ranging from Fortune 50 companies, venture funds and emerging companies to individuals. From disputes involving energy, healthcare, high tech and telecommunications clients to claims relating to construction, corporate and securities matters, torts and personal injury, the firm is prepared to handle any type of dispute. Integrating cutting-edge document processing and review systems with advanced technologies and experienced trial presentation, the firm manages large cases effectively and cost-efficiently.

### Domestic & International Arbitration:

Experienced at all stages of dispute resolution from risk assessment through enforcement of the final judgment, SOHJ lawyers have successfully represented clients in domestic and international arbitral proceedings across the United States and throughout the world in forums such as the AAA, FINRA, ICC, ICDR, ICSID, JAMS, LCIA, and UNCITRAL. Firm lawyers also provide customized risk avoidance strategies, which often enable clients to prevent disputes from arising.

## Industry Expertise:

- Construction
- Corporate & Securities
- Energy
- Healthcare

## Firm Recognition:

Members of the firm have been recognized by Chambers USA, Who's Who Legal, the Global Arbitration Review, Texas Super Lawyers, and the Million Dollar Advocates Forum, among others, for expertise in energy, securities, business and commercial litigation and international arbitration matters. The lawyers have also been designated as leaders in international construction disputes, ranked as leading business lawyers and recognized as among the top 100 lawyers in Texas.

## Key Clients:

- Apache Corporation
- MRC Global Inc.
- Quintana Energy Partners
- Sandridge Energy, Inc.
- SBM Offshore, Inc.

## PRACTICE AREAS

Trials & Appeals
Domestic & International Arbitration

## OFFICES

### TEXAS

**HOUSTON:** Bank of America Center, 700 Louisiana Street, Suite 1200, Texas 77002
Tel: 713 357 5150  Fax: 713 357 5160
Email: aschiffer@sohjlaw.com

### WASHINGTON

**SEATTLE:** 701 Fifth Avenue, Suite 4200, Washington 98104
Tel: 206 262 7677  Fax: 206 262 800
Email: ljohnson@sohjlaw.com

# SHANNON, GRACEY, RATLIFF & MILLER, LLP

www.shannongracey.com **tel:** 817 336 9333 **fax:** 817 336 3735

**Managing Partner:** Richard A Lowe
Number of partners: 55
Number of lawyers: 74
Languages: *English, Spanish*

### Firm Overview:

For more than 80 years, attorneys at Shannon, Gracey, Ratliff & Miller, LLP have built a legacy of working smart, helping its clients make better decisions as they navigate complex legal challenges and a changing business environment. The firm looks at legal challenges practically, allowing it to provide its clients with cost efficient, creative and effective solutions.

Shannon Gracey is a highly diversified Texas firm with offices in Arlington, Austin, Dallas, Fort Worth and Houston. Its state-wide services, coupled with a strong network of regional and global counsel, afford its clients essential legal guidance in the evolving global marketplace. The firm is comprised of well-respected attorneys known for their sound judgment who work efficiently and effectively to provide unvarnished and balanced legal counsel. Shannon Gracey attorneys are committed to the time-honored principles of accessibility and responsiveness.

### Main Areas of Practice:

**Commercial Litigation:**
The Litigation Group works with both individual and business clients from conflict analysis through appeal, whether the matter involves a complex commercial, business, or international dispute; a simple breach of contract; an employment or labor issue; or calls for defense against allegations of white collar crime.

**Corporate:**
Members of the firm's Corporate Group assist clients with legal and practical advice on business entity selection and formation, corporate finance, corporate law compliance, equity based incentives, executive compensation, mergers and acquisitions, private equity, venture capital, restructurings, Security and Exchange Commission reporting, Sarbanes-Oxley, charter and bylaw issues and capitalization.

**Energy:**
The Energy Group represents operators, royalty owners, working interest owners, service providers, lessees, lessors and municipal entities in a variety of energy related matters including production, development, agreements, negotiations, syndications, regulatory concerns and title opinions. The firm has earned a preeminent reputation in the energy industry with a track record of successes appearing before state and federal courts.

**Insurance:**
The Insurance Group has unparalleled depth, including six members with more than twenty years of experience in the field of insurance law. Its attorneys have worked with a diverse portfolio of insurance products, such as commercial liability, excess/umbrella, commercial property, professional and executive liability, product recall, crime and fidelity, and reinsurance. The Group's work includes specialized problems such as the management of issues related to insurance fraud, class action allegations, and insurance regulation, including the numerous technical problems presented by surplus lines and Lloyd's products. Members are also involved with risk management analysis, drafting, and litigation management in connection with real estate, construction, transportation and numerous other types of commercial activities and transactions.

**Mergers & Acquisitions:**
The Mergers & Acquisition Group has extensive experience with a wide variety of complex transactions including acquisitions and dispositions of assets and stock, sales and conversions, exchange offers, spin-offs, recapitalizations, and related due diligence and documentation, working closely with their clients' accountants and financial advisors.

**Real Estate:**
The Real Estate Group provides legal counsel on various real estate matters including acquisitions and dispositions, environmental, finance and securitization, property management and operation, leasing, brokers and salespersons, construction, workouts, development and zoning and land use. The firm represents a broad spectrum of clients, including lenders, purchasers, sellers, lessors, lessees, investors and developers.

## PRACTICE AREAS

Alternative Dispute Resolution
Appellate
Banking & Financial Institutions
Bankruptcy
Construction
Corporate
Energy
Environmental Law
Estate Planning, Probate & Trusts
Government & Municipal Law
Health Care
Hospitality
Insurance
Intellectual Property
International Law
Labor & Employment
Land Use
Litigation
Mergers & Acquisitions
Professional Liability
Real Estate
Securities
Tax
Transportation

## OFFICES

TEXAS
**AUSTIN:** 301 Congress Avenue, Suite 1500, TX 78701
**ARLINGTON:** 1000 Ballpark Way, Suite 300, TX 76011
**DALLAS:** 901 Main Street, Suite 4600, TX 75202
**FORT WORTH:** 777 Main Street, Suite 3800, TX 76102
**HOUSTON:** 1301 McKinney Street, Suite 2900, TX 77010

The firm also has an associated office in Rhome, Texas.

**Tax:**
The Tax Group advises clients on federal and state tax issues. Its members regularly provide counsel on the tax implications of choice of entity, business transactions, estate planning, compensation and retirement issues and sales and use tax matters. The Firm's clients include corporations, partnerships, limited liability companies, professional associations, business trusts, sole proprietorships and individuals.

### International Work:

The International Law Group has substantial experience in a broad range of representation for international and domestic clients with needs in the economic communities in the United States and globally including clients conducting business in and from Europe, Asia, Latin America, Mexico, Canada and the Middle East.

SHANNON, GRACEY, RATLIFF & MILLER, LLP

# SMYSER KAPLAN & VESELKA, LLP

www.skv.com **tel:** 713 221 2322 **fax:** 713 221 2320

Contact for all Practice Areas: Any of the Partners of the firm
Number of partners: 7   Number of lawyers: 13
Languages: *English, Spanish*

## Firm Overview:

Smyser Kaplan & Veselka, LLP ("SKV") lawyers have been at the forefront of Houston trial practice for more than 30 years. SKV fields a team of aggressive, dedicated and creative attorneys at all levels of experience who practice in all areas of commercial litigation. SKV lawyers have outstanding academic credentials and actual trial and appellate experience; they have tried and argued cases on both sides of the docket at every level of the federal and state systems, and also represent clients in appeals, arbitrations and mediations.

## Main Areas of Practice:

The firm handles contract disputes, fraud and securities claims, patent cases, medical malpractice defense, oil and gas, other complex commercial disputes, and white-collar criminal matters, including government investigations. During the past year:

- SKV (Craig Smyser and Larry Veselka). SKV was hired in July 2011 to protect an $18 billion judgment procured in Ecuador against Chevron for decades of pollution to the ecologically sensitive Amazonian rain forest and for damage to the individuals who lived there. Chevron sued the Ecuadorians and others in New York in February 2011. The Ecuadorians hired SKV after entry of a temporary injunction preventing enforcement of the judgment anywhere in the world and set for trial a severed DJA claim challenging the validity of the judgment. The US Court of Appeals for the Second Circuit dissolved the injunction and dismissed the DJA claims. Chevron then sought to attach the Ecuadorians' interests in the judgment in the remaining case. The district court denied Chevron's motion for attachment in May 2012. In July 2012, that court also denied Chevron's motion for summary judgment, declining to rule as a matter of law that the Ecuadorian judgment is not entitled to recognition.

- SKV (Lee Kaplan). Lee Kaplan worked with attorneys from a national firm in a 3-1/2 week trial representing Schlumberger affiliate WesternGeco in a patent infringement case covering state-of-the-art technology for marine seismic surveys. In addition to voir dire, Mr Kaplan conducted the direct examination of plaintiff's damages expert and the cross-examination of the opposing damages expert. After one of the parties settled for a confidential eight-figure amount during trial, on August 16, 2012 the jury returned a verdict in favor of WesternGeco against ION Geophysical on all claims, including willful infringement, and assessed actual damages of $105.9 million ($12.5 million in reasonable royalty and $93.4 million in lost profits).

- SKV (Christina Bryan and Craig Smyser). SKV successfully represented Nabors Industries Ltd. in a shareholder derivative and class action suit arising out of a much-publicized potential $100 million severance obligation contained in its former CEO's employment agreement. Plaintiff attempted to recover damages, to compel the executive to disgorge compensation, and to remedy the alleged oppressive conduct. Defendants filed a motion to dismiss, asserting that because Nabors is domiciled in and organized under the laws of Bermuda, Bermuda law governed Plaintiff's claims. Further, Defendants argued that under Bermuda law, Plaintiff lacked standing to assert derivative or class action claims under the facts alleged. The district court dismissed Plaintiff's Complaint on July 30, 2012. Plaintiff initially filed an appeal with the U.S. Court of Appeals for the Fifth Circuit, but ultimately withdrew the appeal.

- SKV (Craig Smyser and Lee Kaplan) has represented an inventor and his company in patent infringement cases involving random number generators that interface directly with a computer. True random numbers are of increasing value to encrypt computer communications to insure that the information being transmitted cannot be "hacked". After settling one lawsuit against various manufacturers, SKV and a team of lawyers filed suit against Dell, Hewlett Packard and Acer for patent infringement by selling computers that contain true random number generators covered by the patent. The case is set for trial on June 3, 2013.

A broader sampling of illustrative cases follows:

### Commercial Fraud & Securities Litigation:

- SKV successfully defended a large owner of Mexican resort properties in a RICO and fraud class action filed in federal court in Los Angeles. SKV successfully defended the special committee of a logistics company against shareholder claims regarding a $1.5 billion going-private transaction. SKV represented former Enron CFO Andrew Fastow in over 100 civil lawsuits nationwide.

### Contract Disputes:

- SKV obtained substantial confidential settlements for a hospital system against several national insurers with respect to contractual reimbursements. SKV obtained a confidential settlement for a Kansas company against an international construction company for work on an Iraqi pipeline river crossing.

## PRACTICE AREAS

Litigation: Trials, Arbitrations & Appeals

## OFFICES

TEXAS

**HOUSTON:** Bank of America Center, 700 Louisiana, Suite 2300, TX 77002
Tel: 713 221 2300  Fax: 713 221 2320

### International Proceedings & Clients:

- SKV represented an oil field equipment manufacturer in a London arbitration brought by an Indian company involving construction of a manufacturing plant in Hyderabad. SKV represented a Scottish company in the arbitration of a post-audit adjustment. SKV represents officers and directors of the privately owned entities of Yukos Oil International and Yukos Finances B.V. in disputes regarding the nationalization of Yukos.

### Other Energy Litigation:

- SKV successfully defended in Alaska federal court a $100 million dispute over an 'area of mutual interest' agreement, obtaining a summary judgment that was upheld by the US Ninth Circuit Court of Appeals.

### Governmental Investigations & White Collar Criminal Matters:

- SKV represented a former Fortune 500 energy company executive in an SEC investigation of the write-down of oil and gas reserves. SKV represented a client in a government prosecution for alleged Foreign Corrupt Practices Act violations, where the client's employer and others pled guilty and paid to the DOJ and SEC over $1.7 billion. The client's cooperation resulted in a significant reduction in sentence.

### Trade Secrets:

Multiple cases for both plaintiffs and defendants, often involving injunction proceedings.

### Clients:

City of Houston, BHP Billiton Petroleum Great Britain, Limited, Maersk Corp., Penn Virginia Oil & Gas Corporation, Yukos International UK B.V., Celotex, Memorial Hermann Hospital System, Nabors Industries, Inc., Del Monte Fresh Produce NA, Cadent Energy Partners, Enduring Resources LLC.

# STRASBURGER & PRICE LLP

**www.**strasburger.com **tel:** 214 651 4300 **fax:** 214 651 4330

**Managing Partner:** Dan Butcher
Number of partners: 131   Number of lawyers: 227
Languages: *English, French, German, Portuguese, Spanish*

### Firm Overview:

Strasburger & Price LLP (Strasburger) is a full-service law firm recognized as one of the preeminent litigation firms in the Southwestern United States. The firm was founded in 1939 in Dallas, Texas and maintains offices in Austin, Collin County, Houston, and San Antonio, Texas (the latter of which operates under the name Strasburger Price Oppenheimer Blend), New York City, Washington DC, and Mexico City. Strasburger is committed to providing expansive and superior client service. Strasburger attorneys view themselves not only as legal advisors, but also as client partners. This collaborative spirit has driven the firm's success for over 70 years.

With over 200 attorneys practicing across more than 30 practice areas, Strasburger provides comprehensive legal services for a diverse range of clients from growing start-ups to *Fortune* 100 companies both domestically and abroad. Although its reputation as a premier litigation firm has been built on thousands of trials, the firm promotes creative and strategic dispute resolution through arbitration, mediation and negotiated settlements. Strasburger's approach is simple: strive to protect and seek an advantage for clients in an efficient, insightful and thorough manner while adhering to the highest standards of professionalism, integrity and character.

**Lateral Recruiting:** Strasburger actively seeks lateral candidates with more than just outstanding academic records and experience, but those who share the values of the firm. The firm's attorneys have high degrees of personal and professional integrity, superior problem-solving and communication skills and a demonstrated commitment to the community. Strasburger attorneys not only exhibit outstanding legal skills and knowledge, but also reflect the diverse backgrounds of the communities they serve.

**Training:** Strasburger lawyers receive the opportunity to enhance their professional development from the time they join the firm as a summer associate or lateral attorney through partnership and beyond. Strasburger is committed to helping its attorneys achieve success in their careers by providing training opportunities in legal writing, negotiating, business development and client relations, communication and presentation skills, litigation experience, transactional practice including drafting, due diligence and Sarbanes-Oxley compliance, and business and financial statement mastery.

### Main Areas of Practice:

Admiralty and maritime; alternative finance; antitrust; appellate; business reorganization and bankruptcy; construction; corporate and securities; EBS regional centers; eminent domain-condemnation; employee benefits and executive compensation; energy; environmental; estate planning; family office and asset protection; fidelity and surety; food, drug and medical device litigation; franchise and distribution; governmental; health; immigration; international; labor and employment; litigation; pension and employee retirement; private equity; products litigation; professional liability; oil, gas and petroleum; real estate; tax; transportation and logistics; white-collar crime; zoning and land use.

### International Work:

When companies need to move money, products, services, technology or people across a border or operate in another country, Strasburger's international team develops strategies and finds solutions. The team members have been long-time advisors of growing middle market to multinational clients who oversee complex business, financial, trade and regulatory matters in global markets. Strasburger is also a member of ALFA International (www.alfainternational.com), an international law firm alliance, which allows Strasburger to refer clients to capable firms in countries across the globe. Strasburger lawyers speak numerous languages including Spanish, Portuguese, French, and German.

## PRACTICE AREAS

Admiralty & Maritime
Alternative Finance
Antitrust
Appellate
Business Reorganization & Bankruptcy
Construction
Corporate & Securities
Food, Drug & Medical Device Litigation
Eminent Domain-Condemnation
Employee Benefits & Executive Compensation
Energy
Environmental
Estate Planning
Fidelity & Surety
Franchise & Distribution
Governmental
Health
Immigration
International
Labor & Employment
Litigation
Products Litigation
Professional Liability
Oil, Gas & Petroleum
Real Estate
Tax
Transportation & Logistics
White Collar Crime
Zoning & Land Use

## OFFICES

**TEXAS**

**DALLAS:** 901 Main Street, Suite 4400, TX 75202
Tel: 214 651 4300   Fax: 214 651 4330

**AUSTIN:** 720 Brazos Street, Suite 700, TX 78701
Tel: 512 499 3600   Fax 512 499 3660

**COLLIN COUNTY:** 2801 Network Boulevard, Suite 600
Frisco, TX 75034.1872
Tel: 469 287 3900   Fax: 469 287 3999

**HOUSTON:** 909 Fannin Street, Suite 2300, TX 77010
Tel: 713 951 5600   Fax 713 951 5660

**SAN ANTONIO:** Strasburger Price Oppenheimer Blend
300 Convent Street, Suite 900, TX 78205-3715
Tel: 210 250 6000   Fax: 210 250 6100

**SAN ANTONIO:** Strasburger Price Oppenheimer Blend
Travis Park Plaza Building, 711 Navarro, Suite 600,
TX 78205-1796
Tel: 210 224 2000   Fax: 210 224 7540

**DISTRICT OF COLUMBIA**

**WASHINGTON DC:** 1700 K Street, NW, Suite 640,
DC 20006 3817
Tel: 202 742 8600   Fax: 202 742 8699

**NEW YORK**

**NEW YORK:** International Plaza, 750 Lexington Avenue,
6th Floor, NY 10022
Tel: 646 395 8580   Fax: 646 395 8700

**Strasburger**
ATTORNEYS AT LAW

2455

# SUTTON MCAUGHAN DEAVER PLLC

www.smd-iplaw.com **tel:** 713 800 5700 **fax:** 713 800 5699

**Managing Partner:** Al Deaver
**Partners:** Mike Sutton, Bob McAughan, Tanya Chaney, Jeff Andrews
Number of other lawyers: 4

**PRACTICE AREAS**
Intellectual Property Litigation, Prosecution & Counseling

**OFFICES**
TEXAS
Houston: Three Riverway, Suite 900, TX 77056
Tel: 713 800 5700   Fax: 713 800 5699

## Firm Overview:

Sutton McAughan Deaver PLLC is a premier boutique law firm specializing in intellectual property matters. The firm's heritage reaches back to the iconic Houston-based IP boutique of Arnold White & Durkee, PC, where all three name partners were shareholders. Since then, Mike Sutton, Bob McAughan, and Al Deaver have practiced law – together and apart – at large AmLaw 100 firms. As the practice of law has evolved, the firm's founding partners ultimately became convinced that the best way to provide exceptional IP representation is through a firm that specializes in intellectual property law and has the flexibility to customize legal services and fee arrangements to the individualized needs of its clients. This shared philosophy led the founding partners to form SMD in early 2012. The firm practices all aspects of intellectual property law, including litigation, prosecution, licensing, and counseling related to patents, trademarks, copyrights, and trade secrets.

## Main Areas of Practice:

### Intellectual Property Litigation:

SMD's attorneys are seasoned trial attorneys with extensive experience representing clients in jury and bench trials in federal and state courts and other tribunals across the country. SMD's attorneys also represent clients in arbitration, mediation, and other alternative dispute resolution proceedings. The firm handles disputes involving any type of IP claims, including patent, trademark, or copyright infringement; trade secret theft; antitrust; and unfair competition and false advertising.

SMD recognizes that success in the courtroom is possible only through the efforts of a focused and dedicated trial team. SMD's attorneys and staff work tirelessly and aggressively to obtain the best possible result in any litigation. While always ready to go to trial, SMD's attorneys also recognize that their clients' interests are often best served by resolving disputes outside of the courtroom. SMD's attorneys take the time to identify a client's needs, and find creative ways to resolve disputes consistent with those needs – whether in the courtroom or otherwise. SMD aggressively pursues alternative fee arrangements with its clients, including contingent fee representations.

### Intellectual Property Counseling & Procurement:

SMD helps clients advance their business interests through strategic IP asset procurement, creation, and monetization. SMD provides a full range of services related to patents, trademarks, and copyrights. These services include preparation and prosecution of patent applications, as well as post-grant proceedings. All of the firm's attorneys are registered to practice before the US Patent and Trademark Office. SMD also counsels clients regarding the availability of trademarks, and the management and enforcement of trademark portfolios. The firm's attorneys also have significant experience with trademark opposition and cancellation proceedings. SMD also assists clients with registration, licensing, and policing of copyrights, including internet-based and digital technology.

### Awards:

Surveys conducted by legal and business publications consistently rank SMD's attorneys at the top of their profession. Although the firm is young, it was quickly recognized as a leader in providing excellent intellectual property legal services. During its first year, SMD was recognized as a "Leading Law Firm in Texas" by *Chambers USA*, and as a "Go-To Law Firm" for Fortune 500 Companies for intellectual property litigation by Corporate Counsel Magazine. Only seven months after opening its doors, SMD was ranked by US News – Best Lawyers as a top firm in Houston and nationally for intellectual property and patent litigation as well as for patent law.

### Clients:

Located in Houston, the energy capital of the world, Sutton McAughan Deaver represents a large number of clients in the energy sector. But SMD's reputation for excellence has attracted clients in virtually every business sector and in a wide range of technologies, such as neural networks and industrial process control; board-level digital power management; oil and gas exploration, drilling, and production technologies; architectural copyrights; medical devices and compounds; global positioning systems; consumer electronics; children's products; consumer products; signature authentication; and lighting. SMD's clients range from start-ups to mid-size companies to Fortune 50 corporations, in locations across the United States and world. Representative clients include: Emerson Electric Company, General Electric Company, Baker Hughes Incorporated, United Airlines, ION Geophysical Corp., Waste Connections, Inc., Imperial Sugar Company, MD Anderson Cancer Center, Texas United Chemical Co., Riviana Foods (a subsidiary of Ebra Foods, S.A.), Lufkin Industries, and Tribocor Technologies.

# Sutton McAughan Deaver PLLC
*Intellectual Property*
*Trial Lawyers & Counselors*

# THOMPSON, COE, COUSINS & IRONS

**www.**thompsoncoe.com **tel:** 214 871 8200 **fax:** 214 871 8209

**Managing Partner:** Jack M Cleaveland, Jr
Number of partners: 74
Number of lawyers: 140
Languages: *French, German, Korean, Portuguese, Spanish, Vietnamese*

## Firm Overview:

For more than 60 years, Thompson Coe has been recognized as a premier litigation firm and national authority on insurance law. With offices in Dallas, Austin, and Houston, Texas, and Saint Paul, Minnesota, Thompson Coe not only provides a full range of services to the insurance industry but also offers many other client services in labor and employment, commercial litigation, premises and product liability, professional liability, mass tort, appellate, administrative law, construction, commercial transactions, health care, real estate and tax, and estate planning. Clients choose Thompson Coe because the firm provides a total, integrated solution to their legal service needs.

## Main Areas of Practice:

### Insurance Law:

The firm's clients depend on its broad insurance background and knowledge to provide reliable and efficient legal advice and assistance for all insurance business and regulatory matters. Whether giving advice pertaining to insurance laws, representing clients before an insurance regulator, handling mergers and acquisitions or formations of insurance companies and agencies, or drafting or reviewing documents needed for insurance-related transactions, this practice group brings extensive experience to areas of law that are unfamiliar to many.

### Insurance Litigation & Coverage:

This practice group is recognized by the insurance industry for its experience and ability to provide counsel to insurance companies through a broad range of insurance-related litigation, coverage disputes, bad faith and other extra contractual liabilities litigation. Drawing upon the firm's experience in the administrative and regulatory arena, the firm represents carriers facing complex corporate, regulatory and class action litigation. The attorneys have been at the forefront of some of the most important property insurance cases and have unmatched experience helping insurers formulate cost-effective defense strategies to respond to lawsuits and claims after a catastrophe.

### Products & General Litigation:

The firm's trial attorneys have been recognized for their proficiency in the trial and defense of personal injury cases involving premises liability, products liability, medical malpractice, nursing home litigation and healthcare regulatory matters, mass tort litigation, negligence and other tort-related claims. They are committed to excellence in trial advocacy and pride themselves in responding to litigation needs with practical, creative solutions.

### Commercial Litigation:

This practice group has handled every type of commercial dispute – ranging from simple contract matters to complex international disputes. The attorneys share a commitment to do whatever it takes in terms of preparation and development of innovative strategies to ensure the best possible results for their business litigation clients – including trying cases to a conclusion with successful results.

### Governmental & Legislative Advocacy:

The firm's attorneys help clients achieve legislative initiatives and resolve regulatory issues. Their involvement and extensive experience in legislative and governmental processes enables them to effectively represent clients and advocate client positions before the legislature and other governmental agencies.

### Labor & Employment:

The firm's attorneys counsel the management of both private and public sector companies in connection with all employment-related matters, including compliance with the FLSA, Title VII, ADEA, ADA, WARN, OHSA and other federal, state and local laws that regulate employment. They have an active labor litigation practice defending management against EEO claims, wrongful termination, workers' compensation, retaliation, civil rights and other employment-related claims. The firm handles employment and non-competition agreements, as well as collective bargaining, grievance arbitrations, unfair labor practice proceedings and other situations relating to labor and management issues.

### Professional Liability:

Lawsuits involving malpractice claims against attorneys, accountants, insurance agents and brokers, corporate directors and officers and other business professionals are being asserted at an increasing rate. The attorneys in this practice group draw upon years of hands-on experience in dealing with claims to provide the firm's professional clients with the finest quality legal representation.

### Appellate:

Thompson Coe's appellate attorneys have successfully represented litigants in important cases decided by the Texas Supreme Court, federal appellate courts, including the Fifth Circuit, and other appellate courts in Texas and across the country.

### Business Transactions:

This practice group encompasses everything from contractual relationships, including mergers and acquisitions, sales and purchases of ownership interests, shareholder agreements, management compensation arrangements, entity formation and financing, to bankruptcy, real estate transactions, estate planning and tax issues.

## PRACTICE AREAS

Insurance Litigation & Coverage
Products & General Litigation
Commercial Litigation
Governmental & Legislative Advocacy
Labor & Employment
Professional Liability
Appellate
Business Transactions

## OFFICES

**TEXAS**

**DALLAS (HEAD OFFICE):** 700 N Pearl Street, Twenty-fifth Floor, TX 75201-2832
Tel: 214 871 8200 Fax: 214 871 8209

**AUSTIN:** 701 Brazos, Suite 1500, TX 78701
Tel: 512 708 8200 Fax: 512 708 8777

**HOUSTON:** One Riverway, Suite 1600, TX 77056
Tel: 713 403 8210 Fax: 713 403 8299

**MINNESOTA**

**SAINT PAUL:** The Historic Hamm Building, 408 St. Peter Street, Suite 510, MN 55102
Tel: 651 389 5000 Fax: 651 389 5059

THOMPSON
COE

# THOMPSON & KNIGHT LLP

www.tklaw.com **tel:** 214 969 1700 **fax:** 214 969 1751

**Managing Partner:** Emily A Parker
Number of partners: 160 approx. Number of lawyers: 330 approx.
Languages: *Arabic, English, French, German, Gujarati, Hebrew, Italian, Mandarin, Portuguese, Russian, Spanish, Turkish, Vietnamese*

**Firm Overview:**
Since 1887, Thompson & Knight attorneys have been anticipating clients' needs and striving to exceed expectations. With an emphasis on global energy, litigation, tax, and insolvency matters, the firm's attorneys provide clients with innovative, cost-effective legal and business solutions to their issues. Thompson & Knight's experience in these areas establishes it as a leading global energy law firm, with more than two-thirds of its practice relating to the energy industry.

**Main Areas of Practice:**

**Corporate & Securities:**
- Represented majority holder of Frac Tech Services in its $3.7 billion sale of equity to a Singaporean fund
- Represented EnCap Investments in formation of a private equity fund with total commitments of $3.5 billion
- Represented Noble Energy in their $1.85 billion public offering of 4.15% senior notes due 2021

**Bankruptcy & Restructuring:**
- Represented Vitro, S.A.B. de C.V. in its Chapter 11 bankruptcy proceedings in the Northern District of Texas
- Obtained plan confirmation in Baseline Oil & Gas Corp.'s 'pre-pack' Chapter 11 bankruptcy case in 33 days
- Represented Hercules Offshore in its acquisition of Seahawk's drilling rig assets through Sec. 363 purchase

**Oil, Gas & Energy:**
- Represented Brigham Exploration Company in its sale to Statoil ASA for approximately $4.4 billion
- Represented Chief Gathering in its $1 billion sale to Penn Virginia Resource Partners
- Assisted Infinity Energy Resources in oil and gas concessions for 1.4 million acres off Nicaraguan coast

**Environmental:**
- Represent energy firms on environmental issues with E&P, midstream, and downstream operations
- Challenging an ordinance adopted by the Houston City Council on behalf of BNSF, Union Pacific, and HBT
- Representing The Dow Chemical Company in a federal Superfund action involving a former waste oil recovery facility

**Finance:**
- Represented agent bank in $4 billion syndicated revolving credit facility with large E&P company
- Represented Apache Corp. in $3.95 billion financing raised in part to facilitate acquisition of BP assets
- Represented agent bank in $3.5 billion syndicated revolving credit facility for large energy partnership

**Healthcare:**
- Manage more than 150 hospital contract litigation cases nationwide for a *Fortune* 200 hospital company
- Represent hospital systems and healthcare providers in investigations, litigation, and compliance
- Represent a national medical device manufacturer regarding healthcare antitrust and marketing issues

**Intellectual Property & Technology:**
- Represented US air carrier in patent litigation in E. Dist. of Texas involving internet server technology
- Represented semiconductor manufacturer in patent litigation in California involving eight US patents
- Prepared/prosecuted patent applications related to hydrogen hybrid locomotive for national railroad company

**Employment & Labor:**
- Assisted transportation employer in defeating EEOC nationwide investigatory subpoenas
- Multi-jurisdictional litigation of noncompetes for transportation and medical employers
- Handled FLSA matters for food distributor, energy services, and electronics employers

**Real Estate:**
- Represented City of Austin in 2.5 million square feet of mixed use development estimated at $750 million
- Represented C-III Asset Mgmt./Alliance in REO sale transactions for a trust prior to Lehman Bros.' bankruptcy
- Represented Granite Properties in the disposition of its entire $165 million industrial property portfolio

**Tax:**
- Complex tax planning for more than $25 billion of oil and gas transactions
- Represented Brigham Exploration Company in the tax issues related to its $4.4 billion sale to Statoil ASA
- US tax counsel on one of the first Canadian offerings of an income trust acquiring US energy assets

**Trial & Appellate:**
- Represented Petrobras America Inc. and affiliates in an arbitration involving ownership of a joint venture
- Secured a $10 million jury verdict for Resort Development Latin America, Inc. in a breach of fiduciary duty and tortious interference case

## OFFICES

**TEXAS**

**AUSTIN:** 98 San Jacinto Blvd, Suite 1900, TX 78701
Tel: 512 469 6100   Fax 512 469 6180
Email: James.Morriss@tklaw.com

**DALLAS:** 1722 Routh Street, Suite 1500, TX 75201
Tel: 214 969 1700   Fax: 214 969 1751
Email: Larry.Hicks@tklaw.com

**FORT WORTH:** 801 Cherry Street, Unit #1, Burnett Plaza, Suite 1600, TX 76102
Tel: 817 347 1700   Fax: 817 347 1799
Email: Mike.Sheehan@tklaw.com

**HOUSTON:** 333 Clay Street, Suite 3300, TX 77002
Tel: 713 654 8111   Fax: 713 654 1871
Email: Meyerson@tklaw.com

**CALIFORNIA**

**LOS ANGELES:** 10100 Santa Monica Blvd, Suite 950, CA 90067
Tel: 310 203 6900   Fax: 310 203 6980
Email: Shelly.Youree@tklaw.com

**SAN FRANCISCO:** 650 California Street, Fifth Floor, CA 94108
Tel: 415 433 3900   Fax: 415 433 3950

**MICHIGAN**

**BLOOMFIELD HILLS:** 39533 Woodward, Suite 320, MI 48304
Tel: 248 258 7900   Fax: 214 880 3100
Email: Philip.Kessler@tklaw.com

**NEW YORK**

**NEW YORK:** 900 Third Avenue, 20th Floor, NY 10022
Tel: 212 751 3001   Fax: 212 751 3113
Email: Philip.Kessler@tklaw.com

## INTERNATIONAL OFFICES

Algiers, Algeria; Paris, France; Monterrey, Mexico; London, UK

- Represented an international E&P company in an arbitration related to hydrocarbons in Colombia

**Clients:**
BNSF Railway Company, Chief Oil & Gas, The Dow Chemical Company, EnCap Investments L.P., Johnson & Johnson, Lafarge, Lockheed Martin Corporation, Natural Gas Partners, Petróleo Brasileiro S.A. – Petrobras, Royal Bank of Canada, Wells Fargo Bank, Vitro, S.A.B. de C.V.

**International Work:**
The firm represents clients worldwide in a variety of legal matters, particularly those related to energy, dispute resolution, tax, and bankruptcy. In the global energy realm, the firm offers a full range of legal and commercial services, including advice on host government contracts; joint operating, study, and bidding agreements; service contracts; regulatory matters; tax; corporate structure; arbitration; M&A; financings; and pipeline and refinery projects.

Thompson & Knight | Impact
ATTORNEYS AND COUNSELORS

# VINSON & ELKINS

www.velaw.com **tel:** 713 758 2222 **fax:** 713 758 2346

**Chairman:** T Mark Kelly
**Managing Partner:** Scott Neal Wulfe
Number of partners worldwide: 252
Number of other lawyers worldwide: 469

## Firm Overview:

For almost a century, Vinson & Elkins lawyers have provided innovative business solutions for clients whose needs are as diverse as the entities they represent. In today's challenging environment of global markets, volatile economies and complex human and environmental issues, its time-tested role as trusted adviser has become even more critical. The lawyers' extensive experience, combined with the responsiveness and efficiencies of the firm's global reach, enable Vinson & Elkins to serve clients from start-up, to the negotiating table and boardroom, and before legislative and regulatory bodies in the courtroom and beyond.

## Main Areas of Practice:

Core practice areas include: admiralty and maritime; antitrust; appellate; biotechnology; business transactions; capital markets and securities; climate change; condemnation and land use; construction; contracts; corporate governance and compliance; e-commerce/internet; employee benefits (ERISA) and executive compensation; employment, labor and OSHA; energy; environmental; finance; financial institutions; government contracts; infrastructure; intellectual property; international dispute resolution; Islamic finance and investment; litigation; mergers and acquisitions; oil and gas; outsourcing; private equity/venture capital; project finance and development; real estate; regulatory; restructuring and reorganization; securities litigation; structured finance; syndicated finance; tax; technology; telecommunications; and white-collar criminal defense.

## International Work:

Sixteen offices worldwide allow Vinson & Elkins' lawyers to work efficiently across time zones, as well as with local lawyers in foreign jurisdictions to accomplish the client's objectives. In addition to legal experience, the firm has strong personal relationships with business people and other professionals that offer significant benefits to the client including broad experience in transactions spanning multiple jurisdictions, cultures and languages.

The firm efficiently guides its clients through a wide range of transactions, such as mergers and acquisitions, joint ventures and strategic alliances, public and private offerings of securities in the developed and emerging capital markets, as well as development and financing of a variety of projects.

The firm's international dispute resolution team engages in international arbitration under all leading institutional rules as well as international civil litigation in US courts and in other jurisdictions. The firm's lawyers work with their clients to develop effective solutions to the complex problems and unique challenges of international business.

## Clients:

Since the firm was founded in 1917, it has attracted an outstanding and diverse group of lawyers who serve an international clientele. Clients include the governments of sovereign nations and of North American states, cities and municipalities, public and private companies, domestic and international financial institutions, new entities, joint ventures, project companies, and individuals and families.

---

**OFFICES**

CALIFORNIA
**PALO ALTO:** 1841 Page Mill Road, Suite 200-B, CA 94304
Tel: 650 617 8400  Fax: 650 618 1970
Email: bcarano@velaw.com

**SAN FRANCISCO:** 525 Market Street, Suite 2750,
CA 94105
Tel: 415 979 6900  Fax: 415 651 8786
Email: mjacobs@velaw.com

DISTRICT OF COLUMBIA
**WASHINGTON:** 2200 Pennsylvania Avenue NW, Suite 500
West, DC 20037-1701
Tel: 202 639 6500  Fax: 202 639 6604
Email: mcharness@velaw.com

NEW YORK
**NEW YORK:** 666 Fifth Avenue, 26th Floor, NY 10103-0040
Tel: 212 237 0000  Fax: 212 237 0100
Email: cthau@velaw.com

TEXAS
**AUSTIN:** 2801 Via Fortuna, Suite 100, TX 78746-7568
Tel: 512 542 8400  Fax: 512 542 8612
Email: dwood@velaw.com, wvolk@velaw.com

**DALLAS:** Trammell Crow Center, 2001 Ross Avenue, Suite
3700, TX 75201-2975
Tel: 214 220 7700  Fax: 214 220 7716
Email: jwander@velaw.com, byoung@velaw.com

**HOUSTON:** 1001 Fannin, Suite 2500, TX 77002-6760
Tel: 713 758 2222  Fax: 713 758 2346
Email: myeates@velaw.com

**INTERNATIONAL OFFICES**

The firm also has offices in Beijing, Hong Kong, Shanghai, China; Abu Dhabi, Dubai, United Arab Emirates; Moscow, Russia; Tokyo, Japan; Riyadh, Saudi Arabia; and London, United Kingdom.

# WINSTEAD PC

www.winstead.com

**Chairman, CEO:** Kevin A Sullivan
Number of shareholders: 155
Number of other lawyers: 148

**Firm Overview:**

Winstead is a national business law firm with 300 attorneys in Texas, North Carolina, Louisiana and Washington, DC. The firm provides a full range of business legal services to some of the most recognized and respected companies across the country and throughout the world.

Winstead attorneys and consultants serve as trusted advisors to mid-market and large businesses, providing a core range of legal services that are critical to their operation and success. From its well known reputation in the energy, financial services, real estate and technology industries to its corporate and high-stakes litigation practices, Winstead delivers practical knowledge and responsive service.

## Main Areas of Practice:

**BUSINESS & TRANSACTIONS DEPARTMENT:**

**Business Restructuring/Bankruptcy:**
Contact: Phillip L Lamberson Tel: 214 745 5180
Email: plamberson@winstead.com

**Corporate, Securities/Mergers & Acquisitions:**
Contact: Mark G Johnson Tel: 214 745 5600
Email: mgjohnson@winstead.com

**Energy & Environmental Law:**
Contact: Thomas T Hutcheson Tel: 713 650 2717
Email: thutcheson@winstead.com

**Finance & Banking:**
Contact: Jennifer D Knapek Tel: 214 745 5230
Email: jknapek@winstead.com

**Healthcare:**
Contact: T Andrew Dow Tel: 214 745 5387
Email: adow@winstead.com

**Government Relations:**
Contact: Pete Winstead Tel: 512 370 2801
Email: pwinstead@winstead.com

**Intellectual Property:**
Contact: Stanley R Moore Tel: 214 745 5110
Email: smoore@winstead.com

**Planned Community, Mixed-Use & Condominium:**
Contact: Robert D Burton Tel: 512 370 2869
Email: rburton@winstead.com

**Public Finance:**
Contact: Julia R Houston Tel: 512 370 2817
Email: jhouston@winstead.com

**Public & Regulatory Law:**
Contact: Alex Gonzales Tel: 512 370 2887
Email: agonzales@winstead.com

**Real Estate Development & Investments:**
Contact: Greg Erwin Tel: 713 650 2781
Email: gerwin@winstead.com
Contact: Gregory A Zimmerman Tel: 214 745 5658
Email: gzimmerman@winstead.com

**Real Estate Finance:**
Contact: Bradley D Broberg Tel: 214 745 5203
Email: bbroberg@winstead.com

**Syndicated Finance:**
Contact: Melissa Ruman Stewart Tel: 214 745 5200
Email: mstewart@winstead.com

**Taxation, Employee Benefits & Private Business:**
Contact: Nancy W Furney Tel: 214 745 5228
Email: nfurney@winstead.com

**Wealth Preservation:**
Contact: John F Bergner Tel: 214 745 5289
Email: jbergner@winstead.com

**LITIGATION & DISPUTE RESOLUTION DEPARTMENT:**

**Appellate:**
Contact: David Fowler Johnson Tel: 817 420 8223
Email: dfjohnson@winstead.com

**Commercial Litigation:**
Contact: Linda J Burgess (Austin/San Antonio)
Tel: 512 370 2881 Email: lburgess@winstead.com
Contact: Brian T Morris (Dallas/Fort Worth)
Tel: 214 745 5714 Email: bmorris@winstead.com
Contact: Tom Van Arsdel (Houston/The Woodlands)
Tel: 713 650 2728 Email: tvanarsdel@winstead.com

**Construction:**
Contact: Dale E Butler Tel: 214 745 5244
Email: dbutler@winstead.com

**Energy & Environmental Litigation:**
Contact: Thomas T Hutcheson Tel: 713 650 2717
Email: thutcheson@winstead.com

**Fiduciary Litigation:**
Contact: Jay J Madrid Tel: 214 745 5709
Email: jmadrid@winstead.com
Contact: Stephanie Loomis-Price Tel: 713 650 2750
Email: sloomisprice@winstead.com

**Intellectual Property Litigation:**
Contact: Stanley R Moore Tel: 214 745 5110
Email: smoore@winstead.com

**Labor, Employment & Immigration:**
Contact: Thomas E Reddin Tel: 214 745 5650
Email: treddin@winstead.com

**Securities Litigation & Enforcement:**
Contact: John P Kincade Tel: 214 745 5707
Email: jkincade@winstead.com

WINSTEAD

ATTORNEYS

# YETTER COLEMAN LLP

www.yettercoleman.com **tel:** 713 632 8000 **fax:** 713 632 8002

**Managing Partner:** R Paul Yetter
Number of attorneys: 33
Number of partners: 14
Number of other attorneys: 19

## Firm Overview:

Yetter Coleman LLP focuses on high-stakes matters for plaintiffs and defendants involving contract, business tort, appellate, intellectual property, antitrust, and securities litigation, with particular experience in the energy, healthcare, technology and travel industries.

## Main Areas of Practice:

Yetter Coleman has been recognized as one of the nation's best litigation-only firms. Its success for clients generates consistent top rankings, including by the National Law Journal in its 2012 Litigation Boutique Hot List; by the National Law Journal in its 2010 Appellate Hot List; by the American Lawyer in its 2009 and 2005 Litigation Boutiques of the Year; by the US News – Best Lawyers® in the 2013 Best Law Firms for its commercial, appellate, antitrust, intellectual property, and securities litigation practices; and in the 2012 Chambers USA: America's Leading Lawyers for Business and 2013 Best Lawyers in America® Guide for various areas of commercial litigation.

These rankings reflect the firm's strong reputation for representing clients engaged in complex high-profile business disputes, including during 2012:

- Securing a major settlement for American Airlines following three weeks of trial before a Texas state court jury in its $1 billion antitrust lawsuit against the largest US global distribution system
- Winning a complete defense judgment for GE Oil & Gas after a five-week trial in a $59 million breach of warranty case over high-speed reciprocating gas compressors aboard a floating oil production vessel off the coast of West Africa
- Winning three major appellate victories for a major brake manufacturer in asbestos litigation tried in McLean County, Illinois (a venue named by some as a "Judicial Hell Hole"), signaling an end to certain liability conspiracy claims
- Obtaining a key summary judgment for a Texas-based LNG processor in a significant royalty claims dispute with a former investor and partner, which led to a favorable settlement
- Securing a favorable settlement for a global energy company in a fast-track arbitration involving sales pricing of Alaskan North Slope crude oil
- Obtaining reversal of a district court's judgment vacating a $125 million arbitration award arising from an agreement to sell a power plant and further obtaining rendition of judgment confirming the award
- Obtaining conditional certification of up to 15,000 home mortgage consultants pursuing wage claims against Wells Fargo and Wachovia banks. The case is currently on mandamus to the Fifth Circuit

## Clients:

Clients include American Airlines, CenterPoint Energy, ConocoPhillips, ExxonMobil, Freeport LNG, General Electric, IBM, Oxbow Group, Phillips66, and The Methodist Hospital.

**OFFICES**

TEXAS
**AUSTIN:** 221 West 6th Street, Suite 750, TX 78701
Tel: 512 533 0150 Fax: 512 533 0120
**HOUSTON:** 909 Fannin, Suite 3600, TX 77010
Tel: 713 632 8000 Fax: 713 632 8002

## YetterColeman LLP
### TRIALS | APPEALS

## How lawyers are ranked

Every year we carry out thousands of in-depth interviews with clients in order to assess the reputations and expertise of business lawyers worldwide. The qualities we look for (and which determine rankings) include technical legal ability, professional conduct, client service, commercial awareness/astuteness, diligence, commitment, and other qualities most valued by the client. For details of our research team, see p.5.

# CORPORATE/M&A

Commentary about individuals can be found under their firm's paragraph. If the firm has no paragraph (is not ranked) look at Other Notable Practitioners.

### Corporate/M&A
### Leading Firms

**Band 1**
Dorsey & Whitney LLP *
Parr Brown Gee & Loveless, A Professional Corporation *

**Band 2**
Ballard Spahr LLP *
Holland & Hart LLP *
Jones Waldo *
Stoel Rives LLP

**Band 3**
Durham Jones & Pinegar, PC *
Parsons Behle & Latimer PC *
Ray Quinney & Nebeker P.C. *
Snell & Wilmer LLP *
Vantus Law Group

## Band 1

### Dorsey & Whitney LLP
See profile on p.1583

THE FIRM This highly regarded firm's Salt Lake City corporate practice retains an impressive standing in the market thanks to its ability to handle the full range of M&A and finance transactions. The group counsels businesses on public offerings and securities, and also assists private equity funds with formation and investment matters. The team is especially noted for its ability to tackle more complex transactional issues such as spin-offs, making it a go-to for some of the largest corporate entities in the state, often handling work that is international in scope. Clients include HSBC Capital, Healthcare Quality Catalyst and Sorenson Capital.
**Sources say:** *"They have been thorough and responsive in providing us with excellent legal advice and experience."*
**KEY INDIVIDUALS** Corporate department head **Samuel Gardiner** is described as a *"very good lawyer."* He recently acted for Sorenson Capital on a $20 million preferred stock

investment. **Alan Bell** earns high praise from clients for his corporate practice, with one source noting: *"His expertise on private equity funds is unmatched in this market."* **David Marx**'s corporate practice covers company formation, public offerings, M&A and venture capital financing. *"David was always very responsive and thorough, and delivered the highest quality results,"* said one satisfied client. Associate **David Day** focuses his practice on corporate, M&A and securities law. Sources praise *"his experience with venture capital financings, attention to detail and ability to do the job."*

### Parr Brown Gee & Loveless, A Professional Corporation
See profile on p.2479

THE FIRM Parr Brown is considered one of the finest in the state for its corporate expertise, representing leading businesses in a number of sophisticated transactions. The group is known for its strength in the M&A space, and is experienced in work involving private equity funds and investments as well as general corporate counseling and governance. The team is also able to work with other departments within the firm to provide an integrated service to clients. Recent highlights include representing Merit Medical Systems in the $167 million acquisition of Thomas Medical Products.
**Sources say:** *"They have been stellar in all areas."*
**KEY INDIVIDUALS** The highly regarded **Brian Lloyd** advises clients on corporate governance, financing transactions, securities regulation and M&A issues. Sources say he is a *"great thinker with wonderful writing and strong communication skills, who is calm under pressure, fair and equitable."* The *"superbright"* **Bryan Allen** is known for his corporate transactional practice involving securities and intellectual property. **Seth King** focuses on securities law, M&A and finance, and is said to be *"very thorough, with sound business skills."* **Brent Stevenson** has a well-regarded corporate practice focusing on M&A and finance. According

### Corporate/M&A
### Leading Individuals

**Band 1**
| | |
|---|---|
| Anderson P Christian | Ballard Spahr LLP * |
| Lloyd Brian G | Parr Brown Gee & Loveless |

**Band 2**
| | |
|---|---|
| Alston Robinson (Rob) M | Jones Waldo |
| Gardiner Samuel P | Dorsey & Whitney LLP |
| Jones Nathan W | Stoel Rives LLP |
| Moffitt Ronald G | Stoel Rives LLP |
| Poelman Ronald S | Jones Waldo * |
| Topham Reed W | Stoel Rives LLP |
| Wells Matthew | Holland & Hart LLP * |

**Band 3**
| | |
|---|---|
| Allen Bryan T | Parr Brown Gee & Loveless |
| Bell Alan W | Dorsey & Whitney LLP |
| Fredman Stuart A | Vantus Law Group |
| Jacobsen Brad | Vantus Law Group |
| King Seth R | Parr Brown Gee & Loveless |
| Leishman N Todd | Durham Jones & Pinegar, PC |
| Lindley Greg | Holland & Hart LLP * |
| Rudd David R | Ballard Spahr LLP * |
| Stevenson Brent M | Parr Brown Gee & Loveless |
| Taylor Thomas R | Durham Jones & Pinegar, PC * |
| Winger R Gary | Kirton & McConkie (ONP)† |

**Band 4**
| | |
|---|---|
| Bagnasacco Barbara | Ballard Spahr LLP * |
| Flint George | Parsons Behle & Latimer PC * |
| Mangum Geoffrey W | Parsons Behle & Latimer PC * |
| Marx David | Dorsey & Whitney LLP |
| Pinegar Kevin R | Durham Jones & Pinegar, PC * |
| Wilson Randon W | Jones Waldo * |

**Associates to watch**
| | |
|---|---|
| Day David | Dorsey & Whitney LLP |

\* Indicates firm / individual with profile.
†ONP = Other Notable Practitioner.

to sources, his M&A experience *"really is unmatched in our region."*

## Band 2

### Ballard Spahr LLP
See profile on p.2234

**THE FIRM** This firm maintains a strong foothold in Utah's business community with a corporate practice that is international in scope. The group is known for its ability to handle large, complex deals, and for its expertise in the venture capital, technology and life sciences industries. Clients include UpStart Life Sciences Capital, Progressive Finance and Triumph Group. The team has recently been involved in a series of high-value acquisition, loan and investment transactions.
**Sources say:** *"They have a really good team. Highly qualified, well-trained lawyers who have good experience in lots of different areas of corporate law."*
**KEY INDIVIDUALS Chris Anderson** (see p.2472) concentrates on corporate and securities law. He has significant experience working with hi-tech organizations, and is noted to be *"excellent at venture capital"* in that area. **David Rudd** (see p.2475) handles complex corporate transactions that are often international in scope, and earns client praise for his *"great efficiency."* He recently represented C7 Data Centers in a $25 million recapitalization. **Barbara Bagnasacco** (see p.2472) focuses her practice on international and domestic business transactions and M&A. **Sources say:** *"She is highly perceptive and reliable, and she possesses a deep knowledge of her practice area."*

### Holland & Hart LLP
See profile on p.727

**THE FIRM** This strong regional firm covers the full spectrum of corporate securities issues. The group has expertise in M&A, private equity financings and investment transactions in particular, and is experienced in working with emerging growth companies. Clients include Signal Peak Venture Partners, Clear Link Technologies, True Science and Consult Net.
**Sources say:** *"Holland & Hart's service and expertise have been outstanding."*
**KEY INDIVIDUALS Matthew Wells** (see p.2476) focuses his corporate practice on issues pertaining to growing companies. He handles M&A and venture capital financings, often on an international scale. Clients say he is *"extremely knowledgeable and service-oriented."* **Greg Lindley**'s (see p.2474) core practice is in corporate and securities law, advising clients on securities offerings and M&A matters. He has particular expertise in the medical and technological industries.

### Jones Waldo
See profile on p.2478

**THE FIRM** This firm is a key player in the Utah corporate arena and is known for its M&A, finance and securities expertise. The group is also noted for advising companies in the medical and technology industries on startup and

development issues, with recent work including assisting internet marketing software company Qualtrics in a $70 million venture capital financing transaction.
**KEY INDIVIDUALS Rob Alston** is well regarded for his practice involving M&A and corporate reorganizations. Representative clients include Unishippers Global Logistics and Access Information Management. **Ronald Poelman** (see p.2475) heads the corporate securities and emerging company practice groups, and represents clients in securities and contractual issues, with an emphasis on companies in the technology sector. **Randon Wilson** (see p.2476) has a broad practice covering agricultural and real estate law in addition to his corporate, banking and M&A expertise.

### Stoel Rives LLP

**THE FIRM** With a strong regional presence, this corporate practice is able to draw on the firm's network of offices to provide a seamless service to its Utah client base. The group has experience in the energy, utilities, outdoor products and medical devices markets, among others, and is praised for its work involving M&A, business formation and venture capital funding. Clients include Questar Gas, Rocky Mountain Power, Diamond Rental and Huntsman Corporation.
**KEY INDIVIDUALS Nathan Jones** is praised for his M&A expertise and also has a significant practice in securities law and financing. He recently acted for Intermountain Healthcare on a series of investment transactions. **Ronald Moffitt** has a practice that focuses on M&A, commercial contracts and corporate finance. **Reed Topham** has a broad practice encompassing corporate governance, acquisitions and securities law, with expertise in debt and equity financings.

## Band 3

### Durham Jones & Pinegar, PC
See profile on p.2477

**THE FIRM** This firm continues to expand its presence in the corporate and finance spaces with a solid team providing transactional services in the business, tax, securities and finance areas. The group is also able to utilize the firm's banking and creditors' rights teams, providing greater capacity to handle all possible aspects of a deal.
**KEY INDIVIDUALS Todd Leishman**'s broad practice includes representing clients in transactions involving M&A, debt and equity financing, governance and commercial contracts. **Tom Taylor** (see p.2476) handles various issues pertaining to M&A, corporate finance and lending transactions, and often counsels emerging growth and technology companies. **Kevin Pinegar** (see p.2475) is renowned for counseling clients on corporate governance and securities-related matters including M&A, securities offerings and spin-offs.

### Parsons Behle & Latimer PC
See profile on p.2480

**THE FIRM** This firm's corporate and securities practice maintains a solid reputation among the state's business

community and works with its impressive natural resources department to assist key clients in the mining, exploration, energy and utilities industries. The group is known for its acquisitions, sales and financing expertise, representing clients such as Barrick Resources, Rio Tinto America and JPMorgan Chase.
**Sources say:** *"I found their performance highly professional and accommodating. I also found them to be extremely knowledgeable concerning M&A and corporate law and very responsive."*
**KEY INDIVIDUALS George Flint**'s (see p.2473) corporate practice focuses on advising emerging growth companies on issues involving acquisitions, financings and complex commercial transactions. Corporate, securities and tax practice group chair **Geoffrey Mangum** (see p.2475) handles the negotiation and structuring of complex business transactions. He recently represented ClearOne in the $5 million acquisition of VCON Videoconferencing.

### Ray Quinney & Nebeker P.C.
See profile on p.2481

**THE FIRM** This firm has a strong bench of 21 attorneys in its corporate practice, offering transactional services to key corporate clients. The group's expertise covers M&A, tax, company formation and financing, and it is experienced in working with tax-exempt organizations, emerging growth technology companies and healthcare organizations. Representative clients include Dental Select and Keystone Aviation.
**KEY INDIVIDUALS Mark Cotter** and **Bruce Olson** co-head the department.

### Snell & Wilmer LLP
See profile on p.517

**THE FIRM** Snell & Wilmer has a strong business and finance practice covering corporate, banking and securities law. The group has recently handled a significant number of sales and acquisitions, and is praised by clients for its corporate governance, venture capital financing and loan structuring expertise, representing a significant number of companies in the financial and real estate industries.
**Sources say:** *"Snell & Wilmer has shown strong expertise and we are fully confident when it is representing us in legal negotiations with deal counterparties."*
**KEY INDIVIDUALS Brad Merrill** heads Snell & Wilmer's Salt Lake City corporate practice.

### Vantus Law Group

**THE FIRM** This business law boutique offers a unique breadth of experience, making it a firm choice for many of the state's leading corporate clients. The team is able to offer support in the areas of corporate, finance, M&A and securities law, and is also adept in handling complex commercial transactions.
**KEY INDIVIDUALS Stuart Fredman**'s core focus is on M&A; he has additional expertise in strategic business planning and tax law. **Brad Jacobsen**'s broad practice includes the financing and formation of new businesses and real estate, with an emphasis on M&A and securities law.

## Other Notable Practitioners

Client favorite **Gary Winger** of Kirton & McConkie advises on M&A, contracts, securities and corporate finance issues. He recently secured a $12 million line of credit for Sierra Forest Products. *"He is detailed, timely and very tenacious in his work,"* say interviewees.

# ENERGY & NATURAL RESOURCES

Commentary about individuals can be found under their firm's paragraph. If the firm has no paragraph (is not ranked) look at Other Notable Practitioners.

### Energy & Natural Resources
### Leading Firms

**Band 1**
Holland & Hart LLP *
Parsons Behle & Latimer PC *

**Band 2**
Parr Brown Gee & Loveless, A Professional Corporation *
Snell & Wilmer LLP *
Stoel Rives LLP

**Band 3**
Jones Waldo *
Van Cott, Bagley, Cornwall & McCarthy, P.C.

### Senior Statesmen

**Senior Statesmen: distinguished older practitioners**
Parr Clayton J — *Parr Brown Gee & Loveless*

### Leading Individuals

**Band 1**
| | |
|---|---|
| Dragoo Denise | *Snell & Wilmer LLP* |
| Holtkamp James A | *Holland & Hart LLP* * |
| Keller H Michael | *Van Cott, Bagley, Cornwall & McCarthy, P.C.* |
| Pos Hal J | *Parsons Behle & Latimer PC* * |
| Prince William B | *Dorsey & Whitney LLP (ONP)[†]* |

**Band 2**
| | |
|---|---|
| Beless Rosemary J | *Fabian Law (ONP)[†]* |
| Bramhall Christopher | *Kirton & McConkie (ONP)[†]* |
| Butler Jim B | *Parsons Behle & Latimer PC* * |
| Hull Stephen J | *Parsons Behle & Latimer PC* * |
| Jenkins Lucy B | *Jones Waldo* * |
| Jensen Daniel A | *Parr Brown Gee & Loveless* |
| Kirkham John S | *Stoel Rives LLP* |
| Lear Phillip | *Lear & Lear LLP (ONP)[†]* |
| Malmquist Michael J | *Parsons Behle & Latimer PC* * |
| Murray Kevin R | *Chapman and Cutler LLP (ONP)[†]* |
| Winmill Patricia | *Parsons Behle & Latimer PC* * |

**Band 3**
| | |
|---|---|
| Cahoon Brad | *Snell & Wilmer LLP* |
| Christiansen Steven J | *Parr Brown Gee & Loveless* |
| Clawson Thomas | *Van Cott, Bagley, Cornwall & McCarthy, P.C.* |
| Galli Craig D | *Holland & Hart LLP* * |
| Kirschner Lisa | *Parsons Behle & Latimer PC* * |
| Rawson Blaine | *Ray Quinney & Nebeker P.C.* |
| Williams Jody | *Holland & Hart LLP* * |
| Zody Michael A | *Parsons Behle & Latimer PC* * |

### Energy & Natural Resources: Water Law
### Leading Individuals

| | |
|---|---|
| Bramhall Christopher | *Kirton & McConkie (ONP)[†]* |
| Jensen Daniel A | *Parr Brown Gee & Loveless* |
| Keller H Michael | *Van Cott, Bagley, Cornwall & McCarthy, P.C.* |
| Kirschner Lisa | *Parsons Behle & Latimer PC* * |
| Williams Jody | *Holland & Hart LLP* * |

\* Indicates firm / individual with profile.
[†]ONP = Other Notable Practitioner.

## Band 1

### Holland & Hart LLP
See profile on p.727

**THE FIRM** Holland & Hart's environment, energy and natural resources practice is one of the finest in the state. The group has a marked excellence in its environmental litigation offering and is also highly regarded for its permitting and oil and gas work. With a deep bench, the team's breadth of experience allows it to handle matters across the energy and resources spectrum, representing major clients including BP America Productions and ConocoPhillips.

**KEY INDIVIDUALS** The *"excellent"* James Holtkamp (see p.2474) is highly regarded in the areas of air quality regulation and climate change. He has recently represented Red Leaf Resources in the permitting for the commercial development of oil shale. Craig Galli (see p.2473) is regarded as an *"outstanding"* attorney who focuses on issues pertaining to environmental law including permitting, compliance and due diligence. The highly regarded **Jody Williams** (see p.2476) has extensive expertise in the water law arena and recently represented Weber Basin Water Conservancy District in a $150 million water importation project.

### Parsons Behle & Latimer PC
See profile on p.2480

**THE FIRM** This regional firm has an exceptional reputation for its mining practice, with deep experience in the industry, and it continues to establish itself as a leader in the natural resources and energy arenas. The team is also highly regarded for its environmental law and litigation practices, being praised for its work involving energy law, land use, water rights and environmental permitting. The group's clients include Barrick, US Magnesium and Questar, and it has recently represented Kennecott Utah Copper in a substantial expansion and capital investment project to extend the life of the Bingham Canyon Mine.

Sources say: *"They're superb: their knowledge of the mining industry is very good, in terms of both the industry and the applicable laws."*
**KEY INDIVIDUALS** Lisa Kirschner (see p.2474) counsels clients on environmental regulation, with a focus on water quality. A satisfied client comments: *"She is one of the more knowledgeable people on CWA and Section 404 issues and helps maneuver through the very tangled law in that area. She is really quite a specialist."* **Hal Pos** (see p.2475) has expertise in contaminated properties and Superfund liability. He is described as an *"excellent lawyer across the spectrum of environmental issues who is very helpful on due diligence for mineral property transactions with good knowledge on hazardous waste laws."* **Jim Butler** (see p.1681) concentrates on environmental and natural resources matters and has recently assisted Barrick with compliance and permitting issues for the Goldstrike and Cortez Mines in Nevada. Sources say he is an *"excellent attorney who has solid judgment, good experience and great responsiveness."* **Stephen Hull** (see p.2474) *"is an excellent minerals lawyer who has been involved in a lot of large mineral property transactions of all sorts,"* comments one interviewee. He has recently handled major regulatory and transactional work relating to the mining industry. **Michael Malmquist** (see p.2474) is described as a *"top-notch practical lawyer."* He advises clients on environmental permitting, land use and public land issues in natural resource and energy projects. **Patricia Winmill** (see p.2476) focuses on mining and public land issues and is said to *"take a very academic and thorough view of issues and is extremely reliable on core property and core mining law questions."* **Michael Zody** (see p.2476) handles environmental and natural resources litigation and is noted for his deep knowledge and experience, as well as strong relationships with agency personnel.

## Band 2

### Parr Brown Gee & Loveless, A Professional Corporation
See profile on p.2479

**THE FIRM** This firm has a longstanding reputation in Utah for its work involving mining and natural resources law. This group of talented attorneys also offers solid expertise in the environmental, energy and utilities and water law arenas. Representative clients include American Vanadium, Gryphon Gold and Scorpio Gold.

Sources say: *"They have demonstrated an ability to determine the most important issues and deliver intelligent and well-reasoned recommendations on how to solve problems."*

KEY INDIVIDUALS **Daniel Jensen** is recognized for his work involving mineral transactions, title issues and water rights. According to clients, *"he is a consummate professional and delivers high-quality work in a reasonable amount of time. His advice is accurate, measured and appropriate for action."* **Steven Christiansen** is hailed as *"an outstanding environmental lawyer"* whose practice includes permitting, climate change and air emissions credits transactions. The highly respected **Clayton Parr** is an *"excellent minerals lawyer, with an outstanding national reputation in this field, and knows the business thoroughly."*

## Snell & Wilmer LLP
See profile on p.517

THE FIRM Snell & Wilmer has a sophisticated energy and natural resources practice with particular emphasis on environmental compliance, litigation and transactional issues. The group is increasing its presence in the renewable energy space and continues to represent clients in the utilities, oil and gas and mineral industries.

Sources say: *"The legal guidance received has been very satisfactory and we are very pleased with the attention given to these matters by the attorneys."*

KEY INDIVIDUALS The highly regarded **Denise Dragoo** focuses on mining-related issues and is recognized for her public land, coal and water practice. **Brad Cahoon** is a *"seasoned attorney and expert in the environmental field"* with knowledge and experience in water and zoning issues.

## Stoel Rives LLP

THE FIRM Stoel Rives continues to have a strong presence in the energy and mining spaces, representing some of the largest public utility providers in the Intermountain West region. The Salt Lake City team is known for its environmental law and land use expertise pertaining to natural gas, oil, mining and renewable energy. Clients include Graymont Western US, Rocky Mountain Power and Pacificorp Energy.

KEY INDIVIDUALS **John Kirkham** is a highly respected natural resources attorney who offers unparalleled expertise in the coal industry. He is praised by clients for his straightforward approach.

## Band 3

### Jones Waldo
See profile on p.2478

THE FIRM This firm's energy and natural resources practice group continues to expand its presence in the state. Being part of the firm's wider real estate department, the team is able to offer particular expertise in the energy, land use and environmental spaces, with experience in brownfield, Superfund sites and toxic torts.

KEY INDIVIDUALS **Lucy Jenkins** (see p.2474) focuses her practice on environmental law and is experienced in handling related business transactions, climate change issues and air and water quality matters.

### Van Cott, Bagley, Cornwall & McCarthy, P.C.

THE FIRM This firm's energy and natural resources practice offers a seamless service to clients on the West Coast. The group continues to offer solid transactional services and is gaining increasing prominence in the oil and gas

area, adept at handling exploration, production and title examination issues.

KEY INDIVIDUALS The well-regarded **Michael Keller** is known for his environmental practice, advising clients on permitting, compliance and regulatory issues with a focus on mining and water law. **Thomas Clawson** concentrates on handling various transactional issues involving natural resources and public land law.

## Other Notable Practitioners

**William Prince** of Dorsey & Whitney LLP cochairs the Salt Lake City energy group and focuses on natural resources, energy and environmental law, with particular expertise in the coal and uranium industries. Representative clients include Tri-State Generation & Transmission Association and Dundee Securities. The well-regarded **Rosemary Beless** of Fabian Law has a broad natural resource and environmental practice, focusing on mining, oil and gas, public land and condemnation law. **Christopher Bramhall** of Kirton & McConkie concentrates on real estate transactional work and is also held in high regard for his practice in water law. **Phillip Lear** of Lear & Lear LLP is recognized as a leading individual for oil and gas-related work and also practices in the areas of mineral financing and natural resource litigation. **Kevin Murray** of Chapman and Cutler LLP has a broad energy and natural resources practice and is well regarded for his transactional and power generation expertise. **Blaine Rawson** of Ray Quinney & Nebeker P.C. has a broad natural resources practice and is noted for his work involving mining, oil and gas and environmental issues. According to sources, *"he has a firm grasp of satisfying the client's needs and using his expertise to resolve complex problems."*

# INTELLECTUAL PROPERTY

Commentary about individuals can be found under their firm's paragraph. If the firm has no paragraph (is not ranked) look at Other Notable Practitioners.

## Band 1

### Stoel Rives LLP

THE FIRM This firm continues to have one of the finest IP practices in the state, with a particularly strong patent offering. The group is adept at handling the full range of services involving copyright, licensing and IP litigation as well as managing international trademark portfolios for companies such as XanGo and Nature's Sunshine Products. The firm's impressive clientele also includes Exopack, Mindray Medical and Big Cartel.

KEY INDIVIDUALS **Kevin Laurence** is recognized for the high quality of his advice. He concentrates his practice on patent-related issues involving technologies in the pharmaceutical, medical and chemical areas. **Barton Giddings** is recognized for his IP expertise pertaining to the pharmaceutical, biotech and medical industries. **Michael Mangelson** is highly regarded for his trademark practice

and specializes in helping clients protect and enforce their business IP rights. **Kory Christensen** has an international IP practice with clients in Europe and Asia as well as the USA, concentrating on patent prosecution in the technological industries. **Kenneth Black** is a well-regarded commercial litigator with a significant focus on IP disputes.

### Workman Nydegger
See profile on p.2482

THE FIRM This leading IP boutique remains a force to contended with in the Utah market. The group's deep bench and breadth of experience allows it to service its clients in various industries seamlessly. The team is noted for the international scope of its prosecution services as well as its ability to handle complex IP litigation, licensing and transactions.

KEY INDIVIDUALS **Rick Nydegger** has extensive experience in various IP-related issues and his practice is focused

on patent prosecution involving medical devices, software and electronic technologies. **John Stringham** has a broad IP practice and concentrates on the prosecution of patent, trademark and copyright applications.

## Band 2

### Holland & Hart LLP
See profile on p.727

THE FIRM Holland & Hart retains a well-established IP practice which garners high praise from its clients. The group is particularly well regarded for its trademark enforcement, patent prosecution and litigation expertise. Clients include Otto Bock Healthcare, Easton Technical Products, Primos and US Synthetic.

Sources say: *"Their IP practice group is excellent."*

**KEY INDIVIDUALS Brett Foster** (see p.2473) is a highly regarded IP litigator who continues to handle high-profile patent infringement suits for clients including K-Tec and Hydro Engineering. **Grant Foster** (see p.2473) is praised as an *"excellent attorney"* who focuses on trademark and patent prosecution. Representative clients include St. Jude Medical and Symantec.

## TraskBritt, PC

**THE FIRM** This boutique firm continues to receive praise from peers for its IP work covering the full range of IP and related transactional services. The group particularly stands out for its patent offering and represents clients in the biomedical, pharmaceutical, chemical and electronic industries.

**KEY INDIVIDUALS** The highly regarded **Joseph Walkowski** focuses on the acquisition and exploitation of IP rights, with expertise in the electronic and mechanical industries. **Dickson Burton** is an experienced IP litigator and counsels clients on issues involving patents and trade secrets. **Edgar Cataxinos** concentrates on patent law and is highly regarded for his IP litigation practice.

## Band 3

### Parsons Behle & Latimer PC
See profile on p.2480

**THE FIRM** This firm's solid IP practice is well regarded for its trademark and copyright expertise, with attorneys covering the enforcement and licensing of copyright and all areas of trademark prosecution. The group has experience in the biomedical, chemical and technological industries servicing clients such as Dyno Nobel, Iomega and DKI Services.

**KEY INDIVIDUALS David Mangum** (see p.2474) is an experienced IP litigator, with a client describing him as *"a very impressive attorney – a straight shooter, smart and reliable."* **Kevin Speirs** (see p.2475) focuses his practice on patent infringement litigation and also has expertise in antitrust-related issues.

### Ray Quinney & Nebeker P.C.
See profile on p.2481

**THE FIRM** This Utah law firm is recognized in the areas of trademark and copyright registration, licensing and trade secrets and is particularly strong in the IP litigation arena. The group represents clients including Orbit Irrigation Products, Idaho Technology, Mircrosoft and Brigham Young University.

**KEY INDIVIDUALS Arthur Berger** is well regarded for handling IP disputes and is relied on by clients for his patent, trademark and litigation experience. **Mark Bettilyon** is an experienced commercial litigator with a practice emphasis on IP rights disputes. **Samuel Straight** is a reputable IP trial lawyer and represents companies in the technological industries in defending against claims of infringement.

### Thorpe, North & Western LLP

**THE FIRM** This well-regarded IP boutique continues to prove itself a valuable asset among the business community. Its attorneys are adept in patent, trademark and IP litigation in addition to offering strategic business advice and transactional services to its diverse set of clients.

**KEY INDIVIDUALS Peter De Jonge** focuses his practice in the areas of trademark prosecution, IP licensing and litigation.

## Other Notable Practitioners

**Eric Maschoff** of Maschoff Gilmore & Israelsen has a highly regarded patent prosecution practice, with a peer citing his *"tenacity and creativity"* as standout qualities. **Charles Veverka** of Maschoff Gilmore & Israelsen is described as a *"very good lawyer"* who focuses his practice on IP-related disputes and litigation. **Matthew Thayne** of Phillips Ryther & Winchester concentrates on patent law and technologies in the medical, mechanical and electronic industries.

# LABOR & EMPLOYMENT

Commentary about individuals can be found under their firm's paragraph. If the firm has no paragraph (is not ranked) look at Other Notable Practitioners.

| Labor & Employment | |
| --- | --- |
| **Leading Firms** | |
| **Band 1** | |
| Holland & Hart LLP * | |
| Ray Quinney & Nebeker P.C. * | |
| **Band 2** | |
| Jones Waldo * | |
| Parsons Behle & Latimer PC * | |
| **Band 3** | |
| Manning Curtis Bradshaw & Bednar LLC | |
| Stoel Rives LLP | |

| **Leading Individuals** | |
| --- | --- |
| **Band 1** | |
| Baar Lois A | Holland & Hart LLP * |
| Bednar Steven C | Manning Curtis Bradshaw & Bednar LLC |
| O'Brien Michael Patrick | Jones Waldo * |
| Smith Janet Hugie | Ray Quinney & Nebeker P.C. |
| **Band 2** | |
| Blattner-Thompson Elisabeth | Ballard Spahr LLP (ONP)[†] * |
| Dunning Elizabeth | Holland & Hart LLP * |
| Durham Matthew M | Stoel Rives LLP |
| Gavre Mark | Parsons Behle & Latimer PC * |
| Hagen Scott | Ray Quinney & Nebeker P.C. |
| Leithead Heidi E C | Parr Brown Gee & Loveless (ONP)[†] |
| Rice Robert | Ray Quinney & Nebeker P.C. |
| **Band 3** | |
| Benard Bryan | Holland & Hart LLP * |
| Palmer Justin | Stoel Rives LLP |
| Thaler Jr Rick | Ray Quinney & Nebeker P.C. |
| Zody Michael A | Parsons Behle & Latimer PC * |

| Labor & Employment: ERISA | |
| --- | --- |
| **Leading Individuals** | |
| **Band 1** | |
| Babcock Bruce E | Jones Waldo * |
| Barnett James L | Holland & Hart LLP * |
| Gavre Mark | Parsons Behle & Latimer PC * |
| Hagen Scott | Ray Quinney & Nebeker P.C. |
| Lloyd W Waldan | Callister Nebeker & McCullough (ONP)[†] |
| Petersen Scott | Fabian Law (ONP)[†] |

\* Indicates firm / individual with profile.
[†]ONP = Other Notable Practitioner.

## Band 1

### Holland & Hart LLP
See profile on p.727

**THE FIRM** Holland & Hart rises to the top band after gaining high praise from peers and clients. Its Salt Lake City office comprises a deep bench of dedicated attorneys providing a breadth of experience to serve the state's leading employers. The group is particularly impressive in wage and hour, employment litigation and discrimination matters, and has an increasingly strong immigration practice. Clients include Sun Products, Pride Transport and UPS.
**Sources say:** *"I have been very impressed with their performance and would recommend them to anyone. Communication, instructions and follow-up are very impressive."*
**KEY INDIVIDUALS** Highly regarded **Lois Baar** (see p.2472) is an experienced labor and employment lawyer whose practice includes the mediation of employment disputes and workforce training. **Elizabeth Dunning** (see p.2473) handles employment litigation and mediation as well as discrimination-related cases. *"I've never been disappointed with the information she provides or her willingness to tackle any question,"* said one interviewee. Experienced litigator **Bryan Benard** (see p.2472) regularly handles discrimination and harassment-related suits. ERISA practitioner **James Barnett** (see p.2472) has a broad litigation practice encompassing employment and employee benefits disputes.

### Ray Quinney & Nebeker P.C.
See profile on p.2481

**THE FIRM** This firm continues to be recognized as a leader in the state for labor and employment law, housing a team that provides high-quality service to a diverse client base. The group earns praise from clients for its employment litigation practice and handles the full spectrum of issues, including discrimination, wage and hour, immigration and traditional labor law. Notable recent work includes obtaining summary judgment for Verizon Wireless in a suit involving defamation, ADA and FMLA claims brought by a former employee.
**Sources say:** *"The service that we receive from Ray Quinney & Nebeker is first class."*
**KEY INDIVIDUALS** Labor and employment group chair **Scott Hagen** has a broad practice that includes ERISA, labor relations and employment-related litigation. **Janet Smith** is highly regarded in the labor and employment arena, and focuses on discrimination, affirmative action and wrongful termination issues. **Robert Rice** represents employers in various employment-related disputes, and is also noted for his commercial litigation and IP expertise. **Rick Thaler** has a varied practice with significant emphasis on complex commercial and employment litigation. **Sources say:** *"His knowledge of employment and labor issues is encyclopedic."*

## Band 2

### Jones Waldo
See profile on p.2478

**THE FIRM** Jones Waldo's strong labor and employment practice is part of the firm's larger litigation department, enabling the team to assist clients in employment disputes. The group's expertise also covers employee benefits, unfair trade, labor and union issues. Key clients include The Salt Lake Tribune, Zions Bank and MountainStar Healthcare.
**KEY INDIVIDUALS** Experienced tax lawyer **Bruce Babcock** (see p.2472) is recognized for his employee benefits and ERISA expertise. **Michael O'Brien** (see p.2475) is a highly reputable employment lawyer with significant trial experience. Sources describe him as *"a great lawyer and a good person."*

### Parsons Behle & Latimer PC
See profile on p.2480

**THE FIRM** This firm's labor and employment practice has one of the deepest benches in the state, with 16 dedicated attorneys in Salt Lake City. The group provides the full scope of services, handling discrimination and harassment issues, government investigations and preventive advice, and has been praised for its litigation and ERISA work in particular. Rio Tinto and Mountain Medical Physician Specialists are among the major clients benefiting from the team's counseling and advice.
**Sources say:** *"Parsons has always provided quick and on-point advice on our labor matters. They are competitively priced and have various experts to handle different employment matters."*
**KEY INDIVIDUALS Mark Gavre** (see p.2473) has a broad employment practice and is *"excellent in the employment law area as well as ERISA,"* according to interviewees. **Michael Zody** (see p.2476) has a varied practice with a significant focus on employment litigation. He is known for his expertise in retaliation claims.

## Band 3

### Manning Curtis Bradshaw & Bednar LLC

**THE FIRM** This Salt Lake City firm has a solid labor and employment practice, with noted strength in the employment litigation area, representing clients in various employment disputes. The group is adept in a wide range of employment law issues, covering discrimination, wage and hour, employee benefits and harassment.
**KEY INDIVIDUALS** Described as a *"really terrific lawyer,"* **Steven Bednar** is a seasoned trial attorney who focuses on employment-related litigation as well as workforce training.

## Stoel Rives LLP

**THE FIRM** Stoel Rives's well-regarded employment practice earns high praise from clients for its expertise in employment litigation and employee benefits. The group defends employers in complex class action, discrimination and wage and hour claims, representing clients such as Chevron Products, eBay and PacifiCorp Energy.

**KEY INDIVIDUALS Matthew Durham** handles employment disputes in relation to discrimination, harassment

and wage and hour issues. **Justin Palmer** concentrates on employment litigation.

## Other Notable Practitioners

**Waldan Lloyd** of Callister Nebeker & McCullough, A Professional Corporation has expertise in tax law and is also highly regarded for his ERISA practice. **Scott Petersen** of Fabian Law concentrates his employment practice on employee benefits. Sources note that *"he is a very good*

*ERISA lawyer."* **Elisabeth Blattner-Thompson** (see p.2472) of Ballard Spahr LLP is recognized for her expertise in employment law, and is often sought by managers for her advice and counseling on compliance issues. **Heidi Leithead** of Parr Brown Gee & Loveless, A Professional Corporation is an experienced employment lawyer who focuses on counseling, workforce training and litigation. *"Heidi is well known and respected as an exceptional attorney,"* say sources.

# LITIGATION GENERAL COMMERCIAL

Commentary about individuals can be found under their firm's paragraph. If the firm has no paragraph (is not ranked) look at Other Notable Practitioners.

### Litigation: General Commercial
**Leading Firms**

**Band 1**
Burbidge Mitchell & Gross
Parsons Behle & Latimer PC *
Ray Quinney & Nebeker P.C. *
Snell & Wilmer LLP *

**Band 2**
Holland & Hart LLP *
Parr Brown Gee & Loveless, A Professional Corporation *
Stoel Rives LLP

**Band 3**
Anderson & Karrenberg
Dorsey & Whitney LLP *
Jones Waldo *
Magleby & Greenwood PC
Snow, Christensen & Martineau
Van Cott, Bagley, Cornwall & McCarthy, P.C.

## Band 1

### Burbidge Mitchell & Gross

**THE FIRM** This litigation boutique is able to handle complicated disputes with a level of sophistication comparable to its full-service competitors. The group enjoys an exceptional reputation for representing clients in complex commercial disputes and advises a diverse client base with expertise in areas including antitrust, securities, banking, IP and real estate.

**Sources say:** *"A unique firm that does high-end litigation."*

**KEY INDIVIDUALS Richard Burbidge** is a highly experienced trial lawyer with a broad practice which includes securities, antitrust, and complex commercial and patent litigation. Sources say he is *"as good a lawyer as we have in our market."* **Jefferson Gross** is well regarded in the market and focuses his practice on litigating commercial contract disputes and IP cases.

### Parsons Behle & Latimer PC
See profile on p.2480

**THE FIRM** This 75-attorney team is one of the largest litigation practices in Utah. The group's impressive bench strength makes Parsons Behle & Latimer one the firms

most sought in the state for commercial and civil disputes. Its expertise includes environmental, bankruptcy, healthcare and First Amendment lawsuits, representing clients such as Hydro Engineering, Alpine Securities and Chubb Atlantic.

**Sources say:** *"I've always found them to be extremely prompt, always on the spot with our questions and they will identify issues I've not even thought about."*

**KEY INDIVIDUALS Francis Wikstrom** (see p.2476) is a highly regarded trial lawyer who handles complex civil litigation and has significant expertise on patent, real estate and construction issues. **Raymond Etcheverry** (see p.2473) has a broad skill set and focuses on complex business litigation. Sources say: *"He's a strong litigator, certainly on the antitrust side."* **Michael Larsen** (see p.2474) concentrates on IP and IT-related litigation. Clients praise his ability to handle the most sophisticated of disputes. **Michael Bailey**'s (see p.2472) practice centers on political law and commercial litigation. *"He is great,"* say clients.

### Ray Quinney & Nebeker P.C.
See profile on p.2481

**THE FIRM** This firm continues to stand out for its exceptional litigation practice with a large team of talented trial attorneys. The group is well equipped to handle commercial and appellate litigation at all levels with technical expertise in areas including employment, environmental, construction and healthcare. The team's breadth makes it a firm choice for large corporate entities and it has recently handled high-profile cases with over $1 billion at stake on behalf of clients including Microsoft and Huntsman.

**KEY INDIVIDUALS** The *"very talented"* **James Jardine** focuses on commercial litigation and returns to practice after a three-year leave of absence, adding further strength to the team's bench. **Justin Toth** is lauded as *"a terrific lawyer"* and handles commercial litigation, with a specialty in antitrust law. Managing partner **John Adams** concentrates his practice on complex commercial disputes. **Greggory Savage** chairs the firm's litigation group and has a diverse practice which includes business torts, construction, land use and real estate litigation. **Rick Rose**'s litigation practice focuses on the areas of product liability, insurance defense and transport.

### Litigation: General Commercial
**Leading Individuals**

**Band 1**

| | | |
|---|---|---|
| Burbidge Richard D | Burbidge Mitchell & Gross | |
| Haley George M | Holland & Hart LLP * | |
| Jardine James S | Ray Quinney & Nebeker P.C. | |
| Karrenberg Thomas R. | Anderson & Karrenberg | |
| Sullivan Alan | Snell & Wilmer LLP | |
| Toth Justin T | Ray Quinney & Nebeker P.C. | |
| Wikstrom Francis M | Parsons Behle & Latimer PC * | |

**Band 2**

| | |
|---|---|
| Ashton John P | Van Cott, Bagley, Cornwall & McCarthy, P.C. |
| Benard Blaine | Holland & Hart LLP * |
| Benevento Bryon J | Dorsey & Whitney LLP |
| Billings Peter W | Fabian Law (ONP)† |
| Black Kenneth B | Stoel Rives LLP |
| Clark Robert S | Parr Brown Gee & Loveless |
| Etcheverry Raymond J | Parsons Behle & Latimer PC * |
| Hafen Jonathan O | Parr Brown Gee & Loveless |
| Hale Stephen E W | Parr Brown Gee & Loveless |
| Houpt Timothy C | Jones Waldo * |
| Hunt Jeffrey J | Parr Brown Gee & Loveless |
| Lund John R | Snow, Christensen & Martineau |
| Magleby James E | Magleby & Greenwood PC * |
| Marsden Milo Steven | Dorsey & Whitney LLP |
| Moscon D Matthew | Stoel Rives LLP |
| Wheeler Max | Snow, Christensen & Martineau |

**Band 3**

| | |
|---|---|
| Adams John A | Ray Quinney & Nebeker P.C. |
| Anderson John A | Stoel Rives LLP |
| Bailey Michael | Parsons Behle & Latimer PC * |
| Christiansen Stephen | Van Cott, Bagley, Cornwall & McCarthy, P.C. |
| Gaylord Mark | Ballard Spahr LLP (ONP)† * |
| Gross Jefferson W | Burbidge Mitchell & Gross |
| Harrington John P | Holland & Hart LLP * |
| Lalli Matthew L | Snell & Wilmer LLP |
| Larsen Michael L | Parsons Behle & Latimer PC * |
| Rose Rick L | Ray Quinney & Nebeker P.C. |
| Savage Greggory | Ray Quinney & Nebeker P.C. |
| Shields Jeffrey Weston | Snell & Wilmer LLP |
| Sullivan Christopher | Snell & Wilmer LLP |
| Wing Robert | Prince, Yeates & Geldzahler (ONP)† |

* Indicates firm / individual with profile.
† ONP = Other Notable Practitioner.

## Snell & Wilmer LLP
See profile on p.517

**THE FIRM** This 25-strong litigation team earns high praise from peers and clients. The group has expertise in a host of areas catering to its varied client base, representing companies in the healthcare, utilities and finance industries. The group regularly represents a series of significant clients including KPMG, the American Board of Pediatrics and Intermountain HealthCare.

**Sources say:** "*You can trust them to be very effective when they need to represent clients.*"

**KEY INDIVIDUALS Alan Sullivan** is hailed as "*one of the finest litigators in Utah*" and has a wealth of experience in commercial, securities and healthcare litigation. **Matthew Lalli** is an experienced trial attorney and practices in the areas of corporate control, securities and business fraud. **Jeffrey Shields** recently joined the firm from Jones Waldo. He focuses on complex business litigation, specializing in bankruptcy-related disputes. **Christopher Sullivan** has a national practice, litigating complex disputes often on behalf of accounting firms and auditors.

## Band 2

### Holland & Hart LLP
See profile on p.727

**THE FIRM** The Utah practice at this national firm is particularly recognized in IP, environmental and natural resource litigation. The team has been particularly active of late in a series of receivership and banking-related disputes. The firm's client portfolio includes Rolls-Royce, DHL Express and US Oil Sands.

**KEY INDIVIDUALS** Peers are quick to describe **George Haley** (see p.2473) as a "*phenomenal practitioner.*" He has extensive experience in handling complex commercial litigation. The "*terrific*" **Blaine Benard** (see p.2472) focuses his practice on commercial disputes, with expertise in healthcare and IP matters. **John Harrington** (see p.2474) is recognized for his extensive trial experience. He handles complex commercial and civil disputes.

### Parr Brown Gee & Loveless, A Professional Corporation
See profile on p.2479

**THE FIRM** This Utah firm has a well-established litigation practice which handles complex commercial disputes on behalf of clients from a range of industries. The firm's strengths include construction-related disputes, representing a number of large construction companies, as well as corporate and real estate litigation and an increasing depth of experience in IP.

**KEY INDIVIDUALS Robert Clark** has a broad litigation practice which includes representing companies in securities, antitrust and IP disputes on a national scale. The well-regarded **Jonathan Hafen** focuses his practice on litigating cases related to securities and employment law. Established partner **Stephen Hale** is known to handle disputes for clients in technology, construction and manufacturing

industries. **Jeffrey Hunt** continues to earn market praise for his commercial and First Amendment expertise.

## Stoel Rives LLP

**THE FIRM** This firm rates highly among peers and has expertise in a broad range of industry areas, advising clients in sectors including media, technology, renewable energy and life sciences. Notable work includes representing Rocky Mountain Power in a lawsuit against the Sierra Club involving the prevention of over $100 million of pollution control devices being included in the base rate of Utah utility tariffs.

**KEY INDIVIDUALS Matthew Moscon** handles various commercial disputes and has been increasingly involved with issues in the energy and utilities space. **Kenneth Black** handles commercial litigation with a focus on IP-related disputes. Commentators praise **John Anderson**, particularly for his experience in product liability law.

## Band 3

### Anderson & Karrenberg

**THE FIRM** This litigation boutique is well regarded for its ability to handle a range of disputes, serving clients on both a local and regional basis. The group's strengths include complex commercial litigation, as well as real estate-related issues and condemnation litigation.

**KEY INDIVIDUALS Thomas Karrenberg** is a highly regarded trial lawyer whose litigation practice includes commercial disputes, antitrust and securities matters.

### Dorsey & Whitney LLP
See profile on p.1583

**THE FIRM** This firm has the ability to handle a range of commercial disputes with additional expertise in product liability and bankruptcy litigation. The firm's depth gives it the capacity to service clients from various industries including healthcare, real estate and construction.

**KEY INDIVIDUALS** Previously at Snell & Wilmer, **Bryon Benevento** brings his product liability and IP expertise to Dorsey's commercial litigation team. Sources say: "*Bryon is an ideal litigation attorney. He brings a bulldog mentality balanced with a good practical understanding of the best interests of his clients.*" Department head **Steven Marsden** is described as "*a really fine lawyer*" and focuses his practice on commercial litigation involving securities and fraud.

### Jones Waldo
See profile on p.2478

**THE FIRM** This firm has a solid litigation practice with a deep bench of trial lawyers offering a diverse set of technical skills. In addition to general business disputes involving securities, bankruptcy and fraud, clients have praised the team for its insurance defense work. Regence BlueCross BlueShield of Utah, Unishippers Global Logistics, 4Life Research and Cedar Mountain Environmental are among the firm's clientele.

**KEY INDIVIDUALS** The "*terrific*" **Timothy Houpt** (see p.2474) has litigation experience in various areas including IP, ERISA, insurance and securities. Sources say: "*Tim has excellent courtroom and negotiation skills.*"

## Magleby & Greenwood PC

**THE FIRM** This litigation boutique is praised for having a host of talented trial lawyers able to handle complex commercial disputes. Recent work includes representing USA Power in bringing forward a trade secrets suit against PacifiCorp, with a unanimous jury verdict awarding the plaintiffs over $130 million in damages.

**Sources say:** "*Their performance is excellent – very bright lawyers, very good work.*"

**KEY INDIVIDUALS** The well-regarded **James Magleby** (see p.2474) concentrates on IP, commercial and civil litigation. Sources say: "*He brings wicked smarts, uncanny intuition and appropriate passion to the cases he works on.*"

## Snow, Christensen & Martineau

**THE FIRM** This firm has a well-regarded commercial litigation practice representing clients in business disputes both in and out of state. The group has skills in a wide range of issues including antitrust, real estate, class actions, bankruptcy and technology, allowing it to handle cases for clients in various industries.

**KEY INDIVIDUALS John Lund** is well regarded among peers. His practice is centered on commercial disputes, with a specialty in product and professional liability suits. **Max Wheeler** has extensive experience in complex civil and white-collar criminal litigation.

## Van Cott, Bagley, Cornwall & McCarthy, P.C.

**THE FIRM** This firm retains a broad-based practice with expertise in business, construction, First Amendment and product liability law. The group also continues to expand its litigation practice, making inroads to the criminal law space in order to offer clients a more rounded service.

**KEY INDIVIDUALS John Ashton** chairs the firm's litigation group and handles civil and IP disputes. **Stephen Christiansen** has a broad litigation practice, representing clients in commercial disputes pertaining to a diverse range of issues.

## Other Notable Practitioners

**Peter Billings** of Fabian Law is known for handling complex commercial litigation. Sources report: "*He has great judgment and great technical skills. A real top-flight practitioner.*" **Mark Gaylord** (see p.2473) of Ballard Spahr LLP focuses on business litigation and real estate development-related disputes. One interviewee comments: "*His service has been exceptional. He is an important asset to our business.*" The well-regarded **Robert Wing** of Prince, Yeates & Geldzahler represents clients in IP and real estate-related disputes.

# REAL ESTATE

Commentary about individuals can be found under their firm's paragraph. If the firm has no paragraph (is not ranked) look at Other Notable Practitioners.

| Real Estate |
| --- |
| **Leading Firms** |

| **Band 1** |
| --- |
| Jones Waldo * |
| Parr Brown Gee & Loveless, A Professional Corporation * |
| Stoel Rives LLP |

| **Band 2** |
| --- |
| Ballard Spahr LLP * |
| Kirton & McConkie |
| Parsons Behle & Latimer PC * |
| Ray Quinney & Nebeker P.C. * |

| **Band 3** |
| --- |
| Holland & Hart LLP * |
| Van Cott, Bagley, Cornwall & McCarthy, P.C. |

| **Senior Statesmen** |
| --- |

| Senior Statesmen: distinguished older practitioners | |
| --- | --- |
| Maak Charles | Parr Brown Gee & Loveless |

| **Leading Individuals** |
| --- |

| **Band 1** | |
| --- | --- |
| Ellison Thomas A | Stoel Rives LLP |
| Ferrin Shawn | Parsons Behle & Latimer PC * |
| Gee David E | Parr Brown Gee & Loveless |
| Hyde Robert C | Kirton & McConkie |

| **Band 2** | |
| --- | --- |
| Banks Diane | Fabian Law (ONP)[†] |
| Bennett Thomas G | Ballard Spahr LLP * |
| Berggren Tom | Jones Waldo * |
| Broadbent David K | Holland & Hart LLP * |
| Cook Rand | Van Cott, Bagley, Cornwall & McCarthy, P.C. |
| Cunningham Brian D | Snell & Wilmer LLP (ONP)[†] |
| Holmes Ervin R | Stoel Rives LLP |
| Kroesche Guy P | Stoel Rives LLP |
| McConnell Robert A | Parr Brown Gee & Loveless |
| Moore Larry | Ray Quinney & Nebeker P.C. |
| Peterson Steven D | Ballard Spahr LLP * |
| Rowe Keven M | Jones Waldo * |
| Rubinfeld Ira B | Ray Quinney & Nebeker P.C. |
| Watkins Glen | Jones Waldo * |
| Williams Gregory | Van Cott, Bagley, Cornwall & McCarthy, P.C. |

| **Band 3** | |
| --- | --- |
| Barton Carl | Holland & Hart LLP * |
| Harman Paul M | Jones Waldo |
| Hellewell Read | Kirton & McConkie |
| Meaders William A | Kirton & McConkie |
| Owens Kerry L | Parsons Behle & Latimer PC * |
| Whitehead Steven | Kirton & McConkie |

| **Up-and-coming individuals** | |
| --- | --- |
| Evans Nicole C | Ballard Spahr LLP * |

* Indicates individual with profile.

[†]ONP = Other Notable Practitioner.

## Band 1

### Jones Waldo
See profile on p.2478

THE FIRM Jones Waldo's real estate practice continues to be a standout choice in the Utah market. Its deep bench of 23 attorneys is able to deal with the full scope of real estate matters at a national level, handling development, acquisition, financing and leasing aspects of real estate transactions for various developers, investors and lenders. The group has been praised for its work involving loan restructuring, acquisitions and tax credit issues, and recently assisted the Redevelopment Agency of Salt Lake City with the $120 million development of a 2,500 seat theater.

Sources say: *"They are excellent. Very knowledgeable and professional, they draft excellent contracts, understand the issues, protect clients and are responsive."*

KEY INDIVIDUALS **Tom Berggren** (see p.2472) brings extensive commercial lending experience to his real estate practice and is known for his expertise in real estate secured loans. **Keven Rowe** (see p.2475) focuses on corporate law, commercial lending and complex real estate transactions. He has recently acted for Wells Fargo on the restructuring of credit facilities, closing of real estate loans, and property acquisitions and transfers with a combined value of over $400 million. **Glen Watkins** (see p.2476) is an experienced real estate lawyer focusing on complex real estate transactions which often involve commercial, retail or resorts properties. **Paul Harman** has deep experience in acting for retail clients. He has recently handled a series of site acquisitions and leases for Lowe's valued at $40 million.

### Parr Brown Gee & Loveless, A Professional Corporation
See profile on p.2479

THE FIRM Parr Brown remains a formidable force in the state for its highly regarded real estate practice. The group handles commercial, industrial and residential real estate development projects, covering acquisitions, development, financing and leasing issues. The team is also able to utilize its construction and land use expertise to deal with all aspects of a transaction seamlessly for developers, lenders and landowners.

KEY INDIVIDUALS The *"terrific"* **David Gee** has a highly regarded business and finance practice, bringing his expertise in project financing and asset-based and structured lending to his real estate practice. **Robert McConnell** concentrates on financing transactions and real estate development, representing clients in retail and residential real estate matters. The highly respected **Charles Maak** has a wealth of experience in the real estate arena, having represented clients in various issues involving residential, commercial and industrial real estate developments.

### Stoel Rives LLP

THE FIRM This firm's real estate practice continues to be held in high esteem by both clients and peers thanks to its ability to provide exceptional service across the spectrum of real estate-related issues. In addition to handling real property development matters such as acquisitions, leasing and land use, the group is recognized for its work involving PPP, financial restructuring, tax and construction. The team recently handled a host of sophisticated deals including the $47.5 million financing for a construction loan and a timeshare resort development project on behalf of Gardiner Properties.

KEY INDIVIDUALS **Thomas Ellison** is highly regarded for his real estate development and land use expertise. The experienced **Ervin Holmes** focuses on real estate transactions and has expertise in acquisitions, sales and leasing as well as foreclosure and workouts. **Guy Kroesche** has a broad practice which includes real estate, finance and corporate law. Clients appreciate his ability to analyze the risks associated with complex transactions.

## Band 2

### Ballard Spahr LLP
See profile on p.2234

THE FIRM This real estate practice is able to work with its offices on both coasts to provide clients with a full transactional real estate practice that is nationwide in scope. The Utah team is particularly known for its extensive expertise in the resorts and hospitality space as well as its work with timeshares and mixed-use developments. The group's client portfolio includes Diamond Resorts International, Wal-Mart, DCP International and Snowbird Ski and Summer Resort.

Sources say: *"All of them are excellent lawyers. They work hard, provide correct information and are sensitive to the business needs of our organization."*

KEY INDIVIDUALS **Thomas Bennett** (see p.2472) is noted for his traditional real estate practice and is the group's go-to for development-related work, particularly in the resort and hotel industries. **Steven Peterson** (see p.2475) has a national reputation for his expertise in timeshare issues pertaining to resort and hospitality law. **Nicole Evans** (see p.2473) continues to impress with her practice involving real estate. She handles condominium and resorts work, with an increasing focus on timeshare development.

### Kirton & McConkie

THE FIRM This Utah-based firm retains a 22-strong team with the capacity to cover transactional issues in commercial, residential and public real property. The group is recognized, in particular, for its expertise in commercial leasing and agricultural property issues. Notable recent work includes assisting Suburban Land Reserve with a mixed-use development project with an approximate value of $610 million.

**Sources say:** *"The individuals I work with are knowledgeable and efficient in every way. They are also very quick to respond to my inquiries."*

**KEY INDIVIDUALS Robert Hyde** is praised as an *"outstanding"* attorney whose practice includes corporate law and real estate development, often handling complex commercial transactions on behalf of large developers and corporate clients. **Read Hellewell** handles commercial lending, financing and leasing transactions with significant experience in working on condominium projects. **William Meaders** concentrates on commercial real estate transactions and disputes. According to one source, *"he makes my job easier and is a delight to work with. I appreciate his knowledge and experience."* **Steven Whitehead** has a broad real estate practice with an emphasis on land use, and the leasing and development of commercial and residential properties.

## Parsons Behle & Latimer PC
See profile on p.2480

**THE FIRM** This firm has a solid real estate and finance department with a broad range of expertise which serves clients in a diverse set of industries including resorts, retail and mining. The group is adept in the acquisition, permitting, development and finance of real estate projects and is also known for its ability to resolve related disputes with strong litigation capabilities. Clients include The Home Depot, JPMorgan Chase and First Wind.

**KEY INDIVIDUALS Shawn Ferrin** (see p.2473) is a *"top-notch real estate guy,"* according to commentators. He handles real estate transactions involving community, retail and resort developments. **Kerry Owens** (see p.2475) concentrates on the acquisition, sale and development of commercial, residential and industrial real property. Sources say: *"He has great business acumen and is able to cut to the point of what we are looking to achieve."*

## Ray Quinney & Nebeker P.C.
See profile on p.2481

**THE FIRM** This firm has a well-regarded real estate practice which receives high praise from clients for its work involving the acquisition, sale, financing and leasing of commercial real estate. The group is also noted for its ability to handle the zoning and environmental aspects of a transaction, drawing on the firm's various areas of expertise. The group's client portfolio includes Zions First National Bank, Sinclair Oil and Rocky Mountain Power.

**Sources say:** *"They have been excellent to work with. They have excellent skills in the area of real estate transactions."*

**KEY INDIVIDUALS Larry Moore**'s practice covers a wide range of real estate issues and he is particularly noted for his ability to litigate property-related disputes. **Ira Rubinfeld** focuses on real estate transactions including the acquisition, sale and leasing of real property. Sources say he is *"great to work with"* and *"has good judgment as to the risk of certain decisions."*

## Band 3

### Holland & Hart LLP
See profile on p.727

**THE FIRM** Holland & Hart represents clients from various industries on a number of transactional real estate matters. The team's expertise includes the development, financing and acquisition of real estate projects and it also has experience in construction and zoning issues. Recent highlights include the $325 million development, financing and sale of an Idaho-based wind farm on behalf of Cedar Creek Wind.

**KEY INDIVIDUALS Carl Barton** (see p.2472) represents developers, banks and other institutional lenders in the acquisition, financing and leasing of commercial real estate developments. **David Broadbent** (see p.2473) has a broad practice and brings his financing, loan workouts and restructuring expertise to his real estate development work.

### Van Cott, Bagley, Cornwall & McCarthy, P.C.

**THE FIRM** This firm has a well-established real estate practice which is able to assist its clients in significant transactional issues including the acquisition, sale, development and leasing of commercial real property. The group is particularly involved of late with the acquisition and financings of industrial real estate developments, representing clients in a range of industry sectors.

**KEY INDIVIDUALS Gregory Williams** and **Rand Cook** are both hailed as *"outstanding lawyers."* Williams focuses on real property development and business-related real estate transactions, while Cook is known for his commercial real estate and lending practice.

## Other Notable Practitioners

**Diane Banks** of Fabian Law focuses on real estate development and transactions. According to sources, she is *"very experienced and very polished; a good lawyer."* **Brian Cunningham** of Snell & Wilmer LLP has a well-regarded commercial finance and real estate lending practice, representing banks and other financial institutions in structuring secured and unsecured real estate loans.

# Leaders' Profiles in Utah

**ANDERSON, P Christian (Chris)**
Ballard Spahr LLP, Salt Lake City
801 517 6826
andersonc@ballardspahr.com
*Featured in Corporate/M&A (Utah)*
**Practice Areas:** Paul Christian (Chris) Anderson is a partner in the Business and Finance Department, practicing business, securities, and international law. He focuses on venture capital transactions for emerging-growth companies, representing high-technology companies in the initial stages of development and more mature companies in public and private financings, acquisitions, dispositions, recapitalizations, mergers, and other commercial transactions and agreements.
**Professional Memberships:** American Bar Association Utah State Bar Member and past President, International and Securities Sections California State Bar.
**Career:** Admissions: California Utah.
**Personal:** University of Utah, S.J. Quinney College of Law (JD 1978) University of Utah (BA, 1976).

**BAAR, Lois A**
Holland & Hart LLP, Salt Lake City
801 799 5929
labaar@hollandhart.com
*Featured in Labor & Employment (Utah)*
**Practice Areas:** Employment litigation, counseling, training and mediation.
**Professional Memberships:** Fellow, College of Labor and Employment Lawyers; Utah Bar Foundation Board; ABA, Labor and Employment, ADR sections; Utah Bar, Employment, ADR sections; Utah Council on Conflict Resolution; US District Court Mediator/Arbitrator Panel; President Legal Aid Society 1999; Utah Antidiscrimination Advisory Council 1998-2003; Utah Business "Top 100 Legal Elite" since 2004; Best Lawyers in America, Employment Law, since 1994, including 2010 Utah Employment Lawyer of the Year.
**Personal:** University of Utah College of Law (JD 1982); Drexel University (MBA 1973), (BS 1968); Harvard University Negotiation Workshop, 2005.

**BABCOCK, Bruce E**
Jones Waldo, Salt Lake City
801 5347 246
bbabcock@joneswaldo.com
*Featured in Labor & Employment (Utah)*
**Practice Areas:** More than 30 years experience in tax planning for corporations, LLCs, nonprofits, partnerships and individuals. Expertise in employment law includes employment agreements, design and administration of retirement and other benefit plans, compliance issues including ERISA, COBRA and HIPAA.
**Professional Memberships:** Tax Counsel, Utah Housing Corporation - Low Income Housing Tax Credit Program.
**Career:** Practice group leader for tax, executive compensation and employee benefits, and non-profit/tax-exempt organizations, Jones Waldo.

**Personal:** JD, Brigham Young University, 1980, cum laude, Editor, Brigham Young University Law Review, 1979-80; LLM in Taxation, New York University, 1981; BS, Brigham Young University, 1977.

**BAGNASACCO, Barbara**
Ballard Spahr LLP, Salt Lake City
801 517 6831
bagnasaccob@ballardspahr.com
*Featured in Corporate/M&A (Utah)*
**Practice Areas:** Barbara Bagnasacco concentrates on international and domestic business transactions, and mergers and acquisitions, including European business transactions. She also represents domestic and international clients on corporate governance issues, including compliance with the Foreign Corrupt Practices Act.
**Professional Memberships:** American Bar Association Utah State Bar Association Association for Corporate Growth, Utah Board Member Licensed attorney in Italy.
**Career:** Admissions: Utah Italy.
**Personal:** University of Utah, S.J. Quinney College of Law (JD 1998) Institute of European Studies/International Labor Organization (Postgraduate Certificate 1996) University of Turin College of Law (BS 1995).

**BAILEY, Michael**
Parsons Behle & Latimer PC, Salt Lake City
801 532 1234
MBailey@parsonsbehle.com
*Featured in Litigation (Utah)*
**Practice Areas:** Complex commercial litigation and trial practice with an emphasis on environmental litigation and tort litigation. Represents plaintiffs and defendants in state and federal courts in many western states. Has significant arbitration and mediation experience. Also maintains an extensive governmental affairs practice including litigation in the area of election law and expertise in state and federal lobbying.
**Professional Memberships:** Utah State Bar; Arizona State Bar; American Bar Association.
**Career:** Shareholder. Former member of Parsons Behle & Latimer's Board of Directors. Former Chair of firm's Hiring Committee.
**Personal:** JD, Brigham Young University, 1986. BS, Santa Clara University, 1983.

**BARNETT, James L**
Holland & Hart LLP, Salt Lake City
801 799 5826
jbarnett@hollandhart.com
*Featured in Labor & Employment (Utah)*
**Practice Areas:** Practices in the area of complex commercial litigation, including employment litigation, employee benefits litigation, real estate litigation, and bankruptcy litigation.
**Professional Memberships:** American Bar Association, Utah Bar Association.
**Personal:** Received a JD from the University of Utah College of Law (1996) (Order of the Coif) and a BS from the University of Utah (1992) (cum laude - Finance).

**BARTON, Carl**
Holland & Hart LLP, Salt Lake City
801 799 5831
cbarton@hollandhart.com
*Featured in Real Estate (Utah)*
**Practice Areas:** Real estate acquisitions, sales, financing, development, land use and zoning, and 1031 exchanges. Projects include resorts, large ranches and farms, hotels, shopping malls, business parks, energy facilities, restaurants, office buildings, senior and assisted living facilities, and apartment projects. His practice involves retail, office, industrial, and ground leases and real estate loans and workouts. He is also experienced in the purchase, sale, and financing of water rights.
**Professional Memberships:** Real Property and Banking and Finance, Utah State Bar.
**Career:** Admitted to the Utah State Bar (1986).
**Personal:** JD (1986) and two BA degrees (1982) from the University of Utah.

**BENARD, Blaine**
Holland & Hart LLP, Salt Lake City
801 799 5800
BJBenard@hollandhart.com
*Featured in Litigation (Utah)*
**Practice Areas:** Commercial litigation, healthcare and intellectual property litigation. Significant success in cases involving complex business disputes, healthcare providers, patent and trademark litigation, aerospace, and energy. Mr Benard represents an international aerospace and defense contracting company, an international commercial airline, hospitals, financial institutions, manufacturers, energy, and other businesses. Client mix ranges from Fortune 500 and international companies to local businesses. Mr Benard is the former chairman of the litigation department of a large regional law firm.
**Career:** Licensed: Utah (1990).
**Personal:** University of Utah JD (1990); University of Utah BS (1986).

**BENARD, Bryan**
Holland & Hart LLP, Salt Lake City
801 799 5833
bbenard@hollandhart.com
*Featured in Labor & Employment (Utah)*
**Practice Areas:** Labor and employment counseling and litigation, commercial litigation. Regularly represents employers in wrongful termination, harassment, and discrimination claims. Counsels regarding employee relations, employee and non-compete agreements, and employee handbooks. Broad experience in appellate matters, intellectual property, and complex litigation.
**Professional Memberships:** ABA; California, Utah, and Salt Lake County Bar Associations.
**Career:** Admitted: California Bar, US District Courts, Central and Southern Districts of California (1997); Utah State Bar, US District Court, District of Utah (2001); US Court of Appeals, Tenth Circuit, US Supreme Court (2004).
**Personal:** JD (1997), University of Utah; BA (1994), Weber State University.

**BENNETT, Thomas G**
Ballard Spahr LLP, Salt Lake City
801 531 3060
bennett@ballardspahr.com
*Featured in Real Estate (Utah)*
**Practice Areas:** Thomas G Bennett is a partner in the Real Estate Department and a member of the Resort and Hotel Group, Real Estate Development Group, Planned Communities and Condominiums Group, and Zoning and Land Use Group. He concentrates his practice in the development of commercial and resort properties, with an emphasis on property acquisition, financing, zoning and entitlements, construction, state and federal regulatory compliance, and development of planned communities, condominiums, timeshares, private residence clubs, golf courses, and condominium hotels.
**Professional Memberships:** American Resort Development Association.
**Career:** Admissions: Utah.
**Personal:** Brigham Young University, J. Reuben Clark Law School.

**BERGGREN, Tom**
Jones Waldo, Salt Lake City
801 534 7449
tberggren@joneswaldo.com
*Featured in Real Estate (Utah)*
**Practice Areas:** Practice includes the purchase and sale, leasing, financing and development of commercial office buildings, retail space, industrial parks, professional buildings, apartments and mixed-use projects. Represents national retailers acquiring property for stores in the West and Fortune 500 companies in negotiating governmental incentive packages.
**Professional Memberships:** ICSC; NAIOP; ABA's Committee on Legal Opinions; Salt Lake City Board of Adjustment for Zoning Appeals.
**Career:** Four years with Morrison & Foerster (San Francisco and London); Practiced in Utah since 1983. Chair, Real Estate Department; Member of Opinion Letter Committee.
**Personal:** Harvard Law School '78; Harvard College '74.

**BLATTNER-THOMPSON, Elisabeth**
Ballard Spahr LLP, Salt Lake City
801 517 6844
BlattnerThompsonE@BallardSpahr.com
*Featured in Labor & Employment (Utah)*
**Practice Areas:** Partner Elisabeth R Blattner-Thompson practices exclusively in employment law. She advises management on employment law compliance and risk reduction, trains workforces on employment law topics, investigates employee complaints and recommends responses, structures and implements employee training, and defends employers against employee claims.
**Professional Memberships:** American Bar Association, Labor and Employment Law and Litigation sections Litigation Counsel of America, Fellow Senior HR Forum.

**Career:** Admissions: California Utah US District Court for the District of Utah US Court of Appeals for the Tenth Circuit.
**Personal:** Education: University of Utah, S.J. Quinney College of Law, JD University of Utah, BS.

---

**BROADBENT, David K**
Holland & Hart LLP, Salt Lake City
801 799 5806
dbroadbent@hollandhart.com
*Featured in Real Estate (Utah)*
**Practice Areas:** Real estate and corporate law. Represents clients in real estate and corporate acquisition and financing transactions, including conventional, conduit, tax credit, and bond financing. Projects include acquisition, development and financing of shopping centers, office buildings, office park, condominiums, hotels, multi-family housing, wind energy projects and radio stations.
**Professional Memberships:** Real Property and Business Law sections, Utah State Bar; Business Law and Real Property Sections, ABA. Chairman, Real Property Section, Utah State Bar; Board Chairman, Valley Mental Health.
**Career:** Admitted to the Utah State Bar (1979).
**Personal:** Received JD (1979) and BA (1976), University of Utah.

---

**BUTLER, Jim B**
Parsons Behle & Latimer PC, Reno
801 532 1234
JButler@parsonsbehle.com
*Featured in Environment (Nevada), Energy & Natural Resources (Utah)*
See under Nevada for profile.

---

**DUNNING, Elizabeth**
Holland & Hart LLP, Salt Lake City
801 799 5959
ETDunning@hollandhart.com
*Featured in Labor & Employment (Utah)*
**Practice Areas:** Litigates employment and discrimination cases in state and federal courts and before administrative agencies. Advises on employment, privacy, and data protection policies and practices in US and international matters. Serves as an arbitrator and mediator for the Alternative Dispute Resolution Program of the US District Court, District of Utah.
**Professional Memberships:** American Bar Association, Labor and Employment Law Section and International Law Section.
**Career:** Licensed: Massachusetts (1977); New York (1980); Utah (1982); US Court of Appeals, First, Tenth and Federal Circuits; US Supreme Court.
**Personal:** Harvard JD (magna cum laude) (1977); Barnard College BA (magna cum laude) (1968).

---

**ETCHEVERRY, Raymond J**
Parsons Behle & Latimer PC, Salt Lake City
801 532 1234
REtcheverry@parsonsbehle.com
*Featured in Litigation (Utah)*
**Practice Areas:** Complex business litigation with expertise in antitrust and securities defense including class action defense, intellectual proper-

ty disputes involving primarily patents and trade secrets, and insurance coverage disputes.
**Professional Memberships:** Fellow, American Bar Foundation. Member, American Bar Association: Litigation Section; Antitrust Section; Intellectual Property Section. Master of the Bench, American Inns of Court II.
**Career:** President and Chairman of the Board of Directors, 1992-present.
**Personal:** JD, Duke University. Honors BS, magna cum laude, University of Utah.

---

**EVANS, Nicole C**
Ballard Spahr LLP, Salt Lake City
801 531 3058
evansn@ballardspahr.com
*Featured in Real Estate (Utah)*
**Practice Areas:** Nicole C Evans is a partner in the Real Estate Department and member of the Resort and Hotel Group and the Planned Communities and Condominiums Group. Ms Evans has a broad-based practice in resort and hospitality law, including resort development, timesharing, fractionals, condominium hotels and analysis of club structures. She is counsel to owners, franchisors and franchisees with respect to due diligence, branding and development of hospitality properties.
**Professional Memberships:** American Resort Development Association. Member, Utah Chapter of Commercial Real Estate Women.
**Career:** Admissions: Nevada Utah.
**Personal:** University of Utah, S.J. Quinney College of Law (JD 2000).

---

**FERRIN, Shawn**
Parsons Behle & Latimer PC, Salt Lake City
801 532 1234
SFerrin@parsonsbehle.com
*Featured in Real Estate (Utah)*
**Practice Areas:** Real property transactions, with emphasis on retail and resort development, and land use planning. Handles acquisition, lease and financing transactions for numerous clients, including Home Depot, Fidelity Investments, Barrick Mining, Canyons Resort and Micron Technology.
**Professional Memberships:** American Bar Association: Real Property Section. Utah State Bar: Real Property Section.
**Career:** Shareholder and past Chair, Real Estate & Finance department. Executive Committee, Economic Development Corporation of Utah (past). Adjunct Professor, S.J. Quinney College of Law, Advanced Real Estate Drafting.
**Personal:** JD, University of Utah, 1986. BUS, University of Utah, 1982.

---

**FLINT, George**
Parsons Behle & Latimer PC, Salt Lake City
801 532 1234
GFlint@parsonsbehle.com
*Featured in Corporate/M&A (Utah)*
**Practice Areas:** Deal lawyer whose practice focuses on domestic and international transactions including acquisitions, financings, workouts, joint-ventures and commercial agreements, and the ongoing representation of businesses focused on corporate growth through dealmaking.

Extensive M&A and international law background, including nine years with Skadden Arps (NY and London). Counseled clients in over $15 billion in M&A transactions.
**Professional Memberships:** Board Member and Past Chairman, Utah Chapter-Association for Corporate Growth www.acgutah.org
**Personal:** JD, Georgetown University Law Center, 1984, member Georgetown Law Review. A.B., Duke University.

---

**FOSTER, Brett**
Holland & Hart LLP, Salt Lake City
801 799 5836
bfoster@hollandhart.com
*Featured in Intellectual Property (Utah)*
**Practice Areas:** Mr Foster has extensive experience in strategically managing disputes related to patents, trademarks, trade secrets, false advertising, unfair competition and copyrights. He counsels clients on how to build strong intellectual property assets and diligently enforce their rights.
**Professional Memberships:** Utah Bar, IP Section; Arizona Bar; Western District of Michigan, Federal Circuit Court of Appeals; Tenth Circuit Court of Appeals; ABA; AIPLA.
**Career:** IP Litigation Practice Group Manager 2001-12.
**Personal:** Brigham Young University, JD, cum laude, 1990, Student Bar Association President; University of Utah, BS, 1987; Dixie College A.A., 1984, Student Body President.

---

**FOSTER, L Grant**
Holland & Hart LLP, Salt Lake City
801 799 5830
gfoster@hollandhart.com
*Featured in Intellectual Property (Utah)*
**Practice Areas:** As a registered patent attorney, Mr Foster has extensive experience in US and foreign patent and trademark prosecution, IP licensing and litigation, IP opinions and due diligence. By combining his technical knowledge as an engineer and his specialized prosecution skills and litigation experience, he is able to advise clients on the most sophisticated of IP issues.
**Professional Memberships:** Utah State Bar Association; Washington State Bar Association; IP Board, Northwestern School of Law of Lewis & Clark College; AIPLA.
**Personal:** JD Northwestern School of Law of Lewis & Clark College (1989); BS Engineering University of Utah.

---

**GALLI, Craig D**
Holland & Hart LLP, Salt Lake City
801 799 5842
cgalli@hollandhart.com
*Featured in Energy & Natural Resources (Utah)*
**Practice Areas:** Focuses on litigation in a variety of natural resources, environmental, public lands and energy-related civil and criminal cases. Advises a wide range of clients on compliance with NEPA, CWA, RCRA, CERCLA, and ESA.
**Professional Memberships:** Member, Bars of the District of Columbia, Utah, Colorado, and US Courts of Appeals for the 1st, 2nd, 9th, 10th and DC Circuits.

**Career:** Senior Trial Attorney, Environment and Natural Resources Division, Department of Justice (1989-93). Teaches environmental law as an adjunct professor.
**Publications:** Has published numerous articles on environmental issues.
**Personal:** Columbia University (JD 1987); Brigham Young University (MA 1984; BA 1982).

---

**GAVRE, Mark**
Parsons Behle & Latimer PC, Salt Lake City
801 532 1234
MGavre@parsonsbehle.com
*Featured in Labor & Employment (Utah)*
**Practice Areas:** Employment, labor and benefits law, including ERISA litigation, wrongful discharge, workplace discrimination, sexual/other harassment claims, employee pension and benefits, union relations and whistleblower complaints, and alternative dispute resolution.
**Professional Memberships:** Utah State Bar.
**Career:** Shareholder. Intern for Justice Christine Durham of the Utah Supreme Court. Before becoming an attorney, was professor of political science at the University of Utah.
**Personal:** JD, University of Utah, 1985. PhD University of California, Los Angeles, 1978. Fulbright Scholar, University of Madrid. BA, University of California, Berkeley, 1968.

---

**GAYLORD, Mark**
Ballard Spahr LLP, Salt Lake City
801 531 3070
gaylord@ballardspahr.com
*Featured in Litigation (Utah)*
**Practice Areas:** Mr Gaylord focuses on complex civil litigation, at both the trial and appellate levels in federal and state courts throughout the country, with an emphasis on corporate business litigation, land use and development disputes, and construction matters. He handles complex matters in a variety of areas, including environmental, creditor and bankruptcy, and business governance.
**Professional Memberships:** American Bar Association, Federal Bar Association, Utah Bar Association, Utah Trial Lawyers Association.
**Career:** Utah, US Supreme Court, US Court of Appeals for the Ninth and Tenth Circuit.
**Personal:** University of Utah, S.J. Quinney College of Law (JD) Lewis and Clark College (BS).

---

**HALEY, George M**
Holland & Hart LLP, Salt Lake City
801 799 5880
gmhaley@hollandhart.com
*Featured in Litigation (Utah)*
**Practice Areas:** Trial lawyer focusing on complex commercial litigation, including class actions, natural resources/energy litigation, IP disputes, financial fraud, and legal malpractice defense. American Board of Trial Advocate's 2003 Utah Trial Lawyer of the Year; Best Lawyers' 2012 Utah Lawyer of the Year (Environmental Litigation).
**Professional Memberships:** International Academy of Trial Lawyers (Board of Directors); American College of Trial Lawyers; American Board of Trial Advocates.

**Publications:** Annual ABA Survey of State Class Litigation Law, Contributing editor to 'Newberg on Class Actions'; Business & Commercial Litigation in Federal Courts, Third Edition, Energy Chapter.
**Personal:** University of Utah JD (1978).

### HARRINGTON, John P
Holland & Hart LLP, Salt Lake City
801 799 5819
jharrington@hollandhart.com
*Featured in Litigation (Utah)*
**Practice Areas:** Mr Harrington has more than 30 years of experience as a trial lawyer. He represents clients in complex commercial litigation. His extensive experience includes jury and bench trials in state and federal courts in Utah, Nevada, New York, California, and Texas.
**Career:** Mr Harrington is admitted to practice in front of the US Supreme Court, 9th and 10th Circuit Court of Appeals, and the US District Court for the District of Utah and Colorado. He is a member of the Utah, Colorado and Texas bars.
**Personal:** University of Colorado School of Law, 1977; Dartmouth College, AB 1973.

### HOLTKAMP, James A
Holland & Hart LLP, Salt Lake City
801 799 5847
jholtkamp@hollandhart.com
*Featured in Energy & Natural Resources (Utah)*
**Practice Areas:** Represents industry and government clients in various environmental, natural resources and energy project development issues. Extensively involved in air quality and climate change issues including corporate climate change policies, avoided deforestation, carbon credit trading and development of governmental programs.
**Career:** Current Leader of the firm's Climate Change Practice Team. Adjunct professor of law at the University of Utah.
**Publications:** Has published numerous articles on climate change and air pollution control.
**Personal:** George Washington University (JD 1975); Brigham Young University (BA 1972).

### HOUPT, Timothy C
Jones Waldo, Salt Lake City
801 534 7250
thoupt@joneswaldo.com
*Featured in Litigation (Utah)*
**Practice Areas:** Represents individuals and businesses in lawsuits before administrative agencies, federal and state courts and in mediations and arbitrations. Experience in franchising, insurance and personal injury, intellectual property, securities fraud and commercial disputes.
**Professional Memberships:** Former president, Watkiss Sutherland Inn of the American Inns of Court; Fellow, American College of Trial Lawyers.
**Career:** Jones Waldo, Partner, 1988-present; Law Clerk, Chief United States District Judge Willis Ritter; Adjunct Professor of Trial Advocacy, University of Utah College of Law.
**Personal:** JD, University of Utah College of Law, 1977; BA, Northwestern University, 1972.

### HULL, Stephen J
Parsons Behle & Latimer PC, Salt Lake City
801 532 1234
SHull@parsonsbehle.com
*Featured in Energy & Natural Resources (Utah)*
**Practice Areas:** Mining law. Represents small and large mining companies in domestic (United States) and international (principally Central and South America) transactions. Focuses on structuring and negotiating acquisitions, joint ventures and project financings, and has participated in a number of major domestic and international projects. Substantial experience in Unites States Mining Law.
**Professional Memberships:** Utah State Bar Association: Energy, Natural Resources & Environmental Section. American Bar Association: Natural Resources Section.
**Career:** Shareholder, Environmental, Energy and Natural Resources department.
**Personal:** JD, University of Utah, 1978. BS, West Virginia University, 1970.

### JENKINS, Lucy B
Jones Waldo, Salt Lake City
801 534 7356
ljenkins@joneswaldo.com
*Featured in Energy & Natural Resources (Utah)*
**Practice Areas:** Practice focuses on business transactions involving environmentally impaired properties, redevelopment of Brownfields properties, acquisition of military base properties, remediation under state and federal environmental programs, voluntary cleanups, defending EPA and state administrative environmental enforcement actions, environmentall permitting and compliance, clean energy, environmental insurance, cleanup litigation and toxic torts.
**Career:** Jones Waldo, Chair, Energy, Natural Resources and Environmental practice group.
**Personal:** J. Reuben Clark Law School, Brigham Young University, 1979; University of Colorado, 1974; Energy Law Fellowship at the University of Utah College of Law from 1979 to 1980.

### KIRSCHNER, Lisa
Parsons Behle & Latimer PC, Salt Lake City
801 532 1234
LKirschner@parsonsbehle.com
*Featured in Energy & Natural Resources (Utah)*
**Practice Areas:** Environmental matters, with focus on local, state and federal water quality regulation. Works with clients to obtain, comply with and defend permits involving water quality regulation, including surface/groundwater discharges, underground injection, municipal water supply/treatment, wetlands.
**Professional Memberships:** Northwest Mining Association, Board of Trustees; Utah State Bar – Energy, Environment, Natural Resources Section; American Bar Association - Natural Resources and Environmental Law Section (Natural Resources & Environment, Editorial Board).
**Career:** Shareholder, Environmental, Energy & Natural Resources department.
**Personal:** JD, University of Denver College of Law, 1990. Master of Science, University of Arizona, 1984. BA, Williams College, 1981.

### LARSEN, Michael L
Parsons Behle & Latimer PC, Salt Lake City
801 532 1234
MLarsen@parsonsbehle.com
*Featured in Litigation (Utah)*
**Practice Areas:** Complex commercial litigation and trial practice for aerospace, mining, information technology, insurance, business, intellectual property, and manufacturing clients. Maintains a diverse and extensive trial practice representing plaintiffs and defendants in state and federal courts in a number of jurisdictions, while also utilizing his skills in numerous arbitrations and mediations.
**Professional Memberships:** Utah State Bar Association: Litigation Section; American Bar Association: Litigation Section.
**Career:** Shareholder, Parsons Behle & Latimer's Litigation Department—Utah's largest; Litigation Department Chair-1999-2010.
**Personal:** JD, Brigham Young University, 1983. BA, Utah State University 1980.

### LINDLEY, Greg
Holland & Hart LLP, Salt Lake City
801 799 5829
glindley@hollandhart.com
*Featured in Corporate/M&A (Utah)*
**Practice Areas:** Corporate, securities, mergers and acquisitions, and franchise law. Represented numerous companies with bank financings, joint ventures, distributorship, licensing agreements, and general contractual matters. Worked on numerous public and private offerings of securities. Represents public companies in Securities Exchange Act compliance. Represented both buyers and sellers in mergers and acquisitions in numerous industries, including food manufacture and distribution, banking, printing and publishing, insurance, manufacturing, and medical diagnostics. Counseled on organizational, executive compensation, and fundraising issues.
**Career:** Admitted to Utah (1989) and Texas Bar (1983).
**Personal:** JD, Duke University (1983); MBA (1981) and BS (1978), Utah State University.

### MAGLEBY, James E
Magleby & Greenwood PC, Salt Lake City
801 359 9000
magleby@mgpclaw.com
*Featured in Litigation (Utah)*
**Practice Areas:** James E Magleby practices in all areas of intellectual property and complex civil and commercial litigation. Mr Magleby's litigation experience includes disputes involving theft of trade secrets, intellectual property, trademark and unfair competition, trade dress, fiduciary duty, fraud, real property, construction, partnership and business dissolutions, securities, commercial and residential landlord-tenant disputes, and complex probate or estate matters. Recent jury trial and arbitration victories include a $10.5 million trade secret verdict, a $1.3 million civil bench verdict, defense award on a $27 million arbitration claim, a $45 million settlement in a FINRA securities arbitration, and the $134 million jury verdict in USA Power v. PacifiCorp as co-counsel with firm partner Peggy A. Tomsic.
**Professional Memberships:** Mr Magleby is A/V rated by Martindale Hubble, the highest rating available for an attorney from that organization. Mr Magleby has been consistently voted by his peers as one of Utah's "Legal Elite," as published in Utah Business Magazine, and included on the list of Mountain States Super LawyersTM, an honor given to only the top 5% of attorneys practicing in the Mountain States. Mr Magleby has been listed in the Mountain States Top 75, as one of the top 75 lawyers in all of Nevada, Utah, Montana, Idaho, and Wyoming. Mr Magleby has been listed in Best Lawyers® in the area of Litigation-Real Estate. Mr Magleby has been listed as a leading lawyer in Utah in the 2010 through 2013 editions of Chambers USA. (The Magleby & Greenwood, P.C. firm has been listed in Chambers USA as a leading firm for Litigation: General Commercial, since 2011).
**Career:** In 2005, James Magleby and Christine Greenwood formed Magleby & Greenwood, PC, as a boutique litigation firm dedicated to providing its clients with creative and effective solutions to challenging and complex business and civil disputes.

### MALMQUIST, Michael J
Parsons Behle & Latimer PC, Salt Lake City
801 532 1234
MMalmquist@parsonsbehle.com
*Featured in Energy & Natural Resources (Utah)*
**Practice Areas:** Helps clients develop energy, natural resource and transportation projects. Advises on environmental, land use, NEPA, wildlife, and public land permits, issues and strategies. Defends permit appeals and lawsuits involving claims under NEPA, FLPMA, the ESA, the Clean Water and Air Acts and public land laws. Due diligence on energy and natural resource projects.
**Professional Memberships:** Board of Trustees, Rocky Mountain Mineral Law Foundation.
**Career:** Shareholder, former head of Environmental, Energy and Natural Resources department; US Department of Justice, Environment & Natural Resources Division (1988-92).
**Personal:** JD, University of Utah, 1988 (honors); BA, Gustavus Adolphus College, 1977 (honors).

### MANGUM, David G
Parsons Behle & Latimer PC, Salt Lake City
801 532 1234
DMangum@parsonsbehle.com
*Featured in Intellectual Property (Utah)*
**Practice Areas:** Intellectual property and antitrust litigation. Represents clients in intellectual property and antitrust lawsuits in federal courts throughout the United States. Litigates patents pertaining to biological, chemical, electrical and mechanical products and processes in a variety of industries, including oil and gas production, biotechnology, computer software and hardware and medical treatment.

**Professional Memberships:** Utah State Bar and American Bar Associations: Litigation, Intellectual Property and Antitrust Sections.
**Career:** Shareholder, Intellectual Property and Antitrust Practice Group.
**Personal:** JD, magna cum laude, Order of the Coif, Brigham Young University, 1983. BA Economics, magna cum laude, University of Utah, 1980.

### MANGUM, Geoffrey W
Parsons Behle & Latimer PC, Salt Lake City
801 532 1234
GMangum@parsonsbehle.com
*Featured in Corporate/M&A (Utah)*
**Practice Areas:** General corporate and business law, with emphasis on negotiating and structuring complex business transactions, including mergers/acquisitions, joint ventures and commercial real estate financing arrangements. Extensive experience with co-branding identity issues, including co-branded credit and loyalty card programs, supply chain contracting and Foreign Corrupt Practices Act issues.
**Professional Memberships:** Utah State Bar Association; American Bar Association.
**Career:** Shareholder and current Chair of Corporate and Tax Department; former Vice President, Corporate Transactions, American Stores Company (formerly a Fortune 400 company), 1996-99.
**Personal:** JD, Georgetown University Law Center, 1979. BA, magna cum laude, University of Utah, 1976.

### O'BRIEN, Michael Patrick
Jones Waldo, Salt Lake City
801 521 3200
mobrien@joneswaldo.com
*Featured in Labor & Employment (Utah)*
**Practice Areas:** Practice includes counseling businesses and employers on how to minimize and manage risks in all aspects of labor and employment law and representing employers in employment-related litigation. Has extensive experience assisting news and publishing organizations in obtaining access to places and records, and in minimizing risks and responding to claims of defamation, invasion of privacy, tort and other matters related to publishing. Serves as an arbitrator and mediator in employment law disputes. Played an active role in lobbying for Utah's first reporter shield law, receiving a Sunshine award. Listed in Utah Business Legal Elite. Utah Employment Lawyer of the Year.
**Professional Memberships:** Works with the local and national Society for Human Resource Management (SHRM) and has been honored with its Capital Award, given annually to one of SHRM's members worldwide. Also serves as the legal and legislative director for Utah SHRM and Salt Lake SHRM and has been given its Award for Professional Excellence. Member of the Society of Professional Journalists and the National Association of Broadcasters.
**Career:** Practicing in Utah since 1986. Leader, Employment Practice Group and past Chair, Litigation Department.

**Personal:** Personal: University of Notre Dame (1983); University of Utah College of Law (1986).

### OWENS, Kerry L
Parsons Behle & Latimer PC, Salt Lake City
801 532 1234
kowens@parsonsbehle.com
*Featured in Real Estate (Utah)*
**Practice Areas:** Real estate transactions, acquisition, development, leasing and financing for retail, commercial, industrial, renewable energy and master/common interest projects. Land use, zoning and permitting/entitlement. Representative projects: industrial/mining, student housing, renewable energy, large-box retail and resort/golf course. Represents Home Depot in acquisition/development matters. Lead real estate counsel in development/financing of largest utility-scale wind energy project in Utah.
**Professional Memberships:** American Bar Association, Utah State Bar Association, International Conference Shopping Centers.
**Career:** Shareholder. Member, Utah Real Property Section. Department Chair, Real Estate Finance Department.
**Personal:** JD, University of Utah, 1996. BS, magna cum laude, Southern Illinois University, 1992.

### PETERSON, Steven D
Ballard Spahr LLP, Salt Lake City
801 531 3023
petersons@ballardspahr.com
*Featured in Real Estate (Utah)*
**Practice Areas:** Steven D Peterson is a partner in the Real Estate Department and a member of the Resort and Hotel, Planned Communities and Condominiums, Real Estate Development, and Zoning and Land Use Groups. Mr Peterson concentrates his practice in resort and hospitality law, including resort development, timesharing, fractionals, private residence club and destination club creation and operation, condominiums, resort finance, resort-related commercial real estate transactions, planned community development, community associations, ski resorts, golf course development, and zoning.
**Professional Memberships:** American Resort Development Association.
**Career:** Admissions Utah.
**Personal:** Brigham Young University, J. Reuben Clark Law School (JD 1976).

### PINEGAR, Kevin R
Durham Jones & Pinegar, PC, Salt Lake City
801 415 3000
kpinegar@djplaw.com
*Featured in Corporate/M&A (Utah)*
**Practice Areas:** Corporate and securities law, mergers and acquisitions, international law. Experience counseling public and private companies on corporate governance, public company reporting and disclosure, financing, acquisitions and transaction structuring, licensing and distribution agreements, private and public offerings.
**Professional Memberships:** Admitted to practice in Utah; US Supreme Court; Utah State Bar Securities Section and International Section (past President); Idaho State Bar; Washington State Bar;

Board of Governors, Salt Lake Chamber of Commerce.
**Career:** D|J|P Board of Directors (1994-2004), Chairman and President (2007 to present).
**Publications:** Author in trade journals on US and international legal matters Doing Business in North America, co-author (ed., Kluwer; The Export Trading Company Act of 1982, International Business Lawyer, London, November 1983; UK Data Protection Bill: Data Protection under the European Convention, 5 Business Law Review, London, January 1984; Privacy Protection Acts: Privacy Protection or Economic Protectionism? International Business Lawyer, London, April 1984.
**Personal:** JD, J Reuben Clark Law School, Brigham Young University, 1982; BA, Brigham Young University, 1979.

### POELMAN, Ronald S
Jones Waldo, Salt Lake City
801 534 7311
rpoelman@joneswaldo.com
*Featured in Corporate/M&A (Utah)*
**Practice Areas:** Leads the corporate and securities practice focusing on corporate, contractual and securities work for both private and public companies, with an emphasis on technology companies. Experienced with corporate organization and governance, executive compensation, technology licensing, SEC compliance and reporting, mergers and acquisitions, venture capital and other private financings.
**Professional Memberships:** Board of Directors, USANA Health Sciences, Inc. President, Utah Chapter of the National Association of Corporate Directors.
**Career:** Listed in Utah's Legal Elite, Chambers USA and Best Lawyers. AV Martindale-Hubbell. Worked in Silicon Valley before returning to Utah.
**Personal:** JD, University of California at Berkeley, 1981. Speaks Japanese.

### POS, Hal J
Parsons Behle & Latimer PC, Salt Lake City
801 532 1234
HPos@parsonsbehle.com
*Featured in Energy & Natural Resources (Utah)*
**Practice Areas:** Concentrates on environmental and mining matters with particular emphasis on CERCLA liability, environmental cleanups and insurance recovery, Brownfield's development and property acquisition transactions.
**Professional Memberships:** Board of Trustees, TerraLex. Rocky Mountain Mineral Law Foundation. Board of Litigation for Mountain States Legal Foundation. American Bar Association: Natural Resources, Energy and Environmental Law Section; Tort and Insurance Section. Utah Mining Association Environmental Committee. Board Chairman The McGillis School.
**Career:** Vice Chair, Vice President/Treasurer, Board of Directors, Parsons Behle & Latimer.
**Personal:** JD, Washington University, 1984. BA, Carleton College, 1981.

### ROWE, Keven M
Jones Waldo, Salt Lake City
801 534 7333
krowe@joneswaldo.com
*Featured in Real Estate (Utah)*
**Practice Areas:** Practices in complex real estate and asset based lending for institutional and governmental clients, including construction, permanent and securitized financings and restructurings, complex real estate transactions for shopping centers, apartment, residential and resort developments, and office/commercial building acquisition and leasing. Handles business acquisitions and divestures involving real estate and non-real estate assets.
**Professional Memberships:** ICSC, NAIOP.
**Career:** Jones, Waldo, Partner, 1986-present; President, 2003-present; Executive Committee Member, 1996-present; Chair, Real Estate Finance Group.
**Personal:** JD, University of Utah College of Law, 1986, Order of the Coif, William H. Leary Scholar; University of Utah, 1983.

### RUDD, David R
Ballard Spahr LLP, Salt Lake City
801 517 6829
ruddd@ballardspahr.com
*Featured in Corporate/M&A (Utah)*
**Practice Areas:** David R Rudd is a partner in the Business and Finance Department and a member of the Life Sciences and Technology, Energy and Project Finance, Mergers and Acquisitions/Private Equity, P3/Infrastructure, and Securities Groups. He practices exclusively in the area of complex domestic and international business transactions in a wide variety of legal fields and industrial sectors.
**Professional Memberships:** American Bar Association District of Columbia Bar Association Inter-American Bar Association Utah State Bar Association Office of US Senator Orrin G. Hatch.
**Career:** Admissions: District of Columbia Utah.
**Personal:** Pepperdine University School of Law (JD 1982) Brigham Young University (BA 1979).

### SPEIRS, Kevin
Parsons Behle & Latimer PC, Salt Lake City
801 532 1234
KSpeirs@parsonsbehle.com
*Featured in Intellectual Property (Utah)*
**Practice Areas:** Intellectual property, patent infringement, trade secret and antitrust matters. Patent infringement matters covering a range of technologies, including biomedical and surgical devices, explosives and detonators, electrical devices, computer software, oil and gas production devices and processes, water treatment, microbiological products and processes.
**Professional Memberships:** Member, Utah State Bar Association: Intellectual Property Section. Member, American Bar Association: Committee on Intellectual Properties Litigation. Registered to practice before the United States Patent and Trademark Office.
**Career:** Shareholder.
**Personal:** JD, University of Utah, 1988. B.S.E.Eng., University of Utah, cum laude, 1985.

**TAYLOR, Thomas R**
Durham Jones & Pinegar, PC, Salt Lake City
801 297 1370
ttaylor@djplaw.com
*Featured in Corporate/M&A (Utah)*
**Practice Areas:** Corporate, M&A, securities, corporate finance, venture capital and private equity.
**Professional Memberships:** Admitted in Utah (1988), Arizona (1987) and District of Columbia (1990); President, Utah State Bar, Securities Section (2003-04); Chairman of the Board of Directors, MountainWest Capital Network (2009-11), Vice Chairman (2012-13); Member, Board of Trustees, Hale Centre Theatre (2009-present).
**Career:** Joined Durham Jones & Pinegar in 2010.
**Personal:** JD (cum laude), Arizona State University, 1987; MBA (with highest distinction), Brigham Young University Marriott School of Management, 1983; BS (cum laude), University of Utah, 1981 (Management) and 1980 (Accounting and Finance).

**WATKINS, Glen**
Jones Waldo, Salt Lake City
801 521 3200
gwatkins@joneswaldo.com
*Featured in Real Estate (Utah)*
**Practice Areas:** Practice includes the acquisition, financing, development and sale of commercial, retail and resort properties; land use and regulatory matters; corporate and corporate governance matters involving owners and developers associations; and development of resort infrastructure. Extensive experience with multi-state business acquisitions, including real estate assets.
**Professional Memberships:** Salt Lake Chamber Board of Governors, Economic Development Corporation of Uta, Board of Trustees.
**Career:** Chair, Board of Directors, Jones Waldo (2001-present), Chair, Resort/Leisure Practice Group, admitted to practice in Utah and DC.
**Personal:** JD, University of Utah College of Law, 1975; Stanford University / University of Utah, 1972, magna cum laude.

**WELLS, Matthew**
Holland & Hart LLP, Salt Lake City
801 799 5942
mgwells@hollandhart.com
*Featured in Corporate/M&A (Utah)*
**Practice Areas:** Mr Wells helps entrepreneurs and investors form, fund and exit technology and life sciences companies. He advises on a wide range of corporate/securities issues from company start-up through sale, with a particular focus on venture capital financings and middle-market mergers and acquisitions. He has also facilitated cross-border acquisitions involving Canada, Mexico, the UK, Ireland, France, Germany, The Netherlands, Israel and Russia.
**Career:** He previously practiced at Wilson Sonsini Goodrich & Rosati in Palo Alto/Salt Lake City and Ray Quinney & Nebeker, P.C. in Salt Lake City.
**Personal:** University of Virginia School of Law JD 2000.

**WIKSTROM, Francis M**
Parsons Behle & Latimer PC, Salt Lake City
801 532 1234
FWikstrom@parsonsbehle.com
*Featured in Litigation (Utah)*
**Practice Areas:** Complex civil litigation, intellectual property and environmental litigation, white collar criminal defense.
**Professional Memberships:** Fellow, American College of Trial Lawyers (Secretary, Board of Regents). Fellow, International Academy of Trial Lawyers. Fellow, International Society of Barristers, International Association of Defense Counsel. Fellow, American Bar Foundation. Chair, Utah Supreme Court Advisory Committee on the Rules of Civil Procedure. Master of the Bench, American Inns of Court II.
**Career:** Shareholder. Former US Attorney and Assistant US Attorney.
**Personal:** JD, Yale Law School, 1974. BS, Weber State University, 1971.

**WILLIAMS, Jody**
Holland & Hart LLP, Salt Lake City
801 799 5965
JLWilliams@hollandhart.com
*Featured in Energy & Natural Resources (Utah)*
**Practice Areas:** Member of Energy, Environment and Natural Resources Practice Group and advises on water rights, natural resources, and energy law. Represents purchasers and sellers of water rights and water suppliers, including due diligence review, licensing and permitting complex private and public water development projects, permitting energy development, and acquiring approval to use water for new projects and developments.
**Professional Memberships:** Utah State Bar's Energy, Natural Resources & Environmental Law Section and Utah Reclamation Mitigation and Conservation Commission.
**Career:** Licensed: Utah (1978); Colorado (2007); U.S. Supreme Court (1982).
**Personal:** University of Utah JD (1978); BA (1975).

**WILSON, Randon W**
Jones Waldo, Salt Lake City
801 534 7263
rwilson@joneswaldo.com
*Featured in Corporate/M&A (Utah)*
**Practice Areas:** Mergers and acquisitions, agricultural and other cooperatives, complex corporate finance, banking, government relations and general corporate matters.
**Professional Memberships:** National Council of Farmer Cooperatives, Legal Tax and Accounting Committee; Utah State Bar; American Bar Association.
**Career:** Admitted to practice in Utah (1965); US Supreme Court (1968); US District Court of Utah (1968); US Court of Military Appeals (1968); US Court of Appeals, Tenth Circuit (1969).
**Personal:** University of Utah BS (1962); University of Utah College of Law JD (1964).

**WINMILL, Patricia**
Parsons Behle & Latimer PC, Salt Lake City
801 532 1234
PWinmill@parsonsbehle.com
*Featured in Energy & Natural Resources (Utah)*
**Practice Areas:** Mining, mineral title and public lands.
**Professional Memberships:** Director (2010-12) and Trustee (2008-12), Rocky Mountain Mineral Law Foundation; Program Chair, 58th Annual Rocky Mountain Mineral Law Institute (2012); Utah State Bar Association: Energy and Natural Resources Section; ABA: Natural Resources, Energy and Environmental Law Section; President, Alumni Board of Trustees, S.J. Quinney College of Law (2003-04).
**Career:** Shareholder, Environmental, Energy and Natural Resources department.
**Personal:** JD, University of Utah, 1980 (Order of the Coif). BA, Idaho State University, 1976 (Highest Honors).

**ZODY, Michael A**
Parsons Behle & Latimer PC, Salt Lake City
801 532 1234
MZody@parsonsbehle.com
*Featured in Energy & Natural Resources (Utah), Labor & Employment (Utah)*
**Practice Areas:** Environmental litigation, defense of civil and criminal enforcement actions, citizens' suits, landfill litigation, defense of permit challenges, CERCLA cases. Climate change law/policy. Employment litigation, including ADA, ADEA, Title VII, employment contracts and OSHA/MSHA. Whistleblower/retaliation cases, including environmental and Sarbanes-Oxley whistleblower cases.
**Professional Memberships:** American Bar Association: Natural Resources, Energy and Environmental Law Section; Tort Trial and Insurance Practice Section, Toxic Torts and Environmental Law Committee; Employment Law Section.
**Career:** Shareholder. Chair: firm's Environmental Litigation Practice Group.
**Personal:** JD, cum laude, Indiana University, 1990. BA, Purdue University, 1987.

# DURHAM JONES & PINEGAR, PC

www.djplaw.com **tel:** 801 415 3000 **fax:** 801 415 3500

**Chairman:** Kevin R Pinegar
**Managing Partner:** Kevin R Pinegar
Number of shareholders: 55
Number of lawyers: 88
Languages: *Bulgarian, Cape Verdean Creole, Danish, Finnish, French, German, Italian, Japanese, Malagasy, Mandarin Chinese, Mongolian, Portuguese, Romanian, Russian, Serbian, Sign Language (SEE), Spanish, Swedish, Tagalog*

**Firm Overview:**

Durham Jones & Pinegar is a leading law firm with offices in Utah and Nevada, offering legal services in, among other practice areas, business and finance, commercial litigation, intellectual property, government relations, estate planning, real estate, bankruptcy, employment, tax law and family law. Although the firm was founded in 1991, it is one of the largest and fastest growing law firms in Utah.

**Main Areas of Practice:**

**Bankruptcy & Creditors' Rights:**
6 shareholders, 12 fee earners based in the United States
**Contact:** Duane H Gillman **Tel:** 801 297 1208
**Email:** dgillman@djplaw.com

**Business & Finance**
5 Shareholders, 18 fee earners based in the United States
- $2 billion acquisition of Vivint Solar by Blackstone Group – the biggest deal in Utah State History
- Representation of public companies in connection with Securities and Exchange Act of 1934 disclosure filings and corporate governance matters
- Utah counsel for 2GIG Technologies, Inc. in sale to an affiliate of The Blackstone Group, L.P.
- Utah counsel for Vivint Solar in sale to an affiliate of The Blackstone Group, L.P.

**Clients:** iFrogz; Neways; 2GIG Technologies, Inc.; Vivint Solar; Vivint Inc.;USANA Health Sciences
**Contact:** Russell K Smith
**Email:** rsmith@djplaw.com

**Estate Planning:**
6 Shareholders, 12 fee earners based in the United States
**Contact:** Douglas A Taggart
**Email:** dtaggart@djplaw.com

**Intellectual Property:**
6 Shareholders, 10 fee earners based in the United States
**Contact:** Kevin K Johanson
**Email:** kjohanson@djplaw.com

**Litigation:**
20 Shareholders, 27 fee earners based in the United States
- Successful defense of ASUS Tek in a multi-million dollar patent infringement action
**Contact:** Richard M Hymas
**Email:** rhymas@djplaw.com

**Real Estate:**
5 Shareholders, 7 fee earners based in the United States
- Representation of Associated Food Stores, Inc. in its acquisition of 34 full-service Albertson's grocery stores and related properties located in Utah, Idaho, Nevada and Montana in a single transaction from SUPERVALU, Inc.
- Representation of The Homestead, Inc. in its sale of an historic hotel resort and golf course to Legacy Homestead, LLC
**Contact:** Paul M Durham
**Email:** pdurham@djplaw.com

## PRACTICE AREAS

Bankruptcy
Business & Finance
Estate Planning
Intellectual Property
Litigation
Real Estate

## OFFICES

UTAH

**SALT LAKE CITY:** 111 East Broadway, Suite 900, 84111
Tel: 801 415 3000  Fax: 801 415 3500
Email: msmith@djplaw.com

**OGDEN:** 1104 East Country Hills Drive, Suite 710, 84403
Tel: 801 395 2424  Fax: 801 395 2430
Email: msmith@djplaw.com

**PROVO:** 4844 North 300 West, Suite 300, 84604
Tel: 801 375 6600  Fax: 801 375 3865
Email: msmith@djplaw.com

**ST. GEORGE:** 192 East 200 North, 3rd Floor, 84770
Tel: 435 674 0400  Fax: 435 628 1610
Email: ckarr@djplaw.com

NEVADA

**LAS VEGAS:** 10785 West Twain Avenue, Suite 200, 89135
Tel: 702 870 6060  Fax: 702 870 6090
Email: jbooker@djplaw.com

**International Work:**

Durham Jones & Pinegar is a member of the World Services Group organization (WSG), the world's largest interdisciplinary network that is comprised of leading law firms around the world plus investment banking and accounting firms.

Durham Jones & Pinegar is the sole representative for legal services in the states of Nevada and Utah. Membership in WSG enables the firm to have relationships with top-tier law firms and other interdisciplinary firms throughout the world.

A majority of the firm's attorneys have lived in a foreign country and speak a second language, and the firm's attorneys have represented clients with interests in Europe, Asia, Latin America and Australia.

DURHAM
JONES &
PINEGAR

# JONES WALDO

www.joneswaldo.com **tel:** 801 521 3200 **fax:** 801 328 0537

**President:** Keven M Rowe
**Chairman:** Paul M Harman

### Firm Overview:

Since 1875, Jones Waldo has been providing legal services to the businesses and community organizations that support and grow the state's economy. Built on a strong foundation of service and knowledge of Utah's core industries, the firm continues to evolve through meeting new challenges, finding innovative solution and advancing legal trends in the state.

### Main Areas of Practice:

### Real Estate:

Jones Waldo has the largest group of real estate lawyers of any firm in Utah and has extensive experience in virtually all aspects of real estate matters. The department has worked on the negotiation and preparation of documents related to the acquisition and sale of real property (commercial, residential and multi-family), commercial leasing (including shopping center and office building leasing) and the development of real property projects throughout the United States. The real estate team has represented big-box and chain retailers such as Wal-Mart, Albertson's, Lowe's, CVS, Safeway and Kohl's and assisted Extra Space Storage (a Fortune 500 company) in property acquisitions across the US. The firm also provides legal services to national resort and recreation developers. More Jones Waldo lawyers were named by Utah Business magazine to Utah's 2013 Legal Elite in real estate than from any other Utah firm.

### Real Estate Finance:

The firm represents banks, financial institutions and borrowers in a wide range of real property secured lending transactions within and outside of Utah, including negotiating and documenting sophisticated real estate financings, revolving credit facilities, syndicated credit facilities, construction lending, acquisition financings, securitized financings, public finance transactions, tax-credit financings, foreclosures, workouts, bankruptcies and other reorganizations.

### Bankruptcy:

The Jones Waldo Bankruptcy Practice Group has experience in commercial bankruptcy in several jurisdictions around the country which covers representation of secured and unsecured creditors and debtors, service on creditor's committees, representation of bondholders, indenture trustees, landlords, tenants, retail goods suppliers, utilities, state and federal regulatory and enforcement agencies (such as the SEC and the FDIC) and equipment lessors. The team has experience with structuring and implementing debtor-in-possession financing and planning exit financing and cash collateral arrangements and intercreditor relationships.

### Healthcare Law:

Jones Waldo recently added new attorneys to its Healthcare Law Practice Group with the goal of helping clients in all industries manage the burgeoning demands of healthcare laws and regulations.

### Construction Litigation:

Jones Waldo has one of the most active construction law practices in the Intermountain West and is a major player in the construction litigation arena. The Construction Law Practice Group has experience with cost overrun litigation and general representation of construction industry clients.

### Litigation:

Jones Waldo litigators represent clients in state and federal courts, before administrative agencies and in arbitration and mediation. With strong emphasis on commercial and business related litigation, these lawyers act as litigation counsel for national and international corporations in all areas of commercial and business law. The firm also represents clients in real estate and environmental litigation as well as bankruptcy and family law.

### Employment:

The firm represents employers in all industries and virtually all areas of employer-employee relations, including risk avoidance, equal employment opportunity, fair labor standards (wage and hour matters), immigration and wrongful termination. Services provided to employers include litigation, arbitration, mediation, administrative proceedings, training and general counseling.

### Corporate & Securities:

The firm has expertise in handling almost all types of corporate, securities and transactional matters for a wide variety of clients. Expertise includes handling venture capital, private equity, and merger/acquisition transactions, start-up company organization and growth matters, corporate governance matters, private offerings, domestic and international strategic contracting, technology licensing, patent and trademark registrations and executive incentives and compensation matters.

### OFFICES

**ILLINOIS**

**NAPERVILLE:** 608 South Washington Street, Suite 207, IL 60540
Tel: 630 983 5946   Fax: 630 983 5986

**UTAH**

**PARK CITY:** 1441 West Ute Boulevard, Suite 330, UT 84098
Tel: 435 200 0085   Fax: 435 200 0084

**PROVO:** 3325 North University Avenue, Suite 200, UT 84604
Tel: 801 375 9801   Fax: 801 379 1149

**SALT LAKE CITY:** 170 South Main Street, Suite 1500, UT 84101
Tel: 801 521 3200   Fax: 801 328 0537
Email: info@joneswaldo.com

**ST. GEORGE:** 301 North 200 East, Suite 3-A, , UT 84770-3041
Tel: 435 628 1627   Fax: 435 628 5225

### Tax:

Jones Waldo advises businesses, individuals, attorneys, accountants and non-profit organizations nationwide on a wide array of tax matters. Members of the Tax Law Practice Group also have experience drafting and assisting with the administration of all welfare benefit plans subject to ERISA.

### International Work:

The firm represents US companies that are engaged in overseas acquisitions and investments.

### Clients:

4 Life Research, Access Information Management; Albertson's, Inc.; Bonneville International Corporation; Browning; CVS; Deseret Mutual Benefit Administrators; Dick's Sporting Goods; Extra Space Storage, Inc.; Hospital Corporation of America (HCA); LANDesk; Lowe's; Overstock.com; Phillips Edison & Company; Qualtrics Lab; Safeway; Salt Lake City Redevelopment Agency; Tesoro; The Salt Lake Tribune; Stampin' Up!; Unishippers Global Logistics; United Concerts; US Bank; Wells Fargo Bank; Zions National Bank.

JONES WALDO

Attorneys          Est. 1875

# PARR BROWN GEE & LOVELESS

**www**.parrbrown.com **tel:** 801 532 7840 **fax:** 801 532 7750

**President:** Stephen E W Hale
Number of partners: 54   Number of other lawyers: 20

## Firm Overview:

Parr Brown Gee and Loveless, one of Utah's largest commercial law firms, provides comprehensive legal services to a diverse group of corporate and individual clients.

## Main Areas of Practice:

**Mergers & Acquisitions:**

- Represented Merit Medical Systems, Inc. in acquiring Thomas Medical Products, Inc. from GE Healthcare for $167 million. Partners: Brian Lloyd, Matthew Tenney, Michael Schefer, Kenneth Tillou, Lamont Richardson, Steven Christiansen
- Represented Moelis Capital Partners in six acquisitions totalling $450 million. Partners: Kent Larsen, Seth King, Ken Tillou, Lamont Richardson
- Holly Corporation and Holly Energy Partners. Acquisition of Sinclair's Tulsa, OK refinery for $203 million. Partners: Steven Christiansen, Roger Henriksen, Scott Loveless, Seth King
- Sale of iFrogz, Inc. to ZAGG, Inc. in a cash and stock transaction valued at $108 million. Partners: Scott Loveless, Keith Pope, Ken Tillou, Seth King
- Barrick Gold Corporation's acquisition of Cortez joint venture gold mine interest from Rio Tinto for $1.7 billion. Partners: Clay Parr, Scott Loveless, Daniel Jensen, Ken Tillou, Seth King
- SkyWest, Inc. acquisition of Atlantic Southeast Airlines from Delta Air Lines for $1.75 billion in total consideration. Partners: Scott Loveless, Brian Lloyd, Dale Hansen, Seth King

**Contact:** Keith Pope **Tel:** 801 257 7938
**Email:** kpope@parrbrown.com

**Corporate & Securities:**

- Represented SkyWest, Inc. in negotiation of Aircraft Purchase Agreement for 100 MRJ90 regional jet aircraft, with a list value of more than $4 billion, and 100 additional aircraft at SkyWest's option. Partners: Dale Hansen, Michael Schefer, Brian Lloyd
- Represented Pluralsight, Inc. in sale of $27.5 million in preferred equity interests to Insight Venture Partners. Partners: Michael Schefer, Brian Lloyd
- $92.4 million secondary public offering of common stock for Merit Medical Systems, Inc.- underwritten by Piper Jeffray. Partners: Brian Lloyd, Bryan Allen, Greg Nelson
- $102 million secondary public offering of common stock for SkyWest Airlines – underwritten by Merrill Lynch & Co. and Raymond James and Associates. Partners: Brian Lloyd, Dale Hansen, Seth King

**Contact:** Brian Lloyd **Tel:** 801 257 7964
**Email:** blloyd@parrbrown.com

**Real Estate Development & Finance:**

- Represented Merit Medical Systems, Inc., in obtaining a $275 million secured loan – the largest single bank loan made in the US in the 2012 calendar year. Partners: Lamont Richardson, Brian Lloyd
- Represented The Boyer Company in the transfer and contribution of 12 medical office buildings located in 6 states to a Healthcare Properties Inc. (NYSE: HCP) for $182 million. Partners: David Gee, Lamont Richardson
- Combination sale and contribution of six shopping centers in Nevada to Inland Real Estate Group for $294.5 million. Partners: David Gee, Barton Gertsch
- Represented KC Gardner Company in connection with the construction, leasing and partial sale of a 17 storey condominium office building in Boise, Idaho, and a related $48 million construction loan. Partners: David Gee, Lamont Richardson, Barton Gertsch
- Represented The Boyer Company in connection with a ground lease transaction in the City of Phoenix for the development and operation of a biomedical research facility and parking garage, including the negotiation of related development agreements. Partners: David Gee, Lamont Richardson

**Contact:** David Gee **Tel:** 801 257 7914
**Email:** dgee@parrbrown.com

**Litigation:**

- Represented EnergySolutions, Inc. in a Federal False Claims Act case defending allegations of improperly disposing of radioactive waste that resulted in submission of false invoices to the government. Prevailed on motion for partial summary judgment that eliminated the core of the claims, enabling resolution of favorable terms. Partner: Robert Clark
- Represented Deseret Digital Media in defamation action brought in federal court by a former contractor against the UTOPIA, fiber-optic network municipal group, leading on briefing the issues in a motion for judgment on the pleadings. Motion was granted and cases dismissed. Partners: Jeffrey Hunt, David Reyman, Austin Riter
- Represented secured noteholder in multi-million dollar claim against a publicly-traded company in Hawes v. Madison Avenue Media. Prevailed on a contested summary judgment motion and awarded more than $3 million. Partners: Jonathan Hafen, R Jeremy Adamson
- Represented defendants, LeftNRights, in $80 million

---

**PRACTICE AREAS**

Corporate/Securities
Mergers, Acquisitions & Divestitures
Real Estate Development & Finance
Construction Law
Commercial Litigation
Employment
Environmental & Natural Resources
Tax

**OFFICES**

UTAH
**SALT LAKE CITY:** 185 South State Street, Suite 800, UT 84111
Tel: 801 532 7840  Fax: 801 532 7750

litigation involving patent, trade secret and partnership claims relating to internet marketing technology. Successfully opposed a request for a preliminary injuction, successfully moved to dismiss 12 of 15 filed claims, and received a favorable settlement. Partners: Terry Welch, Craig Parry
- Unanimous favorable summary judgment for client, Utah Community Bank, in a mechanic's lien where claimant claimed a lien even though it failed to record a lis pendens until a year after the statute required. Partners: Ron Russell, Matthew Ball
- Successfully defended US Gypsum Company in an oil and gas lease case where plaintiff sought damages of approximately $4.5 million for USG's breach of the lease. Judge awarded nominal damages of $1. Partners: Patricia Christiansen, Matthew Ball

**Contact:** Robert Clark **Tel:** 801 257 7910
**Email:** rclark@parrbrown.com

**Environmental & Natural Resources:**

- Served as US counsel for American Vanadium Corporation in a $170 million advanced-stage vanadium project in Nevada. Partners: Daniel Jensen
- Conducted title review for Gryphon Gold Corporation for a secured gold stream credit facility in connection with a 750-claim gold operation in Nevada ($20 million). Partners: Daniel Jensen
- US counsel for Scorpio Gold Corporation in the $15 million acquisition of gold properties in Nye and Elko Counties, Nevada, including royalty and gold supply agreements and security documents. Partners: Daniel Jensen, Lamont Richardson
- Represented Barrick Gold Corporation in the acquisition of the Mill Canyon mining properties and assets for $24 million from Victoria Gold. Partners: Dan Jensen, Seth King, Ken Tillou, Steven Christiansen

**Contact:** Daniel Jensen **Tel:** 801 257 7922
**Email:** djensen@parrbrown.com

PARR BROWN
GEE & LOVELESS

ATTORNEYS AT LAW

# PARSONS BEHLE & LATIMER

**www.**parsonbehle.com **tel:** 801 532 1234

**Chairman:** Raymond J Etcheverry
**Senior Partner:** James B Lee
Number of shareholders: 92
Number of other lawyers: 40

## Firm Overview:

Parsons Behle & Latimer offers national expertise in a regional law firm. In addition to being the largest Utah-based law firm, Parsons Behle & Latimer is one of the oldest and best known firms in the Intermountain Region, offering litigation and business law services since 1882. The firm's first clients were in the business of mining – one of the major industries that helped fuel the growth of the area. Over time, the firm's reputation and client base have grown with the Intermountain Region. The firm offers the resources and capabilities of a large and diverse firm, coupled with the highest levels of accessibility and responsiveness. With more than 130 attorneys, it brings a depth and range of experience in the major practice areas listed below.

## Main Areas of Practice:

### Corporate & Tax:

Members of the firm's Corporate and Tax Department participate in the negotiation and documentation of complex business transactions, furnishing timely advice about securities, tax, environmental, employment law and other issues. The firm advises clients concerning business, corporate and securities, tax, international business, regulatory and administrative, energy and government relations.

### Employment:

The firm's employment law practice is one of the broadest in the Intermountain Region. Many of its attorneys practice exclusively in the labor and employment area. Areas of representation include wrongful discharge, discrimination, sexual harassment, employee benefits, ERISA, workers' compensation, OSHA and MSHA, and National Labor Relations Act.

### Environmental, Energy & Natural Resources:

With more than 20 attorneys, the firm has one of the largest environmental, energy and natural resources practice groups in the western United States. The practice is national and international in scope with particular emphasis on the western United States and Latin America. Areas of practice include mining, oil and gas, water rights, public lands, energy and electrical power, air and water quality, hazardous waste, Superfund and Brownfields, and occupational issues. In these and other areas the firm advises and assists clients with transactions and finance, project development and closure, property acquisition and title, permitting, compliance, enforcement, cost recovery, rate cases, litigation, rulemakings and legislation.

### Government Relations, Lobbying & Political Law:

Attorneys and lobbyists represent clients before state legislatures, local governments and regulatory agencies on issues including, but not limited to: environmental, natural resources finance, power, real estate telecommunications and transportation. Attorneys and professionals in this practice area, many of whom have significant campaign and election law experience, also advise clients regarding election law, campaign finance, lobbying, procurement and regulatory law.

### Intellectual Property:

The firm handles intellectual property of all types, including patents, trade secrets, trademarks, copyrights, technology licensing and intellectual property agreements. Attorneys assist clients in all industries with intellectual property and technology matters including patent infringement and intellectual property litigation. The firm has the resources to assist clients in patent prosecution, licensing, portfolio management, strategic counseling and other transactions involving intellectual property assets.

### Litigation:

The firm has one of the largest litigation departments in the Intermountain Region. Attorneys practice before federal and state courts, administrative agencies and arbitration panels. Representative areas of trial practice include commercial litigation, natural resources and environmental, intellectual property, antitrust, banking, insolvency, personal injury, products liability, mass media and white-collar criminal law.

### Mining:

With beginnings as a mining firm, Parsons Behle & Latimer has one of the strongest mining practices in western US. From initial stages of a mining project through reclamation and closure, its lawyers have experience assisting clients with mineral title examination and land use authorizations; financing; mergers and acquisitions; joint ventures; exploration, lease, and option agreements; environmental permitting, compliance, and diligence; royalty and refining agreements; joint operating agreements; water rights; electrical power supply and infrastructure; and administrative appeals and litigation.

### Real Estate, Banking & Finance:

Attorneys represent commercial banks, mortgage companies and other financial institutions. They also handle all aspects of real estate transactions, including acquisition, finance, development, condominium and PUD documentation, and zoning and land use regulations.

### International Work:

Parsons Behle & Latimer maintains an active and varied practice internationally, in particular in Latin America.

### Clients:

Representative clients include: ATK; Baker Hughes; Barrick Gold; Bear River Water Conservancy; Boise State University; Chase; Chubb; The Church of Jesus Christ of Latter-day Saints; Danaher Corporation; Davis & Weber Canal; Dyno Nobel; Eaton; Eureka Moly, LLC; First Utah Bank; First Wind; Freeport-McMoran Copper & Gold; Home Depot; Life Technologies; inContact, Inc.; Intermountain Power Agency; Johnson Matthey; Kennecott Utah Copper; LS Power; Merrill Lynch; Newegg, Inc.; Questar Corporation; Regence Blue Cross; RioTinto; Stericycle; Suburban Land Reserve; US Magnesium; ViewSonic Corp.

## OFFICES

### UTAH

**SALT LAKE CITY:** 201 South Main Street, Suite 1800, Salt Lake City, UT 84111
Tel: 801 532 1234   Toll Free: 800 293 9669

### DISTRICT OF COLUMBIA

**WASHINGTON, DC:** 101 Constitution Ave. NW, Ninth Floor East, DC, 20001
Tel: 202 808 7220   Toll Free: 800 293 9669

### IDAHO

**BOISE:** 960 Broadway Avenue, Suite 250, ID, 83706
Tel: 208 562 4900   Toll Free: 800 293 9669

### NEVADA

**RENO:** 50 West Liberty Street, Suite 750, NV 89501
Tel: 775 323 1601   Toll Free: 800 293 9669

**LAS VEGAS:** 3753 Howard Hughes Parkway, Suite 200, NV, 89169
Tel: 702 599 6000   Toll Free: 800 293 9669

### WASHINGTON

**SPOKANE:** 23403 E. Mission Avenue, Liberty Lake, WA, 99019
Tel: 208 562 4900   Toll Free: 800 293 9669

# RAY QUINNEY & NEBEKER P.C.

www.rqn.com **tel:** 801 532 1500 **fax:** 801 532 7543

**Managing Partner:** John A Adams
Number of partners: 77
Number of other lawyers: 25

## Firm Overview:

Since 1940, Ray Quinney & Nebeker PC (RQ&N) has represented clients in many locations and industries, including banks, insurance companies, financial services firms, manufacturers, *Fortune* 500 companies, healthcare providers and hospitals, energy companies and utilities, entrepreneurs and emerging businesses. The firm has nearly 100 attorneys in two offices, and is recognized as one of the 'preeminent' law firms in the United States.

## Main Areas of Practice:

**Litigation:**
The litigation section is the largest practice group at the firm, and includes a number of the most respected trial lawyers in Utah. The practice is diverse, covering commercial litigation, insurance, malpractice defense, personal injury, real estate, employment relations, tax litigation and other areas.
**Contact:** Justin T Toth

**Intellectual Property Law & Litigation:**
The firm represents a wide array of clients in patent, trademark, copyright, piracy, unfair competition and related matters. The firm's attorneys handle litigation, administrative proceedings, technology, licensing, franchising, trade secret, copyright and trademark application matters.
**Contact:** Mark M Bettilyon

**Employment & Labor Law & Litigation:**
The firm has the largest practice group focusing on employment and labor law in Utah. The firm represents clients in matters relating to the workplace, including wage and hour issues, discrimination, unemployment matters, workers' compensation, civil rights, non-competition issues, ERISA, OSHA, labor management relations, and other labor issues.
**Contact:** Scott A Hagen

**Real Estate Transactions & Litigation:**
The firm offers a complete range of services in commercial, industrial and residential real estate matters, including real estate acquisition, development, financing, leasing, title insurance issues and litigation. The firm's Real Estate Group has long been recognized for its successful practice in real estate tax challenges and planning.
**Contact:** Douglas Matsumori

**Mergers & Acquisitions:**
The firm's attorneys are experienced in all facets of purchase and sale transactions, including contract negotiation, structuring, financing, due diligence matters and deal consummation. The firm can handle preparation and negotiation of the contract, through due diligence investigation to the closing.
**Contact:** Mark A Cotter

**Tax Planning & Tax Controversies:**
RQ&N handles a broad variety of tax planning and tax controversy work. The firm's tax attorneys are experienced in both federal and state tax matters, including income and franchise tax, transfer tax, sales and use tax, and property tax.
**Contact:** Bruce L Olson

**Banking & Financial Institutions:**
The firm's Banking and Financial Institutions Practice represents a broad range of financial institutions and other lenders in a wide range of transactions and circumstances including commercial lending, commercial mortgage lending, equipment finance, syndicated credits, warehouse credits, workouts, foreclosures, and other credit transactions.
**Contact:** Kevin G Glade

**Bankruptcy & Creditors' Rights:**
The firm's Bankruptcy and Creditors' Rights Group includes some of the most well-respected bankruptcy and insolvency lawyers in Utah. The group represent creditors, debtors, trustees, receivers and others in bankruptcy reorganizations and insolvencies, debt restructurings and workouts, receivership proceedings and other complex financial matters. In addition, the firm is experienced in insolvency related litigation and appeals.
**Contact:** Michael R Johnson

## Clients:

Representative clients include: Albion Laboratories; Alta Ski Lifts Co.; Bombardier Recreational Products, Inc.; Brigham Young University; Chubb Group of Insurance Companies; C.R. England & Sons, Inc.; Delta Air Lines, Inc.; Eli Lilly & Company; Edwards Lifesciences LLC; Exxon Corp.; Flying J, Inc.; Garff Enterprises, Inc.; Home Depot, Inc.; Huntsman International LLC; Kennecott Utah Copper Corp.; Marriott International, Inc.;

Microsoft Corporation; Morinda Holdings, Inc.; O.C. Tanner Co.; PacifiCorp; Questar Gas Company; Salt Lake Organizing Committee for the Olympic Games of 2002; University of Utah; Utah Transit Authority; Wells Fargo Bank, N.A.; Wells Fargo Equipment Financing, Inc.; Zions Credit Corporation.

**RAY QUINNEY & NEBEKER**
ATTORNEYS AT LAW

# WORKMAN | NYDEGGER

www.workmannydegger.net **tel:** 801 533 9800 **fax:** 801 328 1707

**Managing Partners:** Brent P Lorimer
Number of partners: 33
Number of lawyers: 42
Languages: *French, German, Italian, Japanese, Portuguese, Russian, Spanish, Swedish*

**Firm Overview:**

Founded more than 25 years ago, Workman Nydegger is one of the largest firms in Salt Lake, and has consistently earned recognition as one of the top intellectual property firms in the nation. The firm represents a wide array of clients in all areas of intellectual property law, including patent, trademark, copyright, unfair competition, and related litigation and licensing matters, and in a diverse range of technologies, including computer systems, software, e-commerce and information technology; electronics and electrical engineering; pharmaceutical, neutraceutical, chemical, biotechnology, and medical and life science technologies; physics and optics; mechanics and mechanical engineering and alternative energy.

**MAIN AREAS OF PRACTICE:**

**U.S. & International IP Prosecution:**

W|N represents US and foreign clients in all aspects of US and foreign patent and trademark prosecution. The firm received Top 10 national rankings for the quality of the patents obtained for its clients in several categories by Intellectual Property Magazine. W|N ranked 8th in the US for the quality of its patents granted in the Information Technology sector, and ranked 9th in the US for the quality of its patents across all industries. W|N ranked 35th in the U.S. for the number of patents obtained for its clients by Intellectual Property Today.

**Key Clients:** Microsoft, Abbott, Seiko Epson, ThermoFisher, Ultradent Products, Inc., 3Form.
**Contact:** Patents - Rick D Nydegger
**Email:** rnydegger@wnlaw.com
Trademarks – John C Stringham
**Email:** jstringham@wnlaw.com

**IP Litigation / Enforcement:**

W|N's Litigation Team has enforced patents and trademarks throughout the United States and has coordinated enforcement efforts in the EU and Asia in a wide variety of technologies, including medical devices, dental compositions and appliances, radar, high speed data transmission, agglomerations technologies, wastewater treatment, and nano-catalysts, to name a few.

W|N lawyers have prevailed in major IP litigation, from both plaintiff's and defendant's points of view. Major wins include

- Successful defense of client in e-commerce litigation filed by major on-line retailer
- Successful prosecution of patent litigation against a multinational manufacturer of tooth bleaching products, resulting in large settlement to client
- Defense of patent litigation asserted by one of the largest fitness manufacturers in the US, with summary judgment of no infringement affirmed on appeal
- Preliminary injunction and subsequent $15,000,000 settlement in favor of client
- Prevailed on trademark and false marking claims, resulting in $7,000,000 judgment in favor of client

**Key Clients:** Ultradent Products, Inc., Merit Medical Systems, Inc., Lifetime Products, Inc.
**Contact:** Brent P Lorimer
**Email:** blorimer@wnlaw.com

**Complex Commercial Litigation:**

The same skills W|N brings to bear in IP litigation are evident in our complex commercial litigation practice. We are often involved in complex unfair competition and non-compete litigation. Illustrative successes include:

- Successful defense of claims of breach of contract in data security services in the credit card processing industry, including defeat of motions for Temporary Restraining Order and Preliminary Injunction in two separate actions
- Successful prosecution of claim for injunctive relief against former employees who left client and unfairly competed using former employer's trade secrets.

**Key Clients:** Merit Medical Systems, Inc., Zrii, Inc.
**Contact:** Brent P Lorimer
**Email:** blorimer@wnlaw.com

**Appeals:**

W|N's appellate practice group has successfully handled appeals before the US Supreme Court, the Court of Appeals for the Federal Circuit, and other regional Circuit Courts of Appeal. W|N's lawyers include a number of former law clerks at the Federal Circuit, The firm's reputation in appellate practice is reflected in the slection of its lawyers to author amicus briefs on behalf of institutions like the AIPLA in cased before the U.S. Supreme Court (Metro-Goldwyn-Mayer Studios, Inc. v. Grokster, 2005) and the Federal Circuit (In re Beauregard, 1995 and Phillips v. AWH Corporation, 2004).

## PRACTICE AREAS

U.S. Patent, Trademark & Copyright prosecution
International Patent, Trademark & Copyright prosecution
Patent, Trademark & Copyright Litigation
Complex Commercial Litigation
Appeals
Mediation & Arbitration
Licensing & Transactional Work
IP Counseling

## OFFICES:

**UTAH**

**SALT LAKE CITY:** 60 East South Temple   Suite 1000, UT 84111
Tel: 801 533 9800

**VIRGINIA**

**ALEXANDRIA:** King Street Station, 1800 Diagonal Road, Suite 600, VA 22314
Tel: 703 647 7530

Successful results include:
- Vita-Mix Corp. v. Basic Holding, Inc.
- Nautilus Group, Inc. v. ICON Health and Fitness, Inc.
- Lifetime Products, Inc. v. GSC Technology Corp.

**Contact:** David R Todd
**Email:** dtodd@wnlaw.com

**Mediation & Arbitration:**

W|N regularly participates in mediation and arbitration proceedings as an alternative to costly and time-consuming litigation. Various of our attorneys are qualified as mediators and serve as mediators in complex commercial and IP related disputes.
**Contact:** Rick D Nydegger
**Email:** rnydegger@wnlaw.com

**Licensing & Transactional Work:**

W|N has extensive experience in assessing and advising clients on intellectual property issues surrounding mergers, acquisitions, joint ventures, partnerships, and licensing transactions. W|N also specializes in client counseling matters such as non-infringement and invalidity opinions, design-around strategies to avoid infringement, and clearance searches.
**Contact:** Thomas R Vuksinick
**Email:** tvuksinick@wnlaw.com

**IP Counseling:**

W|N works to develop strategies that optimize revenue and manage exposure so that our clients' businesses can grow and prosper. Attention to detail and decades of experience enable us to guide clients through the maze of options and choices inherent in managing IP.

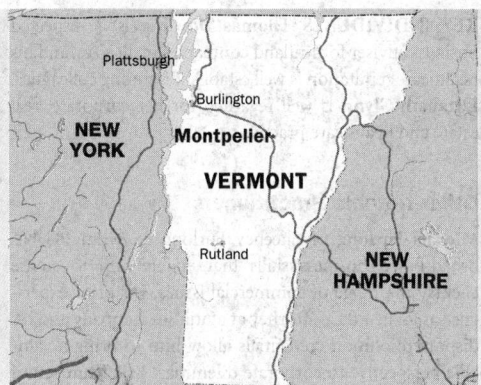

## How lawyers are ranked

Every year we carry out thousands of in-depth interviews with clients in order to assess the reputations and expertise of business lawyers worldwide. The qualities we look for (and which determine rankings) include technical legal ability, professional conduct, client service, commercial awareness/astuteness, diligence, commitment, and other qualities most valued by the client. For details of our research team, see p.5.

# CORPORATE/COMMERCIAL

Commentary about individuals can be found under their firm's paragraph. If the firm has no paragraph (is not ranked) look at Other Notable Practitioners.

### Corporate/Commercial
### Leading Firms

**Band 1**
Dinse, Knapp & McAndrew PC
Downs Rachlin Martin PLLC
Gravel and Shea

**Band 2**
Primmer Piper Eggleston & Cramer PC
Ryan Smith & Carbine, Ltd

### Leading Individuals

**Band 1**

| | |
|---|---|
| Erly Peter | Gravel and Shea |
| McMahan Jeffrey J | Dinse, Knapp & McAndrew PC |
| Moody Thomas H | Downs Rachlin Martin PLLC |
| Murphy Brian R | Dinse, Knapp & McAndrew PC |
| Ode Jr Paul H | Downs Rachlin Martin PLLC |

**Band 2**

| | |
|---|---|
| Eggleston Jon R | Primmer Piper Eggleston & Cramer PC |
| Mason IV William A | Gravel and Shea |

**Band 3**

| | |
|---|---|
| Ahmadi Afi | Dinse, Knapp & McAndrew PC |
| Dowling Thomas M | Ryan Smith & Carbine, Ltd |
| Furlong Michael G | Sheehey Furlong & Behm PC (ONP)[†] |
| Glynn Elizabeth A | Ryan Smith & Carbine, Ltd |
| Knudsen Eric | Langrock Sperry & Wool, LLP (ONP)[†] |
| Melloni Thomas R | Burak, Anderson & Melloni PLC (ONP)[†] |
| Merritt Jr H Kenneth | Merritt & Merritt & Moulton (ONP)[†] |
| Montgomery Margaret | Gravel and Shea |
| Prescott Wm Roger | Downs Rachlin Martin PLLC |
| Sylvester David J | Downs Rachlin Martin PLLC |

**Up-and-coming individuals**

| | |
|---|---|
| Roberts Keith A | Primmer Piper Eggleston & Cramer PC |

### Corporate/Commercial: Captive Insurance
### Leading Firms

**Band 1**
Downs Rachlin Martin PLLC
Primmer Piper Eggleston & Cramer PC

**Band 2**
Paul Frank + Collins P.C.

### Leading Individuals

**Band 1**

| | |
|---|---|
| Davis Kathleen H | Downs Rachlin Martin PLLC |
| Johnson Jeffrey P | Primmer Piper Eggleston & Cramer PC |

**Band 2**

| | |
|---|---|
| Mapes Stephanie J | Paul Frank + Collins P.C. |

**Band 3**

| | |
|---|---|
| Clemons James E | Primmer Piper Eggleston & Cramer PC |
| Moriarty Kevin P | Downs Rachlin Martin PLLC |
| Palmer Bruce | Downs Rachlin Martin PLLC |

**Up-and-coming individuals**

| | |
|---|---|
| Angus II David J | The Angus Firm, PLC (ONP)[†] |
| Young Russell A | Primmer Piper Eggleston & Cramer PC |

[†] ONP = Other Notable Practitioner.

*The editorial is in alphabetical order by firm name.*

## Dinse, Knapp & McAndrew PC

**THE FIRM** This firm has a well-known education and healthcare focus, and its corporate team also advises on an impressive range of sectors and continues to win new clients. Its full-service approach means that the busy team handles diverse commercial challenges, from financing to vendor agreements, with equal aplomb. Some transactions bear eye-catching values and several longstanding clients treat the group as a reliable, one-stop shop for all their legal needs
**Sources say:** *"On par with the best firms I've worked with. They understand my industry and are very well positioned within this community."*

**KEY INDIVIDUALS Jeffrey McMahan** is *"tremendously helpful,"* say clients, who also compliment *"his depth in the area of M&A"* as beneficial in transactions. The *"extraordinary"* **Brian Murphy** is particularly valued for his tax expertise. Peers see him as *"sharp, diligent and ethical"* as well as able to *"get straight to specifics."* **Afi Ahmadi** is *"extremely proficient, knowledgeable and personable"* in the view of clients. He leads local business restructurings as well as advising on significant financing and procurement matters.

## Downs Rachlin Martin PLLC

**THE FIRM** This group has a striking number of senior practitioners in the corporate sphere. It can therefore bring considerable expertise to bear on tax and corporate structuring matters. Its experienced experts are able to handle multiple deals, inside and outside Vermont, comfortably.
**Sources say:** *"It has a roster of good clients."*
**KEY INDIVIDUALS** Head of the firm's insurance practice, **Kathleen Davis** is nearly unrivaled in risk retention and captive insurance matters, and her practice includes regulatory advice for companies and insurers. **Thomas Moody** is *"a very good lawyer"* who sources find *"excellent and good to deal with."* He has a broad-based corporate practice, and also becomes involved in international matters. **Paul Ode** maintains an active and varied corporate practice, with a strong transactional bent, while managing the firm's Burlington office. **Bruce Palmer** is admitted to the Bar of four different states and has US Court of Appeal audience rights. This flexibility enhances his ability to serve on multijurisdictional matters, especially involving environmental and product liability issues, common to insurers. **Roger Prescott** is highlighted for using his specialist tax knowledge and complementary captive insurance expertise to great effect. **David Sylvester** has an established retail and real estate practice that keeps him active on corporate and commercial transactions in those sectors. His admission to New York as well as Vermont enhances his transactional capability and he is especially known for work involving wholesale chains in neighboring New

England states. Of counsel **Kevin Moriarty** brings his considerable reputation and experience to the team in both captive insurance and nonprofit corporate structures.

## Gravel and Shea

**THE FIRM** This agile team has considerable transactional experience covering deals of various sizes, and represents companies across the spectrum of industries. The group has seen particular activity in the alternative energy space, among others.

**Sources say:** "*We continue to run into them; they are busy!*"

**KEY INDIVIDUALS Peter Erly** is an eminent adviser on transactions, and his securities experience makes him a valuable resource for companies seeking to structure their business efficiently to take advantage of Vermont laws. **William Mason** is well known in local financing and M&A circles. **Margaret Montgomery** has in-depth experience with multimillion-dollar financing deals and corporate transactions.

## Paul Frank + Collins P.C.

**THE FIRM** This long-established Burlington firm has captive insurance as an avowed area of focus. Its insurance attorneys are occasionally seen within this specialty as well, demonstrating the team's commitment to use the full slate of Paul Frank + Collins's experience in the service of its flagship practice.

**KEY INDIVIDUALS Stephanie Mapes** is increasingly recognized for both her captive insurance and IP expertise. She leads the firm's captive insurance team.

## Primmer Piper Eggleston & Cramer PC

**THE FIRM** This prestigious team represents several local companies, and its complementary, top-tier captive insurance practice enhances its overall commercial offering. With several bases throughout New England, its reputation is increasingly regional, although still very much concentrated on its niche in providing outstanding regulatory and insurance advice.

**Sources say:** "*I'd give high marks to them.*"

**KEY INDIVIDUALS Jon Eggleston** maintains a diverse practice that encompasses taxation and estates law. **James Clemons** continues to impress with the currency and quality of his captive insurance advice. **Jeffrey Johnson**'s name is synonymous with captive insurance, and he supports a range of companies inside and outside financial services with both regulatory and transactional advice. Clients find **Russell Young** to be "*intelligent, thorough, very thoughtful and articulate,*" and his insurance focus makes him an adviser highly sought by companies seeking to capitalize on Vermont's advantageous captive insurance provisions. **Keith Roberts** is active and prominent in the healthcare industry and his admissions in several New England states support the firm's regional push.

## Ryan Smith & Carbine, Ltd

**THE FIRM** The sole Rutland-headquartered firm in this category benefits from close local links and an accessibility that makes it a favorite for day-to-day commercial challenges.

**KEY INDIVIDUALS Thomas Dowling** is a respected business adviser for Rutland companies of all sizes, and his healthcare reputation is well established among colleagues. **Elizabeth Glynn** is well regarded for her corporate, real estate and healthcare practice.

## Other Notable Practitioners

**Michael Furlong** of Sheehey Furlong & Behm PC has broad-based business skills that enable him to advise clients on a range of commercial issues. His prior experience as an in-house attorney at a utilities company and his dispute resolution credentials allow him to bring a valuable perspective to corporate dilemmas. **Eric Knudsen** of Langrock Sperry & Wool, LLP has built a sound reputation for his deal orientation, as well as for his general commercial advice. **Thomas Melloni** of Burak, Anderson & Melloni PLC is "*very good, very diligent and a smart guy*" who wins particular acclaim for his able representation of banks. **Kenneth Merritt** of Merritt & Merritt & Moulton is particularly valued for his broad-ranging transactional practice, particularly in equity and venture capital-related matters. **David Angus** of The Angus Firm, PLC has been operating in a boutique dedicated to tax, business law and captive insurance since November 2011. He advises on matters with significant overseas elements and has specialist tax law qualifications.

# INTELLECTUAL PROPERTY

Commentary about individuals can be found under their firm's paragraph. If the firm has no paragraph (is not ranked) look at Other Notable Practitioners.

| Intellectual Property | |
|---|---|
| **Leading Firms** | |
| **Band 1** | |
| Downs Rachlin Martin PLLC | |
| **Band 2** | |
| Gravel and Shea | |

| **Leading Individuals** | | |
|---|---|---|
| **Band 1** | | |
| Kunin Peter B | Downs Rachlin Martin PLLC | |
| Meier Lawrence H | Downs Rachlin Martin PLLC | |
| Meyer Stuart P | Fenwick & West LLP (ONP)† * | |
| **Band 2** | | |
| Manitsky Andrew D | Gravel and Shea | |
| Mapes Stephanie J | Paul Frank + Collins P.C. (ONP)† | |
| McMahan Jeffrey J | Dinse, Knapp & McAndrew PC (ONP)† | |
| Merritt Sharon J | Merritt & Merritt & Moulton (ONP)† | |

*\* Indicates firm / individual with profile.*
*†ONP = Other Notable Practitioner.*

## Band 1

### Downs Rachlin Martin PLLC

**THE FIRM** The team is recognized for the breadth of its IP practice and others readily acknowledge its distinction. Its activity in promoting and participating in associations and conferences is praised and its name is a byword for IP excellence. The group handles trademark and licensing matters across industries as diverse as technology and consumer products.

**KEY INDIVIDUALS Peter Kunin** is "*a very good, smart and professional lawyer,*" say sources, who remark on the balance he strikes between being a "*firm advocate for his clients*" yet pleasant to deal with. He is especially valued for his trademark capabilities. **Lawrence Meier** is well known in the market for his patent and trademark expertise, and peers point to him as a key source of the team's strength in that area.

## Band 2

### Gravel and Shea

**THE FIRM** This practice benefits from the firm's top-ranked litigation arm and sources see that as a distinctive advantage in its IP offering, particularly in the trademark prosecution arena. The group is active both on obtaining patents and on offering ongoing advice across the range of IP issues.

**KEY INDIVIDUALS Andrew Manitsky** is a familiar face in IP circles, and peers are quick to point to his level of activity, especially in litigation.

## Other Notable Practitioners

**Jeffrey McMahan** of Dinse, Knapp & McAndrew PC is someone clients say they depend on because he uses "*plain English*" to explain licensing issues in easy-to-understand terms. They also point to him as a "*very successful*" negotiator in IP matters. **Stuart Meyer** (see p.2488) of Fenwick & West LLP maintains an excellent practice in Vermont, while being based primarily in Palo Alto. He counsels on general IP matters but draws on prior experience as a patent litigator. **Stephanie Mapes** of Paul Frank + Collins P.C. successfully balances her insurance work with a well-respected trademark and copyright practice. **Sharon Merritt** of Merritt & Merritt & Moulton is especially adept at assisting companies of all sizes, including emerging companies, with trademark issues.

# LABOR & EMPLOYMENT

## Band 1

### Dinse, Knapp & McAndrew PC

**THE FIRM** This is one of the top teams in Vermont, particularly in the Burlington area. In addition to a level of client service that creates total confidence, it is actively involved in the community. The group's recent work included acting on behalf of a healthcare employer on unemployment benefit liabilities.

**Sources say:** *"No one else can even come close to its depth and ability."*

**KEY INDIVIDUALS Karen McAndrew** is *"responsive, pragmatic, thorough and resourceful,"* according to clients. She represents prominent education and insurance sector employers, among others, in complex disputes. **Robert McKearin** is especially good at sensitive employment issues, where *"he does a superb job in terms of coaching employers on what to expect and how to respond."* **Amy McLaughlin** *"is outstanding,"* say clients, due to her depth of experience working in HR. She is especially adept at helping others *"communicate critical messages and handle difficult conversations with employees."* **Jeffrey Nolan** is able to negotiate reasonable solutions due to his expertise in employment law, and also due to his *"extremely level-headed and practical"* approach. He stays on top of current higher education issues and trends. **Sophie Zdatny** has been particularly involved in contentious labor and employment cases, where her litigation expertise comes especially highly recommended.

### Downs Rachlin Martin PLLC

**THE FIRM** With its statewide resources, Downs Rachlin can provide senior labor expertise throughout New England. From reorganizations to contentious dismissals, this full-service team supports employers in dealing with both routine compliance and significant HR challenges.

**KEY INDIVIDUALS Peter Robb** is venerated for his deep experience in negotiations on the management side. He is qualified to practice in various states and, in addition to managerial duties at the firm, he maintains a national labor practice. **Patricia Sabalis** has been involved in landmark national cases and uses her past experience counseling national household names to provide savvy advice to Vermont companies from her Burlington base. **Johan Maitland** is *"practical in his approach and knowledgeable"* according to sources. He has successfully represented employers in the education and healthcare sectors. **Timothy Copeland** supports employers in a variety of industries, and is especially known for his expertise with union-related issues.

## Other Notable Practitioners

**Kerin Stackpole** of Paul Frank + Collins P.C. is a *"dynamic individual who knows the law."* Others in the market say she *"works collaboratively and is a wonderful advocate for her clients."* **Elizabeth Grant** of Grant Norten PLLC has a longstanding reputation as a steady and methodical practitioner with a deliberate style. Her unflappable qualities serves her employment practice well. **Joseph McNeil** of McNeil Leddy & Sheahan PC is *"extremely knowledgeable, especially about unions."* Clients marvel at his institutional experience and familiarity with key players.

# LITIGATION GENERAL COMMERCIAL

Commentary about individuals can be found under their firm's paragraph. If the firm has no paragraph (is not ranked) look at Other Notable Practitioners.

## Band 1

### Dinse, Knapp & McAndrew PC

**THE FIRM** This litigation practice offers a highly effective, high-value service, say clients. Its work in the healthcare sector is especially well regarded, and interviewees note that it is a top choice for litigation concerned with professional liability and medical malpractice. Notwithstanding this focus, the team is active on a variety of commercial and personal litigation spanning the banking, education and sporting sectors.

**Sources say:** *"Rates are good. To be perfectly honest, they should be paid more!"*

**KEY INDIVIDUALS Karen McAndrew** has had a busy year defending multimillion-dollar claims and bolstering her justifiably superb reputation in the education sector. She recently successfully represented Mountain School in a federal district court personal injury action. **John Monahan** is *"a spectacular attorney both in and out of the courtroom,"* and is capable of keen case analysis and innovative ways to defend, according to sources. **Ritchie Berger** is *"well thought of"* in the market and clients appreciate his assertive style. He heads the litigation department. **Samuel Hoar** leads the firm's Plattsburgh practice in New York state, while maintaining a local presence supporting the litigation team. He is also active in the Vermont Bar Association.

### Downs Rachlin Martin PLLC

**THE FIRM** This litigation group handles a remarkable range of matters for utility, technology and financial services clients. It also has great depth of technical expertise, covering transport and product liability questions, for instance, with extraordinary skill. The team handles notably complex matters, and its deep bench is justly regarded as one of the most seasoned and versatile in the state.

**KEY INDIVIDUALS Marc Heath** has a staggering depth of experience in litigating highly technical cases, including product liability and wrongful death claims. **Andre Bouffard** continues to be recognized for his expertise in financial sector litigation. He used his considerable experience in workouts and complex financial liability matters to lead on a recent multijurisdictional matter involving the recovery of high-value assets caught up in foreign bankruptcy proceedings. **Bradford Fawley** leads on complex environmental, IP and insurance disputes. His expertise covers a range of trademark, copyright, patent, contaminated property and toxic tort disputes. **Walter Judge** has a strong IP slant to his litigation practice, and advises companies on trade secrets, among other commercial matters relevant to manufacturers. **Robert Rachlin** is the firm's senior director and is frequently involved in some of its most high-profile, international engagements.

## Gravel and Shea

**THE FIRM** This four-partner team advises on high-profile matters in the energy sector, with considerable legislative and financial impact. It is as comfortable handling local disputes as it is arguing before the nation's highest judicial authority, and has a justly earned reputation for its involvement in matters to which the State of Vermont is a party. The group is complemented by a set of able associates, so it can staff even complex litigation comfortably.

**KEY INDIVIDUALS Robert Hemley** is lauded as *"a great trial lawyer,"* and features in some of the most prominent cases, including the recent proposed closure of the Vermont Yankee nuclear power plant. **Andrew Manitsky** champions the commercial interests of clients in a range of matters. Although his intellectual property expertise is especially well known, he advises on matters as diverse as personal injury, business torts and employment law. **Robert O'Neill** has significant experience with disputes involving Washington, DC, and is admitted to practice in that jurisdiction. This, along with his tax and environmental expertise, adds valuable depth to the team's business offering. **Matthew Byrne** has excellent litigation expertise covering a diverse range of sectors, including healthcare, securities and projects disputes.

## Sheehey Furlong & Behm PC
See profile on p.2489

**THE FIRM** Sheehey Furlong's litigation and disputes partners are highly active in the local market on a variety of cases. The team is especially accomplished due to its mixture of established, seasoned practitioners and more recent talent. Peers readily refer to this team in case of conflicts, because of confidence in the breadth of its skill set.

**KEY INDIVIDUALS** Peers say that **Jeffrey Behm** is *"insistent on behalf of his clients"* during tough proceedings, and tough to beat. **Eric Miller** is extraordinarily well prepared and confident in court, say sources. Interviewees hail him as *"a future star"* of the sector. **James Spink** brings valuable arbitration and mediation experience to the group. Having also run a litigation boutique, his practice covers the full spectrum of dispute resolution methods.

## Band 2

## Cleary Shahi & Aicher, P.C.

**THE FIRM** This team has a clear litigation focus, flanked by employment and insurance practices. It is especially well known for personal and catastrophic injury work, and is also respected for its insurance and product liability expertise on behalf of defendants.

**KEY INDIVIDUALS** Firm president **David Cleary** has a deep and wide-ranging litigation practice. His preeminent expertise covers all manner of commercial litigation, and he is particularly *"famed for medical malpractice work,"* say sources. **Kaveh Shahi** is admitted to practice in several states and is renowned for accident and injury work. His commercial litigation practice has an insurance emphasis.

## Paul Frank + Collins P.C.

**THE FIRM** Construction, insurance and healthcare companies value this team's disputes experience. Its expertise covers a range of commercial litigation, with product and professional liability and personal injury claims featuring more recently.

**KEY INDIVIDUALS Crocker Bennett** focuses on medical malpractice suits and is praised as an *"extremely good trial lawyer"* for such purposes. **Robert DiPalma** has a strong financial services and corporate disputes offering. Sources describe **John Sartore** as *"a smart guy"* who is frequently seen on landmark decisions in the state.

## Band 3

## Primmer Piper Eggleston & Cramer PC

**THE FIRM** The market is enthusiastic about recent hires to this litigation team, which extend its established practice in Vermont into a strengthening New Hampshire offering. The flagship Burlington office, not to be outdone, is attracting approving attention in commercial disputes.

**KEY INDIVIDUALS Gary Franklin** is a respected litigator who is admitted in three states and whose practice runs the gamut from intellectual property to disputed contracts.

## Theriault & Joslin PC

**THE FIRM** A favorite among insurers, this group's complementary litigation practice is adept in advising on liabilities, whether in personal injury, arson or medical malpractice cases. Its members are also capable of handling alternative dispute resolution, and the team is noted for its mediation activities. The compact practice has carved out a niche in representing doctors and hospitals.

**KEY INDIVIDUALS Peter Joslin** *"is smart and well prepared, and does a good job,"* according to interviewees, many of whom also praise his abilities as a mediator.

## Other Notable Practitioners

**Richard Rubin** of Rubin, Kidney, Myer & DeWolfe has a positive reputation among peers, many of whom *"think highly"* of his litigation capabilities. **Michael Burak** of Burak, Anderson & Melloni PLC is known for his client-friendly style and strategic approach. His utilities experience is a differentiator in this market. **Thomas McCormick** of McCormick, Fitzpatrick, Kasper & Burchard PC wins acclaim for both his eminent litigation skills and his effective and personal style in tense situations. **Richard Wadhams** of Pierson, Wadhams, Quinn, Yates & Coffrin LLP has a vibrant insurance defense practice and is viewed as being extremely experienced. **Peter Langrock** of Langrock Sperry & Wool, LLP is a venerable trial lawyer who remains an important anchor of the firm's litigation group.

# REAL ESTATE

Commentary about individuals can be found under their firm's paragraph. If the firm has no paragraph (is not ranked) look at Other Notable Practitioners.

| Real Estate |  |
| --- | --- |
| **Leading Firms** | |
| **Band 1** | |
| Dinse, Knapp & McAndrew PC | |
| Downs Rachlin Martin PLLC | |
| Gravel and Shea | |
| Murphy Sullivan Kronk | |
| **Band 2** | |
| Kenlan, Schwiebert, Facey & Goss P.C. | |
| Langrock Sperry & Wool, LLP | |
| Primmer Piper Eggleston & Cramer PC | |

| Senior Statesmen | |
| --- | --- |
| **Senior Statesmen: distinguished older practitioners** | |
| Lisman Carl H | Lisman, Webster & Leckerling PC (ONP)[†] |

| Leading Individuals | |
| --- | --- |
| **Band 1** | |
| Farkas Michelle | Gravel and Shea |
| Hart Austin | Dinse, Knapp & McAndrew PC |
| Lebowitz Molly | Dinse, Knapp & McAndrew PC |
| Murphy Liam | Murphy Sullivan Kronk |
| Rushford Robert | Gravel and Shea |
| Schroeder William W | Downs Rachlin Martin PLLC |
| **Band 2** | |
| Conard David | Langrock Sperry & Wool, LLP |
| Farkas Jeremy I | Murphy Sullivan Kronk |
| Jaunich R Prescott | Downs Rachlin Martin PLLC |
| Kenlan Jay | Kenlan, Schwiebert, Facey & Goss P.C. |
| Knudsen Eric | Langrock Sperry & Wool, LLP |
| Kronk Catherine | Murphy Sullivan Kronk |
| **Band 3** | |
| Anderson Jon T | Burak, Anderson & Melloni PLC |
| Eustace Timothy M | Gravel and Shea |
| Facey III John A | Kenlan, Schwiebert, Facey & Goss P.C. |

| Real Estate: Zoning/Land Use | |
| --- | --- |
| **Leading Individuals** | |
| **Band 1** | |
| Kenlan Jay | Kenlan, Schwiebert, Facey & Goss P.C. |
| Murphy Liam | Murphy Sullivan Kronk |
| Reynes Stephen A | Primmer Piper Eggleston & Cramer PC |
| Schwiebert Edward V | Kenlan, Schwiebert, Facey & Goss P.C. |
| Sullivan Brian | Murphy Sullivan Kronk |
| Van Oot Peter D | Downs Rachlin Martin PLLC |
| **Band 2** | |
| Anderson Jon T | Burak, Anderson & Melloni PLC (ONP)[†] |
| Dodge William J | Downs Rachlin Martin PLLC |
| Eustace Timothy M | Gravel and Shea |
| Facey III John A | Kenlan, Schwiebert, Facey & Goss P.C. |
| Grayck David | Cheney, Brock and Saudek, P.C. (ONP)[†] |
| Hall Mark | Paul Frank + Collins P.C. (ONP)[†] |

[†]ONP = Other Notable Practitioner.

## Band 1

### Dinse, Knapp & McAndrew PC

**THE FIRM** Clients are very satisfied with this real estate team and cite its ability to give a real sense of the market overview as a particular strength. The group has recently been active on several substantial deals and projects, covering a range of issues, including financing and transfers, as well as land use permitting.

**Sources say:** *"They are thorough and accurate, and give good guidance."*

**KEY INDIVIDUALS Austin Hart** reflects the firm's reputation for accuracy, timeliness and responsiveness, according to several clients. He also knows how to *"step right in and facilitate a solution to a problem."* Clients are also full of praise for his *"strong real estate background."* **Molly Lebowitz** is a solid real estate transactional lawyer with *"extremely good business sense."* She *"focuses on the important issues,"* say sources, and is also *"responsive, quick and to the point."*

### Downs Rachlin Martin PLLC

**THE FIRM** This team is highly recommended for land acquisition work, and is highlighted for its significant expertise in handling work outside of the state. It devotes a large number of attorneys to this practice and related environmental and land use sectors. In addition to being well resourced, the group is backed by excellent regional coverage with real estate personnel based in four New England offices.

**KEY INDIVIDUALS William Schroeder** is cochair of the firm's real estate practice group. He has a leading presence across a range of real estate financing, leasing, acquisition and regulatory issues, and peers pronounce him to be *"good to work with."* **Peter Van Oot** is based in New Hampshire, but his regulatory and utilities focus earns him a justified eminence in Vermont for his real estate zoning advice. **William Dodge** operates regionally, using his telecom and utilities experience to handle complex zoning requirements for facilities in those industries. **Prescott Jaunich** cochairs this practice group and is *"good for zoning,"* according to market sources. He is also admitted to state and district courts in California, where he practiced for several years prior to joining Downs Rachlin Martin.

### Gravel and Shea

**THE FIRM** Gravel and Shea has a compact and highly effective group of real estate professionals who are nearly all leading lights in the industry with considerable expertise. Its experience spans commercial, residential, utilities and retail matters, usually within Vermont, although its retail work is national in scope.

**KEY INDIVIDUALS Michelle Farkas** is easy to work with and maintains her sterling reputation in the real estate sector. She has in-depth expertise across a range of commercial real estate transactions, covering everything from zoning and land use to acquisitions and condominium issues. **Robert Rushford** has an equally broad and respected real estate practice. He is especially active on commercial leases and developments, and in telecom-related matters. Sources also highlight his expertise in zoning work. **Timothy Eustace** is noted for his excellent expertise across an array of permitting and zoning issues. He also advises on environmental regulations.

### Murphy Sullivan Kronk

**THE FIRM** Real estate forms a noteworthy part of this firm's superb operation, and it offers a dedicated group covering the property and land use sector, from permitting and financing through to litigation. Its team includes a number of recognized specialists and is readily and favorably compared by interviewees to the top-tier practices of full-service neighbors.

**KEY INDIVIDUALS** The highly respected **Liam Murphy** is renowned for all manner of real estate and land use matters. His litigation capabilities are also praised. **Brian Sullivan** is a giant in the area of telecom zoning and permitting work. His practice ranges from regulatory advice to appellate litigation in a variety of state and federal courts. **Jeremy Farkas** is active on both transactional and disputes work, including those relating to residential, hotel and office developments. While passionate in defense of his clients, peers say he is able to *"work out issues cordially."* **Catherine Kronk** *"is excellent, gets things done"* and *"understands negotiations,"* according to interviewees. Sources also highlight her capabilities in representing local developers.

## Band 2

### Kenlan, Schwiebert, Facey & Goss P.C.

**THE FIRM** This team is distinguished for its representation of developers and for its roles in vacation real estate matters. Its Rutland base gives it proximity to this important part of the sector, while its numerous experts in Vermont land use issues ensure others have no hesitation in referring matters to this group.

**KEY INDIVIDUALS Jay Kenlan** is a trusted name in real estate circles and is closely associated with several of the most prominent land use developments in the Rutland area. The tremendously respected **Edward Schwiebert** is an acknowledged expert in zoning and permitting work, and has strong expertise in environmental and administrative law. **John Facey** is adept at real estate issues affecting clients of various sizes, although he is especially known for his work in condominium law and state permitting issues.

## Langrock Sperry & Wool, LLP

**THE FIRM** This local firm serves an extremely diverse group of clients, and is visible on transactions such as lender representations, but is also well known in construction, permitting and disputes. The team is also recognized for its work involving financing, foreclosures and leasing across a range of development types.

**KEY INDIVIDUALS David Conard** has a varied real estate practice covering an array of permitting, finance and acquisition matters, as well as litigation assignments. He is also noted for his work involving construction issues. **Eric Knudsen** *"appreciates making the deal happen,"* say sources. He is highlighted for his excellent transactional and finance practice.

## Primmer Piper Eggleston & Cramer PC

**THE FIRM** This firm incorporates an excellent real estate practice into its broader commercial offering, and its lawyers have complementary finance and corporate expertise to serve their clients. Sales, acquisitions, permitting and leasing all fall within the team's skill set.

**KEY INDIVIDUALS Stephen Reynes** heads the firm's environmental and land use practice group. He has a distinguished record in permitting, and significant utilities, zoning and environmental experience.

## Other Notable Practitioners

**Jon Anderson** of Burak, Anderson & Melloni PLC is famed for his permitting experience and is frequently seen in contentious matters. **David Grayck** of Cheney, Brock and Saudek, P.C. is noted for representing clients in significant land use and zoning permitting and litigation. **Mark Hall** of Paul Frank + Collins P.C. is especially well known for his litigation expertise, including in environmental, land use and construction-related cases. **Carl Lisman** of Lisman, Webster & Leckerling PC continues to feature in significant litigation and lends his decades of experience to developers both in financing and in handling claims.

# Leaders' Profiles in Vermont

## MEYER, Stuart P
Fenwick & West LLP, Mountain View
650 335 7286
smeyer@fenwick.com
*Featured in Intellectual Property (Vermont)*

**Practice Areas:** Stuart P Meyer is a partner in the Intellectual Property and Litigation Groups of Fenwick & West. He counsels clients on intellectual property matters, including technology-based litigation, performing strategic intellectual property planning and intellectual property audits for technology companies, and securing patent, copyright, and other intellectual property rights. Mr Meyer has extensive experience in patent reexaminations and other post-grant disputes. He currently serves on the PTO's pro bono steering committee for California.

**Career:** Mr Meyer was recently named one of The Best Lawyers in America 2012 in Information Technology Law and as a "Leading Individual" for Intellectual Property Law by Chambers USA 2011. He was also named to The International Who's Who of Internet & e-Commerce Lawyers, 2009 and The International Who's Who of Business Lawyers, 2010 published by Who's Who Legal. Intellectual Asset Management magazine includes Mr Meyer in their IAM 250-The World's Leading IP Strategists guide for 2009, 2010 and 2011.

**Publications:** Mr Meyer has contributed to books and authored numerous articles on intellectual property law. He is frequently invited to lecture on this topic throughout the United States and abroad.

**Leading Law Firms Vermont**

# SHEEHEY FURLONG & BEHM P.C.

www.sheeheyvt.com **tel:** 802 864 9891 **fax:** 1 802 864 6815

**Managing Partner:** Diane McCarthy
Number of partners: 9
Number of lawyers: 11
Languages: *English, French*

**OFFICES**

VERMONT

**BURLINGTON:** 30 Main Street, PO Box 66, VT 05402-0066
Tel: +1 802 864 9891  Fax: +1 802 864 6815

**Firm Overview:**

Sheehey Furlong & Behm P.C. and its predecessor firms have, since 1926, enjoyed a reputation for excellence in a variety of practice areas. The firm is mid-sized by Vermont standards, efficient, highly responsive and includes many of the Vermont Bar's most experienced and sought-after leaders in litigation, utility regulatory matters, business, energy, healthcare, employment and real estate matters. The firm prides itself on its proven ability to combine thorough representation of the highest quality with right-sized staffing to obtain optimal results in a cost-effective manner.

**Main Areas of Practice:**

**Banking & Finance:**
The firm regularly represents and advises banks and other financial institutions, including Merchants Bank, TD Bank, and People's United Bank, in financing transactions, operational, security and regulatory (state and FDIC) matters, and litigation matters. On the borrower side, the firm represents business and non-profit corporations in bank loans and bond financing transactions.
**Contacts:** Michael Furlong, Diane McCarthy
**Email:** mfurlong@sheeheyvt.com, dmccarthy@sheeheyvt.com

**Corporate/M&A:**
The firm represents and advises a wide range of business and non-profit clients based in or operating in Vermont in their start-up organization and capitalization and ongoing legal matters, including mergers, acquisitions and reorganizations.
**Contacts:** Michael Furlong, Diane McCarthy
**Email:** mfurlong@sheeheyvt.com, dmccarthy@sheeheyvt.com

**Litigation:**
The firm's litigation team includes two Fellows of the American College of Trial Lawyers. All members of the team have extensive experience in Vermont and other jurisdictions when required. Representative clients include General Electric, Green Mountain Power (Vermont's largest electric utility), Fletcher Allen Health Care (Vermont's leading hospital) and many others. The firm has expertise in representing health care providers, regulated utilities, product manufacturers, insurers, and lending institutions. The firm represents licensed professionals in civil and criminal litigation and before professional practice boards, and its attorneys have extensive experience in criminal defense, including white collar criminal defense. James Spink is one of Vermont's leading ADR specialists with over 1500 mediations completed.
**Contacts:** Jeff Behm, James Spink, Eric Miller, Ian Carleton, Debra Bouffard

**Email:** jbehm@sheeheyvt.com, jspink@sheeheyvt.com, emiller@sheeheyvt.com, icarleton@sheeheyvt.com, dbouffard@sheeheyvt.com

**Real Estate:**
The firm represents clients in the acquisition, leasing, financing, development, management and sale of all types of properties, including shopping centers, office and mixed-use buildings, utility properties and easements, retirement communities and residential properties. The firm performs title examinations and reviews permit compliance, negotiates contracts and leases, assists in permitting and environmental matters, and advises clients on varying and unique aspects related to the ownership, management and development of property in Vermont. Key projects include acquisition of property rights relative to a wind farm, acquisition of property and financing for senior housing developments, redevelopment and leasing of mixed use shopping center and former industrial buildings.
**Contacts:** Diane McCarthy, Michael Furlong
**Email:** dmccarthy@sheeheyvt.com, mfurlong@sheeheyvt.com

**Healthcare:**
The firm's healthcare team represents healthcare providers, partnerships, and institutions, serving as advisors and advocates on a broad range of issues confronting its clients in this complex and quickly evolving area. The firm assists healthcare clients as they form their practices and grow those practices through transitions in ownership or organizational structure, real estate/leasing, and related contractual matters. Representative clients and matters include healthcare institutions and their individual providers in connection with investigations conducted by state and federal authorities with respect to Stark, billing, and licensing issues, criminal prosecutions and civil malpractice actions. The firm also represents institutions in litigation and arbitration concerning contractual and employment-related disputes.
**Contacts:** Michael Furlong, Jeff Behm, Eric Miller
**Email:** mfurlong@sheeheyvt.com, jbehm@sheeheyvt.com, emiller@sheeheyvt.com

**Energy & Natural Resources:**
The firm's energy practice involves representation of electric and gas providers in state and federal regulatory matters involving facilities siting, ratesetting, mergers, transmission reliability, approvals of power contracts and other matters. The practice also includes negotiation of long-term electricity and gas contracts and litigation of energy-related disputes. Peter Zamore has been counsel to the Public Service Board ("PSB") and Public Service Department, and general counsel to an electric utility and a competitive electricity marketer.
**Contacts:** Peter Zamore, Charlotte Ancel
**Email:** pzamore@sheeheyvt.com, cancel@sheeheyvt.com

**Telecom, Broadcast & Satellite:**
The firm's team represents a variety of telecommunications, broadcast and related providers, including the largest incumbent local exchange carrier. The practice includes representation before the PSB in connection with ratesetting, service quality, video franchises, joint use infrastructure and related matters, as well as transactional matters and litigation. The firm represents Vermont's largest television broadcaster in litigating claims related to First Amendment protections, defamation, and access to public records.
**Contacts:** Peter Zamore, Charlotte Ancel
**Email:** pzamore@sheeheyvt.com, cancel@sheeheyvt.com

**Employment:**
The firm advises large and small Vermont employers on all types of employment related questions, including such topics as employee hiring, discipline, discrimination and harassment claims, internal investigations, leave management, and termination. The firm also provides training to management teams to facilitate compliance with state and federal employment laws, works with employers to update and revise employment handbooks, policies and related notices and forms, and frequently represents firm clients in employment related matters before various government agencies and courts.
**Contact:** Debra Bouffard
**Email:** dbouffard@sheeheyvt.com

## How lawyers are ranked

Every year we carry out thousands of in-depth interviews with clients in order to assess the reputations and expertise of business lawyers worldwide. The qualities we look for (and which determine rankings) include technical legal ability, professional conduct, client service, commercial awareness/astuteness, diligence, commitment, and other qualities most valued by the client. For details of our research team, see p.5.

## VIRGINIA: An Introduction

### Contributed by Patrick O. Gottschalk, Partner at Williams Mullen (former Virginia Secretary of Commerce and Trade)

For four of the last six years, Forbes.com ranked Virginia as the "Best State for Business" in America. Virginia was ranked as "America's Top State for Business" by CNBC in 2007, 2009 and 2011. In 2011, Virginia was ranked the "Top Pro-Business State" by Pollina Real Estate. That is why 31 Fortune 1000 companies and 16,900 hi-tech businesses call Virginia home. The capital, Richmond, boasts 11 Fortune 1000 companies alone. Virginia is also a major player in international commerce because of its strong transportation infrastructure and perfectly situated location; over 700 internationally owned companies from over 45 countries have established operations here.

### Pro-Business Climate

Virginia's pro-business climate begins with its right-to-work laws, which allow employees to work regardless of whether they are members of a labor union. Both state and local governments in Virginia have been recognized by the media for excellence in their management and delivery of governmental services (Virginia enjoys an AAA bond rating). Taxes are low across the board (the corporate income tax, at 6%, has not been increased since 1972), and government regulations are less burdensome than in practically any other state in the union. Hence, businesses large and small, public and private, thrive in Virginia's business environment. That is why at least 40 firms with annual revenues over $1 billion are headquartered in Virginia.

### Low Litigation

Virginia is not litigation friendly. For example, the Virginia state courts still recognize contributory negligence as a defense. Virginia ranked sixth in the US Chamber of Commerce's 2010 State Liability Systems Study; as adjudged by corporate America, it is one of the best states in the country for creating a fair and reasonable litigation environment. Virginia has a statutory cap on punitive damages, as well as on medical malpractice claims. State law does not sanction class action suits and attorneys' fees are not recoverable as a matter of course, save a specific contract provision or statute. As a result, businesses find Virginia to be a relatively safe haven from litigation.

### Ideal Location

With a mid-Atlantic location, Virginia is blessed by its close proximity to Washington, DC and the presence of numerous defense facilities in Northern Virginia and Hampton Roads. The largest concentration of federal R&D establishments in the USA is located in Virginia, which equates to 25% of the total number. This concentration includes 20 defense-related labs and R&D centers and 19 federal civilian research centers, such as the new Homeland Security Institute, NASA Langley Research Center and DOE's unique Thomas Jefferson National Accelerator Facility. Virginia ranks third among the 50 states as a recipient of federal R&D funds.

### Excellent Accessibility

Virginia has a strong transportation infrastructure, which includes 11 commercial airports (including two of the nation's busiest), 3,500 miles of railroad, 70,000 miles of interstate, and one of the largest ports on the East Coast. The Port of Virginia in Hampton Roads and Dulles International Airport near Washington, DC are two major international gateways, allowing businesses to deliver goods overnight to 55% of the nation's consumers. Virginia is intersected by I-95, I-85, I-81, I-77, I-66 and I-64, and is served extensively by CSX and Norfolk Southern railroads. The state also offers six foreign trade zones, designed to encourage businesses to participate in international trade by effectively eliminating or reducing customs duties.

### Quality of Life

Virginia's list of attributes would not be complete without mentioning its quality of life, hospitality and abundance of tourism and recreational destinations for all ages and interests. With the Atlantic Ocean and Chesapeake Bay in the east, the Blue Ridge and Appalachian Mountains to the west, and historical landmarks throughout the Commonwealth, Virginia has something for everyone. Four Virginia localities (Alexandria, Centreville, Chesapeake and Suffolk) were named in Money Magazine's 2010 list of the 100 best places to live in the United States.

**Economic Incentives**

The Governor's Opportunity Fund ("GOF") (a deal closing fund) continues to be a popular incentive to attract new business to Virginia and facilitate expansions of existing businesses. In 2010, the legislature appropriated nearly $50 million for the Governor's economic development and job creation plan, and an additional $50 million was included in Virginia's budget for economic development in 2011.

**Conclusion**

Virginia truly is a great state for business. For the past 400 years, it has utilized its unique combination of assets to make it one of the most attractive states for business relocation and expansion.

# CONSTRUCTION

Commentary about individuals can be found under their firm's paragraph. If the firm has no paragraph (is not ranked) look at Other Notable Practitioners.

| Construction | |
| --- | --- |
| **Leading Firms** | |
| **Band 1** | |
| Watt, Tieder, Hoffar & Fitzgerald, LLP * | |
| **Band 2** | |
| Kraftson Caudle | |
| Moore & Lee LLP | |
| Reed Smith LLP | |
| Smith Pachter McWhorter PLC * | |
| **Band 3** | |
| Akerman Senterfitt | |

## Band 1

### Watt, Tieder, Hoffar & Fitzgerald, LLP
See profile on p.2522

**THE FIRM** This 32-partner practice handles a variety of high-value construction matters from its headquarters in McLean. The team's high-profile client portfolio features major names such as Balfour Beatty, Hitachi and AECOM. Areas of focus include project planning, drafting construction contracts, subcontracts, purchase orders and related documents. The team is also well known for its contentious construction practice.

**Sources say:** *"They're a real powerhouse in this field." "They work to a very high standard. Everything they do is excellent."*
**KEY INDIVIDUALS** Construction doyen **Robert Watt** is a mainstay in the *Chambers* rankings. Boasting over 30 years' experience of major infrastructure matters, he is one of the most illustrious names in Virginia's construction scene. Clients describe *"outstanding"* managing partner **Lewis Baker** (see p.2508) as being *"at the top of his game."* Baker has been at the firm for over 25 years, offering clients in-depth experience of all construction, surety and architect/engineer claims. **Paul Varela** (see p.2514) advised Tishman Construction Corporation on a $500 million multiparty dispute pertaining to the 18 million sq ft mixed-use development CityCenter, located in the heart of the Las Vegas Strip. Clients laud him as *"a valuable asset who really understands our business."* **Robert Fitzgerald** (see p.2509) is a veritable leading light in the construction sector. Sources acknowledge him as *"an experienced practitioner who knows construction inside out."* He is well known

for his expertise in construction contracts, as well as in resolving disputes relating to public and private construction projects. **John Tieder** (see p.2514) continues to maintain a stellar profile in the Virginia construction market. He is particularly active on construction matters with an international dimension, advising clients on the construction of infrastructure and energy projects around the world. **Vivian Katsantonis** (see p.2510) specializes in drafting contractual documents, advising on strategies for contract administration, and closeout. A further aspect of her practice is the preparation, negotiation and litigation of major construction claims. Peers describe her as a *"very impressive lawyer."* **Todd Metz** (see p.2512) focuses on contentious matters, advising all parties on construction claims and bid protests throughout the USA and internationally. He is commended by sources as *"a competent practitioner who presents his arguments persuasively."* Sureties expert **Carter Reid** (see p.2513) is hailed by clients as *"an amazing lawyer with real presence"* who *"commands the respect of judges."* Other sources describe him as *"technically very strong and always well prepared."* Peers describe **Mark Sgarlata** (see p.2513) as *"a recognized name in the industry."* He has significant experience in heavy industrial and commercial construction projects. He also offers clients in-depth knowledge of both state and federal environmental law.

## Band 2

### Kraftson Caudle

**THE FIRM** This McLean-based construction and government contracts boutique has been a consistent presence in the Chambers rankings. The team advises public and private owners, contractors, subcontractors, suppliers and design professionals on all aspects of the construction process.

**Sources say:** *"A great firm with real construction expertise."*
**KEY INDIVIDUALS Wayne Lalle** primarily focuses on construction disputes, but is also well known for his project development and contract formation work in relation to transportation projects. Sources acknowledge his *"great reputation in the construction sector."* **Daniel Kraftson's**

| Construction | |
| --- | --- |
| **Senior Statesmen** | |
| **Senior Statesmen: distinguished older practitioners** | |
| Franczek William E | Vandeventer Black LLP (ONP)† |
| Smith Richard F | Smith Pachter McWhorter PLC |
| **Leading Individuals** | |
| **Star individuals** | |
| Watt Robert G | Watt, Tieder, Hoffar & Fitzgerald, LLP |
| **Band 1** | |
| Baker Lewis J | Watt, Tieder, Hoffar & Fitzgerald, LLP * |
| Fitzgerald Robert M | Watt, Tieder, Hoffar & Fitzgerald, LLP * |
| Kraftson Daniel | Kraftson Caudle |
| Lalle Wayne | Kraftson Caudle |
| Loulakis Michael C | Capital Project Strategies LLC (ONP)† |
| McWhorter Val S | Smith Pachter McWhorter PLC |
| Moore Robert M | Moore & Lee LLP |
| Tieder John B | Watt, Tieder, Hoffar & Fitzgerald, LLP * |
| Vella Brian | Smith Pachter McWhorter PLC |
| **Band 2** | |
| Brownell Thomas | Holland & Knight LLP (ONP)† * |
| Cox Robert K | Williams Mullen (ONP)† |
| Gavin Donald G | Akerman Senterfitt |
| Gilmore Jeffrey G | Akerman Senterfitt |
| Hurlbut Stephen | Akerman Senterfitt |
| Lee Charlie C H | Moore & Lee LLP |
| **Band 3** | |
| Barat Scott | Pillsbury Winthrop Shaw Pittman (ONP)† * |
| Briglia Shannon J | BrigliaMcLaughlin, PLLC (ONP)† |
| Caudle Jr Larry W | Kraftson Caudle |
| Folk Thomas R | Reed Smith LLP |
| Hanson Mark E | Smith Pachter McWhorter PLC |
| Howley Sean M | Kraftson Caudle |
| Katsantonis Vivian | Watt, Tieder, Hoffar & Fitzgerald, LLP * |
| Metz Todd R | Watt, Tieder, Hoffar & Fitzgerald, LLP * |
| Reid Carter B | Watt, Tieder, Hoffar & Fitzgerald, LLP * |
| Sgarlata Mark A | Watt, Tieder, Hoffar & Fitzgerald, LLP * |
| Varela Paul A | Watt, Tieder, Hoffar & Fitzgerald, LLP * |

*  Indicates firm / individual with profile.
† ONP = Other Notable Practitioner.

practice focuses on construction and government contracts. Sources laud him as *"an excellent attorney who is 100% focused on construction law."* **Larry Caudle**'s construction work has a strong emphasis on heavy civil and transportation matters. His clientele includes owners, contractors, subcontractors and engineers. His broad practice encompasses claim preparation and analysis, as well as dispute resolution. Sources praise him as *"a promising lawyer who is really working his way up."* **Sean Howley** offers clients a wealth of industry experience. He enjoys a strong reputation for resolving major construction and government contracts matters. Rivals recognize him as *"a strong practitioner who is very active in the state bar."*

## Moore & Lee LLP

**THE FIRM** Clients from across the construction industry seek out this firm for its comprehensive construction law expertise. The team is particularly well known for its contentious construction practice. It also advises clients on all forms of government contracts work, assisting on federal, state and municipal procurement issues.

**Sources say:** *"A strong boutique firm, especially reputable for construction litigation."*

**KEY INDIVIDUALS** Founding partner of the firm, **Robert Moore** is recognized for his expertise across a broad range of construction matters. Areas of focus include advising clients on federal procurement law, as well as on commercial construction contracts and disputes. Fellow founding partner **Charlie Lee** has a broad construction practice, offering advice on all phases of the construction process, from contract formation and negotiation to dispute resolution. His practice encompasses a wide range of heavy industrial and large commercial projects, as well as a specialist focus on healthcare institutions. He is recognized by commentators as *"an extremely talented litigator who is really convincing in court."*

## Reed Smith LLP

**THE FIRM** Working closely with Reed Smith's real estate, litigation, and insurance groups, this 21-lawyer construction practice has extensive experience in all forms of construction-related dispute resolution. The team has worked with public owners, private owners, developers, contractors, and designers on a broad range of large infrastructure, commercial, residential and retail construction projects. Recent high-profile clients include Duke Realty Corporation and The Franklin and Eleanor Roosevelt Institute.

**Sources say:** *"Our go-to firm. They have represented us very well. They are extremely competent and very professional."*

**KEY INDIVIDUALS Thomas Folk** has extensive litigation experience across a broad range of legal disciplines, but he is best known for his contentious construction and public procurement practice. Clients commend him as *"a very strong attorney, experienced in design-build contract development. He listens to his clients' needs and he is very responsive and personable. He is very creative, always looking at new ideas. A genuine and sincere lawyer."*

## Smith Pachter McWhorter PLC
See profile on p.2521

**THE FIRM** This construction and government contracts boutique focuses on high-value, heavy construction and civil works projects. The team boasts longstanding expertise in dealing with Virginia's public agencies in respect of regulatory, audit and compliance issues. The group's practice encompasses all phases of the construction process, from contract bidding and negotiation to contentious claims and litigation.

**Sources say:** *"A good, solid firm with capable lawyers."*

**KEY INDIVIDUALS Val McWhorter** is well known for representing contractors in complex claims arising from public and private sector construction projects. Sources regard him as *"a true stalwart."* **Brian Vella** has more than 25 years' experience of representing contractors and owners in all forms of contentious construction claims. Vella also advises on contract formation and interpretation, as well as counseling clients on developing strategies for analyzing and avoiding risk. **Mark Hanson** has acted on a diverse range of construction projects, including commercial, industrial and heavy civil projects. He also has extensive litigation expertise, having pursued and defended claims before state and federal courts, as well as in international arbitration proceedings. He is acknowledged by rivals as *"a strong attorney who has been on the construction scene for a long time."* **Richard Smith** is a popular choice among clients for construction-related dispute resolution matters. Observers praise his work as a mediator, and he regularly acts as a project neutral and disputes review board member in construction-related issues.

## Band 3

## Akerman Senterfitt
See profile on p.1014

**THE FIRM** This eight-partner practice serves clients from a range of industries, including transportation, energy, public infrastructure and healthcare. The team advises all parties on construction projects, and it often counsels clients in the related field of state and federal procurement process. Recent highlights include advising Architect of the Capitol on a deficiency claim relating to the US Capitol Visitors' Center.

**KEY INDIVIDUALS Donald Gavin**'s experience includes contentious construction claims relating to major oil and gas, chemical, wastewater and power production facilities and infrastructure. Sources describe him as *"a highly active and well-respected practitioner."* Practice chair **Jeffrey Gilmore** handles a broad range of public and private construction matters. He recently advised Washington Metropolitan Area Transit Authority on several matters relating to the construction of a bus maintenance facility. Construction litigation specialist **Stephen Hurlbut** splits his time between the firm's DC and Virginia offices. He has significant experience in resolving delay and other schedule-related claims. He recently represented Carrimex LLC in ICC arbitration proceedings in the British Virgin Islands, in respect of damages and wrongful termination claims relating to a hospital building project.

## Other Notable Practitioners

**Michael Loulakis** of Capital Project Strategies LLC is well known for his extensive experience on design-build and other alternative project delivery systems. Clients describe him as *"extremely personable, very knowledgeable, prompt, and flexible."* **Thomas Brownell** (see p.2508) of Holland & Knight LLP is well known for defending both private and public-sector clients against changes and delay claim litigation relating to major construction projects. Other areas of expertise include defending construction-related product liability claims. **Shannon Briglia** of BrigliaMcLaughlin, PLLC has extensive experience in litigating construction contract disputes and surety cases in various federal and state courts. She is also well versed in alternative dispute resolution, having conducted arbitration and mediation proceedings throughout the USA. *"Top-notch"* **William Franczek** is the managing partner of Vandeventer Black LLP. Clients seek him out for his extensive experience in both construction and public contract law. He is particularly well known for his contentious practice and is recognized by sources as a leading mediator and arbitrator in construction matters. **Robert Cox** is a new addition to the construction practice of Williams Mullen. Cox is recognized as an expert in all construction and surety law matters. He offers clients more than 35 years of experience in preparing and negotiating construction contracts, as well as representing clients in all types of contentious construction claims. **Scott Barat** (see p.2508) of Pillsbury Winthrop Shaw Pittman LLP is head of the firm's construction practice in North Virginia. He has a wide-ranging local and nationwide client base. Sources describe him as *"a very competent attorney who is very good at drafting contracts."*

# CORPORATE/M&A NORTHERN VIRGINIA

## Corporate/M&A: Northern Virginia
### Leading Firms

**Band 1**
Hogan Lovells US LLP

**Band 2**
Cooley LLP
Holland & Knight LLP *
Morrison & Foerster LLP *
Pillsbury Winthrop Shaw Pittman LLP *

**Band 3**
Arnold & Porter LLP *
DLA Piper LLP (US) *
Venable LLP *

### Leading Individuals

**Band 1**

| | |
|---|---|
| Chason Craig | Pillsbury Winthrop Shaw Pittman LLP |
| Horan Richard | Hogan Lovells US LLP |
| Knox Thomas J | Morrison & Foerster LLP * |
| Lehrer Jeffrey K | DLA Piper LLP (US) * |
| Lincoln Michael | Cooley LLP |
| Mutryn William J | Holland & Knight LLP * |
| Yanowitch Lawrence T | Morrison & Foerster LLP * |

**Band 2**

| | |
|---|---|
| Becker Richard K A | Hogan Lovells US LLP |
| Meltzer Steven | Pillsbury Winthrop Shaw Pittman LLP |
| Schmelter Joseph C | Venable LLP * |

**Band 3**

| | |
|---|---|
| France Thomas W | Venable LLP * |
| Giammittorio Gregory | Morrison & Foerster LLP * |
| Katz Charles | Morrison & Foerster LLP * |
| Lustig Andrew | Cooley LLP |
| Segal Randy | Hogan Lovells US LLP |
| Siler Brent B | Cooley LLP |
| Vold Kevin L | Hogan Lovells US LLP |
| Wechselblatt Eric | Holland & Knight LLP * |
| Welp Robert A | Hogan Lovells US LLP |

**Up-and-coming individuals**

| | |
|---|---|
| August Adam J | Holland & Knight LLP * |
| Swartz Matthew B. | Pillsbury Winthrop Shaw Pittman LLP * |

* Indicates firm / individual with profile.
Alphabetical order within each band. Band 1 is the highest.

## Band 1

### Hogan Lovells US LLP

**THE FIRM** Hogan Lovells has one of the largest corporate practice groups in Northern Virginia and is highly rated for its diverse practice, which handles high-level M&A transactions and private equity work. The firm offers services in a number of specialized industry sectors, including telecommunications, media and technology, aerospace, defense and government services. It regularly undertakes cross-border deals, and advised UK-based manufacturing company Cobham on the $350 million sale of its ownership interest in its US-headquartered Analytics Solutions Business to California-based Parsons Corporation.
**Sources say:** *"A world-class firm."*
**KEY INDIVIDUALS** Department head **Richard Horan** is praised by clients for his *"exceptional legal abilities – he is easy to work with, hard working and innovative."* He led the firm in its work for Cobham. **Richard Becker** specializes in private equity, M&A and other commercial transactions, both in the USA and further afield. **Randy Segal**'s broad practice includes M&A, private equity and venture capital work. She continues to advise the government of Mexico on a $1.5 billion satellite program procurement. **Kevin Vold** focuses on corporate governance, M&A and equity capital markets. He represented Public Storage in $1.7 billion preferred stock offerings. **Robert Welp** features on many of the team's key deals. His practice covers financing transactions, fund formation and corporate reorganizations.

## Band 2

### Cooley LLP

**THE FIRM** Cooley maintains a strong reputation for its venture capital practice and emerging company work in Northern Virginia. It also represents publicly held companies in M&A, with a focus on tech sector deals. In recent highlights, the firm advised Millennial Media on its IPO and follow-on offering, and acted for URS on its $260 million acquisition of Apptis Holdings. Other clients include Micromet and Rosetta Stone.
**KEY INDIVIDUALS** The highly respected **Michael Lincoln** is one of the state's top venture capital specialists. He is held in high esteem by commentators for his expertise in the arena, and for his leading negotiation skills. **Andrew Lustig** earns praise for his efficient and effective approach to transactions. He recently acted for Lightyear Acquisition Company on its acquisition of Near Infinity. **Brent Siler** focuses on registered public offerings, corporate governance, M&A and venture capital work. He acted for OPNET Technologies on its $1 billion sale to Riverbed Technology.

### Holland & Knight LLP
See profile on p.1028

**THE FIRM** This group's broad corporate practice covers venture capital finance, middle and upper-market M&A deals and due diligence. It has a strong focus on government contracts, with additional expertise in other industries including healthcare, retail, green tech and life sciences. The firm recently represented management consulting firm Whitney Bradley & Brown (WBB) in its sale to Netstar-1 Government Consulting.
**Sources say:** *"I would use them again and again – they were simply outstanding."*

**KEY INDIVIDUALS** Government contracts specialist **William Mutryn** (see p.2512) is recommended for his *"professional, understated and calm"* approach to his work. One client said: *"He is a superstar."* **Eric Wechselblatt** (see p.2515) is *"a go-to guy"* for emerging growth work. *"Working with Eric was a fantastic experience,"* said one client, adding: *"He is compassionate and strong, he understood me, and made sure I understood everything."* The up-and-coming **Adam August** (see p.2508) is praised for his *"intelligence, responsiveness and focus on delivering good value."* He represents both public and private company clients in merger, acquisition and disposition transactions. One client comments: *"He did a great job in getting us to the finish line."*

### Morrison & Foerster LLP
See profile on p.1990

**THE FIRM** This firm had a busy year in the corporate/M&A market in Northern Virginia. The team has broad expertise, including in representing both public and private companies in securities and financing transactions. Notably, 2012 saw the firm expand its government contracts group with a number of significant lateral hires. Representative work highlights include acting for software company Sonatype on its $25 million Series C venture capital financing, and advising Salient Federal Solutions on its acquisition of ATS.
**KEY INDIVIDUALS** **Thomas Knox** (see p.2511) is the cochair of the firm's East Coast/Europe corporate practice. He is highly rated for his professional approach and involvement in technology and life sciences transactions. He recently advised ManTech International on its acquisition of HBGary. **Lawrence Yanowitch** (see p.2515) is praised for his *"zealous advocacy."* Peers describe him as a *"very skilled, very thorough and very determined"* attorney. He cochairs the firm's global M&A group and was involved in the ManTech/HBGary deal alongside Knox. **Gregory Giammittorio** (see p.2510) is an *"experienced, poised and very effective negotiator,"* say interviewees. He acted for ITT Exelis on its acquisition of Space Computer Corporation. **Charles Katz** (see p.2510) advises on M&A, private equity and venture capital transactions, divestitures and strategic investments. Work highlights include advising Novak Biddle on the sale of its portfolio company Copiun to Good Technology.

### Pillsbury Winthrop Shaw Pittman LLP
See profile on p.2000

**THE FIRM** This firm specializes in government contracts, technology M&A and private equity fund formation. The team is active on both the buy and sell side of transactions, and regularly undertakes multijurisdictional work. It acts for a diverse list of clients, ranging from entrepreneurs to industry-leading multinationals.
**Sources say:** *"An extremely good firm that is focused on achieving results."* *"A strong government group."*

**KEY INDIVIDUALS** Practice group head **Craig Chason** is described by clients as a *"seasoned and knowledgeable"* attorney who is *"very in tune with business objectives."* His clients include technology companies and government contractors. **Steven Meltzer** is *"a trusted adviser and counselor. He understands the bigger picture of very complex transactions and gets to the most critical point of the negotiation."* **Matthew Swartz** (see p.2514) represents middle market and technology companies in a broad range of matters, including M&A, private equity and venture capital investments.

## Band 3

### Arnold & Porter LLP
See profile on p.906

**THE FIRM** Arnold & Porter advises US and international companies on complex domestic and cross-border mergers. Recent work includes advising ManTech International on its acquisition of Evolvent Technologies. Other clients

include DC Capital Partners, Provident Bank New York and AOL.
**Sources say:** *"They understand our business needs and the ethos of our company."*
**KEY INDIVIDUALS** Kevin Lavin is a key contact.

### DLA Piper LLP (US)
See profile on p.1971

**THE FIRM** DLA Piper is a strong competitor in private equity and venture capital work in this market. The firm stands out for its national and international reach, and is often sought out for its cross-border experience. Representative work highlights saw the team act for New Enterprise Associates and New Atlantic Ventures on the $36 million financing of Moda Operandi. It also represented NextNav in a $50 million growth equity financing led by Goldman Sachs and Columbia Capital.
**KEY INDIVIDUALS** The experienced **Jeffrey Lehrer** (see p.2511) cochairs the firm's emerging growth and venture capital group. *"He sees deals from both sides. He is great at client management, very hard-working, responsive and super friendly,"* say sources.

### Venable LLP
See profile on p.927

**THE FIRM** This firm's experience cuts across a diverse cross section of practice areas, from corporate finance to government contracts. Recent work includes representing nonprofit research corporation Noblis in its acquisition of ElanTech Systems. Other clients include WR Grace, Base Technologies and Electronic Consulting Services.
**Sources say:** *"Venable has a great government contracts team."*
**KEY INDIVIDUALS** **Joseph Schmelter** (see p.2513) cochairs the firm's government contractor services industry group. He is *"highly respected and well regarded"* among peers. **Thomas France** (see p.2509) specializes in M&A, banking, financial services and the structuring and formation of new ventures.

# CORPORATE/M&A SOUTHERN VIRGINIA

| Corporate/M&A: Southern Virginia Leading Firms | |
| --- | --- |
| **Band 1** | |
| Hunton & Williams LLP * | |
| McGuireWoods LLP * | |
| **Band 2** | |
| Troutman Sanders LLP | |
| Williams Mullen | |
| **Band 3** | |
| Kaufman & Canoles | |
| LeClairRyan | |
| Willcox & Savage | |

## Band 1

### Hunton & Williams LLP
See profile on p.2517

**THE FIRM** Hunton & Williams is highly respected for its work in the Southern Virginia corporate/M&A market. The firm also has a strong reputation both statewide and nationwide, and regularly undertakes cross-border work. The team offers extensive experience in matters ranging from merger transactions, corporate finance and securities law to corporate governance and commercial contracts.
**Sources say:** *"They provide high-quality work; they are easy to work with and are responsive, and I appreciate that they have reasonable rates." "Our number-one firm for M&A."*
**KEY INDIVIDUALS** **Justin Moore** (see p.2512) is the head of the firm's corporate team. Described by peers as *"diligent and skilled,"* his experience covers public M&A, private equity and go-private transactions. **Gary Thompson** (see p.2514) is *"a superb practitioner"* who demonstrates an exceptional level of *"skill and knowledge*

| Corporate/M&A: Southern Virginia Senior Statesmen | |
| --- | --- |
| **Senior Statesmen: distinguished older practitioners** | |
| Burrus Robert | McGuireWoods LLP |
| Goolsby Allen | Hunton & Williams LLP * |
| Mastracco Vincent | Kaufman & Canoles |

| Leading Individuals | |
| --- | --- |
| **Band 1** | |
| Cutchins IV Clifford A | McGuireWoods LLP |
| Frantz Thomas R | Williams Mullen |
| Inglima Thomas C | Willcox & Savage |
| Moore Justin | Hunton & Williams LLP * |
| **Band 2** | |
| LeClair Gary D | LeClairRyan |
| Oakey David N | McGuireWoods LLP |
| Thompson Gary | Hunton & Williams LLP * |
| Vaughan III C Porter | Hunton & Williams LLP * |
| Whitley George P | LeClairRyan |
| **Band 3** | |
| Old Jr William A | Williams Mullen |
| Van Buren III William R | Kaufman & Canoles |

*Indicates firm / individual with profile.*
*Alphabetical order within each band. Band 1 is the highest.*

*about the industry."* He advises public companies on M&A, corporate governance and corporate finance activities. **Porter Vaughan** (see p.2514) has a wealth of experience representing public companies in M&A, corporate financings, corporate governance and securities. **Allen Goolsby** (see p.2510) is highly regarded as *"the dean of corporate law in Virginia – he has an incredible reputation."*

### McGuireWoods LLP
See profile on p.2519

**THE FIRM** This top law firm is an active player in the Southern Virginia corporate world, with a strong focus on energy M&A. The team also acts on transactions in the life sciences, pharmaceutical and manufacturing sectors and regularly advises international companies on their US mergers and other commercial contracts. In addition to its public and private company clients, McGuireWoods also represents private equity firms.
**KEY INDIVIDUALS** **Clifford Cutchins** is widely regarded by peers as being *"at the top of his field."* One source enthused: *"He is fantastic – he offers a very good perspective on deals and transactions."* **David Oakey** has extensive experience advising public and private companies on their corporate and securities transactions. He also advises on corporate governance and takeover defense. The experienced **Robert Burrus** specializes in M&A, shareholder disputes and fiduciary counseling.

## Band 2

### Troutman Sanders LLP

**THE FIRM** This team handles a range of complex M&A transactions, corporate governance and private equity deals. The firm recently represented Hargray Communications in its acquisition of Falcon Video Communications. Other clients include New Jersey Resources and Lumos Networks.
**KEY INDIVIDUALS** David Carter and Dave Meyers cohead the corporate practice group.

## Williams Mullen

**THE FIRM** This group offers considerable expertise on matters ranging from M&A, corporate restructuring and company formation to venture capital financing and private equity. In recent highlights, the firm represented Lumber Liquidators, the largest specialty retailer of hardwood flooring in the USA, in its acquisition of Sequoia Flooring. Other clients include Markel Ventures and Dollar Tree Stores.

**Sources say:** *"We have been impressed with them. We find them very responsive, and they provide a good service in a fashion that fits well with the deal."*

**KEY INDIVIDUALS Thomas Frantz** is praised for his *"good legal mind and excellent business background."* One client said: *"He is one of the best lawyers that I have ever worked with."* Recent work includes advising Amerigroup on its acquisition of Health Plus Prepaid Health Services Plan as well as on its sale of Amerigroup Virginia to Inova. **William Old** is described by clients as a *"very effective and very clever"* attorney. Recent highlights included acting for Hampton Roads Bankshares on a $50 million private placement and a $45 million rights offering.

## Band 3

### Kaufman & Canoles

**THE FIRM** This firm offers significant experience in transactions involving manufacturers, distributors, defense contractors and healthcare-related businesses. The group recently acted for Harbor Group International on its acquisition of three affiliated commercial real estate companies.

**KEY INDIVIDUALS William Van Buren** is described by clients as an *"excellent attorney."* His practice covers banking and finance, contract negotiation, general corporate and healthcare law. **Vincent Mastracco** is *"one of the pre-eminent corporate lawyers in the business,"* say interviewees. He advises on capital formation, M&A and real estate transactions.

### LeClairRyan

**THE FIRM** This firm advises on a range of small, mid-market and large transactions involving mergers, LBOs, tax and securities.

**KEY INDIVIDUALS George Whitley** is regarded by peers as a *"standout"* lawyer in this market. He is described as *"extremely bright, responsive"* and *"excellent in the banking space."* Founding partner **Gary LeClair** also enjoys a strong reputation and is well known for his representation of emerging growth companies.

### Willcox & Savage

**THE FIRM** This firm has substantial experience advising on M&A and joint venture transactions in the media, information services, industrial equipment and transportation sectors. Notably, it represented Landmark Media Enterprises in the sale of CBS TV affiliate News Channel 5.

**Sources say:** *"Wilcox & Savage does outstanding work. It is very responsive, client-focused and has a very good knowledge and understanding of business matters."*

**KEY INDIVIDUALS** The *"exceptional"* **Thomas Inglima** is acclaimed for his *"responsiveness, dedication and professionalism."* One source enthused: *"He is an excellent lawyer who is extremely diligent. He gives practical advice and leaves no stone unturned."*

# ENVIRONMENT

Commentary about individuals can be found under their firm's paragraph. If the firm has no paragraph (is not ranked) look at Other Notable Practitioners.

| Environment | |
|---|---|
| **Leading Firms** | |
| **Band 1** | |
| Hunton & Williams LLP * | |
| McGuireWoods LLP * | |
| **Band 2** | |
| AquaLaw PLC | |
| Troutman Sanders LLP | |
| Williams Mullen | |

| **Leading Individuals** | |
|---|---|
| **Band 1** | |
| Calamita Paul | AquaLaw PLC |
| Evans David E | McGuireWoods LLP |
| Finto Kevin J | Hunton & Williams LLP * |
| Knauer Thomas E | Law Office of Thomas E. Knauer (ONP) † |
| Martin Channing J | Williams Mullen |
| Slone Daniel K | McGuireWoods LLP |
| Smith Brooks | Hunton & Williams LLP * |
| **Band 2** | |
| Christman James | Hunton & Williams LLP * |
| Daniel II John W | Troutman Sanders LLP |
| Ellis William | William B. Ellis, PLLC (ONP) † |
| Lain John M | McGuireWoods LLP |
| Pomeroy Chris | AquaLaw PLC |
| Thomson Jr Paul R | Woods Rogers PLC (ONP) † |
| Thornhill James | McGuireWoods LLP |
| Varner Shannon | Troutman Sanders LLP |
| **Associates to watch** | |
| Rhode Lynne C. | Troutman Sanders LLP |

\* *Indicates firm / individual with profile.*
† *ONP = Other Notable Practitioner.*

## Band 1

### Hunton & Williams LLP
See profile on p.2517

**THE FIRM** This firm maintains its position at the fore of environmental matters in Virginia. Its large team of dedicated environmental lawyers is regularly engaged by big-name clients to handle a variety of high-profile and complicated matters. It has recently worked for Agrium, Smithfield Foods and Tredegar on a range of issues, and was lead counsel for the Ohio River Basin Water Quality Trading Project, the largest nutrient credit trading initiative in the world, in relation to multiple aspects of its establishment.

**Sources say:** *"A first-rate, world-class team."*

**KEY INDIVIDUALS Kevin Finto** (see p.2509) is *"an excellent air lawyer"* with a *"big national practice,"* according to interviewees. He is highly respected in the market, and his broad practice encompasses environmental issues involved in business transactions, as well as air permitting and enforcement and hazardous waste management. **Brooks Smith** (see p.2514) is cochair of the firm's environmental practice. He receives glowing reviews from clients, with one impressed interviewee claiming: *"He has been a hero on our project."* Smith has particular expertise in CWA-related issues. **James Christman** (see p.2508) is also an expert in the CWA, and is an accomplished litigator. He has a fine reputation in the field, and is commended by peers for the high quality of his work.

### McGuireWoods LLP
See profile on p.2519

**THE FIRM** This diverse practice offers both breadth and depth in its coverage of a broad spectrum of environmental matters. Its client list includes prominent companies involved in a range of industries. It is particularly noted for its work with large energy companies, and has recently worked for PSEG and PPL on the NEPA process of a joint project to build a 500 kV transmission line in Pennsylvania. Alongside this, the team has worked for CSX on the environmental factors of an $850 million clearance of 61 track obstructions, as well as track, tunnel and bridge modifications in a number of states.

**Sources say:** *"Their work is exceptional. They are very talented, intelligent and responsive practitioners. They know their business and they know the law."*

**KEY INDIVIDUALS David Evans** brings more than 35 years of experience to bear in relation to a range of environmental issues. Clients note that he *"tends to settle cases with great skill."* He has undertaken work for Smithfield Foods in numerous high-value suits nationwide. **Daniel Slone** *"is an expert in regulatory law and in a lot of areas that cross into environment law."* He is well recognized in the market, and is particularly renowned for representing developers of green technologies and projects. **John Lain** is acclaimed for his expertise in wetlands permitting, and is also commended for his understanding of clients' business needs. As a regular feature in large transactions with environmental implications, **James Thornhill** has cultivated a reputation for the accurate and insightful nature of his work. He recently advised Huron Consulting Group on the environmental considerations of the sale and closure of foundries in Virginia.

## Band 2

### AquaLaw PLC

**THE FIRM** This Richmond-based boutique specializes in all matters relating to water law, and is also particularly active in municipal wastewater matters. In its ten years of operation, it has become a respected team, widely acknowledged for its impressive capabilities in these areas. It recently represented the Virginia Association of Wastewater Agencies in enacting legislation to expand the state's nutrient trading legislation and program.

**Sources say:** *"The firm is well versed in the areas that I rely on it for. They are responsive and know our business, and their advice has been sound."*

**KEY INDIVIDUALS** Firm cofounder **Paul Calamita** earns the respect of the market at large. One peer said: *"He is someone I really respect; a fierce advocate who is very effective and certainly very knowledgeable."* Calamita recently represented the Hampton Roads Sanitation District in negotiating a federal consent decree for a regional sewer overflow control program. Fellow cofounder **Chris Pomeroy** has carved a niche for himself in the Virginia area. Clients believe that *"he is an expert lawyer with an extensive system of contacts."* He recently represented Fairfax County in litigation against the US EPA challenging water regulation for Accotink Creek.

### Troutman Sanders LLP

**THE FIRM** This compact team has developed valuable links with state and federal authorities in order to provide contact with the relevant agencies for its clients. In addition, the team has recently begun to put in place a framework for its real estate and environment attorneys to work in close proximity in order to offer complete coverage of any environmental issues emerging from real estate developments and purchases.

**KEY INDIVIDUALS** Clients appreciate that **John Daniel** has developed impressive relationships around the region. He is widely regarded as one of the strongest environment lawyers in Virginia. **Shannon Varner** has over two decades of experience in handling complex environment matters. His practice is broad, encompassing environmental audits, compliance issues and brownfield developments. He is also active in handling a number of due diligence matters. **Lynne Rhode** has advised clients on diverse topics, including air and water permitting, alternative energy projects and animal law matters.

### Williams Mullen

**THE FIRM** This team offers support on the full range of environmental matters, and has been particularly active of late representing manufacturers in air and land contamination issues. It has particularly strong experience in matters connected to brownfields developments, CWA and CAA issues. In addition to this, it is a valued adviser in M&A and construction transactions with environmental considerations. It recently assisted Commonwealth Atlantic-Spotsylvania with managing the investigation and remediation of the 38-acre LA Clarke Superfund Site.

**Sources say:** *"We had an outstanding experience with them."*

**KEY INDIVIDUALS Channing Martin** impresses clients, with one saying: *"He helps us really understand our risks and our direction in full; he is very accessible and personable, and gives outstanding advice."* He is involved in a substantial amount of property and cleanup work, as well as enforcement and litigation.

### Other Notable Practitioners

**Thomas Knauer** of Law Office of Thomas E. Knauer, PLLC runs his own practice and is recommended for his expertise in air regulation. He is highly esteemed in this area, with peers observing that *"he is one of the best air lawyers around"* and *"the go-to guy for this industry – the number-one air lawyer in the state."* **William Ellis** of William B. Ellis, PLLC is a senior figure in the market who brings his extensive experience in the field to a variety of cases. He has featured in a large number of wetlands issues of late. **Paul Thomson** of Woods Rogers PLC is praised as *"a great attorney"* and *"a generalist with a good reputation."* He is one of the foremost environment lawyers in Roanoke, and is seen as a key figure in the western part of the state.

# INTELLECTUAL PROPERTY NORTHERN VIRGINIA

Commentary about individuals can be found under their firm's paragraph. If the firm has no paragraph (is not ranked) look at Other Notable Practitioners.

## Band 1

### Finnegan, Henderson, Farabow, Garrett & Dunner LLP
See profile on p.912

**THE FIRM** This firm offers a full-service IP practice. The outstanding team is at the forefront of patent prosecution work, and has a diverse client roster, which includes telecommunications, biotechnology, pharmaceutical and aerospace companies. It recently represented Cephalon against Apotex, Lupin, Sandoz and Watson in Abbreviated New Drug Application litigation concerning the Cephalon's Nuvigil drug. It also represented the plaintiff in InterDigital Communications v ITC.

**Sources say:** *"I have all the respect in the world for them."* *"The leaders in Northern Virginia – one of the best in the country. They are always involved in cutting-edge cases."*

**KEY INDIVIDUALS Christopher Foley** (see p.2509) concentrates his practice on patent and trademark law. In the latter area, he has a wealth of experience in the procurement of trademark registrations, licensing and litigation. **Charles Lipsey** (see p.357) is *"a fabulous lawyer and a top guy."* He is the lead lawyer on the Cephalon matter, and is an expert in IP and patent infringement litigation. **Jay Westermeier**'s (see p.2515) practice spans copyrights, trade secrets, licensing and patent litigation. He has particular expertise in computer software, outsourcing, distribution and e-commerce issues.

### Pillsbury Winthrop Shaw Pittman LLP
See profile on p.2000

**THE FIRM** This preeminent IP team has experts in all areas of counseling, including prosecution, strategy and monetization. The group maintains a strong presence in litigation, and is able to assist clients with both enforcement and defense. The team recently assisted Lenovo with IP due diligence and open source issues related to its partnership with EMC. Further notable activity includes handling IP portfolio management, enforcement and defense for Fellowes. Other key clients include Intel and Disney.

**Sources say:** *"The firm is one of the strongest I've dealt with. Amazingly customer-oriented."* *"They have a great business strategy, and they're very responsive."*

**KEY INDIVIDUALS** The *"outstanding"* **Jack Barufka** (see p.2508) leads the firmwide IP practice and is praised as a *"terrific leader"* by impressed sources. His diverse practice includes copyright protection, pre-litigation advice, dispute resolution, and mining and enforcement. Of late, he has been focusing on issues arising under the America Invents Act (AIA) and patent reform. **William Atkins** is a highly regarded patent attorney with 20 years' experience in the field. Trademark, unfair competition and copyright are among his areas of expertise. He has been playing a crucial role in the team's work for Fellowes. **James Gatto** (see p.2510) is commended for his leadership capabilities and communication skills. He is *"a great mentor and business partner,"* say sources. He was involved in the Lenovo matter, and also recently assisted Catalina Marketing with the IP due diligence aspects of its acquisition of Modiv Media. **George Sirilla** (see p.2513) is renowned for his prowess in technology licensing, patents and trade secrets. He has represented numerous clients before the ITC, including Komatsu, Toyota, Ventra Automotive and the Korean government.

## Band 2

### Arnold & Porter LLP
See profile on p.906
**THE FIRM** The IP team at Arnold & Porter concentrates on transactional matters and has handled issues for clients in an impressive array of industries, including telecommunications, electronics, life sciences, finance, and media and entertainment. It also regularly advises on licensing mat-

ters, research and development arrangements, manufacturing, and technology transfer. It recently represented AOL in its acquisition of several companies, including Outside.in, Pictela, Techcrunch and Thing Labs.
**Sources say:** *"They were very good at taking us with them on strategy. They are all knowledgeable, and bend over backwards to meet you. They were creative, responsive, and good on the technical side of things."*
**KEY INDIVIDUALS Steve Parker** (see p.2513) specializes in life sciences transactions. According to one particularly impressed client, he is *"really creative and sensitive to what your issues are."* **Susan Hendrickson** (see p.2510) was the lead partner on the AOL matter. She has 18 years' experience in the area, and has expertise covering confidentiality, trade secrets and social media.

### Buchanan Ingersoll & Rooney PC
See profile on p.2236
**THE FIRM** This firm's sterling IP team is renowned for its excellence in the highly specialized areas of patent interferences, reexaminations and reissues. Of late, it has been especially active in the renewable energy and power sectors. The group recently acted for BAE Systems on the development of a worldwide IP portfolio, and assisted Siemens Enterprise Communications with patent portfolio management. Other clients include Apple, Alstom Technology and Pfizer.
**KEY INDIVIDUALS Todd Walters** (see p.2514) has significant experience before the USPTO and in federal courts, and is also well versed in patent procurement, infringement and validity analysis. **Erin Dunston**'s (see p.2509) practice covers a range of interferences, district court litigation, opinions and prosecution. Of late, she has been working on a comprehensive patent portfolio for a pharmaceutical company.

### Cooley LLP
**THE FIRM** The IP team at Cooley offers superb prosecution, counseling and litigation services. It is regularly engaged in high-profile patent litigation, and maintains a diverse client list. The group recently secured a key victory for Nintendo of America in an ITC case concerning alleged patent infringement, brought by Creative Kingdom. It has also been assisting Rosetta Stone in patent infringement litigation filed by Englishtown.
**KEY INDIVIDUALS Frank Pietrantonio** is partner-in-charge of the firm's Reston office. His highlights include assisting Millennial Media in a patent infringement suit brought by Streetspace. He has expertise in a broad range of technologies, including graphics processing, network security, telecommunications and digital signal processing. **Scott Talbot** is renowned for his litigation expertise. His broad practice covers patent prosecution and enforcement, and he has an excellent grasp of issues involving the medical technology sector.

### Hogan Lovells US LLP
**THE FIRM** Hogan Lovells' IP practice spans licensing, trademark and domain names, prosecution, audits, social media, outsourcing transactions and M&A-related IP

issues. The team is able to lean on the firm's expansive global reach, bringing to the table experience in myriad sectors, including life sciences, real estate, technology and transportation. Key clients include Time Warner Cable, The College Board and PETNET Solutions.
**Sources say:** *"They have a lot of knowledge and a good database, and the service is speedy."*
**KEY INDIVIDUALS Philip Porter** assists a diverse range of clients in technology, outsourcing, IP and licensing issues.

### Nixon & Vanderhye PC
**THE FIRM** Nixon & Vanderhye is highly regarded for its patent prosecution practice. It has notable experience in patent litigation, and advises on trademarks, IP due diligence, ITC Section 337 investigations, licensing and copyright.
**Sources say:** *"A unique, strong firm."*
**KEY INDIVIDUALS Larry Nixon** is *"very, very well regarded"* by his peers. He has nearly 40 years' experience in the sector and is renowned for his patent prosecution and litigation expertise.

### Oblon Spivak McClelland Maier & Neustadt LLP
See profile on p.2520
**THE FIRM** This firm's sterling IP group handles all manner of patent, trademark, copyright and enforcement proceedings. The firm has a specialist USPTO post-grant patent practice, which concentrates on validity trials arising under the AIA. Recent highlights include successfully defending the TiVo time warp patent. Other key clients include Google, CISCO and Nordstrom.
**KEY INDIVIDUALS Arthur Neustadt** (see p.2512) is a founding member of the firm. He has more than 35 years' experience in IP litigation, and counts SMC as a client. **Charles Gholz** (see p.2510) is applauded for his responsiveness on *"any issue, any question."* He is an immense talent in the IP sector, with sources conveying that *"his authority in the subject is huge."* He has performed significant work for Advanced Voice Recognition Systems. Sources are impressed with **James Kulbaski**'s (see p.2511) tremendous legal knowledge and technical skills. He has assisted a raft of clients in obtaining patent pool royalties. The *"excellent"* **Stephen Kunin** (see p.2511) chairs the firm's post-grant patent practice group. He benefits from over 30 years' experience at the USPTO.

### Other Notable Practitioners

**Barry Bretschneider** (see p.2508) of Baker Hostetler concentrates on patent matters, including infringement litigation, interferences, prosecution and licensing. He represents clients in an array of industries, including electronics and pharmaceuticals. **James Oliff** of Oliff & Berridge PLC has significant experience at the USPTO. He focuses his practice on patent prosecution. **James Heintz** (see p.2510) of DLA Piper LLP (US) is highly respected for his knowledge of electrical and computer technologies. He recently represented Samsung Electronics in district court litigation concerning smart phone technology. He is praised as *"an absolute expert,"* with *"incredible"* responsiveness and *"impeccable"* attention to detail. **Dale Lazar** (see p.2511),

also of DLA Piper LLP (US), has notable experience in patent and copyright issues surrounding computer hard-

ware and software. He is the head of the firm's IP department.

## INTELLECTUAL PROPERTY SOUTHERN VIRGINIA

Commentary about individuals can be found under their firm's paragraph. If the firm has no paragraph (is not ranked) look at Other Notable Practitioners.

### Intellectual Property: Southern Virginia
### Leading Firms

**Band 1**
Hunton & Williams LLP *
McGuireWoods LLP *
Troutman Sanders LLP

**Band 2**
Kaufman & Canoles
Williams Mullen

**Band 3**
Leading-Edge Law Group, PLC

### Leading Individuals

**Band 1**

| | |
|---|---|
| Angle Robert A | Troutman Sanders LLP |
| Carr Dabney | Troutman Sanders LLP |
| Farmer John B | Leading-Edge Law Group, PLC |
| Martinez de Andino J Michael | Hunton & Williams LLP * |
| McDaniel Dana D | Spotts Fain (ONP) † |
| Mugel Christopher J | Kaufman & Canoles |
| Noona Stephen E | Kaufman & Canoles |
| Riopelle Brian C | McGuireWoods LLP |
| Stillman Gregory | Hunton & Williams LLP * |
| Tyler Robert | McGuireWoods LLP |

**Band 2**

| | |
|---|---|
| Demm Stephen P | Hunton & Williams LLP * |
| Eckstein Maya M | Hunton & Williams LLP * |
| Lockhart Timothy J | Willcox & Savage (ONP) † |
| Mytelka Craig L | Williams Mullen |

**Band 3**

| | |
|---|---|
| Finkelson David E | McGuireWoods LLP |

**Up-and-coming individuals**

| | |
|---|---|
| Peyton Janet P | McGuireWoods LLP |
| White Edward T | LeClairRyan (ONP) † |

\* Indicates firm / individual with profile.
† ONP = Other Notable Practitioner

## Band 1

### Hunton & Williams LLP
See profile on p.2517

**THE FIRM** Hunton & Williams has all-around experience in this area. It assists clients with trademark opposition, patent acquisition and enforcement, portfolio management, transactions, technology transfers and domain name disputes. The team recently represented Capital One in a patent infringement action concerning its mobile banking platform. Other notable clients include

Personalized Media Communications, Epic Games and Verizon.

**Sources say:** *"The team is very timely, has excellent responsiveness, and is on top of key issues." "You can ask for assistance, and they'll help you figure out how to get it. The partners are not territorial, they're collegial. They'll get you the best person."*

**KEY INDIVIDUALS** Sources applaud the *"very experienced"* **Michael Martinez de Andino** (see p.2511) for his deft handling of strategic matters. He has an impressive record in patent litigation. The *"brilliant"* **Stephen Demm** (see p.2509) has a sterling practice undertaking IP litigation, including prosecutions, cancellations and trademark issues. His recent highlights include representing lawn and garden products marketer Scotts Miracle-Gro in connection with false advertising claims. **Maya Eckstein** (see p.2509) was the lead partner on the aforementioned Capital One matter. She is a distinguished patent and IP litigator, and has recently handled cases involving hearing aid, smartphone app and electric payment technology. **Gregory Stillman** (see p.2514) is head of the firm's IP department. He is held in high esteem for his excellent litigation practice and his expertise in patents. He was recently involved in the major MercExchange v eBay patent infringement case.

### McGuireWoods LLP
See profile on p.2519

**THE FIRM** This excellent team is renowned for its handling of patent cases concerning telecommunications, and counts Nokia, Siemens and Verizon as major clients. It also has significant experience in trademarks, data privacy and trade secrets. The group successfully represented DuPont in a trade secrets case against Kolon Industries. It also represented the defendant in KGR v Ford Motor Company, a complex patent infringement case.

**Sources say:** *"Their work was outstanding." "Very knowledge and very responsive."*

**KEY INDIVIDUALS Robert Tyler** receives plaudits for his research and writing skills. *"What is impressive is that he can communicate very technical concepts to lay people,"* remark sources. He recently represented General Nutrition Centers in a major trademark infringement matter. The *"first-rate"* **Brian Riopelle** is labeled a *"lion of the Bar."* He recently led in the aforementioned DuPont case, and also acts for Sprint Spectrum. **David Finkelson** knows *"all the intricacies of patent law"* but *"he never loses sight of the forest for the trees,"* according to sources. He was the lead trial lawyer for Ford in a major patent infringement case relating to hybrid automobile visual displays. **Janet Peyton** chairs the firm's transactional IP group, and has assisted

myriad clients in the retail and manufacturing industries with the management of their trademark portfolios. *"She knows her field through and through,"* say interviewees.

### Troutman Sanders LLP

**THE FIRM** The 13-strong team at Troutman Sanders is spread across four offices, in Richmond, Tysons Corner, Virginia Beach and Norfolk. Areas of expertise include trade secret protection and litigation, technology, licensing and cybersquatting issues, among others. In recent highlights, the team represented Baby Jogger in a patent infringement action against Britax Child Safety, and assisted Twitter in its defense of a patent infringement action brought by VS Technologies.

**KEY INDIVIDUALS** Sources class **Robert Angle** as one of eastern Virginia's leading attorneys. He led on both the Baby Jogger and Twitter matters. **Dabney Carr** has practiced for over 20 years and accrued substantial experience in patent litigation. He recently assisted Integrated Medical Systems in a patent infringement action brought by Karl Storz.

## Band 2

### Kaufman & Canoles

**THE FIRM** This team is best known for its patent litigation work but handles all aspects of IP, including trademarks, trade secrets, management, and licensing and technology transfer. It has substantial knowledge of marketing and advertising, and significant expertise in franchising. It has represented countless clients before the Trademark Trial and Appeal Board of the USPTO, and the WIPO.

**KEY INDIVIDUALS Christopher Mugel** is an expert in transactional IP issues, and is frequently involved in major trademark prosecution matters. He is also active in developing licensing and services agreements for clients in an array of industries. **Stephen Noona** *"is an exceptional attorney,"* say sources. He has experience in major cases before federal and state courts, and heads the firm's IP department and its litigation section.

### Williams Mullen

**THE FIRM** The IP group at Williams Mullen is ever-present in trademark and patent cases in the region. The group is well known for its expertise in patent issues, and for its noteworthy experience in IP matters occurring in the gaming and defense technology fields. Its key clients include Agio International, Massimo Zanetti Beverage USA, and Premier Exhibitions.

Sources say: "*They are excellent, with great knowledge and efficiency.*" "*They're professional and very sharp, but they engage with you in a casual and comfortable way.*"
KEY INDIVIDUALS Craig Mytelka heads the IP group and is "*incredibly knowledgeable,*" according to sources, many of whom also highlight his tenacity and accessibility. His far-ranging practice spans trademark, unfair competition, trade secrets, patents, and domestic and international licensing.

## Band 3

### Leading-Edge Law Group, PLC

THE FIRM This specialist IP firm is renowned for its trademarks, patent and patent software licensing practice. It also earns particular praise for its work with trade secrets, and for its recent activities in the healthcare sector.
KEY INDIVIDUALS The "*very bright and very hard-working*" John Farmer is highly regarded for his trademark portfolio practice.

## Other Notable Practitioners

Dana McDaniel of Spotts Fain is said to be "*one of the top IP litigators in Virginia,*" and remains a go-to specialist for referrals from peers. Timothy Lockhart heads the IP practice group at Willcox & Savage. He wins plaudits for his trademark counseling expertise, and for his work in trade secret and e-commerce matters. The highly sought-after Edward White of LeClairRyan excels in trademark, trade dress and copyright matters.

# LABOR & EMPLOYMENT

Employee Benefits & Compensation p.2500

Commentary about individuals can be found under their firm's paragraph. If the firm has no paragraph (is not ranked) look at Other Notable Practitioners.

| Labor & Employment Leading Firms |
| --- |
| **Band 1** |
| Hunton & Williams LLP * |
| McGuireWoods LLP * |
| **Band 2** |
| Isler Dare * |
| Jackson Lewis LLP * |
| Kaufman & Canoles |
| Williams Mullen |
| **Band 3** |
| Hogan Lovells US LLP |
| LeClairRyan |
| Littler Mendelson, PC * |
| Lorenger & Carnell PLC |
| Troutman Sanders LLP |
| Venable LLP * |
| Womble Carlyle Sandridge & Rice, LLP * |
| Woods Rogers PLC |
| * Indicates firm with profile. |
| Alphabetical order within each band. Band 1 is the highest. |

## Band 1

### Hunton & Williams LLP
See profile on p.2517

THE FIRM This leading team continues to impress clients and peers with the sheer breadth of its expertise and market coverage in the labor and employment arena. Its client portfolio encompasses a wide range of industries, demonstrating its ability to handle disputes and advisory work across the board in the space. It continues to house an enviable array of recognized senior attorneys.
Sources say: "*There is real value in having one firm with all that talent.*"
KEY INDIVIDUALS Gregory Robertson (see p.2513) is widely praised for his expertise in all aspects of labor and employment law. Clients applaud his "*excellent technical and legal expertise, common sense, and strong sense of*

urgency." A long-standing doyen of the Virginia Bar, Hill Wellford's (see p.2515) practice encompasses a wide range of labor and employment litigation. He is a highly experienced trial lawyer, and has handled multiple claims at both a state and federal level. Thomas Murphy (see p.2512) is recognized by clients and peers alike as one of Virginia's preeminent labor and employment lawyers. Clients observe: "*He is a problem solver, and brings creative solutions to the table.*" David Mustone (see p.2512) is respected for his long-standing experience in matters related to employee benefits. He works with a wide range of government, nonprofit and for-profit employers, and has particular expertise in tax issues and ERISA. Noted by clients as "*strong, measured and thoughtful,*" leading associate Kurt Larkin (see p.2511) has a broad-based labor and employment practice, with a particular focus on handling union campaign matters for corporate employers.

### McGuireWoods LLP
See profile on p.2519

THE FIRM The labor and employment practice at McGuireWoods remains a stalwart leader in this area. The practice has a reputation for being a full-service team with leading professionals operating across the spectrum of employment law. Its reputation is matched by a list of high-profile clients which include DuPont, Coca-Cola Enterprises and Amgen.
Sources say: "*I know we are important to them. They understand our business as much as we do.*" "*They handle all of our big labor and employment problems, and are first rate.*"
KEY INDIVIDUALS Jonathan Harmon is an established trial lawyer who has handled employer defense cases in a wide range of state and federal courts. His clients include CSX and Verizon. Gary Marshall is a highly respected labor attorney who is well known for his skill in collective bargaining negotiations. Sources describe him as "*very knowledgeable, practical and service oriented.*" Recent notable clients include Catalent Pharma and the Remington Arms Company. James McElligott remains one of Virginia's most respected attorneys in the field of employee benefits and compensation. He recently defend-

ed ITT Excelis in ERISA litigation claims related to disability pensions. Stephen Robinson has been described by peers as "*the best in Virginia.*" Clients are equally enthusiastic, commending his excellent technical skills in a wide range of labor and employment matters. Carter Younger is reported to have "*all the qualities you look for in a lawyer.*" Clients highlight his wealth of knowledge, and particularly value his practical approach. He represents employers in matters as diverse as union management relations, discrimination and international employment.

## Band 2

### Isler Dare
See profile on p.2518

THE FIRM This firm is a compact boutique with a big reputation. It is commended by clients for providing consistently high-level employment work at a reasonable cost. Recent highlights include work done on behalf of the Navy Federal Credit Union in relation to harassment and discrimination cases.
Sources say: "*Their performance level is very high and they are very experienced, practical and business oriented.*"
KEY INDIVIDUALS Edward Isler (see p.2510) is once again celebrated for his deep expertise in the field, and is described as having an "*encyclopedic brain.*" He is highly respected by peers and clients alike, and is considered "*outstanding in the employment space.*" He recently represented the Navy Federal Credit Union in the matter referred to above. Theresa Connolly (see p.2508) is an established employment practitioner who continues to earn praise for her responsive approach to client relationships. She has impressive experience in advising clients on litigation and counseling matters relating to labor and employment law. Mark Dare's (see p.2508) breadth of experience in this field inspires confidence in his clients, one describing how "*any time I have any employment issues I hand them straight over to him.*" Dave has a reputation for being a thoughtful and strategic thinker who is "*tough when he needs to be, but always balanced.*"

## Labor & Employment
### Senior Statesmen

**Senior Statesmen: distinguished older practitioners**

| | |
|---|---|
| Wellford Jr Hill B | Hunton & Williams LLP * |

### Leading Individuals

**Band 1**

| | |
|---|---|
| Bredehoft John M | Kaufman & Canoles |
| Isler Edward Lee | Isler Dare * |
| Lorenger Michael J | Lorenger & Carnell PLC |
| Meath James V | Williams Mullen |
| Morse Clinton S | LeClairRyan |
| Murphy Thomas P | Hunton & Williams LLP * |
| Robertson Gregory | Hunton & Williams LLP * |
| Robinson Stephen W | McGuireWoods LLP |
| Younger Carter | McGuireWoods LLP |

**Band 2**

| | |
|---|---|
| Burton David C | Williams Mullen |
| Connolly Theresa | Isler Dare * |
| Constine III David E | Troutman Sanders LLP |
| Dare Mark | Isler Dare * |
| Flaherty Thomas | Littler Mendelson, PC * |
| Flanagan William P | Hogan Lovells US LLP |
| Marshall Gary | McGuireWoods LLP |
| Nagle David | Jackson Lewis LLP * |
| Sawyer Thomas J | Womble Carlyle Sandridge & Rice, LLP |
| Smith David S | Venable LLP * |
| Webb Eugene | Troutman Sanders LLP |
| Westman Daniel P | Morrison & Foerster LLP (ONP) † * |
| Whitt Burt | Kaufman & Canoles |

**Band 3**

| | |
|---|---|
| Carnell Susanne Harris | Lorenger & Carnell PLC |
| Coleman James M | Constangy, Brooks & Smith, LLP (ONP) † |
| DeCamp Paul | Jackson Lewis LLP * |
| Harmon Jonathan P | McGuireWoods LLP |
| Jacob Lynn F | Williams Mullen |
| Lalik Elizabeth A | Littler Mendelson, PC * |
| Lewis Betsey | Cooley LLP (ONP) † |
| Meyer III Charles G | LeClairRyan |
| North Susan Childers | LeClairRyan |
| Ossi Gregory J | Venable LLP * |
| Tower King | Spilman Thomas & Battle PLLC (ONP) † * |
| Warner David | Venable LLP * |

**Associates to watch**

| | |
|---|---|
| Larkin Kurt G | Hunton & Williams LLP * |
| Wilkinson J Nelson | Williams Mullen |

*\* Indicates individual with profile.*

*† ONP = Other Notable Practitioner*

## Jackson Lewis LLP

See profile on p.1982

**THE FIRM** This practice continues to flourish, and houses expertise in a wide range of matters, including employment discrimination claims, ERISA and labor relations. Its growing team serves a number of noteworthy clients, such as Capital One Financial, Safeway and Goodrich.

**Sources say:** *"They always have time for us, and do wonderful work."*

## Labor & Employment: Employee Benefits & Compensation
### Leading Individuals

**Band 1**

| | |
|---|---|
| McElligott James | McGuireWoods LLP |

**Band 2**

| | |
|---|---|
| Marriott Catherine M | Williams Mullen |
| Mustone David A | Hunton & Williams LLP * |
| Starke Wallace | Troutman Sanders LLP |

**Band 3**

| | |
|---|---|
| Esposito Jewell Lim | Constangy, Brooks & Smith, LLP (ONP) † |

**KEY INDIVIDUALS David Nagle** (see p.2512) is a highly experienced litigator who is admired for being *"technically omniscient"* and someone who *"sees the big picture."* He offers experience across a broad spread of labor and employment matters. **Paul DeCamp** (see p.2508) *"is an expert on wage and hour labor issues, and is just a genius when it comes to this kind of work,"* according to one impressed client. DeCamp has extensive experience in litigating cases for a wide range of clients.

## Kaufman & Canoles

**THE FIRM** This group maintains its impressive presence in the Norfolk area. It offers market-leading expertise in matters such as wage and hour compliance, union avoidance and employee contract negotiation. Recent clients include ECPI and Virginia Oncology Associates.

**KEY INDIVIDUALS John Bredehoft** is a well-established management lawyer. He is credited for his *"high technical skill and inventive approach."* **Burt Whitt** has a strong reputation built on years of experience in this field. He currently chairs the practice group, and represents employers in all aspects of employment law.

## Williams Mullen

**THE FIRM** Williams Mullen is commended for the skill and expertise of its attorneys, and focuses on all aspects of labor law. Its extensive employment law expertise sees it represent management in a wide range of litigation and arbitration. Its recent work includes successfully representing Hampton Roads Transit in a case concerning its collective bargaining agreement.

**Sources say:** *"The attorneys with Williams Mullens have a great Southern charm, and I really can't say enough about them. They have not only met expectations but exceeded them."*

**KEY INDIVIDUALS James Meath** has long-standing experience in advising both private and public sector clients on a range of labor and employment matters. He is lauded by clients as *"highly skilled, very diligent and accessible."* **David Burton** chairs the labor and employment practice. Sources highlight him as a *"knowledgeable, very experienced, responsive and practical"* attorney. **Catherine Marriott** heads the employee benefits practice. Her expertise spans a wide range of matters, including pension and welfare matters as well as incentive and executive compensation. **Lynn Jacob** has expertise in a number of different areas of employment law. She is commended as a particu-

larly effective employment litigator, and also handles non-contentious matters. Enthusiastic peers describe her as *"tenacious"* and *"fantastic at identifying solutions."* Associate **Nelson Wilkinson** is one of the rising stars of the team. He is particularly well versed in employment discrimination matters, including age, race and sex discrimination.

### Band 3

## Hogan Lovells US LLP

**THE FIRM** This practice advises on employment litigation as well as management-side labor relations, and handles matters spanning a wide range of industries. Its expertise includes a broad spread of litigation, counseling and transactional matters, and high-profile clients include the Dana Corporation and the Ford Motor Company.

**Sources say:** *"A very broad-based practice. They are fantastic – very good at handling expectations."*

**KEY INDIVIDUALS William Flanagan** is acknowledged by peers for his expertise in employment litigation. Clients commend him as *"accessible at all times, incredibly thorough and very fair."*

## LeClairRyan

**THE FIRM** This practice handles a variety of labor and employment matters, including wrongful discharge claims, breach of employment contracts and restrictive covenants, and a wide range of litigation claims. Its client base includes such names as Advance Auto Parts and Genworth Financial.

**Sources say:** *"High-level, high-quality work product and service. They are very familiar with local courts and judges, which is a great help."*

**KEY INDIVIDUALS Clinton Morse** is *"a very seasoned and experienced labor lawyer"* whose breadth of expertise garners him particular praise. He is commended by clients as *"collaborative, practical and helpful."* Acclaimed by clients as *"a superb all-around attorney,"* **Charles Meyer** is a stalwart of the practice who offers widespread experience in employment litigation and counseling. Alongside her wide-ranging experience of employment litigation matters, the *"terrific"* **Susan Childers North** also has significant experience in handling mandatory arbitration programs. Clients commend her as being *"very hard-working and conscientious."*

## Littler Mendelson, PC

See profile on p.688

**THE FIRM** Littler's Northern Virginia team plays a key part in the firm's leading national labor and employment practice. The group advises large US and global organizations across a range of industries. Its practice encompasses every and all types of labor and employment work, including wage and hour disputes and unionizing matters.

**Sources say:** *"Skilled practitioners with great client-handling skills. High quality and results-driven."*

**KEY INDIVIDUALS** *"An excellent negotiator who always maintains a calm demeanor and never loses his cool,"*

**Thomas Flaherty** (see p.2509) has extensive experience in class action litigation cases pertaining to discrimination and wage and hour laws, among other types of work. He is also managing partner of the firm's McLean office. **Elizabeth Lalik** (see p.2511) is hailed as a *"very responsive"* attorney who is *"unflappable when standing up to aggressive attorneys on the opposing side."* She is especially well versed in advising UK clients and their US counterparts.

## Lorenger & Carnell PLC

**THE FIRM** This Alexandria-based boutique firm handles the full spectrum of labor matters, including discrimination, workplace harassment, wage and hour law violations, leave entitlements, and wrongful termination.

**KEY INDIVIDUALS Michael Lorenger** garners superb reviews from clients. He is described as *"exceptionally conscientious, incredibly intelligent, and practical."* He has a highly respected practice undertaking a range of labor and employment matters. **Susanne Harris Carnell** is best known for her superb litigation talents, as well as for her preemptive capabilities in helping her clients avoid disputes.

## Troutman Sanders LLP

**THE FIRM** Headquartered in Richmond, this six-partner team advises employers on assorted workplace issues, including breach of contract, noncompete and discrimination matters. The group is also highly active in wage and hour disputes.

**KEY INDIVIDUALS** Deputy group leader of the firm's labor and employment practice **David Constine** is an expert in a broad range of advisory and litigious issues, including noncompetition agreements and employment contracts. **Wallace Starke** is considered an excellent go-to attorney for ERISA, pension and deferred compensation plans, as well as for health and welfare matters. The highly experienced **Eugene Webb** boasts particular expertise in union avoidance and defending employers against union organizing campaigns.

## Venable LLP
See profile on p.927

**THE FIRM** Long recognized for its involvement in labor matters pertaining to the energy industry, this practice also acts for clients from a broad range of industries. The team has recently negotiated a number of health and welfare contracts, including negotiating with drug retail chains to secure pharmacy benefits for employees.

**Sources say:** *"The service has been so, so good. One of the things that impresses you most is their responsiveness and professionalism."*

**KEY INDIVIDUALS David Smith** (see p.2514) is praised by clients as *"very seasoned and very detail oriented, and very proficient in the language of contracts."* He undertakes sophisticated labor work, including collective bargaining and union negotiations. **Gregory Ossi** (see p.2512) is described by clients as *"extremely professional and highly responsive to client needs."* He continues to be highlighted for his collective bargaining expertise, as well as for his work involving retiree health benefits in bankruptcy situations. **David Warner** (see p.2514) enters the rankings on the back of strong praise for his labor and employment disputes expertise. He is acknowledged as *"an extremely helpful and dependable attorney who always reports back in a timely manner."*

## Womble Carlyle Sandridge & Rice, LLP
See profile on p.2049

**THE FIRM** This firm's Tysons Corner office opened in 2001, and has since flourished. A perennial presence in the rankings in recent years, the employment group has an impressive client portfolio including a number of housing companies and educational institutions.

**Sources say:** *"An excellent team of lawyers."*

**KEY INDIVIDUALS Thomas Sawyer** leads the firm's labor and employment group, and is cofounder of its Northern Virginia office. He advises a number of government contractors in Northern Virginia, as well as carrying out multijurisdictional work with noncompete and

employee defection issues. Peers acknowledge him as *"a great attorney and a nice guy."*

## Woods Rogers PLC

**THE FIRM** Woods Rogers continues to develop an excellent reputation in the state, representing management across various industries. Its expertise spans a range of labor law and employment litigation.

**KEY INDIVIDUALS Thomas Winn** is a key contact at the firm.

## Other Notable Practitioners

With over 20 years' experience of employee benefits and tax matters, **Jewell Lim Esposito** of Constangy, Brooks & Smith, LLP is particularly well versed in crossover matters concerning the tax dimension of employment issues such as pensions and payrolls. She is appreciated by clients for being *"very personable."* The *"very collegial"* **Daniel Westman** (see p.2515) is managing partner of the Northern Virginia office of Morrison & Foerster LLP. He has a national practice encompassing employee mobility, noncompete issues and whistle-blower matters. The tremendously experienced **James Coleman** of Constangy, Brooks & Smith, LLP is *"a very responsive attorney who is always available and offers great value for money,"* according to satisfied clients. He is best known for his superb wage and hour practice. **King Tower** (see p.2514) of Spilman Thomas & Battle PLLC is hailed as *"a standout lawyer – really pleasant to work with and easy to understand."* He has a very strong and broad-ranging labor and employment law practice. Reston-based **Betsey Lewis** of Cooley LLP is held in high regard by clients for her responsiveness and up-to-date knowledge. Her expertise encompasses a range of issues, including misconduct allegations and employment agreements.

# LITIGATION

Commentary about individuals can be found under their firm's paragraph. If the firm has no paragraph (is not ranked) look at Other Notable Practitioners.

## Litigation: General Commercial
### Leading Firms

**Band 1**
Hunton & Williams LLP *
McGuireWoods LLP *

**Band 2**
Hogan Lovells US LLP
Troutman Sanders LLP
Williams Mullen

**Band 3**
Christian & Barton LLP
Gentry Locke Rakes & Moore LLP
Kaufman & Canoles
LeClairRyan
Morris & Morris PC
Reed Smith LLP
Spotts Fain
Venable LLP *
Willcox & Savage
Woods Rogers PLC

*The editorial is in alphabetical order by firm name.*

## Bowman and Brooke LLP

**THE FIRM** Bowman and Brooke receives outstanding market praise for its trial expertise, and is considered to be a leader in the field of product liability litigation. The firm enjoys close ties to a range of sectors, including the automotive, medical device, construction and tobacco industries. Notable clients include Toyota and Electrolux, while it recently represented Ford in a three-week trial concerning a claim of unintended acceleration.

**Sources say:** *"They are a very good firm. They are very responsive and focused."*

**KEY INDIVIDUALS** **Sandra Ezell**'s (see p.2509) prowess is flourishing in the area of product liability. She is the managing partner of the Richmond office, and receives excellent feedback from sources, one attesting that she is *"very, very effective, and a great strategist."*

## Christian & Barton LLP

**THE FIRM** This team's trial talents are singled out as a leading reason for its engagement by a broad range of clients. In addition to a strong general commercial litigation practice, the group also advises on real estate, insurance, IP and bankruptcy disputes, among others.

**KEY INDIVIDUALS** Sources note **Michael Smith**'s ability to handle a diverse array of contentious work, and he is described as *"a straight shooter and a guy who will cut to the chase."* **Warren David Harless** attracts impressive praise from market sources, who note that he is *"thorough and meticulous. He has great energy – he's dogged, and not in an abrasive way."* **Craig Merritt** is singled out for his expanding patent litigation presence, which is growing alongside

## Litigation: General Commercial
### Senior Statesmen

**Senior Statesmen: distinguished older practitioners**

| | |
|---|---|
| Morris III James W | Morris & Morris PC |
| Page Rosewell | McGuireWoods LLP |

### Leading Individuals

**Band 1**

| | |
|---|---|
| Allen Everette | LeClairRyan |
| Bayliss William D | Williams Mullen |
| Broaddus William | McGuireWoods LLP |
| Sims Hunter | Kaufman & Canoles |
| Slater Jr Thomas G | Hunton & Williams LLP * |
| Stillman Gregory | Hunton & Williams LLP * |

**Band 2**

| | |
|---|---|
| Anthony David | Troutman Sanders LLP |
| Boland J William | McGuireWoods LLP |
| Burke Jr John K | Setliff Turner & Holland, P.C. (ONP)[†] |
| Connally III N Thomas | Hogan Lovells US LLP |
| Cullen Richard | McGuireWoods LLP |
| Fuhr Edward J | Hunton & Williams LLP * |
| Jennings Jr James W | Woods Rogers PLC |
| Kearfott Joseph C | Hunton & Williams LLP * |
| Lee Tara | DLA Piper LLP (US) (ONP)[†] |
| Lobel Douglas P | Cooley LLP (ONP)[†] |
| Morris Philip | Morris & Morris PC |
| Raphael Stuart A | Hunton & Williams LLP * |
| Rudlin D Alan | Hunton & Williams LLP * |
| Shumadine Conrad M | Willcox & Savage |
| Smith Michael | Christian & Barton LLP * |
| Tata Robert M | Hunton & Williams LLP * |
| Witthoefft Charles | Hirschler Fleischer (ONP)[†] |
| Yinger Emily M | Hogan Lovells US LLP |

**Band 3**

| | |
|---|---|
| Austin J Rudy | Gentry Locke Rakes & Moore LLP |
| Devine William F | Williams Mullen |
| Goewey David W | Venable LLP * |
| Harless Warren David | Christian & Barton LLP |
| Hoptman Virginia Whitner | Womble Carlyle Sandridge (ONP)[†] |
| Hurd William | Troutman Sanders LLP |
| Loftis Mark D | Woods Rogers PLC |
| Merritt Craig | Christian & Barton LLP |
| Robinson Michael W | Venable LLP * |
| Shebelskie Michael | Hunton & Williams LLP * |
| Starr Edward | Troutman Sanders LLP |
| Thomas Alexander | Reed Smith LLP |

his solid general commercial practice. Sources say he is *"a wise and respected lawyer."*

## Gentry Locke Rakes & Moore LLP

**THE FIRM** This firm is noted for its assiduous and intelligent lawyers, and is particularly singled out for its trial skills. The group is based in Roanoke, but advises clients

## Litigation: Products Liability
### Leading Firms

**Band 1**
Bowman and Brooke LLP
McGuireWoods LLP *
Willcox & Savage

**Band 2**
Morris & Morris PC

## Litigation: Products Liability
### Senior Statesmen

**Senior Statesmen: distinguished older practitioners**

| | |
|---|---|
| King William | McGuireWoods LLP |
| Morris III James W | Morris & Morris PC |

### Leading Individuals

**Band 1**

| | |
|---|---|
| Bishop Bruce T | Willcox & Savage |
| Ezell Sandra | Bowman and Brooke LLP * |
| Walker Tracy | McGuireWoods LLP |

**Band 2**

| | |
|---|---|
| Bagley Terrence | McGuireWoods LLP |
| Epps John D | Hunton & Williams LLP * |
| Morris Philip | Morris & Morris PC |
| Williams Steven R | McGuireWoods LLP |

## Litigation: White-Collar Crime Government Investigations
### Leading Individuals

**Band 1**

| | |
|---|---|
| Barger David G | Greenberg Traurig, LLP (ONP)[†] * |
| Cullen Richard | McGuireWoods LLP |
| Dolan William | Venable LLP * |
| Vick Jr Howard C | McGuireWoods LLP |

**Up-and-coming individuals**

| | |
|---|---|
| Adams John | McGuireWoods LLP |

\* Indicates firm / individual with profile.

[†]ONP = Other Notable Practitioner

throughout the commonwealth. The team handles contentious matters in a range of areas, including antitrust, contract law and commercial torts.

**KEY INDIVIDUALS** **Rudy Austin** is a seasoned litigator with particular expertise in transport and construction litigation. One source enthusiastically refers to him as a *"really, really excellent lawyer who is very well respected around the state."*

## Hogan Lovells US LLP

**THE FIRM** This firm's commercial litigators handle a range of disputes. The team has a growing reputation for its defense of businesses operating in highly regulated industries such as media and financial services, while it has

*The editorial is in alphabetical order by firm name.*

particular expertise in class action litigation brought against healthcare providers. A recent notable client is Blue Cross Blue Shield of North Carolina, who it successfully defended in a putative nationwide class action concerning allegations of ERISA violations.

**Sources say:** *"Thanks to the depth of their experience they understand our business, and they know how the company thinks."*

**KEY INDIVIDUALS Thomas Connally** is described as having *"terrific strategic sense complemented by great leadership skills."* He recently successfully defended iStar financial and Dividend Capital in litigation relating to a claim of a right of first offer following the sale of a real estate portfolio. **Emily Yinger** has an increasingly impressive workload. She is described by peers as *"excellent,"* and has recently successfully defended a number of high-profile healthcare providers, including the aforementioned matter for Blue Cross Blue Shield of North Carolina.

## Hunton & Williams LLP
See profile on p.2517

**THE FIRM** This firm is recognized for its exceptional bench strength, and is well placed to handle sophisticated litigation. The group receives praise for its superb commitment to client service, and is noted for its experience in a range of industry sectors, including financial services, energy and manufacturing. It represents a number of local authorities in Virginia, while its impressive roster of commercial clients includes Sodexo.

**Sources say:** *"They are stellar! Their preparation and the way they fight in court hasve been truly world class, both in foundation and presentation."*

**KEY INDIVIDUALS Thomas Slater**'s (see p.2513) position as a leader in this field is reflected in the excellent reputation he holds among peers and in the significance of his high-value workload. He has had recent success in a high-value antitrust litigation. Sources note his *"terrific intellectual skill."* **Gregory Stillman** (see p.2514) has an outstanding reputation as a commercial litigator. He has a wealth of experience in areas including patent litigation, business torts and securities. **John Epps** (see p.2509) is a seasoned litigator with a reputation for product liability disputes. He is described as a *"great product lawyer,"* and is consistently recognized as having excellent technical abilities. The *"outstanding"* **Edward Fuhr** (see p.2510) is an established trial lawyer who is praised by clients for his ability to communicate complex matters in a simple and effective way. His expertise lies in securities litigation, as well as in Securities and Exchange Commission (SEC) and DOJ investigations. **Joseph Kearfott** (see p.2510) has considerable trial and appellate experience, and is noted for his handling of toxic tort litigation. *"He is very smart, able and ethical,"* say sources. **Stuart Raphael** (see p.2513) is held in high esteem by peers and clients alike. One client describes him as a *"superstar litigator,"* and he has considerable experience in litigating on behalf of local authorities. He has also represented businesses in significant antitrust litigation. **Alan Rudlin** (see p.2513) is a respected litigator with a national presence. He has considerable experience in commercial

disputes, including class actions and fiduciary litigation. **Robert Tata** (see p.2514) remains a strong presence in litigation in Virginia. He has an established reputation in complex commercial litigation, notably in breach of contract matters. He is also recognized for his government investigations and product liability work. **Michael Shebelskie** (see p.2513) enters the rankings after receiving excellent praise from the market. Clients and peers alike commend his considerable technical ability, with one describing how *"he can look at a set of facts and see the vulnerabilities straight away."*

## Kaufman & Canoles

**THE FIRM** This firm has a strong presence in the eastern reaches of the commonwealth, and is a heavy hitter in the Norfolk area. The team advises on contract disputes and litigation related to insurance, employment, construction and product liability, among other matters.

**KEY INDIVIDUALS Hunter Sims** is a highly respected trial and litigation lawyer. He advises on general commercial litigation as well as white-collar crime. He is regularly noted by sources as being one of the most skilled and experienced attorneys in Virginia.

## LeClairRyan

**THE FIRM** LeClairRyan has a nationwide litigation footprint. It represents businesses in complex matters, and has a reputation for its strength in antitrust, business tort and financial services litigation.

**KEY INDIVIDUALS Everette Allen** is described as *"one of the best in Virginia"* by peers. His stellar reputation is built upon his energetic and continually successful representation of businesses in large disputes.

## McGuireWoods LLP
See profile on p.2519

**THE FIRM** McGuireWoods has a commanding presence in Virginia in commercial, product liability and white-collar criminal litigation. This considerable depth is highly valued by clients, who are confident that it can meet a diverse range of litigation needs. The team works across a range of commercial sectors, and significant clients include Smithfield Foods, Bank of America and Dominion Resources.

**Sources say:** *"They are extraordinarily effective and professional."*

**KEY INDIVIDUALS William Broaddus** is considered to be a leading figure of the commercial litigation Bar. He has a broad range of expertise in areas that include government contracts, commercial credit and libel. He is also noted for his experience in environmental litigation. **Richard Cullen** has over 30 years of trial experience. He is widely admired for his *"extraordinary work"* in general commercial litigation, as well as in specialized white-collar crime and government investigations. **Howard Vick** chairs the firm's white-collar crime group, and stands out as being an exemplary criminal defense litigator. One source has described him as having *"the best judgment of anybody I have ever worked with."* *"Excellent lawyer"* **Terrence Bagley** has impressive experience in trying product liabili-

ty cases across the country in both state and federal courts. He continues to represent ConAgra Foods in ongoing national litigation relating to Peter Pan Peanut Butter. **William Boland** has an excellent reputation as chair of the businesses and securities litigation department, and has extensive experience in representing financial services. A recent high-profile client is Bank of America. **Tracy Walker** is the lead counsel for a number of high-profile clients in product liability matters, among them Ford and Dominion. Sources enthuse that *"his trial skills, presence in the courtroom, and ability to interact with both the judge and opposing counsel are all exceptional."* **Steven Williams** is credited for his skilled work and expertise in product liability. He is noted for his particular strengths in mass tort litigation. Senior counsel **William King** is highly respected in the field of product liability. **Rosewell Page** is a highly experienced commercial litigator. Clients value the continuity of his presence at the firm and the depth of his legal and commercial expertise. The *"very solid"* **John Adams** is a rising star in the government investigation and white-collar crime practice area, and his excellent reputation continues to grow among clients and peers.

## Morris & Morris PC

**THE FIRM** Morris & Morris is a compact Richmond team with an impressive reputation. Clients value its extensive experience of local courts as well as its fine commercial and product liability litigation capabilities. It has a wealth of experience in the transport, retail and financial sectors.

**Sources say:** *"The results are always excellent. They assess cases well, and they do it early on and provide strong advice."*

**KEY INDIVIDUALS Philip Morris** is an established litigator who handles product liability and general commercial disputes. One commentator notes that he is *"well prepared, honest and analytical."* Seasoned product liability specialist **James Morris** is hailed by one peer as being *"one of the all-time great stand-up trial lawyers."* He continues to be a venerated presence in the Virginia Bar.

## Reed Smith LLP

**THE FIRM** Reed Smith has a respected litigation practice that is now firmly established in Virginia. The team caters for a wide range of business litigation needs, and has trial experience in both state and federal courts. Rosetta Stone and Santander are counted among the firm's growing number of high-profile clients.

**Sources say:** *"I have had nothing but exceptional counsel and guidance from Reed Smith."*

**KEY INDIVIDUALS Alexander Thomas** is the global chair of the firm's litigation practice. He has considerable depth of experience, but is particularly noted for his work in antitrust compliance and competition-related disputes.

## Spotts Fain

**THE FIRM** Spotts Fain defends businesses in a range of commercial litigation matters. It is also recognized for its capabilities in representing businesses involved in IP, employment and construction disputes.

**KEY INDIVIDUALS Hugh Fain** is a key contact.

*The editorial is in alphabetical order by firm name.*

## Troutman Sanders LLP

**THE FIRM** This firm has a prominent team that continues to play a significant role in both the commonwealth and nationwide. Its litigation practice is bolstered by the firm's expertise in financial services, regulatory compliance and IP. It recently represented Bayview Loan Servicing in a significant consumer finance litigation. Other clients include BB&T and Capital One.

**KEY INDIVIDUALS David Anthony** is widely respected throughout the region, and is especially praised for his work on behalf of financial institutions. He recently advised Midland on a large and significant debt collection case alleging violations of RICO and the Fair Debt Collection Practices and Telephone Consumer Protection Acts. **William Hurd** has considerable depth of experience in government and appellate litigation. Clients particularly praise his willingness to go the extra mile in providing them with constructive advice. **Edward Starr** is a highly experienced litigator. He is especially well known for his insurance coverage work.

## Venable LLP

See profile on p.927

**THE FIRM** Venable has a notable presence in Virginia. The firm is well known for its commercial litigation, as well as its handling of government investigations and white-collar crime matters. Clients include Simplexity, Intersections and Slait Consulting.

**Sources say:** *"They are always thoughtful, thorough and timely."*

**KEY INDIVIDUALS William Dolan** (see p.2509) has an outstanding reputation for his white-collar crime and government investigations work. One source describes him as being *"very smart and excellent in court."* **Michael Robinson** (see p.2513) is valued by clients for his effective and down-to-earth style. Sources note that he *"always keeps calm and gets the results."* **David Goewey**'s (see p.2510) clients appreciate his ability to be *"direct"* and *"get to the point."* He recently represented Simplexity in a complicated and high-value litigation and arbitration.

## Willcox & Savage

**THE FIRM** This firm continues to play a leading role in product liability litigation in Virginia, and also has noted depth in general commercial disputes. The compact team has recently successfully defended Honeywell International in a high-value case involving alleged asbestos exposure. Other clients include Dow Union Carbide and Georgia-Pacific Corporation.

**KEY INDIVIDUALS Bruce Bishop** has a national presence, and is regarded by peers as one of the most able and *"standout"* product liability lawyers in the state. He handled the aforementioned matter for Honeywell International. **Conrad Shumadine** has over 35 years of experience as a trial lawyer. His practice is focused on general commercial litigation, with particular expertise in antitrust matters.

## Williams Mullen

**THE FIRM** Clients seek this team out for a full range of advice on commercial litigation and internal investigations. Recent highlights include advising Selective Way Insurance on a case involving an allegedly fraudulent insurance claim following Hurricane Isabel. The group is also representing Honeywell International in a product liability case regarding one of the company's aviation autopilot systems.

**Sources say:** *"I was very impressed. They are responsive, knowledgeable, and their advice is spot on."*

**KEY INDIVIDUALS** Richmond-based **William Bayliss** is known for being a gifted advocate on behalf of his clients. He has a broad commercial litigation practice, but is particularly well known for his professional liability and product liability work. **William Devine** is another practitioner renowned for his breadth of practice. He often advises major national clients on disputes taking place around the country, yet remains a top choice for local clients.

## Woods Rogers PLC

**THE FIRM** This firm has solid litigation capabilities which stretch across a wide range of sectors, including rail, healthcare and energy. It has recently had notable success in breach of warranty and unfair competition cases. Notable clients include Innovative Wireless Technologies and American Electric Power.

**KEY INDIVIDUALS James Jennings** is an established practitioner, and is praised by one source for his ability to *"take the hardest cases and win them."* **Mark Loftis** is a seasoned litigator with recognized expertise in commercial litigation. He recently acted as counsel for Strongwell in a significant insurance dispute.

## Other Notable Practitioners

**Tara Lee** (see p.2511) of DLA Piper LLP (US) is the managing partner of the Northern Virginia office and global cochair of the firm's cross-border litigation group. She is noted for her increasing expertise in US military matters relating to litigation. **Douglas Lobel** of Cooley LLP is known for his skill in complex commercial litigation. Sources name him an exceptional trial lawyer, and praise his dedicated and highly tactical approach to handling cases. **David Barger** (see p.2508) of Greenberg Traurig, LLP has a long-standing reputation for being *"friendly and smart."* He has a wealth of experience in white-collar crime defense litigation, and is widely respected by colleagues. **John Burke** of Setliff Turner & Holland, P.C. is a strong general litigator with significant experience in real estate disputes. **Virginia Whitner Hoptman** of Womble Carlyle Sandridge & Rice, LLP represents clients in a wide range of sectors. She has a particularly strong reputation for her representation of clients in the banking sector. **Charles Witthoefft** of Hirschler Fleischer is praised for his impressive work ethic and ability to *"get results."* He represents plaintiffs and defendants in a variety of commercial litigation matters. He is particularly experienced in the representation of developers and construction companies.

# REAL ESTATE NORTHERN VIRGINIA

Commentary about individuals can be found under their firm's paragraph. If the firm has no paragraph (is not ranked) look at Other Notable Practitioners.

### Real Estate: Northern Virginia
#### Leading Firms

**Band 1**
Cooley LLP
Walsh, Colucci, Lubeley, Emrich & Walsh PC

**Band 2**
McGuireWoods LLP *
Pillsbury Winthrop Shaw Pittman LLP *
Reed Smith LLP
Venable LLP *

**Band 3**
Holland & Knight LLP *
Hunton & Williams LLP *

#### Leading Individuals

**Band 1**

| Lavoie John G | Cooley LLP |
| Miller David | Pillsbury Winthrop Shaw Pittman LLP * |

**Band 2**

| Brennan James C | Reed Smith LLP |
| Dickerman Dorothea W | McGuireWoods LLP |
| Houston David S | Reed Smith LLP |
| Yurow M Jay | Leach Travell Britt PC (ONP)† |

**Band 3**

| Diamond Robert | Reed Smith LLP |
| Fagelson Karen | Reed Smith LLP |
| McDonald Douglas | Venable LLP * |
| Tompkins Benjamin F | Reed Smith LLP |

**Associates to watch**

| Wire Kenneth | McGuireWoods LLP |

* Indicates firm / individual with profile.
† ONP = Other Notable Practitioner

### Real Estate: Zoning/Land Use
#### Leading Individuals

**Star individuals**

| Calabrese Antonio J | Cooley LLP |

**Band 1**

| Foote John H | Walsh, Colucci, Lubeley, Emrich & Walsh |
| McDermott Francis A | Hunton & Williams LLP * |
| McGranahan Jr John C | Hunton & Williams LLP * |
| Milliken John | Venable LLP * |
| Walsh Martin D | Walsh, Colucci, Lubeley, Emrich & Walsh |

**Band 2**

| Banzhaf Michael A | Reed Smith LLP |
| Looney Mark | Cooley LLP |
| Lubeley Michael D | Walsh, Colucci, Lubeley, Emrich & Walsh |
| Mendelsohn Stuart | Holland & Knight LLP * |
| Riegle Gregory | McGuireWoods LLP |
| Rosati Michelle A | Holland & Knight LLP * |
| Tompkins Benjamin F | Reed Smith LLP |
| Walsh Nan | Walsh, Colucci, Lubeley, Emrich & Walsh |

**Up-and-coming individuals**

| Snow Colleen Gillis | Cooley LLP |

## Band 1

### Cooley LLP

**THE FIRM** Cooley continues to set the standard for real estate work in Northern Virginia, and operates a broad practice which includes complex land use, zoning and real estate transactions. Notably, the firm continues to act on the construction of the $5 billion Metrorail extension project, with the first phase scheduled for completion in 2013. In other highlights, the team is advising Verne Global in connection with the development, leasing and construction of its data centers in Iceland.
**KEY INDIVIDUALS** Zoning expert **Antonio Calabrese** is described by peers as one of the leading land use professionals in Northern Virginia. Clients are quick to praise the experience and expertise he brings to working on matters. **John Lavoie** is held in high esteem by clients for his business-focused and pragmatic approach. He has particular experience in all aspects of commercial real estate transactions. **Mark Looney** has an extensive land use practice

which covers retail, office, industrial and mixed-use developments, as well as hotel and large-scale community projects. **Colleen Gillis Snow** continues to impress sources with her real estate practice, and is praised for her extensive knowledge of land transactions in Loudoun County.

### Walsh, Colucci, Lubeley, Emrich & Walsh PC

**THE FIRM** The firm is widely regarded as a major player in the Northern Virginia real estate market. It is best known for its specialization in zoning and land use, where its wide-ranging expertise covers project approvals and entitlements, zoning compliance, due diligence and local government law. The team stands out for its experience in such niche areas of practice as brownfield redevelopment, affordable housing, educational institutions and energy facilities. It also advises on Virginia's land use value assessment program and conservation easement program.
**Sources say:** *"A top-tier firm."*
**KEY INDIVIDUALS** Founding partner **Martin Walsh** offers considerable expertise in land development, urban planning and zoning law. Prince William-based **John Foote** is an experienced litigator who maintains a broad practice in land use, zoning and environmental matters. **Michael Lubeley** has broad expertise in matters ranging from zoning and land use projects to commercial real estate, and is recognized as a go-to person for matters in Prince William County. **Nan Walsh** specializes predominantly in land use and zoning work. Based in Arlington, her experience encompasses hospital campus renovations, retail redevelopments and high-rise residential and office buildings.

## Band 2

### McGuireWoods LLP
See profile on p.2519

**THE FIRM** This group offers broad expertise in matters ranging from commercial real estate to complex land use and zoning issues. The firm maintains a strong focus on real estate finance and bankruptcy-related real estate work, and also advises on PPP. In notable highlights, the team represented Wells Fargo in a post-bankruptcy workout, subdivision and foreclosure of a 514-lot residential site.
**KEY INDIVIDUALS** The *"very capable"* **Dorothea Dickerman** is the head of the firm's distressed real estate practice group. She handles a broad spectrum of commercial real estate transactions including sales and acquisitions, leasing, workouts and loans. With a background in urban planning, **Gregory Riegle** focuses on land use, zoning and redevelopment. He has advised on a wide range of projects, and is noted for his knowledge of transit-oriented real estate development. **Kenneth Wire** focuses on land use, real estate and utility work. *"He is a great attorney,"* say sources.

### Pillsbury Winthrop Shaw Pittman LLP
See profile on p.2000

**THE FIRM** This firm is recognized for its specialization in transactional real estate, and regularly undertakes high-level work in this area. The real estate team works closely with the firm's tax, energy, insolvency and restructuring groups to advise on a variety of projects ranging from mixed-use redevelopments to government-sponsored PPP.
**Sources say:** *"The firm has specific and well-crafted expertise."*
**KEY INDIVIDUALS** **David Miller** (see p.2512) *"is an excellent practitioner with broad experience,"* sources agree. One commentator added: *"He is a very, very smart guy."*

### Reed Smith LLP

**THE FIRM** Reed Smith has considerable expertise in commercial leasing, land use development and zoning work. It has been particularly active with private office and residential work, and recently represented Gateway Holding in a joint venture for a two-phase apartment development. In other highlights, the team acted for Alexandria Waterfront Associates on the refinancing of a leasehold interest in the Torpedo Factory development.
**Sources say:** *"The quality of their work is exemplary. The attorneys are gifted in this area of law and manage our cases with style and success."*
**KEY INDIVIDUALS** **James Brennan** is a key contact in the firm's Falls Church office. His practice covers commercial transactions, leasing and asset-based lending, and he is praised by clients for his detail-oriented and flexible approach. **David Houston** comes highly recommended for his expertise in commercial leasing and retail transactions.

He represents both landlords and tenants in connection with department stores, theaters, restaurants, in-line retail stores and lifestyle centers, among other types of project. **Benjamin Tompkins** is described by clients as *"supportive, easy to work with"* and *"great at navigating the quasi-political negotiations which are implicit in real estate transactions."* **Michael Banzhaf** *"knows the land use business – he understands the politics and the personalities of the county decision makers, from the highest elected officials to the day-to-day staff members."* **Robert Diamond** is considered a *"go-to guy"* for condominium work in Northern Virginia. **Karen Fagelson** is praised for her *"ability to use real-world examples when explaining the potential impact of complex legal issues."* Her commercial real estate practice encompasses PPP, mixed-use development acquisition, financing and leasing.

### Venable LLP
**See profile on p.927**
THE FIRM This firm's Northern Virginia real estate practice group advises on commercial real estate, real estate finance, commercial leasing, zoning and land use. It stands out for its work on behalf of a number of high-profile clients, including Fannie Mae and Marriott International. In recent highlights, the team advised on the land use and zoning aspects of the $1 billion development of PenPlace, the largest remaining vacant parcel for development in Arlington County.

**Sources say:** *"We have been very impressed in working with this firm – they are very client-oriented."*
**KEY INDIVIDUALS** The *"outstanding"* **John Milliken** (see p.2512) advises on complex land use and transportation issues. He is currently leading the team in its work on the aforementioned PenPlace development. Clients describe **Douglas McDonald** (see p.2511) as *"a customer service-oriented, hard-working lawyer who is able to break down the legal issues and achieve consensus."*

### Band 3

### Holland & Knight LLP
**See profile on p.1028**
THE FIRM This firm advises on complex real estate transactions and zoning and related litigation. It recently represented Arlington County Board in a ground lease transaction for the development of an affordable housing complex. Other clients include Washington Properties, Habitat for Humanity Northern Virginia, ING Realty Partners and Burger King.
**Sources say:** *"The quality of the work at this firm is excellent."*
**KEY INDIVIDUALS Michelle Rosati** (see p.2513) is *"truly a standout – she is clear and concise in her work and has a knack for looking at problems from every possible angle. She has a deep breadth of knowledge regarding all aspects of real estate and a gift for resolving adversarial situations."* The

*"thorough and professional"* **Stuart Mendelsohn** (see p.2512) is commended for his *"strong knowledge of the market place"* and described as a *"strategic thinker."*

### Hunton & Williams LLP
**See profile on p.2517**
THE FIRM This 13-strong team focuses on zoning, land use regulation and complex real estate acquisition and finance transactions. The firm also advises on the environmental implications of development work.
**Sources say:** *"The attorneys and other staff are very knowledgeable and very thorough in their provision of services."*
**KEY INDIVIDUALS** The *"extremely experienced"* **Francis McDermott** (see p.2511) *"knows this practice area well and provides excellent service."* His expertise encompasses zoning litigation, public infrastructure issues and water quality regulation. **John McGranahan** (see p.2512) is also highly rated for his zoning and land use regulation practice and has developed a strong following in this field. *"He is a professional expert who treats us like his one and only client,"* say sources.

### Other Notable Practitioners

**Jay Yurow** is the head of the real estate department at Leach Travell Britt PC. He offers extensive experience in real estate law, with a focus on acquisition, development and sales within the hotel and retail industry.

## REAL ESTATE SOUTHERN VIRGINIA

Commentary about individuals can be found under their firm's paragraph. If the firm has no paragraph (is not ranked) look at Other Notable Practitioners.

| Real Estate: Southern Virginia |
|---|
| **Leading Firms** |
| **Band 1** |
| Hirschler Fleischer * |
| Hunton & Williams LLP * |
| McGuireWoods LLP * |
| Williams Mullen |
| **Band 2** |
| Troutman Sanders LLP |
| **Band 3** |
| Kaufman & Canoles |
| Willcox & Savage |
| * Indicates firm / individual with profile. |
| †ONP = Other Notable Practitioner |

| Real Estate: Southern Virginia | |
|---|---|
| **Leading Individuals** | |
| **Star individuals** | |
| Walsh William | Hunton & Williams LLP * |
| **Band 1** | |
| Campbell Daniel M | Hunton & Williams LLP * |
| Johnson Jr Thomas G | Willcox & Savage |
| Kidd Ed | Troutman Sanders LLP |
| Little Nancy | McGuireWoods LLP |
| Tapscott Andrew | Hunton & Williams LLP * |
| Terry Michael H | Hirschler Fleischer |
| **Band 2** | |
| Dewey Robert L. | Willcox & Savage |
| DuVal David V | Spotts Fain (ONP)† |
| Rothenberg Charles | Hirschler Fleischer |
| **Band 3** | |
| Gordon Howard E. | Williams Mullen |
| Nutter R.J. | Troutman Sanders LLP |
| **Up-and-coming individuals** | |
| Payne Charles | Hirschler Fleischer |

| Real Estate: Zoning/Land Use | |
|---|---|
| **Senior Statesmen and Eminent Partners** | |
| **Senior Statesmen:** distinguished older practitioners | |
| Axselle Jr Ralph L | Williams Mullen |
| **Leading Individuals** | |
| **Band 1** | |
| Cogbill III John V | McGuireWoods LLP |
| Condlin Andrew M | Williams Mullen |
| Theobald James | Hirschler Fleischer |
| **Band 2** | |
| Freye Gloria L | McGuireWoods LLP |
| Kidd Ed | Troutman Sanders LLP |
| Rothenberg Charles | Hirschler Fleischer |

### Band 1

### Hirschler Fleischer
**See profile on p.2516**
THE FIRM This firm is a dominant player in the Southern Virginia real estate market. Its diverse practice covers all matters of commercial real estate, ranging from acquisitions, dispositions and construction to financing, leasing, zoning and land use. Notably, Hirschler Fleischer also has

a dedicated team specializing in real estate securities work, including REIT fund formation, public and private offerings and major credit transactions.

**Sources say:** *"Hirschler Fleischer is absolutely wonderful – a top-line firm."*
**KEY INDIVIDUALS Michael Terry** is praised for his *"intelligence, quick and responsive attitude,"* and is described as a *"gentleman to deal with – he is superb."* One source enthused: *"There is no one better in real estate."* Interviewees laud **James Theobald** as *"a peer and a chief rival – a very skilled lawyer."* Widely regarded as *"the dean of land use,"* Theobald is acknowledged as being *"terrific for real estate matters in Richmond – he is very good at dealing*

*with the local community."* **Charles Rothenberg** has an extensive practice covering commercial real estate, acquisition and development, land use and zoning. Based in Fredericksburg, **Charles Payne** offers considerable expertise in commercial real estate and PPPs.

## Hunton & Williams LLP
See profile on p.2517

**THE FIRM** Hunton & Williams is widely regarded as a top firm for real estate work in Southern Virginia. The team offers considerable expertise in matters ranging from real estate planning, urban investment and commercial leasing to real estate finance and commercial lending, and stands out for its multijurisdictional experience. The firm also advises on distressed real estate transactions and natural resources development.
**Sources say:** *"They are timely, efficient, thorough and responsive."*
**KEY INDIVIDUALS** Star individual **William Walsh** (see p.2514) is *"just incredible,"* sources agree. *"He is without doubt one of the top lawyers around."* The *"very talented"* **Andrew Tapscott** (see p.2514) is widely viewed as a top-choice real estate practitioner in Southern Virginia. He regularly advises on distressed real estate work and on matters in the hospitality sector. **Daniel Campbell's** (see p.2508) broad commercial real estate practice includes work on behalf of developers, owners and lenders in connection with a variety of renewable energy projects.

## McGuireWoods LLP
See profile on p.2519

**THE FIRM** McGuireWoods is highly rated for its expertise in commercial real estate, real estate finance, land use and zoning matters. In recent highlights, the firm represented Watkins Land in connection with a mixed-use project in Chesterfield county, and advised the University of Richmond on the approval of a campus master plan amendment.
**Sources say:** *"McGuireWoods does excellent work. They are very detail-oriented and available whenever we need them."*
**KEY INDIVIDUALS** The *"exceptionally talented"* **Nancy Little** is described by peers as a *"tremendous transactional lawyer."* Her practice encompasses real estate finance and capital markets work, PPPs and M&A. **John Cogbill** is a

point person for land use matters. His successful track record has included the development of residential and industrial parks, regional malls and waste facilities, as well as transportation projects. *"Besides his legal knowledge, he understands our business and provides thoughtful suggestions that help manage the legal process,"* said one interviewee. **Gloria Freye** is a *"fine land use attorney."* She recently represented the Riverside on the James Homeowners' Association in connection with subdivision issues and the transfer of ownership interests.

## Williams Mullen

**THE FIRM** This leading firm earns widespread praise for its commercial real estate practice and for its involvement in high-level transactions and land use matters. In notable highlights, the group represented Riverbend Management and S.J. Collins Enterprises in a zoning hearing relating to the Fifth Street Station project. Other clients include Gilbane Development Company and Trinitas Ventures.
**Sources say:** *"They are truly the best in the business."*
**KEY INDIVIDUALS** **Andrew Condlin** leads the firm's Southern Virginia land use practice group. He is described by peers and clients as a *"well-organized and excellent lawyer."* **Howard Gordon** *"delivers top-notch work,"* say sources. His practice covers commercial and multifamily real estate, ground leases and land use planning, and he was recently involved in the development of Wards Corner. **Ralph Axselle** is highly regarded for his long experience in this field. He offers considerable expertise across a wide area of law, including land use, regulatory, lobbying and administrative law.

## Band 2

## Troutman Sanders LLP

**THE FIRM** This firm specializes in real estate development and acquisition, zoning and land use. It advises clients across a range of sectors, with notable experience in entertainment, hospitality and tourism-related work. The group recently represented Green Mountain Coffee in the negotiation of an incentive package for a coffee production and distribution facility in Windsor. It also assisted with the

negotiation of a lease and participation deal for a $200 million entertainment facility in Virginia Beach.
**KEY INDIVIDUALS** **Ed Kidd** earns widespread praise for his commanding presence in the boardroom and his insightful, intelligent approach. Clients describe **R.J. Nutter** as a one-of-a-kind, quality individual. He has handled several major negotiations for Green Mountain Coffee

## Band 3

## Kaufman & Canoles

**THE FIRM** This business law firm is rated for the breadth of its expertise in real estate. The group advises on a wide range of matters, such as commercial transactions, PPPs, zoning matters, leases and healthcare-related projects including senior housing facilities.
**KEY INDIVIDUALS** **Charles Land** is the cochair of the real estate strategies group.

## Willcox & Savage

**THE FIRM** This strong regional firm stands out for its involvement in major commercial real estate development transactions in Southern Virginia. Recent highlights include representing The Salvation Army in its acquisition of property from the city of Norfolk, and in the environmental and construction aspects of the construction of a new community center.
**KEY INDIVIDUALS** **Thomas Johnson** is described as a *"premier lawyer"* with a *"great legal mind."* One source enthused: *"He is simply outstanding."* **Robert Dewey** is a *"phenomenal lawyer"* who *"is bright and has excellent judgment."* He advises on commercial leasing, PPPs and construction finance, among other areas of expertise.

## Other Notable Practitioners

The *"young and talented"* **David DuVal** of Spotts Fain practices within all areas of commercial real estate. He has advised national retailers on transactions across the USA.

## Leaders' Profiles in Virginia

### AUGUST, Adam J
Holland & Knight LLP, Tysons Corner
703 720 8059
adam.august@hklaw.com
*Featured in Corporate/M&A (Northern Virginia)*

**Career:** Adam August counsels public and private company clients in a variety of industries including information technology, government contracting, distribution, software and telecommunications. He has been actively involved in merger, acquisition and disposition transactions with a combined value more than $1 billion, and financing/investment transactions and securities offerings worth more than $750 million. He also has extensive experience in issues related to corporate governance; corporate reorganizations; development, production, and distribution of technology goods and services; employment and equity-based compensation matters; and transactions with distressed entities and business bankruptcy.

### BAKER, Lewis J
Watt, Tieder, Hoffar & Fitzgerald, LLP, McLean
703 749 1000
lbaker@wthf.com
*Featured in Construction (Virginia)*

**Practice Areas:** Domestic and international construction, suretyship, goverment contracts.
**Professional Memberships:** American Bar Association, Fellow - American College of Construction Lawyers, Maryland State Bar Association.
**Career:** Larry Baker is Managing Partner of WTHF. His practice focuses on major construction, surety and architect/engineer claims. Larry also has an active government contracts practice and has litigated bid protests in various local, state and federal forums. Larry has experience as a neutral in mini-trials, as a mediator, and has acted as a special master to resolve disputes.
**Publications:** Larry writes and speaks regularly on construction and government contracting issues within the United States.

### BARAT, Scott
Pillsbury Winthrop Shaw Pittman LLP, McLean
703 770 7995
scott.barat@pillsburylaw.com
*Featured in Construction (Virginia)*

**Practice Areas:** Mr Barat counsels clients involved in all aspects of the construction process and represents owners, developers, and contractors in construction transactions involving private and public projects, both in the Washington, DC metropolitan area and throughout the country. Mr Barat's practice includes drafting and negotiating development, design, construction, and design/build agreements. He is experienced in resolving disputes through negotiation, mediation, litigation, and arbitration.
**Professional Memberships:** ABA Forum on the Construction Industry.
**Career:** Admitted to practice: Commonwealth of Virginia, District of Columbia.

**Personal:** JD, University of Michigan Law School, 1985; BA, University of Virginia, 1982.

### BARGER, David G
Greenberg Traurig, LLP, McLean
703 749 1307
BargerD@gtlaw.com
*Featured in Litigation (Virginia)*

**Practice Areas:** Litigation; white collar criminal defense; environmental; government litigation; business immigration and compliance; commercial and construction litigation, government investigations, corporate compliance, criminal and civil tax controversies.
**Professional Memberships:** Member: American, District of Columbia and Fairfax Bar Associations; Society of CPAs.
**Career:** Rated, AV® Preeminent™ 5.0 out of 5. Selected, Chambers USA Guide, 2009-13. Recipient, numerous awards while with the Department of Justice and the United States Attorneys Office, EDVA.
**Personal:** JD, University of Maryland; MSJA, University of Denver, College of Law; BA, cum laude, University of Maryland.

### BARUFKA, Jack S
Pillsbury Winthrop Shaw Pittman LLP, McLean
703 770 7712
jack.barufka@pillsburylaw.com
*Featured in Intellectual Property (Northern Virginia)*

**Practice Areas:** Firmwide head of Pillsbury's Intellectual Property Practice, with over 90 practitioners. Practice includes strategic patent counseling, litigation, dispute resolution, patent reexaminations, licensing, pre-litigation opinions, patent prosecution, design-arounds, interferences, trade secrets, trademarks and copyright. Represents clients in the areas of electronics, semiconductor manufacturing, medical devices, software, business methods, and mechanical technologies. Frequently quoted in national publications and ranked among the top 15 IP attorneys in the Washington DC area by 'The Legal Times'.
**Career:** Adjunct Professor, George Washington University.
**Personal:** JD, American University, Washington College of Law (cum laude); LLM, George Washington University National Law Center; BS Binghamton University.

### BRETSCHNEIDER, Barry E
Baker & Hostetler LLP, Washington, DC
202 861 1754
bbretschneider@bakerlaw.com
*Featured in Intellectual Property (Northern Virginia)*

**Career:** Barry Bretschneider's practice is concentrated in patent infringement litigation in the district courts and before the International Trade Commission, and includes post grant patent procedures including inter partes review, reexaminations and interferences, patent prosecution, patent licensing and related transactional work, trademark litigation and prosecution. Barry represents US and foreign corporations in various industries,

including electronics, semiconductors, polymers, composite materials, medical device, pharmaceutical and automotive, among others. A well-known interference practitioner, Barry has had a number of notable successes in this field before the US Patent and Trademark Office. He co-authored How to Win Interferences, published by Managing Intellectual Property.

### BROWNELL, Thomas
Holland & Knight LLP, Tysons Corner
703 720 8600
thomas.brownell@hklaw.com
*Featured in Construction (Virginia)*

**Practice Areas:** Partner, Government Contracts Group. He practices in the areas of construction claims/disputes, government contracts, intellectual property law, real estate and business litigation. He is experienced in the preparation and trial of complex civil cases, and in the counseling and drafting of agreements in the areas of government contracts, construction, real estate, and software development and licensing. He has trial experience in the areas of government contracts, patent infringement, trade secret, and copyright infringement in the computer software industry, commercial disputes relating to the delivery and installation of integrated computer systems and a wide range of construction disputes.

### CAMPBELL, Daniel M
Hunton & Williams LLP, Richmond
804 788 8503
dcampbell@hunton.com
*Featured in Real Estate (Southern Virginia)*

**Practice Areas:** Practice is focused on real estate development, including the acquisition and development of office buildings (including corporate headquarters and medical office), hospital bed towers, and manufacturing, mining, and energy generation facilities (including solar, wind, geothermal, biomass and other renewable energy projects). Experienced in the financing, permitting and other attendant steps associated with these projects, including working within the constraints of governmental incentive programs, public-private models, land use restrictions and master planning, conservation easements, and brownfield regulations. Practice frequently involves the management and coordination of acquisitions, dispositions, leasing and financing of assets for clients with significant real estate portfolios.

### CHRISTMAN, James
Hunton & Williams LLP, Richmond
804 788 8368
jchristman@hunton.com
*Featured in Environment (Virginia)*

**Practice Areas:** Mr Christman's practice focuses on environmental, energy, and administrative law, particularly the Clean Water Act, water rights, and laboratory methods for measuring water pollutants.
**Professional Memberships:** ABA; Virginia State Bar; Member and past Chair, State Advisory Board to Virginia Air Pollution Control Board;

past Chair, AWWA Water Rights Committee; past Chair, Virginia Chapter AWMA; former Adjunct Professor, Environmental Law, Marshall-Wythe Law School.
**Publications:** Co-author, Environmental Permitting Guide Book (McGraw Hill 1999); co-author, Eastern Water Rights (AWWA 1998).
**Personal:** JD, University of Michigan, 1973; BS, Physics, University of Illinois, 1970); Phi Beta Kappa.

### CONNOLLY, Theresa
Isler Dare, Vienna
703 748 2690
tconnolly@islerdare.com
*Featured in Labor & Employment (Virginia)*

**Practice Areas:** Represents employers in all labor and employment matters, including discipline management, preventative counseling and training, litigation in state and federal courts, and before administrative agencies. Handles union matters including elections, ULPs, arbitrations, negotiations, and NLRB proceedings.
**Professional Memberships:** Bars of VA, MD, DC, and NY.
**Career:** Partner 2007 – present; Partner - DLA Piper, 1996-2007; Venable, 1994-96; Orrick, Herrington & Sutcliffe, 1990-94; Virginia Super Lawyers, Washingtonian Magazine, Washington Business Journal – Top Employment Lawyer.
**Personal:** JD, Fordham University, 1990; BS, Cornell University, ILR, 1987.

### DARE, Mark
Isler Dare, Vienna
703 748 2690
mdare@islerdare.com
*Featured in Labor & Employment (Virginia)*

**Practice Areas:** Employment litigation and counseling, defending employers before human rights commissions, EEOC, and state and federal courts.
**Professional Memberships:** Member, VBA Labor and Employment Law Section; Fairfax Bar Association President (1994-95), Member, Board of Directors (1995-96).
**Career:** Partner 2006 – present; Reed Smith, LLP, 1974-2006; Listed in Best Lawyers in America, Virginia Super Lawyers, Virginia's Legal Elite, Washingtonian Magazine, and Northern Virginia Magazine.
**Publications:** "Unfair Competition", Employment Law in Virginia (Virginia Law Foundation); "Employment Law: Employee Rights and Employee Responsibilities", in The Virginia Lawyer: A Deskbook For Practitioners.
**Personal:** JD, University of Virginia, 1974; AB, Politics, Princeton University, 1971.

### DECAMP, Paul
Jackson Lewis LLP, Reston
703 483 8305
DeCampP@jacksonlewis.com
*Featured in Labor & Employment (Virginia)*

**Practice Areas:** Focused exclusively on management-side wage and hour law, including class

and collective actions, federal and state agency investigations, and internal compliance reviews.
**Career:** Partner and National Chair, Wage and Hour Practice Group, Jackson Lewis LLP, 2008-present; Administrator, U.S. Department of Labor, Wage and Hour Division, 2006-07; Senior Policy Advisor, US Department of Labor, Employment Standards Administration, 2005-06; Law Clerk to the Honorable Alan E. Norris, US Court of Appeals for the Sixth Circuit, 1995-96.
**Personal:** Columbia University School of Law, JD, Notes Editor, Columbia Law Review, 1995; Harvard College, AB, magna cum laude, 1992.

### DEMM, Stephen P
Hunton & Williams LLP, Richmond
804 788 8331
sdemm@hunton.com
*Featured in Intellectual Property (Southern Virginia)*
**Practice Areas:** Mr Demm's practice focuses on intellectual property and technology litigation, counseling, and prosecution, with emphasis on trademark, trade dress, copyright and domain name litigation and dispute resolution. His practice also includes intellectual property audits and policies; clearance, registration and management of intellectual property assets; intellectual property and technology licenses and agreements; and counseling on advertising and promotions, including consumer sweepstakes.
**Professional Memberships:** International Trademark Association, American Bar Association, ABA Intellectual Property Law Section, American Intellectual Property Law Association, Virginia State Bar, Virginia State Bar Intellectual Property Law Section, Virginia Bar Association, Virginia Bar Association Intellectual Property and Information Technology Law Section, Fourth Circuit Judicial Conference, Merit Selection Panel for US District Court, Eastern District of Virginia.
**Career:** Litigated cases include CFA Institute v. Institute of Chartered Financial Analysts of India, 551 F.3d 285 (4th Cir. 2009); Circuit City Stores, Inc. v. Speedy Car-X, Inc., 35 U.S.P.Q.2d 1703 (E.D. Va. 1995); Georgia-Pacific Consumer Products LP v. von Drehle Corp., 618 F.3d 441 (4th Cir. 2010); Playtex Products, Inc. v. Georgia-Pacific Corp., 67 U.S.P.Q.2d 1923 (S.D.N.Y. 2003), aff'd, 390 F.3d 158 (2d Cir. 2004); Takeall v. Pepsico, Inc., 809 F. Supp. 19 (D. Md. 1992), aff'd, 14 F.3d 596 (4th Cir. 1993), cert. denied, 512 U.S. 1236 (1994).

### DOLAN, William
Venable LLP, Tysons Corner
703 760 1680
wddolan@Venable.com
*Featured in Litigation (Virginia)*
**Practice Areas:** William Dolan concentrates on trial work involving a wide range of civil, business disputes, and white collar criminal matters. His litigation practice is focused primarily in Virginia and the District of Columbia.
**Professional Memberships:** Mr Dolan is a past President of the Virginia State Bar and Chair of the Criminal Law Section. He is a Fellow of the American College of Trial Lawyers, the

International Academy of Trial Lawyers, the American Bar Foundation and the Virginia Law Foundation.
**Personal:** JD, Columbus School of Law, Catholic University of America, 1972; AB, Marquette University, 1967.

### DUNSTON, Erin M
Buchanan Ingersoll & Rooney PC, Alexandria
703 838 6645
erin.dunston@bipc.com
**Career:** Erin is a Shareholder in the firm's Intellectual Property Section and Chair of the Biotechnology Practice Group. Her practice focuses on interferences, district court litigation, opinions, and prosecution – primarily in the fields of biotechnology, pharmaceuticals, and medical devices. Erin has assisted in over 35 interferences before the Patent Trial and Appeal Board and is transitioning that experience to inter partes reviews and post-grant proceedings. Erin also maintains an extensive patent prosecution docket. Her litigation practice includes classic infringement, declaratory judgment, and Paragraph IV cases. She earned her JD from the University of the Pacific, McGeorge School of Law.

### ECKSTEIN, Maya M
Hunton & Williams LLP, Richmond
804 788 8788
meckstein@hunton.com
*Featured in Intellectual Property (Southern Virginia)*
**Practice Areas:** Advises companies and organizations on protecting intellectual property rights. Represents plaintiffs and defendants in patent infringement litigation and other IP matters.
**Professional Memberships:** Virginia State Bar, New York State Bar, John Marshall Inn of Court, Thomas Jefferson Intellectual Property Inn of Court.
**Career:** Judicial Clerk, Hon. Roger L Gregory, US Court of Appeals for the Fourth Circuit, 2001; Hunton & Williams 1997-2001, 2001-present.
**Personal:** JD, Syracuse University College of Law, magna cum laude, Order of the Coif; Associate Notes and Comments Editor, Syracuse Law Review, 1995; BA, Kent State University, cum laude, Journalism, 1991.

### EPPS, John D
Hunton & Williams LLP, Richmond
804 788 8311
jepps@hunton.com
*Featured in Litigation (Virginia)*
**Practice Areas:** Mr Epps' practice focuses on business litigation, including products liability, toxic tort, asbestos, benzene and environmental liability, commercial and construction disputes. He represents clients as national coordinating and national trial counsel. He has tried over 100 jury trials, in state and federal courts, including toxic exposure, commercial disputes, securities fraud, construction and personal injury cases. Mr Epps is licensed in Virginia, West Virginia, Pennsylvania and Texas.
**Professional Memberships:** President, Virginia Bar Association, 2009; President, Virginia Association of Defense Attorneys, 1997-98. Vice

President, Virginia Law Foundation, 2012-13; American Bar Association; Defense Research Institute.

### EZELL, Sandra
Bowman and Brooke LLP, Richmond
804 819 1156
sandra.ezell@bowmanandbrooke.com
*Featured in Litigation (Virginia)*
**Practice Areas:** Sandra Giannone Ezell is a trial lawyer who devotes her seemingly boundless energy to representing corporations in both commercial claims and wrongful death/catastrophic injury product liability claims, often as national trial counsel.
**Professional Memberships:** She is a member of Product Liability Advisory Council, International Association of Defense Counsel, Defense Research Institute (DRI) and National Association of Women Lawyers.
**Career:** In more than 20 years of managing and trying cases she has handled wrongful death and catastrophic injury matters in various arenas including automotive, general transportation, construction, tobacco, child products, medical device, trucking, toxic tort, recreational products, food products, household products and power tools.
**Personal:** She was named to The Legal 500 in 2010 and 2011, a "2010 Influential Women of Virginia" by Virginia Lawyers Weekly, a "2010 Women at the Top" by Virginia American Business Women's Association, the recipient of The Burton Award for Legal Achievement, Distinguished Legal Writing Award in 2008 and a 2012 Virginia Super Lawyer. Sandra attended The University of Michigan Law School and is licensed in Virginia and Illinois.

### FINTO, Kevin J
Hunton & Williams LLP, Richmond
804 788 8568
kfinto@hunton.com
*Featured in Environment (Virginia)*
**Practice Areas:** Kevin Finto's practice focuses on air and water permitting (electric generation facilities, natural gas facilities, pulp and paper mills, steel mills, mining operations and specialty chemical facilities), enforcement (New Source Review) and permit challenges; wetlands; voluntary remediation; economic development; environmental aspects of business transactions; and environmental management system development. He is listed in Best Lawyers in America and Virginia's Superlawyers.
**Professional Memberships:** Fellow, American College of Environmental Lawyers.
**Career:** Engineer, Chevron USA; Adjunct Professor, Virginia Commonwealth University School of Engineering.

### FITZGERALD, Robert M
Watt, Tieder, Hoffar & Fitzgerald, LLP, McLean
703 749 1000
rfitzger@wthf.com
*Featured in Construction (Virginia)*
**Practice Areas:** Construction, government contracts, international construction.

**Professional Memberships:** American Bar Association; New York, Virginia, District of Columbia and Fairfax County Bar Associations; Moles Honorary Underground Construction Society. Honors include Chambers USA - Top Construction Lawyers in Virginia; Best Lawyers in America; International Who's Who of Construction & Business Lawyers; Washington, DC Super Lawyers.
**Career:** Bob's practice focuses primarily on the preparation and negotiation of construction contracts and claims. His practice is international in scope. He has developed a particular expertise in heavy construction contract disputes relating to dams, canals, powerplants, water and sewage treatment plants, and machine mined tunnels.

### FLAHERTY, Thomas
Littler Mendelson, PC, McLean
703 442 8425
TFlaherty@littler.com
*Featured in Labor & Employment (Virginia)*
**Practice Areas:** Complex litigation and jury trials; competition and trade secret law; discrimination and harassment; labor management relations and healthcare.
**Career:** Thomas J Flaherty's practice encompasses most areas of employment and labor law, including litigation and advice involving both individual and class action matters. He represents clients in state and federal courts and in arbitration.
**Publications:** "Virginia Supreme Court Further Narrows Non-Compete Covenant Enforceability", December 16, 2011.
**Personal:** JD, Boston College, 1975; BA, Yale University, 1972.

### FOLEY, Christopher P
Finnegan, Henderson, Farabow, Garrett & Dunner LLP, Reston
571 203 2720
christopher.foley@finnegan.com
*Featured in Intellectual Property (Northern Virginia)*
**Practice Areas:** Practices both trademark and patent law. His trademark practice includes procurement of trademark registrations, participation in inter partes administrative proceedings, evaluating potentially infringing marks, licensing, and litigation. He has coordinated the daily activities of litigations from the initial pleading stage through trials. He has handled patent prosecution and disputes relating to aircraft and automotive parts, packaging designs, injection molding products and equipment, medical products and methods, networking systems, tools and tooling machinery.
**Personal:** United States Naval Academy (BS, 1975); Georgetown University Law Center (JD, 1983).

### FRANCE, Thomas W
Venable LLP, Tysons Corner
703 760 1657
twfrance@Venable.com
*Featured in Corporate/M&A (Northern Virginia)*
**Practice Areas:** Thomas France's practice focuses on public and private offerings of equity and debt securities, mergers and acquisitions,

franchise transactions, corporate reorganizations, the formation of various business entities, banking and securities regulation, and general corporate matters. His clients include public and private companies, with a particular emphasis on companies in the technology, government contracts, hospitality, banking and financial services, and retail industries.

**Personal:** JD, Washington and Lee University School of Law, 1995; BA, summa cum laude, Oregon State University, 1992.

### FUHR, Edward J
Hunton & Williams LLP, Richmond
804 788 8201
efuhr@hunton.com
*Featured in Litigation (Virginia)*

**Practice Areas:** Ed Fuhr is Head of the Securities and Corporate Governance Litigation Practice at Hunton & Williams. His practice focuses on corporate governance and securities litigation, mergers and acquisitions, FCPA business torts, commercial contract disputes and appellate litigation. He has received recognition in Who's Who in American Lawyers, The Best Lawyers In America - Business Litigation, and Virginia's Legal Elite. Prior to joining the firm, Mr Fuhr served as attorney-advisor in the Office of Legal Counsel with the Department of Justice. He received his Law Degree, cum laude, from the University of Chicago.

### GATTO, James
Pillsbury Winthrop Shaw Pittman LLP, McLean
703 770 7754
james.gatto@pillsburylaw.com
*Featured in Intellectual Property (Northern Virginia)*

**Practice Areas:** Leader, Social Media, Entertainment and Technology Team and Video Games Team. Focuses on IP and business strategies, including patents, trademarks, copyrights (including DMCA), trade secrets, and open source software relating to games, social media, internet and software-based technologies. Focuses on emerging legal issues and business strategy associated with user generated content, social media-based contests, sweepstakes and gambling, gamification, virtual goods and virtual currency. Handles high profile litigation, complex prosecution, transactional, regulatory and advisory work and patent portfolio acquisitions, sales and monetization.

**Personal:** JD, Georgetown University, 1988; BE Manhattan College (electrical engineering; physics minor), 1984.

### GHOLZ, Charles
Oblon Spivak McClelland Maier & Neustadt LLP, Alexandria
703 412 6485
cgholz@oblon.com
*Featured in Intellectual Property (Northern Virginia)*

**Personal:** Specializes in patent interferences under 35 USC § 135 before the Patent Trial and Appeal Board (PTAB) and court review of interference decisions by the BPAI. Handles appeals before the Federal Circuit under 35 USC § 141 and civil actions in district courts under 35 USC §

146. Represents a wide variety of clients across a range of technologies including biotech, chemical, electronics, and computers and regularly appears before the BPAI, the Federal Circuit, and various district courts and appears as an expert witness on patent issues. Named by Chambers among the top IP attorneys in Virginia (2005-13).

### GIAMMITTORIO, Gregory
Morrison & Foerster LLP, McLean
703 760 7320
ggiammittorio@mofo.com
*Featured in Corporate/M&A (Northern Virginia)*

**Practice Areas:** Focuses on advising private and publicly held companies on M&A, joint ventures, strategic alliances, venture capital financings, and corporate governance issues. Works with private equity funds on leveraged buyouts and management buyouts. Advises on complex cross-border M&A transactions. Recent matters have involved government services, defense, semiconductor, cleantech, telecommunications, software, IT, and life science businesses. Experience with IP licensing, e-commerce, and other complex commercial agreements. Works with emerging to medium-sized enterprises as outside general counsel.

**Professional Memberships:** Admitted to practice in Virginia and the District of Columbia.

**Personal:** BA, University of Virginia; JD, University of Virginia School of Law.

### GOEWEY, David W
Venable LLP, Tysons Corner
202 344 4853
dwgoewey@venable.com
*Featured in Litigation (Virginia)*

**Practice Areas:** Commercial litigation, including D&O, financial and regulatory and class action defense.

**Professional Memberships:** Admitted to all federal and state courts in Virginia, DC and Maryland.

**Career:** Tried complex civil cases at Venable since 1987. AV® rated (Martindale & Hubbell). Financial services-related litigation and regulatory proceedings; D&O defense work and litigation stemming from M&A, contracts and torts.

**Publications:** Co-author of Compensatory Damages chapter (Business and Commercial Litigation in Federal Courts).

**Personal:** JD, William and Mary (executive editor, William & Mary Law Review), 1987; BA, University of Virginia, 1984.

### GOOLSBY, Allen
Hunton & Williams LLP, Richmond
804 788 8289
agoolsby@hunton.com
*Featured in Corporate/M&A (Southern Virginia)*

**Practice Areas:** Allen Goolsby's practice focuses on corporate governance.

**Professional Memberships:** ABA Board of Governors. ABA Business Law Section's Committee on Corporate Laws, its Committee on Securities Regulation and its Committee on Corporate Documents and Process.

**Career:** Mr Goolsby specializes in assisting publicly-held corporations on matters relating to cor-

porate governance. He also has worked on a variety of acquisition, disposition and financing transactions and served as the principal draftsman of the Virginia Stock Corporation Act.

**Publications:** 'Goolsby on Virginia Corporations' (LexisNexis) (Fourth Edition); 'Virginia Corporation Law and Practice' (Prentice Hall Law & Business).

### HEINTZ, James M
DLA Piper LLP (US), Washington, DC
703 773 4148
jim.heintz@dlapiper.com
*Featured in Intellectual Property (Northern Virginia)*

**Practice Areas:** Intellectual property.

**Career:** He focuses on patent litigation and prosecution with an emphasis on electrical and computer technologies, including encryption technologies, conditional access television systems, computer operating system software, electronic train control and signaling systems, optical sensors, integrated circuits and semiconductors. He has represented clients in patent litigation in the US involving a wide variety of technologies, including satellite television systems, video processing, on-line computer gaming, telecommunications testing equipment and power tools. He counsels clients regarding patentability, validity and infringement issues.

**Personal:** JD, St. John's University (magna cum laude); BSEE, State University of New York at Stony Brook.

### HENDRICKSON, Susan E
Arnold & Porter LLP, McLean
703 720 7010
Susan.Hendrickson@aporter.com
*Featured in Intellectual Property (Northern Virginia)*

**Practice Areas:** Sue Hendrickson is a Partner in the firm's Intellectual Property and Technology Practice Group. Her practice focuses on complicated technology transactions, joint ventures and licensing matters and regularly assists clients ranging from Fortune 100 companies to start-ups in structuring the key business arrangements involving their intellectual property and technology assets. Ms Hendrickson has been involved in technology transactions for over fifteen years and has extensive experience in the information technology, new media, and life sciences sectors.

### ISLER, Edward Lee
Isler Dare, Vienna
703 748 2690
eisler@islerdare.com
*Featured in Labor & Employment (Virginia)*

**Practice Areas:** Practice dedicated exclusively to representing management in all aspects of labor and employment law.

**Professional Memberships:** Virginia Bar Association, Labor and Employment Law Section (Executive Council 2002-12; Chair 2010-11); DC Bar, Labor Relations Section.

**Career:** Founding Partner 1997 – present; Gibson, Dunn & Crutcher, 1988-95; Judicial Clerk, USDC WD Va., 1987-88; Listed in Best Lawyers in America, Virginia Super Lawyers, Virginia's Legal Elite, and Washingtonian Magazine.

**Publications:** Author, Virginia Employment Practices and Forms; Virginia Business Torts; Virginia Wage & Hour Handbook.

**Personal:** JD, William & Mary, 1987 (Law Review, Order of the Coif); BA, University of Virginia, 1983.

### KATSANTONIS, Vivian
Watt, Tieder, Hoffar & Fitzgerald, LLP, McLean
703 749 1000
vkatsant@wthf.com
*Featured in Construction (Virginia)*

**Practice Areas:** Construction, suretyship, government contracts, international construction.

**Professional Memberships:** ABA, ABA Forum on Construction, District of Columbia and Virginia Bar Associations, TIPS.

**Career:** Vivian represents clients in contract procurement, drafting and negotiation, administration, dispute resolution and litigation for a broad range of commercial, construction and government contract matters. She has represented clients on a wide range of heavy industrial and commerical construction projects, including mass transit systems, power plants, public roadways and office complexes.

**Publications:** Vivian has authored numerous works and speaks regularly on issues related to the construction industry in the United States and abroad.

### KATZ, Charles
Morrison & Foerster LLP, McLean
703 760 7319
ckatz@mofo.com
*Featured in Corporate/M&A (Northern Virginia)*

**Practice Areas:** Co-Chair, Emerging Company Venture Capital practice. Focuses on emerging growth and technology companies (public and private) in transactional work, emphasizing M&A, private equity and venture capital transactions, divestitures, recapitalizations and restructurings, debt and equity financings and securities offerings, leveraged and management buyouts, joint ventures and strategic investments. Experience in domestic and international transactions, including with parties in cross-border transactions and with multinational investors.

**Career:** Admitted to practice in Virginia and in the District of Columbia.

**Personal:** AB, Lafayette College, 1989; JD, Washington & Lee University School of Law, 1992; LLM (Securities Regulations), Georgetown University Law School, 1993.

### KEARFOTT, Joseph C
Hunton & Williams LLP, Richmond
804 788 8200
jkearfott@hunton.com
*Featured in Litigation (Virginia)*

**Practice Areas:** Joseph Kearfott's practice focuses on all aspects of civil litigation, both state and federal, at the trial and appellate levels, with particular focus on complex product liability and toxic tort litigation. Other areas of practice include premises liability and other personal injury litigation, commercial disputes, business torts and valuation litigation. He is listed in Who's

Who in America, Who's Who in American Law, Best Lawyers in America - 2010, 2010 Virginia Super Lawyers, and the 2005 BTI Client Service All-Star Team for Law Firms.

### KNOX, Thomas J
Morrison & Foerster LLP, McLean
703 760 7317
tknox@mofo.com
*Featured in Corporate/M&A (Northern Virginia)*
**Practice Areas:** Co-Chair of the firm's East Coast / Europe Corporate Practice. Advises on corporate and securities matters (including venture capital, IPOs and other financings, M&A transactions, and corporate governance and restructuring matters), technology and business process outsourcing (BPO) transactions, and technology transactions (including complex procurements, distribution arrangements, e-commerce deals, and licensing, acquisition and disposition of intellectual property assets). Clients include a wide range of technology, cleantech, telecommunications, life sciences, e-commerce, and network infrastructure companies.
**Career:** Named 'Top Corporate Finance Lawyer' by Washington Business Journal. AV rated.
**Personal:** JD, University of Michigan; BA, Middlebury College.

### KULBASKI, James J
Oblon Spivak McClelland Maier & Neustadt LLP, Alexandria
703 413 3000
jkulbaski@oblon.com
*Featured in Intellectual Property (Northern Virginia)*
**Professional Memberships:** Virginia Bar, registered USPTO patent attorney. Member of IPO, AIPLA, LES and ABA; past Vice-Chair, IPO committee on Standards Setting; past Chair, ABA subcommittee on Trade Secret Protection of Computer Software.
**Personal:** A former USPTO examiner, Kulbaski focuses his practice on electrical technologies, communications standards, computer hardware/software, and digital video encoding. He is a leader in patent pools and obtaining patents related to industry standards and has expertise in obtaining, managing, licensing, and enforcing patents and patent portfolios, and litigation at trial and appellate levels. JD, Columbus School of Law, Catholic University; BS, Electrical Engineering, Rensselaer Polytechnic Institute.

### KUNIN, Stephen
Oblon Spivak McClelland Maier & Neustadt LLP, Alexandria
703 412 6011
skunin@oblon.com
*Featured in Intellectual Property (Northern Virginia)*
**Personal:** As the former Deputy Commissioner for Patent Examination Policy, Kunin has more than three decades of experience within the USPTO and is knowledgeable in all aspects of patent policy, practice and procedure, including USPTO patent post-grant proceedings. He participated in the establishment of patent policy, including changes in patent examination guidelines, revision of the rules of practice and procedure, establishment of examining priorities, classi-

fication of technological arts, and the reexamination and reissue rules and procedures. He is highly skilled in the strategic and tactical use of post-grant proceedings to help clients avoid the high cost of patent litigation.

### LALIK, Elizabeth A
Littler Mendelson, PC, McLean
703 442 8425
elalik@littler.com
*Featured in Labor & Employment (Virginia)*
**Practice Areas:** Business restructuring; complex litigation and jury trials; competition and trade secret law; discrimination and harassment; and international employment law.
**Professional Memberships:** Member, Virginia and District of Columbia Bars; Member, Hispanic Bar Association of Washington, DC.
**Career:** Ms Lalik focuses her practice exclusively on employment and labor law. She has tried several significant cases before federal and state court juries, obtaining wins by both judge and jury verdict.
**Publications:** FMLA Chapter, Employment Law in Virginia, Virginia CLE Publications, 2010.
**Personal:** JD, University of Virginia School of Law, 1993; BS, Cornell University, School of Industrial and Labor Relations, 1990.

### LARKIN, Kurt G
Hunton & Williams LLP, Richmond
804 788 8200
klarkin@hunton.com
*Featured in Labor & Employment (Virginia)*
**Practice Areas:** Mr Larkin's practice focuses on representing management in labor and employment matters. He has extensive experience advising companies facing union corporate campaign activities and developing litigation responses including civil RICO. His experience also includes employment litigation, trade secret and non-compete litigation, and advice and counseling on traditional labor subjects including representation elections, strikes and lockouts and labor arbitrations.
**Professional Memberships:** State Bars of Virginia and New Jersey; Virginia Bar Association.
**Career:** Army Judge Advocate; Special Assistant US Attorney: 2001-05.

### LAZAR, Dale S
DLA Piper LLP (US), Reston
703 773 4149
dale.lazar@dlapiper.com
*Featured in Intellectual Property (Northern Virginia)*
**Practice Areas:** Intellectual property; patent prosecution; patent litigation.
**Professional Memberships:** American Intellectual Property Law Association; International Association for the Protection of Industrial Property; Computer Law Association; Institute of Electrical and Electronics Engineers.
**Career:** He counsels on intellectual property matters concerning a variety of technologies, concentrating on patenting electronic technology, patenting and copyrighting computer hardware and software, litigating patents and copyrights, negotiating and drafting licenses for patents and software, and preparing software-related agree-

ments. He has also been involved in analyzing electronic and computer-related patents and copyright for infringement and validity.
**Personal:** JD, Cornell Law School; BS, Cornell University (with distinction).

### LEE, Tara
DLA Piper LLP (US), Reston
703 773 4150
tara.lee@dlapiper.com
*Featured in Litigation (Virginia)*
**Practice Areas:** Litigation.
**Career:** She is managing partner of the Northern Virginia office and global co-chair of the Cross Border Litigation practice. She focuses on commercial litigation, employment litigation, white-collar and regulatory defense, international law, and government contracts litigation. She has represented clients in contract disputes, government investigations, commercial transactions, intellectual property, business torts, international dispute resolution, and employment law. She is experienced in defense industry issues and with government contractors, and has spoken and written extensively on battlefield contractors' oversight and liability and battlefield torts.
**Personal:** JD, University of San Diego; BS, United States Naval Academy.

### LEHRER, Jeffrey K
DLA Piper LLP (US), Reston
703 773 4182
jeff.lehrer@dlapiper.com
*Featured in Investment Funds (Nationwide),
Corporate/M&A (Northern Virginia)*
**Practice Areas:** Corporate/M&A, venture capital, life sciences, government contracts.
**Career:** He concentrates in representing clients in connection with corporate and securities transactions, including mergers and acquisitions, securities offerings, venture capital, joint ventures, and corporate finance. Clients include a wide range of early stage and later stage companies.
**Personal:** JD, University of Virginia; BA, Rutgers University (with honors).

### LIPSEY, Charles E
Finnegan, Henderson, Farabow, Garrett & Dunner LLP, Reston
571 203 2755
charles.lipsey@finnegan.com
*Featured in Intellectual Property (Northern Virginia), Life Sciences (Nationwide)*
See under Nationwide for profile.

### MARTINEZ DE ANDINO, J Michael
Hunton & Williams LLP, Richmond
804 788 7216
mmartinez@hunton.com
*Featured in Intellectual Property (Southern Virginia)*
**Practice Areas:** Acquisition and enforcement of intellectual property rights, including client counseling, development of anti-counterfeiting and brand protection programs, opinion writing, patent prosecution, due diligence investigations and audits, litigation assistance, joint venture, collaboration and licensing agreements.
**Professional Memberships:** Member of the Board of Directors, American Intellectual Property Law Assn, 2011-14; American Bar Assn,

1992-2013; President, Greater Richmond Intellectual Property Law Assn, 1999-2000; Chair, Professional Programs, American Intellectual Property Law Assn, 2008-10.
**Career:** Received AIPLA's 2011 Mentor of the Year Award. Listed in The Best Lawyers in America and Virginia's Legal Elite. Named one of the 'Leading Law Firm Rainmakers' by Diversity & The Bar, Nov-Dec 2009.
**Publications:** 1/08/2013 'Common Interest Privilege - A View from the Federal Circuits', AIPLA, LEXOLOGY; 2/02/2011 'Common Interest Doctrine in the Fourth Circuit', Virginia Lawyer, Vol. 59, No. 7; 11/01/07 'US Patent Office Delays Creating Limited and Late Protection', IP & Technology Law Journal; 12/01/05 'Privilege of IP Opinions Under the Common Interest Doctrine', Practical Lawyer; 08/01/04 'Conducting an Intellectual Property Due Diligence Investigation', IP & Technology Law Journal.
**Personal:** University of Kansas Law (JD), William & Mary (MBA), University of Virginia (BS).

### MCDERMOTT, Francis A
Hunton & Williams LLP, McLean
703 714 7422
fmcdermott@hunton.com
*Featured in Real Estate (Northern Virginia)*
**Practice Areas:** Mr McDermott's practice focuses on land use, zoning, planning and development; litigation relating to the regulation and use of real property; environmental issues, including water quality regulation; public infrastructure issues, including tax districts, access to public utilities; due diligence assessment of entitled and potential development rights; successful landmark litigation relating to (i) zoning; (ii) sewer, water, and development moratoria; (iii) vested rights; (iv) utility rates; (v) tax assessments; (vi) eminent domain. In fifteen mixed-use projects alone, Frank has obtained rezoning approvals for approximately 26,000 residential units and 27 million square feet of retail, office, hotel, theater, and industrial uses.

### MCDONALD, Douglas
Venable LLP, Tysons Corner
703 760 1639
dbmcdonald@Venable.com
*Featured in Real Estate (Northern Virginia)*
**Practice Areas:** Douglas McDonald focuses his practice on real estate and commercial finance, including workouts, special asset management programs, defaulted loan and REO dispositions, secured financings to government contractors and technology companies and complex CMBS consent matters; real estate transactions, including site acquisition and development and retail and office leasing; and business counseling, including acquisitions and dispositions. Mr McDonald has experience in virtually every aspect of complex real estate and other business transactions, and applies proactive strategies and negotiating skills to achieve creative solutions.
**Personal:** JD, Vanderbilt University School of Law, 1984; BA, College of William and Mary, 1981.

## MCGRANAHAN JR, John C
Hunton & Williams LLP, McLean
703 714 7464
jmcgranahan@hunton.com
*Featured in Real Estate (Northern Virginia)*
**Practice Areas:** John McGranahan's practice focuses on every facet of land use. He has extensive experience with planning and zoning approvals; due diligence and development issues in real estate transactions; infrastructure and utilities; land use litigation; eminent domain; and environmental regulations. Projects include mixed-use communities containing over 10 million square feet of office, hotel, retail and residential uses; a minor league baseball stadium; a hospital and medical campus; planned residential communities; various utility and industrial uses; and a tax district to fund extending Metrorail to Dulles Airport.
**Personal:** Harvard University (JD, 1990); William and Mary (BA, 1987).

## MENDELSOHN, Stuart
Holland & Knight LLP, Tysons Corner
703 720 8071
stuart.mendelsohn@hklaw.com
*Featured in Real Estate (Northern Virginia)*
**Practice Areas:** Partner in the firm's Real Estate Section, leading the Northern Virginia land use practice, he practices in the areas of real estate, land use, litigation, government affairs and corporate law. Clients include a broad range of corporations, non-profit organizations, and developers, especially representing clients in difficult land use cases throughout Northern Virginia. He served as an elected member of the Fairfax County Board of Supervisors in Virginia and also has served on numerous regional boards, authorities and commissions, the Tysons Land Use Task Force, the Tysons Partnership and as Chairman of the Fairfax County Chamber of Commerce.

## METZ, Todd R
Watt, Tieder, Hoffar & Fitzgerald, LLP, McLean
703 749 1000
tmetz@wthf.com
*Featured in Construction (Virginia)*
**Practice Areas:** Construction, government contracts, suretyship.
**Professional Memberships:** ABA; Virginia State Bar, Public Contract Section Vice-Chair; DC and New York Bar Associations.
**Career:** Todd's practice includes dispute resolution, and defense and prosecution of claims related to domestic and international construction contracts. Todd represents contractors and owners in preparation, analysis, and negotiation of complex construction claims; preparation and negotiation of contract documents; and litigation before a broad range of forums. His projects include embassies, tunnels, bridges, powerplants, and sports facilities.
**Publications:** Todd has authored numerous works and lectured on construction matters in the United States and abroad.

## MILLER, David
Pillsbury Winthrop Shaw Pittman LLP, McLean
703 770 7925
david.miller@pillsburylaw.com
*Featured in Real Estate (Northern Virginia)*
**Practice Areas:** Complex real estate and related transactions including portfolio sales, joint ventures, equity funds, financings, and leases, of office, hotel, retail, industrial, transportation, and other income-producing assets; public-private partnerships, privatizations, and cross-border investments.
**Professional Memberships:** ABA; American College of Real Estate Lawyers; NAIOP; Pension Real Estate Association; Urban Land Institute; National Federal Development Association.
**Career:** Admitted: District of Columbia; Virginia.
**Publications:** Wide variety of articles and speeches including US government leasing; privatization; legal opinions.
**Personal:** JD, University of Michigan Law School, 1979 (magna cum laude, Order of the Coif); BA, George Washington University, 1976 (with distinction, phi beta kappa).

## MILLIKEN, John
Venable LLP, Tysons Corner
703 760 1637
jgmilliken@Venable.com
*Featured in Real Estate (Northern Virginia)*
**Practice Areas:** John Milliken's practice focuses on transportation, land use and environmental issues associated with major infrastructure projects, including public private partnerships in several states and on local land use and zoning issues on major development projects in Northern Virginia.
**Career:** Served as Secretary of Transportation for the Commonwealth of Virginia, Chairman of the Board of the Washington Metropolitan Area Transit Authority, ten years on County Board of Arlington County, Virginia, ten years as Chairman of the Board of Commissioners of the Virginia Port Authority.
**Personal:** JD, University of Virginia School of Law, 1970; BA, Haverford College, 1967.

## MOORE, Justin
Hunton & Williams LLP, Richmond
804 788 8464
jmoore@hunton.com
*Featured in Corporate/M&A (Southern Virginia)*
**Practice Areas:** Jay Moore is the Head of the firm's Corporate Team. His practice focuses on mergers and acquisitions, corporate finance, corporate governance and private equity. He represents public and private companies in M&A transactions. His clients also include private equity funds and related portfolio companies. Corporate finance experience includes public and private equity and debt financings. Industry experience encompasses consumer products, software, coal, biotechnology, chemicals and manufacturing. He is listed in The Best Lawyers in America for corporate, mergers and acquisitions, leveraged buyouts, private equity and venture capital, Virginia

Business' 'Legal Elite' and Virginia Super Lawyers selected by Richmond magazine.

## MURPHY, Thomas P
Hunton & Williams LLP, McLean
703 714 7533
tpmurphy@hunton.com
*Featured in Labor & Employment (Virginia)*
**Practice Areas:** Mr Murphy's practice focuses on all areas of labor and employment law, with particular emphasis on the trial of discrimination cases. He is a frequent speaker on labor and employment topics, and the contributing author to three treatises in the labor and employment law field. He has been recognized in The Best Lawyers In America for over 15 years, The Legal Elite by Virginia Business magazine; Chambers USA: America's Leading Lawyers for Business, and Top 100 Washington, DC Super Lawyers by Law & Politics magazine.

## MUSTONE, David A
Hunton & Williams LLP, McLean
703 714 7509
dmustone@hunton.com
*Featured in Labor & Employment (Virginia)*
**Practice Areas:** US federal tax, ERISA and related labor law aspects of employee benefits law (including healthcare reform). Clients include for-profit employers (both publicly-traded and privately-held), as well as non-profit and governmental employers.
**Professional Memberships:** Chair, Employee Benefits Committee, Tax Section (ABA) - 2007-08; Member, IRS Advisory Committee on Tax Exempt and Governmental Entities (2012-present)
**Career:** Partner since 2000; Reed Smith (1990-2000); IRS Office of Chief Counsel (1986-90).
**Publications:** Member, Advisory Board, BNA Pension and Benefits Reporter.
**Personal:** GW Law School (JD, 1977; LLM - Taxation, 1989); University of Notre Dame (BA, 1974).

## MUTRYN, William J
Holland & Knight LLP, Tysons Corner
703 720 8600
william.mutryn@hklaw.com
*Featured in Corporate/M&A (Northern Virginia)*
**Career:** Mr Mutryn is co-leader of the firm's Mergers and Acquisitions Practice Group. His practice emphasizes M&A, corporate governance and equity finance. He served as Lead Counsel for approximately 50 middle market M&A transactions in both buy-side and sell-side engagements over the last five years. Mr Mutryn serves as M&A counsel or principal outside counsel to national businesses in fields including government IT services, healthcare, defense/aerospace, computer software, telecommunications, energy, manufacturing, consumer goods and staffing. In addition to his duties on the firm's Directors Committee, he also represents clients in joint ventures, complex agreements, and divestitures of subsidiaries or divisions.

## NAGLE, David
Jackson Lewis LLP, Richmond
804 648 4077
David.Nagle@jacksonlewis.com
*Featured in Labor & Employment (Virginia)*
**Practice Areas:** Labor and employment law on behalf of management, including workplace arbitration programs (Circuit City Stores v Adams, 532 U.S. 105 (2001)); appellate practice.
**Professional Memberships:** American Arbitration Association (Panel of Arbitrators—Employment); American, Virginia Bar Associations.
**Career:** Thirty years private practice, selected by peers for Best Lawyers in America (Labor & Employment, Appellate Practice), Virginia SuperLawyers, Virginia Business "Legal Elite."
**Publications:** Author of law review articles, weekly newspaper column and op-ed pieces; university lecturer and 300+ presentations.
**Personal:** Georgetown, LLM (Labor Law), 1983; University of Richmond, JD, 1981; William & Mary, AB, 1976.

## NEUSTADT, Arthur I
Oblon Spivak McClelland Maier & Neustadt LLP, Alexandria
703 413 3000
aneustadt@oblon.com
*Featured in Intellectual Property (Northern Virginia)*
**Practice Areas:** Actively involved in IP litigation in courts throughout the US. Successfully tried jury and bench cases in all areas of technology before the federal district courts and the ITC. Argued appeals before the Supreme Court, the Federal Circuit and regional circuit courts of appeal. Successfully argued the landmark Festo case before the Supreme Court and twice before the en banc Federal Circuit.
**Personal:** Selected by Legal Times as one of 15 top IP attorneys in the Washington, DC area (2003); by Chambers among the top IP attorneys in Virginia (2004-13); Best Lawyers in America (2007-13); Super Lawyers (2007-13).

## OSSI, Gregory J
Venable LLP, Tysons Corner
703 760 1957
gossi@Venable.com
*Featured in Labor & Employment (Virginia)*
**Practice Areas:** Focuses on all aspects of labor and employee benefits law. He has negotiated collective bargaining agreements and provided counseling on dealing with union organizing, unfair labor practice charges, employee benefits and labor issues arising in mergers, acquisitions and bankruptcy. He has broad experience with multi-employer pension, drug formulary and health vendor concerns. He has represented employers in labor and employee benefit matters before the NLRB, Department of Labor, Congress, federal courts and arbitrators.
**Personal:** JD, magna cum laude, Catholic University of America Columbus School of Law, 1997; MS, University of Virginia, 1991; BS, Washington and Lee University, 1990.

## PARKER, Steve
Arnold & Porter LLP, McLean
703 720 7006
Steve.Parker@aporter.com
*Featured in Intellectual Property (Northern Virginia), Life Sciences (Nationwide)*
**Practice Areas:** Steve Parker's practice focuses on transactions for pharmaceutical companies, biotechs, medical device companies, universities and other non-profits, including patent licensing, partnerships and joint ventures; R&D and other product development agreements; marketing, distribution, co-marketing and co-promotion agreements; manufacturing and supply agreements; database agreements; and clinical-trial agreements. He has extensive corporate experience, including mergers and acquisitions, investments, employment agreements and related matters, and in corporate governance matters.
**Career:** Represented pharmaceutical companies since the late 1980s, and started in biotech in 1992. He has worked on transactions throughout the US and in Canada, Europe, and Asia, including China, India, and Korea.

## RAPHAEL, Stuart A
Hunton & Williams LLP, McLean
703 714 7463
sraphael@hunton.com
*Featured in Litigation (Virginia)*
**Practice Areas:** Complex trial and appellate litigation, business torts, water rights.
**Professional Memberships:** Virginia Bar; DC Bar.
**Career:** Clients include Fortune 500 companies and governmental bodies. Served as Virginia's Counsel in Virginia v Maryland, 540 U.S. 56 (2003), successfully establishing Virginia's right to use the Potomac River.
**Publications:** Practical Considerations in Original Action Litigation, 12 Wyo. L. Rev. 15 (2012); Recent Developments in Civil Litigation, Virginia CLE (2006-12); Toxic Tort Litigation, Chapter 14, Special Cases: MTBE (2007).
**Personal:** University of Virginia (JD, 1989); Harvard University (BA, magna cum laude, 1986).

## REID, Carter B
Watt, Tieder, Hoffar & Fitzgerald, LLP, McLean
703 749 1000
creid@wthf.com
*Featured in Construction (Virginia)*
**Practice Areas:** Domestic and international construction, suretyship, government contracts.
**Professional Memberships:** American Bar Association, Virginia State Bar, New York State Bar, Georgia State Bar, District of Columbia Bar.
**Career:** Carter Reid focuses on private and public construction contracts, surety and environmental law matters. His practice involves preparation of claims, negotiations, mediations and litigation before dispute review boards, arbitration panels and state and federal courts. He represents contractors, sureties, owners, designers, subcontractors, and suppliers in contract negotiations, claims, claims defense, dispute resolution and litigation.

**Publications:** Carter has authored numerous works and regularly speaks on construction and claims issues worldwide.

## ROBERTSON, Gregory
Hunton & Williams LLP, Richmond
804 788 8200
grobertson@hunton.com
*Featured in Labor & Employment (Virginia)*
**Practice Areas:** Greg Robertson is Head of Hunton & Williams' Labor and Employment Law Practice. His practice focuses on all aspects of labor and employment law including strategic labor relations planning, contract and deal negotiations, corporate campaigns and related RICO litigation, employment advice and litigation, with expertise in the manufacturing, food distribution and service, meatpacking, healthcare, hospitality and gaming industries, and natural resource industries. He is counsel to the Virginia Chamber of Commerce and the Richmond Symphony. Robertson's expertise in labor and employment law has been repeatedly recognized in Chambers and Partners, Best Lawyers in America, Who's Who, Ten Best Labor and Employment Lawyers in Virginia by Virginia Business Magazine, and Virginia Super Lawyers.

## ROBINSON, Michael W
Venable LLP, Tysons Corner
703 760 1988
mwrobinson@Venable.com
*Featured in Litigation (Virginia)*
**Practice Areas:** Commercial/business litigation, trade secret and IP litigation, legal malpractice defense.
**Professional Memberships:** American Bar Association, Fairfax Bar Association.
**Career:** With 25 years of experience, Mr Robinson is an AV Preeminent© rated attorney whose practice focuses on business disputes, business torts, legal malpractice defense, and the protection of intellectual property rights. His practice emphasizes litigation in the federal and state courts in Northern Virginia. He serves on the VSB Council and the VSB Standing Committee on Legal Ethics.
**Personal:** JD, with honors, George Mason University School of Law; BA, Philosophy, George Mason University.

## ROSATI, Michelle A
Holland & Knight LLP, Tysons Corner
703 720 8079
michelle.rosati@hklaw.com
*Featured in Real Estate (Northern Virginia)*
**Practice Areas:** Partner in the firm's Real Estate Section, her practice is focused on land use and real estate development entitlements and related litigation. She has successfully represented applicants in a wide variety of complex land use applications and appeals in jurisdictions throughout Northern Virginia. Michelle has helped clients secure approvals for myriad residential developments, commercial and multi-use developments, and has a rich and varied experience in obtaining high-impact use approvals. She has obtained zoning approvals for her clients in some of the most sensitive areas in suburban and exurban Northern

Virginia, bringing communities, elected officials and landowners to consensus.

## RUDLIN, D Alan
Hunton & Williams LLP, Richmond
804 788 8459
arudlin@hunton.com
*Featured in Litigation (Virginia)*
**Practice Areas:** Alan Rudlin's practice focuses on alternative dispute resolution, including mediation, arbitration, and independent settlement counsel, as well as class actions, mass torts, toxic litigation, and fiduciary trust litigation. Specialty includes national coordinating counsel and management of complex litigation.

## SCHMELTER, Joseph C
Venable LLP, Tysons Corner
703 760 1920
jcschmelter@Venable.com
*Featured in Corporate/M&A (Northern Virginia)*
**Practice Areas:** Practice focuses on mergers and acquisitions and general corporate representation.
**Career:** Partner-in-charge of Venable's Tysons Corner office.
**Publications:** authored "How Best to Incentivize Your Employees to Ensure a Successful Sale Transaction" and "Earnouts: Do They Really Work?" published by the Washington Business Journal and the National Capital Chapter of the Association for Corporate Growth. Spoke on "The dynamics of M&A transactions for technology companies serving the government and public sector industry" as part of the Chesapeake Innovation Center's Business to Government CEO Roundtable Series.
**Personal:** JD, Georgetown University Law Center, 1987; BA, high distinction, University of Virginia, 1984.

## SGARLATA, Mark A
Watt, Tieder, Hoffar & Fitzgerald, LLP, McLean
703 749 1000
msgarlat@wthf.com
*Featured in Construction (Virginia)*
**Practice Areas:** Construction, suretyship, government contracts, international construction.
**Professional Memberships:** American Bar Association, Virginia State Bar Association, CMAA, HCAA.
**Career:** Mark represents clients in contract drafting and negotiations, dispute resolution and litigation on a wide range of heavy industrial and commercial construction projects. His projects include tunnels, cable-stayed bridges, mass transit, process, and heavy civil buildings. Mark has extensive claims negotiation and litigation experience on behalf of contractors, owners and sureties. He lectures nationally.
**Publications:** Mark has authored numerous articles on construction topics and has spoken throughout the United States on the subject.

## SHEBELSKIE, Michael
Hunton & Williams LLP, Richmond
804 788 8716
mshebelskie@hunton.com
*Featured in Litigation (Virginia)*

**Practice Areas:** Mr Shebelskie's litigation practice focuses on complex commercial disputes and appellate proceedings, with particular focus on environmental, energy, intellectual property rights, and business disputes, as well as federal statutory, administrative and constitutional law issues. With nearly 30 years' experience, he has successfully tried scores of cases and handled numerous appeals in federal and state courts in a wide array of subject matters.

## SIRILLA, George M
Pillsbury Winthrop Shaw Pittman LLP, McLean
703 770 7784
george.sirilla@pillsburylaw.com
*Featured in Intellectual Property (Northern Virginia)*
**Practice Areas:** Mr Sirilla has led teams that successfully upheld as well as invalidated patents in numerous cases, both in the federal courts and before the US International Trade Commission. He has considerable experience in technology licensing, patents and trade secrets.
**Professional Memberships:** Bar Association of the District of Columbia, American Bar Association, American Intellectual Property Law Association, Fellow of the American College of Trial Lawyers.
**Personal:** JD, Georgetown University Law Center; BS, Rensselaer Polytechnic Institute (Mechanical Engineering, Tau Beta Pi and Pi Tau Sigma national engineering honor societies).

## SLATER JR, Thomas G
Hunton & Williams LLP, Richmond
804 788 8475
tslater@hunton.com
*Featured in Litigation (Virginia)*
**Practice Areas:** Mr Slater's practice focuses on complex litigation matters with emphasis on antitrust, intellectual property, trade secrets, unfair trade practices, product liability and white collar criminal defense. He has handled over 70 jury trials in courts throughout the US. Mr Slater has handled dozens of civil antitrust cases, many of which were national in scope, including numerous antitrust class action cases that were consolidated by the Judicial Panel on Multidistrict Litigation. He has also handled criminal and civil actions brought by the US Justice Department. In 2005, he was co-lead Counsel in a mock jury trial program sponsored by the American Bar Association Antitrust Section.
**Professional Memberships:** Fellow, American College of Trial Attorneys; Fellow, American Bar Foundation; Fellow, Virginia Law Foundation; Member, Fourth Circuit Judicial Conference; Listed in 'Best Lawyers in America' for over 10 years, antitrust and corporate litigation. He has been listed on numerous occasions in Who's Who in American Law and Who's Who in America, and as a "trial ace" on Lawdragon's Top 500 Leading Litigators list.
**Career:** Mr Slater has been active in Bar and community activities. He is a past President of the Richmond Bar Association and a Former Member of the Virginia State Bar Executive Committee. He currently serves as Member, Central Virginia Legal

Aid Society Board of Directors, Chairman of Board of Trustees of the Virginia Historical Society, and Director, the Virginia 4-H Foundation Board.

### SMITH, Brooks
Hunton & Williams LLP, Richmond
804 787 8086
bsmith@hunton.com
*Featured in Environment (Virginia)*
**Practice Areas:** Brooks Smith co-chairs the firm's environmental practice. He focuses on civil and administrative proceedings and appeals arising out of the Clean Water Act. Brooks also counsels clients on a wide range of regulatory compliance issues in the context of voluntary environmental audits, environmental management systems, permitting, enforcement, transactions and litigation.

### SMITH, David S
Venable LLP, Tysons Corner
703 760 1600
dssmith@Venable.com
*Featured in Labor & Employment (Virginia)*
**Practice Areas:** David Smith's practice emphasizes labor cost savings for clients through strategic planning, collective bargaining, healthcare cost control, lobbying, effective liability allocation related to mergers and acquisitions, restructurings, labor aspects of bankruptcies and other circumstances where labor issues are significant. Additionally, he represents clients before the National Labor Relations Board (NLRB).
**Professional Memberships:** American Bar Association, bar admissions include Virginia, District of Columbia, Tennessee, Court of Appeals for the District of Columbia and the Supreme Court of the United States
**Personal:** JD, University of Tennessee College of Law, 1970; BA, University of Tennessee, 1967.

### STILLMAN, Gregory
Hunton & Williams LLP, Norfolk
757 640 5314
gstillman@hunton.com
*Featured in Intellectual Property (Southern Virginia), Litigation (Virginia)*
**Practice Areas:** Greg Stillman's practice focuses on federal trial and appellate litigation, with emphasis on business torts, intellectual property (copyright and patent), securities and corporate governance. Mr Stillman chairs the firm's Intellectual Property Practice Group.
**Professional Memberships:** Fellow, American College of Trial Lawyers.

### SWARTZ, Matthew B.
Pillsbury Winthrop Shaw Pittman LLP, McLean
703 770 7513
matthew.swartz@pillsburylaw.com
*Featured in Corporate/M&A (Northern Virginia)*
**Practice Areas:** Mr Swartz primarily represents middle market and technology companies, investors in these companies, and the investment banks that serve them. He focuses on mergers and acquisitions, private equity and venture capital investments, public and private securities offerings, and corporate governance. He is a counselor

to closely-held companies in a variety of industries.
**Career:** Admitted: State of California; Commonwealth of Virginia.
**Personal:** JD, University of California, Hastings College of the Law, 1995; BA, University of California, Berkeley, 1990.

### TAPSCOTT, Andrew
Hunton & Williams LLP, Richmond
804 788 8620
atapscott@hunton.com
*Featured in Real Estate (Southern Virginia)*
**Practice Areas:** Andy Tapscott's practice focuses on commercial real estate transactions, including sophisticated finance, development, acquisitions, dispositions, joint ventures, leasing, loan workouts and foreclosures. Mr Tapscott's practice has a special emphasis on the hospitality, REIT, retail and multifamily industries, as well as historic rehabiliation tax credit projects and distressed real estate assets.

### TATA, Robert M
Hunton & Williams LLP, Norfolk
757 640 5328
btata@hunton.com
*Featured in Litigation (Virginia)*
**Practice Areas:** Bob Tata's practice includes complex commercial litigation, intellectual property (copyright, trademark, trade dress, trade secret and patent) litigation, pharmaceutical and other products liability defense, construction and government contracts, government investigations, and other high stakes litigation. Bob's focus is on results. Bob at one time held the record for the largest jury verdict in the history of Virginia. He has won and recovered seven and eight figure awards for his IP and commercial clients and defeated numerous multi-million dollar claims. Bob has taught, spoken and been quoted extensively on IP and other commercial litigation topics.

### THOMPSON, Gary
Hunton & Williams LLP, Richmond
804 788 8787
gthompson@hunton.com
*Featured in Corporate/M&A (Southern Virginia)*
**Practice Areas:** Gary Thompson has over 25 years experience advising public companies in connection with mergers and acquisitions, including consensual and unsolicited transactions, corporate governance issues, public and private securities offerings, and a wide range of corporate finance activities. His representative clients include defense, energy, and consumer products companies. He is Co-Head of the firm's Corporate Finance and Mergers and Acquisitions Practice Group. He was named the 2012 M&A Lawyer of the Year – Americas Middle Markets by the Global M&A Network, and led deal teams that were awarded M&A Atlas Awards in 2011 and 2012.

### TIEDER, John B
Watt, Tieder, Hoffar & Fitzgerald, LLP, McLean
703 749 1000
jtieder@wthf.com
*Featured in Construction (Virginia)*

**Practice Areas:** Construction, government contracts, international construction and arbitration.
**Professional Memberships:** American College of Construction Lawyers, District of Columbia, New York and Virginia Bar Associations, ABA, IBA, IPBA.
**Career:** Jack's practice involves major construction matters with a particular emphasis on international projects. He represents foreign governments, utilities, energy companies and US and international contractors and major equipment manufacturers in all phases of construction. He is recognized for his exceptional negotiating and litigation skills.
**Publications:** Jack has authored numerous publications relating to international and domestic construction, arbitration and litigation and speaks on these matters both within the US and abroad.

### TOWER, King
Spilman Thomas & Battle PLLC, Roanoke
540 512 1830
ktower@spilmanlaw.com
*Featured in Labor & Employment (Virginia)*
**Practice Areas:** Labor and employment law and litigation.
**Professional Memberships:** American Bar Association, Labor and Employment Section; Virginia Bar Association, Employment and Labor Relations; Virginia State Bar, Litigation Section; Roanoke Valley Society for Human Resources Management, Legislative Affairs Chair; Roanoke Public Library, Advisory Board Member; Western Virginia Workforce Development Board, Board Member; Virginia Bar Association's Young Lawyers Division, Former Chair.
**Personal:** University of Virginia; BA, 1990; College of William & Mary, JD, 1995.

### VARELA, Paul A
Watt, Tieder, Hoffar & Fitzgerald, LLP, McLean
703 749 1000
pvarela@wthf.com
*Featured in Construction (Virginia)*
**Practice Areas:** Domestic and international construction, suretyship, government contracts.
**Career:** Paul counsels clients in contract planning, administration and dispute resolution matters nationwide in the engineering and construction industry. His broad range of legal experience includes transportation and infrastructure, power, energy and chemical, stadiums, pharmaceutical, and all types of general building design and construction. Paul has extensive claims negotiation and prosecution experience with private, state and federal government entities.
**Publications:** Co-Author: Chapter 9 - "Pricing of Construction Claims" for the American Bar Association's book "CONSTRUCTION ACCOUNTING - A Guide for Attorneys and Other Professionals."

### VAUGHAN III, C Porter
Hunton & Williams LLP, Richmond
804 788 8285
pvaughan@hunton.com
*Featured in Corporate/M&A (Southern Virginia)*

**Practice Areas:** Mr Vaughan's practice focuses on representing public companies in mergers and acquisitions, corporate financings, corporate governance and securities regulation. He regularly represents Fortune 500 and EU-headquartered manufacturing and distribution companies in M&A transactions, spin-offs and issuer tender offers, and a Fortune 500 medical/surgical distributor in its acquisitions and dispositions and public market financings. He also advises public clients on SEC compliance, corporate governance, restructurings, shareholder activism and and various takeover protective measures. Former Co-Head of firm's Business Practice Group.

### WALSH, William
Hunton & Williams LLP, Richmond
804 788 8378
wwalsh@hunton.com
*Featured in Real Estate (Southern Virginia)*
**Practice Areas:** Bill Walsh's practice focuses on commercial leasing, strategic planning for commercial real estate assets, real estate investments (including non-performing loans) and urban redevelopment. He represents a variety of clients from Fortune 500 companies to organizations and indigent individuals on a pro bono basis. He represents his firm on its leasing matters for its US and international offices. Bill was named Best Real Estate and Construction Lawyer in Virginia by Virginia Business magazine in its inaugural "Legal Elite" edition. He is a member of the American College of Real Estate Lawyers and the head of his firm's Commercial Real Estate Practice Group.

### WALTERS, Todd
Buchanan Ingersoll & Rooney PC, Alexandria
703 838 6556
todd.walters@bipc.com
*Featured in Intellectual Property (Northern Virginia)*
**Career:** Todd is Co-Chair of the firm's Intellectual Property Section, and he previously served as a member of the firm's Executive Management team. His practice has special emphasis on inter partes matters, and he has represented clients in over 100 inter partes matters before the USPTO and in federal courts. Todd has worked on all types of ex parte and inter partes matters in the biotechnology, chemical, electrical, mechanical and pharmaceutical fields. He has aided clients in settlement of proceedings and prevailed on patentability and priority issues. He earned his JD from The George Washington University Law School.

### WARNER, David
Venable LLP, Tysons Corner
703 760 1652
drwarner@Venable.com
*Featured in Labor & Employment (Virginia)*
**Practice Areas:** Labor and employment, commercial litigation.
**Professional Memberships:** ABA, bar associations of Virginia, DC & Maryland.
**Career:** Represents clients in complex labor, employment and commercial disputes with a particular emphasis on the government contractor and non-profit industries. Has significant first-chair experience litigating restrictive covenant,

trade secret, business conspiracy and procurement integrity matters, as well as class and collective actions in the employment context. Routinely advises employers in strategies for minimizing litigation risk through proactive and compliant employment practices.
**Personal:** JD, cum laude, Georgetown University Law Center, 1996; BA, cum laude, Georgetown University, 1993.

### WECHSELBLATT, Eric
Holland & Knight LLP, Tysons Corner
703 720 8600
eric.wechselblatt@hklaw.com
*Featured in Corporate/M&A (Northern Virginia)*
**Career:** Mr Wechselblatt is a Partner in the Business Section, who represents clients in a variety of corporate and securities activities with an emphasis on mergers and acquisitions, venture capital transactions and other private placements, and general corporate matters. He has extensive experience in leading deal teams in complex merger and acquisition transactions, including mergers, asset deals, stock deals, leveraged buyouts, spin-offs, joint ventures and similar transactions. His clients include numerous leading private equity and venture capital funds as well as companies engaged in multiple industry sectors including government contracting, software, social media, telecommunications, financial services, and life sciences.

### WELLFORD JR, Hill B
Hunton & Williams LLP, Richmond
804 788 8518
hwellford@hunton.com
*Featured in Labor & Employment (Virginia)*
**Practice Areas:** Hill Wellford's practice focuses on equal opportunity law, labor relations, labor arbitrations, collective bargaining, executive employment agreements, covenants not to complete/trade secrets, wage-hour law, occupational safety and health law, and litigation of employment claims, including class actions, under federal and state labor and employment statutes. He has been recognized in Best Lawyers in America for labor and employment law; Virginia's Legal Elite; and Virginia Super Lawyers.
**Professional Memberships:** American Bar, Virginia Bar, Virginia State Bar, Fourth Circuit Judicial Conference, Fellow of the Virginia Law Foundation.

### WESTERMEIER, J "Jay" T
Finnegan, Henderson, Farabow, Garrett & Dunner LLP, Reston
571 203 2480
jay.westermeier@finnegan.com
*Featured in Intellectual Property (Northern Virginia)*
**Practice Areas:** Represents clients in the information technology industry on copyright, trade secrets, licensing, and patent litigation issues. He has experience with drafting, negotiating, and all forms of dispute resolutions arising from agree-

ments, licenses, and transactions. His work has involved a range of technical subjects, including computer software, software development, automated databases, complex systems, distribution, the Internet, and e-commerce.
**Personal:** US Military Academy, West Point (BS, 1963); George Washington University (MBA, 1969); American University, Washington College of Law (JD, 1974); George Washington University (LLM, Antitrust and Government Procurement, 1978).

### WESTMAN, Daniel P
Morrison & Foerster LLP, McLean
703 760 7795
dwestman@mofo.com
*Featured in Labor & Employment (Virginia)*
**Practice Areas:** Mr Westman's practice focuses on employment, employee mobility, trade secret, non-competition, Computer Fraud and Abuse Act, whistleblower, and retaliatory discharge litigation.
**Professional Memberships:** Former management co-chair, Sarbanes-Oxley subcommittee of the Fair Labor Standards Legislation Committee, ABA's Labor and Employment Law Section; former chair, Trade Secrets Committee, American Intellectual Property Lawyers Association.
**Career:** Managing partner, NoVA office.
**Publications:** Whistleblowing: The Law of Retaliatory Discharge, Second Edition (BNA

Books 2004/2012 Supp.). Senior editor, Trade Secrets (Law Journal Press 2013).
**Personal:** Stanford University, AB; University of Chicago Law School, JD; Law clerk, Hon. Barbara Crabb (WD Wis, 1981-82).

### YANOWITCH, Lawrence T
Morrison & Foerster LLP, McLean
703 760 7318
lyanowitch@mofo.com
*Featured in Corporate/M&A (Northern Virginia)*
**Practice Areas:** Concentrates on mergers and acquisitions, corporate finance, SEC compliance and corporate counseling. Successfully completed hundreds of M&A transactions. Has expertise with registered public offerings (debt and equity), PIPEs, private equity sponsored transactions and corporate restructurings. Represents emerging companies (private and public), investment banks, special committees and institutional investors.
**Career:** Co-Chair, Global Mergers and Acquisitions Practice. Named a leader in Mergers & Acquisitions Law, The Best Lawyers in America (2011); and "Top Corporate Mergers & Acquisitions Lawyer", Washington Business Journal (2006 and 2007). Founder of M&A University, an interdisciplinary training program for companies using M&A as a growth strategy.

# HIRSCHLER FLEISCHER

www.hf-law.com **tel:** 804 771 9500 **fax:** 804 644 0957

**President:** James L Weinberg
**Chairman:** James W Theobald
Number of lawyers: 69

**OFFICES**

VIRGINIA

**RICHMOND:** The Edgeworth Building, 2100 East Cary Street, VA 23223
Tel: 804 771 9500   Fax: 804 644 0957

**FREDERICKSBURG:** Mill Race North Building, 725 Jackson Street; Suite 200, VA 22401
Tel: 540 604 2100   Fax: 540 604 2101

## Firm Overview:

Hirschler Fleischer is a full-service firm engaged in a diverse and sophisticated legal practice. Founded in 1946 by Edward S Hirschler and Alan G Fleischer, the firm serves clients throughout the US from its headquarters in Richmond, Virginia and offices in Fredericksburg, Virginia. Hirschler Fleischer approaches work with the entrepreneurial spirit established by its founders. The firm embraces a passion for the practice of law that engenders a commitment from its attorneys and staff to provide creative and practical solutions for clients and the community.

## Main Areas of Practice:

**Business:**
Experienced in structuring solutions for all types of business entities, the firm organizes corporations, prepares partnership and shareholder agreements and handles the purchase and sale of businesses. It also handles all forms of capital formation, securities offerings, corporate financing, reorganizations and workouts. Other services include tax counseling, trust and estate planning, wills, employee benefits, health law, bankruptcy, securities law, financial institution regulation, patents, copyrights and trademarks. Hirschler Fleischer is particularly adept at counseling middle market clients. Clients, large and small, new and established, are attracted to the firm by its ability to tailor legal services to meet their needs and to consult with them on important business and financial decisions.

**Real Estate:**
The firm has a pre-eminent reputation in the commercial real estate community resulting from its involvement in the area's most significant real estate developments, transactions and financings. The firm's active involvement in negotiations at all stages of development include: zoning, land use, environmental, leasing, acquisition, construction, contracting and financing. The firm structures and implements tax deferred exchanges, joint ventures, investment partnerships and other innovative approaches to real estate. This experience has helped clients develop many of the premier office parks, shopping centers, residential subdivisions, apartment complexes, downtown office buildings, condominium projects, planned unit developments and mixed-use developments throughout the region. Practice areas include the acquisition and development of mixed use projects, commercial leasing, commercial real estate financing, representation of lenders, representation of REITs, the sale and purchase of loan and servicing pools, securities and the structuring of tax credits.

**Litigation:**
Through the combined skills of advocacy, counseling and judgment, the firm's attorneys are dedicated to achieving the best outcome for clients in challenging circumstances. Hirschler Fleischer combines aggressive promotion of clients' positions with a realistic assessment of success in court. The firm's aim is to achieve the best results for the firm's clients, competently and promptly. The firm's litigators are widely recognized for their work in federal and state courts, at the trial and appellate levels and before federal and state administrative agencies. The firm routinely handles commercial, construction, probate, shareholder, partnership and labor and employment disputes, as well as highly specialized litigation pertaining to zoning and land use, bankruptcy, employment law, immigration, antitrust, securities and constitutional matters. The firm's Catastrophic Injury Practice Group represents plaintiffs in cases involving complex, high-value medical malpractice, product liability and other personal injury.

## Clients:

VerizonWireless; Gumenick Properties; Holladay Properties; Bertram Capital; ChemTreat, Inc.; HHHunt; Bon Secours Health System; Highwood Properties; Silver Companies; Colonial Webb, Hilldrup Moving & Storage, Baskervill.

# HUNTON & WILLIAMS LLP

www.hunton.com  **tel:** 212 309 1000  **fax:** 212 309 1100

**Managing Partner:** Walfrido J Martinez
**Chairman, Executive Committee:** F William Brownell
Number of partners worldwide: 346  Number of other lawyers worldwide: 434

**Firm Overview:**
Founded in 1901, Hunton & Williams LLP is a US law firm with a significant international presence. Hunton & Williams has grown to more than 800 lawyers who work in 19 offices serving clients in over 100 countries in more than 100 separate practice areas.

**Main Areas of Practice:**

**Bankruptcy, Restructuring & Creditors' Rights:**
Hunton & Williams regularly handles significant debtor, trustee, committee, secured creditor and bond holder representations for national clients in bankruptcy and federal courts across the United States. Clients include corporations, partnerships, financial institutions, consulting firms, hedge funds and private equity firms.

**Competition:**
Hunton & Williams' antitrust and competition practice offers the full range of competition law advice. Lawyers come from both of the US antitrust enforcement agencies and include a former Deputy Director of the US Federal Trade Commission's Bureau of Competition, a Deputy Assistant Attorney General and Chief of Staff of the US Department of Justice Antitrust Division, as well as two former senior FTC litigators. The group represents domestic and international companies in competition litigation, merger review, IP matters, consumer protection and privacy, and criminal antitrust defense and related price-fixing litigation.

**Corporate:**
Hunton & Williams' capital markets practice includes public and private offerings of equity and debt, structured financings and securitization transactions. The firm's clients include corporate and governmental issuers, underwriters, financial institutions, REITs, insurers, specialty finance companies and other capital market participants. The firm's mergers and acquisitions practice includes representation of domestic and international clients in contested and negotiated acquisitions, tender offers, proxy fights, takeover defenses, leveraged buyouts, spin-offs, holding company formations, corporate auctions, mergers of equals, going private transactions, and strategic acquisition and divestiture programs.

**Energy:**
Hunton & Williams has represented clients involved in the development of power and infrastructure projects throughout the world for decades. Clients comprise private equity funds and financial institutions, independent power producers, trading companies, ISOs, RTOs, as well as domestic and foreign government agencies. As designated counsel to underwriters for many prominent domestic utilities, the firm represents, most of the major investment banking firms involved in the power sector. In addition, the firm regularly provides counsel to financial institutions in connection with renewable energy tax-equity investments.

**Environmental:**
The firm's environmental practice is among the largest in the nation. Its lawyers have helped clients navigate every major federal environmental statute, and those of most states and many international jurisdictions. The team advises a range of industries on innovative responses to environmental compliance, represents companies in litigation and administrative permitting and regulatory proceedings, and ensures that clients have a voice in shaping policy. The lawyers are active on emerging environmental issues, including climate change and Europe's regulatory program for chemicals. On climate change, firm lawyers address the full range of policy, regulatory and litigation issues, including emissions trading under the Kyoto protocol, defense of public nuisance actions, and legislative and administrative policy developments.

**Labor & Employment:**
Hunton & Williams' nationally recognized labor and employment team has extensive experience in defending class, collective, and mass actions, including multiple first impression cases, and its lawyers are some of the very few in the country who have tried complex representative proof cases to verdict. The team has experience in traditional labor and union corporate campaigns, public accessibility litigation, national and regional docket management, non-competition and trade secrets lawsuits, pay and promotion discrimination matters and Sarbanes-Oxley investigations. It also has extensive trial experience with high-profile governmental agency cases, including defending pattern and practice cases against the Department of Justice, EEOC and multiple state agencies.

**Litigation:**
The firm's litigation practice is recognized as one of the major litigation groups in the country. The practice encompasses virtually every area of law, including antitrust, appellate, bankruptcy, business crimes defense, complex business litigation, corporate governance / mergers and acquisitions, data intrusion, e-discovery, environment and energy litigation, intellectual property and patent litigation, international arbitration, product liability, restructuring and creditors' rights, securities litigation and toxic tort.

**International Work:**
Hunton & Williams has offices in London, Brussels, Bangkok, Tokyo and Beijing. Clients include leading US and foreign corporations, governments and governmental entities, financial institutions, commercial and investment banks, multilateral and bilateral lending and guarantee agencies.

## OFFICES

**CALIFORNIA**
**LOS ANGELES:** 550 South Hope Street, Suite 2000, CA 90071
Tel: 213 532 2000  Fax: 213 532 2020

**SAN FRANCISCO:** 575 Market Street, Suite 3700, CA 94105
Tel: 415 975 3700  Fax: 415 975 3701

**DISTRICT OF COLUMBIA**
**WASHINGTON, DC:** 2200 Pennsylvania Avenue, NW, DC 20037
Tel: 202 955 1500  Fax: 202 778 2201

**FLORIDA**
**MIAMI:** 1111 Brickell Avenue, Suite 2500, FL 33131
Tel: 305 810 2500  Fax: 305 810 2460

**GEORGIA**
**ATLANTA:** Bank of America Plaza, Suite 4100, 600 Peachtree Street, NE, GA 30308
Tel: 404 888 4000  Fax:404 888 4190

**NEW YORK**
**NEW YORK:** 200 Park Avenue, NY 10166
Tel: 212 309 1000  Fax: 212 309 1100

**NORTH CAROLINA**
**CHARLOTTE:** Bank of America Plaza, Suite 3500, 101 South Tryon Street, NC 28280
Tel: 704 378 4700  Fax:704 378 4890

**RALEIGH:** One Bank of America Plaza, Suite 1400, 421 Fayetteville Street, NC 27601
Tel: 919 899 3000  Fax:919 833 6352

**TEXAS**
**AUSTIN:** 111 Congress Avenue, Suite 510, TX 78701
Tel: 512 542 5000  Fax: 512 542 5049

**DALLAS:** 1445 Ross Avenue, Suite 3700, TX 75202
Tel: 214 979 3000  Fax:214 880 0011

**HOUSTON:** Bank of America Center, Suite 4200, 700 Louisiana Street, Texas 77002
Tel: 713 229 5700  Fax: 713 229 5750

**VIRGINIA**
**MCLEAN:** 1751 Pinnacle Drive, Suite 1700, VA 22102
Tel: 703 714 7400  Fax: 703 714 7410

**NORFOLK:** 500 East Main Street, Suite 1000, VA 23510
Tel: 757 640 5300  Fax: 757 625 7720

**RICHMOND:** Riverfront Plaza, East Tower, 951 East Byrd Street, VA 23219
Tel: 804 788 8200  Fax: 804 788 8218

# ISLER DARE, P.C.

www.islerdare.com  **tel:** 703 748 2690  **fax:** 703 748 2695

**Managing Partners:** Edward Lee Isler & Steven W Ray
**Partners:** R Mark Dare, Michelle B Radcliffe, Theresa M Connolly, Andrea I O'Brien, Wayne A Schrader,
Lori H Turner, Mark E Papadopoulos
Number of other lawyers: 5

## Firm Overview:

Isler Dare Ray Radcliffe & Connolly, P.C. is Northern Virginia's premier management-side labor, employment and employee benefits law firm. The firm was formed in 1997 when Steven Ray and Edward (Eddie) Isler, having been associated previously with large national law firms (Epstein Becker and Gibson Dunn, respectively), concluded that they could better serve their management clients by opening their own practice. With the addition of other large firm attorneys, Mark Dare (Reed Smith), Theresa Connolly (DLA Piper), Michelle Radcliffe (Gibson Dunn), Andrea O'Brien (Venable), Wayne Schrader (Gibson Dunn) and Mark Papadopoulos (Gibson Dunn), the practice has grown to 14 full time attorneys, all engaged in the representation of management in labor, employment and employee benefits matters.
Isler Dare prides itself on the individual attention and responsiveness that its attorneys provide to each of the firm's clients. Clients range in size from large companies with more than 10,000 employees to small employers with fewer than 20 employees, and span widespread industries such as government contractors, national homebuilders, technology and software developers, rental car agencies, private schools, medical and veterinary practices, financial institutions, printing companies and restaurants.

## Main Areas of Practice:

### Sound Counsel & Legal Advice:

Isler Dare focuses on partnering with clients to anticipate issues and to develop sound and practical solutions in the increasingly complex realm of employment and employee benefits law. The firm provides counsel to employers in the following areas: dealing with difficult or non-performing employees; responding to claims of discrimination, harassment, or retaliation; offering counsel on labor-management relationships; advising on terminations; navigating laws covering employee illnesses, disabilities, and absences, including the FMLA, ADA and workers comp; ensuring compliance with wage and hour issues (FLSA and SCA); and designing and implementing a wide range of employee benefits, including retirement plans, health and welfare plans and executive compensation arrangements.

### Employment Litigation:

When, despite counseling, employment or employee benefits litigation ensues, Isler Dare attorneys serve as experienced litigators in defending employers against the often meritless claims that are asserted. The firm aggressively defends its clients in all of the employment and benefits areas in which they provide advice and counsel.

### Business Tort & Non-Compete Litigation:

The firm specializes in business tort and related litigation involving employee duty of loyalty, trade secrets and non-competition or non-solicitation agreements. The attorneys of the firm have been involved in dozens of injunction hearings often associated with such litigation.

### Collective Bargaining:

The firm's partners are experienced labor attorneys who effectively support employers in counsel and litigation related to: unfair labor practice charges; negotiation of CBAs; grievance and arbitration; and the National Labor Relations Act (NLRA), including union organizing issues and union avoidance strategy.

### Employee Benefits:

Isler Dare assists private and public employers with employee benefits issues by designing and implementing a wide range of qualified and non-qualified retirement arrangements, health and welfare plans and executive compensation arrangements. The firm also represents plan sponsors in benefit claim disputes, plan audits and compliance matters with the IRS and DOL; the redesign of benefit plans to comply with Federal health reform and other legal and regulatory developments; the employee benefit implications of business transactions; and contract review and negotiation of vendor contracts supporting benefit plans.

### Prevention & Training:

Isler Dare assists its clients in avoiding potential employment claims by reviewing personnel policies and practices, crafting employment agreements and restrictive covenants, and providing training on best practices in managing employees legally and effectively.

### Bar Leadership:

Throughout its 15 year history, the firm's attorneys have served in significant roles in state and local bar activities. Eddie Isler just completed a two year term as Chair of the Labor Relations and Employment Law section of the Virginia Bar Association. Mark Dare and Steve Ray are both past Presidents of the Fairfax Bar Association, the state's largest county bar association, and Steve Ray is the current Chair of the Virginia State Bar Standing Committee on Professionalism. The firm's attorneys are also frequently featured speakers at Continuing Legal Education programs.

### Honors & Awards:

The firm has been rated 'AV' by Martindale-Hubbell, and the firm's lawyers are among the region's most recognized and successful employment and labor attorneys, regularly appearing in 'Super Lawyers,' Virginia Business magazine's 'Virginia Legal Elite,' 'Best Lawyers in America', and Washingtonian magazine.

### Publications:

Isler Dare attorneys have served as authors and/or editors of numerous legal resource materials, such as 'Virginia Wage and Hour Handbook' (2010); 'Virginia Employment Practices and Forms' (2010); 'Virginia Business Torts' (2d edition 2009); 'Employment Law in Virginia' (3d edition 2009); and 'The Virginia Lawyer' - Employment Law Chapter (4th edition 2009).

### Affiliations:

Isler Dare is a member of the Worklaw® Network, an organization of specialty labor and employment law firms located throughout the world.

### Clients:

Representative clients: Serco Inc.; Enterprise Rent-A-Car; SHRM; Navy Federal Credit Union; SAIC; EADS North America; Konica Minolta Business Solutions; SRA International, Inc.; Republican National Committee; Dewberry Companies; OMNIPLEX World Services Corp; Sectek, Inc.; Merkle Inc.; TeleCommunication Systems, Inc.; NJVC; Intelsat Corporation; Zachary Industrial.

IslerDare PC
*Your workplace, our insight*

# MCGUIREWOODS LLP

**www.**mcguirewoods.com

**Chairman:** Richard Cullen
**Managing Partner:** Thomas Cabaniss
Number of partners: 427
Number of other attorneys: 547

**OFFICES**

Atlanta, GA; Austin, TX; Baltimore, MD; Charlotte, NC; Charlottesville, VA; Chicago, IL; Houston, TX; Jacksonville, FL; Los Angeles, CA; New York, NY; Norfolk, VA; Pittsburgh, PA; Raleigh, NC; Richmond, VA; Tysons Corner, VA; Washington, D.C.; Wilmington, NC

**INTERNATIONAL OFFICES**

Brussels and London

## Firm Overview:

For more than 175 years, McGuireWoods has built its reputation on the bedrock of providing clients with the highest quality legal service and sound strategic guidance. Clients include public and private companies, private individuals, and government and nonprofit organizations around the world.

Client trust has been earned by the credentials and experience of McGuireWoods' lawyers and consultants, who include 14 former attorneys general and assistant attorneys general; 19 former US attorneys and assistant U.S. attorneys; and more than 200 first-chair trial lawyers.

In addition, McGuireWoods' lawyers have consistently been recognized for excellence in legal work and client service. The firm received a Tier 1 ranking on U.S. News – Best Lawyers' "Best Law Firms" 2013 list, and the firm is listed among the 2013 "Top 500 Go-To Law Firms" for litigation by American Lawyer Media, the publisher of Corporate Counsel magazine. Consistently ranked in the top 10 firms nationally in syndicated loans by volume of credit exposure and number of deals by Loan Pricing Corporation's Law Firm League Table, the firm ranked eighth nationally in dollar volume of transactions and ranked fifth in the number of deals closed in 2012 (Thomson Reuters, U.S. Lender Law Firm League Tables, 2012). For more than a decade, McGuireWoods has been named a BTI Consulting "Client-Service A-Team," and is ranked No. 4 on the list in 2013. The firm was also again named by Working Mother magazine as a "Best Law Firm for Women," in 2012.

With more than 900 lawyers in 19 offices, the firm has experienced rapid growth, opening offices in Houston and Austin in 2011. The firm has also seen significant growth in its Atlanta, Charlotte, Chicago and Washington, DC, offices.

Internationally, the firm expanded into the European market via a London office in 2009 and offers experienced and varied cross-border relationships — particularly with the Nordic countries, Russia and Eurasia, Eastern Europe, China, Africa, the Middle East, Israel, India, Spain, Portugal and South America. McGuireWoods' clients span six continents, and collectively, firm lawyers speak 22 languages.

The firm also maintain unique cooperative arrangements with Paris law firm KGA, and in Israel with Shenhav Konforti Shavit & Co (SKS). The firm's international practice is further enhanced by our participation in global legal networks Lex Mundi and LNI Oasis. In addition to offering extensive legal capability and experience, the firm also invests significantly in technology and process innovation. This investment enables optimized project management and program delivery. The firm takes aggressive, innovative approaches to value billing arrangements and fee structuring, based on individual needs. More than 25 percent of major firm clients are under one or more alternative fee arrangements.

As part of the firm's commitment to community service, its lawyers provide thousands of hours of pro bono work annually, including death penalty cases, child support enforcement prosecutions, housing law cases, battered spouse representations, wills and powers of attorney, court-appointed criminal defense and general counseling for nonprofit groups. It also provides legal services and support to local community groups everywhere it does business.

To complement legal services, the firm offers solutions outside the legal realm through McGuireWoods Consulting LLC — a full-service public affairs subsidiary — which offers services in federal, state and local government relations; strategic communications; grassroots advocacy and infrastructure and economic development. The combination of the firm's legal practice with these crucial consulting services makes McGuireWoods a valuable resource to businesses worldwide.

## Main Areas of Practice:

### Corporate:

Banking and finance; business tax; corporate governance; data privacy and security; emerging company and venture capital; employee benefits; environmental; executive compensation; intellectual property; international transactions; M&A; private equity; private wealth; real estate and land use; restructuring and insolvency; securities; supply chain; technology and outsourcing.

### Litigation:

Antitrust and trade regulation; appellate; class action litigation; commercial litigation; consumer financial services litigation; discovery counsel services; ERISA; financial services litigation; fraud/anticorruption; government, regulatory and criminal investigations;

immigration; insurance coverage; intellectual property litigation and patent prosecution; international; labor and employment; land use; product and consumer litigation; SEC enforcement defense; securities litigation; toxic tort and environmental litigation; white-collar defense.

### Finance:

Acquisition financing; asset-based lending; debt finance; commercial lending; lease finance; project finance; public finance; real estate finance; structured finance.

### Industries:

Accountants defense; aerospace and defense; automotive and manufacturing; broker-dealers and investment advisers; capital markets; construction; consumer products; data privacy and security;

education; energy, energy regulatory and utilities; energy and climate change; financial services, food and beverage; franchise and distribution; healthcare; hospitality and resorts; life sciences; mining; nonprofit and tax-exempt organizations; political law; private equity; professional and business services; sports; technology and outsourcing; and transportation.

## OBLON, SPIVAK, MCCLELLAND, MAIER & NEUSTADT LLP

www.oblon.com  **tel:** 703 413 3000  **fax:** 703 413 2220

**Managing Partner:** Bradley D Lytle
Number of partners: 47
Number of other lawyers: 55
Languages: *English, Japanese, French, German, Mandarin and Korean*

### Firm Overview:

Companies across the world depend on Oblon Spivak to establish, leverage and protect their intellectual property assets in the US and abroad. Headquartered within steps of the US Patent and Trademark Office's (USPTO) Alexandria Virginia Campus, Oblon Spivak is home to many preeminent practitioners, former USPTO executives and judges. Oblon Spivak is also home to the leading Post Grant Patent Practice group in the US. Since the formation of the USPTO's Patent Trial & Appeal Board, the firm has outpaced other law firms in terms of the number, diversity and commercial importance of post grant proceeding representations.

### Main Areas of Practice:

**Patent Prosecution:**
Some of the most well known technology companies in the world rely on the patent prosecution counsel of Oblon Spivak. It is the world's leading US patent prosecution firm, and for the last 23 consecutive years, has obtained more US patents than any other law firm worldwide (5,767 US patents in 2012 alone).

**Post Grant Patentability Trials:**
The intellectual property law firm Oblon Spivak has established itself as the nation's leading post-grant practice. The firm's post-grant practice builds upon the wealth of USPTO contested proceeding experience amassed over the decades in the area of patent interference. Of all of the individuals recently recognized as the nation's best post-grant practitioners, one third of them are on the Oblon Spivak post-grant team. Major companies across the world have turned to Oblon Spivak to handle their highest stakes matters. Oblon Spivak has far outpaced other firms in terms of the number, diversity and commercial importance of post grant proceeding representations.

**District Court & ITC Litigation:**
Oblon Spivak's litigation team argued the landmark Festo case at the Supreme Court, and is recognized for expertise in proceedings before the International Trade Commission. The Litigation Group provides turnkey patent representation, being well positioned to represent clients simultaneously in both district court or ITC litigation and co-pending post-grant proceedings before the USPTO. The Group has represented many of the world's leading companies in US patent litigation, such as Toyota, Subaru, SMC Corporation, Toshiba and L'Oreal.

**Trademark & Copyright:**
Oblon Spivak's Copyright Group is headed by the former US Register of Copyrights. The firm's Trademark practice group handles portfolios of leading companies and work with US and international clients on a full-range of trademark matters, from prosecuting applications to litigation. The firm understands that trademarks and copyrights are an integral part of a company's IP portfolio and assists clients in balancing protection and costs while taking proactive steps to protect against counterfeits.

**Specialty Patent Prosecution Groups:**
**Electrical:** The firm's Electrical Team is experienced in a vast array of electrical and software disciplines – many holding advanced degrees in electrical engineering, computer and software engineering, physics, and other fields. The team stays current on cutting edge developments.

**Mechanical:** The Mechanical Prosecution Team boasts an impressive team of attorneys, with experience as engineers, scientists, and inventors. Some are former Patent Examiners with the USPTO and bring an insider's perspective on the agency. By combining technical know-how with legal savvy and scientific knowledge, the firm quickly grasps the complexities of its clients' innovations to effectively assert their interests before the USPTO.

**Chemical:** The Chemical Prosecution group leverages chemists and other PhD-level scientists, prosecuting attorneys and litigators to provide an unmatched level of success in protecting its clients' most valuable intellectual property assets in a wide range of chemical industries and clearly understands the various technologies.

**Industrial Designs:** The Industrial Designs Group is comprised of dedicated professionals who focus on protecting its clients' designs using a variety of intellectual property methods, including design patents. Its attorneys have become experts in the field based on experience, both in obtaining industrial design rights and in enforcing them.

**Patent Pools & Standards:** Oblon Spivak has extensive experience obtaining patents that read on standards in a variety of technology areas. The firm has proven experience in drafting claims in view of standards documents ensuring that its clients secure issued patents containing claims that are essential to the practice of a standard.

**Pharmaceutical/Medical Devices:** Oblon Spivak is at the forefront of helping companies identify, protect, license and enforce intellectual property in the medical, pharmaceutical and healthcare fields. Its clients include both domestic and foreign companies, developing medicines, medical devices, procedures and treatments and has the resources to execute global patent protection strategies for its clients.

**Biotechnology:** The Biotechnology group includes skilled attorneys with scientific and industrial experience, many of whom hold doctorates in microbiology, biochemistry, immunology, molecular genetics, molecular biology and life sciences, to help clients navigate the difficult divide between science and the law.

**Patent Trial & Appeal Board (PTAB):** The PTAB practice group is made up of experienced professionals with unmatched expertise in handling appeals before the PTAB, as former Administrative Patent Judges and administrators at the Board of Patent Appeals and Interferences (the predecessor to the PTAB) and with attorneys who have strong technical backgrounds. The group's members are involved in all aspects of appeals in a wide range of technology areas.

### International Work:

For over 40 years, Oblon, Spivak has provided a full range of intellectual property services to companies based in Japan, France, Germany, Italy, the US and other areas of the world. The group's effectiveness is enhanced by the ability of many of its members to speak foreign languages fluently.

**OFFICES**

VIRGINIA
**ALEXANDRIA:** 1940 Duke Street, VA 22314
Tel: 703 413 3000   Fax: 703 413 2220
Email: oblonpat@oblon.com

# SMITH PACHTER McWHORTER PLC

**www.**smithpachter.com **tel:** 703 847 6300 **fax:** 703 847 6312

**Managing Member:** Mark E Hanson
**Founding Members:** Val S McWhorter, John S Pachter
**Senior Counsel:** Richard F Smith
Number of Members: 11
Number of other attorneys: 12

**OFFICES**

VIRGINIA

**TYSONS CORNER:** 8000 Towers Crescent Drive, Suite 900, VA 22182
Tel: 703 847 6300   Fax: 703 847 6312
Email: info@smithpachter.com

## Firm Overview:

Smith Pachter McWhorter PLC represents clients in the construction and government contracts industries. The firm uses its extensive, in-depth knowledge to respond efficiently to a broad range of counseling, compliance, and litigation matters. Founded in 1986, the firm's attorneys are pre-eminent in their fields of practice, receiving recognition from peers, legal and industry associations, and clients for their quality of work and contribution to their fields. The firm has particular expertise in litigating claims on large, complex infrastructure projects, counseling on the whole spectrum of government contract issues, and resolving controversies through the use of alternative dispute resolution.

## Main Areas of Practice:

### Construction:

The firm represents clients in all phases of the construction process, including contract drafting, negotiation, and risk assessment; on-site identification and analysis of geotechnical, design, engineering, specification, and other contract-related problems; and claims and litigation. The firm has prepared, litigated, and resolved complex construction claims and disputes of every type, including delay, disruption, acceleration, and inefficiency. Attorneys in the construction law practice excel before courts, arbitration panels, and in alternative dispute resolution settings such as mediation. The firm is particularly well known for its skill in litigating complex, fact intensive disputes in heavy civil, power, light-rail, transportation, and industrial and process plant projects. The construction practice is both national and international in scope, handling litigation across the United States and extending to arbitration forums in the Middle East and Europe. The firm's clients include a mix of large general contractors, including many firms in the Engineering News-Record Top 500, as well as owners, specialty contractors, subcontractors, and architects and engineers.

### Government Contracts:

With its location in the Washington, DC metropolitan area, the firm is well-positioned to assist clients navigate the ever-growing maze of statutes and regulations characteristic of contracting with the United States Government, as well as state and local governments. The practice also encompasses grants. The firm's attorneys are highly experienced in bid protests; cost accounting issues; contract terminations, suspension, and debarment; compliance audits; procurement integrity investigations, including false claims actions; and claims and litigation, among other matters. The firm represents clients before federal courts, boards of contact appeals and agencies, including the Government Accountability Office. The firm's clients include major defense contractors and civilian agency contractors who sell goods and provide services across all industries. Smith Pachter McWhorter's government contracts clients include large, medium, and small companies based in the United States, Europe, and the Middle East.

### International Disputes:

The firm has an active international arbitration practice in Europe and the Middle East encompassing work for clients in large-scale construction projects and other contract disputes, including those arising out of contracts with the United States Government. The firm is experienced in contingency contracting and disputes arising therefrom. The firm's experience includes representing clients before the International Chamber of Commerce's International Court of Arbitration, the Cairo Regional Centre for International Commercial Arbitration, and the American Arbitration Association's International Centre for Dispute Resolution. The firm also helps European and Middle Eastern companies comply with the myriad regulations applicable to foreign companies performing work for the United States Government in the United States and overseas, as well as resolve claims and disputes arising from such contracts. These matters currently involve contracts throughout the Middle East as well as Europe.

### Alternative Dispute Resolution:

The firm is known for its success in resolving large, complex disputes through alternative dispute resolution, including mediation and arbitration. The firm's members have assisted many clients in successfully resolving complex claims out-of-court and in proactively seeking to resolve disputes in a favorable and economical manner. Founding member Richard F Smith, a Senior Counsel to the firm and former construction litigator, currently serves as a mediator and arbitrator in construction disputes in Virginia and across the nation.

Smith • Pachter • McWhorter PLC
Attorneys At Law

# WATT, TIEDER, HOFFAR & FITZGERALD, LLP

**www.wthf.com** **tel:** 703 749 1000 **fax:** 703 893 8029

**Chairman:** Robert G Watt
**Managing Partner:** Lewis J Baker
Number of partners: 56
Number of lawyers: 87
Languages: *English*

## Firm Overview:

Watt, Tieder, Hoffar & Fitzgerald, LLP (WTHF) was founded in 1978 with six attorneys involved almost exclusively in construction disputes litigation. Now, with over 80 professionals, the firm handles complex design and construction issues and disputes encompassing international and domestic construction, government contracts, suretyship, real estate and commercial transactions, and insolvency throughout the nation and the world. In October 2012, WTHF became a founding member of the Global Construction and Infrastructure Legal Alliance (GCILA) along with top-ranked French construction law firm FRILET-Société d'Avocats. With GCILA's headquarters in Paris, WTHF can service international clients around the world.

Additionally, WTHF opened its seventh domestic office in Chicago, Illinois in January 2013.

WTHF provides its clients with a diverse group of attorneys with backgrounds in government and private industry, as well as some with degrees in engineering and construction management. To further enhance the breadth and depth of its legal service offerings, the firm is vertically integrated with an in-house staff of estimating, engineering and scheduling experts, a sophisticated graphics and electronic presentations group, litigation support services and an extensive library and electronic research department.

WTHF attorneys regularly publish articles, participate in industry groups and speak at seminars throughout the world. The attorneys also develop customized in-house seminars for clients on topics of special interest.

## Main Areas of Practice:

WTHF's attorneys handle complex design and construction issues and disputes encompassing international and domestic construction, government contracts, surety, real estate and commercial transactions, and insolvency throughout the United States and the world. The firm has been involved in every type of major construction project, including tunnels, bridges, sports venues, highways, airports, rail and subway systems, military bases, industrial and chemical facilities, waste-water facilities, power plants and commercial and public buildings. The firm also assists clients in the full spectrum of transactions related to commercial properties, including: leasing, acquisition and development, project owner representation, lending and project finance, portfolio expansions, brokerage, organizational matters, and construction documentation. WTHF's clients include many of the world's leading corporations, developers and contractors on both domestic and international projects. The firm represents 60 percent of the Engineering News Record Top 30 Contractors and seven of the United States' top 10 sureties.

## PRACTICE AREAS

Domestic Construction
International Construction
Suretyship
Government Contracts
Real Estate & Commercial Transactions
Insolvency

## OFFICES

**VIRGINIA**
**MCLEAN:** 8405 Greensboro Drive, Suite 100, McLean, VA 22102
Tel: 703 749 1000   Fax: 703 893 8029

**CALIFORNIA**
**IRVINE:** 2040 Main Street, Suite 300, CA 92614
Tel: 949 852 6700   Fax: 949 261 0771

**SAN FRANCISCO:** 333 Bush Street, Suite 1500, CA 94104
Tel: 415 623 7000   Fax: 415 623 7001

**FLORIDA**
**MIAMI:** 1200 Brickell Avenue, Suite 1800, FL 33131
Tel: 305 777 3572   Fax: 786 693 7797

**ILLINOIS**
**CHICAGO:** 10 South Wacker Drive, Suite 2935, IL 60606
Tel: 312 219 6900   Fax: 312 559 2758

**NEVADA**
**LAS VEGAS:** 3993 Howard Hughes Parkway, Suite 400, NV 89169
Tel: 702 789 3100  Fax: 702 822 2650

**WASHINGTON**
**SEATTLE:** 1215 Fourth Avenue, Suite 2210, WA 98161
Tel: 206 204 5800   Fax: 206 204 0284

## INTERNATIONAL OFFICES

The firm also has an office in Paris, France in conjunction with the GCILA

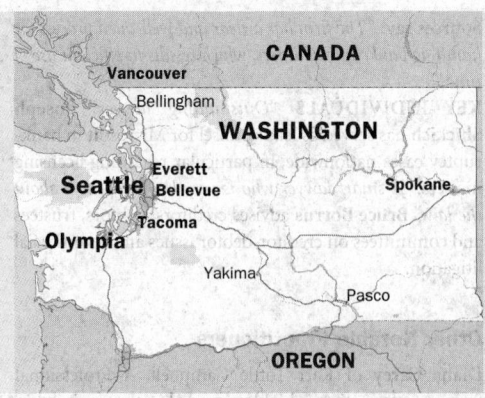

## How lawyers are ranked

Every year we carry out thousands of in-depth interviews with clients in order to assess the reputations and expertise of business lawyers worldwide. The qualities we look for (and which determine rankings) include technical legal ability, professional conduct, client service, commercial awareness/astuteness, diligence, commitment, and other qualities most valued by the client. For details of our research team, see p.5.

# BANKRUPTCY/RESTRUCTURING

Commentary about individuals can be found under their firm's paragraph. If the firm has no paragraph (is not ranked) look at Other Notable Practitioners.

### Bankruptcy/Restructuring
### Leading Firms

**Band 1**
Bush Strout & Kornfeld LLP
Davis Wright Tremaine LLP *
Foster Pepper PLLC *
Lane Powell PC *
Perkins Coie LLP

**Band 2**
K&L Gates *
Riddell Williams PS

### Leading Individuals

**Band 1**

| | | |
|---|---|---|
| Bush Gayle | Bush Strout & Kornfeld LLP | |
| Carey Diana | Karr Tuttle Campbell (ONP)† | |
| Cullen Jack | Foster Pepper PLLC | |
| Ekberg Charles | Lane Powell PC * | |
| Jackson Dillon | Foster Pepper PLLC | |
| Kornfeld Armand J | Bush Strout & Kornfeld LLP | |
| Leaverton Bruce | Lane Powell PC * | |
| Powers Ragan | Davis Wright Tremaine LLP | |
| Shickich Joseph | Riddell Williams PS | |
| Smith Alan | Perkins Coie LLP | |

**Band 2**

| | | |
|---|---|---|
| Alston Christopher | Foster Pepper PLLC | |
| Borrus Bruce | Riddell Williams PS | |
| Crabbe Deborah | Foster Pepper PLLC | |
| Crocker Shelly | Crocker Law Group PLC (ONP)† | |
| Gearin Michael | K&L Gates * | |
| Heston Mary Jo | Lane Powell PC * | |
| Kaplan John | Perkins Coie LLP | |
| Neu David | K&L Gates * | |
| Northrup Mark | Graham & Dunn PC (ONP)† | |
| Rizzardi John | Cairncross & Hempelmann (ONP)† | |

* Indicates firm / individual with profile.
† ONP = Other Notable Practitioner.

## Band 1

### Bush Strout & Kornfeld LLP

**THE FIRM** Bush Strout & Kornfeld is universally admired by peers for having one of the best bankruptcy practices in the state. This boutique law firm represents commercial debtors, as well as companies that are interested in purchasing from insolvency proceedings. The firm is known for conducting the more sophisticated Chapter 11 bankruptcies that happen in the state.
**Sources say:** *"The premier debtor firm in town."*
**KEY INDIVIDUALS** The *"excellent, highly respected"* **Gayle Bush** is an expert in Chapter 11 reorganizations and debtors' rights. He is experienced in a range of high-value bankruptcy issues. The highly regarded **Armand Kornfeld** has a deep knowledge of Chapter 11s and restructurings. He represents clients from an extensive range of industry sectors.

### Davis Wright Tremaine LLP
See profile on p.2544

**THE FIRM** Davis Wright Tremaine's bankruptcy team has a lender-oriented practice, with some involvement in debtor cases also. The Seattle office conducts both local and regional matters, with Seattle lawyers involved across Idaho, Montana, Oregon and California. Clients include AmericanWest Bank, Starbucks and Plum TV.
**Sources say:** *"Very good lawyers. They are hard, tireless workers."*
**KEY INDIVIDUALS** The *"terrific"* **Ragan Powers** is known for his expertise in Chapter 11 bankruptcies and workouts. He recently acted on behalf of Plum TV in its Chapter 11 proceedings.

### Foster Pepper PLLC
See profile on p.2545

**THE FIRM** With its deep bench, this Washington firm is well equipped to deal with a large variety of bankruptcy matters, and is a mainstay in the local insolvency arena. It is especially held in high esteem for its handling of bankruptcy matters pertaining to real estate. The group also houses expertise in litigation arising out of bankruptcy issues.
**Sources say:** *"They've proven to be the best of the best and have always provided us with the most professional, knowledgeable and reliable service out there."*
**KEY INDIVIDUALS Jack Cullen** concentrates his practice on Chapter 11 reorganizations, complex commercial litigation and distressed commercial restructuring transactions. He is described by sources as *"a really great attorney."* The *"very experienced and very good"* **Dillon Jackson**'s bankruptcy practice has a particular emphasis on commercial and multifamily real estate, and Chapter 11 bankruptcies across the country. He is singled out by sources for his ability to understand both creditors' and debtors' perspectives. **Christopher Alston** is a bankruptcy and commercial litigator, and chairs the firm's creditors' rights and bankruptcy practice. He is described by one client as *"calm, reasoned and smart. He has a good background in his field and is very experienced."* *"Excellent bankruptcy and insolvency lawyer"* **Deborah Crabbe** focuses her practice on the representation of creditors and lenders in a variety of matters, including receiverships, workout proceedings and secured transactions.

### Lane Powell PC
See profile on p.2547

**THE FIRM** Lane Powell's Seattle bankruptcy regularly represents national banks and financial institutions, as well as handling international insolvency and Chapter 15 matters. The group is particularly experienced in troubled loan restructuring, and is admired by clients for its deep knowledge of insolvency laws. The firm's client portfolio includes Wells Fargo, Nordstrom and Starbucks.
**Sources say:** *"An excellent, full-service firm with bright people and lots of depth."*
**KEY INDIVIDUALS Bruce Leaverton** (see p.2540) has a wide-ranging bankruptcy practice and is considered to be

an expert in complex bankruptcies and restructurings. One admiring client enthuses: *"Ten out of ten. He is a leader – the conductor of the orchestra. He brings everyone together to draw a resolution."* **Charles Ekberg** (see p.2539) is considered in the market to be *"highly respected and a great practitioner."* He concentrates his practice on bankruptcy cases, workouts and related litigation. **Mary Jo Heston** (see p.2539) has expertise in commercial bankruptcies, workouts and insolvency matters both statewide and internationally. Sources describe her as *"a very solid and professional attorney who is sound in her judgment."*

## Perkins Coie LLP
See profile on p.2548

**THE FIRM** Perkins Coie continues to have one of the region's preeminent bankruptcy and restructuring practices, and handles Chapter 11 reorganizations, risk mitigation strategies and complex insolvency matters for a wide variety of clients, including financial institutions, pension fund administrators and creditors' committees. The firm's impressive roster of clients includes Boeing, Intel and Weyerhaeuser.

**KEY INDIVIDUALS Alan Smith** is highly respected for his bankruptcy and business practice, and recently represented Intel in the Chapter 15 proceedings of Qimonda. **John Kaplan** has a broad practice which includes commercial litigation as well as bankruptcy matters. He represents both lenders and borrowers in a range of matters such as receiverships and restructurings.

## Band 2

## K&L Gates
See profile on p.2245

**THE FIRM** The Seattle office of this international giant has the vast resources required to handle all types of bankruptcy and restructuring matters, with recognized expertise in receivership actions, Ponzi schemes, Chapter 11 reorganizations, and M&A through bankruptcies.

**Sources say:** *"They have a high level of professionalism, and the quality of their legal work is outstanding."*

**KEY INDIVIDUALS Michael Gearin** (see p.2539) focuses his practice on insolvency and workouts, and is commended by clients for his ability to think of creative solutions. One source says: *"He's a very good and knowledgeable lawyer, good at conflict resolution."* **David Neu** (see p.2540) attracts much praise from peers and clients alike, with one source remarking that he is *"one of the sharpest guys that I've had the fortune to be around. He really knows his way in and out of a federal bankruptcy court from a debtor perspective but also, more importantly, from a creditor perspective."*

## Riddell Williams PS

**THE FIRM** Riddell Williams's single Seattle office is known for its experience in working out troubled real estate, and for handling bankruptcy matters on behalf of banks across Washington state. Clients include Philips Healthcare, Washington Federal and Weyerhaeuser Real Estate. The firm has recently represented Union Bank in a series of receiverships, foreclosures and bankruptcies.

**Sources say:** *"The firm has a clear and well-oiled process for handling bankruptcy matters, which results in efficient use of time."*

**KEY INDIVIDUALS** *"Outstanding lawyer"* **Joseph Shickich** has served as lead counsel for Microsoft in bankruptcy cases nationwide, in particular regarding licensing matters. *"A smart lawyer who is very knowledgeable about the law,"* **Bruce Borrus** advises creditors, debtors, trustees and committees on creditor-debtor issues and commercial litigation.

## Other Notable Practitioners

**Diana Carey** of Karr Tuttle Campbell, A Professional Service Corporation is highly regarded in the receivership arena and is described as being *"responsive and pragmatic – she really knows the law well but knows how to do a business deal too."* **Mark Northrup** of Graham & Dunn PC is described by peers as an *"excellent"* bankruptcy lawyer who is *"well respected and smart."* He concentrates his practice on a wide range of insolvency matters, including Chapter 11 reorganizations and receiverships. **John Rizzardi** of Cairncross & Hempelmann, A Professional Service Corporation is a receivership and bankruptcy lawyer who conducts workouts for real estate and hotel developers. According to sources, he is a *"down-to-earth, nondramatic and quiet bankruptcy specialist. No one likes to operate in the bankruptcy world, but to have Mr Rizzardi on your team is a 'steady as she goes' experience."* **Shelly Crocker** of Crocker Law Group PLC is well regarded for conducting receiverships and workouts throughout the state.

# CORPORATE/COMMERCIAL

Commentary about individuals can be found under their firm's paragraph. If the firm has no paragraph (is not ranked) look at Other Notable Practitioners.

| Corporate/Commercial |
| --- |
| **Leading Firms** |
| **Band 1** |
| Davis Wright Tremaine LLP * |
| DLA Piper LLP (US) * |
| K&L Gates * |
| Perkins Coie LLP |
| **Band 2** |
| Dorsey & Whitney LLP * |
| Wilson Sonsini Goodrich & Rosati * |
| **Band 3** |
| Cooley LLP |
| Fenwick & West LLP * |
| Foster Pepper PLLC * |
| Garvey Schubert Barer |
| Lane Powell PC * |
| Stoel Rives LLP |

\* *Indicates firm with profile.*
*Alphabetical order within each band. Band 1 is the highest.*

## Band 1

## Davis Wright Tremaine LLP
See profile on p.2544

**THE FIRM** This preeminent Washington group continues to distinguish itself as one of the region's most successful corporate practices. M&A is a particularly strong area for the firm, with recent major deals involving Microsoft, Starbucks and Double Down Interactive. The team's practice is bolstered by DWT's office in Shanghai, as well as by the firm's connections in Canada.

**Sources say:** *"Very knowledgeable, very experienced and very accessible."*

**KEY INDIVIDUALS Joseph Weinstein** is an expert in corporate matters pertaining to the food-related industries, and is held in high regard by sources, one of whom remarks that he is a *"thoughtful, skillful, excellent lawyer."* **Greg Adams** occupies a senior partner role at the firm, and is corporate counsel to a number of companies, particularly advising them on projects, governance and shareholder rights. Business transaction lawyer **Bruce Bjerke** recently represented Starbucks in its $100 million acquisition of Bay Bread, and is described by sources as a *"very calm"* attorney who *"brings so much credibility to negotiations."* One admiring source describes emerging companies and startup expert **Joseph Whitford** as *"the guy you look to in the Seattle area for securities advice – he can't be beaten."* **Marcus Williams** has a broad corporate practice and recently represented HomeStreet in its $96 million IPO. **LaVerne Woods** is a tax expert who concentrates on acting for tax-exempt organizations, in particular foundations and public charities. According to clients, she is *"very helpful in assisting with tax structures."* **James Wreggelsworth** focuses on federal income tax, partnership work and complex M&A transactions. Clients appreciate his ability to negotiate complex tax issues. **Pamela Charles** handles federal and complex tax issues, as well as advising the firm's energy practice group on all aspects of tax related to energy projects.

## Corporate/Commercial

### Senior Statesmen

**Senior Statesmen: distinguished older practitioners**

| | |
|---|---|
| Dodd Richard | K&L Gates * |
| Strother Jack | Graham & Dunn PC (ONP)† |

### Leading Individuals

**Band 1**

| | |
|---|---|
| Adams Greg | Davis Wright Tremaine LLP |
| Barry Christopher | Dorsey & Whitney LLP |
| Bor Andrew | Perkins Coie LLP |
| Carlson C Kent | K&L Gates * |
| Landefeld Stewart | Perkins Coie LLP |
| Morgan Michael | Lane Powell PC * |
| Schultheis Patrick J | Wilson Sonsini Goodrich & Rosati |
| Steel John M | DLA Piper LLP (US) * |
| Weinstein Joseph D | Davis Wright Tremaine LLP |

**Band 2**

| | |
|---|---|
| Bjerke Bruce | Davis Wright Tremaine LLP |
| Clarke David | Perkins Coie LLP |
| Coonrod Stephan | K&L Gates * |
| Erickson Sonya | Cooley LLP |
| Graham Stephen M | Fenwick & West LLP * |
| Kocher Gary J | K&L Gates * |
| McShea David F | Perkins Coie LLP |
| Robertson John W | Cooley LLP |
| Sherman Craig E | Wilson Sonsini Goodrich & Rosati |
| Smith Alan C | Fenwick & West LLP * |
| Sroufe Evelyn Cruz | Perkins Coie LLP |
| Voss Christopher J | Stoel Rives LLP |
| Yentzer Steven R | DLA Piper LLP (US) * |

**Band 3**

| | |
|---|---|
| Bromfield William | Fenwick & West LLP * |
| Bryant Duff | Stoel Rives LLP |
| Gamsky Michael | Foster Pepper PLLC |
| Greenburg G Scott | K&L Gates * |
| Hutchings Michael | DLA Piper LLP (US) * |
| Israel Allen D | Foster Pepper PLLC |
| Kunold Jr Robert | Foster Pepper PLLC |
| Moore Andrew | Perkins Coie LLP |
| Robertson Bruce | Garvey Schubert Barer |
| Whitford Joseph P | Davis Wright Tremaine LLP |
| Williams Marcus | Davis Wright Tremaine LLP |

**Up-and-coming individuals**

| | |
|---|---|
| Dykes Trenton | DLA Piper LLP (US) * |

## Corporate/Commercial: Tax

### Leading Individuals

**Band 1**

| | |
|---|---|
| Charles Pamela | Davis Wright Tremaine LLP |
| Crow Carl | Perkins Coie LLP |
| Lewis Charles S | Stoel Rives LLP |
| Purcell Charles | K&L Gates * |
| Tober Gary | Garvey Schubert Barer |
| Woods LaVerne | Davis Wright Tremaine LLP |
| Wreggelsworth James | Davis Wright Tremaine LLP |
| Zuccotti Andrew | K&L Gates * |

*\* Indicates individual with profile.*

*†ONP = Other Notable Practitioner.*

### DLA Piper LLP (US)

See profile on p.1971

**THE FIRM** The Seattle office of this international power-house is renowned for its involvement in venture capital firms and emerging companies, in particular technology startups. The corporate team recently oversaw SonicWALL's acquisition by Dell in a deal worth over $1 billion. Other clients include Madrona Venture Group, Eli Lilly and Maveron.

**Sources say:** *"I enjoy working with DLA Piper and feel I've made a great choice. They seem responsive, comprehensive, and well suited to continue to work with as my company changes and grows."*

**KEY INDIVIDUALS John Steel** (see p.2541) has a broad-based corporate finance practice, with public offerings being a particular strong suit. Sources praise him as being *"first rate"* and *"one of the best in town."* The *"phenomenal"* **Steven Yentzer** (see p.2542) is held in high esteem by peers and clients alike, and is often called upon to advise on complex corporate finance matters. One source enthuses: *"He's very practical and very good at the law, but he also understands the business situation."* **Michael Hutchings** (see p.2539) focuses on advising technology companies on all aspects of corporate law, including capital markets and M&A. One client remarks: *"He's very knowledgeable and took the time to understand our business."* Rising star **Trenton Dykes** (see p.2539) is chair of the firm's Northwest emerging growth and venture capital practice. One source describes him as *"spectacular – he's extraordinarily efficient, he doesn't waste my time, and he works to save money for us. He's super-smart and well respected in the industry."*

### K&L Gates

See profile on p.2245

**THE FIRM** The corporate practice at K&L Gates's Seattle office is acknowledged as one of the finest in the Pacific Northwest. The team is particularly known for its work with funds, joint ventures and institutional investors. Clients include HTC, Halliburton and California Public Employees' Retirement System. Recent highlights include the representation of Microsoft in a joint venture interest sale to NBCUniversal.

**Sources say:** *"A superb law firm with a great collection of corporate lawyers."*

**KEY INDIVIDUALS** Described by sources as *"one of the best corporate attorneys in the region,"* the highly respected **Kent Carlson** (see p.2538) is an expert in M&A. He serves as outside general counsel to a number of companies across the country, particularly advising them on joint ventures and sales. **Richard Dodd** (see p.2538) is known as a *"go-to person for corporate and SEC issues,"* and is recognized for his experience in all facets of M&A including financings, divestitures and securities offerings. **Stephan Coonrod** (see p.2538) concentrates his practice on domestic and international acquisitions, trade issues and technology transfers. He recently advised Blue Point Capital Partners on its acquisition of Selmet. **Gary Kocher** (see p.2540) is well regarded for his expertise in all types of corporate matters, with a focus on counseling emerging com-panies on their public and private securities offerings. The *"excellent"* **Scott Greenburg** (see p.2539) has a broad prac-tice which spans IP matters, public offerings and complex commercial transactions. **Andrew Zuccotti** (see p.2542) concentrates his practice on federal income tax and advis-es a variety of clients on complex issues related to this field. **Charles Purcell** (see p.2540) is another of of the group's distinguished tax lawyers. He focuses on fund work, particularly on the representation of entities wishing to create and invest in funds.

### Perkins Coie LLP

See profile on p.2548

**THE FIRM** This established national firm's Seattle base is known for its strong corporate department. The team regularly acts for major clients including Microsoft, Amazon.com and Coinstar. Clients also include startup companies, and the group's expertise in this area was recently displayed by its representation of Donuts, Inc. in its formation and financing.

**KEY INDIVIDUALS Stewart Landefeld** is noted for his experience in corporate governance matters, public offerings and securities compliance. Client favorite **Andrew Bor** is particularly praised his practicality in deals. He has a wide-ranging corporate practice which includes corporate governance, securities regulation and strategic divestitures and spinoffs. **David Clarke** is recognized for his abilities in representing emerging growth companies, private equity funds and public companies. Interviewees admire his commercial approach. **David McShea** is a specialist in handling IPO matters, and represents venture capital firms, emerging technology companies and public companies in a variety of transactional matters such as M&A and financings. **Andrew Moore** is appreciated by clients for his skill in handling securities, public offerings and SEC compliance. He is also held in high regard for his pragmatic approach. **Carl Crow** is a well-regarded tax lawyer who specializes in debt and equity financings and international business transactions. **Evelyn Cruz Sroufe** is well respected for her corporate practice, with a particular emphasis on antitakeover, acquisitions and corporate governance matters.

## Band 2

### Dorsey & Whitney LLP

See profile on p.1583

**THE FIRM** Dorsey & Whitney's Seattle team is particularly noted in the market for its cross-border Canadian work concerning capital markets and M&A. The firm represents many clients in the mining and cleantech industries, and has managed large deals for NovaGold and Bentall Kennedy. The team has also recently been involved in a series of matters for Kodiak Oil & Gas in relation to high-value acquisitions and public offerings, among other issues.

**Sources say:** *"They're responsible, professional, and they get things done."*

**KEY INDIVIDUALS Christopher Barry** is chair of the firm's Canada practice group and earns praise as an "*efficient and knowledgeable*" practitioner. He recently served as US counsel to NovaGold in the high-value spin-off of NovaCopper.

## Wilson Sonsini Goodrich & Rosati
See profile on p.700

**THE FIRM** This firm is admired for its representation of clients from the IT, life sciences and venture capital industries. The firm has a preeminent reputation in particular for managing the requirements of early-stage and startup companies, and has recognized expertise in matters related to state and federal securities laws. Clients include Bungie, Photobucket and Fusion-IO.

**Sources say:** "*While they are certainly hyper-technical, they are also known for providing solid, pragmatic guidance.*"

**KEY INDIVIDUALS Patrick Schultheis** is described by sources as "*one of the leading emerging company lawyers in this area.*" As well as acting for startups, he tackles a wide range range of corporate matters for large public companies, underwriters and venture capital investors. **Craig Sherman** is known by sources to be "*super-knowledgeable about industry norms and legal advice.*" He concentrates his practice on corporate and securities laws, with an emphasis on M&A, joint ventures and public offerings.

## Band 3

## Cooley LLP

**THE FIRM** This team has a solid reputation for handling a wide variety of corporate matters on behalf of emerging companies, with particular expertise in corporate securities, stock issuances and corporate governance.

**KEY INDIVIDUALS Sonya Erickson** has expertise in technology firms, the life sciences and venture capital funds. She is renowned as having a strong reputation for handling matters involving emerging companies and acts as corporate counsel to a variety of these clients, advising them on all aspects of growth, including IPOs and M&A. **John Robertson** is admired by peers and clients for his reputation and practical approach to deals. He has a wide-ranging transactional and corporate practice, with particular emphasis on public offerings, venture capital financings and M&A.

## Fenwick & West LLP
See profile on p.680

**THE FIRM** The Seattle office of this leading California technology and startup firm is reputed for its wealth of experience in the life sciences and emerging companies

spheres. It represents clients from these industries in the full range of corporate matters, including IPOs and M&A.

**KEY INDIVIDUALS Stephen Graham** (see p.2539) is described by sources as "*a pioneer in the life sciences industries here*" and someone who has "*carved out a niche in the biotech arena.*" **Alan Smith** (see p.2541) has recognized expertise in representing emerging and public companies in all manner of corporate matters, including capital markets offerings, M&A and securities matters. He is also known for his experience in venture capital financings. The well-respected **William Bromfield** (see p.2538) concentrates his transactional and corporate practice on emerging companies, private financings and venture capital matters. He advises many clients from the media and digital worlds on general corporate and securities issues.

## Foster Pepper PLLC
See profile on p.2545

**THE FIRM** This Washington law firm, with offices in Seattle and Spokane, has a notable practice which encompasses the full spectrum of corporate matters. The team is especially experienced in conducting work for private equity firms and for the representation of public pensions funds. Key clients include Marlin Equity and Pendulum Investments.

**KEY INDIVIDUALS** Managing partner **Robert Kunold** has a broad transactional practice that covers M&A, joint ventures and deals out of state, particularly with New York-based firms. According to clients, "*he knows how we think, what we want and how to go about making it happen.*" **Michael Gamsky**'s corporate practice particularly focuses on securities and finance matters. He conducts a large amount of work for banks, especially regarding loans and mortgage deals. The "*very strong and smart*" **Allen Israel** is much respected for his skill as a corporate lawyer. He is particularly adept in matters related to real estate and non-profits.

## Garvey Schubert Barer

**THE FIRM** Garvey Schubert Barer's corporate group takes full advantage of its Pacific Rim position, with clients in Japan and cross-border deals in Canada, as well as notable clients in the maritime and fishing fields. The team has noteworthy expertise in representing public, private and family-owned companies in debt and equity financing matters, shareholder rights and regulatory compliance.

**Sources say:** "*Their advice is practical, focused and very helpful.*"

**KEY INDIVIDUALS Gary Tober** is a well-respected tax lawyer praised by clients for being "*precise and informative.*" He counsels both US and foreign clients on all aspects of tax matters, in particular those with cross-border ele-

ments. **Bruce Robertson** is "*very experienced in both corporate and acquisition work, and he brings that wealth of experience to bear on our situation,*" mentioned an impressed client. His practice includes international transactional matters, M&A and joint venture formation, as well as acting as general counsel to a variety of public and privately held companies.

## Lane Powell PC
See profile on p.2547

**THE FIRM** This established Pacific Northwest firm has a healthy corporate practice in Washington, and assists companies from across a variety of industries in the full range of corporate matters. The team also serves as outside general counsel for a number of established local companies. Clients includes Nordstrom, Bank of Hawaii and Wells Fargo.

**Sources say:** "*Very sophisticated on the public company side.*"

**KEY INDIVIDUALS Michael Morgan** (see p.2540) is held in high regard in the Washington market for his broad corporate practice. One client enthuses: "*He understands in depth every aspect of every deal he's supervising and has the uncanny ability to provide practical, business-savvy advice.*"

## Stoel Rives LLP

**THE FIRM** The Seattle office of Pacific Northwest stalwart Stoel Rives has a strong corporate practice, notable for its expertise in international deals, corporate compliance and public and private offerings. The team represents a range of clients from the financial, forestry, energy and natural resources sectors. Clients include Schnitzer Steel, Ecover and Darigold.

**KEY INDIVIDUALS Christopher Voss** is commended for his deep knowledge of public offering and M&A matters, and represents clients from the forest products, life sciences and IT industries. **Duff Bryant** chairs the firm's M&A practice group. He draws plaudits from clients for his experience in complex negotiations. **Charles Lewis** has a well-regarded practice, particularly in relation to federal income tax issues. He assists clients with complex partnerships, mergers and joint ventures in the USA and worldwide.

## Other Notable Practitioners

**Jack Strother** of Graham & Dunn PC is viewed as one of Washington's leading corporate lawyers for banking and financial institutions. He also has vast experience in representing public and private companies in a broad range of corporate matters, including transactions, M&A and venture formation.

vast knowledge of immigration law, and acts as counsel to plaintiffs in a variety of immigration matters.

### MacDonald Hoague & Bayless
THE FIRM This well-respected Seattle firm has a healthy practice covering the full range of business immigration law. The team represents a broad range of clients, and is held in high regard by peers who identify it as a choice for referrals.

KEY INDIVIDUALS Described as *"top-notch in her particular area,"* **Ester Greenfield** is especially well regarded for her expertise in labor certifications. She is also recognized

as an expert in all facets of business immigration law. The *"really smart"* **Felicia Gittleman** counsels companies on a variety of business immigration matters, such as nonimmigrant and immigrant visas.

### Other Notable Practitioners

**Diane Butler** (see p.2538) is manager of Lane Powell PC's immigration and Canada practices. She is held in high regard by peers, while clients praise her responsiveness and round-the-clock availability. She has recently been involved in a range of H-1B issues. **Gregg Rodgers** of

Garvey Schubert Barer is a specialist in employment and immigration law, particularly management-focused immigration. He is especially active in assisting clients from the healthcare, hospitality and entertainment industries. **Carol Edward** of the Law Offices of Carol L Edward & Associates has a wide-ranging immigration practice covering business and family immigration issues. She has particular expertise in deportation defense. **Gregory McCall** of Perkins Coie LLP is an experienced practitioner of business immigration law and is heavily involved in immigrant and nonimmigrant visa matters. His clients include World Vision, Intellectual Ventures and Tagged.

# INTELLECTUAL PROPERTY

Commentary about individuals can be found under their firm's paragraph. If the firm has no paragraph (is not ranked) look at Other Notable Practitioners.

| Intellectual Property Leading Firms |
| --- |
| **Band 1** |
| Perkins Coie LLP |
| **Band 2** |
| Davis Wright Tremaine LLP * |
| Dorsey & Whitney LLP * |
| K&L Gates * |
| **Band 3** |
| Christensen O'Connor Johnson Kindness, PLLC |
| Lowe Graham Jones |
| Seed IP Law Group PLLC |
| Wilson Sonsini Goodrich & Rosati * |
| **Band 4** |
| Lane Powell PC * |

*Indicates firm / individual with profile.*
†*ONP = Other Notable Practitioner.*

| Intellectual Property Leading Individuals | |
| --- | --- |
| **Band 1** | |
| Al-Salam Ramsey | Perkins Coie LLP |
| Bodine Brian G | Lane Powell PC * |
| Meiklejohn Paul | Dorsey & Whitney LLP |
| Rheaume Warren J | Davis Wright Tremaine LLP |
| Riedinger Jerry | Perkins Coie LLP |
| **Band 2** | |
| Bateman David A | K&L Gates * |
| Cumbow Robert C | Graham & Dunn PC (ONP)† |
| Dunwoody Stuart R | Davis Wright Tremaine LLP |
| Ferron Jr William O | Seed IP Law Group PLLC |
| Goto Bruce T | Riddell Williams PS (ONP)† |
| Graham Lawrence | Lowe Graham Jones |
| Hendelman Aaron | Wilson Sonsini Goodrich & Rosati |
| McDonald David | K&L Gates * |
| Nagae Jerald | Christensen O'Connor Johnson Kindness |
| Parker Paul T | Perkins Coie LLP |
| Parris Mark S | Orrick, Herrington & Sutcliffe LLP (ONP)† |
| Tellekson David K | Fenwick & West LLP (ONP)† * |
| **Band 3** | |
| Denkenberger John | Christensen O'Connor Johnson Kindness |
| Eng Kimton | Dorsey & Whitney LLP |
| Jost Shannon | Stokes Lawrence, PS (ONP)† |
| Morgan Kevan | Christensen O'Connor Johnson Kindness |
| Park Brian C | Stoel Rives LLP (ONP)† |
| Siefert Richard C | Garvey Schubert Barer (ONP)† |
| **Associates to watch** | |
| Byer Benjamin | Davis Wright Tremaine LLP |

## Band 1

### Perkins Coie LLP
See profile on p.2548

THE FIRM Perkins Coie's Washington intellectual property practice towers above others in the Pacific Northwest, and has a formidable reputation in both patent prosecution and litigation. A significant amount of the firm's IP work involves semiconductors, medical devices and software, and the team acts for some of the country's most prominent technology companies.

KEY INDIVIDUALS **Jerry Riedinger** is known to be one of the state's leading litigators. He specializes in complex patent disputes, patent infringements and trade secrets. Patent litigator **Ramsey Al-Salam** is universally admired and respected by peers. According to market commentators, he handles IP disputes to an impressively high level. **Paul Parker** is chair of the firm's IP practice, and is a specialist in patent issues relating to semiconductor technologies and emerging companies, particularly those involving medical devices.

## Band 2

### Davis Wright Tremaine LLP
See profile on p.2544

THE FIRM This Seattle-headquartered full-service firm is one of the most influential in the Pacific Northwest, with a thriving and well-respected IP practice. The team has recognized expertise in trademark registration and protection, patent prosecution and litigation for clients from the

life sciences, electronics and software industries. The group has recently acted for major clients including Alaska Airlines, Univar and Pacific Market International.

Sources say: *"Excellent. Very responsive and thorough; they know their subject matter well."*

KEY INDIVIDUALS **Warren Rheaume** is admired by sources as an *"extremely responsive, excellent and thorough litigator."* He conducts IP cases for both plaintiffs and defendants in the state and across the country. He has a broad practice covering general and complex IP litigation, patent and copyright work, especially in the technology field. **Stuart Dunwoody** has a broad IP practice which includes patent, trade secret and copyright litigation. He recently represented Leatherman Tool Group in a false advertising claim against Coast Cutlery. Associate **Benjamin Byer** handles patent litigation and focuses his practice on a wide variety of technologies, including laser devices, search engine ranking algorithms and e-commerce.

### Dorsey & Whitney LLP
See profile on p.1583

THE FIRM The robust IP practice at Dorsey & Whitney's Seattle office is particularly strong in patent and trademark issues. The team is especially experienced in handling patent litigation pertaining to a broad range of technologies. Clients include Robert Bosch Healthcare Systems, Big Fish Games and Smith Optics.

Sources say: *"They provide excellent services in the preparation and prosecution of patent applications with respect to complex electrical inventions."*

KEY INDIVIDUALS **Paul Meiklejohn** heads the firm's Seattle IP litigation group. He is an experienced litigator who represents a number of significant technology companies in disputes across the country. **Kimton Eng** is particularly experienced in patent prosecution, and counsels some of the firm's biggest clients on matters in this area. He is cited by sources as an attorney who produces a *"first-rate work product."*

## K&L Gates

See profile on p.2245

**THE FIRM** This international firm with local roots has a flourishing IP practice across its offices in Seattle and Spokane. Clients benefit from the firm's extensive network of intellectual property expertise. The team is noted for its prowess in patent litigation defense, international and domestic patent prosecution, and internet safety issues.

**KEY INDIVIDUALS David Bateman** (see p.2538) has broad-based expertise in IP and is recognized for his knowledge of cyber and technology law. He often acts for high-profile clients, particularly those from the technology fields, in trademark infringement cases and technology disputes. A patent litigator with substantial experience, **David McDonald** (see p.2540) is especially adept in representing software and technology firms. He is praised by one client for his *"good bedside manner – he works well with the in-house community in our company. He's a very helpful team-mate in implementing issues."*

## Band 3

### Christensen O'Connor Johnson Kindness, PLLC

**THE FIRM** This established Seattle boutique is held in high esteem by clients for its customer service and value for money. The team is notable for its ability across a broad range of patent-related issues, including prosecution, drafting and non-infringement, in addition to handling IP litigation and trademark and copyright matters. Clients include Nintendo, Weyerhaeuser and JBT.

**KEY INDIVIDUALS Jerald Nagae**'s practice covers all facets of IP law, including litigation, patents, copyright and trademarks. He is highly respected in the market and much admired by clients, with one stating: *"I rely heavily on him. If I need general counseling in the patent field, I go to him first."* **John Denkenberger** heads the firm's litigation group and handles patent prosecution and litigation. He draws admiration from both peers and clients, one of whom enthuses: *"He's cost-effective and concentrates on the long-term relationship."* **Kevan Morgan** focuses his IP practice on the enforcement of trademarks, patents and copyrights, particularly advising clients from the electronics, medical devices and telecoms industries.

## Lowe Graham Jones

**THE FIRM** This prominent Seattle-based boutique firm covers all aspects of IP law, including complex patents across the USA and abroad, copyrights, trademarks, trade secrets and litigation. The firm's client portfolio includes Honeywell, Costco and DocuSign.

**Sources say:** *"They have an in-depth knowledge of our products and are able to articulate that in complex patents and filings matters."*

**KEY INDIVIDUALS Lawrence Graham** is praised by clients as a *"smart and strategic IP attorney"* who is *"reliable and meticulous in his work."* He is particularly distinguished by his skill in litigation, having appeared before trial and appellate courts nationwide, and also has a well-respected mediation practice.

## Seed IP Law Group PLLC

**THE FIRM** This Seattle-based group has forged a reputation in patent prosecution in the biotechnology, chemistry and electrical engineering arenas. The team also has recognized expertise in enforcement, trade secrets, copyrights and related litigation. Key clients include Nordstrom, Panasonic and GlaxoSmithKline.

**Sources say:** *"Very good at knowing US and international patent law, and responsive to the client – they're subject matter experts."*

**KEY INDIVIDUALS** The highly respected **William Ferron** specializes in a wide range of IP matters, with a focus on dispute resolution. He is well regarded by peers for his prowess in copyright and trademark issues.

## Wilson Sonsini Goodrich & Rosati

See profile on p.700

**THE FIRM** The lawyers at the Seattle office of this nationally renowned firm have broad knowledge of all aspects of IP law, particularly trademarks, patents, litigation, and retail and consumer protection. The team is particularly known for advising major clients from the life sciences, technology and media industries. Recent highlights include acting for Amazon.com on a range of IP and trademark issues.

**Sources say:** *"Excellent – on time, on budget and very responsive."*

**KEY INDIVIDUALS** Practice head **Aaron Hendelman** is an expert in a wide variety of IP and transactional matters, including those relating to unfair competition, trademarks, rights and licenses. Clients praise his business sense, practicality and responsiveness, with one stating: *"He's prompt, thorough and intuitive. He understands not only what the question is, but what the issue is."*

## Band 4

### Lane Powell PC

See profile on p.2547

**THE FIRM** The 11-partner team at this Pacific Northwest fixture tackles a wide range of IP matters, with clients praising its handling of copyright infringement, trademark portfolios, licensing and worldwide trademark clearance issues. The group has continued to expand its IP practice, with the recent addition of several IP portfolio developers and litigators, and represents clients from the software, pharmaceutical and technology industries.

**Sources say:** *"They've gone above and beyond – they really care about our company."*

**KEY INDIVIDUALS** Litigator **Brian Bodine** (see p.2538) is highly respected in the market for his vast knowledge of patent, trade secrets and trademark matters, and for his mediation practice.

## Other Notable Practitioners

The *"incredibly smart and practical"* **Mark Parris** of Orrick, Herrington & Sutcliffe LLP handles complex commercial litigation, with an emphasis on trade secrets, patents and licensing disputes, particularly in the technology arena. His clients include Expedia and Gamber-Johnson. The *"excellent and responsive"* **Bruce Goto** of Riddell Williams PS is prized by clients for being *"articulate, extremely knowledgeable in his field and an extraordinary resource."* He represents clients from the gaming, software and healthcare industries in a wide variety of IP and corporate matters. **David Tellekson** (see p.2541) of Fenwick & West LLP is held in high regard as an attorney who *"is outstanding and really achieves good results."* He is an expert in patent law and litigation, and represents clients from the biotechnology, medical devices and pharmaceutical industries. **Richard Siefert** of Garvey Schubert Barer is respected for his skills as a litigator in IP and antitrust disputes. He is also involved in mediation and arbitration work. Sources consider the *"professorial"* **Robert Cumbow** of Graham & Dunn PC to be an expert in copyright issues. He also counsels clients from a wide range of industries on trademark, IP litigation and advertising compliance issues. **Shannon Jost** of Stokes Lawrence, PS has a combined IP transactional and litigation practice covering licensing issues, the protection and enforcement of IP rights, and patent infringement litigation. **Brian Park** of Stoel Rives LLP conducts complex IP litigation and dispute resolution. Clients say: *"He knows when to fight and when not to. He knows how to win as well."*

# LABOR & EMPLOYMENT

Commentary about individuals can be found under their firm's paragraph. If the firm has no paragraph (is not ranked) look at Other Notable Practitioners.

| Labor & Employment Leading Firms |
| --- |
| **Band 1** |
| Davis Wright Tremaine LLP * |
| Perkins Coie LLP |
| Sebris Busto James |
| **Band 2** |
| Lane Powell PC * |
| Stoel Rives LLP |
| Winterbauer & Diamond PLLC * |
| **Band 3** |
| Dorsey & Whitney LLP * |
| Jackson Lewis LLP * |
| K&L Gates * |
| Riddell Williams PS |

## Band 1

### Davis Wright Tremaine LLP
**See profile on p.2544**

THE FIRM Davis Wright Tremaine's Washington labor and employment practice operates out of offices in Seattle and Bellevue, and is one of the largest and best in the state. The group consists of many talented attorneys, offering trial, mediation and counseling experience. Clients include Microsoft, Providence Health Services and Virginia Mason Medical Center.
**Sources say:** *"They truly partner with us in finding the right solution."*
**KEY INDIVIDUALS** Described as a *"class act,"* trial lawyer **Michael Reiss** is held in high regard, particularly for his skill in wage and hour class action trials and discrimination cases. He also has an established mediation practice. **Robert Blackstone** is skilled in a wide range of labor matters, including executive employment and separation agreements, labor relations planning, and noncompetition and trade secret matters. The *"excellent"* **Lawton Humphrey** concentrates her practice on a broad range of issues, and is especially adept at labor and employment litigation, dispute resolution and counseling. **Mark Berry** is well respected for his skills in labor and employment counseling, dispute resolution and grievance arbitration. **Henry Farber** specializes in advising and representing employers from the healthcare, hospitality and communications industries in issues such as arbitrations and negotiations. According to clients, *"efficiency is the hallmark of his practice and his advice."* The highly experienced **Mark Hutcheson** is known for his prowess in the traditional labor law arena, including labor planning, strike planning and prevention, and collective bargaining. **Thomas Lemly** is a much-admired trial lawyer with extensive experience in state and federal courts. He also counsels clients on a wide range of issues, such as wage and overtime compliance, sexual harassment and labor relations management.

| Labor & Employment Senior Statesmen | |
| --- | --- |
| **Senior Statesmen:** distinguished older practitioners | |
| Aslin John | Perkins Coie LLP |
| Williams Nancy | Perkins Coie LLP |

| Leading Individuals | |
| --- | --- |
| **Band 1** | |
| Busto Mark | Sebris Busto James |
| Cairns Carolyn | Stokes Lawrence, PS (ONP) † |
| Hutcheson Mark A | Davis Wright Tremaine LLP |
| Reiss Michael | Davis Wright Tremaine LLP |
| **Band 2** | |
| Barnes Clemens H | Graham & Dunn PC (ONP) † |
| Blackstone Robert A | Davis Wright Tremaine LLP |
| Cross Bruce Michael | Perkins Coie LLP |
| Diamond Kenneth J | Winterbauer & Diamond PLLC * |
| Droke Michael | Dorsey & Whitney LLP |
| Hollingsworth Jeff | Perkins Coie LLP |
| Howie Robert M | Riddell Williams PS |
| Humphrey Lawton | Davis Wright Tremaine LLP |
| James Jeffrey | Sebris Busto James |
| Klein III Otto G | Summit Law Group, PLLC (ONP) † |
| Madden Patrick M | K&L Gates * |
| O'Connell Timothy J | Stoel Rives LLP |
| Preston Anne | Garvey Schubert Barer (ONP) † |
| Reilly D. Michael | Lane Powell PC * |
| Rubin Jerome L | Stoel Rives LLP |
| Sebris Robert | Sebris Busto James |
| Shore James M | Stoel Rives LLP |
| Winterbauer Steven | Winterbauer & Diamond PLLC * |
| **Band 3** | |
| Berry Mark W | Davis Wright Tremaine LLP |
| Farber Henry | Davis Wright Tremaine LLP |
| Griffin Michael A | Jackson Lewis LLP * |
| Hamilton Kevin J | Perkins Coie LLP |
| Lemly Thomas A | Davis Wright Tremaine LLP |
| Mautner Gail | Lane Powell PC * |
| Thomas Suzanne | K&L Gates * |

### Perkins Coie LLP
**See profile on p.2548**

THE FIRM This preeminent firm has one of the strongest labor and employment practices in the region. The team is particularly experienced in wage and hour class action cases, ERISA litigation and workplace investigations, and additionally conducts cross-border work in Canada. The group's distinguished roster of clients include Nintendo, Boeing and UPS, which have all been represented in significant matters during the past year.
**KEY INDIVIDUALS Kurt Linsenmayer** is chair of the firm's employee benefits and executive compensation practice group. He has expertise in ERISA, 401(k) plans and benefits related to corporate matters such as M&A.

| Labor & Employment: Employee Benefits & Compensation Leading Individuals | |
| --- | --- |
| **Band 1** | |
| Curtice Melanie | Stoel Rives LLP |
| Linsenmayer Kurt | Perkins Coie LLP |
| Warner Mimi | Stoel Rives LLP |
| **Band 2** | |
| Morgan Sue | Perkins Coie LLP |

*\* Indicates firm / individual with profile.*
*Alphabetical order within each band. Band 1 is the highest.*

Well-regarded litigator **Jeff Hollingsworth** handles complex class employment cases for a variety of businesses. His clients include Les Schwab Tire Centers and Comcast. **Bruce Michael Cross** has a wide-ranging labor law practice, and is considered to be a strong player in wage and hour and employment class action matters. **Sue Morgan** is acclaimed for her vast knowledge of employee benefits, executive and equity compensation, and insider trading compliance. She has represented clients from a range of industries, including software, aviation and retail. Labor and employment practice chair **Kevin Hamilton** is an adept labor and employment litigator. He recently represented Microsoft in a gender discrimination and retaliation lawsuit, and acted for Starbucks in a disability discrimination case. **Nancy Williams** represents high-profile clients in litigation concerning a variety of matters. Clients consistently laud her attentiveness and dedication to their business needs. **John Aslin** is an experienced practitioner of labor and employment law. He is an expert in employment discrimination and equal employment matters, and also has expertise in mediation.

### Sebris Busto James

THE FIRM This compact and highly specialized Seattle labor and employment boutique is known for its ability to offer clients leading subject expertise at competitive rates. The team consists of experienced practitioners who are able to handle a broad range of matters, particularly dispute resolution, with expertise in litigation and arbitration.
**KEY INDIVIDUALS Mark Busto** is experienced in a wide range of labor and employment matters. He has particular expertise in discrimination and harassment cases, as well as union management. **Robert Sebris** focuses exclusively on representing management in strike planning and avoidance, wrongful discharge and unfair labor practice matters. **Jeffrey James** is praised by sources for his skill in labor and employment disputes. According to market commentators, *"he's an exceptionally capable litigator and a standout lawyer."*

## Band 2

### Lane Powell PC

See profile on p.2547

THE FIRM Clients praise the high level of customer service provided by this Washington labor and employment group. The team has experience in advising a wide range of clients, including those from the banking, retail and pharmaceutical industries, on all aspects of employment law and employee benefits. Recent highlights include acting for Nordstrom on an age discrimination claim, and representing Macy's in labor negotiations.

Sources say: "They are completely up-to-date on the latest court decisions."

KEY INDIVIDUALS Michael Reilly (see p.2541) attracts praise for his varied litigation practice, which covers ERISA and non-ERISA employee benefit claims, discrimination and retaliation cases. Clients say: "He gets back to you quickly with clear concise answers that don't just address legal concerns, but state things from a business standpoint." The "outstanding" Gail Mautner (see p.2540) chairs the firm's labor and employment practice group, and advises clients on religious and disability accommodation, employee discipline and termination, and wage and hour compliance.

### Stoel Rives LLP

THE FIRM This labor and employment practice handles litigation and advises on matters such as wage and hour and discrimination class action defense and employee pension plans. The team is especially well regarded by clients for its expertise in issues relating to harassment and labor law. It has recently been involved in a series of matters for MultiCare Health System, including class action disputes and union bargaining.

KEY INDIVIDUALS Seattle office managing partner Melanie Curtice focuses on matters related to health and welfare benefit plans, and the accompanying taxation, HIPAA and ERISA issues. Mimi Warner leads the group's benefits, tax and private client practice group. She has a deep knowledge of employee benefits, particularly relating to ERISA law and 401(k) plans. Labor law specialist Timothy O'Connell is an expert in labor law, and is admired for his skill in negotiating union and management relations, arbitrations, collective bargaining and wrongful discharge litigation. Jerome Rubin is held in high regard for his expertise in labor law matters such as union negotiations, NLRB proceedings and wage and hour issues. Sources praise his deep subject knowledge and experience. James Shore is described as a superb negotiator. His broad labor and employment practice incorporates wrongful termination, noncompetition agreements, and discrimination and harassment cases.

### Winterbauer & Diamond PLLC

See profile on p.2549

THE FIRM This compact, dedicated labor and employment boutique is held in high esteem by clients for providing high-quality work at competitive rates. The firm handles the full scope of employment issues, including regulatory compliance, equal employment opportunity, and labor relations and contract negotiations. Client include Expedia, Walgreens and King County.

Sources say: "They're thorough, cost-conscious and responsive, and get good results."

KEY INDIVIDUALS The "excellent" Kenneth Diamond (see p.2538) is experienced in all facets of employment law, including the removal of high-level executives, FMLA, contract disputes, and recruitment and training. Clients praise his business-savvy approach. Steven Winterbauer's (see p.2541) employment litigation and counseling practice encompasses the defense of companies before state and federal courts, early retirement programs and labor issues arising from M&A. "He's solid, knowledgeable, insightful, reasonable, measured, practical and resourceful," according to clients.

## Band 3

### Dorsey & Whitney LLP

See profile on p.1583

THE FIRM The Washington office of international law firm Dorsey & Whitney has the depth and expertise to handle all facets of labor and employment law. The team has been particularly active in discrimination, breach of contract, unfair labor practices and wage and hour disputes in the past year. Major clients include Wells Fargo, LA Fitness and Orbitz Worldwide.

KEY INDIVIDUALS Michael Droke handles wage and hour issues, unfair labor practices and union-management training. He effectively utilizes his background as an HR professional to also offer employment law training and preventive counseling.

### Jackson Lewis LLP

See profile on p.1982

THE FIRM This national labor and employment firm has an established presence in Seattle. The team represents clients from the automotive, financial services and manufacturing industries in a wide range of labor issues and litigation, such as ERISA cases, employment discrimination and harassment claims and class actions.

Sources say: "I've had very positive experiences with Jackson Lewis."

KEY INDIVIDUALS The "very good" Michael Griffin (see p.2539) is particularly adept at handling discrimination, retaliation and noncompetition agreement cases. He also counsels employers on workplace law issues such as disability and religious accommodation.

### K&L Gates

See profile on p.2245

THE FIRM K&L Gates's Washington team is run out of its offices in Seattle and Spokane. The group offers clients expertise in matters including employment counseling, wrongful termination and discrimination disputes, and traditional labor law issues. The firm regularly acts for high-profile clients, and the Seattle practice recently represented Amazon in litigation against a startup comprised of several of its former employees.

Sources say: "The firm is approachable and flexible to work with, and its national presence is helpful in dealing with our multilocation business structure."

KEY INDIVIDUALS Sources describe Suzanne Thomas (see p.2541) as "an excellent attorney and an excellent person to work with." She has experience in class action litigation, wage and hour payment and compliance, and workforce restructuring issues. Clients strongly praise Patrick Madden (see p.2540) for his expertise in class action cases and wage and hour issues. Clients say he is "incredibly knowledgeable – his knowledge level is frightening. He knows stuff inside-out."

### Riddell Williams PS

THE FIRM This firm represents clients in the full range of labor and employment disputes, in addition to offer counseling and training to companies in the full range of employment issues. Key clients include Microsoft, Boeing and T-Mobile.

Sources say: "The firm is excellent."

KEY INDIVIDUALS The "professional and client-friendly" Robert Howie counsels clients from the healthcare, hospitality and construction industries on matters such as discrimination, wage and hour compliance and workplace safety.

## Other Notable Practitioners

Carolyn Cairns of Stokes Lawrence, PS has extensive expertise in labor and employment dispute resolution, and is known to be one of the region's leading mediators. She also has a healthy litigation and counseling practice. Anne Preston of Garvey Schubert Barer is held in high regard by peers and clients for her talent in labor and employment litigation and counseling. Sources compliment her for being "very knowledgeable and experienced, and an excellent communicator." Clemens Barnes of Graham & Dunn PC has deep experience as a litigator and adviser in labor and employment law, with areas of expertise including employee discipline and termination, government contractor obligations, and wage and hour issues. "Fabulous lawyer" Otto Klein of Summit Law Group, PLLC earns accolades for his experience in labor and employment law. His practice includes grievance arbitration, executive compensation matters and bargaining negotiations.

# LITIGATION

Commentary about individuals can be found under their firm's paragraph. If the firm has no paragraph (is not ranked) look at Other Notable Practitioners.

## Litigation: General Commercial
### Leading Firms

**Band 1**

Byrnes Keller Cromwell LLP

Corr Cronin Michelson Baumgardner & Preece LLP

Davis Wright Tremaine LLP *

Perkins Coie LLP

**Band 2**

Gordon Tilden Thomas & Cordell LLP *

**Band 3**

Calfo Harrigan Leyh & Eakes LLP

Lane Powell PC *

McNaul Ebel Nawrot Helgren & Vance PLLC

Stoel Rives LLP

**Band 4**

DLA Piper LLP (US) *

Dorsey & Whitney LLP *

K&L Gates *

Orrick, Herrington & Sutcliffe LLP *

Savitt Bruce & Willey LLP

Summit Law Group, PLLC

*Indicates firm with profile.*

†*ONP = Other Notable Practitioner.*

## Litigation: General Commercial
### Leading Individuals

**Band 1**

| Burman David J | Perkins Coie LLP |
|---|---|
| Corr Kelly | Corr Cronin Michelson Baumgardner |
| Harrigan Jr Arthur W | Calfo Harrigan Leyh & Eakes LLP |
| Keehnel Stellman | DLA Piper LLP (US) * |
| Keller Brad | Byrnes Keller Cromwell LLP |
| Rummage Stephen M | Davis Wright Tremaine LLP |
| Schneider Jr Harry H | Perkins Coie LLP |
| Taylor Paul R | Byrnes Keller Cromwell LLP |
| Tilden Jeffrey I | Gordon Tilden Thomas & Cordell LLP |

**Band 2**

| Cronin William | Corr Cronin Michelson Baumgardner |
|---|---|
| Englund Rudy A | Lane Powell PC * |
| Gordon Charles C | Gordon Tilden Thomas & Cordell LLP |
| Kaplan Barry M | Wilson Sonsini Goodrich & Rosati (ONP)† |
| Ross Douglas C | Davis Wright Tremaine LLP |
| Sulkin Robert M | McNaul Ebel Nawrot Helgren & Vance PLLC |

**Band 3**

| Berenstain Ronald L | Perkins Coie LLP |
|---|---|
| Boeder Thomas | Perkins Coie LLP |
| Dunne Daniel J | Orrick, Herrington & Sutcliffe LLP * |
| Feldman Leonard | Stoel Rives LLP |
| Folse Parker | Susman Godfrey LLP (ONP)† |
| Goodnight David R | Stoel Rives LLP |
| Greer George E | Orrick, Herrington & Sutcliffe LLP * |
| Guess Philip | K&L Gates * |
| Leyh Timothy | Calfo Harrigan Leyh & Eakes LLP |
| Marchese Lisa | Dorsey & Whitney LLP |
| McNaul Jerry | McNaul Ebel Nawrot Helgren & Vance PLLC |
| Palumbo Ralph H | Summit Law Group, PLLC |
| Parnass John | Davis Wright Tremaine LLP |
| Squires III William R | Corr Cronin Michelson Baumgardner |

**Associates to watch**

| Escobar Andrew | DLA Piper LLP (US) * |
|---|---|
| Francis Rebecca | Davis Wright Tremaine LLP |

## Litigation: White-Collar Crime & Government Investigations
### Leading Individuals

**Band 1**

| Calfo Angelo J | Calfo Harrigan Leyh & Eakes LLP |
|---|---|
| Chadwell Robert G | McKay Chadwell PLLC (ONP)† |
| Finegold Laurence B | Garvey Schubert Barer (ONP)† |
| Mahler Robert | Dorsey & Whitney LLP |
| Robinson Jeffery | Schroeter Goldmark & Bender (ONP)† |
| Schwartz Irwin H | The Law Office of Irwin Schwartz (ONP)† |
| Wolfe John W | DLA Piper LLP (US) * |

## Band 1

### Byrnes Keller Cromwell LLP

**THE FIRM** Composed solely of trial lawyers, Byrnes Keller Cromwell represents clients in a wide variety of litigation, including white-collar criminal defense, securities, business torts and commercial disputes. In addition, this superb boutique is highly esteemed by peers and is often hired by law firms for professional liability defense counsel.

**Sources say:** "*A very good litigation boutique – I think highly of them.*"

**KEY INDIVIDUALS Brad Keller**, one of the founding partners of the firm, is held in high esteem by sources, who describe him as an "*outstanding trial lawyer.*" He is especially praised for his work in legal malpractice cases. **Paul Taylor** attracts admiration throughout the Pacific Northwest for his skill and experience as a trial lawyer. His litigation expertise encompasses condemnation, securities and professional liability defense lawsuits, personal injury and wrongful death claims, and a criminal antitrust and perjury prosecution.

### Corr Cronin Michelson Baumgardner & Preece LLP

**THE FIRM** This formidable, 26-lawyer boutique is a market leader in the state, possessing the ability to compete against Washington's many full-service firms. The firm represents clients in many types of litigation, including class action defense, product liability and insurance coverage cases.

**Sources say:** "*A growing, aggressive and excellent boutique.*"

**KEY INDIVIDUALS** The "*top-notch*" **Kelly Corr** is widely respected for his abilities as a trial lawyer, with a broad practice that encompasses commercial litigation, class actions, product liability, personal injury and employment litigation. **William Squires** is a highly thought-of trial lawyer who is described by one appreciative source as "*a very good lawyer with long experience. I have high regard for him.*" Founding partner **William Cronin** is an impressive litigator who has long-standing expertise in the law, and is complimented by sources as "*a lawyer's lawyer.*"

### Davis Wright Tremaine LLP

See profile on p.2544

**THE FIRM** Davis Wright Tremaine's Washington litigation group is admired for its prowess in the class action defense, healthcare, trade secrets and financial litigation spheres. The group's client roster includes T-Mobile USA, Washington Federal and Clearwire. Recent highlights include representing technology giant Microsoft in a series of class action disputes.

**Sources say:** "*High quality across the board.*"

**KEY INDIVIDUALS** The "*terrific*" **Stephen Rummage** concentrates his litigation practice on class action defense and appellate litigation, focusing on media-related industries such as digital media and telecommunications, as well as other sectors, including financial services. He has recently acted for Microsoft. **Douglas Ross**, identified by one source as "*an exceptional litigator,*" focuses on antitrust and competition work in the healthcare arena, representing Pacific Northwest healthcare systems such as Providence Health & Services, as well as hospitals and health systems outside the region. **John Parnass** is regarded as one of the state's leading construction litigators. He advises clients on public and private infrastructure projects and is an expert in complex construction disputes and transactions. **Rebecca Francis** is an associate who continues to impress with her talent in representing clients in complex civil litigation cases. Her practice spans a broad range of matters, including class action defense, shareholder and derivative litigation, and appellate law.

### Perkins Coie LLP

See profile on p.2548

**THE FIRM** Perkins Coie is firmly established as having one of the Pacific Northwest's outstanding litigation practices. The Washington group, comprised of offices in Seattle and Bellevue, handles an impressive variety of litigation, including white-collar defense, securities and corporate governance, business and IP. The group's client list includes local heavy hitters Boeing, Microsoft and Starbucks.

**KEY INDIVIDUALS** The highly respected **David Burman** has a commercial litigation practice which includes class actions, federal and state false claims acts and consumer protection. **Thomas Boeder**, head of the firm's Washington litigation group, also concentrates his practice on commercial litigation, with areas of expertise including IP, class actions and consumer product liability. **Harry Schneider** has a national profile for his litigation, trial and arbitration practice. His broad expertise particularly focuses on complex financial, IP and professional liability litigation. **Ronald Berenstain** concentrates his practice on securities and corporate governance litigation, such as shareholder class actions, litigation relating to M&A and SEC enforcement proceedings, and internal investigations.

## Band 2

### Gordon Tilden Thomas & Cordell LLP
See profile on p.2546

**THE FIRM** This eminent firm, which devotes itself entirely to litigation and advice related to it, represents a wide variety of high-profile clients in Washington and nationwide. The team particularly focuses on business litigation, personal injury disputes and insurance coverage claims, with added expertise in lawyer malpractice, securities litigation and environmental coverage.
**KEY INDIVIDUALS** The *"outstanding"* **Jeffrey Tilden** commands respect for his experience and abilities as a trial lawyer, with one admiring peer stating he is *"known as a go-to trial lawyer around town."* Described by one source as *"a superb lawyer,"* the much-admired **Charles Gordon** has deep experience in a broad range of civil litigation cases.

## Band 3

### Calfo Harrigan Leyh & Eakes LLP

**THE FIRM** Formerly known as Danielson Harrigan Leyh & Tollefson, this litigation boutique recently welcomed formidable white-collar lawyer Angelo Calfo to its practice. The firm has a strong reputation in the market for its skilled trial lawyers who practice in areas such as whistleblower, marine and complex civil litigation.
**Sources say:** *"Absolutely superb trial lawyers."*
**KEY INDIVIDUALS Angelo Calfo** is a white-collar lawyer who has a reputation as one of the Pacific Northwest's strongest practitioners. Sources say: *"He gets top marks in his skills, how he handles himself and the cases he gets. He's very successful."* **Arthur Harrigan** is a highly respected commercial trial lawyer who has represented a number of illustrious local clients in high-stakes litigation cases. One admiring source describes him as *"smart and has had huge trial experience for many years and is an excellent choice."* The *"excellent"* **Timothy Leyh** draws plaudits for his experience as a trial lawyer who litigates class action defense, business torts and securities cases.

### Lane Powell PC
See profile on p.2547

**THE FIRM** The Seattle office of this Pacific Northwest stalwart covers all facets of commercial and white-collar litiga-

tion, with insurance coverage litigation being a particularly prominent area of work for the firm. The group also has expertise in trials and appeals at the state and federal levels, commercial disputes and class action litigation. Clients include Lloyd's, Nordstrom and AIG.
**Sources say:** *"They do great work – they're responsive and proactive."*
**KEY INDIVIDUALS** The *"wonderful, tenacious, smart and hard-working"* **Rudy Englund** (see p.2539) is respected for his commercial and complex litigation practice which includes securities litigation, IP disputes and consumer fraud.

### McNaul Ebel Nawrot Helgren & Vance PLLC

**THE FIRM** This Seattle-based firm, which principally concentrates on corporate, real estate and technology law, has a broad and well-respected litigation practice. Areas covered include legal malpractice defense, business litigation and insurance coverage matters.
**Sources say:** *"Excellent – they do consistently good work."*
**KEY INDIVIDUALS Robert Sulkin** is described by admiring sources as *"one of the best trial lawyers in town."* He has a wide-ranging litigation practice which incorporates real estate, environmental and securities law litigation. Described by market sources as *"one of the deans of the Seattle community,"* **Jerry McNaul** is much admired for his longstanding litigation practice, which includes commercial, employment and construction litigation.

### Stoel Rives LLP

**THE FIRM** The Washington branch of this Portland-headquartered firm has a litigation group with expertise in an extensive range of litigation, including IP, product liability and breach of contract litigation. The group represents clients from the life sciences, renewable energy and media industries, with clients including King County, American Traffic Solutions and REC Silicon.
**KEY INDIVIDUALS Leonard Feldman** has a complex commercial litigation and appellate practice, and is in particular recognized for the latter. **David Goodnight** has deep experience in various disputes, including land use, tax and commercial litigation.

## Band 4

### DLA Piper LLP (US)
See profile on p.1971

**THE FIRM** This international giant has a healthy practice in Washington which covers the full scope of litigation, including class action defense, civil litigation, criminal defense, and government and internal investigations. Clients include Community Health Systems, United Online and Groupon.
**KEY INDIVIDUALS** The *"very creative and smart"* **Stellman Keehnel** (see p.2540) is an experienced litigator who is particularly known for his work in securities law, including securities class action defense. He recently successfully defended Verizon Corporate Services Group in a software copyright infringement suit brought by Gillani

Consulting. The eminent **John Wolfe** (see p.2541) is described by appreciative clients as a *"stellar"* attorney. He has deep experience as a litigator and white-collar criminal defense lawyer. Rising star **Andrew Escobar** (see p.2539), described by one competitor as *"one to watch,"* attracts praise for his skill as a litigator, particularly in regards to securities litigation and internal investigations.

### Dorsey & Whitney LLP
See profile on p.1583

**THE FIRM** Dorsey & Whitney's Seattle office has an effective litigation practice which is particularly experienced in securities disputes, complex commercial cases and class action matters. The team's clients include Bank of America, Wells Fargo and Comcast.
**Sources say:** *"You'll get top service with this firm. I can't say enough good things about the team."*
**KEY INDIVIDUALS** *"Very fine lawyer"* **Robert Mahler** focuses his practice on white-collar criminal defense, securities litigation, bank fraud and complex civil disputes. He recently successfully represented a client in a federal jury trial brought by the SEC for alleged securities fraud. Client favorite **Lisa Marchese** earns ringing endorsement for her client service and skills as a litigator. *"She is one of the top trial lawyers that I've had the privilege of dealing with. Her responsiveness is unreal. She will do anything that is necessary to get the work done for her client,"* according to clients.

### K&L Gates
See profile on p.2245

**THE FIRM** National giant K&L Gates's 40-strong Washington commercial litigation practice, comprised of offices in Seattle and Spokane, represents clients from hedge funds, startups, class actions and regulatory proceedings in all aspects of commercial litigation. Major clients include a series of household names including T-Mobile and Amazon.com.
**Sources say:** *"We are very happy to know that K&L Gates has our back."*
**KEY INDIVIDUALS Philip Guess** (see p.2539) has a litigation practice which frequently crosses over into the firm's corporate and bankruptcy practices. He attracts praise from clients for his skill and *"business-savvy strength."* According to one source, *"I cannot think of anyone I would rather have on my side in a dispute."*

### Orrick, Herrington & Sutcliffe LLP
See profile on p.1994

**THE FIRM** The Washington branch of this leading national firm is especially well regarded for securities litigation. Other areas the team covers include commercial dispute resolution, professional liability defense and complex contractual disputes. Recent highlights include acting for Residential Capital in lawsuits surrounding an MBS dispute.
**Sources say:** *"Their responsiveness is extremely timely, they speak in plain English and their legal analysis is fantastic."*
**KEY INDIVIDUALS** The *"solid, smart, personable"* **Daniel Dunne** (see p.2538) is a litigator well regarded in the market for his expertise in defending management, financial

institutions and accountants in a variety of securities matters. **George Greer** (see p.2539) conducts complex commercial, securities and professional liability litigation. He is described by one source as enjoying *"a sterling reputation as a securities litigator for years."*

## Savitt Bruce & Willey LLP

THE FIRM This litigation boutique, located in Seattle and comprised of 11 attorneys, handles an impressive variety of litigation both in state and federal court. The team concentrates particularly on IP litigation, corporate governance matters and investor claims.

Sources say: *"They're all experienced lawyers. Why we like to work with them is that you get top-quality counsel in lawyering, but delivered through more cost-effective means."*

KEY INDIVIDUALS David Bruce, James Savitt and Stephen Willey are key contacts at the firm.

## Summit Law Group, PLLC

THE FIRM This Seattle firm is highly respected by peers for the quality of its attorneys. The litigation team handles a wide range of matters, and represents prominent clients in environmental, business and technology litigation.

Sources say: *"Probably one of the best-kept secrets in the market. They're an excellent group."*

KEY INDIVIDUALS *"Excellent lawyer"* **Ralph Palumbo** is held in high esteem for his expertise as a litigator in areas including insurance, complex commercial disputes and environmental cases.

## Other Notable Practitioners

The well-regarded **Parker Folse** of Susman Godfrey LLP is a litigator who focuses on commercial and IP matters. Sources state: *"He's intellectually smart as you come. A wonderful guy who is highly competent."* **Barry Kaplan** of

Wilson Sonsini Goodrich & Rosati has a well-respected litigation practice. According to commentators, *"he's very smart and very good at what he does"* and is a top choice for securities litigation work. The deeply experienced **Robert Chadwell** of McKay Chadwell PLLC has a reputation in the market as a talented criminal defense lawyer. The illustrious **Laurence Finegold** of Garvey Schubert Barer is widely respected for his abilities in white-collar criminal defense and complex business litigation. The *"superb and very smart"* **Irwin Schwartz** of The Law Office of Irwin Schwartz is a litigator who represents companies and individuals in white-collar criminal defense matters. **Jeffery Robinson** of Schroeter Goldmark & Bender is universally acknowledged as one of the state's premier criminal defense attorneys. Sources compliment him as being a *"very fine trial lawyer"* and *"first-rate – careful and outstanding on his feet."*

# REAL ESTATE

Zoning/Land Use p.2536

Commentary about individuals can be found under their firm's paragraph. If the firm has no paragraph (is not ranked) look at Other Notable Practitioners.

## Real Estate
### Leading Firms

**Band 1**

Alston Courtnage & Bassetti LLP
Davis Wright Tremaine LLP *
Foster Pepper PLLC *
K&L Gates *
Perkins Coie LLP

**Band 2**

Jameson Babbitt Stites & Lombard
Lane Powell PC *
Stoel Rives LLP
Van Ness Feldman PC *

\* Indicates firm with profile.
†ONP = Other Notable Practitioner.

## Real Estate
### Leading Individuals

**Band 1**

| Barrett Michael A | Perkins Coie LLP |
| Bassetti Andrew B | Alston Courtnage & Bassetti LLP |
| Kuntz Michael | Foster Pepper PLLC |
| Rockwell David H | Stoel Rives LLP |

**Band 2**

| Ackerman Gary | Foster Pepper PLLC |
| Courtnage Michael S | Alston Courtnage & Bassetti LLP |
| Dial Ellen | Perkins Coie LLP |
| Fluhrer Gary | Foster Pepper PLLC |
| Green William | Perkins Coie LLP |
| Koons Warren | Davis Wright Tremaine LLP |
| Pedreira Virginia M | Stoel Rives LLP |
| Pepple Daniel P | Pepple Cantu & Schmidt, PLLC (ONP)† |
| Percival Donald E | Davis Wright Tremaine LLP |
| Skinner Shannon | K&L Gates * |
| Tanner Gordon W | Stoel Rives LLP |
| Thomas Cynthia | Real Property Law Group PLLC (ONP)† |

**Band 3**

| Clark Beth | Foster Pepper PLLC |
| Cobb Jennifer Dunn | Jameson Babbitt Stites & Lombard |
| de Sa e Silva Marco | Davis Wright Tremaine LLP |
| DeVoe Lawler Anne | Jameson Babbitt Stites & Lombard |
| Fikso Robert | Fikso Kretschmer Smith Dixon (ONP)† |
| Goeltz Thomas | Davis Wright Tremaine LLP |
| Gradel James | Perkins Coie LLP |
| Greenfield Jim | Davis Wright Tremaine LLP |
| Moore Richard | Socius Law Group PLLC (ONP)† |
| Neugebauer Robert | K&L Gates * |
| Read Thomas | Alston Courtnage & Bassetti LLP |
| Shigley Charles E | Alston Courtnage & Bassetti LLP |
| Shrontz Craig H | Perkins Coie LLP |
| Stokke Diane | K&L Gates * |
| Wheeler Douglas | Lane Powell PC * |

**Associates to watch**

| Arefi-Afshar Yousef | Cairncross & Hempelmann |

*The editorial is in alphabetical order by firm name.*

## Alston Courtnage & Bassetti LLP

THE FIRM This eight-attorney boutique is well regarded in the market for its expertise in commercial real estate, especially regarding acquisitions, sales and commercial leasing. The firm has recently been involved in a series of property sales involving significant developments. Clients appreciate the firm's efficient manner in dealing with their real estate issues.

KEY INDIVIDUALS **Andrew Bassetti** is an authority on commercial real estate and real estate financing, and counts several national banks among his clients. **Michael Courtnage** has a broad real estate practice covering office, industrial and mixed-use projects for clients based in the USA and abroad. **Thomas Read** focuses his practice on commercial real estate transactions, including workouts, distressed assets, office and multifamily projects. **Charles**

**Shigley** is singled out by one client as *"a bright guy who is very responsive and cuts to the chase."* He has expertise in commercial real estate transactions and bankruptcy matters, and frequently represents both lenders and borrowers.

## Cairncross & Hempelmann, A Professional Service Corporation

See profile on p.2543

THE FIRM The land use group at this Seattle stalwart is highly regarded for its expertise in the related practice areas of natural resources and environmental law, and for its work for residential developers. Clients also praise the team's expertise in land acquisition and related litigation,

and laud the firm's ability to deliver value for money in its service.

Sources say: *"They are very knowledgeable and professional."*

KEY INDIVIDUALS **John Hempelmann** counsels both large companies and nonprofit developer clients on real estate development projects, ranging from major projects to mixed-use, sustainable developments. **Donald Marcy** has built a solid reputation as a real estate and land use lawyer with particular expertise in complex land use laws. **Yousef Arefi-Afshar** is praised as being *"smart, personable and intelligent."* He is seen in the market as a rising star, known in particular for his skill in real estate insolvencies.

*The editorial is in alphabetical order by firm name.*

## Davis Wright Tremaine LLP
See profile on p.2544

THE FIRM DWT's formidable Washington real estate and land use group is comprised of two offices operating from Bellevue and Seattle. The team has extensive experience in healthcare facilities, hotels, low-income multifamily housing and energy projects. Clients include Comcast, Group Health Cooperative and Rockefeller Group. Recent highlights include representing Alaska Airlines in the establishment of a PPP with the Port of Seattle.
Sources say: *"What I like about DWT is how they solve problems through the lens of a businessman, not just a lawyer."*
KEY INDIVIDUALS John Keegan is a well-respected land use lawyer admired for his ability to navigate his way around the more complex land use laws. He is particularly known for his work with medical institutions and hospital developments. Donald Percival is cochair of the firm's real estate and land use practice, and is held in high esteem by clients, with one enthusing that he is *"a very good lawyer – astute, responsive, thorough, thoughtful, and easy to work with."* Marco de Sa e Silva has a broad real estate practice covering aquatic projects, wind energy projects and commercial real estate purchases and sales, as well as land use

issues such as permitting and representing clients in front of government agencies. Thomas Goeltz has a broad real estate and land use practice ranging from transportation and infrastructure agreements to mixed-use master plan projects. Jim Greenfield represents public, private and nonprofit clients in real estate transactions and land use matters. He is appreciated by clients for his personable nature and astuteness in negotiating the political aspects of real estate law, in particular zoning and neighborhood concerns. Warren Koons has extensive experience in commercial real estate law, and advises clients on timberland, agricultural and medical property issues, as well as real property issues such as easements, logging contracts and title matters. One client enthuses: *"He's a fantastic lawyer – incredible. Couldn't be better."*

## Foster Pepper PLLC
See profile on p.2545
THE FIRM This Washington fixture has the breadth and depth to distinguish itself as one of the state's top real estate and land use practices. From its offices in Seattle and Spokane, the group's attorneys advise clients on all facets of real estate and land use matters, with expertise in sophisticated transactional real estate and municipal bond work.
KEY INDIVIDUALS Michael Kuntz is a highly regarded real estate lawyer who focuses on commercial and residential development and finance. He handles a variety of related matters, including sales, partnerships, and debt and equity financing. He is also noted for his experience in the development and financing of affordable housing. Thomas Walsh is a well-respected lawyer known for representing Seattle's hospital and college institutions in matters pertaining to land use and environmental law. Gary Ackerman concentrates his real estate practice on condominium and homeowner association laws, and represents both land owners and developers. Gary Fluhrer's real estate practice frequently involves a wide variety of projects, from those with a bankruptcy component, to those which require development, leasing and financing, with a particular emphasis on the hospitality and financing sectors. Beth Clark is chair of the firm's real estate group and has a broad practice covering all aspects of real estate law. Judith Runstad is admired for her deep knowledge of land use, real estate development and environmental law. Described by one source as *"the leading scholar in land use,"* Richard Settle has vast experience in land use laws and regulations, and represents landowners and developers before governmental agencies at the trial and appellate levels.

## Hillis Clark Martin & Peterson P.S.
THE FIRM This Seattle-based firm has a healthy real estate and land use practice, with the latter being a particularly strong area for the group. The team handles a wide variety of related matters, including permits, entitlements, land use appeals and litigation. The environmental sector is another key area of expertise for the group.
KEY INDIVIDUALS Melody McCutcheon and Ryan Durkan are two well-respected land use and environmental lawyers, both described by one source as being *"very*

*strong."* McCutcheon concentrates on representing private and public bodies in all aspects of land use and environmental law, while Durkan focuses on land development and permitting. George Kresovich's practice encompasses both real estate and land use law. He is particularly known for conducting litigation in state and federal trial and appellate courts. The *"wonderful"* Richard Wilson is well reputed for his expertise in complex master planned projects, and for his ability to obtain entitlements for major development proposals in Washington.

## Jameson Babbitt Stites & Lombard
THE FIRM This compact Seattle-based firm has a well-respected commercial real estate practice which handles a wide range of related matters, and is ably supported by its land use and construction law groups.
KEY INDIVIDUALS Jennifer Dunn Cobb is experienced in all facets of real estate transactions, and has particular experience in multifamily financing, apartment projects, leasing and entity formation. Anne DeVoe Lawler excels in a wide variety of transactional real estate matters, as well as counseling clients on environmental and hazardous waste issues.

## K&L Gates
See profile on p.2245
THE FIRM The Seattle office of established global firm K&L Gates is well equipped to handle all manner of real estate and land use matters, with particular expertise in purchase and sale agreements, distressed assets and environmental issues. Clients appreciate the firm's capacity to work effectively across state borders.
Sources say: *"Excellent – we're very comfortable."*
KEY INDIVIDUALS Eric Laschever (see p.2540) has a broad practice covering the full spectrum of land use and environmental law. He has expertise in projects, land development and environmental compliance. Shannon Skinner (see p.2541) concentrates her practice on real estate and financing transactions, and is particularly experienced in complex redevelopment projects and troubled loans. Sources say she is *"good at getting to a resolution without it taking forever, and good at separating the business from the legal without anybody having to give up anything."* Real estate attorney Robert Neugebauer (see p.2540) is held in high regard by peers for his proficiency in complex real estate transactions and financings, and advises clients from the hospitality and retail industries seeking locations in Washington and Alaska. Diane Stokke (see p.2541) is noted for her deep knowledge of property law, commercial real estate and mixed-use developments. She advises a number of energy and utilities companies on the real estate and financing aspects of their facilities.

## Lane Powell PC
See profile on p.2547
THE FIRM The real estate team at this Northwest institution is especially adept at handling commercial real estate matters such as leasing transactions, acquisitions and creditor-debtor law. Clients include Wells Fargo, Home Depot and Washington Federal. The team recently represented

*The editorial is in alphabetical order by firm name.*

Key Banks in relation to loan workouts and real estate collateral involving an agricultural borrower.

**Sources say:** *"Unique problem solvers who are available around the clock. We work across six time zones and they're always available."*

**KEY INDIVIDUALS Douglas Wheeler** (see p.2541) is considered by one source to be *"really one of the finest lawyers I've worked with. He's able to work seamlessly with many other people, including those who are difficult."* He has a wide-ranging practice covering real estate, corporate law and M&A.

## McCullough Hill Leary, PS

**THE FIRM** This dynamic, nine-attorney Seattle-based boutique is regarded as one of the state's premier land use firms. It represents both public and private organizations in a variety of projects throughout Washington, including resorts, industrial facilities, urban infill and airports. The team has recently been involved in a series of high-profile developments throughout Seattle.

**KEY INDIVIDUALS Richard Hill** has deep knowledge of Seattle's land use codes and entitlement processes, and is experienced in obtaining governmental approvals for residential, educational and mixed-use developments. The *"super"* and *"really talented"* **Jack McCullough** is admired by commentators for his legal skill in handling a wide variety of land use matters.

## Perkins Coie LLP

See profile on p.2548

**THE FIRM** Perkins Coie's real estate group maintains its reputation as one of the preeminent practices in Washington, with an impressive number of talented attorneys and a roster of high-caliber clients. The firm's client portfolio includes Starbucks, Puget Sound Energy and Boeing. Recent highlights include acting for Brooks Sports on the development of new global headquarters in Seattle, in a high-value office and retail project.

**KEY INDIVIDUALS Michael Barrett** has expertise across all aspects of real estate matters, including acquisitions and dispositions, as well as workouts and insolvencies of hospitality, retail and residential developments. The well-

respected **Ellen Dial** is experienced in real estate development and financing, land use and zoning. Clients are quick to praise her attentiveness and responsiveness to their needs. **William Green** focuses on real estate transactions and is sought after by clients from the biotech, hi-tech and educational industries. **James Gradel** is skilled in dealing with complex real estate transactions, and has deep knowledge of real estate finance. He ably assists a wide variety of clients, including those from the telecoms, energy and timber industries. **Craig Shrontz** is chair of the firm's real estate practice and concentrates on commercial real estate and property development transactions. Sources praise his service-oriented approach.

## Stoel Rives LLP

**THE FIRM** This Pacific Northwest market leader has a thriving real estate and land use practice. It has particular expertise in real estate taxation, condominium and time share issues and a range of sophisticated transactions. Clients include the City of Redmond, Pacific Bioscience Laboratories and Koniag Development.

**KEY INDIVIDUALS** Highly experienced attorney **David Rockwell** has a broad commercial real estate practice. He is held in high regard by peers and clients for his ability to manage large projects. **Virginia Pedreira** is acclaimed for her work in the real estate sphere. She has expertise in agricultural and renewable energy projects, and represents clients throughout the region. **Gordon Tanner** is an expert in all manner of real estate issues, including secured lending, title insurance and community property. He also has deep knowledge of agribusiness.

## Van Ness Feldman PC

See profile on p.926

**THE FIRM** This Seattle-based firm, the erstwhile GordonDerr, recently merged with a firm in DC to become its current namesake. It has a longstanding and reputable land use practice, with particular expertise in environmental and natural resources law, as well as a growing energy and climate change practice.

**Sources say:** *"They're engaged and knowledgeable, and do things in a timely manner."*

**KEY INDIVIDUALS Brent Carson** (see p.2538) is an expert on complex land development, real property disputes and environmental entitlements process issues. He also has a robust environmental litigation practice. **Jay Derr** (see p.2538) is a respected land use and environmental attorney who is adept at obtaining permits for complex development projects regionally and countrywide. He is known for representing municipal clients located in Washington.

## Other Notable Practitioners

**Robert Fikso** of Fikso Kretschmer Smith Dixon Ormseth PS handles all aspects of real estate transactions. Sources praise him as *"a very efficient and practical lawyer who provides excellent legal advice."* **Glenn Amster** of Kantor Taylor Nelson Boyd & Evatt PC handles a wide variety of real estate matters and environmental regulatory issues, such as property acquisitions, development strategies and Endangered Species Act compliance. **Daniel Pepple** of Pepple Cantu & Schmidt, PLLC has vast knowledge of all types of commercial real estate transactions, and frequently represents institutional lenders and developers in construction loan, permanent loan, creditors' rights and workout matters. **Cynthia Thomas** of Real Property Law Group PLLC has built a reputation for handling a wide range of commercial real estate transactional matters, including leasing and financing. **Richard Moore** of Socius Law Group PLLC concentrates his practice on commercial leasing and property management, and represents both landlords and tenants in complex commercial real estate matters.

# Leaders' Profiles in Washington

## BATEMAN, David A
K&L Gates, Seattle
206 370 6682
david.bateman@klgates.com
*Featured in Intellectual Property (Washington)*
**Practice Areas:** Partner David Bateman focuses on the cutting edge of cyberlaw, technology law, and intellectual property litigation. With 20 years of experience in technology, privacy and intellectual property law, he represents clients in high profile litigation matters and investigations. He consults with clients regarding all types of cyberlaw issues and works with wireless carriers, Internet service providers, online retailers, software developers, and hardware manufacturers to create and protect their intellectual property and technologies. He has worked extensively on cyber-forensic investigations, data breaches and instances of trade secret misappropriation.

## BODINE, Brian G
Lane Powell PC, Seattle
206 223 7406
bodineb@lanepowell.com
*Featured in Intellectual Property (Washington)*
**Practice Areas:** Extensive experience litigating patent, trademark and other IP-related disputes in courts throughout the country.
**Professional Memberships:** Past Chair, IP Section of the Washington State Bar Association. Past President, Washington State Patent Law Association.
**Career:** Law Clerk to Hon. Carolyn R Dimmick, US District Court and Hon. Joseph F Baca, New Mexico Supreme Court.
**Publications:** Lectured and written on topics of interest to IP Bar.
**Personal:** JD (magna cum laude), University of Puget Sound (now Seattle University) School of Law. BS in Chemical Engineering, Montana State University. Adjunct Professor Patent and Trade Secret Law, Seattle University School of Law.

## BROMFIELD, William
Fenwick & West LLP, Seattle
206 389 4532
bbromfield@fenwick.com
*Featured in Corporate/Commercial (Washington)*
**Practice Areas:** William H Bromfield is a partner in the Corporate Group of Fenwick & West LLP. He is resident in the firm's Seattle office. Mr Bromfield provides general corporate and securities advice to public and private companies, particularly those in the media, Internet, e-commerce, wireless applications, gaming, SaaS, and other high-technology industries. He represents numerous start-ups with their formations, equity and debt financings, and general corporate matters, as well as counseling management and boards of directors on transactional, fund-raising, employment, fiduciary and other matters. He also regularly represents venture capital and private equity investors in private financings in a broad range of industries.
**Career:** Chambers USA named Mr Bromfield an "Up and Coming" lawyer as well as a leader in his

field for 2012 and the Washington Law and Politics magazine named him a "Rising Star" for four consecutive years.

## BUTLER, Diane
Lane Powell PC, Seattle
206 223 7715
butlerd@lanepowell.com
*Featured in Immigration (Washington)*
**Practice Areas:** Chair, Immigration Practice Group: focus on business immigration and foreign investment, border issue troubleshooting and waivers, employer compliance issues and investigation defense.
**Professional Memberships:** American Immigration Lawyers Association (AILA) Director, Board of Governors (2011-14).
**Career:** Shareholder since 2004; Bull Housser Tupper, Shanghai, China (legal assistant 1988-89).
**Publications:** Lectured, given training and written extensively on immigration law; developed immigration forms and I-9 compliance guidance; quoted in New York Times and other publications on immigration issues.
**Personal:** George Washington University (JD, 1992); University of Wyoming (BA, 1983); Trade Development Alliance Advisory Committee; Gage Academy of Art Advisory Committee.

## CARLSON, C Kent
K&L Gates, Seattle
206 370 6679
kent.carlson@klgates.com
*Featured in Corporate/Commercial (Washington)*
**Practice Areas:** Partner Kent Carlson practices corporate law, primarily focusing on merger and acquisition transactions and on financings and joint venture and other complex strategic relationships. He advises publicly held and private companies on governance and shareholder issues, including bylaw amendments, shareholder proposals, public filings, and proxy contests. He counsels boards of directors regarding fiduciary duties, committee charters, indemnification matters, disclosure and compliance issues. He is a founding member of the state bar association committee that oversees and updates the Washington Business Corporation Act. He also is the Washington liaison to the ABA Committee on Corporate Laws.

## CARSON, Brent
Van Ness Feldman PC, Seattle
206 802 3831
brc@vnf.com
*Featured in Real Estate (Washington)*
**Practice Areas:** Brent advises clients with complex land development, environmental permitting and real property issues. His practice focuses on local, state and federal land use and environmental regulations and issues concerning wetlands, endangered species, shoreline and in-water construction, environmental assessments, rezones, comprehensive plan amendments, and development agreements. Brent's litigation practice includes defense of environmental enforcement

actions and entitlements and real property disputes.
**Personal:** JD, University of Washington School of Law; MS, Harvard School of Public Health; SB, Massachusetts Institute of Technology.

## CHAPMAN, William
K&L Gates, Seattle
206 370 7807
bill.chapman@klgates.com
*Featured in Environment (Washington)*
**Practice Areas:** Bill Chapman, a partner in the environmental, land and natural resources practice group, represents clients performing hazardous waste investigation and cleanup; pursuing or litigating air and water permits; land use permitting and litigation; redevelopment requiring hazardous waste remedy; and permitting and environmental review for major office campus and infrastructure facilities. He advises corporations and municipalities in permitting and environmental compliance matters in the energy, high technology, waste management, and real estate industries. He has chaired or keynoted conferences on hazardous waste cleanup, defending citizen suits under the clean water and clean air acts, permitting and land conservation.

## COONROD, Stephan
K&L Gates, Seattle
206 370 8316
Stephan.coonrod@klgates.com
*Featured in Corporate/Commercial (Washington)*
**Practice Areas:** Stephan Coonrod, a partner in the corporate, mergers and acquisitions and securities practice group, has a domestic and international business practice centering on acquisitions, private equity and venture capital investments, trans-border transactions and technology transfers. He also handles general corporate matters for K&L Gates' clients.

## DERR, Jay
Van Ness Feldman PC, Seattle
206 802 3829
jpd@vnf.com
*Featured in Real Estate (Washington)*
**Practice Areas:** Jay helps public and private sector clients manage and obtain federal, state and local permits for major development projects across Washington State and throughout the United States. He also serves or has served as special land use counsel for several Washington cities and counties.
**Professional Memberships:** Washington State Bar Association, Environmental and Land Use Law Section (Executive Committee).
**Personal:** JD, University of California Berkeley, Boalt School of Law; BS, summa cum laude, Michigan State University.

## DIAMOND, Kenneth J
Winterbauer & Diamond PLLC, Seattle
206 676 8440
ken@winterbauerdiamond.com
*Featured in Labor & Employment (Washington)*

**Practice Areas:** Ken counsels and defends employers across a broad range of industries on the full range of employment law matters. He also has significant experience defending wage and hour class-action cases alleging misclassification of employees.
**Professional Memberships:** Executive Committee–The Worklaw Network, 2009-13; Washington Defense Trial Lawyers Association; Stanford Law School-Board of Visitors, 2006-11; Seattle Country Day School-Board of Trustees, 2004-09; American Bar Association (Employment & Labor Law, Litigation); Washington State Bar Association (Labor & Employment Law); King County Bar Association (Labor & Employment Law, Litigation).
**Career:** Joined Winterbauer & Diamond as a partner in 1997. Before that he served as a judicial clerk to The Honorable J. Frederick Motz, USDC for the District of Maryland, and practiced in Washington, DC with Covington & Burling LLP and Chadbourne & Parke LLP. Listed among top attorneys in Washington Super Lawyers®, Chambers USA, and Best Lawyers in America®. Holds Martindale-Hubbell AV® Preeminent™ peer review rating.
**Personal:** BA, with Distinction, Yale University. MA, Columbia University. JD, Stanford Law School.

## DODD, Richard
K&L Gates, Seattle
206 370 5790
rick.dodd@klgates.com
*Featured in Corporate/Commercial (Washington)*
**Practice Areas:** Partner Rick Dodd has more than 40 years experience in mergers and acquisitions, securities offerings, and other financings, divestitures and spin-offs, joint ventures, and other business organization. Transactions include seven involving between $1 billion and $50 billion in market value. He has been involved in corporate governance issues for a number of public companies including Microsoft, TrueBlue, T-Mobile, Western Wireless, Expedia, Starbucks, Penford, and Univar. He also participates in board and committee meetings dealing with cutting edge corporate governance issues and has a thorough knowledge of Sarbanes Oxley, Dodd-Frank Acts and state corporate law.

## DUNNE, Daniel J
Orrick, Herrington & Sutcliffe LLP, Seattle
206 839 4395
ddunne@orrick.com
*Featured in Litigation (Washington)*
**Practice Areas:** Daniel Dunne, a Partner in Orrick's Seattle office, is a member of the Securities Litigation and Regulatory Enforcement Group. He is currently spending most of his time defending banks in various securities, insurance and breach of contract lawsuits spawned by the financial crisis. Mr Dunne's litigation practice involves defense of financial institutions, technology companies, accountants, and directors and officers in complex litigation in federal and state

courts. Mr Dunne has acted as first and second chair in multiple jury and bench trials, including both civil and felony criminal cases, and has represented numerous clients in consumer class actions.

### DYKES, Trenton
DLA Piper LLP (US), Washington, DC
206 839 4834
trent.dykes@dlapiper.com
*Featured in Corporate/Commercial (Washington)*
**Practice Areas:** Corporate/commercial.
**Career:** He is chair of the firm's Northwest Emerging Growth and Venture Capital practice and concentrates in securities and corporate finance, mergers and acquisitions and general corporate law. His experience ranges from advising startup companies about formation and venture financings to representing public companies with SEC compliance, corporate governance and other related issues. His clients include individual entrepreneurs, early stage, venture-backed and public companies and venture capital investors.
**Personal:** JD, Universit of Washington; BA, University of Washington cum laude; Harvard Business School (Executive Education, DLA Piper Leadership Program).

### EKBERG, Charles
Lane Powell PC, Seattle
206 223 7012
ekbergc@lanepowell.com
*Featured in Bankruptcy/Restructuring (Washington)*
**Practice Areas:** Bankruptcy, creditors' rights, real estate, commercial law, business reorganizations, workouts, creditors' remedies, real estate financing, and litigation.
**Professional Memberships:** Fellow, American College of Bankruptcy; ABA Business Bankruptcy Subcommittee (member); American Bankruptcy Institute, Washington State Bar Association's Creditor/Debtor Section (four-term Executive Committee Member); King County Bar Association's Bankruptcy Section (former Chairperson); Western District Federal Bar Association Bankruptcy Committee (member); Ninth Circuit Judicial Conference (lawyer representative).
**Career:** Joined firm in 1971; Partner since 1978; Chair, Bankruptcy and Creditors' Rights Practice Group (1988-2009).
**Publications:** Lectured and written on bankruptcy.
**Personal:** University of Washington (JD, Order of the Coif, 1971; BA, 1968).

### ENGLUND, Rudy A
Lane Powell PC, Seattle
206 223 7042
englundr@lanepowell.com
*Featured in Litigation (Washington)*
**Practice Areas:** Complex commercial, class action and securities litigation and business dispute resolution. Rudy is one of the Firm's Senior Trial Lawyers and current Director of Wage and Hour and Class Action Litigation.
**Professional Memberships:** Fellow, American College of Trial Lawyers; ABA Standing Committee on Federal Judiciary (member, 1997-

2002); ABA Section of Litigation (council member, 1994-97); ABA Section of Litigation - multiple task forces (2003-present); International Association of Defense Counsel; Fellow, American Bar Foundation.
**Career:** Shareholder since 1984.
**Publications:** Lectured and written extensively on litigation issues.
**Personal:** University of Washington (JD, 1975; BA, magna cum laude, 1972). Phi Beta Kappa.

### ESCOBAR, Andrew
DLA Piper LLP (US), Seattle
206 839 4828
andrew.escobar@dlapiper.com
*Featured in Litigation (Washington)*
**Practice Areas:** Litigation: general commercial.
**Career:** His practice focuses on securities and complex commercial litigation and has represented clients in special committee and internal investigations, white collar criminal matters, real estate disputes, labor litigation, insurance litigation, and bankruptcy proceedings. He has experience in all phases of federal and state court litigation, including expert and lay discovery, dispositive motions, trials and appeals.
**Personal:** JD, Yale Law School; BA, University of Southern California (summa cum laude).

### GEARIN, Michael
K&L Gates, Seattle
206 370 6666
michael.gearin@klgates.com
*Featured in Bankruptcy/Restructuring (Washington)*
**Practice Areas:** Michael Gearin concentrates his practice in insolvency and commercial reorganizations. His practice is broad based, encompassing transactional, litigation and business advice in the insolvency and creditors rights arenas. He has significant experience in the representation of pension interests in municipal bankruptcy cases. He has substantial experience in the resolution of Ponzi schemes through the chapter 11 plan confirmation process. He has represented debtors and purchasers in complex asset sales transactions in chapter 11 cases. Mr Gearin is a past chair of the Seattle-King County Bar Association Bankruptcy Section and is a panel mediator for chapter 11 matters.

### GRAHAM, Stephen M
Fenwick & West LLP, Seattle
206 389 4520
sgraham@fenwick.com
*Featured in Corporate/Commercial (Washington)*
**Practice Areas:** Stephen M Graham is Co-Chair of Fenwick & West's Life Sciences Practice, is a partner in the Corporate Group and is a member of the firm's executive committee. He is resident in the firm's Seattle office where he is Managing Partner. Mr Graham's practice is focused on private and public mergers and acquisitions, public offerings, private placements, and corporate governance matters, including advising boards of directors, audit, compensation and nominating/corporate governance committees, preparation and filing of periodic SEC reports and other securities law compliance, including disclosure issues with respect to Rule 10b-5 and

Regulation FD. His diverse practice is focused on the representation of emerging and established high growth companies. He has represented companies and investment banks in numerous initial public offerings, a wide variety of merger and acquisition transactions, and private offerings of debt and equity.
**Career:** Mr Graham has been recognized by Chambers USA as one of the top corporate and mergers and acquisitions lawyers in Washington. He is a "Super Lawyer" award recipient, 2000-12 and has also been recognized as a "Life Science Superstar" for his outstanding transactional work in Euromoney's LMG Life Sciences 2012.

### GREENBURG, G Scott
K&L Gates, Seattle
206 370 6797
scott.greenburg@klgates.com
*Featured in Corporate/Commercial (Washington)*
**Practice Areas:** Partner Scott Greenburg has more than 25 years experience in mergers and acquisitions, venture capital, public offerings, technology issues, complex commercial transactions and international product distribution. He has completed more than 200 corporate transactions for companies such as Starbucks, HaloSource, VoiceStream Wireless, Sabey Data Centers, iCIMS, Tango Card, Sambazon, Guayaki, Kona Brewing Company, the Seattle Supersonics, and Classmates Online. He also has transactional experience in Internet technology, software and SAAS, specialty retail, consumer brands, natural products, wireless telecommunications, cleantech, and hospitality.

### GREER, George E
Orrick, Herrington & Sutcliffe LLP, Seattle
206 389 6006
ggreer@orrick.com
*Featured in Litigation (Washington)*
**Practice Areas:** George Greer, a Partner in the Securities Litigation and Regulatory Enforcement Group, focuses his practice on complex commercial litigation with an emphasis on securities, corporate governance, professional liability for accounting firms and energy issues. Mr Greer has represented issuers, officers, directors, accountants and underwriters in class action securities litigation and in SEC investigations and enforcement proceedings. Mr Greer's practice also includes representation of companies, Special Litigation Committees and individuals in corporate governance disputes. He has conducted a number of internal investigations on behalf of boards of directors of both public and private companies.

### GRIFFIN, Michael A
Jackson Lewis LLP, Seattle
206 626 6416
GriffinM@jacksonlewis.com
*Featured in Labor & Employment (Washington)*
**Practice Areas:** Serves as lead counsel on broad range of employment litigation matters in state and federal court, including discrimination, harassment, retaliation, and wrongful discharge lawsuits. Provides advice and counsel and conducts management training on many workplace

legal issues, focusing on employee leave and disability management.
**Professional Memberships:** Washington State Bar Association, King County Bar Association.
**Career:** Began career in New York, relocated to Seattle in 1999, joining Davis Grimm & Payne. Joined Jackson Lewis in 2001. Elevated to Partner in 2008, selected Litigation Manager in 2011.
**Personal:** New York Law School, JD 1997; Stony Brook University, BA Sociology, 1993.

### GUESS, Philip
K&L Gates, Seattle
206 370 5834
philg@klgates.com
*Featured in Litigation (Washington)*
**Practice Areas:** Philip Guess represents clients in securities, fraud, and other business disputes. Mr Guess has particular experience in areas pertaining to fraud and insolvency—whether in state, federal district, or bankruptcy courts—including prosecuting and defending claims of fraud, misrepresentation, conversion, and fraudulent conveyance. He has also represented institutions and funds in matters involving the Securities & Exchange Commission, Securities Investor Protection Corporation, and Washington State Department of Financial Institutions. With respect to business litigation, he has represented companies in disputes involving alleged contractual breaches, usurpation of trade secrets, tortious interference and class action allegations.

### HESTON, Mary Jo
Lane Powell PC, Seattle
206 223 7015
hestonm@lanepowell.com
*Featured in Bankruptcy/Restructuring (Washington)*
**Practice Areas:** Business restructuring, business bankruptcy, cross-border insolvency, purchase/sale of financially troubled businesses, financial institution litigation.
**Professional Memberships:** Fellow, American College of Bankruptcy; Current Alternate, TMA Board of Trustees; President, CENTS (WDWA pro bono organization); Former President Northwest TMA; Former INSOL Council Member/ABI Board Member.
**Career:** (1993-Present); US Trustee, Region 18 (1988-93). Licensed in Oregon/Washington.
**Publications:** Frequent speaker and author on bankruptcy, insolvency and debtor-creditor issues.
**Personal:** University of Puget Sound Law school (JD, 1980); University of Washington (BS, 1975); Adjunct Professor, Seattle University Law School (1984-2005);University of Washington School of Law (1997-99).

### HUTCHINGS, Michael
DLA Piper LLP (US), Seattle
206 839 4824
michael.hutchings@dlapiper.com
*Featured in Corporate/Commercial (Washington)*
**Practice Areas:** Corporate/M&A, private equity, finance.
**Career:** He provides general counsel services to public and private technology companies and represents clients on a wide range of transactions. He counsels companies, boards of directors and

board committees on corporate governance matters and securities law compliance. He is a frequent speaker on topics related to corporate finance, mergers and acquistions, securities laws and corporate governance.

**Personal:** JD, Seattle University, MBA, University of Washington, BA, University of Utah.

## KEEHNEL, Stellman
DLA Piper LLP (US), Seattle
206 839 4888
stellman.keehnel@dlapiper.com
*Featured in Litigation (Washington)*

**Practice Areas:** Litigation, life sciences, patent litigation, securities litigation.

**Career:** He specializes in securities litigation, intellectual property and technology litigation, and complex commercial litigation. In securities litigation, he defends class actions and shareholder derivative/fiduciary breach actions; provides representation in SEC and SRO proceedings; and defends incorporate governance litigation. In complex commercial litigation, he defends consumer class actions and defends and prosecutes in high stakes commercial and real estate lawsuits. In intellectual property and technology litigation, he defends and prosecutes lawsuits involving patent infringement, trademark, copyright, and trade secrets.

**Personal:** JD, Yale Law School; AB, Stanford University.

## KOCHER, Gary J
K&L Gates, Seattle
206 370 7809
gary.kocher@klgates.com
*Featured in Corporate/Commercial (Washington)*

**Practice Areas:** Gary Kocher, a partner in K&L Gates' corporate, mergers and acquisitions and securities practice group, focuses on a broad range of M&A and financing transactions with an emphasis on public and private securities offerings for consumer product, technology and life sciences companies. He also has served as US counsel on a number of cross-border transactions for Canadian and Asian companies, and advises on a broad range of transactional matters including joint ventures, strategic alliances and business formation issues.

## LASCHEVER, Eric S
K&L Gates, Seattle
206 623 7022
eric.laschever@klgates.com
*Featured in Real Estate (Washington)*

**Practice Areas:** Eric Laschever, one of the most widely respected land use lawyers in the Pacific Northwest, concentrates his practice in land use planning and permitting and natural resource and environmental law. He advises private and public clients, including energy companies, railways, ports, and corporations, in securing and defending land use and environmental permits and approvals for large infrastructure and other complex projects. In addition to assisting in obtaining approvals at the federal, state, and local levels, he counsels on such related matters as zoning, environmental impact, litigation, and Endangered Species Act and climate change issues.

## LEAVERTON, Bruce
Lane Powell PC, Seattle
206 223 7389
leavertonb@lanepowell.com
*Featured in Bankruptcy/Restructuring (Washington)*

**Practice Areas:** Business bankruptcy, reorganizations, workouts, banking law, commercial litigation, real estate finance and new markets tax credit transactions.

**Professional Memberships:** ABA (Member, subcommittee on technology-related bankruptcies); Creditor/Debtor Section of WSBA (Member, International Insolvency Subcommittee); Director and Secretary, Northwest Chapter, Turnaround Management Association.

**Career:** Joined firm in 1985; Shareholder since 1991. Began career in 1983 with Houston firm Baker and Botts.

**Publications:** Lectured and written extensively on bankruptcy, insolvency and financial matters.

**Personal:** University of Oklahoma (JD, 1983); University of Kansas (BA, 1975; MA, 1978); Chief Articles Editor, Oklahoma Law Review, 1982-83; International Academy of Trial Lawyers Award, 1983. Named Best Lawyers® Seattle Banking and Finance Lawyer of the Year, 2011; Recommended by Chambers USA: America's Leading Lawyers for Business, Bankruptcy/ Restructuring, 2008-13; Named as one of The Best Lawyers in America®, Bankruptcy and Creditor/Debtor Rights, Banking and Finance, Bankruptcy and Creditor Debtor Rights/Insolvency and Reorganization, Banking and Finance Litigation, Bankruptcy Litigation, 2005-13; Named as a "Washington Super Lawyer," Super Lawyers magazine, Bankruptcy and Creditor/Debtor Rights, 2005, 2007-12; Peer Review Rated "AV" in Martindale-Hubbell; Volunteer, Rebuilding Together; Board Member, American Heart Association; 2013 March of Dimes Leadership Cabinet.

## MADDEN, Patrick M
K&L Gates, Seattle
206 370 6795
patrick.madden@klgates.com
*Featured in Labor & Employment (Washington)*

**Practice Areas:** Patrick Madden co-chairs K&L Gates' global labor and employment practice group and leads its wage and hour class action practice. He advises employers on employment issues, including complex contracts, wage compliance, and compensation plan design. In addition to defending employers against agency investigations and individual lawsuits, he has successfully defended clients in over a hundred class, collective, and government enforcement actions, some involving claims for hundreds of thousands of employees and billions of dollars. His knowledge of arcane exemptions and exceptions coupled with early strategic planning help him extinguish these matters while keeping client costs to a minimum.

## MAUTNER, Gail
Lane Powell PC, Seattle
206 223 7099
mautnerg@lanepowell.com
*Featured in Labor & Employment (Washington)*

**Practice Areas:** Chair, Labor and Employment Practice Group. Advises and litigates regarding both labor/employment law and probate, trust and guardianship disputes.

**Professional Memberships:** Washington State Bar Association; King County Bar Association; Estate Planning Council of Seattle; American College of Trust and Estate Counsel.

**Career:** Law Clerk, US District Court for Western Washington, 1982-84; Shareholder since 1991.

**Publications:** Lectures and writes extensively on labor/employment law, and trust and estate disputes.

**Personal:** University of California, Hastings College of Law (JD, 1982), Order of the Coif; Pitzer College, (BA, with honors, 1978). Secretary, Jewish Family Service of Seattle; President, Temple De Hirsch Sinai.

## MCDONALD, David
K&L Gates, Seattle
206 370 7957
david.mcdonald@klgates.com
*Featured in Intellectual Property (Washington)*

**Practice Areas:** David McDonald, a partner in, and global Practice Area Leader of, the firm's Intellectual Property practice, emphasizes technology-related intellectual property litigation, including strategic litigation arising from contract-based disputes. Much of his practice has focused on software-related disputes and litigation adverse to Apple since 1986. He also regularly advises on litigation against patent assertion entities and on matters of constitutional and statutory law relating to political parties. He has led legal teams in significant matters at all levels, including on the merits in the United States Supreme Court.

## MORGAN, Michael
Lane Powell PC, Seattle
206 223 7013
morganm@lanepowell.com
*Featured in Corporate/Commercial (Washington)*

**Practice Areas:** Michael Morgan has extensive experience counseling companies in mergers and acquisitions, securities offerings, venture capital and transactions. He represents various public and private companies in domestic and cross-border transactions, and regularly advises boards of directors and board committees on corporate governance and compliance matters.

**Professional Memberships:** ABA; Washington State Bar Association.

**Career:** Shareholder since 1980.

**Publications:** Lectured and written extensively on corporate and securities law issues.

**Personal:** Loyola University at Los Angeles (JD, cum laude, 1974); University of California at Berkeley (AB, with distinction, 1971). He also serves as Past-Chair and Board member of The Kline Galland Center.

## NESTEROFF, Michael
Lane Powell PC, Seattle
206 223 6242
nesteroffm@lanepowell.com
*Featured in Environment (Washington)*

**Practice Areas:** Environmental, climate change and sustainability, real estate and commercial litigation. Has litigated hazardous substance cleanup and contribution actions and advised on site assessment, cleanup and closure, pipeline safety, natural resource damages, Endangered Species Act, cogeneration contracts and climate change regulation.

**Professional Memberships:** Washington & Oregon State Bars; ABA; Board member: Northwest Environmental Business Council; Western States Petroleum Association - Pacific Northwest Associates.

**Career:** Joined firm in 1988. Shareholder since 1997.

**Personal:** University of Puget Sound (JD, 1983); Washington State University (BA, cum laude, 1975). Board member: Hopelink; Seattle Country Day School; and Leadership Eastside. Chair, Lawyerpalooza Organizing Committee.

## NEU, David
K&L Gates, Seattle
206 370 8125
david.neu@klgates.com
*Featured in Bankruptcy/Restructuring (Washington)*

**Practice Areas:** David Neu is a partner in the firm's Seattle office, where he practices in the area of insolvency and creditor/debtor rights. In his practice, David represents debtors, trustees, committees and asset-purchasers in Chapter 11 bankruptcy proceedings and bankruptcy-related litigation as well as creditors in Chapter 11, 7, and 13 proceedings. He also frequently represents receivers and creditors in state-court receivership actions, and both lenders and borrowers in out-of-court workout negotiations.

## NEUGEBAUER, Robert
K&L Gates, Seattle
206 370 7644
robert.neugebauer@klgates.com
*Featured in Real Estate (Washington)*

**Practice Areas:** Partner Bob Neugebauer focuses on real estate matters, particularly the representation of clients in commercial real estate transactions, including purchases and sales, financings, and leases. He has acted as counsel in connection with purchases, financings, and leases of office buildings, retail properties, data centers, hotels, and warehouse and industrial properties.

## PURCELL, Charles
K&L Gates, Seattle
206 370 8369
charles.purcell@klgates.com
*Featured in Corporate/Commercial (Washington)*

**Practice Areas:** Partner Charles Purcell works extensively in the alternative investments arena with a focus on federal and international tax issues. He has broad experience in the formation of domestic and foreign investment funds (including private equity, venture, real estate, and infrastructure funds); large joint venture transactions; mergers and acquisitions; financing and banking transactions; venture capital investments and start-up companies; and compensation of managers, executives, and promoters. He represents domestic and foreign institutional investors in connection with alternative investment activities. He also works with developers and investors in alternative energy projects, including solar, biomass and wind energy facilities.

## REILLY, D. Michael
Lane Powell PC, Seattle
206 223 7051
reillym@lanepowell.com
*Featured in Labor & Employment (Washington)*

**Practice Areas:** Director, Labor, Employment and Employee Benefits Practice Groups. Reilly was named one of the 2012 "Top 100 Most Powerful Employment Attorneys in the Nation" by Human Resource Executive. Reilly has tried over 60 jury trials and arbitrations, and advises clients and litigates cases for large and small employers in all types of employment, ERISA, wage/hour class actions, breach of fiduciary duty, and trade secret and unfair competition claims. Reilly was named 2012 ERISA Litigation "Lawyer of the Year" by Best Lawyers in America. His clients include Nordstrom, Wyndham, Home Depot, Tesoro, Ferrellgas, Fred Hutchinson Cancer Research Center, Worldpac.
**Professional Memberships:** ABA; Washington State Bar Association; American Employment Law Council.
**Career:** Reilly joined Lane Powell after an appellate court clerkship. Reilly is very active on non-profit boards, including his service as Vice-Chair for the Gonzaga University Board of Regents.
**Publications:** Founder and Contributor, Boom: The ERISA Law Blog; Co-author, "ERISA Fiduciary Claims: Planning, Protecting and Preparing for Class Actions", Emp. Rel. L. J. (2005); "NLRB Protects Many Employee Facebook Postings," Puget Sound Business Journal (November 11, 2011); "Job Nightmare," Newsweek, (July 2003).
**Personal:** Catholic University of America, Washington, DC (JD, 1984); Gonzaga University, Spokane, WA (BBA, cum laude, 1981).

## SKINNER, Shannon
K&L Gates, Seattle
206 370 7657
shannon.skinner@klgates.com
*Featured in Real Estate (Washington)*

**Practice Areas:** K&L Gates' partner Shannon Skinner's practice centers on commercial real estate and financing transactions. Her experience includes the acquisition and financing of regional shopping malls, hotels, office buildings, retail centers, manufacturing facilities and residential complexes, including multi-state transactions. Her practice also includes corporate and margin financing transactions, as well as aviation financing. She has significant experience in public/private developments that are key to urban renewal projects, such as museums, mixed use projects and brownfields redevelopments. The workout and enforcement of distressed commercial mort-

gage loans, including restructurings and foreclosures, are also a part of her practice.

## SMITH, Alan C
Fenwick & West LLP, Seattle
206 389 4530
acsmith@fenwick.com
*Featured in Corporate/Commercial (Washington)*

**Practice Areas:** Alan C Smith is a partner in the Corporate Group of Fenwick & West LLP and he is resident in the firm's Seattle office. His practice focuses on representing emerging and public companies in mergers and acquisitions, capital markets offerings and venture capital and strategic investments. He also has an active venture capital financing practice, having represented many of Seattle area's leading start-ups and venture capital firms.
**Career:** Mr Smith has been recognized as one of the top corporate and mergers and acquisitions lawyers in Washington by Chambers USA, annually as a "Super Lawyer" by Washington Law & Politics since 2003, and as one of the "Top 40 Under 40" by the Puget Sound Business Journal.
**Publications:** Mr Smith is a frequent speaker on corporate finance topics, including the initial public offering process, venture and angel financing and mergers and acquisitions.

## STEEL, John M
DLA Piper LLP (US), Seattle
206 839 4833
john.steel@dlapiper.com
*Featured in Corporate/Commercial (Washington)*

**Practice Areas:** Corporate/M&A, venture capital, private equity, life sciences.
**Career:** He concentrates in structuring and negotiating a wide range of financing transactions, acquisitions, and strategic alliances. He has managed hundreds of private equity financings for issuers and investors and served as lead counsel on approximately 30 public offerings. He is experienced in a broad variety of commercial transactions including commercial finance, licensing, and distribution arrangements.
**Personal:** JD, University of Washington; BA, Stanford University.

## STOKKE, Diane
K&L Gates, Seattle
206 370 5791
diane.stokke@klgates.com
*Featured in Real Estate (Washington)*

**Practice Areas:** Partner Diane Stokke represents real estate developers, owners, public entities and lenders in the acquisition, development, leasing and conventional and tax-exempt financing of commercial real estate including mixed-use developments, shopping centers, office buildings, data centers, industrial and research facilities and multifamily and senior housing. She has represented energy clients on a wide range of real estate issues associated with acquisition, development and financing of wind, solar and other renewable energy generating facilities, transmission and other infrastructure projects. She also has experience in the structuring and financing of public/private partnerships with an emphasis on urban redevelopment and transportation projects.

## TELLEKSON, David K
Fenwick & West LLP, Seattle
206 389 4560
dtellekson@fenwick.com
*Featured in Intellectual Property (Washington)*

**Practice Areas:** David K Tellekson is a partner in the Litigation Group of Fenwick & West LLP. He is resident in the firm's Seattle office and his practice focuses on litigating patent cases for clients in the areas of biotechnology, pharmaceuticals, polymer chemistry, medical devices, industrial chemistry and a wide variety of other technologies including: retroreflective sheeting, orthodontic brackets, silicon chemistry, and electronic printing. In addition to his trial work, he also consults on patent strategy and opinions.
**Career:** Mr Tellekson has been selected as a Washington "Super Lawyer" in the area of intellectual property litigation for the past five consecutive years.
**Publications:** Mr Tellekson is a frequent writer and lecturer in areas of patent law and patent litigation.

## THOMAS, Suzanne
K&L Gates, Seattle
206 370 6642
suzanne.thomas@klgates.com
*Featured in Labor & Employment (Washington)*

**Practice Areas:** A former co-chair of K&L Gates' global labor and employment practice group, Suzanne Thomas represents management with regard to employment litigation and counseling. She defends employers in agency claims and litigation on a wide range of employment issues, including discrimination, harassment, wage and hour payment and compliance, contracts, privacy rights, trade secrets, restrictive covenants, unfair competition, and workforce restructuring. She provides advice to employers regarding all aspects of the employment relationship. Ms Thomas has substantial background in conducting and overseeing independent investigations for publicly traded, regulated, private and public employers, including managing issues of privilege and work product.

## WHEELER, Douglas
Lane Powell PC, Seattle
206 223 7025
wheelerd@lanepowell.com
*Featured in Real Estate (Washington)*

**Practice Areas:** Resort development, timeshare and fractional ownership projects, real estate and business transactions, mergers and acquisitions, secured transactions (including personal property leasing), asset based lending, corporate law, and creditor-debtor law.
**Professional Memberships:** WSBA (member, real property, probate and trust law, business law and IP law sections; member, UCC committee); American Resort Development Association.
**Career:** Joined Lane Powell in 1984; Shareholder since 1993.
**Publications:** "Timeshares" chapter, Washington Real Property Deskbook, WSBA (2009); Washington and Alaska law chapters in the State Compendium of Timeshare Law, ABA (2008).

**Personal:** University of Washington (JD, 1984); University of Puget Sound (BA, 1973).

## WINTERBAUER, Steven
Winterbauer & Diamond PLLC, Seattle
206 676 8440
steven@winterbauerdiamond.com
*Featured in Labor & Employment (Washington)*

**Practice Areas:** Steve has extensive experience counseling employers on all aspects of labor and employment law, and litigating before multiple state and federal courts and enforcement agencies. His arbitration experience ranges from private arbitration pursuant to mandatory arbitration agreements to traditional labor arbitration, to public sector arbitration.
**Professional Memberships:** Executive Committee-Washington State Bar Association Employment and Labor Law Section, 2012-13; Employee Relations Law Journal Editorial Advisory Board, 1996-2013; Washington Defense Trial Lawyer Association; Washington State Bar Association's Annual Employment Law Institute, co-founder and co-chair, 1993-2010; Pacific Coast Labor Law Conference Planning Committee, 1993-95; Mercer Island Civil Service Commission, Commissioner, 1996-2001; JAMS*Endispute, Mediator/Arbitrator, 1996-2001; American Bar Association (Employment & Labor Law; Litigation); Washington State Bar Association (Employment & Labor Law); King County Bar Association (Employment & Labor Law, Litigation).
**Career:** Founded Winterbauer & Diamond in 1996. Before that he was a partner and chairperson of the Employment and Labor Group at Foster Pepper & Shefelman. Listed among top attorneys in Washington Super Lawyers®, Chambers USA, and Best Lawyers in America®. Holds Martindale-Hubbell AV® Preeminent™ peer review rating.
**Personal:** BA, with Distinction, Phi Beta Kappa, Stanford University. JD, Stanford Law School.

## WOLFE, John W
DLA Piper LLP (US), Seattle
206 839 4820
john.wolfe@dlapiper.com
*Featured in Litigation (Washington)*

**Practice Areas:** Litigation, white collar litigation.
**Career:** He has been in practice for more than 30 years, focusing on representing individuals and businesses subject to governmental investigation (criminal and civil) as well as civil litigation related to or paralleling a criminal investigation. He has represented clients in more than 100 jury trials and has appeared in numerous state and federal courts. He has extensive experience representing clients in criminal envirnment and complex financing fraud investigations as well as resolving high-profile problems confronting public officials.
**Personal:** JD, University of Puget Sound Law School; BA, Western Washington University

**YENTZER, Steven R**
DLA Piper LLP (US), Seattle
206 839 4836
steven.yentzer@dlapiper.com
*Featured in Corporate/Commercial (Washington)*
**Practice Areas:** Corporate, international tax, real estate capital markets, private equity.
**Career:** He is the Managing Partner of the firm's Seattle office and focuses on corporate and securities transactions primarily involving private equity securities and finance. He regularly advises investment and private equity funds in all facets of their operations, including fund formation, tax structuring, internal operations, and investment related matters. He represents clients involved in sophisticated tax-sensitive businesses. His representation of these clients covers a broad area of corporate, tax, and finance related matters.
**Personal:** JD, Marquette University School of Law; BA, Gonzaga University (magna cum laude).

**ZUCCOTTI, Andrew**
K&L Gates, Seattle
206 370 6680
andrew.zuccotti@klgates.com
*Featured in Corporate/Commercial (Washington)*
**Practice Areas:** Andrew Zuccotti is a partner in the Seattle office of K&L Gates, where he practices primarily in the area of federal income tax. His experience includes a full range of federal income tax issues including mergers and acquisitions, real estate syndications, international tax, and general corporate transactions.

# CAIRNCROSS & HEMPELMANN

**www.**cairncross.com **tel:** 205 587 0700 **fax:** 206 587 2308

**Chairman:** John Hempelmann
**Managing Partners:** Stephen Van Derhoef, Matt Hanna
Number of principals: 23  Number of lawyers: 40
Languages: *Cantonese, Dutch, English, French, German, Mandarin, Romanian, Russian*

**OFFICES**

WASHINGTON

**SEATTLE:** 524 2nd Avenue, Suite 500, WA 98104-2323
Tel: 206 587 0700   Fax: 206 587 2308
Email: info@cairncross.com

## Firm Overview:

Cairncross & Hempelmann (CH&) is a Seattle-based law firm with offices located on the edge of the city's historic Pioneer Square District. Founded in 1987, CH& employs lawyers who advise companies and individuals in nine practice areas: bankruptcy and creditors' rights; corporate finance and business transactions; employment; land use, natural resources and environmental law; litigation; real estate; tax; technology and intellectual property transactions; and trademarks. The attorneys and staff at CH& are dedicated to providing highly efficient legal assistance and superior service to clients. The firm is a member of Mackrell International, a global network of member firms in 50 countries, providing clients access to 4,000 lawyers worldwide and seamless legal service wherever the client needs it, and it is regularly recognized as a "Best Workplace" by local publications (Washington CEO, Seattle Business Monthly and the Puget Sound Business Journal) as well as various industry groups.

## Main Areas of Practice:

### Bankruptcy & Creditors' Rights:
1 principal, 4 fee earners, Seattle, WA
This group represents debtors, debtors in possession, and Chapter 11 trustees, but also creditors' committees, secured lenders, landlords, suppliers, service providers, and licensors of intellectual property in all aspects of insolvency and bankruptcy law, business planning and turnaround, and litigation.
**Contact:** John Rizzardi  **Tel:** 206 254 4444
**Email:** jrizzardi@cairncross.com

### Corporate Finance & Business Transactions:
8 principals, 15 fee earners, Seattle, WA
The attorneys in this broad-based practice assist both private and public companies with mergers and acquisitions, private offerings, venture and other strategic financings, public offerings, securities compliance, board counsel, finance and operations, and supplier and customer contracts.
**Contact:** Tim Woodland  **Tel:** 206 254 4497
**Email:** twoodland@cairncross.com

### Employment:
1 principal, 1 fee earners, Seattle, WA
Whether your organization needs help with compliance, personnel policies, personnel issues, training, or representation in an administrative proceeding or lawsuit, CH& is well-equipped to assist. CH& understands that employers of all sizes need prompt, cost-effective employment law assistance to stay focused on their businesses and to avoid bigger problems in the future.
**Contact:** Kirsten Daniels  **Tel:** 206 254 4454
**Email:** kdaniels@cairncross.com

### Land Use, Natural Resources & Environmental Law:
4 principals, 6 fee earners, Seattle, WA
The land use group participates in some of this region's most complex and high-profile land use projects. The group has successfully advised clients through all phases of the land use approval process, including planned unit development, rezones, conditional uses, design review, site plan review, master use permits, variances, temporary uses and code interpretations, and analysis of state and federal environmental review requirements.
**Contact:** Nancy Bainbridge Rogers  **Tel:** 206 254 4417
**Email:** nrogers@cairncross.com

### Litigation:
9 principals, 14 fee earners, Seattle, WA
The firm's litigation group advises clients on the following matters: intellectual property, employment disputes, creditors' rights, bankruptcy, receiverships and workouts, internal corporate, partnership and LLC disputes, commercial and residential real estate disputes, land use litigation, real estate, securities broker liability, natural resources litigation, construction disputes, condemnation/eminent domain, antitrust, product and premises liability, and will and trust disputes.
**Contact:** Charles Newton  **Tel:** 206 254 4413
**Email:** cnewton@cairncross.com

### Real Estate:
5 principals, 12 fee earners, Seattle, WA
The real estate group remains at the cutting edge of real estate (and tax) law and also is experienced with advising on 1031/Tenant-in-Common projects, business and real property acquisition and conveyance, leasing, land development, commercial or seller financing, construction and architect contracts, taxation, title insurance, easements, broker liability, escrow issues, joint venture and partner-ships, and all other aspects of commercial real estate.
**Contact:** Sandip Soli  **Tel:** 206 254 4493
**Email:** ssoli@cairncross.com

### Tax:
2 principals, 3 fee earners, Seattle, WA
This group offers clients a comprehensive array of tax services, including: selecting the optimal form and location for business enterprises, structuring compensation programs to attract and retain key personnel, minimizing the tax cost of international transfers of intellectual and tangible property, developing creative strategies for mergers and acquisitions, using tax benefits to improve deal economics, assisting business owners and other individuals with personal tax strategies and estate planning, including transfers of family wealth to younger generations, helping real estate developers find new sources of capital using innovative tax strategies, representing enterprises and individuals in disputes with the Internal Revenue Service, as well as state taxing authorities.
**Contact:** Dawson Taylor  **Tel:** 206 254 4431
**Email:** dtaylor@cairncross.com

### Technology & Intellectual Property Transactions:
4 principals, 7 fee earners, Seattle, WA
The technology team's broad-based experience allows them to provide counsel in the following technology areas: e-commerce and Internet law, trademark and domestic name protection, registration and disputes, website review and develop-ment, intranets, copyright, software development, licensing and distribution, patent licensing, biotechnology, and international licensing, marketing and distribution.
**Contact:** Robert Kaye  **Tel:** 206 254 4467
**Email:** rkaye@cairncross.com

### Trademarks:
1 principal, 1 fee earner, Seattle, WA
The CH& trademarks team advises clients at each stage of the branding process, from selection and registration to protection and monetization of these critical assets. The team has counseled clients with almost all categories of trademarks: single words, taglines, logos, even color schemes and cartoon characters. CH& also provides specialized services for other intellectual property assets, especially software, music and other digital content.
**Contact:** Maureen Burke  **Tel:** 206 254 4463
**Email:** mburke@cairncross.com

# DAVIS WRIGHT TREMAINE LLP

www.dwt.com

**Managing Partner:** David C Baca
Number of partners worldwide: 304
Number of other attorneys worldwide: 199

## Firm Overview:

Davis Wright Tremaine LLP was founded on a simple guiding principle: to provide clients with high value legal services customized to their particular needs. This principle has remained intact for decades as the firm has continued to expand across the nation. Today, its team includes approximately 500 attorneys and nine offices, covering a wide variety of practice and industry areas.

## Main Areas of Practice:

### Business Transactions & Tax:

The firm regularly counsels clients on issues such as: M&A, joint ventures, strategic alliances, corporate finance, securities, corporate governance, and restructuring and reorganization. Members of the group also regularly advise tax-exempt organizations and for- profit businesses on the full range of domestic and international tax issues.

### Employment & Labor:

The firm frequently advises employers of all sizes in traditional employment counseling, litigation matters, immigration matters, and union/labor matters.

### Litigation:

With nearly 200 lawyers in eight offices around the country, the firm has experience in all areas of civil litigation, with particular experience in the communications, media, healthcare, financial services and energy industries. The firm also has broad experience in large-scale litigation involving antitrust and consumer class actions.

### Real Estate:

The firm has decades of experience handling complex real estate transactions nationwide for clients in a wide variety of industries. The team includes strong land use, environmental, construction, finance, tax, bankruptcy/workout and litigation attorneys to provide clients a unified, one-stop solution.

### Energy:

Members of the group provide a full range of transactional, regulatory and litigation services to a wide variety of entities in the electric, natural gas, and renewable energy industries.

### Healthcare:

The team provides clients with comprehensive regulatory and transactional services, along with real estate, labor/employment, benefits, litigation, financing (including tax-exempt financing), bankruptcy and tax work. They also have substantial experience with the rapidly evolving worlds of healthcare reform and health information technology.

### Privacy & Security:

The firm provides counsel on all critical privacy and security issues for media companies, retailers, health care organisations, financial institutions and other clients handling sensitive data – including personally identifiable information. The firm not only helps clients comply with the law, but also custom-designs privacy and security plans to forecast and manage potential legal and regulatory issues germane to their specific workplaces, industries and global technology needs.

### Media & Entertainment:

The firm's media and entertainment attorneys are widely recognized as among the best in the country. Davis Wright is the law firm of choice for many of the nation's most prominent news, information and entertainment companies.

### Telecommunications:

The firm boasts an extremely broad, deep and experienced team focused on critical transactional, regulatory and litigation advice for telecommunications market leaders and emerging companies alike.

### Hospitality:

Members of the team practice exclusively in this space, representing restaurants, wineries, breweries and distilleries, hotels and resorts, gaming companies, and food and beverage producers on the full range of operational, transactional, regulatory and litigation matters.

### Intellectual Property:

The firm provides comprehensive practical advice over the full range of patent, trademark and copyright procurement, registration, licensing and litigation, as well as marketing and trade secret strategies. It also has extensive experience in the IP aspects of all forms of business transactions.

### Environmental:

The firm has the depth and experience to help clients assess risks, assume ongoing compliance and address concerns with project development, business transactions, permitting and government investigations. It works on the full range of environmental and natural resources issues, and the emerging body of climate change regulation.

### Financial Services:

The team provides a full range of counsel on financial services matters, with a particular focus on emerging and mobile payments, as well as defense of consumer class actions.

### Technology & Digital Media:

The firm provides critical operational, transactional, regulatory and litigation counsel to companies in this highly regulated and rapidly evolving industry.

## OFFICES

### WASHINGTON

**SEATTLE:** 1201 Third Avenue, Suite 2200, WA 98101-3045
Tel: 206 622 3150  Fax: 206 757 7700
Email: info@dwt.com

**BELLEVUE:** Suite 2300, 777 108th Avenue NE, WA 98004-5149
Tel: 425 646 6100  Fax: 425 646 6199

### ALASKA

**ANCHORAGE:** 188 West Northern Lights Blvd., 1100, 99503-3985
Tel: 907 257 5300  Fax: 907 257 5399

### CALIFORNIA

**LOS ANGELES:** Suite 2400, 865 South Figueroa Street, CA 90017-2566
Tel: 213 633 6800  Fax: 213 633 6899

**SAN FRANCISCO:** Suite 800, 505 Montgomery Street, CA 94111-6533
Tel: 415 276 6500  Fax: 415 276 6599

### DISTRICT OF COLUMBIA

**WASHINGTON DC:** Suite 800, 1919 Pennsylvania Avenue NW, DC 20006-3401
Tel: 202 973 4200  Fax: 202 973 4499

### NEW YORK

**NEW YORK:** 1633 Broadway, 27th Floor, NY 10019-6708
Tel: 212 489 8230  Fax: 212 489 8340

### OREGON

**PORTLAND:** Suite 2400, 1300 SW Fifth Avenue, OR 97201-5610
Tel: 503 241 2300  Fax: 503 778 5299

## INTERNATIONAL OFFICES

The firm also has an office in Shanghai

Davis Wright Tremaine LLP
DEFINING SUCCESS TOGETHER

# FOSTER PEPPER PLLC

www.foster.com **tel:** 800 995 5902 **fax:** 206 447 9700

**Chairman:** Robert Kunold, Jr
Number of partners: 77  Number of lawyers: 120
Languages: *Afrikaans, Bosnian, Croatian, French, German, Greek, Italian, Japanese, Korean, Laotian, Polish, Russian, Serbian, Spanish, Tagalog, Thai*

## Firm Overview:

Since 1904 Foster Pepper has represented publicly traded corporations, closely held businesses, commercial and investment banks, municipalities, government agencies, professional corporations, partnerships, joint ventures, and individuals. Firm attorneys have extensive legal experience and community involvement that allows them to successfully navigate complex and politically sensitive projects, as well as efficiently staff smaller, less complex matters.

## Main Areas of Practice:

**Business:**
Attorneys have worked in-house or have prior experience with governmental agencies that regulate the complex environment in which businesses operate. They specialize in consumer product safety; general business consulting; corporate finance; mergers, acquisitions, and reorganizations; emerging companies and venture capital; and SEC.

**Creditors' Rights and Bankruptcy:**
The practice is national, with attorneys involved in bankruptcy cases throughout the United States. They have been lead counsel in successful Chapter 11 reorganizations involving regional and national clients in industries such as manufacturing, timber, fishing, real estate, and retailing.

**Employment & Labor Relations:**
Attorneys provide legal services, including adversarial proceedings/litigation; employee benefits, executive compensation and ERISA; employment counseling; and labor relations.

**Environmental:**
Attorneys have experience with many industrial, commercial, and residential projects, including stadiums, hospitals, airport expansions and runways, sewage treatment plants, and landfills. They obtain defensible permits and approvals on time and within budget, and have established relationships with regulatory agencies that are crucial when permitting a complex project. Attorneys have extensive litigation experience in various administrative forums, and in trials and appeals in state and federal courts.

**Financial Institutions:**
Attorneys represent numerous large and small state and federally chartered commercial banks, savings associations, savings banks, and local branches of foreign banks, as well as non-bank lenders. They have particular experience in general business services, loan structuring and documentation, regulatory compliance, debt restructuring and workouts, litigation, director

representation, securities, new bank organization, mergers and acquisitions, and troubled institutions.

**Health Care:**
Attorneys represent providers, including hospitals, physician groups, health care service contractors, trade associations, nursing homes, and others. Particular experience includes governance and organization of public and private hospitals, regulatory compliance, reimbursement, structuring joint ventures, medical staff issues, licensing and accreditation, and state and federal tax and tax-exempt issues. They represent hospitals at each level of the certificate of need process and in the judicial review of planning decisions.

**Intellectual Property:**
Attorneys' practices embrace all aspects of U.S. and international patent, trademark, and copyright preparation, prosecution, litigation, licensing, and counseling in diverse fields of technology. Legal services include patent procurement; acquisition, transfer, and licensing of computer and telecommunications technology equipment; trademark and trade secret protection; and re-examination of an issued patent.

**Investment Management:**
Attorneys support public and private pension funds and other institutions with complex real estate and alternative investments, such as private equity, leveraged buyout funds, venture capital funds, and more. They represent money managers and investment professionals who provide investment services to institutional investors, helping them and fund staff to ensure conformity with investment policies and guidelines.

**Land Use:**
Attorneys are experienced in site acquisition, due diligence, planning/zoning/subdivision regulation, commercial and mixed-use projects, residential plats and subdivisions, large public infrastructure projects, wastewater treatment, Growth Management Act compliance, shorelines and wetlands regulation, water quality and water resources, NEPA/SEPA compliance, and related litigation.

## PRACTICE AREAS

Business
Creditors' Rights & Bankruptcy
Employment & Labor Relations
Environmental
Financial Institutions
Health Care
Intellectual Property
Investment Management
Land Use
Litigation & Dispute Resolution
Municipal Government & Public Finance
Real Estate

## OFFICES

WASHINGTON
**SEATTLE:** 1111 Third Avenue, Suite 3400, WA 98101-3299
Tel: 206 447 4400   Fax: 206 447 9700

**SPOKANE:** US Bank Building, West 422 Riverside Avenue, Suite 1310, WA 99201-0302
Tel: 509 777 1600   Fax: 509 777 1616

Email: info@foster.com
LinkedIn: http://www.linkedin.com/company/foster-pepper-pllc
Twitter: @fosterpepper

**Litigation & Dispute Resolution:**
Attorneys resolve disputes before administrative tribunals, political boards, and trial and appellate courts in the state and federal systems. They apply substantive experience from insurance policyholder law to antitrust/trade regulation, intellectual property law to real property law, construction law to defense of securities and consumer class actions.

**Municipal Government & Public Finance:**
Attorneys provide services to states, counties, cities, school districts, housing authorities, public hospital districts, and other municipal entities throughout the Northwest. Bond counsel attorneys are nationally recognized and are well known to issuers, underwriters, rating agencies, and bond issuers. Attorneys have drafted numerous inter-local contracts, joint operating agreements, and other arrangements among governmental entities on a wide range of legal issues.

**Real Estate:**
Attorneys represent office buildings, corporate and industrial parks, landmarks and special projects, public/private projects, shopping malls, rail companies, hospitals/medical centers, hotels, destination resorts, golf course projects, sports stadiums, marinas, universities, multifamily projects, retirement facilities, and nursing homes. Services range from due diligence and acquisition, financing, tax planning, development, construction, insurance, property management, and leasing agreements through property disposition.

# GORDON TILDEN THOMAS & CORDELL LLP

www.gordontilden.com **tel:** 206 467 6477 **fax:** 206 467 6292

**Managing Partner:** Jeffrey M Thomas
Number of partners: 8
Number of other lawyers: 4

**OFFICES**

WASHINGTON

**SEATTLE:** 1001 Fourth Avenue, Suite 4000, WA 98154-1007
Tel: 206 467 6477   Fax: 206 467 6292

## Firm Overview:

Gordon Tilden Thomas & Cordell LLP is a trial practice firm engaging only in litigation and litigation-oriented advice. GTT&C's lawyers pride themselves on being skilled and experienced litigators and trial lawyers – they believe in the court system and feel that, in some cases, there is no substitute for trial and judgment. However, they recognize that their role is conceiving and implementing cost-effective strategies for resolving disputes, whether through trial, creative approaches to settlement, or use of alternative dispute resolution. The firm has no non-litigation practices and does not 'cross-sell'; the vast majority of their work comes from referrals from satisfied former clients and fellow attorneys.

The firm's Business Litigation Practice is led by partners Chuck Gordon, Jeff Tilden, and Jeff Thomas. Chuck and Jeff Tilden are Fellows of the American College of Trial Lawyers and have collectively tried over 200 cases to verdict. Jeff Thomas likewise is a veteran trial lawyer with over 20 verdicts to his credit.

## Main Areas of Practice:

Gordon Tilden Thomas & Cordell LLP is, first and last, a civil trial-practice firm. The firm's broad range of substantive experience, combined with an emphasis on trial skills, permit them to handle an exceptionally wide variety of matters with equal efficiency and success. Moreover, they often associate as trial counsel to complement the case-specific substantive expertise of co-counsel. Although the firm places great importance on maintaining a general trial practice, they have developed widely recognized expertise in a number of practice areas, as follows.

**Insurance Coverage Advice & Litigation:**
GTT&C's accomplishments in the insurance-coverage arena establish the firm as the premier policyholder-side practice in the Northwest. Their coverage work ranges from large-scale litigation on behalf of international corporate policyholders under complex business coverages, to advising individuals under personal-line policies. The firm's lawyers represented the policyholders in some of the most important insurance coverage decisions to come out of the Washington courts. These and other decisions have made Washington one of the most policyholder-friendly jurisdictions in the country. The firm's Insurance Coverage Practice is led by partners Frank Cordell and Dale Kingman, who collectively have over 50 years of experience in the field.

**Business Ownership, Governance & Contract Disputes:**
The firm regularly represents owners of businesses engaged in conflicts over ownership and governance issues. The firm also is experienced in the litigation and trial of complex, high-stakes contract disputes.

**Securities & Shareholder Derivative Litigation:**
GTT&C's lawyers have developed a national reputation for their securities and derivative litigation representations in high-profile cases. The firm's securities work focuses on protecting the interests of shareholders of public companies and enforcing the fiduciary obligations of directors and officers, thereby helping preserve the integrity of the US financial markets.

**Professional Liability:**
The firm maintains an active practice representing lawyers, hospitals, physicians, insurance brokers, and others in professional negligence cases and billing disputes.

**Product Liability:**
GTT&C's lawyers have represented a broad variety of manufacturer, wholesaler, and retailer defendants named in product liability actions.

**Personal Injury & Sex-Abuse Litigation:**
GTT&C's lawyers regularly represent Washington and national companies, as well as plaintiffs, in high-stakes personal injury litigation. They have substantial experience in the resolution of catastrophic-injury and wrongful-death cases, both in the trial court and through alternative dispute resolution. They also serve as trial counsel to a variety of institutions defending against allegations of negligence in connection with sexual abuse of minors.

**Real Estate Disputes:**
GTT&C maintains an active practice representing parties to real-estate disputes. Their expertise runs the gamut from commercial landlord-tenant disputes, to major condemnation cases, to complex real estate transactions gone awry. They are also active in the representation of taxpayers in significant real and personal property appeals from local tax assessments.

## Clients:

The firm represents individuals, governmental entities and Northwest, national, and international businesses including The Boeing Company, Expeditors, Puget Sound Energy, the State of Washington, Bentall Kennedy (US), LP, Multi Employer Property Trust and Evraz Inc. NA.

# LANE POWELL PC

www.lanepowell.com  **tel:** 206 223 7000  **fax:** 206 223 7107

**President:** Lewis M Horowitz
**Vice President:** Charles W Riley, Jr
Number of partners in the US: 116
Number of other lawyers in the US: 78
Languages: *Afrikaans, Armenian, Catalan, Chinese Mandarin, Dutch, English, French, Hebrew, Italian, Japanese, Kyrgyz, Russian, Spanish*

## Firm Overview:

Lane Powell, Your Pacific Northwest Law Firm®, provides legal solutions for businesses and individuals. The firm's business, employment and litigation attorneys help companies manage growth, build workforces and capitalize on creativity. Founded more than 135 years ago, the firm has approximately 200 attorneys in five offices in the Pacific Northwest, as well as an office in London, England.

## Main Areas of Practice:

### Business:

Lane Powell provides a full range of general business services to individuals, as well as regional, national and international companies. Delivery of legal services is organized around one or more industry teams or areas of practice. Business services the firm provides include: aviation; banking and financial services; anti-trust; construction; cooperative law; corporate finance and securities; dealers and manufacturer relations; electronic discovery, technology and strategy; emerging companies and venture investment; Foreign Corrupt Practices Act, bribery and international anti-corruption; food, beverage and hospitality; franchising; government and regulatory; health care; immigration; intellectual property and technology; international business and investment; international tax; long term care; mergers and acquisitions; real estate and land use; renewable energy and sustainability; retailing, distribution and trade regulation; and tax, compensation and personal planning.

### Labor & Employment:

Lane Powell represents management in the entire range of labor and employment matters and issues. Serving clients in virtually every industry in both the private and public sectors, Lane Powell advises in matters relating to: labor relations, class action defense, employment discrimination, wrongful discharge, unions, civil rights, employee benefits (ERISA, COBRA, etc.), immigration in state and federal courts, wage and hour audits, and before the NLRB, OFCCP, EEOC and all other state and federal agencies involved in employment matters. The firm frequently arbitrates

or represents clients in employment-related jury trials. Whether developing an ERISA plan, amending an existing one or facing litigation involving plan terms, decisions or benefits, Lane Powell's breadth of experience, collaborative approach and extensive resources enable it to be handled in a consistent, efficient and effective manner. The firm also regularly advises in ERISA fiduciary matters and assist clients to address preemption, breach of fiduciary duty, fraud and misrepresentation, reporting and disclosure, and potential financial exposure issues.

### Litigation:

The firm represents clients in all aspects of commercial litigation, including trials and appeals in all state and federal courts; federal, state and self-regulatory administrative proceedings; and arbitrations and mediations. Lane Powell's broad range of litigation matters include: complex litigation (including class actions); securities; commercial disputes; virtually every type of litigation involving financial institutions; intellectual property; bankruptcy and creditors' rights; antitrust; health care; intellectual property and technology; appellate; insurance; products liability; real estate and environmental; trusts and estates; and architects, engineers and construction.

### International Work:

Lane Powell's international business and investment practice provides a full range of legal services to clients whose businesses cross international borders, including: inbound and outbound investments; joint ventures; strategic alliances; licensing and other forms of proprietary protection; distribution arrangements; the establishment, financing and operation of foreign branches and subsidiaries; international business negotiations; trade regulation; compliance with US securities and export laws; immigration matters; cross border IP protection (including trademark, trade dress, copyright and patent matters); and anti-trust compliance and defense.

### Clients:

Lane Powell represents emerging and established businesses. Respected clients – from individuals to small businesses to Fortune 500 companies – turn to the firm for trusted legal counsel. In fact, Fortune 500 companies including Home Depot, Nike, Tesoro, Eli Lilly, Wells Fargo, Aetna and Nordstrom have named Lane Powell as one of the prestigious "Go-To Law Firms of Top US Companies®" in Corporate Counsel magazine.

# PERKINS COIE LLP

www.perkinscoie.com

**Managing Partner:** Robert E Giles

## Firm Overview:

With more than 900 attorneys in 19 offices across United States, China and Taiwan, Perkins Coie provides a full array of corporate, commercial litigation and intellectual property legal services to a broad range of great companies, from Fortune 50 corporations to small, independent start-ups, as well as public and not-for-profit organizations. Perkins Coie has been named one of Fortune magazine's '100 Best Companies to Work For' for 11 years in a row.

## Main Areas of Practice:

### Business:

The firm's 200+ attorneys handle a variety of matters for leading companies, including publicly traded, multi-national, emerging growth and private entities. The group focuses on public and private equity and debt financings, mergers and acquisitions, corporate governance, securities compliance, tax, licensing and technology matters, bankruptcy and workouts, employee benefits and compensation matters and international transactions.

### Environment, Energy & Resources:

The Environment, Energy & Resources Group advises on regulatory and legislative advocacy, project permitting, compliance counseling, due diligence, litigation and enforcement defense. Their expertise covers every area of environmental and energy law, from pollution control and hazardous substances, to conventional and renewable energy, to extractive industries, to wildlife conservation.

### Finance:

The firm represents debtors, borrowers, creditors, lenders, committees, trustees, receivers and asset purchasers in bankruptcy and workout transactions, as well as federally insured financial institutions, CMBS special services, and pension fund administrators in all types of debt financings.

### Insurance:

The firm's insurance attorneys have a record of success in enforcing policyholders' rights to coverage under almost every type of commercial insurance policy for a wide spectrum of losses and liabilities.

### Intellectual Property:

The firm's IP practice includes more than 250 lawyers focused on IP litigation, patent and trademark procurement, technology licensing, copyrights and unfair competition counseling. The patent group includes more than 100 members with advanced degrees. Lawyers have experience in federal courts across the country and before the International Trade Commission. Four IP litigators are Fellows in the American College of Trial Lawyers.

### Labor & Employment:

The firm represents clients on every issue arising in the modern workplace. The firm has exceptional strength in employment litigation, including not only typical discrimination or wrongful termination litigation, but also fast-moving class action, trade secret, and noncompete litigation.

### Life Sciences:

The firm helps biologic, diagnostic, medical device and pharmaceutical companies in a variety of areas including corporate, intellectual property, litigation, real estate, employment and immigration.

### Litigation:

The firm's 400+ litigators have extensive experience in state and federal jurisdictions and at every appellate level including the US Supreme Court. The Litigation practice includes 14 Fellows in the American College of Trial Lawyers and has particular strength in the patent litigation, privacy, product liability (aviation), insurance (policyholder) coverage and class action defense.

### Political Law:

The Political Law group is the largest, most experienced group of its kind in the nation. With extensive experience in the political arena, they have provided advice and counsel to hundreds of candidates for elective office (including seven presidential campaigns), scores of nonprofit and ideological groups and dozens of corporations and businesses.

### Privacy & Data Security:

The firm's Privacy & Data Security attorneys counsel clients on issues such as enforcement, litigation, compliance, incident response and government and third-party requests for information.

### Product Liability:

The firm provides counseling on product liability containment and lawsuit avoidance, litigation and trial representation, global, national and regional claims coordination, and representation before government agencies.

### Real Estate & Land Use:

The firm helps clients with leasing, land use permitting strategies, and the financing, acquisition, development and disposition of national and international projects.

### Retail & Consumer Products:

The firm's wide range of retail clients, from small start-ups to some of the largest Internet and big-box retailers and consumer product companies, come to them for a range of issues, including tax, marketing and advertising, litigation, intellectual property, employment, real estate

and environmental, franchising, consumer protection, ecommerce and social media, and bankruptcy.

# WINTERBAUER & DIAMOND PLLC

www.winterbauerdiamond.com **tel:** 206 676 8440 **fax:** 206 676 8441

**Managing Partner:** Steven H Winterbauer
**Partner:** Kenneth J Diamond
Number of partners: 2
Number of other lawyers: 4
Languages: *English, Spanish*

**PRACTICE AREAS**
Employment & Labor Law

**OFFICES**
WASHINGTON
**SEATTLE:** 1200 Fifth Avenue Suite 1700, WA 98101
Tel: 206 676 8440   Fax: 206 676 8441
Email: mail@winterbauerdiamond.com

## Firm Overview:
Winterbauer & Diamond PLLC is a boutique firm devoted entirely to representing management on all employment and traditional labor matters throughout Seattle, Washington state and the Pacific Northwest. The firm offers experience at a level of personal attention not common to most firms. Counseling, training, and litigation services are tailored to match the needs and goals of each client. The firm is the Washington representative to Worklaw® Network, a national consortium of management-side employment and labor law boutique firms.

## Main Areas of Practice:
Winterbauer & Diamond's substantive areas of expertise extend to every facet of the employer-employee and independent contractor-principal relationships.

## Employment Litigation:
The firm's employment lawyers defend employers against claims and charges brought in court and before regulatory agencies on the full range of legal theories, including employment discrimination, employment torts, wage-related claims, unfair labor practice charges, and claims related to the protection of business information and assets.

## Regulatory Compliance & Administrative Enforcement:
Compliance can be a burden and enforcement actions can be taxing and distracting. However, both offer opportunities. These include recalibrating the labor-management or employee-employer relationship, increasing employee understanding and investment in the compliance process, demonstrating the organization's commitment to certain interests and objectives deeply held and shared by its workers, and educating employees on the business considerations and other reasons behind certain decisions and actions that may otherwise be misunderstood.

## Proprietary Information & Executive Mobility:
In an increasingly information-based economy populated with an ever more mobile and transitory workforce, the retention of key employees and the protection of proprietary information and other business assets have become essential to the long-term success of nearly every enterprise. The firm's lawyers have years of experience assisting employers in meeting these objectives, in both the boardroom and the court room.

## Public Employment:
The firm's lawyers counsel and litigate with respect to all facets of federal, state and local government employment. Public sector clients include, and have included, cities, counties, police departments, firefighter departments, public housing authorities, public utility districts, educational institutions, public hospital districts, and most local government bodies that fall under the Washington Interlocal Cooperation Act.

## Labor Relations:
The firm provides the full range of industrial relations and traditional labor law services for public and private sector employers across nearly all industries. Services include counseling and representation in connection with preemption issues, employee solicitation and distribution rules, non-employee access to private employer property, rules governing the display of union insignia, union organizing and recognition, collective bargaining, labor contract administration and interpretation, prevailing wage issues, unfair labor practice charges before the National Labor Relations Board and the Public Employment Relations Commission, grievance administration and arbitration, and the labor implications of corporate restructuring, plant closures, mass layoffs and other reductions in force, and mergers and acquisitions. The firm also advises employers regarding the application of traditional labor principles to the non-union workforce.

## Planning, Training & Investigations:
In the employment and labor law arena, the adage that an ounce of prevention is worth a pound of cure is particularly true. Many work-related legal issues are preventable. They start small and appear routine: an employee complains of being treated differently or too harshly by a supervisor; two employees begin to date; a manager offends a subordinate with ribald jokes and comments; or an employee complains of back pain and asks to be temporarily relieved of certain tasks. Too often these types of circumstances, readily navigable at inception, fester and ultimately morph into difficult legal matters due to employer inaction. Avoiding this self-defeating tendency through planning, training and self-examination is a major focus of the firm's practice.

## Clients:
Winterbauer & Diamond PLLC represents public and private employers, from sole proprietorships and start-ups to Fortune 500 corporations, throughout Washington and the Pacific Northwest across a broad range of industries, including hospitality, healthcare, retail, local government, law enforcement, education, technology and insurance. Key clients include Costco Wholesale Corporation, Expedia, Inc., King County Sheriff's Office, MultiCare Health System, Safeway Inc., Les Schwab Tire Centers, Schweitzer Engineering Laboratories, Inc., and Walgreen Co.

# WINTERBAUER & DIAMOND PLLC

EMPLOYMENT & LABOR LAW

## How lawyers are ranked

Every year we carry out thousands of in-depth interviews with clients in order to assess the reputations and expertise of business lawyers worldwide. The qualities we look for (and which determine rankings) include technical legal ability, professional conduct, client service, commercial awareness/astuteness, diligence, commitment, and other qualities most valued by the client. For details of our research team, see p.5.

## CORPORATE/COMMERCIAL

Commentary about individuals can be found under their firm's paragraph. If the firm has no paragraph (is not ranked) look at Other Notable Practitioners.

### Corporate/Commercial
### Leading Firms

**Band 1**
Bowles Rice LLP *
Jackson Kelly PLLC
Spilman Thomas & Battle, PLLC *
Steptoe & Johnson PLLC *

**Band 2**
Huddleston Bolen LLP

**Band 3**
Campbell Woods, PLLC
Dinsmore & Shohl LLP
Kay Casto & Chaney PLLC
Phillips Gardill Kaiser & Altmeyer
Robinson & McElwee PLLC

### Leading Individuals

**Band 1**

| | |
|---|---|
| Cappellanti Ellen | Jackson Kelly PLLC |
| Graff Jr F Thomas | Bowles Rice LLP * |
| Heywood Thomas A | Bowles Rice LLP * |
| Lord Elizabeth Osenton | Jackson Kelly PLLC |
| Murray Thomas J | Huddleston Bolen LLP |

**Band 2**

| | |
|---|---|
| Basile Michael | Spilman Thomas & Battle, PLLC * |
| Deem Patrick D | Steptoe & Johnson PLLC * |
| Maxwell-Hoffman Ellen | Bowles Rice LLP * |
| Plybon Christopher J | Huddleston Bolen LLP |
| Williams Jr L Frederick | Steptoe & Johnson PLLC * |

**Band 3**

| | |
|---|---|
| Helmick Brian C | Spilman Thomas & Battle, PLLC * |
| Higgins David K | Robinson & McElwee PLLC |
| Perry Jr Audy M | Huddleston Bolen LLP |

**Up-and-coming individuals**

| | |
|---|---|
| Alsop Jessica | Jackson Kelly PLLC |

### Corporate/Commercial: Banking & Finance
### Leading Individuals

**Band 1**

| | |
|---|---|
| Booker William | Kay Casto & Chaney PLLC |
| Dunbar Charles | Jackson Kelly PLLC |
| Gardill James | Phillips Gardill Kaiser & Altmeyer |
| Hill Lee O | Spilman Thomas & Battle, PLLC * |
| Murphy Sandra M | Bowles Rice LLP * |
| Murray Thomas J | Huddleston Bolen LLP |

**Band 2**

| | |
|---|---|
| Chincheck Julia A | Bowles Rice LLP * |
| Gee Samme | Jackson Kelly PLLC |
| King Jr Evans L | Steptoe & Johnson PLLC * |
| Siegrist Camden P | Bowles Rice LLP * |
| Stump John C | Steptoe & Johnson PLLC * |
| Thomas David M | Dinsmore & Shohl LLP |

**Up-and-coming individuals**

| | |
|---|---|
| King Condaras Amy R | Spilman Thomas & Battle, PLLC * |

### Corporate/Commercial: Healthcare
### Leading Individuals

**Band 1**

| | |
|---|---|
| Coffield Robert L | Flaherty Sensabaugh Bonasso (ONP)[†] |
| Heywood Thomas A | Bowles Rice LLP * |
| Thomas James W | Jackson Kelly PLLC |

**Band 2**

| | |
|---|---|
| Moore John S | Bowles Rice LLP * |
| Williams Walter L | Steptoe & Johnson PLLC * |
| Willis-Miller Taunja | Jackson Kelly PLLC |

### Corporate/Commercial: Tax
### Leading Individuals

**Band 1**

| | |
|---|---|
| Caryl Michael E | Bowles Rice LLP * |
| Kiss Robert S | Bowles Rice LLP * |
| Southworth II Louis S | Jackson Kelly PLLC |
| Tweel Robert | Jackson Kelly PLLC |
| Williams Jr L Frederick | Steptoe & Johnson PLLC * |

**Band 2**

| | |
|---|---|
| Allevato John | Spilman Thomas & Battle, PLLC * |
| Hussell IV John F | Dinsmore & Shohl LLP |
| Kay Craig | Kay Casto & Chaney PLLC |
| Monteleone Marc A | Bowles Rice LLP * |
| Perry Jr Audy M | Huddleston Bolen LLP |

\* Indicates firm / individual with profile.
[†]ONP = Other Notable Practitioner.

## Band 1

### Bowles Rice LLP
See profile on p.2568

**THE FIRM** This well-resourced, full-service firm is highly recommended, offering expertise to energy, healthcare, manufacturing and banking clients on various commercial and corporate matters. As well as business transactions and financing, they are well recognized for real estate-related work. The practice has a traditional strength in the energy sector and has been capitalizing on the recent regional boom in this space, resulting in increased banking transactions, inbound investments, and general corporate work. Its work highlights from the past year include advising First Community Bancshares on its $26.3 million acquisition of People's Bank of Virginia.

**Sources say:** *"There is a very strong partnership and business relationship between us which we very much encourage and appreciate."* *"They are very easy to deal with. If you run into issues, they can always give you helpful advice with a balanced approach, and provide good guidance."*

**KEY INDIVIDUALS** Based in the firm's Martinsburg office, **Michael Caryl** (see p.2561) enjoys an excellent reputation for his top-notch tax practice. His expertise in state and federal taxation is highly appreciated by corporate clients. Former managing partner of the firm, **Thomas Graff** (see p.2563) has over 40 years of experience in general business and commercial matters. His energy background coupled with his broad commercial practice makes him a go-to lawyer for many key businesses in the state. **Thomas Heywood** (see p.2563) is the firm's managing partner in combination with what one commentator called his *"high-level corporate work."* He is best known for serving primary corporate clients on high-end corporate commercial work, healthcare matters and government relations. **Julia Chincheck** (see p.2562) is regarded as one of the premier bankruptcy experts in the region. Additionally, she handles loan workouts and commercial lending. Her busy year included assisting clients on a range of acquisition and loan transactions. **Sandra Murphy** (see p.2565) enjoys a reputation as a *"top banking lawyer who does a great job."* As well as advising banks on commercial transactions, she also guides clients through the regulatory landscape. She was a lead adviser on the acquisition of People's Bank of Virginia by First Community Bancshares as mentioned above. **Robert Kiss** (see p.2563) is well known and respected for his tax practice. He brings many years of experience assisting clients with their business development, advising on all aspects of state and federal tax law. **Ellen Maxwell-Hoffman** (see p.2564), who is the new head of the practice group, has a traditional, full-service corporate practice. She acts for a range of local and multinational clients, including Japanese investors, and also advises on commercial lending. One appreciative client commented: *"She is very down to earth, responsive and a big help. She knows the background of my company and the hot-button issues."* Another source noted: *"She has a very strong skill set and is a pleasure to work with."* Charleston-based commercial generalist **Camden Siegrist** (see p.2565) makes a debut this year on the list. He has extensive experience in the banking transactional area, and is particularly known for his commercial financing work. **Marc Monteleone** (see p.2564) has a broad corporate practice across the construction and oil and natural gas sectors. He is also known for his experience in entity formation and corporate tax. Healthcare specialist **John Moore** (see p.2564) is praised for being *"very bright and skilled."* He impresses clients, including nonprofit entities with his grasp of all aspects of healthcare issues and regulations.

## Jackson Kelly PLLC

**THE FIRM** Jackson Kelly is highly respected for the sheer depth of its commercial practice, which is deeply rooted in West Virginia. With offices in a number of other states, it is one of the largest and longest-established corporate commercial practices in the region. The group offers expertise in every aspect of corporate practice to clients ranging from local businesses to multinationals. Clients are drawn from industries as diverse as natural resources, biotechnology and media, and it has been particularly active in the oil sector.

**KEY INDIVIDUALS Ellen Cappellanti** stands out in the market for her excellent bankruptcy work. Sources praise her *"great counseling skills, quality work, solid background and particular expertise in real estate"* together with her *"business sense."* **Louis Southworth** is identified as another excellent corporate practitioner who specializes in taxation and is also active in government relations matters. *"He has savvy business sense and great drafting and analytic skills,"* enthused one source. **Samme Gee** is one of the most pop-

ular players in the state's financing arena. She is especially well regarded for her bond-related work and is also heavily engaged in governmental and public development project financing transactions. The *"efficient and pleasant"* **Charles Dunbar** focuses his practice primarily on banking and finance. As a long-standing and highly regarded practitioner, he offers 30 years of experience in the banking, finance and regulatory arenas. Sources consider him *"top-notch"* and have no hesitation in referring matters to him. The highly experienced **Elizabeth Osenton Lord** is regarded as *"a very strong, very able and very talented"* lawyer. She specializes in transactional work, with a strong focus on securities-related matters. Charleston-based **James Thomas** stands out as one of the foremost healthcare specialists in the state. He represents hospitals, clinics, health centers and trade associations in various matters, including regulatory compliance, acquisitions and general administrative issues. **Robert Tweel**, who chairs the firm's tax practice, has a broad practice but is particularly known for his skills in respect of federal taxation. He acts for a range of corporates and partnerships, advising on corporate and partnership tax and state planning. **Jessica Alsop** has been identified as an up-and-coming tax practitioner who is well regarded for her capability in a range of taxation issues, including income, partnership and corporate tax. She is also identified for her bond and securities work, with one source commenting: *"She is bright, talented and capable."* Morgantown-based **Taunja Willis-Miller**'s practice spans both healthcare and finance. She is best known for representing nonprofit entities, healthcare providers and universities in M&A, financing and bond transactions.

## Spilman Thomas & Battle, PLLC
### See profile on p.2569

**THE FIRM** This highly regarded and growing regional firm has a broad commercial corporate practice. The group provides a full-service corporate offering from general corporate issues and major business transactions to employment, wealth management and tax planning matters. In 2012 its team was strengthened further by the addition of two commercial partners who brought expertise in banking, regulatory matters and securities. A recent highlight was its role as adviser to Chico Enterprises on the sale of its convenience store chain to Circle K.

**Sources say:** *"I would recommend this strong, solid and experienced firm for major transactions. They can adapt and are good at planning. They add value to transactions." "I am also impressed with the high-quality work they are able to deliver."*

**KEY INDIVIDUALS Michael Basile** (see p.2561) has the role of managing partner as well as enjoying an excellent all-around reputation as a corporate lawyer. He is considered a first choice for government relations issues as well as corporate matters. He wins high acclaim from market sources, who say: *"He is very experienced, a great strategic thinker and a very able communicator; he does a great job leading the firm."* **Lee Hill** (see p.2563) is a senior player in the firm's public financing team who is *"easily regarded as one of the deans in the bond and financing space."* He has been involved in healthcare public financing transactions

of late, and also advises clients from various sectors on all aspects of tax-exempt and taxable bonds. **John Allevato** (see p.2561) heads the firm's wealth management and tax practice. With over 30 years of experience, he has impressive capability in state planning, wealth management and taxation counseling in M&A transactions. One client commented: *"He was a critical component of our transaction, and dramatically improved our financial situation with his knowledge. He is my first call."* One of the recent highlights is his representation of Ohio Precious Metals in its merger with NTR Metals, involving complex corporate and federal tax planning. **Brian Helmick** (see p.2563) heads the practice group and concentrates his practice primarily on public project financing representing state issuers. Sources reveal: *"He is a very experienced and good business lawyer, an extremely able guy."* He led the team advising Paradigm Development on all aspects of the West Virginia University student housing project, involving acquisition of real property, project financing and construction contracts. Co-head of the banking and finance group, **Amy King Condaras** (see p.2563) is considered *"smart, tough and committed"* and as having *"business savvy."* She has a busy healthcare public financing practice, and continues to develop her federal tax compliance strength. In addition, she also handles securities and commercial loans for clients. Recent highlights include representing West Virginia United Health System on the issuance of its $66 million hospital refunding bonds.

## Steptoe & Johnson PLLC
### See profile on p.2570

**THE FIRM** Steptoe & Johnson maintains its position at the forefront of the West Virginia market, representing energy, banking, real estate, commercial developers and business clients. The firm's commercial capabilities have been bolstered by a number of new hires and internal promotions in the past year. It has seen an uptick in mandates in relation to the energy sector, including public finance and public development work in the oil and gas arenas.

**Sources say:** *"Its service is very personable, its team is knowledgeable and professional, and they understand our needs."*

**KEY INDIVIDUALS** General counsel **Evans King** (see p.2563) offers all-around expertise in M&A with an emphasis on banking and finance. He represents clients in diverse sectors and is particularly known for his knowledge of the energy industry. **John Stump** (see p.2566) is a well-known player in the market, focusing his practice on public financing. He is highly regarded in the bond market, with extensive experience in handling bond issues for local governments. **Frederick Williams** (see p.2566) is considered to be *"among the most highly regarded bond lawyers"* in the market and commentators are quick to praise his substantial strength in finance work. Sources are also very impressed with his broad talents in banking, public financing and state and federal taxation. **Patrick Deem**'s (see p.2562) broad commercial practice has a strong reputation in the West Virginia market. *"He is able, well regarded and produces quality work,"* one commentator enthused. He advises on M&A, real estate acquisitions and general corporate matters, with an emphasis on the oil and gas industries. **Walter Williams** (see p.2566) heads the firm's healthcare practice, and has many years' experience of general commercial transactions. He currently concentrates on healthcare and is highly regarded in this field, advising healthcare providers on all aspects of their business.

## Band 2

### Huddleston Bolen LLP

**THE FIRM** With a strong presence, particularly in the Huntington market, this group is considered a strong competitor by many peers. Its commercial group enjoys an excellent reputation in both the corporate and banking arenas, and most recently has been particularly active in the coal mining sector. It advises on significant acquisitions, regulations, securities laws and public listings, and in the past year it has won mandates from the likes of Premier Financial Bancorp, Partners Insurance and Early Construction.

**KEY INDIVIDUALS Thomas Murray** heads the firm's M&A practice and its federal securities group, regularly acting on general commercial and corporate matters. He is equally well regarded for his securities work and solid tax understanding, being described as *"a very talented lawyer."* **Audy Perry** oversees the firm's business state planning department and has been involved in a range of financing and construction projects for Marshall University in the past year. He offers a strong skill set and impresses clients with his *"professionalism and intelligence."* **Christopher Plybon** enjoys a fine reputation for his banking and finance skills and remains involved in a range of projects for Marshall University. Of late, he led the team advising the university on the bond financing for the construction of a number of properties, valued at over $20 million. Sources say: *"He is a pleasure to work with"* and *"he is a very confident business generalist."*

### Campbell Woods, PLLC

**THE FIRM** This Huntington-based boutique enjoys an excellent reputation within the local market. The group is traditionally known for its tax strength in relation to commercial transactions and general corporate issues, and in the past year the team has handled a increasing level of work in the oil and gas sectors. Its extensive local knowledge and connections are appreciated by diverse clients, including Doctor's Associates, Sysco and Persinger Supply.
**KEY INDIVIDUALS** Department head **Howard Crews** is a key contact.

### Dinsmore & Shohl LLP

**THE FIRM** This growing firm has developed a strong presence in West Virginia with three offices in the state. The team offers a full range of commercial transactional and tax expertise with a particular focus on the healthcare sector; it includes Health Services of the Virginias among its clients. It is also highly regarded for its solid tax background, and is becoming increasingly active in the natural gas and coal industries. A key highlight in the past year saw the team represent BCBank, the creditor, on a commercial collection and foreclosure matter valued at $5 million.
**KEY INDIVIDUALS John Hussell** is the well-regarded managing partner of the firm. His corporate commercial practice includes particular expertise in family wealth planning, trust and state tax planning and trust administration work. Morgantown-based **David Thomas** enjoys a fine reputation for his solid banking work, representing banks in commercial deals, loan structuring, collections and bankruptcy cases. His notable work includes representing Citizens Bank of West Virginia in a collection action, bankruptcy and foreclosure matter.

### Kay Casto & Chaney PLLC

**THE FIRM** With offices in Charleston and Morgantown, this firm houses a team of excellent practitioners, offering experience and savvy advice on corporate, bankruptcy, real estate and taxation matters. The corporate/commercial group works closely with other practice groups, including employment and healthcare, offering multidisciplinary expertise to clients. Of late, it has been particularly active representing banks in commercial lending deals as well as litigation matters.

**KEY INDIVIDUALS** The experienced **William Booker** *"stands out in the market"* for his fine reputation and for *"being well prepared."* He has a diverse practice, covering bankruptcy law, commercial lending and mortgage lending, with a particular focus on representing banking clients. **Craig Kay** is recognized for his tax and accounting expertise, and primarily concentrates his practice on federal and state tax planning together with estate and business planning.

### Phillips Gardill Kaiser & Altmeyer

**THE FIRM** This long-established, Wheeling-based firm offers a skill set in general corporate and commercial law, business transactions, tax and banking. Its team is well regarded in the market and is particularly known for handling banking and financing transactions. Some of its clients include WesBanco, Mull Industries and Belmont Savings Bank.
**KEY INDIVIDUALS** Managing partner **James Gardill** is praised as *"a superb lawyer."* He specializes in banking matters and is also known for his taxation and estate planning skills.

### Robinson & McElwee PLLC

**THE FIRM** This firm operates from three offices in West Virginia, and is home to some well-regarded practitioners within the business and commercial practice group. Its teams offer expertise across commercial transactions, banking, bankruptcy and tax matters with the aim of counseling clients on all phases of the life of a business. It is best known for its strength in serving clients in the utilities and energy sectors.
**KEY INDIVIDUALS** Founding partner **David Higgins** is based in the Charleston office and is widely recognized as an excellent corporate and commercial lawyer. He is *"hardworking and very experienced,"* advising on state and federal taxation, securities and other general business matters.

### Other Notable Practitioners

**Robert Coffield** of Flaherty Sensabaugh Bonasso PLLC specializes in healthcare-related corporate and commercial work, and has particular expertise in regulatory compliance and medical malpractice. His practice is highly regarded by various healthcare clients in West Virginia, including hospitals, clinics, healthcare providers and trade organizations.

# LABOR & EMPLOYMENT

Commentary about individuals can be found under their firm's paragraph. If the firm has no paragraph (is not ranked) look at Other Notable Practitioners.

| Labor & Employment |
| --- |
| **Leading Firms** |

| **Band 1** | |
| --- | --- |
| Steptoe & Johnson PLLC * | |

| **Band 2** | |
| --- | --- |
| Dinsmore & Shohl LLP | |
| Spilman Thomas & Battle, PLLC * | |

| **Band 3** | |
| --- | --- |
| Bowles Rice LLP * | |
| Jackson Kelly PLLC | |
| Kay Casto & Chaney PLLC | |

| **Senior Statesmen** | |
| --- | --- |
| **Senior Statesmen: distinguished older practitioners** | |
| Steptoe Jr Robert M | Steptoe & Johnson PLLC * |

| **Leading Individuals** | |
| --- | --- |

| **Band 1** | |
| --- | --- |
| Brown Ricklin | Bailey & Glasser LLP (ONP)† |
| Carter Mark | Dinsmore & Shohl LLP |
| Cokeley Bryan R | Steptoe & Johnson PLLC * |
| Morrison C David | Steptoe & Johnson PLLC * |
| Roles Forrest | Dinsmore & Shohl LLP |

| **Band 2** | |
| --- | --- |
| Bean Rodney L | Steptoe & Johnson PLLC * |
| Carr Kevin | Spilman Thomas & Battle, PLLC * |
| Dailey Anna M | Dinsmore & Shohl LLP |
| Iskra Eric | Spilman Thomas & Battle, PLLC * |
| Magee Erin E | Jackson Kelly PLLC |
| Price Joseph | Robinson & McElwee PLLC (ONP)† |
| Slaughter Christopher L | Steptoe & Johnson PLLC * |
| Weber Stephen A | Kay Casto & Chaney PLLC |
| Wolfe Roger | Jackson Kelly PLLC |
| Woody Charles | Spilman Thomas & Battle, PLLC * |

| **Band 3** | |
| --- | --- |
| Dellinger Mark H | Bowles Rice LLP * |
| Dick David E | Steptoe & Johnson PLLC * |
| Heath Mark E | Spilman Thomas & Battle, PLLC * |
| Kinder Eric | Spilman Thomas & Battle, PLLC * |
| Merinar Jr John R | Steptoe & Johnson PLLC * |
| Nelson Kevin A | Huddleston Bolen LLP (ONP)† |
| Sebok Al F | Jackson Kelly PLLC |
| Sheets Scott K | Huddleston Bolen LLP (ONP)† |
| Weber Constance H | Kay Casto & Chaney PLLC |

| **Up-and-coming individuals** | |
| --- | --- |
| Peterson Brian | Bowles Rice LLP * |
| Wallace Rick | Spilman Thomas & Battle, PLLC * |

\* Indicates firm / individual with profile.

†ONP = Other Notable Practitioner.

## Band 1

### Steptoe & Johnson PLLC
See profile on p.2570

**THE FIRM** This substantial, leading practice provides a full service across the labor and employment arena. A deep bench of talent offers expertise from collective bargaining and wage and hour disputes to occupational injuries and counseling employers on compliance and employment policy issues. The group is enhanced by the firm's litigation strength and is increasingly handling matters arising from the energy and resources sectors as well as such diverse sectors as healthcare, education and construction.

**Sources say:** *"The firm has a good range of lawyers, from junior associates to senior partner level. It is able to staff cases properly."*

**KEY INDIVIDUALS Robert Steptoe** (see p.2565) is one of the most experienced members of the team and is regarded as a go-to lawyer when it comes to labor and employment matters. *"He can do anything and he has done everything,"* according to one source. **Bryan Cokeley** (see p.2562) heads the firm's labor and employment department and maintains a highly active employment litigation practice. He is regarded as a *"top-notch"* and dedicated litigator. **David Morrison** (see p.2564) is the former chair of the labor and employment department at this firm and has over 30 years of experience in this field. He covers both labor and employment counseling and litigation and is particularly active representing energy and coal industry clients. For ten years, **Rodney Bean** (see p.2561) has primarily focused his practice on providing healthcare and energy clients with labor and employment counseling. He serves as principal outside counsel to a major natural gas company in connection with all its employment and labor-related requirements. **Christopher Slaughter** (see p.2565) has a broad practice encompassing both advisory work and litigation. Of late, he has been heavily engaged in traditional labor issues, labor negotiations and employment disputes, in particular representing employers from the energy, healthcare, manufacturing and construction sectors. **David Dick** (see p.2562) heads the firm's workplace safety team and concentrates his practice on labor and employment-related counseling. Clients appreciate his hands-on experience; he brings some 15 years of HR management experience in various industries, including manufacturing and pharmaceuticals. **John Merinar** (see p.2564) is the well-regarded team leader who specializes in employer counseling and labor work. He is currently heavily engaged with clients in the education sector, handling a suite of employment-related matters.

## Band 2

### Dinsmore & Shohl LLP

**THE FIRM** This firm is recognized as a real force in the West Virginia market. It is known for its strong traditional labor law practice in addition to handling employment and benefits matters. The practice has been further strengthened by the expansion of the team at the Charleston office, continuing to serve labor-intense clients, especially in the coal industry, in respect of both counseling and litigation. Its diverse client roster includes Sysco Corporation, Chesapeake Energy, Essar Minerals and Frontier Communications.

**Sources say:** *"Strategically they gave us the best results we have ever had." "The judges are always pleased to know that they are in the courtroom, because judges know that they will be reasonable and prepared, with reasonable expectations. They will not waste the judge's and courtroom's valuable time."*

**KEY INDIVIDUALS Mark Carter** is recognized as a leading labor law practitioner in the state. His skill set encompasses negotiating union contracts, advising on collective bargaining, general labor law and arbitrations. One commentator remarked: *"He is knowledgeable, a good communicator and strategically minded."* Work highlights include acting for Frontier West Virginia in connection with a claim of breach of a collective bargaining agreement. With some 40 years' experience, **Forrest Roles** continues to serve clients on a range of labor and employment matters. He is also highly regarded for his mediation skills, with one source commenting: *"He is brilliant at bringing people together"* and *"he is the calmest person in the world and the one you would want to be with in a storm."* **Anna Dailey** brings a wealth of experience to clients across a range of industries on the labor and employment fronts and is also a highly regarded litigator. Her busy year included successfully representing Frasure Creek Mining with regard to UMWA election proceedings and subsequent unfair labor practice cases filed by UMWA.

### Spilman Thomas & Battle, PLLC
See profile on p.2569

**THE FIRM** Spilman is one of the largest employment and labor practices in the region and is widely acknowledged for its all-around employment work, together with a labor law capacity including acting on collective bargaining negotiations. It attracts clients of the order of the Coca-Cola Bottling Company, DuPont and Mylan Pharmaceuticals. Highlights of late include defending Lockheed Martin in an age discrimination claim from a highly ranked former employee.

**Sources say:** *"They are very attentive, work very hard and do their best to achieve the best results for us. They really seem to care about their clients. It is their first priority and it shows* in their work." "It is a very strong practice with a strong skill-ful team."

KEY INDIVIDUALS Charles Woody (see p.2566) is a well-regarded labor and employment practitioner who is widely known for his litigation and appellate work. He recently successfully defended Chase Investment Services in a disability discrimination claim. Kevin Carr (see p.2561) offers a broad skill set, advising clients on employment and traditional labor issues. "He really gets to the bottom of the cases, understands the facts and is a good legal technician in this area." In the past year, he was mandated by Fairmont General Hospital on collective bargaining negotiations, achieving over $1.5 million in savings and enhancements. New to the list, Mark Heath (see p.2563) enjoys a fine reputation for being "very detail-oriented, knowledgeable and experienced." His practice has a strong focus on occupational health and safety, especially in the energy industries. Eric Iskra (see p.2563) heads the practice group and is particularly active in respect of employment-related litigation as well as counseling in matters such as class actions, healthcare and disability. Significant work of late includes acting for DuPont in a high-profile age discrimination and national origin discrimination claim, obtaining a victory for the client. A source noted of Eric Kinder (see p.2563): "He is responsive and has a thorough understanding of West Virginia labor laws." He is a key member of the team who has very broad employment and labor law experience coupled with a strong litigation background. Rick Wallace (see p.2566) is a young partner who was promoted recently and specializes in labor and employment-related litigation. His expertise extends to advising on labor relations, and he took a role in the collective bargaining negotiations for Fairmont General Hospital as mentioned above.

## Band 3

### Bowles Rice LLP
See profile on p.2568

THE FIRM This firm maintains its position in the employment and labor market, representing leading healthcare providers, energy, insurance and banking clients. The team is active in the employment negotiation arena, and saw an uptake in the areas of collective wage and hour matters, as well as employment litigation cases. In the last year it acted for Verizon Services on a number of unemployment compensation claims and also counts Highmark Blue Cross Blue Shield West Virginia and FedEx among its clients.
Sources say: "They are very responsive on employment-related matters and the partner we work with is very personable."

KEY INDIVIDUALS Mark Dellinger (see p.2562) is a very experienced practitioner whose particular forte is employment litigation and union contract-related matters. Notable work of late includes representing the City of Ravenswood in its collective bargaining negotiations with the United Steelworkers Union in respect of a new labor agreement. Martinsburg-based Brian Peterson (see p.2565) is building an increasingly notable labor and employment practice and has attracted praise for doing "an excellent job." His busy year included successfully defending United Bank against wage payment claims filed by two former employees.

### Jackson Kelly PLLC

THE FIRM Jackson Kelly has a traditional strength in the labor and employment arenas in both litigation and counseling. It is also growing its consultation practice, offering advice to employers on all aspects of employee relations. The team's clients include United Coal, Alpha Natural Resources, West Virginia University and Azimuth.
KEY INDIVIDUALS Erin Magee heads the firm's labor and employment practice and is considered a leading player in this field. She handles a broad range of issues, including traditional labor work and union negotiations, with a particular focus on employment litigation. The well-regarded Roger Wolfe has extensive experience of traditional labor matters, employment counseling and litigation, particularly in the energy industries. He has also served as a mediator in an array of employment disputes. Al Sebok is a longtime practitioner who has traditional strength in dealing with labor issues in the energy arena, particularly coal sector clients. He is also recognized as an excellent employment litigator, with one source commenting: "He is exceptionally responsive and a very good counsel for our business in addition to being a clear expert in labor law."

### Kay Casto & Chaney PLLC

THE FIRM This long-established and relatively compact practice is particularly specialized in employment counseling and litigation. On the counseling front it also offers risk management in combination with alternative dispute resolution. The team is best known for representing major healthcare providers and banking clients in the state.
KEY INDIVIDUALS Stephen Weber's decades of experience have largely focused on employment law, handling advisory and mediation work for employers, as well as litigation. He continues to serve as a contact point for his long-standing clients, and with his wealth of knowledge and experience he is in demand as a lecturer by both business and professional groups. Constance Weber, who is a key member of the team, concentrates primarily on employment law-related work. She is representing numerous hospital clients including advising on policy and human resources matters and is also a member of the firm's healthcare and litigation groups.

### Other Notable Practitioners

Joseph Price of Robinson & McElwee PLLC is a long-time labor and employment lawyer with over 30 years of experience in this field. He concentrates on traditional labor work together with some complex employment litigation cases. He also teaches labor and employment law at Marshall University. Ricklin Brown of Bailey & Glasser LLP is considered to be a "premier lawyer in the state." For more than 35 years, he has represented management and employers in an extensive range of industries, in all facets of labor and employment relations law, including negotiating collective bargaining agreements. Huntington-based Kevin Nelson of Huddleston Bolen LLP is recognized as a principal member of the team with many years of experience representing both employers and employees. His clients include the Thomson Reuters subsidiary West Publishing (dba Thomson West) in a wrongful dismissal claim. Scott Sheets of Huddleston Bolen LLP focuses in the main on employment law, representing employers across a number of industries, including those in the energy sectors. In the past year, he has handled a range of matters, including race discrimination and wrongful terminations.

# LITIGATION

Commentary about individuals can be found under their firm's paragraph. If the firm has no paragraph (is not ranked) look at Other Notable Practitioners.

## Litigation: General Commercial
### Leading Firms

**Band 1**
Bowles Rice LLP *
Flaherty Sensabaugh Bonasso PLLC
Jackson Kelly PLLC
Steptoe & Johnson PLLC *

**Band 2**
Bailey & Glasser LLP
Dinsmore & Shohl LLP
Farrell, White & Legg PLLC
Spilman Thomas & Battle, PLLC *
Thomas Combs & Spann

**Band 3**
Hendrickson & Long PLLC
Huddleston Bolen LLP
Jenkins Fenstermaker, PLLC

## Litigation: Healthcare
### Leading Individuals

**Band 1**

| Hurney Jr Thomas J | Jackson Kelly PLLC |
| Sensabaugh Don | Flaherty Sensabaugh Bonasso PLLC |

**Band 2**

| Brewer Susan Slenker | Steptoe & Johnson PLLC * |
| Jones Richard D | Flaherty Sensabaugh Bonasso PLLC |
| Martin Edward | Flaherty Sensabaugh Bonasso PLLC |
| White Tammy | Farrell, White & Legg PLLC * |

## Litigation: Mass Tort
### Senior Statesmen

**Senior Statesmen: distinguished older practitioners**

| Love III Charles M | Bowles Rice LLP * |

### Leading Individuals

**Band 1**

| Betts Rebecca A | Kay Casto & Chaney PLLC (ONP)[†] |
| Hendrickson David K | Hendrickson & Long PLLC |
| Long R Scott | Hendrickson & Long PLLC |
| Thomas David | Thomas Combs & Spann |

* Indicates firm / individual with profile.
[†] ONP = Other Notable Practitioner.

## Litigation: General Commercial
### Senior Statesmen

**Senior Statesmen: distinguished older practitioners**

| Love III Charles M | Bowles Rice LLP * |
| Stickler Daniel | Jackson Kelly PLLC |
| Tinney John | The Tinney Law Firm (ONP)[†] |

### Leading Individuals

**Star individuals**

| Emch A L | Jackson Kelly PLLC |

**Band 1**

| Bailey Benjamin | Bailey & Glasser LLP |
| Farmer Stephen | Farmer, Cline & Campbell PLLC (ONP)[†] |
| Farrell Michael J | Farrell, White & Legg PLLC * |
| Flaherty Thomas | Flaherty Sensabaugh Bonasso PLLC |
| Galeota William E | Steptoe & Johnson PLLC * |
| George Shawn P | George & Lorensen (ONP)[†] |
| Jernigan Jr W Henry | Dinsmore & Shohl LLP |
| Stowers Gerard R | Bowles Rice LLP * |
| Thomas David | Thomas Combs & Spann |
| Williams Marc E | Nelson Mullins Riley & Scarborough (ONP)[†] * |

**Band 2**

| Betts Rebecca A | Kay Casto & Chaney PLLC |
| Bonasso Michael | Flaherty Sensabaugh Bonasso PLLC |
| Carey Michael W | Carey, Scott & Douglas, PLLC (ONP)[†] |
| Glasser Brian | Bailey & Glasser LLP |
| LaCagnin Stephen | Jackson Kelly PLLC |
| Miller Timothy | Robinson & McElwee PLLC (ONP)[†] |
| Paul Niall | Spilman Thomas & Battle, PLLC * |
| Phillips Jeffrey K | Steptoe & Johnson PLLC * |
| Scarr Thomas | Jenkins Fenstermaker, PLLC |
| Spann Bryant J | Thomas Combs & Spann |
| Tabit Joanna I | Steptoe & Johnson PLLC * |
| Wakefield Jeffrey M | Flaherty Sensabaugh Bonasso PLLC |

**Band 3**

| Bailey Charles R | Bailey & Wyant PLLC (ONP)[†] * |
| Bolen Richard J | Huddleston Bolen LLP |
| Combs Philip J | Thomas Combs & Spann |
| Hall Lee Murray | Jenkins Fenstermaker, PLLC |
| Hoblitzell John R | Kay Casto & Chaney PLLC (ONP)[†] |
| Jones Heather Heiskell | Spilman Thomas & Battle, PLLC * |
| Konrad Angela | Huddleston Bolen LLP |
| Lusk Neva | Spilman Thomas & Battle, PLLC * |
| Mahaney John H | Huddleston Bolen LLP |
| Printz Charles F | Bowles Rice LLP * |
| Ramey Ancil G | Steptoe & Johnson PLLC * |
| Sweeney Robert | Jenkins Fenstermaker, PLLC |
| Walls James | Spilman Thomas & Battle, PLLC * |

**Up-and-coming individuals**

| Callas Gretchen M | Jackson Kelly PLLC |
| Foster Bird Melissa | Nelson Mullins Riley & Scarborough (ONP)[†] |
| Legg Erik | Farrell, White & Legg PLLC * |

**Associates to watch**

| Ellis Jonathan | Steptoe & Johnson PLLC * |

## Band 1

### Bowles Rice LLP
**See profile on p.2568**

**THE FIRM** The firm's substantial litigation team continues to thrive and in concert with other teams, the litigators tackle a diverse range of matters, including mass torts, class actions, property disputes and product liability in sectors such as oil and gas, banking, insurance and construction. As well as appearing before state and federal courts and administrative tribunals, it argues appeals before the West Virginia Supreme Court. Its impressive client roster includes The MENTOR Network, CONSOL Energy and Century Aluminum.

**Sources say:** "*They are intelligent, pragmatic and knowledgeable about the law.*"

**KEY INDIVIDUALS Charles Love** (see p.2564) is a senior, "*top-notch*" commercial litigator who garners widespread respect for his many years of experience in class actions, mass toxic tort and product liability cases. Considered one of "*the chief litigators of the firm,*" **Gerard Stowers** (see p.2566) is based in the Charleston office and focuses on commercial litigation, covering both plaintiff and defense work. He is actively engaged in representing insurance brokers and governing boards, and acting in product liability cases. "*He is a very intelligent, knowledgeable and experienced litigator, who seems to excel when it gets the toughest,*" one source said. Based in Martinbury, **Charles Printz** (see p.2565) has a statewide practice and is considered to have vast local knowledge of West Virginia. He is a highly experienced litigator with a broad practice including complex insurance coverage disputes.

### Flaherty Sensabaugh Bonasso PLLC

**THE FIRM** This litigation boutique, which operates from three offices in West Virginia, is recognized as a real force in the market. It acts for an array of clients, from individuals to large corporates in all aspects of the litigation process. The group possesses established expertise in class actions and mass tort, and is also known for its medical malpractice, product liability defense and commercial litigation experience.

**KEY INDIVIDUALS** Sources are impressed by **Thomas Flaherty**'s robust commercial litigation practice, and praise his particular strength in coal mining-related cases, workplace liability and personal injury litigation. **Don Sensabaugh** enjoys a reputation as one of the best medical malpractice defense lawyers around. With some 30 years' experience, he offers vast experience in the healthcare sector. The highly regarded **Michael Bonasso** is known for his general commercial litigation practice with an emphasis on product liability, especially in the automobile industry. **Richard Jones** has built up a particularly extensive reputation in medical malpractice defense cases, including medical device defense work and, more generally, product liability matters. Likewise, **Edward Martin** is a lead trial lawyer with extensive experience representing hospitals, insurers and doctors in medical malpractice defense cases. He also provides counsel to the healthcare sector on matters such as risk management in respect of professional liability. **Jeffrey Wakefield** is considered an "*outstanding*" litigator who is particularly sought out for personal injury and accident-related cases as well as product liability and insurance-related cases.

## Jackson Kelly PLLC

**THE FIRM** This sizable team is widely acknowledged as being among the leading commercial litigation practices in West Virginia. The team has recently seen an increase in oil and gas-related litigation for major regional clients. It represents clients in an array of sectors but has a particularly well-established strength in the energy and natural resources sectors.

**Sources say:** "*They are very practical, and do a nice job of navigating us through the litigation field.*" "*They are a wonderful firm.*"

**KEY INDIVIDUALS Daniel Stickler** is a leading partner in the arbitration group. He has 40 years' experience in the coal industry, both in private practice and in-house, and so understands the industry inside and out. He serves clients in both arbitration and litigation matters involving toxic torts, personal injuries, environmental disputes and contractual matters. **A L Emch** is fêted as one of the very best litigators in West Virginia. His broad practice is concentrated predominantly on defense work, which he has litigated at state, federal and appellate level. One interviewee pointed out that "*he is an exceptional communicator, who has the communication skills that most people can only wish to have.*" **Thomas Hurney** heads the firm's healthcare group and is particularly sought out for his medical malpractice expertise. His practice also encompasses cases involving defective pharmaceuticals and other products, and mass torts. Based in Morgantown, **Stephen LaCagnin** is recognized as one of the finest commercial litigators in the state. He handles a diverse range of litigation from personal injuries and wrongful deaths to employment and product liability. New to the list, **Gretchen Callas** is building an ever-increasing profile as a commercial litigator, especially in defending employers in workplace injuries and industrial accidents as well as in product liability cases. She is also a member of the Product Liability Advisory Council.

## Steptoe & Johnson PLLC
See profile on p.2570

**THE FIRM** This sizable group continues to win a substantial number of mandates flowing from the energy industry, ranging across contractual disputes, property issues, employment and regulatory matters. The practice also handles product liability and professional liability cases for clients in the mining sector. The team's industry knowledge attracts clients from diverse areas including healthcare, rail, natural resources and financial services.

**Sources say:** "*One of their strengths is they analyze the claim at the outset and formulate a game plan early on, and head*

it in the direction we want rather than where the other side takes us.*"

**KEY INDIVIDUALS** Morgantown-based **William Galeota** (see p.2562) leads the medical malpractice department and is especially experienced in healthcare-related litigation including medical malpractice defense, personal injuries and insurance defense work. Managing partner **Susan Slenker Brewer** (see p.2561) brings decades of experience to her clients in the healthcare arena, particularly with regard to medical malpractice work. Her experience includes taking cases to the West Virginia Supreme Court of Appeals and the US Court of Appeals. **Jeffrey Phillips** (see p.2565) is considered a top-notch litigator who is heavily engaged in personal injury work for natural resources clients. "*Jeff has adapted to how I want things done, so any time I have called with an issue, it is dealt with quickly and it goes away,*" an impressed client remarked. **Joanna Tabit** (see p.2566) is a general commercial litigator, who provides advice on a range of disputes in relation to employment, mass torts, property damage and workplace accidents. She is particularly experienced and active in the personal injury area. With many years of experience as a clerk of the Supreme Court of Appeals of West Virginia prior to his private practice, **Ancil Ramey** (see p.2565) is in demand for appellate matters. He has handled a huge number of appeals, with one source commenting: "*He is highly respected for appellate litigation.*" New to the list this year, **Jonathan Ellis** (see p.2562) focuses on the energy and mining industries and is experienced at handling MSHA issues and injury cases. Clients are attracted by his excellent understanding of the mining industry, with one source commenting: "*He saves us money because he understands what people are talking about so we don't have to explain it to him.*"

## Band 2

## Bailey & Glasser LLP

**THE FIRM** This specialist practice is widely respected for the quality and range of its litigation skills. The team represents both plaintiffs and defendants in matters ranging from product liability disputes and consumer class actions to environmental and energy-related actions.

**KEY INDIVIDUALS Benjamin Bailey** "*is considered one of the premier commercial litigators*" in West Virginia. A hugely experienced trial and appellate lawyer, he handles cases for clients ranging from the State of West Virginia to major corporates in the insurance, energy, healthcare and general commercial arenas. **Brian Glasser** practices commercial litigation exclusively, representing both plaintiffs and defendants. He has handled a range of high-stakes commercial disputes and is highly valued by clients. "*He is a very bright litigator who leaves no stone unturned,*" according to interviewees.

## Dinsmore & Shohl LLP

**THE FIRM** With a strong business background, commercial litigation is a core practice area for this firm. Its client base includes leading banks and healthcare providers and over the past year the team has been especially active with

healthcare and pharmaceutical-related work. Additionally, the practice is handling increasing levels of oil and gas-related disputes.

**KEY INDIVIDUALS Henry Jernigan** is a principal litigator whose practice serves banks, healthcare providers and the pharmaceutical industries. Most recently, he has been occupied with cases involving the pricing of drugs and regulatory disputes.

## Farrell, White & Legg PLLC

**THE FIRM** This respected group has a particular reputation for handling major product liability, medical and legal malpractice actions as well as class actions and general commercial matters. The group has acted on a number of pharmaceutical-related cases and has taken on a number of significant new clients. It also has extensive experience representing insurance companies; most recently, it acted as defense counsel for West Virginia Mutual Insurance in a medical professional liability case.

**Sources say:** "*The firm's strength is the thoroughness of its work and competencies of its lawyers.*"

**KEY INDIVIDUALS** Impressed interviewees describe **Michael Farrell** (see p.2562) as "*an exceptionally talented lawyer.*" His commercial litigation practice covers a range of issues with a particular focus on liability defense work in the chemical, pharmaceutical and coal mining industries. Over the past few years, he has been conducting a class action defense case involving thousands of former coal miners. Other notable work includes defending Robinson & McElwee and its managing member in a legal malpractice action. Healthcare litigation specialist **Tammy White** (see p.2566) heads the firm's medical defense group and "*has a good reputation*" among her peers. She is regularly engaged in major liability defense cases in relation to the pharmaceutical and healthcare industries. Recent highlights include acting in a multiparty medical negligence and wrongful death case. Young litigator **Erik Legg** (see p.2564) is considered "*exceptional*" and "*a future superstar.*" He focuses largely on pharmaceutical product liability defense and medical liability defense matters and most recently represented two physicians in a multiparty medical negligence case.

## Spilman Thomas & Battle, PLLC
See profile on p.2569

**THE FIRM** Over the past year, Spilman's robust litigation practice has been increasingly popular in the areas of toxic tort, medical care disputes and a natural gas-related class action. It also continues to see a steady stream of insurance and employment disputes work. The group takes pride in its early assessment approach to evaluating cases and serves an impressive client roster including DuPont, Coca-Cola Bottling and Alpha Natural Resources.

**Sources say:** "*Spilman has always got good results for us in West Virginia and understands our business well. They really vigorously represent our interests and care a lot about their clients. It is their first priority and it shows in their work.*"

**KEY INDIVIDUALS Niall Paul** (see p.2565) is praised by sources as an "*excellent lawyer*" and for having "*an impressive client base.*" He leads the practice group and can handle high-risk matters heading to trial. His primary areas of practice are complex torts, and commercial and employment disputes. Charleston-based **Neva Lusk** (see p.2564) regularly represents clients in diverse commercial litigation and has also been busy in her role with the board of directors of DRI, an international organization of attorneys defending the interests of businesses and individuals in civil litigation. **Heather Heiskell Jones** (see p.2563) heads the firm's litigation department and enjoys a fine reputation, particularly in dealing with mass torts and class actions related to the chemical and medical industries. *"She is a tough litigator and a good listener who really cares: what separates her from other lawyers is how much she really cares about the client's goals."* Morgantown-based **James Walls** (see p.2566) brings experience working in-house for the coal industry to his private practice. He is singled out by sources for his adept handling of high-value commercial disputes in relation to the oil, gas and coal industries. Notable work of late includes defending ArcelorMittal against employment discrimination claims brought by its former employees.

## Thomas Combs & Spann

**THE FIRM** Following the dissolution of Guthrie & Thomas in June 2012, key members of its litigation group created this boutique firm. Continuing its successful commercial litigation practice, the group has inherited traditional strengths in mass tort and product liability defense matters with a strong emphasis on the pharmaceutical and healthcare industries. It is also increasingly recognized for its expertise in the banking and finance sectors. Notable clients include Johnson & Johnson, Yamaha Motors, GE and 3M.
**KEY INDIVIDUALS** Managing partner **David Thomas** is highly respected for his expertise in mass torts in relation to a range of issues, including toxic exposure and personal injuries as well as commercial litigation. He is lead counsel for Johnson & Johnson in the pelvic mesh federal multidistrict litigation, which is a consolidation of over 2,200 federal lawsuits. **Bryant Spann**'s practice features product liability defense, toxic tort cases and defending financial institutions against individual consumer claims. Over the past year, he has served as leading counsel for 3M in the asbestos cases in West Virginia and Kentucky. **Philip Combs** is a rising litigator who is building considerable product liability expertise, especially in the pharmaceutical and medical devices sectors. He is also acting for Johnson & Johnson, and in other work he recently represented Subaru, successfully defending his client in respect of contractual claims brought by a terminated dealer.

## Band 3

## Hendrickson & Long PLLC

**THE FIRM** This forward-looking and growing group is increasingly active in the energy and construction sectors with respect to general commercial and product liability litigation. The group has an impressive breadth of experience across diverse sectors from natural resources to hos-

pitality and healthcare. As well as experienced trial lawyers, the practice also offers arbitration and mediation services.
**KEY INDIVIDUALS David Hendrickson** garners widespread respect for his vast experience, particularly mass torts, product liability and insurance-related litigation. He has acted for a wide range of industries, including pharmaceuticals, energy and coal mining. He is especially knowledgeable in cases involving toxic substances. **Scott Long** also enjoys a great reputation for his mass tort practice. Of late he has been dealing with class action cases involving toxic torts.

## Huddleston Bolen LLP

**THE FIRM** This highly experienced group acts for a diverse range of national and international clients in matters such as chemical spills, product liability, class actions and train derailments. It has a niche in the transportation sector, particularly in the railroad industry, as well as handling significant work in energy and construction. Its clients include Speedway, Ashland, Clorox, Marathon Oil and CSX Transportation.
**Sources say:** *"The people I used are very smart, have great presence in the courtroom and remain energized about defending us. The firm has done such a great job that the plaintiff attorneys are looking elsewhere for other defendants to sue."*
**KEY INDIVIDUALS** With a broad litigation practice, **Richard Bolen** is one of the most senior commercial litigators in the coal industry, whose enviable clients *"have relied on him for years and consider him as their in-house lawyer."* He focuses on representing energy clients in general torts, product liability cases and coal lease disputes. Over the past year, **Angela Konrad** has been heavily engaged in an employment mass tort litigation for a local retail chain. She brings many years of experience to the table and is a primary litigator in the firm who handles mass tort cases for manufacturing and transportation clients. With a solid mass tort background, **John Mahaney** heads the firm's commercial litigation practice and specializes in mass product liability defense. He is also known for handling complex commercial litigation and environmental claims. Recently he has represented a large gas producer in a significant class action.

## Jenkins Fenstermaker, PLLC

**THE FIRM** This relatively compact Huntington-based firm has a long-established reputation for its defense work. It regularly represents insurance companies defending clients in product liability and medical malpractice cases.
**KEY INDIVIDUALS Thomas Scarr** is considered an excellent litigator who is particularly experienced in employment matters. He also handles white-collar criminal work, construction disputes and product liability as well as medical malpractice defense and personal injury litigation. **Robert Sweeney** enjoys a fine reputation for handling mass tort litigation and complex litigation in the construction sector. Based in Huntington, **Lee Murray Hall**'s commercial litigation practice has a strong focus on the insurance industry, dealing with a wide range of disputes, including insurance coverage, defense and bad faith

defense work. She is also known for her expertise in product liability and mass tort cases.

## Other Notable Practitioners

The recent arrival of **Rebecca Betts** at Kay Casto & Chaney PLLC has further strengthened the firm's litigation practice group. She is a *"bright"* litigator who is highly respected in the state and regularly advises on mass tort litigation in relation to product liability, chemical sector and toxic exposure. The *"outstanding"* and *"skillful"* **Shawn George** of George & Lorensen is a well-respected general commercial litigator whose broad practice covers mass tort, product liability defense and toxic tort together with general business disputes. **Stephen Farmer** of Farmer, Cline & Campbell PLLC enjoys an excellent reputation among his peers. His practice covers product liability and personal injuries as well as general commercial litigation, acting for both plaintiffs and defendants. Founding member **Marc Williams** (see p.2566) of Nelson Mullins Riley & Scarborough has a great reputation in the state, best known for large-scale class action cases and representation of railroad clients in personal injury cases. Market sources also praise his skills in front of juries. Interviewees have high regard for **Michael Carey** of Carey, Scott & Douglas, PLLC, widely considering him as a leading litigator and describing him as *"intelligent, experienced, sophisticated and hard-working."* He has a broad litigation practice, covering general business and contract disputes, product liability, litigation in relation to the natural gas and energy industries, and white-collar criminal defense. **Timothy Miller** of Robinson & McElwee PLLC is recognized as a leading commercial litigation player in the state. He offers many years of specialized experience in the energy and natural resources industries, being best known for representing natural gas and timber producers in commercial litigation. **Charles Bailey** (see p.2561) of Bailey & Wyant PLLC has extensive experience in insurance defense, employment disputes and representing state agents. Interviewees recommend him as a forceful lawyer who is simply *"very good at what he does."* **John Hoblitzell** of Kay Casto & Chaney PLLC offers a multifaceted commercial litigation skills, advising clients on contract disputes, payment disputes and employment litigation. He also has solid expertise in energy-related litigation and is regularly involved in complex tort cases. **John Tinney** of The Tinney Law Firm is a senior commercial litigator who is still actively practicing. He was heavily engaged in a fraud defense and breach of contract dispute for a high-profile individual over the past year. Huntington-based **Melissa Foster Bird** (see p.2562) of Nelson Mullins Riley & Scarborough offers increasing levels of expertise in workplace sexual harassment and termination cases. She also represents railroad, chemical and manufacturing clients in product liability, professional malpractice and toxic tort cases.

# NATURAL RESOURCES

Commentary about individuals can be found under their firm's paragraph. If the firm has no paragraph (is not ranked) look at Other Notable Practitioners.

## Natural Resources
### Leading Firms

**Band 1**

Bowles Rice LLP *

Jackson Kelly PLLC

Steptoe & Johnson PLLC *

**Band 2**

Dinsmore & Shohl LLP

Spilman Thomas & Battle, PLLC *

**Band 3**

Huddleston Bolen LLP

Robinson & McElwee PLLC

### Leading Individuals

**Band 1**

| | |
|---|---|
| Deem Patrick D | Steptoe & Johnson PLLC * |
| Flanery Sharon O | Steptoe & Johnson PLLC * |
| Graff Jr F Thomas | Bowles Rice LLP * |
| Herlihy William | Spilman Thomas & Battle, PLLC * |
| Lane J Thomas | Bowles Rice LLP * |

**Band 2**

| | |
|---|---|
| Bolen Richard J | Huddleston Bolen LLP |
| Fluharty Robert | Jackson Kelly PLLC |
| Kelly Donna C | Dinsmore & Shohl LLP |
| Patterson III George A | Bowles Rice LLP * |
| Rubenstein Thomas | Dinsmore & Shohl LLP |
| Russell James A | Steptoe & Johnson PLLC * |
| Tawney Kenneth E | Jackson Kelly PLLC |

**Up-and-coming individuals**

| | |
|---|---|
| Stonestreet Robert | Dinsmore & Shohl LLP |
| Summers Scott | Huddleston Bolen LLP |
| Wilson Seth | Bowles Rice LLP * |

## Natural Resources: Environment
### Leading Individuals

**Band 1**

| | |
|---|---|
| Bradley Ann | Spilman Thomas & Battle, PLLC * |
| Flannery David | Jackson Kelly PLLC |
| Knee Leonard B | Bowles Rice LLP * |
| McLusky Robert G | Jackson Kelly PLLC |
| Power Christopher B | Dinsmore & Shohl LLP |
| Turner Allyn | Spilman Thomas & Battle, PLLC * |
| Yaussy David L | Robinson & McElwee PLLC |

* Indicates firm / individual with profile.
Alphabetical order within each band. Band 1 is the highest.

## Band 1

### Bowles Rice LLP
See profile on p.2568

**THE FIRM** This fine team garners universal praise for its depth of experience and resources, thus maintaining its position among the front runners of the West Virginia market. The group has huge experience in advising the coal, oil and gas industries on issues such as energy-related loans, investments, property and regulatory work. Over the past year it has handled a considerable volume of resources-related M&A work as well as litigation in relation to mine health and safety. Its client roster includes CONSOL Energy, Trans Energy and the Independent Oil & Gas Association of West Virginia.

**Sources say:** *"Overall, I really cannot say enough positive things about Bowles Rice. It's a great firm with great people. I continue to think very highly of them."*

**KEY INDIVIDUALS** Former managing partner **Thomas Graff** (see p.2563) is widely recognized as a leader in the energy market. He is known for his extensive experience and knowledge in M&A transactions and property development in relation to the mining and coal industries. **Leonard Knee** (see p.2564) heads the firm's environmental practice and regularly advises on environmental litigation and toxic tort cases. On the non-litigation side, he is particularly active in state environmental policy making and regulatory work. **Thomas Lane** (see p.2564) is sought out for his transactional and regulatory expertise in relation to the oil and gas sectors as well as for his litigation skills. He has taught extensively on oil and gas law. **George Patterson** (see p.2565) focuses his practice on oil and gas-related matters and plays an active role in the West Virginia Independent Oil and Gas Association. Additionally, he enjoys a good reputation for representing coal companies, particularly in real estate-related matters. **Seth Wilson** (see p.2566) chairs the firm's energy department and devotes his time to work related to the oil, gas and coal industries. He also has an active finance practice, and has been involved in financing the sale of a natural gas plant and several oil and gas M&A transactions. An appreciative client commented: *"He is knowledgeable, experienced and professional."*

### Jackson Kelly PLLC

**THE FIRM** This substantial firm has a broad-based natural resources practice, providing comprehensive services nationwide. The West Virginia team is long established and is especially respected for serving the coal industry; it offers clients a specialist coal industry group, covering both litigation and advisory work. It can also assist clients with mine safety, permits, labor and employment, regulations as well as tax.

**Sources say:** *"This full-service firm's strength is that they know the coal industry very well."*

**KEY INDIVIDUALS** The *"well-respected"* **David Flannery** enjoys an excellent reputation for his extensive environmental practice. In the energy and natural resources arena, he offers vast experience in advising coal and railroad companies on environmental regulation, environmental litigation, enforcement and tort cases. Charleston-based **Robert McLusky** is considered to be a leading expert when it comes to the chemical and coal industries. He specializes in obtaining coal and water discharge permits and also handles litigation. He is praised as *"very bright and knowledgeable"* and because *"he has been through the wars on the issues that the industry faces, so has a breadth of knowledge that is unparalleled."* Offering litigation skills combined with energy expertise, **Kenneth Tawney** chairs the firm's oil and gas industry group. He concentrates on representing oil and gas producers and distributors in a broad range of disputes related to sale, purchase and operating contracts, leases and title issues. He also has extensive experience advising on transactional and regulatory issues. Head of the firm's land and natural resources development department, **Robert Fluharty** enjoys a fine reputation for his transactional work in this arena, especially for coal industry clients. He also offers solid expertise in financing matters.

### Steptoe & Johnson PLLC
See profile on p.2570

**THE FIRM** This full-service firm offers one of the largest and most impressive groups in the region which has further expanded as a result of a number of new hires. It is particularly highly regarded for its strength in the coal, oil and natural gas sectors, handling matters such as property acquisitions and sales. It can field teams to advise on the most complex of transactions and handles major energy investment matters for both national and international clients.

**Sources say:** *"We use its services because it is one of the leading firms in this field and is staffed to meet all our needs. We really rely on its expertise. The team pays attention to what clients want."*

**KEY INDIVIDUALS** **Patrick Deem** (see p.2562) is considered to be a *"top-notch"* oil and gas lawyer who enjoys an excellent reputation for assisting clients on M&A and financing transactions, as well as real estate-related matters. Peers are consistently impressed by the quality of his work, and recent highlights include assisting a provider of gas transportation and storage services on all aspects of its property acquisition for the construction of a gas extraction facility. **Sharon Flanery** (see p.2562) focuses her practice on energy-related business transactions and regulatory work, including negotiating joint venture agreements. She is particularly knowledgeable about the oil and gas industry and leads the firm's energy practice. Clients rate her highly because *"she is not only a lawyer, but also a petroleum engineer. She understands the full scope of our business"* and *"she is very fast and attentive and knows how to structure the deal."* **James Russell** (see p.2565) is based in the firm's Morgantown office and is highly rated for his skills in natural resources-related commercial transactions and litigation. He offers extensive experience in the coal, oil and gas industries, representing developers and land owners in natural resources matters and coal field developments.

## Band 2

### Dinsmore & Shohl LLP

**THE FIRM** The Dinsmore & Shohl team is widely recognized as one of the most impressive in this field, particularly in the coal industry and increasingly also in the natural gas sector. It also provides advice on the full gamut of environmental issues including the many regulatory and safety regimes. It represents a range of companies, including producers and developers, with a client roster including Alpha Natural Resources, Coal River Energy and Consol Energy. **KEY INDIVIDUALS** Senior partner **Christopher Power** specializes in the natural gas and coal industries, assisting clients on a range of environmental matters including litigation. Offering 27 years of experience, he enjoys an excellent reputation with key work including assisting a group of coal companies in appeals related to compliance orders issued by the Department of Environmental Protection, involving water quality-based effluent limits and enforcement actions. Senior partner, **Donna Kelly** is particularly sought after for her mine health and safety work for coal companies. Her recent highlights include representing a number of mining companies in challenging unwarrantable failure orders, and other matters under the Mine Act. **Thomas Rubenstein** is the "*well-respected*" managing partner of the firm's Morgantown office and his previous experience as in-house counsel with a coal company is an additional attraction for clients. Of late, he has been heavily engaged in a range of issues arising under the Mine Act as well as handling general corporate issues for coal and natural gas clients, including investment transactions and leasing issues. Young natural resources lawyer **Robert Stonestreet** was made partner in 2012 and is building a profile, particularly representing clients in civil litigation and environmental defense cases. Recently, he was part of the team representing a group of coal companies in appeals in relation to compliance orders issued by the West Virginia Department of Environmental Protection.

### Spilman Thomas & Battle, PLLC
See profile on p.2569

**THE FIRM** This well-established practice is recognized as a real force in the West Virginia market, acting for an impressive range of clients such as DuPont, Penn Virginia Resource Partners and Independent Oil & Gas Association of West Virginia. It is singled out for its traditional strength in coal-related environmental defense work, commercial disputes and government lobbying practice. Recently, the team has seen a uptick in instructions with regard to negotiating with financial institutions on business consolidation deals for oil and gas clients. **Sources say:** "*Our experience has been good across the board, a very good performance.*" **KEY INDIVIDUALS Ann Bradley** (see p.2561) concentrates her practice on environment-related regulatory advice to oil, gas and coal companies. She is highly regarded as a fine environmental lawyer with one source noting: "*She is outstanding, very astute and has a wide range of experience and skills.*" Her recent highlights include representing DuPont in an appeal before the West Virginia Environmental Quality Board, involving a modification to certain permits. Practice head, **William Herlihy** (see p.2563) enjoys a fine reputation for coal, oil and gas-related matters, especially coal sector transactions. His work includes advising on environmental issues and defending mine owners in various civil claims. On the oil and gas side, he assists clients on operational issues, including drilling permits and litigation as well as financial and business transactions. Former regulator, **Allyn Turner** (see p.2566) specializes in environmental regulatory work, particularly advising coal companies on water and waste management. She is highly regarded by sources with one commenting: "*She has a tremendous amount of expertise and experience in this area.*" Recently, she defended Penn Virginia Operating Company in a non-compliant water pollution matter under the Clean Water Act.

## Band 3

### Huddleston Bolen LLP

**THE FIRM** This relatively compact team offers impressive natural resources skills. It is best known for acting for land owners in mining and railroad development leasing matters, mineral leasing and transactional matters. It also handles a range of litigation and arbitration work, attracting clients from the coal, natural gas, timber, and mineral industries. Its roster of clients includes Alpha Natural Resources, Arch Coal and Natural Resource Partners. **Sources say:** "*A very well-rounded firm with expertise in every area we have needed.*" "*I really like the relationship we have, they are very responsive and helpful, very good at what they do. Their strength is that they know the local culture and systems.*" **KEY INDIVIDUALS Richard Bolen**, who heads the natural resources department, is considered "*an excellent litigator.*" He enjoys a fine reputation for representing land owners in property rights matters, defending coal companies against commercial claims, as well as advising on leasing issues. **Scott Summers** is an experienced litigator in the natural resources arena. He focuses largely on the coal industry, defending major coal companies in personal injury claims and commercial disputes. Clients report that they appreciate his skill in helping them through the litigation process.

### Robinson & McElwee PLLC

**THE FIRM** This local boutique is especially well regarded for its environmental expertise. The team is known for advising oil, gas and manufacturing clients on environmental issues in relation to redevelopments, recycling and water pollution. Recently, it has also been handling increasing levels of environment-related litigation, defending coal companies, farmers as well as oil and gas developers. Highlights from the past year include acting for Marathon Oil in a statewide class action for alleged $750 million damage to underground storage tanks. **Sources say:** "*They are a very good smaller and local firm.*" **KEY INDIVIDUALS David Yaussy** has a robust environment practice, representing natural resources and energy companies in a range of litigation, including flood, sewage license and air permit matters. Notable work from the past year includes acting for a group of clients who sought an order from the West Virginia Supreme Court against state officials in connection with the elimination of straight pipe discharge from private homes.

# REAL ESTATE

Commentary about individuals can be found under their firm's paragraph. If the firm has no paragraph (is not ranked) look at Other Notable Practitioners.

## Band 1

### Bowles Rice LLP
See profile on p.2568

**THE FIRM** This group continues to offer clients an outstanding service, especially with regard to large title projects. The team has a particular niche in energy-related real estate transactions, often representing banks as lenders as well as national and international energy corporates. Of late, it has been involved in title work as a result of the development of Marcellus and Utica Shale. Notable clients include United Bank, First American Title Insurance and WesBanco Bank.
**Sources say:** "Several of our customers that I have referred to Bowles Rice have been so impressed with the firm that they have engaged them for other work." "They are very knowledgeable and sophisticated."
**KEY INDIVIDUALS Stephen Mathias** (see p.2564) heads the firm's real estate practice and is regarded as having "excellent knowledge and underwriting skills." He is heavily involved in advising a major regional builder on residential projects. Over the past year, he has also handled increasing levels of commercial development work as well as refinancing projects, title work and significant shopping mall deals. Charleston-based **Carl Andrews** (see p.2561) earns high respect for "being results-oriented" and for his excellent title insurance work. He represents banks in commercial real estate transactions and financing matters, in addition to handling various title work for national and international clients on Marcellus Shale-related transactions.

### Jackson Kelly PLLC
**THE FIRM** This sizable, multistate firm is home to an excellent team, which has maintained its position at the forefront of the market. The group's expertise covers mineral rights matters and project financing, and it has been especially active on transactions relating to the energy and natural resources industries. It is also well regarded for its extensive experience in complex title projects for large coal companies.
**KEY INDIVIDUALS Robert Fluharty** heads the firm's land and natural resource development practice group and has a reputation for being "good to work with and knowledgeable." He advises coal, gas and oil clients on a broad range of transactional real estate and financing projects. Interviewees are impressed by **Charles Loeb**'s broad commercial expertise, covering corporate, M&A and banking transactions. He is particularly experienced in handling commercial real estate transactions and financing projects for coal, oil and natural gas clients.

### Spilman Thomas & Battle, PLLC
See profile on p.2569

**THE FIRM** This statewide firm's long-established real estate practice group benefits from the firm's full-service commercial practice, working closely with tax, environmental and corporate teams to provide a one-stop service to clients. It focuses on the energy and natural resources industries, handling a broad range of commercial and mineral real estate transactions for lenders, developers, businesses and individuals.
**KEY INDIVIDUALS Joyce Ofsa** (see p.2565) is based in the Charleston office and concentrates her practice on real estate transactions, development projects, land use, zoning and title insurance. Sources agree that "she is very good to work with in terms of being results-oriented and getting a rational result."

### Steptoe & Johnson PLLC
See profile on p.2570

**THE FIRM** Steptoe & Johnson is recognized as a real force in the West Virginia market for its sizable team and robust commercial practice. Its real estate group advises on commercial and mineral real estate transactions for energy and natural resources clients, and is known for its capabilities in handling complex projects and litigious matters.

**KEY INDIVIDUALS Patrick Deem** (see p.2562) is well known in West Virginia for his commercial real estate practice, and is particularly active in the energy and natural resources sectors. Over the past year, he has been heavily engaged in assisting oil and gas producers with various land and lease issues, and property and mineral acquisitions. He also acts for title insurance companies and their clients. **Louis Enderle** (see p.2562) focuses his commercial property practice primarily on the energy and natural resources industries. He is also a licensed title insurance agent. **Randall Light** (see p.2564) is also a title insurance agent, and represents national title insurance companies in a range of matters. He focuses on energy and natural resources-related transactions.

## Band 2

### Huddleston Bolen LLP
**THE FIRM** This medium-sized firm has an excellent reputation in West Virginia for offering a full suite of commercial real estate expertise. Combining transactional and financing skills, the team is especially valued by sources for its strength in dealing with commercial development projects, property acquisitions and financing arrangements for the coal, oil and gas sectors. Additionally, the team has seen an expansion of its mineral-related work over the past year. Highlights include acting for Marshall University on the development of an international student center.
**KEY INDIVIDUALS Thomas Gilpin** is a key player in the team. He focuses his commercial real estate practice largely on providing business and financing advice to clients in the mineral and healthcare sectors on property developments and real estate transactions. **Christopher Plybon** heads the firm's real estate practice and has particular expertise in commercial developments. He is renowned for his strength in financing and has recently been engaged on the redevelopment of an abandoned mining site and the development of a local community center.

### Reeder & Shuman
**THE FIRM** Operating from its Morgantown office, this firm's compact real estate team has a fine reputation in West Virginia. It is particularly known for handling mineral real estate transactions and smaller sized projects.
**KEY INDIVIDUALS Robert Shuman** focuses primarily on commercial real estate and advises on the gamut of development projects. He is widely recognized in West Virginia, and is praised as being "beyond outstanding." **Stephen Shuman** is the senior member of the team and is particularly sought out for mineral property deals by clients.

## Robinson & McElwee PLLC

**THE FIRM** This highly respected team has experienced a steady growth of its Charleston-based real estate group over the past year. The team counsels oil and gas companies and is known for its traditional strength in the coal and other power sectors. Its practitioners are well respected in the state for their in-depth experience and industry knowledge.

**KEY INDIVIDUALS** With a solid natural resources background, **Douglas McElwee** has a long-established real estate practice, advising on a range of sectors, including coal, oil, gas, chemical and solid waste energy. *"He is very knowledgeable and good to work with, and his practical approach is very beneficial to clients,"* according to one interviewee.

### Other Notable Practitioners

**Richard Pill** is Pill & Pill, PLLC's leading real estate practitioner and has a particularly excellent reputation for his residential property expertise. He advises on the gamut of transactions, together with real estate financing.

# Leaders' Profiles in West Virginia

**ALLEVATO, John**
Spilman Thomas & Battle, PLLC, Charleston
304 340 3885
jallevato@spilmanlaw.com
*Featured in Corporate/Commercial (West Virginia)*
**Practice Areas:** Federal taxation, estate planning, corporate, health care law, and public finance.
**Professional Memberships:** Board Member, Charleston Estate Planning Council; American Health Lawyers Association; National Association of Bond Lawyers; Probate Committee, West Virginia State Bar.
**Career:** Adjunct Lecturer, West Virginia University College of Law, Morgantown, West Virginia, teaching Estate Planning, 2002-06; Partner and Associate, Kegler, Brown, Hill & Ritter, Columbus, Ohio, 1984-97; Adjunct Professor, Capital University Law School and Capital University Graduate Tax Program, Columbus, Ohio, teaching classes in Estate Planning, Federal Estate and Gift Taxation, Advanced Income Taxation, 1982-97.

**ANDREWS, Carl D**
Bowles Rice LLP, Charleston
304 347 1109
candrews@bowlesrice.com
*Featured in Real Estate (West Virginia)*
**Practice Areas:** Commercial and real estate issues including coal, oil, natural gas and timber; title insurance; zoning issues; and general property law.
**Career:** Mr Andrews is a senior member of the firm's Real Estate Practice Group. He has issued more than $500 million in title insurance since 1982 as a title insurance agent. He focuses his practice on commercial transactions involving real estate as collateral; industrial parks; 1031 tax-free exchanges; zoning; land development and commercial and residential loaning for construction.
**Personal:** West Virginia University College of Law (1974).

**BAILEY, Charles R**
Bailey & Wyant PLLC, Charleston
304 345 4222
cbailey@baileywyant.com
*Featured in Litigation (West Virginia)*

**Practice Areas:** Labor and employment law, medical malpractice, governmental liability, toxic torts, products liability, aviation, employment benefits, professional liability, construction defects, insurance coverage, lending liability and consumer protection.
**Professional Memberships:** Defense Research Institute, West Virginia Chamber of Commerce, Charleston Area Business Alliance, West Virginia Independent Oil and Gas Association, American Bar Association committee on Litigation and Employment Law, Board of Directors for the West Virginia Defense Trial Counsel and is a Member of the Employment and Labor Law Committee.
**Career:** Managing Member Bailey & Wyant, PLLC 1999-Present General Counsel West Virginia School of Osteopathic Medicine 2006-09 Partner Shuman Annand Bailey Wyant & Earles 1985-2001 Named former Governor Manchin's "Go To" lawyer.
**Publications:** Bailey, Charles R. "Toward a More Complete Notice of Proposed Rulemaking: A Judicial Overview and Suggestions for Change," 84 West Virginia Law Review 277, 1981. Bailey, Charles R. "Human Resource Policies That Prevent Law Suits." Charleston, West Virginia. 16 May 2007. Bailey, Charles R. "Political Subdivision Immunities in West Virginia under the Governmental Tort Claims and Insurance Reform Act." Charleston, West Virginia. 27 March 2012. Bailey, Charles R. "Public Contracts and Procurement Regulations." Charleston, West Virginia. 16 August 2011. Bailey, Charles R. "Recent Changes to the Americans with Disabilities Act – the 2008 Amendments to the ADA." Charleston, West Virginia. 28 May 2009. Bailey, Charles R. "Successfully Litigating Employment Discrimination Claims." Charleston, West Virginia. 28 April 2009.

**BASILE, Michael**
Spilman Thomas & Battle, PLLC, Charleston
304 340 3854
mbasile@spilmanlaw.com
*Featured in Corporate/Commercial (West Virginia)*
**Practice Areas:** Government, business, land use planning/administrative law centering on Marcellus Shale resource development.

**Professional Memberships:** Charleston Inter-Regional Chamber of Commerce, Chairman, Board of Directors; Charleston Area Alliance, Board of Directors; Vision Shared, Board of Directors; Discover the Real West Virginia, Board of Directors; Young President's Organization, Mountain State Chapter.
**Career:** Managing Member. Previously Associate General Counsel, General Counsel and Deputy Chief of Staff to the Office of Governor Gaston Caperton, General Counsel to the West Virginia Development Office and assistant and senior assistant Attorneys General.
**Personal:** West Virginia University (BS in Finance, 1987), University of Pittsburgh (JD, 1991).

**BEAN, Rodney L**
Steptoe & Johnson PLLC, Morgantown
304 598 8140
rodney.bean@steptoe-johnson.com
*Featured in Labor & Employment (West Virginia)*
**Practice Areas:** Bean maintains a broad employment litigation and counseling practice. He has represented clients in state and federal trial and appellate courts and administrative agencies across the region for many years.
**Professional Memberships:** Defense Research Institute; Defense Trial Counsel of West Virginia; Society of Human Resource Management; West Virginia Health Care Human Resource Association; West Virginia Oil & Natural Gas Association; Independent Oil & Gas Association; West Virginia State Bar; Pennsylvania Bar Association; The Best Lawyers in America®; Super Lawyers®.
**Personal:** West Virginia University College of Law; West Virginia University Perley Isaac Reed School of Journalism.

**BRADLEY, Ann**
Spilman Thomas & Battle, PLLC, Charleston
304 340 3882
abradley@spilmanlaw.com
*Featured in Natural Resources (West Virginia)*
**Practice Areas:** Representing business interests in all aspects of environmental law/regulations for over 25 years.
**Professional Memberships:** WV State Bar, Chair, Environmental Law Committee; WV

Chamber of Commerce, Chair, Environmental Committee.
**Publications:** Coauthor, "West Virginia's Antidegradation Policy for State Waters: From Theoretical Construct to Implementation Procedures," 103 W. Va. L. Rev. 331 (2001) Coauthor, "The Voluntary Remediation and Redevelopment Act – WV Restructures Environmental Liability," 99 W. Va. L. Rev. 455 (1997) "WV Supreme Court Clarifies Deadlines for Enforcement of Environmental Laws/Regulations," WV Manufacturers Association Digest, August (1997)
**Personal:** Miami University (BS, 1969); University of Miami (JD, 1976).

**BREWER, Susan Slenker**
Steptoe & Johnson PLLC, Morgantown
304 598 8103
susan.brewer@steptoe-johnson.com
*Featured in Litigation (West Virginia)*
**Practice Areas:** Brewer is CEO of the firm and focuses her practice in the area of professional liability defense litigation. She has tried over 100 cases in state and federal courts and numerous appellate proceedings before the West Virginia Supreme Court of Appeals and the United States Court of Appeals.
**Professional Memberships:** Fellow, American College of Trial Lawyers; National Association of Women Lawyers; Board of Directors, West Virginia University Foundation; American Board of Trial Advocates; West Virginia State Bar; Virginia State Bar; The Best Lawyers in America®; Super Lawyers®.
**Personal:** George Mason University School of Law; Duke University.

**CARR, Kevin**
Spilman Thomas & Battle, PLLC, Charleston
304 340 3877
kcarr@spilmanlaw.com
*Featured in Labor & Employment (West Virginia)*
**Practice Areas:** Co-chair of the Labor and Employment Practice Group; traditional labor and union issues, trial work in employment matters, complex immigration litigation, wage and hour law.
**Professional Memberships:** Kanawha County Bar Association; American Bar Association.

**Career:** Member; Co-chair of the Labor and Employment Practice Group; collective bargaining, union decertification, unfair labor practice charges and appeals to the NLRB, labor/employment due diligence reviews in connection with mergers/acquisitions, lead trial counsel in over 200 employment cases in various jurisdictions.
**Personal:** West Virginia University (BA, cum laude, honors graduate, Presidential Scholar, 1992), West Virginia University (JD, 1995).

### CARYL, Michael E
Bowles Rice LLP, Martinsburg
304 264 4225
mcaryl@bowlesrice.com
*Featured in Corporate/Commercial (West Virginia)*
**Practice Areas:** Federal, state and local tax planning and litigation; economic development; government relations; trusts and estate planning and litigation.
**Career:** Mr Caryl served as the West Virginia State Tax Commissioner, 1985-88, as well as President of the 12-state Southeastern Association of Tax Administrators, 1987-88. He is an elected Fellow of the American College of Tax Counsel and previously served as vice-chair of the Governor's Commission on Fair Taxation. He is a frequent speaker and published author on a variety of taxation topics.
**Personal:** Yale Law School (1974).

### CHINCHECK, Julia A
Bowles Rice LLP, Charleston
304 347 1713
jchincheck@bowlesrice.com
*Featured in Corporate/Commercial (West Virginia)*
**Practice Areas:** Creditors' rights and bankruptcy; commercial and financial services; banking; litigation; economic development.
**Professional Memberships:** American Bankruptcy Institute; American Bar Association; Commercial Law League of America.
**Career:** Ms Chincheck assisted in the drafting and review of local changes to Article 9 of the Uniform Commercial Code. She serves as an adjunct professor at West Virginia University College of Law. She is a frequent lecturer on bankruptcy issues and the Uniform Commercial Code.
**Publications:** Contributing author to the American Bankruptcy Institute's Health Care Insolvency Manual; authored numerous publications on bankruptcy and commercial issues.

### COKELEY, Bryan R
Steptoe & Johnson PLLC, Charleston
304 353 8116
bryan.cokeley@steptoe-johnson.com
*Featured in Labor & Employment (West Virginia)*
**Practice Areas:** Cokeley concentrates his practice in labor and employment law and has experience in defending employers in protected class litigation. He appears before administrative agencies such as the West Virginia Human Rights Commission and the EEOC. Cokeley is Chair of the firm's Labor Department.
**Professional Memberships:** Society of Human Resource Management; Human Resource Committee, West Virginia Chamber of Commerce; West Virginia Coal Association; West

Virginia State Bar; Ohio State Bar Association; Kentucky Bar Association; The Best Lawyers in America®; Super Lawyers®.
**Personal:** West Virginia University College of Law; West Virginia University, summa cum laude.

### DEEM, Patrick D
Steptoe & Johnson PLLC, Bridgeport
304 933 8121
pat.deem@steptoe-johnson.com
*Featured in Real Estate (West Virginia),*
*Corporate/Commercial (West Virginia), Natural Resources (West Virginia)*
**Practice Areas:** Deem has practiced with the firm since 1969, with primary emphasis in the areas of real estate and minerals, commercial transactions and business organizations. Deem's experience includes significant involvement in mergers, acquisitions and all aspects of financing.
**Professional Memberships:** Energy & Mineral Law Foundation; Fellow, American Bar Association; Fellow, West Virginia Bar Foundation; Executive Committee, West Virginia Bar Association; Corporations, Banking and Business Law Committees, West Virginia State Bar; Independent Oil & Gas Association; The Best Lawyers in America®; Super Lawyers®.
**Personal:** West Virginia University College of Law; Marietta College (economics and accounting).

### DELLINGER, Mark H
Bowles Rice LLP, Charleston
304 347 1178
mdellinger@bowlesrice.com
*Featured in Labor & Employment (West Virginia)*
**Practice Areas:** Labor and employment law, litigation.
**Career:** Mr Dellinger is the co-chair of the firm's Employers' Legal Services Group and serves as a member of the firm's human resources committee. He regularly represents private and public sector employers in matters of labor and employment law, including preventative counseling, employment litigation and traditional labor relations matters. He has obtained multiple summary judgment rulings in federal and state courts, and successfully handled trials and appeals. He has substantial experience representing employers in administrative proceedings involving EEO investigations and public hearings, unemployment compensation claims and state employee grievances.

### DICK, David E
Steptoe & Johnson PLLC, Morgantown
304 598 8104
david.dick@steptoe-johnson.com
*Featured in Labor & Employment (West Virginia)*
**Practice Areas:** Dick has a unique background of "hands on" executive experience prior to entering the practice of law. Dick maintains a broad counseling practice, offering significant experience in labor negotiations, safety and health (OSHA) litigation, and compliance with FMLA, ADA and discrimination laws.
**Professional Memberships:** Society of Human Resource Management; Morgantown Chamber of Commerce; West Virginia State Bar; The Best Lawyers in America® Super Lawyers®.

**Personal:** West Virginia University College of Law; Pennsylvania State University.

### ELLIS, Jonathan
Steptoe & Johnson PLLC, Charleston
304 353 8118
jonathan.ellis@steptoe-johnson.com
*Featured in Litigation (West Virginia)*
**Practice Areas:** Ellis focuses his practice in the areas of mine safety and health law, deliberate intent and premises liability litigation, and environmental law.
**Professional Memberships:** Energy & Mineral Law Foundation; National Mining Association; American Inns of Court; West Virginia Coal Association; MENSA.
**Personal:** Washington & Lee University; Concord College, summa cum laude.

### ENDERLE JR, Louis E
Steptoe & Johnson PLLC, Bridgeport
304 933 8172
lee.enderle@steptoe-johnson.com
*Featured in Real Estate (West Virginia)*
**Practice Areas:** Enderle's practice focuses on energy law, real estate law, mineral law, commercial transactions, and business law, including acquisitions, financing, and commercial leasing. Enderle is an agent for several title insurance companies and works with their customers on commercial real estate projects.
**Professional Memberships:** Corporations, Banking and Business Law Committees, West Virginia State Bar; Rotary Club of Clarksburg; Harrison County Chamber of Commerce; Humane Society of Harrison County; The Best Lawyers in America®; Super Lawyers®.
**Personal:** Washington & Lee School of Law; Albright College, cum laude.

### FARRELL, Michael J
Farrell, White & Legg PLLC, Huntington
304 781 1809
MJF@farrell3.com
*Featured in Litigation (West Virginia)*
**Practice Areas:** Product liability, pharmaceutical, chemical and business litigation, class actions, medical malpractice, employment law and insurance bad faith.
**Professional Memberships:** American College of Trial Lawyers. Career includes Presidency of the Defense Trial Counsel of West Virginia and the West Virginia Chapter of ABOTA. He has served as a member of the Board of Governors for the West Virginia State Bar and Defense Trial Counsel of West Virginia. He was the Interim President of Marshall University in 2005. Three West Virginia Governors have appointed him to multiple higher education governing boards including the Marshall University Board of Governors.
**Career:** In 1995, Mike founded and became managing Member of Farrell & Farrell, LC. He formed Farrell, Farrell & Farrell, PLLC in 1997, which became Farrell, White & Legg PLLC in 2011. Prior to that, he was Partner in charge of litigation Jenkins, Fenstermaker, Krieger, Kayes, Farrell & Agee. He was recently elected to the Marshall University Lewis College of Business Hall of Fame.

**Publications:** Among his dozens of publications are a chapter regarding the Joint Defense Doctrine published by the International Association of Defense Counsel in Advocacy in the 21st Century, a featured article in the Defense Research Institute's Medical Malpractice Monograph and the Civil Litigation Chapter in the West Virginia Practice Handbook.

### FLANERY, Sharon O
Steptoe & Johnson PLLC, Charleston
304 353 8155
sharon.flanery@steptoe-johnson.com
*Featured in Natural Resources (West Virginia)*
**Practice Areas:** Flanery is Chair of the firm's Energy Department and concentrates her practice in the areas of energy and natural resources law. As a petroleum engineer, she brings industry experience to her practice, including acquisitions and divestitures, mineral leases, joint ventures, contract mining agreements, joint operating agreements, sales and marketing agreements, as well as gathering, transportation and processing agreements. She has substantial experience in land and legal due diligence associated with mineral transactions, as well as in legislative and regulatory arenas.
**Professional Memberships:** Energy & Mineral Law Foundation; Women in Energy; Independent Petroleum Association of America; Outstanding Alumni of the Year, WVU Minerals & Energy Resources Department; West Virginia State Bar; Pennsylvania Bar Association; Ohio Bar Association; The Best Lawyers in America®.
**Publications:** Co-author, "National Survey of Pooling and Unitization Affecting Appalachian Shale Development," 2010; Co-author, "Recent Legal Developments in Carbon Sequestration," 2008 Society of Petroleum Engineers Eastern Regional/American Association of Petroleum Geologists; Co-author, "The Balancing of Coal and Coalbed Methane Interests Within the Coalbed Methane Statutory Schemes of Virginia, West Virginia and Kentucky," Journal of Natural Resources & Environmental Law, University of Kentucky College of Law, 2004-05.
**Personal:** Duquesne University School of Law; West Virginia University, cum laude.

### FOSTER BIRD, Melissa
Nelson Mullins Riley & Scarborough
304 526 3503
melissa.fosterbird@nelsonmullins.com
*Featured in Litigation (West Virginia)*
**Practice Areas:** Litigation, general commercial. Practices in West Virginia, Kentucky, and Ohio.
**Professional Memberships:** Defense Research Institute; National Association of Railroad Trial Counsel; Defense Trial Counsel of West Virginia; Fellow, Litigation Counsel of America.
**Career:** Extensive trial background in cases for railroads, trucking companies, chemical companies, manufacturers and retailers in the most difficult venues in the nation; practice concentrated in workplace discrimination, harassment and retaliatory termination; broad experience in railroad defense litigation, products liability, premises lia-

bility, professional malpractice, and toxic tort cases.
**Personal:** Juris Doctor, The Ohio State University; BS, Miami University in Oxford, Ohio.

## GALEOTA, William E
Steptoe & Johnson PLLC, Morgantown
304 598 8109
bill.galeota@steptoe-johnson.com
*Featured in Litigation (West Virginia)*
**Practice Areas:** Galeota devotes his practice to personal injury and commercial litigation, particularly medical professional and hospital liability, commercial disputes, and fiduciary litigation. He has tried a variety of civil actions in state and federal district courts and has argued cases at the appellate level.
**Professional Memberships:** West Virginia State Bar; Defense Trial Counsel of West Virginia; American Board of Trial Advocates; Defense Research Institute; WVU College of Law Development Council; The Best Lawyers in America®; Super Lawyers®.
**Personal:** West Virginia University College of Law; West Virginia University.

## GRAFF JR, F Thomas
Bowles Rice LLP, Charleston
304 347 1103
tgraff@bowlesrice.com
*Featured in Corporate/Commercial (West Virginia), Natural Resources (West Virginia)*
**Practice Areas:** Energy and mineral law, business and commercial law, real estate law and banking.
**Career:** Mr Graff is a Senior Partner in the firm's Charleston office. He has broad experience in negotiations, contracts, strategic planning, mergers and acquisitions and capital funding involving commercial, banking and coal, oil and gas transactions. As the firm's former Managing Partner (1986-2006), he has significant experience in law firm administration operations, practice management, client development, total quality management and recruiting. He is Chairman, Chemical Alliance Zone; Director Emeritus, West Virginia Roundtable; and Director, United Bankshares, Inc.
**Personal:** West Virginia University College of Law (1964).

## HEATH, Mark E
Spilman Thomas & Battle, PLLC, Charleston
304 340 3843
mheath@spilmanlaw.com
*Featured in Labor & Employment (West Virginia)*
**Practice Areas:** Safety issues (MSHA and OSHA), labor and employment law and litigation. His work involves federal and state court actions, as well as administrative cases before federal and state agencies.
**Professional Memberships:** Energy & Mineral Law Foundation; Kentucky Coal Association, Safety, Environmental and Legal Committees; West Virginia Coal Association, Safety Committee; Tug Valley Mining Institute; American Bar Association; Kentucky Bar Association.
**Career:** Member.
**Publications:** "Pattern of Violation: The Changing Dynamic of Enforcement and

Regulation Under the Mine Act," 32 Energy & Min. L. Inst. (2011).

## HELMICK, Brian C
Spilman Thomas & Battle, PLLC, Charleston
304 340 3826
bhelmick@spilmanlaw.com
*Featured in Corporate/Commercial (West Virginia)*
**Practice Areas:** Business expansion, economic development, government relations and public finance.
**Career:** Member, Corporate Department Chair. Formerly Deputy Secretary and General Counsel, West Virginia Department of Commerce, May 2005 - July 2006; Counsel to Committee on Government Organization, West Virginia House of Delegates, 2003.
**Personal:** West Virginia University, BS in Resource Management, 1994. West Virginia University College of Law, JD, 2001.

## HERLIHY, William
Spilman Thomas & Battle, PLLC, Charleston
304 340 3838
wherlihy@spilmanlaw.com
*Featured in Natural Resources (West Virginia)*
**Practice Areas:** More than 25 years of experience in natural resources, energy and general business acquisitions.
**Professional Memberships:** West Virginia and Kanawha County Bar Associations; Trustee, Energy & Mineral Law Foundation.
**Career:** US Department of Justice (Administrative Division); clerk to the US Court of Appeals for the Fourth Circuit; General Counsel to the West Virginia Economic Development Authority.
**Personal:** University of Virginia (BA, Economics with Honors, 1977, Phi Beta Kappa), University of Virginia (JD, 1981).

## HEYWOOD, Thomas A
Bowles Rice LLP, Charleston
304 347 1702
theywood@bowlesrice.com
*Featured in Corporate/Commercial (West Virginia)*
**Practice Areas:** Corporate, commercial and finance law; government relations; healthcare law.
**Career:** Mr Heywood is Managing Partner of Bowles Rice. He joined the firm in 1983 and returned after serving as Chief of Staff to Governor Gaston Caperton, 1990-93. He was recognized in 2012 as one of the "10 Most Influential Business Leaders in West Virginia" and chaired the successful election campaigns of West Virginia Governor Earl Ray Tomblin (2011, 2012). He is an active leader in many civic organizations and has received numerous awards for public service.
**Personal:** Harvard Law School (1982). BA, International Relations, Stanford University (1978).

## HILL, Lee O
Spilman Thomas & Battle, PLLC, Charleston
304 340 3802
lhill@spilmanlaw.com
*Featured in Corporate/Commercial (West Virginia)*
**Practice Areas:** Public finance, electrical generating facility development and related legislation.

**Professional Memberships:** National Association of Bond Lawyers.
**Career:** Past President, Charleston Estate Planning Council; Panelist and Moderator, National Association of Bond Lawyers Workshop. Participating in public finance issues over a period of more than 30 years in the role of bond counsel, underwriter's counsel, issuer's counsel, user's counsel, trustee's counsel, letter of credit issuer's counsel, insurer's counsel and related roles.
**Personal:** West Virginia University, BS in Business Administration, 1959; West Virginia University, JD, 1961.

## ISKRA, Eric
Spilman Thomas & Battle, PLLC, Charleston
304 340 3875
eiskra@spilmanlaw.com
*Featured in Labor & Employment (West Virginia)*
**Practice Areas:** Trial work/litigation - emphasis on employment, class actions, labor, healthcare/disability, and complex matters.
**Professional Memberships:** American Bar Association; Employee Rights and Responsibilities Committee, Administrative Chair (201011), Program Chair (2012-present); Labor & Employment Annual Conference, Vice Chair (2011), Co-Chair (2012); Past Chair, YLD Labor & Employment Committee; American Employment Law Council; World Services Group, Board of Trustees.
**Career:** Chair, Labor and Employment Group; Member-in-Charge of Client Relations.
**Publications:** Editorial Advisory Board, Mental & Physical Disability Law Reporter; BNA publications.
**Personal:** College of William and Mary (BA, 1991); Wake Forest University School of Law (JD, 1994).

## JONES, Heather Heiskell
Spilman Thomas & Battle, PLLC, Charleston
304 340 3842
hheiskell@spilmanlaw.com
*Featured in Litigation (West Virginia)*
**Practice Areas:** Litigation defense, including toxic tort, medical monitoring class actions, employment discrimination claims, product liability, including medical device and pharmaceutical products, employer liability, deliberate intent and insurance bad faith.
**Professional Memberships:** Defense Research Institute; American Bar Association; Permanent Member of the Fourth Circuit Judicial Conference; Defense Trial Counsel of West Virginia.
**Career:** Member. Litigation Department Chair.
**Personal:** West Virginia University, BA, cum laude, 1984; University of Richmond, T. C. Williams School of Law, JD, 1987.

## KINDER, Eric
Spilman Thomas & Battle, PLLC, Charleston
304 340 3893
ekinder@spilmanlaw.com
*Featured in Labor & Employment (West Virginia)*
**Practice Areas:** Labor and employment law with an emphasis on wage and hour, employee benefits, ERISA litigation, and USERRA.

**Professional Memberships:** American Bar Association; DRI, Employment Law Committee; SHRM, West Virginia State Council.
**Publications:** Co-author, "The Pessimist's Guide to Employment Litigation," For the Defense, August 2012. Co-author, chapter on West Virginia, Employment At Will: A State-by-State Survey, (ABA Section of Labor and Employment Law, 2011).
**Personal:** Cornell University, School of Industrial and Labor Relations, BS, 1988; Case Western Reserve School of Law, JD, summa cum laude, 1994; University of Virginia Trial Advocacy School, 2004.

## KING CONDARAS, Amy R
Spilman Thomas & Battle, PLLC, Charleston
304 340 3781
acondaras@spilmanlaw.com
*Featured in Corporate/Commercial (West Virginia)*
**Practice Areas:** Public finance, commercial lending, private equity and general corporate matters.
**Professional Memberships:** National Association of Bond Lawyers; American Bar Association, Business Law Section; American Health Lawyers Association; West Virginia and North Carolina Bar Associations.
**Career:** Co-chair of the Banking and Finance Practice Group. Former Senior Associate with PricewaterhouseCoopers, LLP.
**Personal:** University of Richmond, BS in Business Administration, Concentration in Accounting, cum laude, 1996. Washington and Lee University School of Law, JD, 2002.

## KING JR, Evans L
Steptoe & Johnson PLLC, Bridgeport
304 933 8132
evans.king@steptoe-johnson.com
*Featured in Corporate/Commercial (West Virginia)*
**Practice Areas:** King concentrates his practice in the areas of mergers and acquisitions, banking, workouts, and commercial litigation. His experience includes serving as lead counsel in numerous mergers and acquisitions and commercial lending transactions. King serves as General Counsel to the firm, as well as on several of its major committees.
**Professional Memberships:** Medbrook Children's Charity; Sacred Heart Children's Center; Clarksburg Mission, Inc.; Harrison County Chamber of Commerce; Clarksburg Kiwanis; West Virginia State Bar; The Best Lawyers in America®; Super Lawyers®.
**Personal:** William & Mary College of Law; University of Virginia.

## KISS, Robert S
Bowles Rice LLP, Charleston
304 347 1736
rkiss@bowlesrice.com
*Featured in Corporate/Commercial (West Virginia)*
**Practice Areas:** State tax litigation, estate planning, state and federal taxpayer representation, business planning, commercial law, economic development.
**Career:** Mr Kiss is a member of the firm's Tax Team. He is a former Speaker of the West Virginia

House of Delegates (1997-2006) and served as House Finance Chairman from 1993 to 1996. He was extensively involved in over a decade of major economic and fiscal legislation, including the West Virginia School Building Authority, water and sewer infrastructure development, state tax policy, state health care plans and state retirement systems.

**Personal:** The Ohio State University Law School (JD, 1982).

### KNEE, Leonard B
Bowles Rice LLP, Charleston
304 347 1726
lknee@bowlesrice.com
*Featured in Natural Resources (West Virginia)*

**Practice Areas:** Environmental litigation; water pollution issues; ground water hydrology; mining and quarrying; landfills and industrial facilities; environmental compliance, liability and permitting; and public utility law.

**Career:** Mr Knee has participated in the defense of several environmental criminal cases and represents clients in civil litigation. He handles a variety of administrative hearings before the Surface Mine Board, Environmental Quality Board, Public Service Commission and the Air Quality Board. Significant experience with the legislature in developing and lobbying environmental laws and regulations. Advises clients about environmental permitting process and successful strategies in dealing with controversial environmental projects.

### LANE, J Thomas
Bowles Rice LLP, Charleston
304 347 1111
tlane@bowlesrice.com
*Featured in Natural Resources (West Virginia)*

**Practice Areas:** Coal, oil and gas law; energy transactions, sales and acquisitions; mineral litigation; environmental law; natural resources; zoning and land development.

**Career:** Mr Lane is President of the Charleston City Council, where he has been an elected member since 1987. He is trustee and past President of the Energy and Mineral Law Foundation and the Chairman of the Charleston Land Trust. He served as adjunct professor of coal, oil and gas law for more than 20 years at West Virginia University College of Law. He is a frequent speaker at industry meetings and the author of numerous articles.

### LEGG, Erik
Farrell, White & Legg PLLC, Huntington
304 522 9100
ewl@farrell3.com
*Featured in Litigation (West Virginia)*

**Practice Areas:** Product liability defense, health care and medical malpractice defense, class action litigation, commercial business litigation, and employment litigation.

**Professional Memberships:** Erik is admitted in West Virginia and Ohio, as well as the federal courts for the Northern and Southern Districts of West Virginia. He is a member of the International Association of Defense Counsel, Defense Trial Counsel of West Virginia (Board Member), and the Defense Research Institute, as

well as the American Bar Association and state and local bar associations.

**Career:** Erik has been with the firm for over twelve years, having become a Member of Farrell, Farrell & Farrell, PLLC, which then became Farrell, White & Legg PLLC in 2011. He has been a frequent lecturer on issues relating to federal jurisdiction, civil litigation discovery practice including electronic discovery, and medical negligence avoidance and defense. He has represented several Fortune 500 pharmaceutical companies in drug and medical device litigations in West Virginia which experience has included management of numerous individual pharmaceutical cases as well as class action/mass action claims.

**Publications:** Erik has prepared course material articles in conjunction with a number of continuing legal education programs, including programs on electronic discovery (for West Virginia Continuing Legal Education and for Defense Trial Counsel of West Virginia), federal jurisdiction (for West Virginia Continuing Legal Education), witness examination at trial (for the West Virginia State Bar; co-author), the use of expert witnesses in litigation (for National Business Institute) and litigation ethics (for National Business Institute).

**Personal:** Erik is active in various civic and charitable programs, including Kiwanis and the Salvation Army (local Advisory Board member). As the parents of four, Erik and his wife are actively involved in volunteerism and administration in youth sports and wellness programs including Little League Baseball and YMCA-sponsored programs.Currently, Erik is teaching an undergraduate business law course as an adjunct instructor in the Marshall University Lewis College of Business.

### LIGHT, Randall C
Steptoe & Johnson PLLC, Bridgeport
304 933 8125
randy.light@steptoe-johnson.com
*Featured in Real Estate (West Virginia)*

**Practice Areas:** Light focuses his practice in the areas of commercial, corporate, real estate, energy, and natural resources law. Light advises clients about commercial and mineral property transactions and the formation, capitalization, operation, and management of their commercial enterprises. He works with lenders and borrowers in the structuring and collateralization of commercial loans. Light is a title insurance agent for two national title insurance companies.

**Professional Memberships:** American Bar Association; Allohak Council, Boy Scouts of America; West Virginia State Bar; The Best Lawyers in America®; Super Lawyers®.

**Personal:** Washington & Lee School of Law; West Virginia Wesleyan College.

### LOVE III, Charles M
Bowles Rice LLP, Charleston
304 347 1104
clove@bowlesrice.com
*Featured in Litigation (West Virginia)*

**Practice Areas:** Commercial litigation, mass and toxic tort litigation, alternative dispute resolution.

**Professional Memberships:** Kanawha County, West Virginia and American Bar Associations; American Board of Trial Advocates.

**Career:** Mr Love has more than 40 years of legal experience. He served as President of both the West Virginia State Bar and the West Virginia Bar Association, is a Fellow of the American Bar Association and is a permanent Member of the Fourth Circuit Judicial Conference. He is an experienced mediator in dispute resolution for business, financial, personal injury, professional liability and condemnation matters.

**Personal:** West Virginia University College of Law (1965).

### LUSK, Neva
Spilman Thomas & Battle, PLLC, Charleston
304 340 3866
nlusk@spilmanlaw.com
*Featured in Litigation (West Virginia)*

**Practice Areas:** General litigation with emphasis on product liability, toxic torts and class actions.

**Professional Memberships:** DRI, National Director & Member, Public Policy Committee, State Representatives Task Force, Minority Scholarship Committee, Women in the Law Steering Committee; Lawyers for Civil Justice, Member; Defense Trial Counsel of West Virginia, past President; West Virginia Bar Foundation, past member of Board of Directors; West Virginia State Bar, past member of the Board of Governors; American Bar Association, Member.

**Career:** Member since 1994; former assistant prosecuting attorney for Kanawha County, WV, 1981-91.

**Personal:** Marshall University (BA, 1977); West Virginia University (JD, 1980).

### MATHIAS, Stephen M
Bowles Rice LLP, Martinsburg
304 264 4234
smathias@bowlesrice.com
*Featured in Real Estate (West Virginia)*

**Practice Areas:** Real estate law; commercial and financial services law; workers' compensation law.

**Professional Memberships:** American Bar Association; West Virginia Bar Association; Eastern Panhandle Bar Association.

**Career:** Mr Mathias has more than 30 years' experience in the practice of law. Prior to joining Bowles Rice in 1985, he served as Assistant Attorney General for the State of West Virginia, 1983-85. He is recognized by Best Lawyers in America for his work in Real Estate Law.

**Personal:** West Virginia University College of Law (1982).

### MAXWELL-HOFFMAN, Ellen
Bowles Rice LLP, Charleston
304 347 1186
emaxwell@bowlesrice.com
*Featured in Corporate/Commercial (West Virginia)*

**Practice Areas:** Commercial and financial services, economic development and municipal bonds and finance.

**Professional Memberships:** American Bar Association, Fourth Circuit Judicial Conference.

**Career:** Ms Maxwell-Hoffman focuses her practice in the areas of general corporate and commercial law, including acquisitions and finance, and corporate governance. She frequently provides legal counsel regarding the West Virginia Governmental Ethics Act and federal and state election laws relating to political action committees. She has been recognized by Best Lawyers in the area of ethics and professional responsibility law. She has considerable experience assisting clients with business interests in both Japan and the United States.

### MERINAR JR, John R
Steptoe & Johnson PLLC, Bridgeport
304 933 8135
jack.merinar@steptoe-johnson.com
*Featured in Labor & Employment (West Virginia)*

**Practice Areas:** Merinar's practice combines employer counseling, traditional labor law matters, and employment litigation. He also defends ski areas in personal injury civil actions and is the leader of the firm's NLRA team.

**Professional Memberships:** National Association of College and University Attorneys; American Bar Association; Board of Directors, Associated Builders & Contractors; Association of Ski Defense Attorneys; West Virginia State Bar; Pennsylvania Bar Association; The Best Lawyers in America®.

**Personal:** University of Pittsburgh School of Law; Pennsylvania State University.

### MONTELEONE, Marc A
Bowles Rice LLP, Charleston
304 347 1132
mmonteleone@bowlesrice.com
*Featured in Corporate/Commercial (West Virginia)*

**Practice Areas:** Oil and gas law; commercial law; tax law; construction law; real estate development; small business development; estate planning.

**Career:** Mr Monteleone serves as in-house counsel to one of West Virginia's largest independent oil and gas producers. His responsibilities include strategic planning, acquisition and leasing of mineral interests and pipeline right of ways, and permitting for new wells. He oversees the company's Marcellus Shale exploration, including negotiation of gas sales contracts and supervision of mineral acquisitions. He wrote the West Virginia Design-Build Law and is chairman of the West Virginia Design-Build Review Board.

### MOORE, John S
Bowles Rice LLP, Charleston
304 347 1716
jmoore@bowlesrice.com
*Featured in Corporate/Commercial (West Virginia)*

**Practice Areas:** Healthcare Law; Physician and Hospital Managed Care Contracts; Physician Employment Agreements; Not-for-Profit Organizational Development.

**Professional Memberships:** Medical Group Management Association; Health Finance Managers Association.

**Career:** Mr Moore has significant experience in many health care-related areas and frequently advises hospitals and physicians on a wide variety of health care legal issues and business matters. He brings hands-on knowledge and practical solutions to challenging issues related to managed care contracting and physician employment. **Personal:** West Virginia University College of Law (1973).

## MORRISON, C David
Steptoe & Johnson PLLC, Bridgeport
304 933 8113
david.morrison@steptoe-johnson.com
*Featured in Labor & Employment (West Virginia)*
**Practice Areas:** Morrison focuses his practice in the area of labor and employment law, including NLRA proceedings, including elections and unfair labor practice litigation. He has litigate over 50 cases and arbitrations, and over 20 appeals before the West Virginia Supreme Court of Appeals and The United State Court of Appeals for the Fourth Circuit. **Professional Memberships:** Fellow, American College of Labor & Employment Lawyers; Past President; Energy & Mineral Law Foundation; Fourth Circuit Judicial Conference; West Virginia Coal Association; The Best Lawyers in America®; Super Lawyers. **Personal:** University of Kentucky School of Law; Transylvania University.

## MURPHY, Sandra M
Bowles Rice LLP, Charleston
304 347 1131
smurphy@bowlesrice.com
*Featured in Corporate/Commercial (West Virginia)*
**Practice Areas:** Banking; commercial and financial services; corporate law; and securities. **Professional Memberships:** American Bar Association; West Virginia Bankers Association; Chair, PIECES Advisory Council. **Career:** Ms Murphy represents clients in all aspects of banking transactions, and assists clients with compliance issues and various other legal matters that arise in the operation of business. She has authored several articles related to banking, securities law, and commercial and financial services, and was selected as 2013 West Virginia Lawyer of the Year in Financial Services Regulation Law by Best Lawyers in America. **Personal:** Brooklyn Law School (JD, 1986); Yale University (BA, 1981).

## OFSA, Joyce
Spilman Thomas & Battle, PLLC, Charleston
304 340 3847
jofsa@spilmanlaw.com
*Featured in Real Estate (West Virginia)*
**Practice Areas:** Commercial/mineral/residential real estate law, zoning, land use/development, eminent domain, landlord/tenant law, title insurance. **Professional Memberships:** Kanawha County Bar Association; West Virginia Bar Association; American Bar Association, Member, Real Property/Probate/Trust Law; American College of Mortgage Attorneys, Fellow, State Chairperson; American College of Real Estate Lawyers, Fellow. **Career:** Member. **Publications:** Contributing author, "Navigating Rough Waters: Successful Lending in Challenging

Finanical Times," Lorman, 2009; "Commercial and Real Estate Loan Documents in West Virginia," Lorman, 2007; "Challenges in Title Transfers," PESI, 2002, 2003. **Personal:** West Virginia University (BA, magna cum laude, 1975); West Virginia University (JD, 1979).

## PATTERSON III, George A
Bowles Rice LLP, Charleston
304 347 1118
gpatterson@bowlesrice.com
*Featured in Natural Resources (West Virginia)*
**Practice Areas:** Coal, oil and gas law; commercial real estate; natural resources. **Professional Memberships:** Trustee, Energy and Mineral Law Foundation (EMLF). **Career:** Mr Patterson has a wide variety of legal experience, but now limits his practice to matters involving oil and gas, coal, and commercial real estate law. He serves as general counsel for the Independent Oil and Gas Association of West Virginia (IOGAWV) and is frequently invited to write for legal and industry publications and speak at industry meetings. **Personal:** West Virginia University College of Law (1979).

## PAUL, Niall
Spilman Thomas & Battle, PLLC, Charleston
304 340 3874
npaul@spilmanlaw.com
*Featured in Litigation (West Virginia)*
**Practice Areas:** Trial work, litigation/appellate practice focusing on complex tort, class actions, medical monitoring, commercial and employment litigation. **Professional Memberships:** IADC, ABA, LCA. **Career:** Member. **Publications:** Spoken and published on jury trials, managing e-discovery, litigating complex water contamination, toxic and environmental torts. Spoken internationally on Sarbanes-Oxley litigation. Organized and moderated annual workshops for the ABA in 2006-08 - "Contamination Examination: Changing Face of Chemical Product Liability Claims", "The Chemical Products Liability Trial: Winning At Every Stage" and "Mass, Class or Pass - Making Strategic Decisions in the Big Chemical Case". **Personal:** Bridgewater College (BA, cum laude, 1987); University of Richmond,(JD, 1990).

## PETERSON, Brian
Bowles Rice LLP, Martinsburg
304 264 4223
bpeterson@bowlesrice.com
*Featured in Labor & Employment (West Virginia)*
**Practice Areas:** Labor and employment, litigation. **Professional Memberships:** American Bar Association, Labor and Employment Section; Defense Trial Counsel of West Virginia. **Career:** Mr Peterson regularly counsels clients in a variety of employment-related matters, including contracts, handbooks and policy manuals, workplace harassment investigations, hiring and discharge of employees and wrongful discharge claims. He also defends employers against claims

such as discrimination, harassment and retaliation, and has obtained summary judgments in areas including FMLA, ADA, ADEA, Section 1981, Title VII of the Civil Rights Act of 1964, and the WV Human Rights Act. **Personal:** Chair of the Bowles Rice Technology Committee.

## PHILLIPS, Jeffrey K
Steptoe & Johnson PLLC, Lexington
859 219 8210
jeff.phillips@steptoe-johnson.com
*Featured in Litigation (West Virginia)*
**Practice Areas:** Phillips concentrates his practice on complex litigation including the defense of energy companies in issues such as deliberate intent, personal injury, and MSHA regulations. He has tried over 45 cases to verdict and has been involved in appellate proceedings before state and federal courts. He is Managing Member of the Lexington, Kentucky office. **Professional Memberships:** Energy & Mineral Law Foundation; Kentucky Coal Association; Lexington Coal Exchange; West Virginia Coal Association; Kentucky Bar Association; West Virginia State Bar; Pennsylvania Bar Association; The Best Lawyers in America®; Super Lawyers®. **Personal:** University of Pittsburgh School of Law; Point Park College.

## PRINTZ, Charles F
Bowles Rice LLP, Martinsburg
304 264 4222
cprintz@bowlesrice.com
*Featured in Litigation (West Virginia)*
**Practice Areas:** Business litigation; labor and employment law (defense); product liability litigation; workplace safety and deliberate intent; condemnation and eminent domain. **Professional Memberships:** American Bar Association; Board of Governors, Defense Trial Counsel of West Virginia, Inc.; DRI; Board Member, Friends of the National Conservation Training Center, Inc. and Shenandoah Valley Medical Systems, Inc. **Career:** Mr Printz is a permanent member of the US 4th Circuit Judicial Conference and a 2008 West Virginia Bar Foundation Fellow. He is a member of the Bowles Rice Executive Committee. **Personal:** JD, West Virginia University College of Law (1975); BA, University of Virginia (1972).

## RAMEY, Ancil G
Steptoe & Johnson PLLC, Huntington
304 526 8133
ancil.ramey@steptoe-johnson.com
*Featured in Litigation (West Virginia)*
**Practice Areas:** Ramey concentrates his efforts in the areas of appellate litigation, having handled over 250 appellate matters, as well as matters involving commercial litigation and insurance litigation. For more than a decade, he served as Clerk of the Supreme Court of Appeals of West Virginia. **Professional Memberships:** Distinguished Service Award, West Virginia Trial Lawyers Association; Distinguished Service Award, West Virginia State Bar; Foundation Fellow, West Virginia Bar Foundation, 2009; Fellow, Litigation Counsel of America; Journal of College and

University Law; National Conference of Appellate Court Clerks; The Best Lawyers in America®; Super Lawyers®. **Personal:** West Virginia University; Marshall University.

## RUSSELL, James A
Steptoe & Johnson PLLC, Morgantown
304 598 8105
james.russell@steptoe-johnson.com
*Featured in Natural Resources (West Virginia)*
**Practice Areas:** Russell's primary emphasis is in the areas of natural resources (coal, oil and gas), commercial transactions and litigation. Russell has acted as counsel for various syndications involving the development of real estate. **Professional Memberships:** Energy & Mineral Law Foundation; West Virginia State Bar; Morgantown Area Chamber of Commerce; Vision 20/20 Riverfront Development Committee; The Best Lawyers in America®. **Personal:** West Virginia University College of Law; United States Military Academy.

## SIEGRIST, Camden P
Bowles Rice LLP, Charleston
304 347 1129
csiegrist@bowlesrice.com
*Featured in Corporate/Commercial (West Virginia)*
**Practice Areas:** Municipal bonds and public finance; banking; economic development; commercial and financial services. **Professional Memberships:** National Association of Bond Lawyers; West Virginia Society of Certified Public Accountants. **Career:** Mr Siegrist is a partner in the Charleston, West Virginia office of Bowles Rice. He focuses his practice in the areas of municipal bonds and related governmental financings, securities, and commercial transactions. He earned his law degree in 1984 and received CPA certification in 1985. He is a retired Lieutenant Colonel in the West Virginia Army National Guard.

## SLAUGHTER, Christopher L
Steptoe & Johnson PLLC, Huntington
304 526 8140
chris.slaughter@steptoe-johnson.com
*Featured in Labor & Employment (West Virginia)*
**Practice Areas:** Slaughter represents employers in labor and employment law as well as arbitration matters. Slaughter has tried cases before state and federal courts and administrative agencies, and he regularly litigates arbitration matters. **Professional Memberships:** Energy & Mineral Law Foundation; American Bar Association; Advantage Valley, Inc.; Commerce Lexington; Kentucky Coal Association; Human Resources Committee, West Virginia Chamber of Commerce; Huntington Regional Chamber of Commerce; Tri-State Society for Human Resource Management; Kentucky Bar Association; Ohio State Bar Association; West Virginia State Bar; The Best Lawyers in America®; Super Lawyers®. **Personal:** University of Kentucky College of Law; Marshall University, cum laude.

## STEPTOE JR, Robert M
Steptoe & Johnson PLLC, Bridgeport
304 933 8142
bob.steptoe@steptoe-johnson.com
*Featured in Labor & Employment (West Virginia)*
**Practice Areas:** For over 40 years, he has focused his practice in the areas of labor and employment law. In addition to counseling clients, Steptoe has tried over 100 cases and has argued over 50 appeals in the West Virginia Supreme Court and the United States Courts of Appeals.
**Professional Memberships:** Fellow, American College of Trial Lawyers; Fellow, College of Labor & Employment Lawyers; Fourth Circuit Judicial Conference; Fellow, American Bar Foundation; Fellow, West Virginia Bar Foundation; Association of Ski Defense Attorneys; AAA National Roster of Neutrals; Chairman, West Virginia Chapter of The Nature Conservancy; Pennsylvania Bar Association; Virginia State Bar; West Virginia State Bar; 2007 Who's Who in WV Business; The Best Lawyers in America®; Super Lawyers®.
**Personal:** West Virginia University College of Law; University of Virginia; Officer in the United States Naval Reserve.

## STOWERS, Gerard R
Bowles Rice LLP, Charleston
304 347 1112
gstowers@bowlesrice.com
*Featured in Litigation (West Virginia)*
**Practice Areas:** Business litigation; insurance coverage disputes; professional liability defense; products liability litigation.
**Professional Memberships:** Charter member and immediate past president, WV Defense Trial Counsel.
**Career:** Mr Stowers' experience includes more than 100 civil jury and bench trials in federal and state courts, and appeals before the Supreme Court of Appeals of West Virginia and the US Court of Appeals for the Fourth Circuit. He has more than 35 years' experience in all aspects of civil litigation, including insurance coverage disputes; personal injury defense; automotive cases; work-place accidents, including mining; commercial disputes; legal malpractice defense and employer liability litigation.

## STUMP, John C
Steptoe & Johnson PLLC, Charleston
304 353 8196
john.stump@steptoe-johnson.com
*Featured in Corporate/Commercial (West Virginia)*
**Practice Areas:** Stump concentrates his practice in the areas of project finance, economic development, utility regulation, and corporate law. Stump's experience includes significant involvement in tax-exempt and taxable bond issues of all types, as well as a variety of economic development projects, and providing legal representation to utilities, financial institutions and municipal and other public bodies.
**Professional Memberships:** National Association of Bond Lawyers; Council of Development Finance Agencies; Mid-Atlantic Technology Research & Innovation Center, Board

Member; West Virginia State Bar; The Best Lawyers in America®.
**Personal:** Washington & Lee University School of Law; West Virginia University.

## TABIT, Joanna I
Steptoe & Johnson PLLC, Charleston
304 353 8142
joanna.tabit@steptoe-johnson.com
*Featured in Litigation (West Virginia)*
**Practice Areas:** Tabit focuses her practice in trial and appellate advocacy. She has tried scores of cases in federal and state courts and has argued approximately 60 appeals in state and federal appellate courts.
**Professional Memberships:** John A Field, Jr., American Inns of Court; Defense Trial Counsel of West Virginia; Defense Research Institute; Women's Energy Network; United States Supreme Court Historical Society; City of Charleston Human Rights Commission; Governor's Council on Literacy; The Cystic Fibrosis Foundation; West Virginia State Bar; The Best Lawyers in America®; Super Lawyers®.
**Personal:** West Virginia University College of Law; Marshall University.

## TURNER, Allyn
Spilman Thomas & Battle, PLLC, Charleston
304 340 3856
aturner@spilmanlaw.com
*Featured in Natural Resources (West Virginia)*
**Practice Areas:** Environmental law.
**Professional Memberships:** Admitted to the United States Court of Appeals for the Fourth Circuit, the United States District Courts for the Northern and Southern Districts of West Virginia, and the West Virginia Supreme Court of Appeals.
**Career:** Formerly Director of the West Virginia Department of Environmental Protection's Division of Water and Waste Management; Managing Attorney for the DEP's Office of Legal Services.
**Personal:** University of Virginia, BA, Environmental Sciences, 1986 Wake Forest University School of Law, JD, 1990.

## WALLACE, Rick
Spilman Thomas & Battle, PLLC, Charleston
304 340 3865
rwallace@spilmanlaw.com
*Featured in Labor & Employment (West Virginia)*
**Practice Areas:** Labor and employment law and general litigation.
**Career:** Extensive traditional labor law experience, including assisting and advice prior to and during union organizing campaigns and strikes, prosecution and defense of labor litigation in federal court, and representation of employers in proceedings before the National Labor Relations Board.
**Personal:** University of Virginia, BA in Foreign Affairs, 2002; Wake Forest University School of Law, JD, 2005.

## WALLS, James
Spilman Thomas & Battle, PLLC, Morgantown
304 291 7947
jwalls@spilmanlaw.com
*Featured in Litigation (West Virginia)*
**Practice Areas:** Natural resources law, commercial litigation, and labor and employment discrimination litigation.
**Professional Memberships:** American Bar Association, Litigation Section; Admitted to practice in all state and federal courts in West Virginia, the US Courts of Appeals for the Third, Fourth and Sixth Circuits and the US District Court for the Northern District of Ohio.
**Career:** Member in Charge of the Morgantown Office. Previously General Counsel for Anker Energy Corporation.
**Personal:** West Virginia University (BS/BA, 1984; JD, 1989).

## WHITE, Tammy
Farrell, White & Legg PLLC, Huntington
304 781 1821
TJW@farrell3.com
*Featured in Litigation (West Virginia)*
**Practice Areas:** Healthcare law and regulation counseling; and medical negligence defense; business, corporate and risk management and compliance; Health policy; Product liability defense and risk management; business and commercial litigation; employment law.
**Professional Memberships:** She is admitted before United States Supreme Court; Fourth and Sixth Circuits (US Federal Courts); and is licensed in West Virginia, Kentucky and Ohio. She is a member of several advisory boards including the West Virginia Women's Education Forum Marshall University Forensic Science Advisor; International Association of Defense Counsel; Marshall University School of Pharmacy curriculum developer and lecturer (Pharmacy Law).
**Career:** She is a founding Member of Farrell & Farrell, LC which became Farrell, Farrell & Farrell PLLC in 1997 and then Farrell, White and Legg PLLC in 2011. Prior to becoming a lawyer, she practiced in clinical nursing and hospital administration as a Registered Nurse.
**Publications:** She has numerous publications. By example, Chapter Pharmaceutical Law and Policy (2007 to date); ABA Health Law Division; Defense Law Journal - "The Medicare Secondary Payer Act" and West Virginia University Law Review.
**Personal:** In May, 2011, Tammy achieved a Master's in Public Health from the Bloomberg School of Public Health, John Hopkins University, Baltimore, Maryland with an emphasis on insurance, economics and policy.

## WILLIAMS, Marc E
Nelson Mullins Riley & Scarborough, Huntington
304 526 3501
marc.williams@nelsonmullins.com
*Featured in Litigation (West Virginia)*

## WILLIAMS, Walter L
Steptoe & Johnson PLLC, Bridgeport
304 933 8152
walter.williams@steptoe-johnson.com
*Featured in Corporate/Commercial (West Virginia)*
**Practice Areas:** Williams' experience includes involvement in real estate, commercial transactions and financings. His practice includes health care and business transactions, particularly in transactions involving for-profit and tax-exempt health care providers. Williams counsels clients regarding acquisitions, financings, confidentiality issues (including HIPAA), medical staff and bylaws issues, medical records, licensure, fraud and abuse and self-referral issues and general health care issues. Williams is leader of the firm's Health Care Team.
**Professional Memberships:** American Health Lawyers Association; Fourth Circuit Judicial Conference; West Virginia State Bar; The Best Lawyers in America®; Super Lawyers®.
**Personal:** William & Mary College of Law; University of Virginia.

## WILLIAMS JR, L Frederick
Steptoe & Johnson PLLC, Charleston
304 353 8178
fred.williams@steptoe-johnson.com
*Featured in Corporate/Commercial (West Virginia)*
**Practice Areas:** Williams concentrates his practice in tax, business, public finance and government relations. His experience includes complex business transactions, public and private offerings, economic development, drafting legislation on tax and public law matters, and public finance.
**Professional Memberships:** American Institute of Certified Public Accountants; State Bar of Arizona; Kentucky Bar Association; West Virginia State Bar; Ohio State Bar Association; "Distinguished West Virginian" 1992; Secretary, West Virginia Department of Revenue and State Tax Commissioner (1990-91); The Best Lawyers in America®.
**Personal:** West Virginia University College of Law; University of Florida, Masters of Taxation; Wheeling Jesuit University; Certified Public Accountant (WV).

## WILSON, Seth
Bowles Rice LLP, Morgantown
304 285 2531
swilson@bowlesrice.com
*Featured in Natural Resources (West Virginia)*
**Practice Areas:** Natural resources law, with emphasis in oil and natural gas; real estate law; tax law; economic development; and commercial and financial services.
**Professional Memberships:** Energy and Mineral Law Foundation.
**Career:** Mr Wilson is the head of the Bowles Rice Energy and Real Estate Development Department and is licensed to practice in West Virginia and Pennsylvania. He divides his practice between the firm's offices in Morgantown, West Virginia and Southpointe, Pennsylvania and regularly assists clients in matters related to exploration and development of the Marcellus and Utica Shale formations.

**Personal:** West Virginia University College of Law (2001); President.

---

**WOODY, Charles**
Spilman Thomas & Battle, PLLC, Charleston
304 340 3862
cwoody@spilmanlaw.com
*Featured in Labor & Employment (West Virginia)*
**Practice Areas:** Litigation, labor/employment, appellate.
**Professional Memberships:** American Bar Foundation, Fellow; American Bar Association, Labor & Employment and Litigation Sections; Member, Fourth Circuit Judicial Conference.
**Career:** Adjunct Professor of Law, Washington and Lee University Law School and Charleston School of Law, Charleston, S.C.
**Publications:** "How to Handle Difficult Opposing Counsel," and "How to Second Chair Trial," ABA YLS, Online Products Liability Articles, 2006; "Early Case Assessment," Counsel to Counsel, 2006; "NLRB Alters Successor Bar Rule," WV Lawyer (2002).
**Personal:** University of Virginia (BA, 1969); Florida State University (JD, 1972).

# BOWLES RICE LLP

www.bowlesrice.com **tel:** 304 347 1100 **fax:** 304 343 3058

**Managing Partner:** Thomas A Heywood
Number of partners: 82  Number of lawyers: 135

## Firm Overview:

Bowles Rice, founded in 1920, is a full service, business-focused law firm providing high quality and efficient legal services. The firm is strategically located throughout the Appalachian Basin, with eight locations to serve its clients in business and industry. The firm is AV Peer Review Rated by Martindale Hubbell.

## Main Areas of Practice:

### Energy:

Coal, oil and natural gas matters are a significant part of the firm's practice. The firm has a wealth of knowledge regarding the Marcellus and Utica Shale formations and extensive experience in energy-related mergers and acquisitions. They represent owners, operators, producers and contractors, ranging from small, locally-owned businesses to international corporations. The firm's energy practice includes public utility and regulatory law, mineral related issues, real estate and land use development, as well as mine safety and health issues.

### Litigation:

More than 50 Bowles Rice lawyers are engaged in litigation on behalf of individuals, businesses and large multinational corporations. The firm prosecutes and defends lawsuits in federal and state courts and administrative agencies of all branches of government in the region. It aggressively seeks to resolve commercial, professional or business disputes for its clients through all available means, including negotiation, mediation, arbitration or, when necessary, trial, in an ethical, competent, cost effective manner. The firm's trial lawyers are engaged in real property and mineral disputes and lawsuits regarding the following: the defense of personal injury, products liability; workplace injuries; construction and condemnation; environmental and toxic torts; lender liability; complex commercial disputes; legal and other professional malpractice; RICO; and white-collar criminal defense.

### Commercial & Corporate:

Among the complex areas in which Bowles Rice attorneys provide assistance are: acquisitions and mergers; bankruptcy; bond financing; business structure; contracts; creditor's rights; economic development; leases; planning and zoning; securities; small business development; and venture capital.

### Banking:

The firm serves as general counsel to banks, bank holding companies and other banking organizations, including the West Virginia Bankers Association and the Community Bankers of West Virginia, and is active in formations, mergers and acquisitions, branch expansions, de novo banking, and special projects. They regularly draft loan agreements, notes and security instruments, and assist banks in complying with regulatory matters.

### Labor & Employment:

The firm assists private and public sector employers in all aspects of labor and employment law, including human resources advice; counseling and training; representation in wrongful discharge and all other forms of employment-related litigation; preparation of contracts and policies; collective bargaining negotiations and traditional labor relations matters; employee benefits issues; and workers' compensation claims. The firm's lawyers work strategically with their clients to achieve work force objectives and prevent litigation. Nevertheless, when employment related litigation arises, they provide experienced and aggressive representation in courts and administrative agencies.

### Environmental & Regulatory:

Environmental representation encompasses commercial transactional structuring, compliance counseling, judicial and administrative proceedings, legislative activity, and technical services. The firm has extensive experience in environmental policy formulation, implementation, interpretation and enforcement.

### Real Estate:

The real estate practice includes purchase and sale transactions and related financing, litigation involving real estate, title and mineral law issues, contract preparation, title insurance, zoning issues and title examinations. Developers proposing industrial, commercial and residential projects receive counsel in land use and development law, planning and zoning, compliance with state and federal sales registration requirements and filings, approvals, permits, and other governmental requirements.

### Taxation and Trusts & Estate Planning:

Tax practitioners advise and represent clients in the formation, purchase, sale, and reorganization of businesses; mergers and acquisitions; property, sales and use tax; issues related to federal, state, and local taxation; and in the ongoing operations of large and small businesses and nonprofit organizations. The firm also has significant experience in estate planning and administration.

### Government Relations:

The firm provides advocacy and counsel on issues related to economic development, banking, energy, environmental and regulatory issues, education, employment, tax and health care-related issues. Services include bill drafting and in-depth review, technical presentations and issue advocacy. They have significant experience in dealing with government officials at the local, state and federal levels.

### Healthcare:

The firm assists providers, employers and payors in regulatory and contractual matters, is experienced in medicine and health benefits, and represents individuals and groups of physicians, hospitals, insurance companies, benefit administrators, associations and companies offering healthcare coverage to employees.

### Employee Benefits, Executive Compensation & ERISA:

Services include drafting of individually designed, qualified defined contribution and defined benefit plans and amending them as changes in the law require. They assist in the preparation of non-qualified deferred compensation arrangements, incentive stock option plans and nonincentive stock option plans for highly compensated executives. They represent employers, insurers and third party administrators in all phases of ERISA litigation.

## OFFICES

**WEST VIRGINIA**

**CHARLESTON:** 600 Quarrier Street, WV 25301
Tel: 304 347 1100   Fax: 304 343 3058

**MARTINSBURG:** 101 South Queen Street, WV 25401
Tel: 304 263 0836

**MORGANTOWN:** 7000 Hampton Center, WV 26505
Tel: 304 285 2500

**MOUNDSVILLE:** 511 7th Street, WV 26041
Tel: 304 845 1040

**PARKERSBURG:** 501 Avery Street, WV 26102
Tel: 304 485 8500

**PENNSYLVANIA**

**CANONSBURG:** 6000 Town Center Boulevard, Suite 210, PA 15317
Tel: 724 514 8915

**KENTUCKY**

**LEXINGTON:** 333 West Vine Street, Suite 1700, KY 40507
Tel: 859 252 2202

**VIRGINIA**

**WINCHESTER:** 480 West Jubal Early Drive, Suite 130, VA 22601
Tel: 540 723 8877

# SPILMAN THOMAS & BATTLE, PLLC

www.spilmanlaw.com **tel:** 800 967 8251 **fax:** 304 340 3801

**Managing Member:** Michael J Basile
**Member in Charge of Lawyer Administration:** David P Ferretti
**Member in Charge of Client Relations:** Eric W Iskra
Number of members: 67
Number of non-members: 78

## Firm Overview:

Spilman Thomas & Battle, PLLC is a full-service law firm with more than 140 attorneys. Founded in 1864, the firm has seven offices located throughout the Mid-Atlantic Inland Basin. Spilman is one of the region's largest law firms and has a diverse client base – one that includes Fortune 500™ companies, smaller entrepreneurial businesses and everything in between. Spilman attorneys and staff are carefully trained to serve as an extension of the client's management team – to help prevent problems and to provide guidance through the legal process. The firm's commitment to excellent service has been a tradition for nearly 150 years, and today that commitment is coupled with a passion for delivering value.

## Main Areas of Practice:

**Corporate:**
28 members; 20 non-members
- Handled all aspects of developing, negotiating and documenting a joint venture relationship and project contracts for a $70,000,000+ construction and commercial retail/development project
- Represented the West Virginia Jobs Investment Trust Board on all corporate, governance, and debt and equity financing transactions, including the closing and disbursement of $13,168,350 of funding
- Represented West Virginia United Health System as bond counsel for the issuance of the West Virginia Hospital Finance Authority's $66,005,000 Hospital Refunding Bonds

**Key Clients:** Branch Banking and Trust Company, Charleston Area Medical Center, Inc., Protea Biosciences, Inc., The Greenbrier.
**Contact:** Brian C Helmick   **Tel:** 304 340 3826
**Email:** bhelmick@spilmanlaw.com

**Labor & Employment:**
16 members; 13 non-members
- Successful summary judgment victories in high-profile wrongful discharge lawsuits
- Go-to counsel for West Virginia-based labor and employment litigation for a Fortune 10™ client
- Strategic, traditional labor guidance and lead negotiator in collective bargaining negotiations resulting in contracts with multimillion dollar savings

**Key Clients:** Lockheed Martin, Lowes Home Centers, Inc., E.I. DuPont de Nemours and Company, Res-Care, Inc.
**Contact:** Eric W Iskra   **Tel:** 304 340 3875
**Email:** eiskra@spilmanlaw.com

**Litigation:**
32 members; 41 non-members
- Obtained award of $3 million for City of Charleston, WV, against prominent engineering firm for faulty design of multimillion dollar compost facility
- Obtained pivotal decision from the WV Supreme Court about what insurance coverage workers' compensation insurers in WV must offer employers. Absent this ruling, insurers would be required to offer deliberate intent coverage to every employer they insured. This requirement would be a serious setback to the workers' compensation insurers privatization law enacted by WV several years ago.
- Obtained multimillion dollar settlement for Mid Vol Coal Sales Inc. in breach of contact case. Defendants denied Mid Vol its exclusive right to purchase a coal prep plant that was constructed at its request.
- Obtained momentous ruling for Feroleto Steel regarding application of ad valorem tax. The question presented was whether a piece of steel cut to customer specifications in WV and shipped to out-of-state customer is a new product such that it can be taxed by the state. The WV Supreme Court ruled that it should not be taxed. This case impacts any business that does warehousing in the state.

**Key Clients:** Cytec, DuPont, Chase Bank, AIG (now Chartis), General Electric.
**Contact:** Heather Heiskell Jones   **Tel:** 304 340 3842
**Email:** hheiskell@spilmanlaw.com

**Natural Resources & Environmental:**
26 natural resources members; 14 non-members
9 environmental members; 6 non-members
- Negotiated a settlement favorable to a West Virginia operating coal company in which a federal Clean Water Act citizens action suit was dismissed without any award of damages
- Successfully lobbied on behalf of a West Virginia oil and gas industry trade association to prevent the passage of proposed oil and gas regulations that would have impeded Marcellus Shale development in West Virginia
- Successfully prosecuted civil trespass actions against environmental activists who unlawfully entered and remained upon active mining properties, including permanent injunction orders against 43 named defendants
- Negotiated and documented transactions in multiple states involving oil and gas and coal assets, including related due diligence activities for real property, environmental and regulatory aspects of these transactions

**Key Clients:** DuPont, Chesapeake Energy, Independent Oil & Gas Association of West Virginia, Alpha Natural Resources.
**Contact:** William M Herlihy (Natural Resources)
**Tel:** 304 340 3838   **Email:** wherlihy@spilmanlaw.com
**Contact:** Allyn G Turner (Environmental)
**Tel:** 304 340 3856   **Email:** aturner@spilmanlaw.com

## PRACTICE AREAS

Banking & Finance
Bonds
Consumer Finance
Corporate & Business Law
Energy
Environmental
Government Relations
Healthcare
Insurance
Labor & Employment
Litigation
Natural Resources
OSHA & MSHA
Real Estate
Tax

## OFFICES

**WEST VIRGINIA**
**CHARLESTON:** 300 Kanawha Blvd., East, WV 25301
Tel: 304 340 3800   Fax: 304 340 3801
Email: stb@spilmanlaw.com

**MORGANTOWN:** 48 Donley Street, Suite 800, WV 26501
Tel: 304 291 7920   Fax: 304 291 7979

**WHEELING:** Century Centre Building, 1233 Main Street, Suite 4000, WV 26003
Tel: 304 230 6950   Fax: 304 230 6951

**NORTH CAROLINA**
**WINSTON-SALEM:** 110 Oakwood Dr., Suite 500, NC 27103
Tel: 336 725 4710   Fax: 336 725 4476

**PENNSYLVANIA**
**PITTSBURGH:** One Oxford Centre, Suite 3440, 301 Grant Street, PA 15219
Tel: 412 325 3301   Fax: 412 325 3324

**MECHANICSBURG:** 1100 Bent Creek Blvd., Suite 101, PA 17050
Tel: 717 795 2740   Fax: 717 795 2743

**VIRGINIA**
**ROANOKE:** 310 First Street, Suite 1100, VA 24011
Tel: 540 512 1800   Fax: 540 342 4480

SPILMAN
ATTORNEYS AT LAW

# STEPTOE & JOHNSON PLLC

**CEO:** Susan S Brewer

## Firm Overview:

Steptoe & Johnson PLLC is nationally recognized as an energy firm serving the industry with its core strengths in Energy Law, Labor and Employment Law, Litigation, and Transactional Law. In 2013, Steptoe & Johnson celebrates serving clients for 100 years.

## Main Areas of Practice:

### Energy:

Firm attorneys represent Fortune 500 energy producers and are nationally recognized for excellence in shale gas law. The group is ranked #1 in energy-related practice areas by The Best Lawyers in America® 2013.
Steptoe & Johnson's Energy Team:
- 12th largest energy practice in the US by Energy Law 360
- Multi-billion dollar oil and gas transactions in the Marcellus and Utica shales
- Governmental affairs support to national energy developers
- One of the largest mineral title groups in the nation
Experience:
- Represent regional and national entities in both the purchase and sale of mineral properties including producing coal properties and oil and gas leaseholds and producing wells
- FERC and midstream compliance management for major energy clients
- Employment and labor services to the extractive mineral industry
- Experience in private placements for natural gas drilling programs with IDC tax credits
- Litigated quiet title action relating to enforcement of a right of reconveyance found in prior assignment with respect to various oil and gas leasehold estates

### Labor & Employment:

Steptoe & Johnson's Labor and Employment Law Practice Group represents employers in all aspects of labor, employment, employee benefits, and occupational injury law. Group lawyers assist clients in industries such as energy, manufacturing, education, health care, and construction. The labor and employment practice is ranked #1 by The Best Lawyers in America® 2013.
Experience:
- Defended oil and gas, timbering, manufacturing, and coal industry clients in deliberate intent cases involving companion claims of retaliatory discharge
- Negotiated pre-suit settlements for clients in sensitive employment matters

### Real Estate & Natural Resources:

Steptoe & Johnson provides comprehensive legal services to real estate developers, commercial banks and lending institutions, governmental entities, energy companies, buyers and sellers of business assets and investors. The group's broad experience positions the firm at the forefront of the legal profession in the region. The real estate practice is ranked #1 by The Best Lawyers in America® 2013. The natural resources practice is also ranked #1 in Ohio and West Virginia by The Best Lawyers in America® 2013.
Experience:
- Managed large abstracting teams in multiple states to assist a major energy client in meeting an extensive drilling plan
- Lead teams responsible for numerous asset and stock transactions, lease transactions, and land and legal due diligence for acquisitions as lead or local counsel involving over 1,000,000 gross acres

### Litigation:

Steptoe & Johnson litigators have built a reputation in trial and appellate courts based on a strong record in dealing with complex cases. Knowing that cost control is a critical factor in any successful strategy, the firm's attorneys are also adept at analysis, budgeting and alternative dispute resolution.
Experience:
- Lead counsel energy litigation experience, including defense of claims in excess of $250 million regarding allegations of contract breach, fraud and tortious interference in a natural gas measurement dispute
- Defended an oil and gas producer in a dispute over ownership of oil and gas rights worth over $70 million
- Defended a Fortune 100 coal company in a $100 million fraud and breach of contract action
- Represented oil and gas producers in over 100 mineral title and other litigation matters

### Environmental:

Steptoe & Johnson's environmental attorneys are seasoned litigators who handle commercial and energy related litigation in high profile cases, and experienced counselors who help clients to meet environmental

obligations. The group counsels clients on environmental issues including industry and penalty and enforcement actions, site remediation and planning, hazardous and solid waste disposal permitting and enforcement. Five attorneys are recognized by The Best Lawyers in America® 2013 in environmental law.

## OFFICES

### WEST VIRGINIA

**BRIDGEPORT:** 400 White Oaks Boulevard, WV 26330
Tel: 304 933 8000  Fax: 304 933 8183
Email: gary.nickerson@steptoe-johnson.com

**CHARLESTON:** Chase Tower - Eighth Floor, 707 Virginia Street E., WV 25301
Tel: 304 353 8000  Fax: 304 353 8180
Email: bryan.cokeley@steptoe-johnson.com

**HUNTINGTON:** Chase Center-Second Floor, 1000 Fifth Avenue, Suite 250, WV 25701
Tel: 304 522 8290  Fax: 304 526 8089
Email: chris.slaughter@steptoe-johnson.com

**MARTINSBURG:** Edwin Miller Professional Centre, 1250 Edwin Miller Boulevard, Suite 300, WV 25404
Tel: 304 263 6991  Fax: 304 262 3541
Email: bridget.cohee@steptoe-johnson.com

**MORGANTOWN:** United Center, 1085 Van Voorhis Road, Suite 400, WV 26507
Tel: 304 598 8000  Fax: 304 598 8116
Email: brian.gallagher@steptoe-johnson.com

**WHEELING:** 1233 Main Street, Suite 3000, WV 26003
Tel: 304 233 0000  Fax: 304 233 0014
Email: william.wilmoth@steptoe-johnson.com

### KENTUCKY

**LEXINGTON:** One Paragon Centre, Suite 300, 2525 Harrodsburg Road, KY 40513
Email: jeff.phillips@steptoe-johnson.com

### OHIO

**CANTON:** 4580 Stephen Circle NW Suite 300, OH 44718
Tel: 330 498 3000
Email: dan.kostrub@steptoe-johnson.com

**COLUMBUS:** Huntington Center, 41 South High St., Suite 2200, OH 43215
Tel: 614 221 5100  Fax: 614 221 0952
Email: kevin.west@steptoe-johnson.com

### PENNSYLVANIA

**CANONSBURG:** 11 Grandview Circle, Suite 200, PA 15317
Tel: 724 873 3140  Fax: 724 873 3143
Email: kristian.white@steptoe-johnson.com

**MEADVILLE:** 201 Chestnut Street, Suite 200, PA 16335
Tel: 814 333 4900  Fax: 814 336 6570
Email: russell.schetroma@steptoe-johnson.com

### TEXAS

**HOUSTON:** Two Allen Center, 1200 Smith Street, 16th Floor, TX 77002
Tel: 713 3533911
Email: andrew.graham@steptoe-johnson.com

## How lawyers are ranked

Every year we carry out thousands of in-depth interviews with clients in order to assess the reputations and expertise of business lawyers worldwide. The qualities we look for (and which determine rankings) include technical legal ability, professional conduct, client service, commercial awareness/astuteness, diligence, commitment, and other qualities most valued by the client. For details of our research team see p.5.

# CORPORATE/M&A

## Corporate/M&A
### Leading Firms

**Band 1**
Foley & Lardner LLP *

**Band 2**
Godfrey & Kahn, SC *
Quarles & Brady LLP *
Reinhart Boerner Van Deuren s.c. *

**Band 3**
Michael Best & Friedrich LLP *
Whyte Hirschboeck Dudek S.C. *

## Band 1

### Foley & Lardner LLP
See profile on p.2588

**THE FIRM** Foley & Lardner's transactional and securities team is considered Wisconsin's leading corporate practice. It provides market-leading advice across a broad spectrum of matters, including M&A, corporate governance and public offerings. The group is particularly active in the professional sports sector, and recently acted for Guggenheim Baseball Management on its acquisition of the Los Angeles Dodgers for over $2 billion. The group has also provided corporate counsel to Harley-Davidson, Johnson Controls and Quad/Graphics.
**Sources say:** *"Foley & Lardner are the ones I turn to for the most difficult, sophisticated transactions."*
**KEY INDIVIDUALS Benjamin Garmer** is a celebrated transactional lawyer. He recently assisted Regal Beloit with the $875 million acquisition of A.O. Smith Electrical Products. **Jay Rothman** has an excellent reputation for handing M&A, public offerings and other corporate matters. He recently advised MAKO Surgical on a $50 million facility agreement. Clients report that corporate counselor **Patrick Quick** has a *"strong command of the requirements of the law and the practical implications of compliance,"* as well as *"good business sense."* **James Peterson** handles a range of corporate transactions, with a particular empha-

sis on private equity and venture capital matters. Clients are impressed by his energetic and intelligent approach. **John Wilson** is another key player at the firm and was recently called upon to advise Pentair on its merger with a spun-off subsidiary of Tyco International. Clients admire his *"tremendous work ethic."* **Bill Abraham** is a well-regarded transactional lawyer with extensive experience in the field. He is noted for his M&A expertise.

## Band 2

### Godfrey & Kahn, SC
See profile on p.2590

**THE FIRM** This well-respected group has a strong reputation for handling midmarket transactions. It is well equipped to advise public and private companies on a variety of corporate matters, ranging from M&A and securities to issues concerning recapitalizations and venture capital. The team was recently called upon to act for Johnson Controls on the disposal of its marine division. Other key clients include Khol's, BMO Harris Bank and ManpowerGroup.
**Sources say:** *"Dedicated, insightful and thorough."*
**KEY INDIVIDUALS John Dickens** is a highly esteemed practitioner. He is particularly known for his private equity expertise and recently advised investment firm Lubar & Co on its purchase of Erdman Holdings. Well-respected practitioner **Patricia Falb** handles a range of M&A and financing transactions. She recently represented a subsidiary of Landec in a $63 million stock purchase. **Christopher Noyes** is described as an *"extremely bright"* lawyer with *"a great reputation for M&A."* Recent work highlights include advising Walker Forge on its acquisition of limited liability company PMT Industries. **Mark Witt** has a strong reputation in the field of M&A. He provided corporate counsel to Johnson Controls on the disposal mentioned above. **Peter Sommerhauser** is an iconic figure in the Wisconsin legal community. He recently assisted Magnum Products with its $80 million sale of assets to Generac.

## Corporate/M&A
### Senior Statesmen

**Senior Statesmen:** distinguished older practitioners
Sommerhauser Peter   *Godfrey & Kahn, SC*

### Leading Individuals

**Band 1**

| | |
|---|---|
| Buono Kathryn M | *Quarles & Brady LLP* * |
| Dickens John A | *Godfrey & Kahn, SC* |
| Garmer III Benjamin F | *Foley & Lardner LLP* |
| Linstroth Tod B | *Michael Best & Friedrich LLP* * |
| Rothman Jay O | *Foley & Lardner LLP* |

**Band 2**

| | |
|---|---|
| Abraham Bill | *Foley & Lardner LLP* |
| Bedore James M | *Reinhart Boerner Van Deuren s.c.* * |
| Falb Patricia L | *Godfrey & Kahn, SC* |
| Noyes Christopher | *Godfrey & Kahn, SC* |
| Pepke Michael T | *Reinhart Boerner Van Deuren s.c.* * |
| Quick Patrick G | *Foley & Lardner LLP* |

**Band 3**

| | |
|---|---|
| Burnett Lawrence J | *Reinhart Boerner Van Deuren s.c.* * |
| Emanuel John F | *Whyte Hirschboeck Dudek S.C.* * |
| Fraser Alexander P | *Michael Best & Friedrich LLP* * |
| Hutter Patricia M | *Quarles & Brady LLP* * |
| Lundgren K Thor | *Michael Best & Friedrich LLP* * |
| Myers Thomas A | *Reinhart Boerner Van Deuren s.c.* * |
| Peterson James | *Foley & Lardner LLP* |
| Roang Sverre | *Whyte Hirschboeck Dudek S.C.* * |
| Silverthorn Richard W | *Whyte Hirschboeck Dudek S.C.* * |
| Skipper Walter J | *Quarles & Brady LLP* * |
| Wilson John K | *Foley & Lardner LLP* |
| Witt Mark | *Godfrey & Kahn, SC* |

**Up-and-coming individuals**

| | |
|---|---|
| Van Den Elzen Ryan L | *Quarles & Brady LLP* * |

*Indicates firm / individual with profile.*
*Alphabetical order within each band. Band 1 is the highest.*

## Quarles & Brady LLP
See profile on p.2593

**THE FIRM** This firm is well versed in a wide range of corporate matters, and has notable experience handling M&A and securities issues. It is particularly active in the sphere of private equity, and has recently advised private equity investor Mason Wells on a number of substantial transactions. The group is also called upon to represent significant clients from the food and beverage, manufacturing and technology sectors, including MillerCoors, Menasha and Westell Technologies.
**Sources say:** *"Especially client-focused and eager to learn and understand our business."*
**KEY INDIVIDUALS Kathryn Buono** (see p.2581) is a *"well-respected"* attorney with a *"significant private equity practice."* Clients report that *"she combines a terrific legal mind with a practical, businesslike approach."* Clients agree that **Patricia Hutter** (see p.2583) is *"extremely good on the documents side, really great at mastering the details and a strong negotiator."* She is a notable M&A practitioner and recently advised Mason Wells on its acquisition of Eddy Packing and Beeman Transportation. **Walter Skipper** (see p.2586) has broad transactional and compliance expertise. Clients praise him as *"an outstanding negotiator and deal lead,"* who is *"very in tune with the business and what points are important to us."* Clients describe **Ryan Van Den Elzen** (see p.2587) as *"smart, practical and hard-working."* He handles a wide variety of corporate matters, and has considerable experience in the private equity arena.

## Reinhart Boerner Van Deuren s.c.
See profile on p.2594

**THE FIRM** This well-regarded group has a broad business practice, encompassing M&A and corporate finance matters. It places a particular emphasis on the representation of private equity clients in midmarket transactions, and

has significant experience of handling recapitalizations and ESOP issues. The team has recently provided corporate counsel to Merit Capital Partners, Chicago Growth Partners and Johnson Outdoors.
**Sources say:** *"It is a terrific organization and highly regarded in financial circles in Wisconsin."*
**KEY INDIVIDUALS James Bedore** (see p.2580) is a well-regarded business lawyer. He concentrates his practice on corporate transactional matters, including M&A and securities. **Michael Pepke** (see p.2585) is another key player at the firm. He handles M&A, private equity matters and general corporate counseling. M&A specialist **Thomas Myers** (see p.2585) is regularly called upon to represent medical technology companies and family-owned businesses. Clients are impressed by **Lawrence Burnett**'s (see p.2581) proactivity and attentiveness. He is cochair of the firm's business law group and focuses on corporate finance and M&A.

### Band 3

## Michael Best & Friedrich LLP
See profile on p.2592

**THE FIRM** This group is particularly active in the field of corporate finance, and has notable experience in securities, reorganizations and tax credits. It is also equipped to advise on M&A matters, and has notable experience of handling strategic investments and asset transactions. Recent matters include advising Odyne Systems on a substantial strategic investment into the company by Allison Transmissions.
**Sources say:** *"I hold them in very high regard. I have recommended them many times."*
**KEY INDIVIDUALS Tod Linstroth** (see p.2584) has an excellent reputation in the market. He is well versed in pri-

vate equity and venture capital, and has a particular interest in the technology sector. Clients report that **Thor Lundgren** (see p.2584) has *"great business sense"* and gives *"good, practical advice."* His practice encompasses a broad range of transactional and compliance-related issues. Head of the firm's banking and financial services team, **Alexander Fraser** (see p.2582) is identified by sources as a *"very good lawyer."* He focuses his practice on commercial lending and M&A matters.

## Whyte Hirschboeck Dudek S.C.
See profile on p.2595

**THE FIRM** This group is recommended for its transactional capabilities. It has experience of handling a range of M&A matters, including strategic acquisitions, buyouts and asset transactions. It is also active in the corporate finance area, and has recently advised on stock offerings, bond issuances and tax-exempt matters. The team acts for clients from a variety of industries, ranging from manufacturing to energy and natural resources.
**Sources say:** *"They have been very good at listening to what our issues and concerns are and proposing strategies that make sense given what we're trying to accomplish."*
**KEY INDIVIDUALS** *"Master negotiator"* **John Emanuel** (see p.2582) is praised by clients for his *"ability to see the big picture on transactions."* He advises clients on a range of M&A and finance-related issues. Sources observe that **Sverre Roang** (see p.2585) *"has a solid command of corporate law and special expertise in agricultural transactions."* His practice is focused on transactional matters. *"Practical and solutions-focused counselor"* **Richard Silverthorn** (see p.2586) also concentrates his practice on transactional work, and has particular experience in the chemical and energy industries. Clients appreciate that *"he is deeply experienced in both the legal and market elements of transactions."*

# INTELLECTUAL PROPERTY

Commentary about individuals can be found under their firm's paragraph. If the firm has no paragraph (is not ranked) look at Other Notable Practitioners.

### Band 1

## Michael Best & Friedrich LLP
See profile on p.2592

**THE FIRM** This group is widely regarded as having one of Wisconsin's leading IP practices. It has a broad range of expertise, with notable experience in the fields of patent infringement defense, patent prosecution, licensing and IP issues arising from corporate transactions. The team is also sought after to handle general portfolio management and has recently assisted clients of the caliber of Harley-Davidson, Ingersoll Rand and ACCO Brands.
**Sources say:** *"They appreciate the business aspects of legal matters and offer solid, useful, informed suggestions to solve real-world problems."*

**KEY INDIVIDUALS Jonathan Margolies** (see p.2584) is highly esteemed in the field of IP litigation and has recently been engaged to act for Modine on a patent infringement claim. **David De Bruin** (see p.2582) is another well-respected litigator, with experience at trial and appellate levels. He also assists in patent applications and general IP counseling. **Donald Best** (see p.2581) is known for his IP litigation expertise. He has a particular interest in biotechnology patent issues. **Christopher Austin** (see p.2580) is a much-praised patent prosecutor, with a focus on mechanical, software and medical technology. *"Well-respected IP lawyer"* **Kevin Moran** (see p.2584) handles patent prosecution and defense. Clients value his *"good strategic advice."* His areas of expertise include mechanical, electro-mechanical and biomedical technologies. **Derek Stettner** (see

p.2587) is viewed as *"very good"* in the fields of IP protection and licensing. He has notable experience of software-related issues. *"Exceptional attorney"* **Richard Kaiser** (see p.2583) is singled out for his *"in-depth patent prosecution knowledge."* His practice focuses on patent prosecution.

## Quarles & Brady LLP
See profile on p.2593

**THE FIRM** Quarles & Brady has an excellent reputation in the market. The firm has an acknowledged tradition of patent law expertise and is particularly recommended for its life sciences, medical and technology capabilities. In the past year, it has prosecuted patents on behalf of Mayo Clinic, Roche Diagnostics and Steelcase. The team has a strong track record of working with research institutions,

## Intellectual Property
### Leading Firms

**Band 1**

Michael Best & Friedrich LLP *

Quarles & Brady LLP *

**Band 2**

Boyle Fredrickson

Foley & Lardner LLP *

Perkins Coie LLP

Whyte Hirschboeck Dudek S.C. *

**Band 3**

Andrus, Sceales, Starke & Sawall, LLP

Godfrey & Kahn, SC *

Reinhart Boerner Van Deuren s.c. *

Ryan Kromholz & Manion SC

### Leading Individuals

**Band 1**

| | |
|---|---|
| Baker Jean C | Quarles & Brady LLP * |
| Boyle James F | Boyle Fredrickson |
| Hanson David G | Reinhart Boerner Van Deuren s.c. * |
| Margolies Jonathan H | Michael Best & Friedrich LLP * |
| Skilton John S | Perkins Coie LLP |

**Band 2**

| | |
|---|---|
| Carter Eugenia | Whyte Hirschboeck Dudek S.C. * |
| De Bruin David L | Michael Best & Friedrich LLP * |
| McConnell Andrew | Boyle Fredrickson |

**Band 3**

| | |
|---|---|
| Austin Christopher B | Michael Best & Friedrich LLP * |
| Baxter Keith M | Boyle Fredrickson |
| Berson Bennett J | Quarles & Brady LLP * |
| Best J Donald | Michael Best & Friedrich LLP * |
| Fredrickson John P | Boyle Fredrickson |
| Gundersen Jeffrey S | Foley & Lardner LLP |
| Hanewicz Christopher G | Perkins Coie LLP |
| Heino Joseph S. | Davis & Kuelthau, SC (ONP) [†] |
| Jaskolski Michael A | Quarles & Brady LLP * |
| Kassel Mark | Foley & Lardner LLP |
| Kromholz Joseph A | Ryan Kromholz & Manion SC |
| Moran Kevin | Michael Best & Friedrich LLP * |
| Morrow James G | Reinhart Boerner Van Deuren s.c. * |
| Newholm Timothy E | Boyle Fredrickson |
| Pienkos John T | Whyte Hirschboeck Dudek S.C. * |
| Simmons Jeffrey | Foley & Lardner LLP |

**Up-and-coming individuals**

| | |
|---|---|
| Kaiser Richard L. | Michael Best & Friedrich LLP * |
| Stettner Derek C. | Michael Best & Friedrich LLP * |

**Associates to watch**

| | |
|---|---|
| Cronin Michael J. | Whyte Hirschboeck Dudek S.C. * |
| Gregor Jennifer L. | Godfrey & Kahn, SC |

* Indicates firm / individual with profile.

[†] ONP = Other Notable Practitioner.

## Intellectual Property: Litigation
### Leading Individuals

| | |
|---|---|
| Arntsen Allen A | Foley & Lardner LLP |
| Best J Donald | Michael Best & Friedrich LLP * |
| Boyle James F | Boyle Fredrickson |
| Carter Eugenia | Whyte Hirschboeck Dudek S.C. * |
| Hanson David G | Reinhart Boerner Van Deuren s.c. * |
| Margolies Jonathan H | Michael Best & Friedrich LLP * |
| Skilton John S | Perkins Coie LLP |

ground gives her an advantage in prosecuting biotechnology, material science and medical patents. **Bennett Berson** (see p.2581) is singled out for his life sciences expertise. He also has experience of prosecuting electrical and mechanical patents. He recently worked closely with Baker on the prosecution of a portfolio of patent applications for the Wisconsin Alumni Research Foundation. **Michael Jaskolski** (see p.2583) is known for handling patent prosecution and enforcement strategies. Clients say: *"You feel confident when he's doing your patent prosecution that he has an eye towards litigation and will make your patent as strong as it could be."*

### Band 2

#### Boyle Fredrickson

**THE FIRM** This Milwaukee IP boutique is a well-established adviser to Wisconsin's manufacturing industry and has experience of working with agricultural, engine, paper and construction equipment manufacturers. It is also active in the area of industrial controls. The group's practice is heavily patent-oriented.

**KEY INDIVIDUALS James Boyle** is a talented litigator. He handles both patent and trademark disputes, in addition to prosecution and counseling. **Andrew McConnell** has a strong reputation for patent prosecution. He has a particular interest in the mechanical, electromechanical and chemical sectors. *"Smart, thoughtful and pragmatic,"* **Keith Baxter** focuses on prosecuting and advising on technology patents. Clients report that *"he is very good at crafting applications that get to the point."* Experienced litigator **John Fredrickson** is a trademark and copyright expert. He is also experienced as a mediator in intellectual property disputes. **Timothy Newholm** is another respected patent prosecutor. His practice places an emphasis on mechanical technology.

#### Foley & Lardner LLP
See profile on p.2588

**THE FIRM** This diverse practice is equipped to act for clients on a variety of IP matters. It has notable experience in the fields of patent infringement litigation, trademark issues and copyright disputes, and is particularly active in handling IP due diligence arising from corporation transactions. The group has extensive technology expertise and has recently acted for Spectrum Brands, Johnson Controls and BASF. Recent highlights include representing Sloan Global Holdings in a multimillion-dollar patent infringement dispute.

**KEY INDIVIDUALS** Noted patent specialist **Jeffrey Gundersen** counsels client on a range of issues, including opinions, licensing, protection and transactional due diligence. He is well recognized for his knowledge of the nuclear engineering space, and also handles matters in other areas of mechanics and biomechanics. **Mark Kassel** is head of Foley's Madison IP group and chairs its chemical, biotechnology and pharmaceutical practice firmwide. He handles a variety of IP counseling and litigation, with a focus on the areas mentioned above. **Allen Arntsen** is a highly regarded IP litigator. He is well versed in patent, trademark and copyright matters, and recently represented TreeHouse Foods in a $20 million patent, trademark and false advertising dispute. **Jeffrey Simmons** is praised for his handling of IP disputes. Clients value his ability to find *"resolutions that avoid unnecessary litigation."*

#### Perkins Coie LLP
See profile on p.2548

**THE FIRM** Perkins Coie's Madison office has a strong focus on IP law and is noted for its breadth of practice and geographical reach. It is particularly active in the field of patent infringement litigation and has a notable track record of handling copyright and trade secret matters. The group places a heavy emphasis on life sciences, and has significant experience of litigating disputes under the Hatch-Waxman Act. Recent clients include Ruud Lighting, Mylan and Palmetto Pharmaceuticals.

**KEY INDIVIDUALS John Skilton** devotes his practice to patent litigation. Clients prize his ability to break down highly sophisticated technical issues into more understandable concepts. **Christopher Hanewicz** also focuses on patent litigation. He is praised by clients for his tireless approach and extensive knowledge and ability as a litigator.

#### Whyte Hirschboeck Dudek S.C.
See profile on p.2595

**THE FIRM** This firm handles a wide range of IP matters, including patent, trademark and copyright law, and has a notable interest in information technology issues. It is also well versed in trade secret agreements and disputes. Recent clients include Lake Region Medical, Acme United and Illinois Tool Works.

**Sources say:** *"The service we have received from them has been outstanding."*

**KEY INDIVIDUALS Eugenia Carter** (see p.2581) litigates a wide variety of contentious IP matters. Clients praise her management of patent, trademark, copyright and trade secret disputes. **John Pienkos** (see p.2585) is a *"highly skilled and knowledgeable"* IP counselor with a focus on the electrical engineering sector. Associate to watch **Michael Cronin** (see p.2581) is singled out by clients as being *"absolutely outstanding in the realm of patent prosecution."* He is described as *"extremely detailed and extremely customer-focused."*

and has recently acted for the Wisconsin Alumni Research Foundation.

**Sources say:** *"They cross-pollinate ideas, which is helpful to get the best patent applications."*

**KEY INDIVIDUALS Jean Baker** (see p.2580) is recognized as a *"very good"* patent lawyer. Her scientific back-

## Band 3

### Andrus, Sceales, Starke & Sawall, LLP

THE FIRM This well-respected IP boutique has offices in Milwaukee and Madison. It handles patent, trademark and copyright matters, in addition to trade secret issues and IP concerns arising from corporate transactions. The group has broad experience of a diverse range of technology areas.

KEY INDIVIDUALS George Solveson is a key contact at the firm.

### Godfrey & Kahn, SC
See profile on p.2590

THE FIRM This group is recommended for its litigation, trademark prosecution and general counseling capabilities. It is well equipped to handle IP matters across a wide variety of client industries, ranging from research institutions to consumer goods manufacturers and retailers. The team has recently provided IP counsel to Johnsonville Sausage, Pacific Swim and Kohl's.

Sources say: *"They do a really great job with client service."*

KEY INDIVIDUALS Associate to watch **Jennifer Gregor** is recognized for her *"excellent"* work in connection to trademark applications. Clients appreciate her knowledge of their businesses.

### Reinhart Boerner Van Deuren s.c.
See profile on p.2594

THE FIRM This firm is particularly active in the area of patent infringement defense litigation. It also places an emphasis on patent prosecution, in addition to trademark, copyright and trade secret issues. The group has experience of a number of different technology areas, most notably biological sciences. Recent clients include Silgan and Amerisource Bergen.

KEY INDIVIDUALS Team leader **David Hanson** (see p.2583) is acknowledged as a *"very good"* IP litigator. He has a broad practice, which encompasses patent, trademark and copyright matters, in addition to false advertising. **James Morrow** (see p.2584) advises on a wide variety of IP issues. Clients appreciate that he is *"clearly centered on the business purpose"* and *"very strategic with regard to the*

*patent process, from the beginning to the potential allowance of the patent and how well it could be defended in the future."*

### Ryan Kromholz & Manion SC

THE FIRM This Brookfield IP boutique is known for its work with independent inventors. It covers a wide variety of IP matters, including patent, trademark and copyright law. The group has experience of working within a range of sectors, including engineering, medical technology, industrial controls and computer software.

KEY INDIVIDUALS **Joseph Kromholz** is a well-regarded IP litigator. He handles both enforcement and infringement defense cases for clients from a diverse range of industries.

### Other Notable Practitioners

**Joseph Heino** of Davis & Kuelthau s.c. is well versed in a wide variety of IP issues, including patent and trademark infringement litigation. Clients describe him as being *"adept at providing both legal and business strategy advice."*

# LABOR & EMPLOYMENT

Commentary about individuals can be found under their firm's paragraph. If the firm has no paragraph (is not ranked) look at Other Notable Practitioners.

| Labor & Employment Leading Firms |
|---|
| **Band 1** |
| Michael Best & Friedrich LLP * |
| Quarles & Brady LLP * |
| **Band 2** |
| Foley & Lardner LLP * |
| **Band 3** |
| Godfrey & Kahn, SC * |
| Reinhart Boerner Van Deuren s.c. * |
| **Band 4** |
| Krukowski & Costello, S.C. |
| Lindner & Marsack, SC * |
| Littler Mendelson, PC * |

* Indicates firm / individual with profile.
Alphabetical order within each band. Band 1 is the highest.

## Band 1

### Michael Best & Friedrich LLP
See profile on p.2592

THE FIRM This firm has one of Wisconsin's premier labor and employment practices, and counsels employers on a diverse range of issues. It is particularly active in the fields of employment discrimination litigation, noncompete agreements and traditional labor law matters, and is increasingly called upon to defend wage and hour class actions. The group recently obtained a favorable summary judgment for Wheaton Franciscan Healthcare in a dis-

crimination and retaliation case. Other key clients include Briess, KS Energy and ThyssenKrupp Waupaca.

Sources say: *"A very strong labor and employment practice."*

KEY INDIVIDUALS *"Leading benefits lawyer"* **Charles Stevens** (see p.2587) is well versed in employee pension and welfare plans, including new federal healthcare legislation. *"Highly regarded"* lawyer **Tom Scrivner** (see p.2586) handles a variety of labor and employment issues, including employment discrimination litigation and union avoidance counseling. **José Olivieri** (see p.2585) is held in high esteem in the market. He specializes in immigration law, in addition to general employment matters, and is particularly knowledgeable of issues relating to higher education institutions. **Scott Beightol** (see p.2580) focuses on employment discrimination and noncompete litigation, in addition to general labor and employment counseling. One interviewee reports being *"really impressed with his sensitivity towards our situation as a client."* **David Croysdale** (see p.2581) is considered a *"great labor practitioner."* His practice encompasses labor collective bargaining, union avoidance and NLRB representation. *"Topnotch"* attorney **Eric Hobbs** (see p.2583) is recognized for his OSHA expertise. He is also experienced in matters concerning the ADA, the FMLA and wage and hour disputes. **Amy Schmidt-Jones** (see p.2586) is a rising star who focuses her practice on employment litigation. Her expertise includes discrimination, FMLA and contractual matters.

### Quarles & Brady LLP
See profile on p.2593

THE FIRM This group has an excellent reputation across a wide variety of practice specialisms and has significant experience of discrimination, harassment, FMLA, and immigration matters, in addition to wage and hour class actions. It is also well versed in NLRB and EEOC proceedings. The team was recently called upon to advise Oshkosh Corporation on a number of labor and employment issues, including arbitrations, civil rights litigation, and NLRA matters. In the past year, it has also acted for MillerCoors, GE Healthcare and Actuant.

Sources say: *"We feel like we get a lot of special attention. It's the personal level of service that they provide for us that makes us happy with them."*

KEY INDIVIDUALS **David Kern** (see p.2583) is recommended as a *"very strong labor practitioner"* by impressed sources. Clients describe him as *"incredibly balanced,"* *"incredibly prepared"* and *"always proactive."* Clients report that **Ely Leichtling** (see p.2583) is *"very responsive, very knowledgeable and very easy to work with."* He concentrates on traditional labor law, and leads the firm's NLRA team. He is also experienced in employment law matters. **David Olson** (see p.2585) is a leading employee benefits lawyer. He focuses his practice on executive compensation and retirement plan matters. **Robert Rothacker** (see p.2586) is also a preeminent employee benefits lawyer with a focus on executive compensation and retirement plans. He is particularly noted for his experience in the healthcare sector. **Robert Duffy** (see p.2582) handles both labor and

## Labor & Employment
### Senior Statesmen

**Senior Statesmen:** distinguished older practitioners

| | |
|---|---|
| Marsack Gary | Lindner & Marsack, SC |

### Leading Individuals

**Band 1**

| | |
|---|---|
| Bobber Bernard J | Foley & Lardner LLP |
| Kern David B | Quarles & Brady LLP * |
| Leichtling Ely A | Quarles & Brady LLP * |
| Levine Jonathan O | Littler Mendelson, PC * |
| Scrivner Tom | Michael Best & Friedrich LLP * |
| Sholl Robert K | Reinhart Boerner Van Deuren s.c. * |

**Band 2**

| | |
|---|---|
| Beightol Scott C | Michael Best & Friedrich LLP * |
| Croysdale David | Michael Best & Friedrich LLP * |
| Duffy Robert H | Quarles & Brady LLP * |
| Kaplan Daniel A | Foley & Lardner LLP |
| Pence Thomas C | Foley & Lardner LLP |

**Band 3**

| | |
|---|---|
| Fischer Michael J | Quarles & Brady LLP * |
| Hobbs Eric | Michael Best & Friedrich LLP * |
| Kinney Kevin J | Krukowski & Costello, S.C. |
| Lindner Laura A | Littler Mendelson, PC * |
| Mackenzie Thomas W | Lindner & Marsack, SC |
| McLaughlin Christine Liu | Godfrey & Kahn, SC |
| Ploor Pamela M | Quarles & Brady LLP * |
| Scullen Sean M | Quarles & Brady LLP * |
| Stathas Lynn M | Reinhart Boerner Van Deuren sc * |

**Up-and-coming individuals**

| | |
|---|---|
| Schmidt-Jones Amy | Michael Best & Friedrich LLP * |
| Tilkens Mark | Constangy, Brooks & Smith, LLP (ONP)[†] |

*\* Indicates firm / individual with profile.*

*[†]ONP = Other Notable Practitioner.*

## Labor & Employment:
### Employee Benefits & Compensation
### Leading Individuals

**Band 1**

| | |
|---|---|
| Olson David P | Quarles & Brady LLP * |
| Rothacker Robert D | Quarles & Brady LLP * |
| Stevens Charles P | Michael Best & Friedrich LLP * |

## Labor & Employment: Immigration
### Leading Individuals

**Band 1**

| | |
|---|---|
| Hochstatter Tom | Hochstatter, McCarthy, Rivas (ONP)[†] |
| Olivieri José A | Michael Best & Friedrich LLP * |

**Band 2**

| | |
|---|---|
| Sovern Grant S | Quarles & Brady LLP * |

---

employment issues, including civil rights litigation and labor arbitrations. Sources say: *"He does a great job and is well regarded by his clients."* **Grant Sovern** (see p.2586) is singled out as an *"excellent"* labor attorney. His clients range from international research organizations to energy companies. **Michael Fischer** (see p.2582) focuses his practice on employer counseling and training, and is recommended for his FMLA and ADA expertise. He also handles contentious matters. Employment specialist **Pamela Ploor** (see p.2585) has notable experience of OFCCP matters. Clients appreciate that she *"really takes the time to get to know the organization and its culture and leadership."* Group leader **Sean Scullen** (see p.2586) has a strong track record of handling noncompete and wage and hour matters. He also defends employers against discrimination claims.

### Band 2

## Foley & Lardner LLP
See profile on p.2588

**THE FIRM** This well-respected group counsels clients on a broad range of labor and employment issues, and has notable experience of ERISA, FMLA, wage and hour, immigration, OSHA and discrimination matters. The team has a distinguished litigation practice at trial and appellate levels, and has been engaged to act for Nestlé in its challenge to the 2011 NLRB ruling on the scope of units organized by unions. Other recent clients include Kraft, Spectrum Brands and Harley-Davidson.

**Sources say:** *"They really work at partnering with our company. You feel like you get individualized attention rather than a cookie-cutter approach."*

**KEY INDIVIDUALS** *"Top-drawer"* attorney **Bernard Bobber** is considered *"a highly credentialed labor attorney and very respected."* He anchored the team's aforementioned work for Nestlé. Clients report that **Daniel Kaplan** *"truly understands OSHA and how it operates."* He is a respected employment litigator and recently handled a wage and hour class action on behalf of Kraft Foods Global. *"Strong practitioner"* **Thomas Pence** handles a variety of labor and employment issues, including labor negotiations, ADA and FMLA matters. Clients report that he is *"practical and able to work towards realistic solutions."*

### Band 3

## Godfrey & Kahn, SC
See profile on p.2590

**THE FIRM** Godfrey & Kahn has a diverse labor and employment practice, with an emphasis on high risk litigation, the healthcare sector and issues arising from corporate transactions. It has considerable experience of handling discrimination, OSHA, FLSA, restrictive covenant and wage and hour matters. Notable clients include Kimberly-Clark, ManpowerGroup and Mercy Health System.

**Sources say:** *"Very good! Knowledgeable and able to provide common-sense solutions and guidance."*

**KEY INDIVIDUALS** **Christine Liu McLaughlin** devotes her practice to employment law. She is particularly active in the transactional and OFCCP arenas.

## Reinhart Boerner Van Deuren s.c.
See profile on p.2594

**THE FIRM** This firm handles a range of labor and employment matters, including discrimination, immigration, FMLA and trade secret issues. The group recently prevailed in the Illinois Supreme Court on behalf of Reliable Fire Equipment Company, securing a judgment that redefined the standard that state courts must apply to the enforceability of restrictive covenants. Other clients include Milliman, Mercury Marine and KishHealth System.

**Sources say:** *"They are very thorough and their responses give us a lot of insight and options."*

**KEY INDIVIDUALS** Clients report that **Robert Sholl** (see p.2586) is *"good at showing different perspectives."* He has a strong reputation for handling a wide variety of labor and employment matters. **Lynn Stathas** (see p.2586) is recognized for her employment litigation practice. Her experience encompasses discrimination, wage and hour, whistleblower and noncompete issues.

### Band 4

## Krukowski & Costello, S.C.

**THE FIRM** This Milwaukee labor and employment boutique represents employers in a variety of matters. It handles discrimination, FMLA, OFCCP, OSHA and employee benefit-related matters, in addition to labor arbitrations and collective bargaining. The firm has experience of advising clients from the financial, healthcare, retail and manufacturing industries.

**KEY INDIVIDUALS** **Kevin Kinney** is a notable labor specialist with broad NLRA expertise. His practice also covers a variety of employment and OSHA matters.

## Lindner & Marsack, SC
See profile on p.2591

**THE FIRM** This labor and employment boutique is based in Milwaukee. Its wide-ranging experience encompasses NLRB representation, union avoidance and collective bargaining, as well as employment discrimination, restrictive covenants, immigration and employee benefits.

**KEY INDIVIDUALS** *"Great"* attorney **Thomas Mackenzie** is a well-regarded labor lawyer with considerable experience of arbitrations and negotiations. Senior statesman **Gary Marsack** counsels clients on both labor and employment matters. His areas of focus include issues arising from corporate transactions.

## Littler Mendelson, PC
See profile on p.688

**THE FIRM** The Milwaukee office of this national labor and employment boutique is recommended for its labor negotiation, wage and hour, discrimination and ERISA expertise. The group has notable experience of FLSA matters and labor arbitrations, and is also particularly active in the area of FMLA litigation. It recently defended AT&T against a number of FMLA-related claims. Other key clients include Navistar, Assurant Health Systems and Hospira.

**Sources say:** *"They are very smart, they understand the business side of things and their work product has been excellent."*

**KEY INDIVIDUALS** Labor and employment expert **Jonathan Levine** (see p.2583) has an *"excellent reputation"* in the market. Clients say: *"He is extremely responsive and his legal advice is very pragmatic. He is very good at helping us develop strategy rather than just reporting on the law."*

Clients report that **Laura Lindner** (see p.2584) *"is super smart and absolutely knows this area of the law inside and out."* She concentrates her practice on employment and employee benefits litigation.

## Other Notable Practitioners

**Tom Hochstatter** of Hochstatter, McCarthy, Rivas & Runde SC is considered *"the dean of immigration lawyers in Wisconsin."* He is considered an expert in handling busi-

ness immigration matters. **Mark Tilkens** of Constangy, Brooks & Smith LLP is a much-praised labor counselor and litigator. He *"displays a high level of emotional intelligence and understanding of how to identify and meet my company's needs in employment and litigation matters,"* said one client.

# LITIGATION GENERAL COMMERCIAL

Commentary about individuals can be found under their firm's paragraph. If the firm has no paragraph (is not ranked) look at Other Notable Practitioners.

### Litigation: General Commercial
### Leading Firms

**Band 1**
Foley & Lardner LLP *

**Band 2**
Gass Weber Mullins LLC *
Godfrey & Kahn, SC *
Quarles & Brady LLP *

**Band 3**
Reinhart Boerner Van Deuren s.c. *
Whyte Hirschboeck Dudek S.C. *

**Band 4**
Michael Best & Friedrich LLP *
Stafford Rosenbaum LLP

## Band 1

### Foley & Lardner LLP
See profile on p.2588

**THE FIRM** Foley & Lardner's litigation group is universally acknowledged as the leading practice in Wisconsin. It is recognized for its excellence across a broad range of contentious matters and is particularly outstanding in the fields of shareholder disputes, securities litigation, and distribution and franchising issues. The team is also preeminent in the insurance arena and was called upon to represent Wisconsin's Commissioner of Insurance in the Ambac Assurance insolvency proceedings. Honda, GE Healthcare and Fiskars are among its other key clients.

**Sources say:** *"They work collaboratively to find solutions."*

**KEY INDIVIDUALS** *"Leading practitioner"* **Nancy Sennett** has a strong reputation in the area of securities litigation. She has extensive experience of acting for traders, investment advisers, corporations and individuals. **James Clark** handles professional malpractice, product liability and contractual disputes in his broad litigation practice. Clients report that he *"is very thorough, pays attention to detail, prepares exceptionally well and is aggressive, yet professional, in representing his client."* Well-regarded attorney **Thomas Shriner** is an experienced appellate, trial and bankruptcy lawyer. He also specializes in constitutional matters and recently represented Wisconsin's Republican

### Litigation: General Commercial
### Senior Statesmen

**Senior Statesmen: distinguished older practitioners**

| | |
|---|---|
| Butler Brian | *Stafford Rosenbaum LLP* |
| Levit William | *Godfrey & Kahn, SC* |

### Leading Individuals

**Band 1**

| | |
|---|---|
| Clark James R | *Foley & Lardner LLP* |
| Conley Daniel E | *Quarles & Brady LLP* * |
| Conway Gregory B | *Liebmann, Conway, Olejniczak (ONP)[†]* |
| Curtis Jr Charles G | *Arnold & Porter LLP (ONP)[†] ** |
| Hansen Scott W. | *Reinhart Boerner Van Deuren s.c. ** |
| Shriner Jr Thomas L | *Foley & Lardner LLP* |
| Weber Ralph A | *Gass Weber Mullins LLC ** |

**Band 2**

| | |
|---|---|
| McGinnity Maureen A | *Foley & Lardner LLP* |
| Sennett Nancy J | *Foley & Lardner LLP* |
| Williamson Brady C | *Godfrey & Kahn, SC* |

**Band 3**

| | |
|---|---|
| Bowen Michael A | *Foley & Lardner LLP* |
| Cameli Mark A | *Reinhart Boerner Van Deuren s.c. ** |
| Flaherty Daniel T | *Godfrey & Kahn, SC* |
| Gass J Ric | *Gass Weber Mullins LLC ** |
| Kirtley John | *Godfrey & Kahn, SC* |
| Maher Ann | *Whyte Hirschboeck Dudek S.C. ** |
| McCarthy Amelia L | *Gass Weber Mullins LLC ** |
| McGrath Brian W | *Foley & Lardner LLP* |
| O'Neill Matthew W | *Fox O'Neill & Shannon S.C. (ONP)[†]* |
| Rothstein John A | *Quarles & Brady LLP ** |
| Van Sicklen Michael B | *Foley & Lardner LLP* |
| Van Vugt Eric J | *Quarles & Brady LLP.** |

**Up-and-coming individuals**

| | |
|---|---|
| Baish Anthony S. | *Godfrey & Kahn, SC* |
| Schlinsog Allen C | *Reinhart Boerner Van Deuren s.c. ** |

* Indicates firm / individual with profile.
[†] ONP = Other Notable Practitioner.

members of the House of Representatives in defending the state legislature's redistricting process. **Maureen McGinnity** is singled out as a talented tax litigator. She recently succeeded in securing $1.2 million in property tax refunds on behalf of the Delavan Lake Taxpayers

Association. **Michael Bowen** is known for handling complex dealership disputes at trial and appellate levels. He is also well versed in lender liability and false advertising claims. **Brian McGrath** is praised for providing *"practical advice, strategy and analysis,"* with a client-oriented approach. His practice is focused on real estate, dealership and general commercial litigation. **Michael Van Sicklen** is head of the firm's Madison litigation team. He handles a range of business litigation, with a focus on bankruptcy, lender liability, and creditor's rights. Sources note that he is *"a very good litigator."*

## Band 2

### Gass Weber Mullins LLC
See profile on p.2589

**THE FIRM** This much-praised Milwaukee boutique is known for the quality of its practitioners. It fields experts in a number of niche areas, including complex personal injury and food safety litigation, and has a strong reputation for handling a range of challenging commercial disputes. The group recently secured $50 million damages for Aqua Finance in a high-profile professional negligence claim against accounting firm Baker Tilly. Other notable clients include Coca-Cola, Cargill and Humana.

**Sources say:** *"They were outstanding. They were extremely diligent in preparation and very good in both their written and oral arguments."*

**KEY INDIVIDUALS** Ralph Weber (see p.2587) is an *"outstanding"* practitioner in the fields of complex commercial and tort litigation. Clients admire his *"persuasive ability,"* *"calm demeanor"* and *"command of a courtroom."* **Ric Gass** (see p.2582) is another well-respected attorney, and devotes his practice to insurance defense litigation. He recently represented the County of Maui, Hawaii, in a case claiming $1 million in damages following a death in custody. Clients describe *"strong advocate"* **Amelia McCarthy** (see p.2584) as *"very smart, very diligent and tenacious."* Her practice is focused on general commercial and product liability litigation.

## Godfrey & Kahn, SC
See profile on p.2590

THE FIRM This diverse practice is well equipped to assist with a broad range of contentious matters, including corporate governance, financial services and tort litigation, and is particularly recommended for handling insurance coverage disputes. The group recently defended Wells Fargo in a $7.7 million breach of fiduciary duty case. Other clients include Marshall & Isley, Kimberly-Clark and Liberty Mutual.

Sources say: "They are very skilled and have great expertise in insurance."

KEY INDIVIDUALS Experienced practitioner **Brady Williamson** is known for his bankruptcy and restructuring expertise. He is also a distinguished constitutional litigator, and recently represented a group of 23 citizens in a complaint that the redistricting of Wisconsin violated the state constitution. Co-head of the firm's litigation group **Daniel Flaherty** has distinguished himself in the fields of white-collar criminal defense and IP litigation. **John Kirtley** is another well-respected attorney. He chairs the firm's financial services litigation group and receives praise for his adept handling of depositions. He played a leading role in the aforementioned matter for Wells Fargo. Senior statesman **William Levit** is known as an experienced and talented litigator. He has a broad practice encompassing antitrust, insurance and securities matters. Rising star **Anthony Baish** is characterized by clients as "smart and thoughtful." He handles a range of complex commercial disputes and is particularly active in the area of IP litigation.

## Quarles & Brady LLP
See profile on p.2593

THE FIRM This firm acts for clients in a variety of commercial disputes, with a heavy emphasis on product liability issues. It also has considerable class action experience and recently defended Harley-Davidson in a $230 million punitive class action concerning allegations of instability in a class of motorcycles. Other active clients include Bank of America, Menasha and agricultural manufacturer CNH.

Sources say: "Each of the lawyers I have worked with is talented, efficient and client-focused."

KEY INDIVIDUALS **Daniel Conley** (see p.2581) is described by sources as "a very good lawyer." He has a wide-ranging business litigation practice, with a strong focus on class action defense. **John Rothstein** (see p.2586) has distinguished himself in the fields of corporate disputes and

product liability litigation. He is experienced at both trial and appellate level. **Eric Van Vugt** (see p.2587) is also highly regarded. He concentrates his practice on insurance coverage, product liability and professional negligence litigation.

## Band 3

### Reinhart Boerner Van Deuren s.c.
See profile on p.2594

THE FIRM This well-respected group handles a wide range of commercial litigation, including white-collar, ERISA, insurance, fiduciary and securities matters. It has significant experience in the product liability arena and recently defended Cargotec in relation to a high-value series of product liability claims. Other key clients include Milliman, SC Johnson and Harley-Davidson.

Sources say: "They are diligent and tireless."

KEY INDIVIDUALS The highly regarded **Scott Hansen** (see p.2583) is praised by clients for "consistently delivering outstanding results." He handles a broad range of complex litigation, including disputes relating to trade secrets, antitrust and breach of contract. Clients value **Mark Cameli**'s (see p.2581) ability to offer "practical solutions to problems large and small." He leads the firm's white-collar litigation and corporate compliance team. **Allen Schlinsog** (see p.2586) is recognized as an up-and-coming product liability expert. Clients identify him as someone who is committed to understanding the unique issues of every case he handles.

### Whyte Hirschboeck Dudek S.C.
See profile on p.2595

THE FIRM This 40-strong team has offices in Milwaukee and Madison, and has experience of litigating a broad spectrum of contentious matters, including IP, white-collar crime, bankruptcy, product liability, professional liability and insurance coverage. It recently acted for Enbridge Energy on a dispute concerning the remediation of property following the construction of an oil pipeline.

Sources say: "They are extremely thorough and are very prepared for court hearings."

KEY INDIVIDUALS Well-respected attorney **Ann Maher** (see p.2584) focuses her practice on antitrust, distribution and dealership litigation.

## Band 4

### Michael Best & Friedrich LLP
See profile on p.2592

THE FIRM This group provides representation in a wide range of commercial litigation. Its experience includes false advertising, electoral redistricting and securities litigation. The team has also handled class actions and recently defended National Presto Industries in a nationwide class action concerning allegations of false advertising. Other notable clients include TTi Power Tools and Harley-Davidson.

Sources say: "They did a very good job of explaining the process, legal reasoning and prospects of success at a grass roots level."

KEY INDIVIDUALS Daniel Vaccaro is a key contact at the firm.

### Stafford Rosenbaum LLP

THE FIRM Stafford Rosenbaum's litigators advise clients from offices in Madison and Milwaukee. The group has a diverse practice, covering general business litigation, franchise and dealership issues, product liability, utilities, insurance coverage and shareholder disputes.

KEY INDIVIDUALS Senior statesman **Brian Butler** has distinguished himself in the fields of antitrust, business torts and dealership litigation. He also acts as an arbitrator of commercial disputes.

### Other Notable Practitioners

"Powerful advocate" **Charles Curtis** (see p.2582) of Arnold & Porter LLP receives glowing praise from peers, who describe him as an "excellent counselor" and an "extraordinarily good writer and researcher." He is widely regarded as one of the state's leading authorities on Native American law. **Gregory Conway** of Liebmann, Conway, Olejniczak & Jerry SC has an excellent reputation in the fields of personal injury and general commercial litigation. Sources praise him as "a very good lawyer." **Matthew O'Neill** of Fox O'Neill & Shannon SC is an experienced and respected attorney. He handles a range of complex commercial litigation and has a notable appellate practice.

# NATURAL RESOURCES & ENVIRONMENT

Commentary about individuals can be found under their firm's paragraph. If the firm has no paragraph (is not ranked) look at Other Notable Practitioners.

## Natural Resources & Environment

### Leading Firms

**Band 1**

Foley & Lardner LLP *

Quarles & Brady LLP *

**Band 2**

DeWitt Ross & Stevens SC

Godfrey & Kahn, SC *

Michael Best & Friedrich LLP *

Reinhart Boerner Van Deuren s.c. *

Whyte Hirschboeck Dudek S.C. *

### Senior Statesmen

**Senior Statesmen: distinguished older practitioners**

| | |
|---|---|
| Peshek Peter | DeWitt Ross & Stevens SC |

### Leading Individuals

**Band 1**

| | |
|---|---|
| Benfield Linda E | Foley & Lardner LLP |
| Bochert Linda | Michael Best & Friedrich LLP * |
| Harrington Arthur | Godfrey & Kahn, SC |
| Kent Paul | Stafford Rosenbaum LLP (ONP)† |
| McCauley Michael S | Quarles & Brady LLP * |
| Palmer Todd | Michael Best & Friedrich LLP * |
| Thimke Mark | Foley & Lardner LLP |
| Vogel, Jr Arthur A | Quarles & Brady LLP * |

**Band 2**

| | |
|---|---|
| Buzecky Jennifer | Whyte Hirschboeck Dudek S.C. * |
| Carlton Michael P | von Briesen & Roper SC (ONP)† |
| Gallo Donald P | Reinhart Boerner Van Deuren sc * |
| Grzezinski Dennis | Dennis Grzezinski (ONP)† |
| Handzel Henry | DeWitt Ross & Stevens SC |
| McElligott Thomas P | Quarles & Brady LLP * |
| Peterson Nancy K | Quarles & Brady LLP * |
| Van Lieshout John M | Reinhart Boerner Van Deuren s.c. * |
| Witte Edward | Gonzalez Saggio & Harlan LLP (ONP)† |

**Band 3**

| | |
|---|---|
| Flanagan Mike | Foley & Lardner LLP |
| Simpson Michael H | Reinhart Boerner Van Deuren s.c. * |
| Tomasi Peter | Quarles & Brady LLP * |

**Up-and-coming individuals**

| | |
|---|---|
| Potts Brian H. | Foley & Lardner LLP |

\* Indicates firm / individual with profile.

†ONP = Other Notable Practitioner.

## Band 1

### Foley & Lardner LLP

See profile on p.2588

**THE FIRM** Foley & Lardner's environmental regulation team has an excellent reputation in Wisconsin. It handles a diverse range of environmental matters and has notable experience in the fields of compliance and enforcement, redevelopment and remediation, due diligence and insurance-related matters. The group was recently called upon to represent an intervening party in the State of Minnesota v 3M river pollution litigation. In the past year, it has also acted for Buckeye, Maxus Energy and Winsert.

**KEY INDIVIDUALS** Managing partner of the Wisconsin office **Linda Benfield** is an experienced environmental litigator. She is well versed in permitting and compliance disputes. "*Top air attorney*" **Mark Thimke** is admired by clients for his environmental knowledge and diplomatic approach to negotiations. He is also sought after to advise on major remediation projects. **Brian Potts** is singled out as one of Wisconsin's up-and-coming environmental lawyers. He deals with a range of compliance and enforcement issues, in addition to contentious matters. **Mike Flanagan** is also well respected in the market. He advises clients on compliance and due diligence, as well as handling related litigation.

### Quarles & Brady LLP

See profile on p.2593

**THE FIRM** Quarles & Brady benefits from one of Wisconsin's premier environment and energy practices. It has extensive experience of a variety of matters, with a focus in the areas of electrical utilities, historic remediation and natural resources. The group is particularly known for its water expertise and recently engaged by the Lake Carriers' Association to advise on the development of the regulation of ballast water discharges. Other key clients include Domtar, MillerCoors and Rexnord.

**Sources say:** "*Outstanding – good legal knowledge, good depth and very sensitive to clients' concerns.*"

**KEY INDIVIDUALS Michael McCauley** (see p.2584) is recognized as a leading air permitting and compliance expert. **Arthur Vogel** (see p.2587) is considered a "*leading attorney for waste issues.*" Clients characterize him as "*a strong, technical environmental lawyer with precise attention to detail.*" Clients describe **Thomas McElligott** (see p.2584) as "*very knowledgeable, with the seasoned ability to create solutions to complex matters.*" He has a broad environmental practice, which encompasses litigation and permitting issues. "*Terrific*" practitioner **Nancy Peterson** (see p.2585) handles compliance, litigation and crisis management. Clients report that she has "*an innate ability to stay focused on a successful outcome*" and "*does an A-plus job in court.*" **Peter Tomasi** (see p.2587) is another key player at the firm. His practice comprises of litigation and permitting work, and he has significant experience with air permitting and environmental impact assessments.

## Band 2

### DeWitt Ross & Stevens SC

**THE FIRM** This well-regarded group is equipped to advise on a broad range of environmental matters. It is particularly knowledgeable about regulatory issues relating to the mining of iron ore and sand for the purposes of fracking. The group is also active in the areas of renewable energy and environmental litigation. It has offices in Milwaukee and Madison.

**KEY INDIVIDUALS Henry Handzel** continues to be recognized for his air regulation expertise. Senior statesman **Peter Peshek** is noted for his extensive experience of governmental relations. Recent work highlights include advising on significant litigation relating to the CWA.

### Godfrey & Kahn, SC

See profile on p.2590

**THE FIRM** This firm is particularly known for its work in the areas of energy law and environmental issues arising from corporate transactions. It also has significant experience with air and solid waste permitting, environmental due diligence, renewable energy projects, urban redevelopment and general environmental compliance counseling. The group recently advised Domtar on its intervention in support of a $250 million cogeneration facility. Other notable clients include the Forest County Potawatomi Community, Kohl's Department Stores and Johnson Controls.

**KEY INDIVIDUALS** Chair of the firm's environmental and energy practice, **Arthur Harrington** is particularly active in the areas of brownfield redevelopment and environmental contamination.

### Michael Best & Friedrich LLP

See profile on p.2592

**THE FIRM** This multiservice practice is particularly active in the fields of water law, air emissions, toxic torts and the defense of enforcement actions and class action law suits. The group has significant clients in the utilities, agricultural and food industries, and serves as general counsel to the Wisconsin Paper Council. It is also noted for its renewable energy expertise.

**KEY INDIVIDUALS Linda Bochert** (see p.2581) focuses her practice on regulatory matters and is noted for her experience of permitting, zoning and enforcement issues. **Todd Palmer** (see p.2585) is considered a leading expert on air-related matters.

### Reinhart Boerner Van Deuren s.c.

See profile on p.2594

**THE FIRM** This group is well versed in a range of environmental matters, encompassing compliance, permitting, due diligence and remediation. Recent work highlights include advising Green Whey Energy on a $29 million anaerobic digester and waste treatment project. It has also recently acted for Advanced Waste Services, Waukesha Water Utility and the Polyurethane Manufacturers Association. The team is also recommended for its environmental litigation capabilities.

**Sources say:** "*Their responsiveness is outstanding.*"

KEY INDIVIDUALS **Donald Gallo** (see p.2582) is an environmental expert and recently advised the City of Waukesha on its application for the diversion and return flow of the Great Lakes water supply. Clients admire his *"creative"* arguments and *"cool, calm, collected"* approach. Clients describe **John Van Lieshout** (see p.2587) as *"very attentive, very responsive and very knowledgeable."* He focuses his environmental practice on issues relating to real estate. *"Fantastic"* attorney **Michael Simpson** (see p.2586) has notable experience of enforcement defense litigation and land use issues. Clients value the way *"he makes sure all angles of an issue are thought through thoroughly."*

## Whyte Hirschboeck Dudek S.C.
See profile on p.2595

THE FIRM This group is recommended for its ongoing compliance counseling. It also has experience of handling the environmental aspects of corporate transactions within the natural resources sector, including environmental due diligence and permit transfers. In addition to this, the team is active in the area of permitting, and is well equipped to advise clients on permit applications and related defense litigation.

KEY INDIVIDUALS Clients characterize **Jennifer Buzecky** (see p.2581) as an *"extremely helpful,"* *"proactive"* counselor. She has a broad practice, which encompasses compliance, permitting, utilities and renewable energy projects.

## Other Notable Practitioners

*"Outstanding"* practitioner **Paul Kent** of Stafford Rosenbaum LLP is viewed as one of Wisconsin's top water attorneys and is an expert on wetland issues. **Michael Carlton** is chair of the environmental practice at von Briesen & Roper SC and is called upon to handle both regulatory litigation and transactional matters. He has wide-ranging experience of issues relating to air, water, waste and wetlands. Sole practitioner **Dennis Grzezinski** is best known for representing governmental entities and environmental organizations in public interest litigation. **Edward Witte** of Gonzalez Saggio & Harlan LLP is a notable environmental practitioner, with extensive experience with compliance, due diligence and transactional matters.

# REAL ESTATE

Commentary about individuals can be found under their firm's paragraph. If the firm has no paragraph (is not ranked) look at Other Notable Practitioners.

| Real Estate |
|---|
| **Leading Firms** |
| **Band 1** |
| Foley & Lardner LLP * |
| Quarles & Brady LLP * |
| Reinhart Boerner Van Deuren s.c. * |
| **Band 2** |
| Godfrey & Kahn, SC * |
| Whyte Hirschboeck Dudek S.C. * |
| **Band 3** |
| Davis & Kuelthau, SC |
| Michael Best & Friedrich LLP * |

| Real Estate | |
|---|---|
| **Senior Statesmen** | |
| Senior Statesmen: distinguished older practitioners | |
| Marcuvitz Alan H | *Michael Best & Friedrich LLP* * |
| **Leading Individuals** | |
| **Band 1** | |
| Block Bruce T | *Reinhart Boerner Van Deuren s.c.* * |
| Chernof Steve | *Godfrey & Kahn, SC* |
| Dwyer Michael | *Godfrey & Kahn, SC* |
| Hatch Michael W | *Foley & Lardner LLP* |
| Ishikawa Jesse S | *Reinhart Boerner Van Deuren sc* * |
| **Band 2** | |
| Dallet Bradley I | *Whyte Hirschboeck Dudek S.C.* * |
| Jelencic Sarah O | *Foley & Lardner LLP* |
| Karas Hal | *Whyte Hirschboeck Dudek S.C.* * |
| Ostermeyer Michael J | *Quarles & Brady LLP* * |
| Puchner Joseph E | *Quarles & Brady LLP* * |
| Tomczyk Deborah C | *Reinhart Boerner Van Deuren s.c.* * |
| **Band 3** | |
| Comer Ann K | *Quarles & Brady LLP* * |
| Delorey Kevin A | *Quarles & Brady LLP* * |
| Hoffman Nathaniel A | *Whyte Hirschboeck Dudek S.C.* * |
| Langlois Scott L | *Quarles & Brady LLP* * |
| O'Halloran Hugh J | *Foley & Lardner LLP* |
| Richards Dean B | *Reinhart Boerner Van Deuren sc* * |
| Roge Bret A | *Michael Best & Friedrich LLP* * |
| Temkin Harvey L | *Reinhart Boerner Van Deuren sc* * |
| **Associates to watch** | |
| Mitch Rebecca H | *Whyte Hirschboeck Dudek S.C.* * |

\* Indicates firm / individual with profile.
Alphabetical order within each band. Band 1 is the highest.

## Band 1

### Foley & Lardner LLP
See profile on p.2588

THE FIRM This highly regarded firm has an excellent reputation across a broad spectrum of real estate matters, with a strong focus on financing. Its expertise includes acquisitions, economic development incentives and troubled loan workouts. The group recently advised Marcus Corporation on the tax incremental financing of a $150 million shopping center development in Brookfield, Wisconsin. The group has also provided real estate counsel to U.S. Bancorp, Mandel Group and Van Buren Management.
Sources say: *"They are very talented and knowledgeable."*
KEY INDIVIDUALS Finance specialist **Sarah Jelencic** impresses clients with her diligent approach. She has notable experience of handling New Markets Tax Credits and multi-tiered financings. **Hugh O'Halloran** is another key player at the firm. He is particularly active in the sphere of economic development incentives and has notable experience of handling golf course developments. **Michael Hatch** was engaged to act as lead counsel to Marcus Corporation on the development described above. Clients report that he *"brings a strong, knowledgeable, practical and experienced perspective to his work."*

### Quarles & Brady LLP
See profile on p.2593

THE FIRM This much-admired group is eminently well equipped to advise on a wide variety of real estate matters, with a particular emphasis on complex development and financing issues. It regularly represents corporate and healthcare clients, and recently acted for Baker Tilly Virchow Krause on the multimillion-dollar lease of an office building in Milwaukee. Other key clients include the Wisconsin Alumni Research Foundation, Canyon Capital Partners and JPMorgan Chase.
Sources say: *"Absolutely fantastic to work with."*
KEY INDIVIDUALS **Michael Ostermeyer** (see p.2585) is singled out for his *"solution-oriented"* approach. He was recently engaged to act for Marcus Center on the PPP and project development of a mixed-use arts facility. Well-regarded attorney **Joseph Puchner** (see p.2585) focuses his practice on commercial real estate development. He is particularly active within the energy sector, and recently represented Wisconsin Electric Power Company in the development of a $250 million biomass-fueled power facility. **Ann Comer** (see p.2581) is another key player at the firm. She has extensive experience in a range of issues relating to real estate financing and tax credits. **Kevin Delorey** (see p.2582) has a strong reputation in the Wisconsin market. He has considerable construction-related expertise and is regularly called upon to handle development projects with significant construction components. Clients report that **Scott Langlois** (see p.2583) is *"absolutely amazing"* at keeping them up to date and *"provides a very good work product."* He is sought after to handle office building leases, and acted for Baker Tilly on the matter described above.

### Reinhart Boerner Van Deuren s.c.
See profile on p.2594

THE FIRM This highly esteemed firm is well versed in a broad range of real estate matters. Its impressive development and financing activities are complemented by its specialist expertise in zoning and land use, economic development incentives and PPPs. The group was recently engaged to advise Kohl's on the multimillion-dollar development of its new head office. Other key clients include Opus Development, the University of Wisconsin Milwaukee Real Estate Foundation and commercial contractor J.H. Findorff & Son.

Sources say: *"A very high-quality, professional-oriented firm."*

KEY INDIVIDUALS Bruce Block (see p.2581) is considered one of Milwaukee's top real estate practitioners. Clients report that he is *"exceptionally knowledgeable about the substantive law and extremely practical."* Jesse Ishikawa (see p.2583) is also viewed as a leading real estate attorney in Wisconsin. He is recognized for his land use, tax incremental financing and condominium expertise. Clients praise Deborah Tomczyk's (see p.2587) knowledge, pragmatism and client-focused approach. Her practice focuses on zoning and land use. Harvey Temkin (see p.2587) is another prominent individual in the practice. He handles a range of real estate financing matters and is noted for his tax expertise. Dean Richards (see p.2585) is known for his extensive experience of zoning and land use issues. Clients say he is *"extremely knowledgeable in real estate law,"* and value his *"excellent negotiation skills."*

## Band 2

### Godfrey & Kahn, SC
See profile on p.2590

THE FIRM This Wisconsin firm is recognized as having a strong real estate practice. It has wide-ranging experience of a variety of real estate issues, including acquisition, financing and contentious matters. It is particularly active in the area of leasing, and recently represented Clysmic Properties in the tax-exempt financing and lease negotiation relating to a student housing development. The team has also provided real estate counsel to BMO Harris Bank, Kaufman Jacobs and the Livesey Company.

Sources say: *"They have been thorough and responsive in every case, and have always maintained excellent communication."*

KEY INDIVIDUALS Eminent practitioner Steve Chernof has extensive experience across a broad range of real estate matters. Clients observe that *"he has a unique ability to pick up on the most minute and nuanced details of a deal structure."* Clients report that Michael Dwyer is *"very intelligent and a very hard worker."* He focuses his practice on development and leasing, and was lead counsel to Clysmic in the matter described above.

### Whyte Hirschboeck Dudek S.C.
See profile on p.2595

THE FIRM This well-respected group advises clients on a wide range of real estate matters. It is regularly called upon to advise on development issues, with a particular focus on economic incentives, including New Markets Tax Credits and Low Income Housing Tax Credits. Clients include Greywolf Partners and Roundy's Supermarkets.

Sources say: *"They bring a very good business sense to the table. They understand where the risks and where the rewards are."*

KEY INDIVIDUALS Impressed clients observe that Bradley Dallet (see p.2582) *"is very practical and understands our company and needs well."* He has a broad practice, which encompasses development, financing and leasing. Hal Karas (see p.2583) is regularly engaged to advise on development projects involving complex financing and tax credits. Clients describe him as *"exceptional, both as an attorney and as a business adviser."* Associate to watch Rebecca Mitich (see p.2584) is reported to be *"very helpful and very pleasant to work with."* She recently assisted in the representation of River Vision Partnership in connection to a multi-use development. *"Top-notch"* attorney Nathaniel Hoffman (see p.2583) continues to be recognized for his leasing expertise. His recent experience includes retail, residential, offices and business premises.

## Band 3

### Davis & Kuelthau, SC

THE FIRM This Wisconsin firm is known for representing local developers in the acquisition, financing, developing and leasing of real estate projects. It is particularly active in the healthcare arena and recently advised Hammes Company on a multimillion-dollar hospital office development. Other notable clients include Fiduciary Real Estate Development and Continental Properties.

Sources say: *"Good quality lawyers."*

KEY INDIVIDUALS Timothy Kronquist chairs the firm's real estate department.

### Michael Best & Friedrich LLP
See profile on p.2592

THE FIRM This practice places a particular emphasis on development, financing and land use. It has significant experience of advising on acquisitions, tax credits and land use issues, and recently acted for Gebhardt Development on a redevelopment project involving incremental tax financing, New Markets Tax Credits and other economic development incentives. In the past year, it has also provided real estate counsel to ABS Global, ACCO Brands and Andis.

KEY INDIVIDUALS Clients describe Bret Roge (see p.2586) as a *"very smart"* attorney who *"gives great advice."* He is noted for his transactional practice. Senior statesman Alan Marcuvitz (see p.2584) has an excellent reputation in Wisconsin for his eminent domain and tax appeal expertise.

# Leaders' Profiles in Wisconsin

## AUSTIN, Christopher B
Michael Best & Friedrich LLP, Milwaukee
414 225 8266
cbaustin@michaelbest.com
*Featured in Intellectual Property (Wisconsin)*

**Practice Areas:** Chris Austin focuses his practice on intellectual property with an emphasis on domestic and international patent matters relating to mechanical, electro-mechanical, medical, materials science, software, and business method technologies. He also helps clients acquire and enforce United States and foreign trademark rights, copyrights and trade secrets, negotiates intellectual property licenses and technology transfers and prepares patentability and non-infringement opinions. His work applies strategic planning to intellectual property protection to help clients achieve their business goals.

## BAKER, Jean C
Quarles & Brady LLP, Milwaukee
414 277 5709
jean.baker@quarles.com
*Featured in Intellectual Property (Wisconsin)*

**Practice Areas:** Intellectual property.
**Professional Memberships:** State Bar of Wisconsin (elected Board Member of Intellectual Property Section, 2000-present; elected Vice-Chairman, 2002-03, Chairman, 2003-04); Wisconsin Intellectual Property Law Association (Secretary-Treasurer, 1995-97; President, 1997-98).
**Career:** Partner since 1999. Head of Quarles & Brady IP Group since 2007.
**Personal:** University of Wisconsin (JD, with honors, 1990); University of Georgia (PhD, 1987; BS, 1979).

## BEDORE, James M
Reinhart Boerner Van Deuren s.c., Milwaukee
414 298 8196
jbedore@reinhartlaw.com
*Featured in Corporate/M&A (Wisconsin)*

**Practice Areas:** Corporate/M&A, securities and corporate governance.
**Professional Memberships:** State Bar of Wisconsin, Securities Law Committee Member; Society of Corporate Secetaries and Governance Professionals, Securities Law Committee.
**Career:** Shareholder who works with corporate clients and in-house counsel to manage daily corporate, transactional and securities law needs, including mergers and acquisitions, takeover defense, public securities offerings, private placements, corporate governance and preparing and filing quarterly and annual reports, proxy statements and other filings required by the SEC. Works with clients on executive compensation, strategic planning and general corporate issues. Frequently advises Special Committees in various types of transactions or investigations.

## BEIGHTOL, Scott C
Michael Best & Friedrich LLP, Milwaukee
414 225 4994
scbeightol@michaelbest.com
*Featured in Labor & Employment (Wisconsin)*

**Practice Areas:** Scott Beightol is Chairman of Michael Best's Management Committee. He represents businesses in all aspects of employment/labor relations, focusing on litigation of discrimination, non-compete and other matters before federal and state courts, the NLRB, the OFCCP, and arbitrators. He has obtained multiple verdicts in jury and bench trials in various federal and state courts. Mr Beightol counsels clients on workforce structure, HR audits and best practices, complex termination and disability, FMLA matters, union avoidance, and union relation matters involving labor negotiations and arbitrations. He has experience representing national businesses in industries including manufacturing, transportation, paper, financial and healthcare.

### BERSON, Bennett J
Quarles & Brady LLP, Madison
608 283 2418
bennett.berson@quarles.com
*Featured in Intellectual Property (Wisconsin)*
**Practice Areas:** Intellectual property (patent and trademark) prosecution and litigation relating principally to health and life sciences, biotechnology, embryonic and induced pluripotent stem cells, bioinformatics, biofuels, clean energy, medical devices
**Professional Memberships:** American Bar Association, IP Section; Member, State Bar of Wisconsin, IP Section; American Intellectual Property Law Association; International Trademark Association.
**Career:** Counsels clients in leading-edge fields on a full range of intellectual property issues; obtains, manages, and enforces large patent and trademark portfolios.
**Personal:** University of Wisconsin Law School (JD, cum laude); University of Wisconsin (MS, Oncology/molecular retrovirology); Haverford College (BS, Biology, molecular).

### BEST, J Donald
Michael Best & Friedrich LLP, Madison
608 283 2272
jdbest@michaelbest.com
*Featured in Intellectual Property (Wisconsin)*
**Practice Areas:** Don Best is a trial lawyer with over 20 years of experience handling complex, high profile IP cases representing national and international businesses in diverse industry sectors. Mr Best has extensive trial, arbitration and mediation experience, including matters involving patents, trade secrets and trademarks. His practice includes providing IP counseling and litigation services to clients in highly technical fields involving mechanical arts, biotechnology, telecommunications, electronics, pharmaceuticals, computer products, chemical processing, medical devices, and commercial products. He also frequently counsels clients on IP matters in Europe and Asia.

### BLOCK, Bruce T
Reinhart Boerner Van Deuren s.c., Milwaukee
414 298 8130
bblock@reinhartlaw.com
*Featured in Real Estate (Wisconsin)*
**Practice Areas:** Real estate.
**Professional Memberships:** American College of Real Estate Lawyers, Member since 1992; Wisconsin State Bar, eight years as Construction and Public Law Section Board Member.
**Career:** Real Estate Practice Chair who represents private developers and investors, institutional developers and investors, lenders, municipalities and community development authorities. Bruce's contacts in all sectors contribute to his ability to navigate complex transactions to successful and creative conclusions.
**Personal:** UWM Real Estate Foundation, Chairman; National Trust Community

Investment Corporation, Board Member and Investment Committee Chair; Greater Milwaukee Committee, Member; Wisconsin Preservation Fund, Inc., President; Froedtert Hospital Foundation, Chairman.

### BOCHERT, Linda
Michael Best & Friedrich LLP, Milwaukee
608 283 2271
lhbochert@michaelbest.com
*Featured in Natural Resources (Wisconsin)*
**Practice Areas:** Linda Bochert is a partner in the Land and Resources Group, focusing on environmental law. Prior to joining the firm, she served 17 years in state government with the Departments of Natural Resources and Justice. Her practice includes wastewater and air permitting; stormwater, wetlands and navigable waters regulation; landfill, pipeline, transmission line, wind farm and power plant siting. She co-chairs the firm's Sustainability Initiative, and is the current Chair of the Dean's Advisory Council at UW-Stevens Point College of Natural Resources, a DNR Green Tier Advisor, and a Founding Regent of the American College of Environmental Lawyers.

### BUONO, Kathryn M
Quarles & Brady LLP, Milwaukee
414 277 5109
kathie.buono@quarles.com
*Featured in Corporate/M&A (Wisconsin)*
**Practice Areas:** Mergers and acquisitions, private equity and general corporate services.
**Professional Memberships:** Milwaukee Bar Association; American Bar Association; State Bar of Wisconsin; Association for Corporate Growth; Marquette Law School Alumni Board.
**Career:** Corporate partner since 1995. Has represented both buyers and sellers, strategic and financial, in dozens of acquisition and divestiture transactions, principally in manufacturing and service businesses. Also works with institutional and individual investors with regard to private equity investment transactions.
**Personal:** Marquette University (JD, 1986); University of Dayton (BS, 1983).

### BURNETT, Lawrence J
Reinhart Boerner Van Deuren s.c., Milwaukee
414 298 8175
lburnett@reinhartlaw.com
*Featured in Corporate/M&A (Wisconsin)*
**Practice Areas:** Corporate law.
**Professional Memberships:** Milwaukee Bar Association, State Bar of Wisconsin.
**Career:** Lawrence Burnett is a shareholder who provides counsel on business matters relating to mergers, acquisitions and corporate finance. Larry has a talent for corporate finance and identifying and solving capital needs problems. He has structured highly creative deals to help clients achieve their business goals with maximum financial efficiency and minimum legal and business headaches. Larry functions as a member of his clients' upper management teams, identifying and preempting difficulties and providing timely guid-

ance to protect their interests and maximize their bottom line.

### BUZECKY, Jennifer
Whyte Hirschboeck Dudek S.C., Milwaukee
414 978 5749
jbuzecky@whdlaw.com
*Featured in Natural Resources (Wisconsin)*
**Practice Areas:** Environmental (air permitting, regulatory compliance, transactional risk assessment, remediation and brownfields development, mobile sources, solid and hazardous waste, wetlands and waterways, state and federal enforcement), endangered and cultural resources, energy and public utilities (state and federal permits and authorizations), sustainability and renewable energy.
**Professional Memberships:** State Bar of Wisconsin, Milwaukee Bar Association, Federation of Environmental Technologists, Air and Waste Management Association, American Bar Association Section of Environment, Energy and Resources.
**Career:** 1992-95 US Environmental Protection Agency (air permit program); 1995-present, Whyte Hirschboeck Dudek S.C.
**Personal:** University of Wisconsin-Madison, Loyola University Chicago School of Law.

### CAMELI, Mark A
Reinhart Boerner Van Deuren s.c., Milwaukee
414 298 8155
mcameli@reinhartlaw.com
*Featured in Litigation (Wisconsin)*
**Practice Areas:** Complex commercial and white collar criminal litigation.
**Professional Memberships:** State Bar of Wisconsin; United States District Court for the Eastern and Western Districts of Wisconsin (Past President of the Western District Bar Association; Board of Governors Eastern District Bar Association); United States Court of Appeals for the Seventh Circuit; Past President and Board of Directors, Wisconsin Justinian Society of Lawyers.
**Career:** Former Assistant United States Attorney, Criminal Division; Chief, Civil Division; substantial trial and federal appellate experience; Clients include manufacturing, health care, and government contracting sectors; Co-Counseled 2008 civil fraud prosecution leading to largest verdict in Wisconsin's history.

### CARTER, Eugenia
Whyte Hirschboeck Dudek S.C., Madison
608 234 6058
gcarter@whdlaw.com
*Featured in Intellectual Property (Wisconsin)*
**Career:** Gina Carter is a shareholder at WHD where she leads the Intellectual Property Counseling and Protection Team. She represents a wide array of clients, including high technology and computer software companies, on-line retailers and manufacturers, in all aspects of intellectual property law protection and rights enforcement. She has litigated patent, trademark, copyright, and trade secret cases in federal trial and appeals courts across the country. She also counsels and litigates in the area of unfair advertising and com-

petition. She has been a Chambers designated lawyer since 2005. She received her JD from Georgetown University with honors.

### COMER, Ann K
Quarles & Brady LLP, Milwaukee
414 277 5509
ann.comer@quarles.com
*Featured in Real Estate (Wisconsin)*
**Practice Areas:** Real estate and commercial finance, project finance, real estate, tax credit (low-income housing and new markets).
**Professional Memberships:** State Bar of Wisconsin and State Bar of Michigan; Fellow, American College of Mortgage Attorneys.
**Career:** Partner since 1996.
**Personal:** University of Wisconsin (JD, 1983); Marquette University (BA, 1980).

### CONLEY, Daniel E
Quarles & Brady LLP, Milwaukee
414 277 5609
dec@quarles.com
*Featured in Litigation (Wisconsin)*
**Practice Areas:** Crisis Management, Class Actions, Complex Litigation, Contracts, Business Disputes, , Legal Ethics and Malpractice, Securities, Trade Secrets and Unfair Competition, ADR.
**Professional Memberships:** Court Appointed Member to E.D. Wis. and 7th Circuit Local Rules Committees, E.D. Wis. Indigent Defense Committee; Past President, Seventh Circuit Bar; Program Chair and Past Board Member, E.D. Wis. Bar; Former Chair of Courts and CLE Committees of Milwaukee Bar Association.
**Career:** Law Clerk to Hon. John Reynolds (E.D. Wis.); Quarles & Brady Partner since 1993.
**Personal:** University of Wisconsin (JD, cum laude, 1985); University of Wisconsin (BA, with distinction, 1981).

### CRONIN, Michael J.
Whyte Hirschboeck Dudek S.C., Milwaukee
608 258 7393
mcronin@whdlaw.com
*Featured in Intellectual Property (Wisconsin)*
**Practice Areas:** Assists universities and biotechnology companies of all sizes in transferring innovation from the laboratory to the marketplace. Works primarily in biochemistry and molecular biology where he combines his scientific and legal training to secure patent protection for new technologies.
**Professional Memberships:** Association of University Technology Managers; American Intellectual Property Association.
**Career:** Earned his doctoral degree in molecular biology from the University of California, San Francisco. Earned his law degree from George Mason University. Began his career with an IP law firm in Washington DC. Joined Whyte Hirschboeck Dudek in 2006.

### CROYSDALE, David
Michael Best & Friedrich LLP, Milwaukee
414 271 6560
dwcroysdale@michaelbest.com
*Featured in Labor & Employment (Wisconsin)*

**Practice Areas:** David Croysdale has more than 35 years experience representing management in matters relating to labor relations, defense to employment claims, severance arrangements, non-compete issues and employee benefits. Mr Croysdale negotiates collective bargaining agreements, provides representation in arbitration, NLRB, and EEOC proceedings, and counsels regarding welfare benefit and health reform issues. Mr Croysdale has served publishers, manufacturers, defense contractors, non-profit agencies, health care providers, transportation companies, retail food concerns, meat processors, the construction industry, and benefit consulting firms.

### CURTIS JR, Charles G
Arnold & Porter LLP, Washington, DC
608 257 1922
Charles.Curtis@aporter.com
*Featured in Native American Law (Nationwide), Litigation (Wisconsin)*
**Practice Areas:** Mr Curtis practices out of offices in Madison, WI and Washington, DC. He has over 25 years of experience in counseling and litigating in a diversity of areas, including constitutional, administrative, antitrust, intellectual property, telecommunications, environmental and natural resource, Native American, and general commercial law. He focuses his practice on the briefing and argument of complex issues at the agency, trial, and appellate levels. He clerked for Senior Judge David L Bazelon (DC Circuit) and for Justice William J Brennan, Jr.
**Personal:** JD, University of Chicago Law School, 1982; BA, History, Harvard University, 1978.

### DALLET, Bradley I
Whyte Hirschboeck Dudek S.C., Milwaukee
414 978 5525
bdallet@whdlaw.com
*Featured in Real Estate (Wisconsin)*
**Career:** Brad Dallet is a shareholder at WHD and Chair of the firm's Real Estate Practice. He focuses on real estate and real estate finance law, representing developers, companies and individuals in the purchase, sale, leasing and development of commercial and residential real estate. Recently, he assisted several local developers in the acquisition and development of retail shopping centers, including extensive work negotiating national retail leases, and assisted with the roll out and leasing of a national retail chain as a new retail concept in over 20 locations throughout the region. He received his JD from Case Western Reserve University.

### DE BRUIN, David L
Michael Best & Friedrich LLP, Milwaukee
414 225 2776
dldebruin@michaelbest.com
*Featured in Intellectual Property (Wisconsin)*
**Practice Areas:** David DeBruin has successfully lead complex patent trials before juries and courts and argued numerous patent cases before the Federal Circuit Court of Appeals. Dave also practices from Chicago, representing clients from across the country and abroad. His practice includes opinion and counseling work. He has served as an arbitrator and as a Markman expert.

His education includes physics at MIT and public policy and law (law review) at Michigan. With early experience as a law clerk and with complex financial litigation and fraud, Mr. DeBruin offers clients a high level of perspective, creativity and tenacity.

### DELOREY, Kevin A
Quarles & Brady LLP, Madison
608 283 2424
kevin.delorey@quarles.com
*Featured in Real Estate (Wisconsin)*
**Practice Areas:** Real estate/construction.
**Career:** His practice includes all aspects of commercial real estate development, including purchase and sale; finance; annexation, eminent domain and land use and zoning approval; subdivision and condominium documentation and approval; design and construction contract negotiation and drafting, including multiparty integrated project delivery (IPD) contracts, contracts associated with building information modeling (BIM) and lean construction.
**Personal:** University of Wisconsin Law School (JD, magna cum laude); University of Wisconsin-Stevens Point (BS, highest honors).

### DUFFY, Robert H
Quarles & Brady LLP, Milwaukee
414 277 5647
robert.duffy@quarles.com
*Featured in Labor & Employment (Wisconsin)*
**Practice Areas:** Bob Duffy, a Quarles & Brady Partner, assists employers in all labor and employment areas, providing front-end employment solutions and defending employers from civil rights, wrongful discharge, breach of contract and union-related litigation. Bob frequently speaks on employment matters, has handled hundreds of cases before state and federal courts, administrative agencies and private arbitrators, and is nationally recognized for "combining exceptional legal expertise with practical advise, business savvy and creative solutions—all of which make his clients' lives easier."
**Personal:** Marquette University, JD (magna cum laude), BA (cum laude).

### EMANUEL, John F
Whyte Hirschboeck Dudek S.C., Milwaukee
414 978 5430
jemanuel@whdlaw.com
*Featured in Corporate/M&A (Wisconsin)*
**Career:** John Emanuel is a shareholder at WHD and a member of its Corporate Practice Group. He has more than 30 years experience representing investors, business owners and entrepreneurs in the areas of business acquisitions, divestitures and reorganizations, capital raising, tax planning, succession planning, and general corporate and business counseling. Mr Emanuel was one of 86 attorneys nationwide named to the 2008 BTI Consulting Group's "Client Services All-Star Team" for his work in corporate transactions. Since 2007 he has taught the course in mergers and acquisitions at Marquette University Law School. Mr Emanuel received his JD from Stanford University.

### FISCHER, Michael J
Quarles & Brady LLP, Milwaukee
414 277 5639
mike.fischer@quarles.com
*Featured in Labor & Employment (Wisconsin)*
**Practice Areas:** Mike Fischer is a Partner in Quarles & Brady's Labor and Employment Group. He counsels employers on labor and employment issues, focusing on Title VII discrimination as well as family medical leave, state and federal disability law, and military leave. In addition to representing clients before administrative agencies and courts, Mr Fischer emphasizes the delivery of practical, front-end solutions through numerous counseling and training sessions conducted for clients ranging from Fortune 500 Companies to small non-profits and the EEOC.
**Personal:** Harvard University (JD, magna cum laude); University of Michigan (MA, English); Yale University (BA, summa cum laude).

### FRASER, Alexander P
Michael Best & Friedrich LLP, Milwaukee
414 347 4757
apfraser@michaelbest.com
*Featured in Corporate/M&A (Wisconsin)*
**Practice Areas:** Alec Fraser leads the firm's Banking and Financial Services Group. His practice is focused on commercial lending, derivatives and corporate finance. He has represented financial institutions and borrowers in secured and unsecured credit transactions of all sizes and types, venture capital and leveraged buyout financing, interest rate swaps, foreign exchange and other derivatives transactions, reorganizations and workouts, loan syndications and participations, correspondent banking, equipment finance and credit enhancement facilities for bond offerings. He is a founding member of the firm's VentureBest practice, focused on early-stage high technology companies, and the investors and universities that launch them.

### GALLO, Donald P
Reinhart Boerner Van Deuren sc, Waukesha
262 951 4555
dgallo@reinhartlaw.com
*Featured in Natural Resources (Wisconsin)*
**Practice Areas:** Real estate, environmental.
**Professional Memberships:** Ozaukee-Washington Land Trust, Inc., Board Member; member of ABA, State and Milwaukee Environmental Law Section; Milwaukee County Local Emergency Planning Committee; DERF Governor's Council; Tall Pines Conservancy, Secretary; Water Council Committee, Co-Chair.
**Career:** Shareholder concentrating on environmental matters, including litigation, development of legislation, regulatory compliance and permitting. Named one of the top construction lawyers by The Daily Reporter and Wisconsin Law Journal.
**Personal:** Authored several books and articles, including Brownfields Initiatives, Drycleaning and PECFA legislation, and the 1999 Budget Bill, as well as the Great Lakes Diversion Application for the City of Waukesha.

### GASS, J Ric
Gass Weber Mullins LLC, Milwaukee
414 224 7697
gass@gasswebermullins.com
*Featured in Litigation (Wisconsin)*
**Practice Areas:** Serves as both national trial and supervising counsel for a number of insurers and self-insured corporations and represents corporations and insurers to bring affirmative claims for relief. Specialty areas include catastrophic injuries, trucking, products liability, and bad faith. His practice is nationwide with cases pending from Miami to Hawaii. He also accepts assignments to provide expert testimony. Approximately 75% of his practice is for corporations and insurance carriers with 25% of his practice representing corporations and insurers as plaintiffs. Representing a corporation and municipality as clients Ric won the largest verdict in the history of the State of Wisconsin: $104.4 million.
**Professional Memberships:** American Board of Trial Advocates (Diplomate), Fellow American College of Trial Lawyers, Litigation Counsel of America (President 2012) & International Society of Barristers, The American College of Barristers, Federation of Defense & Corporate Counsel (Past President), International Association of Defense Counsel, Defense Research Institute, Lawyers for Civil Justice (Past President), American Arbitration Association, National Board of Trial Advocacy, Milwaukee, Wisconsin and American Bar Associations.
**Career:** A founding member of Gass Weber Mullins.
**Publications:** Defending Against Damages Claims (FDCC Quarterly, Winter 2008); Damages Caused by Wrongful Death (Wisconsin Law of Damages, published 1988 and updated bi-annually); Defending Against Catastrophic Damages: Challenges and Choices (For The Defense, June 1997).
**Personal:** In addition to his active trial practice Mr Gass has served as an Adjunct Associate Professor of Law at Marquette University Law School and has been regularly invited to do ten or more presentations a year at national legal conferences in his specialty area of trial presentation. He has spoken to the annual conventions of more than 25 state and local defense organizations, he is regularly the highest rated speaker at DRI seminars and has presented at the annual conventions of all national defense and insurance organizations. He frequently is the featured speaker at such events. He has authored more than 30 articles and book chapters and holds an AV rating from Martindale. He has been selected for inclusion in Leading American Attorneys and Who's Who in American Law. Mr Gass' practice is national in scope, and he has taken almost 300 cases to verdict, winning ninety-five percent of them. His areas of specialty are catastrophic injury, bad faith, products liability and punitive damages. Mr Gass has been listed in The Best Lawyers of America for over a decade and has been selected for inclusion in the listing of the top 50 Wisconsin SuperLawyers and in "The Best Lawyers in Milwaukee." He was selected in the inaugural class

of "The Leaders of Wisconsin Law." He has been described by Milwaukee Magazine as "the man who can talk to juries." He has been descibed by clients and other lawyers as: "One of the few lawyers who can take his facts and beat you with them or trade facts with you and beat you with your facts"; "There are superstars and there are megastars. Ric Gass is a megastar; a true mentor of the art of advocacy whose cutting edge approaches are ahead of the curve – without a doubt a lawyer's lawyer"; "A personality the jury wants to listen to". University of Wisconsin-Stevens Point (BS). Marquette University Law School (JD, 1970).

### HANSEN, Scott W.
Reinhart Boerner Van Deuren s.c., Milwaukee
414 298 8123
shansen@reinhartlaw.com
*Featured in Litigation (Wisconsin)*
**Practice Areas:** Complex litigation.
**Career:** Named a 2010 Leader in the Law for successfully litigating some of the most complex and high-stakes civil cases in Wisconsin. Bio with sample published cases is at www.reinhartlaw.com. Recognition - Chambers: Tier One 2004-12; SuperLawyers: since inception (Wisconsin Top 50 2008-12); Best Lawyers: Antitrust Lawyer of the Year.
**Publications:** Representative Presentations: 'The Art of Persuasion in Complex Litigation', 'The Use of Jury Studies in Franchise Litigation', 'Contract Litigation', Selecting, Presenting and Examining Financial Expert Witnesses'.

### HANSON, David G
Reinhart Boerner Van Deuren s.c., Milwaukee
414 298 8324
dhanson@reinhartlaw.com
*Featured in Intellectual Property (Wisconsin)*
**Practice Areas:** Intellectual property litigation.
**Professional Memberships:** Past Chair, Intellectual Property Section of the State Bar of Wisconsin.
**Career:** IP Litigation Practice Chair with significant IP trial experience, including trials in the "rocket docket" of the Western District of Wisconsin. Works nationwide with domestic and foreign companies on patent, trademark, trade secret and copyright controversies. Has served as AAA arbitrator and as expert witness (reasonableness of fees) in IP disputes.
**Personal:** Adjunct Professor of IP Litigation, 15 years, Marquette University Law School. Named "Wisconsin Super Lawyer." Frequent speaker, including "IP Year in Review," at Wisconsin Sate Bar convention.

### HOBBS, Eric
Michael Best & Friedrich LLP, Milwaukee
414 225 4991
eehobbs@michaelbest.com
*Featured in Labor & Employment (Wisconsin)*
**Practice Areas:** Eric Hobbs' national practice focuses on labor and employment law, with an emphasis on employment counseling and policy development, occupational safety and health,

employment discrimination litigation, worker's compensation, and clergy abuse investigation and related litigation. He also has experience in wage-hour, employment discrimination and multi-district class action cases and has tried cases before state and federal agencies and courts throughout the United States.

### HOFFMAN, Nathaniel A
Whyte Hirschboeck Dudek S.C., Milwaukee
414 978 5634
nhoffman@whdlaw.com
*Featured in Real Estate (Wisconsin)*
**Career:** Nathaniel Hoffman is a shareholder at WHD and a member of the firm's Real Estate Group. He focuses on representing national, regional and local landlords and tenants in all aspects of leasing office, retail, industrial, residential, medical, and other properties. He handles real estate purchases and sales, management contracts, easements, licenses and land development. Before joining private practice, Mr Hoffman served as Special Counsel for urban redevelopment for numerous California cities and as Counsel to the New York Public Development Corporation. He received his JD from the University of Michigan and is admitted to practice in Wisconsin and California.

### HUTTER, Patricia M
Quarles & Brady LLP, Milwaukee
414 277 5117
patricia.hutter@quarles.com
*Featured in Corporate/M&A (Wisconsin)*
**Practice Areas:** Mergers and acquisitions, private equity/venture capital, corporate services, corporate finance/securities, health & life sciences law and commercial law.
**Professional Memberships:** American Bar Association, State Bar of Wisconsin, Association for Corporate Growth.
**Career:** Partner since 2007. Chair of the Firm's Mergers & Acquisitions Team since 2011.
**Publications:** Co-Author, "Management Equity: Aligning Interests in Private Equity Buyouts," The Milwaukee Business Journal, August 2, 2012. Speaker, "Creating Competitive Advantage in the Deal Process Building Blocks of Success: Structuring Deals to Gain a Competitive Advantage."
**Personal:** University of Illinois College of Law (JD, cum laude, 1997); University of Illinois (BA, 1994).

### ISHIKAWA, Jesse S
Reinhart Boerner Van Deuren sc, Madison
608 229 2208
jishikaw@reinhartlaw.com
*Featured in Real Estate (Wisconsin)*
**Practice Areas:** Real estate.
**Professional Memberships:** State Bar of Wisconsin, American College of Real Estate Lawyers.
**Career:** Represents developers, mortgage lenders and businesses in all aspects of real estate law, including purchases, sales, commercial leasing, development transactions. Consistently ranked as a top real estate lawyer in Madison, frequently called upon to assist lawyers throughout

Wisconsin as a condominium, tax incremental financing and easement law expert. Currently teaching Advanced Real Estate Transactions at the University of Wisconsin Law School.
**Personal:** Wrote three books and numerous articles on real estate topics. Madison Museum of Contemporary Art, Past President.

### JASKOLSKI, Michael A
Quarles & Brady LLP, Milwaukee
414 277 5000
michael.jaskolski@quarles.com
*Featured in Intellectual Property (Wisconsin)*
**Practice Areas:** Intellectual property.
**Professional Memberships:** State Bar of Wisconsin.
**Career:** Partner since 2001.
**Personal:** University of Wisconsin Law School (JD, 1992); Marquette University (BSEE, 1989).

### KAISER, Richard L.
Michael Best & Friedrich LLP, Milwaukee
262 956 6576
rlkaiser@michaelbest.com
*Featured in Intellectual Property (Wisconsin)*
**Practice Areas:** Richard Kaiser is a partner in the Intellectual Property Practice Group, focusing on patent prosecution for mechanical arts, with extensive experience with utility and design patents. Mr Kaiser works closely with clients to provide meaningful and practical guidance on both US and foreign patent strategies. He is proficient with all steps of the patenting process, from initial patentability searching and analysis, to patent application drafting, and finally with the nuances of prosecuting the pending patent applications before the various patent offices. Mr Kaiser also has experience with post-grant proceedings, such as US re-examination proceedings and European opposition proceedings.

### KARAS, Hal
Whyte Hirschboeck Dudek S.C., Milwaukee
414 978 5499
hkaras@whdlaw.com
*Featured in Real Estate (Wisconsin)*
**Career:** Hal Karas is a shareholder at WHD and a member of the Corporate and Real Estate Teams. For over 30 years, he has been involved in all facets of business and real estate transactions, including the purchase and sale of numerous manufacturing businesses, transactions involving New Markets Tax Credits and other tax incentives, placement of securitized auto loan pools, construction loans for downtown and suburban buildings, community associations and redevelopment projects involving mixed-use development. He has provided representation in many states, among them exchange transactions, ground leases and public-component financing projects. Mr Karas received his JD from Northeastern University.

### KERN, David B
Quarles & Brady LLP, Milwaukee
414 277 5653
david.kern@quarles.com
*Featured in Labor & Employment (Wisconsin)*
**Practice Areas:** David Kern is a Partner with Quarles & Brady and chairs the Labor Section's

National Labor Relations Act Practice Team. Mr Kern represents employers in a variety of industries on union avoidance issues, collective bargaining, grievance arbitration, defense of discrimination and unfair labor practice claims, and counseling on all aspects of labor and employment law. Mr Kern is a Member of the ABA's Committee on the Development of the Law under the National Relations Act.
**Personal:** University of Michigan Law School (JD, magna cum laude); Marquette University (BA, summa cum laude).

### LANGLOIS, Scott L
Quarles & Brady LLP, Milwaukee
414 277 5619
scott.langlois@quarles.com
*Featured in Real Estate (Wisconsin)*
**Practice Areas:** Real estate.
**Professional Memberships:** Board of Directors and Secretary, NAIOP Wisconsin Chapter.
**Career:** Scott Langlois has practiced at Quarles & Brady LLP for over 20 years and is the Chairman of the Wisconsin Real Estate Group, beginning his practice at Jones Day in Dallas, Texas. He practices in all areas involving commercial real estate, specializing in real estate development, purchase and sale, financing, land use, condominiums and leasing. He is listed in the Best Lawyers in America (2009-present) and is Martindale-Hubbell AV Preeminent Peer Review Rated.
**Publications:** Co-author, "Wisconsin Condominium Law Handbook," Wisconsin State Bar Publication.

### LEICHTLING, Ely A
Quarles & Brady LLP, Milwaukee
414 277 5681
ely.leichtling@quarles.com
*Featured in Labor & Employment (Wisconsin)*
**Practice Areas:** Ely Leichtling, a Partner with Quarles & Brady, represents employers in all aspects of labor and employment law. Mr Leichtling's practice emphasizes defense of discrimination claims, preparation and review of affirmative action programs and consultation and representation during government audits of AAPs, planning for and defending reductions-in-force and business reorganization, and challenges to employer "testing" procedures, in addition to providing day-to-day advice solving sticky human resources problems. Mr Leichtling founded the Department of Labor's OFCCP Milwaukee Industry Liaison Group with government contractors and chaired it for over 10 years.
**Personal:** University of Virginia (JD); Wesleyan University (BA).

### LEVINE, Jonathan O
Littler Mendelson, PC, Milwaukee
414 277 5536
jlevine@littler.com
*Featured in Labor & Employment (Wisconsin)*
**Practice Areas:** Labor and employment.
**Career:** Mr Levine has a national practice representing the interests of management in labor law, and labor relations matters for 25 years. His practice includes advising clients on mergers/acquisi-

tions, restructuring, and other strategic planning, collective bargaining, contract administration and labor arbitration, matters of all types before the NLRB and DOL, and counsels clients, globally, concerning positive employee relations in creating and maintaining a positive union free environment.
**Personal:** JD, Georgetown University, 1988, Note and Comment Editor, Georgetown Journal of Legal Ethics; BA, University of Wisconsin-Madison, 1985.

## LINDNER, Laura A
Littler Mendelson, PC, Milwaukee
414 291 5536
LLindner@littler.com
*Featured in Labor & Employment (Wisconsin)*
**Practice Areas:** Employment and Labor Law; Employment Litigation, including discrimination, retaliation, and unfair competition claims.
**Professional Memberships:** Tempo Milwaukee, Member (2005-10).
**Career:** Prior to joining Littler, Laura was a shareholder at Lindner & Marsack, S.C. She was also Senior Counsel at SBC Communications Inc. (now AT&T).
**Publications:** The Family and Medical Leave Act, BNA Books (2007, 2008, 2009, 2010) (Supplements); Contributing Author, EEOC Litigation and Charge Resolution, BNA Books 2005.
**Personal:** JD, 1993, University of Wisconsin Law School, cum laude, Order of the Coif; BA, 1990, University of Notre Dame, summa cum laude, Phi Beta Kappa.

## LINSTROTH, Tod B
Michael Best & Friedrich LLP, Madison
608 283 2242
tblinstroth@michaelbest.com
*Featured in Corporate/M&A (Wisconsin)*
**Practice Areas:** Tod Linstroth, a member of the Management Committee, is lead corporate counsel to many corporate and technology clients, and founded the firm's VentureBest practice. He provides advice on financing strategies, mergers and acquisitions, strategic partnering, shareholder and director issues, corporate structure, and governance. He handles complex transactions involving leveraged buyouts, divestitures, recapitalizations, and securities offerings. He served as lead counsel to: MSI Systems Integrators in its merger with Sirius Computer Solutions, creating a $1 billion sales company; The Pleasant Company in it's $700 million sale to Mattel; and Berbee Information Networks in it's $180 million sale to CDW.

## LUNDGREN, K Thor
Michael Best & Friedrich LLP, Milwaukee
414 225 4952
ktlundgren@mbf-law.com
*Featured in Corporate/M&A (Wisconsin)*
**Practice Areas:** K Thor Lundgren is a partner in the Transactional Group and a member of the Management Committee. His practice concentrates on all aspects of corporate law, business transactions and finance, including domestic and foreign mergers and acquisitions, joint ventures, debt and equity restructuring and financing under

securities and banking laws. He regularly advises companies boards of directors on strategic and corporate governance matters and has conducted internal investigations worldwide. He recently advised clients concerning strategic acquisitions, a successful resolution of a contested FDIC matter and counseled the independent directors of a public company regarding management succession matters.

## MAHER, Ann
Whyte Hirschboeck Dudek S.C., Milwaukee
414 978 5410
amaher@whdlaw.com
*Featured in Litigation (Wisconsin)*
**Career:** Ann Maher is a shareholder at WHD and a member of its Business Litigation Practice Group. She practices in the area of business litigation and advises business clients in dealership, distribution and antitrust related matters. She has represented clients as trial counsel in a wide variety of cases involving employment, real estate and commercial contracts, intellectual property, trade secrets and franchise and dealer termination laws. She serves as the firm's General Counsel, has served on its Board of Directors and has managed the Litigation Department. Ms Maher received her JD, cum laude, from Marquette University Law School in 1988.

## MARCUVITZ, Alan H
Michael Best & Friedrich LLP, Milwaukee
414 225 4927
ahmarcuvitz@michaelbest.com
*Featured in Real Estate (Wisconsin)*
**Practice Areas:** Alan Marcuvitz is a partner in the Land and Resources Practice Group. His areas of practice include eminent domain, property taxation and real estate development, in all of which he is acknowledged as exemplary counsel. While most of his practice is on behalf of the private sector, he has also provided significant representation to local governments.

## MARGOLIES, Jonathan H
Michael Best & Friedrich LLP, Milwaukee
414 225 2784
jhmargolies@michaelbest.com
*Featured in Intellectual Property (Wisconsin)*
**Practice Areas:** Jon Margolies practices primarily in the area of intellectual property litigation, represents large commercial clients in patent and trademark cases in Federal courts throughout the country. Mr Margolies is also an adjunct professor at Marquette Law School.

## MCCARTHY, Amelia L
Gass Weber Mullins LLC, Milwaukee
414 224 7699
mccarthy@gasswebermullins.com
*Featured in Litigation (Wisconsin)*
**Career:** Amelia McCarthy is a Member of Gass Weber Mullins LLC where she practices in the areas of commercial litigation and products liability litigation. Ms McCarthy is listed in Best Lawyers in America for Commercial Litigation and is a Fellow of the Litigation Counsel of America, an invitation-only honorary trial lawyer association. She also received an AV Preeminent peer rating from Martindale-Hubbell and she has

been selected as a Wisconsin Super Lawyer for eight years. Ms McCarthy was also recognized as one of Milwaukee's top 40 Under 40 business leaders by The Milwaukee Business Journal. Ms McCarthy formerly served as a Municipal Prosecutor for a Wisconsin community and has served as a Public Service Special Prosecutor for two District Attorney's offices. Ms McCarthy has tried over 50 court and jury trials. She also successfully defended four class action lawsuits, obtaining three dismissals with prejudice and one nuisance value settlement without having to proceed through class certification. Ms McCarthy received her undergraduate degree, magna cum laude, from Carthage College and her law degree from Marquette University Law School, where she served as an editor for the Marquette Law Review and competed in the Phillip Jessup International Law Moot Court competition.
**Personal:** Ms McCarthy recently returned from a sabbatical in Ondangwa, Namibia (Africa) where she served as an NGO Advisor to Oonte Orphans and Vulnerable Children Organization through the United States Peace Corps. While in Namibia, she also assisted Namibia's Legal Assistance Centre and lawyers and judges from across southern Africa to develop Namibia's Child Care and Protection Bill. The Bill will reform Namibia's existing Child Care and Protection laws which were all enacted during apartheid and prior to Namibia's Independence. Ms McCarthy received a 2011 Pro Bono award from Super Lawyers for her work in Namibia. Ms McCarthy is licensed to practice in Wisconsin and Colorado. She serves as an advisor to the Humanities Division at Carthage College and she is a member of the Carthage College Alumni Council.

## MCCAULEY, Michael S
Quarles & Brady LLP, Milwaukee
414 277 5525
michael.mccauley@quarles.com
*Featured in Natural Resources (Wisconsin)*
**Practice Areas:** Environmental.
**Professional Memberships:** American College of Environmental Lawyers; American Bar Association Air Quality Committee; Wisconsin Bar Environmental Law Section; Environmental Law Institute; Wisconsin Environmental Working Group.
**Career:** He counsels corporate clients in all aspects of environmental management and dispute resolution. His practice includes special emphasis on the Clean Air Act, Clean Energy and Sustainability issues, environmental assessments in business and real estate transactions and providing advice on environmental compliance issues.
**Personal:** University of Iowa College of Law (JD, with highest distinction); Harvard University (MPA); University of Notre Dame (BA, magna cum laude).

## MCELLIGOTT, Thomas P
Quarles & Brady LLP, Milwaukee
414 277 5531
thomas.mcelligott@quarles.com
*Featured in Natural Resources (Wisconsin)*

**Practice Areas:** Environmental.
**Professional Memberships:** Member, State Bar of Wisconsin; Member, American Bar Association; Member, Federation of Environmental Technologists.
**Career:** He has significant experience in environmental law including: negotiating air and water discharge permits, administrative and judicial litigation regarding air and water permits, defense of governmental and third party enforcement actions, representing private and municipal clients in remedial projects involving state and federal authorities. He is also an Adjunct Professor of Law at Marquette University Law School teaching a Clean Water Act Workshop.
**Personal:** Marquette University (JD, cum laude; BA).

## MITICH, Rebecca H.
Whyte Hirschboeck Dudek S.C., Milwaukee
414 978 5367
rmitich@whdlaw.com
*Featured in Real Estate (Wisconsin)*
**Career:** Rebecca Mitich is an associate at WHD and a member of the firm's Real Estate, Finance and Condominium & HOA Law teams. Ms Mitich assists clients in all manner of real estate transactions, including purchase and sale transactions, leasing and development. Recently, Rebecca has focused her practice on community economic development, representing developers in transactions using New Markets Tax Credits and other tax incentives and guiding a quasi-governmental state agency in the creation and implementation of federally funded venture debt and venture equity programs. Ms Mitich received her JD magna cum laude from Marquette University.

## MORAN, Kevin
Michael Best & Friedrich LLP, Milwaukee
262 956 6510
kpmoran@michaelbest.com
*Featured in Intellectual Property (Wisconsin)*
**Practice Areas:** Kevin Moran is a partner in the firm's Intellectual Property Practice. Mr Moran's practice includes the acquisition and enforcement of United States and foreign patents, with an emphasis on mechanical, electro-mechanical and biomedical technologies. Mr Moran also counsels clients in challenging the validity and enforcement of competitors' patents, including challenging patents through ex parte and inter partes reexamination proceedings. His practice further involves the acquisition of, enforcement of, and counseling regarding United States and foreign trademark rights, copyrights and trade secrets, negotiation of and counseling regarding worldwide intellectual property licenses and technology transfers, and product development counseling.

## MORROW, James G
Reinhart Boerner Van Deuren s.c., Milwaukee
414 298 8136
jmorrow@reinhartlaw.com
*Featured in Intellectual Property (Wisconsin)*
**Practice Areas:** Intellectual property.
**Professional Memberships:** State Bar of Wisconsin, State Bar of Illinois, State Bar of

Arizona, American Intellectual Property Law Association, Licensing Executives Society, American Society of Mechanical Engineers.
**Career:** James Morrow is a shareholder with 25 years of IP law experience. His practice includes infringement risk assessment and evaluation, IP litigation risk management; IP agreement negotiation and counseling; and intellectual capital protection counseling. He provides complex prosecution services, including US reissues and reexaminations, including the use of these procedures for litigation management. He also served as an adjunct professor of law at Marquette University Law School.

**MYERS, Thomas A**
Reinhart Boerner Van Deuren s.c., Milwaukee
414 298 8120
tmyers@reinhartlaw.com
*Featured in Corporate/M&A (Wisconsin)*
**Practice Areas:** Corporate/M&A.
**Professional Memberships:** Serves as a Board Chair for Cardinal Stritch University, and board member for the Ozaukee County Economic Development Corporation and Girl Scouts of Wisconsin Southeast, Inc. Member of both the Wisconsin and the Illinois Bars.
**Career:** Serves a variety of clients, including the following industries: Medical devices and data, software, plastics, chemicals, paper and pulp, heavy equipment, large retail and financial services.
**Personal:** Routinely provides pro bono services to a number of community agencies. Speaks regularly to business groups regarding all legal aspects of the business purchase process, with particular emphasis on Mergers and Acquisitions.

**OLIVIERI, José A**
Michael Best & Friedrich LLP, Milwaukee
414 225 4967
jaolivieri@michaelbest.com
*Featured in Labor & Employment (Wisconsin)*
**Practice Areas:** José Olivieri is Chair of the Labor and Employment Relations Practice Group and Immigration & International Migration subgroup. His experience includes handling all temporary immigration categories, permanent labor certification, national interest waiver, adjustment of status, consular processing, citizenship and naturalization and I-9 compliance. He counsels management in other aspects of employment law including federal and state discrimination law; NLRB and WERC law; the Fair Labor Standards Act; employee termination and discipline; unemployment compensation; and labor contract administration. Additionally, he leads Michael Best's Higher Education Practice, counseling colleges and universities on the broad spectrum of issues affecting their organizations.

**OLSON, David P**
Quarles & Brady LLP, Milwaukee
414 277 5671
david.olson@quarles.com
*Featured in Labor & Employment (Wisconsin)*
**Practice Areas:** Employee benefits and executive compensation law.

**Professional Memberships:** American Bar Association; State Bar of Wisconsin; Milwaukee Bar Association; National Association of Stock Plan Professionals.
**Career:** Partner since 1993.
**Publications:** "Employee Benefit Changes You Need To Think About Now: New Tax Rules For SERPs, Options, Restricted Stocks, SARs, Severance And Other Non-Qualified Deferred Compensation Arrangements," Quarles & Brady Employee Benefits Seminar, 2005.
**Personal:** Northern Illinois University (JD, 1985; BS, 1979).

**OSTERMEYER, Michael J**
Quarles & Brady LLP, Milwaukee
414 277 5521
michael.ostermeyer@quarles.com
*Featured in Real Estate (Wisconsin)*
**Practice Areas:** Public-private development; corporate real estate; project finance.
**Professional Memberships:** American College of Real Estate Lawyers; American Law Institute - American Bar Association (ALI-ABA), Editorial Board, 'The Practical Real Estate Lawyer'; Acquisitions Editor, 'Real Property, Trusts & Estates Law Journal'; CoreNet (MCR Candidate).
**Career:** Partner since 1998.
**Publications:** 'Recent Developments in Project Financing under the American Recovery and Reinvestment Act of 2009' (2009); Protect Your Rights and Remedies with Owner Default Clause' (2005); 'A Primer on Remedies for Landlord Defaults' (2004).
**Personal:** University of Notre Dame (MBA, 2011); Vanderbilt University (JD, 1989); University of Notre Dame (MA, 1984).

**PALMER, Todd**
Michael Best & Friedrich LLP, Madison
608 283 4432
tepalmer@michaelbest.com
*Featured in Natural Resources (Wisconsin)*
**Practice Areas:** Todd Palmer is a member of the Energy and Sustainability Practice Group and leads the sub-group on Clean Air Act matters, such as repowering industrial facilities. Mr Palmer's clients benefit from his unique experience as both a lawyer and technical consultant. During the last 20 years, Mr Palmer has relied on his varied experience to assist clients representing numerous industries. Mr Palmer has focused his legal career on Clean Air Act matters and has helped numerous clients with their efforts to remain in compliance with all aspects of the complex and dynamic Clean Air Act regulatory program.

**PEPKE, Michael T**
Reinhart Boerner Van Deuren s.c., Milwaukee
414 298 8133
mpepke@reinhartlaw.com
*Featured in Corporate/M&A (Wisconsin)*
**Practice Areas:** Corporate/M&A.
**Professional Memberships:** State Bar of Wisconsin, Member. Participates in five clients' Boards of Directors.

**Career:** Business Law Practice Chair representing businesses in all phases, including start-up/acquisition, growth financing, add-on acquisitions, recapitalization and exit strategies through sale or public offering. Representation includes banking relationships, customer and supplier relationships, manufacturing and distribution matters, employee and key executive relationships, owner relationships and strategic and succession planning.
**Personal:** On Boards of Directors for Junior Achievement and Children's Hospital and Health Systems, Inc.

**PETERSON, Nancy K**
Quarles & Brady LLP, Milwaukee
414 277 5515
nancy.peterson@quarles.com
*Featured in Natural Resources (Wisconsin)*
**Practice Areas:** Environmental; litigation.
**Professional Memberships:** Member, State Bar of Wisconsin; Chair, Milwaukee Arts High School Board; Greater Milwaukee Women's Fund Board; Quarles & Brady Executive Committee.
**Career:** She has successfully resolved complex, multi-party claims under environmental and insurance laws through negotiation, mediation and litigation. She is lead counsel for a client at a river/harbor site involving litigated cleanup and natural resource damage claims exceeding $1 billion, and mediated insurance claims. She helps clients manage environmental risks and counsels on transactions and environmental compliance.
**Personal:** University of Wisconsin Law School (JD); University of Wisconsin (BA).

**PIENKOS, John T**
Whyte Hirschboeck Dudek S.C., Milwaukee
414 978 5630
jpienkos@whdlaw.com
*Featured in Intellectual Property (Wisconsin)*
**Career:** John Pienkos is a shareholder at WHD and focuses his practice on intellectual property law, particularly patent law. John has extensive experience preparing and prosecuting patent applications and preparing patent-related opinions involving numerous technologies, including wireless communications, engines and motors, and computer hardware, software and e-commerce. He has counseled clients in relation to a variety of transactional and other IP issues. John has held leadership roles in the Licensing Executives Society Wisconsin chapter, and authored The Patent Guidebook published by the ABA. His background includes a Master's degree from the University of Wisconsin-Madison and JD from Harvard Law School.

**PLOOR, Pamela M**
Quarles & Brady LLP, Milwaukee
414 277 5661
pamela.ploor@quarles.com
*Featured in Labor & Employment (Wisconsin)*
**Practice Areas:** Pamela Ploor is a Partner with Quarles & Brady, with concentrations in client representation in court and administrative agencies, OFCCP affirmative action plan creation and defense during audit, leave laws, and electronic discovery/employer record retention practices. Named 2009 and 2010 BTI Client Service star for

delivering superior client service based on Fortune 1000 corporate counsel interviews. Representative litigation cases include Beamon v M&I, 411 F.3d 854 (7th Cir, 2005); Schneiker v Fortis, 200 F.3d 1055 (7th Cir, 2000); Hoeller v Eaton, 149 F.3d 621 (7th Cir, 1998).
**Personal:** Harvard University (JD); UCLA (BA, magna cum laude).

**PUCHNER, Joseph E**
Quarles & Brady LLP, Milwaukee
414 277 5533
joseph.puchner@quarles.com
*Featured in Real Estate (Wisconsin)*
**Practice Areas:** Real estate, international business.
**Professional Memberships:** State Bar of California; State Bar of Wisconsin (International Section Board Member).
**Career:** Partner since 1999.
**Personal:** Stanford University (JD, with distinction, 1986); Marquette University (BA, summa cum laude,1983).

**RICHARDS, Dean B**
Reinhart Boerner Van Deuren sc, Waukesha
262 951 4561
drichards@reinhartlaw.com
*Featured in Real Estate (Wisconsin)*
**Practice Areas:** Real estate.
**Professional Memberships:** State Bar of Wisconsin, US District Court for the Eastern & Western Districts of Wisconsin, Seventh Circuit US Court of Appeals.
**Career:** Represents developers and landowners throughout Wisconsin, principally in connection with development, zoning and land division activities. Practice includes obtaining governmental approvals and permits for developments and land use projects, resolving property and land use disputes and adjudicating land use conflicts and zoning violations.
**Personal:** Fire Chief of Town of Delafield Fire Department (1998-2010), former Waukesha County Economic Development Corporation Director, former Director of Greater Delafield Community Fund.

**ROANG, Sverre**
Whyte Hirschboeck Dudek S.C., Madison
608 234 6079
sroang@whdlaw.com
*Featured in Corporate/M&A (Wisconsin)*
**Career:** Sverre is a consummate deal attorney who teams with his clients to find creative, practical solutions to get deals done. He particularly excels at obtaining a deep knowledge about his clients and their industries and tailoring deals to his clients' unique business objectives. Sverre has worked in many industries, including manufacturing, publishing, energy and banking, and has developed an internationally recognized expertise in large agricultural transactions, with emphasis on the production, marketing and licensing of seed products. Sverre is also especially adept at working with family businesses through ownership transitions, helping families to build lasting, generational wealth.

## ROGE, Bret A
Michael Best & Friedrich LLP, Milwaukee
414 271 6560
baroge@michaelbest.com
*Featured in Real Estate (Wisconsin)*
**Practice Areas:** Bret Roge focuses his practice extensively on matters concerning business, real estate and tax law, and is skilled in resolving problems encountered in acquiring, structuring, forming, owning and operating real estate and operating businesses through such entities as corporations, general and limited partnerships, limited liability partnerships and limited liability companies.

## ROTHACKER, Robert D
Quarles & Brady LLP, Milwaukee
414 277 5643
robert.rothacker@quarles.com
*Featured in Labor & Employment (Wisconsin)*
**Practice Areas:** Employee benefits.
**Professional Memberships:** Milwaukee and American Bar Associations; State Bar of Wisconsin, Wisconsin Retirement Plan Professionals (past President).
**Career:** Partner since 2006.
**Personal:** University of Michigan Law School (JD); College of William and Mary (AB).

## ROTHSTEIN, John A
Quarles & Brady LLP, Milwaukee
414 277 5351
john.rothstein@quarles.com
*Featured in Litigation (Wisconsin)*
**Practice Areas:** Litigation; class actions; commercial transactions litigation; financial institutions and fiduciary/trust litigation; insurance coverage litigation (liability, casualty, error/omissions, title, directors and officer, property); products liability; mass toxic torts; real estate, land use and construction; professional malpractice; securities/corporate litigation; arbitrations and mediations; internal corporate investigations.
**Professional Memberships:** US Supreme Court; US Courts of Appeals (7th & 8th); US Dist. Courts (multiple states); Wisconsin Supreme Court; American Bar; Wisconsin Bar; Milwaukee Bar.
**Career:** Partner Quarles & Brady since 1986.
**Personal:** 2013 Recipient of "Leader in the Law", Wisconsin Law Journal; Marquette Univ. (JD/valedictorian 1979; BA 1976).

## SCHLINSOG, Allen C
Reinhart Boerner Van Deuren s.c., Milwaukee
414 298 8214
aschlinsog@reinhartlaw.com
*Featured in Litigation (Wisconsin)*
**Practice Areas:** Litigation.
**Professional Memberships:** President, Eastern District of Wisconsin Bar Association; Defense Research Institute; Wisconsin Civil Defense Counsel; State Bar of Wisconsin and Illinois.
**Career:** Chair of Reinhart's Litigation Practice and Product Liability and Safety Group. Practices product liability defense and complex commercial litigation. Has represented drug and device companies in significant product liability, multi-dis-

trict litigation and mass tort proceedings. In addition to medical devices and pharmaceuticals, Al has defended a variety of products in highly regulated industries. Represents clients involved in significant commercial and intellectual property disputes, and has acted as national and regional counsel for several clients.

## SCHMIDT-JONES, Amy
Michael Best & Friedrich LLP, Milwaukee
414 225 2771
asjones@michaelbest.com
*Featured in Labor & Employment (Wisconsin)*
**Practice Areas:** Amy Schmidt Jones is a partner whose practice includes representation of management in all aspects of employment and labor law, with special emphasis in employment litigation, employment counseling, and employee/supervisor training. Ms Jones's litigation practice has involved representing and defending financial institutions and other employers in employment discrimination, contract, and other litigation matters before federal and state courts (at the trial and appellate level), federal and state administrative agencies, the NLRB, and arbitrators. Ms Jones's trial experience includes government enforcement (EEOC) and individual plaintiff actions (jury and non-jury).

## SCRIVNER, Tom
Michael Best & Friedrich LLP, Milwaukee
414 225 4965
twscrivner@michaelbest.com
*Featured in Labor & Employment (Wisconsin)*
**Practice Areas:** Tom Scrivner led the firm's Labor and Employment Relations Practice Group from 1998-2001. His practice includes all aspects of labor law and employment litigation. Industries where Mr Scrivner has provided substantial legal services include construction, health care, printing, education, manufacturing and the service and not-for-profit sectors. He is a frequent speaker on topics including wrongful discharge, employment litigation, work force reduction, drug and alcohol testing, disability and family medical leave laws, sexual harassment and labor relations planning.

## SCULLEN, Sean M
Quarles & Brady LLP, Milwaukee
414 277 5421
sean.scullen@quarles.com
*Featured in Labor & Employment (Wisconsin)*
**Practice Areas:** Sean Scullen is a Partner with Quarles & Brady and Chair of the Milwaukee Labor & Employment Group and Co-Chair of the National Class Action Subgroup. He represents private and public sector employers in all areas of labor and employment law, including multi-jurisdictional defense of employment discrimination and whistleblower claims; federal/state wage and hour law compliance and litigation (including FLSA collective and class action defense); FMLA; USERRA and Sarbanes-Oxley compliance and litigation; grievance arbitration; and non-competition litigation.
**Personal:** University of Wisconsin (JD, cum laude/Order of the Coif); Santa Clara University (BS-Honors Program, magna cum laude/Phi Beta Kappa).

## SHOLL, Robert K
Reinhart Boerner Van Deuren s.c., Milwaukee
414 298 8143
rsholl@reinhartlaw.com
*Featured in Labor & Employment (Wisconsin)*
**Practice Areas:** Labor and employment.
**Career:** For 30 years has vigorously defended employers against employment discrimination, workplace harassment, and breach of noncompete agreement or employment contract lawsuits before state and federal agencies and courts. Represents employers in unemployment and worker's compensation hearings and wage/hour disputes. Labor practice includes collective bargaining, unfair labor practice hearings before NLRB, and labor arbitrations.
**Publications:** Co-author of Wisconsin Employment Law and Hiring and Firing in Wisconsin, each published by State Bar of Wisconsin and updated bi-annually.
**Personal:** Board Member of Milwaukee Children's Choir and Associate Council Member of Milwaukee County Council, Boy Scouts of America.

## SILVERTHORN, Richard W
Whyte Hirschboeck Dudek S.C., Milwaukee
414 978 5419
rsilverthorn@whdlaw.com
*Featured in Corporate/M&A (Wisconsin)*
**Career:** Rich Silverthorn focuses his practice on representing privately held and publicly traded companies in domestic and international business transactions, and general business and finance related matters. Mr Silverthorn has extensive experience in negotiating and structuring complex corporate and commercial transactions, including mergers and acquisitions, strategic alliance transactions, manufacturing, distribution and supply arrangements, licensing transactions, general business matters, and dispute resolution proceedings relating to the foregoing transactions. Mr Silverthorn has represented companies in the manufacturing, mining, chemical, entertainment, amusement/theme park, energy, water treatment, utility (gas, electric and water), electronics, automotive, trucking, food, and financial/hedge fund industries.

## SIMPSON, Michael H
Reinhart Boerner Van Deuren s.c., Milwaukee
414 298 8124
msimpson@reinhartlaw.com
*Featured in Natural Resources (Wisconsin)*
**Practice Areas:** Environmental.
**Professional Memberships:** State Bar of Wisconsin (former chairperson of Environmental Law Section), Wisconsin Small Business Environmental Council (former chairperson), Waukesha County Economic Development Corporation (director).
**Career:** As chair of the firm's Environmental Practice, Mike works with clients to creatively solve environmental, sustainability and land use issues. He advises clients on compliance with all aspects of federal and state environmental laws and represents clients in enforcement actions and

litigation involving environmental issues. Mike also advises clients on development projects, particularly those involving brownfields and sustainability issues. He is a former member of Wisconsin's Green Tier Advisors Group.

## SKIPPER, Walter J
Quarles & Brady LLP, Milwaukee
414 277 5119
walter.skipper@quarles.com
*Featured in Corporate/M&A (Wisconsin)*
**Practice Areas:** Mergers and acquisitions, private equity, securities, and business law services.
**Career:** Equity partner since 1999. Regularly represents purchasers and sellers, strategic and financial, in over 200 transactions, primarily in manufacturing and service businesses. Forms private equity funds and counsels funds on compliance and business operations matters. Counsels businesses on operating strategies and dispute resolution, helps businesses solve problems and take advantage of opportunities.
**Personal:** University of Wisconsin (JD, 1990); Marquette University (BS, 1985).

## SOVERN, Grant S
Quarles & Brady LLP, Madison
608 283 2668
grant.sovern@quarles.com
*Featured in Labor & Employment (Wisconsin)*
**Practice Areas:** Immigration.
**Professional Memberships:** Served on the American Immigration Lawyers Association's national Verification Liaison Committee,Interagency Taskforce, E-Verify Legislative Taskforce, and was Chair of AILA's national Social Security Administration Liaison Committee.
**Career:** He practices in the area of immigration law and is Chair of Quarles & Brady's national immigration practice. His area of concentration is immigration for employers and employees, including developing I-9 and E-Verify compliance programs. He is an Adjunct Professor at the University of Wisconsin Law School, teaching Immigration Law.
**Personal:** University of Michigan Law School (JD); Tufts University (BA, magna cum laude).

## STATHAS, Lynn M
Reinhart Boerner Van Deuren sc, Madison
608 229 2205
lstathas@reinhartlaw.com
*Featured in Labor & Employment (Wisconsin)*
**Practice Areas:** Labor and employment.
**Professional Memberships:** Immediate Past President, US District Court, Western District of Wisconsin Bar Association; James E. Doyle Inns of Court; Wisconsin State Bar; ABA; Executive Committee Member and Trustee, Memorial Union Building Association; Director, Madison Symphony Orchestra Board; Past President, LAW; TEMPO.
**Career:** Shareholder Lynn Stathas represents management in all areas of employment law, litigating and representing businesses before state and federal courts and agencies. Recognized in Wisconsin Super Lawyers (Labor & Employment Law), Best Lawyers in America, and is the Best

Lawyers in America 2013 Madison Employee Benefits (ERISA) Law "Lawyer of the Year."

## STETTNER, Derek C.
Michael Best & Friedrich LLP, Milwaukee
414 225 4947
dcstettner@michaelbest.com
*Featured in Intellectual Property (Wisconsin)*
**Practice Areas:** Derek Stettner is a partner focusing his practice on intellectual property and information technology matters and has over 15 years of experience in patent prosecution and technology transfer and licensing. He secures patent, copyright, and other intellectual property protection for electrical, computer, software, business method, and mechanical inventions. Mr Stettner regularly provides or assists with invention harvesting, patent portfolio management and strategy, IP due diligence, product clearance, and litigation support. His practice also involves competitive landscaping and patentability and infringement analysis. Mr Stettner has prepared, analyzed, and negotiated hundreds of software and other intellectual property licenses.

## STEVENS, Charles P
Michael Best & Friedrich LLP, Milwaukee
414 271 6560
cpstevens@michaelbest.com
*Featured in Labor & Employment (Wisconsin)*
**Practice Areas:** Charlie Stevens is a partner with over 25 years of experience in all aspects of Employee Benefits law and heads Michael Best's Employee Benefits Group. His practice focuses on the resolution of employee benefit problems arising through collective bargaining, benefit plan noncompliance, ERISA litigation, and multiemployer pension plans including contribution demands and withdrawal liability. Mr Stevens has counseled numerous employers and plan administrators on the Patient Protection and Affordable Care Act. His practice also involves strategizing with employers concerning the Americans with Disabilities Act, the Family and Medical Leave Act, Workers Compensation and similar areas of legal complexity.

## TEMKIN, Harvey L
Reinhart Boerner Van Deuren sc, Madison
608 229 2210
htemkin@reinhartlaw.com
*Featured in Real Estate (Wisconsin)*
**Practice Areas:** Real estate.
**Professional Memberships:** Fellow, American College of Mortgage Attorneys; Fellow, American College of Real Estate Lawyers (Title Insurance Coverage Subcommittee); American Bar Association; State Bar of Wisconsin.
**Career:** Shareholder in the firm's Madison office, represents real estate developers, lenders, businesses and healthcare providers since 1978. Areas of concentration include acquisitions, sales, zoning, land division and development, leasing, real estate litigation, commercial finance, business organizations and tax-deferred exchanges. Frequently named a top real estate lawyer in Madison Magazine's survey of Madison lawyers.

**Personal:** A former law professor, Harvey still enjoys teaching at real estate programs throughout the country.

## TOMASI, Peter
Quarles & Brady LLP, Milwaukee
414 277 5677
peter.tomasi@quarles.com
*Featured in Natural Resources (Wisconsin)*
**Practice Areas:** Environmental, energy, utilities, litigation.
**Career:** He practices in the areas of environmental permitting and litigation, with an emphasis on environmental issues for utility and independent power producers located in the Midwest and Southwest. He has advised energy-related clients on environmental compliance issues under the Clean Air Act, Clean Water Act, NEPA, and the Resource Conservation and Recovery Act. He represents clients in state and federal courts, and before the Wisconsin DNR, U.S. EPA, Department of Energy, and other state and federal environmental agencies.
**Personal:** Duke University (JD, cum laude); Duke University (MEM); University of Chicago (BA, cum laude).

## TOMCZYK, Deborah C
Reinhart Boerner Van Deuren s.c., Milwaukee
414 298 8331
dtomczyk@reinhartlaw.com
*Featured in Real Estate (Wisconsin)*
**Practice Areas:** Real estate.
**Professional Memberships:** Past President of Wisconsin Commercial Real Estate Women; Board of Directors, NAIOP (Commercial Real Estate Development Association) (Wisconsin chapter); Treasurer, Real Property, Probate, Trust Section of State Bar of Wisconsin.
**Career:** Shareholder representing local, regional and national developers and retailers in all aspects of real estate development. Areas of concentration include entitlements, zoning, land use, government relations, licensing, eminent domain and public financing, including tax incremental financing. Chairs firm's entitlements subpractice group.
**Personal:** Business Journal of Milwaukee 'Forty Under 40' award recipient, WCREW Women in Real Estate Leadership Award.

## VAN DEN ELZEN, Ryan L
Quarles & Brady LLP, Milwaukee
414 277 5455
ryan.vandenelzen@quarles.com
*Featured in Corporate/M&A (Wisconsin)*
**Practice Areas:** Mergers and acquisitions, private equity and venture capital, institutional investor services, securities, general corporate services.
**Professional Memberships:** American Bar Association, State Bar of Wisconsin, Association for Corporate Growth.
**Career:** Partner since 2010. Extensive experience representing privately and publicly held businesses, private fund sponsors, and institutional investors in various significant transactions, including acquisitions and divestitures, fund for-

mation, investments in private funds and other alternative asset classes, secondary market transactions, and private placements.
**Personal:** University of Notre Dame (JD, summa cum laude, 2002) University of Wisconsin (BS, 1999).

## VAN LIESHOUT, John M
Reinhart Boerner Van Deuren s.c., Milwaukee
414 298 8182
jvanlieshout@reinhartlaw.com
*Featured in Natural Resources (Wisconsin)*
**Practice Areas:** Environmental, litigation, real estate.
**Professional Memberships:** State Bar of Wisconsin (Board of Directors of the Environmental Law Section), Federation of Environmental Technologist.
**Career:** Shareholder focusing on real estate litigation and environmental clean-up issues. Lectures on mortgage forclosures and loan workouts, eminent domain and environmental issues. Taught environmental compliance at the Wisconsin Bankers Association Commercial Banking School and Agricultural Lending School. Litigates cases involving mortgage/loan workouts and foreclosures, eminent domain/condemnation underground storage tanks, landfills and wetlands. Counsels corporate officers, lenders and trustees on environmental matters.
**Publications:** Co-author, "Condemnation Law and Practice in Wisconsin" for the State Bar of Wisconsin.

## VAN VUGT, Eric J
Quarles & Brady LLP, Milwaukee
414 277 5625
eric.vanvugt@quarles.com
*Featured in Litigation (Wisconsin)*
**Practice Areas:** Litigation and dispute resolution; professional liability.
**Professional Memberships:** Fellow, American College of Trial Lawyers.
**Career:** He is a trial lawyer who handles complex commercial litigation, specializing in professional liability, insurance coverage and product liability matters. He has been lead counsel in more than 100 cases tried to verdict in state and federal courts across the country and has extensive arbitration and appellate experience.
**Personal:** Marquette University Law School (JD); Calvin College (BA).

## VOGEL, JR, Arthur A
Quarles & Brady LLP, Milwaukee
414 277 5545
arthur.vogel@quarles.com
*Featured in Natural Resources (Wisconsin)*
**Practice Areas:** Environmental.
**Professional Memberships:** Member, American Bar Association, State Bar of Wisconsin; Chair, 2005-06, Governor Doyle's "Blue Ribbon Task Force on Waste Materials Recovery and Disposal".
**Career:** He focuses his practice on environmental matters, including solid and hazardous waste, environmental due diligence, climate change and sustainability, site investigations and remediation

(including contaminated sediment), agency and private party negotiations relating to environmental liabilities (including mediation), Superfund management, and general regulatory compliance. Since 2007, he has chaired the national environmental practice group of Quarles & Brady LLP.
**Personal:** University of Notre Dame Law School (JD, cum laude); Northwestern University (BA).

## WEBER, Ralph A
Gass Weber Mullins LLC, Milwaukee
414 224 7698
weber@gasswebermullins.com
*Featured in Litigation (Wisconsin)*
**Career:** Mr Weber has represented clients in several of Wisconsin's highest profile lawsuits over the past several decades, and recently won a $50 million verdict after a five week jury trial. He also represents companies in cases nationwide. For example, Mr Weber won a multi-million dollar award in Portland, Maine for a food company whose supplier caused a widespread foodborne illness outbreak. Mr Weber has tried many lengthy jury and court trials. His appellate experience includes multiple oral arguments before the Wisconsin Supreme Court and intermediate appellate courts. The prestigious international lawyer reference, Chambers Guide-USA, identifies Mr Weber as a top commercial litigator. He also has been recognized by his peers through selection to Best Lawyers in America, Wisconsin Super Lawyers, and has been selected as a "Best of Class" service provider in the United States. An Adjunct Professor at Marquette University Law School, he has taught Trial Advocacy for more than 15 years, and created a jury research and courtroom facility, the Trial Science Institute. In addition to speaking about litigation subjects, Mr Weber co-edited a best selling book, Dear Americans: Letters from the Desk of Ronald Reagan (Doubleday, 2003). Mr Weber serves on the Northwestern Mutual Board of Trustees and the Board of Directors of the Wisconsin Conservatory of Music. Mr Weber founded and worked with several charitable and nonprofit groups, including the Marquette University National Alumni Board, the Marquette University College of Arts & Sciences Alumni Board, and the FC Milwaukee Soccer Club. He also served on the Board of Directors of Pius XI High School and chaired the Education Committee. Mr. Weber served on the Law Review at Columbia University Law School, graduating in 1982, and then served as a Law Clerk for the Hon. Richard D. Cudahy, United States Court of Appeals for the Seventh Circuit. He graduated summa cum laude from Marquette University in 1978, when he became a member of Phi Beta Kappa.

# FOLEY & LARDNER LLP

www.foley.com

**Chairman and CEO:** Jay O Rothman
Number of partners: 436
Number of other attorneys: 436

## Firm Overview:

Foley provides award-winning business and legal insight to clients across the country and around the world. The firm's exceptional client service, thought-leadership, value, and innovative technology are continually recognized by their clients and the legal industry. Foley's client-focused, industry-specific approach enables them to provide comprehensive, customized, and high-value legal solutions that help meet clients' needs today – and anticipate challenges tomorrow.

## Main Areas of Practice:

### Business Law:

Foley's Business Law Department is organized and staffed to provide comprehensive legal advice and business counseling. From corporate legal services such as mergers and acquisitions, finance, and securities to tax and individual planning, real estate, environmental regulation, and general commercial transactions and business counseling, nearly 400 Business Law attorneys are highly skilled in addressing today's most sophisticated business and legal issues.

### Government & Public Policy:

In addition to offering a full range of legal counsel to clients seeking to do business with federal, state, and local government, Foley also provides services covering the full spectrum of public policy — combining comprehensive counsel with proficiency in government relations, political law, strategic positioning, and communications coupled with the practice of law, when needed.

### Intellectual Property:

With nearly 200 IP lawyers — many with advanced technical degrees and experience — Foley delivers an innovative life cycle of IP services to obtain, protect, and add value to clients' IP. They provide product clearance opinions; conduct licensing programs; and handle the IP due diligence for corporate transactions. When and if their clients must litigate to enforce or defend their IP rights, the firm's experienced IP trial lawyers have handled hundreds of patent and IP litigation matters.

### Litigation:

With more than 300 litigators practicing nationwide, Foley has one of the largest and most comprehensive litigation departments in the United States. Their attorneys represent and counsel corporations in nearly every industry, and they provide complete state and federal trial and appellate representation, arbitration, mediation, and alternative dispute resolution (ADR) services. They also counsel and represent clients in administrative adjudications and in regulatory investigations and hearings.

### Industry Teams:

Each of Foley's integrated, industry-focused teams encompass a range of service offerings, enabling them to take a comprehensive view of their clients' industries and bring together the right practitioners and competencies to address their needs. Foley's industry teams focus on the airport and aviation, automotive, emerging technologies, energy, food and beverage, health care, hospitality, resort and golf, insurance and reinsurance, life sciences, medical devices, nanotechnology, senior living, and sports industries.

### Recent Accolades:

- Recognized as one of the elite BTI Client Service 30 for nine of the past 10 years (BTI Client Service A-Team survey, The BTI Consulting Group, Wellesley, MA)
- Twenty national first-tier rankings, 134 metropolitan first-tier rankings, and named "Law Firm of the Year — Health Care Law" for the second consecutive year on the 2013 U.S. News – Best Lawyers® "Best Law Firms" list
- Twenty practices and 73 attorneys recognized in The Legal 500 guide for the United States (2012)
- Named to the InformationWeek 500 list for innovative, client-focused technology (2012)

### Clients:

Bank of America; Carbonite; Citigroup; CVS Caremark; Google; Hanger Orthopedic Group; Harley-Davidson; Johnson Controls; Integrys Energy Group; Major League Baseball; Pentair; Takeda Pharmaceutical; Wellpoint.

## OFFICES

### CALIFORNIA

**LOS ANGELES**
Tel: 213 972 4500   Fax: 213 486 0065

**SACRAMENTO**
Tel: 916 443 8005   Fax: 916 443 2240

**SAN DIEGO**
Tel: 619 234 6655   Fax: 619 234 3510

**SAN DIEGO/DEL MAR**
Tel: 858 847 6700   Fax: 858-792 6773

**SAN FRANCISCO**
Tel: 415 434 4484   Fax: 415 434 4507

**SILICON VALLEY**
Tel: 650 856 3700   Fax: 650 856 3710

### DISTRICT OF COLUMBIA

**WASHINGTON, DC**
Tel: 202 672 5300   Fax: 202 672 5399

### FLORIDA

**JACKSONVILLE**
Tel: 904 359 2000   Fax: 904 359 8700

**MIAMI**
Tel: 305 482 8400   Fax: 305 482 8600

**ORLANDO**
Tel: 407 423 7656   Fax: 407 648 1743

**TALLAHASSEE**
Tel: 850 222 6100   Fax: 850 561 6475

**TAMPA**
Tel: 813 229 2300   Fax: 813 221 4210

### ILLINOIS

**CHICAGO**
Tel: 312 832 4500   Fax: 312 832 4700

### MASSACHUSETTS

**BOSTON**
Tel: 617 342 4000   Fax: 617 342 4001

### MICHIGAN

**DETROIT**
Tel: 313 234 7100   Fax: 313 234 2800

### NEW YORK

**NEW YORK**
Tel: 212 682 7474   Fax: 212 687 2329

### WISCONSIN

**MADISON**
Tel: 608 257 5035   Fax: 608 258 4258

**MILWAUKEE**
Tel: 414 271 2400   Fax: 414 297 4900

### INTERNATIONAL OFFICES

Brussels, Belgium; Shanghai, China; and Tokyo, Japan

# GASS WEBER MULLINS

**Managing Partner:** Michael B Brennan
Number of partners: 9
Number of other lawyers: 4

**OFFICES**

WISCONSIN

**MILWAUKEE:** 309 North Water Street, WI 53202
Tel: 414 223 3300  Fax: 414 224 6116

### Firm Overview:

Gass Weber Mullins is a litigation boutique of 13 innovative lawyers with decades of trial experience. Since opening in 2004, the firm's lawyers have prosecuted and defended cases in 36 states encompassing complex issues of national and international scope. The founding members set out to create a firm of lawyers with the intelligence and creativity to solve the most difficult factual and legal issues. They assembled lawyers with a deep reservoir of courtroom skills and experience because some cases need to be tried - and all cases resolve on better terms when your opponent realizes that you are ready for trial. Firm lawyers also have significant experience conducting mock trials and other jury research. This research helps secure great trial results by giving the attorneys the added dimension of understanding what motivates jurors beyond the bare facts and the law.

### Main Areas of Practice:

The firm's trial lawyers concentrate on civil litigation, including food safety, product liability, catastrophic injuries, bad faith, commercial and construction lawsuits, appellate, and life, health and disability insurance litigation.

### Clients:

Representative clients include: American Cyanamid, Aqua Finance, Inc., Cargill, Inc., CBS Corporation, Crown Equipment Corporation, Dupont, Humana Insurance Company, Joy Global Inc., RSUI Group, Inc., Stifel, Nicolaus, and Company, Inc. and Trek Bicycle Corporation.

# GODFREY & KAHN, S.C.

**www.**gklaw.com **tel:** 414 273 3500 **fax:** 414 273 5198

**Managing Partner:** Nicholas P Wahl
Number of partners: 94
Number of other lawyers (in US offices): 81
Languages: *English*

## Firm Overview:

Godfrey & Kahn provides business-oriented, comprehensive advice to clients ranging from emerging growth companies, venture capital and buyout funds to large, privately and publicly held national and international corporations, and high net worth individuals and executives. The firm is a member of TerraLex®, an international network of independent law firms.

## Main Areas of Practice:

### Corporate:

- Sale of a division of Johnson Controls Denmark ApS to Emerson Electric Co.
- Purchase of stock of GreenLine Foods, Inc. by Apio, Inc. (a subsidiary of Landec Corporation) for $63 million

**Key Clients:** Kohl's Corp., Johnson Controls, Inc., Quad/Graphics, Inc., BMO Harris Bank, N.A., ManpowerGroup, The Mark Travel Corporation, Allen Edmonds Shoe Corporation, Diageo, Robert W. Baird & Co. Incorporated, Pinstripe, Inc., Walker Forge, Inc.
**Contact:** Chris Noyes **Tel:** 414 287 9530
**Email:** cnoyes@gklaw.com

### Intellectual Property:

- Represented Pacific Cycle in the global protection including enforcement and defense, of its Schwinn, Mongoose, GT, Iron Horse, InSTEP, and other brands of bicycles and recreational products
- Enforcement of patent portfolio for automotive OEM Asyst Technologies against aftermarket parts companies

**Key Clients:** Johnsonville Sausage, LLC, Pacific Cycle, Allen Edmonds Shoe Corporation, Kohl's Corp., Wisconsin Alumni Research Foundation, Extreme Networks, Inc., The Art Commission, LLC.
**Contact:** Brian Gilpin **Tel:** 414 287 9317
**Email:** bgilpin@gklaw.com

### Litigation:

- Defended Wells Fargo Bank, N.A., as trustee, from claims of breach of fiduciary duty by beneficiaries claiming that the bank engaged in self-dealing and imprudent investments, and was awarded actual attorney fees
- Represented Quad/Graphics, Inc. prosecuting claims against former agents of its subsidiary, Openfirst, claiming the defendants had breached their contractual and fiduciary duties to Openfirst by secretly diverting Openfirst's customers away from Openfirst to the defendants. A jury awarded Quad/Graphics $14 million

**Key Clients:** Journal Communications, Inc., Kimberly-Clark Corporation, Liberty Mutual Insurance Co., Fiserv, Inc., Oshkosh Corporation, Manpower, Inc., Forest County Potawatomi Community,

Quad/Graphics, Inc., Wisconsin Physicians Service Insurance Corporation, Kohl's Corp.
**Contact:** James Friedman **Tel:** 608 284 2617
**Email:** jfriedman@gklaw.com

### Real Estate:

- Represented a developer/landlord in a build-to-suit development and lease of a 230-bed student housing project for Carroll University in Waukesha, Wisconsin. Further, negotiated a long-term lease of the facility to Carroll University and assisted with the project financing using Midwest Disaster Relief Bonds
- Assisted regional healthcare provider with the discrete land assemblage project to be developed into a suburban healthcare campus. Representation included negotiation of a development agreement and tax incremental financing package with the City of Middleton, Wisconsin

**Key Clients:** BMO Harris Bank N.A., Irgens Development Partners, LLC, Kaufman Jacobs, LLC, US Bank National Association, PrivateBank Trust & Company, Cobalt Partners, Crown Court Properties, Ltd., Meriter Hospital, Inc., The Livesey Company, Forest County Potawatomi Community.
**Contact:** Mark O'Neill **Tel:** 414 287 9233
**Email:** moneill@gklaw.com

### Environmental & Energy:

- Assisted client in obtaining numerous competitive grants and other incentives totaling more than $9 million toward energy independence projects and provided legal advice for all aspects of development of biogas, solar and other energy projects
- Provided national bank with strategic advice regarding the environmental issues with distressed properties as part of its foreclosure process and served as a single point of contact to help ensure consistency of its evaluation and decision making

**Key Clients:** Forest County Potawatomi Community, Quad/Graphics Inc., Johnson Controls, Inc., Kohl's Corp., American Transmission Company, A.O. Smith Corporation, Wisconsin Power & Light, Co., City of Kenosha, City of Oak Creek.

**Contact:** John Clancy **Tel:** 414 287 9256
**Email:** jclancy@gklaw.com

### Labor & Employment:

- Provided advice related to interpretation and implementation of 2010 Wisconsin Act 10. Assisted employers in developing comprehensive personnel policies in politically charged public environment
- Assisted one of the largest mortgage lenders in the country with implementing comprehensive employment practices, innovative employment policies, and complex restrictive covenant agreements to support the company's rapid employment growth

**Key Clients:** Waterstone Mortgage Corporation, a wholly owned subsidiary of WaterStone Bank SSB (NASDAQ: WSBF), Kimberly-Clark Corporation, ManpowerGroup, Oshkosh Corporation, Mercy Health System Corporation, Allen Edmonds Shoe Corporation, Cambridge Major Laboratories, Inc., Dane County, Wisconsin, ZBB Energy Corporation, School Speciality, Inc.
**Contact:** Jon Anderson **Tel:** 608 284 2610
**Email:** janderson@gklaw.com

# GODFREY ■ KAHN S.C.

# LINDNER & MARSACK, S.C.

WWW.lindner-marsack.com **tel:** 414 273 3910 **fax:** 414 273 0522

**Chairman:** Gary A Marsack
**President & CEO:** Jonathan T Swain
Number of partners: 9
Number of other lawyers: 8

**PRACTICE AREAS**
Labor & Employment

**OFFICES**
WISCONSIN
**MILWAUKEE:** 411 East Wisconsin Avenue, Suite 1800,
Milwaukee, WI 53202-4498
Tel: 414 273 3910   Fax: 414 273 0522

## Firm Overview:

Lindner & Marsack, S.C. is one of the nation's preeminent law firms specializing in labor, employment and benefits law. Established in 1908 in Milwaukee, Wisconsin, the firm's experience and talents are uniformly respected in the business and legal communities. Serving as labor and employment law advisors, negotiators, and litigators, the attorneys of Lindner & Marsack, S.C. represent employers of all sizes in industries ranging from traditional manufacturing to emerging hi-tech concerns, wholesale distribution to retail, and from trucking to construction, as well as municipalities and other governmental entities. The firm believes that its labor and employment legal experience is virtually unmatched; partners average over 25 years in the practice of workplace law. Lindner & Marsack, S.C. is a member of the Worklaw® Network, an organization of specialty labor and employment law firms located throughout the USA, Canada and Europe, and Asia which focus their practices exclusively in the area of labor and employment law. As a member of this network, Lindner & Marsack, S.C. is able to offer management high quality and cost effective representation with national and international expertise. Lindner & Marsack, S.C. lawyers have been regularly recognized as 'Best Lawyers in America' and 'Super Lawyers' in Wisconsin.

## Main Areas of Practice:

### General Labor & Union Representation Matters:
Lindner & Marsack, S.C. aggressively represents employers in union organizing and decertification matters, as well as clients seeking to maintain their non-union status. The firm also represents employers in matters before the NLRB in representation matters and in the defense of unfair labor practice charges.

### Collective Bargaining & Contract Administration:
The firm has been successfully representing management at the bargaining table for over 75 years. Its attorneys are recognized as firm, passionate negotiators with the experience to skillfully negotiate collective bargaining agreements that address today's complex global economic issues.

### Employment Counseling:
The attorneys of Lindner & Marsack, S.C. help management find creative solutions for all of its human resource and employee relations challenges, seeking to avoid costly litigation and employee relations problems by ensuring that its clients' policies, practices and employment decisions are legally compliant and properly enforced.

### Labor, Employment, & Benefits Litigation:
The attorneys of Lindner & Marsack, S.C. are also experienced, innovative and aggressive litigators in defending the rights of management in all facets of labor, employment and employee benefits litigation, including employment discrimination and harassment, whistleblower and retaliation claims, FMLA issues, wage and hour matters, ERISA/employee benefits litigation, contract and labor disputes, including multiple-plaintiff and class/collective actions.

### Employee Benefits:
The firm assists businesses in addressing the dynamic and critical issues of implementing, administering and maintaining cost-effective employee benefits plans.

### Business Immigration Law:
The firm assists with the full range of immigration and guest worker issues.

### Work Injury Defense:
The firm represents businesses in the defense of worksite injury and illness claims. The firm's experienced worker's compensation team aggressively fights fraudulent claims and represents employers seeking subrogation or reimbursement following a workplace injury.

### Non-Compete Agreements & Trade Secrets:
Lindner & Marsack, S.C. assists employers in drafting and enforcing non-compete and confidentiality agreements. When necessary, the firm's attorneys serve as aggressive litigators in the enforcement of such agreements.

## Clients:
Arandell Corp.; Badger Meter Mfg.; Bemis Manufacturing Company; Besse Forest Products; Brenntag; City of Sheboygan; Cleaver Brooks; Domtar, Inc.; Fairbanks Morse; General Electric Medical Systems; Guardian Life Insurance Company of America; Louisiana-Pacific Corporation; Marcus Center; Masonite, Inc.; Michels Pipeline; Milwaukee County; Milwaukee Metropolitan Sewerage District; Newell Rubbermaid, Inc.; Norwich Pharmaceutical; Ocean Spray, Inc.; Overture Center; Printpack, Inc.; Roundy's Supermarkets, Inc., d/b/a Rainbow Foods and Pick 'N Save; Sargento Foods, Inc.; Snap-On, Inc.; Strattec Security Corp.; Voith Paper; Walgreen Co.; Wisconsin County Mutual Insurance Corporation; W.S. Darley & Co.

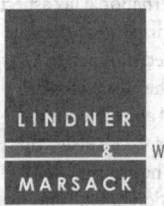

LINDNER & MARSACK   Winning strategies for employers since 1908

# MICHAEL BEST & FRIEDRICH LLP

www.michaelbest.com **tel:** 414 271 6560 **fax:** 414 277 0656

**Managing Partner:** David A Krutz
**Chair of the Management Committee:** Scott C Beightol
Number of partners: 142  Number of attorneys: 223

## Firm Overview:

Michael Best & Friedrich LLP has earned a reputation as a leading law firm in the Midwest due to the firm's long commitment to delivering results for clients. By guiding businesses through complex legal problems in diverse economic environments, the firm's attorneys possess a solid foundation for understanding the constantly evolving business environments facing clients today. Michael Best is ideally positioned to handle a wide range of legal matters across the practice areas identified below. In addition, the firm offers sophisticated counsel to cutting-edge industries, including advanced manufacturing, banking and financial services, energy and sustainability and technology.

## Main Areas of Practice:

### Transactional Corporate & Business:

The firm's Transactional Practice Group includes a broad range of services. Corporate and business law is a core competency of the firm. The range of services involves individuals, partnerships, limited liability companies and corporations and includes assisting in the organization, financing and operation of business ventures, through and including mergers, acquisitions, divestitures and joint ventures. Experience in corporate finance has resulted in representation of venture capital investors, mezzanine lenders and start-up companies.
**Contact:** Michael S Green
**Email:** msgreen@michaelbest.com

### Land & Resources:

Michael Best's land and resources attorneys practice in all areas of environmental, construction, development, real estate law and climate change, serving property owners, developers, all types of manufacturers and industrial operations, public utilities, construction and agribusiness companies.
**Contact:** Michael S Green
**Email:** msgreen@michaelbest.com

### Tax:

Michael Best's Tax Group is comprised of some of the most pre-eminent practitioners in the Midwest. In the tax planning area, attorneys advise organizations with respect to the federal, state and international tax aspects of structuring acquisitions, reorganizations, real estate developments, exchanges and related transactions. In the tax controversy area, members of the group regularly appear in federal and state trial and appellate courts, litigating all aspects of income taxes, excise taxes, sales and use taxes and property taxes. The group is well known for its sought-after publication titled, "The Complete Guide to Wisconsin Sales and Use Taxes".
**Contact:** Timothy G Schally
**Email:** tgschally@michaelbest.com

### Wealth Planning Services:

Michael Best provides high quality, cost effective and innovative services regarding business succession planning, financial planning, asset protection planning, retirement planning, estate litigation and family counseling. The attorneys in this group consult with clients to determine short-term and long-term objectives regarding asset protection and management, minimization of taxes and disposition of wealth.
**Contact:** Mark S Poker
**Email:** mspoker@michaelbest.com

### Intellectual Property:

Michael Best has one of the nation's leading intellectual property practices. Nearly 100 professionals offer a complete range of services to clients throughout the nation and around the world. Michael Best's Intellectual Property Practice Group offers legal and technical experience in areas such as patent, trademark and copyright prosecution and counseling; intellectual property litigation; internet and e-commerce; technology transfer and joint venture agreements; computer software and system acquisition agreements; M&A due diligence; biotechnology and trade secrets. Michael Best ranks among the leading trademark law firms in the nation.
**Contact:** Billie Jean Smith
**Email:** bjsmith@michaelbest.com

### Labor & Employment:

Michael Best's labor and employment attorneys represent some of the most innovative businesses, public sector and non-profit organizations in the nation. The attorneys continually strive to develop close partnerships with clients, focusing on litigation prevention and the achievement of strategic objectives through human resources counseling, planning and training. The attorneys are recognized by their clients and peers as among the best and most respected management-side labor, employment, and employee benefits attorneys in the Midwest, providing legal defense in all aspects of labor and employment litigation; union organizing, collective bargaining, and grievance arbitration; wage-hour issues; safety and workers compensation; employee benefits and immigration. They have decades of experience practicing in state and federal trial courts, appellate and Supreme courts, administrative agencies and arbitrators, and designing compensation, retirement, pension, stock and health plans.
**Contact:** José A Olivieri
**Email:** jaolivieri@michaelbest.com

### Litigation:

Michael Best's Litigation Practice Group has an unmatched depth of experience and success with more than 150 published cases at every level of State and Federal Courts in recent years. Its members include a host of former judicial law clerks, law review editors, a former Wisconsin Supreme Court Justice and board members and officers of local, state and national bar associations. The attorneys are consistently honored by publications as among the best counsel in their fields. More than 70 members strong, Michael Best's Litigation Practice Group is equipped to provide clients with first class representation in any type of complex commercial litigation.
**Contact:** Daniel J Vaccaro
**Email:** djvaccaro@michaelbest.com

### International Work:

Through various international legal affiliations, Michael Best has the ability to bring global resources to clients. Michael Best is the exclusive Wisconsin member of Lex Mundi ('Law of the World'), enabling the firm to arrange effective representation for clients around the world.
**Contact:** Thomas A Miller
**Email:** tamiller@michaelbest.com

## OFFICES

### WISCONSIN

**MADISON:** One South Pinckney Street, Suite 700, WI 53703-4257
Tel: 608 257 3501  Fax: 608 283 2275

**MANITOWOC:** 1000 Maritime Drive, WI 54220-2922
Tel: 920 686 2800  Fax: 920 686 2810

**MILWAUKEE:** 100 East Wisconsin Avenue, Suite 3300, WI 53202-4108
Tel: 414 271 6560  Fax: 414 277 0656

**WAUKESHA:** Two Riverwood Place, Suite 200, N19 W24133 Riverwood Drive, WI 53188-1174
Tel: 262 956 6560  Fax: 262 956 6565

### ILLINOIS

**CHICAGO:** Two Prudential Plaza, 180 North Stetson Avenue, Suite 2000, IL 60601
Tel: 312 222 0800  Fax: 312 222 0818

MICHAEL BEST & FRIEDRICH LLP

# QUARLES & BRADY LLP

www.quarles.com **tel:** 414 277 5000 **fax:** 414 271 3552

**Chairman:** John W Daniels Jr
**Managing Partner:** Fredrick G Lautz
Number of partners: 274
Number of lawyers: 436

### Firm Overview:

Quarles & Brady provides broad-based, multi-disciplinary international services through a strong network of regional practices across the United States. In its distinguished 120-year history, Quarles has grown from a small, well-respected local Milwaukee law firm to achieve a place among the Am Law 200, building a national practice and earning a comparable reputation throughout the United States.

The firm's success is based on the strength of its client relationships, as Quarles places a commitment to help among its highest priorities. Effecting positive legal outcomes is merely the means to the firm's primary end, which is to help clients fully achieve *all* objectives of which their legal needs are a part, in any way possible. As a result, in addition to its listings in *Chambers USA*, 160 of the firm's partners have been recognized by *The Best Lawyers in America* in 2013, including 24 of whom were ranked as "Lawyers of the Year" in their respective practices. Quarles continuously seeks to add value through a variety of operational efficiencies and complimentary service offerings, defining "success" only according to each client's specific criteria, and seeking to better represent all clients through a thorough understanding of their businesses, industries, and competitive environments.

### Main Areas of Practice:

Quarles & Brady provides comprehensive legal services in the general practice areas of Bankruptcy, Commercial Litigation, Corporate Services, Environmental, Health, Intellectual Property, Labor & Employment, Product Liability, Public Finance, Real Estate & Land Use, and Trust & Estates Law.

The firm has further developed distinguishing experience and knowledge in the areas of Energy, Financial Services, Franchising, Health & Life Sciences, IP Litigation, Middle-Market Business Services, Public Finance, and Research Institutions, employing attorneys, engineers, scientists, and other subject-matter authorities in order to practice in these areas at a particularly high level.

### Diversity:

Attracting and retaining a diverse workforce is integral to the way in which Quarles & Brady sees itself, and its partners and employees see one another. The firm's wholehearted commitment to diversity & inclusion is reflected in the chairman's motto, "Everybody counts, every day," in its substantial and formal diversity program, and in its frequent recognition for its dedication and achievements. In the 2013 edition of the *Vault Guide to the Top 100 Law Firms*, Quarles was ranked No. 13 in "Best Law Firms for Diversity," No. 8 in "Diversity for Women," and No. 14 in "Diversity for Minorities." The firm has further received "Gold Standard Certification" from the Women in Law

Enforcement Forum and has earned a 100% rating in both the 2010 and 2011 editions of the Human Rights Campaign Foundation's *Corporate Equality Index*. Quarles as a firm, as well as its individual attorneys, has received numerous citations and awards from both clients and the legal industry.

### Pro Bono & Community Service:

Quarles & Brady attorneys and staff are encouraged to support their neighborhood and professional communities; leadership and volunteer opportunities are available to employees at every level. Whether providing pro bono legal counsel to the indigent, mentoring children, leading through diversity, developing educational programs for industry groups, or supporting non-profit organizations through board service, the firm gives back to its communities with the same dedication devoted to its clients.

### Clients:

The firm's clients include major national and multinational corporations, high-tech companies, educational and research institutions, municipalities and government agencies, charitable organizations, industry executives and high-net-worth individuals. They are industry leaders in high-tech, energy, financial services, health care, insurance, pharmaceuticals, real estate and manufacturing, to name just a few.

**OFFICES**

**WISCONSIN**

**MILWAUKEE (HEAD OFFICE):** 411 East Wisconsin Avenue, Suite 2350, WI 53202-4426
Tel: 414 277 5000   Fax: 414 271 3552

**MADISON:** 33 East Main Street, Suite 900, WI 53703-3095
Tel: 608 251 5000   Fax: 608 251 9166

**ARIZONA**

**PHOENIX:** One Renaissance Square, Two North Central Avenue, AZ 85004-2391
Tel: 602 229 5200   Fax: 602 229 5690

**TUCSON:** One South Church Avenue, Suite 1700, AZ 85701-1621
Tel 520 770 8700 Fax 520 623 2418

**DISTRICT OF COLUMBIA**

**WASHINGTON DC:** 1700 K Street, NW, Suite 825, DC 20006
Tel: 202 372 9600   Fax: 202 372 9599

**FLORIDA**

**NAPLES:** 1395 Panther Lane, Suite 300, FL 34109-7874
Tel: 239 262 5959   Fax: 239 434 4999

**TAMPA:** 101 East Kennedy Blvd., Suite 3400, FL 33602-5187
Tel: 813 387 0300   Fax: 813 387 1800

**ILLINOIS**

**CHICAGO:** 300 N. LaSalle Street, Suite 4000, IL 60654-3406
Tel: 312 715 5000   Fax: 312 715 5155

**INTERNATIONAL OFFICES**

The firm also has an office in Shanghai

# REINHART BOERNER VAN DEUREN S.C.

www.reinhartlaw.com **tel:** 414 298 1000 **fax:** 414 298 8097

**Chief Executive Officer:** Jerome M Janzer

Number of partners: 137  Number of associates: 65

Total number of attorneys: 202  Total number of support staff: 217

## Firm Overview:

Reinhart Boerner Van Deuren s.c. serves business needs with innovation, focus and commitment. The firm's attorneys are dedicated to providing strategic, comprehensive and cost-effective legal services to clients throughout the world. Founded in 1894, Reinhart serves public and privately held corporations, financial institutions, family-owned businesses, retirement plans, exempt organizations and individuals.

## Main Areas of Practice:

### Banking & Finance:

Reinhart goes beyond providing counsel on state and regulatory compliance. The firm brings together lenders and borrowers to meet the needs of businesses and help municipalities finance projects.

### Business Law:

The firm's deal makers and problem solvers have the insight and contacts to help clients achieve goals and add value at any stage in the life of their business.

### Business Reorganization:

With a pre-eminent reputation and proven track record of success in insolvency matters, the firm represents lenders, borrowers, creditors, debtors, committees, trustees, receivers, landlords, buyers, sellers, shareholders and other equity holders and bondholders.

### Employee Benefits:

Reinhart was one of the first law firms to represent employee benefit plans more than 40 years ago and now has clients in almost every state.

### Environmental Law:

The firm has experienced attorneys, scientists, engineers and other technical professionals who provide one-stop shopping for resolution of environmental problems.

### Government Relations:

When businesses or not-for-profit organizations need access to local, state or federal officials, Reinhart delivers through lobbying, government procurement opportunities or building strategic partnerships.

### Healthcare:

With 150 years of combined insight, the firm's healthcare teams offer both industry-focused support and guidance into traditional and niche legal practice areas.

### Insurance:

The firm represents clients before state insurance departments and helps organizations navigate complex regulations and address the unique aspects of insurance related transactions. The firm's attorneys also have extensive experience in a wide range of insurance related litigation.

### Intellectual Property:

The firm offers strategic solutions to develop customized and forward-thinking intellectual property protection. The firm's philosophy involves not only obtaining traditional protection for its clients, but also offers a synergistic approach with intangible asset management.

### International:

The firm advises clients on compliance with business, tax and immigration laws around the world, and has the connections to compete in a wide range of foreign political or economic systems.

### Labor & Employment:

Reinhart advises clients on the entire spectrum of labor and employment issues and helps employers prevent problems and avoid costly litigation. Reinhart represents management before federal and state courts and administrative agencies.

### Litigation:

Winning efficiently requires a trial team with case-specific experience. The firm understands the difference between bloated strategies that sound good and creative solutions that produce results. The firm believes in early evaluation and negotiated solutions to reduce legal fees.

### Mergers & Acquisitions:

Reinhart offers a broad spectrum of services ranging from counseling purchasers and sellers of middle-market companies to negotiating and structuring complex transactions involving publicly held and multinational companies.

### Private Equity, Venture Capital & Corporate Finance:

Efficiency, responsiveness and the ability to get involved in the early stages of financing are what sets Reinhart apart. Firm attorneys do more than structure and negotiate financial transactions; they help clients raise capital by assisting them to locate the right source.

### Product Distribution & Franchise:

The firm's unique interdisciplinary team of trial and corporate attorneys solve distribution and franchise law problems for companies that buy or sell products or services at retail or wholesale.

### Public Finance:

The firm serves as bond counsel and as counsel to 501(c)(3) borrowers, letter of credit banks and underwriters in tax-exempt bond financings.

### Real Estate:

Reinhart offers clients custom-tailored real estate counsel through subspecialty groups so that its broad experience and depth of knowledge apply to every matter.

### Tax:

The firm is dedicated to saving clients money, whether at the international, domestic, federal or state levels. The firm's Tax Controversy Group enjoys a reputation for winning large reductions from tax agencies.

### Tax-Exempt Organizations:

Serving several industries, Reinhart provides corporate, formational, governance endowment, tax, financing, employee benefit, litigation and employment legal advice.

### Telecommunications & Energy:

The firm's attorneys help clients compete successfully in the complex world of heavily regulated industries.

### Trusts & Estates:

Reinhart helps clients build and preserve wealth both for themselves and their heirs. Many successful family-owned businesses rely on Reinhart for business succession and continuation planning. They also rely on Reinhart for their personal estate and tax planning, as well as for estate and trust administration.

## OFFICES

### WISCONSIN

**MILWAUKEE:** 1000 North Water Street, Suite 1700, Milwaukee, WI 53202
Tel: 414 298 1000  Fax: 414 298 8097

**WAUKESHA:** N16W23250 Stone Ridge Drive, Suite 1, Waukesha, WI 53188
Tel: 262 951 4500  Fax: 262 951 4690

**MADISON:** 22 East Mifflin Street, Suite 600, Madison, WI 53703
Tel: 608 229 2200  Fax: 608 229 2100

### ILLINOIS

**CHICAGO:** 233 South Wacker Drive, Suite 9400, IL 60606
Tel: 312 207 5456  Fax: 414 298 8097

**ROCKFORD:** 2215 Perrygreen Way, Rockford, IL 61107
Tel: 815 633 5300  Fax: 815 654 5770

### ARIZONA

**PHOENIX:** 16220 North Scottsdale Road, Suite 290, Scottsdale, AZ 85254
Tel: 480 860 0414  Fax: 414 298 8097

### COLORADO

**DENVER:** 8400 East Prentice Avenue, Penthouse, Greenwood Village, CO 80111
Tel: 303 843 6042  Fax: 303 721 1083

# WHYTE HIRSCHBOECK DUDEK S.C.

**Chief Executive:** Paul J Eberle
Number of partners: 75 Number of other attorneys: 51

**Firm Overview:**

Whyte Hirschboeck Dudek S.C. is a full-service law firm committed to delivering client success with innovative yet practical solutions to complex legal problems. WHD has over 150 professionals practicing in more than 50 industry and specialty teams.

**Main Areas of Practice:**

**Corporate:**

The firm works with publicly traded companies to emerging, entrepreneurial and closely held businesses. WHD does significant M&A work, tailors deals to the unique needs of its clients and their industries, and gets deals done. WHD works closely with its clients, along with the clients' owners and advisors, to help them fully understand and address the legal and business aspects of starting, operating, acquiring and selling a business, including issues relating to financing and capital structures, ownership structures and succession.

**Litigation:**

The firm successfully represents business clients' interests in federal and state trial and appellate courts throughout the country and before federal and state agencies and national and international arbitrators. WHD handles business disputes in a variety of areas, including: intellectual property, theft of trade secrets, patent, trademark and copyright, information technology and e-commerce, ERISA, tax, franchise and dealership, products liability, construction, shareholder disputes, employment disputes, condemnation, unfair competition, antitrust, fraud and environmental, health and safety, transportation, toxic tort and catastrophic personal injury, constitutional law and professional liability claims.

**Human Resources Law:**

The firm advises clients on all aspects of the employer-employee relationship, including collective bargaining and union matters, employment contracts, noncompetition agreements, discrimination claims, worker's compensation and employee benefits. WHD takes an integrated approach to ensure proper consideration of all employee-related legal issues that may impact the client's business.

**Intellectual Property:**

The firm represents national and international clients in all areas of intellectual property law. WHD has substantial experience representing clients in connection with obtaining, maintaining, and enforcing intellectual property rights, as well as negotiating licenses and other intellectual property agreements. Technical experience extends to chemical products and processes, mechanical and electrical devices, life sciences, biotechnology, medical devices, software, computers and integrated circuits, and business methods.

**Technology:**

The firm addresses the unique challenges inherent in contracting and claims resolution processes involving the design, development, implementation, operation and maintenance of complex information technology, telecommunications and ecommerce solutions. WHD is experienced in software and business method patents, trademarks and copyrights and have industry experience in engineering and consulting in both the wireless and wireline segments of the telecommunications industry.

**Real Estate:**

The firm represents developers, purchasers, sellers, tenants, landlords, municipalities, contractors and lenders across the spectrum of real estate matters. WHD is intimately involved in the real estate community and has the technical expertise and ability to complete the most sophisticated transactions.

**Finance:**

The firm provides a full spectrum of legal services to banks and savings institutions, commercial and consumer finance companies, insurance companies, equity funds and other institutional lenders and investors. WHD has nationally recognized Public Finance, Credit Union and Consumer Financial Services practices.

**Reorganization:**

The experience of the firm's Business Restructuring, Creditors' Rights & Bankruptcy practice extends to all matters that concern advising, consulting or doing business with financially troubled enterprises. WHD represents lenders, creditors' committees, suppliers, lessors, purchasers, equity holders, corporate and individual creditors and debtors, and has successfully represented many regional and national clients in some notable reorganizations.

**Trusts & Estates:**

The firm provides comprehensive legal services for estate planning and estate and trust administration for individuals, families, business owners and professionals. WHD helps clients evaluate their assets and create a plan that maximizes the transfer of wealth and minimizes taxes while avoiding future legal difficulties and unnecessary costs.

**OFFICES**

**WISCONSIN**
**MADISON:** 33 East Main Street, Suite 300, P.O. Box 1379, WI 53701-1379
Tel: 608 255 4440 Fax: 608 258 7138

**MILWAUKEE:** 555 East Wells Street, Suite 1900, WI 53202-3819
Tel: 414 273 2100 Fax: 414 223 5000

**ILLINOIS**
**CHICAGO:** 161 North Clark Street, Suite 4700, IL 60601-3206
Tel: 312 523 2080 Fax: 414 223 5000
www.whdlaw.com

**Tax - Federal, State & Local Tax Planning, Audit Defense, Litigation:**

The firm represents clients in federal, state and local income, franchise, sales and property tax planning and dispute resolution, including issues involving multi-state taxation, nexus and related matters. WHD's transactional tax attorneys focus on providing practical and efficient solutions to complex tax problems for large and midsize companies. The team collaborates with lawyers in the corporate transactions and business law areas to develop and implement optimal tax planning strategies for complex corporate transactions such as acquisitions, mergers, divestitures and other reorganizations. Several of the team members have in-depth experience in the taxation of S corporations, limited liability companies, partnerships and similar 'pass-through' entities. In addition, the firm's transactional team represents tax-exempt entities of varying sizes including both public charities and private foundations on a range of income tax matters and in securing and maintaining tax-exempt status. WHD's contested tax team has appeared before almost all levels of state and federal tribunals on civil and criminal matters, and consists of several experienced attorneys, including a former IRS trial attorney, and former tax manager for two *Fortune* 500 companies.

**Clients:**

Acuity, A Mutual Insurance Company, BMO Harris Bank N.A., Cleaver-Brooks Inc., Enbridge Energy Partnership, J.F. Brennan Company, Inc., Roundy's Supermarkets, Inc., Safway Services Inc., Standard Process Inc., and United Healthcare of Wisconsin, Inc.

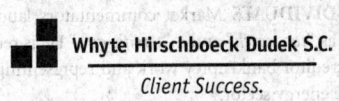

Whyte Hirschboeck Dudek S.C.

*Client Success.*

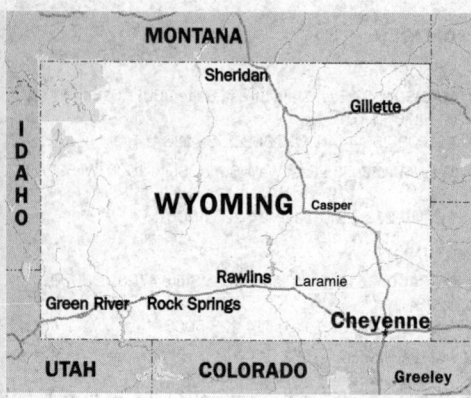

## How lawyers are ranked

Every year we carry out thousands of in-depth interviews with clients in order to assess the reputations and expertise of business lawyers worldwide. The qualities we look for (and which determine rankings) include technical legal ability, professional conduct, client service, commercial awareness/astuteness, diligence, commitment, and other qualities most valued by the client. For details of our research team, see p.5.

# CORPORATE/M&A

Commentary about individuals can be found under their firm's paragraph. If the firm has no paragraph (is not ranked) look at Other Notable Practitioners.

### Corporate/M&A
#### Leading Firms

**Band 1**

Belcher & Boomgaarden LLP
Dray, Dyekman, Reed & Healey, P.C.
Hirst Applegate
Holland & Hart LLP *
Long Reimer Winegar Beppler LLP

#### Leading Individuals

**Band 1**

| | |
|---|---|
| Belcher James | Belcher & Boomgaarden LLP |
| Buffington Teresa | Holland & Hart LLP * |
| Cottam Dale | Hirst Applegate |
| Dray W Perry | Dray, Dyekman, Reed & Healey, P.C. |
| Dyekman Gregory C | Dray, Dyekman, Reed & Healey, P.C. |
| Long Thomas N | Long Reimer Winegar Beppler LLP |
| Toner Tom C | Yonkee & Toner LLP (ONP)† |

**Band 2**

| | |
|---|---|
| Barbe J Kenneth | Welborn Sullivan Meck & Tooley (ONP)† |
| Reed Randall B | Dray, Dyekman, Reed & Healey, P.C. |
| Reimer Christopher M | Long Reimer Winegar Beppler LLP |
| Winegar Natalie K | Long Reimer Winegar Beppler LLP |

* Indicates firm / individual with profile.
† ONP = Other Notable Practitioner.

## Band 1

### Belcher & Boomgaarden LLP

**THE FIRM** This team's stellar Cheyenne practice earns particular recognition for its expertise in corporate, renewable energy and bankruptcy matters. The firm is also highly regarded for representing clients in the mining industry. **KEY INDIVIDUALS** Market commentators laud **James Belcher** as *"top notch"* and a *"terrific guy."* He is renowned for his creditor bankruptcy work and representing clients from the energy sector.

### Corporate/M&A: Bankruptcy
#### Leading Individuals

**Band 1**

| | |
|---|---|
| Belcher James | Belcher & Boomgaarden LLP |
| Cottam Dale | Hirst Applegate |
| Dyekman Gregory C | Dray, Dyekman, Reed & Healey, P.C. |

### Corporate/M&A: Tax
#### Leading Individuals

**Band 1**

| | |
|---|---|
| Long Thomas N | Long Reimer Winegar Beppler LLP |
| Metzke John | Hirst Applegate |
| Reed Randall B | Dray, Dyekman, Reed & Healey, P.C. |
| Reimer Christopher M | Long Reimer Winegar Beppler LLP |
| Wolfe Lawrence J | Holland & Hart LLP * |

### Dray, Dyekman, Reed & Healey, P.C.

**THE FIRM** This full-service firm has an exceptional reputation in the corporate realm. The team is highly experienced assisting with securities law, mineral taxation and business planning issues across national borders.
**Sources say:** *"They carry on a very strong tradition of excellent client service."*
**KEY INDIVIDUALS** Sources praise market veteran **Perry Dray** as a *"very fine lawyer."* He has an impressive practice covering all areas of corporate and tax law. **Gregory Dyekman** remains a highly respected attorney and is recognized as having particular strength in bankruptcy and creditor work. In addition to his comprehensive corporate experience, he is highly sought after for his expertise in financing agreements. Sources single out **Randall Reed** as a *"very competent guy."* His diverse practice includes handling mineral taxation, oil and gas transactions and various corporate matters.

### Hirst Applegate

**THE FIRM** This longstanding Cheyenne institution scores highly with clients for its talented team. It offers dedicated expertise in a broad range of corporate matters, including assisting corporations set up a presence in Wyoming. The firm also advises on public utilities and trust and estate planning matters.
**Sources say:** *"They have expertise in many areas and they are very quick. We are very comfortable with the level of expertise across the firm."*
**KEY INDIVIDUALS** Clients praise **Dale Cottam** for his effective style of representation, with one saying: *"When we have asked him to represent us, he clearly stands his ground and is not confrontational. He looks for solutions and we like that."* Cottam has recently assisted creditor clients with bankruptcy matters. **John Metzke**'s strength lies in corporate tax matters, in which he advises on the federal tax aspects of various business transactions. His work also regularly involves advising high net worth individuals on matters relating to corporate taxation.

### Holland & Hart LLP
See profile on p.727

**THE FIRM** This regional powerhouse's Jackson and Cheyenne teams play an instrumental role in the firm's national presence. The group maintains impressive expertise in finance and corporate matters, and is also highlighted for its strength in representing clients from the coal, energy and mining industries.
**KEY INDIVIDUALS** **Teresa Buffington** (see p.2601) is held in high regard by clients for her thorough approach to real estate matters. She has recently been assisting with financing activities and representing clients from the natural gas, wind development and electrical industries. **Lawrence Wolfe** (see p.2601) is widely recognized as a *"standout in state mineral taxation."* He is also viewed as a solid choice for advising on credit facilities and natural resource transactions.

## Long Reimer Winegar Beppler LLP

**THE FIRM** With four offices in Wyoming, this firm is well situated to provide unparalleled local advice on tax policy, business planning and all major aspects of corporate law. In addition to representing private and public companies in the Rocky Mountain region, the firm is renowned for its national and international work.

**KEY INDIVIDUALS** *"Very fine and sophisticated business lawyer"* **Thomas Long** *"always stands out in federal taxation,"* according to sources. His practice also covers complex business and estate planning. **Christopher Reimer** is respected for his strength in the international tax field. Peers also acknowledge that he is a *"superb lawyer doing very specialized corporate and estate work."* Managing partner **Natalie Winegar** is viewed as a *"really great lawyer."* She lends her extensive knowledge to clients from the healthcare, mineral and financial services industries.

## Other Notable Practitioners

**Kenneth Barbe** of Welborn Sullivan Meck & Tooley, P.C. is known for his expertise in handling business acquisitions, insurance coverage matters and divestitures. The *"fantastic"* **Tom Toner** of Yonkee & Toner LLP has deep experience in the corporate practice and maintains a healthy reputation among peers.

# LABOR & EMPLOYMENT

| Labor & Employment | |
|---|---|
| **Leading Firms** | |
| **Band 1** | |
| Davis & Cannon | |
| Hirst Applegate | |
| Holland & Hart LLP * | |
| Williams, Porter, Day & Neville PC | |

| **Leading Individuals** | |
|---|---|
| **Band 1** | |
| Cave Bradley | Holland & Hart LLP * |
| Fox Kate | Davis & Cannon |
| Jarosh Robert | Hirst Applegate |
| Ortiz Scott E | Williams, Porter, Day & Neville PC |
| Scott Gary | Hirst Applegate |
| Vilos Joanna | Holland & Hart LLP * |
| **Associates to watch** | |
| Esch Amanda | Davis & Cannon |

\* Indicates firm / individual with profile.
Alphabetical order within each band. Band 1 is the highest.

## Band 1

### Davis & Cannon

**THE FIRM** This leading labor and employment practice receives strong endorsement from its clients as a genuine market leader. The team regularly assists clients on matters ranging from hospital privileges and medical practice agreements, noncompete agreements and state or federal claims. Other areas of expertise include discrimination and wrongful termination issues.

Sources say: *"My overall experience with Davis & Cannon has been very positive. They are good, hard-working lawyers."* **KEY INDIVIDUALS Kate Fox** enjoys a healthy reputation for employment work. She has been active defending employers against discriminatory work environments and wrongful termination allegations. According to clients, *"she combines an ebullient personality with a deep understanding of legal intricacies."* Associate **Amanda Esch** is admired by clients as a *"bright young lawyer, who provides excellent support and assistance."*

### Hirst Applegate

**THE FIRM** This firm houses an enviable labor and employment practice in its Cheyenne office, which is capable of handling complex employment litigation matters. The team is also well versed in assisting a diverse clientele ranging from large multinationals to municipalities with disability discrimination, wrongful discharge and retaliation claims.

**KEY INDIVIDUALS Robert Jarosh** has built up a strong presence in Wyoming's employment law market. He handles contentious and noncontentious matters. Market sources praise **Gary Scott** as *"great to work with."* He is a key figure in the state and has a particular strength in handling employment litigation.

### Holland & Hart LLP
See profile on p.727

**THE FIRM** Holland & Hart is widely regarded as a preeminent labor and employment firm. It has a distinguished record handling EEOC investigations, timecard audits and complex employment litigation. The firm counsels a range of illustrious clients from the healthcare, mining and industrial chemical industries.

Sources say: *"The attorneys are very responsive and timely in responding to requests and turning around an excellent final product and advice."*

**KEY INDIVIDUALS Joanna Vilos** (see p.2601) is *"quick on her feet and a graceful navigator, who is a pleasure to work with,"* according to clients. She has been active assisting clients with drafting OSHA complaint responses, advising on internal investigations and handling sexual harassment litigation. **Bradley Cave** (see p.2601) inspires confidence in clients with his deep experience, which *"brings real-world knowledge into the picture."* He is highly experienced handling WARN Act and discrimination matters and is noted for his experience assisting clients from the mining and healthcare industries.

### Williams, Porter, Day & Neville PC

**THE FIRM** This impressive team remains particularly strong across the entire gamut of labor and employment issues. The group is heavily involved in defending First Amendment, harassment and discrimination and whistleblower retaliation claims. In addition, the firm also regularly handles workers' compensation defense matters.

**KEY INDIVIDUALS Scott Ortiz** maintains a fine reputation for his experience in defending private and public employers in litigation. He is particularly knowledgeable in representing clients from the transportation industry.

# LITIGATION

Commentary about individuals can be found under their firm's paragraph. If the firm has no paragraph (is not ranked) look at Other Notable Practitioners.

## Litigation: General Commercial
### Leading Firms

**Band 1**
Davis & Cannon
Gifford & Brinkerhoff
Hirst Applegate
Holland & Hart LLP *
Williams, Porter, Day & Neville PC

**Band 2**
Hickey & Evans LLP
Lathrop & Rutledge
Rothgerber Johnson & Lyons LLP
Sundahl, Powers, Kapp & Martin LLC

## Litigation: General Commercial
### Senior Statesmen

**Senior Statesmen:** distinguished older practitioners

| | |
|---|---|
| Day Richard E | Williams, Porter, Day & Neville PC |

### Leading Individuals

**Band 1**

| | |
|---|---|
| Brinkerhoff Jeffrey C | Gifford & Brinkerhoff |
| Cannon Kim D | Davis & Cannon |
| Day Patrick | Holland & Hart LLP * |
| Fox Kate | Davis & Cannon |
| Hickey Paul | Hickey & Evans LLP |
| Mincer Richard | Hirst Applegate |
| Murphy Patrick J | Williams, Porter, Day & Neville PC |
| Neville Frank D | Williams, Porter, Day & Neville PC |
| Scott Gary | Hirst Applegate |
| Sundahl John Alan | Sundahl, Powers, Kapp & Martin LLC |
| Toner Tom C | Yonkee & Toner LLP (ONP)† |

**Band 2**

| | |
|---|---|
| Gifford Mark W | Gifford & Brinkerhoff |
| Jarosh Robert | Hirst Applegate |
| Ortiz Scott E | Williams, Porter, Day & Neville PC |
| Powers Jr George E | Sundahl, Powers, Kapp & Martin LLC |
| Rutledge Kent | Lathrop & Rutledge |
| Schneebeck Richard | Richard G Schneebeck PC (ONP)† |
| Studer Judith | Schwartz, Bon, Walker & Studer (ONP)† |
| Sullivan Michael J | Rothgerber Johnson & Lyons LLP |
| Teig Joe M | Holland & Hart LLP * |

**Band 3**

| | |
|---|---|
| Bestol Kay Lynn | Sundahl, Powers, Kapp & Martin LLC |
| Eggers III Walter F | Holland & Hart LLP * |
| Kapp Paul | Sundahl, Powers, Kapp & Martin LLC |
| Martin Raymond | Sundahl, Powers, Kapp & Martin LLC |
| Masterson John | Rothgerber Johnson & Lyons LLP |
| Stubson Timothy M | Crowley Fleck PLLP (ONP)† * |

**Up-and-coming individuals**

| | |
|---|---|
| Addleman Billie L M | Hirst Applegate |

## Litigation: Mediators
### Leading Individuals

**Band 1**

| | |
|---|---|
| Gifford Mark W | Gifford & Brinkerhoff |
| Sullivan Michael J | Rothgerber Johnson & Lyons LLP |

## Litigation: Medical Malpractice Defense
### Leading Individuals

**Star individuals**

| | |
|---|---|
| Brinkerhoff Jeffrey C | Gifford & Brinkerhoff |

**Band 1**

| | |
|---|---|
| Neville Frank D | Williams, Porter, Day & Neville PC |
| Ortiz Scott E | Williams, Porter, Day & Neville PC |
| Powers Jr George E | Sundahl, Powers, Kapp & Martin LLC |
| Rutledge Corinne | Lathrop & Rutledge |
| Rutledge Kent | Lathrop & Rutledge |
| Sundahl John Alan | Sundahl, Powers, Kapp & Martin LLC |

*  Indicates firm / individual with profile.
† ONP = Other Notable Practitioner.

## Band 1

### Davis & Cannon

**THE FIRM** With three offices in Wyoming, this firm has a formidable presence across the state in a wide range of litigation matters. Clients are generous in their praise for the team's dedicated service. The group has had an active year representing clients involved in employment and civil rights litigation and has also defended municipalities in various disputes.

**Sources say:** "*They were very responsive and very sensitive to client needs in terms of billing. Overall an excellent group to work with.*"

**KEY INDIVIDUALS Kim Cannon** is a highly respected authority in the litigation sphere. He evokes glowing praise from clients, who say: "*Wyoming has its own unique concepts and Kim was able to present them to us in a manner that made sense to us.*" He is also recognized for his "*ability to distill an issue quickly, respond to judges' questions and present an argument.*" Clients can rely on **Kate Fox** for "*straightforward legal advice under any circumstances.*" She continues to impress with her ability to handle a diverse range of cases related to various employment law disputes and complex tort litigation.

### Gifford & Brinkerhoff

**THE FIRM** This Casper-based litigation boutique is sought after for its expertise in a wide variety of dispute resolution and its ability to handle complex litigation matters. The talented two-partner team is renowned for representing clients in medical malpractice and various civil litigation issues.

**Sources say:** "*They are excellent.*"

**KEY INDIVIDUALS Jeffrey Brinkerhoff** earns praise from peers and clients, with one commentator highlighting that he "*does an incredible job defending and is one of the top medical malpractice attorneys in the state.*" He is known as an experienced authority on appellate and trial work and has niche knowledge of oilfield accidents. **Mark**

**Gifford** is widely recommended as a preeminent performer in mediation and arbitration.

### Hirst Applegate

**THE FIRM** Hirst Applegate enjoys a sterling reputation in litigation. The team has had a busy year assisting clients with a wide variety of disputes. Most recently it successfully handled sophisticated issues related to several oil and gas interests and leases. Clients include hospitals, insurance and reinsurance companies and significant national corporations.

**Sources say:** "*I have worked with them for years and they have always provided stellar representation to my company.*"

**KEY INDIVIDUALS Richard Mincer** stands out as a versatile litigator with a practice spanning product liability, premises liability and insurance matters. **Gary Scott** is a

prominent litigator with a healthy reputation in wrongful death defense and employment litigation. He recently won a defense verdict that addressed the Federal Employers Liability Act. **Robert Jarosh** continues to develop his practice and is becoming a trusted name assisting with complex litigation. He recently handled a high-profile federal due process and wrongful termination case and obtained summary judgment on behalf of a former state government administrator in a civil conspiracy and federal RICO matter. Rising star **Billie Addleman** recently acted as lead partner in a successful appeal to the Wyoming Supreme Court relating to a complex conspiracy to commit fraud action on behalf of a major Wyoming realtor.

### Holland & Hart LLP
See profile on p.727

**THE FIRM** With two offices in Wyoming, this established firm earns a strong reputation for handling a broad spectrum of litigation matters. Its litigators have developed niche practices in labor and employment, complex commercial, natural resources and oil and gas disputes. The team is also equipped to defend clients before various Wyoming administrative agencies. Clients include Basin Electric Power Cooperative and the Coalition for Responsible Regulation.

**Sources say:** "*You know at the end of the day you are going to get excellent options. When you litigate you get top-notch advice.*"

**KEY INDIVIDUALS Patrick Day** (see p.2601) "*presents oral arguments with clarity and confidence,*" according to clients. He is a renowned specialist in royalty and tax litigation with added expertise in the mining and oil and gas sectors. **Joe Teig** (see p.2601) currently heads the firm's emergency response team and is renowned for his prowess defending large-scale personal injury matters and industrial actions. **Walter Eggers** (see p.2601) is lauded by clients as being *"very personable, strong technically and very responsive."* He devotes his practice to assisting clients from the oil and gas sector and is noted for his extensive experience handling regulatory issues before various state agencies.

### Williams, Porter, Day & Neville PC

**THE FIRM** This firm continues to house one of the most highly regarded litigation practices in Wyoming. Its lawyers have represented clients in state and federal courts nationally and also before several regulatory agencies. It offers a comprehensive civil litigation service and is also frequently called upon to advise on energy, product liability and professional malpractice disputes.

**KEY INDIVIDUALS** Shareholder **Patrick Murphy** is renowned for his skill in relation to medical malpractice, product liability and personal injury disputes. He has extensive experience representing clients before the Wyoming Supreme Court and is also noted for his ability to handle complex litigation related to insurance claims. **Frank Neville** is the firm's leading name for medical malpractice matters and also has considerable experience assisting with oil and gas, environmental and product liability litigation. *"I enjoy using him as a mediator as he knows all the issues,"* says one source. Medical malpractice specialist **Scott Ortiz** is a highly experienced litigator, who has defended over 50 jury trials in federal and state court. Esteemed practitioner **Richard Day** is lauded by peers as *"a legend in Wyoming."* He has spent his distinguished career representing companies and individuals in criminal and civil proceedings.

## Band 2

### Hickey & Evans LLP

**THE FIRM** Hickey & Evans continues to enjoy a healthy presence in Wyoming. The team continues to attract clients with its extensive trial experience and expert knowledge of the oil and gas, insurance and construction industries.

**KEY INDIVIDUALS Paul Hickey** has extensive experience in the courtroom and handles a wide array of disputes.

### Lathrop & Rutledge

**THE FIRM** This compact group has a robust litigation practice and undertakes trials across a broad range of sectors. It is best known for its expertise in handling medical malpractice cases.

**Sources say:** *"They have skilled medical malpractice attorneys."*

**KEY INDIVIDUALS Corinne Rutledge** is a well-regarded litigator who devotes her practice to complex disputes. She is highly sought after for her strength in medical malpractice matters in Wyoming. **Kent Rutledge** is a known presence in medical malpractice defense. He is also adept at handling insurance coverage, product liability and commercial litigation.

### Rothgerber Johnson & Lyons LLP

**THE FIRM** This Colorado firm's Casper office handles a broad range of disputes. The firm earns particular recognition for its ability to handle energy and mineral rights litigation and to represent clients before regulatory agencies and state and federal courts.

**Sources say:** *"I have worked with a lot of attorneys over the years and these guys have been top-notch."*

**KEY INDIVIDUALS Michael Sullivan** enjoys a healthy reputation for his mediation and arbitration practice addressing water law, land use and public policy. **John Masterson** is hailed as a *"very good litigator"* by his peers. Clients praise his extensive understanding of all facets of dispute resolution.

### Sundahl, Powers, Kapp & Martin LLC

**THE FIRM** This Cheyenne boutique firm is a respected player in the state and is noted for its civil litigation expertise. The team assists a variety of clients that range from family businesses to large corporations.

**Sources say:** *"A good litigation firm."*

**KEY INDIVIDUALS** Peers acknowledge leading medical malpractice lawyer **George Powers** as *"an incredibly sharp and hard-working attorney."* He is also sought after for his experience in trucking and railroad litigation. **John Sundahl** is held in high esteem for his ability to handle complex litigation. He has a strong record for litigation relating to medical malpractice, land disputes and banking. **Paul Kapp** is valued for his expertise and experience in insurance defense work. He frequently assists clients from the construction, trucking and oil and gas sectors. **Kay Lynn Bestol** is an experienced trial lawyer who handles a broad range of disputes. She is particularly active handling personal injury matters. Having considerable experience in the construction industry, **Raymond Martin** remains the top choice for clients in this area.

### Other Notable Practitioners

**Judith Studer** of Schwartz, Bon, Walker & Studer LLC is known among peers to be *"very easy to get along with and very professional."* Her long-standing expertise in insurance defense and in trust and estate litigation is highly respected. **Tom Toner** of Yonkee & Toner LLP stands out as a *"top litigation attorney"* in the state. He is a respected authority in disputes and has a practice that spans a range of industries. Sole practitioner **Richard Schneebeck** is a trusted hand for litigation. He brings with him a wealth of experience in handling product liability, toxic torts and oil and gas litigation. Casper-based **Timothy Stubson** (see p.2601) of Crowley Fleck LLP is a respected figure in the state. He is recognized for his experience in both trial and appellate court.

# REAL ESTATE

Commentary about individuals can be found under their firm's paragraph. If the firm has no paragraph (is not ranked) look at Other Notable Practitioners.

| Real Estate | | |
| --- | --- | --- |
| **Leading Firms** | | |
| **Band 1** | | |
| Dray, Dyekman, Reed & Healey, P.C. | | |
| Holland & Hart LLP * | | |
| **Band 2** | | |
| Davis & Cannon | | |
| Lonabaugh and Riggs | | |
| Long Reimer Winegar Beppler LLP | | |
| MacPherson Kelly & Thompson | | |
| Mullikin, Larson & Swift | | |

| Senior Statesmen | | |
| --- | --- | --- |
| **Senior Statesmen:** distinguished older practitioners | | |
| Davis Jr Richard M | Davis & Cannon | |
| MacPherson John A | MacPherson Kelly & Thompson | |

| Leading Individuals | | |
| --- | --- | --- |
| **Band 1** | | |
| Barbe J Kenneth | Welborn Sullivan Meck & Tooley (ONP)[†] | |
| Riggs Dan B | Lonabaugh and Riggs | |
| **Band 2** | | |
| Buffington Teresa | Holland & Hart LLP * | |
| Dray W Perry | Dray, Dyekman, Reed & Healey, P.C. | |
| Dyekman Gregory C | Dray, Dyekman, Reed & Healey, P.C. | |
| Hawks Christopher H | Hawks & Associates LC (ONP)[†] | |
| Larson David K | Mullikin, Larson & Swift | |
| Phibbs Henry | Phibbs Law Office PC (ONP)[†] | |
| Swift Jr Phelps H | Mullikin, Larson & Swift | |
| Tyler Keith | Keith P. Tyler (ONP)[†] | |
| Winegar Natalie K | Long Reimer Winegar Beppler LLP | |

* Indicates firm / individual with profile.
[†] ONP = Other Notable Practitioner.

## Band 1

### Dray, Dyekman, Reed & Healey, P.C.

**THE FIRM** This leading real estate team offers genuine expertise and depth. Its attorneys routinely advise a range of clients and are able to assist with a varied mix of real estate work, such as mineral rights, condominium projects and annexation appeals and litigation.

**KEY INDIVIDUALS Gregory Dyekman** actively serves clients from the wind energy industry and maintains an impressive profile assisting with business and ranching sales. He is also lauded by sources for being *"very good with financing agreements."* Of counsel **Perry Dray** is a well-regarded senior lawyer with a broad real estate practice. He is particularly adept at handling ranching transactions and knowledgeable about wind leasing.

### Holland & Hart LLP
See profile on p.727

**THE FIRM** The real estate team at Holland & Hart is held in high esteem by clients. Its lawyers are highly experienced representing builders, buyers and sellers, developers and lenders in financing, land owner issues and acquisitions. The team is adept at guiding clients through purchases of refineries, retail space and large companies.

**Sources say:** *"Multiple people there have corporate, energy and real estate cross-knowledge. We definitely felt we had their attention and were a priority."*

**KEY INDIVIDUALS** Clients appreciate that **Teresa Buffington** (see p.2601) *"spends time to think about things and is thoughtful in her responses."* She is well renowned for her grasp of the wind energy sphere and her ability to assist with complex real estate financings.

## Band 2

### Davis & Cannon

**THE FIRM** Operating from three Wyoming offices, this team is well positioned to advise local clients on the full spectrum of real estate transactions, including condominium law, foreclosure and title disputes. Clients particularly praise the firm's capability in handling estate planning, land sales and easement matters.

**Sources say:** *"The firm has always been knowledgeable in the matters we have instructed it in and has offered sound guidance and counsel."*

**KEY INDIVIDUALS Richard Davis** is a distinguished attorney who can draw on decades of experience. *"He has offered us sound counsel, guidance and representation in all matters,"* say sources. He has recently assisted clients with easements and acquisition contracts.

### Lonabaugh and Riggs

**THE FIRM** This longstanding practice is known for expertly conducting real estate work out of Sheridan. The team routinely assists with liens and mortgages, mineral leasing and property acquisitions.

**KEY INDIVIDUALS** Peers respect **Dan Riggs**'s manner in real estate negotiations. He is known for representing land owners and is very knowledgeable in land transactions.

### Long Reimer Winegar Beppler LLP

**THE FIRM** This well-known team provides an impressive real estate service. The lawyers are well equipped to handle financing, commercial and residential leasing, and land use regulatory issues.

**KEY INDIVIDUALS Natalie Winegar** splits her time between the firm's Cheyenne and Denver offices. She is highly recommended for conveyancing, financing and real property transactions.

### MacPherson Kelly & Thompson

**THE FIRM** MacPherson Kelly & Thompson is a dominant player in the Rawlins real estate area. The team is known for its strength in assisting clients from the agricultural, ranching and wind energy sectors.

**KEY INDIVIDUALS John MacPherson** has a longstanding reputation in Wyoming for real estate work. He has a wealth of experience in the field, with a niche focus on ranching law.

### Mullikin, Larson & Swift

**THE FIRM** This Jackson-based team offers the full range of real estate services. It is noted for its ability to act for sellers and buyers on disclosure statements, mortgages, adverse possession and financing.

**KEY INDIVIDUALS David Larson** combines his banking and finance knowledge with real estate expertise when advising on lending transactions. He is highly regarded for his work in the Jackson Hole vicinity. **Phelps Swift** is another vital member of the firm's real estate practice. He deals with a wide range of real estate issues, including zoning and various land use matters.

### Other Notable Practitioners

**Christopher Hawks** of Hawks & Associates LC is a highly renowned Jackson attorney with extensive real estate experience. **Kenneth Barbe** of Welborn Sullivan Meck & Tooley, P.C. is recommended for his expertise in assisting clients with acquisitions and real estate planning documents. He also has particular strength in the healthcare and wind energy industries. Jackson attorney **Henry Phibbs** of Phibbs Law Office PC is a notable figure in the state for real estate work. Sole practitioner **Keith Tyler** is based in Casper. He has a varied practice, but is particularly noted for his real estate expertise.

# Leaders' Profiles in Wyoming

**BUFFINGTON, Teresa**
Holland & Hart LLP, Cheyenne
307 778 4237
tbuffington@hollandhart.com
*Featured in Real Estate (Wyoming), Corporate/M&A (Wyoming)*
**Practice Areas:** Partner practicing commercial transactions, including real estate, business and finance. Practice includes acquisitions and sales, contract preparation and negotiation, energy project transactions including wind project development, rights of way for gathering and pipelines, commercial financing, entity formation and continuation, design, engineering and construction contracting, transactional due diligence, and legal opinions.
**Professional Memberships:** Member, Laramie County Bar Association; Wyoming Bar Association; Colorado Bar Association; ABA.
**Career:** Admitted to Colorado (1985) and Wyoming Bar (1991). Past Administrative Partner of Cheyenne Office. Former Manager of Business Entities and Transactions Practice Group.
**Personal:** JD, University of Colorado (1985); BA, Ohio University (1977).

**CAVE, Bradley**
Holland & Hart LLP, Cheyenne
307 778 4210
bcave@hollandhart.com
*Featured in Labor & Employment (Wyoming)*
**Practice Areas:** Employer-based employment law and litigation. Represents employers in matters involving discrimination, harassment, wage/hour disputes, defamation, wrongful discharge, breach of contract and employment-related torts. Advises employers on employee handbooks and personnel policies, supervisory training, compliance with federal and state statutes and regulations, employee investigations, discipline and termination.
**Professional Memberships:** Wyoming, Colorado, and American Bar Association; The College of Labor and Employment Lawyers, 2009; Employment Law Alliance.
**Career:** Admitted to Colorado (1988) Wyoming (1991) Bars. Editor, Wyoming Employment Law

Letter. Leader of firm's Labor & Employment Group.
**Personal:** JD (with honors), George Washington University (1988); BS, University of Wyoming (1985).

**DAY, Patrick**
Holland & Hart LLP, Cheyenne
307 778 4209
pday@hollandhart.com
*Featured in Litigation (Wyoming)*
**Practice Areas:** Mr Day's practice involves commercial and environmental litigation, arbitration and mediation for the firm's energy clients, which include coal producers, oil and gas companies, pipelines, refineries and gas plants. He is also involved in ad valorem and mineral severance tax litigation for the energy industry.
**Professional Memberships:** Admitted to practice in the Ninth, Tenth, and DC Circuit Courts of Appeal.
**Personal:** JD University of Wyoming (1984), BA University of Michigan (1980).

**EGGERS III, Walter F**
Holland & Hart LLP, Cheyenne
307 778 4208
weggers@hollandhart.com
*Featured in Litigation (Wyoming)*
**Practice Areas:** Mr Eggers' practice focuses on administrative and regulatory litigation before Wyoming administrative agencies. He appears regularly before the Wyoming Oil & Gas Conservation Commission on permitting and other issues. He also represents clients before the Wyoming Public Service Commission, Wyoming tax agencies and Wyoming courts.
**Professional Memberships:** Wyoming Bar Association; appointed by the Wyoming Supreme Court to the Access to Justice Commission (2009-present).
**Career:** Admitted to the Wyoming Bar (1997). Before joining Holland & Hart, he was an Assistant District Attorney in Cheyenne, Wyoming.
**Personal:** JD University of Wyoming College of Law (1997), BA American University (1992).

**STUBSON, Timothy M**
Crowley Fleck PLLP, Casper
307 265 2279
tstubson@crowleyfleck.com
*Featured in Litigation (Wyoming)*
**Practice Areas:** Partner. Work includes commercial litigation, employment litigation and creditor's bankruptcy. Also handles numerous appeals before the Wyoming Supreme Court.
**Professional Memberships:** Wyoming Bar Association.
**Career:** Licensed in Wyoming 1997. Clerk for the Hon. William Downes, US District Court for the District of Wyoming. Practiced with Brown, Drew, & Massey, LLP 1998-2011. Joined Crowley Fleck PLLP 2011. Currently Contact Partner for the Casper, Wyoming office.
**Publications:** The Life, Death and Rebirth of Co-employee Immunity, Wyoming Bar Journal, June 2009.
**Personal:** Born August 9, 1971. Member Wyoming House of Representatives, 2008-Present. House Majority Whip, 2013-14.

**TEIG, Joe M**
Holland & Hart LLP, Jackson
307 734 4512
jteig@hollandhart.com
*Featured in Litigation (Wyoming)*
**Practice Areas:** Mr Teig's practice focuses primarily on the defense of catastrophic personal injury cases and has developed extensive experience defending companies in personal injury cases arising out of accidents in the mining, oil and gas production, refining and railroad industries. Mr Teig has also developed considerable experience in the area of pharmaceutical/products liability defense.
**Professional Memberships:** American, Wyoming and Colorado Bar Associations. Former President, Defense Lawyers Association of Wyoming.
**Career:** Listed in Best Lawyers in America for Personal Injury Litigation.
**Personal:** JD - University of Wyoming, 1985. MPA - University of Wyoming, 1982. BA - Bemidji State University, 1979.

**VILOS, Joanna**
Holland & Hart LLP, Cheyenne
307 778 4261
jvilos@hollandhart.com
*Featured in Labor & Employment (Wyoming)*
**Practice Areas:** Ms Vilos advises and defends employers in matters involving discrimination, harassment, retaliation, wrongful discharge, breach of contract, employment-related torts, workers' compensation, family and medical leave, wage and hour disputes, non-compete agreements, trade secrets, First Amendment retaliation and Equal Protection.
**Professional Memberships:** American Bar Association, Colorado Bar Association, Wyoming Bar Association.
**Publications:** Ms Vilos has authored numerous employment law-related articles and currently serves as co-editor of the Wyoming Employment Law Letter.
**Personal:** Harvard Law School (JD 2003), University of Maryland (BA 1999).

**WOLFE, Lawrence J**
Holland & Hart LLP, Cheyenne
307 778 4218
lwolfe@hollandhart.com
*Featured in Corporate/M&A (Wyoming)*
**Practice Areas:** Mr Wolfe has Wyoming's premier governmental affairs practice for conventional and renewable energy and natural resources. He advises energy and mineral extraction developers on environmental, tax, royalties, financing, administrative law and government relations. His extensive litigation experience includes over 25 cases decided by the Wyoming Supreme Court.
**Professional Memberships:** University of Wyoming Foundation Board; President, Cheyenne LEADS.
**Career:** Holland & Hart experience: joined, 1985; Chairman, Natural Resources Department, 2001-2006; Managing Partner, 2007-08. Additional: Chief, Natural Resources Division, Wyoming Attorney General's Office, 1983-85; Wyoming Assistant Attorney General, 1980-85.
**Personal:** JD, University of Wyoming; BA, UC Davis.

# INDEX TO THE RANKED LAW FIRMS

**Barnett, Bolt, Kirkwood, Long & McBride**
Table(s): **Florida:** Tax **Band 3** p.979

**Barran Liebman LLP**
Profile: p.2180
Table(s): **Oregon:** Labor & Employment **Band 1** p.2168

**Barrasso Usdin Kupperman Freeman & Sarver LLC**
Profile: p.1373
Table(s): **Louisiana:** Litigation **Band 1** p.1352

**Barris, Sott, Denn & Driker, PLLC**
Table(s): **Michigan:** Litigation **Band 2** p.1544, Real Estate **Band 3** p.1546

**Barst Mukamal & Kleiner LLP**
Table(s): **New York:** Immigration **Band 3** p.1813

**Bartlit Beck Herman Palenchar & Scott LLP**
Table(s): **Colorado:** Corporate/M&A **Band 3** p.702, Litigation **Band 1** p.708, **Illinois:** Litigation **Band 1** p.1179, **Nationwide:** Product Liability & Mass Torts **Band 1** p.207

**Bass, Berry & Sims PLC**
Profile: p.2314
Table(s): **Tennessee:** Banking & Finance **Band 1** p.2287, Corporate/M&A **Band 1** p.2288, Environment **Band 1** p.2290, Healthcare **Band 1** p.2291, Labor & Employment **Band 1** p.2293, Litigation **Band 1** p.2295, Real Estate **Band 1** p.2299

**Bassford Remele, A Professional Association**
Table(s): **Minnesota:** Litigation **Band 3** p.1573

**Bateman Seidel Miner Blomgren Chellis & Gram, P.C.**
Table(s): **Oregon:** Real Estate **Band 3** p.2173

**Bates Carey Nicolaides LLP**
Table(s): **Illinois:** Insurance **Band 2** p.1167

**Bayard, P.A.**
Profile: p.779
Table(s): **Delaware:** Bankruptcy/Restructuring **Band 3** p.754, Intellectual Property **Band 2** p.763, Real Estate **Band 2** p.766

**Bays Lung Rose & Holma**
Table(s): **Hawaii:** Litigation **Band 2** p.1118

**Beasley, Allen, Crow, Methvin, Portis & Miles, PC**
Table(s): **Alabama:** Litigation **Band 1** p.463

**Beck Redden LLP**
Table(s): **Texas:** Litigation **Band 1** p.2361

**Becker & Poliakoff PA**
Profile: p.1016
Table(s): **Florida:** Construction **Band 2** p.944

**Bedell, Dittmar, DeVault, Pillans & Coxe**
Table(s): **Florida:** Litigation **Band 2** p.965

**Beirne Maynard & Parsons, LLP**
Profile: p.2428
Table(s): **Louisiana:** Bankruptcy/Restructuring **Band 3** p.1337, **Texas:** Insurance **Band 4** p.2350

**Belcher & Boomgaarden LLP**
Table(s): **Wyoming:** Corporate/M&A **Band 1** p.2596

**Belin McCormick PC**
Table(s): **Iowa:** Corporate/M&A **Band 1** p.1282, Labor & Employment **Band 2** p.1285, Litigation **Band 1** p.1287, Real Estate **Band 1** p.1290

**Bell, Davis & Pitt, P.A.**
Table(s): **North Carolina:** Litigation **Band 4** p.2033

**Belles Graham Proudfoot Wilson & Chun**
Table(s): **Hawaii:** Real Estate **Band 2** p.1120

**Bello, Black & Welsh LLP**
Table(s): **Massachusetts:** Labor & Employment **Band 3** p.1466

**Benesch, Friedlander, Coplan & Aronoff LLP**
Profile: p.2120
Table(s): **Indiana:** Real Estate **Band 2** p.1274, **Ohio:** Banking & Finance **Band 1** p.2056, Construction **Band 2** p.2062, Corporate/M&A **Band 3** p.2064, Healthcare **Band 2** p.2069, Intellectual Property **Band 4** p.2071, Labor & Employment **Band 3** p.2073, Real Estate **Band 3** p.2085

**Benjamin, Bain, Howard & Cohen LLC**
Profile: p.724
Table(s): **Colorado:** Real Estate **Band 2** p.714

**Bercow Radell & Fernandez P.A.**
Table(s): **Florida:** Real Estate **Band 2** p.975

**Berger & Montague PC**
Table(s): **Pennsylvania:** Antitrust **Band 2** p.2184

**Berger Singerman**
Profile: p.1017
Table(s): **Florida:** Bankruptcy/Restructuring **Band 1** p.939, Corporate/M&A & Private Equity **Band 3** p.947, Environment **Band 3** p.951, Litigation **Band 3** p.965, Real Estate **Band 4** p.974

**Berkowitz Oliver Williams Shaw & Eisenbrandt LLP**
Table(s): **Missouri:** Litigation **Band 2** p.1628

**Berman & Simmons**
Table(s): **Maine:** Litigation **Band 1** p.1393

**Berns, Ockner & Greenberger**
Table(s): **Ohio:** Real Estate **Band 2** p.2086

**Bernstein Litowitz Berger & Grossmann LLP**
Profile: p.1957
Table(s): **Nationwide:** Securities **Band 1** p.233, **New York:** Litigation **Band 1** p.1835

**Bernstein Shur**
Profile: p.1406
Table(s): **Maine:** Corporate/M&A **Band 1** p.1385, Energy & Natural Resources **Band 1** p.1387, Environment **Band 3** p.1388, Labor & Employment **Band 2** p.1390, Litigation **Band 2** p.1392, Real Estate **Band 1** p.1395, **New Hampshire:** Labor & Employment **Band 2** p.1688, Litigation **Band 3** p.1689

**Berry & Damore LLC**
Table(s): **Arizona:** Real Estate **Band 1** p.504

**Berry Appleman & Leiden LLP**
Table(s): **California:** Immigration **Band 1** p.571, **Nationwide:** Immigration **Band 2** p.131, **Texas:** Immigration **Band 1** p.2349

**Best Best & Krieger LLP**
Table(s): **California:** Environment **Band 4** p.564

**Beus Gilbert PLLC**
Table(s): **Arizona:** Real Estate **Band 1** p.504

**Beveridge & Diamond PC**
Profile: p.907
Table(s): **District of Columbia:** Environment **Band 2** p.804, **Massachusetts:** Environment **Band 3** p.1457, **Nationwide:** Environment **Band 2** p.89, **Texas:** Environment **Band 4** p.2343

**Bickel & Brewer**
Table(s): **Nationwide:** Leisure & Hospitality **Band 4** p.178

**Bierce & Kenerson, P.C.**
Table(s): **New York:** Technology & Outsourcing **Band 4** p.1868

**Biggs, Ingram, Solop & Carlson, PLLC**
Table(s): **Mississippi:** Energy & Natural Resources **Band 3** p.1593

**Bilzin Sumberg Baena Price & Axelrod LLP**
Profile: p.1018
Overview(s): **Florida:** p.933
Table(s): **Florida:** Antitrust **Band 3** p.934, Bankruptcy/Restructuring **Band 1** p.939, Construction **Band 4** p.944, Corporate/M&A & Private Equity **Band 3** p.947, Litigation **Band 2** p.965, Real Estate **Band 1** p.974, Tax **Band 3** p.979

**Bingham Greenebaum Doll LLP**
Profile: p.1281
Table(s): **Indiana:** Corporate/M&A **Band 3** p.1268, Environment **Band 2** p.1270, Litigation **Band 2** p.1273, Real Estate **Band 3** p.1274, **Kentucky:** Corporate/M&A **Band 2** p.1305, Environment, Natural Resources & Utilities **Band 1** p.1307, Intellectual Property **Band 3** p.1308, Labor & Employment **Band 2** p.1309, Litigation **Band 3** p.1311, Real Estate **Band 3** p.1314

**Bingham McCutchen LLP**
Profile: p.1515
Table(s): **California:** Antitrust **Band 3** p.535, Banking & Finance **Band 2** p.539, Corporate/M&A **Band 3** p.553, Environment **Band 1** p.564, Intellectual Property **Band 3** p.577, Litigation **Band 3** p.593, **Connecticut:** Real Estate **Band 1** p.740, **District of Columbia:** Corporate/M&A & Private Equity **Band 4** p.797, Environment **Band 3** p.804, Real Estate **Band 3** p.834, Tax **Band 1** p.838, Telecom, Broadcast & Satellite **Band 2** p.844, **Massachusetts:** Antitrust **Band 1** p.1444, Banking & Finance **Band 2** p.1445, Bankruptcy/Restructuring **Band 3** p.1449, Corporate/M&A **Band 3** p.1452, Employee Benefits & Executive Compensation **Band 2** p.1455, Hedge & Mutual Funds **Band 1** p.1461, Litigation **Band 1** p.1470, Private Equity **Band 3** p.1476, Tax **Band 2** p.1481, **Nationwide:** Antitrust **Band 4** p.22, Banking & Finance **Band 5** p.31, Bankruptcy/Restructuring **Band 3** p.38, Capital Markets **Band 1** p.58, Corporate/M&A **Band 2** p.67, Environment **Band 4** p.89, Financial Services Regulation **Band 2** p.95, Government **Band 3** p.121, Investment Funds **Band 2** p.169, Projects **Band 3** p.217, Real Estate **Band 3** p.225, Securities **Band 2** p.233, Tax **Band 1** p.243, **New York:** Bankruptcy/Restructuring **Band 4** p.1781, Litigation **Band 3** p.1834, Real Estate **Band 4** p.1853

**Birch, Horton, Bittner & Cherot**
Table(s): **Alaska:** Corporate/M&A **Band 1** p.487, Litigation **Band 1** p.490, Real Estate **Band 2** p.491

**Bird, Marella, Boxer, Wolpert, Nessim, Drooks & Lincenberg PC**
Profile: p.675
Table(s): **California:** Litigation **Band 2** p.601

**Black Helterline LLP**
Table(s): **Oregon:** Labor & Employment **Band 1** p.2168

**Black, Srebnick, Kornspan & Stumpf, P.A.**
Table(s): **Florida:** Litigation **Band 1** p.967

**Blair & Bondurant, PA**
Table(s): **Mississippi:** Energy & Natural Resources **Band 2** p.1593

**Blank Rome LLP**
Profile: p.2235
Table(s): **Delaware:** Bankruptcy/Restructuring **Band 2** p.754, **Nationwide:** Investment Funds **Band 4** p.173, Transportation **Band 3** p.259, Transportation **Band 1** p.260, **Pennsylvania:** Banking & Finance **Band 1** p.2186, Bankruptcy/Restructuring **Band 1** p.2188, Corporate/M&A & Private Equity **Band 2** p.2191, Labor & Employment **Band 3** p.2200, Litigation **Band 3** p.2203, Real Estate **Band 2** p.2207

**Blish & Cavanagh, LLP**
Table(s): **Rhode Island:** Litigation **Band 2** p.2254

**Bloom Hergott Diemer Rosenthal LaViolette & Feldman, LLP**
Table(s): **California:** Media & Entertainment **Band** 2 p.609

**Bodman PLC**
Profile: p.1557
Table(s): **Michigan:** Banking & Finance **Band 1** p.1536, Corporate/M&A **Band 2** p.1538, Labor & Employment **Band 3** p.1541, Litigation **Band 2** p.1544, Real Estate **Band 2** p.1546

**Boehl Stopher & Graves, LLP**
Profile: p.1328
Table(s): **Kentucky:** Litigation **Band 1** p.1312

**Boies, Schiller & Flexner LLP**
Profile: p.1958
Table(s): **Florida:** Antitrust **Band 2** p.934, Litigation **Band 2** p.965, **Nationwide:** Antitrust **Band 4** p.22, **New York:** Antitrust **Band 3** p.1777, Litigation **Band 2** p.1833

**Bond, Schoeneck & King, PLLC**
Table(s): **New York:** Environment **Band 3** p.1807, Labor & Employment **Band 4** p.1826

**Bondurant, Mixson & Elmore, LLP**
Table(s): **Georgia:** Antitrust **Band 2** p.1037, Litigation **Band 1** p.1065

**Boone Karlberg PC**
Table(s): **Montana:** Corporate/M&A **Band 2** p.1646, Litigation **Band 1** p.1649, Real Estate **Band 1** p.1652

**Bose McKinney & Evans LLP**
Table(s): **Indiana:** Corporate/M&A **Band 3** p.1268, Environment **Band 1** p.1270, Labor & Employment **Band 2** p.1271, Real Estate **Band 3** p.1274

**Bouchard Margules & Friedlander PA**
Table(s): **Delaware:** Chancery **Band 2** p.758

**Bowles Rice LLP**
Profile: p.2568
Table(s): **West Virginia:** Corporate/Commercial **Band 1** p.2550, Labor & Employment **Band 3** p.2553, Litigation **Band 1** p.2555, Natural Resources **Band 1** p.2558, Real Estate **Band 1** p.2560

**Bowman and Brooke LLP**
Table(s): **Nationwide:** Product Liability & Mass Torts **Band 2** p.207, **Virginia:** Litigation **Band 1** p.2502

**Boyce, Greenfield, Pashby & Welk LLP**
Table(s): **South Dakota:** Corporate/Commercial **Band 2** p.2281, Labor & Employment **Band 1** p.2283, Litigation **Band 1** p.2284, Real Estate **Band 2** p.2286

**Boyle Fredrickson**
Table(s): **Wisconsin:** Intellectual Property **Band 2** p.2573

**Bracewell & Giuliani LLP**
Profile: p.2429
Table(s): **District of Columbia:** Environment **Band 3** p.804, **Nationwide:** Climate Change **Band 2** p.62, Corporate/M&A **Band 3** p.67, Energy & Natural Resources **Band 2** p.75, Environment **Band 3** p.89, Financial Services Regulation **Band 4** p.95, Projects **Band 3** p.217, **New York:** Corporate/M&A **Band 4** p.1794, **Texas:** Banking & Finance **Band 1** p.2325, Bankruptcy/Restructuring **Band 2** p.2328, Capital Markets **Band 3** p.2333, Corporate/M&A **Band 3** p.2337, Energy **Band 3** p.2340, Environment **Band 2** p.2343, Intellectual Property **Band 3** p.2354, Labor & Employment **Band 3** p.2358, Litigation **Band 4** p.2361, Real Estate **Band 2** p.2367, Tax **Band 3** p.2371, Technology **Band 3** p.2374

**Brach Eichler L.L.C.**
Table(s): **New Jersey:** Healthcare **Band 1** p.1714, Real Estate **Band 3** p.1728

**Bradley & Riley PC**
Table(s): **Iowa:** Corporate/M&A **Band 2** p.1282, Labor & Employment **Band 2** p.1285, Litigation **Band 1** p.1287, Real Estate **Band 3** p.1290

**Bradley Arant Boult Cummings LLP**
Profile: p.476
Table(s): **Alabama:** Banking & Finance **Band 1** p.455, Bankruptcy/Restructuring **Band 1** p.457, Corporate/Commercial **Band 1** p.458, Labor & Employment **Band 3** p.460, Litigation **Band 1** p.462, Real Estate **Band 1** p.465, **District of Columbia:** Construction **Band 2** p.795, **Mississippi:** Litigation **Band 1** p.1596, **North Carolina:** Banking & Finance **Band 4** p.2021, **Tennessee:** Banking & Finance **Band 2** p.2287, Corporate/M&A **Band 3** p.2288, Healthcare **Band 1** p.2291, Litigation **Band 2** p.2295, Media & Entertainment **Band 2** p.2297, Real Estate **Band 1** p.2299

**Bradley Murchison Kelly & Shea**
Profile: p.1374
Table(s): **Louisiana:** Energy & Natural Resources **Band 2** p.1344

**Bradshaw, Fowler, Proctor & Fairgrave, PC**
Table(s): **Iowa:** Litigation **Band 1** p.1288

**Breazeale, Sachse & Wilson, LLP**
Table(s): **Louisiana:** Construction **Band 2** p.1339, Gaming & Licensing **Band 2** p.1348, Labor & Employment **Band 2** p.1349, Litigation **Band 3** p.1352

**Bricker & Eckler LLP**
Table(s): **Ohio:** Bankruptcy/Restructuring **Band 3** p.2058, Construction **Band 2** p.2062, Healthcare **Band 1** p.2069, Labor & Employment **Band 3** p.2073, Litigation **Band 3** p.2078, Natural Resources & Environment **Band 2** p.2082, Real Estate **Band 2** p.2085

**Briggs and Morgan**
Profile: p.1581
Table(s): **Minnesota:** Construction **Band 2** p.1567, Corporate/M&A **Band 2** p.1568, Labor & Employment **Band 1** p.1570, Litigation **Band 2** p.1573, Real Estate **Band 3** p.1576

**Brinks Hofer Gilson & Lione**
Profile: p.1242
Table(s): **Illinois:** Intellectual Property **Band 2** p.1171

**Broad and Cassel**
Table(s): **Florida:** Banking & Finance **Band 4** p.936, Bankruptcy/Restructuring **Band 4** p.939, Construction **Band 3** p.944, Corporate/M&A & Private Equity **Band 3** p.947, Environment **Band 3** p.951, Healthcare **Band 1** p.953, Litigation **Band 4** p.965, Real Estate **Band 2** p.974

**Brooks Wilkins Sharkey & Turco, PLLC**
Profile: p.1558
Table(s): **Michigan:** Litigation **Band 3** p.1544

**Brooks, Pierce, McLendon, Humphrey & Leonard LLP**
Table(s): **North Carolina:** Antitrust **Band 1** p.2020, Banking & Finance **Band 4** p.2021, Corporate/M&A **Band 3** p.2025, Environment **Band 2** p.2027, Intellectual Property **Band 4** p.2030, Labor & Employment **Band 3** p.2031, Litigation **Band 1** p.2033

**Brown & Kornegay LLP**
Table(s): **Texas:** Insurance **Band 2** p.2350

**Brown Law Firm PC**
Table(s): **Montana:** Labor & Employment **Band 3** p.1647, Litigation **Band 3** p.1649

**Brown McCarroll, L.L.P.**
Profile: p.2430
Table(s): **Texas:** Energy **Band 2** p.2340, Environment **Band 2** p.2343, Healthcare **Band 2** p.2347

**Brown Rudnick LLP**
Profile: p.437
Table(s): **Connecticut:** Environment **Band 2** p.733, **Massachusetts:** Bankruptcy/Restructuring **Band 2** p.1449, Employee Benefits & Executive Compensation **Band 3** p.1455, **Nationwide:** Bankruptcy/Restructuring **Band 3** p.38, **New York:** Bankruptcy/Restructuring **Band 3** p.1781

**Brown, Winick, Graves, Gross, Baskerville and Schoenebaum PLC**
Table(s): **Iowa:** Corporate/M&A **Band 2** p.1282, Labor & Employment **Band 3** p.1285, Litigation **Band 3** p.1287, Real Estate **Band 3** p.1290

**Browning, Kaleczyc, Berry & Hoven PC**
Table(s): **Montana:** Corporate/M&A **Band 1** p.1646, Labor & Employment **Band 2** p.1647, Litigation **Band 2** p.1649, Natural Resources & Environment **Band 1** p.1651, Real Estate **Band 2** p.1652

**Brownstein Hyatt Farber Schreck, LLP**
Profile: p.725
Table(s): **California:** Environment **Band 4** p.564, **Colorado:** Corporate/M&A **Band 2** p.702, Labor & Employment **Band 3** p.706, Litigation **Band 3** p.708, Natural Resources & Environment **Band 2** p.712, Real Estate **Band 1** p.714, **Nevada:** Corporate/Commercial **Band 1** p.1672, Gaming & Licensing **Band 1** p.1674, Litigation **Band 2** p.1676, Real Estate **Band 3** p.1679, **New Mexico:** Corporate/Commercial **Band 1** p.1764

**Brune & Richard LLP**
Profile: p.1959
Table(s): **New York:** Litigation **Band 2** p.1835

**Brunini, Grantham, Grower & Hewes, PLLC**
Profile: p.1611
Table(s): **Mississippi:** Corporate/Commercial **Band 2** p.1591, Energy & Natural Resources **Band 1** p.1593, Environment **Band 1** p.1594, Litigation **Band 1** p.1596, Real Estate **Band 3** p.1600

**Bryan Cave LLP**
Table(s): **Arizona:** Corporate/M&A **Band 4** p.494, Litigation **Band 3** p.501, **California:** Media & Entertainment **Band 3** p.605, **Colorado:** Corporate/M&A **Band 2** p.702, Labor & Employment **Band 3** p.706, Litigation **Band 4** p.708, Natural Resources & Environment **Band 2** p.712, Real Estate **Band 2** p.714, **Georgia:** Antitrust **Band 3** p.1037, Banking & Finance **Band 1** p.1039, Bankruptcy/Restructuring **Band 3** p.1041, Corporate/M&A **Band 4** p.1046, Litigation **Band 4** p.1065, Real Estate **Band 3** p.1069, **Illinois:** Environment **Band 3** p.1162, Labor & Employment **Band 4** p.1174, Media & Entertainment **Band 3** p.1185, **Missouri:** Corporate/M&A **Band 1** p.1618, Environment **Band 2** p.1621, Intellectual Property **Band 2** p.1623, Labor & Employment **Band 1** p.1625, Litigation **Band 1** p.1628, Real Estate **Band 1** p.1633, **Nationwide:** Franchising **Band 3** p.111, Sports Law **Band 3** p.240, **New York:** Environment **Band 1** p.1807, Real Estate **Band 4** p.1855

**Buchalter Nemer**
Profile: p.676
Table(s): **California:** Banking & Finance **Band 3** p.539, Bankruptcy/Restructuring **Band 3** p.542, Healthcare **Band 4** p.567

**Buchanan Angeli Altschul & Sullivan LLP**
Table(s): **Oregon:** Labor & Employment **Band 2** p.2168

**Buchanan Ingersoll & Rooney PC**
Profile: p.2236
Table(s): **Northern Virginia:** Intellectual Property **Band 2** p.2496, **Pennsylvania:** Antitrust **Band 2** p.2184, Banking & Finance **Band 3** p.2186, Bankruptcy/Restructuring **Band 4** p.2188, Corporate/M&A & Private Equity **Band 3** p.2191, Environment **Band 4** p.2194, Intellectual Property **Band 4** p.2197, Labor & Employment **Band 2** p.2200, Litigation **Band 3** p.2203

# Index of firms

**Buchman Law Firm, LLP**
Table(s): **Nationwide:** Food & Beverages **Band 2** p.109

**BuckleySandler LLP**
Profile: p.908
Table(s): **Nationwide:** Financial Services Regulation **Band 1** p.97

**Bullard Law**
Profile: p.2181
Table(s): **Oregon:** Labor & Employment **Band 2** p.2168

**Bullivant Houser Bailey PC**
Table(s): **California:** Insurance **Band 3** p.573

**Burbidge Mitchell & Gross**
Table(s): **Utah:** Litigation **Band 1** p.2468

**Burch & Cracchiolo**
Profile: p.513
Table(s): **Arizona:** Real Estate **Band 1** p.504

**Burch, Porter & Johnson PLLC**
Table(s): **Tennessee:** Litigation **Band 3** p.2295, Real Estate **Band 3** p.2299

**Burke & Parsons**
Table(s): **Nationwide:** Transportation **Band 2** p.260

**Burr & Forman LLP**
Profile: p.477
Table(s): **Alabama:** Banking & Finance **Band 2** p.455, Bankruptcy/Restructuring **Band 1** p.457, Corporate/Commercial **Band 1** p.458, Labor & Employment **Band 1** p.460, Litigation **Band 2** p.462, Real Estate **Band 1** p.465, **Florida:** Bankruptcy/Restructuring **Band 4** p.939, **Georgia:** Banking & Finance **Band 4** p.1039, Bankruptcy/Restructuring **Band 4** p.1041

**Bush Strout & Kornfeld LLP**
Table(s): **Washington:** Bankruptcy/Restructuring **Band 1** p.2523

**Butler Pappas Weihmuller Katz Craig LLP**
Table(s): **Florida:** Insurance **Band 3** p.957

**Butler Rubin Saltarelli & Boyd LLP**
Profile: p.1243
Table(s): **Illinois:** Insurance **Band 1** p.1168

**Butler, Snow, O'Mara, Stevens & Cannada, PLLC**
Profile: p.1613
Table(s): **Mississippi:** Corporate/Commercial **Band 1** p.1591, Environment **Band 1** p.1594, Labor & Employment **Band 2** p.1595, Litigation **Band 1** p.1596, Real Estate **Band 1** p.1600, **Nationwide:** Product Liability & Mass Torts **Band 3** p.207, **Tennessee:** Healthcare **Band 2** p.2291, Labor & Employment **Band 2** p.2293, Litigation **Band 3** p.2295, Real Estate **Band 3** p.2299

**Butzel Long**
Table(s): **Michigan:** Corporate/M&A **Band 4** p.1538, Employee Benefits & Executive Compensation **Band 2** p.1540, Labor & Employment **Band 3** p.1541, Litigation **Band 3** p.1544

**Byrnes Keller Cromwell LLP**
Table(s): **Washington:** Litigation **Band 1** p.2533

## C

**Cable Huston Benedict Haagensen & Lloyd LLP**
Table(s): **Oregon:** Environment **Band 2** p.2165

**Cades Schutte LLP**
Table(s): **Hawaii:** Bankruptcy/Restructuring **Band 1** p.1114, Corporate/Commercial **Band 1** p.1115, Labor & Employment **Band 2** p.1117, Litigation **Band 1** p.1118, Real Estate **Band 1** p.1120

**Cadwalader, Wickersham & Taft LLP**
Profile: p.438
Table(s): **District of Columbia:** Antitrust **Band 4** p.786, Bankruptcy/Restructuring **Band 1** p.792, **Nationwide:** Bankruptcy/Restructuring **Band 3** p.38, Capital Markets **Band 2** p.51, Corporate/M&A **Band 2** p.67, Energy & Natural Resources **Band 4** p.75, Financial Services Regulation **Band 2** p.98, Real Estate **Band 3** p.225, Tax **Band 3** p.248, **New York:** Bankruptcy/Restructuring **Band 3** p.1781, Corporate/M&A **Band 3** p.1794, Employee Benefits & Executive Compensation **Band 4** p.1802, Healthcare **Band 3** p.1811, Intellectual Property **Band 3** p.1820, Litigation **Band 3** p.1833, Real Estate **Band 2** p.1853, Tax **Band 3** p.1860, **North Carolina:** Real Estate **Band 2** p.2037

**Cadwell Sanford Deibert & Garry LLP**
Table(s): **South Dakota:** Corporate/Commercial **Band 2** p.2281, Litigation **Band 1** p.2284

**Caesar, Rivise, Bernstein, Cohen & Pokotilow Ltd**
Table(s): **Pennsylvania:** Intellectual Property **Band 2** p.2197

**Cahill Gordon & Reindel LLP**
Profile: p.1960
Table(s): **District of Columbia:** Telecom, Broadcast & Satellite **Band 4** p.844, **Nationwide:** Banking & Finance **Band 2** p.31, Capital Markets **Band 1** p.46, Insurance **Band 3** p.134, **New York:** Antitrust **Band 4** p.1777, Insurance **Band 1** p.1815, Litigation **Band 3** p.1833, Media & Entertainment **Band 1** p.1851

**Cairncross & Hempelmann, A Professional Service Corporation**
Profile: p.2543
Table(s): **Washington:** Real Estate **Band 1** p.2536

**Caldwell Leslie & Proctor, PC**
Profile: p.677
Table(s): **California:** Litigation **Band 5** p.593, Litigation **Band 3** p.601

**Calfee, Halter & Griswold LLP**
Profile: p.2121
Table(s): **Ohio:** Banking & Finance **Band 2** p.2056, Bankruptcy/Restructuring **Band 3** p.2058, Construction **Band 3** p.2062, Corporate/M&A **Band 3** p.2064, Employee Benefits & Executive Compensation **Band 2** p.2067, Intellectual Property **Band 2** p.2071, Litigation **Band 3** p.2078

**Calfo Harrigan Leyh & Eakes LLP**
Table(s): **Washington:** Litigation **Band 3** p.2533

**Campbell & Levine**
Table(s): **Pennsylvania:** Bankruptcy/Restructuring **Band 4** p.2188

**Campbell & Wells, P.A.**
Table(s): **New Mexico:** Real Estate **Band 3** p.1772

**Campbell & Williams**
Table(s): **Nevada:** Litigation **Band 1** p.1676

**Campbell Campbell Edwards & Conroy PC**
Profile: p.1516
Table(s): **Nationwide:** Product Liability & Mass Torts **Band 3** p.207

**Campbell Woods, PLLC**
Table(s): **West Virginia:** Corporate/Commercial **Band 3** p.2550

**Camrud, Maddock, Olson & Larson, Ltd.**
Table(s): **North Dakota:** Litigation **Band 3** p.2053

**Canterbury, Elder, Gooch, Surratt, Shapiro & Stein, P. C.**
Profile: p.2431
Table(s): **Texas:** Construction **Band 2** p.2334

**Caplin & Drysdale**
Profile: p.909
Table(s): **District of Columbia:** Bankruptcy/Restructuring **Band 2** p.792, Tax **Band 2** p.838, **Nationwide:** Government **Band 2** p.124, Tax **Band 3** p.243

**Carlsmith Ball LLP**
Profile: p.1127
Table(s): **Hawaii:** Bankruptcy/Restructuring **Band 2** p.1114, Corporate/Commercial **Band 1** p.1115, Labor & Employment **Band 2** p.1117, Litigation **Band 2** p.1118, Real Estate **Band 1** p.1120

**Carlton Fields, P.A.**
Profile: p.1020
Table(s): **Florida:** Antitrust **Band 2** p.934, Bankruptcy/Restructuring **Band 4** p.939, Construction **Band 1** p.944, Corporate/M&A & Private Equity **Band 3** p.947, Environment **Band 2** p.951, Healthcare **Band 3** p.953, Insurance **Band 1** p.957, Litigation **Band 1** p.965, Real Estate **Band 2** p.974, Tax **Band 2** p.979

**Carmagnola & Ritardi LLC**
Table(s): **New Jersey:** Labor & Employment **Band 3** p.1718

**Carmody & Torrance LLP**
Table(s): **Connecticut:** Labor & Employment **Band 3** p.736, Litigation **Band 2** p.738

**Carpenter Lipps & Leland LLP**
Table(s): **Ohio:** Litigation **Band 4** p.2078

**Carrington, Coleman, Sloman & Blumenthal, LLP**
Table(s): **Texas:** Litigation **Band 4** p.2361

**Carroll Warren & Parker PLLC**
Profile: p.1614
Table(s): **Mississippi:** Litigation **Band 3** p.1596

**Carter Ledyard & Milburn LLP**
Profile: p.1961
Table(s): **Nationwide:** Wealth Management **Band 4** p.266, **New York:** Environment **Band 3** p.1807

**Carver, Darden, Koretzky, Tessier, Finn, Blossman & Areaux LLC**
Table(s): **Louisiana:** Banking & Finance **Band 3** p.1335, Bankruptcy/Restructuring **Band 3** p.1337, Energy & Natural Resources **Band 2** p.1344

**Cascadia Law Group**
Table(s): **Washington:** Environment **Band 1** p.2527

**Case Lombardi & Pettit**
Profile: p.1128
Table(s): **Hawaii:** Bankruptcy/Restructuring **Band 1** p.1114, Corporate/Commercial **Band 2** p.1115, Litigation **Band 2** p.1118, Real Estate **Band 2** p.1120

**Cassem Tierney Adams Gotch & Douglas**
Table(s): **Nebraska:** Litigation **Band 1** p.1664

**Cassidy Levy Kent LLP**
Table(s): **Nationwide:** International Trade **Band 4** p.152

**Chadbourne & Parke LLP**
Profile: p.1962
Table(s): **District of Columbia:** Insurance **Band 2** p.816, **Nationwide:** Bankruptcy/Restructuring **Band 5** p.38, Energy & Natural Resources **Band 3** p.75, International Arbitration **Band 4** p.144, Projects **Band 1** p.217, **New York:** Bankruptcy/Restructuring **Band 4** p.1781, Latin American Investment **Band 3** p.1829

**Chaffetz Lindsey LLP**
Table(s): **Nationwide:** International Arbitration **Band 4** p.144, **New York:** Insurance **Band 2** p.1815

**Chamberlain, Hrdlicka, White, Williams & Aughtry**
Profile: p.2432
Table(s): **Georgia:** Tax **Band 1** p.1072, **Nationwide:** Tax **Band 3** p.243, **Texas:** Tax **Band 4** p.2371

**Chapman and Cutler LLP**
Profile: p.1244
Table(s): **Illinois:** Banking & Finance **Band 4** p.1145, **Nationwide:** Capital Markets **Band 3** p.58

**Cheng Cohen LLC**
Table(s): **Nationwide:** Franchising **Band 4** p.111

**Chilivis, Cochran, Larkins & Bever LLP**
Table(s): **Georgia:** Litigation **Band 4** p.1065

**Chimicles & Tikellis**
Table(s): **Delaware:** Chancery **Band 2** p.759

**Choate Hall & Stewart LLP**
Profile: p.1517
Table(s): **Massachusetts:** Antitrust **Band 2** p.1444, Banking & Finance **Band 2** p.1445, Bankruptcy/Restructuring **Band 2** p.1449, Corporate/M&A **Band 3** p.1452, Intellectual Property **Band 3** p.1462, Litigation **Band 2** p.1470, Private Equity **Band 3** p.1474, Tax **Band 3** p.1481

**Christensen O'Connor Johnson Kindness, PLLC**
Table(s): **Washington:** Intellectual Property **Band 3** p.2529

**Christian & Barton LLP**
Table(s): **Virginia:** Litigation **Band 3** p.2502

**Christian & Small LLP**
Profile: p.479
Table(s): **Alabama:** Litigation **Band 4** p.462

**Chun Yoshimoto LLP**
Table(s): **Hawaii:** Corporate/Commercial **Band 2** p.1115, Real Estate **Band 2** p.1120

**Chun, Kerr, Dodd, Beaman & Wong**
Table(s): **Hawaii:** Corporate/Commercial **Band 2** p.1115, Real Estate **Band 2** p.1120

**Ciklin Lubitz Martens & O'Connell**
Table(s): **Florida:** Construction **Band 2** p.944

**Clarence Dyer & Cohen, LLP**
Table(s): **California:** Litigation **Band 2** p.601

**Clark & Elbing**
Table(s): **Massachusetts:** Intellectual Property **Band 3** p.1462

**Clark Hill PLC**
Profile: p.1559
Table(s): **Michigan:** Corporate/M&A **Band 4** p.1538, Labor & Employment **Band 2** p.1541, Real Estate **Band 3** p.1546

**Cleary Gottlieb Steen & Hamilton LLP**
Profile: p.1963
Table(s): **District of Columbia:** Antitrust **Band 1** p.786, Corporate/M&A & Private Equity **Band 3** p.797, **Nationwide:** Antitrust **Band 1** p.22, Banking & Finance **Band 3** p.31, Bankruptcy/Restructuring **Band 2** p.38, Capital Markets **Band 1** p.46, Corporate/M&A **Band 2** p.67, Employee Benefits & Executive Compensation **Band 1** p.72, Energy & Natural Resources **Band 1** p.77, Financial Services Regulation **Band 1** p.95, International Arbitration **Band 3** p.144, Investment Funds **Band 2** p.165, Private Equity **Band 2** p.203, Projects **Band 4** p.217, Real Estate **Band 3** p.225, Securities **Band 2** p.231, Securities **Band 1** p.231, Tax **Band 1** p.248, **New York:** Bankruptcy/Restructuring **Band 2** p.1781, Corporate/M&A **Band 2** p.1792, Employee Benefits & Executive Compensation **Band 1** p.1802, Latin American Investment **Band 1** p.1829, Litigation **Band 1** p.1833, Real Estate **Band 1** p.1853, Tax **Band 1** p.1860

**Cleary Shahi & Aicher, P.C.**
Table(s): **Vermont:** Litigation **Band 2** p.2485

**Clifford Chance LLP**
Profile: p.439
Table(s): **Nationwide:** Banking & Finance **Band 2** p.32, Capital Markets **Band 1** p.55, Investment Funds **Band 4** p.165, Projects **Band 3** p.217, Transportation **Band 2** p.251, **New York:** Corporate/M&A **Band 3** p.1794, Insurance **Band 3** p.1816, Latin American Investment **Band 3** p.1829, Tax **Band 4** p.1860

**Cline, Williams, Wright, Johnson & Oldfather LLP**
Table(s): **Nebraska:** Corporate/Commercial **Band 1** p.1659, Healthcare **Band 3** p.1661, Labor & Employment **Band 2** p.1662, Litigation **Band 1** p.1663

**Clyde & Co LLP**
Profile: p.440
Table(s): **Nationwide:** Transportation **Band 2** p.253, **New Jersey:** Litigation **Band 2** p.1723, **New York:** Insurance **Band 3** p.1815

**Coats Rose Yale Ryman Lee**
Table(s): **Louisiana:** Labor & Employment **Band 2** p.1349, **Texas:** Construction **Band 2** p.2334

**Coblentz, Patch, Duffy & Bass LLP**
Table(s): **California:** Real Estate **Band 4** p.611, Real Estate **Band 1** p.611

**Coffey Burlington**
Table(s): **Florida:** Litigation **Band 4** p.965

**Cohen & Gresser LLP**
Profile: p.1964
Table(s): **New York:** Litigation **Band 4** p.1835

**Cohen & Grigsby PC**
Table(s): **Pennsylvania:** Labor & Employment **Band 4** p.2200

**Cohen and Wolf, PC**
Table(s): **Connecticut:** Litigation **Band 3** p.738, Real Estate **Band 3** p.740

**Cokinos, Bosien and Young**
Table(s): **Texas:** Construction **Band 1** p.2334

**Cole, Schotz, Meisel, Forman & Leonard PA**
Profile: p.1752
Table(s): **Delaware:** Bankruptcy/Restructuring **Band 1** p.754, **New Jersey:** Bankruptcy/Restructuring **Band 1** p.1704, Litigation **Band 2** p.1722, Real Estate **Band 1** p.1728

**Collora LLP**
Profile: p.1518
Table(s): **Massachusetts:** Litigation **Band 2** p.1470

**Colodny, Fass, Talenfeld, Karlinsky, Abate & Webb PA**
Profile: p.1021
Table(s): **Florida:** Insurance **Band 2** p.957

**Colson Hicks Eidson**
Profile: p.1022
Table(s): **Florida:** Litigation **Band 1** p.965

**Comiter Singer Baseman & Braun LLP**
Table(s): **Florida:** Tax **Band 3** p.979

**Commercial Law Group**
Table(s): **Oklahoma:** Corporate/Commercial **Band 2** p.2134

**Condon & Forsyth LLP**
Profile: p.1965
Table(s): **Nationwide:** Transportation **Band 1** p.253

**Conklin, Woodcock & Ziegler, P.C.**
Table(s): **New Mexico:** Labor & Employment **Band 2** p.1767

**Conley Rose, P.C.**
Table(s): **Texas:** Intellectual Property **Band 4** p.2354

**Conmy Feste Ltd**
Table(s): **North Dakota:** Corporate/Commercial **Band 2** p.2051, Real Estate **Band 1** p.2055

**Connelly Baker Wotring LLP**
Table(s): **Texas:** Environment **Band 4** p.2343

**Conner & Winters, LLP**
Table(s): **Oklahoma:** Corporate/Commercial **Band 2** p.2134, Energy & Natural Resources **Band 2** p.2136, Labor & Employment **Band 1** p.2139

**Conrad O'Brien**
Table(s): **Pennsylvania:** Litigation **Band 2** p.2203

**Constangy, Brooks & Smith, LLP**
Table(s): **Alabama:** Labor & Employment **Band 3** p.460, **Florida:** Labor & Employment **Band 3** p.959, **Georgia:** Labor & Employment **Band 3** p.1059, **Missouri:** Labor & Employment **Band 3** p.1624, **North Carolina:** Labor & Employment **Band 1** p.2031, **South Carolina:** Labor & Employment **Band 3** p.2262, **Tennessee:** Labor & Employment **Band 3** p.2293, **Texas:** Labor & Employment **Band 4** p.2358

**Conway & Mrowiec**
Table(s): **Illinois:** Construction **Band 3** p.1154

**Cook, Little, Rosenblatt & Manson PLLC**
Table(s): **New Hampshire:** Corporate/Commercial **Band 1** p.1685, Labor & Employment **Band 3** p.1688, Litigation **Band 3** p.1689

**Cooley LLP**
Table(s): **California:** Capital Markets **Band 2** p.547, Corporate/M&A **Band 1** p.553, Employee Benefits & Executive Compensation **Band 3** p.560, Intellectual Property **Band 3** p.577, IT & Outsourcing **Band 2** p.583, Life Sciences **Band 1** p.590, Litigation **Band 3** p.593, **Colorado:** Corporate/M&A **Band 2** p.702, Intellectual Property **Band 2** p.704, **District of Columbia:** Corporate/M&A & Private Equity **Band 3** p.797, **Massachusetts:** Private Equity **Band 3** p.1474, **Nationwide:** Intellectual Property **Band 3** p.140, Investment Funds **Band 1** p.173, Life Sciences **Band 1** p.182, Projects **Band 4** p.218, **New York:** Litigation **Band 2** p.1832, Litigation **Band 3** p.1832, **Northern Virginia:** Corporate/M&A **Band 2** p.2493, Intellectual Property **Band 2** p.2496, Real Estate **Band 1** p.2505, **Washington:** Corporate/Commercial **Band 3** p.2524

**Cooper & Scully PC**
Profile: p.2433
Table(s): **Texas:** Insurance **Band 2** p.2350

**Copeland Cook Taylor & Bush, A Professional Association**
Table(s): **Mississippi:** Energy & Natural Resources **Band 1** p.1593, Litigation **Band 2** p.1596

**Coppersmith Schermer & Brockelman PLC**
Table(s): **Arizona:** Labor & Employment **Band 3** p.499

**Corbyn Hampton PLLC**
Table(s): **Oklahoma:** Litigation **Band 2** p.2141

**Corlew Munford & Smith PLLC**
Table(s): **Mississippi:** Environment **Band 2** p.1594, Litigation **Band 3** p.1596

**Corr Cronin Michelson Baumgardner & Preece LLP**
Table(s): **Washington:** Litigation **Band 1** p.2533

**Cotchett, Pitre & McCarthy**
Table(s): **California:** Litigation **Band 1** p.593

**Friedman Kaplan Seiler & Adelman LLP**
Table(s): **New York:** Litigation **Band 2** p.1832

**Fross Zelnick Lehrman & Zissu PC**
Profile: p.1976
Table(s): **Nationwide:** Intellectual Property **Band 1** p.141, **New York:** Intellectual Property **Band 1** p.1821

**Frost Brown Todd LLC**
Profile: p.1329
Table(s): **Indiana:** Litigation **Band 3** p.1273, **Kentucky:** Corporate/M&A **Band 1** p.1305, Environment, Natural Resources & Utilities **Band 1** p.1307, Intellectual Property **Band 2** p.1308, Labor & Employment **Band 1** p.1309, Litigation **Band 2** p.1311, Real Estate **Band 1** p.1314, **Ohio:** Banking & Finance **Band 3** p.2056, Bankruptcy/Restructuring **Band 2** p.2058, Construction **Band 3** p.2062, Healthcare **Band 2** p.2069, Intellectual Property **Band 2** p.2071, Labor & Employment **Band 1** p.2073, Natural Resources & Environment **Band 1** p.2082, Real Estate **Band 2** p.2085

**Fulbright & Jaworski LLP**
Profile: p.2435
Table(s): **California:** Environment **Band 4** p.564, Healthcare **Band 4** p.567, **District of Columbia:** Healthcare **Band 2** p.809, **Nationwide:** Banking & Finance **Band 3** p.32, Bankruptcy/Restructuring **Band 5** p.38, Energy & Natural Resources **Band 3** p.78, Healthcare **Band 4** p.126, Intellectual Property **Band 4** p.140, International Arbitration **Band 3** p.144, Product Liability & Mass Torts **Band 3** p.207, Projects **Band 2** p.217, Projects **Band 2** p.217, Retail **Band 2** p.229, Tax **Band 3** p.243, Transportation **Band 3** p.251, **Texas:** Antitrust **Band 1** p.2322, Banking & Finance **Band 5** p.2325, Bankruptcy/Restructuring **Band 1** p.2328, Corporate/M&A **Band 4** p.2337, Environment **Band 2** p.2343, Healthcare **Band 1** p.2347, Insurance **Band 2** p.2350, Intellectual Property **Band 2** p.2354, Labor & Employment **Band 1** p.2358, Litigation **Band 2** p.2361, Real Estate **Band 3** p.2367, Tax **Band 2** p.2371, Technology **Band 2** p.2374

**Fullenkamp, Doyle & Jobeun**
Table(s): **Nebraska:** Real Estate **Band 1** p.1666

**Fultz Maddox Hovious & Dickens PLC**
Table(s): **Kentucky:** Litigation **Band 3** p.1311

---

## G

**GableGotwals**
Table(s): **Oklahoma:** Energy & Natural Resources **Band 2** p.2136, Litigation **Band 2** p.2141

**Gainsburgh, Benjamin, David, Meunier & Warshauer, L.L.C.**
Table(s): **Louisiana:** Litigation **Band 3** p.1352

**Gallagher & Kennedy PA**
Table(s): **Arizona:** Corporate/M&A **Band 4** p.494, Environment (including water rights) **Band 1** p.496, Litigation **Band 1** p.501, Real Estate **Band 2** p.504

**Gallagher, Evelius & Jones, LLP**
Table(s): **Maryland:** Healthcare **Band 2** p.1415, Litigation **Band 3** p.1419, Real Estate **Band 2** p.1422

**Gallivan, White & Boyd, PA**
Profile: p.2274
Table(s): **South Carolina:** Litigation **Band 2** p.2264

**Gammage & Burnham, PLC**
Table(s): **Arizona:** Real Estate **Band 1** p.504

**Gang, Tyre, Ramer & Brown, Inc.**
Table(s): **California:** Media & Entertainment **Band 1** p.609

**Gardere Wynne Sewell LLP**
Profile: p.2436
Table(s): **Nationwide:** Energy & Natural Resources **Band 4** p.79, Leisure & Hospitality **Band 3** p.178, **Texas:** Antitrust **Band 3** p.2322, Bankruptcy/Restructuring **Band 2** p.2328, Construction **Band 3** p.2334, Corporate/M&A **Band 5** p.2337, Environment **Band 4** p.2343, Insurance **Band 1** p.2350, Real Estate **Band 3** p.2367, Tax **Band 4** p.2371

**Garfunkel Wild P.C.**
Table(s): **New Jersey:** Healthcare **Band 2** p.1714, **New York:** Healthcare **Band 3** p.1811

**Garlington, Lohn & Robinson, PLLP**
Profile: p.1657
Table(s): **Montana:** Corporate/M&A **Band 2** p.1646, Labor & Employment **Band 1** p.1647, Litigation **Band 1** p.1649, Real Estate **Band 2** p.1652

**Garofalo Goerlich Hainbach PC**
Table(s): **Nationwide:** Transportation **Band 2** p.255

**Garvey Schubert Barer**
Table(s): **Washington:** Corporate/Commercial **Band 3** p.2524

**Gass Weber Mullins LLC**
Profile: p.2589
Table(s): **Wisconsin:** Litigation **Band 2** p.2576

**Gelber, Gelber & Ingersoll, A Law Corporation**
Table(s): **Hawaii:** Bankruptcy/Restructuring **Band 2** p.1114

**Genova, Burns & Giantomasi**
Table(s): **New Jersey:** Labor & Employment **Band 3** p.1718

**Genovese Joblove & Battista, PA**
Table(s): **Florida:** Bankruptcy/Restructuring **Band 1** p.939

**Gentry Locke Rakes & Moore LLP**
Table(s): **Virginia:** Litigation **Band 3** p.2502

**Gibbons P.C.**
Profile: p.1754
Overview(s): **New Jersey:** p.1703
Table(s): **New Jersey:** Bankruptcy/Restructuring **Band 2** p.1704, Corporate/M&A **Band 2** p.1707, Environment **Band 2** p.1711, Healthcare **Band 3** p.1714, Intellectual Property **Band 2** p.1716, Labor & Employment **Band 2** p.1718, Litigation **Band 1** p.1722, Real Estate **Band 2** p.1728

**Gibbs & Bruns LLP**
Profile: p.2437
Table(s): **Texas:** Litigation **Band 1** p.2361

**Gibbs Giden Locher Turner Senet & Wittbrodt LLP.**
Profile: p.681
Table(s): **California:** Construction **Band 2** p.549

**Gibbs Houston Pauw**
Table(s): **Washington:** Immigration **Band 2** p.2528

**Gibney, Anthony & Flaherty LLP**
Table(s): **New York:** Immigration **Band 3** p.1813

**Gibson, Dunn & Crutcher LLP**
Profile: p.682
Table(s): **California:** Antitrust **Band 1** p.535, Banking & Finance **Band 2** p.539, Bankruptcy/Restructuring **Band 2** p.542, Capital Markets **Band 2** p.547, Corporate/M&A **Band 1** p.553, Employee Benefits & Executive Compensation **Band 2** p.560, Environment **Band 2** p.564, Insurance **Band 4** p.573, Intellectual Property **Band 3** p.577, IT & Outsourcing **Band 1** p.583, Labor & Employment **Band 2** p.586, Litigation **Band 1** p.593, Media & Entertainment **Band 1** p.605, Real Estate **Band 1** p.611, Tax **Band 1** p.616, **Colorado:** Corporate/M&A **Band 2** p.702, Litigation **Band 3** p.708, **District of Columbia:** Antitrust **Band 3** p.786, Corporate/M&A & Private Equity **Band 1** p.797, Employee Benefits & Executive Compensation **Band 3** p.801, Environment **Band 4** p.804, Labor & Employment **Band 1** p.824, Litigation **Band 2** p.826, **Nationwide:** Antitrust **Band 1** p.22, Appellate Law **Band 1** p.26, Banking & Finance **Band 5** p.31, Capital Markets **Band 4** p.46, Corporate/M&A **Band 2** p.67, ERISA Litigation **Band 2** p.92, Government **Band 2** p.117, International Trade **Band 2** p.152, Investment Funds **Band 3** p.165, Labor & Employment **Band 3** p.176, Outsourcing **Band 1** p.195, Privacy & Data Security **Band 1** p.199, Private Equity **Band 3** p.203, Real Estate **Band 3** p.225, Retail **Band 2** p.229, Securities **Band 1** p.231, Tax **Band 2** p.248, Transportation **Band 1** p.258, **New York:** Antitrust **Band 4** p.1777, Corporate/M&A **Band 5** p.1792, Intellectual Property **Band 4** p.1820, Litigation **Band 2** p.1833, Media & Entertainment **Band 1** p.1851, Real Estate **Band 3** p.1853, Technology & Outsourcing **Band 4** p.1868, **Texas:** Antitrust **Band 1** p.2322, Corporate/M&A **Band 3** p.2337, Litigation **Band 4** p.2361

**Gifford & Brinkerhoff**
Table(s): **Wyoming:** Litigation **Band 1** p.2598

**Gignilliat, Savitz & Bettis LLP**
Table(s): **South Carolina:** Labor & Employment **Band 2** p.2262

**Gilbert LLP**
Profile: p.914
Table(s): **District of Columbia:** Insurance **Band 3** p.818

**Gill Ragon Owen, P.A.**
Table(s): **Arkansas:** Corporate/Commercial **Band 3** p.518, Real Estate **Band 3** p.524

**Gilmartin, Poster & Shafto LLP**
Table(s): **Nationwide:** Transportation **Band 3** p.259

**Giordano Halleran & Ciesla PC**
Table(s): **New Jersey:** Corporate/M&A **Band 3** p.1707, Environment **Band 2** p.1711, Healthcare **Band 1** p.1714, Intellectual Property **Band 4** p.1716, Real Estate **Band 2** p.1728

**Givens Pursley LLP**
Table(s): **Idaho:** Bankruptcy/Restructuring **Band 1** p.1131, Corporate/Commercial **Band 2** p.1132, Labor & Employment **Band 2** p.1132, Litigation **Band 2** p.1134, Natural Resources & Environment **Band 1** p.1136, Real Estate **Band 1** p.1136

**Gjording Fouser PLLC**
Table(s): **Idaho:** Litigation p.1134

**Glankler Brown, PLLC**
Table(s): **Tennessee:** Real Estate **Band 2** p.2299

**Glaser, Weil, Fink, Jacobs, Howard, Avchen & Shapiro, LLP**
Table(s): **California:** Media & Entertainment **Band 3** p.605

**Glenn Rasmussen, P.A.**
Profile: p.1023
Table(s): **Florida:** Bankruptcy/Restructuring **Band 3** p.939, Corporate/M&A & Private Equity **Band 4** p.947

**Godfrey & Kahn, SC**
Profile: p.2590
Table(s): **Wisconsin:** Corporate/M&A **Band 2** p.2571, Intellectual Property **Band 3** p.2573, Labor & Employment **Band 3** p.2574, Litigation **Band 2** p.2576, Natural Resources & Environment **Band 2** p.2578, Real Estate **Band 2** p.2579

**Goetz Fitzpatrick LLP**
Profile: p.1977
Table(s): **New York:** Construction **Band 3** p.1790

**Goldberg Godles Wiener & Wright**
Table(s): **District of Columbia:** Telecom, Broadcast & Satellite **Band 4** p.844

## H

**Haddon, Morgan and Foreman, P.C.**
Table(s): **Colorado:** Litigation **Band 1** p.708

**Hahn Loeser & Parks LLP**
Profile: p.2123
Table(s): **Ohio:** Bankruptcy/Restructuring **Band 2** p.2058, Construction **Band 4** p.2062, Corporate/M&A **Band 3** p.2064, Intellectual Property **Band 4** p.2071, Litigation **Band 3** p.2078

**Hall Maines Lugrin, P.C.**
Table(s): **Texas:** Insurance **Band 3** p.2350

**Hall, Estill, Hardwick, Gable, Golden & Nelson, PC**
Profile: p.2160
Table(s): **Oklahoma:** Corporate/Commercial **Band 2** p.2134, Energy & Natural Resources **Band 1** p.2136, Intellectual Property **Band 1** p.2138, Labor & Employment **Band 1** p.2139, Native American Law **Band 2** p.2144

**Hangley Aronchick Segal Pudlin & Schiller**
Profile: p.2243
Table(s): **Pennsylvania:** Bankruptcy/Restructuring **Band 2** p.2188, Environment **Band 3** p.2194, Litigation **Band 2** p.2203, Real Estate **Band 4** p.2207

**Hansen, Jacobson, Teller, Hoberman, Newman, Warren & Richman, LLP**
Table(s): **California:** Media & Entertainment **Band 1** p.609

**Hanson Bridgett LLP**
Table(s): **California:** Construction **Band 2** p.549, Healthcare **Band 3** p.567

**Harding & Shultz PC**
Table(s): **Nebraska:** Labor & Employment **Band 2** p.1662

**Hare, Wynn, Newell & Newton LLP**
Profile: p.480
Table(s): **Alabama:** Litigation **Band 1** p.463

**Harkavy Shainberg Kaplan & Dunstan PLC**
Table(s): **Tennessee:** Real Estate **Band 3** p.2299

**Harkins Cunningham LLP**
Profile: p.2244
Table(s): **Nationwide:** Transportation **Band 3** p.256, **Pennsylvania:** Litigation **Band 3** p.2203

**Harper Meyer Perez Hagen O'Connor Albert & Dribin LLP**
Profile: p.1026
Table(s): **Florida:** Latin American Investment **Band 3** p.962

**Harris Martin Jones P.A.**
Table(s): **Tennessee:** Media & Entertainment **Band 2** p.2297

**Harris Winick LLP**
Table(s): **Illinois:** Construction **Band 3** p.1154

**Harter, Secrest & Emery LLP**
Profile: p.1979
Table(s): **New York:** Immigration **Band 3** p.1813

**Hartzog Conger Cason & Neville, LLP**
Profile: p.2161
Table(s): **Oklahoma:** Corporate/Commercial **Band 2** p.2134, Litigation **Band 2** p.2141

**Harwell Howard Hyne Gabbert & Manner, PC**
Table(s): **Tennessee:** Corporate/M&A **Band 2** p.2288, Healthcare **Band 3** p.2291, Litigation **Band 3** p.2295

**Hatchett & Hauck LLP**
Table(s): **Indiana:** Environment **Band 1** p.1270

**Hawley Troxell Ennis & Hawley LLP**
Table(s): **Idaho:** Corporate/Commercial **Band 1** p.1132, Labor & Employment **Band 1** p.1132, Litigation **Band 2** p.1134, Real Estate **Band 2** p.1136

**Haynes and Boone, LLP**
Profile: p.444
Table(s): **Nationwide:** Bankruptcy/Restructuring **Band 5** p.38, Franchising **Band 2** p.111, Intellectual Property **Band 4** p.140, **New York:** Real Estate **Band 4** p.1853, **Texas:** Antitrust **Band 1** p.2322, Banking & Finance **Band 2** p.2325, Bankruptcy/Restructuring **Band 1** p.2328, Capital Markets **Band 3** p.2333, Construction **Band 3** p.2334, Corporate/M&A **Band 3** p.2337, Energy **Band 2** p.2340, Environment **Band 2** p.2343, Insurance **Band 1** p.2350, Intellectual Property **Band 2** p.2354, Labor & Employment **Band 3** p.2358, Litigation **Band 3** p.2361, Real Estate **Band 1** p.2367, Tax **Band 4** p.2371, Technology **Band 2** p.2376

**Haynsworth Sinkler Boyd PA**
Table(s): **South Carolina:** Corporate/M&A **Band 1** p.2260, Litigation **Band 3** p.2264, Real Estate **Band 2** p.2266

**Heim, Payne & Chorush LLP**
Profile: p.2440
Table(s): **Texas:** Intellectual Property **Band 4** p.2354

**Heley, Duncan & Melander, PLLP**
Table(s): **Minnesota:** Construction **Band 2** p.1567

**Heller, Draper, Patrick & Horn, LLC**
Table(s): **Louisiana:** Bankruptcy/Restructuring **Band 1** p.1337

**Helmsing, Leach, Herlong, Newman & Rouse, PC**
Profile: p.481
Table(s): **Alabama:** Litigation **Band 2** p.462

**Hendrick, Phillips, Salzman & Flatt P.C.**
Table(s): **Georgia:** Construction **Band 3** p.1044

**Hendrickson & Long PLLC**
Table(s): **West Virginia:** Litigation **Band 3** p.2555

**Herman, Herman & Katz LLC**
Table(s): **Louisiana:** Litigation **Band 3** p.1352

**Herrick, Feinstein LLP**
Table(s): **New Jersey:** Litigation **Band 3** p.1722, **New York:** Real Estate **Band 4** p.1855

**Hickey & Evans LLP**
Table(s): **Wyoming:** Litigation **Band 2** p.2598

**Hill & Robbins PC**
Table(s): **Colorado:** Litigation **Band 4** p.708

**Hill Rivkins LLP**
Table(s): **Nationwide:** Transportation **Band 2** p.260

**Hill Wallack LLP**
Table(s): **New Jersey:** Real Estate **Band 3** p.1728

**Hill Ward Henderson**
Profile: p.1027
Table(s): **Florida:** Corporate/M&A & Private Equity **Band 3** p.947, Litigation **Band 2** p.965, Real Estate **Band 2** p.974, Tax **Band 3** p.979

**Hillis Clark Martin & Peterson P.S.**
Table(s): **Washington:** Real Estate **Band 1** p.2536

**Hinckley, Allen & Snyder LLP**
Table(s): **New Hampshire:** Corporate/Commercial **Band 3** p.1685, Litigation **Band 2** p.1689, **Rhode Island:** Corporate/Commercial **Band 2** p.2251, Labor & Employment **Band 2** p.2253, Litigation **Band 1** p.2254, Real Estate **Band 1** p.2255

**Hinkle Hensley Shanor & Martin LLP**
Table(s): **New Mexico:** Environment, Natural Resources & Regulated Industries **Band 1** p.1765, Litigation **Band 3** p.1769

**Hinkle Law Firm LLC**
Table(s): **Kansas:** Litigation **Band 2** p.1295, Real Estate **Band 3** p.1297

**Hinman & Carmichael LLP**
Table(s): **Nationwide:** Food & Beverages **Band 2** p.109

**Hirsch Roberts Weinstein LLP**
Table(s): **Massachusetts:** Labor & Employment **Band 4** p.1466

**Hirsch Wallerstein Hayum Matlof & Fishman**
Table(s): **California:** Media & Entertainment **Band 2** p.609

**Hirschler Fleischer**
Profile: p.2516
Table(s): **Southern Virginia:** Real Estate **Band 1** p.2506

**Hirst Applegate**
Table(s): **Wyoming:** Corporate/M&A **Band 1** p.2596, Labor & Employment **Band 1** p.2597, Litigation **Band 1** p.2598

**Hiscock & Barclay LLP**
Profile: p.1980
Table(s): **New York:** Energy & Natural Resources **Band 2** p.1806

**Hite, Fanning & Honeyman LLP**
Table(s): **Kansas:** Litigation **Band 2** p.1295

**Hobbs Straus Dean & Walker LLP**
Table(s): **Nationwide:** Native American Law **Band 2** p.191

**Hochman Salkin Rettig Toscher & Perez**
Table(s): **California:** Tax **Band 3** p.616

**Hodge Dwyer & Driver**
Table(s): **Illinois:** Environment **Band 3** p.1162

**Hodgson Russ LLP**
Table(s): **New York:** Environment **Band 3** p.1807, Healthcare **Band 3** p.1811

**Hogan Lovells**
Table(s): **California:** Litigation **Band 3** p.593, **Colorado:** Corporate/M&A **Band 1** p.702, Intellectual Property **Band 3** p.704, Litigation **Band 2** p.708, Natural Resources & Environment **Band 1** p.712, **District of Columbia:** Antitrust **Band 3** p.786, Bankruptcy/Restructuring **Band 3** p.792, Corporate/M&A & Private Equity **Band 1** p.797, Employee Benefits & Executive Compensation **Band 4** p.801, Environment **Band 2** p.804, Healthcare **Band 1** p.809, Immigration **Band 3** p.814, Insurance **Band 3** p.816, Litigation **Band 2** p.826, Real Estate **Band 2** p.834, Telecom, Broadcast & Satellite **Band 2** p.844, **Florida:** Corporate/M&A & Private Equity **Band 2** p.947, Healthcare **Band 2** p.953, Labor & Employment **Band 4** p.959, Latin American Investment **Band 2** p.962, Litigation **Band 2** p.965, **Maryland:** Corporate/M&A **Band 1** p.1412, Healthcare **Band 3** p.1415, Litigation **Band 1** p.1419, **Nationwide:** Antitrust **Band 3** p.22, Appellate Law **Band 3** p.26, Capital Markets **Band 1** p.55, Climate Change **Band 3** p.62, Corporate/M&A **Band 4** p.67, Energy & Natural Resources **Band 3** p.75, Environment **Band 3** p.89, Financial Services Regulation **Band 3** p.95, Food & Beverages **Band 1** p.107, Government **Band 2** p.117, Government **Band 1** p.121, Healthcare **Band 2** p.126, Insurance **Band 4** p.134, International Arbitration **Band 5** p.144, International Trade **Band 4** p.152, Investment Funds **Band 3** p.173, Leisure & Hospitality **Band 3** p.178, Life Sciences **Band 2** p.182, Native American Law **Band 3** p.191, Privacy & Data Security **Band 1** p.199, Product Liability & Mass Torts **Band 3** p.207, Projects **Band 3** p.218, Real Estate **Band 4** p.225, Securities **Band 3** p.233, Transportation **Band 1** p.255, **New York:** Corporate/M&A **Band 3** p.1794, Healthcare **Band 3** p.1811, Insurance **Band 3** p.1815, Litigation **Band**

**Kaufmann Gildin Robbins & Oppenheim LLP**
Table(s): **Nationwide:** Franchising **Band** 4 p.111

**Kay Casto & Chaney PLLC**
Table(s): **West Virginia:** Corporate/Commercial **Band** 3 p.2550, Labor & Employment **Band** 3 p.2553

**Kaye Scholer LLP**
Profile: p.1984
Table(s): **Illinois:** Bankruptcy/Restructuring **Band** 3 p.1148, **Nationwide:** Capital Markets **Band** 3 p.58, Intellectual Property **Band** 4 p.140, International Trade **Band** 4 p.152, Life Sciences **Band** 2 p.182, Product Liability & Mass Torts **Band** 1 p.207, Real Estate **Band** 4 p.225, Securities **Band** 4 p.231, Transportation **Band** 4 p.251, **New York:** Corporate/M&A **Band** 3 p.1794, Intellectual Property **Band** 3 p.1820, Litigation **Band** 1 p.1832, Real Estate **Band** 2 p.1853, Technology & Outsourcing **Band** 4 p.1868

**Kazmarek Geiger & Laseter LLP**
Table(s): **Georgia:** Environment **Band** 2 p.1050

**Kean Miller LLP**
Profile: p.1379
Table(s): **Louisiana:** Corporate/M&A **Band** 3 p.1341, Energy & Natural Resources **Band** 2 p.1344, Environment **Band** 1 p.1346, Labor & Employment **Band** 2 p.1349, Litigation **Band** 3 p.1352, Real Estate **Band** 3 p.1355

**Keating Muething & Klekamp PLL**
Profile: p.2124
Table(s): **Ohio:** Bankruptcy/Restructuring **Band** 3 p.2058, Corporate/M&A **Band** 2 p.2064, Litigation **Band** 3 p.2078

**Keesal, Young & Logan PC**
Table(s): **Nationwide:** Transportation **Band** 1 p.263

**Kegler, Brown, Hill & Ritter**
Profile: p.2125
Table(s): **Ohio:** Banking & Finance **Band** 3 p.2056, Bankruptcy/Restructuring **Band** 3 p.2058, Construction **Band** 3 p.2062, Corporate/M&A **Band** 2 p.2064, Intellectual Property **Band** 4 p.2071, Labor & Employment **Band** 3 p.2073, Litigation **Band** 3 p.2078, Real Estate **Band** 4 p.2085

**Keker & Van Nest LLP**
Table(s): **California:** Intellectual Property **Band** 2 p.577, Litigation **Band** 1 p.593, **Nationwide:** Intellectual Property **Band** 3 p.140

**Keleher & McLeod, PA**
Table(s): **New Mexico:** Litigation **Band** 2 p.1769

**Keller and Heckman LLP**
Profile: p.920
Table(s): **Nationwide:** Food & Beverages **Band** 2 p.107

**Kelley Drye & Warren LLP**
Profile: p.1985
Table(s): **District of Columbia:** Insurance **Band** 4 p.818, Telecom, Broadcast & Satellite **Band** 4 p.844, **Illinois:** Communications **Band** 2 p.1153, **Nationwide:** Advertising **Band** 2 p.19, International Trade **Band** 4 p.152, Privacy & Data Security **Band** 2 p.199, **New York:** Bankruptcy/Restructuring **Band** 5 p.1781

**Kellogg, Huber, Hansen, Todd, Evans & Figel, PLLC**
Table(s): **District of Columbia:** Telecom, Broadcast & Satellite **Band** 1 p.844, **Nationwide:** Appellate Law **Band** 2 p.26

**Kelly Hart & Hallman LLP**
Table(s): **Texas:** Environment **Band** 3 p.2343

**Kemp Smith LLP**
Table(s): **Texas:** Labor & Employment **Band** 3 p.2358

**Kemp, Jones & Coulthard, LLP**
Table(s): **Nevada:** Litigation **Band** 1 p.1676

**Kendall, Brill & Klieger LLP**
Table(s): **California:** Media & Entertainment **Band** 3 p.605

**Kenlan, Schwiebert, Facey & Goss P.C.**
Table(s): **Vermont:** Real Estate **Band** 2 p.2487

**Kennelly & O'Keeffe Attorneys**
Table(s): **North Dakota:** Real Estate **Band** 1 p.2055

**Kenny Nachwalter PA**
Profile: p.1029
Table(s): **Florida:** Antitrust **Band** 1 p.934, Litigation **Band** 1 p.965

**Kenyon & Kenyon LLP**
Table(s): **Nationwide:** Intellectual Property **Band** 4 p.140, International Trade **Band** 4 p.159, **New York:** Intellectual Property **Band** 3 p.1820

**Kienbaum Opperwall Hardy & Pelton, P.L.C.**
Profile: p.1562
Table(s): **Michigan:** Labor & Employment **Band** 1 p.1541

**Kilpatrick Townsend & Stockton LLP**
Profile: p.1109
Table(s): **California:** Intellectual Property **Band** 2 p.578, **Colorado:** Intellectual Property **Band** 1 p.704, **District of Columbia:** Employee Benefits & Executive Compensation **Band** 4 p.801, Intellectual Property **Band** 1 p.820, Intellectual Property **Band** 4 p.820, **Georgia:** Bankruptcy/Restructuring **Band** 2 p.1041, Construction **Band** 1 p.1044, Corporate/M&A **Band** 3 p.1046, Environment **Band** 3 p.1050, Intellectual Property **Band** 1 p.1056, Labor & Employment **Band** 2 p.1059, Litigation **Band** 2 p.1065, Real Estate **Band** 2 p.1069, Tax **Band** 2 p.1072, **Nationwide:** Construction **Band** 1 p.65, Franchising **Band** 4 p.111, Intellectual Property **Band** 2 p.141, Native American Law **Band** 3 p.191,

Outsourcing **Band** 4 p.195, **New York:** Intellectual Property **Band** 3 p.1821, **North Carolina:** Corporate/M&A **Band** 4 p.2025, Environment **Band** 2 p.2027, Intellectual Property **Band** 1 p.2030, Labor & Employment **Band** 3 p.2031, Litigation **Band** 3 p.2033

**King & Ballow**
Table(s): **Tennessee:** Labor & Employment **Band** 3 p.2293

**King & Schickli**
Table(s): **Kentucky:** Intellectual Property **Band** 2 p.1308

**King & Spalding LLP**
Profile: p.445
Table(s): **District of Columbia:** Healthcare **Band** 2 p.809, Healthcare **Band** 1 p.809, **Georgia:** Antitrust **Band** 1 p.1037, Banking & Finance **Band** 1 p.1039, Bankruptcy/Restructuring **Band** 1 p.1041, Corporate/M&A **Band** 1 p.1046, Environment **Band** 1 p.1050, Healthcare **Band** 1 p.1052, Intellectual Property **Band** 3 p.1056, Labor & Employment **Band** 3 p.1059, Litigation **Band** 1 p.1065, Real Estate **Band** 1 p.1069, Tax **Band** 1 p.1072, **Nationwide:** Appellate Law **Band** 3 p.26, Capital Markets **Band** 4 p.55, Corporate/M&A **Band** 3 p.67, Energy & Natural Resources **Band** 2 p.75, Environment **Band** 3 p.89, Food & Beverages **Band** 3 p.107, Government **Band** 3 p.121, Healthcare **Band** 2 p.126, International Arbitration **Band** 2 p.144, International Trade **Band** 3 p.152, Product Liability & Mass Torts **Band** 2 p.207, Projects **Band** 3 p.217, Tax **Band** 5 p.248, **New York:** Intellectual Property **Band** 4 p.1820, **North Carolina:** Banking & Finance **Band** 4 p.2021, **Texas:** Bankruptcy/Restructuring **Band** 3 p.2328, Construction **Band** 3 p.2334, Environment **Band** 4 p.2343, Healthcare **Band** 2 p.2347, Litigation **Band** 3 p.2361

**King, Blackwell, Zehnder & Wermuth, PA**
Table(s): **Florida:** Litigation **Band** 3 p.965

**Kirk & Chaney**
Table(s): **Oklahoma:** Litigation **Band** 3 p.2141

**Kirkland & Ellis LLP**
Profile: p.1254
Table(s): **California:** Banking & Finance **Band** 4 p.539, Corporate/M&A **Band** 1 p.553, Intellectual Property **Band** 5 p.577, IT & Outsourcing **Band** 4 p.583, Litigation **Band** 3 p.593, **District of Columbia:** Antitrust **Band** 3 p.786, Corporate/M&A & Private Equity **Band** 1 p.797, Environment **Band** 3 p.804, Intellectual Property **Band** 3 p.820, Litigation **Band** 3 p.826, Media & Entertainment **Band** 2 p.832, **Illinois:** Antitrust **Band** 1 p.1142, Banking & Finance **Band** 2 p.1145, Bankruptcy/Restructuring **Band** 1 p.1148, Corporate/M&A **Band** 1 p.1156, Insurance **Band** 1 p.1167, Intellectual Property **Band** 1 p.1171, Litigation **Band** 1 p.1179, Real Estate **Band** 2 p.1187, Tax **Band** 1 p.1192, Technology & Outsourcing **Band** 2 p.1194, **Nationwide:** Advertising **Band** 3 p.19, Antitrust **Band** 3 p.22, Appellate Law **Band** 3 p.26, Banking & Finance **Band** 3 p.31, Bankruptcy/Restructuring **Band** 1

p.38, Capital Markets **Band** 3 p.46, Capital Markets **Band** 4 p.58, Climate Change **Band** 2 p.62, Corporate/M&A **Band** 2 p.67, Energy & Natural Resources **Band** 2 p.77, Environment **Band** 3 p.89, Intellectual Property **Band** 1 p.140, International Trade **Band** 3 p.159, Investment Funds **Band** 1 p.165, Life Sciences **Band** 4 p.182, Outsourcing **Band** 3 p.195, Private Equity **Band** 1 p.203, Product Liability & Mass Torts **Band** 2 p.207, Real Estate **Band** 4 p.225, Tax **Band** 1 p.248, Transportation **Band** 3 p.253, Wealth Management **Band** 4 p.266, **New York:** Bankruptcy/Restructuring **Band** 1 p.1781, Corporate/M&A **Band** 3 p.1792, Intellectual Property **Band** 1 p.1820, Litigation **Band** 3 p.1833, Media & Entertainment **Band** 2 p.1851, Real Estate **Band** 4 p.1853, Tax **Band** 2 p.1860

**Kirton & McConkie**
Table(s): **Utah:** Real Estate **Band** 2 p.2470

**Kirwin Norris PA**
Table(s): **Florida:** Construction **Band** 3 p.944

**Klarquist Sparkman, LLP**
Table(s): **Oregon:** Intellectual Property **Band** 1 p.2166

**Klasko Rulon Stock & Seltzer**
Table(s): **Nationwide:** Immigration **Band** 2 p.131

**Klee, Tuchin, Bogdanoff & Stern LLP**
Profile: p.687
Table(s): **California:** Bankruptcy/Restructuring **Band** 1 p.542, **Nationwide:** Bankruptcy/Restructuring **Band** 4 p.38

**Klehr Harrison Harvey Branzburg LLP**
Table(s): **Pennsylvania:** Bankruptcy/Restructuring **Band** 3 p.2188, Real Estate **Band** 3 p.2207

**Kleinfeld, Kaplan & Becker LLP**
Table(s): **District of Columbia:** Healthcare **Band** 3 p.810

**Klevansky Piper, LLP**
Table(s): **Hawaii:** Bankruptcy/Restructuring **Band** 1 p.1114

**Kluger, Kaplan, Silverman, Katzen & Levine, P.L.**
Profile: p.1030
Table(s): **Florida:** Litigation **Band** 4 p.965

**Knobbe Martens Olson & Bear**
Table(s): **California:** Intellectual Property **Band** 1 p.577, Intellectual Property **Band** 4 p.577, Life Sciences **Band** 3 p.590, **Nationwide:** Intellectual Property **Band** 4 p.140

**Kobayashi, Sugita & Goda**
Table(s): **Hawaii:** Labor & Employment **Band** 3 p.1117

**Kobre & Kim LLP**
Profile: p.1031
Table(s): **Florida:** Litigation **Band** 2 p.967, **New York:** Litigation **Band** 3 p.1835

**Kohn Swift & Graf, PC**
Table(s): **Pennsylvania:** Antitrust **Band 3** p.2184

**Kohn, Shands, Elbert, Gianoulakis & Giljum, LLP**
Table(s): **Missouri:** Litigation **Band 3** p.1629

**Koley Jessen P.C.**
Table(s): **Nebraska:** Corporate/Commercial **Band 1** p.1659, Healthcare **Band 3** p.1661, Real Estate **Band 3** p.1666

**Kollman & Saucier PA**
Table(s): **Maryland:** Labor & Employment **Band 2** p.1417

**Kostelanetz & Fink LLP**
Table(s): **Nationwide:** Tax **Band 3** p.243

**Kozyak Tropin & Throckmorton**
Table(s): **Florida:** Bankruptcy/Restructuring **Band 1** p.939, Litigation **Band 2** p.965

**Kraftson Caudle**
Table(s): **Virginia:** Construction **Band 2** p.2491

**Kramer & Alfano PC**
Table(s): **Georgia:** Immigration **Band 3** p.1054

**Kramer Levin Naftalis & Frankel LLP**
Profile: p.1987
Table(s): **Nationwide:** Advertising **Band 1** p.19, Bankruptcy/Restructuring **Band 2** p.38, Immigration **Band 2** p.131, Investment Funds **Band 3** p.169, **New York:** Bankruptcy/Restructuring **Band 1** p.1781, Corporate/M&A **Band 3** p.1794, Immigration **Band 1** p.1813, Litigation **Band 2** p.1833, Real Estate **Band 2** p.1855, Tax **Band 4** p.1860

**Kramer Rayson LLP**
Profile: p.2316
Table(s): **Tennessee:** Labor & Employment **Band 2** p.2293

**Kramon & Graham, PA**
Profile: p.1436
Table(s): **Maryland:** Litigation **Band 1** p.1419

**Krebs, Farley & Pelleteri PLLC**
Profile: p.1380
Table(s): **Louisiana:** Construction **Band 1** p.1339

**Krieg DeVault LLP**
Table(s): **Indiana:** Corporate/M&A **Band 3** p.1268, Real Estate **Band 3** p.1274

**Krovatin Klingeman LLC**
Table(s): **New Jersey:** Litigation **Band 2** p.1723

**Krukowski & Costello, S.C.**
Table(s): **Wisconsin:** Labor & Employment **Band 4** p.2574

**Kuck Immigration Partners LLC**
Table(s): **Georgia:** Immigration **Band 2** p.1054

**Kurzban, Kurzban, Weinger, Tetzeli & Pratt**
Table(s): **Florida:** Immigration **Band 1** p.956

**Kutak Rock LLP**
Profile: p.1670
Table(s): **Arkansas:** Corporate/Commercial **Band 1** p.518, Real Estate **Band 2** p.524, **Kansas:** Labor & Employment **Band 2** p.1293, **Nebraska:** Corporate/Commercial **Band 1** p.1659, Healthcare **Band 2** p.1661, Litigation **Band 1** p.1663, Real Estate **Band 1** p.1666

## L

**Labaton Sucharow LLP**
Profile: p.1988
Table(s): **Nationwide:** Securities **Band 1** p.233, **New York:** Litigation **Band 1** p.1835

**Lamberth, Cifelli, Stokes & Stout, P.A.**
Table(s): **Georgia:** Bankruptcy/Restructuring **Band 4** p.1041

**Lamson, Dugan & Murray, LLP**
Table(s): **Nebraska:** Litigation **Band 1** p.1664

**Landis Rath & Cobb LLP**
Profile: p.781
Table(s): **Delaware:** Bankruptcy/Restructuring **Band 2** p.754

**Landye Bennett Blumstein LLP**
Table(s): **Oregon:** Environment **Band 3** p.2165

**Lane & Waterman LLP**
Table(s): **Iowa:** Corporate/M&A **Band 2** p.1282, Labor & Employment **Band 3** p.1285, Litigation **Band 2** p.1287, Real Estate **Band 1** p.1290

**Lane Powell PC**
Profile: p.2547
Table(s): **Alaska:** Litigation **Band 3** p.490, **Oregon:** Corporate/M&A **Band 2** p.2163, Labor & Employment **Band 4** p.2168, Litigation **Band 3** p.2171, Real Estate **Band 3** p.2173, **Washington:** Bankruptcy/Restructuring **Band 1** p.2523, Corporate/Commercial **Band 3** p.2524, Intellectual Property **Band 4** p.2529, Labor & Employment **Band 2** p.2531, Litigation **Band 3** p.2533, Real Estate **Band 2** p.2535

**Laner Muchin, Ltd**
Profile: p.1255
Table(s): **Illinois:** Labor & Employment **Band 3** p.1174

**Langer, Grogan & Diver PC**
Table(s): **Pennsylvania:** Antitrust **Band 3** p.2184

**Langrock Sperry & Wool, LLP**
Table(s): **Vermont:** Real Estate **Band 2** p.2487

**Lanier Ford Shaver & Payne P.C.**
Table(s): **Alabama:** Litigation **Band 3** p.462

**Lankler Siffert & Wohl LLP**
Profile: p.1989
Table(s): **New York:** Litigation **Band 1** p.1835

**Larkin Hoffman Daly & Lindgren, Ltd.**
Profile: p.1586
Table(s): **Nationwide:** Franchising **Band 3** p.111

**Larrabee Mehlman Albi Coker LLP**
Table(s): **California:** Immigration **Band 2** p.571

**Latham & Watkins LLP**
Profile: p.446
Table(s): **California:** Antitrust **Band 1** p.535, Banking & Finance **Band 1** p.539, Bankruptcy/Restructuring **Band 1** p.542, Capital Markets **Band 1** p.547, Corporate/M&A **Band 1** p.553, Employee Benefits & Executive Compensation **Band 1** p.560, Environment **Band 1** p.564, Healthcare **Band 1** p.567, Insurance **Band 3** p.575, IT & Outsourcing **Band 1** p.583, Life Sciences **Band 1** p.590, Litigation **Band 1** p.601, Real Estate **Band 1** p.611, Tax **Band 1** p.616, **District of Columbia:** Antitrust **Band 3** p.786, Corporate/M&A & Private Equity **Band 1** p.797, Environment **Band 2** p.804, Healthcare **Band 2** p.809, Intellectual Property **Band 3** p.820, Litigation **Band 4** p.826, Media & Entertainment **Band 2** p.832, Tax **Band 2** p.838, Technology & Outsourcing **Band 2** p.842, Telecom, Broadcast & Satellite **Band 2** p.844, **Illinois:** Banking & Finance **Band 1** p.1145, Bankruptcy/Restructuring **Band 2** p.1148, Corporate/M&A **Band 1** p.1156, Litigation **Band 2** p.1179, Real Estate **Band 4** p.1187, Tax **Band 3** p.1192, **Massachusetts:** Corporate/M&A **Band 3** p.1452, Private Equity **Band 2** p.1474, **Nationwide:** Antitrust **Band 2** p.22, Appellate Law **Band 1** p.26, Banking & Finance **Band 2** p.31, Bankruptcy/Restructuring **Band 2** p.38, Capital Markets **Band 1** p.55, Climate Change **Band 1** p.62, Corporate/M&A **Band 1** p.67, Employee Benefits & Executive Compensation **Band 3** p.72, Energy & Natural Resources **Band 1** p.75, Environment **Band 1** p.89, Financial Services Regulation **Band 3** p.98, Healthcare **Band 4** p.126, Insurance **Band 3** p.136, Intellectual Property **Band 3** p.140, International Trade **Band 5** p.152, Investment Funds **Band 2** p.173, Leisure & Hospitality **Band 3** p.178, Life Sciences **Band 1** p.182, Outsourcing **Band 2** p.195, Private Equity **Band 2** p.203, Projects **Band 1** p.217, Real Estate **Band 4** p.225, Retail **Band 3** p.229, Securities **Band 3** p.231, Tax **Band 1** p.243, **New Jersey:** Litigation **Band 3** p.1722, **New York:** Bankruptcy/Restructuring **Band 3** p.1781, Corporate/M&A **Band 2** p.1792, Employee Benefits & Executive Compensation **Band 4** p.1802, Latin American Investment **Band 3** p.1829, Litigation **Band 3** p.1833, Real Estate **Band 3** p.1853, Tax **Band 3** p.1860, **Texas:** Banking & Finance **Band 2** p.2325, Capital Markets **Band 1** p.2333, Corporate/M&A **Band 2** p.2337

**Latham, Shuker, Barker, Eden & Beaudine LLP**
Table(s): **Florida:** Bankruptcy/Restructuring **Band 4** p.939

**Lathrop & Gage LLP**
Table(s): **Illinois:** Media & Entertainment **Band 2** p.1184, **Kansas:** Corporate/M&A **Band 3** p.1292, Litigation **Band 3** p.1295, Real Estate **Band 2** p.1297, **Missouri:** Corporate/M&A **Band 2** p.1618, Environment **Band 1** p.1621, Labor & Employment **Band 1** p.1624, Litigation **Band 2** p.1628, Real Estate **Band 2** p.1632, **Nationwide:** Transportation **Band 3** p.256

**Lathrop & Rutledge**
Table(s): **Wyoming:** Litigation **Band 2** p.2598

**Lau, Lane, Pieper, Conley & McCreadie PA**
Table(s): **Nationwide:** Transportation **Band 1** p.263

**Laura Devine Solicitors**
Table(s): **New York:** Immigration **Band 3** p.1813

**Laurie & Brennan, LLP**
Table(s): **Illinois:** Construction **Band 2** p.1154

**Lavely & Singer PC**
Table(s): **California:** Media & Entertainment **Band 2** p.605

**Law Offices of Richard A Gump Jr PC**
Table(s): **Texas:** Immigration **Band 2** p.2349

**Lawler, Metzger, Keeney & Logan LLC**
Table(s): **District of Columbia:** Telecom, Broadcast & Satellite **Band 2** p.844

**Leading-Edge Law Group, PLC**
Table(s): **Southern Virginia:** Intellectual Property **Band 3** p.2498

**Leavens, Strand & Glover, Adler LLC**
Table(s): **Illinois:** Media & Entertainment **Band 1** p.1185

**LeClairRyan**
Table(s): **Southern Virginia:** Corporate/M&A **Band 3** p.2494, **Virginia:** Labor & Employment **Band 3** p.2499, Litigation **Band 3** p.2502

**Lederer Weston Craig PLC**
Table(s): **Iowa:** Litigation **Band 3** p.1287, Litigation **Band 1** p.1287

**Lehr Middlebrooks & Vreeland, P.C.**
Table(s): **Alabama:** Labor & Employment **Band 1** p.460

**Leitman, Siegal, Payne & Campbell, P.C.**
Table(s): **Alabama:** Real Estate **Band 2** p.465

**Leonard, Street and Deinard Professional Association**
Table(s): **Minnesota:** Construction **Band 2** p.1567, Corporate/M&A **Band 2** p.1568, Labor & Employment **Band 3** p.1570, Litigation **Band 3** p.1573, Real Estate **Band 2** p.1576

**Magleby & Greenwood PC**
Table(s): **Utah:** Litigation **Band 3** p.2468

**Maguire & Pearce, PLLC**
Table(s): **Arizona:** Environment (including water rights) **Band 2** p.496

**Manatt Phelps & Phillips LLP**
Profile: p.690
Table(s): **California:** Healthcare **Band 2** p.567, Labor & Employment **Band 4** p.586, Litigation **Band 4** p.593, Media & Entertainment **Band 2** p.608, Real Estate **Band 2** p.611, **Nationwide:** Advertising **Band 2** p.19, Healthcare **Band 4** p.126, **New York:** Healthcare **Band 1** p.1811

**Mancini Welch & Geiger LLP**
Table(s): **Hawaii:** Real Estate **Band 2** p.1120

**Manko, Gold, Katcher & Fox LLP**
Table(s): **Pennsylvania:** Environment **Band 1** p.2194

**Manning Curtis Bradshaw & Bednar LLC**
Table(s): **Utah:** Labor & Employment **Band 3** p.2467

**Manning Fulton & Skinner PA**
Table(s): **North Carolina:** Real Estate **Band 3** p.2036

**Marger Johnson & McCollom PC**
Table(s): **Oregon:** Intellectual Property **Band 2** p.2166

**Maring Williams Law Office PC**
Table(s): **North Dakota:** Litigation **Band 2** p.2053

**Markowitz Ringel Trusty + Hartog P.A.**
Table(s): **Florida:** Bankruptcy/Restructuring **Band 4** p.939

**Markowitz, Herbold, Glade & Mehlhaf PC**
Table(s): **Oregon:** Litigation **Band 1** p.2171

**Marks & Klein, LLP**
Table(s): **Nationwide:** Franchising **Band 2** p.114

**Markus & Markus, PLLC**
Table(s): **Florida:** Litigation **Band 3** p.967

**Marr Jones & Wang LLLLP**
Profile: p.1129
Table(s): **Hawaii:** Labor & Employment **Band 1** p.1117

**Marsh, Rickard & Bryan P.C**
Table(s): **Alabama:** Litigation **Band 1** p.463

**Marshall, Dennehey, Warner, Coleman & Goggin**
Table(s): **Nationwide:** Transportation **Band 3** p.260

**Marshall, Gerstein & Borun LLP**
Table(s): **Illinois:** Intellectual Property **Band 3** p.1171

**Marten Law PLLC**
Table(s): **Washington:** Environment **Band 2** p.2527

**Martin & Chioffi LLP**
Table(s): **Connecticut:** Corporate/M&A **Band 3** p.731

**Martin, Disiere, Jefferson & Wisdom, LLP**
Profile: p.2445
Table(s): **Texas:** Insurance **Band 1** p.2350

**Martin, Pringle, Oliver, Wallace & Bauer, L.L.P.**
Table(s): **Kansas:** Labor & Employment **Band 2** p.1293, Litigation **Band 2** p.1295

**Maslon Edelman Borman & Brand, LLP**
Table(s): **Minnesota:** Construction **Band 2** p.1567, Corporate/M&A **Band 3** p.1568, Labor & Employment **Band 3** p.1570, Litigation **Band 2** p.1573

**Mautino & Mautino**
Table(s): **California:** Immigration **Band 2** p.571

**May, Adam, Gerdes & Thompson, L.L.P.**
Table(s): **South Dakota:** Litigation **Band 2** p.2284

**Mayer Brown LLP**
Profile: p.1257
Table(s): **District of Columbia:** Antitrust **Band 4** p.786, Intellectual Property **Band 4** p.820, Litigation **Band 4** p.826, Real Estate **Band 2** p.834, Technology & Outsourcing **Band 1** p.842, **Illinois:** Antitrust **Band 1** p.1142, Banking & Finance **Band 2** p.1145, Bankruptcy/Restructuring **Band 4** p.1148, Communications **Band 1** p.1153, Corporate/M&A **Band 2** p.1156, Environment **Band 3** p.1162, Insurance **Band 2** p.1168, Intellectual Property **Band 3** p.1171, Labor & Employment **Band 2** p.1176, Litigation **Band 2** p.1179, Real Estate **Band 2** p.1187, Tax **Band 2** p.1192, Technology & Outsourcing **Band 1** p.1194, **Nationwide:** Antitrust **Band 3** p.22, Appellate Law **Band 1** p.26, Bankruptcy/Restructuring **Band 5** p.38, Capital Markets **Band 1** p.58, Employee Benefits & Executive Compensation **Band 4** p.72, Financial Services Regulation **Band 4** p.95, Government **Band 3** p.117, International Arbitration **Band 5** p.144, International Trade **Band 4** p.152, Investment Funds **Band 4** p.165, Outsourcing **Band 1** p.195, Product Liability & Mass Torts **Band 2** p.207, Projects **Band 1** p.217, Real Estate **Band 4** p.225, Tax **Band 1** p.243, Transportation **Band 1** p.258, Wealth Management **Band 4** p.266, **New York:** Bankruptcy/Restructuring **Band 5** p.1781, Insurance **Band 3** p.1816, Latin American Investment **Band 3** p.1829, Litigation **Band 2** p.1832, Tax **Band 4** p.1860, **North Carolina:** Banking & Finance **Band 3** p.2021, Real Estate **Band 3** p.2037, **Texas:** Banking & Finance **Band 4** p.2325, Capital Markets **Band 3** p.2333, Corporate/M&A **Band 4** p.2337, Real Estate **Band 2** p.2367, Technology **Band 3** p.2374

**Maynard, Cooper & Gale, P.C.**
Profile: p.483
Table(s): **Alabama:** Banking & Finance **Band 2** p.455, Bankruptcy/Restructuring **Band 2** p.457, Corporate/Commercial **Band 1** p.458, Labor & Employment **Band 1** p.460, Litigation **Band 2** p.462, Real Estate **Band 1** p.465

**Mazur Carp & Rubin PC**
Table(s): **New York:** Construction **Band 2** p.1790

**McAfee & Taft**
Profile: p.2162
Table(s): **Oklahoma:** Corporate/Commercial **Band 1** p.2134, Energy & Natural Resources **Band 1** p.2136, Intellectual Property **Band 1** p.2138, Labor & Employment **Band 1** p.2139, Litigation **Band 1** p.2141, Native American Law **Band 2** p.2144, Real Estate **Band 1** p.2145

**McAndrews, Held & Malloy, Ltd**
Table(s): **Illinois:** Intellectual Property **Band 3** p.1171

**McBrayer, McGinnis, Leslie & Kirkland, PLLC**
Table(s): **Kentucky:** Real Estate **Band 3** p.1314

**McCarter & English, LLP**
Profile: p.1759
Table(s): **Connecticut:** Corporate/M&A **Band 3** p.731, Environment **Band 2** p.733, Labor & Employment **Band 3** p.736, Litigation **Band 2** p.738, Real Estate **Band 3** p.740, **Massachusetts:** Banking & Finance **Band 1** p.1446, Intellectual Property **Band 3** p.1462, **New Jersey:** Bankruptcy/Restructuring **Band 2** p.1704, Corporate/M&A **Band 2** p.1707, Employee Benefits & Executive Compensation **Band 1** p.1710, Environment **Band 1** p.1711, Healthcare **Band 2** p.1714, Intellectual Property **Band 2** p.1716, Litigation **Band 1** p.1722, Real Estate **Band 1** p.1728, **New York:** Construction **Band 3** p.1790, **Pennsylvania:** Bankruptcy/Restructuring **Band 4** p.2188

**McCorriston Miller Mukai MacKinnon LLP**
Table(s): **Hawaii:** Corporate/Commercial **Band 2** p.1115, Litigation **Band 1** p.1118, Real Estate **Band 2** p.1120

**McCullough Hill Leary, PS**
Table(s): **Washington:** Real Estate **Band 1** p.2536

**McDermott Will & Emery LLP**
Profile: p.1258
Table(s): **California:** Banking & Finance **Band 4** p.539, Healthcare **Band 1** p.567, Intellectual Property **Band 3** p.577, Life Sciences **Band 4** p.590, Litigation **Band 3** p.593, Tax **Band 2** p.601, Tax **Band 2** p.616, **District of Columbia:** Antitrust **Band 4** p.786, Employee Benefits & Executive Compensation **Band 4** p.801, Healthcare **Band 1** p.809, Insurance **Band 2** p.816, Intellectual Property **Band 2** p.820, Tax **Band 2** p.838, **Florida:** Corporate/M&A & Private Equity **Band 3** p.947, Healthcare **Band 1** p.953, **Illinois:** Antitrust **Band 1** p.1142, Banking & Finance **Band 4** p.1145, Corporate/M&A **Band 2**

p.1156, Environment **Band 4** p.1162, Healthcare **Band 1** p.1165, Intellectual Property **Band 2** p.1171, Labor & Employment **Band 1** p.1176, Litigation **Band 2** p.1179, Tax **Band 1** p.1192, **Massachusetts:** Employee Benefits & Executive Compensation **Band 2** p.1455, Healthcare **Band 1** p.1459, Litigation **Band 2** p.1470, **Nationwide:** Antitrust **Band 3** p.22, Corporate/M&A **Band 2** p.67, Employee Benefits & Executive Compensation **Band 2** p.72, ERISA Litigation **Band 2** p.92, Food & Beverages **Band 1** p.109, Government **Band 3** p.124, Healthcare **Band 1** p.126, Intellectual Property **Band 3** p.140, International Trade **Band 4** p.152, Life Sciences **Band 3** p.182, Privacy & Data Security **Band 3** p.199, Projects **Band 4** p.217, Tax **Band 2** p.243, Wealth Management **Band 1** p.266, **New York:** Corporate/M&A **Band 3** p.1794, Tax **Band 3** p.1860, **Texas:** Antitrust **Band 3** p.2322, Tax **Band 4** p.2371

**McDonald Carano Wilson LLP**
Table(s): **Nevada:** Environment **Band 3** p.1673, Gaming & Licensing **Band 3** p.1674, Litigation **Band 1** p.1676, Real Estate **Band 2** p.1679

**McDonald Hopkins LLC**
Table(s): **Ohio:** Banking & Finance **Band 3** p.2056, Bankruptcy/Restructuring **Band 2** p.2058

**McDonnell Boehnen Hulbert & Berghoff LLP**
Profile: p.1259
Table(s): **Illinois:** Intellectual Property **Band 2** p.1171

**McDowell Knight Roedder & Sledge LLC**
Table(s): **Alabama:** Litigation **Band 2** p.462

**McElroy, Deutsch, Mulvaney & Carpenter, LLP**
Profile: p.1760
Table(s): **New Jersey:** Healthcare **Band 1** p.1714, Labor & Employment **Band 1** p.1718, **Pennsylvania:** Bankruptcy/Restructuring **Band 4** p.2188

**McElroy, Sullivan & Miller LLP**
Table(s): **Texas:** Energy **Band 1** p.2341

**McEwen Gisvold LLP**
Table(s): **Oregon:** Real Estate **Band 4** p.2173

**McGee Hankla Backes & Dobrovolny P.C.**
Table(s): **North Dakota:** Litigation **Band 3** p.2053

**McGill, Gotsdiner, Workman & Lepp PC LLO**
Profile: p.1671
Table(s): **Nebraska:** Corporate/Commercial **Band 2** p.1659

**McGinnis Lochridge & Kilgore LLP**
Table(s): **Texas:** Energy **Band 1** p.2341

**McGlinchey Stafford PLLC**
Profile: p.1382
Table(s): **Louisiana:** Banking & Finance **Band 2**
p.1335, Bankruptcy/Restructuring **Band 2** p.1337,
Corporate/M&A **Band 3** p.1341, Gaming &
Licensing **Band 2** p.1348, Litigation **Band 3**
p.1352, Real Estate **Band 2** p.1355,
**Mississippi:** Litigation **Band 3** p.1596,
**Nationwide:** Financial Services Regulation **Band
3** p.99

**McGrath North Mullin & Kratz PC**
Table(s): **Nebraska:** Corporate/Commercial **Band
1** p.1659, Labor & Employment **Band 2** p.1662,
Litigation **Band 1** p.1663, Real Estate **Band 2**
p.1666

**McGuireWoods LLP**
Profile: p.2519
Table(s): **Georgia:** Labor & Employment **Band 4**
p.1059, **Illinois:** Antitrust **Band 4** p.1142,
Healthcare **Band 2** p.1165, Labor & Employment
**Band 3** p.1174, Litigation **Band 5** p.1179,
**Maryland:** Labor & Employment **Band 3** p.1417,
**Nationwide:** Product Liability & Mass Torts **Band
4** p.207, Wealth Management **Band 1** p.266,
**North Carolina:** Banking & Finance **Band 2**
p.2021, Bankruptcy/Restructuring **Band 1** p.2023,
Corporate/M&A **Band 3** p.2025, Environment **Band
2** p.2027, Litigation **Band 1** p.2033, Real Estate
**Band 3** p.2036, **Northern Virginia:** Real Estate
**Band 2** p.2505, **Southern Virginia:**
Corporate/M&A **Band 1** p.2494, Intellectual
Property **Band 1** p.2498, Real Estate **Band 1**
p.2506, **Virginia:** Environment **Band 1** p.2495,
Labor & Employment **Band 1** p.2499, Litigation
**Band 1** p.2502

**McKenna Long & Aldridge LLP**
Profile: p.922
Table(s): **California:** Insurance **Band 4** p.573,
Real Estate **Band 3** p.611, **District of
Columbia:** Bankruptcy/Restructuring **Band 3**
p.792, **Georgia:** Bankruptcy/Restructuring **Band
2** p.1041, Corporate/M&A **Band 3** p.1046, Energy
**Band 2** p.1049, Environment **Band 3** p.1050,
Healthcare **Band 2** p.1052, Immigration **Band 3**
p.1054, Labor & Employment **Band 3** p.1059,
Litigation **Band 3** p.1065, Real Estate **Band 3**
p.1069, Tax **Band 2** p.1072, **Nationwide:**
Government **Band 1** p.117, International Trade
**Band 5** p.152

**McKool Smith**
Profile: p.2446
Table(s): **Nationwide:** Intellectual Property **Band
3** p.140, **Texas:** Intellectual Property **Band 1**
p.2354, Litigation **Band 2** p.2361

**McLane, Graf, Raulerson & Middleton
Professional Association**
Profile: p.1700
Table(s): **New Hampshire:**
Corporate/Commercial **Band 1** p.1685,
Environment **Band 1** p.1687, Labor & Employment
**Band 1** p.1688, Litigation **Band 1** p.1689, Real
Estate **Band 1** p.1692

**McMahon DeGulis LLP**
Profile: p.2126
Table(s): **Ohio:** Natural Resources & Environment
**Band 1** p.2082

**McManus Darden & Felsen LLP**
Table(s): **District of Columbia:** Construction
**Band 3** p.795

**McNair Law Firm PA**
Table(s): **South Carolina:** Corporate/M&A **Band
1** p.2260, Litigation **Band 3** p.2264, Real Estate
**Band 1** p.2266

**McNaul Ebel Nawrot Helgren & Vance
PLLC**
Table(s): **Washington:** Litigation **Band 3** p.2533

**Meadows, Collier, Reed, Cousins,
Crouch & Ungerman, L.L.P.**
Table(s): **Texas:** Tax **Band 3** p.2371

**Meagher & Geer, P.L.L.P.**
Table(s): **Minnesota:** Litigation **Band 3** p.1573

**Meckler Bulger Tilson Marick &
Pearson LLP**
Table(s): **Illinois:** Insurance **Band 2** p.1167, Labor
& Employment **Band 2** p.1174

**Meland Russin & Budwick PA**
Table(s): **Florida:** Bankruptcy/Restructuring **Band
3** p.939

**Mercer Thompson LLC**
Table(s): **Georgia:** Energy **Band 2** p.1049

**Merchant & Gould PC**
Table(s): **Colorado:** Intellectual Property **Band 3**
p.704

**Messing, Rudavsky & Weliky PC**
Table(s): **Massachusetts:** Labor & Employment
**Band 2** p.1467

**Meuleman Mollerup LLP**
Table(s): **Idaho:** Real Estate **Band 3** p.1136

**Meunier Carlin & Curfman, LLC**
Table(s): **Georgia:** Intellectual Property **Band 3**
p.1056

**Meyer Capel, PC**
Table(s): **Illinois:** Communications **Band 3** p.1153

**Michael Best & Friedrich LLP**
Profile: p.2592
Table(s): **Illinois:** Media & Entertainment **Band 3**
p.1185, **Wisconsin:** Corporate/M&A **Band 3**
p.2571, Intellectual Property **Band 1** p.2573,
Labor & Employment **Band 1** p.2574, Litigation
**Band 4** p.2576, Natural Resources & Environment
**Band 2** p.2578, Real Estate **Band 3** p.2579

**Middleton Reutlinger PSC**
Table(s): **Kentucky:** Intellectual Property **Band 1**
p.1308, Litigation **Band 3** p.1311, Real Estate
**Band 2** p.1314

**Milbank, Tweed, Hadley & McCloy LLP**
Profile: p.448
Table(s): **California:** Bankruptcy/Restructuring
**Band 1** p.542, Corporate/M&A **Band 3** p.553,
**District of Columbia:** Telecom, Broadcast &
Satellite **Band 3** p.844, **Nationwide:** Banking &
Finance **Band 1** p.31, Bankruptcy/Restructuring
**Band 1** p.38, Capital Markets **Band 3** p.52, Energy
& Natural Resources **Band 2** p.77, Financial
Services Regulation **Band 4** p.98, International
Arbitration **Band 5** p.144, Leisure & Hospitality
**Band 3** p.178, Projects **Band 1** p.215, Securities
**Band 4** p.231, Tax **Band 4** p.248, Transportation
**Band 1** p.251, Wealth Management **Band 2** p.266,
**New York:** Bankruptcy/Restructuring **Band 1**
p.1781, Corporate/M&A **Band 2** p.1794,
Intellectual Property **Band 4** p.1820, Latin
American Investment **Band 2** p.1829, Litigation
**Band 2** p.1833, Tax **Band 3** p.1860

**Miles & Stockbridge PC**
Profile: p.1438
Overview(s): **Maryland:** p.1411
Table(s): **Maryland:** Corporate/M&A **Band 2**
p.1412, Employee Benefits & Executive
Compensation **Band 2** p.1414, Labor &
Employment **Band 3** p.1417, Litigation **Band 2**
p.1419, Real Estate **Band 3** p.1422

**Miley & Brown PC**
Table(s): **Texas:** Immigration **Band 2** p.2349

**Miller & Chevalier Chartered**
Profile: p.923
Table(s): **District of Columbia:** Employee
Benefits & Executive Compensation **Band 2**
p.801, Litigation **Band 4** p.826, Tax **Band 2** p.838,
**Nationwide:** International Trade **Band 4** p.152,
Tax **Band 3** p.243

**Miller & Martin PLLC**
Profile: p.2317
Table(s): **Georgia:** Labor & Employment **Band 4**
p.1059, **Tennessee:** Corporate/M&A **Band 2**
p.2288, Labor & Employment **Band 3** p.2293,
Litigation **Band 3** p.2295

**Miller Johnson**
Table(s): **Michigan:** Corporate/M&A **Band 4**
p.1538, Employee Benefits & Executive
Compensation **Band 2** p.1540, Labor &
Employment **Band 2** p.1541, Litigation **Band 3**
p.1544

**Miller Mayer LLP**
Table(s): **New York:** Immigration **Band 3** p.1813

**Miller Nash LLP**
Profile: p.2182
Table(s): **Oregon:** Corporate/M&A **Band 3**
p.2163, Labor & Employment **Band 4** p.2168,
Litigation **Band 2** p.2171

**Miller, Balis & O'Neil, PC**
Table(s): **Nationwide:** Energy & Natural
Resources **Band 5** p.75

**Miller, Canfield, Paddock and Stone,
P.L.C.**
Profile: p.1563
Table(s): **Michigan:** Banking & Finance **Band 2**
p.1536, Corporate/M&A **Band 2** p.1538,
Employee Benefits & Executive Compensation
**Band 1** p.1540, Labor & Employment **Band 2**
p.1541, Litigation **Band 1** p.1544, Real Estate
**Band 2** p.1546

**Mills Paskert Divers PA**
Table(s): **Florida:** Construction **Band 4** p.944

**Milom Horsnell Crow Rose Kelley PLC**
Table(s): **Tennessee:** Media & Entertainment
**Band 1** p.2297

**Mintz Levin Cohn Ferris Glovsky and
Popeo PC**
Profile: p.1523
Table(s): **District of Columbia:** Healthcare
**Band 3** p.809, Telecom, Broadcast & Satellite **Band
3** p.844, **Massachusetts:** Banking & Finance
**Band 1** p.1446, Bankruptcy/Restructuring **Band 1**
p.1449, Corporate/M&A **Band 3** p.1452,
Employee Benefits & Executive Compensation
**Band 2** p.1455, Environment **Band 2** p.1457,
Healthcare **Band 2** p.1459, Labor & Employment
**Band 3** p.1466, Litigation **Band 2** p.1470, Real
Estate **Band 2** p.1477, **Nationwide:** Healthcare
**Band 1** p.128, Immigration **Band 3** p.131, Life
Sciences **Band 4** p.182, **New York:** Healthcare
**Band 2** p.1811

**Mitchell Silberberg & Knupp LLP**
Table(s): **California:** Labor & Employment **Band 3**
p.586, Media & Entertainment **Band 3** p.605,
**District of Columbia:** Media & Entertainment
**Band 3** p.832

**Mitchell, McNutt & Sams PA**
Profile: p.1616
Table(s): **Mississippi:** Litigation **Band 2** p.1596

**Mitchell, Williams, Selig, Gates
Woodyard, PLLC**
Profile: p.531
Table(s): **Arkansas:** Corporate/Commercial **Band
1** p.518, Labor & Employment **Band 2** p.520,
Litigation **Band 2** p.522, Real Estate **Band 1** p.524

**Mock, Schwabe, Waldo, Elder, Reeves
& Bryant**
Table(s): **Oklahoma:** Real Estate **Band 2** p.2145

**Modrall, Sperling, Roehl, Harris & Sisk,
PA**
Table(s): **Nationwide:** Native American Law
**Band 2** p.191, **New Mexico:**
Corporate/Commercial **Band 1** p.1764,
Environment, Natural Resources & Regulated
Industries **Band 1** p.1765, Labor & Employment
**Band 2** p.1767, Litigation **Band 1** p.1769, Native
American Law **Band 1** p.1771, Real Estate **Band 1**
p.1772

**Moffatt Thomas Barrett Rock & Fields**
Table(s): **Idaho:** Bankruptcy/Restructuring **Band 1** p.1131, Corporate/Commercial **Band 2** p.1132, Labor & Employment **Band 1** p.1132, Litigation **Band 3** p.1134, Natural Resources & Environment **Band 2** p.1136, Real Estate **Band 3** p.1136

**Monteleone & McCrory, LLP**
Table(s): **California:** Construction **Band 2** p.549

**Montgomery & Andrews, PA**
Table(s): **New Mexico:** Environment, Natural Resources & Regulated Industries **Band 1** p.1765

**Montiel Davis & Fonte, P.L.**
Table(s): **Florida:** Immigration **Band 3** p.956

**Moody & Warner PC**
Table(s): **New Mexico:** Labor & Employment **Band 3** p.1767

**Moore & Lee LLP**
Table(s): **Virginia:** Construction **Band 2** p.2491

**Moore & Van Allen, PLLC**
Table(s): **North Carolina:** Banking & Finance **Band 1** p.2021, Bankruptcy/Restructuring **Band 1** p.2023, Corporate/M&A **Band 1** p.2025, Environment **Band 4** p.2027, Intellectual Property **Band 1** p.2030, Litigation **Band 2** p.2033, Real Estate **Band 1** p.2036

**Moore, Cockrell, Goicoechea & Axelberg, P.C.**
Table(s): **Montana:** Litigation **Band 1** p.1649

**Morgan, Brown and Joy LLP**
Profile: p.1524
Overview(s): **Massachusetts:** p.1443
Table(s): **Massachusetts:** Labor & Employment **Band 1** p.1466

**Morgan, Lewis & Bockius LLP**
Profile: p.2246
Table(s): **California:** Corporate/M&A **Band 4** p.554, Employee Benefits & Executive Compensation **Band 1** p.560, Immigration **Band 2** p.571, Insurance **Band 3** p.575, IT & Outsourcing **Band 3** p.583, Labor & Employment **Band 2** p.586, Litigation **Band 3** p.593, Tax **Band 3** p.616, **District of Columbia:** Employee Benefits & Executive Compensation **Band 2** p.801, Environment **Band 3** p.804, Healthcare **Band 3** p.809, Immigration **Band 1** p.814, Insurance **Band 3** p.818, Labor & Employment **Band 1** p.824, Tax **Band 3** p.838, **Florida:** Labor & Employment **Band 3** p.959, **Illinois:** Labor & Employment **Band 1** p.1174, **Massachusetts:** Banking & Finance **Band 2** p.1445, **Nationwide:** Appellate Law **Band 4** p.26, Corporate/M&A **Band 1** p.67, Employee Benefits & Executive Compensation **Band 1** p.72, Energy & Natural Resources **Band 1** p.75, Environment **Band 3** p.89, ERISA Litigation **Band 1** p.92, Financial Services Regulation **Band 2** p.98, Immigration **Band 3** p.131, Insurance **Band 3** p.136, Investment Funds **Band 3** p.162, Labor & Employment **Band 1** p.176, Life Sciences **Band 3** p.182, Outsourcing **Band 2** p.195, Product Liability & Mass Torts **Band 4** p.207, Projects **Band 4** p.218, Retail **Band 2** p.229, Securities **Band 3**

p.233, **New Jersey:** Corporate/M&A **Band 2** p.1707, Labor & Employment **Band 2** p.1718, Litigation **Band 3** p.1722, **New York:** Corporate/M&A **Band 1** p.1794, Employee Benefits & Executive Compensation **Band 4** p.1802, Insurance **Band 3** p.1816, Labor & Employment **Band 2** p.1826, Media & Entertainment **Band 3** p.1848, Technology & Outsourcing **Band 4** p.1868, **Pennsylvania:** Antitrust **Band 3** p.2184, Bankruptcy/Restructuring **Band 4** p.2188, Corporate/M&A & Private Equity **Band 1** p.2191, Environment **Band 3** p.2194, Labor & Employment **Band 1** p.2200, Litigation **Band 1** p.2203, Real Estate **Band 3** p.2207, **Texas:** Intellectual Property **Band 3** p.2354, Labor & Employment **Band 1** p.2358, Litigation **Band 4** p.2361

**Morris & Morris PC**
Table(s): **Virginia:** Litigation **Band 3** p.2502, Litigation **Band 2** p.2502

**Morris James LLP**
Profile: p.782
Table(s): **Delaware:** Bankruptcy/Restructuring **Band 3** p.754, Chancery **Band 2** p.758, Labor & Employment **Band 3** p.765

**Morris Peterson**
Table(s): **Nevada:** Litigation **Band 3** p.1676

**Morris, Laing, Evans, Brock & Kennedy, Chartered**
Table(s): **Kansas:** Labor & Employment **Band 2** p.1293, Litigation **Band 3** p.1295, Real Estate **Band 3** p.1297

**Morris, Manning & Martin, LLP**
Table(s): **Georgia:** Bankruptcy/Restructuring **Band 3** p.1041, Corporate/M&A **Band 4** p.1046, Environment **Band 3** p.1050, Healthcare **Band 3** p.1052, Intellectual Property **Band 4** p.1056, Labor & Employment **Band 4** p.1059, Litigation **Band 4** p.1065, Real Estate **Band 2** p.1069, Tax **Band 3** p.1072, **Nationwide:** Capital Markets **Band 4** p.55, International Trade **Band 4** p.152

**Morris, Nichols, Arsht & Tunnell LLP**
Profile: p.783
Table(s): **Delaware:** Bankruptcy/Restructuring **Band 1** p.754, Chancery **Band 1** p.758, Corporate/M&A **Band 1** p.761, Intellectual Property **Band 1** p.763

**Morrison & Foerster LLP**
Profile: p.1990
Table(s): **California:** Antitrust **Band 3** p.535, Banking & Finance **Band 4** p.539, Corporate/M&A **Band 3** p.553, Employee Benefits & Executive Compensation **Band 3** p.560, Energy **Band 2** p.562, Environment **Band 2** p.564, Intellectual Property **Band 1** p.577, IT & Outsourcing **Band 1** p.583, Labor & Employment **Band 3** p.586, Life Sciences **Band 2** p.590, Litigation **Band 1** p.593, Real Estate **Band 3** p.611, Tax **Band 3** p.616, **Colorado:** Corporate/M&A **Band 3** p.702, **District of Columbia:** Antitrust **Band 5** p.786, Corporate/M&A & Private Equity **Band 4** p.797, Intellectual Property **Band 4** p.820, Technology &

Outsourcing **Band 2** p.842, **Nationwide:** Antitrust **Band 4** p.22, Appellate Law **Band 4** p.26, Bankruptcy/Restructuring **Band 3** p.38, Capital Markets **Band 3** p.51, Climate Change **Band 3** p.62, Corporate/M&A **Band 4** p.67, Financial Services Regulation **Band 1** p.95, Intellectual Property **Band 2** p.140, International Arbitration **Band 5** p.144, International Trade **Band 3** p.159, Life Sciences **Band 3** p.182, Outsourcing **Band 2** p.195, Privacy & Data Security **Band 1** p.199, Product Liability & Mass Torts **Band 4** p.207, Projects **Band 4** p.218, Securities **Band 4** p.231, Tax **Band 4** p.243, Transportation **Band 2** p.253, **New York:** Bankruptcy/Restructuring **Band 3** p.1781, Corporate/M&A **Band 3** p.1794, Litigation **Band 2** p.1832, Tax **Band 4** p.1860, Technology & Outsourcing **Band 1** p.1868, **Northern Virginia:** Corporate/M&A **Band 2** p.2493

**Morse, Barnes-Brown & Pendleton PC**
Table(s): **Massachusetts:** Private Equity **Band 3** p.1474

**Morvillo Abramowitz Grand Iason & Anello P.C**
Profile: p.1991
Table(s): **New York:** Litigation **Band 1** p.1835

**Moscowitz & Moscowitz, PA**
Table(s): **Florida:** Litigation **Band 1** p.967

**Moseley Biehl Tsugawa Lau & Muzzi**
Table(s): **Hawaii:** Bankruptcy/Restructuring **Band 2** p.1114

**Moseley Prichard Parrish Knight & Jones**
Table(s): **Nationwide:** Transportation **Band 1** p.263

**Moulton Bellingham PC**
Table(s): **Montana:** Litigation **Band 3** p.1649, Real Estate **Band 2** p.1652

**Mound Cotton Wollan & Greengrass**
Profile: p.1992
Table(s): **New York:** Insurance **Band 3** p.1815

**Mowrey Meezan Coddington Cloud LLP**
Table(s): **Georgia:** Environment **Band 3** p.1050

**Moye, O'Brien, O'Rourke, Pickert & Dillon, LLP**
Profile: p.1032
Table(s): **Florida:** Construction **Band 1** p.944, **Nationwide:** Construction **Band 4** p.65

**Mullikin, Larson & Swift**
Table(s): **Wyoming:** Real Estate **Band 2** p.2600

**Munck Wilson Mandala LLP**
Profile: p.2447
Table(s): **Texas:** Intellectual Property **Band 4** p.2354

**Munger & Stone**
Table(s): **Georgia:** Labor & Employment **Band 3** p.1059

**Munger, Tolles & Olson LLP**
Profile: p.691
Table(s): **California:** Antitrust **Band 2** p.535, Corporate/M&A **Band 2** p.554, Energy **Band 2** p.562, Labor & Employment **Band 2** p.586, Litigation **Band 1** p.593, Media & Entertainment **Band 1** p.605, Real Estate **Band 4** p.611, Tax **Band 3** p.616, **Nationwide:** Securities **Band 3** p.231

**Munsch Hardt Kopf & Harr, P.C.**
Profile: p.2448
Table(s): **Texas:** Bankruptcy/Restructuring **Band 3** p.2328, Healthcare **Band 4** p.2347, Real Estate **Band 3** p.2367

**Murphy & King, P.C.**
Profile: p.1525
Table(s): **Massachusetts:** Bankruptcy/Restructuring **Band 1** p.1449

**Murphy Sullivan Kronk**
Table(s): **Vermont:** Real Estate **Band 1** p.2487

**Murphy, Goldammer & Prendergast LLP**
Table(s): **South Dakota:** Corporate/Commercial **Band 2** p.2281, Litigation **Band 2** p.2284, Real Estate **Band 3** p.2286

**Murtha Cullina LLP**
Table(s): **Connecticut:** Corporate/M&A **Band 3** p.731, Environment **Band 1** p.733, Healthcare **Band 2** p.735, Labor & Employment **Band 3** p.736, Litigation **Band 3** p.738

**Myers Bigel**
Table(s): **North Carolina:** Intellectual Property **Band 1** p.2030

**Myers Oliver & Price**
Table(s): **New Mexico:** Real Estate **Band 1** p.1772

# N

**Neal & Harwell, PLC**
Table(s): **Tennessee:** Litigation **Band 2** p.2295

**Neal, Gerber & Eisenberg LLP**
Profile: p.1260
Overview(s): **Illinois:** p.1141
Table(s): **Illinois:** Bankruptcy/Restructuring **Band 5** p.1148, Corporate/M&A **Band 4** p.1156, Insurance **Band 2** p.1167, Intellectual Property **Band 3** p.1171, Labor & Employment **Band 3** p.1174, Litigation **Band 4** p.1179, Real Estate **Band 3** p.1187, Tax **Band 3** p.1192, Technology & Outsourcing **Band 3** p.1194

**Nelson Kinder + Mosseau, PC**
Table(s): **New Hampshire:** Litigation **Band 3** p.1689

**Parker Poe Adams & Bernstein LLP**
Table(s): **North Carolina:** Antitrust **Band 2** p.2020, Banking & Finance **Band 3** p.2021, Bankruptcy/Restructuring **Band 1** p.2023, Corporate/M&A **Band 3** p.2025, Environment **Band 2** p.2027, Intellectual Property **Band 2** p.2030, Labor & Employment **Band 3** p.2031, Litigation **Band 2** p.2033, Real Estate **Band 2** p.2036

**Parker, Hudson, Rainer & Dobbs LLP**
Table(s): **Georgia:** Banking & Finance **Band 1** p.1039, Bankruptcy/Restructuring **Band 2** p.1041, Healthcare **Band 1** p.1052, Litigation **Band 3** p.1065

**Parr Brown Gee & Loveless, A Professional Corporation**
Profile: p.2479
Table(s): **Utah:** Corporate/M&A **Band 1** p.2462, Energy & Natural Resources **Band 2** p.2464, Litigation **Band 2** p.2468, Real Estate **Band 1** p.2470

**Parrilli Renison**
Table(s): **Oregon:** Labor & Employment **Band 1** p.2168

**Parsley Coffin Renner, LLP**
Table(s): **Texas:** Energy **Band 1** p.2340

**Parsons Behle & Latimer PC**
Profile: p.2480
Table(s): **Nevada:** Environment **Band 1** p.1673, Litigation **Band 3** p.1676, **Utah:** Corporate/M&A **Band 3** p.2462, Energy & Natural Resources **Band 1** p.2464, Intellectual Property **Band 3** p.2466, Labor & Employment **Band 2** p.2467, Litigation **Band 1** p.2468, Real Estate **Band 2** p.2470

**Partridge Snow & Hahn LLP**
Table(s): **Rhode Island:** Corporate/Commercial **Band 2** p.2251, Labor & Employment **Band 2** p.2253, Litigation **Band 2** p.2254, Real Estate **Band 2** p.2255

**Patterson Belknap Webb & Tyler LLP**
Profile: p.1995
Table(s): **Nationwide:** Advertising **Band 1** p.19, **New York:** Intellectual Property **Band 3** p.1820, Intellectual Property **Band 2** p.1820, Litigation p.1836, Media & Entertainment **Band 2** p.1851, Real Estate **Band 4** p.1855

**Pattishall, McAuliffe, Newbury, Hilliard & Geraldson LLP**
Table(s): **Illinois:** Intellectual Property **Band 3** p.1171

**Patton Boggs LLP**
Table(s): **Alaska:** Litigation **Band 2** p.490, **Nationwide:** Construction **Band 4** p.65, Food & Beverages **Band 3** p.107, Government **Band 1** p.121, Native American Law **Band 3** p.191, Privacy & Data Security **Band 3** p.199

**Paul Frank + Collins P.C.**
Table(s): **Vermont:** Corporate/Commercial **Band 2** p.2483, Litigation **Band 2** p.2485

**Paul Hastings LLP**
Profile: p.1996
Table(s): **California:** Antitrust **Band 4** p.535, Banking & Finance **Band 2** p.539, Capital Markets **Band 3** p.547, Corporate/M&A **Band 4** p.554, Employee Benefits & Executive Compensation **Band 2** p.560, Environment **Band 3** p.564, Healthcare **Band 3** p.567, Labor & Employment **Band 1** p.586, Litigation **Band 3** p.593, Real Estate **Band 1** p.611, Tax **Band 2** p.616, **District of Columbia:** Antitrust **Band 5** p.786, Labor & Employment **Band 2** p.824, **Georgia:** Banking & Finance **Band 2** p.1039, Bankruptcy/Restructuring **Band 4** p.1041, Corporate/M&A **Band 2** p.1046, Labor & Employment **Band 1** p.1059, Litigation **Band 4** p.1065, Tax **Band 2** p.1072, **Illinois:** Corporate/M&A **Band 5** p.1156, Real Estate **Band 4** p.1187, **Nationwide:** Banking & Finance **Band 4** p.31, Corporate/M&A **Band 3** p.67, ERISA Litigation **Band 3** p.92, Financial Services Regulation **Band 5** p.95, International Arbitration **Band 5** p.144, Investment Funds **Band 4** p.165, Labor & Employment **Band 1** p.176, Leisure & Hospitality **Band 1** p.178, Real Estate **Band 2** p.225, **New York:** Corporate/M&A **Band 3** p.1794, Intellectual Property **Band 3** p.1820, Labor & Employment **Band 2** p.1826, Latin American Investment **Band 4** p.1829, Litigation **Band 2** p.1832, Real Estate **Band 2** p.1855

**Paul, Weiss, Rifkind, Wharton & Garrison LLP**
Profile: p.1997
Table(s): **District of Columbia:** Antitrust **Band 4** p.786, **Nationwide:** Antitrust **Band 4** p.22, Banking & Finance **Band 4** p.31, Bankruptcy/Restructuring **Band 2** p.38, Capital Markets **Band 3** p.46, Corporate/M&A **Band 3** p.67, ERISA Litigation **Band 3** p.92, Financial Services Regulation **Band 3** p.97, Investment Funds **Band 2** p.165, Private Equity **Band 3** p.203, Retail **Band 3** p.229, Securities **Band 1** p.231, Tax **Band 2** p.248, Wealth Management **Band 3** p.266, **New York:** Antitrust **Band 3** p.1777, Bankruptcy/Restructuring **Band 1** p.1781, Corporate/M&A **Band 3** p.1792, Employee Benefits & Executive Compensation **Band 3** p.1802, Intellectual Property **Band 3** p.1820, Litigation **Band 1** p.1833, Media & Entertainment **Band 1** p.1848, Real Estate **Band 2** p.1853, Tax **Band 2** p.1860

**Pearce & Dow LLC**
Table(s): **Maine:** Corporate/M&A **Band 4** p.1385

**Pearce & Durick**
Table(s): **North Dakota:** Litigation **Band 3** p.2053

**Pearl Law Group**
Table(s): **California:** Immigration **Band 1** p.571, **Nationwide:** Immigration **Band 3** p.131

**Pearne & Gordon**
Table(s): **Ohio:** Intellectual Property **Band 4** p.2071

**Peckar & Abramson, P.C.**
Profile: p.1998
Table(s): **California:** Construction **Band 3** p.549, **District of Columbia:** Construction **Band 1** p.795, **Florida:** Construction **Band 1** p.944, **Nationwide:** Construction **Band 1** p.65, **New York:** Construction **Band 1** p.1790

**Peifer, Hanson & Mullins PA**
Table(s): **New Mexico:** Litigation **Band 2** p.1769

**Peitzman Weg LLP**
Profile: p.695
Table(s): **California:** Bankruptcy/Restructuring **Band 3** p.542

**Pennington, P.A.**
Table(s): **Florida:** Insurance **Band 2** p.957

**Pepper Hamilton LLP**
Profile: p.2248
Table(s): **Delaware:** Bankruptcy/Restructuring **Band 3** p.754, **Nationwide:** Construction **Band 4** p.65, Product Liability & Mass Torts **Band 2** p.207, **New Jersey:** Labor & Employment **Band 4** p.1718, **Pennsylvania:** Antitrust **Band 2** p.2184, Bankruptcy/Restructuring **Band 3** p.2188, Corporate/M&A & Private Equity **Band 2** p.2191, Intellectual Property **Band 3** p.2197, Labor & Employment **Band 3** p.2200, Litigation **Band 1** p.2203

**Perkins Coie LLP**
Profile: p.2548
Table(s): **Alaska:** Environment, Natural Resources & Regulated Industries **Band 1** p.488, Labor & Employment **Band 1** p.489, Litigation **Band 3** p.490, **Arizona:** Corporate/M&A **Band 4** p.494, Litigation **Band 1** p.501, Real Estate **Band 3** p.504, **California:** Life Sciences **Band 4** p.590, Real Estate **Band 2** p.612, **Colorado:** Corporate/M&A **Band 2** p.702, Intellectual Property **Band 3** p.704, Litigation **Band 3** p.710, **District of Columbia:** Insurance **Band 3** p.818, **Idaho:** Corporate/Commercial **Band 1** p.1132, Labor & Employment **Band 2** p.1132, Litigation **Band 2** p.1134, Natural Resources & Environment **Band 1** p.1136, **Illinois:** Bankruptcy/Restructuring **Band 4** p.1148, Litigation **Band 2** p.1181, Real Estate **Band 4** p.1187, **Nationwide:** Environment **Band 4** p.89, Government **Band 1** p.124, Intellectual Property **Band 4** p.140, Investment Funds **Band 3** p.173, Leisure & Hospitality **Band 2** p.178, Privacy & Data Security **Band 2** p.199, Product Liability & Mass Torts **Band 4** p.207, Retail **Band 3** p.229, Transportation **Band 1** p.253, **Oregon:** Corporate/M&A **Band 1** p.2163, Environment **Band 1** p.2165, Intellectual Property **Band 2** p.2166, Litigation **Band 1** p.2171, Real Estate **Band 2** p.2173, **Washington:** Bankruptcy/Restructuring **Band 1** p.2523, Corporate/Commercial **Band 1** p.2524, Environment **Band 1** p.2527, Intellectual Property **Band 1** p.2529, Labor & Employment **Band 1** p.2531, Litigation **Band 1** p.2533, Real Estate **Band 1** p.2535, **Wisconsin:** Intellectual Property **Band 2** p.2573

**Perkins Thompson**
Table(s): **Maine:** Corporate/M&A **Band 4** p.1385

**Pettiette, Armand, Dunkelman, Woodley, Byrd & Cromwell LLP**
Table(s): **Louisiana:** Banking & Finance **Band 3** p.1335

**Phelps Dunbar LLP**
Profile: p.1383
Table(s): **Florida:** Construction **Band 4** p.944, Labor & Employment **Band 4** p.959, **Louisiana:** Banking & Finance **Band 1** p.1335, Bankruptcy/Restructuring **Band 3** p.1337, Construction **Band 2** p.1339, Corporate/M&A **Band 3** p.1341, Energy & Natural Resources **Band 2** p.1344, Environment **Band 1** p.1346, Gaming & Licensing **Band 2** p.1348, Labor & Employment **Band 1** p.1349, Litigation **Band 2** p.1352, Real Estate **Band 1** p.1355, **Mississippi:** Corporate/Commercial **Band 2** p.1591, Labor & Employment **Band 1** p.1595, Litigation **Band 3** p.1596, Real Estate **Band 3** p.1600, **Nationwide:** Transportation **Band 1** p.263, **Texas:** Insurance **Band 3** p.2350

**Phillips Gardill Kaiser & Altmeyer**
Table(s): **West Virginia:** Corporate/Commercial **Band 3** p.2550

**Phillips Lytle LLP**
Profile: p.1999
Table(s): **New York:** Environment **Band 2** p.1807

**Phillips Murrah P.C.**
Table(s): **Oklahoma:** Real Estate **Band 2** p.2145

**Piccarreta Davis PC**
Table(s): **Arizona:** Litigation **Band 1** p.501

**Pierce Atwood LLP**
Profile: p.1408
Overview(s): **Maine:** p.1384
Table(s): **Maine:** Corporate/M&A **Band 1** p.1385, Energy & Natural Resources **Band 1** p.1387, Environment **Band 1** p.1388, Labor & Employment **Band 1** p.1390, Litigation **Band 1** p.1392, Real Estate **Band 1** p.1395

**Pillsbury Winthrop Shaw Pittman LLP**
Profile: p.2000
Table(s): **California:** Capital Markets **Band 3** p.547, Construction **Band 3** p.549, Corporate/M&A **Band 3** p.553, Corporate/M&A **Band 4** p.553, Energy & Natural Resources **Band 3** p.562, Environment **Band 3** p.564, IT & Outsourcing **Band 3** p.583, Life Sciences **Band 3** p.590, Real Estate **Band 3** p.611, Tax **Band 3** p.616, **District of Columbia:** Construction **Band 2** p.795, Corporate/M&A & Private Equity **Band 3** p.797, Environment **Band 4** p.804, Real Estate **Band 2** p.834, Technology & Outsourcing **Band 1** p.842, Telecom, Broadcast & Satellite **Band 4** p.844, **Nationwide:** Banking & Finance **Band 2** p.32, Construction **Band 4** p.65, Corporate/M&A **Band 3** p.67, Energy & Natural Resources **Band 4** p.77, Environment **Band 3** p.89, Food & Beverages **Band 2** p.109, Government **Band 3** p.124, International Trade **Band 4** p.152, Investment Funds **Band 3** p.173, Life Sciences **Band 3** p.182, Native American Law **Band 3** p.191, Outsourcing **Band 1** p.195, Privacy & Data Security **Band 3** p.199, Projects **Band 4** p.217, Real Estate **Band 4** p.225, Tax **Band 4** p.243,

**Reed, Claymon, Meeker & Hargett, PLLC**
Table(s): **Texas:** Healthcare **Band 2** p.2347

**Reeder & Shuman**
Table(s): **West Virginia:** Real Estate **Band 2** p.2560

**Reilly Pozner LLP**
Table(s): **Colorado:** Litigation **Band 1** p.708

**Reinhart Boerner Van Deuren s.c.**
Profile: p.2594
Table(s): **Wisconsin:** Corporate/M&A **Band 2** p.2571, Intellectual Property **Band 3** p.2573, Labor & Employment **Band 3** p.2574, Litigation **Band 3** p.2576, Natural Resources & Environment **Band 2** p.2578, Real Estate **Band 1** p.2579

**Renner, Otto, Boisselle & Sklar LLP**
Table(s): **Ohio:** Intellectual Property **Band 4** p.2071

**Reynolds, Frizzell, Black, Doyle, Allen & Oldham, LLP**
Profile: p.2451
Table(s): **Texas:** Litigation **Band 3** p.2361

**Rhoades McKee**
Profile: p.1565
Table(s): **Michigan:** Litigation **Band 3** p.1544

**Rhodes, Hieronymus, Jones, Tucker & Gable PLLC**
Table(s): **Oklahoma:** Litigation **Band 3** p.2141

**Rice Pugatch Robinson & Schiller, PA**
Table(s): **Florida:** Bankruptcy/Restructuring **Band 3** p.939

**Rice Reuther Sullivan & Carroll, LLP**
Table(s): **Nevada:** Real Estate **Band 2** p.1679

**Richards Kibbe & Orbe LLP**
Profile: p.2002
Table(s): **Nationwide:** Securities **Band 4** p.233, **New York:** Litigation **Band 2** p.1832

**Richards, Layton & Finger PA**
Profile: p.785
Table(s): **Delaware:** Bankruptcy/Restructuring **Band 1** p.754, Chancery **Band 1** p.758, Corporate/M&A **Band 1** p.761, Intellectual Property **Band 2** p.763, Labor & Employment **Band 3** p.765, Real Estate **Band 1** p.766

**Richardson, Whitman, Large & Badger**
Table(s): **Maine:** Litigation **Band 3** p.1392

**Richilano Shea LLC**
Table(s): **Colorado:** Litigation **Band 2** p.710

**Richman Greer PA**
Profile: p.1034
Table(s): **Florida:** Litigation **Band 2** p.965

**Riddell Williams PS**
Table(s): **Washington:**
Bankruptcy/Restructuring **Band 2** p.2523, Environment **Band 3** p.2527

**Riemer & Braunstein LLP**
Table(s): **Massachusetts:** Banking & Finance **Band 2** p.1445

**Rifkin and Fox-Isicoff PA**
Table(s): **Florida:** Immigration **Band 2** p.956

**Riker Danzig Scherer Hyland & Perretti LLP**
Profile: p.1761
Table(s): **New Jersey:** Bankruptcy/Restructuring **Band 2** p.1704, Corporate/M&A **Band 2** p.1707, Environment **Band 1** p.1711, Intellectual Property **Band 4** p.1716, Labor & Employment **Band 4** p.1718, Litigation **Band 1** p.1722, Real Estate **Band 3** p.1728

**Riley Warnock & Jacobson, PLC**
Profile: p.2318
Table(s): **Tennessee:** Litigation **Band 1** p.2295

**Roach & Newton, L.L.P.**
Table(s): **Texas:** Insurance **Band 4** p.2350

**Robbins Geller Rudman & Dowd LLP**
Profile: p.696
Table(s): **California:** Litigation **Band 1** p.593, **Nationwide:** Securities **Band 1** p.233, **New York:** Litigation **Band 1** p.1835

**Robbins, Russell, Englert, Orseck, Untereiner & Sauber LLP**
Table(s): **Nationwide:** Appellate Law **Band 3** p.26

**Roberts & Holland LLP**
Table(s): **New York:** Tax **Band 4** p.1860

**Robins, Kaplan, Miller & Ciresi LLP**
Profile: p.1588
Table(s): **California:** Media & Entertainment **Band 3** p.605, **Minnesota:** Litigation **Band 1** p.1573

**Robinson & Cole LLP**
Profile: p.751
Table(s): **Connecticut:** Corporate/M&A **Band 2** p.731, Environment **Band 1** p.733, Healthcare **Band 2** p.735, Litigation **Band 2** p.738, Real Estate **Band 1** p.740

**Robinson & McElwee PLLC**
Table(s): **West Virginia:** Corporate/Commercial **Band 3** p.2550, Natural Resources **Band 3** p.2558, Real Estate **Band 2** p.2560

**Robinson, Bradshaw & Hinson PA**
Table(s): **North Carolina:** Antitrust **Band 1** p.2020, Banking & Finance **Band 2** p.2021, Bankruptcy/Restructuring **Band 1** p.2023, Corporate/M&A **Band 1** p.2025, Environment **Band 3** p.2027, Labor & Employment **Band 2** p.2031, Litigation **Band 1** p.2033, Real Estate **Band 1** p.2036

**Rodey, Dickason, Sloan, Akin & Robb, PA**
Profile: p.1775
Table(s): **New Mexico:** Corporate/Commercial **Band 1** p.1764, Environment, Natural Resources & Regulated Industries **Band 2** p.1765, Labor & Employment **Band 1** p.1767, Litigation **Band 1** p.1769, Real Estate **Band 1** p.1772

**Roetzel & Andress, LPA**
Profile: p.2128
Table(s): **Ohio:** Litigation **Band 4** p.2078, Natural Resources & Environment **Band 2** p.2082

**Rogers & Hardin LLP**
Profile: p.1111
Table(s): **Georgia:** Antitrust **Band 3** p.1037, Corporate/M&A **Band 2** p.1046, Labor & Employment **Band 3** p.1059, Litigation **Band 2** p.1065

**Rogers Joseph O'Donnell**
Profile: p.697
Table(s): **Nationwide:** Government **Band 2** p.117

**Rogers Towers PA**
Table(s): **Florida:** Real Estate **Band 4** p.974, Real Estate **Band 3** p.974

**Rooney Rippie & Ratnaswamy LLP**
Table(s): **Illinois:** Energy & Natural Resources **Band 1** p.1161

**Ropes & Gray LLP**
Profile: p.1528
Table(s): **California:** Corporate/M&A **Band 3** p.553, Healthcare **Band 3** p.567, Intellectual Property **Band 3** p.577, Life Sciences **Band 4** p.590, **District of Columbia:** Antitrust **Band 5** p.786, Healthcare **Band 2** p.809, **Massachusetts:** Antitrust **Band 2** p.1444, Banking & Finance **Band 1** p.1445, Bankruptcy/Restructuring **Band 1** p.1449, Corporate/M&A **Band 1** p.1452, Employee Benefits & Executive Compensation **Band 1** p.1455, Healthcare **Band 2** p.1459, Hedge & Mutual Funds **Band 1** p.1461, Intellectual Property **Band 2** p.1462, Labor & Employment **Band 1** p.1466, Litigation **Band 1** p.1470, Private Equity **Band 1** p.1474, Private Equity **Band 1** p.1476, Real Estate **Band 3** p.1477, Tax **Band 1** p.1481, **Nationwide:** Banking & Finance **Band 3** p.31, Bankruptcy/Restructuring **Band 5** p.38, Capital Markets **Band 4** p.46, Corporate/M&A **Band 3** p.67, Employee Benefits & Executive Compensation **Band 4** p.72, Healthcare **Band 3** p.126, Intellectual Property **Band 2** p.140, Investment Funds **Band 1** p.169, Life Sciences **Band 1** p.182, Privacy & Data Security **Band 3** p.199, Privacy & Data Security p.199, Private Equity **Band 2** p.203, Securities **Band 4** p.231, Tax **Band 2** p.248, Wealth Management **Band 4** p.266, **New York:** Bankruptcy/Restructuring **Band 4** p.1781, Corporate/M&A **Band 2** p.1794, Healthcare **Band 1** p.1811, Intellectual Property **Band 2** p.1820

**Rose Law Firm**
Table(s): **Arkansas:** Corporate/Commercial **Band 2** p.518, Labor & Employment **Band 2** p.520, Litigation **Band 2** p.522, Real Estate **Band 2** p.524

**Rose Walker, L.L.P.**
Table(s): **Texas:** Litigation **Band 4** p.2361

**Rosenberg Martin Greenberg, LLP**
Table(s): **Maryland:** Litigation **Band 2** p.1419, Real Estate **Band 3** p.1422

**Rosenthal, Monhait & Goddess PA**
Table(s): **Delaware:** Chancery **Band 2** p.759

**Rothgerber Johnson & Lyons LLP**
Table(s): **Colorado:** Litigation **Band 2** p.708, Wyoming: Litigation **Band 2** p.2598

**Rouse Hendricks German May PC**
Profile: p.1642
Table(s): **Missouri:** Litigation **Band 1** p.1628

**Rudman Winchell**
Table(s): **Maine:** Corporate/M&A **Band 3** p.1385, Labor & Employment **Band 3** p.1390, Litigation **Band 3** p.1392, Real Estate **Band 3** p.1395

**Rumberger, Kirk & Caldwell**
Table(s): **Florida:** Litigation **Band 4** p.965

**Rush Moore LLP**
Table(s): **Hawaii:** Bankruptcy/Restructuring **Band 2** p.1114

**Rushton, Stakely, Johnston & Garrett**
Table(s): **Alabama:** Litigation **Band 3** p.462, Real Estate **Band 2** p.465

**Ryan Kromholz & Manion SC**
Table(s): **Wisconsin:** Intellectual Property **Band 3** p.2573

**Ryan Smith & Carbine, Ltd**
Table(s): **Vermont:** Corporate/Commercial **Band 2** p.2483

**Ryan Swanson**
Table(s): **Washington:** Immigration **Band 1** p.2528

**Ryan Whaley Coldiron Shandy**
Table(s): **Oklahoma:** Litigation **Band 3** p.2141

**Ryley Carlock & Applewhite**
Profile: p.515
Table(s): **Arizona:** Environment (including water rights) **Band 2** p.496, Labor & Employment **Band 2** p.499, Real Estate **Band 3** p.504, **Colorado:** Natural Resources & Environment **Band 3** p.712

## S

**Sabo & Zahn**
Table(s): **Illinois:** Construction **Band 3** p.1154

Markets **Band 1** p.46, Corporate/M&A **Band 1** p.67, Employee Benefits & Executive Compensation **Band 2** p.72, Energy & Natural Resources **Band 1** p.77, Financial Services Regulation **Band 1** p.95, Insurance **Band 2** p.138, International Arbitration **Band 4** p.144, International Trade **Band 5** p.152, Investment Funds **Band 3** p.169, Projects **Band 1** p.215, Real Estate **Band 1** p.225, Securities **Band 1** p.231, Tax **Band 1** p.248, Wealth Management **Band 3** p.266, **New York:** Antitrust **Band 2** p.1777, Bankruptcy/Restructuring **Band 5** p.1781, Corporate/M&A **Band 1** p.1792, Employee Benefits & Executive Compensation **Band 1** p.1802, Environment **Band 2** p.1808, Insurance **Band 2** p.1815, Insurance **Band 3** p.1815, Labor & Employment **Band 3** p.1826, Latin American Investment **Band 2** p.1829, Litigation **Band 1** p.1833, Real Estate **Band 1** p.1853, Tax **Band 1** p.1860

**Sullivan & Worcester LLP**
Profile: p.1534
Table(s): **Massachusetts:** Banking & Finance **Band 3** p.1445, Bankruptcy/Restructuring **Band 4** p.1449, Tax **Band 2** p.1481, **Nationwide:** Tax **Band 5** p.248

**Sulloway & Hollis PLLC**
Table(s): **New Hampshire:** Labor & Employment **Band 3** p.1688, Litigation **Band 2** p.1689, Real Estate **Band 3** p.1692

**Summit Law Group, PLLC**
Table(s): **Washington:** Litigation **Band 4** p.2533

**Sundahl, Powers, Kapp & Martin LLC**
Table(s): **Wyoming:** Litigation **Band 2** p.2598

**Susman Godfrey LLP**
Table(s): **Texas:** Antitrust **Band 1** p.2322, Intellectual Property **Band 3** p.2354, Litigation **Band 1** p.2361

**Sutherland Asbill & Brennan LLP**
Table(s): **District of Columbia:** Tax **Band 3** p.838, **Georgia:** Banking & Finance **Band 4** p.1039, Construction **Band 1** p.1044, Corporate/M&A **Band 2** p.1046, Energy **Band 2** p.1049, Intellectual Property **Band 2** p.1056, Labor & Employment **Band 4** p.1059, Litigation **Band 2** p.1065, Real Estate **Band 1** p.1069, Tax **Band 1** p.1072, **Nationwide:** Capital Markets **Band 4** p.51, Construction **Band 3** p.65, Energy & Natural Resources **Band 4** p.75, Insurance **Band 3** p.138, Investment Funds **Band 3** p.169, Outsourcing **Band 4** p.195, Tax **Band 2** p.243, **New York:** Corporate/M&A **Band 5** p.1794, **Texas:** Energy **Band 3** p.2340, Insurance **Band 4** p.2350

**Sutin, Thayer & Browne**
Table(s): **New Mexico:** Corporate/Commercial **Band 1** p.1764, Litigation **Band 2** p.1769, Native American Law **Band 2** p.1771

**Sutton McAughan Deaver, PLLC**
Profile: p.2456
Table(s): **Texas:** Intellectual Property **Band 4** p.2354

**Swanson & McNamara LLP**
Table(s): **California:** Litigation **Band 1** p.601

## Tachau Meek PLC
Table(s): **Kentucky:** Litigation **Band 3** p.1311

**Tafapolsky & Smith**
Table(s): **California:** Immigration **Band 3** p.571

**Taft Stettinius & Hollister LLP**
Profile: p.2130
Table(s): **Indiana:** Corporate/M&A **Band 2** p.1268, Environment **Band 2** p.1270, Litigation **Band 3** p.1273, Real Estate **Band 3** p.1274, **Ohio:** Banking & Finance **Band 3** p.2056, Bankruptcy/Restructuring **Band 3** p.2058, Construction **Band 4** p.2062, Corporate/M&A **Band 3** p.2064, Employee Benefits & Executive Compensation **Band 2** p.2067, Healthcare **Band 3** p.2069, Intellectual Property **Band 4** p.2071, Labor & Employment **Band 1** p.2073, Litigation **Band 3** p.2078, Natural Resources & Environment **Band 3** p.2082, Real Estate **Band 4** p.2085

**Tarter Krinsky & Drogin LLP**
Table(s): **New York:** Construction **Band 4** p.1790

**Taylor English Duma LLP**
Table(s): **Georgia:** Labor & Employment **Band 4** p.1059

**Taylor, Porter, Brooks & Phillips, LLP**
Table(s): **Louisiana:** Environment **Band 1** p.1346, Litigation **Band 3** p.1352

**Temkin Wielga & Hardt LLP**
Table(s): **Colorado:** Natural Resources & Environment **Band 2** p.712

**Tew Cardenas LLP**
Table(s): **Florida:** Litigation **Band 3** p.965

**The Bennett Law Firm PA**
Table(s): **Maine:** Labor & Employment **Band 4** p.1390

**The Center for Economic Development Law**
Table(s): **Oklahoma:** Real Estate **Band 2** p.2145

**The Health Law Consultancy**
Profile: p.1250
Table(s): **Illinois:** Healthcare **Band 3** p.1165

**The Kullman Firm PLC**
Table(s): **Louisiana:** Labor & Employment **Band 1** p.1349, **Mississippi:** Labor & Employment **Band 3** p.1595

**The Law Offices of Carl Shusterman**
Table(s): **California:** Immigration **Band 3** p.571

**The Steeg Law Firm, LLC**
Table(s): **Louisiana:** Real Estate **Band 2** p.1355

**The Webb Law Firm**
Table(s): **Pennsylvania:** Intellectual Property **Band 4** p.2197

**Theriault & Joslin PC**
Table(s): **Vermont:** Litigation **Band 3** p.2485

**Thomas Combs & Spann**
Table(s): **West Virginia:** Litigation **Band 2** p.2555

**Thompson & Knight LLP**
Profile: p.2458
Table(s): **Nationwide:** Energy & Natural Resources **Band 4** p.79, **Texas:** Antitrust **Band 2** p.2322, Banking & Finance **Band 3** p.2325, Bankruptcy/Restructuring **Band 2** p.2328, Capital Markets **Band 3** p.2333, Corporate/M&A **Band 3** p.2337, Environment **Band 2** p.2343, Healthcare **Band 4** p.2347, Intellectual Property **Band 2** p.2354, Labor & Employment **Band 3** p.2358, Litigation **Band 4** p.2361, Real Estate **Band 1** p.2367, Tax **Band 2** p.2371, Technology **Band 3** p.2376

**Thompson Coburn LLP**
Table(s): **Illinois:** Litigation **Band 5** p.1179, **Missouri:** Corporate/M&A **Band 1** p.1619, Environment **Band 1** p.1621, Intellectual Property **Band 2** p.1623, Labor & Employment **Band 2** p.1625, Litigation **Band 1** p.1629, Real Estate **Band 1** p.1633, **Nationwide:** Energy & Natural Resources **Band 5** p.75

**Thompson Hine LLP**
Profile: p.2131
Table(s): **Nationwide:** Construction **Band 4** p.65, Transportation **Band 1** p.257, **Ohio:** Banking & Finance **Band 1** p.2056, Bankruptcy/Restructuring **Band 2** p.2058, Construction **Band 1** p.2062, Corporate/M&A **Band 2** p.2064, Employee Benefits & Executive Compensation **Band 1** p.2067, Intellectual Property **Band 3** p.2071, Litigation **Band 3** p.2078, Natural Resources & Environment **Band 1** p.2082, Real Estate **Band 1** p.2085

**Thompson, Coe, Cousins & Irons, LLP**
Profile: p.2457
Table(s): **Texas:** Insurance **Band 1** p.2350

**Thompson, Loss & Judge LLP**
Table(s): **District of Columbia:** Insurance **Band 3** p.816

**Thompson, Sizemore, Gonzalez & Hearing, PA**
Table(s): **Florida:** Labor & Employment **Band 3** p.959

**Thorpe, North & Western LLP**
Table(s): **Utah:** Intellectual Property **Band 3** p.2466

**Tilden McCoy + Dilweg LLP**
Table(s): **Nationwide:** Native American Law **Band 3** p.191

**Tinnin Law Firm**
Table(s): **New Mexico:** Labor & Employment **Band 3** p.1767

**TLP: Telecommunications Law Professionals PLLC**
Table(s): **District of Columbia:** Telecom, Broadcast & Satellite **Band 4** p.844

**Tollefson Bradley Ball & Mitchell, LLP**
Table(s): **Texas:** Insurance **Band 3** p.2350

**Tom Quitiquit Chee & Watts, LLP**
Table(s): **Hawaii:** Real Estate **Band 2** p.1120

**Tonkon Torp LLP**
Profile: p.2183
Table(s): **Oregon:** Corporate/M&A **Band 2** p.2163, Environment **Band 2** p.2165, Intellectual Property **Band 2** p.2166, Labor & Employment **Band 1** p.2168, Litigation **Band 2** p.2171, Real Estate **Band 3** p.2173

**Torkildson, Katz, Moore, Hetherington & Harris**
Table(s): **Hawaii:** Labor & Employment **Band 1** p.1117

**TraskBritt, PC**
Table(s): **Utah:** Intellectual Property **Band 2** p.2466

**Trenam Kemker, Attorneys**
Table(s): **Florida:** Bankruptcy/Restructuring **Band 2** p.939, Corporate/M&A & Private Equity **Band 4** p.947, Real Estate **Band 3** p.974

**Triplett, Woolf & Garretson LLC**
Profile: p.1304
Table(s): **Kansas:** Corporate/M&A **Band 2** p.1292, Litigation **Band 3** p.1295, Real Estate **Band 1** p.1297

**Troutman Sanders LLP**
Table(s): **California:** Insurance **Band 4** p.573, **District of Columbia:** Insurance **Band 2** p.816, **Georgia:** Banking & Finance **Band 2** p.1039, Bankruptcy/Restructuring **Band 3** p.1041, Construction **Band 2** p.1044, Corporate/M&A **Band 3** p.1046, Energy **Band 1** p.1049, Environment **Band 1** p.1050, Immigration **Band 2** p.1054, Intellectual Property **Band 4** p.1056, Labor & Employment **Band 2** p.1059, Litigation **Band 2** p.1065, Real Estate **Band 2** p.1069, **Illinois:** Insurance **Band 3** p.1167, **Nationwide:** Climate Change **Band 2** p.62, Energy & Natural Resources **Band 3** p.75, Insurance **Band 3** p.134, **Southern Virginia:** Corporate/M&A **Band 2** p.2494, Intellectual Property **Band 1** p.2498, Real Estate **Band 2** p.2506, **Virginia:** Environment **Band 2** p.2495, Labor & Employment **Band 3** p.2499, Litigation **Band 2** p.2502

**Trucker Huss PC**
Table(s): **California:** Employee Benefits & Executive Compensation **Band 2** p.560

**Tschider & Smith**
Table(s): **North Dakota:** Corporate/Commercial **Band 2** p.2051

**Tucker Ellis**
Table(s): **Nationwide**: Product Liability & Mass Torts **Band 4** p.207, **Ohio**: Litigation **Band 3** p.2078

**Turner, Padget, Graham & Laney, P.A.**
Profile: p.2279
Table(s): **South Carolina**: Labor & Employment **Band 3** p.2262, Litigation **Band 3** p.2264

## U

**Ugrin, Alexander, Zadick & Higgins, PC**
Table(s): **Montana**: Labor & Employment **Band 3** p.1647, Litigation **Band 2** p.1649

**Ulmer & Berne LLP**
Profile: p.2132
Table(s): **Ohio**: Employee Benefits & Executive Compensation **Band 2** p.2067, Litigation **Band 2** p.2078, Real Estate **Band 4** p.2085

**Ungaretti & Harris LLP**
Profile: p.1265
Table(s): **Illinois**: Banking & Finance **Band 4** p.1145, Corporate/M&A **Band 4** p.1156, Healthcare **Band 2** p.1165

**Upton and Hatfield LLP**
Table(s): **New Hampshire**: Litigation **Band 3** p.1689, Real Estate **Band 3** p.1692

## V

**Van Cott, Bagley, Cornwall & McCarthy, P.C.**
Table(s): **Utah**: Energy & Natural Resources **Band 3** p.2464, Litigation **Band 3** p.2468, Real Estate **Band 3** p.2470

**Van Hoy Reutlinger Adams & Dunn**
Table(s): **North Carolina**: Labor & Employment **Band 3** p.2031

**Van Kley & Walker**
Table(s): **Ohio**: Natural Resources & Environment **Band 3** p.2082

**Van Ness Feldman LLP**
Profile: p.926
Table(s): **District of Columbia**: Environment **Band 2** p.804, **Nationwide**: Climate Change **Band 1** p.62, Energy & Natural Resources **Band 2** p.75, Environment **Band 4** p.89, Government **Band 3** p.121, Native American Law **Band 3** p.191, Transportation **Band 2** p.257, **Washington**: Real Estate **Band 2** p.2535, Real Estate **Band 2** p.2535

**Vantus Law Group**
Table(s): **Utah**: Corporate/M&A **Band 3** p.2462

**Varnum LLP**
Table(s): **Michigan**: Corporate/M&A **Band 4** p.1538, Labor & Employment **Band 3** p.1541, Litigation **Band 3** p.1544

**Vaughan & Murphy**
Table(s): **Georgia**: Antitrust **Band 3** p.1037

**Vedder Price PC**
Profile: p.1266
Table(s): **Illinois**: Banking & Finance **Band 3** p.1145, Bankruptcy/Restructuring **Band 4** p.1148, Construction **Band 3** p.1154, Corporate/M&A **Band 4** p.1156, Labor & Employment **Band 2** p.1174, Labor & Employment **Band 3** p.1174, **Nationwide**: Banking & Finance **Band 1** p.32, Transportation **Band 1** p.251

**Venable LLP**
Profile: p.927
Table(s): **District of Columbia**: Corporate/M&A & Private Equity **Band 4** p.797, Employee Benefits & Executive Compensation **Band 4** p.801, Environment **Band 2** p.804, Intellectual Property **Band 1** p.820, Real Estate **Band 1** p.834, Technology & Outsourcing **Band 2** p.842, **Maryland**: Corporate/M&A **Band 1** p.1412, Employee Benefits & Executive Compensation **Band 1** p.1414, Healthcare **Band 1** p.1415, Labor & Employment **Band 1** p.1417, Litigation **Band 2** p.1419, Real Estate **Band 1** p.1422, **Nationwide**: Advertising **Band 2** p.19, Capital Markets **Band 1** p.55, Energy & Natural Resources **Band 4** p.78, Financial Services Regulation **Band 2** p.95, Government **Band 3** p.117, Leisure & Hospitality **Band 4** p.178, Privacy & Data Security **Band 2** p.199, Product Liability & Mass Torts **Band 4** p.207, **New York**: Technology & Outsourcing **Band 3** p.1868, **Northern Virginia**: Corporate/M&A **Band 3** p.2493, Real Estate **Band 2** p.2505, **Virginia**: Labor & Employment **Band 3** p.2499, Litigation **Band 3** p.2502

**Vercruysse Murray & Calzone, PC**
Profile: p.1566
Table(s): **Michigan**: Labor & Employment **Band 1** p.1541

**Verrill Dana, LLP**
Profile: p.1410
Table(s): **Maine**: Corporate/M&A **Band 1** p.1385, Energy & Natural Resources **Band 1** p.1387, Environment **Band 2** p.1388, Labor & Employment **Band 1** p.1390, Litigation **Band 3** p.1392, Real Estate **Band 1** p.1395

**Vezina Lawrence & Piscitelli PA**
Table(s): **Florida**: Construction **Band 2** p.944

**Vinson & Elkins LLP**
Profile: p.2459
Table(s): **District of Columbia**: Antitrust **Band 5** p.786, Environment **Band 4** p.804, **Nationwide**: Appellate Law **Band 4** p.26, Bankruptcy/Restructuring **Band 5** p.38, Capital Markets **Band 3** p.46, Climate Change **Band 3** p.62, Corporate/M&A **Band 4** p.67, Energy & Natural Resources **Band 1** p.75, Environment **Band 3** p.89, Government **Band 4** p.117, Intellectual Property **Band 4** p.140, International Trade **Band 5** p.152, Projects **Band 1** p.217, Tax **Band 4** p.243, **New York**: Corporate/M&A **Band 3** p.1794, **Texas**: Antitrust **Band 3** p.2322, Banking & Finance **Band 2** p.2325, Bankruptcy/Restructuring

**Band 1** p.2328, Capital Markets **Band 1** p.2333, Corporate/M&A **Band 1** p.2337, Energy **Band 1** p.2340, Environment **Band 1** p.2343, Intellectual Property **Band 2** p.2354, Labor & Employment **Band 2** p.2358, Litigation **Band 1** p.2361, Real Estate **Band 1** p.2367, Tax **Band 1** p.2371, Technology **Band 2** p.2374

**Vogel Law Firm**
Table(s): **North Dakota**:
Bankruptcy/Restructuring **Band 1** p.2050, Corporate/Commercial **Band 1** p.2051, Labor & Employment **Band 1** p.2052, Litigation **Band 1** p.2053, Real Estate **Band 1** p.2055

**Volpe and Koenig, PC**
Table(s): **Pennsylvania**: Intellectual Property **Band 3** p.2197

**Vorys, Sater, Seymour and Pease LLP**
Profile: p.2133
Table(s): **Ohio**: Banking & Finance **Band 2** p.2056, Bankruptcy/Restructuring **Band 2** p.2058, Corporate/M&A **Band 2** p.2064, Employee Benefits & Executive Compensation **Band 1** p.2067, Healthcare **Band 2** p.2069, Labor & Employment **Band 2** p.2073, Litigation **Band 2** p.2078, Natural Resources & Environment **Band 1** p.2082, Real Estate **Band 1** p.2085

## W

**Wachtell, Lipton, Rosen & Katz**
Profile: p.2012
Table(s): **Nationwide**: Antitrust **Band 2** p.22, Bankruptcy/Restructuring **Band 2** p.38, Capital Markets **Band 3** p.55, Corporate/M&A **Band 1** p.67, Financial Services Regulation **Band 1** p.99, Securities **Band 2** p.231, Tax **Band 1** p.248, **New York**: Antitrust **Band 2** p.1777, Bankruptcy/Restructuring **Band 2** p.1781, Corporate/M&A **Band 1** p.1792, Employee Benefits & Executive Compensation **Band 2** p.1802, Litigation **Band 1** p.1833, Tax **Band 1** p.1860

**Wadleigh, Starr & Peters PLLC**
Profile: p.1702
Table(s): **New Hampshire**: Real Estate **Band 2** p.1692

**Wagner Choi & Verbrugge**
Table(s): **Hawaii**: Bankruptcy/Restructuring **Band 1** p.1114

**Wakelin, Hallock & O'Donovan LLP**
Table(s): **Maine**: Labor & Employment **Band 3** p.1390

**Walder, Hayden & Brogan P.A.**
Table(s): **New Jersey**: Litigation **Band 1** p.1723

**Walker, Tipps & Malone**
Profile: p.2319
Table(s): **Tennessee**: Litigation **Band 1** p.2295

**Wallace, Jordan, Ratliff & Brandt, LLC**
Table(s): **Alabama**: Banking & Finance **Band 3** p.455

**Wallack Somers & Haas PC**
Table(s): **Indiana**: Real Estate **Band 2** p.1274

**Waller Lansden Dortch & Davis**
Profile: p.2320
Table(s): **Tennessee**: Banking & Finance **Band 2** p.2287, Corporate/M&A **Band 1** p.2288, Environment **Band 1** p.2290, Healthcare **Band 1** p.2291, Labor & Employment **Band 2** p.2293, Litigation **Band 2** p.2295, Media & Entertainment **Band 2** p.2297, Real Estate **Band 1** p.2299

**Walsh, Colucci, Lubeley, Emrich & Walsh PC**
Table(s): **Northern Virginia**: Real Estate **Band 1** p.2505

**Warner Norcross & Judd LLP**
Table(s): **Michigan**: Banking & Finance **Band 3** p.1536, Corporate/M&A **Band 3** p.1538, Employee Benefits & Executive Compensation **Band 1** p.1540, Litigation **Band 2** p.1544

**Watanabe Ing LLP**
Table(s): **Hawaii**: Labor & Employment **Band 3** p.1117, Real Estate **Band 2** p.1120

**Watkins & Eager PLLC**
Profile: p.1617
Table(s): **Mississippi**: Corporate/Commercial **Band 1** p.1591, Environment **Band 3** p.1594, Labor & Employment **Band 2** p.1595, Litigation **Band 1** p.1596, Real Estate **Band 1** p.1600, **Nationwide**: Product Liability & Mass Torts **Band 4** p.207

**Watson, Farley & Williams**
Profile: p.450
Table(s): **Nationwide**: Transportation **Band 1** p.259

**Watt, Tieder, Hoffar & Fitzgerald, LLP**
Profile: p.2522
Table(s): **California**: Construction **Band 1** p.549, **Nationwide**: Construction **Band 1** p.65, **Virginia**: Construction **Band 1** p.2491

**Weaver Schlenger Mazel LLP**
Table(s): **California**: Immigration **Band 2** p.571

**Weber & Rose, PSC**
Table(s): **Kentucky**: Real Estate **Band 3** p.1314

**Weil, Gotshal & Manges LLP**
Profile: p.2015
Table(s): **California**: Corporate/M&A **Band 2** p.553, Intellectual Property **Band 2** p.577, IT & Outsourcing **Band 4** p.583, **District of Columbia**: Antitrust **Band 2** p.786, Environment **Band 4** p.804, Intellectual Property **Band 4** p.820, **Florida**: Litigation **Band 3** p.965, **Massachusetts**: Corporate/M&A **Band 2** p.1452, Private Equity **Band 1** p.1474, **Nationwide**: Antitrust **Band 3** p.22, Banking & Finance **Band 3** p.31, Bankruptcy/Restructuring **Band 1** p.38, Capital Markets **Band 3** p.58,

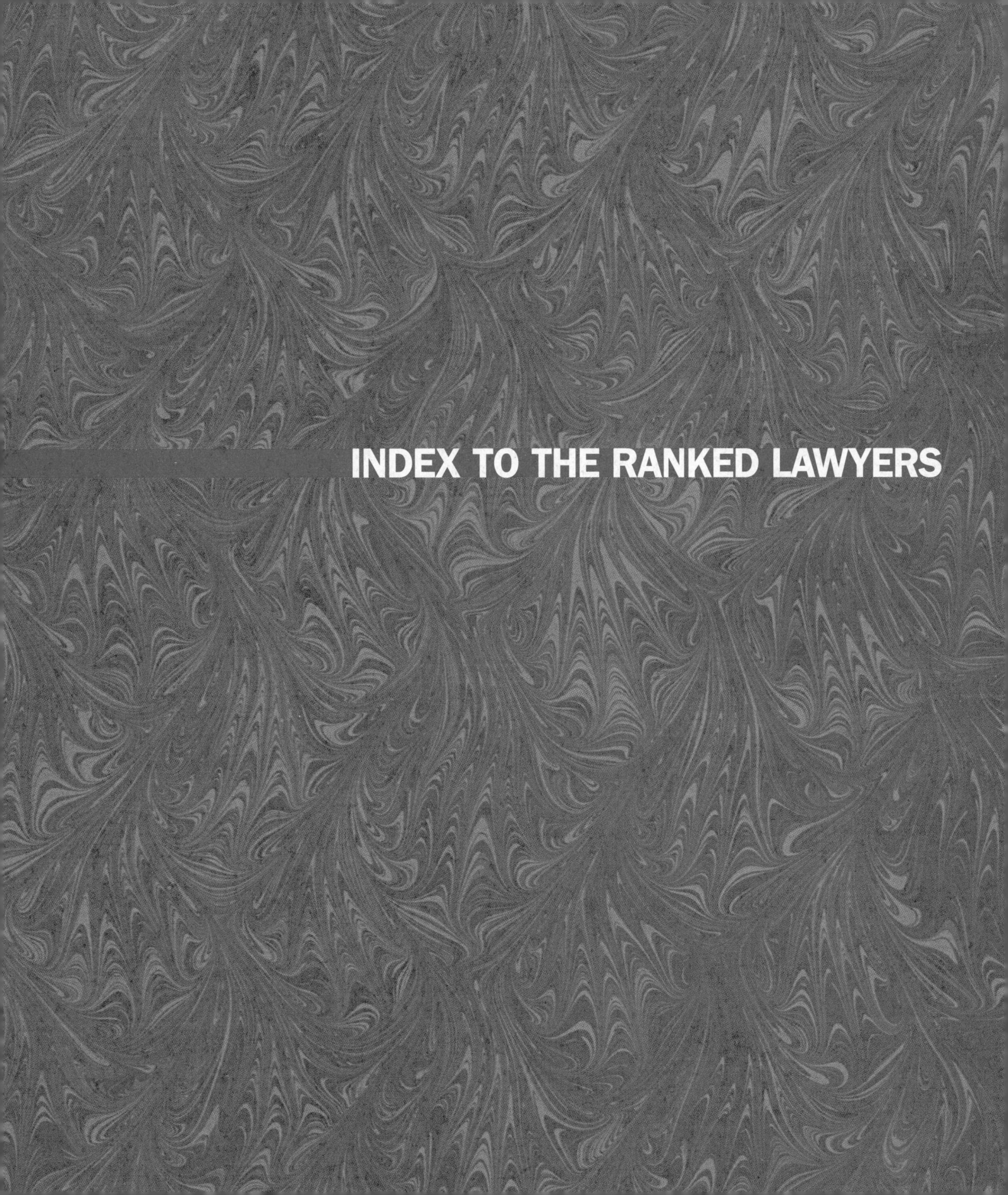

# INDEX TO THE RANKED LAWYERS

## A

**Aamoth, Robert J**
Table(s): **District of Columbia:** Telecom,
Broadcast & Satellite **Band 3** p.844

**Aaron, Wayne M**
Profile: p.271
Table(s): **Nationwide:** Financial Services
Regulation: Broker Dealer (Enforcement) **Band 3**
p.98

**Aaron, William**
Table(s): **Florida:** Litigation: White-Collar Crime &
Government Investigations **Band 3** p.967

**Aaronson, Anne Marie**
Table(s): **Pennsylvania:**
Bankruptcy/Restructuring **Band 4** p.2188

**Abate, Mark J**
Profile: p.1871
Table(s): **New York:** Intellectual Property: Patent
**Band 3** p.1820

**Abaunza, Donald R**
Table(s): **Louisiana:** Litigation: General
Commercial **Band 1** p.1352

**Abbott, David F**
Table(s): **Nationwide:** Tax: Controversy **Band 3**
p.244

**Abbott, Derek C**
Table(s): **Delaware:** Bankruptcy/Restructuring
**Band 1** p.754

**Abbott, James E**
Profile: p.1871
Table(s): **New York:** Corporate/M&A **Band 5**
p.1793

**Abbott, Scott M**
Table(s): **Nevada:** Labor & Employment **Band 2**
p.1675

**Abbott, Thomas M**
Table(s): **Nationwide:** Government: Government
Contracts **Band 4** p.117

**Abbott Jr, Ralph F**
Table(s): **Massachusetts:** Labor & Employment
**Band 3** p.1466

**Abdallah, Scott**
Table(s): **South Dakota:** Litigation: General
Commercial **Band 3** p.2284

**Abel, Ashley B**
Profile: p.2267
Table(s): **South Carolina:** Labor & Employment
**Band 3** p.2262

**Abel, Kenneth**
Table(s): **Maryland:** Corporate/M&A **Band 3**
p.1412

**Abel, Sally**
Profile: p.620
Table(s): **California:** Intellectual Property:
Trademark, Copyright & Trade Secrets **Band 1**
p.578

**Abel, Steven W**
Table(s): **Oregon:** Real Estate: Zoning/Land Use
**Band 1** p.2173

**Abell, Nancy L**
Table(s): **California:** Labor & Employment **Star
individuals** p.587

**Abelson, Barry M**
Profile: p.2210
Table(s): **Pennsylvania:** Corporate/M&A &
Private Equity **Star individuals** p.2191,
**Pennsylvania:** Corporate/M&A: Securities **Star
individuals** p.2191

**Abelson, Ned**
Table(s): **Massachusetts:** Environment **Band 1**
p.1457

**Abelson, Philip**
Table(s): **New York:** Bankruptcy/Restructuring
**Up-and-coming individuals** p.1782

**Abendroth, Thomas W.**
Table(s): **Nationwide:** Wealth Management:
Central Region **Band 2** p.266

**Abernathy, Terry J**
Table(s): **Iowa:** Litigation: General Commercial
**Band 4** p.1288

**Abernathy, Thomas E**
Profile: p.1074
Table(s): **Georgia:** Construction **Senior Statesmen:**
p.1044

**Abernethy, Jonathan S.**
Profile: p.1871
Table(s): **New York:** Litigation: White-Collar
Crime & Government Investigations **Up-and-coming
individuals** p.1836

**Abernethy, Phil B**
Profile: p.1601
Table(s): **Mississippi:** Litigation: Construction
**Band 2** p.1596, **Mississippi:** Litigation: General
Commercial **Band 3** p.1596

**Abowitz, Murray E**
Table(s): **Oklahoma:** Litigation: General
Commercial **Band 1** p.2141

**Abraham, Aaron N**
Table(s): **New York:** Construction **Band 3** p.1791

**Abraham, Bill**
Table(s): **Wisconsin:** Corporate/M&A **Band 2**
p.2571

**Abrahamson, Joel**
Table(s): **Minnesota:** Labor & Employment **Band 3**
p.1571

**Abramczyk, Jon E**
Table(s): **Delaware:** Chancery **Band 3** p.758

**Abramov, Hope**
Table(s): **Missouri:** Labor & Employment **Up-and-
coming individuals** p.1625

**Abramowitz, Elkan**
Profile: p.1871
Table(s): **New York:** Litigation: White-Collar
Crime & Government Investigations **Senior
Statesmen:** p.1836

**Abramowitz, Robert**
Profile: p.2210
Table(s): **Pennsylvania:** Labor & Employment:
Employee Benefits & Compensation **Band 1**
p.2200

**Abrams, Donald-Bruce**
Profile: p.1483
Table(s): **Massachusetts:** Tax **Band 2** p.1481

**Abrams, Floyd**
Profile: p.271
Table(s): **Nationwide:** First Amendment
Litigation **Star individuals** p.105, **New York:** Media
& Entertainment: First Amendment Litigation
**Star individuals** p.1851

**Abrams, Jeffrey A**
Profile: p.1276
Table(s): **Indiana:** Real Estate **Band 2** p.1275

**Abrams, Kevin G**
Table(s): **Delaware:** Chancery **Band 1** p.758

**Abrams, Lee N**
Table(s): **Nationwide:** Franchising: Mainly
Franchisee **Band 1** p.114, **Illinois:** Antitrust **Senior
Statesmen:** p.1143

**Abrams, Marc**
Profile: p.271
Table(s): **Nationwide:** Bankruptcy/Restructuring
**Band 2** p.39, **New York:**
Bankruptcy/Restructuring **Band 2** p.1782

**Abrams, Marc**
Profile: p.1871
Table(s): **New York:** Insurance: Dispute
Resolution: Insurer **Band 3** p.1816

**Abrams, Robert G**
Profile: p.849
Table(s): **District of Columbia:** Antitrust **Band 5**
p.787

**Abrams, William F**
Profile: p.620
Table(s): **California:** Intellectual Property: Patent
**Band 4** p.578, **California:** Intellectual Property:
Trademark, Copyright & Trade Secrets **Band 3**
p.578

**Abramson, Gil**
Profile: p.1424
Table(s): **Maryland:** Labor & Employment **Band 2**
p.1417

**Abramson, Richard W**
Profile: p.1731
Table(s): **New Jersey:** Real Estate **Band 1** p.1728

**Abrao, Cybil**
Table(s): **North Carolina:** Banking & Finance
**Associates to watch** p.2021

**Abuhoff, Daniel M**
Table(s): **New York:** Antitrust **Band 4** p.1778

**Aciman, Carole**
Table(s): **New York:** Technology & Outsourcing
**Band 3** p.1868

**Acker, Lawrence G**
Profile: p.271
Table(s): **Nationwide:** Energy: Electricity
(Regulatory & Litigation) **Band 2** p.76,
**Nationwide:** Energy: Oil & Gas (Regulatory &
Litigation) **Band 2** p.76

**Acker, Rodney**
Profile: p.2377
Table(s): **Texas:** Litigation: General Commercial
**Band 2** p.2362

**Ackerbaum Cox, Joyce**
Profile: p.983
Table(s): **Florida:** Labor & Employment **Band 3**
p.959

**Ackerman, David**
Profile: p.1196
Table(s): **Illinois:** Labor & Employment:
Employee Benefits & Compensation **Band 3**
p.1176

**Ackerman, Gary**
Table(s): **Washington:** Real Estate **Band 2** p.2535

**Ackerman, Jill Robb**
Table(s): **Nebraska:** Litigation: Intellectual
Property **Band 1** p.1664

**Ackourey, Mary Anne**
Table(s): **Georgia:** Labor & Employment **Band 4**
p.1060

**Acord Noland, Bobbi**
Table(s): **Georgia:** Banking & Finance **Band 1**
p.1039

**Adamek, Andrew**
Table(s): **Montana:** Labor & Employment **Band 3**
p.1648

**Adamo, Kenneth R**
Profile: p.1196
Table(s): **Illinois:** Intellectual Property **Band 1**
p.1171

**Adams, Alfred G**
Table(s): **North Carolina:** Real Estate **Band 1**
p.2037

**Adams, Bert**
Table(s): **New York:** Corporate/M&A **Band 5**
p.1793

**Adams, Bryan**
Table(s): **North Carolina:** Labor & Employment
**Band 2** p.2031

**Adams, Deborah**
Profile: p.2089
Table(s): **Ohio:** Labor & Employment **Band 1**
p.2074

**Adams, Eben**
Profile: p.1397
Table(s): **Maine:** Real Estate **Band 3** p.1395

**Adams, Garth**
Table(s): **Iowa:** Corporate/M&A **Band 1** p.1283

**Adams, Greg**
Table(s): **Washington:** Corporate/Commercial
**Band 1** p.2525

**Adams, H Mark**
Profile: p.1357
Table(s): **Louisiana:** Labor & Employment **Band 2**
p.1350

**Adams, Joe**
Profile: p.1196
Table(s): **Illinois:** Labor & Employment:
Employee Benefits & Compensation **Band 2**
p.1176

**Adams, John**
Table(s): **Virginia:** Litigation: White-Collar Crime
& Government Investigations **Up-and-coming individu-
als** p.2502

**Adams, John A**
Table(s): **Utah:** Litigation: General Commercial
**Band 3** p.2468

**Adams, Marguerite L**
Table(s): **Louisiana:** Real Estate **Band 2** p.1355

**Adams, Mark K**
Profile: p.1773
Table(s): New Mexico: Environment, Natural Resources & Regulated Industries: Water Law **Band 1** p.1766

**Adams, Matthew**
Profile: p.271
Table(s): Nationwide: Climate Change **Up-and-coming individuals** p.63

**Adams, Richard**
Profile: p.2377
Table(s): Texas: Energy: State Regulatory & Litigation (Electricity) **Band 2** p.2341

**Adams, Robert**
Table(s): Missouri: Litigation: General Commercial **Band 1** p.1628

**Adams Jr, Alfred G**
Table(s): Georgia: Real Estate **Band 1** p.1070

**Adas, Craig**
Profile: p.620
Table(s): California: Corporate/M&A **Band 4** p.553

**Addison, Linda L**
Profile: p.1871
Table(s): New York: Litigation: General Commercial **Band 4** p.1833

**Addleman, Billie L M**
Table(s): Wyoming: Litigation: General Commercial **Up-and-coming individuals** p.2598

**Adducci, Steven**
Profile: p.271
Table(s): Nationwide: Energy: Oil & Gas (Regulatory & Litigation) **Band 5** p.78

**Adduci II, V James**
Table(s): Nationwide: International Trade: Intellectual Property (Section 337) **Band 1** p.160

**Addy, Meredith Martin**
Table(s): Illinois: Intellectual Property **Band 1** p.1171

**Adelfio, Marco**
Profile: p.271
Table(s): Nationwide: Investment Funds: Registered Funds **Band 3** p.170

**Adelman, Howard**
Profile: p.1196
Table(s): Illinois: Bankruptcy/Restructuring **Band 3** p.1148

**Adelman, S Allan**
Table(s): Maryland: Healthcare **Band 2** p.1415

**Adinata, Geetha**
Profile: p.1074
Table(s): Georgia: Immigration **Up-and-coming individuals** p.1055

**Adkins, Edward J**
Profile: p.1424
Table(s): Maryland: Employee Benefits & Executive Compensation **Band 1** p.1414

**Adler, Arthur S**
Profile: p.271
Table(s): Nationwide: Capital Markets: REITs **Band 4** p.55, Nationwide: Real Estate **Band 2** p.225, New York: Real Estate: Finance **Band 2** p.1855

**Adler, David F**
Profile: p.2089
Table(s): Ohio: Litigation: General Commercial **Band 4** p.2078

**Adler, Howard B**
Profile: p.849
Table(s): Nationwide: Capital Markets: REITs **Band 4** p.55, District of Columbia: Corporate/M&A & Private Equity **Band 1** p.797

**Adler, Kenneth A**
Profile: p.1872
Table(s): Nationwide: Outsourcing **Band 3** p.195, New York: Technology & Outsourcing **Band 2** p.1868

**Adler, Sheldon S**
Profile: p.271
Table(s): Nationwide: Energy: Electricity (Transactional) **Band 1** p.77

**Advani, Suresh**
Profile: p.1196
Table(s): Illinois: Tax **Band 3** p.1192

**Aframe, Karen**
Table(s): New Hampshire: Labor & Employment **Associates to watch** p.1688

**Aftanas, Richard**
Profile: p.272
Table(s): Nationwide: Capital Markets: Debt & Equity **Up-and-coming individuals** p.46

**Agneshwar, Anand**
Profile: p.272
Table(s): Nationwide: Product Liability & Mass Torts **Band 5** p.208

**Agoglia, Michael J**
Profile: p.272
Table(s): Nationwide: Financial Services Regulation: Consumer Finance (Litigation) **Band 2** p.99

**Agran, Raymond**
Table(s): Pennsylvania: Corporate/M&A & Private Equity **Band 4** p.2191

**Agron, Adam**
Table(s): Colorado: Corporate/M&A **Band 2** p.703

**Agsten, Melinda**
Table(s): Connecticut: Healthcare **Band 1** p.735

**Aguilar, Richard A**
Profile: p.1357
Table(s): Louisiana: Bankruptcy/Restructuring **Band 2** p.1337, Louisiana: Litigation: General Commercial **Band 3** p.1352

**Aguilar Jr, Rodolfo J**
Profile: p.1357
Table(s): Louisiana: Corporate/M&A **Band 3** p.1341

**Aguilar-Alvarez, Guillermo**
Profile: p.272
Table(s): Nationwide: International Arbitration **Band 3** p.145, Nationwide: International Arbitration: Arbitrators **Band 1** p.145

**Aguirre, John E**
Table(s): California: Employee Benefits & Executive Compensation **Band 2** p.560

**Ahari, Leslie**
Table(s): District of Columbia: Insurance: Insurer **Band 3** p.816

**Ahearn, Dale**
Profile: p.1315
Table(s): Kentucky: Real Estate **Band 1** p.1314

**Ahern, Janice M**
Table(s): New Mexico: Real Estate **Band 3** p.1772

**Ahern, Patrick**
Table(s): Illinois: Antitrust **Band 3** p.1143

**Ahern III, Lawrence R**
Table(s): Tennessee: Litigation: Bankruptcy **Senior Statesmen:** p.2295

**Ahlers, Vickie Brady**
Table(s): Nebraska: Healthcare **Band 2** p.1661

**Ahmadi, Afi**
Table(s): Vermont: Corporate/Commercial **Band 3** p.2483

**Ahnert, Janell M.**
Profile: p.467
Table(s): Alabama: Labor & Employment **Up-and-coming individuals** p.460

**Ahrens, Matthew**
Profile: p.1872
Table(s): New York: Environment: Mainly Transactional **Band 3** p.1808

**Ahrens, Michael**
Table(s): California: Bankruptcy/Restructuring **Band 2** p.542

**Ahrens, Philip FW**
Profile: p.1397
Table(s): Maine: Environment **Band 2** p.1389

**Ahrens, Richard A.**
Profile: p.1635
Table(s): Missouri: Environment **Band 3** p.1621

**Aiello, Anthony**
Profile: p.1196
Table(s): Illinois: Real Estate **Band 3** p.1187

**Aiello, John**
Table(s): New Jersey: Corporate/M&A **Band 1** p.1707

**Aiello, Michael**
Profile: p.1872
Table(s): New York: Corporate/M&A **Band 2** p.1793

**Aiello LeBeau, Josephine**
Table(s): Nationwide: International Trade: Export Controls & Economic Sanctions **Band 2** p.153

**Ainslie, Elizabeth K**
Table(s): Pennsylvania: Litigation: General Commercial **Band 2** p.2203

**Aisenbrey, John C**
Table(s): Missouri: Litigation: General Commercial **Band 2** p.1628, Missouri: Litigation: White-Collar Crime & Government Investigations **Band 1** p.1628

**Aizenstein, Neal**
Profile: p.1196
Table(s): Illinois: Corporate/M&A **Band 3** p.1156

**Ajamie, Thomas**
Table(s): Texas: Litigation: General Commercial **Band 3** p.2362

**Aksamit, Roger D**
Profile: p.2377
Table(s): Texas: Tax **Band 4** p.2371

**Aksen, Gerald**
Table(s): Nationwide: International Arbitration: Arbitrators **Band 1** p.146

**Al-Salam, Ramsey**
Table(s): Washington: Intellectual Property **Band 1** p.2529

**Alam, Joel**
Table(s): Michigan: Corporate/M&A **Band 3** p.1538

**Alamuddin, Sari M**
Profile: p.1196
Table(s): Illinois: Labor & Employment **Band 2** p.1175

**Albano, Jonathan M**
Profile: p.1483
Table(s): Nationwide: First Amendment Litigation **Band 3** p.105, Massachusetts: Litigation: General Commercial **Band 2** p.1470

**Albano, Michael J**
Profile: p.1872
Table(s): New York: Employee Benefits & Executive Compensation **Band 4** p.1802

**Albarracín, Carlos**
Profile: p.1872
Table(s): New York: Latin American Investment **Band 2** p.1829

**Alberg, James L**
Profile: p.272
Table(s): Nationwide: Outsourcing **Band 1** p.195, District of Columbia: Technology & Outsourcing **Band 2** p.842

**Albergotti, Robert**
Table(s): Nationwide: Bankruptcy/Restructuring **Band 2** p.39, Texas: Bankruptcy/Restructuring **Band 1** p.2328

**Alberino, Scott L**
Profile: p.849
Table(s): District of Columbia: Bankruptcy/Restructuring **Band 4** p.792

**Albers, Matthew**
Profile: p.2089
Table(s): Ohio: Healthcare **Associates to watch** p.2069

**Albers, Michael F**
Profile: p.2377
Table(s): Texas: Construction **Band 2** p.2335

**Albert, Lauren S**
Profile: p.1872
Table(s): New York: Antitrust **Band 4** p.1778

**Albert, Richard**
Profile: p.1872
Table(s): New York: Litigation: White-Collar Crime & Government Investigations **Band 3** p.1836

**Albert, Rory**
Table(s): New York: Employee Benefits & Executive Compensation **Band 3** p.1802

**Albert, Victor**
Table(s): Oklahoma: Labor & Employment **Band 3** p.2140

**Alberts, Barry S**
Table(s): Illinois: Litigation: General Commercial **Band 4** p.1180

**Alberts, David**
Table(s): New York: Insurance: Transactional & Regulatory **Band 3** p.1816

**Alberts, Sam J**
Profile: p.849
Table(s): District of Columbia: Bankruptcy/Restructuring **Band 3** p.792

**Albertson, Terry**
Profile: p.272
Table(s): Nationwide: Government: Government Contracts **Band 1** p.117, Nationwide: Government: Government Contracts: Costs Disputes p.117

**Albi, Fausta M**
Table(s): California: Immigration **Band 3** p.571

**Albin, David I**
Table(s): Connecticut: Corporate/M&A **Band 1** p.732

**Albrecht, Kristy L**
Table(s): North Dakota: Labor & Employment **Band 1** p.2052

**Albrecht, Virginia S**
Profile: p.849
Table(s): District of Columbia: Environment **Band 2** p.804

**Albright, Alan D**
Profile: p.2377
Table(s): Texas: Intellectual Property **Band 3** p.2354

**Albright, Val J**
Profile: p.2378
Table(s): Texas: Tax: Litigation **Band 1** p.2371

**Alden, John W**
Table(s): Georgia: Labor & Employment **Band 4** p.1060

**Alderman, Silvia M**
Table(s): Florida: Environment **Band 1** p.951

**Aldock, John D**
Profile: p.849
Table(s): District of Columbia: Litigation: General Commercial **Band 2** p.826

**Aldrich, Marcy Levine**
Table(s): Florida: Insurance **Band 1** p.957

**Aldrich, Thomas A**
Profile: p.2089
Table(s): Ohio: Corporate/M&A **Band 3** p.2064

**Aldridge, Richard B**
Profile: p.2210
Table(s): Pennsylvania: Corporate/M&A & Private Equity **Band 3** p.2191

**Alessandra, M Nan**
Table(s): Louisiana: Labor & Employment **Band 1** p.1350

**Alessi, Robert**
Profile: p.1872
Table(s): New York: Environment **Band 3** p.1807

**Alessio, Michael**
Profile: p.2378
Table(s): Texas: Real Estate **Band 2** p.2367

**Alexander, Bruce**
Table(s): Florida: Construction **Star individuals** p.944

**Alexander, Dina E**
Table(s): Oregon: Real Estate **Band 3** p.2173

**Alexander, Douglas W**
Profile: p.2378
Table(s): Texas: Litigation: Appellate **Band 2** p.2361

**Alexander, Frederick H**
Table(s): Delaware: Corporate/M&A **Band 1** p.761

**Alexander, Jim**
Profile: p.849
Table(s): District of Columbia: Immigration **Band 3** p.814

**Alexander, Joseph**
Profile: p.1074
Table(s): Georgia: Corporate/M&A **Up-and-coming individuals** p.1046

**Alexander, Lee**
Profile: p.272
Table(s): Nationwide: Energy: Oil & Gas (Regulatory & Litigation) **Band 3** p.78

**Alexander, Lori**
Table(s): Connecticut: Labor & Employment **Band 2** p.736

**Alexander, Mason**
Profile: p.2039
Table(s): North Carolina: Labor & Employment **Band 3** p.2031

**Alexander, Miles**
Table(s): Georgia: Intellectual Property **Band 1** p.1056

**Alexander, Nelson D**
Profile: p.1276
Table(s): Indiana: Litigation: General Commercial **Up-and-coming individuals** p.1273

**Alexander, Richard M**
Profile: p.272
Table(s): Nationwide: Financial Services Regulation: Banking (Enforcement & Investigations) **Band 1** p.97

**Alexander, Todd E**
Profile: p.272
Table(s): Nationwide: Projects **Band 3** p.216, Nationwide: Projects: Renewables & Alternative Energy **Band 2** p.216

**Alexander, Troy**
Profile: p.272
Table(s): Nationwide: Projects **Band 1** p.216, New York: Latin American Investment **Band 4** p.1829

**Alexandrov, Stanimir A**
Profile: p.272
Table(s): Nationwide: International Arbitration **Band 2** p.145

**Alexis, Geraldine M**
Table(s): California: Antitrust **Band 4** p.536

**Alfano, Lea**
Table(s): Georgia: Immigration **Band 3** p.1055

**Alfert, Jr, Robert**
Table(s): Florida: Construction **Band 2** p.944

**Alford, Carolyn Zander**
Profile: p.1074
Table(s): Georgia: Banking & Finance **Band 1** p.1039

**Alfred, Richard**
Profile: p.1483
Table(s): Massachusetts: Labor & Employment **Band 1** p.1466

**Ali, Arif H**
Profile: p.272
Table(s): Nationwide: International Arbitration **Band 2** p.145

**Alioto Jr, Joseph M**
Table(s): California: Antitrust **Band 4** p.536, California: Antitrust: Mainly Plaintiff p.536

**Alito, Rosemary**
Profile: p.1731
Table(s): New Jersey: Labor & Employment **Band 1** p.1718

**Alke, John L**
Table(s): Montana: Natural Resources & Environment **Band 1** p.1651

**Alker, Susan C**
Table(s): California: Banking & Finance **Band 4** p.539

**Allan, John M**
Profile: p.1074
Table(s): Georgia: Tax **Band 2** p.1072

**Allan, Richard H**
Table(s): Oregon: Environment **Band 3** p.2165

**Allard, Nicholas W**
Table(s): Nationwide: Government: Government Relations **Band 3** p.121

**Allcock, John**
Profile: p.620
Table(s): California: Intellectual Property: Patent **Band 2** p.578

**Allderdice, Linda**
Profile: p.620
Table(s): California: Labor & Employment **Band 4** p.587

**Alleman, Thomas B**
Table(s): Texas: Insurance **Band 3** p.2351

**Allen, Ben M**
Table(s): New Mexico: Litigation: Medical Malpractice & Insurance Defense **Band 1** p.1769

**Allen, Bryan T**
Table(s): Utah: Corporate/M&A **Band 3** p.2462

**Allen, Everette**
Table(s): Virginia: Litigation: General Commercial **Band 1** p.2502

**Allen, Gary**
Table(s): Idaho: Natural Resources & Environment **Band 2** p.1136, Idaho: Real Estate: Zoning/Land Use **Band 1** p.1138

**Allen, James W**
Table(s): Missouri: Corporate/M&A **Band 3** p.1618

**Allen, Julie M**
Table(s): Nationwide: Capital Markets: Debt & Equity **Band 4** p.46

**Allen, Rand L**
Profile: p.272
Table(s): Nationwide: Government: Government Contracts **Band 1** p.117

**Allen, Randall L**
Profile: p.1074
Table(s): Georgia: Antitrust **Band 1** p.1037

**Allen, Tom**
Table(s): Ohio: Bankruptcy/Restructuring **Band 2** p.2058

**Allen, Trudy B**
Profile: p.1601
Table(s): Mississippi: Environment **Band 3** p.1594

**Allen, William**
Table(s): Arkansas: Litigation: General Commercial **Band 1** p.522

**Allen, Zachary W**
Profile: p.2146
Table(s): Oklahoma: Real Estate **Band 2** p.2145

**Allender, John R**
Profile: p.2378
Table(s): Texas: Tax **Band 1** p.2371

**Allensworth, William**
Table(s): Texas: Construction **Band 1** p.2335

**Allerhand, Joseph S**
Profile: p.273
Table(s): Nationwide: Securities: Litigation **Band 2** p.232, New York: Litigation: Securities **Band 2** p.1834

**Alletag, Gary M**
Profile: p.2378
Table(s): Texas: Real Estate **Band 3** p.2367

**Allevato, John**
Profile: p.2561
Table(s): West Virginia: Corporate/Commercial: Tax **Band 2** p.2550

**Allgeyer, David A**
Table(s): Minnesota: Litigation: Intellectual Property **Band 1** p.1574

**Allgood, Michele S**
Table(s): Arkansas: Corporate/Commercial: Municipal Bonds **Band 2** p.518

**Alli Jr, Richard J**
Table(s): Oregon: Labor & Employment **Band 3** p.2168

**Allingham II, Thomas J**
Profile: p.767
Table(s): Delaware: Chancery **Band 1** p.758

**Allison, Benjamin**
Table(s): New Mexico: Litigation: General Commercial **Up-and-coming individuals** p.1769

**Allison, Christopher F**
Profile: p.2378
Table(s): Texas: Tax **Band 2** p.2371

**Allison, Sonny**
Table(s): Colorado: Corporate/M&A **Band 3** p.703

**Allison, William**
Table(s): Arizona: Real Estate: Zoning/Land Use **Band 3** p.504

**Allotta, John J**
Profile: p.2089
Table(s): Ohio: Corporate/M&A **Up-and-coming individuals** p.2064

**Arado, Frank E**
Table(s): North Carolina: Real Estate: Finance
Up-and-coming individuals p.2037

**Aragon, Rudolph F**
Profile: p.983
Table(s): Florida: Litigation: General Commercial
Band 2 p.966

**Arar, Roger M**
Profile: p.1874
Table(s): New York: Media & Entertainment:
Film & Television Band 2 p.1849

**Arash, Dora**
Profile: p.620
Table(s): California: Tax Band 3 p.617

**Arbery, W Christopher**
Profile: p.1074
Table(s): Georgia: Labor & Employment Band 3
p.1060

**Arca, Emil**
Table(s): New York: Latin American Investment
Band 4 p.1829

**Arcano, Stephen F**
Profile: p.1874
Table(s): New York: Corporate/M&A Band 3
p.1793

**Arcella, Craig F**
Profile: p.274
Table(s): Nationwide: Capital Markets: Debt &
Equity Band 4 p.46

**Archer, Judith A**
Profile: p.1874
Table(s): New York: Litigation: General
Commercial Band 4 p.1833

**Archer, Matt**
Profile: p.274
Table(s): Nationwide: Projects Band 4 p.216

**Archibald, Jeanne S**
Table(s): Nationwide: International Trade: CFIUS
Experts Band 2 p.152, Nationwide: International
Trade: Export Controls & Economic Sanctions
Band 3 p.152

**Ardelean, Paula Graves**
Profile: p.1601
Table(s): Mississippi: Labor & Employment Band
1 p.1595

**Ardinger, William F J**
Table(s): New Hampshire:
Corporate/Commercial: Tax Band 1 p.1685

**Arefi-Afshar, Yousef**
Table(s): Washington: Real Estate Associates to
watch p.2535

**Arellano, Joseph C**
Table(s): Oregon: Litigation: General
Commercial Band 2 p.2171

**Arfmann, Dennis**
Table(s): Colorado: Natural Resources &
Environment Band 2 p.712

**Arguedas, Cristina C**
Table(s): Nationwide: Litigation: Trial Lawyers
Band 1 p.187, California: Litigation: White-Collar
Crime & Government Investigations Star individu-
als p.601

**Arkell, Betty**
Profile: p.716
Table(s): Colorado: Corporate/M&A Band 2 p.703

**Arkell, J David**
Table(s): Colorado: Real Estate: Construction
Band 1 p.714

**Armas, Oliver J**
Profile: p.274
Table(s): Nationwide: International Arbitration
Band 3 p.145

**Armenio, Peter J**
Table(s): New York: Intellectual Property: Patent
Band 2 p.1820

**Armentrout, Randall**
Table(s): Iowa: Labor & Employment Band 2
p.1285

**Armour, Jonathan W. J.**
Profile: p.1578
Table(s): Minnesota: Real Estate Band 3 p.1576

**Armstrong, David J**
Profile: p.507
Table(s): Arizona: Environment (including water
rights) Band 3 p.497

**Armstrong, Dwight L**
Profile: p.620
Table(s): California: Labor & Employment Band 3
p.587

**Armstrong, James M**
Profile: p.1299
Table(s): Kansas: Litigation: General
Commercial Band 1 p.1295

**Armstrong, Jane E**
Table(s): Louisiana: Labor & Employment:
Employee Benefits & Compensation Band 2
p.1350

**Arndt, Randall S**
Table(s): Ohio: Real Estate Band 3 p.2086

**Arnhols, William C**
Table(s): Florida: Banking & Finance:
Transactional Band 3 p.937

**Arnholz, John**
Profile: p.274
Table(s): Nationwide: Capital Markets:
Securitisation Band 1 p.59

**Arnold, Beth E**
Profile: p.1483
Table(s): Massachusetts: Intellectual Property
Band 2 p.1463

**Arnold, Dennis**
Profile: p.620
Table(s): California: Real Estate Band 1 p.611

**Arnold, Douglas S**
Profile: p.1074
Table(s): Georgia: Environment Band 2 p.1051

**Arnold, James S**
Table(s): Ohio: Litigation: General Commercial
Band 2 p.2078

**Arnold, John K**
Profile: p.2378
Table(s): Texas: Energy: State Regulatory &
Litigation (Electricity) Band 2 p.2341

**Arnold, Mark**
Profile: p.2378
Table(s): Texas: Real Estate Band 3 p.2367

**Arnold, Richard**
Table(s): Florida: Antitrust Band 1 p.935

**Arnold III, Edward H (Hank)**
Profile: p.1357
Table(s): Louisiana: Banking & Finance: Marine
Finance Band 1 p.1335

**Arnone, James L**
Table(s): California: Real Estate: Zoning/Land
Use Band 3 p.612

**Arntsen, Allen A**
Table(s): Wisconsin: Intellectual Property:
Litigation p.2573

**Aro, Edwin**
Profile: p.716
Table(s): Colorado: Litigation: General
Commercial Band 3 p.709

**Aronchick, Mark Alan**
Profile: p.2210
Table(s): Pennsylvania: Litigation: General
Commercial Band 2 p.2203

**Aronoff, James B**
Profile: p.2089
Table(s): Ohio: Real Estate Band 2 p.2086

**Aronov, Mary L**
Profile: p.2301
Table(s): Tennessee: Real Estate Band 2 p.2299

**Aronson, Clifford H**
Profile: p.1874
Table(s): New York: Antitrust Band 1 p.1778

**Aronson, Daniel H**
Profile: p.983
Table(s): Florida: Corporate/M&A & Private
Equity Band 1 p.947

**Aronson, Seth**
Table(s): Nationwide: Securities: Litigation Band
2 p.232, California: Litigation: General
Commercial Band 2 p.593, California: Litigation:
Securities Band 1 p.593

**Aronstam, Brad**
Table(s): Delaware: Chancery Up-and-coming individuals p.758

**Aronzon, Paul S**
Profile: p.620
Table(s): Nationwide: Bankruptcy/Restructuring
Band 2 p.39, California:
Bankruptcy/Restructuring Band 1 p.542

**Arovas, Gregory S**
Profile: p.1874
Table(s): Nationwide: International Trade:
Intellectual Property (Section 337) Band 3 p.160,
New York: Intellectual Property: Patent Band 2
p.1820

**Arp, D Jarrett**
Profile: p.850
Table(s): District of Columbia: Antitrust Band 3
p.787

**Arquit, Kevin J**
Profile: p.1874
Table(s): New York: Antitrust Band 1 p.1778

**Arrajj, David R**
Table(s): Nationwide: Gaming & Licensing Band 3
p.115, Nevada: Gaming & Licensing Band 1
p.1674

**Arrieta, Alejandro M**
Table(s): Florida: Corporate/M&A & Private
Equity Associates to watch p.947

**Arrington, Scott J**
Profile: p.274
Table(s): Nationwide: Projects Band 3 p.216

**Arrowood, Catharine Biggs**
Table(s): North Carolina: Litigation: General
Commercial Band 2 p.2033

**Arrowood, Lisa G**
Table(s): Massachusetts: Litigation: General
Commercial Band 3 p.1470

**Arseneault, Jack**
Table(s): New Jersey: Litigation: White-Collar
Crime & Government Investigations Band 1
p.1723

**Arumi, Cristina**
Table(s): Nationwide: Capital Markets: REITs
Band 2 p.55

**Asaad, Peter F.**
Table(s): District of Columbia: Immigration Band
3 p.814

**Asaro, Michael**
Profile: p.1874
Table(s): New York: Litigation: White-Collar
Crime & Government Investigations Up-and-coming
individuals p.1836

**Asbill, Henry W**
Profile: p.850
Table(s): District of Columbia: Litigation: White-
Collar Crime & Government Investigations Band 3
p.827

**Asensio, M.J.**
Profile: p.2089
Table(s): Ohio: Labor & Employment Band 4
p.2074

**Ash, David**
Table(s): Mississippi: Real Estate Band 3 p.1600

**Ash, James**
Table(s): Missouri: Corporate/M&A Band 1 p.1618

**Ashburn, Mark**
Table(s): Alaska: Litigation: General Commercial
Senior Statesmen: p.490

**Ashburner, Clifford**
Profile: p.1315
Table(s): Kentucky: Real Estate: Zoning/Land
Use Up-and-coming individuals p.1314

**Ashby, Kimberly**
Table(s): Florida: Construction Band 1 p.944

**Ashby, Lawrence C**
Profile: p.767
Table(s): Delaware: Chancery Senior Statesmen:
p.758

**Ashcraft, Howard W**
Profile: p.621
Table(s): California: Construction Band 1 p.550

**Ashe, Barry W**
Table(s): Louisiana: Litigation: General
Commercial Band 3 p.1352

**Ashe, Brian T**
Profile: p.621
Table(s): California: Labor & Employment **Band 3**
p.587

**Ashe Jr, R Lawrence**
Profile: p.1074
Table(s): Georgia: Labor & Employment **Band 1**
p.1060

**Asher Jr, William B**
Profile: p.1483
Table(s): Massachusetts: Corporate/M&A **Band 2**
p.1452

**Ashford, Leon**
Table(s): Alabama: Litigation: Mainly Plaintiff
**Band 1** p.463

**Ashinoff, Reid**
Profile: p.274
Table(s): Nationwide: Insurance: Dispute
Resolution: Insurer **Band 2** p.134, New York:
Insurance: Dispute Resolution: Insurer **Band 2**
p.1816

**Ashley, Thomas**
Table(s): New Jersey: Litigation: White-Collar
Crime & Government Investigations **Band 1**
p.1723

**Ashman Jr, Berton W**
Profile: p.767
Table(s): Delaware: Chancery **Associates to watch**
p.758

**Ashmore, Daniel E**
Table(s): South Dakota: Labor & Employment:
Workers' Compensation **Band 1** p.2283, South
Dakota: Litigation: General Commercial **Band 2**
p.2284

**Ashmus, Keith A**
Profile: p.2089
Table(s): Ohio: Labor & Employment **Band 4**
p.2074

**Ashraf, Saba**
Profile: p.1074
Table(s): Georgia: Tax **Band 2** p.1072

**Ashton, John P**
Table(s): Utah: Litigation: General Commercial
**Band 2** p.2468

**Ashworth, John P**
Table(s): Oregon: Environment **Band 3** p.2165

**Askew, Anthony B**
Table(s): Georgia: Intellectual Property **Band 1**
p.1056

**Askew III, Jess**
Table(s): Arkansas: Litigation: General
Commercial **Band 3** p.522

**Aslani-Far, Adel**
Profile: p.1874
Table(s): New York: Corporate/M&A **Band 3**
p.1793

**Aslin, John**
Table(s): Washington: Labor & Employment
**Senior Statesmen:** p.2531

**Asmar, Charles M**
Table(s): District of Columbia: Construction **Band
2** p.795

**Asmus, David**
Profile: p.274
Table(s): Nationwide: Energy: Oil & Gas
(Transactional) **Star individuals** p.79, Nationwide:
Projects **Band 1** p.216, Texas: Corporate/M&A
**Band 4** p.2337

**Asner, Marcus**
Profile: p.1875
Table(s): New York: Litigation: White-Collar
Crime & Government Investigations **Band 3**
p.1836

**Asperger, James**
Table(s): California: Litigation: White-Collar
Crime & Government Investigations **Band 1** p.601

**Assaf, Eugene F**
Profile: p.850
Table(s): District of Columbia: Litigation:
General Commercial **Band 2** p.826

**Asselin, Thomas H**
Profile: p.1075
Table(s): Georgia: Construction **Senior Statesmen:**
p.1044

**Astigarraga, José I**
Profile: p.275
Table(s): Nationwide: International Arbitration
**Band 1** p.145

**Astle, Richard W**
Profile: p.1197
Table(s): Illinois: Energy & Natural Resources:
Transactional **Band 1** p.1161

**Atchison, W Michael**
Table(s): Alabama: Litigation: General
Commercial **Band 1** p.463

**Athanas, Josef S**
Table(s): Illinois: Bankruptcy/Restructuring **Band
2** p.1148

**Atkins, Peter Allan**
Profile: p.1875
Table(s): New York: Corporate/M&A **Band 1**
p.1793

**Atkins, Sean**
Profile: p.275
Table(s): Nationwide: Energy: Electricity
(Regulatory & Litigation) **Band 5** p.76

**Atkins, William P**
Table(s): Northern Virginia: Intellectual Property
**Band 2** p.2497

**Atkinson, Clifford K.**
Table(s): New Mexico: Litigation: General
Commercial **Band 2** p.1769

**Atkinson, Kathryn Cameron**
Profile: p.275
Table(s): Nationwide: International Trade: FCPA
Experts **Band 3** p.153

**Atkinson Jr., David R**
Table(s): Florida: Litigation: General Commercial
**Band 4** p.966

**Atlas, Harry I**
Profile: p.1424
Table(s): Maryland: Employee Benefits &
Executive Compensation **Band 2** p.1414

**Atnipp, Douglas C**
Profile: p.275
Table(s): Nationwide: Energy: Oil & Gas
(Transactional) **Band 3** p.79

**Ator, Michelle**
Profile: p.525
Table(s): Arkansas: Litigation: Medical
Malpractice Defense **Band 2** p.522

**Attai, Robert**
Table(s): Colorado: Corporate/M&A **Band 3** p.703

**Attanasio, Donna**
Profile: p.275
Table(s): Nationwide: Energy: Electricity
(Regulatory & Litigation) **Band 2** p.76

**Attridge, Daniel F**
Profile: p.850
Table(s): District of Columbia: Intellectual
Property: Litigation **Band 4** p.821

**Attwell, Gwilym**
Table(s): Delaware: Intellectual Property **Up-and-
coming individuals** p.763

**Aube, John R**
Table(s): Hawaii: Corporate/Commercial:
Finance **Band 1** p.1116, Hawaii: Real Estate **Band
2** p.1120

**Auberry, E Kent**
Profile: p.2039
Table(s): North Carolina: Corporate/M&A **Band 3**
p.2025

**Aucutt, Ronald D**
Table(s): Nationwide: Wealth Management:
Eastern Region **Band 1** p.267

**Auerbach, Dennis B**
Profile: p.850
Table(s): District of Columbia:
Bankruptcy/Restructuring **Band 4** p.792

**Auerbach, Marc H**
Profile: p.983
Table(s): Florida: Healthcare **Band 2** p.954

**Auerbach, Reed D**
Profile: p.275
Table(s): Nationwide: Capital Markets:
Securitisation **Band 1** p.59

**Aughtry, David D**
Profile: p.1075
Table(s): Nationwide: Tax: Controversy **Band 2**
p.244, Georgia: Tax **Star individuals** p.1072

**August, Adam J**
Profile: p.2508
Table(s): Northern Virginia: Corporate/M&A **Up-
and-coming individuals** p.2493

**August, Jerald David**
Profile: p.983
Table(s): Florida: Tax **Band 1** p.979

**Augustin, David R.**
Table(s): Pennsylvania: Real Estate **Band 4**
p.2208

**Augustine, Mary Jane**
Profile: p.1875
Table(s): New York: Construction **Band 2** p.1791

**Ausherman, Larry P**
Table(s): New Mexico: Environment, Natural
Resources & Regulated Industries **Band 1** p.1766

**Auslander, Mitchell J**
Profile: p.1875
Table(s): New York: Insurance: Dispute
Resolution: Policyholder **Band 3** p.1816

**Auspitz, Jack**
Profile: p.1875
Table(s): New York: Litigation: Securities **Band 2**
p.1834

**Austin, Brad**
Table(s): Iowa: Real Estate **Band 3** p.1290

**Austin, Christopher B**
Profile: p.2580
Table(s): Wisconsin: Intellectual Property **Band 3**
p.2573

**Austin, Christopher E**
Profile: p.1875
Table(s): Nationwide: Private Equity: Buyouts
**Band 5** p.203, New York: Corporate/M&A **Band 4**
p.1793

**Austin, David M**
Table(s): Maine: Corporate/M&A **Band 3** p.1385

**Austin, J Rudy**
Table(s): Virginia: Litigation: General
Commercial **Band 3** p.2502

**Austin, Jesse**
Profile: p.1075
Table(s): Georgia: Bankruptcy/Restructuring
**Band 1** p.1042

**Auvil, Steven**
Profile: p.2089
Table(s): Ohio: Intellectual Property **Band 2**
p.2071

**Avallone, Vincent N**
Profile: p.1731
Table(s): New Jersey: Labor & Employment **Band
2** p.1718

**Averch, Craig H**
Profile: p.621
Table(s): California: Bankruptcy/Restructuring
**Band 4** p.542

**Avery, Alan**
Profile: p.275
Table(s): Nationwide: Financial Services
Regulation: Banking (Compliance) **Band 4** p.96

**Avil, Richard**
Profile: p.275
Table(s): Nationwide: Energy: Oil & Gas
(Regulatory & Litigation) **Band 4** p.78

**Avila, Alcides**
Table(s): Florida: Banking & Finance: Regulatory
**Band 1** p.937, Florida: Banking & Finance:
Transactional **Band 2** p.937, Florida: Latin
American Investment **Band 2** p.963

**Aviv, Joseph**
Table(s): Michigan: Litigation: General
Commercial **Band 1** p.1544

**Avram, Randall D**
Table(s): North Carolina: Labor & Employment
**Band 2** p.2031

**Awner, Jonathan L**
Table(s): Florida: Corporate/M&A & Private
Equity **Band 1** p.947

# Index of Lawyers

**Axe, Albert**
Profile: p.2379
Table(s): Texas: Environment **Band 2** p.2343

**Axelberg, Tracy**
Table(s): Montana: Litigation: Mediators **Band 1** p.1649

**Axelrad, Alexis S**
Table(s): New York: Immigration **Band 2** p.1814

**Axelrad, David M**
Profile: p.621
Table(s): Nationwide: Appellate Law **Band 3** p.26, California: Litigation: Appellate **Band 2** p.599

**Axelrad, Jonathan**
Profile: p.275
Table(s): Nationwide: Investment Funds: Venture Capital **Band 2** p.174, California: Corporate/M&A: Venture Capital **Band 2** p.555

**Axelrod, Alan D**
Profile: p.983
Table(s): Florida: Corporate/M&A & Private Equity **Band 2** p.947

**Axelrod, David W**
Table(s): Oregon: Intellectual Property **Band 3** p.2167, Oregon: Litigation: General Commercial **Band 3** p.2171

**Axelrod, Gary**
Table(s): Nationwide: Leisure & Hospitality **Band 2** p.179, Illinois: Real Estate **Band 3** p.1187

**Axinn, Stephen**
Profile: p.1875
Table(s): New York: Antitrust **Band 2** p.1778

**Axselle Jr, Ralph L**
Table(s): Southern Virginia: Real Estate: Zoning/Land Use **Senior Statesmen**: p.2506

**Ayabe, Gail O**
Table(s): Hawaii: Real Estate **Band 2** p.1120

**Ayabe, Sidney K**
Table(s): Hawaii: Litigation: General Commercial **Band 3** p.1119

**Ayali, Noam**
Profile: p.275
Table(s): Nationwide: Projects **Band 3** p.216

**Ayanian, John V**
Profile: p.275
Table(s): Nationwide: Financial Services Regulation: Broker Dealer (Compliance) **Band 3** p.97

**Ayer, Donald**
Profile: p.276
Table(s): Nationwide: Appellate Law **Band 3** p.26

**Ayers, David L**
Profile: p.1601
Table(s): Mississippi: Litigation: General Commercial **Band 2** p.1597

**Ayers, G Randall**
Profile: p.2090
Table(s): Ohio: Labor & Employment **Band 3** p.2074

**Ayers, Gary L**
Profile: p.1299
Table(s): Kansas: Litigation: General Commercial **Band 2** p.1295

**Ayoob, Richard**
Table(s): California: Tax: State & Local **Band 2** p.617

**Ayoub, Paul**
Profile: p.1483
Table(s): Massachusetts: Real Estate **Band 3** p.1478

**Ayres, Jeffrey P**
Profile: p.1424
Table(s): Maryland: Labor & Employment **Band 1** p.1417

**Aziz, Azam**
Profile: p.276
Table(s): Nationwide: Capital Markets: Derivatives **Band 3** p.51

**Azzollini, Phillip J**
Profile: p.276
Table(s): Nationwide: Capital Markets: Structured Products **Band 3** p.52

## B

**Baach, Martin**
Table(s): District of Columbia: Insurance: Insurer **Band 2** p.816

**Baader, Michael**
Profile: p.1425
Table(s): Maryland: Corporate/M&A **Band 2** p.1412

**Baar, Lois A**
Profile: p.2472
Table(s): Utah: Labor & Employment **Band 1** p.2467

**Babb, Bryan H.**
Table(s): Indiana: Litigation: Appellate **Up-and-coming individuals** p.1273

**Babbitt, Bradford**
Profile: p.741
Table(s): Connecticut: Litigation: General Commercial **Band 3** p.738

**Babbo, Thomas**
Table(s): Illinois: Healthcare **Band 3** p.1165

**Babcock, Bruce E**
Profile: p.2472
Table(s): Utah: Labor & Employment: ERISA **Band 1** p.2467

**Babcock, Charles**
Profile: p.276
Table(s): Nationwide: First Amendment Litigation **Band 1** p.105, Nationwide: Litigation: Trial Lawyers **Band 2** p.187, Texas: Litigation: General Commercial **Band 1** p.2362

**Baber, Bruce**
Profile: p.1075
Table(s): Georgia: Intellectual Property **Band 2** p.1056

**Babineau, Anne S**
Table(s): New Jersey: Real Estate **Band 2** p.1728

**Babington, Joseph**
Profile: p.467
Table(s): Alabama: Litigation: General Commercial **Band 4** p.463

**Babson, Marshall B**
Profile: p.1875
Table(s): New York: Labor & Employment **Band 3** p.1826

**Babst III, Chester**
Table(s): Pennsylvania: Environment **Band 1** p.2194

**Baca, Elena**
Table(s): California: Labor & Employment **Band 3** p.587

**Bacchus, James**
Profile: p.276
Table(s): Nationwide: International Trade: Trade Remedies & Trade Policy **Band 4** p.154

**Bach, Jonathan**
Table(s): New York: Litigation: White-Collar Crime & Government Investigations **Band 3** p.1836

**Bach, Robert H**
Table(s): Colorado: Real Estate **Band 1** p.714

**Bachelder, Stephan G**
Table(s): Maine: Labor & Employment: Employee Benefits & Compensation **Band 1** p.1390

**Bacheller, Chester E**
Profile: p.983
Table(s): Florida: Corporate/M&A & Private Equity **Band 3** p.947

**Bachman, Gary**
Profile: p.276
Table(s): Nationwide: Energy: Electricity (Regulatory & Litigation) **Band 3** p.76

**Bachman, John Q**
Table(s): Nebraska: Real Estate **Band 2** p.1666, Nebraska: Real Estate: Zoning/Land Use **Band 2** p.1666

**Bachman, Katharine E**
Profile: p.1483
Table(s): Massachusetts: Real Estate **Band 1** p.1478

**Backstrom, William**
Profile: p.1357
Table(s): Louisiana: Corporate/M&A: Tax **Band 1** p.1341

**Backus, Marcia E**
Profile: p.276
Table(s): Nationwide: Energy: Electricity (Transactional) **Band 3** p.77, Nationwide: Energy: Oil & Gas (Transactional) **Band 1** p.77

**Bacon, Christopher V**
Profile: p.2379
Table(s): Texas: Labor & Employment **Band 3** p.2359

**Bacon, J Douglas**
Table(s): Illinois: Bankruptcy/Restructuring **Band 2** p.1148

**Bacot, Samuel A**
Profile: p.1357
Table(s): Louisiana: Real Estate **Band 2** p.1355

**Bader, Gregory K.**
Table(s): Florida: Banking & Finance: Regulatory **Band 3** p.937

**Badgerow, J Nick**
Table(s): Kansas: Labor & Employment **Band 1** p.1294, Kansas: Litigation: General Commercial **Band 2** p.1295

**Badke, Bradford J**
Table(s): New York: Intellectual Property: Patent **Band 3** p.1820

**Baecher, John**
Profile: p.276
Table(s): Nationwide: Projects **Band 4** p.216

**Baechtold, Robert L**
Profile: p.276
Table(s): Nationwide: Life Sciences: IP/Patent Litigation **Senior Statesmen**: p.183, New York: Intellectual Property: Patent **Senior Statesmen**: p.1820

**Baena, Scott L**
Profile: p.984
Table(s): Florida: Bankruptcy/Restructuring **Band 1** p.939

**Baer, John RF**
Table(s): Nationwide: Franchising **Band 1** p.111

**Bagbey, Francis C**
Profile: p.2039
Table(s): North Carolina: Real Estate **Band 2** p.2037

**Bagley, Terrence**
Table(s): Virginia: Litigation: Products Liability **Band 2** p.2502

**Bagnasacco, Barbara**
Profile: p.2472
Table(s): Utah: Corporate/M&A **Band 4** p.2462

**Bahlke, Conrad G**
Table(s): Nationwide: Capital Markets: Derivatives **Band 2** p.51

**Baier, Kelly**
Table(s): Iowa: Labor & Employment **Band 1** p.1285

**Bail, Lisa A**
Table(s): Hawaii: Real Estate: Environment **Band 2** p.1120

**Bailey, Arthur L**
Table(s): Nationwide: Tax: Controversy **Band 2** p.244, District of Columbia: Tax **Band 4** p.838

**Bailey, Benjamin**
Table(s): West Virginia: Litigation: General Commercial **Band 1** p.2555

**Bailey, Charles R**
Profile: p.2561
Table(s): West Virginia: Litigation: General Commercial **Band 3** p.2555

**Bailey, Elizabeth A.**
Profile: p.1694
Table(s): New Hampshire: Labor & Employment **Band 3** p.1688

**Bailey, John**
Table(s): Idaho: Litigation: General Commercial **Band 2** p.1134

**Bailey, John**
Table(s): Nevada: Litigation: General Commercial **Band 3** p.1677

**Bailey, K Brock**
Profile: p.2379
Table(s): **Texas: Real Estate Band 3** p.2367

**Bailey, Michael**
Profile: p.2472
Table(s): **Utah: Litigation: General Commercial
Band 3** p.2468

**Bain, Michael D**
Profile: p.1483
Table(s): **Massachusetts: Private Equity: Venture
Capital Investment Band 3** p.1474

**Baine, Kevin T**
Table(s): **Nationwide: First Amendment
Litigation Band 1** p.105, **District of Columbia:
Media & Entertainment Band 1** p.832

**Bains, Kay K**
Table(s): **Alabama: Banking & Finance Band 2**
p.455, **Alabama: Real Estate Band 2** p.466

**Bains Jr, Lee E**
Profile: p.467
Table(s): **Alabama: Litigation: General
Commercial Band 3** p.463

**Baird, Bruce**
Profile: p.276
Table(s): **Nationwide: Securities: Regulation:
Enforcement Band 2** p.233

**Baird, Joseph H**
Table(s): **Idaho: Natural Resources &
Environment Band 1** p.1136

**Baird, Stanford D**
Profile: p.2039
Table(s): **North Carolina: Environment Band 3**
p.2028

**Baish, Anthony S.**
Table(s): **Wisconsin: Litigation: General
Commercial Up-and-coming individuals** p.2576

**Baker, Andrew M**
Profile: p.2379
Table(s): **Texas: Corporate/M&A Band 1** p.2337

**Baker, Charles H**
Profile: p.276
Table(s): **Nationwide: Sports Law Band 3** p.241

**Baker, Charles S**
Profile: p.2379
Table(s): **Texas: Intellectual Property Band 3**
p.2354

**Baker, Constance H**
Profile: p.1425
Table(s): **Maryland: Healthcare Band 1** p.1415

**Baker, D J (Jan)**
Profile: p.277
Table(s): **Nationwide: Bankruptcy/Restructuring
Band 1** p.39, **New York:
Bankruptcy/Restructuring Band 1** p.1782

**Baker, David**
Table(s): **Ohio: Real Estate Band 1** p.2086

**Baker, David A**
Profile: p.277
Table(s): **Nationwide: Wealth Management:
Central Region Band 3** p.266

**Baker, Debra**
Table(s): **Texas: Environment Band 2** p.2343

**Baker, Derek J**
Profile: p.277
Table(s): **Pennsylvania:
Bankruptcy/Restructuring Band 4** p.2188

**Baker, Douglas**
Table(s): **New Mexico: Litigation: General
Commercial Band 1** p.1769

**Baker, Hayden**
Profile: p.1875
Table(s): **New York: Environment: Mainly
Transactional Up-and-coming individuals** p.1808

**Baker, James P**
Profile: p.621
Table(s): **California: Employee Benefits &
Executive Compensation Band 2** p.560

**Baker, Jean C**
Profile: p.2580
Table(s): **Wisconsin: Intellectual Property Band 1**
p.2573

**Baker, John K**
Table(s): **Arkansas: Litigation: General
Commercial Band 3** p.522

**Baker, Lewis J**
Profile: p.2508
Table(s): **Virginia: Construction Band 1** p.2491

**Baker, Mark**
Profile: p.277
Table(s): **Nationwide: International Arbitration
Band 2** p.145

**Baker, Michael**
Table(s): **Nationwide: Banking & Finance Band 4**
p.31

**Baker, Michael J**
Profile: p.621
Table(s): **California: Construction Band 3** p.550

**Baker, Miller**
Profile: p.277
Table(s): **Nationwide: Appellate Law Band 4** p.26

**Baker, Pamela**
Profile: p.1197
Table(s): **Nationwide: Employee Benefits &
Executive Compensation Band 2** p.73, **Illinois:
Labor & Employment: Employee Benefits &
Compensation Star individuals** p.1176

**Baker, Stewart**
Table(s): **Nationwide: International Trade: CFIUS
Experts Band 2** p.152

**Baker, Tammy L**
Profile: p.467
Table(s): **Alabama: Labor & Employment Band 3**
p.460

**Baker, Thomas William**
Profile: p.1075
Table(s): **Georgia: Healthcare Band 3** p.1052

**Baker, Tyler A**
Profile: p.621
Table(s): **California: Antitrust Band 2** p.536

**Baker III, William R**
Table(s): **Nationwide: Securities: Regulation:
Enforcement Band 2** p.233

**Baker Jr, William T**
Profile: p.277
Table(s): **Nationwide: Energy: Electricity
(Transactional) Senior Statesmen:** p.77

**Baker-Shenk, Philip M.**
Profile: p.277
Table(s): **Nationwide: Native American Law Band
2** p.192

**Bakke, Randall J**
Table(s): **North Dakota: Litigation: General
Commercial Band 1** p.2053

**Bakker, Jeffrey J**
Profile: p.1197
Table(s): **Illinois: Labor & Employment:
Employee Benefits & Compensation Band 2**
p.1176

**Bakker, Mark W**
Profile: p.2267
Table(s): **South Carolina: Labor & Employment
Band 3** p.2262

**Balaban, Witold**
Profile: p.277
Table(s): **Nationwide: Capital Markets:
Derivatives Band 2** p.51

**Balabanian, David M**
Profile: p.621
Table(s): **California: Litigation: General
Commercial Senior Statesmen:** p.593

**Baldauf Sr, Kent E**
Table(s): **Pennsylvania: Intellectual Property
Band 4** p.2197

**Baldiga, William R**
Table(s): **Massachusetts:
Bankruptcy/Restructuring Band 1** p.1449

**Baldner, Mike**
Table(s): **Idaho: Real Estate Band 3** p.1138

**Baldwin, Charles B**
Profile: p.1276
Table(s): **Indiana: Labor & Employment Band 1**
p.1271

**Baldwin, George**
Table(s): **Texas: Construction Band 1** p.2335

**Bale, Morgan**
Profile: p.277
Table(s): **Nationwide: Banking & Finance Band 4**
p.31

**Balfour, Clark I**
Table(s): **Oregon: Environment Band 3** p.2165

**Balick, Steven J**
Profile: p.767
Table(s): **Delaware: Intellectual Property Band 1**
p.763

**Balin, Robert**
Table(s): **Nationwide: First Amendment
Litigation Band 3** p.105

**Ball, Corinne**
Profile: p.277
Table(s): **Nationwide: Bankruptcy/Restructuring
Band 1** p.39, **New York:
Bankruptcy/Restructuring Band 1** p.1782

**Ball, Dan H**
Table(s): **Missouri: Litigation: General
Commercial Band 1** p.1629

**Ball, David A**
Profile: p.741
Table(s): **Connecticut: Litigation: General
Commercial Band 2** p.738

**Ballack, Karen N**
Profile: p.621
Table(s): **California: IT & Outsourcing Band 2**
p.583

**Ballan, Harry**
Profile: p.1875
Table(s): **New York: Tax Band 4** p.1862

**Ballantine, Douglas C**
Profile: p.1315
Table(s): **Kentucky: Litigation: General
Commercial Band 3** p.1312, **Kentucky: Litigation:
Tort & Insurance Defense Band 1** p.1312

**Ballantine, Frank D**
Profile: p.1197
Table(s): **Illinois: Corporate/M&A: Private Equity
Band 2** p.1157

**Ballantine, John T**
Profile: p.1315
Table(s): **Kentucky: Litigation: General
Commercial Senior Statesmen:** p.1312

**Ballard, Brian**
Table(s): **Idaho: Real Estate Band 1** p.1138

**Ballard, Catherine**
Table(s): **Ohio: Healthcare Band 3** p.2069

**Ballard, Wade E**
Profile: p.2267
Table(s): **South Carolina: Labor & Employment
Band 1** p.2262

**Ballati, Deborah S**
Table(s): **California: Construction Band 1** p.550

**Ballenger, J Scott**
Profile: p.277
Table(s): **Nationwide: Appellate Law Up-and-coming
individuals** p.26

**Ballis, Jon A**
Profile: p.1197
Table(s): **Illinois: Corporate/M&A: Private Equity
Band 1** p.1157

**Ballon, Ian C**
Profile: p.621
Table(s): **Nationwide: Privacy & Data Security
Band 3** p.199, **California: IT & Outsourcing Band 2**
p.583

**Ballou, Vicki A**
Profile: p.2175
Table(s): **Oregon: Intellectual Property Band 2**
p.2167

**Balloun, J Eugene**
Table(s): **Missouri: Litigation: General
Commercial Senior Statesmen:** p.1628

**Balser, David L**
Profile: p.1075
Table(s): **Georgia: Litigation: General
Commercial Band 2** p.1065

**Baltz, Raymond E**
Profile: p.1075
Table(s): **Georgia: Corporate/M&A Band 3** p.1046

**Band, Ian P**
Profile: p.850
Table(s): **District of Columbia: Immigration Band
3** p.814

**Barnes, Clemens H**
Table(s): Washington: Labor & Employment **Band 2** p.2531

**Barnes, David H**
Table(s): New Hampshire: Corporate/Commercial: Finance **Band 1** p.1685

**Barnes, Geoffrey K**
Profile: p.2090
Table(s): Ohio: Natural Resources & Environment **Band 2** p.2083

**Barnes, John Kelly**
Profile: p.2379
Table(s): Texas: Healthcare **Associates to watch** p.2347

**Barnes, Robert M**
Table(s): Missouri: Corporate/M&A **Band 2** p.1618

**Barnes Jr, Dale E**
Profile: p.622
Table(s): California: Litigation: Securities **Band 3** p.594

**Barnett, Barry C**
Table(s): Texas: Antitrust **Band 3** p.2323, Texas: Litigation: General Commercial **Band 3** p.2362

**Barnett, Benjamin R**
Profile: p.278
Table(s): Nationwide: Litigation: E-Discovery **Band 3** p.187

**Barnett, Bonnie Allyn**
Profile: p.2210
Table(s): Pennsylvania: Environment **Band 1** p.2194

**Barnett, Carol**
Table(s): Missouri: Labor & Employment **Band 3** p.1625

**Barnett, James L**
Profile: p.2472
Table(s): Utah: Labor & Employment: ERISA **Band 1** p.2467

**Barnett, Leslie**
Table(s): Florida: Tax **Band 2** p.979

**Barnett, Robert B**
Table(s): District of Columbia: Media & Entertainment **Band 2** p.832

**Barnett, Thomas O**
Profile: p.851
Table(s): District of Columbia: Antitrust **Band 2** p.787

**Barnett, Timothy M**
Profile: p.1578
Table(s): Minnesota: Corporate/M&A **Band 4** p.1569

**Barnhart, Richard A**
Table(s): Ohio: Banking & Finance **Band 3** p.2056

**Barnwell, Francis T**
Table(s): Oregon: Labor & Employment **Band 4** p.2168

**Baron, Collin**
Profile: p.741
Table(s): Connecticut: Healthcare **Band 1** p.735

**Baron, Robert**
Profile: p.278
Table(s): Nationwide: Securities: Litigation **Band 2** p.232, New York: Litigation: General Commercial **Band 2** p.1833, New York: Litigation: Securities **Band 2** p.1833

**Baron, Steven**
Table(s): Texas: Energy: State Regulatory & Litigation (Electricity) **Band 1** p.2341

**Baron Jr, Robert R**
Profile: p.2210
Table(s): Pennsylvania: Intellectual Property **Band 4** p.2197

**Baronsky, Kenneth**
Profile: p.622
Table(s): California: Corporate/M&A: Private Equity **Band 3** p.553, California: Corporate/M&A **Band 3** p.553

**Barr, Christopher J.**
Table(s): Nationwide: Energy: Oil & Gas (Regulatory & Litigation) **Band 4** p.78

**Barr, Evan**
Table(s): New York: Litigation: White-Collar Crime & Government Investigations **Band 2** p.1836

**Barr, Lynne B**
Profile: p.278
Table(s): Nationwide: Financial Services Regulation: Banking (Compliance) **Band 3** p.96, Nationwide: Financial Services Regulation: Consumer Finance (Compliance) **Band 1** p.96, Massachusetts: Banking & Finance: Corporate & Regulatory **Band 1** p.1446

**Barr, Matthew S**
Profile: p.1876
Table(s): Nationwide: Bankruptcy/Restructuring **Band 4** p.39, New York: Bankruptcy/Restructuring **Band 3** p.1782

**Barr, Michael H**
Profile: p.278
Table(s): Nationwide: Insurance: Dispute Resolution: Insurer **Band 2** p.134, New York: Insurance: Dispute Resolution: Insurer **Band 2** p.1816

**Barr, Michael R**
Profile: p.622
Table(s): California: Environment **Band 1** p.564

**Barr, Neil J**
Profile: p.1876
Table(s): New York: Tax **Band 3** p.1862

**Barr, P Douglas**
Profile: p.1315
Table(s): Kentucky: Intellectual Property **Band 2** p.1308

**Barr, Stuart A.**
Table(s): Nationwide: Capital Markets: REITs **Band 4** p.55

**Barr Jr, John H**
Profile: p.2379
Table(s): Texas: Intellectual Property **Band 3** p.2354

**Barragate, Brett**
Profile: p.2090
Table(s): Nationwide: Banking & Finance **Band 3** p.31, Ohio: Banking & Finance **Band 1** p.2056

**Barrall, James**
Table(s): Nationwide: Employee Benefits & Executive Compensation **Band 1** p.73, California: Employee Benefits & Executive Compensation **Star individuals** p.560

**Barran, Paula**
Profile: p.2175
Table(s): Oregon: Labor & Employment **Band 1** p.2168

**Barrasso, Judy Y**
Profile: p.1357
Table(s): Louisiana: Litigation: General Commercial **Band 1** p.1352

**Barrett, Gayle**
Table(s): Oklahoma: Labor & Employment **Band 2** p.2140

**Barrett, James**
Profile: p.984
Table(s): Florida: Tax **Band 1** p.979

**Barrett, James**
Profile: p.1484
Table(s): Massachusetts: Private Equity: Venture Capital Investment **Band 4** p.1474

**Barrett, Michael A**
Table(s): Washington: Real Estate **Band 1** p.2535

**Barrett, Patrick J**
Table(s): Nebraska: Labor & Employment **Band 1** p.1662

**Barrett, Terry**
Profile: p.2146
Table(s): Oklahoma: Energy & Natural Resources **Band 2** p.2136

**Barrier, W Christopher**
Table(s): Arkansas: Real Estate **Band 1** p.524

**Barriere, Brent B**
Profile: p.1357
Table(s): Louisiana: Bankruptcy/Restructuring **Band 3** p.1337, Louisiana: Litigation: General Commercial **Band 1** p.1352

**Barringer, William H**
Profile: p.279
Table(s): Nationwide: International Trade: Trade Remedies & Trade Policy **Band 1** p.154

**Barris, William G**
Table(s): Michigan: Real Estate **Band 1** p.1546

**Barron, Anthony**
Profile: p.622
Table(s): California: Construction **Band 4** p.550, California: Litigation: General Commercial **Band 5** p.593

**Barrow, Peter H**
Profile: p.1197
Table(s): Illinois: Banking & Finance **Band 2** p.1145

**Barrowes, Brooksany**
Profile: p.279
Table(s): Nationwide: Energy: Electricity (Regulatory & Litigation) **Band 4** p.76

**Barry, Andre**
Table(s): Nebraska: Litigation: General Commercial **Band 3** p.1664

**Barry, Christopher**
Table(s): Washington: Corporate/Commercial **Band 1** p.2525

**Barry, David**
Profile: p.1397
Table(s): Maine: Litigation: General Commercial **Band 3** p.1393

**Barry, Dennis M**
Profile: p.279
Table(s): Nationwide: Healthcare: Regulatory & Litigation **Band 1** p.127, District of Columbia: Healthcare **Band 1** p.809

**Barry, James R**
Table(s): Illinois: Tax **Band 3** p.1192

**Barry, John P**
Table(s): New Jersey: Labor & Employment **Band 3** p.1718

**Barry, Michael**
Profile: p.1075
Table(s): Georgia: Healthcare **Up-and-coming individuals** p.1052

**Barry Jr, Desmond T**
Table(s): Nationwide: Transportation: Aviation: Litigation **Band 1** p.254

**Barsh, Kerri**
Profile: p.984
Table(s): Florida: Environment **Band 1** p.951

**Barshay, Lawrence N**
Profile: p.279
Table(s): Nationwide: Investment Funds: Hedge Funds **Band 1** p.162, Nationwide: Investment Funds: Private Equity: Fund Formation **Band 2** p.166

**Barshay, Scott A**
Profile: p.1876
Table(s): New York: Corporate/M&A **Band 1** p.1793

**Barshefsky, Charlene**
Profile: p.279
Table(s): Nationwide: International Trade: Trade Remedies & Trade Policy **Band 1** p.154

**Barshop, Melissa**
Profile: p.622
Table(s): California: Banking & Finance **Associates to watch** p.539

**Barsky, Wayne**
Profile: p.622
Table(s): California: Intellectual Property: Patent **Band 3** p.578

**Barson, Leon R**
Profile: p.2211
Table(s): Pennsylvania: Bankruptcy/Restructuring **Band 2** p.2188

**Barsotti, Stephen C**
Table(s): Ohio: Intellectual Property **Up-and-coming individuals** p.2071

**Bart, Andrew**
Profile: p.1876
Table(s): New York: Media & Entertainment: Copyright & Contract Disputes **Band 2** p.1851

**Bart, Susan T**
Profile: p.279
Table(s): Nationwide: Wealth Management: Central Region **Band 2** p.266

**Barta, Michael J**
Table(s): District of Columbia: Litigation: White-Collar Crime & Government Investigations **Band 3** p.827

**Bartelsmeyer, Fred W**
Table(s): Missouri: Corporate/M&A **Band 2** p.1619

**Bartfeld, Daniel D**
Profile: p.1876
Table(s): Nationwide: Projects **Band 3** p.216, New York: Latin American Investment **Band 2** p.1829

**Barth, Giselle**
Profile: p.279
Table(s): Nationwide: Capital Markets: Securitisation **Up-and-coming individuals** p.59

**Bartholomew, Christian**
Profile: p.851
Table(s): District of Columbia: Litigation: Securities **Up-and-coming individuals** p.826

**Bartine, William**
Table(s): Iowa: Real Estate **Band 1** p.1290

**Bartlett, Brett C**
Profile: p.1075
Table(s): Georgia: Labor & Employment **Band 4** p.1060

**Bartlett, Maurine R**
Profile: p.279
Table(s): Nationwide: Financial Services Regulation: Broker Dealer (Compliance) **Band 3** p.97

**Bartley, Kelly D**
Profile: p.1315
Table(s): Kentucky: Environment, Natural Resources & Utilities: Environment **Associates to watch** p.1307

**Bartley, Sherry P**
Table(s): Arkansas: Litigation: General Commercial **Band 3** p.522

**Bartlit Jr, Fred**
Table(s): Nationwide: Litigation: Trial Lawyers **Senior Statesmen:** p.186, Colorado: Litigation: General Commercial **Senior Statesmen:** p.709, Illinois: Litigation: General Commercial **Senior Statesmen:** p.1180

**Bartner, Douglas**
Profile: p.1876
Table(s): New York: Bankruptcy/Restructuring **Band 3** p.1782

**Barton, Bernard**
Profile: p.984
Table(s): Florida: Tax: State & Local **Band 1** p.979

**Barton, Carl**
Profile: p.2472
Table(s): Utah: Real Estate **Band 3** p.2470

**Barton, Elizabeth C**
Profile: p.741
Table(s): Connecticut: Environment **Band 1** p.733

**Barton, Peter**
Table(s): Idaho: Natural Resources & Environment **Band 2** p.1136

**Barton, Thomas J**
Profile: p.2211
Table(s): Pennsylvania: Labor & Employment **Band 3** p.2200

**Bartrum, Thomas E**
Profile: p.2301
Table(s): Tennessee: Healthcare: Regulatory **Band 1** p.2291

**Barufka, Jack S**
Profile: p.2508
Table(s): Northern Virginia: Intellectual Property **Band 1** p.2497

**Barzilai, Laura M**
Profile: p.1876
Table(s): New York: Tax **Band 4** p.1862

**Barzoukas, Nicolas G**
Profile: p.2380
Table(s): Texas: Intellectual Property **Band 2** p.2354

**Basarrate, Armando L**
Table(s): Georgia: Healthcare **Band 2** p.1052

**Bash, Brian A**
Profile: p.2090
Table(s): Ohio: Bankruptcy/Restructuring **Band 2** p.2058

**Bash, Roy**
Table(s): Missouri: Litigation: General Commercial **Band 2** p.1628

**Bashaw, John R**
Table(s): Connecticut: Environment **Band 2** p.733

**Basich, Anthony M**
Table(s): California: Media & Entertainment: Litigation **Band 3** p.606

**Basile, Edward**
Profile: p.851
Table(s): Nationwide: Life Sciences: Regulatory/Compliance **Band 3** p.183, District of Columbia: Healthcare: Pharmaceutical/Medical Products Regulatory **Band 1** p.810

**Basile, Joseph**
Profile: p.1484
Table(s): Massachusetts: Corporate/M&A **Band 3** p.1452, Massachusetts: Private Equity: Buyouts **Band 3** p.1474

**Basile, Michael**
Table(s): Florida: Banking & Finance: Regulatory **Band 2** p.937

**Basile, Michael**
Profile: p.2561
Table(s): West Virginia: Corporate/Commercial **Band 2** p.2550

**Baskin, Stephen E.**
Table(s): District of Columbia: Intellectual Property: Litigation **Band 4** p.821

**Baskin, Stuart**
Table(s): Nationwide: Securities: Litigation **Band 3** p.232, New York: Litigation: Securities **Band 3** p.1834

**Bason Jr, George R**
Profile: p.279
Table(s): Nationwide: Financial Services Regulation: Financial Institutions M&A **Band 1** p.99, Nationwide: Private Equity: Buyouts **Band 3** p.203, New York: Corporate/M&A **Band 1** p.1793

**Bass, David**
Profile: p.1731
Table(s): New Jersey: Bankruptcy/Restructuring **Band 4** p.1705

**Bass, Fred**
Profile: p.279
Table(s): Nationwide: Banking & Finance: Equipment Finance & Leasing **Band 2** p.32, Nationwide: Transportation: Aviation: Finance **Band 2** p.252

**Bass, Hilarie**
Profile: p.984
Table(s): Florida: Litigation: General Commercial **Band 1** p.966

**Bass, Jeffrey S**
Table(s): Florida: Real Estate: Zoning/Land Use **Band 2** p.975

**Bass, Scott**
Profile: p.280
Table(s): Nationwide: Life Sciences: Regulatory/Compliance **Band 2** p.183, District of Columbia: Healthcare: Pharmaceutical/Medical Products Regulatory **Band 3** p.810

**Bass Jr, Robert C**
Profile: p.2380
Table(s): Texas: Construction **Star individuals** p.2335

**Bass Jr, Ross F**
Table(s): Mississippi: Litigation: General Commercial **Band 2** p.1597

**Basseches, Robert T**
Profile: p.280
Table(s): Nationwide: Transportation: Shipping: Regulatory (outside New York) **Senior Statesmen:** p.264

**Bassen, Ned**
Profile: p.1876
Table(s): New York: Labor & Employment **Band 3** p.1826

**Bassett, Barton**
Profile: p.622
Table(s): California: Tax **Band 3** p.617

**Bassett, David**
Profile: p.1876
Table(s): New York: Intellectual Property: Patent **Band 3** p.1820

**Bassett, Michael**
Table(s): Nationwide: Banking & Finance **Band 4** p.31

**Bassett, W Randall**
Profile: p.280
Table(s): Nationwide: Product Liability & Mass Torts **Band 5** p.208

**Bassetti, Andrew B**
Table(s): Washington: Real Estate **Band 1** p.2535

**Bast, Cynthia**
Profile: p.2380
Table(s): Texas: Real Estate **Band 3** p.2367

**Bast, Jeffrey P**
Table(s): Florida: Bankruptcy/Restructuring **Band 3** p.939

**Basta, Paul M**
Profile: p.280
Table(s): Nationwide: Bankruptcy/Restructuring **Band 2** p.39, New York: Bankruptcy/Restructuring **Band 2** p.1782

**Bastianelli III, Adrian L**
Profile: p.851
Table(s): District of Columbia: Construction **Band 1** p.795

**Baswell, Karen**
Profile: p.1876
Table(s): New York: Insurance: Dispute Resolution: Insurer **Associates to watch** p.1816

**Batchelor, Dan**
Table(s): Oklahoma: Real Estate **Band 2** p.2145

**Batchelor, Leslie V**
Table(s): Oklahoma: Real Estate **Band 2** p.2145

**Bateman, David A**
Profile: p.2538
Table(s): Washington: Intellectual Property **Band 2** p.2529

**Bateman, Randall**
Table(s): Oregon: Real Estate **Band 2** p.2173

**Bateman, Thomas**
Profile: p.280
Table(s): Nationwide: Energy: Oil & Gas (Transactional) **Band 4** p.79

**Bates, Brian K**
Table(s): Texas: Immigration **Band 1** p.2349

**Bates, David G.**
Table(s): Florida: Corporate/M&A & Private Equity **Band 2** p.947

**Bates, Douglas**
Profile: p.984
Table(s): Florida: Bankruptcy/Restructuring **Band 4** p.939

**Bates, Walter W**
Profile: p.467
Table(s): Alabama: Litigation: Medical Malpractice Defense **Band 2** p.463

**Bates Jr, Robert J**
Table(s): Illinois: Insurance: Dispute Resolution **Band 1** p.1168, Illinois: Insurance: Dispute Resolution: Reinsurance **Band 2** p.1168

**Bath, Thomas J**
Table(s): Kansas: Litigation: White-Collar Crime & Government Investigations **Band 1** p.1295

**Battcher, Fritz R**
Profile: p.1681
Table(s): Nevada: Corporate/Commercial **Band 3** p.1672

**Batten, Mark W**
Table(s): Massachusetts: Labor & Employment **Band 2** p.1466

**Batter III, John F**
Profile: p.1484
Table(s): Massachusetts: Litigation: Securities **Band 2** p.1470

**Batterman, Robert**
Table(s): Nationwide: Sports Law **Band 1** p.241

**Battista, Gregory J.**
Profile: p.1876
Table(s): New York: Environment: Mainly Transactional **Band 3** p.1808

**Battista, Paul J**
Table(s): Florida: Bankruptcy/Restructuring **Band 1** p.939

**Batty, E Jerome**
Table(s): Rhode Island: Real Estate **Band 1** p.2255

**Baty, Donald**
Table(s): Michigan: Banking & Finance: Bankruptcy **Band 2** p.1536

**Bauer, Charles P**
Table(s): New Hampshire: Litigation: General Commercial **Band 3** p.1690

**Bauer, Robert F**
Table(s): Nationwide: Government: Political Law **Band 1** p.124

**Bauer, Steven M**
Profile: p.622
Table(s): California: Litigation: White-Collar Crime & Government Investigations **Band 2** p.601

**Bauer, Steven M**
Table(s): Massachusetts: Intellectual Property **Band 1** p.1463

**Baugh, Robert R**
Profile: p.467
Table(s): Alabama: Litigation: General Commercial **Band 4** p.463

**Baum, David R**
Profile: p.1877
Table(s): New York: Media & Entertainment: Copyright & Contract Disputes **Up-and-coming individuals** p.1851

**Bauman, Mary V**
Table(s): Michigan: Employee Benefits & Executive Compensation **Band 2** p.1540

**Bauman, Todd**
Table(s): Oregon: Corporate/M&A **Band 1** p.2164

**Baumann, Frederick J**
Table(s): Colorado: Litigation: General Commercial **Band 1** p.709, Colorado: Litigation: White-Collar Crime & Government Investigations **Band 1** p.709

**Baumann, Linda**
Profile: p.851
Table(s): District of Columbia: Healthcare **Band 3** p.809

**Baumel, Jeffrey**
Profile: p.1731
Table(s): New Jersey: Corporate/M&A **Band 3** p.1707

**Baumer, Steven M**
Table(s): Missouri: Corporate/M&A **Band 3** p.1619

**Baumert, Michaelle L**
Table(s): Nebraska: Labor & Employment **Up-and-coming individuals** p.1662

**Baumgardner, John E**
Profile: p.280
Table(s): Nationwide: Investment Funds: Registered Funds **Band 1** p.170

**Baumgarten, Joseph**
Table(s): New York: Labor & Employment **Band 3** p.1826

**Bausch, James M**
Table(s): Nebraska: Litigation: General Commercial **Band 1** p.1664

**Bausch, Trenten P**
Table(s): Nebraska: Litigation: General Commercial **Band 2** p.1664

**Bautista, John**
Profile: p.622
Table(s): California: Corporate/M&A: Venture Capital **Band 4** p.555

**Baxley, C William**
Profile: p.1075
Table(s): Georgia: Corporate/M&A **Star individuals** p.1046

**Baxter, David**
Table(s): Nationwide: Energy: Electricity (Finance) **Band 1** p.75

**Baxter, John B**
Table(s): Indiana: Real Estate **Band 2** p.1275

**Baxter, Keith M**
Table(s): Wisconsin: Intellectual Property **Band 3** p.2573

**Baxter, Michael St Patrick**
Profile: p.851
Table(s): District of Columbia: Bankruptcy/Restructuring **Band 1** p.792

**Baxter, Samuel F**
Profile: p.2380
Table(s): Texas: Intellectual Property **Band 1** p.2354, Texas: Litigation: General Commercial **Band 2** p.2362

**Baxter, Tom**
Table(s): California: Banking & Finance **Band 3** p.539

**Bayer, Mark W**
Profile: p.2380
Table(s): Texas: Antitrust **Band 3** p.2323

**Bayer Jr, Jacob W**
Table(s): Missouri: Corporate/M&A **Band 3** p.1618

**Bayko, Tom**
Table(s): Texas: Litigation: Energy & Natural Resources **Band 2** p.2361, Texas: Litigation: General Commercial **Band 3** p.2361

**Bayless, David**
Profile: p.622
Table(s): California: Litigation: General Commercial **Band 5** p.593

**Bayliss, A. Thompson**
Table(s): Delaware: Chancery **Band 4** p.758

**Bayliss, William D**
Table(s): Virginia: Litigation: General Commercial **Band 1** p.2502

**Bayman, Andrew T**
Profile: p.280
Table(s): Nationwide: Product Liability & Mass Torts **Band 4** p.208

**Bayouth, Frank E**
Profile: p.2380
Table(s): Texas: Corporate/M&A **Band 3** p.2337

**Baysinger, Kara**
Profile: p.622
Table(s): California: Insurance: Insurer **Band 3** p.574

**Bayt, Phillip**
Table(s): Indiana: Real Estate **Band 1** p.1275

**Bazar, Jason S.**
Table(s): New York: Tax **Up-and-coming individuals** p.1862

**Beach, Peter T**
Profile: p.1694
Table(s): New Hampshire: Corporate/Commercial: Tax **Band 1** p.1685

**Beach, R Scott**
Profile: p.741
Table(s): Connecticut: Corporate/M&A **Band 2** p.732

**Beach Jr, Robert B**
Profile: p.525
Table(s): Arkansas: Corporate/Commercial: Municipal Bonds **Band 1** p.518

**Beale, R Daniel**
Profile: p.1076
Table(s): Georgia: Labor & Employment **Band 3** p.1060

**Beall, Christopher**
Profile: p.716
Table(s): Colorado: Intellectual Property **Band 2** p.704

**Beals, John P**
Profile: p.1484
Table(s): Massachusetts: Private Equity: Fund Formation **Band 2** p.1476, New Hampshire: Corporate/Commercial **Band 3** p.1685

**Beamon, Martine**
Profile: p.1877
Table(s): New York: Litigation: White-Collar Crime & Government Investigations **Band 3** p.1836

**Bean, Lori Ann**
Profile: p.280
Table(s): Nationwide: Projects **Band 4** p.216

**Bean, Rodney L**
Profile: p.2561
Table(s): West Virginia: Labor & Employment **Band 2** p.2553

**Beane, Jerry**
Profile: p.2380
Table(s): Texas: Antitrust **Band 1** p.2323

**Bearce, Nicole Denise**
Profile: p.1731
Table(s): New Jersey: Litigation: General Commercial **Up-and-coming individuals** p.1722

**Beard, Brian**
Table(s): Texas: Technology: Corporate & Commercial **Band 1** p.2375

**Beard, James**
Profile: p.1198
Table(s): Nationwide: Real Estate **Band 2** p.225, Illinois: Real Estate **Band 1** p.1187

**Beard III, RT**
Table(s): Arkansas: Litigation: Medical Malpractice Defense **Band 1** p.522

**Beardsley, Kate C**
Table(s): Nationwide: Life Sciences: Regulatory/Compliance **Band 1** p.183

**Bearman Jr, Leo**
Profile: p.2301
Table(s): Tennessee: Litigation: General Commercial **Band 1** p.2295

**Beasley, Jere L**
Table(s): Alabama: Litigation: Mainly Plaintiff **Band 1** p.463

**Beasley, Kathleen**
Table(s): Texas: Antitrust **Band 3** p.2323

**Beaton, Kevin**
Table(s): Idaho: Natural Resources & Environment **Band 1** p.1136

**Beattie, Nina**
Profile: p.1877
Table(s): New York: Litigation: White-Collar Crime & Government Investigations **Band 3** p.1836

**Beattie, Richard I**
Profile: p.280
Table(s): Nationwide: Private Equity: Buyouts **Senior Statesmen:** p.203, New York: Corporate/M&A **Senior Statesmen:** p.1793

**Beatty, J Robert**
Profile: p.2380
Table(s): Texas: Litigation: Energy & Natural Resources **Band 3** p.2361

**Beatty, Kim**
Table(s): Montana: Corporate/M&A **Band 2** p.1646

**Beaty, John B**
Profile: p.280
Table(s): Nationwide: Financial Services Regulation: Banking (Compliance) **Band 4** p.96

**Beaubien, Mark J**
Table(s): Illinois: Real Estate **Band 3** p.1187

**Beauchamp, David G**
Table(s): Arizona: Corporate/M&A **Band 3** p.495

**Beaudoin, Thomas A**
Profile: p.1484
Table(s): Massachusetts: Private Equity: Fund Formation **Band 2** p.1476

**Beaupain, Dean**
Table(s): Maine: Real Estate: Timberland/Conservation **Band 1** p.1396

**Beavers Jr, Charles AJ**
Table(s): Alabama: Real Estate: Zoning/Land Use **Band 1** p.466

**Beavin, C Joseph**
Profile: p.1316
Table(s): Kentucky: Labor & Employment **Band 3** p.1310

**Beber, Howard J.**
Table(s): Massachusetts: Private Equity: Fund Formation **Band 3** p.1476

**Becerra, Jacqueline**
Profile: p.984
Table(s): Florida: Litigation: General Commercial **Band 4** p.966

**Beck, David J**
Table(s): Nationwide: Litigation: Trial Lawyers **Band 1** p.187, Texas: Litigation: Energy & Natural Resources **Band 1** p.2361, Texas: Litigation: General Commercial **Band 1** p.2361

**Beck, Henry**
Table(s): Connecticut: Corporate/M&A **Band 3** p.732

**Bell, Crayton L**
Profile: p.281
Table(s): **Nationwide:** Energy: Electricity
(Transactional) **Band 3** p.77

**Bell, Jerry**
Profile: p.2380
Table(s): **Nationwide:** Healthcare: Transactional
**Band 3** p.128, **Texas:** Healthcare **Band 1** p.2347

**Bell, Katherine E.**
Table(s): **California:** Banking & Finance
**Associates to watch** p.539

**Bell, Ken**
Table(s): **North Carolina:** Litigation: White-Collar
Crime & Government Investigations **Band 1**
p.2034

**Bell, Lewis**
Profile: p.1601
Table(s): **Mississippi:** Litigation: General
Commercial **Band 4** p.1597

**Bell, Robert B**
Profile: p.851
Table(s): **District of Columbia:** Antitrust **Band 4**
p.787

**Bell, Rodney H**
Profile: p.984
Table(s): **Florida:** Corporate/M&A & Private
Equity **Band 2** p.947

**Bell, Steven**
Table(s): **Nationwide:** Transportation: Aviation:
Litigation **Band 2** p.254

**Bell, Suzanne Y**
Table(s): **California:** IT & Outsourcing **Band 1**
p.583

**Bell, Thomas**
Profile: p.281
Table(s): **Nationwide:** Investment Funds: Private
Equity: Fund Formation **Band 1** p.166

**Bell Jr, Albert R**
Table(s): **North Carolina:** Labor & Employment
**Band 2** p.2031

**Bellah Maguire, Jennifer**
Profile: p.623
Table(s): **Nationwide:** Private Equity: Buyouts
**Band 4** p.203, **California:** Corporate/M&A: Private
Equity **Band 2** p.553, **California:** Corporate/M&A
**Band 4** p.553

**Bellamy, Fredric D**
Table(s): **Arizona:** Environment (including water
rights) **Band 3** p.497

**Beller, Alan**
Profile: p.281
Table(s): **Nationwide:** Capital Markets: Debt &
Equity **Star Individuals** p.46, **Nationwide:**
Securities: Regulation: Advisory **Band 1** p.232

**Beller, Daniel J**
Profile: p.1877
Table(s): **New York:** Litigation: General
Commercial **Band 4** p.1833

**Beller, Herbert N**
Table(s): **District of Columbia:** Tax **Band 4** p.838

**Beller, Jude J.**
Table(s): **Nebraska:** Real Estate **Up-and-coming individuals** p.1666

**Belles, Michael J**
Table(s): **Hawaii:** Real Estate **Band 1** p.1120,
**Hawaii:** Real Estate: Zoning/Land Use **Band 1**
p.1120

**Bello, Kenneth**
Table(s): **Massachusetts:** Labor & Employment
**Band 4** p.1466

**Belnavis, Clarence**
Profile: p.2176
Table(s): **Oregon:** Labor & Employment **Band 2**
p.2168

**Beloff, Donn A**
Profile: p.984
Table(s): **Florida:** Corporate/M&A & Private
Equity **Band 1** p.947

**Belt, David L**
Profile: p.741
Table(s): **Connecticut:** Litigation: General
Commercial **Band 1** p.738

**Beltzer, Howard S**
Table(s): **New York:** Bankruptcy/Restructuring
**Band 4** p.1782

**Belval, Paul**
Table(s): **Nationwide:** Energy: Electricity
(Transactional) **Band 4** p.77

**Belz, Saul**
Profile: p.2301
Table(s): **Tennessee:** Litigation: General
Commercial **Band 2** p.2295

**Belzer, Irvin V**
Table(s): **Missouri:** Litigation: General
Commercial **Band 2** p.1628

**Ben-Ami, Leora**
Profile: p.282
Table(s): **Nationwide:** Life Sciences: IP/Patent
Litigation **Band 1** p.183, **New York:** Intellectual
Property: Patent **Band 1** p.1820

**Ben-Jacob, Michael**
Profile: p.282
Table(s): **Nationwide:** Wealth Management:
Eastern Region **Up-and-coming individuals** p.267

**Benach, Andres**
Table(s): **District of Columbia:** Immigration **Band 2** p.814

**Benard, Blaine**
Profile: p.2472
Table(s): **Utah:** Litigation: General Commercial
**Band 2** p.2468

**Benard, Bryan**
Profile: p.2472
Table(s): **Utah:** Labor & Employment **Band 3**
p.2467

**Benck, Jennifer**
Profile: p.1122
Table(s): **Hawaii:** Real Estate **Up-and-coming individuals** p.1120

**Bender, Jack**
Profile: p.1316
Table(s): **Kentucky:** Environment, Natural
Resources & Utilities: Environment **Band 1** p.1307

**Bender, Jay R**
Table(s): **Alabama:** Bankruptcy/Restructuring
**Band 2** p.457

**Bender, Jean**
Table(s): **South Dakota:** Labor & Employment
**Band 1** p.2283

**Bender, Jeanne Matthews**
Profile: p.1653
Table(s): **Montana:** Labor & Employment **Senior Statesmen:** p.1648

**Bender, Lawrence**
Table(s): **North Dakota:** Litigation: Energy &
Natural Resources **Band 1** p.2053

**Bender, Ron**
Table(s): **California:** Bankruptcy/Restructuring
**Band 2** p.542

**Bender, Ronald**
Table(s): **Montana:** Labor & Employment **Band 2**
p.1648, **Montana:** Litigation: General
Commercial **Band 3** p.1649

**Bender Jr, Thomas J**
Table(s): **Pennsylvania:** Labor & Employment
**Band 2** p.2200

**Bendicksen III, Perry E**
Table(s): **New Mexico:** Corporate/Commercial
**Band 1** p.1764

**Bendinger, Gary F**
Profile: p.1877
Table(s): **New York:** Litigation: Securities **Band 3**
p.1834

**Benedict, James**
Profile: p.1877
Table(s): **Nationwide:** Securities: Litigation **Band 2** p.232, **New York:** Litigation: Securities **Band 1**
p.1834

**Benedict, James E**
Table(s): **Oregon:** Environment **Band 2** p.2165

**Benedict, Philippe**
Profile: p.1877
Table(s): **New York:** Tax **Band 4** p.1862

**Benevento, Bryon J**
Table(s): **Utah:** Litigation: General Commercial
**Band 2** p.2468

**Benfield, Linda E**
Table(s): **Wisconsin:** Natural Resources &
Environment **Band 1** p.2578

**Benford, Norman J**
Profile: p.985
Table(s): **Nationwide:** Wealth Management:
Eastern Region **Band 3** p.267, **Florida:** Tax: Estate
Planning **Band 1** p.979

**Benge, Malcolm**
Table(s): **Nationwide:** Transportation: Aviation:
Regulatory **Band 3** p.256

**Bengtson, David E**
Table(s): **Kansas:** Corporate/M&A **Band 3** p.1292,
**Kansas:** Litigation: General Commercial **Band 3**
p.1295

**Benham III, Paul B**
Profile: p.525
Table(s): **Arkansas:** Corporate/Commercial **Band 2** p.518

**Benjamin, Alan**
Profile: p.623
Table(s): **California:** Banking & Finance **Band 2**
p.539

**Benjamin, James G.**
Profile: p.716
Table(s): **Colorado:** Real Estate: Construction
**Band 1** p.714

**Benjamin, Thomas M**
Table(s): **Louisiana:** Gaming & Licensing **Band 2**
p.1348

**Benjamin, Jr, James J**
Profile: p.1878
Table(s): **New York:** Litigation: White-Collar
Crime & Government Investigations **Band 1**
p.1836

**Benner, C Jonathan**
Table(s): **Nationwide:** Transportation: Shipping:
Regulatory (outside New York) **Band 1** p.264

**Bennett, Alan**
Table(s): **District of Columbia:** Healthcare:
Pharmaceutical/Medical Products Regulatory
**Band 2** p.810

**Bennett, Bruce S**
Profile: p.282
Table(s): **Nationwide:** Bankruptcy/Restructuring
**Band 1** p.39, **California:**
Bankruptcy/Restructuring **Band 1** p.542

**Bennett, Crocker**
Table(s): **Vermont:** Litigation: General
Commercial **Band 2** p.2486

**Bennett, David M**
Profile: p.2380
Table(s): **Texas:** Bankruptcy/Restructuring **Band 2**
p.2328

**Bennett, Frank B**
Table(s): **Minnesota:** Corporate/M&A **Band 3**
p.1569

**Bennett, Herbert B.**
Table(s): **New Jersey:** Environment **Band 3** p.1711

**Bennett, J David**
Table(s): **Oregon:** Real Estate **Band 2** p.2173

**Bennett, Jackie**
Profile: p.1276
Table(s): **Indiana:** Litigation: General
Commercial **Band 3** p.1273

**Bennett, Jim**
Profile: p.1635
Table(s): **Missouri:** Litigation: General
Commercial **Band 2** p.1629, **Missouri:** Litigation:
White-Collar Crime & Government Investigations
**Band 3** p.1629

**Bennett, John K**
Profile: p.1731
Table(s): **New Jersey:** Labor & Employment **Band 2** p.1718

**Bennett, Lynda**
Profile: p.1731
Table(s): **New Jersey:** Litigation: Insurance **Band 1** p.1723

**Bennett, Mark J**
Profile: p.1122
Table(s): **Hawaii:** Litigation: General Commercial
**Band 1** p.1119

**Bennett, Mary**
Profile: p.851
Table(s): **District of Columbia:** Tax **Band 4** p.838

**Bennett, Michael P**
Profile: p.1198
Table(s): **Illinois:** Technology & Outsourcing **Band 3** p.1194

**Bennett, Peter**
Table(s): **Maine:** Labor & Employment **Band 3** p.1390

**Bennett, Robert S**
Table(s): **District of Columbia:** Litigation: White-Collar Crime & Government Investigations **Band 1** p.827

**Bennett, Thomas G**
Profile: p.2472
Table(s): **Utah:** Real Estate **Band 2** p.2470

**Bennett, Wm Blake**
Table(s): **Louisiana:** Banking & Finance **Band 3** p.1335, **Louisiana:** Banking & Finance: Marine Finance **Band 1** p.1335

**Bennett Jr, Charles R**
Profile: p.1484
Table(s): **Massachusetts:** Bankruptcy/Restructuring **Band 2** p.1449

**Benoit, Wilfred J**
Profile: p.1484
Table(s): **Massachusetts:** Labor & Employment **Band 1** p.1466

**Benshoof, Ward L**
Profile: p.623
Table(s): **California:** Environment **Band 4** p.564

**Benson, Amy**
Table(s): **Colorado:** Litigation: General Commercial **Up-and-coming individuals** p.709

**Benson, Jeffrey A**
Table(s): **North Carolina:** Real Estate **Band 2** p.2037

**Benson, Matthew H**
Table(s): **New Hampshire:** Corporate/Commercial **Band 3** p.1685

**Benson, Robert E**
Profile: p.716
Table(s): **Colorado:** Real Estate: Construction **Senior Statesmen:** p.714

**Bentivoglio, John T**
Profile: p.851
Table(s): **District of Columbia:** Healthcare: Pharmaceutical/Medical Products Regulatory **Band 2** p.810

**Bentley, Kassandra**
Profile: p.2146
Table(s): **Oklahoma:** Corporate/Commercial **Associates to watch** p.2134

**Benton, Mary T**
Profile: p.1076
Table(s): **Georgia:** Tax **Band 3** p.1072

**Benudiz, P Peter**
Profile: p.282
Table(s): **Nationwide:** Leisure & Hospitality **Band 1** p.179, **California:** Real Estate **Band 2** p.611

**Benvenutti, Peter J**
Profile: p.623
Table(s): **California:** Bankruptcy/Restructuring **Band 2** p.542

**Beran, Richard**
Profile: p.1731
Table(s): **New Jersey:** Litigation: General Commercial **Band 3** p.1722

**Berberian, H Nicholas**
Profile: p.1198
Table(s): **Illinois:** Litigation: General Commercial **Band 3** p.1180

**Bercow, Jeffrey**
Table(s): **Florida:** Real Estate: Zoning/Land Use **Band 1** p.975

**Bercun Bohm, Stacy**
Table(s): **Florida:** Construction **Band 3** p.944

**Berens, Kelvin C**
Profile: p.1667
Table(s): **Nebraska:** Labor & Employment **Band 3** p.1662

**Berenstain, Ronald L**
Table(s): **Washington:** Litigation: General Commercial **Band 3** p.2533

**Berenstein, Marvin**
Table(s): **Iowa:** Corporate/M&A **Band 2** p.1283

**Berenter, Steven**
Table(s): **Idaho:** Labor & Employment **Band 1** p.1132

**Beres, Joel T**
Profile: p.1316
Table(s): **Kentucky:** Intellectual Property **Band 1** p.1308

**Berg, Andrew**
Table(s): **New York:** Tax **Band 4** p.1862

**Berg, Eric L**
Profile: p.282
Table(s): **Nationwide:** Banking & Finance **Band 1** p.31

**Berg, Robert N**
Table(s): **Georgia:** Healthcare **Band 2** p.1052

**Berg, Sara**
Table(s): **Montana:** Litigation: General Commercial **Band 4** p.1649

**Bergdolt, Robert H**
Profile: p.282
Table(s): **Nationwide:** Capital Markets: REITs **Band 4** p.55

**Berge, Amy B**
Profile: p.1316
Table(s): **Kentucky:** Intellectual Property **Band 2** p.1308

**Berge, Bradford**
Profile: p.1773
Table(s): **New Mexico:** Litigation: General Commercial **Band 2** p.1769

**Berger, Arthur B**
Table(s): **Utah:** Intellectual Property **Band 2** p.2466

**Berger, Bill**
Table(s): **Colorado:** Labor & Employment **Band 3** p.706

**Berger, David**
Table(s): **Florida:** Immigration **Band 3** p.956

**Berger, Donald I**
Table(s): **California:** Real Estate **Band 3** p.611

**Berger, Frances C.**
Table(s): **New York:** Immigration **Band 3** p.1814

**Berger, James L**
Profile: p.985
Table(s): **Florida:** Real Estate **Band 3** p.974

**Berger, Max W**
Profile: p.1878
Table(s): **Nationwide:** Securities: Litigation: Mainly Plaintiff **Star individuals** p.234, **New York:** Litigation: Securities Mainly Plaintiff **Star individuals** p.1835

**Berger, Mitchell W**
Profile: p.985
Table(s): **Florida:** Litigation: General Commercial **Band 3** p.966

**Berger, Paul**
Table(s): **Nationwide:** Securities: Regulation: Enforcement **Band 1** p.233

**Berger, Ritchie**
Table(s): **Vermont:** Litigation: General Commercial **Band 1** p.2486

**Berger, Scott A**
Profile: p.1878
Table(s): **New York:** Real Estate: Corporate **Band 3** p.1854

**Berger, Stephen L**
Profile: p.1198
Table(s): **Illinois:** Real Estate **Band 3** p.1187

**Bergère, Timothy J**
Table(s): **Pennsylvania:** Environment **Band 2** p.2194

**Bergeron, Keith J**
Table(s): **Louisiana:** Construction **Band 2** p.1339

**Bergeson, Donna P**
Profile: p.1076
Table(s): **Georgia:** Healthcare **Band 3** p.1052

**Bergeson, Lynn L**
Profile: p.852
Table(s): **District of Columbia:** Environment **Band 1** p.804

**Berggren, Tom**
Profile: p.2472
Table(s): **Utah:** Real Estate **Band 2** p.2470

**Bergin, Edward H**
Profile: p.1358
Table(s): **Louisiana:** Energy & Natural Resources: Utilities **Band 1** p.1344

**Berglund II, James**
Profile: p.2380
Table(s): **Texas:** Antitrust **Band 3** p.2323

**Bergman, Nicholas J**
Table(s): **Nationwide:** Food & Beverages: Alcohol **Band 2** p.109

**Bergstrom, Brian D**
Table(s): **Iowa:** Corporate/M&A **Band 3** p.1283

**Bergstrom, Rick**
Profile: p.623
Table(s): **California:** Labor & Employment **Band 4** p.587

**Bergstrom, Thomas A**
Profile: p.2211
Table(s): **Pennsylvania:** Litigation: White-Collar Crime & Government Investigations **Band 1** p.2204

**Berhold, Jeffrey L**
Table(s): **Georgia:** Antitrust **Band 3** p.1037

**Beringer, Ashlie**
Profile: p.282
Table(s): **Nationwide:** Privacy & Data Security **Up-and-coming individuals** p.199

**Berke, Barry H**
Profile: p.282
Table(s): **Nationwide:** Litigation: Trial Lawyers **Band 1** p.187, **New York:** Litigation: General Commercial **Band 2** p.1833, **New York:** Litigation: White-Collar Crime & Government Investigations **Band 1** p.1833

**Berke, Elliot**
Table(s): **Nationwide:** Government: Political Law **Band 3** p.124

**Berkeley, Jill B**
Profile: p.1198
Table(s): **Nationwide:** Insurance: Dispute Resolution: Policyholder **Band 3** p.137, **Illinois:** Insurance: Dispute Resolution **Band 1** p.1168

**Berkman, Jerome**
Profile: p.742
Table(s): **Connecticut:** Real Estate **Band 1** p.740

**Berkoff, Mark A**
Profile: p.1198
Table(s): **Illinois:** Bankruptcy/Restructuring **Band 2** p.1148

**Berkowitz, Alan D**
Profile: p.2211
Table(s): **Pennsylvania:** Labor & Employment **Band 1** p.2200

**Berkowitz, Philip M**
Table(s): **New York:** Labor & Employment **Band 4** p.1826

**Berkowitz, Sean M**
Table(s): **Illinois:** Litigation: General Commercial **Band 2** p.1180, **Illinois:** Litigation: White-Collar Crime & Government Investigations **Band 1** p.1180

**Berkowitz, William N**
Profile: p.1484
Table(s): **Massachusetts:** Antitrust **Band 1** p.1444

**Berlin, Howard J**
Profile: p.985
Table(s): **Florida:** Bankruptcy/Restructuring **Band 3** p.939

**Berlin, Seth D**
Profile: p.852
Table(s): **District of Columbia:** Media & Entertainment **Band 2** p.832

**Berlin, Stephen R**
Table(s): **North Carolina:** Environment **Band 2** p.2028

**Berman, Brad L**
Profile: p.282
Table(s): **Nationwide:** Transportation: Shipping: Finance (New York) **Band 2** p.260

**Berman, Bruce J**
Profile: p.985
Table(s): **Florida:** Litigation: General Commercial **Band 4** p.966

**Berman, David**
Table(s): **Massachusetts:** Banking & Finance **Band 1** p.1445

**Berman, Garry C**
Profile: p.742
Table(s): **Connecticut:** Real Estate **Band 1** p.740

**Berman, Jeffrey**
Profile: p.623
Table(s): **California:** Labor & Employment **Band 2** p.587

**Berman, Kenneth J**
Table(s): **Nationwide:** Investment Funds: Registered Funds **Band 2** p.170

**Berman, Mark N**
Profile: p.1484
Table(s): **Massachusetts:** Bankruptcy/Restructuring **Band 2** p.1449

**Berman, Michael P**
Table(s): **Arizona:** Labor & Employment **Band 4** p.499

**Berman, Stan**
Profile: p.282
Table(s): **Nationwide:** Energy: Electricity (Regulatory & Litigation) **Band 4** p.76

**Bermann, George A**
Table(s): **Nationwide:** International Arbitration: Arbitrators **Band 1** p.146

**Bernard, G Wogan**
Profile: p.1358
Table(s): **Louisiana:** Banking & Finance **Associates to watch** p.1335

**Bernard, J Michael**
Table(s): **Michigan:** Corporate/M&A **Band 2** p.1538

**Berne, Gary**
Table(s): **Oregon:** Litigation: General Commercial **Band 1** p.2171

**Berner, Donald**
Profile: p.1299
Table(s): **Kansas:** Labor & Employment **Band 3** p.1294

**Bernick, Carol**
Table(s): **Oregon:** Labor & Employment **Band 1** p.2168

**Berns, Sheldon**
Table(s): **Ohio:** Real Estate: Zoning/Land Use **Band 2** p.2086

**Bernstein, Andrew**
Profile: p.1878
Table(s): **New York:** Employee Benefits & Executive Compensation **Band 3** p.1802

**Bernstein, David**
Table(s): **Nationwide:** Advertising: Litigation **Band 2** p.19, **New York:** Intellectual Property: Trade Mark & Copyright **Band 1** p.1821

**Bernstein, Donald S**
Profile: p.282
Table(s): **Nationwide:** Bankruptcy/Restructuring **Band 1** p.39, **New York:** Bankruptcy/Restructuring **Band 1** p.1782

**Bernstein, Glen S**
Profile: p.283
Table(s): **Nationwide:** Energy: Electricity (Regulatory & Litigation) **Band 5** p.76

**Bernstein, H Bruce**
Profile: p.1198
Table(s): **Illinois:** Banking & Finance **Senior Statesmen:** p.1145

**Bernstein, Howard L**
Profile: p.1198
Table(s): **Illinois:** Labor & Employment **Band 2** p.1175

**Bernstein, Jay L**
Profile: p.283
Table(s): **Nationwide:** Capital Markets: REITs **Band 1** p.55

**Bernstein, Kevin M**
Profile: p.1878
Table(s): **New York:** Environment **Band 2** p.1807

**Bernstein, Leonard A**
Table(s): **Pennsylvania:** Banking & Finance: Mainly Regulatory **Band 1** p.2186

**Bernstein, Michael**
Profile: p.852
Table(s): **District of Columbia:** Bankruptcy/Restructuring **Band 1** p.792

**Bernstein, Michael I**
Profile: p.1878
Table(s): **New York:** Labor & Employment **Senior Statesmen:** p.1826

**Bernstein, Stanley**
Table(s): **Nationwide:** Securities: Litigation: Mainly Plaintiff **Band 2** p.234, **New York:** Litigation: Securities Mainly Plaintiff **Band 2** p.1835

**Bernstein, Stephen W**
Profile: p.1484
Table(s): **Nationwide:** Healthcare: Transactional **Band 2** p.128, **Massachusetts:** Healthcare **Band 1** p.1460

**Bernstein, Steve**
Profile: p.985
Table(s): **Florida:** Labor & Employment **Band 4** p.959

**Bernstein, Steven K**
Profile: p.852
Table(s): **District of Columbia:** Antitrust **Band 4** p.787

**Bernstein, Warren J**
Profile: p.1878
Table(s): **New York:** Real Estate: Finance **Band 2** p.1855

**Bernstein, William S**
Table(s): **Nationwide:** Healthcare: Regulatory & Litigation **Band 3** p.127, **New York:** Healthcare **Band 1** p.1811

**Bernthal, Eric L**
Profile: p.852
Table(s): **District of Columbia:** Media & Entertainment **Band 3** p.832, **District of Columbia:** Media & Entertainment: Mainly Regulatory **Band 2** p.832

**Berrie, Peter**
Table(s): **Minnesota:** Real Estate **Band 3** p.1576

**Berrios, Ariel**
Profile: p.623
Table(s): **California:** Banking & Finance **Band 4** p.539

**Berrodin, Frank**
Table(s): **Michigan:** Employee Benefits & Executive Compensation **Band 3** p.1540

**Berry, David P**
Table(s): **Nationwide:** Immigration **Band 2** p.131, **California:** Immigration **Band 2** p.571

**Berry, Jennifer L. Ivester**
Profile: p.2146
Table(s): **Oklahoma:** Real Estate **Band 2** p.2145

**Berry, John V**
Table(s): **Arizona:** Real Estate: Zoning/Land Use **Band 1** p.504

**Berry, Leo**
Table(s): **Montana:** Natural Resources & Environment **Band 2** p.1651

**Berry, Mark W**
Table(s): **Washington:** Labor & Employment **Band 3** p.2531

**Berry IV, C Dewees**
Profile: p.2301
Table(s): **Tennessee:** Real Estate **Band 1** p.2299, **Tennessee:** Real Estate: Zoning/Land Use **Band 1** p.2299

**Berryman, Cathryn A**
Profile: p.2381
Table(s): **Texas:** Intellectual Property: Trade Mark & Copyright **Band 2** p.2354

**Bershad, Russell B**
Table(s): **New Jersey:** Real Estate **Band 1** p.1728

**Berson, Bennett J**
Profile: p.2581
Table(s): **Wisconsin:** Intellectual Property **Band 3** p.2573

**Berson, Susan**
Profile: p.852
Table(s): **District of Columbia:** Healthcare **Band 3** p.809

**Berthou, Erica**
Table(s): **Nationwide:** Investment Funds: Private Equity: Fund Formation **Band 3** p.166

**Berz, David**
Profile: p.852
Table(s): **District of Columbia:** Environment: Mainly Transactional **Band 1** p.805

**Berzon, David**
Table(s): **Illinois:** Real Estate **Band 3** p.1187

**Beshar, Sarah**
Profile: p.283
Table(s): **Nationwide:** Capital Markets: Debt & Equity **Band 3** p.46

**Bessette-Smith, Suzanne**
Table(s): **Illinois:** Real Estate **Band 2** p.1187

**Best, Edward S**
Table(s): **Nationwide:** Capital Markets: Debt & Equity **Band 3** p.46, **Illinois:** Insurance: Transactional & Regulatory **Band 3** p.1168

**Best, J Donald**
Profile: p.2581
Table(s): **Wisconsin:** Intellectual Property **Band 3** p.2573, **Wisconsin:** Intellectual Property: Litigation p.2573

**Best, Stephen A**
Table(s): **District of Columbia:** Litigation: White-Collar Crime & Government Investigations **Band 4** p.827

**Bestol, Kay Lynn**
Table(s): **Wyoming:** Litigation: General Commercial **Band 3** p.2598

**Betensky, Gary**
Profile: p.985
Table(s): **Florida:** Litigation: General Commercial **Band 4** p.966

**Betow, Gary**
Table(s): **Oklahoma:** Corporate/Commercial **Band 3** p.2134

**Bettencourt, Mark T**
Profile: p.1484
Table(s): **Massachusetts:** Corporate/M&A **Band 2** p.1452

**Bettilyon, Mark M**
Table(s): **Utah:** Intellectual Property **Band 2** p.2466

**Bettinger, Michael**
Profile: p.623
Table(s): **California:** Intellectual Property: Patent **Band 4** p.578

**Bettis, Vance J**
Table(s): **South Carolina:** Labor & Employment **Band 2** p.2262

**Betts, Rebecca A**
Table(s): **West Virginia:** Litigation: General Commercial **Band 2** p.2555, **West Virginia:** Litigation: Mass Tort **Band 1** p.2555

**Betzen, Mark E**
Profile: p.2381
Table(s): **Texas:** Corporate/M&A **Band 2** p.2337

**Beulick, John**
Table(s): **Missouri:** Intellectual Property **Band 3** p.1623

**Beus, Karl**
Profile: p.2090
Table(s): **Ohio:** Banking & Finance **Band 3** p.2056

**Beus, Leo R**
Table(s): **Arizona:** Litigation: General Commercial **Band 2** p.501

**Bevan III, William**
Table(s): **Pennsylvania:** Labor & Employment **Band 2** p.2200

**Bever, Thomas Dean**
Table(s): **Georgia:** Litigation: White-Collar Crime & Government Investigations **Band 2** p.1066

**Beveridge, Cathy**
Table(s): **Florida:** Labor & Employment **Band 2**
p.959

**Beveridge, David**
Table(s): **Nationwide:** Capital Markets: Debt &
Equity **Band 3** p.46

**Bevilacqua, Louis J**
Profile: p.1878
Table(s): **New York:** Corporate/M&A **Band 5**
p.1793

**Bevilacqua, Michael J**
Profile: p.1485
Table(s): **Massachusetts:** Intellectual Property:
Licensing **Band 1** p.1463

**Bey, Sheryl**
Profile: p.1601
Table(s): **Mississippi:** Litigation: General
Commercial **Band 4** p.1597

**Beyda, Richard**
Table(s): **District of Columbia:** Real Estate **Senior
Statesmen:** p.835

**Beyer, David**
Profile: p.283
Table(s): **Nationwide:** Franchising **Band 4** p.111

**Beyer, Ruth**
Table(s): **Oregon:** Corporate/M&A **Band 1** p.2164

**Beyer, Timothy R**
Table(s): **Colorado:** Litigation: General
Commercial **Band 2** p.709

**Bezet, Gary A**
Profile: p.1358
Table(s): **Louisiana:** Litigation: General
Commercial **Band 3** p.1352

**Bezold, Richard**
Table(s): **Florida:** Real Estate **Band 4** p.974

**Biagini, Ray**
Profile: p.283
Table(s): **Nationwide:** Government: Government
Contracts **Band 4** p.117

**Bialick, Mark**
Table(s): **Oklahoma:** Litigation: General
Commercial **Band 2** p.2141

**Bianchi, Alden J**
Profile: p.1485
Table(s): **Nationwide:** Employee Benefits &
Executive Compensation **Band 3** p.73,
**Massachusetts:** Employee Benefits & Executive
Compensation **Band 1** p.1455

**Biasetti, Jon**
Profile: p.1199
Table(s): **Illinois:** Insurance: Transactional &
Regulatory **Band 2** p.1168

**Bibb, Julian L**
Profile: p.2301
Table(s): **Tennessee:** Banking & Finance **Band 1**
p.2287, **Tennessee:** Real Estate **Band 2** p.2299

**Bible, Paul**
Table(s): **Nevada:** Gaming & Licensing **Band 2**
p.1674

**Bibler, Gregory A**
Profile: p.1485
Table(s): **Massachusetts:** Environment **Band 1**
p.1457

**Bice, Todd L**
Table(s): **Nevada:** Litigation: General
Commercial **Band 2** p.1677

**Bice, William B**
Profile: p.283
Table(s): **Nationwide:** Projects **Band 2** p.216

**Bick, John**
Profile: p.1878
Table(s): **New York:** Corporate/M&A **Band 5**
p.1793

**Bickel, John**
Table(s): **Nationwide:** Leisure & Hospitality **Band
4** p.179

**Bickel, John M**
Table(s): **Iowa:** Litigation: General Commercial
**Band 4** p.1288

**Bickerstaff, Alan**
Profile: p.2381
Table(s): **Texas:** Technology: Corporate &
Commercial **Band 3** p.2375

**Bickerton, James J**
Table(s): **Hawaii:** Litigation: General Commercial
**Band 2** p.1119

**Bickford IV, Warren F**
Table(s): **Oklahoma:** Litigation: General
Commercial **Band 3** p.2141

**Bicks, Peter A**
Profile: p.283
Table(s): **Nationwide:** Product Liability & Mass
Torts **Band 2** p.208, **Nationwide:** Product Liability:
Toxic Torts p.208

**Bidart, Michael J**
Table(s): **California:** Insurance: Policyholder **Band
4** p.576

**Biegel, Adam J**
Profile: p.1076
Table(s): **Georgia:** Antitrust **Band 2** p.1037

**Biek, John A**
Profile: p.1199
Table(s): **Illinois:** Tax **Band 3** p.1192

**Bieke, James R**
Profile: p.852
Table(s): **District of Columbia:** Environment **Band
3** p.804

**Bienenstock, Martin J**
Table(s): **Nationwide:** Bankruptcy/Restructuring
**Band 1** p.39, **New York:**
Bankruptcy/Restructuring **Band 1** p.1782

**Bienstock, Floyd P**
Table(s): **Arizona:** Litigation: General
Commercial **Band 3** p.501

**Bierce, William B**
Profile: p.1878
Table(s): **New York:** Technology & Outsourcing
**Band 3** p.1868

**Bierig, Jack R**
Profile: p.1199
Table(s): **Illinois:** Antitrust **Band 3** p.1143

**Bierman, Ivy Kagan**
Profile: p.623
Table(s): **California:** Labor & Employment **Band 3**
p.587

**Biesterfeld, Craig**
Table(s): **Missouri:** Real Estate **Band 2** p.1633

**Bigel, Mitchell S.**
Table(s): **North Carolina:** Intellectual Property
**Band 1** p.2030

**Biggio, Charles E**
Table(s): **New York:** Antitrust **Band 5** p.1778

**Biggs, Jude**
Profile: p.717
Table(s): **Colorado:** Labor & Employment **Band 2**
p.706

**Bigler, C Stephen**
Profile: p.767
Table(s): **Delaware:** Corporate/M&A **Band 2** p.761

**Biles, Blake A**
Profile: p.852
Table(s): **District of Columbia:** Environment **Band
2** p.804

**Bilitski, Deborah A**
Profile: p.1316
Table(s): **Kentucky:** Real Estate: Zoning/Land
Use **Band 1** p.1314

**Bilkis, David**
Profile: p.283
Table(s): **Nationwide:** Banking & Finance **Band 3**
p.31

**Billings, Peter W**
Table(s): **Utah:** Litigation: General Commercial
**Band 2** p.2468

**Bilzin, Brian L**
Profile: p.985
Table(s): **Florida:** Real Estate **Band 1** p.974

**Binhak, Stephen J**
Table(s): **Florida:** Litigation: White-Collar Crime &
Government Investigations **Band 3** p.967

**Binnig, Christian F**
Table(s): **Illinois:** Communications **Band 2** p.1153

**Birchall, James L**
Profile: p.468
Table(s): **Alabama:** Banking & Finance: Public
Finance **Band 1** p.455

**Birchfield, Thomas J**
Profile: p.1316
Table(s): **Kentucky:** Labor & Employment **Band 2**
p.1310

**Birchfield Jr, Andy**
Table(s): **Nationwide:** Product Liability: Plaintiffs
**Band 3** p.209

**Bird, Geron J**
Table(s): **Kansas:** Litigation: General
Commercial **Up-and-coming individuals** p.1295

**Bird, Kelly Ann**
Table(s): **New Jersey:** Labor & Employment **Band
3** p.1718

**Bird, Paul S**
Table(s): **Nationwide:** Private Equity: Buyouts
**Band 2** p.203, **New York:** Corporate/M&A **Band 3**
p.1793

**Bird, Terry W**
Profile: p.283
Table(s): **Nationwide:** Litigation: Trial Lawyers
**Senior Statesmen:** p.186, **California:** Litigation:
White-Collar Crime & Government Investigations
**Senior Statesmen:** p.601

**Birenbaum, Charles S**
Profile: p.624
Table(s): **California:** Labor & Employment **Band 4**
p.587

**Birkenstock, Joseph**
Table(s): **Nationwide:** Government: Political Law
**Band 2** p.124

**Birley, Cindy**
Profile: p.717
Table(s): **Colorado:** Labor & Employment:
Employee Benefits & Compensation **Band 2**
p.706

**Birnbaum, Gary L**
Profile: p.507
Table(s): **Arizona:** Litigation: General
Commercial **Band 1** p.501

**Birnbaum, Sheila L**
Profile: p.283
Table(s): **Nationwide:** Product Liability & Mass
Torts **Star individuals** p.208

**Birnkrant, Henry**
Profile: p.852
Table(s): **District of Columbia:** Tax **Band 4** p.838

**Biron, Thomas E**
Profile: p.2211
Table(s): **Pennsylvania:**
Bankruptcy/Restructuring **Band 1** p.2188

**Birsic, Thomas E**
Profile: p.2211
Table(s): **Pennsylvania:** Litigation: General
Commercial **Band 3** p.2203

**Bisbee, Dana**
Table(s): **New Hampshire:** Environment **Band 2**
p.1687

**Bisceglia, Joseph G**
Profile: p.1199
Table(s): **Illinois:** Construction **Band 2** p.1154

**Biser, Sarah**
Profile: p.1879
Table(s): **New York:** Construction **Band 3** p.1791

**Bisgaier, Carl S**
Table(s): **New Jersey:** Real Estate: Zoning/Land
Use **Band 1** p.1728

**Bishop, Bruce T**
Table(s): **Virginia:** Litigation: Products Liability
**Band 1** p.2502

**Bishop, Cynthia J**
Table(s): **Texas:** Environment **Band 3** p.2343

**Bishop, Doak**
Profile: p.283
Table(s): **Nationwide:** International Arbitration
**Band 1** p.145, **Texas:** Litigation: General
Commercial **Band 3** p.2362

**Bishop, Jeannine T**
Table(s): **Pennsylvania:** Real Estate **Up-and-coming
individuals** p.2208

**Bishop, L Randall**
Table(s): Montana: Litigation: Mainly Plaintiff
**Band 1** p.1649

**Bishop, Leah M**
Profile: p.624
Table(s): **Nationwide:** Wealth Management:
Western Region **Band 1** p.267, **California:** Tax:
Estate Planning **Star individuals** p.617

**Bishop, Martin**
Table(s): **Illinois:** Litigation: General Commercial
**Band 4** p.1180

**Bishop, Timothy S**
Table(s): **Illinois:** Environment: Litigation **Band 1**
p.1162

**Bishop III, George W**
Profile: p.2301
Table(s): **Tennessee:** Healthcare **Band 1** p.2291

**Biskind, Neil**
Table(s): **Arizona:** Real Estate **Band 2** p.504

**Bissinger, Charles**
Profile: p.2090
Table(s): **Ohio:** Real Estate **Band 4** p.2086

**Bistram, Gregory**
Profile: p.1578
Table(s): **Minnesota:** Construction **Band 1** p.1567

**Bithell, Walter**
Profile: p.1138
Table(s): **Idaho:** Litigation: General Commercial
**Band 1** p.1134

**Bittman, Michael J**
Table(s): **Florida:** Healthcare **Band 2** p.954

**Bivens, Donald**
Table(s): **Arizona:** Litigation: General
Commercial **Band 3** p.501

**Bixenstine, Barton A**
Profile: p.2090
Table(s): **Ohio:** Labor & Employment **Band 2**
p.2074

**Bixler, Albert G**
Table(s): **Pennsylvania:** Litigation: General
Commercial **Band 4** p.2203

**Bizar, Steven E**
Profile: p.2211
Table(s): **Pennsylvania:** Antitrust **Band 1** p.2184,
**Pennsylvania:** Litigation: General Commercial
**Band 3** p.2203

**Bjerke, Bruce**
Table(s): **Washington:** Corporate/Commercial
**Band 2** p.2525

**Bjork, Jeffrey E**
Profile: p.624
Table(s): **California:** Bankruptcy/Restructuring
**Band 3** p.542

**Black, Allen**
Profile: p.284
Table(s): **Nationwide:** Transportation: Shipping:
Regulatory (outside New York) **Band 2** p.264

**Black, Allen**
Table(s): **Pennsylvania:** Antitrust **Senior Statesmen:**
p.2184, **Pennsylvania:** Litigation: General
Commercial **Band 3** p.2203

**Black, Amos**
Table(s): **Oklahoma:** Native American Law **Band 3**
p.2144

**Black, Carl E**
Profile: p.2090
Table(s): **Ohio:** Bankruptcy/Restructuring **Band 4**
p.2058

**Black, Daniel H**
Profile: p.624
Table(s): **California:** Media & Entertainment:
Transactional **Band 3** p.608

**Black, David**
Profile: p.284
Table(s): **Nationwide:** Government: Government
Contracts **Band 4** p.117

**Black, David**
Profile: p.985
Table(s): **Florida:** Corporate/M&A & Private
Equity **Associates to watch** p.947

**Black, Edward**
Table(s): **Massachusetts:** Intellectual Property
**Band 3** p.1463

**Black, Josiah M**
Table(s): **Massachusetts:** Labor & Employment
**Band 4** p.1466

**Black, Kathryn A**
Profile: p.492
Table(s): **Alaska:** Corporate/M&A **Band 1** p.487,
**Alaska:** Real Estate **Band 1** p.491

**Black, Kenneth B**
Table(s): **Utah:** Intellectual Property **Band 3**
p.2466, **Utah:** Litigation: General Commercial
**Band 2** p.2468

**Black, Margaret F**
Profile: p.1731
Table(s): **New Jersey:** Real Estate **Band 2** p.1728

**Black, Martin J**
Profile: p.2211
Table(s): **Pennsylvania:** Intellectual Property
**Band 2** p.2197

**Black, Roy**
Table(s): **Florida:** Litigation: White-Collar Crime &
Government Investigations **Star individuals** p.967

**Black Franzoni, Dorothy**
Table(s): **Georgia:** Energy **Band 2** p.1049

**Black III, James I.**
Profile: p.284
Table(s): **Nationwide:** Wealth Management:
Eastern Region **Band 4** p.267

**Black Jr, Creed C**
Table(s): **Pennsylvania:** Litigation: White-Collar
Crime & Government Investigations **Band 1**
p.2204

**Blackaby, Nigel**
Profile: p.284
Table(s): **Nationwide:** International Arbitration
**Band 1** p.145

**Blackburn, Thomas**
Table(s): **Nationwide:** Energy: Electricity
(Regulatory & Litigation) **Band 2** p.76

**Blackburn, W Stanley**
Table(s): **Georgia:** Corporate/M&A **Band 2** p.1046

**Blackhurst, Steven**
Table(s): **Oregon:** Litigation: General
Commercial **Band 1** p.2171

**Blacklow, Kimberly B**
Profile: p.1879
Table(s): **New York:** Real Estate **Up-and-coming individuals** p.1854

**Blackstone, Robert A**
Table(s): **Washington:** Labor & Employment **Band 2** p.2531

**Blackwell, Bruce B**
Table(s): **Florida:** Litigation: General Commercial
**Band 4** p.966

**Blackwood, Kelly**
Table(s): **Mississippi:** Environment **Band 2** p.1594

**Bladh, Wayne**
Table(s): **New Mexico:** Native American Law
**Band 1** p.1771

**Blaesser, Brian**
Profile: p.1485
Table(s): **Massachusetts:** Real Estate:
Zoning/Land Use **Band 2** p.1478

**Blain, Russell**
Profile: p.985
Table(s): **Florida:** Bankruptcy/Restructuring **Band 2** p.939

**Blair, Bonnie S**
Table(s): **Nationwide:** Energy: Electricity
(Regulatory & Litigation) **Band 5** p.76

**Blair, Mitchell G**
Profile: p.2090
Table(s): **Ohio:** Litigation: General Commercial
**Band 2** p.2078

**Blair, Stephanie**
Profile: p.284
Table(s): **Nationwide:** Litigation: E-Discovery **Band 3** p.187

**Blair, William**
Table(s): **Mississippi:** Energy & Natural
Resources **Band 1** p.1593

**Blake, T Michael**
Profile: p.2146
Table(s): **Oklahoma:** Corporate/Commercial: Tax
**Band 1** p.2134

**Blalock, Tom**
Table(s): **Oklahoma:** Corporate/Commercial **Band 2** p.2134

**Blanchard, Gerald L**
Table(s): **Georgia:** Banking & Finance: Mainly
Regulatory **Band 2** p.1039

**Blanchard, James J**
Profile: p.284
Table(s): **Nationwide:** Government: Government
Relations **Band 3** p.121

**Blanchard, Kimberly S**
Profile: p.1879
Table(s): **New York:** Tax **Band 2** p.1862

**Blanco, Leyza**
Profile: p.986
Table(s): **Florida:** Bankruptcy/Restructuring **Band 2** p.939

**Bland, Douglas S**
Profile: p.284
Table(s): **Nationwide:** Energy: Oil & Gas
(Transactional) **Band 1** p.79

**Blandford, David B.**
Table(s): **Kentucky:** Litigation: Construction **Band 1** p.1312

**Blaney, Brian H**
Profile: p.507
Table(s): **Arizona:** Corporate/M&A **Band 3** p.495

**Blank, Jonathan**
Table(s): **Nationwide:** Transportation: Shipping:
Regulatory (outside New York) **Band 2** p.264

**Blankenship, Kimberly H**
Table(s): **Iowa:** Labor & Employment:
Immigration **Up-and-coming individuals** p.1285

**Blankenstein, Paul**
Profile: p.284
Table(s): **Nationwide:** ERISA Litigation **Band 3**
p.92

**Blanton, M Stanford**
Table(s): **Nationwide:** Energy: Nuclear
(Regulatory & Litigation) **Band 2** p.77

**Blanton, WC**
Table(s): **Missouri:** Environment **Band 2** p.1621

**Blaser, Michael R**
Table(s): **Iowa:** Corporate/M&A **Band 2** p.1283

**Blashek, Robert D**
Table(s): **California:** Tax **Band 1** p.617

**Blass, Michael S**
Profile: p.1879
Table(s): **New York:** Healthcare **Band 3** p.1811

**Blassberg, Franci J**
Table(s): **Nationwide:** Private Equity: Buyouts
**Band 1** p.203

**Blaszak, James S**
Table(s): **District of Columbia:** Telecom,
Broadcast & Satellite **Band 3** p.844

**Blatt, Lisa**
Profile: p.284
Table(s): **Nationwide:** Appellate Law **Band 1** p.26

**Blattner, Wray**
Profile: p.2090
Table(s): **Ohio:** Natural Resources &
Environment **Band 1** p.2083

**Blattner-Thompson, Elisabeth**
Profile: p.2472
Table(s): **Utah:** Labor & Employment **Band 2**
p.2467

**Blau, Michael L**
Table(s): **Nationwide:** Healthcare: Transactional
**Band 2** p.128, **Massachusetts:** Healthcare **Band 1**
p.1460

**Blau, Richard M**
Profile: p.284
Table(s): **Nationwide:** Food & Beverages: Alcohol
**Band 1** p.109

**Blauch, Kevin C**
Profile: p.284
Table(s): **Nationwide:** Capital Markets:
Securitisation **Band 2** p.59

# Index of Lawyers

**Blears, Norman J**
Table(s): California: Litigation: Securities **Band 2** p.594

**Blecha, Kirk S**
Table(s): Nebraska: Litigation: General Commercial **Band 1** p.1664

**Blecher, Maxwell M**
Table(s): Nationwide: Litigation: Trial Lawyers **Senior Statesmen:** p.186, California: Antitrust **Senior Statesmen:** p.536, California: Antitrust: Mainly Plaintiff p.536, California: Litigation: General Commercial **Senior Statesmen:** p.593

**Blechman, William**
Table(s): Florida: Antitrust **Band 1** p.935

**Bleck, Daniel**
Profile: p.1485
Table(s): Massachusetts: Bankruptcy/Restructuring **Band 2** p.1449

**Bledsoe, David**
Table(s): Oregon: Environment **Band 2** p.2165

**Blefeld, Bruce**
Profile: p.2381
Table(s): Texas: Antitrust **Band 3** p.2323

**Bleier, Michael E**
Table(s): Pennsylvania: Banking & Finance: Mainly Regulatory **Band 1** p.2186

**Blessing, Peter H**
Table(s): New York: Tax **Band 1** p.1862

**Blewett III, Alexander**
Table(s): Montana: Litigation: Mainly Plaintiff **Band 1** p.1649

**Bley, Kenneth B**
Table(s): California: Real Estate: Zoning/Land Use **Senior Statesmen:** p.612

**Blickman, Michael A**
Table(s): Indiana: Labor & Employment **Band 2** p.1271

**Blinderman, Harold M**
Profile: p.742
Table(s): Connecticut: Environment **Band 3** p.733

**Blissard, Judith M**
Profile: p.2381
Table(s): Texas: Tax **Band 4** p.2371

**Blittner, David**
Profile: p.285
Table(s): Nationwide: Private Equity: Buyouts **Band 5** p.203

**Blitz, Jeffrey**
Table(s): Alabama: Real Estate **Band 1** p.466

**Blizzard, Edward F**
Table(s): Nationwide: Product Liability: Plaintiffs **Band 2** p.209

**Bloch, Emily**
Table(s): Maine: Litigation: Medical Malpractice & Insurance **Band 3** p.1393

**Bloch, Matthew**
Profile: p.285
Table(s): Nationwide: Capital Markets: Debt & Equity **Band 4** p.46

**Bloch, Robert E**
Table(s): District of Columbia: Antitrust **Band 5** p.787

**Block, Bruce T**
Profile: p.2581
Table(s): Wisconsin: Real Estate **Band 1** p.2579

**Block, David**
Profile: p.986
Table(s): Florida: Labor & Employment **Band 3** p.959

**Block, Dennis J**
Profile: p.1879
Table(s): New York: Corporate/M&A **Band 1** p.1793

**Block, Ken**
Table(s): New York: Construction **Band 4** p.1791

**Block, Mark A**
Profile: p.1076
Table(s): Georgia: Real Estate **Band 2** p.1070

**Blocker, Mark B**
Profile: p.285
Table(s): Nationwide: ERISA Litigation **Band 3** p.92

**Blond, Irwin E**
Table(s): Missouri: Real Estate **Band 2** p.1633

**Bloodworth, Darryl**
Table(s): Florida: Litigation: General Commercial **Band 3** p.966

**Bloom, Allan S.**
Table(s): New York: Labor & Employment **Band 4** p.1826

**Bloom, David I**
Table(s): Nationwide: Energy: Electricity (Regulatory & Litigation) **Band 4** p.76

**Bloom, Elise M**
Table(s): New York: Labor & Employment **Band 4** p.1826

**Bloom, Jacob A**
Table(s): California: Media & Entertainment: Transactional: Mainly Talent **Band 1** p.609

**Bloom, Jerry**
Profile: p.285
Table(s): Nationwide: Projects: Renewables & Alternative Energy **Band 1** p.218, California: Energy: State Regulatory & Litigation **Band 1** p.562

**Bloom, Mark D**
Profile: p.986
Table(s): Nationwide: Bankruptcy/Restructuring **Band 4** p.39, Florida: Bankruptcy/Restructuring **Band 1** p.939

**Bloom, Michael**
Table(s): Pennsylvania: Bankruptcy/Restructuring **Band 3** p.2188

**Bloom, Mitchell S**
Profile: p.1485
Table(s): Massachusetts: Corporate/M&A **Band 4** p.1452

**Bloom, Warren S**
Profile: p.986
Table(s): Florida: Banking & Finance: Public Finance **Band 1** p.936

**Bloomquist, John**
Table(s): Montana: Natural Resources & Environment **Band 1** p.1651

**Bloostein, Marc J**
Table(s): Nationwide: Wealth Management: Eastern Region **Band 3** p.267

**Blount, David L**
Table(s): Oregon: Environment **Band 1** p.2165

**Blount, Gregory W**
Table(s): Georgia: Environment **Band 2** p.1051

**Bloxom IV, John M**
Table(s): Delaware: Real Estate **Band 2** p.766

**Blue, Rachel**
Profile: p.2147
Table(s): Oklahoma: Intellectual Property **Band 1** p.2138

**Blue Jr, William A**
Table(s): Tennessee: Labor & Employment **Band 2** p.2293

**Bluedorn II, Donald C**
Table(s): Pennsylvania: Environment **Band 2** p.2194

**Bluhm, Mark A**
Table(s): Missouri: Corporate/M&A **Band 2** p.1618

**Blum, Theodore I**
Profile: p.1076
Table(s): Georgia: Corporate/M&A **Band 4** p.1046

**Blume, Fred**
Profile: p.2211
Table(s): Pennsylvania: Corporate/M&A & Private Equity **Senior Statesmen:** p.2191

**Blume, Robert**
Profile: p.717
Table(s): Colorado: Litigation: White-Collar Crime & Government Investigations **Band 2** p.710

**Blumen, Rick D**
Profile: p.1076
Table(s): Georgia: Banking & Finance **Band 1** p.1039

**Blumenfeld, Charles**
Table(s): Washington: Environment **Senior Statesmen:** p.2527

**Blumenfeld, Jack B**
Table(s): Delaware: Intellectual Property **Star individuals** p.763

**Blumenthal, Jon**
Table(s): Nebraska: Real Estate **Band 2** p.1666

**Blumenthal, Michael L**
Table(s): Missouri: Labor & Employment **Band 2** p.1625

**Blumenthal, William**
Profile: p.853
Table(s): District of Columbia: Antitrust **Band 5** p.787

**Blumling, Sheldon J**
Profile: p.624
Table(s): California: Employee Benefits & Executive Compensation **Band 3** p.560

**Blumrosen, Eric A**
Profile: p.2381
Table(s): Texas: Corporate/M&A **Band 4** p.2337

**Blumstein, Philip**
Table(s): Alaska: Corporate/M&A **Band 1** p.487

**Boardman, Richard**
Table(s): Idaho: Litigation: General Commercial **Band 2** p.1134

**Boast, Molly S**
Profile: p.1879
Table(s): New York: Antitrust **Band 4** p.1778

**Boatright, Daniel**
Profile: p.1635
Table(s): Missouri: Labor & Employment **Band 2** p.1625

**Bobber, Bernard J**
Table(s): Wisconsin: Labor & Employment **Band 1** p.2575

**Bobo, Stephen**
Table(s): Illinois: Bankruptcy/Restructuring **Band 4** p.1148

**Bobrow, Jared**
Profile: p.624
Table(s): California: Intellectual Property: Patent **Band 2** p.578

**Bobys, Matthew**
Profile: p.285
Table(s): Nationwide: Government: Political Law **Up-and-coming individuals** p.124

**Boch, David C**
Profile: p.285
Table(s): Nationwide: Financial Services Regulation: Broker Dealer (Compliance) **Band 3** p.97, Nationwide: Financial Services Regulation: Broker Dealer (Enforcement) **Band 2** p.97, Nationwide: Securities: Regulation: Enforcement **Band 4** p.233

**Bochert, Linda**
Profile: p.2581
Table(s): Wisconsin: Natural Resources & Environment **Band 1** p.2578

**Bochner, Steven**
Table(s): Nationwide: Investment Funds: Venture Capital **Band 2** p.174, California: Corporate/M&A: Venture Capital **Band 3** p.555

**Bock, Joel N**
Profile: p.1732
Table(s): New Jersey: Intellectual Property **Band 2** p.1716

**Bocock, Joseph H**
Profile: p.2147
Table(s): Oklahoma: Litigation: General Commercial **Band 2** p.2141

**Bodansky, Robert**
Profile: p.853
Table(s): District of Columbia: Real Estate **Band 4** p.835

**Boden, Kelly**
Profile: p.1397
Table(s): Maine: Environment **Band 3** p.1389

**Bodian, Robert**
Profile: p.1879
Table(s): New York: Litigation: General Commercial **Band 3** p.1833

**Bodine, Brian G**
Profile: p.2538
Table(s): Washington: Intellectual Property **Band 1** p.2529

**Bodner, Randall W**
Table(s): Nationwide: Securities: Litigation **Band 2** p.232, Massachusetts: Litigation: Securities **Band 1** p.1470

**Bodney, David J.**
Table(s): Nationwide: First Amendment Litigation **Band 3** p.105

**Bodor, Brian R**
Profile: p.853
Table(s): District of Columbia: Technology & Outsourcing **Band 3** p.842

**Boe, Tim**
Table(s): Arkansas: Labor & Employment **Band 1** p.520

**Boeder, Thomas**
Table(s): Washington: Litigation: General Commercial **Band 3** p.2533

**Boeglin, Daniel L**
Table(s): Indiana: Corporate/M&A **Band 1** p.1268

**Boehm, Lisa**
Profile: p.1397
Table(s): Maine: Labor & Employment: Employee Benefits & Compensation **Band 3** p.1390

**Boehm, Steven B**
Table(s): Nationwide: Investment Funds: Registered Funds **Band 2** p.170

**Boehnen, Daniel A**
Profile: p.1199
Table(s): Illinois: Intellectual Property **Band 2** p.1171

**Boehning, H Christopher**
Profile: p.285
Table(s): Nationwide: International Arbitration **Up-and-coming individuals** p.145

**Boehrer, Charles B**
Profile: p.1199
Table(s): Illinois: Banking & Finance **Band 2** p.1145

**Boeke, Noel**
Profile: p.986
Table(s): Florida: Bankruptcy/Restructuring **Band 4** p.939

**Bogan III, James F**
Table(s): Georgia: Litigation: General Commercial **Band 4** p.1065

**Bogarad, Cynthia**
Table(s): Nationwide: Energy: Electricity (Regulatory & Litigation) **Band 5** p.76

**Bogdanoff, Lee R**
Table(s): Nationwide: Bankruptcy/Restructuring **Band 4** p.39, California: Bankruptcy/Restructuring **Band 1** p.542

**Bogdanow, Alan J**
Profile: p.2381
Table(s): Texas: Corporate/M&A **Band 4** p.2337

**Boggs, Craig**
Table(s): Illinois: Labor & Employment **Band 4** p.1175

**Boggs, Jack**
Table(s): Florida: Tax **Senior Statesmen** p.979

**Boggs Jr, Thomas Hale**
Table(s): Nationwide: Government: Government Relations **Star individuals** p.121

**Bogin, Michael S**
Table(s): New York: Environment **Band 4** p.1807

**Bogue, Stevenson**
Table(s): Nebraska: Labor & Employment **Band 1** p.1662

**Bohannon, C Tad**
Profile: p.525
Table(s): Arkansas: Corporate/Commercial: Municipal Bonds **Band 2** p.518, Arkansas: Corporate/Commercial: Tax **Band 2** p.518, Arkansas: Real Estate **Band 3** p.524

**Bohannon, Paul**
Profile: p.2381
Table(s): Texas: Environment **Band 3** p.2343

**Bohler, William J**
Table(s): California: Intellectual Property: Patent **Band 4** p.578

**Bohm, Richard D**
Table(s): New York: Media & Entertainment: Corporate **Band 2** p.1848

**Bohnhoff, Henry M**
Profile: p.1773
Table(s): New Mexico: Litigation: General Commercial **Band 3** p.1769

**Bohrer, Barry A**
Profile: p.1879
Table(s): New York: Litigation: White-Collar Crime & Government Investigations **Band 1** p.1836

**Bohrer, Sanford**
Profile: p.986
Table(s): Florida: Litigation: General Commercial **Band 2** p.966

**Boice, William**
Table(s): Georgia: Intellectual Property **Band 2** p.1056, Georgia: Litigation: General Commercial **Band 2** p.1065

**Boies, Bill**
Profile: p.285
Table(s): Nationwide: ERISA Litigation **Band 3** p.92

**Boies, David**
Table(s): Nationwide: Litigation: Trial Lawyers **Star individuals** p.187, New York: Antitrust **Band 2** p.1778, New York: Litigation: General Commercial **Star individuals** p.1833

**Boisseau, Richard**
Table(s): Georgia: Labor & Employment **Senior Statesmen** p.1060

**Boisvert Jr, Robert C**
Table(s): Minnesota: Labor & Employment **Band 2** p.1571

**Bojko, Andrew**
Profile: p.2091
Table(s): Ohio: Banking & Finance **Up-and-coming individuals** p.2056

**Bokhari, Zulfiqar**
Profile: p.1199
Table(s): Illinois: Banking & Finance **Band 3** p.1145

**Bokor, Bruce**
Table(s): Florida: Tax **Band 2** p.979, Florida: Tax: Estate Planning **Band 2** p.979

**Boland, Beth**
Profile: p.1485
Table(s): Massachusetts: Litigation: Securities **Band 2** p.1470

**Boland, J William**
Table(s): Virginia: Litigation: General Commercial **Band 2** p.2502

**Boland, Sean F X**
Profile: p.853
Table(s): District of Columbia: Antitrust **Band 4** p.787

**Bolding, Grady**
Table(s): California: Tax **Band 3** p.617

**Boldt, Michael**
Table(s): Indiana: Labor & Employment **Band 2** p.1271

**Bolen, Christopher**
Table(s): North Carolina: Intellectual Property **Band 2** p.2030

**Bolen, Richard J**
Table(s): West Virginia: Litigation: General Commercial **Band 3** p.2555, West Virginia: Natural Resources **Band 2** p.2558

**Boles, H Hampton**
Table(s): Alabama: Banking & Finance: Mainly Regulatory **Band 1** p.455

**Boles, Janet**
Table(s): Louisiana: Gaming & Licensing **Band 3** p.1348

**Bolger, Katherine M**
Profile: p.1879
Table(s): New York: Media & Entertainment: First Amendment Litigation **Band 2** p.1851

**Bolinder, Clint**
Table(s): Idaho: Corporate/Commercial **Up-and-coming individuals** p.1132

**Bollinger, Bernard**
Profile: p.624
Table(s): California: Bankruptcy/Restructuring **Band 4** p.542

**Bollweg, Pamela**
Table(s): South Dakota: Litigation: General Commercial **Up-and-coming individuals** p.2284

**Bolstein, Joel**
Profile: p.2211
Table(s): Pennsylvania: Environment **Band 2** p.2194

**Bolt, Preston**
Table(s): Alabama: Banking & Finance: Public Finance **Band 1** p.455

**Bolton, Richard M**
Profile: p.1548
Table(s): Michigan: Corporate/M&A **Band 3** p.1538

**Bomhoff, Timothy J**
Profile: p.2147
Table(s): Oklahoma: Energy & Natural Resources **Band 2** p.2136

**Bomse, Stephen**
Table(s): California: Antitrust **Band 2** p.536

**Bonano, William E**
Table(s): Nationwide: Tax: Controversy **Band 4** p.244

**Bonasso, Michael**
Table(s): West Virginia: Litigation: General Commercial **Band 2** p.2555

**Bond, Thomas J**
Profile: p.2381
Table(s): Texas: Insurance: Regulation **Band 1** p.2351

**Bond, W Michael**
Profile: p.1879
Table(s): New York: Real Estate: Corporate **Band 2** p.1854

**Bonder, Teresa T**
Profile: p.1076
Table(s): Georgia: Antitrust **Band 2** p.1037

**Bondurant, Emmet J**
Table(s): Georgia: Antitrust **Senior Statesmen:** p.1037, Georgia: Litigation: General Commercial **Senior Statesmen:** p.1065

**Bondurant, Si Morgan**
Table(s): Mississippi: Energy & Natural Resources **Band 1** p.1593

**Bonebrake, Stephen J**
Table(s): Illinois: Environment: Litigation **Band 3** p.1162

**Bonifay, Cecelia**
Table(s): Florida: Real Estate: Zoning/Land Use **Band 1** p.975

**Bonner, Michael J**
Profile: p.1681
Table(s): Nevada: Corporate/Commercial **Band 1** p.1672, Nevada: Gaming & Licensing **Band 2** p.1674

**Bonner, Raymond A**
Profile: p.853
Table(s): District of Columbia: Healthcare: Pharmaceutical/Medical Products Regulatory **Band 2** p.810

**Bonnie, Joshua Ford**
Profile: p.285
Table(s): Nationwide: Capital Markets: Debt & Equity **Band 4** p.46

**Bonser, David W**
Table(s): Nationwide: Capital Markets: REITs **Band 1** p.55

**Bonsib, Robert**
Table(s): Maryland: Litigation: General Commercial **Band 3** p.1419

**Booe, J Michael**
Profile: p.2039
Table(s): North Carolina: Bankruptcy/Restructuring **Band 1** p.2023

**Booker, Daniel I**
Table(s): Pennsylvania: Antitrust **Band 2** p.2184

**Booker, William**
Table(s): West Virginia: Corporate/Commercial: Banking & Finance **Band 1** p.2550

**Bookin, Daniel**
Table(s): California: Litigation: White-Collar Crime & Government Investigations **Band 1** p.601

**Bookman, Lloyd A**
Table(s): Nationwide: Healthcare: Regulatory & Litigation **Band 2** p.127, California: Healthcare **Band 1** p.568

**Boone, Michael**
Table(s): **Texas: Corporate/M&A Senior Statesmen:** p.2337

**Boone, Thomas**
Table(s): **Montana: Corporate/M&A Band 1** p.1646, **Montana: Real Estate Band 1** p.1652

**Boone Jr, Sidney**
Table(s): **South Carolina: Real Estate Band 1** p.2266

**Boonin, Robert A**
Table(s): **Michigan: Labor & Employment Band 3** p.1542

**Boonstra, Brian**
Profile: p.717
Table(s): **Colorado: Corporate/M&A Band 3** p.703

**Booth, Karyn A**
Profile: p.285
Table(s): **Nationwide: Transportation: Rail (for Shippers) Band 2** p.258

**Booth, Susan J**
Profile: p.624
Table(s): **California: Real Estate Band 4** p.611

**Bopp, Gregory M**
Profile: p.2381
Table(s): **Texas: Corporate/M&A Band 4** p.2337, **Texas: Tax Band 3** p.2371

**Bopp III, Fred W**
Table(s): **Maine: Corporate/M&A: Bankruptcy Band 2** p.1385

**Bor, Andrew**
Table(s): **Washington: Corporate/Commercial Band 1** p.2525

**Bord, Eric S**
Profile: p.853
Table(s): **District of Columbia: Immigration Band 2** p.814

**Borden, Barbara**
Table(s): **California: Corporate/M&A Band 4** p.554

**Borden, Mark**
Profile: p.1485
Table(s): **Massachusetts: Corporate/M&A Band 1** p.1452, **Massachusetts: Private Equity: Venture Capital Investment Band 1** p.1474

**Borden, Paul**
Table(s): **California: Employee Benefits & Executive Compensation Band 2** p.560

**Borders, Sarah**
Profile: p.1076
Table(s): **Georgia: Bankruptcy/Restructuring Band 1** p.1042

**Borders, Thomas**
Profile: p.285
Table(s): **Nationwide: Tax: Controversy Band 2** p.244, **Illinois: Tax Band 2** p.1192

**Boren, Alison C**
Profile: p.2381
Table(s): **Texas: Banking & Finance Band 3** p.2325

**Born, Michael**
Table(s): **Ohio: Natural Resources & Environment Band 3** p.2083

**Borod, Don**
Profile: p.742
Table(s): **Connecticut: Corporate/M&A Band 2** p.732

**Borrus, Bruce**
Table(s): **Washington: Bankruptcy/Restructuring Band 2** p.2523

**Bortstein, Lawrence**
Profile: p.1879
Table(s): **New York: Technology & Outsourcing Band 3** p.1868

**Bos, William**
Profile: p.2381
Table(s): **Texas: Banking & Finance Band 3** p.2325

**Bosch, William M.**
Table(s): **Nationwide: Leisure & Hospitality Band 4** p.179

**Boschee, Larry**
Table(s): **North Dakota: Litigation: General Commercial Band 2** p.2053

**Boschert, Neville H**
Profile: p.1601
Table(s): **Mississippi: Litigation: General Commercial Band 3** p.1597

**Boshkoff, Ellen**
Table(s): **Indiana: Labor & Employment Band 2** p.1271

**Boss, Barry**
Profile: p.853
Table(s): **District of Columbia: Litigation: White-Collar Crime & Government Investigations Band 3** p.827

**Boston, David**
Profile: p.1880
Table(s): **New York: Corporate/M&A Band 3** p.1793

**Boston, Robert E**
Profile: p.2301
Table(s): **Tennessee: Labor & Employment Band 1** p.2293, **Tennessee: Litigation: General Commercial Band 1** p.2295

**Bostwick, Gary L**
Table(s): **California: Media & Entertainment: First Amendment Litigation Band 1** p.606

**Bostwick, Janet E**
Table(s): **Massachusetts: Bankruptcy/Restructuring Band 3** p.1449

**Bothe, Robert**
Table(s): **Nebraska: Litigation: General Commercial Band 3** p.1664

**Bothwick, Jay**
Profile: p.1485
Table(s): **Massachusetts: Corporate/M&A Band 2** p.1452

**Botica, Matthew J**
Profile: p.1199
Table(s): **Illinois: Bankruptcy/Restructuring Band 3** p.1148

**Botnick, Michael**
Profile: p.1358
Table(s): **Louisiana: Construction Band 2** p.1339

**Bott, April**
Table(s): **Ohio: Natural Resources & Environment Band 2** p.2083

**Botter, David H**
Profile: p.1880
Table(s): **New York: Bankruptcy/Restructuring Band 4** p.1782

**Botti, James**
Profile: p.2091
Table(s): **Ohio: Bankruptcy/Restructuring Band 4** p.2058

**Bottrell, Lowell**
Table(s): **North Dakota: Bankruptcy/Restructuring Band 1** p.2050, **North Dakota: Corporate/Commercial Band 1** p.2051

**Bouchard, Andre G**
Table(s): **Delaware: Chancery Band 1** p.758

**Bouchard, Sarah**
Profile: p.2212
Table(s): **Pennsylvania: Labor & Employment Band 4** p.2200

**Boucher, Jamie L**
Profile: p.285
Table(s): **Nationwide: Financial Services Regulation: Banking (Enforcement & Investigations) Band 2** p.97

**Bouffard, Andre D**
Table(s): **Vermont: Litigation: General Commercial Band 3** p.2486

**Boulden, Michael R**
Profile: p.2381
Table(s): **Texas: Real Estate Band 2** p.2367

**Boulger, Sean T**
Profile: p.1485
Table(s): **Massachusetts: Real Estate Band 3** p.1478

**Boulos, Nader**
Profile: p.1199
Table(s): **Illinois: Insurance: Dispute Resolution Band 2** p.1168

**Boulware, Margaret A**
Table(s): **Texas: Intellectual Property: Trade Mark & Copyright Band 3** p.2354

**Boulware, R Dan**
Table(s): **Missouri: Litigation: General Commercial Band 3** p.1628

**Bouma, John Jacob**
Table(s): **Arizona: Litigation: General Commercial Band 1** p.501

**Bourdeau, Karl S**
Profile: p.853
Table(s): **District of Columbia: Environment Band 2** p.804

**Bourgeois, John A**
Profile: p.1425
Table(s): **Maryland: Litigation: General Commercial Band 3** p.1419

**Bourtin, Nicolas**
Profile: p.1880
Table(s): **New York: Litigation: White-Collar Crime & Government Investigations Up-and-coming individuals** p.1836

**Bouthillier, Reggie L**
Profile: p.986
Table(s): **Florida: Real Estate: Zoning/Land Use Band 4** p.975

**Bouton, Paul E**
Profile: p.1485
Table(s): **Massachusetts: Real Estate Band 3** p.1478

**Boutrous Jr, Theodore J**
Profile: p.624
Table(s): **Nationwide: Appellate Law Band 2** p.26, **Nationwide: First Amendment Litigation Band 2** p.105, **Nationwide: Product Liability & Mass Torts Band 2** p.208, **California: Litigation: Appellate Star individuals** p.599, **California: Media & Entertainment: First Amendment Litigation Band 1** p.606

**Bowden, William P**
Profile: p.767
Table(s): **Delaware: Bankruptcy/Restructuring Band 2** p.754

**Bowe Jr, James F**
Profile: p.286
Table(s): **Nationwide: Energy: Oil & Gas (Regulatory & Litigation) Band 2** p.78

**Bowen, James N**
Table(s): **Tennessee: Litigation: General Commercial Associates to watch** p.2295

**Bowen, Michael A**
Table(s): **Wisconsin: Litigation: General Commercial Band 3** p.2576

**Bowen, Stephen S**
Table(s): **Illinois: Tax Senior Statesmen:** p.1192

**Bower, R Bruce**
Profile: p.1076
Table(s): **Georgia: Intellectual Property Band 3** p.1056

**Bowers, Chris**
Profile: p.853
Table(s): **District of Columbia: Tax Band 4** p.838

**Bowers, Michael J**
Table(s): **Georgia: Litigation: General Commercial Band 2** p.1065

**Bowers, Terree**
Profile: p.624
Table(s): **California: Litigation: White-Collar Crime & Government Investigations Band 3** p.601

**Bowers, William**
Profile: p.2382
Table(s): **Texas: Tax Band 1** p.2371

**Bowers, William C**
Table(s): **Nationwide: Banking & Finance: Equipment Finance & Leasing Band 2** p.32, **Nationwide: Transportation: Aviation: Finance Band 2** p.252

**Bowie, Scott O**
Table(s): **Nationwide: Investment Funds: Private Equity: Fund Formation Band 2** p.166

**Bowman, Andy**
Profile: p.1276
Table(s): **Indiana: Environment Band 2** p.1270

**Bowman, Carl**
Table(s): **Nebraska: Healthcare Band 2** p.1661

**Bowman, Everett J**
Table(s): **North Carolina**: Antitrust **Band 1** p.2020

**Bowman, John**
Profile: p.286
Table(s): **Nationwide**: International Arbitration **Band 2** p.145

**Bowman, Ryan**
Profile: p.525
Table(s): **Arkansas**: Corporate/Commercial: Municipal Bonds **Band 3** p.518

**Bowser, William W**
Table(s): **Delaware**: Labor & Employment **Band 1** p.765

**Box, Dennis R.**
Table(s): **Oklahoma**: Real Estate **Band 2** p.2145

**Boxer, Leonard**
Table(s): **New York**: Real Estate **Senior Statesmen**: p.1854

**Boyajian, Victor**
Profile: p.1732
Table(s): **New Jersey**: Corporate/M&A **Band 1** p.1707

**Boyar, Brand**
Table(s): **Montana**: Corporate/M&A **Up-and-coming Individuals** p.1646

**Boyd, David R**
Table(s): **Alabama**: Litigation: General Commercial **Band 2** p.463

**Boyd, Eric E**
Profile: p.1199
Table(s): **Illinois**: Environment: Litigation **Band 2** p.1162

**Boyd, Felicia**
Profile: p.1578
Table(s): **Minnesota**: Litigation: Intellectual Property **Band 1** p.1574

**Boyd, Michael**
Profile: p.2382
Table(s): **Texas**: Real Estate **Band 3** p.2367

**Boyd, Paul**
Table(s): **Idaho**: Corporate/Commercial **Band 1** p.1132

**Boyd, Thomas H**
Profile: p.1578
Table(s): **Minnesota**: Litigation: Appellate **Band 1** p.1573

**Boyd, Thomas M**
Profile: p.286
Table(s): **Nationwide**: Government: Government Relations **Band 3** p.121, **Nationwide**: Privacy & Data Security **Band 3** p.199

**Boyd, William**
Table(s): **South Carolina**: Corporate/M&A **Senior Statesmen**: p.2260

**Boyd III, Willard L**
Table(s): **Iowa**: Corporate/M&A **Band 3** p.1283

**Boydston, Richard**
Profile: p.2091
Table(s): **Ohio**: Bankruptcy/Restructuring **Band 4** p.2058

**Boyett, Christopher W**
Profile: p.986
Table(s): **Florida**: Tax: Estate Planning **Band 2** p.979

**Boyken, Quentin**
Table(s): **Iowa**: Corporate/M&A **Band 2** p.1283

**Boykins, Michael L**
Profile: p.1199
Table(s): **Illinois**: Banking & Finance **Band 4** p.1145

**Boyko, Stephen A**
Table(s): **Massachusetts**: Banking & Finance **Band 2** p.1445

**Boyle, Brian**
Profile: p.286
Table(s): **Nationwide**: ERISA Litigation **Band 3** p.92

**Boyle, Christopher W**
Profile: p.2212
Table(s): **Pennsylvania**: Environment **Band 3** p.2194

**Boyle, Edward**
Profile: p.1880
Table(s): **New York**: Litigation: General Commercial **Band 4** p.1833

**Boyle, James F**
Table(s): **Wisconsin**: Intellectual Property **Band 1** p.2573, **Wisconsin**: Intellectual Property: Litigation p.2573

**Boyle, Kim M**
Table(s): **Louisiana**: Labor & Employment **Band 2** p.1350

**Boyle, Lisa**
Profile: p.742
Table(s): **Connecticut**: Healthcare **Band 1** p.735

**Boyle, Philip G**
Profile: p.1485
Table(s): **Massachusetts**: Labor & Employment **Band 4** p.1466

**Boyles, William**
Profile: p.986
Table(s): **Florida**: Healthcare **Band 3** p.954

**Bracken, Andrew J**
Table(s): **Iowa**: Labor & Employment **Band 3** p.1285

**Bracken II, Lawrence J**
Profile: p.1076
Table(s): **Georgia**: Litigation: General Commercial **Band 3** p.1065

**Bradbury, Steve**
Table(s): **Idaho**: Real Estate: Zoning/Land Use **Band 1** p.1138

**Braddock, James D**
Table(s): **Texas**: Environment **Band 1** p.2343

**Braden, Gregory C**
Profile: p.286
Table(s): **Nationwide**: ERISA Litigation **Band 2** p.92

**Bradford, David**
Profile: p.1199
Table(s): **Illinois**: Litigation: General Commercial **Band 3** p.1180

**Bradley, Ann**
Profile: p.2561
Table(s): **West Virginia**: Natural Resources: Environment **Band 1** p.2558

**Bradley, Beth D**
Table(s): **Texas**: Insurance **Band 2** p.2351

**Bradley, Craig C**
Profile: p.1200
Table(s): **Illinois**: Corporate/M&A: Private Equity **Band 2** p.1157

**Bradley, James P**
Profile: p.2382
Table(s): **Texas**: Intellectual Property **Band 2** p.2354

**Bradley, Patrick E**
Table(s): **Nationwide**: Transportation: Aviation: Litigation **Band 2** p.254

**Bradley, Wayne N**
Profile: p.1077
Table(s): **Georgia**: Corporate/M&A **Band 3** p.1046

**Bradley III, Francis 'Frank' R**
Profile: p.2382
Table(s): **Texas**: Banking & Finance **Band 2** p.2325

**Bradley Jr, C Craig**
Profile: p.1316
Table(s): **Kentucky**: Corporate/M&A **Band 2** p.1305

**Bradshaw, Brian A**
Profile: p.286
Table(s): **Nationwide**: Projects **Band 4** p.216

**Bradshaw, Penni Pearson**
Table(s): **North Carolina**: Labor & Employment **Band 2** p.2031, **North Carolina**: Labor & Employment: Immigration **Band 1** p.2031

**Bradshaw II, Jean Paul**
Table(s): **Missouri**: Litigation: White-Collar Crime & Government Investigations **Band 2** p.1629

**Brady, Francis**
Table(s): **Connecticut**: Litigation: General Commercial **Band 1** p.738

**Brady, Jennifer G**
Profile: p.768
Table(s): **Delaware**: Labor & Employment **Band 2** p.765

**Brady, Kevin F**
Table(s): **Nationwide**: Litigation: E-Discovery **Band 2** p.187

**Brady, Patrick G**
Table(s): **New Jersey**: Labor & Employment **Band 1** p.1718

**Brady, Robert P**
Table(s): **Nationwide**: Life Sciences: Regulatory/Compliance **Senior Statesmen**: p.183, **District of Columbia**: Healthcare: Pharmaceutical/Medical Products Regulatory **Senior Statesmen**: p.810

**Brady, Robert S**
Table(s): **Delaware**: Bankruptcy/Restructuring **Band 1** p.754

**Brady, Thomas P**
Table(s): **Michigan**: Labor & Employment **Band 3** p.1542

**Braemer, Richard J**
Profile: p.2212
Table(s): **Pennsylvania**: Corporate/M&A & Private Equity **Band 3** p.2191

**Braga, Stephen**
Table(s): **District of Columbia**: Litigation: White-Collar Crime & Government Investigations **Band 4** p.827

**Braham, Denis Clive**
Profile: p.286
Table(s): **Nationwide**: Sports Law **Band 3** p.241

**Brahm, Richard**
Table(s): **Ohio**: Real Estate: Zoning/Land Use **Band 2** p.2086

**Brahmst, Oliver**
Profile: p.286
Table(s): **Nationwide**: Private Equity: Buyouts **Band 5** p.203

**Braid, Frederick**
Profile: p.1880
Table(s): **New York**: Labor & Employment **Band 3** p.1826

**Brailsford, Amanda**
Table(s): **Idaho**: Labor & Employment **Band 2** p.1132

**Brainard, Barbara A**
Table(s): **Oregon**: Labor & Employment **Band 3** p.2168

**Braiterman, Andrew H**
Profile: p.1880
Table(s): **New York**: Tax **Band 2** p.1862

**Brakke, Jon**
Table(s): **North Dakota**: Bankruptcy/Restructuring **Band 1** p.2050

**Bramblett Jr, George W**
Table(s): **Texas**: Litigation: General Commercial **Band 1** p.2362

**Bramhall, Christopher**
Table(s): **Utah**: Energy & Natural Resources **Band 2** p.2464, **Utah**: Energy & Natural Resources: Water Law p.2464

**Bramlett, Jeffrey**
Table(s): **Georgia**: Litigation: General Commercial **Band 2** p.1065

**Bramnick, James**
Table(s): **Florida**: Labor & Employment **Band 2** p.959

**Brams, Robert**
Table(s): **District of Columbia**: Construction **Band 3** p.795

**Bran, Paul Bennett**
Profile: p.853
Table(s): **District of Columbia**: Bankruptcy/Restructuring **Band 2** p.792

**Branca, John G**
Table(s): **California**: Media & Entertainment: Transactional: Mainly Talent **Band 1** p.609

**Branca, Michael A**
Profile: p.853
Table(s): **District of Columbia**: Construction **Band 3** p.795

**Branciforte, Jason**
Profile: p.853
Table(s): District of Columbia: Labor &
Employment Band 3 p.824

**Brand, Richard L**
Profile: p.286
Table(s): Nationwide: Sports Law Band 3 p.241

**Brand, Walter J**
Profile: p.1601
Table(s): Mississippi: Labor & Employment Band
2 p.1595

**Brandow, John M**
Profile: p.286
Table(s): Nationwide: Capital Markets:
Derivatives Band 1 p.51

**Brandt, A Peter**
Table(s): Florida: Construction Band 2 p.944

**Brandt, James E**
Profile: p.1880
Table(s): New York: Litigation: General
Commercial Band 3 p.1833

**Brandt, Michael**
Table(s): Alabama: Banking & Finance Band 2
p.455

**Brandt, William Perry**
Table(s): Missouri: Litigation: General
Commercial Band 2 p.1628

**Brandt-Erichsen, Svend**
Table(s): Washington: Environment Band 2
p.2527

**Branigan, Thomas P**
Profile: p.1548
Table(s): Michigan: Litigation: General
Commercial Band 3 p.1544

**Brannock, Steven L**
Table(s): Florida: Litigation: Appellate Band 2
p.972

**Brannon, Leah**
Profile: p.854
Table(s): District of Columbia: Antitrust Band 5
p.787

**Brantley IV, Joseph P.**
Table(s): Louisiana: Gaming & Licensing Band 3
p.1348

**Branzburg, Morton R**
Table(s): Pennsylvania:
Bankruptcy/Restructuring Band 3 p.2188

**Brasher, Lance T**
Profile: p.286
Table(s): Nationwide: Projects Band 3 p.216

**Brassey, Andrew C**
Table(s): Idaho: Litigation: Medical Malpractice
& Insurance Band 1 p.1134

**Braswell, David W**
Table(s): Missouri: Corporate/M&A Band 2 p.1619

**Bratcher, Timothy**
Profile: p.1077
Table(s): Georgia: Banking & Finance Band 4
p.1039

**Braude, Herman**
Table(s): District of Columbia: Construction Band
3 p.795

**Brauerman, Stephen B.**
Profile: p.768
Table(s): Delaware: Chancery Associates to watch
p.758, Delaware: Intellectual Property Band Star
Associate p.763

**Braukmann, Michele**
Table(s): Montana: Litigation: General
Commercial Up-and-coming individuals p.1649

**Braun, Bruce R**
Profile: p.1200
Table(s): Illinois: Litigation: General Commercial
Band 3 p.1180

**Braun, Lawrence M**
Table(s): California: Corporate/M&A Band 2 p.554

**Braun, Lonnie R**
Table(s): South Dakota: Litigation: Medical
Malpractice Defense Band 1 p.2284

**Braun, Stephen T**
Table(s): Tennessee: Healthcare Band 1 p.2291

**Brauwerman, Jeffrey N**
Table(s): Florida: Immigration Band 3 p.956

**Bravin, Mark N**
Profile: p.286
Table(s): Nationwide: International Arbitration
Band 4 p.145

**Bray, Gregory A**
Profile: p.625
Table(s): California: Bankruptcy/Restructuring
Band 3 p.542

**Bray, John**
Profile: p.854
Table(s): District of Columbia: Litigation:
General Commercial Band 3 p.826

**Bray, Thomas**
Profile: p.1578
Table(s): Minnesota: Real Estate Band 3 p.1576

**Braza, Mary K**
Table(s): Nationwide: Sports Law Band 2 p.241

**Brazell, Cindy**
Profile: p.1077
Table(s): Georgia: Banking & Finance Band 3
p.1039

**Breach, David A**
Profile: p.625
Table(s): California: Corporate/M&A: Private
Equity Band 2 p.553

**Brearton, Christopher**
Table(s): California: Media & Entertainment:
Transactional Band 1 p.608

**Breaux, Ronald W**
Table(s): Texas: Antitrust Band 2 p.2323

**Breay, James**
Table(s): Michigan: Banking & Finance Band 3
p.1536

**Bredehoft, John M**
Table(s): Virginia: Labor & Employment Band 1
p.2500

**Bredehoft, Patrick**
Profile: p.2382
Table(s): Texas: Healthcare Band 3 p.2347

**Breed, Logan M**
Table(s): District of Columbia: Antitrust Up-and-
coming individuals p.787

**Breedlove, Gregory B**
Table(s): Alabama: Litigation: Mainly Plaintiff
Band 2 p.463

**Breedlove, Roy C**
Table(s): Oklahoma: Intellectual Property Band 2
p.2138

**Breen, Justin**
Table(s): Nationwide: Capital Markets: Debt &
Equity Up-and-coming individuals p.46

**Breen, Kenneth M**
Table(s): New York: Litigation: White-Collar
Crime & Government Investigations Band 3
p.1836

**Breene, Paul Evan**
Table(s): New York: Insurance: Dispute
Resolution: Policyholder Band 3 p.1816

**Bregstein, Henry**
Table(s): Nationwide: Investment Funds: Hedge
Funds Band 3 p.162

**Breheny, Brian V.**
Profile: p.286
Table(s): Nationwide: Securities: Regulation:
Advisory Band 2 p.232

**Bremer, Cynthia**
Profile: p.1578
Table(s): Minnesota: Labor & Employment Band 3
p.1571

**Brennan, Daniel**
Table(s): Illinois: Construction Band 2 p.1154

**Brennan, Elise**
Table(s): Oklahoma: Corporate/Commercial:
Healthcare Band 1 p.2134

**Brennan, J. Michael**
Table(s): Maryland: Real Estate Band 3 p.1422

**Brennan, James C**
Table(s): Northern Virginia: Real Estate Band 2
p.2505

**Brennan, Jeffrey W**
Profile: p.854
Table(s): District of Columbia: Antitrust Band 4
p.787

**Brennan, Matthew J**
Profile: p.1880
Table(s): New York: Environment: Mainly
Transactional Band 1 p.1808

**Brennan, Maureen A**
Profile: p.2091
Table(s): Ohio: Natural Resources &
Environment Band 2 p.2083

**Brennan, Michael G**
Profile: p.287
Table(s): Nationwide: Franchising Band 2 p.111

**Brennan, Terrence L.**
Table(s): Louisiana: Construction Band 1 p.1339

**Brennan Jr, John T**
Profile: p.287
Table(s): Nationwide: Healthcare: Regulatory &
Litigation Band 1 p.127, District of Columbia:
Healthcare Band 1 p.809

**Brenner, Alan Gordon**
Profile: p.287
Table(s): Nationwide: Transportation: Aviation:
Finance Band 3 p.252

**Brenner, Benjamin**
Table(s): Arkansas: Litigation: General
Commercial Band 4 p.522

**Brenner, Jeffrey S**
Profile: p.2256
Table(s): Rhode Island: Litigation: General
Commercial Band 2 p.2254

**Brentani, William B**
Profile: p.625
Table(s): California: Capital Markets: Debt &
Equity Band 3 p.547

**Brescher, John B**
Profile: p.1732
Table(s): New Jersey: Employee Benefits &
Executive Compensation Band 2 p.1710

**Breslow, Stephanie R**
Profile: p.287
Table(s): Nationwide: Investment Funds: Hedge
Funds Band 1 p.162

**Bresnick, Sandra A**
Table(s): New York: Intellectual Property: Patent
Band 3 p.1820

**Bressler, Barry E**
Table(s): Pennsylvania:
Bankruptcy/Restructuring Band 3 p.2188

**Bressler, Gary D**
Profile: p.2212
Table(s): Pennsylvania:
Bankruptcy/Restructuring Band 3 p.2188

**Bressler, Todd N**
Profile: p.625
Table(s): California: Construction Band 4 p.550

**Bressman, Robert I**
Profile: p.1880
Table(s): New York: Real Estate Band 3 p.1854

**Bressman, Stuart**
Table(s): Nationwide: Capital Markets: Debt &
Equity Band 3 p.46

**Bretschneider, Barry E**
Profile: p.2508
Table(s): Northern Virginia: Intellectual Property
Band 1 p.2497

**Bretz, Daniel**
Table(s): Michigan: Labor & Employment Band 1
p.1542

**Breuning, Jonathan R.**
Table(s): Nebraska: Labor & Employment Band 3
p.1662

**Brew, John B.**
Profile: p.287
Table(s): Nationwide: International Trade:
Customs Band 3 p.155

**Brew, Sarah L.**
Table(s): Nationwide: Food & Beverages:
Regulatory & Litigation Band 3 p.107

**Brewer, Bill**
Table(s): Nationwide: Leisure & Hospitality Band
4 p.179

**Brewer, Cassady V**
Table(s): Georgia: Tax **Band 3** p.1072

**Brewer, John N**
Profile: p.1681
Table(s): Nevada: Corporate/Commercial **Band 3** p.1672

**Brewer, Susan Slenker**
Profile: p.2561
Table(s): West Virginia: Litigation: Healthcare **Band 2** p.2555

**Brewer Jr, Robert G**
Profile: p.1425
Table(s): Maryland: Real Estate: Land Use **Band 1** p.1422

**Brewer Jr, Robert S**
Profile: p.625
Table(s): California: Litigation: White-Collar Crime & Government Investigations **Band 2** p.601

**Brewington, Lori**
Profile: p.768
Table(s): Delaware: Labor & Employment **Associates to watch** p.765

**Brewster, Christopher L.**
Table(s): Texas: Energy: State Regulatory & Litigation (Electricity) **Up-and-coming individuals** p.2341

**Brewster, William H**
Table(s): Georgia: Intellectual Property **Band 2** p.1056

**Brian, Brad D**
Profile: p.625
Table(s): Nationwide: Litigation: Trial Lawyers **Band 1** p.187, California: Litigation: General Commercial **Star individuals** p.593, California: Litigation: White-Collar Crime & Government Investigations **Band 1** p.601

**Brian Jr, William J**
Table(s): North Carolina: Real Estate: Zoning/Land Use **Band 1** p.2037

**Brice, Susan E.**
Table(s): Illinois: Environment: Mainly Transactional **Up-and-coming individuals** p.1162

**Bricklemyer, Keith**
Table(s): Florida: Real Estate: Zoning/Land Use **Band 3** p.975

**Brickman, Steven A**
Profile: p.468
Table(s): Alabama: Real Estate **Band 2** p.466

**Brickner, Jed**
Profile: p.1880
Table(s): New York: Employee Benefits & Executive Compensation **Band 4** p.1802

**Bridge, Catherine L**
Profile: p.1276
Table(s): Indiana: Corporate/M&A **Band 1** p.1268

**Bridges, Andrew P**
Profile: p.625
Table(s): California: Intellectual Property: Trademark, Copyright & Trade Secrets **Band 1** p.578

**Bridston, Kevin**
Profile: p.717
Table(s): Colorado: Real Estate: Construction **Band 1** p.714

**Brigagliano, James**
Profile: p.287
Table(s): Nationwide: Financial Services Regulation: Broker Dealer (Compliance) **Band 3** p.97

**Briggs, Benjamin**
Profile: p.1077
Table(s): Georgia: Labor & Employment **Up-coming individuals** p.1060

**Briggs, David W**
Profile: p.854
Table(s): District of Columbia: Real Estate: Zoning/Land Use **Band 2** p.835

**Brigham, Johan V**
Table(s): Massachusetts: Corporate/M&A **Band 4** p.1452

**Brightbill, Timothy C**
Profile: p.287
Table(s): Nationwide: International Trade: Trade Remedies & Trade Policy **Band 4** p.154

**Brightmire, Jon**
Profile: p.2147
Table(s): Oklahoma: Labor & Employment **Band 3** p.2140

**Brightmire, Kristen**
Profile: p.2147
Table(s): Oklahoma: Labor & Employment **Band 1** p.2140

**Briglia, Shannon J**
Table(s): Virginia: Construction **Band 3** p.2491

**Brignone, Andrew S**
Table(s): Nevada: Labor & Employment: ERISA **Band 1** p.1675

**Brill, Matthew**
Profile: p.854
Table(s): District of Columbia: Telecom, Broadcast & Satellite **Band 2** p.844

**Brilliant, Allan S**
Profile: p.1880
Table(s): New York: Bankruptcy/Restructuring **Band 3** p.1782

**Brimer, Jeffrey A**
Table(s): Nationwide: Franchising **Band 4** p.111

**Brindell, James R.**
Table(s): Florida: Real Estate: Zoning/Land Use **Band 2** p.975

**Brinkerhoff, Jeffrey C**
Table(s): Wyoming: Litigation: General Commercial **Band 1** p.2598, Wyoming: Litigation: Medical Malpractice Defense **Star individuals** p.2598

**Brinkman, David**
Table(s): Ohio: Intellectual Property **Band 3** p.2071

**Brinkman, Kathleen**
Profile: p.2091
Table(s): Ohio: Litigation: White-Collar Crime & Government Investigations **Band 3** p.2079

**Brinkman, Paul F**
Table(s): Nationwide: International Trade: Intellectual Property (Section 337) **Band 2** p.160

**Brinkman, Scott W**
Profile: p.1316
Table(s): Kentucky: Corporate/M&A **Band 1** p.1305

**Brisson, Jean-Philippe**
Table(s): Nationwide: Climate Change **Band 2** p.63

**Brister, Scott**
Profile: p.2382
Table(s): Texas: Litigation: Appellate **Band 2** p.2361

**Brito, Michael James**
Table(s): Nationwide: Outsourcing **Band 2** p.195, Texas: Technology: Outsourcing **Band 1** p.2376

**Britt III, Louis P**
Profile: p.2301
Table(s): Tennessee: Labor & Employment **Band 2** p.2293

**Brittain, David R**
Table(s): Florida: Real Estate **Band 2** p.974

**Brittain, Max**
Table(s): Illinois: Labor & Employment **Senior Statesmen:** p.1175

**Brittenham, David**
Table(s): Nationwide: Banking & Finance **Band 2** p.31, Nationwide: Capital Markets: Debt & Equity **Band 4** p.46

**Brittenham, Harry M**
Table(s): California: Media & Entertainment: Transactional: Mainly Talent **Band 1** p.609

**Brittingham IV, Smith R**
Profile: p.287
Table(s): Nationwide: International Trade: Intellectual Property (Section 337) **Band 2** p.160

**Broadbent, David K**
Profile: p.2473
Table(s): Utah: Real Estate **Band 2** p.2470

**Broaddus, William**
Table(s): Virginia: Litigation: General Commercial **Band 1** p.2502

**Broadfoot, Alexander L**
Table(s): Arizona: Real Estate **Band 3** p.504

**Broadhurst, John**
Table(s): Nationwide: Investment Funds: Hedge Funds **Band 2** p.162

**Broadwin, David**
Profile: p.1486
Table(s): Massachusetts: Private Equity: Venture Capital Investment **Band 3** p.1474

**Brocato, Thomas L.**
Table(s): Texas: Energy: State Regulatory & Litigation (Electricity) **Band 2** p.2341

**Broccolo, Bernadette**
Profile: p.1200
Table(s): Nationwide: Healthcare: Transactional **Band 2** p.128, Illinois: Healthcare **Band 1** p.1165

**Brochin, Gregg**
Profile: p.1880
Table(s): New York: Labor & Employment **Up-and-coming individuals** p.1826

**Brochin, Robert M**
Table(s): Florida: Litigation: General Commercial **Band 3** p.966

**Brock, Robert C.**
Profile: p.287
Table(s): Nationwide: Product Liability & Mass Torts **Band 1** p.208

**Brockelman, Kent**
Table(s): Arizona: Labor & Employment **Band 2** p.499

**Brockhaus, Marc A**
Profile: p.2147
Table(s): Oklahoma: Intellectual Property **Band 1** p.2138

**Brockhoff, Wallace E**
Table(s): Missouri: Corporate/M&A **Band 3** p.1618

**Brockland, John P**
Profile: p.625
Table(s): Nationwide: Outsourcing **Band 4** p.195, California: IT & Outsourcing **Band 1** p.583

**Brockman, Christopher C**
Profile: p.987
Table(s): Florida: Real Estate **Band 4** p.974

**Brockman, Richard J**
Table(s): Alabama: Corporate/Commercial **Band 2** p.459

**Brockway, David H**
Profile: p.854
Table(s): District of Columbia: Tax **Band 3** p.838

**Brockway, James**
Table(s): Nationwide: Wealth Management: Eastern Region **Band 4** p.267

**Brod, Craig B**
Profile: p.287
Table(s): Nationwide: Capital Markets: Debt & Equity **Band 3** p.46

**Brodeen, Karen A.**
Table(s): Florida: Real Estate: Zoning/Land Use **Band 4** p.975

**Broder, James N**
Table(s): Maine: Energy & Natural Resources **Band 3** p.1388

**Broderick, David F**
Profile: p.1732
Table(s): New Jersey: Corporate/M&A **Band 3** p.1707

**Broderick, James M**
Profile: p.1486
Table(s): Massachusetts: Real Estate **Band 3** p.1478

**Broderick, JJ**
Table(s): Pennsylvania: Real Estate **Band 2** p.2208

**Broders, John J**
Profile: p.1358
Table(s): Louisiana: Banking & Finance: Marine Finance **Band 1** p.1335

**Brodsky, David E**
Profile: p.1881
Table(s): New York: Litigation: White-Collar Crime & Government Investigations **Band 2** p.1836

**Brodsky, Richard E**
Table(s): Florida: Litigation: General Commercial **Band 4** p.966

**Bryant, David**
Table(s): Illinois: Real Estate **Band 4** p.1187

**Bryant, David L**
Table(s): Oklahoma: Litigation: General Commercial **Band 2** p.2141

**Bryant, Duff**
Table(s): Washington: Corporate/Commercial **Band 3** p.2525

**Bryson, Susan J**
Profile: p.742
Table(s): Connecticut: Real Estate **Band 1** p.740

**Buatt, Louis**
Profile: p.1358
Table(s): Louisiana: Environment **Band 3** p.1346

**Buchan Jr, Jonathan E**
Table(s): North Carolina: Litigation: First Amendment **Band 1** p.2033

**Buchanan, Brandon L**
Profile: p.2147
Table(s): Oklahoma: Litigation: General Commercial **Up-and-coming individuals** p.2141

**Buchanan, John**
Profile: p.855
Table(s): Nationwide: Insurance: Dispute Resolution: Policyholder **Band 2** p.137, **District of Columbia: Insurance: Policyholder Band 1** p.818

**Buchanan, Paul**
Table(s): Oregon: Labor & Employment **Band 1** p.2168

**Buchanan, Thomas G.**
Profile: p.2212
Table(s): Pennsylvania: Corporate/M&A & Private Equity **Band 3** p.2191

**Buchanan Jr, Robert M**
Profile: p.1486
Table(s): Massachusetts: Antitrust **Band 1** p.1444

**Buchenroth, Stephen**
Profile: p.2091
Table(s): Ohio: Real Estate **Band 1** p.2086

**Bucher, Elaine M**
Table(s): Florida: Tax: Estate Planning **Band 2** p.979

**Buchholtz, David P**
Table(s): New Mexico: Corporate/Commercial **Band 1** p.1764

**Buchman, Barry I**
Profile: p.855
Table(s): District of Columbia: Insurance: Policyholder **Band 3** p.818

**Buchman, Emil**
Profile: p.289
Table(s): Nationwide: Banking & Finance **Band 3** p.31

**Bucholtz, Harold**
Profile: p.855
Table(s): District of Columbia: Tax **Band 4** p.838

**Buck, Charles**
Profile: p.1486
Table(s): Massachusetts: Healthcare **Band 2** p.1460

**Buck, David**
Profile: p.2383
Table(s): Texas: Corporate/M&A **Band 2** p.2337

**Buck, Frank W**
Profile: p.2091
Table(s): Ohio: Labor & Employment **Band 4** p.2074

**Buck, Peter**
Table(s): North Carolina: Banking & Finance **Band 1** p.2021, North Carolina: Corporate/M&A **Band 1** p.2025

**Buck, Willis**
Profile: p.289
Table(s): Nationwide: Capital Markets: Securitisation **Band 3** p.59

**Buck Richard, Molly**
Table(s): Texas: Intellectual Property: Trade Mark & Copyright **Band 1** p.2354

**Buckholz Jr, Robert E**
Profile: p.289
Table(s): Nationwide: Capital Markets: Debt & Equity **Band 1** p.46

**Bucking, James W**
Profile: p.1486
Table(s): Massachusetts: Labor & Employment **Band 1** p.1466

**Buckler, Robert H**
Table(s): Georgia: Labor & Employment **Band 3** p.1060

**Buckley, Daniel J**
Profile: p.2091
Table(s): Ohio: Litigation: General Commercial **Band 2** p.2078

**Buckley, Jeremiah S**
Profile: p.289
Table(s): Nationwide: Financial Services Regulation: Consumer Finance (Compliance) **Senior Statesmen:** p.98

**Buckley, Joseph L**
Profile: p.1732
Table(s): New Jersey: Litigation: General Commercial **Band 2** p.1722

**Buckley, Kevin J**
Profile: p.289
Table(s): Nationwide: Capital Markets: Securitisation **Band 2** p.59

**Buckley, Mert**
Table(s): Kansas: Real Estate **Band 1** p.1297

**Buckley, Michael E**
Table(s): Nevada: Real Estate **Band 1** p.1679

**Buckley, Susan**
Profile: p.1881
Table(s): New York: Media & Entertainment: First Amendment Litigation **Band 2** p.1851

**Bucy, Rhea**
Table(s): Tennessee: Litigation: Bankruptcy **Band 2** p.2295

**Buday, Robert**
Table(s): Illinois: Real Estate **Band 3** p.1187

**Buddie, Raymond M**
Profile: p.626
Table(s): California: Construction **Band 3** p.550

**Budny, Terrence**
Table(s): Illinois: Real Estate **Band 3** p.1187

**Budofsky, Daniel**
Profile: p.289
Table(s): Nationwide: Capital Markets: Derivatives **Band 1** p.51

**Budwick, Michael**
Table(s): Florida: Bankruptcy/Restructuring **Band 3** p.939

**Buechler, Bruce**
Profile: p.1732
Table(s): New Jersey: Bankruptcy/Restructuring **Band 2** p.1705

**Bueide, Daniel**
Table(s): North Dakota: Real Estate **Band 1** p.2055

**Buente, David**
Profile: p.855
Table(s): Nationwide: Product Liability & Mass Torts **Band 5** p.208, Nationwide: Product Liability: Toxic Torts p.208, District of Columbia: Environment **Band 1** p.804

**Buerstetta, Grant E**
Profile: p.289
Table(s): Nationwide: Banking & Finance **Band 4** p.31

**Buesing, Karen Meyer**
Table(s): Florida: Labor & Employment **Band 2** p.959

**Buffenstein, Daryl**
Table(s): Nationwide: Immigration **Band 1** p.131, Georgia: Immigration **Star individuals** p.1055

**Buffier, Beau W**
Table(s): New York: Antitrust **Up-and-coming individuals** p.1778

**Buffington, Teresa**
Profile: p.2601
Table(s): Wyoming: Corporate/M&A **Band 1** p.2596, Wyoming: Real Estate **Band 2** p.2600

**Buford, Calvin D**
Table(s): Ohio: Corporate/M&A **Band 3** p.2064

**Buford Jr, C Douglas**
Table(s): Arkansas: Corporate/Commercial **Band 1** p.518

**Bulger, Brian**
Table(s): Illinois: Labor & Employment **Band 2** p.1175

**Bull, Edwin**
Profile: p.507
Table(s): Arizona: Real Estate: Zoning/Land Use **Band 1** p.504

**Bullard, Randy A**
Profile: p.987
Table(s): Florida: Latin American Investment **Band 3** p.963

**Bulleit, Kristy**
Profile: p.855
Table(s): District of Columbia: Environment **Band 5** p.804

**Bulleit Jr, Thomas N**
Table(s): Nationwide: Healthcare: Regulatory & Litigation **Band 1** p.127, District of Columbia: Healthcare **Band 1** p.809

**Bullen, Linda M**
Table(s): Nevada: Environment **Band 1** p.1673

**Bullock, Brentley**
Table(s): Oregon: Corporate/M&A **Band 2** p.2164

**Bullock, David**
Table(s): Tennessee: Environment **Band 3** p.2290

**Bulman, John**
Table(s): Rhode Island: Litigation: General Commercial **Band 2** p.2254

**Bult, Teresa Rider**
Table(s): Tennessee: Labor & Employment **Band 3** p.2293

**Bumpass, T Merritt**
Profile: p.2091
Table(s): Ohio: Labor & Employment **Band 2** p.2074

**Bumpers, Heidi**
Profile: p.855
Table(s): District of Columbia: Environment **Band 5** p.804

**Bumpers, William**
Table(s): Nationwide: Climate Change **Band 1** p.63, District of Columbia: Environment **Band 1** p.804

**Bundy, David H**
Table(s): Alaska: Corporate/M&A: Bankruptcy **Band 1** p.487

**Bundy, Kerry**
Table(s): Nationwide: Franchising **Band 3** p.111

**Bundy, Robert C**
Table(s): Alaska: Litigation: General Commercial **Senior Statesmen:** p.490

**Bunn, Andrew**
Table(s): Hawaii: Real Estate **Up-and-coming individuals** p.1120

**Bunn, Andrew O**
Profile: p.1732
Table(s): New Jersey: Litigation: General Commercial **Band 3** p.1722

**Bunnell, Stevan E**
Table(s): District of Columbia: Litigation: White-Collar Crime & Government Investigations **Band 3** p.827

**Bunning, David W.**
Profile: p.1881
Table(s): New York: Tax **Band 4** p.1862

**Bunsow, Henry**
Table(s): California: Intellectual Property: Patent **Band 2** p.578

**Buntain, David**
Table(s): Nebraska: Labor & Employment **Band 3** p.1662

**Buoncristiani, David**
Profile: p.626
Table(s): California: Construction **Band 1** p.550

**Buongiorno, Diana**
Table(s): New Jersey: Environment **Up-and-coming individuals** p.1711

**Buono, Francis**
Profile: p.855
Table(s): District of Columbia: Telecom, Broadcast & Satellite **Band 4** p.844

**Buono, Kathryn M**
Profile: p.2581
Table(s): **Wisconsin: Corporate/M&A Band 1**
p.2571

**Burack, Marshall R**
Table(s): **Florida: Healthcare Band 3** p.954

**Burak, Michael L**
Table(s): **Vermont: Litigation: General
Commercial Band 3** p.2486

**Burbach, Max**
Table(s): **Nebraska: Real Estate Band 3** p.1666

**Burbidge, Richard D**
Table(s): **Utah: Litigation: General Commercial
Band 1** p.2468

**Burcat, Joel R**
Table(s): **Pennsylvania: Environment Band 2**
p.2194

**Burchfield, Bobby R**
Profile: p.289
Table(s): **Nationwide: Government: Political Law
Band 3** p.124, **District of Columbia: Litigation:
General Commercial Band 3** p.826

**Burdick, Rick L**
Profile: p.855
Table(s): **District of Columbia: Corporate/M&A &
Private Equity Band 3** p.797

**Burdumy, Stephen T**
Profile: p.2212
Table(s): **Pennsylvania: Corporate/M&A &
Private Equity Band 4** p.2191

**Burg, Michael S**
Table(s): **Pennsylvania: Real Estate Band 2**
p.2208

**Burge, Jason**
Profile: p.1359
Table(s): **Louisiana: Litigation: General
Commercial Associates to watch** p.1352

**Burger, Peter**
Table(s): **New Hampshire:
Corporate/Commercial Band 1** p.1685

**Burgert, David**
Profile: p.2383
Table(s): **Texas: Intellectual Property Band 3**
p.2354

**Burgess, Kevin**
Profile: p.2383
Table(s): **Texas: Intellectual Property Up-and-com-
ing individuals** p.2354

**Burgess, Linda J**
Profile: p.2383
Table(s): **Texas: Insurance Band 3** p.2351

**Burgess, Rick J.**
Table(s): **Florida: Environment Band 1** p.951

**Burgin, Sara**
Profile: p.2383
Table(s): **Texas: Environment Band 1** p.2343

**Burgoyne, Robert**
Profile: p.855
Table(s): **District of Columbia: Litigation:
General Commercial Band 3** p.826

**Burke, Arthur J**
Profile: p.626
Table(s): **California: Antitrust Band 2** p.536, **New
York: Antitrust Band 3** p.1778

**Burke, David P**
Profile: p.987
Table(s): **Florida: Tax Band 1** p.979

**Burke, Denise D**
Profile: p.2302
Table(s): **Tennessee: Healthcare: Regulatory
Band 1** p.2291

**Burke, James E**
Profile: p.2091
Table(s): **Ohio: Litigation: General Commercial
Band 1** p.2078

**Burke, Kim**
Profile: p.2092
Table(s): **Ohio: Natural Resources &
Environment Band 1** p.2083

**Burke, Lawrence B**
Table(s): **Oregon: Environment Band 2** p.2165

**Burke, Meghan**
Profile: p.1486
Table(s): **Massachusetts: Banking & Finance:
Public Finance Band 1** p.1446

**Burke, P John**
Profile: p.626
Table(s): **California: Media & Entertainment:
Transactional Band 2** p.608

**Burke, Patrick J**
Table(s): **Colorado: Litigation: White-Collar Crime
& Government Investigations Band 2** p.710

**Burke, Peter S**
Table(s): **California: Banking & Finance Band 3**
p.539

**Burke, Robert**
Profile: p.1486
Table(s): **Massachusetts: Tax Band 2** p.1481

**Burke, Steven M**
Profile: p.1694
Table(s): **New Hampshire:
Corporate/Commercial Band 3** p.1685, **New
Hampshire: Corporate/Commercial: Tax Band 1**
p.1685

**Burke, Thomas H**
Table(s): **Iowa: Corporate/M&A: Banking &
Finance Band 2** p.1283

**Burke, Thomas R**
Table(s): **California: Media & Entertainment:
First Amendment Litigation Band 2** p.606

**Burke, Timothy P**
Profile: p.289
Table(s): **Nationwide: Securities: Regulation:
Enforcement Band 4** p.233

**Burke Jr, John K**
Table(s): **Virginia: Litigation: General
Commercial Band 2** p.2502

**Burke Jr, Raymond J**
Table(s): **Nationwide: Transportation: Shipping:
Litigation (New York) Band 1** p.261

**Burkett, Teresa M.**
Table(s): **Oklahoma: Corporate/Commercial:
Healthcare Band 1** p.2134

**Burks, Ashby Q**
Profile: p.2302
Table(s): **Tennessee: Healthcare Band 2** p.2291

**Burleigh, Jennifer J**
Table(s): **Nationwide: Investment Funds: Private
Equity: Fund Formation Band 2** p.166

**Burling, James**
Profile: p.1486
Table(s): **Massachusetts: Antitrust Band 1** p.1444

**Burman, David J**
Table(s): **Washington: Litigation: General
Commercial Band 1** p.2533

**Burmeister, Edward**
Profile: p.626
Table(s): **Nationwide: Employee Benefits &
Executive Compensation Band 2** p.73, **California:
Employee Benefits & Executive Compensation
Band 1** p.560

**Burmood, Brent C**
Profile: p.1667
Table(s): **Nebraska: Real Estate Band 3** p.1666

**Burnett, Henry Guy**
Profile: p.290
Table(s): **Nationwide: International Arbitration
Band 5** p.145

**Burnett, Lawrence J**
Profile: p.2581
Table(s): **Wisconsin: Corporate/M&A Band 3**
p.2571

**Burnett, LeAnne**
Profile: p.2147
Table(s): **Oklahoma: Energy & Natural
Resources: Environment Band 1** p.2136

**Burnett, Mark**
Profile: p.1487
Table(s): **Nationwide: Private Equity: Buyouts
Band 5** p.203, **Massachusetts: Corporate/M&A
Band 2** p.1452, **Massachusetts: Private Equity:
Buyouts Band 3** p.1474

**Burnham, Rebecca Lynne**
Profile: p.507
Table(s): **Arizona: Real Estate Band 2** p.504

**Burns, C B**
Table(s): **Texas: Labor & Employment Band 3**
p.2359

**Burns, Caleb P**
Profile: p.290
Table(s): **Nationwide: Government: Political Law
Band 3** p.124

**Burns, Kevin**
Table(s): **Arkansas: Corporate/Commercial Band
1** p.518

**Burns, Paul D**
Table(s): **Iowa: Litigation: General Commercial
Band 3** p.1288

**Burns, Robert**
Table(s): **Idaho: Real Estate Band 2** p.1138

**Burns, Stephen L**
Profile: p.290
Table(s): **Nationwide: Capital Markets: Debt &
Equity Band 2** p.46

**Burns, Timothy W**
Table(s): **Nationwide: Insurance: Dispute
Resolution: Policyholder Band 2** p.137

**Burns, W. Morgan**
Table(s): **Minnesota: Corporate/M&A Band 2**
p.1569

**Burnstein, Matthew R**
Profile: p.2302
Table(s): **Tennessee: Corporate/M&A Band 2**
p.2288

**Buroker, Brian M**
Profile: p.855
Table(s): **District of Columbia: Intellectual
Property: Litigation Band 4** p.821

**Burrage, Michael**
Table(s): **Oklahoma: Litigation: General
Commercial Band 1** p.2141, **Oklahoma: Litigation:
Mediators Band 1** p.2141

**Burrell, Lizabeth L**
Profile: p.290
Table(s): **Nationwide: Transportation: Shipping:
Litigation (New York) Band 2** p.261

**Burroughs, Allison**
Profile: p.1487
Table(s): **Massachusetts: Litigation: White-Collar
Crime & Government Investigations Band 2**
p.1471

**Burroughs, Harold R**
Table(s): **Missouri: Real Estate Band 3** p.1633

**Burrow, Patrick**
Profile: p.526
Table(s): **Arkansas: Corporate/Commercial Band
3** p.518

**Burrus, Robert**
Table(s): **Southern Virginia: Corporate/M&A
Senior Statesmen:** p.2494

**Bursky, Daniel J**
Profile: p.290
Table(s): **Nationwide: Capital Markets: Debt &
Equity Band 4** p.46

**Burstein, Richard**
Table(s): **Michigan: Real Estate Band 1** p.1546

**Burt, Antony S**
Table(s): **Illinois: Insurance: Dispute Resolution:
Reinsurance Band 3** p.1168

**Burton, David C**
Table(s): **Virginia: Labor & Employment Band 2**
p.2500

**Burton, Doug**
Profile: p.1487
Table(s): **Massachusetts: Real Estate Up-and-com-
ing individuals** p.1478

**Burton, H. Dickson**
Table(s): **Utah: Intellectual Property Band 3**
p.2466

**Burton, J Mark**
Profile: p.1317
Table(s): **Kentucky: Real Estate Band 1** p.1314

**Burton, Michael L**
Table(s): **Nationwide: International Trade: Export
Controls & Economic Sanctions Band 3** p.153

**Burton, Preston**
Table(s): District of Columbia: Litigation: White-Collar Crime & Government Investigations Band 2 p.827

**Burton, Richard A**
Profile: p.290
Table(s): Nationwide: Capital Markets: REITs Band 4 p.55

**Burton Jr, John H**
Table(s): Alabama: Banking & Finance: Public Finance Band 2 p.455

**Burwell, Linda G**
Profile: p.1548
Table(s): Michigan: Labor & Employment Band 2 p.1542

**Busenkell, Michael**
Table(s): Delaware: Bankruptcy/Restructuring Band 4 p.754

**Buser, James D**
Table(s): Nebraska: Real Estate Band 2 p.1666

**Busey, Brian**
Profile: p.290
Table(s): Nationwide: International Trade: Intellectual Property (Section 337) Band 3 p.160

**Busey, Roxane C**
Table(s): Illinois: Antitrust Band 2 p.1143

**Busey, Stephen D**
Table(s): Florida: Bankruptcy/Restructuring Band 1 p.939, Florida: Litigation: General Commercial Band 3 p.966

**Bush, Christine K**
Table(s): Rhode Island: Litigation: General Commercial Band 3 p.2254

**Bush, Derek M**
Profile: p.290
Table(s): Nationwide: Financial Services Regulation: Banking (Compliance) Band 1 p.96, Nationwide: Financial Services Regulation: Financial Institutions M&A Band 2 p.96

**Bush, Gayle**
Table(s): Washington: Bankruptcy/Restructuring Band 1 p.2523

**Bush, Glenn**
Table(s): Mississippi: Energy & Natural Resources Band 2 p.1593

**Bush, John**
Table(s): Idaho: Litigation: Medical Malpractice & Insurance Band 2 p.1134

**Bush III, F M**
Table(s): Mississippi: Corporate/Commercial Band 2 p.1591

**Bushnell, Laura**
Profile: p.626
Table(s): California: Corporate/M&A: Venture Capital Band 4 p.555

**Busis, Richard J**
Profile: p.2212
Table(s): Pennsylvania: Corporate/M&A: Securities Band 2 p.2191

**Bussard, Donald A**
Profile: p.768
Table(s): Delaware: Corporate/M&A Band 1 p.761

**Bustamante III, Alberto S**
Profile: p.987
Table(s): Florida: Real Estate: Zoning/Land Use Band 4 p.975

**Busto, Mark**
Table(s): Washington: Labor & Employment Band 1 p.2531

**Butcher, Rebecca**
Profile: p.768
Table(s): Delaware: Chancery Up-and-coming individuals p.758

**Butler, Brian**
Table(s): Wisconsin: Litigation: General Commercial Senior Statesmen: p.2576

**Butler, Christopher**
Profile: p.1200
Table(s): Illinois: Banking & Finance Band 2 p.1145

**Butler, Diane**
Profile: p.2538
Table(s): Washington: Immigration Band 1 p.2528

**Butler, Edward**
Profile: p.1732
Table(s): New Jersey: Real Estate Band 2 p.1728

**Butler, Jim B**
Profile: p.1681
Table(s): Nevada: Environment Band 2 p.1673, Utah: Energy & Natural Resources Band 2 p.2464

**Butler, JoAnn**
Table(s): Idaho: Real Estate: Zoning/Land Use Star Individuals p.1138

**Butler III, A Bates**
Table(s): Arizona: Litigation: White-Collar Crime & Government Investigations Band 2 p.501

**Butler Jr, James R**
Table(s): Nationwide: Leisure & Hospitality Band 3 p.179

**Butler Jr, John Wm**
Profile: p.290
Table(s): Nationwide: Bankruptcy/Restructuring Band 1 p.39, Illinois: Bankruptcy/Restructuring Band 1 p.1148

**Butler, III, James F**
Profile: p.1077
Table(s): Georgia: Construction Band 2 p.1044

**Butswinkas, Dane**
Table(s): District of Columbia: Litigation: General Commercial Band 3 p.826

**Butte, Dagmar**
Table(s): Oregon: Labor & Employment: Immigration Band 1 p.2168

**Butwin, Bradley**
Profile: p.1882
Table(s): New York: Litigation: General Commercial Band 2 p.1833, New York: Litigation: Securities Band 4 p.1833

**Butzier, Stuart**
Table(s): New Mexico: Environment, Natural Resources & Regulated Industries Band 1 p.1766

**Buxton, Anthony**
Profile: p.1397
Table(s): Maine: Energy & Natural Resources Band 1 p.1388

**Buydens, Robert**
Table(s): Michigan: Employee Benefits & Executive Compensation Band 3 p.1540

**Buzecky, Jennifer**
Profile: p.2581
Table(s): Wisconsin: Natural Resources & Environment Band 2 p.2578

**Buzzell, David W**
Table(s): Pennsylvania: Environment Band 2 p.2194

**Byer, Benjamin**
Table(s): Washington: Intellectual Property Associates to watch p.2529

**Byergo, Anthony B**
Profile: p.1635
Table(s): Missouri: Labor & Employment Band 2 p.1625

**Byers, Boyd**
Profile: p.1299
Table(s): Kansas: Labor & Employment Band 2 p.1294

**Bylund, Jacob**
Table(s): Iowa: Litigation: General Commercial Band 4 p.1288

**Byowitz, Michael H**
Profile: p.1882
Table(s): New York: Antitrust Band 2 p.1778

**Byrd, Brian**
Profile: p.2039
Table(s): North Carolina: Real Estate Band 3 p.2037

**Byrd, Michael**
Profile: p.291
Table(s): Nationwide: Energy: Oil & Gas (Transactional) Band 4 p.79

**Byrd, William C**
Table(s): Alabama: Real Estate Band 2 p.466

**Byrne, Brian**
Profile: p.855
Table(s): District of Columbia: Antitrust Band 5 p.787

**Byrne, Jane**
Table(s): New York: Insurance: Dispute Resolution: Insurer Band 2 p.1816

**Byrne, Lawrence**
Profile: p.1882
Table(s): New York: Litigation: White-Collar Crime & Government Investigations Band 2 p.1836

**Byrne, Matthew B**
Table(s): Vermont: Litigation: General Commercial Band 3 p.2486

**Byrne, Michael P**
Profile: p.742
Table(s): Connecticut: Real Estate Band 2 p.740

**Byrne, Richard L**
Table(s): Pennsylvania: Intellectual Property Band 2 p.2197

**Byrne, William**
Profile: p.291
Table(s): Nationwide: Transportation: Rail (for Railroads) Band 2 p.257, Nationwide: Transportation: Road (Carriage/Commercial) Band 3 p.259

## C

**Cable, Stuart M**
Profile: p.1487
Table(s): Massachusetts: Corporate/M&A Band 1 p.1452

**Cabot, Anthony N**
Table(s): Nationwide: Gaming & Licensing Star Individuals p.115, Nevada: Gaming & Licensing Band 1 p.1674

**Cabot, Howard Ross**
Table(s): Arizona: Litigation: General Commercial Band 2 p.501

**Cabou, Jean-Jacques**
Table(s): Arizona: Litigation: White-Collar Crime & Government Investigations Band 3 p.501

**Cabraser, Elizabeth J**
Table(s): Nationwide: Product Liability: Plaintiffs Band 1 p.209

**Caccia, John**
Profile: p.291
Table(s): Nationwide: Investment Funds: Private Equity: Fund Formation Band 4 p.166

**Cacciabeve, Charles J**
Profile: p.987
Table(s): Florida: Construction Band 1 p.944

**Cacheris, Plato**
Table(s): District of Columbia: Litigation: White-Collar Crime & Government Investigations Senior Statesmen: p.827

**Cadwalader, Lynn K**
Profile: p.291
Table(s): Nationwide: Leisure & Hospitality Band 3 p.179

**Cadwallader, John I**
Profile: p.2092
Table(s): Ohio: Real Estate Band 2 p.2086

**Cagle, Molly**
Profile: p.2383
Table(s): Texas: Environment Band 1 p.2343

**Cagle, Steve**
Profile: p.2383
Table(s): Texas: Intellectual Property Band 4 p.2354

**Cagney, Lawrence K**
Table(s): Nationwide: Employee Benefits & Executive Compensation Band 1 p.73, New York: Employee Benefits & Executive Compensation Band 1 p.1802

**Cahalan, Scott D**
Profile: p.1077
Table(s): Georgia: Construction Band 3 p.1044

**Cahan, James N**
Profile: p.1200
Table(s): Illinois: Environment: Mainly Transactional Band 2 p.1162

**Cahill, Mark D**
Profile: p.1487
Table(s): Massachusetts: Litigation: General
Commercial **Band 3** p.1470

**Cahill Jr, Elwood**
Table(s): Louisiana: Real Estate **Band 2** p.1355

**Cahoon, Brad**
Table(s): Utah: Energy & Natural Resources **Band 3** p.2464

**Cahoon, Susan**
Table(s): Georgia: Litigation: General
Commercial **Band 2** p.1065

**Cain, Hugh**
Table(s): Iowa: Labor & Employment **Band 3** p.1285

**Cain, Patricia S**
Profile: p.1200
Table(s): Illinois: Labor & Employment:
Employee Benefits & Compensation **Band 2** p.1176

**Caiola, Paul S**
Table(s): Maryland: Litigation: General
Commercial **Band 3** p.1419

**Cairns, Carolyn**
Table(s): Washington: Labor & Employment **Band 1** p.2531

**Calabrese, Antonio J**
Table(s): Northern Virginia: Real Estate:
Zoning/Land Use **Star individuals** p.2505

**Calabrese, Joseph**
Table(s): Nationwide: Sports Law **Band 2** p.241,
California: Media & Entertainment:
Transactional **Band 1** p.608

**Calamari, Peter E**
Table(s): New York: Litigation: General
Commercial **Band 3** p.1833

**Calamita, Paul**
Table(s): Virginia: Environment **Band 1** p.2495

**Calcagni, Anthony M**
Profile: p.1398
Table(s): Maine: Real Estate **Band 2** p.1395

**Calderin, Jacqueline**
Table(s): Florida: Bankruptcy/Restructuring **Up-and-coming individuals** p.939

**Calderone, Lynda**
Table(s): Pennsylvania: Intellectual Property **Band 3** p.2197

**Caldwell, Charles**
Profile: p.291
Table(s): Nationwide: Energy: Oil & Gas
(Regulatory & Litigation) **Band 1** p.78

**Caldwell, Christopher**
Table(s): California: Litigation: General
Commercial **Band 5** p.593

**Caldwell, Joe R**
Profile: p.856
Table(s): District of Columbia: Litigation:
General Commercial **Band 3** p.826

**Calfo, Angelo J**
Table(s): Washington: Litigation: White-Collar
Crime & Government Investigations **Band 1** p.2533

**Calhoun, Clark**
Profile: p.1077
Table(s): Georgia: Tax **Associates to watch** p.1072

**Califano, Thomas**
Profile: p.1882
Table(s): New York: Bankruptcy/Restructuring **Band 4** p.1782

**Calk, Jeffrey A**
Profile: p.2302
Table(s): Tennessee: Real Estate **Band 2** p.2299

**Calkins, Charles**
Table(s): North Carolina: Intellectual Property **Band 1** p.2030

**Calkins, Mary Craig**
Profile: p.626
Table(s): California: Insurance: Policyholder **Band 2** p.576

**Calkins II, George D**
Table(s): California: Construction: Mediators **Band 2** p.550

**Call, Gregory**
Table(s): California: Litigation: General
Commercial **Band 4** p.593

**Callahan, David K**
Profile: p.1200
Table(s): Illinois: Intellectual Property **Band 3** p.1171

**Callahan, John M**
Profile: p.1200
Table(s): Illinois: Healthcare **Band 3** p.1165

**Callahan, Michael R**
Table(s): Nationwide: Healthcare: Regulatory &
Litigation **Band 3** p.127, Illinois: Healthcare **Band 1** p.1165

**Callahan, Michael R**
Table(s): New Hampshire: Litigation: General
Commercial **Senior Statesmen:** p.1690

**Callahan, Timothy P**
Table(s): Nationwide: Projects **Band 4** p.216

**Calland, Dean**
Table(s): Pennsylvania: Environment **Band 1** p.2194

**Callas, Gretchen M**
Table(s): West Virginia: Litigation: General
Commercial **Up-and-coming individuals** p.2555

**Callaway, Edward M**
Profile: p.2302
Table(s): Tennessee: Environment **Band 2** p.2290

**Callaway Jr, William H**
Table(s): Nationwide: Transportation: Aviation:
Finance **Band 3** p.252

**Callcott, W Hardy**
Profile: p.291
Table(s): Nationwide: Financial Services
Regulation: Broker Dealer (Compliance) **Band 1** p.97, Nationwide: Financial Services Regulation:
Broker Dealer (Enforcement) **Band 2** p.97

**Calli, Paul**
Profile: p.987
Table(s): Florida: Litigation: White-Collar Crime &
Government Investigations **Band 3** p.967

**Callobre, Anthony R**
Profile: p.626
Table(s): California: Banking & Finance **Band 3** p.539

**Calloway, Mark T**
Profile: p.2039
Table(s): North Carolina: Litigation: White-Collar
Crime & Government Investigations **Band 1** p.2034

**Calmann, Arnold B**
Table(s): New Jersey: Litigation: General
Commercial **Band 3** p.1722

**Calsyn, Jeremy**
Profile: p.856
Table(s): District of Columbia: Antitrust **Band 5** p.787

**Calvani, Terry**
Profile: p.856
Table(s): District of Columbia: Antitrust **Band 5** p.787

**Calvaruso, Andrea**
Table(s): New York: Intellectual Property: Trade
Mark & Copyright **Band 3** p.1821

**Calvert, Matthew J**
Profile: p.1077
Table(s): Georgia: Litigation: General
Commercial **Band 3** p.1065

**Calvin, Charles D**
Table(s): Colorado: Real Estate **Band 2** p.714

**Calzacorta, Carmen**
Table(s): Oregon: Corporate/M&A **Band 3** p.2164

**Calzone, David B**
Table(s): Michigan: Labor & Employment **Band 2** p.1542

**Camahort, Steve L**
Profile: p.626
Table(s): California: Corporate/M&A **Band 2** p.553

**Cambridge, James**
Table(s): Michigan: Corporate/M&A **Band 3** p.1538

**Cameli, Mark A**
Profile: p.2581
Table(s): Wisconsin: Litigation: General
Commercial **Band 3** p.2576

**Cameron, E Colby**
Table(s): Rhode Island: Corporate/Commercial **Band 2** p.2251

**Cameron, John**
Profile: p.1548
Table(s): Michigan: Real Estate **Band 3** p.1546

**Cameron, Patrick K**
Table(s): Maryland: Corporate/M&A **Band 3** p.1412

**Cameron Jr, Donald B**
Table(s): Nationwide: International Trade: Trade
Remedies & Trade Policy **Band 2** p.154

**Camp, Jacqueline E**
Table(s): North Carolina: Banking & Finance **Band 3** p.2021

**Camp, John W**
Table(s): Texas: Energy: State Regulatory &
Litigation (Oil & Gas) **Band 2** p.2341

**Camp, Lawton**
Table(s): Nationwide: Capital Markets:
Securitisation **Band 4** p.59

**Camp, Leo**
Profile: p.1317
Table(s): Kentucky: Real Estate **Band 3** p.1314

**Campagna, Larry A**
Table(s): Nationwide: Tax: Fraud **Band 1** p.244,
Texas: Tax: Litigation **Band 1** p.2371

**Campana, Jeremy M**
Profile: p.2092
Table(s): Ohio: Bankruptcy/Restructuring **Band 4** p.2058

**Campbell, Andrew**
Profile: p.2383
Table(s): Texas: Real Estate **Band 3** p.2367

**Campbell, Bruce**
Table(s): Nationwide: Transportation: Aviation:
Litigation **Band 1** p.254

**Campbell, Daniel M**
Profile: p.2508
Table(s): Southern Virginia: Real Estate **Band 1** p.2506

**Campbell, David**
Profile: p.1276
Table(s): Indiana: Litigation: General
Commercial **Senior Statesmen:** p.1273

**Campbell, Donald**
Table(s): Nevada: Litigation: General
Commercial **Band 1** p.1677

**Campbell, Douglas A**
Table(s): Pennsylvania:
Bankruptcy/Restructuring **Band 2** p.2188

**Campbell, Drew**
Table(s): Ohio: Litigation: General Commercial **Band 3** p.2078

**Campbell, Frederick K**
Table(s): Arkansas: Corporate/Commercial **Band 3** p.518

**Campbell, Glenn C**
Table(s): Maryland: Corporate/M&A **Band 2** p.1412

**Campbell, James M**
Table(s): Nationwide: Product Liability & Mass
Torts **Band 2** p.208, Nationwide: Product Liability:
Automobile p.208

**Campbell, John W**
Profile: p.627
Table(s): California: Life Sciences:
Corporate/Commercial **Band 3** p.590

**Campbell, Kevin B**
Table(s): Tennessee: Healthcare **Band 3** p.2291,
Tennessee: Healthcare: Regulatory **Band 1** p.2291

**Campbell, Leah**
Profile: p.1882
Table(s): New York: Insurance: Transactional &
Regulatory **Band 3** p.1816

**Campbell, Margaret Claiborne**
Table(s): Georgia: Environment **Band 1** p.1051

**Campbell, Margaret H**
Profile: p.1078
Table(s): Georgia: Labor & Employment **Band 2** p.1060

**Campbell, Michael**
Table(s): New Mexico: Environment, Natural Resources & Regulated Industries **Band 1** p.1766, New Mexico: Litigation: General Commercial **Band 3** p.1769

**Campbell, Michael G**
Profile: p.1548
Table(s): Michigan: Banking & Finance **Band 2** p.1536

**Campbell, Michael R**
Table(s): Oregon: Environment **Band 2** p.2165

**Campbell, Patrick S**
Profile: p.856
Table(s): District of Columbia: Telecom, Broadcast & Satellite **Band 4** p.844

**Campbell, Rhett G**
Profile: p.2383
Table(s): Texas: Bankruptcy/Restructuring **Band 1** p.2328

**Campbell, Ronald L**
Table(s): Kansas: Litigation: General Commercial **Band 2** p.1295

**Campbell, Roy**
Table(s): Mississippi: Litigation: General Commercial **Band 2** p.1597

**Campbell, Scott**
Table(s): Idaho: Natural Resources & Environment **Band 2** p.1136

**Campbell, Terence**
Table(s): Illinois: Litigation: White-Collar Crime & Government Investigations **Band 3** p.1181

**Campbell, Thomas**
Table(s): Illinois: Antitrust **Senior Statesmen:** p.1143

**Campbell, William**
Table(s): New York: Real Estate: Finance **Band 2** p.1855

**Campbell II, L Webb**
Table(s): Tennessee: Litigation: General Commercial **Band 2** p.2295

**Campbell Jr, Boyd**
Table(s): North Carolina: Banking & Finance **Band 2** p.2021, North Carolina: Corporate/M&A **Band 2** p.2025

**Campbell Jr, Robert R**
Profile: p.2302
Table(s): Tennessee: Real Estate **Band 1** p.2299

**Campellone, Paul**
Profile: p.2256
Table(s): Rhode Island: Corporate/Commercial: Intellectual Property **Band 2** p.2251

**Campion, Kevin**
Profile: p.291
Table(s): Nationwide: Financial Services Regulation: Broker Dealer (Compliance) **Band 3** p.97

**Campion, Thomas**
Profile: p.1732
Table(s): Nationwide: Product Liability & Mass Torts **Band 5** p.208, New Jersey: Litigation: General Commercial **Band 1** p.1722, New Jersey: Litigation: Products Liability **Band 2** p.1722

**Campos, Lorraine**
Table(s): Nationwide: Government: Government Contracts **Band 4** p.117

**Canan, Michael J**
Table(s): Florida: Tax: Employee Benefits **Band 2** p.979

**Cancienne, Phyllis G**
Profile: p.1359
Table(s): Louisiana: Labor & Employment **Band 2** p.1350

**Candler, James**
Profile: p.1548
Table(s): Michigan: Real Estate **Band 2** p.1546

**Cane, Paul**
Table(s): California: Labor & Employment **Band 2** p.587

**Canfield, Kenneth**
Table(s): Georgia: Litigation: General Commercial **Band 2** p.1065

**Canfield, Peter C**
Profile: p.291
Table(s): Nationwide: First Amendment Litigation **Band 2** p.105

**Cannada, Don B**
Profile: p.1602
Table(s): Mississippi: Real Estate **Star individuals** p.1600

**Cannada, R Barry**
Profile: p.1602
Table(s): Mississippi: Corporate/Commercial **Band 1** p.1591

**Cannon, James**
Table(s): North Carolina: Intellectual Property **Band 1** p.2030

**Cannon, Kathleen**
Table(s): Nationwide: International Trade: Trade Remedies & Trade Policy **Band 5** p.154

**Cannon, Kim D**
Table(s): Wyoming: Litigation: General Commercial **Band 1** p.2598

**Cannon, William**
Table(s): North Carolina: Intellectual Property **Associates to watch** p.2030

**Cannon III, John J**
Table(s): New York: Employee Benefits & Executive Compensation **Band 2** p.1802

**Cannon Jr, George D**
Profile: p.291
Table(s): Nationwide: Energy: Electricity (Regulatory & Litigation) **Band 5** p.76

**Cannone, Frank T**
Profile: p.1732
Table(s): New Jersey: Corporate/M&A **Band 4** p.1707

**Cannuscio, Robert**
Profile: p.2212
Table(s): Pennsylvania: Intellectual Property **Band 4** p.2197

**Canterbury Jr, Joseph F**
Table(s): Texas: Construction **Senior Statesmen:** p.2335

**Cantero, Raoul**
Profile: p.987
Table(s): Nationwide: Appellate Law **Band 4** p.26, Florida: Litigation: Appellate **Band 1** p.972

**Cantlin, Richard**
Table(s): Oregon: Real Estate **Senior Statesmen:** p.2173

**Canton, Doreen**
Profile: p.2092
Table(s): Ohio: Labor & Employment **Band 2** p.2074

**Capel, Christopher**
Profile: p.2039
Table(s): North Carolina: Corporate/M&A **Band 3** p.2025

**Capell, David C**
Table(s): California: Insurance: Insurer **Band 3** p.574

**Capelouto, Richard**
Profile: p.627
Table(s): Nationwide: Private Equity: Buyouts **Band 2** p.203, California: Corporate/M&A **Band 3** p.553, California: Corporate/M&A: Private Equity **Band 1** p.553

**Capers, John**
Profile: p.1078
Table(s): Georgia: Corporate/M&A **Band 2** p.1046

**Caplan, David L**
Profile: p.1882
Table(s): New York: Corporate/M&A **Band 2** p.1793

**Caplan, Gordon**
Profile: p.1882
Table(s): Nationwide: Private Equity: Buyouts **Band 4** p.203, New York: Technology & Outsourcing **Band 3** p.1868

**Caplan, Stuart A**
Profile: p.291
Table(s): Nationwide: Energy: Electricity (Regulatory & Litigation) **Band 2** p.76

**Caples, Michael D**
Profile: p.1602
Table(s): Mississippi: Environment **Band 2** p.1594

**Capone Kirk, Shannon**
Table(s): Nationwide: Litigation: E-Discovery **Band 3** p.187

**Caporizzo, A William**
Profile: p.1487
Table(s): Massachusetts: Tax **Band 2** p.1481

**Cappellanti, Ellen**
Table(s): West Virginia: Corporate/Commercial **Band 1** p.2550

**Cappello, Juan Pablo**
Profile: p.988
Table(s): Florida: Latin American Investment **Band 1** p.963

**Cappola, Jeffrey**
Table(s): New Jersey: Environment **Band 3** p.1711

**Capps, Bryan**
Table(s): Florida: Construction **Band 3** p.944

**Capraro Jr, Joseph A**
Table(s): Massachusetts: Intellectual Property **Band 3** p.1463

**Capshaw, Richard A**
Table(s): Texas: Construction **Band 3** p.2335

**Capute, Courtney G**
Profile: p.292
Table(s): Nationwide: Leisure & Hospitality **Band 4** p.179

**Carden, Donald**
Profile: p.1882
Table(s): New York: Tax **Band 4** p.1862

**Cárdenas, M. Cristina**
Profile: p.292
Table(s): Nationwide: International Arbitration **Up-and-coming individuals** p.145

**Carder-Thompson, Elizabeth**
Table(s): Nationwide: Healthcare: Regulatory & Litigation **Band 1** p.127, District of Columbia: Healthcare **Band 1** p.809

**Cardonick, Andrew**
Profile: p.1201
Table(s): Illinois: Banking & Finance **Band 4** p.1145

**Caresani, Ann M.**
Profile: p.2092
Table(s): Ohio: Employee Benefits & Executive Compensation **Band 3** p.2067

**Carey, Diana**
Table(s): Washington: Bankruptcy/Restructuring **Band 1** p.2523

**Carey, Jason**
Profile: p.292
Table(s): Nationwide: Government: Government Contracts **Up-and-coming individuals** p.117

**Carey, Michael R**
Table(s): Florida: Construction **Band 2** p.944

**Carey, Michael W**
Table(s): West Virginia: Litigation: General Commercial **Band 2** p.2555

**Carey, Robert**
Profile: p.2176
Table(s): Oregon: Labor & Employment **Band 2** p.2168

**Carey, Scott**
Table(s): Illinois: Insurance: Dispute Resolution **Band 2** p.1168

**Carey, Stevens**
Table(s): California: Real Estate **Band 1** p.611

**Cargile, Ann Peldo**
Table(s): Tennessee: Real Estate **Band 1** p.2299

**Carickhoff, David**
Profile: p.768
Table(s): Delaware: Bankruptcy/Restructuring **Band 4** p.754

**Carter, Francis L**
Table(s): Florida: Bankruptcy/Restructuring
Senior Statesmen: p.939

**Carter, J. Kenneth**
Profile: p.2268
Table(s): South Carolina: Litigation: General
Commercial Band 4 p.2264

**Carter, James H**
Profile: p.292
Table(s): Nationwide: International Arbitration
Senior Statesmen: p.145, Nationwide: International
Arbitration: Arbitrators Senior Statesmen: p.145

**Carter, Leon**
Table(s): Texas: Litigation: General Commercial
Band 4 p.2362

**Carter, Mark**
Table(s): West Virginia: Labor & Employment
Band 1 p.2553

**Carter, Peter W**
Table(s): Minnesota: Litigation: General
Commercial Band 1 p.1574

**Carter Jr, Winstol D**
Profile: p.2383
Table(s): Texas: Litigation: General Commercial
Band 4 p.2362

**Caruso II, Ralph A**
Profile: p.1276
Table(s): Indiana: Corporate/M&A Band 3 p.1268

**Carver, M Hampton**
Table(s): Louisiana: Energy & Natural
Resources: Oil & Gas Senior Statesmen: p.1344

**Carver, Mark**
Table(s): Tennessee: Real Estate Band 2 p.2299

**Carvin, Michael A**
Profile: p.292
Table(s): Nationwide: Appellate Law Band 2 p.26

**Cary, George S**
Profile: p.856
Table(s): District of Columbia: Antitrust Band 1
p.787

**Cary, Robert**
Table(s): District of Columbia: Litigation: White-
Collar Crime & Government Investigations Band 4
p.827

**Caryl, Michael E**
Profile: p.2561
Table(s): West Virginia: Corporate/Commercial:
Tax Band 1 p.2550

**Casablanca, Maria Isabel**
Table(s): Florida: Immigration Band 3 p.956

**Casarona, Robert B**
Profile: p.2092
Table(s): Ohio: Litigation: General Commercial
Band 4 p.2078, Ohio: Natural Resources &
Environment Band 4 p.2083

**Cascarilla, Ralph E**
Profile: p.2092
Table(s): Ohio: Litigation: White-Collar Crime &
Government Investigations Band 1 p.2079

**Casciari, Mark**
Profile: p.292
Table(s): Nationwide: ERISA Litigation Band 3
p.92

**Case, Charles D**
Profile: p.2040
Table(s): North Carolina: Environment Star Individ-
uals p.2028

**Casey, Barbara A**
Profile: p.1732
Table(s): New Jersey: Real Estate Band 2 p.1728

**Casey, David**
Profile: p.1487
Table(s): Massachusetts: Labor & Employment
Band 1 p.1466

**Casey, Edward J**
Profile: p.627
Table(s): California: Real Estate: Zoning/Land
Use Band 3 p.612

**Casey, George**
Profile: p.1883
Table(s): New York: Corporate/M&A Band 5
p.1793

**Casey, James A**
Table(s): Nationwide: Wealth Management:
Central Region Up-and-coming Individuals p.266

**Casey, Kevin**
Table(s): Pennsylvania: Intellectual Property
Band 2 p.2197

**Casey, Michael W**
Table(s): Florida: Labor & Employment Star individuals p.959

**Casey, Richard D**
Table(s): South Dakota: Labor & Employment
Band 1 p.2283

**Casey, Robert**
Profile: p.1359
Table(s): Louisiana: Corporate/M&A: Tax Star indi-
viduals p.1341

**Casey, Robert P**
Profile: p.1201
Table(s): Illinois: Labor & Employment Band 3
p.1175

**Casey, Warren J**
Profile: p.1733
Table(s): New Jersey: Corporate/M&A Band 2
p.1707

**Casey, William J**
Table(s): California: Insurance: Insurer Band 2
p.574

**Cashdan, Jeffrey**
Profile: p.1078
Table(s): Georgia: Antitrust Band 1 p.1037

**Cashen, John C**
Profile: p.1548
Table(s): Michigan: Labor & Employment Band 3
p.1542

**Casiello Jr, Nicholas**
Profile: p.292
Table(s): Nationwide: Gaming & Licensing Band 1
p.115

**Cason, Len**
Profile: p.2147
Table(s): Oklahoma: Corporate/Commercial: Tax
Band 1 p.2134

**Casper Jr, Paul W**
Table(s): Ohio: Natural Resources &
Environment Senior Statesmen: p.2083

**Cassada, Garland S**
Table(s): North Carolina:
Bankruptcy/Restructuring Band 1 p.2023

**Cassanos, Robert**
Profile: p.1883
Table(s): New York: Tax Band 2 p.1862

**Casserly, James L**
Profile: p.856
Table(s): District of Columbia: Telecom,
Broadcast & Satellite Band 1 p.844

**Cassidy, Bart**
Table(s): Pennsylvania: Environment Band 2
p.2194

**Cassidy, David R**
Table(s): Louisiana: Corporate/M&A: Tax Band 2
p.1341

**Cassilly, Lisa H**
Profile: p.1078
Table(s): Georgia: Labor & Employment Band 3
p.1060

**Castaldo, Paula**
Table(s): New Jersey: Labor & Employment Up-
and-coming Individuals p.1718

**Caster, Lauren James**
Table(s): Arizona: Environment (including water
rights) Band 4 p.497

**Castle, Bruce**
Table(s): New Mexico: Real Estate Band 2 p.1772

**Castrodale, Joseph A**
Profile: p.2092
Table(s): Ohio: Litigation: General Commercial
Band 4 p.2078

**Catalano, Richard**
Profile: p.292
Table(s): Nationwide: Capital Markets: REITs
Band 1 p.55, New York: Tax Band 4 p.1862

**Cataxinos, Edgar R**
Table(s): Utah: Intellectual Property Band 3
p.2466

**Caterine, Melinda J**
Profile: p.1398
Table(s): Maine: Labor & Employment Band 2
p.1390

**Cates, C Thomas**
Table(s): Tennessee: Real Estate Band 3 p.2299

**Cathcart, Patrick**
Table(s): California: Insurance: Insurer Band 2
p.574

**Catillaz, Margaret A**
Table(s): Nationwide: Immigration Band 3 p.131,
New York: Immigration Band 2 p.1814

**Catino, Ann M**
Table(s): Connecticut: Environment Band 3 p.733

**Catlett, Steven T**
Table(s): Illinois: Labor & Employment Band 3
p.1175

**Cattel, Thomas A**
Profile: p.1548
Table(s): Michigan: Labor & Employment Band 3
p.1542

**Catullo, Kim M**
Table(s): New Jersey: Litigation: Products
Liability Band 2 p.1723

**Caudill, William H**
Profile: p.2383
Table(s): Texas: Tax Band 3 p.2371

**Caudle Jr, Larry W**
Table(s): Virginia: Construction Band 3 p.2491

**Cauley, Michelle**
Table(s): Arkansas: Litigation: Medical
Malpractice Defense Band 2 p.522

**Caulkins, Charles**
Profile: p.988
Table(s): Florida: Labor & Employment Band 1
p.959

**Cavalieri, Nick V**
Table(s): Ohio: Bankruptcy/Restructuring Band 2
p.2058

**Cavanagh, Rita A**
Profile: p.857
Table(s): District of Columbia: Tax Band 3 p.838

**Cavanagh, William G**
Profile: p.1883
Table(s): New York: Tax Band 4 p.1862

**Cavanagh Jr, Joseph V**
Table(s): Rhode Island: Litigation: General
Commercial Star individuals p.2254

**Cavanaugh, David L**
Profile: p.857
Table(s): District of Columbia: Intellectual
Property: Litigation Band 4 p.821

**Cavanaugh Jr, William (Chip) T**
Table(s): Texas: Real Estate Band 2 p.2367

**Cavazos, Edward A**
Profile: p.2384
Table(s): Texas: Technology: Corporate &
Commercial Band 3 p.2375

**Cave, Bradley**
Profile: p.2601
Table(s): Wyoming: Labor & Employment Band 1
p.2597

**Cavender, C Paul**
Table(s): Alabama: Litigation: General
Commercial Band 3 p.463

**Caverly, Joseph L**
Table(s): Louisiana: Corporate/M&A Band 2
p.1341

**Caviani Pease, Ann M**
Profile: p.293
Table(s): Nationwide: Life Sciences: IP/Patent
Litigation Band 3 p.183

**Cawley, Douglas**
Profile: p.2384
Table(s): Texas: Intellectual Property Band 1
p.2354

**Cayne, Howard N**
Profile: p.293
Table(s): **Nationwide**: Financial Services Regulation: Banking (Enforcement & Investigations) **Band 3** p.97

**Cecere, Dominic J**
Table(s): **Minnesota**: Labor & Employment **Band 3** p.1571

**Cederoth, Richard A**
Profile: p.1201
Table(s): **Illinois**: Intellectual Property **Band 2** p.1171

**Celebrezze, Bruce**
Table(s): **California**: Insurance: Insurer **Band 3** p.574

**Cendali, Dale**
Profile: p.1883
Table(s): **New York**: Intellectual Property: Trade Mark & Copyright **Band 1** p.1821, **New York**: Media & Entertainment: Copyright & Contract Disputes **Band 1** p.1851

**Centrella, Nicholas M**
Table(s): **Pennsylvania**: Litigation: General Commercial **Band 4** p.2203

**Cerabino, Thomas M**
Profile: p.1883
Table(s): **New York**: Corporate/M&A **Band 3** p.1793

**Cerasani, Denise**
Profile: p.1883
Table(s): **New York**: Corporate/M&A **Band 5** p.1793

**Cerasia II, Ed**
Profile: p.1883
Table(s): **New York**: Labor & Employment **Band 3** p.1826

**Cereghini, Paul G**
Profile: p.293
Table(s): **Nationwide**: Product Liability & Mass Torts **Band 2** p.208, **Nationwide**: Product Liability: Automobile p.208

**Ceresney, Andrew J**
Table(s): **Nationwide**: Securities: Regulation: Enforcement **Band 2** p.233, **New York**: Litigation: White-Collar Crime & Government Investigations **Band 2** p.1836

**Cerezo, Francisco**
Table(s): **Florida**: Latin American Investment **Band 3** p.963

**Cermak Jr, John F**
Profile: p.627
Table(s): **California**: Environment **Band 3** p.564

**Cernelich, John R**
Profile: p.2092
Table(s): **Ohio**: Labor & Employment **Band 4** p.2074

**Cerone, Rudy**
Profile: p.1359
Table(s): **Louisiana**: Bankruptcy/Restructuring **Band 2** p.1337

**Cerra, Suzanne**
Profile: p.1733
Table(s): **New Jersey**: Labor & Employment **Band 2** p.1718

**Cerrito, Chris**
Profile: p.742
Table(s): **Connecticut**: Corporate/M&A **Band 3** p.732

**Chadwell, Robert G**
Table(s): **Washington**: Litigation: White-Collar Crime & Government Investigations **Band 1** p.2533

**Chadwick, James**
Table(s): **California**: Media & Entertainment: First Amendment Litigation **Band 2** p.606

**Chae, Meryl K**
Profile: p.627
Table(s): **California**: Real Estate **Band 4** p.611

**Chaffetz, Peter**
Profile: p.293
Table(s): **Nationwide**: Insurance: Dispute Resolution: Reinsurance **Band 1** p.135, **New York**: Insurance: Dispute Resolution: Insurer **Band 2** p.1816

**Chaiken, Frank D**
Profile: p.2092
Table(s): **Ohio**: Corporate/M&A **Band 4** p.2064

**Chaiken, Paul**
Table(s): **Maine**: Litigation: General Commercial **Band 3** p.1393

**Chaikovsky, Yar R**
Profile: p.627
Table(s): **California**: Intellectual Property: Patent **Band 3** p.578

**Chalk, Wm David**
Profile: p.1425
Table(s): **Maryland**: Corporate/M&A **Band 2** p.1412

**Chalmers, Arthur S**
Table(s): **Kansas**: Litigation: General Commercial **Band 3** p.1295

**Chalos, Michael G**
Table(s): **Nationwide**: Transportation: Shipping: Litigation (New York) **Band 3** p.261

**Chalsen, Christopher**
Profile: p.1883
Table(s): **New York**: Intellectual Property: Patent **Band 3** p.1820

**Chambers, J Michael**
Table(s): **Nationwide**: Capital Markets: Debt & Equity **Band 4** p.46, **Texas**: Capital Markets: Debt & Equity **Band 3** p.2333

**Chambers, Lawrence**
Profile: p.2148
Table(s): **Oklahoma**: Corporate/Commercial **Band 3** p.2134

**Chambers, Matthew**
Table(s): **North Carolina**: Corporate/M&A **Associates to watch** p.2025

**Chambers, Reid**
Table(s): **Nationwide**: Native American Law **Band 1** p.192

**Chambers, Robert C**
Profile: p.1078
Table(s): **Georgia**: Construction **Band 2** p.1044

**Chamlin, Marc**
Profile: p.1883
Table(s): **New York**: Media & Entertainment: Film & Television **Band 1** p.1849

**Champlin, Steve**
Table(s): **Minnesota**: Construction **Band 1** p.1567

**Champoux, David**
Profile: p.1398
Table(s): **Maine**: Corporate/M&A **Band 1** p.1385

**Chan, Ashely M**
Profile: p.2212
Table(s): **Pennsylvania**: Bankruptcy/Restructuring **Band 3** p.2188

**Chandler, John A**
Profile: p.1078
Table(s): **Georgia**: Litigation: General Commercial **Band 1** p.1065

**Chandler, L Kay**
Table(s): **California**: Life Sciences: Corporate/Commercial **Band 3** p.590

**Chaney, James**
Table(s): **Oklahoma**: Litigation: General Commercial **Band 3** p.2141

**Chang, Carmen I**
Profile: p.627
Table(s): **California**: Corporate/M&A: Deals in Asia **Band 3** p.553

**Chang, Corlis J**
Table(s): **Hawaii**: Litigation: General Commercial **Band 2** p.1119

**Chang, Leo**
Table(s): **Nationwide**: Transportation: Shipping: Finance (New York) **Band 1** p.260

**Chang, Wesley Y S**
Table(s): **Hawaii**: Real Estate **Band 1** p.1120

**Chanin, Jeffrey R**
Table(s): **California**: Intellectual Property: Trademark, Copyright & Trade Secrets **Band 1** p.578

**Chanin, Leonard**
Profile: p.293
Table(s): **Nationwide**: Financial Services Regulation: Consumer Finance (Compliance) **Band 3** p.98

**Chao, Cedric**
Profile: p.293
Table(s): **Nationwide**: International Arbitration **Band 4** p.145

**Chao, Howard**
Table(s): **California**: Corporate/M&A: Deals in Asia **Band 1** p.553

**Chapin, David C**
Table(s): **Nationwide**: Private Equity: Buyouts **Band 1** p.203, **Massachusetts**: Corporate/M&A **Band 1** p.1452, **Massachusetts**: Private Equity: Buyouts **Band 1** p.1474

**Chaplick, Trevor J**
Table(s): **District of Columbia**: Corporate/M&A & Private Equity **Band 3** p.797

**Chapman, Drew G L**
Profile: p.293
Table(s): **Nationwide**: Investment Funds: Hedge Funds **Band 3** p.162

**Chapman, Jeffrey A**
Profile: p.2384
Table(s): **Texas**: Capital Markets: Debt & Equity **Band 3** p.2333, **Texas**: Corporate/M&A **Star Individuals** p.2337

**Chapman, William**
Profile: p.2538
Table(s): **Washington**: Environment **Band 2** p.2527

**Chapman, William L**
Table(s): **New Hampshire**: Litigation: General Commercial **Band 2** p.1690

**Chapman Jr, Ron**
Profile: p.2384
Table(s): **Texas**: Labor & Employment **Band 3** p.2359

**Chappelear, Stephen**
Profile: p.2092
Table(s): **Ohio**: Litigation: General Commercial **Band 4** p.2078

**Chappell, Brian**
Table(s): **Nationwide**: Projects: Renewables & Alternative Energy **Band 2** p.218

**Charbonneau, Robert**
Table(s): **Florida**: Bankruptcy/Restructuring **Band 3** p.939

**Charles, Pamela**
Table(s): **Washington**: Corporate/Commercial: Tax **Band 1** p.2525

**Charles, Scott K**
Profile: p.293
Table(s): **Nationwide**: Bankruptcy/Restructuring **Band 2** p.39, **New York**: Bankruptcy/Restructuring **Band 2** p.1782

**Charlton, Paul**
Table(s): **Arizona**: Litigation: White-Collar Crime & Government Investigations **Band 2** p.501

**Charnes, Adam H**
Table(s): **North Carolina**: Litigation: General Commercial **Band 3** p.2033

**Charness, Michael**
Profile: p.293
Table(s): **Nationwide**: Government: Government Contracts **Band 2** p.117

**Charney, Steven M**
Profile: p.1883
Table(s): **New York**: Construction **Band 2** p.1791

**Charnley, Richard**
Profile: p.627
Table(s): **California**: Media & Entertainment: Litigation **Band 4** p.606

**Charyk, William**
Profile: p.857
Table(s): **District of Columbia**: Employee Benefits & Executive Compensation **Band 3** p.801

**Chase, Jeffrey**
Table(s): **Colorado**: Litigation: General Commercial **Band 1** p.709

**Chase, Terri L**
Profile: p.1884
Table(s): **New York**: Labor & Employment **Band 4** p.1826

**Childs Jr, James W**
Table(s): **Alabama:** Corporate/Commercial **Band 3** p.459

**Chiles IV, E B (Chip)**
Profile: p.526
Table(s): **Arkansas:** Labor & Employment **Band 3** p.520, **Arkansas:** Litigation: General Commercial **Band 2** p.522

**Chilton, Frederick**
Profile: p.628
Table(s): **California:** Tax **Band 1** p.617

**Chimento, George L**
Profile: p.1487
Table(s): **Massachusetts:** Employee Benefits & Executive Compensation **Band 1** p.1455

**Chincheck, Julia A**
Profile: p.2562
Table(s): **West Virginia:** Corporate/Commercial: Banking & Finance **Band 2** p.2550

**Chine, Jeffrey**
Profile: p.628
Table(s): **California:** Real Estate: Zoning/Land Use **Band 3** p.612

**Chip, William W**
Profile: p.857
Table(s): **District of Columbia:** Tax **Band 4** p.838

**Chiperfield, Robert N**
Profile: p.294
Table(s): **Nationwide:** Capital Markets: Structured Products **Band 3** p.52

**Chipman, William E**
Table(s): **Delaware:** Bankruptcy/Restructuring **Up-and-coming individuals** p.754

**Chisholm, David**
Table(s): **Montana:** Corporate/M&A **Band 1** p.1646

**Chittick, Michael D**
Profile: p.2256
Table(s): **Rhode Island:** Labor & Employment **Band 2** p.2253

**Chlebus, Andrew J**
Profile: p.2256
Table(s): **Rhode Island:** Corporate/Commercial: Banking & Finance **Band 1** p.2251

**Choi, Byung**
Table(s): **Massachusetts:** Banking & Finance **Band 3** p.1445

**Choi, Chuck C**
Table(s): **Hawaii:** Bankruptcy/Restructuring **Band 1** p.1114

**Choi, Paul L**
Profile: p.1201
Table(s): **Illinois:** Corporate/M&A **Band 2** p.1156

**Chopra, Apalla**
Table(s): **California:** Labor & Employment **Band 3** p.587

**Chory, John**
Table(s): **Nationwide:** Investment Funds: Venture Capital **Band 3** p.174, **Massachusetts:** Private Equity: Venture Capital Investment **Band 1** p.1474

**Chriss, Timothy**
Table(s): **Maryland:** Real Estate **Band 2** p.1422

**Christen, Amy M**
Table(s): **Michigan:** Employee Benefits & Executive Compensation **Band 3** p.1540

**Christensen, Amy D**
Table(s): **Montana:** Labor & Employment **Band 2** p.1648

**Christensen, Craig W**
Table(s): **Idaho:** Bankruptcy/Restructuring **Band 2** p.1131

**Christensen, Douglas**
Table(s): **North Dakota:** Corporate/Commercial **Band 2** p.2051

**Christensen, Douglas R**
Table(s): **Minnesota:** Labor & Employment **Band 2** p.1571

**Christensen, Kory D**
Table(s): **Utah:** Intellectual Property **Band 3** p.2466

**Christensen, Larry E**
Profile: p.294
Table(s): **Nationwide:** International Trade: Export Controls & Economic Sanctions **Band 2** p.153

**Christensen, Mark A**
Table(s): **Nebraska:** Litigation: Insurance **Band 2** p.1664, **Nebraska:** Litigation: Mediators **Band 1** p.1664

**Christensen, Wallace A**
Table(s): **District of Columbia:** Insurance: Insurer **Band 3** p.816

**Christensen III, Henry**
Profile: p.294
Table(s): **Nationwide:** Wealth Management: Eastern Region **Band 1** p.267

**Christian, Betty Jo**
Table(s): **Nationwide:** Transportation: Rail (for Railroads) **Senior Statesmen:** p.257

**Christian, Edward R**
Table(s): **Alabama:** Corporate/Commercial **Band 2** p.459

**Christian, Elizabeth H**
Table(s): **New Jersey:** Healthcare **Band 2** p.1715

**Christian, Thomas W**
Table(s): **Alabama:** Litigation: General Commercial **Band 1** p.463

**Christiansen, Brian D.**
Profile: p.294
Table(s): **Nationwide:** Financial Services Regulation: Financial Institutions M&A **Up-and-coming individuals** p.99

**Christiansen, Mark D**
Profile: p.2148
Table(s): **Oklahoma:** Energy & Natural Resources **Band 1** p.2136

**Christiansen, Stephen**
Table(s): **Utah:** Litigation: General Commercial **Band 3** p.2468

**Christiansen, Steven J**
Table(s): **Utah:** Energy & Natural Resources **Band 3** p.2464

**Christianson, Cabot**
Table(s): **Alaska:** Corporate/M&A: Bankruptcy **Band 1** p.487

**Christie, R. Lee**
Profile: p.1201
Table(s): **Illinois:** Tax **Band 3** p.1192

**Christie, Scott**
Profile: p.1733
Table(s): **New Jersey:** Intellectual Property **Band 2** p.1716

**Christman, James**
Profile: p.2508
Table(s): **Virginia:** Environment **Band 2** p.2495

**Christopher, Thomas H**
Table(s): **Georgia:** Labor & Employment **Band 4** p.1060

**Christy, Angela M**
Table(s): **Minnesota:** Real Estate **Band 1** p.1576

**Christy, Walter W**
Profile: p.1359
Table(s): **Louisiana:** Labor & Employment **Band 2** p.1350

**Christy Jr, David S**
Profile: p.294
Table(s): **Nationwide:** International Trade: Trade Remedies & Trade Policy **Band 5** p.154

**Chu, Morgan**
Profile: p.628
Table(s): **Nationwide:** Litigation: Trial Lawyers **Band 1** p.187, **California:** Intellectual Property: Patent **Star individuals** p.578

**Chu, Wilson**
Profile: p.2384
Table(s): **Texas:** Technology: Corporate & Commercial **Band 3** p.2375

**Chumrau, Gary B**
Profile: p.1653
Table(s): **Montana:** Corporate/M&A **Band 1** p.1646

**Chun, Deborah**
Table(s): **Hawaii:** Corporate/Commercial: Finance **Band 1** p.1116, **Hawaii:** Real Estate **Star individuals** p.1120

**Chun, Ed**
Table(s): **Hawaii:** Real Estate **Senior Statesmen:** p.1120

**Chung, Ernest**
Profile: p.294
Table(s): **Nationwide:** Projects **Band 4** p.216

**Chung, Steven**
Profile: p.295
Table(s): **Nationwide:** Transportation: Aviation: Finance **Up-and-coming individuals** p.252

**Chuquimia, Ruben K**
Table(s): **Missouri:** Corporate/M&A **Band 3** p.1619

**Church, Pamela**
Table(s): **New York:** Intellectual Property: Trade Mark & Copyright **Band 3** p.1821

**Churchill, David A**
Profile: p.295
Table(s): **Nationwide:** Government: Government Contracts **Band 1** p.117

**Ciabarra, Laura G**
Profile: p.1884
Table(s): **New York:** Real Estate: Finance **Band 2** p.1855

**Ciardi, Albert**
Table(s): **Pennsylvania:** Bankruptcy/Restructuring **Band 4** p.2188

**Cicarella, Thomas**
Profile: p.2092
Table(s): **Ohio:** Banking & Finance **Band 1** p.2056

**Cicchillo Jr, Richard**
Table(s): **Georgia:** Corporate/M&A **Band 4** p.1046

**Cieri, Richard M**
Profile: p.295
Table(s): **Nationwide:** Bankruptcy/Restructuring **Band 1** p.39, **New York:** Bankruptcy/Restructuring **Band 1** p.1782

**Ciesla, Frank R**
Table(s): **New Jersey:** Healthcare **Band 1** p.1715

**Cifelli, James**
Table(s): **Georgia:** Bankruptcy/Restructuring **Band 2** p.1042

**Cimino Jr, Thomas P.**
Profile: p.1201
Table(s): **Illinois:** Litigation: General Commercial **Band 4** p.1180

**Cimo, David C**
Table(s): **Florida:** Bankruptcy/Restructuring **Band 2** p.939

**Cino, Vincent**
Profile: p.1733
Table(s): **New Jersey:** Labor & Employment **Band 2** p.1718

**Cinquegrana, Jack**
Profile: p.1487
Table(s): **Massachusetts:** Litigation: White-Collar Crime & Government Investigations **Band 1** p.1471

**Cipolla, John S**
Profile: p.2093
Table(s): **Ohio:** Intellectual Property **Band 2** p.2071

**Cipriano, Renee**
Table(s): **Illinois:** Environment: Mainly Transactional **Band 1** p.1162

**Ciraolo, Caroline**
Profile: p.295
Table(s): **Nationwide:** Tax: Fraud **Up-and-coming individuals** p.244

**Ciresi, Michael V**
Profile: p.1578
Table(s): **Nationwide:** Product Liability: Plaintiffs **Band 3** p.209, **Minnesota:** Litigation: General Commercial **Band 1** p.1574, **Minnesota:** Litigation: Intellectual Property **Band 1** p.1574

**Ciriaco, Anthony C**
Profile: p.2093
Table(s): **Ohio:** Employee Benefits & Executive Compensation **Band 2** p.2067

**Ciucci, Joseph A**
Table(s): **Georgia:** Labor & Employment **Band 4** p.1060

**Cividanes, Emilio W**
Profile: p.295
Table(s): **Nationwide:** Privacy & Data Security **Band 2** p.199

# Index of Lawyers

**Cohen, H Rodgin**
Profile: p.297
Table(s): Nationwide: Financial Services Regulation: Banking (Compliance) **Star Individuals** p.96, Nationwide: Financial Services Regulation: Banking (Enforcement & Investigations) **Band 1** p.96, Nationwide: Financial Services Regulation: Financial Institutions M&A **Star Individuals** p.96, New York: Corporate/M&A **Star Individuals** p.1793

**Cohen, Harry P**
Profile: p.1885
Table(s): New York: Insurance: Dispute Resolution: Insurer **Band 3** p.1816

**Cohen, James I.**
Profile: p.1398
Table(s): Maine: Energy & Natural Resources **Band 2** p.1388

**Cohen, Jay**
Profile: p.1885
Table(s): New York: Media & Entertainment: Copyright & Contract Disputes **Band 2** p.1851

**Cohen, Jay G**
Table(s): Maryland: Corporate/M&A **Band 4** p.1412

**Cohen, Jeffrey**
Profile: p.717
Table(s): Colorado: Litigation: General Commercial **Band 4** p.709

**Cohen, Jeffrey H**
Profile: p.628
Table(s): California: Corporate/M&A: Private Equity **Band 2** p.553, California: Corporate/M&A **Band 3** p.553

**Cohen, Jill**
Table(s): California: Media & Entertainment: Transactional **Band 2** p.608

**Cohen, Joel M**
Profile: p.1885
Table(s): New York: Antitrust **Band 3** p.1778

**Cohen, Jon**
Table(s): Arizona: Corporate/M&A **Band 2** p.495

**Cohen, Jules**
Table(s): Florida: Bankruptcy/Restructuring **Senior Statesmen:** p.939

**Cohen, Kimberly**
Table(s): Massachusetts: Tax: Estate Planning **Band 1** p.1481

**Cohen, Lewis**
Profile: p.297
Table(s): Nationwide: Capital Markets: Securitisation **Band 3** p.59

**Cohen, Lori G**
Profile: p.1078
Table(s): Nationwide: Product Liability & Mass Torts **Band 2** p.208, Nationwide: Product Liability: Pharmaceutical p.208, Georgia: Litigation: General Commercial **Band 1** p.1065

**Cohen, Louis**
Profile: p.1202
Table(s): Illinois: Real Estate **Band 2** p.1187

**Cohen, Marc S**
Profile: p.629
Table(s): California: Bankruptcy/Restructuring **Band 2** p.542

**Cohen, Margaret R**
Profile: p.1488
Table(s): Massachusetts: Corporate/M&A **Band 4** p.1452

**Cohen, Mark S**
Profile: p.1885
Table(s): New York: Litigation: White-Collar Crime & Government Investigations **Band 3** p.1836

**Cohen, Matthew**
Table(s): Washington: Environment **Band 1** p.2527

**Cohen, Michael**
Table(s): New Jersey: Litigation: Insurance **Band 2** p.1723

**Cohen, Michael P A**
Table(s): District of Columbia: Antitrust **Band 4** p.787

**Cohen, Murry B**
Profile: p.2385
Table(s): Texas: Litigation: Appellate **Band 3** p.2361

**Cohen, N Jerold**
Table(s): Nationwide: Tax: Controversy **Band 1** p.244, Georgia: Tax **Star Individuals** p.1072

**Cohen, Nancy S**
Table(s): Nationwide: Insurance: Dispute Resolution: Policyholder **Band 2** p.137, California: Insurance: Policyholder **Band 3** p.576

**Cohen, Nelson C**
Table(s): District of Columbia: Bankruptcy/Restructuring **Band 3** p.792

**Cohen, R Scott**
Profile: p.2385
Table(s): Texas: Corporate/M&A **Band 2** p.2337

**Cohen, Richard S**
Profile: p.507
Table(s): Arizona: Labor & Employment **Band 1** p.499

**Cohen, Robert**
Profile: p.1667
Table(s): Nebraska: Healthcare **Band 1** p.1661

**Cohen, Robin L**
Profile: p.297
Table(s): Nationwide: Insurance: Dispute Resolution: Policyholder **Band 1** p.137, New York: Insurance: Dispute Resolution: Policyholder **Band 1** p.1816

**Cohen, Ronald Jay**
Table(s): Arizona: Litigation: General Commercial **Band 3** p.501

**Cohen, Stanley H**
Table(s): Pennsylvania: Intellectual Property **Senior Statesmen:** p.2197

**Cohen, Stephen M L**
Profile: p.1488
Table(s): Massachusetts: Private Equity: Buyouts **Band 2** p.1474

**Cohen, Steve**
Table(s): Colorado: Real Estate **Band 3** p.714

**Cohen, Steven**
Table(s): New Hampshire: Corporate/Commercial **Band 1** p.1685, New Hampshire: Corporate/Commercial: Tax **Band 1** p.1685

**Cohen, Steven**
Profile: p.1733
Table(s): New Jersey: Corporate/M&A **Band 1** p.1707

**Cohen, Steven M.**
Table(s): New York: Litigation: White-Collar Crime & Government Investigations **Band 3** p.1836

**Cohen, Steven N**
Profile: p.297
Table(s): Nationwide: Banking & Finance **Band 4** p.31

**Cohen, Susan**
Profile: p.297
Table(s): Nationwide: Immigration **Band 2** p.131

**Cohen (formerly Flowe), Carol Connor**
Profile: p.297
Table(s): Nationwide: ERISA Litigation **Band 2** p.92

**Cohn, Daniel C**
Table(s): Massachusetts: Bankruptcy/Restructuring **Band 1** p.1449

**Cohn, Joel M**
Profile: p.857
Table(s): District of Columbia: Labor & Employment **Band 3** p.824

**Cohn, Joshua**
Table(s): Nationwide: Capital Markets: Derivatives **Band 1** p.51

**Cohn, Lawrence B**
Table(s): California: Life Sciences: Corporate/Commercial **Band 3** p.590

**Cohn, Robert**
Table(s): Nationwide: Transportation: Aviation: Regulatory **Band 2** p.256

**Coil, James**
Table(s): Georgia: Labor & Employment **Band 1** p.1060

**Cokeley, Bryan R**
Profile: p.2562
Table(s): West Virginia: Labor & Employment **Band 1** p.2553

**Coker, Diana Vellos**
Table(s): California: Immigration **Band 3** p.571

**Cokinos, Gregory**
Table(s): Texas: Construction **Band 1** p.2335

**Colacino, Antonio**
Table(s): Iowa: Real Estate **Band 2** p.1290

**Colagiovanni, Joseph**
Profile: p.1636
Table(s): Missouri: Real Estate **Band 2** p.1633

**Colaizzi, Roger**
Profile: p.297
Table(s): Nationwide: Advertising: Litigation **Band 2** p.19

**Colbo, Kimberlee A**
Table(s): Alaska: Labor & Employment **Band 2** p.489

**Coldwell, Deborah S**
Table(s): Nationwide: Franchising **Band 2** p.111

**Cole, Alexandra**
Table(s): Nationwide: Leisure & Hospitality **Band 4** p.179, Illinois: Construction **Band 2** p.1154, Illinois: Real Estate **Band 4** p.1187

**Cole, Christopher**
Profile: p.297
Table(s): Nationwide: Advertising: Litigation **Band 2** p.19

**Cole, Christopher**
Profile: p.1694
Table(s): New Hampshire: Litigation: General Commercial **Band 4** p.1690

**Cole, Clark**
Table(s): Missouri: Litigation: General Commercial **Band 2** p.1629

**Cole, Danielle J**
Profile: p.1078
Table(s): Georgia: Construction **Up-and-coming individuals** p.1044

**Cole, Edward**
Table(s): Florida: Environment **Up-and-coming individuals** p.951

**Cole, J Chase**
Table(s): Tennessee: Corporate/M&A **Band 1** p.2288

**Cole, Terry**
Table(s): Florida: Environment **Band 1** p.951

**Cole, Thomas A**
Profile: p.1202
Table(s): Illinois: Corporate/M&A **Star Individuals** p.1156

**Cole, William**
Table(s): California: Labor & Employment **Band 2** p.587

**Cole, William**
Table(s): Idaho: Corporate/Commercial **Band 1** p.1132

**Colella, Paul**
Table(s): New Jersey: Corporate/M&A **Band 3** p.1707

**Coleman, C Payson**
Table(s): Nationwide: Banking & Finance: Equipment Finance & Leasing **Band 2** p.32, Nationwide: Transportation: Aviation: Finance **Band 2** p.252

**Coleman, Charles T**
Profile: p.526
Table(s): Arkansas: Litigation: General Commercial **Band 2** p.522

**Coleman, Graham**
Table(s): New York: Media & Entertainment: Theatre **Band 2** p.1850

**Coleman, Ira**
Profile: p.297
Table(s): Nationwide: Healthcare: Transactional **Band 1** p.128, Florida: Healthcare **Band 1** p.954

**Coleman, James**
Table(s): Texas: Litigation: General Commercial **Senior Statesmen:** p.2362

**Coleman, James M**
Table(s): Virginia: Labor & Employment **Band 3**
p.2500

**Coleman, Jeffrey**
Table(s): Minnesota: Construction **Band 1** p.1567

**Coleman, Jill A**
Table(s): Illinois: Banking & Finance **Band 4**
p.1145

**Coleman, John**
Table(s): Alabama: Labor & Employment **Band 2**
p.460

**Coleman, Joseph M**
Profile: p.2385
Table(s): Texas: Bankruptcy/Restructuring **Band 2**
p.2328

**Coleman, Ken**
Table(s): New York: Bankruptcy/Restructuring
**Band 3** p.1782

**Coleman, Patrick D**
Profile: p.988
Table(s): Florida: Labor & Employment **Senior
Statesmen**: p.959

**Coleman, Stuart H**
Table(s): Nationwide: Investment Funds:
Registered Funds **Band 1** p.170

**Coleman, Tony C**
Profile: p.1317
Table(s): Kentucky: Labor & Employment **Band 2**
p.1310

**Coleman, W Chris**
Profile: p.2148
Table(s): Oklahoma: Corporate/Commercial **Band
1** p.2134

**Coleman IV, J Walker**
Profile: p.2268
Table(s): South Carolina: Labor & Employment
**Band 2** p.2262

**Coleman Jr, Ronald T**
Table(s): Georgia: Litigation: General
Commercial **Band 4** p.1065

**Coleman, Jr, Aubrey L**
Profile: p.1079
Table(s): Georgia: Construction **Band 1** p.1044

**Colen, Frederick H**
Table(s): Pennsylvania: Intellectual Property
**Band 2** p.2197

**Coletti, Robert E**
Profile: p.2093
Table(s): Ohio: Corporate/M&A **Band 2** p.2064

**Colgin Jr, William F**
Profile: p.297
Table(s): Nationwide: Tax: Controversy **Band 3**
p.244, California: Tax **Band 3** p.617

**Colin-Antonini, Carolina**
Table(s): Georgia: Immigration **Band 1** p.1055

**Colker, David**
Profile: p.629
Table(s): California: Tax **Band 3** p.617

**Colletta, Anthony J**
Profile: p.298
Table(s): Nationwide: Capital Markets: REITs
**Band 3** p.55, Nationwide: Real Estate **Band 2**
p.225, New York: Real Estate: Corporate **Band 2**
p.1854

**Colley, Mark**
Profile: p.298
Table(s): Nationwide: Government: Government
Contracts **Band 2** p.117

**Collier, H Guy**
Profile: p.857
Table(s): District of Columbia: Healthcare **Band 2**
p.809

**Collier, Philip W**
Profile: p.1317
Table(s): Kentucky: Litigation: General
Commercial **Band 1** p.1312

**Collier, Stacie B**
Profile: p.2256
Table(s): Rhode Island: Labor & Employment
**Band 1** p.2253

**Collier, William H**
Table(s): Nationwide: Transportation: Shipping:
Litigation (outside New York) **Band 3** p.263

**Collin, Thomas J**
Profile: p.2093
Table(s): Nationwide: Franchising **Band 4** p.111,
Ohio: Litigation: Antitrust **Band 1** p.2078

**Collings, Robert L**
Table(s): Pennsylvania: Environment **Band 2**
p.2194

**Collins, Brendan K**
Profile: p.2213
Table(s): Pennsylvania: Environment **Band 2**
p.2194

**Collins, Christopher H**
Profile: p.857
Table(s): District of Columbia: Real Estate:
Zoning/Land Use **Band 3** p.835

**Collins, Daniel**
Profile: p.298
Table(s): Nationwide: Appellate Law **Band 3** p.26

**Collins, Dennis G**
Table(s): Missouri: Labor & Employment **Band 2**
p.1625

**Collins, Erika C**
Table(s): New York: Labor & Employment **Band 3**
p.1826

**Collins, Jeffrey D**
Profile: p.1488
Table(s): Massachusetts: Hedge & Mutual
Funds **Band 2** p.1461

**Collins, Joseph**
Profile: p.1202
Table(s): Illinois: Litigation: General Commercial
**Band 4** p.1180

**Collins, Kevin H**
Table(s): Iowa: Litigation: General Commercial
**Band 3** p.1288

**Collins, Mark D**
Profile: p.768
Table(s): Delaware: Bankruptcy/Restructuring
**Star Individuals** p.754

**Collins, Michael**
Profile: p.857
Table(s): District of Columbia: Employee
Benefits & Executive Compensation **Band 3** p.801

**Collins, Patrick**
Table(s): Illinois: Litigation: White-Collar Crime &
Government Investigations **Band 3** p.1181

**Collins, Patrick**
Profile: p.1886
Table(s): New York: Labor & Employment **Band 4**
p.1826

**Collins, Thomas**
Profile: p.1488
Table(s): Massachusetts: Banking & Finance:
Public Finance **Band 2** p.1446

**Collins, Wayne Dale**
Table(s): New York: Antitrust **Band 2** p.1778

**Collins Jr, P Clarkson**
Table(s): Delaware: Chancery **Band 3** p.758

**Collora, Michael A**
Table(s): Massachusetts: Litigation: White-Collar
Crime & Government Investigations **Band 2**
p.1471

**Collyer, Glenn**
Table(s): California: Banking & Finance **Band 4**
p.539

**Colman, Jeffrey D**
Profile: p.1202
Table(s): Illinois: Litigation: General Commercial
**Band 4** p.1180

**Colodny, Mike**
Profile: p.988
Table(s): Florida: Insurance **Band 3** p.957

**Colomb, P. Kevin**
Profile: p.1360
Table(s): Louisiana: Gaming & Licensing **Band 3**
p.1348

**Colson, Dean**
Table(s): Florida: Litigation: General Commercial
**Senior Statesmen**: p.966

**Colson, Randall E**
Table(s): Texas: Technology: Outsourcing **Band 3**
p.2376

**Colton, Neal**
Profile: p.2213
Table(s): Pennsylvania:
Bankruptcy/Restructuring **Band 2** p.2188

**Colton, Roberta**
Table(s): Florida: Bankruptcy/Restructuring **Band
1** p.939

**Columbia, Sarah Chapin**
Profile: p.1488
Table(s): Massachusetts: Intellectual Property
**Band 2** p.1463

**Colvin, R Keith**
Profile: p.1360
Table(s): Louisiana: Real Estate **Band 1** p.1355

**Combs, Philip J**
Table(s): West Virginia: Litigation: General
Commercial **Band 3** p.2555

**Combs, Terri**
Table(s): Iowa: Litigation: General Commercial
**Band 4** p.1288

**Comella, Philip L.**
Profile: p.1202
Table(s): Illinois: Environment: Litigation **Band 3**
p.1162

**Comer, Ann K**
Profile: p.2581
Table(s): Wisconsin: Real Estate **Band 3** p.2579

**Comerford, David L**
Profile: p.2213
Table(s): Pennsylvania: Litigation: Securities
**Band 2** p.2204

**Comiter, Richard**
Table(s): Florida: Tax **Band 1** p.979, Florida: Tax:
Estate Planning **Band 2** p.979

**Comizio, V. Gerard**
Table(s): Nationwide: Financial Services
Regulation: Banking (Compliance) **Band 4** p.96

**Comodeca, Peter J**
Profile: p.2093
Table(s): Ohio: Construction **Band 3** p.2062

**Compernolle, Paul**
Profile: p.1202
Table(s): Illinois: Labor & Employment:
Employee Benefits & Compensation **Band 3**
p.1176

**Compton, Gregory A**
Table(s): Kentucky: Real Estate **Band 2** p.1314

**Compton, Paul**
Table(s): Alabama: Banking & Finance **Band 1**
p.455, Alabama: Banking & Finance: Mainly
Regulatory **Band 1** p.455

**Comstock, David**
Table(s): Idaho: Litigation: Medical Malpractice
& Insurance **Band 2** p.1134

**Conard, David**
Table(s): Vermont: Real Estate **Band 2** p.2487

**Conde, Dominick A**
Profile: p.1886
Table(s): New York: Intellectual Property: Patent
**Band 3** p.1820

**Conde, Kathryn Keough**
Profile: p.1488
Table(s): Massachusetts: Antitrust **Band 3** p.1444

**Condlin, Andrew M**
Table(s): Southern Virginia: Real Estate:
Zoning/Land Use **Band 1** p.2506

**Condo, James**
Table(s): Arizona: Litigation: General
Commercial **Band 3** p.501

**Confalone, Perry W**
Table(s): Hawaii: Labor & Employment **Band 1**
p.1117

**Congdon, Charles B**
Profile: p.2213
Table(s): Pennsylvania: Banking & Finance **Band
2** p.2186

**Conigliaro, Matthew J**
Profile: p.988
Table(s): Florida: Litigation: Appellate **Band 2**
p.972

**Cooper, Donald D**
Profile: p.1488
Table(s): Massachusetts: Environment Band 3
p.1457

**Cooper, Elizabeth A**
Profile: p.298
Table(s): Nationwide: Financial Services
Regulation: Financial Institutions M&A Up-and-
coming individuals p.99

**Cooper, Felise**
Table(s): New York: Environment: Mainly
Transactional Associates to watch p.1808

**Cooper, Glenn M.**
Profile: p.988
Table(s): Florida: Immigration Up-and-coming indi-
viduals p.956

**Cooper, H Wayne**
Profile: p.2148
Table(s): Oklahoma: Corporate/Commercial Band
2 p.2134

**Cooper, James**
Profile: p.2385
Table(s): Texas: Insurance Band 2 p.2351

**Cooper, James D**
Profile: p.298
Table(s): Nationwide: Banking & Finance Band 1
p.31

**Cooper, James W**
Profile: p.858
Table(s): District of Columbia: Litigation: White-
Collar Crime & Government Investigations Band 4
p.827

**Cooper, Jay L**
Profile: p.629
Table(s): California: Media & Entertainment:
Transactional: Mainly Talent Band 1 p.609

**Cooper, Jenny**
Profile: p.1488
Table(s): Massachusetts: Labor & Employment
Up-and-coming individuals p.1466

**Cooper, John H**
Profile: p.468
Table(s): Alabama: Corporate/Commercial Band
2 p.459

**Cooper, Jonathan**
Profile: p.1203
Table(s): Illinois: Banking & Finance Band 4
p.1145

**Cooper, M Scott**
Profile: p.629
Table(s): California: Real Estate Band 3 p.611

**Cooper, Mary Quinn**
Profile: p.2148
Table(s): Oklahoma: Litigation: General
Commercial Band 2 p.2141

**Cooper, Richard J**
Profile: p.1886
Table(s): New York: Latin American Investment
Band 1 p.1829

**Cooper, Richard M**
Table(s): District of Columbia: Healthcare:
Pharmaceutical/Medical Products Regulatory
Band 1 p.810

**Cooper, Robert E**
Profile: p.298
Table(s): Nationwide: Litigation: Trial Lawyers
Senior Statesmen: p.186, California: Antitrust Senior
Statesmen: p.536

**Cooper, Samuel W**
Profile: p.2385
Table(s): Texas: Litigation: Securities Band 2
p.2362

**Cooper, Scott**
Profile: p.1488
Table(s): Massachusetts: Real Estate Band 2
p.1478

**Cooper, Scott**
Profile: p.2213
Table(s): Pennsylvania: Labor & Employment
Band 2 p.2200

**Cooper, Tammy**
Profile: p.2386
Table(s): Texas: Energy: State Regulatory &
Litigation (Electricity) Band 2 p.2341

**Cooperman, Harriet E**
Table(s): Maryland: Labor & Employment Band 3
p.1417

**Cooperman, Marc S**
Profile: p.1203
Table(s): Illinois: Intellectual Property Band 3
p.1171

**Cope, Gerald**
Table(s): Florida: Litigation: Appellate Band 3
p.972

**Copeland, Greg**
Table(s): Mississippi: Litigation: General
Commercial Band 2 p.1597

**Copeland, Gregory**
Profile: p.2386
Table(s): Texas: Litigation: Energy & Natural
Resources Band 1 p.2361

**Copeland Jr, Timothy E**
Table(s): Vermont: Labor & Employment Band 3
p.2485

**Copen, Robert A**
Profile: p.298
Table(s): Nationwide: Banking & Finance Band 4
p.31

**Copenhaver, Karen F**
Profile: p.1489
Table(s): Massachusetts: Intellectual Property:
Licensing Band 1 p.1463

**Copenhaver, W Andrew**
Table(s): North Carolina: Antitrust Band 1 p.2020,
North Carolina: Litigation: General Commercial
Band 2 p.2033

**Copenhefer, Lea Anne**
Profile: p.299
Table(s): Nationwide: Investment Funds:
Registered Funds Band 2 p.170, Massachusetts:
Hedge & Mutual Funds Band 2 p.1461

**Coran, Michael**
Table(s): Pennsylvania: Litigation: General
Commercial Band 3 p.2203

**Corash, Michèle B**
Profile: p.629
Table(s): California: Environment Band 1 p.564

**Corbett, Sherrill A**
Profile: p.2176
Table(s): Oregon: Corporate/M&A Band 2 p.2164

**Corbin, Peter**
Profile: p.988
Table(s): Florida: Labor & Employment Band 4
p.959

**Corbin, Robert L**
Table(s): California: Litigation: White-Collar
Crime & Government Investigations Band 2 p.601

**Corbyn, George**
Table(s): Oklahoma: Litigation: General
Commercial Band 1 p.2141

**Cordell, David R**
Table(s): Oklahoma: Labor & Employment Band 1
p.2140

**Cordell, Ruffin**
Table(s): Nationwide: International Trade:
Intellectual Property (Section 337) Band 1 p.160,
District of Columbia: Intellectual Property:
Litigation Band 1 p.821

**Cordero, Frank**
Table(s): Florida: Tax Band 3 p.979

**Cordero, Luis A**
Table(s): Florida: Immigration Band 2 p.956

**Cordiano, Dean M**
Profile: p.742
Table(s): Connecticut: Environment Band 3 p.733

**Cordone, Michael J**
Table(s): Pennsylvania:
Bankruptcy/Restructuring Band 4 p.2188

**Corgan, Brian**
Table(s): Georgia: Construction Band 1 p.1044

**Corlew, John**
Table(s): Mississippi: Environment Band 2
p.1594, Mississippi: Litigation: General
Commercial Band 1 p.1597

**Corman, Karen L**
Profile: p.629
Table(s): California: Labor & Employment Band 4
p.587

**Corn-Revere, Robert**
Table(s): Nationwide: First Amendment
Litigation Band 3 p.105, District of Columbia:
Media & Entertainment Band 1 p.832, District of
Columbia: Media & Entertainment: Mainly
Regulatory Band 1 p.832

**Cornelius, O Ray**
Profile: p.1360
Table(s): Louisiana: Banking & Finance: Public
Finance Band 1 p.1335

**Cornell, James L**
Table(s): Texas: Insurance Band 2 p.2351

**Cornell, Laurel**
Profile: p.1317
Table(s): Kentucky: Labor & Employment
Associates to watch p.1310

**Cornish, Kelley A**
Profile: p.1886
Table(s): New York: Bankruptcy/Restructuring
Band 4 p.1782

**Cornwell, David KS**
Table(s): District of Columbia: Intellectual
Property: Patent Prosecution Band 2 p.820

**Corr, Kelly**
Table(s): Washington: Litigation: General
Commercial Band 1 p.2533

**Corrales, Carmen Amalia**
Profile: p.1886
Table(s): New York: Latin American Investment
Band 3 p.1829

**Corrigan, Sean F**
Profile: p.299
Table(s): Nationwide: Transportation: Aviation:
Finance Band 3 p.252

**Corrigan Jr, William M**
Table(s): Missouri: Litigation: General
Commercial Band 3 p.1629

**Corson, Samantha R**
Profile: p.2213
Table(s): Pennsylvania: Environment Band 4
p.2194

**Cortell, Nina**
Table(s): Texas: Litigation: Appellate Band 1
p.2361

**Cortes, Jessica**
Profile: p.1886
Table(s): New York: Labor & Employment Up-and-
coming individuals p.1826

**Cortesio, John**
Table(s): Iowa: Corporate/M&A Senior Statesmen:
p.1283

**Coruzzi, Laura A**
Profile: p.1886
Table(s): New York: Intellectual Property: Patent
Band 2 p.1820

**Coryell II, Cornelius E**
Profile: p.1317
Table(s): Kentucky: Litigation: General
Commercial Band 3 p.1312

**Cosby, Cameron**
Profile: p.299
Table(s): Nationwide: Capital Markets: REITs
Band 4 p.55

**Coscarelli, Dianne S**
Profile: p.2093
Table(s): Ohio: Real Estate Band 2 p.2086

**Cosper Jr, Harvey L**
Table(s): North Carolina: Litigation: Healthcare
& Medical Malpractice Band 1 p.2034

**Costello, James**
Table(s): Maine: Energy & Natural Resources
Band 3 p.1388

**Costello, Joseph J**
Profile: p.2213
Table(s): Pennsylvania: Labor & Employment
Band 2 p.2200

**Costello, Kenneth R**
Table(s): Nationwide: Franchising Band 2 p.111

**Costello Slovak, Patricia**
Table(s): Illinois: Labor & Employment Band 2
p.1175

**Costley, Kevin**
Table(s): Minnesota: Corporate/M&A Band 4
p.1569

**Coston, William**
Profile: p.858
Table(s): District of Columbia: Intellectual
Property: Litigation Band 4 p.821

**Cotchett, Joseph**
Table(s): Nationwide: Litigation: Trial Lawyers
Band 2 p.187, California: Litigation: General
Commercial Band 1 p.593, California: Litigation:
Securities Band 1 p.593

**Cotney, Trenton**
Table(s): Florida: Construction Band 3 p.944

**Cotropia, Charles S**
Profile: p.2386
Table(s): Texas: Intellectual Property: Trade
Mark & Copyright Band 3 p.2354

**Cottam, Dale**
Table(s): Wyoming: Corporate/M&A Band 1
p.2596, Wyoming: Corporate/M&A: Bankruptcy
Band 1 p.2596

**Cottingham, Dale E.**
Table(s): Oklahoma: Energy & Natural
Resources Band 2 p.2136

**Cottingham III, T Thomas**
Profile: p.2040
Table(s): North Carolina: Litigation: General
Commercial Band 2 p.2033

**Cottle, Lisa A**
Profile: p.629
Table(s): California: Energy: State Regulatory &
Litigation Band 3 p.562

**Cotton, Raymond**
Profile: p.858
Table(s): District of Columbia: Employee
Benefits & Executive Compensation Band 3 p.801

**Cotton, Stuart**
Table(s): New York: Insurance: Dispute
Resolution: Insurer Band 3 p.1816

**Cottrell III, Frederick L**
Profile: p.769
Table(s): Delaware: Intellectual Property Band 1
p.763

**Couch, Kimberly S**
Profile: p.1398
Table(s): Maine: Labor & Employment: Employee
Benefits & Compensation Band 3 p.1390

**Coughlin, Jennifer**
Profile: p.492
Table(s): Alaska: Litigation: General Commercial
Band 3 p.490

**Coughlin, Kevin**
Table(s): New Jersey: Litigation: Insurance Band
2 p.1723

**Coughlin, Patrick J**
Profile: p.629
Table(s): California: Litigation: Securities Senior
Statesmen: p.594

**Coughlin, William E**
Profile: p.2093
Table(s): Ohio: Natural Resources &
Environment Band 4 p.2083

**Coulson, David A**
Profile: p.989
Table(s): Florida: Litigation: General Commercial
Band 4 p.966

**Coulter, Nate**
Table(s): Arkansas: Litigation: General
Commercial Band 2 p.522

**Coupe, Bradford W**
Profile: p.1398
Table(s): Maine: Labor & Employment Band 3
p.1390

**Court, Leonard**
Table(s): Oklahoma: Labor & Employment Band 1
p.2140

**Courtnage, Michael S**
Table(s): Washington: Real Estate Band 2 p.2535

**Courtney, Keith**
Profile: p.2386
Table(s): Texas: Environment Band 3 p.2343

**Cousins, Scott**
Table(s): Delaware: Bankruptcy/Restructuring
Band 3 p.754

**Coutroulis, Chris S**
Profile: p.989
Table(s): Florida: Antitrust Band 1 p.935, Florida:
Litigation: General Commercial Band 4 p.966

**Coverdale, Brent**
Table(s): Missouri: Labor & Employment Band 3
p.1625

**Covey, J Tyson**
Table(s): Illinois: Communications Band 2 p.1153

**Covit, Barrie B**
Profile: p.299
Table(s): Nationwide: Investment Funds: Private
Equity: Fund Formation Band 2 p.166

**Cowan, Cameron**
Profile: p.299
Table(s): Nationwide: Capital Markets:
Securitisation Senior Statesmen: p.59

**Cowan, H Mitchell**
Profile: p.1602
Table(s): Mississippi: Litigation: General
Commercial Band 3 p.1597

**Cowan, Kevin**
Table(s): Florida: Real Estate Band 3 p.974

**Cowan, Pamela S**
Table(s): Washington: Immigration Band 1 p.2528

**Cowan, Peter S**
Profile: p.1694
Table(s): New Hampshire: Litigation: General
Commercial Band 4 p.1690

**Cowan, Stephen A**
Profile: p.630
Table(s): California: Real Estate Band 2 p.611

**Cowart, Richard**
Profile: p.2302
Table(s): Tennessee: Healthcare Band 1 p.2291

**Cowden, John**
Profile: p.1636
Table(s): Missouri: Litigation: General
Commercial Band 2 p.1628

**Cowen, Stephen**
Profile: p.1079
Table(s): Georgia: Litigation: White-Collar Crime
& Government Investigations Band 1 p.1066

**Cowling, David**
Profile: p.2386
Table(s): Texas: Tax Band 3 p.2371

**Cowlishaw, Patrick R**
Profile: p.2386
Table(s): Texas: Energy: State Regulatory &
Litigation (Electricity) Band 2 p.2341

**Cox, Brian**
Profile: p.299
Table(s): Nationwide: Capital Markets:
Securitisation Up-and-coming Individuals p.59

**Cox, David**
Table(s): Tennessee: Corporate/M&A Band 2
p.2288

**Cox, David S**
Table(s): South Carolina: Litigation: General
Commercial Band 3 p.2264

**Cox, Donald**
Table(s): Kentucky: Litigation: General
Commercial Band 1 p.1312

**Cox, Randy**
Table(s): Montana: Litigation: General
Commercial Band 1 p.1649

**Cox, Rob**
Table(s): North Carolina:
Bankruptcy/Restructuring Band 2 p.2023

**Cox, Robert K**
Table(s): Virginia: Construction Band 2 p.2491

**Cox, Trey**
Profile: p.2386
Table(s): Texas: Litigation: General Commercial
Band 3 p.2362

**Cox, W Donald**
Table(s): Florida: Insurance Senior Statesmen:
p.957

**Cox, Walter B**
Table(s): Arkansas: Litigation: Medical
Malpractice Defense Band 1 p.522

**Cox, Yvette**
Table(s): Ohio: Bankruptcy/Restructuring Band 4
p.2058

**Cox Jr, Robert D**
Table(s): Massachusetts: Environment Band 2
p.1457

**Coxe, Henry M**
Table(s): Florida: Litigation: White-Collar Crime &
Government Investigations Band 1 p.967

**Coyle, Michael F**
Table(s): Nebraska: Litigation: General
Commercial Band 1 p.1664, Nebraska: Litigation:
Insurance Band 1 p.1664

**Coyne, Thomas J**
Profile: p.2093
Table(s): Ohio: Real Estate Band 1 p.2086

**Cozen, Stephen A**
Profile: p.299
Table(s): Nationwide: Insurance: Dispute
Resolution: Insurer Band 3 p.134

**Crabb, Joseph**
Profile: p.507
Table(s): Arizona: Corporate/M&A Band 3 p.495

**Crabbe, Deborah**
Table(s): Washington: Bankruptcy/Restructuring
Band 2 p.2523

**Crabtree, Daniel D**
Table(s): Kansas: Litigation: General
Commercial Band 3 p.1295

**Craco, Louis A**
Table(s): Nationwide: International Arbitration:
Arbitrators Band 1 p.146

**Craft, Randal Robert**
Profile: p.299
Table(s): Nationwide: Transportation: Aviation:
Litigation Band 1 p.254

**Craig, Ashley**
Profile: p.299
Table(s): Nationwide: Transportation: Shipping:
Regulatory (outside New York) Up-and-coming individuals p.264

**Craig, Barbara**
Table(s): Oregon: Environment Band 3 p.2165

**Craig, Carolyn**
Table(s): California: IT & Outsourcing Band 3
p.583

**Craig, Molly Hood**
Profile: p.2268
Table(s): South Carolina: Litigation: General
Commercial Band 4 p.2264

**Craig III, Allen B**
Profile: p.2386
Table(s): Texas: Tax Band 4 p.2371

**Crain, Stephen B**
Profile: p.2386
Table(s): Texas: Litigation: General Commercial
Band 4 p.2362

**Cramer, Eric**
Table(s): Pennsylvania: Antitrust Band 2 p.2184

**Crane, R Max**
Profile: p.1733
Table(s): New Jersey: Corporate/M&A Band 3
p.1707

**Crane, Steven**
Table(s): California: Insurance: Insurer Band 1
p.574

**Cranford, Bryant K**
Table(s): Arkansas: Labor & Employment:
Employee Benefits & Compensation Band 2
p.521

**Cranmer, Thomas W**
Profile: p.1549
Table(s): Michigan: Litigation: White-Collar Crime
& Government Investigations Band 1 p.1544

**Cranshaw, David W**
Table(s): Georgia: Bankruptcy/Restructuring
Band 2 p.1042

**Cranston, David**
Profile: p.630
Table(s): California: Environment Band 4 p.564

**Crapo, David**
Profile: p.1733
Table(s): New Jersey: Bankruptcy/Restructuring Band 4 p.1705

**Crass, Kevin**
Profile: p.526
Table(s): Arkansas: Litigation: General Commercial Band 1 p.522

**Craven, George W**
Table(s): Illinois: Tax Band 3 p.1192

**Crawford, Bradley C**
Profile: p.630
Table(s): California: Banking & Finance Band 4 p.539

**Crawford, Joseph C**
Profile: p.2213
Table(s): Pennsylvania: Litigation: General Commercial Band 3 p.2203

**Crawford, Nick**
Table(s): Idaho: Litigation: Medical Malpractice & Insurance Band 2 p.1134

**Crawford, Nicole A**
Table(s): North Carolina: Labor & Employment Band 3 p.2031

**Crawford, Roy J**
Table(s): Alabama: Corporate/Commercial Band 3 p.459

**Crawford, Vaughn**
Table(s): Nationwide: Product Liability & Mass Torts Band 5 p.208

**Crawshaw-Sparks, Sandra**
Table(s): New York: Media & Entertainment: Copyright & Contract Disputes Band 3 p.1851

**Creamer, Michael**
Table(s): Idaho: Natural Resources & Environment Band 2 p.1136

**Creamer Jr, Ronald E**
Profile: p.1886
Table(s): New York: Tax Band 2 p.1862

**Creed, John J**
Profile: p.1887
Table(s): New York: Tax Band 4 p.1862

**Creem, Gary**
Table(s): Massachusetts: Banking & Finance Band 3 p.1445

**Creighton, Susan A**
Table(s): District of Columbia: Antitrust Band 2 p.787

**Cremin, Pat**
Profile: p.2148
Table(s): Oklahoma: Labor & Employment Band 1 p.2140

**Crenshaw Jr, Waverly D**
Profile: p.2302
Table(s): Tennessee: Labor & Employment Band 2 p.2293

**Creps, Clay**
Profile: p.2176
Table(s): Oregon: Labor & Employment Band 2 p.2168

**Creswell, Randy**
Table(s): Maine: Corporate/M&A: Bankruptcy Band 2 p.1385

**Crew, Eugene**
Table(s): California: Antitrust Senior Statesmen: p.536

**Crewdson, Robert L**
Profile: p.1079
Table(s): Georgia: Construction Band 2 p.1044

**Cribley, James M**
Profile: p.1122
Table(s): Hawaii: Corporate/Commercial Band 2 p.1116

**Crider, Marcus**
Profile: p.2303
Table(s): Tennessee: Labor & Employment Band 3 p.2293

**Crimmins, Stephen J**
Profile: p.299
Table(s): Nationwide: Securities: Regulation: Enforcement Band 3 p.233

**Cripps Jr, Jesse A**
Profile: p.630
Table(s): California: Labor & Employment Band 4 p.587

**Crisafi, Frank A**
Table(s): Georgia: Tax Band 3 p.1072

**Crisman Jr, C Benjamin**
Profile: p.858
Table(s): District of Columbia: Antitrust Band 3 p.787

**Crist, John G**
Table(s): Montana: Labor & Employment Band 2 p.1648

**Crist, Thomas O**
Profile: p.2093
Table(s): Ohio: Construction Band 4 p.2062

**Critchley, Sr., Michael**
Table(s): New Jersey: Litigation: White-Collar Crime & Government Investigations Band 1 p.1723

**Critchlow, Richard H**
Table(s): Florida: Litigation: General Commercial Band 1 p.966

**Critelli Jr, Nicholas**
Table(s): Iowa: Litigation: General Commercial Band 3 p.1288

**Croall, David T**
Profile: p.2093
Table(s): Ohio: Labor & Employment Band 4 p.2074

**Crochet, Anne J**
Table(s): Louisiana: Environment Band 1 p.1346

**Crochet, Vicki**
Table(s): Louisiana: Labor & Employment Band 2 p.1350

**Crocker, Shelly**
Table(s): Washington: Bankruptcy/Restructuring Band 2 p.2523

**Crocker, Thomas E**
Profile: p.299
Table(s): Nationwide: International Trade: Export Controls & Economic Sanctions Band 2 p.153

**Croke, James**
Table(s): Nationwide: Capital Markets: Securitisation Band 2 p.59

**Cromwell, David**
Table(s): Louisiana: Banking & Finance Band 1 p.1335, Louisiana: Real Estate Band 2 p.1355

**Cronan, Todd**
Profile: p.1489
Table(s): Massachusetts: Litigation: White-Collar Crime & Government Investigations Band 2 p.1471

**Cronan IV, Charles J**
Profile: p.1318
Table(s): Kentucky: Litigation: General Commercial Star Individuals p.1312

**Cronic, Jason P**
Profile: p.858
Table(s): District of Columbia: Insurance: Insurer Band 4 p.816

**Cronin, Denis**
Profile: p.1887
Table(s): New York: Bankruptcy/Restructuring Senior Statesmen: p.1782

**Cronin, Michael J.**
Profile: p.2581
Table(s): Wisconsin: Intellectual Property Associates to watch p.2573

**Cronin, William**
Table(s): Washington: Litigation: General Commercial Band 2 p.2533

**Cronk, Peter J**
Table(s): Pennsylvania: Intellectual Property Band 2 p.2197

**Crook Martin, Linda**
Profile: p.2148
Table(s): Oklahoma: Energy & Natural Resources: Environment Band 1 p.2136

**Crosby, Dani**
Table(s): Alaska: Litigation: General Commercial Band 3 p.490

**Crosby, E Howell**
Profile: p.1360
Table(s): Louisiana: Real Estate Band 3 p.1355

**Crosby, Lisa A**
Profile: p.299
Table(s): Nationwide: International Trade: Export Controls & Economic Sanctions Band 2 p.153

**Cross, Bruce Michael**
Table(s): Washington: Labor & Employment Band 2 p.2531

**Cross, J Bruce**
Table(s): Arkansas: Labor & Employment Band 2 p.520

**Cross, James**
Profile: p.300
Table(s): Nationwide: Banking & Finance Band 1 p.31, Nationwide: Private Equity: Buyouts Band 3 p.203

**Cross, Jeffery M**
Profile: p.1203
Table(s): Illinois: Antitrust Band 2 p.1143

**Cross, Patrick**
Table(s): Indiana: Corporate/M&A Band 2 p.1268

**Crossley, John**
Table(s): Missouri: Real Estate Up-and-coming individuals p.1633

**Crost, Katharine I**
Profile: p.300
Table(s): Nationwide: Capital Markets: Securitisation Band 3 p.59

**Crotty, Jonathan**
Table(s): North Carolina: Labor & Employment Band 3 p.2031

**Crough, Maureen**
Profile: p.1887
Table(s): New York: Environment: Mainly Transactional Band 2 p.1808

**Crouter, Jerrol A**
Profile: p.1398
Table(s): Maine: Litigation: General Commercial Band 2 p.1393

**Crow, Carl**
Table(s): Washington: Corporate/Commercial: Tax Band 1 p.2525

**Crow, Carter**
Profile: p.2386
Table(s): Texas: Labor & Employment Band 2 p.2359

**Crow, David**
Table(s): Tennessee: Media & Entertainment Up-and-coming individuals p.2297

**Crow, William**
Table(s): Oregon: Litigation: General Commercial Senior Statesmen: p.2171

**Crowell, C Wesley**
Table(s): Maine: Real Estate Band 4 p.1395

**Crowl, Matthew**
Table(s): Illinois: Litigation: White-Collar Crime & Government Investigations Band 3 p.1181

**Crowley, Frank**
Table(s): Montana: Natural Resources & Environment Band 2 p.1651

**Crowley, Lisanne**
Table(s): Nationwide: Energy: Oil & Gas (Regulatory & Litigation) Band 3 p.78

**Croysdale, David**
Profile: p.2581
Table(s): Wisconsin: Labor & Employment Band 2 p.2575

**Cruger, James R**
Table(s): Illinois: Corporate/M&A: Private Equity Band 3 p.1157

**Crum, Bruce**
Profile: p.2148
Table(s): Oklahoma: Corporate/Commercial Band 3 p.2134

**Crumbaugh, David G**
Table(s): Nationwide: Banking & Finance Band 2 p.31, Illinois: Banking & Finance Band 1 p.1145

**Crutcher Jr, Robert Pepper**
Table(s): Mississippi: Labor & Employment Band 1 p.1595

**Cruz, John E**
Profile: p.1636
Table(s): Missouri: Real Estate Band 3 p.1633

**Cruz-Brown, Kelly A**
Profile: p.989
Table(s): Florida: Insurance Band 2 p.957

**Curtz, Chauncey**
Table(s): Kentucky: Environment, Natural
Resources & Utilities: Natural Resources **Band 1**
p.1307

**Curvin, Thomas W**
Table(s): Georgia: Litigation: General
Commercial **Band 4** p.1065

**Curzon, Thomas H**
Profile: p.507
Table(s): Arizona: Corporate/M&A **Band 1** p.495

**Cushing, Paul M**
Profile: p.1079
Table(s): Georgia: Banking & Finance **Band 1**
p.1039

**Cusick, Michael F**
Table(s): Nationwide: Energy: Electricity
(Transactional) **Band 3** p.77

**Cussen, Deborah**
Profile: p.630
Table(s): California: Real Estate **Band 3** p.611

**Custer, William V**
Table(s): Georgia: Litigation: General
Commercial **Band 3** p.1065

**Cutchins IV, Clifford A**
Table(s): Southern Virginia: Corporate/M&A **Band
1** p.2494

**Cutler, Kenneth**
Table(s): Minnesota: Corporate/M&A **Band 1**
p.1569

**Cutler, Louisiana**
Profile: p.492
Table(s): Alaska: Litigation: General Commercial
**Band 3** p.490

**Cutler, Richard A**
Table(s): South Dakota: Corporate/Commercial
**Senior Statesmen:** p.2281, South Dakota: Real
Estate **Senior Statesmen:** p.2286

**Cutter, David F**
Table(s): Illinois: Insurance: Dispute Resolution
**Band 3** p.1168

**Cuva, Anthony J**
Table(s): Nationwide: Transportation: Shipping:
Litigation (outside New York) **Band 1** p.263

**Cymrot, Mark A**
Profile: p.300
Table(s): Nationwide: International Arbitration
**Band 5** p.145

**Cyphert, Michael**
Profile: p.2094
Table(s): Ohio: Natural Resources &
Environment **Band 2** p.2083

**Cyr, Joe**
Table(s): New York: Litigation: General
Commercial **Band 4** p.1833

**Czajka, Terri Ann**
Table(s): Indiana: Environment **Band 2** p.1270

**Czarniak, Julia A**
Profile: p.300
Table(s): Nationwide: Projects **Band 2** p.216

## D

**D'Amante, Raymond**
Table(s): New Hampshire: Real Estate: Land Use
**Band 1** p.1692

**D'Amato, John J**
Table(s): Hawaii: Labor & Employment:
Employee Benefits & Compensation **Band 1**
p.1117

**D'Angelo Jr, Alfred J**
Profile: p.2214
Table(s): Pennsylvania: Labor & Employment
**Band 1** p.2200

**D'Aquila, Barbara**
Profile: p.1578
Table(s): Minnesota: Labor & Employment **Band 2**
p.1571

**D'Avolio, Lisa**
Profile: p.1887
Table(s): New York: Immigration **Band 3** p.1814

**D'Cruz, Jason**
Table(s): Georgia: Labor & Employment **Band 2**
p.1060

**Dabney, James W**
Profile: p.1887
Table(s): New York: Intellectual Property: Patent
**Band 3** p.1820

**Daccord, Deborah**
Profile: p.1489
Table(s): Massachusetts: Healthcare **Band 2**
p.1460

**Dace, Robert W**
Profile: p.2148
Table(s): Oklahoma: Litigation: General
Commercial **Band 3** p.2141

**Dadakis, John D**
Profile: p.300
Table(s): Nationwide: Wealth Management:
Eastern Region **Band 3** p.267

**Dady, J Michael**
Profile: p.301
Table(s): Nationwide: Franchising: Mainly
Franchisee **Band 1** p.114

**Dafoe, Colette A**
Profile: p.859
Table(s): District of Columbia: Real Estate
**Associates to watch** p.835

**Dagenais, Don F**
Table(s): Missouri: Real Estate **Band 1** p.1633

**Dagenhart, Larry**
Table(s): North Carolina: Corporate/M&A **Senior
Statesmen:** p.2025

**Dagle, Paul**
Table(s): Oregon: Real Estate **Band 3** p.2173

**Dagley, Michael L**
Profile: p.2303
Table(s): Tennessee: Litigation: General
Commercial **Band 2** p.2295

**Dahl, Sherri**
Profile: p.2094
Table(s): Ohio: Bankruptcy/Restructuring
**Associates to watch** p.2058

**Dahlgren, Jeffery C**
Profile: p.1299
Table(s): Kansas: Corporate/M&A **Band 3** p.1292,
Kansas: Real Estate **Band 2** p.1297

**Dahlk, Thomas**
Profile: p.1667
Table(s): Nebraska: Litigation: General
Commercial **Band 1** p.1664

**Dahlson, Richard**
Profile: p.2386
Table(s): Texas: Corporate/M&A **Band 4** p.2337

**Dailey, Anna M**
Table(s): West Virginia: Labor & Employment
**Band 2** p.2553

**Dailey, Robert**
Table(s): Nebraska: Real Estate **Band 3** p.1666

**Dakin, Carol**
Table(s): Ohio: Employee Benefits & Executive
Compensation **Band 3** p.2067

**Dakin-Grimm, Linda**
Profile: p.630
Table(s): California: Insurance: Reinsurance
**Band 1** p.574

**Dale, Angelyn**
Profile: p.2148
Table(s): Oklahoma: Labor & Employment **Band 2**
p.2140

**Dale, Eric**
Profile: p.742
Table(s): Connecticut: Corporate/M&A **Band 2**
p.732

**Dale, Gregory N**
Table(s): Indiana: Labor & Employment **Band 3**
p.1271

**Dale, James C**
Table(s): Idaho: Labor & Employment **Star individuals** p.1132

**Dale III, Charles A**
Profile: p.1489
Table(s): Massachusetts:
Bankruptcy/Restructuring **Band 1** p.1449

**Daley, Annamarie**
Profile: p.1578
Table(s): Minnesota: Litigation: General
Commercial **Band 3** p.1574

**Daley, Susan J**
Table(s): Illinois: Labor & Employment:
Employee Benefits & Compensation **Band 1**
p.1176

**Dalgleish, Douglas**
Table(s): Missouri: Litigation: General
Commercial **Band 1** p.1628

**Daliere, Mark**
Profile: p.301
Table(s): Nationwide: Leisure & Hospitality **Band
4** p.179

**Dallas, Bruce**
Profile: p.630
Table(s): Nationwide: Capital Markets: Debt &
Equity **Band 3** p.46, California: Capital Markets:
Debt & Equity **Band 1** p.547

**Dallet, Bradley I**
Profile: p.2582
Table(s): Wisconsin: Real Estate **Band 2** p.2579

**Dalton, John**
Table(s): Georgia: Litigation: General
Commercial **Senior Statesmen:** p.1065

**Daluz, Tobey**
Profile: p.769
Table(s): Delaware: Bankruptcy/Restructuring
**Band 2** p.754

**Daly, Bryan D**
Table(s): California: Litigation: White-Collar
Crime & Government Investigations **Band 2** p.601

**Daly, Erik**
Profile: p.1549
Table(s): Michigan: Corporate/M&A **Associates to
watch** p.1538

**Daly, James R**
Profile: p.1203
Table(s): Illinois: Litigation: General Commercial
**Band 4** p.1180

**Daly, Lawrence**
Profile: p.1653
Table(s): Montana: Litigation: General
Commercial **Band 3** p.1649

**Dame, Thomas C**
Table(s): Maryland: Litigation: Bankruptcy **Band 2**
p.1419

**Dameris, Thad**
Table(s): Nationwide: Product Liability & Mass
Torts **Band 5** p.208, Nationwide: Transportation:
Aviation: Litigation **Band 1** p.254, Texas:
Litigation: General Commercial **Band 4** p.2362

**Damgaard, Roger**
Table(s): South Dakota: Corporate/Commercial
**Band 1** p.2281, South Dakota:
Corporate/Commercial:
Bankruptcy/Restructuring **Band 1** p.2281

**Damm, Jacqueline**
Table(s): Oregon: Labor & Employment **Band 3**
p.2168

**Damon, Doneene Keemer**
Profile: p.769
Table(s): Delaware: Corporate/M&A: Alternative
Entities **Band 3** p.761

**Damon, Lisa J.**
Profile: p.1489
Table(s): Massachusetts: Labor & Employment
**Band 1** p.1466

**Damschroder, Timothy R**
Profile: p.1549
Table(s): Michigan: Corporate/M&A **Band 1**
p.1538

**Danaher, Michael**
Table(s): Nationwide: Investment Funds: Venture
Capital **Band 3** p.174

**Danco, Sharon Docherty**
Table(s): Florida: Corporate/M&A & Private
Equity **Band 2** p.947

**Daneker, Michael D**
Profile: p.859
Table(s): District of Columbia: Environment **Band
5** p.804

**Davis, Cindy JK**
Profile: p.1079
Table(s): Georgia: Banking & Finance **Band 2**
p.1039

**Davis, Doreen**
Profile: p.2214
Table(s): Pennsylvania: Labor & Employment
**Band 2** p.2200

**Davis, Edward J**
Table(s): New York: Intellectual Property: Trade
Mark & Copyright **Band 3** p.1821

**Davis, Gardner F**
Table(s): Florida: Corporate/M&A & Private
Equity **Band 2** p.947

**Davis, Gary**
Profile: p.2148
Table(s): Oklahoma: Litigation: General
Commercial **Senior Statesmen:** p.2141, Oklahoma:
Litigation: Mediators **Senior Statesmen:** p.2141

**Davis, Gary Scott**
Profile: p.301
Table(s): Nationwide: Healthcare: Transactional
**Band 1** p.128, Florida: Healthcare **Band 1** p.954

**Davis, Geoffrey B**
Table(s): Nationwide: Life Sciences:
Corporate/Commercial **Band 2** p.182

**Davis, Geoffrey M**
Profile: p.1203
Table(s): Illinois: Tax **Band 3** p.1192

**Davis, George A**
Profile: p.1887
Table(s): Nationwide: Bankruptcy/Restructuring
**Band 3** p.39, New York:
Bankruptcy/Restructuring **Band 2** p.1782

**Davis, J Daniel**
Table(s): Nationwide: Food & Beverages: Alcohol
**Band 2** p.109

**Davis, James B**
Table(s): Florida: Tax: Employee Benefits **Band 1**
p.979

**Davis, James M**
Table(s): Illinois: Insurance: Dispute Resolution
**Band 2** p.1168

**Davis, Jeffrey J**
Table(s): North Carolina: Litigation: General
Commercial **Band 2** p.2033

**Davis, John**
Table(s): Montana: Natural Resources &
Environment **Band 2** p.1651

**Davis, John D**
Profile: p.526
Table(s): Arkansas: Labor & Employment **Band 1**
p.520, Arkansas: Labor & Employment:
Employee Benefits & Compensation **Band 2**
p.520

**Davis, Joshua M**
Table(s): Massachusetts: Labor & Employment
**Band 3** p.1466

**Davis, Kathleen H**
Table(s): Vermont: Corporate/Commercial:
Captive Insurance **Band 1** p.2483

**Davis, Kearns**
Table(s): North Carolina: Litigation: White-Collar
Crime & Government Investigations **Band 1**
p.2034

**Davis, Kirk S**
Table(s): Florida: Healthcare **Band 2** p.954

**Davis, Lee C**
Table(s): Georgia: Construction **Band 1** p.1044

**Davis, Mark**
Profile: p.1602
Table(s): Mississippi: Real Estate **Band 1** p.1600

**Davis, Mark G**
Profile: p.301
Table(s): Nationwide: International Trade:
Intellectual Property (Section 337) **Band 2** p.160,
District of Columbia: Intellectual Property:
Litigation **Band 2** p.821

**Davis, Maxon**
Table(s): Montana: Litigation: General
Commercial **Band 2** p.1649

**Davis, Michael M**
Profile: p.1489
Table(s): Massachusetts: Tax **Band 2** p.1481

**Davis, Michael W**
Profile: p.302
Table(s): Nationwide: Product Liability & Mass
Torts **Band 2** p.208

**Davis, Richard F**
Profile: p.302
Table(s): Nationwide: Leisure & Hospitality **Band
3** p.179

**Davis, Robert P**
Profile: p.1887
Table(s): New York: Corporate/M&A **Band 5**
p.1793

**Davis, Robert P**
Table(s): New York: Labor & Employment **Band 3**
p.1826

**Davis, Robert S**
Table(s): New York: Real Estate: Zoning/Land
Use **Band 2** p.1855

**Davis, Scott E**
Table(s): Oregon: Intellectual Property **Band 3**
p.2167

**Davis, Scott J**
Table(s): Illinois: Corporate/M&A **Band 2** p.1156

**Davis, Steven C**
Profile: p.2149
Table(s): Oklahoma: Corporate/Commercial: Tax
**Band 1** p.2134

**Davis, Steven G**
Profile: p.1489
Table(s): Massachusetts: Intellectual Property
**Band 3** p.1463

**Davis, Thomas A**
Profile: p.468
Table(s): Alabama: Labor & Employment **Band 2**
p.460

**Davis, Timothy A**
Table(s): Missouri: Labor & Employment **Band 2**
p.1625

**Davis, Tony**
Table(s): Texas: Bankruptcy/Restructuring **Band 3**
p.2328

**Davis, Trayton M**
Profile: p.302
Table(s): Nationwide: Capital Markets:
Securitisation **Band 3** p.59

**Davis, W Ryan**
Table(s): Pennsylvania: Corporate/M&A &
Private Equity **Band 4** p.2191

**Davis, Wendy**
Profile: p.631
Table(s): California: Employee Benefits &
Executive Compensation **Band 3** p.560

**Davis, Will**
Table(s): Texas: Insurance: Regulation **Senior
Statesmen:** p.2351

**Davis, William K**
Table(s): North Carolina: Litigation: General
Commercial **Band 1** p.2033

**Davis Jones, Laura**
Table(s): Delaware: Bankruptcy/Restructuring
**Band 1** p.754

**Davis Jr, Richard M**
Table(s): Wyoming: Real Estate **Senior Statesmen:**
p.2600

**Davis Jr, Theodore H**
Table(s): Georgia: Intellectual Property **Band 4**
p.1056

**Davis Jr, William C**
Table(s): Nevada: Real Estate **Band 3** p.1679

**Davis Lux, Melinda**
Profile: p.2268
Table(s): South Carolina: Corporate/M&A **Up-and-
coming individuals** p.2260

**Davis Varner, Chilton**
Profile: p.302
Table(s): Nationwide: Litigation: Trial Lawyers
**Band 2** p.187, Nationwide: Product Liability &
Mass Torts **Band 1** p.208, Georgia: Litigation:
General Commercial **Band 1** p.1065

**Davis, Jr, W Kenneth**
Table(s): Illinois: Healthcare **Band 2** p.1165

**Davison, Bruce C**
Profile: p.1636
Table(s): Missouri: Corporate/M&A **Band 2** p.1618

**Davison, Douglas**
Profile: p.302
Table(s): Nationwide: Securities: Litigation **Band
3** p.232

**Davison, Kimberly A**
Table(s): Texas: Construction **Band 3** p.2335

**Davison, Walter C**
Table(s): Hawaii: Bankruptcy/Restructuring **Band
2** p.1114

**Dawahare, Debra**
Profile: p.1318
Table(s): Kentucky: Labor & Employment **Band 2**
p.1310

**Dawda, Edward C**
Profile: p.1549
Table(s): Michigan: Real Estate **Band 1** p.1546

**Dawkins, Michael**
Profile: p.1602
Table(s): Mississippi: Environment **Band 3** p.1594

**Dawley, Kris**
Table(s): Ohio: Healthcare **Band 3** p.2069

**Dawson, Alistair**
Table(s): Texas: Litigation: General Commercial
**Band 4** p.2362

**Dawson, Cari K**
Profile: p.1079
Table(s): Georgia: Litigation: General
Commercial **Band 3** p.1065

**Dawson, James**
Table(s): Minnesota: Labor & Employment **Band 1**
p.1571

**Dawson, Jon S**
Table(s): Alaska: Corporate/M&A **Band 1** p.487,
Alaska: Litigation: General Commercial **Band 3**
p.490, Alaska: Real Estate **Band 2** p.491

**Dawson, R Alec**
Profile: p.1888
Table(s): Nationwide: Private Equity: Buyouts
**Band 5** p.203, New York: Corporate/M&A **Band 4**
p.1793

**Dawson, Stephen E**
Profile: p.1549
Table(s): Michigan: Real Estate **Band 2** p.1546

**Dawson, William B**
Profile: p.2387
Table(s): Texas: Litigation: General Commercial
**Band 2** p.2362

**Dawson III, Amos C**
Table(s): North Carolina: Environment **Band 1**
p.2028

**Dax, John**
Table(s): New York: Energy: State Regulatory &
Wholesale Electric Market **Band 1** p.1806

**Day, Alison**
Profile: p.2094
Table(s): Ohio: Labor & Employment **Band 4**
p.2074

**Day, Barton D**
Table(s): Arizona: Environment (including water
rights) **Band 3** p.497

**Day, David**
Table(s): Utah: Corporate/M&A **Associates to
watch** p.2462

**Day, John G**
Profile: p.769
Table(s): Delaware: Intellectual Property **Band 3**
p.763

**Day, Kate**
Profile: p.2387
Table(s): Texas: Banking & Finance **Up-and-coming
individuals** p.2325

**Day, Michael**
Table(s): California: Energy: State Regulatory &
Litigation **Band 2** p.562

**Day, Patrick**
Profile: p.2601
Table(s): Wyoming: Litigation: General
Commercial **Band 1** p.2598

**Day, Richard E**
Table(s): **Wyoming**: Litigation: General
Commercial **Senior Statesmen**: p.2598

**Dayan, Michael D**
Profile: p.302
Table(s): **Nationwide**: Capital Markets:
Derivatives **Star individuals** p.51

**Dayanim, Behnam**
Table(s): **Nationwide**: Gaming & Licensing **Band 3**
p.115

**Dayton, Peter S**
Table(s): **Montana**: Real Estate **Band 1** p.1652

**de Armas, Luis A**
Table(s): **Florida**: Corporate/M&A & Private
Equity **Band 1** p.947

**De Blasi, Michelle A**
Profile: p.508
Table(s): **Arizona**: Environment (including water
rights) **Band 3** p.497

**de Bodo, Richard**
Profile: p.631
Table(s): **Nationwide**: Life Sciences: IP/Patent
Litigation **Band 3** p.183, **California**: Life Sciences:
IP/Patent Litigation **Band 2** p.590

**de Brito, Carl A**
Profile: p.302
Table(s): **Nationwide**: Investment Funds: Private
Equity: Fund Formation **Band 4** p.166

**De Bruin, David L**
Profile: p.2582
Table(s): **Wisconsin**: Intellectual Property **Band 2**
p.2573

**De Buys Jr, John**
Table(s): **Alabama**: Real Estate: Zoning/Land
Use **Band 1** p.466

**De Chiara, Michael K**
Table(s): **New York**: Construction **Band 2** p.1791

**De Ghenghi, Luigi L**
Profile: p.302
Table(s): **Nationwide**: Financial Services
Regulation: Banking (Compliance) **Band 3** p.96

**de Gramont, Alexandre**
Profile: p.302
Table(s): **Nationwide**: International Arbitration
**Band 5** p.145

**de Groot, Jay**
Profile: p.631
Table(s): **California**: Corporate/M&A: Venture
Capital **Band 3** p.555

**De Jonge, Peter M**
Table(s): **Utah**: Intellectual Property **Band 3**
p.2466

**De Leo, Charles G**
Table(s): **Nationwide**: Transportation: Shipping:
Litigation (outside New York) **Band 1** p.263

**de Lipkau, Ross E**
Profile: p.1681
Table(s): **Nevada**: Environment **Band 1** p.1673

**De Lorenzi, David E**
Table(s): **New Jersey**: Intellectual Property **Band
2** p.1716

**de Sa e Silva, Marco**
Table(s): **Washington**: Real Estate **Band 3** p.2535

**De Simone, Dominic**
Profile: p.2214
Table(s): **Pennsylvania**: Real Estate **Band 3**
p.2208

**De Simone, Joseph**
Table(s): **New York**: Litigation: Securities **Band 4**
p.1834

**De Vore, Bradford A**
Table(s): **North Carolina**: Environment **Band 2**
p.2028

**Deakins Jr, Homer L**
Profile: p.1080
Table(s): **Georgia**: Labor & Employment **Senior
Statesmen**: p.1060

**Dean, Cathy J**
Table(s): **Missouri**: Litigation: General
Commercial **Band 3** p.1628

**Dean, Richard N**
Profile: p.302
Table(s): **Nationwide**: International Trade: FCPA
Experts **Band 3** p.153

**Deane Jr, Richard H**
Profile: p.1080
Table(s): **Georgia**: Litigation: White-Collar Crime
& Government Investigations **Band 1** p.1066

**Dearlove, Catherine**
Profile: p.769
Table(s): **Delaware**: Chancery **Band 4** p.758

**DeArment, Roderick**
Profile: p.302
Table(s): **Nationwide**: Government: Government
Relations **Band 3** p.121

**Deatherage, Scott D**
Profile: p.2387
Table(s): **Texas**: Environment **Band 3** p.2343

**DeBaecke, Michael D**
Profile: p.769
Table(s): **Delaware**: Bankruptcy/Restructuring
**Band 4** p.754

**DeBarge, Michelle Wilcox**
Profile: p.742
Table(s): **Connecticut**: Healthcare **Band 2** p.735

**DeBaugh, Arthur**
Table(s): **North Carolina**: Intellectual Property
**Band 2** p.2030

**Debbeler, Michael**
Table(s): **Ohio**: Bankruptcy/Restructuring **Band 2**
p.2058

**deBeers, Kimberly A**
Profile: p.1203
Table(s): **Illinois**: Corporate/M&A: Private Equity
**Band 3** p.1157

**DeBlasio, Joseph**
Table(s): **New Jersey**: Labor & Employment **Band
3** p.1718

**Debolt, Paul A**
Profile: p.303
Table(s): **Nationwide**: Government: Government
Contracts **Band 4** p.117

**DeBorde, Frank W**
Table(s): **Georgia**: Bankruptcy/Restructuring
**Band 2** p.1042

**Debruge, Marcel**
Table(s): **Alabama**: Labor & Employment **Band 3**
p.460

**DeBusk, F Amanda**
Profile: p.303
Table(s): **Nationwide**: International Trade: Export
Controls & Economic Sanctions **Band 2** p.153

**DeCamp, Paul**
Profile: p.2508
Table(s): **Virginia**: Labor & Employment **Band 3**
p.2500

**DeCelle, Arthur J**
Profile: p.303
Table(s): **Nationwide**: Food & Beverages: Alcohol
**Band 3** p.109

**Decker, Jeffrey E**
Profile: p.989
Table(s): **Florida**: Corporate/M&A & Private
Equity **Band 4** p.947

**Decker, John S**
Profile: p.303
Table(s): **Nationwide**: Energy: Electricity
(Regulatory & Litigation) **Band 3** p.76,
**Nationwide**: Energy: Oil & Gas (Regulatory &
Litigation) **Band 5** p.76

**DeConti, Elizabeth A**
Profile: p.303
Table(s): **Nationwide**: Food & Beverages: Alcohol
**Band 3** p.109

**DeConti Jr, Giulio A**
Table(s): **Massachusetts**: Intellectual Property
**Band 2** p.1463

**Dedman, Linda**
Table(s): **Texas**: Insurance **Band 3** p.2351

**Dedyo, John**
Profile: p.303
Table(s): **Nationwide**: Capital Markets:
Securitisation **Band 3** p.59

**Dee, David S**
Table(s): **Florida**: Environment **Band 2** p.951

**Dee, Francis X**
Profile: p.1734
Table(s): **New Jersey**: Labor & Employment **Star
individuals** p.1718

**Deem, Patrick D**
Profile: p.2562
Table(s): **West Virginia**: Corporate/Commercial
**Band 2** p.2550, **West Virginia**: Natural Resources
**Band 1** p.2558, **West Virginia**: Real Estate **Band 1**
p.2560

**Deems, Nyal**
Table(s): **Michigan**: Real Estate **Band 3** p.1546

**Deeny, Raymond**
Table(s): **Colorado**: Labor & Employment **Band 2**
p.706

**Dees, C Stanley**
Table(s): **Nationwide**: Government: Government
Contracts **Senior Statesmen**: p.117

**DeFranceschi, Daniel J**
Profile: p.769
Table(s): **Delaware**: Bankruptcy/Restructuring
**Band 2** p.754

**DeFranco, Denise W**
Profile: p.1489
Table(s): **Massachusetts**: Intellectual Property
**Band 3** p.1463

**Degan, Michael**
Table(s): **Nebraska**: Litigation: General
Commercial **Band 3** p.1664

**Degan, Nancy**
Profile: p.1360
Table(s): **Louisiana**: Litigation: General
Commercial **Band 3** p.1352

**Degnan, Donald**
Profile: p.717
Table(s): **Colorado**: Intellectual Property **Band 3**
p.704

**Degnan, Frederick H**
Profile: p.303
Table(s): **Nationwide**: Food & Beverages:
Regulatory & Litigation **Band 1** p.107

**Degnan, Peter**
Profile: p.1080
Table(s): **Georgia**: Energy **Band 2** p.1049

**DeGrandis, William D**
Table(s): **Nationwide**: Energy: Electricity
(Regulatory & Litigation) **Band 5** p.76

**DeGulis, Gregory J**
Profile: p.2094
Table(s): **Ohio**: Natural Resources &
Environment **Band 3** p.2083

**DeHaven, Dara L**
Profile: p.1080
Table(s): **Georgia**: Labor & Employment **Band 4**
p.1060

**DeHihns III, Lee A**
Profile: p.1080
Table(s): **Georgia**: Environment **Senior Statesmen**:
p.1051

**Dehney, Robert J**
Table(s): **Delaware**: Bankruptcy/Restructuring
**Band 1** p.754

**Deibert, Doug**
Table(s): **South Dakota**: Litigation: General
Commercial **Band 2** p.2284

**Deibert, Edward**
Profile: p.631
Table(s): **California**: Corporate/M&A **Up-and-com-
ing individuals** p.553

**Deitch, Laurence B**
Profile: p.1549
Table(s): **Michigan**: Corporate/M&A **Band 2**
p.1538

**DeJong, Ralph E**
Profile: p.1203
Table(s): **Illinois**: Healthcare **Band 2** p.1165

**Dekker, David T**
Table(s): **District of Columbia**: Construction **Band
1** p.795

**del Calvo, Jorge**
Table(s): **Nationwide**: Investment Funds: Venture
Capital **Band 1** p.174, **California**: Capital Markets:
Debt & Equity **Band 2** p.547, **California**:
Corporate/M&A **Band 3** p.553, **California**:
Corporate/M&A: Venture Capital **Band 1** p.553

**Del Casino, Casey**
Table(s): Tennessee: Media & Entertainment **Band 1** p.2297

**del Castillo, Albert A**
Profile: p.989
Table(s): Florida: Banking & Finance: Public Finance **Band 1** p.936

**Del Pino, Antonio**
Profile: p.1888
Table(s): New York: Latin American Investment **Band 3** p.1829

**Del Rey-Cone, Christie**
Table(s): New York: Labor & Employment **Up-and-coming individuals** p.1826

**Delaney, Jeffrey J**
Table(s): Nationwide: Energy: Electricity (Finance) **Band 1** p.75

**Delaney, John**
Profile: p.1888
Table(s): Nationwide: Outsourcing **Band 2** p.195, New York: Technology & Outsourcing **Band 1** p.1868

**Delaney, Thomas J**
Table(s): Nationwide: Financial Services Regulation: Banking (Enforcement & Investigations) **Band 3** p.97

**DeLaney III, Ernest S (Mike)**
Table(s): North Carolina: Corporate/M&A **Band 1** p.2025

**DelDuca, Matthew V**
Profile: p.1734
Table(s): New Jersey: Labor & Employment **Band 3** p.1718

**Delegal, Mark**
Table(s): Florida: Insurance **Band 1** p.957

**Delegal, Susan F**
Table(s): Florida: Real Estate: Zoning/Land Use **Band 3** p.975

**Deligans, Julianna**
Profile: p.2149
Table(s): Oklahoma: Intellectual Property **Up-and-coming individuals** p.2138

**Delikat, Michael**
Profile: p.1888
Table(s): New York: Labor & Employment **Band 1** p.1826

**DeLisle, Joe**
Profile: p.1080
Table(s): Georgia: Corporate/M&A **Band 4** p.1046

**Dell-Powell, Denise**
Table(s): Florida: Bankruptcy/Restructuring **Band 3** p.939

**Dellinger, Mark H**
Profile: p.2562
Table(s): West Virginia: Labor & Employment **Band 3** p.2553

**Dellinger, Walter**
Table(s): Nationwide: Appellate Law **Senior Statesmen** p.26

**DelNero, Matthew**
Profile: p.859
Table(s): District of Columbia: Media & Entertainment: Mainly Regulatory **Up-and-coming individuals** p.832, District of Columbia: Telecom, Broadcast & Satellite **Up-and-coming individuals** p.844

**Delorey, Kevin A**
Profile: p.2582
Table(s): Wisconsin: Real Estate **Band 3** p.2579

**DelPriore, Robert J**
Profile: p.2303
Table(s): Tennessee: Corporate/M&A **Band 3** p.2288

**DeLuca, Jean M.**
Profile: p.1490
Table(s): Massachusetts: Banking & Finance: Public Finance **Band 1** p.1446

**DeLuca, Mark**
Profile: p.2214
Table(s): Pennsylvania: Intellectual Property **Band 3** p.2197

**DeLucia, Richard L**
Table(s): New York: Intellectual Property: Patent **Band 2** p.1820

**DeMarco, Daniel A**
Profile: p.2094
Table(s): Ohio: Bankruptcy/Restructuring **Band 1** p.2058

**DeMarco, Joseph V**
Profile: p.303
Table(s): Nationwide: Privacy & Data Security **Band 2** p.199

**DeMaria, Gerald C**
Table(s): Rhode Island: Litigation: General Commercial **Band 3** p.2254

**DeMars, Greg**
Table(s): Michigan: Real Estate **Band 3** p.1546

**DeMarte, Luke W**
Profile: p.1203
Table(s): Illinois: Media & Entertainment: Transactional **Band 2** p.1185

**DeMeo, Chris**
Table(s): Texas: Healthcare **Band 3** p.2347

**DeMeo, Ralph A**
Table(s): Florida: Environment **Band 2** p.951

**Demerath, Jeffrey T**
Table(s): Missouri: Litigation: White-Collar Crime & Government Investigations **Band 1** p.1629

**Demetriou, Andrew James**
Table(s): California: Healthcare **Band 2** p.568

**deMeza Jr, William B**
Profile: p.989
Table(s): Florida: Labor & Employment **Band 2** p.959

**Deming, N Karen**
Table(s): Georgia: Litigation: General Commercial **Band 3** p.1065

**Demitrack, Thomas**
Profile: p.2094
Table(s): Ohio: Litigation: Antitrust **Band 1** p.2078

**Demm, Stephen P**
Profile: p.2509
Table(s): Southern Virginia: Intellectual Property **Band 2** p.2498

**Demmo, Nicholas G**
Profile: p.303
Table(s): Nationwide: Financial Services Regulation: Financial Institutions M&A **Band 2** p.99

**Dempster, Hazen H**
Table(s): Georgia: Banking & Finance **Band 2** p.1039

**Denaburg, Charles L**
Table(s): Alabama: Bankruptcy/Restructuring **Senior Statesmen** p.457

**Denaro, Jack M**
Table(s): Florida: Litigation: White-Collar Crime & Government Investigations **Band 2** p.967

**DeNatale, Richard**
Table(s): California: Insurance: Policyholder **Band 4** p.576

**Denehy, Mark O**
Profile: p.2256
Table(s): Rhode Island: Litigation: General Commercial **Band 3** p.2254

**Denenberg, Alan**
Profile: p.631
Table(s): Nationwide: Capital Markets: Debt & Equity **Band 2** p.46, California: Capital Markets: Debt & Equity **Band 1** p.547, California: Corporate/M&A **Band 2** p.553

**Denham, Robert E**
Profile: p.631
Table(s): California: Corporate/M&A **Band 2** p.554

**Denious, David S**
Profile: p.2214
Table(s): Pennsylvania: Corporate/M&A & Private Equity **Band 4** p.2191

**Denis, Paul T**
Profile: p.859
Table(s): District of Columbia: Antitrust **Band 2** p.787

**Denitzio Jr, Thomas J**
Table(s): New Jersey: Real Estate **Band 3** p.1728

**Denkenberger, John**
Table(s): Washington: Intellectual Property **Band 3** p.2529

**Denmon, Richard A**
Profile: p.989
Table(s): Florida: Corporate/M&A & Private Equity **Band 4** p.947

**Dennis, Patrick W**
Profile: p.631
Table(s): California: Environment **Band 1** p.564

**Dennison, Karen D**
Profile: p.1681
Table(s): Nevada: Real Estate **Band 1** p.1679

**Denny, Otway**
Profile: p.2387
Table(s): Nationwide: Product Liability & Mass Torts **Band 3** p.208, Nationwide: Product Liability: Toxic Torts p.208, Texas: Litigation: General Commercial **Band 2** p.2362

**DeNovio, Nicholas J**
Profile: p.859
Table(s): District of Columbia: Tax **Band 4** p.838

**Densborn, Donald**
Profile: p.1276
Table(s): Indiana: Corporate/M&A **Band 2** p.1268

**Dent, Leslie**
Table(s): Georgia: Labor & Employment **Band 2** p.1060

**Dent, Miriam**
Profile: p.1080
Table(s): Georgia: Real Estate **Band 2** p.1070

**DeOrchis, Vincent M**
Table(s): Nationwide: Transportation: Shipping: Litigation (New York) **Band 3** p.261

**DePaoli, Gordon**
Table(s): Nevada: Environment **Band 1** p.1673

**DePillis, Mark S**
Profile: p.2214
Table(s): Pennsylvania: Real Estate **Band 4** p.2208

**DePrez, Anne**
Profile: p.1276
Table(s): Indiana: Litigation: General Commercial **Band 3** p.1273

**Derevan, Richard**
Table(s): California: Litigation: Appellate **Band 3** p.599

**Deringer, Joshua**
Profile: p.303
Table(s): Nationwide: Investment Funds: Registered Funds **Band 3** p.170

**Derman, Andrew B**
Profile: p.304
Table(s): Nationwide: Energy: Oil & Gas (Transactional) **Band 4** p.79

**DeRosa, Franca L**
Table(s): Connecticut: Environment **Band 2** p.733

**Derosby, Anthony R**
Profile: p.1399
Table(s): Maine: Labor & Employment: Immigration **Band 1** p.1390

**Derouin, James G**
Table(s): Arizona: Environment (including water rights) **Senior Statesmen** p.497

**Derr, Jay**
Profile: p.2538
Table(s): Washington: Real Estate: Zoning/Land Use **Band 2** p.2536

**Derrick, Gary W**
Table(s): Oklahoma: Corporate/Commercial **Band 1** p.2134

**Des Laurier, Victor A.**
Table(s): Illinois: Banking & Finance **Band 4** p.1145

**des Rosiers, Jared S.**
Profile: p.1399
Table(s): Maine: Energy & Natural Resources **Band 1** p.1388

**DeSantis, Victor J**
Profile: p.304
Table(s): Nationwide: Projects **Band 1** p.216

**Dickerson, Christopher L**
Profile: p.1204
Table(s): Illinois: Bankruptcy/Restructuring **Band 3** p.1148

**Dickerson Jr, W Brinkley**
Table(s): Georgia: Corporate/M&A **Band 3** p.1046

**Dickey, M Jane**
Table(s): Arkansas: Corporate/Commercial: Municipal Bonds **Band 1** p.518

**Dickinson, Christopher C**
Profile: p.1204
Table(s): Illinois: Insurance: Dispute Resolution **Band 3** p.1168

**Dickinson, John**
Table(s): Florida: Labor & Employment **Band 1** p.959

**Dickinson, Mark**
Table(s): Iowa: Corporate/M&A **Band 2** p.1283

**Dickinson, Timothy L**
Table(s): Nationwide: International Trade: FCPA Experts **Band 1** p.153

**Dickman, David G**
Profile: p.304
Table(s): Nationwide: Transportation: Shipping: Regulatory (outside New York) **Band 3** p.264

**Dickson, Robert J**
Table(s): Alaska: Litigation: Construction **Band 1** p.490

**Dickson, Roger W**
Profile: p.2303
Table(s): Tennessee: Litigation: General Commercial **Band 2** p.2295

**Dickstein, Beth**
Profile: p.1204
Table(s): Illinois: Labor & Employment: Employee Benefits & Compensation **Band 2** p.1176

**Dickstein, Howard**
Table(s): Nationwide: Native American Law **Band 3** p.192

**Diehl Jr, Robert J**
Profile: p.1549
Table(s): Michigan: Banking & Finance: Bankruptcy **Band 1** p.1536

**Diehl Jr, William K**
Table(s): North Carolina: Litigation: General Commercial **Band 1** p.2033

**Diekmann Jr, Gilmore F**
Profile: p.632
Table(s): California: Labor & Employment **Band 2** p.587

**Dienelt, John F**
Profile: p.304
Table(s): Nationwide: Franchising **Band 1** p.111

**Dietderich, Andrew G**
Profile: p.305
Table(s): Nationwide: Bankruptcy/Restructuring **Band 3** p.39, New York: Bankruptcy/Restructuring **Band 3** p.1782

**Dietrich, Stephen J**
Profile: p.717
Table(s): Colorado: Corporate/M&A **Band 2** p.703

**Dietz, Wallace W**
Profile: p.2303
Table(s): Tennessee: Litigation: General Commercial **Band 2** p.2295

**Diffen, Becky H**
Profile: p.2387
Table(s): Texas: Energy: State Regulatory & Litigation (Electricity) **Associates to watch** p.2341

**Diffenderfer, Robert P**
Table(s): Florida: Environment **Band 3** p.951

**Diggins, Timothy W**
Table(s): Massachusetts: Hedge & Mutual Funds **Band 2** p.1461

**DiGiovanni, Francis**
Table(s): Delaware: Intellectual Property **Band 3** p.763

**DiGiovanni, Nick J**
Profile: p.1204
Table(s): Illinois: Insurance: Dispute Resolution: Reinsurance **Band 1** p.1168

**DiGiovanni, Peter**
Profile: p.1636
Table(s): Missouri: Real Estate **Band 1** p.1633

**Digirolamo, Sam**
Table(s): Missouri: Intellectual Property **Band 1** p.1623

**DiLeo, Anthony M**
Table(s): Louisiana: Corporate/M&A **Band 4** p.1341

**Dillard, Michael E**
Table(s): Texas: Capital Markets: Debt & Equity **Band 2** p.2333, Texas: Corporate/M&A **Band 2** p.2337

**Dillard, Stephen C**
Profile: p.2387
Table(s): Texas: Litigation: General Commercial **Band 3** p.2362

**Diller, Edward D**
Profile: p.2094
Table(s): Ohio: Real Estate **Band 3** p.2086

**Diller, Nicole A**
Profile: p.632
Table(s): California: Employee Benefits & Executive Compensation **Band 3** p.560

**Dilloff, Neil**
Profile: p.1426
Table(s): Maryland: Litigation: General Commercial **Band 1** p.1419

**Dillon, Bradley E**
Profile: p.1318
Table(s): Kentucky: Environment, Natural Resources & Utilities: Environment **Band 2** p.1307

**Dillon, Carol K**
Profile: p.632
Table(s): California: Real Estate **Band 2** p.611

**Dillon, Christopher D**
Profile: p.632
Table(s): California: Corporate/M&A **Band 4** p.553

**Dillon, Liz**
Table(s): Nationwide: Franchising **Up-and-coming individuals** p.111

**Dillon, Sean M**
Profile: p.990
Table(s): Florida: Construction **Band 2** p.944

**Dillow, John**
Table(s): Nationwide: Product Liability & Mass Torts **Band 5** p.208, Nationwide: Transportation: Aviation: Litigation **Band 1** p.254

**Dillworth, Drew M**
Table(s): Florida: Bankruptcy/Restructuring **Band 3** p.939

**DiLorenzo, Louis P**
Profile: p.1888
Table(s): New York: Labor & Employment **Band 2** p.1826

**Dilworth, George Toby**
Profile: p.1399
Table(s): Maine: Litigation: General Commercial **Band 2** p.1393

**DiMatteo, John M**
Profile: p.1888
Table(s): New York: Intellectual Property: Patent **Band 3** p.1820

**DiMichael, Nicholas J**
Profile: p.305
Table(s): Nationwide: Transportation: Rail (for Shippers) **Senior Statesmen** p.258

**Dimling, Robert A**
Profile: p.2094
Table(s): Ohio: Labor & Employment **Band 3** p.2074

**Dimon, Samuel**
Profile: p.1888
Table(s): New York: Tax **Band 2** p.1862

**DiNardo, Lawrence**
Profile: p.1204
Table(s): Illinois: Labor & Employment **Band 1** p.1175

**Dinardo, Patrick P**
Profile: p.1490
Table(s): Massachusetts: Bankruptcy/Restructuring **Band 3** p.1449

**Dinkins, Carol**
Profile: p.2387
Table(s): Texas: Environment **Star individuals** p.2343

**Dinkoff, Allan**
Profile: p.1888
Table(s): New York: Labor & Employment **Band 4** p.1826

**Dintzer, Jeffrey D**
Profile: p.632
Table(s): California: Environment **Band 3** p.564

**DiNucci, Jennifer Fonner**
Table(s): California: Corporate/M&A **Band 4** p.553

**Dinwiddie, Thomas**
Profile: p.1277
Table(s): Indiana: Real Estate **Band 1** p.1275

**DiPalma, Robert**
Table(s): Vermont: Litigation: General Commercial **Band 3** p.2486

**DiPrinzio, Eugene A**
Table(s): Delaware: Real Estate **Band 1** p.766

**Director, Mark D**
Profile: p.859
Table(s): District of Columbia: Corporate/M&A & Private Equity **Band 2** p.797

**Disiere, David D**
Table(s): Texas: Insurance **Band 3** p.2351

**Diskant, Gregory L**
Profile: p.1888
Table(s): New York: Intellectual Property: Patent **Band 1** p.1820

**Disler, Joan A**
Profile: p.1734
Table(s): New Jersey: Employee Benefits & Executive Compensation **Band 1** p.1710

**DiStefano, Emily C**
Table(s): Nationwide: Transportation: Aviation: Finance **Band 3** p.252

**DiStefano, Joseph R**
Profile: p.2256
Table(s): Rhode Island: Real Estate **Band 2** p.2255

**Dittmar, James S**
Profile: p.1490
Table(s): Massachusetts: Litigation: Securities **Band 1** p.1470

**Dittrick, William G**
Table(s): Nebraska: Litigation: General Commercial **Band 1** p.1664

**DiVarco, Sandra**
Profile: p.1204
Table(s): Illinois: Healthcare **Up-and-coming individuals** p.1165

**Divola, Julie**
Table(s): California: Tax **Band 1** p.617

**Diwik, James**
Table(s): California: Construction **Band 4** p.550

**Dixon, Aaron J**
Table(s): Indiana: Real Estate **Band 3** p.1275

**Dixon, Augustus M**
Table(s): South Carolina: Corporate/M&A **Band 1** p.2260

**Dixon, Bradley J**
Table(s): Idaho: Litigation: General Commercial **Up-and-coming individuals** p.1134

**Dixon, Dale**
Profile: p.1667
Table(s): Nebraska: Corporate/Commercial **Band 2** p.1659

**Dixon, David L**
Profile: p.632
Table(s): California: Corporate/M&A: Private Equity **Up-and-coming individuals** p.553

**Dixon, Gary**
Table(s): Nationwide: Insurance: Dispute Resolution: Insurer **Band 1** p.134, District of Columbia: Insurance: Insurer **Band 1** p.816

**Dixon, Joyce A**
Profile: p.1667
Table(s): Nebraska: Corporate/Commercial **Band 1** p.1659

**Dixon, Megan**
Table(s): California: Antitrust **Band 4** p.536

**Dixon, Sharon Quinn**
Table(s): **Florida:** Tax: Employee Benefits **Band 1**
p.979

**Dizengoff, Ira S**
Profile: p.305
Table(s): **Nationwide:** Bankruptcy/Restructuring
**Band 2** p.39, **New York:**
Bankruptcy/Restructuring **Band 2** p.1782

**Djaha, David**
Profile: p.1889
Table(s): **New York:** Real Estate: Corporate **Band
3** p.1854

**Djuric, Nikola R**
Table(s): **Nationwide:** Wealth Management:
Eastern Region **Band 4** p.267

**Dlugie, David**
Table(s): **Illinois:** Real Estate **Band 3** p.1187

**Dobbins, Carolyn B**
Profile: p.1080
Table(s): **Georgia:** Real Estate **Band 3** p.1070

**Dobbs, C Edward**
Table(s): **Nationwide:** Bankruptcy/Restructuring
**Band 4** p.39, **Georgia:** Banking & Finance **Band 1**
p.1039, **Georgia:** Bankruptcy/Restructuring **Star
individuals** p.1042

**Dobrowski, Stanley J**
Profile: p.2094
Table(s): **Ohio:** Construction **Band 4** p.2062

**Dockery, Michael**
Profile: p.1653
Table(s): **Montana:** Real Estate **Band 1** p.1652

**Docks, Adam**
Table(s): **Nationwide:** Leisure & Hospitality **Up-
and-coming individuals** p.179

**Docksey, Ross**
Profile: p.1204
Table(s): **Nationwide:** Outsourcing **Band 2** p.195,
**Illinois:** Technology & Outsourcing **Band 1** p.1194

**Dockterman, Michael**
Profile: p.1204
Table(s): **Illinois:** Litigation: General Commercial
**Band 2** p.1180

**Dodd, Jan E**
Profile: p.305
Table(s): **Nationwide:** Product Liability & Mass
Torts **Band 5** p.208

**Dodd, Jeff**
Profile: p.2387
Table(s): **Texas:** Intellectual Property **Band 3**
p.2354

**Dodd, Richard**
Profile: p.2538
Table(s): **Washington:** Corporate/Commercial
**Senior Statesmen:** p.2525

**Dodds, John C**
Profile: p.2214
Table(s): **Pennsylvania:** Litigation: White-Collar
Crime & Government Investigations **Band 1**
p.2204

**Dodge, William J**
Table(s): **Vermont:** Real Estate: Zoning/Land
Use **Band 2** p.2487

**Doehrmann, Carrie**
Profile: p.1277
Table(s): **Indiana:** Environment **Band 2** p.1270

**Doerner, Brian D**
Profile: p.2214
Table(s): **Pennsylvania:** Corporate/M&A &
Private Equity **Band 4** p.2191

**Doetsch, Douglas A**
Table(s): **Illinois:** Banking & Finance **Band 3**
p.1145

**Doffermyre, Everette L**
Table(s): **Georgia:** Litigation: General
Commercial **Band 2** p.1065

**Dogali, Andy**
Table(s): **Florida:** Construction **Band 3** p.944

**Dohner Smith, Mary**
Table(s): **Tennessee:** Labor & Employment **Up-
and-coming individuals** p.2293

**Doke Jr, Marshall J**
Profile: p.305
Table(s): **Nationwide:** Government: Government
Contracts **Senior Statesmen:** p.117

**Dokos, Daniel S**
Profile: p.305
Table(s): **Nationwide:** Banking & Finance **Band 2**
p.31

**Dolan, Edward**
Table(s): **District of Columbia:**
Bankruptcy/Restructuring **Band 2** p.792

**Dolan, William**
Profile: p.2509
Table(s): **Virginia:** Litigation: White-Collar Crime
& Government Investigations **Band 1** p.2502

**Dolin, Kenneth R**
Profile: p.1204
Table(s): **Illinois:** Labor & Employment **Band 3**
p.1175

**Dolin, Mitchell F**
Profile: p.305
Table(s): **Nationwide:** Insurance: Dispute
Resolution: Policyholder **Band 1** p.137, **District of
Columbia:** Insurance: Policyholder **Band 1** p.818

**Doliner, Nathaniel L**
Profile: p.990
Table(s): **Florida:** Corporate/M&A & Private
Equity **Band 1** p.947

**Dollinger, Martin E**
Table(s): **New Jersey:** Real Estate **Band 1** p.1728

**Dolson, Scott**
Profile: p.1318
Table(s): **Kentucky:** Corporate/M&A **Band 1**
p.1305

**Domby, Arthur H**
Table(s): **Nationwide:** Energy: Nuclear
(Regulatory & Litigation) **Band 4** p.77

**Domina, David A**
Table(s): **Nebraska:** Litigation: General
Commercial **Band 1** p.1664

**Dominguez, Manuel J**
Table(s): **Florida:** Antitrust **Up-and-coming individuals**
p.935

**Domzalski, Shawn**
Profile: p.632
Table(s): **California:** Corporate/M&A **Associates to
watch** p.554

**Donadio, Donald A**
Table(s): **North Carolina:** Real Estate **Band 2**
p.2037

**Donahey, Michael**
Table(s): **Arizona:** Corporate/M&A **Band 3** p.495

**Donahue, Douglas**
Profile: p.305
Table(s): **Nationwide:** Capital Markets:
Derivatives **Up-and-coming individuals** p.51

**Donahue, Joseph G**
Profile: p.1399
Table(s): **Maine:** Energy & Natural Resources
**Band 2** p.1388

**Donaldson, Robert W**
Table(s): **Oregon:** Labor & Employment:
Immigration **Band 2** p.2168

**Donarski, Michelle**
Table(s): **North Dakota:** Labor & Employment
**Band 2** p.2052

**Donhauser, Linda V**
Profile: p.1426
Table(s): **Maryland:** Litigation: Bankruptcy **Band 1**
p.1419

**Donley, Charles F**
Profile: p.305
Table(s): **Nationwide:** Transportation: Aviation:
Regulatory **Band 2** p.256

**Donnelly, Dennis C**
Table(s): **Missouri:** Labor & Employment **Senior
Statesmen:** p.1625

**Donnelly, Paul**
Table(s): **Missouri:** Labor & Employment **Band 1**
p.1625

**Donnelly, Thomas M**
Profile: p.632
Table(s): **California:** Environment **Band 3** p.564

**Donoghue, Laurence J**
Profile: p.1490
Table(s): **Massachusetts:** Labor & Employment
**Band 3** p.1466

**Donohue, P Daniel**
Table(s): **South Dakota:** Corporate/Commercial
**Band 3** p.2281, **South Dakota:** Real Estate **Band 1**
p.2286

**Donohue Jr, John P**
Profile: p.2214
Table(s): **Pennsylvania:** Intellectual Property
**Band 2** p.2197

**Donovan, David M**
Table(s): **Arkansas:** Labor & Employment **Band 3**
p.520

**Donovan, Donald Francis**
Table(s): **Nationwide:** International Arbitration
**Band 1** p.145, **Nationwide:** International
Arbitration: Arbitrators **Band 1** p.145

**Donovan, Edward C**
Profile: p.859
Table(s): **District of Columbia:** Intellectual
Property: Litigation **Band 3** p.821

**Donovan, John D**
Table(s): **Nationwide:** Securities: Litigation **Band
2** p.232, **Massachusetts:** Litigation **Band 1** p.1470, **Massachusetts:**
Litigation: Securities **Star individuals** p.1470

**Donovan, John M**
Profile: p.305
Table(s): **Nationwide:** Capital Markets:
Securitisation **Band 4** p.59

**Donovan, Martha N**
Profile: p.1734
Table(s): **New Jersey:** Environment **Band 2** p.1711

**Donovan, Richard E**
Table(s): **New York:** Antitrust **Band 5** p.1778

**Donovan, Richard T**
Table(s): **Arkansas:** Litigation: General
Commercial **Band 2** p.522

**Donovan, Thomas J**
Profile: p.1694
Table(s): **New Hampshire:** Litigation: General
Commercial **Band 2** p.1690

**Donovan Esq, Colleen R**
Profile: p.1734
Table(s): **New Jersey:** Environment **Band 3**
p.1711, **New Jersey:** Real Estate **Band 2** p.1728

**Donovan Jr, Lawrence**
Table(s): **Colorado:** Real Estate **Band 1** p.714

**Donson, Jack**
Profile: p.2094
Table(s): **Ohio:** Litigation: Antitrust **Band 1** p.2078

**Doogal, Daljit**
Table(s): **Michigan:** Corporate/M&A **Band 3**
p.1538

**Doot, David T**
Profile: p.305
Table(s): **Nationwide:** Energy: Electricity
(Regulatory & Litigation) **Band 3** p.76

**Doran, James**
Table(s): **Illinois:** Banking & Finance **Band 3**
p.1145

**Doran, John Alan**
Table(s): **Arizona:** Labor & Employment **Band 2**
p.499

**Doran, Scott**
Profile: p.2094
Table(s): **Ohio:** Natural Resources &
Environment **Band 3** p.2083

**Doran Jr, James M**
Profile: p.2303
Table(s): **Tennessee:** Litigation: General
Commercial **Band 2** p.2295

**Dore, Michael**
Profile: p.1734
Table(s): **New Jersey:** Environment **Band 2** p.1711

**Doren, Richard J**
Profile: p.632
Table(s): **California:** Insurance: Insurer **Band 3**
p.574

**Dorf, Michael**
Profile: p.632
Table(s): **California:** Corporate/M&A **Band 3** p.553

**Dori, Yaron**
Profile: p.860
Table(s): District of Columbia: Telecom, Broadcast & Satellite **Band 3** p.844

**Dorn, Joseph W**
Profile: p.306
Table(s): Nationwide: International Trade: Trade Remedies & Trade Policy **Band 1** p.154

**Dornette, W Stuart**
Profile: p.2095
Table(s): Ohio: Litigation: General Commercial **Band 3** p.2078

**Dorris, Malcolm S**
Profile: p.306
Table(s): Nationwide: Capital Markets: Securitisation **Band 2** p.59

**Dorris, William**
Table(s): Georgia: Construction **Band 1** p.1044

**Dorsey, Rufus Thomas**
Table(s): Georgia: Bankruptcy/Restructuring **Band 2** p.1042

**Dorsi, Carla**
Profile: p.1734
Table(s): New Jersey: Labor & Employment **Up-and-coming individuals** p.1718

**Dorton, David R**
Table(s): North Carolina: Real Estate **Band 3** p.2037

**Dost, Patricia**
Table(s): Oregon: Environment **Band 1** p.2165

**Dotson Jr, Albert E**
Profile: p.990
Table(s): Florida: Real Estate: Zoning/Land Use **Band 3** p.975

**Dottori, Mario F**
Table(s): District of Columbia: Technology & Outsourcing **Band 3** p.842

**Dougherty, Brian**
Profile: p.2214
Table(s): Pennsylvania: Labor & Employment: Employee Benefits & Compensation **Band 3** p.2200

**Dougherty, Lucia A**
Profile: p.990
Table(s): Florida: Real Estate: Zoning/Land Use **Band 3** p.975

**Dougherty, Thomas J**
Profile: p.1490
Table(s): Nationwide: Securities: Litigation **Band 2** p.232, Massachusetts: Litigation: Securities **Star individuals** p.1470

**Dougherty, III, Clifford C**
Profile: p.2149
Table(s): Oklahoma: Intellectual Property **Band 2** p.2138

**Douglas, Charles W**
Profile: p.1204
Table(s): Illinois: Antitrust **Band 3** p.1143, Illinois: Litigation: General Commercial **Band 3** p.1180

**Douglas, John R**
Table(s): Nebraska: Litigation: Insurance **Band 1** p.1664

**Douglas, Robert J**
Table(s): Iowa: Real Estate **Band 1** p.1290

**Douglas, Sue**
Profile: p.2095
Table(s): Ohio: Labor & Employment **Band 3** p.2074

**Douglass, Duncan B**
Profile: p.306
Table(s): Nationwide: Financial Services Regulation: Consumer Finance (Compliance) **Up-and-coming individuals** p.98

**Douglass, Susan Upton**
Table(s): New York: Intellectual Property: Trade Mark & Copyright **Band 2** p.1821

**Dove, Luke**
Table(s): Mississippi: Litigation: General Commercial **Band 3** p.1597

**Dove, Agnes**
Table(s): Nationwide: Government: Government Contracts **Band 4** p.117

**Dow, Joshua R**
Table(s): Maine: Corporate/M&A: Bankruptcy **Band 3** p.1385

**Dow, Melvin**
Table(s): Texas: Real Estate **Senior Statesmen:** p.2367

**Dow, Rebecca W**
Profile: p.717
Table(s): Colorado: Real Estate **Band 1** p.714

**Dow, T Andrew**
Profile: p.2387
Table(s): Texas: Real Estate **Band 3** p.2367

**Dowd, David F**
Table(s): Nationwide: Government: Government Contracts **Band 4** p.117

**Dowd, Kelvin J**
Profile: p.306
Table(s): Nationwide: Transportation: Rail (for Shippers) **Band 2** p.258

**Dowd, Martin F**
Profile: p.1734
Table(s): New Jersey: Real Estate **Band 1** p.1728

**Dowd, Mary Joanne**
Profile: p.860
Table(s): District of Columbia: Bankruptcy/Restructuring **Band 2** p.792

**Dowd Jr, Edward**
Profile: p.1636
Table(s): Missouri: Litigation: White-Collar Crime & Government Investigations **Band 2** p.1629

**Dowdall, Colleen**
Table(s): Montana: Real Estate **Band 3** p.1652

**Dowdell, Thomas E**
Profile: p.860
Table(s): District of Columbia: Healthcare **Band 2** p.809

**Dowdy, L Craig**
Profile: p.1080
Table(s): Georgia: Energy **Band 1** p.1049

**Dowling, Charles T**
Profile: p.306
Table(s): Nationwide: Wealth Management: Eastern Region **Band 4** p.267

**Dowling, Donald C**
Profile: p.1889
Table(s): New York: Labor & Employment **Band 4** p.1826

**Dowling, Sarah T**
Profile: p.2257
Table(s): Rhode Island: Corporate/Commercial **Band 3** p.2251

**Dowling, Thomas M**
Table(s): Vermont: Corporate/Commercial **Band 3** p.2483

**Downes, Robert W**
Profile: p.306
Table(s): Nationwide: Capital Markets: Debt & Equity **Band 4** p.46

**Downey, Alicia L**
Table(s): Massachusetts: Antitrust **Band 3** p.1444

**Downey, Kevin**
Table(s): Nationwide: Securities: Litigation **Band 3** p.232, District of Columbia: Litigation: Securities **Band 1** p.826, District of Columbia: Litigation: White-Collar Crime & Government Investigations **Band 3** p.826

**Downey III, Charles J**
Table(s): Connecticut: Corporate/M&A **Band 2** p.732

**Downs, Andrew**
Table(s): California: Insurance: Insurer **Band 3** p.574

**Downs, J Anthony**
Profile: p.1490
Table(s): Massachusetts: Intellectual Property **Band 2** p.1463

**Downs, Jeremy**
Profile: p.1205
Table(s): Illinois: Bankruptcy/Restructuring **Band 4** p.1148

**Downs III, Joseph W**
Table(s): Florida: Construction **Band 1** p.944

**Dowsley III, Felix R**
Profile: p.2303
Table(s): Tennessee: Banking & Finance **Band 2** p.2287

**Doyle, David C**
Profile: p.633
Table(s): California: Intellectual Property: Patent **Band 4** p.578

**Doyle, David P**
Profile: p.1734
Table(s): New Jersey: Employee Benefits & Executive Compensation **Band 2** p.1710

**Doyle, Diana**
Table(s): Illinois: Tax **Band 3** p.1192

**Doyle, Kathryn R**
Table(s): Pennsylvania: Intellectual Property **Band 2** p.2197

**Doyle, Linda**
Profile: p.1205
Table(s): Illinois: Labor & Employment **Band 4** p.1175

**Doyle, Patrick**
Profile: p.306
Table(s): Nationwide: Financial Services Regulation: Banking (Compliance) **Band 2** p.96

**Doyle, Thomas R**
Profile: p.1399
Table(s): Maine: Environment **Band 1** p.1389

**Doyle Jr, John**
Table(s): North Carolina: Labor & Employment **Band 1** p.2031

**Dozeman, Douglas A**
Table(s): Michigan: Litigation: General Commercial **Band 2** p.1544

**Drablos, Scott**
Table(s): Texas: Tax **Band 4** p.2371

**Draeger, Scot**
Table(s): Maine: Corporate/M&A **Band 3** p.1385

**Dragna, James J**
Profile: p.633
Table(s): California: Environment **Band 1** p.564

**Dragoo, Denise**
Table(s): Utah: Energy & Natural Resources **Band 1** p.2464

**Drake, Denise K**
Profile: p.1636
Table(s): Missouri: Labor & Employment **Band 1** p.1625

**Drake, Stuart AC**
Profile: p.306
Table(s): Nationwide: Climate Change **Band 3** p.63, District of Columbia: Environment **Band 3** p.804

**Dranoff, David**
Profile: p.1205
Table(s): Illinois: Banking & Finance **Band 3** p.1145

**Draper, Douglas S**
Profile: p.1360
Table(s): Louisiana: Bankruptcy/Restructuring **Band 1** p.1337

**Draper, Hayward L**
Table(s): Iowa: Litigation: General Commercial **Band 3** p.1288

**Draper, John B**
Table(s): New Mexico: Environment, Natural Resources & Regulated Industries: Water Law **Star individuals** p.1766

**Draper, Thomas B**
Table(s): Nationwide: Banking & Finance **Band 4** p.31, Massachusetts: Banking & Finance **Band 1** p.1445

**Draper IV, Clare H**
Profile: p.1080
Table(s): Georgia: Labor & Employment **Band 3** p.1060

**Drapkin, Steven**
Table(s): California: Labor & Employment **Band 2** p.587

**Drasco, Dennis J**
Profile: p.1734
Table(s): New Jersey: Litigation: General Commercial **Band 1** p.1722

**Duncan, J Kelly**
Profile: p.1361
Table(s): Nationwide: Gaming & Licensing **Band 2** p.115, Louisiana: Banking & Finance: Marine Finance **Band 1** p.1335, Louisiana: Gaming & Licensing **Band 1** p.1348

**Duncan, James**
Profile: p.1889
Table(s): New York: Tax **Band 2** p.1862

**Duncan, Margaret M**
Profile: p.1205
Table(s): Illinois: Intellectual Property **Band 3** p.1171

**Duncan III, Brooke**
Profile: p.1361
Table(s): Louisiana: Labor & Employment **Band 2** p.1350

**Dunham, Edward Wood**
Profile: p.307
Table(s): Nationwide: Franchising **Band 1** p.111, Connecticut: Litigation: General Commercial **Band 1** p.738

**Dunham Jr, Wolcott B**
Table(s): Nationwide: Insurance: Transactional & Regulatory **Senior Statesmen:** p.139, New York: Insurance: Transactional & Regulatory **Senior Statesmen:** p.1816

**Dunkle, Mark F**
Table(s): Delaware: Real Estate: Zoning/Land Use **Band 2** p.766

**Dunlay, Catherine**
Profile: p.2095
Table(s): Ohio: Healthcare **Band 3** p.2069

**Dunlay, Jon**
Profile: p.2387
Table(s): Texas: Real Estate **Star individuals** p.2367

**Dunlevie, Steven S**
Table(s): Georgia: Banking & Finance: Mainly Regulatory **Band 2** p.1039

**Dunlop, Fred**
Profile: p.2388
Table(s): Texas: Real Estate **Senior Statesmen:** p.2367

**Dunlop, Lisl J**
Table(s): New York: Antitrust **Band 5** p.1778

**Dunn, Christopher A**
Profile: p.307
Table(s): Nationwide: International Trade: Trade Remedies & Trade Policy **Band 4** p.154

**Dunn, Daniel**
Table(s): Colorado: Natural Resources & Environment **Band 1** p.712

**Dunn, Daniel J**
Table(s): North Dakota: Litigation: General Commercial **Band 1** p.2053

**Dunn, Deborah**
Table(s): Nationwide: Wealth Management: Central Region **Up-and-coming individuals** p.266

**Dunn, Glenn H**
Table(s): North Carolina: Environment **Band 2** p.2028

**Dunn, K Kristine**
Profile: p.633
Table(s): California: Banking & Finance **Band 2** p.539

**Dunn, Loren R**
Table(s): Washington: Environment **Band 2** p.2527

**Dunn, Martin**
Profile: p.307
Table(s): Nationwide: Securities: Regulation: Advisory **Band 1** p.232

**Dunn, Matthew S**
Profile: p.1889
Table(s): New York: Immigration **Band 3** p.1814

**Dunn, Stephen**
Table(s): North Carolina: Labor & Employment **Band 2** p.2031

**Dunn, William**
Profile: p.1549
Table(s): Michigan: Real Estate **Senior Statesmen:** p.1546

**Dunne, Carey R**
Profile: p.1889
Table(s): New York: Litigation: General Commercial **Band 3** p.1833, New York: Litigation: White-Collar Crime & Government Investigations **Band 2** p.1833

**Dunne, Daniel J**
Profile: p.2538
Table(s): Washington: Litigation: General Commercial **Band 3** p.2533

**Dunne, Dennis**
Profile: p.307
Table(s): Nationwide: Bankruptcy/Restructuring **Band 1** p.39, New York: Bankruptcy/Restructuring **Band 1** p.1782

**Dunne, Kim**
Table(s): Alaska: Labor & Employment **Band 3** p.489

**Dunne, Kimberly A**
Profile: p.633
Table(s): California: Litigation: White-Collar Crime & Government Investigations **Band 2** p.601

**Dunne, Michael J**
Profile: p.1735
Table(s): New Jersey: Corporate/M&A **Band 3** p.1707

**Dunner, Donald R**
Profile: p.860
Table(s): Nationwide: Appellate Law **Band 4** p.26, District of Columbia: Intellectual Property: Litigation **Star individuals** p.821

**Dunning, Elizabeth**
Profile: p.2473
Table(s): Utah: Labor & Employment **Band 2** p.2467

**Dunsizer, Jennifer**
Profile: p.2095
Table(s): Ohio: Employee Benefits & Executive Compensation **Band 2** p.2067

**Dunston, Erin M.**
Profile: p.2509
Table(s): Northern Virginia: Intellectual Property **Up-and-coming individuals** p.2497

**Dunwoody, Stuart R**
Table(s): Washington: Intellectual Property **Band 2** p.2529

**Duplantis, Bob J.**
Profile: p.1361
Table(s): Louisiana: Energy & Natural Resources: Oil & Gas **Band 1** p.1344

**Dupler, Mitchell S**
Profile: p.307
Table(s): Nationwide: Capital Markets: Securitisation **Band 3** p.59

**Dupré, Marc F.**
Table(s): Massachusetts: Private Equity: Venture Capital Investment **Band 4** p.1474

**Dupree Jr, Thomas**
Profile: p.307
Table(s): Nationwide: Appellate Law **Up-and-coming individuals** p.26

**Duprey, Susan V**
Table(s): New Hampshire: Real Estate: Land Use **Band 2** p.1692

**Durant, E Terry**
Table(s): Connecticut: Labor & Employment **Senior Statesmen:** p.736

**Durham, Albert F**
Table(s): North Carolina: Bankruptcy/Restructuring **Band 1** p.2023

**Durham, Matthew M**
Table(s): Utah: Labor & Employment **Band 2** p.2467

**Durham, Phillip**
Profile: p.307
Table(s): Nationwide: Transportation: Aviation: Finance **Up-and-coming individuals** p.252

**Durham, Thomas C**
Table(s): Nationwide: Tax: Controversy **Band 2** p.244

**Durick, Patrick**
Table(s): North Dakota: Litigation: General Commercial **Senior Statesmen:** p.2053

**Durie, Daralyn J**
Table(s): California: Intellectual Property: Patent **Band 2** p.578

**Durkan, Ryan**
Table(s): Washington: Real Estate: Zoning/Land Use **Band 2** p.2536

**Durkin, Denis L**
Profile: p.990
Table(s): Florida: Construction **Band 2** p.944

**Durkin, Thomas M**
Table(s): Illinois: Litigation: General Commercial **Band 3** p.1180

**Durlacher, Erich N**
Table(s): Georgia: Bankruptcy/Restructuring **Band 2** p.1042

**Durling, James P**
Profile: p.307
Table(s): Nationwide: International Trade: Trade Remedies & Trade Policy **Band 4** p.154

**Durocher, Skip**
Table(s): Nationwide: Native American Law **Band 2** p.192

**Durrell, Brian**
Table(s): Alaska: Corporate/M&A **Band 1** p.487, Alaska: Real Estate **Band 1** p.491

**Durrer II, Van C**
Profile: p.633
Table(s): California: Bankruptcy/Restructuring **Band 2** p.542

**Durso, John**
Profile: p.1205
Table(s): Illinois: Healthcare **Band 2** p.1165

**Dutro, James R**
Profile: p.633
Table(s): California: Healthcare **Band 1** p.568

**Dutton, David J**
Table(s): Iowa: Litigation: General Commercial **Band 1** p.1288

**Dutton, Melinda J.**
Table(s): New York: Healthcare **Up-and-coming individuals** p.1811

**Dutton, Thomas E**
Profile: p.2095
Table(s): Ohio: Healthcare **Band 2** p.2069

**DuVal, David V**
Table(s): Southern Virginia: Real Estate **Band 2** p.2506

**Duvall, Scot A**
Table(s): Kentucky: Intellectual Property **Band 2** p.1308

**Duwe, Brian W**
Profile: p.1205
Table(s): Illinois: Corporate/M&A **Band 3** p.1156

**Dvorak, Thomas E**
Table(s): Idaho: Bankruptcy/Restructuring **Band 2** p.1131

**Dweck, Erwin**
Table(s): New York: Real Estate: Corporate **Up-and-coming individuals** p.1854

**Dworetzky, Joseph A**
Profile: p.2215
Table(s): Pennsylvania: Bankruptcy/Restructuring **Star individuals** p.2188

**Dworkin, Adam**
Profile: p.307
Table(s): Nationwide: Banking & Finance **Band 4** p.31

**Dworsky, Marc**
Profile: p.633
Table(s): California: Litigation: Securities **Band 4** p.594

**Dwyer, James R**
Table(s): New York: Insurance: Transactional & Regulatory **Band 3** p.1816

**Dwyer, John**
Table(s): California: Litigation: General Commercial **Band 3** p.593, California: Litigation: Securities **Band 4** p.593

**Dwyer, John V**
Table(s): New Hampshire: Environment **Band 1** p.1687

**Dwyer, Maureen**
Table(s): District of Columbia: Real Estate: Zoning/Land Use **Band 1** p.835

**Edison-Smith, Lisa**
Table(s): North Dakota: Labor & Employment
Band 1 p.2052

**Edlin, Richard A**
Profile: p.1889
Table(s): New York: Litigation: General
Commercial Band 3 p.1833

**Edvalson, Ian B**
Table(s): California: Life Sciences:
Corporate/Commercial Band 3 p.590

**Edward, Carol L**
Table(s): Washington: Immigration Band 2 p.2528

**Edwards, A Clifford**
Table(s): Montana: Litigation: Mainly Plaintiff
Band 1 p.1649

**Edwards, Amy L**
Profile: p.860
Table(s): District of Columbia: Environment Band
4 p.804

**Edwards, Brady**
Profile: p.2388
Table(s): Texas: Litigation: General Commercial
Band 4 p.2362

**Edwards, Charles L**
Profile: p.1205
Table(s): Illinois: Real Estate Senior Statesmen:
p.1187

**Edwards, Christine A**
Profile: p.308
Table(s): Nationwide: Financial Services
Regulation: Banking (Compliance) Band 4 p.96

**Edwards, James M**
Table(s): Alabama: Real Estate Band 3 p.466

**Edwards, Katherine**
Table(s): Nationwide: Energy: Oil & Gas
(Regulatory & Litigation) Band 4 p.78

**Edwards, Linda Pearce**
Table(s): South Carolina: Labor & Employment
Band 3 p.2262

**Edwards, Michael L**
Table(s): Alabama: Litigation: General
Commercial Band 1 p.463

**Edwards, Steve**
Table(s): California: Real Estate Band 3 p.611

**Edwards Jr, Robert**
Table(s): Georgia: Energy Band 1 p.1049

**Egan, Michael**
Profile: p.1081
Table(s): Georgia: Corporate/M&A Band 1 p.1046

**Egan, Peter**
Profile: p.1890
Table(s): New York: Healthcare Up-and-coming indi-
viduals p.1811

**Egan III, John J**
Profile: p.1490
Table(s): Nationwide: Investment Funds: Venture
Capital Band 2 p.174, Massachusetts:
Corporate/M&A Band 3 p.1452, Massachusetts:
Private Equity: Venture Capital Investment Band
1 p.1474

**Egan Jr, James C**
Profile: p.860
Table(s): District of Columbia: Antitrust Band 5
p.787

**Egerton, Charles**
Table(s): Florida: Tax Band 1 p.979

**Eggers III, Walter F**
Profile: p.2601
Table(s): Wyoming: Litigation: General
Commercial Band 3 p.2598

**Eggert, Russell R**
Table(s): Illinois: Environment: Litigation Band 1
p.1162

**Eggleston, Jon R**
Table(s): Vermont: Corporate/Commercial Band 2
p.2483

**Eggleston, W Neil**
Profile: p.860
Table(s): Nationwide: Securities: Litigation Band
2 p.232, Nationwide: Securities: Regulation:
Enforcement Band 2 p.232, District of Columbia:
Litigation: Securities Band 1 p.826, District of
Columbia: Litigation: White-Collar Crime &
Government Investigations Band 1 p.826

**Eggleton, Keith**
Table(s): California: Litigation: General
Commercial Band 5 p.593

**Ehrenberg, Peter H**
Profile: p.1735
Table(s): New Jersey: Corporate/M&A Band 1
p.1707

**Ehrgott, Catherine**
Profile: p.634
Table(s): California: Healthcare Band 4 p.568

**Ehrhard, T Gregory**
Profile: p.1318
Table(s): Kentucky: Real Estate Band 3 p.1314

**Ehrhart, Kevin M**
Table(s): California: Real Estate Band 3 p.611

**Ehrlich, Gayle**
Profile: p.1490
Table(s): Massachusetts:
Bankruptcy/Restructuring Band 3 p.1449

**Ehrlich, Kenneth**
Profile: p.1490
Table(s): Massachusetts: Banking & Finance:
Corporate & Regulatory Band 1 p.1446

**Ehrlich, Miles F**
Table(s): California: Litigation: White-Collar
Crime & Government Investigations Band 3 p.601

**Eichel, Steven P**
Profile: p.1490
Table(s): Massachusetts: Tax Band 3 p.1481

**Eid, Troy A**
Profile: p.309
Table(s): Nationwide: Native American Law Band
2 p.192, Colorado: Natural Resources &
Environment Band 3 p.712

**Eidelman, Gary B**
Table(s): Maryland: Labor & Employment Band 2
p.1417

**Eidelman, Michael M**
Profile: p.1205
Table(s): Illinois: Bankruptcy/Restructuring Band
3 p.1148

**Eidson, Mike**
Table(s): Florida: Litigation: General Commercial
Band 2 p.966

**Eiland, Gary**
Profile: p.2388
Table(s): Nationwide: Healthcare: Regulatory &
Litigation Band 3 p.127, Texas: Healthcare Band 1
p.2347

**Eimer, Nathan P**
Profile: p.1205
Table(s): Illinois: Antitrust Star individuals p.1143

**Einbinder, Michael**
Table(s): Nationwide: Franchising: Mainly
Franchisee Band 3 p.114

**Einhorn, Alan**
Table(s): Massachusetts: Healthcare Band 3
p.1460

**Einhorn, Robert M**
Table(s): Nationwide: Franchising: Mainly
Franchisee Band 3 p.114

**Einhorn, Theresa A**
Table(s): Texas: Banking & Finance Band 4
p.2325

**Einowski, Edward**
Table(s): Nationwide: Projects: Renewables &
Alternative Energy Band 2 p.218

**Einsiedler Jr, Charles S**
Profile: p.1399
Table(s): Maine: Labor & Employment Band 3
p.1390, Maine: Labor & Employment: Employee
Benefits & Compensation Band 3 p.1390

**Eisdorfer, Stephen M**
Table(s): New Jersey: Real Estate: Zoning/Land
Use Band 2 p.1728

**Eiseman, Byron**
Profile: p.526
Table(s): Arkansas: Corporate/Commercial: Tax
Senior Statesmen: p.518

**Eiseman, Neal M**
Table(s): New York: Construction Band 3 p.1791

**Eisen, Rebecca**
Profile: p.634
Table(s): California: Labor & Employment Band 2
p.587

**Eisen, Steven J**
Profile: p.2304
Table(s): Tennessee: Banking & Finance Band 2
p.2287, Tennessee: Banking & Finance:
Regulatory Band 1 p.2287

**Eisenberg, Joe**
Table(s): California: Bankruptcy/Restructuring
Band 4 p.542

**Eisenberg, Jon B**
Profile: p.634
Table(s): California: Litigation: Appellate Band 3
p.599

**Eisenberg, Susan Nadler**
Table(s): Florida: Labor & Employment Band 1
p.959

**Eisenbiegler, Frederick F**
Profile: p.309
Table(s): Nationwide: Banking & Finance Band 4
p.31

**Eisenbrandt, James**
Table(s): Missouri: Litigation: White-Collar Crime
& Government Investigations Band 1 p.1629

**Eisenhauer, Margaret P**
Table(s): Nationwide: Privacy & Data Security
Band 3 p.199

**Eisenhofer, Jay W**
Profile: p.770
Table(s): Nationwide: Securities: Litigation:
Mainly Plaintiff Band 1 p.234, Delaware:
Chancery: Mainly Plaintiff Band 1 p.759, New
York: Litigation: Securities Mainly Plaintiff Band 1
p.1835

**Eisenstat, Larry**
Profile: p.309
Table(s): Nationwide: Energy: Electricity
(Regulatory & Litigation) Band 1 p.76

**Eisert, Richard**
Profile: p.309
Table(s): Nationwide: Advertising: Transactional
& Regulatory Band 2 p.20

**Eisner, Rebecca S**
Table(s): Nationwide: Outsourcing Band 1 p.195,
Illinois: Technology & Outsourcing Band 1 p.1194

**Eitel, Mitchell S**
Profile: p.309
Table(s): Nationwide: Financial Services
Regulation: Banking (Compliance) Band 2 p.96,
Nationwide: Financial Services Regulation:
Financial Institutions M&A Band 1 p.96, New
York: Corporate/M&A Band 4 p.1793

**Eizenstat, Stuart E**
Profile: p.309
Table(s): Nationwide: International Trade: Trade
Remedies & Trade Policy Band 1 p.154

**Ek, Dale**
Table(s): New Mexico: Real Estate Senior
Statesmen: p.1772

**Ekberg, Charles**
Profile: p.2539
Table(s): Washington: Bankruptcy/Restructuring
Band 1 p.2523

**Elacqua, James J**
Profile: p.634
Table(s): California: Intellectual Property: Patent
Band 3 p.578

**Elbaum, Steven**
Profile: p.743
Table(s): Connecticut: Real Estate Band 2 p.740

**Elberger, Ronald**
Table(s): Indiana: Litigation: General
Commercial Band 3 p.1273

**Elbert, Angela R**
Profile: p.1206
Table(s): Illinois: Insurance: Dispute Resolution
Band 2 p.1168

**Elbing, Karen L.**
Table(s): Massachusetts: Intellectual Property
Band 3 p.1463

**Elder, James**
Table(s): Oklahoma: Real Estate **Band 1** p.2145

**Elderkin, Dianne B**
Profile: p.2215
Table(s): Pennsylvania: Intellectual Property **Band 1** p.2197

**Eldridge, John R**
Table(s): Texas: Environment **Band 3** p.2343

**Elento-Sneed, Anna**
Profile: p.1122
Table(s): Hawaii: Labor & Employment **Band 1** p.1117

**Elfman Esq, Eric M**
Table(s): Massachusetts: Tax **Band 1** p.1481

**Elias, Marc Erik**
Table(s): Nationwide: Government: Political Law **Band 1** p.124

**Eliopoulos, Elias**
Profile: p.1890
Table(s): New York: Real Estate **Up-and-coming individuals** p.1854

**Elkin, Michael**
Profile: p.1890
Table(s): New York: Intellectual Property: Patent **Band 3** p.1820, New York: Intellectual Property: Trade Mark & Copyright **Band 3** p.1820, New York: Media & Entertainment: Copyright & Contract Disputes **Band 3** p.1851

**Elkow, Pamela K**
Profile: p.743
Table(s): Connecticut: Environment **Band 1** p.733

**Ellefson, Anne**
Table(s): South Carolina: Real Estate **Band 2** p.2266

**Ellenberg, Mark C**
Profile: p.860
Table(s): Nationwide: Bankruptcy/Restructuring **Band 3** p.39, District of Columbia: Bankruptcy/Restructuring **Band 1** p.792

**Ellett, E Tazewell**
Table(s): Nationwide: Transportation: Aviation: Regulatory **Band 2** p.256

**Elligett, Raymond**
Table(s): Florida: Litigation: Appellate **Band 3** p.972

**Ellin, Howard L**
Profile: p.1890
Table(s): New York: Corporate/M&A **Band 2** p.1793

**Elliot, Thomas**
Table(s): District of Columbia: Immigration **Band 3** p.814

**Elliott, E Donald**
Profile: p.861
Table(s): District of Columbia: Environment **Band 2** p.804

**Elliott, Richard W**
Table(s): Washington: Environment **Band 1** p.2527

**Ellis, Emmett N**
Profile: p.309
Table(s): Nationwide: Energy: Electricity (Finance) **Band 1** p.75

**Ellis, Jonathan**
Profile: p.2562
Table(s): West Virginia: Litigation: General Commercial **Associates to watch** p.2555

**Ellis, Richard W**
Table(s): North Carolina: Litigation: General Commercial **Band 1** p.2033

**Ellis, Steven M**
Table(s): Massachusetts: Banking & Finance **Band 1** p.1445

**Ellis, William**
Table(s): Virginia: Environment **Band 2** p.2495

**Ellis, Jr., Harvey D.**
Profile: p.2149
Table(s): Oklahoma: Litigation: General Commercial **Band 3** p.2141

**Ellison, Christopher T**
Table(s): California: Energy: State Regulatory & Litigation **Band 1** p.562

**Ellison, John N**
Table(s): Pennsylvania: Litigation: General Commercial **Band 3** p.2203

**Ellison, Morris**
Table(s): South Carolina: Real Estate **Band 3** p.2266

**Ellison, Scott W**
Table(s): New Hampshire: Corporate/Commercial **Band 2** p.1685

**Ellison, Thomas A**
Table(s): Utah: Real Estate **Band 1** p.2470

**Ellman, Howard**
Profile: p.634
Table(s): California: Real Estate: Zoning/Land Use **Senior Statesmen:** p.612

**Ellsworth, Kathryn**
Table(s): New York: Insurance: Dispute Resolution: Insurer **Band 3** p.1816

**Ellsworth, Laura**
Profile: p.2215
Table(s): Pennsylvania: Litigation: General Commercial **Band 3** p.2203

**Ellzey, Daniel**
Profile: p.2268
Table(s): South Carolina: Labor & Employment **Senior Statesmen:** p.2262

**Elrifi, Ivor R**
Profile: p.309
Table(s): Nationwide: Life Sciences: IP/Patent Litigation **Band 3** p.183, Massachusetts: Intellectual Property **Band 3** p.1463

**Elrod, Eugene R**
Profile: p.309
Table(s): Nationwide: Energy: Oil & Gas (Regulatory & Litigation) **Band 1** p.78

**Elrod, John**
Profile: p.1081
Table(s): Georgia: Bankruptcy/Restructuring **Up-and-coming individuals** p.1042

**Elrod, John R**
Table(s): Arkansas: Litigation: General Commercial **Band 3** p.522

**Elrod, Steven M**
Profile: p.1206
Table(s): Illinois: Real Estate: Zoning/Land Use **Band 2** p.1188

**Elsaesser, Ford**
Table(s): Idaho: Bankruptcy/Restructuring **Band 1** p.1131

**Elwood, John**
Profile: p.309
Table(s): Nationwide: Appellate Law **Band 3** p.26

**Ely III, Hiram**
Table(s): Kentucky: Litigation: General Commercial **Band 4** p.1312

**Ely Jr, Clausen**
Profile: p.310
Table(s): Nationwide: Food & Beverages: Regulatory & Litigation **Senior Statesmen:** p.107

**Emanuel, Craig A**
Profile: p.634
Table(s): California: Media & Entertainment: Transactional: Mainly Talent **Band 2** p.609

**Emanuel, John F**
Profile: p.2582
Table(s): Wisconsin: Corporate/M&A **Band 3** p.2571

**Emch, A L**
Table(s): West Virginia: Litigation: General Commercial **Star individuals** p.2555

**Emerick, Steven P**
Profile: p.508
Table(s): Arizona: Corporate/M&A **Band 3** p.495

**Emerson, J. Russell**
Table(s): Texas: Intellectual Property **Band 4** p.2354

**Emmanuel, John**
Table(s): Florida: Bankruptcy/Restructuring **Band 3** p.939

**Emmerich, Adam O**
Profile: p.1890
Table(s): Nationwide: Capital Markets: REITs **Band 2** p.55, New York: Corporate/M&A **Band 1** p.1793

**Emory Jr, Frank E**
Profile: p.2040
Table(s): North Carolina: Litigation: General Commercial **Band 2** p.2033

**Enderle Jr, Louis E**
Profile: p.2562
Table(s): West Virginia: Real Estate **Band 2** p.2560

**Eng, Kimton**
Table(s): Washington: Intellectual Property **Band 3** p.2529

**Engel, John**
Table(s): District of Columbia: Real Estate **Band 2** p.835

**Engellenner, Thomas J**
Profile: p.1490
Table(s): Massachusetts: Intellectual Property **Band 3** p.1463

**Engh, Anna**
Profile: p.861
Table(s): District of Columbia: Insurance: Policyholder **Band 3** p.818

**England, John F**
Profile: p.1602
Table(s): Mississippi: Corporate/Commercial: Municipal Finance **Band 2** p.1591

**Englander, John C**
Profile: p.1491
Table(s): Massachusetts: Intellectual Property **Band 3** p.1463

**Engle, Craig**
Profile: p.310
Table(s): Nationwide: Government: Political Law **Band 2** p.124

**Engle, Daniel T**
Table(s): Missouri: Real Estate **Band 2** p.1633

**Engler, Bruce M**
Table(s): Minnesota: Corporate/M&A **Band 1** p.1569

**Englert Jr, Roy**
Table(s): Nationwide: Appellate Law **Star individuals** p.26

**English, Holly**
Profile: p.1735
Table(s): New Jersey: Labor & Employment **Band 3** p.1718

**English, Stephen**
Table(s): Oregon: Litigation: General Commercial **Star individuals** p.2171

**Englund, Rudy A**
Profile: p.2539
Table(s): Washington: Litigation: General Commercial **Band 2** p.2533

**Engros Jr, Charles E**
Profile: p.1890
Table(s): New York: Corporate/M&A **Band 5** p.1793, New York: Media & Entertainment: Corporate **Band 2** p.1848

**Engstrom, Eric**
Table(s): Kansas: Corporate/M&A **Senior Statesmen:** p.1292

**Engstrom, Stephen**
Table(s): Arkansas: Litigation: General Commercial **Band 3** p.522

**Enns, Rodrick J**
Table(s): North Carolina: Antitrust **Band 1** p.2020

**Enoch, Craig T**
Table(s): Texas: Litigation: Appellate **Band 3** p.2361

**Enriquez, Maria G**
Table(s): Illinois: Insurance: Dispute Resolution **Band 3** p.1168

**Ensor, R Steve**
Profile: p.1081
Table(s): Georgia: Labor & Employment **Band 2** p.1060

**Entenman, John A**
Table(s): Michigan: Labor & Employment **Band 3** p.1542

**Entin, Seth J**
Profile: p.990
Table(s): Florida: Tax **Band 2** p.979

**Epps, John D**
Profile: p.2509
Table(s): Virginia: Litigation: Products Liability
**Band 2** p.2502

**Epstein, Gary M**
Profile: p.991
Table(s): Florida: Corporate/M&A & Private
Equity **Star individuals** p.947

**Epstein, Joseph G**
Profile: p.2388
Table(s): Texas: Bankruptcy/Restructuring **Band 4**
p.2328

**Epstein, Michael**
Profile: p.1890
Table(s): New York: Technology & Outsourcing
**Band 2** p.1868

**Epstein, Roger H**
Table(s): Hawaii: Corporate/Commercial: Tax
**Band 1** p.1115

**Epstein, Ruth S**
Table(s): Nationwide: Investment Funds:
Registered Funds **Band 3** p.170

**Epstein, Steven B**
Table(s): District of Columbia: Healthcare **Band 2**
p.809

**Epstien, Jay**
Profile: p.310
Table(s): Nationwide: Real Estate **Band 1** p.225,
District of Columbia: Real Estate **Band 1** p.835

**Erb, Thomas C**
Profile: p.1636
Table(s): Missouri: Corporate/M&A **Band 2** p.1619

**Erde, Joanne B**
Table(s): Nationwide: Healthcare: Regulatory &
Litigation **Band 3** p.127, Florida: Healthcare **Band
1** p.954

**Erens, Brad B**
Profile: p.1206
Table(s): Illinois: Bankruptcy/Restructuring **Band
3** p.1148

**Erf, Stephen**
Profile: p.1206
Table(s): Illinois: Labor & Employment **Band 4**
p.1175

**Erickson, David**
Table(s): Iowa: Real Estate **Band 2** p.1290

**Erickson, David**
Table(s): Missouri: Environment **Band 1** p.1621

**Erickson, Randall L**
Profile: p.634
Table(s): California: Construction: Mediators
**Band 2** p.550

**Erickson, Sonya**
Table(s): Washington: Corporate/Commercial
**Band 2** p.2525

**Ericsson, Richard J**
Profile: p.1735
Table(s): New Jersey: Environment **Band 2** p.1711

**Erker, Christopher E**
Table(s): Missouri: Environment **Band 3** p.1621

**Erly, Peter**
Table(s): Vermont: Corporate/Commercial **Band 1**
p.2483

**Ernst, Andrew**
Table(s): Georgia: Environment **Band 3** p.1051

**Ernst, David A**
Table(s): Oregon: Litigation: General
Commercial **Band 3** p.2171

**Ervin, James M**
Profile: p.991
Table(s): Florida: Tax: State & Local **Band 1** p.979

**Erwin, Greg**
Profile: p.2388
Table(s): Texas: Real Estate **Band 2** p.2367

**Erwin, James R**
Profile: p.1399
Table(s): Maine: Labor & Employment **Band 2**
p.1390

**Esch, Amanda**
Table(s): Wyoming: Labor & Employment
**Associates to watch** p.2597

**Eschels, Philip**
Profile: p.1318
Table(s): Kentucky: Labor & Employment **Band 2**
p.1310

**Escobar, Andrew**
Profile: p.2539
Table(s): Washington: Litigation: General
Commercial **Associates to watch** p.2533

**Escue, Michael T**
Profile: p.310
Table(s): Nationwide: Financial Services
Regulation: Banking (Compliance) **Band 2** p.96

**Esdorn, Joerg**
Profile: p.310
Table(s): Nationwide: Banking & Finance **Band 4**
p.31

**Eskenazi, Bonnie**
Profile: p.634
Table(s): California: Media & Entertainment:
Litigation **Band 3** p.606

**Esposito, Jewell Lim**
Table(s): Virginia: Labor & Employment:
Employee Benefits & Compensation **Band 3**
p.2500

**Esposito, Joseph P.**
Profile: p.861
Table(s): District of Columbia: Litigation:
General Commercial **Band 3** p.826

**Esseks, David**
Table(s): New York: Litigation: White-Collar
Crime & Government Investigations **Band 3**
p.1836

**Esser, William**
Table(s): North Carolina:
Bankruptcy/Restructuring **Up-and-coming individuals**
p.2023

**Esserman, Sander L**
Table(s): Texas: Bankruptcy/Restructuring **Band 2**
p.2328

**Esserman, Susan**
Table(s): Nationwide: International Trade: Trade
Remedies & Trade Policy **Band 2** p.154

**Esteban, Amor A.**
Table(s): Nationwide: Litigation: E-Discovery **Band
1** p.187

**Estes, Allen**
Table(s): Alabama: Litigation: General
Commercial **Up-and-coming individuals** p.463

**Estes III, John N**
Profile: p.310
Table(s): Nationwide: Energy: Electricity
(Regulatory & Litigation) **Band 1** p.76

**Estevez, Anne Marie**
Profile: p.991
Table(s): Florida: Labor & Employment **Band 2**
p.959

**Estrada, Miguel A**
Profile: p.310
Table(s): Nationwide: Appellate Law **Band 1** p.26

**Estridge, Larry D**
Table(s): South Carolina: Real Estate **Band 1**
p.2266

**Etchart, Mark**
Table(s): Montana: Real Estate **Band 3** p.1652

**Etcheverry, Raymond J**
Profile: p.2473
Table(s): Utah: Litigation: General Commercial
**Band 2** p.2468

**Etem, Craig E**
Table(s): Nevada: Corporate/Commercial **Band 3**
p.1672

**Eth, Jordan**
Profile: p.634
Table(s): Nationwide: Securities: Litigation **Band
2** p.232, California: Litigation: Securities **Band 1**
p.594

**Etkin, Michael S**
Profile: p.1735
Table(s): New Jersey: Bankruptcy/Restructuring
**Band 3** p.1705

**Ettelson, Bruce I**
Profile: p.310
Table(s): Nationwide: Investment Funds: Private
Equity: Fund Formation **Band 1** p.166

**Ettinger, Mitchell S**
Profile: p.861
Table(s): District of Columbia: Litigation: White-
Collar Crime & Government Investigations **Band 3**
p.827

**Ettredge, Katherine**
Profile: p.2388
Table(s): Texas: Banking & Finance **Band 4**
p.2325

**Eurich, Gregory**
Profile: p.718
Table(s): Colorado: Labor & Employment **Band 1**
p.706

**Eustace, Timothy M**
Table(s): Vermont: Real Estate **Band 3** p.2487,
Vermont: Real Estate: Zoning/Land Use **Band 2**
p.2487

**Evans, Beverly**
Table(s): Iowa: Corporate/M&A **Band 3** p.1283

**Evans, Brian P**
Profile: p.2040
Table(s): North Carolina: Real Estate **Band 2**
p.2037

**Evans, Craig L**
Table(s): Missouri: Corporate/M&A **Band 2** p.1618

**Evans, David**
Profile: p.310
Table(s): Nationwide: Projects **Band 4** p.216

**Evans, David E**
Table(s): Virginia: Environment **Band 1** p.2495

**Evans, Edwin E**
Table(s): South Dakota: Litigation: General
Commercial **Band 1** p.2284, South Dakota:
Litigation: Medical Malpractice Defense **Star indi-
viduals** p.2284

**Evans, Elizabeth H**
Profile: p.310
Table(s): Nationwide: Transportation: Aviation:
Finance **Band 3** p.252

**Evans, Kevin D**
Table(s): Colorado: Litigation: White-Collar Crime
& Government Investigations **Band 1** p.710

**Evans, Mark**
Table(s): Ohio: Construction **Band 4** p.2062

**Evans, Mark C**
Profile: p.2388
Table(s): Texas: Banking & Finance **Senior
Statesmen:** p.2325

**Evans, Nicole C**
Profile: p.2473
Table(s): Utah: Real Estate **Up-and-coming individu-
als** p.2470

**Evans, Parthenia B**
Table(s): Missouri: Environment **Band 2** p.1621

**Evans, Stephanie C**
Profile: p.861
Table(s): District of Columbia: Corporate/M&A &
Private Equity **Band 2** p.797

**Evans, William J**
Table(s): Alaska: Labor & Employment **Band 1**
p.489

**Evans III, Edward S**
Profile: p.1426
Table(s): Maryland: Real Estate **Up-and-coming indi-
viduals** p.1422

**Evans III, Jesse P**
Table(s): Alabama: Real Estate: Zoning/Land
Use **Band 1** p.466

**Evans III, Robert**
Table(s): Nationwide: Capital Markets: Debt &
Equity **Band 2** p.46

**Evans Jr, Robert M**
Profile: p.1636
Table(s): Missouri: Intellectual Property **Band 1**
p.1623

**Everett, Carl B**
Table(s): Pennsylvania: Environment **Band 3**
p.2194

**Everett, Denise M**
Table(s): Kentucky: Intellectual Property **Band 2**
p.1308

**Farmer, Stephen**
Table(s): West Virginia: Litigation: General
Commercial **Band 1** p.2555

**Farmer II, Guy O**
Profile: p.991
Table(s): Florida: Labor & Employment **Band 3**
p.959

**Farmer III, Malcolm**
Table(s): Rhode Island: Corporate/Commercial:
Banking & Finance **Senior Statesmen:** p.2251

**Farnan, Brian**
Table(s): Delaware: Intellectual Property **Up-and-
coming Individuals** p.763

**Farney, Bryan**
Table(s): Texas: Intellectual Property **Band 3**
p.2354

**Farolino, Shane A**
Profile: p.2095
Table(s): Ohio: Natural Resources &
Environment **Band 1** p.2083

**Farquhar, Michele C**
Table(s): District of Columbia: Telecom,
Broadcast & Satellite **Band 2** p.844

**Farr, Bartow**
Table(s): Nationwide: Appellate Law **Band 3** p.26

**Farr, Lucy W**
Profile: p.1891
Table(s): New York: Tax **Band 3** p.1862

**Farr, Thomas A**
Profile: p.2040
Table(s): North Carolina: Labor & Employment
**Band 1** p.2031

**Farrar, Steven E**
Profile: p.2268
Table(s): South Carolina: Litigation: General
Commercial **Band 3** p.2264

**Farrell, Margaret D**
Table(s): Rhode Island: Corporate/Commercial
**Band 2** p.2251

**Farrell, Michael J**
Profile: p.2562
Table(s): West Virginia: Litigation: General
Commercial **Band 1** p.2555

**Farren, Patricia**
Profile: p.1891
Table(s): New York: Antitrust **Band 5** p.1778

**Farris, Gary W**
Table(s): Georgia: Real Estate **Band 3** p.1070

**Farris Jr, James G**
Profile: p.1081
Table(s): Georgia: Real Estate **Band 2** p.1070

**Faruki, Charles J**
Profile: p.2095
Table(s): Ohio: Litigation: General Commercial
**Band 1** p.2078

**Fasman, Zachary D**
Table(s): New York: Labor & Employment **Band 1**
p.1826

**Fass, Peter M**
Table(s): Nationwide: Capital Markets: REITs
**Senior Statesmen:** p.55, New York: Real Estate:
Finance **Senior Statesmen:** p.1855

**Fassett, Brent**
Table(s): Colorado: Corporate/M&A **Up-and-coming
Individuals** p.703

**Fastow, Jay N**
Profile: p.1891
Table(s): New York: Antitrust **Band 2** p.1778

**Fatell, Bonnie Glantz**
Profile: p.770
Table(s): Delaware: Bankruptcy/Restructuring
**Band 1** p.754

**Fathe, Fred C**
Profile: p.508
Table(s): Arizona: Real Estate **Band 1** p.504

**Fatica, Kimberly A**
Table(s): Arizona: Labor & Employment **Band 3**
p.499

**Faucher, Robert A**
Profile: p.1138
Table(s): Idaho: Bankruptcy/Restructuring **Band 2**
p.1131

**Faulk, Richard O**
Profile: p.2388
Table(s): Texas: Environment **Band 2** p.2343

**Faulkner, Andrew M**
Profile: p.311
Table(s): Nationwide: Capital Markets:
Securitisation **Band 2** p.59

**Faure, Jean E**
Table(s): Montana: Labor & Employment **Band 2**
p.1648

**Faust, Scott**
Table(s): Massachusetts: Labor & Employment
**Band 2** p.1466

**Favretto, Richard J**
Table(s): District of Columbia: Antitrust **Band 4**
p.787

**Fawley, R Bradford**
Table(s): Vermont: Litigation: General
Commercial **Band 3** p.2486

**Faxon, Robert S**
Profile: p.2096
Table(s): Ohio: Litigation: General Commercial
**Band 4** p.2078

**Fay, Terrence M**
Profile: p.2096
Table(s): Ohio: Natural Resources &
Environment **Band 4** p.2083

**Fazio, Christine A**
Table(s): New York: Environment **Band 3** p.1807

**Fazio, Joseph M**
Profile: p.1549
Table(s): Michigan: Real Estate **Band 2** p.1546

**Feagles, Prentiss**
Table(s): Nationwide: Capital Markets: REITs
**Band 1** p.55, District of Columbia: Tax **Band 3**
p.838

**Featherly, Walter T**
Table(s): Nationwide: Native American Law **Band
3** p.192

**Fechner, Holly**
Profile: p.311
Table(s): Nationwide: Government: Government
Relations **Up-and-coming Individuals** p.121

**Feder, Gary H**
Table(s): Missouri: Real Estate **Band 2** p.1633

**Feder, Philip**
Table(s): California: Real Estate **Band 3** p.611

**Feder, Samuel L**
Profile: p.861
Table(s): District of Columbia: Telecom,
Broadcast & Satellite **Band 3** p.844

**Federhar, Andrew M**
Table(s): Arizona: Litigation: General
Commercial **Band 3** p.501

**Fee, Jon**
Profile: p.311
Table(s): Nationwide: International Trade:
Customs **Band 3** p.155

**Fee, Michael K**
Table(s): Massachusetts: Litigation: White-Collar
Crime & Government Investigations **Band 2**
p.1471

**Feeney, Carolyn**
Profile: p.2215
Table(s): Pennsylvania: Antitrust **Band 3** p.2184

**Feeney, James**
Table(s): Michigan: Litigation: General
Commercial **Band 1** p.1544

**Feeney, Matthew**
Table(s): Arizona: Corporate/M&A **Band 1** p.495

**Feheley, Lawrence F**
Table(s): Ohio: Labor & Employment **Band 2**
p.2074

**Feher, David G**
Profile: p.312
Table(s): Nationwide: Sports Law **Band 3** p.241

**Feher, Kristine**
Profile: p.1735
Table(s): New Jersey: Labor & Employment **Band
3** p.1718

**Feibel, Edward**
Table(s): Maine: Labor & Employment: Employee
Benefits & Compensation **Band 2** p.1390

**Feibelman, Jef**
Table(s): Tennessee: Litigation: General
Commercial **Band 1** p.2295

**Feigin, Samuel E**
Profile: p.861
Table(s): District of Columbia: Corporate/M&A &
Private Equity **Band 4** p.797

**Feiman, Ronald**
Profile: p.312
Table(s): Nationwide: Investment Funds:
Registered Funds **Band 3** p.170

**Fein, Scott N**
Table(s): New York: Environment **Band 3** p.1807

**Feinberg, David**
Table(s): Massachusetts: Corporate/M&A **Band 4**
p.1452

**Feinberg, Robert J**
Table(s): New Jersey: Litigation: General
Commercial **Band 3** p.1722

**Feingerts, Sandra Mills**
Profile: p.1361
Table(s): Louisiana: Labor & Employment:
Employee Benefits & Compensation **Band 1**
p.1350

**Feinstein, Deborah**
Profile: p.861
Table(s): District of Columbia: Antitrust **Band 1**
p.787

**Feinstein, Robert J**
Table(s): New York: Bankruptcy/Restructuring
**Band 4** p.1782

**Feirman, Steven**
Profile: p.312
Table(s): Nationwide: Franchising **Band 4** p.111

**Feirson, Steven B**
Profile: p.2215
Table(s): Pennsylvania: Litigation: General
Commercial **Band 3** p.2203, Pennsylvania:
Litigation: Securities **Band 1** p.2203

**Feldberg, Michael**
Table(s): New York: Litigation: General
Commercial **Band 3** p.1833, New York: Litigation:
White-Collar Crime & Government Investigations
**Band 3** p.1833

**Felderstein, Steven H**
Table(s): California: Bankruptcy/Restructuring
**Band 3** p.542

**Feldewert, Michael**
Profile: p.1773
Table(s): New Mexico: Environment, Natural
Resources & Regulated Industries **Band 3** p.1766

**Feldkamp, Janet**
Profile: p.2096
Table(s): Ohio: Healthcare **Band 3** p.2069

**Feldman, Boris**
Table(s): Nationwide: Securities: Litigation **Band
2** p.232, California: Litigation: Securities **Band 1**
p.594

**Feldman, Bret**
Table(s): Florida: Construction **Up-and-coming Individuals** p.944

**Feldman, David**
Profile: p.1891
Table(s): New York: Bankruptcy/Restructuring
**Band 4** p.1782

**Feldman, Elliot J**
Profile: p.312
Table(s): Nationwide: International Trade: Trade
Remedies & Trade Policy **Band 4** p.154

**Feldman, Eric N**
Profile: p.770
Table(s): Delaware: Corporate/M&A: Alternative
Entities **Band 3** p.761

**Feldman, Gary M**
Profile: p.1491
Table(s): Massachusetts: Labor & Employment
**Band 4** p.1466

**Feldman, Glenn M.**
Profile: p.312
Table(s): Nationwide: Native American Law **Band
2** p.192

**Feldman, Jeffrey M**
Table(s): **Alaska**: Litigation: General Commercial **Band 1** p.490

**Feldman, Joan**
Table(s): **Connecticut**: Healthcare **Band 1** p.735

**Feldman, Larry**
Profile: p.635
Table(s): **California**: Litigation: General Commercial **Band 3** p.593

**Feldman, Leonard**
Table(s): **Washington**: Litigation: General Commercial **Band 3** p.2533

**Feldman, Lewis G**
Profile: p.635
Table(s): **California**: Real Estate **Band 2** p.611

**Feldman, Mark I**
Profile: p.1206
Table(s): **Illinois**: Intellectual Property **Band 1** p.1171

**Feldman, Matthew A**
Profile: p.1891
Table(s): **Nationwide**: Bankruptcy/Restructuring **Band 3** p.39, **New York**: Bankruptcy/Restructuring **Band 2** p.1782

**Feldman, Murray**
Profile: p.1138
Table(s): **Idaho**: Natural Resources & Environment **Band 1** p.1136

**Feldman, Paul L**
Profile: p.1491
Table(s): **Massachusetts**: Litigation: General Commercial **Band 3** p.1470

**Feldman, Richard E**
Table(s): **Missouri**: Real Estate **Band 3** p.1633

**Feldman, Roger D**
Table(s): **Massachusetts**: Corporate/M&A **Band 4** p.1452

**Feldman, Ron**
Table(s): **Tennessee**: Real Estate **Band 3** p.2299

**Felger, Mark E**
Profile: p.770
Table(s): **Delaware**: Bankruptcy/Restructuring **Band 1** p.754

**Fellas, John**
Profile: p.312
Table(s): **Nationwide**: International Arbitration: Arbitrators **Band 1** p.145

**Feller, Sean C**
Profile: p.635
Table(s): **California**: Employee Benefits & Executive Compensation **Up-and-coming individuals** p.560

**Fellner, Baruch A**
Profile: p.862
Table(s): **District of Columbia**: Labor & Employment **Band 2** p.824

**Fellows, Henry**
Profile: p.1081
Table(s): **Georgia**: Litigation: General Commercial **Band 1** p.1065

**Felman, David S**
Profile: p.991
Table(s): **Florida**: Corporate/M&A & Private Equity **Band 1** p.947

**Felmly, Bruce W**
Profile: p.1695
Table(s): **New Hampshire**: Litigation: General Commercial **Band 1** p.1690

**Felsenthal, David**
Profile: p.312
Table(s): **Nationwide**: Capital Markets: Derivatives **Band 2** p.51

**Felsten, Nancy J**
Table(s): **Nationwide**: Advertising: Transactional & Regulatory **Band 2** p.20

**Felter, John Kenneth**
Table(s): **Massachusetts**: Litigation: General Commercial **Band 3** p.1470

**Felton, W Raymond**
Table(s): **New Jersey**: Corporate/M&A **Band 2** p.1707

**Femia, Rocco V**
Profile: p.862
Table(s): **District of Columbia**: Tax **Band 4** p.838

**Fendrick, Keith**
Profile: p.991
Table(s): **Florida**: Bankruptcy/Restructuring **Band 4** p.939

**Fenley, David A**
Table(s): **Missouri**: Real Estate **Band 1** p.1633

**Fenn, Tim**
Table(s): **Texas**: Tax **Band 3** p.2371

**Fenning, Lisa Hill**
Profile: p.635
Table(s): **California**: Bankruptcy/Restructuring **Band 3** p.542

**Fentin, Susan G**
Profile: p.1491
Table(s): **Massachusetts**: Labor & Employment **Band 4** p.1466

**Fenton, Kathryn M**
Profile: p.862
Table(s): **District of Columbia**: Antitrust **Band 2** p.787

**Fenzel, Mark S**
Table(s): **Kentucky**: Litigation: Tort & Insurance Defense **Band 1** p.1312

**Feola, Phil**
Table(s): **District of Columbia**: Real Estate: Zoning/Land Use **Band 2** p.835

**Feore, John R**
Profile: p.862
Table(s): **District of Columbia**: Media & Entertainment: Mainly Regulatory **Band 3** p.832, **District of Columbia**: Telecom, Broadcast & Satellite **Band 2** p.844

**Ferdinands, Paul K**
Profile: p.1081
Table(s): **Georgia**: Bankruptcy/Restructuring **Band 1** p.1042

**Fereday, Jeffrey**
Table(s): **Idaho**: Natural Resources & Environment **Band 1** p.1136

**Ferencik, Robert E**
Table(s): **Florida**: Construction **Band 1** p.944

**Fergemann, Brian**
Profile: p.1206
Table(s): **Illinois**: Media & Entertainment: Transactional **Up-and-coming individuals** p.1185

**Ferguson, James R**
Table(s): **Illinois**: Litigation: General Commercial **Band 4** p.1180

**Ferguson, Mark A**
Table(s): **Kansas**: Labor & Employment **Band 3** p.1294

**Ferguson, Thomas**
Table(s): **Illinois**: Corporate/M&A **Band 4** p.1156

**Ferland, Roger**
Profile: p.508
Table(s): **Arizona**: Environment (including water rights) **Senior Statesmen**: p.497

**Fernandez, Andres A.**
Table(s): **Florida**: Banking & Finance: Regulatory **Up-and-coming individuals** p.937

**Fernandez, Manuel A**
Table(s): **Florida**: Real Estate **Band 2** p.974

**Fernandez, Robert L**
Profile: p.1206
Table(s): **Illinois**: Real Estate **Band 4** p.1187

**Fernandez, Segundo J**
Profile: p.991
Table(s): **Florida**: Environment **Band 3** p.951

**Fernandez Jr, Jack E**
Table(s): **Florida**: Litigation: White-Collar Crime & Government Investigations **Band 3** p.967

**Fernhoff, Michael**
Table(s): **California**: Tax **Band 2** p.617

**Fernicola, Gregory**
Profile: p.312
Table(s): **Nationwide**: Capital Markets: Debt & Equity **Band 4** p.46

**Ferrara, Ralph C**
Table(s): **Nationwide**: Securities: Litigation **Band 3** p.232, **Nationwide**: Securities: Regulation: Enforcement **Band 2** p.232

**Ferrari, Renata**
Table(s): **Massachusetts**: Employee Benefits & Executive Compensation **Band 3** p.1455

**Ferrario, Mark E**
Profile: p.1681
Table(s): **Nevada**: Litigation: General Commercial **Band 2** p.1677

**Ferrazzano, Dennis**
Table(s): **Illinois**: Real Estate **Senior Statesmen**: p.1187

**Ferrell, Charles S**
Table(s): **Minnesota**: Real Estate **Star individuals** p.1576

**Ferrell, Kathleen**
Profile: p.1891
Table(s): **New York**: Tax **Band 3** p.1862

**Ferrer, Barbara**
Profile: p.991
Table(s): **Florida**: Real Estate **Up-and-coming individuals** p.974

**Ferri, Marco**
Table(s): **Florida**: Latin American Investment **Band 2** p.963

**Ferrill, Michael**
Table(s): **Texas**: Antitrust **Band 2** p.2323

**Ferrin, Shawn**
Profile: p.2473
Table(s): **Utah**: Real Estate **Band 1** p.2470

**Ferris, Kassim**
Table(s): **Oregon**: Intellectual Property **Band 2** p.2167

**Ferron Jr, William O**
Table(s): **Washington**: Intellectual Property **Band 2** p.2529

**Fersko, Jack**
Table(s): **New Jersey**: Real Estate: Zoning/Land Use **Band 1** p.1728

**Fetscher, Candace**
Profile: p.1654
Table(s): **Montana**: Labor & Employment **Band 1** p.1648

**Fetterman, Daniel J**
Profile: p.1892
Table(s): **New York**: Litigation: General Commercial **Band 3** p.1833, **New York**: Litigation: White-Collar Crime & Government Investigations **Band 2** p.1833

**Feuerstein, Eric M**
Profile: p.1892
Table(s): **New York**: Real Estate **Band 3** p.1854

**Feuerstein, Howard**
Table(s): **Oregon**: Real Estate **Band 1** p.2173

**Few Jr, Richard L**
Profile: p.2268
Table(s): **South Carolina**: Corporate/M&A **Band 3** p.2260

**Fiala, Marie L**
Profile: p.635
Table(s): **California**: Antitrust **Band 4** p.536

**Fiebach, H Robert**
Profile: p.2215
Table(s): **Pennsylvania**: Litigation: General Commercial **Band 4** p.2203

**Field, Andrea Bear**
Profile: p.862
Table(s): **District of Columbia**: Environment **Band 2** p.804

**Fields, Bertram**
Table(s): **California**: Media & Entertainment: Litigation **Senior Statesmen**: p.606

**Fields, Craig**
Profile: p.1892
Table(s): **New York**: Tax **Band 4** p.1862

**Fields, Henry M**
Profile: p.312
Table(s): **Nationwide**: Financial Services Regulation: Banking (Compliance) **Band 3** p.96, **Nationwide**: Financial Services Regulation: Financial Institutions M&A **Band 3** p.96

**Fields, Leslie A**
Table(s): **Colorado**: Real Estate **Band 2** p.714

**Fields, Wendy**
Table(s): **District of Columbia:** Real Estate **Band 2** p.835

**Fiero, John D**
Table(s): **California:** Bankruptcy/Restructuring **Band 4** p.542

**Fife, Lori R**
Profile: p.312
Table(s): **Nationwide:** Bankruptcy/Restructuring **Band 2** p.39, **New York:** Bankruptcy/Restructuring **Band 2** p.1782

**Fifer, Samuel**
Profile: p.1206
Table(s): **Illinois:** Intellectual Property **Band 4** p.1171, **Illinois:** Media & Entertainment: Litigation **Band 1** p.1184

**Figenshaw, Michael H**
Table(s): **Iowa:** Litigation: Insurance **Senior Statesmen:** p.1288

**Fijolek, Richard M**
Table(s): **Texas:** Tax **Band 4** p.2371

**Fikso, Robert**
Table(s): **Washington:** Real Estate **Band 3** p.2535

**Filardi, Edward V**
Profile: p.1892
Table(s): **New York:** Intellectual Property: Patent **Band 2** p.1820

**Fildes, Richard J**
Table(s): **Florida:** Real Estate **Band 4** p.974

**Fileti, Thomas**
Profile: p.635
Table(s): **California:** Real Estate **Band 2** p.611

**Filip, Mark**
Profile: p.1206
Table(s): **Illinois:** Litigation: General Commercial **Band 1** p.1180, **Illinois:** Litigation: White-Collar Crime & Government Investigations **Band 1** p.1180

**Filippi, David E**
Table(s): **Oregon:** Environment **Band 2** p.2165

**Filippini, Victor P**
Profile: p.1206
Table(s): **Illinois:** Real Estate: Zoning/Land Use **Band 2** p.1188

**Finberg, Frederick**
Table(s): **Maine:** Labor & Employment **Band 3** p.1390

**Finch, Andrew**
Profile: p.1892
Table(s): **New York:** Antitrust **Band 5** p.1778

**Fine, Drew S**
Profile: p.312
Table(s): **Nationwide:** Banking & Finance: Equipment Finance & Leasing **Band 1** p.32, **Nationwide:** Transportation: Aviation: Finance **Band 1** p.252

**Fine, Stanley S**
Profile: p.1426
Table(s): **Maryland:** Real Estate: Land Use **Band 2** p.1422

**Finegan, Thomas S**
Table(s): **New York:** Construction **Band 4** p.1791

**Finegold, Laurence B**
Table(s): **Washington:** Litigation: White-Collar Crime & Government Investigations **Band 1** p.2533

**Finestone, Ben**
Table(s): **New York:** Bankruptcy/Restructuring **Up-and-coming individuals** p.1782

**Fingeret, Kevin**
Profile: p.312
Table(s): **Nationwide:** Capital Markets: Securitisation **Band 3** p.59

**Fink, Marc J**
Profile: p.313
Table(s): **Nationwide:** Transportation: Shipping: Regulatory (outside New York) **Band 1** p.264

**Fink, Neil**
Table(s): **Michigan:** Litigation: White-Collar Crime & Government Investigations **Band 2** p.1544

**Fink, Robert S**
Table(s): **Nationwide:** Tax: Fraud **Band 1** p.244

**Fink, Stephen F**
Profile: p.2388
Table(s): **Texas:** Labor & Employment **Band 2** p.2359

**Finkel, Robert**
Profile: p.313
Table(s): **Nationwide:** Outsourcing **Band 1** p.195, **New York:** Technology & Outsourcing **Band 1** p.1868

**Finkelman, Daniel P**
Table(s): **Massachusetts:** Private Equity: Fund Formation **Band 1** p.1476

**Finkelson, David E.**
Table(s): **Southern Virginia:** Intellectual Property **Band 3** p.2498

**Finkelstein, Joseph**
Profile: p.2215
Table(s): **Pennsylvania:** Real Estate **Band 2** p.2208

**Finkelstein, Stuart M**
Profile: p.1892
Table(s): **New York:** Tax **Band 3** p.1862

**Finley, Joseph M**
Table(s): **Minnesota:** Real Estate **Band 3** p.1576

**Finley, Thomas A**
Table(s): **Iowa:** Litigation: Insurance **Senior Statesmen:** p.1288

**Finley, Zachary S**
Profile: p.635
Table(s): **California:** Banking & Finance **Associates to watch** p.539

**Finn, Terrence**
Profile: p.2096
Table(s): **Ohio:** Natural Resources & Environment **Band 2** p.2083

**Finn, William**
Table(s): **Louisiana:** Bankruptcy/Restructuring **Band 3** p.1337

**Finn Braddock, Patricia**
Profile: p.2388
Table(s): **Texas:** Environment **Band 1** p.2343

**Finn III, Harold**
Table(s): **Connecticut:** Corporate/M&A **Band 1** p.732

**Finnegan IV, William N**
Table(s): **Texas:** Capital Markets: Debt & Equity **Band 1** p.2333, **Texas:** Corporate/M&A **Band 1** p.2337

**Finto, Kevin J**
Profile: p.2509
Table(s): **Virginia:** Environment **Band 1** p.2495

**Finucane, Brian J**
Profile: p.1636
Table(s): **Missouri:** Labor & Employment **Band 1** p.1625

**Finzi, Roberto**
Profile: p.1892
Table(s): **New York:** Litigation: White-Collar Crime & Government Investigations **Band 3** p.1836

**Fiorentino, Mark H**
Table(s): **Nevada:** Real Estate: Zoning/Land Use **Band 1** p.1679

**Firestone, Frederic**
Profile: p.313
Table(s): **Nationwide:** Securities: Regulation: Enforcement **Band 4** p.233

**Fisch, Alan**
Table(s): **District of Columbia:** Intellectual Property: Litigation **Band 2** p.821

**Fisch, Peter E**
Profile: p.1892
Table(s): **New York:** Real Estate **Band 4** p.1854

**Fischer, A Robert**
Profile: p.2388
Table(s): **Texas:** Labor & Employment **Band 4** p.2359

**Fischer, Bruce**
Profile: p.635
Table(s): **California:** Real Estate **Band 3** p.611

**Fischer, David**
Profile: p.1207
Table(s): **Illinois:** Bankruptcy/Restructuring **Band 4** p.1148

**Fischer, Eric R**
Profile: p.1491
Table(s): **Massachusetts:** Banking & Finance: Corporate & Regulatory **Band 2** p.1446

**Fischer, Jeremy R.**
Table(s): **Maine:** Corporate/M&A: Bankruptcy **Associates to watch** p.1385

**Fischer, L Richard**
Profile: p.313
Table(s): **Nationwide:** Financial Services Regulation: Consumer Finance (Compliance) **Star individuals** p.98, **Nationwide:** Privacy & Data Security **Band 1** p.199

**Fischer, Matthew E**
Profile: p.770
Table(s): **Delaware:** Chancery **Band 4** p.758

**Fischer, Michael J**
Profile: p.2582
Table(s): **Wisconsin:** Labor & Employment **Band 3** p.2575

**Fischer, Nancy A**
Profile: p.313
Table(s): **Nationwide:** International Trade: Export Controls & Economic Sanctions **Band 3** p.153

**Fischer, Rebecca**
Table(s): **Colorado:** Real Estate: Hotels & Leisure **Band 1** p.714

**Fischer, Samuel N**
Table(s): **California:** Media & Entertainment: Transactional: Mainly Talent **Band 1** p.609

**Fishbein, Matthew E**
Table(s): **New York:** Litigation: White-Collar Crime & Government Investigations **Band 2** p.1836

**Fishbein, Stephen**
Profile: p.1892
Table(s): **New York:** Litigation: General Commercial **Band 4** p.1833, **New York:** Litigation: White-Collar Crime & Government Investigations **Band 3** p.1833

**Fisher, Alice S**
Profile: p.862
Table(s): **District of Columbia:** Litigation: White-Collar Crime & Government Investigations **Band 4** p.827

**Fisher, Daniel E**
Table(s): **Kentucky:** Corporate/M&A **Band 3** p.1305

**Fisher, Duane**
Profile: p.1122
Table(s): **Hawaii:** Real Estate **Band 2** p.1120

**Fisher, Frederick**
Profile: p.1207
Table(s): **Illinois:** Banking & Finance **Up-and-coming individuals** p.1145

**Fisher, Gregory**
Table(s): **Alaska:** Labor & Employment **Band 3** p.489

**Fisher, J Matthew**
Table(s): **Ohio:** Bankruptcy/Restructuring **Band 4** p.2058

**Fisher, Kenneth**
Table(s): **Ohio:** Construction **Band 4** p.2062

**Fisher, Lane**
Profile: p.313
Table(s): **Nationwide:** Franchising **Band 4** p.111

**Fisher, Mark**
Table(s): **Illinois:** Bankruptcy/Restructuring **Band 4** p.1148

**Fisher, Miriam L**
Profile: p.313
Table(s): **Nationwide:** Tax: Controversy **Band 1** p.244, **Nationwide:** Tax: Fraud **Band 1** p.244, **District of Columbia:** Tax **Band 2** p.838

**Fisher, Robert**
Profile: p.1636
Table(s): **Missouri:** Corporate/M&A **Senior Statesmen:** p.1618

**Fisher, Ruth**
Profile: p.635
Table(s): **California:** Media & Entertainment: Transactional **Band 2** p.608

**Fleischman, Dana G**
Profile: p.314
Table(s): **Nationwide**: Financial Services
Regulation: Broker Dealer (Compliance) **Band 1**
p.97

**Fleischmann, Stuart K**
Table(s): **New York**: Latin American Investment
**Band 3** p.1829

**Fleishman, Robert S**
Profile: p.314
Table(s): **Nationwide**: Energy: Oil & Gas
(Regulatory & Litigation) **Band 4** p.78

**Fleissig, Steven D**
Profile: p.1735
Table(s): **New Jersey**: Real Estate **Band 2** p.1728

**Fleming, John H**
Table(s): **Georgia**: Litigation: General
Commercial **Band 2** p.1065

**Fleming, Joseph R**
Profile: p.314
Table(s): **Nationwide**: Investment Funds:
Registered Funds **Band 2** p.170, **Massachusetts**:
Hedge & Mutual Funds **Band 2** p.1461

**Fleming, Joseph Z**
Profile: p.991
Table(s): **Florida**: Labor & Employment **Senior
Statesmen** p.959

**Fleming, Terrence J**
Table(s): **Minnesota**: Litigation: General
Commercial **Band 2** p.1574

**Fletcher, Jennifer W**
Table(s): **Georgia**: Construction **Star individuals**
p.1044

**Fletcher, Martin T**
Table(s): **Maryland**: Litigation: Bankruptcy **Band 2**
p.1419

**Fletcher, N Scott**
Profile: p.2389
Table(s): **Texas**: Litigation: Securities **Band 1**
p.2362

**Fletman, Abbe F**
Table(s): **Pennsylvania**: Intellectual Property
**Band 4** p.2197

**Flexner, Donald L**
Table(s): **New York**: Antitrust **Band 2** p.1778

**Flick II, Lawrence**
Profile: p.2216
Table(s): **Pennsylvania**: Banking & Finance **Band
1** p.2186

**Flics, Martin**
Table(s): **New York**: Bankruptcy/Restructuring
**Band 3** p.1782

**Flinn, Patrick J**
Profile: p.1081
Table(s): **Georgia**: Intellectual Property **Band 1**
p.1056

**Flint, Andrew P**
Profile: p.2389
Table(s): **Texas**: Banking & Finance **Band 3**
p.2325

**Flint, George**
Profile: p.2473
Table(s): **Utah**: Corporate/M&A **Band 4** p.2462

**Florack, James A**
Profile: p.314
Table(s): **Nationwide**: Banking & Finance **Band 1**
p.31, **New York**: Latin American Investment **Band
4** p.1829

**Flores, Daniel F**
Profile: p.1735
Table(s): **New Jersey**: Bankruptcy/Restructuring
**Band 4** p.1705

**Florey, Michael**
Table(s): **Minnesota**: Litigation: Intellectual
Property **Band 1** p.1574

**Florie, Michael A**
Profile: p.469
Table(s): **Alabama**: Litigation: General
Commercial **Band 3** p.463, **Alabama**: Litigation:
Medical Malpractice Defense **Band 1** p.463

**Florin, Kenneth R**
Profile: p.314
Table(s): **Nationwide**: Advertising: Transactional
& Regulatory **Band 1** p.20

**Flowe Jr, Benjamin H**
Table(s): **Nationwide**: International Trade: Export
Controls & Economic Sanctions **Band 1** p.153

**Flowers, Drew C.**
Profile: p.636
Table(s): **California**: Real Estate **Up-and-coming individ-
viduals** p.611

**Floyd, Jeffery B**
Profile: p.2389
Table(s): **Texas**: Corporate/M&A **Band 4** p.2337

**Floyd, John**
Table(s): **Georgia**: Litigation: General
Commercial **Band 3** p.1065

**Fluharty, Robert**
Table(s): **West Virginia**: Natural Resources **Band
2** p.2558, **West Virginia**: Real Estate **Band 1**
p.2560

**Fluhrer, Gary**
Table(s): **Washington**: Real Estate **Band 2** p.2535

**Flumenbaum, Martin**
Profile: p.1893
Table(s): **New York**: Litigation: General
Commercial **Band 2** p.1833

**Flynn, David P**
Profile: p.1893
Table(s): **New York**: Environment **Band 3** p.1807

**Flynn, Guy E**
Profile: p.1426
Table(s): **Maryland**: Real Estate **Band 3** p.1422

**Flynn, James**
Table(s): **Ohio**: Healthcare **Band 1** p.2069

**Flynn, John T**
Profile: p.1081
Table(s): **Georgia**: Construction **Band 2** p.1044

**Flynn, Thomas L**
Table(s): **Iowa**: Corporate/M&A: Banking &
Finance **Band 2** p.1283

**Flynn, William**
Table(s): **New York**: Energy: State Regulatory &
Wholesale Electric Market **Band 3** p.1806

**Flynn III, William J**
Table(s): **Florida**: Immigration **Band 1** p.956

**Focht, Jack**
Profile: p.1299
Table(s): **Kansas**: Litigation: White-Collar Crime
& Government Investigations **Senior Statesmen**
p.1295

**Fodor, Susanna S**
Profile: p.1893
Table(s): **New York**: Construction **Band 3** p.1791,
**New York**: Real Estate **Band 4** p.1854

**Fogarty, James**
Table(s): **Connecticut**: Litigation: General
Commercial **Band 3** p.738

**Fogarty, Robert J**
Profile: p.2096
Table(s): **Ohio**: Litigation: General Commercial
**Band 2** p.2078

**Fogel, Eric M.**
Table(s): **Illinois**: Corporate/M&A **Band 4** p.1156

**Fogg, William V**
Profile: p.314
Table(s): **Nationwide**: Capital Markets: Debt &
Equity **Band 3** p.46

**Foggan, Laura A**
Profile: p.862
Table(s): **District of Columbia**: Insurance:
Insurer **Band 2** p.816

**Fogle Jr, H Glenn**
Table(s): **Georgia**: Immigration **Band 2** p.1055

**Fogler, Murray**
Table(s): **Texas**: Litigation: Energy & Natural
Resources **Band 1** p.2361, **Texas**: Litigation:
General Commercial **Band 1** p.2361

**Fognani, John D**
Table(s): **Colorado**: Natural Resources &
Environment **Band 1** p.712

**Folb, Kerri**
Profile: p.1893
Table(s): **New York**: Environment **Associates to
watch** p.1807

**Foley, Allison D**
Profile: p.862
Table(s): **District of Columbia**: Environment
**Associates to watch** p.804

**Foley, Christopher P**
Profile: p.2509
Table(s): **Northern Virginia**: Intellectual Property
**Band 1** p.2497

**Foley, Mark J**
Profile: p.2216
Table(s): **Pennsylvania**: Labor & Employment
**Band 2** p.2200

**Foley, Shawn P**
Profile: p.1735
Table(s): **New Jersey**: Intellectual Property **Band
3** p.1716

**Foley Gannon, Ella**
Profile: p.636
Table(s): **California**: Environment **Band 4** p.564

**Folk, Mark D**
Table(s): **Tennessee**: Healthcare **Band 3** p.2291

**Folk, Thomas R.**
Table(s): **Virginia**: Construction **Band 3** p.2491

**Folland, Robert C**
Profile: p.2096
Table(s): **Ohio**: Bankruptcy/Restructuring **Band 3**
p.2058

**Follansbee, Daniel**
Profile: p.1491
Table(s): **Massachusetts**: Corporate/M&A **Up-and-
coming individuals** p.1452

**Folluo, Dan S.**
Profile: p.2149
Table(s): **Oklahoma**: Litigation: General
Commercial **Band 3** p.2141

**Folse, Parker**
Table(s): **Washington**: Litigation: General
Commercial **Band 3** p.2533

**Foltyn, David**
Table(s): **Michigan**: Corporate/M&A **Band 1**
p.1538

**Foltz, Joseph B**
Table(s): **Georgia**: Real Estate **Band 2** p.1070

**Fong, Kevin M**
Table(s): **California**: Litigation: Appellate **Band 2**
p.599

**Fons, Randy**
Profile: p.718
Table(s): **Colorado**: Litigation: General
Commercial **Band 2** p.709

**Fonseca, Roger W**
Table(s): **Hawaii**: Labor & Employment:
Employee Benefits & Compensation **Band 1**
p.1117

**Fontaine, Mary C**
Table(s): **Nationwide**: Capital Markets:
Securitisation **Band 3** p.59

**Fontana, Angela L**
Profile: p.2389
Table(s): **Nationwide**: Banking & Finance **Band 2**
p.31, **Texas**: Banking & Finance **Band 1** p.2325

**Fontham, Michael R**
Table(s): **Louisiana**: Energy & Natural
Resources: Utilities **Band 1** p.1344

**Foote, John H**
Table(s): **Northern Virginia**: Real Estate:
Zoning/Land Use **Band 1** p.2505

**Foradas, Michael P**
Profile: p.1207
Table(s): **Illinois**: Insurance: Dispute Resolution
**Star individuals** p.1168

**Forbes, Amy R**
Profile: p.636
Table(s): **California**: Real Estate: Zoning/Land
Use **Band 1** p.612

**Forbes, Nancy E**
Table(s): **Massachusetts**: Healthcare **Band 2**
p.1460

**Ford, Ann K**
Profile: p.862
Table(s): **District of Columbia**: Intellectual
Property: Trademark, Copyright & Trade Secrets
**Band 1** p.820

**Fox, J Nixon**
Table(s): Texas: Technology: Corporate &
Commercial **Band 2** p.2375

**Fox, Kate**
Table(s): Wyoming: Labor & Employment **Band 1**
p.2597, Wyoming: Litigation: General
Commercial **Band 1** p.2598

**Fox, Michael W**
Profile: p.2389
Table(s): Texas: Labor & Employment **Band 1**
p.2359

**Fox, Paul W**
Profile: p.315
Table(s): Nationwide: Energy: Electricity
(Regulatory & Litigation) **Band 5** p.76

**Fox, Robert**
Table(s): Pennsylvania: Environment **Band 1**
p.2194

**Fox, Steven E**
Profile: p.1081
Table(s): Georgia: Corporate/M&A **Band 1** p.1046

**Fox, Thomas**
Table(s): District of Columbia: Healthcare **Band 2**
p.809

**Fox IV, Charles D**
Table(s): Nationwide: Wealth Management:
Eastern Region **Band 2** p.267

**Fox-Isicoff, Tammy**
Table(s): Nationwide: Immigration **Band 2** p.131,
Florida: Immigration **Band 1** p.956

**Foy, Stacey W E**
Profile: p.1123
Table(s): Hawaii: Real Estate **Band 1** p.1120

**Fozzard, Peter**
Table(s): Georgia: Energy **Band 2** p.1049

**Frackman, Andrew**
Table(s): New York: Litigation: General
Commercial **Band 3** p.1833, New York: Litigation:
Securities **Band 4** p.1833

**Frackman, Russell**
Table(s): California: Media & Entertainment:
Litigation **Band 1** p.606

**Fradin, Scott R**
Table(s): Illinois: Construction **Band 2** p.1154

**Fragomen Jr, Austin T**
Table(s): Nationwide: Immigration **Band 2** p.131,
New York: Immigration **Band 2** p.1814

**Fraidin, Stephen**
Profile: p.1894
Table(s): New York: Corporate/M&A **Band 3**
p.1793

**Fraiser, Andrew**
Table(s): Nationwide: Projects: PPP **Band 2** p.217

**Fram, Robert**
Profile: p.636
Table(s): California: Intellectual Property: Patent
**Band 3** p.578

**France, Thomas W**
Profile: p.2509
Table(s): Northern Virginia: Corporate/M&A **Band
3** p.2493

**Francescani, David**
Table(s): New York: Intellectual Property: Patent
**Band 3** p.1820

**Franchina, David A**
Profile: p.2040
Table(s): North Carolina: Environment **Band 1**
p.2028

**Franchini, John D.**
Profile: p.1894
Table(s): New York: Corporate/M&A **Up-and-com-
ing Individuals** p.1793

**Francis, Rebecca**
Table(s): Washington: Litigation: General
Commercial **Associates to watch** p.2533

**Franck, Douglas C**
Table(s): Tennessee: Corporate/M&A **Band 3**
p.2288

**Franco, Philip A**
Profile: p.1361
Table(s): Louisiana: Construction **Band 2** p.1339

**Franco, Sandra**
Profile: p.863
Table(s): District of Columbia: Environment **Up-
and-coming individuals** p.804

**Franczek, William E**
Table(s): Virginia: Construction **Senior Statesmen:**
p.2491

**Franczek, Jr, James C**
Profile: p.1207
Table(s): Illinois: Labor & Employment **Band 1**
p.1175

**Frandsen, Nancy**
Profile: p.2216
Table(s): Pennsylvania: Intellectual Property
**Band 3** p.2197

**Frank, Daniel**
Table(s): Nationwide: Energy: Electricity
(Regulatory & Litigation) **Band 5** p.76

**Frank, Ian H**
Profile: p.2096
Table(s): Ohio: Construction **Band 3** p.2062

**Frank, Michael T**
Table(s): California: Employee Benefits &
Executive Compensation **Band 2** p.560

**Frank, Monte**
Profile: p.743
Table(s): Connecticut: Litigation: General
Commercial **Band 2** p.738

**Frank, Richard L**
Profile: p.315
Table(s): Nationwide: Food & Beverages:
Regulatory & Litigation **Band 2** p.107

**Frank, Steven J**
Profile: p.1491
Table(s): Massachusetts: Intellectual Property
**Band 2** p.1463

**Frank Jr, Robert S**
Profile: p.1492
Table(s): Massachusetts: Intellectual Property
**Band 1** p.1463, Massachusetts: Litigation:
General Commercial **Band 2** p.1470

**Frankel, Amelia**
Table(s): Missouri: Real Estate **Up-and-coming individuals** p.1633

**Frankel, Jamie**
Profile: p.1894
Table(s): New York: Construction **Band 4** p.1791

**Frankel, Michael I**
Table(s): Nationwide: Wealth Management:
Eastern Region **Band 3** p.267

**Frankel, Paul H**
Profile: p.315
Table(s): Nationwide: Tax: Controversy **Band 4**
p.244, New York: Tax **Band 4** p.1862

**Frankel, Roger**
Profile: p.863
Table(s): Nationwide: Bankruptcy/Restructuring
**Band 3** p.39, District of Columbia:
Bankruptcy/Restructuring **Band 1** p.792

**Frankel, William H**
Profile: p.1207
Table(s): Illinois: Intellectual Property **Band 4**
p.1171

**Frankenheimer, John T**
Profile: p.636
Table(s): California: Media & Entertainment:
Transactional **Band 1** p.608

**Frankle, Diane H**
Profile: p.636
Table(s): California: Corporate/M&A **Band 3** p.553

**Franklin, Cassandra**
Profile: p.636
Table(s): California: Insurance: Policyholder **Band
4** p.576

**Franklin, Gary L**
Table(s): Vermont: Litigation: General
Commercial **Band 3** p.2486

**Franklin, Jonathan S**
Profile: p.316
Table(s): Nationwide: Appellate Law **Band 4** p.26

**Franklin, Peter**
Table(s): New Mexico: Corporate/Commercial
**Band 3** p.1764

**Franklin, Samuel H**
Table(s): Alabama: Litigation: General
Commercial **Band 1** p.463

**Franklin, Steven R**
Table(s): Nationwide: Investment Funds: Venture
Capital **Band 1** p.174, California: Corporate/M&A:
Venture Capital **Band 1** p.555

**Franklin III, Denson N**
Table(s): Alabama: Corporate/Commercial **Band
2** p.459

**Frankovich, John**
Table(s): Nevada: Real Estate **Band 2** p.1679

**Franse, Nelson**
Profile: p.1773
Table(s): New Mexico: Litigation: General
Commercial **Band 2** p.1769, New Mexico:
Litigation: Medical Malpractice & Insurance
Defense **Band 2** p.1769

**Frantz, Mary Ann**
Table(s): Oregon: Corporate/M&A **Band 2** p.2164

**Frantz, Michael**
Profile: p.2096
Table(s): Ohio: Labor & Employment **Band 1**
p.2074

**Frantz, Steven P**
Profile: p.316
Table(s): Nationwide: Energy: Nuclear
(Regulatory & Litigation) **Band 2** p.77

**Frantz, Thomas R**
Table(s): Southern Virginia: Corporate/M&A **Band
1** p.2494

**Frantze, David**
Table(s): Missouri: Real Estate **Band 1** p.1633

**Franz, Holly**
Table(s): Montana: Natural Resources &
Environment **Band 1** p.1651

**Franzetti, Susan M**
Table(s): Illinois: Environment: Litigation **Band 1**
p.1162

**Fraser, Alexander P**
Profile: p.2582
Table(s): Wisconsin: Corporate/M&A **Band 3**
p.2571

**Fraser, Thomas S**
Table(s): Minnesota: Litigation: General
Commercial **Band 1** p.1574

**Frawley, Alfred**
Table(s): Maine: Litigation: General Commercial
**Band 3** p.1393

**Frazen, Laurence M**
Table(s): Missouri: Corporate/M&A **Band 3** p.1618

**Frazer, A Danner**
Table(s): Alabama: Litigation: Medical
Malpractice Defense **Band 2** p.463

**Frazier, James**
Profile: p.1894
Table(s): New York: Employee Benefits &
Executive Compensation **Band 4** p.1802

**Frazier, Keith D**
Profile: p.2304
Table(s): Tennessee: Labor & Employment **Band
2** p.2293

**Frazier, Randal B**
Profile: p.526
Table(s): Arkansas: Real Estate **Band 2** p.524,
Arkansas: Real Estate: Zoning/Land Use **Band 1**
p.524

**Frazier III, James H.**
Table(s): Kentucky: Real Estate: Zoning/Land
Use **Band 1** p.1314

**Frazier Jr, Sydney F**
Table(s): Alabama: Labor & Employment **Band 3**
p.460

**Frederick, David C**
Table(s): Nationwide: Appellate Law **Band 1** p.26

**Frederick, Robin G**
Table(s): Connecticut: Labor & Employment **Band
2** p.736

**Frederick, Thomas**
Profile: p.316
Table(s): Nationwide: Product Liability & Mass
Torts **Band 4** p.208

**Friedman, Peter**
Profile: p.1208
Table(s): Illinois: Real Estate: Zoning/Land Use **Band 2** p.1188

**Friedman, Peter M**
Profile: p.863
Table(s): District of Columbia: Bankruptcy/Restructuring **Band 2** p.792

**Friedman, Robert J**
Profile: p.992
Table(s): Florida: Tax: Employee Benefits **Band 2** p.979

**Friedman, Steven A**
Profile: p.2096
Table(s): Ohio: Construction **Band 3** p.2062

**Friedrich, Ira**
Profile: p.1579
Table(s): Minnesota: Labor & Employment **Band 3** p.1571

**Friedrich, Laura S**
Profile: p.317
Table(s): Nationwide: Investment Funds: Private Equity: Fund Formation **Band 4** p.166

**Friedrich, William R**
Table(s): California: Insurance: Policyholder **Band 3** p.576

**Friel Jr, Thomas J**
Table(s): California: Intellectual Property: Patent **Band 3** p.578

**Frier, Daniel B.**
Table(s): New Jersey: Healthcare **Band 3** p.1715

**Fries, David K**
Table(s): New Hampshire: Corporate/Commercial **Band 3** p.1685

**Fries, Elizabeth Shea**
Profile: p.1492
Table(s): Nationwide: Investment Funds: Hedge Funds **Band 3** p.162, Massachusetts: Hedge & Mutual Funds **Band 2** p.1461

**Fries, Richard S**
Profile: p.317
Table(s): Nationwide: Real Estate **Band 1** p.225, New York: Real Estate: Finance **Band 1** p.1855

**Friesen, Connie M**
Profile: p.317
Table(s): Nationwide: Financial Services Regulation: Banking (Compliance) **Band 4** p.96

**Friesen, Daniel**
Table(s): Colorado: Labor & Employment **Band 2** p.706

**Friestedt, Matthew M**
Profile: p.1895
Table(s): New York: Employee Benefits & Executive Compensation **Band 2** p.1802

**Frimmer, Paul N**
Profile: p.317
Table(s): Nationwide: Wealth Management: Western Region **Band 1** p.267, California: Tax: Estate Planning **Band 1** p.617

**Frisbie Jr, Curtis L**
Profile: p.2389
Table(s): Texas: Antitrust **Band 1** p.2323

**Frisch, John B**
Profile: p.1426
Table(s): Maryland: Corporate/M&A **Band 2** p.1412

**Frischling, Carl**
Profile: p.317
Table(s): Nationwide: Investment Funds: Registered Funds **Band 2** p.170

**Friscia, Michael R**
Profile: p.1735
Table(s): New Jersey: Intellectual Property **Band 3** p.1716

**Fritton, Karl**
Table(s): Pennsylvania: Labor & Employment **Band 2** p.2200

**Fritts, Laura**
Profile: p.1081
Table(s): Georgia: Intellectual Property **Up-and-coming individuals** p.1056

**Fritz, Thomas G**
Table(s): South Dakota: Litigation: General Commercial **Band 1** p.2284

**Fritze, Daniel J**
Profile: p.2269
Table(s): South Carolina: Corporate/M&A **Band 2** p.2260

**Frizell, Edward E 'Trip'**
Table(s): Missouri: Corporate/M&A **Band 3** p.1618

**Frizzell, Jean C**
Profile: p.2389
Table(s): Texas: Litigation: General Commercial **Band 3** p.2362

**Froelich, Edward**
Profile: p.317
Table(s): Nationwide: Tax: Controversy **Band 4** p.244

**Froelich Jr, Jerome J**
Table(s): Georgia: Litigation: White-Collar Crime & Government Investigations **Band 2** p.1066

**Froio, Nicholas I**
Profile: p.770
Table(s): Delaware: Corporate/M&A: Alternative Entities **Band 3** p.761

**Fromm O'Brien, Eva**
Profile: p.2390
Table(s): Texas: Environment **Band 1** p.2343

**Frongillo, Thomas C**
Profile: p.1492
Table(s): Massachusetts: Litigation: White-Collar Crime & Government Investigations **Band 2** p.1471

**Frost, Claudia Wilson**
Profile: p.2390
Table(s): Texas: Litigation: Appellate **Band 2** p.2361

**Frost, Daniel**
Table(s): Colorado: Real Estate: Construction **Band 1** p.714

**Frost Jr, Don J**
Profile: p.863
Table(s): District of Columbia: Environment: Mainly Transactional **Band 1** p.805

**Froy, Michael M**
Profile: p.1208
Table(s): Illinois: Corporate/M&A **Band 3** p.1156

**Frumkin, Joseph B**
Profile: p.317
Table(s): Nationwide: Energy: Electricity (Transactional) **Band 1** p.77, New York: Corporate/M&A **Band 1** p.1793

**Fruth, Terence**
Table(s): Minnesota: Litigation: General Commercial **Senior Statesmen** p.1574

**Fry, John**
Table(s): Georgia: Intellectual Property **Band 4** p.1056

**Fry, Roger**
Table(s): Ohio: Litigation: General Commercial **Band 3** p.2078

**Frye, Paul**
Table(s): New Mexico: Native American Law **Band 1** p.1771

**Fryer, Gregory**
Profile: p.1399
Table(s): Maine: Corporate/M&A **Band 1** p.1385

**Fryer, Judith D**
Profile: p.317
Table(s): Nationwide: Capital Markets: REITs **Band 2** p.55

**Fryman, David S**
Profile: p.2216
Table(s): Pennsylvania: Labor & Employment **Band 2** p.2200

**Fuchs, Jack F**
Profile: p.2096
Table(s): Ohio: Employee Benefits & Executive Compensation **Band 2** p.2067

**Fuchs, Nancy E**
Profile: p.1895
Table(s): New York: Corporate/M&A **Band 5** p.1793

**Fugate, Lee**
Table(s): Florida: Litigation: White-Collar Crime & Government Investigations **Band 3** p.967

**Fuhr, Edward J**
Profile: p.2510
Table(s): Virginia: Litigation: General Commercial **Band 2** p.2502

**Fuhrer, Loriann E.**
Table(s): Ohio: Litigation: General Commercial **Up-and-coming individuals** p.2078

**Fuhrman, Steven M**
Profile: p.1895
Table(s): New York: Bankruptcy/Restructuring **Band 4** p.1782

**Fujimoto, Wesley M**
Table(s): Hawaii: Labor & Employment **Band 2** p.1117

**Fulkerson, Sam**
Profile: p.2149
Table(s): Oklahoma: Labor & Employment **Band 2** p.2140

**Fullenkamp, John**
Table(s): Nebraska: Real Estate **Band 1** p.1666, Nebraska: Real Estate: Zoning/Land Use **Band 1** p.1666

**Fullenweider, Keith**
Profile: p.2390
Table(s): Nationwide: Energy: Oil & Gas (Transactional) **Band 4** p.79, Texas: Corporate/M&A **Band 3** p.2337

**Fuller, Gary**
Profile: p.2149
Table(s): Oklahoma: Corporate/Commercial: Tax **Senior Statesmen** p.2134

**Fuller, James P**
Profile: p.637
Table(s): California: Tax **Star individuals** p.617

**Fuller, Robert**
Table(s): North Carolina: Litigation: General Commercial **Band 1** p.2033

**Fuller, William P**
Table(s): South Dakota: Litigation: General Commercial **Band 1** p.2284

**Fuller III, William H**
Profile: p.2041
Table(s): North Carolina: Banking & Finance **Band 2** p.2021

**Fullmer, David R**
Profile: p.637
Table(s): California: Immigration **Band 2** p.571

**Fullmer, Mark A**
Table(s): Louisiana: Corporate/M&A **Band 1** p.1341

**Fultz, Benjamin C**
Table(s): Kentucky: Litigation: General Commercial **Band 2** p.1312

**Funes, Kelsey**
Table(s): Louisiana: Construction **Up-and-coming individuals** p.1339

**Funk, Markus T**
Table(s): Colorado: Litigation: White-Collar Crime & Government Investigations **Up-and-coming individuals** p.710

**Funk, Mary E**
Table(s): Iowa: Labor & Employment **Band 2** p.1285

**Funk, Samuel**
Table(s): Tennessee: Litigation: General Commercial **Band 2** p.2295

**Fuqua, James A**
Table(s): Delaware: Real Estate: Zoning/Land Use **Band 2** p.766

**Furci, Peter**
Table(s): New York: Tax **Band 2** p.1862

**Furey, Michael K**
Table(s): New Jersey: Labor & Employment **Band 2** p.1718

**Furletti, Mark J.**
Profile: p.318
Table(s): Nationwide: Financial Services Regulation: Consumer Finance (Compliance) **Associates to watch** p.98, Pennsylvania: Banking & Finance: Mainly Regulatory **Associates to watch** p.2186

**Furlong, Matthew**
Profile: p.1492
Table(s): **Massachusetts: Banking & Finance**
**Band 2** p.1445

**Furlong, Michael G**
Table(s): **Vermont: Corporate/Commercial Band 3**
p.2483

**Furman, Marc**
Table(s): **Pennsylvania: Labor & Employment**
**Band 4** p.2200

**Furr, Brett P**
Table(s): **Louisiana: Bankruptcy/Restructuring**
**Band 3** p.1337

**Furr, Jeffrey L**
Profile: p.2041
Table(s): **North Carolina: Litigation: General**
**Commercial Band 4** p.2033

**Furr, Susan W**
Table(s): **Louisiana: Labor & Employment Band 2**
p.1350

**Fuson, Bradley S.**
Table(s): **Indiana: Real Estate Band 3** p.1275

**Fussell, Herman L**
Table(s): **Georgia: Construction Band 3** p.1044

**Futrell, Elizabeth J**
Profile: p.1362
Table(s): **Louisiana: Bankruptcy/Restructuring**
**Band 2** p.1337

## G

**Gaba, Michael M**
Profile: p.863
Table(s): **District of Columbia: Healthcare:**
**Pharmaceutical/Medical Products Regulatory**
**Band 3** p.810

**Gabay, Donald**
Table(s): **New York: Insurance: Transactional &**
**Regulatory Senior Statesmen:** p.1816

**Gabbay, Carolyn Jacoby**
Profile: p.1492
Table(s): **Massachusetts: Healthcare Band 2**
p.1460

**Gabbert Jr, Craig V**
Table(s): **Tennessee: Litigation: Bankruptcy Band**
**1** p.2295

**Gabelman, Thomas**
Table(s): **Ohio: Construction Band 4** p.2062

**Gabric, Ralph J**
Profile: p.1208
Table(s): **Illinois: Intellectual Property Band 4**
p.1171

**Gabriel, Andrew S**
Table(s): **Nevada: Corporate/Commercial Band 2**
p.1672, **Nevada: Real Estate Band 2** p.1679

**Gabrio, Gino L**
Table(s): **Hawaii: Real Estate Band 1** p.1120

**Gadbois, Barbara**
Profile: p.637
Table(s): **California: Construction Band 2** p.550

**Gage, Larry**
Profile: p.863
Table(s): **District of Columbia: Healthcare Band 2**
p.809

**Gage, Robert J**
Profile: p.864
Table(s): **District of Columbia: Real Estate Band**
**2** p.835

**Gagliano, Bill J**
Profile: p.2097
Table(s): **Ohio: Real Estate Band 3** p.2086

**Gagliardo, Joseph M**
Profile: p.1208
Table(s): **Illinois: Labor & Employment Band 2**
p.1175

**Gagnon, Bruce**
Table(s): **Alaska: Litigation: General Commercial**
**Senior Statesmen:** p.490

**Gaillard, W Foster**
Table(s): **South Carolina: Real Estate Band 1**
p.2266

**Gaines, Andrew L**
Profile: p.1895
Table(s): **New York: Employee Benefits &**
**Executive Compensation Band 2** p.1802

**Gair, Chris**
Table(s): **Illinois: Litigation: White-Collar Crime &**
**Government Investigations Band 3** p.1181

**Gajer, Paul**
Profile: p.318
Table(s): **Nationwide: Investment Funds: Venture**
**Capital Band 3** p.174

**Gajkowski, Andrew J**
Profile: p.2390
Table(s): **Texas: Technology: Corporate &**
**Commercial Associates to watch** p.2375

**Galante, Linda Ann**
Table(s): **Pennsylvania: Real Estate Band 3**
p.2208

**Galardi, Gregg M**
Profile: p.770
Table(s): **Nationwide: Bankruptcy/Restructuring**
**Band 3** p.39, **Delaware:**
**Bankruptcy/Restructuring Band 1** p.754

**Galati, Vito**
Table(s): **Hawaii: Corporate/Commercial: Tax**
**Band 1** p.1115

**Galchus, Donna Smith**
Table(s): **Arkansas: Labor & Employment Band 3**
p.520

**Galdean, Trinidad**
Table(s): **Kansas: Labor & Employment Band 3**
p.1294

**Gale, Catherine C**
Table(s): **Colorado: Real Estate Band 3** p.714

**Gale, Kelley**
Profile: p.318
Table(s): **Nationwide: Projects Band 3** p.216,
**Nationwide: Projects: Renewables & Alternative**
**Energy Band 2** p.216

**Galeota, William E**
Profile: p.2562
Table(s): **West Virginia: Litigation: General**
**Commercial Band 1** p.2555

**Galgay, David**
Profile: p.1399
Table(s): **Maine: Real Estate Band 4** p.1395

**Gall, John R**
Profile: p.2097
Table(s): **Ohio: Litigation: General Commercial**
**Band 4** p.2078

**Gallagher, Gregory W.**
Profile: p.1208
Table(s): **Illinois: Tax Up-and-coming individuals**
p.1192

**Gallagher, James J**
Profile: p.318
Table(s): **Nationwide: Government: Government**
**Contracts Band 2** p.117

**Gallagher, Michael J**
Profile: p.718
Table(s): **Colorado: Litigation: General**
**Commercial Band 2** p.709

**Gallagher, Patrick C**
Profile: p.1895
Table(s): **New York: Tax Band 2** p.1862

**Gallagher, Thomas M**
Profile: p.2216
Table(s): **Pennsylvania: Litigation: White-Collar**
**Crime & Government Investigations Band 2**
p.2204

**Gallegos, J. E.**
Table(s): **New Mexico: Litigation: General**
**Commercial Band 2** p.1769

**Galli, Craig D**
Profile: p.2473
Table(s): **Utah: Energy & Natural Resources Band**
**3** p.2464

**Gallion, Michael L**
Table(s): **California: Labor & Employment Band 4**
p.587

**Gallion, Theresa M**
Profile: p.992
Table(s): **Florida: Labor & Employment Band 2**
p.959

**Gallo, Barbara**
Profile: p.1082
Table(s): **Georgia: Environment Band 3** p.1051

**Gallo, Donald P**
Profile: p.2582
Table(s): **Wisconsin: Natural Resources &**
**Environment Band 2** p.2578

**Gallo, John N**
Profile: p.1208
Table(s): **Illinois: Litigation: White-Collar Crime &**
**Government Investigations Band 3** p.1181

**Gallo, Kenneth A**
Profile: p.864
Table(s): **District of Columbia: Antitrust Band 3**
p.787

**Gallogly, Maggie**
Table(s): **Arizona: Environment: Water Rights**
**Band 2** p.497

**Galloway, Robert C**
Profile: p.1603
Table(s): **Mississippi: Litigation: General**
**Commercial Band 2** p.1597

**Gallozzi, Marialuisa**
Profile: p.864
Table(s): **District of Columbia: Insurance:**
**Policyholder Band 3** p.818

**Galvan, Hilda**
Profile: p.2390
Table(s): **Texas: Intellectual Property Band 2**
p.2354

**Galvan, Ramon P**
Profile: p.318
Table(s): **Nationwide: Native American Law Band**
**3** p.192

**Galvin, Martin Jay**
Table(s): **Michigan: Labor & Employment Band 3**
p.1542

**Galvis, Sergio J**
Profile: p.1895
Table(s): **Nationwide: Projects Band 3** p.216, **New**
**York: Latin American Investment Band 1** p.1829

**Gambino, Lucas**
Profile: p.469
Table(s): **Alabama: Banking & Finance Up-and-**
**coming individuals** p.455

**Gamble, Robert A**
Table(s): **Iowa: Corporate/M&A: Banking &**
**Finance Band 1** p.1283

**Gamboli, Michael**
Table(s): **Rhode Island: Labor & Employment**
**Band 1** p.2253

**Gambro, Michael S**
Profile: p.318
Table(s): **Nationwide: Capital Markets:**
**Securitisation Band 1** p.59

**Gammage Jr, Grady**
Table(s): **Arizona: Real Estate: Zoning/Land Use**
**Senior Statesmen:** p.504

**Gamsky, Michael**
Table(s): **Washington: Corporate/Commercial**
**Band 3** p.2525

**Ganchan, Leigh**
Profile: p.2390
Table(s): **Texas: Immigration Band 3** p.2349

**Gandhi, Samir A**
Profile: p.318
Table(s): **Nationwide: Capital Markets: Debt &**
**Equity Band 3** p.46

**Gang, Robert C**
Profile: p.992
Table(s): **Florida: Banking & Finance: Public**
**Finance Band 3** p.936

**Gangemi Jr, Columbus R**
Profile: p.1208
Table(s): **Illinois: Labor & Employment Senior**
**Statesmen:** p.1175

**Gans, Gary E**
Table(s): **California: Media & Entertainment:**
**Litigation Band 4** p.606

**Gans, Jeffrey R**
Table(s): District of Columbia: Construction Up-
and-coming individuals p.795

**Ganske, Lyle G**
Profile: p.2097
Table(s): Ohio: Corporate/M&A Band 1 p.2064

**Ganulin, Neil**
Profile: p.2097
Table(s): Ohio: Corporate/M&A Band 2 p.2064

**Ganz, Howard**
Table(s): Nationwide: Sports Law Band 1 p.241,
New York: Labor & Employment Band 2 p.1826

**Gaquin, Dan**
Profile: p.1492
Table(s): Massachusetts: Real Estate Band 3
p.1478

**Garber, Kevin J**
Table(s): Pennsylvania: Environment Band 2
p.2194

**Garbrecht, Robert L**
Profile: p.2149
Table(s): Oklahoma: Real Estate Band 2 p.2145

**Garcia, David A**
Profile: p.1681
Table(s): Nevada: Corporate/Commercial Band 1
p.1672

**Garcia, Rodrigo**
Table(s): Texas: Insurance Band 3 p.2351

**Garcia, Victoria M**
Profile: p.2390
Table(s): Texas: Immigration Band 2 p.2349

**Garcia Linares, Manuel A**
Profile: p.992
Table(s): Florida: Litigation: General Commercial
Band 4 p.966

**Garcia-Serra, Mario**
Profile: p.992
Table(s): Florida: Real Estate: Zoning/Land Use
Up-and-coming individuals p.975

**Garciadiaz, Manuel**
Profile: p.1895
Table(s): New York: Latin American Investment
Band 2 p.1829

**Gardels, David E**
Table(s): Nebraska: Corporate/Commercial Band
2 p.1659

**Gardill, James**
Table(s): West Virginia: Corporate/Commercial:
Banking & Finance Band 1 p.2550

**Gardiner, John L**
Profile: p.318
Table(s): Nationwide: International Arbitration
Band 2 p.145

**Gardiner, Kent A**
Profile: p.864
Table(s): District of Columbia: Antitrust Band 3
p.787

**Gardiner, Samuel P**
Table(s): Utah: Corporate/M&A Band 2 p.2462

**Gardner, Bryant**
Profile: p.318
Table(s): Nationwide: Transportation: Shipping:
Regulatory (outside New York) Up-and-coming indi-
viduals p.264

**Gardner, James K**
Profile: p.1208
Table(s): Illinois: Antitrust Band 3 p.1143

**Gardner, Price C**
Profile: p.526
Table(s): Arkansas: Corporate/Commercial Band
2 p.518, Arkansas: Corporate/Commercial: Tax
Band 1 p.518, Arkansas: Real Estate Band 2 p.524

**Gardner, Ronald K**
Profile: p.318
Table(s): Nationwide: Franchising: Mainly
Franchisee Band 1 p.114

**Gardner, Russell H**
Profile: p.1426
Table(s): Maryland: Labor & Employment Band 2
p.1417

**Gardner, Stephen D**
Table(s): Nationwide: Tax: Controversy Band 1
p.244

**Gardner, Steven**
Table(s): North Carolina: Intellectual Property
Band 1 p.2030

**Gardner, Terri**
Profile: p.2041
Table(s): North Carolina:
Bankruptcy/Restructuring Band 2 p.2023

**Garfield, Gerald**
Profile: p.318
Table(s): Nationwide: Energy: Nuclear
(Regulatory & Litigation) Band 3 p.77

**Garfinkel, Barry H**
Profile: p.318
Table(s): Nationwide: International Arbitration:
Arbitrators Band 1 p.146

**Garibaldi, Oscar M**
Profile: p.319
Table(s): Nationwide: International Arbitration
Band 2 p.145

**Garland, David W**
Profile: p.1736
Table(s): New Jersey: Labor & Employment Band
2 p.1718

**Garmer III, Benjamin F**
Table(s): Wisconsin: Corporate/M&A Band 1
p.2571

**Garmey, Terrence D**
Table(s): Maine: Litigation: Medical Malpractice
& Insurance Band 1 p.1393, Maine: Litigation:
Mainly Plaintiff Band 1 p.1393

**Garner, James**
Table(s): Louisiana: Litigation: General
Commercial Band 2 p.1352

**Garner, W. Michael**
Table(s): Nationwide: Franchising: Mainly
Franchisee Band 2 p.114

**Garofalo, Beverly W**
Profile: p.743
Table(s): Connecticut: Labor & Employment Band
1 p.736

**Garofalo, Gary B**
Table(s): Nationwide: Transportation: Aviation:
Regulatory Band 1 p.256

**Garon, Philip S**
Table(s): Minnesota: Corporate/M&A Senior
Statesmen: p.1569

**Garone, Michael**
Table(s): Oregon: Labor & Employment Band 3
p.2168

**Garre, Gregory**
Profile: p.319
Table(s): Nationwide: Appellate Law Band 1 p.26

**Garretson, Thomas P**
Profile: p.1299
Table(s): Kansas: Corporate/M&A Senior
Statesmen: p.1292

**Garrett, G Lee**
Profile: p.1082
Table(s): Georgia: Litigation: General
Commercial Band 3 p.1065

**Garrett, Robert A**
Profile: p.864
Table(s): Nationwide: Sports Law Band 3 p.241,
District of Columbia: Media & Entertainment
Band 2 p.832

**Garrett, Theodore**
Profile: p.864
Table(s): District of Columbia: Environment
Senior Statesmen: p.804

**Garrett, Tim K**
Profile: p.2304
Table(s): Tennessee: Labor & Employment Band
2 p.2293

**Garrity, James**
Profile: p.1895
Table(s): New York: Bankruptcy/Restructuring
Band 3 p.1782

**Garrity, Paul**
Table(s): New York: Intellectual Property: Trade
Mark & Copyright Band 3 p.1821

**Garrote, Nora**
Profile: p.864
Table(s): District of Columbia: Technology &
Outsourcing Band 3 p.842

**Garry, William C**
Table(s): South Dakota: Litigation: General
Commercial Band 1 p.2284

**Gart, Brian**
Profile: p.992
Table(s): Florida: Bankruptcy/Restructuring Band
2 p.939

**Gart, Ron**
Profile: p.864
Table(s): District of Columbia: Real Estate Band
2 p.835

**Gartin, Timothy L**
Table(s): Iowa: Real Estate Band 3 p.1290

**Gartman, John**
Table(s): California: Intellectual Property: Patent
Band 3 p.578

**Gartner, Gary J**
Profile: p.1895
Table(s): New York: Tax Band 4 p.1862

**Gartner, Steven J**
Profile: p.319
Table(s): Nationwide: Private Equity: Buyouts
Band 2 p.203

**Garton, Thomas W**
Table(s): Minnesota: Corporate/M&A Band 3
p.1569

**Garvin, Michael**
Profile: p.2097
Table(s): Ohio: Intellectual Property Band 3
p.2071

**Garvin, Michele M**
Table(s): Nationwide: Healthcare: Transactional
Band 3 p.128, Massachusetts: Healthcare Band 1
p.1460

**Garwood, Suzanne**
Profile: p.319
Table(s): Nationwide: Financial Services
Regulation: Consumer Finance (Compliance) Up-
and-coming individuals p.98

**Garwood, Thomas**
Profile: p.992
Table(s): Florida: Labor & Employment Band 1
p.959

**Gary, T Bart**
Table(s): Georgia: Construction Band 3 p.1044

**Garza, Deborah A**
Profile: p.864
Table(s): District of Columbia: Antitrust Band 2
p.787

**Garza, Oscar**
Profile: p.637
Table(s): California: Bankruptcy/Restructuring
Band 2 p.542

**Gass, J Ric**
Profile: p.2582
Table(s): Wisconsin: Litigation: General
Commercial Band 3 p.2576

**Gassenheimer, James D**
Profile: p.992
Table(s): Florida: Litigation: General Commercial
Band 3 p.966

**Gaswirth, Ronald M**
Profile: p.2390
Table(s): Texas: Labor & Employment Band 4
p.2359

**Gately, Mark**
Table(s): Maryland: Litigation: General
Commercial Band 1 p.1419

**Gates, Allan**
Table(s): Arkansas: Litigation: Environmental
Band 1 p.522

**Gates, Edward R**
Table(s): Massachusetts: Intellectual Property
Band 3 p.1463

**Gates, Jennifer L**
Table(s): Oregon: Environment Band 3 p.2165

**Gates, Martin S**
Profile: p.2097
Table(s): Ohio: Banking & Finance Band 3 p.2056

**Gates, Melodi**
Table(s): Nationwide: Privacy & Data Security
Associates to watch p.199

**Gerber, Dean N**
Profile: p.319
Table(s): **Nationwide:** Banking & Finance: Equipment Finance & Leasing **Band 1** p.32, **Nationwide:** Transportation: Aviation: Finance **Band 1** p.252, **Illinois:** Banking & Finance **Band 2** p.1145

**Gerber, Toby L**
Profile: p.2390
Table(s): **Nationwide:** Bankruptcy/Restructuring **Band 4** p.39, **Texas:** Bankruptcy/Restructuring **Band 1** p.2328

**Gerecke, Edward W**
Profile: p.993
Table(s): **Florida:** Litigation: General Commercial **Band 4** p.966

**Gergely, Peter A**
Table(s): **Colorado:** Intellectual Property **Band 3** p.704

**Gergen, Michael**
Profile: p.320
Table(s): **Nationwide:** Energy: Electricity (Regulatory & Litigation) **Band 2** p.76

**Gerlach, C. Andrew**
Profile: p.320
Table(s): **Nationwide:** Financial Services Regulation: Financial Institutions M&A **Up-and-coming individuals** p.99

**Germain, Kenneth B**
Table(s): **Ohio:** Intellectual Property **Senior Statesmen:** p.2071

**German, Charles**
Table(s): **Missouri:** Litigation: General Commercial **Band 1** p.1628, **Missouri:** Litigation: White-Collar Crime & Government Investigations **Band 1** p.1628

**Germann, Hans J**
Table(s): **Illinois:** Communications **Band 2** p.1153

**Gerrish, Jeffrey**
Table(s): **Tennessee:** Banking & Finance: Regulatory **Band 2** p.2287

**Gersch, David**
Profile: p.864
Table(s): **District of Columbia:** Litigation: General Commercial **Band 3** p.826

**Gershanik, Maureen**
Profile: p.1362
Table(s): **Louisiana:** Corporate/M&A **Up-and-coming individuals** p.1341

**Gersich, Bradley J**
Profile: p.637
Table(s): **California:** Corporate/M&A **Up-and-coming individuals** p.553

**Gerson, David**
Profile: p.2217
Table(s): **Pennsylvania:** Corporate/M&A & Private Equity **Band 1** p.2191

**Gerson, Herb**
Profile: p.2304
Table(s): **Tennessee:** Labor & Employment **Band 2** p.2293

**Gerstein, John R**
Table(s): **District of Columbia:** Insurance: Insurer **Band 2** p.816

**Gerstein, Mark D**
Table(s): **Illinois:** Corporate/M&A **Band 1** p.1156

**Gerstell, Glenn S**
Profile: p.865
Table(s): **District of Columbia:** Telecom, Broadcast & Satellite **Band 2** p.844

**Gerstenzang, Michael A**
Profile: p.320
Table(s): **Nationwide:** Investment Funds: Private Equity: Fund Formation **Band 1** p.166

**Gerstmayr, John W**
Table(s): **Nationwide:** Investment Funds: Registered Funds **Band 3** p.170, **Massachusetts:** Hedge & Mutual Funds **Band 1** p.1461

**Gertler, Gary B**
Profile: p.637
Table(s): **California:** Healthcare **Band 4** p.568

**Gertzman, Stephen**
Profile: p.865
Table(s): **District of Columbia:** Tax **Band 2** p.838

**Gessner, Douglas C**
Profile: p.320
Table(s): **Nationwide:** Private Equity: Buyouts **Band 3** p.203, **Illinois:** Corporate/M&A: Private Equity **Band 3** p.1157

**Geston, Mark S**
Table(s): **Idaho:** Litigation: General Commercial **Band 2** p.1134

**Gettleman, Chad H**
Profile: p.1208
Table(s): **Illinois:** Bankruptcy/Restructuring **Band 3** p.1148

**Gevertz, David**
Profile: p.1082
Table(s): **Georgia:** Labor & Employment **Band 4** p.1060

**Gewin, James**
Table(s): **Alabama:** Litigation: General Commercial **Band 1** p.463

**Ghegan, David W**
Table(s): **Georgia:** Banking & Finance: Mainly Regulatory **Up-and-coming individuals** p.1039

**Gherlein, John M**
Profile: p.2097
Table(s): **Ohio:** Corporate/M&A **Band 1** p.2064

**Gholz, Charles**
Profile: p.2510
Table(s): **Northern Virginia:** Intellectual Property **Band 2** p.2497

**Giammittorio, Gregory**
Profile: p.2510
Table(s): **Northern Virginia:** Corporate/M&A **Band 3** p.2493

**Giannelli, Karen A**
Table(s): **New Jersey:** Bankruptcy/Restructuring **Band 1** p.1705

**Giannotto, Michael S**
Profile: p.865
Table(s): **District of Columbia:** Environment **Band 4** p.804

**Gianoulakis, John**
Table(s): **Missouri:** Litigation: General Commercial **Band 1** p.1629

**Gianvecchio, Natasha**
Profile: p.320
Table(s): **Nationwide:** Energy: Electricity (Regulatory & Litigation) **Band 5** p.76

**Giarrusso III,, Joseph I.**
Table(s): **Louisiana:** Litigation: General Commercial **Up-and-coming individuals** p.1352

**Gibbons, John**
Table(s): **New Jersey:** Litigation: General Commercial **Senior Statesmen:** p.1722

**Gibbons, M Colette**
Table(s): **Ohio:** Bankruptcy/Restructuring **Band 2** p.2058

**Gibbons, Ray D**
Table(s): **Alabama:** Banking & Finance **Band 2** p.455

**Gibbons, Susanna**
Table(s): **North Carolina:** Labor & Employment **Band 3** p.2031

**Gibbs, Charles R**
Table(s): **Nationwide:** Bankruptcy/Restructuring **Band 4** p.39, **Texas:** Bankruptcy/Restructuring **Band 1** p.2328

**Gibbs, Jeffrey N**
Table(s): **District of Columbia:** Healthcare: Pharmaceutical/Medical Products Regulatory **Band 3** p.810

**Gibbs, Kenneth C**
Table(s): **California:** Construction: Mediators **Band 1** p.550

**Gibbs, Kirstin E**
Profile: p.320
Table(s): **Nationwide:** Energy: Oil & Gas (Regulatory & Litigation) **Band 4** p.78

**Gibbs, Lawrence B**
Profile: p.865
Table(s): **District of Columbia:** Tax **Band 2** p.838

**Gibbs, Robert**
Table(s): **Washington:** Immigration **Band 1** p.2528

**Gibbs, Robin C**
Profile: p.2391
Table(s): **Nationwide:** Litigation: Trial Lawyers **Band 2** p.187, **Texas:** Litigation: Energy & Natural Resources **Band 1** p.2361, **Texas:** Litigation: General Commercial **Band 1** p.2361

**Gibby, Darin J**
Table(s): **Colorado:** Intellectual Property **Band 1** p.704

**Giblin, Pamela**
Profile: p.2391
Table(s): **Texas:** Environment **Star Individuals** p.2343

**Giblin Jr, Thomas P**
Profile: p.320
Table(s): **Nationwide:** Energy: Electricity (Finance) **Band 1** p.75

**Gibson, Christopher R**
Profile: p.1736
Table(s): **New Jersey:** Environment **Band 2** p.1711

**Gibson, Douglas G**
Profile: p.320
Table(s): **Nationwide:** Sports Law **Band 2** p.241

**Gibson Jr, C Allen**
Table(s): **South Carolina:** Litigation: General Commercial **Band 3** p.2264

**Gidari, Albert**
Table(s): **Nationwide:** Privacy & Data Security **Band 1** p.199

**Giddens, James W**
Profile: p.1896
Table(s): **Nationwide:** Bankruptcy/Restructuring **Band 4** p.39, **New York:** Bankruptcy/Restructuring **Band 3** p.1782

**Giddens, Jared D**
Table(s): **Oklahoma:** Litigation: General Commercial **Band 3** p.2141

**Giddings, Barton**
Table(s): **Utah:** Intellectual Property **Band 2** p.2466

**Giddings, Katherine E**
Table(s): **Florida:** Litigation: Appellate **Band 2** p.972

**Gideon, Benjamin**
Table(s): **Maine:** Litigation: Medical Malpractice & Insurance **Band 3** p.1393, **Maine:** Litigation: Mainly Plaintiff **Band 2** p.1393

**Gideon, CJ**
Table(s): **Tennessee:** Litigation: Medical Malpractice Defense **Band 1** p.2295

**Gideon, Kenneth W**
Profile: p.320
Table(s): **Nationwide:** Tax: Controversy **Band 1** p.244, **District of Columbia:** Tax **Band 1** p.838

**Gidley, J Mark**
Profile: p.865
Table(s): **District of Columbia:** Antitrust **Band 3** p.787

**Gidley, James**
Table(s): **Oregon:** Litigation: General Commercial **Band 2** p.2171

**Giebelstein, Terry M**
Table(s): **Iowa:** Corporate/M&A **Band 4** p.1283

**Giegerich, Thomas**
Profile: p.1896
Table(s): **New York:** Tax **Band 4** p.1862

**Giese, Jeffrey W**
Profile: p.2391
Table(s): **Texas:** Real Estate **Band 3** p.2367

**Giese, Michael J**
Profile: p.2269
Table(s): **South Carolina:** Litigation: General Commercial **Band 3** p.2264

**Giesel, James A**
Profile: p.1318
Table(s): **Kentucky:** Corporate/M&A **Band 2** p.1305

**Gietz, Raymond**
Profile: p.1896
Table(s): **New York:** Corporate/M&A **Band 5** p.1793

**Giffin, John D**
Table(s): **Nationwide:** Transportation: Shipping: Litigation (outside New York) **Band 3** p.263

**Gifford, David B**
Profile: p.2217
Table(s): Pennsylvania: Real Estate **Band 1**
p.2208

**Gifford, Mark W**
Table(s): Wyoming: Litigation: General
Commercial **Band 2** p.2598, Wyoming: Litigation:
Mediators **Band 1** p.2598

**Gignilliat, R Read**
Table(s): Georgia: Labor & Employment **Band 3**
p.1060

**Gilberg, David J**
Profile: p.320
Table(s): Nationwide: Capital Markets:
Derivatives **Band 2** p.51

**Gilbert, Alan**
Table(s): Minnesota: Corporate/M&A **Band 4**
p.1569

**Gilbert, Andrew P**
Profile: p.1736
Table(s): New Jersey: Corporate/M&A **Band 1**
p.1707

**Gilbert, Donald R**
Table(s): Arizona: Labor & Employment **Band 3**
p.499

**Gilbert, Françoise**
Table(s): Nationwide: Privacy & Data Security
**Band 2** p.199

**Gilbert, Jan S.**
Table(s): Nationwide: Franchising **Band 4** p.111

**Gilbert, Leonard H**
Profile: p.993
Table(s): Florida: Bankruptcy/Restructuring
**Senior Statesmen:** p.939

**Gilbert, Paul E**
Table(s): Arizona: Real Estate: Zoning/Land Use
**Band 1** p.504

**Gilbert, Robert N**
Profile: p.993
Table(s): Florida: Bankruptcy/Restructuring **Band
3** p.939

**Gilbert, Scott D**
Profile: p.865
Table(s): District of Columbia: Insurance:
Policyholder **Band 1** p.818

**Gilchrist, Bruce**
Table(s): Nationwide: Capital Markets: REITs
**Band 4** p.55

**Gilden, David M**
Table(s): Rhode Island: Corporate/Commercial
**Band 1** p.2251, Rhode Island: Real Estate **Band 2**
p.2255

**Giles, Stephen R**
Table(s): Arkansas: Real Estate: Zoning/Land
Use **Band 1** p.524

**Gilford, Steven R**
Table(s): Illinois: Insurance: Dispute Resolution
**Star individuals** p.1168, Illinois: Insurance: Dispute
Resolution: Reinsurance **Band 2** p.1168

**Gilhuly, Morgan**
Profile: p.637
Table(s): California: Environment **Band 4** p.564

**Gilhuly, Peter**
Table(s): Nationwide: Bankruptcy/Restructuring
**Band 3** p.39, California:
Bankruptcy/Restructuring **Band 1** p.542

**Gill, Clayton**
Table(s): Idaho: Corporate/Commercial **Band 3**
p.1132

**Gill, Richard**
Table(s): Alabama: Litigation: General
Commercial **Band 3** p.463

**Gill, Sartaj**
Profile: p.320
Table(s): Nationwide: Banking & Finance **Band 3**
p.31

**Gillece Jr, James P**
Table(s): Maryland: Labor & Employment **Band 3**
p.1417

**Gillen, Craig A**
Table(s): Georgia: Litigation: White-Collar Crime
& Government Investigations **Band 2** p.1066

**Gillen, Dennis L**
Table(s): Kansas: Litigation: General
Commercial **Band 1** p.1295

**Gillen, Stephen E**
Table(s): Ohio: Intellectual Property **Band 1**
p.2071

**Gillespie, Michael J**
Table(s): New York: Latin American Investment
**Band 4** p.1829, New York: Media &
Entertainment: Corporate **Band 1** p.1848

**Gillette, Patricia**
Profile: p.637
Table(s): California: Labor & Employment **Band 3**
p.587

**Gilliam, James H**
Profile: p.1291
Table(s): Iowa: Labor & Employment **Band 2**
p.1285

**Gilliam, Robert S**
Table(s): Louisiana: Energy & Natural
Resources: Utilities **Band 1** p.1344

**Gilligan, John P**
Table(s): Ohio: Litigation: General Commercial
**Band 3** p.2078

**Gilligan, Leigh A**
Profile: p.1492
Table(s): Massachusetts: Environment **Band 2**
p.1457

**Gilligan, Michael**
Table(s): New York: Corporate/M&A **Band 5**
p.1793

**Gilluly III, John J**
Profile: p.2391
Table(s): Texas: Technology: Corporate &
Commercial **Up-and-coming individuals** p.2375

**Gilman, Charles A**
Profile: p.1896
Table(s): New York: Litigation: General
Commercial **Band 2** p.1833

**Gilmore, Jeffrey G**
Table(s): Virginia: Construction **Band 2** p.2491

**Gilmore, Patrick**
Table(s): Alaska: Litigation: General Commercial
**Band 2** p.490, Alaska: Real Estate **Band 2** p.491

**Gilpin, Thomas**
Table(s): West Virginia: Real Estate **Band 1**
p.2560

**Gilson, Gary**
Table(s): Missouri: Corporate/M&A **Band 2** p.1618

**Gilson, Jerome**
Profile: p.1209
Table(s): Illinois: Intellectual Property **Senior
Statesmen:** p.1171

**Gindler, David I**
Profile: p.638
Table(s): California: Intellectual Property: Patent
**Band 4** p.578, California: Life Sciences: IP/Patent
Litigation **Band 2** p.590

**Ginensky, Amy B**
Profile: p.2217
Table(s): Pennsylvania: Litigation: General
Commercial **Band 2** p.2203

**Ginn, Gregg H**
Profile: p.1399
Table(s): Maine: Labor & Employment: Employee
Benefits & Compensation **Senior Statesmen:**
p.1390

**Ginsberg, Benjamin L**
Table(s): Nationwide: Government: Political Law
**Band 1** p.124

**Ginsberg, Beth S**
Table(s): Washington: Environment **Band 1**
p.2527

**Ginsberg, Paul D**
Profile: p.1896
Table(s): New York: Corporate/M&A **Band 5**
p.1793

**Ginsberg, Ross D**
Profile: p.1082
Table(s): Georgia: Construction **Band 2** p.1044

**Ginsburg, Dennis**
Table(s): Florida: Tax **Band 2** p.979

**Ginsburg, Jonathan**
Table(s): Nationwide: Immigration **Band 3** p.131

**Ginsburg, Roy**
Table(s): Minnesota: Labor & Employment **Band 2**
p.1571

**Gioia, Paul L**
Table(s): New York: Energy: State Regulatory &
Wholesale Electric Market **Senior Statesmen:**
p.1806

**Giordano, Cynthia**
Table(s): District of Columbia: Real Estate:
Zoning/Land Use **Band 3** p.835

**Giordano, P Gregory**
Table(s): Nevada: Gaming & Licensing **Band 2**
p.1674

**Giotto, Thomas S**
Profile: p.2217
Table(s): Pennsylvania: Labor & Employment
**Band 1** p.2200

**Giovannone, Lauren**
Table(s): Nationwide: Leisure & Hospitality
**Associates to watch** p.179

**Giove, Stephen**
Table(s): Nationwide: Capital Markets: Debt &
Equity **Band 4** p.46

**Gips, Robert**
Profile: p.320
Table(s): Nationwide: Native American Law **Band
1** p.192

**Girard, Robert D**
Table(s): California: Healthcare **Band 3** p.568

**Girardi, Thomas V**
Table(s): Nationwide: Product Liability: Plaintiffs
**Band 2** p.209

**Gire, Michael**
Table(s): Ohio: Healthcare **Band 1** p.2069

**Gische, David**
Table(s): District of Columbia: Insurance:
Insurer **Band 3** p.816

**Gisser, Michael**
Profile: p.638
Table(s): California: Corporate/M&A: Deals in
Asia **Band 1** p.553, California: Corporate/M&A
**Band 3** p.553

**Gisvold, Dean P**
Table(s): Oregon: Real Estate **Senior Statesmen:**
p.2173

**Gitlin, David**
Profile: p.321
Table(s): Nationwide: Investment Funds: Venture
Capital **Band 3** p.174, Pennsylvania:
Corporate/M&A & Private Equity **Band 3** p.2191

**Gitomer, Deborah**
Profile: p.321
Table(s): Nationwide: Energy: Oil & Gas
(Transactional) **Band 3** p.79

**Gittleman, Felicia**
Table(s): Washington: Immigration **Band 2** p.2528

**Gittler, Amy J**
Profile: p.508
Table(s): Arizona: Labor & Employment **Band 3**
p.499

**Giudicessi, Michael A**
Table(s): Iowa: Labor & Employment **Band 2**
p.1285

**Giuffra Jr, Robert J**
Profile: p.321
Table(s): Nationwide: Securities: Litigation **Band
1** p.232, New York: Litigation: General
Commercial **Band 1** p.1833, New York: Litigation:
Securities **Band 1** p.1833

**Giuliani, Richard W**
Profile: p.1492
Table(s): Massachusetts: Tax **Band 3** p.1481

**Giunco Jr, John A**
Table(s): New Jersey: Real Estate: Zoning/Land
Use **Band 2** p.1728

**Giunta, Tara K**
Table(s): District of Columbia: Telecom,
Broadcast & Satellite **Band 4** p.844

**Given, David A**
Table(s): Indiana: Labor & Employment **Band 2**
p.1271

**Givens, Leonard D**
Profile: p.1550
Table(s): Michigan: Labor & Employment Band 2 p.1542

**Gjording, Jack**
Table(s): Idaho: Litigation: Medical Malpractice & Insurance Band 1 p.1134

**Glad, Paul E B**
Profile: p.321
Table(s): Nationwide: Insurance: Dispute Resolution: Insurer Band 1 p.134, California: Insurance: Insurer Band 1 p.574

**Glade, Peter**
Table(s): Oregon: Litigation: General Commercial Band 2 p.2171

**Glahn III, Wilbur A**
Profile: p.1695
Table(s): New Hampshire: Litigation: General Commercial Band 1 p.1690

**Glancz, Ronald R**
Profile: p.321
Table(s): Nationwide: Financial Services Regulation: Banking (Compliance) Band 2 p.96, Nationwide: Financial Services Regulation: Banking (Enforcement & Investigations) Band 1 p.96

**Glascock, Thomas B**
Table(s): Nationwide: Projects Band 4 p.216

**Glaser, D Louis**
Table(s): Illinois: Healthcare Band 2 p.1165

**Glaser, Michael**
Table(s): Nationwide: Investment Funds: Venture Capital Band 3 p.174, California: Corporate/M&A: Venture Capital Up-and-coming individuals p.555

**Glaser, Patricia**
Table(s): California: Litigation: General Commercial Band 3 p.593, California: Media & Entertainment: Litigation Band 1 p.606

**Glaser, Peter**
Table(s): Nationwide: Climate Change Band 1 p.63

**Glaser, Steven**
Profile: p.1896
Table(s): New York: Litigation: White-Collar Crime & Government Investigations Up-and-coming individuals p.1836

**Glaser Jr, Richard S**
Table(s): North Carolina: Litigation: White-Collar Crime & Government Investigations Band 1 p.2034

**Glasgow Jr, Norman**
Profile: p.865
Table(s): District of Columbia: Real Estate: Zoning/Land Use Band 1 p.835

**Glass, Robert**
Table(s): Oklahoma: Corporate/Commercial: Healthcare Band 2 p.2134

**Glass, Todd**
Table(s): Nationwide: Projects: Renewables & Alternative Energy Band 1 p.218

**Glasscock, C Edward**
Profile: p.1318
Table(s): Kentucky: Corporate/M&A Star individuals p.1305

**Glasser, Brian**
Table(s): West Virginia: Litigation: General Commercial Band 2 p.2555

**Glasser, James**
Table(s): Connecticut: Litigation: General Commercial Band 3 p.738

**Glasser, Mark K**
Profile: p.2391
Table(s): Texas: Litigation: General Commercial Band 2 p.2362

**Glassman, Andrew C**
Profile: p.743
Table(s): Connecticut: Corporate/M&A Band 2 p.732

**Glassman, Jacqueline**
Table(s): Nationwide: Transportation: Road (Carriage/Commercial) Band 1 p.259

**Glassman, Michael S**
Table(s): Ohio: Labor & Employment Band 3 p.2074

**Glassman, Neil B**
Profile: p.771
Table(s): Delaware: Bankruptcy/Restructuring Band 2 p.754

**Glazer, Anne W**
Table(s): Oregon: Intellectual Property Band 3 p.2167

**Glazer, Daniel C**
Profile: p.1896
Table(s): New York: Technology & Outsourcing Band 3 p.1868

**Glazer, David G**
Profile: p.1736
Table(s): New Jersey: Corporate/M&A Band 4 p.1707

**Glazer, Dennis**
Profile: p.1896
Table(s): New York: Litigation: General Commercial Band 3 p.1833

**Glazer, Edward**
Profile: p.321
Table(s): Nationwide: Capital Markets: REITs Band 2 p.55

**Glazer, Michael**
Profile: p.321
Table(s): Nationwide: Investment Funds: Registered Funds Band 3 p.170

**Glazer, Michael H**
Profile: p.1493
Table(s): Nationwide: Real Estate Band 2 p.225, Massachusetts: Real Estate Band 1 p.1478

**Glazer, Ronald B**
Table(s): Pennsylvania: Real Estate Band 3 p.2208

**Glazier, Robert**
Table(s): Florida: Litigation: Appellate Band 2 p.972

**Gleason, Daniel J**
Profile: p.1493
Table(s): Massachusetts: Litigation: General Commercial Band 3 p.1470

**Gleicher, Brian**
Profile: p.321
Table(s): Nationwide: Tax: Controversy Up-and-coming individuals p.244

**Gleklen, Jonathan**
Profile: p.865
Table(s): District of Columbia: Antitrust Band 2 p.787

**Glendenning, Don M**
Profile: p.2391
Table(s): Texas: Corporate/M&A Band 3 p.2337

**Glenn, Robert B**
Table(s): Florida: Bankruptcy/Restructuring Band 1 p.939

**Glenney, Jeffrey W**
Table(s): North Carolina: Real Estate Band 2 p.2037

**Glenos, Chris**
Table(s): Alabama: Bankruptcy/Restructuring Band 3 p.457

**Glerum, Charles L**
Profile: p.1493
Table(s): Massachusetts: Bankruptcy/Restructuring Band 1 p.1449

**Gliatta, Stephen**
Profile: p.1896
Table(s): New York: Real Estate: Finance Band 2 p.1855

**Glick, Anna H.**
Profile: p.321
Table(s): Nationwide: Capital Markets: Securitisation Band 1 p.59

**Glick, Marty**
Profile: p.638
Table(s): California: Intellectual Property: Patent Band 4 p.578

**Glick, Richard M**
Table(s): Oregon: Environment Band 1 p.2165

**Glickson, Andrew A**
Profile: p.743
Table(s): Connecticut: Real Estate Band 3 p.740

**Glickstein, David**
Profile: p.1209
Table(s): Illinois: Real Estate Band 3 p.1187

**Glickstein, Steven**
Profile: p.321
Table(s): Nationwide: Product Liability & Mass Torts Band 3 p.208

**Glincher, Andrew**
Profile: p.1493
Table(s): Massachusetts: Real Estate Band 3 p.1478

**Gline, Gerald**
Profile: p.1736
Table(s): New Jersey: Bankruptcy/Restructuring Band 2 p.1705

**Glisson, Gary**
Table(s): Oregon: Intellectual Property Band 2 p.2167

**Glist, Paul**
Table(s): District of Columbia: Telecom, Broadcast & Satellite Band 3 p.844

**Glosband, Daniel M**
Profile: p.1493
Table(s): Massachusetts: Bankruptcy/Restructuring Star individuals p.1449

**Glover, Jerry W**
Table(s): Illinois: Media & Entertainment: Transactional Band 1 p.1185

**Glover, Stephen I**
Profile: p.865
Table(s): District of Columbia: Corporate/M&A & Private Equity Band 1 p.797

**Glucoft, Frida P**
Table(s): California: Immigration Band 4 p.571

**Glynn, Elizabeth A**
Table(s): Vermont: Corporate/Commercial Band 3 p.2483

**Godar, Daniel**
Table(s): Missouri: Corporate/M&A Band 3 p.1619

**Godar, Michael E**
Profile: p.1637
Table(s): Missouri: Intellectual Property Band 1 p.1623

**Godby, Herbert R**
Table(s): Ohio: Real Estate Band 4 p.2086

**Goddard, J. Andrew**
Profile: p.2304
Table(s): Tennessee: Environment Band 1 p.2290

**Godfrey, H Lee**
Table(s): Nationwide: Litigation: Trial Lawyers Band 2 p.187, Texas: Antitrust Band 2 p.2323, Texas: Litigation: Energy & Natural Resources Band 1 p.2361, Texas: Litigation: General Commercial Band 1 p.2361

**Godfrey, Richard C**
Profile: p.1209
Table(s): Illinois: Litigation: General Commercial Band 1 p.1180

**Godiner, Clifford A**
Table(s): Missouri: Labor & Employment Band 1 p.1625

**Godman, James**
Profile: p.1896
Table(s): New York: Real Estate Band 4 p.1854

**Godshall, Craig L**
Profile: p.2217
Table(s): Pennsylvania: Corporate/M&A & Private Equity Band 3 p.2191

**Godwin, Jeremy H**
Table(s): North Carolina: Corporate/M&A Band 4 p.2025

**Goe, Oliver**
Table(s): Montana: Labor & Employment Band 2 p.1648

**Goebel, Teresa**
Profile: p.321
Table(s): Nationwide: Leisure & Hospitality Band 3 p.179

**Goeltz, Thomas**
Table(s): Washington: Real Estate Band 3 p.2535

**Goering, Gail**
Table(s): Illinois: Insurance: Dispute Resolution: Reinsurance Band 3 p.1168

**Goettel, Timothy S**
Profile: p.2041
Table(s): **North Carolina: Corporate/M&A Band 3** p.2025

**Goetz, James**
Table(s): **Montana: Litigation: Mainly Plaintiff Band 1** p.1649

**Goetz, John D.**
Profile: p.321
Table(s): **Nationwide: Transportation: Aviation: Litigation Band 3** p.254

**Goetz, Peter**
Table(s): **New York: Construction Senior Statesmen:** p.1791

**Goetz, Richard**
Table(s): **Nationwide: Insurance: Dispute Resolution: Insurer Band 3** p.134, **California: Insurance: Insurer Band 2** p.574

**Goetzinger, Patrick**
Table(s): **South Dakota: Corporate/Commercial Band 1** p.2281, **South Dakota: Real Estate Band 2** p.2286

**Goewey, David W**
Profile: p.2510
Table(s): **Virginia: Litigation: General Commercial Band 3** p.2502

**Goff, Christopher**
Table(s): **Missouri: Intellectual Property Band 1** p.1623

**Goffman, Jay M**
Profile: p.322
Table(s): **Nationwide: Bankruptcy/Restructuring Band 1** p.39, **New York: Bankruptcy/Restructuring Band 1** p.1782

**Goggin, James G**
Profile: p.1399
Table(s): **Maine: Litigation: General Commercial Band 3** p.1393

**Goicoechea, Sean**
Table(s): **Montana: Litigation: General Commercial Band 2** p.1649

**Gold, Brian J**
Profile: p.1209
Table(s): **Illinois: Labor & Employment Band 3** p.1175

**Gold, Frederick**
Table(s): **Connecticut: Litigation: General Commercial Band 2** p.738

**Gold, Jason**
Profile: p.865
Table(s): **District of Columbia: Bankruptcy/Restructuring Band 2** p.792

**Gold, Marc**
Table(s): **Pennsylvania: Environment Band 1** p.2194

**Gold, Martin**
Profile: p.322
Table(s): **Nationwide: Government: Government Relations Band 3** p.121

**Gold, Michael**
Profile: p.1209
Table(s): **Illinois: Banking & Finance Band 2** p.1145

**Gold, Michael A**
Profile: p.865
Table(s): **District of Columbia: Corporate/M&A & Private Equity Band 4** p.797

**Gold, Richard M**
Profile: p.322
Table(s): **Nationwide: Government: Government Relations Band 3** p.121

**Gold, Ronald**
Profile: p.2097
Table(s): **Ohio: Bankruptcy/Restructuring Band 1** p.2058

**Gold, Stephen**
Table(s): **Illinois: Technology & Outsourcing Band 3** p.1194

**Goldammer, Vance RC**
Table(s): **South Dakota: Corporate/Commercial Band 1** p.2281, **South Dakota: Real Estate Band 1** p.2286

**Goldberg, Catherine T**
Profile: p.1773
Table(s): **New Mexico: Real Estate Band 1** p.1772

**Goldberg, Charles**
Table(s): **Colorado: Litigation: General Commercial Band 3** p.709

**Goldberg, Daniel L**
Profile: p.1493
Table(s): **Massachusetts: Antitrust Band 1** p.1444, **Massachusetts: Litigation: General Commercial Band 2** p.1470

**Goldberg, Gregory E**
Profile: p.718
Table(s): **Colorado: Litigation: White-Collar Crime & Government Investigations Band 2** p.710

**Goldberg, Henry**
Table(s): **District of Columbia: Telecom, Broadcast & Satellite Band 2** p.844

**Goldberg, Jerrold F**
Profile: p.1897
Table(s): **New York: Labor & Employment Band 4** p.1826

**Goldberg, Joel H**
Table(s): **Nationwide: Investment Funds: Registered Funds Band 3** p.170

**Goldberg, Joseph**
Table(s): **New Mexico: Litigation: General Commercial Band 2** p.1769

**Goldberg, Louis L**
Profile: p.1897
Table(s): **New York: Corporate/M&A Band 3** p.1793

**Goldberg, Michael**
Table(s): **Massachusetts: Bankruptcy/Restructuring Band 2** p.1449

**Goldberg, Michael I**
Table(s): **Florida: Bankruptcy/Restructuring Band 1** p.939

**Goldberg, Michael S**
Profile: p.322
Table(s): **Nationwide: International Arbitration Band 3** p.145

**Goldberg, Richard M**
Profile: p.1427
Table(s): **Maryland: Litigation: Bankruptcy Band 2** p.1419

**Goldberg, Stephen**
Profile: p.322
Table(s): **Nationwide: Insurance: Dispute Resolution: Policyholder Band 3** p.137, **California: Insurance: Policyholder Band 3** p.576

**Goldberg, Steven H**
Profile: p.1897
Table(s): **New York: Corporate/M&A Band 5** p.1793

**Goldberg Jr, Fred T**
Profile: p.322
Table(s): **Nationwide: Tax: Controversy Band 1** p.244, **District of Columbia: Tax Band 1** p.838

**Goldberger, M Norman**
Profile: p.2217
Table(s): **Pennsylvania: Litigation: Securities Band 2** p.2204

**Goldblatt, Craig**
Profile: p.866
Table(s): **District of Columbia: Bankruptcy/Restructuring Band 1** p.792

**Golden, Adam**
Profile: p.322
Table(s): **Nationwide: Life Sciences: Corporate/Commercial Band 2** p.182

**Golden, Arthur F**
Profile: p.1897
Table(s): **New York: Antitrust Band 2** p.1778

**Golden, Daniel H**
Profile: p.322
Table(s): **Nationwide: Bankruptcy/Restructuring Band 1** p.39, **New York: Bankruptcy/Restructuring Band 1** p.1782

**Golden, Eric**
Table(s): **Florida: Bankruptcy/Restructuring Band 4** p.939

**Golden, Gerald A**
Profile: p.1209
Table(s): **Illinois: Labor & Employment Band 3** p.1175

**Golden, Jonathan**
Profile: p.1082
Table(s): **Georgia: Corporate/M&A Band 3** p.1046

**Golden, William**
Table(s): **New York: Intellectual Property: Trade Mark & Copyright Band 3** p.1821

**Goldfarb, Steven A.**
Profile: p.2097
Table(s): **Ohio: Litigation: General Commercial Band 3** p.2078

**Goldfein, Shepard**
Profile: p.322
Table(s): **Nationwide: Sports Law Band 1** p.241, **New York: Antitrust Band 2** p.1778

**Goldman, Andrew N**
Profile: p.1897
Table(s): **New York: Bankruptcy/Restructuring Band 4** p.1782

**Goldman, Geoffrey B**
Profile: p.322
Table(s): **Nationwide: Capital Markets: Derivatives Band 2** p.51

**Goldman, Howard**
Table(s): **New York: Real Estate: Zoning/Land Use Band 2** p.1855

**Goldman, Joel S**
Profile: p.638
Table(s): **California: Healthcare Band 2** p.568

**Goldman, Joseph**
Profile: p.866
Table(s): **District of Columbia: Tax Band 4** p.838

**Goldman, Matthew R**
Profile: p.2097
Table(s): **Ohio: Bankruptcy/Restructuring Band 2** p.2058

**Goldman, Michael D**
Profile: p.771
Table(s): **Delaware: Chancery Senior Statesmen:** p.758

**Goldman, Michael P**
Profile: p.1209
Table(s): **Nationwide: Insurance: Transactional & Regulatory Band 2** p.139, **Illinois: Insurance: Transactional & Regulatory Band 1** p.1168

**Goldman, Michael S**
Profile: p.322
Table(s): **Nationwide: Banking & Finance Band 1** p.31

**Goldman, Richard A**
Profile: p.1493
Table(s): **Nationwide: Investment Funds: Hedge Funds Band 3** p.162, **Massachusetts: Hedge & Mutual Funds Band 1** p.1461

**Goldman, Robert J**
Table(s): **California: Intellectual Property: Patent Band 4** p.578

**Goldman, Robert S**
Table(s): **Florida: Tax: State & Local Band 1** p.979

**Goldman, Roger**
Profile: p.866
Table(s): **District of Columbia: Healthcare Band 2** p.809

**Goldman, William L**
Profile: p.322
Table(s): **Nationwide: Tax: Controversy Senior Statesmen:** p.244

**Goldner, Bruce J**
Profile: p.1897
Table(s): **New York: Intellectual Property: Trade Mark & Copyright Band 2** p.1821

**Goldring, Stuart J**
Profile: p.1897
Table(s): **New York: Tax Band 1** p.1862

**Goldschmidt, David J**
Profile: p.323
Table(s): **Nationwide: Capital Markets: Debt & Equity Band 2** p.46, **Nationwide: Capital Markets: REITs Band 2** p.55

**Goldsmith, Barry**
Profile: p.323
Table(s): **Nationwide: Securities: Regulation: Enforcement Band 1** p.233

**Goldsmith, Robert S**
Table(s): New Jersey: Real Estate: Zoning/Land Use **Band 2** p.1728

**Goldsmith, Willis J**
Profile: p.1897
Table(s): New York: Labor & Employment **Band 1** p.1826

**Goldstein, Aimee H**
Profile: p.1897
Table(s): New York: Antitrust **Band 4** p.1778

**Goldstein, Andrew**
Profile: p.1209
Table(s): Illinois: Media & Entertainment: Transactional **Band 1** p.1185

**Goldstein, Andrew M**
Profile: p.1427
Table(s): Maryland: Real Estate **Band 3** p.1422

**Goldstein, Arthur S**
Table(s): New Jersey: Litigation: General Commercial **Band 3** p.1722

**Goldstein, Bruce**
Table(s): District of Columbia: Bankruptcy/Restructuring **Band 3** p.792

**Goldstein, David A**
Profile: p.323
Table(s): Nationwide: Investment Funds: Private Equity: Fund Formation **Band 4** p.166

**Goldstein, Heidi B**
Profile: p.2097
Table(s): Ohio: Natural Resources & Environment **Band 3** p.2083

**Goldstein, Howard W**
Profile: p.1897
Table(s): New York: Litigation: White-Collar Crime & Government Investigations **Band 3** p.1836

**Goldstein, Jane D**
Table(s): Massachusetts: Corporate/M&A **Band 3** p.1452

**Goldstein, Jeremy**
Profile: p.1897
Table(s): New York: Employee Benefits & Executive Compensation **Band 3** p.1802

**Goldstein, Jorge A**
Table(s): Nationwide: Life Sciences: IP/Patent Litigation **Band 1** p.183, District of Columbia: Intellectual Property: Patent Prosecution **Band 2** p.820

**Goldstein, Joseph**
Profile: p.993
Table(s): Florida: Real Estate: Zoning/Land Use **Band 1** p.975

**Goldstein, Linda A**
Table(s): Nationwide: Advertising: Transactional & Regulatory **Star individuals** p.20

**Goldstein, Marcia**
Profile: p.323
Table(s): Nationwide: Bankruptcy/Restructuring **Band 1** p.39, New York: Bankruptcy/Restructuring **Band 1** p.1782

**Goldstein, Mark**
Table(s): Nevada: Real Estate **Band 3** p.1679

**Goldstein, Marvin**
Table(s): Nationwide: Capital Markets: Derivatives **Band 3** p.51

**Goldstein, Marvin M**
Table(s): New Jersey: Labor & Employment **Band 2** p.1718

**Goldstein, Maura**
Profile: p.323
Table(s): Nationwide: Projects **Band 3** p.216

**Goldstein, Michael R**
Table(s): Florida: Environment **Band 2** p.951

**Goldstein, Richard J**
Profile: p.1736
Table(s): New Jersey: Real Estate **Band 3** p.1728

**Goldstein, Richard M**
Profile: p.993
Table(s): Florida: Tax **Band 2** p.979

**Goldstein, Sandra C**
Profile: p.1898
Table(s): New York: Litigation: Securities **Band 3** p.1834

**Goldstein, Stephanie J**
Profile: p.1898
Table(s): New York: Litigation: General Commercial **Band 4** p.1833

**Goldstein, Steven J**
Profile: p.2097
Table(s): Ohio: Intellectual Property **Band 1** p.2071

**Goldstein, Stuart N**
Profile: p.323
Table(s): Nationwide: Capital Markets: Securitisation **Band 4** p.59

**Goldstein, Thomas C**
Table(s): Nationwide: Appellate Law **Band 2** p.26

**Goldstein, Wendy C**
Profile: p.1898
Table(s): New York: Healthcare **Band 2** p.1811

**Golumbic, Lars**
Profile: p.323
Table(s): Nationwide: ERISA Litigation **Band 3** p.92

**Gomez, Armando**
Profile: p.866
Table(s): District of Columbia: Tax **Band 4** p.838

**Gomez, Paul A.**
Table(s): California: Healthcare **Up-and-coming individuals** p.568

**Gonchar, Meryl A G**
Table(s): New Jersey: Real Estate: Zoning/Land Use **Band 1** p.1728

**Gonsoulin Jr, Dewey J**
Profile: p.2391
Table(s): Texas: Banking & Finance **Band 2** p.2325

**Gonzales, Alex**
Profile: p.2391
Table(s): Texas: Insurance: Regulation **Band 2** p.2351

**Gonzales O'Kelly, Cathy**
Profile: p.323
Table(s): Nationwide: Investment Funds: Registered Funds **Band 3** p.170

**Gonzalez, Edward E**
Profile: p.1898
Table(s): New York: Tax **Band 2** p.1862

**Gonzalez, Enrique**
Table(s): Florida: Immigration **Band 1** p.956

**Gonzalez, Ervin A**
Table(s): Florida: Litigation: General Commercial **Band 1** p.966

**Gonzalez, Josie**
Table(s): Nationwide: Immigration **Band 2** p.131, California: Immigration **Band 1** p.571

**Gonzalez, Thomas M**
Table(s): Florida: Labor & Employment **Band 1** p.959

**González, Arturo J**
Profile: p.638
Table(s): California: Litigation: General Commercial **Band 4** p.593

**González, Daniel E**
Table(s): Nationwide: International Arbitration **Band 4** p.145, Florida: Litigation: General Commercial **Band 3** p.966

**Gooch, W Kyle**
Table(s): Texas: Construction **Band 1** p.2335

**Good, John A**
Profile: p.323
Table(s): Nationwide: Capital Markets: REITs **Band 3** p.55, Tennessee: Corporate/M&A **Band 3** p.2288

**Good, Samantha**
Profile: p.638
Table(s): California: Banking & Finance **Band 3** p.539

**Goodchild, John**
Profile: p.2217
Table(s): Pennsylvania: Bankruptcy/Restructuring **Band 4** p.2188

**Goode, Jason**
Profile: p.323
Table(s): Nationwide: Capital Markets: REITs **Up-and-coming individuals** p.55

**Goodell Jr, Charles P**
Profile: p.323
Table(s): Nationwide: Product Liability & Mass Torts **Band 4** p.208, Nationwide: Product Liability: Pharmaceutical p.208

**Goodgame, John**
Profile: p.2391
Table(s): Texas: Capital Markets: Debt & Equity **Band 3** p.2333

**Goodheart, Jodi R**
Table(s): Nevada: Real Estate **Band 3** p.1679

**Goodheart, Lisa**
Profile: p.1493
Table(s): Massachusetts: Environment **Band 1** p.1457

**Gooding, Douglas R**
Profile: p.1493
Table(s): Massachusetts: Bankruptcy/Restructuring **Band 1** p.1449

**Gooding, Gregory**
Table(s): New York: Latin American Investment **Band 4** p.1829

**Goodison, Eric**
Profile: p.324
Table(s): Nationwide: Banking & Finance **Band 4** p.31

**Goodling, Jonathon L**
Profile: p.2176
Table(s): Oregon: Real Estate **Band 2** p.2173

**Goodman, Alan H**
Table(s): Louisiana: Bankruptcy/Restructuring **Band 2** p.1337, Louisiana: Litigation: General Commercial **Band 3** p.1352

**Goodman, Amy**
Profile: p.324
Table(s): Nationwide: Securities: Regulation: Advisory **Band 2** p.232

**Goodman, Jack N**
Table(s): District of Columbia: Media & Entertainment: Mainly Regulatory **Band 3** p.832

**Goodman, Jeffrey H**
Profile: p.324
Table(s): Nationwide: Projects **Band 4** p.216

**Goodman, Jerald M**
Profile: p.2217
Table(s): Pennsylvania: Real Estate **Band 4** p.2208

**Goodman, Jimmy**
Profile: p.2149
Table(s): Oklahoma: Litigation: General Commercial **Band 2** p.2141

**Goodman, Lisa**
Table(s): Delaware: Real Estate: Zoning/Land Use **Band 1** p.766

**Goodman, Louis A**
Profile: p.1493
Table(s): Massachusetts: Corporate/M&A **Band 1** p.1452

**Goodman, Marcia E**
Table(s): Illinois: Labor & Employment **Band 4** p.1175

**Goodman, Mark R**
Profile: p.1209
Table(s): Illinois: Insurance: Transactional & Regulatory **Band 2** p.1168

**Goodman, Robert D**
Table(s): New York: Insurance: Dispute Resolution: Insurer **Band 3** p.1816

**Goodman, Ronald**
Profile: p.324
Table(s): Nationwide: International Arbitration **Band 4** p.145

**Goodman, Saul**
Profile: p.866
Table(s): District of Columbia: Insurance: Policyholder **Band 2** p.818

**Goodman, Scott Warren**
Profile: p.1736
Table(s): New Jersey: Corporate/M&A **Band 4** p.1707

**Goodman, Stanley**
Profile: p.1736
Table(s): New Jersey: Labor & Employment **Band 2** p.1718

**Goodman, Stephen M**
Table(s): Pennsylvania: Corporate/M&A &
Private Equity **Senior Statesmen:** p.2191

**Goodman, William M**
Profile: p.638
Table(s): California: Litigation: White-Collar
Crime & Government Investigations **Band 3** p.601

**Goodman III, Will**
Profile: p.324
Table(s): Nationwide: Product Liability & Mass
Torts **Band 3** p.208, Mississippi: Litigation:
General Commercial **Band 3** p.1597

**Goodman Jr, William F**
Profile: p.1603
Table(s): Mississippi: Litigation: General
Commercial **Senior Statesmen:** p.1597

**Goodnight, David R**
Profile: p.2304
Table(s): Washington: Litigation: General
Commercial **Band 3** p.2533

**Goodrich, James E**
Table(s): Maryland: Real Estate **Band 4** p.1422

**Goodrich, Robert**
Profile: p.2304
Table(s): Tennessee: Litigation: Bankruptcy **Band
1** p.2295

**Goodsell, Verne**
Table(s): South Dakota: Litigation: General
Commercial **Band 3** p.2284

**Goodwin, David B**
Profile: p.324
Table(s): Nationwide: Insurance: Dispute
Resolution: Policyholder **Band 1** p.137, California:
Insurance: Policyholder **Band 1** p.576

**Goodwin, Michael**
Profile: p.866
Table(s): Nationwide: Leisure & Hospitality **Band
4** p.179, District of Columbia: Real Estate **Star
individuals** p.835

**Goodwin, T Daniel**
Table(s): Arkansas: Corporate/Commercial **Band
3** p.518, Arkansas: Real Estate **Band 2** p.524

**Goodwin, Timothy J**
Profile: p.1082
Table(s): Georgia: Real Estate **Band 2** p.1070

**Googe Jr, Charles H**
Profile: p.1898
Table(s): New York: Media & Entertainment:
Film & Television **Band 1** p.1849

**Googins, Mark K**
Profile: p.1399
Table(s): Maine: Corporate/M&A **Star individuals**
p.1385

**Goold, Barry**
Table(s): Nevada: Real Estate **Band 2** p.1679

**Goolsby, Allen**
Profile: p.2510
Table(s): Southern Virginia: Corporate/M&A
**Senior Statesmen:** p.2494

**Goolsby, Bryan L**
Profile: p.324
Table(s): Nationwide: Capital Markets: REITs
**Band 3** p.55

**Goranin, Aleksander J.**
Profile: p.2217
Table(s): Pennsylvania: Intellectual Property **Up-
and-coming individuals** p.2197

**Gordet, Richard E**
Table(s): Massachusetts: Real Estate **Band 3**
p.1478

**Gordian, Carmelo**
Profile: p.2391
Table(s): Texas: Technology: Corporate &
Commercial **Band 1** p.2375

**Gordon, Andrew K**
Table(s): Nationwide: Insurance: Dispute
Resolution: Insurer **Band 3** p.134, California:
Insurance: Insurer **Band 2** p.574

**Gordon, Andrew P**
Table(s): Nevada: Litigation: General
Commercial **Band 3** p.1677

**Gordon, Charles C**
Table(s): Washington: Litigation: General
Commercial **Band 2** p.2533

**Gordon, Dana M**
Profile: p.1493
Table(s): Massachusetts: Intellectual Property
**Band 2** p.1463

**Gordon, David A**
Profile: p.324
Table(s): Nationwide: Projects **Band 1** p.216

**Gordon, David L**
Profile: p.1082
Table(s): Georgia: Labor & Employment **Band 3**
p.1060

**Gordon, David S**
Table(s): New Jersey: Real Estate **Band 1** p.1728

**Gordon, Eric B**
Profile: p.638
Table(s): Nationwide: Healthcare: Regulatory &
Litigation **Band 2** p.127, California: Healthcare
**Band 1** p.568

**Gordon, George G**
Profile: p.2217
Table(s): Pennsylvania: Antitrust **Band 2** p.2184

**Gordon, Gregory M**
Profile: p.2391
Table(s): Texas: Bankruptcy/Restructuring **Band 2**
p.2328

**Gordon, Howard E.**
Table(s): Southern Virginia: Real Estate **Band 3**
p.2506

**Gordon, Jack B**
Table(s): District of Columbia: Insurance:
Insurer **Band 4** p.816

**Gordon, Jill H**
Profile: p.638
Table(s): California: Healthcare **Band 3** p.568

**Gordon, Kevin D**
Table(s): Oklahoma: Corporate/Commercial:
Healthcare **Band 2** p.2134

**Gordon, Lynn**
Profile: p.1209
Table(s): Illinois: Healthcare **Band 3** p.1165

**Gordon, Nicholas**
Table(s): New York: Media & Entertainment:
Music **Band 1** p.1849

**Gordon, Patricia**
Table(s): North Carolina: Banking & Finance
**Band 4** p.2021

**Gordon, Paul A**
Profile: p.638
Table(s): California: Healthcare **Band 3** p.568

**Gordon, Phillip**
Table(s): Nationwide: Leisure & Hospitality **Band
3** p.179

**Gordon, Randy D**
Profile: p.2392
Table(s): Texas: Antitrust **Band 3** p.2323

**Gordon, Rebecca**
Table(s): Nationwide: Government: Political Law
**Up-and-coming individuals** p.124

**Gordon, Robert B**
Table(s): Massachusetts: Labor & Employment
**Band 1** p.1466

**Gordon, Robert J**
Table(s): Nationwide: Product Liability: Plaintiffs
**Band 2** p.209

**Gordon, Roberta G**
Table(s): New York: Environment: Mainly
Transactional **Band 2** p.1808

**Gordon, Scott D**
Profile: p.1773
Table(s): New Mexico: Labor & Employment
**Band 1** p.1767

**Gordon, Stephen L**
Profile: p.1898
Table(s): New York: Environment **Band 4** p.1807

**Gordon, Stephen L**
Profile: p.1898
Table(s): New York: Tax **Band 1** p.1862

**Gorelick, Jamie**
Profile: p.324
Table(s): Nationwide: Government: Government
Relations **Band 1** p.121

**Gorham, Anne E**
Profile: p.1318
Table(s): Kentucky: Litigation: Construction **Band
1** p.1312

**Gorman, Sean**
Profile: p.2392
Table(s): Texas: Litigation: General Commercial
**Band 4** p.2362

**Gorrell, Joseph M**
Table(s): New Jersey: Healthcare **Band 1** p.1715

**Gorrell Jr, J Warren**
Table(s): Nationwide: Capital Markets: REITs
**Band 1** p.55, District of Columbia:
Corporate/M&A & Private Equity **Band 1** p.797

**Gorson, Matthew B**
Profile: p.993
Table(s): Florida: Real Estate **Band 1** p.974

**Gorton, William T**
Profile: p.1319
Table(s): Kentucky: Environment, Natural
Resources & Utilities: Environment **Band 1** p.1307

**Gortz, Albert W**
Table(s): Nationwide: Wealth Management:
Eastern Region **Band 4** p.267, Florida: Tax: Estate
Planning **Band 3** p.979

**Gosfield, Gregory G**
Table(s): Pennsylvania: Real Estate **Band 3**
p.2208

**Goshko, Mark**
Profile: p.1494
Table(s): Massachusetts: Hedge & Mutual
Funds **Band 2** p.1461

**Gosnell, Guy R.**
Profile: p.2041
Table(s): North Carolina: Intellectual Property
**Band 1** p.2030

**Goss, Patrick**
Table(s): Arkansas: Litigation: General
Commercial **Band 3** p.522

**Gosselink, Paul**
Table(s): Texas: Environment **Band 4** p.2343

**Gossett, David**
Table(s): South Carolina: Real Estate **Band 2**
p.2266

**Gotch, Charles F**
Table(s): Nebraska: Litigation: Insurance **Senior
Statesmen:** p.1664

**Goto, Bruce T**
Table(s): Washington: Intellectual Property **Band
2** p.2529

**Gotsdiner, Gary M**
Profile: p.1668
Table(s): Nebraska: Corporate/Commercial **Band
2** p.1659

**Gottlieb, Gail**
Table(s): New Mexico: Litigation: General
Commercial **Band 3** p.1769

**Gottlieb, Ira**
Profile: p.1736
Table(s): New Jersey: Environment **Band 2**
p.1711, New Jersey: Litigation: Insurance **Band 2**
p.1723

**Gottlieb, Joel E**
Table(s): South Carolina: Real Estate **Band 1**
p.2266

**Gottlieb, Richard E**
Table(s): Nationwide: Financial Services
Regulation: Consumer Finance (Litigation) **Band 2**
p.99

**Gottlieb, Robert G**
Profile: p.866
Table(s): District of Columbia: Real Estate **Band
2** p.835

**Gotts, Ilene Knable**
Profile: p.1898
Table(s): New York: Antitrust **Band 1** p.1778

**Gotts, Lawrence J**
Profile: p.866
Table(s): District of Columbia: Intellectual
Property: Litigation **Band 2** p.821

**Gottschalk, Hugh**
Profile: p.718
Table(s): Colorado: Litigation: General
Commercial **Band 2** p.709

**Gottshall, Justine**
Profile: p.1209
Table(s): Illinois: Media & Entertainment: Transactional **Band 2** p.1185

**Goudie, Federico**
Profile: p.993
Table(s): Florida: Latin American Investment **Band 4** p.963

**Gould, Edward**
Table(s): Maine: Litigation: Medical Malpractice & Insurance **Band 3** p.1393

**Gourley, Sara J**
Profile: p.325
Table(s): Nationwide: Product Liability & Mass Torts **Band 2** p.208

**Govett, Brett C**
Profile: p.2392
Table(s): Texas: Intellectual Property **Band 3** p.2354

**Gowan, Thomas W**
Profile: p.325
Table(s): Nationwide: Sports Law **Band 3** p.241

**Gowland, Kimbal L**
Table(s): Idaho: Real Estate **Band 2** p.1138

**Goyne, Roderick**
Profile: p.2392
Table(s): Texas: Banking & Finance **Band 1** p.2325

**Grabar, Nicolas**
Profile: p.1898
Table(s): Nationwide: Capital Markets: Debt & Equity **Band 3** p.46, New York: Latin American Investment **Band 1** p.1829

**Grace, David W**
Profile: p.638
Table(s): California: Intellectual Property: Trademark, Copyright & Trade Secrets **Band 3** p.578

**Graceffa, Charles M**
Profile: p.1400
Table(s): Maine: Corporate/M&A **Band 3** p.1385

**Gracer, Jeffrey B**
Table(s): New York: Environment **Band 2** p.1807

**Grachuk, Jeanine L G**
Profile: p.1494
Table(s): Massachusetts: Environment **Band 3** p.1457

**Gradel, James**
Table(s): Washington: Real Estate **Band 3** p.2535

**Grady, Jack**
Profile: p.1082
Table(s): Georgia: Environment **Band 3** p.1051

**Grady, Keith**
Table(s): Missouri: Intellectual Property **Band 1** p.1623

**Grady, Timothy**
Profile: p.2097
Table(s): Ohio: Banking & Finance **Band 2** p.2056

**Graff Jr, F Thomas**
Profile: p.2563
Table(s): West Virginia: Corporate/Commercial **Band 1** p.2550, West Virginia: Natural Resources **Band 1** p.2558

**Grafton, Susan**
Profile: p.325
Table(s): Nationwide: Financial Services Regulation: Broker Dealer (Compliance) **Band 3** p.97, Nationwide: Financial Services Regulation: Broker Dealer (Enforcement) **Band 3** p.97

**Graham, Andrew Jay**
Profile: p.1427
Table(s): Maryland: Litigation: General Commercial **Band 1** p.1419

**Graham, Bruce**
Table(s): Hawaii: Real Estate **Band 1** p.1120

**Graham, Christopher**
Profile: p.2257
Table(s): Rhode Island: Corporate/Commercial **Band 2** p.2251

**Graham, Daniel P**
Profile: p.325
Table(s): Nationwide: Government: Government Contracts **Band 4** p.117

**Graham, David F**
Profile: p.1209
Table(s): Illinois: Antitrust **Band 4** p.1143, Illinois: Litigation: General Commercial **Band 3** p.1180

**Graham, F Brian**
Table(s): Texas: Immigration **Band 2** p.2349

**Graham, Lawrence**
Table(s): Washington: Intellectual Property **Band 2** p.2529

**Graham, Mary B**
Table(s): Delaware: Intellectual Property **Band 2** p.763

**Graham, Max**
Table(s): Hawaii: Real Estate: Zoning/Land Use **Band 1** p.1120

**Graham, Morgan G**
Profile: p.1899
Table(s): New York: Environment **Band 3** p.1807

**Graham, Robert L**
Profile: p.1210
Table(s): Illinois: Environment: Mainly Transactional **Band 1** p.1162

**Graham, Stanley E**
Profile: p.2304
Table(s): Tennessee: Labor & Employment **Band 3** p.2293

**Graham, Stephen M**
Profile: p.2539
Table(s): Washington: Corporate/Commercial **Band 2** p.2525

**Grais, David J**
Table(s): New York: Insurance: Dispute Resolution: Insurer **Band 2** p.1816

**Grala, Bronislaw E**
Profile: p.325
Table(s): Nationwide: Employee Benefits & Executive Compensation **Band 1** p.73, New York: Employee Benefits & Executive Compensation **Band 1** p.1802

**Gram, Chresten**
Table(s): Oregon: Real Estate **Band 3** p.2173

**Grammig, Robert J**
Profile: p.993
Table(s): Florida: Corporate/M&A & Private Equity **Star Individuals** p.947

**Granda, John A**
Table(s): Missouri: Corporate/M&A **Band 1** p.1618

**Granik, Gary L**
Table(s): Nationwide: Investment Funds: Registered Funds **Band 3** p.170

**Grant, Denise M**
Table(s): New York: Latin American Investment **Band 3** p.1829

**Grant, Elizabeth J**
Table(s): Vermont: Labor & Employment **Band 3** p.2485

**Grant, Eugene L**
Table(s): Oregon: Real Estate **Band 2** p.2173

**Grant, Harry**
Table(s): Washington: Environment **Band 2** p.2527

**Grant, James C**
Profile: p.1082
Table(s): Georgia: Litigation: General Commercial **Band 3** p.1065

**Grant, Jill E**
Table(s): Nationwide: Native American Law **Band 3** p.192

**Grant, Maximillian**
Profile: p.866
Table(s): District of Columbia: Intellectual Property: Litigation **Band 3** p.821

**Grant, Stuart M**
Profile: p.771
Table(s): Nationwide: Securities: Litigation: Mainly Plaintiff **Band 1** p.234, Delaware: Chancery: Mainly Plaintiff **Band 1** p.759, New York: Litigation: Securities Mainly Plaintiff **Band 1** p.1835

**Grantham, Mark E**
Profile: p.1083
Table(s): Georgia: Litigation: General Commercial **Band 4** p.1065

**Granwell, Alan Winston**
Profile: p.866
Table(s): District of Columbia: Tax **Band 4** p.838

**Grassgreen, Debra**
Table(s): California: Bankruptcy/Restructuring **Band 4** p.542

**Grasso, Jeanne**
Profile: p.325
Table(s): Nationwide: Transportation: Shipping: Regulatory (outside New York) **Band 3** p.264

**Gratton, Scott**
Table(s): Montana: Litigation: General Commercial **Band 2** p.1649

**Grauer, David W**
Profile: p.2098
Table(s): Ohio: Healthcare **Band 3** p.2069

**Graves, Judson**
Profile: p.1083
Table(s): Georgia: Litigation: General Commercial **Band 1** p.1065

**Graves, Kathlyn**
Table(s): Arkansas: Labor & Employment **Band 1** p.520

**Graves, Robert**
Profile: p.1210
Table(s): Illinois: Banking & Finance **Band 4** p.1145

**Graw, Andrew E**
Profile: p.1736
Table(s): New Jersey: Employee Benefits & Executive Compensation **Band 1** p.1710

**Gray, Douglas G**
Profile: p.2257
Table(s): Rhode Island: Corporate/Commercial **Band 2** p.2251

**Gray, Elizabeth P.**
Profile: p.325
Table(s): Nationwide: Securities: Regulation: Enforcement **Band 3** p.233

**Gray, Elizabeth Van Doren**
Profile: p.2269
Table(s): South Carolina: Litigation: General Commercial **Band 1** p.2264

**Gray, James**
Profile: p.1427
Table(s): Maryland: Litigation: General Commercial **Band 3** p.1419

**Gray, Jeffrey**
Table(s): California: Energy: State Regulatory & Litigation **Band 2** p.562

**Gray, Jeffry W**
Profile: p.1362
Table(s): Louisiana: Real Estate **Band 3** p.1355

**Gray, Katie**
Profile: p.1400
Table(s): Maine: Energy & Natural Resources **Associates to watch** p.1388

**Gray, Kenneth F**
Profile: p.1400
Table(s): Maine: Environment **Band 1** p.1389

**Gray, Kevin**
Profile: p.469
Table(s): Alabama: Bankruptcy/Restructuring **Band 3** p.457

**Gray, Kyle**
Profile: p.1654
Table(s): Montana: Natural Resources & Environment **Band 2** p.1651

**Gray, Mark R**
Table(s): Iowa: Real Estate **Band 4** p.1290

**Gray, Michael B**
Profile: p.1210
Table(s): Illinois: Corporate/M&A: Private Equity **Band 3** p.1157

**Gray, Michael J**
Profile: p.1210
Table(s): Illinois: Labor & Employment **Band 2** p.1175

**Gray, Peter**
Profile: p.866
Table(s): District of Columbia: Environment **Band 5** p.804

**Gray, Robert F**
Table(s): Texas: Corporate/M&A **Band 2** p.2337, Texas: Technology: Corporate & Commercial **Band 1** p.2375

**Gray, Todd**
Profile: p.866
Table(s): District of Columbia: Telecom, Broadcast & Satellite **Band 4** p.844

**Gray, Tracy**
Profile: p.718
Table(s): Colorado: Intellectual Property **Band 2** p.704

**Gray, William**
Profile: p.325
Table(s): Nationwide: Capital Markets: Derivatives **Band 3** p.51

**Graybeal, John F**
Table(s): North Carolina: Antitrust **Senior Statesmen:** p.2020

**Grayck, David**
Table(s): Vermont: Real Estate: Zoning/Land Use **Band 2** p.2487

**Grayson, E Lynn**
Profile: p.1210
Table(s): Illinois: Environment: Mainly Transactional **Band 1** p.1162

**Grayson, Neil E**
Profile: p.2269
Table(s): South Carolina: Corporate/M&A **Band 2** p.2260, South Carolina: Corporate/M&A: Banking & Finance **Band 1** p.2260

**Graziano, Michael C**
Profile: p.2217
Table(s): Pennsylvania: Banking & Finance **Band 2** p.2186

**Graziano, Salvatore J**
Profile: p.1899
Table(s): Nationwide: Securities: Litigation: Mainly Plaintiff **Band 2** p.234, New York: Litigation: Securities Mainly Plaintiff **Band 2** p.1835

**Greaney, William**
Profile: p.325
Table(s): Nationwide: Insurance: Dispute Resolution: Policyholder **Band 1** p.137, District of Columbia: Insurance: Policyholder **Band 1** p.818

**Greeley, Jack**
Table(s): Florida: Banking & Finance: Regulatory **Band 2** p.937, Florida: Banking & Finance: Transactional **Band 2** p.937

**Green, Allen B.**
Profile: p.325
Table(s): Nationwide: International Arbitration **Band 5** p.145

**Green, Barry D**
Table(s): Massachusetts: Real Estate **Band 2** p.1478

**Green, Christopher O.**
Table(s): Georgia: Intellectual Property **Up-and-coming individuals** p.1056

**Green, David W**
Table(s): Oregon: Real Estate **Band 1** p.2173

**Green, Douglas G**
Table(s): Nationwide: Energy: Electricity (Regulatory & Litigation) **Band 1** p.76

**Green, Douglas H**
Profile: p.867
Table(s): District of Columbia: Environment **Band 2** p.804

**Green, Elizabeth A**
Profile: p.993
Table(s): Florida: Bankruptcy/Restructuring **Band 2** p.939

**Green, Frederick S**
Profile: p.1899
Table(s): New York: Corporate/M&A **Band 5** p.1793

**Green, James**
Table(s): Oklahoma: Litigation: General Commercial **Band 3** p.2141

**Green, Jonathan**
Profile: p.325
Table(s): Nationwide: Banking & Finance **Band 4** p.31, Nationwide: Projects **Band 1** p.216

**Green, Jonathan S**
Profile: p.1550
Table(s): Michigan: Banking & Finance: Bankruptcy **Band 1** p.1536

**Green, Jordan**
Table(s): Arizona: Litigation: White-Collar Crime & Government Investigations **Senior Statesmen:** p.501

**Green, Rachelle R**
Table(s): Rhode Island: Litigation: General Commercial **Band 2** p.2254

**Green, Ronald M**
Table(s): New York: Labor & Employment **Band 3** p.1826

**Green, Thomas C**
Profile: p.326
Table(s): Nationwide: Litigation: Trial Lawyers **Band 1** p.187, District of Columbia: Litigation: White-Collar Crime & Government Investigations **Band 1** p.827

**Green, William**
Table(s): Washington: Real Estate **Band 2** p.2535

**Green-Kelly, Diane**
Table(s): Nationwide: Franchising: Mainly Franchisee **Band 2** p.114

**Greenbaum, Jack A**
Profile: p.326
Table(s): Nationwide: Transportation: Shipping: Litigation (New York) **Band 3** p.261

**Greenbaum, Jeffrey A**
Profile: p.326
Table(s): Nationwide: Advertising: Transactional & Regulatory **Band 1** p.20

**Greenbaum, Jeffrey J**
Profile: p.1736
Table(s): New Jersey: Litigation: General Commercial **Band 2** p.1722

**Greenbaum, William**
Profile: p.1736
Table(s): New Jersey: Labor & Employment **Band 3** p.1718

**Greenberg, Barry C**
Profile: p.1427
Table(s): Maryland: Real Estate **Band 2** p.1422

**Greenberg, Bennett D**
Profile: p.867
Table(s): District of Columbia: Construction **Band 1** p.795

**Greenberg, Eric Dodson**
Table(s): District of Columbia: Telecom, Broadcast & Satellite **Band 3** p.844

**Greenberg, Gary**
Table(s): Ohio: Labor & Employment **Band 3** p.2074

**Greenberg, Gerald**
Profile: p.2098
Table(s): Ohio: Corporate/M&A **Band 2** p.2064

**Greenberg, Gordon A**
Profile: p.639
Table(s): Nationwide: Litigation: Trial Lawyers **Band 2** p.187, California: Litigation: White-Collar Crime & Government Investigations **Star individuals** p.601

**Greenberg, Jeffrey**
Table(s): Nationwide: Projects **Band 1** p.216

**Greenberg, Joel I**
Profile: p.1899
Table(s): New York: Corporate/M&A **Band 4** p.1793

**Greenberg, Leo M.**
Profile: p.1899
Table(s): New York: Corporate/M&A **Up-and-coming individuals** p.1793

**Greenberg, Marilynn R**
Table(s): New Jersey: Environment **Band 3** p.1711

**Greenberg, William S**
Table(s): New Jersey: Litigation: General Commercial **Band 3** p.1722

**Greenburg, G Scott**
Profile: p.2539
Table(s): Washington: Corporate/Commercial **Band 3** p.2525

**Greendyke, William**
Profile: p.2392
Table(s): Texas: Bankruptcy/Restructuring **Band 2** p.2328

**Greene, Clifford M**
Table(s): Minnesota: Litigation: General Commercial **Band 2** p.1574

**Greene, Kenneth**
Table(s): North Carolina: Banking & Finance **Band 1** p.2021

**Greene, Kevin C**
Table(s): Georgia: Energy **Star individuals** p.1049

**Greene, Mark I**
Profile: p.1899
Table(s): New York: Corporate/M&A **Band 5** p.1793

**Greene, Nathan J**
Profile: p.326
Table(s): Nationwide: Investment Funds: Registered Funds **Band 3** p.170

**Greene, Robert M**
Profile: p.1899
Table(s): New York: Healthcare **Band 3** p.1811

**Greene, Thomas M**
Profile: p.1494
Table(s): Massachusetts: Employee Benefits & Executive Compensation **Band 2** p.1455

**Greener, Richard**
Table(s): Idaho: Litigation: General Commercial **Senior Statesmen:** p.1134

**Greenfield, Andrew B**
Table(s): District of Columbia: Immigration **Band 2** p.814

**Greenfield, Ester**
Table(s): Washington: Immigration **Band 1** p.2528

**Greenfield, Gregg S**
Table(s): South Dakota: Corporate/Commercial **Band 2** p.2281, South Dakota: Real Estate **Band 1** p.2286

**Greenfield, Harry**
Table(s): Ohio: Bankruptcy/Restructuring **Band 4** p.2058

**Greenfield, Jim**
Table(s): Washington: Real Estate **Band 3** p.2535

**Greenfield, Leon B**
Profile: p.867
Table(s): District of Columbia: Antitrust **Band 4** p.787

**Greenfield, Rebecca**
Profile: p.1400
Table(s): Maine: Real Estate **Up-and-coming individuals** p.1395

**Greenfield, Robert A**
Table(s): California: Bankruptcy/Restructuring **Senior Statesmen:** p.542

**Greengrass, Lawrence S**
Profile: p.1899
Table(s): New York: Insurance: Dispute Resolution: Insurer **Band 3** p.1816

**Greenhalgh, Duncan**
Profile: p.1494
Table(s): Massachusetts: Intellectual Property **Band 2** p.1463

**Greenhalgh, Walter J**
Table(s): New Jersey: Bankruptcy/Restructuring **Band 2** p.1705

**Greenman, Ronald L**
Profile: p.2176
Table(s): Oregon: Corporate/M&A **Band 2** p.2164

**Greenstein, Abraham**
Table(s): District of Columbia: Real Estate **Band 2** p.835

**Greenthal, John**
Profile: p.1899
Table(s): New York: Environment **Band 2** p.1807

**Greenwald, John D**
Profile: p.326
Table(s): Nationwide: International Trade: Trade Remedies & Trade Policy **Band 2** p.154

**Greenwald, Steven**
Table(s): California: Energy: State Regulatory & Litigation **Band 1** p.562

**Greenwell, Charles D**
Table(s): Kentucky: Litigation: General
Commercial **Band 4** p.1312

**Greenwell, Karen J**
Profile: p.1319
Table(s): Kentucky: Environment, Natural
Resources & Utilities: Natural Resources **Band 1**
p.1307

**Greer, Alan**
Profile: p.993
Table(s): Florida: Litigation: General Commercial
**Band 1** p.966

**Greer, David**
Table(s): Ohio: Litigation: General Commercial
**Senior Statesmen:** p.2078

**Greer, George E**
Profile: p.2539
Table(s): Washington: Litigation: General
Commercial **Band 3** p.2533

**Greer, Scott A**
Profile: p.2392
Table(s): Texas: Construction **Band 1** p.2335

**Gregg, Joseph**
Table(s): Ohio: Natural Resources &
Environment **Band 4** p.2083

**Gregg, Timothy W.**
Profile: p.469
Table(s): Alabama: Corporate/Commercial **Band
3** p.459

**Gregor, Jennifer L.**
Table(s): Wisconsin: Intellectual Property
**Associates to watch** p.2573

**Gregorie Jr, Isaac McPherson**
Profile: p.1362
Table(s): Louisiana: Real Estate **Band 2** p.1355

**Gregory, Cleburne E**
Profile: p.1083
Table(s): Georgia: Tax **Band 2** p.1072

**Gregory, Donald**
Table(s): Ohio: Construction **Band 1** p.2062

**Gregory, H Watt**
Profile: p.526
Table(s): Arkansas: Corporate/Commercial **Band
1** p.518

**Gregory, Julie Ann**
Table(s): Kentucky: Intellectual Property **Band 2**
p.1308

**Gregson, Gabriel F**
Profile: p.639
Table(s): California: Banking & Finance **Up-and-
coming individuals** p.539

**Greig, Brian**
Profile: p.2392
Table(s): Texas: Labor & Employment **Star individ-
uals** p.2359

**Greising, Robert**
Table(s): Indiana: Corporate/M&A **Band 2** p.1268

**Grenfell, Matthew H**
Profile: p.1603
Table(s): Mississippi: Real Estate **Associates to
watch** p.1600

**Grenier, John B**
Table(s): Alabama: Corporate/Commercial **Band
2** p.459

**Grever, Thomas**
Table(s): Missouri: Environment **Band 2** p.1621

**Gribble II, Don D**
Table(s): Kansas: Litigation: General
Commercial **Band 3** p.1295

**Grice, Richard**
Profile: p.1083
Table(s): Georgia: Banking & Finance **Band 2**
p.1039

**Gries, Matthew J**
Table(s): Georgia: Tax **Up-and-coming individuals**
p.1072

**Griesing, Francine Friedman**
Table(s): Pennsylvania: Litigation: General
Commercial **Band 3** p.2203

**Griffin, Daniel P**
Profile: p.1083
Table(s): Georgia: Litigation: White-Collar Crime
& Government Investigations **Band 3** p.1066

**Griffin, James**
Table(s): Missouri: Litigation: General
Commercial **Band 1** p.1628

**Griffin, Michael A**
Profile: p.2539
Table(s): Washington: Labor & Employment **Band
3** p.2531

**Griffin III, Malvern U**
Table(s): Georgia: Intellectual Property **Band 3**
p.1056

**Griffin III, Thomas N**
Table(s): North Carolina: Environment **Band 1**
p.2028

**Griffin Jr, John J**
Profile: p.2149
Table(s): Oklahoma: Energy & Natural
Resources **Band 2** p.2136

**Griffinger, Michael R**
Table(s): New Jersey: Litigation: General
Commercial **Band 1** p.1722

**Griffith, Calvin P**
Profile: p.2098
Table(s): Ohio: Intellectual Property **Band 2**
p.2071

**Griffith, Gerald M**
Profile: p.1210
Table(s): Illinois: Healthcare **Band 2** p.1165

**Griffith, James**
Profile: p.2217
Table(s): Pennsylvania: Litigation: General
Commercial **Band 3** p.2203

**Griffith, Kevin**
Profile: p.2098
Table(s): Ohio: Labor & Employment **Band 2**
p.2074

**Griffith, Patricia**
Profile: p.1083
Table(s): Georgia: Labor & Employment **Band 1**
p.1060

**Griffith, Richard G**
Profile: p.1319
Table(s): Kentucky: Labor & Employment **Band 1**
p.1310

**Griffith, Robert W**
Profile: p.1319
Table(s): Kentucky: Litigation: General
Commercial **Band 4** p.1312

**Griffith, Scott**
Table(s): Texas: Construction **Band 3** p.2335

**Griffith, Vanessa**
Profile: p.2392
Table(s): Texas: Labor & Employment **Band 4**
p.2359

**Griffith Jr, Stephen M**
Profile: p.2098
Table(s): Ohio: Real Estate **Band 3** p.2086

**Griffith, Jr, Steven F**
Profile: p.1362
Table(s): Louisiana: Labor & Employment **Band 3**
p.1350

**Griffiths, Sean P.**
Profile: p.326
Table(s): Nationwide: Private Equity: Buyouts
**Band 5** p.203

**Griffiths, Walter L**
Profile: p.1668
Table(s): Nebraska: Real Estate **Band 3** p.1666

**Grigera Naón, Horacio**
Table(s): Nationwide: International Arbitration:
Arbitrators **Band 1** p.146

**Griggs, Linda L**
Table(s): Nationwide: Securities: Regulation:
Advisory **Band 2** p.232

**Griggs, Sean**
Profile: p.1277
Table(s): Indiana: Environment **Band 2** p.1270

**Grignon, Margaret**
Table(s): California: Litigation: Appellate **Band 1**
p.599

**Grigorian, Christopher**
Table(s): Nationwide: Transportation: Road
(Carriage/Commercial) **Band 3** p.259

**Grikscheit, Alyssa A**
Profile: p.1900
Table(s): New York: Latin American Investment
**Band 4** p.1829

**Grillo, Phillip E**
Table(s): Oregon: Real Estate: Zoning/Land Use
**Band 2** p.2173

**Grime, Richard**
Table(s): Nationwide: International Trade: FCPA
Experts **Band 2** p.153

**Grimes, Dale**
Profile: p.2304
Table(s): Tennessee: Litigation: General
Commercial **Band 3** p.2295

**Grimes, Gordon F**
Table(s): Maine: Energy & Natural Resources
**Band 1** p.1388

**Grimm, Bernie**
Table(s): District of Columbia: Litigation: White-
Collar Crime & Government Investigations **Band 4**
p.827

**Grimm, Thomas C**
Table(s): Delaware: Intellectual Property **Band 3**
p.763

**Grimmer, Gary**
Table(s): Hawaii: Litigation: General Commercial
**Band 3** p.1119

**Grimshaw, Thomas T**
Table(s): Colorado: Real Estate: Zoning/Land
Use **Senior Statesmen:** p.714

**Grindstaff, Michael J**
Table(s): Florida: Real Estate: Zoning/Land Use
**Band 2** p.975

**Griner, G Christopher**
Profile: p.326
Table(s): Nationwide: International Trade: CFIUS
Experts **Band 1** p.152

**Grinfas, Dan**
Table(s): Oregon: Labor & Employment **Band 2**
p.2168

**Groban Jr, Robert S**
Profile: p.1900
Table(s): New York: Immigration **Band 3** p.1814

**Grochal, Alan M**
Table(s): Maryland: Litigation: Bankruptcy **Band 2**
p.1419

**Grofman, Udi**
Profile: p.326
Table(s): Nationwide: Investment Funds: Hedge
Funds **Band 2** p.162

**Grogan, Gregory**
Profile: p.1900
Table(s): New York: Employee Benefits &
Executive Compensation **Band 4** p.1802

**Grogan, Michael K**
Table(s): Florida: Labor & Employment **Band 2**
p.959

**Grohsgal, Bruce**
Table(s): Delaware: Bankruptcy/Restructuring
**Band 2** p.754

**Groll, Christina**
Profile: p.718
Table(s): Colorado: Corporate/M&A **Band 3** p.703

**Groll, Michael**
Profile: p.326
Table(s): Nationwide: Insurance: Transactional &
Regulatory **Band 2** p.139, New York: Insurance:
Transactional & Regulatory **Band 2** p.1816

**Gromacki, Joseph P**
Profile: p.1210
Table(s): Illinois: Corporate/M&A **Band 4** p.1156

**Gronauer, Bob**
Table(s): Nevada: Real Estate: Zoning/Land Use
**Band 2** p.1679

**Groobey, Christopher**
Table(s): Nationwide: Projects **Band 3** p.216

**Groombridge, Nicholas**
Profile: p.1900
Table(s): New York: Intellectual Property: Patent
**Band 1** p.1820

**Grooms, Timothy W**
Profile: p.526
Table(s): **Arkansas:** Corporate/Commercial **Band 2** p.518, **Arkansas:** Real Estate **Star individuals** p.524

**Groos, Richard J**
Profile: p.2392
Table(s): **Texas:** Intellectual Property: Trade Mark & Copyright **Band 3** p.2354

**Groskaufmanis, Karl A**
Profile: p.326
Table(s): **Nationwide:** Securities: Regulation: Advisory **Band 2** p.232

**Gross, David JF**
Table(s): **Minnesota:** Litigation: Intellectual Property **Band 1** p.1574

**Gross, Doug**
Table(s): **Iowa:** Corporate/M&A **Band 1** p.1283

**Gross, Edward K.**
Profile: p.326
Table(s): **Nationwide:** Banking & Finance: Equipment Finance & Leasing **Band 2** p.32

**Gross, Jefferson W**
Table(s): **Utah:** Litigation: General Commercial **Band 3** p.2468

**Gross, Joel M**
Profile: p.867
Table(s): **District of Columbia:** Environment **Band 1** p.804

**Gross, John**
Table(s): **New York:** Insurance: Dispute Resolution: Policyholder **Band 2** p.1816

**Gross, Jonathan**
Table(s): **California:** Real Estate **Band 3** p.611

**Gross, Kenneth A**
Profile: p.327
Table(s): **Nationwide:** Government: Political Law **Band 1** p.124

**Gross, Michael J**
Table(s): **New Jersey:** Environment **Band 1** p.1711

**Gross, Mike**
Table(s): **Missouri:** Intellectual Property **Band 3** p.1623

**Gross, Steven E**
Profile: p.1736
Table(s): **New Jersey:** Corporate/M&A **Band 2** p.1707

**Gross, Steven R**
Table(s): **New York:** Bankruptcy/Restructuring **Band 3** p.1782

**Grossbauer, John F**
Profile: p.771
Table(s): **Delaware:** Corporate/M&A **Band 3** p.761

**Grossenburg, Bradley C**
Table(s): **South Dakota:** Corporate/Commercial **Band 2** p.2281

**Grosshandler, Seth**
Profile: p.327
Table(s): **Nationwide:** Capital Markets: Derivatives **Star individuals** p.51

**Grossi, Peter**
Profile: p.327
Table(s): **Nationwide:** Product Liability & Mass Torts **Senior Statesmen** p.208

**Grossman, Daryn A**
Table(s): **Nationwide:** Life Sciences: Corporate/Commercial **Band 3** p.182

**Grossman, Marshall B**
Profile: p.639
Table(s): **Nationwide:** Litigation: Trial Lawyers **Band 2** p.187, **California:** Litigation: General Commercial **Band 1** p.593, **California:** Media & Entertainment: Litigation **Band 3** p.606

**Grossman, Maura**
Profile: p.327
Table(s): **Nationwide:** Litigation: E-Discovery **Band 3** p.187

**Grossman, Paul**
Table(s): **California:** Labor & Employment **Star individuals** p.587

**Grossman, Scott M**
Profile: p.993
Table(s): **Florida:** Bankruptcy/Restructuring **Up-and-coming individuals** p.939

**Grossman, Shukie**
Profile: p.327
Table(s): **Nationwide:** Investment Funds: Private Equity: Fund Formation **Band 4** p.166

**Grossman, Theodore**
Profile: p.2098
Table(s): **Nationwide:** Product Liability & Mass Torts **Band 4** p.208, **Nationwide:** Product Liability: Tobacco p.208, **Ohio:** Litigation: General Commercial **Band 2** p.2078

**Groten, Eric**
Profile: p.2392
Table(s): **Texas:** Environment **Band 2** p.2343

**Grove, Roger A**
Table(s): **Oklahoma:** Energy & Natural Resources **Band 2** p.2136

**Grover, Gavin B**
Profile: p.639
Table(s): **California:** Corporate/M&A **Band 4** p.553

**Groves, KC**
Table(s): **Colorado:** Litigation: General Commercial **Band 3** p.709

**Grovier, Tina M**
Profile: p.492
Table(s): **Alaska:** Environment, Natural Resources & Regulated Industries **Band 2** p.488

**Grow, Michael A**
Profile: p.867
Table(s): **District of Columbia:** Intellectual Property: Trademark, Copyright & Trade Secrets **Band 2** p.820

**Grubin, John**
Table(s): **New York:** Construction **Band 4** p.1791

**Grubman, Allen**
Table(s): **New York:** Media & Entertainment: Music **Band 2** p.1849

**Gruemmer, Brooks B**
Profile: p.1210
Table(s): **Illinois:** Corporate/M&A: Private Equity **Band 3** p.1157

**Gruendel, Stephen E**
Table(s): **North Carolina:** Bankruptcy/Restructuring **Band 1** p.2023

**Grueneberg, Susan A**
Table(s): **Nationwide:** Franchising **Band 2** p.111

**Gruenglas, Michael H**
Profile: p.1900
Table(s): **New York:** Litigation: General Commercial **Band 4** p.1833

**Gruhin, Mark I**
Table(s): **District of Columbia:** Corporate/M&A & Private Equity **Band 3** p.797

**Grumbine, D Allen**
Table(s): **South Carolina:** Corporate/M&A **Band 2** p.2260

**Grunblatt, David**
Table(s): **Nationwide:** Immigration **Band 1** p.131, **New York:** Immigration **Band 1** p.1814

**Grundy, J Mark**
Profile: p.1319
Table(s): **Kentucky:** Litigation: Construction **Band 1** p.1312

**Gryboski, Thomas**
Table(s): **Georgia:** Real Estate **Band 3** p.1070

**Grymes Thompson, Christie**
Table(s): **Nationwide:** Advertising: Transactional & Regulatory **Band 3** p.20

**Grzezinski, Dennis**
Table(s): **Wisconsin:** Natural Resources & Environment **Band 2** p.2578

**Guadagnoli, David A**
Profile: p.1494
Table(s): **Massachusetts:** Employee Benefits & Executive Compensation **Band 1** p.1455

**Guaragna, John M**
Profile: p.2392
Table(s): **Texas:** Intellectual Property **Band 3** p.2354

**Guarcini, Gerald J**
Profile: p.2218
Table(s): **Pennsylvania:** Corporate/M&A: Securities **Band 2** p.2191

**Guariglia, Dale A**
Table(s): **Missouri:** Environment **Band 1** p.1621

**Guattery, Peter**
Profile: p.1427
Table(s): **Maryland:** Labor & Employment **Band 3** p.1417

**Guay, Joseph**
Profile: p.327
Table(s): **Nationwide:** Leisure & Hospitality **Band 4** p.179

**Guben, Jerrold K**
Table(s): **Hawaii:** Bankruptcy/Restructuring **Band 1** p.1114

**Guedry, David N**
Profile: p.327
Table(s): **Nationwide:** Outsourcing **Band 1** p.195, **Texas:** Technology: Outsourcing **Band 1** p.2376

**Guenthner, Robert**
Profile: p.1210
Table(s): **Illinois:** Healthcare **Up-and-coming individuals** p.1165

**Guernsey, John (Jack)**
Profile: p.2218
Table(s): **Pennsylvania:** Litigation: General Commercial **Band 3** p.2203

**Guerrera, Sal**
Profile: p.327
Table(s): **Nationwide:** Banking & Finance **Band 2** p.31

**Guerry, David L**
Profile: p.1362
Table(s): **Louisiana:** Energy & Natural Resources: Utilities **Band 1** p.1344

**Guess, Philip**
Profile: p.2539
Table(s): **Washington:** Litigation: General Commercial **Band 3** p.2533

**Guevara, Gregory W.**
Table(s): **Indiana:** Labor & Employment **Band 3** p.1271

**Guggenheim, Miriam J**
Profile: p.327
Table(s): **Nationwide:** Food & Beverages: Regulatory & Litigation **Band 3** p.107

**Gugig, Michael**
Table(s): **New Jersey:** Litigation: Insurance **Band 2** p.1723

**Guida, Joseph**
Table(s): **Texas:** Environment **Band 2** p.2343

**Guinasso, John**
Table(s): **Oregon:** Real Estate **Band 2** p.2173

**Guinn, Guy**
Profile: p.2098
Table(s): **Ohio:** Banking & Finance **Band 1** p.2056

**Gullace, John**
Table(s): **Pennsylvania:** Environment **Band 4** p.2194

**Gulland, Eugene D**
Profile: p.327
Table(s): **Nationwide:** International Arbitration **Band 4** p.145

**Gullickson, Charles D**
Table(s): **South Dakota:** Corporate/Commercial **Band 1** p.2281

**Gullikson, Rosemary L**
Profile: p.1210
Table(s): **Nationwide:** Outsourcing **Band 3** p.195, **Illinois:** Technology & Outsourcing **Band 2** p.1194

**Gulliver, John W**
Profile: p.1400
Table(s): **Maine:** Energy & Natural Resources **Band 1** p.1388

**Gumbel, Jon M**
Profile: p.1083
Table(s): **Georgia:** Labor & Employment **Band 4** p.1060

**Gumbert, Gregg C**
Profile: p.2304
Table(s): **Tennessee:** Real Estate **Band 3** p.2299

**Gumbs, Keir D**
Profile: p.328
Table(s): **Nationwide:** Securities: Regulation: Advisory **Up-and-coming individuals** p.232

**Gump Jr, Richard**
Table(s): Texas: Immigration **Band 1** p.2349

**Gundersen, Glenn A**
Profile: p.2218
Table(s): Pennsylvania: Intellectual Property **Band 2** p.2197

**Gundersen, Jeffrey S**
Table(s): Wisconsin: Intellectual Property **Band 3** p.2573

**Gunderson, Bob**
Table(s): Nationwide: Investment Funds: Venture Capital **Band 1** p.174, California: Corporate/M&A: Venture Capital **Band 2** p.555

**Gunn, Brian**
Profile: p.328
Table(s): Nationwide: Native American Law **Band 3** p.192

**Gunn, David M**
Table(s): Texas: Litigation: Appellate **Band 1** p.2361

**Gunn, Paul L**
Profile: p.1603
Table(s): Mississippi: Real Estate **Band 1** p.1600

**Gunnell, Bret**
Table(s): Colorado: Real Estate: Construction **Band 1** p.714

**Gunning, Vicky**
Profile: p.2392
Table(s): Texas: Real Estate **Band 3** p.2367

**Gunsett, Daniel J**
Profile: p.2098
Table(s): Ohio: Natural Resources & Environment **Band 4** p.2083

**Gunter, Russell**
Table(s): Arkansas: Labor & Employment **Band 1** p.520

**Gunter III, J Clifford**
Profile: p.2393
Table(s): Texas: Litigation: Energy & Natural Resources **Senior Statesmen**: p.2361, Texas: Litigation: General Commercial **Senior Statesmen**: p.2361

**Gunther Jr, Robert J**
Profile: p.1900
Table(s): New York: Intellectual Property: Patent **Band 2** p.1820

**Gupta, Paul R**
Table(s): New York: Intellectual Property: Patent **Band 3** p.1820

**Gupton III, John A**
Profile: p.2305
Table(s): Tennessee: Real Estate **Band 2** p.2299

**Gurbst, Richard**
Profile: p.2098
Table(s): Ohio: Litigation: General Commercial **Band 4** p.2078

**Gurley, John M**
Table(s): Nationwide: International Trade: Trade Remedies & Trade Policy **Band 5** p.154

**Gurney, Scott**
Profile: p.2098
Table(s): Ohio: Construction **Band 4** p.2062

**Guryan, Peter**
Profile: p.1900
Table(s): New York: Antitrust **Band 4** p.1778

**Guso, Jordi**
Profile: p.994
Table(s): Florida: Bankruptcy/Restructuring **Band 1** p.939

**Gussack, Nina M**
Profile: p.328
Table(s): Nationwide: Product Liability & Mass Torts **Band 1** p.208, Nationwide: Product Liability: Pharmaceutical p.208, Pennsylvania: Litigation: General Commercial **Band 1** p.2203

**Gust, Michael**
Table(s): North Dakota: Bankruptcy/Restructuring **Band 2** p.2050

**Gustafson, Donald R**
Table(s): Connecticut: Real Estate **Band 3** p.740

**Gustman, David C**
Profile: p.1210
Table(s): Illinois: Antitrust **Band 4** p.1143

**Guthman, Jack**
Table(s): Illinois: Real Estate: Zoning/Land Use **Senior Statesmen**: p.1188

**Guthrie, LB**
Table(s): Minnesota: Real Estate **Band 2** p.1576

**Guthrie, Mark C**
Profile: p.2393
Table(s): Texas: Construction **Band 2** p.2335

**Gutierrez, Jay M**
Profile: p.328
Table(s): Nationwide: Energy: Nuclear (Regulatory & Litigation) **Band 1** p.77

**Gutierrez, Steve**
Profile: p.719
Table(s): Colorado: Labor & Employment **Band 2** p.706

**Gutmacher, Norman**
Profile: p.2098
Table(s): Ohio: Real Estate **Band 3** p.2086

**Gutman, Olga**
Profile: p.328
Table(s): Nationwide: Investment Funds: Hedge Funds **Band 3** p.162

**Gutowski, Peter**
Profile: p.328
Table(s): Nationwide: Transportation: Shipping: Litigation (New York) **Band 1** p.261

**Gutter, Samuel**
Profile: p.867
Table(s): District of Columbia: Environment **Band 3** p.804

**Guttilla, Phillip P**
Table(s): Arizona: Corporate/M&A **Band 4** p.495

**Guy, Jonathan P**
Profile: p.867
Table(s): District of Columbia: Bankruptcy/Restructuring **Band 3** p.792

**Guy III, G Hopkins**
Profile: p.639
Table(s): California: Intellectual Property: Patent **Band 4** p.578

**Guynn, Randall**
Profile: p.328
Table(s): Nationwide: Financial Services Regulation: Banking (Compliance) **Band 1** p.96, Nationwide: Financial Services Regulation: Financial Institutions M&A **Band 1** p.96

**Gwynne, Kurt F**
Table(s): Delaware: Bankruptcy/Restructuring **Band 1** p.754

**Gyorke, Scott P**
Profile: p.1550
Table(s): Michigan: Banking & Finance **Band 3** p.1536

## H

**Haab, Eric**
Table(s): Illinois: Insurance: Dispute Resolution: Reinsurance **Band 2** p.1168

**Haag, Lee**
Table(s): Texas: Construction **Band 2** p.2335

**Haas, Buddy**
Profile: p.2393
Table(s): Texas: Banking & Finance **Band 4** p.2325

**Haas, Colleen**
Profile: p.2098
Table(s): Ohio: Real Estate **Band 4** p.2086

**Haas, Erik**
Profile: p.1900
Table(s): New York: Litigation: General Commercial **Band 4** p.1833

**Haas, Karl P**
Table(s): Indiana: Real Estate **Band 2** p.1275

**Haas, Michael**
Profile: p.2098
Table(s): Ohio: Real Estate **Band 4** p.2086

**Haas III, W Melvin**
Table(s): Georgia: Labor & Employment **Band 3** p.1060

**Habbart, Ellisa Opstbaum**
Table(s): Delaware: Corporate/M&A: Alternative Entities **Band 1** p.761

**Habel, Christopher S**
Profile: p.2098
Table(s): Ohio: Natural Resources & Environment **Band 3** p.2083

**Haber, Scott R**
Profile: p.639
Table(s): California: Corporate/M&A: Private Equity **Band 2** p.553

**Haberl, Heather**
Profile: p.867
Table(s): District of Columbia: Real Estate **Band 4** p.835

**Hachigian, Jay**
Table(s): Massachusetts: Private Equity: Venture Capital Investment **Band 2** p.1474

**Hack, Marion T**
Profile: p.639
Table(s): California: Construction **Band 4** p.550

**Hack, Randall A**
Profile: p.1210
Table(s): Illinois: Antitrust **Band 4** p.1143

**Hacker, Jonathan**
Table(s): Nationwide: Appellate Law **Band 4** p.26

**Hackett, Robert J**
Table(s): Arizona: Corporate/M&A **Band 3** p.495

**Hackman, Stephen**
Table(s): Indiana: Corporate/M&A **Band 1** p.1268

**Hackmann, Frank H**
Profile: p.1637
Table(s): Missouri: Environment **Band 2** p.1621

**Hackney, Hamilton H**
Profile: p.1494
Table(s): Massachusetts: Environment **Band 2** p.1457

**Haddad, Mark**
Profile: p.639
Table(s): California: Litigation: Appellate **Band 4** p.599

**Haddad, Mark**
Profile: p.1494
Table(s): Massachusetts: Corporate/M&A **Band 4** p.1452

**Haddon, Harold**
Table(s): Colorado: Litigation: White-Collar Crime & Government Investigations **Senior Statesmen**: p.710

**Haden Jr, William H**
Profile: p.1319
Table(s): Kentucky: Real Estate **Band 1** p.1314

**Hader, Cheryl**
Profile: p.328
Table(s): Nationwide: Wealth Management: Eastern Region **Band 4** p.267

**Hadjilogiou, Steven**
Profile: p.994
Table(s): Florida: Tax **Associates to watch** p.979

**Hadjis, Alexander J**
Profile: p.328
Table(s): Nationwide: International Trade: Intellectual Property (Section 337) **Band 3** p.160, District of Columbia: Intellectual Property: Litigation **Band 3** p.821

**Hadley, Joseph P**
Profile: p.328
Table(s): Nationwide: Projects **Band 4** p.216

**Hafen, Jonathan O**
Table(s): Utah: Litigation: General Commercial **Band 2** p.2468

**Hafer, Randall F**
Table(s): Georgia: Construction **Band 1** p.1044

**Hafets, Richard J**
Profile: p.1427
Table(s): Maryland: Labor & Employment **Band 1** p.1417

**Hafetz, Fred**
Table(s): New York: Litigation: White-Collar Crime & Government Investigations **Band 3** p.1836

**Haff, Jeffery S.**
Profile: p.328
Table(s): **Nationwide: Franchising: Mainly Franchisee Band 3** p.114

**Haffey, Dennis M**
Table(s): **Michigan: Litigation: General Commercial Band 2** p.1544

**Hafter, Jerome C**
Table(s): **Mississippi: Corporate/Commercial Band 2** p.1591

**Hagaman, David C**
Profile: p.1083
Table(s): **Georgia: Labor & Employment Band 4** p.1060

**Hage, Jamie N**
Table(s): **New Hampshire: Litigation: General Commercial Band 3** p.1690

**Hagen, Daniel C**
Profile: p.2099
Table(s): **Ohio: Employee Benefits & Executive Compensation Band 1** p.2067

**Hagen, Howard O**
Table(s): **Iowa: Corporate/M&A: Banking & Finance Star individuals** p.1283

**Hagen, Paul**
Profile: p.867
Table(s): **District of Columbia: Environment Band 2** p.804

**Hagen, Scott**
Table(s): **Utah: Labor & Employment Band 2** p.2467, **Utah: Labor & Employment: ERISA Band 1** p.2467

**Hager, Ashley Z**
Table(s): **Georgia: Labor & Employment Band 3** p.1060

**Hagerty, George**
Table(s): **Colorado: Corporate/M&A Band 2** p.703

**Hagerty, Timothy J**
Profile: p.1319
Table(s): **Kentucky: Environment, Natural Resources & Utilities: Environment Band 1** p.1307

**Haggart, Todd**
Table(s): **North Dakota: Litigation: General Commercial Band 1** p.2053

**Haggerty, John**
Profile: p.1494
Table(s): **Massachusetts: Corporate/M&A: Capital Markets Band 2** p.1453

**Hagle, Jennifer**
Profile: p.639
Table(s): **California: Bankruptcy/Restructuring Band 3** p.542

**Haglund, Benjamin E**
Profile: p.1737
Table(s): **New Jersey: Litigation: Products Liability Band 2** p.1723

**Haglund, Michael E**
Table(s): **Oregon: Litigation: General Commercial Band 2** p.2171

**Hagner, John D**
Table(s): **District of Columbia: Real Estate Band 1** p.835

**Hahn, Howard F**
Profile: p.1668
Table(s): **Nebraska: Healthcare Band 3** p.1661

**Hahn, James H**
Table(s): **Rhode Island: Corporate/Commercial Band 1** p.2251

**Hahn, Martin J**
Table(s): **Nationwide: Food & Beverages: Regulatory & Litigation Band 2** p.107

**Hahn, Richard**
Table(s): **Nationwide: Bankruptcy/Restructuring Band 4** p.39, **New York: Bankruptcy/Restructuring Band 3** p.1782

**Hahn, W Patton**
Profile: p.469
Table(s): **Alabama: Bankruptcy/Restructuring Up-and-coming individuals** p.457

**Haigh, Mark W**
Table(s): **South Dakota: Litigation: Medical Malpractice Defense Band 1** p.2284

**Haight, Catherine L**
Table(s): **California: Immigration Band 1** p.571

**Haile, Lisa A**
Profile: p.639
Table(s): **California: Intellectual Property: Patent Band 4** p.578, **California: Life Sciences: IP/Patent Litigation Band 2** p.590

**Hailey, Jay**
Profile: p.2393
Table(s): **Texas: Real Estate Band 2** p.2367

**Haimm, Neil K**
Profile: p.2218
Table(s): **Pennsylvania: Corporate/M&A & Private Equity Band 3** p.2191

**Haimo, Adam**
Profile: p.994
Table(s): **Florida: Construction Band 3** p.944

**Hainbach, Don H**
Table(s): **Nationwide: Transportation: Aviation: Regulatory Band 2** p.256

**Haines, Lisa**
Table(s): **Missouri: Real Estate Band 3** p.1633

**Haines, Sigrid**
Profile: p.1427
Table(s): **Maryland: Healthcare Band 2** p.1415

**Haines, Spencer**
Profile: p.2150
Table(s): **Oklahoma: Corporate/Commercial: Tax Up-and-coming individuals** p.2134

**Hainline III, Forrest A**
Profile: p.639
Table(s): **California: Litigation: General Commercial Band 4** p.593

**Hainline Jr, Theodore**
Table(s): **Florida: Real Estate: Zoning/Land Use Band 3** p.975

**Hainsfurther, A Michael**
Table(s): **Texas: Corporate/M&A Band 2** p.2337

**Haire, Dirk D**
Profile: p.867
Table(s): **District of Columbia: Construction Band 3** p.795

**Hajek, Douglas J**
Table(s): **South Dakota: Corporate/Commercial Band 1** p.2281

**Hakki, Adam S**
Table(s): **New York: Litigation: Securities Band 2** p.1834

**Halberstadter, David**
Table(s): **California: Media & Entertainment: Litigation Band 4** p.606

**Halbleib Jr, W Thomas**
Profile: p.1319
Table(s): **Kentucky: Corporate/M&A Band 2** p.1305

**Halbreich, David M**
Table(s): **Nationwide: Insurance: Dispute Resolution: Policyholder Band 2** p.137, **California: Insurance: Policyholder Band 2** p.576

**Hale, Robert**
Profile: p.1494
Table(s): **Massachusetts: Labor & Employment Band 1** p.1466

**Hale, Russell**
Table(s): **Florida: Banking & Finance: Regulatory Band 3** p.937, **Florida: Tax Band 3** p.979, **Florida: Tax: State & Local Band 2** p.979

**Hale, Stephen E W**
Table(s): **Utah: Litigation: General Commercial Band 2** p.2468

**Hale Jr, Ben W**
Table(s): **Ohio: Real Estate: Zoning/Land Use Band 2** p.2086

**Hale-Eagland, Jennifer**
Profile: p.2218
Table(s): **Pennsylvania: Labor & Employment Up-and-coming individuals** p.2200

**Hales Jr, H Edward**
Table(s): **Georgia: Real Estate Band 3** p.1070

**Halevy, Amy Karff**
Profile: p.2393
Table(s): **Texas: Labor & Employment Band 3** p.2359

**Haley, George M**
Profile: p.2473
Table(s): **Utah: Litigation: General Commercial Band 1** p.2468

**Haley, Nedom A**
Profile: p.1083
Table(s): **Georgia: Tax Band 3** p.1072

**Haley, Victor P**
Table(s): **Georgia: Real Estate Band 2** p.1070

**Haley III, Raymond**
Profile: p.1319
Table(s): **Kentucky: Labor & Employment Band 2** p.1310

**Haley Jr, James F**
Table(s): **New York: Intellectual Property: Patent Band 3** p.1820

**Halford, James L**
Table(s): **Mississippi: Energy & Natural Resources Band 2** p.1593

**Hall, Alan**
Profile: p.1773
Table(s): **New Mexico: Corporate/Commercial Band 2** p.1764

**Hall, Bruce**
Profile: p.1773
Table(s): **New Mexico: Litigation: General Commercial Senior Statesmen:** p.1769

**Hall, Charles**
Profile: p.328
Table(s): **Nationwide: Tax: Controversy Senior Statesmen:** p.244, **Texas: Tax: Litigation Senior Statesmen:** p.2371

**Hall, Christopher R**
Profile: p.2218
Table(s): **Pennsylvania: Litigation: White-Collar Crime & Government Investigations Band 2** p.2204

**Hall, Donald R**
Table(s): **Florida: Real Estate: Zoning/Land Use Band 2** p.975

**Hall, Eric B.**
Profile: p.2393
Table(s): **Texas: Intellectual Property Band 4** p.2354

**Hall, Greg R**
Profile: p.508
Table(s): **Arizona: Corporate/M&A Band 2** p.495

**Hall, Henderson**
Table(s): **Mississippi: Energy & Natural Resources Band 3** p.1593

**Hall, Joseph A**
Profile: p.329
Table(s): **Nationwide: Capital Markets: Debt & Equity Band 4** p.46

**Hall, Lawrence A**
Profile: p.2393
Table(s): **Texas: Corporate/M&A Band 4** p.2337

**Hall, Lee Murray**
Table(s): **West Virginia: Litigation: General Commercial Band 3** p.2555

**Hall, Mark**
Table(s): **Vermont: Real Estate: Zoning/Land Use Band 2** p.2487

**Hall, Martin**
Table(s): **Nationwide: Wealth Management: Eastern Region Band 4** p.267

**Hall, Michael L**
Table(s): **Alabama: Bankruptcy/Restructuring Band 1** p.457

**Hall, Richard**
Profile: p.1900
Table(s): **New York: Corporate/M&A Band 1** p.1793

**Hall, Richard E**
Table(s): **Idaho: Litigation: General Commercial Senior Statesmen:** p.1134

**Hall, Richard R**
Table(s): **Idaho: Natural Resources & Environment Up-and-coming individuals** p.1136

**Hall, Scott**
Table(s): **New Mexico: Environment, Natural Resources & Regulated Industries Band 2** p.1766

**Hall, Stephen C**
Profile: p.1319
Table(s): Kentucky: Intellectual Property **Band 2**
p.1308

**Hall, Thomas Jay**
Profile: p.1737
Table(s): New Jersey: Real Estate: Zoning/Land
Use **Senior Statesmen:** p.1728

**Hall III, J Clifton**
Table(s): Texas: Insurance **Band 2** p.2351

**Hall Jr, Cary H**
Profile: p.2269
Table(s): South Carolina: Corporate/M&A **Band 2**
p.2260

**Hall Jr, Warren R**
Profile: p.1083
Table(s): Georgia: Labor & Employment **Band 4**
p.1060

**Haller, Anthony**
Profile: p.2218
Table(s): Pennsylvania: Labor & Employment
**Band 1** p.2200

**Haller, Diane**
Profile: p.508
Table(s): Arizona: Real Estate **Band 1** p.504

**Halligan, R Mark**
Profile: p.1211
Table(s): Illinois: Intellectual Property **Band 4**
p.1171

**Halling, Gary L**
Table(s): California: Antitrust **Band 3** p.536

**Hallock, Leslie C**
Table(s): Maine: Labor & Employment: Employee
Benefits & Compensation **Band 3** p.1390

**Hallos, Jeffrey L**
Profile: p.1319
Table(s): Kentucky: Corporate/M&A **Band 2**
p.1305

**Halloway, Lorraine B**
Profile: p.329
Table(s): Nationwide: Transportation: Aviation:
Regulatory **Band 1** p.256

**Halls, Peter C**
Table(s): Minnesota: Construction **Band 2** p.1567

**Hallward-Driemeier, Douglas**
Table(s): Nationwide: Appellate Law **Band 4** p.26

**Halper, Jason M**
Profile: p.1900
Table(s): New York: Litigation: Securities **Band 4**
p.1834

**Halperin, Alan D**
Table(s): New York: Bankruptcy/Restructuring
**Band 4** p.1782

**Halperin, Alan S**
Profile: p.329
Table(s): Nationwide: Wealth Management:
Eastern Region **Band 1** p.267

**Halpern, Marcelo**
Table(s): Illinois: Technology & Outsourcing **Band
2** p.1194

**Halpert, James J**
Profile: p.329
Table(s): Nationwide: Privacy & Data Security
**Band 2** p.199

**Halsey, Douglas**
Profile: p.994
Table(s): Florida: Environment **Band 1** p.951

**Halsey, Susan A**
Profile: p.2393
Table(s): Texas: Real Estate **Band 3** p.2367

**Halula, John F**
Profile: p.994
Table(s): Florida: Real Estate **Band 1** p.974

**Hamann, Lee**
Table(s): Nebraska: Real Estate **Band 1** p.1666

**Hamborg, Kelly D**
Table(s): Iowa: Real Estate **Band 4** p.1290

**Hamburger, Paul M**
Table(s): Nationwide: Employee Benefits &
Executive Compensation **Band 2** p.73, District of
Columbia: Employee Benefits & Executive
Compensation **Band 1** p.801

**Hamel, Douglas**
Profile: p.2393
Table(s): Texas: Labor & Employment **Band 2**
p.2359

**Hamel, Mark**
Table(s): Minnesota: Real Estate **Star individuals**
p.1576

**Hament, Andrew**
Profile: p.994
Table(s): Florida: Labor & Employment **Band 2**
p.959

**Hamermesh, Matthew A**
Profile: p.2218
Table(s): Pennsylvania:
Bankruptcy/Restructuring **Band 4** p.2188

**Hamersmith, Harold**
Table(s): California: Construction **Band 4** p.550

**Hamid, Jyotin**
Table(s): New York: Labor & Employment **Up-and-
coming individuals** p.1826

**Hamilton, Jeffrey A**
Table(s): Kentucky: Real Estate **Band 2** p.1314

**Hamilton, John W**
Profile: p.1277
Table(s): Indiana: Real Estate **Band 3** p.1275

**Hamilton, Joseph L**
Profile: p.1319
Table(s): Kentucky: Litigation: Tort & Insurance
Defense **Band 1** p.1312

**Hamilton, Kevin J.**
Table(s): Washington: Labor & Employment **Band
3** p.2531

**Hamilton, Larry**
Table(s): Illinois: Insurance: Transactional &
Regulatory **Band 3** p.1168

**Hamilton, Lawrence**
Profile: p.329
Table(s): Nationwide: Transportation: Road
(Carriage/Commercial) **Band 3** p.259

**Hamilton, Michael D**
Profile: p.640
Table(s): California: Real Estate **Up-and-coming indi-
viduals** p.611

**Hamilton, P Andrew**
Table(s): Maine: Environment **Band 2** p.1389

**Hamilton, Shannon Antle**
Profile: p.1320
Table(s): Kentucky: Labor & Employment **Band 3**
p.1310

**Hamilton, Trudie**
Table(s): Connecticut: Litigation: General
Commercial **Band 3** p.738

**Hamlin, Harold W**
Table(s): Arkansas: Real Estate **Band 1** p.524

**Hamme, Joel**
Table(s): District of Columbia: Healthcare **Band 2**
p.809

**Hammell, Joseph W**
Table(s): Minnesota: Labor & Employment **Band 2**
p.1571

**Hammer, Aaron**
Profile: p.1211
Table(s): Illinois: Bankruptcy/Restructuring **Band
4** p.1148

**Hammer, Alan R**
Table(s): New Jersey: Real Estate **Band 1** p.1728

**Hammer, Michael H**
Profile: p.867
Table(s): District of Columbia: Telecom,
Broadcast & Satellite **Band 3** p.844

**Hammer, Stuart**
Table(s): New York: Environment: Mainly
Transactional **Band 2** p.1808

**Hammes, Jeffrey C**
Profile: p.1211
Table(s): Nationwide: Private Equity: Buyouts
**Band 2** p.203, Illinois: Corporate/M&A: Private
Equity **Senior Statesmen:** p.1157

**Hammes, Patricia**
Table(s): Nationwide: Projects **Band 3** p.216

**Hammond, Craig**
Profile: p.1550
Table(s): Michigan: Banking & Finance **Band 3**
p.1536

**Hammond, Denise**
Profile: p.868
Table(s): Nationwide: Immigration **Band 3** p.131,
District of Columbia: Immigration **Band 1** p.814

**Hammond, Edward**
Profile: p.1550
Table(s): Michigan: Employee Benefits &
Executive Compensation **Band 3** p.1540

**Hammond, Herbert J**
Profile: p.2393
Table(s): Texas: Intellectual Property **Band 3**
p.2354

**Hammond, Larry A**
Profile: p.508
Table(s): Arizona: Litigation: White-Collar Crime
& Government Investigations **Band 1** p.501

**Hammond, Steven A**
Profile: p.329
Table(s): Nationwide: International Arbitration
**Band 3** p.145

**Hamner, Herschel**
Table(s): Texas: Banking & Finance **Up-and-coming
individuals** p.2325

**Hampton, Jeffrey C**
Table(s): Pennsylvania:
Bankruptcy/Restructuring **Band 3** p.2188

**Hampton, Joe M**
Table(s): Oklahoma: Litigation: General
Commercial **Band 2** p.2141

**Hancock, Nancy**
Profile: p.744
Table(s): Connecticut: Corporate/M&A **Band 2**
p.732

**Hancock, Nicole C**
Table(s): Idaho: Litigation: General Commercial
**Up-and-coming individuals** p.1134

**Hancock, William K**
Profile: p.469
Table(s): Alabama: Labor & Employment **Band 3**
p.460

**Hancock Jr, John P**
Table(s): Michigan: Labor & Employment **Band 2**
p.1542

**Hand, Lloyd**
Profile: p.329
Table(s): Nationwide: Government: Government
Relations **Senior Statesmen:** p.121

**Hand, Jr., Albert M.**
Profile: p.1362
Table(s): Louisiana: Environment: Litigation **Band
3** p.1346

**Handlan, Allen**
Table(s): Ohio: Banking & Finance **Band 2** p.2056,
Ohio: Real Estate **Band 3** p.2086

**Handler, David A**
Profile: p.329
Table(s): Nationwide: Wealth Management:
Central Region **Band 1** p.266

**Handlos, Bryan G**
Profile: p.1668
Table(s): Nebraska: Corporate/Commercial **Band
3** p.1659

**Handman, Laura R**
Table(s): Nationwide: First Amendment
Litigation **Band 1** p.105, District of Columbia:
Media & Entertainment **Band 1** p.832

**Handrinos, Peter N**
Table(s): Massachusetts: Corporate/M&A:
Capital Markets **Band 2** p.1453

**Handwerker, Jeffrey L**
Profile: p.868
Table(s): District of Columbia: Healthcare:
Pharmaceutical/Medical Products Regulatory
**Band 3** p.810

**Handzel, Henry**
Table(s): Wisconsin: Natural Resources &
Environment **Band 2** p.2578

**Handzlik, Jan Lawrence**
Profile: p.640
Table(s): California: Litigation: White-Collar
Crime & Government Investigations **Band 2** p.601

**Hane, John**
Table(s): District of Columbia: Telecom,
Broadcast & Satellite **Band 4** p.844

**Hanessian, Grant**
Profile: p.329
Table(s): Nationwide: International Arbitration
**Band 3** p.145

**Hanewicz, Christopher G**
Table(s): Wisconsin: Intellectual Property **Band 3**
p.2573

**Haney, Dennis R**
Profile: p.1681
Table(s): Nevada: Litigation: Construction **Senior
Statesmen:** p.1676

**Hangley, William T**
Profile: p.2218
Table(s): Pennsylvania: Litigation: General
Commercial **Band 1** p.2203

**Hanify, John D**
Profile: p.1494
Table(s): Massachusetts: Litigation: General
Commercial **Band 1** p.1470

**Hanisch, Douglas L**
Profile: p.1299
Table(s): Kansas: Labor & Employment **Band 2**
p.1294

**Hankins, Richard B**
Profile: p.1083
Table(s): Georgia: Labor & Employment **Band 2**
p.1060

**Hankins, Stuart**
Table(s): Arkansas: Real Estate **Band 3** p.524

**Hankinson, Deborah G**
Profile: p.2393
Table(s): Texas: Litigation: Appellate **Band 2**
p.2361

**Hanks, Gregg**
Table(s): Arizona: Real Estate **Band 1** p.504

**Hanks, James**
Table(s): Iowa: Labor & Employment **Band 2**
p.1285

**Hanks, Jr, James J**
Profile: p.329
Table(s): Nationwide: Capital Markets: REITs
**Band 1** p.55, Maryland: Corporate/M&A **Band 1**
p.1412

**Hanley, Elizabeth A**
Profile: p.1494
Table(s): Massachusetts: Intellectual Property
**Band 2** p.1463

**Hanley, Mark A**
Table(s): Florida: Labor & Employment **Band 2**
p.959

**Hanlon, Michael J**
Profile: p.2218
Table(s): Pennsylvania: Labor & Employment
**Band 3** p.2200

**Hanlon-Leh, Natalie**
Table(s): Colorado: Intellectual Property **Band 1**
p.704

**Hanna, Nicola T**
Profile: p.640
Table(s): California: Litigation: White-Collar
Crime & Government Investigations **Band 3** p.601

**Hanna III, George V**
Table(s): North Carolina: Litigation: General
Commercial **Senior Statesmen:** p.2033

**Hannon, Bob**
Table(s): Tennessee: Banking & Finance **Up-and-
coming individuals** p.2287

**Hannum III, William E**
Profile: p.1494
Table(s): Massachusetts: Labor & Employment
**Band 4** p.1466

**Hanover, John D**
Profile: p.640
Table(s): California: Construction **Band 2** p.550

**Hanrahan, Marc P**
Profile: p.330
Table(s): Nationwide: Banking & Finance **Band 1**
p.31

**Hanrahan, Michael**
Table(s): Delaware: Chancery **Band 2** p.758

**Hansberry, Charles**
Profile: p.1654
Table(s): Montana: Labor & Employment **Band 3**
p.1648

**Hanschen, Peter**
Profile: p.640
Table(s): California: Energy: State Regulatory &
Litigation **Band 2** p.562

**Hansel, Greg**
Profile: p.1400
Table(s): Maine: Litigation: General Commercial
**Band 3** p.1393

**Hansell, Edgar**
Table(s): Iowa: Corporate/M&A **Senior Statesmen:**
p.1283

**Hanselman, Suzanne K**
Profile: p.2099
Table(s): Ohio: Corporate/M&A **Band 2** p.2064

**Hansen, Brian**
Profile: p.1139
Table(s): Idaho: Corporate/Commercial **Band 2**
p.1132

**Hansen, Christian W**
Profile: p.330
Table(s): Nationwide: Transportation: Aviation:
Finance **Band 3** p.252, Florida: Latin American
Investment **Band 4** p.963

**Hansen, David**
Profile: p.640
Table(s): California: Intellectual Property: Patent
**Band 4** p.578

**Hansen, Edward J**
Profile: p.1900
Table(s): Nationwide: Outsourcing **Band 2** p.195,
New York: Technology & Outsourcing **Band 1**
p.1868

**Hansen, Gregory**
Profile: p.1123
Table(s): Hawaii: Labor & Employment:
Employee Benefits & Compensation **Band 2**
p.1117

**Hansen, Kenneth W**
Profile: p.330
Table(s): Nationwide: Projects **Band 3** p.216

**Hansen, Kristopher M**
Table(s): Nationwide: Bankruptcy/Restructuring
**Band 3** p.39, New York:
Bankruptcy/Restructuring **Band 2** p.1782

**Hansen, Max A**
Table(s): Montana: Real Estate **Band 2** p.1652

**Hansen, Russell C**
Profile: p.640
Table(s): California: Corporate/M&A **Band 2** p.553

**Hansen, Scott W.**
Profile: p.2583
Table(s): Wisconsin: Litigation: General
Commercial **Band 1** p.2576

**Hansen, Stephanie L**
Table(s): Delaware: Real Estate: Zoning/Land
Use **Up-and-coming individuals** p.766

**Hansen, Thomas**
Table(s): California: Media & Entertainment:
Transactional: Mainly Talent **Band 1** p.609

**Hansen, William**
Table(s): New York: Intellectual Property: Trade
Mark & Copyright **Band 3** p.1821

**Hanson, David G**
Profile: p.2583
Table(s): Wisconsin: Intellectual Property **Band 1**
p.2573, Wisconsin: Intellectual Property:
Litigation p.2573

**Hanson, John N**
Profile: p.868
Table(s): District of Columbia: Environment **Band
4** p.804

**Hanson, Mark E**
Table(s): Virginia: Construction **Band 3** p.2491

**Hanson, Mark R**
Table(s): North Dakota: Litigation: General
Commercial **Band 1** p.2053

**Hanson, Mark V**
Table(s): Iowa: Real Estate **Band 2** p.1290

**Hanson, Randall S**
Table(s): North Dakota: Litigation: Medical
Malpractice Defense **Band 2** p.2053

**Hanson, Samuel**
Profile: p.1579
Table(s): Minnesota: Litigation: Appellate **Senior
Statesmen:** p.1573

**Hanson, Sandra**
Table(s): South Dakota: Labor & Employment
**Band 2** p.2283

**Hanson, Thomas D**
Table(s): Iowa: Litigation: General Commercial
**Band 4** p.1288

**Hanson, Tom S**
Table(s): Maine: Real Estate **Band 2** p.1395

**Hanson, Vivian L**
Profile: p.330
Table(s): Nationwide: Outsourcing **Band 2** p.195,
New York: Technology & Outsourcing **Band 2**
p.1868

**Hanson, William H**
Table(s): Maine: Real Estate:
Timberland/Conservation **Band 1** p.1396

**Harakas, Andrew**
Table(s): Nationwide: Transportation: Aviation:
Litigation **Band 1** p.254

**Haraldson, Comet**
Table(s): South Dakota: Labor & Employment:
Workers' Compensation **Band 1** p.2283

**Harbison, William L**
Table(s): Tennessee: Litigation: General
Commercial **Band 1** p.2295

**Harbourt, Maureen N**
Profile: p.1362
Table(s): Louisiana: Environment **Band 1** p.1346

**Harburg, Stephen J**
Profile: p.330
Table(s): Nationwide: Product Liability & Mass
Torts **Band 5** p.208

**Harckham, Finley**
Profile: p.1901
Table(s): New York: Insurance: Dispute
Resolution: Policyholder **Band 3** p.1816

**Hardcastle, Jay**
Table(s): Tennessee: Healthcare **Band 2** p.2291,
Tennessee: Healthcare: Regulatory **Band 1**
p.2291

**Harder, Patrick D**
Table(s): Nationwide: Projects: PPP **Band 2** p.217

**Hardesty, Stephen**
Table(s): Idaho: Corporate/Commercial **Band 1**
p.1132

**Hardin, Charles**
Profile: p.2099
Table(s): Ohio: Corporate/M&A **Band 2** p.2064

**Hardin, Edward J**
Profile: p.1083
Table(s): Georgia: Corporate/M&A **Band 1** p.1046

**Hardin, Elizabeth**
Profile: p.330
Table(s): Nationwide: Capital Markets:
Securitisation **Band 4** p.59

**Hardin, Pauline**
Profile: p.1363
Table(s): Louisiana: Litigation: White-Collar
Crime & Government Investigations **Band 1**
p.1352

**Hardin, Steven D**
Table(s): Indiana: Real Estate **Band 3** p.1275

**Hardin, William M**
Profile: p.508
Table(s): Arizona: Corporate/M&A **Band 1** p.495

**Hardin III, Harry S**
Profile: p.1363
Table(s): Louisiana: Litigation: General
Commercial **Band 2** p.1352

**Hardin, Jr, A Edward**
Profile: p.1363
Table(s): **Louisiana**: Labor & Employment **Band 3** p.1350

**Harding, Major B**
Table(s): **Florida**: Litigation: Appellate **Senior Statesmen**: p.972

**Harding, William A**
Table(s): **Nebraska**: Labor & Employment **Band 2** p.1662

**Hardwick, James C T**
Profile: p.2150
Table(s): **Oklahoma**: Energy & Natural Resources **Band 1** p.2136

**Hardy, Elizabeth P**
Profile: p.1550
Table(s): **Michigan**: Labor & Employment **Band 1** p.1542

**Hardy, Kelly Tubman**
Profile: p.1427
Table(s): **Maryland**: Corporate/M&A **Up-and-coming individuals** p.1412

**Hardy, Michael L**
Profile: p.2099
Table(s): **Ohio**: Natural Resources & Environment **Senior Statesmen**: p.2083

**Hardy, Sharon C**
Table(s): **Kentucky**: Real Estate **Band 3** p.1314

**Hardy, Timothy**
Table(s): **Louisiana**: Environment **Band 2** p.1346

**Hare, Gregory J**
Profile: p.1084
Table(s): **Georgia**: Labor & Employment **Band 4** p.1060

**Harens, John**
Table(s): **Minnesota**: Construction **Band 2** p.1567

**Hargens, William F**
Table(s): **Nebraska**: Litigation: General Commercial **Band 2** p.1664

**Hargrove, John**
Table(s): **Alabama**: Labor & Employment **Band 3** p.460

**Haridi, Samaa**
Profile: p.330
Table(s): **Nationwide**: International Arbitration **Band 5** p.145

**Hariton, David P**
Profile: p.1901
Table(s): **New York**: Tax **Band 1** p.1862

**Harkavy, Ronald**
Table(s): **Tennessee**: Real Estate **Band 2** p.2299, **Tennessee**: Real Estate: Zoning/Land Use **Band 1** p.2299

**Harkins, Aaron J**
Table(s): **Nationwide**: Native American Law **Up-and-coming individuals** p.192

**Harkins, Deborah**
Profile: p.1363
Table(s): **Louisiana**: Gaming & Licensing **Band 2** p.1348

**Harkins Jr, John G**
Profile: p.2218
Table(s): **Pennsylvania**: Litigation: General Commercial **Senior Statesmen**: p.2203

**Harkrider, John D**
Profile: p.1901
Table(s): **New York**: Antitrust **Band 2** p.1778

**Harless, Warren David**
Table(s): **Virginia**: Litigation: General Commercial **Band 3** p.2502

**Harlev, Shayla K.**
Profile: p.1495
Table(s): **Massachusetts**: Corporate/M&A **Up-and-coming individuals** p.1452

**Harman, Paul M**
Table(s): **Utah**: Real Estate **Band 3** p.2470

**Harman, Thomas**
Profile: p.330
Table(s): **Nationwide**: Investment Funds: Registered Funds **Band 2** p.170

**Harmon, Christopher B**
Profile: p.469
Table(s): **Alabama**: Corporate/Commercial **Band 2** p.459

**Harmon, Jason C**
Profile: p.1427
Table(s): **Maryland**: Corporate/M&A **Band 3** p.1412

**Harmon, Jonathan P**
Table(s): **Virginia**: Labor & Employment **Band 3** p.2500

**Harms, David B**
Profile: p.330
Table(s): **Nationwide**: Capital Markets: Debt & Equity **Band 1** p.46

**Harnden, Edwin**
Profile: p.2176
Table(s): **Oregon**: Labor & Employment **Band 1** p.2168

**Harnden, Ronald H**
Profile: p.1299
Table(s): **Kansas**: Real Estate **Band 1** p.1297

**Harner, Paul E**
Profile: p.1901
Table(s): **New York**: Bankruptcy/Restructuring **Band 4** p.1782

**Harold, Edward F**
Profile: p.1363
Table(s): **Louisiana**: Labor & Employment **Band 3** p.1350

**Harper, A John**
Profile: p.2393
Table(s): **Texas**: Labor & Employment **Senior Statesmen**: p.2359

**Harper, George R**
Table(s): **Florida**: Latin American Investment **Band 2** p.963

**Harper, Keith**
Table(s): **Nationwide**: Native American Law **Band 2** p.192

**Harper, Marty**
Table(s): **Arizona**: Litigation: General Commercial **Band 3** p.501

**Harper, Sue Erwin**
Profile: p.2269
Table(s): **South Carolina**: Labor & Employment **Band 3** p.2262

**Harrell, J Hayden**
Table(s): **North Carolina**: Real Estate: Finance **Band 1** p.2037

**Harrell, Michael P**
Table(s): **Nationwide**: Investment Funds: Private Equity: Fund Formation **Band 1** p.166

**Harrie, William**
Table(s): **North Dakota**: Litigation: General Commercial **Band 3** p.2053

**Harrigan, Kenneth**
Table(s): **New Mexico**: Litigation: General Commercial **Senior Statesmen**: p.1769

**Harrigan Jr, Arthur W**
Table(s): **Washington**: Litigation: General Commercial **Band 1** p.2533

**Harrington, Arthur**
Table(s): **Wisconsin**: Natural Resources & Environment **Band 1** p.2578

**Harrington, Carol A**
Profile: p.330
Table(s): **Nationwide**: Wealth Management: Central Region **Band 1** p.266

**Harrington, John P**
Profile: p.2474
Table(s): **Utah**: Litigation: General Commercial **Band 3** p.2468

**Harrington, Michael S**
Profile: p.2219
Table(s): **Pennsylvania**: Corporate/M&A & Private Equity **Band 3** p.2191

**Harrington, Susan D**
Profile: p.330
Table(s): **Nationwide**: Wealth Management: Eastern Region **Band 3** p.267

**Harris, Adam C**
Profile: p.1901
Table(s): **Nationwide**: Bankruptcy/Restructuring **Band 3** p.39, **New York**: Bankruptcy/Restructuring **Band 2** p.1782

**Harris, Alan**
Table(s): **California**: Construction **Senior Statesmen**: p.550, **California**: Construction: Mediators **Senior Statesmen**: p.550

**Harris, Amy**
Profile: p.994
Table(s): **Florida**: Bankruptcy/Restructuring **Up-and-coming individuals** p.939

**Harris, Arlene**
Profile: p.330
Table(s): **Nationwide**: Wealth Management: Eastern Region **Band 3** p.267

**Harris, Brett**
Table(s): **New Jersey**: Corporate/M&A **Band 3** p.1707

**Harris, Brian M.**
Table(s): **Georgia**: Labor & Employment **Up-and-coming individuals** p.1060

**Harris, David**
Table(s): **Missouri**: Litigation: General Commercial **Band 2** p.1629

**Harris, David L**
Profile: p.1737
Table(s): **New Jersey**: Litigation: General Commercial **Band 2** p.1722

**Harris, Glenn A**
Profile: p.1737
Table(s): **New Jersey**: Environment **Band 1** p.1711

**Harris, Gregg**
Profile: p.331
Table(s): **Nationwide**: Projects **Band 2** p.216

**Harris, Ivan P**
Table(s): **Florida**: Litigation: White-Collar Crime & Government Investigations **Band 3** p.967

**Harris, James B**
Profile: p.2394
Table(s): **Texas**: Environment **Band 2** p.2343

**Harris, Jeffery D**
Table(s): **California**: Energy: State Regulatory & Litigation **Band 2** p.562

**Harris, Kari K.**
Profile: p.1495
Table(s): **Massachusetts**: Private Equity: Fund Formation **Up-and-coming individuals** p.1476

**Harris, Kenneth L**
Profile: p.1211
Table(s): **Illinois**: Tax **Band 3** p.1192

**Harris, Larry D**
Profile: p.868
Table(s): **District of Columbia**: Construction **Band 1** p.795

**Harris, Linda C**
Profile: p.1211
Table(s): **Illinois**: Corporate/M&A **Band 3** p.1156

**Harris, Marc S**
Table(s): **California**: Litigation: White-Collar Crime & Government Investigations **Band 2** p.601

**Harris, Marcia**
Profile: p.640
Table(s): **California**: Media & Entertainment: Litigation **Band 4** p.606

**Harris, Mark A**
Profile: p.1211
Table(s): **Illinois**: Corporate/M&A: Private Equity **Band 2** p.1157

**Harris, Martha**
Profile: p.2394
Table(s): **Texas**: Real Estate **Band 3** p.2367

**Harris, Matthew T**
Profile: p.2305
Table(s): **Tennessee**: Real Estate **Band 2** p.2299

**Harris, Morton A**
Table(s): **Georgia**: Tax **Band 2** p.1072

**Harris, Patricia A**
Profile: p.1427
Table(s): **Maryland**: Real Estate: Land Use **Band 3** p.1422

**Harris, Philip H**
Profile: p.331
Table(s): **Nationwide**: Investment Funds: Hedge Funds **Band 1** p.162

**Hastie, John D**
Table(s): Oklahoma: Real Estate **Senior Statesmen**:
p.2145

**Hastings, Craig R**
Table(s): Iowa: Real Estate **Band 3** p.1290

**Hastings, Douglas A**
Profile: p.331
Table(s): Nationwide: Healthcare: Transactional
**Band 1** p.128, District of Columbia: Healthcare
**Band 1** p.809

**Hastings, Kerry P**
Profile: p.2099
Table(s): Ohio: Labor & Employment **Band 4**
p.2074

**Hastings, Susan C**
Profile: p.2099
Table(s): Ohio: Labor & Employment **Band 2**
p.2074

**Haston, Tripp**
Table(s): Alabama: Litigation: General
Commercial **Band 3** p.463

**Hasty, Robert**
Profile: p.868
Table(s): District of Columbia: Technology &
Outsourcing **Band 3** p.842

**Hataway, C Scott**
Table(s): District of Columbia: Antitrust **Up-and-
coming individuals** p.787

**Hatch, M Sean**
Profile: p.527
Table(s): Arkansas: Corporate/Commercial **Band
2** p.518

**Hatch, Michael W**
Table(s): Wisconsin: Real Estate **Band 1** p.2579

**Hatchell, Mike A**
Profile: p.2394
Table(s): Nationwide: Appellate Law **Band 3** p.26,
Texas: Litigation: Appellate **Band 1** p.2361

**Hatcher, Julia**
Profile: p.868
Table(s): District of Columbia: Environment **Band
5** p.804

**Hatcher, Merrick**
Profile: p.1211
Table(s): Illinois: Corporate/M&A **Band 4** p.1156

**Hatchett, David**
Table(s): Indiana: Environment **Band 1** p.1270

**Hatfield, C Kent**
Profile: p.1320
Table(s): Kentucky: Environment, Natural
Resources & Utilities: Utilities **Band 2** p.1307

**Hatfield, William S**
Profile: p.1737
Table(s): New Jersey: Environment **Band 2** p.1711

**Hathaway, Gregory S**
Table(s): Oregon: Real Estate: Zoning/Land Use
**Band 1** p.2173

**Hathaway, Thomas M J**
Table(s): Michigan: Labor & Employment **Band 2**
p.1542

**Hathaway III, James E**
Profile: p.527
Table(s): Arkansas: Corporate/Commercial:
Municipal Bonds **Band 2** p.518

**Hathorn, Meredith L**
Table(s): Louisiana: Banking & Finance: Public
Finance **Band 1** p.1335

**Hattaway, Ashley**
Table(s): Alabama: Labor & Employment **Up-and-
coming individuals** p.460

**Hatten, Eric**
Table(s): Mississippi: Litigation: General
Commercial **Band 4** p.1597

**Hattenbach, Benjamin**
Profile: p.640
Table(s): California: Intellectual Property: Patent
**Band 4** p.578

**Hattersley III, Thomas E**
Table(s): Montana: Labor & Employment **Band 1**
p.1648

**Hauber, Catherine**
Table(s): Missouri: Real Estate **Band 3** p.1633

**Hauberg, Kyle R**
Table(s): Michigan: Real Estate **Band 3** p.1546

**Haubert, William J**
Profile: p.771
Table(s): Delaware: Corporate/M&A **Band 2** p.761

**Hauck, Terry**
Table(s): Oregon: Real Estate **Band 1** p.2173

**Hauer, Richard**
Profile: p.2099
Table(s): Ohio: Employee Benefits & Executive
Compensation **Band 3** p.2067

**Haueter, Eric S**
Profile: p.640
Table(s): Nationwide: Capital Markets: Debt &
Equity **Band 4** p.46, California: Capital Markets:
Debt & Equity **Band 2** p.547

**Haughey, Stephen N**
Profile: p.2099
Table(s): Ohio: Natural Resources &
Environment **Band 2** p.2083

**Hauser, James**
Table(s): Massachusetts: Employee Benefits &
Executive Compensation **Band 2** p.1455

**Hauser, Mark R**
Table(s): Michigan: Real Estate **Band 3** p.1546

**Hauser III, Wade**
Table(s): Iowa: Litigation: General Commercial
**Band 2** p.1288

**Havel, Richard W**
Profile: p.641
Table(s): California: Bankruptcy/Restructuring
**Band 2** p.542

**Havens, Jolie**
Profile: p.2099
Table(s): Ohio: Healthcare **Up-and-coming individuals**
p.2069

**Havlick, Scott**
Profile: p.719
Table(s): Colorado: Intellectual Property **Band 3**
p.704

**Hawk, Sarah J**
Profile: p.1084
Table(s): Georgia: Immigration **Band 3** p.1055

**Hawke Jr, John D**
Profile: p.332
Table(s): Nationwide: Financial Services
Regulation: Banking (Enforcement &
Investigations) **Senior Statesmen**: p.97

**Hawkins, Ann A**
Profile: p.332
Table(s): Nationwide: Energy: Electricity
(Transactional) **Band 4** p.77

**Hawkins, Barry**
Table(s): Connecticut: Real Estate **Band 1** p.740

**Hawkins, Brent**
Profile: p.1211
Table(s): Illinois: Intellectual Property **Up-and-com-
ing individuals** p.1171

**Hawkins, Holmes**
Profile: p.1084
Table(s): Georgia: Intellectual Property **Band 1**
p.1056

**Hawkins, Howard**
Profile: p.1902
Table(s): New York: Litigation: Securities **Band 4**
p.1834

**Hawkins, Michael**
Table(s): Ohio: Labor & Employment **Band 2**
p.2074

**Hawks, Christopher H**
Table(s): Wyoming: Real Estate **Band 2** p.2600

**Hawks-Ladds, Joshua A**
Profile: p.744
Table(s): Connecticut: Labor & Employment **Band
3** p.736

**Hawley, Thomas**
Table(s): Nationwide: Transportation: Shipping:
Finance (New York) **Band 2** p.260

**Haworth, Gregory R**
Table(s): New Jersey: Litigation: General
Commercial **Band 3** p.1722

**Hay, Jeff**
Table(s): North Carolina: Corporate/M&A **Band 4**
p.2025

**Haycraft, Donald**
Table(s): Louisiana: Litigation: General
Commercial **Band 3** p.1352

**Hayden, Donald J**
Table(s): Florida: Litigation: General Commercial
**Band 3** p.966

**Hayden, Jan M**
Profile: p.1363
Table(s): Louisiana: Bankruptcy/Restructuring
**Band 2** p.1337

**Hayden, Joseph**
Table(s): New Jersey: Litigation: White-Collar
Crime & Government Investigations **Band 1**
p.1723

**Hayden, Raymond P**
Table(s): Nationwide: Transportation: Shipping:
Litigation (New York) **Band 1** p.261

**Hayes, David L**
Profile: p.641
Table(s): California: Intellectual Property:
Trademark, Copyright & Trade Secrets **Band 1**
p.578, California: IT & Outsourcing **Band 1** p.583

**Hayes, J Kevin**
Profile: p.2150
Table(s): Oklahoma: Energy & Natural
Resources **Band 2** p.2136

**Hayes, Jeffrey**
Profile: p.2099
Table(s): Ohio: Real Estate **Band 4** p.2086

**Hayes, Robert E**
Table(s): South Dakota: Corporate/Commercial
**Band 1** p.2281, South Dakota:
Corporate/Commercial:
Bankruptcy/Restructuring **Band 1** p.2281, South
Dakota: Real Estate **Band 1** p.2286

**Hayes, William D**
Profile: p.2099
Table(s): Ohio: Natural Resources &
Environment **Band 1** p.2083

**Haygood, Paul M**
Profile: p.1363
Table(s): Louisiana: Corporate/M&A **Senior
Statesmen**: p.1341

**Haygood, Richard D**
Table(s): North Carolina: Labor & Employment
**Band 4** p.2031

**Hayhurst, Matthew B**
Table(s): Montana: Litigation: General
Commercial **Band 2** p.1649

**Hayman, Russell**
Profile: p.641
Table(s): California: Litigation: White-Collar
Crime & Government Investigations **Band 2** p.601

**Haymer, Robert**
Table(s): California: Media & Entertainment:
Transactional **Band 3** p.608

**Haynam, Douglas**
Table(s): Ohio: Natural Resources &
Environment **Band 3** p.2083

**Hayne Jr, C Peck**
Profile: p.1364
Table(s): Louisiana: Energy & Natural
Resources: Oil & Gas **Band 2** p.1344

**Haynes, Craig A**
Profile: p.2394
Table(s): Texas: Litigation: Energy & Natural
Resources **Band 3** p.2361

**Haynes, Greg**
Profile: p.1320
Table(s): Kentucky: Litigation: General
Commercial **Band 1** p.1312

**Haynes, John**
Table(s): Tennessee: Real Estate **Band 2** p.2299

**Haynor, Charles**
Profile: p.1579
Table(s): Minnesota: Real Estate **Band 3** p.1576

**Hayutin, Marc I**
Profile: p.641
Table(s): California: Real Estate **Band 3** p.611

**Helfand, Thomas**
Profile: p.2395
Table(s): Texas: Tax Band 3 p.2371

**Heller, Amy Erenrich**
Profile: p.333
Table(s): Nationwide: Wealth Management:
Eastern Region Up-and-coming individuals p.267

**Heller, Dan**
Profile: p.1084
Table(s): Georgia: Real Estate Band 3 p.1070

**Heller, David S**
Table(s): Nationwide: Bankruptcy/Restructuring
Band 2 p.39, Illinois: Bankruptcy/Restructuring
Band 1 p.1148

**Heller, Lawrence H**
Profile: p.333
Table(s): Nationwide: Wealth Management:
Western Region Band 3 p.267

**Heller, Mark A**
Profile: p.868
Table(s): District of Columbia: Healthcare:
Pharmaceutical/Medical Products Regulatory
Band 1 p.810

**Heller, Michael**
Profile: p.2219
Table(s): Pennsylvania: Corporate/M&A &
Private Equity Band 3 p.2191

**Heller, Richard B**
Profile: p.1902
Table(s): New York: Media & Entertainment:
Film & Television Band 1 p.1849

**Heller, Ron**
Table(s): Hawaii: Corporate/Commercial: Tax
Band 1 p.1115

**Heller, William**
Table(s): Texas: Capital Markets: Debt & Equity
Band 3 p.2333

**Heller, William P**
Table(s): Florida: Litigation: General Commercial
Band 3 p.966

**Hellerer, Mark R**
Table(s): Nationwide: Securities: Regulation:
Enforcement Band 4 p.233

**Hellewell, Read**
Table(s): Utah: Real Estate Band 3 p.2470

**Hellman, Dolph**
Profile: p.641
Table(s): California: Banking & Finance Band 4
p.539

**Hellow, John R**
Table(s): California: Healthcare Band 3 p.568

**Helm, Christopher R**
Table(s): Washington: Immigration Band 1 p.2528

**Helm, Robert W**
Profile: p.333
Table(s): Nationwide: Investment Funds:
Registered Funds Band 1 p.170

**Helm III, Kennedy**
Profile: p.1320
Table(s): Kentucky: Corporate/M&A Band 1
p.1305

**Helman, Robert A**
Table(s): Illinois: Corporate/M&A Senior Statesmen:
p.1156

**Helmer, Maureen**
Profile: p.1902
Table(s): New York: Energy: State Regulatory &
Wholesale Electric Market Band 2 p.1806

**Helmick, Brian C**
Profile: p.2563
Table(s): West Virginia: Corporate/Commercial
Band 3 p.2550

**Helmreich, Richard J**
Profile: p.2100
Table(s): Ohio: Employee Benefits & Executive
Compensation Band 1 p.2067

**Helms, Katherine Dudley**
Profile: p.2269
Table(s): South Carolina: Labor & Employment
Band 2 p.2262

**Helms, Shawn C**
Profile: p.2395
Table(s): Nationwide: Outsourcing Up-and-coming
individuals p.195, Texas: Technology: Outsourcing
Band 2 p.2376

**Helton, Jeanne**
Table(s): Florida: Healthcare Band 3 p.954

**Heltzer, Harold J**
Profile: p.868
Table(s): Nationwide: Tax: Controversy Band 4
p.244, District of Columbia: Tax Band 3 p.838

**Helvestine, William A**
Profile: p.641
Table(s): California: Healthcare Band 2 p.568

**Hembree, G. Dewey**
Profile: p.1603
Table(s): Mississippi: Litigation: General
Commercial Band 4 p.1597

**Hemley, Robert**
Table(s): Vermont: Litigation: General
Commercial Band 1 p.2486

**Hemlock, Adam C.**
Profile: p.1902
Table(s): New York: Antitrust Up-and-coming individ-
uals p.1778

**Hemmersbaugh, Paul A**
Profile: p.333
Table(s): Nationwide: Transportation: Rail (for
Railroads) Band 2 p.257

**Hemming, Seth M**
Table(s): Illinois: Corporate/M&A: Private Equity
Band 3 p.1157

**Hempelmann, John**
Table(s): Washington: Real Estate: Zoning/Land
Use Band 1 p.2536

**Hemr, Kurt Wm**
Profile: p.1495
Table(s): Massachusetts: Litigation: Securities
Band 2 p.1470

**Henchey, Brian**
Profile: p.2395
Table(s): Texas: Technology: Outsourcing Band 3
p.2376

**Hendelman, Aaron**
Table(s): Washington: Intellectual Property Band
2 p.2529

**Henderson, Derek**
Table(s): Mississippi: Corporate/Commercial:
Bankruptcy Band 1 p.1591

**Henderson, Douglas A**
Table(s): Georgia: Environment Band 1 p.1051

**Henderson III, Thomas N**
Profile: p.994
Table(s): Florida: Real Estate Band 1 p.974

**Henderson Jr, Donald B**
Profile: p.333
Table(s): Nationwide: Insurance: Transactional &
Regulatory Band 3 p.139, New York: Insurance:
Transactional & Regulatory Band 3 p.1816

**Hendler, Clifford B**
Profile: p.868
Table(s): Nationwide: Insurance: Dispute
Resolution: Insurer Band 3 p.134, District of
Columbia: Insurance: Insurer Band 2 p.816

**Hendren, Jason**
Profile: p.527
Table(s): Arkansas: Litigation: Medical
Malpractice Defense Up-and-coming individuals
p.522

**Hendrick, David R**
Table(s): Georgia: Construction Band 2 p.1044

**Hendricks, Randall**
Table(s): Missouri: Litigation: General
Commercial Band 2 p.1628

**Hendricks, Sharon J**
Table(s): California: Employee Benefits &
Executive Compensation Band 2 p.560

**Hendrickson, David K**
Table(s): West Virginia: Litigation: Mass Tort
Band 1 p.2555

**Hendrickson, Robert C**
Table(s): California: Construction Band 4 p.550

**Hendrickson, Susan E**
Profile: p.2510
Table(s): Northern Virginia: Intellectual Property
Band 3 p.2497

**Hendrix, Glenn P**
Profile: p.1084
Table(s): Georgia: Healthcare Band 2 p.1052

**Hendrix, Lynn P**
Table(s): Colorado: Natural Resources &
Environment Band 3 p.712

**Hendrix, Steven M**
Profile: p.1603
Table(s): Mississippi: Real Estate Band 2 p.1600

**Henegan, John C**
Profile: p.1604
Table(s): Mississippi: Litigation: Appellate Band 2
p.1596, Mississippi: Litigation: General
Commercial Band 3 p.1596

**Henegar, Matthew**
Profile: p.333
Table(s): Nationwide: Projects Band 4 p.216

**Henes, Jonathan S**
Profile: p.1902
Table(s): Nationwide: Bankruptcy/Restructuring
Band 3 p.39, New York:
Bankruptcy/Restructuring Band 2 p.1782

**Hengen, Nancy L**
Profile: p.333
Table(s): Nationwide: Banking & Finance:
Equipment Finance & Leasing Band 1 p.32,
Nationwide: Transportation: Shipping: Finance
(New York) Band 1 p.260

**Hengesbaugh, Brian**
Profile: p.333
Table(s): Nationwide: Privacy & Data Security
Band 3 p.199, Illinois: Technology & Outsourcing
Band 3 p.1194

**Henn Jr, R Charles**
Table(s): Nationwide: Sports Law Band 3 p.241,
Georgia: Intellectual Property Band 3 p.1056

**Henneburg, Frank H**
Table(s): District of Columbia: Real Estate Band
2 p.835

**Hennes, David**
Profile: p.1902
Table(s): New York: Litigation: General
Commercial Up-and-coming individuals p.1833

**Henney, Raymond W**
Table(s): Michigan: Litigation: General
Commercial Band 3 p.1544

**Hennigan, Brian J**
Profile: p.641
Table(s): California: Litigation: White-Collar
Crime & Government Investigations Band 1 p.601

**Hennigan, J Michael**
Profile: p.333
Table(s): Nationwide: Litigation: Trial Lawyers
Band 1 p.187, California: Litigation: General
Commercial Band 1 p.593

**Henning, Mark G**
Profile: p.1212
Table(s): Illinois: Real Estate Band 4 p.1187

**Henrichs, Ragna**
Profile: p.2395
Table(s): Texas: Environment Band 4 p.2343

**Henrie, Michelle**
Table(s): New Mexico: Environment, Natural
Resources & Regulated Industries: Water Law
Band 1 p.1766

**Henry, D Steven**
Profile: p.2395
Table(s): Texas: Construction Band 3 p.2335

**Henry, Judy**
Profile: p.527
Table(s): Arkansas: Litigation: General
Commercial Band 2 p.522

**Henry, Matthew C**
Profile: p.2395
Table(s): Texas: Energy: State Regulatory &
Litigation (Electricity) Band 2 p.2341

**Henry, Roxann E**
Table(s): District of Columbia: Antitrust Band 3
p.787

**Hensel, Jan E**
Table(s): **Ohio:** Labor & Employment **Band 3**
p.2074

**Hensler, David**
Table(s): **District of Columbia:** Insurance:
Insurer **Band 2** p.816, **District of Columbia:**
Litigation: General Commercial **Band 2** p.826

**Hensley, Dennis C**
Profile: p.333
Table(s): **Nationwide:** Financial Services
Regulation: Broker Dealer (Compliance) **Band 3**
p.97, **Nationwide:** Securities: Regulation:
Advisory **Band 2** p.232

**Hensley Jr, Harold**
Table(s): **New Mexico:** Environment, Natural
Resources & Regulated Industries **Band 1** p.1766

**Henthorne, D. Michael**
Profile: p.2269
Table(s): **South Carolina:** Labor & Employment
**Band 3** p.2262

**Hentoff, Thomas G**
Table(s): **District of Columbia:** Media &
Entertainment **Band 2** p.832

**Henze, Tom**
Table(s): **Arizona:** Litigation: White-Collar Crime
& Government Investigations **Band 1** p.501

**Henze II, William F**
Profile: p.333
Table(s): **Nationwide:** Energy: Electricity
(Transactional) **Band 3** p.77

**Hepworth, Charles**
Table(s): **Idaho:** Litigation: Medical Malpractice
& Insurance **Band 2** p.1134

**Herbert, Mark D**
Profile: p.1604
Table(s): **Mississippi:** Litigation: Construction
**Band 3** p.1596

**Herdzina, John W**
Table(s): **Nebraska:** Corporate/Commercial **Band
2** p.1659

**Herfort, John**
Profile: p.1902
Table(s): **New York:** Antitrust **Band 4** p.1778

**Hering, Louis G**
Table(s): **Delaware:** Corporate/M&A: Alternative
Entities **Band 1** p.761

**Heringer, Michael**
Table(s): **Montana:** Labor & Employment **Band 2**
p.1648

**Herlihy, Edward D**
Profile: p.334
Table(s): **Nationwide:** Financial Services
Regulation: Financial Institutions M&A **Star indi-
viduals** p.99, **New York:** Corporate/M&A **Band 1**
p.1793

**Herlihy, Scott C**
Profile: p.334
Table(s): **Nationwide:** Capital Markets: REITs
**Band 3** p.55

**Herlihy, William**
Profile: p.2563
Table(s): **West Virginia:** Natural Resources **Band
1** p.2558

**Herling, Michael J**
Table(s): **Connecticut:** Corporate/M&A **Band 1**
p.732

**Herlong, Warren**
Profile: p.470
Table(s): **Alabama:** Real Estate: Zoning/Land
Use **Band 1** p.466

**Herman, Andrew M**
Profile: p.869
Table(s): **District of Columbia:** Corporate/M&A &
Private Equity **Band 4** p.797

**Herman, Howard R.**
Table(s): **New York:** Corporate/M&A **Band 5**
p.1793

**Herman, Jason**
Profile: p.334
Table(s): **Nationwide:** Investment Funds: Private
Equity: Fund Formation **Up-and-coming individuals**
p.166

**Herman, John H**
Table(s): **Minnesota:** Real Estate: Zoning/Land
Use **Band 1** p.1576

**Herman, Jordan J**
Table(s): **Texas:** Technology: Outsourcing **Band 3**
p.2376

**Herman, Matthew**
Profile: p.1902
Table(s): **New York:** Corporate/M&A **Up-and-com-
ing individuals** p.1793

**Herman, Philip A**
Table(s): **Massachusetts:** Banking & Finance
**Band 1** p.1445

**Herman, Russ M**
Table(s): **Nationwide:** Product Liability: Plaintiffs
**Band 2** p.209, **Louisiana:** Litigation: General
Commercial **Band 1** p.1352

**Herman, Sarah Andrews**
Table(s): **North Dakota:** Labor & Employment
**Star individuals** p.2052, **North Dakota:** Litigation:
General Commercial **Band 2** p.2053

**Hermann, Brian S**
Profile: p.1902
Table(s): **New York:** Bankruptcy/Restructuring
**Band 4** p.1782

**Hermann, Christopher R.**
Table(s): **Nationwide:** Food & Beverages: Alcohol
**Band 2** p.109

**Hermes, John N**
Profile: p.2150
Table(s): **Oklahoma:** Litigation: General
Commercial **Band 1** p.2141

**Hermes, Robert N**
Profile: p.1212
Table(s): **Illinois:** Insurance: Dispute Resolution:
Reinsurance **Band 2** p.1168

**Hermle, Lynne C.**
Profile: p.642
Table(s): **California:** Labor & Employment **Band 1**
p.587

**Hernand, David**
Table(s): **California:** Corporate/M&A: Venture
Capital **Band 4** p.555

**Hernandez, Eugenio**
Table(s): **Florida:** Immigration **Band 2** p.956

**Hernandez, Jennifer L**
Profile: p.642
Table(s): **California:** Environment **Band 2** p.564,
**California:** Real Estate: Zoning/Land Use **Band 1**
p.612

**Hernandez, Louis**
Table(s): **Illinois:** Banking & Finance **Band 4**
p.1145

**Hernandez, Patricia M**
Table(s): **Florida:** Banking & Finance: Regulatory
**Band 3** p.937, **Florida:** Latin American Investment
**Band 3** p.963

**Heroy, David**
Profile: p.1212
Table(s): **Illinois:** Bankruptcy/Restructuring **Band
4** p.1148

**Herpe, David**
Profile: p.334
Table(s): **Nationwide:** Wealth Management:
Central Region **Band 3** p.266

**Herr, David**
Table(s): **Minnesota:** Litigation: Appellate **Band 1**
p.1573

**Herr, Robert**
Table(s): **California:** Real Estate **Band 3** p.611

**Herren, Mitch**
Table(s): **Kansas:** Litigation: General
Commercial **Band 2** p.1295

**Herrin, Barry S**
Profile: p.1084
Table(s): **Georgia:** Healthcare **Band 3** p.1052

**Herring II, Wade W**
Table(s): **Georgia:** Labor & Employment **Band 3**
p.1060

**Herrington, Daniel**
Profile: p.527
Table(s): **Arkansas:** Labor & Employment **Band 1**
p.520

**Herrington Jr, Alex P**
Profile: p.1320
Table(s): **Kentucky:** Corporate/M&A **Band 3**
p.1305

**Herrmann, Judith**
Table(s): **Iowa:** Labor & Employment **Band 3**
p.1285

**Herrmann, Richard K**
Table(s): **Delaware:** Intellectual Property **Band 3**
p.763

**Herschman, Gary W**
Profile: p.1737
Table(s): **New Jersey:** Healthcare **Band 1** p.1715

**Hershkowitz, Benjamin**
Profile: p.1902
Table(s): **New York:** Intellectual Property: Patent
**Band 3** p.1820

**Hershman, Douglas M**
Profile: p.771
Table(s): **Delaware:** Real Estate **Band 2** p.766

**Hershman, Jordan D**
Profile: p.1495
Table(s): **Massachusetts:** Litigation: Securities
**Band 1** p.1470

**Hershman, Stuart**
Profile: p.334
Table(s): **Nationwide:** Franchising **Band 3** p.111

**Hertlein Jr, Charles F**
Table(s): **Ohio:** Corporate/M&A **Band 4** p.2064

**Hertz, Clifford**
Table(s): **Florida:** Real Estate: Zoning/Land Use
**Band 2** p.975

**Hertz, Mitchell F**
Table(s): **Nationwide:** Energy: Electricity
(Transactional) **Band 1** p.77

**Hertzke, Adam**
Table(s): **Iowa:** Corporate/M&A **Associates to
watch** p.1283

**Heryford, Craig S**
Profile: p.2219
Table(s): **Pennsylvania:** Banking & Finance **Band
2** p.2186

**Herz, Andrew L**
Profile: p.1903
Table(s): **New York:** Real Estate **Band 3** p.1854

**Herzeca, Lois F**
Profile: p.1903
Table(s): **New York:** Insurance: Transactional &
Regulatory **Band 3** p.1816

**Herzog, Barry**
Profile: p.1903
Table(s): **New York:** Tax **Band 4** p.1862

**Herzog, David K**
Table(s): **Indiana:** Litigation: General
Commercial **Band 1** p.1273

**Herzog Jr, Richard B**
Profile: p.1084
Table(s): **Georgia:** Bankruptcy/Restructuring
**Band 3** p.1042

**Hess, Kristofer**
Profile: p.1903
Table(s): **New York:** Tax **Band 4** p.1862

**Hess, W Ashley**
Profile: p.2100
Table(s): **Ohio:** Corporate/M&A **Band 4** p.2064

**Hesse, Karl N**
Profile: p.1299
Table(s): **Kansas:** Real Estate **Band 3** p.1297

**Hester, Theodore M**
Profile: p.334
Table(s): **Nationwide:** Government: Government
Relations **Band 2** p.121

**Heston, Mary Jo**
Profile: p.2539
Table(s): **Washington:** Bankruptcy/Restructuring
**Band 2** p.2523

**Hetland, Janice E**
Table(s): **Missouri:** Real Estate **Band 2** p.1633

**Hetrick, Stephen M**
Profile: p.2150
Table(s): **Oklahoma:** Real Estate **Up-and-coming
individuals** p.2145

**Hettinger, Glen**
Profile: p.2395
Table(s): Texas: Corporate/M&A **Band 2** p.2337

**Hettinger, Kyle**
Table(s): Arizona: Real Estate **Band 4** p.504

**Heusel, Cornelius**
Profile: p.1364
Table(s): Louisiana: Labor & Employment **Senior Statesmen** p.1350

**Heuser, Peter E**
Table(s): Oregon: Intellectual Property **Band 2** p.2167

**Hevener, Mary**
Profile: p.869
Table(s): District of Columbia: Employee Benefits & Executive Compensation **Band 3** p.801

**Hewey, Melissa**
Profile: p.1400
Table(s): Maine: Labor & Employment **Band 2** p.1390, Maine: Litigation: General Commercial **Band 2** p.1393

**Hewitt, Henry**
Table(s): Oregon: Corporate/M&A **Senior Statesmen**: p.2164

**Hewitt, John**
Table(s): Nebraska: Labor & Employment **Band 3** p.1662

**Hewitt, Lester L**
Table(s): Texas: Intellectual Property **Band 4** p.2354

**Hewitt, William**
Profile: p.1400
Table(s): Maine: Energy & Natural Resources **Band 3** p.1388

**Heyl, Jonathan**
Profile: p.2041
Table(s): North Carolina: Litigation: General Commercial **Up-and-coming individuals** p.2033

**Heyman, Kurt M**
Table(s): Delaware: Chancery **Band 3** p.758

**Heyman, Robert**
Table(s): New Mexico: Corporate/Commercial **Senior Statesmen**: p.1764

**Heywood, Thomas A**
Profile: p.2563
Table(s): West Virginia: Corporate/Commercial **Band 1** p.2550, West Virginia: Corporate/Commercial: Healthcare **Band 1** p.2550

**Hibey, Richard**
Profile: p.869
Table(s): District of Columbia: Litigation: White-Collar Crime & Government Investigations **Senior Statesmen**: p.827

**Hickey, Andrew**
Profile: p.1495
Table(s): Massachusetts: Banking & Finance **Up-and-coming individuals** p.1445

**Hickey, Kathleen O'Callaghan**
Profile: p.1550
Table(s): Michigan: Banking & Finance **Band 3** p.1536

**Hickey, Matthew**
Table(s): Oklahoma: Corporate/Commercial: Tax **Associates to watch** p.2134

**Hickey, Michael**
Table(s): South Dakota: Litigation: General Commercial **Band 2** p.2284

**Hickey, Patrick F**
Table(s): Michigan: Labor & Employment **Band 2** p.1542, Michigan: Litigation: General Commercial **Band 2** p.1544

**Hickey, Paul**
Table(s): Wyoming: Litigation: General Commercial **Band 1** p.2598

**Hickey Jr, John T**
Profile: p.1212
Table(s): Illinois: Litigation: General Commercial **Band 2** p.1180

**Hickok, Robert L**
Profile: p.2219
Table(s): Pennsylvania: Litigation: General Commercial **Band 1** p.2203, Pennsylvania: Litigation: Securities **Band 1** p.2203

**Hicks, Alvin J**
Table(s): Nevada: Gaming & Licensing **Band 1** p.1674

**Hicks, Hal**
Profile: p.869
Table(s): District of Columbia: Tax **Band 2** p.838

**Hicks, John S**
Profile: p.2305
Table(s): Tennessee: Litigation: General Commercial **Band 2** p.2295

**Hicks, M Maxine**
Profile: p.1084
Table(s): Georgia: Real Estate **Band 2** p.1070

**Hicks, Matthew**
Profile: p.1139
Table(s): Idaho: Real Estate **Band 2** p.1138

**Hicks, Patrick H**
Profile: p.1681
Table(s): Nevada: Labor & Employment **Band 1** p.1675

**Hicks, Robert J**
Profile: p.1277
Table(s): Indiana: Corporate/M&A **Band 1** p.1268

**Hicks Jr, M Lawrence**
Profile: p.2395
Table(s): Texas: Real Estate **Band 1** p.2367

**Hieb, Dixie**
Table(s): South Dakota: Corporate/Commercial **Band 3** p.2281

**Hieb, Jack H**
Table(s): South Dakota: Litigation: General Commercial **Band 2** p.2284

**Higbee, Robert Alan**
Table(s): Florida: Corporate/M&A & Private Equity **Band 3** p.947

**Higdon, Gerald D**
Profile: p.2395
Table(s): Texas: Environment **Band 2** p.2343

**Higgins, Claudia R**
Profile: p.869
Table(s): District of Columbia: Antitrust **Band 5** p.787

**Higgins, Daniel B**
Table(s): Nationwide: Healthcare: Transactional **Band 2** p.128, California: Healthcare **Band 1** p.568

**Higgins, David K**
Table(s): West Virginia: Corporate/Commercial **Band 3** p.2550

**Higgins, John**
Profile: p.2100
Table(s): Ohio: Construction **Band 4** p.2062

**Higgins, John**
Profile: p.2395
Table(s): Texas: Bankruptcy/Restructuring **Band 1** p.2328

**Higgins, Keith F**
Table(s): Massachusetts: Corporate/M&A: Capital Markets **Band 1** p.1453

**Higgins, Roger**
Table(s): Texas: Insurance **Band 2** p.2351

**Higgins, Stephen**
Table(s): Missouri: Litigation: General Commercial **Band 2** p.1629, Missouri: Litigation: White-Collar Crime & Government Investigations **Band 2** p.1629

**Higgins, Tara A**
Table(s): Nationwide: Projects **Band 3** p.216

**Higgins Jr, James R**
Table(s): Kentucky: Intellectual Property **Band 1** p.1308

**High, Mark R**
Profile: p.1550
Table(s): Michigan: Corporate/M&A **Band 3** p.1538

**High, Michael E**
Profile: p.1400
Table(s): Maine: Corporate/M&A **Star individuals** p.1385

**High Jr, Charles C**
Table(s): Texas: Labor & Employment **Band 1** p.2359

**Hildebrand, Mary J**
Profile: p.1737
Table(s): New Jersey: Intellectual Property **Band 2** p.1716

**Hildebrandt, Jennifer B**
Table(s): California: Banking & Finance **Up-and-coming individuals** p.539

**Hildreth, Thomas W**
Profile: p.1695
Table(s): New Hampshire: Real Estate: Land Use **Band 2** p.1692

**Hiles, Bradley**
Table(s): Missouri: Labor & Employment **Band 2** p.1625

**Hilfers, Eric W.**
Profile: p.1903
Table(s): New York: Employee Benefits & Executive Compensation **Band 4** p.1802

**Hilgers, David W**
Table(s): Nationwide: Healthcare: Regulatory & Litigation **Band 3** p.127, Texas: Healthcare **Band 1** p.2347

**Hill, David W**
Profile: p.869
Table(s): District of Columbia: Intellectual Property: Patent Prosecution **Band 2** p.820

**Hill, Eva H**
Profile: p.1428
Table(s): Maryland: Corporate/M&A **Band 3** p.1412

**Hill, Frank**
Profile: p.2150
Table(s): Oklahoma: Real Estate **Band 1** p.2145

**Hill, Hollister Anne**
Table(s): Georgia: Environment **Band 2** p.1051

**Hill, J Reginald**
Profile: p.2305
Table(s): Tennessee: Healthcare **Band 1** p.2291

**Hill, James M**
Profile: p.2100
Table(s): Ohio: Corporate/M&A **Band 3** p.2064

**Hill, James S**
Table(s): North Dakota: Litigation: General Commercial **Band 1** p.2053

**Hill, James W**
Profile: p.642
Table(s): California: Life Sciences: Corporate/Commercial **Band 3** p.590

**Hill, Jeremy**
Profile: p.1277
Table(s): Indiana: Corporate/M&A **Band 3** p.1268

**Hill, Lawrence**
Table(s): Nationwide: Tax: Controversy **Band 2** p.244

**Hill, Lee O**
Profile: p.2563
Table(s): West Virginia: Corporate/Commercial: Banking & Finance **Band 1** p.2550

**Hill, Michael R**
Table(s): Tennessee: Healthcare **Band 3** p.2291

**Hill, Richard**
Table(s): Washington: Real Estate: Zoning/Land Use **Band 1** p.2536

**Hill, Robert F**
Table(s): Colorado: Litigation: General Commercial **Band 1** p.709

**Hill, Sean J**
Table(s): Massachusetts: Private Equity: Fund Formation **Band 3** p.1476

**Hill, Stephen L**
Table(s): Missouri: Litigation: White-Collar Crime & Government Investigations **Band 2** p.1629

**Hill, Teresa A**
Table(s): Idaho: Natural Resources & Environment **Band 2** p.1136

**Hill, Thomas**
Table(s): Ohio: Litigation: General Commercial **Band 1** p.2078

**Hill, Timothy J**
Table(s): Iowa: Litigation: Insurance **Band 1**
p.1288

**Hill, William K**
Table(s): Florida: Litigation: General Commercial
**Band 4** p.966

**Hill III, Benjamin H**
Profile: p.994
Table(s): Florida: Litigation: General Commercial
**Band 1** p.966

**Hill Jr, William B**
Profile: p.1084
Table(s): Georgia: Labor & Employment **Band 3**
p.1060, Georgia: Litigation: General Commercial
**Band 2** p.1065

**Hiller, Thomas R**
Table(s): Nationwide: Investment Funds:
Registered Funds **Band 3** p.170, Massachusetts:
Hedge & Mutual Funds **Band 2** p.1461

**Hilliard, David C**
Table(s): Illinois: Intellectual Property **Senior
Statesmen:** p.1171

**Hilliard, Hugh**
Table(s): Nationwide: Energy: Electricity
(Regulatory & Litigation) **Band 5** p.76

**Hilliard, Michael**
Profile: p.2396
Table(s): Texas: Banking & Finance **Band 2**
p.2325

**Hilliard, Russell**
Table(s): New Hampshire: Litigation: General
Commercial **Band 1** p.1690

**Hillman, David M**
Profile: p.1903
Table(s): New York: Bankruptcy/Restructuring
**Band 4** p.1782

**Hillman, Robert**
Table(s): Massachusetts: Intellectual Property
**Senior Statesmen:** p.1463

**Hills, Bethany J.**
Table(s): New York: Healthcare **Up-and-coming individuals** p.1811

**Hilmes, Jack**
Table(s): Iowa: Litigation: General Commercial
**Band 3** p.1288

**Hilson, John F**
Table(s): Nationwide: Banking & Finance **Band 3**
p.31, California: Banking & Finance **Star individuals** p.539

**Hilton, Paul**
Table(s): Colorado: Corporate/M&A **Band 1** p.703

**Himeles, Martin**
Table(s): Maryland: Litigation: General
Commercial **Band 2** p.1419

**Himmel, Michael B**
Profile: p.1737
Table(s): New Jersey: Litigation: White-Collar
Crime & Government Investigations **Band 1**
p.1723

**Hindman, Kathryn M**
Table(s): Oregon: Labor & Employment **Band 4**
p.2168

**Hindus, Michael**
Table(s): California: Energy: State Regulatory &
Litigation **Band 3** p.562

**Hinebaugh, Jeffrey P**
Table(s): Ohio: Litigation: General Commercial
**Band 4** p.2078

**Hiner, Thomas Y**
Profile: p.334
Table(s): Nationwide: Capital Markets:
Securitisation **Band 3** p.59

**Hinerman, Philip L**
Profile: p.2219
Table(s): Pennsylvania: Environment **Band 2**
p.2194

**Hines, Barry A**
Profile: p.1320
Table(s): Kentucky: Real Estate **Band 1** p.1314

**Hines, Robert L**
Table(s): California: Environment **Band 3** p.564

**Hiney, Jesse**
Profile: p.1903
Table(s): New York: Environment **Up-and-coming
individuals** p.1807

**Hingle, Charles**
Profile: p.1654
Table(s): Montana: Corporate/M&A **Band 1**
p.1646

**Hink, John**
Table(s): Arizona: Real Estate **Band 3** p.504

**Hinkle IV, Samuel D**
Profile: p.1320
Table(s): Kentucky: Litigation: General
Commercial **Band 2** p.1312

**Hinkle, Jr., Buckner**
Profile: p.1320
Table(s): Kentucky: Litigation: Construction **Band
1** p.1312

**Hinkley, Gerry**
Table(s): Nationwide: Healthcare: Transactional
**Band 3** p.128, California: Healthcare **Band 1** p.568

**Hinman, Frank M**
Profile: p.642
Table(s): California: Antitrust **Band 3** p.536

**Hinman, John A**
Table(s): Nationwide: Food & Beverages: Alcohol
**Band 1** p.109

**Hinman Jr, William H**
Profile: p.642
Table(s): Nationwide: Capital Markets: Debt &
Equity **Band 2** p.46, California: Capital Markets:
Debt & Equity **Band 1** p.547

**Hinson, Edward T**
Table(s): North Carolina: Litigation: General
Commercial **Band 1** p.2033

**Hinson, H Douglas**
Profile: p.334
Table(s): Nationwide: ERISA Litigation **Band 2**
p.92

**Hinton, Melissa**
Table(s): South Dakota: Litigation: Medical
Malpractice Defense **Band 2** p.2284

**Hintze, John**
Table(s): Iowa: Corporate/M&A **Band 4** p.1283

**Hipp, David W**
Profile: p.1551
Table(s): Michigan: Real Estate **Band 2** p.1546

**Hird, David B**
Profile: p.869
Table(s): District of Columbia: Environment **Band
2** p.804

**Hirsch, Barry L**
Table(s): California: Media & Entertainment:
Transactional: Mainly Talent **Band 1** p.609

**Hirsch, Jeffrey L**
Table(s): Massachusetts: Labor & Employment
**Band 3** p.1466

**Hirsch, Reece**
Profile: p.642
Table(s): California: Healthcare **Band 2** p.568

**Hirsch, Steven A**
Table(s): Arizona: Litigation: General
Commercial **Band 3** p.501

**Hirschfeld, Michael A**
Table(s): Ohio: Corporate/M&A **Band 2** p.2064

**Hirschfeld, Stephen J**
Table(s): California: Labor & Employment **Band 4**
p.587

**Hirschfield, Marc E**
Profile: p.1903
Table(s): New York: Bankruptcy/Restructuring
**Band 4** p.1782

**Hirschson, Linda B.**
Profile: p.334
Table(s): Nationwide: Wealth Management:
Eastern Region **Band 2** p.267

**Hirsh, Robert M**
Profile: p.334
Table(s): Nationwide: Investment Funds: Private
Equity: Fund Formation **Band 3** p.166

**Hirshman, Michele**
Profile: p.1903
Table(s): New York: Litigation: White-Collar
Crime & Government Investigations **Band 2**
p.1836

**Hirshman, Neil S**
Profile: p.334
Table(s): Nationwide: Outsourcing **Band 2** p.195,
Illinois: Technology & Outsourcing **Band 2** p.1194

**Hirzel, Samuel**
Table(s): Delaware: Chancery **Up-and-coming individuals** p.758

**Hise, Daniel G**
Profile: p.1604
Table(s): Mississippi: Corporate/Commercial:
Gaming & Licensing **Band 1** p.1591

**Hisert, George A**
Profile: p.642
Table(s): California: Banking & Finance **Senior
Statesmen:** p.539

**Hishon, Robert H**
Table(s): Georgia: Tax **Band 1** p.1072

**Hisiger, James I**
Profile: p.1903
Table(s): New York: Real Estate **Band 4** p.1854,
New York: Real Estate: Finance **Band 3** p.1854

**Hite, Richard**
Table(s): Kansas: Litigation: General
Commercial **Senior Statesmen:** p.1295

**Hitselberger, Carol A**
Table(s): Nationwide: Capital Markets:
Securitisation **Band 2** p.59, North Carolina:
Banking & Finance **Band 2** p.2021

**Hix, Richard P**
Profile: p.2150
Table(s): Oklahoma: Litigation: General
Commercial **Band 3** p.2141

**Hjelm, Lars-Erik A**
Profile: p.334
Table(s): Nationwide: International Trade:
Customs **Band 2** p.155

**Hluchan, Richard M**
Table(s): New Jersey: Environment **Band 1**
p.1711, New Jersey: Real Estate: Zoning/Land
Use **Band 1** p.1728

**Hnath, Gary**
Table(s): Nationwide: International Trade:
Intellectual Property (Section 337) **Band 3** p.160

**Ho, Allyson N**
Profile: p.2396
Table(s): Nationwide: Appellate Law **Band 4** p.26,
Texas: Litigation: Appellate **Band 2** p.2361

**Ho, James**
Profile: p.2396
Table(s): Texas: Litigation: Appellate **Band 3**
p.2361

**Hoar Jr, Samuel**
Table(s): Vermont: Litigation: General
Commercial **Band 2** p.2486

**Hobbs, Eric**
Profile: p.2583
Table(s): Wisconsin: Labor & Employment **Band 3**
p.2575

**Hobbs, James R**
Table(s): Missouri: Litigation: White-Collar Crime
& Government Investigations **Band 1** p.1629

**Hobbs Jr, Michael D**
Table(s): Georgia: Intellectual Property **Band 3**
p.1056

**Hobby, Scott M**
Table(s): Nationwide: Outsourcing **Band 2** p.195

**Hobel, Lawrence**
Profile: p.335
Table(s): Nationwide: Insurance: Dispute
Resolution: Policyholder **Band 2** p.137, California:
Insurance: Policyholder **Band 2** p.576

**Hobel, Michael**
Table(s): California: Media & Entertainment:
Transactional **Band 2** p.608

**Hoblitzell, John R**
Table(s): West Virginia: Litigation: General
Commercial **Band 3** p.2555

**Hochberg, Kevin J**
Profile: p.335
Table(s): Nationwide: Capital Markets:
Securitisation **Band 3** p.59

**Hochstatter, Tom**
Table(s): Wisconsin: Labor & Employment:
Immigration **Band 1** p.2575

**Hockeimer Jr, Henry E**
Profile: p.2219
Table(s): Pennsylvania: Litigation: White-Collar Crime & Government Investigations **Band 2** p.2204

**Hockenbury, John C**
Profile: p.869
Table(s): District of Columbia: Insurance: Insurer **Band 3** p.816

**Hockett, Christopher**
Profile: p.642
Table(s): California: Antitrust **Band 2** p.536

**Hockley, Michael D**
Table(s): Missouri: Environment **Band 1** p.1621

**Hodara, Fred S**
Profile: p.335
Table(s): Nationwide: Bankruptcy/Restructuring **Band 2** p.39, New York: Bankruptcy/Restructuring **Band 2** p.1782

**Hodes, Joel**
Table(s): New York: Healthcare **Band 4** p.1811

**Hodes, Scott**
Table(s): Illinois: Media & Entertainment: Transactional **Band 1** p.1185

**Hodess, Ronald E**
Profile: p.1551
Table(s): Michigan: Real Estate **Band 3** p.1546

**Hodge, Katherine D**
Table(s): Illinois: Environment: Mainly Transactional **Band 1** p.1162

**Hodge Jr, E Clifton**
Profile: p.1604
Table(s): Mississippi: Corporate/Commercial **Band 3** p.1591

**Hodges, Charles**
Table(s): Georgia: Tax **Band 2** p.1072

**Hodges Taylor, Laura C**
Profile: p.1495
Table(s): Massachusetts: Private Equity: Buyouts **Band 1** p.1474

**Hodgkins, Scott**
Table(s): California: Capital Markets: Debt & Equity **Band 2** p.547

**Hodgman, David R**
Table(s): Nationwide: Wealth Management: Central Region **Band 3** p.266

**Hoeflich, Adam**
Table(s): Nationwide: Product Liability & Mass Torts **Band 4** p.208, Illinois: Litigation: General Commercial **Band 4** p.1180

**Hoey, Barbara**
Table(s): New York: Labor & Employment **Band 4** p.1826

**Hoff, Jonathan M**
Profile: p.1904
Table(s): New York: Litigation: Securities **Band 2** p.1834

**Hoffinger, Adam S**
Profile: p.869
Table(s): District of Columbia: Litigation: White-Collar Crime & Government Investigations **Band 2** p.827

**Hoffman, A Kimberly**
Table(s): Delaware: Real Estate: Zoning/Land Use **Band 2** p.766

**Hoffman, D Bruce**
Profile: p.869
Table(s): District of Columbia: Antitrust **Band 4** p.787

**Hoffman, Debra B**
Table(s): Illinois: Labor & Employment: Employee Benefits & Compensation **Band 2** p.1176

**Hoffman, Gary M**
Profile: p.869
Table(s): District of Columbia: Intellectual Property: Litigation **Band 3** p.821

**Hoffman, Jerome**
Profile: p.995
Table(s): Florida: Antitrust **Band 1** p.935

**Hoffman, John W.**
Table(s): Missouri: Real Estate **Band 3** p.1633

**Hoffman, Kenneth R**
Profile: p.1428
Table(s): Maryland: Employee Benefits & Executive Compensation **Band 1** p.1414

**Hoffman, Lee D**
Profile: p.744
Table(s): Connecticut: Environment **Band 2** p.733

**Hoffman, Michael K**
Profile: p.335
Table(s): Nationwide: Investment Funds: Registered Funds **Band 3** p.170

**Hoffman, Nathaniel A**
Profile: p.2583
Table(s): Wisconsin: Real Estate **Band 3** p.2579

**Hoffman, Robert**
Profile: p.1428
Table(s): Maryland: Real Estate: Land Use **Band 2** p.1422

**Hoffman, Timothy**
Table(s): Ohio: Natural Resources & Environment **Band 4** p.2083

**Hoffmann, Christian**
Profile: p.509
Table(s): Arizona: Corporate/M&A **Band 3** p.495

**Hoffmann, Thomas**
Profile: p.335
Table(s): Nationwide: Projects: Renewables & Alternative Energy **Band 2** p.218

**Hoffmann, Warren**
Profile: p.1320
Table(s): Kentucky: Environment, Natural Resources & Utilities: Natural Resources **Band 1** p.1307

**Hofstetter, Richard**
Profile: p.1904
Table(s): New York: Media & Entertainment: Film & Television **Band 1** p.1849

**Hogan, Carol C**
Table(s): Illinois: Healthcare **Band 3** p.1165

**Hogan, E. Desmond**
Table(s): District of Columbia: Litigation: General Commercial **Up-and-coming individuals** p.826

**Hogan, Edward A**
Profile: p.1737
Table(s): New Jersey: Environment **Band 1** p.1711

**Hogan, John M**
Profile: p.995
Table(s): Florida: Litigation: White-Collar Crime & Government Investigations **Band 1** p.967

**Hogan, Kevin M**
Profile: p.1904
Table(s): New York: Environment **Band 4** p.1807

**Hogan, Timothy C**
Table(s): Iowa: Real Estate **Band 4** p.1290

**Hogan III, Dennis P**
Table(s): Nebraska: Real Estate: Zoning/Land Use **Band 1** p.1666

**Hogans, Daniel L**
Profile: p.869
Table(s): District of Columbia: Employee Benefits & Executive Compensation **Band 2** p.801

**Hoganson, Jon J**
Profile: p.1579
Table(s): Minnesota: Real Estate **Band 2** p.1576

**Hogen, Vanya**
Table(s): Nationwide: Native American Law **Band 2** p.192

**Hogewood, Lee**
Profile: p.2041
Table(s): North Carolina: Bankruptcy/Restructuring **Band 2** p.2023

**Hogfoss, Robert**
Profile: p.1084
Table(s): Georgia: Environment **Band 2** p.1051

**Hogue Jr, P Mason**
Profile: p.2270
Table(s): South Carolina: Corporate/M&A **Band 2** p.2260

**Hohenstein, James**
Profile: p.335
Table(s): Nationwide: Transportation: Shipping: Litigation (New York) **Band 3** p.261

**Hohn, Christopher**
Table(s): Missouri: Litigation: General Commercial **Band 3** p.1629

**Hohnbaum, Cory**
Profile: p.2041
Table(s): North Carolina: Litigation: General Commercial **Band 4** p.2033

**Holcomb, James M**
Table(s): Iowa: Real Estate **Senior Statesmen:** p.1290

**Holcomb, Mark E**
Table(s): Florida: Tax: State & Local **Band 1** p.979

**Holcomb, Ryan S**
Profile: p.335
Table(s): Nationwide: Projects **Band 4** p.216

**Hold-Weiss, Rachel**
Profile: p.1904
Table(s): New York: Healthcare **Up-and-coming individuals** p.1811

**Holden, G Graham**
Profile: p.1084
Table(s): Georgia: Environment **Band 2** p.1051

**Holden, Robert E**
Table(s): Louisiana: Environment **Band 1** p.1346

**Holden, S Craig**
Table(s): Nationwide: Healthcare: Regulatory & Litigation **Band 3** p.127, Maryland: Healthcare **Band 2** p.1415

**Holden Jr, Frederick D**
Profile: p.642
Table(s): California: Bankruptcy/Restructuring **Band 3** p.542

**Holden-Davis, Julia**
Table(s): Alaska: Litigation: Construction **Up-and-coming individuals** p.490

**Holdenried, John R**
Table(s): Nebraska: Healthcare **Band 1** p.1661

**Holewinski, Kevin**
Profile: p.870
Table(s): District of Columbia: Environment **Band 4** p.804

**Holland, Elizabeth**
Table(s): New York: Intellectual Property: Patent **Band 3** p.1820

**Holland, James**
Profile: p.1637
Table(s): Missouri: Labor & Employment **Band 3** p.1625

**Holland, Mark**
Profile: p.335
Table(s): Nationwide: Securities: Litigation **Band 2** p.232, New York: Litigation: Securities **Band 2** p.1834

**Holland, Michael**
Table(s): Nationwide: Transportation: Aviation: Litigation **Band 3** p.254

**Holland, Patricia L**
Profile: p.2041
Table(s): North Carolina: Labor & Employment **Band 2** p.2031

**Hollander, Adam K**
Profile: p.1212
Table(s): Illinois: Insurance: Dispute Resolution **Band 3** p.1168

**Hollander, Ross**
Table(s): Kansas: Labor & Employment **Band 1** p.1294

**Hollander, William H**
Profile: p.1320
Table(s): Kentucky: Intellectual Property **Band 2** p.1308

**Hollender, Victor**
Profile: p.1904
Table(s): New York: Tax **Band 4** p.1862

**Holley, Steven L**
Profile: p.1904
Table(s): New York: Antitrust **Band 3** p.1778

**Holley II, William J**
Table(s): Georgia: Litigation: General Commercial **Band 2** p.1065

**Hollingsworth, Jeff**
Table(s): Washington: Labor & Employment **Band 2** p.2531

**Hollingsworth II, Michael E**
Profile: p.1084
Table(s): Georgia: Corporate/M&A **Band 4** p.1046

**Hollis, Sheila Slocum**
Table(s): Nationwide: Energy: Electricity
(Regulatory & Litigation) **Band 5** p.76

**Hollister, Timothy S**
Table(s): Connecticut: Real Estate **Band 2** p.740

**Holloman Jr, James H**
Table(s): Oklahoma: Corporate/Commercial: Tax
**Band 1** p.2134

**Hollyfield, John S**
Profile: p.2396
Table(s): Texas: Real Estate **Senior Statesmen:**
p.2367

**Holm, Kristi Geisler**
Table(s): South Dakota: Labor & Employment:
Workers' Compensation **Band 2** p.2283

**Holman, James J**
Table(s): Pennsylvania:
Bankruptcy/Restructuring **Band 3** p.2188

**Holmes, Barbara**
Table(s): Tennessee: Litigation: Bankruptcy **Band
2** p.2295

**Holmes, Ervin R**
Table(s): Utah: Real Estate **Band 2** p.2470

**Holmes, Hillary H.**
Profile: p.335
Table(s): Nationwide: Energy: Oil & Gas
(Transactional) **Up-and-coming individuals** p.79

**Holmes, Joshua**
Profile: p.1904
Table(s): New York: Tax **Band 3** p.1862

**Holmes, Lock**
Table(s): California: Construction **Band 4** p.550

**Holmes, Patricia**
Table(s): Illinois: Litigation: White-Collar Crime &
Government Investigations **Band 3** p.1181

**Holmes, Robert A.**
Table(s): Colorado: Real Estate **Band 1** p.714

**Holmes, Whitney**
Table(s): Colorado: Corporate/M&A **Band 2** p.703

**Holmstead, Jeffrey R**
Profile: p.335
Table(s): Nationwide: Climate Change **Band 1**
p.63, District of Columbia: Environment **Band 2**
p.804

**Holo, Robert**
Profile: p.1904
Table(s): New York: Tax **Band 4** p.1862

**Holscher, Mark**
Profile: p.642
Table(s): California: Litigation: White-Collar
Crime & Government Investigations **Band 1** p.601

**Holshouser, Eric J**
Table(s): Florida: Labor & Employment **Band 2**
p.959

**Holt, Scott**
Table(s): Delaware: Labor & Employment **Band 2**
p.765

**Holt, Whitman**
Table(s): California: Bankruptcy/Restructuring
**Up-and-coming individuals** p.542

**Holt III, Berry**
Table(s): Tennessee: Healthcare **Band 3** p.2291,
Tennessee: Healthcare: Regulatory **Band 1**
p.2291

**Holtkamp, James A**
Profile: p.2474
Table(s): Utah: Energy & Natural Resources **Band
1** p.2464

**Holtman, Stephen**
Table(s): Iowa: Litigation: General Commercial
**Band 4** p.1288

**Holtzer, Gary T**
Profile: p.1904
Table(s): Nationwide: Bankruptcy/Restructuring
**Band 3** p.39, New York:
Bankruptcy/Restructuring **Band 2** p.1782

**Holub, Cynthia A**
Profile: p.2396
Table(s): Texas: Insurance **Band 3** p.2351

**Holzer, Walter S**
Profile: p.1212
Table(s): Illinois: Corporate/M&A: Private Equity
**Band 3** p.1157

**Homburger, Thomas C**
Profile: p.1212
Table(s): Illinois: Real Estate **Band 3** p.1187

**Hommer, Scott**
Profile: p.335
Table(s): Nationwide: Government: Government
Contracts **Band 4** p.117

**Honan, William J**
Profile: p.335
Table(s): Nationwide: Transportation: Shipping:
Litigation (New York) **Band 1** p.261

**Honeyman, Jason M**
Table(s): Massachusetts: Intellectual Property
**Band 3** p.1463

**Honeyman, Richard**
Table(s): Kansas: Litigation: General
Commercial **Band 2** p.1295

**Hong, Ji Hoon**
Table(s): Nationwide: Banking & Finance:
Equipment Finance & Leasing **Band 2** p.32,
Nationwide: Transportation: Aviation: Finance
**Band 2** p.252

**Hong, Ki P**
Profile: p.336
Table(s): Nationwide: Government: Political Law
**Band 1** p.124

**Hood, James**
Profile: p.1695
Table(s): New Hampshire:
Corporate/Commercial **Band 1** p.1685

**Hood, James**
Profile: p.2270
Table(s): South Carolina: Litigation: General
Commercial **Up-and-coming individuals** p.2264

**Hood, John T**
Profile: p.336
Table(s): Nationwide: Energy: Electricity
(Transactional) **Band 3** p.77

**Hood, Robert**
Profile: p.2270
Table(s): South Carolina: Litigation: General
Commercial **Band 2** p.2264

**Hood, Roger W**
Table(s): Rhode Island: Corporate/Commercial
**Band 1** p.2251

**Hood, Vicki V**
Profile: p.1212
Table(s): Illinois: Labor & Employment:
Employee Benefits & Compensation **Band 2**
p.1176

**Hooker, Richard A**
Table(s): Michigan: Labor & Employment **Band 2**
p.1542

**Hooper, Chester D**
Profile: p.336
Table(s): Nationwide: Transportation: Shipping:
Litigation (outside New York) **Band 1** p.263

**Hooper, James E.**
Profile: p.336
Table(s): Nationwide: Product Liability & Mass
Torts **Band 5** p.208

**Hooper, John**
Table(s): Nationwide: Product Liability & Mass
Torts **Band 5** p.208

**Hooper, Patric**
Table(s): Nationwide: Healthcare: Regulatory &
Litigation **Band 2** p.127, California: Healthcare
**Band 1** p.568

**Hoort, Steven T**
Table(s): Massachusetts:
Bankruptcy/Restructuring **Band 1** p.1449

**Hootsell III, Sessions Ault**
Table(s): Louisiana: Bankruptcy/Restructuring
**Band 2** p.1337

**Hoover, Craig A**
Table(s): District of Columbia: Litigation:
General Commercial **Band 2** p.826

**Hope, Stephen D**
Table(s): North Carolina: Corporate/M&A **Band 2**
p.2025

**Hopkins, Mariam T**
Table(s): Arkansas: Litigation: Medical
Malpractice Defense **Band 2** p.522

**Hopkins, Timothy**
Table(s): Idaho: Litigation: General Commercial
**Senior Statesmen:** p.1134

**Hopkinson, Christine A**
Profile: p.1085
Table(s): Georgia: Antitrust **Associates to watch**
p.1037

**Hopkinson, R Ronald**
Profile: p.336
Table(s): Nationwide: Private Equity: Buyouts
**Band 5** p.203

**Hopson, Edwin**
Profile: p.1320
Table(s): Kentucky: Labor & Employment **Band 1**
p.1310

**Hopson, Keith**
Table(s): Texas: Environment **Band 2** p.2343

**Hopson, Mark D**
Profile: p.870
Table(s): District of Columbia: Litigation: White-
Collar Crime & Government Investigations **Band 2**
p.827

**Hoptman, Virginia Whitner**
Table(s): Virginia: Litigation: General
Commercial **Band 3** p.2502

**Horacek, Joseph**
Table(s): California: Media & Entertainment:
Transactional: Mainly Talent **Band 2** p.609

**Horan, Richard**
Table(s): Northern Virginia: Corporate/M&A **Band
1** p.2493

**Hord, Charles**
Profile: p.336
Table(s): Nationwide: Energy: Electricity
(Transactional) **Band 3** p.77

**Horder, Richard**
Table(s): Georgia: Environment **Band 1** p.1051

**Hori, Susan K**
Table(s): California: Real Estate: Zoning/Land
Use **Band 3** p.612

**Horkovich, Robert M**
Profile: p.336
Table(s): Nationwide: Insurance: Dispute
Resolution: Policyholder **Band 1** p.137, New York:
Insurance: Dispute Resolution: Policyholder **Band
1** p.1816

**Horlick, Gary N**
Table(s): Nationwide: International Trade: Trade
Remedies & Trade Policy **Band 1** p.154

**Horn, Charles M**
Profile: p.336
Table(s): Nationwide: Financial Services
Regulation: Banking (Compliance) **Band 2** p.96

**Horn, Lawrence S**
Profile: p.1737
Table(s): New Jersey: Litigation: White-Collar
Crime & Government Investigations **Band 1**
p.1723

**Horn, Todd J**
Profile: p.1428
Table(s): Maryland: Labor & Employment **Band 1**
p.1417

**Horne, Daniel**
Table(s): California: Immigration **Up-and-coming
individuals** p.571

**Horneman, H Carl**
Profile: p.1320
Table(s): Kentucky: Environment, Natural
Resources & Utilities: Environment **Band 2** p.1307

**Hornreich, Michael**
Profile: p.995
Table(s): Florida: Construction **Band 1** p.944

**Horoschak, Mark J**
Table(s): North Carolina: Antitrust **Band 1** p.2020,
North Carolina: Litigation: Healthcare & Medical
Malpractice **Band 1** p.2034

**Horowitz, Alan**
Profile: p.336
Table(s): Nationwide: Tax: Controversy **Band 3**
p.244

**Horowitz, Douglas S.**
Profile: p.336
Table(s): Nationwide: Capital Markets: Debt & Equity **Band 4** p.46

**Horowitz, Gary I**
Profile: p.336
Table(s): Nationwide: Private Equity: Buyouts **Band 1** p.203, New York: Corporate/M&A **Band 2** p.1793, New York: Insurance: Transactional & Regulatory **Band 3** p.1816

**Horowitz, Gregory**
Profile: p.1737
Table(s): New Jersey: Litigation: Insurance **Band 3** p.1723

**Horowitz, Mitchell**
Table(s): Florida: Tax **Band 2** p.979

**Horowitz, Philip**
Profile: p.870
Table(s): District of Columbia: Real Estate **Band 2** p.835

**Horowitz, Steven G**
Profile: p.337
Table(s): Nationwide: Real Estate **Band 1** p.225, New York: Real Estate: Corporate **Band 2** p.1854, New York: Real Estate: Finance **Band 1** p.1854

**Horsch, Richard**
Profile: p.1905
Table(s): New York: Environment: Mainly Transactional **Band 3** p.1808

**Horsnell, Chris**
Table(s): Tennessee: Media & Entertainment **Band 2** p.2297

**Horst, Jeffrey D**
Profile: p.1085
Table(s): Georgia: Litigation: General Commercial **Band 4** p.1065

**Horton, Bob**
Profile: p.2305
Table(s): Tennessee: Labor & Employment **Band 3** p.2293

**Horton, Michel Yves**
Profile: p.337
Table(s): Nationwide: Insurance: Dispute Resolution: Policyholder **Band 2** p.137, California: Insurance: Policyholder **Band 2** p.576

**Horwitz, Debbie**
Table(s): Massachusetts: Real Estate **Band 3** p.1478

**Horwitz, Jeffrey A**
Table(s): Nationwide: Leisure & Hospitality **Band 2** p.179

**Horwitz, Justin A**
Profile: p.1773
Table(s): New Mexico: Corporate/Commercial **Band 3** p.1764

**Horwitz, Richard L**
Profile: p.771
Table(s): Delaware: Intellectual Property **Band 1** p.763

**Hosch, Heyward C**
Profile: p.470
Table(s): Alabama: Banking & Finance: Public Finance **Band 2** p.455

**Hosenpud, David**
Profile: p.2176
Table(s): Oregon: Labor & Employment **Band 4** p.2168

**Hosking, James**
Profile: p.337
Table(s): Nationwide: International Arbitration **Band 4** p.145

**Hotz, Jr., Robert H.**
Profile: p.1905
Table(s): New York: Litigation: White-Collar Crime & Government Investigations **Band 3** p.1836

**Houghton, Robert**
Table(s): Iowa: Litigation: General Commercial **Band 3** p.1288

**Houk, D Reed**
Profile: p.2305
Table(s): Tennessee: Real Estate **Band 2** p.2299

**Houle, Jeffrey R**
Profile: p.870
Table(s): District of Columbia: Corporate/M&A & Private Equity **Band 4** p.797

**Houpt, Timothy C**
Profile: p.2474
Table(s): Utah: Litigation: General Commercial **Band 2** p.2468

**House, George W**
Table(s): North Carolina: Environment **Band 1** p.2028

**House, Holly A**
Table(s): California: Antitrust **Band 3** p.536

**House, W Michael**
Table(s): Nationwide: Government: Government Relations **Band 1** p.121

**Houser, Bradley D**
Table(s): Florida: Banking & Finance: Transactional **Band 2** p.937, Florida: Corporate/M&A & Private Equity **Band 4** p.947

**Houser, Douglas**
Table(s): Oregon: Litigation: General Commercial **Senior Statesmen:** p.2171

**Houston, David S**
Table(s): Northern Virginia: Real Estate **Band 2** p.2505

**Houston III, Jamie G**
Profile: p.1604
Table(s): Mississippi: Corporate/Commercial **Band 2** p.1591

**Hoven, Daniel**
Table(s): Montana: Litigation: General Commercial **Band 1** p.1649

**Hovermale, Kenneth**
Table(s): Maine: Litigation: Medical Malpractice & Insurance **Band 2** p.1393

**Hovious, R Gregg**
Table(s): Kentucky: Litigation: General Commercial **Band 1** p.1312

**Hovis, James W**
Table(s): North Carolina: Banking & Finance **Band 1** p.2021

**Howard, Christopher E**
Profile: p.1400
Table(s): Maine: Corporate/M&A **Band 1** p.1385

**Howard, Douglas P**
Table(s): Maryland: Corporate/M&A **Associates to watch** p.1412

**Howard, Geoffrey M**
Profile: p.642
Table(s): California: Intellectual Property: Trademark, Copyright & Trade Secrets **Band 2** p.578

**Howard, Lindsay**
Table(s): Pennsylvania: Environment **Band 3** p.2194

**Howard, Nigel L**
Profile: p.337
Table(s): Nationwide: Outsourcing **Band 1** p.195, New York: Technology & Outsourcing **Band 1** p.1868

**Howard, Oliver S**
Table(s): Oklahoma: Litigation: General Commercial **Band 2** p.2141

**Howard, R Craig**
Profile: p.1682
Table(s): Nevada: Real Estate **Band 3** p.1679

**Howard, Robert**
Profile: p.642
Table(s): California: Environment **Band 3** p.564

**Howard Jr, George S**
Profile: p.643
Table(s): California: Labor & Employment **Band 2** p.587

**Howe, Joseph**
Profile: p.337
Table(s): Nationwide: Capital Markets: REITs **Band 3** p.55, District of Columbia: Tax **Band 3** p.838

**Howell, D Clayton**
Profile: p.1085
Table(s): Georgia: Real Estate **Band 3** p.1070

**Howell, John E**
Profile: p.337
Table(s): Nationwide: Outsourcing **Star Individuals** p.195, Texas: Technology: Outsourcing **Star individuals** p.2376

**Howell, Steven G**
Profile: p.1551
Table(s): Michigan: Banking & Finance: Bankruptcy **Band 2** p.1536

**Howell, Trent**
Table(s): New Mexico: Labor & Employment **Band 3** p.1767

**Howell III, George C**
Profile: p.337
Table(s): Nationwide: Capital Markets: REITs **Band 1** p.55

**Howie, Robert M.**
Table(s): Washington: Labor & Employment **Band 2** p.2531

**Howitt, John P**
Profile: p.337
Table(s): Nationwide: Banking & Finance: Equipment Finance & Leasing **Band 1** p.32, Nationwide: Transportation: Aviation: Finance **Band 1** p.252

**Howlett, Timothy**
Profile: p.1551
Table(s): Michigan: Labor & Employment **Band 2** p.1542

**Howley, Sean M**
Table(s): Virginia: Construction **Band 3** p.2491

**Howley, Thomas A**
Profile: p.2396
Table(s): Texas: Bankruptcy/Restructuring **Band 3** p.2328

**Hoyme, Christopher**
Profile: p.1668
Table(s): Nebraska: Labor & Employment **Band 3** p.1662

**Hoyne, Andrew**
Table(s): Missouri: Corporate/M&A **Band 3** p.1619

**Hoyng, Charles F**
Profile: p.643
Table(s): Nationwide: Life Sciences: IP/Patent Litigation **Band 3** p.183, California: Life Sciences: Corporate/Commercial **Band 2** p.590

**Hoyns, John K**
Profile: p.337
Table(s): Nationwide: Banking & Finance: Equipment Finance & Leasing **Band 2** p.32, Nationwide: Transportation: Aviation: Finance **Band 2** p.252

**Hoyos, Maite**
Table(s): Florida: Immigration **Band 3** p.956

**Hribernick, Paul R**
Table(s): Oregon: Labor & Employment: Immigration **Band 1** p.2168

**Hroblak, Kevin G**
Profile: p.1428
Table(s): Maryland: Litigation: Bankruptcy **Up-and-coming individuals** p.1419, Maryland: Litigation: General Commercial **Up-and-coming individuals** p.1419

**Hsiao, Peter**
Profile: p.643
Table(s): California: Environment **Band 4** p.564

**Hsing, Benjamin**
Profile: p.1905
Table(s): New York: Intellectual Property: Patent **Band 3** p.1820

**Huard, David**
Table(s): California: Energy: State Regulatory & Litigation **Band 3** p.562

**Hubbard, Heidi K**
Table(s): Nationwide: Product Liability & Mass Torts **Band 2** p.208

**Hubbard, Paul**
Table(s): North Dakota: Real Estate **Band 1** p.2055

**Huber, Betty Moy**
Profile: p.1905
Table(s): New York: Environment: Mainly Transactional **Band 1** p.1808

**Hurley, Patrick**
Table(s): New Mexico: Real Estate Senior
Statesmen: p.1772

**Hurley, Timothy J**
Profile: p.2100
Table(s): Ohio: Bankruptcy/Restructuring Band 1
p.2058

**Hurney Jr, Thomas J**
Table(s): West Virginia: Litigation: Healthcare
Band 1 p.2555

**Hurst, Annette**
Table(s): California: Intellectual Property:
Trademark, Copyright & Trade Secrets Band 2
p.578

**Hurst, James F**
Profile: p.1212
Table(s): Illinois: Intellectual Property Band 2
p.1171

**Hurst Jr, Joseph B**
Profile: p.527
Table(s): Arkansas: Labor & Employment:
Employee Benefits & Compensation Band 2
p.521

**Hurt, Jeffrey**
Profile: p.1300
Table(s): Kansas: Labor & Employment Band 2
p.1294

**Hurt, Richard T**
Table(s): Florida: Tax: Employee Benefits Band 2
p.979

**Hurtuk, Edward**
Table(s): Ohio: Real Estate Band 4 p.2086

**Hurvitz, John A**
Profile: p.338
Table(s): Nationwide: Life Sciences:
Corporate/Commercial Band 1 p.182

**Hurwitz, Ann**
Profile: p.338
Table(s): Nationwide: Franchising Band 2 p.111

**Husar, Linda S**
Table(s): California: Labor & Employment Band 4
p.587

**Husband, John**
Profile: p.719
Table(s): Colorado: Labor & Employment Band 1
p.706

**Husch, Gerald T**
Table(s): Idaho: Labor & Employment Band 1
p.1132

**Husid, Douglas M**
Table(s): Massachusetts: Real Estate:
Zoning/Land Use Band 1 p.1478

**Huss, R Bradford**
Table(s): California: Employee Benefits &
Executive Compensation Band 2 p.560

**Husseini, Richard**
Table(s): Nationwide: Tax: Controversy Band 4
p.244

**Hussell IV, John F**
Table(s): West Virginia: Corporate/Commercial:
Tax Band 2 p.2550

**Hussle, Robert C**
Profile: p.1085
Table(s): Georgia: Corporate/M&A Band 3 p.1046

**Huston, Thomas C**
Table(s): Nebraska: Real Estate Band 3 p.1666,
Nebraska: Real Estate: Zoning/Land Use Band 2
p.1666

**Hutcheson, Mark A**
Table(s): Washington: Labor & Employment Band
1 p.2531

**Hutchings, Jeffrey D**
Profile: p.870
Table(s): District of Columbia: Technology &
Outsourcing Band 2 p.842

**Hutchings, Julie**
Profile: p.338
Table(s): Nationwide: Projects Associates to watch
p.216

**Hutchings, Michael**
Profile: p.2539
Table(s): Washington: Corporate/Commercial
Band 3 p.2525

**Hutchings, Stephen H**
Profile: p.492
Table(s): Alaska: Litigation: Construction Band 1
p.490, Alaska: Litigation: General Commercial
Band 3 p.490

**Hutchings Reed, Mary**
Profile: p.1212
Table(s): Illinois: Media & Entertainment:
Transactional Band 1 p.1185

**Hutchinson, James A**
Profile: p.870
Table(s): District of Columbia: Corporate/M&A &
Private Equity Band 3 p.797

**Hutchinson Jr, Joseph F**
Profile: p.2100
Table(s): Ohio: Bankruptcy/Restructuring Band 1
p.2058

**Hutchison, Fred D**
Profile: p.2041
Table(s): North Carolina: Corporate/M&A Band 3
p.2025

**Hutnik, Alysa Zeltzer**
Table(s): Nationwide: Privacy & Data Security
Band 3 p.199

**Hutson, Benne C**
Table(s): North Carolina: Environment Band 1
p.2028

**Hutt, Peter Barton**
Profile: p.870
Table(s): Nationwide: Food & Beverages:
Regulatory & Litigation Band 1 p.107, District of
Columbia: Healthcare: Pharmaceutical/Medical
Products Regulatory Senior Statesmen: p.810

**Hutter, Patricia M**
Profile: p.2583
Table(s): Wisconsin: Corporate/M&A Band 3
p.2571

**Hutton, Lee J**
Profile: p.2100
Table(s): Ohio: Labor & Employment Band 3
p.2074

**Hutton III, John B**
Profile: p.995
Table(s): Florida: Bankruptcy/Restructuring Band
3 p.939

**Hutz, Rudolf E**
Table(s): Delaware: Intellectual Property Senior
Statesmen: p.763

**Huvelle, Jeffrey**
Profile: p.338
Table(s): Nationwide: ERISA Litigation Band 2
p.92

**Hyatt, Thomas**
Profile: p.870
Table(s): District of Columbia: Healthcare Band 3
p.809

**Hyatt, Townsend**
Table(s): Nationwide: Native American Law Band
1 p.192

**Hyatt, Jr, William H**
Profile: p.1738
Table(s): New Jersey: Environment Band 1 p.1711

**Hyde, James Dudley**
Profile: p.2150
Table(s): Oklahoma: Labor & Employment Band 3
p.2140

**Hyde, Kevin E**
Table(s): Florida: Labor & Employment Band 2
p.959

**Hyde, Robert C**
Table(s): Utah: Real Estate Band 1 p.2470

**Hyman, Milt**
Profile: p.643
Table(s): California: Tax Senior Statesmen: p.617

**Hynes, Patricia**
Table(s): New York: Litigation: General
Commercial Band 3 p.1833

**Hynes, Terence M**
Profile: p.338
Table(s): Nationwide: Transportation: Rail (for
Railroads) Band 2 p.257

# I

**Iancu, Andrei**
Profile: p.643
Table(s): California: Intellectual Property: Patent
Band 4 p.578

**Iani, John**
Table(s): Washington: Environment Band 2
p.2527

**Iannaccone, Carmine A**
Profile: p.1738
Table(s): New Jersey: Labor & Employment Band
2 p.1718

**Ianniello, Antonia B**
Table(s): District of Columbia: Insurance:
Insurer Band 2 p.816

**Ianno Jr, Joseph**
Profile: p.995
Table(s): Florida: Litigation: General Commercial
Band 4 p.966

**Iason, Lawrence**
Profile: p.1905
Table(s): New York: Litigation: White-Collar
Crime & Government Investigations Band 3
p.1836

**Ibarra, Yosbel A**
Profile: p.995
Table(s): Florida: Latin American Investment
Band 4 p.963

**Ibrahim, Ray**
Profile: p.338
Table(s): Nationwide: Capital Markets:
Derivatives Band 2 p.51

**Ice, Thomas**
Table(s): Kentucky: Real Estate Band 2 p.1314

**Ichel, David W**
Profile: p.1905
Table(s): Nationwide: Product Liability & Mass
Torts Band 4 p.208, New York: Litigation: General
Commercial Band 2 p.1833

**Ifrah, A Jeff**
Profile: p.870
Table(s): District of Columbia: Litigation: White-
Collar Crime & Government Investigations Band 3
p.827

**Ignacio, Vanessa**
Profile: p.1738
Table(s): New Jersey: Intellectual Property
Associates to watch p.1716

**Ihrig, Richard**
Table(s): Minnesota: Litigation: General
Commercial Band 3 p.1574

**Imes, Linda**
Table(s): New York: Litigation: White-Collar
Crime & Government Investigations Band 3
p.1836

**Immelt, Stephen**
Table(s): Nationwide: Healthcare: Regulatory &
Litigation Band 3 p.127, Maryland: Healthcare
Band 1 p.1415, Maryland: Litigation: General
Commercial Band 2 p.1419

**Immerman, Leon Andrew**
Profile: p.1085
Table(s): Georgia: Tax Band 2 p.1072

**Imperato, Gabriel L**
Table(s): Nationwide: Healthcare: Regulatory &
Litigation Band 1 p.127, Florida: Healthcare Band
1 p.954

**Imse, Peter**
Table(s): New Hampshire: Real Estate Band 1
p.1692

**Imus, Neil W**
Profile: p.870
Table(s): District of Columbia: Antitrust Band 5
p.787

**Indek, Ben**
Profile: p.338
Table(s): Nationwide: Securities: Regulation:
Enforcement Band 3 p.233

**Infinger, Marvin D**
Table(s): South Carolina: Litigation: General
Commercial Band 4 p.2264

**Jackson, Thomas R**
Profile: p.2397
Table(s): Texas: Antitrust **Band 3** p.2323

**Jackson, William**
Table(s): Texas: Environment **Band 4** p.2343

**Jackson, William Stuart**
Profile: p.527
Table(s): Arkansas: Labor & Employment **Band 2** p.520

**Jacob, Clyde**
Profile: p.1364
Table(s): Louisiana: Labor & Employment **Band 1** p.1350

**Jacob, Cynthia M**
Profile: p.1738
Table(s): New Jersey: Labor & Employment **Senior Statesmen**: p.1718

**Jacob, John**
Profile: p.871
Table(s): District of Columbia: Healthcare **Band 2** p.809

**Jacob, Lynn F**
Table(s): Virginia: Labor & Employment **Band 3** p.2500

**Jacob, Valerie Ford**
Profile: p.339
Table(s): Nationwide: Capital Markets: Debt & Equity **Band 1** p.46

**Jacobs, Bruce D**
Profile: p.871
Table(s): District of Columbia: Telecom, Broadcast & Satellite **Band 3** p.844

**Jacobs, Caryn**
Profile: p.1213
Table(s): Illinois: Litigation: General Commercial **Band 4** p.1180

**Jacobs, Charles P**
Profile: p.339
Table(s): Nationwide: Investment Funds: Private Equity: Fund Formation **Band 2** p.166

**Jacobs, Donna Brown**
Profile: p.1604
Table(s): Mississippi: Litigation: Appellate **Band 3** p.1596

**Jacobs, Gina**
Profile: p.1604
Table(s): Mississippi: Corporate/Commercial **Band 3** p.1591

**Jacobs, Hara K**
Profile: p.2220
Table(s): Pennsylvania: Intellectual Property **Band 4** p.2197

**Jacobs, Howard L**
Profile: p.339
Table(s): Nationwide: Sports Law: Athletic Disputes **Band 1** p.241

**Jacobs, Matthew L**
Profile: p.871
Table(s): District of Columbia: Insurance: Policyholder **Band 2** p.818

**Jacobs, Michael A**
Profile: p.644
Table(s): California: Intellectual Property: Patent **Band 1** p.578

**Jacobs, Neil**
Profile: p.1496
Table(s): Massachusetts: Labor & Employment **Senior Statesmen**: p.1466

**Jacobs, Paul**
Table(s): Colorado: Real Estate **Band 1** p.714

**Jacobs, Robert A**
Profile: p.644
Table(s): California: Media & Entertainment: Litigation **Band 4** p.606

**Jacobs, Robert P**
Table(s): District of Columbia: Insurance: Policyholder **Band 2** p.818

**Jacobs, Ronald**
Profile: p.339
Table(s): Nationwide: Government: Political Law **Band 3** p.124

**Jacobs, Stephen C**
Profile: p.2397
Table(s): Texas: Real Estate **Band 2** p.2367

**Jacobs-Meadway, Roberta**
Table(s): Pennsylvania: Intellectual Property **Band 1** p.2197

**Jacobsen, Brad**
Table(s): Utah: Corporate/M&A **Band 3** p.2462

**Jacobsen, Wayne**
Table(s): California: Employee Benefits & Executive Compensation **Band 2** p.560

**Jacobsen Jr, Raymond A**
Profile: p.871
Table(s): District of Columbia: Antitrust **Band 3** p.787

**Jacobson, Craig**
Table(s): California: Media & Entertainment: Transactional: Mainly Talent **Band 2** p.609

**Jacobson, Doug**
Table(s): Nationwide: International Trade: Export Controls & Economic Sanctions **Band 3** p.153

**Jacobson, Fruman**
Profile: p.1213
Table(s): Illinois: Bankruptcy/Restructuring **Band 3** p.1148

**Jacobson, Hillel**
Profile: p.1906
Table(s): New York: Tax **Up-and-coming individuals** p.1862

**Jacobson, John R**
Table(s): Tennessee: Litigation: General Commercial **Band 2** p.2295

**Jacobson, Jonathan**
Table(s): New York: Antitrust **Band 1** p.1778

**Jacobson, Marc**
Profile: p.1906
Table(s): New York: Media & Entertainment: Music **Band 1** p.1849

**Jacobson, Michael A**
Table(s): Illinois: Banking & Finance **Band 3** p.1145

**Jacobson, Michele L**
Table(s): New York: Insurance: Dispute Resolution: Insurer **Band 3** p.1816

**Jacobson, Ronald H**
Profile: p.1213
Table(s): Illinois: Banking & Finance **Band 2** p.1145

**Jacobson, Seth E**
Profile: p.1213
Table(s): Illinois: Banking & Finance **Band 3** p.1145

**Jacoby, Aaron**
Profile: p.339
Table(s): Nationwide: Transportation: Road (Carriage/Commercial) **Band 3** p.259

**Jacus, John R**
Profile: p.719
Table(s): Colorado: Natural Resources & Environment **Band 2** p.712

**Jaeger, Lisa M**
Profile: p.871
Table(s): District of Columbia: Environment **Band 5** p.804

**Jaffe, Arvin J**
Table(s): Florida: Banking & Finance: Transactional **Band 2** p.937

**Jaffe, Helene D**
Table(s): New York: Antitrust **Band 3** p.1778

**Jaffe, Kenneth G**
Profile: p.340
Table(s): Nationwide: Energy: Electricity (Regulatory & Litigation) **Band 1** p.76

**Jaffe, Marc D**
Profile: p.340
Table(s): Nationwide: Capital Markets: Debt & Equity **Band 1** p.46

**Jaffe, Michael Evan**
Table(s): District of Columbia: Construction **Band 1** p.795

**Jaffe, Richard P**
Table(s): Pennsylvania: Corporate/M&A & Private Equity **Band 3** p.2191

**Jaffe, Seth D**
Profile: p.1496
Table(s): Massachusetts: Environment **Band 1** p.1457

**Jaffe Bloom, Suzanne**
Profile: p.1906
Table(s): New York: Litigation: White-Collar Crime & Government Investigations **Band 3** p.1836

**Jahn, Paul E**
Profile: p.644
Table(s): California: IT & Outsourcing **Band 2** p.583

**Jahnke, Mark J**
Table(s): Ohio: Corporate/M&A **Band 1** p.2064

**Jahrling III, Robert V**
Profile: p.1496
Table(s): Massachusetts: Corporate/M&A **Band 4** p.1452

**Jain, Samir**
Profile: p.871
Table(s): District of Columbia: Telecom, Broadcast & Satellite **Band 3** p.844

**Jakes, J Michael**
Profile: p.871
Table(s): District of Columbia: Intellectual Property: Litigation **Band 2** p.821

**Jakubowicz, Janet P**
Profile: p.1321
Table(s): Kentucky: Litigation: General Commercial **Band 2** p.1312

**Jakubowski, Paul**
Profile: p.1496
Table(s): Massachusetts: Real Estate **Band 3** p.1478

**Jalinous, Farhad**
Profile: p.340
Table(s): Nationwide: International Trade: CFIUS Experts **Band 1** p.152

**James, Bruce A**
Table(s): Colorado: Real Estate: Hotels & Leisure **Band 1** p.714

**James, Doug**
Table(s): Montana: Corporate/M&A **Band 2** p.1646

**James, Dwight W**
Table(s): Iowa: Litigation: General Commercial **Senior Statesmen**: p.1288

**James, Eric A**
Profile: p.1123
Table(s): Hawaii: Real Estate **Band 1** p.1120

**James, Jeffrey**
Table(s): Washington: Labor & Employment **Band 2** p.2531

**James, Kurt F**
Profile: p.1637
Table(s): Missouri: Intellectual Property **Band 2** p.1623

**James, Norman D**
Table(s): Arizona: Environment (including water rights) **Band 1** p.497

**James, Robert F**
Table(s): Montana: Litigation: General Commercial **Band 2** p.1649

**Jameson, John**
Table(s): California: Banking & Finance **Band 2** p.539

**Jameson, Louis Norwood**
Table(s): Georgia: Intellectual Property **Band 2** p.1056

**Jamieson, Brewster**
Profile: p.492
Table(s): Alaska: Litigation: General Commercial **Band 2** p.490

**Janick III, Herbert F**
Profile: p.340
Table(s): Nationwide: Securities: Regulation: Enforcement **Band 1** p.233

**Janik, Stephen**
Table(s): Oregon: Real Estate **Star individuals** p.2173, Oregon: Real Estate: Zoning/Land Use **Star individuals** p.2173

**Janis, John**
Table(s): Idaho: Litigation: Medical Malpractice & Insurance **Band 2** p.1134

**Janis, Ronald H**
Profile: p.1738
Table(s): New Jersey: Corporate/M&A **Band 1**
p.1707

**Janka, John P**
Profile: p.871
Table(s): District of Columbia: Telecom,
Broadcast & Satellite **Band 2** p.844

**Jankowsky, Joel**
Profile: p.340
Table(s): Nationwide: Government: Government
Relations **Band 1** p.121

**Janos, Ellen L**
Profile: p.1496
Table(s): Massachusetts: Healthcare **Band 2**
p.1460

**Janove, Jathan**
Profile: p.2176
Table(s): Oregon: Labor & Employment **Band 4**
p.2168

**Janowitz, James**
Table(s): New York: Media & Entertainment:
Film & Television **Band 3** p.1849

**Janowitz, Robert**
Table(s): Missouri: Labor & Employment **Band 2**
p.1625

**Jansonius, John V**
Profile: p.2397
Table(s): Texas: Labor & Employment **Band 1**
p.2359

**Januszewski, David**
Profile: p.1906
Table(s): New York: Litigation: General
Commercial **Band 4** p.1833

**Jaqua, David P**
Profile: p.2306
Table(s): Tennessee: Labor & Employment **Band 1** p.2293

**Jardine, James S**
Table(s): Utah: Litigation: General Commercial
**Band 1** p.2468

**Jarin, Kenneth M**
Profile: p.2220
Table(s): Pennsylvania: Labor & Employment
**Band 3** p.2200

**Jaros, Tom**
Table(s): Illinois: Real Estate **Band 3** p.1187

**Jarosh, Robert**
Table(s): Wyoming: Labor & Employment **Band 1**
p.2597, Wyoming: Litigation: General
Commercial **Band 2** p.2598

**Jarpe, Geoffrey P**
Table(s): Minnesota: Litigation: General
Commercial **Band 2** p.1574

**Jarrell, Brenda H**
Profile: p.1496
Table(s): Massachusetts: Intellectual Property
**Band 2** p.1463

**Jarrell, Eric E.**
Table(s): Louisiana: Environment **Band 3** p.1346

**Jarrett, Danny W**
Profile: p.1773
Table(s): New Mexico: Labor & Employment
**Band 2** p.1767

**Jarrett, R. Keith**
Table(s): Louisiana: Litigation: General
Commercial **Band 3** p.1352

**Jarvis, Thomas L**
Profile: p.340
Table(s): Nationwide: International Trade:
Intellectual Property (Section 337) **Band 1** p.160

**Jasaitis, James E**
Profile: p.1738
Table(s): New Jersey: Corporate/M&A **Band 3**
p.1707

**Jaskolski, Michael A**
Profile: p.2583
Table(s): Wisconsin: Intellectual Property **Band 3**
p.2573

**Jauffret, Jennifer C**
Profile: p.771
Table(s): Delaware: Labor & Employment **Band 2**
p.765

**Jaunich, R Prescott**
Table(s): Vermont: Real Estate **Band 2** p.2487

**Jebejian, Sarkis**
Profile: p.1906
Table(s): New York: Corporate/M&A **Up-and-coming Individuals** p.1793

**Jedrey, Christopher M**
Profile: p.1496
Table(s): Nationwide: Healthcare: Transactional
**Band 2** p.128, Massachusetts: Healthcare **Band 1**
p.1460

**Jeffcoat III, Otis Allen**
Profile: p.2270
Table(s): South Carolina: Real Estate **Band 3**
p.2266

**Jeffery, D Ethan**
Profile: p.1496
Table(s): Massachusetts:
Bankruptcy/Restructuring **Band 3** p.1449

**Jeffery, Stephen G**
Table(s): Missouri: Environment **Band 2** p.1621

**Jeffress Jr, William H**
Table(s): Nationwide: Litigation: Trial Lawyers
**Band 1** p.187, District of Columbia: Litigation:
General Commercial **Band 1** p.826, District of
Columbia: Litigation: White-Collar Crime &
Government Investigations **Band 1** p.826

**Jeffries, M Hill**
Profile: p.1085
Table(s): Georgia: Corporate/M&A **Band 2** p.1046

**Jeffry, Thomas**
Profile: p.644
Table(s): California: Healthcare **Band 4** p.568

**Jelencic, Sarah O**
Table(s): Wisconsin: Real Estate **Band 2** p.2579

**Jellinek, Charles B**
Table(s): Missouri: Labor & Employment **Band 2**
p.1625

**Jelsma, Franklin**
Profile: p.1321
Table(s): Kentucky: Corporate/M&A **Band 3**
p.1305

**Jenett, Bruce W**
Profile: p.644
Table(s): California: Life Sciences:
Corporate/Commercial **Band 2** p.590

**Jenkins, David**
Table(s): Delaware: Chancery: Mainly Plaintiff
**Band 2** p.759

**Jenkins, Dennis L**
Profile: p.1496
Table(s): Massachusetts:
Bankruptcy/Restructuring **Band 3** p.1449

**Jenkins, John**
Profile: p.2100
Table(s): Ohio: Corporate/M&A **Band 2** p.2064

**Jenkins, Lucy B**
Profile: p.2474
Table(s): Utah: Energy & Natural Resources **Band 2** p.2464

**Jenkins, Maurice**
Profile: p.1551
Table(s): Michigan: Labor & Employment **Band 3**
p.1542

**Jenkins, Stephen E**
Profile: p.771
Table(s): Delaware: Chancery **Band 2** p.758

**Jenkins, Steve**
Table(s): Texas: Real Estate **Band 1** p.2367

**Jenkins III, Robert M**
Table(s): Nationwide: Transportation: Rail (for
Railroads) **Band 1** p.257

**Jenner, Jesse J**
Table(s): New York: Intellectual Property: Patent
**Band 1** p.1820

**Jennings, Deborah E**
Profile: p.872
Table(s): District of Columbia: Environment **Band 4** p.804

**Jennings, John M.**
Profile: p.2270
Table(s): South Carolina: Corporate/M&A **Band 3**
p.2260

**Jennings, Paul G**
Profile: p.2306
Table(s): Tennessee: Litigation: Bankruptcy **Band 1** p.2295

**Jennings Jr, James W**
Table(s): Virginia: Litigation: General
Commercial **Band 2** p.2502

**Jennis, David**
Table(s): Florida: Bankruptcy/Restructuring **Band 4** p.939

**Jensen, Curtis S**
Table(s): South Dakota: Real Estate **Band 1**
p.2286

**Jensen, Daniel A**
Table(s): Utah: Energy & Natural Resources **Band 2** p.2464, Utah: Energy & Natural Resources:
Water Law p.2464

**Jensen, David S**
Table(s): Idaho: Corporate/Commercial **Band 2**
p.1132, Idaho: Real Estate **Band 2** p.1138

**Jensen, Eric**
Table(s): Nationwide: Investment Funds: Venture
Capital **Band 2** p.174, California: Capital Markets:
Debt & Equity **Band 3** p.547, California:
Corporate/M&A: Venture Capital **Band 4** p.555

**Jensen, Garth B.**
Table(s): Colorado: Corporate/M&A **Band 2** p.703

**Jensen, J Christopher**
Table(s): New York: Intellectual Property: Trade
Mark & Copyright **Band 3** p.1821

**Jensen, Jill Gossin**
Table(s): Nebraska: Healthcare **Band 2** p.1661

**Jensen, John E**
Table(s): Nationwide: Government: Government
Contracts **Band 4** p.117

**Jensen-Welch, Jill R**
Table(s): Iowa: Labor & Employment **Band 2**
p.1285

**Jepson Jr, Edward C**
Profile: p.1213
Table(s): Illinois: Labor & Employment **Band 2**
p.1175

**Jernigan, John L**
Profile: p.2041
Table(s): North Carolina: Corporate/M&A **Band 1**
p.2025

**Jernigan Jr, W Henry**
Table(s): West Virginia: Litigation: General
Commercial **Band 1** p.2555

**Jernstedt, Kenneth**
Table(s): Oregon: Labor & Employment **Senior Statesmen:** p.2168

**Jerome, John**
Profile: p.1906
Table(s): New York: Bankruptcy/Restructuring
**Senior Statesmen:** p.1782

**Jessen, Polly**
Profile: p.719
Table(s): Colorado: Natural Resources &
Environment **Band 3** p.712

**Jessup Jr, Clifton R**
Profile: p.2397
Table(s): Texas: Bankruptcy/Restructuring **Band 2**
p.2328

**Jester, Amanda**
Table(s): Florida: Healthcare **Up-and-coming Individuals** p.954

**Jew, Quana**
Profile: p.872
Table(s): District of Columbia: Employee
Benefits & Executive Compensation **Band 3** p.801

**Jewell, Robert V**
Profile: p.2397
Table(s): Texas: Capital Markets: Debt & Equity
**Band 3** p.2333, Texas: Corporate/M&A **Band 1**
p.2337

**Jewett, Steve**
Table(s): Colorado: Intellectual Property **Band 2**
p.704

**Jezouit, Debra**
Profile: p.872
Table(s): **District of Columbia:** Environment **Band 5** p.804

**Jiménez, Marcos Daniel**
Profile: p.995
Table(s): **Florida:** Litigation: General Commercial **Band 3** p.966

**Jobeun, Larry**
Table(s): **Nebraska:** Real Estate **Band 2** p.1666, **Nebraska:** Real Estate: Zoning/Land Use **Band 1** p.1666

**Joblove, Michael D**
Table(s): **Nationwide:** Franchising **Band 2** p.111

**Jochim, Tim**
Table(s): **Ohio:** Employee Benefits & Executive Compensation **Band 3** p.2067

**Joe, Harry**
Profile: p.2397
Table(s): **Texas:** Immigration **Band 1** p.2349

**Johns, Daniel**
Profile: p.1654
Table(s): **Montana:** Labor & Employment **Band 3** p.1648

**Johns, Daniel V.**
Profile: p.2220
Table(s): **Pennsylvania:** Labor & Employment **Up-and-coming individuals** p.2200

**Johnson, Boyd**
Profile: p.1906
Table(s): **New York:** Litigation: White-Collar Crime & Government Investigations **Band 3** p.1836

**Johnson, Bruce**
Table(s): **Nationwide:** First Amendment Litigation **Band 2** p.105

**Johnson, Charles E**
Table(s): **North Carolina:** Labor & Employment **Band 2** p.2031

**Johnson, Cheryl**
Table(s): **Connecticut:** Corporate/M&A **Band 2** p.732

**Johnson, Christopher D**
Profile: p.509
Table(s): **Arizona:** Corporate/M&A **Band 1** p.495

**Johnson, Daniel**
Table(s): **Delaware:** Real Estate **Band 2** p.766

**Johnson, Daniel**
Table(s): **Texas:** Insurance **Up-and-coming individuals** p.2351

**Johnson, David**
Table(s): **New York:** Energy: State Regulatory & Wholesale Electric Market **Band 2** p.1806

**Johnson, David L**
Table(s): **North Dakota:** Bankruptcy/Restructuring **Band 1** p.2050

**Johnson, David R**
Profile: p.340
Table(s): **Nationwide:** Government: Government Contracts **Band 4** p.117, **Nationwide:** International Trade: Export Controls & Economic Sanctions **Band 2** p.153

**Johnson, Deidre**
Table(s): **Massachusetts:** Antitrust **Band 3** p.1444

**Johnson, Dennis A**
Profile: p.1277
Table(s): **Indiana:** Real Estate **Band 2** p.1275

**Johnson, Dixie L**
Profile: p.340
Table(s): **Nationwide:** Securities: Regulation: Enforcement **Band 2** p.233

**Johnson, Edward D**
Table(s): **California:** Litigation: General Commercial **Band 5** p.593

**Johnson, Glenn E**
Table(s): **Texas:** Energy: State Regulatory & Litigation (Oil & Gas) **Band 2** p.2341

**Johnson, Greg L.**
Table(s): **Louisiana:** Environment **Band 3** p.1346

**Johnson, Jeffrey P**
Table(s): **Vermont:** Corporate/Commercial: Captive Insurance **Band 1** p.2483

**Johnson, Jeffrey R**
Profile: p.340
Table(s): **Nationwide:** Capital Markets: Securitisation **Band 4** p.59

**Johnson, Jeffrey T**
Profile: p.719
Table(s): **Colorado:** Labor & Employment **Band 2** p.706

**Johnson, Jennifer A**
Profile: p.872
Table(s): **District of Columbia:** Telecom, Broadcast & Satellite **Band 3** p.844

**Johnson, Keith H**
Table(s): **North Carolina:** Environment **Band 4** p.2028

**Johnson, Kenneth**
Table(s): **Ohio:** Bankruptcy/Restructuring **Band 4** p.2058

**Johnson, Kevin**
Table(s): **California:** Intellectual Property: Patent **Band 4** p.578

**Johnson, Linda**
Table(s): **Alaska:** Labor & Employment **Band 3** p.489

**Johnson, Linda S**
Profile: p.1695
Table(s): **New Hampshire:** Labor & Employment **Band 1** p.1688

**Johnson, Louisa**
Profile: p.1086
Table(s): **Georgia:** Labor & Employment **Up-and-coming individuals** p.1060

**Johnson, Mark A**
Profile: p.2101
Table(s): **Ohio:** Litigation: General Commercial **Band 4** p.2078

**Johnson, Mark R**
Profile: p.1213
Table(s): **Illinois:** Energy & Natural Resources: Regulatory **Band 3** p.1161

**Johnson, Michael R**
Profile: p.2397
Table(s): **Texas:** Construction **Band 3** p.2335

**Johnson, Paul H.**
Table(s): **Oklahoma:** Intellectual Property **Senior Statesmen:** p.2138

**Johnson, Rene M**
Profile: p.1738
Table(s): **New Jersey:** Labor & Employment **Band 2** p.1718

**Johnson, Robert C**
Profile: p.1213
Table(s): **Illinois:** Insurance: Dispute Resolution **Band 1** p.1168

**Johnson, Robert K**
Profile: p.644
Table(s): **California:** Employee Benefits & Executive Compensation **Senior Statesmen:** p.560

**Johnson, Robert N**
Profile: p.1086
Table(s): **Georgia:** Immigration **Band 3** p.1055

**Johnson, Rodman C**
Table(s): **Texas:** Environment **Band 2** p.2343

**Johnson, Ross W**
Table(s): **Iowa:** Litigation: General Commercial **Band 4** p.1288

**Johnson, Steven**
Table(s): **North Dakota:** Corporate/Commercial **Band 1** p.2051

**Johnson, Steven**
Table(s): **South Dakota:** Litigation: General Commercial **Band 1** p.2284

**Johnson, Thomas**
Table(s): **Oregon:** Litigation: General Commercial **Up-and-coming individuals** p.2171

**Johnson, Thomas E**
Table(s): **Nebraska:** Litigation: General Commercial **Band 3** p.1664, **Nebraska:** Litigation: Insurance **Band 2** p.1664

**Johnson, Thora A**
Profile: p.1428
Table(s): **Maryland:** Employee Benefits & Executive Compensation **Band 2** p.1414

**Johnson, Tom**
Profile: p.719
Table(s): **Colorado:** Litigation: General Commercial **Band 3** p.709

**Johnson, V Duncan**
Profile: p.2257
Table(s): **Rhode Island:** Corporate/Commercial **Senior Statesmen:** p.2251

**Johnson, W Stanfield**
Profile: p.340
Table(s): **Nationwide:** Government: Government Contracts **Senior Statesmen:**

**Johnson, Walker**
Table(s): **Nationwide:** Tax: Controversy **Band 4** p.244

**Johnson, Weyman**
Table(s): **Georgia:** Labor & Employment **Senior Statesmen:** p.1060

**Johnson, William**
Table(s): **Nebraska:** Litigation: Insurance **Band 2** p.1664

**Johnson, William**
Profile: p.1906
Table(s): **New York:** Litigation: White-Collar Crime & Government Investigations **Band 2** p.1836

**Johnson III, Charles F**
Profile: p.1604
Table(s): **Mississippi:** Corporate/Commercial **Band 3** p.1591

**Johnson III, Joseph L**
Profile: p.1496
Table(s): **Massachusetts:** Corporate/M&A **Band 3** p.1452

**Johnson III, W.H. "Kip"**
Table(s): **North Carolina:** Corporate/M&A **Band 3** p.2025

**Johnson Jr, Alexander C**
Table(s): **Oregon:** Intellectual Property **Band 3** p.2167

**Johnson Jr, Daniel**
Profile: p.644
Table(s): **California:** Intellectual Property: Patent **Band 4** p.578

**Johnson Jr, John H**
Table(s): **Georgia:** Environment **Band 1** p.1051

**Johnson Jr, Patrick**
Profile: p.1364
Table(s): **Louisiana:** Bankruptcy/Restructuring **Band 2** p.1337

**Johnson Jr, Thomas G**
Table(s): **Southern Virginia:** Real Estate **Band 1** p.2506

**Johnson Lario, Wendy**
Profile: p.1738
Table(s): **New Jersey:** Labor & Employment **Band 2** p.1718

**Johnson, Jr., James H.**
Table(s): **Georgia:** Intellectual Property **Band 4** p.1056

**Johnston, Elaine**
Table(s): **New York:** Antitrust **Band 3** p.1778

**Johnston, Gordon**
Table(s): **Ohio:** Banking & Finance **Band 3** p.2056

**Johnston, James L**
Profile: p.1907
Table(s): **New York:** Media & Entertainment: Film & Television **Band 3** p.1849

**Johnston, James O**
Profile: p.644
Table(s): **California:** Bankruptcy/Restructuring **Band 2** p.542

**Johnston, Kenneth C**
Profile: p.2397
Table(s): **Texas:** Litigation: General Commercial **Band 4** p.2362

**Johnston, Michael**
Profile: p.1086
Table(s): **Georgia:** Labor & Employment **Band 1** p.1060

**Johnston, Pamela L**
Table(s): **California:** Litigation: White-Collar Crime & Government Investigations **Band 3** p.601

**Johnston, Ronald**
Profile: p.644
Table(s): **California**: Intellectual Property: Trademark, Copyright & Trade Secrets **Band 2** p.578

**Johnston, Susan A**
Table(s): **Massachusetts**: Tax **Band 1** p.1481

**Johnston, Thomas D**
Table(s): **Nationwide**: Tax: Controversy **Band 3** p.244

**Johnstone, Debbi M**
Profile: p.2397
Table(s): **Nationwide**: Healthcare: Transactional **Band 2** p.128, **Texas**: Healthcare **Band 1** p.2347

**Jolly, Ieuan**
Profile: p.340
Table(s): **Nationwide**: Privacy & Data Security **Band 3** p.199

**Jones, Alicia Grahn**
Table(s): **Nationwide**: Sports Law **Up-and-coming individuals** p.241

**Jones, Celeste**
Table(s): **South Carolina**: Litigation: General Commercial **Band 2** p.2264

**Jones, Christopher**
Profile: p.2101
Table(s): **Ohio**: Natural Resources & Environment **Band 3** p.2083

**Jones, Christy D**
Profile: p.341
Table(s): **Nationwide**: Litigation: Trial Lawyers **Band 2** p.187, **Nationwide**: Product Liability & Mass Torts **Star individuals** p.208, **Nationwide**: Product Liability: Pharmaceutical p.208, **Mississippi**: Litigation: General Commercial **Star individuals** p.1597

**Jones, David F**
Profile: p.2220
Table(s): **Pennsylvania**: Labor & Employment: Employee Benefits & Compensation **Band 1** p.2200

**Jones, Erika Z**
Table(s): **Nationwide**: Transportation: Road (Carriage/Commercial) **Band 1** p.259

**Jones, Evan M**
Table(s): **California**: Bankruptcy/Restructuring **Band 3** p.542

**Jones, Haskins W**
Table(s): **Alabama**: Banking & Finance **Band 3** p.455, **Alabama**: Real Estate **Band 3** p.466

**Jones, Heather Heiskell**
Profile: p.2563
Table(s): **West Virginia**: Litigation: General Commercial **Band 3** p.2555

**Jones, J Randall**
Table(s): **Nevada**: Litigation: General Commercial **Band 1** p.1677

**Jones, J Wesley**
Profile: p.2397
Table(s): **Texas**: Technology: Corporate & Commercial **Band 3** p.2375

**Jones, Jerald N**
Profile: p.1364
Table(s): **Louisiana**: Environment **Band 3** p.1346

**Jones, John**
Table(s): **Montana**: Real Estate **Band 3** p.1652

**Jones, Joseph E**
Table(s): **Nebraska**: Litigation: General Commercial **Band 2** p.1664, **Nebraska**: Litigation: Insurance **Band 2** p.1664

**Jones, Julie H**
Table(s): **Nationwide**: Private Equity: Buyouts **Band 3** p.203, **Massachusetts**: Corporate/M&A **Band 2** p.1452, **Massachusetts**: Private Equity: Buyouts **Band 3** p.1474

**Jones, Karen Samuels**
Table(s): **Colorado**: Real Estate **Band 2** p.714

**Jones, Kimberly**
Table(s): **Missouri**: Labor & Employment **Band 2** p.1625

**Jones, Laura Ellen**
Profile: p.341
Table(s): **Nationwide**: Projects: Renewables & Alternative Energy **Band 1** p.218

**Jones, Leslie Terry**
Table(s): **Nevada**: Real Estate **Senior Statesmen**: p.1679

**Jones, Lewis B**
Profile: p.1086
Table(s): **Georgia**: Environment **Band 2** p.1051

**Jones, Linda B**
Profile: p.1139
Table(s): **Idaho**: Natural Resources & Environment **Band 2** p.1136

**Jones, Maria**
Profile: p.1907
Table(s): **New York**: Tax **Band 4** p.1862

**Jones, Michael R**
Table(s): **Arkansas**: Labor & Employment **Band 2** p.520

**Jones, Nathan W**
Table(s): **Utah**: Corporate/M&A **Band 2** p.2462

**Jones, Patrick H**
Profile: p.1123
Table(s): **Hawaii**: Labor & Employment **Band 1** p.1117

**Jones, Richard D**
Profile: p.1907
Table(s): **New York**: Real Estate: Finance **Band 3** p.1855, **Pennsylvania**: Real Estate **Band 3** p.2208

**Jones, Richard D**
Table(s): **West Virginia**: Litigation: Healthcare **Band 2** p.2555

**Jones, Richard L.**
Profile: p.1496
Table(s): **Massachusetts**: Tax **Band 3** p.1481

**Jones, Robert**
Table(s): **Nationwide**: Life Sciences: Corporate/Commercial **Band 1** p.182, **California**: Life Sciences: Corporate/Commercial **Band 1** p.590

**Jones, Robert**
Table(s): **Massachusetts**: Litigation: Securities **Band 2** p.1470

**Jones, Robert C**
Profile: p.341
Table(s): **Nationwide**: Government: Government Relations **Band 3** p.121

**Jones, Rod**
Table(s): **Florida**: Banking & Finance: Regulatory **Band 3** p.937

**Jones, Roger**
Table(s): **Mississippi**: Energy & Natural Resources **Band 2** p.1593

**Jones, Roger**
Table(s): **Tennessee**: Litigation: Bankruptcy **Band 2** p.2295

**Jones, Roger J**
Table(s): **Nationwide**: Tax: Controversy **Band 3** p.244, **Illinois**: Tax **Band 3** p.1192

**Jones, Russell A.**
Table(s): **Tennessee**: Media & Entertainment **Band 1** p.2297

**Jones, Scott S**
Table(s): **Massachusetts**: Tax **Band 3** p.1481

**Jones, Sean M**
Profile: p.2042
Table(s): **North Carolina**: Corporate/M&A **Band 3** p.2025

**Jones, Stephen C**
Table(s): **Missouri**: Corporate/M&A **Band 2** p.1619

**Jones, Thomas**
Profile: p.872
Table(s): **District of Columbia**: Telecom, Broadcast & Satellite **Band 3** p.844

**Jones, Thomas M**
Profile: p.1213
Table(s): **Nationwide**: Insurance: Transactional & Regulatory **Band 3** p.139, **Illinois**: Insurance: Transactional & Regulatory **Band 2** p.1168

**Jones, Walker (Bill)**
Profile: p.1604
Table(s): **Mississippi**: Litigation: General Commercial **Band 1** p.1597

**Jones, Wilson G**
Profile: p.2397
Table(s): **Texas**: Healthcare **Band 2** p.2347

**Jones Jr, Lawrence R**
Table(s): **Texas**: Tax: Litigation **Band 2** p.2371

**Jones Jr, Philip K**
Table(s): **Louisiana**: Bankruptcy/Restructuring **Band 1** p.1337

**Jones Jr, Russell S**
Table(s): **Missouri**: Litigation: General Commercial **Band 2** p.1628

**Jones Jr, Stanley S**
Profile: p.1086
Table(s): **Georgia**: Healthcare **Band 3** p.1052

**Jones Van Buren, Carolyn A**
Table(s): **North Carolina**: Environment **Band 2** p.2028

**Jones, III, Gladstone N.**
Table(s): **Louisiana**: Environment: Litigation **Band 3** p.1346

**Jontz, Dennis**
Table(s): **New Mexico**: Corporate/Commercial **Band 3** p.1764

**Jordaan, Hendrik**
Profile: p.719
Table(s): **Colorado**: Corporate/M&A **Band 2** p.703

**Jordan, Carey**
Profile: p.2397
Table(s): **Texas**: Intellectual Property **Band 3** p.2354

**Jordan, Hilary P**
Table(s): **Georgia**: Banking & Finance **Band 2** p.1039

**Jordan, James B**
Table(s): **Georgia**: Real Estate **Band 1** p.1070

**Jordan, Nora**
Profile: p.341
Table(s): **Nationwide**: Investment Funds: Hedge Funds **Band 2** p.162

**Jordan, Saskia A**
Table(s): **Colorado**: Litigation: White-Collar Crime & Government Investigations **Band 2** p.710

**Jordan, Shelby**
Table(s): **Texas**: Bankruptcy/Restructuring **Band 4** p.2328

**Jordan, W. Carl**
Profile: p.2398
Table(s): **Texas**: Labor & Employment **Band 1** p.2359

**Jorissen, Paul A**
Table(s): **Nationwide**: Capital Markets: Securitisation **Band 2** p.59

**Joscelyn, Alan L**
Table(s): **Montana**: Natural Resources & Environment **Band 1** p.1651

**Joseffer, Daryl**
Profile: p.341
Table(s): **Nationwide**: Appellate Law **Band 3** p.26

**Josefsberg, Robert C**
Profile: p.995
Table(s): **Florida**: Litigation: General Commercial **Band 1** p.966, **Florida**: Litigation: White-Collar Crime & Government Investigations **Star individuals** p.966

**Joseph, Allan J**
Table(s): **Nationwide**: Government: Government Contracts **Band 1** p.117

**Joseph, Bruce G**
Profile: p.872
Table(s): **District of Columbia**: Intellectual Property: Trademark, Copyright & Trade Secrets **Band 2** p.820

**Joseph, Gregory P**
Table(s): **New York**: Litigation: General Commercial **Band 1** p.1833

**Joseph, James P**
Profile: p.872
Table(s): **District of Columbia**: Tax **Band 4** p.838

**Joseph, Joe A**
Table(s): **Alabama**: Bankruptcy/Restructuring **Band 2** p.457

**Joseph, Matthew P**
Profile: p.341
Table(s): Nationwide: Capital Markets:
Securitisation Band 3 p.59

**Joseph, Michael E**
Profile: p.2150
Table(s): Oklahoma: Corporate/Commercial:
Healthcare Band 1 p.2134

**Joseph, Robert T**
Profile: p.341
Table(s): Nationwide: Franchising Band 3 p.111

**Joseph, Roger P**
Profile: p.1496
Table(s): Nationwide: Investment Funds:
Registered Funds Band 2 p.170, Massachusetts:
Hedge & Mutual Funds Band 1 p.1461

**Joseph, Stephen M**
Table(s): Kansas: Litigation: White-Collar Crime
& Government Investigations Band 2 p.1295

**Joseph III, Alfred S**
Profile: p.1321
Table(s): Kentucky: Real Estate Senior Statesmen:
p.1314

**Joseph Pedersen, Amy**
Table(s): Oregon: Labor & Employment Band 1
p.2168

**Josepher, Richard**
Table(s): Florida: Tax Band 2 p.979

**Josephson, Anne**
Table(s): Massachusetts: Labor & Employment:
Mainly Plaintiffs Representation Band 2 p.1467

**Josephson, Richard**
Profile: p.2398
Table(s): Texas: Litigation: General Commercial
Band 4 p.2362

**Joslin, Peter B**
Table(s): Vermont: Litigation: General
Commercial Band 1 p.2486

**Jospin, Walter**
Table(s): Georgia: Corporate/M&A Band 2 p.1046

**Jossen, Robert J**
Profile: p.1907
Table(s): New York: Litigation: White-Collar
Crime & Government Investigations Band 3
p.1836

**Jost, Shannon**
Table(s): Washington: Intellectual Property Band
3 p.2529

**Joswick, Theresa C**
Profile: p.1551
Table(s): Michigan: Employee Benefits &
Executive Compensation Band 2 p.1540

**Joy, Robert**
Profile: p.1497
Table(s): Massachusetts: Labor & Employment
Band 2 p.1466

**Joy, William**
Profile: p.1497
Table(s): Massachusetts: Labor & Employment
Band 2 p.1466

**Joyce, David E**
Profile: p.341
Table(s): Nationwide: Banking & Finance Band 4
p.31

**Joyce, Edward M**
Profile: p.1907
Table(s): New York: Insurance: Dispute
Resolution: Policyholder Band 3 p.1816

**Joyce, Jeb**
Profile: p.527
Table(s): Arkansas: Corporate/Commercial Band
3 p.518

**Joyce, Katherine**
Table(s): Maine: Environment Up-and-coming individuals p.1389

**Joyce, Robert**
Profile: p.2150
Table(s): Oklahoma: Energy & Natural
Resources: Environment Band 2 p.2136

**Joyce, William F**
Table(s): Washington: Environment Band 1
p.2527

**Joyner, Gary**
Table(s): North Carolina: Real Estate Band 2
p.2037

**Joyner III, G. William**
Table(s): North Carolina: Corporate/M&A Band 4
p.2025

**Juantorena, Jorge U**
Profile: p.1907
Table(s): New York: Latin American Investment
Band 3 p.1829

**Judge, John P**
Table(s): Pennsylvania: Environment Band 2
p.2194

**Judge, Thomas J**
Table(s): District of Columbia: Insurance:
Insurer Band 2 p.816

**Judge Esq, Marty**
Table(s): New Jersey: Environment Band 2 p.1711

**Judge Jr, Walter E**
Table(s): Vermont: Litigation: General
Commercial Band 3 p.2486

**Juelke, Robert C**
Profile: p.2220
Table(s): Pennsylvania: Corporate/M&A &
Private Equity Band 3 p.2191

**Julin, Thomas R**
Profile: p.341
Table(s): Nationwide: First Amendment
Litigation Band 2 p.105

**Juliussen, James H**
Table(s): Alaska: Labor & Employment Band 2
p.489

**Junewicz, James J**
Profile: p.1213
Table(s): Illinois: Corporate/M&A Band 3 p.1156

**Jung, P Michael**
Table(s): Texas: Litigation: Appellate Band 2
p.2361

**Jung, William F**
Table(s): Florida: Litigation: White-Collar Crime &
Government Investigations Band 1 p.967

**Junghans, Paula**
Table(s): Nationwide: Tax: Fraud Band 1 p.244

**Jurgensmeyer, Randy R**
Profile: p.2398
Table(s): Texas: Real Estate Star Individuals p.2367

**Juska Jr, William L**
Profile: p.341
Table(s): Nationwide: Transportation: Shipping:
Litigation (New York) Band 3 p.261

**Justice, Max E**
Table(s): North Carolina: Environment Band 2
p.2028

# K

**Kabnick, Lisa D**
Table(s): Pennsylvania: Banking & Finance Band
1 p.2186

**Kachmar, Shawn A**
Table(s): Georgia: Labor & Employment Band 4
p.1060

**Kadaba, Wab P**
Table(s): Georgia: Intellectual Property Band 2
p.1056

**Kaden, Alan S**
Profile: p.872
Table(s): District of Columbia: Tax Band 3 p.838

**Kaden, Greg**
Table(s): Massachusetts:
Bankruptcy/Restructuring Associates to watch
p.1449

**Kadish, Scott P**
Profile: p.2101
Table(s): Ohio: Real Estate Band 4 p.2086

**Kadlick, Richard F**
Profile: p.341
Table(s): Nationwide: Capital Markets:
Securitisation Band 3 p.59

**Kadue, David**
Profile: p.644
Table(s): California: Labor & Employment Band 2
p.587

**Kadzielski, Mark A**
Profile: p.644
Table(s): Nationwide: Healthcare: Regulatory &
Litigation Band 3 p.127, California: Healthcare
Band 1 p.568

**Kaemmerling, Michelle M**
Table(s): Arkansas: Labor & Employment Band 3
p.520

**Kaempfer, Christopher L**
Table(s): Nevada: Real Estate: Zoning/Land Use
Band 1 p.1679

**Kafin, Robert**
Table(s): New York: Environment Senior
Statesmen: p.1807

**Kafka, Gerald A**
Profile: p.342
Table(s): Nationwide: Tax: Controversy Band 1
p.244, District of Columbia: Tax Band 1 p.838

**Kagan, Stewart**
Profile: p.342
Table(s): Nationwide: Private Equity: Buyouts
Band 5 p.203

**Kahale III, George**
Profile: p.342
Table(s): Nationwide: International Arbitration
Band 5 p.145

**Kahan, Jonathan S**
Table(s): District of Columbia: Healthcare:
Pharmaceutical/Medical Products Regulatory
Band 2 p.810

**Kahle, Thomas W**
Profile: p.2101
Table(s): Ohio: Healthcare Band 3 p.2069

**Kahn, Adam**
Profile: p.1497
Table(s): Massachusetts: Environment Band 1
p.1457

**Kahn, Ben**
Table(s): North Carolina:
Bankruptcy/Restructuring Band 1 p.2023

**Kahn, Benita A**
Profile: p.342
Table(s): Nationwide: Privacy & Data Security
Band 3 p.199

**Kahn, David S**
Profile: p.872
Table(s): District of Columbia: Real Estate Band
2 p.835

**Kahn, Henry D**
Table(s): Maryland: Corporate/M&A Band 1
p.1412

**Kahn, Michael A.**
Profile: p.645
Table(s): California: Litigation: General
Commercial Band 5 p.593

**Kahn, Richard R**
Table(s): New Jersey: Real Estate Band 2 p.1728

**Kahn, Ronald L**
Profile: p.2101
Table(s): Ohio: Employee Benefits & Executive
Compensation Band 2 p.2067

**Kahn, Sarah E**
Profile: p.872
Table(s): District of Columbia: Corporate/M&A &
Private Equity Band 4 p.797

**Kahnke, Randall E**
Table(s): Minnesota: Litigation: General
Commercial Band 3 p.1574, Minnesota: Litigation:
Intellectual Property Band 1 p.1574

**Kailes, Howard**
Profile: p.1738
Table(s): New Jersey: Corporate/M&A Band 2
p.1707

**Kaim, Henry**
Table(s): Texas: Bankruptcy/Restructuring Band 1
p.2328

**Kaiser, Richard L.**
Profile: p.2583
Table(s): Wisconsin: Intellectual Property Up-and-
coming Individuals p.2573

**Kaiser, Robert**
Table(s): **Missouri**: Labor & Employment **Band 3** p.1625

**Kaitz, Nathan**
Profile: p.1497
Table(s): **Massachusetts**: Labor & Employment **Band 4** p.1466

**Kalb MD, Paul E**
Profile: p.872
Table(s): **District of Columbia**: Healthcare **Band 1** p.809

**Kaleczyc, Stanley**
Table(s): **Montana**: Corporate/M&A **Band 1** p.1646, **Montana**: Litigation: General Commercial **Band 2** p.1649

**Kaler, Robert**
Profile: p.1497
Table(s): **Massachusetts**: Litigation: General Commercial **Band 3** p.1470

**Kalicki, Jean E**
Profile: p.342
Table(s): **Nationwide**: International Arbitration **Band 2** p.145

**Kalina, Ira M**
Profile: p.1213
Table(s): **Illinois**: Technology & Outsourcing **Band 3** p.1194

**Kalish, Paul W**
Profile: p.873
Table(s): **Nationwide**: Insurance: Dispute Resolution: Insurer **Band 3** p.134, **District of Columbia**: Insurance: Insurer **Band 2** p.816

**Kalison, Michael J**
Profile: p.1738
Table(s): **New Jersey**: Healthcare **Senior Statesmen**: p.1715

**Kallas, Hani R**
Profile: p.2101
Table(s): **Ohio**: Banking & Finance **Band 2** p.2056

**Kallas, Jay**
Profile: p.1214
Table(s): **Illinois**: Insurance: Transactional & Regulatory **Up-and-coming individuals** p.1168

**Kallianis, James**
Table(s): **Illinois**: Insurance: Dispute Resolution **Band 3** p.1168

**Kallos, Chris P**
Profile: p.342
Table(s): **Nationwide**: Investment Funds: Private Equity: Fund Formation **Band 4** p.166

**Kallstrom, D Ward**
Profile: p.645
Table(s): **Nationwide**: ERISA Litigation **Band 3** p.92, **California**: Employee Benefits & Executive Compensation **Band 2** p.560

**Kalmykov, Kate**
Profile: p.1907
Table(s): **New York**: Immigration **Up-and-coming individuals** p.1814

**Kalyvas, James R**
Table(s): **California**: IT & Outsourcing **Band 3** p.583

**Kamantauskas-Holder, Katrina**
Table(s): **Maryland**: Employee Benefits & Executive Compensation **Band 1** p.1414

**Kamb, Barclay**
Table(s): **California**: Life Sciences: Corporate/Commercial **Band 3** p.590

**Kamen, Steven R**
Profile: p.1738
Table(s): **New Jersey**: Corporate/M&A **Band 2** p.1707

**Kamer, Gregory**
Table(s): **Nevada**: Labor & Employment **Band 1** p.1675

**Kamikawa, Ray K**
Table(s): **Hawaii**: Corporate/Commercial: Tax **Star individuals** p.1115

**Kamin, Joshua M**
Profile: p.1086
Table(s): **Georgia**: Real Estate **Band 2** p.1070

**Kaminsky, Neal**
Profile: p.2398
Table(s): **Texas**: Banking & Finance **Band 4** p.2325

**Kamp, David**
Table(s): **Ohio**: Litigation: General Commercial **Band 3** p.2078

**Kanaly, Mark C**
Profile: p.1086
Table(s): **Georgia**: Banking & Finance: Mainly Regulatory **Band 1** p.1039

**Kanan, Gregory B**
Table(s): **Colorado**: Litigation: General Commercial **Band 3** p.709

**Kane, Ivan P**
Table(s): **Illinois**: Real Estate **Band 1** p.1187

**Kane, Jon**
Table(s): **Florida**: Bankruptcy/Restructuring **Band 4** p.939

**Kane, Larry**
Profile: p.1278
Table(s): **Indiana**: Environment **Band 2** p.1270

**Kane, Meredith J**
Profile: p.1907
Table(s): **New York**: Real Estate **Band 2** p.1854

**Kane, Raymond J**
Profile: p.2398
Table(s): **Texas**: Real Estate **Band 3** p.2367

**Kane, T Richard**
Table(s): **North Carolina**: Environment **Band 3** p.2028

**Kang Ansbach, Cindy**
Profile: p.2398
Table(s): **Texas**: Immigration **Band 2** p.2349

**Kanji, Riyaz**
Table(s): **Nationwide**: Native American Law **Band 1** p.192

**Kannel, William**
Profile: p.1497
Table(s): **Massachusetts**: Bankruptcy/Restructuring **Band 2** p.1449

**Kanner, Allan**
Profile: p.1364
Table(s): **Louisiana**: Environment: Litigation **Band 1** p.1346

**Kant, Robert S**
Profile: p.509
Table(s): **Arizona**: Corporate/M&A **Band 1** p.495

**Kanter, Jane A**
Profile: p.342
Table(s): **Nationwide**: Investment Funds: Registered Funds **Band 3** p.170

**Kanter, Jonathan**
Profile: p.873
Table(s): **District of Columbia**: Antitrust **Band 5** p.787

**Kanter, Rod**
Table(s): **Alabama**: Banking & Finance: Public Finance **Up-and-coming individuals** p.455

**Kanter, Stacy J**
Profile: p.342
Table(s): **Nationwide**: Capital Markets: Debt & Equity **Band 2** p.46

**Kanter, Stanley**
Profile: p.2257
Table(s): **Rhode Island**: Real Estate **Band 1** p.2255

**Kantor, Hal**
Table(s): **Florida**: Real Estate: Zoning/Land Use **Senior Statesmen**: p.975

**Kantor, Mark**
Table(s): **Nationwide**: International Arbitration: Arbitrators **Band 1** p.146

**Kantor, Michael**
Table(s): **Nationwide**: International Trade: Trade Remedies & Trade Policy **Band 4** p.154

**Kantrow, Lee**
Table(s): **Louisiana**: Corporate/M&A **Band 1** p.1341

**Kaplan, Barbara T**
Profile: p.342
Table(s): **Nationwide**: Tax: Controversy **Band 3** p.244, **New York**: Tax **Band 4** p.1862

**Kaplan, Barry M**
Table(s): **Washington**: Litigation: General Commercial **Band 2** p.2533

**Kaplan, Daniel A**
Table(s): **Wisconsin**: Labor & Employment **Band 2** p.2575

**Kaplan, David M**
Profile: p.2220
Table(s): **Pennsylvania**: Labor & Employment: Employee Benefits & Compensation **Band 2** p.2200

**Kaplan, Donald**
Profile: p.342
Table(s): **Nationwide**: Energy: Electricity (Regulatory & Litigation) **Band 4** p.76

**Kaplan, Edward**
Table(s): **New Hampshire**: Labor & Employment **Band 2** p.1688, **New Hampshire**: Litigation: General Commercial **Band 3** p.1690

**Kaplan, Gary L**
Profile: p.1907
Table(s): **New York**: Bankruptcy/Restructuring **Band 4** p.1782

**Kaplan, Gary P**
Profile: p.645
Table(s): **California**: Tax **Band 3** p.617

**Kaplan, Gilbert**
Profile: p.343
Table(s): **Nationwide**: International Trade: Trade Remedies & Trade Policy **Band 2** p.154

**Kaplan, H Deen**
Table(s): **Nationwide**: International Trade: Trade Remedies & Trade Policy **Band 3** p.154

**Kaplan, Harold L**
Table(s): **Illinois**: Bankruptcy/Restructuring **Band 3** p.1148

**Kaplan, Harvey**
Table(s): **Nationwide**: Product Liability & Mass Torts **Band 1** p.208, **Nationwide**: Product Liability: Pharmaceutical p.208, **Missouri**: Litigation: General Commercial **Band 1** p.1628

**Kaplan, Ira C**
Profile: p.2101
Table(s): **Ohio**: Corporate/M&A **Band 3** p.2064

**Kaplan, Jared**
Profile: p.1214
Table(s): **Illinois**: Labor & Employment: Employee Benefits & Compensation **Senior Statesmen**: p.1176

**Kaplan, Joel**
Profile: p.1214
Table(s): **Illinois**: Labor & Employment **Band 1** p.1175

**Kaplan, John**
Table(s): **Washington**: Bankruptcy/Restructuring **Band 2** p.2523

**Kaplan, Jonathan E**
Profile: p.2306
Table(s): **Tennessee**: Labor & Employment **Band 2** p.2293

**Kaplan, Lawrence**
Profile: p.1497
Table(s): **Massachusetts**: Real Estate: Zoning/Land Use **Band 2** p.1478

**Kaplan, Lee**
Profile: p.2398
Table(s): **Texas**: Litigation: General Commercial **Band 2** p.2362

**Kaplan, Michael**
Profile: p.343
Table(s): **Nationwide**: Capital Markets: Debt & Equity **Band 1** p.46

**Kaplan, Philip**
Table(s): **Arkansas**: Labor & Employment **Star individuals** p.520, **Arkansas**: Litigation: General Commercial **Band 1** p.522

**Kaplan, Stephen H**
Profile: p.719
Table(s): **Colorado**: Real Estate: Zoning/Land Use **Band 1** p.714

**Kaplan, Steven**
Profile: p.873
Table(s): **District of Columbia:** Corporate/M&A & Private Equity **Band 1** p.797

**Kaplan, Steven M**
Profile: p.343
Table(s): **Nationwide:** Financial Services Regulation: Consumer Finance (Compliance) **Band 2** p.98

**Kaplan, Tamsin R**
Profile: p.1497
Table(s): **Massachusetts:** Labor & Employment **Band 4** p.1466

**Kaplan-Gross, Kimberley**
Table(s): **Massachusetts:** Private Equity: Fund Formation **Band 3** p.1476

**Kaplinsky, Alan S**
Profile: p.343
Table(s): **Nationwide:** Financial Services Regulation: Consumer Finance (Compliance) **Band 1** p.98, **Pennsylvania:** Banking & Finance: Mainly Regulatory **Band 1** p.2186

**Kapoor, Rahul**
Profile: p.645
Table(s): **California:** IT & Outsourcing **Band 1** p.583

**Kapoor, Romy**
Table(s): **Georgia:** Immigration **Band 1** p.1055

**Kapp, Jeffrey L**
Profile: p.2101
Table(s): **Ohio:** Healthcare **Band 3** p.2069

**Kapp, Paul**
Table(s): **Wyoming:** Litigation: General Commercial **Band 3** p.2598

**Kapsner, John**
Table(s): **North Dakota:** Litigation: General Commercial **Senior Statesmen:** p.2053

**Karalis, Aris J**
Table(s): **Pennsylvania:** Bankruptcy/Restructuring **Band 2** p.2188

**Karamali, Riaz**
Table(s): **California:** IT & Outsourcing **Band 3** p.583

**Karas, Hal**
Profile: p.2583
Table(s): **Wisconsin:** Real Estate **Band 2** p.2579

**Karbowski, Patrick A**
Table(s): **Michigan:** Real Estate **Band 3** p.1546

**Karcazes, Dimitri**
Profile: p.1214
Table(s): **Illinois:** Bankruptcy/Restructuring **Band 4** p.1148

**Karell, Allan L**
Table(s): **Montana:** Real Estate **Band 1** p.1652

**Karen, James**
Profile: p.2398
Table(s): **Texas:** Litigation: General Commercial **Band 3** p.2362

**Karig, Adele M**
Table(s): **New York:** Tax **Band 3** p.1862

**Karlinsky, Fred**
Profile: p.995
Table(s): **Florida:** Insurance **Band 2** p.957

**Karmel, Philip E**
Table(s): **New York:** Environment **Band 2** p.1807

**Karotkin, Stephen**
Profile: p.343
Table(s): **Nationwide:** Bankruptcy/Restructuring **Band 1** p.39, **New York:** Bankruptcy/Restructuring **Band 1** p.1782

**Karp, Brad S**
Profile: p.343
Table(s): **Nationwide:** Financial Services Regulation: Banking (Enforcement & Investigations) **Band 3** p.97, **Nationwide:** Securities: Litigation **Star individuals** p.232, **New York:** Litigation: General Commercial **Band 3** p.1833, **New York:** Litigation: Securities **Star individuals** p.1833

**Karp, Eric H**
Table(s): **Nationwide:** Franchising: Mainly Franchisee **Band 2** p.114

**Karp, Joseph**
Profile: p.645
Table(s): **California:** Energy: State Regulatory & Litigation **Band 2** p.562

**Karp, Marvin L**
Profile: p.2101
Table(s): **Ohio:** Litigation: General Commercial **Senior Statesmen:** p.2078

**Karp, Susan C.**
Profile: p.1739
Table(s): **New Jersey:** Environment **Band 3** p.1711

**Karpeles, Michael D**
Profile: p.1214
Table(s): **Illinois:** Labor & Employment **Band 4** p.1175

**Karpenko, Gregory**
Table(s): **Minnesota:** Litigation: General Commercial **Band 3** p.1574

**Karpf, Jeffrey D**
Profile: p.343
Table(s): **Nationwide:** Capital Markets: Debt & Equity **Band 3** p.46

**Karrenberg, Thomas R.**
Table(s): **Utah:** Litigation: General Commercial **Band 1** p.2468

**Karter, Philip**
Table(s): **Nationwide:** Tax: Controversy **Band 2** p.244

**Kartheiser, Robert**
Table(s): **Nationwide:** Projects **Band 3** p.216, **New York:** Latin American Investment **Band 2** p.1829

**Karzmer, Steve**
Profile: p.2101
Table(s): **Ohio:** Corporate/M&A **Band 4** p.2064

**Kasdin, Neisen**
Table(s): **Florida:** Real Estate: Zoning/Land Use **Band 4** p.975

**Kashatus, Jennifer**
Profile: p.343
Table(s): **Nationwide:** Privacy & Data Security **Band 3** p.199

**Kashtan, Michael F**
Table(s): **Florida:** Construction **Band 2** p.944

**Kasle, Jeffrey**
Table(s): **Rhode Island:** Labor & Employment **Band 2** p.2253

**Kaslow, Howard**
Table(s): **Nebraska:** Corporate/Commercial **Band 1** p.1659

**Kasner, Jay B**
Profile: p.1907
Table(s): **Nationwide:** Securities: Litigation **Band 1** p.232, **New York:** Litigation: Securities **Star individuals** p.1834

**Kasowitz, Marc E**
Profile: p.1907
Table(s): **New York:** Litigation: General Commercial **Band 2** p.1833

**Kasper, David**
Profile: p.1278
Table(s): **Indiana:** Litigation: General Commercial **Band 3** p.1273

**Kass, Geoffrey R**
Profile: p.343
Table(s): **Nationwide:** Transportation: Aviation: Finance **Band 3** p.252

**Kass, Mark**
Profile: p.873
Table(s): **District of Columbia:** Corporate/M&A & Private Equity **Band 4** p.797

**Kass, Stephen**
Table(s): **New York:** Environment **Senior Statesmen:** p.1807

**Kassel, Mark**
Table(s): **Wisconsin:** Intellectual Property **Band 3** p.2573

**Kassin, Thomas**
Profile: p.1086
Table(s): **Georgia:** Labor & Employment **Band 3** p.1060

**Kassinger, Theodore**
Table(s): **Nationwide:** International Trade: CFIUS Experts **Band 1** p.152

**Kassner, Andrew C**
Profile: p.2220
Table(s): **Pennsylvania:** Bankruptcy/Restructuring **Star individuals** p.2188

**Kastenberg, Stephen J**
Profile: p.2220
Table(s): **Pennsylvania:** Litigation: General Commercial **Band 2** p.2203

**Kastner, Ken**
Table(s): **District of Columbia:** Environment **Band 3** p.804

**Katelman, John**
Table(s): **Nebraska:** Real Estate **Band 1** p.1666

**Katsantonis, Vivian**
Profile: p.2510
Table(s): **Virginia:** Construction **Band 3** p.2491

**Kattan, Joseph**
Profile: p.873
Table(s): **District of Columbia:** Antitrust **Band 2** p.787

**Katyal, Neal**
Table(s): **Nationwide:** Appellate Law **Band 3** p.26

**Katz, A Sidney**
Table(s): **Illinois:** Intellectual Property **Senior Statesmen:** p.1171

**Katz, Alvin**
Table(s): **Illinois:** Real Estate **Band 1** p.1187

**Katz, Brian M**
Profile: p.2220
Table(s): **Pennsylvania:** Corporate/M&A: Securities **Band 2** p.2191

**Katz, Charles**
Profile: p.2510
Table(s): **Northern Virginia:** Corporate/M&A **Band 3** p.2493

**Katz, David A**
Profile: p.1908
Table(s): **New York:** Corporate/M&A **Band 1** p.1793

**Katz, Elai**
Profile: p.1908
Table(s): **New York:** Antitrust **Band 4** p.1778

**Katz, Hal**
Table(s): **Texas:** Healthcare **Band 3** p.2347

**Katz, Jeffrey**
Profile: p.1908
Table(s): **New York:** Intellectual Property: Trade Mark & Copyright **Band 3** p.1821

**Katz, Jerome C**
Table(s): **New York:** Litigation: General Commercial **Band 4** p.1833

**Katz, Joel A**
Profile: p.1086
Table(s): **Georgia:** Intellectual Property **Band 2** p.1056

**Katz, Lawrence**
Table(s): **Arizona:** Labor & Employment **Band 1** p.499

**Katz, M Marvin**
Table(s): **Texas:** Real Estate **Senior Statesmen:** p.2367

**Katz, Mark M**
Profile: p.873
Table(s): **District of Columbia:** Real Estate **Band 3** p.835

**Katz, Marty**
Table(s): **California:** Media & Entertainment: Litigation **Band 2** p.606

**Katz, Mitch A**
Profile: p.1086
Table(s): **Georgia:** Intellectual Property **Band 4** p.1056

**Katz, Ori**
Table(s): **California:** Bankruptcy/Restructuring **Up-and-coming individuals** p.542

**Katz, Robert S**
Table(s): **Hawaii:** Labor & Employment **Band 1** p.1117

**Katz, Stuart M**
Profile: p.744
Table(s): **Connecticut:** Labor & Employment **Band 3** p.736

**Katz, Wayne D**
Table(s): **Nationwide:** Sports Law **Band 2** p.241

**Katz Jr, William M**
Profile: p.2398
Table(s): **Texas**: Antitrust **Band 2** p.2323

**Katz-Leavy, Charlie**
Profile: p.1401
Table(s): **Maine**: Real Estate:
Timberland/Conservation **Associates to watch**
p.1396

**Katzenstein, Andrew M**
Table(s): **Nationwide**: Wealth Management:
Western Region **Band 2** p.267

**Katzenstein, Lawrence P**
Table(s): **Nationwide**: Wealth Management:
Central Region **Band 2** p.266

**Kauffman, Douglas B.**
Table(s): **Alabama**: Labor & Employment **Band 3**
p.460

**Kaufman, Beth Shapiro**
Table(s): **Nationwide**: Wealth Management:
Eastern Region **Band 2** p.267

**Kaufman, Bonni F**
Profile: p.873
Table(s): **District of Columbia**: Environment **Band
5** p.804

**Kaufman, Christopher L**
Profile: p.343
Table(s): **Nationwide**: Investment Funds: Venture
Capital **Band 1** p.174, **California**: Corporate/M&A
**Band 3** p.553, **California**: Corporate/M&A:
Venture Capital **Band 1** p.553

**Kaufman, D William**
Table(s): **Minnesota**: Corporate/M&A **Band 4**
p.1569

**Kaufman, David**
Profile: p.343
Table(s): **Nationwide**: Capital Markets:
Derivatives **Band 3** p.51

**Kaufman, David**
Table(s): **Mississippi**: Litigation: General
Commercial **Band 1** p.1597

**Kaufman, David J**
Table(s): **Illinois**: Corporate/M&A **Band 4** p.1156

**Kaufman, Kenneth M**
Table(s): **District of Columbia**: Media &
Entertainment **Band 3** p.832

**Kaufman, Mark D**
Table(s): **Georgia**: Corporate/M&A **Band 3** p.1046

**Kaufman, Mark S**
Profile: p.1086
Table(s): **Georgia**: Bankruptcy/Restructuring
**Band 2** p.1042

**Kaufman, Steven M**
Table(s): **District of Columbia**: Telecom,
Broadcast & Satellite **Band 2** p.844

**Kaufman, Steven S**
Table(s): **Ohio**: Litigation: General Commercial
**Band 2** p.2078

**Kaufman, Thomas F**
Table(s): **District of Columbia**: Real Estate **Band
3** p.835

**Kaufmann, David J**
Table(s): **Nationwide**: Franchising **Band 3** p.111

**Kaufmann, Mark L**
Profile: p.1214
Table(s): **Illinois**: Technology & Outsourcing **Band
2** p.1194

**Kauss, Andrew**
Table(s): **Georgia**: Real Estate **Band 2** p.1070

**Kavaler, Thomas J**
Profile: p.1908
Table(s): **New York**: Litigation: General
Commercial **Band 2** p.1833

**Kavanagh, John**
Table(s): **Nationwide**: Transportation: Shipping:
Litigation (outside New York) **Band 2** p.263

**Kavoukjian, Michael E**
Profile: p.995
Table(s): **Nationwide**: Wealth Management:
Eastern Region **Band 4** p.267, **Florida**: Tax: Estate
Planning **Band 2** p.979

**Kawanabe, Kenzo S**
Profile: p.719
Table(s): **Colorado**: Litigation: General
Commercial **Band 2** p.709

**Kawashima, Ellen**
Table(s): **Hawaii**: Labor & Employment:
Employee Benefits & Compensation **Band 2**
p.1117

**Kawata, Yukako**
Profile: p.344
Table(s): **Nationwide**: Investment Funds: Private
Equity: Fund Formation **Band 1** p.166

**Kay, Craig**
Table(s): **West Virginia**: Corporate/Commercial:
Tax **Band 2** p.2550

**Kay, Minta E**
Profile: p.1497
Table(s): **Massachusetts**: Real Estate **Band 2**
p.1478

**Kay, Richard A**
Table(s): **Michigan**: Litigation: General
Commercial **Band 2** p.1544

**Kayatta Jr, William**
Profile: p.1401
Table(s): **Maine**: Litigation: General Commercial
**Star Individuals** p.1393

**Kaye, Barbara**
Table(s): **Michigan**: Corporate/M&A **Band 3**
p.1538

**Kaye, Joshua**
Profile: p.995
Table(s): **Florida**: Healthcare **Band 2** p.954

**Kayle, Bruce E**
Profile: p.1908
Table(s): **New York**: Tax **Band 2** p.1862

**Kayukov, Edward V**
Profile: p.344
Table(s): **Nationwide**: Projects **Band 3** p.216,
**Nationwide**: Projects: Renewables & Alternative
Energy **Band 1** p.216

**Kaywood, Sam K**
Profile: p.1086
Table(s): **Georgia**: Tax **Band 1** p.1072

**Kazakis, Georgia**
Profile: p.873
Table(s): **District of Columbia**: Insurance:
Policyholder **Band 3** p.818

**Kazaks, Julia M**
Profile: p.645
Table(s): **Nationwide**: Tax: Controversy **Band 4**
p.244, **California**: Tax **Band 3** p.617

**Kazanoff, Peter E**
Profile: p.1908
Table(s): **New York**: Litigation: Securities **Band 3**
p.1834

**Kazmarek, E A Skip**
Table(s): **Georgia**: Environment **Band 1** p.1051

**Keach, Robert J**
Table(s): **Maine**: Corporate/M&A: Bankruptcy
**Star Individuals** p.1385

**Kean, Warren**
Profile: p.2042
Table(s): **North Carolina**: Corporate/M&A **Band 4**
p.2025

**Keane, Edward A**
Table(s): **Nationwide**: Transportation: Shipping:
Litigation (New York) **Band 3** p.261

**Keane, Jennifer**
Profile: p.2398
Table(s): **Texas**: Environment **Band 3** p.2343

**Keane, Margaret E**
Profile: p.1321
Table(s): **Kentucky**: Litigation: General
Commercial **Band 4** p.1312, **Kentucky**: Litigation:
Tort & Insurance Defense **Band 1** p.1312

**Keane, Paul**
Table(s): **Nationwide**: Transportation: Shipping:
Litigation (New York) **Band 4** p.261

**Kearfott, Joseph C**
Profile: p.2510
Table(s): **Virginia**: Litigation: General
Commercial **Band 2** p.2502

**Kearney, Dennis T**
Profile: p.1739
Table(s): **New Jersey**: Litigation: General
Commercial **Band 3** p.1722

**Kearney, John B**
Profile: p.1739
Table(s): **New Jersey**: Litigation: General
Commercial **Band 3** p.1722

**Kearney, Sean P**
Table(s): **Minnesota**: Corporate/M&A **Band 4**
p.1569

**Keating, Con M**
Table(s): **Nebraska**: Litigation: Mediators **Band 1**
p.1664

**Keating, David C**
Profile: p.344
Table(s): **Nationwide**: Privacy & Data Security
**Band 3** p.199

**Keating, Geoffrey T**
Profile: p.873
Table(s): **District of Columbia**: Construction **Band
3** p.795

**Keating, Gregory C**
Profile: p.1497
Table(s): **Massachusetts**: Labor & Employment
**Band 3** p.1466

**Keating, Michael**
Profile: p.1497
Table(s): **Massachusetts**: Litigation: General
Commercial **Senior Statesmen** p.1470

**Keefe, Jo**
Table(s): **New Hampshire**: Real Estate **Band 3**
p.1692

**Keefe, Robert D**
Profile: p.1497
Table(s): **Massachusetts**: Litigation: White-Collar
Crime & Government Investigations **Band 1**
p.1471

**Keegan, JoDee**
Table(s): **Oregon**: Corporate/M&A **Up-and-coming
individuals** p.2164

**Keegan, John E**
Table(s): **Washington**: Real Estate: Zoning/Land
Use **Band 1** p.2536

**Keehnel, Stellman**
Profile: p.2540
Table(s): **Washington**: Litigation: General
Commercial **Band 1** p.2533

**Keeler, Dennis C**
Profile: p.1401
Table(s): **Maine**: Real Estate **Band 1** p.1395

**Keen, C Matthew**
Profile: p.2042
Table(s): **North Carolina**: Labor & Employment
**Band 1** p.2031

**Keenan, Mark L**
Profile: p.1087
Table(s): **Georgia**: Labor & Employment **Band 4**
p.1060

**Keenan, Robert M**
Profile: p.1087
Table(s): **Georgia**: Healthcare **Band 2** p.1052

**Keene, Thomas**
Table(s): **Alabama**: Litigation: Medical
Malpractice Defense **Band 1** p.463

**Keener, Mark P**
Table(s): **Maryland**: Real Estate **Band 3** p.1422

**Keeney, Jeffrey H**
Profile: p.2176
Table(s): **Oregon**: Real Estate **Band 2** p.2173

**Keeney, Regina**
Table(s): **District of Columbia**: Telecom,
Broadcast & Satellite **Band 2** p.844

**Keesal Jr, Samuel A**
Table(s): **Nationwide**: Transportation: Shipping:
Litigation (outside New York) **Band 2** p.263

**Keeton, Charles R**
Table(s): **Kentucky**: Corporate/M&A **Band 3**
p.1305

**Kegler, Charles**
Table(s): **Ohio**: Corporate/M&A **Band 2** p.2064

**Kegler, Todd**
Table(s): **Ohio**: Corporate/M&A **Band 3** p.2064

**Kehoe, Edward**
Profile: p.344
Table(s): Nationwide: International Arbitration
**Band 2** p.145

**Kehoe, Gerald J**
Profile: p.1498
Table(s): Massachusetts: Private Equity: Fund
Formation **Band 3** p.1476

**Kehoe, Greg W**
Profile: p.995
Table(s): Florida: Litigation: White-Collar Crime &
Government Investigations **Band 3** p.967

**Keidan Martin, Laura**
Table(s): Illinois: Antitrust **Band 3** p.1143, Illinois:
Healthcare **Band 1** p.1165

**Keim, Clay**
Profile: p.2270
Table(s): South Carolina: Labor & Employment
**Band 3** p.2262

**Keim Jr, Thomas E**
Table(s): Illinois: Corporate/M&A **Band 4** p.1156

**Keim Jr, Thomas H**
Profile: p.2270
Table(s): South Carolina: Labor & Employment
**Band 3** p.2262

**Keiner, Jeffrey**
Profile: p.996
Table(s): Florida: Construction **Band 2** p.944

**Keiper, Jeffrey B**
Profile: p.2101
Table(s): Ohio: Labor & Employment **Band 4**
p.2074

**Keisler, Peter**
Profile: p.344
Table(s): Nationwide: Appellate Law **Band 2** p.26

**Keitelman, Jeffrey R**
Profile: p.873
Table(s): District of Columbia: Real Estate **Band
2** p.835

**Keith, Calvin L**
Table(s): Oregon: Labor & Employment **Band 3**
p.2168

**Keith, James A**
Profile: p.1604
Table(s): Mississippi: Labor & Employment **Band
3** p.1595

**Keithley, Bradford G**
Table(s): Alaska: Environment, Natural
Resources & Regulated Industries **Band 2** p.488

**Keker, John**
Table(s): Nationwide: Litigation: Trial Lawyers
**Band 1** p.187, California: Intellectual Property:
Patent **Band 2** p.578, California: Litigation:
General Commercial **Star individuals** p.593,
California: Litigation: White-Collar Crime &
Government Investigations **Star individuals** p.601

**Kelbon, Regina Stango**
Profile: p.2220
Table(s): Delaware: Bankruptcy/Restructuring
**Band 4** p.754, Pennsylvania:
Bankruptcy/Restructuring **Band 2** p.2188

**Keleher, William B.**
Table(s): New Mexico: Real Estate **Senior
Statesmen:** p.1772

**Keliher, Cynthia**
Profile: p.1498
Table(s): Massachusetts: Real Estate **Band 2**
p.1478

**Kelleher, Michael F**
Profile: p.344
Table(s): Nationwide: Tax: Controversy **Band 4**
p.244

**Kelleher, Rory**
Profile: p.344
Table(s): Nationwide: Banking & Finance:
Equipment Finance & Leasing **Senior Statesmen:**
p.32, Nationwide: Transportation: Aviation:
Finance **Senior Statesmen:** p.252

**Kelleher, Jr, Thomas J**
Profile: p.1087
Table(s): Georgia: Construction **Senior Statesmen:**
p.1044

**Keller, Brad**
Table(s): Washington: Litigation: General
Commercial **Band 1** p.2533

**Keller, Bruce P**
Table(s): Nationwide: Sports Law **Band 2** p.241,
New York: Intellectual Property: Trade Mark &
Copyright **Band 1** p.1821, New York: Media &
Entertainment: Copyright & Contract Disputes
**Band 1** p.1851

**Keller, Donald**
Table(s): Ohio: Labor & Employment **Band 4**
p.2074

**Keller, Eric R**
Table(s): District of Columbia: Employee
Benefits & Executive Compensation **Up-and-com-
ing individuals** p.801

**Keller, H Michael**
Table(s): Utah: Energy & Natural Resources **Band
1** p.2464, Utah: Energy & Natural Resources:
Water Law p.2464

**Keller, Jennifer P**
Profile: p.2306
Table(s): Tennessee: Labor & Employment **Band
3** p.2293

**Keller, John**
Profile: p.2101
Table(s): Ohio: Natural Resources &
Environment **Band 4** p.2083

**Keller, Karen E**
Table(s): Delaware: Intellectual Property **Up-and-
coming individuals** p.763

**Keller, Kent**
Table(s): California: Insurance: Insurer **Band 1**
p.574

**Keller, Mary**
Profile: p.2398
Table(s): Texas: Insurance **Band 2** p.2351, Texas:
Insurance: Regulation **Band 1** p.2351

**Keller, Natalie**
Profile: p.344
Table(s): Nationwide: Tax: Controversy **Up-and-
coming individuals** p.244, Illinois: Tax **Up-and-coming
individuals** p.1192

**Keller, Stanley**
Profile: p.1498
Table(s): Massachusetts: Corporate/M&A **Senior
Statesmen:** p.1452

**Keller, Tobias S**
Profile: p.645
Table(s): California: Bankruptcy/Restructuring
**Band 3** p.542

**Kelley, Anne Marie P**
Table(s): New Jersey: Bankruptcy/Restructuring
**Band 3** p.1705

**Kelley, Bernard J**
Profile: p.772
Table(s): Delaware: Corporate/M&A: Alternative
Entities **Band 1** p.761

**Kelley, David**
Table(s): Minnesota: Real Estate **Band 3** p.1576

**Kelley, David N**
Profile: p.1908
Table(s): New York: Litigation: White-Collar
Crime & Government Investigations **Band 1**
p.1836

**Kelley, James R**
Table(s): Tennessee: Litigation: Bankruptcy **Band
1** p.2295

**Kelley, Jay D**
Table(s): Nationwide: Projects **Band 4** p.216

**Kelley, Jeffrey W**
Table(s): Georgia: Bankruptcy/Restructuring
**Band 2** p.1042

**Kelley, John J**
Table(s): Georgia: Corporate/M&A **Band 2** p.1046

**Kelley, Kevin**
Table(s): Colorado: Real Estate **Band 3** p.714

**Kelley, Kevin**
Profile: p.1908
Table(s): New York: Latin American Investment
**Band 4** p.1829

**Kelley, Kevin L**
Profile: p.2399
Table(s): Texas: Real Estate **Band 2** p.2367

**Kelley, Thomas**
Profile: p.344
Table(s): Nationwide: First Amendment
Litigation **Band 1** p.105

**Kellman, Sandra Y**
Profile: p.344
Table(s): Nationwide: Leisure & Hospitality **Band
2** p.179

**Kellmeyer, Joseph M**
Table(s): Missouri: Environment **Band 3** p.1621

**Kellner, Leon B**
Table(s): Nationwide: Insurance: Dispute
Resolution: Policyholder **Band 3** p.137, District of
Columbia: Insurance: Policyholder **Band 2** p.818

**Kellner, Robert**
Table(s): Maryland: Labor & Employment **Band 2**
p.1417

**Kellner, Stuart**
Table(s): Montana: Litigation: Mediators **Band 1**
p.1649

**Kellogg, Amy E**
Profile: p.2101
Table(s): Ohio: Real Estate **Band 3** p.2086

**Kellogg, Michael**
Table(s): Nationwide: Appellate Law **Band 3** p.26,
District of Columbia: Telecom, Broadcast &
Satellite **Band 1** p.844

**Kelly, Adam G**
Profile: p.1214
Table(s): Illinois: Intellectual Property **Up-and-com-
ing individuals** p.1171

**Kelly, Andrew P**
Profile: p.509
Table(s): Arizona: Corporate/M&A **Band 3** p.495

**Kelly, Ashley**
Profile: p.1087
Table(s): Georgia: Labor & Employment **Band 3**
p.1060

**Kelly, Brian**
Profile: p.2102
Table(s): Ohio: Labor & Employment **Band 3**
p.2074

**Kelly, Christopher G**
Profile: p.344
Table(s): Nationwide: Transportation: Aviation:
Litigation **Band 2** p.254

**Kelly, Deborah**
Profile: p.873
Table(s): District of Columbia: Labor &
Employment **Band 3** p.824

**Kelly, Donna C**
Table(s): West Virginia: Natural Resources **Band
2** p.2558

**Kelly, Edward J**
Table(s): Massachusetts: Intellectual Property
**Band 2** p.1463

**Kelly, Henry**
Table(s): Illinois: Communications **Band 2** p.1153

**Kelly, Henry**
Table(s): New Mexico: Corporate/Commercial:
Tax **Band 1** p.1764

**Kelly, James**
Table(s): New York: Corporate/M&A **Band 5**
p.1793

**Kelly, James P**
Table(s): Georgia: Healthcare **Band 2** p.1052

**Kelly, Mark**
Profile: p.2042
Table(s): North Carolina: Corporate/M&A **Band 3**
p.2025

**Kelly, Robert**
Profile: p.873
Table(s): District of Columbia: Telecom,
Broadcast & Satellite **Band 4** p.844

**Kelly, Samuel**
Table(s): Mississippi: Litigation: Construction
**Band 2** p.1596

**Kelly, Sarah A**
Profile: p.2220
Table(s): Pennsylvania: Labor & Employment
**Band 4** p.2200

**Kelly, Shawn L**
Table(s): New Jersey: Litigation: Insurance **Band
1** p.1723

**Kersh, Candice**
Profile: p.345
Table(s): Nationwide: Advertising: Transactional & Regulatory Band 2 p.20

**Kershaw Jr., Newton H**
Table(s): New Hampshire: Labor & Employment: Employee Benefits & Compensation Band 1 p.1688

**Kerwin, Brian P**
Table(s): Illinois: Corporate/M&A: Private Equity Band 3 p.1157

**Kerwin, Gregory J**
Profile: p.719
Table(s): Colorado: Litigation: General Commercial Band 2 p.709

**Keshian, Richard J**
Table(s): North Carolina: Litigation: General Commercial Band 4 p.2033

**Kesslen, Mark**
Profile: p.1739
Table(s): New Jersey: Intellectual Property Band 3 p.1716

**Kessler, David**
Profile: p.346
Table(s): Nationwide: Litigation: E-Discovery Band 1 p.187

**Kessler, Elizabeth P**
Profile: p.2102
Table(s): Ohio: Litigation: General Commercial Band 4 p.2078

**Kessler, Jeffrey L**
Profile: p.346
Table(s): Nationwide: Sports Law Band 1 p.241, New York: Antitrust Band 2 p.1778

**Kessler, Judd**
Profile: p.346
Table(s): Nationwide: International Arbitration: Arbitrators Band 1 p.146

**Kessler, Marc**
Profile: p.2102
Table(s): Ohio: Litigation: General Commercial Band 4 p.2078

**Kessler, Philip J**
Profile: p.1551
Table(s): Michigan: Litigation: General Commercial Band 1 p.1544

**Kestner, R Steven**
Profile: p.2102
Table(s): Ohio: Corporate/M&A Band 3 p.2064

**Ketchum, Elena**
Profile: p.996
Table(s): Florida: Bankruptcy/Restructuring Up-and-coming individuals p.939

**Ketterling, Keith A**
Table(s): Oregon: Litigation: General Commercial Band 2 p.2171

**Kettlewell, William H**
Table(s): Massachusetts: Litigation: White-Collar Crime & Government Investigations Band 2 p.1471

**Ketzback, Thor W**
Table(s): Illinois: Environment: Mainly Transactional Band 3 p.1162

**Keville, John**
Profile: p.2399
Table(s): Texas: Intellectual Property Band 2 p.2354

**Keville, Terri D**
Table(s): California: Healthcare Band 3 p.568

**Keyes, David**
Table(s): Texas: Banking & Finance Band 3 p.2325

**Keyes, Judith Droz**
Table(s): California: Labor & Employment Band 3 p.587

**Keyes, Kevin M**
Profile: p.874
Table(s): District of Columbia: Tax Band 3 p.838

**Keyser, Denise M**
Profile: p.1739
Table(s): New Jersey: Labor & Employment Band 2 p.1718

**Keyte, James**
Profile: p.1908
Table(s): New York: Antitrust Band 4 p.1778

**Khadavi, Steven**
Table(s): New York: Corporate/M&A Band 4 p.1793

**Khedekar, Sameer**
Table(s): California: Immigration Band 3 p.571

**Khil, John C**
Profile: p.1123
Table(s): Hawaii: Labor & Employment: Employee Benefits & Compensation Band 1 p.1117

**Khorey, David E**
Table(s): Michigan: Labor & Employment Band 2 p.1542

**Khoury, Paul F**
Profile: p.346
Table(s): Nationwide: Government: Government Contracts Band 1 p.117, Nationwide: Government: Government Contracts: Bid Protests p.117

**Khuri, Walid**
Profile: p.346
Table(s): Nationwide: Investment Funds: Hedge Funds Band 3 p.162

**Kibert, Nicole C**
Profile: p.996
Table(s): Florida: Real Estate: Zoning/Land Use Up-and-coming individuals p.975

**Kicenuik, Maryann P**
Table(s): New Jersey: Healthcare Band 3 p.1715

**Kichline, Michael L**
Profile: p.2221
Table(s): Pennsylvania: Litigation: Securities Band 2 p.2204

**Kickham, Edward F.**
Table(s): Michigan: Real Estate Band 3 p.1546

**Kidd, Ed**
Table(s): Southern Virginia: Real Estate Band 1 p.2506, Southern Virginia: Real Estate: Zoning/Land Use Band 2 p.2506

**Kiefer, Matthew J**
Table(s): Massachusetts: Real Estate: Zoning/Land Use Band 1 p.1478

**Kiefer, Richard**
Table(s): Hawaii: Real Estate Band 1 p.1120

**Kienbaum, Thomas G**
Profile: p.1551
Table(s): Michigan: Labor & Employment Star individuals p.1542

**Kierkut, Galit**
Profile: p.1739
Table(s): New Jersey: Labor & Employment Up-and-coming individuals p.1718

**Kiern, Larry**
Profile: p.346
Table(s): Nationwide: Transportation: Shipping Regulatory (outside New York) Band 3 p.264

**Kiernan, John S**
Table(s): New York: Litigation: General Commercial Band 2 p.1833

**Kiernan, Vincent M**
Profile: p.744
Table(s): Connecticut: Corporate/M&A Band 3 p.732

**Kieselstein, Marc**
Profile: p.1909
Table(s): Nationwide: Bankruptcy/Restructuring Band 4 p.39, New York: Bankruptcy/Restructuring Band 3 p.1782

**Kiesewetter, Jay W**
Profile: p.2306
Table(s): Tennessee: Labor & Employment Band 2 p.2293

**Kiessling, B Robbins**
Profile: p.346
Table(s): Nationwide: Banking & Finance Band 1 p.31

**Kiggans, Thomas H**
Table(s): Louisiana: Labor & Employment Band 2 p.1350

**Kilb, Brian D**
Profile: p.646
Table(s): California: Banking & Finance Band 2 p.539

**Kilberg, William J**
Profile: p.874
Table(s): Nationwide: ERISA Litigation Band 2 p.92, District of Columbia: Employee Benefits & Executive Compensation Band 3 p.801, District of Columbia: Labor & Employment Band 1 p.824

**Kilbreth, James**
Profile: p.1401
Table(s): Maine: Environment Band 3 p.1389, Maine: Litigation: General Commercial Band 2 p.1393

**Kilduff, Jeffrey**
Table(s): Nationwide: Securities: Litigation Band 3 p.232, District of Columbia: Litigation: Securities Band 2 p.826

**Kilgore, Scott**
Profile: p.874
Table(s): District of Columbia: Employee Benefits & Executive Compensation Band 3 p.801

**Kilgore III, Leonard L**
Profile: p.1364
Table(s): Louisiana: Environment Band 1 p.1346

**Kilkenney, Michelle**
Profile: p.1214
Table(s): Illinois: Banking & Finance Band 4 p.1145

**Killebrew, Denise**
Profile: p.470
Table(s): Alabama: Real Estate Band 2 p.466

**Killian, James**
Table(s): Minnesota: Construction Band 2 p.1567

**Killion, William L**
Table(s): Nationwide: Franchising Band 2 p.111

**Killworth, Richard**
Table(s): Ohio: Intellectual Property Senior Statesmen: p.2071

**Kilmer, Brian**
Table(s): Texas: Bankruptcy/Restructuring Band 4 p.2328

**Kilmer, Paul**
Profile: p.874
Table(s): District of Columbia: Intellectual Property: Trademark, Copyright & Trade Secrets Band 1 p.820

**Kilpatrick, J Thomas**
Profile: p.1087
Table(s): Georgia: Labor & Employment Band 3 p.1060

**Kilroy, W Terrence**
Table(s): Missouri: Labor & Employment Band 1 p.1625

**Kilroy Jr, John M**
Table(s): Missouri: Litigation: General Commercial Band 3 p.1628

**Kim, Eduardo**
Profile: p.2102
Table(s): Ohio: Banking & Finance Band 3 p.2056

**Kim, Gregory R**
Table(s): Hawaii: Corporate/Commercial Band 1 p.1116

**Kim, Jane**
Profile: p.527
Table(s): Arkansas: Labor & Employment Associates to watch p.520

**Kim, Jay**
Table(s): Nationwide: Banking & Finance Band 3 p.31

**Kim, Jay**
Table(s): Florida: Litigation: General Commercial Band 4 p.966

**Kim, Mark**
Profile: p.646
Table(s): California: Corporate/M&A Up-and-coming individuals p.554

**Kim, Michael S**
Profile: p.1909
Table(s): New York: Litigation: White-Collar Crime & Government Investigations Band 2 p.1836

**Kirk, Richard D**
Profile: p.772
Table(s): Delaware: Intellectual Property **Band 3**
p.763

**Kirk, WL**
Table(s): Florida: Litigation: General Commercial
**Band 3** p.966

**Kirkbride, Rick S**
Table(s): Nationwide: Leisure & Hospitality **Band 1** p.179

**Kirkham, Christopher W**
Profile: p.646
Table(s): California: Banking & Finance **Band 2** p.539

**Kirkham, John S**
Table(s): Utah: Energy & Natural Resources **Band 2** p.2464

**Kirkland, Byron B**
Profile: p.2042
Table(s): North Carolina: Corporate/M&A **Band 2** p.2025

**Kirkland, David**
Profile: p.2399
Table(s): Texas: Corporate/M&A **Band 1** p.2337

**Kirkpatrick, Deanna**
Profile: p.347
Table(s): Nationwide: Capital Markets: Debt & Equity **Band 4** p.46

**Kirkwood, Peter**
Table(s): Florida: Tax: Estate Planning **Band 3** p.979

**Kirkwood, Thomas J**
Profile: p.2102
Table(s): Ohio: Construction **Band 2** p.2062

**Kirmis, Lyle W**
Table(s): North Dakota: Litigation: General Commercial **Band 1** p.2053

**Kirpalani, Susheel**
Table(s): Nationwide: Bankruptcy/Restructuring **Band 1** p.39, New York: Bankruptcy/Restructuring **Band 1** p.1782

**Kirsch, Gregory J**
Table(s): Georgia: Intellectual Property **Band 3** p.1056

**Kirsch, Kevin W**
Profile: p.2102
Table(s): Ohio: Intellectual Property **Band 3** p.2071

**Kirsch, Laurence S**
Profile: p.874
Table(s): District of Columbia: Environment **Band 3** p.804

**Kirsch, Mark**
Profile: p.1909
Table(s): Nationwide: Securities: Litigation **Band 2** p.232, New York: Litigation: Securities **Band 1** p.1834

**Kirsch, Mark**
Profile: p.744
Table(s): Connecticut: Real Estate **Band 3** p.740

**Kirsch, Robert**
Profile: p.1498
Table(s): Massachusetts: Environment **Band 1** p.1457

**Kirschbaum, Howard**
Table(s): Illinois: Real Estate **Band 1** p.1187

**Kirschner, Lisa**
Profile: p.2474
Table(s): Utah: Energy & Natural Resources **Band 3** p.2464, Utah: Energy & Natural Resources: Water Law p.2464

**Kirshenbaum, Mark**
Profile: p.1498
Table(s): Massachusetts: Tax **Band 2** p.1481

**Kirson, Sarah E**
Profile: p.347
Table(s): Nationwide: Investment Funds: Private Equity: Fund Formation **Band 4** p.166

**Kirsons, Mark**
Profile: p.1215
Table(s): Illinois: Banking & Finance **Up-and-coming individuals** p.1145

**Kirtley, John**
Table(s): Wisconsin: Litigation: General Commercial **Band 3** p.2576

**Kirwin, Brian P**
Table(s): Florida: Construction **Band 1** p.944

**Kisch, Victor J**
Table(s): Oregon: Labor & Employment **Band 1** p.2168

**Kiser, Chérie Renee**
Profile: p.874
Table(s): District of Columbia: Telecom, Broadcast & Satellite **Band 2** p.844

**Kisicki, Mark G**
Profile: p.509
Table(s): Arizona: Labor & Employment **Band 3** p.499

**Kiss, Robert S**
Profile: p.2563
Table(s): West Virginia: Corporate/Commercial: Tax **Band 1** p.2550

**Kissinger, William D**
Profile: p.646
Table(s): California: Energy: State Regulatory & Litigation **Band 3** p.562

**Kistenbroker, David H**
Profile: p.1215
Table(s): Illinois: Litigation: General Commercial **Band 4** p.1180

**Kistler, David**
Profile: p.1739
Table(s): New Jersey: Litigation: General Commercial **Up-and-coming individuals** p.1722

**Kitchel, Chris**
Table(s): Oregon: Labor & Employment **Band 2** p.2168

**Kitchen, David**
Profile: p.646
Table(s): California: Banking & Finance **Band 2** p.539

**Kitchen, F Damon**
Table(s): Florida: Labor & Employment **Band 2** p.959

**Kitchens, Dean**
Profile: p.347
Table(s): Nationwide: Securities: Litigation **Band 2** p.232, California: Litigation: General Commercial **Band 2** p.593, California: Litigation: Securities **Band 2** p.593

**Kitslaar, Elizabeth C**
Profile: p.1215
Table(s): Illinois: Corporate/M&A **Band 2** p.1156

**Kittle-Kamp, Thomas L**
Table(s): Nationwide: Tax: Controversy **Band 4** p.244

**Kizziar Jr, James H**
Profile: p.2399
Table(s): Texas: Labor & Employment **Band 4** p.2359

**Klaas, Paul B**
Table(s): Minnesota: Litigation: General Commercial **Band 3** p.1574

**Klahr, Robert**
Table(s): Missouri: Real Estate **Band 3** p.1633

**Klapper, Richard**
Profile: p.1909
Table(s): New York: Litigation: General Commercial **Band 3** p.1833, New York: Litigation: Securities **Band 4** p.1833

**Klarfeld, Peter J**
Table(s): Nationwide: Franchising **Band 2** p.111

**Klasko, H Ronald**
Table(s): Nationwide: Immigration **Band 1** p.131

**Klasmeier, Coleen**
Profile: p.347
Table(s): Nationwide: Life Sciences: Regulatory/Compliance **Band 2** p.183, District of Columbia: Healthcare: Pharmaceutical/Medical Products Regulatory **Band 2** p.810

**Klauberg, John G**
Profile: p.347
Table(s): Nationwide: Energy: Electricity (Transactional) **Band 1** p.77

**Klausner, Robert A**
Profile: p.1739
Table(s): New Jersey: Real Estate **Band 2** p.1728

**Klawiter, Donald C**
Table(s): District of Columbia: Antitrust **Band 4** p.787

**Klawiter, Richard F**
Profile: p.1215
Table(s): Illinois: Real Estate: Zoning/Land Use **Band 1** p.1188

**Kleban, Barry**
Profile: p.2221
Table(s): Pennsylvania: Bankruptcy/Restructuring **Band 1** p.2188

**Klee, Kenneth N**
Table(s): Nationwide: Bankruptcy/Restructuring **Band 1** p.39, California: Bankruptcy/Restructuring **Band 1** p.542

**Klee, Peter**
Profile: p.646
Table(s): California: Insurance: Insurer **Band 2** p.574

**Klegerman, Neal A**
Table(s): Nevada: Corporate/Commercial **Band 2** p.1672

**Klein, Adam**
Table(s): Nationwide: Sports Law **Band 2** p.241

**Klein, Allen**
Profile: p.874
Table(s): Nationwide: Outsourcing **Band 2** p.195, District of Columbia: Technology & Outsourcing **Band 1** p.842

**Klein, Anthony**
Profile: p.646
Table(s): California: IT & Outsourcing **Band 2** p.583

**Klein, Barry L**
Profile: p.2221
Table(s): Pennsylvania: Labor & Employment: Employee Benefits & Compensation **Band 2** p.2200

**Klein, Daniel L**
Profile: p.772
Table(s): Delaware: Real Estate **Band 1** p.766

**Klein, David F**
Table(s): District of Columbia: Insurance: Policyholder **Band 3** p.818

**Klein, Deborah**
Table(s): California: Media & Entertainment: Transactional: Mainly Talent **Band 2** p.609

**Klein, Eric A**
Table(s): California: Healthcare **Band 3** p.568

**Klein, Frederick L**
Profile: p.347
Table(s): Nationwide: Real Estate **Band 1** p.225, District of Columbia: Real Estate **Band 1** p.835

**Klein, Howard Bruce**
Profile: p.2221
Table(s): Pennsylvania: Litigation: White-Collar Crime & Government Investigations **Band 1** p.2204

**Klein, Howard M**
Profile: p.2221
Table(s): Pennsylvania: Litigation: General Commercial **Band 3** p.2203

**Klein, Jeffrey**
Profile: p.1909
Table(s): New York: Labor & Employment **Band 1** p.1826

**Klein, Jordan A**
Profile: p.347
Table(s): Nationwide: Wealth Management: Central Region **Band 3** p.266

**Klein, Joshua T**
Profile: p.2221
Table(s): Pennsylvania: Bankruptcy/Restructuring **Up-and-coming individuals** p.2188

**Klein, Justin**
Table(s): Nationwide: Franchising: Mainly Franchisee **Band 3** p.114

**Knudsen, Donald P**
Table(s): South Dakota: Labor & Employment
Band 2 p.2283

**Knudsen, Eric**
Table(s): Vermont: Corporate/Commercial Band 3
p.2483, Vermont: Real Estate Band 2 p.2487

**Knudson, Kathryn L**
Table(s): Georgia: Banking & Finance: Mainly
Regulatory Band 1 p.1039

**Knueve, Mark**
Profile: p.2102
Table(s): Ohio: Labor & Employment Band 3
p.2074

**Knull, William H**
Table(s): Nationwide: International Arbitration
Band 4 p.145, Texas: Litigation: Energy & Natural
Resources Band 3 p.2361

**Knutson, Becky S**
Table(s): Iowa: Labor & Employment Band 3
p.1285

**Knutson, Julie**
Table(s): Nebraska: Healthcare Band 2 p.1661

**Kobak, Scott M**
Profile: p.1910
Table(s): New York: Real Estate: Corporate Band
3 p.1854

**Kobayashi Jr, Bert T**
Table(s): Hawaii: Litigation: General Commercial
Senior Statesmen: p.1119

**Kobert, Roy**
Table(s): Florida: Bankruptcy/Restructuring Band
3 p.939

**Kobler, Scott A**
Profile: p.1740
Table(s): New Jersey: Healthcare Band 3 p.1715

**Kobre, Steven G**
Profile: p.1910
Table(s): New York: Litigation: White-Collar
Crime & Government Investigations Band 2
p.1836

**Kobus III, Theodore J**
Profile: p.348
Table(s): Nationwide: Privacy & Data Security
Band 3 p.199

**Koch, Amelia W**
Profile: p.1365
Table(s): Louisiana: Labor & Employment Band 3
p.1350

**Koch, David W**
Table(s): Nationwide: Franchising Band 3 p.111

**Koch, Elaine Drodge**
Table(s): Missouri: Labor & Employment Band 2
p.1625

**Koch, Gary**
Table(s): Florida: Healthcare Band 3 p.954

**Kochanek, Joseph J**
Profile: p.1551
Table(s): Michigan: Banking & Finance Band 1
p.1536

**Kochanski, David**
Table(s): Maryland: Real Estate Band 2 p.1422

**Kocher, Gary J**
Profile: p.2540
Table(s): Washington: Corporate/Commercial
Band 2 p.2525

**Kociubes, Joseph L**
Profile: p.1498
Table(s): Massachusetts: Litigation: General
Commercial Band 1 p.1470

**Kocoras, John**
Profile: p.1215
Table(s): Illinois: Litigation: White-Collar Crime &
Government Investigations Up-and-coming individu-
als p.1181

**Kodish, Thad C**
Table(s): Georgia: Intellectual Property Band 4
p.1056

**Koehler, Kristin Graham**
Profile: p.874
Table(s): District of Columbia: Litigation: White-
Collar Crime & Government Investigations Up-
and-coming individuals p.827

**Koen, Robert**
Table(s): New York: Real Estate: Finance Band 3
p.1855

**Koenigs, Christopher**
Table(s): Colorado: Litigation: General
Commercial Band 2 p.709

**Koenigsberg, Benjamin Y**
Profile: p.348
Table(s): Nationwide: Projects Band 4 p.216

**Koenigsknecht, John K.**
Profile: p.1215
Table(s): Illinois: Corporate/M&A Up-and-coming
individuals p.1156

**Koepff, Paul**
Table(s): Nationwide: Insurance: Dispute
Resolution: Insurer Band 2 p.134, New York:
Insurance: Dispute Resolution: Insurer Band 2
p.1816

**Koeppel, John**
Profile: p.348
Table(s): Nationwide: Investment Funds: Private
Equity: Fund Formation Band 4 p.166, New York:
Corporate/M&A Band 5 p.1793

**Koerner, Andrew**
Table(s): New York: Immigration Up-and-coming
individuals p.1814

**Koestler, Mark D**
Profile: p.1910
Table(s): Nationwide: Immigration Band 3 p.131,
New York: Immigration Band 2 p.1814

**Koff, Douglas I**
Table(s): New York: Litigation: White-Collar
Crime & Government Investigations Band 3
p.1836

**Kofman, Robert**
Table(s): Florida: Labor & Employment Band 1
p.959

**Kogut, Barry R**
Profile: p.1910
Table(s): New York: Environment Band 3 p.1807

**Koh, Jin-Kyu**
Table(s): Michigan: Corporate/M&A Band 3
p.1538

**Kohn, Alan C**
Table(s): Missouri: Litigation: General
Commercial Senior Statesmen: p.1629

**Kohn, Arthur H**
Profile: p.348
Table(s): Nationwide: Employee Benefits &
Executive Compensation Band 1 p.73, New York:
Employee Benefits & Executive Compensation
Band 1 p.1802

**Kohn, Jeffrey**
Table(s): New York: Labor & Employment Band 2
p.1826

**Kohn, Joseph**
Table(s): Pennsylvania: Antitrust Band 2 p.2184

**Kohn, Richard**
Profile: p.1215
Table(s): Illinois: Banking & Finance Band 3
p.1145

**Kohn Ross, Susan**
Table(s): Nationwide: International Trade:
Customs Band 3 p.155

**Kohnen, Ralph**
Profile: p.2103
Table(s): Ohio: Litigation: White-Collar Crime &
Government Investigations Band 3 p.2079

**Kok, Peter**
Table(s): Michigan: Labor & Employment Band 2
p.1542

**Kokoruda, Thomas G**
Table(s): Missouri: Litigation: General
Commercial Band 2 p.1628

**Kolar, Joseph M**
Profile: p.348
Table(s): Nationwide: Financial Services
Regulation: Consumer Finance (Compliance)
Band 1 p.98

**Kolasky, William J**
Profile: p.875
Table(s): District of Columbia: Antitrust Band 2
p.787

**Kolb, William R**
Profile: p.1499
Table(s): Massachusetts: Corporate/M&A Band 3
p.1452

**Kolenic Jr, Anthony**
Table(s): Michigan: Employee Benefits &
Executive Compensation Band 2 p.1540

**Kolesar, Andrew L**
Profile: p.1910
Table(s): Ohio: Natural Resources &
Environment Band 2 p.2083

**Kolkey, Daniel M**
Profile: p.647
Table(s): Nationwide: Appellate Law Band 4 p.26,
California: Litigation: Appellate Band 1 p.599

**Kollman, Frank L**
Table(s): Maryland: Labor & Employment Band 3
p.1417

**Kolman, Mark H**
Profile: p.875
Table(s): District of Columbia: Insurance:
Policyholder Band 2 p.818

**Koltun, Timothy**
Profile: p.1551
Table(s): Michigan: Real Estate Band 3 p.1546

**Kolyer, Steven**
Profile: p.348
Table(s): Nationwide: Capital Markets:
Structured Products Band 3 p.52

**Kominers, William**
Profile: p.1428
Table(s): Maryland: Real Estate: Land Use Band 2
p.1422

**Komoroski, Kenneth S**
Profile: p.2221
Table(s): Pennsylvania: Environment Band 3
p.2194

**Komoroski-Wiwi, Amy**
Profile: p.1740
Table(s): New Jersey: Labor & Employment Up-
and-coming individuals p.1718

**Komrower, Stuart**
Profile: p.1740
Table(s): New Jersey: Bankruptcy/Restructuring
Band 3 p.1705

**Koneck, John**
Table(s): Minnesota: Real Estate Band 1 p.1576

**Konopka, Patricia A**
Table(s): Missouri: Labor & Employment Band 3
p.1625

**Konrad, Angela**
Table(s): West Virginia: Litigation: General
Commercial Band 3 p.2555

**Kontio, Peter**
Profile: p.1087
Table(s): Georgia: Antitrust Band 3 p.1037,
Georgia: Litigation: General Commercial Band 3
p.1065

**Kontrimas, Andrius**
Profile: p.2399
Table(s): Texas: Tax Band 4 p.2371

**Konvisser, Joshua B**
Profile: p.1910
Table(s): Nationwide: Outsourcing Band 4 p.195,
New York: Technology & Outsourcing Band 2
p.1868

**Koogler, Mark**
Profile: p.2103
Table(s): Ohio: Corporate/M&A Band 3 p.2064

**Kooistra, John**
Table(s): Arkansas: Corporate/Commercial Band
3 p.518, Arkansas: Real Estate Band 3 p.524

**Koonce, Jeffrey**
Table(s): Louisiana: Corporate/M&A: Tax Band 2
p.1341

**Koons, Warren**
Table(s): Washington: Real Estate Band 2 p.2535

**Koons Jr, Robert A**
Profile: p.2221
Table(s): Pennsylvania: Intellectual Property
Band 3 p.2197

**Koontz, Eric A**
Table(s): Georgia: Corporate/M&A Band 4 p.1046

**Kopecky, Robert J**
Profile: p.1215
Table(s): **Illinois:** Litigation: General Commercial **Band 2** p.1180

**Kopf, Rick O**
Table(s): **Texas:** Real Estate **Band 3** p.2367

**Kopp, Steven**
Profile: p.1910
Table(s): **New York:** Tax **Band 4** p.1862

**Korando, Kimberly J**
Profile: p.2042
Table(s): **North Carolina:** Labor & Employment **Band 2** p.2031

**Korb, Donald L**
Profile: p.349
Table(s): **Nationwide:** Tax: Controversy **Band 4** p.244, **District of Columbia:** Tax **Band 4** p.838

**Korb, Philip B**
Profile: p.2222
Table(s): **Pennsylvania:** Real Estate **Band 2** p.2208

**Korbey, Mitchell**
Table(s): **New York:** Real Estate: Zoning/Land Use **Band 2** p.1855

**Korby, Mary**
Profile: p.2399
Table(s): **Texas:** Corporate/M&A **Band 2** p.2337

**Korda, Peter**
Profile: p.1910
Table(s): **New York:** Real Estate **Band 4** p.1854

**Koren, Bennet S**
Profile: p.349
Table(s): **Nationwide:** Financial Services Regulation: Consumer Finance (Compliance) **Band 1** p.98

**Koren, Edward**
Profile: p.997
Table(s): **Nationwide:** Wealth Management: Eastern Region **Band 2** p.267, **Florida:** Tax: Estate Planning **Band 1** p.979

**Koretzky, I Harold**
Table(s): **Louisiana:** Labor & Employment **Band 2** p.1350

**Korff, Joshua N**
Profile: p.349
Table(s): **Nationwide:** Capital Markets: Debt & Equity **Band 2** p.46

**Korff, Phyllis G**
Profile: p.349
Table(s): **Nationwide:** Capital Markets: Debt & Equity **Band 1** p.46

**Korman, Martin W**
Table(s): **California:** Corporate/M&A **Band 2** p.553

**Korman, Paul**
Profile: p.349
Table(s): **Nationwide:** Energy: Oil & Gas (Regulatory & Litigation) **Band 4** p.78

**Kornberg, Alan W**
Profile: p.349
Table(s): **Nationwide:** Bankruptcy/Restructuring **Band 1** p.39, **New York:** Bankruptcy/Restructuring **Band 1** p.1782

**Kornblau, David**
Profile: p.349
Table(s): **Nationwide:** Securities: Regulation: Enforcement **Band 3** p.233

**Kornblith, Richard L**
Profile: p.647
Table(s): **California:** Tax **Band 3** p.617

**Kornegay, Nancy**
Profile: p.2399
Table(s): **Texas:** Insurance **Up-and-coming individuals** p.2351

**Kornfeld, Armand J**
Table(s): **Washington:** Bankruptcy/Restructuring **Band 1** p.2523

**Kornfeld, Linda D**
Profile: p.647
Table(s): **California:** Insurance: Policyholder **Band 3** p.576

**Kornfeld, Lynn M**
Table(s): **Colorado:** Natural Resources & Environment **Band 3** p.712

**Kornfeld, Rick**
Table(s): **Colorado:** Litigation: White-Collar Crime & Government Investigations **Band 2** p.710

**Korniczky, Stephen S**
Table(s): **California:** Intellectual Property: Patent **Band 4** p.578

**Kornreich, Craig**
Table(s): **Texas:** Banking & Finance **Band 2** p.2325

**Kornreich, David**
Profile: p.997
Table(s): **Florida:** Labor & Employment **Band 3** p.959

**Kornreich, Edward S**
Table(s): **Nationwide:** Healthcare: Regulatory & Litigation **Band 1** p.127, **Nationwide:** Healthcare: Transactional **Band 1** p.127, **New York:** Healthcare **Band 1** p.1811

**Kortanek, Steven K**
Table(s): **Delaware:** Bankruptcy/Restructuring **Band 3** p.754

**Korzenowski, Scott E**
Profile: p.349
Table(s): **Nationwide:** Franchising: Mainly Franchisee **Band 2** p.114

**Kosacz, Barbara**
Table(s): **Nationwide:** Investment Funds: Venture Capital **Band 2** p.174, **Nationwide:** Life Sciences: Corporate/Commercial **Band 1** p.182, **California:** Life Sciences: Corporate/Commercial **Band 1** p.590

**Koschik, David N**
Profile: p.349
Table(s): **Nationwide:** Banking & Finance **Band 3** p.31

**Koski, Ceridwen**
Table(s): **New York:** Immigration **Associates to watch** p.1814

**Kosnitzky, Michael**
Table(s): **Florida:** Tax **Band 2** p.979

**Kotler, Bradley E**
Table(s): **Illinois:** Banking & Finance **Band 3** p.1145

**Kotler, David**
Profile: p.1740
Table(s): **New Jersey:** Litigation: General Commercial **Band 3** p.1722

**Kotler, Lawrence J**
Table(s): **Pennsylvania:** Bankruptcy/Restructuring **Band 3** p.2188

**Kotovsky, Stanley**
Table(s): **New Mexico:** Labor & Employment **Band 3** p.1767

**Kotran, Stephen M**
Profile: p.1910
Table(s): **New York:** Corporate/M&A **Band 3** p.1793, **New York:** Insurance: Transactional & Regulatory **Band 3** p.1816

**Kott, David R**
Profile: p.1740
Table(s): **New Jersey:** Litigation: Products Liability **Band 1** p.1723

**Kouimelis, Eleni**
Profile: p.1215
Table(s): **Illinois:** Environment: Mainly Transactional **Band 2** p.1162

**Koury, Joseph S**
Table(s): **Nationwide:** Energy: Oil & Gas (Regulatory & Litigation) **Band 3** p.78

**Kovacich, Thomas**
Profile: p.647
Table(s): **California:** Construction **Band 4** p.550

**Kovacs, Paul**
Table(s): **Missouri:** Litigation: General Commercial **Senior Statesmen:** p.1629

**Kovner, Mark L**
Profile: p.875
Table(s): **District of Columbia:** Antitrust **Band 3** p.787

**Kovner, Victor A**
Table(s): **Nationwide:** First Amendment Litigation **Band 2** p.105, **New York:** Media & Entertainment: First Amendment Litigation **Band 1** p.1851

**Kowalski, Jack**
Table(s): **Georgia:** Construction **Band 3** p.1044

**Kozak, John W**
Profile: p.1216
Table(s): **Illinois:** Intellectual Property **Band 2** p.1171

**Kozlowski, Holly D**
Profile: p.2103
Table(s): **Ohio:** Intellectual Property **Band 2** p.2071

**Kozminski, Brian**
Table(s): **Illinois:** Real Estate **Band 3** p.1187

**Kozusko, Donald**
Table(s): **Nationwide:** Wealth Management: Eastern Region **Band 3** p.267

**Kozyak, John W**
Profile: p.997
Table(s): **Florida:** Bankruptcy/Restructuring **Band 1** p.939

**Kracov, Daniel**
Profile: p.875
Table(s): **District of Columbia:** Healthcare: Pharmaceutical/Medical Products Regulatory **Band 2** p.810

**Kraemer, Michael F**
Table(s): **Rhode Island:** Labor & Employment **Band 2** p.2253

**Kraeutler, Eric**
Profile: p.2222
Table(s): **Pennsylvania:** Litigation: General Commercial **Band 4** p.2203

**Kraft, Barbara Simpson**
Table(s): **Alaska:** Corporate/M&A **Band 2** p.487, **Alaska:** Real Estate **Band 2** p.491

**Kraft, Denise**
Profile: p.772
Table(s): **Delaware:** Intellectual Property **Band 4** p.763

**Kraft, Jeffrey G**
Profile: p.1216
Table(s): **Illinois:** Healthcare **Band 3** p.1165

**Kraft, Kenneth H**
Table(s): **Georgia:** Real Estate **Band 3** p.1070

**Krafte, Lori E**
Table(s): **Ohio:** Intellectual Property **Band 3** p.2071

**Kraftson, Daniel**
Table(s): **Virginia:** Construction **Band 1** p.2491

**Kraiem, Rubén**
Profile: p.349
Table(s): **Nationwide:** Climate Change **Band 3** p.63, **New York:** Latin American Investment **Band 4** p.1829

**Krakauer, Bryan**
Profile: p.1216
Table(s): **Illinois:** Bankruptcy/Restructuring **Band 3** p.1148

**Krakaur, Keith D**
Profile: p.1910
Table(s): **New York:** Litigation: White-Collar Crime & Government Investigations **Band 2** p.1836

**Krakoff, David S.**
Profile: p.875
Table(s): **District of Columbia:** Litigation: White-Collar Crime & Government Investigations **Band 2** p.827

**Krakus, Beata**
Table(s): **Nationwide:** Franchising **Up-and-coming individuals** p.111

**Kramer, Andrea S**
Profile: p.1216
Table(s): **Illinois:** Tax **Band 3** p.1192

**Kramer, Ann**
Table(s): **New York:** Insurance: Dispute Resolution: Policyholder **Band 3** p.1816

**Kramer, Barry J**
Profile: p.350
Table(s): **Nationwide:** Investment Funds: Venture Capital **Band 3** p.174, **California:** Corporate/M&A: Venture Capital **Band 4** p.555

**Kramer, Daniel J**
Profile: p.350
Table(s): Nationwide: Securities: Litigation Band 1 p.232, New York: Litigation: Securities Band 1 p.1834

**Kramer, David H**
Table(s): California: Intellectual Property: Trademark, Copyright & Trade Secrets Band 1 p.578

**Kramer, Howard L**
Profile: p.350
Table(s): Nationwide: Financial Services Regulation: Broker Dealer (Compliance) Band 2 p.97

**Kramer, James**
Profile: p.647
Table(s): California: Litigation: Securities Up-and-coming individuals p.594

**Kramer, Jay S**
Table(s): Arizona: Real Estate Band 1 p.504

**Kramer, Mary E**
Table(s): Florida: Immigration Band 3 p.956

**Kramer, Morris J**
Profile: p.1911
Table(s): New York: Corporate/M&A Senior Statesmen: p.1793

**Kramer, Myron**
Table(s): Georgia: Immigration Band 1 p.1055

**Kramer, Samuel**
Profile: p.1216
Table(s): Nationwide: Outsourcing Band 4 p.195, Illinois: Technology & Outsourcing Band 2 p.1194

**Kramer, Steven E**
Profile: p.2306
Table(s): Tennessee: Labor & Employment Band 2 p.2293

**Kramer, Thomas I**
Table(s): Oregon: Labor & Employment Band 3 p.2168

**Krantz, Richard**
Profile: p.744
Table(s): Connecticut: Corporate/M&A Band 3 p.732

**Krantz, Stefan**
Profile: p.350
Table(s): Nationwide: Energy: Oil & Gas (Regulatory & Litigation) Band 4 p.78

**Krapf, Daniel H**
Table(s): Delaware: Real Estate Band 2 p.766

**Krapf, Robert J**
Profile: p.772
Table(s): Delaware: Real Estate Band 1 p.766

**Kraske, Paul S**
Profile: p.350
Table(s): Nationwide: Projects Band 4 p.216

**Krasnow, Jordan**
Table(s): Massachusetts: Real Estate Senior Statesmen: p.1478

**Krasny, Leslie T.**
Table(s): Nationwide: Food & Beverages: Regulatory & Litigation Band 3 p.107

**Krassen, Glenn**
Table(s): Ohio: Natural Resources & Environment Band 4 p.2083

**Kratz, Erwin D**
Table(s): Arizona: Labor & Employment Band 4 p.499

**Krauland, Edward**
Table(s): Nationwide: International Trade: Export Controls & Economic Sanctions Band 1 p.153

**Kraus, Alan E**
Table(s): New Jersey: Litigation: General Commercial Band 1 p.1722

**Krause, Jeffrey**
Profile: p.647
Table(s): California: Bankruptcy/Restructuring Band 4 p.542

**Krausman, Jeffrey A**
Table(s): Iowa: Labor & Employment Band 3 p.1285

**Krauss, Joseph G**
Table(s): District of Columbia: Antitrust Band 4 p.787

**Kravetz, Jonathan**
Profile: p.350
Table(s): Nationwide: Life Sciences: Corporate/Commercial Band 2 p.182, Massachusetts: Corporate/M&A: Capital Markets Band 2 p.1453

**Kravitt, Jason H P**
Table(s): Nationwide: Capital Markets: Securitisation Senior Statesmen: p.59

**Krebs, David J.**
Profile: p.1365
Table(s): Louisiana: Construction Band 2 p.1339

**Krebs, Michael**
Profile: p.1499
Table(s): Massachusetts: Banking & Finance: Corporate & Regulatory Band 2 p.1446

**Kreger, Michael E**
Table(s): Alaska: Litigation: Construction Band 1 p.490

**Kreider, Gary P**
Profile: p.2103
Table(s): Ohio: Corporate/M&A Senior Statesmen: p.2064

**Kreider, Kenneth**
Profile: p.2103
Table(s): Ohio: Real Estate Band 4 p.2086

**Kreiger, Arthur**
Table(s): Massachusetts: Environment Band 3 p.1457

**Kreindler, Marla**
Profile: p.1216
Table(s): Illinois: Labor & Employment: Employee Benefits & Compensation Band 3 p.1176

**Kreisler, David**
Profile: p.1499
Table(s): Massachusetts: Private Equity: Fund Formation Band 2 p.1476

**Kreitman, Robert M**
Profile: p.1911
Table(s): New York: Tax Band 4 p.1862

**Kreitzer, Michael N**
Profile: p.997
Table(s): Florida: Litigation: General Commercial Band 3 p.966

**Kreller, Thomas R**
Profile: p.648
Table(s): California: Bankruptcy/Restructuring Band 2 p.542

**Kremen, Richard M**
Profile: p.1429
Table(s): Maryland: Litigation: Bankruptcy Band 2 p.1419

**Krendl, Cathy S**
Table(s): Colorado: Corporate/M&A Senior Statesmen: p.703

**Kresge, Raymond**
Profile: p.2222
Table(s): Pennsylvania: Labor & Employment Band 3 p.2200

**Kresovich, George**
Table(s): Washington: Real Estate: Zoning/Land Use Band 2 p.2536

**Kress, Alan H**
Profile: p.1911
Table(s): New York: Media & Entertainment: Music Band 2 p.1849

**Kreusler-Walsh, Jane**
Table(s): Florida: Litigation: Appellate Band 1 p.972

**Krevans, Rachel**
Profile: p.648
Table(s): California: Intellectual Property: Patent Band 2 p.578

**Krevitt, Josh**
Profile: p.1911
Table(s): New York: Intellectual Property: Patent Band 2 p.1820

**Krevolin, Douglas P**
Profile: p.1087
Table(s): Georgia: Real Estate Band 3 p.1070

**Kriegel, Jeremy**
Table(s): Illinois: Intellectual Property Band 4 p.1171

**Krieger, Paul**
Profile: p.2400
Table(s): Texas: Intellectual Property Band 2 p.2354

**Kriesberg, Simeon M**
Table(s): Nationwide: International Trade: Export Controls & Economic Sanctions Band 2 p.153

**Krieser, Jason D**
Profile: p.2400
Table(s): Nationwide: Outsourcing Band 2 p.195, Texas: Technology: Outsourcing Band 1 p.2376

**Krimminger, Michael**
Profile: p.350
Table(s): Nationwide: Financial Services Regulation: Banking (Compliance) Band 3 p.96

**Kriss, Ronald A.**
Table(s): Florida: Real Estate Band 4 p.974

**Kritenbrink, Lawrence E**
Table(s): Nebraska: Real Estate Band 3 p.1666

**Kroculick, George J**
Table(s): Pennsylvania: Real Estate Band 4 p.2208

**Kroener, William F**
Profile: p.350
Table(s): Nationwide: Financial Services Regulation: Banking (Compliance) Band 3 p.96

**Kroesche, Guy P**
Table(s): Utah: Real Estate Band 2 p.2470

**Kroger, William**
Table(s): Texas: Energy: State Regulatory & Litigation (Electricity) Band 2 p.2341

**Kromer, John**
Profile: p.350
Table(s): Nationwide: Financial Services Regulation: Consumer Finance (Compliance) Band 3 p.98

**Kromholz, Joseph A**
Table(s): Wisconsin: Intellectual Property Band 3 p.2573

**Kroncke-Moore, Barbara J.**
Profile: p.1499
Table(s): Massachusetts: Banking & Finance: Public Finance Band 2 p.1446

**Kronk, Catherine**
Table(s): Vermont: Real Estate Band 2 p.2487

**Kronk, Edward M**
Profile: p.1551
Table(s): Michigan: Litigation: General Commercial Band 2 p.1544

**Kroon, David**
Table(s): South Dakota: Labor & Employment Band 2 p.2283

**Kroupa, Sharon A**
Profile: p.350
Table(s): Nationwide: Capital Markets: REITs Band 2 p.55

**Krouse, Bradley A**
Table(s): Pennsylvania: Real Estate Band 3 p.2208

**Krovatin, Gerald**
Table(s): New Jersey: Litigation: White-Collar Crime & Government Investigations Band 1 p.1723

**Krpata, Kyle C**
Profile: p.648
Table(s): California: Corporate/M&A Band 4 p.553

**Krueger, Allyson S**
Table(s): Oregon: Labor & Employment Band 3 p.2168

**Krueger, Herbert W**
Table(s): Illinois: Labor & Employment: Employee Benefits & Compensation Band 1 p.1176

**Kruger, Lewis**
Table(s): New York: Bankruptcy/Restructuring Band 4 p.1782

**Krugman, Edward B**
Table(s): Georgia: Antitrust Band 3 p.1037, Georgia: Litigation: General Commercial Band 4 p.1065

**Krugman, Edward P**
Profile: p.350
Table(s): **Nationwide:** Insurance: Dispute
Resolution: Insurer **Band 2** p.134, **Nationwide:**
Insurance: Dispute Resolution: Reinsurance
**Band 1** p.134, **New York:** Insurance: Dispute
Resolution: Insurer **Band 1** p.1816

**Krugman, Gary**
Table(s): **District of Columbia:** Intellectual
Property: Trademark, Copyright & Trade Secrets
**Band 2** p.820

**Krumholz, Dennis J**
Table(s): **New Jersey:** Environment **Band 1** p.1711

**Krumholz, Joshua C**
Profile: p.1499
Table(s): **Massachusetts:** Intellectual Property
**Band 3** p.1463

**Krupka, Catherine M**
Table(s): **Nationwide:** Energy: Electricity
(Regulatory & Litigation) **Band 4** p.76

**Krupp, Peter C**
Profile: p.1216
Table(s): **Illinois:** Corporate/M&A: Private Equity
**Band 1** p.1157

**Krus, Cynthia M**
Table(s): **District of Columbia:** Corporate/M&A &
Private Equity **Band 4** p.797

**Kruse, Alvin**
Profile: p.1216
Table(s): **Illinois:** Real Estate **Band 3** p.1187

**Kruse, C Thomas**
Profile: p.2400
Table(s): **Texas:** Litigation: General Commercial
**Band 4** p.2362

**Kruse, Layne**
Profile: p.2400
Table(s): **Texas:** Antitrust **Star individuals** p.2323

**Krutz, Fred**
Profile: p.1605
Table(s): **Mississippi:** Litigation: General
Commercial **Band 2** p.1597

**Krysinski, Mark**
Table(s): **Michigan:** Real Estate **Band 2** p.1546

**Kubat, Rod**
Table(s): **Iowa:** Corporate/M&A **Band 3** p.1283,
**Iowa:** Corporate/M&A: Banking & Finance **Band
2** p.1283

**Kubehl, Douglas M**
Table(s): **Texas:** Intellectual Property **Band 4**
p.2354

**Kubek, Gary W**
Table(s): **New York:** Antitrust **Band 4** p.1778

**Kubetz, Bernard J**
Table(s): **Maine:** Litigation: General Commercial
**Band 2** p.1393

**Kubicek, David W**
Table(s): **Iowa:** Real Estate **Band 1** p.1290

**Kubin, Karen**
Profile: p.648
Table(s): **California:** Labor & Employment **Band 3**
p.587

**Kubota, Carolyn**
Table(s): **California:** Litigation: White-Collar
Crime & Government Investigations **Band 3** p.601

**Kucera, William**
Table(s): **Illinois:** Corporate/M&A **Band 4** p.1156

**Kuck, Charles H**
Table(s): **Nationwide:** Immigration **Band 2** p.131,
**Georgia:** Immigration **Band 1** p.1055

**Kudenholdt, Stephen S**
Profile: p.351
Table(s): **Nationwide:** Capital Markets:
Securitisation **Band 1** p.59

**Kudlac, Kevin**
Profile: p.2400
Table(s): **Texas:** Intellectual Property **Band 2**
p.2354

**Kudo, Benjamin**
Table(s): **Hawaii:** Real Estate: Zoning/Land Use
**Band 1** p.1120

**Kuebel III, Omer F (Rick)**
Profile: p.1365
Table(s): **Louisiana:** Bankruptcy/Restructuring
**Band 2** p.1337

**Kuehnle, Kenton**
Table(s): **Ohio:** Real Estate **Band 3** p.2086

**Kuester, Jeffrey R**
Table(s): **Georgia:** Intellectual Property **Band 3**
p.1056

**Kuffel, John C**
Table(s): **Delaware:** Real Estate **Associates to
watch** p.766

**Kugell, Jaclyn L**
Profile: p.1499
Table(s): **Massachusetts:** Labor & Employment
**Band 3** p.1466

**Kulbaski, James J**
Profile: p.2511
Table(s): **Northern Virginia:** Intellectual Property
**Band 3** p.2497

**Kummer, Thomas F**
Profile: p.1682
Table(s): **Nevada:** Litigation: General
Commercial **Band 3** p.1677

**Kumpe, Peter G**
Table(s): **Arkansas:** Litigation: General
Commercial **Band 2** p.522

**Kun, Michael S**
Profile: p.648
Table(s): **California:** Labor & Employment **Band 4**
p.587

**Kuney, David**
Profile: p.875
Table(s): **District of Columbia:**
Bankruptcy/Restructuring **Senior Statesmen:** p.792

**Kunin, Peter B**
Table(s): **Vermont:** Intellectual Property **Band 1**
p.2484

**Kunin, Stephen**
Profile: p.2511
Table(s): **Northern Virginia:** Intellectual Property
**Band 3** p.2497

**Kunkel, Anne**
Table(s): **Idaho:** Real Estate **Up-and-coming individuals** p.1138

**Kunkel, Daniel H**
Table(s): **Florida:** Labor & Employment **Band 3**
p.959

**Kunold Jr, Robert**
Table(s): **Washington:** Corporate/Commercial
**Band 3** p.2525

**Kuntamukkala, Ajay**
Table(s): **Nationwide:** Energy: Nuclear
(Regulatory & Litigation) **Up-and-coming individuals**
p.77

**Kuntz, Michael**
Table(s): **Washington:** Real Estate **Band 1** p.2535

**Kunz, Donald**
Table(s): **Michigan:** Corporate/M&A **Band 1**
p.1538

**Kunz III, Carl N**
Table(s): **Delaware:** Bankruptcy/Restructuring
**Band 3** p.754

**Kunzman, Kathleen**
Table(s): **California:** Immigration **Band 4** p.571

**Kupec, Christopher C**
Table(s): **North Carolina:** Banking & Finance
**Band 1** p.2021

**Kupietzky, Moshe J**
Profile: p.648
Table(s): **California:** Banking & Finance **Band 4**
p.539, **California:** Corporate/M&A **Band 4** p.554

**Kupperman, Stephen H**
Profile: p.1365
Table(s): **Louisiana:** Litigation: General
Commercial **Band 2** p.1352

**Kurlander, Stuart**
Profile: p.875
Table(s): **District of Columbia:** Healthcare **Band 2**
p.809

**Kurnit, Rick**
Profile: p.351
Table(s): **Nationwide:** Advertising: Transactional
& Regulatory **Star individuals** p.20

**Kurth, Mette**
Profile: p.648
Table(s): **California:** Bankruptcy/Restructuring
**Up-and-coming individuals** p.542

**Kurtz, David**
Profile: p.1365
Table(s): **Louisiana:** Construction **Band 2** p.1339

**Kurtz, Glenn M**
Profile: p.1911
Table(s): **New York:** Litigation: General
Commercial **Band 4** p.1833

**Kurtz, John F**
Table(s): **Idaho:** Bankruptcy/Restructuring **Band 2**
p.1131

**Kurtz, Marcy E**
Profile: p.2400
Table(s): **Texas:** Bankruptcy/Restructuring **Band 3**
p.2328

**Kurtzman, Jeffrey**
Table(s): **Pennsylvania:**
Bankruptcy/Restructuring **Band 3** p.2188

**Kurtzon, Michael S**
Table(s): **Illinois:** Real Estate **Band 2** p.1187

**Kurucza, Robert M**
Profile: p.351
Table(s): **Nationwide:** Investment Funds:
Registered Funds **Band 2** p.170

**Kuryla, Matthew**
Profile: p.2400
Table(s): **Texas:** Environment **Band 2** p.2343

**Kurzban, Ira J**
Table(s): **Nationwide:** Immigration **Band 1** p.131,
**Florida:** Immigration **Star individuals** p.956

**Kurzweil, David**
Profile: p.1088
Table(s): **Georgia:** Bankruptcy/Restructuring
**Band 1** p.1042

**Kurzweil, Harvey**
Profile: p.1911
Table(s): **New York:** Litigation: General
Commercial **Band 4** p.1833

**Kurzweil, Lanny S**
Profile: p.1740
Table(s): **New Jersey:** Environment **Band 1** p.1711

**Kus, Edward J**
Table(s): **Illinois:** Real Estate: Zoning/Land Use
**Band 1** p.1188

**Kushan, Jeffrey P**
Profile: p.875
Table(s): **District of Columbia:** Intellectual
Property: Litigation **Band 2** p.821

**Kushman, Moshe J**
Profile: p.648
Table(s): **California:** Tax **Band 2** p.617

**Kushner, Gary Jay**
Table(s): **Nationwide:** Food & Beverages:
Regulatory & Litigation **Band 2** p.107

**Kushner, Harold**
Table(s): **Alabama:** Corporate/Commercial **Band
1** p.459

**Kushner, Margaret B**
Table(s): **Oregon:** Corporate/M&A **Band 2** p.2164

**Kushner, Philip**
Table(s): **Ohio:** Litigation: White-Collar Crime &
Government Investigations **Band 3** p.2079

**Kutler, Marilyn**
Table(s): **Pennsylvania:** Real Estate **Band 2**
p.2208

**Kutrow, Bradley R**
Table(s): **North Carolina:** Litigation: General
Commercial **Band 3** p.2033

**Kutzschbach, George**
Profile: p.351
Table(s): **Nationwide:** Energy: Oil & Gas
(Transactional) **Senior Statesmen:** p.79

**Kuylenstierna, Jan M**
Table(s): **Nationwide:** Transportation: Shipping:
Litigation (outside New York) **Band 2** p.263

**Kwan-Gett, Mei Lin**
Profile: p.1911
Table(s): **New York:** Litigation: White-Collar
Crime & Government Investigations **Up-and-coming
individuals** p.1836

**Kwasnick, Raymond**
Table(s): Massachusetts: Real Estate Band 3
p.1478

**Kwon, Julie K**
Profile: p.351
Table(s): Nationwide: Wealth Management:
Western Region Up-and-coming individuals p.267

**Kyle, Amy L**
Profile: p.1499
Table(s): Massachusetts: Banking & Finance
Band 1 p.1445

**Kyle, John**
Profile: p.1278
Table(s): Indiana: Environment Band 1 p.1270

**Kyper, James R**
Profile: p.2222
Table(s): Pennsylvania: Intellectual Property
Band 2 p.2197

**Kyrwood, Jason**
Profile: p.351
Table(s): Nationwide: Banking & Finance Band 3
p.31

## L

**La Suer, Gene**
Table(s): Iowa: Labor & Employment Band 2
p.1285

**Labate, Robert J**
Profile: p.1216
Table(s): Illinois: Media & Entertainment:
Transactional Band 1 p.1185

**Labe, Monica**
Profile: p.1552
Table(s): Michigan: Real Estate Band 3 p.1546

**LaBianca, Margaret B.**
Table(s): Arizona: Environment (including water
rights) Up-and-coming individuals p.497

**LaBine, Jeffrey L**
Profile: p.1552
Table(s): Michigan: Corporate/M&A Up-and-coming
individuals p.1538

**LaBrie, Michael J.**
Profile: p.2151
Table(s): Oklahoma: Intellectual Property Band 1
p.2138

**LaBriola, Stephen T**
Profile: p.1088
Table(s): Georgia: Litigation: General
Commercial Band 4 p.1065

**Labson, Michael S**
Profile: p.875
Table(s): District of Columbia: Healthcare:
Pharmaceutical/Medical Products Regulatory
Band 2 p.810

**LaCagnin, Stephen**
Table(s): West Virginia: Litigation: General
Commercial Band 2 p.2555

**Lacey, Jason P**
Profile: p.1300
Table(s): Kansas: Labor & Employment Up-and-
coming individuals p.1294

**Lackey, Michael**
Table(s): Nationwide: Litigation: E-Discovery Band
2 p.187

**Lacktman, Nathaniel M.**
Table(s): Florida: Healthcare Up-and-coming individuals p.954

**Lacovara, Philip Allen**
Table(s): Nationwide: International Arbitration:
Arbitrators Band 1 p.146

**Lacy, John R**
Table(s): Hawaii: Litigation: General Commercial
Band 2 p.1119

**Lacy Jr, Peyton**
Profile: p.470
Table(s): Alabama: Labor & Employment Senior
Statesmen: p.460

**Ladig, Peter B**
Table(s): Delaware: Chancery Band 3 p.758

**Ladik, Steven M**
Table(s): Nationwide: Immigration Band 3 p.131,
Texas: Immigration Band 1 p.2349

**Ladner, Gregory W**
Profile: p.772
Table(s): Delaware: Corporate/M&A: Alternative
Entities Band 2 p.761

**Ladner, Mark P**
Profile: p.351
Table(s): Nationwide: Financial Services
Regulation: Consumer Finance (Litigation) Band 2
p.99, New York: Antitrust Band 5 p.1778

**Lafferty, Latour**
Table(s): Florida: Litigation: White-Collar Crime &
Government Investigations Band 2 p.967

**Lafferty, William M**
Table(s): Delaware: Chancery Band 2 p.758

**LaFiandra, Aldo L**
Profile: p.1088
Table(s): Georgia: Banking & Finance Band 2
p.1039

**LaFiura, Dennis R**
Profile: p.1740
Table(s): Nationwide: Franchising Band 4 p.111,
New Jersey: Litigation: General Commercial
Band 2 p.1722

**LaFollette, Christine B**
Profile: p.2400
Table(s): Nationwide: Energy: Oil & Gas
(Transactional) Band 3 p.79, Texas:
Corporate/M&A Band 2 p.2337

**LaFuze, William L**
Profile: p.2400
Table(s): Texas: Intellectual Property Band 1
p.2354

**LaGory, Dennis**
Table(s): Illinois: Insurance: Dispute Resolution:
Reinsurance Band 3 p.1168

**Lahey, William L**
Table(s): Massachusetts: Environment Band 2
p.1457

**Lahlou, Yasmine**
Profile: p.351
Table(s): Nationwide: International Arbitration
Up-and-coming individuals p.145

**Lahoud, Charbel**
Table(s): Nationwide: Native American Law Band
3 p.192

**Lain, John M**
Table(s): Virginia: Environment Band 2 p.2495

**Laing, Michael**
Profile: p.2103
Table(s): Ohio: Employee Benefits & Executive
Compensation Band 2 p.2067

**Laird, Michael S**
Profile: p.2151
Table(s): Oklahoma: Real Estate Band 1 p.2145

**Lalik, Elizabeth A**
Profile: p.2511
Table(s): Virginia: Labor & Employment Band 3
p.2500

**Lalle, Wayne**
Table(s): Virginia: Construction Band 1 p.2491

**Lalli, Matthew L**
Table(s): Utah: Litigation: General Commercial
Band 3 p.2468

**Lally, Amy**
Profile: p.648
Table(s): California: Environment Band 4 p.564

**Lamar, Jayna Partain**
Profile: p.470
Table(s): Alabama: Bankruptcy/Restructuring
Band 1 p.457

**Lamar III, Howard H**
Profile: p.2306
Table(s): Tennessee: Corporate/M&A Band 2
p.2288

**Lamb, Bruce D.**
Table(s): Florida: Healthcare Band 2 p.954

**Lamb, Christopher J**
Profile: p.772
Table(s): Delaware: Real Estate Band 2 p.766

**Lamb, William S**
Profile: p.351
Table(s): Nationwide: Energy: Electricity
(Transactional) Band 1 p.77

**Lambert, Arthur**
Profile: p.2400
Table(s): Texas: Labor & Employment Band 4
p.2359

**Lambert, Kent A**
Profile: p.1365
Table(s): Louisiana: Litigation: General
Commercial Band 3 p.1352

**Lamdin III, William**
Profile: p.1654
Table(s): Montana: Corporate/M&A Band 1
p.1646

**Lamken, Jeffrey A**
Profile: p.351
Table(s): Nationwide: Appellate Law Band 1 p.26

**Lamm, Carolyn B**
Profile: p.351
Table(s): Nationwide: International Arbitration
Band 1 p.145, Nationwide: International
Arbitration: Arbitrators Band 1 p.145

**Lamont, Charlotte**
Profile: p.1774
Table(s): New Mexico: Labor & Employment
Band 3 p.1767

**Lamontagne, Ovide M**
Table(s): New Hampshire: Litigation: General
Commercial Band 4 p.1690

**Lampe, Donald C**
Table(s): Nationwide: Financial Services
Regulation: Consumer Finance (Compliance)
Band 2 p.98, North Carolina: Banking & Finance
Band 3 p.2021

**Lampe, Matthew W**
Profile: p.1911
Table(s): New York: Labor & Employment Band 3
p.1826

**Lamson, William**
Table(s): Nebraska: Litigation: Insurance Band 1
p.1664

**Lancaster, Stephen R**
Profile: p.527
Table(s): Arkansas: Litigation: General
Commercial Band 4 p.522

**Lancaster Jr, Ralph I**
Profile: p.1401
Table(s): Maine: Litigation: General Commercial
Senior Statesmen: p.1393

**Lance, Andrew A**
Profile: p.1911
Table(s): New York: Real Estate Band 2 p.1854

**Land, Allison**
Profile: p.772
Table(s): Delaware: Corporate/M&A: Alternative
Entities Band 3 p.761

**Land, Brian R**
Profile: p.875
Table(s): District of Columbia: Environment:
Mainly Transactional Band 2 p.805

**Landa, Leor**
Profile: p.351
Table(s): Nationwide: Investment Funds: Hedge
Funds Band 2 p.162, Nationwide: Investment
Funds: Private Equity: Fund Formation Band 2
p.166

**Landau, Christopher**
Profile: p.352
Table(s): Nationwide: Appellate Law Band 2 p.26

**Landau, David E**
Table(s): Pennsylvania: Litigation: General
Commercial Band 4 p.2203

**Landau, Eric R**
Table(s): New York: Real Estate Band 3 p.1854

**Landefeld, Stewart**
Table(s): Washington: Corporate/Commercial
Band 1 p.2525

**Landfair, Stan**
Table(s): California: Environment Band 3 p.564

**Landis, Adam G**
Profile: p.772
Table(s): Delaware: Bankruptcy/Restructuring
Band 1 p.754

# Index of Lawyers

**Landis, John M**
Table(s): **Louisiana:** Bankruptcy/Restructuring
**Band 3** p.1337

**Landon, Stephen**
Table(s): **South Dakota:** Litigation: General
Commercial **Band 1** p.2284

**Landow-Esser, Janine**
Profile: p.1216
Table(s): **Illinois:** Environment: Mainly
Transactional **Band 3** p.1162

**Landreth, Lloyd**
Table(s): **Oklahoma:** Energy & Natural
Resources: Environment **Band 2** p.2136

**Landrum, Craig**
Profile: p.1605
Table(s): **Mississippi:** Corporate/Commercial:
Banking & Finance **Band 1** p.1591

**Landry, Andrew**
Profile: p.1401
Table(s): **Maine:** Energy & Natural Resources
**Band 3** p.1388

**Landry, Charles**
Profile: p.1365
Table(s): **Louisiana:** Real Estate **Band 2** p.1355

**Landsberg, Barry S**
Table(s): **California:** Healthcare **Band 3** p.568

**Landsman, Stephen A**
Profile: p.1216
Table(s): **Illinois:** Corporate/M&A **Band 4** p.1156

**Landy, Douglas J**
Profile: p.352
Table(s): **Nationwide:** Financial Services
Regulation: Banking (Compliance) **Band 3** p.96

**Lane, Brian**
Profile: p.352
Table(s): **Nationwide:** Securities: Regulation:
Advisory **Band 1** p.232

**Lane, J Thomas**
Profile: p.2564
Table(s): **West Virginia:** Natural Resources **Band
1** p.2558

**Lane, Joe**
Table(s): **Florida:** Construction **Band 3** p.944

**Lane, Michael L**
Profile: p.1401
Table(s): **Maine:** Real Estate **Band 4** p.1395

**Lane, Patrick**
Table(s): **Ohio:** Litigation: General Commercial
**Band 4** p.2078

**Lane, William F**
Table(s): **North Carolina:** Environment **Up-and-coming individuals** p.2028

**Lang, Richard A**
Profile: p.352
Table(s): **Nationwide:** Wealth Management:
Central Region **Band 2** p.266

**Langan, J Andrew**
Profile: p.1216
Table(s): **Illinois:** Antitrust **Band 3** p.1143

**Langdon, Larry R**
Table(s): **Nationwide:** Tax: Controversy **Band 3**
p.244, **California:** Tax **Band 2** p.617

**Lange, Cynthia J**
Table(s): **California:** Immigration **Band 3** p.571

**Lange, Mark S**
Profile: p.1088
Table(s): **Georgia:** Tax **Band 1** p.1072

**Langel, John B**
Profile: p.2222
Table(s): **Pennsylvania:** Labor & Employment
**Band 1** p.2200

**Langer, Howard**
Table(s): **Pennsylvania:** Antitrust **Band 1** p.2184

**Langer, Leonard W**
Profile: p.1401
Table(s): **Maine:** Litigation: General Commercial
**Band 3** p.1393

**Langer, Paul**
Table(s): **Illinois:** Insurance: Dispute Resolution
**Band 2** p.1168

**Langevin, Judith Bevis**
Table(s): **Minnesota:** Labor & Employment **Band 3**
p.1571

**Langlois, Jack J**
Profile: p.352
Table(s): **Nationwide:** Energy: Oil & Gas
(Transactional) **Band 2** p.79

**Langlois, Scott L**
Profile: p.2583
Table(s): **Wisconsin:** Real Estate **Band 3** p.2579

**Langrock, Peter F**
Table(s): **Vermont:** Litigation: General
Commercial **Senior Statesmen** p.2486

**Laniado, Sam**
Table(s): **New York:** Energy: State Regulatory &
Wholesale Electric Market **Band 2** p.1806

**Lanier, Randolph H**
Table(s): **Alabama:** Real Estate **Band 2** p.466

**Lanier, W Mark**
Table(s): **Nationwide:** Product Liability: Plaintiffs
**Band 1** p.209

**Lansdale, Daryl**
Profile: p.2401
Table(s): **Texas:** Technology: Corporate &
Commercial **Band 3** p.2375

**Lansky, David**
Profile: p.509
Table(s): **Arizona:** Real Estate **Band 1** p.504

**Lantry, Kevin T**
Profile: p.648
Table(s): **California:** Bankruptcy/Restructuring
**Band 4** p.542

**Lanusse, Leslie A**
Profile: p.1365
Table(s): **Louisiana:** Labor & Employment **Band 2**
p.1350

**Lanza, John D**
Table(s): **Massachusetts:** Intellectual Property
**Band 3** p.1463

**Lanznar, Howard S**
Table(s): **Illinois:** Corporate/M&A **Band 3** p.1156

**Lapatin, Philip**
Profile: p.1499
Table(s): **Massachusetts:** Real Estate **Band 3**
p.1478

**Lapeze, James**
Table(s): **Louisiana:** Energy & Natural
Resources: Oil & Gas **Up-and-coming individuals**
p.1344, **Louisiana:** Environment: Litigation **Up-and-coming individuals** p.1346

**Lapicola, Michael**
Table(s): **Minnesota:** Construction **Band 2** p.1567

**Laporte, Claire**
Profile: p.1499
Table(s): **Massachusetts:** Intellectual Property
**Band 2** p.1463

**Lapowsky, Robert**
Table(s): **Pennsylvania:**
Bankruptcy/Restructuring **Band 2** p.2188

**Lapushchik, Tatiana**
Profile: p.352
Table(s): **Nationwide:** Banking & Finance **Up-and-coming individuals** p.31

**Laracy, Ward**
Profile: p.1740
Table(s): **New Jersey:** Corporate/M&A **Band 4**
p.1707

**Laramore, Jon**
Table(s): **Indiana:** Litigation: Appellate **Band 1**
p.1273

**Larason, Timothy M**
Table(s): **Oklahoma:** Corporate/Commercial: Tax
**Band 1** p.2134

**Larcamp, Daniel**
Table(s): **Nationwide:** Energy: Electricity
(Regulatory & Litigation) **Band 3** p.76

**Lardakis, Terry**
Profile: p.2103
Table(s): **Ohio:** Labor & Employment **Band 3**
p.2074

**Large, Wendell G**
Table(s): **Maine:** Litigation: General Commercial
**Band 3** p.1393, **Maine:** Litigation: Medical
Malpractice & Insurance **Band 2** p.1393

**Laria, Jon M**
Profile: p.1429
Table(s): **Maryland:** Real Estate: Land Use **Band 2**
p.1422

**Larimore, James W**
Profile: p.2151
Table(s): **Oklahoma:** Corporate/Commercial **Band
3** p.2134

**Lark, Eric I**
Table(s): **Michigan:** Corporate/M&A **Band 3**
p.1538

**Larkin, Kurt G**
Profile: p.2511
Table(s): **Virginia:** Labor & Employment
**Associates to watch** p.2500

**LaRocca, Anthony J**
Table(s): **Nationwide:** Transportation: Rail (for
Railroads) **Band 2** p.257

**Larose, Cynthia**
Profile: p.352
Table(s): **Nationwide:** Privacy & Data Security
**Band 3** p.199

**LaRose, Robert M**
Table(s): **Missouri:** Corporate/M&A **Band 2** p.1619

**Larrabee, Matthew L**
Profile: p.648
Table(s): **California:** Litigation: General
Commercial **Band 5** p.593, **California:** Litigation:
Securities **Band 4** p.593

**Larsen, Michael L**
Profile: p.2474
Table(s): **Utah:** Litigation: General Commercial
**Band 3** p.2468

**Larsen, Paul E**
Table(s): **Nevada:** Real Estate: Zoning/Land Use
**Band 2** p.1679

**Larsen, Peter O**
Table(s): **Florida:** Tax: State & Local **Band 1** p.979

**Larsen, Tracy T**
Profile: p.1552
Table(s): **Michigan:** Corporate/M&A **Band 1**
p.1538

**Larson, Charles**
Table(s): **South Dakota:** Labor & Employment:
Workers' Compensation **Band 2** p.2283

**Larson, David K**
Table(s): **Wyoming:** Real Estate **Band 2** p.2600

**Larson, Joseph D**
Profile: p.1911
Table(s): **New York:** Antitrust **Band 3** p.1778

**Larson, Keith D**
Table(s): **Nationwide:** Projects **Band 4** p.216

**Larson, Linda R.**
Table(s): **Washington:** Environment **Band 2**
p.2527

**Larson, Mary Jo**
Table(s): **Michigan:** Employee Benefits &
Executive Compensation **Band 1** p.1540

**Larson, Steve D**
Table(s): **Oregon:** Litigation: General
Commercial **Band 3** p.2171

**LaRue, James D**
Table(s): **Idaho:** Litigation: Medical Malpractice
& Insurance **Band 1** p.1134

**LaSala, Joseph P**
Profile: p.1740
Table(s): **New Jersey:** Litigation: General
Commercial **Band 2** p.1722

**LaSala, Todd A**
Table(s): **Missouri:** Real Estate **Band 2** p.1633

**Lasater Jr, W Robert**
Profile: p.1774
Table(s): **New Mexico:** Litigation: Medical
Malpractice & Insurance Defense **Band 1** p.1769

**Laschever, Eric S**
Profile: p.2540
Table(s): **Washington:** Real Estate: Zoning/Land
Use **Band 2** p.2536

**Laseter, Scott**
Table(s): **Georgia:** Environment **Band 2** p.1051

**Lash, Nancy B**
Profile: p.997
Table(s): **Florida**: Real Estate **Band 2** p.974

**Lassar, Scott R**
Profile: p.1217
Table(s): **Illinois**: Litigation: White-Collar Crime & Government Investigations **Band 1** p.1181

**Lastowski, Michael R**
Table(s): **Delaware**: Bankruptcy/Restructuring **Band 4** p.754

**Latham, John L**
Profile: p.1088
Table(s): **Georgia**: Litigation: General Commercial **Band 3** p.1065

**Latham, Myrna**
Profile: p.2151
Table(s): **Oklahoma**: Real Estate **Band 2** p.2145

**Latham, William Larry**
Table(s): **Mississippi**: Litigation: General Commercial **Band 3** p.1597

**Lathram, Brook**
Profile: p.2306
Table(s): **Tennessee**: Litigation: General Commercial **Band 3** p.2295

**Latman, Marc D**
Profile: p.352
Table(s): **Nationwide**: Transportation: Aviation: Finance **Up-and-coming individuals** p.252

**LaTour, Randall D**
Profile: p.2103
Table(s): **Ohio**: Bankruptcy/Restructuring **Band 4** p.2058

**Latta, Bob**
Table(s): **California**: Corporate/M&A: Venture Capital **Band 3** p.555

**Latza, William**
Table(s): **New York**: Insurance: Transactional & Regulatory **Band 3** p.1816

**Laubach, Larry P**
Profile: p.2222
Table(s): **Pennsylvania**: Corporate/M&A & Private Equity **Band 4** p.2191

**Laudano, Paul**
Table(s): **Massachusetts**: Real Estate **Band 3** p.1478

**Lauderdale, Michael F**
Profile: p.2151
Table(s): **Oklahoma**: Labor & Employment **Band 3** p.2140

**Lauer, Katherine A.**
Profile: p.648
Table(s): **California**: Healthcare **Band 3** p.568

**Lauer, Robert A.**
Table(s): **Nationwide**: Franchising **Up-and-coming individuals** p.111

**Laughlin, Alexander M**
Profile: p.875
Table(s): **District of Columbia**: Bankruptcy/Restructuring **Band 4** p.792

**Laughlin, Mark C**
Table(s): **Nebraska**: Litigation: Insurance **Band 2** p.1664

**Laughner, Catherine A.**
Table(s): **Montana**: Natural Resources & Environment **Band 2** p.1651

**Laupheimer, Ann Blair**
Profile: p.2222
Table(s): **Pennsylvania**: Litigation: General Commercial **Band 2** p.2203

**Laurence, Kevin B**
Table(s): **Utah**: Intellectual Property **Band 1** p.2466

**Lauria, Thomas E**
Profile: p.352
Table(s): **Nationwide**: Bankruptcy/Restructuring **Band 2** p.39, **Florida**: Bankruptcy/Restructuring **Band 2** p.939, **New York**: Bankruptcy/Restructuring **Band 2** p.1782

**Laurie, Ty D**
Table(s): **Illinois**: Construction **Band 1** p.1154

**Laurin, Samuel**
Table(s): **Indiana**: Litigation: General Commercial **Band 3** p.1273

**Lauro, John**
Profile: p.997
Table(s): **Florida**: Litigation: White-Collar Crime & Government Investigations **Band 2** p.967

**Lause, Michael F**
Table(s): **Missouri**: Corporate/M&A **Band 2** p.1619

**Lautzenhiser, Roger**
Profile: p.2103
Table(s): **Ohio**: Corporate/M&A **Band 4** p.2064

**LaValle, Kathleen**
Profile: p.2401
Table(s): **Texas**: Energy: State Regulatory & Litigation (Electricity) **Band 2** p.2341

**Lavelle, Joseph**
Profile: p.876
Table(s): **District of Columbia**: Intellectual Property: Litigation **Band 4** p.821

**LaVelle, Michael N**
Profile: p.744
Table(s): **Connecticut**: Labor & Employment **Band 3** p.736

**Lavelle Jr, John P**
Profile: p.2222
Table(s): **Nationwide**: Product Liability & Mass Torts **Band 4** p.208, **Pennsylvania**: Litigation: General Commercial **Band 2** p.2203

**Lavely Jr, John H**
Table(s): **California**: Media & Entertainment: Litigation **Band 3** p.606

**Lavin, Kevin J**
Profile: p.876
Table(s): **District of Columbia**: Corporate/M&A & Private Equity **Band 3** p.797

**LaVine, Jordan A**
Table(s): **Pennsylvania**: Intellectual Property **Band 2** p.2197

**Lavoie, John G**
Table(s): **Northern Virginia**: Real Estate **Band 1** p.2505

**Lavoie, Mark G**
Table(s): **Maine**: Litigation: Medical Malpractice & Insurance **Star individuals** p.1393

**Lavorgna, Gregory J**
Profile: p.2222
Table(s): **Pennsylvania**: Intellectual Property **Band 2** p.2197

**Law, Kathleen K**
Table(s): **Iowa**: Real Estate **Band 4** p.1290

**Law, Rhea**
Table(s): **Florida**: Real Estate: Zoning/Land Use **Band 2** p.975

**Lawall, Francis J**
Profile: p.2222
Table(s): **Pennsylvania**: Bankruptcy/Restructuring **Band 2** p.2188

**Lawler, Kathy A**
Profile: p.1740
Table(s): **New Jersey**: Employee Benefits & Executive Compensation **Band 1** p.1710

**Lawler, Martin J**
Table(s): **California**: Immigration **Band 3** p.571

**Lawless, J Mark**
Table(s): **Texas**: Insurance **Band 1** p.2351

**Lawless, Thomas**
Profile: p.2306
Table(s): **Tennessee**: Litigation: Bankruptcy **Band 2** p.2295

**Lawlor, James S**
Table(s): **Pennsylvania**: Banking & Finance **Band 2** p.2186

**Lawlor, John F**
Table(s): **Illinois**: Banking & Finance **Band 3** p.1145

**Lawlor, William G**
Profile: p.2222
Table(s): **Pennsylvania**: Corporate/M&A & Private Equity **Band 2** p.2191

**Lawniczak, James**
Profile: p.2103
Table(s): **Ohio**: Bankruptcy/Restructuring **Band 2** p.2058

**Lawrence, Carmen J**
Profile: p.352
Table(s): **Nationwide**: Securities: Regulation: Enforcement **Band 3** p.233, **New York**: Litigation: White-Collar Crime & Government Investigations **Band 3** p.1836

**Lawrence, Dylan B**
Table(s): **Idaho**: Natural Resources & Environment **Up-and-coming individuals** p.1136

**Lawrence, Gregory**
Profile: p.352
Table(s): **Nationwide**: Energy: Electricity (Regulatory & Litigation) **Band 5** p.76

**Lawrence, James K L**
Table(s): **Ohio**: Labor & Employment **Band 2** p.2074

**Lawrence, Jeffrey F**
Profile: p.353
Table(s): **Nationwide**: Transportation: Shipping: Regulatory (outside New York) **Band 1** p.264

**Lawrence, Maurie**
Profile: p.2270
Table(s): **South Carolina**: Real Estate **Up-and-coming individuals** p.2266

**Lawrence, Nancy M**
Table(s): **District of Columbia**: Immigration **Band 3** p.814

**Lawrence, Paul F**
Profile: p.648
Table(s): **California**: Healthcare **Band 4** p.568

**Lawrence, Robert W**
Profile: p.720
Table(s): **Colorado**: Natural Resources & Environment **Band 1** p.712

**Lawrence, Steven T**
Table(s): **Arizona**: Corporate/M&A **Band 4** p.495

**Lawrence II, Joseph W**
Table(s): **Florida**: Construction **Band 2** p.944

**Lawrence III, Robert C**
Profile: p.353
Table(s): **Nationwide**: Wealth Management: Eastern Region **Band 1** p.267

**Lawrence Jr, John H**
Table(s): **Connecticut**: Corporate/M&A **Band 2** p.732, **Connecticut**: Healthcare **Band 2** p.735

**Lawrence-Hardy, Allegra J**
Table(s): **Georgia**: Labor & Employment **Band 3** p.1060

**Lawson, David L**
Profile: p.876
Table(s): **District of Columbia**: Telecom, Broadcast & Satellite **Band 2** p.844

**Lawson, Kurt**
Table(s): **District of Columbia**: Employee Benefits & Executive Compensation **Band 2** p.801

**Lawson, Margaret**
Profile: p.2103
Table(s): **Ohio**: Intellectual Property **Band 3** p.2071

**Lawton, David B**
Table(s): **Nationwide**: Transportation: Shipping: Litigation (outside New York) **Band 1** p.263

**Lax, Charles**
Table(s): **Michigan**: Employee Benefits & Executive Compensation **Band 1** p.1540

**Lay, John T.**
Profile: p.2270
Table(s): **South Carolina**: Litigation: General Commercial **Band 4** p.2264

**Lay, Wood W**
Profile: p.2043
Table(s): **North Carolina**: Labor & Employment **Band 2** p.2031

**Layne, Jonathan K**
Profile: p.649
Table(s): **California**: Capital Markets: Debt & Equity **Band 2** p.547, **California**: Corporate/M&A **Band 1** p.554

**Layng, Karen P**
Profile: p.1217
Table(s): **Illinois**: Construction **Band 3** p.1154

**Layson, Frank**
Profile: p.1088
Table(s): **Georgia**: Corporate/M&A **Band 2** p.1046

**Laytin, Daniel E**
Profile: p.1217
Table(s): **Illinois**: Antitrust **Band 2** p.1143

**Lazar, Dale S**
Profile: p.2511
Table(s): Northern Virginia: Intellectual Property
Band 2 p.2497

**Lazar, Kathy**
Profile: p.2104
Table(s): Ohio: Employee Benefits & Executive
Compensation Band 3 p.2067

**Lazar, Vincent**
Profile: p.1217
Table(s): Illinois: Bankruptcy/Restructuring Band
3 p.1148

**Lazarow, Warren T**
Table(s): California: Corporate/M&A: Venture
Capital Band 4 p.555

**Lazaruk, Ken**
Table(s): New York: Construction Band 4 p.1791

**Lazarus, Larry S**
Table(s): Arizona: Real Estate: Zoning/Land Use
Band 1 p.504

**Lazarus, Lewis H**
Table(s): Delaware: Chancery Band 3 p.758

**Lazarus, Robert**
Profile: p.1605
Table(s): Mississippi: Corporate/Commercial:
Municipal Finance Star individuals p.1591

**Lazarus, Scott R**
Table(s): New York: Media & Entertainment:
Theatre Band 1 p.1850

**Lazear, Sherri Blank**
Profile: p.2104
Table(s): Ohio: Bankruptcy/Restructuring Band 4
p.2058

**Lazos, Nicholas J**
Table(s): New Hampshire: Real Estate Band 2
p.1692

**Lazovich, Jennifer**
Table(s): Nevada: Real Estate: Zoning/Land Use
Up-and-coming individuals p.1679

**Le Cren, Danelle**
Table(s): Nationwide: Banking & Finance Up-and-
coming individuals p.31

**Le Sage, Jeffrey**
Profile: p.649
Table(s): California: Corporate/M&A Band 3 p.554

**Lea, Haynes**
Table(s): North Carolina: Corporate/M&A Band 3
p.2025

**Leace, Benjamin**
Table(s): Pennsylvania: Intellectual Property
Band 2 p.2197

**Leach, Donald**
Table(s): Ohio: Construction Band 2 p.2062

**Leach, William S**
Profile: p.2151
Table(s): Oklahoma: Litigation: General
Commercial Band 3 p.2141

**Leach Jr, John N**
Profile: p.470
Table(s): Alabama: Litigation: General
Commercial Band 4 p.463

**Leachman, Tamsen L**
Profile: p.2176
Table(s): Oregon: Labor & Employment Band 3
p.2168

**Leahy, Carrie**
Profile: p.1552
Table(s): Michigan: Corporate/M&A Up-and-coming
individuals p.1538

**Leahy, James R**
Profile: p.2401
Table(s): Texas: Litigation: General Commercial
Band 3 p.2362

**Leahy, Michael H**
Profile: p.876
Table(s): District of Columbia: Real Estate Band
3 p.835

**Leake, Paul**
Profile: p.353
Table(s): Nationwide: Bankruptcy/Restructuring
Band 2 p.39, New York:
Bankruptcy/Restructuring Band 2 p.1782

**Lear, Phillip**
Table(s): Utah: Energy & Natural Resources Band
2 p.2464

**Lear, Steven D**
Profile: p.997
Table(s): Florida: Corporate/M&A & Private
Equity Band 4 p.947

**Leason, Chris S**
Table(s): Arizona: Environment (including water
rights) Band 3 p.497

**Leatherbury, Thomas S**
Profile: p.353
Table(s): Nationwide: First Amendment
Litigation Band 3 p.105

**Leavens, Thomas**
Table(s): Illinois: Media & Entertainment:
Transactional Band 1 p.1185

**Leaverton, Bruce**
Profile: p.2540
Table(s): Washington: Bankruptcy/Restructuring
Band 1 p.2523

**Leavitt, Jeffrey M**
Profile: p.353
Table(s): Nationwide: Investment Funds: Venture
Capital Band 3 p.174

**Leavitt, Jeffrey S**
Profile: p.2104
Table(s): Ohio: Employee Benefits & Executive
Compensation Band 3 p.2067

**Leavitt, Josh**
Profile: p.1217
Table(s): Illinois: Construction Band 2 p.1154

**Leavy, Richard A.**
Profile: p.1912
Table(s): New York: Tax Band 3 p.1862

**LeBey, Daniel M**
Profile: p.353
Table(s): Nationwide: Capital Markets: REITs
Band 2 p.55

**Leblanc, Andrew**
Profile: p.876
Table(s): District of Columbia:
Bankruptcy/Restructuring Band 3 p.792

**Leblang, Kevin B**
Profile: p.1912
Table(s): New York: Labor & Employment Band 2
p.1826

**Leblang, Stuart E**
Profile: p.1912
Table(s): New York: Tax Band 2 p.1862

**Lebovitz, James A**
Profile: p.2222
Table(s): Nationwide: Capital Markets: Debt &
Equity Band 3 p.46, Pennsylvania:
Corporate/M&A & Private Equity Band 2 p.2191

**Lebow, Patricia**
Table(s): Florida: Litigation: General Commercial
Band 3 p.966

**Lebowitz, Molly**
Table(s): Vermont: Real Estate Band 1 p.2487

**LeBreton, Rose**
Table(s): Louisiana: Real Estate Band 3 p.1355

**Leccese, Joseph M**
Table(s): Nationwide: Sports Law Band 1 p.241

**LeClair, Gary D**
Table(s): Southern Virginia: Corporate/M&A Band
2 p.2494

**LeClair, Lewis**
Profile: p.2401
Table(s): Texas: Litigation: General Commercial
Band 2 p.2362

**LeClaire, John R**
Profile: p.1499
Table(s): Nationwide: Private Equity: Buyouts
Band 4 p.203, Massachusetts: Private Equity:
Buyouts Band 1 p.1474

**Leddy, Mark**
Profile: p.876
Table(s): District of Columbia: Antitrust Band 1
p.787

**Lederer, Gregory**
Table(s): Iowa: Litigation: General Commercial
Band 1 p.1288

**Lederman, Alan S.**
Table(s): Florida: Tax Band 1 p.979

**Lederman, Henry D**
Profile: p.649
Table(s): California: Labor & Employment Band 4
p.587

**Lederman, Kevin**
Table(s): Washington: Immigration Band 2 p.2528

**Ledig, Robert H**
Profile: p.353
Table(s): Nationwide: Financial Services
Regulation: Banking (Compliance) Band 4 p.96,
Nationwide: Financial Services Regulation:
Banking (Enforcement & Investigations) Band 2
p.96

**Ledoux, Stephen R**
Table(s): Oregon: Real Estate Band 3 p.2173

**LeDuc, André**
Profile: p.876
Table(s): District of Columbia: Tax Band 4 p.838

**Lee, Alexander**
Table(s): California: Tax Band 3 p.617

**Lee, Bennett J**
Profile: p.649
Table(s): California: Construction Band 2 p.550

**Lee, Carl B**
Table(s): Texas: Real Estate Band 2 p.2367

**Lee, Carolyn Joy**
Profile: p.1912
Table(s): New York: Tax Band 2 p.1862

**Lee, Charles**
Table(s): North Carolina: Banking & Finance
Band 3 p.2021

**Lee, Charlie C H**
Table(s): Virginia: Construction Band 2 p.2491

**Lee, Don**
Table(s): Montana: Natural Resources &
Environment Band 1 p.1651

**Lee, Franklin G**
Table(s): Idaho: Real Estate Band 3 p.1138

**Lee, Gary**
Profile: p.1912
Table(s): New York: Bankruptcy/Restructuring
Band 4 p.1782

**Lee, Harry**
Table(s): District of Columbia: Insurance:
Insurer Band 2 p.816

**Lee, James J**
Profile: p.2401
Table(s): Texas: Bankruptcy/Restructuring Band 3
p.2328

**Lee, John R**
Profile: p.1654
Table(s): Montana: Natural Resources &
Environment Band 2 p.1651

**Lee, Judith**
Profile: p.353
Table(s): Nationwide: International Trade: CFIUS
Experts Band 3 p.152, Nationwide: International
Trade: Export Controls & Economic Sanctions
Band 2 p.152

**Lee, Judy J**
Table(s): Texas: Immigration Band 1 p.2349

**Lee, Mary M.**
Table(s): Oklahoma: Intellectual Property Band 2
p.2138

**Lee, Michael**
Table(s): Massachusetts: Banking & Finance Up-
and-coming individuals p.1445

**Lee, Michael P**
Table(s): Illinois: Corporate/M&A Band 4 p.1156

**Lee, Paul L**
Table(s): Nationwide: Financial Services
Regulation: Banking (Compliance) Band 1 p.96

**Lee, Rebecca A**
Profile: p.1499
Table(s): Massachusetts: Real Estate:
Zoning/Land Use Band 2 p.1478

**Lee, Robert C**
Profile: p.1217
Table(s): Illinois: Real Estate Band 1 p.1187

**Lee, Ronald D**
Profile: p.353
Table(s): **Nationwide:** Privacy & Data Security **Band 2** p.199

**Lee, Stephen W**
Profile: p.1278
Table(s): **Indiana:** Real Estate **Band 1** p.1275

**Lee, Steven J**
Table(s): **New York:** Intellectual Property: Patent **Band 3** p.1820

**Lee, Tara**
Profile: p.2511
Table(s): **Virginia:** Litigation: General Commercial **Band 2** p.2502

**Lee, Victoria**
Profile: p.649
Table(s): **California:** IT & Outsourcing **Band 3** p.583

**Lee, Wayne J**
Table(s): **Louisiana:** Litigation: General Commercial **Band 1** p.1352

**Lee, William F**
Profile: p.353
Table(s): **Nationwide:** International Trade: Intellectual Property (Section 337) **Band 3** p.160, **Nationwide:** Life Sciences: IP/Patent Litigation **Star Individuals** p.183, **Nationwide:** Litigation: Trial Lawyers **Band 2** p.187, **Massachusetts:** Intellectual Property **Star Individuals** p.1463

**Lee, William S**
Profile: p.2401
Table(s): **Texas:** Tax: Litigation **Band 2** p.2371

**Lee, Yoon-Young**
Profile: p.353
Table(s): **Nationwide:** Financial Services Regulation: Broker Dealer (Compliance) **Band 1** p.97

**Lee, Young J**
Table(s): **Nationwide:** Projects: PPP **Band 3** p.217

**Lee II, Thomas H**
Profile: p.2222
Table(s): **Pennsylvania:** Litigation: White-Collar Crime & Government Investigations **Band 1** p.2204

**Lee-Lim, Jiyeon**
Profile: p.1912
Table(s): **New York:** Tax **Band 3** p.1862

**Leeds, Edward I**
Profile: p.2223
Table(s): **Pennsylvania:** Labor & Employment: Employee Benefits & Compensation **Band 2** p.2200

**Leeming, Simon C**
Profile: p.1696
Table(s): **New Hampshire:** Real Estate **Band 2** p.1692

**Leeper, Charles S**
Profile: p.876
Table(s): **District of Columbia:** Litigation: White-Collar Crime & Government Investigations **Band 4** p.827

**Lees, C. Ray**
Table(s): **Oklahoma:** Corporate/Commercial **Band 3** p.2134

**Leet, Alan C**
Profile: p.1088
Table(s): **Georgia:** Corporate/M&A **Band 4** p.1046

**Leet, Byron E**
Profile: p.1321
Table(s): **Kentucky:** Litigation: General Commercial **Band 2** p.1312

**Lefeber, Peter J**
Profile: p.744
Table(s): **Connecticut:** Labor & Employment **Band 1** p.736

**Leff, Neil M**
Profile: p.1912
Table(s): **New York:** Employee Benefits & Executive Compensation **Band 2** p.1802

**Leffert, Kim A**
Table(s): **Illinois:** Labor & Employment **Band 4** p.1175

**Lefkowitz, David S**
Profile: p.354
Table(s): **Nationwide:** Capital Markets: Debt & Equity **Band 3** p.46

**Lefkowitz, Jay**
Profile: p.1912
Table(s): **New York:** Litigation: General Commercial **Band 3** p.1833

**Lefkowitz, Ken**
Profile: p.1912
Table(s): **New York:** Corporate/M&A **Band 4** p.1793

**Lefkowitz, Stephen A**
Profile: p.1912
Table(s): **New York:** Real Estate: Zoning/Land Use **Band 1** p.1855

**Legg, Erik**
Profile: p.2564
Table(s): **West Virginia:** Litigation: General Commercial **Up-and-coming individuals** p.2555

**Leggette, Poe**
Profile: p.354
Table(s): **Nationwide:** Energy: Oil & Gas (Regulatory & Litigation) **Band 2** p.78

**Lehfeldt, Richard**
Profile: p.354
Table(s): **Nationwide:** Energy: Electricity (Regulatory & Litigation) **Band 4** p.76

**Lehman, Michael P**
Table(s): **New Hampshire:** Litigation: General Commercial **Band 2** p.1690

**Lehman, Robert T**
Profile: p.1740
Table(s): **New Jersey:** Environment **Band 3** p.1711

**Lehman, Steven**
Profile: p.1654
Table(s): **Montana:** Labor & Employment **Band 1** p.1648

**Lehman, Thomas**
Table(s): **Florida:** Bankruptcy/Restructuring **Band 4** p.939

**Lehot, Louis**
Table(s): **California:** Capital Markets: Debt & Equity **Band 3** p.547

**Lehr, Matthew**
Profile: p.649
Table(s): **California:** Intellectual Property: Patent **Band 4** p.578

**Lehr, Richard**
Table(s): **Alabama:** Labor & Employment **Band 1** p.460

**Lehrer, Jeffrey K**
Profile: p.2511
Table(s): **Nationwide:** Investment Funds: Venture Capital **Band 3** p.174, **Northern Virginia:** Corporate/M&A **Band 1** p.2493

**Lehrer, Joseph D**
Table(s): **Missouri:** Corporate/M&A **Band 3** p.1619

**Lehv, Richard**
Table(s): **New York:** Intellectual Property: Trade Mark & Copyright **Band 3** p.1821

**Leibenluft, Robert F**
Table(s): **Nationwide:** Healthcare: Regulatory & Litigation **Band 1** p.127, **District of Columbia:** Healthcare **Band 1** p.809

**Leibert, Burton**
Table(s): **Nationwide:** Investment Funds: Registered Funds **Band 3** p.170

**Leibowitz, Hal J**
Profile: p.1499
Table(s): **Massachusetts:** Corporate/M&A **Band 2** p.1452

**Leibowitz, Lewis E**
Table(s): **Nationwide:** International Trade: Trade Remedies & Trade Policy **Band 4** p.154

**Leibowitz, Richard D**
Table(s): **Louisiana:** Banking & Finance: Public Finance **Band 1** p.1335

**Leibrock, Fred A.**
Table(s): **Oklahoma:** Litigation: General Commercial **Band 2** p.2141

**Leiby, Larry R**
Table(s): **Florida:** Construction **Senior Statesmen:** p.944

**Leich, Christopher M**
Table(s): **Massachusetts:** Tax **Band 1** p.1481

**Leicht, Eric F**
Profile: p.354
Table(s): **Nationwide:** Banking & Finance **Band 4** p.31

**Leichtling, Ely A**
Profile: p.2583
Table(s): **Wisconsin:** Labor & Employment **Band 1** p.2575

**Leiden, Warren R**
Table(s): **Nationwide:** Immigration **Band 1** p.131, **California:** Immigration **Band 1** p.571

**Leiken, Jonathan**
Profile: p.2104
Table(s): **Ohio:** Litigation: White-Collar Crime & Government Investigations **Band 3** p.2079

**Leishman, N Todd**
Table(s): **Utah:** Corporate/M&A **Band 3** p.2462

**Leithead, Heidi E C**
Table(s): **Utah:** Labor & Employment **Band 2** p.2467

**Leitman, Matthew**
Profile: p.1552
Table(s): **Michigan:** Litigation: White-Collar Crime & Government Investigations **Band 2** p.1544

**Leitman Bailey, Adam**
Profile: p.1912
Table(s): **New York:** Real Estate **Band 4** p.1854

**Leland, Richard G**
Profile: p.1913
Table(s): **New York:** Environment **Band 2** p.1807

**Lele, Sachin A**
Profile: p.1217
Table(s): **Illinois:** Technology & Outsourcing **Up-and-coming individuals** p.1194

**Lelong, Rivers**
Profile: p.1365
Table(s): **Louisiana:** Banking & Finance **Band 2** p.1335

**Lemasters, P. Reid**
Profile: p.2104
Table(s): **Ohio:** Real Estate **Band 4** p.2086

**LeMay, David M.**
Table(s): **New York:** Bankruptcy/Restructuring **Band 4** p.1782

**Lemein, Gregg D**
Profile: p.354
Table(s): **Nationwide:** Tax: Controversy **Band 2** p.244, **Illinois:** Tax **Band 2** p.1192

**Lemley, Gregg M**
Profile: p.1637
Table(s): **Missouri:** Labor & Employment **Band 2** p.1625

**Lemley, Mark**
Table(s): **California:** Intellectual Property: Patent **Band 3** p.578

**Lemly, Thomas A**
Table(s): **Washington:** Labor & Employment **Band 3** p.2531

**Lemon, Neel**
Profile: p.2401
Table(s): **Texas:** Corporate/M&A **Band 2** p.2337

**Lenas, Elizabeth**
Profile: p.354
Table(s): **Nationwide:** Investment Funds: Private Equity: Fund Formation **Band 4** p.166

**Lenck, Eric**
Profile: p.354
Table(s): **Nationwide:** Transportation: Shipping: Litigation (New York) **Band 4** p.261

**Lender, David**
Profile: p.1913
Table(s): **New York:** Litigation: General Commercial **Band 4** p.1833

**Leney, Douglas**
Profile: p.1740
Table(s): **New Jersey:** Bankruptcy/Restructuring **Associates to watch** p.1705

**Lenhard, Kirk B**
Table(s): **Nevada:** Litigation: General Commercial **Band 1** p.1677

**Lenhard, Robert**
Profile: p.354
Table(s): Nationwide: Government: Political Law
**Band 3** p.124

**Lenhart, Benedict M**
Profile: p.876
Table(s): District of Columbia: Insurance:
Policyholder **Band 2** p.818

**Lenhart, Benjamin**
Profile: p.2176
Table(s): Oregon: Corporate/M&A **Band 3** p.2164

**Lenihan, Brian P**
Profile: p.1500
Table(s): Massachusetts: Private Equity: Venture
Capital Investment **Band 2** p.1474

**Lennon, Daniel**
Profile: p.876
Table(s): Nationwide: Private Equity: Buyouts
**Band 2** p.203, District of Columbia:
Corporate/M&A & Private Equity **Band 1** p.797

**Lennon, Michael**
Table(s): New York: Intellectual Property: Patent
**Band 3** p.1820

**Lennon, Patrick F**
Table(s): Nationwide: Transportation: Shipping:
Litigation (New York) **Band 3** p.261

**Lennon Jr, Michael P**
Profile: p.354
Table(s): Nationwide: International Arbitration
**Band 5** p.145

**Lennox, Heather**
Profile: p.2104
Table(s): Nationwide: Bankruptcy/Restructuring
**Band 3** p.39, New York:
Bankruptcy/Restructuring **Band 3** p.1782, Ohio:
Bankruptcy/Restructuring **Band 1** p.2058

**Lenobel, Jeffrey A**
Profile: p.1913
Table(s): New York: Real Estate **Band 2** p.1854

**Lents, Don G**
Table(s): Missouri: Corporate/M&A **Band 1** p.1619

**Leo, Thomas Glen**
Table(s): California: Media & Entertainment:
Transactional **Band 3** p.608

**Leon, Christopher E**
Table(s): North Carolina: Banking & Finance
**Band 1** p.2021

**Leon, Michael**
Profile: p.1500
Table(s): Massachusetts: Environment **Band 2**
p.1457

**Leon, Norman**
Profile: p.354
Table(s): Nationwide: Franchising **Band 4** p.111

**Leonard, Emily I**
Profile: p.354
Table(s): Nationwide: Life Sciences:
Corporate/Commercial **Band 2** p.182, California:
Life Sciences: Corporate/Commercial **Band 2**
p.590

**Leonard, Jeffrey A**
Profile: p.2223
Table(s): Pennsylvania: Real Estate **Band 4**
p.2208

**Leone, Eugene**
Table(s): Illinois: Real Estate **Band 4** p.1187

**Leonetti, Kenneth**
Profile: p.1500
Table(s): Massachusetts:
Bankruptcy/Restructuring **Band 3** p.1449

**Leong, Ronald Y K**
Table(s): Hawaii: Labor & Employment **Band 2**
p.1117

**Leonhardt, Frederick**
Profile: p.997
Table(s): Florida: Real Estate: Zoning/Land Use
**Band 3** p.975

**LePage, Margaret Coughlin**
Profile: p.1401
Table(s): Maine: Labor & Employment **Band 1**
p.1390

**Lepene, Alan R**
Profile: p.2104
Table(s): Ohio: Bankruptcy/Restructuring **Star**
**Individuals** p.2058

**Leppo, Jeffrey W**
Table(s): Washington: Environment **Band 1**
p.2527

**Lerman, Cary**
Profile: p.649
Table(s): California: Insurance: Policyholder **Band**
**2** p.576

**Lerman, Steven A**
Table(s): District of Columbia: Telecom,
Broadcast & Satellite **Band 3** p.844

**Lerner, Arthur N**
Profile: p.876
Table(s): Nationwide: Healthcare: Regulatory &
Litigation **Band 3** p.127, District of Columbia:
Healthcare **Band 1** p.809

**Lerner, Brian L**
Table(s): Florida: Labor & Employment **Band 4**
p.959

**Lerner, James**
Table(s): Massachusetts: Banking & Finance
**Band 3** p.1445

**Lerner, Jonathan J**
Profile: p.355
Table(s): Nationwide: Securities: Litigation **Senior**
**Statesmen** p.232, New York: Litigation: General
Commercial **Senior Statesmen** p.1833, New York:
Litigation: Securities **Senior Statesmen** p.1833

**Lerner, Matthew D**
Table(s): Nationwide: Tax: Controversy **Band 3**
p.244

**Lerner, Stephen D**
Profile: p.2104
Table(s): Ohio: Bankruptcy/Restructuring **Star**
**individuals** p.2058

**Lesemann, Ellis R**
Table(s): South Carolina: Litigation: General
Commercial **Band 4** p.2264

**LeSeur, John H**
Profile: p.355
Table(s): Nationwide: Transportation: Rail (for
Shippers) **Band 2** p.258

**Leshaw, James P S**
Table(s): Florida: Bankruptcy/Restructuring **Band**
**2** p.939

**Leslie, John W**
Profile: p.649
Table(s): California: Energy: State Regulatory &
Litigation **Band 3** p.562

**Leslie, Michael R**
Table(s): California: Environment **Band 4** p.564

**Leslie, Stephen R**
Table(s): Florida: Bankruptcy/Restructuring **Band**
**4** p.939

**Lessard, Mark N**
Table(s): Nationwide: Transportation: Aviation:
Finance **Band 3** p.252

**Lesser, Bruce**
Profile: p.2223
Table(s): Pennsylvania: Banking & Finance **Senior**
**Statesmen** p.2186

**Lesser, Henry**
Profile: p.649
Table(s): California: Corporate/M&A **Band 4** p.553

**Lesser, Lori E**
Profile: p.1913
Table(s): New York: Technology & Outsourcing
**Band 2** p.1868

**Lesser, Steven**
Table(s): Florida: Construction **Band 1** p.944

**Lessner, Martin**
Table(s): Delaware: Chancery **Band 4** p.758

**Lester, R David**
Profile: p.1321
Table(s): Kentucky: Corporate/M&A **Band 2**
p.1305

**Lester Jr, Edgel C**
Profile: p.997
Table(s): Florida: Real Estate **Band 3** p.974

**Letchinger, John S**
Profile: p.1217
Table(s): Illinois: Intellectual Property **Band 4**
p.1171

**Leto, Bruce G**
Table(s): Nationwide: Investment Funds:
Registered Funds **Band 2** p.170

**Letscher, Tom**
Table(s): Minnesota: Corporate/M&A **Band 2**
p.1569

**Leukart, Barbara**
Profile: p.2104
Table(s): Ohio: Labor & Employment **Band 4**
p.2074

**Levander, Andrew J**
Profile: p.1913
Table(s): Nationwide: Litigation: Trial Lawyers
**Band 2** p.187, Nationwide: Securities: Litigation
**Band 3** p.232, Nationwide: Securities: Regulation:
Enforcement **Band 1** p.232, New York: Litigation:
White-Collar Crime & Government Investigations
**Star individuals** p.1836

**Levasseur, Eric**
Profile: p.2104
Table(s): Ohio: Construction **Up-and-coming individu-**
**als** p.2062

**LeVee, Jeffrey A**
Profile: p.649
Table(s): California: Antitrust **Band 2** p.536

**Leveille, Michael**
Profile: p.1088
Table(s): Georgia: Banking & Finance **Band 3**
p.1039

**Levengood, J Michael**
Profile: p.1088
Table(s): Georgia: Bankruptcy/Restructuring
**Band 2** p.1042

**Levenson, Fred**
Profile: p.997
Table(s): Florida: Corporate/M&A & Private
Equity **Band 4** p.947

**Levenstein, Gary**
Profile: p.1217
Table(s): Illinois: Corporate/M&A **Band 3** p.1156

**Leventhal, F Daniel**
Profile: p.649
Table(s): California: Banking & Finance **Band 3**
p.539

**Leventhal, Norman P**
Profile: p.876
Table(s): District of Columbia: Telecom,
Broadcast & Satellite **Band 4** p.844

**Leventhal, Robert A**
Table(s): Florida: Litigation: White-Collar Crime &
Government Investigations **Band 2** p.967

**Lever, Chauncey**
Table(s): Florida: Banking & Finance **Band 3**
p.936

**Levi, Stuart D**
Profile: p.1913
Table(s): Nationwide: Outsourcing **Band 2** p.195,
New York: Technology & Outsourcing **Band 1**
p.1868

**Levin, Adam**
Table(s): California: Labor & Employment **Band 3**
p.587

**Levin, Barry S**
Table(s): California: Insurance: Policyholder **Band**
**2** p.576

**Levin, Christine C**
Profile: p.2223
Table(s): Pennsylvania: Antitrust **Band 2** p.2184

**Levin, Edward J**
Table(s): Maryland: Real Estate **Band 1** p.1422

**Levin, Irwin B**
Table(s): Indiana: Litigation: General
Commercial **Band 1** p.1273

**Levin, Jay J**
Table(s): Georgia: Real Estate **Band 3** p.1070

**Levin, Matthew W**
Table(s): Georgia: Bankruptcy/Restructuring
**Band 3** p.1042

**Levin, Oscar**
Profile: p.998
Table(s): Florida: Immigration **Band 1** p.956

**Levin, Richard**
Profile: p.355
Table(s): Nationwide: Bankruptcy/Restructuring **Band 2** p.39, New York: Bankruptcy/Restructuring **Band 2** p.1782

**Levin, Timothy W**
Profile: p.355
Table(s): Nationwide: Investment Funds: Registered Funds **Band 2** p.170

**Levin Mesard, Nicole**
Table(s): New York: Real Estate: Corporate **Band 3** p.1854

**Levine, A Kenneth**
Profile: p.998
Table(s): Florida: Insurance **Band 3** p.957

**Levine, Alan**
Table(s): New York: Litigation: General Commercial **Band 2** p.1833

**Levine, Barry Wm**
Profile: p.877
Table(s): District of Columbia: Litigation: White-Collar Crime & Government Investigations **Band 3** p.827

**Levine, David**
Profile: p.744
Table(s): Connecticut: Healthcare **Band 2** p.735

**Levine, David**
Profile: p.877
Table(s): District of Columbia: Employee Benefits & Executive Compensation **Band 3** p.801

**Levine, David**
Table(s): Nevada: Corporate/Commercial **Band 3** p.1672

**Levine, David J**
Profile: p.355
Table(s): Nationwide: International Trade: Export Controls & Economic Sanctions **Band 2** p.153

**Levine, David M**
Table(s): Florida: Bankruptcy/Restructuring **Band 4** p.939

**Levine, Gregory**
Table(s): District of Columbia: Healthcare: Pharmaceutical/Medical Products Regulatory **Band 2** p.810

**Levine, Harvey R**
Table(s): California: Insurance: Policyholder **Band 4** p.576

**Levine, Henry D**
Table(s): District of Columbia: Telecom, Broadcast & Satellite **Band 2** p.844

**Levine, Howard J**
Table(s): Illinois: Labor & Employment: Employee Benefits & Compensation **Band 2** p.1176

**Levine, James D**
Profile: p.1088
Table(s): Georgia: Immigration **Band 3** p.1055

**Levine, Janet**
Profile: p.650
Table(s): California: Litigation: White-Collar Crime & Government Investigations **Band 1** p.601

**Levine, Jerome L**
Profile: p.355
Table(s): Nationwide: Native American Law **Band 1** p.192

**Levine, Jonathan O**
Profile: p.2583
Table(s): Wisconsin: Labor & Employment **Band 1** p.2575

**Levine, Josh**
Profile: p.1913
Table(s): New York: Litigation: White-Collar Crime & Government Investigations **Band 3** p.1836

**Levine, Lee**
Profile: p.355
Table(s): Nationwide: First Amendment Litigation **Star individuals** p.105, District of Columbia: Media & Entertainment **Band 1** p.832

**Levine, Richard E**
Profile: p.1429
Table(s): Maryland: Real Estate **Band 1** p.1422

**Levine, Richard L**
Table(s): Massachusetts: Bankruptcy/Restructuring **Senior Statesmen:** p.1449

**Levine, Ronald J**
Table(s): New Jersey: Litigation: Products Liability **Band 2** p.1723

**Levine, Roxanne**
Table(s): New York: Immigration **Band 3** p.1814

**Levine, Russell E**
Profile: p.1217
Table(s): Illinois: Intellectual Property **Band 2** p.1171

**Levine, Sharon L**
Profile: p.1741
Table(s): New Jersey: Bankruptcy/Restructuring **Band 1** p.1705

**Levine, Stanley E**
Table(s): Pennsylvania: Bankruptcy/Restructuring **Band 2** p.2188

**Levine, Steve J**
Table(s): Louisiana: Environment **Band 1** p.1346, Louisiana: Environment: Litigation **Band 2** p.1346

**Levine II, Ronald R**
Profile: p.720
Table(s): Colorado: Corporate/M&A **Band 1** p.703

**Levinson, Marc A**
Profile: p.650
Table(s): Nationwide: Bankruptcy/Restructuring **Band 3** p.39, California: Bankruptcy/Restructuring **Band 1** p.542

**Levinson, Michael**
Profile: p.1217
Table(s): Illinois: Litigation: General Commercial **Band 3** p.1180

**Levinson, Michael P**
Table(s): Florida: Healthcare **Band 2** p.954

**Levinson, Sidney P**
Profile: p.650
Table(s): California: Bankruptcy/Restructuring **Band 3** p.542

**Levinstein, Mark S**
Table(s): Nationwide: Sports Law **Band 3** p.241

**Levit, William**
Table(s): Wisconsin: Litigation: General Commercial **Senior Statesmen:** p.2576

**Levitan, Shari**
Profile: p.1500
Table(s): Massachusetts: Tax: Estate Planning **Band 1** p.1481

**Levitan, Steve**
Profile: p.355
Table(s): Nationwide: Capital Markets: Securitisation **Band 3** p.59

**Levitas, Steven J**
Table(s): North Carolina: Environment **Band 1** p.2028

**Levitin, Joel H**
Profile: p.1913
Table(s): New York: Bankruptcy/Restructuring **Band 4** p.1782

**Levitt, Joseph A**
Table(s): Nationwide: Food & Beverages: Regulatory & Litigation **Band 1** p.107

**Levitt, Michael**
Profile: p.355
Table(s): Nationwide: Capital Markets: Debt & Equity **Band 4** p.46

**Levy, Andrew H**
Profile: p.1913
Table(s): New York: Real Estate **Band 3** p.1854

**Levy, Bruce A**
Table(s): New Jersey: Healthcare **Band 3** p.1715

**Levy, David**
Profile: p.1217
Table(s): Illinois: Tax **Band 3** p.1192

**Levy, David**
Table(s): Nebraska: Real Estate: Zoning/Land Use **Band 2** p.1666

**Levy, David**
Profile: p.2401
Table(s): Texas: Intellectual Property **Band 3** p.2354

**Levy, Evan R**
Profile: p.1914
Table(s): New York: Real Estate: Finance **Up-and-coming individuals** p.1855

**Levy, Gregg**
Profile: p.355
Table(s): Nationwide: Sports Law **Band 1** p.241

**Levy, Jack A**
Profile: p.356
Table(s): Nationwide: International Trade: Trade Remedies & Trade Policy **Band 5** p.154

**Levy, Jay M**
Table(s): Florida: Litigation: Appellate **Band 3** p.972

**Levy, Joshua S**
Table(s): Massachusetts: Litigation: White-Collar Crime & Government Investigations **Band 1** p.1471

**Levy, Mark P**
Profile: p.2104
Table(s): Ohio: Intellectual Property **Band 3** p.2071

**Levy, Michael N**
Profile: p.877
Table(s): District of Columbia: Litigation: White-Collar Crime & Government Investigations **Band 2** p.827

**Levy, Neil L**
Profile: p.356
Table(s): Nationwide: Energy: Electricity (Regulatory & Litigation) **Band 1** p.76, Nationwide: Energy: Oil & Gas (Regulatory & Litigation) **Band 4** p.76

**Levy, Richard A**
Table(s): Illinois: Bankruptcy/Restructuring **Band 2** p.1148

**Levy, Sally**
Table(s): Massachusetts: Healthcare **Band 3** p.1460

**Levy, Seth D**
Profile: p.650
Table(s): California: Life Sciences: Corporate/Commercial **Band 3** p.590

**Lew, Darryl**
Profile: p.356
Table(s): Nationwide: International Arbitration **Band 5** p.145

**Lewand, F Thomas**
Profile: p.1552
Table(s): Michigan: Corporate/M&A **Band 3** p.1538

**Lewczak, Joseph J**
Profile: p.356
Table(s): Nationwide: Advertising: Transactional & Regulatory **Band 2** p.20

**Lewin, Matthew R**
Profile: p.1217
Table(s): Illinois: Banking & Finance **Band 3** p.1145

**Lewin, Robert**
Table(s): New York: Insurance: Dispute Resolution: Insurer **Band 3** p.1816

**Lewin, Ross A**
Profile: p.1741
Table(s): New Jersey: Environment **Band 3** p.1711

**Lewis, Betsey**
Table(s): Virginia: Labor & Employment **Band 3** p.2500

**Lewis, Brooke E.**
Table(s): Florida: Environment **Associates to watch** p.951

**Lewis, Charles B**
Table(s): Illinois: Construction **Band 1** p.1154

**Lewis, Charles S**
Table(s): Washington: Corporate/Commercial: Tax **Band 1** p.2525

**Lewis, Dan**
Profile: p.1218
Table(s): Illinois: Technology & Outsourcing **Associates to watch** p.1194

**Lilien, Warren H**
Profile: p.357
Table(s): Nationwide: Projects **Band 4** p.216

**Lillehaug, David**
Table(s): Minnesota: Litigation: Appellate **Band 2** p.1573

**Lillehaug, Duane A.**
Table(s): North Dakota: Litigation: General Commercial **Band 3** p.2053

**Lillie, Mark S**
Profile: p.1218
Table(s): Illinois: Environment: Litigation **Band 3** p.1162

**Lillis, William**
Table(s): Iowa: Real Estate **Band 1** p.1290

**Liloia, Gerald A**
Table(s): New Jersey: Litigation: General Commercial **Band 2** p.1722

**Lilyestrom, John**
Profile: p.357
Table(s): Nationwide: Energy: Electricity (Regulatory & Litigation) **Band 4** p.76

**Lim, Glen**
Table(s): California: Banking & Finance **Up-and-coming individuals** p.539

**Lim, Stephanie**
Profile: p.357
Table(s): Nationwide: Energy: Electricity (Regulatory & Litigation) **Up-and-coming individuals** p.76

**Liman, Lewis J**
Profile: p.1914
Table(s): New York: Litigation: Securities **Band 4** p.1834, New York: Litigation: White-Collar Crime & Government Investigations **Band 2** p.1834

**Limbeck, Randal**
Profile: p.1668
Table(s): Nebraska: Labor & Employment: ERISA **Band 1** p.1662

**Limeres, Amy**
Profile: p.492
Table(s): Alaska: Labor & Employment **Band 2** p.489

**Lin, Raymond Y**
Profile: p.357
Table(s): Nationwide: Private Equity: Buyouts **Band 4** p.203

**Lincenberg, Gary**
Profile: p.650
Table(s): California: Litigation: White-Collar Crime & Government Investigations **Band 3** p.601

**Lincer, Richard S**
Profile: p.357
Table(s): Nationwide: Projects **Band 4** p.216, Nationwide: Projects: PPP **Band 2** p.216

**Lincoln, Michael**
Table(s): District of Columbia: Corporate/M&A & Private Equity **Band 3** p.797, Northern Virginia: Corporate/M&A **Band 1** p.2493

**Lind, Dennis**
Table(s): Montana: Litigation: Mediators **Band 1** p.1649

**Lindauer, Erik D**
Profile: p.357
Table(s): Nationwide: Banking & Finance **Band 2** p.31

**Lindberg, Lawrence V**
Profile: p.2105
Table(s): Ohio: Real Estate **Band 3** p.2086

**Lindemann, Steven R**
Table(s): Minnesota: Construction **Band 2** p.1567

**Linder, David M**
Profile: p.650
Table(s): California: Real Estate **Band 4** p.611

**Lindgren, Jay**
Table(s): Minnesota: Real Estate: Zoning/Land Use **Band 1** p.1576

**Lindley, Greg**
Profile: p.2474
Table(s): Utah: Corporate/M&A **Band 3** p.2462

**Lindley, Tom**
Table(s): Oregon: Environment **Band 1** p.2165

**Lindner, Laura A**
Profile: p.2584
Table(s): Wisconsin: Labor & Employment **Band 3** p.2575

**Lindquist, Teri**
Table(s): Illinois: Corporate/M&A: Private Equity **Band 3** p.1157

**Lindsay, Colin Hugh**
Table(s): Kentucky: Litigation: General Commercial **Band 3** p.1312

**Lindsay, David**
Table(s): North Carolina: Labor & Employment **Up-and-coming individuals** p.2031

**Lindsay, Timothy W**
Profile: p.1605
Table(s): Mississippi: Labor & Employment **Band 2** p.1595

**Lindsey, David**
Profile: p.357
Table(s): Nationwide: International Arbitration **Band 2** p.145

**Lindsey, Michael K**
Table(s): Nationwide: Franchising **Band 2** p.111

**Lindsmith, Quintin**
Table(s): Ohio: Litigation: General Commercial **Band 2** p.2078

**Linebaugh, Jesse**
Table(s): Iowa: Litigation: General Commercial **Up-and-coming individuals** p.1288

**Linenbroker, David A**
Table(s): Missouri: Real Estate **Band 3** p.1633

**Linfield, James**
Table(s): Colorado: Corporate/M&A **Band 1** p.703

**Linnan, Nancy G**
Profile: p.998
Table(s): Florida: Real Estate: Zoning/Land Use **Band 1** p.975

**Linsenmayer, Kurt**
Table(s): Washington: Labor & Employment: Employee Benefits & Compensation **Band 1** p.2531

**Linsky, Heath**
Table(s): Nationwide: Capital Markets: REITs **Up-and-coming individuals** p.55

**Linstroth, Tod B**
Profile: p.2584
Table(s): Wisconsin: Corporate/M&A **Band 1** p.2571

**Linton, John**
Table(s): South Carolina: Litigation: General Commercial **Senior Statesmen:** p.2264

**Linton, Robert C**
Table(s): Illinois: Real Estate **Band 4** p.1187

**Linville, Ronald G**
Profile: p.2105
Table(s): Ohio: Labor & Employment **Band 2** p.2074

**Linxwiler, James**
Table(s): Alaska: Environment, Natural Resources & Regulated Industries **Band 2** p.488

**Linzy, Howard S**
Table(s): Louisiana: Labor & Employment **Band 3** p.1350

**Lipe, Guy**
Profile: p.2401
Table(s): Texas: Litigation: Energy & Natural Resources **Band 2** p.2361

**Lipinsky, Lino**
Profile: p.720
Table(s): Colorado: Litigation: General Commercial **Band 4** p.709

**Lipke, Douglas J**
Profile: p.1218
Table(s): Illinois: Bankruptcy/Restructuring **Band 3** p.1148

**Lipman, Andrew D**
Profile: p.877
Table(s): District of Columbia: Telecom, Broadcast & Satellite **Band 2** p.844

**Lipsey, Charles E**
Profile: p.357
Table(s): Nationwide: Life Sciences: IP/Patent Litigation **Band 1** p.183, Northern Virginia: Intellectual Property **Band 1** p.2497

**Lipsey, Christine**
Profile: p.1366
Table(s): Louisiana: Litigation: General Commercial **Band 3** p.1352

**Lipshie, Samuel D**
Table(s): Tennessee: Media & Entertainment **Band 1** p.2297

**Lipsig, Ethan**
Table(s): Nationwide: Employee Benefits & Executive Compensation **Band 2** p.73, California: Employee Benefits & Executive Compensation **Band 1** p.560

**Lipsitz, Alan M**
Table(s): South Carolina: Corporate/M&A: Banking & Finance **Band 1** p.2260

**Lipsky, Abbott (Tad)**
Profile: p.877
Table(s): District of Columbia: Antitrust **Band 4** p.787

**Lipsky, Joshua**
Table(s): Washington: Environment **Band 2** p.2527

**Lipson, Kevin J**
Profile: p.357
Table(s): Nationwide: Energy: Oil & Gas (Regulatory & Litigation) **Band 2** p.78

**Lipton, Joshua**
Profile: p.877
Table(s): District of Columbia: Antitrust **Band 5** p.787

**Lipton, M Steven**
Table(s): Nationwide: Healthcare: Regulatory & Litigation **Band 2** p.127, California: Healthcare **Band 2** p.568

**Lipton, Martin**
Profile: p.1914
Table(s): New York: Corporate/M&A **Senior Statesmen:** p.1793

**Lipton, Richard**
Profile: p.1218
Table(s): Illinois: Tax **Band 2** p.1192

**Lipton, Stuart**
Profile: p.650
Table(s): California: Tax **Band 2** p.617

**Lischer, Dale**
Profile: p.1088
Table(s): Georgia: Intellectual Property **Band 4** p.1056

**Liscio, Mark F**
Profile: p.1914
Table(s): New York: Bankruptcy/Restructuring **Band 4** p.1782

**Liset, J Robert**
Table(s): California: Healthcare **Band 3** p.568

**Lisher, Mary**
Table(s): Indiana: Real Estate **Band 1** p.1275

**Lisker, Steven L**
Profile: p.509
Table(s): Arizona: Real Estate **Band 2** p.504

**Lisman, Carl H**
Table(s): Vermont: Real Estate **Senior Statesmen:** p.2487

**Liss-Riordan, Shannon**
Table(s): Massachusetts: Labor & Employment: Mainly Plaintiffs Representation **Band 1** p.1467

**Litchford, Hal**
Profile: p.998
Table(s): Florida: Antitrust **Band 1** p.935

**Litt, Daniel**
Profile: p.877
Table(s): District of Columbia: Bankruptcy/Restructuring **Band 2** p.792

**Litt, Paula E**
Profile: p.1218
Table(s): Illinois: Insurance: Dispute Resolution **Band 2** p.1168

**Littauer, Dwayne O.**
Table(s): Louisiana: Labor & Employment: Employee Benefits & Compensation **Band 2** p.1350

**Litten, Elizabeth**
Profile: p.1741
Table(s): New Jersey: Healthcare **Band 3** p.1715

**Littenberg, Joseph S**
Profile: p.1741
Table(s): New Jersey: Intellectual Property **Band 1** p.1716

**Little, Catherine**
Profile: p.1088
Table(s): Georgia: Environment **Band 2** p.1051

**Little, Christopher**
Table(s): Rhode Island: Litigation: General Commercial **Band 3** p.2254

**Little, Edward JM**
Profile: p.1914
Table(s): New York: Litigation: White-Collar Crime & Government Investigations **Band 3** p.1836

**Little, Jan Nielsen**
Table(s): California: Litigation: White-Collar Crime & Government Investigations **Band 1** p.601

**Little, Kathleen C**
Profile: p.357
Table(s): Nationwide: International Trade: Export Controls & Economic Sanctions **Band 1** p.153

**Little, Nancy**
Table(s): Southern Virginia: Real Estate **Band 1** p.2506

**Little, Robert B**
Profile: p.2401
Table(s): Texas: Corporate/M&A **Band 4** p.2337

**Little Hoffman, Nancy**
Table(s): Florida: Litigation: Appellate **Band 3** p.972

**Little Jr, Curtis W**
Table(s): New Hampshire: Corporate/Commercial **Band 1** p.1685

**Little Jr, Marion H**
Table(s): Ohio: Litigation: General Commercial **Band 3** p.2078

**Littlejohn, James R**
Profile: p.2402
Table(s): Texas: Banking & Finance **Band 2** p.2325

**Littlepage, Zoe**
Table(s): Nationwide: Product Liability: Plaintiffs **Band 3** p.209

**Littman, Bernice**
Table(s): Hawaii: Corporate/Commercial: Finance **Band 2** p.1116, Hawaii: Real Estate **Band 2** p.1120

**Litwak, Lawrence B**
Table(s): Massachusetts: Healthcare **Senior Statesmen:** p.1460

**Litwin, Edward R**
Table(s): California: Immigration **Band 2** p.571

**Litwin, Ethan**
Profile: p.1914
Table(s): New York: Antitrust **Band 5** p.1778

**Litwin, Frank**
Table(s): Massachusetts: Real Estate **Band 3** p.1478

**Litwin, Sharen**
Table(s): Massachusetts: Labor & Employment: Mainly Plaintiffs Representation **Band 2** p.1467

**Litwin, Stuart M**
Table(s): Nationwide: Capital Markets: Securitisation **Band 2** p.59

**Litz, Thomas A**
Table(s): Missouri: Corporate/M&A **Band 1** p.1619

**Liu, Gilbert**
Profile: p.357
Table(s): Nationwide: Capital Markets: Securitisation **Band 4** p.59

**Lively, Leah C**
Profile: p.2177
Table(s): Oregon: Labor & Employment **Band 2** p.2168

**Livingston, Donald R**
Profile: p.877
Table(s): District of Columbia: Labor & Employment **Band 2** p.824

**Livingston, Theodore A**
Table(s): Illinois: Communications **Band 1** p.1153

**Lizotte, Andrew G**
Profile: p.1500
Table(s): Massachusetts: Bankruptcy/Restructuring **Band 3** p.1449

**Lizza, Charles M**
Table(s): New Jersey: Intellectual Property **Band 2** p.1716

**Llorens Jr, Hector E**
Profile: p.1088
Table(s): Georgia: Banking & Finance **Band 3** p.1039

**Lloyd, Brian G**
Table(s): Utah: Corporate/M&A **Band 1** p.2462

**Lloyd, Diana K**
Profile: p.1500
Table(s): Massachusetts: Litigation: White-Collar Crime & Government Investigations **Band 2** p.1471

**Lloyd, Dominic A**
Profile: p.720
Table(s): Colorado: Corporate/M&A **Band 3** p.703

**Lloyd, W Waldan**
Table(s): Utah: Labor & Employment: ERISA **Band 1** p.2467

**Lobb, James T**
Table(s): Kentucky: Real Estate **Band 2** p.1314

**Lobel, Douglas P**
Table(s): Virginia: Litigation: General Commercial **Band 2** p.2502

**Lobel, William N**
Table(s): California: Bankruptcy/Restructuring **Band 2** p.542

**Loble, Jason**
Profile: p.1654
Table(s): Montana: Corporate/M&A **Band 3** p.1646

**Lobrano, John D**
Profile: p.357
Table(s): Nationwide: Capital Markets: Debt & Equity **Band 3** p.46

**LoBue, Robert P**
Profile: p.1915
Table(s): New York: Intellectual Property: Trade Mark & Copyright **Band 2** p.1821

**LoCascio, Gregg F**
Profile: p.877
Table(s): District of Columbia: Intellectual Property: Litigation **Band 3** p.821

**Locke, Chris**
Table(s): California: Environment **Band 4** p.564

**Locker, Nina**
Table(s): California: Litigation: Securities **Band 3** p.594

**Lockerby, Michael J**
Table(s): Nationwide: Franchising **Band 2** p.111

**Lockett, Laurel E**
Profile: p.998
Table(s): Florida: Environment **Band 1** p.951

**Lockhart, Timothy J**
Table(s): Southern Virginia: Intellectual Property **Band 2** p.2498

**Locklear, Arlinda**
Table(s): Nationwide: Native American Law **Band 2** p.192

**Loder, John M**
Table(s): Nationwide: Investment Funds: Registered Funds **Band 1** p.170, Massachusetts: Hedge & Mutual Funds **Band 1** p.1461

**Loeb, Christopher**
Table(s): North Carolina: Real Estate **Band 3** p.2037

**Loeb, Jeffrey M**
Profile: p.650
Table(s): California: Tax: Estate Planning **Band 1** p.617

**Loeb, Steven B**
Table(s): Louisiana: Construction **Band 2** p.1339

**Loeb Jr, Charles W**
Table(s): West Virginia: Real Estate **Band 2** p.2560

**Loeffler, Robert H**
Table(s): Nationwide: Energy: Oil & Gas (Regulatory & Litigation) **Senior Statesmen:** p.78

**Loepere, Carol**
Table(s): District of Columbia: Healthcare **Band 2** p.809

**Loeser, Julius**
Profile: p.358
Table(s): Nationwide: Financial Services Regulation: Banking (Compliance) **Band 3** p.96

**Loewenson Jr, Carl H**
Profile: p.1915
Table(s): New York: Litigation: White-Collar Crime & Government Investigations **Band 2** p.1836

**Loewinger, Andrew P**
Profile: p.358
Table(s): Nationwide: Franchising **Band 2** p.111

**Lofchie, Steven**
Profile: p.358
Table(s): Nationwide: Capital Markets: Derivatives **Band 1** p.51, Nationwide: Financial Services Regulation: Broker Dealer (Compliance) **Band 1** p.97

**Loftis, James**
Profile: p.358
Table(s): Nationwide: International Arbitration **Band 5** p.145

**Loftis, Mark D**
Table(s): Virginia: Litigation: General Commercial **Band 3** p.2502

**Loftis Jr, W Randolph**
Table(s): North Carolina: Labor & Employment **Band 1** p.2031

**Loftus, C Michael**
Profile: p.358
Table(s): Nationwide: Transportation: Rail (for Shippers) **Senior Statesmen:** p.258

**Loftus, Nora**
Profile: p.2105
Table(s): Ohio: Construction **Associates to watch** p.2062

**Logan, Catherine P.**
Table(s): Kansas: Real Estate **Band 3** p.1297

**Logan III, Ben H**
Table(s): Nationwide: Bankruptcy/Restructuring **Band 4** p.39, California: Bankruptcy/Restructuring **Band 1** p.542

**LoGiudice, Susan E**
Profile: p.1401
Table(s): Maine: Corporate/M&A **Band 2** p.1385

**Logue, Kelly**
Table(s): California: Media & Entertainment: Transactional **Up-and-coming individuals** p.608

**Lohmann, Walter H**
Profile: p.878
Table(s): District of Columbia: Environment: Mainly Transactional **Band 1** p.805

**Lohr Jr, Walter**
Table(s): Maryland: Corporate/M&A **Senior Statesmen:** p.1412

**Lokey Jr, James**
Profile: p.1089
Table(s): Georgia: Tax **Band 2** p.1072

**Lokting, David**
Table(s): Oregon: Real Estate **Band 2** p.2173

**Lomax Jr, John F**
Table(s): Arizona: Labor & Employment **Band 2** p.499

**Lombardi, David**
Table(s): Idaho: Litigation: General Commercial **Band 2** p.1134

**Lombardi, Dennis M**
Profile: p.1123
Table(s): Hawaii: Real Estate **Band 1** p.1120

**Lombardi, George C**
Profile: p.1218
Table(s): Illinois: Intellectual Property **Band 1** p.1171

**Lubetkin, Jay**
Profile: p.1741
Table(s): New Jersey: Bankruptcy/Restructuring
Band 4 p.1705

**Lubin, Andrew R**
Table(s): Connecticut: Real Estate Band 2 p.740

**Lubin, Donald G**
Profile: p.1219
Table(s): Illinois: Corporate/M&A Senior Statesmen: p.1156

**Lubit, Beverly W**
Table(s): New Jersey: Intellectual Property Band 3 p.1716

**Lubowitz, Michael**
Profile: p.1915
Table(s): New York: Corporate/M&A Band 5 p.1793

**Lucas, Carol**
Profile: p.651
Table(s): California: Healthcare Band 4 p.568

**Lucas, Edwin F**
Table(s): North Carolina: Banking & Finance Band 2 p.2021

**Lucas, Kathleen**
Table(s): Indiana: Environment Band 2 p.1270

**Lucas, Michael L**
Table(s): Alabama: Labor & Employment Band 2 p.460

**Lucchesi, Thomas R**
Profile: p.2105
Table(s): Ohio: Litigation: General Commercial Band 4 p.2078

**Lucci, Joseph**
Profile: p.2223
Table(s): Pennsylvania: Intellectual Property Band 4 p.2197

**Luce, Gregory M**
Profile: p.359
Table(s): Nationwide: Healthcare: Regulatory & Litigation Band 1 p.127, District of Columbia: Healthcare Band 1 p.809

**Luce, Michael L**
Table(s): South Dakota: Litigation: General Commercial Band 1 p.2284

**Lucero, Gene**
Table(s): California: Environment Band 2 p.564

**Luchs, Richard W**
Table(s): District of Columbia: Real Estate Band 4 p.835

**Luchsinger, Dan**
Profile: p.878
Table(s): District of Columbia: Tax Band 4 p.838

**Lucic, Robert R**
Profile: p.1696
Table(s): New Hampshire: Environment Band 3 p.1687

**Luck, Bradley**
Profile: p.1654
Table(s): Montana: Labor & Employment Band 2 p.1648, Montana: Litigation: General Commercial Band 2 p.1649

**Lucking, David**
Table(s): Nationwide: Capital Markets: Derivatives Up-and-coming individuals p.51

**Luckoff, Howard N**
Table(s): Michigan: Real Estate Band 1 p.1546

**Ludwiszewski, Raymond B**
Profile: p.878
Table(s): Nationwide: Climate Change Band 3 p.63, District of Columbia: Environment Band 2 p.804

**Lueck, Martin**
Profile: p.1579
Table(s): Minnesota: Litigation: Intellectual Property Band 1 p.1574

**Luedke IV, William T**
Profile: p.359
Table(s): Nationwide: Financial Services Regulation: Financial Institutions M&A Band 3 p.99

**Luger, Andrew**
Table(s): Minnesota: Litigation: General Commercial Band 1 p.1574

**Luginbill, David H**
Table(s): Iowa: Litigation: General Commercial Band 2 p.1288

**Lui, Elwood**
Profile: p.651
Table(s): California: Litigation: Appellate Senior Statesmen: p.599

**Lukas, Edwin J.**
Profile: p.1552
Table(s): Michigan: Corporate/M&A Band 3 p.1538

**Lukey, Joan**
Table(s): Nationwide: Litigation: Trial Lawyers Band 2 p.187, Massachusetts: Litigation: General Commercial Band 1 p.1470

**Lukin, Mitch**
Profile: p.2402
Table(s): Texas: Intellectual Property Band 4 p.2354

**Lum, Dale**
Profile: p.359
Table(s): Nationwide: Capital Markets: Securitisation Band 4 p.59

**Lumish, Douglas E**
Profile: p.651
Table(s): California: Intellectual Property: Patent Band 3 p.578

**Lumish, Wendy F**
Profile: p.998
Table(s): Nationwide: Product Liability & Mass Torts Band 4 p.208, Florida: Litigation: Appellate Band 2 p.972

**Lumpkin, Cristina**
Profile: p.999
Table(s): Florida: Environment Associates to watch p.951

**Luna, Jones Wilson (J W)**
Table(s): Tennessee: Environment Band 2 p.2290

**Lund, Daniel**
Profile: p.1366
Table(s): Louisiana: Litigation: General Commercial Senior Statesmen: p.1352

**Lund, John R**
Table(s): Utah: Litigation: General Commercial Band 2 p.2468

**Lundberg, G Andrew**
Table(s): Nationwide: Insurance: Dispute Resolution: Policyholder Band 1 p.137, California: Insurance: Policyholder Band 1 p.576

**Lundgren, K Thor**
Profile: p.2584
Table(s): Wisconsin: Corporate/M&A Band 3 p.2571

**Lundsten, E Hans**
Profile: p.2257
Table(s): Rhode Island: Corporate/Commercial Band 3 p.2251

**Lundvall, Pat**
Table(s): Nevada: Litigation: General Commercial Band 2 p.1677

**Lundy, Robert W**
Table(s): California: Healthcare Band 1 p.568

**Lundy, Seth H**
Profile: p.878
Table(s): District of Columbia: Healthcare Band 2 p.809

**Lung, Harvey J**
Table(s): Hawaii: Litigation: General Commercial Band 3 p.1119

**Lunn, Gregory**
Table(s): Ohio: Intellectual Property Band 3 p.2071

**Lunsford III, Rodgers**
Profile: p.1089
Table(s): Georgia: Intellectual Property Band 2 p.1056

**Lunt, Gregory O**
Table(s): California: Bankruptcy/Restructuring Band 3 p.542

**Lupinacci, Timothy M**
Profile: p.470
Table(s): Alabama: Bankruptcy/Restructuring Band 1 p.457

**Lupo, Anthony V**
Profile: p.878
Table(s): District of Columbia: Intellectual Property: Trademark, Copyright & Trade Secrets Band 1 p.820

**Lupo, Dickson**
Table(s): North Carolina: Intellectual Property Band 1 p.2030

**Lupo, Raphael**
Profile: p.878
Table(s): District of Columbia: Intellectual Property: Litigation Senior Statesmen: p.821

**Lurey, Alfred**
Table(s): Georgia: Bankruptcy/Restructuring Band 1 p.1042

**Lurie, Dawn M**
Table(s): District of Columbia: Immigration Band 3 p.814

**Lurie, Jonathan C**
Profile: p.651
Table(s): Nationwide: Wealth Management: Western Region Band 2 p.267, California: Tax: Estate Planning Band 1 p.617

**Lurie, Paul**
Table(s): Illinois: Construction Senior Statesmen: p.1154

**Lusk, Neva**
Profile: p.2564
Table(s): West Virginia: Litigation: General Commercial Band 3 p.2555

**Luskin, Martin**
Profile: p.1915
Table(s): New York: Real Estate: Corporate Band 3 p.1854

**Luskin, Michael**
Table(s): New York: Bankruptcy/Restructuring Band 3 p.1782

**Lust, David E**
Table(s): South Dakota: Corporate/Commercial Band 3 p.2281

**Lustberg, Lawrence S**
Table(s): New Jersey: Litigation: White-Collar Crime & Government Investigations Band 1 p.1723

**Lustig, Andrew**
Table(s): Northern Virginia: Corporate/M&A Band 3 p.2493

**Lustigman, Andrew B**
Profile: p.359
Table(s): Nationwide: Advertising: Transactional & Regulatory Band 2 p.20

**Lustrin, Robert E**
Profile: p.359
Table(s): Nationwide: Transportation: Shipping: Finance (New York) Band 2 p.260

**Lutes, Mark**
Table(s): District of Columbia: Healthcare Band 2 p.809

**Luthey, Dean**
Table(s): Oklahoma: Native American Law Band 1 p.2144

**Lutsky, Jeffrey A**
Table(s): Pennsylvania: Litigation: General Commercial Band 3 p.2203

**Luttinger Jr, David A**
Profile: p.1915
Table(s): New York: Insurance: Dispute Resolution: Policyholder Band 3 p.1816

**Lutton, Katherine**
Table(s): California: Intellectual Property: Patent Band 3 p.578

**Lutz, Douglas L**
Profile: p.2105
Table(s): Ohio: Bankruptcy/Restructuring Band 2 p.2058

**Lutz, Holley Thames**
Profile: p.878
Table(s): District of Columbia: Healthcare Band 2 p.809

**Makinen, Marita A**
Profile: p.1916
Table(s): New York: Corporate/M&A Up-and-coming individuals p.1793

**Makoulian, Tina R**
Profile: p.2223
Table(s): Pennsylvania: Real Estate Band 3 p.2208

**Malecek, Michael**
Profile: p.651
Table(s): California: Intellectual Property: Patent Band 4 p.578

**Maledon, William J**
Profile: p.509
Table(s): Nationwide: Litigation: Trial Lawyers Band 2 p.187, Arizona: Litigation: General Commercial Star individuals p.501

**Malefatto, Alfred J**
Table(s): Florida: Environment Band 1 p.951

**Malester, Ann**
Profile: p.879
Table(s): District of Columbia: Antitrust Band 3 p.787

**Maley, John**
Profile: p.1278
Table(s): Indiana: Labor & Employment Band 2 p.1271, Indiana: Litigation: General Commercial Band 1 p.1273

**Malfitano, Michael**
Table(s): Florida: Labor & Employment Band 2 p.959

**Malheiro, Sharon**
Table(s): Iowa: Labor & Employment Band 2 p.1285

**Malicki, Thomas J**
Table(s): Nebraska: Corporate/Commercial Band 3 p.1659

**Malik, Thaddeus**
Table(s): Illinois: Corporate/M&A Band 3 p.1156

**Malin, Steven**
Profile: p.2402
Table(s): Texas: Intellectual Property Band 4 p.2354

**Malkerson, Bruce**
Table(s): Minnesota: Real Estate: Zoning/Land Use Band 1 p.1576

**Malkin, Joseph**
Profile: p.651
Table(s): California: Energy: State Regulatory & Litigation Band 1 p.562

**Mallard, Lynwood**
Table(s): North Carolina: Corporate/M&A Band 3 p.2025

**Mallery, Mark N**
Profile: p.1366
Table(s): Louisiana: Labor & Employment Band 2 p.1350

**Mallin, John**
Profile: p.745
Table(s): Connecticut: Real Estate Band 2 p.740

**Mallory, Richard C**
Profile: p.651
Table(s): California: Real Estate Band 2 p.611

**Mallow, Michael**
Profile: p.651
Table(s): California: Litigation: General Commercial Band 5 p.593

**Malloy, Elizabeth A**
Profile: p.2223
Table(s): Pennsylvania: Labor & Employment Band 2 p.2200

**Malloy, Michael**
Profile: p.361
Table(s): Nationwide: Investment Funds: Registered Funds Band 3 p.170

**Malloy, Sean**
Table(s): Ohio: Bankruptcy/Restructuring Band 2 p.2058

**Malloy, Timothy J**
Profile: p.1219
Table(s): Illinois: Intellectual Property Band 1 p.1171

**Malm, Richard**
Table(s): Iowa: Corporate/M&A Band 3 p.1283

**Malmen, Erika**
Table(s): Idaho: Natural Resources & Environment Up-and-coming individuals p.1136

**Malmquist, Michael J**
Profile: p.2474
Table(s): Utah: Energy & Natural Resources Band 2 p.2464

**Malone, Michael L**
Profile: p.2402
Table(s): Texas: Healthcare Band 3 p.2347

**Malone, Raymond M**
Profile: p.2105
Table(s): Ohio: Employee Benefits & Executive Compensation Band 2 p.2067

**Malone, Robert**
Profile: p.1741
Table(s): New Jersey: Bankruptcy/Restructuring Band 2 p.1705

**Malone Jr, Ernest**
Table(s): Louisiana: Labor & Employment Band 1 p.1350

**Malone Jr, Gayle**
Table(s): Tennessee: Litigation: General Commercial Band 2 p.2295

**Maloney, James**
Profile: p.2403
Table(s): Texas: Litigation: Securities Band 2 p.2362

**Maloney, John T**
Table(s): Hawaii: Labor & Employment: Employee Benefits & Compensation Band 1 p.1117

**Maloney, Timothy P**
Profile: p.1219
Table(s): Illinois: Intellectual Property Band 4 p.1171

**Maloney MacKenzie, Pamela**
Table(s): Massachusetts: Banking & Finance Band 3 p.1445

**Maloy, Bruce**
Table(s): Georgia: Litigation: White-Collar Crime & Government Investigations Band 1 p.1066

**Malt, R Bradford**
Table(s): Nationwide: Private Equity: Buyouts Senior Statesmen: p.203, Massachusetts: Corporate/M&A Senior Statesmen: p.1452, Massachusetts: Private Equity: Buyouts Senior Statesmen: p.1474

**Maltby, Stephen J O**
Profile: p.1916
Table(s): New York: Immigration Band 2 p.1814

**Malyshev, Peter**
Profile: p.361
Table(s): Nationwide: Capital Markets: Derivatives Band 3 p.51

**Mammarella, Thomas**
Table(s): Delaware: Real Estate Band 2 p.766

**Manahan, Matthew**
Profile: p.1401
Table(s): Maine: Environment Band 1 p.1389

**Manard, Jr, John P**
Table(s): Louisiana: Environment: Litigation Band 3 p.1346

**Manaut, Pete**
Profile: p.1123
Table(s): Hawaii: Litigation: General Commercial Band 3 p.1119

**Manchester, Susan A**
Profile: p.1696
Table(s): New Hampshire: Real Estate Band 1 p.1692, New Hampshire: Real Estate: Land Use Band 1 p.1692

**Mancini, David C**
Profile: p.879
Table(s): District of Columbia: Construction Band 4 p.795

**Mancini, Mary Ann**
Profile: p.361
Table(s): Nationwide: Wealth Management: Eastern Region Band 4 p.267

**Mancini, Paul**
Table(s): Hawaii: Real Estate Band 1 p.1120, Hawaii: Real Estate: Zoning/Land Use Band 1 p.1120

**Mancino, David A**
Profile: p.2105
Table(s): Ohio: Intellectual Property Band 3 p.2071

**Mancino, Douglas M**
Profile: p.651
Table(s): Nationwide: Healthcare: Transactional Band 2 p.128, California: Healthcare Band 1 p.568

**Mancusi, Michael A.**
Table(s): Nationwide: Financial Services Regulation: Banking (Enforcement & Investigations) Up-and-coming individuals p.97

**Mandel, David M**
Table(s): Massachusetts: Labor & Employment Band 2 p.1466

**Mandel, David S**
Table(s): Florida: Litigation: White-Collar Crime & Government Investigations Band 2 p.967

**Mandel, Gary B**
Profile: p.1916
Table(s): New York: Tax Band 3 p.1862

**Mandel, Jeffrey E**
Profile: p.999
Table(s): Florida: Labor & Employment Band 3 p.959

**Mandelbaum, David G**
Profile: p.2224
Table(s): Pennsylvania: Environment Band 1 p.2194

**Mandell, Floyd A**
Table(s): Illinois: Intellectual Property Band 1 p.1171

**Mandell, Steven P**
Table(s): Illinois: Media & Entertainment: Litigation Band 2 p.1184

**Mangelson, Michael E**
Table(s): Utah: Intellectual Property Band 2 p.2466

**Mangen Jr, Christopher**
Profile: p.1654
Table(s): Montana: Natural Resources & Environment Band 2 p.1651

**Manger, J Anthony**
Table(s): New Jersey: Healthcare Band 1 p.1715

**Mangino, Brian**
Profile: p.879
Table(s): Nationwide: Private Equity: Buyouts Band 5 p.203, District of Columbia: Corporate/M&A & Private Equity Band 3 p.797

**Mangum, David G**
Profile: p.2474
Table(s): Utah: Intellectual Property Band 2 p.2466

**Mangum, Geoffrey W**
Profile: p.2475
Table(s): Utah: Corporate/M&A Band 4 p.2462

**Manheim, Jr., Bruce S.**
Table(s): District of Columbia: Healthcare: Pharmaceutical/Medical Products Regulatory Band 3 p.810

**Manheimer, Jacob A**
Profile: p.1402
Table(s): Maine: Corporate/M&A: Bankruptcy Band 1 p.1385

**Manigan, Mark**
Table(s): New Jersey: Healthcare Up-and-coming individuals p.1715

**Manitsky, Andrew D**
Table(s): Vermont: Intellectual Property Band 2 p.2484, Vermont: Litigation: General Commercial Band 2 p.2486

**Manko, Joseph M**
Table(s): Pennsylvania: Environment Senior Statesmen: p.2194

**Mann, Barry D**
Table(s): North Carolina: Real Estate Band 2 p.2037

**Mann, Christopher L**
Profile: p.361
Table(s): Nationwide: Projects Band 2 p.216, New York: Latin American Investment Band 3 p.1829

**Mann, James E**
Table(s): Texas: Energy: State Regulatory & Litigation (Oil & Gas) Band 1 p.2341

**Mann, Michael D**
Table(s): **Nationwide: Securities: Regulation: Enforcement Band 2** p.233, **District of Columbia: Litigation: Securities Band 2** p.826

**Mann, Phillip L**
Profile: p.879
Table(s): **District of Columbia: Tax Band 3** p.838

**Mann, Terry**
Table(s): **Kansas: Labor & Employment Band 1** p.1294

**Mannal, Douglas**
Profile: p.1916
Table(s): **New York: Bankruptcy/Restructuring Up-and-coming individuals** p.1782

**Manne, Neal**
Table(s): **Texas: Litigation: General Commercial Band 2** p.2362

**Manner, Mark**
Table(s): **Tennessee: Corporate/M&A Band 1** p.2288, **Tennessee: Healthcare Band 2** p.2291

**Mannheimer, Douglas L**
Table(s): **Florida: Healthcare Band 3** p.954

**Manning, Amy**
Table(s): **Illinois: Antitrust Band 4** p.1143

**Manning, Fred**
Profile: p.2271
Table(s): **South Carolina: Labor & Employment Band 3** p.2262

**Manning, Jack**
Table(s): **Montana: Corporate/M&A Star individuals** p.1646

**Manning, Meredith**
Table(s): **District of Columbia: Healthcare: Pharmaceutical/Medical Products Regulatory Band 3** p.810

**Manning, William E**
Table(s): **Delaware: Real Estate: Zoning/Land Use Band 1** p.766

**Manolopoulos, Lynn T**
Table(s): **Washington: Environment Band 1** p.2527

**Manos, Karen L**
Profile: p.361
Table(s): **Nationwide: Government: Government Contracts Band 1** p.117, **Nationwide: Government: Government Contracts: Costs Disputes** p.117

**Manos, Marc**
Table(s): **South Carolina: Litigation: General Commercial Band 2** p.2264

**Mansfield, Alan**
Profile: p.1916
Table(s): **New York: Litigation: General Commercial Band 3** p.1833

**Mansfield, Melainie K**
Profile: p.652
Table(s): **California: Banking & Finance Band 3** p.539

**Mansfield, Stephen A**
Profile: p.652
Table(s): **California: Litigation: White-Collar Crime & Government Investigations Band 3** p.601

**Manson, Thomas P**
Table(s): **New Hampshire: Corporate/Commercial Band 1** p.1685

**Manter, Gregory A**
Table(s): **Illinois: Technology & Outsourcing Up-and-coming individuals** p.1194

**Manthei, John**
Profile: p.879
Table(s): **District of Columbia: Healthcare: Pharmaceutical/Medical Products Regulatory Band 3** p.810

**Manthey, Ron**
Profile: p.2403
Table(s): **Texas: Labor & Employment Band 2** p.2359

**Manthey, Tristan E**
Profile: p.1366
Table(s): **Louisiana: Bankruptcy/Restructuring Band 3** p.1337

**Manuel, J William**
Table(s): **Mississippi: Litigation: General Commercial Band 3** p.1597

**Manulik, Mark**
Table(s): **Oregon: Real Estate Band 3** p.2173

**Manwaring, Jed W**
Table(s): **Idaho: Bankruptcy/Restructuring Band 2** p.1131

**Mapes, Stephanie J**
Table(s): **Vermont: Corporate/Commercial: Captive Insurance Band 2** p.2483, **Vermont: Intellectual Property Band 2** p.2484

**Marandett, Eric J**
Profile: p.1500
Table(s): **Massachusetts: Intellectual Property Band 3** p.1463

**Marathas, Peter J**
Table(s): **Massachusetts: Employee Benefits & Executive Compensation Band 1** p.1455

**Marcello III, Matthew T**
Table(s): **Rhode Island: Corporate/Commercial: Banking & Finance Band 2** p.2251

**March, Aaron**
Table(s): **Missouri: Real Estate Band 2** p.1633

**March, Bruce I**
Profile: p.999
Table(s): **Florida: Corporate/M&A & Private Equity Band 2** p.947

**March, Jon G**
Table(s): **Michigan: Labor & Employment Band 2** p.1542

**Marchese, Lisa**
Table(s): **Washington: Litigation: General Commercial Band 3** p.2533

**Marchetta, Anthony J**
Profile: p.1741
Table(s): **New Jersey: Litigation: General Commercial Band 2** p.1722

**Marcil, Jack G**
Table(s): **North Dakota: Litigation: General Commercial Senior Statesmen** p.2053

**Marco, Frank J**
Table(s): **Connecticut: Corporate/M&A Band 1** p.732

**Marcu, Aaron R**
Profile: p.1916
Table(s): **New York: Litigation: White-Collar Crime & Government Investigations Band 2** p.1836

**Marcus, Benjamin E**
Profile: p.1402
Table(s): **Maine: Corporate/M&A Band 2** p.1385, **Maine: Corporate/M&A: Bankruptcy Band 1** p.1385

**Marcus, Courtney**
Profile: p.2403
Table(s): **Texas: Banking & Finance Band 2** p.2325

**Marcus, Craig**
Table(s): **Nationwide: Private Equity: Buyouts Band 5** p.203, **Massachusetts: Private Equity: Buyouts Band 3** p.1474

**Marcus, George J**
Table(s): **Maine: Corporate/M&A: Bankruptcy Band 1** p.1385

**Marcus, Jacqueline**
Profile: p.1916
Table(s): **New York: Bankruptcy/Restructuring Band 3** p.1782

**Marcus, Jeffrey**
Table(s): **Florida: Litigation: White-Collar Crime & Government Investigations Up-and-coming individuals** p.967

**Marcus, Kenneth B**
Profile: p.1123
Table(s): **Hawaii: Real Estate Band 1** p.1120

**Marcus, Robert R**
Profile: p.2043
Table(s): **North Carolina: Litigation: General Commercial Band 3** p.2033

**Marcus, Stephen**
Profile: p.2403
Table(s): **Texas: Tax Band 3** p.2371

**Marcuvitz, Alan H**
Profile: p.2584
Table(s): **Wisconsin: Real Estate Senior Statesmen** p.2579

**Marcy, Donald E**
Table(s): **Washington: Real Estate: Zoning/Land Use Band 1** p.2536

**Marell, Jeffrey D**
Profile: p.1917
Table(s): **New York: Corporate/M&A Up-and-coming individuals** p.1793

**Marella, Vincent J**
Profile: p.652
Table(s): **California: Litigation: White-Collar Crime & Government Investigations Senior Statesmen** p.601

**Marenberg, Steven**
Profile: p.652
Table(s): **California: Media & Entertainment: Litigation Band 1** p.606

**Marett, Louis J**
Profile: p.1501
Table(s): **Massachusetts: Tax Band 2** p.1481

**Margalit, Nir**
Table(s): **Nationwide: Leisure & Hospitality Band 4** p.179

**Margie, Paul**
Profile: p.880
Table(s): **District of Columbia: Telecom, Broadcast & Satellite Band 3** p.844

**Margo, Robert C.**
Table(s): **Oklahoma: Litigation: Mediators Band 2** p.2141

**Margolies, Jonathan H**
Profile: p.2584
Table(s): **Wisconsin: Intellectual Property Band 1** p.2573, **Wisconsin: Intellectual Property: Litigation** p.2573

**Margolis, Jeremy**
Profile: p.1219
Table(s): **Illinois: Litigation: White-Collar Crime & Government Investigations Band 3** p.1181

**Margulies, Jeffrey Brian**
Profile: p.652
Table(s): **California: Environment Band 3** p.564

**Marhofer, Michael**
Profile: p.2106
Table(s): **Ohio: Corporate/M&A Band 3** p.2064

**Marick, Michael**
Table(s): **Illinois: Insurance: Dispute Resolution Band 3** p.1168

**Marigo, Noiana Paula**
Profile: p.361
Table(s): **Nationwide: International Arbitration Up-and-coming individuals** p.145

**Maring, David**
Table(s): **North Dakota: Litigation: General Commercial Band 1** p.2053

**Marino, James J**
Profile: p.1741
Table(s): **New Jersey: Corporate/M&A Band 3** p.1707

**Marino, Kevin H**
Table(s): **New Jersey: Litigation: White-Collar Crime & Government Investigations Band 2** p.1723

**Marinuzzi, Lorenzo**
Profile: p.1917
Table(s): **New York: Bankruptcy/Restructuring Up-and-coming individuals** p.1782

**Marion, David H**
Profile: p.2224
Table(s): **Pennsylvania: Litigation: General Commercial Senior Statesmen** p.2203

**Marionneaux, Kyle**
Table(s): **Louisiana: Energy & Natural Resources: Utilities Band 2** p.1344

**Mark, Etan**
Profile: p.999
Table(s): **Florida: Litigation: General Commercial Up-and-coming individuals** p.966

**Mark, Wayne J**
Table(s): **Nebraska: Litigation: General Commercial Senior Statesmen** p.1664

**Mastro, Randy**
Profile: p.1917
Table(s): New York: Litigation: General
Commercial Band 2 p.1833

**Masucci, Michele**
Profile: p.1917
Table(s): New York: Healthcare Band 3 p.1811

**Masur, Daniel A**
Table(s): Nationwide: Outsourcing Band 1 p.195,
District of Columbia: Technology & Outsourcing
Band 1 p.842

**Masyr, Jesse**
Table(s): New York: Real Estate: Zoning/Land
Use Band 2 p.1855

**Matava, George G**
Table(s): Colorado: Intellectual Property Band 2
p.704

**Matays, Steven J.**
Profile: p.1917
Table(s): New York: Tax Band 4 p.1862

**Matchett, Sam**
Profile: p.1089
Table(s): Georgia: Labor & Employment Band 3
p.1060

**Matejka, Michael**
Table(s): Nebraska: Real Estate Band 3 p.1666

**Matheny, Richard**
Profile: p.363
Table(s): Nationwide: International Trade: Export
Controls & Economic Sanctions Band 3 p.153

**Mather, Barbara W**
Profile: p.2224
Table(s): Pennsylvania: Antitrust Star individuals
p.2184, Pennsylvania: Litigation: General
Commercial Band 1 p.2203

**Matheson, David S**
Table(s): Oregon: Corporate/M&A Band 2 p.2164

**Mathews, Daniel A**
Table(s): Nationwide: Projects Band 3 p.216,
Nationwide: Projects: PPP Band 1 p.216

**Mathews, Kristen**
Table(s): Nationwide: Privacy & Data Security
Band 2 p.199, New York: Technology &
Outsourcing Band 3 p.1868

**Mathews, Mark**
Table(s): Colorado: Natural Resources &
Environment Band 2 p.712

**Mathias, James D**
Profile: p.1429
Table(s): Maryland: Litigation: General
Commercial Band 3 p.1419

**Mathias, Robert J**
Profile: p.1429
Table(s): Maryland: Litigation: General
Commercial Band 1 p.1419

**Mathias, Stephen M**
Profile: p.2564
Table(s): West Virginia: Real Estate Band 1
p.2560

**Mathias Jr, John H**
Profile: p.1220
Table(s): Illinois: Insurance: Dispute Resolution
Band 1 p.1168

**Mathiason, Garry G**
Profile: p.652
Table(s): California: Labor & Employment Band 1
p.587

**Mathis, Ben**
Table(s): Georgia: Labor & Employment Band 2
p.1060

**Matichak, Jill**
Table(s): California: Banking & Finance Band 2
p.539

**Matkins, Michael L**
Profile: p.652
Table(s): California: Real Estate Band 1 p.611

**Matour, James M**
Profile: p.2224
Table(s): Pennsylvania:
Bankruptcy/Restructuring Band 2 p.2188

**Matovich, Carey E**
Table(s): Montana: Litigation: General
Commercial Band 1 p.1649

**Matricciani, Rose M**
Profile: p.1429
Table(s): Maryland: Healthcare Band 2 p.1415

**Matsushige, Cary**
Table(s): Hawaii: Corporate/Commercial:
Finance Band 1 p.1116

**Mattei, Ivan E**
Table(s): Nationwide: Projects Band 2 p.216,
Nationwide: Projects: PPP Band 2 p.216, New
York: Latin American Investment Band 4 p.1829

**Matteo-Boehm, Rachel E**
Table(s): California: Media & Entertainment:
First Amendment Litigation Band 2 p.606

**Matterer, Mary B**
Table(s): Delaware: Intellectual Property Band 4
p.763

**Matthews, David R**
Table(s): Arkansas: Litigation: General
Commercial Band 1 p.522

**Matthews, Frank E**
Table(s): Florida: Environment Band 1 p.951

**Matthews, John E**
Profile: p.363
Table(s): Nationwide: Energy: Nuclear
(Regulatory & Litigation) Band 3 p.77

**Matthews, Joseph M**
Table(s): Florida: Litigation: General Commercial
Band 1 p.966

**Matthews, Mark E**
Table(s): Nationwide: Tax: Controversy Band Star
Associate p.244, Nationwide: Tax: Fraud Band 1
p.244

**Matthews, Philip R**
Table(s): Nationwide: Insurance: Dispute
Resolution: Insurer Band 1 p.134, California:
Insurance: Insurer Band 1 p.574

**Matthews, Scott**
Table(s): Delaware: Corporate/M&A Up-and-coming
individuals p.761

**Matthews Jr, William**
Table(s): North Carolina: Real Estate Band 3
p.2037

**Matthias, Michael R**
Profile: p.653
Table(s): California: Litigation: General
Commercial Band 4 p.593

**Mattingly, Patrick W**
Profile: p.1322
Table(s): Kentucky: Corporate/M&A Band 2
p.1305, Kentucky: Environment, Natural
Resources & Utilities: Natural Resources Band 2
p.1307

**Mattox, Sharon**
Profile: p.2403
Table(s): Texas: Environment Band 2 p.2343

**Mattson, Eric S**
Profile: p.1220
Table(s): Illinois: Media & Entertainment:
Litigation Band 2 p.1184

**Matula, Michael L.**
Profile: p.1637
Table(s): Missouri: Labor & Employment Band 3
p.1625

**Matyas, David E**
Table(s): District of Columbia: Healthcare Band 2
p.809

**Mauel, John G**
Table(s): Nationwide: Projects Band 2 p.216,
Nationwide: Projects: LNG Band 1 p.216

**Mauer, Kimberly K**
Profile: p.2106
Table(s): Ohio: Banking & Finance Band 3 p.2056

**Maurelli, Gino**
Table(s): Colorado: Corporate/M&A Band 2 p.703

**Maurer, Thomas K.**
Table(s): Florida: Environment Band 3 p.951

**Mautino, Kathrin**
Table(s): California: Immigration Band 2 p.571

**Mautino, Robert A**
Table(s): California: Immigration Band 2 p.571

**Mautner, Gail**
Profile: p.2540
Table(s): Washington: Labor & Employment Band
3 p.2531

**Maxwell, Robin JH**
Table(s): Nationwide: Financial Services
Regulation: Banking (Compliance) Band 3 p.96

**Maxwell-Hoffman, Ellen**
Profile: p.2564
Table(s): West Virginia: Corporate/Commercial
Band 2 p.2550

**May, Arnold P**
Table(s): Massachusetts: Tax Band 2 p.1481

**May, Gregory**
Profile: p.880
Table(s): District of Columbia: Tax Band 2 p.838

**May, Jane Wells**
Profile: p.1220
Table(s): Illinois: Tax Band 3 p.1192

**May, Kirk**
Table(s): Missouri: Litigation: General
Commercial Band 2 p.1628

**May, Walter**
Table(s): Arkansas: Corporate/Commercial Band
2 p.518

**May Jr, Henry S**
Profile: p.363
Table(s): Nationwide: Energy: Oil & Gas
(Regulatory & Litigation) Senior Statesmen: p.78

**Mayberry, David**
Table(s): District of Columbia: Intellectual
Property: Trademark, Copyright & Trade Secrets
Band 1 p.820

**Mayer, Marc**
Table(s): California: Intellectual Property:
Trademark, Copyright & Trade Secrets Band 3
p.578

**Mayer, Sylvia**
Profile: p.2404
Table(s): Texas: Bankruptcy/Restructuring Band 4
p.2328

**Mayer, Theodore VH**
Profile: p.363
Table(s): Nationwide: Product Liability & Mass
Torts Band 3 p.208

**Mayer, Thomas Moers**
Profile: p.363
Table(s): Nationwide: Bankruptcy/Restructuring
Band 1 p.39, New York:
Bankruptcy/Restructuring Band 1 p.1782

**Mayer, William P**
Profile: p.1501
Table(s): Nationwide: Financial Services
Regulation: Financial Institutions M&A Band 3
p.99, Massachusetts: Banking & Finance:
Corporate & Regulatory Band 1 p.1446

**Mayerle, Thomas M**
Table(s): Minnesota: Real Estate Band 3 p.1576

**Mayerson, Marc S**
Table(s): District of Columbia: Insurance:
Policyholder Band 2 p.818

**Mayerson, Mickey A**
Profile: p.653
Table(s): California: Media & Entertainment:
Transactional Band 1 p.608

**Mayes, Gregory E**
Table(s): Kentucky: Real Estate Band 2 p.1314

**Mayesh, Jay**
Profile: p.363
Table(s): Nationwide: Product Liability & Mass
Torts Band 3 p.208

**Maynard, Deanne**
Profile: p.363
Table(s): Nationwide: Appellate Law Band 3 p.26

**Maynard, Robert**
Table(s): Idaho: Natural Resources &
Environment Band 1 p.1136

**Maynard Jr, Joe**
Profile: p.1654
Table(s): Montana: Labor & Employment Band 2
p.1648

**Maynes, Todd F**
Profile: p.1220
Table(s): Nationwide: Tax: Controversy Band 4
p.244, Illinois: Tax Band 2 p.1192

**McCollum, James**
Table(s): Alaska: Real Estate **Band 1** p.491

**McCombs, David**
Table(s): Texas: Intellectual Property **Band 1** p.2354

**McConnell, Alan**
Table(s): North Carolina: Environment **Band 2** p.2028

**McConnell, Andrew**
Table(s): Wisconsin: Intellectual Property **Band 2** p.2573

**McConnell, Karen C**
Profile: p.510
Table(s): Arizona: Corporate/M&A **Band 1** p.495

**McConnell, Mark S**
Table(s): Nationwide: International Trade: Trade Remedies & Trade Policy **Band 2** p.154

**McConnell, Michael J**
Profile: p.1090
Table(s): Georgia: Litigation: General Commercial **Band 4** p.1065

**McConnell, Robert A**
Table(s): Utah: Real Estate **Band 2** p.2470

**McConnell, Timothy**
Profile: p.2307
Table(s): Tennessee: Labor & Employment **Band 3** p.2293

**McConnell-Corbyn, Laura**
Profile: p.2151
Table(s): Oklahoma: Litigation: General Commercial **Band 2** p.2141

**McConville, Tom**
Profile: p.653
Table(s): California: Litigation: White-Collar Crime & Government Investigations **Up-and-coming individuals** p.601

**McCool, Steven**
Table(s): District of Columbia: Litigation: White-Collar Crime & Government Investigations **Band 4** p.827

**McCord, Thomas**
Profile: p.1501
Table(s): Massachusetts: Employee Benefits & Executive Compensation **Band 2** p.1455

**McCormack, Aidan**
Profile: p.1918
Table(s): New York: Insurance: Dispute Resolution: Insurer **Band 3** p.1816

**McCormack, Christopher**
Profile: p.745
Table(s): Connecticut: Environment **Band 3** p.733

**McCormack, David B**
Table(s): South Carolina: Labor & Employment **Band 2** p.2262

**McCormack, Thomas**
Profile: p.1918
Table(s): New York: Litigation: General Commercial **Band 4** p.1833

**McCormack, William F**
Table(s): Nationwide: Investment Funds: Private Equity: Fund Formation **Band 4** p.166

**McCormally, Brian C**
Profile: p.364
Table(s): Nationwide: Financial Services Regulation: Banking (Enforcement & Investigations) **Band 2** p.97

**McCormick, Alan**
Profile: p.1655
Table(s): Montana: Real Estate **Band 2** p.1652

**McCormick, Kevin C**
Profile: p.1429
Table(s): Maryland: Labor & Employment **Band 3** p.1417

**McCormick, Mark**
Table(s): Iowa: Litigation: General Commercial **Band 1** p.1288

**McCormick, Thomas**
Table(s): Vermont: Litigation: General Commercial **Band 2** p.2486

**McCormick, Timothy R**
Profile: p.2404
Table(s): Texas: Litigation: General Commercial **Band 3** p.2362

**McCorriston, William C**
Table(s): Hawaii: Litigation: General Commercial **Star individuals** p.1119

**McCourt, Terence**
Profile: p.1501
Table(s): Massachusetts: Labor & Employment **Band 4** p.1466

**McCowan, Charles**
Profile: p.1366
Table(s): Louisiana: Environment: Litigation **Senior Statesmen:** p.1346, Louisiana: Litigation: General Commercial **Senior Statesmen:** p.1352

**McCown, Steven R**
Profile: p.2404
Table(s): Texas: Labor & Employment **Band 3** p.2359

**McCoy, Michael D**
Profile: p.2043
Table(s): North Carolina: Intellectual Property **Band 2** p.2030

**McCoy, Padraic I**
Table(s): Nationwide: Native American Law **Band 2** p.192

**McCrary, Dan H**
Table(s): Georgia: Energy **Band 2** p.1049

**McCrea, Keith R**
Table(s): Nationwide: Energy: Electricity (Regulatory & Litigation) **Band 3** p.76

**McCrea Jr, Richard C**
Profile: p.1000
Table(s): Florida: Labor & Employment **Star individuals** p.959

**McCreadie, David W**
Table(s): Nationwide: Transportation: Shipping: Litigation (outside New York) **Band 1** p.263

**McCreary, Charles 'Dusty'**
Table(s): Ohio: Real Estate **Band 1** p.2086

**McCreary, Jean H**
Profile: p.1918
Table(s): New York: Environment **Band 2** p.1807

**McCue, Judith W**
Profile: p.365
Table(s): Nationwide: Wealth Management: Central Region **Band 1** p.266

**McCue, Mark S**
Table(s): New Hampshire: Corporate/Commercial **Band 2** p.1685

**McCullough, David**
Profile: p.2152
Table(s): Oklahoma: Native American Law **Band 2** p.2144

**McCullough, Jack**
Table(s): Washington: Real Estate: Zoning/Land Use **Band 1** p.2536

**McCullough, James J**
Profile: p.365
Table(s): Nationwide: Government: Government Contracts **Band 1** p.117, Nationwide: Government: Government Contracts: Bid Protests p.117

**McCullough, Joe**
Profile: p.1221
Table(s): Illinois: Insurance: Dispute Resolution: Reinsurance **Band 3** p.1168

**McCullough, Kim**
Profile: p.365
Table(s): Nationwide: Franchising **Band 4** p.111

**McCune, Andrew W**
Profile: p.1221
Table(s): Illinois: Corporate/M&A: Private Equity **Band 2** p.1157

**McCusker, Anthony**
Profile: p.653
Table(s): California: Corporate/M&A **Up-and-coming individuals** p.553, California: Corporate/M&A: Venture Capital **Up-and-coming individuals** p.553

**McCutchen, Tammy D**
Profile: p.881
Table(s): District of Columbia: Labor & Employment **Band 3** p.824

**McCutcheon, Mary E**
Table(s): California: Insurance: Policyholder **Band 4** p.576

**McCutcheon, Melody**
Table(s): Washington: Real Estate: Zoning/Land Use **Band 2** p.2536

**McDaniel, Dana D**
Table(s): Southern Virginia: Intellectual Property **Band 1** p.2498

**McDaniel, Janet Lawler**
Profile: p.720
Table(s): Colorado: Real Estate: Construction **Band 1** p.714

**McDaniel Jr, Dan M**
Profile: p.1606
Table(s): Mississippi: Corporate/Commercial: Gaming & Licensing **Band 1** p.1591

**McDaniels, William E**
Table(s): District of Columbia: Litigation: General Commercial **Band 2** p.826

**McDavid, Janet L**
Table(s): District of Columbia: Antitrust **Band 2** p.787

**McDermett Jr, Don J**
Profile: p.2404
Table(s): Texas: Technology: Corporate & Commercial **Band 2** p.2375

**McDermott, Brian L**
Profile: p.1278
Table(s): Indiana: Labor & Employment **Band 2** p.1271

**McDermott, Daniel**
Table(s): Nationwide: Transportation: Shipping: Litigation (New York) **Band 4** p.261

**McDermott, Francis A**
Profile: p.2511
Table(s): Northern Virginia: Real Estate: Zoning/Land Use **Band 1** p.2505

**McDermott, James T**
Table(s): Oregon: Litigation: General Commercial **Band 2** p.2171

**McDermott, John V**
Table(s): Colorado: Litigation: General Commercial **Band 2** p.709

**McDermott, Matt**
Table(s): Iowa: Litigation: General Commercial **Up-and-coming individuals** p.1288

**McDermott III, Stanley**
Profile: p.365
Table(s): Nationwide: Transportation: Shipping: Litigation (New York) **Band 3** p.261

**McDonald, Bruce**
Profile: p.2404
Table(s): District of Columbia: Antitrust **Band 5** p.787, Texas: Antitrust **Band 1** p.2323

**McDonald, Daniel**
Table(s): Minnesota: Litigation: Intellectual Property **Band 1** p.1574

**McDonald, David**
Profile: p.2540
Table(s): Washington: Intellectual Property **Band 2** p.2529

**McDonald, Derek**
Profile: p.2404
Table(s): Texas: Environment **Band 2** p.2343

**McDonald, Douglas**
Profile: p.2511
Table(s): Northern Virginia: Real Estate **Band 3** p.2505

**McDonald, John**
Table(s): Ohio: Litigation: General Commercial **Band 3** p.2078

**McDonald, John D**
Profile: p.1221
Table(s): Illinois: Tax **Band 3** p.1192

**McDonald, Michael R**
Table(s): New Jersey: Litigation: General Commercial **Band 3** p.1722

**McDonald, Paul**
Table(s): Maine: Litigation: General Commercial **Band 3** p.1393

**McDonald, Scott**
Profile: p.2404
Table(s): Texas: Labor & Employment **Band 3** p.2359

**McIlvaine III, John W**
Table(s): Pennsylvania: Intellectual Property
Band 4 p.2197

**McInerney, Patrick**
Table(s): Missouri: Litigation: White-Collar Crime
& Government Investigations Band 3 p.1629

**McInerney, Tim**
Table(s): California: Construction Band 4 p.550

**McInerney, William P**
Profile: p.365
Table(s): Nationwide: Real Estate Band 2 p.225,
New York: Real Estate: Finance Band 2 p.1855

**McInerny, Daniel**
Table(s): Indiana: Environment Band 1 p.1270

**McInnis, Judith**
Table(s): South Carolina: Real Estate Band 3
p.2266

**McInnis, Terrence R**
Table(s): California: Insurance: Insurer Band 4
p.574

**McIntosh, Carolyn L**
Table(s): Colorado: Natural Resources &
Environment Band 3 p.712

**McIntosh, Ian**
Profile: p.1655
Table(s): Montana: Litigation: General
Commercial Band 1 p.1649

**McIntyre, Kenneth J.**
Profile: p.1553
Table(s): Michigan: Litigation: General
Commercial Band 3 p.1544

**McIntyre, Krista K**
Table(s): Idaho: Natural Resources &
Environment Band 1 p.1136

**McIntyre, Paul R.**
Profile: p.2224
Table(s): Pennsylvania: Environment Up-and-coming Individuals p.2194

**McIsaac, Christopher**
Profile: p.365
Table(s): Nationwide: Projects Band 1 p.216

**McIver, Tex**
Profile: p.1090
Table(s): Georgia: Labor & Employment Band 2
p.1060

**McJunkin, John**
Profile: p.881
Table(s): District of Columbia:
Bankruptcy/Restructuring Band 3 p.792

**McKane, Mark**
Profile: p.653
Table(s): California: Litigation: General
Commercial Band 5 p.593

**McKay, Daniel G**
Table(s): Maine: Corporate/M&A Band 1 p.1385

**McKay, Hugh E**
Profile: p.2106
Table(s): Ohio: Litigation: General Commercial
Band 4 p.2078

**McKearin, Robert**
Table(s): Vermont: Labor & Employment Band 3
p.2485

**McKee, Bill**
Profile: p.881
Table(s): District of Columbia: Tax Band 1 p.838

**McKee, Thomas F**
Profile: p.2106
Table(s): Ohio: Corporate/M&A Senior Statesmen:
p.2064

**McKeeman, Michael T**
Profile: p.653
Table(s): California: Construction Band 3 p.550

**McKeithen, Ward**
Table(s): North Carolina: Litigation: General
Commercial Senior Statesmen: p.2033

**McKellar, James W**
Profile: p.2404
Table(s): Texas: Banking & Finance Band 1
p.2325

**McKelvey, Jr., Steven**
Profile: p.366
Table(s): Nationwide: Transportation: Road
(Carriage/Commercial) Band 3 p.259

**McKelvie, Roderick R**
Profile: p.881
Table(s): District of Columbia: Intellectual
Property: Litigation Band 4 p.821

**McKendall, Miriam**
Profile: p.1501
Table(s): Massachusetts: Labor & Employment
Band 4 p.1466

**McKendry Jr, John H**
Table(s): Michigan: Employee Benefits &
Executive Compensation Band 2 p.1540

**McKenna, John J**
Table(s): District of Columbia: Construction Band
4 p.795

**McKenna, Kathleen**
Table(s): New York: Labor & Employment Band 2
p.1826

**McKenna, Keith**
Profile: p.1918
Table(s): New York: Insurance: Dispute
Resolution: Policyholder Up-and-coming Individuals
p.1816

**McKenna, Susan**
Profile: p.1000
Table(s): Florida: Labor & Employment Band 1
p.959

**McKenzie, James**
Profile: p.2224
Table(s): Pennsylvania: Corporate/M&A:
Securities Band 1 p.2191

**Mckenzie, Jeffrey A**
Table(s): Kentucky: Corporate/M&A Band 2
p.1305

**McKeon, Michael J**
Table(s): Nationwide: International Trade:
Intellectual Property (Section 337) Band 2 p.160,
District of Columbia: Intellectual Property:
Litigation Band 3 p.821

**McKeon, Tina Williams**
Table(s): Georgia: Intellectual Property Band 3
p.1056

**McKinney, Kathleen**
Table(s): South Carolina: Corporate/M&A:
Banking & Finance Band 1 p.2260

**McKinney II, J Cliff**
Profile: p.528
Table(s): Arkansas: Real Estate Band 2 p.524

**McKinney Jr, John A**
Table(s): New Jersey: Environment Band 2 p.1711

**McKinnon, Michele**
Table(s): Nationwide: Wealth Management:
Eastern Region Band 4 p.267

**McKinstry Jr, Robert B**
Profile: p.2224
Table(s): Nationwide: Climate Change Band 3
p.63, Pennsylvania: Environment Band 2 p.2194

**McKirgan, Robert H**
Table(s): Arizona: Litigation: General
Commercial Band 3 p.501

**McKnight, Frederick (Rick)**
Profile: p.653
Table(s): California: Litigation: General
Commercial Band 4 p.593

**McKnight, Michael S**
Table(s): South Dakota: Labor & Employment:
Workers' Compensation Band 1 p.2283

**McKool, Mike**
Profile: p.2405
Table(s): Nationwide: Litigation: Trial Lawyers
Band 2 p.187, Texas: Intellectual Property Band 1
p.2354, Texas: Litigation: General Commercial
Band 1 p.2362

**McLamb, Dan J**
Table(s): North Carolina: Litigation: Healthcare
& Medical Malpractice Band 1 p.2034

**McLaughlin, Alan L**
Profile: p.1278
Table(s): Indiana: Labor & Employment Band 2
p.1271

**McLaughlin, Alex**
Table(s): Idaho: Litigation: General Commercial
Band 2 p.1134

**McLaughlin, Amy M**
Table(s): Vermont: Labor & Employment Band 3
p.2485

**McLaughlin, Cathleen**
Table(s): New York: Latin American Investment
Band 3 p.1829

**McLaughlin, Christine Liu**
Table(s): Wisconsin: Labor & Employment Band 3
p.2575

**McLaughlin, Ellen E**
Profile: p.1221
Table(s): Illinois: Labor & Employment Band 3
p.1175

**McLaughlin, Joseph**
Profile: p.366
Table(s): Nationwide: Securities: Regulation:
Advisory Band 2 p.232

**McLaughlin, Kevin T**
Table(s): Missouri: Labor & Employment Band 2
p.1625

**McLaughlin, Lawrence**
Table(s): Michigan: Real Estate Star Individuals
p.1546

**McLaughlin, Patrick**
Table(s): Ohio: Litigation: General Commercial
Band 4 p.2078, Ohio: Litigation: White-Collar
Crime & Government Investigations Band 1
p.2078

**McLaughlin, T Mark**
Table(s): Illinois: Antitrust Band 2 p.1143

**McLaughlin, Theresa M**
Table(s): Florida: Real Estate Band 3 p.974

**McLaughlin, Thomas J**
Table(s): Nationwide: Transportation: Aviation:
Litigation Band 3 p.254

**McLean, David**
Table(s): Montana: Labor & Employment Band 2
p.1648, Montana: Litigation: General
Commercial Up-and-coming Individuals p.1649

**McLean, David J**
Table(s): New Jersey: Litigation: General
Commercial Band 3 p.1722

**McLean, Michael**
Profile: p.2225
Table(s): Pennsylvania: Corporate/M&A:
Securities Band 2 p.2191

**McLean, Ronald**
Table(s): North Dakota: Litigation: General
Commercial Star Individuals p.2053

**McLeay, Bartholomew L**
Profile: p.1668
Table(s): Nebraska: Litigation: General
Commercial Band 1 p.1664

**McLeod, David K**
Table(s): Michigan: Banking & Finance Band 3
p.1536

**McLoon, Christopher**
Profile: p.1402
Table(s): Maine: Corporate/M&A Band 3 p.1385

**McLoughlin, Jean**
Profile: p.1918
Table(s): New York: Employee Benefits &
Executive Compensation Band 2 p.1802

**McLoughlin Jr, James P**
Table(s): North Carolina: Litigation: General
Commercial Band 2 p.2033

**McLucas, William**
Profile: p.366
Table(s): Nationwide: Securities: Regulation:
Enforcement Star Individuals p.233

**McLusky, Robert G**
Table(s): West Virginia: Natural Resources:
Environment Band 1 p.2558

**McMackin III, James H**
Table(s): Delaware: Labor & Employment Up-and-coming Individuals p.765

**McMahan, Jeffrey J**
Table(s): Vermont: Corporate/Commercial Band 1
p.2483, Vermont: Intellectual Property Band 2
p.2484

**McMahon, Brian J**
Table(s): New Jersey: Litigation: General
Commercial Band 3 p.1722

**Meeder, James**
Profile: p.654
Table(s): California: Environment **Band 4** p.564

**Meehan, Wayne D**
Profile: p.366
Table(s): Nationwide: Transportation: Shipping: Litigation (New York) **Band 2** p.261

**Meek, Derek**
Table(s): Alabama: Bankruptcy/Restructuring **Band 3** p.457

**Meek, Dustin**
Table(s): Kentucky: Litigation: General Commercial **Band 4** p.1312

**Meek, Kevin J**
Profile: p.2405
Table(s): Texas: Intellectual Property **Band 3** p.2354

**Meeker, Heather J**
Profile: p.654
Table(s): California: Intellectual Property: Patent **Band 4** p.578, California: IT & Outsourcing **Band 1** p.583

**Meeker, Suzanne**
Profile: p.1402
Table(s): Maine: Labor & Employment: Employee Benefits & Compensation **Band 1** p.1390

**Meeks, Thomas J**
Profile: p.1000
Table(s): Florida: Litigation: General Commercial **Band 3** p.966

**Meeks, William**
Table(s): Ohio: Litigation: White-Collar Crime & Government Investigations **Band 3** p.2079

**Meenan, Timothy J**
Table(s): Florida: Insurance **Band 2** p.957

**Meezan, David M**
Table(s): Georgia: Environment **Band 3** p.1051

**Mehalko, Megan**
Profile: p.2106
Table(s): Ohio: Corporate/M&A **Band 3** p.2064

**Mehlman, Mark**
Profile: p.1221
Table(s): Illinois: Real Estate **Band 2** p.1187

**Mehlman, Nancy**
Profile: p.1918
Table(s): New York: Tax **Band 3** p.1862

**Mehlman, Sharon R**
Table(s): Nationwide: Immigration **Band 2** p.131, California: Immigration **Band 1** p.571

**Mehr, Matthew**
Profile: p.510
Table(s): Arizona: Real Estate **Band 4** p.504

**Mehra, Shailesh (Shaalu)**
Table(s): California: IT & Outsourcing **Band 3** p.583

**Mehrara, Sasan**
Profile: p.1919
Table(s): New York: Real Estate: Corporate **Up-and-coming individuals** p.1854

**Mehta, Amit**
Table(s): Illinois: Corporate/M&A: Private Equity **Band 3** p.1157

**Mehta, Cyrus D**
Profile: p.366
Table(s): Nationwide: Immigration **Band 3** p.131, New York: Immigration **Band 1** p.1814

**Mehta, Eileen B**
Profile: p.1000
Table(s): Florida: Real Estate **Band 4** p.974

**Mehta, Kiran H**
Profile: p.2043
Table(s): North Carolina: Litigation: General Commercial **Band 2** p.2033

**Mehta, Prakash**
Profile: p.366
Table(s): Nationwide: Investment Funds: Private Equity: Fund Formation **Band 3** p.166

**Mei, James M**
Table(s): Oregon: Labor & Employment: Immigration **Band 2** p.2168

**Meier, Joseph M**
Table(s): Idaho: Bankruptcy/Restructuring **Band 1** p.1131

**Meier, Lawrence H**
Table(s): Vermont: Intellectual Property **Band 1** p.2484

**Meiklejohn, Paul**
Table(s): Washington: Intellectual Property **Band 1** p.2529

**Meir, Dennis**
Table(s): Georgia: Bankruptcy/Restructuring **Senior Statesmen**: p.1042

**Meisel, Michael S**
Profile: p.1742
Table(s): New Jersey: Litigation: General Commercial **Band 2** p.1722

**Meiser, Kenneth E**
Table(s): New Jersey: Real Estate: Zoning/Land Use **Band 2** p.1728

**Meisler, Ron E**
Profile: p.1221
Table(s): Illinois: Bankruptcy/Restructuring **Band 4** p.1148

**Meister, Margaret L**
Table(s): New Mexico: Real Estate **Band 1** p.1772

**Meklinsky, Ian D**
Profile: p.1742
Table(s): New Jersey: Labor & Employment **Band 3** p.1718

**Meland, Creighton**
Table(s): Illinois: Banking & Finance **Band 3** p.1145

**Melbinger, Michael S**
Profile: p.1222
Table(s): Illinois: Labor & Employment: Employee Benefits & Compensation **Band 1** p.1176

**Melby, Barbara Murphy**
Profile: p.366
Table(s): Nationwide: Outsourcing **Band 1** p.195

**Mele, Dennis**
Table(s): Florida: Real Estate: Zoning/Land Use **Band 1** p.975

**Melgaard, Robert J**
Table(s): Oklahoma: Corporate/Commercial **Band 3** p.2134

**Melicharek Jr, John**
Profile: p.366
Table(s): Nationwide: Leisure & Hospitality **Band 2** p.179

**Melillo, Cynthia A**
Table(s): Idaho: Real Estate **Up-and-coming individuals** p.1138

**Melko, John P**
Profile: p.2405
Table(s): Texas: Bankruptcy/Restructuring **Band 3** p.2328

**Meller, Bruce**
Profile: p.1919
Table(s): New York: Construction **Band 4** p.1791

**Mellin, Matthew P**
Table(s): Maryland: Employee Benefits & Executive Compensation **Band 2** p.1414

**Mellits, Bart**
Profile: p.2225
Table(s): Pennsylvania: Real Estate **Band 3** p.2208

**Mello, James**
Table(s): Missouri: Real Estate **Band 2** p.1633

**Melloni, Thomas R**
Table(s): Vermont: Corporate/Commercial **Band 3** p.2483

**Melmed, Lynden**
Table(s): District of Columbia: Immigration **Band 3** p.814

**Melodia, Mark S**
Table(s): Nationwide: Privacy & Data Security **Band 3** p.199

**Meloy, Michael M**
Table(s): Pennsylvania: Environment **Band 1** p.2194

**Melsheimer, Tom**
Table(s): Texas: Intellectual Property **Band 2** p.2354

**Meltebeke, Brenda**
Table(s): Oregon: Corporate/M&A **Band 3** p.2164

**Melton, Timothy J**
Profile: p.1222
Table(s): Illinois: Corporate/M&A **Band 3** p.1156

**Meltzer, Ronald**
Profile: p.366
Table(s): Nationwide: International Trade: Export Controls & Economic Sanctions **Band 2** p.153

**Meltzer, Steven**
Table(s): Northern Virginia: Corporate/M&A **Band 2** p.2493

**Melville, James C**
Table(s): Minnesota: Corporate/M&A **Band 2** p.1569

**Melvin, Daniel**
Profile: p.1222
Table(s): Illinois: Healthcare **Band 3** p.1165

**Melvin Jr, Charles E**
Profile: p.2043
Table(s): North Carolina: Real Estate: Zoning/Land Use **Band 1** p.2037

**Menchel, Matthew I**
Profile: p.1000
Table(s): Florida: Litigation: White-Collar Crime & Government Investigations **Band 2** p.967

**Mencio Jr, George**
Profile: p.1000
Table(s): Florida: Latin American Investment **Band 3** p.963

**Mendel, Linda**
Profile: p.2107
Table(s): Ohio: Employee Benefits & Executive Compensation **Band 1** p.2067

**Mendelsohn, David**
Profile: p.1222
Table(s): Illinois: Insurance: Transactional & Regulatory **Band 1** p.1168

**Mendelsohn, Mark F.**
Profile: p.367
Table(s): Nationwide: International Trade: FCPA Experts **Band 2** p.153

**Mendelsohn, Stuart**
Profile: p.2512
Table(s): Northern Virginia: Real Estate: Zoning/Land Use **Band 2** p.2505

**Mendelson, Alan C**
Profile: p.367
Table(s): Nationwide: Life Sciences: Corporate/Commercial **Star Individuals** p.182, California: Corporate/M&A: Venture Capital **Band 1** p.555, California: Life Sciences: Corporate/Commercial **Band 1** p.590

**Mendelson, Barbara R**
Profile: p.367
Table(s): Nationwide: Financial Services Regulation: Banking (Compliance) **Band 3** p.96

**Mendelson, Richard C**
Profile: p.654
Table(s): California: Real Estate **Band 3** p.611

**Mendelson, Richard P**
Table(s): Nationwide: Food & Beverages: Alcohol **Senior Statesmen**: p.109

**Mendelson, Robert C**
Profile: p.367
Table(s): Nationwide: Financial Services Regulation: Broker Dealer (Compliance) **Band 2** p.97

**Mendenhall, William**
Profile: p.1606
Table(s): Mississippi: Corporate/Commercial **Band 2** p.1591, Mississippi: Real Estate **Band 3** p.1600

**Mendez, John E**
Table(s): Nationwide: Banking & Finance **Band 2** p.31, California: Banking & Finance **Band 1** p.539

**Mendez, Mark**
Profile: p.367
Table(s): Nationwide: Capital Markets: Derivatives **Band 1** p.51

**Méndez-Peñate, Carlos**
Table(s): New York: Latin American Investment **Band 4** p.1829

**Mendiola III, Lino**
Profile: p.2405
Table(s): Texas: Energy: State Regulatory & Litigation (Electricity) **Band 1** p.2341

**Mendoza, Julie C**
Table(s): **Nationwide**: International Trade: Trade Remedies & Trade Policy **Band 3** p.154

**Mendoza, Mary S**
Table(s): **Texas**: Environment **Band 3** p.2343

**Meneghello, Richard**
Profile: p.2177
Table(s): **Oregon**: Labor & Employment **Band 2** p.2168

**Menendez, Kenneth G**
Profile: p.1090
Table(s): **Georgia**: Litigation: General Commercial **Band 4** p.1065

**Menéndez-Cambó, Patricia**
Profile: p.1001
Table(s): **Florida**: Latin American Investment **Band 1** p.963

**Menges, Kenneth**
Table(s): **Texas**: Corporate/M&A **Band 4** p.2337

**Menkowitz, Michael**
Profile: p.2225
Table(s): **Pennsylvania**: Bankruptcy/Restructuring **Band 2** p.2188

**Menna, Gilbert G**
Profile: p.367
Table(s): **Nationwide**: Capital Markets: REITs **Star individuals** p.55, **Massachusetts**: Corporate/M&A: Capital Markets **Band 1** p.1453

**Menotti, David E**
Profile: p.881
Table(s): **District of Columbia**: Environment **Band 2** p.804

**Mensch, Linda S.**
Table(s): **Illinois**: Media & Entertainment: Transactional **Band 1** p.1185

**Mensik, Michael S**
Profile: p.367
Table(s): **Nationwide**: Outsourcing **Band 1** p.195, **Illinois**: Technology & Outsourcing **Band 1** p.1194

**Menting, Mark J**
Profile: p.367
Table(s): **Nationwide**: Financial Services Regulation: Banking (Compliance) **Band 3** p.96, **Nationwide**: Financial Services Regulation: Financial Institutions M&A **Band 2** p.96

**Mentlik, William L**
Profile: p.1742
Table(s): **New Jersey**: Intellectual Property **Band 1** p.1716

**Menz, David F**
Table(s): **Arkansas**: Corporate/Commercial: Municipal Bonds **Band 1** p.518

**Menzie, Edward G**
Table(s): **South Carolina**: Corporate/M&A **Band 1** p.2260, **South Carolina**: Real Estate **Band 1** p.2266

**Mercante, Mark W**
Profile: p.1366
Table(s): **Louisiana**: Construction **Up-and-coming individuals** p.1339

**Mercer, John T W**
Table(s): **Georgia**: Energy **Band 1** p.1049

**Mercer, Joy**
Table(s): **New Jersey**: Employee Benefits & Executive Compensation **Band 1** p.1710

**Mercer, Robert M. D.**
Table(s): **Georgia**: Bankruptcy/Restructuring **Up-and-coming individuals** p.1042

**Merchant, Michael J**
Profile: p.773
Table(s): **Delaware**: Bankruptcy/Restructuring **Up-and-coming individuals** p.754

**Mercier Vargas, Rebecca**
Table(s): **Florida**: Litigation: Appellate **Band 3** p.972

**Meredith, Stephen O**
Profile: p.1502
Table(s): **Massachusetts**: Private Equity: Buyouts **Band 2** p.1474

**Merinar Jr, John R**
Profile: p.2564
Table(s): **West Virginia**: Labor & Employment **Band 3** p.2553

**Merkle, Alan**
Table(s): **Nationwide**: Projects: Renewables & Alternative Energy **Band 2** p.218

**Merkle, Craig**
Profile: p.1430
Table(s): **Maryland**: Healthcare: Medical Malpractice **Band 2** p.1415

**Mermelstein, Joshua**
Profile: p.367
Table(s): **Nationwide**: Real Estate **Band 1** p.225, **New York**: Real Estate **Band 1** p.1854

**Meron, Daniel**
Profile: p.881
Table(s): **District of Columbia**: Healthcare **Band 3** p.809

**Merriam, Dwight**
Profile: p.745
Table(s): **Connecticut**: Real Estate **Band 1** p.740

**Merrigan, John A**
Profile: p.367
Table(s): **Nationwide**: Government: Government Relations **Band 2** p.121

**Merrill, Erich**
Profile: p.2177
Table(s): **Oregon**: Corporate/M&A **Band 3** p.2164

**Merrill, Frank**
Table(s): **Ohio**: Natural Resources & Environment **Band 2** p.2083

**Merrill, Susan**
Profile: p.367
Table(s): **Nationwide**: Financial Services Regulation: Broker Dealer (Enforcement) **Band 1** p.98

**Merrills, Andrew W**
Profile: p.2043
Table(s): **North Carolina**: Labor & Employment: Immigration **Band 1** p.2031

**Merriman, Mark**
Profile: p.1919
Table(s): **New York**: Media & Entertainment: Theatre **Band 3** p.1850

**Merritt, Craig**
Table(s): **Virginia**: Litigation: General Commercial **Band 3** p.2502

**Merritt, Mark**
Table(s): **North Carolina**: Antitrust **Band 1** p.2020, **North Carolina**: Litigation: General Commercial **Band 1** p.2033

**Merritt, Sharon J**
Table(s): **Vermont**: Intellectual Property **Band 2** p.2484

**Merritt, William Lee**
Table(s): **Nebraska**: Corporate/Commercial **Band 3** p.1659

**Merritt Jr, H Kenneth**
Table(s): **Vermont**: Corporate/Commercial **Band 3** p.2483

**Merryman, Bryan A**
Profile: p.654
Table(s): **California**: Litigation: General Commercial **Band 5** p.593

**Mersol, Gregory V**
Profile: p.2107
Table(s): **Ohio**: Labor & Employment **Band 2** p.2074

**Merten, Howard**
Table(s): **Rhode Island**: Litigation: General Commercial **Band 3** p.2254

**Mertens, Anton F**
Table(s): **Georgia**: Immigration **Band 3** p.1055

**Merwin, Bruce**
Table(s): **Texas**: Construction **Band 3** p.2335

**Meserve, Richard**
Profile: p.367
Table(s): **Nationwide**: Energy: Nuclear (Regulatory & Litigation) **Band 4** p.77

**Mesires, George**
Profile: p.1222
Table(s): **Illinois**: Bankruptcy/Restructuring **Band 4** p.1148

**Messerly, Robert**
Profile: p.1222
Table(s): **Illinois**: Real Estate **Band 3** p.1187

**Messerschmidt, Michael G**
Profile: p.1402
Table(s): **Maine**: Labor & Employment **Band 2** p.1390

**Messersmith, Michael**
Profile: p.1222
Table(s): **Illinois**: Bankruptcy/Restructuring **Band 4** p.1148

**Metalitz, Steven**
Table(s): **District of Columbia**: Media & Entertainment **Band 3** p.832

**Meth, Richard**
Profile: p.1742
Table(s): **New Jersey**: Bankruptcy/Restructuring **Band 2** p.1705

**Metheny, Bryance**
Table(s): **Alabama**: Labor & Employment **Up-and-coming individuals** p.460

**Metropoulos, Demetrios G**
Table(s): **Illinois**: Communications **Band 2** p.1153

**Metz, Eric B**
Profile: p.1300
Table(s): **Kansas**: Labor & Employment **Band 1** p.1294

**Metz, Todd R**
Profile: p.2512
Table(s): **Virginia**: Construction **Band 3** p.2491

**Metzger Jr, A Richard**
Table(s): **District of Columbia**: Telecom, Broadcast & Satellite **Band 1** p.844

**Metzke, John**
Table(s): **Wyoming**: Corporate/M&A: Tax **Band 1** p.2596

**Meunier, Gerald E**
Table(s): **Louisiana**: Litigation: General Commercial **Band 1** p.1352

**Meusey, Joseph K**
Table(s): **Nebraska**: Litigation: General Commercial **Senior Statesmen:** p.1664

**Meyer, Bruce D**
Profile: p.654
Table(s): **California**: Corporate/M&A **Band 4** p.554

**Meyer, Bruce S**
Profile: p.368
Table(s): **Nationwide**: Sports Law **Band 3** p.241

**Meyer, Christopher**
Table(s): **Idaho**: Natural Resources & Environment **Band 1** p.1136

**Meyer, David L.**
Table(s): **District of Columbia**: Antitrust **Band 5** p.787

**Meyer, Dianne A**
Table(s): **Pennsylvania**: Banking & Finance **Band 3** p.2186

**Meyer, G Christopher**
Profile: p.2107
Table(s): **Ohio**: Bankruptcy/Restructuring **Band 1** p.2058

**Meyer, George J**
Profile: p.1001
Table(s): **Florida**: Construction **Band 1** p.944

**Meyer, Jill P**
Profile: p.2107
Table(s): **Ohio**: Litigation: General Commercial **Band 4** p.2078

**Meyer, John W**
Table(s): **Texas**: Immigration **Band 2** p.2349

**Meyer, Lindsay**
Profile: p.368
Table(s): **Nationwide**: International Trade: Customs **Band 3** p.155

**Meyer, Malcolm A**
Profile: p.1367
Table(s): **Louisiana**: Real Estate **Band 3** p.1355

**Meyer, Michael E**
Profile: p.654
Table(s): **California**: Real Estate **Band 1** p.611

**Meyer, Paul**
Profile: p.1919
Table(s): **Nationwide**: Insurance: Transactional & Regulatory **Band 3** p.139, **New York**: Insurance: Transactional & Regulatory **Band 2** p.1816

**Meyer, Paul E**
Table(s): Illinois: Real Estate **Band 3** p.1187

**Meyer, Richard**
Table(s): District of Columbia: Intellectual Property: Litigation **Band 4** p.821

**Meyer, Stuart P**
Profile: p.2488
Table(s): Vermont: Intellectual Property **Band 1** p.2484

**Meyer, Theodore D**
Table(s): Texas: Labor & Employment **Band 2** p.2359

**Meyer III, Charles G**
Table(s): Virginia: Labor & Employment **Band 3** p.2500

**Meyer Jr, Robert A**
Profile: p.2107
Table(s): Ohio: Real Estate: Zoning/Land Use **Band 2** p.2086

**Meyers, Arthur S**
Profile: p.1502
Table(s): Massachusetts: Employee Benefits & Executive Compensation **Band 1** p.1455

**Meyers, D Kent**
Profile: p.2152
Table(s): Oklahoma: Litigation: General Commercial **Senior Statesmen:** p.2141

**Meyers, Jim**
Profile: p.881
Table(s): District of Columbia: Litigation: Securities **Band 2** p.826

**Meyers, Melanie**
Profile: p.1919
Table(s): New York: Real Estate: Zoning/Land Use **Band 2** p.1855

**Meyers, Thomas**
Table(s): Massachusetts: Intellectual Property **Band 3** p.1463

**Meyers, Todd**
Table(s): Georgia: Bankruptcy/Restructuring **Band 1** p.1042

**Meyerson, Alfred M**
Profile: p.2405
Table(s): Texas: Real Estate **Band 3** p.2367

**Meyerson, Edward P**
Profile: p.471
Table(s): Alabama: Litigation: Construction **Band 1** p.462

**Meyerson, Lee**
Profile: p.368
Table(s): Nationwide: Financial Services Regulation: Banking (Compliance) **Band 2** p.96, Nationwide: Financial Services Regulation: Financial Institutions M&A **Band 1** p.96, New York: Corporate/M&A **Band 3** p.1793

**Mezzanotte, Joseph J**
Profile: p.1430
Table(s): Maryland: Real Estate **Band 4** p.1422

**Mezzullo, Louis A**
Profile: p.368
Table(s): Nationwide: Wealth Management: Western Region **Band 1** p.267

**Miano, Steven T**
Profile: p.2225
Table(s): Pennsylvania: Environment **Band 1** p.2194

**Micallef, Joseph**
Profile: p.881
Table(s): District of Columbia: Intellectual Property: Litigation **Up-and-coming individuals** p.821

**Micciche, Daniel J**
Table(s): Texas: Tax **Band 2** p.2371

**Michaels, Jane**
Profile: p.720
Table(s): Colorado: Intellectual Property **Band 2** p.704, Colorado: Litigation: General Commercial **Band 2** p.709

**Michaels, Joel**
Profile: p.368
Table(s): Nationwide: Healthcare: Regulatory & Litigation **Band 1** p.127, Nationwide: Healthcare: Transactional **Band 1** p.127, District of Columbia: Healthcare **Band 1** p.809

**Michalchuk, Daniel J**
Profile: p.368
Table(s): Nationwide: Projects **Up-and-coming individuals** p.216

**Michalopoulos, Pantelis**
Table(s): District of Columbia: Telecom, Broadcast & Satellite **Band 2** p.844

**Michaud, Elaine M**
Table(s): New Hampshire: Litigation: General Commercial **Band 3** p.1690

**Michel, Scott D**
Table(s): Nationwide: Tax: Fraud **Band 1** p.244, District of Columbia: Tax **Band 3** p.838

**Michetti, Michael E**
Table(s): Nationwide: Banking & Finance **Band 2** p.31

**Michon, Katherine J**
Profile: p.1502
Table(s): Massachusetts: Labor & Employment: Mainly Plaintiffs Representation **Band 1** p.1467

**Micoleau, Charles J.**
Table(s): Maine: Energy & Natural Resources **Band 3** p.1388

**Middlebrooks, David J**
Table(s): Alabama: Labor & Employment **Band 1** p.460

**Middleton, Jack B**
Profile: p.1696
Table(s): New Hampshire: Litigation: General Commercial **Senior Statesmen:** p.1690

**Midvidy, David H**
Profile: p.368
Table(s): Nationwide: Capital Markets: Securitisation **Band 4** p.59

**Mierzewski, Michael B**
Profile: p.368
Table(s): Nationwide: Financial Services Regulation: Banking (Enforcement & Investigations) **Band 3** p.97, Nationwide: Financial Services Regulation: Consumer Finance (Compliance) **Band 2** p.97, Nationwide: Financial Services Regulation: Consumer Finance (Litigation) **Band 2** p.97

**Migdal, Nelson F**
Profile: p.368
Table(s): Nationwide: Leisure & Hospitality **Band 2** p.179, District of Columbia: Real Estate **Band 3** p.835

**Mihlsten, George**
Table(s): California: Real Estate: Zoning/Land Use **Band 1** p.612

**Mikels, Richard**
Profile: p.1502
Table(s): Massachusetts: Bankruptcy/Restructuring **Star individuals** p.1449

**Milam, Kenneth E**
Profile: p.1606
Table(s): Mississippi: Labor & Employment **Band 2** p.1595

**Milcetic, Paul B**
Table(s): Pennsylvania: Intellectual Property **Band 4** p.2197

**Milch, Thomas**
Profile: p.882
Table(s): District of Columbia: Environment **Band 1** p.804

**Miles, Craig**
Profile: p.368
Table(s): Nationwide: International Arbitration **Band 5** p.145

**Miles, John C.**
Table(s): Nebraska: Corporate/Commercial **Band 3** p.1659

**Miles, John J**
Table(s): Nationwide: Healthcare: Regulatory & Litigation **Band 1** p.127, District of Columbia: Healthcare **Band 1** p.809

**Miles, Steven**
Profile: p.368
Table(s): Nationwide: Projects **Band 3** p.216, Nationwide: Projects: LNG **Band 1** p.216

**Miley, Claire F**
Profile: p.2307
Table(s): Tennessee: Healthcare: Regulatory **Band 1** p.2291

**Miley, Craig**
Table(s): Texas: Immigration **Band 2** p.2349

**Milgrom Jr, Brent M**
Table(s): North Carolina: Real Estate **Band 2** p.2037

**Milkes, Jay**
Table(s): New York: Tax **Band 4** p.1862

**Millard, Alden**
Profile: p.369
Table(s): Nationwide: Banking & Finance **Band 4** p.31

**Millard, David B**
Profile: p.1278
Table(s): Indiana: Corporate/M&A **Band 2** p.1268

**Millen, Pressly M**
Table(s): North Carolina: Litigation: General Commercial **Band 2** p.2033

**Miller, Alan S**
Table(s): Pennsylvania: Environment **Band 2** p.2194

**Miller, Alison W**
Table(s): Florida: Corporate/M&A & Private Equity **Band 4** p.947

**Miller, Allen**
Profile: p.1919
Table(s): New York: Latin American Investment **Band 3** p.1829

**Miller, Barbara S**
Table(s): Connecticut: Environment **Band 3** p.733

**Miller, Barry**
Profile: p.2107
Table(s): Ohio: Construction **Band 1** p.2062

**Miller, Brad P**
Table(s): Idaho: Labor & Employment **Band 2** p.1132

**Miller, Bradley**
Table(s): Oregon: Real Estate **Band 1** p.2173

**Miller, Brett**
Profile: p.369
Table(s): Nationwide: Bankruptcy/Restructuring **Band 3** p.39, New York: Bankruptcy/Restructuring **Band 3** p.1782

**Miller, Britt**
Table(s): Illinois: Antitrust **Band 4** p.1143

**Miller, Camille**
Profile: p.2225
Table(s): Pennsylvania: Intellectual Property **Band 3** p.2197

**Miller, Carole G**
Profile: p.471
Table(s): Alabama: Labor & Employment **Band 2** p.460

**Miller, Charles E**
Table(s): Maine: Real Estate **Band 1** p.1395

**Miller, Charles F**
Profile: p.1637
Table(s): Missouri: Real Estate **Band 1** p.1633

**Miller, Charles G**
Profile: p.369
Table(s): Nationwide: Franchising **Band 4** p.111

**Miller, Christopher S**
Profile: p.2225
Table(s): Pennsylvania: Corporate/M&A & Private Equity **Band 4** p.2191

**Miller, Clifford J**
Table(s): Hawaii: Real Estate **Band 1** p.1120

**Miller, Craig S**
Profile: p.2107
Table(s): Ohio: Real Estate: Zoning/Land Use **Band 2** p.2086

**Miller, David**
Profile: p.2512
Table(s): Northern Virginia: Real Estate **Band 1** p.2505

**Miller, David S**
Profile: p.1919
Table(s): New York: Tax **Band 2** p.1862

**Miller, Dennis**
Profile: p.1606
Table(s): Mississippi: Energy & Natural Resources **Band 3** p.1593

**Miller, E Powell**
Table(s): Michigan: Litigation: General
Commercial Band 1 p.1544

**Miller, Eric**
Table(s): Vermont: Litigation: General
Commercial Band 2 p.2486

**Miller, Evan**
Profile: p.369
Table(s): Nationwide: ERISA Litigation Band 2
p.92, District of Columbia: Employee Benefits &
Executive Compensation Band 2 p.801

**Miller, George**
Profile: p.1322
Table(s): Kentucky: Labor & Employment Band 3
p.1310

**Miller, Gregory P**
Profile: p.2225
Table(s): Pennsylvania: Litigation: General
Commercial Band 3 p.2203, Pennsylvania:
Litigation: White-Collar Crime & Government
Investigations Band 1 p.2203

**Miller, Harvey R**
Profile: p.369
Table(s): Nationwide: Bankruptcy/Restructuring
Star individuals p.39, New York:
Bankruptcy/Restructuring Star individuals p.1782

**Miller, James C**
Profile: p.1001
Table(s): Florida: Construction Band 3 p.944

**Miller, Jessica Davidson**
Profile: p.369
Table(s): Nationwide: Product Liability & Mass
Torts Band 4 p.208

**Miller, Kenneth W**
Table(s): Illinois: Corporate/M&A: Private Equity
Band 2 p.1157

**Miller, L Edward**
Table(s): Idaho: Real Estate Band 1 p.1138

**Miller, Lance R**
Table(s): Arkansas: Litigation: General
Commercial Band 4 p.522

**Miller, Laura Ariane**
Profile: p.882
Table(s): District of Columbia: Litigation: White-
Collar Crime & Government Investigations Senior
Statesmen: p.827

**Miller, Laura Beth**
Profile: p.1222
Table(s): Illinois: Intellectual Property Band 3
p.1171

**Miller, Lloyd**
Table(s): Nationwide: Native American Law Band
3 p.192

**Miller, Marie-Bernarde**
Table(s): Arkansas: Litigation: General
Commercial Band 3 p.522

**Miller, Michael**
Profile: p.1579
Table(s): Minnesota: Labor & Employment Band 2
p.1571

**Miller, Michael**
Table(s): New York: Litigation: General
Commercial Band 3 p.1833

**Miller, Michael J**
Table(s): New York: Tax Band 4 p.1862

**Miller, Michelle**
Profile: p.1502
Table(s): Massachusetts: Antitrust Band 1 p.1444

**Miller, Morris H**
Profile: p.1001
Table(s): Florida: Healthcare Band 2 p.954

**Miller, Nicholas**
Table(s): Idaho: Corporate/Commercial Band 1
p.1132

**Miller, O'Malley**
Profile: p.654
Table(s): California: Real Estate Band 2 p.611

**Miller, Peter A**
Profile: p.1919
Table(s): New York: Real Estate Band 3 p.1854

**Miller, Rick**
Table(s): Georgia: Corporate/M&A Band 4 p.1046

**Miller, Robert**
Table(s): California: Corporate/M&A Band 4 p.554

**Miller, Robert N**
Table(s): Colorado: Litigation: General
Commercial Band 4 p.709

**Miller, Rod**
Profile: p.369
Table(s): Nationwide: Capital Markets: Debt &
Equity Band 2 p.46

**Miller, Roger**
Table(s): Nebraska: Labor & Employment Senior
Statesmen: p.1662

**Miller, Samuel R**
Profile: p.655
Table(s): California: Antitrust Band 4 p.536

**Miller, Stephen**
Profile: p.2405
Table(s): Texas: Construction Band 3 p.2335

**Miller, Stephen M**
Table(s): Delaware: Bankruptcy/Restructuring
Band 3 p.754

**Miller, Steven M.**
Profile: p.2225
Table(s): Pennsylvania: Banking & Finance Band
2 p.2186

**Miller, Steven S**
Table(s): Washington: Immigration Band 1 p.2528

**Miller, T Kurt**
Table(s): Alabama: Banking & Finance: Mainly
Regulatory Band 2 p.455

**Miller, T Matthew**
Table(s): Alabama: Labor & Employment Band 3
p.460

**Miller, Timothy**
Table(s): West Virginia: Litigation: General
Commercial Band 2 p.2555

**Miller, Travis L**
Table(s): Florida: Insurance Band 3 p.957

**Miller, W Timothy**
Profile: p.2107
Table(s): Ohio: Bankruptcy/Restructuring Band 4
p.2058

**Miller, William**
Profile: p.369
Table(s): Nationwide: Banking & Finance Band 4
p.31

**Miller, Winston**
Profile: p.1322
Table(s): Kentucky: Litigation: General
Commercial Band 2 p.1312, Kentucky: Litigation:
Tort & Insurance Defense Band 1 p.1312

**Miller, Zach C**
Profile: p.720
Table(s): Colorado: Natural Resources &
Environment Band 1 p.712

**Miller Jr, Ben R**
Profile: p.1367
Table(s): Louisiana: Corporate/M&A Band 4
p.1341

**Miller Jr, Max M**
Profile: p.2177
Table(s): Oregon: Environment Band 2 p.2165

**Millet, Craig H**
Profile: p.655
Table(s): California: Bankruptcy/Restructuring
Band 3 p.542

**Millett, Patricia A**
Profile: p.369
Table(s): Nationwide: Appellate Law Band 2 p.26

**Millikan, Jess**
Table(s): California: Insurance: Insurer Band 3
p.574

**Milliken, John**
Profile: p.2512
Table(s): Northern Virginia: Real Estate:
Zoning/Land Use Band 1 p.2505

**Millikin, Margaret**
Profile: p.2152
Table(s): Oklahoma: Intellectual Property Band 2
p.2138

**Millisor, Richard A**
Profile: p.2107
Table(s): Ohio: Labor & Employment Band 3
p.2074

**Millner, Robert B**
Profile: p.1222
Table(s): Illinois: Bankruptcy/Restructuring Band
3 p.1148

**Millock, Peter J**
Profile: p.1919
Table(s): Nationwide: Healthcare: Regulatory &
Litigation Band 2 p.127, New York: Healthcare
Band 1 p.1811

**Mills, Craig**
Profile: p.1502
Table(s): Massachusetts: Banking & Finance
Band 3 p.1445

**Mills, Elizabeth M**
Table(s): Illinois: Healthcare Band 2 p.1165

**Mills, Gail L**
Table(s): Alabama: Banking & Finance Band 3
p.455, Alabama: Real Estate Band 2 p.466

**Mills, John S**
Table(s): Florida: Litigation: Appellate Band 2
p.972

**Mills, John W**
Profile: p.1090
Table(s): Georgia: Bankruptcy/Restructuring
Band 3 p.1042

**Mills, Lori**
Profile: p.1742
Table(s): New Jersey: Environment Band 3 p.1711

**Mills, Michael**
Table(s): Alaska: Corporate/M&A Band 2 p.487,
Alaska: Corporate/M&A: Bankruptcy Band 1
p.487

**Mills, Phillip R**
Profile: p.1919
Table(s): New York: Corporate/M&A Band 3
p.1793

**Mills Jr, Osborne**
Profile: p.2107
Table(s): Ohio: Banking & Finance Band 1 p.2056

**Millsap, Charles E.**
Table(s): Kansas: Litigation: General
Commercial Band 2 p.1295

**Millspaugh, Thomas E D**
Profile: p.882
Table(s): District of Columbia: Real Estate Band
4 p.835

**Millstein, Julian S**
Table(s): Nationwide: Outsourcing Senior
Statesmen: p.195, New York: Technology &
Outsourcing Senior Statesmen: p.1868

**Millstone, David J**
Profile: p.2107
Table(s): Ohio: Labor & Employment Band 3
p.2074

**Milmed, Paul K**
Profile: p.1920
Table(s): New York: Environment: Mainly
Transactional Band 3 p.1808

**Milmoe, J Gregory**
Profile: p.369
Table(s): Nationwide: Bankruptcy/Restructuring
Senior Statesmen: p.39, New York:
Bankruptcy/Restructuring Senior Statesmen:
p.1782

**Milne, Karen**
Profile: p.882
Table(s): District of Columbia: Telecom,
Broadcast & Satellite Associates to watch p.844

**Milne, Robert A**
Profile: p.1920
Table(s): New York: Antitrust Band 5 p.1778

**Milner, Ann L**
Table(s): Nationwide: Investment Funds: Private
Equity: Fund Formation Band 3 p.166,
Massachusetts: Private Equity: Fund Formation
Band 1 p.1476

**Milner, John**
Table(s): Mississippi: Environment Band 1 p.1594

**Milom, W Michael**
Table(s): Tennessee: Media & Entertainment
Star individuals p.2297

**Milone, Richard D.**
Table(s): District of Columbia: Insurance:
Policyholder Band 2 p.818

**Milton, Christopher H**
Profile: p.1502
Table(s): Massachusetts: Real Estate **Band 3**
p.1478

**Mimms, Malcolm**
Table(s): Tennessee: Media & Entertainment
**Band 2** p.2297

**Mims, Peter E**
Profile: p.2405
Table(s): Texas: Intellectual Property **Band 3**
p.2354

**Mince, Loretta G**
Profile: p.1367
Table(s): Louisiana: Litigation: General
Commercial **Band 2** p.1352

**Mincer, Richard**
Table(s): Wyoming: Litigation: General
Commercial **Band 1** p.2598

**Minch, Roger J**
Table(s): North Dakota:
Bankruptcy/Restructuring **Band 1** p.2050

**Minchella, Michael F**
Table(s): California: Construction **Band 2** p.550

**Mindlin, Philip**
Profile: p.1920
Table(s): New York: Bankruptcy/Restructuring
**Band 3** p.1782

**Miner, Curtis B**
Table(s): Florida: Litigation: General Commercial
**Band 3** p.966

**Miner, Martin P**
Profile: p.1920
Table(s): New York: Real Estate **Band 4** p.1854

**Miner, Tracy A**
Profile: p.1502
Table(s): Massachusetts: Litigation: White-Collar
Crime & Government Investigations **Band 2**
p.1471

**Minesinger, Kenneth M**
Profile: p.369
Table(s): Nationwide: Energy: Oil & Gas
(Regulatory & Litigation) **Band 2** p.78

**Minias, Joseph G.**
Profile: p.1920
Table(s): New York: Bankruptcy/Restructuring
Up-and-coming individuals p.1782

**Minion, Robert G**
Profile: p.1742
Table(s): New Jersey: Corporate/M&A **Band 3**
p.1707

**Minisman Jr, B G**
Profile: p.471
Table(s): Alabama: Corporate/Commercial **Band
2** p.459

**Minkin, David J**
Table(s): Hawaii: Litigation: General Commercial
**Band 3** p.1119

**Minkoff, Jared M**
Table(s): Missouri: Real Estate Up-and-coming individuals p.1633

**Minkus, Daniel H**
Table(s): Michigan: Corporate/M&A **Band 1**
p.1538

**Minnick, M David**
Profile: p.655
Table(s): California: Bankruptcy/Restructuring
**Band 3** p.542

**Minogue, Thomas J**
Table(s): Missouri: Corporate/M&A **Band 2** p.1619

**Minor, J Douglas**
Table(s): Mississippi: Litigation: General
Commercial **Band 3** p.1597

**Minor, William**
Profile: p.369
Table(s): Nationwide: Government: Political Law
**Band 2** p.124

**Minsk, Alan**
Profile: p.370
Table(s): Nationwide: Life Sciences:
Regulatory/Compliance **Band 3** p.183

**Minsker, Helen Hill**
Profile: p.1222
Table(s): Illinois: Intellectual Property **Band 4**
p.1171

**Minton, Michael B.**
Table(s): Missouri: Litigation: General
Commercial **Band 3** p.1629

**Minton, Michael D**
Table(s): Florida: Tax **Band 2** p.979

**Mintz, Douglas S**
Profile: p.882
Table(s): District of Columbia:
Bankruptcy/Restructuring Up-and-coming individuals
p.792

**Mintz, Jeffrey M**
Profile: p.1090
Table(s): Georgia: Labor & Employment **Band 4**
p.1060

**Mintz, Josef**
Profile: p.2225
Table(s): Pennsylvania:
Bankruptcy/Restructuring Associates to watch
p.2188

**Mintz, Robert A**
Profile: p.1742
Table(s): New Jersey: Litigation: White-Collar
Crime & Government Investigations **Band 2**
p.1723

**Minuskin, Heidi S**
Table(s): New Jersey: Environment **Band 3** p.1711

**Minuti, Mark**
Table(s): Delaware: Bankruptcy/Restructuring
**Band 1** p.754

**Miraldi, Leslee W**
Profile: p.2107
Table(s): Ohio: Banking & Finance **Band 1** p.2056

**Mirchandani, Dolly**
Table(s): Nationwide: Projects: PPP **Band 2** p.217

**Mirvis, Theodore N**
Profile: p.370
Table(s): Nationwide: Securities: Litigation **Band
1** p.232, New York: Litigation: Securities **Band 1**
p.1834

**Miscimarra, Philip A**
Profile: p.1222
Table(s): Illinois: Labor & Employment **Band 1**
p.1175

**Mishkin, Jeffrey A**
Profile: p.370
Table(s): Nationwide: Sports Law **Band 1** p.241

**Mishkind, Charles S**
Profile: p.1553
Table(s): Michigan: Labor & Employment Senior
Statesmen: p.1542

**Misken, Ken**
Profile: p.1430
Table(s): Maryland: Litigation: Bankruptcy Up-and-
coming individuals p.1419

**Misko, Charles**
Table(s): Missouri: Real Estate **Band 2** p.1633

**Mitchell, Barry D**
Table(s): Arizona: Litigation: White-Collar Crime
& Government Investigations **Band 1** p.501

**Mitchell, Beth H**
Profile: p.1502
Table(s): Massachusetts: Real Estate **Band 2**
p.1478

**Mitchell, Chris**
Profile: p.471
Table(s): Alabama: Labor & Employment Senior
Statesmen: p.460

**Mitchell, Cleta D**
Table(s): Nationwide: Government: Political Law
**Band 3** p.124

**Mitchell, David S**
Profile: p.370
Table(s): Nationwide: Capital Markets:
Derivatives **Band 2** p.51

**Mitchell, Marvin**
Table(s): Indiana: Real Estate Senior Statesmen:
p.1275

**Mitchell, Michael H**
Profile: p.370
Table(s): Nationwide: Capital Markets:
Securitisation **Band 2** p.59

**Mitchell, Michael S**
Profile: p.1367
Table(s): Louisiana: Labor & Employment **Band 3**
p.1350

**Mitchell, Nancy A**
Profile: p.1920
Table(s): New York: Bankruptcy/Restructuring
**Band 4** p.1782

**Mitchell, Patrick**
Table(s): Massachusetts: Private Equity: Venture
Capital Investment **Band 3** p.1474

**Mitchell, Stephen C**
Profile: p.2271
Table(s): South Carolina: Labor & Employment
**Band 3** p.2262

**Mitchell, Stephen G**
Table(s): Missouri: Real Estate **Band 3** p.1633

**Mitchell, Stephen J**
Profile: p.1001
Table(s): Florida: Real Estate **Band 2** p.974

**Mitchell, Thomas L**
Table(s): North Carolina: Banking & Finance
**Band 3** p.2021

**Mitchell, W Scott**
Profile: p.1655
Table(s): Montana: Natural Resources &
Environment **Band 2** p.1651

**Mitchelson Jr, William (Mitch) R**
Profile: p.1090
Table(s): Georgia: Healthcare **Band 2** p.1052,
Georgia: Litigation: White-Collar Crime &
Government Investigations **Band 2** p.1066

**Mitich, Rebecca H.**
Profile: p.2584
Table(s): Wisconsin: Real Estate Associates to
watch p.2579

**Mitnick, Joel**
Profile: p.1920
Table(s): New York: Antitrust **Band 5** p.1778

**Mitrione, Michael V**
Table(s): Florida: Banking & Finance:
Transactional **Band 3** p.937, Florida:
Corporate/M&A & Private Equity **Band 2** p.947

**Mittelstaedt, Robert A**
Profile: p.655
Table(s): California: Antitrust **Band 2** p.536,
California: Litigation: General Commercial **Band 3**
p.593

**Mitz, Daniel R.**
Profile: p.655
Table(s): California: Corporate/M&A **Band 4** p.553

**Mixson, Dwight**
Table(s): Alabama: Banking & Finance **Band 2**
p.455, Alabama: Real Estate **Band 2** p.466

**Mixson, H Lamar**
Table(s): Georgia: Litigation: General
Commercial **Band 2** p.1065

**Mixter, Christian J**
Profile: p.370
Table(s): Nationwide: Securities: Regulation:
Enforcement **Band 4** p.233

**Mixter, Stephen**
Profile: p.2108
Table(s): Ohio: Real Estate **Band 4** p.2086

**Miziolek, Aleksandra A**
Table(s): Michigan: Corporate/M&A **Band 2**
p.1538

**Mo, Curtis L**
Profile: p.655
Table(s): California: Corporate/M&A: Venture
Capital **Band 4** p.555

**Moates, G Paul**
Profile: p.370
Table(s): Nationwide: Transportation: Rail (for
Railroads) **Band 1** p.257

**Moberly, Michael D**
Table(s): Arizona: Labor & Employment **Band 2**
p.499

**Moche, Richard**
Profile: p.1502
Table(s): Massachusetts: Banking & Finance:
Public Finance **Band 2** p.1446

**Mock, Randall D**
Table(s): Oklahoma: Corporate/Commercial: Tax **Band 1** p.2134

**Mockbee, David**
Table(s): Mississippi: Litigation: Construction **Band 1** p.1596

**Modell, Charles S**
Table(s): Nationwide: Franchising **Band 2** p.111

**Modlin, James**
Profile: p.1920
Table(s): New York: Corporate/M&A **Band 5** p.1793

**Moe, Michelle**
Table(s): Kansas: Labor & Employment **Associates to watch** p.1294

**Moeckel, Jennifer Shea**
Table(s): New Hampshire: Labor & Employment **Band 2** p.1688

**Moeling, Walter G**
Table(s): Georgia: Banking & Finance: Mainly Regulatory **Star individuals** p.1039

**Moellenberg, Dalva**
Table(s): New Mexico: Environment, Natural Resources & Regulated Industries **Band 2** p.1766

**Moeller, Elizabeth V**
Profile: p.370
Table(s): Nationwide: Government: Government Relations **Band 3** p.121

**Moeller Jr, Armin J**
Table(s): Mississippi: Labor & Employment **Star individuals** p.1595

**Moerdler, Jeffrey**
Profile: p.1920
Table(s): New York: Real Estate **Band 4** p.1854

**Moffatt, J Curtis**
Profile: p.370
Table(s): Nationwide: Energy: Oil & Gas (Regulatory & Litigation) **Band 2** p.78

**Moffet, Brian**
Table(s): Maryland: Litigation: General Commercial **Up-and-coming individuals** p.1419

**Moffitt, Ronald G**
Table(s): Utah: Corporate/M&A **Band 2** p.2462

**Moglin, Neal**
Table(s): Illinois: Insurance: Dispute Resolution: Reinsurance **Band 2** p.1168

**Mohan, Daniel J**
Table(s): Georgia: Healthcare **Band 3** p.1052

**Mohr, Peter**
Profile: p.2177
Table(s): Oregon: Environment **Band 3** p.2165

**Moir, Katharine P.**
Profile: p.655
Table(s): California: Tax **Up-and-coming individuals** p.617

**Molen, Chris D**
Table(s): Georgia: Banking & Finance **Band 1** p.1039

**Molen, John K**
Table(s): Alabama: Corporate/Commercial **Band 2** p.459

**Molinaro, Michael L**
Table(s): Illinois: Bankruptcy/Restructuring **Band 4** p.1148

**Moll, Brian K.**
Table(s): Arizona: Corporate/M&A **Band 4** p.495

**Moll, Charles J**
Profile: p.655
Table(s): California: Tax: State & Local **Band 1** p.617

**Mollaaghababa, Reza**
Profile: p.1502
Table(s): Massachusetts: Intellectual Property **Up-and-coming individuals** p.1463

**Mollen, Neal D**
Table(s): District of Columbia: Labor & Employment **Band 2** p.824

**Mollerup, Richard W**
Table(s): Idaho: Real Estate **Band 2** p.1138

**Mollerus, Michael**
Profile: p.1920
Table(s): New York: Tax **Band 3** p.1862

**Molloy, Brian J**
Table(s): New Jersey: Litigation: General Commercial **Band 3** p.1722

**Moloney, Thomas J**
Profile: p.1920
Table(s): New York: Litigation: General Commercial **Band 3** p.1833

**Moltenbrey, MJ**
Table(s): District of Columbia: Antitrust **Band 4** p.787

**Monaco, Daniel A**
Profile: p.2225
Table(s): Pennsylvania: Intellectual Property **Band 4** p.2197

**Monaco, Francis**
Table(s): New York: Insurance: Dispute Resolution: Insurer **Up-and-coming individuals** p.1816

**Monaco, Stephanie**
Table(s): Nationwide: Investment Funds: Registered Funds **Band 3** p.170

**Monaco Jr, Frank A**
Table(s): Delaware: Bankruptcy/Restructuring **Band 3** p.754

**Monaghan, John J**
Profile: p.1502
Table(s): Massachusetts: Bankruptcy/Restructuring **Band 1** p.1449

**Monaghan, Maura**
Table(s): New York: Litigation: General Commercial **Band 4** p.1833

**Monaghan, Sean**
Profile: p.1743
Table(s): New Jersey: Environment **Band 2** p.1711

**Monahan Jr, John**
Table(s): Vermont: Litigation: General Commercial **Band 2** p.2486

**Monahan Jr, Thomas V**
Profile: p.1430
Table(s): Maryland: Healthcare: Medical Malpractice **Band 2** p.1415

**Monhait, Norman**
Table(s): Delaware: Chancery: Mainly Plaintiff **Band 2** p.759

**Monico, Michael D**
Table(s): Illinois: Litigation: White-Collar Crime & Government Investigations **Band 1** p.1181

**Monk, Stephen**
Table(s): Alabama: Real Estate **Band 1** p.466

**Monk, William**
Table(s): Louisiana: Environment: Litigation **Band 3** p.1346

**Monk II, Charles O**
Table(s): Maryland: Litigation: Bankruptcy **Band 2** p.1419, Maryland: Litigation: General Commercial **Band 3** p.1419

**Monnat, Dan**
Profile: p.1300
Table(s): Kansas: Litigation: White-Collar Crime & Government Investigations **Band 1** p.1295

**Monnheimer, Donald B**
Profile: p.1774
Table(s): New Mexico: Corporate/Commercial **Band 2** p.1764

**Monnin, Paul N**
Profile: p.1090
Table(s): Georgia: Litigation: White-Collar Crime & Government Investigations **Band 3** p.1066

**Monohan, David**
Table(s): Kentucky: Litigation: General Commercial **Band 2** p.1312

**Monroe, C Robert**
Table(s): Missouri: Corporate/M&A **Band 2** p.1618

**Monroe Jr, John L**
Profile: p.1090
Table(s): Georgia: Labor & Employment **Band 4** p.1060

**Monroy, Gladys H**
Profile: p.655
Table(s): California: Life Sciences: IP/Patent Litigation **Band 1** p.590

**Montag, Brian S**
Profile: p.1743
Table(s): New Jersey: Environment **Band 2** p.1711

**Montague Jr, H Laddie**
Table(s): Pennsylvania: Antitrust **Band 1** p.2184

**Monteleone, Marc A**
Profile: p.2564
Table(s): West Virginia: Corporate/Commercial: Tax **Band 2** p.2550

**Montgomery, Cromwell**
Profile: p.655
Table(s): California: Banking & Finance **Band 2** p.539

**Montgomery, David**
Table(s): New York: Construction **Senior Statesmen:** p.1791

**Montgomery, James L**
Profile: p.2405
Table(s): Texas: Technology: Corporate & Commercial **Band 3** p.2375

**Montgomery, John T**
Table(s): Massachusetts: Litigation: General Commercial **Senior Statesmen:** p.1470

**Montgomery, Judson**
Table(s): Idaho: Corporate/Commercial **Band 3** p.1132

**Montgomery, Malcolm K**
Table(s): New York: Real Estate: Finance **Band 2** p.1855

**Montgomery, Margaret**
Table(s): Vermont: Corporate/Commercial **Band 3** p.2483

**Montgomery, Sandra Lee**
Profile: p.655
Table(s): California: Banking & Finance **Band 4** p.539

**Montgomery III, John H**
Table(s): Maine: Litigation: General Commercial **Band 3** p.1393

**Montiel Davis, Magda**
Table(s): Florida: Immigration **Band 2** p.956

**Montjoy II, R Wilson**
Profile: p.1606
Table(s): Mississippi: Energy & Natural Resources **Band 1** p.1593

**Moody, Christopher M**
Table(s): New Mexico: Labor & Employment **Band 2** p.1767

**Moody, Thomas H**
Table(s): Vermont: Corporate/Commercial **Band 1** p.2483

**Moon, Richard G**
Profile: p.1402
Table(s): Maine: Labor & Employment **Band 1** p.1390

**Mooney, Jenna L**
Table(s): Oregon: Labor & Employment **Band 3** p.2168

**Mooney, Marilyn**
Profile: p.882
Table(s): District of Columbia: Corporate/M&A Private Equity **Band 3** p.797

**Mooney, Michael E**
Profile: p.1503
Table(s): Massachusetts: Tax **Band 3** p.1481

**Mooney Carroll, Katherine**
Profile: p.370
Table(s): Nationwide: Financial Services Regulation: Banking (Compliance) **Up-and-coming individuals** p.96

**Mooradian, George T**
Profile: p.655
Table(s): California: Tax: Estate Planning **Band 1** p.617

**Moore, Amy N**
Profile: p.882
Table(s): District of Columbia: Employee Benefits & Executive Compensation **Band 2** p.801

**Moore, Andrew**
Table(s): Washington: Corporate/Commercial **Band 3** p.2525

**Moore, Bryan**
Profile: p.2406
Table(s): Texas: Environment **Band 4** p.2343

**Moore, Charles A**
Profile: p.370
Table(s): Nationwide: Energy: Oil & Gas
(Regulatory & Litigation) **Band 1** p.78

**Moore, Christopher**
Profile: p.1367
Table(s): Louisiana: Labor & Employment **Band 2**
p.1350

**Moore, Christopher J**
Table(s): Nationwide: Projects: Renewables &
Alternative Energy **Band 2** p.218

**Moore, Dan**
Table(s): Iowa: Real Estate **Band 1** p.1290

**Moore, David E**
Profile: p.773
Table(s): Delaware: Intellectual Property **Band 4**
p.763

**Moore, David M**
Table(s): Georgia: Environment **Band 2** p.1051

**Moore, Deirdre E**
Profile: p.1743
Table(s): New Jersey: Real Estate **Band 2** p.1728

**Moore, Duncan Joseph**
Table(s): California: Real Estate: Zoning/Land
Use **Associates to watch** p.612

**Moore, Ernest C.**
Table(s): Hawaii: Labor & Employment **Band 2**
p.1117

**Moore, Gary H**
Table(s): California: IT & Outsourcing **Senior
Statesmen:** p.583

**Moore, George**
Table(s): New Hampshire: Litigation: General
Commercial **Band 3** p.1690

**Moore, Harold F**
Profile: p.371
Table(s): Nationwide: Projects **Band 1** p.216

**Moore, James E**
Table(s): South Dakota: Litigation: General
Commercial **Band 1** p.2284

**Moore, Jean C.**
Table(s): New Mexico: Real Estate **Up-and-coming
individuals** p.1772

**Moore, John S**
Profile: p.2564
Table(s): West Virginia: Corporate/Commercial:
Healthcare **Band 2** p.2550

**Moore, John T**
Profile: p.2271
Table(s): South Carolina: Corporate/M&A:
Banking & Finance **Band 1** p.2260

**Moore, Justin**
Profile: p.2512
Table(s): Southern Virginia: Corporate/M&A **Band
1** p.2494

**Moore, Kevin J**
Profile: p.1743
Table(s): New Jersey: Real Estate: Zoning/Land
Use **Band 2** p.1728

**Moore, Larry**
Table(s): Utah: Real Estate **Band 2** p.2470

**Moore, Lynnwood**
Table(s): Oklahoma: Corporate/Commercial **Band
1** p.2134

**Moore, Malcolm A**
Table(s): Nationwide: Wealth Management:
Western Region **Band 1** p.267

**Moore, Margaret**
Profile: p.371
Table(s): Nationwide: Energy: Electricity
(Regulatory & Litigation) **Band 2** p.76

**Moore, Marie**
Table(s): Louisiana: Real Estate **Band 3** p.1355

**Moore, Mary Margaret**
Table(s): Illinois: Labor & Employment **Band 3**
p.1175

**Moore, Matthew**
Profile: p.882
Table(s): District of Columbia: Intellectual
Property: Litigation **Up-and-coming individuals** p.821

**Moore, Michael**
Profile: p.528
Table(s): Arkansas: Labor & Employment **Band 2**
p.520

**Moore, Mikel L**
Table(s): Montana: Litigation: General
Commercial **Band 1** p.1649

**Moore, Pamela**
Profile: p.745
Table(s): Connecticut: Labor & Employment **Band
2** p.736

**Moore, Paul D**
Table(s): Massachusetts:
Bankruptcy/Restructuring **Band 1** p.1449

**Moore, Read M**
Profile: p.371
Table(s): Nationwide: Wealth Management:
Central Region **Band 3** p.266

**Moore, Richard**
Table(s): Washington: Real Estate **Band 3** p.2535

**Moore, Robert**
Profile: p.655
Table(s): California: Bankruptcy/Restructuring
**Band 2** p.542

**Moore, Robert M**
Table(s): Virginia: Construction **Band 1** p.2491

**Moore, Rodney L**
Profile: p.371
Table(s): Nationwide: Energy: Oil & Gas
(Transactional) **Band 4** p.79

**Moore, Schuyler M**
Table(s): California: Media & Entertainment:
Transactional **Band 2** p.608

**Moore, Scott S**
Table(s): Nebraska: Labor & Employment **Band 2**
p.1662

**Moore, Steven W**
Profile: p.720
Table(s): Colorado: Labor & Employment **Band 3**
p.706

**Moore, Thomas J**
Profile: p.371
Table(s): Nationwide: Energy: Oil & Gas
(Transactional) **Band 2** p.79

**Moore III, Randolph A**
Profile: p.1090
Table(s): Georgia: Corporate/M&A **Band 4** p.1046

**Moore III, Thomas O**
Profile: p.371
Table(s): Nationwide: Projects **Band 3** p.216,
Nationwide: Projects: PPP **Band 3** p.216

**Moorefield Jr, Harold**
Table(s): Florida: Bankruptcy/Restructuring **Band
2** p.939

**Moorehead, Paul**
Profile: p.371
Table(s): Nationwide: Native American Law **Band
1** p.192

**Moorman, Robert**
Table(s): Oregon: Corporate/M&A **Band 1** p.2164

**Moorse, Charles P**
Table(s): Minnesota: Corporate/M&A **Band 2**
p.1569

**Moos, Rebecca E**
Table(s): Minnesota: Litigation: General
Commercial **Band 3** p.1574

**Moot, John S**
Profile: p.371
Table(s): Nationwide: Energy: Electricity
(Regulatory & Litigation) **Band 1** p.76

**Mora, Mindy A**
Profile: p.1001
Table(s): Florida: Bankruptcy/Restructuring **Band
1** p.939

**Morales, Gerard**
Table(s): Arizona: Labor & Employment **Band 4**
p.499

**Moran, Anne**
Table(s): District of Columbia: Employee
Benefits & Executive Compensation **Band 2** p.801

**Moran, Charles R**
Profile: p.1430
Table(s): Nationwide: Capital Markets: REITs
**Band 3** p.55, Maryland: Corporate/M&A **Band 2**
p.1412

**Moran, Jeffrey G**
Table(s): Illinois: Banking & Finance **Band 4**
p.1145

**Moran, Kevin**
Profile: p.2584
Table(s): Wisconsin: Intellectual Property **Band 3**
p.2573

**Moran, Mark**
Table(s): Nationwide: International Trade: Trade
Remedies & Trade Policy **Band 1** p.154

**Moran, Michael W.**
Profile: p.2406
Table(s): Texas: Construction **Up-and-coming individuals** p.2335

**Moran, Patricia**
Profile: p.1920
Table(s): New York: Corporate/M&A **Band 5**
p.1793

**Moran, Patrick G**
Profile: p.1222
Table(s): Illinois: Real Estate **Band 1** p.1187

**Morell, Avram E**
Table(s): Nationwide: Immigration **Band 3** p.131,
New York: Immigration **Band 2** p.1814

**Morency, Paula J**
Table(s): Nationwide: Franchising **Band 2** p.111

**Moreno, Jeffrey O**
Profile: p.371
Table(s): Nationwide: Transportation: Rail (for
Shippers) **Band 1** p.258

**Morey, Richard J.**
Profile: p.371
Table(s): Nationwide: Franchising **Up-and-coming
individuals** p.111

**Morford, J Mark**
Table(s): Oregon: Environment **Band 1** p.2165

**Morgan, Charles H**
Profile: p.1091
Table(s): Georgia: Labor & Employment **Band 4**
p.1060

**Morgan, Christine M**
Profile: p.1091
Table(s): Georgia: Environment **Band 2** p.1051

**Morgan, Donna**
Table(s): Nationwide: Wealth Management:
Central Region **Band 3** p.266

**Morgan, Jennifer M**
Profile: p.1920
Table(s): New York: Real Estate: Corporate **Up-and-coming individuals** p.1854

**Morgan, Kevan**
Table(s): Washington: Intellectual Property **Band
3** p.2529

**Morgan, Linda**
Table(s): Nationwide: Transportation: Rail (for
Railroads) **Band 1** p.257

**Morgan, Michael**
Profile: p.2540
Table(s): Washington: Corporate/Commercial
**Band 1** p.2525

**Morgan, Pauline**
Table(s): Delaware: Bankruptcy/Restructuring
**Band 1** p.754

**Morgan, Sue**
Table(s): Washington: Labor & Employment:
Employee Benefits & Compensation **Band 2**
p.2531

**Morgan, Vincent E**
Profile: p.2406
Table(s): Texas: Insurance **Band 1** p.2351

**Morgan II, Kirk D**
Profile: p.371
Table(s): Nationwide: Energy: Oil & Gas
(Regulatory & Litigation) **Band 5** p.78

**Morgan III, Mack J**
Table(s): Oklahoma: Litigation: General
Commercial **Band 2** p.2141

**Morgenbesser, Henry**
Table(s): New York: Employee Benefits &
Executive Compensation **Band 3** p.1802

**Morgenstern, Saul P**
Profile: p.1921
Table(s): New York: Antitrust **Band 3** p.1778

**Moriarty, Kevin P**
Table(s): **Vermont:** Corporate/Commercial:
Captive Insurance **Band 3** p.2483

**Morphy, James C**
Profile: p.1921
Table(s): **New York:** Corporate/M&A **Band 1**
p.1793

**Morreale, Matthew**
Profile: p.1921
Table(s): **New York:** Environment: Mainly
Transactional **Band 2** p.1808

**Morriello, Henry G**
Profile: p.371
Table(s): **Nationwide:** Capital Markets:
Securitisation **Band 2** p.59

**Morrier, John**
Table(s): **Massachusetts:**
Bankruptcy/Restructuring **Band 2** p.1449

**Morris, Bruce H**
Table(s): **Georgia:** Litigation: White-Collar Crime
& Government Investigations **Band 2** p.1066

**Morris, E Lee**
Table(s): **Texas:** Bankruptcy/Restructuring **Band 4**
p.2328

**Morris, Emily**
Profile: p.1322
Table(s): **Kentucky:** Labor & Employment
**Associates to watch** p.1310

**Morris, Jason**
Table(s): **Arizona:** Real Estate: Zoning/Land Use
**Band 4** p.504

**Morris, Jeffrey D.**
Table(s): **Missouri:** Litigation: White-Collar Crime
& Government Investigations **Band 1** p.1629

**Morris, John G**
Table(s): **Georgia:** Real Estate **Band 3** p.1070

**Morris, Mark L**
Profile: p.2225
Table(s): **Pennsylvania:** Real Estate **Band 4**
p.2208

**Morris, Philip**
Table(s): **Virginia:** Litigation: General
Commercial **Band 2** p.2502, **Virginia:** Litigation:
Products Liability **Band 2** p.2502

**Morris, Ralph A**
Table(s): **Illinois:** Labor & Employment **Band 4**
p.1175

**Morris, Robert**
Profile: p.745
Table(s): **Connecticut:** Corporate/M&A **Band 3**
p.732

**Morris, Steve**
Table(s): **Nevada:** Litigation: General
Commercial **Band 1** p.1677

**Morris III, James W**
Table(s): **Virginia:** Litigation: General
Commercial **Senior Statesmen:** p.2502, **Virginia:**
Litigation: Products Liability **Senior Statesmen:**
p.2502

**Morrison, C David**
Profile: p.2564
Table(s): **West Virginia:** Labor & Employment
**Band 1** p.2553

**Morrison, Edgar C**
Profile: p.2406
Table(s): **Texas:** Healthcare **Band 2** p.2347

**Morrison, John**
Profile: p.2055
Table(s): **North Dakota:** Litigation: Energy &
Natural Resources **Band 1** p.2053

**Morrison, Kenneth P**
Profile: p.372
Table(s): **Nationwide:** Capital Markets:
Securitisation **Band 2** p.59

**Morrison, Stephen G**
Profile: p.2271
Table(s): **Nationwide:** Product Liability & Mass
Torts **Band 4** p.208, **South Carolina:** Litigation:
General Commercial **Band 1** p.2264

**Morrison, Thomas C**
Table(s): **Nationwide:** Advertising: Litigation
**Senior Statesmen:** p.19

**Morrison, Valerie P**
Profile: p.882
Table(s): **District of Columbia:**
Bankruptcy/Restructuring **Band 3** p.792

**Morrison III, Francis H**
Profile: p.745
Table(s): **Connecticut:** Litigation: General
Commercial **Band 2** p.738

**Morriss III, James C**
Profile: p.2406
Table(s): **Texas:** Environment **Band 1** p.2343

**Morrissey, Jennifer M**
Table(s): **Oregon:** Labor & Employment:
Immigration **Band 2** p.2168

**Morrow, James G**
Profile: p.2584
Table(s): **Wisconsin:** Intellectual Property **Band 3**
p.2573

**Morrow, Lynn**
Profile: p.2307
Table(s): **Tennessee:** Media & Entertainment
**Band 2** p.2297

**Morrow, Randall**
Profile: p.471
Table(s): **Alabama:** Banking & Finance **Band 2**
p.455

**Morse, Clinton S**
Table(s): **Virginia:** Labor & Employment **Band 1**
p.2500

**Morse, Judy Hamilton**
Table(s): **Oklahoma:** Litigation: General
Commercial **Band 2** p.2141

**Morse, M Howard**
Table(s): **District of Columbia:** Antitrust **Band 5**
p.787

**Morse, Peter A**
Profile: p.1279
Table(s): **Indiana:** Labor & Employment **Band 3**
p.1271

**Morton, Edmon L.**
Table(s): **Delaware:** Bankruptcy/Restructuring
**Band 4** p.754

**Morton, Mark A**
Profile: p.773
Table(s): **Delaware:** Corporate/M&A **Band 2** p.761

**Morton, Richard E**
Table(s): **North Carolina:** Environment **Band 2**
p.2028

**Morton Jr, Charles J**
Profile: p.1430
Table(s): **Maryland:** Corporate/M&A **Band 4**
p.1412

**Morvillo, Richard J**
Table(s): **Nationwide:** Securities: Regulation:
Enforcement **Band 3** p.233

**Moschel, Michael**
Profile: p.2307
Table(s): **Tennessee:** Labor & Employment **Band**
**3** p.2293

**Moscon, D Matthew**
Table(s): **Utah:** Litigation: General Commercial
**Band 2** p.2468

**Moscowitz, Jane W**
Table(s): **Florida:** Litigation: White-Collar Crime &
Government Investigations **Band 1** p.967

**Moscowitz, Norman A**
Table(s): **Florida:** Litigation: White-Collar Crime &
Government Investigations **Band 1** p.967

**Moseley, Thomas**
Table(s): **Nationwide:** Immigration **Band 3** p.131,
**New York:** Immigration **Band 2** p.1814

**Moseley Jr, James F**
Table(s): **Nationwide:** Transportation: Shipping:
Litigation (outside New York) **Band 1** p.263

**Moser, Eric K**
Profile: p.372
Table(s): **Nationwide:** Capital Markets:
Structured Products **Band 2** p.52

**Moser, Joel H**
Profile: p.372
Table(s): **Nationwide:** Projects: PPP **Band 3** p.217

**Moskatel, Ira D**
Profile: p.656
Table(s): **California:** IT & Outsourcing **Band 3**
p.583

**Moskowitz, Adam M**
Profile: p.1001
Table(s): **Florida:** Litigation: General Commercial
**Band 4** p.966

**Moskowitz, Ross F**
Table(s): **New York:** Real Estate: Zoning/Land
Use **Band 2** p.1855

**Moskowitz, Steven**
Table(s): **New York:** Real Estate **Band 3** p.1854

**Mosley, Daniel L**
Profile: p.372
Table(s): **Nationwide:** Wealth Management:
Eastern Region **Band 4** p.267

**Mosner, Anita**
Profile: p.372
Table(s): **Nationwide:** Transportation: Aviation:
Regulatory **Band 1** p.256

**Moss, Edward A**
Table(s): **Florida:** Litigation: General Commercial
**Band 2** p.966

**Moss, Gary**
Profile: p.1682
Table(s): **Nevada:** Labor & Employment **Band 1**
p.1675

**Moss, Philip J**
Profile: p.1402
Table(s): **Maine:** Labor & Employment **Band 3**
p.1390

**Moss, Ron H**
Profile: p.2406
Table(s): **Texas:** Energy: State Regulatory &
Litigation (Electricity) **Band 1** p.2341

**Mosseau, Peter**
Table(s): **New Hampshire:** Litigation: General
Commercial **Band 1** p.1690

**Mostow, Peter**
Table(s): **Nationwide:** Projects: Renewables &
Alternative Energy **Band 2** p.218

**Moticka, John W.**
Table(s): **Missouri:** Litigation: General
Commercial **Band 3** p.1629

**Motley, Ronald L**
Table(s): **Nationwide:** Product Liability: Plaintiffs
**Senior Statesmen:** p.209

**Motley, Warren**
Profile: p.372
Table(s): **Nationwide:** Capital Markets:
Structured Products **Band 2** p.52

**Mott, Cassandra**
Profile: p.2406
Table(s): **Texas:** Banking & Finance **Up-and-coming**
**individuals** p.2325

**Mottesi, Marcelo A**
Profile: p.1921
Table(s): **New York:** Latin American Investment
**Band 2** p.1829

**Moulthrop, Samuel P**
Table(s): **New Jersey:** Environment **Band 3**
p.1711, **New Jersey:** Litigation: White-Collar
Crime & Government Investigations **Band 2**
p.1723

**Mounteer, Thomas R**
Table(s): **District of Columbia:** Environment:
Mainly Transactional **Band 2** p.805

**Mourning, Paul W.**
Profile: p.1921
Table(s): **New York:** Healthcare **Band 3** p.1811

**Mousavi, Nader A**
Profile: p.656
Table(s): **California:** IT & Outsourcing **Band 2**
p.583

**Mow Jr, Robert H**
Profile: p.2406
Table(s): **Texas:** Litigation: General Commercial
**Senior Statesmen:** p.2362

**Mowe, Gregory**
Table(s): **Oregon:** Litigation: General
Commercial **Band 2** p.2171

**Mowrey, Robert**
Table(s): **Georgia:** Environment **Band 2** p.1051

**Moy, Eric R**
Profile: p.1279
Table(s): **Indiana:** Corporate/M&A **Band 3** p.1268

**Moye, James E**
Profile: p.1001
Table(s): Florida: Construction **Band 1** p.944

**Moyer, Dennis K**
Profile: p.882
Table(s): District of Columbia: Real Estate **Band 2** p.835

**Moyer, Jeffrey L**
Profile: p.773
Table(s): Delaware: Intellectual Property **Band 4** p.763

**Moyer Jr, Homer E**
Profile: p.372
Table(s): Nationwide: International Trade: FCPA Experts **Band 1** p.153

**Moynihan, Carla M**
Profile: p.1503
Table(s): Massachusetts: Real Estate **Band 3** p.1478

**Mrachek, L Louis**
Table(s): Florida: Litigation: General Commercial **Band 2** p.966

**Mrkonich, Marko**
Profile: p.1579
Table(s): Minnesota: Labor & Employment **Band 2** p.1571

**Mrowiec, John S**
Profile: p.1223
Table(s): Illinois: Construction **Band 2** p.1154

**Muchmore, Clyde A**
Profile: p.2152
Table(s): Oklahoma: Litigation: General Commercial **Band 1** p.2141

**Muchmore, Iris**
Table(s): Iowa: Labor & Employment **Band 1** p.1285

**Muckenfuss, Robert A**
Table(s): North Carolina: Litigation: General Commercial **Up-and-coming individuals** p.2033

**Muedeking, Mark**
Profile: p.1430
Table(s): Maryland: Employee Benefits & Executive Compensation **Band 2** p.1414

**Mueller, Bernhard**
Profile: p.2271
Table(s): South Carolina: Labor & Employment **Band 3** p.2262

**Mueller, John M**
Profile: p.2108
Table(s): Ohio: Intellectual Property **Band 3** p.2071

**Mueller, Kathleen T**
Table(s): Missouri: Real Estate **Band 3** p.1633

**Mueller, Michael**
Table(s): Nebraska: Labor & Employment: ERISA **Band 1** p.1662

**Mueller, Thomas**
Table(s): District of Columbia: Antitrust **Band 3** p.787

**Muench, John E**
Table(s): Illinois: Communications **Band 3** p.1153

**Mugel, Christopher J**
Table(s): Southern Virginia: Intellectual Property **Band 1** p.2498

**Muir, Bruce**
Table(s): Colorado: Labor & Employment: Employee Benefits & Compensation **Band 2** p.706

**Muirhead, Chris**
Table(s): New Mexico: Corporate/Commercial **Band 2** p.1764

**Mulaney Jr, Charles W**
Profile: p.1223
Table(s): Illinois: Corporate/M&A **Star individuals** p.1156

**Mulcahy, Benjamin R**
Table(s): Nationwide: Advertising: Transactional & Regulatory **Band 3** p.20

**Mulcahy, Michael D**
Profile: p.1553
Table(s): Michigan: Real Estate **Band 3** p.1546

**Muldoon Jr, Robert J**
Table(s): Massachusetts: Litigation: General Commercial **Senior Statesmen:** p.1470

**Muldowney, Patrick M**
Profile: p.1001
Table(s): Florida: Labor & Employment **Band 4** p.959

**Muldrow, Lee J**
Profile: p.528
Table(s): Arkansas: Labor & Employment **Band 3** p.520, Arkansas: Labor & Employment: Employee Benefits & Compensation **Band 2** p.520

**Mulitz, Michael C**
Profile: p.372
Table(s): Nationwide: Transportation: Aviation: Finance **Band 3** p.252

**Mullen, Kevin**
Profile: p.372
Table(s): Nationwide: Government: Government Contracts **Band 4** p.117

**Mullen, Robert A**
Table(s): Iowa: Corporate/M&A: Banking & Finance **Band 1** p.1283

**Mullen, Thomas A**
Table(s): Delaware: Corporate/M&A **Band 3** p.761, Delaware: Corporate/M&A: Alternative Entities **Band 2** p.761

**Muller, Scott**
Profile: p.372
Table(s): Nationwide: International Trade: FCPA Experts **Band 2** p.153, New York: Litigation: White-Collar Crime & Government Investigations **Band 2** p.1836

**Mullin, David C.**
Table(s): Nebraska: Litigation: Insurance **Up-and-coming individuals** p.1664

**Mullin, Joel A**
Table(s): Oregon: Litigation: General Commercial **Band 1** p.2171

**Mullin, Michael G**
Profile: p.1668
Table(s): Nebraska: Litigation: Mediators **Band 1** p.1664

**Mullin Jr, Robert D**
Table(s): Nebraska: Litigation: Insurance **Band 1** p.1664

**Mullins, Todd**
Table(s): Nationwide: Energy: Electricity (Regulatory & Litigation) **Band 4** p.76

**Mulroy II, James R**
Profile: p.2307
Table(s): Tennessee: Labor & Employment **Band 2** p.2293

**Mulvaney, James M**
Profile: p.1743
Table(s): New Jersey: Litigation: General Commercial **Band 3** p.1722

**Mulvaney, Karl**
Profile: p.1279
Table(s): Indiana: Litigation: Appellate **Band 1** p.1273

**Mulvaney, Michael**
Profile: p.471
Table(s): Alabama: Litigation: General Commercial **Band 4** p.463

**Mumaugh, Brian**
Profile: p.720
Table(s): Colorado: Labor & Employment **Band 3** p.706

**Mumford, Kerri K**
Profile: p.773
Table(s): Delaware: Bankruptcy/Restructuring **Up-and-coming individuals** p.754

**Mummery, Daniel**
Profile: p.656
Table(s): Nationwide: Outsourcing **Band 1** p.195, California: IT & Outsourcing **Star individuals** p.583

**Munck, William A**
Table(s): Texas: Intellectual Property **Band 4** p.2354

**Muncy, Dennis**
Table(s): Illinois: Communications **Senior Statesmen:** p.1153

**Munford, Luther T**
Profile: p.1606
Table(s): Mississippi: Litigation: Appellate **Band 1** p.1596

**Munford, Virginia**
Table(s): Mississippi: Environment **Band 1** p.1594

**Munger, Lisa Woods**
Table(s): Hawaii: Litigation: General Commercial **Band 3** p.1119, Hawaii: Real Estate: Environment **Band 1** p.1120

**Munger, Stephen X**
Profile: p.1091
Table(s): Georgia: Labor & Employment **Band 4** p.1060

**Munger, Tom**
Table(s): Georgia: Labor & Employment **Band 2** p.1060

**Mungovan, Timothy W**
Table(s): Massachusetts: Litigation: General Commercial **Band 2** p.1470

**Munoz, Jeff**
Table(s): Nationwide: Energy: Oil & Gas (Transactional) **Band 4** p.79

**Munsch, Martha Hartle**
Table(s): Pennsylvania: Labor & Employment **Band 2** p.2200

**Munsch, Russell L**
Table(s): Texas: Bankruptcy/Restructuring **Band 3** p.2328

**Munsell, Michael**
Table(s): Missouri: Intellectual Property **Band 3** p.1623

**Munther, Merrily**
Table(s): Idaho: Labor & Employment **Band 2** p.1132

**Murashige, Kate H**
Profile: p.372
Table(s): Nationwide: Life Sciences: IP/Patent Litigation **Senior Statesmen:** p.183, California: Life Sciences: IP/Patent Litigation **Senior Statesmen:** p.590

**Murdock III, John E**
Table(s): Tennessee: Banking & Finance **Band 1** p.2287

**Muris, Timothy J**
Profile: p.882
Table(s): District of Columbia: Antitrust **Band 2** p.787

**Murnane, Don P**
Profile: p.372
Table(s): Nationwide: Transportation: Shipping: Litigation (New York) **Band 2** p.261

**Murov, Ellis B**
Table(s): Louisiana: Labor & Employment **Band 2** p.1350

**Murphy, Barbara A**
Profile: p.373
Table(s): Nationwide: International Trade: Intellectual Property (Section 337) **Band 2** p.160

**Murphy, Brian**
Profile: p.373
Table(s): Nationwide: Advertising: Transactional & Regulatory **Band 3** p.20

**Murphy, Brian R**
Table(s): Vermont: Corporate/Commercial **Band 1** p.2483

**Murphy, Brooke S**
Table(s): Oklahoma: Litigation: General Commercial **Band 2** p.2141

**Murphy, Gerald**
Profile: p.373
Table(s): Nationwide: Transportation: Aviation: Regulatory **Band 3** p.256

**Murphy, Gerald**
Table(s): Montana: Litigation: General Commercial **Band 2** p.1649

**Murphy, Harold B**
Profile: p.1503
Table(s): Massachusetts: Bankruptcy/Restructuring **Star individuals** p.1449

**Murphy, Jack W**
Profile: p.373
Table(s): Nationwide: Investment Funds: Registered Funds **Band 1** p.170

**Murphy, John**
Table(s): Florida: Latin American Investment
Band 4 p.963

**Murphy, Joseph**
Table(s): Illinois: Communications Band 3 p.1153

**Murphy, Kathleen**
Profile: p.373
Table(s): Nationwide: International Trade:
Customs Band 3 p.155

**Murphy, Lawrence J**
Table(s): Michigan: Labor & Employment Band 2
p.1542

**Murphy, Lewis F**
Profile: p.1001
Table(s): Florida: Litigation: General Commercial
Band 3 p.966

**Murphy, Liam**
Table(s): Vermont: Real Estate Band 1 p.2487,
Vermont: Real Estate: Zoning/Land Use Band 1
p.2487

**Murphy, Marc S**
Profile: p.1322
Table(s): Kentucky: Litigation: Tort & Insurance
Defense Band 1 p.1312

**Murphy, Martin F**
Profile: p.1503
Table(s): Massachusetts: Litigation: White-Collar
Crime & Government Investigations Band 2
p.1471

**Murphy, Mary**
Profile: p.656
Table(s): California: Real Estate: Zoning/Land
Use Band 1 p.612

**Murphy, Michael**
Profile: p.373
Table(s): Nationwide: International Trade:
Customs Up-and-coming individuals p.155

**Murphy, Michael**
Profile: p.373
Table(s): Nationwide: Outsourcing Band 2 p.195,
California: IT & Outsourcing Band 2 p.583

**Murphy, Michael**
Profile: p.1921
Table(s): New York: Insurance: Dispute
Resolution: Insurer Band 3 p.1816

**Murphy, Michael J**
Table(s): California: IT & Outsourcing Band 3
p.583

**Murphy, Patrick J**
Table(s): Wyoming: Litigation: General
Commercial Band 1 p.2598

**Murphy, Paul B**
Profile: p.1091
Table(s): Georgia: Litigation: White-Collar Crime
& Government Investigations Band 2 p.1066

**Murphy, Sandra M**
Profile: p.2565
Table(s): West Virginia: Corporate/Commercial:
Banking & Finance Band 1 p.2550

**Murphy, Sean M**
Profile: p.1921
Table(s): New York: Litigation: Securities Band 3
p.1834

**Murphy, Terrence H**
Profile: p.2226
Table(s): Pennsylvania: Labor & Employment
Band 2 p.2200

**Murphy, Thomas P**
Profile: p.2512
Table(s): Virginia: Labor & Employment Band 1
p.2500

**Murphy, William**
Table(s): Maryland: Litigation: General
Commercial Band 1 p.1419

**Murphy III, James L**
Table(s): Tennessee: Real Estate: Zoning/Land
Use Band 1 p.2299

**Murphy Jr, Charles C**
Profile: p.1091
Table(s): Georgia: Antitrust Band 1 p.1037

**Murphy Jr, George L**
Table(s): Georgia: Litigation: General
Commercial Band 4 p.1065

**Murphy PE, Michael G**
Profile: p.1002
Table(s): Florida: Construction Band 3 p.944

**Murray, Christopher**
Table(s): California: Media & Entertainment:
Transactional Band 2 p.608

**Murray, Craig**
Profile: p.2406
Table(s): Texas: Banking & Finance Senior
Statesmen: p.2325

**Murray, Daniel**
Profile: p.1223
Table(s): Illinois: Bankruptcy/Restructuring Band
3 p.1148

**Murray, George E**
Table(s): Missouri: Real Estate Band 1 p.1633

**Murray, Gregory S**
Profile: p.1223
Table(s): Illinois: Banking & Finance Band 1
p.1145

**Murray, Gregory V**
Table(s): Michigan: Labor & Employment Band 2
p.1542

**Murray, Hugh**
Table(s): Connecticut: Labor & Employment Band
3 p.736

**Murray, James R**
Profile: p.883
Table(s): District of Columbia: Insurance:
Policyholder Band 2 p.818

**Murray, Jordan C**
Table(s): Nationwide: Investment Funds: Private
Equity: Fund Formation Band 4 p.166

**Murray, Kevin R**
Table(s): Utah: Energy & Natural Resources Band
2 p.2464

**Murray, Saranne**
Table(s): Connecticut: Labor & Employment Band
3 p.736

**Murray, Thomas J**
Table(s): West Virginia: Corporate/Commercial
Band 1 p.2550, West Virginia:
Corporate/Commercial: Banking & Finance Band
1 p.2550

**Murray Jr, William G**
Profile: p.656
Table(s): California: Real Estate Band 3 p.611

**Murrell, Dennis D**
Table(s): Kentucky: Litigation: General
Commercial Band 2 p.1312

**Murtaugh, Christopher D**
Profile: p.1223
Table(s): Illinois: Real Estate Band 3 p.1187

**Musgrave, Bobbee J.**
Table(s): Colorado: Litigation: General
Commercial Band 4 p.709

**Musiker, Jean**
Profile: p.1503
Table(s): Massachusetts: Labor & Employment
Band 4 p.1466

**Musil, Greg L**
Table(s): Kansas: Litigation: General
Commercial Band 1 p.1295

**Musoff, Scott**
Profile: p.373
Table(s): Nationwide: Securities: Litigation Band
2 p.232, New York: Litigation: Securities Band 2
p.1834

**Musser, William**
Table(s): South Carolina: Corporate/M&A Band 3
p.2260, South Carolina: Corporate/M&A:
Banking & Finance Band 1 p.2260

**Mustone, David A**
Profile: p.2512
Table(s): Virginia: Labor & Employment:
Employee Benefits & Compensation Band 2
p.2500

**Mutchnik, James H**
Profile: p.1223
Table(s): Illinois: Antitrust Band 1 p.1143

**Muth, Jon R**
Table(s): Michigan: Litigation: General
Commercial Senior Statesmen: p.1544

**Muto, Fred**
Table(s): Nationwide: Investment Funds: Venture
Capital Band 3 p.174, Nationwide: Life Sciences:
Corporate/Commercial Band 2 p.182, California:
Capital Markets: Debt & Equity Band 3 p.547,
California: Corporate/M&A: Venture Capital Band
2 p.555, California: Life Sciences:
Corporate/Commercial Band 1 p.590

**Mutryn, William J**
Profile: p.2512
Table(s): Northern Virginia: Corporate/M&A Band
1 p.2493

**Mutterperl, Mark**
Profile: p.1921
Table(s): New York: Intellectual Property: Trade
Mark & Copyright Band 2 p.1821

**Muzzi, Christopher J**
Table(s): Hawaii: Bankruptcy/Restructuring Band
2 p.1114

**Myatt, Christine**
Table(s): North Carolina:
Bankruptcy/Restructuring Band 1 p.2023

**Myers, Donald J**
Profile: p.883
Table(s): District of Columbia: Employee
Benefits & Executive Compensation Band 3 p.801

**Myers, Elizabeth Murdock**
Table(s): Rhode Island: Corporate/Commercial
Band 3 p.2251

**Myers, Gary M**
Table(s): Iowa: Real Estate Band 3 p.1290

**Myers, John A**
Table(s): New Mexico: Real Estate Band 1 p.1772

**Myers, Kimberly L**
Profile: p.1091
Table(s): Georgia: Antitrust Band 2 p.1037

**Myers, Lawrence J**
Profile: p.1091
Table(s): Georgia: Healthcare Band 3 p.1052

**Myers, Linda K**
Profile: p.1223
Table(s): Nationwide: Banking & Finance Band 4
p.31, Illinois: Banking & Finance Band 1 p.1145

**Myers, Louis**
Table(s): Massachusetts: Intellectual Property
Band 1 p.1463

**Myers, Marlee**
Profile: p.2226
Table(s): Pennsylvania: Corporate/M&A &
Private Equity Band 2 p.2191

**Myers, Martin H**
Profile: p.656
Table(s): California: Insurance: Policyholder Band
4 p.576

**Myers, Roger**
Table(s): California: Media & Entertainment:
First Amendment Litigation Band 2 p.606

**Myers, Thomas A**
Profile: p.2585
Table(s): Wisconsin: Corporate/M&A Band 3
p.2571

**Myers, Thomas W**
Table(s): Texas: Construction Band 1 p.2335

**Myers II, John W**
Table(s): Tennessee: Banking & Finance Band 1
p.2287

**Myers III, William G**
Profile: p.1139
Table(s): Idaho: Natural Resources &
Environment Band 1 p.1136

**Myerson, Toby S**
Profile: p.1921
Table(s): New York: Corporate/M&A Band 3
p.1793

**Mytelka, Craig L**
Table(s): Southern Virginia: Intellectual Property
Band 2 p.2498

## N

**Naar, Alan S**
Table(s): New Jersey: Litigation: General
Commercial **Band 3** p.1722

**Nachbar, Kenneth J**
Table(s): Delaware: Chancery **Band 1** p.758

**Nachwalter, Michael**
Table(s): Florida: Antitrust **Senior Statesmen**: p.935,
Florida: Litigation: General Commercial **Senior
Statesmen**: p.966

**Nadeau, Mark A**
Profile: p.510
Table(s): Arizona: Litigation: General
Commercial **Band 3** p.501

**Nadel, Alan S**
Profile: p.2226
Table(s): Pennsylvania: Intellectual Property
**Band 2** p.2197

**Nadel, Darren**
Profile: p.721
Table(s): Colorado: Labor & Employment:
Employee Benefits & Compensation **Band 2**
p.706

**Nadel, Peter F**
Table(s): Nationwide: Healthcare: Regulatory &
Litigation **Senior Statesmen**: p.127, New York:
Healthcare **Senior Statesmen**: p.1811

**Nadel, Steven B**
Profile: p.373
Table(s): Nationwide: Investment Funds: Hedge
Funds **Band 3** p.162

**Nadell, Bernhardt**
Table(s): New York: Insurance: Transactional &
Regulatory **Band 3** p.1816

**Nadler, David**
Profile: p.374
Table(s): Nationwide: Government: Government
Contracts **Band 3** p.117

**Naeve, Clifford M**
Profile: p.374
Table(s): Nationwide: Energy: Electricity
(Regulatory & Litigation) **Star individuals** p.76,
Nationwide: Energy: Oil & Gas (Regulatory &
Litigation) **Band 1** p.76

**Naftalis, Gary P**
Profile: p.1921
Table(s): Nationwide: Litigation: Trial Lawyers
**Band 1** p.187, New York: Litigation: General
Commercial **Band 2** p.1833, New York: Litigation:
White-Collar Crime & Government Investigations
**Star individuals** p.1833

**Nagae, Jerald**
Table(s): Washington: Intellectual Property **Band
2** p.2529

**Nagel, Trevor**
Profile: p.374
Table(s): Nationwide: Outsourcing **Band 1** p.195,
District of Columbia: Technology & Outsourcing
**Band 1** p.842

**Nagelberg, Howard**
Table(s): Illinois: Real Estate **Band 2** p.1187

**Nager, Glen**
Profile: p.374
Table(s): Nationwide: Appellate Law **Band 2** p.26,
District of Columbia: Labor & Employment **Band
2** p.824

**Nagin, Stephen**
Table(s): Florida: Antitrust **Band 2** p.935

**Nagle, David**
Profile: p.2512
Table(s): Virginia: Labor & Employment **Band 2**
p.2500

**Nagle, David J**
Profile: p.1503
Table(s): Massachusetts: Tax **Band 3** p.1481

**Nagle, James W**
Profile: p.1503
Table(s): Massachusetts: Labor & Employment
**Band 1** p.1466

**Nagle Jr, David W**
Profile: p.1322
Table(s): Kentucky: Intellectual Property **Band 2**
p.1308

**Nagy Jr, Tibor**
Profile: p.510
Table(s): Arizona: Labor & Employment **Band 2**
p.499

**Nahra, Kirk J**
Profile: p.374
Table(s): Nationwide: Privacy & Data Security
**Band 1** p.199

**Naimon, Jeffrey**
Profile: p.374
Table(s): Nationwide: Financial Services
Regulation: Consumer Finance (Compliance)
**Band 3** p.98

**Najder, Kenneth**
Profile: p.1367
Table(s): Louisiana: Corporate/M&A **Band 3**
p.1341

**Nakahata, John T**
Profile: p.883
Table(s): District of Columbia: Telecom,
Broadcast & Satellite **Band 1** p.844

**Nakashima, David A**
Profile: p.1124
Table(s): Hawaii: Litigation: General Commercial
**Band 3** p.1119

**Nakasian, Stacey**
Table(s): Rhode Island: Litigation: General
Commercial **Band 2** p.2254

**Nakayama, Granta Y**
Profile: p.883
Table(s): District of Columbia: Environment **Band
3** p.804

**Nalda, Carlos M**
Profile: p.883
Table(s): District of Columbia: Telecom,
Broadcast & Satellite **Band 4** p.844

**Namorato, Cono R**
Table(s): Nationwide: Tax: Fraud **Band 1** p.244

**Nannes, John M**
Profile: p.883
Table(s): District of Columbia: Antitrust **Band 2**
p.787

**Napolitano, Steven V**
Profile: p.1223
Table(s): Illinois: Corporate/M&A: Private Equity
**Band 2** p.1157

**Napper, Kevin J**
Profile: p.1002
Table(s): Florida: Litigation: White-Collar Crime &
Government Investigations **Band 3** p.967

**Nardi, Karen**
Profile: p.656
Table(s): California: Environment **Band 3** p.564

**Nardone, Susan L**
Table(s): New Jersey: Labor & Employment **Band
3** p.1718

**Nardoni, Stanley C.**
Table(s): Illinois: Insurance: Dispute Resolution
**Band 3** p.1168

**Narducci, Lucas J**
Table(s): Arizona: Environment (including water
rights) **Band 1** p.497

**Nash, Bernard**
Profile: p.374
Table(s): Nationwide: Government: Government
Relations **Band 2** p.121

**Nash, Daniel L**
Profile: p.374
Table(s): Nationwide: Sports Law **Band 3** p.241,
District of Columbia: Labor & Employment **Band
3** p.824

**Nash, David**
Profile: p.2108
Table(s): Ohio: Natural Resources &
Environment **Band 2** p.2083

**Nash, Glenn**
Profile: p.656
Table(s): Nationwide: Outsourcing **Band 2** p.195,
California: IT & Outsourcing **Star individuals** p.583

**Nash, Gordon B**
Profile: p.1223
Table(s): Illinois: Litigation: General Commercial
**Band 3** p.1180

**Nash, Walter**
Table(s): Arizona: Litigation: White-Collar Crime
& Government Investigations **Band 2** p.501

**Nash, Jr, Patrick**
Profile: p.1223
Table(s): Illinois: Bankruptcy/Restructuring **Band
4** p.1148

**Nashelsky, Larren M**
Profile: p.1922
Table(s): New York: Bankruptcy/Restructuring
**Band 4** p.1782

**Nasi, Michael**
Profile: p.2406
Table(s): Texas: Environment **Band 4** p.2343

**Nason, Leigh M**
Profile: p.2271
Table(s): South Carolina: Labor & Employment
**Band 2** p.2262

**Nassau, Henry N**
Profile: p.2226
Table(s): Nationwide: Private Equity: Buyouts
**Band 5** p.203, Pennsylvania: Corporate/M&A &
Private Equity **Band 1** p.2191

**Nassen, John W**
Table(s): Texas: Construction **Band 2** p.2335

**Nassif, Joseph G**
Table(s): Missouri: Environment **Band 1** p.1621

**Nassikas, John**
Profile: p.883
Table(s): District of Columbia: Litigation: White-
Collar Crime & Government Investigations **Band 3**
p.827

**Natale, Andrew J**
Profile: p.2108
Table(s): Ohio: Construction **Band 1** p.2062

**Nathan, Arthur M**
Table(s): Texas: Corporate/M&A **Band 4** p.2337

**Nathanson, Kirsten L**
Profile: p.883
Table(s): District of Columbia: Environment **Up-
and-coming individuals** p.804

**Nation, Floyd**
Profile: p.2406
Table(s): Texas: Intellectual Property **Band 3**
p.2354

**Natsis, Anton N**
Profile: p.656
Table(s): California: Real Estate **Band 1** p.611

**Naughton, Laurence P**
Profile: p.1503
Table(s): Massachusetts: Corporate/M&A **Band 3**
p.1452

**Naugle, Louis**
Table(s): Pennsylvania: Environment **Band 2**
p.2194

**Navia, Talbert I**
Profile: p.1922
Table(s): New York: Latin American Investment
**Band 3** p.1829

**Naylor, Greg A**
Table(s): Iowa: Labor & Employment **Band 2**
p.1285

**Nazarenus, Brian**
Table(s): Colorado: Natural Resources &
Environment **Band 3** p.712

**Nazareth, Annette**
Profile: p.374
Table(s): Nationwide: Financial Services
Regulation: Broker Dealer (Compliance) **Star indi-
viduals** p.97, Nationwide: Financial Services
Regulation: Broker Dealer (Enforcement) **Band 1**
p.97, Nationwide: Securities: Regulation:
Advisory **Band 1** p.232

**Nazette, Adam R**
Profile: p.2108
Table(s): Ohio: Banking & Finance **Up-and-coming
individuals** p.2056

**Neaher Jr, Ned**
Profile: p.374
Table(s): Nationwide: Projects **Band 2** p.216

**Neal, Austin**
Table(s): Florida: Insurance **Band 3** p.957

**Neal, Kathy R**
Profile: p.2152
Table(s): Oklahoma: Labor & Employment **Band 2**
p.2140

**Norwood, E Andrew**
Profile: p.2307
Table(s): Tennessee: Media & Entertainment **Band 2** p.2297

**Norwood Jr, Colvin G**
Profile: p.377
Table(s): Nationwide: Product Liability & Mass Torts **Band 4** p.208, Nationwide: Product Liability: Automobile p.208

**Noteboom, Lowell**
Table(s): Minnesota: Construction **Senior Statesmen:** p.1567

**Noteboom, Todd**
Table(s): Minnesota: Litigation: General Commercial **Band 2** p.1574

**Notkin, Deborah**
Table(s): Nationwide: Immigration **Band 3** p.131, New York: Immigration **Band 2** p.1814

**Noto, Margaret Hill**
Table(s): Oregon: Corporate/M&A **Band 2** p.2164

**Notopoulos, Philip**
Profile: p.1504
Table(s): Massachusetts: Real Estate **Band 2** p.1478

**Nourse, David A**
Table(s): Nationwide: Transportation: Shipping: Litigation (New York) **Senior Statesmen:** p.261

**Nouss Jr, James L**
Table(s): Missouri: Corporate/M&A **Band 1** p.1619

**Novacek, Stephen V**
Profile: p.1682
Table(s): Nevada: Real Estate **Band 3** p.1679

**Novack, Stephen**
Table(s): Illinois: Litigation: General Commercial **Band 3** p.1180

**Novak, Edward F**
Table(s): Arizona: Litigation: White-Collar Crime & Government Investigations **Band 1** p.501

**Novak, Frank A**
Table(s): New York: Immigration **Band 3** p.1814

**Novak, Ira S**
Table(s): New Jersey: Healthcare **Band 3** p.1715

**Novak, Tabor**
Table(s): Alabama: Litigation: General Commercial **Band 2** p.463

**Novak, Theodore**
Profile: p.1224
Table(s): Illinois: Real Estate **Band 1** p.1187, Illinois: Real Estate: Zoning/Land Use **Band 1** p.1187

**Novetsky, Terry D**
Profile: p.377
Table(s): Nationwide: Capital Markets: Securitisation **Band 4** p.59

**Novick, Robert T**
Profile: p.378
Table(s): Nationwide: International Trade: Trade Remedies & Trade Policy **Band 3** p.154

**Novikoff, Harold S**
Profile: p.378
Table(s): Nationwide: Bankruptcy/Restructuring **Band 1** p.39, New York: Bankruptcy/Restructuring **Band 1** p.1782

**Novogrod, John C**
Profile: p.378
Table(s): Nationwide: Wealth Management: Eastern Region **Band 4** p.267

**Nowak, Gregory J**
Profile: p.378
Table(s): Nationwide: Investment Funds: Hedge Funds **Band 3** p.162

**Noyes, Christopher**
Table(s): Wisconsin: Corporate/M&A **Band 2** p.2571

**Nuechterlein, Jonathan**
Profile: p.884
Table(s): District of Columbia: Telecom, Broadcast & Satellite **Band 1** p.844

**Nuechterlein, Michael F**
Profile: p.1002
Table(s): Florida: Construction **Senior Statesmen:** p.944

**Nugent, Eileen T**
Profile: p.378
Table(s): Nationwide: Private Equity: Buyouts **Band 2** p.203, New York: Corporate/M&A **Band 2** p.1793

**Nukk-Freeman, Katherin**
Profile: p.1743
Table(s): New Jersey: Labor & Employment **Band 3** p.1718

**Null, Amy A**
Profile: p.1504
Table(s): Massachusetts: Employee Benefits & Executive Compensation **Band 2** p.1455

**Nunnelley, Richard A**
Profile: p.1322
Table(s): Kentucky: Real Estate **Band 3** p.1314

**Nurnberg, D Tyler**
Profile: p.1224
Table(s): Illinois: Bankruptcy/Restructuring **Band 4** p.1148

**Nusbaum, Jack H**
Profile: p.1924
Table(s): New York: Corporate/M&A **Senior Statesmen:** p.1793

**Nussbaum, Andrew J**
Profile: p.1924
Table(s): New York: Corporate/M&A **Band 3** p.1793

**Nussbaum, Bernard W**
Profile: p.378
Table(s): Nationwide: Litigation: Trial Lawyers **Senior Statesmen:** p.186, New York: Litigation: General Commercial **Senior Statesmen:** p.1833

**Nussbaum, Martin**
Profile: p.1924
Table(s): New York: Corporate/M&A **Band 5** p.1793

**Nussbaum, Mitchell S**
Profile: p.1924
Table(s): New York: Corporate/M&A **Band 5** p.1793

**Nussbaum, Paul M**
Profile: p.1430
Table(s): Maryland: Litigation: Bankruptcy **Band 1** p.1419

**Nussbaum, Peter**
Table(s): New Jersey: Intellectual Property **Band 3** p.1716

**Nussdorf, Melanie**
Table(s): Nationwide: Employee Benefits & Executive Compensation **Band 1** p.73, District of Columbia: Employee Benefits & Executive Compensation **Star Individuals** p.801

**Nutter, R.J.**
Table(s): Southern Virginia: Real Estate **Band 3** p.2506

**Nydegger, Rick D**
Table(s): Utah: Intellectual Property **Band 1** p.2466

**Nye, Marcus**
Table(s): Idaho: Litigation: General Commercial **Band 1** p.1134

**Nyhan, Christopher D**
Profile: p.1402
Table(s): Maine: Litigation: Medical Malpractice & Insurance **Band 1** p.1393

**Nyhan, Lawrence**
Profile: p.378
Table(s): Nationwide: Bankruptcy/Restructuring **Band 1** p.39, Illinois: Bankruptcy/Restructuring **Band 1** p.1148

**Nylen Jr, Richard A**
Table(s): Massachusetts: Real Estate: Zoning/Land Use **Band 2** p.1478

**Nylund, Jessica A**
Profile: p.1696
Table(s): New Hampshire: Real Estate **Band 3** p.1692

**Nyquist, Peter A**
Profile: p.657
Table(s): California: Environment **Band 3** p.564

# O

**O'Bannon, James E**
Profile: p.2407
Table(s): Texas: Corporate/M&A **Band 3** p.2337

**O'Brien, Anne**
Profile: p.378
Table(s): Nationwide: Wealth Management: Eastern Region **Band 2** p.267

**O'Brien, Clare**
Profile: p.1924
Table(s): New York: Corporate/M&A **Band 3** p.1793

**O'Brien, Claudia**
Profile: p.884
Table(s): District of Columbia: Environment **Band 4** p.804

**O'Brien, George**
Profile: p.745
Table(s): Connecticut: Labor & Employment **Band 1** p.736

**O'Brien, Harry**
Table(s): California: Real Estate: Zoning/Land Use **Band 2** p.612

**O'Brien, James**
Profile: p.379
Table(s): Nationwide: Tax: Controversy **Band 2** p.244

**O'Brien, Jeannemarie**
Profile: p.1924
Table(s): New York: Employee Benefits & Executive Compensation **Band 2** p.1802

**O'Brien, Kevin**
Profile: p.884
Table(s): District of Columbia: Construction **Band 3** p.795

**O'Brien, Kevin**
Table(s): District of Columbia: Employee Benefits & Executive Compensation **Band 3** p.801

**O'Brien, Maria**
Table(s): New Mexico: Environment, Natural Resources & Regulated Industries: Water Law **Band 1** p.1766

**O'Brien, Michael Patrick**
Profile: p.2475
Table(s): Utah: Labor & Employment **Band 1** p.2467

**O'Brien, Michelle N**
Table(s): Massachusetts: Environment **Band 1** p.1457

**O'Brien, Patrick**
Table(s): Massachusetts: Corporate/M&A: Capital Markets **Band 2** p.1453

**O'Brien, Peter**
Profile: p.379
Table(s): Nationwide: Energy: Electricity (Finance) **Band 1** p.75

**O'Brien, Richard**
Profile: p.1224
Table(s): Illinois: Media & Entertainment: Litigation **Band 1** p.1184

**O'Brien, Timothy J**
Table(s): Maine: Labor & Employment **Band 3** p.1390

**O'Brien, Vincent**
Profile: p.379
Table(s): Nationwide: Food & Beverages: Alcohol **Senior Statesmen:** p.109

**O'Brien, William**
Profile: p.379
Table(s): Nationwide: International Arbitration **Band 5** p.145

**O'Brien III, Thomas P**
Profile: p.1322
Table(s): Kentucky: Intellectual Property **Band 2** p.1308

**O'Bryan, Michael**
Profile: p.657
Table(s): California: Corporate/M&A **Band 3** p.553

**O'Bryan, Rory**
Table(s): Indiana: Real Estate **Band 2** p.1275

**O'Bryant, Ramona Cunningham**
Profile: p.2043
Table(s): North Carolina: Environment **Band 3** p.2028

**O'Connell, Ann**
Table(s): California: Healthcare **Band 3** p.568

**O'Shaughnessy, William J**
Profile: p.1743
Table(s): New Jersey: Litigation: General
Commercial Senior Statesmen: p.1722

**O'Shea, Kevin**
Table(s): New York: Real Estate: Finance Band 2
p.1855

**O'Sullivan, Maura**
Table(s): Nationwide: Banking & Finance Band 2
p.31

**O'Toole, Daniel K**
Table(s): Missouri: Labor & Employment Band 1
p.1625

**O'Toole, Matthew J**
Table(s): Delaware: Corporate/M&A: Alternative
Entities Band 2 p.761

**O'Toole, Patrick**
Profile: p.1504
Table(s): Massachusetts: Litigation: General
Commercial Band 3 p.1470

**O'Toole, Terence J**
Profile: p.1124
Table(s): Hawaii: Litigation: General Commercial
Star Individuals p.1119

**Oade, K Preston**
Table(s): Colorado: Labor & Employment Senior
Statesmen: p.706

**Oakes, Jared E**
Profile: p.2108
Table(s): Ohio: Real Estate Associates to watch
p.2086

**Oakes, Leslie**
Profile: p.1092
Table(s): Georgia: Environment Band 2 p.1051

**Oakes, Royal F**
Table(s): California: Insurance: Insurer Band 2
p.574

**Oakey, David N**
Table(s): Southern Virginia: Corporate/M&A Band
2 p.2494

**Oates, J Christopher**
Table(s): North Carolina: Real Estate Band 2
p.2037

**Oates, Mark A**
Profile: p.378
Table(s): Nationwide: Tax: Controversy Band 1
p.244

**Oberkfell, Keith F**
Table(s): Nationwide: Capital Markets:
Securitisation Band 2 p.59, North Carolina:
Banking & Finance Band 2 p.2021

**Oberschmidt, E Richard**
Profile: p.2108
Table(s): Ohio: Real Estate Band 2 p.2086

**Oberstein, Gary J**
Profile: p.1504
Table(s): Massachusetts: Labor & Employment
Band 4 p.1466

**Occhino, Lennine**
Table(s): Illinois: Labor & Employment:
Employee Benefits & Compensation Band 2
p.1176

**Ochs, Timothy E**
Table(s): Indiana: Real Estate Band 3 p.1275

**Ocker, Jonathan M**
Table(s): California: Employee Benefits &
Executive Compensation Band 2 p.560

**Ockner, Ben**
Table(s): Ohio: Real Estate: Zoning/Land Use
Band 2 p.2086

**Ode Jr, Paul H**
Table(s): Vermont: Corporate/Commercial Band 1
p.2483

**Odell, Francesca**
Profile: p.1925
Table(s): New York: Latin American Investment
Band 2 p.1829

**Odell, Herbert**
Table(s): Nationwide: Tax: Controversy Band 3
p.244

**Odle, Kathleen**
Table(s): Colorado: Labor & Employment:
Employee Benefits & Compensation Band 1
p.706

**Odoner, Ellen J**
Profile: p.379
Table(s): Nationwide: Securities: Regulation:
Advisory Band 2 p.232

**Odorizzi, Michele L**
Table(s): Illinois: Litigation: General Commercial
Band 2 p.1180

**Oellermann, Charles M**
Profile: p.2108
Table(s): Ohio: Bankruptcy/Restructuring Band 3
p.2058

**Oelman, David**
Profile: p.2407
Table(s): Nationwide: Capital Markets: Debt &
Equity Band 4 p.46, Texas: Capital Markets: Debt
& Equity Band 1 p.2333, Texas: Corporate/M&A
Band 2 p.2337

**Oertel, Ken**
Profile: p.1002
Table(s): Florida: Environment Band 3 p.951

**Oesting, David W**
Table(s): Alaska: Litigation: General Commercial
Band 1 p.490

**Oestreicher, Charles R**
Profile: p.1402
Table(s): Maine: Real Estate Senior Statesmen:
p.1395

**Ofsa, Joyce**
Profile: p.2565
Table(s): West Virginia: Real Estate Band 1
p.2560

**Ogden, David W**
Profile: p.884
Table(s): District of Columbia: Litigation:
General Commercial Band 3 p.826

**Ogilby, Anne Phillips**
Table(s): Massachusetts: Banking & Finance:
Public Finance Band 2 p.1446, Massachusetts:
Healthcare Band 1 p.1460

**Ogilvy, George**
Table(s): Nevada: Litigation: Construction Band 1
p.1676

**Ogletree, Powell G**
Profile: p.1606
Table(s): Mississippi: Real Estate Band 1 p.1600

**Ogrosky, Kirk**
Profile: p.884
Table(s): District of Columbia: Healthcare Band 3
p.809

**Ohlenforst, Cynthia**
Profile: p.2407
Table(s): Texas: Tax: Litigation Band 2 p.2371

**Ohm, Michael K**
Table(s): Illinois: Environment: Mainly
Transactional Band 2 p.1162

**Okinaga, Lawrence S**
Profile: p.1124
Table(s): Hawaii: Corporate/Commercial:
Finance Band 1 p.1116

**Okumura, Miki**
Table(s): Hawaii: Corporate/Commercial: Tax
Band 1 p.1115

**Oland, Mark**
Profile: p.746
Table(s): Connecticut: Real Estate Band 2 p.740

**Olcott, Bruce**
Profile: p.884
Table(s): District of Columbia: Telecom,
Broadcast & Satellite Band 4 p.844

**Old, Gareth**
Profile: p.379
Table(s): Nationwide: Capital Markets:
Derivatives Up-and-coming Individuals p.51

**Old Jr, William A**
Table(s): Southern Virginia: Corporate/M&A Band
3 p.2494

**Oldham, Phillip G**
Profile: p.2407
Table(s): Texas: Energy: State Regulatory &
Litigation (Electricity) Band 2 p.2341

**Oldham, William K**
Table(s): Kentucky: Litigation: Tort & Insurance
Defense Band 1 p.1312

**Olejko, Mitchell J**
Profile: p.657
Table(s): California: Healthcare Band 2 p.568

**Olenn, J Renn**
Table(s): Rhode Island: Litigation: General
Commercial Band 3 p.2254

**Oleynik, Jeffrey E**
Table(s): North Carolina: Antitrust Band 1 p.2020,
North Carolina: Litigation: General Commercial
Band 2 p.2033

**Olian, Robert**
Profile: p.1224
Table(s): Illinois: Environment: Litigation Band 1
p.1162

**Oliff, James A**
Table(s): Northern Virginia: Intellectual Property
Band 3 p.2497

**Olinsky, Mark S**
Profile: p.1743
Table(s): New Jersey: Litigation: White-Collar
Crime & Government Investigations Band 2
p.1723

**Oliphant, Fred**
Profile: p.884
Table(s): District of Columbia: Employee
Benefits & Executive Compensation Band 2 p.801

**Olivar, Harry**
Table(s): California: Litigation: Securities Band 4
p.594

**Oliver, Craig**
Table(s): Tennessee: Labor & Employment Band
3 p.2293

**Oliver, David**
Table(s): Missouri: Litigation: General
Commercial Band 2 p.1628

**Oliver, George J**
Profile: p.2043
Table(s): North Carolina: Labor & Employment
Band 2 p.2031

**Oliver, James**
Table(s): Maryland: Real Estate Band 1 p.1422

**Oliver, James D**
Profile: p.1300
Table(s): Kansas: Litigation: General
Commercial Band 2 p.1295

**Oliver Jr, Samuel**
Table(s): North Carolina: Real Estate Band 1
p.2037

**Olivier, Elizabeth**
Profile: p.1402
Table(s): Maine: Labor & Employment Up-and-com-
ing Individuals p.1390

**Olivieri, José A**
Profile: p.2585
Table(s): Wisconsin: Labor & Employment:
Immigration Band 1 p.2575

**Oller, Shawn**
Profile: p.510
Table(s): Arizona: Labor & Employment Up-and-
coming Individuals p.499

**Olsen, Eric T**
Table(s): Florida: Environment Band 3 p.951

**Olsen, Peter C**
Table(s): New York: Real Estate Band 3 p.1854

**Olsen, Theodore**
Table(s): Colorado: Labor & Employment Band 2
p.706

**Olshan, Regina**
Profile: p.1925
Table(s): Nationwide: Employee Benefits &
Executive Compensation Band 3 p.73, New York:
Employee Benefits & Executive Compensation
Band 1 p.1802

**Olson, Camille A**
Profile: p.1224
Table(s): Illinois: Labor & Employment Band 1
p.1175

**Ottenweller, Chris R**
Table(s): California: Intellectual Property: Patent Band 3 p.578

**Ottinger, Patrick S**
Table(s): Louisiana: Energy & Natural Resources: Oil & Gas Band 3 p.1344

**Otto, Angela Turriciano**
Table(s): Nevada: Real Estate Band 3 p.1679

**Ouellette, Robert R**
Table(s): Ohio: Corporate/M&A Band 4 p.2064

**Outten, Samuel W.**
Table(s): South Carolina: Litigation: General Commercial Band 2 p.2264

**Overberg, Nathan**
Table(s): Iowa: Labor & Employment Band 3 p.1285

**Overby, J Allen**
Profile: p.2307
Table(s): Tennessee: Corporate/M&A Band 3 p.2288

**Overly, Michael**
Table(s): California: IT & Outsourcing Band 3 p.583

**Overman, Robert**
Table(s): Kansas: Labor & Employment Band 1 p.1294

**Overstreet, David**
Profile: p.2226
Table(s): Pennsylvania: Environment Band 4 p.2194

**Overstreet, Mark R**
Profile: p.1322
Table(s): Kentucky: Environment, Natural Resources & Utilities: Utilities Band 2 p.1307

**Owen, Charles**
Table(s): Arkansas: Corporate/Commercial: Tax Band 2 p.518

**Owen, Robert D**
Table(s): Nationwide: Litigation: E-Discovery Band 1 p.187

**Owens, Andre**
Profile: p.381
Table(s): Nationwide: Financial Services Regulation: Broker Dealer (Compliance) Band 2 p.97

**Owens, James F**
Table(s): California: Healthcare Band 1 p.568

**Owens, Kerry L**
Profile: p.2475
Table(s): Utah: Real Estate Band 3 p.2470

**Owens, Richard D**
Profile: p.1925
Table(s): New York: Litigation: White-Collar Crime & Government Investigations Band 2 p.1836

**Owren, Turid**
Profile: p.2177
Table(s): Oregon: Labor & Employment: Immigration Band 1 p.2168

**Owren-Wiest, Nicole J**
Profile: p.381
Table(s): Nationwide: Government: Government Contracts Up-and-coming individuals p.117

**Oxley, William W**
Profile: p.658
Table(s): California: Litigation: General Commercial Band 5 p.593

**Oxton, Glen T.**
Table(s): Nationwide: Transportation: Shipping: Finance (New York) Band 2 p.260

**Ozdogan, Catherine**
Table(s): Texas: Banking & Finance Band 2 p.2325

**Ozier, William N**
Profile: p.2308
Table(s): Tennessee: Labor & Employment Band 1 p.2293

**Ozinga, Martin G.**
Table(s): Oklahoma: Intellectual Property Band 2 p.2138

# P

**Pace, Christopher**
Profile: p.1002
Table(s): Florida: Litigation: General Commercial Band 4 p.966

**Pace, Stanley Dan**
Profile: p.2109
Table(s): Ohio: Labor & Employment Band 3 p.2074

**Pachter, John**
Table(s): Nationwide: Government: Government Contracts Band 2 p.117

**Pachulski, Isaac M**
Table(s): California: Bankruptcy/Restructuring Band 2 p.542

**Pachulski, Richard M**
Table(s): Nationwide: Bankruptcy/Restructuring Band 2 p.39, California: Bankruptcy/Restructuring Band 1 p.542

**Pacitti, Domenic E**
Table(s): Delaware: Bankruptcy/Restructuring Band 3 p.754

**Packer, Leslie**
Profile: p.2044
Table(s): North Carolina: Litigation: Healthcare & Medical Malpractice Band 1 p.2034

**Packer, Rosetta B**
Profile: p.2226
Table(s): Pennsylvania: Bankruptcy/Restructuring Band 3 p.2188

**Packman, Kevin**
Profile: p.1002
Table(s): Florida: Tax: Estate Planning Band 3 p.979

**Packman, Stephen M**
Profile: p.1744
Table(s): New Jersey: Bankruptcy/Restructuring Band 1 p.1705

**Padgett, Mike**
Profile: p.1279
Table(s): Indiana: Labor & Employment Band 2 p.1271

**Page, Brian J**
Table(s): Michigan: Real Estate Band 3 p.1546

**Page, Edward J**
Profile: p.1002
Table(s): Florida: Litigation: White-Collar Crime & Government Investigations Band 3 p.967

**Page, Gregory P**
Table(s): Iowa: Corporate/M&A: Banking & Finance Band 2 p.1283

**Page, Marshall**
Profile: p.1367
Table(s): Louisiana: Banking & Finance Band 2 p.1335

**Page, Michael**
Table(s): California: Intellectual Property: Trademark, Copyright & Trade Secrets Band 1 p.578

**Page, Rosewell**
Table(s): Virginia: Litigation: General Commercial Senior Statesmen: p.2502

**Page, Thomas**
Table(s): Oregon: Real Estate Band 1 p.2173

**Pagel, Martha O**
Table(s): Oregon: Environment Band 1 p.2165

**Paget, David**
Table(s): New York: Environment Senior Statesmen: p.1807

**Paget, Joel**
Table(s): Washington: Immigration Band 2 p.2528

**Pagliaro, James**
Profile: p.2226
Table(s): Pennsylvania: Litigation: General Commercial Band 3 p.2203

**Pagliuca, Jeffrey S.**
Table(s): Colorado: Litigation: General Commercial Band 4 p.709

**Paine, James**
Table(s): Nationwide: Outsourcing Band 4 p.195

**Paine, William H**
Profile: p.1504
Table(s): Massachusetts: Litigation: Securities Band 1 p.1470

**Painter, Ann Marie**
Profile: p.2408
Table(s): Texas: Labor & Employment Band 4 p.2359

**Painter, Brett**
Profile: p.721
Table(s): Colorado: Labor & Employment Band 2 p.706

**Painter, Robin A**
Table(s): Nationwide: Investment Funds: Private Equity: Fund Formation Band 2 p.166, Massachusetts: Private Equity: Fund Formation Star Individuals p.1476

**Painter, William S**
Profile: p.1606
Table(s): Mississippi: Corporate/Commercial Band 1 p.1591

**Paisley, Bonnie J**
Table(s): New Mexico: Corporate/Commercial Band 2 p.1764

**Pak, Byung**
Profile: p.1092
Table(s): Georgia: Litigation: White-Collar Crime & Government Investigations Up-and-coming individuals p.1066

**Pakalka, William**
Profile: p.2408
Table(s): Texas: Antitrust Band 1 p.2323

**Pakenham, Kathleen M**
Table(s): Nationwide: Tax: Controversy Band 4 p.244

**Pakenham, Timothy J**
Profile: p.1092
Table(s): Georgia: Real Estate Band 1 p.1070

**Palan, Stephen**
Profile: p.885
Table(s): District of Columbia: Intellectual Property: Patent Prosecution Up-and-coming individuals p.820

**Palecki, Scott C.**
Profile: p.1300
Table(s): Kansas: Corporate/M&A Band 3 p.1292

**Palenchar, James**
Table(s): Colorado: Corporate/M&A Band 1 p.703

**Paliotta, Armand**
Profile: p.2152
Table(s): Oklahoma: Corporate/Commercial Band 1 p.2134

**Palladino, Peter M**
Profile: p.1504
Table(s): Massachusetts: Banking & Finance Band 1 p.1445

**Palma, Laura**
Profile: p.381
Table(s): Nationwide: Capital Markets: Securitisation Band 1 p.59

**Palmer, Bruce**
Table(s): Vermont: Corporate/Commercial: Captive Insurance Band 3 p.2483

**Palmer, Christopher E**
Profile: p.381
Table(s): Nationwide: Investment Funds: Registered Funds Band 2 p.170

**Palmer, Crisman**
Table(s): South Dakota: Corporate/Commercial Band 3 p.2281, South Dakota: Litigation: General Commercial Band 1 p.2284

**Palmer, David G**
Profile: p.721
Table(s): Colorado: Litigation: General Commercial Band 1 p.709

**Palmer, Deryck A**
Table(s): Nationwide: Bankruptcy/Restructuring Band 3 p.39, New York: Bankruptcy/Restructuring Band 3 p.1782

**Palmer, Drew T.**
Profile: p.2152
Table(s): Oklahoma: Intellectual Property Associates to watch p.2138

**Palmer, James C**
Profile: p.1403
Table(s): Maine: Real Estate Band 4 p.1395

2801

**Palmer, Justin**
Table(s): Utah: Labor & Employment **Band 3**
p.2467

**Palmer, Stephen D**
Profile: p.1092
Table(s): Georgia: Banking & Finance **Band 4**
p.1039

**Palmer, Thomas**
Profile: p.2177
Table(s): Oregon: Corporate/M&A **Band 2** p.2164

**Palmer, Timothy A**
Profile: p.2308
Table(s): Tennessee: Labor & Employment **Band 3** p.2293

**Palmer, Todd**
Profile: p.2585
Table(s): Wisconsin: Natural Resources &
Environment **Band 1** p.2578

**Palmer, Jr, James I**
Profile: p.1606
Table(s): Mississippi: Environment **Band 3** p.1594

**Palms, Stephen G**
Profile: p.1554
Table(s): Michigan: Real Estate **Band 1** p.1546

**Paltell, Eric**
Table(s): Maryland: Labor & Employment **Band 1**
p.1417

**Palumbo, Ralph H**
Table(s): Washington: Litigation: General
Commercial **Band 3** p.2533

**Panagakis, George N**
Profile: p.1224
Table(s): Nationwide: Bankruptcy/Restructuring
**Band 4** p.39, Illinois: Bankruptcy/Restructuring
**Band 2** p.1148

**Panahy, Dara A**
Profile: p.885
Table(s): District of Columbia: Telecom,
Broadcast & Satellite **Band 2** p.844

**Pangborn, Susan W**
Table(s): Georgia: Labor & Employment **Band 4**
p.1060

**Panitch, Ronald L**
Profile: p.2226
Table(s): Pennsylvania: Intellectual Property
**Band 2** p.2197

**Panoff, Robert**
Table(s): Florida: Tax **Band 1** p.979

**Panos, Christopher J**
Table(s): Massachusetts:
Bankruptcy/Restructuring **Band 3** p.1449

**Panovka, Robin**
Profile: p.1925
Table(s): Nationwide: Capital Markets: REITs
**Band 2** p.55, New York: Real Estate: Corporate
**Band 1** p.1854

**Pantaleo, Peter V**
Profile: p.381
Table(s): Nationwide: Bankruptcy/Restructuring
**Band 2** p.39, New York:
Bankruptcy/Restructuring **Band 2** p.1782

**Pantano, Paul**
Profile: p.381
Table(s): Nationwide: Capital Markets:
Derivatives **Band 3** p.51, Nationwide: Energy:
Electricity (Regulatory & Litigation) **Band 1** p.76

**Pantel, Glenn S**
Profile: p.1744
Table(s): New Jersey: Real Estate: Zoning/Land
Use **Band 1** p.1728

**Panter, Danielle**
Table(s): New Mexico: Labor & Employment:
Employee Benefits & Compensation **Band 1**
p.1767

**Papa, Ronald**
Table(s): New York: Corporate/M&A **Band 5**
p.1793

**Papalia, Vincent**
Table(s): New Jersey: Bankruptcy/Restructuring
**Band 3** p.1705

**Paparella, Christopher**
Profile: p.381
Table(s): Nationwide: International Arbitration
**Band 5** p.145

**Paparelli, Angelo**
Profile: p.658
Table(s): Nationwide: Immigration **Band 1** p.131,
California: Immigration **Star individuals** p.571

**Papavizas, Constantine G**
Profile: p.381
Table(s): Nationwide: Transportation: Shipping:
Regulatory (outside New York) **Band 1** p.264

**Pape, Stuart M**
Table(s): Nationwide: Food & Beverages:
Regulatory & Litigation **Band 1** p.107

**Papel, Laurence M**
Profile: p.2308
Table(s): Tennessee: Real Estate **Band 3** p.2299

**Papermaster, Daniel**
Profile: p.746
Table(s): Connecticut: Corporate/M&A **Band 3**
p.732

**Papier, David J**
Profile: p.1744
Table(s): New Jersey: Corporate/M&A **Band 3**
p.1707

**Pappas, Dean C**
Profile: p.658
Table(s): California: Real Estate **Band 2** p.611

**Pappas, Edward H**
Profile: p.1554
Table(s): Michigan: Litigation: General
Commercial **Band 1** p.1544

**Pappas, George F**
Profile: p.885
Table(s): District of Columbia: Intellectual
Property: Litigation **Band 1** p.821

**Pappas, M Lynn**
Table(s): Florida: Real Estate: Zoning/Land Use
**Band 1** p.975

**Pappas, Nicholas**
Profile: p.1279
Table(s): Indiana: Litigation: Appellate **Up-and-com-
ing individuals** p.1273

**Pappas, Peter G**
Table(s): Georgia: Intellectual Property **Band 3**
p.1056

**Pappas, Thomas J**
Table(s): New Hampshire: Litigation: General
Commercial **Band 3** p.1690

**Pappert, Michael J**
Profile: p.2408
Table(s): Texas: Real Estate **Band 3** p.2367

**Pappone, Michael J**
Profile: p.1504
Table(s): Massachusetts:
Bankruptcy/Restructuring **Band 1** p.1449

**Papson, Thomas C**
Profile: p.381
Table(s): Nationwide: Government: Government
Contracts **Band 2** p.117, Nationwide:
Government: Government Contracts: Bid
Protests p.117

**Paradee, John W**
Table(s): Delaware: Real Estate: Zoning/Land
Use **Band 2** p.766

**Paradiso, Robert**
Profile: p.1744
Table(s): New Jersey: Intellectual Property **Band**
**3** p.1716

**Parascandola, Stephen T**
Profile: p.2044
Table(s): North Carolina: Environment **Band 4**
p.2028

**Paravano, Jeffrey H**
Profile: p.885
Table(s): District of Columbia: Tax **Band 3** p.838

**Pardo, James A**
Profile: p.1926
Table(s): New York: Environment **Band 4** p.1807

**Pardo Jr, James**
Table(s): Georgia: Bankruptcy/Restructuring
**Band 1** p.1042

**Paré Jr, Armand M**
Table(s): Nationwide: Transportation: Shipping:
Litigation (New York) **Band 2** p.261

**Parel, S Scott**
Profile: p.2408
Table(s): Texas: Corporate/M&A **Up-and-coming**
**individuals** p.2337

**Parent, Jennifer L**
Profile: p.1696
Table(s): New Hampshire: Labor & Employment
**Band 3** p.1688

**Parham, David**
Profile: p.2408
Table(s): Texas: Bankruptcy/Restructuring **Band 4**
p.2328

**Pari, Joseph**
Table(s): District of Columbia: Tax **Band 2** p.838

**Paris, Ted W**
Profile: p.2408
Table(s): Texas: Corporate/M&A **Band 3** p.2337

**Paris, Zachary**
Profile: p.2109
Table(s): Ohio: Real Estate **Band 1** p.2086

**Parise, Michael J**
Profile: p.493
Table(s): Alaska: Corporate/M&A **Band 2** p.487,
Alaska: Corporate/M&A: Bankruptcy **Band 1**
p.487

**Parisi, Donna**
Profile: p.382
Table(s): Nationwide: Capital Markets:
Derivatives **Band 3** p.51

**Park, Brian C**
Table(s): Washington: Intellectual Property **Band**
**3** p.2529

**Park, Corey**
Table(s): Hawaii: Litigation: General Commercial
**Band 3** p.1119

**Park, Steven**
Table(s): Georgia: Intellectual Property **Up-and-
coming individuals** p.1056

**Park, Tai H**
Table(s): New York: Litigation: White-Collar
Crime & Government Investigations **Band 2**
p.1836

**Park, William W**
Profile: p.382
Table(s): Nationwide: International Arbitration:
Arbitrators **Band 1** p.146

**Parker, Anne S**
Table(s): Arkansas: Corporate/Commercial:
Municipal Bonds **Band 2** p.518

**Parker, Bruce**
Profile: p.382
Table(s): Nationwide: Product Liability & Mass
Torts **Band 5** p.208

**Parker, C Allen**
Profile: p.382
Table(s): Nationwide: Banking & Finance **Senior**
**Statesmen:** p.31

**Parker, Clayton**
Profile: p.1003
Table(s): Florida: Corporate/M&A & Private
Equity **Band 4** p.947

**Parker, Dallas**
Table(s): Texas: Corporate/M&A **Band 4** p.2337,
Texas: Technology: Corporate & Commercial
**Band 3** p.2375

**Parker, David L**
Table(s): Texas: Intellectual Property **Band 2**
p.2354

**Parker, Doug**
Profile: p.493
Table(s): Alaska: Labor & Employment **Band 2**
p.489

**Parker, Emily A**
Profile: p.2408
Table(s): Texas: Tax: Litigation **Band 1** p.2371

**Parker, Gilbert E**
Table(s): Oregon: Real Estate **Band 1** p.2173

**Parker, James**
Table(s): New Mexico: Corporate/Commercial
**Band 2** p.1764, New Mexico:
Corporate/Commercial: Tax **Band 1** p.1764, New
Mexico: Labor & Employment: Employee
Benefits & Compensation **Band 1** p.1767

**Parker, Jeffrey**
Table(s): California: Environment **Band 4** p.564

**Parker, John**
Table(s): Georgia: Healthcare **Band 1** p.1052

**Parker, Kimberly**
Profile: p.382
Table(s): Nationwide: International Trade: FCPA
Experts **Band 3** p.153

**Parker, Myles A**
Profile: p.1606
Table(s): Mississippi: Litigation: General
Commercial **Band 3** p.1597

**Parker, Paul T**
Table(s): Washington: Intellectual Property **Band 2** p.2529

**Parker, Richard G**
Table(s): District of Columbia: Antitrust **Band 1** p.787

**Parker, Stephanie**
Profile: p.1092
Table(s): Georgia: Litigation: General
Commercial **Band 2** p.1065

**Parker, Steve**
Profile: p.2513
Table(s): Nationwide: Life Sciences:
Corporate/Commercial **Band 3** p.182, Northern
Virginia: Intellectual Property **Band 2** p.2497

**Parkins, Lenard**
Table(s): New York: Bankruptcy/Restructuring
**Band 4** p.1782

**Parks, John R**
Table(s): Georgia: Real Estate **Band 2** p.1070

**Parks, Randall S**
Profile: p.382
Table(s): Nationwide: Outsourcing **Band 2** p.195

**Parks, Timothy M**
Table(s): Oregon: Real Estate **Band 2** p.2173

**Parliman, Gregory C**
Profile: p.1744
Table(s): New Jersey: Labor & Employment **Band 1** p.1718

**Parmley, Bruce E**
Table(s): Nationwide: Leisure & Hospitality **Band 2** p.179, District of Columbia: Real Estate **Band 1** p.835

**Parnass, John**
Table(s): Washington: Litigation: General
Commercial **Band 3** p.2533

**Parnes, Lydia B.**
Table(s): Nationwide: Privacy & Data Security
**Band 3** p.199

**Parobek, Drew**
Profile: p.2109
Table(s): Ohio: Bankruptcy/Restructuring **Band 1** p.2058

**Parr, Clayton J**
Table(s): Utah: Energy & Natural Resources
**Senior Statesmen:** p.2464

**Parr, Keith D**
Profile: p.1224
Table(s): Illinois: Intellectual Property **Band 4** p.1171

**Parr, Jr, Henry L**
Profile: p.2271
Table(s): South Carolina: Litigation: General
Commercial **Band 2** p.2264

**Parrilli, Tifani**
Table(s): Oregon: Labor & Employment:
Immigration **Band 2** p.2168

**Parrino, Richard**
Table(s): District of Columbia: Corporate/M&A &
Private Equity **Band 4** p.797

**Parris, Mark S**
Table(s): Washington: Intellectual Property **Band 2** p.2529

**Parrish, Jimmy D**
Profile: p.1003
Table(s): Florida: Bankruptcy/Restructuring **Up-and-coming individuals** p.939

**Parrish, Robert B**
Table(s): Nationwide: Transportation: Shipping:
Litigation (outside New York) **Band 1** p.263

**Parrish, Theresa W**
Profile: p.1774
Table(s): New Mexico: Labor & Employment
**Band 2** p.1767

**Parrott, Charles N**
Profile: p.1607
Table(s): Mississippi: Corporate/Commercial:
Banking & Finance **Band 1** p.1591

**Parry, Stanley W**
Profile: p.1682
Table(s): Nevada: Litigation: General
Commercial **Band 3** p.1677

**Parsigian, David N**
Table(s): Michigan: Corporate/M&A **Band 2** p.1538

**Parsigian, Kenneth J**
Table(s): Nationwide: Product Liability & Mass
Torts **Band 4** p.208, Nationwide: Product Liability:
Tobacco **Band 2** p.208, Massachusetts: Litigation:
General Commercial **Band 2** p.1470

**Parsley, Julie**
Profile: p.2409
Table(s): Texas: Energy: State Regulatory &
Litigation (Electricity) **Band 2** p.2341

**Parsonage, Ronald K**
Table(s): Nebraska: Corporate/Commercial **Band 3** p.1659

**Parsons, Gary S**
Table(s): North Carolina: Litigation: General
Commercial **Band 3** p.2033

**Parsons, Jeffrey R**
Profile: p.2409
Table(s): Texas: Insurance **Band 3** p.2351

**Parsons, Paul**
Table(s): Texas: Immigration **Band 2** p.2349

**Parsons, Philip S**
Table(s): Florida: Environment **Band 1** p.951

**Parsons, Ron**
Table(s): South Dakota: Litigation: General
Commercial **Band 3** p.2284

**Partnow, Peter C**
Profile: p.493
Table(s): Alaska: Labor & Employment **Band 3** p.489

**Partridge, John J**
Table(s): Rhode Island: Corporate/Commercial
**Band 2** p.2251

**Partridge, Scott**
Profile: p.2409
Table(s): Texas: Intellectual Property **Band 1** p.2354

**Parvis, Peter P**
Profile: p.1431
Table(s): Maryland: Healthcare **Band 2** p.1415

**Pasahow, Lynn H**
Profile: p.658
Table(s): California: Intellectual Property: Patent
**Band 4** p.578

**Pasano, Michael S**
Profile: p.1003
Table(s): Florida: Litigation: White-Collar Crime &
Government Investigations **Star individuals** p.967

**Pascual, Rey**
Table(s): Georgia: Corporate/M&A **Band 3** p.1046

**Pasek, Jeffrey**
Profile: p.2227
Table(s): Pennsylvania: Labor & Employment
**Band 2** p.2200

**Pashby, Gary**
Table(s): South Dakota: Litigation: General
Commercial **Band 1** p.2284

**Pasich, Kirk A**
Profile: p.382
Table(s): Nationwide: Insurance: Dispute
Resolution: Policyholder **Band 1** p.137, California:
Insurance: Policyholder **Band 1** p.576

**Pass, Brian J**
Table(s): California: IT & Outsourcing **Band 2** p.583

**Passannante, William G**
Profile: p.382
Table(s): Nationwide: Insurance: Dispute
Resolution: Policyholder **Band 2** p.137, New York:
Insurance: Dispute Resolution: Policyholder **Band 2** p.1816

**Passantino, Stefan**
Table(s): Nationwide: Government: Political Law
**Band 3** p.124

**Passarelli, John P**
Profile: p.1668
Table(s): Nebraska: Litigation: Intellectual
Property **Band 1** p.1664

**Passman, Donald S**
Table(s): California: Media & Entertainment:
Transactional: Mainly Talent **Band 1** p.609

**Pasternack, Marshall**
Profile: p.1003
Table(s): Florida: Corporate/M&A & Private
Equity **Band 3** p.947

**Pasternak, Daniel B**
Profile: p.510
Table(s): Arizona: Labor & Employment **Band 4** p.499

**Pastor, Sherilyn**
Profile: p.1744
Table(s): New Jersey: Litigation: Insurance **Band 1** p.1723

**Pastuszenski, Brian E**
Profile: p.1504
Table(s): Nationwide: Securities: Litigation **Band 2** p.232, Massachusetts: Litigation: Securities
**Band 1** p.1470

**Patberg, William L**
Table(s): Ohio: Natural Resources &
Environment **Band 3** p.2083

**Pate, Stephen**
Profile: p.2409
Table(s): Texas: Insurance **Band 1** p.2351

**Patel, Anjana D**
Profile: p.1744
Table(s): New Jersey: Healthcare **Band 3** p.1715

**Patel, Nikesh R**
Table(s): Nationwide: Projects: Renewables &
Alternative Energy **Band 2** p.218

**Patel, Rahul**
Profile: p.1092
Table(s): Georgia: Corporate/M&A **Band 4** p.1046

**Patella, Raymond**
Profile: p.1744
Table(s): New Jersey: Bankruptcy/Restructuring
**Band 4** p.1705

**Patin, Douglas L**
Table(s): District of Columbia: Construction **Band 2** p.795

**Patrick, Diane**
Table(s): Massachusetts: Labor & Employment
**Band 1** p.1466

**Patrick, Kathy**
Profile: p.2409
Table(s): Nationwide: Securities: Litigation **Band 2** p.232, Texas: Litigation: General Commercial
**Band 1** p.2362, Texas: Litigation: Securities **Band 1** p.2362

**Patrick, Michael D**
Table(s): Nationwide: Immigration **Band 3** p.131,
New York: Immigration **Band 1** p.1814

**Patrick, Tandy**
Profile: p.1322
Table(s): Kentucky: Real Estate **Band 2** p.1314

**Patrick III, William H**
Profile: p.1367
Table(s): Louisiana: Bankruptcy/Restructuring
**Band 1** p.1337

**Patrikis, Ernest T**
Profile: p.382
Table(s): Nationwide: Financial Services
Regulation: Banking (Compliance) **Band 3** p.96

**Patterson, Carol J**
Table(s): New York: Construction **Band 4** p.1791

**Patterson, Donna**
Profile: p.885
Table(s): District of Columbia: Antitrust **Band 5** p.787

# Index of Lawyers

**Patterson, J Randall**
Profile: p.1607
Table(s): **Mississippi**: Labor & Employment **Band 3** p.1595

**Patterson, Jeffrey**
Table(s): **Nevada**: Real Estate **Band 2** p.1679

**Patterson, John**
Table(s): **New Mexico**: Real Estate **Band 2** p.1772

**Patterson, Nancy L**
Profile: p.2409
Table(s): **Texas**: Labor & Employment **Band 1** p.2359

**Patterson, Paul**
Table(s): **Pennsylvania**: Bankruptcy/Restructuring **Band 3** p.2188

**Patterson, Robert S**
Table(s): **Tennessee**: Litigation: General Commercial **Band 2** p.2295

**Patterson, Stephen J**
Profile: p.1505
Table(s): **Massachusetts**: Banking & Finance **Band 3** p.1445

**Patterson, Thomas E**
Table(s): **California**: Bankruptcy/Restructuring **Band 2** p.542

**Patterson III, George A**
Profile: p.2565
Table(s): **West Virginia**: Natural Resources **Band 2** p.2558

**Patterson Jr, Carl N**
Profile: p.2044
Table(s): **North Carolina**: Litigation: General Commercial **Band 3** p.2033

**Pattiz, Keith**
Profile: p.1926
Table(s): **New York**: Real Estate **Band 3** p.1854

**Patton, David**
Profile: p.382
Table(s): **Nationwide**: Energy: Oil & Gas (Transactional) **Band 4** p.79

**Patton, Glenn G**
Profile: p.1093
Table(s): **Georgia**: Labor & Employment **Band 4** p.1060

**Patton Jr, James L**
Table(s): **Delaware**: Bankruptcy/Restructuring **Star individuals** p.754

**Pauken, Patrick J**
Profile: p.2109
Table(s): **Ohio**: Real Estate **Band 4** p.2086

**Paul, Chris A**
Profile: p.2152
Table(s): **Oklahoma**: Energy & Natural Resources: Environment **Band 2** p.2136

**Paul, Deborah L**
Profile: p.1926
Table(s): **New York**: Tax **Band 2** p.1862

**Paul, Marcia B**
Table(s): **New York**: Intellectual Property: Trade Mark & Copyright **Band 2** p.1821, **New York**: Media & Entertainment: Copyright & Contract Disputes **Band 2** p.1851

**Paul, Niall**
Profile: p.2565
Table(s): **West Virginia**: Litigation: General Commercial **Band 2** p.2555

**Paul, Patrick**
Table(s): **Arizona**: Environment (including water rights) **Band 2** p.497

**Paul, William M**
Profile: p.885
Table(s): **District of Columbia**: Tax **Band 2** p.838

**Paulk, Joseph H.**
Table(s): **Oklahoma**: Litigation: Mediators **Band 1** p.2141

**Paulsen, Bruce G.**
Profile: p.383
Table(s): **Nationwide**: Transportation: Shipping: Litigation (New York) **Band 4** p.261

**Paulson, Matthew**
Table(s): **Nationwide**: Climate Change **Band 3** p.63, **Texas**: Environment **Band 4** p.2343

**Pautler, Paul**
Table(s): **Missouri**: Labor & Employment **Band 3** p.1625

**Pauw, Robert**
Table(s): **Washington**: Immigration **Band 2** p.2528

**Pavey, Judith**
Profile: p.1124
Table(s): **Hawaii**: Litigation: General Commercial **Band 2** p.1119

**Pawlosky, Mollie M**
Table(s): **Iowa**: Litigation: General Commercial **Band 3** p.1288

**Pawlow, Jean A**
Profile: p.383
Table(s): **Nationwide**: Tax: Controversy **Band 3** p.244

**Payne, Allan**
Table(s): **Montana**: Natural Resources & Environment **Band 2** p.1651

**Payne, Charles**
Table(s): **Southern Virginia**: Real Estate **Up-and-coming individuals** p.2506

**Payne, Clare Hudson**
Table(s): **Maine**: Labor & Employment **Band 3** p.1390

**Paynter, Craig**
Profile: p.2109
Table(s): **Ohio**: Construction **Band 3** p.2062

**Pear, Charles**
Table(s): **Hawaii**: Real Estate **Band 1** p.1120

**Pearce, Michael J**
Table(s): **Arizona**: Environment: Water Rights **Band 1** p.497

**Pearce, Michael J**
Table(s): **Maine**: Corporate/M&A: Bankruptcy **Band 2** p.1385

**Peard, Patricia A**
Table(s): **Maine**: Labor & Employment **Band 3** p.1390

**Pearigen, Michael**
Table(s): **Tennessee**: Environment **Band 2** p.2290

**Pearl, Julie**
Table(s): **Nationwide**: Immigration **Band 2** p.131, **California**: Immigration **Star individuals** p.571

**Pearl, Nicole M.**
Profile: p.383
Table(s): **Nationwide**: Wealth Management: Western Region **Up-and-coming individuals** p.267

**Pearlman, Samuel**
Table(s): **Ohio**: Real Estate **Band 3** p.2086

**Pearlson, Jonathan Z**
Table(s): **Massachusetts**: Environment **Band 3** p.1457

**Pearlstein, Andrew M**
Profile: p.1505
Table(s): **Massachusetts**: Real Estate **Band 3** p.1478

**Pearlstein, Mark D**
Table(s): **Illinois**: Real Estate **Band 4** p.1187

**Pearlstein, Mark W**
Profile: p.1505
Table(s): **Massachusetts**: Litigation: White-Collar Crime & Government Investigations **Band 1** p.1471

**Pearse, Richard W**
Profile: p.1224
Table(s): **Illinois**: Construction **Band 2** p.1154

**Pearson, Jonathan**
Profile: p.2271
Table(s): **South Carolina**: Labor & Employment **Band 2** p.2262

**Pearson, Nick**
Profile: p.1926
Table(s): **New York**: Insurance: Transactional & Regulatory **Band 3** p.1816

**Pearson, Richard**
Table(s): **Alabama**: Banking & Finance: Mainly Regulatory **Band 2** p.455

**Pearson, Ronald C**
Profile: p.658
Table(s): **California**: Tax: Estate Planning **Band 1** p.617

**Peaslee, James M**
Profile: p.1926
Table(s): **New York**: Tax **Band 1** p.1862

**Pecht, Gerard**
Profile: p.2409
Table(s): **Texas**: Litigation: Energy & Natural Resources **Band 3** p.2361, **Texas**: Litigation: Securities **Band 2** p.2361

**Peck, Anne**
Table(s): **California**: Intellectual Property: Trademark, Copyright & Trade Secrets **Band 3** p.578

**Peck, Ian**
Table(s): **Texas**: Bankruptcy/Restructuring **Up-and-coming individuals** p.2328

**Peck, Kathy A**
Table(s): **Oregon**: Labor & Employment **Band 2** p.2168

**Peck, S Michael**
Profile: p.1224
Table(s): **Illinois**: Corporate/M&A: Private Equity **Band 1** p.1157

**Peck, Steven**
Profile: p.1505
Table(s): **Massachusetts**: Private Equity: Buyouts **Band 2** p.1474

**Peck, Stewart F**
Table(s): **Louisiana**: Bankruptcy/Restructuring **Band 2** p.1337

**Peckar, Robert S**
Profile: p.1926
Table(s): **New York**: Construction **Band 1** p.1791

**Pecoraro, Jessica**
Table(s): **Minnesota**: Labor & Employment **Band 3** p.1571

**Peden, David**
Profile: p.2409
Table(s): **Texas**: Construction **Band 1** p.2335

**Pederson, Jan**
Table(s): **District of Columbia**: Immigration **Band 3** p.814

**Pedowitz, Lawrence B**
Profile: p.1926
Table(s): **New York**: Litigation: White-Collar Crime & Government Investigations **Star individuals** p.1836

**Pedreira, Virginia M**
Table(s): **Washington**: Real Estate **Band 2** p.2535

**Pedrick, Michael J**
Profile: p.2227
Table(s): **Pennsylvania**: Banking & Finance **Band 2** p.2186

**Pedrow, Brian D**
Profile: p.2227
Table(s): **Pennsylvania**: Labor & Employment **Band 3** p.2200

**Peek, J Stephen**
Profile: p.1682
Table(s): **Nevada**: Litigation: General Commercial **Band 1** p.1677

**Peek, Michael S**
Profile: p.2308
Table(s): **Tennessee**: Real Estate **Band 2** p.2299

**Peifer, Charles**
Table(s): **New Mexico**: Litigation: General Commercial **Band 1** p.1769

**Peikes, Lawrence**
Profile: p.746
Table(s): **Connecticut**: Labor & Employment **Band 3** p.736

**Peikin, Steven R**
Profile: p.1927
Table(s): **New York**: Litigation: White-Collar Crime & Government Investigations **Band 2** p.1836

**Peirano, John J**
Profile: p.1744
Table(s): **New Jersey**: Labor & Employment **Band 1** p.1718

**Peirce, Richard**
Table(s): **Pennsylvania**: Intellectual Property **Band 4** p.2197

**Peitzman, Lawrence**
Profile: p.658
Table(s): **California**: Bankruptcy/Restructuring **Senior Statesmen**: p.542

**Pelavin, Alyse N**
Profile: p.658
Table(s): **California**: Tax: Estate Planning **Up-and-coming individuals** p.617

**Pelczarski, Karen A**
Table(s): **Rhode Island**: Litigation: General Commercial **Band 3** p.2254

**Pelfrey, D Patton**
Profile: p.1323
Table(s): **Kentucky**: Labor & Employment **Band 1** p.1310

**Pelham, Zachary**
Table(s): **North Dakota**: Litigation: General Commercial **Up-and-coming individuals** p.2053

**Pelle, Anthony**
Profile: p.1003
Table(s): **Florida**: Insurance **Band 3** p.957

**Pellerin, Bryan**
Table(s): **New Hampshire**: Real Estate **Band 3** p.1692

**Pelletier, Raymond A**
Profile: p.1403
Table(s): **Maine**: Real Estate **Band 4** p.1395, **Maine**: Real Estate: Timberland/Conservation **Band 2** p.1395

**Pels, Gerald J**
Profile: p.2409
Table(s): **Texas**: Environment **Band 3** p.2343

**Pelta, Eleanor**
Profile: p.885
Table(s): **Nationwide**: Immigration **Band 1** p.131, **District of Columbia**: Immigration **Band 1** p.814

**Pelton, Eric J**
Profile: p.1554
Table(s): **Michigan**: Labor & Employment **Band 3** p.1542

**Peltonen, John E**
Profile: p.1697
Table(s): **New Hampshire**: Environment **Band 1** p.1687

**Pemberton, Alan**
Profile: p.383
Table(s): **Nationwide**: Government: Government Contracts **Band 4** p.117

**Pence, Linda L**
Table(s): **Indiana**: Litigation: General Commercial **Band 2** p.1273

**Pence, Thomas C**
Table(s): **Wisconsin**: Labor & Employment **Band 2** p.2575

**Pence, William L**
Profile: p.1003
Table(s): **Florida**: Environment **Band 2** p.951

**Penchina, Robert**
Profile: p.1927
Table(s): **New York**: Intellectual Property: Trade Mark & Copyright **Band 3** p.1821

**Penick, Bridget R**
Table(s): **Iowa**: Labor & Employment **Band 2** p.1285, **Iowa**: Labor & Employment: Immigration **Band 1** p.1285

**Penna, Richard A**
Profile: p.885
Table(s): **District of Columbia**: Environment **Band 3** p.804

**Penne, Jeffrey S.**
Table(s): **Nebraska**: Corporate/Commercial **Up-and-coming individuals** p.1659

**Pennington, James C**
Profile: p.471
Table(s): **Alabama**: Labor & Employment **Band 2** p.460

**Pennington, Michael**
Table(s): **Alabama**: Litigation: General Commercial **Band 3** p.463

**Penny, William**
Profile: p.2308
Table(s): **Tennessee**: Environment **Band 1** p.2290

**Pentelovitch, William**
Table(s): **Minnesota**: Litigation: General Commercial **Band 1** p.1574

**Penza Jr, Joseph F**
Table(s): **Rhode Island**: Litigation: General Commercial **Band 3** p.2254

**Penzer, Michèle**
Profile: p.383
Table(s): **Nationwide**: Banking & Finance **Band 2** p.31

**Pepke, Michael T**
Profile: p.2585
Table(s): **Wisconsin**: Corporate/M&A **Band 2** p.2571

**Peponis, Margaret S**
Profile: p.383
Table(s): **Nationwide**: Banking & Finance **Band 2** p.31

**Pepper, David E**
Profile: p.2152
Table(s): **Oklahoma**: Energy & Natural Resources **Band 1** p.2136

**Pepple, Daniel P**
Table(s): **Washington**: Real Estate **Band 2** p.2535

**Pera, Lucian**
Profile: p.2308
Table(s): **Tennessee**: Litigation: General Commercial **Band 3** p.2295

**Percival, Donald E**
Table(s): **Washington**: Real Estate **Band 2** p.2535

**Peregrine, Michael W**
Profile: p.1225
Table(s): **Nationwide**: Healthcare: Transactional **Band 2** p.128, **Illinois**: Healthcare **Band 1** p.1165

**Perellis, Andrew H**
Profile: p.1225
Table(s): **Illinois**: Environment: Litigation **Band 2** p.1162

**Perelman, Richard S**
Profile: p.2227
Table(s): **Pennsylvania**: Banking & Finance **Band 2** p.2186

**Perez, Alfredo R**
Profile: p.2409
Table(s): **Nationwide**: Bankruptcy/Restructuring **Band 4** p.39, **Texas**: Bankruptcy/Restructuring **Band 1** p.2328

**Perez, Luis J**
Table(s): **Florida**: Corporate/M&A & Private Equity **Band 2** p.947, **Florida**: Latin American Investment **Band 4** p.963

**Perez, Tania**
Profile: p.383
Table(s): **Nationwide**: Energy: Oil & Gas (Regulatory & Litigation) **Up-and-coming individuals** p.78

**Pergola, Anthony O**
Profile: p.1744
Table(s): **New Jersey**: Corporate/M&A **Band 2** p.1707

**Perich, Thomas J**
Profile: p.2409
Table(s): **Texas**: Banking & Finance **Band 3** p.2325

**Perkins, Alan**
Profile: p.2410
Table(s): **Texas**: Corporate/M&A **Band 4** p.2337

**Perkins, Alan Curtis**
Profile: p.2177
Table(s): **Oregon**: Labor & Employment: Immigration **Band 2** p.2168

**Perkins, Eric**
Table(s): **New Jersey**: Bankruptcy/Restructuring **Band 4** p.1705

**Perkins, G Alan**
Table(s): **Arkansas**: Litigation: Environmental **Band 1** p.522

**Perkins, Jennifer**
Profile: p.885
Table(s): **District of Columbia**: Real Estate **Band 3** p.835

**Perkins, Michael**
Table(s): **Texas**: Insurance: Regulation **Band 2** p.2351

**Perkins, Nancy L**
Profile: p.383
Table(s): **Nationwide**: Privacy & Data Security **Band 2** p.199

**Perkins Jr, Joseph J**
Table(s): **Alaska**: Environment, Natural Resources & Regulated Industries **Band 1** p.488

**Perl, Arnold E**
Profile: p.2308
Table(s): **Tennessee**: Labor & Employment **Band 3** p.2293

**Perl, Sanford E**
Profile: p.1225
Table(s): **Illinois**: Corporate/M&A: Private Equity **Band 1** p.1157

**Perling, Lester**
Table(s): **Florida**: Healthcare **Band 2** p.954

**Perlis, Mark**
Profile: p.383
Table(s): **Nationwide**: Energy: Electricity (Regulatory & Litigation) **Band 3** p.76

**Perlman, Daniel J**
Profile: p.1225
Table(s): **Illinois**: Real Estate **Band 2** p.1187

**Perlman, Felicia G**
Profile: p.1225
Table(s): **Illinois**: Bankruptcy/Restructuring **Band 3** p.1148

**Perloff, Hal**
Table(s): **District of Columbia**: Construction **Up-and-coming individuals** p.795

**Perlowski, Henry M**
Profile: p.1093
Table(s): **Georgia**: Labor & Employment **Band 2** p.1060

**Permut, Barry**
Table(s): **Colorado**: Real Estate **Band 2** p.714

**Pernick, John D**
Profile: p.658
Table(s): **California**: Litigation: Securities **Band 4** p.594

**Pernick, Norman L**
Profile: p.773
Table(s): **Delaware**: Bankruptcy/Restructuring **Band 1** p.754

**Perrault, Jean-Paul**
Profile: p.1367
Table(s): **Louisiana**: Corporate/M&A **Band 4** p.1341

**Perrenoud, Scott**
Table(s): **South Dakota**: Corporate/Commercial **Band 2** p.2281, **South Dakota**: Corporate/Commercial: Bankruptcy/Restructuring **Band 1** p.2281

**Perrin, Harry**
Profile: p.2410
Table(s): **Texas**: Bankruptcy/Restructuring **Band 2** p.2328

**Perrochet, Lisa**
Profile: p.658
Table(s): **California**: Litigation: Appellate **Band 3** p.599

**Perrone, William A**
Profile: p.746
Table(s): **Connecticut**: Corporate/M&A **Band 2** p.732

**Perry, Alan W**
Profile: p.1607
Table(s): **Mississippi**: Litigation: Appellate **Band 2** p.1596, **Mississippi**: Litigation: General Commercial **Star individuals** p.1596

**Perry, C Jones**
Table(s): **Nationwide**: Wealth Management: Eastern Region **Band 4** p.267

**Perry, Donna**
Table(s): **Kentucky**: Labor & Employment **Band 1** p.1310

**Perry, Mark A**
Profile: p.384
Table(s): **Nationwide**: Appellate Law **Band 3** p.26

**Perry Jr, Audy M**
Table(s): **West Virginia**: Corporate/Commercial **Band 3** p.2550, **West Virginia**: Corporate/Commercial: Tax **Band 2** p.2550

**Person, Barbara E**
Table(s): Nebraska: Healthcare **Band 2** p.1661

**Persons, Ray**
Profile: p.1093
Table(s): Georgia: Litigation: General
Commercial **Band 1** p.1065

**Perwin, Joel**
Table(s): Florida: Litigation: Appellate **Band 1**
p.972

**Perwin, Scott**
Table(s): Florida: Antitrust **Band 1** p.935

**Perzek, Philip**
Table(s): Illinois: Banking & Finance **Band 4**
p.1145

**Pesch, Ellen**
Profile: p.384
Table(s): Nationwide: Capital Markets:
Structured Products **Band 3** p.52

**Peshek, Peter**
Table(s): Wisconsin: Natural Resources &
Environment **Senior Statesmen:** p.2578

**Pestaina, Cora-Ann V.**
Table(s): New York: Immigration **Associates to
watch** p.1814

**Peterman, David**
Profile: p.2410
Table(s): Texas: Technology: Corporate &
Commercial **Band 3** p.2375

**Peterman, Nancy A**
Profile: p.1225
Table(s): Illinois: Bankruptcy/Restructuring **Band
2** p.1148

**Peterman, Randall**
Table(s): Idaho: Bankruptcy/Restructuring **Band 1**
p.1131

**Peters, Christopher**
Profile: p.1927
Table(s): New York: Tax **Band 4** p.1862

**Peters, Elliot**
Table(s): California: Litigation: White-Collar
Crime & Government Investigations **Band 2** p.601

**Peters, Georgeann G**
Profile: p.2109
Table(s): Ohio: Employee Benefits & Executive
Compensation **Band 2** p.2067

**Peters, Gerald**
Profile: p.659
Table(s): California: Healthcare **Band 2** p.568

**Peters, M Beth**
Table(s): Nationwide: International Trade: Export
Controls & Economic Sanctions **Band 2** p.153,
District of Columbia: Immigration **Band 3** p.814

**Peters, William J**
Profile: p.384
Table(s): Nationwide: Outsourcing **Band 1** p.195,
California: IT & Outsourcing **Band 1** p.583

**Petersen, Curtis J**
Table(s): Kansas: Real Estate **Up-and-coming individuals** p.1297

**Petersen, James L**
Table(s): Indiana: Litigation: General
Commercial **Band 2** p.1273

**Petersen, John D**
Table(s): Kansas: Real Estate **Band 1** p.1297

**Petersen, Joseph**
Table(s): New York: Intellectual Property: Trade
Mark & Copyright **Band 3** p.1821

**Petersen, Larry**
Profile: p.1655
Table(s): Montana: Corporate/M&A **Band 1**
p.1646

**Petersen, Scott**
Table(s): Utah: Labor & Employment: ERISA **Band
1** p.2467

**Peterson, Andrew**
Profile: p.2153
Table(s): Oklahoma: Intellectual Property
**Associates to watch** p.2138

**Peterson, Brad L**
Table(s): Nationwide: Outsourcing **Band 1** p.195,
Illinois: Technology & Outsourcing **Band 1** p.1194

**Peterson, Brian**
Profile: p.2565
Table(s): West Virginia: Labor & Employment **Up-
and-coming individuals** p.2553

**Peterson, Charles**
Table(s): Nationwide: Energy: Nuclear
(Regulatory & Litigation) **Band 3** p.77

**Peterson, Edward**
Table(s): Florida: Bankruptcy/Restructuring **Up-
and-coming individuals** p.939

**Peterson, Edward**
Profile: p.2410
Table(s): Texas: Real Estate **Band 2** p.2367

**Peterson, James**
Table(s): Wisconsin: Corporate/M&A **Band 3**
p.2571

**Peterson, John M.**
Table(s): Nationwide: International Trade:
Customs **Band 2** p.155

**Peterson, Ken**
Table(s): Kansas: Litigation: General
Commercial **Band 1** p.1295

**Peterson, Kurt**
Table(s): California: Healthcare **Band 4** p.568

**Peterson, Matthew**
Table(s): Alaska: Litigation: General Commercial
**Band 3** p.490

**Peterson, Nancy K**
Profile: p.2585
Table(s): Wisconsin: Natural Resources &
Environment **Band 2** p.2578

**Peterson, R Alan**
Table(s): South Dakota: Litigation: General
Commercial **Band 3** p.2284

**Peterson, Ralph**
Table(s): Florida: Labor & Employment **Band 2**
p.959

**Peterson, Ronald R**
Profile: p.1225
Table(s): Illinois: Bankruptcy/Restructuring **Band
3** p.1148

**Peterson, Steven D**
Profile: p.2475
Table(s): Utah: Real Estate **Band 2** p.2470

**Peterson Jr, John M**
Profile: p.659
Table(s): Nationwide: Tax: Controversy **Band 3**
p.244, California: Tax **Band 1** p.617

**Petesch, Bruce A**
Profile: p.2044
Table(s): North Carolina: Labor & Employment
**Band 3** p.2031

**Peticolas, Susanne**
Table(s): New Jersey: Environment **Band 3** p.1711

**Petranovich, Milo**
Profile: p.2178
Table(s): Oregon: Litigation: General
Commercial **Band 2** p.2171

**Petretti, Vito**
Profile: p.1927
Table(s): New York: Technology & Outsourcing
**Up-and-coming individuals** p.1868

**Petrich, Louis P**
Table(s): California: Media & Entertainment:
Litigation **Band 2** p.606

**Petricoff, Howard**
Profile: p.2109
Table(s): Ohio: Natural Resources &
Environment **Band 4** p.2083

**Petrie, James**
Table(s): Ohio: Labor & Employment **Band 4**
p.2074

**Petrik, Michael T**
Profile: p.1093
Table(s): Georgia: Tax **Band 1** p.1072

**Petrikin, Ronald**
Table(s): Oklahoma: Labor & Employment **Band 1**
p.2140

**Petrillo, Guy**
Table(s): New York: Litigation: White-Collar
Crime & Government Investigations **Band 2**
p.1836

**Petro, John J**
Table(s): Ohio: Construction **Senior Statesmen:**
p.2062

**Petrocelli, Daniel**
Table(s): California: Litigation: General
Commercial **Band 1** p.593, California: Media &
Entertainment: Litigation **Band 2** p.606

**Petroff, Laura R**
Profile: p.659
Table(s): California: Labor & Employment **Band 3**
p.587

**Petros, Gerald J**
Table(s): Rhode Island: Litigation: General
Commercial **Band 1** p.2254

**Petrosky, Edward F**
Profile: p.384
Table(s): Nationwide: Capital Markets: Debt &
Equity **Band 2** p.46, Nationwide: Capital Markets:
REITs **Band 2** p.55

**Petrovich, Michael P**
Table(s): Florida: Environment **Band 3** p.951

**Petruccelli, Gerald**
Table(s): Maine: Litigation: General Commercial
**Band 1** p.1393

**Petrus, Barbara**
Table(s): Hawaii: Labor & Employment **Band 1**
p.1117

**Pettibone, Jon E**
Profile: p.510
Table(s): Arizona: Labor & Employment **Band 1**
p.499

**Pettit, Debra**
Table(s): Iowa: Litigation: General Commercial
**Band 4** p.1288

**Pettit, Ted N**
Profile: p.1124
Table(s): Hawaii: Bankruptcy/Restructuring **Band
1** p.1114

**Petty, W Scott**
Profile: p.1093
Table(s): Georgia: Intellectual Property **Band 4**
p.1056

**Petumenos, Timothy J**
Profile: p.493
Table(s): Alaska: Litigation: General Commercial
**Band 1** p.490

**Peyton, Janet P**
Table(s): Southern Virginia: Intellectual Property
**Up-and-coming individuals** p.2498

**Pezanosky, Stephen**
Table(s): Texas: Bankruptcy/Restructuring **Band 3**
p.2328

**Pfeffer, David J**
Table(s): New York: Construction **Band 3** p.1791

**Pfefferle III, Ben L**
Profile: p.2109
Table(s): Ohio: Natural Resources &
Environment **Band 4** p.2083

**Pfeifer, Michael**
Table(s): Nationwide: Wealth Management:
Eastern Region **Band 4** p.267

**Pfeiffer, Alfred**
Profile: p.659
Table(s): California: Antitrust **Band 2** p.536

**Pfeiffer, Hudnall A**
Table(s): Indiana: Labor & Employment **Band 1**
p.1271

**Pfeiffer, Philip J**
Profile: p.2410
Table(s): Texas: Labor & Employment **Senior
Statesmen:** p.2359

**Pfeiffer, Steven L**
Table(s): Oregon: Real Estate: Zoning/Land Use
**Band 1** p.2173

**Pfister, Helen R**
Profile: p.1927
Table(s): New York: Healthcare **Up-and-coming indi-
viduals** p.1811

**Pfohl, Peter A**
Profile: p.384
Table(s): Nationwide: Transportation: Rail (for
Shippers) **Up-and-coming individuals** p.258

**Plybon, Christopher J**
Table(s): West Virginia: Corporate/Commercial **Band 2** p.2550, West Virginia: Real Estate **Band 1** p.2560

**Pocino Kelly, Amy**
Profile: p.2227
Table(s): Pennsylvania: Labor & Employment: Employee Benefits & Compensation **Up-and-coming individuals** p.2200

**Podgorsky, Arnold**
Table(s): Nationwide: Energy: Electricity (Regulatory & Litigation) **Band 3** p.76

**Podhurst, Aaron S**
Profile: p.1003
Table(s): Florida: Litigation: General Commercial **Band 1** p.966

**Poe, Gregory L**
Table(s): District of Columbia: Litigation: White-Collar Crime & Government Investigations **Band 2** p.827

**Poelman, Ronald S**
Profile: p.2475
Table(s): Utah: Corporate/M&A **Band 2** p.2462

**Poff, Adam**
Table(s): Delaware: Intellectual Property **Band 4** p.763

**Pogue, Mark**
Profile: p.2258
Table(s): Rhode Island: Labor & Employment **Band 2** p.2253, Rhode Island: Litigation: General Commercial **Band 1** p.2254

**Pohl, Beverly**
Table(s): Florida: Litigation: Appellate **Band 2** p.972

**Pohl, Paul M**
Profile: p.385
Table(s): Nationwide: Product Liability & Mass Torts **Band 4** p.208, Pennsylvania: Litigation: General Commercial **Band 4** p.2203

**Pohlen, Patrick A**
Profile: p.659
Table(s): Nationwide: Investment Funds: Venture Capital **Band 3** p.174, California: Capital Markets: Debt & Equity **Band 2** p.547, California: Corporate/M&A: Venture Capital **Band 3** p.555

**Pointer, Ann Margaret**
Profile: p.1093
Table(s): Georgia: Labor & Employment **Band 4** p.1060

**Pokorski, Jody**
Table(s): Arizona: Real Estate **Band 1** p.504

**Pokotilow, Manny D**
Table(s): Pennsylvania: Intellectual Property **Star individuals** p.2197

**Pokotilow, Steven**
Table(s): New York: Intellectual Property: Trade Mark & Copyright **Band 3** p.1821

**Polak, Jonathan**
Profile: p.1279
Table(s): Indiana: Litigation: General Commercial **Band 3** p.1273

**Polcyn, Thomas A**
Table(s): Missouri: Intellectual Property **Band 1** p.1623

**Pole, Debra E**
Profile: p.386
Table(s): Nationwide: Product Liability & Mass Torts **Band 2** p.208

**Polebaum, Elliot E**
Profile: p.386
Table(s): Nationwide: International Arbitration **Band 3** p.145

**Polevoy, Martin D**
Profile: p.1928
Table(s): New York: Real Estate **Band 2** p.1854

**Poliakoff, Abba**
Table(s): Maryland: Corporate/M&A **Band 4** p.1412

**Policastro, Marc**
Table(s): New Jersey: Environment **Band 3** p.1711

**Polidora, Roxane A**
Table(s): California: Antitrust **Band 4** p.536

**Poliquin, James**
Table(s): Maine: Litigation: Medical Malpractice & Insurance **Band 1** p.1393

**Politano, Frank L**
Profile: p.1745
Table(s): New Jersey: Intellectual Property **Band 2** p.1716

**Polite Jr., Kenneth Allen**
Table(s): Louisiana: Litigation: White-Collar Crime & Government Investigations **Band 1** p.1352

**Polizzi, Catherine**
Profile: p.659
Table(s): California: Life Sciences: IP/Patent Litigation **Band 2** p.590

**Polkes, Jonathan**
Profile: p.386
Table(s): Nationwide: Securities: Litigation **Band 2** p.232, New York: Litigation: General Commercial **Band 3** p.1833, New York: Litigation: Securities **Band 2** p.1833, New York: Litigation: White-Collar Crime & Government Investigations **Band 3** p.1833

**Pollack, Barry J**
Profile: p.886
Table(s): District of Columbia: Litigation: White-Collar Crime & Government Investigations **Band 3** p.827

**Pollack, Barry S**
Table(s): Massachusetts: Litigation: White-Collar Crime & Government Investigations **Band 2** p.1471

**Pollack, David**
Table(s): Florida: Litigation: General Commercial **Band 4** p.966

**Pollack, Elliott B**
Profile: p.746
Table(s): Connecticut: Healthcare **Band 2** p.735

**Pollack, Martin D**
Profile: p.1928
Table(s): New York: Tax **Band 4** p.1862

**Pollack, Richard A**
Profile: p.386
Table(s): Nationwide: Private Equity: Buyouts **Band 5** p.203

**Pollak, Mark**
Profile: p.1431
Table(s): Maryland: Real Estate **Band 1** p.1422

**Polley, John W**
Profile: p.1580
Table(s): Minnesota: Labor & Employment **Band 3** p.1571

**Pollock, Jeffrey M**
Profile: p.1745
Table(s): New Jersey: Environment **Band 2** p.1711, New Jersey: Litigation: General Commercial **Band 3** p.1722, New Jersey: Litigation: Insurance **Band 2** p.1722

**Polly Jr, Ronald G**
Table(s): Georgia: Labor & Employment **Band 4** p.1060

**Poloncarz, Kevin**
Table(s): California: Environment **Band 4** p.564

**Polonsky, Alex**
Profile: p.386
Table(s): Nationwide: Energy: Nuclear (Regulatory & Litigation) **Band 4** p.77

**Polsinelli, James A**
Table(s): Missouri: Corporate/M&A **Band 3** p.1618

**Polster, David**
Profile: p.1226
Table(s): Illinois: Tax **Band 2** p.1192

**Polvino, Kathlynn Butler**
Profile: p.1093
Table(s): Georgia: Healthcare **Band 2** p.1052

**Pomerantz, Glenn D**
Profile: p.660
Table(s): California: Antitrust **Band 2** p.536, California: Media & Entertainment: Litigation **Band 1** p.606

**Pomerantz, Jeffrey N**
Table(s): California: Bankruptcy/Restructuring **Band 2** p.542

**Pomerantz, Mark F**
Profile: p.1928
Table(s): Nationwide: Litigation: Trial Lawyers **Band 2** p.187, New York: Litigation: White-Collar Crime & Government Investigations **Star individuals** p.1836

**Pomeroy, Chris**
Table(s): Virginia: Environment **Band 2** p.2495

**Pomeroy, Emily**
Table(s): Oklahoma: Real Estate **Up-and-coming individuals** p.2145

**Pommerening, David**
Profile: p.886
Table(s): District of Columbia: Corporate/M&A & Private Equity **Band 2** p.797

**Pompeo, Paul E**
Profile: p.386
Table(s): Nationwide: Government: Government Contracts **Band 3** p.117

**Ponader, Erick**
Profile: p.1279
Table(s): Indiana: Real Estate **Band 3** p.1275

**Ponce, Mario**
Profile: p.1928
Table(s): New York: Corporate/M&A **Band 3** p.1793

**Pond, George M**
Profile: p.1928
Table(s): New York: Energy: State Regulatory & Wholesale Electric Market **Band 2** p.1806

**Ponda, Ameek Ashok**
Profile: p.1505
Table(s): Nationwide: Capital Markets: REITs **Band 4** p.55, Massachusetts: Tax **Band 1** p.1481

**Ponder, Anita**
Profile: p.1226
Table(s): Illinois: Construction **Band 3** p.1154

**Pongrace, Donald R**
Profile: p.386
Table(s): Nationwide: Native American Law **Band 1** p.192

**Ponikvar, Dale L**
Profile: p.1928
Table(s): New York: Tax **Band 4** p.1862

**Pontone, Kathleen**
Table(s): Maryland: Labor & Employment **Band 2** p.1417

**Pool, Terry W**
Profile: p.528
Table(s): Arkansas: Real Estate **Band 2** p.524

**Poole, Jeanine L**
Table(s): New Hampshire: Labor & Employment **Band 3** p.1688

**Poole, Samuel E.**
Profile: p.1003
Table(s): Florida: Environment **Band 3** p.951

**Poon, Julian**
Profile: p.660
Table(s): California: Labor & Employment **Band 4** p.587

**Poonja, Zaitun**
Profile: p.660
Table(s): California: Employee Benefits & Executive Compensation **Band 3** p.560

**Poorak, Sharon**
Profile: p.1093
Table(s): Georgia: Immigration **Band 2** p.1055

**Poore, William A**
Table(s): Rhode Island: Litigation: General Commercial **Band 3** p.2254

**Pope, Alan W**
Table(s): North Carolina: Bankruptcy/Restructuring **Band 1** p.2023

**Pope, Michael**
Profile: p.1226
Table(s): Illinois: Litigation: General Commercial **Band 2** p.1180

**Pope, Nicholas A**
Table(s): Florida: Real Estate **Band 2** p.974

**Popeo, R Robert**
Profile: p.1505
Table(s): Massachusetts: Litigation: General Commercial **Senior Statesmen** p.1470

**Poplar, Carl**
Table(s): New Jersey: Litigation: White-Collar Crime & Government Investigations **Band 2** p.1723

**Poplawski, Edward G**
Profile: p.660
Table(s): California: Intellectual Property: Patent **Band 4** p.578

**Poplawski, Steven J.**
Table(s): Missouri: Environment **Band 2** p.1621

**Popofsky, Laurence**
Table(s): California: Antitrust **Senior Statesmen:** p.536

**Popofsky, Mark**
Table(s): District of Columbia: Antitrust **Band 3** p.787

**Popowitz, Allen J**
Table(s): New Jersey: Real Estate **Band 3** p.1728

**Poppick, David**
Table(s): Connecticut: Labor & Employment **Band 2** p.736

**Poppitt, Kathy L**
Table(s): Texas: Healthcare **Band 2** p.2347

**Popplewell, Thomas**
Profile: p.2411
Table(s): Texas: Tax **Band 4** p.2371

**Porcelli, Frank P**
Table(s): Massachusetts: Intellectual Property **Band 1** p.1463

**Porsborg, Scott**
Table(s): North Dakota: Litigation: General Commercial **Band 2** p.2053

**Port, Gail S**
Table(s): New York: Environment: Mainly Transactional **Band 2** p.1808

**Porter, Daniel L**
Profile: p.386
Table(s): Nationwide: International Trade: Trade Remedies & Trade Policy **Band 4** p.154

**Porter, J William**
Table(s): North Carolina: Bankruptcy/Restructuring **Band 1** p.2023

**Porter, Jeffrey R**
Profile: p.1506
Table(s): Massachusetts: Environment **Band 1** p.1457

**Porter, John**
Profile: p.386
Table(s): Nationwide: Tax: Controversy **Band 4** p.244, Nationwide: Wealth Management: Central Region **Band 1** p.266, Texas: Tax: Litigation **Band 2** p.2371

**Porter, Maibeth**
Profile: p.471
Table(s): Alabama: Litigation: General Commercial **Band 3** p.463

**Porter, Philip**
Table(s): Nationwide: Outsourcing **Band 3** p.195, Northern Virginia: Intellectual Property **Band 3** p.2497

**Porter, Sue**
Table(s): Ohio: Labor & Employment **Band 4** p.2074

**Porter II, William G**
Profile: p.2110
Table(s): Ohio: Litigation: General Commercial **Band 4** p.2078

**Porter Jr, Joseph T**
Table(s): Missouri: Corporate/M&A **Band 3** p.1619

**Porterfield, Curtis D**
Profile: p.660
Table(s): California: Insurance: Policyholder **Band 4** p.576

**Portnoy, Jeffrey**
Table(s): Hawaii: Litigation: General Commercial **Band 1** p.1119

**Portnoy, Lawrence**
Profile: p.1928
Table(s): Nationwide: Securities: Litigation **Band 2** p.232, New York: Litigation: Securities **Band 1** p.1834

**Pos, Hal J**
Profile: p.2475
Table(s): Utah: Energy & Natural Resources **Band 1** p.2464

**Pose, Christopher**
Table(s): Iowa: Real Estate **Band 2** p.1290

**Posey, Tim**
Profile: p.2153
Table(s): Oklahoma: Native American Law **Band 2** p.2144

**Positan, Wayne J**
Profile: p.1745
Table(s): New Jersey: Labor & Employment **Band 1** p.1718

**Poss, Stephen D**
Profile: p.1506
Table(s): Massachusetts: Litigation: General Commercial **Band 2** p.1470, Massachusetts: Litigation: Securities **Band 1** p.1470

**Possinger, Paul**
Table(s): Illinois: Bankruptcy/Restructuring **Band 4** p.1148

**Post, Russell**
Table(s): Texas: Litigation: Appellate **Band 3** p.2361

**Poster, Robert L**
Profile: p.386
Table(s): Nationwide: Transportation: Shipping: Finance (New York) **Band 1** p.260

**Posthumus, John R**
Table(s): Colorado: Intellectual Property **Band 2** p.704

**Postler, Charles**
Profile: p.1003
Table(s): Florida: Bankruptcy/Restructuring **Band 4** p.939

**Potenza, Joseph M**
Profile: p.886
Table(s): District of Columbia: Intellectual Property: Litigation **Band 2** p.821

**Potter, Geoffrey**
Profile: p.1928
Table(s): New York: Intellectual Property: Trade Mark & Copyright **Band 3** p.1821

**Potter, John**
Table(s): California: Litigation: White-Collar Crime & Government Investigations **Band 1** p.601

**Potter, Nicholas F**
Table(s): Nationwide: Financial Services Regulation: Financial Institutions M&A **Band 2** p.99, Nationwide: Insurance: Transactional & Regulatory **Band 1** p.139, New York: Insurance: Transactional & Regulatory **Band 1** p.1816

**Potter, Trevor**
Table(s): Nationwide: Government: Political Law **Band 2** p.124

**Pottle, Steven L**
Profile: p.1093
Table(s): Georgia: Healthcare **Band 3** p.1052

**Potts, Brian H.**
Table(s): Wisconsin: Natural Resources & Environment **Up-and-coming individuals** p.2578

**Potts, Dylan**
Table(s): Arkansas: Labor & Employment **Up-and-coming individuals** p.520

**Poulos, Denise A**
Table(s): New Hampshire: Real Estate **Band 2** p.1692

**Poulos, Theodore T**
Table(s): Illinois: Litigation: White-Collar Crime & Government Investigations **Band 3** p.1181

**Pouncey Jr, Gerald L**
Table(s): Georgia: Environment **Band 2** p.1051

**Powar, Lee**
Profile: p.2110
Table(s): Ohio: Bankruptcy/Restructuring **Band 3** p.2058

**Powell, Benjamin**
Profile: p.387
Table(s): Nationwide: International Trade: CFIUS Experts **Band 3** p.152

**Powell, Bryan**
Profile: p.2178
Table(s): Oregon: Real Estate **Band 3** p.2173

**Powell, Charles D**
Profile: p.2411
Table(s): Texas: Technology: Corporate & Commercial **Band 2** p.2375

**Powell, David L**
Table(s): Florida: Real Estate: Zoning/Land Use **Band 1** p.975

**Powell, David M**
Table(s): Arkansas: Litigation: General Commercial **Band 2** p.522

**Powell, Fred**
Table(s): Alabama: Real Estate **Senior Statesmen:** p.466

**Powell, Kurt**
Profile: p.1093
Table(s): Georgia: Labor & Employment **Band 3** p.1060

**Powell, Michael J**
Profile: p.1093
Table(s): Georgia: Intellectual Property **Band 4** p.1056

**Powell, Michael V**
Profile: p.2411
Table(s): Texas: Litigation: Energy & Natural Resources **Band 3** p.2361, Texas: Litigation: General Commercial **Band 3** p.2361

**Powell, Norman**
Table(s): Delaware: Corporate/M&A: Alternative Entities **Band 3** p.761

**Powell, Roy A**
Profile: p.2227
Table(s): Pennsylvania: Litigation: General Commercial **Band 4** p.2203

**Powell, Thomas O**
Table(s): Georgia: Banking & Finance: Mainly Regulatory **Band 1** p.1039

**Powell, Tracy**
Table(s): Tennessee: Healthcare **Band 3** p.2291

**Powell, Wesley**
Profile: p.1928
Table(s): New York: Antitrust **Band 5** p.1778

**Powell IV, Charles A**
Profile: p.471
Table(s): Alabama: Labor & Employment **Band 2** p.460

**Powell Jr, David D**
Profile: p.721
Table(s): Colorado: Labor & Employment **Band 1** p.706

**Power, Christopher B**
Table(s): West Virginia: Natural Resources: Environment **Band 1** p.2558

**Power, James H**
Profile: p.387
Table(s): Nationwide: Transportation: Shipping: Litigation (New York) **Band 4** p.261

**Powers, Claudia K**
Table(s): Oregon: Environment **Band 1** p.2165

**Powers, James G**
Table(s): Nebraska: Litigation: General Commercial **Band 3** p.1664

**Powers, Matthew D**
Table(s): California: Intellectual Property: Patent **Star individuals** p.578

**Powers, Patricia O**
Profile: p.2308
Table(s): Tennessee: Healthcare: Regulatory **Senior Statesmen:** p.2291

**Powers, Ragan**
Table(s): Washington: Bankruptcy/Restructuring **Band 1** p.2523

**Powers, Raymond D**
Table(s): Idaho: Litigation: Medical Malpractice & Insurance **Band 1** p.1134

**Powers, Richard**
Profile: p.387
Table(s): Nationwide: Energy: Oil & Gas (Regulatory & Litigation) **Band 4** p.78

**Powers, Timothy**
Table(s): Texas: Banking & Finance **Band 3** p.2325

**Powers, Tony G**
Profile: p.1094
Table(s): Georgia: Antitrust **Band 2** p.1037,
Georgia: Litigation: General Commercial **Band 3**
p.1065

**Powers, Victoria E**
Table(s): Ohio: Bankruptcy/Restructuring **Band 1**
p.2058

**Powers, Werner**
Table(s): Texas: Insurance **Band 3** p.2351

**Powers Jr, George E**
Table(s): Wyoming: Litigation: General
Commercial **Band 2** p.2598, Wyoming: Litigation:
Medical Malpractice Defense **Band 1** p.2598

**Poynor, Daniel**
Table(s): Nationwide: Energy: Oil & Gas
(Regulatory & Litigation) **Band 3** p.78

**Pozner, Larry**
Table(s): Colorado: Litigation: White-Collar Crime
& Government Investigations **Band 1** p.710

**Pozza Jr, Clarence L**
Profile: p.1554
Table(s): Michigan: Litigation: General
Commercial **Band 2** p.1544

**Pozzerle, Sergio A**
Profile: p.387
Table(s): Nationwide: Projects **Band 3** p.216,
Nationwide: Projects: Renewables & Alternative
Energy **Band 1** p.216

**Prager, Dietmar**
Table(s): Nationwide: International Arbitration
**Up-and-coming individuals** p.145

**Praitis, Judith**
Profile: p.660
Table(s): California: Environment **Band 3** p.564

**Prame, Michael**
Profile: p.387
Table(s): Nationwide: ERISA Litigation **Band 2**
p.92

**Prater, Harlan**
Table(s): Alabama: Litigation: General
Commercial **Band 2** p.463

**Prather, Paul E**
Profile: p.2309
Table(s): Tennessee: Labor & Employment **Band
1** p.2293

**Prather, R Anthony**
Profile: p.1279
Table(s): Indiana: Labor & Employment **Band 3**
p.1271

**Prats, Luis**
Profile: p.1004
Table(s): Florida: Construction **Band 1** p.944

**Pratt, Aaron**
Profile: p.1403
Table(s): Maine: Corporate/M&A **Band 3** p.1385

**Pratt, David**
Table(s): Nationwide: Wealth Management:
Eastern Region **Band 2** p.267, Florida: Tax: Estate
Planning **Band 1** p.979

**Pratt, Donald**
Table(s): Texas: Construction **Band 3** p.2335

**Pratt, Jason**
Table(s): New York: Environment **Up-and-coming
individuals** p.1807

**Pratt, John**
Table(s): Georgia: Intellectual Property **Band 1**
p.1056

**Pratt, John Patrick**
Table(s): Florida: Immigration **Band 2** p.956

**Pratt, Neal F**
Table(s): Maine: Litigation: General Commercial
**Band 3** p.1393

**Pratt, William**
Profile: p.1928
Table(s): New York: Litigation: General
Commercial **Band 4** p.1833

**Pravda, Susan**
Table(s): Massachusetts: Private Equity: Venture
Capital Investment **Band 3** p.1474

**Praw, Douglas**
Profile: p.660
Table(s): California: Real Estate **Up-and-coming indi-
viduals** p.611

**Precella, Karen S**
Table(s): Texas: Litigation: Appellate **Band 3**
p.2361

**Prechtel, David**
Profile: p.1279
Table(s): Indiana: Corporate/M&A **Band 2** p.1268

**Preis Jr, E Fredrick**
Table(s): Louisiana: Labor & Employment **Band 3**
p.1350

**Prendergast, Terry N**
Table(s): South Dakota: Corporate/Commercial
**Band 2** p.2281

**Prentice, Richard D**
Profile: p.1403
Table(s): Maine: Real Estate **Band 3** p.1395

**Preovolos, Penelope A**
Table(s): California: Antitrust **Band 2** p.536

**Presant, Sanford C**
Profile: p.660
Table(s): California: Tax **Band 3** p.617

**Prescott, Andrew**
Profile: p.2258
Table(s): Rhode Island: Labor & Employment
**Band 1** p.2253

**Prescott, Wm Roger**
Table(s): Vermont: Corporate/Commercial **Band 3**
p.2483

**Presley, J Hobson**
Table(s): Alabama: Banking & Finance: Public
Finance **Band 1** p.455

**Press, Martin R**
Table(s): Florida: Tax **Band 2** p.979

**Pressley Jr, Fred G**
Profile: p.2110
Table(s): Ohio: Labor & Employment **Band 2**
p.2074

**Pressman, Arthur L**
Profile: p.387
Table(s): Nationwide: Franchising **Band 1** p.111

**Pressman, Stewart**
Table(s): Hawaii: Corporate/Commercial **Band 1**
p.1116

**Prester, Jackie**
Profile: p.2309
Table(s): Tennessee: Banking & Finance **Band 2**
p.2287

**Prestia, Paul F**
Table(s): Pennsylvania: Intellectual Property
**Senior Statesmen** p.2197

**Preston, Anne**
Table(s): Washington: Labor & Employment **Band
2** p.2531

**Preston, Richard**
Profile: p.886
Table(s): District of Columbia: Construction **Band
1** p.795

**Preston, Susan T**
Profile: p.1431
Table(s): Maryland: Healthcare: Medical
Malpractice **Band 2** p.1415

**Preston, William D**
Table(s): Florida: Environment **Band 2** p.951

**Prevost, Lauren**
Table(s): Nationwide: Capital Markets: REITs
**Band 4** p.55

**Prezioso, Giovanni**
Profile: p.387
Table(s): Nationwide: Financial Services
Regulation: Broker Dealer (Compliance) **Band 2**
p.97, Nationwide: Financial Services Regulation:
Broker Dealer (Enforcement) **Band 3** p.97,
Nationwide: Securities: Regulation: Advisory
**Band 1** p.232, Nationwide: Securities: Regulation:
Enforcement **Band 2** p.232

**Price, Alan H**
Profile: p.387
Table(s): Nationwide: International Trade: Trade
Remedies & Trade Policy **Band 2** p.154

**Price, Bill**
Table(s): California: Litigation: General
Commercial **Band 3** p.593

**Price, Charles**
Table(s): New Mexico: Real Estate **Senior
Statesmen** p.1772

**Price, Christopher B**
Profile: p.1929
Table(s): New York: Real Estate: Corporate **Band
3** p.1854

**Price, Gene**
Table(s): Alabama: Corporate/Commercial **Band
2** p.459

**Price, James**
Table(s): Missouri: Environment **Band 1** p.1621

**Price, Joseph**
Table(s): West Virginia: Labor & Employment
**Band 2** p.2553

**Price, Joseph M**
Table(s): Nationwide: Product Liability & Mass
Torts **Band 4** p.208

**Price, Scott D**
Profile: p.1929
Table(s): New York: Employee Benefits &
Executive Compensation **Band 2** p.1802

**Price, Stanley B**
Profile: p.1004
Table(s): Florida: Real Estate: Zoning/Land Use
**Band 1** p.975

**Price III, Warren**
Table(s): Hawaii: Litigation: General Commercial
**Band 2** p.1119

**Price Jr, Glenn A**
Profile: p.1323
Table(s): Kentucky: Real Estate: Zoning/Land
Use **Band 1** p.1314

**Price Jr, Joel A**
Table(s): Alabama: Banking & Finance **Band 3**
p.455

**Priestley, Robert**
Table(s): New Jersey: Litigation: Insurance **Band
2** p.1723

**Prieto, Peter**
Profile: p.1004
Table(s): Florida: Litigation: General Commercial
**Band 4** p.966, Florida: Litigation: White-Collar
Crime & Government Investigations **Band 2** p.966

**Primavera, Carl**
Table(s): Pennsylvania: Real Estate:
Zoning/Land Use **Band 1** p.2208

**Prince, Allison**
Table(s): District of Columbia: Real Estate:
Zoning/Land Use **Band 2** p.835

**Prince, James**
Profile: p.2411
Table(s): Texas: Bankruptcy/Restructuring **Band 4**
p.2328

**Prince, James M**
Profile: p.2411
Table(s): Texas: Capital Markets: Debt & Equity
**Band 3** p.2333, Texas: Corporate/M&A **Band 3**
p.2337

**Prince, Kenneth S**
Table(s): New York: Antitrust **Band 3** p.1778

**Prince, Larry E**
Profile: p.1139
Table(s): Idaho: Bankruptcy/Restructuring **Star
individuals** p.1131, Idaho: Corporate/Commercial
**Band 2** p.1132

**Prince, Rebekah**
Table(s): Nationwide: Franchising **Up-and-coming
individuals** p.111

**Prince, William B**
Table(s): Utah: Energy & Natural Resources **Band
1** p.2464

**Princi, Anthony**
Profile: p.1929
Table(s): New York: Bankruptcy/Restructuring
**Band 4** p.1782

**Principe, William K**
Table(s): Georgia: Labor & Employment **Band 4**
p.1060

**Quinn, James W**
Profile: p.388
Table(s): Nationwide: Litigation: Trial Lawyers
**Band 1** p.187, Nationwide: Sports Law **Band 2**
p.241, New York: Litigation: General Commercial
**Band 1** p.1833

**Quinn, John B**
Table(s): Nationwide: Litigation: Trial Lawyers
**Band 1** p.187, California: Intellectual Property:
Patent **Band 4** p.578, California: Litigation:
General Commercial **Band 1** p.593

**Quinn, Jonathan**
Table(s): Illinois: Litigation: General Commercial
**Up-and-coming individuals** p.1180

**Quinn, Kenneth P**
Table(s): Nationwide: Transportation: Aviation:
Regulatory **Band 1** p.256

**Quinn, Lawrence J.**
Table(s): Maryland: Labor & Employment **Band 3**
p.1417

**Quinn, Michael J**
Profile: p.1697
Table(s): New Hampshire: Environment **Band 2**
p.1687

**Quinn, Patrick T**
Profile: p.388
Table(s): Nationwide: Capital Markets:
Securitisation **Band 2** p.59

**Quinn, Paul**
Table(s): Illinois: Corporate/M&A: Private Equity
**Band 2** p.1157

**Quinn, Thomas**
Profile: p.1745
Table(s): New Jersey: Litigation: Insurance **Band
1** p.1723

**Quinn, Yvonne S**
Profile: p.1929
Table(s): New York: Antitrust **Band 2** p.1778

**Quinn Jr, Louis S**
Profile: p.1368
Table(s): Louisiana: Real Estate **Band 3** p.1355

**Quiñon, Jose M**
Table(s): Florida: Litigation: White-Collar Crime &
Government Investigations **Band 1** p.967

**Quinter, Peter**
Profile: p.388
Table(s): Nationwide: International Trade:
Customs **Band 3** p.155

**Quintiere, Gary G**
Profile: p.886
Table(s): District of Columbia: Employee
Benefits & Executive Compensation **Band 2** p.801

**Quirk, Marion**
Profile: p.774
Table(s): Delaware: Bankruptcy/Restructuring
**Up-and-coming individuals** p.754

**Quitiquit, Bud**
Table(s): Hawaii: Real Estate **Band 2** p.1120

# R

**Raab, David S**
Profile: p.1929
Table(s): New York: Tax **Band 3** p.1862

**Raabe, Craig**
Profile: p.746
Table(s): Connecticut: Litigation: General
Commercial **Band 2** p.738

**Raattama, Henry**
Table(s): Florida: Tax **Band 1** p.979

**Rabalais, Robert René**
Profile: p.2411
Table(s): Texas: Banking & Finance **Band 1**
p.2325

**Raber, Stephen**
Table(s): Nationwide: Product Liability & Mass
Torts **Band 3** p.208

**Rabinovitz, Joel**
Profile: p.660
Table(s): California: Tax **Senior Statesmen**: p.617

**Rabinowitz, Jonathan**
Profile: p.1745
Table(s): New Jersey: Bankruptcy/Restructuring
**Band 2** p.1705

**Rabinowitz, Mark A**
Profile: p.1226
Table(s): Illinois: Litigation: General Commercial
**Band 4** p.1180

**Rabinowitz, Mark I**
Profile: p.2227
Table(s): Pennsylvania: Banking & Finance **Band
2** p.2186

**Rabinowitz, Mitchell L**
Profile: p.887
Table(s): District of Columbia: Corporate/M&A &
Private Equity **Band 3** p.797

**Rabinowitz, Stephen L**
Profile: p.1929
Table(s): New York: Real Estate **Band 2** p.1854

**Rabitz, Steven**
Table(s): New York: Employee Benefits &
Executive Compensation **Band 2** p.1802

**Rabon, Bob**
Table(s): Oklahoma: Native American Law **Band 1**
p.2144

**Rachal, Robert**
Table(s): Louisiana: Labor & Employment:
Employee Benefits & Compensation **Band 2**
p.1350

**Rachlin, Robert D**
Table(s): Vermont: Litigation: General
Commercial **Senior Statesmen**: p.2486

**Racioppi Jr, Nicholas**
Table(s): New Jersey: Real Estate **Band 2** p.1728

**Raciti-Knapp, Melissa**
Profile: p.388
Table(s): Nationwide: Projects **Band 4** p.216

**Radcliffe, Mark F**
Profile: p.660
Table(s): Nationwide: Outsourcing **Band 3** p.195,
California: IT & Outsourcing **Star Individuals** p.583

**Rademacher, Kurt G**
Profile: p.388
Table(s): Nationwide: Wealth Management:
Central Region **Up-and-coming individuals** p.266

**Rader, Kermit L**
Table(s): Pennsylvania: Environment **Band 4**
p.2194

**Rader, Michael**
Table(s): Massachusetts: Intellectual Property
**Up-and-coming individuals** p.1463

**Radford, William R**
Profile: p.1004
Table(s): Florida: Labor & Employment **Band 3**
p.959

**Radke, Kirk A**
Profile: p.388
Table(s): Nationwide: Private Equity: Buyouts
**Band 1** p.203

**Radler, Barbara**
Table(s): Oregon: Real Estate **Band 1** p.2173

**Radloff, Jill**
Table(s): Minnesota: Corporate/M&A **Band 4**
p.1569

**Radolinski, Anne M**
Table(s): Minnesota: Labor & Employment **Band 3**
p.1571

**Radovich, Scott D**
Table(s): Hawaii: Real Estate **Band 1** p.1120

**Radulescu, David**
Table(s): New York: Intellectual Property: Patent
**Band 3** p.1820

**Radzely, Edward S**
Table(s): New Jersey: Real Estate **Senior
Statesmen**: p.1728

**Radzik, Edward C**
Table(s): Nationwide: Transportation: Shipping:
Litigation (New York) **Band 3** p.261

**Rae, Mark N**
Table(s): Nationwide: Capital Markets:
Derivatives **Band 3** p.51

**Rafatjoo, Hamid**
Profile: p.660
Table(s): California: Bankruptcy/Restructuring
**Band 3** p.542

**Raff, Joshua E**
Profile: p.388
Table(s): Nationwide: Capital Markets:
Securitisation **Band 2** p.59

**Raffa, Connie A**
Profile: p.1929
Table(s): New York: Healthcare **Band 2** p.1811

**Raffkind, Eliot D**
Table(s): Nationwide: Investment Funds: Hedge
Funds **Band 3** p.162

**Raffman, Mark S**
Profile: p.887
Table(s): District of Columbia: Litigation:
General Commercial **Band 3** p.826

**Raforth, John H**
Table(s): South Dakota: Corporate/Commercial
**Band 2** p.2281, South Dakota: Real Estate **Band 2**
p.2286

**Rafte, G Alan**
Profile: p.389
Table(s): Nationwide: Energy: Oil & Gas
(Transactional) **Band 1** p.79, Nationwide: Projects
**Band 2** p.216, Texas: Banking & Finance **Band 3**
p.2325

**Rafter, John**
Table(s): Oregon: Intellectual Property **Band 2**
p.2167

**Rafter, Michael**
Profile: p.1094
Table(s): Georgia: Corporate/M&A **Band 4** p.1046

**Rafuse, Nancy E**
Profile: p.1094
Table(s): Georgia: Labor & Employment **Band 1**
p.1060

**Ragalevsky, Stanley V**
Profile: p.1506
Table(s): Massachusetts: Banking & Finance:
Corporate & Regulatory **Band 1** p.1446

**Ragland Jr, William M**
Table(s): Georgia: Intellectual Property **Band 3**
p.1056, Georgia: Litigation: General Commercial
**Band 4** p.1065

**Ragon III, Heartsill**
Table(s): Arkansas: Corporate/Commercial **Band
3** p.518

**Ragonetti, Thomas J**
Table(s): Colorado: Real Estate **Band 1** p.714,
Colorado: Real Estate: Zoning/Land Use **Band 1**
p.714

**Ragsdale, Terry D.**
Table(s): Oklahoma: Energy & Natural
Resources **Band 2** p.2136

**Rahal, Linda**
Table(s): District of Columbia: Immigration **Band
3** p.814

**Raher, Patrick M**
Table(s): Nationwide: Transportation: Road
(Carriage/Commercial) **Band 1** p.259, District of
Columbia: Environment **Band 2** p.804

**Rahhal, Anthony**
Profile: p.2153
Table(s): Oklahoma: Intellectual Property **Band 2**
p.2138

**Raim, David**
Profile: p.389
Table(s): Nationwide: Insurance: Dispute
Resolution: Reinsurance **Band 1** p.135, District of
Columbia: Insurance: Insurer **Band 1** p.816

**Rain, John W**
Profile: p.2411
Table(s): Nationwide: Energy: Oil & Gas
(Transactional) **Band 4** p.79, Texas: Banking &
Finance **Band 1** p.2325

**Rainer, Marbury**
Table(s): Georgia: Litigation: General
Commercial **Band 4** p.1065

**Rainero, Julian**
Profile: p.389
Table(s): Nationwide: Financial Services
Regulation: Broker Dealer (Compliance) **Band 3**
p.97

**Rattner, Andrea S.**
Table(s): New York: Employee Benefits & Executive Compensation **Band 3** p.1802

**Rauh, Carl S**
Table(s): District of Columbia: Litigation: White-Collar Crime & Government Investigations **Band 3** p.827

**Raul, Alan Charles**
Profile: p.389
Table(s): Nationwide: Privacy & Data Security **Band 1** p.199

**Raulston, Keith R**
Profile: p.1607
Table(s): Mississippi: Litigation: General Commercial **Band 2** p.1597

**Raval, Abhilash**
Profile: p.1930
Table(s): New York: Bankruptcy/Restructuring **Band 4** p.1782

**Rave, Michael T**
Profile: p.1745
Table(s): New Jersey: Corporate/M&A **Band 2** p.1707

**Rawlins, Justin**
Profile: p.661
Table(s): California: Bankruptcy/Restructuring **Up-and-coming individuals** p.542

**Rawlinson, Dennis P**
Profile: p.2178
Table(s): Oregon: Litigation: General Commercial **Band 3** p.2171

**Rawls, James C**
Profile: p.1094
Table(s): Georgia: Healthcare **Band 3** p.1052

**Rawls III, John C.**
Table(s): Texas: Intellectual Property: Trade Mark & Copyright **Band 3** p.2354

**Rawson, Blaine**
Table(s): Utah: Energy & Natural Resources **Band 3** p.2464

**Rawson, Rachel**
Table(s): Ohio: Banking & Finance **Band 1** p.2056

**Rawson, Richard**
Table(s): Washington: Immigration **Band 1** p.2528

**Rawson, Robert**
Profile: p.2110
Table(s): Ohio: Litigation: Antitrust **Senior Statesmen:** p.2078

**Rawson, William**
Profile: p.887
Table(s): District of Columbia: Environment **Band 5** p.804

**Ray, Brennan**
Table(s): Arizona: Real Estate: Zoning/Land Use **Associates to watch** p.504

**Ray, Claudia**
Profile: p.1930
Table(s): New York: Intellectual Property: Trade Mark & Copyright **Band 3** p.1821

**Ray, Eric**
Table(s): Alabama: Bankruptcy/Restructuring **Up-and-coming individuals** p.457

**Ray, Frank**
Table(s): Ohio: Litigation: General Commercial **Band 3** p.2078

**Ray, Hugh M**
Profile: p.2412
Table(s): Texas: Bankruptcy/Restructuring **Band 2** p.2328

**Ray, James**
Profile: p.746
Table(s): Connecticut: Environment **Band 2** p.733

**Ray, Stephen E**
Table(s): Illinois: Construction **Band 2** p.1154

**Ray, William F**
Profile: p.1607
Table(s): Mississippi: Litigation: General Commercial **Band 3** p.1597

**Rayback, Brian**
Profile: p.1404
Table(s): Maine: Environment **Up-and-coming individuals** p.1389

**Rayburn, Charles (Trey)**
Table(s): North Carolina: Bankruptcy/Restructuring **Associates to watch** p.2023

**Rayburn Jr, C Richard**
Table(s): North Carolina: Bankruptcy/Restructuring **Band 1** p.2023

**Rayis, John D**
Profile: p.389
Table(s): Nationwide: Capital Markets: REITs **Band 1** p.55, Illinois: Tax **Band 2** p.1192

**Raymond, James F**
Table(s): New Hampshire: Real Estate **Band 2** p.1692

**Raymond, Mark F**
Table(s): Florida: Litigation: General Commercial **Band 2** p.966

**Raymond, Robert J**
Profile: p.1930
Table(s): New York: Employee Benefits & Executive Compensation **Band 3** p.1802

**Raymond III, F Douglas**
Profile: p.2227
Table(s): Pennsylvania: Corporate/M&A & Private Equity **Band 2** p.2191, Pennsylvania: Corporate/M&A: Securities **Band 2** p.2191

**Raysman, Richard**
Profile: p.1930
Table(s): Nationwide: Outsourcing **Band 3** p.195, New York: Technology & Outsourcing **Band 2** p.1868

**Rayson, G Scott**
Profile: p.2309
Table(s): Tennessee: Healthcare **Band 3** p.2291

**Razzak, Amr**
Profile: p.661
Table(s): California: Corporate/M&A **Band 3** p.553

**Re, Joseph R**
Table(s): California: Intellectual Property: Patent **Band 4** p.578

**Rea, Anne E**
Profile: p.390
Table(s): Nationwide: ERISA Litigation **Band 3** p.92

**Read, Charles**
Profile: p.661
Table(s): California: Energy: State Regulatory & Litigation **Band 3** p.562

**Read, Thomas**
Table(s): Washington: Real Estate **Band 3** p.2535

**Reamer, David C**
Profile: p.661
Table(s): Nationwide: Banking & Finance **Band 4** p.31, California: Banking & Finance **Band 1** p.539

**Reames, Wayne E**
Table(s): Iowa: Corporate/M&A **Band 3** p.1283

**Reardon, Marc A**
Profile: p.390
Table(s): Nationwide: Projects **Band 3** p.216

**Reaser, Dan R**
Table(s): Nevada: Gaming & Licensing **Band 2** p.1674

**Reasoner, Barrett**
Profile: p.2412
Table(s): Texas: Litigation: Energy & Natural Resources **Band 2** p.2361, Texas: Litigation: General Commercial **Band 2** p.2361

**Reasoner, Harry M**
Profile: p.390
Table(s): Nationwide: Litigation: Trial Lawyers **Senior Statesmen:** p.186, Texas: Antitrust **Senior Statesmen:** p.2323, Texas: Litigation: Energy & Natural Resources **Senior Statesmen:** p.2361, Texas: Litigation: General Commercial **Senior Statesmen:** p.2361

**Reasor Jr, Charles B**
Table(s): Tennessee: Real Estate **Band 2** p.2299

**Reaves, Lacy H**
Profile: p.2044
Table(s): North Carolina: Real Estate: Zoning/Land Use **Band 1** p.2037

**Rebein, David**
Table(s): Kansas: Litigation: General Commercial **Band 1** p.1295

**Rebein, Joseph**
Table(s): Missouri: Litigation: General Commercial **Band 1** p.1628

**Rebel, Thomas P**
Profile: p.1094
Table(s): Georgia: Labor & Employment **Band 4** p.1060

**Reber, David J**
Table(s): Hawaii: Corporate/Commercial **Band 1** p.1116

**Rechen, Thomas J**
Profile: p.746
Table(s): Connecticut: Litigation: General Commercial **Band 3** p.738

**Recht, Daniel N.**
Table(s): Colorado: Litigation: General Commercial **Band 3** p.709

**Rechtin Jr, Michael**
Profile: p.1226
Table(s): Illinois: Real Estate **Up-and-coming individuals** p.1187

**Reck, Michael**
Table(s): Iowa: Labor & Employment **Band 1** p.1285

**Recker, Catherine M**
Table(s): Pennsylvania: Litigation: White-Collar Crime & Government Investigations **Band 2** p.2204

**Rector, Jay**
Profile: p.1300
Table(s): Kansas: Labor & Employment **Band 1** p.1294

**Rector, Richard P**
Profile: p.390
Table(s): Nationwide: Government: Government Contracts **Band 2** p.117

**Rector, Susan D**
Table(s): Ohio: Intellectual Property **Band 2** p.2071

**Redcay, Ronald**
Profile: p.661
Table(s): California: Antitrust **Band 2** p.536

**Redd, Charles A**
Table(s): Nationwide: Wealth Management: Central Region **Band 2** p.266

**Redden, Joe**
Table(s): Texas: Litigation: General Commercial **Band 2** p.2362

**Reddick, C N Franklin**
Profile: p.661
Table(s): California: Corporate/M&A **Band 4** p.554

**Reder, Henry**
Table(s): Ohio: Construction **Band 3** p.2062

**Redgrave, Jonathan**
Profile: p.390
Table(s): Nationwide: Litigation: E-Discovery **Band 1** p.187

**Rediker, J Michael**
Table(s): Alabama: Litigation: General Commercial **Band 2** p.463

**Redlick, David E**
Profile: p.390
Table(s): Nationwide: Life Sciences: Corporate/Commercial **Band 1** p.182, Massachusetts: Corporate/M&A **Band 1** p.1452

**Redmond, Patricia**
Table(s): Florida: Bankruptcy/Restructuring **Band 1** p.939

**Redwine, R Kevin**
Table(s): Oklahoma: Energy & Natural Resources **Band 2** p.2136

**Reece, Joseph**
Table(s): Alaska: Corporate/M&A **Band 1** p.487, Alaska: Real Estate **Band 2** p.491

**Reed, G Darryl**
Profile: p.1226
Table(s): Illinois: Energy & Natural Resources: Regulatory **Band 3** p.1161

**Reed, Glen**
Profile: p.1094
Table(s): **Nationwide**: Healthcare: Regulatory & Litigation **Band 3** p.127, **Georgia**: Healthcare **Band 1** p.1052

**Reed, Janet E**
Profile: p.774
Table(s): **Delaware**: Intellectual Property **Band 4** p.763

**Reed, John L**
Profile: p.774
Table(s): **Delaware**: Chancery **Band 4** p.758

**Reed, John S**
Table(s): **Kentucky**: Litigation: General Commercial **Band 1** p.1312

**Reed, Kevin A**
Profile: p.2412
Table(s): **Texas**: Healthcare **Band 1** p.2347

**Reed, Margery N**
Table(s): **Pennsylvania**: Bankruptcy/Restructuring **Band 1** p.2188

**Reed, Michael**
Profile: p.887
Table(s): **District of Columbia**: Corporate/M&A & Private Equity **Band 4** p.797

**Reed, Michael H**
Profile: p.2227
Table(s): **Pennsylvania**: Bankruptcy/Restructuring **Band 3** p.2188

**Reed, Orville**
Table(s): **Ohio**: Litigation: General Commercial **Band 4** p.2078

**Reed, Randall B**
Table(s): **Wyoming**: Corporate/M&A **Band 2** p.2596, **Wyoming**: Corporate/M&A: Tax **Band 1** p.2596

**Reed, Stanley J**
Profile: p.1431
Table(s): **Maryland**: Litigation: General Commercial **Band 3** p.1419

**Reed, Steven**
Table(s): **Nationwide**: Energy: Oil & Gas (Regulatory & Litigation) **Band 1** p.78

**Reed, Walter G D**
Profile: p.2258
Table(s): **Rhode Island**: Corporate/Commercial **Band 2** p.2251

**Reed, Wendy N**
Table(s): **Nationwide**: Energy: Electricity (Regulatory & Litigation) **Band 3** p.76

**Reed, William N (Bill)**
Profile: p.1607
Table(s): **Mississippi**: Litigation: General Commercial **Band 2** p.1597

**Reeder III, Robert W**
Profile: p.391
Table(s): **Nationwide**: Capital Markets: Derivatives **Band 3** p.51

**Reeder Jr, James A**
Profile: p.2412
Table(s): **Texas**: Antitrust **Band 3** p.2323

**Reedy, Robert**
Profile: p.2412
Table(s): **Texas**: Capital Markets: Debt & Equity **Band 2** p.2333, **Texas**: Corporate/M&A **Band 4** p.2337

**Reemer, Ellis L**
Profile: p.391
Table(s): **Nationwide**: Tax: Controversy **Band 3** p.244

**Reese, Michael T.**
Profile: p.391
Table(s): **Nationwide**: Projects **Up-and-coming individuals** p.216

**Reeves, Edward**
Table(s): **Oregon**: Labor & Employment **Band 3** p.2168

**Reeves, Susan**
Table(s): **Alaska**: Environment, Natural Resources & Regulated Industries **Band 2** p.488

**Reger Jr, Robert J**
Profile: p.391
Table(s): **Nationwide**: Energy: Electricity (Finance) **Band 1** p.75

**Regier, John**
Profile: p.1506
Table(s): **Massachusetts**: Banking & Finance: Public Finance **Band 1** p.1446

**Regner, William D**
Table(s): **New York**: Corporate/M&A **Band 5** p.1793

**Rego, John A**
Profile: p.2110
Table(s): **Ohio**: Natural Resources & Environment **Band 2** p.2083

**Rehnquist, James C**
Profile: p.1506
Table(s): **Massachusetts**: Litigation: White-Collar Crime & Government Investigations **Band 2** p.1471

**Reich, Judith E**
Profile: p.2227
Table(s): **Pennsylvania**: Banking & Finance **Band 2** p.2186

**Reich, William Z**
Table(s): **New York**: Immigration **Band 3** p.1814

**Reich, Yaron Z**
Profile: p.1930
Table(s): **New York**: Tax **Band 2** p.1862

**Reich Esq, Abraham C**
Profile: p.2228
Table(s): **Pennsylvania**: Litigation: General Commercial **Band 1** p.2203

**Reid, Benjamine**
Profile: p.1004
Table(s): **Florida**: Litigation: General Commercial **Band 2** p.966

**Reid, Carter B**
Profile: p.2513
Table(s): **Virginia**: Construction **Band 3** p.2491

**Reid, Spencer**
Table(s): **New Mexico**: Litigation: General Commercial **Band 2** p.1769

**Reid Jr, Glen G**
Profile: p.2309
Table(s): **Tennessee**: Litigation: General Commercial **Band 2** p.2295

**Reider, Alan E**
Profile: p.887
Table(s): **District of Columbia**: Healthcare **Band 2** p.809

**Reidy, Andrew**
Profile: p.887
Table(s): **Nationwide**: Insurance: Dispute Resolution: Policyholder **Band 3** p.137, **District of Columbia**: Insurance: Policyholder **Band 2** p.818

**Reidy, Daniel E**
Profile: p.1226
Table(s): **Nationwide**: Litigation: Trial Lawyers **Band 2** p.187, **Illinois**: Litigation: General Commercial **Band 1** p.1180, **Illinois**: Litigation: White-Collar Crime & Government Investigations **Band 1** p.1180

**Reidy, James P**
Profile: p.1697
Table(s): **New Hampshire**: Labor & Employment **Band 1** p.1688

**Reidy, Joseph M**
Table(s): **Ohio**: Natural Resources & Environment **Band 2** p.2083

**Reierson, Kent**
Profile: p.2055
Table(s): **North Dakota**: Litigation: Energy & Natural Resources **Band 1** p.2053

**Reif, David**
Profile: p.747
Table(s): **Connecticut**: Litigation: General Commercial **Band 3** p.738

**Reiff, Laura Foote**
Profile: p.887
Table(s): **Nationwide**: Immigration **Band 3** p.131, **District of Columbia**: Immigration **Band 2** p.814

**Reifman, David L**
Profile: p.1226
Table(s): **Illinois**: Real Estate: Zoning/Land Use **Band 1** p.1188

**Reilly, D. Michael**
Profile: p.2541
Table(s): **Washington**: Labor & Employment **Band 2** p.2531

**Reilly, Daniel**
Table(s): **Colorado**: Litigation: General Commercial **Star individuals** p.709

**Reilly, Kenneth J**
Table(s): **Nationwide**: Product Liability & Mass Torts **Band 3** p.208, **Nationwide**: Product Liability: Tobacco p.208, **Florida**: Litigation: General Commercial **Band 1** p.966

**Reilly, Michael J**
Profile: p.391
Table(s): **Nationwide**: Bankruptcy/Restructuring **Band 3** p.39, **New York**: Bankruptcy/Restructuring **Band 3** p.1782

**Reilly, Patricia**
Profile: p.747
Table(s): **Connecticut**: Labor & Employment **Band 3** p.736

**Reilly, Timothy P**
Profile: p.2110
Table(s): **Ohio**: Labor & Employment **Band 1** p.2074

**Reimer, Christopher M**
Table(s): **Wyoming**: Corporate/M&A **Band 2** p.2596, **Wyoming**: Corporate/M&A: Tax **Band 1** p.2596

**Reimer, Eric R**
Table(s): **California**: Banking & Finance **Band 4** p.539

**Reindel, F William**
Profile: p.391
Table(s): **Nationwide**: Banking & Finance **Band 2** p.31

**Reinert, Peter**
Table(s): **Florida**: Corporate/M&A & Private Equity **Band 4** p.947

**Reines, Edward R**
Profile: p.661
Table(s): **California**: Intellectual Property: Patent **Band 2** p.578

**Reinhardt, Daniel S**
Table(s): **Georgia**: Litigation: General Commercial **Band 2** p.1065

**Reinhart, Joe**
Table(s): **Pennsylvania**: Environment **Band 3** p.2194

**Reinhold, Richard L**
Profile: p.1930
Table(s): **New York**: Tax **Band 2** p.1862

**Reisch, Scott H**
Table(s): **Colorado**: Natural Resources & Environment **Band 2** p.712

**Reische, Alan L**
Profile: p.1697
Table(s): **New Hampshire**: Corporate/Commercial **Band 1** p.1685

**Reisdorff, Kerri S.**
Profile: p.1638
Table(s): **Missouri**: Labor & Employment **Up-and-coming individuals** p.1625

**Reisenfeld, Kenneth B**
Table(s): **Nationwide**: International Arbitration **Band 5** p.145

**Reiser, Bert C**
Profile: p.391
Table(s): **Nationwide**: International Trade: Intellectual Property (Section 337) **Band 3** p.160

**Reisman, Stephen H**
Profile: p.1004
Table(s): **Florida**: Construction **Band 1** p.944

**Reisman, Steven J**
Profile: p.1930
Table(s): **New York**: Bankruptcy/Restructuring **Band 3** p.1782

**Reisman, W Michael**
Table(s): **Nationwide**: International Arbitration: Arbitrators **Band 1** p.146

**Reisner, Carl L**
Profile: p.391
Table(s): **Nationwide**: Private Equity: Buyouts **Band 4** p.203

**Reisner, Jeffrey M**
Profile: p.661
Table(s): California: Bankruptcy/Restructuring
**Band 2** p.542

**Reiss, John**
Profile: p.1930
Table(s): Nationwide: Private Equity: Buyouts
**Band 3** p.203, New York: Corporate/M&A **Band 2**
p.1793

**Reiss, Michael**
Table(s): Washington: Labor & Employment **Band
1** p.2531

**Reisz, Cynthia Y**
Profile: p.2309
Table(s): Tennessee: Healthcare **Band 1** p.2291,
Tennessee: Healthcare: Regulatory **Band 1**
p.2291

**Reitano, Anthony**
Table(s): New Jersey: Environment **Band 3** p.1711

**Reiter, Glenn M**
Profile: p.391
Table(s): Nationwide: Capital Markets: Debt &
Equity **Band 2** p.46, New York: Latin American
Investment **Band 2** p.1829

**Reiter, Harvey L**
Table(s): Nationwide: Energy: Electricity
(Regulatory & Litigation) **Band 4** p.76

**Reiter, Luis**
Profile: p.1004
Table(s): Florida: Banking & Finance: Public
Finance **Band 1** p.936

**Reitzfeld, Alan D**
Profile: p.391
Table(s): Nationwide: Transportation: Aviation:
Litigation **Band 3** p.254

**Reive, Chris**
Profile: p.2178
Table(s): Oregon: Environment **Band 3** p.2165

**Remar, Robert B**
Profile: p.1094
Table(s): Georgia: Litigation: General
Commercial **Band 2** p.1065

**Remele Jr, Lewis A**
Table(s): Minnesota: Litigation: General
Commercial **Band 1** p.1574

**Remensperger, Eric**
Table(s): California: Real Estate **Band 4** p.611

**Remer, Gary**
Table(s): Michigan: Employee Benefits &
Executive Compensation **Band 3** p.1540

**Remington, Rob**
Profile: p.2110
Table(s): Ohio: Construction **Band 2** p.2062, Ohio:
Litigation: General Commercial **Band 4** p.2078

**Remsburg, Edward W**
Table(s): Iowa: Litigation: General Commercial
**Band 1** p.1288

**Rendell, Robert**
Table(s): Texas: Banking & Finance **Band 4**
p.2325

**Renehan, Richard**
Table(s): Massachusetts: Litigation: General
Commercial **Senior Statesmen:** p.1470

**Renfrew, Charles B**
Table(s): Nationwide: International Arbitration:
Arbitrators **Senior Statesmen:** p.146

**Renfroe, Tracie**
Profile: p.2412
Table(s): Texas: Environment **Band 4** p.2343

**Renison, Brent**
Table(s): Oregon: Labor & Employment:
Immigration **Band 1** p.2168

**Rentz, Rebecca J**
Profile: p.2412
Table(s): Texas: Environment **Band 4** p.2343

**Repass, James**
Profile: p.2412
Table(s): Texas: Intellectual Property **Band 4**
p.2354

**Repka, David A**
Profile: p.391
Table(s): Nationwide: Energy: Nuclear
(Regulatory & Litigation) **Band 1** p.77

**Reschly, Jason**
Table(s): Missouri: Corporate/M&A **Band 3** p.1618

**Resnick, Brian**
Profile: p.1930
Table(s): New York: Bankruptcy/Restructuring
**Up-and-coming individuals** p.1782

**Resnick, Donald I**
Profile: p.1227
Table(s): Illinois: Real Estate **Band 2** p.1187

**Resnick, Stephanie**
Profile: p.2228
Table(s): Pennsylvania: Litigation: General
Commercial **Band 4** p.2203

**Ressa, Gregory J**
Profile: p.392
Table(s): Nationwide: Leisure & Hospitality **Band
4** p.179, Nationwide: Real Estate **Band 1** p.225,
New York: Real Estate: Corporate **Band 1** p.1854

**Ressler, Alison S**
Profile: p.661
Table(s): California: Capital Markets: Debt &
Equity **Band 2** p.547, California: Corporate/M&A:
Private Equity **Band 2** p.553, California:
Corporate/M&A **Band 1** p.553

**Rester, Daniel K**
Profile: p.1368
Table(s): Louisiana: Gaming & Licensing **Band 3**
p.1348

**Rettig, Charles P**
Table(s): Nationwide: Tax: Fraud **Band 1** p.244,
California: Tax **Band 1** p.617

**Reuter, F Mark**
Profile: p.2110
Table(s): Ohio: Corporate/M&A **Band 4** p.2064

**Revels, Jr., Richard W.**
Table(s): Louisiana: Energy & Natural
Resources: Oil & Gas **Band 2** p.1344

**Rey-Bear, Dan**
Table(s): Nationwide: Native American Law **Band
3** p.192, New Mexico: Native American Law **Band
2** p.1771

**Reymond III, Leon J**
Table(s): Louisiana: Corporate/M&A **Band 3**
p.1341

**Reymond Jr, Leon J**
Table(s): Louisiana: Real Estate **Band 2** p.1355

**Reynaud, Jr, Claude F**
Table(s): Louisiana: Litigation: General
Commercial **Band 3** p.1352

**Reynes, Stephen A**
Table(s): Vermont: Real Estate: Zoning/Land
Use **Band 1** p.2487

**Reynolds, Chris**
Profile: p.2412
Table(s): Texas: Litigation: Energy & Natural
Resources **Band 2** p.2361, Texas: Litigation:
General Commercial **Band 2** p.2361

**Reynolds, Don**
Table(s): North Carolina: Corporate/M&A **Band 3**
p.2025

**Reynolds, Kevin**
Table(s): Iowa: Litigation: General Commercial
**Band 2** p.1288

**Reynolds, Timothy G**
Profile: p.1931
Table(s): New York: Insurance: Dispute
Resolution: Insurer **Band 3** p.1816

**Reynolds III, John B**
Profile: p.392
Table(s): Nationwide: International Trade: CFIUS
Experts **Band 2** p.152, Nationwide: International
Trade: Export Controls & Economic Sanctions
**Band 1** p.152

**Reynoldson, Laurie**
Profile: p.1139
Table(s): Idaho: Real Estate **Band 3** p.1138

**Reznick, Robert P**
Table(s): District of Columbia: Antitrust **Band 5**
p.787

**Rheaume, Warren J**
Table(s): Washington: Intellectual Property **Band
1** p.2529

**Rhee, Hansel H**
Table(s): Ohio: Construction **Band 4** p.2062

**Rhiel, Susan**
Table(s): Ohio: Bankruptcy/Restructuring **Band 4**
p.2058

**Rhode, Lynne C.**
Table(s): Virginia: Environment **Associates to watch**
p.2495

**Rhodes, Linda**
Table(s): District of Columbia: Technology &
Outsourcing **Band 3** p.842

**Rhodes, Michael G**
Table(s): California: Intellectual Property: Patent
**Band 4** p.578, California: Litigation: General
Commercial **Band 5** p.593

**Rhodes, Thomas**
Profile: p.1094
Table(s): Georgia: Antitrust **Band 3** p.1037

**Rhodes Jr, Forrest T**
Profile: p.1300
Table(s): Kansas: Labor & Employment **Up-and-
coming individuals** p.1294

**Rhorer Jr, John R**
Table(s): Kentucky: Environment, Natural
Resources & Utilities: Natural Resources **Band 2**
p.1307

**Rhyne, Katherine L**
Profile: p.887
Table(s): District of Columbia: Environment **Band
4** p.804

**Riback, Ronald H**
Profile: p.1554
Table(s): Michigan: Banking & Finance **Band 3**
p.1536

**Ribaudo, Anthony**
Profile: p.1227
Table(s): Illinois: Insurance: Transactional &
Regulatory **Band 3** p.1168

**Ribeiro, Mariana R.**
Table(s): Florida: Immigration **Associates to watch**
p.956

**Ricci, Richard F**
Profile: p.1745
Table(s): New Jersey: Environment **Band 1** p.1711

**Ricciardi, Mark J**
Profile: p.1682
Table(s): Nevada: Labor & Employment **Band 1**
p.1675

**Ricciardi, Walter G**
Profile: p.392
Table(s): Nationwide: Securities: Regulation:
Enforcement **Band 3** p.233

**Rice, Arthur Halsey**
Table(s): Florida: Bankruptcy/Restructuring **Band
3** p.939

**Rice, Edwin G**
Table(s): Florida: Bankruptcy/Restructuring **Band
3** p.939

**Rice, Emily Gray**
Table(s): New Hampshire: Labor & Employment
**Band 3** p.1688, New Hampshire: Litigation:
General Commercial **Band 2** p.1690

**Rice, James**
Profile: p.392
Table(s): Nationwide: Energy: Oil & Gas
(Transactional) **Band 3** p.79

**Rice, Robert**
Table(s): Utah: Labor & Employment **Band 2**
p.2467

**Rice, Stephen M**
Table(s): Nevada: Real Estate **Band 1** p.1679

**Rice, Thomas C**
Profile: p.1931
Table(s): New York: Litigation: Securities **Band 4**
p.1834

**Rich, Brian G**
Profile: p.1004
Table(s): Florida: Bankruptcy/Restructuring **Band
4** p.939

**Rich, Christopher W**
Table(s): Oregon: Environment **Band 2** p.2165

**Rich, Frederic C**
Profile: p.392
Table(s): Nationwide: Projects **Band 1** p.216

**Ringler, Michael S**
Profile: p.662
Table(s): California: Corporate/M&A **Band 2** p.553

**Riopelle, Brian C**
Table(s): Southern Virginia: Intellectual Property **Band 1** p.2498

**Riordan, J Michael**
Profile: p.1745
Table(s): New Jersey: Labor & Employment **Band 2** p.1718

**Riordan, Robert P**
Profile: p.1094
Table(s): Georgia: Labor & Employment **Band 4** p.1060

**Rios, Edward**
Table(s): Texas: Immigration **Associates to watch** p.2349

**Ripp, Michael**
Table(s): Arizona: Real Estate **Band 4** p.504

**Rippey, Edward**
Profile: p.392
Table(s): Nationwide: Litigation: E-Discovery **Band 3** p.187

**Rippie, E Glenn**
Profile: p.1227
Table(s): Illinois: Energy & Natural Resources: Regulatory **Band 1** p.1161

**Rishwain, James**
Profile: p.662
Table(s): California: Real Estate **Band 3** p.611

**Risman, Clifford J**
Profile: p.392
Table(s): Nationwide: Leisure & Hospitality **Band 2** p.179, Texas: Real Estate **Band 2** p.2367

**Rist, Steven L**
Profile: p.1638
Table(s): Missouri: Corporate/M&A **Band 2** p.1618

**Ritardi, Steven F**
Table(s): New Jersey: Labor & Employment **Band 3** p.1718

**Ritchie, Jason S**
Profile: p.1655
Table(s): Montana: Labor & Employment **Associates to watch** p.1648

**Ritchie, Stephen L**
Profile: p.1227
Table(s): Illinois: Corporate/M&A: Private Equity **Band 1** p.1157

**Riter, Charles**
Table(s): South Dakota: Real Estate **Band 1** p.2286

**Ritok Jr, Joseph A**
Table(s): Michigan: Labor & Employment **Band 1** p.1542

**Ritt, Roger M**
Profile: p.1506
Table(s): Massachusetts: Tax **Band 2** p.1481

**Ritter, David B**
Profile: p.1227
Table(s): Illinois: Labor & Employment **Band 3** p.1175

**Ritterband, Alan**
Profile: p.2228
Table(s): Pennsylvania: Real Estate **Band 3** p.2208

**Ritzer, Lonnie M**
Profile: p.1431
Table(s): Maryland: Real Estate **Band 3** p.1422

**Rivkin, David W**
Table(s): Nationwide: International Arbitration **Band 1** p.145, Nationwide: International Arbitration: Arbitrators **Band 1** p.145

**Rivlin, Kenneth**
Table(s): New York: Environment: Mainly Transactional **Band 2** p.1808

**Rizek, Christopher**
Table(s): Nationwide: Tax: Controversy **Band 4** p.244

**Rizzardi, John**
Table(s): Washington: Bankruptcy/Restructuring **Band 2** p.2523

**Rizzo, Sandra E**
Profile: p.393
Table(s): Nationwide: Energy: Electricity (Regulatory & Litigation) **Band 4** p.76

**Rizzotti, Anthony D**
Profile: p.1506
Table(s): Massachusetts: Labor & Employment **Band 2** p.1466

**Roach, Gerald F**
Profile: p.2044
Table(s): North Carolina: Corporate/M&A **Band 1** p.2025

**Roach, Steven A**
Profile: p.1554
Table(s): Michigan: Banking & Finance: Bankruptcy **Band 3** p.1536

**Roach Jr, Robert M**
Table(s): Texas: Insurance **Band 2** p.2351

**Roady, Celia**
Profile: p.888
Table(s): District of Columbia: Tax **Band 2** p.838

**Roang, Sverre**
Profile: p.2585
Table(s): Wisconsin: Corporate/M&A **Band 3** p.2571

**Roark, Brian D.**
Profile: p.2309
Table(s): Tennessee: Healthcare: Government Investigations & Fraud **Band 1** p.2291

**Robb, Kathy**
Profile: p.1931
Table(s): New York: Environment **Band 3** p.1807

**Robb, Peter B**
Table(s): Vermont: Labor & Employment **Band 1** p.2485

**Robbins, Brett A**
Table(s): Massachusetts: Private Equity: Fund Formation **Band 3** p.1476, Massachusetts: Tax **Band 3** p.1481

**Robbins, Brian D**
Profile: p.1931
Table(s): Nationwide: Employee Benefits & Executive Compensation **Band 2** p.73, New York: Employee Benefits & Executive Compensation **Band 1** p.1802

**Robbins, Darren J**
Table(s): California: Litigation: Securities **Band 3** p.594

**Robbins, Kenneth S**
Profile: p.1124
Table(s): Hawaii: Litigation: General Commercial **Band 2** p.1119

**Robbins, Larry E**
Table(s): North Carolina: Corporate/M&A **Band 2** p.2025

**Robbins, Lawrence**
Table(s): Nationwide: Appellate Law **Band 2** p.26, District of Columbia: Litigation: White-Collar Crime & Government Investigations **Band 2** p.827

**Robbins, Patrick D**
Table(s): California: Litigation: White-Collar Crime & Government Investigations **Band 3** p.601

**Robbins, Robert B**
Profile: p.888
Table(s): District of Columbia: Corporate/M&A & Private Equity **Band 3** p.797

**Robbins, Virginia C**
Profile: p.1931
Table(s): New York: Environment **Band 3** p.1807

**Robbins Jr, William S**
Table(s): Missouri: Labor & Employment **Band 3** p.1625

**Robbins, Jr, E Hutchinson**
Profile: p.1431
Table(s): Maryland: Litigation: General Commercial **Band 3** p.1419

**Robenalt, James D**
Profile: p.2110
Table(s): Ohio: Litigation: General Commercial **Band 3** p.2078

**Roberson, Richard M**
Profile: p.2413
Table(s): Texas: Bankruptcy/Restructuring **Band 1** p.2328

**Roberti, John**
Table(s): District of Columbia: Antitrust **Up-and-coming individuals** p.787

**Roberts, Carley A**
Table(s): California: Tax: State & Local **Band 2** p.617

**Roberts, Gary M**
Profile: p.662
Table(s): California: Environment **Band 4** p.564

**Roberts, Harrison**
Table(s): Georgia: Banking & Finance **Up-and-coming individuals** p.1039

**Roberts, Jennifer**
Table(s): Nevada: Gaming & Licensing **Up-and-coming individuals** p.1674

**Roberts, Keith A**
Table(s): Vermont: Corporate/Commercial **Up-and-coming individuals** p.2483

**Roberts, Kenneth M**
Table(s): Illinois: Construction **Band 1** p.1154

**Roberts, Michele A**
Profile: p.393
Table(s): Nationwide: Litigation: Trial Lawyers **Band 1** p.187, District of Columbia: Litigation: General Commercial **Band 1** p.826

**Roberts, Richard**
Table(s): Nationwide: Energy: Electricity (Regulatory & Litigation) **Band 1** p.76

**Roberts, Steven L**
Table(s): Texas: Insurance **Band 3** p.2351

**Roberts, Thomas A**
Profile: p.1931
Table(s): New York: Corporate/M&A **Band 3** p.1793

**Roberts III, Hardy L**
Profile: p.1005
Table(s): Florida: Construction **Band 3** p.944

**Roberts Jr, Harry M**
Profile: p.2413
Table(s): Texas: Real Estate **Senior Statesmen:** p.2367

**Robertson, Allen K**
Table(s): North Carolina: Banking & Finance **Band 2** p.2021

**Robertson, Bruce**
Table(s): Washington: Corporate/Commercial **Band 3** p.2525

**Robertson, Elihu**
Profile: p.393
Table(s): Nationwide: Banking & Finance: Equipment Finance & Leasing **Band 2** p.32, Nationwide: Transportation: Aviation: Finance **Band 2** p.252

**Robertson, Eric**
Table(s): Illinois: Energy & Natural Resources: Regulatory **Band 1** p.1161

**Robertson, Gregory**
Profile: p.2513
Table(s): Virginia: Labor & Employment **Band 1** p.2500

**Robertson, James**
Table(s): Mississippi: Litigation: Appellate **Band 3** p.1596

**Robertson, James A.**
Profile: p.1745
Table(s): New Jersey: Healthcare **Band 3** p.1715

**Robertson, John D**
Profile: p.2153
Table(s): Oklahoma: Corporate/Commercial **Band 2** p.2134

**Robertson, John W**
Table(s): Washington: Corporate/Commercial **Band 2** p.2525

**Robertson, Robert**
Table(s): District of Columbia: Antitrust **Band 4** p.787

**Robertson Jr, James K**
Table(s): Connecticut: Litigation: General Commercial **Band 1** p.738

**Rodgers, Scott W**
Profile: p.511
Table(s): **Arizona: Labor & Employment Band 3** p.499

**Rodgers, W Stanley**
Table(s): **Alabama: Litigation: General Commercial Band 3** p.463, **Alabama: Litigation: Medical Malpractice Defense Band 2** p.463

**Rodi, David**
Profile: p.2413
Table(s): **Texas: Antitrust Band 3** p.2323

**Rodriguez, Antonio J**
Profile: p.394
Table(s): **Nationwide: Transportation: Shipping: Litigation (outside New York) Band 3** p.263

**Rodriguez, Carlos A**
Profile: p.394
Table(s): **Nationwide: Capital Markets: Securitisation Band 2** p.59

**Rodriguez, Denise Rios**
Table(s): **California: Healthcare Band 3** p.568

**Rodriguez, Gabriel M**
Table(s): **Illinois: Environment: Litigation Band 4** p.1162

**Rodriguez, Grace**
Profile: p.888
Table(s): **District of Columbia: Antitrust Band 5** p.787

**Rodriguez, Raquel**
Table(s): **Florida: Litigation: General Commercial Band 4** p.966

**Rodriguez Aldort, Julie**
Profile: p.1227
Table(s): **Illinois: Insurance: Dispute Resolution: Reinsurance Band 3** p.1168

**Rodriques, Louis A**
Profile: p.1507
Table(s): **Massachusetts: Labor & Employment Band 2** p.1466

**Roe, Christopher M**
Profile: p.2228
Table(s): **Pennsylvania: Environment Band 3** p.2194

**Roe, Kathryn**
Profile: p.1227
Table(s): **Illinois: Healthcare Band 3** p.1165

**Roe, Michael**
Table(s): **Idaho: Corporate/Commercial Band 3** p.1132

**Roe Jr, Clifford A**
Table(s): **Ohio: Corporate/M&A Senior Statesmen:** p.2064

**Roe Jr, John H**
Table(s): **Tennessee: Real Estate Band 2** p.2299

**Roeder, Craig A**
Profile: p.1227
Table(s): **Illinois: Corporate/M&A Band 4** p.1156

**Roeder, Kim H**
Profile: p.1094
Table(s): **Georgia: Healthcare Band 2** p.1052

**Roellke, Jon R**
Profile: p.888
Table(s): **District of Columbia: Antitrust Band 4** p.787

**Roeper, Jennifer G**
Table(s): **Florida: Immigration Up-and-coming individuals** p.956

**Roesch, Charles M**
Table(s): **Ohio: Labor & Employment Band 3** p.2074

**Roesch, Lynda E**
Table(s): **Ohio: Intellectual Property Band 1** p.2071

**Roesser, Tom E**
Profile: p.1124
Table(s): **Hawaii: Bankruptcy/Restructuring Band 1** p.1114, **Hawaii: Corporate/Commercial: Finance Band 2** p.1116

**Rogan, Michael P**
Profile: p.888
Table(s): **District of Columbia: Corporate/M&A & Private Equity Band 1** p.797

**Roge, Bret A**
Profile: p.2586
Table(s): **Wisconsin: Real Estate Band 3** p.2579

**Rogers, Alan T**
Table(s): **Alabama: Litigation: General Commercial Band 2** p.463

**Rogers, Bruce F**
Table(s): **Alabama: Litigation: General Commercial Band 2** p.463

**Rogers, CB**
Profile: p.1095
Table(s): **Georgia: Litigation: General Commercial Senior Statesmen:** p.1065

**Rogers, Charles**
Profile: p.1580
Table(s): **Minnesota: Litigation: General Commercial Band 3** p.1574

**Rogers, E Mabry**
Table(s): **Alabama: Litigation: Construction Band 1** p.462

**Rogers, Ed**
Table(s): **District of Columbia: Real Estate Band 2** p.835

**Rogers, Elizabeth N**
Profile: p.2413
Table(s): **Texas: Healthcare Band 2** p.2347

**Rogers, Gregory Parker**
Profile: p.2110
Table(s): **Ohio: Labor & Employment Band 2** p.2074

**Rogers, Guy W**
Table(s): **Montana: Litigation: General Commercial Band 3** p.1649

**Rogers, Karla**
Profile: p.2111
Table(s): **Ohio: Real Estate Band 4** p.2086

**Rogers, Patricia A.**
Profile: p.2153
Table(s): **Oklahoma: Corporate/Commercial: Healthcare Up-and-coming individuals** p.2134

**Rogers, Randy**
Profile: p.662
Table(s): **California: Bankruptcy/Restructuring Band 3** p.542

**Rogers Jr, Theodore O**
Profile: p.1932
Table(s): **New York: Labor & Employment Band 1** p.1826

**Rogers Jr, William P**
Profile: p.394
Table(s): **Nationwide: Capital Markets: Debt & Equity Band 2** p.46

**Rogoff, Adam**
Profile: p.1932
Table(s): **New York: Bankruptcy/Restructuring Band 4** p.1782

**Rogoff, Michael A.**
Profile: p.1932
Table(s): **New York: Litigation: White-Collar Crime & Government Investigations Band 3** p.1836

**Rogow, Bruce S**
Table(s): **Nationwide: Appellate Law Band 3** p.26, **Florida: Litigation: Appellate Band 1** p.972

**Rogowski, Patricia Smink**
Table(s): **Delaware: Intellectual Property Band 4** p.763

**Roh, Charles E**
Profile: p.394
Table(s): **Nationwide: International Trade: Trade Remedies & Trade Policy Band 3** p.154

**Rohan, Brendon**
Table(s): **Montana: Litigation: General Commercial Band 4** p.1649

**Rohback, Thomas G**
Profile: p.747
Table(s): **Connecticut: Litigation: General Commercial Band 2** p.738

**Rohde, Wayne**
Profile: p.394
Table(s): **Nationwide: Transportation: Shipping: Regulatory (outside New York) Band 3** p.264

**Rohn, Frederick**
Profile: p.1932
Table(s): **New York: Construction Band 1** p.1791

**Rohn, James J**
Profile: p.2228
Table(s): **Pennsylvania: Litigation: White-Collar Crime & Government Investigations Band 1** p.2204

**Rohrbacher, Blake**
Profile: p.774
Table(s): **Delaware: Chancery Up-and-coming individuals** p.758

**Rohrer, Paul**
Profile: p.662
Table(s): **California: Real Estate: Zoning/Land Use Band 3** p.612

**Rohrer, William D**
Profile: p.1005
Table(s): **Florida: Tax Band 3** p.979

**Roisman, Natalie**
Profile: p.888
Table(s): **District of Columbia: Telecom, Broadcast & Satellite Up-and-coming individuals** p.844

**Rolando, Margaret A.**
Table(s): **Florida: Real Estate Band 3** p.974

**Rolapp, Todd J**
Profile: p.2309
Table(s): **Tennessee: Corporate/M&A Band 3** p.2288

**Roles, Forrest**
Table(s): **West Virginia: Labor & Employment Band 1** p.2553

**Roll, Michael**
Table(s): **Nationwide: International Trade: Customs Band 3** p.155

**Roller, Sarah E (Taylor)**
Table(s): **Nationwide: Food & Beverages: Regulatory & Litigation Band 2** p.107

**Rollin, Michael**
Table(s): **Colorado: Litigation: General Commercial Up-and-coming individuals** p.709

**Rollnick, Neil S**
Table(s): **Florida: Real Estate Band 3** p.974

**Rollo, Marc A**
Profile: p.1746
Table(s): **New Jersey: Environment Band 2** p.1711

**Rolnick, Lawrence M**
Profile: p.1746
Table(s): **New Jersey: Litigation: General Commercial Band 2** p.1722

**Rolston, Chad G.**
Profile: p.662
Table(s): **California: Corporate/M&A Associates to watch** p.553

**Rom, Fred**
Table(s): **North Carolina: Litigation: General Commercial Band 4** p.2033

**Roma, Amy C**
Table(s): **Nationwide: Energy: Nuclear (Regulatory & Litigation) Associates to watch** p.77

**Roman, Terry**
Table(s): **Arizona: Corporate/M&A Band 2** p.495

**Román Griffith, Marissa**
Profile: p.662
Table(s): **California: Media & Entertainment: Transactional Band 3** p.608

**Romano, Benito**
Profile: p.1932
Table(s): **New York: Litigation: White-Collar Crime & Government Investigations Band 2** p.1836

**Romano, Carmen J**
Profile: p.2228
Table(s): **Pennsylvania: Corporate/M&A & Private Equity Band 2** p.2191

**Romano, Robert M**
Profile: p.394
Table(s): **Nationwide: Securities: Regulation: Enforcement Band 4** p.233

**Rosenberg, Robert**
Profile: p.395
Table(s): Nationwide: Transportation: Rail (for Shippers) **Band 2** p.258

**Rosenberg, Sheli**
Profile: p.1228
Table(s): Illinois: Real Estate **Senior Statesmen:** p.1187

**Rosenberg, Sumner**
Profile: p.1095
Table(s): Georgia: Intellectual Property **Band 2** p.1056

**Rosenberg, Thomas L**
Profile: p.2111
Table(s): Ohio: Construction **Band 4** p.2062

**Rosenblatt, Arnold**
Table(s): New Hampshire: Litigation: General Commercial **Band 1** p.1690

**Rosenblatt, Brett P**
Profile: p.395
Table(s): Nationwide: Leisure & Hospitality **Band 4** p.179

**Rosenblatt, Paul M**
Table(s): Georgia: Bankruptcy/Restructuring **Band 3** p.1042

**Rosenblatt, Philip R**
Profile: p.1507
Table(s): Massachusetts: Banking & Finance **Band 3** p.1445

**Rosenblatt, Richard**
Profile: p.1668
Table(s): Nebraska: Real Estate **Band 2** p.1666

**Rosenblatt, Richard G**
Profile: p.1746
Table(s): New Jersey: Labor & Employment **Band 1** p.1718

**Rosenblatt, Stephen W**
Profile: p.1607
Table(s): Mississippi: Corporate/Commercial: Bankruptcy **Band 1** p.1591

**Rosenbloom, David**
Profile: p.1228
Table(s): Illinois: Litigation: General Commercial **Band 2** p.1180, Illinois: Litigation: White-Collar Crime & Government Investigations **Band 1** p.1180

**Rosenbloom, H David**
Table(s): Nationwide: Tax: Controversy **Band 2** p.244, District of Columbia: Tax **Band 1** p.838

**Rosenbloom, James B**
Profile: p.1228
Table(s): Illinois: Real Estate **Band 2** p.1187

**Rosenbloum, Robert**
Profile: p.1095
Table(s): Georgia: Intellectual Property **Band 3** p.1056

**Rosenblum, Carl D**
Profile: p.1368
Table(s): Louisiana: Energy & Natural Resources: Oil & Gas **Band 1** p.1344

**Rosenblum, Howard S**
Profile: p.1507
Table(s): Massachusetts: Private Equity: Fund Formation **Band 3** p.1476

**Rosenblum, Jay**
Table(s): New Mexico: Corporate/Commercial **Band 2** p.1764

**Rosenblum, Jeremy T**
Profile: p.395
Table(s): Nationwide: Financial Services Regulation: Consumer Finance (Litigation) **Band 1** p.99, Pennsylvania: Banking & Finance: Mainly Regulatory **Band 1** p.2186

**Rosenblum, Peter**
Profile: p.1507
Table(s): Massachusetts: Corporate/M&A **Band 2** p.1452, Massachusetts: Private Equity: Venture Capital Investment **Band 1** p.1474

**Rosenblum, Rick**
Profile: p.2413
Table(s): Texas: Insurance **Band 2** p.2351

**Rosenblum, Steven A**
Profile: p.1933
Table(s): New York: Corporate/M&A **Band 4** p.1793

**Rosendorf, David L**
Table(s): Florida: Bankruptcy/Restructuring **Band 4** p.939

**Rosenfeld, Dana**
Table(s): Nationwide: Privacy & Data Security **Band 2** p.199

**Rosenfeld, Jonathan**
Profile: p.1507
Table(s): Massachusetts: Labor & Employment **Band 4** p.1466

**Rosenfeld, Lawrence**
Profile: p.511
Table(s): Arizona: Labor & Employment **Band 1** p.499

**Rosenfeld, Margaret**
Profile: p.2044
Table(s): North Carolina: Corporate/M&A **Band 4** p.2025

**Rosenfeld, Robert**
Table(s): California: Antitrust **Band 2** p.536

**Rosenfeldt, Philip**
Profile: p.2228
Table(s): Pennsylvania: Real Estate **Band 3** p.2208

**Rosenkranz, Joshua**
Table(s): Nationwide: Appellate Law **Band 2** p.26

**Rosenstein, Mace J**
Profile: p.888
Table(s): District of Columbia: Media & Entertainment: Mainly Regulatory **Band 1** p.832, District of Columbia: Telecom, Broadcast & Satellite **Band 1** p.844

**Rosenthal, Barry P**
Profile: p.888
Table(s): Nationwide: Real Estate **Band 2** p.225, District of Columbia: Real Estate **Band 1** p.835

**Rosenthal, Brian**
Table(s): Arkansas: Corporate/Commercial **Band 3** p.518, Arkansas: Litigation: Environmental **Band 1** p.522

**Rosenthal, Brian**
Table(s): District of Columbia: Intellectual Property: Litigation **Up-and-coming individuals** p.821

**Rosenthal, Daniel G**
Table(s): Ohio: Labor & Employment **Band 1** p.2074

**Rosenthal, David S**
Profile: p.1507
Table(s): Massachusetts: Labor & Employment **Band 3** p.1466

**Rosenthal, Edward H**
Profile: p.395
Table(s): Nationwide: Advertising: Litigation **Band 3** p.19

**Rosenthal, Jeffrey**
Profile: p.395
Table(s): Nationwide: International Arbitration **Band 4** p.145

**Rosenthal, John J**
Profile: p.395
Table(s): Nationwide: Litigation: E-Discovery **Band 1** p.187

**Rosenthal, Marc**
Table(s): Illinois: Insurance: Dispute Resolution **Band 1** p.1168

**Rosenthal, Michael D**
Table(s): Nationwide: Investment Funds: Venture Capital **Band 2** p.174, Illinois: Corporate/M&A: Private Equity **Band 2** p.1157

**Rosenthal, Michael L**
Profile: p.395
Table(s): Nationwide: Transportation: Rail (for Railroads) **Band 1** p.257

**Rosenthal, Paul C**
Table(s): Nationwide: International Trade: Trade Remedies & Trade Policy **Band 2** p.154

**Rosenthal, Stephen F**
Profile: p.1005
Table(s): Florida: Litigation: Appellate **Band 2** p.972

**Rosenthal, Thorn**
Profile: p.1933
Table(s): Nationwide: Insurance: Dispute Resolution: Insurer **Band 3** p.134, New York: Insurance: Dispute Resolution: Insurer **Band 2** p.1816

**Rosenwasser, Michael**
Profile: p.395
Table(s): Nationwide: Energy: Oil & Gas (Transactional) **Band 2** p.79

**Rosh, Kenneth I**
Profile: p.395
Table(s): Nationwide: Investment Funds: Private Equity: Fund Formation **Band 2** p.166

**Roska, Kay**
Profile: p.2413
Table(s): Texas: Environment **Band 4** p.2343

**Rosman, Mark**
Table(s): District of Columbia: Antitrust **Up-and-coming individuals** p.787

**Rosner, David S**
Profile: p.1933
Table(s): Nationwide: Bankruptcy/Restructuring **Band 4** p.39, New York: Bankruptcy/Restructuring **Band 3** p.1782

**Rosner, Douglas**
Table(s): Massachusetts: Bankruptcy/Restructuring **Band 1** p.1449

**Rosner, Ira N**
Profile: p.1005
Table(s): Florida: Corporate/M&A & Private Equity **Band 2** p.947

**Ross, Allen J**
Table(s): New York: Construction **Senior Statesmen:** p.1791

**Ross, Bruce S**
Profile: p.395
Table(s): Nationwide: Wealth Management: Western Region **Band 1** p.267

**Ross, David L**
Profile: p.1005
Table(s): Florida: Antitrust **Band 2** p.935, Florida: Litigation: General Commercial **Band 1** p.966

**Ross, Douglas C**
Table(s): Washington: Litigation: General Commercial **Band 2** p.2533

**Ross, Jane**
Profile: p.663
Table(s): California: Corporate/M&A **Up-and-coming individuals** p.553

**Ross, Jeffrey**
Profile: p.1933
Table(s): New York: Employee Benefits & Executive Compensation **Band 4** p.1802

**Ross, Jeffrey E.**
Table(s): Nationwide: Banking & Finance **Up-and-coming individuals** p.31

**Ross, Jerry W**
Profile: p.2413
Table(s): Texas: Environment **Band 3** p.2343

**Ross, Joel L**
Profile: p.2414
Table(s): Texas: Real Estate **Band 2** p.2367

**Ross, John Walker**
Table(s): Montana: Natural Resources & Environment **Band 2** p.1651

**Ross, Judith**
Profile: p.2414
Table(s): Texas: Bankruptcy/Restructuring **Band 4** p.2328

**Ross, Lauri Waldman**
Table(s): Florida: Litigation: Appellate **Band 1** p.972

**Ross, Nancy**
Table(s): Nationwide: ERISA Litigation **Band 2** p.92, Illinois: Labor & Employment: Employee Benefits & Compensation **Band 2** p.1176

**Ross, Rebecca L**
Table(s): Illinois: Insurance: Dispute Resolution **Band 2** p.1168

**Ross, Richard**
Table(s): Minnesota: Labor & Employment **Band 2** p.1571

**Ross, Richard F**
Profile: p.396
Table(s): Nationwide: Leisure & Hospitality **Band 1** p.179

**Royse, David T**
Profile: p.1323
Table(s): Kentucky: Litigation: General
Commercial **Band 4** p.1312

**Rozansky, Daniel**
Table(s): California: Media & Entertainment:
Litigation **Band 4** p.606

**Rozell, William B**
Table(s): Alaska: Environment, Natural
Resources & Regulated Industries **Band 2** p.488

**Rubalcava, Sharon**
Profile: p.663
Table(s): California: Environment **Band 1** p.564

**Rubel, Eric**
Profile: p.396
Table(s): Nationwide: Product Liability & Mass
Torts **Band 4** p.208

**Rubenfire, Mark**
Table(s): Michigan: Real Estate **Band 3** p.1546

**Rubenstein, Joshua**
Table(s): Nationwide: Wealth Management:
Eastern Region **Band 1** p.267

**Rubenstein, Marc A**
Table(s): Nationwide: Life Sciences:
Corporate/Commercial **Band 1** p.182

**Rubenstein, Thomas**
Table(s): West Virginia: Natural Resources **Band 2** p.2558

**Rubenstein, William S**
Profile: p.396
Table(s): Nationwide: Financial Services
Regulation: Banking (Compliance) **Band 3** p.96,
Nationwide: Financial Services Regulation:
Financial Institutions M&A **Band 2** p.96

**Rubin, Aaron P.**
Profile: p.663
Table(s): California: IT & Outsourcing **Up-and-coming Individuals** p.583

**Rubin, Amy M**
Profile: p.1934
Table(s): New York: Employee Benefits &
Executive Compensation **Band 4** p.1802

**Rubin, Blake D**
Profile: p.889
Table(s): District of Columbia: Tax **Band 1** p.838

**Rubin, Charles**
Table(s): Florida: Tax **Band 2** p.979

**Rubin, David J**
Table(s): Rhode Island: Real Estate **Band 1** p.2255

**Rubin, David S**
Table(s): Louisiana: Bankruptcy/Restructuring
**Band 1** p.1337

**Rubin, Gary L.**
Table(s): New York: Construction **Band 4** p.1791

**Rubin, Howard**
Profile: p.1934
Table(s): New York: Labor & Employment **Band 4** p.1826

**Rubin, Howard**
Profile: p.2178
Table(s): Oregon: Labor & Employment **Band 3** p.2168

**Rubin, James I**
Profile: p.1228
Table(s): Nationwide: Insurance: Dispute
Resolution: Reinsurance **Band 1** p.135, Illinois:
Insurance: Dispute Resolution: Reinsurance **Star individuals** p.1168

**Rubin, Jamie**
Profile: p.1229
Table(s): Illinois: Media & Entertainment:
Transactional **Band 1** p.1185

**Rubin, Jerome L**
Table(s): Washington: Labor & Employment **Band 2** p.2531

**Rubin, Joel D**
Profile: p.1229
Table(s): Illinois: Real Estate **Band 1** p.1187

**Rubin, Michael H**
Profile: p.1369
Table(s): Louisiana: Banking & Finance **Band 1** p.1335

**Rubin, Peter J**
Table(s): Maine: Litigation: General Commercial
**Band 1** p.1393

**Rubin, Richard**
Table(s): Vermont: Litigation: General
Commercial **Band 3** p.2486

**Rubin, Robert A**
Profile: p.1934
Table(s): New York: Construction **Senior Statesmen:** p.1791

**Rubin, Stephen W**
Table(s): Nationwide: Private Equity: Buyouts
**Band 5** p.203

**Rubinfeld, Ira B**
Table(s): Utah: Real Estate **Band 2** p.2470

**Rubinger, Hedy S**
Profile: p.1095
Table(s): Georgia: Healthcare **Band 2** p.1052

**Rubinoff, Edward L**
Profile: p.396
Table(s): Nationwide: International Trade: Export
Controls & Economic Sanctions **Band 1** p.153

**Rubinstein, Aaron**
Profile: p.1934
Table(s): New York: Litigation: General
Commercial **Band 3** p.1833

**Rubinstein, Joel S**
Table(s): District of Columbia: Construction **Band 3** p.795

**Rubocki, Melanie G**
Table(s): Idaho: Corporate/Commercial **Band 1** p.1132

**Ruby, Allen J**
Profile: p.396
Table(s): Nationwide: Litigation: Trial Lawyers
**Band 1** p.187, California: Litigation: General
Commercial **Band 1** p.593, California: Litigation:
White-Collar Crime & Government Investigations
**Band 1** p.601

**Ruby, Jay C**
Profile: p.1095
Table(s): Georgia: Immigration **Band 2** p.1055

**Ruby, Joseph**
Table(s): District of Columbia: Insurance:
Insurer **Band 4** p.816

**Ruck, Charles K**
Profile: p.663
Table(s): California: Corporate/M&A **Band 1** p.554

**Ruckman, Deirdre B**
Profile: p.2414
Table(s): Texas: Bankruptcy/Restructuring **Band 3** p.2328

**Ruckman, Robert**
Profile: p.396
Table(s): Nationwide: Transportation: Aviation:
Litigation **Band 3** p.254

**Rudd, David R**
Profile: p.2475
Table(s): Utah: Corporate/M&A **Band 3** p.2462

**Rudder, Richard D**
Profile: p.397
Table(s): Nationwide: Capital Markets:
Securitisation **Band 3** p.59

**Rudell, Michael**
Table(s): New York: Media & Entertainment:
Film & Television **Band 1** p.1849

**Rudlin, D Alan**
Profile: p.2513
Table(s): Virginia: Litigation: General
Commercial **Band 2** p.2502

**Rudman, Jeffrey**
Profile: p.1507
Table(s): Nationwide: Securities: Litigation **Band 2** p.232, Massachusetts: Litigation: Securities
**Star individuals** p.1470

**Rudman, Richard D**
Profile: p.1508
Table(s): Massachusetts: Real Estate **Band 1** p.1478

**Rudman, Samuel**
Profile: p.1934
Table(s): Nationwide: Securities: Litigation:
Mainly Plaintiff **Band 2** p.234, New York:
Litigation: Securities Mainly Plaintiff **Band 2** p.1835

**Rudnick, Amy G**
Profile: p.397
Table(s): Nationwide: Financial Services
Regulation: Banking (Enforcement &
Investigations) **Band 2** p.97

**Rudnick, Robert**
Table(s): District of Columbia: Tax **Band 2** p.838

**Rudo, Saul E**
Table(s): Illinois: Tax **Band 3** p.1192

**Rudolph, Andrew J**
Profile: p.2228
Table(s): Pennsylvania: Labor & Employment:
Employee Benefits & Compensation **Band 1** p.2200

**Ruediger, David L**
Profile: p.1508
Table(s): Massachusetts: Banking & Finance
**Band 2** p.1445

**Rueff Jr, David A**
Profile: p.1607
Table(s): Mississippi: Real Estate **Band 3** p.1600

**Ruegger, Philip T**
Profile: p.1934
Table(s): New York: Corporate/M&A **Band 5** p.1793

**Ruehlmann, Mark J**
Profile: p.2111
Table(s): Ohio: Litigation: General Commercial
**Band 4** p.2078

**Ruff, Randolph E**
Profile: p.1229
Table(s): Illinois: Construction **Band 2** p.1154

**Ruffatto, Steven P**
Profile: p.1655
Table(s): Montana: Natural Resources &
Environment **Band 1** p.1651

**Ruge, Mark**
Profile: p.397
Table(s): Nationwide: Transportation: Shipping:
Regulatory (outside New York) **Band 3** p.264

**Rugg, Joseph W N**
Table(s): Florida: Healthcare **Band 3** p.954

**Ruggeri, James**
Table(s): Nationwide: Insurance: Dispute
Resolution: Insurer **Band 2** p.134, District of
Columbia: Insurance: Insurer **Band 2** p.816

**Ruggiero, Jeffrey**
Profile: p.1934
Table(s): New York: Healthcare **Band 3** p.1811

**Ruhland, Christopher**
Profile: p.663
Table(s): California: Litigation: General
Commercial **Up-and-coming individuals** p.593

**Rule, Charles F**
Profile: p.889
Table(s): District of Columbia: Antitrust **Band 2** p.787

**Ruley, Alan M**
Table(s): North Carolina: Litigation: General
Commercial **Band 3** p.2033

**Rumeld, Myron D**
Table(s): Nationwide: ERISA Litigation **Band 2** p.92

**Rummage, Stephen M**
Table(s): Washington: Litigation: General
Commercial **Band 1** p.2533

**Running, Andrew R**
Profile: p.1229
Table(s): Illinois: Environment: Litigation **Band 2** p.1162

**Runstad, Judith M**
Table(s): Washington: Real Estate: Zoning/Land
Use **Senior Statesmen:** p.2536

**Rupe, Alan L**
Profile: p.1300
Table(s): Kansas: Labor & Employment **Band 1** p.1294

**Rupert, Anton**
Table(s): Oklahoma: Litigation: General
Commercial **Band 2** p.2141

**Rupp, Anthony F**
Table(s): Kansas: Litigation: General
Commercial **Band 2** p.1295

**Sackett, Christopher R**
Profile: p.1291
Table(s): Iowa: Corporate/M&A **Band 3** p.1283

**Sackheim, Michael**
Profile: p.398
Table(s): Nationwide: Capital Markets: Derivatives **Band 2** p.51

**Sacks, Ivan A**
Profile: p.663
Table(s): Nationwide: Wealth Management: Eastern Region **Band 3** p.267

**Sacks, Robert A**
Profile: p.663
Table(s): Nationwide: Securities: Litigation **Band 2** p.232, California: Litigation: General Commercial **Band 3** p.593, California: Litigation: Securities **Band 1** p.593

**Sacks, Russell**
Profile: p.398
Table(s): Nationwide: Financial Services Regulation: Broker Dealer (Compliance) **Band 3** p.97

**Sacripanti, Peter**
Profile: p.1935
Table(s): New York: Environment **Band 4** p.1807

**Sadat, Ellen Radow**
Profile: p.1747
Table(s): New Jersey: Environment **Band 3** p.1711

**Sadler, Alex E**
Profile: p.889
Table(s): District of Columbia: Tax **Band 4** p.838

**Sadler, Thomas C**
Table(s): California: Corporate/M&A **Band 3** p.554

**Saeed, Faiza J**
Profile: p.1935
Table(s): New York: Corporate/M&A **Band 1** p.1793, New York: Media & Entertainment: Corporate **Band 1** p.1848

**Saegert, Ann**
Table(s): Texas: Real Estate **Band 2** p.2367

**Safer, Ronald S**
Table(s): Illinois: Litigation: White-Collar Crime & Government Investigations **Band 1** p.1181

**Saferstein, Jeffrey D**
Profile: p.1935
Table(s): New York: Bankruptcy/Restructuring **Band 4** p.1782

**Saffer, David**
Profile: p.1323
Table(s): Kentucky: Real Estate **Band 2** p.1314

**Saffer, Ian**
Table(s): Colorado: Intellectual Property **Band 3** p.704

**Saffery, Edmund K**
Table(s): Hawaii: Litigation: General Commercial **Band 2** p.1119

**Safir, Peter O**
Profile: p.889
Table(s): Nationwide: Life Sciences: Regulatory/Compliance **Band 2** p.183, District of Columbia: Healthcare: Pharmaceutical/Medical Products Regulatory **Band 1** p.810

**Safron, Robert M**
Profile: p.1935
Table(s): New York: Real Estate **Band 4** p.1854

**Saft, Stuart M**
Profile: p.1935
Table(s): New York: Real Estate **Band 4** p.1854

**Sage, Michael**
Profile: p.1935
Table(s): New York: Bankruptcy/Restructuring **Band 3** p.1782

**Sager, David S**
Profile: p.398
Table(s): Nationwide: Franchising **Band 4** p.111

**Sager, Kelli L**
Table(s): Nationwide: First Amendment Litigation **Star individuals** p.105, California: Media & Entertainment: First Amendment Litigation **Star individuals** p.606

**Sagerman, Eric E**
Profile: p.663
Table(s): California: Bankruptcy/Restructuring **Band 2** p.542

**Sahr, David**
Table(s): Nationwide: Financial Services Regulation: Banking (Compliance) **Band 2** p.96

**Sahr, Evelyn**
Table(s): Nationwide: Transportation: Aviation: Regulatory **Band 3** p.256

**Saia, Doreen U**
Profile: p.1935
Table(s): New York: Energy: State Regulatory & Wholesale Electric Market **Band 2** p.1806

**Saibert, Frank J**
Profile: p.1229
Table(s): Illinois: Labor & Employment **Band 4** p.1175

**Saines, Richard**
Table(s): Nationwide: Climate Change **Band 1** p.63, Illinois: Environment: Mainly Transactional **Band 3** p.1162

**Saint-Antoine, Paul**
Profile: p.2229
Table(s): Pennsylvania: Antitrust **Band 3** p.2184

**Sakalo, Jay M**
Profile: p.1005
Table(s): Florida: Bankruptcy/Restructuring **Band 3** p.939

**Sakamoto, Ronald**
Table(s): Hawaii: Corporate/Commercial: Tax **Band 2** p.1115

**Salaman, Christian A**
Profile: p.398
Table(s): Nationwide: Leisure & Hospitality **Band 3** p.179

**Salamone, Mary**
Profile: p.663
Table(s): California: Construction **Band 3** p.550

**Salazar, John F**
Table(s): Kentucky: Intellectual Property **Band 2** p.1308

**Salazar, John P**
Profile: p.1774
Table(s): New Mexico: Real Estate **Band 1** p.1772

**Salazar, Luis**
Profile: p.1005
Table(s): Florida: Bankruptcy/Restructuring **Band 2** p.939

**Salcido, Robert S**
Profile: p.398
Table(s): Nationwide: Healthcare: Regulatory & Litigation **Band 1** p.127, District of Columbia: Healthcare **Band 1** p.809

**Sale, Jon A**
Table(s): Florida: Litigation: White-Collar Crime & Government Investigations **Band 1** p.967

**Saleh, Anis N**
Table(s): Florida: Immigration **Band 1** p.956

**Salehi, Nader H**
Profile: p.398
Table(s): Nationwide: Securities: Regulation: Enforcement **Band 4** p.233

**Sales, Bruce**
Profile: p.1747
Table(s): New Jersey: Intellectual Property **Band 1** p.1716

**Sales, Walter L**
Profile: p.1323
Table(s): Kentucky: Labor & Employment **Band 1** p.1310

**Salesin, Lowell D**
Table(s): Michigan: Real Estate **Band 1** p.1546

**Salimone, Shannon Hartsfield**
Profile: p.1005
Table(s): Florida: Healthcare **Band 2** p.954

**Salinger, Jeffrey L**
Table(s): New York: Environment: Mainly Transactional **Band 2** p.1808

**Salky, Steven M**
Table(s): District of Columbia: Litigation: White-Collar Crime & Government Investigations **Band 2** p.827

**Sallemi, Kelli**
Profile: p.398
Table(s): Nationwide: Banking & Finance: Equipment Finance & Leasing **Associates to watch** p.32

**Salomon, Claudia T**
Profile: p.399
Table(s): Nationwide: International Arbitration **Band 4** p.145

**Salomon, Peter**
Table(s): Florida: Tax: Employee Benefits **Band 2** p.979

**Salpeter, Alan N**
Profile: p.1229
Table(s): Illinois: Litigation: General Commercial **Band 2** p.1180

**Salter, Christopher**
Table(s): Nationwide: Financial Services Regulation: Broker Dealer (Compliance) **Band 3** p.97

**Salter, Dean**
Table(s): Colorado: Corporate/M&A **Band 1** p.703

**Saltiel, David M**
Table(s): Illinois: Media & Entertainment: Transactional **Band 2** p.1185

**Saltzman, Stephen L**
Profile: p.664
Table(s): California: Media & Entertainment: Transactional **Band 3** p.608

**Saltzstein, Susan L**
Profile: p.1935
Table(s): New York: Litigation: General Commercial **Band 4** p.1833, New York: Litigation: Securities **Band 3** p.1833

**Salvatore, Paul**
Table(s): New York: Labor & Employment **Band 1** p.1826

**Salvi, Lucantonio**
Table(s): District of Columbia: Corporate/M&A & Private Equity **Band 3** p.797

**Salyers, Douglas D**
Table(s): Georgia: Intellectual Property **Band 3** p.1056

**Salzman, Jerrold E**
Profile: p.399
Table(s): Nationwide: Capital Markets: Derivatives **Senior Statesmen:** p.51

**Sama, Vincent A**
Profile: p.1935
Table(s): New York: Litigation: Securities **Band 3** p.1834

**Samay, Christian**
Profile: p.1747
Table(s): New Jersey: Intellectual Property **Band 3** p.1716

**Samole, David**
Profile: p.1005
Table(s): Florida: Bankruptcy/Restructuring **Up-and-coming individuals** p.939

**Sampson, Ellen G**
Table(s): Minnesota: Labor & Employment **Senior Statesmen:** p.1571

**Sampson, Phillip L**
Profile: p.2414
Table(s): Texas: Construction **Band 3** p.2335

**Sampson, William**
Table(s): Missouri: Litigation: General Commercial **Band 1** p.1628

**Sams Jr, L F**
Table(s): Mississippi: Litigation: General Commercial **Band 1** p.1597

**Samson, Gary D.**
Table(s): California: Banking & Finance **Band 3** p.539

**Samson, Russell**
Table(s): Iowa: Labor & Employment **Band 1** p.1285

**Samuel, Donald F**
Table(s): Georgia: Litigation: White-Collar Crime & Government Investigations **Band 1** p.1066

**Samuels, Don**
Table(s): Colorado: Labor & Employment **Band 3** p.706

**Samuels, Jeffrey B**
Profile: p.1935
Table(s): New York: Tax **Band 3** p.1862

**Sartore, John T**
Table(s): Vermont: Litigation: General Commercial **Band 3** p.2486

**Sartori, Michael**
Profile: p.889
Table(s): District of Columbia: Intellectual Property: Patent Prosecution **Band 2** p.820

**Sarver, Richard E**
Profile: p.1369
Table(s): Louisiana: Litigation: General Commercial **Band 1** p.1352

**Sasine, Joan B**
Table(s): Georgia: Environment **Band 3** p.1051

**Saslaw, Michael A**
Profile: p.2414
Table(s): Texas: Corporate/M&A **Band 2** p.2337

**Sasser, Jonathan D**
Profile: p.2045
Table(s): North Carolina: Litigation: General Commercial **Band 2** p.2033

**Sasso, Gary L**
Profile: p.1006
Table(s): Florida: Litigation: General Commercial **Band 3** p.966

**Sassower, Edward O**
Profile: p.400
Table(s): Nationwide: Bankruptcy/Restructuring **Band 4** p.39, New York: Bankruptcy/Restructuring **Band 4** p.1782

**Sastre, Hildy**
Table(s): Florida: Litigation: General Commercial **Up-and-coming individuals** p.966

**Sathy, Anup**
Profile: p.1229
Table(s): Nationwide: Bankruptcy/Restructuring **Band 4** p.39, Illinois: Bankruptcy/Restructuring **Band 2** p.1148

**Satinsky, Barnett**
Profile: p.2229
Table(s): Pennsylvania: Labor & Employment **Band 4** p.2200

**Sato, Gregory M**
Table(s): Hawaii: Labor & Employment **Band 2** p.1117

**Satorius, John A**
Table(s): Minnesota: Corporate/M&A **Band 4** p.1569

**Satriana, Daniel**
Table(s): Colorado: Labor & Employment **Band 1** p.706

**Satterfield Jr, Andreas N**
Profile: p.2272
Table(s): South Carolina: Labor & Employment **Band 2** p.2262

**Satterlee, Terry J**
Table(s): Missouri: Environment **Band 1** p.1621

**Saturley, William C**
Profile: p.1697
Table(s): New Hampshire: Litigation: General Commercial **Band 3** p.1690

**Satyr, Allison J**
Profile: p.1230
Table(s): Illinois: Banking & Finance **Band 4** p.1145

**Sauer, Ari J.**
Table(s): Nationwide: Immigration **Up-and-coming individuals** p.131

**Sauermilch, Thomas**
Profile: p.1936
Table(s): New York: Corporate/M&A **Band 5** p.1793

**Saul, Gary**
Profile: p.1006
Table(s): Florida: Real Estate **Band 1** p.974

**Saul, H Carol**
Profile: p.1095
Table(s): Georgia: Healthcare **Band 3** p.1052

**Saunders, Eric F**
Table(s): Maine: Corporate/M&A **Band 2** p.1385

**Saunders, Robert S**
Profile: p.774
Table(s): Delaware: Chancery **Band 2** p.758

**Saupe, A William**
Table(s): Alaska: Environment, Natural Resources & Regulated Industries **Band 2** p.488

**Savage, Christine G**
Profile: p.1508
Table(s): Massachusetts: Healthcare **Band 2** p.1460

**Savage, Diane**
Table(s): California: IT & Outsourcing **Senior Statesmen:** p.583

**Savage, Greggory**
Table(s): Utah: Litigation: General Commercial **Band 3** p.2468

**Savage, Janet A**
Profile: p.722
Table(s): Colorado: Labor & Employment **Band 2** p.706

**Savage, Joseph F**
Profile: p.1508
Table(s): Massachusetts: Litigation: White-Collar Crime & Government Investigations **Band 1** p.1471

**Savarese, John F**
Profile: p.1936
Table(s): New York: Litigation: White-Collar Crime & Government Investigations **Band 2** p.1836

**Savarise, Jeffrey A**
Profile: p.1324
Table(s): Kentucky: Labor & Employment **Band 2** p.1310

**Savin, James R**
Profile: p.889
Table(s): District of Columbia: Bankruptcy/Restructuring **Band 2** p.792

**Savitz, Stephen**
Table(s): South Carolina: Labor & Employment **Band 2** p.2262

**Savrin, Daniel S**
Profile: p.1508
Table(s): Massachusetts: Antitrust **Band 2** p.1444

**Savva, John L**
Profile: p.664
Table(s): California: Capital Markets: Debt & Equity **Band 3** p.547

**Sawchak, Matthew W**
Profile: p.2045
Table(s): North Carolina: Antitrust **Band 1** p.2020

**Sawtelle, James G**
Table(s): Colorado: Litigation: General Commercial **Band 3** p.709

**Sawyer, Douglas L.**
Table(s): Colorado: Intellectual Property **Up-and-coming individuals** p.704

**Sawyer, Ed**
Profile: p.1006
Table(s): Florida: Tax **Band 2** p.979

**Sawyer, Sheila**
Profile: p.2309
Table(s): Tennessee: Healthcare: Government Investigations & Fraud **Band 1** p.2291

**Sawyer, Thomas J**
Table(s): Virginia: Labor & Employment **Band 2** p.2500

**Sawyers, Al B**
Profile: p.400
Table(s): Nationwide: Capital Markets: Structured Products **Band 2** p.52

**Sawyler, David R**
Profile: p.400
Table(s): Nationwide: Investment Funds: Hedge Funds **Band 1** p.162

**Saxbe, Charles**
Profile: p.2111
Table(s): Ohio: Litigation: General Commercial **Band 4** p.2078

**Saxton, James**
Profile: p.528
Table(s): Arkansas: Real Estate **Band 1** p.524

**Sayles, Richard A 'Dick'**
Table(s): Texas: Litigation: General Commercial **Band 3** p.2362

**Sayre, Russell S.**
Profile: p.2111
Table(s): Ohio: Litigation: General Commercial **Band 4** p.2078

**Scafidel, Amy Garrity**
Profile: p.1369
Table(s): Louisiana: Banking & Finance **Up-and-coming individuals** p.1335

**Scalia, Eugene**
Profile: p.890
Table(s): District of Columbia: Labor & Employment **Band 1** p.824

**Scallen, Tim**
Table(s): Minnesota: Corporate/M&A **Band 4** p.1569

**Scallet, Edward**
Profile: p.400
Table(s): Nationwide: ERISA Litigation **Band 3** p.92

**Scanlon, Chris**
Table(s): Indiana: Litigation: General Commercial **Band 1** p.1273

**Scanlon, Tara A**
Profile: p.890
Table(s): District of Columbia: Real Estate **Band 4** p.835

**Scanna, Karen**
Table(s): New York: Real Estate **Band 4** p.1854

**Scannell, J Gordon**
Table(s): Maine: Real Estate: Timberland/Conservation **Band 2** p.1396

**Scarano Jr, R Michael**
Table(s): California: Healthcare **Band 3** p.568

**Scarboro, James E**
Profile: p.722
Table(s): Colorado: Litigation: General Commercial **Senior Statesmen:** p.709

**Scarborough, Lawrence G**
Table(s): Arizona: Litigation: General Commercial **Band 2** p.501

**Scarborough, Robert**
Profile: p.1936
Table(s): New York: Tax **Band 3** p.1862

**Scarpulla, Francis O**
Table(s): California: Antitrust **Band 4** p.536, California: Antitrust: Mainly Plaintiff p.536

**Scarr, Thomas**
Table(s): West Virginia: Litigation: General Commercial **Band 2** p.2555

**Scarsella, Carla**
Profile: p.1230
Table(s): Illinois: Energy & Natural Resources: Regulatory **Up-and-coming individuals** p.1161

**Scavone, Arthur A**
Profile: p.400
Table(s): Nationwide: Projects **Band 1** p.216

**Scavone Jr, Nicholas P**
Profile: p.1554
Table(s): Michigan: Real Estate **Band 3** p.1546

**Schaaf, Douglas A**
Table(s): California: Tax **Band 2** p.617

**Schaberg, Richard A**
Table(s): Nationwide: Financial Services Regulation: Banking (Compliance) **Band 4** p.96

**Schachter, Michael**
Profile: p.1936
Table(s): New York: Litigation: White-Collar Crime & Government Investigations **Band 3** p.1836

**Schacter, Ira J**
Profile: p.400
Table(s): Nationwide: Capital Markets: Securitisation **Band 3** p.59

**Schaedle, Michael B.**
Profile: p.2229
Table(s): Pennsylvania: Bankruptcy/Restructuring **Band 3** p.2188

**Schaefer, David S**
Profile: p.1936
Table(s): New York: Corporate/M&A **Band 4** p.1793

**Schaefer, Georgette A**
Profile: p.400
Table(s): Nationwide: Investment Funds: Private Equity: Fund Formation **Band 3** p.166

**Schimmel, Seth M**
Table(s): Florida: Construction **Band 3** p.944

**Schindler, Barry J**
Profile: p.1747
Table(s): New Jersey: Intellectual Property **Band 2** p.1716

**Schindler, David J**
Table(s): California: Litigation: White-Collar Crime & Government Investigations **Band 2** p.601

**Schindler, Ozzie A**
Profile: p.1006
Table(s): Florida: Tax **Band 1** p.979

**Schindler, Paul D**
Profile: p.1937
Table(s): New York: Media & Entertainment: Music **Band 2** p.1849

**Schlack, Carl J**
Table(s): Hawaii: Real Estate **Band 1** p.1120

**Schlaff, Barbara E**
Profile: p.1431
Table(s): Maryland: Employee Benefits & Executive Compensation **Band 1** p.1414

**Schlager, Ivan A**
Profile: p.401
Table(s): Nationwide: International Trade: CFIUS Experts **Band 1** p.152, District of Columbia: Telecom, Broadcast & Satellite **Band 4** p.844

**Schlauch Stark, Lucy**
Profile: p.722
Table(s): Colorado: Corporate/M&A **Band 3** p.703

**Schlenger, Kirsten**
Table(s): California: Immigration **Band 2** p.571

**Schler, Michael L**
Profile: p.1937
Table(s): New York: Tax **Band 1** p.1862

**Schlerf, Jeffrey M**
Profile: p.774
Table(s): Delaware: Bankruptcy/Restructuring **Band 3** p.754

**Schleuning, Elizabeth A**
Table(s): Oregon: Labor & Employment **Band 2** p.2168

**Schlinsog, Allen C**
Profile: p.2586
Table(s): Wisconsin: Litigation: General Commercial **Up-and-coming individuals** p.2576

**Schloemer, Jeffrey S**
Profile: p.2112
Table(s): Ohio: Banking & Finance **Band 3** p.2056

**Schloendorn, Daniel**
Profile: p.401
Table(s): Nationwide: Investment Funds: Hedge Funds **Band 2** p.162

**Schlossberg, Bob**
Profile: p.890
Table(s): District of Columbia: Antitrust **Band 3** p.787

**Schlossman, William**
Table(s): North Dakota: Corporate/Commercial **Band 2** p.2051

**Schlumberger, Charles L**
Profile: p.529
Table(s): Arkansas: Litigation: General Commercial **Band 3** p.522

**Schmall, Deborah J**
Table(s): California: Environment **Band 2** p.564

**Schmarak, Bradley**
Table(s): Illinois: Corporate/M&A: Private Equity **Band 2** p.1157

**Schmelter, Joseph C**
Profile: p.2513
Table(s): Northern Virginia: Corporate/M&A **Band 2** p.2493

**Schmidt, Donald R**
Profile: p.1006
Table(s): Nationwide: Healthcare: Regulatory & Litigation **Band 3** p.127, Florida: Healthcare **Band 2** p.954

**Schmidt, Jeffrey**
Table(s): New York: Antitrust **Band 4** p.1778

**Schmidt, John R**
Table(s): Nationwide: Projects **Band 3** p.216, Nationwide: Projects: PPP **Band 1** p.216

**Schmidt, Justin B**
Profile: p.1369
Table(s): Louisiana: Real Estate **Band 3** p.1355

**Schmidt, Kevin M**
Table(s): Nationwide: Private Equity: Buyouts **Band 4** p.203

**Schmidt, Paul**
Profile: p.890
Table(s): District of Columbia: Tax **Band 3** p.838

**Schmidt, Paul W**
Profile: p.401
Table(s): Nationwide: Product Liability & Mass Torts **Band 4** p.208

**Schmidt, William**
Profile: p.890
Table(s): District of Columbia: Employee Benefits & Executive Compensation **Band 2** p.801

**Schmidt Jr, Robert J**
Profile: p.2112
Table(s): Ohio: Natural Resources & Environment **Band 3** p.2083

**Schmidt-Jones, Amy**
Profile: p.2586
Table(s): Wisconsin: Labor & Employment **Up-and-coming individuals** p.2575

**Schmidtberger, Michael J**
Profile: p.401
Table(s): Nationwide: Investment Funds: Hedge Funds **Band 1** p.162

**Schmit, David E**
Profile: p.2112
Table(s): Ohio: Intellectual Property **Band 2** p.2071

**Schnabel, David H**
Table(s): New York: Tax **Band 2** p.1862

**Schnall, Matthew D**
Profile: p.1508
Table(s): Massachusetts: Tax **Band 3** p.1481

**Schnapp, Daniel E**
Profile: p.1937
Table(s): New York: Media & Entertainment: Corporate **Up-and-coming individuals** p.1848

**Schnapp, Karlyn**
Profile: p.2112
Table(s): Ohio: Intellectual Property **Band 2** p.2071

**Schnapp, Mark P**
Profile: p.1006
Table(s): Florida: Litigation: White-Collar Crime & Government Investigations **Band 1** p.967

**Schneebeck, Richard**
Table(s): Wyoming: Litigation: General Commercial **Band 2** p.2598

**Schneider, Bruce H**
Table(s): New York: Antitrust **Band 5** p.1778

**Schneider, David P**
Table(s): New Jersey: Environment **Band 2** p.1711

**Schneider, Jeffrey G**
Table(s): Nationwide: Healthcare: Regulatory & Litigation **Band 1** p.127, New York: Healthcare **Band 1** p.1811

**Schneider, John**
Profile: p.1095
Table(s): Georgia: Banking & Finance **Band 2** p.1039

**Schneider, Lawrence**
Profile: p.401
Table(s): Nationwide: International Trade: Trade Remedies & Trade Policy **Band 2** p.154

**Schneider, Leslie**
Profile: p.890
Table(s): District of Columbia: Tax **Band 1** p.838

**Schneider, Lisa**
Profile: p.401
Table(s): Nationwide: Investment Funds: Hedge Funds **Up-and-coming individuals** p.162

**Schneider, Mark**
Profile: p.890
Table(s): District of Columbia: Telecom, Broadcast & Satellite **Band 2** p.844

**Schneider, Mark**
Profile: p.1580
Table(s): Minnesota: Labor & Employment **Band 3** p.1571

**Schneider, Mark**
Table(s): Washington: Environment **Band 1** p.2527

**Schneider, Michael R**
Table(s): Louisiana: Real Estate **Band 2** p.1355

**Schneider, Pam H**
Table(s): Nationwide: Wealth Management: Eastern Region **Band 1** p.267

**Schneider, Paul H**
Table(s): New Jersey: Environment **Band 2** p.1711

**Schneider, Richard A**
Profile: p.1096
Table(s): Nationwide: Product Liability & Mass Torts **Band 5** p.208, Georgia: Litigation: General Commercial **Band 4** p.1065

**Schneider, Robert F**
Table(s): Hawaii: Corporate/Commercial: Finance **Band 1** p.1116, Hawaii: Real Estate **Band 1** p.1120

**Schneider, Timothy**
Profile: p.1404
Table(s): Maine: Energy & Natural Resources **Associates to watch** p.1388

**Schneider Jr, Harry H**
Table(s): Washington: Litigation: General Commercial **Band 1** p.2533

**Schneidman, Edward J**
Profile: p.1230
Table(s): Illinois: Corporate/M&A **Band 4** p.1156

**Schneirov, Allison R**
Profile: p.402
Table(s): Nationwide: Private Equity: Buyouts **Band 3** p.203

**Schnell, Anthony L**
Profile: p.1324
Table(s): Kentucky: Real Estate **Band 2** p.1314

**Schnell, Paul**
Profile: p.1937
Table(s): New York: Corporate/M&A **Band 1** p.1793, New York: Healthcare **Band 3** p.1811, New York: Latin American Investment **Band 1** p.1829

**Schnell, Jr, Robert L**
Table(s): Minnesota: Litigation: General Commercial **Band 3** p.1574

**Schnoor, William J**
Profile: p.1508
Table(s): Massachusetts: Corporate/M&A **Band 4** p.1452, Massachusetts: Private Equity: Venture Capital Investment **Band 1** p.1474

**Schochet, Harvey**
Table(s): California: Bankruptcy/Restructuring **Band 3** p.542

**Schoen, Ann G.**
Profile: p.2112
Table(s): Ohio: Intellectual Property **Band 3** p.2071

**Schoen, George F**
Profile: p.1937
Table(s): New York: Corporate/M&A **Band 5** p.1793

**Schoenberg, Robert J**
Table(s): New Jersey: Intellectual Property **Band 2** p.1716

**Schoenbrun, Gary**
Profile: p.1938
Table(s): New York: Tax **Band 4** p.1862

**Schoenbrun, Larry**
Profile: p.2415
Table(s): Texas: Corporate/M&A **Senior Statesmen:** p.2337

**Schoenholz, William**
Profile: p.664
Table(s): California: Banking & Finance **Band 4** p.539

**Scholer, Randal J**
Table(s): Iowa: Corporate/M&A **Band 3** p.1283

**Schwartz, David L**
Profile: p.402
Table(s): Nationwide: Energy: Electricity (Regulatory & Litigation) **Band 2** p.76

**Schwartz, Donald**
Profile: p.1230
Table(s): Illinois: Banking & Finance **Band 2** p.1145

**Schwartz, Eric J.**
Table(s): District of Columbia: Media & Entertainment **Band 3** p.832

**Schwartz, Erich T**
Profile: p.402
Table(s): Nationwide: Securities: Regulation: Enforcement **Band 3** p.233

**Schwartz, Irwin H**
Table(s): Washington: Litigation: White-Collar Crime & Government Investigations **Band 1** p.2533

**Schwartz, Jaimie Paul**
Table(s): Maine: Real Estate **Band 1** p.1395

**Schwartz, James R**
Table(s): Nationwide: Healthcare: Transactional **Band 3** p.128, California: Healthcare **Band 2** p.568

**Schwartz, Jodi J**
Profile: p.1938
Table(s): New York: Tax **Band 1** p.1862

**Schwartz, Jordan M**
Profile: p.402
Table(s): Nationwide: Capital Markets: Securitisation **Band 1** p.59

**Schwartz, Joseph L**
Table(s): New Jersey: Bankruptcy/Restructuring **Band 2** p.1705

**Schwartz, Jurate**
Table(s): Florida: Labor & Employment **Associates to watch** p.959

**Schwartz, Lanny**
Profile: p.402
Table(s): Nationwide: Financial Services Regulation: Broker Dealer (Compliance) **Band 1** p.97

**Schwartz, Max J**
Profile: p.402
Table(s): Nationwide: Employee Benefits & Executive Compensation **Senior Statesmen:** p.73, New York: Employee Benefits & Executive Compensation **Senior Statesmen:** p.1802

**Schwartz, Michael**
Profile: p.2229
Table(s): Pennsylvania: Litigation: White-Collar Crime & Government Investigations **Band 2** p.2204

**Schwartz, Niki Z**
Table(s): Ohio: Litigation: White-Collar Crime & Government Investigations **Senior Statesmen:** p.2079

**Schwartz, Paul**
Profile: p.722
Table(s): Colorado: Litigation: White-Collar Crime & Government Investigations **Band 2** p.710

**Schwartz, Paul D**
Profile: p.1509
Table(s): Massachusetts: Real Estate **Band 3** p.1478

**Schwartz, Richard**
Profile: p.891
Table(s): District of Columbia: Environment **Band 3** p.804

**Schwartz, Richard M**
Profile: p.1938
Table(s): New York: Environment: Mainly Transactional **Band 2** p.1808

**Schwartz, Robert**
Table(s): California: Media & Entertainment: Litigation **Band 2** p.606

**Schwartz, Sara Goldsmith**
Profile: p.1509
Table(s): Massachusetts: Labor & Employment **Band 2** p.1466

**Schwartz, Steven**
Profile: p.403
Table(s): Nationwide: Insurance: Dispute Resolution: Reinsurance **Band 1** p.135, New York: Insurance: Dispute Resolution: Insurer **Band 2** p.1816

**Schwartz, Tessa**
Profile: p.664
Table(s): California: IT & Outsourcing **Up-and-coming individuals** p.583

**Schwartz, Wallace L**
Profile: p.1938
Table(s): New York: Real Estate **Band 2** p.1854

**Schwartz, William**
Profile: p.664
Table(s): California: IT & Outsourcing **Band 1** p.583

**Schwartz, William J**
Table(s): New York: Litigation: White-Collar Crime & Government Investigations **Band 2** p.1836

**Schwartzbaum, David M**
Profile: p.1939
Table(s): New York: Corporate/M&A **Band 4** p.1793

**Schwarz, Dan P**
Profile: p.1698
Table(s): New Hampshire: Labor & Employment **Band 3** p.1688

**Schwarz, Helfried**
Profile: p.403
Table(s): Nationwide: Banking & Finance: Equipment Finance & Leasing **Band 1** p.32, Nationwide: Transportation: Aviation: Finance **Band 1** p.252

**Schwarz, James H**
Profile: p.1279
Table(s): Indiana: Real Estate **Band 2** p.1275

**Schwarze, William W**
Profile: p.2229
Table(s): Pennsylvania: Intellectual Property **Band 3** p.2197

**Schwechter, Melvin S**
Profile: p.403
Table(s): Nationwide: International Trade: Export Controls & Economic Sanctions **Band 2** p.153, Nationwide: International Trade: Customs **Band 2** p.153

**Schwed, Robert**
Profile: p.403
Table(s): Nationwide: Private Equity: Buyouts **Band 4** p.203

**Schweitzer, Lisa M**
Profile: p.1939
Table(s): Nationwide: Bankruptcy/Restructuring **Band 4** p.39, New York: Bankruptcy/Restructuring **Band 3** p.1782

**Schwenke, Roger D**
Profile: p.1006
Table(s): Florida: Environment **Band 1** p.951

**Schwenkel, Robert C**
Profile: p.403
Table(s): Nationwide: Private Equity: Buyouts **Band 2** p.203

**Schwert, James J**
Table(s): Minnesota: Real Estate **Band 3** p.1576

**Schwiebert, Edward V**
Table(s): Vermont: Real Estate: Zoning/Land Use **Band 1** p.2487

**Schwolsky, John**
Profile: p.1939
Table(s): Nationwide: Insurance: Transactional & Regulatory **Band 3** p.139, New York: Insurance: Transactional & Regulatory **Band 2** p.1816

**Schworer, Philip**
Profile: p.1324
Table(s): Kentucky: Environment, Natural Resources & Utilities: Environment **Band 2** p.1307

**Scimia, Joseph**
Table(s): Indiana: Real Estate **Band 1** p.1275

**Scofield, Eileen MG**
Profile: p.1096
Table(s): Georgia: Immigration **Band 1** p.1055

**Scofield, George W**
Profile: p.2415
Table(s): Texas: Tax **Band 4** p.2371

**Scoggins, Linda G.**
Table(s): Oklahoma: Corporate/Commercial: Healthcare **Band 1** p.2134

**Scolnic, David**
Profile: p.2229
Table(s): Pennsylvania: Real Estate **Band 3** p.2208

**Scott, Ami G**
Table(s): Illinois: Banking & Finance **Band 3** p.1145

**Scott, Craig M**
Table(s): Rhode Island: Litigation: General Commercial **Band 3** p.2254

**Scott, Donald E**
Table(s): Nationwide: Product Liability & Mass Torts **Band 4** p.208, Colorado: Litigation: General Commercial **Band 2** p.709

**Scott, Dwight**
Table(s): Texas: Healthcare **Band 3** p.2347

**Scott, Gary**
Table(s): Wyoming: Labor & Employment **Band 1** p.2597, Wyoming: Litigation: General Commercial **Band 1** p.2598

**Scott, John W**
Profile: p.472
Table(s): Alabama: Litigation: General Commercial **Band 4** p.463

**Scott, Michael T**
Table(s): Nationwide: Product Liability & Mass Torts **Band 4** p.208, Pennsylvania: Litigation: General Commercial **Band 3** p.2203

**Scott, Thane D**
Profile: p.1509
Table(s): Massachusetts: Antitrust **Band 1** p.1444

**Scott, Timothy H.**
Profile: p.1369
Table(s): Louisiana: Labor & Employment **Band 3** p.1350

**Scott, W Rowlett**
Table(s): Tennessee: Real Estate **Band 2** p.2299

**Scott, William C**
Table(s): New Mexico: Environment, Natural Resources & Regulated Industries **Band 1** p.1766, New Mexico: Native American Law **Band 2** p.1771

**Scott, Zaldwaynaka**
Profile: p.1230
Table(s): Illinois: Litigation: White-Collar Crime & Government Investigations **Band 3** p.1181

**Scribner, John E**
Profile: p.891
Table(s): District of Columbia: Antitrust **Band 5** p.787

**Scrivner, Tom**
Profile: p.2586
Table(s): Wisconsin: Labor & Employment **Band 1** p.2575

**Scrutton, Suzanne**
Profile: p.2112
Table(s): Ohio: Healthcare **Band 3** p.2069

**Scull, Nancy**
Profile: p.664
Table(s): California: Real Estate **Band 4** p.611

**Scull, Timothy B**
Table(s): Colorado: Intellectual Property **Band 2** p.704

**Scullen, Sean M**
Profile: p.2586
Table(s): Wisconsin: Labor & Employment **Band 3** p.2575

**Scully, Patrick J**
Table(s): Maine: Energy & Natural Resources **Band 1** p.1388

**Scully, Thomas A.**
Profile: p.891
Table(s): District of Columbia: Healthcare **Band 3** p.809

**Sczudlo, Paul**
Table(s): California: Tax **Band 3** p.617

**Seabaugh, William F**
Table(s): Missouri: Corporate/M&A **Band 1** p.1619

**Sensabaugh, Don**
Table(s): West Virginia: Litigation: Healthcare **Band 1** p.2555

**Serbaroli, Francis J**
Profile: p.1939
Table(s): New York: Healthcare **Band 2** p.1811

**Serdahely, Douglas J**
Table(s): Alaska: Environment, Natural Resources & Regulated Industries **Band 2** p.488, Alaska: Litigation: General Commercial **Band 1** p.490

**Serell, Andrew W**
Table(s): New Hampshire: Litigation: General Commercial **Band 2** p.1690

**Serino, Jr, Joseph**
Profile: p.1940
Table(s): New York: Litigation: Securities **Band 4** p.1834

**Sernau, Ronald D**
Table(s): New York: Real Estate **Band 2** p.1854

**Serota, James I**
Profile: p.1940
Table(s): New York: Antitrust **Band 5** p.1778

**Serota, Susan P**
Table(s): Nationwide: Employee Benefits & Executive Compensation **Band 1** p.73, New York: Employee Benefits & Executive Compensation **Star individuals** p.1802

**Servodidio, Thomas G**
Table(s): Pennsylvania: Labor & Employment **Band 2** p.2200

**Serwin, Andrew B**
Table(s): Nationwide: Privacy & Data Security **Band 2** p.199

**Seryak, Richard J**
Profile: p.1554
Table(s): Michigan: Labor & Employment **Band 2** p.1542

**Session, William T**
Table(s): Missouri: Environment **Band 2** p.1621

**Sessions, Rex L**
Profile: p.1231
Table(s): Illinois: Labor & Employment **Band 2** p.1175

**Settelmayer, Daniel K**
Table(s): California: Healthcare **Band 2** p.568

**Settle, Richard**
Table(s): Washington: Real Estate: Zoning/Land Use **Senior Statesmen**: p.2536

**Seuch, William M**
Table(s): Massachusetts: Environment **Band 1** p.1457

**Sewell Jr., Henry F**
Profile: p.1096
Table(s): Georgia: Bankruptcy/Restructuring **Band 3** p.1042

**Sexton, Robert R**
Profile: p.472
Table(s): Alabama: Real Estate **Band 1** p.466

**Seyfer, Greg**
Table(s): Iowa: Real Estate **Band 3** p.1290

**Seyferth, Paul D**
Table(s): Missouri: Labor & Employment **Band 1** p.1625

**Seymour, Brian**
Table(s): Florida: Real Estate **Band 4** p.974

**Seymour, Karen Patton**
Profile: p.1940
Table(s): Nationwide: Financial Services Regulation: Banking (Enforcement & Investigations) **Band 3** p.97, New York: Litigation: White-Collar Crime & Government Investigations **Band 1** p.1836

**Seymour, Samuel W**
Profile: p.1940
Table(s): Nationwide: Financial Services Regulation: Banking (Enforcement & Investigations) **Band 3** p.97, New York: Litigation: White-Collar Crime & Government Investigations **Band 1** p.1836

**Sferra, Anne Marie**
Table(s): Ohio: Litigation: General Commercial **Band 3** p.2078

**Sfregola, Michael F**
Profile: p.665
Table(s): California: Real Estate **Band 1** p.611

**Sgarlata, Mark A**
Profile: p.2513
Table(s): Virginia: Construction **Band 3** p.2491

**Shachar, Avishai**
Profile: p.1940
Table(s): New York: Tax **Band 1** p.1862

**Shackelford, Richard L**
Profile: p.1096
Table(s): Nationwide: Healthcare: Regulatory & Litigation **Band 3** p.127, Georgia: Healthcare **Band 1** p.1052

**Shad, Kerry**
Profile: p.2045
Table(s): North Carolina: Labor & Employment **Band 3** p.2031

**Shadley, Frederic X**
Profile: p.2112
Table(s): Ohio: Litigation: General Commercial **Band 4** p.2078

**Shadwick, Jay**
Table(s): Kansas: Real Estate **Band 2** p.1297

**Shaffer, Brent**
Table(s): Delaware: Real Estate **Band 2** p.766

**Shafferman, Howard H**
Profile: p.404
Table(s): Nationwide: Energy: Electricity (Regulatory & Litigation) **Band 5** p.76

**Shaft, Grant**
Table(s): North Dakota: Real Estate **Band 2** p.2055

**Shahi, Kaveh**
Table(s): Vermont: Litigation: General Commercial **Band 2** p.2486

**Shainberg, Raymond**
Table(s): Tennessee: Real Estate **Band 3** p.2299

**Shalhoub, Paul V**
Profile: p.1940
Table(s): New York: Bankruptcy/Restructuring **Band 4** p.1782

**Shalton, Lonnie J**
Table(s): Missouri: Real Estate **Band 1** p.1633

**Shandy, Donald**
Table(s): Oklahoma: Energy & Natural Resources: Environment **Band 2** p.2136

**Shane, Jeffrey N**
Table(s): Nationwide: Transportation: Aviation: Regulatory **Band 2** p.256

**Shane, Michael**
Table(s): Florida: Immigration **Band 2** p.956

**Shane, Penny**
Profile: p.1940
Table(s): New York: Litigation: Securities **Band 2** p.1834

**Shank, Mark**
Profile: p.2415
Table(s): Texas: Labor & Employment **Band 2** p.2359

**Shanmugam, Kannon**
Table(s): Nationwide: Appellate Law **Band 2** p.26

**Shannon, Joseph J**
Profile: p.1554
Table(s): Michigan: Litigation: General Commercial **Band 3** p.1544

**Shannon, Kevin R**
Profile: p.775
Table(s): Delaware: Chancery **Band 3** p.758

**Shanor, Stuart D**
Table(s): New Mexico: Litigation: General Commercial **Band 1** p.1769

**Shapiro, Clifford J**
Profile: p.1231
Table(s): Illinois: Construction **Band 1** p.1154

**Shapiro, David**
Profile: p.1940
Table(s): Nationwide: Capital Markets: REITs **Up-and-coming individuals** p.55, New York: Corporate/M&A **Band 5** p.1793

**Shapiro, David I**
Profile: p.1940
Table(s): Nationwide: Investment Funds: Private Equity: Fund Formation **Band 4** p.166, New York: Tax **Band 3** p.1862

**Shapiro, Hal S**
Profile: p.404
Table(s): Nationwide: International Trade: Trade Remedies & Trade Policy **Band 4** p.154

**Shapiro, Howard**
Profile: p.404
Table(s): Nationwide: Energy: Electricity (Regulatory & Litigation) **Band 3** p.76

**Shapiro, Howard**
Table(s): Nationwide: ERISA Litigation **Band 1** p.92, Louisiana: Labor & Employment: Employee Benefits & Compensation **Star individuals** p.1350

**Shapiro, Hy**
Table(s): Florida: Litigation: White-Collar Crime & Government Investigations **Band 3** p.967

**Shapiro, J Ben**
Profile: p.1096
Table(s): Georgia: Construction **Senior Statesmen**: p.1044

**Shapiro, Jay B**
Table(s): Florida: Litigation: General Commercial **Band 4** p.966

**Shapiro, Joel Charles**
Profile: p.2230
Table(s): Pennsylvania: Bankruptcy/Restructuring **Band 2** p.2188

**Shapiro, Jonathan**
Profile: p.1404
Table(s): Maine: Labor & Employment **Band 1** p.1390, Maine: Labor & Employment: Employee Benefits & Compensation **Band 3** p.1390

**Shapiro, Jonathan A**
Profile: p.665
Table(s): California: Litigation: Securities **Band 3** p.594

**Shapiro, Keith J**
Profile: p.1231
Table(s): Illinois: Bankruptcy/Restructuring **Band 2** p.1148

**Shapiro, Mark D**
Table(s): New Jersey: Real Estate **Band 2** p.1728

**Shapiro, Mark L**
Profile: p.1231
Table(s): Illinois: Labor & Employment **Band 4** p.1175

**Shapiro, Noah D**
Table(s): New York: Real Estate **Up-and-coming individuals** p.1854

**Shapiro, Raymond**
Profile: p.2230
Table(s): Pennsylvania: Bankruptcy/Restructuring **Senior Statesmen**: p.2188

**Shapiro, Robert**
Profile: p.404
Table(s): Nationwide: Energy: Electricity (Regulatory & Litigation) **Band 4** p.76

**Shapiro, Robyn**
Profile: p.404
Table(s): Nationwide: Life Sciences: Regulatory/Compliance **Band 3** p.183

**Shapiro, Saul B**
Profile: p.1940
Table(s): New York: Media & Entertainment: Copyright & Contract Disputes **Band 3** p.1851

**Shapiro, Stephen Brett**
Profile: p.891
Table(s): District of Columbia: Construction **Band 2** p.795

**Shapiro, Stephen M**
Table(s): Nationwide: Appellate Law **Band 2** p.26, Illinois: Litigation: General Commercial **Band 2** p.1180

**Shapiro, Stuart**
Table(s): New York: Litigation: Securities **Band 4** p.1834

**Shapiro Snyder, Lynn**
Table(s): District of Columbia: Healthcare **Band 1** p.809

# Index of Lawyers

**Shapiro-Cyr, Lila**
Profile: p.1432
Table(s): Maryland: Real Estate **Up-and-coming individuals** p.1422

**Shapiro, Esq., Howard**
Profile: p.891
Table(s): District of Columbia: Litigation: White-Collar Crime & Government Investigations **Band 2** p.827

**Shapley, Christopher**
Table(s): Mississippi: Litigation: General Commercial **Band 1** p.1597

**Sharbaugh, Charles**
Profile: p.1096
Table(s): Georgia: Real Estate **Band 2** p.1070

**Sharber, Hugh**
Profile: p.2309
Table(s): Tennessee: Corporate/M&A **Band 3** p.2288

**Share, Daniel M**
Table(s): Michigan: Real Estate **Band 3** p.1546

**Sharf, Jesse**
Profile: p.404
Table(s): Nationwide: Real Estate **Band 1** p.225, California: Real Estate **Band 1** p.611

**Sharff, Dawn Helms**
Table(s): Alabama: Banking & Finance **Band 3** p.455, Alabama: Real Estate **Band 3** p.466

**Shargel, Jason M**
Profile: p.2230
Table(s): Pennsylvania: Corporate/M&A: Securities **Band 1** p.2191

**Sharkey, Dan**
Profile: p.1555
Table(s): Michigan: Litigation: General Commercial **Band 3** p.1544

**Sharko, Susan M**
Profile: p.1747
Table(s): New Jersey: Litigation: Products Liability **Band 2** p.1723

**Sharp, DeArmond**
Table(s): Nevada: Real Estate **Band 2** p.1679

**Sharp, Gregory A**
Table(s): Connecticut: Environment **Senior Statesmen** p.733

**Sharp, Joseph**
Profile: p.1096
Table(s): Georgia: Litigation: General Commercial **Band 4** p.1065

**Sharp, Lisa J**
Table(s): Alabama: Labor & Employment **Band 3** p.460

**Sharp, Richard T**
Profile: p.405
Table(s): Nationwide: Financial Services Regulation: Broker Dealer (Compliance) **Band 3** p.97, Nationwide: Financial Services Regulation: Broker Dealer (Enforcement) **Band 2** p.97

**Sharpe, Jeremy**
Table(s): Iowa: Real Estate **Band 1** p.1290

**Sharpe, Mark S**
Table(s): South Carolina: Real Estate **Band 3** p.2266

**Sharpe, Ralph E**
Profile: p.405
Table(s): Nationwide: Financial Services Regulation: Banking (Compliance) **Band 4** p.96, Nationwide: Financial Services Regulation: Banking (Enforcement & Investigations) **Band 3** p.96

**Sharrer, Elizabeth**
Profile: p.722
Table(s): Colorado: Real Estate **Band 2** p.714

**Sharrock, James W**
Profile: p.2154
Table(s): Oklahoma: Real Estate **Band 2** p.2145

**Sharron, Stephanie L**
Profile: p.665
Table(s): California: IT & Outsourcing **Band 2** p.583

**Sharry, Janice V**
Table(s): Texas: Corporate/M&A **Band 3** p.2337

**Shashy, Abraham N M**
Profile: p.891
Table(s): District of Columbia: Tax **Band 3** p.838

**Shaughnessy, Kevin W**
Profile: p.1007
Table(s): Florida: Labor & Employment **Band 2** p.959

**Shaulson, Samuel S**
Profile: p.1940
Table(s): New York: Labor & Employment **Band 2** p.1826

**Shavinsky, Mandy**
Table(s): Nevada: Real Estate **Up-and-coming individuals** p.1679

**Shaw, Cuyler**
Table(s): Hawaii: Bankruptcy/Restructuring **Band 2** p.1114

**Shaw, Danny**
Profile: p.1369
Table(s): Louisiana: Construction **Star individuals** p.1339

**Shaw, John**
Table(s): Delaware: Intellectual Property **Band 1** p.763

**Shaw, Paul W**
Profile: p.1509
Table(s): Massachusetts: Healthcare **Band 3** p.1460

**Shaw, Russell C**
Profile: p.2112
Table(s): Ohio: Employee Benefits & Executive Compensation **Band 3** p.2067

**Shaw-Lorello, Loretta**
Profile: p.405
Table(s): Nationwide: Investment Funds: Private Equity: Fund Formation **Band 4** p.166

**Shawe, Stephen D**
Profile: p.1432
Table(s): Maryland: Labor & Employment **Band 1** p.1417

**Shay, Kathleen M**
Table(s): Pennsylvania: Corporate/M&A & Private Equity **Band 2** p.2191

**Shea, Daniel F**
Table(s): Nationwide: Securities: Litigation **Band 3** p.232, Nationwide: Securities: Regulation: Enforcement **Band 4** p.232, Colorado: Litigation: White-Collar Crime & Government Investigations **Band 1** p.710

**Shea, James**
Profile: p.1432
Table(s): Maryland: Litigation: General Commercial **Band 3** p.1419

**Shea, John**
Table(s): Massachusetts: Environment **Band 2** p.1457

**Shea, Kara E.**
Profile: p.2310
Table(s): Tennessee: Labor & Employment **Band 3** p.2293

**Shea, Kevin M**
Table(s): Colorado: Litigation: White-Collar Crime & Government Investigations **Band 1** p.710

**Shea, Patrick W**
Table(s): New York: Labor & Employment **Band 1** p.1826

**Shea, Richard C**
Profile: p.892
Table(s): District of Columbia: Employee Benefits & Executive Compensation **Band 2** p.801

**Shea, Jr, Joseph L**
Profile: p.1369
Table(s): Louisiana: Energy & Natural Resources: Oil & Gas **Band 3** p.1344

**Sheanshang, George L**
Table(s): New York: Media & Entertainment: Film & Television **Band 1** p.1849

**Shearin, James T**
Profile: p.747
Table(s): Connecticut: Litigation: General Commercial **Band 2** p.738

**Shebelskie, Michael**
Profile: p.2513
Table(s): Virginia: Litigation: General Commercial **Band 3** p.2502

**Shechtman, Paul**
Table(s): New York: Litigation: White-Collar Crime & Government Investigations **Band 1** p.1836

**Sheeder, Robert E**
Profile: p.2415
Table(s): Texas: Labor & Employment **Band 1** p.2359

**Sheeder III, Frank E**
Profile: p.2415
Table(s): Texas: Healthcare **Band 3** p.2347

**Sheehan, Bartholomew**
Profile: p.405
Table(s): Nationwide: Capital Markets: REITs **Band 3** p.55

**Sheehan, Gregory D**
Table(s): Nationwide: Investment Funds: Registered Funds **Band 2** p.170, Massachusetts: Hedge & Mutual Funds **Band 1** p.1461

**Sheehan, Michael J**
Profile: p.1231
Table(s): Illinois: Labor & Employment **Band 4** p.1175

**Sheehan Jr, Gary R**
Table(s): Georgia: Environment **Band 3** p.1051

**Sheeran, Timothy J**
Profile: p.2112
Table(s): Ohio: Labor & Employment **Band 4** p.2074

**Sheets, D Mark**
Profile: p.2310
Table(s): Tennessee: Real Estate **Band 3** p.2299

**Sheets, Scott K**
Table(s): West Virginia: Labor & Employment **Band 3** p.2553

**Sheffield, Frank**
Table(s): North Carolina: Environment **Band 3** p.2028

**Sheffield, Jeffrey T**
Profile: p.1231
Table(s): Illinois: Tax **Band 1** p.1192

**Shein, David E**
Profile: p.511
Table(s): Arizona: Real Estate **Band 4** p.504

**Sheldon, Jerry**
Profile: p.1607
Table(s): Mississippi: Energy & Natural Resources **Band 2** p.1593

**Sheley, Raymond**
Table(s): Georgia: Real Estate **Band 2** p.1070

**Sheller, John**
Profile: p.1324
Table(s): Kentucky: Labor & Employment **Band 3** p.1310

**Shelley, Anthony**
Profile: p.405
Table(s): Nationwide: ERISA Litigation **Band 2** p.92

**Shelley, Linda Loomis**
Table(s): Florida: Real Estate: Zoning/Land Use **Band 1** p.975

**Shelley, William**
Table(s): Nationwide: Insurance: Dispute Resolution: Insurer **Band 3** p.134

**Shelton, Dana**
Table(s): Louisiana: Energy & Natural Resources: Utilities **Band 2** p.1344

**Shelton, Lisa**
Profile: p.2415
Table(s): Texas: Environment **Band 3** p.2343

**Shemano, David B**
Profile: p.665
Table(s): California: Bankruptcy/Restructuring **Band 4** p.542

**Shemin, Kenneth R**
Table(s): Arkansas: Litigation: General Commercial **Band 1** p.522

**Shenberg, Michael**
Profile: p.405
Table(s): Nationwide: Energy: Electricity (Transactional) **Band 2** p.77

**Shenker, Joseph C**
Profile: p.1941
Table(s): **Nationwide**: Capital Markets: REITs
**Band 3** p.55, **New York**: Real Estate: Corporate
**Band 1** p.1854

**Shenson, Jonathan**
Table(s): **California**: Bankruptcy/Restructuring
**Band 4** p.542

**Shepard, Michael J**
Table(s): **Nationwide**: Securities: Regulation:
Enforcement **Band 4** p.233, **California**: Litigation:
White-Collar Crime & Government Investigations
**Band 3** p.601

**Shepherd, Bill**
Profile: p.1007
Table(s): **Florida**: Litigation: White-Collar Crime &
Government Investigations **Band 3** p.967

**Shepherd, Kerry**
Table(s): **Oregon**: Litigation: General
Commercial **Band 2** p.2171

**Shepherd, Kevin**
Profile: p.1432
Table(s): **Maryland**: Real Estate **Band 1** p.1422

**Shepherd, Robert G**
Table(s): **New Jersey**: Intellectual Property **Band
3** p.1716

**Shepherd, Stewart R**
Profile: p.1231
Table(s): **Illinois**: Labor & Employment:
Employee Benefits & Compensation **Band 2**
p.1176

**Shepherd III, Thomas B**
Profile: p.1608
Table(s): **Mississippi**: Corporate/Commercial:
Gaming & Licensing **Band 1** p.1591

**Sheppard, Hale E**
Profile: p.1096
Table(s): **Georgia**: Tax **Band 3** p.1072

**Sheppard, Lee**
Profile: p.472
Table(s): **Alabama**: Real Estate **Associates to watch**
p.466

**Shepro, Richard Warren**
Table(s): **Illinois**: Corporate/M&A **Band 4** p.1156

**Sher, Barry G**
Table(s): **New York**: Litigation: General
Commercial **Band 4** p.1833

**Sher, Joel I**
Profile: p.1432
Table(s): **Maryland**: Litigation: Bankruptcy **Band 1**
p.1419

**Sher, Leopold**
Table(s): **Louisiana**: Real Estate **Band 1** p.1355

**Sher, Michael D**
Profile: p.1231
Table(s): **Illinois**: Litigation: White-Collar Crime &
Government Investigations **Band 3** p.1181

**Sher, Scott**
Table(s): **District of Columbia**: Antitrust **Band 3**
p.787

**Sher, Stanley O**
Profile: p.405
Table(s): **Nationwide**: Transportation: Shipping:
Regulatory (outside New York) **Senior Statesmen**:
p.264

**Sherbill, Esq, Raymond J**
Profile: p.1432
Table(s): **Maryland**: Corporate/M&A **Band 4**
p.1412

**Sherck, Timothy C**
Table(s): **Illinois**: Tax **Band 2** p.1192

**Sheridan, Mark D**
Table(s): **New Jersey**: Litigation: Insurance **Band
3** p.1723

**Sheridan, Mark F**
Profile: p.1774
Table(s): **Nationwide**: Native American Law **Band
3** p.192, **New Mexico**: Native American Law **Band
2** p.1771

**Sheridan, Paul**
Profile: p.892
Table(s): **District of Columbia**: Corporate/M&A &
Private Equity **Band 2** p.797

**Sheridan, Rachel W**
Table(s): **District of Columbia**: Corporate/M&A &
Private Equity **Up-and-coming individuals** p.797

**Sheridan, Robert E**
Profile: p.1655
Table(s): **Montana**: Litigation: General
Commercial **Band 1** p.1649, **Montana**: Litigation:
Mediators **Band 1** p.1649

**Sherlock, Emily**
Table(s): **North Carolina**: Environment **Associates
to watch** p.2028

**Sherman, Andrew H**
Profile: p.1747
Table(s): **New Jersey**: Bankruptcy/Restructuring
**Band 2** p.1705

**Sherman, Andrew J**
Profile: p.892
Table(s): **District of Columbia**: Corporate/M&A &
Private Equity **Band 3** p.797

**Sherman, Craig E**
Table(s): **Washington**: Corporate/Commercial
**Band 2** p.2525

**Sherman, Davis VR**
Profile: p.1432
Table(s): **Maryland**: Healthcare **Band 3** p.1415

**Sherman, Gina S**
Profile: p.1655
Table(s): **Montana**: Real Estate **Up-and-coming indi-
viduals** p.1652

**Sherman, Kyle**
Table(s): **Georgia**: Immigration **Band 2** p.1055

**Sherman, Leslie E**
Table(s): **Nationwide**: Projects: Renewables &
Alternative Energy **Band 2** p.218

**Sherman, Morris**
Table(s): **Minnesota**: Corporate/M&A **Senior
Statesmen**: p.1569

**Sherman, Robert L**
Table(s): **New York**: Intellectual Property: Trade
Mark & Copyright **Band 3** p.1821

**Sherman, Ryan**
Profile: p.2112
Table(s): **Ohio**: Litigation: General Commercial
**Up-and-coming individuals** p.2078

**Sherman, Steven E**
Table(s): **Nationwide**: Banking & Finance **Band 3**
p.31, **California**: Banking & Finance **Band 2** p.539

**Sherman, William**
Profile: p.892
Table(s): **District of Columbia**: Antitrust **Band 5**
p.787

**Sherman, William**
Profile: p.1007
Table(s): **Florida**: Tax **Band 2** p.979

**Shernoff, William M**
Table(s): **California**: Insurance: Policyholder
**Senior Statesmen**: p.576

**Sherrard III, Thomas J**
Table(s): **Tennessee**: Corporate/M&A **Band 1**
p.2288

**Sherrill, John A**
Profile: p.1096
Table(s): **Georgia**: Litigation: General
Commercial **Band 4** p.1065

**Sherwin, Peter J W**
Table(s): **Nationwide**: International Arbitration
**Band 3** p.145

**Sherwood, John K**
Profile: p.1747
Table(s): **New Jersey**: Bankruptcy/Restructuring
**Band 4** p.1705

**Shetterly, Mike M**
Profile: p.2272
Table(s): **South Carolina**: Labor & Employment
**Band 3** p.2262

**Shevin, Maurice L**
Profile: p.472
Table(s): **Alabama**: Banking & Finance **Band 3**
p.455

**Shevnock, Colleen M**
Profile: p.1555
Table(s): **Michigan**: Banking & Finance **Band 2**
p.1536

**Sheyka, Joseph W**
Profile: p.405
Table(s): **Nationwide**: Franchising **Band 3** p.111

**Shibata, David**
Table(s): **Hawaii**: Real Estate **Band 2** p.1120

**Shickich, Joseph**
Table(s): **Washington**: Bankruptcy/Restructuring
**Band 1** p.2523

**Shidlofsky, Lee H**
Table(s): **Texas**: Insurance **Band 1** p.2351

**Shield Jr, William P**
Profile: p.1555
Table(s): **Michigan**: Banking & Finance **Band 1**
p.1536

**Shields, Jeffrey Weston**
Table(s): **Utah**: Litigation: General Commercial
**Band 3** p.2468

**Shields, Lloyd N.**
Table(s): **Louisiana**: Construction **Band 2** p.1339

**Shields, Patricia**
Table(s): **North Carolina**: Litigation: General
Commercial **Band 4** p.2033

**Shields, Robert**
Table(s): **Georgia**: Litigation: General
Commercial **Band 4** p.1065

**Shields, William M.**
Table(s): **Massachusetts**: Private Equity:
Buyouts **Up-and-coming individuals** p.1474

**Shigley, Charles E**
Table(s): **Washington**: Real Estate **Band 3** p.2535

**Shilepsky, Nancy S**
Profile: p.1509
Table(s): **Massachusetts**: Labor & Employment:
Mainly Plaintiffs Representation **Band 1** p.1467

**Shilling, Cameron G**
Profile: p.1698
Table(s): **New Hampshire**: Labor & Employment
**Band 3** p.1688

**Shilling, Monica J**
Table(s): **California**: Corporate/M&A: Private
Equity **Band 3** p.553, **California**: Corporate/M&A
**Band 4** p.553

**Shim, Paul J**
Profile: p.405
Table(s): **Nationwide**: Private Equity: Buyouts
**Band 2** p.203, **New York**: Corporate/M&A **Band 2**
p.1793

**Shimada, Charlene S**
Profile: p.665
Table(s): **California**: Litigation: Securities **Band 4**
p.594

**Shimshak, Stephen J**
Profile: p.1941
Table(s): **New York**: Bankruptcy/Restructuring
**Band 3** p.1782

**Shinay, Richard**
Profile: p.1404
Table(s): **Maine**: Real Estate **Band 2** p.1395

**Shindell, James W**
Profile: p.1007
Table(s): **Florida**: Real Estate **Band 2** p.974

**Shinderman, Mark**
Profile: p.665
Table(s): **California**: Bankruptcy/Restructuring
**Band 2** p.542

**Shine, David N**
Profile: p.1941
Table(s): **New York**: Corporate/M&A **Band 3**
p.1793

**Shipley, George**
Table(s): **Texas**: Litigation: General Commercial
**Band 3** p.2362

**Shipley III, Benjamin H**
Table(s): **Arkansas**: Labor & Employment **Band 3**
p.520

**Shirazi, Ray**
Profile: p.405
Table(s): **Nationwide**: Capital Markets:
Derivatives **Band 1** p.51, **Nationwide**: Capital
Markets: Structured Products **Band 2** p.51

**Siefert, Richard C**
Table(s): **Washington:** Intellectual Property **Band 3** p.2529

**Siegal, F Don**
Table(s): **Alabama:** Real Estate **Senior Statesmen:** p.466

**Siegel, Adam**
Profile: p.1941
Table(s): **New York:** Litigation: White-Collar Crime & Government Investigations **Band 3** p.1836

**Siegel, Bradd N**
Profile: p.2113
Table(s): **Ohio:** Labor & Employment **Band 1** p.2074

**Siegel, David**
Profile: p.665
Table(s): **Nationwide:** Securities: Litigation **Band 2** p.232, **California:** Litigation: Securities **Star Individuals** p.594

**Siegel, Howard**
Table(s): **New York:** Media & Entertainment: Music **Band 2** p.1849

**Siegel, Mort**
Table(s): **Nationwide:** Food & Beverages: Alcohol **Senior Statesmen:** p.109

**Siegel, Nathan E**
Profile: p.892
Table(s): **District of Columbia:** Media & Entertainment **Band 2** p.832

**Siegel, Robert**
Table(s): **California:** Labor & Employment **Band 3** p.587

**Siegel, Robert M**
Profile: p.1007
Table(s): **Florida:** Banking & Finance: Transactional **Band 2** p.937

**Siegel, Stephen H**
Table(s): **Florida:** Healthcare **Band 3** p.954

**Sieger, John**
Table(s): **Illinois:** Bankruptcy/Restructuring **Band 4** p.1148

**Siegfried, Steven**
Table(s): **Florida:** Construction **Senior Statesmen:** p.944

**Siegler, Douglas L.**
Table(s): **Nationwide:** Wealth Management: Eastern Region **Band 2** p.267

**Siegrist, Camden P**
Profile: p.2565
Table(s): **West Virginia:** Corporate/Commercial: Banking & Finance **Band 2** p.2550

**Siemens, Reynold M**
Profile: p.665
Table(s): **California:** Insurance: Policyholder **Band 3** p.576

**Siemers, John C**
Table(s): **Alaska:** Corporate/M&A: Bankruptcy **Band 1** p.487

**Siemon, Charles L**
Table(s): **Florida:** Real Estate: Zoning/Land Use **Senior Statesmen:** p.975

**Siffert, John S**
Profile: p.1941
Table(s): **New York:** Litigation: White-Collar Crime & Government Investigations **Band 2** p.1836

**Sigel, Gabrielle**
Profile: p.1231
Table(s): **Illinois:** Environment: Litigation **Band 2** p.1162

**Sigel, John**
Profile: p.1509
Table(s): **Massachusetts:** Bankruptcy/Restructuring **Band 2** p.1449

**Sigman, Adam J**
Profile: p.472
Table(s): **Alabama:** Real Estate **Band 3** p.466

**Sigmund, Rebecca L**
Profile: p.1096
Table(s): **Georgia:** Immigration **Band 2** p.1055

**Signoracci, Diane**
Table(s): **Ohio:** Healthcare **Band 3** p.2069

**Sikkel, Robert W**
Profile: p.1555
Table(s): **Michigan:** Labor & Employment **Band 2** p.1542

**Sikora, Clifford S**
Table(s): **Nationwide:** Energy: Electricity (Regulatory & Litigation) **Band 4** p.76

**Silane, Frank A**
Table(s): **Nationwide:** Transportation: Aviation: Litigation **Band 3** p.254

**Silber, Frank**
Table(s): **North Carolina:** Intellectual Property **Band 2** p.2030

**Silberg, Jay**
Profile: p.406
Table(s): **Nationwide:** Energy: Nuclear (Regulatory & Litigation) **Band 1** p.77

**Silberglied, Russell C**
Profile: p.775
Table(s): **Delaware:** Bankruptcy/Restructuring **Band 3** p.754

**Silberman, Alan H**
Profile: p.406
Table(s): **Nationwide:** Franchising **Senior Statesmen:** p.111, **Illinois:** Antitrust **Senior Statesmen:** p.1143

**Silberman, Mickey**
Profile: p.722
Table(s): **Colorado:** Labor & Employment **Band 3** p.706

**Silberstein, Rebecca F**
Table(s): **Nationwide:** Investment Funds: Private Equity: Fund Formation **Band 2** p.166

**Silbert, Earl J**
Profile: p.892
Table(s): **District of Columbia:** Litigation: White-Collar Crime & Government Investigations **Senior Statesmen:** p.827

**Siler, Brent B**
Table(s): **Northern Virginia:** Corporate/M&A **Band 3** p.2493

**Siler Jr, W Thomas**
Table(s): **Mississippi:** Labor & Employment **Band 1** p.1595

**Silfen, Richard A**
Table(s): **Pennsylvania:** Corporate/M&A: Securities **Band 2** p.2191

**Silin, Steven**
Table(s): **Maine:** Litigation: Medical Malpractice & Insurance **Band 1** p.1393, **Maine:** Litigation: Mainly Plaintiff **Band 2** p.1393

**Silliman, Todd**
Profile: p.1097
Table(s): **Georgia:** Environment **Band 2** p.1051

**Silman, Ruth**
Profile: p.1510
Table(s): **Massachusetts:** Environment **Band 3** p.1457

**Silva, David A**
Profile: p.1941
Table(s): **New York:** Insurance: Dispute Resolution: Insurer **Band 3** p.1816

**Silva, Michael**
Profile: p.1007
Table(s): **Florida:** Tax **Band 3** p.979

**Silver, David C**
Profile: p.892
Table(s): **District of Columbia:** Real Estate **Band 2** p.835

**Silver, Hayden J**
Table(s): **North Carolina:** Litigation: General Commercial **Band 3** p.2033

**Silver, Jeffrey**
Profile: p.1683
Table(s): **Nationwide:** Gaming & Licensing **Band 3** p.115, **Nevada:** Gaming & Licensing **Band 1** p.1674

**Silver, Joseph**
Profile: p.1097
Table(s): **Georgia:** Corporate/M&A **Up-and-coming individuals** p.1046

**Silver, Michael J**
Table(s): **Maryland:** Corporate/M&A **Band 1** p.1412

**Silver, Robert S**
Table(s): **Pennsylvania:** Intellectual Property **Band 3** p.2197

**Silver, Ross Z**
Profile: p.1941
Table(s): **New York:** Real Estate **Band 4** p.1854

**Silvera, Harry R**
Profile: p.1941
Table(s): **New York:** Real Estate **Band 4** p.1854

**Silverberg, Philip C**
Profile: p.1942
Table(s): **New York:** Insurance: Dispute Resolution: Insurer **Band 3** p.1816

**Silverman, Arthur C**
Table(s): **New York:** Construction **Band 3** p.1791

**Silverman, Donald J**
Profile: p.406
Table(s): **Nationwide:** Energy: Nuclear (Regulatory & Litigation) **Band 4** p.77

**Silverman, Eric**
Profile: p.406
Table(s): **Nationwide:** Projects **Band 3** p.216

**Silverman, Gary R**
Profile: p.1231
Table(s): **Illinois:** Corporate/M&A: Private Equity **Band 2** p.1157

**Silverman, Jeremy C**
Profile: p.1097
Table(s): **Georgia:** Corporate/M&A **Band 4** p.1046

**Silverman, Karen E**
Profile: p.666
Table(s): **California:** Antitrust **Band 2** p.536

**Silverman, Lawrence D**
Table(s): **Florida:** Antitrust **Band 1** p.935

**Silverman, Leslie N**
Profile: p.406
Table(s): **Nationwide:** Capital Markets: Debt & Equity **Band 1** p.46

**Silverman, Mark**
Table(s): **District of Columbia:** Tax **Band 1** p.838

**Silverman, Moses**
Profile: p.1942
Table(s): **New York:** Antitrust **Band 3** p.1778

**Silverman, Richard S**
Table(s): **Nationwide:** Food & Beverages: Regulatory & Litigation **Band 2** p.107

**Silverman, Robert A**
Profile: p.2230
Table(s): **Pennsylvania:** Real Estate **Band 2** p.2208

**Silverman, Scott T**
Table(s): **Florida:** Labor & Employment **Band 4** p.959

**Silverman, Steve I**
Profile: p.1007
Table(s): **Florida:** Litigation: General Commercial **Band 3** p.966

**Silvernale III, Grant**
Table(s): **Nationwide:** Transportation: Aviation: Litigation **Band 3** p.254

**Silverstein, Amy**
Table(s): **California:** Tax: State & Local **Band 2** p.617

**Silverstein, Bruce L**
Table(s): **Delaware:** Chancery **Band 3** p.758

**Silverstein, Laurie Selber**
Profile: p.775
Table(s): **Delaware:** Bankruptcy/Restructuring **Star Individuals** p.754

**Silverthorn, Richard W**
Profile: p.2586
Table(s): **Wisconsin:** Corporate/M&A **Band 3** p.2571

**Silvestri, Stephen**
Profile: p.1432
Table(s): **Maryland:** Labor & Employment **Band 2** p.1417

**Silvestri Jr, Frank J**
Table(s): **Connecticut:** Litigation: General Commercial **Band 1** p.738

**Silvey, Michael**
Profile: p.2178
Table(s): **Oregon:** Real Estate **Band 3** p.2173

**Silvyn, Keri**
Table(s): **Arizona:** Real Estate: Zoning/Land Use **Band 3** p.504

**Simala, Jodi A**
Table(s): **Illinois:** Corporate/M&A **Band 4** p.1156

**Simard, Kevin J**
Profile: p.1510
Table(s): **Massachusetts:** Banking & Finance **Band 3** p.1445

**Simkin, Steven**
Profile: p.1942
Table(s): **New York:** Real Estate **Band 1** p.1854

**Simmons, Doreen A**
Table(s): **New York:** Environment **Band 3** p.1807

**Simmons, F Chase**
Table(s): **Missouri:** Real Estate **Band 3** p.1633

**Simmons, Jack**
Table(s): **Maine:** Litigation: General Commercial **Senior Statesmen:** p.1393

**Simmons, Jeffrey**
Table(s): **Wisconsin:** Intellectual Property **Band 3** p.2573

**Simmons, Rebecca J**
Profile: p.406
Table(s): **Nationwide:** Capital Markets: Derivatives **Band 2** p.51

**Simmons, Richard**
Table(s): **California:** Labor & Employment **Band 2** p.587

**Simmons, Robert W**
Table(s): **North Carolina:** Real Estate **Band 2** p.2037

**Simmons, Teri A**
Profile: p.1097
Table(s): **Georgia:** Immigration **Band 1** p.1055

**Simon, Bruce**
Table(s): **California:** Antitrust **Band 4** p.536, **California:** Antitrust: Mainly Plaintiff p.536

**Simon, Mark C**
Table(s): **Illinois:** Real Estate **Band 2** p.1187

**Simon, Norman**
Profile: p.407
Table(s): **Nationwide:** Advertising: Litigation **Up-and-coming individuals** p.19

**Simon Jr, Lawrence P**
Table(s): **Louisiana:** Energy & Natural Resources: Oil & Gas **Band 1** p.1344

**Simonds, David**
Profile: p.666
Table(s): **California:** Bankruptcy/Restructuring **Band 4** p.542

**Simonetti, D J**
Profile: p.472
Table(s): **Alabama:** Corporate/Commercial **Band 2** p.459

**Simonetti, Marc**
Table(s): **New York:** Tax **Up-and-coming individuals** p.1862

**Simons, Joseph J**
Profile: p.892
Table(s): **District of Columbia:** Antitrust **Band 3** p.787

**Simons, Robert D**
Table(s): **Georgia:** Real Estate **Band 3** p.1070

**Simonsen, Karen**
Profile: p.1231
Table(s): **Illinois:** Labor & Employment: Employee Benefits & Compensation **Band 3** p.1176

**Simonson, James S**
Table(s): **Minnesota:** Litigation: General Commercial **Band 3** p.1574

**Simonson, Mary Ellen**
Table(s): **Arizona:** Labor & Employment **Band 4** p.499

**Simpler, Gary**
Profile: p.1432
Table(s): **Maryland:** Labor & Employment **Band 2** p.1417

**Simpson, Aaron P.**
Profile: p.407
Table(s): **Nationwide:** Privacy & Data Security **Up-and-coming individuals** p.199

**Simpson, James**
Profile: p.529
Table(s): **Arkansas:** Litigation: General Commercial **Band 2** p.522

**Simpson, James A**
Profile: p.1555
Table(s): **Michigan:** Real Estate **Band 2** p.1546

**Simpson, Linda A**
Profile: p.407
Table(s): **Nationwide:** Capital Markets: Structured Products **Band 2** p.52

**Simpson, Michael H**
Profile: p.2586
Table(s): **Wisconsin:** Natural Resources & Environment **Band 3** p.2578

**Simpson, Patrick**
Table(s): **Oregon:** Corporate/M&A **Band 3** p.2164

**Simpson, Reagan**
Profile: p.2416
Table(s): **Texas:** Litigation: Appellate **Band 1** p.2361, **Texas:** Litigation: Energy & Natural Resources **Band 2** p.2361

**Simpson, William**
Table(s): **California:** Corporate/M&A: Private Equity **Band 2** p.553

**Sims, Charles**
Table(s): **New York:** Media & Entertainment: Copyright & Contract Disputes **Band 2** p.1851

**Sims, Hunter**
Table(s): **Virginia:** Litigation: General Commercial **Band 1** p.2502

**Sims, Joe**
Profile: p.892
Table(s): **District of Columbia:** Antitrust **Band 1** p.787

**Sims, Roger**
Profile: p.1007
Table(s): **Florida:** Environment **Band 1** p.951

**Sims, Steven O**
Table(s): **New Mexico:** Environment, Natural Resources & Regulated Industries: Water Law **Band 2** p.1766

**Sims, William D**
Profile: p.2416
Table(s): **Texas:** Litigation: General Commercial **Band 2** p.2362

**Sinak, David**
Profile: p.2416
Table(s): **Texas:** Tax **Band 2** p.2371

**Sinatra, Geraldine**
Profile: p.2230
Table(s): **Pennsylvania:** Corporate/M&A & Private Equity **Band 3** p.2191

**Sinclair, J Walter**
Table(s): **Idaho:** Litigation: General Commercial **Band 1** p.1134

**Sinclair, Paul H**
Table(s): **Indiana:** Labor & Employment **Band 3** p.1271

**Sinclair, Stacey**
Profile: p.1748
Table(s): **New Jersey:** Environment **Up-and-coming individuals** p.1711

**Sinder, Scott**
Table(s): **Nationwide:** Government: Government Relations **Band 2** p.121

**Singer, Alan**
Profile: p.2230
Table(s): **Pennsylvania:** Corporate/M&A: Securities **Band 1** p.2191

**Singer, Eric L**
Table(s): **Illinois:** Construction **Band 3** p.1154

**Singer, Fern H**
Table(s): **Alabama:** Labor & Employment **Band 1** p.460

**Singer, Jonathan E**
Table(s): **Minnesota:** Litigation: Intellectual Property **Band 1** p.1574

**Singer, Leonard**
Table(s): **New York:** Energy: State Regulatory & Wholesale Electric Market **Band 2** p.1806

**Singer, Louis H**
Profile: p.407
Table(s): **Nationwide:** Investment Funds: Private Equity: Fund Formation **Band 2** p.166

**Singer, Martin D**
Table(s): **California:** Media & Entertainment: Litigation **Band 1** p.606

**Singer, Paul**
Table(s): **Pennsylvania:** Bankruptcy/Restructuring **Band 1** p.2188

**Singer, Randi W**
Profile: p.1942
Table(s): **New York:** Media & Entertainment: Copyright & Contract Disputes **Band 3** p.1851

**Singer, Robert A**
Table(s): **North Carolina:** Banking & Finance **Band 2** p.2021

**Singer, Roger**
Profile: p.407
Table(s): **Nationwide:** Investment Funds: Private Equity: Fund Formation **Band 3** p.166

**Singer, Steven**
Profile: p.1942
Table(s): **Nationwide:** Securities: Litigation: Mainly Plaintiff **Band 2** p.234, **New York:** Litigation: Securities Mainly Plaintiff **Band 2** p.1835

**Singer, Steven D**
Profile: p.407
Table(s): **Nationwide:** Life Sciences: Corporate/Commercial **Star individuals** p.182

**Singer, Stuart**
Table(s): **Florida:** Antitrust **Band 1** p.935, **Florida:** Litigation: General Commercial **Band 1** p.966

**Singer, Toby G**
Profile: p.892
Table(s): **Nationwide:** Healthcare: Regulatory & Litigation **Band 2** p.127, **District of Columbia:** Healthcare **Band 1** p.809

**Singerman, Paul Steven**
Profile: p.1007
Table(s): **Nationwide:** Bankruptcy/Restructuring **Band 4** p.39, **Florida:** Bankruptcy/Restructuring **Star individuals** p.939

**Sinha, Pankaj K**
Profile: p.407
Table(s): **Nationwide:** Energy: Electricity (Transactional) **Band 2** p.77, **District of Columbia:** Corporate/M&A & Private Equity **Band 3** p.797

**Sinick, Marshall S**
Profile: p.407
Table(s): **Nationwide:** Transportation: Aviation: Regulatory **Band 2** p.256

**Siniscalco, Gary**
Profile: p.666
Table(s): **California:** Labor & Employment **Band 2** p.587

**Sink, Charles**
Table(s): **California:** Construction **Band 1** p.550

**Sink, Robert C**
Table(s): **North Carolina:** Real Estate **Band 2** p.2037

**Sinkfield, Richard H**
Profile: p.1097
Table(s): **Georgia:** Litigation: General Commercial **Band 1** p.1065

**Sinnard, Kara M**
Table(s): **Iowa:** Real Estate **Band 4** p.1290

**Sinor, Howard**
Profile: p.1370
Table(s): **Louisiana:** Litigation: General Commercial **Band 2** p.1352

**Siok, Jan**
Profile: p.666
Table(s): **California:** IT & Outsourcing **Associates to watch** p.583

**Sipe, Donald J**
Profile: p.1404
Table(s): **Maine:** Energy & Natural Resources **Band 2** p.1388

# Index of Lawyers

**Sipe Jr, Samuel M**
Table(s): Nationwide: Transportation: Rail (for Railroads) Band 1 p.257

**Sipiora, David E**
Table(s): Colorado: Intellectual Property Band 2 p.704

**Sires, Carlos**
Table(s): Florida: Litigation: General Commercial Band 2 p.966

**Sirilla, George M**
Profile: p.2513
Table(s): Northern Virginia: Intellectual Property Senior Statesmen: p.2497

**Sirkin, Michael**
Table(s): Nationwide: Employee Benefits & Executive Compensation Band 1 p.73, New York: Employee Benefits & Executive Compensation Star Individuals p.1802

**Siros, Steven**
Profile: p.1232
Table(s): Illinois: Environment: Litigation Band 3 p.1162

**Sirota, Michael**
Profile: p.1748
Table(s): New Jersey: Bankruptcy/Restructuring Band 1 p.1705

**Sirus, Richard A**
Profile: p.1232
Table(s): Illinois: Labor & Employment: Employee Benefits & Compensation Band 3 p.1176

**Sirven, José E**
Profile: p.1008
Table(s): Florida: Banking & Finance: Transactional Band 1 p.937

**Sisk, Bart N**
Profile: p.2310
Table(s): Tennessee: Labor & Employment Band 2 p.2293

**Siskind, Harris C**
Profile: p.1008
Table(s): Florida: Corporate/M&A & Private Equity Band 2 p.947

**Sit, Po**
Profile: p.1942
Table(s): New York: Tax Band 2 p.1862

**Sitarchuk, Eric W**
Profile: p.2230
Table(s): Pennsylvania: Litigation: White-Collar Crime & Government Investigations Band 1 p.2204

**Sitton, Larry B**
Profile: p.2045
Table(s): North Carolina: Litigation: General Commercial Band 2 p.2033

**Skarlatos, Bryan**
Table(s): Nationwide: Tax: Fraud Band 1 p.244

**Skeffington, James J**
Profile: p.2258
Table(s): Rhode Island: Corporate/Commercial Band 1 p.2251

**Skelley, Douglas**
Table(s): Texas: Insurance Associates to watch p.2351

**Skelly, Paul**
Table(s): District of Columbia: Labor & Employment Band 3 p.824

**Skerritt, Daniel**
Profile: p.2179
Table(s): Oregon: Litigation: General Commercial Senior Statesmen: p.2171

**Skidmore, Jonathan B**
Profile: p.407
Table(s): Nationwide: Product Liability & Mass Torts Band 4 p.208

**Skidmore, Micah**
Table(s): Texas: Insurance Associates to watch p.2351

**Skigen, Gloria**
Table(s): Connecticut: Corporate/M&A Band 3 p.732

**Skillman, Richard W**
Table(s): District of Columbia: Tax Band 3 p.838

**Skilton, John S**
Table(s): Wisconsin: Intellectual Property Band 1 p.2573, Wisconsin: Intellectual Property: Litigation p.2573

**Skilton III, Robert H**
Table(s): Michigan: Banking & Finance: Bankruptcy Band 2 p.1536

**Skinner, Honey J**
Profile: p.1232
Table(s): Illinois: Healthcare Band 3 p.1165

**Skinner, Philip G**
Profile: p.1097
Table(s): Georgia: Real Estate Band 3 p.1070

**Skinner, Shannon**
Profile: p.2541
Table(s): Washington: Real Estate Band 2 p.2535

**Skinner, Thomas V**
Profile: p.1232
Table(s): Illinois: Environment: Litigation Band 4 p.1162

**Skinner, William P**
Profile: p.407
Table(s): Nationwide: Insurance: Dispute Resolution: Policyholder Band 1 p.137, District of Columbia: Insurance: Policyholder Band 1 p.818

**Skipper, Walter J**
Profile: p.2586
Table(s): Wisconsin: Corporate/M&A Band 3 p.2571

**Sklar, Alan C**
Table(s): Nevada: Corporate/Commercial Band 2 p.1672

**Sklar, Bradley J**
Profile: p.472
Table(s): Alabama: Corporate/Commercial Band 3 p.459

**Sklar, Daniel W**
Profile: p.1698
Table(s): New Hampshire: Corporate/Commercial Band 3 p.1685, New Hampshire: Corporate/Commercial: Bankruptcy Band 1 p.1685

**Sklaroff, Michael**
Profile: p.2230
Table(s): Pennsylvania: Real Estate Band 1 p.2208, Pennsylvania: Real Estate: Zoning/Land Use Band 1 p.2208

**Sklaroff, Neil**
Profile: p.2230
Table(s): Pennsylvania: Real Estate: Zoning/Land Use Band 1 p.2208

**Sklarsky, Charles B**
Profile: p.1232
Table(s): Illinois: Litigation: General Commercial Band 3 p.1180, Illinois: Litigation: White-Collar Crime & Government Investigations Band 1 p.1180

**Skolnick, Holly R**
Profile: p.1008
Table(s): Florida: Litigation: White-Collar Crime & Government Investigations Band 1 p.967

**Skrocki, Melissa**
Table(s): New Jersey: Intellectual Property Associates to watch p.1716

**Slade, David**
Table(s): Nationwide: Projects Band 3 p.216, Nationwide: Projects: PPP Band 2 p.216

**Slade, Georgiana J**
Profile: p.407
Table(s): Nationwide: Wealth Management: Eastern Region Band 2 p.267

**Slade, Lynn H**
Table(s): Nationwide: Native American Law Band 2 p.192, New Mexico: Native American Law Star Individuals p.1771

**Slafsky, John**
Table(s): California: Intellectual Property: Trademark, Copyright & Trade Secrets Band 3 p.578

**Slater, James**
Table(s): Florida: Real Estate Band 2 p.974

**Slater, Paul**
Table(s): Illinois: Antitrust Band 1 p.1143

**Slater, Scott S.**
Table(s): California: Environment Band 3 p.564

**Slater, Valerie A**
Profile: p.408
Table(s): Nationwide: International Trade: Trade Remedies & Trade Policy Band 3 p.154

**Slater Jr, Thomas G**
Profile: p.2513
Table(s): Virginia: Litigation: General Commercial Band 1 p.2502

**Slattery, Alan D**
Table(s): Nebraska: Corporate/Commercial Band 3 p.1659

**Slattery, Kerrin**
Profile: p.1232
Table(s): Illinois: Healthcare Band 2 p.1165

**Slattery Jr, Gerald**
Table(s): Louisiana: Energy & Natural Resources: Oil & Gas Band 3 p.1344

**Slaughter, Christopher L**
Profile: p.2565
Table(s): West Virginia: Labor & Employment Band 2 p.2553

**Slaughter, Thomas L**
Table(s): Iowa: Corporate/M&A Band 4 p.1283

**Slaughter Jr, Harrison T**
Table(s): Florida: Litigation: White-Collar Crime & Government Investigations Band 3 p.967

**Slavich, John**
Table(s): Texas: Environment Band 2 p.2343

**Slavin, Leslie**
Table(s): Massachusetts: Employee Benefits & Executive Compensation Band 3 p.1455

**Slavin, Richard**
Profile: p.747
Table(s): Connecticut: Litigation: General Commercial Band 3 p.738

**Slifkin, Daniel**
Profile: p.1942
Table(s): New York: Litigation: Securities Band 4 p.1834

**Sligar, James S**
Profile: p.408
Table(s): Nationwide: Wealth Management: Eastern Region Band 4 p.267

**Sloan, Cliff**
Profile: p.892
Table(s): District of Columbia: Media & Entertainment Band 3 p.832

**Sloan, David Scott**
Profile: p.1510
Table(s): Massachusetts: Tax: Estate Planning Band 1 p.1481

**Sloan, Mark M**
Profile: p.2416
Table(s): Texas: Real Estate Band 2 p.2367

**Slonaker, Norman**
Profile: p.408
Table(s): Nationwide: Capital Markets: Debt & Equity Senior Statesmen: p.46

**Slone, Daniel K**
Table(s): Virginia: Environment Band 1 p.2495

**Sloss, John**
Table(s): New York: Media & Entertainment: Film & Television Band 2 p.1849

**Slotkin, David P**
Profile: p.408
Table(s): Nationwide: Capital Markets: REITs Band 3 p.55

**Slotnick, Barry I**
Profile: p.1942
Table(s): New York: Media & Entertainment: Copyright & Contract Disputes Band 2 p.1851

**Slovek, Robert M**
Profile: p.1669
Table(s): Nebraska: Litigation: General Commercial Band 2 p.1664

**Slover, William**
Profile: p.408
Table(s): Nationwide: Transportation: Rail (for Shippers) Band 2 p.258

# Index of Lawyers

**Slovin, Gary M**
Table(s): Hawaii: Real Estate: Zoning/Land Use **Band 1** p.1120

**Slusser, William C**
Profile: p.2416
Table(s): Texas: Intellectual Property **Band 1** p.2354

**Slutzky, Lorence H**
Table(s): Illinois: Construction **Band 2** p.1154

**Slutzky, Steven J**
Table(s): Nationwide: Capital Markets: Debt & Equity **Band 4** p.46

**Small, Andrew D**
Profile: p.1232
Table(s): Illinois: Real Estate **Band 2** p.1187

**Small, Daniel W**
Table(s): Tennessee: Banking & Finance: Regulatory **Band 2** p.2287

**Small, John H**
Table(s): Delaware: Corporate/M&A **Band 3** p.761, Delaware: Corporate/M&A: Alternative Entities **Band 3** p.761

**Small, John H**
Table(s): North Carolina: Bankruptcy/Restructuring **Band 1** p.2023

**Smallwood, Mary F**
Profile: p.1008
Table(s): Florida: Environment **Band 1** p.951

**Smart, Skip**
Table(s): North Carolina: Corporate/M&A **Band 3** p.2025

**Smedinghoff, Thomas J**
Profile: p.1232
Table(s): Nationwide: Privacy & Data Security **Band 2** p.199, Illinois: Technology & Outsourcing **Band 1** p.1194

**Smethurst, Ryan**
Profile: p.893
Table(s): District of Columbia: Insurance: Insurer **Band 4** p.816

**Smiley, Cynthia M**
Table(s): Texas: Environment **Band 4** p.2343

**Smit, Robert H**
Profile: p.408
Table(s): Nationwide: International Arbitration **Band 2** p.145

**Smith, Alan**
Table(s): Washington: Bankruptcy/Restructuring **Band 1** p.2523

**Smith, Alan C**
Profile: p.2541
Table(s): Washington: Corporate/Commercial **Band 2** p.2525

**Smith, Alfred**
Table(s): Connecticut: Environment **Band 2** p.733

**Smith, Alison L**
Profile: p.2416
Table(s): Texas: Antitrust **Band 2** p.2323

**Smith, Andrew**
Profile: p.2113
Table(s): Ohio: Labor & Employment **Band 4** p.2074

**Smith, Andrew M**
Profile: p.408
Table(s): Nationwide: Privacy & Data Security **Band 3** p.199

**Smith, Bradford J**
Profile: p.1510
Table(s): Massachusetts: Labor & Employment **Band 2** p.1466

**Smith, Bradley Y**
Profile: p.408
Table(s): Nationwide: Banking & Finance **Band 1** p.31

**Smith, Brooks**
Profile: p.2514
Table(s): Virginia: Environment **Band 1** p.2495

**Smith, Bruce**
Table(s): Massachusetts: Bankruptcy/Restructuring **Band 3** p.1449

**Smith, Bruce M**
Table(s): Idaho: Natural Resources & Environment **Band 2** p.1136

**Smith, Chris M**
Table(s): New York: Real Estate **Band 1** p.1854

**Smith, Christopher J**
Table(s): Connecticut: Real Estate **Band 3** p.740

**Smith, Colin P**
Profile: p.408
Table(s): Nationwide: Product Liability & Mass Torts **Band 4** p.208, Nationwide: Product Liability: Automobile p.208

**Smith, Craig**
Table(s): Florida: Healthcare **Band 2** p.954

**Smith, Darrell C**
Table(s): Florida: Corporate/M&A & Private Equity **Band 3** p.947

**Smith, David M**
Profile: p.473
Table(s): Alabama: Labor & Employment **Band 1** p.460

**Smith, David S**
Profile: p.2514
Table(s): Virginia: Labor & Employment **Band 2** p.2500

**Smith, Douglas**
Profile: p.408
Table(s): Nationwide: Energy: Electricity (Regulatory & Litigation) **Band 2** p.76

**Smith, Douglas D**
Profile: p.666
Table(s): California: Capital Markets: Debt & Equity **Band 2** p.547

**Smith, Duncan C**
Profile: p.408
Table(s): Nationwide: Transportation: Shipping Regulatory (outside New York) **Band 3** p.264

**Smith, E Kendrick**
Profile: p.1097
Table(s): Georgia: Litigation: General Commercial **Band 4** p.1065

**Smith, Edwin E**
Profile: p.1510
Table(s): Nationwide: Banking & Finance **Band 2** p.31, Massachusetts: Banking & Finance **Star individuals** p.1445, Massachusetts: Bankruptcy/Restructuring **Band 1** p.1449

**Smith, Felton W**
Table(s): Alabama: Real Estate **Band 2** p.466

**Smith, George Anthony**
Profile: p.1097
Table(s): Georgia: Construction **Band 2** p.1044

**Smith, Glenn**
Table(s): New Jersey: Labor & Employment **Band 3** p.1718

**Smith, Gregory**
Table(s): Nevada: Labor & Employment **Band 2** p.1675

**Smith, Gregory A**
Table(s): Nationwide: Government: Government Contracts **Band 2** p.117, Nationwide: Government: Government Contracts: Costs Disputes p.117

**Smith, Gregory H**
Profile: p.1698
Table(s): New Hampshire: Environment **Band 1** p.1687

**Smith, Gregory K**
Table(s): Nationwide: Projects **Band 3** p.216

**Smith, Gregory R**
Table(s): Missouri: Real Estate **Band 1** p.1633

**Smith, Holly**
Table(s): Nationwide: Financial Services Regulation: Broker Dealer (Compliance) **Band 3** p.97

**Smith, J Theodore (Ted)**
Profile: p.2113
Table(s): Ohio: Real Estate **Band 3** p.2086

**Smith, James**
Table(s): Arkansas: Corporate/Commercial **Band 2** p.518, Arkansas: Corporate/Commercial: Tax **Band 2** p.518

**Smith, James E**
Profile: p.2416
Table(s): Texas: Environment **Band 2** p.2343

**Smith, James T**
Profile: p.2231
Table(s): Pennsylvania: Litigation: General Commercial **Band 3** p.2203

**Smith, Jane S**
Profile: p.2416
Table(s): Texas: Real Estate **Band 3** p.2367

**Smith, Janet Hugie**
Table(s): Utah: Labor & Employment **Band 1** p.2467

**Smith, Jason**
Profile: p.408
Table(s): Nationwide: Capital Markets: Securitisation **Band 2** p.59

**Smith, Jeffery**
Profile: p.2113
Table(s): Ohio: Corporate/M&A **Band 4** p.2064

**Smith, Jeffrey**
Profile: p.1942
Table(s): Nationwide: Climate Change **Band 3** p.63, New York: Environment: Mainly Transactional **Band 1** p.1808

**Smith, Jeffrey**
Profile: p.409
Table(s): Nationwide: Government: Government Contracts **Band 4** p.117

**Smith, Jeffrey**
Profile: p.1232
Table(s): Illinois: Corporate/M&A: Private Equity **Band 3** p.1157

**Smith, Jeffrey Q**
Profile: p.409
Table(s): Nationwide: Securities: Litigation **Band 2** p.232, New York: Litigation: Securities **Band 2** p.1834

**Smith, Jennifer M**
Profile: p.409
Table(s): Nationwide: International Arbitration **Band 4** p.145

**Smith, Jodie**
Profile: p.473
Table(s): Alabama: Banking & Finance: Public Finance **Band 2** p.455

**Smith, Joel H**
Profile: p.2272
Table(s): Nationwide: Product Liability & Mass Torts **Band 4** p.208, Nationwide: Product Liability: Automobile p.208, South Carolina: Litigation: General Commercial **Band 2** p.2264

**Smith, John F Sandy**
Table(s): Georgia: Corporate/M&A **Band 3** p.1046

**Smith, Joseph A**
Profile: p.409
Table(s): Nationwide: Investment Funds: Private Equity: Fund Formation **Band 3** p.166

**Smith, Joshua D.**
Profile: p.2154
Table(s): Oklahoma: Corporate/Commercial **Up-and-coming individuals** p.2134

**Smith, Kathryn**
Table(s): Ohio: Intellectual Property **Band 3** p.2071

**Smith, Kevin**
Table(s): Kentucky: Labor & Employment **Band 2** p.1310

**Smith, Laura**
Profile: p.529
Table(s): Arkansas: Litigation: Medical Malpractice Defense **Star individuals** p.522

**Smith, Laurence**
Table(s): New Jersey: Corporate/M&A **Band 4** p.1707

**Smith, Leslie M**
Profile: p.409
Table(s): Nationwide: Product Liability & Mass Torts **Band 5** p.208

**Smith, Mary Leslie**
Table(s): Nationwide: Franchising **Band 4** p.111

**Smith, Michael**
Table(s): Virginia: Litigation: General Commercial **Band 2** p.2502

**Smith, Michael E**
Profile: p.2154
Table(s): Oklahoma: Energy & Natural
Resources **Band 1** p.2136

**Smith, Michael H**
Profile: p.2154
Table(s): Oklahoma: Intellectual Property
**Associates to watch** p.2138

**Smith, Michael W**
Profile: p.409
Table(s): Nationwide: Banking & Finance:
Equipment Finance & Leasing **Band 2** p.32,
Nationwide: Transportation: Aviation: Finance
**Band 1** p.252

**Smith, Nathan H**
Table(s): Maine: Real Estate **Band 1** p.1395

**Smith, Patricia A**
Profile: p.1748
Table(s): New Jersey: Labor & Employment **Band
2** p.1718

**Smith, Paul M**
Profile: p.409
Table(s): Nationwide: Appellate Law **Band 2** p.26,
Nationwide: First Amendment Litigation **Band 1**
p.105, District of Columbia: Media &
Entertainment **Band 1** p.832

**Smith, Paul T**
Table(s): California: Healthcare **Band 4** p.568

**Smith, R Jeffrey**
Profile: p.747
Table(s): Connecticut: Real Estate **Band 1** p.740

**Smith, Raymond G**
Profile: p.1324
Table(s): Kentucky: Litigation: General
Commercial **Band 4** p.1312

**Smith, Richard**
Table(s): Maine: Real Estate **Band 3** p.1395

**Smith, Richard F**
Table(s): Virginia: Construction **Senior Statesmen:**
p.2491

**Smith, Robert A**
Profile: p.409
Table(s): Nationwide: Franchising **Band 4** p.111

**Smith, Robert J**
Profile: p.893
Table(s): District of Columbia: Labor &
Employment **Band 3** p.824

**Smith, Robert W.**
Profile: p.1748
Table(s): New Jersey: Intellectual Property **Band
3** p.1716

**Smith, Rodger**
Table(s): Delaware: Intellectual Property **Band 3**
p.763

**Smith, Russell L**
Profile: p.409
Table(s): Nationwide: Government: Government
Relations **Band 3** p.121

**Smith, Scott**
Profile: p.1942
Table(s): New York: Corporate/M&A **Band 3**
p.1793

**Smith, Sean**
Table(s): North Dakota: Corporate/Commercial
**Band 1** p.2051, North Dakota: Real Estate **Band 2**
p.2055

**Smith, Stephen**
Table(s): District of Columbia: Antitrust **Band 3**
p.787

**Smith, Steven**
Table(s): Nationwide: International Arbitration
**Band 4** p.145

**Smith, Steven B.**
Table(s): Nationwide: Sports Law **Band 3** p.241

**Smith, Taylor**
Table(s): Mississippi: Labor & Employment **Star
individuals** p.1595

**Smith, Thomas S**
Table(s): Oregon: Real Estate **Band 2** p.2173

**Smith, Tyson**
Profile: p.409
Table(s): Nationwide: Energy: Nuclear
(Regulatory & Litigation) **Up-and-coming individuals**
p.77

**Smith, W Lindsay**
Table(s): South Carolina: Real Estate **Band 1**
p.2266

**Smith, Wade M**
Table(s): North Carolina: Litigation: White-Collar
Crime & Government Investigations **Band 1**
p.2034

**Smith, Wayne**
Profile: p.666
Table(s): California: Litigation: Securities **Band 2**
p.594

**Smith, William Calvin**
Profile: p.1097
Table(s): Georgia: Corporate/M&A **Band 3** p.1046

**Smith, William L**
Table(s): Mississippi: Litigation: General
Commercial **Band 4** p.1597

**Smith, William P**
Profile: p.1232
Table(s): Illinois: Bankruptcy/Restructuring **Band
3** p.1148

**Smith, Wm. Randolph**
Profile: p.893
Table(s): District of Columbia: Antitrust **Band 2**
p.787

**Smith III, Frank G**
Profile: p.1097
Table(s): Georgia: Intellectual Property **Band 2**
p.1056

**Smith III, Henry A**
Table(s): Maryland: Employee Benefits &
Executive Compensation **Band 1** p.1414

**Smith III, James U**
Table(s): Kentucky: Labor & Employment **Band 1**
p.1310

**Smith III, William C**
Profile: p.1608
Table(s): Mississippi: Real Estate **Band 1** p.1600

**Smith Jr, Arthur B**
Profile: p.1232
Table(s): Illinois: Labor & Employment **Band 2**
p.1175

**Smith Jr, Jay**
Profile: p.1433
Table(s): Maryland: Corporate/M&A **Band 1**
p.1412

**Smith Jr, Richard K**
Profile: p.409
Table(s): Nationwide: Banking & Finance:
Equipment Finance & Leasing **Band 2** p.32,
Nationwide: Transportation: Aviation: Finance
**Band 2** p.252

**Smith Jr, Skottowe W**
Table(s): North Carolina: Real Estate **Band 3**
p.2037

**Smith-Lalla, Lori**
Profile: p.1008
Table(s): Florida: Banking & Finance **Band 3**
p.936

**Smith, Jr, J David**
Profile: p.1324
Table(s): Kentucky: Corporate/M&A **Band 3**
p.1305

**Smoak, Lewis T**
Profile: p.2272
Table(s): South Carolina: Labor & Employment
**Senior Statesmen:** p.2262

**Smolinsky, Joseph H**
Profile: p.1942
Table(s): New York: Bankruptcy/Restructuring
**Band 3** p.1782

**Smulian, Andrew**
Table(s): Florida: Real Estate **Band 2** p.974

**Smutny, Abby Cohen**
Profile: p.409
Table(s): Nationwide: International Arbitration
**Band 2** p.145

**Smylie, Sallie G**
Profile: p.1232
Table(s): Illinois: Litigation: General Commercial
**Band 4** p.1180

**Smyser, Craig**
Profile: p.2416
Table(s): Texas: Litigation: General Commercial
**Band 2** p.2362

**Smythe, Susan**
Table(s): South Carolina: Real Estate **Band 2**
p.2266

**Smythe Jr, Henry B**
Table(s): South Carolina: Litigation: General
Commercial **Band 2** p.2264

**Snapp, Randall J**
Profile: p.2154
Table(s): Oklahoma: Labor & Employment **Band 2**
p.2140

**Snapper, Michael**
Profile: p.1555
Table(s): Michigan: Labor & Employment **Band 3**
p.1542

**Sneed, Spencer**
Table(s): Alaska: Corporate/M&A **Band 1** p.487,
Alaska: Corporate/M&A: Bankruptcy **Band 1**
p.487, Alaska: Litigation: General Commercial
**Band 2** p.490

**Sneed, William M**
Profile: p.1233
Table(s): Illinois: Insurance: Dispute Resolution:
Reinsurance **Band 1** p.1168

**Snell, Dietrich**
Table(s): New York: Litigation: White-Collar
Crime & Government Investigations **Band 3**
p.1836

**Snell, Virginia**
Profile: p.1324
Table(s): Kentucky: Litigation: General
Commercial **Band 3** p.1312

**Snider, Teresa**
Profile: p.1233
Table(s): Illinois: Insurance: Dispute Resolution:
Reinsurance **Band 3** p.1168

**Sniff, Kirk F**
Table(s): Texas: Environment **Band 4** p.2343

**Sniffen, Robert J.**
Table(s): Florida: Labor & Employment **Band 4**
p.959

**Snipes, James C**
Profile: p.666
Table(s): Nationwide: Life Sciences:
Corporate/Commercial **Band 3** p.182, California:
Life Sciences: Corporate/Commercial **Band 1**
p.590

**Snow, Colleen Gillis**
Table(s): Northern Virginia: Real Estate:
Zoning/Land Use **Up-and-coming individuals** p.2505

**Snow, Edgar**
Table(s): Georgia: Banking & Finance **Band 2**
p.1039

**Snow, Steven E**
Table(s): Rhode Island: Litigation: General
Commercial **Band 2** p.2254

**Snyder, Allison**
Profile: p.2416
Table(s): Texas: Construction **Band 1** p.2335

**Snyder, David R**
Profile: p.666
Table(s): California: Capital Markets: Debt &
Equity **Band 3** p.547, California: Life Sciences:
Corporate/Commercial **Band 4** p.590

**Snyder, Jeffrey L**
Profile: p.410
Table(s): Nationwide: International Trade: Export
Controls & Economic Sanctions **Band 1** p.153

**Snyder, Joan P**
Table(s): Oregon: Environment **Band 1** p.2165

**Snyder, John L**
Profile: p.1638
Table(s): Missouri: Real Estate **Band 2** p.1633

**Snyder, Nicole**
Profile: p.1140
Table(s): Idaho: Corporate/Commercial **Band 2**
p.1132

**Snyder, Orin**
Profile: p.1942
Table(s): **New York:** Litigation: General
Commercial **Band 2** p.1833, **New York:** Media &
Entertainment: Copyright & Contract Disputes
**Band 1** p.1851

**Snyder, Randye C.**
Table(s): **Louisiana:** Labor & Employment:
Employee Benefits & Compensation **Band 2**
p.1350

**Snyder, Sheryl**
Profile: p.1324
Table(s): **Kentucky:** Litigation: General
Commercial **Band 1** p.1312

**Sobel, Gerald**
Profile: p.410
Table(s): **Nationwide:** Life Sciences: IP/Patent
Litigation **Senior Statesmen:** p.183, **New York:**
Intellectual Property: Patent **Senior Statesmen:**
p.1820

**Sobel, Stuart**
Table(s): **Florida:** Construction **Band 2** p.944

**Sobin, Sturgis M**
Profile: p.410
Table(s): **Nationwide:** International Trade:
Intellectual Property (Section 337) **Band 2** p.160

**Socha, Charles Q**
Table(s): **Nationwide:** Product Liability & Mass
Torts **Band 5** p.208

**Sofaer, Abraham D**
Table(s): **Nationwide:** International Arbitration:
Arbitrators **Band 1** p.146

**Soffer, Gil M**
Table(s): **Illinois:** Litigation: White-Collar Crime &
Government Investigations **Band 2** p.1181

**Sogn, Jon C**
Table(s): **South Dakota:** Labor & Employment
**Band 2** p.2283, **South Dakota:** Litigation: General
Commercial **Band 2** p.2284

**Sohn, Michael N**
Profile: p.893
Table(s): **District of Columbia:** Antitrust **Senior
Statesmen:** p.787

**Sokler, Bruce D**
Profile: p.893
Table(s): **District of Columbia:** Antitrust **Band 5**
p.787

**Sokol, Jerry J**
Profile: p.1008
Table(s): **Florida:** Healthcare **Band 2** p.954

**Sokul Jr, John H**
Table(s): **New Hampshire:** Real Estate **Band 2**
p.1692

**Solada, Mary E**
Profile: p.1280
Table(s): **Indiana:** Real Estate **Band 3** p.1275

**Solander, William**
Profile: p.1943
Table(s): **New York:** Intellectual Property: Patent
**Band 3** p.1820

**Sold, Kenneth W**
Profile: p.1943
Table(s): **New York:** Real Estate **Band 4** p.1854

**Soldo, Linda J**
Profile: p.410
Table(s): **Nationwide:** Financial Services
Regulation: Banking (Enforcement &
Investigations) **Band 3** p.97

**Solecki, Mike**
Profile: p.2113
Table(s): **Ohio:** Corporate/M&A **Band 4** p.2064

**Soler, Jonathon G**
Profile: p.410
Table(s): **Nationwide:** Investment Funds: Private
Equity: Fund Formation **Band 3** p.166

**Solimine, Louis F**
Profile: p.2113
Table(s): **Ohio:** Bankruptcy/Restructuring **Band 2**
p.2058

**Solish, Jonathan C**
Table(s): **Nationwide:** Franchising **Band 1** p.111

**Sollins, Howard L**
Table(s): **Maryland:** Healthcare **Band 2** p.1415

**Sollner, Richard**
Table(s): **Florida:** Real Estate **Band 3** p.974

**Solomon, Adam**
Profile: p.410
Table(s): **Nationwide:** Advertising: Transactional
& Regulatory **Band 3** p.20

**Solomon, Andrew**
Table(s): **Oregon:** Real Estate **Band 3** p.2173

**Solomon, Andrew P**
Profile: p.1943
Table(s): **New York:** Tax **Band 2** p.1862

**Solomon, David H**
Profile: p.893
Table(s): **District of Columbia:** Telecom,
Broadcast & Satellite **Band 3** p.844

**Solomon, Jay**
Table(s): **Georgia:** Immigration **Band 1** p.1055

**Solomon, Louis M**
Profile: p.1943
Table(s): **New York:** Litigation: General
Commercial **Band 3** p.1833

**Solomon, Randall L**
Profile: p.2113
Table(s): **Ohio:** Litigation: General Commercial
**Band 4** p.2078

**Solomon, Ronni**
Profile: p.410
Table(s): **Nationwide:** Litigation: E-Discovery **Band
3** p.187

**Solomon, Steven J**
Profile: p.1008
Table(s): **Florida:** Bankruptcy/Restructuring **Band
4** p.939

**Solow, Alan P**
Profile: p.1233
Table(s): **Illinois:** Bankruptcy/Restructuring **Band
3** p.1148

**Solow, Michael**
Profile: p.1233
Table(s): **Illinois:** Bankruptcy/Restructuring **Band
2** p.1148

**Solow, Sheldon L**
Profile: p.1233
Table(s): **Illinois:** Bankruptcy/Restructuring **Band
4** p.1148

**Solow, Steven P**
Table(s): **District of Columbia:** Environment **Band
4** p.804

**Soltis, Michael**
Profile: p.747
Table(s): **Connecticut:** Labor & Employment **Band
2** p.736

**Somers, George W**
Table(s): **Indiana:** Real Estate **Band 2** p.1275

**Somerstein, Barry**
Table(s): **Florida:** Real Estate **Band 1** p.974

**Somerstein, Mark R.**
Table(s): **New York:** Bankruptcy/Restructuring
**Band 4** p.1782

**Somerville III, William G**
Profile: p.473
Table(s): **Alabama:** Labor & Employment **Band 3**
p.460

**Sommer, Dean**
Table(s): **New York:** Environment **Band 1** p.1807

**Sommerhauser, Peter**
Table(s): **Wisconsin:** Corporate/M&A **Senior
Statesmen:** p.2571

**Sommers, William W**
Table(s): **Texas:** Construction **Band 3** p.2335

**Song, Stephanie Koo**
Profile: p.2416
Table(s): **Texas:** Banking & Finance **Band 4**
p.2325

**Song, Wayne W**
Profile: p.410
Table(s): **Nationwide:** Projects **Band 4** p.216,
**Nationwide:** Projects: Renewables & Alternative
Energy **Band 2** p.216

**Songy, Randall**
Table(s): **Louisiana:** Energy & Natural
Resources: Oil & Gas **Band 3** p.1344

**Sonnenberg, Stephen**
Table(s): **New York:** Labor & Employment **Band 3**
p.1826

**Sonnenfeld, Marc**
Profile: p.2231
Table(s): **Pennsylvania:** Litigation: General
Commercial **Band 1** p.2203, **Pennsylvania:**
Litigation: Securities **Band 1** p.2203

**Sonnenschein, Edward**
Table(s): **Nationwide:** Energy: Electricity
(Transactional) **Band 2** p.77

**Sonnett, Neal R**
Table(s): **Florida:** Litigation: White-Collar Crime &
Government Investigations **Senior Statesmen:**
p.967

**Sonsini, Larry W**
Table(s): **Nationwide:** Investment Funds: Venture
Capital **Band 2** p.174, **California:** Capital Markets:
Debt & Equity **Band 1** p.547, **California:**
Corporate/M&A **Star individuals** p.553

**Sontag, Scott M**
Profile: p.1943
Table(s): **New York:** Tax **Band 4** p.1862

**Soobert, Allan**
Table(s): **District of Columbia:** Intellectual
Property: Litigation **Band 4** p.821

**Sooy, Kathleen Taylor**
Profile: p.893
Table(s): **District of Columbia:** Litigation:
General Commercial **Band 3** p.826

**Sopher, Edward D**
Profile: p.410
Table(s): **Nationwide:** Investment Funds: Private
Equity: Fund Formation **Band 2** p.166

**Sophir, Eric**
Profile: p.893
Table(s): **District of Columbia:** Intellectual
Property: Patent Prosecution **Band 2** p.820

**Sopko, Jeffrey J**
Table(s): **Ohio:** Intellectual Property **Band 2**
p.2071

**Sorabella, William B**
Profile: p.1943
Table(s): **New York:** Corporate/M&A **Up-and-com-
ing individuals** p.1793

**Soref, Randye**
Table(s): **California:** Bankruptcy/Restructuring
**Band 4** p.542

**Sorensen, David F.**
Table(s): **Pennsylvania:** Antitrust **Band 3** p.2184

**Sorensen, Harvey**
Profile: p.1300
Table(s): **Kansas:** Corporate/M&A **Band 1** p.1292

**Sorensen, Nick H**
Profile: p.2417
Table(s): **Texas:** Banking & Finance **Band 2**
p.2325

**Sorensen, Sharp**
Profile: p.1233
Table(s): **Illinois:** Tax **Band 2** p.1192

**Sorenson, Derek L**
Profile: p.511
Table(s): **Arizona:** Real Estate **Band 2** p.504

**Soriano, Robert A**
Profile: p.1008
Table(s): **Florida:** Bankruptcy/Restructuring **Band
2** p.939

**Sorin, Robert J**
Profile: p.1943
Table(s): **New York:** Real Estate **Band 1** p.1854

**Sorini, Marc**
Profile: p.410
Table(s): **Nationwide:** Food & Beverages: Alcohol
**Star individuals** p.109

**Sorkin, Ira Lee**
Profile: p.1943
Table(s): **New York:** Litigation: White-Collar
Crime & Government Investigations **Band 3**
p.1836

**Sorkin, John E**
Profile: p.1943
Table(s): **New York:** Corporate/M&A **Band 5**
p.1793

**Sorkin, Laurence T**
Profile: p.1943
Table(s): New York: Antitrust **Band 4** p.1778

**Sorocco, Douglas J**
Profile: p.2154
Table(s): Oklahoma: Intellectual Property **Band 1** p.2138

**Soroko, John J**
Table(s): Pennsylvania: Litigation: General Commercial **Band 3** p.2203, Pennsylvania: Litigation: Securities **Band 2** p.2203

**Sorondo Jr, Rodolfo**
Profile: p.1008
Table(s): Florida: Litigation: Appellate **Band 1** p.972

**Sosin, Jeremy**
Table(s): Ohio: Real Estate **Up-and-coming individuals** p.2086

**Sosland, Martin**
Profile: p.2417
Table(s): Nationwide: Bankruptcy/Restructuring **Band 2** p.39, Texas: Bankruptcy/Restructuring **Band 1** p.2328

**Soslow, Joanne R**
Profile: p.2231
Table(s): Pennsylvania: Corporate/M&A: Securities **Band 2** p.2191

**Sostek, Bruce S**
Profile: p.2417
Table(s): Texas: Intellectual Property **Band 2** p.2354

**Sostrin, Rita**
Table(s): California: Immigration **Band 4** p.571

**Soto, Edward**
Profile: p.1008
Table(s): Florida: Litigation: General Commercial **Band 1** p.966

**Sotsky, Lester**
Profile: p.893
Table(s): District of Columbia: Environment **Band 4** p.804

**Sottile, James**
Table(s): New York: Insurance: Dispute Resolution: Insurer **Band 3** p.1816

**Sotto, Lisa J**
Profile: p.410
Table(s): Nationwide: Privacy & Data Security **Star individuals** p.199

**Soussloff, Andrew D**
Profile: p.410
Table(s): Nationwide: Capital Markets: Debt & Equity **Band 4** p.46

**Southworth II, Louis S**
Table(s): West Virginia: Corporate/Commercial: Tax **Band 1** p.2550

**Sovern, Grant S**
Profile: p.2586
Table(s): Wisconsin: Labor & Employment: Immigration **Band 2** p.2575

**Sowatzka, Adam G**
Profile: p.1097
Table(s): Georgia: Environment **Band 2** p.1051

**Sowell, Thornwell F**
Profile: p.2272
Table(s): South Carolina: Litigation: General Commercial **Band 2** p.2264

**Sozio, Stephen**
Profile: p.2113
Table(s): Ohio: Litigation: White-Collar Crime & Government Investigations **Band 1** p.2079

**Spaanstra, James R**
Table(s): Colorado: Natural Resources & Environment **Band 1** p.712

**Spahn Jr, Jeff C**
Table(s): Kansas: Litigation: General Commercial **Band 2** p.1295

**Spak, Gregory J**
Profile: p.411
Table(s): Nationwide: International Trade: Trade Remedies & Trade Policy **Band 4** p.154

**Spak, Walter J**
Profile: p.411
Table(s): Nationwide: International Trade: Trade Remedies & Trade Policy **Band 4** p.154

**Spalj, Gregory**
Table(s): Minnesota: Construction **Band 2** p.1567

**Spandorf, Rochelle Buchsbaum**
Table(s): Nationwide: Franchising **Band 2** p.111

**Spangler, Georlen**
Table(s): Nevada: Litigation: Construction **Band 1** p.1676

**Spangler III, John I**
Profile: p.1098
Table(s): Georgia: Construction **Band 1** p.1044

**Spann, Bryant J**
Table(s): West Virginia: Litigation: General Commercial **Band 2** p.2555

**Spanos, Peter R**
Table(s): Georgia: Labor & Employment **Band 4** p.1060

**Spansel, Mark J**
Profile: p.1370
Table(s): Louisiana: Environment: Litigation **Band 2** p.1346

**Sparagna, Giovanna T**
Table(s): District of Columbia: Tax **Band 3** p.838

**Sparkman, Jon B**
Table(s): New Hampshire: Corporate/Commercial: Tax **Band 2** p.1685

**Sparks, Brian**
Profile: p.1009
Table(s): Florida: Tax: Estate Planning **Band 2** p.979

**Sparks, Daniel**
Table(s): Alabama: Bankruptcy/Restructuring **Band 3** p.457

**Sparks, Kenneth F**
Profile: p.1233
Table(s): Illinois: Labor & Employment **Band 4** p.1175

**Sparks, Stephen S**
Table(s): Missouri: Real Estate **Band 2** p.1633

**Sparks III, A Gilchrist**
Table(s): Delaware: Chancery **Senior Statesmen:** p.758, Delaware: Corporate/M&A **Senior Statesmen:** p.761

**Spatt, Robert E**
Profile: p.1944
Table(s): New York: Corporate/M&A **Band 3** p.1793

**Spears, Berry**
Profile: p.2417
Table(s): Texas: Bankruptcy/Restructuring **Band 2** p.2328

**Spears, David**
Table(s): New York: Litigation: White-Collar Crime & Government Investigations **Band 2** p.1836

**Spears, L Gene**
Profile: p.2417
Table(s): Texas: Intellectual Property **Band 3** p.2354

**Spears, Larry**
Table(s): Oklahoma: Litigation: Mediators **Band 1** p.2141

**Spears, Natalie**
Profile: p.1233
Table(s): Illinois: Media & Entertainment: Litigation **Band 2** p.1184

**Spears Jr, James B**
Profile: p.2045
Table(s): North Carolina: Labor & Employment **Band 3** p.2031

**Specht, Scott A**
Profile: p.1098
Table(s): Georgia: Real Estate **Band 2** p.1070

**Spector, Barry S**
Table(s): Nationwide: Energy: Electricity (Regulatory & Litigation) **Band 1** p.76

**Spector, David**
Table(s): Illinois: Insurance: Dispute Resolution: Reinsurance **Star individuals** p.1168

**Spector, David I**
Table(s): Florida: Labor & Employment **Band 4** p.959, Florida: Litigation: General Commercial **Band 4** p.966

**Spector, Scott**
Profile: p.666
Table(s): California: Employee Benefits & Executive Compensation **Band 1** p.560

**Speer, John**
Profile: p.2310
Table(s): Tennessee: Litigation: General Commercial **Band 3** p.2295

**Speier, Anthony**
Profile: p.411
Table(s): Nationwide: Energy: Oil & Gas (Transactional) **Associates to watch** p.79

**Speights, Grace E**
Profile: p.893
Table(s): District of Columbia: Labor & Employment **Band 3** p.824

**Speirs, Kevin**
Profile: p.2475
Table(s): Utah: Intellectual Property **Band 2** p.2466

**Spelios, Louis C.**
Table(s): Georgia: Corporate/M&A **Band 4** p.1046

**Spell, Cynthia L**
Profile: p.1433
Table(s): Maryland: Real Estate **Band 4** p.1422

**Spelliscy, M J**
Profile: p.411
Table(s): Nationwide: Transportation: Aviation: Finance **Band 3** p.252

**Spencer, Aaron**
Table(s): North Carolina: Corporate/M&A **Up-and-coming individuals** p.2025

**Spencer, Steven D**
Profile: p.2231
Table(s): Pennsylvania: Labor & Employment: Employee Benefits & Compensation **Band 2** p.2200

**Sperber, Marc F**
Table(s): Illinois: Corporate/M&A **Band 3** p.1156

**Spergel, Jonathan**
Table(s): Pennsylvania: Environment **Band 4** p.2194

**Sperling, Joy Harmon**
Profile: p.1748
Table(s): New Jersey: Litigation: General Commercial **Band 3** p.1722

**Sperling, Robert Y**
Profile: p.1233
Table(s): Illinois: Litigation: General Commercial **Band 3** p.1180

**Speth II, Charles T**
Profile: p.2272
Table(s): South Carolina: Labor & Employment **Band 1** p.2262

**Spevacek, Charles**
Table(s): Minnesota: Litigation: Appellate **Band 2** p.1573

**Spiegel, Bennett**
Profile: p.666
Table(s): California: Bankruptcy/Restructuring **Band 4** p.542

**Spiegel, John**
Profile: p.666
Table(s): Nationwide: Securities: Litigation **Band 2** p.232, California: Litigation: General Commercial **Band 2** p.593, California: Litigation: Securities **Band 1** p.593, California: Litigation: White-Collar Crime & Government Investigations **Band 2** p.601

**Spiegel, Lisa**
Table(s): California: Immigration **Band 3** p.571

**Spielberg, David C**
Table(s): Nationwide: Projects: Renewables & Alternative Energy **Band 2** p.218

**Spielman, Andrew L**
Table(s): Colorado: Natural Resources & Environment **Band 2** p.712

**Spiers, Jeffrey E**
Profile: p.2417
Table(s): Texas: Bankruptcy/Restructuring **Band 4** p.2328

**Stanko, Joe**
Profile: p.894
Table(s): District of Columbia: Environment Band 5 p.804

**Stanley, Douglas L**
Profile: p.1301
Table(s): Kansas: Labor & Employment Band 1 p.1294

**Stanley, Hugh**
Table(s): Ohio: Litigation: General Commercial Band 4 p.2078

**Stanley, Richard**
Table(s): Louisiana: Litigation: General Commercial Band 1 p.1352

**Stanley, Robert K**
Table(s): Indiana: Litigation: General Commercial Band 1 p.1273

**Stansbury, Claude B**
Profile: p.894
Table(s): District of Columbia: Tax Band 4 p.838

**Stansbury, Ronald C**
Profile: p.2113
Table(s): Ohio: Employee Benefits & Executive Compensation Band 2 p.2067

**Stanton, David**
Table(s): Nationwide: Litigation: E-Discovery Band 2 p.187

**Stanton, Joseph**
Table(s): Florida: Banking & Finance: Public Finance Band 2 p.936

**Stanton, Patricia**
Profile: p.2417
Table(s): Texas: Real Estate Band 1 p.2367

**Stanton, Patrick M**
Profile: p.1748
Table(s): New Jersey: Labor & Employment Senior Statesmen: p.1718

**Stanton, W Clark**
Table(s): California: Healthcare Band 2 p.568

**Stanziale, Charles**
Profile: p.1748
Table(s): New Jersey: Bankruptcy/Restructuring Band 1 p.1705

**Staples, J. Peter**
Table(s): Oregon: Intellectual Property Band 3 p.2167

**Starcher, Doug**
Table(s): Florida: Corporate/M&A & Private Equity Band 3 p.947

**Stark, Beau**
Profile: p.722
Table(s): Colorado: Corporate/M&A Band 3 p.703

**Stark, Robert**
Table(s): Nationwide: Bankruptcy/Restructuring Band 3 p.39, New York: Bankruptcy/Restructuring Band 2 p.1782

**Stark, Sanford W**
Profile: p.411
Table(s): Nationwide: Tax: Controversy Band 4 p.244

**Stark, Stephen**
Table(s): Kansas: Real Estate Band 2 p.1297

**Starke, Wallace**
Table(s): Virginia: Labor & Employment: Employee Benefits & Compensation Band 2 p.2500

**Starkey, J Shane**
Profile: p.2114
Table(s): Ohio: Employee Benefits & Executive Compensation Band 1 p.2067

**Starling III, M Jefferson**
Table(s): Alabama: Labor & Employment Band 2 p.460

**Starn, Peter**
Profile: p.1125
Table(s): Hawaii: Corporate/Commercial Band 2 p.1116, Hawaii: Real Estate Band 2 p.1120

**Starr, Edward**
Table(s): Virginia: Litigation: General Commercial Band 3 p.2502

**Starr, Judson**
Profile: p.894
Table(s): District of Columbia: Environment Band 1 p.804

**Starr, Kelly. A**
Profile: p.1234
Table(s): Illinois: Labor & Employment: Employee Benefits & Compensation Band 3 p.1176

**Starr, Michael**
Profile: p.1944
Table(s): New York: Labor & Employment Band 3 p.1826

**Starrett, Cindy**
Table(s): California: Real Estate: Zoning/Land Use Band 2 p.612

**Starshak, James L**
Profile: p.1125
Table(s): Hawaii: Labor & Employment: Employee Benefits & Compensation Band 2 p.1117

**Stathas, Lynn M**
Profile: p.2586
Table(s): Wisconsin: Labor & Employment Band 3 p.2575

**Statman, Alan**
Table(s): Nationwide: Energy: Electricity (Regulatory & Litigation) Band 5 p.76

**Staudenmaier, Heidi M**
Table(s): Nationwide: Gaming & Licensing Band 2 p.115, Nationwide: Native American Law Band 2 p.192

**Staudenmaier, L William**
Table(s): Arizona: Environment: Water Rights Band 1 p.497

**Stayer, Mark**
Table(s): Oregon: Real Estate Band 3 p.2173

**Stearn Jr, Robert J**
Profile: p.775
Table(s): Delaware: Bankruptcy/Restructuring Band 4 p.754

**Stearns, Eugene**
Table(s): Florida: Litigation: General Commercial Star Individuals p.966

**Stearns, Scott M**
Table(s): Montana: Litigation: General Commercial Band 4 p.1649

**Steeg, Robert M**
Profile: p.1370
Table(s): Louisiana: Real Estate Band 1 p.1355

**Steege, Catherine L**
Profile: p.1234
Table(s): Illinois: Bankruptcy/Restructuring Band 3 p.1148

**Steel, John M**
Profile: p.2541
Table(s): Washington: Corporate/Commercial Band 1 p.2525

**Steel, Michael**
Profile: p.667
Table(s): California: Environment Band 2 p.564

**Steel Jr, Adrian L**
Table(s): Nationwide: Transportation: Rail (for Railroads) Band 2 p.257

**Steele, Robert M.**
Profile: p.2310
Table(s): Tennessee: Environment Band 2 p.2290

**Steele, Tracy L**
Table(s): Pennsylvania: Real Estate Band 4 p.2208

**Steen, Bruce**
Table(s): North Carolina: Labor & Employment Band 4 p.2031

**Steenrod, Ralston W**
Profile: p.1325
Table(s): Kentucky: Corporate/M&A Senior Statesmen: p.1305

**Stefani, Randall**
Table(s): Iowa: Litigation: General Commercial Band 3 p.1288

**Steffes, William E**
Table(s): Louisiana: Bankruptcy/Restructuring Band 1 p.1337

**Stegemoeller, Mark**
Table(s): California: Capital Markets: Debt & Equity Band 2 p.547

**Steger, S Martijn**
Table(s): Ohio: Corporate/M&A Band 2 p.2064

**Stegich, Stephen R**
Table(s): Nationwide: Transportation: Aviation: Litigation Band 3 p.254

**Stein, Barry**
Table(s): Pennsylvania: Intellectual Property Band 3 p.2197

**Stein, Craig**
Profile: p.412
Table(s): Nationwide: Capital Markets: Derivatives Band 2 p.51

**Stein, David**
Table(s): Nationwide: Wealth Management: Eastern Region Up-and-coming Individuals p.267

**Stein, Gary M**
Profile: p.1009
Table(s): Florida: Construction Band 3 p.944

**Stein, Grant T**
Profile: p.1098
Table(s): Georgia: Bankruptcy/Restructuring Band 1 p.1042

**Stein, Jane Wallison**
Table(s): Nationwide: Projects Band 4 p.216

**Stein, Jay**
Table(s): New Mexico: Environment, Natural Resources & Regulated Industries: Water Law Band 1 p.1766

**Stein, Jeffrey**
Profile: p.1098
Table(s): Georgia: Corporate/M&A Band 3 p.1046

**Stein, Joshua**
Table(s): New York: Real Estate Band 2 p.1854

**Stein, Laurence J**
Table(s): California: Tax Band 2 p.617

**Stein, Lee**
Table(s): Arizona: Litigation: White-Collar Crime & Government Investigations Band 1 p.501

**Stein, Mark**
Profile: p.1944
Table(s): New York: Litigation: White-Collar Crime & Government Investigations Band 2 p.1836

**Stein, Marta**
Table(s): Illinois: Litigation: General Commercial Band 4 p.1180

**Stein, Michael**
Profile: p.1748
Table(s): New Jersey: Litigation: General Commercial Band 3 p.1722

**Stein, Pamela B**
Profile: p.2417
Table(s): Texas: Real Estate Band 3 p.2367

**Stein, Peter**
Profile: p.748
Table(s): Connecticut: Labor & Employment Band 2 p.736

**Stein, Stanton 'Larry'**
Profile: p.667
Table(s): California: Media & Entertainment: Litigation Band 1 p.606

**Stein, Steven GM**
Table(s): Illinois: Construction Band 1 p.1154

**Stein, Stuart**
Table(s): Nationwide: Financial Services Regulation: Banking (Compliance) Band 2 p.96, Nationwide: Financial Services Regulation: Banking (Enforcement & Investigations) Band 3 p.96, Nationwide: Financial Services Regulation: Financial Institutions M&A Band 3 p.96

**Steinberg, Arthur**
Profile: p.1944
Table(s): New York: Bankruptcy/Restructuring Band 4 p.1782

**Steinberg, Donald R**
Profile: p.1510
Table(s): Massachusetts: Intellectual Property Band 3 p.1463

**Steuber, David W**
Profile: p.412
Table(s): Nationwide: Insurance: Dispute
Resolution: Policyholder **Band 1** p.137, California:
Insurance: Policyholder **Band 1** p.576

**Steuer, Richard M**
Table(s): New York: Antitrust **Band 2** p.1778

**Stevens, Charla B**
Profile: p.1698
Table(s): New Hampshire: Labor & Employment
**Band 3** p.1688

**Stevens, Charles P**
Profile: p.2587
Table(s): Wisconsin: Labor & Employment:
Employee Benefits & Compensation **Band 1**
p.2575

**Stevens, Hugh**
Table(s): North Carolina: Litigation: First
Amendment **Band 1** p.2033

**Stevens, James W**
Table(s): Georgia: Banking & Finance: Mainly
Regulatory **Up-and-coming individuals** p.1039

**Stevens, Jane**
Table(s): New York: Media & Entertainment:
Copyright & Contract Disputes **Band 3** p.1851

**Stevens, Mark C**
Profile: p.412
Table(s): Nationwide: Investment Funds: Venture
Capital **Band 2** p.174, California: Corporate/M&A:
Venture Capital **Band 2** p.555

**Stevens, Michael L**
Profile: p.894
Table(s): District of Columbia: Labor &
Employment **Band 3** p.824

**Stevens, Pauline M**
Profile: p.667
Table(s): California: Banking & Finance **Band 3**
p.539

**Stevens, Robert C.**
Profile: p.1098
Table(s): Georgia: Labor & Employment **Band 4**
p.1060

**Stevens, William**
Table(s): Georgia: Real Estate **Band 3** p.1070

**Stevens III, N L (Larry)**
Profile: p.412
Table(s): Nationwide: Energy: Oil & Gas
(Transactional) **Band 4** p.79

**Stevenson, Brent M**
Table(s): Utah: Corporate/M&A **Band 3** p.2462

**Stevenson, Jill M**
Table(s): Iowa: Real Estate **Band 4** p.1290

**Stevenson, Randy RJ**
Table(s): Nebraska: Labor & Employment **Band 1**
p.1662

**Stevenson, Robert B**
Profile: p.1555
Table(s): Michigan: Employee Benefits &
Executive Compensation **Band 1** p.1540

**Stevenson III, Theodore**
Profile: p.2417
Table(s): Texas: Intellectual Property **Band 2**
p.2354

**Stever, Donald W**
Profile: p.1944
Table(s): New York: Environment **Band 3** p.1807

**Steverson, Randall**
Table(s): Hawaii: Corporate/Commercial:
Finance **Band 2** p.1116, Hawaii: Real Estate **Band
1** p.1120

**Stewart, Amy Lee**
Table(s): Arkansas: Litigation: General
Commercial **Band 3** p.522

**Stewart, Cynthia L**
Profile: p.1325
Table(s): Kentucky: Intellectual Property **Band 2**
p.1308

**Stewart, Dan**
Profile: p.2417
Table(s): Nationwide: Bankruptcy/Restructuring
**Band 4** p.39, Texas: Bankruptcy/Restructuring
**Band 1** p.2328

**Stewart, Donald**
Profile: p.473
Table(s): Alabama: Bankruptcy/Restructuring
**Band 3** p.457

**Stewart, James**
Profile: p.1748
Table(s): New Jersey: Environment **Band 2** p.1711

**Stewart, Jefferson**
Profile: p.1608
Table(s): Mississippi: Energy & Natural
Resources **Band 1** p.1593

**Stewart, Robert**
Table(s): Texas: Environment **Band 3** p.2343

**Stewart, Robert K**
Table(s): Alaska: Labor & Employment **Band 2**
p.489

**Stewart, Scott M**
Table(s): Nationwide: Tax: Controversy **Band 4**
p.244

**Stewart, Terence P**
Table(s): Nationwide: International Trade: Trade
Remedies & Trade Policy **Band 2** p.154

**Stewart III, J Hamilton**
Profile: p.2272
Table(s): South Carolina: Labor & Employment
**Senior Statesmen:** p.2262

**Stichter, Don M**
Profile: p.1009
Table(s): Florida: Bankruptcy/Restructuring
**Senior Statesmen:** p.939

**Stichter, Scott**
Profile: p.1009
Table(s): Florida: Bankruptcy/Restructuring **Band
4** p.939

**Stickler, Daniel**
Table(s): West Virginia: Litigation: General
Commercial **Senior Statesmen:** p.2555

**Stickles, Kate**
Profile: p.775
Table(s): Delaware: Bankruptcy/Restructuring
**Band 3** p.754

**Stidham, Erik**
Profile: p.1140
Table(s): Idaho: Litigation: General Commercial
**Band 2** p.1134

**Stief, James**
Table(s): Ohio: Banking & Finance **Band 3** p.2056

**Stieglitz, Graham H**
Table(s): Georgia: Bankruptcy/Restructuring
**Band 3** p.1042

**Stier Jr, Robert H**
Profile: p.1404
Table(s): Maine: Litigation: General Commercial
**Band 2** p.1393

**Stiles, Matthew**
Table(s): Alabama: Labor & Employment **Band 3**
p.460

**Stillman, Charles**
Table(s): New York: Litigation: White-Collar
Crime & Government Investigations **Senior
Statesmen:** p.1836

**Stillman, Gregory**
Profile: p.2514
Table(s): Southern Virginia: Intellectual Property
**Band 1** p.2498, Virginia: Litigation: General
Commercial **Band 1** p.2502

**Stillman, Nina G**
Profile: p.1234
Table(s): Illinois: Labor & Employment **Band 1**
p.1175

**Stillwell, R Newcomb**
Table(s): Nationwide: Private Equity: Buyouts
**Band 2** p.203, Massachusetts: Private Equity:
Buyouts **Band 1** p.1474

**Stinson, C David**
Profile: p.2154
Table(s): Oklahoma: Energy & Natural
Resources **Band 2** p.2136

**Stiss, Carey A**
Profile: p.1009
Table(s): Florida: Real Estate **Band 3** p.974

**Stock, Eric J**
Table(s): New York: Antitrust **Up-and-coming individuals** p.1778

**Stock, Stuart C**
Profile: p.413
Table(s): Nationwide: Financial Services
Regulation: Banking (Compliance) **Band 1** p.96,
Nationwide: Financial Services Regulation:
Banking (Enforcement & Investigations) **Band 2**
p.96

**Stock, William**
Table(s): Nationwide: Immigration **Band 2** p.131

**Stockdale, Don**
Table(s): District of Columbia: Telecom,
Broadcast & Satellite **Band 4** p.844

**Stocker II, Robert W**
Profile: p.413
Table(s): Nationwide: Gaming & Licensing **Band 1**
p.115

**Stocks, Bruce D**
Profile: p.722
Table(s): Colorado: Corporate/M&A **Band 1** p.703

**Stockton, David**
Table(s): Georgia: Corporate/M&A **Band 1** p.1046

**Stockwell, Mitchell G**
Table(s): Georgia: Intellectual Property **Band 2**
p.1056

**Stoddard, Marshall C**
Profile: p.667
Table(s): Nationwide: Banking & Finance **Band 4**
p.31, California: Banking & Finance **Band 2** p.539

**Stohler, Charles**
Table(s): Connecticut: Labor & Employment **Band
1** p.736

**Stohner, Ken**
Profile: p.2418
Table(s): Texas: Bankruptcy/Restructuring **Band 4**
p.2328

**Stokdyk, Steven B**
Table(s): California: Capital Markets: Debt &
Equity **Band 3** p.547

**Stokes, James C**
Profile: p.1510
Table(s): Massachusetts: Corporate/M&A **Band 4**
p.1452

**Stokes, Macey Reasoner**
Profile: p.2418
Table(s): Texas: Litigation: Appellate **Band 2**
p.2361

**Stokes, Randall**
Table(s): Arizona: Real Estate **Band 3** p.504

**Stokke, Diane**
Profile: p.2541
Table(s): Washington: Real Estate **Band 3** p.2535

**Stolkin, Ronald J**
Table(s): Arizona: Labor & Employment **Band 1**
p.499

**Stoll, David J**
Profile: p.413
Table(s): Nationwide: Wealth Management:
Eastern Region **Band 3** p.267

**Stoll, Neal R**
Profile: p.1945
Table(s): New York: Antitrust **Band 5** p.1778

**Stoll, R Ryan**
Profile: p.1234
Table(s): Illinois: Litigation: General Commercial
**Band 3** p.1180

**Stoll, Richard G**
Table(s): District of Columbia: Environment **Band
2** p.804

**Stoll, Robert**
Table(s): Oregon: Litigation: General
Commercial **Senior Statesmen:** p.2171

**Stolper, Antonia E**
Table(s): Nationwide: Capital Markets: Debt &
Equity **Band 4** p.46, New York: Latin American
Investment **Band 1** p.1829

**Stoltman, Thomas P.**
Table(s): Minnesota: Real Estate **Band 3** p.1576

**Stolzman, Robert**
Profile: p.2258
Table(s): Rhode Island: Real Estate **Band 1**
p.2255

**Stone, Alan G.**
Table(s): **Maine:** Energy & Natural Resources **Band 2** p.1388

**Stone, Ben H**
Table(s): **Mississippi:** Litigation: General Commercial **Band 4** p.1597

**Stone, Benjamin**
Table(s): **Georgia:** Labor & Employment **Band 2** p.1060

**Stone, Bruce M**
Table(s): **Florida:** Tax: Estate Planning **Band 1** p.979

**Stone, David S**
Profile: p.1234
Table(s): **Illinois:** Corporate/M&A **Band 4** p.1156

**Stone, Greg**
Profile: p.667
Table(s): **California:** Intellectual Property: Patent **Band 3** p.578

**Stone, James**
Profile: p.2114
Table(s): **Ohio:** Labor & Employment **Band 4** p.2074

**Stone, Jason M**
Table(s): **Iowa:** Corporate/M&A **Band 3** p.1283

**Stone, Jeffrey E**
Profile: p.1234
Table(s): **Illinois:** Litigation: General Commercial **Band 2** p.1180, **Illinois:** Litigation: White-Collar Crime & Government Investigations **Band 2** p.1180

**Stone, Lincoln**
Table(s): **California:** Immigration **Band 4** p.571

**Stone, Richard L**
Profile: p.667
Table(s): **California:** Media & Entertainment: Litigation **Band 3** p.606

**Stone, Steven M**
Table(s): **Missouri:** Real Estate **Band 2** p.1633

**Stone, Steven W**
Profile: p.413
Table(s): **Nationwide:** Financial Services Regulation: Broker Dealer (Compliance) **Band 1** p.97

**Stone, Susan**
Profile: p.413
Table(s): **Nationwide:** Insurance: Dispute Resolution: Reinsurance **Band 1** p.135, **Illinois:** Insurance: Dispute Resolution: Reinsurance **Band 1** p.1168

**Stone, Susan**
Table(s): **Texas:** Tax **Band 3** p.2371

**Stonecipher, Thomas**
Table(s): **Montana:** Corporate/M&A **Band 3** p.1646

**Stoneman, Mark**
Table(s): **Missouri:** Corporate/M&A **Up-and-coming individuals** p.1619

**Stoner, Wayne L**
Profile: p.1510
Table(s): **Massachusetts:** Intellectual Property **Band 2** p.1463

**Stonestreet, Robert**
Table(s): **West Virginia:** Natural Resources **Up-and-coming individuals** p.2558

**Stong, Roger A**
Profile: p.2154
Table(s): **Oklahoma:** Corporate/Commercial **Band 1** p.2134

**Stopher, Edward H**
Profile: p.1325
Table(s): **Kentucky:** Litigation: Tort & Insurance Defense **Star individuals** p.1312

**Stopher, Robert E**
Profile: p.1325
Table(s): **Kentucky:** Litigation: Tort & Insurance Defense **Band 1** p.1312

**Storey, Lee**
Profile: p.511
Table(s): **Arizona:** Environment: Water Rights **Band 1** p.497

**Storey, Lesa J**
Profile: p.511
Table(s): **Arizona:** Real Estate **Band 1** p.504

**Stork, Anita F**
Profile: p.668
Table(s): **California:** Antitrust **Band 3** p.536

**Storke, Charles A**
Table(s): **California:** Employee Benefits & Executive Compensation **Band 3** p.560

**Storms, Justin**
Table(s): **Nationwide:** Investment Funds: Private Equity: Fund Formation **Associates to watch** p.166

**Storslee, Steven**
Table(s): **North Dakota:** Litigation: General Commercial **Band 1** p.2053

**Story, Thomas L**
Table(s): **Missouri:** Real Estate **Band 2** p.1633

**Stotts, Stacy**
Table(s): **Missouri:** Environment **Band 2** p.1621

**Stough, John**
Table(s): **Nationwide:** Energy: Electricity (Regulatory & Litigation) **Band 5** p.76

**Stout, Bradley A**
Table(s): **Kansas:** Litigation: General Commercial **Band 3** p.1295, **Kansas:** Real Estate **Band 3** p.1297

**Stout, Mikel**
Profile: p.1301
Table(s): **Kansas:** Litigation: General Commercial **Band 1** p.1295

**Stovall, Gerald L.**
Table(s): **Kentucky:** Litigation: Construction **Band 1** p.1312

**Stovall, Richard**
Table(s): **Ohio:** Bankruptcy/Restructuring **Band 3** p.2058

**Stowers, Gerard R**
Profile: p.2566
Table(s): **West Virginia:** Litigation: General Commercial **Band 1** p.2555

**Strafer, Richard**
Table(s): **Florida:** Litigation: Appellate **Band 1** p.972

**Straight, Samuel C**
Table(s): **Utah:** Intellectual Property **Band 3** p.2466

**Strain, James A**
Profile: p.1280
Table(s): **Indiana:** Corporate/M&A **Band 1** p.1268

**Strain, Paul**
Profile: p.1433
Table(s): **Nationwide:** Product Liability & Mass Torts **Band 4** p.208, **Maryland:** Litigation: General Commercial **Band 2** p.1419

**Strait, Hawley**
Table(s): **Maine:** Real Estate **Associates to watch** p.1395

**Strand, Margaret**
Profile: p.894
Table(s): **District of Columbia:** Environment **Band 3** p.804

**Strand, Peter**
Table(s): **Illinois:** Media & Entertainment: Transactional **Band 1** p.1185

**Strand, Robert**
Profile: p.1125
Table(s): **Hawaii:** Real Estate **Band 2** p.1120

**Strange, Margaret 'Peggy'**
Profile: p.748
Table(s): **Connecticut:** Labor & Employment **Band 3** p.736

**Strangis, Ralph**
Table(s): **Minnesota:** Corporate/M&A **Senior Statesmen:** p.1569

**Strassberg, Richard M**
Profile: p.1945
Table(s): **New York:** Litigation: White-Collar Crime & Government Investigations **Band 1** p.1836

**Strassner, Peter S**
Table(s): **Missouri:** Environment **Band 1** p.1621

**Stratton, David B**
Profile: p.775
Table(s): **Delaware:** Bankruptcy/Restructuring **Band 1** p.754

**Straus, Jerry C**
Table(s): **Nationwide:** Native American Law **Senior Statesmen:** p.192

**Straus, R James**
Profile: p.1325
Table(s): **Kentucky:** Corporate/M&A **Band 1** p.1305

**Strauss, Bettina**
Table(s): **Missouri:** Litigation: General Commercial **Band 3** p.1629

**Strauss, David J**
Profile: p.2114
Table(s): **Ohio:** Real Estate **Senior Statesmen:** p.2086

**Strauss, Stuart**
Profile: p.413
Table(s): **Nationwide:** Investment Funds: Registered Funds **Band 3** p.170

**Strecker, David**
Table(s): **Oklahoma:** Labor & Employment **Band 1** p.2140

**Street, Phillip**
Table(s): **Georgia:** Healthcare **Band 3** p.1052

**Streff Jr, William A**
Profile: p.1234
Table(s): **Illinois:** Intellectual Property **Band 2** p.1171

**Streicker, James R**
Table(s): **Illinois:** Litigation: White-Collar Crime & Government Investigations **Band 2** p.1181

**Streisand, Adam F**
Profile: p.668
Table(s): **California:** Tax: Estate Planning **Band 1** p.617

**Streit, Gary J**
Table(s): **Iowa:** Corporate/M&A **Band 1** p.1283

**Streitz, Mary**
Table(s): **Nationwide:** Native American Law **Band 3** p.192

**Strelau, Nancy**
Table(s): **Colorado:** Labor & Employment: Employee Benefits & Compensation **Band 1** p.706

**Strench, William G**
Profile: p.1325
Table(s): **Kentucky:** Corporate/M&A **Band 2** p.1305

**Strickland, Nate Wesley**
Table(s): **Florida:** Insurance **Up-and-coming individuals** p.957

**Strickland, Rachel C**
Profile: p.1945
Table(s): **New York:** Bankruptcy/Restructuring **Band 4** p.1782

**Stricklin, Cliff**
Table(s): **Colorado:** Litigation: White-Collar Crime & Government Investigations **Band 2** p.710

**Stricklin, Samuel M**
Profile: p.2418
Table(s): **Texas:** Bankruptcy/Restructuring **Band 3** p.2328

**Stride, Jon P**
Profile: p.2179
Table(s): **Oregon:** Litigation: General Commercial **Band 3** p.2171

**Striefsky, Linda A**
Profile: p.2114
Table(s): **Ohio:** Real Estate **Band 1** p.2086

**Strinden, Jon E**
Table(s): **North Dakota:** Corporate/Commercial **Band 1** p.2051

**Stringer, N Martin**
Profile: p.2154
Table(s): **Oklahoma:** Corporate/Commercial **Band 2** p.2134

**Stringfellow, James S**
Profile: p.413
Table(s): **Nationwide:** Capital Markets: Structured Products **Band 2** p.52

**Stringham, John C**
Table(s): **Utah:** Intellectual Property **Band 2** p.2466

**Kirk, Richard D**
Profile: p.772
Table(s): **Delaware:** Intellectual Property **Band 3** p.763

**Kirk, WL**
Table(s): **Florida:** Litigation: General Commercial **Band 3** p.966

**Kirkbride, Rick S**
Table(s): **Nationwide:** Leisure & Hospitality **Band 1** p.179

**Kirkham, Christopher W**
Profile: p.646
Table(s): **California:** Banking & Finance **Band 2** p.539

**Kirkham, John S**
Table(s): **Utah:** Energy & Natural Resources **Band 2** p.2464

**Kirkland, Byron B**
Profile: p.2042
Table(s): **North Carolina:** Corporate/M&A **Band 2** p.2025

**Kirkland, David**
Profile: p.2399
Table(s): **Texas:** Corporate/M&A **Band 1** p.2337

**Kirkpatrick, Deanna**
Profile: p.347
Table(s): **Nationwide:** Capital Markets: Debt & Equity **Band 4** p.46

**Kirkwood, Peter**
Table(s): **Florida:** Tax: Estate Planning **Band 3** p.979

**Kirkwood, Thomas J**
Profile: p.2102
Table(s): **Ohio:** Construction **Band 2** p.2062

**Kirmis, Lyle W**
Table(s): **North Dakota:** Litigation: General Commercial **Band 1** p.2053

**Kirpalani, Susheel**
Table(s): **Nationwide:** Bankruptcy/Restructuring **Band 1** p.39, **New York:** Bankruptcy/Restructuring **Band 1** p.1782

**Kirsch, Gregory J**
Table(s): **Georgia:** Intellectual Property **Band 3** p.1056

**Kirsch, Kevin W**
Profile: p.2102
Table(s): **Ohio:** Intellectual Property **Band 3** p.2071

**Kirsch, Laurence S**
Profile: p.874
Table(s): **District of Columbia:** Environment **Band 3** p.804

**Kirsch, Mark**
Profile: p.1909
Table(s): **Nationwide:** Securities: Litigation **Band 2** p.232, **New York:** Litigation: Securities **Band 1** p.1834

**Kirsch, Mark**
Profile: p.744
Table(s): **Connecticut:** Real Estate **Band 3** p.740

**Kirsch, Robert**
Profile: p.1498
Table(s): **Massachusetts:** Environment **Band 1** p.1457

**Kirschbaum, Howard**
Table(s): **Illinois:** Real Estate **Band 1** p.1187

**Kirschner, Lisa**
Profile: p.2474
Table(s): **Utah:** Energy & Natural Resources **Band 3** p.2464, **Utah:** Energy & Natural Resources: Water Law p.2464

**Kirshenbaum, Mark**
Profile: p.1498
Table(s): **Massachusetts:** Tax **Band 2** p.1481

**Kirson, Sarah E**
Profile: p.347
Table(s): **Nationwide:** Investment Funds: Private Equity: Fund Formation **Band 4** p.166

**Kirsons, Mark**
Profile: p.1215
Table(s): **Illinois:** Banking & Finance **Up-and-coming individuals** p.1145

**Kirtley, John**
Table(s): **Wisconsin:** Litigation: General Commercial **Band 3** p.2576

**Kirwin, Brian P**
Table(s): **Florida:** Construction **Band 1** p.944

**Kisch, Victor J**
Table(s): **Oregon:** Labor & Employment **Band 1** p.2168

**Kiser, Chérie Renee**
Profile: p.874
Table(s): **District of Columbia:** Telecom, Broadcast & Satellite **Band 2** p.844

**Kisicki, Mark G**
Profile: p.509
Table(s): **Arizona:** Labor & Employment **Band 3** p.499

**Kiss, Robert S**
Profile: p.2563
Table(s): **West Virginia:** Corporate/Commercial: Tax **Band 1** p.2550

**Kissinger, William D**
Profile: p.646
Table(s): **California:** Energy: State Regulatory & Litigation **Band 3** p.562

**Kistenbroker, David H**
Profile: p.1215
Table(s): **Illinois:** Litigation: General Commercial **Band 4** p.1180

**Kistler, David**
Profile: p.1739
Table(s): **New Jersey:** Litigation: General Commercial **Up-and-coming individuals** p.1722

**Kitchel, Chris**
Table(s): **Oregon:** Labor & Employment **Band 2** p.2168

**Kitchen, David**
Profile: p.646
Table(s): **California:** Banking & Finance **Band 2** p.539

**Kitchen, F Damon**
Table(s): **Florida:** Labor & Employment **Band 2** p.959

**Kitchens, Dean**
Profile: p.347
Table(s): **Nationwide:** Securities: Litigation **Band 2** p.232, **California:** Litigation: General Commercial **Band 2** p.593, **California:** Litigation: Securities **Band 2** p.593

**Kitslaar, Elizabeth C**
Profile: p.1215
Table(s): **Illinois:** Corporate/M&A **Band 2** p.1156

**Kittle-Kamp, Thomas L**
Table(s): **Nationwide:** Tax: Controversy **Band 4** p.244

**Kizziar Jr, James H**
Profile: p.2399
Table(s): **Texas:** Labor & Employment **Band 4** p.2359

**Klaas, Paul B**
Table(s): **Minnesota:** Litigation: General Commercial **Band 3** p.1574

**Klahr, Robert**
Table(s): **Missouri:** Real Estate **Band 3** p.1633

**Klapper, Richard**
Profile: p.1909
Table(s): **New York:** Litigation: General Commercial **Band 3** p.1833, **New York:** Litigation: Securities **Band 4** p.1833

**Klarfeld, Peter J**
Table(s): **Nationwide:** Franchising **Band 2** p.111

**Klasko, H Ronald**
Table(s): **Nationwide:** Immigration **Band 1** p.131

**Klasmeier, Coleen**
Profile: p.347
Table(s): **Nationwide:** Life Sciences: Regulatory/Compliance **Band 2** p.183, **District of Columbia:** Healthcare: Pharmaceutical/Medical Products Regulatory **Band 2** p.810

**Klauberg, John G**
Profile: p.347
Table(s): **Nationwide:** Energy: Electricity (Transactional) **Band 1** p.77

**Klausner, Robert A**
Profile: p.1739
Table(s): **New Jersey:** Real Estate **Band 2** p.1728

**Klawiter, Donald C**
Table(s): **District of Columbia:** Antitrust **Band 4** p.787

**Klawiter, Richard F**
Profile: p.1215
Table(s): **Illinois:** Real Estate: Zoning/Land Use **Band 1** p.1188

**Kleban, Barry**
Profile: p.2221
Table(s): **Pennsylvania:** Bankruptcy/Restructuring **Band 1** p.2188

**Klee, Kenneth N**
Table(s): **Nationwide:** Bankruptcy/Restructuring **Band 1** p.39, **California:** Bankruptcy/Restructuring **Band 1** p.542

**Klee, Peter**
Profile: p.646
Table(s): **California:** Insurance: Insurer **Band 2** p.574

**Klegerman, Neal A**
Table(s): **Nevada:** Corporate/Commercial **Band 2** p.1672

**Klein, Adam**
Table(s): **Nationwide:** Sports Law **Band 2** p.241

**Klein, Allen**
Profile: p.874
Table(s): **Nationwide:** Outsourcing **Band 2** p.195, **District of Columbia:** Technology & Outsourcing **Band 1** p.842

**Klein, Anthony**
Profile: p.646
Table(s): **California:** IT & Outsourcing **Band 2** p.583

**Klein, Barry L**
Profile: p.2221
Table(s): **Pennsylvania:** Labor & Employment: Employee Benefits & Compensation **Band 2** p.2200

**Klein, Daniel L**
Profile: p.772
Table(s): **Delaware:** Real Estate **Band 1** p.766

**Klein, David F**
Table(s): **District of Columbia:** Insurance: Policyholder **Band 3** p.818

**Klein, Deborah**
Table(s): **California:** Media & Entertainment: Transactional: Mainly Talent **Band 2** p.609

**Klein, Eric A**
Table(s): **California:** Healthcare **Band 3** p.568

**Klein, Frederick L**
Profile: p.347
Table(s): **Nationwide:** Real Estate **Band 1** p.225, **District of Columbia:** Real Estate **Band 1** p.835

**Klein, Howard Bruce**
Profile: p.2221
Table(s): **Pennsylvania:** Litigation: White-Collar Crime & Government Investigations **Band 1** p.2204

**Klein, Howard M**
Profile: p.2221
Table(s): **Pennsylvania:** Litigation: General Commercial **Band 3** p.2203

**Klein, Jeffrey**
Profile: p.1909
Table(s): **New York:** Labor & Employment **Band 1** p.1826

**Klein, Jordan A**
Profile: p.347
Table(s): **Nationwide:** Wealth Management: Central Region **Band 3** p.266

**Klein, Joshua T**
Profile: p.2221
Table(s): **Pennsylvania:** Bankruptcy/Restructuring **Up-and-coming individuals** p.2188

**Klein, Justin**
Table(s): **Nationwide:** Franchising: Mainly Franchisee **Band 3** p.114

**O'Shaughnessy, William J**
Profile: p.1743
Table(s): New Jersey: Litigation: General
Commercial **Senior Statesmen**: p.1722

**O'Shea, Kevin**
Table(s): New York: Real Estate: Finance **Band 2**
p.1855

**O'Sullivan, Maura**
Table(s): Nationwide: Banking & Finance **Band 2**
p.31

**O'Toole, Daniel K**
Table(s): Missouri: Labor & Employment **Band 1**
p.1625

**O'Toole, Matthew J**
Table(s): Delaware: Corporate/M&A: Alternative
Entities **Band 2** p.761

**O'Toole, Patrick**
Profile: p.1504
Table(s): Massachusetts: Litigation: General
Commercial **Band 3** p.1470

**O'Toole, Terence J**
Profile: p.1124
Table(s): Hawaii: Litigation: General Commercial
**Star Individuals** p.1119

**Oade, K Preston**
Table(s): Colorado: Labor & Employment **Senior
Statesmen**: p.706

**Oakes, Jared E**
Profile: p.2108
Table(s): Ohio: Real Estate **Associates to watch**
p.2086

**Oakes, Leslie**
Profile: p.1092
Table(s): Georgia: Environment **Band 2** p.1051

**Oakes, Royal F**
Table(s): California: Insurance: Insurer **Band 2**
p.574

**Oakey, David N**
Table(s): Southern Virginia: Corporate/M&A **Band
2** p.2494

**Oates, J Christopher**
Table(s): North Carolina: Real Estate **Band 2**
p.2037

**Oates, Mark A**
Profile: p.378
Table(s): Nationwide: Tax: Controversy **Band 1**
p.244

**Oberkfell, Keith F**
Table(s): Nationwide: Capital Markets:
Securitisation **Band 2** p.59, North Carolina:
Banking & Finance **Band 2** p.2021

**Oberschmidt, E Richard**
Profile: p.2108
Table(s): Ohio: Real Estate **Band 2** p.2086

**Oberstein, Gary J**
Profile: p.1504
Table(s): Massachusetts: Labor & Employment
**Band 4** p.1466

**Occhino, Lennine**
Table(s): Illinois: Labor & Employment:
Employee Benefits & Compensation **Band 2**
p.1176

**Ochs, Timothy E**
Table(s): Indiana: Real Estate **Band 3** p.1275

**Ocker, Jonathan M**
Table(s): California: Employee Benefits &
Executive Compensation **Band 2** p.560

**Ockner, Ben**
Table(s): Ohio: Real Estate: Zoning/Land Use
**Band 2** p.2086

**Ode Jr, Paul H**
Table(s): Vermont: Corporate/Commercial **Band 1**
p.2483

**Odell, Francesca**
Profile: p.1925
Table(s): New York: Latin American Investment
**Band 2** p.1829

**Odell, Herbert**
Table(s): Nationwide: Tax: Controversy **Band 3**
p.244

**Odle, Kathleen**
Table(s): Colorado: Labor & Employment:
Employee Benefits & Compensation **Band 1**
p.706

**Odoner, Ellen J**
Profile: p.379
Table(s): Nationwide: Securities: Regulation:
Advisory **Band 2** p.232

**Odorizzi, Michele L**
Table(s): Illinois: Litigation: General Commercial
**Band 2** p.1180

**Oellermann, Charles M**
Profile: p.2108
Table(s): Ohio: Bankruptcy/Restructuring **Band 3**
p.2058

**Oelman, David**
Profile: p.2407
Table(s): Nationwide: Capital Markets: Debt &
Equity **Band 4** p.46, Texas: Capital Markets: Debt
& Equity **Band 1** p.2333, Texas: Corporate/M&A
**Band 2** p.2337

**Oertel, Ken**
Profile: p.1002
Table(s): Florida: Environment **Band 3** p.951

**Oesting, David W**
Table(s): Alaska: Litigation: General Commercial
**Band 1** p.490

**Oestreicher, Charles R**
Profile: p.1402
Table(s): Maine: Real Estate **Senior Statesmen**:
p.1395

**Ofsa, Joyce**
Profile: p.2565
Table(s): West Virginia: Real Estate **Band 1**
p.2560

**Ogden, David W**
Profile: p.884
Table(s): District of Columbia: Litigation:
General Commercial **Band 3** p.826

**Ogilby, Anne Phillips**
Table(s): Massachusetts: Banking & Finance:
Public Finance **Band 2** p.1446, Massachusetts:
Healthcare **Band 1** p.1460

**Ogilvy, George**
Table(s): Nevada: Litigation: Construction **Band 1**
p.1676

**Ogletree, Powell G**
Profile: p.1606
Table(s): Mississippi: Real Estate **Band 1** p.1600

**Ogrosky, Kirk**
Profile: p.884
Table(s): District of Columbia: Healthcare **Band 3**
p.809

**Ohlenforst, Cynthia**
Profile: p.2407
Table(s): Texas: Tax: Litigation **Band 2** p.2371

**Ohm, Michael K**
Table(s): Illinois: Environment: Mainly
Transactional **Band 2** p.1162

**Okinaga, Lawrence S**
Profile: p.1124
Table(s): Hawaii: Corporate/Commercial:
Finance **Band 1** p.1116

**Okumura, Miki**
Table(s): Hawaii: Corporate/Commercial: Tax
**Band 1** p.1115

**Oland, Mark**
Profile: p.746
Table(s): Connecticut: Real Estate **Band 2** p.740

**Olcott, Bruce**
Profile: p.884
Table(s): District of Columbia: Telecom,
Broadcast & Satellite **Band 4** p.844

**Old, Gareth**
Profile: p.379
Table(s): Nationwide: Capital Markets:
Derivatives **Up-and-coming individuals** p.51

**Old Jr, William A**
Table(s): Southern Virginia: Corporate/M&A **Band
3** p.2494

**Oldham, Phillip G**
Profile: p.2407
Table(s): Texas: Energy: State Regulatory &
Litigation (Electricity) **Band 2** p.2341

**Oldham, William K**
Table(s): Kentucky: Litigation: Tort & Insurance
Defense **Band 1** p.1312

**Olejko, Mitchell J**
Profile: p.657
Table(s): California: Healthcare **Band 2** p.568

**Olenn, J Renn**
Table(s): Rhode Island: Litigation: General
Commercial **Band 3** p.2254

**Oleynik, Jeffrey E**
Table(s): North Carolina: Antitrust **Band 1** p.2020,
North Carolina: Litigation: General Commercial
**Band 2** p.2033

**Olian, Robert**
Profile: p.1224
Table(s): Illinois: Environment: Litigation **Band 1**
p.1162

**Oliff, James A**
Table(s): Northern Virginia: Intellectual Property
**Band 3** p.2497

**Olinsky, Mark S**
Profile: p.1743
Table(s): New Jersey: Litigation: White-Collar
Crime & Government Investigations **Band 2**
p.1723

**Oliphant, Fred**
Profile: p.884
Table(s): District of Columbia: Employee
Benefits & Executive Compensation **Band 2** p.801

**Olivar, Harry**
Table(s): California: Litigation: Securities **Band 4**
p.594

**Oliver, Craig**
Table(s): Tennessee: Labor & Employment **Band
3** p.2293

**Oliver, David**
Table(s): Missouri: Litigation: General
Commercial **Band 2** p.1628

**Oliver, George J**
Profile: p.2043
Table(s): North Carolina: Labor & Employment
**Band 2** p.2031

**Oliver, James**
Table(s): Maryland: Real Estate **Band 1** p.1422

**Oliver, James D**
Profile: p.1300
Table(s): Kansas: Litigation: General
Commercial **Band 2** p.1295

**Oliver Jr, Samuel**
Table(s): North Carolina: Real Estate **Band 1**
p.2037

**Olivier, Elizabeth**
Profile: p.1402
Table(s): Maine: Labor & Employment **Up-and-coming
individuals** p.1390

**Olivieri, José A**
Profile: p.2585
Table(s): Wisconsin: Labor & Employment:
Immigration **Band 1** p.2575

**Oller, Shawn**
Profile: p.510
Table(s): Arizona: Labor & Employment **Up-and-
coming individuals** p.499

**Olsen, Eric T**
Table(s): Florida: Environment **Band 3** p.951

**Olsen, Peter C**
Table(s): New York: Real Estate **Band 3** p.1854

**Olsen, Theodore**
Table(s): Colorado: Labor & Employment **Band 2**
p.706

**Olshan, Regina**
Profile: p.1925
Table(s): Nationwide: Employee Benefits &
Executive Compensation **Band 3** p.73, New York:
Employee Benefits & Executive Compensation
**Band 1** p.1802

**Olson, Camille A**
Profile: p.1224
Table(s): Illinois: Labor & Employment **Band 1**
p.1175

# Index of Lawyers

**Olson, David P**
Profile: p.2585
Table(s): Wisconsin: Labor & Employment: Employee Benefits & Compensation **Band 1** p.2575

**Olson, Eric**
Table(s): Colorado: Litigation: General Commercial **Up-and-coming individuals** p.709

**Olson, Eugene E**
Table(s): Iowa: Real Estate **Band 3** p.1290

**Olson, Jeffrey M**
Profile: p.657
Table(s): California: Intellectual Property: Patent **Band 4** p.578

**Olson, John**
Profile: p.380
Table(s): Nationwide: Securities: Regulation: Advisory **Band 1** p.232

**Olson, Nancy M**
Profile: p.1224
Table(s): Illinois: Real Estate **Band 4** p.1187

**Olson, Richard**
Table(s): North Dakota: Bankruptcy/Restructuring **Star individuals** p.2050, North Dakota: Corporate/Commercial **Band 1** p.2051

**Olson, Robert J**
Table(s): Minnesota: Real Estate **Band 3** p.1576

**Olson, Ronald**
Profile: p.657
Table(s): California: Litigation: General Commercial **Band 2** p.593, California: Media & Entertainment: Litigation **Band 3** p.606

**Olson, Theodore B**
Profile: p.380
Table(s): Nationwide: Appellate Law **Star individuals** p.26

**Olson, Wanda J**
Profile: p.1925
Table(s): New York: Latin American Investment **Band 3** p.1829

**Olsson, Patricia**
Table(s): Idaho: Labor & Employment **Band 2** p.1132

**Oncidi, Anthony J**
Table(s): California: Labor & Employment **Band 2** p.587

**Ondeck, Christopher**
Profile: p.884
Table(s): District of Columbia: Antitrust **Band 5** p.787

**Ondrasik, Paul**
Table(s): Nationwide: ERISA Litigation **Band 1** p.92, District of Columbia: Employee Benefits & Executive Compensation **Band 3** p.801

**Onorato, David J**
Profile: p.1925
Table(s): New York: Litigation: Securities **Band 4** p.1834

**Oostema, John R.**
Table(s): Michigan: Litigation: General Commercial **Band 3** p.1544

**Oosterhuis, Paul W**
Profile: p.885
Table(s): District of Columbia: Tax **Band 1** p.838

**Opincar, Scott**
Table(s): Ohio: Bankruptcy/Restructuring **Band 2** p.2058

**Opler, Stephen**
Profile: p.1092
Table(s): Georgia: Corporate/M&A **Band 4** p.1046

**Oppenheim, Charles B**
Table(s): California: Healthcare **Band 3** p.568

**Oppenheim, David**
Table(s): Nationwide: Franchising **Band 4** p.111

**Opperwall, Theodore**
Profile: p.1553
Table(s): Michigan: Labor & Employment **Band 2** p.1542

**Oram, Jon**
Table(s): Nationwide: Sports Law **Band 2** p.241

**Orava, Stephen J**
Profile: p.380
Table(s): Nationwide: International Trade: Trade Remedies & Trade Policy **Band 3** p.154

**Ording, Michael K**
Profile: p.2109
Table(s): Ohio: Real Estate **Band 2** p.2086

**Ordway, Eric**
Profile: p.380
Table(s): Nationwide: International Arbitration **Band 4** p.145

**Oringer, Andrew L**
Profile: p.380
Table(s): Nationwide: Employee Benefits & Executive Compensation **Band 2** p.73, New York: Employee Benefits & Executive Compensation **Band 2** p.1802

**Orlansky, C Lawrence**
Table(s): Louisiana: Gaming & Licensing **Band 2** p.1348

**Orlansky, Susan**
Table(s): Alaska: Litigation: General Commercial **Band 1** p.490

**Orleans, Jonathan**
Profile: p.746
Table(s): Connecticut: Labor & Employment **Band 2** p.736

**Orloff, Gary W**
Profile: p.2408
Table(s): Texas: Corporate/M&A **Band 4** p.2337

**Orloff, Laurence B**
Table(s): New Jersey: Litigation: General Commercial **Band 1** p.1722

**Orlofsky, Stephen**
Profile: p.1743
Table(s): New Jersey: Litigation: General Commercial **Band 2** p.1722

**Orme, Shawn**
Table(s): Texas: Immigration **Band 3** p.2349

**Ormseth, Kris J**
Table(s): Idaho: Corporate/Commercial **Band 1** p.1132

**Orr, Dennis P**
Profile: p.1925
Table(s): New York: Antitrust **Band 5** p.1778, New York: Litigation: General Commercial **Band 3** p.1833

**Orr, Kevyn D**
Profile: p.885
Table(s): District of Columbia: Bankruptcy/Restructuring **Band 2** p.792

**Orr, Rick W**
Table(s): South Dakota: Labor & Employment: Workers' Compensation **Band 1** p.2283

**Orr III, A Summey**
Table(s): Georgia: Real Estate **Band 2** p.1070

**Orshefsky, Debbie M**
Profile: p.1002
Table(s): Florida: Real Estate: Zoning/Land Use **Band 2** p.975

**Ortelere, Brian T**
Profile: p.380
Table(s): Nationwide: ERISA Litigation **Band 2** p.92

**Ortiz, Scott E**
Table(s): Wyoming: Labor & Employment **Band 1** p.2597, Wyoming: Litigation: General Commercial **Band 2** p.2598, Wyoming: Litigation: Medical Malpractice Defense **Band 1** p.2598

**Ortmann, Dale**
Table(s): California: Construction **Band 3** p.550

**Ortner, Charles B**
Table(s): New York: Media & Entertainment: Copyright & Contract Disputes **Band 2** p.1851

**Ortwein, William Scott**
Profile: p.1092
Table(s): Georgia: Corporate/M&A **Band 3** p.1046

**Osborn, John W**
Profile: p.380
Table(s): Nationwide: Capital Markets: Derivatives **Band 1** p.51

**Osborn, William Sheffield**
Table(s): Texas: Energy: State Regulatory & Litigation (Oil & Gas) **Band 2** p.2341

**Osborn II, Jones**
Profile: p.510
Table(s): Arizona: Real Estate **Band 3** p.504

**Oscar, Lawrence E**
Profile: p.2109
Table(s): Ohio: Bankruptcy/Restructuring **Band 1** p.2058

**Osendarp, Joanne**
Profile: p.380
Table(s): Nationwide: International Trade: Trade Remedies & Trade Policy **Band 3** p.154

**Oser, Aaron M**
Table(s): Nationwide: Outsourcing **Band 2** p.195, District of Columbia: Technology & Outsourcing **Band 1** p.842

**Oshinsky, Jerold**
Profile: p.380
Table(s): Nationwide: Insurance: Dispute Resolution: Policyholder **Star individuals** p.137, California: Insurance: Policyholder **Band 1** p.576

**Oshman, Gene**
Table(s): Texas: Corporate/M&A **Band 3** p.2337

**Osias, Brian J**
Profile: p.1743
Table(s): New Jersey: Litigation: Insurance **Band 3** p.1723

**Osman, Lee R**
Table(s): Colorado: Intellectual Property **Band 2** p.704

**Osman, Lisa**
Table(s): Colorado: Intellectual Property **Band 3** p.704

**Ossi, Gregory J**
Profile: p.2512
Table(s): Virginia: Labor & Employment **Band 3** p.2500

**Ossip, Michael J**
Profile: p.2226
Table(s): Pennsylvania: Labor & Employment **Band 2** p.2200

**Osterberg, Edward**
Profile: p.2408
Table(s): Texas: Tax **Senior Statesmen** p.2371

**Osterman, Jeffrey D**
Profile: p.1925
Table(s): Nationwide: Outsourcing **Band 4** p.195, New York: Technology & Outsourcing **Band 2** p.1868

**Ostermeyer, Michael J**
Profile: p.2585
Table(s): Wisconsin: Real Estate **Band 2** p.2579

**Ostlund, Richard**
Table(s): Minnesota: Litigation: General Commercial **Band 2** p.1574

**Ostolaza, Yvette**
Profile: p.2408
Table(s): Texas: Litigation: General Commercial **Band 2** p.2362

**Ostrager, Barry R**
Profile: p.381
Table(s): Nationwide: Insurance: Dispute Resolution: Insurer **Band 1** p.134, Nationwide: Insurance: Dispute Resolution: Reinsurance **Band 1** p.134, Nationwide: Litigation: Trial Lawyers **Band 2** p.187, New York: Insurance: Dispute Resolution: Insurer **Band 1** p.1816, New York: Litigation: General Commercial **Band 1** p.1833

**Ostrau, Mark S**
Profile: p.658
Table(s): California: Antitrust **Band 3** p.536

**Otero, Camille**
Profile: p.1744
Table(s): New Jersey: Environment **Up-and-coming individuals** p.1711

**Ottaviani, John E**
Profile: p.2258
Table(s): Rhode Island: Corporate/Commercial: Intellectual Property **Band 1** p.2251

**Ottaviano, Kenneth**
Table(s): Illinois: Bankruptcy/Restructuring **Band 4** p.1148

**Strober, Frederick D**
Table(s): Pennsylvania: Real Estate **Band 2** p.2208

**Strochak, Adam**
Profile: p.894
Table(s): District of Columbia: Bankruptcy/Restructuring **Band 4** p.792

**Strock, William**
Table(s): Texas: Labor & Employment **Senior Statesmen:** p.2359

**Strohschein, Stephen P**
Profile: p.1370
Table(s): Louisiana: Bankruptcy/Restructuring **Band 3** p.1337

**Stromfeld, Lary**
Profile: p.413
Table(s): Nationwide: Capital Markets: Derivatives **Band 1** p.51

**Strong, Kenneth F**
Table(s): California: Construction **Band 3** p.550

**Strother, Jack**
Table(s): Washington: Corporate/Commercial **Senior Statesmen:** p.2525

**Stroup, Robert L**
Table(s): North Dakota: Real Estate **Band 1** p.2055

**Strubeck, Lou**
Profile: p.2418
Table(s): Nationwide: Bankruptcy/Restructuring **Band 3** p.39, Texas: Bankruptcy/Restructuring **Band 1** p.2328

**Strunk, Sarah A**
Table(s): Arizona: Corporate/M&A **Band 2** p.495

**Struve, Robin**
Table(s): Illinois: Labor & Employment: Employee Benefits & Compensation **Up-and-coming individuals** p.1176

**Struxness, Gregory E**
Table(s): Oregon: Corporate/M&A **Band 3** p.2164

**Stuart, Glen R**
Profile: p.2231
Table(s): Pennsylvania: Environment **Band 4** p.2194

**Stuart III, Claude**
Table(s): Texas: Insurance **Band 2** p.2351

**Stuart III, James R**
Profile: p.895
Table(s): District of Columbia: Corporate/M&A & Private Equity **Band 4** p.797

**Stubbs, Sidney A**
Profile: p.1009
Table(s): Florida: Litigation: General Commercial **Band 1** p.966

**Stubson, Timothy M**
Profile: p.2601
Table(s): Wyoming: Litigation: General Commercial **Band 3** p.2598

**Stuck, Haven L**
Table(s): South Dakota: Real Estate **Band 2** p.2286

**Stucker, Robert J**
Profile: p.1234
Table(s): Nationwide: Employee Benefits & Executive Compensation **Band 3** p.73, Illinois: Labor & Employment: Employee Benefits & Compensation **Band 1** p.1176

**Stuckey, James A**
Table(s): Louisiana: Banking & Finance **Band 1** p.1335

**Studer, Judith**
Table(s): Wyoming: Litigation: General Commercial **Band 2** p.2598

**Stump, John C**
Profile: p.2566
Table(s): West Virginia: Corporate/Commercial: Banking & Finance **Band 2** p.2550

**Stump, T. Douglas**
Table(s): Nationwide: Immigration **Band 3** p.131

**Stumpf, Larry**
Table(s): Florida: Litigation: General Commercial **Band 2** p.966

**Stumpff, Andrew**
Profile: p.1555
Table(s): Michigan: Employee Benefits & Executive Compensation **Band 3** p.1540

**Sturc, John**
Profile: p.413
Table(s): Nationwide: Securities: Regulation: Enforcement **Band 2** p.233

**Sturdivant, James**
Table(s): Oklahoma: Litigation: General Commercial **Senior Statesmen:** p.2141

**Stutts, Charles**
Profile: p.1009
Table(s): Florida: Banking & Finance: Regulatory **Band 3** p.937

**Stutts, Phillip**
Table(s): Alabama: Real Estate **Band 3** p.466

**Styles, Angela B**
Profile: p.414
Table(s): Nationwide: Government: Government Contracts **Band 4** p.117

**Styles, Mark**
Table(s): New Mexico: Real Estate **Band 2** p.1772

**Suarez, Jesus**
Table(s): Florida: Bankruptcy/Restructuring **Associates to watch** p.939

**Suárez, Fradyn**
Profile: p.1009
Table(s): Florida: Latin American Investment **Up-and-coming individuals** p.963

**Suarez Anzorena, Ignacio**
Profile: p.414
Table(s): Nationwide: International Arbitration **Band 5** p.145

**Subin, Ben**
Profile: p.1009
Table(s): Florida: Construction **Band 1** p.944

**Sucharow, Lawrence**
Profile: p.1945
Table(s): Nationwide: Securities: Litigation: Mainly Plaintiff **Senior Statesmen:** p.233, New York: Litigation: Securities Mainly Plaintiff **Senior Statesmen:** p.1835

**Suchman, E Gail**
Table(s): New York: Environment **Band 3** p.1807

**Sucoff, Andrew**
Profile: p.1510
Table(s): Massachusetts: Real Estate **Band 3** p.1478

**Sudbeck, Roger**
Table(s): South Dakota: Litigation: General Commercial **Band 1** p.2284, South Dakota: Litigation: Medical Malpractice Defense **Band 1** p.2284

**Sudbury, Deborah A**
Profile: p.1098
Table(s): Georgia: Labor & Employment **Band 2** p.1060

**Suddath Jr, Thomas H**
Table(s): Pennsylvania: Litigation: White-Collar Crime & Government Investigations **Band 2** p.2204

**Suelthaus, Kenneth H**
Table(s): Missouri: Corporate/M&A **Band 3** p.1619

**Suffoletta Jr, J Robert**
Table(s): Texas: Technology: Corporate & Commercial **Band 3** p.2375

**Suflas, Steven W**
Profile: p.1748
Table(s): New Jersey: Labor & Employment **Band 1** p.1718

**Sugarman, Myron**
Table(s): Nationwide: Wealth Management: Western Region **Band 3** p.267

**Sugarman, Roger P**
Table(s): Ohio: Litigation: General Commercial **Band 3** p.2078

**Suggs Jr, Fred W**
Profile: p.2272
Table(s): South Carolina: Labor & Employment **Band 1** p.2262

**Suh, Maurice**
Profile: p.414
Table(s): Nationwide: Sports Law: Athletic Disputes **Band 1** p.241

**Sukin, Michael**
Table(s): New York: Media & Entertainment: Music **Band 1** p.1849

**Sulds, Jonathan L**
Profile: p.1945
Table(s): New York: Labor & Employment **Band 4** p.1826

**Sulkin, Robert M**
Table(s): Washington: Litigation: General Commercial **Band 2** p.2533

**Sullenberger, Douglas R**
Profile: p.1098
Table(s): Georgia: Labor & Employment **Band 3** p.1060

**Sullivan, Alan**
Table(s): Utah: Litigation: General Commercial **Band 1** p.2468

**Sullivan, Brian**
Table(s): Vermont: Real Estate: Zoning/Land Use **Band 1** p.2487

**Sullivan, Christopher**
Table(s): Utah: Litigation: General Commercial **Band 3** p.2468

**Sullivan, David**
Profile: p.2155
Table(s): Oklahoma: Intellectual Property **Band 1** p.2138

**Sullivan, David C**
Table(s): Nationwide: Investment Funds: Registered Funds **Band 3** p.170

**Sullivan, Diane P**
Profile: p.414
Table(s): Nationwide: Product Liability & Mass Torts **Band 1** p.208, Nationwide: Product Liability: Pharmaceutical p.208, New Jersey: Litigation: General Commercial **Band 3** p.1722, New Jersey: Litigation: Products Liability **Band 1** p.1722

**Sullivan, Douglas**
Profile: p.668
Table(s): California: Litigation: General Commercial **Band 5** p.593

**Sullivan, Edward J**
Table(s): Oregon: Real Estate: Zoning/Land Use **Band 1** p.2173

**Sullivan, Jeffrey**
Profile: p.414
Table(s): Nationwide: Capital Markets: REITs **Band 4** p.55

**Sullivan, John**
Table(s): Montana: Labor & Employment **Band 1** p.1648, Montana: Litigation: Mediators **Band 1** p.1649

**Sullivan, John L**
Profile: p.1511
Table(s): Massachusetts: Real Estate **Band 1** p.1478

**Sullivan, John M**
Profile: p.1698
Table(s): New Hampshire: Corporate/Commercial: Bankruptcy **Band 1** p.1685

**Sullivan, Jon**
Table(s): Iowa: Real Estate **Band 2** p.1290

**Sullivan, Kathleen**
Profile: p.1698
Table(s): New Hampshire: Real Estate **Band 2** p.1692, New Hampshire: Real Estate: Land Use **Band 2** p.1692

**Sullivan, Kathleen M**
Table(s): Nationwide: Appellate Law **Band 1** p.26

**Sullivan, Kevin A**
Profile: p.2418
Table(s): Texas: Real Estate **Band 3** p.2367

**Sullivan, Kevin J**
Profile: p.1511
Table(s): Massachusetts: Private Equity: Buyouts **Band 3** p.1474

**Swanson, David M**
Table(s): South Carolina: Real Estate **Band 2** p.2266

**Swanson, Edward**
Profile: p.668
Table(s): California: Litigation: White-Collar Crime & Government Investigations **Band 2** p.601

**Swanson, James R**
Profile: p.1370
Table(s): Louisiana: Litigation: General Commercial **Band 1** p.1352, Louisiana: Litigation: Securities **Band 1** p.1352

**Swanson, M Anne**
Profile: p.895
Table(s): District of Columbia: Telecom, Broadcast & Satellite **Band 2** p.844

**Swanstrom, Bill**
Profile: p.2418
Table(s): Texas: Corporate/M&A **Band 2** p.2337

**Swapp, Russell**
Profile: p.415
Table(s): Nationwide: Immigration **Band 3** p.131

**Swartley, Christopher**
Table(s): Montana: Real Estate **Band 3** p.1652

**Swartz, Linda Z**
Profile: p.1945
Table(s): New York: Tax **Band 3** p.1862

**Swartz, Matthew B.**
Profile: p.2514
Table(s): Northern Virginia: Corporate/M&A **Up-and-coming individuals** p.2493

**Sweeney, Jill K**
Table(s): New Mexico: Corporate/Commercial **Band 2** p.1764

**Sweeney, John F**
Profile: p.1946
Table(s): New York: Intellectual Property: Patent **Band 2** p.1820

**Sweeney, Kevin**
Table(s): Nationwide: Energy: Oil & Gas (Regulatory & Litigation) **Band 5** p.78

**Sweeney, Kevin R**
Table(s): Missouri: Corporate/M&A **Band 2** p.1618

**Sweeney, Maureen E**
Profile: p.1235
Table(s): Illinois: Banking & Finance **Band 4** p.1145

**Sweeney, Michael F**
Table(s): Rhode Island: Corporate/Commercial **Band 1** p.2251, Rhode Island: Corporate/Commercial: Intellectual Property **Band 2** p.2251

**Sweeney, Neal**
Table(s): Georgia: Construction **Band 1** p.1044

**Sweeney, Patrick J**
Profile: p.2114
Table(s): Ohio: Construction **Band 3** p.2062

**Sweeney, Robert**
Table(s): West Virginia: Litigation: General Commercial **Band 3** p.2555

**Sweeney, Sheryl A**
Table(s): Arizona: Environment (including water rights) **Band 3** p.497, Arizona: Environment: Water Rights **Band 2** p.497

**Sweeney III, James F**
Table(s): Nationwide: Transportation: Shipping: Litigation (New York) **Band 3** p.261

**Sweet, Julian**
Table(s): Maine: Litigation: Medical Malpractice & Insurance **Band 1** p.1393, Maine: Litigation: Mainly Plaintiff **Band 2** p.1393

**Sweet Jr, William J**
Profile: p.415
Table(s): Nationwide: Financial Services Regulation: Banking (Compliance) **Star individuals** p.96, Nationwide: Financial Services Regulation: Financial Institutions M&A **Band 1** p.96

**Swerdloff, David A**
Profile: p.748
Table(s): Connecticut: Corporate/M&A **Band 1** p.732

**Swerdloff, Nicolas**
Profile: p.1010
Table(s): Florida: Litigation: General Commercial **Band 3** p.966

**Swetnam, Dan**
Table(s): Ohio: Bankruptcy/Restructuring **Band 3** p.2058

**Swett, Brian I**
Profile: p.1235
Table(s): Illinois: Bankruptcy/Restructuring **Band 2** p.1148

**Swett, Trevor**
Table(s): District of Columbia: Bankruptcy/Restructuring **Band 4** p.792

**Swhier, Claudia V**
Profile: p.1280
Table(s): Indiana: Corporate/M&A **Band 1** p.1268

**Swider, David**
Table(s): Indiana: Labor & Employment **Band 2** p.1271

**Swift, Betsy**
Table(s): Ohio: Labor & Employment **Band 4** p.2074

**Swift Jr, Phelps H**
Table(s): Wyoming: Real Estate **Band 2** p.2600

**Swill, Douglas B**
Profile: p.1235
Table(s): Illinois: Healthcare **Band 3** p.1165

**Swimley, Susan**
Table(s): Montana: Real Estate **Band 3** p.1652

**Swinton, David**
Table(s): Iowa: Litigation: General Commercial **Band 2** p.1288

**Swirbalus, Mark**
Table(s): Massachusetts: Litigation: General Commercial **Band 3** p.1470

**Swirski, Alan J J**
Profile: p.415
Table(s): Nationwide: Tax: Controversy **Band 4** p.244

**Switzer, Carl**
Table(s): California: Construction **Band 4** p.550

**Sykes, Jeffrey A**
Table(s): California: Construction **Band 2** p.550

**Sykes, Phillip S**
Profile: p.1608
Table(s): Mississippi: Litigation: General Commercial **Band 3** p.1597

**Sylvester, David J**
Table(s): Vermont: Corporate/Commercial **Band 3** p.2483

**Sylvester, William**
Profile: p.473
Table(s): Alabama: Real Estate **Band 2** p.466

**Sylvia, Jack**
Profile: p.1511
Table(s): Massachusetts: Litigation: Securities **Band 2** p.1470

**Sylwestrzak, Theodore**
Profile: p.1555
Table(s): Michigan: Banking & Finance: Bankruptcy **Band 2** p.1536

**Symes, David PR**
Profile: p.2179
Table(s): Oregon: Labor & Employment **Band 2** p.2168

**Symon, Robert**
Table(s): District of Columbia: Construction **Band 3** p.795

**Symonds Jr, Robert L**
Table(s): Delaware: Corporate/M&A: Alternative Entities **Band 1** p.761

**Symons, Howard**
Profile: p.895
Table(s): District of Columbia: Telecom, Broadcast & Satellite **Band 2** p.844

**Symons, Noel**
Table(s): Nationwide: Energy: Electricity (Regulatory & Litigation) **Band 5** p.76

**Symons, Robin**
Table(s): Florida: Labor & Employment **Band 4** p.959

**Synenberg, Roger M**
Table(s): Ohio: Litigation: White-Collar Crime & Government Investigations **Band 1** p.2079

**Synnott, Aidan**
Profile: p.1946
Table(s): New York: Antitrust **Band 3** p.1778

**Syring-Petrocchi, Tina A.**
Profile: p.1580
Table(s): Minnesota: Labor & Employment **Up-and-coming individuals** p.1571

**Szabo, David S**
Profile: p.1511
Table(s): Massachusetts: Healthcare **Band 2** p.1460

**Szabo, Robert G.**
Profile: p.415
Table(s): Nationwide: Transportation: Rail (for Shippers) **Band 2** p.258

**Szalkowski, Charles**
Profile: p.2418
Table(s): Texas: Technology: Corporate & Commercial **Senior Statesmen** p.2375

## T

**Tabacchi, Tina M**
Profile: p.1235
Table(s): Illinois: Litigation: General Commercial **Band 4** p.1180

**Tabacco Jr, Joseph J**
Table(s): California: Litigation: Securities **Band 2** p.594

**Tabacopoulos, Diana**
Profile: p.668
Table(s): California: Labor & Employment **Band 4** p.587

**Tabak, Jeffrey E**
Profile: p.415
Table(s): Nationwide: Investment Funds: Private Equity: Fund Formation **Band 2** p.166

**Tabit, Joanna I**
Profile: p.2566
Table(s): West Virginia: Litigation: General Commercial **Band 2** p.2555

**Tabor, Bert**
Profile: p.415
Table(s): Nationwide: Energy: Oil & Gas (Regulatory & Litigation) **Senior Statesmen:** p.78

**Tabor, Jay**
Profile: p.2418
Table(s): Texas: Corporate/M&A **Band 1** p.2337

**Tachau, David**
Table(s): Kentucky: Litigation: General Commercial **Band 2** p.1312

**Tafapolsky, Alan**
Table(s): California: Immigration **Band 2** p.571

**Taffet, Richard S**
Profile: p.1946
Table(s): New York: Antitrust **Band 4** p.1778

**Taft, Kingsley L**
Profile: p.415
Table(s): Nationwide: Life Sciences: Corporate/Commercial **Band 2** p.182

**Tager, Evan M**
Table(s): Nationwide: Appellate Law **Band 2** p.26

**Taggart, David R**
Profile: p.1370
Table(s): Louisiana: Energy & Natural Resources: Oil & Gas **Band 3** p.1344

**Taggi, Christopher A.**
Table(s): District of Columbia: Construction **Up-and-coming individuals** p.795

**Tagliabue, Paul**
Profile: p.415
Table(s): Nationwide: Sports Law **Senior Statesmen:** p.240

**Tague, Brian**
Table(s): Florida: Real Estate **Band 1** p.974

**Tahyar, Margaret**
Profile: p.415
Table(s): Nationwide: Financial Services Regulation: Banking (Compliance) **Band 2** p.96

**Taintor, Christopher**
Table(s): Maine: Litigation: Medical Malpractice & Insurance **Band 3** p.1393

**Taladay, John**
Profile: p.895
Table(s): **District of Columbia: Antitrust Band 4** p.787

**Talbert, Jeffrey**
Profile: p.1404
Table(s): **Maine: Environment Band 2** p.1389

**Talbot, Scott**
Table(s): **Northern Virginia: Intellectual Property Band 3** p.2497

**Taleff, Ward E**
Table(s): **Montana: Litigation: General Commercial Band 2** p.1649, **Montana: Litigation: Mediators Band 1** p.1649

**Talley, Steven K**
Profile: p.722
Table(s): **Colorado: Corporate/M&A Band 2** p.703

**Talley, Susan G**
Table(s): **Louisiana: Banking & Finance Band 2** p.1335, **Louisiana: Real Estate Band 1** p.1355

**Tambe, Jayant**
Profile: p.1946
Table(s): **New York: Litigation: Securities Band 4** p.1834

**Tamkin, Greg**
Table(s): **Colorado: Intellectual Property Band 2** p.704

**Tan, Daniel**
Table(s): **Nationwide: International Arbitration Up-and-coming individuals** p.145

**Tan, Gregory**
Table(s): **Nationwide: Projects Band 3** p.216, **New York: Latin American Investment Band 3** p.1829

**Tanaka, Tod**
Table(s): **Hawaii: Corporate/Commercial Band 2** p.1116, **Hawaii: Real Estate Band 2** p.1120

**Tanenbaum, Edward**
Profile: p.1946
Table(s): **New York: Tax Band 3** p.1862

**Tanenbaum, James**
Profile: p.415
Table(s): **Nationwide: Capital Markets: Debt & Equity Senior Statesmen** p.46

**Tanenbaum, Jeffrey M**
Profile: p.668
Table(s): **California: Labor & Employment Band 4** p.587

**Tanenbaum, William A**
Profile: p.1946
Table(s): **Nationwide: Outsourcing Band 2** p.195, **New York: Technology & Outsourcing Band 1** p.1868

**Tangeman, Jill S**
Profile: p.2114
Table(s): **Ohio: Real Estate: Zoning/Land Use Band 1** p.2086

**Tangri, Ragesh K**
Table(s): **California: Intellectual Property: Trademark, Copyright & Trade Secrets Band 3** p.578

**Tanis, Elizabeth Vranicar**
Profile: p.1098
Table(s): **Georgia: Litigation: General Commercial Band 1** p.1065

**Tank, David**
Table(s): **Iowa: Litigation: General Commercial Band 1** p.1288

**Tanner, Gordon W**
Table(s): **Washington: Real Estate Band 2** p.2535

**Tannous, Robert**
Profile: p.2114
Table(s): **Ohio: Corporate/M&A Band 4** p.2064

**Tanoury, Mark**
Table(s): **Nationwide: Investment Funds: Venture Capital Band 1** p.174, **California: Corporate/M&A: Venture Capital Band 1** p.555

**Tapscott, Andrew**
Profile: p.2514
Table(s): **Southern Virginia: Real Estate Band 1** p.2506

**Tarabicos, Larry J**
Table(s): **Delaware: Real Estate: Zoning/Land Use Band 2** p.766

**Tarantino, John**
Profile: p.2258
Table(s): **Rhode Island: Litigation: General Commercial Star Individuals** p.2254

**Taranto, Richard**
Table(s): **Nationwide: Appellate Law Band 1** p.26

**Tardy III, Thomas W**
Profile: p.1608
Table(s): **Mississippi: Litigation: General Commercial Band 3** p.1597

**Tarkow, Howard**
Table(s): **Minnesota: Labor & Employment Band 3** p.1571

**Tarpley, George**
Table(s): **Texas: Bankruptcy/Restructuring Band 3** p.2328

**Tarullo, Michael**
Table(s): **Ohio: Construction Band 2** p.2062

**Tarun, Robert W**
Profile: p.416
Table(s): **Nationwide: International Trade: FCPA Experts Band 3** p.153

**Tata, Robert M**
Profile: p.2514
Table(s): **Virginia: Litigation: General Commercial Band 2** p.2502

**Tate, Granville**
Table(s): **Mississippi: Corporate/Commercial: Banking & Finance Band 1** p.1591

**Tate, Joseph A**
Profile: p.2231
Table(s): **Pennsylvania: Antitrust Star individuals** p.2184, **Pennsylvania: Litigation: General Commercial Band 1** p.2203, **Pennsylvania: Litigation: White-Collar Crime & Government Investigations Band 1** p.2203

**Tate Jr, James S**
Profile: p.2310
Table(s): **Tennessee: Banking & Finance Band 1** p.2287

**Tato, Joseph A**
Profile: p.416
Table(s): **Nationwide: Projects Band 4** p.216

**Tatum, John**
Table(s): **Georgia: Litigation: General Commercial Band 4** p.1065

**Taub, Philip B**
Profile: p.1698
Table(s): **New Hampshire: Corporate/Commercial Band 2** p.1685

**Tavel, Andrew G**
Table(s): **New York: Media & Entertainment: Music Band 2** p.1849

**Tavss, John**
Profile: p.416
Table(s): **Nationwide: Investment Funds: Hedge Funds Band 2** p.162

**Tavzel, Erik R**
Profile: p.416
Table(s): **Nationwide: Capital Markets: Debt & Equity Band 4** p.46

**Tawney, Kenneth E**
Table(s): **West Virginia: Natural Resources Band 2** p.2558

**Taylor, Allan B**
Profile: p.748
Table(s): **Connecticut: Litigation: General Commercial Band 2** p.738

**Taylor, Bernard**
Profile: p.1098
Table(s): **Georgia: Litigation: General Commercial Band 3** p.1065

**Taylor, Byron**
Profile: p.1235
Table(s): **Illinois: Environment: Litigation Band 3** p.1162

**Taylor, Consuella Simmons**
Profile: p.2418
Table(s): **Texas: Real Estate Band 3** p.2367

**Taylor, Dan**
Table(s): **North Carolina: Litigation: General Commercial Band 2** p.2033

**Taylor, Errol B**
Profile: p.1946
Table(s): **New York: Intellectual Property: Patent Band 3** p.1820

**Taylor, Glenn**
Table(s): **Mississippi: Energy & Natural Resources Band 1** p.1593

**Taylor, James D**
Profile: p.416
Table(s): **Nationwide: Advertising: Transactional & Regulatory Band 1** p.20

**Taylor, Jasper**
Profile: p.2418
Table(s): **Nationwide: Tax: Controversy Band 2** p.244, **Texas: Tax: Litigation Band 1** p.2371

**Taylor, Jay**
Profile: p.529
Table(s): **Arkansas: Real Estate Band 1** p.524

**Taylor, Joseph**
Profile: p.668
Table(s): **California: Media & Entertainment: Litigation Band 4** p.606

**Taylor, Mark**
Table(s): **Georgia: Labor & Employment Band 4** p.1060

**Taylor, Mark**
Table(s): **Montana: Corporate/M&A Band 3** p.1646

**Taylor, Mark D**
Table(s): **District of Columbia: Bankruptcy/Restructuring Band 4** p.792

**Taylor, Matthew A**
Table(s): **Pennsylvania: Litigation: General Commercial Band 3** p.2203

**Taylor, Paige**
Table(s): **Texas: Immigration Band 3** p.2349

**Taylor, Pamela**
Profile: p.1235
Table(s): **Illinois: Antitrust Band 4** p.1143

**Taylor, Paul R**
Table(s): **Washington: Litigation: General Commercial Band 1** p.2533

**Taylor, Robert P**
Profile: p.668
Table(s): **California: Antitrust Band 3** p.536

**Taylor, Roger D**
Profile: p.1098
Table(s): **Georgia: Intellectual Property Band 1** p.1056

**Taylor, Ronald W**
Profile: p.1433
Table(s): **Maryland: Labor & Employment Band 2** p.1417

**Taylor, Ryan J**
Table(s): **South Dakota: Corporate/Commercial Up-and-coming individuals** p.2281

**Taylor, Thomas R**
Profile: p.2476
Table(s): **Utah: Corporate/M&A Band 3** p.2462

**Taylor, Timothy C.**
Profile: p.2418
Table(s): **Texas: Real Estate Band 3** p.2367

**Taylor, Trent**
Profile: p.1556
Table(s): **Michigan: Banking & Finance Band 3** p.1536

**Taylor, William**
Table(s): **South Dakota: Litigation: General Commercial Band 2** p.2284

**Taylor, William E**
Profile: p.1404
Table(s): **Maine: Environment Band 1** p.1389

**Taylor, Zachary**
Profile: p.1609
Table(s): **Mississippi: Corporate/Commercial: Municipal Finance Band 1** p.1591

**Taylor III, George M**
Table(s): **Alabama: Banking & Finance Band 3** p.455, **Alabama: Corporate/Commercial Band 3** p.459

**Taylor III, William W**
Table(s): District of Columbia: Litigation: White-Collar Crime & Government Investigations Band 1 p.827

**Taylor Jr, Andrew E**
Profile: p.1511
Table(s): Massachusetts: Private Equity: Fund Formation Band 3 p.1476

**Taylor Jr, James D**
Table(s): Delaware: Labor & Employment Band 2 p.765

**Tayon, Kathy**
Table(s): Florida: Healthcare Band 3 p.954

**Teblum, Gary**
Table(s): Florida: Corporate/M&A & Private Equity Band 2 p.947

**Tegeler, David W**
Table(s): Massachusetts: Private Equity: Fund Formation Band 2 p.1476

**Teig, Joe M**
Profile: p.2601
Table(s): Wyoming: Litigation: General Commercial Band 2 p.2598

**Tein, Michael**
Table(s): Florida: Litigation: White-Collar Crime & Government Investigations Band 3 p.967

**Teitelbaum, David E**
Profile: p.416
Table(s): Nationwide: Financial Services Regulation: Consumer Finance (Compliance) Band 2 p.98

**Teitelbaum, Marc**
Profile: p.1946
Table(s): New York: Tax Band 4 p.1862

**Telegen, Arthur**
Profile: p.1511
Table(s): Massachusetts: Labor & Employment Band 1 p.1466

**Telle, Michael S**
Profile: p.2419
Table(s): Texas: Capital Markets: Debt & Equity Band 2 p.2333, Texas: Corporate/M&A Band 4 p.2337

**Tellekson, David K**
Profile: p.2541
Table(s): Washington: Intellectual Property Band 2 p.2529

**Temel, Alexander B**
Table(s): Massachusetts: Private Equity: Buyouts Band 3 p.1474

**Temin, Michael L**
Profile: p.2231
Table(s): Pennsylvania: Bankruptcy/Restructuring Senior Statesmen: p.2188

**Temkin, Elizabeth H**
Table(s): Colorado: Natural Resources & Environment Band 1 p.712

**Temkin, Harvey L**
Profile: p.2587
Table(s): Wisconsin: Real Estate Band 3 p.2579

**Temkin, Jeremy**
Profile: p.1946
Table(s): New York: Litigation: White-Collar Crime & Government Investigations Band 3 p.1836

**Temple, Elizabeth O**
Table(s): South Carolina: Corporate/M&A Band 3 p.2260

**Tenen, Jeffrey S**
Table(s): Nationwide: Transportation: Aviation: Finance Band 3 p.252

**Tenev, Jovi**
Profile: p.416
Table(s): Nationwide: Transportation: Shipping: Finance (New York) Band 2 p.260

**Tenn, Mary Elizabeth**
Table(s): New Hampshire: Litigation: General Commercial Band 3 p.1690

**Tenn Jr, James J**
Table(s): New Hampshire: Litigation: General Commercial Band 4 p.1690

**Tenpas, Ronald J**
Profile: p.895
Table(s): District of Columbia: Environment Band 4 p.804

**Teplin, Lawrence**
Table(s): California: Real Estate Band 3 p.611

**Teplitzky, Ronald J**
Table(s): Ohio: Banking & Finance Band 3 p.2056

**Teplitzky, Sanford V**
Table(s): Nationwide: Healthcare: Regulatory & Litigation Band 1 p.127, Maryland: Healthcare Band 1 p.1415

**Ter Molen, Mark R**
Table(s): Illinois: Environment: Litigation Band 3 p.1162

**Terapak, Rich**
Profile: p.2115
Table(s): Ohio: Healthcare Band 3 p.2069

**Ternes, Mary Ellen**
Profile: p.2155
Table(s): Oklahoma: Energy & Natural Resources: Environment Band 1 p.2136

**Terp, Thomas T**
Profile: p.2115
Table(s): Ohio: Natural Resources & Environment Band 2 p.2083

**Terr, Leonard**
Profile: p.895
Table(s): District of Columbia: Tax Band 2 p.838

**Terraciano, Annmarie M**
Profile: p.1946
Table(s): New York: Environment: Mainly Transactional Band 3 p.1808

**Terrell, Irv**
Profile: p.416
Table(s): Nationwide: Litigation: Trial Lawyers Senior Statesmen: p.186, Texas: Litigation: General Commercial Senior Statesmen: p.2362

**Terrell, J Anthony**
Table(s): Nationwide: Energy: Electricity (Finance) Band 1 p.75

**Terrell, Michael**
Profile: p.1280
Table(s): Indiana: Labor & Employment Band 2 p.1271

**Terry, James W.**
Table(s): Nationwide: Food & Beverages: Alcohol Band 3 p.109

**Terry, Joseph H**
Table(s): Kentucky: Corporate/M&A Band 3 p.1305

**Terry, Michael B**
Table(s): Georgia: Litigation: General Commercial Band 4 p.1065

**Terry, Michael H**
Table(s): Southern Virginia: Real Estate Band 1 p.2506

**Terzo, Frank**
Profile: p.1010
Table(s): Florida: Bankruptcy/Restructuring Band 4 p.939

**Tescher, Donald**
Table(s): Nationwide: Wealth Management: Eastern Region Band 4 p.267, Florida: Tax: Estate Planning Band 1 p.979

**Tessier, Frank A**
Table(s): Louisiana: Banking & Finance Band 2 p.1335, Louisiana: Real Estate Band 3 p.1355

**Tessier, Troy A**
Profile: p.2273
Table(s): South Carolina: Litigation: General Commercial Band 3 p.2264

**Testa, Jeffrey**
Profile: p.1749
Table(s): New Jersey: Bankruptcy/Restructuring Band 3 p.1705

**Teti II, J Leonard (Len)**
Profile: p.1946
Table(s): New York: Tax Up-and-coming individuals p.1862

**Tetrick Jr, David**
Profile: p.1098
Table(s): Georgia: Labor & Employment Band 4 p.1060

**Tetzeli, Helena**
Table(s): Florida: Immigration Band 2 p.956

**Tew, Thomas**
Table(s): Florida: Litigation: General Commercial Band 2 p.966

**Tewksbury, David**
Profile: p.416
Table(s): Nationwide: Energy: Electricity (Regulatory & Litigation) Band 2 p.76

**Thal, John**
Table(s): New Mexico: Litigation: General Commercial Band 3 p.1769

**Thalacker, Laura**
Table(s): Nevada: Labor & Employment Band 3 p.1675

**Thaler Jr, Rick**
Table(s): Utah: Labor & Employment Band 3 p.2467

**Thames, Lee Davis**
Profile: p.1609
Table(s): Mississippi: Litigation: General Commercial Band 1 p.1597

**Tharnish, Deborah**
Table(s): Iowa: Labor & Employment Band 2 p.1285, Iowa: Litigation: General Commercial Band 2 p.1288

**Thatch, David**
Profile: p.416
Table(s): Nationwide: Capital Markets: Securitisation Band 3 p.59

**Thau, Clifford**
Profile: p.1947
Table(s): New York: Litigation: Securities Band 4 p.1834

**Thau, Stephen B**
Profile: p.668
Table(s): California: Corporate/M&A: Venture Capital Band 4 p.555, California: Life Sciences: Corporate/Commercial Band 2 p.590

**Thayer, M Patricia**
Profile: p.669
Table(s): California: Intellectual Property: Patent Band 4 p.578

**Thayne, Matthew**
Table(s): Utah: Intellectual Property Band 3 p.2466

**Theis, B Lawrence**
Table(s): Colorado: Litigation: General Commercial Band 3 p.709

**Theis, Michael**
Table(s): Colorado: Litigation: General Commercial Band 3 p.709, Colorado: Litigation: White-Collar Crime & Government Investigations Band 1 p.709

**Theis, Roger L**
Table(s): Kansas: Real Estate Band 2 p.1297

**Theiss, Paul W**
Table(s): Illinois: Corporate/M&A Band 4 p.1156

**Thek, Raymond P**
Profile: p.1749
Table(s): New Jersey: Corporate/M&A Band 3 p.1707

**Thelen, Trisha A**
Profile: p.1301
Table(s): Kansas: Labor & Employment Band 3 p.1294

**Thengvall, Andrew**
Profile: p.1301
Table(s): Kansas: Corporate/M&A Band 3 p.1292

**Theobald, James**
Table(s): Southern Virginia: Real Estate: Zoning/Land Use Band 1 p.2506

**Theodorou, Nicholas C**
Profile: p.1511
Table(s): Massachusetts: Litigation: White-Collar Crime & Government Investigations Band 1 p.1471

**Theriot, Chad V**
Table(s): Georgia: Construction Up-and-coming individuals p.1044

**Thomson Jr, Paul R**
Table(s): Virginia: Environment Band 2 p.2495

**Thomson, Jr., John A**
Table(s): Georgia: Bankruptcy/Restructuring Band 3 p.1042

**Thoren-Peden, Deborah S**
Profile: p.417
Table(s): Nationwide: Privacy & Data Security Band 3 p.199

**Thornburgh, John**
Table(s): Indiana: Corporate/M&A Band 1 p.1268

**Thorne, René**
Profile: p.1370
Table(s): Louisiana: Labor & Employment: Employee Benefits & Compensation Band 1 p.1350

**Thornhill, James**
Table(s): Virginia: Environment Band 2 p.2495

**Thornton, Charles**
Table(s): California: Real Estate Band 3 p.611

**Thornton, D McCarty**
Profile: p.896
Table(s): District of Columbia: Healthcare Senior Statesmen: p.809

**Thornton, M Robert**
Profile: p.1099
Table(s): Georgia: Litigation: General Commercial Band 3 p.1065

**Thornton, Robert D**
Table(s): California: Environment Band 4 p.564

**Thornton, Timothy**
Profile: p.1580
Table(s): Minnesota: Litigation: General Commercial Band 2 p.1574

**Thorpe, Gregory**
Table(s): Nationwide: Projects Band 4 p.216

**Thorpe, Jane F**
Profile: p.417
Table(s): Nationwide: Food & Beverages: Regulatory & Litigation Band 3 p.107, Nationwide: Product Liability & Mass Torts Band 5 p.208

**Thorpe, Sara**
Table(s): California: Insurance: Insurer Band 4 p.574

**Thorstenson, Craig**
Profile: p.1235
Table(s): Illinois: Labor & Employment Band 4 p.1175

**Thrall, Michael W**
Table(s): Iowa: Litigation: General Commercial Band 3 p.1288

**Thrapp, Richard**
Table(s): Indiana: Corporate/M&A Band 1 p.1268

**Thrasher, Dana**
Table(s): Alabama: Labor & Employment Band 3 p.460

**Threadgill, Timothy M**
Profile: p.1609
Table(s): Mississippi: Labor & Employment Band 2 p.1595

**Threlkeld, Robert C**
Table(s): Georgia: Healthcare Band 3 p.1052

**Throckmorton, Charles W**
Profile: p.1010
Table(s): Florida: Bankruptcy/Restructuring Band 1 p.939

**Thrope, Jeff**
Table(s): New York: Healthcare Band 4 p.1811

**Thum, Robert B**
Profile: p.669
Table(s): California: Construction Band 1 p.550

**Thunhorst, David G**
Profile: p.1099
Table(s): Georgia: Corporate/M&A Band 4 p.1046

**Thurber, Mark**
Profile: p.417
Table(s): Nationwide: Projects Band 4 p.216, Nationwide: Projects: Renewables & Alternative Energy Band 2 p.216

**Thurston, Rosemarie A**
Profile: p.417
Table(s): Nationwide: Capital Markets: REITs Band 3 p.55

**Thurston, Sally A**
Profile: p.1947
Table(s): New York: Tax Band 4 p.1862

**Thuston, Lee**
Table(s): Alabama: Corporate/Commercial Band 2 p.459

**Tibbets, Gaye B**
Table(s): Kansas: Labor & Employment Band 3 p.1294

**Tichner, Jerome B**
Profile: p.1511
Table(s): Massachusetts: Healthcare Up-and-coming individuals p.1460

**Tichy, George**
Profile: p.669
Table(s): California: Labor & Employment Band 4 p.587

**Ticknor, George**
Profile: p.1512
Table(s): Massachusetts: Banking & Finance Band 3 p.1445

**Tiedemann, Charles Welch (Chad)**
Profile: p.896
Table(s): District of Columbia: Real Estate Band 3 p.835

**Tieder, John B**
Profile: p.2514
Table(s): Virginia: Construction Band 1 p.2491

**Tietz, W John**
Table(s): Montana: Natural Resources & Environment Associates to watch p.1651

**Tiffany, Michael E.**
Profile: p.512
Table(s): Arizona: Real Estate Band 3 p.504

**Tigges, Steven W**
Table(s): Ohio: Litigation: General Commercial Band 2 p.2078

**Tighe, J Hagood**
Profile: p.2273
Table(s): South Carolina: Labor & Employment Band 2 p.2262

**Tigue, Michael F**
Table(s): Kentucky: Real Estate: Zoning/Land Use Band 1 p.1314

**Tikellis, Pamela S.**
Table(s): Delaware: Chancery: Mainly Plaintiff Band 2 p.759

**Tilden, Jeffrey I**
Table(s): Washington: Litigation: General Commercial Band 1 p.2533

**Tilden, Mark**
Table(s): Nationwide: Native American Law Band 3 p.192

**Tilkens, Mark**
Table(s): Wisconsin: Labor & Employment Up-and-coming individuals p.2575

**Tillery, M Kelly**
Profile: p.2232
Table(s): Pennsylvania: Intellectual Property Band 2 p.2197

**Tillotson, Jeff**
Profile: p.2419
Table(s): Texas: Litigation: General Commercial Band 3 p.2362

**Tilner, Mitchell C**
Profile: p.669
Table(s): California: Insurance: Insurer Band 2 p.574, California: Litigation: Appellate Band 3 p.599

**Tilson, Joseph**
Table(s): Illinois: Labor & Employment Band 1 p.1175

**Timperio, John M**
Profile: p.417
Table(s): Nationwide: Capital Markets: Securitisation Band 3 p.59

**Timpone, Michael**
Profile: p.417
Table(s): Nationwide: Transportation: Shipping: Finance (New York) Band 2 p.260

**Timpone, Walter F**
Profile: p.1749
Table(s): New Jersey: Litigation: White-Collar Crime & Government Investigations Band 2 p.1723

**Tindall, John H**
Table(s): Alaska: Corporate/M&A Band 2 p.487, Alaska: Real Estate Band 2 p.491

**Tingle, Philip**
Profile: p.1010
Table(s): Florida: Tax Band 3 p.979

**Tinney, John**
Table(s): West Virginia: Litigation: General Commercial Senior Statesmen: p.2555

**Tinnin Jr, Robert P**
Table(s): New Mexico: Labor & Employment Band 3 p.1767

**Tinsley, Randall**
Table(s): North Carolina: Environment Band 3 p.2028

**Tippens, Terry W**
Table(s): Oklahoma: Litigation: General Commercial Senior Statesmen: p.2141

**Tipps, Mark**
Table(s): Tennessee: Litigation: General Commercial Band 2 p.2295

**Tipps, Maynard E**
Profile: p.2046
Table(s): North Carolina: Real Estate Band 3 p.2037

**Tisdale, John R**
Profile: p.529
Table(s): Arkansas: Corporate/Commercial: Municipal Bonds Band 2 p.518, Arkansas: Corporate/Commercial: Tax Band 1 p.518, Arkansas: Real Estate Band 3 p.524

**Tisdale Jr, Charles H**
Table(s): Georgia: Environment Band 1 p.1051

**Title, Gail**
Table(s): California: Media & Entertainment: Litigation Band 2 p.606

**Tittle, David O**
Profile: p.1280
Table(s): Indiana: Litigation: General Commercial Senior Statesmen: p.1273

**Titus, John**
Table(s): Tennessee: Corporate/M&A Band 3 p.2288

**Tius, Susan**
Table(s): Hawaii: Bankruptcy/Restructuring Band 1 p.1114

**To, My Chi**
Table(s): New York: Bankruptcy/Restructuring Band 4 p.1782

**Tober, Gary**
Table(s): Washington: Corporate/Commercial: Tax Band 1 p.2525

**Tobias, Paul R**
Table(s): Texas: Technology: Corporate & Commercial Band 1 p.2375

**Tobin, Charles D**
Profile: p.418
Table(s): Nationwide: First Amendment Litigation Band 1 p.105, District of Columbia: Media & Entertainment Band 2 p.832

**Tobisman, Stuart P**
Profile: p.669
Table(s): Nationwide: Wealth Management: Western Region Band 2 p.267, California: Tax: Estate Planning Band 1 p.617

**Tobocman, Sarah Lea**
Table(s): Nationwide: Immigration Band 3 p.131, Florida: Immigration Band 1 p.956

**Tobor, Ben D**
Profile: p.2419
Table(s): Texas: Intellectual Property Band 3 p.2354

**Todd, Aimee**
Table(s): Georgia: Immigration Band 1 p.1055

**Todd, Jeff L**
Profile: p.2155
Table(s): Oklahoma: Litigation: General Commercial Band 3 p.2141

**Tractenberg, Craig R**
Profile: p.418
Table(s): Nationwide: Franchising **Band 4** p.111

**Tracy, David J**
Table(s): Rhode Island: Real Estate **Band 1** p.2255

**Tracy, Timothy J**
Table(s): Alabama: Corporate/Commercial **Band 2** p.459

**Trafford, Kathleen M**
Profile: p.2115
Table(s): Ohio: Litigation: General Commercial **Band 3** p.2078

**Trafford, Robert W**
Profile: p.2115
Table(s): Ohio: Litigation: General Commercial **Band 3** p.2078

**Trager, Michael D**
Profile: p.418
Table(s): Nationwide: Securities: Regulation: Enforcement **Band 2** p.233

**Trahan, Samantha**
Profile: p.2419
Table(s): Texas: Insurance **Band 3** p.2351

**Tramont, Bryan N**
Profile: p.896
Table(s): District of Columbia: Telecom, Broadcast & Satellite **Band 1** p.844

**Tranter, Jack C**
Table(s): Maryland: Healthcare **Band 1** p.1415

**Tranter, Richard**
Table(s): Ohio: Real Estate: Zoning/Land Use **Band 2** p.2086

**Traub, Amy**
Profile: p.1947
Table(s): New York: Labor & Employment **Up-and-coming individuals** p.1826

**Trautman, Tucker**
Table(s): Colorado: Litigation: General Commercial **Band 2** p.709

**Travostino, Joan**
Profile: p.493
Table(s): Alaska: Real Estate **Band 2** p.491

**Traylor, Patrick D**
Table(s): District of Columbia: Environment **Up-and-coming individuals** p.804

**Treece, John**
Profile: p.1236
Table(s): Illinois: Antitrust **Band 1** p.1143

**Treece, Lawrence W**
Table(s): Colorado: Litigation: General Commercial **Band 3** p.709

**Trela Jr, Constantine L**
Profile: p.1236
Table(s): Illinois: Litigation: General Commercial **Band 4** p.1180

**Trenkle, William**
Profile: p.1301
Table(s): Kansas: Corporate/M&A **Band 2** p.1292

**Trent, Steven H**
Profile: p.2311
Table(s): Tennessee: Labor & Employment **Band 3** p.2293

**Trent, Tom**
Table(s): Tennessee: Real Estate **Band 1** p.2299

**Trentham, Robert**
Profile: p.2311
Table(s): Tennessee: Litigation: Medical Malpractice Defense **Band 1** p.2295

**Tresh, Eric S**
Table(s): Georgia: Tax **Band 3** p.1072

**Trevino, Marc R**
Profile: p.1947
Table(s): Nationwide: Employee Benefits & Executive Compensation **Band 3** p.73, New York: Employee Benefits & Executive Compensation **Band 1** p.1802

**Tribble, Max**
Table(s): Texas: Intellectual Property **Band 4** p.2354

**Trigg, John**
Profile: p.419
Table(s): Nationwide: Product Liability & Mass Torts **Band 2** p.208

**Trigg, Mark G**
Profile: p.1099
Table(s): Georgia: Litigation: General Commercial **Band 4** p.1065

**Trilling, Barry J**
Profile: p.748
Table(s): Connecticut: Environment **Band 1** p.733

**Trilling, Helen R**
Table(s): District of Columbia: Healthcare **Band 2** p.809

**Trinder, Rachel B**
Table(s): Nationwide: Transportation: Aviation: Regulatory **Band 3** p.256

**Tringali, Joseph**
Profile: p.1947
Table(s): New York: Antitrust **Band 3** p.1778

**Trinklein, Jeffrey M**
Profile: p.1947
Table(s): New York: Tax **Band 4** p.1862

**Trip, Warren**
Table(s): Florida: Construction **Band 3** p.944

**Triplett, Thomas C**
Profile: p.1301
Table(s): Kansas: Corporate/M&A **Senior Statesmen:** p.1292

**Tripodoro, John A**
Profile: p.419
Table(s): Nationwide: Capital Markets: Debt & Equity **Band 2** p.46

**Tripp, David**
Table(s): Missouri: Environment **Band 1** p.1621

**Tripp, Mark**
Table(s): Iowa: Litigation: Insurance **Band 1** p.1288

**Tritt, Cheryl**
Profile: p.896
Table(s): District of Columbia: Telecom, Broadcast & Satellite **Band 1** p.844

**Trock, Jennifer E**
Table(s): Nationwide: Transportation: Aviation: Regulatory **Band 2** p.256

**Trombley, Gary**
Table(s): Florida: Litigation: White-Collar Crime & Government Investigations **Band 2** p.967

**Trooboff, Peter D**
Profile: p.419
Table(s): Nationwide: International Trade: Export Controls & Economic Sanctions **Senior Statesmen:** p.153

**Tropin, Harley S**
Profile: p.1011
Table(s): Florida: Litigation: General Commercial **Band 1** p.966

**Tropp, Paul D**
Profile: p.419
Table(s): Nationwide: Capital Markets: Debt & Equity **Band 4** p.46

**Tross, Scott**
Table(s): New Jersey: Litigation: General Commercial **Band 3** p.1722

**Trotter, Jeffrey**
Profile: p.1609
Table(s): Mississippi: Energy & Natural Resources **Band 3** p.1593

**Trout, Robert P**
Table(s): District of Columbia: Litigation: White-Collar Crime & Government Investigations **Band 2** p.827

**Trow, Steve**
Table(s): District of Columbia: Immigration **Band 2** p.814

**Truax, Tim**
Table(s): California: Construction **Band 3** p.550

**Trucker, Lee A**
Table(s): California: Employee Benefits & Executive Compensation **Senior Statesmen:** p.560

**Truesdell, Richard D**
Profile: p.419
Table(s): Nationwide: Capital Markets: Debt & Equity **Star Individuals** p.46

**Truett, Charla**
Table(s): Texas: Immigration **Band 3** p.2349

**Truitt, Raymond G**
Profile: p.1433
Table(s): Maryland: Real Estate **Band 1** p.1422

**Trust, Brian**
Table(s): Nationwide: Bankruptcy/Restructuring **Band 4** p.39, New York: Bankruptcy/Restructuring **Band 3** p.1782

**Tryniecki, Timothy J**
Table(s): Missouri: Real Estate **Band 1** p.1633

**Tse, Marian A**
Profile: p.1512
Table(s): Nationwide: Employee Benefits & Executive Compensation **Band 3** p.73, Massachusetts: Employee Benefits & Executive Compensation **Band 1** p.1455

**Tubach, Michael**
Table(s): California: Antitrust **Band 2** p.536, California: Litigation: White-Collar Crime & Government Investigations **Band 3** p.601

**Tucci, Peter J.**
Profile: p.2232
Table(s): Pennsylvania: Corporate/M&A & Private Equity **Band 4** p.2191

**Tucci, Theodore**
Profile: p.748
Table(s): Connecticut: Healthcare **Band 2** p.735

**Tuchin, Michael L**
Table(s): Nationwide: Bankruptcy/Restructuring **Band 3** p.39, California: Bankruptcy/Restructuring **Band 1** p.542

**Tucker, Charles F**
Table(s): New Hampshire: Real Estate **Band 3** p.1692

**Tucker, H. Glenn**
Table(s): New Jersey: Corporate/M&A **Band 4** p.1707

**Tucker, Hugh**
Profile: p.419
Table(s): Nationwide: Energy: Oil & Gas (Transactional) **Band 3** p.79

**Tucker, John H**
Profile: p.2155
Table(s): Oklahoma: Litigation: General Commercial **Band 2** p.2141

**Tucker, Laurence**
Table(s): Missouri: Litigation: General Commercial **Band 3** p.1628

**Tucker, Robert**
Table(s): Nationwide: Product Liability & Mass Torts **Band 2** p.208

**Tucker, Roy**
Table(s): Oregon: Corporate/M&A **Star individuals** p.2164

**Tucker, Stefan**
Profile: p.897
Table(s): District of Columbia: Real Estate **Senior Statesmen:** p.835

**Tucker, William C**
Profile: p.1698
Table(s): New Hampshire: Corporate/Commercial: Finance **Band 2** p.1685, New Hampshire: Real Estate **Band 1** p.1692, New Hampshire: Real Estate: Land Use **Band 1** p.1692

**Tuggle, Curtis L**
Profile: p.2115
Table(s): Ohio: Bankruptcy/Restructuring **Associates to watch** p.2058

**Tukel, Daniel B**
Table(s): Michigan: Labor & Employment **Band 3** p.1542

**Tull III, John E**
Profile: p.529
Table(s): Arkansas: Litigation: General Commercial **Band 1** p.522

**Tulley, Frederick R.**
Table(s): Louisiana: Litigation: Securities **Band 1** p.1352

**Tully, W Bradley**
Table(s): California: Healthcare **Band 3** p.568

**Tumas, Michael B**
Profile: p.775
Table(s): Delaware: Corporate/M&A **Band 2** p.761

**Urgenson, Laurence A**
Profile: p.420
Table(s): Nationwide: International Trade: FCPA
Experts **Band 2** p.153

**Uris, Harvey R**
Profile: p.420
Table(s): Nationwide: Real Estate **Band 1** p.225,
New York: Real Estate: Finance **Band 1** p.1855

**Urness, Thor**
Table(s): Tennessee: Litigation: General
Commercial **Band 2** p.2295

**Urofsky, Philip**
Table(s): Nationwide: International Trade: FCPA
Experts **Band 3** p.153

**Urowsky, Richard J**
Profile: p.1948
Table(s): New York: Antitrust **Band 4** p.1778

**Urquhart, A William**
Table(s): California: Litigation: General
Commercial **Band 3** p.593

**Urquhart, Douglas**
Profile: p.420
Table(s): Nationwide: Banking & Finance **Band 3**
p.31

**Urquhart, Jr., Quentin F.**
Table(s): Nationwide: Product Liability & Mass
Torts **Band 4** p.208

**Usatine, Warren A.**
Profile: p.1749
Table(s): New Jersey: Bankruptcy/Restructuring
**Band 4** p.1705

**Usdin, Steven W**
Profile: p.1370
Table(s): Louisiana: Litigation: General
Commercial **Band 2** p.1352

**Usow, Jeffrey A**
Table(s): Illinois: Real Estate **Band 2** p.1187

**Utken, Gregory**
Table(s): Indiana: Labor & Employment **Senior
Statesmen:** p.1271

**Utley, Frederick**
Profile: p.420
Table(s): Nationwide: Capital Markets:
Structured Products **Band 3** p.52, Nationwide:
Capital Markets: Securitisation **Band 4** p.59

**Utrecht, Lyn**
Table(s): Nationwide: Government: Political Law
**Senior Statesmen:** p.124

**Utton, John W.**
Table(s): New Mexico: Environment, Natural
Resources & Regulated Industries: Water Law
**Band 2** p.1766

**Utzschneider, John R**
Profile: p.1512
Table(s): Massachusetts: Corporate/M&A **Band 2**
p.1452

**Uyesato, Daniel E**
Profile: p.2046
Table(s): North Carolina: Environment **Band 4**
p.2028

**Uzzi, Gerard**
Profile: p.1948
Table(s): Nationwide: Bankruptcy/Restructuring
**Band 3** p.39, New York:
Bankruptcy/Restructuring **Band 2** p.1782

# V

**Vacketta, Carl Lee**
Profile: p.420
Table(s): Nationwide: Government: Government
Contracts **Senior Statesmen:** p.117

**Vacura, Richard J**
Profile: p.420
Table(s): Nationwide: Government: Government
Contracts **Band 3** p.117

**Vafidis, Matthew P**
Profile: p.420
Table(s): Nationwide: Transportation: Shipping:
Litigation (outside New York) **Band 2** p.263

**Vainder, Steven**
Profile: p.1011
Table(s): Florida: Real Estate **Band 4** p.974

**Valderrama, Teresa S**
Profile: p.2419
Table(s): Texas: Labor & Employment **Band 2**
p.2359

**Valdivia III, José**
Table(s): Florida: Latin American Investment
**Band 3** p.963

**Vale, Shannon**
Table(s): Texas: Intellectual Property: Trade
Mark & Copyright **Band 2** p.2354

**Valentine, Nancy**
Profile: p.2115
Table(s): Ohio: Bankruptcy/Restructuring **Band 3**
p.2058

**Valiant, Carrie**
Profile: p.897
Table(s): District of Columbia: Healthcare **Band 2**
p.809

**Valihura, Karen**
Profile: p.775
Table(s): Delaware: Chancery **Band 3** p.758

**Valukas, Anton R**
Profile: p.1236
Table(s): Nationwide: Litigation: Trial Lawyers
**Band 2** p.187, Illinois: Litigation: General
Commercial **Band 1** p.1180, Illinois: Litigation:
White-Collar Crime & Government Investigations
**Band 1** p.1180

**van Aelstyn, Nicholas**
Table(s): California: Environment **Band 4** p.564

**Van Arnam, Rob**
Table(s): North Carolina: Intellectual Property
**Band 2** p.2030

**Van Buren III, William R**
Table(s): Southern Virginia: Corporate/M&A **Band
3** p.2494

**Van Den Elzen, Ryan L**
Profile: p.2587
Table(s): Wisconsin: Corporate/M&A **Up-and-com-
ing individuals** p.2571

**Van Der Hout, Marc**
Table(s): California: Immigration **Band 1** p.571

**Van Deventer, Kenneth M**
Table(s): New Jersey: Litigation: General
Commercial **Band 3** p.1722

**Van Dongen, Troy**
Profile: p.670
Table(s): California: Tax: State & Local **Up-and-
coming individuals** p.617

**Van Dyck, Timothy P**
Profile: p.1512
Table(s): Massachusetts: Labor & Employment
**Band 4** p.1466

**Van Dyke, Alan**
Table(s): Illinois: Tax **Band 3** p.1192

**Van Dyke, Michael J**
Profile: p.1638
Table(s): Missouri: Corporate/M&A **Band 2** p.1618

**Van Dyke, Peter**
Profile: p.2155
Table(s): Oklahoma: Labor & Employment **Senior
Statesmen:** p.2140

**Van Dyke, Thomas W**
Table(s): Missouri: Corporate/M&A **Band 1** p.1618

**Van Fleet, G Allan**
Profile: p.2419
Table(s): Texas: Antitrust **Band 1** p.2323

**Van Gelder, Barbara**
Profile: p.897
Table(s): District of Columbia: Litigation: White-
Collar Crime & Government Investigations **Band 4**
p.827

**Van Gorp, Jon D**
Table(s): Nationwide: Capital Markets:
Securitisation **Band 2** p.59

**Van Hemel, Peter**
Table(s): Maine: Real Estate **Band 3** p.1395

**Van Hoy, Philip M**
Table(s): North Carolina: Labor & Employment
**Band 1** p.2031

**Van Kley, Jack A**
Table(s): Ohio: Natural Resources &
Environment **Band 2** p.2083

**Van Lieshout, John M**
Profile: p.2587
Table(s): Wisconsin: Natural Resources &
Environment **Band 2** p.2578

**Van Meir, Ellen M**
Table(s): Texas: Insurance **Up-and-coming individuals**
p.2351

**Van Nest, Robert**
Table(s): California: Intellectual Property: Patent
**Band 1** p.578, California: Litigation: General
Commercial **Band 3** p.593

**Van Norden Lockwood, Peter**
Table(s): District of Columbia:
Bankruptcy/Restructuring **Band 2** p.792

**Van Oort, Aaron D**
Table(s): Minnesota: Litigation: Appellate **Band 2**
p.1573

**Van Oot, Martha**
Profile: p.1698
Table(s): New Hampshire: Labor & Employment
**Band 3** p.1688

**Van Oot, Peter D**
Table(s): Vermont: Real Estate: Zoning/Land
Use **Band 1** p.2487

**Van Sicklen, Michael B**
Table(s): Wisconsin: Litigation: General
Commercial **Band 3** p.2576

**Van Slyke, David**
Profile: p.1405
Table(s): Maine: Environment **Band 1** p.1389

**Van Valen, Timothy**
Table(s): New Mexico: Corporate/Commercial:
Tax **Band 1** p.1764

**Van Valkenburg, Wally**
Table(s): Oregon: Intellectual Property **Band 2**
p.2167

**Van Vooren, Scott**
Table(s): Iowa: Corporate/M&A **Band 3** p.1283

**Van Vugt, Eric J**
Profile: p.2587
Table(s): Wisconsin: Litigation: General
Commercial **Band 3** p.2576

**Van Winkle, Jr, Kenneth**
Table(s): Arizona: Real Estate **Band 2** p.504

**Van Zant, Jennifer K**
Table(s): North Carolina: Antitrust **Band 1** p.2020

**VanCanagan, William K**
Table(s): Montana: Corporate/M&A **Band 2**
p.1646

**Vance, Alison**
Profile: p.1609
Table(s): Mississippi: Labor & Employment **Band
3** p.1595

**Vance, Janet**
Profile: p.420
Table(s): Nationwide: Banking & Finance **Band 3**
p.31

**Vance, Kim**
Profile: p.2311
Table(s): Tennessee: Labor & Employment **Band
3** p.2293

**Vance, R Patrick**
Profile: p.1371
Table(s): Louisiana: Bankruptcy/Restructuring
**Band 1** p.1337, Louisiana: Litigation: General
Commercial **Band 1** p.1352

**Vandenberg, John D**
Table(s): Oregon: Intellectual Property **Band 1**
p.2167

**Vander Laan, Mark A**
Table(s): Ohio: Litigation: General Commercial
**Band 2** p.2078

**Vander Tuig, Marc W**
Profile: p.1638
Table(s): Missouri: Intellectual Property **Up-and-
coming individuals** p.1623

**VanDeusen, Darrell R**
Table(s): Maryland: Labor & Employment **Band 2**
p.1417

**Vandevelde, John**
Profile: p.670
Table(s): **California:** Litigation: White-Collar Crime & Government Investigations **Senior Statesmen:** p.601

**Vandiver, Brian**
Table(s): **Arkansas:** Labor & Employment **Up-and-coming individuals** p.520

**VanMiddlesworth, Rex D**
Profile: p.2419
Table(s): **Texas:** Energy: State Regulatory & Litigation (Electricity) **Band 1** p.2341

**Vann, Ryan**
Profile: p.1236
Table(s): **Illinois:** Labor & Employment **Associates to watch** p.1175

**Vanyo, Bruce G**
Table(s): **California:** Litigation: Securities **Band 3** p.594

**Varallo, Gregory V**
Profile: p.775
Table(s): **Delaware:** Chancery **Band 2** p.758

**Vardaman, John W**
Table(s): **District of Columbia:** Litigation: General Commercial **Senior Statesmen:** p.826

**Vardell III, James C**
Profile: p.420
Table(s): **Nationwide:** Banking & Finance **Band 1** p.31

**Varela, Paul A**
Profile: p.2514
Table(s): **Virginia:** Construction **Band 3** p.2491

**Vargo, Ernest E**
Profile: p.2115
Table(s): **Ohio:** Litigation: General Commercial **Band 4** p.2078

**Varn, Jacob D**
Table(s): **Florida:** Environment **Senior Statesmen:** p.951

**Varner, Shannon**
Table(s): **Virginia:** Environment **Band 2** p.2495

**Varner, Thad W**
Profile: p.1609
Table(s): **Mississippi:** Corporate/Commercial: Municipal Finance **Band 2** p.1591

**Varner III, Joseph H.**
Profile: p.1011
Table(s): **Florida:** Litigation: General Commercial **Band 4** p.966

**Varney, Andrew**
Profile: p.897
Table(s): **District of Columbia:** Corporate/M&A & Private Equity **Band 2** p.797

**Varney, Christine**
Profile: p.1948
Table(s): **New York:** Antitrust **Band 4** p.1778

**Vartanian, Thomas**
Profile: p.420
Table(s): **Nationwide:** Financial Services Regulation: Banking (Compliance) **Band 1** p.96, **Nationwide:** Financial Services Regulation: Banking (Enforcement & Investigations) **Band 1** p.96, **Nationwide:** Financial Services Regulation: Financial Institutions M&A **Band 2** p.96

**Vasile, James**
Table(s): **Nationwide:** Energy: Electricity (Regulatory & Litigation) **Band 4** p.76

**Vasily, John M**
Table(s): **Nationwide:** Financial Services Regulation: Financial Institutions M&A **Band 2** p.99

**Vasquez Jr, Juan F**
Table(s): **Nationwide:** Tax: Controversy **Band 4** p.244

**Vatis, Michael A**
Table(s): **Nationwide:** Privacy & Data Security **Band 3** p.199

**Vaughan, James F**
Table(s): **Georgia:** Intellectual Property **Band 3** p.1056

**Vaughan, Keith W**
Table(s): **North Carolina:** Litigation: General Commercial **Band 4** p.2033

**Vaughan III, C Porter**
Profile: p.2514
Table(s): **Southern Virginia:** Corporate/M&A **Band 2** p.2494

**Vaughn, Christina M**
Profile: p.2155
Table(s): **Oklahoma:** Native American Law **Associates to watch** p.2144

**Vaughn, Jonathan R**
Profile: p.2115
Table(s): **Ohio:** Labor & Employment **Band 4** p.2074

**Vaughn, Matthew**
Profile: p.2419
Table(s): **Texas:** Bankruptcy/Restructuring **Band 4** p.2328

**Vaughn, Nancy E.**
Table(s): **Oklahoma:** Labor & Employment **Band 3** p.2140

**Vaughn, Scott**
Table(s): **North Carolina:** Bankruptcy/Restructuring **Band 1** p.2023

**Vazquez, Steven W**
Table(s): **Florida:** Corporate/M&A & Private Equity **Band 3** p.947

**Vázquez-Azpiri, A James**
Profile: p.670
Table(s): **Nationwide:** Immigration **Band 3** p.131, **California:** Immigration **Band 1** p.571

**Vázquez-Bello, Clemente L.**
Table(s): **Florida:** Banking & Finance: Regulatory **Band 1** p.937

**Veber, Jeffrey T**
Profile: p.420
Table(s): **Nationwide:** Transportation: Aviation: Finance **Band 3** p.252

**Vebman, Yossi**
Profile: p.421
Table(s): **Nationwide:** Capital Markets: Derivatives **Band 3** p.51

**Vecchione, Frank J**
Table(s): **New Jersey:** Bankruptcy/Restructuring **Senior Statesmen:** p.1705

**Veerman, Louis R**
Table(s): **Alaska:** Environment, Natural Resources & Regulated Industries **Band 1** p.488

**Velasquez-Heller, Kate**
Table(s): **Massachusetts:** Environment **Associates to watch** p.1457

**Vella, Brian**
Table(s): **Virginia:** Construction **Band 1** p.2491

**Velocci, Frank**
Profile: p.1749
Table(s): **New Jersey:** Bankruptcy/Restructuring **Band 4** p.1705

**Vendsel, Jason R**
Table(s): **North Dakota:** Litigation: General Commercial **Band 3** p.2053

**Venezia, Gina**
Profile: p.421
Table(s): **Nationwide:** Transportation: Shipping: Litigation (New York) **Band 4** p.261

**Venker, Paul**
Table(s): **Missouri:** Litigation: General Commercial **Band 3** p.1629

**Vento, John**
Table(s): **Florida:** Construction **Band 3** p.944

**Ventola, John F**
Profile: p.1512
Table(s): **Massachusetts:** Bankruptcy/Restructuring **Band 2** p.1449

**Vercruysse, Robert**
Table(s): **Michigan:** Labor & Employment **Band 1** p.1542

**Vergilii, Jennifer**
Profile: p.2115
Table(s): **Ohio:** Corporate/M&A **Up-and-coming individuals** p.2064

**Verhoeven, Charles K**
Table(s): **California:** Intellectual Property: Patent **Band 1** p.578

**Vering III, John A**
Table(s): **Missouri:** Labor & Employment **Band 2** p.1625

**Vermeys, Gregg**
Profile: p.1683
Table(s): **Nevada:** Real Estate **Band 3** p.1679

**Vernaglia, Lawrence**
Table(s): **Massachusetts:** Healthcare **Band 1** p.1460

**Vernick, Scott**
Profile: p.2232
Table(s): **Pennsylvania:** Litigation: General Commercial **Band 3** p.2203

**Veroneau, John K**
Profile: p.421
Table(s): **Nationwide:** International Trade: Trade Remedies & Trade Policy **Band 4** p.154

**Verrill Jr, Charles Owen**
Profile: p.421
Table(s): **Nationwide:** International Trade: Trade Remedies & Trade Policy **Senior Statesmen:** p.154

**Verschelden, Matthew J**
Table(s): **Missouri:** Litigation: General Commercial **Band 3** p.1628

**Vesely, Jeffrey M**
Profile: p.670
Table(s): **California:** Tax: State & Local **Band 1** p.617

**Veta, D Jean**
Profile: p.421
Table(s): **Nationwide:** Financial Services Regulation: Banking (Enforcement & Investigations) **Band 1** p.97

**Vettel, Steven L**
Table(s): **California:** Real Estate: Zoning/Land Use **Band 3** p.612

**Vetter, Jeffrey R**
Profile: p.670
Table(s): **California:** Capital Markets: Debt & Equity **Band 3** p.547, **California:** Corporate/M&A: Venture Capital **Band 4** p.555

**Veverka, Charles J**
Table(s): **Utah:** Intellectual Property **Band 3** p.2466

**Vezeau, Timothy**
Table(s): **Illinois:** Intellectual Property **Band 2** p.1171

**Vezina, III, W Robert**
Table(s): **Florida:** Construction **Band 2** p.944

**Viana, Carlos**
Profile: p.1011
Table(s): **Florida:** Banking & Finance: Transactional **Band 2** p.937, **Florida:** Latin American Investment **Band 1** p.963

**Vice, Robert B**
Table(s): **Kentucky:** Real Estate **Band 1** p.1314

**Vice Jr, Robert B**
Profile: p.1325
Table(s): **Kentucky:** Real Estate **Associates to watch** p.1314

**Vicinanzo, David**
Profile: p.1698
Table(s): **New Hampshire:** Litigation: General Commercial **Band 2** p.1690

**Vick Jr, Howard C**
Table(s): **Virginia:** Litigation: White-Collar Crime & Government Investigations **Band 1** p.2502

**Vickers, F Thomas**
Table(s): **Ohio:** Construction **Band 3** p.2062

**Vickery, Ann Morgan**
Table(s): **Nationwide:** Healthcare: Regulatory & Litigation **Band 2** p.127, **District of Columbia:** Healthcare **Band 1** p.809

**Victor, A Paul**
Profile: p.1948
Table(s): **New York:** Antitrust **Band 4** p.1778

**Victory, Nancy J**
Profile: p.897
Table(s): **District of Columbia:** Telecom, Broadcast & Satellite **Band 4** p.844

**Vidmar, Jacqueline M**
Profile: p.1236
Table(s): **Illinois:** Environment: Mainly Transactional **Band 2** p.1162

**Vigdor, William R**
Profile: p.897
Table(s): District of Columbia: Antitrust Band 5
p.787

**Vigil, Charles J**
Profile: p.1774
Table(s): New Mexico: Labor & Employment
Band 3 p.1767

**Vilhauer Jr, Jacob E**
Table(s): Oregon: Intellectual Property Band 2
p.2167

**Villa, John K**
Table(s): Nationwide: Financial Services
Regulation: Banking (Enforcement &
Investigations) Band 1 p.97, Nationwide:
Securities: Litigation Band 3 p.232, District of
Columbia: Litigation: General Commercial Band 1
p.826, District of Columbia: Litigation:
Securities Band 1 p.826

**Villafranco, John E**
Table(s): Nationwide: Advertising: Litigation Band
2 p.19

**Villareal, Patricia J**
Profile: p.2420
Table(s): Texas: Litigation: Securities Band 1
p.2362

**Villeneuve, Tom**
Table(s): California: IT & Outsourcing Band 1
p.583

**Vilos, Joanna**
Profile: p.2601
Table(s): Wyoming: Labor & Employment Band 1
p.2597

**Vince, Clinton A**
Profile: p.421
Table(s): Nationwide: Energy: Electricity
(Regulatory & Litigation) Band 5 p.76

**Vincent, George H**
Table(s): Ohio: Corporate/M&A Band 1 p.2064

**Vincenti, Michael**
Profile: p.1325
Table(s): Kentucky: Real Estate Band 1 p.1314

**Vine, John M**
Profile: p.897
Table(s): District of Columbia: Employee
Benefits & Executive Compensation Senior
Statesmen: p.801

**Vine, Stephen M**
Profile: p.421
Table(s): Nationwide: Investment Funds: Hedge
Funds Band 1 p.162

**Vinegrad, Alan**
Profile: p.1948
Table(s): New York: Litigation: White-Collar
Crime & Government Investigations Band 2
p.1836

**Vines, Leonard D.**
Table(s): Nationwide: Franchising Band 3 p.111

**Vines, Monte**
Table(s): Kansas: Litigation: General
Commercial Band 2 p.1295

**Vineyard, Daniel**
Profile: p.2420
Table(s): Texas: Environment Band 4 p.2343

**Vinson, Laurence D**
Table(s): Alabama: Banking & Finance Band 1
p.455, Alabama: Banking & Finance: Mainly
Regulatory Band 1 p.455

**Virjee, Framroze**
Table(s): California: Labor & Employment Band 2
p.587

**Virtel, James J**
Table(s): Missouri: Litigation: General
Commercial Band 1 p.1629

**Virtue, Paul**
Table(s): Nationwide: Immigration Senior
Statesmen: p.131, District of Columbia:
Immigration Senior Statesmen: p.814

**Viscarello, Kenneth A**
Profile: p.1699
Table(s): New Hampshire: Real Estate Band 2
p.1692

**Viscounty, Perry J**
Profile: p.670
Table(s): California: Intellectual Property:
Trademark, Copyright & Trade Secrets Band 1
p.578

**Vishneski, John S**
Table(s): Nationwide: Insurance: Dispute
Resolution: Policyholder Band 1 p.137, Illinois:
Insurance: Dispute Resolution Band 1 p.1168

**Visser, Kevin**
Table(s): Iowa: Labor & Employment Band 2
p.1285

**Visser, Randolph C**
Table(s): California: Environment Band 3 p.564

**Vitale, Joseph P**
Profile: p.421
Table(s): Nationwide: Financial Services
Regulation: Banking (Compliance) Band 3 p.96,
Nationwide: Financial Services Regulation:
Financial Institutions M&A Band 3 p.96

**Vitarelli, Richard F**
Profile: p.748
Table(s): Connecticut: Labor & Employment Band
3 p.736

**Vitkowsky, Vincent J**
Profile: p.1948
Table(s): New York: Insurance: Dispute
Resolution: Insurer Band 3 p.1816

**Viviani, Gregory J**
Profile: p.2115
Table(s): Ohio: Employee Benefits & Executive
Compensation Band 2 p.2067

**Vizcarrondo Jr, Paul**
Profile: p.421
Table(s): Nationwide: Securities: Litigation Band
2 p.232, New York: Litigation: Securities Band 3
p.1834

**Voboril, Joseph**
Profile: p.2179
Table(s): Oregon: Real Estate Band 2 p.2173

**Vobornik, Donna**
Profile: p.1236
Table(s): Illinois: Insurance: Dispute Resolution
Band 2 p.1168

**Vogel, David C**
Table(s): Missouri: Labor & Employment Band 2
p.1625

**Vogel, Gary**
Profile: p.1405
Table(s): Maine: Real Estate Band 4 p.1395

**Vogel, Mart Daniel**
Table(s): North Dakota: Litigation: General
Commercial Band 3 p.2053

**Vogel, Miriam A.**
Profile: p.670
Table(s): California: Litigation: Appellate Band 1
p.599

**Vogel, Peter S**
Profile: p.2420
Table(s): Texas: Technology: Corporate &
Commercial Band 3 p.2375

**Vogel III, Edward W**
Profile: p.1011
Table(s): Florida: Banking & Finance: Public
Finance Band 1 p.936

**Vogel, Jr, Arthur A**
Profile: p.2587
Table(s): Wisconsin: Natural Resources &
Environment Band 1 p.2578

**Vogtle Jr., Jesse S.**
Table(s): Alabama: Bankruptcy/Restructuring
Band 2 p.457

**Voigt, John**
Table(s): Tennessee: Healthcare Band 1 p.2291

**Voigt, Richard**
Profile: p.748
Table(s): Connecticut: Labor & Employment Band
2 p.736

**Voigts, Gene**
Table(s): Missouri: Litigation: General
Commercial Band 2 p.1628

**Vold, Kevin L**
Table(s): Northern Virginia: Corporate/M&A Band
3 p.2493

**Volinsky, Andru H**
Table(s): New Hampshire: Litigation: General
Commercial Band 2 p.1690

**Volk, William R**
Profile: p.2420
Table(s): Texas: Technology: Corporate &
Commercial Band 1 p.2375

**Volling, James L**
Table(s): Minnesota: Litigation: General
Commercial Band 2 p.1574

**Volpe, Anthony S**
Table(s): Pennsylvania: Intellectual Property
Band 3 p.2197

**Volpe, Michele**
Table(s): Connecticut: Healthcare Band 2 p.735

**Voltmer, Ralph C**
Profile: p.897
Table(s): District of Columbia: Telecom,
Broadcast & Satellite Band 2 p.844

**von Bergen, Mark**
Profile: p.2179
Table(s): Oregon: Corporate/M&A Band 2 p.2164

**von Ende, Carl H**
Profile: p.1556
Table(s): Michigan: Litigation: General
Commercial Senior Statesmen: p.1544

**von Mehren, Robert B**
Table(s): Nationwide: International Arbitration:
Arbitrators Senior Statesmen: p.146

**von Stamwitz, George**
Table(s): Missouri: Environment Band 1 p.1621

**Voorhees Jr, Theodore**
Profile: p.421
Table(s): Nationwide: Product Liability & Mass
Torts Band 5 p.208

**Vorys, John**
Profile: p.2115
Table(s): Ohio: Corporate/M&A Band 3 p.2064

**Voss, Christopher J**
Table(s): Washington: Corporate/Commercial
Band 2 p.2525

**Voss, Wendy K**
Profile: p.775
Table(s): Delaware: Labor & Employment Band 2
p.765

**Votaw, James G**
Profile: p.897
Table(s): District of Columbia: Environment Band
5 p.804

**Voth Blankenship, Patricia**
Profile: p.1301
Table(s): Kansas: Real Estate Band 2 p.1297

**Voxman, W. Alex**
Table(s): California: Corporate/M&A: Venture
Capital Band 3 p.555

**Voyles, Robb L**
Profile: p.2420
Table(s): Texas: Litigation: General Commercial
Band 3 p.2362

**Vreeland, Albert L**
Table(s): Alabama: Labor & Employment Band 2
p.460

**Vuocolo, Diane E**
Profile: p.2232
Table(s): Pennsylvania:
Bankruptcy/Restructuring Band 4 p.2188

**Vyskocil, Mary Kay**
Profile: p.422
Table(s): Nationwide: Insurance: Dispute
Resolution: Insurer Band 1 p.134, Nationwide:
Insurance: Dispute Resolution: Reinsurance
Band 1 p.134, New York: Insurance: Dispute
Resolution: Insurer Band 1 p.1816

**Vyverberg, Robert**
Profile: p.1236
Table(s): Illinois: Labor & Employment Band 4
p.1175

# W

**Wachen, Kimberly**
Profile: p.897
Table(s): Nationwide: Leisure & Hospitality Band
4 p.179, District of Columbia: Real Estate Band 3
p.835

# Index of Lawyers

**Wachs, Amy L**
Table(s): Missouri: Environment **Band 2** p.1621

**Wachsberger, Chaim**
Profile: p.422
Table(s): Nationwide: Projects **Band 1** p.216

**Wachtell, Herbert M**
Profile: p.422
Table(s): Nationwide: Litigation: Trial Lawyers **Senior Statesmen:** p.186, New York: Litigation: General Commercial **Senior Statesmen:** p.1833

**Wachuta, Amanda G**
Table(s): Iowa: Labor & Employment **Up-and-coming individuals** p.1285

**Wada, Ronald**
Table(s): California: Immigration **Band 2** p.571

**Waddell, David**
Table(s): Nationwide: Gaming & Licensing **Band 3** p.115

**Waddell, Paul**
Table(s): Arkansas: Litigation: Medical Malpractice Defense **Band 2**

**Waddell Jr, William A**
Profile: p.529
Table(s): Arkansas: Litigation: General Commercial **Band 1** p.522

**Wade, James A**
Profile: p.748
Table(s): Connecticut: Litigation: General Commercial **Senior Statesmen:** p.738

**Wade, Stephen B**
Table(s): Maine: Litigation: Medical Malpractice & Insurance **Band 2** p.1393, Maine: Litigation: Mainly Plaintiff **Band 2** p.1393

**Wade, Steven T**
Table(s): Montana: Natural Resources & Environment **Band 2** p.1651

**Wadhams Jr, Richard H**
Table(s): Vermont: Litigation: General Commercial **Band 3** p.2486

**Wadzinski, Kevin**
Profile: p.422
Table(s): Nationwide: Native American Law **Band 1** p.192

**Waeger, Ann M**
Table(s): New Jersey: Environment **Band 2** p.1711, New Jersey: Real Estate: Zoning/Land Use **Band 2** p.1728

**Wagenbach, Jeffrey B**
Table(s): New Jersey: Environment **Band 3** p.1711

**Waggoner, Dennis P**
Profile: p.1011
Table(s): Florida: Litigation: General Commercial **Band 3** p.966

**Wagman, Philip**
Profile: p.1949
Table(s): New York: Tax **Up-and-coming individuals** p.1862

**Wagner, James A**
Table(s): Hawaii: Bankruptcy/Restructuring **Band 1** p.1114

**Wagner, Theodore R**
Table(s): Nationwide: Wealth Management: Eastern Region **Band 4** p.267

**Wagner, William**
Profile: p.1655
Table(s): Montana: Real Estate **Band 1** p.1652

**Waguespack, David F**
Table(s): Louisiana: Bankruptcy/Restructuring **Band 2** p.1337

**Wahl, Barbara S**
Profile: p.897
Table(s): District of Columbia: Litigation: General Commercial **Band 3** p.826

**Wahlquist, Andrea K**
Profile: p.1949
Table(s): New York: Employee Benefits & Executive Compensation **Band 3** p.1802

**Waite, Joel**
Table(s): Delaware: Bankruptcy/Restructuring **Band 4** p.754

**Wajert, Sean P**
Table(s): Nationwide: Product Liability & Mass Torts **Band 5** p.208

**Wakefield, Jeffrey M**
Table(s): West Virginia: Litigation: General Commercial **Band 2** p.2555

**Wakelin, David S**
Table(s): Maine: Labor & Employment: Employee Benefits & Compensation **Band 1** p.1390

**Waks, Jay W**
Profile: p.1949
Table(s): New York: Labor & Employment **Band 1** p.1826

**Wakshlag, Stanley**
Table(s): Florida: Litigation: General Commercial **Band 1** p.966

**Walbolt, Sylvia H**
Profile: p.1011
Table(s): Florida: Litigation: Appellate **Band 1** p.972

**Walbridge, Jeffrey**
Table(s): California: Employee Benefits & Executive Compensation **Band 3** p.560

**Walch, Greg**
Profile: p.1683
Table(s): Nevada: Environment **Band 1** p.1673

**Wald, Douglas**
Profile: p.898
Table(s): District of Columbia: Antitrust **Band 4** p.787

**Wald, Peter A**
Profile: p.422
Table(s): Nationwide: Securities: Litigation **Band 2** p.232, California: Litigation: Securities **Band 2** p.594

**Walder, Justin**
Table(s): New Jersey: Litigation: White-Collar Crime & Government Investigations **Band 1** p.1723

**Waldman, Craig**
Profile: p.670
Table(s): California: Antitrust **Band 3** p.536

**Waldman, Ira J**
Table(s): California: Real Estate **Band 1** p.611

**Waldron, Jonathan K**
Profile: p.422
Table(s): Nationwide: Transportation: Shipping: Regulatory (outside New York) **Band 1** p.264

**Waldrop Jr, Norman E**
Table(s): Alabama: Litigation: Medical Malpractice Defense **Band 2** p.463

**Wales, David**
Profile: p.898
Table(s): District of Columbia: Antitrust **Band 4** p.787

**Walker, Adrienne K**
Profile: p.1512
Table(s): Massachusetts: Bankruptcy/Restructuring **Up-and-coming individuals** p.1449

**Walker, Andrew R**
Profile: p.1949
Table(s): New York: Tax **Band 3** p.1862

**Walker, Charles**
Profile: p.2420
Table(s): Texas: Intellectual Property **Band 4** p.2354

**Walker, Christopher A**
Table(s): Ohio: Natural Resources & Environment **Band 2** p.2083

**Walker, Helgi C**
Profile: p.898
Table(s): Nationwide: Appellate Law **Band 4** p.26, District of Columbia: Telecom, Broadcast & Satellite **Band 2** p.844

**Walker, Homer Lee**
Table(s): Georgia: Real Estate **Band 3** p.1070

**Walker, James A**
Profile: p.1301
Table(s): Kansas: Litigation: General Commercial **Band 2** p.1295

**Walker, Jeffrey A**
Profile: p.1610
Table(s): Mississippi: Labor & Employment **Band 2** p.1595

**Walker, Kathleen Campbell**
Table(s): Nationwide: Immigration **Band 1** p.131, Texas: Immigration **Star individuals** p.2349

**Walker, Kim J**
Table(s): Iowa: Litigation: General Commercial **Band 3** p.1288

**Walker, Mark L**
Table(s): Oklahoma: Energy & Natural Resources **Band 1** p.2136

**Walker, Paul**
Profile: p.671
Table(s): California: Real Estate **Band 1** p.611

**Walker, Robert**
Profile: p.2116
Table(s): Ohio: Litigation: General Commercial **Band 4** p.2078

**Walker, Robert**
Table(s): Tennessee: Litigation: General Commercial **Star individuals** p.2295

**Walker, Steve**
Table(s): Florida: Environment **Band 2** p.951

**Walker, Tracy**
Table(s): Virginia: Litigation: Products Liability **Band 1** p.2502

**Walker, Trenholm G**
Table(s): South Carolina: Litigation: General Commercial **Band 1** p.2264

**Walker, W Jason**
Table(s): Texas: Construction **Band 3** p.2335

**Walker, Will**
Table(s): North Carolina: Banking & Finance **Up-and-coming individuals** p.2021

**Walker Jr, F Mitchell**
Profile: p.2311
Table(s): Tennessee: Corporate/M&A **Band 1** p.2288

**Walker Jr, H William**
Profile: p.1011
Table(s): Florida: Real Estate **Senior Statesmen:** p.974

**Walker-Bright, Paul R**
Table(s): Illinois: Insurance: Dispute Resolution **Band 3** p.1168

**Walkowski, Joseph A**
Table(s): Utah: Intellectual Property **Band 1** p.2466

**Wall, Christopher R**
Profile: p.422
Table(s): Nationwide: International Trade: CFIUS Experts **Band 3** p.152, Nationwide: International Trade: Export Controls & Economic Sanctions **Band 1** p.152

**Wall, Daniel**
Profile: p.671
Table(s): California: Antitrust **Band 1** p.536

**Wall, Ethan**
Profile: p.1011
Table(s): Florida: Litigation: General Commercial **Associates to watch** p.966

**Wall, Randall**
Profile: p.1610
Table(s): Mississippi: Corporate/Commercial: Municipal Finance **Band 2** p.1591

**Wall, Robert F**
Profile: p.1236
Table(s): Illinois: Corporate/M&A **Band 1** p.1156

**Wall, Steven R**
Profile: p.2232
Table(s): Pennsylvania: Labor & Employment **Band 1** p.2200

**Wallace, Barbara C**
Table(s): Mississippi: Labor & Employment **Band 2** p.1595

**Wallace, David H**
Profile: p.2116
Table(s): Ohio: Litigation: General Commercial **Band 3** p.2078

**Wallace, Michael B**
Table(s): Mississippi: Litigation: Appellate **Band 1** p.1596, Mississippi: Litigation: General Commercial **Band 1** p.1596

**Wallace, Rick**
Profile: p.2566
Table(s): West Virginia: Labor & Employment **Up-and-coming individuals** p.2553

**Wallace, W Kirk**
Profile: p.1949
Table(s): New York: Tax **Band 3** p.1862

**Wallace Jr, James H**
Profile: p.898
Table(s): District of Columbia: Intellectual Property: Litigation **Band 3** p.821

**Wallach, Eric J**
Profile: p.1949
Table(s): New York: Labor & Employment **Band 4** p.1826

**Wallach, Kenneth**
Profile: p.422
Table(s): Nationwide: Capital Markets: Debt & Equity **Band 4** p.46

**Wallach, Mark**
Profile: p.2116
Table(s): Ohio: Litigation: General Commercial **Band 3** p.2078

**Wallach, William D**
Profile: p.1749
Table(s): New Jersey: Litigation: General Commercial **Band 3** p.1722

**Wallack, Barry Z**
Table(s): Indiana: Real Estate **Band 2** p.1275

**Wallack, James F**
Table(s): Massachusetts: Bankruptcy/Restructuring **Band 1** p.1449

**Wallander, William**
Profile: p.2420
Table(s): Texas: Bankruptcy/Restructuring **Band 1** p.2328

**Wallenstein, James H**
Table(s): Texas: Real Estate **Star Individuals** p.2367

**Waller, Michael**
Profile: p.2055
Table(s): North Dakota: Litigation: Medical Malpractice Defense **Band 1** p.2053

**Waller Jr, Edward M**
Table(s): Florida: Healthcare **Band 2** p.954

**Walls, David S**
Table(s): North Carolina: Bankruptcy/Restructuring **Band 1** p.2023

**Walls, James**
Profile: p.2566
Table(s): West Virginia: Litigation: General Commercial **Band 3** p.2555

**Walmsley, Robert**
Profile: p.1371
Table(s): Louisiana: Corporate/M&A **Band 2** p.1341

**Walper, Thomas**
Profile: p.671
Table(s): California: Bankruptcy/Restructuring **Band 3** p.542

**Walsh, Elaine**
Table(s): Nationwide: Energy: Electricity (Regulatory & Litigation) **Band 4** p.76, Nationwide: Energy: Electricity (Transactional) **Band 2** p.76

**Walsh, Gerard J**
Profile: p.671
Table(s): California: Real Estate **Band 4** p.611

**Walsh, Kevin**
Profile: p.1949
Table(s): New York: Insurance: Dispute Resolution: Insurer **Band 3** p.1816

**Walsh, Kevin J**
Profile: p.1512
Table(s): Massachusetts: Bankruptcy/Restructuring **Band 3** p.1449

**Walsh, Linda**
Profile: p.422
Table(s): Nationwide: Energy: Electricity (Regulatory & Litigation) **Band 3** p.76

**Walsh, Martin D**
Table(s): Northern Virginia: Real Estate: Zoning/Land Use **Band 1** p.2505

**Walsh, Nan**
Table(s): Northern Virginia: Real Estate: Zoning/Land Use **Band 2** p.2505

**Walsh, Thomas**
Table(s): Washington: Real Estate: Zoning/Land Use **Band 1** p.2536

**Walsh, Thomas C**
Table(s): Missouri: Litigation: General Commercial **Band 1** p.1629

**Walsh, William**
Profile: p.2514
Table(s): Southern Virginia: Real Estate **Star Individuals** p.2506

**Walsh, William J**
Profile: p.898
Table(s): District of Columbia: Environment **Band 4** p.804

**Walsh II, Joseph A**
Table(s): Nationwide: Transportation: Shipping: Litigation (outside New York) **Band 1** p.263

**Walsh Jr, Peter J**
Profile: p.775
Table(s): Delaware: Chancery **Band 2** p.758

**Walter, Daniel M**
Table(s): Kentucky: Real Estate **Band 3** p.1314

**Walter, Teri A**
Table(s): Montana: Labor & Employment **Band 2** p.1648

**Walters, David B**
Profile: p.1556
Table(s): Michigan: Employee Benefits & Executive Compensation **Band 3** p.1540

**Walters, Neal**
Profile: p.1749
Table(s): Nationwide: Product Liability & Mass Torts **Band 5** p.208, New Jersey: Litigation: Products Liability **Band 2** p.1723

**Walters, Robert**
Profile: p.2420
Table(s): Texas: Antitrust **Band 2** p.2323, Texas: Litigation: General Commercial **Band 4** p.2362

**Walters, Todd**
Profile: p.2514
Table(s): Northern Virginia: Intellectual Property **Band 2** p.2497

**Walther-Meade, Carolina**
Profile: p.422
Table(s): Nationwide: Projects **Band 4** p.216

**Walton, Gib**
Table(s): Texas: Litigation: General Commercial **Band 2** p.2362

**Walton, Leigh**
Profile: p.2311
Table(s): Tennessee: Healthcare **Band 1** p.2291

**Waltz, Judith A**
Table(s): California: Healthcare **Band 3** p.568

**Waltzman, Howard**
Table(s): Nationwide: Government: Government Relations **Up-and-coming individuals** p.121

**Walz, Monte**
Table(s): South Dakota: Corporate/Commercial **Band 3** p.2281

**Wamsley, James**
Profile: p.2116
Table(s): Ohio: Intellectual Property **Band 2** p.2071

**Wand, Barbara Freedman**
Profile: p.1513
Table(s): Massachusetts: Tax: Estate Planning **Band 1** p.1481

**Wander, Herbert S**
Table(s): Illinois: Corporate/M&A **Senior Statesmen** p.1156

**Wang, Nina**
Table(s): Colorado: Intellectual Property **Band 3** p.704

**Wang, R. Randall**
Table(s): Missouri: Corporate/M&A **Band 2** p.1619

**Wang, Sarah O**
Profile: p.1125
Table(s): Hawaii: Labor & Employment **Band 2** p.1117

**Wanner, David**
Table(s): North Dakota: Real Estate **Band 1** p.2055

**Ward, Alton C**
Profile: p.1011
Table(s): Florida: Tax: Employee Benefits **Band 1** p.979

**Ward, Alysa**
Table(s): Florida: Labor & Employment **Band 4** p.959

**Ward, Catherine M.**
Table(s): New Jersey: Environment **Band 3** p.1711

**Ward, Christopher A**
Table(s): Delaware: Bankruptcy/Restructuring **Band 3** p.754

**Ward, Dale**
Table(s): Kansas: Corporate/M&A **Band 3** p.1292, Kansas: Real Estate **Band 3** p.1297

**Ward, Daniel A**
Profile: p.2116
Table(s): Ohio: Labor & Employment **Band 3** p.2074

**Ward, J Marc**
Table(s): Iowa: Corporate/M&A **Band 3** p.1283

**Ward, Leo S**
Table(s): Montana: Labor & Employment **Band 1** p.1648

**Ward, Patrick**
Table(s): North Dakota: Labor & Employment **Band 2** p.2052

**Ward, R Lawrence**
Table(s): Missouri: Litigation: General Commercial **Star Individuals** p.1628

**Ward, Sarah M**
Profile: p.423
Table(s): Nationwide: Banking & Finance **Band 3** p.31

**Ward, Stephen R.**
Table(s): Oklahoma: Native American Law **Band 3** p.2144

**Ward Brown, Jay**
Profile: p.898
Table(s): District of Columbia: Media & Entertainment **Band 3** p.832

**Wardle, Geoffrey**
Table(s): Idaho: Real Estate: Zoning/Land Use **Band 1** p.1138

**Ware, Donald**
Profile: p.1513
Table(s): Massachusetts: Intellectual Property **Band 1** p.1463

**Ware, Paul**
Table(s): Alabama: Corporate/Commercial **Band 2** p.459

**Ware, Rex D**
Table(s): Florida: Tax: State & Local **Band 1** p.979

**Ware Jr, Paul F**
Profile: p.1513
Table(s): Nationwide: Litigation: Trial Lawyers **Band 2** p.187, Massachusetts: Intellectual Property **Band 1** p.1463, Massachusetts: Litigation: General Commercial **Band 1** p.1470

**Warin, Edward G**
Profile: p.1669
Table(s): Nebraska: Litigation: General Commercial **Band 3** p.1664

**Warin, Joseph**
Profile: p.423
Table(s): Nationwide: International Trade: FCPA Experts **Band 1** p.153, Nationwide: Securities: Litigation **Band 1** p.232, Nationwide: Securities: Regulation: Enforcement **Band 1** p.232, District of Columbia: Litigation: Securities **Band 1** p.826, District of Columbia: Litigation: White-Collar Crime & Government Investigations **Band 1** p.826

**Warin, Roger**
Table(s): Nationwide: Insurance: Dispute Resolution: Insurer **Band 1** p.134, District of Columbia: Insurance: Insurer **Band 1** p.816

**Waxenberg, Jay D**
Table(s): Nationwide: Wealth Management: Eastern Region **Band 2** p.267

**Waxman, Eric S**
Profile: p.671
Table(s): California: Litigation: Securities **Band 3** p.594

**Waxman, J Mark**
Table(s): Massachusetts: Healthcare **Band 2** p.1460

**Waxman, Scott E**
Profile: p.775
Table(s): Delaware: Corporate/M&A: Alternative Entities **Band 1** p.761

**Waxman, Seth**
Profile: p.423
Table(s): Nationwide: Appellate Law **Star Individuals** p.26

**Wayland, R Eddie**
Table(s): Tennessee: Labor & Employment **Band 2** p.2293

**Weakland, Alan W**
Table(s): California: Real Estate **Band 3** p.611

**Wearsch, Thomas M**
Profile: p.2116
Table(s): Ohio: Bankruptcy/Restructuring **Band 4** p.2058

**Weathersby, E Woods**
Table(s): Tennessee: Real Estate **Band 3** p.2299

**Weaver, David**
Profile: p.2421
Table(s): Texas: Intellectual Property **Band 4** p.2354

**Weaver, Elizabeth**
Profile: p.671
Table(s): California: Environment **Band 2** p.564

**Weaver, James M**
Profile: p.2311
Table(s): Tennessee: Environment **Band 1** p.2290

**Weaver, Mary Jane**
Table(s): California: Immigration **Band 2** p.571

**Weaver, Maureen**
Profile: p.748
Table(s): Connecticut: Healthcare **Band 1** p.735

**Weaver, Robin G**
Profile: p.2116
Table(s): Ohio: Litigation: General Commercial **Band 3** p.2078

**Weaver, Ronald**
Table(s): Florida: Real Estate **Band 4** p.974, Florida: Real Estate: Zoning/Land Use **Band 1** p.974

**Webb, Dan K**
Profile: p.1236
Table(s): Nationwide: Litigation: Trial Lawyers **Band 1** p.187, Nationwide: Product Liability & Mass Torts **Band 1** p.208, Illinois: Antitrust **Band 3** p.1143, Illinois: Litigation: General Commercial **Star Individuals** p.1180, Illinois: Litigation: White-Collar Crime & Government Investigations **Star Individuals** p.1180

**Webb, Elizabeth**
Table(s): California: Employee Benefits & Executive Compensation **Band 3** p.560

**Webb, Eugene**
Table(s): Virginia: Labor & Employment **Band 2** p.2500

**Webb, Katherine**
Profile: p.1011
Table(s): Florida: Insurance **Up-and-coming individuals** p.957

**Webb, Robert J**
Profile: p.423
Table(s): Nationwide: Leisure & Hospitality **Band 4** p.179

**Webb, Thompson**
Profile: p.1433
Table(s): Maryland: Corporate/M&A **Band 2** p.1412

**Webb, Trent**
Table(s): Missouri: Intellectual Property **Band 1** p.1623

**Webber, A Duane**
Profile: p.423
Table(s): Nationwide: Tax: Controversy **Band 2** p.244

**Webber, Charles F**
Table(s): Minnesota: Litigation: Appellate **Band 1** p.1573, Minnesota: Litigation: General Commercial **Band 1** p.1573

**Webber, Daniel**
Table(s): Oklahoma: Litigation: General Commercial **Band 2** p.2141

**Webber, Erin**
Profile: p.723
Table(s): Colorado: Labor & Employment **Band 2** p.706

**Weber, Constance H**
Table(s): West Virginia: Labor & Employment **Band 3** p.2553

**Weber, Paul L**
Profile: p.423
Table(s): Nationwide: Projects **Band 3** p.216

**Weber, Ralph A**
Profile: p.2587
Table(s): Wisconsin: Litigation: General Commercial **Band 1** p.2576

**Weber, Stephen A**
Table(s): West Virginia: Labor & Employment **Band 2** p.2553

**Weber, Steven D.**
Table(s): North Carolina: Environment **Band 2** p.2028

**Weber, Victoria**
Table(s): Florida: Tax: State & Local **Band 1** p.979

**Weber, William**
Profile: p.1012
Table(s): Florida: Real Estate **Band 3** p.974

**Weber III, Louis J**
Profile: p.1236
Table(s): Illinois: Tax **Band 3** p.1192

**Webking, Catherine**
Profile: p.2421
Table(s): Texas: Energy: State Regulatory & Litigation (Electricity) **Band 2** p.2341

**Webster, James**
Table(s): Nationwide: Food & Beverages: Alcohol **Band 2** p.109

**Webster, Pamela K**
Profile: p.671
Table(s): California: Bankruptcy/Restructuring **Band 2** p.542

**Webster, Scott A**
Profile: p.1513
Table(s): Massachusetts: Employee Benefits & Executive Compensation **Band 2** p.1455

**Webster, Stephanie**
Profile: p.898
Table(s): District of Columbia: Healthcare **Band 3** p.809

**Webster, Susan**
Profile: p.423
Table(s): Nationwide: Securities: Regulation: Advisory **Band 2** p.232

**Webster, Timothy K**
Profile: p.898
Table(s): District of Columbia: Environment **Band 4** p.804

**Wechselblatt, Eric**
Profile: p.2515
Table(s): Northern Virginia: Corporate/M&A **Band 3** p.2493

**Wechsler, Ernest**
Profile: p.1949
Table(s): New York: Corporate/M&A **Band 5** p.1793

**Weddington, Keith M**
Table(s): North Carolina: Labor & Employment **Band 2** p.2031

**Weddle, Jennifer H**
Profile: p.424
Table(s): Nationwide: Native American Law **Band 3** p.192

**Weedon, Luke A**
Profile: p.2421
Table(s): Texas: Banking & Finance **Band 3** p.2325

**Weeks, Susan**
Table(s): Louisiana: Banking & Finance: Public Finance **Band 1** p.1335

**Weems, Walter S**
Table(s): Mississippi: Corporate/Commercial **Band 2** p.1591

**Weese, Charles W**
Table(s): Colorado: Labor & Employment **Band 2** p.706

**Weese, Esther Chang**
Profile: p.671
Table(s): California: Healthcare **Band 4** p.568

**Weg, Howard J**
Profile: p.671
Table(s): California: Bankruptcy/Restructuring **Band 2** p.542

**Wege, Mark**
Profile: p.2421
Table(s): Texas: Bankruptcy/Restructuring **Band 4** p.2328

**Wehrer, Susan K**
Table(s): California: Immigration **Up-and-coming individuals** p.571

**Wehrli, John**
Profile: p.671
Table(s): California: Life Sciences: IP/Patent Litigation **Up-and-coming individuals** p.590

**Wehrum, William L**
Profile: p.898
Table(s): District of Columbia: Environment **Band 2** p.804

**Weibel, Mark**
Profile: p.2421
Table(s): Texas: Real Estate **Band 3** p.2367

**Weible, Robert A**
Profile: p.2116
Table(s): Ohio: Corporate/M&A **Band 2** p.2064

**Weidhaas, Andrew J**
Profile: p.1949
Table(s): New York: Corporate/M&A **Band 5** p.1793

**Weigel, Kenneth**
Profile: p.424
Table(s): Nationwide: International Trade: Export Controls & Economic Sanctions **Band 3** p.153, Nationwide: International Trade: Customs **Band 1** p.153

**Weil, Alan S**
Profile: p.424
Table(s): Nationwide: Leisure & Hospitality **Band 3** p.179, New York: Real Estate **Band 3** p.1854

**Weil, Andrew L**
Profile: p.1237
Table(s): Illinois: Corporate/M&A **Band 3** p.1156

**Weimer, John**
Profile: p.2117
Table(s): Ohio: Banking & Finance **Band 3** p.2056

**Wein, Howard J**
Profile: p.2232
Table(s): Pennsylvania: Environment **Band 2** p.2194

**Weinberg, David B**
Profile: p.898
Table(s): District of Columbia: Environment **Band 2** p.804

**Weinberg, J D**
Profile: p.1950
Table(s): New York: Corporate/M&A **Band 4** p.1793

**Weinberg, James**
Profile: p.2117
Table(s): Ohio: Intellectual Property **Band 3** p.2071

**Weinberg, Richard D.**
Profile: p.1950
Table(s): New York: Litigation: White-Collar Crime & Government Investigations **Band 3** p.1836

**Weitz, Mark**
Table(s): Minnesota: Corporate/M&A Band 4 p.1569

**Weitz, Perry**
Table(s): Nationwide: Product Liability: Plaintiffs Band 2 p.209

**Weitzel, Mark P**
Table(s): Nationwide: Projects Band 2 p.216, Nationwide: Projects: Renewables & Alternative Energy Band 1 p.216

**Weitzman, Allan H**
Table(s): Florida: Labor & Employment Band 1 p.959

**Weitzman, Patricia D**
Table(s): Connecticut: Healthcare Band 2 p.735

**Welbaum, R Earl**
Table(s): Florida: Construction Senior Statesmen: p.944

**Welby, Thomas H**
Table(s): New York: Construction Band 4 p.1791

**Welch, Brian**
Profile: p.1280
Table(s): Indiana: Litigation: General Commercial Band 3 p.1273

**Welch, Edward P**
Profile: p.776
Table(s): Delaware: Chancery Band 1 p.758

**Welch, John**
Profile: p.899
Table(s): District of Columbia: Corporate/M&A & Private Equity Band 3 p.797

**Welch, Richard J**
Profile: p.672
Table(s): Nationwide: Private Equity: Buyouts Band 5 p.203, California: Corporate/M&A: Private Equity Band 3 p.553

**Welch, Sara**
Table(s): Missouri: Labor & Employment Band 3 p.1625

**Welch, Sidney Summers**
Profile: p.1100
Table(s): Georgia: Healthcare Band 3 p.1052

**Welch, Thomas**
Table(s): Hawaii: Real Estate Band 1 p.1120

**Welch, W Scott**
Profile: p.1610
Table(s): Mississippi: Litigation: General Commercial Band 1 p.1597

**Welch, William M**
Table(s): Maine: Real Estate Band 2 p.1395

**Weld, Chris**
Table(s): Massachusetts: Litigation: General Commercial Band 3 p.1470

**Weld King, Carol**
Table(s): Nationwide: Leisure & Hospitality Band 2 p.179, District of Columbia: Real Estate Band 2 p.835

**Weldon, John B**
Table(s): Arizona: Environment: Water Rights Band 1 p.497

**Welin, Peter D**
Table(s): Ohio: Construction Band 3 p.2062

**Welk, Thomas**
Table(s): South Dakota: Litigation: General Commercial Band 1 p.2284

**Welke, William R**
Profile: p.1237
Table(s): Illinois: Tax Band 2 p.1192

**Welker, Mark D**
Table(s): Missouri: Labor & Employment Band 3 p.1625

**Wellen, Robert H**
Profile: p.899
Table(s): District of Columbia: Tax Band 2 p.838

**Weller, David L**
Profile: p.424
Table(s): Nationwide: International Trade: Trade Remedies & Trade Policy Band 5 p.154

**Weller, Giovanna**
Table(s): Connecticut: Labor & Employment Band 3 p.736

**Weller, Philip D**
Profile: p.2421
Table(s): Texas: Real Estate Band 1 p.2367

**Wellford, Buckner**
Profile: p.2311
Table(s): Tennessee: Litigation: Medical Malpractice Defense Band 1 p.2295

**Wellford, Hill**
Profile: p.899
Table(s): District of Columbia: Antitrust Band 5 p.787

**Wellford Jr, Harry W**
Profile: p.1639
Table(s): Missouri: Labor & Employment Band 2 p.1625

**Wellford Jr, Hill B**
Profile: p.2515
Table(s): Virginia: Labor & Employment Senior Statesmen: p.2500

**Wellington, Martin**
Table(s): California: Corporate/M&A Up-and-coming individuals p.553

**Wellner, John P**
Profile: p.2117
Table(s): Ohio: Real Estate Band 2 p.2086

**Wells, Ben F**
Table(s): Ohio: Employee Benefits & Executive Compensation Band 2 p.2067

**Wells, Catherine**
Table(s): New Jersey: Labor & Employment Band 2 p.1718

**Wells, Christopher M**
Table(s): Nationwide: Investment Funds: Hedge Funds Band 2 p.162

**Wells, David E**
Profile: p.1012
Table(s): Florida: Corporate/M&A & Private Equity Band 4 p.947

**Wells, David M.**
Table(s): Florida: Litigation: General Commercial Band 3 p.966

**Wells, Della Wager**
Profile: p.1100
Table(s): Georgia: Energy Band 2 p.1049

**Wells, J Tullos**
Profile: p.2421
Table(s): Texas: Labor & Employment Band 4 p.2359

**Wells, Lawrence**
Table(s): New Mexico: Real Estate Band 1 p.1772

**Wells, Matthew**
Profile: p.2476
Table(s): Utah: Corporate/M&A Band 2 p.2462

**Wells, Roger W**
Table(s): Nebraska: Corporate/Commercial Band 1 p.1659

**Wells, Stephen E**
Profile: p.899
Table(s): District of Columbia: Tax Band 2 p.838

**Wells, Steve**
Table(s): Minnesota: Litigation: General Commercial Band 2 p.1574

**Wells, W David**
Table(s): Missouri: Litigation: General Commercial Band 2 p.1629

**Wells Jr, Theodore V**
Profile: p.424
Table(s): Nationwide: Litigation: Trial Lawyers Star individuals p.187, New York: Litigation: General Commercial Star individuals p.1833, New York: Litigation: White-Collar Crime & Government Investigations Star individuals p.1833

**Welp, Robert A**
Table(s): Northern Virginia: Corporate/M&A Band 3 p.2493

**Welsh, John F**
Table(s): Massachusetts: Labor & Employment Band 2 p.1466

**Welsh, Patrick J**
Profile: p.1325
Table(s): Kentucky: Corporate/M&A Band 3 p.1305

**Welsh, W Russell**
Table(s): Missouri: Litigation: General Commercial Band 2 p.1628

**Welsh Jr, Robert E**
Table(s): Pennsylvania: Litigation: White-Collar Crime & Government Investigations Band 1 p.2204

**Welshimer, Mark J**
Profile: p.424
Table(s): Nationwide: Capital Markets: Structured Products Band 3 p.52

**Welty, Todd**
Profile: p.2421
Table(s): Nationwide: Tax: Controversy Band 4 p.244, Texas: Tax: Litigation Band 2 p.2371

**Wendel, Diana**
Table(s): Colorado: Real Estate Band 2 p.714

**Wenger, Brian**
Profile: p.1580
Table(s): Minnesota: Corporate/M&A Band 2 p.1569

**Wenick, George D**
Profile: p.1100
Table(s): Georgia: Construction Band 2 p.1044

**Wenik, Jack**
Profile: p.1749
Table(s): New Jersey: Healthcare Band 3 p.1715

**Wenner, Adam**
Table(s): Nationwide: Energy: Electricity (Regulatory & Litigation) Band 3 p.76

**Wenthe, Lucas**
Table(s): Missouri: Intellectual Property Associates to watch p.1623

**Wentsler, Stephen S**
Table(s): Ohio: Intellectual Property Band 2 p.2071

**Werbner, Mark**
Table(s): Texas: Litigation: General Commercial Band 3 p.2362

**Werder Jr, Richard I**
Table(s): New York: Litigation: General Commercial Band 3 p.1833

**Werner, John D**
Profile: p.1371
Table(s): Louisiana: Banking & Finance Band 3 p.1335, Louisiana: Corporate/M&A Band 4 p.1341

**Werner, Kathleen L**
Profile: p.424
Table(s): Nationwide: Capital Markets: REITs Band 3 p.55

**Wertam, John**
Table(s): Connecticut: Environment Band 2 p.733

**Wertheimer, Robert J**
Table(s): New York: Real Estate Band 2 p.1854

**Werther, Barbara G**
Table(s): District of Columbia: Construction Band 2 p.795

**Wesely, Marissa C**
Profile: p.425
Table(s): Nationwide: Banking & Finance Band 2 p.31

**Wesloh, Steven**
Profile: p.2117
Table(s): Ohio: Natural Resources & Environment Band 4 p.2083

**Wessel, Paul J**
Profile: p.1950
Table(s): New York: Employee Benefits & Executive Compensation Band 3 p.1802

**West, Christina S**
Table(s): New Mexico: Native American Law Band 2 p.1771

**West, Glenn D**
Profile: p.2421
Table(s): Nationwide: Private Equity: Buyouts Band 3 p.203, Texas: Corporate/M&A Band 1 p.2337

**West, Joseph D**
Profile: p.899
Table(s): Nationwide: Government: Government Contracts Band 2 p.117, District of Columbia: Construction Band 1 p.795

**West, Kevin**
Profile: p.1140
Table(s): Idaho: Labor & Employment Band 2 p.1132

**White, Tammy**
Profile: p.2566
Table(s): West Virginia: Litigation: Healthcare
**Band 2** p.2555

**White, Thomas V**
Table(s): Tennessee: Real Estate: Zoning/Land
Use **Band 1** p.2299

**White, W Christopher**
Profile: p.1951
Table(s): New York: Real Estate: Finance **Band 3**
p.1855

**White, Wendelin A**
Profile: p.899
Table(s): District of Columbia: Real Estate **Band
2** p.835

**White, William A**
Table(s): North Carolina: Environment **Band 4**
p.2028

**Whitehead, Steven**
Table(s): Utah: Real Estate **Band 3** p.2470

**Whitehead, Stewart**
Profile: p.2422
Table(s): Texas: Construction **Band 3** p.2335

**Whitesell, Anne Marie**
Profile: p.425
Table(s): Nationwide: International Arbitration
**Band 5** p.145

**Whitestone, David**
Profile: p.426
Table(s): Nationwide: Government: Government
Relations **Band 3** p.121

**Whiteway, Andrea**
Profile: p.899
Table(s): District of Columbia: Tax **Band 4** p.838

**Whitfield, George L**
Table(s): Michigan: Employee Benefits &
Executive Compensation **Band 2** p.1540

**Whitford, Joseph P**
Table(s): Washington: Corporate/Commercial
**Band 3** p.2525

**Whitham, Michele A**
Profile: p.1513
Table(s): Massachusetts: Labor & Employment
**Band 3** p.1466

**Whitledge, William H**
Profile: p.1513
Table(s): Massachusetts: Tax **Band 1** p.1481

**Whitley, George P**
Table(s): Southern Virginia: Corporate/M&A **Band
2** p.2494

**Whitley, Joe D**
Profile: p.1100
Table(s): Georgia: Litigation: White-Collar Crime
& Government Investigations **Band 3** p.1066

**Whitlock, David C**
Profile: p.1100
Table(s): Georgia: Immigration **Band 3** p.1055

**Whitlow, Mark**
Table(s): Oregon: Real Estate: Zoning/Land Use
**Band 2** p.2173

**Whitman, John S**
Table(s): Maine: Litigation: General Commercial
**Band 2** p.1393, Maine: Litigation: Medical
Malpractice & Insurance **Band 2** p.1393

**Whitman, Lee M**
Table(s): North Carolina: Litigation: Healthcare
& Medical Malpractice **Band 1** p.2034

**Whitman, W Ray**
Profile: p.2422
Table(s): Texas: Litigation: Energy & Natural
Resources **Band 3** p.2361

**Whitney, Diane W**
Profile: p.748
Table(s): Connecticut: Environment **Band 1** p.733

**Whitt, Burt**
Table(s): Virginia: Labor & Employment **Band 2**
p.2500

**Whittaker, David M**
Table(s): Ohio: Bankruptcy/Restructuring **Band 4**
p.2058

**Whittaker, Scott T**
Table(s): Louisiana: Corporate/M&A **Band 2**
p.1341

**Whittemore, Edward B**
Table(s): Connecticut: Corporate/M&A **Band 3**
p.732

**Whittemore, Ellen**
Table(s): Nevada: Gaming & Licensing **Band 2**
p.1674

**Whittle, Jeffrey S**
Profile: p.2422
Table(s): Texas: Intellectual Property **Band 4**
p.2354

**Whitty, Paul B**
Table(s): Kentucky: Real Estate: Zoning/Land
Use **Band 1** p.1314

**Whitworth, H. Philip**
Table(s): Texas: Energy: State Regulatory &
Litigation (Oil & Gas) **Band 1** p.2341

**Wiacek, Raymond**
Profile: p.899
Table(s): District of Columbia: Tax **Band 2** p.838

**Wickers IV, Alonzo**
Table(s): California: Media & Entertainment:
First Amendment Litigation **Band 1** p.606

**Wickliff Jr, A Martin**
Profile: p.2422
Table(s): Texas: Labor & Employment **Band 2**
p.2359

**Wider, Jedd H**
Profile: p.426
Table(s): Nationwide: Investment Funds: Hedge
Funds **Band 2** p.162

**Widger, Stanley**
Profile: p.1951
Table(s): New York: Energy: State Regulatory &
Wholesale Electric Market **Band 1** p.1806

**Widmayer, Warren**
Table(s): Michigan: Employee Benefits &
Executive Compensation **Band 3** p.1540

**Widom, Mitchell E**
Profile: p.1012
Table(s): Florida: Litigation: General Commercial
**Band 4** p.966

**Wieczorek, Dennis E**
Profile: p.426
Table(s): Nationwide: Franchising **Band 1** p.111

**Wiederrich, James**
Table(s): South Dakota: Corporate/Commercial
**Band 1** p.2281, South Dakota: Real Estate **Band 1**
p.2286

**Wieland, Diana**
Profile: p.1699
Table(s): New Hampshire: Labor & Employment
**Band 2** p.1688

**Wielebinski, Joseph J**
Table(s): Texas: Bankruptcy/Restructuring **Band 2**
p.2328

**Wielinski, Patrick J**
Table(s): Texas: Construction **Band 2** p.2335,
Texas: Insurance **Band 2** p.2351

**Wieman, Lawrence E**
Profile: p.426
Table(s): Nationwide: Banking & Finance **Band 3**
p.31

**Wiener, Todd**
Profile: p.1237
Table(s): Illinois: Environment: Litigation **Band 2**
p.1162

**Wiesen, Jeffrey M**
Profile: p.426
Table(s): Nationwide: Life Sciences:
Corporate/Commercial **Band 1** p.182,
Massachusetts: Corporate/M&A **Band 2** p.1452

**Wiggins, Dena E**
Profile: p.426
Table(s): Nationwide: Energy: Oil & Gas
(Regulatory & Litigation) **Band 4** p.78

**Wigmore, Michael B**
Profile: p.900
Table(s): District of Columbia: Environment **Band
4** p.804

**Wigner Jr, Harry E**
Table(s): Kansas: Real Estate **Band 2** p.1297

**Wikstrom, Francis M**
Profile: p.2476
Table(s): Utah: Litigation: General Commercial
**Band 1** p.2468

**Wilbourn, Gordon**
Profile: p.529
Table(s): Arkansas: Corporate/Commercial:
Municipal Bonds **Band 1** p.518

**Wilcox, Deborah A**
Profile: p.2117
Table(s): Ohio: Intellectual Property **Band 3**
p.2071

**Wilcox, Gregory B**
Table(s): Iowa: Corporate/M&A **Band 3** p.1283

**Wilcox, Justine E**
Profile: p.900
Table(s): District of Columbia: Real Estate **Band
3** p.835

**Wilcox, Kirby**
Table(s): California: Labor & Employment **Band 1**
p.587

**Wilcox, Steven A**
Table(s): Nationwide: Life Sciences:
Corporate/Commercial **Band 2** p.182

**Wilcox, Thomas W**
Table(s): Nationwide: Transportation: Rail (for
Shippers) **Band 1** p.258

**Wilcox, Tony**
Table(s): Arkansas: Litigation: General
Commercial **Band 4** p.522

**Wild, Jeffrey J**
Profile: p.1749
Table(s): New Jersey: Litigation: General
Commercial **Band 3** p.1722

**Wild, Jeffrey J**
Profile: p.2117
Table(s): Ohio: Real Estate **Band 4** p.2086

**Wild, Robert Andrew**
Table(s): Nationwide: Healthcare: Regulatory &
Litigation **Band 3** p.127, New York: Healthcare
**Band 1** p.1811

**Wilder, Marcy**
Table(s): Nationwide: Privacy & Data Security
**Band 2** p.199

**Wildman, William R**
Table(s): Georgia: Construction **Band 3** p.1044

**Wildung, Wendy J**
Table(s): Minnesota: Litigation: General
Commercial **Band 3** p.1574

**Wiley, Jay**
Table(s): Arizona: Real Estate **Band 4** p.504

**Wiley, Richard E**
Profile: p.900
Table(s): District of Columbia: Media &
Entertainment: Mainly Regulatory **Band 1** p.832,
District of Columbia: Telecom, Broadcast &
Satellite **Star Individuals** p.844

**Wilford, Frank L**
Profile: p.1326
Table(s): Kentucky: Real Estate **Band 2** p.1314

**Wilgus, Lauren**
Profile: p.426
Table(s): Nationwide: Transportation: Shipping:
Litigation (New York) **Associates to watch** p.261

**Wilhelm, William**
Profile: p.900
Table(s): District of Columbia: Telecom,
Broadcast & Satellite **Band 4** p.844

**Wilhoit, Adrienne W.**
Profile: p.512
Table(s): Arizona: Corporate/M&A **Band 4** p.495

**Wilk, Corey**
Table(s): Nationwide: Leisure & Hospitality
**Associates to watch** p.179

**Wilkerson, John**
Profile: p.2273
Table(s): South Carolina: Litigation: General
Commercial **Band 3** p.2264

**Wilkins, Michael**
Table(s): Indiana: Litigation: General
Commercial **Band 3** p.1273

**Wilson, Brent**
Table(s): Georgia: Labor & Employment **Band 2** p.1060

**Wilson, Bruce S**
Profile: p.427
Table(s): Nationwide: Sports Law **Band 2** p.241

**Wilson, Christine**
Profile: p.900
Table(s): District of Columbia: Antitrust **Band 5** p.787

**Wilson, Craig P**
Profile: p.2233
Table(s): Pennsylvania: Environment **Band 2** p.2194

**Wilson, David D**
Profile: p.529
Table(s): Arkansas: Litigation: General Commercial **Band 4** p.522

**Wilson, David H**
Table(s): Oregon: Labor & Employment **Band 2** p.2168

**Wilson, Eric**
Table(s): New York: Bankruptcy/Restructuring **Band 4** p.1782

**Wilson, Heather L**
Profile: p.1280
Table(s): Indiana: Labor & Employment **Band 3** p.1271

**Wilson, James**
Profile: p.2117
Table(s): Ohio: Litigation: Antitrust **Band 1** p.2078

**Wilson, Jane A**
Table(s): Maryland: Real Estate **Band 4** p.1422

**Wilson, Jéan E**
Profile: p.1012
Table(s): Florida: Banking & Finance: Public Finance **Band 3** p.936

**Wilson, John**
Table(s): California: Capital Markets: Debt & Equity **Band 1** p.547

**Wilson, John K**
Table(s): Wisconsin: Corporate/M&A **Band 3** p.2571

**Wilson, Jonathan**
Profile: p.2422
Table(s): Texas: Labor & Employment **Band 4** p.2359

**Wilson, Kate**
Profile: p.1580
Table(s): Minnesota: Labor & Employment **Band 3** p.1571

**Wilson, Michael**
Table(s): Florida: Construction **Band 1** p.944

**Wilson, Randon W**
Profile: p.2476
Table(s): Utah: Corporate/M&A **Band 4** p.2462

**Wilson, Reid**
Table(s): Texas: Real Estate **Band 3** p.2367

**Wilson, Richard R**
Table(s): Washington: Real Estate: Zoning/Land Use **Band 1** p.2536

**Wilson, Robert**
Table(s): Texas: Real Estate **Band 1** p.2367

**Wilson, Seth**
Profile: p.2566
Table(s): West Virginia: Natural Resources **Up-and-coming individuals** p.2558

**Wilson, Stanford**
Table(s): Georgia: Labor & Employment **Band 1** p.1060

**Wilson, Stephen M**
Table(s): Mississippi: Corporate/Commercial **Band 2** p.1591

**Wilson, Thomas H**
Profile: p.2422
Table(s): Texas: Labor & Employment **Band 3** p.2359

**Wilson, Virginia B**
Profile: p.2312
Table(s): Tennessee: Banking & Finance: Regulatory **Band 2** p.2287

**Wilson, W Russell**
Profile: p.2117
Table(s): Ohio: Real Estate **Band 4** p.2086

**Wilson, William**
Profile: p.1012
Table(s): Florida: Litigation: General Commercial **Band 3** p.966

**Wilson III, Harry M**
Table(s): Florida: Real Estate **Band 3** p.974

**Wilton, Jim**
Table(s): Massachusetts: Bankruptcy/Restructuring **Band 2** p.1449

**Wiltshire, William M**
Profile: p.900
Table(s): District of Columbia: Telecom, Broadcast & Satellite **Band 4** p.844

**Wimmer, Kurt A**
Profile: p.427
Table(s): Nationwide: First Amendment Litigation **Band 2** p.105, District of Columbia: Media & Entertainment **Band 2** p.832

**Winarsky, Karen**
Table(s): Georgia: Immigration **Band 2** p.1055

**Winburne, Blake H**
Profile: p.427
Table(s): Nationwide: Projects **Band 3** p.216

**Wincek, Mark D**
Table(s): District of Columbia: Employee Benefits & Executive Compensation **Band 3** p.801

**Wind, Todd A**
Table(s): Minnesota: Litigation: General Commercial **Band 3** p.1574

**Windham, Darrell R**
Profile: p.2422
Table(s): Texas: Technology: Corporate & Commercial **Band 3** p.2375

**Wine, James C**
Table(s): Iowa: Real Estate **Band 2** p.1290

**Winegar, Natalie K**
Table(s): Wyoming: Corporate/M&A **Band 2** p.2596, Wyoming: Real Estate **Band 2** p.2600

**Winer, Samuel J**
Table(s): Nationwide: Securities: Regulation: Enforcement **Band 2** p.233

**Winer, Steven L**
Table(s): New Hampshire: Labor & Employment **Band 3** p.1688

**Wing, David**
Table(s): Missouri: Labor & Employment **Band 2** p.1625

**Wing, John R**
Profile: p.1951
Table(s): New York: Litigation: White-Collar Crime & Government Investigations **Senior Statesmen** p.1836

**Wing, Robert**
Table(s): Utah: Litigation: General Commercial **Band 3** p.2468

**Winger, R Gary**
Table(s): Utah: Corporate/M&A **Band 3** p.2462

**Winick, Jeffrey**
Table(s): Illinois: Construction **Band 3** p.1154

**Wink, Stephen**
Profile: p.427
Table(s): Nationwide: Financial Services Regulation: Broker Dealer (Compliance) **Band 2** p.97

**Winkler, Peter**
Profile: p.512
Table(s): Arizona: Real Estate **Band 3** p.504

**Winmill, Patricia**
Profile: p.2476
Table(s): Utah: Energy & Natural Resources **Band 2** p.2464

**Winning Jr, William J**
Profile: p.2233
Table(s): Pennsylvania: Litigation: White-Collar Crime & Government Investigations **Band 2** p.2204

**Winokur, Barton J**
Profile: p.2233
Table(s): Pennsylvania: Corporate/M&A & Private Equity **Star individuals** p.2191

**Winokur, Derek**
Profile: p.1951
Table(s): New York: Corporate/M&A **Up-and-coming individuals** p.1793

**Winokur, Laurence**
Profile: p.1556
Table(s): Michigan: Real Estate **Band 3** p.1546

**Winsberg, Harris Bryan**
Profile: p.1100
Table(s): Georgia: Bankruptcy/Restructuring **Band 2** p.1042

**Winslow III, Edward**
Table(s): North Carolina: Banking & Finance **Senior Statesmen** p.2021

**Winsten, I W**
Table(s): Michigan: Litigation: General Commercial **Band 3** p.1544

**Winston, Eric**
Table(s): California: Bankruptcy/Restructuring **Band 4** p.542

**Winston, Richard L**
Profile: p.1012
Table(s): Florida: Latin American Investment **Band 2** p.963

**Winston, Roger D**
Profile: p.1433
Table(s): Maryland: Real Estate **Band 1** p.1422

**Winter, David A**
Table(s): Nationwide: Investment Funds: Private Equity: Fund Formation **Band 3** p.166

**Winter, John D**
Profile: p.427
Table(s): Nationwide: Product Liability & Mass Torts **Band 4** p.208

**Winterbauer, Steven**
Profile: p.2541
Table(s): Washington: Labor & Employment **Band 2** p.2531

**Winters, Karen A**
Profile: p.2118
Table(s): Ohio: Natural Resources & Environment **Band 2** p.2083

**Winters, Michael G**
Profile: p.2046
Table(s): North Carolina: Real Estate **Band 2** p.2037

**Winters, Vernon M**
Profile: p.672
Table(s): California: Intellectual Property: Patent **Band 4** p.578

**Winterscheid, Joseph F**
Profile: p.900
Table(s): District of Columbia: Antitrust **Band 4** p.787

**Winterscheidt, Rebecca**
Table(s): Arizona: Labor & Employment **Band 3** p.499

**Wintringham, Drew**
Profile: p.1951
Table(s): New York: Intellectual Property: Patent **Band 3** p.1820

**Wire, Kenneth**
Table(s): Northern Virginia: Real Estate **Associates to watch** p.2505

**Wisdom, Rachel Wendt**
Table(s): Louisiana: Labor & Employment **Band 3** p.1350

**Wise, Andy**
Profile: p.900
Table(s): District of Columbia: Litigation: White-Collar Crime & Government Investigations **Up-and-coming individuals** p.827

**Wise, Julian**
Profile: p.1951
Table(s): New York: Real Estate: Corporate **Band 3** p.1854

**Wise, Marc S**
Table(s): Michigan: Employee Benefits & Executive Compensation **Band 3** p.1540

**Wise, Michael**
Table(s): Nationwide: Life Sciences: IP/Patent Litigation **Band 3** p.183, California: Life Sciences: IP/Patent Litigation **Band 2** p.590

**Wolitzer, Michael**
Profile: p.428
Table(s): Nationwide: Investment Funds: Private Equity: Fund Formation **Band 1** p.166

**Wolk, Michael D**
Profile: p.428
Table(s): Nationwide: Securities: Regulation: Enforcement **Band 4** p.233

**Wolkoff, Harvey J**
Table(s): Massachusetts: Litigation: General Commercial **Band 3** p.1470

**Wollin, David A**
Profile: p.2258
Table(s): Rhode Island: Litigation: General Commercial **Band 3** p.2254

**Wollman, Diana L**
Profile: p.1952
Table(s): New York: Tax **Band 2** p.1862

**Woloson, Kenneth**
Profile: p.1683
Table(s): Nevada: Corporate/Commercial **Band 2** p.1672

**Wolowitz, David**
Profile: p.1699
Table(s): New Hampshire: Litigation: General Commercial **Band 3** p.1690

**Wolowitz, Steven**
Table(s): New York: Litigation: General Commercial **Band 4** p.1833

**Wolsk, Jeremiah M**
Profile: p.901
Table(s): District of Columbia: Technology & Outsourcing **Band 3** p.842

**Wommack, Trevor**
Profile: p.2422
Table(s): Texas: Banking & Finance **Associates to watch** p.2325

**Wong, Carolyn K**
Table(s): Hawaii: Labor & Employment **Band 2** p.1117

**Wong, Danton S**
Table(s): Hawaii: Real Estate **Band 1** p.1120

**Wong, David W**
Profile: p.1125
Table(s): Hawaii: Corporate/Commercial: Tax **Band 1** p.1115

**Wong, Karen**
Profile: p.428
Table(s): Nationwide: Projects **Band 3** p.216

**Wong, Ray L**
Table(s): California: Insurance: Insurer **Band 2** p.574

**Wood, Douglas J**
Table(s): Nationwide: Advertising: Transactional & Regulatory **Band 1** p.20

**Wood, Elizabeth Scott**
Profile: p.2156
Table(s): Oklahoma: Labor & Employment **Band 3** p.2140

**Wood, Ivan**
Table(s): Texas: Healthcare **Band 2** p.2347

**Wood, Lisa C**
Profile: p.1514
Table(s): Massachusetts: Antitrust **Band 3** p.1444

**Wood, Mark**
Table(s): California: Insurance: Insurer **Band 3** p.574

**Wood, Nancy**
Table(s): Iowa: Labor & Employment **Band 3** p.1285

**Wood, Nicholas J**
Table(s): Arizona: Real Estate: Zoning/Land Use **Band 2** p.504

**Wood, Robert**
Table(s): Tennessee: Real Estate **Band 2** p.2299

**Wood, Stacy K**
Table(s): North Carolina: Labor & Employment **Band 2** p.2031

**Wood, Thomas R**
Table(s): Oregon: Environment **Band 1** p.2165

**Wood, William**
Profile: p.1301
Table(s): Kansas: Corporate/M&A **Band 1** p.1292, Kansas: Real Estate **Band 1** p.1297

**Wood, William**
Profile: p.2423
Table(s): Texas: Litigation: Energy & Natural Resources **Band 1** p.2361

**Wood III, William A**
Profile: p.2423
Table(s): Texas: Bankruptcy/Restructuring **Band 2** p.2328

**Wood Jr, Fred M**
Profile: p.2046
Table(s): North Carolina: Litigation: General Commercial **Band 4** p.2033

**Woodbury, Judith Fletcher**
Profile: p.1405
Table(s): Maine: Real Estate **Band 2** p.1395

**Woodcock, Jacqueline M**
Table(s): New Mexico: Labor & Employment **Band 2** p.1767

**Wooding, David S**
Table(s): Kansas: Litigation: General Commercial **Band 3** p.1295

**Woodruff, Joseph A**
Profile: p.2312
Table(s): Tennessee: Litigation: General Commercial **Band 2** p.2295

**Woods, Curtis E**
Profile: p.1639
Table(s): Missouri: Litigation: General Commercial **Band 2** p.1628, Missouri: Litigation: White-Collar Crime & Government Investigations **Band 2** p.1628

**Woods, Daniel**
Table(s): California: Litigation: General Commercial **Band 4** p.593

**Woods, John**
Table(s): Nationwide: Transportation: Shipping: Litigation (New York) **Band 2** p.261

**Woods, John W**
Table(s): Nationwide: Litigation: E-Discovery **Band 2** p.187

**Woods, LaVerne**
Table(s): Washington: Corporate/Commercial: Tax **Band 1** p.2525

**Woods, Sharon M**
Table(s): Michigan: Litigation: General Commercial **Band 1** p.1544

**Woods, Will K**
Profile: p.428
Table(s): Nationwide: Franchising **Band 4** p.111

**Woods III, C Laurence**
Profile: p.1326
Table(s): Kentucky: Labor & Employment **Band 2** p.1310

**Woodside III, Frank C**
Table(s): Ohio: Litigation: General Commercial **Band 4** p.2078

**Woodson, R Duke**
Table(s): Florida: Real Estate: Zoning/Land Use **Band 2** p.975

**Woodworth, Stanley N**
Table(s): Kansas: Real Estate **Band 2** p.1297

**Woody, Charles**
Profile: p.2566
Table(s): West Virginia: Labor & Employment **Band 2** p.2553

**Wooley, James**
Profile: p.2118
Table(s): Ohio: Litigation: White-Collar Crime & Government Investigations **Band 1** p.2079

**Woolley, Patrick C.**
Table(s): Missouri: Intellectual Property **Band 2** p.1623

**Woronoff, Michael A**
Table(s): Nationwide: Capital Markets: Debt & Equity **Band 4** p.46, Nationwide: Private Equity: Buyouts **Band 3** p.203, California: Capital Markets: Debt & Equity **Band 3** p.547, California: Corporate/M&A: Private Equity **Band 1** p.553, California: Corporate/M&A **Band 2** p.553

**Worrell, Danny**
Table(s): Texas: Environment **Band 2** p.2343

**Worrell, David**
Table(s): Indiana: Corporate/M&A **Band 2** p.1268

**Wortel, William J**
Table(s): Illinois: Labor & Employment **Band 4** p.1175

**Worth, Diane**
Table(s): Kansas: Labor & Employment **Band 1** p.1294

**Worth Jr, Thomas C**
Table(s): North Carolina: Real Estate: Zoning/Land Use **Band 1** p.2037

**Wortley, Michael**
Profile: p.2423
Table(s): Texas: Corporate/M&A **Band 1** p.2337

**Wovsaniker, Alan**
Profile: p.1750
Table(s): New Jersey: Corporate/M&A **Band 2** p.1707

**Wozniak, Todd**
Profile: p.1100
Table(s): Georgia: Labor & Employment **Band 2** p.1060

**Wray, Christopher A**
Profile: p.1101
Table(s): Georgia: Litigation: White-Collar Crime & Government Investigations **Band 1** p.1066

**Wreggelsworth, James**
Table(s): Washington: Corporate/Commercial: Tax **Band 1** p.2525

**Wren, William C**
Table(s): Texas: Energy: State Regulatory & Litigation (Electricity) **Band 1** p.2341

**Wright, Andrew**
Profile: p.428
Table(s): Nationwide: Investment Funds: Private Equity: Fund Formation **Band 4** p.166

**Wright, Christopher**
Profile: p.901
Table(s): District of Columbia: Telecom, Broadcast & Satellite **Band 2** p.844

**Wright, Corey**
Profile: p.428
Table(s): Nationwide: Banking & Finance **Up-and-coming individuals** p.31

**Wright, David C**
Profile: p.428
Table(s): Nationwide: Capital Markets: REITs **Band 1** p.55

**Wright, Douglas R**
Table(s): Colorado: Corporate/M&A **Band 2** p.703

**Wright, James**
Profile: p.1434
Table(s): Maryland: Real Estate **Band 1** p.1422

**Wright, Jefferson V**
Profile: p.1434
Table(s): Maryland: Litigation: General Commercial **Band 3** p.1419

**Wright, Joyce**
Table(s): Arizona: Real Estate **Band 2** p.504

**Wright, Kenneth C**
Profile: p.1012
Table(s): Florida: Corporate/M&A & Private Equity **Band 4** p.947

**Wright, Michael D**
Profile: p.1237
Table(s): Illinois: Banking & Finance **Band 4** p.1145

**Wright, Richard**
Profile: p.474
Table(s): Alabama: Bankruptcy/Restructuring **Band 3** p.457

**Wright, Robert**
Profile: p.2423
Table(s): Texas: Real Estate **Band 1** p.2367

**Wright, W. Scott**
Table(s): Georgia: Tax **Band 3** p.1072

**Wright, Wm Cary**
Profile: p.1012
Table(s): Florida: Construction **Band 1** p.944

**Wright, Wyatt**
Profile: p.1301
Table(s): Kansas: Labor & Employment **Band 3** p.1294

**Yingling, Ed**
Profile: p.429
Table(s): **Nationwide:** Financial Services
Regulation: Banking (Compliance) **Band 3** p.96

**Yingling, Gary L**
Profile: p.901
Table(s): **District of Columbia:** Healthcare:
Pharmaceutical/Medical Products Regulatory
**Senior Statesmen:** p.810

**Yoder, Lowell D**
Profile: p.1238
Table(s): **Illinois:** Tax **Band 1** p.1192

**Yogodzinski, Debra D**
Table(s): **District of Columbia:** Real Estate **Band 3** p.835

**Yoken, Stephen**
Table(s): **Nevada:** Real Estate **Band 2** p.1679

**Yon, David A**
Table(s): **Florida:** Insurance **Band 1** p.957

**Yood, Kenneth J**
Table(s): **California:** Healthcare **Band 2** p.568

**Yoon, Andrew J**
Profile: p.430
Table(s): **Nationwide:** Banking & Finance **Up-and-coming individuals** p.31

**Yoshimoto, Janel**
Table(s): **Hawaii:** Real Estate **Band 2** p.1120

**Yoskin, Neil**
Table(s): **New Jersey:** Environment **Band 1** p.1711

**Yost, Daniel**
Profile: p.673
Table(s): **California:** IT & Outsourcing **Up-and-coming individuals** p.583

**Yost, Nicholas C**
Profile: p.430
Table(s): **Nationwide:** Native American Law **Band 2** p.192, **California:** Environment **Band 4** p.564

**Youchah, Elayna J**
Profile: p.1683
Table(s): **Nevada:** Labor & Employment **Band 1** p.1675

**Young, Barbara A**
Table(s): **Connecticut:** Corporate/M&A **Band 2** p.732

**Young, Cynthia W**
Profile: p.1326
Table(s): **Kentucky:** Corporate/M&A **Band 1** p.1305

**Young, Douglas R**
Table(s): **California:** Litigation: General
Commercial **Band 2** p.593, **California:** Litigation:
White-Collar Crime & Government Investigations
**Band 1** p.601

**Young, Edward R**
Profile: p.2312
Table(s): **Tennessee:** Labor & Employment **Band 2** p.2293

**Young, Evan**
Profile: p.2423
Table(s): **Texas:** Litigation: Appellate **Associates to watch** p.2361

**Young, George**
Table(s): **Texas:** Capital Markets: Debt & Equity
**Band 3** p.2333

**Young, Greg**
Profile: p.2312
Table(s): **Tennessee:** Environment **Up-and-coming individuals** p.2290

**Young, Howard J**
Profile: p.901
Table(s): **District of Columbia:** Healthcare **Band 2** p.809

**Young, J Randy**
Profile: p.1371
Table(s): **Louisiana:** Energy & Natural
Resources: Utilities **Band 2** p.1344

**Young, Jason**
Profile: p.430
Table(s): **Nationwide:** Sports Law **Up-and-coming individuals** p.241

**Young, Jonathan**
Profile: p.1238
Table(s): **Illinois:** Bankruptcy/Restructuring **Band 4** p.1148

**Young, Kevin**
Table(s): **New York:** Environment **Band 4** p.1807

**Young, Malcolm D**
Profile: p.1101
Table(s): **Georgia:** Real Estate **Band 3** p.1070

**Young, Marc D**
Profile: p.673
Table(s): **California:** Real Estate **Band 3** p.611

**Young, Meryl L**
Profile: p.673
Table(s): **California:** Litigation: Securities **Band 4** p.594

**Young, Michael**
Profile: p.1952
Table(s): **Nationwide:** Securities: Litigation **Band 2** p.232, **New York:** Litigation: Securities **Band 1** p.1834

**Young, Richard R**
Table(s): **Nationwide:** Sports Law: Athletic
Disputes **Band 1** p.241

**Young, Rodger D**
Table(s): **Michigan:** Litigation: General
Commercial **Band 1** p.1544

**Young, Russell A**
Table(s): **Vermont:** Corporate/Commercial:
Captive Insurance **Up-and-coming individuals** p.2483

**Young, Sherilyn Burnett**
Table(s): **New Hampshire:** Environment **Band 1** p.1687

**Young, Terry C**
Table(s): **Florida:** Litigation: General Commercial
**Band 3** p.966

**Young, Theodore D C**
Table(s): **Hawaii:** Bankruptcy/Restructuring **Band 2** p.1114

**Young Jr, Rutledge**
Table(s): **South Carolina:** Litigation: General
Commercial **Band 2** p.2264

**Youngberg, Angela C.**
Table(s): **Tennessee:** Healthcare **Band 3** p.2291

**Younger, Carter**
Table(s): **Virginia:** Labor & Employment **Band 1** p.2500

**Youngman, Stephen A**
Profile: p.2423
Table(s): **Texas:** Bankruptcy/Restructuring **Band 2** p.2328

**Youngren, Nancy**
Profile: p.1125
Table(s): **Hawaii:** Real Estate **Band 2** p.1120

**Youngstrom, Karen D**
Profile: p.2118
Table(s): **Ohio:** Employee Benefits & Executive
Compensation **Band 1** p.2067

**Youngwood, Jonathan K**
Profile: p.1952
Table(s): **Nationwide:** Securities: Litigation **Band 3** p.232, **New York:** Litigation: Securities **Band 2** p.1834

**Yount, Jennifer S**
Table(s): **California:** Banking & Finance **Band 2** p.539

**Yudkin, Felice**
Profile: p.1750
Table(s): **New Jersey:** Bankruptcy/Restructuring
**Associates to watch** p.1705

**Yuen, Leighton**
Table(s): **Hawaii:** Real Estate **Band 1** p.1120

**Yuengert, Anne**
Table(s): **Alabama:** Labor & Employment **Band 3** p.460

**Yuffee, Michael**
Profile: p.430
Table(s): **Nationwide:** Energy: Electricity
(Regulatory & Litigation) **Band 4** p.76

**Yund, George**
Profile: p.2118
Table(s): **Ohio:** Labor & Employment **Band 2** p.2074

**Yungblut, Stephen K**
Table(s): **Texas:** Construction **Band 3** p.2335

**Yurow, M Jay**
Table(s): **Northern Virginia:** Real Estate **Band 2** p.2505

# Z

**Zabaneh, Sam**
Profile: p.2424
Table(s): **Texas:** Technology: Corporate &
Commercial **Band 2** p.2375

**Zabloudil, Susanne**
Table(s): **Florida:** Real Estate **Up-and-coming individuals** p.974

**Zabowsky, Michael D**
Profile: p.1514
Table(s): **Massachusetts:** Real Estate **Band 2** p.1478

**Zabriskie, Mims Maynard**
Profile: p.2233
Table(s): **Pennsylvania:** Labor & Employment:
Employee Benefits & Compensation **Band 2** p.2200

**Zabriskie, Wendy L**
Profile: p.1556
Table(s): **Michigan:** Banking & Finance **Band 2** p.1536

**Zachary, Heather**
Profile: p.901
Table(s): **District of Columbia:** Telecom,
Broadcast & Satellite **Up-and-coming individuals** p.844

**Zackin, Jack M**
Profile: p.1750
Table(s): **New Jersey:** Bankruptcy/Restructuring
**Senior Statesmen:** p.1705

**Zacks, David M**
Table(s): **Georgia:** Litigation: General
Commercial **Band 3** p.1065

**Zadick, Gary M**
Table(s): **Montana:** Litigation: General
Commercial **Band 1** p.1649, **Montana:** Litigation:
Mainly Plaintiff **Band 1** p.1649

**Zaelke, Edward W**
Profile: p.430
Table(s): **Nationwide:** Projects **Band 3** p.216,
**Nationwide:** Projects: Renewables & Alternative
Energy **Band 1** p.216

**Zagore, David A**
Profile: p.2118
Table(s): **Ohio:** Corporate/M&A **Band 3** p.2064

**Zagrans, Eric**
Table(s): **Ohio:** Litigation: General Commercial
**Band 4** p.2078

**Zahler, Robert**
Table(s): **Nationwide:** Outsourcing **Star individuals** p.195, **District of Columbia:** Technology &
Outsourcing **Star individuals** p.842

**Zahn, Jim**
Table(s): **Illinois:** Construction **Band 3** p.1154

**Zaiger, Mark L**
Table(s): **Iowa:** Labor & Employment **Band 1** p.1285

**Zaino, Domenico**
Table(s): **Connecticut:** Labor & Employment **Band 3** p.736

**Zakarian, Albert**
Profile: p.749
Table(s): **Connecticut:** Labor & Employment **Band 1** p.736

**Zakupowsky, Alexander**
Profile: p.901
Table(s): **District of Columbia:** Tax **Band 4** p.838

**Zaldivar, Miguel A**
Table(s): **Florida:** Latin American Investment
**Band 2** p.963

**Zalenski, Walter E**
Profile: p.430
Table(s): **Nationwide:** Financial Services
Regulation: Consumer Finance (Compliance)
**Band 1** p.98

**Zalesin, Steven A**
Profile: p.430
Table(s): **Nationwide:** Advertising: Litigation **Band 1** p.19

**Zmitrovich, Gretchen**
Profile: p.1610
Table(s): Mississippi: Environment **Up-and-coming individuals** p.1594

**Zobitz, George (Jed) E**
Profile: p.431
Table(s): **Nationwide:** Banking & Finance **Band 3** p.31

**Zochowski, T Robert**
Profile: p.431
Table(s): **Nationwide:** Capital Markets: Securitisation **Band 4** p.59

**Zody, Michael A**
Profile: p.2476
Table(s): Utah: Energy & Natural Resources **Band 3** p.2464, Utah: Labor & Employment **Band 3** p.2467

**Zohn, Martin S**
Table(s): California: Bankruptcy/Restructuring **Band 3** p.542

**Zola, Jared**
Profile: p.1953
Table(s): New York: Insurance: Dispute Resolution: Insurer **Up-and-coming individuals** p.1816

**Zoli, Elise N**
Profile: p.1514
Table(s): **Massachusetts:** Environment **Band 1** p.1457

**Zolno, Mark**
Table(s): **Nationwide:** International Trade: Customs **Band 2** p.155

**Zorn, Jonathan M**
Table(s): **Nationwide:** Employee Benefits & Executive Compensation **Band 2** p.73, Massachusetts: Employee Benefits & Executive Compensation **Band 1** p.1455

**Zorn, William V A**
Profile: p.1699
Table(s): New Hampshire: Corporate/Commercial: Tax **Band 2** p.1685

**Zornow, David M**
Profile: p.1953
Table(s): **Nationwide:** Securities: Regulation: Enforcement **Band 4** p.233, New York: Litigation: White-Collar Crime & Government Investigations **Band 1** p.1836

**Zott, David J**
Profile: p.1238
Table(s): Illinois: Antitrust **Band 3** p.1143

**Zottola, A.J.**
Profile: p.902
Table(s): **District of Columbia:** Technology & Outsourcing **Band 3** p.842

**Zovickian, Stephen**
Profile: p.673
Table(s): California: Construction **Band 2** p.550

**Zubairi, Junaid A.**
Profile: p.1239
Table(s): Illinois: Litigation: White-Collar Crime & Government Investigations **Up-and-coming individuals** p.1181

**Zuber, Scott A**
Profile: p.1750
Table(s): **New Jersey:** Bankruptcy/Restructuring **Band 2** p.1705

**Zubkoff, Daniel J**
Profile: p.431
Table(s): **Nationwide:** Banking & Finance **Band 2** p.31

**Zuccotti, Andrew**
Profile: p.2542
Table(s): **Washington:** Corporate/Commercial: Tax **Band 1** p.2525

**Zucker, Carol**
Table(s): **Nevada:** Labor & Employment **Band 2** p.1675

**Zucker, Ellen**
Table(s): **Massachusetts:** Labor & Employment: Mainly Plaintiffs Representation **Band 2** p.1467

**Zucker, Jeffrey**
Table(s): **Nevada:** Corporate/Commercial **Band 1** p.1672, Nevada: Real Estate **Band 1** p.1679

**Zucker, Richard M**
Table(s): **Pennsylvania:** Banking & Finance **Band 3** p.2186

**Zucker, Sam**
Table(s): **Nationwide:** Life Sciences: Corporate/Commercial **Band 3** p.182, California: Life Sciences: Corporate/Commercial **Band 3** p.590

**Zuckerbrot, Kenneth**
Profile: p.1953
Table(s): New York: Tax **Band 4** p.1862

**Zuckerman, Richard**
Table(s): Michigan: Litigation: White-Collar Crime & Government Investigations **Band 2** p.1544

**Zuckerman, Roger E**
Table(s): **District of Columbia:** Litigation: White-Collar Crime & Government Investigations **Band 2** p.827

**Zuckerman Williams, Susan**
Profile: p.673
Table(s): California: Media & Entertainment: Transactional **Band 3** p.608

**Zuklie, Mitchell**
Profile: p.673
Table(s): California: Corporate/M&A **Band 4** p.553, California: Corporate/M&A: Venture Capital **Band 3** p.553

**Zulkie, Paul L**
Table(s): **Nationwide:** Immigration **Band 2** p.131

**Zumbach, Steven E**
Table(s): Iowa: Corporate/M&A **Star individuals** p.1283

**Zumwalt, Jim**
Table(s): Tennessee: Media & Entertainment **Band 2** p.2297

**Zuppone, Michael L**
Table(s): **Nationwide:** Capital Markets: REITs **Band 4** p.55

**Zurik III, Samuel**
Table(s): Louisiana: Labor & Employment **Band 3** p.1350

**Zusmann, Samuel J**
Table(s): Florida: Bankruptcy/Restructuring **Senior Statesmen:** p.939

**Zussman, Gary T**
Profile: p.1239
Table(s): Illinois: Banking & Finance **Band 4** p.1145

**Zussman, Richard**
Table(s): Michigan: Real Estate **Band 2** p.1546

**Zutz, Robert**
Profile: p.431
Table(s): **Nationwide:** Investment Funds: Registered Funds **Band 2** p.170

**Zweifach, Lawrence J.**
Profile: p.1953
Table(s): **Nationwide:** Securities: Regulation: Enforcement **Band 4** p.233, New York: Litigation: Securities **Band 3** p.1834

**Zwillinger, Marc J**
Table(s): **Nationwide:** Privacy & Data Security **Band 2** p.199

**Zwisler, Carl**
Table(s): **Nationwide:** Franchising **Band 4** p.111

**Zwisler, Margaret**
Profile: p.902
Table(s): **District of Columbia:** Antitrust **Band 2** p.787

**Zygmont, C Max**
Table(s): Georgia: Environment **Associates to watch** p.1051

| | |
|---|---|
| AAA | American Arbitration Association |
| ABA | American Bar Association |
| ADA | Americans with Disabilities Act |
| ADEA | Age Discrimination in Employment Act |
| AMA | American Medical Association |
| CAA | Clean Air Act |
| CERCLA | The Comprehensive Environmental Response, Compensation, and Liability Act |
| CWA | Clean Water Act |
| DEP | Department of Environmental Protection |
| DMCA | Digital Millennium Copyright Act |
| D&O | Directors and Officers (insurance) |
| ERISA | Employee Retirement Income Security Act of 1974 |
| EU | European Union |
| FCC | Federal Communications Commission |
| FDA | Food and Drug Administration |
| FERC | Federal Energy Regulatory Commission |
| FLSA | Fair Labor Standards Act |
| FMLA | Family and Medical Leave Act |
| FTC | Federal Trade Commission |
| ICC | International Criminal Court |
| ICSID | International Centre for Settlement of Investment Disputes |
| IP | Intellectual Property |
| IPP | Independent Power Producer |
| IRS | Internal Revenue Service |
| ITC | International Trade Commission |
| LCIA | London Court of International Arbitration |
| MSHA | Mine Safety and Health Administration |
| NAFTA | North American Free Trade Agreement |
| NEPA | National Environmental Policy Act |
| NLRA | National Labor Relations Act |
| NLRB | National Labor Relations Board |
| OECD | Organisation for Economic Co-operation and Development |
| OFCCP | Office of Federal Contract Compliance Programs |
| OSHA | Occupational Safety and Health Act/Administration |
| RCRA | Resource Conservation and Recovery Act |
| REIT | Real Estate Investment Trust |
| REOC | Real Estate Operating Company |
| RICO | Racketeer Influenced and Corrupt Organizations Act |
| SEC | Securities and Exchange Commission |
| SLAPPs | Strategic Lawsuits against Public Participation |
| UNCITRAL | United Nations Commission on International Trade Law |
| USPTO | United States Patent and Trademark Office |
| WIPO | World Intellectual Property Organization |
| WTO | World Trade Organization |